C000037328

R.E.D.
CD CATALOGUE edition *18*

R.E.D.
CD CATALOGUE edition 18

Retail Entertainment Data Publishing Limited
Paulton House, 8 Shepherdess Walk, London N1 7LB, UK
Tel: +44 (0)171 566 8216   Fax: +44 (0)171 566 8259

Editor	Matthew Garbutt
Assistant Editor	Gary Ford
Researcher	Howard Richardson
Editorial Assistants	Chris Evans
	Jeremy Hammett
	Simon Liss
	Adrian Perkins
Sales Executives	Abigail Clarkson
	Nick Griffiths
Sales & Marketing Manager	Becca Bailey
Circulation Co-Ordinator	Michelle Tarrant
Production Manager	Keith Hawkins
Publisher	Brenda Daly

All enquiries:
Retail Entertainment Data Publishing Ltd,
Paulton House, 8 Shepherdess Walk, London N1 7LB, UK
Tel: +44 (0)171 566 8216   Fax: +44 (0)171 566 8259

Front cover image supplied by The Image Bank, London, UK
Photographer P. E. Berglund

Printed and bound by BPC Digital Information, Exeter, UK

ISBN 1 900105 11 X

DPA
DIRECTORY & DATABASE
PUBLISHERS ASSOCIATION
MEMBER

Contents

Introduction

Welcome to the 18th edition of the R.E.D. CD Catalogue, the UK's only comprehensive listing of currently available albums on CD.

The data for this edition has been extracted from the world famous R.E.D. pop database and contains details on over 82,000 titles released and still available in the UK.

Since the publication of the last edition in October 1997, the R.E.D. CD Catalogue has been redesigned - the new page layout being more reader friendly, allowing for speedier referencing of recording information. In addition to this, a lot of work has been undertaken to confirm the availability status of the albums listed in this catalogue - making the R.E.D. CD Catalogue as accurate as it is beautiful !

As ever, the CD catalogue covers all forms of popular music - Blues, Country, Dance, Folk, Indie, Jazz, Pop, Reggae, Rock, Soul and Soundtracks and is therefore the ideal reference source for collectors, enthusiasts and music lovers in general throughout the world.

How To Use

The R.E.D. CD Catalogue is divided into the following sections:

The **Main Section** contains the majority of the recording information. The 'black-strip' artist headings and subsequent recording titles are arranged alphabetically. After the recording title, tracks are listed where we have been advised. The catalogue number is displayed in bold, followed by release date and the issuing label.

Recording Title

'Black Strip' Heading

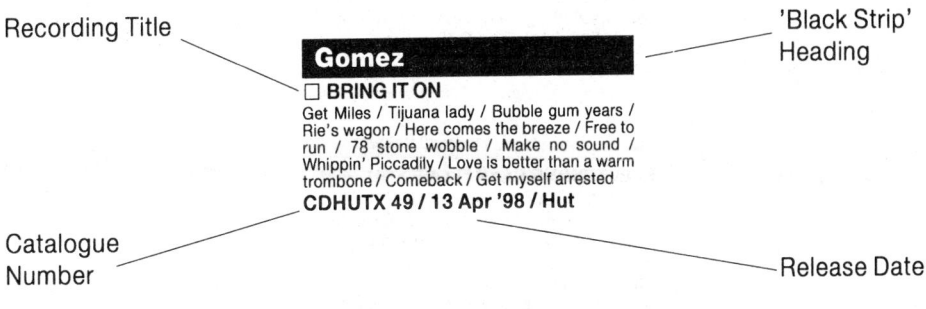

Gomez

☐ **BRING IT ON**
Get Miles / Tijuana lady / Bubble gum years / Rie's wagon / Here comes the breeze / Free to run / 78 stone wobble / Make no sound / Whippin' Piccadily / Love is better than a warm trombone / Comeback / Get myself arrested
CDHUTX 49 / 13 Apr '98 / Hut

Catalogue Number

Release Date

The **Compilations** section is arranged alphabetically by recording title and thereafter the layout is as the Main Section.

Subheading

Track Listing

☐ **AND THIS TIME IT'S FOR REAL (36 Classic R'n'B Standards - 2CD Set)**
Soulful dress: Desanto, Sugar Pie / First I look at the purse: Contours / He was really saying something: Velvelettes / Don't mess up a good thing: Bass, Fontella & Bobby McClure / Hey Leroy your Mama's calling you: Castor, Jimmy / Cleo's mood: Walker, Junior / Devil with the blue dress: Long, Shorty / Mohair Sam: Rich, Charlie / Thread your needle: Dean & Jean / Out of sight: Brown, James / Uptight good woman: Lee, Laura / Ain't nobody home: Tate, Howard / Got to get you off my mind: Burke, Solomon / Every little bit hurts: Holloway, Brenda / Baby I'm for real: Originals / Hey Western Union man: Butler, Jerry / Nowhere to run: Martha & The Vandellas / It's better to have and don't need: Covay, Don / Stealing in the name of the Lord: Kelly, Paul / Who's gonna help brother get further: Dorsey, Lee / I'll take you there: Staple Singers / Buffalo soldiers: Flamingos / War: Starr, Edwin / Bring the boys back home: Payne, Freda / Tell me what you want: Ruffin, Jimmy / Got to get enough: Roy C / Groovy situation: Chandler, Gene / Think (about it): Collins, Lyn / Rubberband man: Detroit Spinners / Deception: Dynamic Superiors / Sneakin' Sally through the alley: Palmer, Robert / Rock steady: Franklin, Aretha / Meet de boys on teh battlefront: Wild Tchoupitoulas / 18 with a bullet: Wingfield, Pete
5531002 / Jul '98 / Debutante

Label

How To Use

The **Soundtracks** section is arranged into three separate parts:

1 : **Soundtracks** - an alphabetical listing by title of film, show and TV soundtrack recordings.

Recording Title

☐ **MY FAIR LADY (Harrison, Rex & Julie Andrews/Stanley Holloway/ 1959 London Cast)**
Loewe, Frederick c —————————————— Composer
Lerner, Alan Jay l
Overture / Why can't the English / Wouldn't it be loverly / With a little bit of luck / I'm just an ordinary man / Just you wait / Rain in Spain / I could have danced all night / Ascot gavotte / On the street where you live / You did it / Show me / Get me to the church on time / Hymn to him / Without you / I've grown accustomed to her face
SK 60539 / Jul '98 / Columbia
Catalogue Number
Broadway Masterworks

Artist/s

☐ **EVERYONE SAYS I LOVE YOU (Alda, Alan & Woody Allen/Goldie Hawn/Julia Roberts/Tim Roth/Dick Hyman & New York Studio Players)**
Allen, Woody c
Allen, Woody l — Lyricist
Just you just me / Everyone says I love you / My baby just cares for me / I'm a dreamer aren't we all / I'm thru with love / Just say I love her / Venetian scene / Recurrence / All my life / Cuddle up a little closer / Looking at you / No lover no friend (that's the end) / I can't believe that you're in love with me / What a little moonlight can do / Chinatown my Chinatown / Cocktails for two / Chiquita banana / Mimi / Louise / You brought a new kind of love to me / Hooray for Captain Spaulding
09026687562 / Apr '97 / RCA Victor

2 : **Collections** - soundtrack compilations listed by recording title.

☐ **BIG SCORE, THE (A Soundtrack To** ————— Subheading
The Black Films Of The Seventies)
Call me Mr.Tibbs: *Jones, Quincy* / Superfly: *Mayfield, Curtis* / Theme from Cleopatra Jones: *Simon, Joe* / Brothers gonna work it out: *Hutch, Willie* / Across 110th Street: *Womack, Bobby* /
Track Listing
Freddie's dead: *Mayfield, Curtis* / Easing in: *Starr, Edwin* / People get up and drive your funky soul: *Brown, James* / Mama feel good: *Collins, Lyn* / Shaft: *Hayes, Isaac* / Sweetback's theme: *Van Peebles, Melvin* / Final comedown: *Green, Grant* / Are you man enough: *Four Tops* / Coffy is the colour: *Ayers, Roy* / Together brother: *White, Barry* / Flying machine: *War* / car wash: *Rose Royce*
4936292 / 30 Mar '98 / EMI

x

3 : **Composer Collections** - compilation recordings devoted to the work of specific composers. Listed alphabetically by composer.

'Black Strip'
Composer Heading

Steiner, Max

☐ FLAME AND THE ARROW, THE (The Classic Film Music Of Max Steiner) (City Of Prague Philharmonic Orchestra

Alwyn, Kenneth *con*

Spencer's Mountain / Dark At The Top Of The Stairs / Mildred Pierce / Ice Palace / Life With Father / Now Voyager / FBI Story / Sergeant York / Hanging Tree / Parrish / Johnny Belinda / Flame And The Arrow

SFC 1502 / May '98 / Silva Screen

Conductor

Release Date

Label

C.D. and CASSETTE PACKAGING

At **LOW LOW** Prices!

Product Description	Box Qty	Unit Price
CD Album Case	200	6.5p
CD Single Case	220	8.3p
*CD Tray	320	3p
**2CD Tray for Album Case	228	10p
CD Multi x 2/3 (not slimline)	64	13p
Single Cassette Case - Clear Pinless	500	4p
Clip to hold 2 Single Cassette Cases Back to Back	615	8p
Double Side by Side Cassette Case	250	14p
Single D.A.T. Case	500	14p

* Tray Colours available: Grey, Clear, Black, Yellow, Blue, Green and Red.
** Makes a Slimline double using a standard Album Case. Colours available: Black and Clear.

Discount available on large orders.

Above prices exclude V.A.T. and delivery.

The prices below are examples of **TOTAL** costs which include VAT and delivery to UK mainland:-

200 CD Cases	£20.06	500 Cassette Cases	£28.28
220 CD Singles	£26.24	228 2CD Tray	£31.57
320 CD Tray	£16.06	615 Clips	£62.59
64 CD Multi x 2/3	£14.56	500 Dat Cases	£87.03

All prices correct as at August 1998

We can also supply: Custom wound R-D.A.T. and Cassettes, 1/4" tape and CDR's.

Please call Lee or Norman to place an order or for more information on
01349 853857.

Credit card facilities available.
Office Hours: Monday - Friday 8am to 5pm

Zonal Audio Plastics Ltd.,
FREEPOST SCO2945
Invergordon IV18 0BR
Tel: 01349 853857   Fax: 01349 853712   Email: zonalap@compuserve.com

Numerical

1 Love

☐ TIME
MGOUTCD 9 / Dec '96 / Granite

1 Sec

☐ SWAMP NIGGAS
MRCCD 1007 / 17 Nov '97 / Marston

2 Bad

☐ ANSWERMACHINE
XM 039CD / Jul '93 / X-Mist

2 Bad Card

☐ HUSTLING ABILITY
ONUCD 78 / Sep '95 / On-U Sound

2 Foot Flame

☐ 2 FOOT FLAME
Lindauer / To the sea / Already walking / MR II / Reinvention / Compass / Arbitrator / Cordoned off / Chisel
OLE 1622 / Oct '95 / Matador

☐ ULTRA DROWNING
Sample stars / Lunar intuition / Dance alone / Salt doubt / Ultra drowning / Pipeline to vertigo / Everwilling / I think you're the weird one / Peacock coal / Resin box
OLE 2092 / Apr '97 / Matador

2 Live Crew

☐ REAL ONE
2247102312 / 7 Apr '98 / Little Joe

2 Rocks

☐ WHEN SANITY IS ACTING KIND OF WILD
WKFMXD 174 / Jul '91 / FM

2 Unlimited

☐ LIMITED 2 TECHNO (A Tribute To 2 Unlimited) (Megatek)
Get ready for this / Twilight zone / Real thing / Let the beat control your body / Tribal dance / Maximum overdrive / Faces / Do what's good for me / No one / Jump for joy / Magic friend / Nothing like the rain / Spread your love / Here I go / No limit
SUMCD 4064 / Nov '96 / Summit

2nd Communication

☐ 2ND COMMUNICATION
KK 038CD / '89 / KK

☐ INTERACTION
KK 066CD / Feb '94 / KK

☐ MY CHROMOSOMAL FRIEND
KK 044CD / Aug '90 / KK

2nd Voice

☐ APPROACHING LUNA
HY 39100682 / Nov '93 / Hyperium

2Pac

☐ 1 IN 21 (2Pac - A Tupac Shakur Story)
Static / Panther power / Never be beat / Case of the misplaced mic / My burnin' heart / Static / Static / Static
AIM 4001CD / Sep '97 / Aim

☐ 2PACALYPSE NOW
Young black male / Trapped / Soulja's story / I don't give a fuck / Violent / Words of wisdom / Something wicked / Crooked ass nigga / If my homie calls / Brenda's got a baby / Lunatic / Rebel of the underground / Part time mutha
CHIP 199 / 2 Mar '98 / Jive

☐ ALL EYEZ ON ME (2CD Set)
Ambitionz az a ridah / All about U / Skandalouz / Got my mind made up / How do U want it / 2 of Amerikaz most wanted / No more pain / Heartz of men / Life goes on / Only God can judge me / Tradin' war stories / California love / I ain't mad at cha / What'z ya phone number / Can't c me / Shorty wanna be a thug / Holla at me / Wonda why they call u bytch / When they ride / Thug passion / Picture me rollin' / Check out time / Ratha be ya nigga / All eyez on me / Run tha streetz / Ain't hard 2 find / Heaven ain't hard 2 find
5242492 / Mar '96 / Death Row/Island

☐ DON KILLUMINATI, THE (Makaveli)
Intro / Bomb first (my second reply) / Hail Mary / Toss it up / To live and die in LA / Blasphemy / Life of an outlaw / Just like daddy / Krazy / White man'z world / Me and my girlfriend / Hold ya head / Against all odds
IND 90039 / Feb '97 / Interscope

☐ IN HIS OWN WORDS
EAGCD 050 / 27 Jul '98 / Eagle

☐ ME AGAINST THE WORLD
Intro / If I die 2nite / Me against the world / So many tears / Temptations / Young niggaz / Heavy in the game / Lord knows / Dear Mama / It ain't easy / Can U get away / Old school / Fuck the world / Death around the corner / Outlaw
CHIP 200 / 2 Mar '98 / Jive

☐ R U STILL DOWN (REMEMBER ME) (2CD Set)
Open fire / R U still down (remember me) / I wonder if Heaven got a ghetto / Fuck all y'all / Fake ass bitches / Hellrazor / Nothing to lose / I'm gettin' money / Lie to kick it / Crooked nigga too / Don't make enemies with me / Is it cool to fuck / Ready 4 whatever / When I get free (soulja's revenge) / Hold on be strong / I'm losin' it / Thug style / What you won't do for love / Po' nigga blues / Thugs 4 life / Nothin' but love / 16 on death row / Let them thangs go / When I get free II / Only fear of death
CHIP 195 / 24 Nov '97 / Jive

☐ STRICTLY 4 MY NIGGAZ
Holler if ya hear me / 2 Pac's theme / Point the finga / Something 2 die 4 / Last wordz / Souljah's revenge / Peep game / Strugglin' / Guess who's back / Representin' / Keep ya head up / Strictly 4 my NIGGAZ / Streetz R deathrow / I get around / Papa'z song / Five deadly venomz
CHIP 197 / 2 Mar '98 / Jive

☐ THUG LIFE VOL.1 (Thug Life)
Bury me a G / Don't get it twisted / Shit don't stop: Thug Life & YNV / Pour out a little liquor / Stay true / Under pressure / Street fame / Cradle to the grave / Str8 ballin'
CHIP 198 / 2 Mar '98 / Jive

☐ WHO SHOT YA (2Pac & Notorious BIG)
CMBCD 1 / 15 Jun '98 / Cashmoneybruthas

3 Colours Red

☐ PURE
This my Hollywood / Nerve gas / Nuclear holiday / Copper girl / Sixty mile smile / Sunny in England / Alright Ma / Mental blocks / Fit boy and faint girl / Halfway up the downs / Hateslick / Love's cradle / Aniseed
CRECD 208 / May '97 / Creation

3 Grand

☐ 3 BAD BROTHERS
GRA 4157CD / May '94 / Ichiban

3 Mustaphas 3

☐ BAM - BIG MUSTAPHAS PLAY STEREOLOCALMUSIC
Intro/Lebedik un treylekh / Singe tema / To tilefono tis xentias / Mehmeteli / Chilling tale / Thalasso p'ola ta nera / Vranjanski ekspres / O memetis / Hora lui marin / Besarabia / Niska banja / Any la la/Ah ya ass mar el lawn / Cabra / Svadba / Bam
CDFEZ 005 / Apr '97 / Fez-O-Phone

☐ FRIENDS, FIENDS AND FRONDS
Si vous passez par la / Starehe Mustapha I, II and III / Maldita guajira / Linda Linda / Fiz'n / DJ Trouble Fezz meets 3 Mustaphas 3 / Buke e kripe ne vater tone / Kalaxhojne / Anapse to Tsigaro / Shouffi rhirou / Niska banja / Kac kuzulu Ceylan / Selma
CDORB 070 / May '91 / Globestyle

☐ HEART OF UNCLE
Awara hoon / Mama O / Anapse to tsigaro / Yeni yol / Kaba mustafa / Taxi driver / Aj zajdi zajdi jasno sonce / Sitna Lisa / Ovcepolsko oro / Kem kem / Trois fois trois (city version) / Vi bist du geveyzn far prohibish'n / Benga taxi / Trois fois trois (country version)
CDORB 043 / May '89 / Globestyle

☐ SHOPPING
Ljubav kraj izvora/zvezdanova (skupovo) kolo / Shika shika / Xamenh evtexia/Fiz'n / Musafir / Szegerely farewell / Night off Beirut / Selver / Shouffi rhirou / Valle e pogradecit / Darling don't say no / Voulez vous danser
CDORB 022 / Aug '87 / Globestyle

☐ SOUP OF THE CENTURY
Hey kripe ne vater tone / Kalaxhojne / Zohar no.2 / Soba song / Golden clarinet / Ti citron / Sadio mome / Tropnalo oro / This city is very exciting / Madre / Ya habibi, ya ghaybine / Mamo, snezhets navalyalo / Yogurt koydum dolaba / Televizyon / Upovacko kolo
CDFEZ 004 / Aug '90 / Fez-O-Phone

3 O'Clock Heroes

☐ ESTONIA
WB 1172CD / 16 Mar '98 / We Bite

☐ KERRANGGGG
LBT 210 / Jun '97 / LBT

3 Phase

☐ SCHLANGEN FARM (2CD Set)
Schwabenfarm / Voo doo pop / Dog days / Current loop / Rota / Road 6 / Sec 3 in / Drei - schlange / Kaa / Dog days / Space generator
NOMU 23CD / Nov '93 / Mute

☐ STRAIGHT ROAD
EFA 017552 / Jun '94 / Tresor

---

3 Way Cum

☐ KILLING THE LIFE
POLLUTE 22 / Aug '97 / Sound Pollution

3rd Bass

☐ DERELICTS OF DIALECT
Merchant of grooves / Derelicts of dialect / Ace in the hole / French toast / Portrait of the artist as a hood / Pop goes the weasel / Sea vessel soliloquy / Daddy rich in the land of 1210 / Word to the third / Herbalz in your mouth / Al's a b cee'z / No master plan no master race / Come in / No static at all / Eye jammie / Microphone techniques / Problem child / Three strikes 5000 / Kick 'em in the grill / Green eggs and swine / Check yourself
5235022 / Jan '96 / Def Jam

3rd Eye

☐ PLANETS
Movin' and shakin' / If it ain't rough it ain't rough / Circles / Reality / Dear Lord / Troopers represent / Scared of revolution / Show me where you're coming from / 360 degrees / Naw mean / One day / Put your boots on
8456842 / 25 Apr '98 / Dec Lic

3rd Force

☐ VITAL FORCE
HOMCD 77591 / 10 Nov '97 / Higher Octave

3rd Rail

☐ ID MUSIC
CREV 053CD / 15 Dec '97 / Rev-Ola

3T

☐ BROTHERHOOD
Anything / 24/7 / Why: 3T & Michael Jackson / Gotta be you / With you / Sexual attention / Memories / I need you / Give me all your lovin' / Tease me / Words without meaning / Brotherhood
4816942 / Feb '96 / MJJ Music

4

☐ UNUSUAL WARMTH
HED 076 / 18 Sep '97 / Headhunter

4 Hero

☐ EARTH PIONEERS EP
Hal's children / Grand river / Plantaria / Dauntless / Loveless
TLCD 24 / 20 Oct '97 / Talkin' Loud

☐ PARALLEL UNIVERSE
RIVETCD 4 / Jun '94 / Reinforced

☐ TWO PAGES (2CD Set)
Loveless / Golden age of life / Planeteria / 3rd Stream / Escape that / Cosmic tree / Spirits in transit / Action / Star chasers / Wishful thinking / We are not as others / Humans / In the shadows / Mathematical probability / Greys / Pegasus 51 / 3005 / Worm holes / Dauntless
5584652 / 10 Aug '98 / Talkin' Loud
5584622 / 13 Jul '98 / Talkin' Loud

4 Mat 4

☐ GET DOWN GET BUSY
MA 009 / Apr '97 / M

4 Non Blondes

☐ BIGGER, BETTER, FASTER, MORE
Train / Superfly / What's up / Pleasantly blue / Morphine and chocolate / Spaceman / Old Mr.Heffer / Calling all the people / Dear Mr. President / Drifting / No place like home
IND 92112 / 8 Sep '97 / Interscope

4 Runner

☐ 4 RUNNER
5273792 / May '95 / A&M

4 Skins

☐ FEW 4 SKINS MORE VOL.2, A
STEPCD 016 / 23 Feb '98 / Step 1

☐ FISTFUL OF 4 SKINS, A
Five more years / Waiting for a friend / Johnny go joggin' / I'll stick to my guns / On file / Forgotten hero / Spy from Alaska / HMP / No excuse / Betrayed / City boy / New war / On the streets / Saturday
AHOYCD 008 / 18 May '98 / Captain Oi

☐ GOOD THE BAD AND THE 4 SKINS, THE
Plastic gangsters / Jealousy / Yesterday's heroes / Justice / Jack the lad / Remembrance day / Manifesto / Wonderful world / Sorry / Evil / I don't wanna die / ACAB / Chaos / One law for them
AHOYCD 003 / 9 Mar '98 / Captain Oi

☐ ONE LAW FOR THEM
Chaos / Wonderful world / 1984 / Sorry / Clockwork skinhead / One law for them / Evil / Yesterday's heroes / Jack the lad / Low life / Seems to me / Bread or blood / On the streets / Five more years / Waiting for a friend / No excuse / Betrayed / Cuty boy / Plastic gangsters / Dambusters / England belongs to me
CANCAN 006CD / 3 Nov '97 / Can Can

☐ SINGALONG-A-4 SKINS
Wonderful world / 1984 / Sorry / Evil / I don't wanna die / Acab / Chaos / Jealousy / On the streets / Johnny go home / Bread or blood / Saturday / City boy / Five more years / On file / Clockwork skinhead
PINCD 102 / 13 Jul '98 / PinHead

☐ WONDERFUL WORLD (The Best Of The 4 Skins)
STEPCD 027 / 4 May '98 / Step 1

4 Walls Falling

☐ GREED
LF 293CD / 27 Oct '97 / Lost & Found

4-Sight

☐ 4-SIGHT
Parabola / First love only love / Sweet / In the flow / Re:Evaluation / Vision of the past / Beyond yesterday's tomorrows / Mastery through love / Love endures / Marti / En jai jai
N2K 10029 / 29 Jun '98 / N2K

4.0

☐ 4.0
5490342 / 20 Oct '97 / A&M

4D

☐ PURE IDEAS
DBMLABCD 7 / Feb '96 / Labworks

4E

☐ 4E 4 ME 4 YOU
EFA 080502 / 18 May '98 / Mille Plateau

☐ BLUE NOTE
HE 010 / Dec '96 / Home Entertainment

4HIM

☐ OBVIOUS
Let the lion run free / I can't get past the evidence / Voice in the wilderness / Mystery of grace / Before the river came / Signs and wonders of the heart / Great awakening / That kind of love / Obvious / Who's at the wheel / Hand of God
8441822052 / Jun '98 / Benson

4PM

☐ LIGHT IN THE DARK
NP 54952 / 8 Dec '97 / Next Plateau

5 Day Week Straw People

☐ 5 DAY WEEK STRAW PEOPLE
MER II / Jun '97 / Merlin

5-6-7-8's

☐ 5-6-7-8'S, THE
ANDA 179CD / Apr '97 / Au-Go-Go

5ive Style

☐ 5IVE STYLE
SP 309B / Sep '95 / Sub Pop

5th Dimension

☐ BEST OF THE 5TH DIMENSION, THE
Last night I didn't get to sleep at all / One less bell to answer / Aquarius / Let the sunshine in / Wedding bell blues / Save the country / Love's lines, angles and rhymes / Puppet man / Up, up and away / Never my love / Together let's find love / Light sings / If I could reach you / Go where you wanna go / Sweet blindness / Working on a groovy thing / MacArthur park
74321225452 / Oct '94 / Arista

5U4

☐ U-TURN
TUMICD 058 May '96 / Tumi

1

5UU's

☐ CRISIS IN CLAY
RER5UUS / Jan '98 / ReR/ Recommended

☐ HUNGER'S TEETH
RER5UU 1 / May '94 / ReR/ Recommended

6th Sense Approach

☐ RELAX 2000
REL 972002 / Jun '97 / Reload

007

☐ LANDSCAPES (007 & The Scene)
DRCD 005 / Mar '96 / Detour

7 Hills Clash

☐ SIGNALS FROM THE SHEFFIELD UNDERGROUND
DON 1 / Jan '97 / DON

7 Kings

☐ GOVERNMENT, THE
ORG 027CD / 23 Feb '98 / Organico

7th Avenue

☐ BEST OF 7TH AVENUE, THE
Miami heatwave / New York's on fire / Midnight in Manhatten / From Chicago to the sky / LA at the end of the day / I hear thunder / Ending up on a high / No man's land / Footprints in the sand / Armed robbery / Right combination / Love I lost / Standing by your side / Love's gone mad
HTCD 29 / 20 Apr '98 / Hot Productions

8 Bold Souls

☐ ANT FARM
Half life / Little encouragement / Antfarm / Corner of walk and don't walk / Furthest from my mind / Big dig
AJ 0114 / Feb '95 / Arabesque

☐ SIDESHOW
AJ 0103 / Jul '94 / Arabesque

8 Eyed Spy

☐ LIVE (8 Eyed Spy & Lydia Lunch)
DANCD 087 / Jun '97 / ROIR

8 Frozen Modules

☐ CONFUSED ELECTRICIAN
Warm and the cold electrified angel / New sensitivity / Short dub / Premature wig / Delivery four / White mud arrival / Under the palace
049992 / 26 Jan '98 / City Slang

8 Storey Window

☐ 8 STOREY WINDOW
TOPPCD 006 / Apr '94 / Ultimate

8 Up

☐ LIE DOWN AND STAY CALM
Rubberneckin' / Ya don't quit / Not cometh of goest / Bottom end (buy the big issue) / Bup / Rip's rub / Keep it like that / Stan Gettes / Bright moments
SJRCD 021 / Oct '94 / Soul Jazz

9 Invisibles

☐ PUREHEADSPACE
King dubby / Dreadnought / Gliding silently / Velvet mind flush / Gandwanaland (water song) / Outback sunset / Social narcotics / Meltdown / Power from the sun / Zero zero / Dolphin / Highway 9 / Earth mother (instruction)
DELECCD 053 / Apr '97 / Delerium

9th Dream

☐ RHYTHM AND IRRELEVANCE
Canfield / Play garden / Red of fire / Summer offering / Benediction / Letter in three parts / La lune de miel / Life a stormy point
4509962572 / May '94 / Warner Bros.

10 Seconds

☐ 10 SECONDS
DGM 9603 / Apr '96 / Discipline

10 Zen

☐ ECSTASY ODYSSEY
TRND 501972 / 12 May '98 / TRND

10cc

☐ ALIVE - GREATEST HITS PERFORMED LIVE
CMCD 0010 / Mar '94 / Creative Man

☐ BLOODY TOURISTS
Dreadlock holiday / For you and I / Take these chains / Shock on the tube / Last night / Anonymous alcoholic / Reds in my bed / Life line / Tokyo / Old mister time / From Rochdale to Ocho Rios / Everything you've wanted to know about / Nothing can move me
5349732 / 14 Jul '97 / Mercury

☐ CHANGING FACES (The Very Best Of 10cc/Godley & Creme) (10cc & Godley & Creme)
Dreadlock holiday: *10cc* / Wall Street shuffle: *10cc* / Under your thumb: *Godley & Creme* / Life is a minestrone: *10cc* / Englishman in New York: *Godley & Creme* / Art for art's sake: *10cc* / Donna: *10cc* / Snack attack: *Godley & Creme* / Cry: *Godley & Creme* / Things we do for love: *10cc* / Wedding bells: *Godley & Creme* / I'm Mandy fly me: *10cc* / Good morning judge: *10cc* / Rubber bullets: *10cc* / Save a mountain for me: *Godley & Creme* / I'm not in love: *10cc*
8163552 / Mar '94 / Polydor

☐ DECEPTIVE BENDS
Good morning Judge / Things we do for love / Marriage bureau rendezvous / People in love / Modern man blues / Honeymoon with B troop / I bought a flat guitar tutor / You've got a cold / Feel the benefit / Hot to trot / Don't squeeze me like toothpaste / I'm so laid back I'm laid out
5349742 / 9 Jul '97 / Mercury

☐ HOW DARE YOU
Art for art's sake / Don't hang up / Head room / How dare you / I wanna rule the world / Iceberg / I'm Mandy fly me / Lazy ways / Rock 'n' roll lullaby / Get it while you can
5349752 / Jul '97 / Mercury

☐ KING BISCUIT PRESENTS...
Intro / Silly love / Baron samedi / Old wild men / Sacro Iliac / Somewhere in Hollywood / Donna / Ships don't disappear in the night do they / Worst band in the world / Wall street shuffle / Rubber bullets
KBFHCD 015 / 3 Aug '98 / King Biscuit

☐ LIVE AND LET LIVE
Second sitting for the last supper / You've got a cold / Honeymoon with B troop / Art for art's sake / People in love / Wall Street shuffle / Ships don't disappear in the night / I'm Mandy fly me / Good morning judge / Feel the benefit / Things we do for love / Waterfall / I'm not in love / Modern man blues
8388612 / Feb '94 / Mercury

☐ LIVE IN CONCERT VOL.1
Wall Street shuffle / I'm Mandy fly me / Good morning Judge / Welcome to paradise / Night the stars didn't show / Dreadlock holiday / Shine a light in the dark / Feel the benefit
QED 018 / Nov '96 / Tring
100012 / May '97 / A-Play Collection

☐ LIVE IN CONCERT VOL.2
I'm not in love / Things we do for love / Across the universe / Art for art's sake / Paperback writer / Slow down / Bullets medley
QED 019 / Nov '96 / Tring
100022 / May '97 / A-Play Collection

☐ ORIGINAL SOUNDTRACK, THE
Une nuit a Paris / I'm not in love / Blackmail / Second sitting for the last supper / Brand new day / Flying junk / Life is a minestrone / Film of my love / Channel swimmer / Good news
5329642 / Sep '96 / Mercury

☐ VERY BEST OF 10CC, THE
Donna / Rubber bullets / Dean and I / Wall Street shuffle / Silly love / Life is a minestrone / Une nuit a Paris / I'm not in love / Art for art's sake / I'm Mandy fly me / Things we do for love / Good morning judge / Dreadlock holiday / People in love / Under your thumb: *Godley & Creme* / Wedding bells: *Godley & Creme* / Cry: *Godley & Creme* / Neanderthal man: *Hotlegs*
5346122 / Mar '97 / Mercury

☐ VERY BEST OF THE EARLY YEARS, THE
Rubber bullets / Wall street shuffle / Waterfall / Headline hustler / Somewhere in hollywood / Donna / Ships don't disappear in the night / Fresh air for my mama / Johnny don't do it / Silly love / Sand in my face / Speed kills / Hospital song / Dean and I / Old wild men / Worst band in the world / Hot sun rock / Bee in my bonnet / 4% of something / Clockwork creep
MCCD 107 / May '93 / Music Club

12 From A Dozen

☐ HALF THE MONEY TWICE THE GUILT
Fondle to finish / Loves ugly head / Himalayan poppy blue / Oscar winners / Save me / Afrique / Space talk / Hope tree / I say / Paparazzi killer / Finish to fondle
KOBICD 008 / 23 Mar '98 / Delancey Street

12 Rods

☐ GAY
VVR 1000982 / 3 Nov '97 / V2

12 Rounds

☐ JITTER JUICE
Spitting in the sunshine / Pleasant smell / Fits nicely / Hesitate / Mug / Strange daze / Dog / Keeling over / Something's burning / Business / Barbed wire hair / Holed / Joyous
5318942 / Jul '96 / Polydor

13 Candles

☐ COME OUT AND...
NIGHTCD 008 / Nov '95 / Nightbreed

13 Ghosts

☐ LEGEND OF THE BLOOD YETI (13 Ghosts & Thurston Moore/Derek Bailey)
CHUGCD 5 / May '97 / Infinite Chug

13th Floor Elevators

☐ ALL TIME HIGHS
You're gonna miss me / Roller coaster / Splash 1 / Reverberation / Fire engine / Kingdom of heaven / Monkey island / Tried to hide / Slip inside this house / Slide machine / She lives (in a time of her own) / Nobody to love / Baby blue / Earthquake / Levitation / Pictures (leave your body behind) / Till then / Never another / Street song / May the circle remain unbroken
MCCD 324 / Nov '97 / Music Club

☐ BEST OF THE 13TH FLOOR ELEVATORS, THE
You're gonna miss me / I had to tell you / Never another / Thru the rhythm / Slip inside this house / Splash / Dr. Doom / Earthquake / May the circle remain unbroken / Levitation / She lives (in a time of her own) / I'm gonna love you too / Kingdom of heaven / Monkey island / Fire engine / Roller coaster / Reverberation (doubt) / You're gonna miss me (live)
642370 / Jun '94 / EVA
REMCD 507 / Feb '98 / Reactive

☐ BULL OF THE WOODS
Livin' on / Barnyard blues / Till then / Never another / Rose and the thorn / Down by the river / Scarlet and gold / Street song / Dr. Doom / With you / May the circle remain unbroken
CDGR 113 / Feb '97 / Charly
14886 / Jul '97 / Spalax

☐ EASTER EVERYWHERE
Slip inside this house / Slide machine / She lives in a time of her own / Nobody to love / It's all over now baby blue / Earthquake / Dust / I had to tell you / Postures (leave your body behind)
CDGR 111 / Feb '97 / Charly
14888 / Jul '97 / Spalax

☐ ELEVATORS LIVE
Before you accuse me / She lives in a time of her own / Tried to hide / You gotta take that girl / I'm gonna love you too / Everybody needs somebody to love / I've got levitation / You can't hurt me anymore / Rollercoaster / You're gonna miss me
CDGR 112 / Feb '97 / Charly

☐ I'VE SEEN YOUR FACE BEFORE
Fire engine / Tried to hide / Levitation / Don't fall down / Kingdom of heaven / You're gonna miss me / Reverberation (doubt) / Monkey Island / Splash / She lives in a time of her own / Rollercoaster
CDWIK 82 / Oct '88 / Big Beat

☐ INTERPRETER
Fire in my bones / Don't fall down / Thru' the rhythm / Dust / Monkey island / You don't know / Roller coaster / Levitation blues / Tried to hide / Fire engine / You're gonna miss me / Catch the wind / For Brian Jones / Lay down your weary tune / Right track now / May the circle remain unbroken / Levitation / Radio commercial / Stand for the fire demon / Interpreter / Don't shake me Lucifer / Wind and more / Interview / Bopping bopping back / Sputnik / Bermuda
CDTB 508 / Sep '96 / Thunderbolt

☐ LEVITATION - IN CONCERT
Levitation / Rollercoaster / Fire engine / Reverberation (doubt) / Don't fall down / Tried to hide / Splash 1 / You're gonna miss me / Monkey island / Kingdom of heaven / She lives in a time of her own
CDTB 147 / Mar '94 / Thunderbolt

☐ MASTERS, THE
EABCD 069 / 24 Nov '97 / Eagle

☐ OUT OF ORDER
Everybody needs somebody / To love / Before you accuse me / You don't know / I'm gonna love you too / You really got me / Splash / Fire engine / Roll over Beethoven / Word / Monkey island / Rollercoaster
CDTB 124 / Jun '93 / Thunderbolt

☐ PSYCHEDELIC SOUNDS OF 13TH FLOOR ELEVATORS, THE
You're gonna miss me / Rollercoaster / Splash 1 / Reverberation (doubt) / Don't fall down / Fire engine / Thru the rhythm / You don't know / Kingdom of heaven / Monkey island / Tried to hide
CDGR 119 / Jun '96 / Charly
SPALAX 14819 / Nov '96 / Spalax

☐ REUNION CONCERT, THE
Beast / Splash 1 / Don't slander me / You're gonna miss me / Clear night for love / Don't shake me lucifer / Bloody hammer / Two headed dog
CDTB 153 / Apr '95 / Thunderbolt

13th Sign

☐ DA STORY NEVER ENDS
Take me to a distant bass / Pressures / Have you met the glisses / Happytime / Hysteria / Moonweed / Come of this trip / Someday / Rainbow / Too far gone / 90 Infinity / Dittonia blue / Back in a day
KOBICD 003 / Nov '96 / On Delancey Street

16

☐ BLAZE OF INCOMPETENCE
T 63CD / 10 Nov '97 / Theologian

16 Horsepower

☐ 16 HORSEPOWER
5404362 / Jun '96 / Paradox

☐ LOW ESTATE
Brimstone rock / My narrow mind / Low estate / For Heaven's sake / Sac of religion / Denver grab / Coal black horses / Pure clob road / Phyllis Ruth / Black lung / Dead run / Golden rope / Hang my teeth on your door
5407092 / Sep '97 / Paradox

☐ SACKCLOTH AND ASHES
Seen what I saw / Black soul choir / Haw / Scrawled in sap / Horse head / Ruthie Lingle / Harm's way / Black bush / Heel on the shovel / American wheeze / Red neck reel / Prison show romp / Neck on the new blade / Strong man
5405912 / Apr '97 / Paradox

16 Volt

☐ LETDOWNCRUSH
REC 022 / Oct '96 / Re-Constriction

16-17

☐ GYATSO
PATH 12CD / Feb '94 / Big Cat

16B

☐ SOUNDS FROM ANOTHER ROOM
Change / New start / Another day / It doesn't have to end / Water ride / Moment to stop / Falling / Remote control / TR mood / Black hole / For c
EYEUKCD 016 / 27 Apr '98 / Eye Q

17 Years

☐ 17 YEARS
GMM 117 / Jul '97 / GMM

18 Wheeler

☐ TWIN ACTION
Sweet tooth / Nature girl / Kum back / Golden candles / Revealer / Honey mink / Gram / Prock shake / Hotel 167 / Suncrush / Frosty hands / Life is strange / I won't let you down / Wet dream
CRECD 164 / Jul '94 / Creation

☐ YEAR ZERO
CRECD 192 / Mar '97 / Creation

18th Dye

☐ CRAYON
Aug / Sixteen ink / Ray / Mystics 11 / Crank / Nuit N
OLE 1182 / Dec '94 / Matador

20th Century Zoo

☐ THUNDER ON A CLEAR DAY
AFT 16 / Nov '97 / Afterglow

22 Brides

☐ DEMOLITION DAY
ZERCD 3010 / 20 Apr '98 / Zero Hour

22 Jacks

☐ UNCLE BOB
SD 1203 / Feb '97 / Side One

23 Degrees

☐ ENDLESS SEARCHING FOR SUBSTANCE, AN
SR 9467 / Oct '94 / Silent

24 Carat Black

☐ GHETTO: MISFORTUNE'S WEALTH
Synopsis One: In the Ghetto/God save the world / Poverty's paradise / Brown-baggin' / Synopsis Two: Mother's Day / Mother's Day / Foodstamps / Ghetto: Misfortune's wealth / 24 Carat Black / God save the world
CDSXE 090 / Sep '93 / Stax

24-7 Spyz

☐ 6
EMY 1552 / Sep '97 / Enemy

☐ TEMPORARILY DISCONNECTED
EMY 1502 / Sep '97 / Enemy

25 Ta Life

☐ KEEPIN' IT REAL
WB 2137CD / Jan '96 / We Bite

☐ SHORT FUSE
SFT 08CD / 6 Apr '98 / Striving For Togetherness

☐ STRENGTH THRU UNITY - THE SPIRIT REMAINS
ED 018CD / 10 Nov '97 / Good Life

30 Amp Fuse

☐ SATURDAY NIGHT AT THE ATOMIC SPEEDWAY
Punk virtuoso / Love is a catch 22 / Stereogram / I fall down / Sleeping with the enemy / Whatever it was / All day afternoon / Till a whirl / For you / Perfect hindsight / Blastin' room / Over the hill / Truth hits hard / Down down / Sound on sound
DEDCD 032 / 20 Oct '97 / Dedicated

30 Foot Fall
☐ DIVIDED WE STAND
F 031CD / 27 Apr '98 / Fearless

.38 Special
☐ RESOLUTION
SPV 08518752 / Aug '97 / SPV

44 Xes
☐ BANISH SILENCE
WENCD 002 / Jun '95 / When

45 Grave
☐ DEBASEMENT TAPES
CLEO 2143CD / Jan '94 / Cleopatra

49th Parallel
☐ 49TH PARALLEL
FLASH 008 / Jun '97 / Flashback

☐ COMPLETE
PACE 019 / 15 Dec '97 / Pacemaker

50ft Hose
☐ CAULDRON
And after / If not this time / Opus 777 / Things that concern you / Opus 11 / Red the sign post / For Paula / Rose / Fantasy / God bless the child / Cauldron / Fly free / Desire / Bad trip / Skins
CDWIKD 158 / Jan '96 / Chiswick

☐ LIVE AND UNRELEASED
CTCD 052 / Jun '97 / Captain Trip

54.40
☐ SMILIN' BUDDHA CABARET
Blame your parents / Radio luv song / Assoholic / Daisy / Once a killer / Punk grass / Lucy / Beyond the outsider / Don't listen to that / Ocean pearl / Higher / Friends end / What Buddy was / Save yoruself / Nice to love you / You don't get away (that easy) / She la
REVXD 1001 / Nov '94 / Black

☐ SOUND OF TRUTH, THE (The Independent Collection)
Set the fire / Big idea / What to do now / Sound of truth / Around the bend / One place set / Cha cha / Lost my hand / Broken pieces / Yank / He's got / Vows sobs tears and kisses / Selection / Re-in-living / (Jamming with) Lawrence
REVXD 240 / Feb '98 / Revolver

☐ TRUSTED BY MILLIONS
Lies to me / Cheer up / Stick to Milly / Love you all / Couldn't be sorry / This is my haircut / Desperately seeking anyone / Crossing a canyon / I love candy / Frank's revenge / Nothing ever happens / I wish I knew / Puddle of love
REVXD 5440 / Sep '97 / Revolver

59 Times The Pain
☐ BLIND ANGER AND HATE
BHR 013CD / Aug '95 / Burning Heart

☐ MORE OUT OF TODAY
BHR 029CD / May '95 / Burning Heart

☐ MUSIC FOR HARDCORE PUNK
BHR 069CD / 19 Jan '98 / Burning Heart

☐ TWENTY PER CENT OF MY HAND
BHR 052CD / Dec '96 / Burning Heart

60ft Dolls
☐ JOYA MAGICA
DOLLS 008CD / 29 Jun '98 / Indolent

68 Comeback
☐ BRIDGE TOO FUCKIN' FAR, A
SFTRI 422CD / 1 Jun '98 / Sympathy For The Record Industry

69
☐ SOUND OF MUSIC, THE
My machines / Microlour / Jam the box / Desire / Rushed / Sub seducer / Sound on sound / Poi et pas / Filter king / Highs / Finale / No
RS 95078CD / Jul '95 / R&S

70 Gwen Party
☐ PEEL SESSIONS, THE
SR 013 / Apr '95 / Snape

78th Fraser Highlander's Pipe Band
☐ LIVE IN SCOTLAND
Slow airs / 4/4 Marches / Waulking songs medley / Solo pipe set / Reels-band, solo pipe, duet / Jigs / Slow air / Piobaireachd / Medley / Drum fanfare / Cape Breton medley / Journey to Skye
LCOM 8016 / Jan '95 / Lismor

☐ NOO THAT'S WHIT A CA'CEILIDH VOL.1
Dashing white sergeant / Dashing white sergeant (Encore) / Polka / Gay Gordons / Gay Gordons (encore) / St. Bernard's waltz / Eightsome reel / Strip the willow / Strip the willow (Encore) / Canadian barn dance / Canadian barn dance encore / Holley ganz jig / Boston two step / Boston two step encore / Virginia reel / Military two step
LISMOR 8016 / Jan '95 / Lismor

80's Ladies
☐ LADIES OF THE 80'S
CDGR 236 / 27 May '98 / Charly

88 Fingers Louie
☐ 88 FINGERS UP YOUR ASS
HR 6192 / Jun '97 / Hopeless

☐ BACK ON THE STREET
HR 635CD / 7 Sep '98 / Hopeless

☐ BEHIND BARS
BTR 011CD / Oct '96 / Bad Taste

92 Degrees
☐ 92 DEGREES
BV 192952 / Nov '96 / Black Vinyl

98 Degrees
☐ 98 DEGREES
5307962 / 1 Dec '97 / Motown

100 Proof (Aged In Soul)
☐ 100 PROOF AGED IN SOUL
Somebody's been sleeping in my bed / Love is sweeter / One man's leftovers / I've come to save you / Ain't that lovin' you / Not enough love to satisfy / Age ain't nothing but a number / She's not just another woman / Too many cooks (spoil the soup) / I can't sit and wait / Backtrack / If I could see the light in the window / Driveway / Ninety day freeze / Everything good is bad / I'd rather fight than switch / Don't scratch (where it don't itch) / Nothing sweeter than love / Since you been gone / Never my love
HDHCD 504 / Apr '92 / HDH

100 Watt Smile
☐ AND REASON FLEW
TR 20082 / 27 Apr '98 / Trocadero

101 Strings
☐ ARE YOU LONESOME TONIGHT
Love me tender / I want you, I need you, I love you / I really don't want to know / Love letters / Are you lonesome tonight / Blue hawaii / Heartbreak hotel / Peace in the valley / No more (la paloma) / Frankie and johnny / Hawaiian wedding song / It's impossible / I'll never fall in love again / Hound dog / Beyond the reef / Make the world go away / I'll take you home again kathleen / Spanish eyes / Swing low, sweet chariot / True love / Your cheatin' heart / What now my love
EMPRCD 009 / Feb '94 / Emporio

☐ ASTRO SOUNDS (From Beyond The Year 2000)
SCP 9717 / Nov '97 / Scamp

☐ COUNTRY COLLECTION, THE
Lovesick blues / Your cheatin' heart / I can't stop loving you / Jambalaya / Have you ever been lonely / Kaw-liga / Bouquet of roses / Wabash cannonball / Cold cold heart / Half as much / King of the road / Crazy / Send me the pillow that you dream on / Little green apples / Take these chains from my heart / Tennessee waltz / Ode to billie joe / I don't hurt anymore / Four walls / You are my sunshine / In the jailhouse now / American trilogy
EMPRCD 017 / Feb '94 / Emporio

☐ GREAT AMERICAN COMPOSERS, THE
Embraceable you / How deep is the ocean / I've got you under my skin / Some enchanted evening / On the street where you live / Way you look tonight / Stardust / Pink panther theme / With a song in my heart / Tea for two / Around the world in eighty days / Mood indigo / Jeannie with the light brown hair / Donkey serenade / Raindrops keep falling on my head / Call me irresponsible / Over the rainbow / Autumn leaves / New york, new york / People / Mame / Yankee doodle dandy
EMPRCD 016 / Feb '94 / Emporio

☐ GREAT LOVE SONGS, THE
Tenderly / Way we were / Autumn leaves / We've only just begun / This guy's in love with you / As time goes by / Night and day / Love for sale / Strangers in the night / When I fall in love / Love story / Romeo and juliet (love theme) / With a song in my heart / Easy to love / You do something to me / Someone to watch over me / Almost like being in love / If ever I would leave you / You're nobody till somebody loves you / Second time around / La mer (beyond the sea)
EMPRCD 008 / Feb '94 / Emporio

☐ GREAT STRAUSS WALTZES, THE
Tales from the vienna woods / Blue danube waltz (strauss) / Emperor waltz, the (strauss) / Treasure waltz / Perpetual motion / Die fledermaus overture (johann strauss ii) / Roses from the south / Wine, women and song / Acceleration waltz / Thousand and one nights / An artist's life / Village swallows / Tric trac waltz / Voices of spring / Radetsky waltz / Tennessee waltz / Pizzicato waltz / Hawaiian magic waltz
EMPRCD 015 / Feb '94 / Emporio

☐ MAGIC OF HAWAII, THE
Blue hawaii / Aloha oe / Hawaiian war chant / Song of the islands / Little grass shack / Hawaiian bells / Beyond the reef / Sweet hawaiian kisses / Orchid lagoon / Sweet leilani / Hawaiian magic / Stars over maui / Now is the hour / Hawaiian wedding song / Lovely hula hands / Torchlight / Hano hano / Hawaii five-o / Maria elena / Bali ha'I / Hawaiian magic waltz
EMPRCD 014 / Feb '94 / Emporio

☐ MEMORIES ARE MADE OF THIS - THE 50'S
Memories are made of this / Mona lisa / Mack the knife / Passing strangers / Cry / Misty / All the way / Canadian sunset / Love is a many splendored thing / Till / More / Blue tango / Cara mia / Love me tender / Cherry pink and apple blossom white / Put your head on my shoulder / O mein papa / Three coins in the fountain / Secret love / Volare / That's amore / My foolish heart
EMPRCD 013 / Feb '94 / Emporio

☐ MEMORIES ARE MADE OF THIS - THE 60'S
Stop in the name of love / Sweets for my sweet / Whiter shade of pale / Feelin' groovy (59th bridge street song) / Good vibrations / She loves you / Everybody's talkin' / Can't take my eyes off you / 'in' crowd / California dreamin' / Are you lonesome tonight / My cherie amour / I want to hold your hand / Baby love / Peter gunn / Somethin' stupid / Penny lane / Spinning wheel / San francisco (flowers in your hair) / All you need is love / I hear a symphony / Hard day's night
EMPRCD 012 / Feb '94 / Emporio

☐ MEMORIES ARE MADE OF THIS - THE 70'S
Joy to the world / Seasons in the sun / You are the sunshine of my life / Goodbye to love / Honky cat / Theme from 'shaft' / Best thing that ever happened to me / I'd like to teach the world to sing / Top of the world / Theme from mahogany (do you know where you're going to) / Living for the city / Don't let the sun go down on me / Love's theme / I honestly love you / Rainy days and mondays / Yesterday once more / Tie a yellow ribbon round the old oak tree / Sunshine on my shoulders / Philadelphia freedom / I won't last a day without you / Bridge over troubled water
EMPRCD 011 / Feb '94 / Emporio

☐ MOONLIGHT SERENADES
Chapel in the moonlight / Harbour lights / Moonlight serenade / Moon was yellow / Orchids in the moonlight / Moonlight becomes you / Moonlight sonata (beethoven) / Some enchanted evening / Moonlight in vermont / Night on the riviera / Moonlight love / Moonlight and you / Night is young and you're so beautiful / Are you lonesome tonight / Moon beams / Evening star / Deep purple / Moon river / Romantic nights / Red sails in the sunset / Noche de ronda
EMPRCD 002 / Feb '94 / Emporio

☐ MUSIC FOR SWINGIN' LOVERS
Young at heart / Always / My funny valentine / Dear heart / Ebb tide / Everybody loves somebody / Fly me to the moon / I've got my love to keep me warm / Fools rush in / Friendly persuasion (thee I love) / Honey / I left my heart in san francisco / I've got you under my skin / If I loved you / I wonder who's kissing her now / It's impossible / Mona lisa / Feelings / Close to you / Can't take my eyes off you / Anniversary song / Come fly with me
EMPRCD 020 / Feb '94 / Emporio

☐ MUSIC OF THE WORLD
Around the world in eighty days / Arrivederci roma / Zorba the greek / Guadalajara / Chopin's polonaise anthem / Gigi / Night in buenos aires / Volare / Malaguena / Skye boat song / Guantanamera / Hava nagila / Canadian sunset / Auf wiedersehen / Quando, quando, quando (tell me when) / Vienna, city of my dreams (sieczyinski) / Cornish rhapsody / Brazil / La vie en rose
EMPRCD 006 / Feb '94 / Emporio

☐ POWER & THE GLORY, THE
All people that on earth do dwell / Let us humbly sing our praises / Onward christian soldiers / O holy night / American trilogy / Impossible dream / Peace in the valley / Praise, praise the lord / Dream of peace / All in the april evening / Praise, my soul, the king of heaven / Ave maria / Oh lord most holy / Battle hymn of the republic / Jesu, joy of man's desiring / Unfold your portals / Hallelujah / Lord, hear our prayer / Our wedding / Lord is my shepherd / Rock of ages / Lord's prayer
EMPRCD 005 / Feb '94 / Emporio

☐ RHAPSODY AND BLUES
Rhapsody in blue / Definitely blue / Blue skies / Blue danube waltz (strauss) / Serenade in blue / Love is blue / Midnight rhapsody / Swedish rhapsody / Where the blue of the night meets the gold of the day / Blue bolero / Blues for nat / Blue grass on fire / Our first rhapsody / Have you ever been lonely / Lover's rhapsody / Blue tango / Mammy blue / Blue coast / Blues in the shadows / Blue twilight
EMPRCD 003 / Feb '94 / Emporio

☐ THAT LATIN SOUND
Guantanamera / Guadalajara / El condor pasa / La bamba / Breeze and I / La cucaracha / Be mine tonight / La cumparsita / Affair in arruba / You belong to my heart / Night in buenos aires / Felicia my love / Adios muchachos / Malaguena / Quando, quando, quando (tell me when) / Cu cu rru cu cu paloma / Adios / Brazil / Puerto valtarta / Adios mariquita linda / Jalousie / Girl from ipanema
EMPRCD 004 / Feb '94 / Emporio

☐ THEY WRITE THE SONGS
Eleanor rigby / Hey jude / Yesterday / Michelle / Goodbye yellow brick road / Honky cat / Benny and the jets / Sound of silence / Homeward bound / I am a rock / Bridge over troubled water / Boxer / By the time I get to Phoenix / Galveston / Wichita lineman / Macarthur park / Up, up and away / Leaving on a jet plane / Take me home country roads / Rocky mountain high / I don't know how to love him / Don't cry for me argentina
EMPRCD 019 / Feb '94 / Emporio

108
☐ CURSE OF INSTINCT
LF 251CD / Dec '96 / Lost & Found

☐ HOLYNAME
EVR 005CD / Apr '97 / Equal Vision

☐ SONGS OF SEPARATION
LF 096CD / Jun '94 / Lost & Found

☐ THREEFOLD MISERY
LF 230CD / May '96 / Lost & Found

108 Grand
☐ ALBUM, THE
OMCD 002 / Nov '94 / OM

112
☐ 112
112 Intro / Now that we're done / Pleasure and pain / Why / Cupid / Call my name / Come see me / Sexy you / Can I touch you / I can't believe: 112 & Faith Evans / Keep it real / Only you: 112 & Notorious BIG/ Mase / I will be there / In love with you / Just a little while / Why does / This is your day / Throw it all away / Only you: 112 & Notorious BIG
74321418362 / Sep '96 / RCA

123 Stab Wounds
☐ DEITY OF PERVERSION, THE
HNF 023CD / Jul '96 / Head Not Found

187
☐ WHEN WORLDS COLLIDE
Worlds apart / Wake up / Def con / When worlds collide / Atmosphere / Dragonfly / Blueshift / Ghetto style / Distant storm approaching / 5 am rinse
JS 123CD / 23 Sep '97 / Jungle Sky

311
☐ 311
Down / Random / Jack O'Lantern's weather / All mixed up / Hive / Guns / Misdirected hostility / Purpose / Loco / Brodels / Don't stay home / DLMD / Sweet / T and P combo
5325302 / Oct '96 / Capricorn

☐ TRANSISTOR
Transistor / Prisoner / Galaxy / Beautiful disaster / Inner light spectrum / Electricity / What was I thinking / Jupiter / Use of time / Continous life / No control / Running / Color / Light years / Creature feature / Tune in / Rub a dub / Starshines / Strangers / Borders / Stealing happy hour
5361812 / Aug '97 / Capricorn

$400 Suits
☐ NEVER GIVE WHAT YOU CAN'T TAKE BACK
CMCD 77144 / Mar '97 / Century Media

454 Big Block
☐ YOUR JESUS
CMCD 77084 / Sep '95 / Century Media

601
☐ MOTION ARCHAOS
JUNK 002 / Apr '96 / Totem

☐ RUB-A-DUB
JUNK 001 / Mar '96 / Totem

702
☐ NO DOUBT
5307382 / Nov '96 / Motown

707
☐ 707
RMED 00195 / 20 Apr '98 / Renaissance

764-Hero
☐ WE'RE SOLIDS
UP 046 / 20 Jul '98 / Up

808 State
☐ 808:88:98
ZTT 100CD / 18 May '98 / ZTT

☐ DON SOLARIS
Intro / Bond / Bird / Azura / Black D'Artagnan / Joyrider / Lopez / Balboa / Kohoutek / Mooz / Jerusahat / Banacheq
ZTT 105CD / 15 Jun '98 / ZTT

☐ DON SOLARIS (US Version)
CLP 0094 / 6 Oct '97 / Hypnotic

☐ EX.EL
San Francisco / Spanish heart / Leo Leo / Qmart / Nephatiti / Lift / Ooops / Empire / In yer face / Cubik / Lambrusco / Techno bell / Olympic
ZTT 103CD / 15 Jun '98 / ZTT

☐ **GORGEOUS**
Plan 9 / Moses / Contrique / Ten times ten / Timebomb / One in ten / Europa / Orbit / Black morpheus / Southern cross / Nimbus / Colony
ZTT 104CD / 15 Jun '98 / ZTT

☐ **NINETY**
Magical dream / Ancodia / Cobra bora / Pacific 202 / Donkey doctor / 808080808 / Sunrise / Fat shadow
ZTT 102CD / 15 Jun '98 / ZTT

911

☐ **JOURNEY, THE**
Don't make me wait / Bodyshakin' / Can't stop / Day we find love / Our last goodbye / Night to remember / Take good care / Love sensation / One more try / Swing / Rhythm of the night / Journey
CDV 2820 / Feb '97 / Virgin

☐ **MOVING ON**
All I want is you / Baby come back to me / Nothing stops the rain / How do you want me to love you / Moving on / New groove generation / That's the way / Party people...Friday night / Don't walk away / Hold on / Should have been the one / Make you my baby
CDV 2852 / 6 Jul '98 / Ginga

999

☐ **999**
Me and my desire / Chicane destiny / Crazy / Your number is my number / Hit me / Titanic (My over) reaction / Pick it up / Emergency / No pity / Direct action / Briefing / Nobody knows
DOJOCD 149 / Sep '93 / Dojo

☐ **BIGGEST PRIZE IN SPORT, THE**
Boys in the gang / Inside out / Trouble / So long / Fun thing / Biggest prize in sport / Hollywood / Stranger / Lie lie lie / Found out too late / Made a fool of you / Boiler / Shake / English wipeout / Stop stop
CDPUNK 67 / Nov '95 / Anagram

☐ **EMERGENCY**
Don't know I love you / Crazy / Feeling alright with the crew / Emergency / Pick it up / Indian reservation / Quite disappointing / My street stinks / Rael raen / Subterfuge / Hollywood / Inside out / Biggest prize in sport / Chicane destination / Obsessed / Hit me / Nasty nasty / Tulse Hill nights / Mercy mercy / English wipeout / Fun thing / Titanic reaction / Boys in the gang / Lil red riding hood / Me and my desire / Homicide / Let's face it / I'm alive / Found out too late
RRCD 245 / 25 Aug '97 / Receiver

☐ **INDEPENDENT PUNK SINGLES COLLECTION**
CDPUNK 78 / Jun '96 / Anagram

☐ **LIVE AT THE NASHVILLE 1979**
Brent Cross / Quite disappointing / Let's face it / Hit me / Biggest prize in sport / Me and my desire / Lie lie lie / Trouble / Crazy / Boys in the gang / Ain't gonna tell / Feelin' alright with the crew / Inside out / Titanic (my over) reaction
CDPUNK 93 / Apr '97 / Anagram

☐ **SEPARATES**
Homicide / Tulse Hill night / Rael rean / Let's face it / Crime / Feelin' alright with the crew / Out of reach / Subterfuge / Wolf / Brightest view / High energy plan
DOJOCD 150 / Sep '93 / Dojo

☐ **TAKEOVER**
CDPUNK 92 / Apr '97 / Anagram

☐ **YOU US IT**
Black flowers for the bride / (There is no glory in) Mary's story / Signed dangerous of Hollywood / Bye bye bones / Everybody needs it / It's over now / Bye bye England / All of the days / Big fast car / Absolution / Deep in the shadow / Run for your life / Don't tell me / Crazy crazy crazy / White light
CDPUNK 92 / Apr '97 / Anagram

1910 Fruitgum Company

☐ **SIMON SAYS**
REP 4019 / Aug '91 / Repertoire

2002

☐ **LAND OF FOREVER**
4628688012 / 19 May '98 / REM

2066 & Then

☐ **REFLECTIONS**
SB 025 / Jun '97 / Second Battle

3080 Yen

☐ **HUMANOID HA HA**
EFA 123042 / Dec '95 / Vince Lombard

5000 Watts

☐ **LIFE OF CHOICE**
HGCD 0957 / 15 Jun '98 / High Gain

7669

☐ **EAST FROM A BAD BLOCK**
Heree ah cumm / Session (interlude) / 69 ways to love a (black) man / Ma, I luv him (interlude) / Joy / Shoot the MF in his kneecap (interlude) / Changes / Conversation fo yo ass (interlude) / RMA (Will you remember me) / Crossover message (interlude) / Last song / Who dez bytches anyway (interlude) / So high / Tic away / By your side / Cabaret (interlude) / Cloud 69 / 1-800 dial f... / King size bed / Shmoken' em up y'all (interlude) / Phillies, 40's and 69
5328422 / Mar '94 / Motown

10,000 Maniacs

☐ **BLIND MAN'S ZOO**
Eat for two / Please forgive us / Big parade / Trouble me / You happy puppet / Headstrong / Poison in the well / Dust bowl / Lion's share / Hateful hate / Jubilee
9608152 / May '89 / Elektra

☐ **IN MY TRIBE**
What's the matter here / Hey Jack Kerouac / Like the weather / Cherry tree / Painted desert / Don't talk / Peace train / Gun shy / My sister Rose / Campfire song / City of angels / Verdi cries
9607382 / Aug '87 / Elektra

☐ **LOVE AMONG THE RUINS**
GED 25009 / 3 Oct '97 / Geffen

☐ **MTV UNPLUGGED**
These are days / Eat for two / Candy everybody wants / I'm not the man / Don't talk / Hey Jack Kerouac / What's the matter here / Gold rush brides / Like the weather / Trouble me / Jezebel / Because the night / Stockton gala days / Noah's dove
7559615692 / Oct '93 / Elektra

☐ **OUR TIME IN EDEN**
Noah's dove / These are days / Eden / Few and far between / Stockton gala days / Gold rush brides / Jezebel / How you've grown / Candy everybody wants / Tolerance / Circle dream / If you intend / I'm not the man
7559613852 / Oct '92 / Elektra

☐ **WISHING CHAIR, THE**
Can't ignore the train / Just as the tide was flowing / Scorpio rising / Lilydale / Maddox table / Everyone a puzzle lover / Arbor day / Back o' the moon / Tension makes a tangle / Among the Americans / Grey victory / Cotton Alley / My mother the war
9604282 / '89 / Elektra

35007

☐ **35007**
PSYBAB 011CD / 20 Oct '97 / Stickman

A

A

☐ HOW ACE ARE BUILDINGS
Turn it up / Foghorn / Cheeky monkey / No.1 / Bad idea / Singalong / Winter of '96 / Out of tune / Fistral / House under the ground / Five in the morning / Ender
8289162 / 29 Jun '98 / Tycoon

A-House

☐ NO MORE APOLOGIES
Start / Into the light / Cry easily / No more apologies / My sweet life / Sister's song / Twist and squeeze / Love is... / Without dreams / Just because / I can't change / Clothes horse / My mind / Broken / Happy ending
SETCD 028 / Sep '96 / Setanta

A-Ha

☐ EAST OF THE SUN, WEST OF THE MOON
Crying in the rain / I call your name / East of the sun and west of the moon / Waiting for her / Way we talk / Seemingly nonstop July / Early mornings / Slender frame / Sycamore leaves / Cold river / Rolling thunder
7599263142 / Dec '96 / WEA

☐ HEADLINES AND DEADLINES
Take on me / Cry wolf / Touchy / You are the one / Manhattan skyline / Blood that moves the body / Early morning / Hunting high and low / Move to memphis / I've been losing you / Living daylights / Crying in the rain / I call your name / Stay on these roads / Train of thought / Sun always shines on TV
7599267732 / Dec '96 / WEA

☐ HUNTING HIGH AND LOW
Take on me / Train of thought / Hunting high and low / Blue sky / Living a boy's adventures tale / Sun always shines on TV / And you tell me / Love is reason / Dream myself alive / Here I stand and face the rain
9253002 / Nov '85 / WEA

☐ MEMORIAL BEACH
Dark is the night / Move to Memphis / Cold as stone / Angel in the snow / Locust / Lie down in darkness / How sweet it was / Lamb to the slaughter / Between your mama and yourself / Memorial beach
9362452292 / Jun '93 / WEA

☐ SCOUNDREL DAYS
Scoundrel days / Swing of things / I've been losing you / October / Manhattan skyline / Cry wolf / Looking for the whales / Weight of the wind / Maybe maybe / Soft rains of April
9255012 / Feb '95 / WEA

☐ STAY ON THESE ROADS
Blood that moves the body / Touchy / This alone is love / Hurry home / Living daylights / There's never a forever thing / Out of blue comes green / You are the one / You'll end up crying / Stay on these roads
9257332 / Feb '95 / WEA

A-La-Tex

☐ ROUGH 'N' TUMBLE
Just sit back and laugh / Young dogs / Don't stop at the borderline / Signpost / Set me free / Girl from the west country / Gold of Eldorado / Loving chain / Don't leave me again / In the doghouse / I'll follow you / Parchman farm / I've got my foolhead on
ZNCD 1008 / Oct '95 / Zane

A-One

☐ FREE ASSOCIATION
ZEN 004CD / Aug '95 / Indochina

A1 People

☐ FRESH JUICE
DUKE 046CD / 10 Aug '98 / Hydrogen Dukebox

Aag

☐ FIRE
OZ 002CD / Jul '90 / Ozone

Aaliyah

☐ AGE AIN'T NOTHING BUT A NUMBER
Throw your hands up / Back and forth / Age ain't nothing but a number / Down with the clique / At your best you are love / Me quite like you do / I'm so into you / Street thing / Young nation / Old scool / I'm down / Thing I like
CHIP 149 / Mar '97 / Jive

☐ ONE IN A MILLION
Got to give it up / Hot like fire / If your girl only knew / One in a million / Choosey lover (old school new school) / Everything's gonna be alright / Heartbroken / I gotcha' back / Never givin' up / Came to give love / Beats 4 da streets / One I gave my heart to / Ladies in da house / Never comin' back / Giving you more / 4 page letter / Girl like you
7567927152 / Aug '96 / Blackground

Aaly Trio

☐ HIDDEN IN THE STOMACH (Aaly Trio & Ken Vandermark)
SHCD 149 / Oct '97 / Silkheart

Aardvark Jazz Orchestra

☐ PSALMS AND ELEGIES
LEOLABCD 028 / May '97 / Leo Lab

Aardvarks

☐ BARGAIN
Bargain day / Cheyenne woman / Office no.1 / Girl on a bike / Fly my plane / Mr. Inertia / Arthur C Clarke / When the morning comes / Fifty hertz man / You're my loving way / Merry go round / Time to fly
DELECCD 029 / Jun '95 / Delerium

Aaron, Lee

☐ CALL OF THE WILD
Rock me all over / Running from the fire / Champion / Barely holding on / Burning love / Beat 'em up / Paradise / Evil game / Danger zone / Hot to be rocked / Line of fire
ACD 1212 / Nov '97 / Attic

☐ EMOTIONAL RAIN
341952 / Nov '95 / No Bull

☐ LEE AARON
Powerline / Hands are tied / Only human / Empty heart / Number one / Don't rain on my parade / Going off the deep end / If this is love / Eye for an eye / Heartbeat of the world / Dream with me
ACDM 1231 / May '97 / Attic

☐ METAL QUEEN
Metal Queen / Lady of the darkest night / Head above water / Got to be the one / Shake it up / Deceiver / Steal away your love / Hold out / Breakdown / We will be rockin'
ACDM 1188 / May '97 / Attic

☐ SOME GIRLS DO
ACD 1322 / May '97 / Attic

Aarset, Eivind

☐ ELECTRONIQUE NOIRE
Dark moisture / Entrance / U-bahn / Lost and found / Superstrings / Electronique noire / Wake up call / Namib / Spooky Danish waltz / Porcupine night walk
5581282 / 26 May '98 / EmArCy

Aatabou, Najat

☐ COUNTRY GIRLS AND CITY WOMEN
Wind (Ar-rih) / Spare me (Taqi fia Allah) / No way out (La hila bidi) / God meant it to be that way (Hekda rad Allah) / Ever since that night (Min deek leela) / Burning pain (Baadou Ihih) / Go find another guy (Shoufi Ghirou)
ROUCD 5077 / Feb '97 / Rounder

☐ VOICE OF THE ATLAS, THE
Baghi narjah / Finetriki / Shouffi rhirou / Lila ya shaba / Ouardatte Lajnane / Zourouni lilah / Ditih
CDORBD 069 / Sep '91 / Globestyle

AB Bars

☐ VERDERAME
GEESTCD 17 / Aug '97 / Bvhaast

AB Skhy

☐ AB SKHY
OW 30011 / Jul '94 / One Way

Aba Shanti

☐ JAH LIGHTNING AND THUNDER
ABACD 003 / Dec '96 / Aba Shanti

☐ WRATH OF JAH, THE
ABACD 001 / Mar '96 / Falasha

Abadzi, Rita

☐ RITA ABADZI 1933-1938
HTCD 36 / May '96 / Heritage

Abana Ba Nasery

☐ NURSERY BOYS GO AHEAD
Esiessi siolle / Abakambl / Omusiele sumila / Mwana wambell / Tumeobeba / Esimiti khusilenje / Abakhasi bano / Eliira yesu ndayanza / Mapingwa / Abandu bandl / Abebi betsing'ombe
CDORBD 076 / Feb '92 / Globestyle

Abate, Greg

☐ BOP CITY - LIVE AT BIRDLAND (Abate, Greg Quartet)
Bop city / Minorism / What is this thing called love / Gypsy / Peaks beaks / Basting the bird / Andromeda / These foolish things / Young 'uns / Opportunity / Gemini / Sax O'Brien
CCD 79513 / Feb '97 / Candid

☐ DR. JEKYLL AND MR. HYDE (Abate, Greg Quintet & Richie Cole)
Fast lane rhythm / From the heart / CCA / Dr. Jekyll and Mr. Hyde / Chan's house of Jazz / My friend from Rio / I'll remember Murph / Tommyhawk / Parallel / For Tony / Vera's song / Bebop baby
CCD 79715 / Feb '97 / Candid

☐ HAPPY SAMBA
3139740042 / 21 Apr '98 / Blue Chip

☐ STRAIGHT AHEAD
Straight ahead / Kelly blue / Denise Marie / Nica's dream / Jessica / 2-22 / Con alma / Bossa for Gregory / It's all right with me
CCD 79530 / Feb '97 / Candid

Abba

☐ AGNETHA & FRIDA - THE SOUND OF ABBA
Heat is on: *Faltskog, Agnetha* / I know there's something going on: *Frida* / You're there: *Faltskog, Agnetha* / To turn the stone: *Frida* / Just one heart: *Faltskog, Agnetha* / That's tough: *Frida* / Turn the world around: *Faltskog, Agnetha* / I got something: *Frida* / We should be together: *Faltskog, Agnetha* / Shine: *Frida* / I won't let you go: *Faltskog, Agnetha* / Here we'll stay: *Frida* / Wrap your arms around me: *Faltskog, Agnetha* / Heart of the country: *Frida*
5502122 / Mar '94 / Spectrum

☐ AND THE MUSIC STILL GOES ON
Does your Mother know / Ring ring / On and on and on / When I kissed the teacher / If it wasn't for the nights / As good as new / Eagle / Dance (while the music still goes on) / Visitors / When all is said and done / So long / Bang a boomerang / Me and I / Move on / Gonna sing you my love song / Arrival
5511092 / Mar '96 / Spectrum

☐ FOREVER GOLD (2CD Set)
5330832 / 17 Nov '97 / Polydor

☐ GOLD (Greatest Hits)
Dancing queen / Knowing me, knowing you / Take a chance on me / Mamma mia / Lay all your love on me / Super trouper / I have a dream / Winner takes it all / Money, money, money / SOS / Chiquitita / Fernando / Voulez vous / Gimme gimme gimme / Does your mother know / One of us / Name of the game / Thank you for the music / Waterloo
5170072 / 9 Mar '98 / Polydor

☐ GREATEST HITS VOL.1
Fernando / SOS / He is your brother / Hasta manana / Dance (while the music still goes on) / Another town another train / Mamma mia / Waterloo / I do I do I do I do I do / Honey honey / People need love / Ring ring / Bang-a-boomerang / Nina, pretty ballerina / So long
ORGAN 034CD / 17 Nov '97 / Org

☐ INSTRUMENTAL MEMORIES (Various Artists)
Waterloo / Fernando / Mamma mia / Does your mother know / Lay all your love on me / Name of the game / Winner takes it all / Dancing queen / Voulez vous / Money money money / Knowing me knowing you / SOS / Take a chance on me / Thank you for the music
308712 / 20 Apr '98 / Hallmark

☐ INTERVIEW DISC
SAM 7021 / Nov '96 / Sound & Media

☐ KLINGA MINA KLOCKOR (Andersson, Benny)
MMCD 001 / Dec '97 / Mono

☐ LATAR AV (Bjorn & Benny)
1047 / 11 May '98 / MIA

☐ MORE ABBA GOLD
5193532 / May '93 / Polydor

☐ NOVEMBER 1989 (Andersson, Benny)
MMCD 003 / Dec '97 / Mono

☐ PLAY ABBA/BEATLES/QUEEN (Royal Philharmonic Orchestra)
HRCD 8011 / Nov '92 / Kenwest

☐ ROYAL PHILHARMONIC ORCHESTRA PERFORM CLASSIC ABBA (Royal Philharmonic Orchestra)
Abbature / SOS / Mamma mia / Eagle / I have a dream / Does your mother know / Money, money, money / Knowing me, knowing you / Gimme, gimme, gimme / Summer night city / Chiquitita / Finale
QED 037 / Nov '96 / Tring

☐ ROYAL PHILHARMONIC ORCHESTRA PLAY ABBA (Royal Philharmonic Orchestra)
Waterloo/Dancing queen/Fernando / SOS / Mamma mia / Eagle / I have a dream / Does your mother know / Money money money / Knowing me knowing you / Gimme gimme gimme/Summer night city / Chiquitita / Waterloo/Name of the game/Take a chance on me
CD 6033 / Sep '96 / Music

☐ RPO PLAYS ABBA (Royal Philharmonic Orchestra)
Abbature / Waterloo / Dancing Queen / Fernando / SOS / Mamma mia / Eagle / I have a dream / Does your mother know / Money money money / Knowing knowing you / Gimme gimme gimme / Summer night city / Chiquitita / Finale
EMPRCD 585 / Oct '95 / Emporio

☐ SALUTE TO ABBA (Various Artists)
Money money money / Chiquitita / Waterloo / I have a dream / Mama mia / Super trouper / Gimme gimme gimme (A man after midnight) / Winner takes it all / Knowing me knowing you / I do I do I do I do I do / Dancing queen / Does your Mother know / Day before you came / Fernando / SOS / Thank you for the music
306772 / May '97 / Hallmark

☐ THANK YOU FOR THE MUSIC
5234722 / Nov '94 / Polydor

Abbacadabra

☐ ABBACADABRA
ALMYCD 03 / Jan '93 / Almighty

☐ ABBACADABRA REVIVAL
ALMYCD 18 / 25 Jul '98 / Almighty

☐ FLIGHT 2
ALMYCD 22 / 2 Feb '98 / Almighty

Abbasi, Rez

☐ THIRD EAR
EFA 015042 / Jul '95 / Ozone

Abbfinoosty

☐ FUTURE
Owl / Future / Medusa / Workshop / Drink with the Devil / Arabian sales / Wild ones / Wish song / Wake up / Mama don't send / Khatra dream / Wizard
CYCL 005 / 22 Sep '97 / Cyclops

☐ STORM
CYCL 034 / Aug '96 / Cyclops

Abbott, Bobby

☐ WELCOME TO GLENSHARRAGH
Isa (scottish waltz) / Galdie's welcome to cleuch head-granach pipers (68 marches / Cromlix house-jim cleland (24 marches) / On parade (two-step) / George purves-mr and mrs j mclean (128 marches) / Woodgrange pipe band-mcneillstown pipe band (44 marches) / Meadowbank two-step (two-step) / Bavarian piper / Willie ross smith-into the circle (68 and 128 marches) / Jacky's two-step (two-step) / Twa dugs (polka)
LCOM 9046 / Jul '91 / Lismor

Abbud, Malik Ahmel

☐ JAZZ SAHARA
Ya annas (oh people) / Ya annas (oh people) / El haris (anxious) / Farah 'alaiyna (joy upon us)
OJCCD 182 / Jun '95 / Original Jazz Classics

ABC

☐ ABSOLUTELY ABC (The Greatest Hits)
Poison arrow / Look of love / All of my heart / Tears are not enough / That was then but this is now / SOS / How to be a millionaire / Be near me / When Smokey sings / Night you murdered love / King without a crown / One better world / Look of love (1990 remix) / When Smokey sings (12" mix) / Be near me (12" remix) / One better world (12" remix) / Ocean blue
8429672 / Apr '90 / Neutron

☐ COLLECTION, THE
Poison arrow / Look of love / Night you murdered love / Tears are not enough / Be near me / I'm in love with you / Real thing / Love's a dangerous language / Greatest love of all / When smokey sings / One better world / Vanity kills / Bite the hand / Chicago / Minneapolis / Think again / Never more than now / All of my heart
5518312 / Mar '96 / Spectrum

☐ LEXICON OF LOVE (Remastered)
Show me / Poison arrow / Many happy returns / Tears are not enough / Valentine's day / Look of love (part one) / Date stamp / All of my heart / 4 ever 2 gether / Look of love (part four) / Tears are not enough / Poison arrow / Look of love / Alphabet soup / Theme from Mantrap / Look of love
5149422 / Mar '96 / Mercury

☐ LEXICON OF LOVE, THE/BEAUTY STAB (2CD Set)
Show me / Poison arrow / Many happy returns / Tears are not enough / Valentine's day / Look of love / Date stamp / All of my heart / 4 ever 2 gether / Look of love (pt 4) / That was them but this is now / Love's a dangerous language / If ever I thought you'd be lonely / Power of persuasion / Beauty stab / By default, by design / Hey citizen / King money / Bite the hand / Unzip / SOS / United Kingdom
5286002 / Aug '95 / Neutron

☐ SKYSCRAPING
Stranger things / Ask a thousand times / Skyscraping / Who can I turn to / Rolling sevens / Only the best will do / Love is its own reward / Light years / Seven day weekend / Heaven knows / Faraway
74321456532 / Mar '97 / Blatant

ABC Diablo

☐ GIVE RISE TO DOUBTS
EFA 124052 / Sep '95 / Common Cause

☐ LAST INTOXICATION OF THE SENSES
CC 001CD / Jun '93 / Common Cause

Abcess

☐ URINE JUNKIES
RR 6923CD / Nov '95 / Relapse

Abdel-Al, Aboud

☐ BEST OF MODERN BELLYDANCE FROM ARABIA
EUCD 1244 / Nov '93 / ARC

Abdelli

☐ NEW MOON
Adarghal introduction / Adarghal / Achaah / Lawan / Walagh / Ayafrouk / Imanza / JSK / Iggantiw / Amegh asinigh
CDRW 54 / Jun '95 / Realworld

Abdelwahab, Mohamed

☐ KOLINA NEHIB ELQAMAR 1920-1935
829132 / Feb '96 / BUDA

Abdul, Paula

☐ FOREVER YOUR GIRL
Way that you love me / Knocked out / Opposites attract: Abdul, Paula & The Wild Pair / State of attraction / I need you / Forever your girl / Straight up / Next to you / Hard hearted / One or the other
CDSRN 19 / Apr '92 / Siren

☐ HEAD OVER HEELS
Crazy cool / My love is for real / Ain't never gonna give you up / Love don't come easy / If I were your girl / Sexy thoughts / Choice is yours / Ho-down / Under the influence / I never knew it / Get your groove on / Missing you / It's all about tonight / Cry for me
CDVUS 90 / Jun '95 / Virgin

☐ SPELLBOUND
Promise of a new day / Rock house / Rush rush / Spellbound / Vibeology / Will you marry me / U / My foolish heart / Blowing kisses in the wind / To you / Alright tonight / Goodnight my love (pleasant dreams)
CDVUS 33 / Jul '91 / Virgin

Abdulai, Alhaji Ibrahim

☐ MASTER DRUMMERS OF DAGBON
ROUCD 5016 / '88 / Rounder

Abe, Kaoru

☐ JAZZ BED
PSFD 66 / Dec '94 / PSF

Abeng

☐ UNCONQUEREBEL
LRCD 001 / Oct '94 / Lush

Abercrombie, John

☐ ANIMATO
Right now / Single moon / Agitato / First light / Last light / For hope of hope / Bright reign / Ollie Mention
8417792 / Mar '90 / ECM

☐ CHARACTERS
Parable / Memoir / Telegram / Backward glance / Ghost dance / Paramour / Afterthoughts / Evensong
8293722 / '88 / ECM

☐ CURRENT EVENTS
Clint / Alice in Wonderland / Ralph's piano waltz / Lisa / Hippityville / Killing time / Still
8277702 / Jun '86 / ECM

☐ FAREWELL
500462 / Nov '93 / Musidisc

☐ GATEWAY
Backwoods song / Waiting / May dance / Unshielded desire / Jamala / Sorcery I
8291922 / Jun '87 / ECM

☐ GATEWAY VOL.2
Opening / Sing song / Blue / Reminiscence / Nexus
8473232 / Dec '95 / ECM

☐ GETTING THERE
Sidekick / Upon a time / Getting there / Remember hymn / Thalia / Furs on ice / Chance / Labour day
8334942 / Feb '88 / ECM

☐ JOHN ABERCROMBIE TRIO (Abercrombie, John & Marc Johnson/Peter Erskine)
Furs on ice / Alice in Wonderland / Innerplay / Drum solo / Samurai hee-haw / Stella by starlight / Beautiful love / Light beam / Four on one / Haunted heart
8377562 / Apr '89 / ECM

☐ NIGHT
Etherreggae / Night / Three East / Look around / Believe you me / Four on one
8232122 / Nov '84 / ECM

☐ NOVEMBER
Cat's back / JS / Right brain patrol / Prelude / November / Rise and fall / John's walts / Ogeda / Tuesday afternoon / To be / Come rain or come shine / Big music
5190732 / Oct '93 / ECM

☐ SPEAK OF THE DEVIL (Abercrombie, John Trio)
Angel food / Now and again / Mahat / Chorale / Farewell / BT-U / Early to bed / Dreamland / Hell's gare
8496482 / May '94 / ECM

☐ TACTICS (Abercrombie, John & Dan Wall/Adam Nussbaum)
Sweet sixteen / Last waltz / Bo Diddley / You and the night and the music / Chumbioh / Dear rain / Mr. Magoo / Long ago and far away
5336802 / Feb '97 / ECM

☐ TIMELESS
Lungs / Love song / Ralph's piano waltz / Red and orange / Remembering / Timeless
8291142 / '87 / ECM

☐ WORKS
Red and orange / Night / Ralph's piano waltz / Backward glance / Nightlake / Dreamstalker / Isla / Sing song
8372752 / Jun '89 / ECM

Aberdeen FC

☐ COME ON YOU REDS (Aberdeen FC/Supporters)
Up the Dons: Shepherd, Robbie / Northern lights: Shepherd, Robbie / European song: Aberdeen FC / Northern lights: Aberdeen FC / Pride of Aberdeen: Ames, Paul / Aberdeen: Red Brigade / Wee red devils: Red Brigade / Ye canna beat us: Red Balloon Soccer Crew / Rap up: Red Balloon Soccer Crew / Tae the Dons frae Donside: Cath & Jean / Aberdeen vs Queens Park: Gordon, Harry & Jack Holden / Don't tell me it's over: Scammels / Football statistcion: Stephen, Graham / It's half past four and we're two nil down: Stephen, Graham / What a happy day: Bagry / Here we go: Aberdeen FC
CDGAFFER 15 / Apr '97 / Cherry Red

Aberdeen Youth Choir

☐ MY SONG IS LOVE
25004 / Dec '96 / Divine Art

Aberg, Lennart

☐ GREEN PRINTS
12762 / Oct '87 / Caprice

Aberjaber

☐ Y BWCED PERFFAITH
Taith Madoc / Medley / Braint / Medley / Medley / Medley / Rmbling pitchfork / Medley / O Mama / Bread man / Perfect bucket
SCD 2157 / May '97 / Sain

ABH

☐ OI COLLECTION (ABH/Subculture)
Country boy rocker: ABH / Wanna riot: ABH / Don't mess with the SAS: ABH / 999: ABH / Teenage aggression: ABH / Concrete jungle: ABH / Kids of the nation: ABH / Pissed on arrival: ABH / Stick together: Subculture / Loud and clear: Subculture / Rogue trooper: Subculture / University city: Subculture / In my time: Subculture / Better than you: Subculture / Harmonics: Subculture / University city: Subculture / Voice of the young: Subculture / Better than you: Subculture / Harmonics: Subculture
AHOYCD 085 / 13 Apr '98 / Captain Oi

Abhinanda

☐ ABHINANDA
DFR 16 / May '97 / Desperate Flight

☐ SENSELESS
DFR 4 / Jun '97 / Desperate Flight

Abhorder

☐ ZYGOTICAL SABBATORY ANABAPT
CYBSR 1012CD / Jun '96 / Cyber

Abies Alba

☐ IN PUNTO ALLA MEZZANOTTE
MMSCD 105 / Aug '96 / MMS

Abigail

☐ FEEL GOOD
GAILCD 1 / Oct '94 / Rumour

Abigail

☐ INTERCOURSE AND LUST
MIM 7342CD / Jun '97 / Modern Invasion

Abigor

☐ INVOKE THE DARK AGE
SPV 08407962 / Apr '95 / Napalm

☐ OPUS 4
NPR 020 / Jul '96 / Napalm

☐ ORKBLUT...THE RETALIATION
SPV 08007992 / May '95 / SPV

☐ SUPREME IMMORTAL ART
Satan in me / Supreme immortal art / Soul of souls / Eclipse of my heart / Spirit of Venus / Blood and soil / Magic glass monument / Exhausted remnants
NPR 040CD / 15 Jun '98 / Napalm

Abisko

☐ SAMHRADH
829012 / Mar '96 / Muance

Ablaze My Sorrow

☐ IF EMOTIONS STILL BURN
NFR 015CD / Jun '96 / No Fashion

☐ PLAGUE
NFR 026CD / 16 Mar '98 / No Fashion

Abomination

☐ ABOMINATION
NB 028CD / '92 / Nuclear Blast

☐ TRAGEDY STRIKES
NB 050CD / Jul '91 / Nuclear Blast

Abou-Khalil, Rabih

☐ AL-JADIDA
Catania / Nashwa / Evening with Jerry / When the lights go out / Storyteller / Ornette never sleeps / Nadim / Wishing well
ENJ 60902 / Oct '91 / Enja

☐ ARABIAN WALTZ
Arabian waltz / Dreams of a dying city / Ornette never sleeps / Georgina / No visa / Pain after
ENJ 90592 / Apr '96 / Enja

☐ BETWEEN DUSK AND DAWN
MMP 170886CD / Mar '89 / MMP

☐ BLUE CAMEL
Sahara / Tsarka / Ziriab / Blue camel / On time / Night in the mountains / Rabou Abou Kabou / Beriut
ENJ 70532 / Oct '92 / Enja

☐ BUKRA
MMP 170889CD / Feb '89 / MMP

☐ NAFAS
8357812 / Sep '88 / ECM

☐ ODD TIMES
Sphinx and I / Dr. Ghialer's prescription / Elephant hips / Q-tips / Son of Ben Hur / Happy sheik / One of those days / Rabou-Abou-Kabou
ENJ 93302 / 17 Nov '97 / Enja

☐ ROOTS AND SPROUTS
Remembering Machghara / Walking on air / Nida / Revelation / Wordless / Sweet tain / Outlook / Caravan / Dreams of a dying city
MMP 170890CD / Jul '90 / MMP

☐ SULTAN'S PICNIC, THE
Sunrise in Montreal / Solitude / Dog river / Moments / Lamentation / Nocturne au villaret / Happy sheik / Snake soup
ENJ 80782 / Oct '94 / Enja

☐ TARAB
Bushman in the desert / After dinner / Awakening / Hamsa maharam / Lost centuries / In search of the well / Orange fields / Tooth lost / Arabian waltz
ENJ 70832 / Oct '93 / Enja

Above All

☐ DOMAIN
RR 88822 / May '96 / Roadrunner

Above The Law

☐ LEGENDS
Floetry / XO / Set trippin' / Promise me / Be about yo bizniz / Clinic niggaz / Soliciting / Deep az the root / Streetz / Summer days / LA vibe / Worldwide / Karma / Soul searching / Adventures of... / In God we trust
TBCD 1233 / 16 Feb '98 / Tommy Boy

☐ TIME WILL REVEAL
TBCD 1154 / Oct '96 / Tommy Boy

Above The Ruins

☐ SONGS OF THE WOLF
ATR 1 / Oct '96 / Above The Ruins

Abrahams, Brian

☐ IMGOMA YABANTWANA (Abrahams, Brian District Six)
McGregorian chant / Home in a home / Maras dance / Django's jungle / Opskud (Let's jump) / Imgoma yabantwana (Song for the children) / Out of the question
D6 002 / Jan '90 / District 6

Abrahams, Mick

☐ AT LAST
When I get back / Absent friends / Time now to decide / Whole wide world / Up and down (part 1) / Up and down (part 2) / Maybe because / Good old days / You'll never get it from me
EDCD 335 / Sep '91 / Edsel

☐ LIVE - ALL TORE DOWN
IGOCD 2011 / Nov '94 / Indigo

☐ LIVE IN MADRID
Let's get down to business / Wanna know how to love / Let me love you baby / Stay with me / Automobile / Blues / Steel blues / Cat squirrel / Guitar boogie / Rock me
IGOCD 2065 / Jul '97 / Indigo

☐ MICK ABRAHAMS
Greyhound Bus / Awake / Winds of change / Why do you do me this way / Big queen / Not to rearrange / Seasons
BGOCD 95 / Aug '94 / Beat Goes On

☐ MICK'S BACK
River's invitation / Bad feeling / Cold women with warm hearts / Time to love / Leaving home blues / Long grey mare / You'd be a millionaire / Send me some lovin' / Yolanda / Little red rooster / Ain't no love in the heart of the city / So much hard luck / Skyline drive
IGOXCD 501 / Aug '96 / Indigo

☐ ONE
ANDCD 7 / Feb '97 / A New Day

☐ PIG IN THE MIDDLE (Abrahams, Mick & Blodwyn Pig)
ANDCD 10 / Feb '97 / A New Day

Abram, Vic

☐ SERENISSIMA
HYCD 200104 / Sep '93 / Hypertension

Abrams, Muhal Richard

☐ 1-0 QA + 19
Charlie in the parker / Balladl / Arhythm / Songy / Oqa / Ritob
1200172 / Oct '90 / Black Saint

☐ BLU BLU BLU
1201172 / Jan '92 / Black Saint

☐ BLUES FOREVER
BSR 0061 / Jun '86 / Black Saint

☐ DUET WITH AMINA CLAUDINE MYERS
1200512 / Jan '94 / Black Saint

☐ FAMILYTALK
1201322 / Nov '93 / Black Saint

☐ LEVELS AND DEGREES OF LIGHT
Levels and degrees of light / Bird song / My thoughts are my future-now and forever
DD 413 / Mar '97 / Delmark

☐ ONE LINE, TWO VIEWS
804692 / Dec '95 / New World

☐ OPEN AIR MEETING, THE (Abrams, Muhal Richard & Marty Ehrlich)
Marching with honor / Dark sestina / Crossbeams / Price of the ticket / Bright canto / Blues is you
805122 / May '97 / New World

☐ SONG FOR ALL
Song for all / Dabadubada / Marching for honor / GMBR / Over the same over / Linetime / Steamin' up the road / Imagine
1201612 / May '97 / Black Saint

☐ THINGS TO COME FROM THOSE NOW GONE
DELMARK 430 / Sep '89 / Delmark

☐ VIEW FROM WITHIN
BSR 0081 / Jun '86 / Black Saint

☐ YOUNG AT HEART/WISE IN TIME
DE 423 / Nov '96 / Delmark

Abrasive Wheels

☐ VICIOUS CIRCLE
AABT 807CD / May '92 / Abstract

☐ WHEN THE PUNKS GO MARCHING IN
Vicious circle / 1982 / Danger danger / BBC / May Day / Voice of youth / Just another punk band / Gotta run / Burn 'em down / Attack / When the punks go marching in / Army song / Juvenile / So far away / Vicious circle / Attack / Voice of youth / Urban rebel / Criminal youth
AHOY 025 / 8 Jun '98 / Captain Oi

Abraxas

☐ **TOMORROWS WORLD**
SPV 08528642 / May '98 / SPV

Abraxas Pool

☐ **ABRAXAS POOL**
Boom ba ya ya / Million miles away / Baila mi cha cha / Waiting for you / Going home / Szabo / Guajirona / Cruzin / Don't give up / Liego / Jingo
IRS 993172 / Apr '97 / IRS

Abreast

☐ **TIME TO SEE**
LF 307CD / 6 Jul '98 / Lost & Found

Abruptum

☐ **IN UMBRA MALFTJAE**
ANTIMOSH 009CD / Apr '94 / Deathlike Silence

Abscess

☐ **IN YOUR MIND**
EFA 112812 / May '95 / Glasnost

☐ **SEMINAL VAMPIRES AND MAGGOT MEN**
RR 69452 / Feb '97 / Relapse

Abshire, Nathan

☐ **FRENCH BLUES (Abshire, Nathan & The Pinegrove Boys)**
Pine grove blues / Kaplan waltz / French blues / New orleans waltz / Pine grove boogie / Hathaway waltz / Step it fast / Jolie, petite juilette / Choupique two step / La valse de belezere / Pine grove blues no. 2 / La valse de holly beach / Iota two step / La valse de bayou tech / Musical five special / Avalon waltz / Tee per coine (keep a knocking, but you can't come in) / New jolie blon / Point de lou two-step / Texas waltz / Lu lu boogie / Carolina blues / Shamrock waltz / Mama rosin / I. s. u. french waltz / Crying pine grove blues / Red rock waltz / Cannon ball special
ARHCD 373 / Apr '95 / Arhoolie

☐ **GREAT CAJUN ACCORDIONIST, THE**
La valse de meche / La valse de bayou teche / La valse du kaplan / T'en as eu mais t'en n'auras plus / La calse de belezaire / Le two-step de l'acadien / Cher ti-monde / Allons tuer la tortue / La valse des valses / Le blues francais / La valse de grand basile / Le two-step de choupique / Pauvre hobo / J'aimerais connaitre / La valse de la porte ouverte / Blues du tac tac / La valse du reveur / Hip et taiau / Jolie blon / Pine grove blues / La valse de choupique / Les flames d'enfer / Le temps est apres fini
CDCHD 401 / Apr '93 / Ace

☐ **PINEGROVE BLUES/THE GOOD TIMES ARE KILLING ME**
Pine grove blues / La valse de Holly Beach / Games people play / Service blues / Musician's life / Fee-fee pon-cho / Lemonade song / La valse de bayou teche / Sur la courtableau / I don't hurt anymore / Phil's waltz / Shamrock / Choupique two step / Tracks of my buggy / Nathan's lafayette two step / Dying in misery / Tramp sur la rue / Partie a grand basile / J'ai etais au balle / Valse de kaplan / If you don't love me / Off shore blues / Let me hold your hand / La noce a Rosalie
CDCHD 329 / Nov '93 / Ace

Abstinence

☐ **FRIGID**
SR 9468 / Jan '95 / Silent

☐ **REVOLT OF CYBERCHRIST**
SR 9440 / Sep '94 / Silent

Absu

☐ **BARATHRUM VITRIOL**
OPCD 020 / Apr '94 / Osmose

☐ **SUN OF TIPERETH, THE**
OPCD 029 / May '95 / Osmose

☐ **THIRD STORM OF...**
OPCD 045 / Feb '97 / Osmose

Absurdus

☐ **NO HEAVEN IN SIGHT**
CANDLE 024CD / 25 May '98 / Candlelight

Abunai

☐ **UNIVERSAL MIND DECODER**
CAM 006CD / 24 Nov '97 / Camera Obscura

Abyss

☐ **OTHER SIDE, THE**
NB 1262 / Mar '95 / Nuclear Blast

☐ **SUMMON THE BEAST**
NB 209CD / Nov '96 / Nuclear Blast

Abyssinians

☐ **BEST OF THE ABYSSINIANS, THE**
Leggo beast / Let's my days be long / Satta a masagana / Jason Whyte / Reason time / Crashie sweeps / Jerusalem / Satta me born ya / Love comes and goes / Tena yistillin
111922 / Mar '94 / Musidisc

☐ **ORIGINAL ABYSSINIANS**
021101 / Apr '97 / Graylan

☐ **SATTA DUB**
3036572 / 30 Mar '98 / Tabou

☐ **SATTA MASSAGANA**
HBCD 120 / Mar '93 / Heartbeat

AC

☐ **40 MORE REASONS TO HATE US**
Face it, you're a metal band / Steroids guy / Trapped / Theme from Three's Company / Metamorphosis / I'm sick of you / Tom Arnold / Your family is dumb / Everyone in the underground music scene is stupid / Gloves of metal
MOSH 149CD / 1 Sep '97 / Earache

☐ **EVERYONE SHOULD BE KILLED**
Some songs / Some more songs / Blur including new HC song / Even more songs / Tim / Judge / Spin cycle / Song 8 / Pavarotti / Unbelievable / Music sucks / Newest HC song / Chiffon and chips / Guy Smiley / Seth / I'm not allowed to like AC anymore / EXA Blur / GMOTR / I'm wicked underground / Blur including G / Shut up Mike / Abomination of unnecessarily augmented... / Radio hit / Loser / When I think of the true punk rock bands / Eddy Grant / MTV is my source for new music / Song titles are fucking stupid / Having to make up song titles sucks / Well you know, mean Gene / Song 5 / Iron funeral / Chapel of gristle / Hellbent for leatherman / Alcoholic / Chump change / Slow song for split 7" / Des Bink's hairstyle / Newest HC song / Greatful dead / Aging disgracefully / Brutally morbid axe of Satan / Surfer / You must be wicked underground if you own this / Choke edge / Otis Sistrunk / Russty knoife / Fred Bash / Guess which 10 of these are actual song titles / Our band is wicked sick (we have flu) / Guy le Fleur / Song 3 / Empire sandwich shop / Morrisey / Selling out by having song titles / Grindcore is very terrifying / Song 6 / Guy Lombardo
MOSH 101CD / 1 Sep '97 / Earache

☐ **I LIKE IT WHEN YOU DIE**
MOSH 169CD / Mar '97 / Earache

☐ **TOP 40 HITS**
Some hits / Some more hits / Pepe, the gay waiter / Even more hits / MJC / Flower shop guy / Living colour is my favourite black metal band / Lenny's in my neighbourhood / Stayin' alive (oi version) / Benchpressing the effects on Kevin Sharp's vocal's / Josue / Delicious face style / Nineteen to go / Stealing Seth's idea (The new book by John Chang) / Morbid dead guy / Believe in the King / Don't call Japanese hardcore Jap core / Shut up Mike / Hey, aren't you Gary Spivey / Breastfeeding JMJ Bullocks' toenail collection / Fore play with a tree shredder / Two down five to go / I liked Earache better when Dig answered the phone / Brain dead / Newest HC Song / Sultry ways of Steve Berger / Escape (Pina colada song) / Lives ruined by music / Still a freshman after all these years / I'm still standing / Art fag / John / Newest HC song / Song 9 / Cleft palate / A-Team / Old lady across the hall with no life / Shut up Paul / Lazy eye (once a hank, always a hank) / American woman
MOSH 129CD / 1 Sep '97 / Earache

Ac Dhonncha, Sean

☐ **AN SPAILPIN FANACH**
CICD 006 / Jan '92 / Clo Iar-Chonnachta

AC Marias

☐ **ONE OF OUR GIRLS HAS GONE MISSING**
Trilby's couch / Just talk / There's a scent of rain in the air / Our dust / So soon / Give me / To sleep / Looks like / Sometime / One of our girls has gone missing / Time was
CDSTUMM 68 / Aug '89 / Mute

AC Temple

☐ **SOURPUSS**
Sundown pet corner / Miss Sky / Stymied / Mother tongue / Crayola / Devil you know / Horsetrading / Mouthful / Faith is a windsock / Ringpiece / (Dirty) weekend
BFFP 45CD / Sep '89 / Blast First

AC/DC

☐ **74 JAILBREAK**
Jailbreak / You ain't got a hold on me / Soul stripper / Baby please don't go / Show business
7567924492 / Sep '94 / Atlantic

☐ **BACK IN BLACK**
Back in black / Hell's bells / Shoot to thrill / Give the dog a bone / What do you do for money honey / Rock 'n' roll ain't noise pollution / Let me put my love into you / You shook me all night long / Shake a leg / Have a drink on me
4951532 / 8 Jun '98 / EMI

☐ **BALLBREAKER**
Hard as a rock / Cover you in oil / Honey roll / Burnin' alive / Hail Caesar / Love bomb / Caught with your pants down / Whiskey on the rocks / Ballbreaker
4951492 / 8 Jun '98 / EMI

☐ **BLOW UP YOUR VIDEO**
Heatseeker / That's the way I wanna rock 'n' roll / Meanstreak / Go zone / Kissin' dynamite / Nick of time / Some sin for nuthin' / Ruff stuff / Two's up / This means war
7818282 / Feb '88 / Atlantic

☐ **BONFIRE (5CD Set)**
Live wire / Problem child / High voltage / Hell ain't a bad place to be / Dog eat dog / Jack / Whole lotta Rosie / Rocker / Live wire / Shot down in flames / Hell ain't a bad place to be / Sin city / Walk all over you / Bad boy boogie / Jack / Highway to hell / Girls got rhythm / High voltage / WHole lotta Rosie / Rocker / TNT / Let there be rock / Dirty eyes / Touch too much / If you want blood you got it / Back seat confidential / Get it hot / Sin city / She's got balls / School days / It's a long way to the top if you wanna rock 'n' roll / Ride on / Hell bells / Shoot to thrill / What do you do for money honey / Give the dog a bone / Let me put my love into you / Back in black / You shook me all night long / Have a drink on me / Shake a leg / Rock 'n' rock / Ain't noise pollution
4932732 / 8 Dec '97 / EMI

☐ **BONFIRE (4CD Set)**
Live wire / Problem child / High voltage / Hell ain't a bad place to be / Dog eat dog / Jack / Whole lotta Rosie / Rocker / Live wire / Shot down in flames / Hell ain't a bad place to be / Sin city / Walk all over you / Bad boy boogie / Jack / Highway to hell / Girl's got rhythm / High voltage / Whole lotta Rosie / Rocker / TNT / Let there be rock / Dirty eyes / Touch too much / If you want blood you got it / Back seat confidential / Get it hot / Sin city / She's got balls / School days / It's a long way to the top / If you wanna rock 'n' roll / Ride on
4932902 / 8 Dec '97 / EMI

☐ **COMPLETE SESSIONS 1971-1972 (2CD Set) (Scott, Bon & The Fraternity)**
RVCD 56 / 24 Nov '97 / Raven

☐ **COVERED IN BLACK (A Tribute To AC/DC) (Various Artists)**
CLP 9811 / Oct '96 / Cleopatra

☐ **DIRTY DEEDS DONE DIRT CHEAP**
Dirty deeds done dirt cheap / Love at first feel / Big balls / Rocker / Problem child / There's gonna be some rockin' / Ain't no fun waiting round to be a millionaire / Ride on / Squealer
7567924142 / Jul '94 / Atlantic
4946702 / 4 May '98 / EMI

☐ **DIRTY WORDS (Interview)**
3D 006 / Dec '96 / Network

☐ **EARLY YEARS (Scott, Bon & The Valentines)**
To know you is to love you / She said / Everyday I have to cry / I can't dance with you / Peculiar hole in the sky / Love makes sweet music / I can hear raindrops / Why me / Sookie sookie
C5CD520 / Sep '91 / See For Miles

☐ **FLICK OF THE SWITCH**
Rising power / Badlands / Brain shake / Flick of the switch / Deep in the hole / Landslide / Guns for hire / Bedlam in Belgium
4770912 / 26 Jan '98 / EMI

☐ **FLY ON THE WALL**
Fly on the wall / Shake your foundations / First blood / Danger / Sink the pink / Playing with girls / Stand up / Hell or high water / Back in business / Send for the man
4770922 / 26 Jan '98 / EMI

☐ **FOR THOSE ABOUT TO ROCK (WE SALUTE YOU)**
For those about to rock (we salute you) / Put the finger on you / Let's get it up / Inject the venom / Snowballed / Evil walk / COD / Breaking the rules / Night of the long knives / Spellbound
4770902 / 26 Jan '98 / EMI

☐ **HIGH VOLTAGE**
It's a long way to the top (if you wanna rock 'n' roll) / Rock 'n' roll singer / Jack / TNT / Can I sit next to you girl / Little lover / She's got balls / High voltage / Live wire
4946712 / 4 May '98 / EMI

☐ **HIGHWAY TO HELL**
Highway to Hell / Girl's got rhythm / Touch too much / Beating around the bush / Shot down in flames / Get it hot / If you want blood (you've got it) / Love hungry / Night prowler
4770882 / 26 Jan '98 / EMI

☐ **HISTORICAL DOCUMENT (Scott, Bon & The Spectors)**
SEACD 6 / Oct '92 / See For Miles

☐ **IF YOU WANT BLOOD YOU'VE GOT IT**
Riff raff / Hell ain't a bad place to be / Bad boy boogie / Jack / Problem child / Whole lotta Rosie / Rock 'n' roll damnation / High voltage / Let there be rock / Rocker
4946692 / 4 May '98 / EMI

☐ **LET THERE BE ROCK**
Go down / Dog eat dog / Let there be rock / Bad boy boogie / Overdose / Crapsody in blue / Hell ain't a bad place to be / Whole lotta Rosie
7567924452 / Sep '94 / Atlantic

☐ **LIVE (2CD Set)**
Thunderstruck / Shoot to thrill / Back in black / Sin City / Who made who / Heatseeker / Fire your guns / Jailbreak / Jack / Razor's edge / Dirty deeds done dirt cheap / Moneytalks / Hell's bells / Are you ready / That's the way I wanna rock 'n' roll / High voltage / You shook me all night long / Whole lotta Rosie / Let there be rock / Bonny / Highway to hell / TNT / For those about to rock (we salute you)
4951462 / 8 Jun '98 / EMI

☐ **LIVE (Highlights)**
Thunderstruck / Shoot to thrill / Back in black / Who made who / Heatseeker / Jack / Moneytalks / Hell's bells / Dirty deeds done dirt cheap / Whole lotta Rosie / You shook me all night long / Highway to hell / TNT / For those about to rock (we salute you)
4951452 / 8 Jun '98 / EMI

☐ **POWERAGE**
Gimme a bullet / Down payment blues / Gone shootin' / Riff raff / Sin City / Up to my neck in you / What's next to the Moon / Cold hearted man / Kicked in the teeth
4946722 / 4 May '98 / EMI

☐ **RAZOR'S EDGE, THE**
Thunderstruck / Fire your guns / Moneytalks / Razor's edge / Mistress for Christmas / Rock your heart out / Are you ready / Got you by the balls / Shot of love / Let's make it / Goodbye and good riddance to bad luck / If you dare
4951442 / 8 Jun '98 / EMI

☐ **THUNDERBOLT (A Tribute To AC/DC) (Various Artists)**
Whole lotta Rosie / Back in black / Little lover / Live wire / Sin city / Shake a leg / It's a long way to the top / Ride on / TNT / Walk all over you / Highway to hell / Night prowler
DERCD 099 / 17 Nov '97 / Derock

☐ **TRIBUTE TO AC/DC, A (Various Artists)**
Riff raff: *AB/CD* / Razor's edge: *Belt* / Hell's bells: *Violent Work Of Art* / Hell ain't a bad place to be: *Straitjackets* / You shook me all night long: *Diamond Dogs* / Whole lotta Rosie: *Masquerade* / Jailbreak: *Tornado Babies* / Sin city: *Trilogy* / Back in black: *Fistfunk* / Overdose: *Downstroke* / Let there be rock: *Transport League* / Send for the man: *Feed*
TR 005CD / Oct '96 / Tribute

☐ **WHO MADE WHO (Film Soundtrack For Maximum Overdrive)**
Who made who / You shook me all night long / DT / Sink the pink / Ride on / Hell's bells / Shake your foundations / Chase the ace / For those about to rock (we salute you)
7816502 / May '88 / Atlantic

Acacia

☐ **CRADLE**
Wired / I'm in love with love / More you ignore me / Sway / Maddening shroud / Unfulfilled desire / Yellow is the colour of my cowardice / Sympathy / Hate / Boils down to money / Woe woe song / You nothing / Wire
3984204802 / 13 Oct '97 / WEA

Acanto

☐ **LABIRINTO**
BRAM 1989022 / Nov '93 / Brambus

☐ **VERSO SERA**
BRAM 1991232 / Nov '93 / Brambus

Acapella

☐ **WE HAVE SEEN HIS GLORY**
Sing to the glory / We have seen his glory / Glory in his name / We will see Jesus / How can I truly say / Good livin' / Talk to Jah / Angels long to look / I understood / To him who sits on the throne
7019299601 / Mar '92 / Word

Acceleration

☐ **ACCELERATION**
8334732 / May '88 / ECM

Accelerators

☐ **DREAM TRAIN**
FILERCD 404 / Jun '91 / Profile

Accept

☐ **ACCEPT**
Lady Lou / Tired of me / Seawinds / Take him in my heart / Sounds of war / Free me now / Glad to be alone / That's rock 'n' roll / Hell driver / Street fighter
CLACD 404 / Nov '95 / Castle

☐ **ALL AREAS WORLDWIDE (2CD Set)**
GUN 150CD / 17 Nov '97 / Gun

☐ **BREAKER**
Starlight / Breaker / Run if you can / Can't stand the night / Son of a bitch / Burning / Feelings / Midnight highway / Breaking up again / Down and out
CLACD 245 / Apr '92 / Castle

☐ **HUNGRY YEARS**
Fast as a shark / Burning / Son of a bitch / Princess of the dawn / I'm a rebel / Breaker / Restless and wild / King / Midnight highway
CLACD 405 / Oct '95 / Castle

☐ **I'M A REBEL**
I'm a rebel / Save us / No time to lose / Thunder and lightning / China lady / I wanna be no hero / King / Do it
CLACD 244 / '92 / Castle

☐ **RESTLESS AND WILD**
Fast as a shark / Restless and wild / Demon's night / Ahead of the pack / Shake your hands / Neon nights / Get ready / Flash rockin' man / Don't go stealing my soul away / Princess of the dawn
HMIXD 6 / Apr '87 / Heavy Metal

☐ **STEEL GLOVE**
Fast as a shark / I'm a rebel / Restless and wild / Princess of the dawn / Lady lou / King / Starlight / China lady / Save us / Down and out / No time to lose / I wanna be no hero / Free me now / Do it / Can't stand the night / Street fighter / Breaker / Son of a bitch / Helldriver / Burning / Thunder and lightning
CCSCD 422 / Oct '95 / Castle

Accord Singers

☐ DOWN BY THE RIVERSIDE
Down by the riverside / Joshua / Milky white way / When the saints / You better mind / Happy day / Soon one morning / Amen / No more sorrow / Couldn't be contented / Swing low sweet chariot
FA 425 / 21 Aug '97 / Fremeaux

Accordion Tribe

☐ ACCORDION TRIBE
Altered landscapes / Wave hill / Gunks / Sackamra / 3/4 suite / Doloeres / Netzwerk / Jane / SSofias / Istunpa sankys laitalla / Mita sina laitoit / Ellin polkka / Utflykt m Damcykel / Nydoina/Quirk / Cirkus II / Fathom / Boeves psalm / Cirkus / Mad cow / Inte quanta / Die wintersonnenwende II
INT 32202 / 23 Mar '98 / Intuition

Accroche Note

☐ LIVE IN BERLIN
FMPCD 83 / May '97 / Full Moon

Accused

☐ MARTHA SPLATTERHEAD'S MADDEST STORIES EVER TOLD
Psychomania / Bag lady song / Inherit the earth / Deception / Molly's x-mas '72-I'd love to change the world / You only die once / Sick boy / Chicago / Starved to death / War=death '88 / Maddest story ever told / Intro-scared of the dark / Losing your mind / Smothered her trust / Lights out / Hearse
WB 043CD / Feb '89 / We Bite

☐ SPLATTER ROCK
Two hours till sunrise / Stick in a hole / No choice / Lettin' go / Blind hate-blind rage / Greenwood house of medicine-don't you have a woman / She's back / Tearin' me apart / Green eyed lady / Brutality and corruption / Living, dying, living-in a zombie world
NMR 7103CD / Jun '92 / Nasty Mix

Accuser

☐ TAKEN BY THE THROAT
341682 / Oct '95 / No Bull

Ace

☐ BEST OF ACE, THE
How long / I'm a man / Ain't gonna stand for this no more / Rock 'n' roll runaway / Real feeling / Rock 'n' roll singer / You're all that I need / Twenty four hours / Crazy world / No future in your eyes / Tongue tied / Time ain't long / Sail on my brother / I think it's gonna last
SEECD 214 / May '93 / See For Miles

☐ VERY BEST OF ACE
How long / I think it's gonna last / Does it hurt you / Why / Message to you / This is what you find / You're all that I need / 24 hours / Tongue tied / I'm not takin' it out on you / You can't lose / Movin' / Ain't gonna stand for this no more / Sniffin' about / Crazy world / So sorry baby
MCCD 123 / Aug '93 / Music Club

Ace Of Base

☐ BRIDGE, THE
Beautiful life / Never gonna say I'm sorry / Lucky love / Edge of heaven / Strange ways / Ravine / Perfect world / Angels eyes / Whispers in blindness / My deja vu / Wave wet sand / Que sera / Just 'n' image / Experiemental / Blooming
5296552 / Nov '95 / London

☐ FLOWERS
Life is a flower / Always have always will / Cruel Summer / Travel to Romantis / Adventures in Paradise / Dr. Sun / Cecilia / He decides / I pray / Tokyo girl / Don't go away / Captain Nemo / Donnie
5576912 / 10 Aug '98 / London

Aceto, Robby

☐ CODE
Equation / Trust / Into indigo / Bells / Being there / Dog it was / Shane heads for the immaculate mountains / Black roses / Archangel
ALCD 1006 / Aug '97 / Alchemy

Acetone

☐ ACETONE
Every kiss / All the time / Germs / Might as well / Shobud / All you know / Good life / Dee / Waltz / Another minute / So slow / Chew
9362468182 / 2 Mar '98 / Vapour

☐ CINDY
Come on / Pinch / Sundown / Chills / Endless summer / Intermission / Louise / Don't cry / No need swim / Barefoot on Sunday
CDHUT 13 / Oct '93 / Hut

☐ I GUESS I WOULD
Juanita / Late John Garfield blues / I guess I would / Sometimes you just can't win / All for the love of a girl / How sweet I roamed / Border lord
HUTMCD 21 / Jan '95 / Hut

☐ IF YOU ONLY KNEW
If you only knew / I don't really care / In the light / I've enjoyed as much of this as I can stand / Final say / When you're gone / Hound dog / 99 / What I see / Nothing at all / Esque / Always late
CDHUT 31 / Mar '96 / Hut

Aceyalone

☐ BOOK OF HUMAN LANGUAGE
PBR 00022 / 30 Mar '98 / Project Blowed

Achenza, Paolo

☐ DO IT (Achenza, Paolo Trio)
RTCD 401 / Jul '96 / Right Tempo

Acheron

☐ THOSE WHO HAVE RISEN
FMP 019CD / 6 Jul '98 / Full Moon

Achiary, Benat

☐ BASQUE MUSIC OF TODAY, THE
Canto de picat / Argi ttirrintan / Obabatxue / Ur ferdez / Bazko / Maitia nun zira / Tira corda / Bihar / Dantza / Gaztetasunak bainerabila / Taos / Esku batean / Urzo bat jin izan da / Lord Byron / Lo ezin eginaren / Liluraren kontra / Tio vivo / Ba-nin adixkide bat / Indien / Pigalle / Cancion de jinete / Django / Jo al pont da mirabel / Lili purprea / Urmiraila
Y 225069 / Nov '97 / Silex

Achkar, Elie

☐ MIDDLE EAST QANUN SONGS
925582 / Jun '93 / BUDA

Acid Farm

☐ SILVER SPIRAL, THE
PROPSCD 013 / Jun '96 / Proper

Acid Mothers Temple

☐ ACID MOTHERS TEMPLE & THE MELTING PARAISO UFO (Acid Mothers Temple/The Melting Paraiso UFO)
PSFD 93 / Jan '98 / PSF

Acid Reign

☐ FEAR, THE/MOSHKINSTEIN
You never know (performed by ringo starr) / Reflection of truths / Insane ecstasy / Humanoia / Fear / Blind aggression / Life in forms / All I see / Lost in solitude / Goddess / Suspended sentence / Motherly love / Respect the dead / Chaos (lambs to the slaughter)
CDFLAG 31 / Mar '89 / Under One Flag

☐ OBNOXIOUS
Creative restraint / Joke chain / Thoughtful sleep / You are your enemy / Phantasm / My open mind / Codes of conformity / This is serious
CDFLAG 39 / Jul '92 / Under One Flag

☐ WORST OF ACID REIGN, THE
Bully boy-lucifer's hammer / Motherly love / Two minded takeover / R.f.y.s. / Amnesiac / Magic roundabout / Argument / Sabbath medley / Reflection of truths / Hangin' on the telephone / Warriors of genghis khan / Three year war / Joke's on us / Big white teeth
CDFLAG 60 / Sep '91 / Under One Flag

Acid Scout

☐ MUSIK FOR MILLIONEN
EFA 122882 / Oct '96 / Disko B

☐ SAFARI
EFA 122672 / Feb '95 / Disko B

Ackerman, Will

☐ OPENING OF DOORS, THE
01934111142 / Sep '95 / Windham Hill

☐ SOUND OF WIND DRIVEN RAIN
Shella's picture / Child's song / Driving / Lion's in the sky / Unconditional / Sound of the wind driven rain / Wings on the water / Pontchatrain / I know the river / Hawk circle / Mr. Jacksons hat
019341125020 / 9 Mar '98 / Windham Hill

☐ WINDHAM HILL RETROSPECTIVE, A
Bricklayer's beautiful daughter / Processional / Ventana / Santos and the well travelled bear / Slow motion roast beef restaurant seduction / Visiting / Anne's song / Impending death of the virgin spirit / Climbing in geometry / Opening of doors / Brother A teaches 7 / Seattle / Lago de montans (mountain lake) / Hawk circle / Region of clouds
01934111212 / Mar '93 / Windham Hill

ACME

☐ TO REDUCE THE CHOIR TO ONE SOLOIST
Blind / Attempt / Injection / Ordinary / Cathode / Bastardiser / Repress / Attempt
EDISON 002 / 16 Feb '98 / Edison

Aconcha, Leandro

☐ PIANO BAR (Aconcha, Leandro & Remi Chaudagne)
Entertainer / Don't start now / Seven days blues / Up to my house / All of me / Come in please / Give me a little peace / Don't try this / My baby's town / On the sunny side of the street / Nothing today / So tender for me / My little girl / C'est si bon
CDSGP 0161 / Sep '95 / Prestige

Acorn 2

☐ ACORN 2
RIVETCD 8 / 15 Oct '97 / Reinforced

Acoustic Alchemy

☐ AGAINST THE GRAIN
Against the grain / Lazeez / Different kind of freedom / Lady Laynda / Road dogs / Shot the loop / Papillion / Silent partner / Nouveau tango
GRP 97832 / Oct '94 / GRP

☐ BACK ON THE CASE
Alchemist / Jamaica heartbeat / Georgia Peach / Playing for time / When lights go out / Clear air for miles / Fire of the heart / Freeze frame / On the case / Break for the border
GRP 96482 / Aug '91 / GRP

☐ BLUE CHIP
Catalina kiss / Blue chip bop / Making waves / With you in mind / Bright tiger / Ariane / Highland / Boulder coaster / Hearts in chains / No more nachos (por favor)
GRP 01402 / 8 Jun '98 / GRP

☐ EARLY ALCHEMY
Santiago / Sarah Victoria / Last Summer song / Slap it down / Sira's song / Moonstone / Wind it up / Casino / Little bercheres / Amanecer / Waiting for you / Return flight / Daybreak / Dream of fair women
GRP 96662 / Feb '92 / GRP

☐ NATURAL ELEMENTS
Drake's dream / Overnight sleeper / Natural elements / Casino / If only / Ballad for Kay / Evil the weasel / Late night duke street
GRP 01412 / 8 Jun '98 / GRP

☐ NEW EDGE
Oceans apart / Notting Hill two-step / Slow ride home / Cool as a rule / Santa cafe / Arc en ciel / London skyline / Liason / Until always / Rive gauche / Act of innocence
GRP 97112 / Mar '93 / GRP

☐ POSITIVE THINKING
Passionelle / Rainwatching / Cadaques / Five card trick / Positive thinking / Better shoes / Vapour trails / Augustrasse / Time gentlemen please / Limited excess
GRP 99072 / 8 Jun '98 / GRP

☐ RED DUST AND SPANISH LACE
Mr. Chow / Ricochet / Stone circle / Rideout / Girl with a red carnation / Colonel and the ashes / One for the road / Sarah Victoria / Red dust and spanish lace
GRP 01392 / 8 Jun '98 / GRP

☐ REFERENCE POINT
Reference point / Missing your touch / Take five / Same road, same reason / Make my day / Caravan of dreams / Homecoming / Cuban heels / Lullaby for the first born
GRP 96142 / Aug '90 / GRP

Acoustic Art

☐ INTERLUDE
BEST 1024CD / Nov '93 / Acoustic Music

Acquaragia Drom

☐ ZINGARI
SN 0044CD / Aug '96 / Sudnord

Acrimony

☐ ACID ELEPHANT, THE
GOD 019 / Oct '95 / Godhead

☐ HYMNS TO THE STONE
GOD 010 / May '95 / Godhead

☐ TUMULI SHROOMAROOM
CDVILE 68 / Jul '97 / Peaceville

Acro

☐ REMIX
FT 6 / Aug '97 / Future Tense

Acrylic Tones

☐ ABOVE THE STREETS AND HOUSES
Weekend freeks / Ode to an aviator / Majestic 12 / Tell me / Last year's man / Radio tones / Delivery / Into the stone / Lies / Tabasco fiasco / Shopping / Carol Anne
DRCD 014 / 20 Oct '97 / Detour

☐ ACRYLIC TONES
DRCD 002 / Jan '95 / Detour

Act Of Faith

☐ ONE VISION
Whole thing / Lost on a breeze / Doing it with love / Love not love / Soul love / Perfect world / Dream about you / Summer in the city / What'cha gonna do for me / Lite up your life / All for love / Looking at the world
BRCD 613 / Mar '95 / 4th & Broadway

☐ RELEASE YOURSELF
Release yourself / All over now / If u believe / From me to u / Do it right / Find your love / Do u remember / Only a child / Lost in love / Pleasure / Free / Forever sing / If u believe / Only a drum and a bass
EXCDP 11 / Feb '97 / Expansion

Action

☐ ROLLED GOLD
DIGCD 01 / Jul '98 / Dig The Fuzz

☐ ULTIMATE ACTION, THE
I'll keep holding on / Harlem shuffle / Never ever / Twenty fourth hour / Since I lost my baby / My lonely room / Hey Sha-lo-ney / Shadows and reflections / Something has hit me / Place / Cissy / Baby you got it / I love you (yeah) / Land of 1000 dances
EDCD 101 / 30 Apr '90 / Edsel

Action Figures

☐ BIG WONDERFUL
ER 008CD / Nov '97 / Eggbert

☐ LITTLE CITIZENS
ER 80016CD / Nov '97 / Eggbert

Action Swingers

☐ DECIMATION BOULEVARD
TOAD 6CD / Jun '94 / Newt

☐ QUIT WHILE YOUR AHEAD
TOAD 7CD / Oct '94 / Newt

Acuff, Roy

☐ KING OF COUNTRY MUSIC, THE (2CD Set)
Tied down / What will I do / Is it love or is it lies / Lonesome Joe / Sweep around your back door / Don't say goodbye / Swamp Lily / Sixteen chickens and a tamborine / Rushing around / Whoa mule / Sunshine special / I closed my heart's door / I'm planting a rose / River of crystal / Please daddy forgive / Streamline heartbreaker / Six more days / Thief upon thee tree / Don't judge your neighbor / Night spots (Of the town) / Great speckled bird / Lonely mound of clay / Pins and needles (In my heart) / Wabash cannonball / Great judgement morning / Wreck on the highway / Precious jewel / Night train to Memphis / That's what makes the jukebox play / Little Moses / What do you think about me / Oh those tombs / Come back little pal / Fireball mail / I'm building a home (In the sky) / Great Titanic / Goodbye Mr. Brown / Mother hold me tight / Crazy worried mind / Along the China coast / It's hard to love / Plant some flowers by my graveside / I wanta to be loved / I like mountain music / Jesus died for me / Thank god / Were you there when they crucified my Lord / How beautiful heaven must be / Unclouded day / Hold to God's unchanging hand / Lord build me a cabin / Where the soul never dies / Shake my mother's hand for me / Take my hand, Precious Lord / This world is not my home / Where could I go but to the Lord
BCD 15652 / Mar '93 / Bear Family

☐ KING OF COUNTRY MUSIC, THE
Wabash cannon ball / Great speckle bird / Freight train blues / Beautiful brown eyes / Living on the mountain baby mine / Eyes are watching you / Streamlined cannon ball / Precious jewel / Mule skinner blues (blue yodel no.8) / Be honest with me / Worried mind / Brother take warning / Wreck on the highway / I'll reap my harvest in Heaven / Night train to Memphis / Prodigal son / Low and lonely / Write me sweetheart / Not a word from home / I'll forgive you but I can't forget / Wait for the light to shine / We live in two different worlds / Pins and needles / Waiting for my call to glory / Our own Jole Blon
CDAJA 5244 / Jul '98 / Living Era

Acuff's Rose

☐ SON OF THE NORTH WIND
422444 / Jan '97 / Last Call

Acustic

☐ ACUSTIC VOL.1
APR 012CD / Feb '97 / April

☐ STAR QUALITY
APR 031CD / 2 Feb '98 / April

AD

☐ AD
RGE 101 / Nov '94 / Enemy

AD

☐ ART OF THE STATE
NUMA 0002 / Mar '97 / Numavox

AD

☐ KNOCKIN' BOOTS VOL.1&2 (AD & James Barth)
SKCD 005 / 18 May '98 / Svek

Ad Vielle Que Pourra

☐ AD VIELLE QUE POURRA
GLCD 1099 / Mar '90 / Green Linnet

☐ COME WHAT MAY
GLCD 1112 / Apr '92 / Green Linnet

☐ MENAGE A QUATRE
Menage a quatre / Les bois noirs / Ar vestrez kollet / Je ne voulais voir l'oiseau / La turlutte de la dure lutte / Ca manque pas de celtes / Ecoutez les mamans / Kalamatiano / Petite solo du matin / La fille du marechal de france / Cine citta / Le cultiv ateur / Flambee Saint-Marcoise / Un froncas au kebak / Ad va que pour elle / Bransle bas le con bas / Tarondelle / Andromadere
XENO 4048CD / Mar '97 / Xenophile

☐ MUSAIQUE
GLCD 4017 / Apr '94 / Green Linnet

Adair, Tina

☐ JUST YOU WAIT AND SEE
Midst of the morning rain / Just me / Pray with Mama and Daddy / Another heartache / By the time it gets dark / Arrow / Crazy love / Nobody but me / When my time comes to go / These tears / How many roads / Some people's lives
SHCD 3868 / Mar '98 / Sugar Hill

Adam Ant

☐ ANTICS IN THE FORBIDDEN ZONE
Zerox / Whip in my valise / Car trouble / Kick / Kings of the wild frontier / Ant music / Dog eat dog / Los Rancheros / Killer in the home / Stand and deliver / Beat my guest / Prince Charming / Ant rap / Desperate but not serious / Place in the country / Friend or foe / Goody two shoes / Strip / Puss 'n' boots / Apollo 9 / Vive le rock
4687622 / Jun '91 / Columbia

☐ DIRK WEARS WHITE SOX (Adam & The Ants)
Car trouble / Nine plan failed / Catholic day / Idea / Never trust a man / Animals and men / Family of noise / Table talk / Day I met God
4805212 / Jul '95 / Columbia

☐ FRIEND OR FOE
Friend or foe / Something girls / Place in the country / Desperate but not serious / Here comes the grump / Hello I love you / Goody two shoes / Crackpot history and the right to lie / Made of money / Cajun twisters / Try this for sighs / Man called Marco
4844362 / Jul '96 / Columbia

☐ HITS
Kings of the wild frontier / Dog eat dog / Ant music / Stand and deliver / Prince Charming / Ant rap / Goody two shoes / Friend or foe / Desperate but not serious / Puss 'n' boots / Strip / Apollo 9 / Vive le rock
4500742 / 27 Jul '98 / Columbia

☐ KINGS OF THE WILD FRONTIER (Adam & The Ants)
Dog eat dog / Ant music / Feed me to the lions / Los rancheros / Ants invasion / Killer in the home / Kings of the wild frontier / Magnificent five / Don't be square / Jolly Roger / Making history / Human beings
4779022 / Oct '94 / Columbia

☐ PRINCE CHARMING (Adam & The Ants)
Prince Charming / Scorpios / Picasso visita el planeta de los Simios / Five guns west / That voodoo / Stand and deliver / Mile high club / Ant rap / Mowhok / SEX
4746062 / Mar '96 / Columbia

☐ STRIP
Baby let me scream at you / Libertine / Spanish games / Vanity / Puss 'n' boots / Playboy / Strip / Montreal / Naval to neck / Amazon
4872392 / Mar '97 / Columbia

☐ VIVE LE ROCK
Vive le rock / Miss thing / Razor keen / Rip down / Scorpio rising / Apollo 9 / Hell's eight acres / Mohair lockeroom pin-up boys / No zap / POE / Human bondage den
4785042 / Feb '95 / Columbia

Adam Bomb

☐ PURE SEX
WKFMCD 140 / Mar '90 / FM

Adam F

☐ COLOURS
Intro / Seventy three / Metropolis / Music in my mind / Jaxx / Mother earth / Trees know everything / Circles / Dirty Harry / F jam / Colours / Aromatherapy
8217252 / 27 Oct '97 / Positiva

Adamaki, Lila

☐ SONGS OF MY HOMELAND
ML 0199 / 11 May '98 / Musurgia Graeca

Adamo

☐ LES MEILLEURS
Vous permettez, monsieur / La nuit / Laissons dire / J'aime une fleur / Les files du bord de mer / Car je veux / Une larme aux nuages / Ma tete / Vivre / Amour perdu / Sans toi, ma mie / Le barbu sans barbe / Il n'est pas fou / Les mal aimes / Quand tu reviendras / Femme aux yeux d'amour
DCA 864502 / Nov '96 / Disky

Adamo, Salvatore

☐ LA VIE COMME ELLE PASSE
472359 / Jul '96 / Flarenasch

Adams, Bryan

☐ 18 'TIL I DIE
Only thing that looks good on me is you / Do to you / Let's make a night to remember / 18 'til I die / Star / (I wanna be your) Underwear / We're gonna win / I think about you / I'll always be right there / It ain't a party...if ya can't come round / Black pearl / You're still beautiful to me / Have you ever really loved a woman
5406752 / Feb '97 / A&M

☐ BRYAN ADAMS
Hidin' from love / Win some lose some / Wait and see / Give me your love / Wastin' time / Don't ya say it / Remember / State of mind / Try to see it my way
CDMID 100 / Oct '92 / A&M

☐ CUTS LIKE A KNIFE
Only one / Take me back / This time / Straight from the heart / Cuts like a knife / I'm ready / What's it gonna be / Don't leave me lonely / Best was yet to come
CDMID 102 / Oct '92 / A&M

☐ INTERVIEW DISC
SAM 7030 / Mar '97 / Sound & Media

☐ INTO THE FIRE
Heat of the night / Into the fire / Victim of love / Another day / Native son / Only the strong survive / Rebel / Remembrance day / Hearts on fire / Home again
CDMID 185 / '92 / A&M

☐ LIVE LIVE LIVE
She's only happy when she's dancin' / It's only love / Cuts like a knife / Kids wanna rock / Hearts on fire / Take me back / Best was yet to come / Heaven / Heat of the night / Run to you / One night love affair / Long gone / Summer of '69 / Somebody / Walkin' after midnight / I fought the law / Into the fire
3970942 / Aug '94 / A&M

☐ RECKLESS
One night love affair / She's only happy when she's dancin' / Run to you / Heaven / Somebody / Summer of '69 / Kids wanna rock / It's only love: *Adams, Bryan & Tina Turner* / Long gone / Ain't gonna cry
3950132 / 15 Sep '97 / A&M

☐ SO FAR SO GOOD (Collection Of The Best Of Bryan Adams)
5401572 / Nov '93 / A&M

☐ UNPLUGGED
Summer of '69 / Back to you / Cuts like a knife / I'm ready / Fits ya good / When you love someone / 18 'til I die / I think about you / If ya wanna be bad ya gotta be good / Let's make a night to remember / Only thing that looks good on me is you / Little love / Heaven / I'll always be right there
5408312 / 1 Dec '97 / A&M

☐ WAKING UP THE NEIGHBOURS
Is your mama gonna miss ya / Hey honey I'm packin' you in / Can't stop this thing we started / Thought I'd died and gone to heaven / Not guilty / Vanishing / House arrest / Do I have to say the words / There will never be another tonight / All I want is you / Depend on me / (Everything I do) I do it for you / If you wanna leave me (can I come too) / Touch the hand / Don't drop that bomb on me
3971642 / Oct '91 / A&M

☐ YOU WANT IT, YOU GOT IT
Lonely nights / One good reason / Don't look now / Coming home / Fits ya good / Tonight / Jealousy / You want it, you got it / Last chance / No one makes it right
CDMID 101 / Oct '92 / A&M

Adams, Cliff

☐ AT YOUR REQUEST
We'll gather lilacs / It had to be you / Barcarolle / Entertainer/Solace / Come rain or come shine / That old black magic / Bewitched, bothered and bewildered / Air on a G string / Dancing in the dark / Lonely Man theme / Ole buttermilk sky / Intermezzo from Cavalleria Rusticana / La vie en rose / Unforgettable/They didn't believe me / They can't take that away from me / Sophisticated lady / Adagio in G minor / Satin doll / East of the sun and west of the moon
CDMFP 6135 / Oct '94 / Music For Pleasure

☐ FORTIES ON PARADE, THE (Adams, Cliff Singers)
White cliffs of Dover / You'll never know / If I didn't care / I don't want to walk without you / When they sound the last all clear / I'll be with you in apple blossom time / Bless 'em all / It's a lovely day tomorrow / Hut sut song / Yes, my darling daughter / Don't sit under the apple tree / I'll never smile again / I don't want to set the world on fire / I'll walk alone / It's been a long, long time / Nightingale sang in Berkeley Square / We're gonna hang the washing out on the Siegfried line / This is the army Mr Jones / Ma I miss your apple pie / Kiss me goodnight Sergeant Major / I know why / At last / Elmer's tune / Tuxedo junction / Chattanooga choo choo / Little on the lonely side / Tangerine / Dolores / Who's taking you home tonight / If I should fall in love again / I yi yi yi yi I like you very much / Lili Marlene / Maybe / I'm gonna get lit up when the lights go on in London / You'd be so nice to come home to / You say the sweetest things baby / Yours / More I see you / Coming home / Roll out the barrel / Quarter master's store / Roll me over / Glorious victorious / She'll be coming round the mountain / Underneath the arches / Dreaming / Run rabbit run / London pride / Take me back to dear old blighty / Pack up your troubles (In your old kit bag) / It's a long way to Tipperary / Goodbye-ee / I'll get by / I'll be seeing you / We'll meet again
303600912 / Apr '97 / Carlton

☐ GOLDEN YEARS OF SONG, THE (Adams, Cliff Singers)
I hear you calling me / Drink to me only / Mighty like a rose / My old Kentucky home / Deep river / Sylvia / Will ye no come back again / Little yellow bird / Rosary / Can I forget you / Brown bird singing / Parted / Eriskay love lilt / Just a-wearyin' for you / Until / Old rustic bridge / Love's old sweet song / I'll take you home again, Kathleen / Kashmiri song / White wings / Lost chord / Good night ladies / Home sweet home
306252 / Jan '97 / Hallmark

☐ SING SOMETHING CHRISTMAS VOL.2 (Adams, Cliff Singers)
Let it snow, let it snow, let it snow / It's gonna be a cold, cold Christmas / Deck the halls with boughs of holly / Angels from the realms of glory / Amazing Grace / I saw three ships / Here we come a-wassailing / Morning has broken / Miner's dream of home / Do they know it's Christmas / Itty bitty baby / My ain folk / Mister Santa / When Santa got stuck up the chimney / Walking in the air / Christians awake / Sleigh ride / Sleep, baby, sleep / God rest ye merry gentlemen / Everything is beautiful / Lift a glass to friendship / It came upon a midnight clear / See amid the Winters snow / Happy Xmas (war is over) / Auld Lang Syne
CDMFP 6244 / Oct '96 / Music For Pleasure

☐ SING SOMETHING COUNTRY (Adams, Cliff Singers)
Hey won't you play another somebody done somebody wrong song / Sweet dreams / I fall to pieces / He'll have to go / Sing me an old fashioned song / Don't it make my brown eyes blue / Red River Valley / Your cheatin' heart / Gentle on my mind / Don't let the stars get in your eyes / You're the only good thing that's happened / Rose garden / Rhinestone cowboy / I'm just a country boy / Hey good lookin' / Heartaches by the number / Jambalaya / Little bitty tear / Lucille / You're my best friend / Tip of my fingers / Help me make it through the night / It ain't me babe / Crazy / I love you because / Moonlight and roses / Most beautiful girl in the world / Galveston / Tennessee waltz / I recall a gypsy woman / Blanket on the ground / Honey come back / Fallen start / Walk on by / All I have to do is dream / Welcome to my world / King of the road / Story of my life
PWKS 4188 / Feb '93 / Carlton

☐ SING SOMETHING SIMPLE - AS TIME GOES BY (Adams, Cliff Singers)
WMEM 00062 / 3 Nov '97 / BBC Worldwide

☐ SING SOMETHING SIMPLE - SAY IT WITH MUSIC (Adams, Cliff Singers)
WMEM 00082 / 3 Nov '97 / BBC Worldwide

☐ SING SOMETHING SIMPLE - THANKS FOR THE MEMORY (Adams, Cliff Singers)
WMEM 00052 / 3 Nov '97 / BBC Worldwide

☐ SING SOMETHING SIMPLE - TIME AFTER TIME (Adams, Cliff Singers)
WMEM 00072 / 3 Nov '97 / BBC Worldwide

☐ SING SOMETHING SIMPLE AT CHRISTMAS (Adams, Cliff Singers)
Sing something seasonal / Christmas alphabet / Winter wonderland / Have yourself a merry little Christmas / First Noel / Past three o'clock / Mary's boy child / Little donkey / When a child is born / Twelve days of Christmas / Little boy that Santa Claus forgot / I'm going home for Christmas / Jingle bells / Little drummer boy / Ding dong merrily on high / Good Christian men rejoice / Coventry carol / We wish you a merry Christmas / I saw Mommy kissing Santa Claus / All I want for Christmas (is my two front teeth) / Rudolph the red nosed reindeer / Do you hear what I hear / We three kings / While shepherds watched their flocks by night / Once in Royal David's City / Hark the herald angels sing / Good King Wenceslas / Santa Claus is coming to town / Rockin' around the Christmas tree / Wonderful Christmas time / Silent night / Mistletoe and wine / Saviour's day / Holly and the ivy / In the bleak midwinter / Away in a manger / O come all ye faithful (Adeste Fidelis) / Christmas song / White Christmas
CDPR 104 / Dec '94 / Premier/MFP

☐ SING SOMETHING SIMPLE FROM THE SHOWS (Adams, Cliff Singers)
PWKS 4148 / '95 / Carlton

☐ VERY BEST OF SING SOMETHING SIMPLE VOL.1 (Adams, Cliff Singers)
Sing something simple / Mame / One / Hello dolly / Give my regards to Broadway / Together / Let me call you sweetheart / Daisy bell / Three o'clock in the morning / After the ball / September song / It don't mean a thing if it ain't got that swing / Lookie lookie lookie here comes cookie / Chili bom bom / Let's all go to Mary's house / Five foot two / Your mother should know / Penny Lane / I want to hold your hand / All my loving / Green grow the rushes oh / Rainy days and Mondays / We've only just begun / I won't last a day without you / Top of the world / Moonlight and roses / I'll see you in my dreams / Down by the old mill stream / Row row row / Paddlin' Madelin' home / Bless this house / Broken doll / Shine on harvest moon / Show me the way to go home / California here I come / By the beautiful sea / You are the sunshine of my life / By the rivers of Babylon / Green green / Tie a yellow ribbon around the old oak tree / Love me tender / Return to sender / Good luck charm / Wooden heart / Updee / Old Macdonald had a farm / Little brown jug / What shall we do with the drunken sailor / There is a tavern in the town / Jesu joy of man's desiring / Cathy's clown / All I have to do is dream / Walk right back / Singing in the rain / Side by side / Way we were
PWKS 4187 / Mar '94 / Carlton

☐ VERY BEST OF SING SOMETHING SIMPLE VOL.2 (Adams, Cliff Singers)
I don't want to walk without you / Mandy / Down by the riverside / Marianne / Love is my reason / We'll gather lilacs / My truly, truly fair / Chicka boom / Liverpool lou / How do you do it / A little bit of heaven / Too-ra-loo-ra-loo-ral (that's an irish lullaby) / That's am irish lullaby / If you're irish come into the parlour / I want a girl just like the girl that married dear old dad / M.o.t.h.e.r. / Darling, je vous aime beaucoup / Under the bridges of paris / Chanson d'amour / Let the rest of the world go by / In the good old summertime / Beautiful dreamer / Camptown races / Poor old joe / My old dutch / One of the ruins that cromwell knocked about a bit / Down at the old bull and bush / Boiled beef and carrots / Over the rainbow / Can't smile without you / If I had a hammer / He's got the whole world in his hands / I can give you the starlight / Someday my heart will awake / Singing the blues / Feet up (pat him on the po-po) / My love is like a red, red rose / Little children / Ferry cross the mersey / It's a great day for the irish / My mother's eyes / Roses of picardy / Pigalle / Michelle / Always / Till we meet again / Little annie rooney / Old folks at home / Oh suzannah / Silver threads among the gold / Call round any old time / Any old iron / In the evening by the moonlight / You made me love you
PWKS 4189 / Mar '94 / Carlton

Adams, Clifford

☐ MASTER POWER
Darshan's love / I can't get started / Graceful feeling / ReRenatyah / Lord is always with them / With his grace / Walkin' / Elixer of life / Precious jewel / Master power
860152 / Jul '98 / Naxos Jazz

Adams, Dave

☐ DAVE ADAMS STORY, THE (The Joe Meek Collection)
Old red lion: *Kids* / Whoopee: *Joy & David* / My oh my: *Joy & David* / Rocking away the blues: *Joy & David* / If you pass me by: *Joy & David* / Let's go see gran'ma: *Joy & David* / Believe me: *Joy & David* / My very good friend the milkman: *Joy & David* / Doopey darling: *Joy & David* / Joe's been a-gittin' there: *Joy & David* / They tell us not to love: *Joy & David* / They tell us not to love: *Joy & David* / Chahawki: *Joy & David* / Diamond Joe: *Joy & David* / San Francisco: *Bailey, Burr & The Six Shooters* / Like a bird without feathers: *Bailey, Burr & The Six Shooters* / Chahawki: *Bailey, Burr* / You made me cry: *Bailey, Burr* / It feels funny it feels good: *Dooley, Silas Jr.* / You just can't do it on your own: *Dooley, Silas Jr.* / Clean clean clean: *Dooley, Silas Jr.* / Birds and the bees: *Dooley, Silas Jr.* / Don't put all your eggs in one basket: *Dooley, Silas Jr.* / Oh what a party: *Dooley, Silas Jr.* / Let me in: *Dooley, Silas Jr.* / They're all up to it: *Dooley, Silas Jr.* / Signs and posters: *Dooley, Silas Jr.* / Out behind the barn: *Dooley, Silas Jr.* / There's something at the bottom of the garden: *Dooley, Silas Jr.* / Bathroom: *Dooley, Silas Jr.* / Telstar: *Adams, Dave & The Outlaws*
GEMCD 013 / 27 Oct '97 / Diamond

Adams, Don

☐ GET SMART
Washington 4 Indians 3 / School days / Satan place / Cone of silence / Too many chiefs/Countersign / Latest devices / All in the mind / Incredible Harry Hoo / I'm only human / Kisses for kaos / Plane sequence / Too many chiefs/Hotel sequence / Weekend vampire / Sorry 'bout that / 99 / Max / Get smart
RVCD 61 / Dec '96 / Raven

Adams, Elliott

☐ THAT DEMON RAG
SOSCD 1299 / Jul '96 / Stomp Off

Adams, Gayle

☐ GAYLE ADAMS/LOVE FEVER
Your love is a life saver / Stretchin' out / For the love of my man / You brought it on yourself / I don't wanna hear it / Plain out of luck / Baby I need your loving / Don't blame it on me / You don't owe me nothing / Let's go all the way / Love fever / I can't get enough of you / Don't jump to conclusions / I loved every minute of it
DEEPM 027 / Apr '97 / Deep Beats

Adams, George

☐ CITY GATES (Adams, George & Don Pullen Quartet)
Mingus metamorphosis / Samba for now / Thank you very much Mr. Monk / Nobody knows the trouble I've seen / City gates
CDSJP 181 / Aug '91 / Timeless Jazz

☐ DECISIONS (Adams, George & Don Pullen Quartet)
Trees and grass and things / His eye is on the sparrow / Message urgent / Decisions / Triple over time / I could really for you
CDSJP 205 / Feb '91 / Timeless Jazz

☐ DON'T LOSE CONTROL (Adams, George & Don Pullen Quartet)
SNCD 1004 / Jan '87 / Soul Note

☐ EARTH BEAMS (Adams, George & Don Pullen Quartet)
Magnetic love / Dionysus / Saturday nite in the cosmos / More flowers / Sophisticated Alice
CDSJP 147 / Mar '90 / Timeless Jazz

☐ HAND TO HAND (Adams, George & Danny Richmond Quartet)
SNCD 1007 / Jun '86 / Soul Note

☐ LIVE AT MONTMARTRE (Adams, George & Don Pullen Quartet)
CDSJP 219 / Jan '88 / Timeless Jazz

☐ LIVE AT THE VILLAGE VANGUARD (Adams, George & Don Pullen Quartet)
Necessary blues / Solitude / Intentions / Diane
SNCD 1094 / May '85 / Soul Note

☐ SOUND SUGGESTIONS
5177552 / Jul '94 / ECM

Adams, John

☐ CHAIRMAN DANCES, THE
Chairman dances / Christian zeal and activity / Two fanfares for orchestra / Tromba lontana / Short ride in a fast machine / Common tones in simple time
7559791442 / Jan '95 / Nonesuch

☐ CHAMBER SYMPHONY/GRAND PIANOLA MUSIC
7559792192 / Jan '95 / Nonesuch

☐ **DEATH OF KLINGHOFFER, THE**
7559792812 / Jan '95 / Nonesuch

☐ **FEARFUL SYMMETRIES/THE WOUND DRESSER**
7559792182 / Jan '95 / Nonesuch

☐ **GNARLY BUTTONS/ALLEGED DANCES (Adams, John & The Kronos Quartet/The London Sinfonietta)**
7559794652 / 20 Apr '98 / Nonesuch

☐ **HARMONIELEHRE**
7559791152 / Dec '95 / Nonesuch

☐ **HARMONIUM**
Negative love (part one) / Because I could not stop for death - Wild nights (part 2) / Negative love / Because I could not stop for death / Wild nights / Why do I / Laughin' and clownin' / If I ever had a good time / Scarred knees / Your love is so doggone good / We don't see eye to eye / Roadblock / Teach me to forget
8214652 / Apr '87 / ECM

☐ **HOODOO ZEPHYR**
Hoodoo zephyr / Coast / Disappointment lake / Tourist song / Tundra / Bump / Cerulean / Hoodoo zephyr
7559793112 / Jan '95 / Nonesuch

☐ **NIXON IN CHINA (3CD Set)**
7559791772 / Jan '95 / Nonesuch

Adams, Johnny

☐ **AFTER DARK**
Lovers will / I don't know you / Fortune teller / Missing you / Do right woman, do right man / Give a broken heart a break / She said the same things to me / Garbage man / Dancing man / Snap your fingers
ROUCD 2049 / '88 / Rounder

☐ **BEST OF NEW ORLEANS RHYTHM & BLUES VOL.1**
MG 9007 / Feb '95 / Mardi Gras

☐ **FROM THE HEART**
I feel like breaking up somebody's home / Why do I / Laughin' and clownin' / If I ever had a good thing / Scarred knees / From the heart / Your love is so doggone good / We don't see eye to eye / Roadblock / Teach me to forget
ROUCD 2044 / '88 / Rounder

☐ **GOOD MORNING HEARTACHE**
ROUCD 2125 / Oct '93 / Rounder

☐ **ONE FOOT IN THE BLUES**
Won't pass me by / One foot in the blues / Baby don't you cry / Ill wind / Road block / Angel eyes / Half awoke / I wonder where our love has gone / Two years of torture / Cookin' in style / I know what I've got
ROUCD 2144 / Oct '96 / Rounder

☐ **ROOM WITH A VIEW OF THE BLUES**
Room with a view / I don't want to do wrong / Not trustworthy / Neither one of us / Body and fender man / I owe you / Wished I'd never loved you at all / Hunt is on / World I never made
ROUCD 2059 / '88 / Rounder

☐ **VERDICT, THE**
ROUCD 2135 / Feb '95 / Rounder

Adams, Oleta

☐ **CIRCLE OF ONE**
Rhythm of life / Get here / Circle of one / You've got to give me room / I've got to sing my song / I've got a right / Will we ever learn / Everything must change
8487402 / Aug '91 / Fontana

☐ **COME WALK WITH ME**
Holy is the lamb / I will love you / What price / Come and walk with me / If you're willing / This love won't fail / Wash o God our sons and daughters / Captain of my ship / Never far away / Beams of heaven
HRD 1601 / 6 Oct '97 / EMI

☐ **EVOLUTION**
5149652 / Jun '93 / Fontana

☐ **MOVING ON**
Never knew love / Once in a lifetime / I knew you when / You need to be loved / Slow motion / We will meet again / This is real / Life keeps moving on / Long distance love / Love begins at home / If this love should ever end / New star / Between hello and goodbye / Don't let the sun go down on me
5289902 / 15 Sep '97 / Fontana

Adams, Pepper

☐ **10 TO 4 AT THE 5-SPOT (Adams, Pepper Quintet)**
'Tis / You're my thrill / Long two-four / Hastings street bounce / Yourna
OJCCD 312 / Sep '93 / Original Jazz Classics

☐ **CONJURATION/FAT TUESDAY'S SESSION**
RSRCD 113 / Nov '94 / Reservoir

☐ **COOL SOUND OF PEPPER ADAMS, THE**
Bloos booze / Blues seein' red / Like...what's this / Skippy
SV 0198 / Oct '97 / Savoy Jazz

☐ **MASTER, THE**
Enchilada / Chelsea Bridge / Bossallegro / Rue Serpente / Lovers of their time / My shining hour
MCD 5213 / Sep '92 / Muse

☐ **OUT OF THIS WORLD**
FSRCD 137 / Dec '90 / Fresh Sound

☐ **PEPPER**
Twelfth and pingree / Child is born / Well you needn't / Bossa nouveau / Osage Autumn / My funny valentine
ENJ 90792 / Sep '96 / Enja

☐ **PEPPER ADAMS LIVE**
IHLCP 2003 / 8 Jun '98 / Rhino

☐ **STARDUST (The Bethlehem Blues) (Adams, Pepper & Donald Byrd)**
BET 6000 / Jan '95 / Bethlehem

Adams, Terry

☐ **TERRIBLE**
804732 / Aug '95 / New World

Adams, Tom

☐ **RIGHT HAND MAN**
Bluegrass breakdown / John Hardy / You are my sunshine / Fiddle and the banjo / I saw the light / Old rugged cross / Old Joe Clark / Fireball mail / Polk country breakdown / Little Maggie / Cumberland gap
ROUCD 0282 / '90 / Rounder

Adamson, Barry

☐ **AS ABOVE SO BELOW**
Can't get loose / What it means / Deja voodoo / Come hell or high water / Jazz devil / Still I rise / Girl / Monkey speaks his mind / Goddess of love / Jesus wept
CDSTUMM 161 / 1 Jun '98 / Mute

☐ **DELUSION (Original Soundtrack)**
IONIC 4CD / Aug '91 / The Fine Line

☐ **MOSS-SIDE STORY**
Ring's the thing / Real deep cool / Final Irony / For your ears only
CDSTUMM 53 / Feb '89 / Mute

☐ **NEGRO INSIDE ME**
Snowball effect / Dead heat / Busted / Cold black preach / Je t'aime...mon non plus / A perfectly natural union
CDSTUMM 120 / Jun '93 / Mute

☐ **OEDIPUS SCHMOEDIPUS**
CDSTUMM 134 / Jul '96 / Mute

☐ **SOUL MURDER**
Preface / Split / Violation of expectation / Suspicion / A gentle man of colour / Trance of hatred / Checkpoint charlie / Reverie / Un petit miracle / 007, a fantasy bond theme / Adamson family / Cool green world / On the edge of atonement / Epilogue
CDSTUMM 105 / Apr '92 / Mute

Adamson, Deirdre

☐ **COME SCOTTISH COUNTRY DANCING (Adamson, Deirdre Quartet)**
DACD 9614 / Oct '96 / Dee-Ay

☐ **PERFECT BLEN**
DACD 9817 / May '98 / Deeay Music

Adcock, Mike

☐ **LOST FOR WORDS (Adcock, Mike & Last Dance Orchestra)**
33WM 105 / Aug '97 / 33 Jazz

Add N To X

☐ **ON THE WIRES OF OUR NERVES**
We are Add N To X / Murmur one / Sound of accelerating concrete / Gentle Germans / Black regent / Planet Munich / Nevermind / King wasp / Orgy of bubastis / Green gun grey body / On the wires of our nerves / Hit me / Sir ape
STL 010CD / 16 Feb '98 / Satellite

☐ **VERO ELECTRONICS**
BLOWUP 4CD / 18 Aug '97 / Blow Up

Adderley, Cannonball

☐ **AFRICAN WALTZ**
African waltz / Barefoot Sunday blues / Kelly blue
OJCCD 258 / Sep '93 / Original Jazz Classics

☐ **BEBOP JAZZ CLASSICS**
BN 001 / Apr '98 / Blue Nite

☐ **CANNONBALL ADDERLEY COLLECTION VOL.3 (Jazz Workshop Revisited)**
Pimitiva / Jessica's day / Unit 7 / Jive samba / Marney / Mellow buno / Lillie
LCD 13032 / Jul '88 / Landmark

☐ **CANNONBALL ADDERLEY COLLECTION VOL.4 (The Poll Winners)**
Chant / Azule serape / Heart alone / Lolita / Au privave / Never will I marry
LCD 13042 / Apr '91 / Landmark

☐ **CANNONBALL ADDERLEY COLLECTION VOL.5 (At The Lighthouse)**
Sack o' woe / Azule serape / Our delight / Big P / Blue Daniel / Exodus / What is this thing called love
LCD 13052 / Apr '91 / Landmark

☐ **CANNONBALL ADDERLEY COLLECTION VOL.6 (Cannonball Takes Charge)**
If this isn't love / I guess I'll hang my tears out to dry / Serenata / I've told every little star / Barefoot Sunday blues / Poor butterfly / I remember you
LCD 13062 / Apr '91 / Landmark

☐ **CANNONBALL ADDERLEY COLLECTION VOL.7 (Cannonball In Europe)**
P Bouk / Gemini / Work song / Trouble in mind / Dizzy's business
LCD 13072 / Apr '91 / Landmark

☐ **CANNONBALL ADDERLEY IN CONCERT**
RTE 10042CD / Apr '95 / RTE/Europe 1

☐ **CANNONBALL ADDERLEY SAMPLER**
Work song / Brother John / Just one of those things / Sounds for Sid / Straight no chaser
OJCX 014 / Jan '98 / Original Jazz Classics

☐ **CANNONBALL AND COLTRANE (Adderley, Cannonball & John Coltrane)**
Limehouse blues / Stars fell on Alabama / Wabash / Grand Central / You're a weaver of dreams / Sleeper
8345882 / Jul '92 / Mercury

☐ **COUNTRY PREACHER**
This here / Jive samba / Miles away / Walk tall / Fiddler on the roof / Mellow buono / Country preacher / Mercy, mercy, mercy
CD 56053 / Mar '95 / Jazz Roots

☐ **DEEP GROOVE - BEST OF CANNONBALL ADDERLEY**
Walk tall / Shake a lady / Why am I treated so bad / Mercy mercy mercy / Do do do (what now is next) / I'm on my way / Games / Happy people / Up and at it / Aries / Taurus
CDP 8307252 / Sep '94 / Blue Note

☐ **DISCOVERIES**
With apologies to Oscar / Bohemia after dark / Chasm / Late entry / Little taste / Caribbean cutie / Spontaneous combustion
SV 0251 / Oct '97 / Savoy Jazz

☐ **DIZZY'S BUSINESS**
Autumn leaves / Dizzy's business / Primitivo / Jive samba / This here / Bohemia after dark / Never say yes / Peter and the goats / New delhi
MCD 47069 / Oct '93 / Milestone

☐ **IN NEW YORK (Adderley, Cannonball Quintet)**
Introduction / Gemini / Planet Earth / Dizzy's business / Syn-anthesia / Scotch and water / Cannon's theme
OJCCD 142 / Feb '92 / Original Jazz Classics

☐ **IN SAN FRANCISCO (Adderley, Cannonball Quintet)**
This here / Spontaneous combustion / Hi fly / You got it / Bohemia / After dark / Straight no chaser
OJCCD 352 / Feb '92 / Original Jazz Classics
OJC20 0352 / Sep '98 / Original Jazz Classics

☐ **INSIDE STRAIGHT (Adderley, Cannonball Quintet)**
Introduction / Inside straight / Saudade / Inner journey / Snakin' the grass / Five of a kind / Second son / End
OJCCD 750 / Oct '93 / Original Jazz Classics

☐ **JAZZ MASTERS**
5226512 / 5 May '98 / Verve

☐ **JAZZ MASTERS**
CDMFP 6305 / Mar '97 / Music For Pleasure

☐ **JULIAN 'CANNONBALL' ADDERLEY QUINTET (Adderley, Cannonball Quintet)**
COD 020 / Jun '92 / Jazz View

☐ **KNOW WHAT I MEAN**
Waltz for Debby / Goodbye / Who cares / Elsa / Venice toy / Nancy / Know what I mean
OJCCD 105 / Feb '92 / Original Jazz Classics
OJC20 1052 / Sep '98 / Original Jazz Classics

☐ **LIVE IN PARIS APRIL 1966**
087172 / Sep '95 / Ulysse

☐ **LUGANO 1963**
Jessica's birthday / Jive samba / Bohemia after dark / Dizzy's business / Trouble in mind / Work song / Unit seven
TCB 02032 / Sep '95 / TCB

☐ **MERCY, MERCY, MERCY**
Fun / Games / Mercy mercy mercy / Sticks / Hippodelphia / Sack o' woe
CDP 8299152 / Jul '95 / Capitol Jazz

☐ **NIPPON SOUL**
OJCCD 435 / Feb '92 / Original Jazz Classics

☐ **PARIS 1960 (Adderley, Cannonball Quintet)**
Intro / Jeannine / Dis here / Blue Daniel / Chant / Bohemia after dark / Work song
PACD 5303 / Aug '97 / Pablo

☐ **PORTRAIT OF CANNONBALL (Adderley, Cannonball Quintet)**
Minority / Minority (Take 2) / Minority (Take 3) / Straight life / Blue funk / Little taste / People will say we're in love / Nardis (take 5) / Nardis (take 4)
OJCCD 361 / Apr '93 / Original Jazz Classics

☐ **PRESENTING CANNONBALL ADDERLEY**
Spontaneous combustion / Still talkin' to ya / Little taste / Caribbean / Flamingo / With apologies to Oscar / Late entry / Bohemia after dark
SV 0108 / Oct '97 / Savoy Jazz
CY 78989 / Jun '98 / Savoy Jazz

☐ **PYRAMID**
Phases / My lady blue / Book ends / Pyramid / Suite cannon / Oh Bess where's my Bess
OJCCD 952 / 26 Jan '98 / Original Jazz Classics

☐ **QUINTET PLUS**
Arriving soon / Well you needn't / New delhl / Winetone / Star eyes / Lisa (take 8) / Lisa (take 3) / O.p.
OJCCD 306 / Feb '92 / Original Jazz Classics

☐ **SOMETHIN' ELSE (Adderley, Cannonball & Miles Davis)**
Autumn leaves / Love for sale / Something else / One for Daddy O / Dancing in the dark / Alison's uncle
CDP 7463382 / Mar '95 / Blue Note

☐ **SPONTANEOUS COMBUSTION**
Still talkin' to ya / Little taste / Caribbean cutie / Bohemia after dark / Chasm / Willow weep for me / Late entry / Spontaneous combustion / Flamingo / Hear me talkin' to ya / With apologies to Oscar / We'll be together again
VGCD 650104 / Oct '93 / Vogue

☐ **THINGS ARE GETTING BETTER (Adderley, Cannonball & Milt Jackson)**
OJCCD 322 / Feb '92 / Original Jazz Classics

Adderley, Nat

☐ **BLUE AUTUMN (Adderley, Nat Quintet)**
For Duke and Cannon / Fifth labour of Hercules / Book's bossa / Blue autumn / Tallahassee kid
ECD 220352 / Sep '92 / Evidence

☐ **GOOD COMPANY (Adderley, Nat Quintet)**
CHR 70009 / Jun '95 / Challenge

☐ **IN THE BAG (Adderley, Nat Sextet)**
In the bag, Sister Wilson / R.s.v.p. / Low brown / Mozart-in / New arrival / Chatterbox / Popeye / Gospel truth
OJCCD 648 / Nov '95 / Original Jazz Classics

☐ **LIVE AT THE 1994 FLOATING JAZZ FESTIVAL**
CRD 334 / Jun '96 / Chiaroscuro

☐ **MUCH BRASS (Adderley, Nat Sextet)**
OJCCD 848 / Nov '95 / Original Jazz Classics

☐ **ON THE MOVE (Adderley, Nat Quintet)**
Malandro / Boy with the sad eyes / To wisdom, the prize / Naturally / Scene / Come in out of the rain
ECD 220642 / Nov '93 / Evidence

☐ **TALKIN' ABOUT YOU (Adderley, Nat Quintet)**
Talkin' about you, Cannon / I can't give you anything but love / Arriving soon / Plum street / Azule serape / Ill wind / Mo's theme / Big P
LCD 15282 / May '91 / Landmark

Addict

☐ **STONES**
ABB 145CD / 4 May '98 / Big Cat

Addrisi Brothers

☐ **CHERRYSTONE**
DFCD 71254 / Apr '97 / Del-Fi

Addy, Obo

☐ **LET ME PLAY MY DRUMS (Addy, Obo & Kukrudu)**
BCA 00102 / Jul '96 / Burnside

☐ **RHYTHM OF WHICH..., THE**
42561 / Aug '96 / Earthbeat

☐ **TRADITIONAL MUSIC OF GHANA**
CDEB 2500 / May '93 / Earthbeat

Ade, King Sunny

☐ **LIVE JUJU**
RCD 10047 / Aug '91 / Rykodisc

☐ ODU
Jigi jigi isapa / Easy motion tourist / Alaji rasaki / Mo ri keke kan / Kiti kiti / Natuba / Aiye nreti eleya mi / Ibi won ri o / Kawa to bere / Eri okan (conscience) / Kini mba ro
7567927962 / 6 Jul '98 / Reprise

☐ OGUN
ALA 211 / 12 Jan '98 / Avid

Adelphi

☐ TRUTH TO BE TOLD
KSRCD 2 / 13 Oct '97 / Kingsize

Aden

☐ ADEN
FOR 42 / Jun '97 / Fortune 4

Adeva

☐ ALL THE HITS IN YA FACE
Respect / Musical freedom: *Adeva & Paul Simpson/ Carmen Marie* / Warning / I thank you / Beautiful love / Treat me right / Ring my bell: *Adeva & Monie Love* / It should've been me / Don't let it show on your face / I'm the one for you / Until you come back to me / Respect (Mix)
MOCD 3005 / Feb '95 / More Music

☐ ULTIMATE ADEVA
Respect / I thank you / Warning / Beautiful love / Musical freedom / I'm the one for you / It should've been me / Don't let it show on your face / Until you come back to me / You've got the best of my love / Ring my bell: *Adeva & Monie Love* / Treat me right / It should've been me / I thank you
CDGOLD 1035 / May '96 / EMI Gold

Adhesive

☐ SIDEBURNERS
ASR 8 / Jun '97 / Ampersand

☐ YOGURT
BROOL 009CD / Mar '96 / Adhesive

Adicts

☐ 27
Angel / Love sucks / Do it / That's happiness / Shangri-La / Football fairy story / Rossini / Breakdown / Give me more / Fuck it up / GIRL / What am I to do / Rockers in rags / Let's dance / 7.27 / Bog / Come out to play / Just wanna dance with you
CDPUNK 87 / Feb '97 / Anagram

☐ BEST OF THE ADICTS, THE
DOJOCD 263 / May '96 / Dojo

☐ COMPLETE ADICTS SINGLES COLLECTION, THE
This week / Easy way out / Straight jacket / Organised confusion / Viva la revolution / Steamroller / Numbers / Chinese takeaway / You'll never walk alone / Too young / Bad boy / Joker in the pack / Shake rattle bang your head / Tokyo / Old couple / ADX Medley / Falling in love / It's a laugh / Saturday night / Champ elysees / Sound of music / Who split my beer / Cowboy
CDPUNK 33 / Jun '94 / Anagram

☐ SONGS OF PRAISE
England / Hurt / Just like me / Tango / Telepathic people / Mary Whitehouse / Distortion / Get addicted / Viva la revolution / Calling calling / In the background / Dynasty / Peculiar music numbers / Sensitive / Songs of praise
CLEO 2481CD / Jan '94 / Cleopatra

☐ SOUND OF MUSIC
CLEO 3315CD / Jan '94 / Cleopatra

☐ SOUND OF MUSIC/SMART ALEX
How sad / 4321 / Chinese takeaway / Johnny was a soldier / Disco / Eyes in the back of your head / Joker in the pack / Lullaby / My baby got run over by a steamroller / Man's gotta do / Let's go / Easy way out / Shake rattle bang your head / Ode to joy / Smart Alex / Troubadour / Tokyo / California / Crazy / Bad boy / Jelly babies / Maybe maybe not / Rocking wrecker / Runaway / You're all fools
AHOYCD 088 / 11 May '98 / Captain Oi

☐ ULTIMATE ADICTION (The Best Of The Adicts)
CLP 9963 / Jul '97 / Cleopatra

☐ VERY BEST OF THE ADICTS, THE
Easy way out / Straight jacket / Viva la revolution / Steamroller / Songs of praise / England / Get addicted / Chinese takeaway / Joker in the pack / How sad / Let's go / Bad boy / Tokyo / Odd couple / Smart Alex / Troubadour / Runaway / Champ Elysees / Angel / Love sucks
CDPUNK 105 / 29 Jun '98 / Cherry Red

Adiemus

☐ ADIEMUS II - CANTATA MUNDI
Song of tears / Chorale 1 / Song of the spirit / Chorale 2 / Song of the trinity / Chorale 3 / Song of the odyssey / Chorale 4 / Song of the plains / Chorale 5 / Song of invocation / Chorale 6 / Song of Aeolus / Chorale 7 / Elegia / Song of tears
CDVEX 932 / 10 Nov '97 / Virgin

Aditi

☐ ENTER THE UNEXPECTED
DC 881932 / Oct '97 / Disky

Adjusters

☐ POLITICS OF STYLE, THE
JUMP 014 / 15 Sep '97 / Jump Up

Adkins, Hasil

☐ WHAT THE HELL WAS I THINKING
Your memories / Ugly woman / No shoes / You're gonna miss me / Beautiful hills / Stay with me / Somehow you'll find your way / Gone gone gone / Up on mars / Talkin' to my lord
03142 / 30 Mar '98 / Fat Possum

Adkins, Trace

☐ BIG TIME
Big time / Took her to the moon / Rest of mine / Snowball in El Paso / See Jane run / Twenty four seven / Hold you now / Nothin' but tailights / Lonely won't leave me alone / Out of my dreams / Wayfaring stranger
8558562 / 10 Aug '98 / EMI

Adler, Larry

☐ BEST OF LARRY ADLER, THE
SWNCD 004 / Oct '95 / Sound Waves

☐ BEST OF LARRY ADLER, THE
Genevieve waltz / Love themes and blues / Caravan / Stormy weather / I've got my love to keep me warm / Slumming on Park Avenue / Night and day / Tiger rag / It ain't necessarily so / Continental (you kiss while you're dancing) / Smoke gets in your eyes / I've got you under my skin / St. Louis blues / Shadow blues / Romance for harmonica and orchestra / Why was s I born / Pam-Poo day / Body and soul / Malaguena / Theme on four notes / Weeping willows (I'm stepping thro' plate glass windows) / Rhapsody in blue
CDMFP 6259 / Sep '96 / Music For Pleasure

☐ GOLDEN ERA OF LARRY ADLER VOL.1
Continental / Smoke gets in your eyes / I won't dance / Why was I born / They all laughed / Caravan / Rhapsody in blue / Stormy weather / I've got my love to keep me warm/Slumming on Park Avenue / I've got you under my skin / Night and day / Tiger rag / Body and soul / Love come back to me / My melancholy baby / I got rhythm
CDSGP 0119 / Aug '94 / Prestige

☐ GOLDEN ERA OF LARRY ADLER VOL.2
How high the moon / Blues in the night / Girl friend / Love for sale / My funny valentine / Le grisbi / This can't be love / Summertime / There's a boat dat's leaving for New York / Sophisticated lady / Little girl blue / Genevieve / Begin the beguine
CDSGP 0120 / Oct '94 / Prestige

☐ GREAT LARRY ADLER
PASTCD 7081 / Feb '96 / Flapper

☐ HARMONICA GENIUS
Stormy weather / Caravan / I've got you under my skin / They all laughed / Why was I born / You hit the spot / Creole love call / Sophisticated lady / September in the rain / Moon at sea / Hometown / Isn't this a lovely day / Top hat / Smoke gets in your eyes / I won't dance / Lovely to look at / Continental / My melancholy babe / They can't take that away from me / With plenty of money and you / Body and soul / Love me forever / South American Joe / Night and day / Tiger rag / Goody goody
307952 / 15 Sep '97 / Hallmark

☐ MOUTH ORGAN VIRTUOSO, THE
I won't dance / Foggy day / Smoke gets in your eyes / Genevieve waltz / I got rhythm / Bolero / It ain't necessarily so / Continental / Londonderry air / Bach goes to town / Rifiti / My melancholy baby / Someone to watch over me / Hora staccato / They all laughed / They can't take that away from me / Le grisbi / Lover come back to me / La mer / Ritual fire dance / Bess you is my woman now / Tiger rag / Rhapsody in blue / Gershwin - King of rhythm
CDEMS 1543 / Nov '94 / EMI

☐ PIANO ROLL RECORDINGS, THE
Our love is here to stay / My funny valentine / How high the moon / Begin the beguine / I can't get started / Rhapsody in blue / Minuet from L'Arlesienne / Blues in the night / As time goes by / Little girl blue / Mountain greenery / When day is done / Summertime / Man I love / It ain't necessarily so / I got rhythm / Tea for two
CDSGP 0143 / Mar '95 / Prestige

☐ RHAPSODY IN BLUE
Continental / Smoke gets in your eyes / Sophisticated lady / Night and day / Tiger rag / Rhapsody in blue / Caravan / September in the rain / Moon at sea / Home town / Creole love call / Isn't this a lovely day (to be caught in the rain) / Rubenstein's melody in F / Love me forever / Solitude / They all laughed / I've got you under my skin / I know now / Whispers in the dark / It looks like rain in Cherry Blossom Lane / Hungarian dance / They can't take that away from me / With plenty of money and you / Why was I born / Stormy weather / I won't dance
RAJCD 835 / 6 Oct '97 / Empress

☐ SUMMERTIME (The Best Of Larry Adler)
PLSCD 131 / Apr '96 / Pulse

Admiral Tibet

☐ EXCITEMENT
Call upon Jah Jah / Burn in flames / Set me free / Keep the fire burning / Not a fool for you / Want to talk / Never overcome / Excitement / Since you've been gone / Rude boys
117502 / Aug '95 / Musidisc UK
VPCD 1432 / Sep '95 / VP

☐ REALITY TIME
VYDCD 5 / Sep '95 / Vine Yard

☐ THINGS THAT YOU DO
SPCD 0128 / 17 Nov '97 / Superpower

☐ TIME IS GOING TO COME, THE
RNCD 2031 / Dec '93 / Rhino

☐ WEEPING AND MOURNING
794022 / Jul '97 / Melodie

Adolescents

☐ ADOLESCENTS, THE
I hate children / Who is who / Wreckin' crew / LA girl / Self destruct / Kids of the black hole / No way / Amoeba / Word attack / Rip it up / Democracy / No friends / Creatures
01022 / May '97 / Epitaph

☐ RETURN TO BLACK HOLE
512252 / 5 Jan '98 / Amsterdamned

Adorable

☐ AGAINST PERFECTION
Glorious / Favourite fallen idol / A to fade in / I know you too well / Homeboy / Sistine chapel ceiling / Cut / Crash sight / Still life / Breathless
CRECD 138 / Mar '93 / Creation

☐ FAKE
Feed me / Vendetta / Man in a suitcase / Submarine / Lettergo / Kangaroo court / Radio days / Go easy on her / Road movie / Have you seen the light
CRECD 165 / Sep '94 / Creation

Adorjan, Andras

☐ LAS FLAUTAS DE BUENOS AIRES (Adorjan, Andras & Jorge De La Vega)
Sur / Canaro en Paris / Cuando tu no estas / Jalousie / Fuimos / Palomita blanca / El choclo / El dia que me quieras / Taquito militar / Los mareados / A fuego lento
74321428122 / Jul '97 / Milan

Adrenalin Kick

☐ MASSACRE THE MAINSTREAM
NM 028 / 18 May '98 / Neat Metal

Adulescents UK

☐ SOCIETY OWES ME A LIVING
Society owes me a living / No no / Jelly machete / Witch of insanity / No war no more / Deathwish
REPCD 001 / Oct '94 / Rage

Advent

☐ ADVENT PRESENTS KOMBINATION PHUNK (Mixed By Advent) (Various Artists)
Porno actress: *Dopplereffekt* / Quexos: *RAC* / Metaphysica: *DJ K1* / Elektra fix: *Advent* / Plastiphilia: *Dopplereffekt* / C on: *Advent* / Waveterm: *Wild, Damon* / Believer: *JB3* / Scorn: *Surgeon* / Flower child: *Morgan*
ADVENT 1 / 17 Nov '97 / Metalbox
74321532742 / 24 Nov '97 / Metalbox

☐ ELEMENTZ OF LIFE
There's no danger / Where in heaven / Audio illusion / Spaceism / Mad dog / It one jah / Overseyah / Bad boy / Farencounters / Electric jazz / Heights / Rhythm / Anno domini / Call God / Lie / City limits
TRUCD 8 / Sep '96 / Internal

☐ SHADED ELEMENTZ
Bad boy / It one jah / Mad dog / It one jah / Overseyah / It one yah / Overseyah / Mad dog
TRCDR 8 / Sep '96 / Internal

Adventures

☐ SEA OF LOVE, THE
Drowning in the sea of love / Broken land / You don't have to cry / Trip to bountiful / Heaven knows which way / Hold me now / Sound of Summer / When your heart was young / One step from heaven
9607722 / Apr '88 / Elektra

Adventures In Stereo

☐ ADVENTURES IN STEREO
BENT 015 / Mar '97 / Creeping Bent

☐ ALTERNATIVE STEREO SOUNDS
Silence falls / Down in the traffic / Dominique K / I once knew / When you're gone / Everything / Out of sight / Brand new day / Here together / Said you said / Hang out / This time / Dream surf baby / O sister / I see / Catch my soul / Long you live / Silence is
BENT 030CD / 4 May '98 / Creeping Bent

Adverse, Anthony

☐ SPIN
Paradise lost / Best friend / Wednesday's child / Cold winds / Centre of your world / Good girl / Night and day / No sweet surrender / Wastelands of your soul / Spin
ACME 22CD / Sep '89 / El

Adverts

☐ CAST OF THOUSANDS
Cast of thousands / Adverts / My place / Male assault / Television's over / Fate of criminals / Love songs / I surrender / I looked at the sun / I will walk you home / Television's over / Back from the dead / New church / Cast of thousands
CDPUNK 102 / 9 Feb '98 / Anagram

☐ CROSSING THE RED SEA WITH THE ADVERTS
One chord wonders / Bored teenagers / New church / On the roof / New boys / Bombsite boys / No time to be 21 / Safety in numbers / Drowning men / On wheels / Great British mistake / Gary Gilmore's eyes / We who wait / New day dawning
ESMCD 451 / Mar '97 / Essential

☐ LIVE AT THE ROXY
Safety in numbers / New boys / One chord wonders / On the roof / New day dawning / Great british mistake / Bombsite boys / No time to be 21 / Quick step / We who wait / New church / Bored teenagers / Gary gilmore's eyes
RRCD 136 / Jul '93 / Receiver

☐ PUNK SINGLES COLLECTION, THE
One chord wonders / Quick step / Gary Gilmore's eyes / Bored teenagers / Safety in numbers / We who wait / No time to be 21 / New day dawning / Television's over / Back from the dead / My place / New church / Cast of thousands / I will walk you home
CDPUNK 95 / May '97 / Anagram

☐ RADIO SESSIONS
One chord wonders / Bored teenagers / Gary Gilmore's eyes / New boys / Quickstep / We who wait / New church / Safety in numbers / Great British mistake / Fate of criminals / Television's over / Love songs / Back from the dead / I surrender / Adverts / I looked at the sun / Cast of thousands / I will walk you home
PILOT 003 / Jun '97 / Burning Airlines

ADZ

☐ PIPER AT THE GATES OF DAWN
TX 70001CD / 8 Dec '97 / Triple XXX

☐ TRANSMISSIONS FROM PLANET SPEEDBALL
TX 70014CD / 8 Jun '98 / Triple XXX

Adzido

☐ AKWAABA
EUCD 1263 / Mar '94 / ARC

☐ SIYE GOLI (Adzido Pan African Dance Ensemble)
EUCD 1223 / Sep '93 / ARC

☐ UNDER AFRICAN SKIES
EUCD 1127 / '91 / ARC

Aerial-M

☐ AERIAL-M
Dazed and awake / Aass / Wedding song no.2 / Rachmaninoff / Skrag theme / Compassion for M / Always farewell
WIGCD 037 / 29 Sep '97 / Domino

Aerosmith

☐ AEROSMITH
Make it / Somebody / Dream on / One way street / Mama Kin / Write me a letter / Movin' out / Walking the dog
4749622 / May '97 / Columbia

☐ BIG ONES
Walk on water / Love in an elevator / Rag doll / What it takes / Dude (looks like a lady) / Janie's got a gun / Cryin' / Amazing / Blind man / Deuces are wild / Other side / Crazy / Eat the rich / Angel / Livin' on the edge / Dude (looks like a lady) (live)
GED 24546 / Oct '94 / Geffen

☐ BOX OF FIRE (13CD Set)
4778032 / May '97 / Columbia

☐ CLASSICS LIVE VOL.2
Back in the saddle / Walk this way / Movin' out / Draw the line / Same old song and dance / Last child / Let the music do the talking / Toys in the attic
4749722 / Nov '93 / Columbia

☐ DONE WITH MIRRORS
Let the music do the talking / My fist, your face / Shame on you / Reason a dog / She La / Gypsy boots / She's on fire / Hop / Darkness
GFLD 19052 / 2 Feb '98 / Geffen

☐ DRAW THE LINE
Draw the line / I wanna know why / Critical mass / Get it up / Bright light fright / Kings and Queens / Hand that feeds / Sight for sore eyes / Milk cow blues
4749662 / May '97 / Columbia

☐ GEMS
Rats in the cellar / Lick and a promise / Chip away the stone / No surprize / Mama kin / Adam's apple / Nobody's fault / Round and round / Critical mass / Lord of the Thighs / Jailbait / Train kept a rollin'
4912362 / 11 May '98 / Columbia

☐ GET A GRIP
Intro / Eat the rich / Get a grip / Fever / Livin' on the edge / Flesh / Walk on down / Shut up and dance / Cryin' / Gotta love it / Crazy / Line up / Can't stop messin' / Amazing / Boogie man
GED 24444 / Apr '93 / Geffen

☐ GET YOUR WINGS
Same old song and dance / Lord of the thighs / Woman of the world / Train kept a rollin' / Spaced / SOS (too bad) / Seasons of wither / Pandora's box
4749632 / May '97 / Columbia

☐ GREATEST HITS
Dream on / Same old song and dance / Sweet emotion / Walk this way / Remember (walkin' in the sand) / Back in the saddle / Draw the line / Kings and Queens / Come together / Last child / Mama Kin / Lightning strikes / Chip away the stone / Sweet emotion / One way street / Big ten inch record / Seasons of wither
4873502 / May '97 / Columbia

☐ LIVE BOOTLEG
Back in the saddle / Sweet emotion / Lord of the thighs / Toys in the attic / Last child / Come together / Walk this way / Sick as a dog / Dream on / Mama kin / SOS / Train kept a rollin' / Sight for sore eyes / Chip away the stone / I ain't got you / Mother popcorn
4749672 / May '97 / Columbia

☐ NIGHT IN THE RUTS
No surprize / Chiquita / Remember (walkin' in the sand) / Cheese cake / Three mile smile / Reefer head woman / Bone to bone (Coney Island white fish boy) / Mia / Think about it
4749682 / May '97 / Columbia

☐ NINE LIVES
Nine lives / Falling in love (is hard on the knees) / Hole in my soul / Taste of India / Full circle / Something's gotta give / Ain't that a bitch / Farm / Crash / Kiss your past good-bye / Pink / Falling off / Attitude adjustment / Fallen angels
4850206 / Mar '97 / Columbia

☐ PANDORA'S BOX
When I needed you / Make it / Movin' out / One way street / On the road again / Mama kin / Same old song and dance / Train kept a rollin' / Seasons of wither / Write me a letter / Dream on / Pandora's box / Rattlesnake shake / Walking the dog / Lord of the Thighs / Toys in the attic / Round and round / Krawhitham / You see me crying/Sweet emotion / No more no more / Walk this way / I wanna know why / Big ten inch record / Rats in the cellar / Last child / All your love / Soul saver / Nobody's fault / Lick and a promise / Adam's apple / Draw the line / Critical mass / Kings and Queens / Milkcow blues / I live in Connecticut / Three mile smile / Let it slide / Cheese cake / Bone to bone (Coney Island white fish boy) / No surprize / Come together / Downtown Charlie / Sharpshooter / Shithouse shuffle / South station blues / Riff and roll / Jailbait / Major Barbara / Chip away the stone / Helter skelter / Back in the saddle
4692932 / Dec '91 / Columbia

☐ PANDORA'S TOYS
Sweet emotion / Draw the line / Walk this way / Dream on / Train kept a rollin' / Mama Kin / Seasons of wither / Big ten inch record / All your love / Helter skelter / Chip away the stone / Rattlesnake shake
4769562 / Jun '94 / Columbia

☐ PERMANENT VACATION
Hearts done time / Magic touch / Rag doll / Simoriah / Dude (looks like a lady) / St. John / Hangman jury / Girl keeps comin' apart / Angel / Permanent vacation / I'm down / Movie
GFLD 19254 / May '94 / Geffen

☐ PUMP
Young lust / FINE / Love in an elevator / Monkey on my back / Janie's got a gun / Other side / My girl / Don't get mad get even / Voodoo medicine man / What it takes
GFLD 19255 / May '94 / Geffen

☐ ROCK IN A HARD PLACE
Jailbait / Bitches brew / Cry me a river / Jig is up / Push comes to shove / Lightning strikes / Bolivian ragamuffin / Prelude to Joanie / Joanie's butterfly / Rock in a hard place
4749702 / May '97 / Columbia

☐ ROCKS
Back in the saddle / Last child / Rats in the cellar / Combination / Sick as a dog / Nobody's fault / Get the lead out / Lick and a promise / Home tonight
4749652 / May '97 / Columbia

☐ TELLTALES (Interview Disc)
TELL 12 / Jun '97 / Network

☐ TOYS IN THE ATTIC
Toys in the attic / Uncle Salty / Adam's apple / Walk this way / Big ten inch record / Sweet emotion / No more no more / Round and round / You see me crying
4749642 / May '97 / Columbia

☐ TOYS IN THE ATTIC/DRAW THE LINE/ ROCKS (3CD Set)
Toys in the attic / Uncle salty / Adam's apple / Walk this way / Big ten inch record / Sweet emotion / No more no more / Round and round / You see me crying / Draw the line / I wanna know why / Critical mass / Get it up / Bright light fright / Kings and Queens / Hand that feeds / Sight for sore eyes / Milk cow blues / Back in the saddle / Last child / Rats in the cellar / Combination / Sick as a dog / Nobody's fault / Get the lead out / Lick and a promise / Home tonight
4853122 / 3 Nov '97 / Columbia

Affif, Ron

☐ 52ND STREET (Affif, Ron Trio)
Bohemia after dark / Stompin' at the Savoy / Moonray / Nightingale sang in Berkeley Square / I'll be seeing you / Yardbird suite / You don't know what love is / Steeplechase / Tadd's delight / Eric's zinc bar blues
23109582 / Nov '96 / Pablo

☐ RINGSIDE
If I were a bell / Don't make me pull that tongue out / Love walked in / Farewell / Uncle Joe / I should care / Alone together
CD 2310962 / Nov '97 / Pablo

Affinity

☐ THIS IS OUR LUNCH
CD 940 / Apr '97 / Music & Arts

☐ TRIBUTE TO ERIC DOLPHY, A
CD 939 / Oct '96 / Music & Arts

☐ TRIBUTE TO ORNETTE COLEMAN, A
CD 938 / Oct '96 / Music & Arts

Afflicted

☐ DAWN OF GLORY
MASSCD 055 / Mar '95 / Massacre

☐ PRODIGAL SUN
NB 063CD / Nov '92 / Nuclear Blast

Afghan Whigs

☐ BLACK LOVE
CDSTUMM 143 / Mar '96 / Mute

☐ GENTLEMEN
BFFP 90CD / Oct '93 / Blast First

Afi

☐ ANSWER TO THAT AND SAY
158112 / May '97 / Nitro

☐ SHUT YOUR MOUTH AND OPEN YOUR EYES
158152 / 8 Dec '97 / Nitro

☐ VERY PROUD OF YA
158052 / Oct '96 / Nitro

Africa System Dance

☐ AFRICA SYSTEM DANCE VOL.2
CD 77172 / Jan '97 / Eddy Black/ Sonodisc

African Children's Choir

☐ ARMS AROUND THE WORLD
It takes the whole village / Arms around the world / John 3:16 / Not too far from here / Abataka / Spread his love / Lord be magnified / Piletek / Take up your cross / Wanabino / Because he lives / I live
ALD 078 / Oct '96 / Alliance Music

☐ WALKING IN THE LIGHT
Walking in the light / Man of the Lord / Be bold, be strong / Ndyahimbisa / Jubulant Africa / Awesome God / Generation song / Steal away / Seed to sow / Nimoljwe kana / Mpulia Ebiwobe (cries of the Lord) / From a distance / We are the world
ALD 030 / Jun '95 / Alliance Music

African Dream

☐ AFRICAN DREAM, THE
EBCD 30 / Jan '95 / Eightball

African Headcharge

☐ AKWAABA
Can't waste time / Yes I / Glory dawn / To fari hail / More peace / Power from Zion / World peace / Cheer up / Walking thrill / All of the love / Irie day / Live good / Child's play
JAZIDCD 129 / Nov '95 / Acid Jazz

☐ DRASTIC SEASON
ONUCD 0027 / 2 Mar '98 / On-U Sound

☐ ENVIRONMENTAL STUDIES
ONUCD 18619 / 29 Sep '97 / On-U Sound

☐ GREAT VINTAGE VOL.1
ONUCD 2 / Jul '89 / On-U Sound

☐ GREAT VINTAGE VOL.2
ONUCD 3 / Sep '89 / On-U Sound

☐ IN PURSUIT OF SHASAMANE LAND
ONUCD 25 / Nov '93 / On-U Sound

☐ NOAH HOUSE OF DREAD (Noah House Of Dread)
BONJO 3CD / 6 Oct '97 / Bonjo I

☐ OFF THE BEATEN TRACK
ONUCD 40 / 6 Jul '98 / On-U Sound

☐ SONGS OF PRAISE
ONUCD 12 / '92 / On-U Sound

African Jazz Pioneers

☐ AFRICAN JAZZ PIONEERS
Nonto sangoma / Yeka yeka / Hellfire / Hosh / Mzabalazo (hometown) / Ten ten special / Riverside special / Mbombela
CDN 1005 / 27 Apr '98 / Camden

Africando

☐ GOMBO SALSA
SV 9604 / Jan '97 / Syllart

Afro Blue Band

☐ IMPRESSIONS
MCD 92372 / Feb '96 / Milestone

Afro Celt Sound System

☐ VOL.1 (Sound Magic)
Saor/Free / News from nowhere / Whirl y reel 1 / Inion/Daughter / Sure as not / Sure as knot (Jungle segue) / Nil cead againn dul abhaile/We cannot go home / Dark moon, high tide (Including farewell to Eireann) / Whirl y reel 2 / House of the ancestors / Eistigh liomas sealand/Listen to me / Soar reprise
CDRW 61 / Jul '96 / Realworld

Afro Cuba

☐ ECLECTICISM
JHCD 039 / Mar '95 / Ronnie Scott's Jazz House

After 7

☐ AFTER 7
Don't cha think / In the heat of the moment / Can't stop / My only woman / Love's been so nice / One night / Ready or not / Sayonara
CDVUS 7 / Sep '89 / Virgin

☐ REFLECTIONS
Till you do me right / Cryin' for it / Save it up / Damn thing called love / How did he love you / What U R 2 me / How do you tell the one / Sprung on it / How could you leave / Givin' up this good thing / I like it like that / Honey (oh how I need you)
CDVUS 88 / Jul '95 / Virgin

☐ VERY BEST OF AFTER 7, THE
Sara smile / Ready or not / Can't stop / Heat of the moment / One night / Baby I'm for real (natural high) / Not enough hours in the night / Can he love u like this / Takin' my time / Gonna love you right / Nights like this / 'Til you do me right
CDVUS 121 / Mar '97 / Virgin

After Dinner

☐ AFTER DINNER
After dinner / Sepia-ture / Accelerating etude / Soknya doll / Shovel and little lady / Cymbals at dawn / Glass tube / Dessert / Sepia-ture II / Walnut / Cymbals at dawn II / RE / Kitchen life / Glass tube II / Variation of Would you like some mushrooms / Ironclad mermaid / After dinner II / Room of hair-mobile
RERADCD / Apr '91 / ReR/ Recommended

☐ PARADISE OF REPLICA
RECDEC 28 / Oct '95 / Rec Rec

After Hours

☐ HUNG UP AND DRY
CMCD 067 / Dec '97 / Celtic Music

☐ UP TO HERE
CMCD 069 / Mar '94 / Celtic Music

After Hours

☐ TAKE OFF
Love attack / Better late than never / Stay by my side / Take off / Game / Another lonely night / Paint it black / Without you
WKFMXD 89 / Aug '88 / FM

After Tea

☐ AFTER TEA
REP 4236 / Aug '91 / Repertoire

Afterlife

☐ JUST TRIP
VIRUS 192CD / Jun '97 / Alternative Tentacles

Afternoons

☐ HOMAGE
CBM 008CD / Jan '94 / Cross Border Media

Agathodaimon

☐ BLACKEN THE ANGEL
Tristeta vehementa / Banner of blasphemy / Near dark / Of an imaginary guilt / Die nacht des unwesens / Contemplation song / Sfintit cu roua suferintii / Stingher/Alone / After dark / Ribbons/Requiem
NB 2982 / 6 Jul '98 / Nuclear Blast

Age

☐ ISOLATION
EFA 044252 / 9 Mar '98 / Force Inc.

☐ ORION YEARS
EFA 006532 / Jul '94 / Force Inc.

Agent

☐ AGENT
ESM 009 / 2 Mar '98 / Escape

☐ EVIDENCE
ESM 024 / 2 Mar '98 / Escape

Agent 99

☐ LITTLE PIECES 1993-1995
Get a grip / Walk / Words / Little pieces / You already know / Kingston on my mind / Murder for rent / Elektra / Little rude ridinghood / Biggest boy / River Cobain / Murder for rent / Happy / Back to the underground / Look at you know / Alzheimers ska / Little rude ridinghood / Theme / Sweet dreams
SHANCD 5731 / Jun '98 / Shanachie

Agent Orange

☐ INDESTRUCTIBLE
REVXD 220 / Feb '98 / Revolver

☐ REAL LIVE SOUND
725292 / Feb '95 / Restless

☐ THIS IS THE VOICE
725402 / Feb '95 / Restless

☐ VIRTUALLY INDESTRUCTIBLE
245T4 / Jan '97 / Gunka Disc

☐ WHEN YOU LEAST EXPECT IT
722182 / Feb '95 / Restless

Agent Provocateur

☐ WHERE THE WILD THINGS ARE
Where the wild things are / Red tape / Spinning / Agent Dan / Kicks / Sabotage / Elvis economics / Sandpit / Hercules / You're no good / Dumb / Red tape / Agent Dan / Sabotage / Dumb
AGENTP 1CD / Mar '97 / Wall Of Sound/ Epic

Agent Steel

☐ UNSTOPPABLE FORCE
Unstoppable force / Never surrender / Indestructive / Chosen to stay / Still searching / Rager / Day at guyana / Nothing left / Traveller
CDMFN 66 / Aug '89 / Music For Nations

Agerskov, Flemming

☐ TAKUAN (Agerskov, Flemming & Jakob Davidsen/Lars Juul)
MECCACD 2032 / Oct '97 / Music Mecca

Agincourt

☐ FLY AWAY
HBG 123/6 / Jun '97 / Background

Agnew, David

☐ CELTIC MOODS (Agnew, David & David Downes)
Mo ghile mear / Katie / Lift the wings / Move on / Into the mist / Death of Richard-In-Irons / Riverdance / Celtic dawn / Winter's end / Airwaves / Bright blue rose / My Lagan love / In this heart / Still haven't found what I'm looking for / My Rathfarnham darlin's
KCD 405 / Jan '97 / Celtic Collections

Agnostic Front

☐ CAUSE FOR ALARM
Eliminator / Existance of hate / Time will come / Growing concern / Your mistake / Out for blood / Toxic shock / Bomber zee / Public assistance / Shoot his load
CDJUST 3 / May '86 / Rough Justice

☐ RAW UNLEASHED
GTA 002R051 / Jul '95 / Grand Theft Auto

☐ SOMETHING'S GOTTA GIVE
Something's gotta give / Believe / Gotta go / Before my eyes / No fear / Blinded / Voices / Do or die / My war / Bloodsucker / Blame / Today tomorrow forever / Rage / Pauly the dog / Crucified
65362 / 26 May '98 / Epitaph

Agony Column

☐ BRAVE WORDS AND BLOODY KNUCKLES
341422 / Oct '95 / No Bull

Agoraphobic Nosebleed

☐ HONKY REDUCTION
Black ink on black paper / Polished turd / Filthy murder shack / Withering of skin / Empowerment / House of feasting / Die and get the fuck out of my way / Insipid conversations / Vexed / Circus mutt / Lives ruined through sex / Clawhammer and an ether rag / NYC always reminds me / Her despair reeks of alcohol / Chump slap / Burned away in sleep / Grief is not quantifiable / Cloved in twain / Torn apart by dingos / Pagan territories / Hat full of shit / McWorld / How Sean threw his back out sneezing / Bones in one bag / Acute awareness / Two shits to the moon
RR 69812 / 13 Apr '98 / Relapse

Agothocles

☐ BLACK CLOUDS DETERMINATE
CYBERCD 10 / Aug '94 / Cyber

☐ THEATRICAL SYMBOLIZATION
CYBERCD 2 / Jun '92 / Cyber

Agression

☐ DON'T BE MISTAKEN
BYO 003CD / Jan '97 / Better Youth
Organisation

Agressor

☐ SATAN'S SODOMY
BMCD 36 / Jun '94 / Black Mark

☐ SYMPOSIUM OF REBIRTH
BMCD 55 / Oct '94 / Black Mark

☐ TOWARDS BEYOND
Intro / Forteress / Positronic showering / Antediluvian / Epileptic aura / Hyaloid / Crypt / Future past/Eldest things / Turkish march
BMCD 23 / Sep '92 / Black Mark

Agudo, Luis

☐ DONA FIA
123442 / Apr '93 / Red

Aguilera, Paco

☐ GUITARRA AND CANTO FLAMENCO
KAR 983 / Sep '96 / IMP

Agyeman, Eric

☐ HIGH LIFE SAFARI
STCD 3002 / Nov '92 / Stern's

Ah Club

☐ KISS THE SKY GOODBYE
SHR 76CD / Feb '97 / Shrimper

Ahbez, Eden

☐ EDEN'S ISLAND
712112 / Sep '97 / Del-Fi

Ahlam

☐ LES RIAM
BARBARITY 012 / Jan '97 / Barbarity

Ahmed, Mahmoud

☐ ERE MELA MELA
CRAW 9 / Feb '96 / Crammed Discs

☐ LIVE IN PARIS
3026712 / 5 Jan '98 / Arcade

Ain Soph

☐ KSHATRIYA
EEE 21 / Aug '94 / Musica Maxima
Magnetica

Ainsworth, Alyn

☐ MOTOWN PARTY (30 Blockbuster Hits)
Standing in the shadows of love / It's the same old song / Reach out, I'll be there / Walk away Renee / Supremes medley / Ain't no mountain high enough / I'm still waiting / Sir Duke / Superstition / Living for the city / I'm gonna make you love me / Signed, sealed, delivered (I'm yours) / With you I'm born again / Dancing in the street / What becomes of the broken hearted / I hear a symphony / My cherie amour / Stop in the name of love / Baby love / Where did our love go / You can't hurry love / Still water (love) / You are the sunshine of my life / Yester-me, yester-you, yesterday / I was made to love her / I just called to say I love you / Reach out and touch / Tears of a clown
CDSIV 1127 / Jul '95 / Horatio Nelson

Ain't

☐ SLAP THE JUDGE
SEMAPHORE 36162 / Nov '96 / Subway

Aints

☐ ASCENSION
It's still nowhere / What's it like out there / Good soundtrack / Like an oil spill / Both worlds / Ascension
HOT 1035CD / May '97 / Hot

☐ AUTOCANNIBALISM
You can't please everybody / Other side of the creek / Linda and Abilene / Ill wind / Red aces / Aints go pop camping
HOT 1037CD / May '97 / Hot

☐ MOST PRIMITIVE BAND IN THE WORLD, THE (Live From The Twilight Zone, Brisbane 1974)
Wild about you / Do the robot / One way street / Knock on wood / Lies / Misunderstood / Messin' with the kid / Stranded
HOT 1053CD / May '97 / Hot

☐ SHELF LIFE UNLIMITED - HOTTER THAN BLAZING PISTOLS
Like an oil spill / Ill wind / River deep, mountain high / It's still nowhere / Erotic neurotic / Aints go pop dancing / What's it like out there / Linda and Abilene
HOT 1054CD / Aug '95 / Hot

Aion

☐ MIDIAN
MASSCD 131 / 28 Jul '97 / Massacre

Air

☐ AIR TIME
NCD 12 / Jun '97 / Nessa

Air

☐ MOON SAFARI
La femme d'argent / Sexy boy / All I need / Kelly watch the stars / Talisman / Remember / You make it easy / Ce matin la / New star in the sky / Le voyage de Penelope
CDV 2848 / 19 Jan '98 / Source

Air Command Band Canadian Forces

☐ SILENT SKY
John Gay suite / Gordon Lightfoot medley / Far and Away / Copland portrait / Wind beneath my wings / Music for a tattoo / White cliffs of Dover / Airman's prayer / RCAF march past
BNA 5100 / Jul '95 / Bandleader

Air Liquide

☐ AIR LIQUIDE
8597082 / 10 Nov '97 / Harvest

☐ AIR LIQUIDE LIVE
RSNCD 37 / Jul '95 / Rising High

☐ SONIC WEATHER MACHINE
RSNCD 38 / Jun '96 / Rising High

Air Miami

☐ ME ME ME
GAD 5011CD / 6 Jul '98 / 4AD

Air Supply

☐ MAKING LOVE (The Best Of Air Supply)
Lost in love / Even the nights are better / One that you love / Every woman in the world / Two less lonely people in the world / Chances / Making love out of nothing at all / All out of love / Here I am / Sweet dreams / Keeping the love alive / Now and forever
260757 / May '90 / Arista

Airbomb

☐ LOOKOUT
RCD 016 / 20 Jul '98 / Retch

Airdash

☐ BOTH ENDS OF THE PATH
BMCD 14 / '92 / Black Mark

Airstream

☐ RICKY TICK
Bright lights / Stay with me / I'll dream of you / Airstream / Follow through / Statue Queen / Fortuna / Jessica / My eyes / Brush your hair
TPLP 36CD / Mar '93 / One Little Indian

Aisha

☐ DAUGHTERS OF ZION
NG 538CD / May '93 / Twinkle

☐ RAISE YOUR VOICE
NGCD 551 / Jul '96 / Twinkle

☐ TRUE ROOTS
ARICD 084 / Mar '94 / Ariwa Sounds

Aislers Set

☐ TERRIBLE THINGS HAPPEN
SL 55CD / 22 Jun '98 / Slumberland

Ait

☐ MODERN BERBER SONGS
AAA 145 / Apr '97 / Club Du Disque Arabe

Aitken, Laurel

☐ GODFATHER OF SKA
GAZCD 009 / Apr '95 / Gaz's Rockin' Records

☐ LONG HOT SUMMER (Aitken, Laurel & The Skatalites)
PHZCD 59 / Nov '93 / Unicorn

☐ RINGO THE GRINGO
PHZCD 50 / Jun '93 / Unicorn

☐ RISE AND FALL/IT'S TOO LATE
PHZCD 71 / Jun '93 / Unicorn

☐ ROCKSTEADY PARTY
Rocksteady party / That was then / Do the jerk / Burnin' fire / Pancho / Bluebeat suit / Things that I do / Dial m for murder / Re-burial / Car chase / Got to go / He man versus
CDBM 115 / 28 Nov '97 / Blue Moon

☐ STORY SO FAR, THE
GROCD 008 / 10 Nov '97 / Grover

☐ WOPPI KING - REGGAE VOL.1
TRRCD 02 / Jul '97 / Trybute

AK1200

☐ FULLY AUTOMATIC (Various Artists)
78568800822 / 14 Apr '98 / Moonshine

Akabu

☐ WARRIOR QUEEN
ONUCD 71 / Oct '95 / On-U Sound

Akademia

☐ ANCIENT ECHOES
09026680552 / May '95 / RCA Victor

Akagi, Kei

☐ MIRROR PUZZLE
AQ 1028 / Apr '95 / Audioquest

Akasha

☐ CINEMATIQUE
Akasha theme / Soft and melting / Crazy baby / Sweet child of mine / Spanish fly / Maximun karma / Mescalin / Brown sugar / Cold fusion / Blues / Jazzadelica reprise
WALLCD 016 / 27 Apr '98 / Wall Of Sound

Akchote, Noel

☐ LUST CORNER
9100192 / Feb '98 / Winter & Winter

Akendague, Pierre

☐ MALADALITE
669762 / Jul '96 / Melodie

Akers, Karen

☐ JUST IMAGINE
Night, make my day / Nightingale sang in Berkeley Square / Remind me / Just imagine/You're nearer / Ain't misbehavin' / I'd rather be blue / More than you know / Angels, punks and raging queen / Twentieth century blues / I see the world through your eyes / My ship / I am your child / Two for the road
DRGCD 5231 / Sep '94 / DRG

☐ LIVE FROM THE RAINBOW AND STARS
DRGCD 91450 / Sep '97 / DRG

☐ UNCHAINED MELODIES
If I sing / Sooner or later / Blame it on the summer night / I fall in love too easily / I never know when to say when / I waltz alone / How sad no one waltzes anymore / Picture in the hall / Life story / Unchained melody / Bewitched, bothered and bewildered / L'Annee ou Piccoli / Isn't it a pity / Every time we say goodbye / Here I'll stay / Falling in love again / What'll I do / Dream a little dream of me
CDSL 5214 / Mar '92 / DRG

Akhbari, Djalal

☐ ART OF THE PERSIAN SANTUR
ARN 60351 / Sep '96 / Arion

Akhenation

☐ DIVINE SYMPHONIES
CDAR 030 / Jan '96 / Adipocre

Akipa, Bryan

☐ FLUTE PLAYER, THE
14941 / Jun '97 / Spalax

Akita, Masami

☐ PROSPERITY OF VICE, THE MISFORTUNE OF VIRTUE
IRE 2022 / Mar '97 / Ire

Akiyoshi, Toshiko

☐ AKIYOSHI/MARIANO QUARTET (Akiyoshi, Toshiko & Charlie Mariano Quartet)
CCD 9012 / Jun '88 / Candid

☐ INTERLUDE
Interlude / I know who loves you / Blue and sentimental / I ain't gonna ask no more / Pagliacci / Solitude / So in love / You stepped out of a dream
CCD 4324 / Sep '87 / Concord Jazz

☐ LIVE AT MAYBECK RECITAL HALL VOL.36
Village / Come Sunday / Con alma / Polka dots and moonbeams / It was a very good year / Things we did last summer / Old devil moon / Sophisticated lady / Quadrille, anyone / Tempous fugit
CCD 4635 / Feb '95 / Concord Jazz

☐ REMEMBERING BUD
ECD 220342 / Sep '92 / Evidence

☐ TOSHIKO MARIANO QUARTET (Akiyoshi, Toshiko & Charlie Mariano Quartet)
When you meet her / Little T / Toshiko's elegy / Deep river / Long yellow road
CCD 79012 / Feb '97 / Candid

Akkerman, Jan

☐ 1000 CLOWNS ON A RAINY DAY (2CD Set)
PM 97002 / Oct '97 / Patio

☐ CAN'T STAND THE NOISE
Pietons / Everything must change / Back to the factory / Journey (a real elegant gypsy) / Heavy treasure / Just because / Crackers / Burger blues / Prima donna / Sketches of pleasure
INAK 11001CD / Jul '97 / In Akustik

☐ COMPLETE GUITARIST, THE
Old tennis shoes / Come closer / Funkology / It could happen to you / Pietons / Journey (a real elegant gypsy)
CDCHARLY 17 / Jun '86 / Charly

☐ FOCUS IN TIME
PM 96500 / 16 Feb '98 / Patio

☐ KIEL/STUTTGART LIVE (Akkerman, Jan & Joachim Kuhn)
Santa Barbara / Santa Barbara
INAK 868CD / Jul '97 / In Akustik

☐ LIVE
CDP 1034DD / Jun '97 / Pseudonym

☐ PUCCINI'S CAFE
Burger's eyes / Your eyes in the whisky / Spanish roads / Key to the highway / It comes and goes / Albatross / Blue train / Love is uneven / Puccini's cafe
INAK 9027 / May '95 / In Akustik

Akotcha

☐ SOUNDBURGER
PORK 047 / 8 Sep '97 / Pork

Al Junayd, Hamud

☐ TRADITIONAL YEMENI SONGS
NI 5481 / Apr '96 / Nimbus

Al-Andalus

☐ ILLUMINATION
CD 374162 / Nov '97 / Koch World

Al-Dhil, Nuba Rasd

☐ AL-ALA
W 260029 / Feb '96 / Inedit

Al-Rais, Haj Abdelkrim

☐ AL-ALA ANTHOLOGY VOL.8 (7CD Set) (Al-Rais, Haj Abdelkrim & Al Brihi Orchestra)
W 260031 / Sep '97 / Inedit

Alabama

☐ DANCING ON THE BOULEVARD
Dancin' shaggin' on the boulevard / Sad lookin' moon / Anytime / She's got that look in her eyes / My girl / Of course I'm alright / I just couldn't say no / Is the magic still there / Calling all angels / One more time around
07863674262 / Apr '97 / RCA

Alabama 3

☐ EXILE ON COLDHARBOUR LANE
ELM 40CDL
ELM 40CD / 17 Nov '97 / Elemental

Alabama Thunder Pussy

☐ RISE AGAIN
MR 102 / 22 Jun '98 / Man's Ruin

Alady

☐ EL REY DEL MUSIC HALL ESPANOL
BMCD 7607 / 1 Jun '98 / Blue Moon

Alagna, Roberto

☐ SERENADES
CDC 5564262 / 20 Oct '97 / EMI Classics

Alaitz Eta Maider

☐ ALAITZ ETA MAIDER
KD 468CD / Dec '97 / Elkar

Alameda, Joel

☐ CUBA - THE TROVA (Alameda, Joel Trio)
Aquella tarde / Canto por mi montuna / Amorosa guajira / Olvido / Longina / La tarde / El arbol / Veinte anos
NI 5565 / 1 Jul '98 / Nimbus

Alanski, Jay H.
☐ HONEY ON A RAZOR BLADE
592204 / Oct '93 / FNAC

Alarm
☐ BEST OF THE ALARM & MIKE PETERS, THE (Alarm & Mike Peters)
68 Guns / Spirit of '76 / Down the road / Rain in the summertime / Strength / Breathe / Sold me down the river / New South Wales / 21st Century / Stand / Where were you hiding when the storm broke / Majority / Deceiver / Blaze of glory / Walk forever by my side / One step closer to home / No better than this / Presence of love / Absolute reality / Rescue me (tearing the bonds assunder)
4937512 / 13 Apr '98 / EMI

Alaska
☐ HEART OF THE STORM
Whiteout / Don't say it's over / Voice on the radio / Susie blue / Heart of the storm / Need your love / Can't let go / Other side of midnight / Headlines / Sorcerer
CLACD 423 / Nov '96 / Castle

Alastis
☐ AND DEATH SMILED
CDAR 029 / May '95 / Adipocre

☐ REVENGE
CM 77223CD / 20 Jul '98 / Century Media

Alba, Haydee
☐ L'EPOQUE TANGO
PS 65198 / May '98 / PlayaSound

Albanatchie
☐ NATIVE
CDLDL 1242 / Aug '96 / Lochshore

Albania
☐ LIFE AFTER DEATH IS ON THE PHONE
So OK / Albania (are you all mine) / Addicts of the first night / Take it away / French farewell / Cold light of day / Great Zambesi / Kaytie King / Men in a million / Deathwatch / Word is out / Today and tomorrow / I told you so / Little baby / Could this be love / Go go go
CDWIKD 157 / Nov '96 / Chiswick

Albany, Joe
☐ BIRD LIVES
STCD 4164 / Feb '90 / Storyville

Albatross
☐ C'EST LA VIE LIVE IN FRANCE
BSCD 4714 / '92 / Blue Shadow

Albert, Christine
☐ UNDERNEATH THE LONE STAR SKY
DOS 7014 / Sep '95 / Dos

Albertbridge Accordian Band
☐ ONWARD TO THE FIELD
COCD 7002 / Aug '96 / Outlet

AlbertoY Los Trios Paranoias
☐ RADIO SWEAT
OVER 56CD / Feb '97 / Overground

☐ SNUFF ROCK: THE BEST OF THE ALBERTOS
Old trust / Brrrr / I'll come if you let me / Invocation of the fundamental Orifice of St. Agnes / No change / Peon in the neck / Happy to be on (an island away from) Demis Roussos / Teenager in schtuck / Italians from outer space / Ballad of Colonel Callen / Fistful of spaghetti / Mandrax sunset variations, part VI / Neville / Breakfast / Whole food love / Holiday frog / Teenage promise / Willie Baxter's blues / It never rains in El Paso / Whispering grass / Death of rock and roll / Heads down no nonsense mindless boogie / Jesus wept / Kill / Gobbing on life / Snuffin' like that / Snuffin' in a Babylon / Twenty three / Dead meat / Juan Lopez / Anadin / Pavlov / Anarchy in the UK
MAUCD 604 / 21 Nov '94 / Mau Mau

Alberto, Jose
☐ DE PUEBLO Y CON CLASE
Hacerte feliz / Eso parte del alma / Juego de amor / Hace falta tiempo / Pesando Todo El Dia En Ti / Te repetiste / El temor me hizo perderte / Baila que baila
RMD 81394 / 24 Mar '98 / RMM

☐ ON TIME
Fotos y recuerdos / Quien como tu / Estas a tiempo / Como ellas son / A la hora que me llamen voy / Como fue / Con sandra en la cama / Celia / Cuestion
66058093 / Feb '96 / RMM

Albesteanu, Ion
☐ DISTRICTS OF YESTERYEAR (Romania)
926612 / Feb '97 / BUDA

Albion Band
☐ 1990
Yellow dress / Power and the glory / Fairford breakdown / Fossie shuffle / Ramble away / Flood / Nameless kind of hell / Adam and Eve / Lock up your daughters / Party's over
TSCD 457 / Aug '90 / Topic

☐ ACOUSTICITY
HTDCD 13 / Oct '93 / HTD

☐ ALBION HEART
HTDCD 30 / 9 Mar '98 / HTD

☐ ALONG THE PILGRIMS WAY
CRESTCD 028 / 19 Jan '98 / Mooncrest

☐ BATTLE OF THE FIELD
BGOCD 354 / Apr '97 / Beat Goes On

☐ BBC SESSIONS, THE
New St.George / Harvest home/Gas almost works / I'll go and list for a soldier / Hanged I shall be / An estampie / Hopping down in Kent / Horses brawl / Old sir Simon the king / Holm's fancy/Cuckolds all awry / Poor old horse / Postman's knock / Bouree / Time to ring some changes / Rainbow over the hill / Down the road / Albion sunrise/Uncle Bernard's/ Badcup tune/Jenny Lind
SFRSCD 050 / 26 Jan '98 / Strange Fruit

☐ BEST OF THE ALBION BAND 1993-1997, THE
Love is an abandoned car / Reels / Man of war / Devil in me / Rainbow over the hill / Dancer to the drum / Ivory tower / Forester's medley / Willow / Along the pilgrim's way / Albion heart / Head-smashed-in / Front porch game / We lie / White water running / Circle round the sun / Oak / Bedtime at Bryn Rhodyn / 36 miles
HTDCD 74 / Jul '97 / HTD

☐ CAPTURED (The Albions Who Nearly Got Away)
Ball, anchor and chain / Yellow dress / Horseshoe hornpipe/Chasing the jack / Party's over / Adam and Eve / Nameless kind of hell / Fossie shuffle / Go north / Chapel keithack/House in the county / Up the crooked spire / Set their mouths to twisting / Hanging tree / Fireman's song
HTDCD 19 / Apr '94 / HTD

☐ DEMI-PARADISE
HTDCD 54 / Mar '96 / HTD

☐ HAPPY ACCIDENT
Wings / Midsummer night dreams / Daeth is just a dream / Sun is a god / Heart of coal / Half each / Landslide / Chromosome or two / Wooden O / I'm going away love / Coming home to me / Ken's hornpipes / Pear tree
HTDCD 82 / 30 Mar '98 / HTD

☐ I GOT NEW SHOES
SPINCD 132 / Dec '97 / Spindrift

☐ LARK RISE TO CANDLEFORD (A Country Tapestry)
Girl I left behind me / Lemady/arise and pick a posy / All of a row / Tommytoes / John Dory / Witch Elder / Abroad for pleasure / Day thou gavest Lord is ended / Battle of the Somme / Grand circle dance / Speed the plough / Snow falls / Cart music / Holly and the ivy / Postman's knock / Hunt music / Scarlet and the blue / Dare to be a Daniel / Jacob's well
CDSCD 4020 / Aug '92 / Charisma

☐ LIVE AT THE CAMBRIDGE FOLK FESTIVAL
Boycott's bouree / Y'acre of land / La sexte extampie royale / Postman's knock/Black joker / Merry Sherwood rangers / Gentleman's agreement/Busy / Gardener/Falling star / Harvest anthem / Shipwreck / Orion's belt / Rose and the rock / Gresford disaster
CAFECD 002 / 27 Jul '98 / Strange Fruit

☐ RISE UP LIKE THE SUN
Ragged heroes / Poor old horse / Afro blues/Danse Royale / Ampleforth/Lay me low / Time to ring some changes / House in the country / Primrose / Gresford disaster / Postman's knock / Pain and paradise / Lay me low / Rainbow over the hill
CDEMS 1460 / Aug '92 / EMI

☐ SONGS FROM THE SHOWS
Here we come a wassailing / While shepherds watched / Rudolph blues / Run rudolph run / Broom dance / In the cross of Christ / Tramp on the street / Lamb of God / Sweet theme run softly / Poor old horse / Swan upping song / Lemady/Arise and pick a posy / Foxy comes to town / Dominion of the sword / When the fighting is over / Rumour hill / Bells of paradise / Snow falls / Ket to the north / Life on the river / Sheep shearing song / Building of our bridge / Twickenham ferry / Letters / Horse music / Burning the clavie / Speed the plough / All in the morning / Judas / Jesus and shall it ever be / Poor old man / Wastelands of England / Big yellow taxi/New Jerusalem / Wayfaring stranger / Dragonfly / Haxey hood game/estample / 15 Louisiana
RGFDCD 006 / May '97 / Road Goes On Forever

☐ SONGS FROM THE SHOWS VOL.1
RGFCD 006 / Feb '91 / Road Goes On Forever

☐ SONGS FROM THE SHOWS VOL.2
RGFCD 007 / Feb '91 / Road Goes On Forever

☐ STELLA MARIS
SPINCD 130 / Oct '94 / Spindrift

☐ UNDER THE ROSE
SPINCD 110 / Aug '96 / Spindrift

☐ WILD SIDE OF TOWN, THE
CMCD 042 / Dec '97 / Celtic Music

Albion Ensemble
☐ MISSISSIPPI FIVE
Mississippi five / Spring moonlight and flowers over the river / Partita for wind quartet / Quintet for wind instruments Op43 (1922) FS 100
PROUCD 142 / May '96 / Proudsound

Albion Jazz Band
☐ ONE FOR THE GUV'NOR
SOSCD 1206 / Oct '92 / Stomp Off

☐ THEY'RE ALL NICE TUNES
SOSCD 1249 / May '93 / Stomp Off

Albita
☐ NO SE PARECE A NADA
Que manera de quererte / No se parece a nada / Que culpa tengo yo / La esperanza / Bolero para nostalgiar / Solo porque vivo / Para que me beses tu / Quien le prohibe / Un solo beso / Mi guaguanco
4809432 / Oct '95 / Epic

Alboth
☐ AMOR FATI
PAN 020 / 20 Apr '98 / Pandemonium

Albrigtsen, Steinar
☐ BOUND TO WANDER
I just wanna fall in love / Now and then / Strawberry creek / Beginning of the end / Bound to wander / That sudden stop / Cruise control / Brown eyed girl / Standing by the waterfall / Say when / Street of blue rain / Bad luck blues / Old flame burns / I can't get close to you / Habit of my heart / Still one broken heart / Close call
RTMCD 52 / Jan '94 / Round Tower

Alcapone, Dennis
☐ FOREVER VERSION
Nanny version / Run run / Riddle I this / Baby version / Sunday version / Version I can feel / Forever version / Baby why version / Dancing version / Midnight version / Sweet talking version / Version you to the ball
CD 3505 / Nov '91 / Heartbeat

☐ GOOD OLD DAYS OF THE 70'S, THE (Alcapone, Dennis & Jah Lloyd)
EAPCD 01 / 27 Jul '98 / Teams

☐ PEACE AND LOVE
RB 3014 / Apr '95 / Reggae Best

☐ SOUL TO SOUL (DJ's Choice) (Various Artists)
DJ's choice: *Alcapone, Dennis* / Funky tang: *Alcapone, Dennis* / Picture on the wall: *Alcapone, Dennis* / Cry tough: *Anderson, Lizzy & Dennis Alcapone* / Jungle skank: *Natural Youth* / Tricks of the trade (I see your face): *Anderson, Lizzy* / Wake up Jamaica: *Alcapone, Dennis* / Love is a treasure: *Anderson, Lizzy* / Ba ba ri ba skank: *Anderson, Lizzy & Dennis Alcapone* / Right song: *Anderson, Lizzy & Dennis Alcapone* / Engine no.9: *Alcapone, Dennis* / Wedding song: *Alcapone, Dennis* / Rock to the beat: *Alcapone, Dennis* / Love is not a gamble: *Alcapone, Dennis* / Super boss: *U-Roy* / Teach the children: *Alcapone, Dennis* / Do it right: *U-Roy* / True true: *U-Roy* / Great woggie: *Alcapone, Dennis* / Judgement day: *Alcapone, Dennis & Hopeton Lewis*
CDTRL 356 / Jul '95 / Trojan

☐ UNIVERSAL ROCKERS
RASCD 3221 / Nov '92 / Ras

☐ WAKE UP JAMAICA
RNCD 2118 / Sep '95 / Rhino

Alcatraz
☐ DC IN THE MIX
SUB 20D / Sep '96 / Subversive

Alcatrazz
☐ BEST OF ALCATRAZZ, THE
Island in the sun / General hospital / Hiroshima mon amour / All night long / Since you've been gone / Night games / Stripper / Painted love / Sons and lovers / God blessed video / Mercy / It's my life / Dangerous games / Undercover / No imagination
CRIDE 1 / 15 Jun '98 / Dream Catcher
RMED 01012CD / 8 Jun '98 / Renaissance

☐ LIVE SENTENCE
Too young to die, too drunk to live / Hiroshima mon amour / Night games / Island in the sun / Kree nakoorie / Coming bach / Since you've been gone / Evil eye / All night long
CDMFN 134 / Jun '92 / Music For Nations

☐ NO PAROLE FROM ROCK'N'ROLL
Island in the sun / General hospital / Jet to jet / Hiroshima mon amour / Kree nakoorie / Incubus / Too young to die, too drunk to live / Big foot / Starcarr lane / Suffer me
CDMFN 133 / Jul '92 / Music For Nations

Alchemy
☐ CELTIC PANPIPES
Ride on / Spinning wheel / Love thee dearest / Spancil Hill / She moved thru' the fair / Flight of the earls / My Lagan love / Steal away / Mountains of Mourne / Sally gardens / Ag criost an siol / Carrickfergus / Derry air / Lonesome boatman / Mise Eire
KCD 415 / Jan '97 / Celtic Collections

Alchemysts
☐ OVER AND OUT
CAM 009CD / 9 Feb '98 / Camera Obscura

Alcione
☐ GAROTO MAROTO
ML 51020 / 14 Apr '98 / Musica Latina

Alcoholics Unanimous
☐ DR. KEGGER MD
TEAR 009CD / Jan '96 / Tear It Up

Alcorn, Alvin
☐ GAY PARIS STOMPER
AMCD 65 / Aug '94 / American Music

☐ SOUNDS OF NEW ORLEANS VOL.5
STCD 6012 / Jul '96 / Storyville

Alden, Howard
☐ 13 STRINGS (Alden, Howard & George Van Eps)
Just you, just me / My ideal / I hadn't anyone till you / Beautiful friendship / Touch of your lips / Ain't misbehavin' / Too marvellous for words / Love walked in / Queerology / How long has this been going on / Mine / Embraceable you / Emaline
CCD 4464 / Jun '91 / Concord Jazz

☐ CONCORD JAZZ GUITAR COLLECTIVE, THE (Alden, Howard/ Jimmy Bruno/Frank Vignola)
Bittersweet / Strictly confidential / String thing / Mating call / Seven come eleven / Body and soul / Donna Lee / Perdido / Swing 39 / Four brothers / Song d'autumne / Ornithology
CCD 4672 / Dec '95 / Concord Jazz

☐ ENCORE (Alden, Howard & Ken Peplowski)
It all depends on you / Palo alto / Since we met / I hear a rhapsody / Dolphin / Wabash / Fading star / With every breath I take / You
CCD 4654 / Jul '95 / Concord Jazz

☐ HAND CRAFTED SWING (Alden, Howard & George Van Eps)
Stompin' at the savoy / What's new / It's wonderful / Lap piano / I could write a book / Tenderly / Can't we be friends / Ll'l darlin' / Just in time / Forty-eight / Nearness of you (take 3) / I've got a crush on you / All the things you are / Moonglow
CCD 4513 / Jul '92 / Concord Jazz

☐ JAZZ CONCORD/FULL CIRCLE (2CD Set) (Alden, Howard & Jimmy Bruno/ Herb Ellis/Joe Pass)
Benedetto blues / I'm glad there is you / Something latin for Patterson / Polkadots and moonbeams / Terrie's tune / Always / Jaguar / Manoir de mes reves / Crushed pepper / I can't give you anything but love / Sixty four bars on wilshire / Look for the silver lining / Shadow of your smile / Good news blues / Honeysuckle rose / Happiness is the Concord Jazz Festival / Stuffy / Georgia on my mind / Love for sale / Bad news blues
CCD 247882 / 6 Apr '98 / Concord Jazz

☐ MISTERIOSO (Alden, Howard Trio)
Song of the dove / Misterioso / Everything but you / Waltz for Julie / This can't be love / Reflections in D
CCD 4487 / Nov '91 / Concord Jazz

☐ NO AMPS ALLOWED (Alden, Howard & Jack Lesberg)
CRD 303 / Mar '96 / Chiaroscuro

☐ SEVEN AND SEVEN (Alden, Howard & George Van Eps)
Surrender dear / I may be wrong, but I think you're wonderful / Lullaby of Birdland / Stella by starlight / Skylark / My romance / Last night when we were young / Salute to Basie / Night and day / Ja da / Just friends
CCD 4584 / Dec '93 / Concord Jazz

☐ SNOWY MORNING BLUES (Alden, Howard Trio)
One morning in May / I'm through with love / Bye-ya / Melancholia / Sleepy time gal / Le sucrier velours / Dancers in love / Snowy morning blues / Ask me now / You leave me breathless / Swing '39
CCD 4424 / Aug '90 / Concord Jazz

☐ TAKE YOUR PICK
I concentrate on you / UMMG (Upper Manhattan Medical Group) / House party starting / Warm valley / Gig / My funny valentine / Sweet and lovely / You're my thrill / How deep is the ocean / After all
CCD 47432 / Feb '97 / Concord Jazz

☐ YOUR STORY (The Music Of Bill Evans) (Alden, Howard & Frank Wess)
Tune for a lyric / Loose bloose / Displacement / Time remembered / Two lonely people / Funkallero / Only child / Laurie / Maxine / Five / Your story
CCD 4621 / Nov '94 / Concord Jazz

Alder

☐ ALDER
AW 21CD / Aug '97 / Tongang

Alec Empire

☐ DESTROYER, THE
Intro / We all die / Suicide / Bang your head / Don't lie white girl / Firebombing / I just wanna destroy / Bonus beats / Nobody gets out alive / My body cannot die / Peak / Heartbeat that isn't there / I don't care what happens / My face would crack / Pleasure is our business / Ending
DHRCD 004 / Jun '96 / Digital Hardcore

☐ GEIST OF ALEC EMPIRE, THE (3CD Set)
22.24 / Kick some soul / Kick some dirt / I die if I fall asleep / God told me how to kiss / Many bars and no money / No name / Sweet / 3 bullets in the back / City of lights / Sieg uber die Mayday HJ / Get some / Low on ice / Backside of my brain / Maschinen volk / Civilisation virus / Metall dub / 13465 / Stahl und blaussaure / Lash the nineties / Sun hurts my eyes / Report / No name / Slowly falling in love / Walk the apocalypse / La villes de filles mortes / Opus 28 - Pour la liberte / Des milles universes / La guere d'opium / Swimming through nails / We have arrived / Clean circuit
GEIST 001 / 6 Oct '97 / Digital Hardcore

☐ GENERATION STAR WARS
EFA 006612 / Mar '95 / Mille Plateau

☐ LOW ON ICE
EFA 006882 / Oct '95 / Mille Plateau

☐ LTD EDITIONS
EFA 006522 / May '94 / Mille Plateau

☐ SQUEEZE THE TRIGGER (2CD Set)
Squeeze the trigger / Silver pills / Fuck the shit up / Streets of gold / King of the street / Brothers crush / Drum and the bass / Generate / Euphoric / Destroyer / Burn Babylon burn / Destruction / I am you (identity)
DHRCD 011 / 17 Nov '97 / Digital Hardcore

Aleman, Oscar

☐ SWING GUITAR MASTERPIECES (2CD Set)
ACD 29 / 7 Apr '98 / Acoustic Disc

Alemany, Jesus

☐ CUBANISMO
Descarga de hoy meta y guaguanco / Tumbao de coqueta / Aprovecha / Pa que goven / Paca y pa ya / Recordando a arcano / La rumba y el tumbador / Cicuta tibia / Ahora me voy
HNCD 1390 / Nov '96 / Hannibal

Ales, Brian

☐ CREATURE OF HABIT
Your small kindnesses / Older road than this / Happy town / Cinema saga / Waltz fatale / Cinema saga / Aho dze
INT 31622 / Feb '97 / Intuition

Alesini, Nicola

☐ MARCO POLO VOL.1 (Alesini, Nicola & Pier Luigi Andreoni)
Come morning / Quinsai / Yangchow / Golden way / Sumatra / M Polo / Il Libro dell'incessante accordo con Il cielo / Maya / Buchara / Kubilay khan / Samarca / Valley of Pamir
MASOCD 90069 / Sep '97 / Materiali Sonori

☐ MARCO POLO VOL.2 (Alesini, Nicola & Pier Luigi Andreoni)
MASOCD 90073 / 2 Mar '98 / Materiali Sonori

Alex P

☐ IBIZA ANTHEMS (Mixed By Alex P & Brandon Block - 2CD Set) (Various Artists)
Free: *Ultra Nate* / Feel it: *Tamperer & Maya* / Give me luv: *Alcatraz* / Bomb: *Gonzalez, Kenny 'Dope'* / Magic caroet ride: *Mighty Dub Katz* / Sugar is sweeter: *Bolland, C.J.* / Spin spin sugar: *Sneaker Pimps* / Keep on jumpin': *Terry, Todd* / Open up: *Leftfield & John Lydon* / Nightmare: *Brainbug* / Plastic dreams: *Jaydee* / Naked in the rain: *Blue Pearl* / Open your mind: *Usura* / Waterfall: *Atlantic Ocean* / Break of dawn: *Rhythm On The Loose* / Isomnia: *Faithless* / Seven days and one week: *BBE* / Equador: *Sash* / Vindaloo: *Fat Les* / Passion: *Gat Decor* / Let me show you: *Camisra* / Testament 1: *Chubby Chunks* / Technocat: *Technocat* / Renegade master: *Wildchild* / Disco's revenge: *Gusto* / Read my lips: *Alex Party* / Let the music (lift you up): *Loveland* / Feel my body: *O'Moiraghi, Frank* / Higher state of conciousness: *Wink, Josh* / I'm alive: *Stretch n' Vern* / Freed from desire: *Gala* / Deep menace: *D'Menace* / Dreamer: *Livin' Joy* / So in love with you: *Duke* / Been a long time: *Fog* / Encore une fois: *Sash* / Want love: *Hysteric Ego*
TTVCD 2965 / 29 Jun '98 / Telstar TV

Alex Party

☐ ALEX PARTY
8288212 / Oct '96 / Systematic

Alexander Brothers

☐ ALEXANDER BROTHERS
Amazing grace / Amazing grace / Margaret's waltz - leezie lindsay / Big kilmarnock bunnet / Oh my papa (o mein papa) / Way old friends do / Nola / Auld lang syne / Song of the clyde / Rothesay o' / Polkas (jigtime) / Rothesay bay / M.s.r. (drunken pipers) / These are my mountains / March hare-irish washerwoman / Song of the clyde / Rothesay bay / These are my mountains / March hare-irish washerwoman / Amazing grace / Let's have a ceilidh / Margaret's waltz - leezie lindsay / Big kilmarnock bunnet / Oh my papa (o mein papa) / Way old friends do / Nola / Auld lang syne
CDITV 568 / May '93 / Scotdisc

☐ BEST OF THE ALEXANDER BROTHERS
Scotland, Scotland / Any dream will do / Mull of Kintyre / Oil rigger / Road to Dundee / Wild side of life / All along Loch Long / Nobody's child / Flying Scotsman / Caledonia / Northern lights of Aberdeen / Medley / Reels / Blackboard of my heart / He bought my soul at Calvary / Come by the hills / Jigs / Cornkisters / Farewell my love / Hiking song
TRTCD 135 / Oct '94 / TrueTrax

☐ BEST OF THE ALEXANDER BROTHERS, THE
PLSCD 226 / Jul '97 / Pulse

☐ GLORIOUS NORTH, THE
Glorious North / Caledonia / Hill o'Benachie / Lass of bon accord / Oil rigger / Northern lights of old Aberdeen / Dark island / Lonely scapa flow / Jigs medley / Farewell my love / McGinty's meal and ale
CDITV 593 / Nov '94 / Scotdisc

☐ NOW
Welcome medley / Nobody's child / Old button box / Pistonette / Gentle Annie / Inverary Inn / Daisy a day / Dark island / Doon in the wee room / When you and I were young Maggie / Sing along medley / Way old friends do / Home from the sea / On the rebound / Goodnight Bobby / Mary mack / Could I have this dance / Glencoe / Flying Scotsman / Bunch of thyme / Catch me if you can / Flower of Scotland
LCDM 9023 / Aug '90 / Lismor

☐ TOAST TO ABSENT FRIENDS, A
Opening medley / Any dream will do / Midges / After the ball / High level hornpipe / Absent friends / Take me back / Working man / After all these years / Tartan / It is no secret / Jaqueline waltz / Helen of Invergarry / Marching through the heather / Bricklayer's song / Fisherman's son
LCOM 6035 / Sep '92 / Lismor

Alexander D. Great

☐ PANORAMA ATTACK (Alexander D. Great & The Great Band)
SARCD 004 / Sep '97 / Lion Valley

Alexander, Arthur

☐ GREATEST, THE
Anna / Soldier of love / You don't care / Call me lonesome / Where have you been / Don't you know / All I need is you / Keep her guessing / In the middle of it all / Without a song / Black night / You're the reason / I hang my head and cry / Dream girl / Are you / Shot of rhythm and blues / You better move on / Detroit city / Go home girl / Whole lot of trouble / I wonder where you are tonight
CDCHD 922 / Jun '89 / Ace

☐ LONELY JUST LIKE ME
If it's really got to be this way / Go home girl / Sally Sue Brown / Mr. John / Lonely just like me / Every day I have to cry / In the middle of it all / Genie in the jug / Johnny Heartbreak / All the time / There is a road / I believe in miracles
7559614752 / Jul '93 / Nonesuch

☐ WARNER BROS. RECORDINGS, THE
Rainbow road / Down the backroads / I'm coming home in the middle of it all / Call me honey / Lover please / You got me knockin' / It hurts to want it so bad / Love's where life begins / Come along with me / Burning love / Go home girl / They'll do it every time / Mr. John / Thank God he came
9362455812 / Jul '96 / Warner Bros.

Alexander, David

☐ BEST OF DAVID ALEXANDER VOL.1 (20 Great Songs)
She wears my ring / Endlessly / Till / We should be together / If I could see the rhondda / Not one minute more / Taste the wine / Solitaire / You'll never find another love like mine / Let there be love / Heaven is my woman's love / Feelings / Think about it baby / She believes in me / Ravishing ruby / I love you, goodbye / Baby don't get hooked on me / Hurt / Help me make it through the night / So many ways
DARCD 4 / Apr '96 / One Stop

☐ BEST OF DAVID ALEXANDER VOL.2 (18 Great Songs)
DARCD 6 / Apr '96 / One Stop

☐ CONCERT, THE
DARCD 11 / Apr '96 / One Stop

☐ FEED THE FIRE STOKE THE COAL
DARCD 7 / Apr '96 / One Stop

☐ IF I NEVER SING ANOTHER SONG
No sacrifice / Rose / You were always on my mind / Lady lay down beside me / I can see clearly now / It must have been love / A working man / Living years / (if I could) hold on to love / First time ever I saw your face / If you go away / Islands in the stream / If I never sing another song
DARCD 3 / Apr '96 / One Stop

☐ INSPIRATIONS
DARCD 16 / 2 Feb '98 / One Stop

☐ MORE & MORE
DARCD 8 / Apr '96 / One Stop

☐ ONE DAY
DARCD 9 / Apr '96 / One Stop

☐ THERE YOU ARE
DARCD 10 / Apr '96 / One Stop

Alexander, Eric

☐ MODE FOR MABES
Mode for mabes / Sugar ray / For heaven's sake / Erik thered / Love thy neighbour / Stay straight / Stairway to the stairs / Naima
DE 500 / 9 Mar '98 / Delmark

☐ NEW YORK CALLING (Alexander, Eric Quintet)
CRISS 1077CD / Nov '93 / Criss Cross

☐ STABLEMATES (Alexander, Eric & Lin Halliday)
Eternal triangle / Blue bird / Polka dots and moonbeams/Old folks / Speak low / Like someone in love / Night has a thousand eyes / Stablemates
DE 488 / Jun '97 / Delmark

☐ STRAIGHT UP
Straight up / What are you doing the rest of your life / Be my love / Blues waltz / Laura / Oscar for Treadwell / End of a love affair / Love is a many splendored thing
DE 461 / Mar '97 / Delmark

☐ TWO OF A KIND (Alexander, Eric Quartet)
Happy song / Pentimento / Mr. Harris / I can't get started / Cecil's slide / Angel eyes / Beautiful things / Kick-a-poo
CRISS 1133CD / Sep '97 / Criss Cross

Alexander, Monty

☐ ECHOES OF JILLY'S
I've got you under my skin / Summer wind / You make me feel so young / I'm a fool to want you / Just one of those things / All the way / Fly me to the moon / In the wee small hours of the morning / Call me irresponsible / Angel eyes / Come fly with me / Here's that rainy day / Strangers in the night
CCD 47692 / Aug '97 / Concord Jazz

☐ FACETS
When Johnny comes marching home / Lost April / I'm walkin' / Hard times / Hold 'em Joe / Consider / Speak low / Tune up / Blues for Dewey / To the ends of the earth
CCD 4108 / Nov '96 / Concord Jazz

☐ IVORY AND STEEL
CCD 4124 / Jul '88 / Concord Jazz

☐ JAMBOREE
Sly mongoose / Reggae-later / No woman no cry / Look up / Accompong / You can see / Big yellow taxi / Think twice crying / Linstead market
CCD 4359 / Oct '88 / Concord Picante

☐ JAMENTO
Accompany / Slippery / Sugar Loaf at twilight / Weekend in LA / Jamento / Mango rengue
OJCCD 9042 / May '98 / Original Jazz Classics

☐ JUST IN TIME (2CD Set)
Out of many one people / Work song / Bossa nova do marilla / Tricrotism / Angel eyes / Body and soul / That's the way it is / Just in time / Soft winds / On Green Dolphin Street / Black orpheus / Blue bossa
JLR 103605 / May '96 / Live At EJ's

☐ LIVE AT MAYBECK RECITAL HALL VOL.40
When the saints go marching in / When I grow too old to dream / Close enough for love / Serpent / Where is love / Renewal / Island in the sun / Estate / (I love you) for sentimental reasons / Speak low / Smile
CCD 4658 / Aug '95 / Concord Jazz

☐ OVERSEAS SPECIAL
But not for me / Time for love / Orange in pain / F S R / For all we know / CC rider
CCD 4253 / Nov '96 / Concord Jazz

☐ REUNION IN EUROPE (Alexander, Monty Quartet)
Two bass hit / Got my mojo working / Smile / Yesterdays / Blues for Stephanie / Love you madly / Ben / Eleuthra / That's why
CCD 4231 / May '97 / Concord Jazz

☐ RIVER, THE
Stand up, stand up for Jesus / River / Serpent / Ave Maria / David danced before the Lord with all his might / Renewal / Ain't gonna study war no more / Holy Holy Lord God Almighty / What a friend we have in Jesus / How great thou art
CCD 4422 / Aug '90 / Concord Jazz

☐ SATURDAY NIGHT (Alexander, Monty Quartet)
Bolivia / Close enough / Funjii mama / Old folks / Just in time / What's new / S.k.j.
MCD 024 / May '89 / Timeless Jazz

☐ SO WHAT
591482 / Jun '91 / Black & Blue

☐ SOLO
BLR 84006 / May '91 / L&R

☐ STEAMIN'
Pure imagination / Just a little bit / Dear Diz / 3000 Miles / Lively up yourself / Make believe / I'll never stop loving you / Maybe September / Tucker avenue stomp / Theme from Prawnbroker / Honest I do / When you go / Young at heart
CCD 4636 / Apr '95 / Concord Jazz

☐ TO NAT WITH LOVE
Unforgettable / What is this thing called love / Moonlight in Vermont / Honeysuckle rose / Three little words / Nature boy / Straighten up and fly right / Too marvellous for words / Yes sir that's my baby
CHECD 12 / Oct '91 / Master Mix

☐ TO THE ENDS OF THE EARTH
To the ends of the earth / One love / Old devil moon / Island Ray / When I fall in love / Mangorengue / Reunion blues / Body and soul / Boogsie's bounce / September song / Killer Joe
CCD 4721 / Oct '96 / Concord Picante

☐ TRIO (Alexander / Brown / Ellis)
CCD 4136 / Dec '90 / Concord Jazz

☐ TRIPLE TREAT VOL.2 (Alexander, Monty & Ray Brown/Herb Ellis)
Lined with a groove / Straighten up and fly right / It might as well be Spring / Seven come eleven / Smile / I'll remember April / Trip man (tracer and inst. mix) / Lester leaps in
CCD 4338 / May '88 / Concord Jazz

☐ TRIPLE TREAT VOL.3 (Alexander, Monty & Ray Brown/Herb Ellis)
I told ya I love ya, now get out / In the wee small hours of the morning / Renewal / My one and only love / There will never be another you / Secret love / Hi-heel sneakers / I love you / Corcovado
CCD 4394 / '89 / Concord Jazz

☐ YARD MOVEMENT
Exodus / Regulator / Crying / Moonlight city / Love notes / Sneaky steppers
IJCD 4001 / May '96 / Island Jamaica Jazz

Alexander, Peter

☐ EBENFALLS ERHALTLICH (4CD Set)
Das machen nur die Beine von Dolores / Bye bye mein Hawaii / Ich lade dich ein in die kleine Taverne / Erzahl mir keine Marchen / Im weissen weissen schnee / Sag es mit Musik Fahr auf dem Zigeunerwagen / Es ist ein abschied nur fur heut / Der alte Liebesbrief / Wenn ich dich seh' / Ich hab' nach dir soviel Heimweh Addio / Donna Grazia / Santa Fe / Wo am weg die apfel reifen ein musikus / Bumms / Weil du schon bist / Ich kusse ihre hand, Madame / Ich weiss es nicht / So ein kleines bisschen liebe / Isabella / Die sussesten fruchte (fressen nur die) / Braucht dein Herz keinen freund / Komm mit nach Palermo / Verliebte music / Ach, Herr Kuhn / Bolero (geheimnis der sudichen nachte) / Die panne panne mit Susanne / Gross kann sie sein, klein kann sie sein / Was versteht denn ein Cowboy von liebe / Margarita / Ich weiss was du dir denkst / Damais in Rom Angelina / Pony serenade / Tabak und Rum / Hannelore / Bella bella Donna / Optimisten boogie / Die alte kuckucksuhr / Es war das letzte mal / Alte lieder traute weisen / Das lied vom sonntag / Ein italiano / Nein nein ich will night bitte lass mich / Bella musica / Der alte stiefel / Ach hatt ich das gefuhl, doch mal / Keine angst vor grossen tieren / Immer wieder du / Jambalaya / Jonathan boogie / Kotettier nicht mit mir / Mein grosser bruder / Ich lieb dich so wie du bist / Die frau kommt direkt aus Spanien / Uno momento Maria / Plim plim, plum plum / Die sussesten fruchte (fressen nur die) / Wir wir wir haben ein klavier / Was hat der Bobby mit der Lisa gemacht / Oh Mister Swoboda / Dann ist er furchtbar mude / In sorrent / Nicolo Nicolo Nicolo / Jede frau in bogota / Die treuen augen / Die schonen frauen haben immer recht / Es war in Napoli vor vielen Jahren / Continental / Es liegt was in der luft / Ich finde dich / Ich sing' heut vergnugt vor mich hin / Du bist die Richtige / Ich hap vor'm kussen immer lampenfieber / Der primas / Agustino / Der bunte traum / Schlager revue No. 8 / Weinlied/ Sagbiem abschied leise servus
BCD 15455 / Jul '96 / Bear Family

☐ FILMTREFFER VOL.1
Margarita / Gluck muss man haben / Blauer tango / Die sussesten Fruchte / Bongo boogie / Wenn sie wollen, bringen sie mal Stein in's roll'n / Ich finde dich... / Ich sing 'Heut' vergnugt vor mich hin / Sing, baby sing / Eventuell / Damit haben sie gluck in der Bundesrepublik / Komm' ein bisschen mit nach Italien / Gespensterblues / Ein mann muss nicht immer schon sein / Kleines Haus auf der Sierra Nevada / Ich weiss was dir fehlt / Im hafen uns'rer traume / Mamma-di-mandolin / Schin wieder mal / Weil du mir sympathisch bist / Grosses finale
BCD 15992 / Jun '97 / Bear Family

☐ FILMTREFFER VOL.2
Das ist alles langst vorbei / Vergiss mich nicct so schnell / Mamitscka / Das ganze Haus ist schief / Vergiss mich nicht so schnell / O Josefin, die nacht in Napoli / Jassa Bobo / Probier dein gluck mit mir / Das grosse Gluckskarussel / Wenn das die andern wussten / Wehe, wenn sie losgelassen / Das schonste auf der Welt / Du hast mir heut mein Herz gestohlen / Der freundliche Franz / Wir sehen uns wieder / Venga, Venga musica / Fabelhaft / Tun sie's nicht / Er war ein Musikant / Hab'n sie nicht ein schones grosses Fass da / Lass mich nie, nie, nie mehr allein / Wir tanzen Huckepack / Die Reblaus / Mann musste Klavier spielen konnen / Ich wunsch' dir einen schlaflosen Abend / In der Schweiz / See you later alligator
BCD 15993 / Jun '97 / Bear Family

☐ ROT-WEISS-ROT AUFNAHMEN
Guten morgen, Frauline Scholz / Ich lad sie ein, faulein / Ich mocht von dir ein foto / Warum sagt dein mund / Jo der kleine Julius / Was die kleinen madchen singen / Eine kleine mansarde / Oh Donna Clara / Nachts sind die strassen so leer / Deine liebe is zuckersuss (Quien sera) / Chef, wir brauchen bitte vorschuss / Komm, wir fahren mit 10ps / Manuela Mambo / Adieu, Mimi / Mule train / Bunny hop
BCD 15998 / Jul '96 / Bear Family

☐ STRASSE MEINER LEIDER
Someone, someone / Love's made a fool of you / I fought the law / A sweet love / Time will tell / When you ask about love / Deborah / Why did you leave / Just this once / Ting a ling / Great balls of fire / Rockin' pneumonia and the boogie woogie flu / And the boogie woogie flu / Rockin' pneumonia and the boogie woogie flu / Smooth guy / After it's over / So you're in love / Baby my heart / So you're in love / More than I can say / Baby my heart / Don't cha know / Peggy sue got married
BCD 15599 / Feb '90 / Bear Family

Alexander, Ray
☐ RAIN IN JUNE (Alexander, Ray Sextet)
Dizzy atmosphere / Nightingale sang in Berkeley Square / Lamp is low / Our love is here to stay / Let's fall in love / Rain in June / Angelique / Easy to love / Twinkletoes / Oh lady be good / Swinging on a star
CDSGP 0139 / Jun '95 / Prestige

Alexander, Sara
☐ ERGA
3004082 / 24 Apr '98 / IMP

☐ HAMSIN
KAR 985 / Nov '96 / IMP

Alexandria, Lorez
☐ ALEXANDRIA THE GREAT
Show me / I've never been in love before / Satin doll / My one and only love / Over the rainbow / Get me to the church on time / Best is yet to come / I've grown accustomed to his face / Give me the simple life / I'm through with love / But beautiful / Little boat / Dancing on the ceiling / It might as well be Spring / Once / Wildest gal in town / Angel eyes / This could be the start of something big / No more / That far away look
MCAD 33116 / Jan '90 / Impulse Jazz

☐ TALK ABOUT COPY
Best is yet to come / Talk about cozy / Something / I'll remember april / Street of dreams / Be a sweet pumpkin / Alfie / I've never been in love before / I've got a right to cry / Night song / Didn't we / Here, there and everywhere / My way
HCD 605 / Oct '95 / Hindsight

Alexia
☐ PARTY, THE
Uh la la la / Gimme love / Music I like / Keep on movin' bad boy / Crazy for you / Claro de luna / Everything / Feelings / Everyday / I love my boy / Don't love me baby / Don't love my baby / If you say goodbye / Dame amor
ALEX 1LPD / 15 Jun '98 / Incredible

Alexiades, Minas
☐ STORIES AMONG FRIENDS
ML 0643 / 11 May '98 / Musurgia Graeca

Alfano, Jorge
☐ INTI-MYSTICAL MUSIC OF THE ANDESA
LYRCD 7429 / Nov '97 / Lyrichord

☐ ONE HEART
LYRCD 7431 / Nov '97 / Lyrichord

Alfonso, Juan Carlos
☐ DANDEN
TUMI 069 / 27 Jul '98 / Tumi

☐ SALSA EN ATARE
TUMICD 069 / 27 Jul '98 / Tumi

Alford, Clem
☐ MIRROR IMAGE
MC 1003CD / Oct '96 / Magic Carpet

Alfred, Jerry
☐ ETSI SHON (Grandfather Song) (Alfred, Jerry & The Medicine Beat)
RHRCD 93 / Aug '96 / Red House

☐ NENDAA (Alfred, Jerry & The Medicine Beat)
RHRCD 97 / Apr '97 / Red House

Alger, Pat
☐ SEEDS
SHCD 1041 / Jan '94 / Sugar Hill

☐ TRUE LOVE AND OTHER STORIES
True love / Lone star state of mind / Goin' gone / Like a hurricane / This town / Love can be a dangerous thing / I do / She came from Fort Worth / Forever lovin' you / Small town Saturday night / Once in a very blue moon / Blue highway 29
SHCD 1029 / Aug '96 / Sugar Hill
ETCD 193 / Dec '97 / Etude

Algiz
☐ CLAIRE VOIE
Claire voie / Sans titre / Dehors la plentitude / Les heures aveugles / Les seigneurs des sentiers / Organique / La chaise (sur l'eau) / Fall apart / Fin de siecle
TURSA 015CD / Feb '98 / Tursa

Alguimia
☐ U
FSNT 023 / 5 Jan '98 / Fresh Sound New Talent

Alhaits, Jean-Michel
☐ FANTAISIE (Alhaits, Jean-Michel & J.P. Rolland)
868CD / May '97 / Escalibur

Alhambra
☐ ART OF JUDEO-SPANISH SONG
GV 127CD / Nov '93 / Global Village

Ali
☐ CRUCIAL
5379332 / 1 Jun '98 / Wild Card

Ali Khan, Badar
☐ LOST IN QAWWALI
5747192 / 5 Jan '98 / Triloka

Ali, Rajab
☐ FEELINGS
DMUT 1051 / Mar '96 / Multitone

☐ UMANG
DMUT 1250 / Mar '96 / Multitone

Ali, Salamat
☐ NAZAKAT AND SALAMAT ALI (Ali, Salamat & Nazakat)
Rag megh / Rag bairagi bhairav
HNCD 1332 / Sep '91 / Hannibal

Alias Ron Kavana
☐ COMING DAYS
Galtee mor / Irish ways / Saddle the pony / Merrily kiss the quaker / Kinnegad slashers / Annie Mulligan's / Thoughts of Abilene / Psycho Mary's voodoo blues / Ain't that peculiar / Fox hunter's reel / Pennies for black babies / Cajun ceili / Freedom crazy / Walk don't walk / Hand me down / Connemara / Handcuffs / Johnny / If I had a rocket launcher
CDWIKD 94 / Mar '91 / Chiswick

☐ GALWAY TO GRACELAND
CDARK 002 / Oct '95 / Alias

☐ HOME FIRE
SPDCD 1043 / Jun '91 / Special Delivery

☐ ROLLIN' AND COASTIN' (In Search Of America)
APCD 042 / Apr '94 / Appaloosa

☐ THINK LIKE A HERO
Waxin' the gaza / Every man is a king (in the US of A) / Gone shopping / Soweto trembles (the Jo'burg jig) / Felice / This is the night (fair dues to "The Man") / Midnight on the water / Caoineadh roisin / Four horsemen / Rap 'n' reel / Tre ceather a hocht / Ochra at Killarney point to points / Reconciliation
CDWIK 88 / Oct '89 / Chiswick

Alice
☐ ALICE
280827 / Jul '97 / Magic

Alice Donut
☐ BUCKETFULS OF SICKNESS AND HORROR (In An Otherwise Meaningless Life)
VIRUS 73CD / Jul '89 / Alternative Tentacles

☐ DONUT COMES ALIVE
VIRUS 61CD / '92 / Alternative Tentacles

☐ DRY HUMPING THE CASH COW
Green meat stew / Hose / Tingler / Dorothy / Every body is on sale / My best friend's wife / Mrs. hayes / Dead river / Mother of christ / Helter skelter / American lips / Egg / Demonologist / Buckets, pock, fork
VIRUS 143CD / 10 Nov '97 / Alternative Tentacles

☐ MULE
VIRUS 82CD / Nov '90 / Alternative Tentacles

☐ PURE ACID PARK
Millennium / Dreaming in Cuban / Freaks in love / Big cars and blow jobs / I walked with a zombie / Senator and the cabin boy / Mummenschantz pachinko / Insane / Shining path / Unspeakable pleasure of being me / Lost in space / Cain
VIRUS 163CD / 10 Nov '97 / Alternative Tentacles

☐ UNTIDY SUICIDES OF YOUR DEGENERATE CHILDREN
VIRUS 115CD / Sep '92 / Alternative Tentacles

Alice In Chains
☐ ALICE IN CHAINS
Grind / Brush away / Sludge factory / Heaven beside you / Head creeps / Again / Shame in you / God am / So close / Nothin' song / Frogs / Over now
4811142 / Nov '95 / Columbia

☐ DIRT
Them bones / Dam that river / Rain when I die / Down in a hole / Sick man / Rooster / Junkhead / Dirt / God smack / Hate to feel / Angry chair / Would
4723302 / Oct '92 / Columbia

☐ FACELIFT
We die young / Man in the box / Sea of sorrow / Bleed the freak / I can't remember / Love hate love / It ain't like that / Sunshine / Put you down / Confusion / I know somethin' ('bout you) / Real thing
4672012 / Mar '96 / Columbia

☐ JAR OF FLIES/SAP (2CD Set)
Rotten apple / Nutshell / I stay away / No excuses / Whale and wasp / Don't follow / Swing on this / Brother / Got me wrong / Right turn / Am I inside / Love story
4757132 / Jan '94 / Columbia

☐ MTV UNPLUGGED
Nutshell / Brother / No excuses / Sludge factory / Down in a hole / Angry chair / Rooster / Got me wrong / Heaven beside you / Would / Frogs / Over now / Killer is me
4843002 / Jul '96 / Columbia

Alien
☐ PLEASURE OF LEISURE
BR 070 / 10 Aug '98 / Blue Room

Alien Boys
☐ SEEDS OF DECAY
SR 330391CD / '91 / Semaphore

Alien Factory
☐ ALIEN TRAX
TIMECD 0402 / 2 Mar '98 / Time Unlimited

Alien Mutation
☐ DNA
Dubula technoid / Dreamscape / Exotic ocean / Shimmer / Marijuana / Sea of colours / Water
KINXCD 9 / Jun '97 / Kinetix

Alien Nation
☐ MICROCOSM MICROCOSM
KINXCD 4 / Apr '96 / Kinetix

Alien Planetscapes
☐ LIFE ON EARTH
G/AP 107 / 27 Apr '98 / Galactus

Alien Rebels
☐ STRANGE FEELINGS
AREB 001 / Feb '97 / Alien Rebels

Alien Sex Fiend
☐ ACID BATH
In God we trust / Dead and reburied / She's a killer / Hee-haw (here come the bone people) / Smoke my bones / Breakdown and cry (lay down and die goodbye) / EST (trip to the moon) / Attack / Boneshaker baby / I'm a product / Thirty second coma
CDMGRAM 18 / Jun '97 / Anagram

☐ ALL OUR YESTERDAYS (The Singles Collection 1983-1987)
Ignore the machine / Lips can't go / RIP / Dead and buried / EST (trip to the moon) / Drive my rocket (up Uranus) / I'm doing time in a maximum security twilight home / I walk the line / Smells like... / Hurricane fighter plane
CDGRAM 34 / May '93 / Anagram

☐ ANOTHER PLANET
Bun ho / Everybody's dream / Radiant city / Spot your lucky warts / Sample my sausage / Outer limits / Instant Karma Sutra / So much to do, so little time / Alien / Wild green fiendy liquid / Nightmare zone / Another planet / Silver machine
CDGRAM 38 / Jun '97 / Anagram

☐ BAT CAVE MASTERS
CLP 232 / Jun '98 / Cleopatra

☐ CURSE
Katch 22 / Now I'm feeling zombiefied / Stress / Blessings / Eat eat eat (an eye for an eye) / Ain't got no time to bleed / Bleeding reprise / Dalisms / Burger bar baby / I think I / Mad daddy drives a UFO / Wuthering wind / Radio Jimi / Hand of the silken / Blessing in disguise
CDGRAM 46 / Sep '90 / Anagram

☐ DRIVE MY ROCKET
CLEO 94122 / Aug '94 / Cleopatra

☐ FIRST ALIEN SEX FIEND CD
I'm doing time in a maximum security twilight home / Mine's full of maggots / In and out of my mind / Spies / Fly in the ointment / Seconds to nowhere / Beaver destroys forests / Do you sleep / Depravity lane / EST (Trip to the moon) / Boneshaker baby / Ignore the machine / Attack
CDGRAM 25 / Apr '94 / Anagram

☐ HERE CUM GERMS
Here cum germs / Camel camel / Impossible mission / Isolation / My brain is in the cupboard above the kitchen sink / You are soul / Death / Boots on / They all call me crazee / Stuff the turkey
CDGRAM 31 / May '92 / Anagram

☐ I'M HER FRANKENSTEIN
CLEO 9508CD / Jun '95 / Cleopatra

☐ IT
Smells like... / Manic depression / Believe it or not / April showers / Wop-bop / Get into it / Lesson one / Do it right / To be continued / Buggin' me / Hurricane fighter plane / It lives again
CDGRAM 26 / Nov '91 / Anagram

☐ LEGENDARY BATCAVE TAPES, THE
Wardance of the Alien Sex Fiend / In heaven / I walk alone / Outta control / I'm her Frankenstein / Boneshaker baby / RIP / Wild women of Wongo / Funk in hell / Drive my rocket (up Uranus) / School's out
CDMGRAM 69 / Oct '93 / Anagram

☐ LIQUID HEAD IN TOKYO
RIP (blue crime truck) / EST (trip to the Moon) / Dead and re-buried / In God we trust (in cars we rust) / Back to the egg / Attack / Lips can't go / Wild women
SUMCD 4087 / Jan '97 / Summit

☐ NOCTURNAL EMISSIONS
FULLCD 1301 / Mar '97 / 13th Moon

☐ OPEN HEAD SURGERY
Clockwork banana, banana-moon / Magic / Class of '69 / Alien sex fiend / Coma / Lickin' ma bone / Stressed out / B-B-bone boogie
CDGRAM 51 / Mar '92 / Anagram

☐ SINGLES 1983-1995, THE (2CD Set)
Ignore the machine / Lips can't go / RIP / New Christian music / Dead and buried / EST (trip to the moon) / I'm doing time in a maximum security twilight home / I walk the line / Smells like... / Hurricane fighter plane / Impossible mission / Here cum germs / Stuff the turkey / Bun ho / Haunted house / Now I'm feeling zombiefied / Magic / Inferno
CDGRAM 99 / Oct '95 / Anagram

☐ TOO MUCH ACID
It lives again / I walk the line / Nightmare zone / Get into it / EST (trip to the moon) / So much to do, so little time / Haunted house / Smells like... / Hurricane fighter plane / Sample my sausage / Boneshaker baby
CDGRAM 41 / May '93 / Anagram

☐ WARDANCE OF THE... (2CD Set)
SMDCD 133 / 9 Feb '98 / Snapper

☐ WHO'S BEEN SLEEPING IN MY BRAIN
Wish I woz a dog / Wild women / I'm not mad / New christian music / Wigwam wipeout / I'm her frankenstein / I am a product / Ignore the machine / Lips can't go / Black rabbit / New christian music (live) / Crazee
CDGRAM 10 / '88 / Anagram

Alienstalk
☐ ALIENSTALK
SCD 28025 / 6 Apr '98 / Sargasso

Alimatov, Turgen
☐ TURGEN ALIMATOV
C 560086 / Jan '96 / Ocora

Alisha's Attic
☐ ALISHA RULES THE WORLD
Irresistable U R / Intense / I am, I feel / Alisha rules the world / White room / Stone in my shoe / Personality lines / Indestructible / I won't miss you / Golden rule / Just the way you like it / Air we breathe / Adore u
5340272 / Nov '96 / Mercury

Alison's Halo
☐ EYEDAZZLER
SINGE 018 / 29 Jun '98 / Burnt Hair

Alkaholiks
☐ LIKWIDATION
Likwidation / Captain hook / NAS skit / Tore down / Off the wall / Killin' it / LL Cool J / Feel the real / Hip hop junkies / Awww shit / J ro late skit / Keep it pourin' / Likwit ridas / Funny style / Commercial skit / Allnight / Debarge skit / Pass out / 20th caller skit / Rockin' with the best / Contents under pressure
74321512252 / 8 Sep '97 / RCA

Alkaline Trio
☐ FOR YOUR LUNGS ONLY
AM 028CD / 22 Jun '98 / Asian Man

Alke, Bjorn
☐ FOREVER LULU
DRCD 217 / Oct '89 / Dragon

☐ JAZZ IN SWEDEN
10722 / Oct '90 / Caprice

All
☐ ALLROY FOR PREZ
CRZ 004CD / Jan '90 / Cruz

☐ ALLROY SEZ...
CRZ 001CD / Jan '90 / Cruz

☐ ALLROY'S REVENGE
Gnutheme / Fool / Check one / Scary sad / Man-o-steel / Box / Copping z / Hot rod lincoln / She's my ex / Bubble gum / Mary / Net / No traffic / Carnage
CRZ 006CD / Jan '90 / Cruz

☐ BREAKING THINGS
CRZ 031CD / Sep '93 / Cruz

☐ DOT
CRZ 024CD / May '93 / Cruz

☐ MASS NERDER
World's on heroin / I'll gre there / Life on the road / Fairweather friend / Perfection / Greedy / Until I say so / Think the world / Honey peeps / Refrain / Silly me / Romantic junkie / Vida blue / Until then / Good as my word / Silence
65312 / 11 May '98 / Epitaph

☐ PERCOLATER
CRZ 022CD / May '93 / Cruz

All 4 One

☐ ALL 4 ONE
So much in love / Oh girl / Better man / I swear / Down to the last drop / Without you (she's got) skillz / Breathless / Something about you / Bomb / Here if you're ready
7567825882 / Apr '94 / Atlantic

☐ AND THE MUSIC SPEAKS
I can love you like that / Giving you my heart forever / I'm your man / These arms / I'm sorry / Here for you / Could this be magic / Roll call / We dedicate / Colors of love / Think you're the one for me / Love is more than just another four-letter word
7567827462 / May '95 / Atlantic

All About Eve

☐ ALL ABOUT EVE
Flowers in our hair / Gypsy dance / In the clouds / Martha's harbour / Every angel / Shelter from the rain / She moved through the fair / Wild hearted woman / Never promise / What kind of fool
8342602 / Aug '95 / Mercury

☐ SCARLET AND OTHER STORIES
Road to your soul / Dream now / Gold and silver / Scarlet / December / Blind lemon Sam / More than the blues / Tuesday's child / Empty dancehall / Only one reason / Pearl fishermen
8389652 / Aug '95 / Mercury

☐ TOUCHED BY JESUS
Strange way / Farewell Mr. Sorrow / Wishing the hours away / Touched by Jesus / Dreamer / Rhythm of life / Mystery we are / Hide child / Ravens / Are you lonely / Share it with me
5101462 / Aug '91 / Mercury

☐ WINTER WORDS, HITS AND RARITIES
Our summer (unreleased version) / Flowers in our hair / In the clouds / Wild hearted women / Every angel / Martha's harbour / What kind of fool / Road to your soul / December / Scarlet / Farewell mr. sorrow / Strange way / Dreamer / Paradise / Candy tree / Drowning / Wild flowers / Theft / Different sky
5141542 / Oct '92 / Mercury

All Day

☐ NOBODY LIKES A QUITTER
Smells like Long Beach / One way ticket / Cry for help / Number 56 / Insane love commandos / Get some / Nobody knows my name / Spain / War on the boulevard / Kim's dead/Michael / Hell no / Daddy / How does it feel / Ain't she sweet / Doreen Shelton / Friends are forever / Thank you
KNR 115 / Apr '97 / Know

All Living Fear

☐ MINIMUM RESISTANCE
FEAR 005CD / 3 Oct '97 / Resurrection

All Natural Lemon & Lime Flavours

☐ ALL NATURAL LEMON & LIME FLAVOURS
GERNCD 36V / 16 Mar '98 / Gern Blandsten

All Out War

☐ TRUTH IN THE AGE OF LIES
GAIN 011CD / 17 Nov '97 / Gain Ground

All Saints

☐ ALL SAINTS
8289792 / 24 Nov '97 / London

☐ INTERVIEW
RVCD 324 / 4 May '98 / Quantum Rockview

All Scars

☐ EARLY AMBIENT
DIS 1185CD / 22 Sep '97 / Dischord

All Souls' Orchestra

☐ KENDRICK COLLECTION, THE (All Souls' Orchestra & Choir)
Lord is King: *Wilson, Precious/All Souls' Orchestra/Choir* / Servant King: *Wilson, Precious/All Souls' Orchestra/Choir* / Such love: *Wilson, Precious/All Souls' Orchestra/Choir* / Burn on: *Richard, Cliff/All Souls' Orchestra/Choir* / Fighter: *Richard, Cliff/All Souls' Orchestra/Choir* / May our worship be acceptable: *Kendrick, Graham/All Souls' Orchestra/Choir* / May the fragrance of Jesus fill this place: *Kendrick, Graham/All Souls' Orchestra/Choir* / Meekness and majesty: *Kendrick, Graham/All Souls' Orchestra/Choir*
LANGD 003 / '89 / Myrrh

All Stars

☐ DREAM SESSION (The All Stars Play Miles Davis Classics)
Autumn leaves / So what / All blues / I thought about you / 'Round midnight / Davis / My funny Valentine / Dear old Stockholm
MCD 92642 / Jan '98 / Milestone

Alla, Tanakoul

☐ UD AND PERCUSSION
ALCD 190 / Sep '96 / Al Sur

Allan, Davie

☐ FUZZ FEST (Allan, Davie & The Arrows)
NER 3016CD / 29 Jun '98 / Total Energy

Allan, Johnnie

☐ FROM LOUISIANA TO THE PROMISED LAND
DECD 2002 / '96 / Deep Elem

☐ PROMISED LAND
Promised land / South to Louisiana / She's gone / Let's do it / Cry foolish heart / What'cha do / Your picture / Somebody else / Please accept my love / You got me whistling / I'll never love again / Secrets of love / Nights of misery / Cajun man / Graduation night (as you pass me by) / Please help me, I'm falling / Somewhere on Skid Row / Isle of Capri / Sweet dreams / I cried / Stranger to you / I can't wait / I'm missing you / Little fat man / Today I started loving you again / Homebound train / Let's go get drunk / Tennessee blues
CDCHD 380 / Jun '92 / Ace

Allan, Laura

☐ HOLD ON TO YOUR DREAMS
SE 1020CD / Apr '96 / Skyline

Allan/Hallberg/Riedel

☐ TRIO CONTROMBA
DRCD226 / May '88 / Dragon

Allaway/Antonia Quartet

☐ SAMIZDAT
Crossing the rubicon / Next time round / Groovin' / Coopers calling / Blues for BB / Let this one go / Cogito ergo sum / Trick of the light / Leonard B / Peel me a grape / Samizdat / Seal it
CDAA 001 / Jan '95 / Mapa Music

Allcock, Martin

☐ MAART
Miltown maid/Jenny's wedding / Minosegi boro / Yow diddley / North Country girl / Planxty Madam Crofton / Con Casey's jig/Tripping up the stairs / Reluctant barman / Why did I leave my home / Overseer's reply / On the floor / Flaherty's hornpipe/ 8 pints of Guinness / Lowlands of Holland
AMARA 109CD / Oct '97 / Amara

Alldis, Dominic

☐ TURN OUT THE STARS
Peri's scope / Waltz for Debby / You and the night and the music / Very early / Like someone in love / Two lonely people / Emily / My bells / You must believe in spring / Turn out the stars / My foolish heart / Days of wine and roses / Laurie / For Nenette (In April)
CANZCD 1 / Apr '96 / Canzona

Allegiance

☐ BLODORNSOFFER
NFR 021CD / Apr '97 / No Fashion

☐ HYMN TILL HANGAGUD
NFR 014CD / May '96 / No Fashion

Allegro Milano

☐ ALLEGRO MILANO PLAYS RONDO VENEZIANO
Magica melodia / La serenissima / Rondo Veneziano / Scaramucce / Visioni di venezia / Fantasia Venezia / Misteriosa Venezia / Rosso Veneziano / Musica...fantasia / Capriccio venziano / Odissea Veneziana / Carme veneziano / Venezia lunare / Andante Milano / Molto allegro / Alla turca
GRF 190 / Jan '93 / Tring

Allen, Carl

☐ PICCADILLY SQUARE (Allen, Carl & Manhattan Projects)
Piccadilly Square / Autumn leaves / 'Round midnight / Lullaby of birdland / Annie's mood / Biscuit man / New joy / What's new / In the still of the night / Afterthoughts
SJP 406 / Oct '93 / Timeless Jazz

Allen, Daevid

☐ BANANA MOON
Time of your life / Memories / All I want is out of here / Fred the fish / White neck blooze / Stoned innocent Frankenstein / His adventures in the land of Flip / I am a bowl
CDCRH 110 / Feb '97 / Charly
14945 / Jul '97 / Spalax

☐ DEATH OF ROCK AND OTHER ENTRANCES, THE
Death of rock / Poet for sale / Tally's birthday song / You never existed at all / Afraid / Radio gnome concert intro loop / Switch doctor / Gong ORFT invasion 1971
BP 114CD / Aug '96 / Blueprint

☐ DIVIDED ALIEN CLOCKWORK BAND
Preface / SQ invocation / When / Well / Bell / Boom / Dab / Gay / Poet for sale / I am a freud / Fastfather / Disguise / Gone and wandering waltz / Sex is a careless sea / Death of rock / Tally's birthday party / Pearle / Bodygas / Froghello / Strong woman / Smile
BP 269CD / 20 Oct '97 / Blueprint

☐ DIVIDEDALIENPLAYBAX 8
When / Well / Bell / Boon / Dab / Gay / Rude / Disguise / Pearls / Bodygas / Froghello / Fast-father / Smile
14837 / Jul '96 / Spalax

☐ DREAMIN' A DREAM
CLP 0106 / Oct '97 / Cleopatra

☐ DREAMING A DREAM
AGASCD 007 / Oct '96 / GAS

☐ GLISSANDO SPIRIT (Invisible Opera Company Of Tibet)
Landing / Uluwatu / Electric bird / Baliman energy / Cosmic dancer / Inner voice / High mountains dance / Dreaming / Moon in the sky / Mirage / Distant shore / Stars can frighten you / 7 keys / Wizard's garden / Eastside
VP 147CD / Mar '97 / Voiceprint

☐ JEWEL IN THE LOTUS (Invisible Opera Company Of Tibet)
AGASCD 006 / Sep '96 / GAS

☐ LIVE 1963 (Allen, Daevid Trio)
Love is a careless sea / My head is a nightclub / Capacity travel (parts 1 - 4) / Song of the jazzman / Dear olde Benny Green is a-turning in his grave / Ya sunny WOT / Frederique la Poissonavec Frite sur le dos
VP 122CD / Mar '94 / Voiceprint

☐ LIVE AT SQUAT THEATRE NEW YORK AUGUST 1980 (Divided Alien Clockwork Band)
Preface / SQ invocation / When / Well / Bell / Boom / Dab / Gay / Poet for sale / I am a freud / Fastfather / Disguise / Gone and wandering waltz / Sex is a careless sea / Death of rock / Tally's birthday party / Pearle / Bodygas / Froghello / Strong woman / Smile
AGASCD 005 / 3 Nov '97 / GAS

☐ N'EXISTE PAS
542817 / May '96 / Spalax

☐ NOW IS THE HAPPIEST TIME OF YOUR LIFE
Flamenco zero / Why do we treat ourselves like we do / Tally and Orlando meet the coconut pixie / See you on the moontower / Poet for sale / Only make love if you want to / I am / Deya Goddess / Crocodile nonsense poem
542825 / May '96 / Spalax
CDCRH 116 / Feb '97 / Charly

☐ OPIUM FOR THE PEOPLE/ALIEN IN NEW YORK
14844 / Oct '96 / Spalax

☐ OWL AND THE TREE, THE (Allen, Daevid & Gong)
I am a tree / Lament for the future of the forest / Hands / Unseen ally / La dea madri / Owly song / I am my own lover / Tudor love poem
CDTB 118 / Feb '92 / Thunderbolt

☐ SHE (Australia Aquaria)
DMCD 1025 / 13 Oct '97 / Demi-Monde

☐ TWELVE SELVES
Introdrone / Mystico Fanatico / Away away away / Colage/Bellyful of telephone / She/Isis is calling / Collage patafisico/Divided alien manifesto / I love sex but / Wargasm / Children of the new world / O Wichitio / Sexual blueprint / Gaia / My heart's song
VP 111CD / Nov '93 / Voiceprint

☐ VOICEPRINT RADIO SESSION
VPR 012CD / Oct '94 / Voiceprint

Allen, Eddie

☐ R & B
Frick and frack / As quiet a it's kept / Clairvoyant / Almost you / Schism / Seduction / Quest
ENJ 90332 / Aug '95 / Enja

Allen, Ernestine

☐ LET IT ROLL
Let it roll / I want a little boy / Lullaby of Broadway / Mean and evil / Love for sale / Miss Allen's blues / Baubles, bangles and beads / Man I love / Tea for two
OBCCD 539 / Nov '92 / Original Blues Classics

Allen, Geri

☐ EYES IN THE BACK OF YOUR HEAD
Mother wit / New eyes opening / Vertical flowing / MOPE / FMFFMF / Dark eyes / Little waltz / In the back of your head / Windows to the soul / Eyes have it
CDP 8382972 / Jun '97 / Blue Note

☐ LIVE AT THE VILLAGE VANGUARD (Allen, Geri & Charlie Haden/Paul Motian)
DIW 847 / Jul '91 / DIW

☐ SOME ASPECTS OF WATER (Allen, Geri Trio/1996 Jazzpar Nonet)
STCD 4212 / May '97 / Storyville

Allen, Harry

☐ CELEBRATION OF SAM FAIN (Allen, Harry Trio)
ACD 261 / Jan '93 / Audiophile

☐ CELEBRATION OF STRAYHORN (Allen, Harry & Keith Ingham)
PCD 7101 / Apr '94 / Progressive

☐ CELEBRATION OF STRAYHORN NO.2 (Allen, Harry & Keith Ingham)
PCD 7102 / Apr '94 / Progressive

☐ HARRY ALLEN MEETS THE JOHN PIZZARELLI TRIO
Pennies from heaven / Dear old Stockholm / P-town / you're driving me crazy / Early autumn / I want to be happy / These foolish things / Blue Lou / Body and soul / Sunday / Dot's cheese cake / When Harry met Martin / Polka dots and moonbeams / Limehouse blues
74321373972 / 1 Jun '98 / RCA Victor

☐ HOW LONG HAS THIS BEEN GOING ON
PCD 7082 / '92 / Progressive

☐ I KNOW THAT YOU KNOW (Allen, Harry Trio)
CHECD 00104 / Jul '92 / Master Mix

☐ I'LL NEVER BE THE SAME (Allen, Harry & Howard Alden)
All through the night / I won't dance / I'll close my eyes
CHECD 106 / Jun '93 / Master Mix

☐ JAZZ IN AMERIKA HAUS VOL.1 (Allen, Harry Quartet)
CD 011 / May '96 / Nagel Heyer

☐ LITTLE TOUCH OF HARRY, A (Allen, Harry Quartet)
From this moment on / Luck be a lady tonight / Nobody's heart / Just like another dream / All god's chillun' got rhythm / I wanna be around / This is all I ask / I never knew / It might as well be spring / Spring can really hang up the most / Easy to love / I get along without you very well
CHECD 00118 / Sep '97 / Master Mix

☐ LIVE AT RENOUF'S (Allen, Harry Quartet)
In a mellowtone / Man I love / Nightingale sang in Berkeley Square / Shadow of your smile / Too close for comfort / Ev'ry time we say goodbye / One note samba / Danny boy
CHECD 00117 / Nov '96 / Master Mix

☐ NIGHT AT BIRDLAND VOL.1 (Allen, Harry Quintet)
CD 007 / May '96 / Nagel Heyer

☐ NIGHT AT BIRDLAND VOL.2 (Allen, Harry Quintet)
CD 010 / May '96 / Nagel Heyer

☐ SOMEONE TO LIGHT UP YOUR LIFE (Allen, Harry Quartet)
CHECD 00100 / Apr '92 / Master Mix

☐ TENORS ANYONE
It was just one of those things / Blue and sentimental / Flying home / My favourite things / Lester leaps in / Somewhere over the rainbow / America / Beautiful / Peacocks / Tea for two / If I'm lucky / Cool man chu / Four brothers
74321506842 / 1 Jun '98 / RCA Victor

Allen, Henry 'Red'

☐ CLASSIC YEARS, THE
Bugle call rag / Doggin' that thing / (New) call of the freaks / Sweet sorrow blues / I feel in love with you / Ride Red ride / Whose honey are you / Roamin' / Lookin' good but feelin' bad / Yes yes / Get goin' / Singing pretty songs / Patrol wagon blues / Sweet Sue / Jersey lightning / Feelin' the spirit
CDSGP 0169 / 4 May '98 / Prestige

☐ CLASSICS 1929-1933
CLASSICS 540 / Dec '90 / Classics

☐ CLASSICS 1933-1935
CLASSICS 551 / Dec '90 / Classics

☐ CLASSICS 1935-1936
CLASSICS 575 / Oct '91 / Classics

☐ CLASSICS 1936-1937
CLASSICS 590 / Sep '91 / Classics

☐ CLASSICS 1937-1941
CLASSICS 628 / Oct '92 / Classics

☐ COLLECTION VOL.1, THE
COCD 01 / Dec '89 / Collector's Classics

☐ COLLECTION VOL.2, THE
COCD 02 / Sep '92 / Collector's Classics

☐ COLLECTION VOL.3, THE
COCD 13 / Oct '89 / Collector's Classics

☐ COLLECTION VOL.5 1937-1941, THE
COCD 23 / Oct '97 / Collector's Classics

☐ COLLECTION VOL.6 1941-1946, THE
COCD 24 / Oct '97 / Collector's Classics

☐ DOCTOR JAZZ VOL.9
STCD 6049 / Jul '96 / Storyville

☐ INTRODUCTION TO HENRY 'RED' ALLEN 1929-1941, AN
4031 / Mar '96 / Best Of Jazz

☐ MUSIC OF THE TRUMPET KINGS, THE (Allen, Henry & Randy Sandke/RIAS Big Band Berlin)
I love louis / Cloudy / Echoes of Harlem / Little jazz boogie / I can't get started / Melancholy rhapsody / Randy's Rolls Royce / Shaw'nuff / All blues / Relaxin' at Clifford's / Moontrane / Bird like
CD 037 / Aug '97 / Nagel Heyer

☐ ORIGINAL 1933-1941
River's takin' care of me / Believe it, beloved / Rosetta / Body and soul / He ain't got rhythm / KK boogie / Jack the bellboy / When my dreamboat comes home
TAXS 32 / Aug '94 / Tax

☐ SWING OUT
TPZ 1037 / Jan '96 / Topaz Jazz

Allen, Pete

☐ ALL ABOARD FOR ALABAMA (Allen, Pete Jazz Band)
LOTCD 4306 / Feb '98 / Loose Tie

☐ BEAU SEJOUR
Seagull strut / Body and soul / I'm gonna sit right down and write myself a letter / St. Phillip's street breakdown / Elephant stomp / Roses of Picardy
PAR 492CD / Apr '91 / PAR

☐ BIG CHIEF (Allen, Pete Jazz Band)
LOTCD 4305 / Nov '96 / Loose Tie

☐ JAZZ YOU LIKE IT (Allen, Pete & Clinton Ford)
Royal Garden blues / Melancholy baby / Swanee River / Apple blossom time / Mood indigo / Sailing down the Chesapeake Bay / Georgia / Wreck of ol' 97
PAR 491CD / Apr '91 / PAR

☐ OH PLAY THAT THING (Allen, Pete Jazz Band)
South Rampart Street Parade / Creole love call / Dans les rues d'antibes / Sunshine of love / Buddy's habits / On the sunny side of the street / White cliffs of Dover / Annie May's cakewalk / My cross eyed cutie / Promenade aux Champs Elysees / Black bottom stomp / Last night on the back porch / St, Philip street breakdown / Creole belles / My Monday date / Just a wearyin' for you / Dippermouth blues
LOTCD 4311 / Jun '98 / Loose Tie

Allen, Peter

☐ PETER ALLEN
RVCD 53 / Mar '96 / Raven

Allen, Red

☐ KITCHEN TAPES, THE (Allen, Red & Frank Wakefield)
ACD 11 / Jul '97 / Acoustic Disc

Allen, Rex

☐ VOICE OF THE WEST
Tyin' knots in the Devil's tail / Moonshine steer / Fireman cowboy / Today I started loving you again / Windy Bill / Little Joe the wrangler / When the work's all done this fall / Droop ears / Streets of Laredo / Braggin' drunk from Wilcox / Gone girl / Catfish John / You never did give up on me / Just call me lonesome / Reflex reaction
BCD 15284 / Aug '86 / Bear Family

Allen, Rex

☐ REX ALLEN & HIS SWING EXPRESS
CD 016 / May '96 / Nagel Heyer

Allen, Steve

☐ STEVE ALLEN PLAYS JAZZ TONIGHT
Tangerine / One I love (belongs to somebody else) / Body and soul / After you've gone / Don't cry little girl / Steve's blues / Gone with the wind / Sinner kissed an angel / You go to my head / I can't get started (with you) / Everyone can see how much I love you / I should have told you so / Fine and dandy
CCD 4548 / May '93 / Concord Jazz

Allen, Terry

☐ HUMAN REMAINS
SHCD 1050 / Feb '96 / Sugar Hill

☐ LUBBOCK (ON EVERYTHING)
Amarillo highway / Highplains jamboree / Great Joe Bob / Wolfman of del rio / Lubbock woman / Girl who danced Oklahoma / Truckload of art / Collector (and the art mob) / Oui / Rendevous USA / Cocktails for three / Beautiful waitress / Blue asian reds / New Delhi freight rain / FFA / Flatland farmer / My amigo / Pink and black song / Thirty years waltz / I just left myself
SHCD 1047 / Mar '98 / Sugar Hill

☐ PEDAL STEAL (Allen, Terry & The Panhandle Mystery Band)
FATE 7655266 / Apr '93 / Fate

☐ SILENT MAJORITY, THE
FATE 7453266 / May '93 / Fate

☐ SMOKIN' THE DUMMY
Heart of California / Cocaine cowboy / Whatever happened to jesus / Helena Montana / Texas tears / Cajun roll / Feelin' easy / Night Cafe / Roll truck roll / Red bird / Lubbock tornado (I don't know)
FRCD 02 / '92 / Fate

☐ SMOKIN' THE DUMMY/BLOODLINES (Allen, Terry & The Panhandle Mystery Band)
Heart of California / Whatever happened to Jesus (and Maybellene) / Helena Montana / Texas tears / Feelin easy / Night cafe / Rock truck roll / Red bird / Lubbock tornado (I don't know) / Bloodlines / Gimme a ride to heaven boy / Cantina Carlotta / Ourland / Oh Hally Lou / Oh what a dangerous life / Manhatten bluebird / There outta be a law against sunny Southern California / Bloodlines
SHCD 1057 / Mar '98 / Sugar Hill

Allen, Thomas

☐ IF I LOVED YOU (Allen, Thomas & Valerie Masterson)
VIRCD 8317 / Nov '93 / Shanachie

Alleyne-Johnson, Ed

☐ 20-20 VISION (Alleyne-Johnson, Ed & Denyze)
WINGCD 002 / 26 Jan '98 / Wingspan

☐ FLY BEFORE DAWN
WINGCD 001 / Jul '95 / Wingspan

☐ PURPLE ELECTRIC VIOLIN CONCERTO
Oxford suite / Inner city music / Improvisation / Concrete eden
EQCD 001 / Feb '93 / Equation

☐ ULTRAVIOLET
EQCD 002 / Jun '94 / Equation

Alliance

☐ ALLIANCE
ESM 012 / 2 Mar '98 / Escape

Alligators

☐ HISTORY OF ROCK 'N' ROLL, THE
POCD 015 / Aug '96 / Popcorn

Allin, G.G.

☐ HATED IN THE NATION
RE 148CD / Nov '94 / ROIR

☐ HATED IN THE NATION
RUSCD 8242 / 20 Jul '98 / ROIR

☐ MURDER JUNKIES
422008 / May '94 / New Rose

☐ TERROR IN AMERICA
OVER 43CD / Nov '95 / Overground

☐ TROUBLED TROUBADOUR
MCDLP 008 / Nov '97 / Mountain

Allin, Ralph

☐ TEA FOR THREE
Nightingale sang in Berkeley square / Hungarian dance no.5 / Liebesleid / Cheek to cheek / Misty / Ain't misbehavin' / Play gypsy dance / Georgia on my mind / Tango / Czardas / Memory / Entertainer / Salut d'amour / I can't give you anything but love / Way down yonder in New Orleans / Largo from Winter, four seasons / Yesterday / Josika / I know him so well / Tea for two / Summertime / Fiddler on the roof
CDGRS 1246 / '91 / Grosvenor

Allis, Julie

☐ TRANQUIL SOUND OF THE HARP, THE
PLSCD 288 / 1 Jun '98 / Pulse

Allison

☐ WAILING
NGCD 544 / Jul '94 / Twinkle

Allison, Amy

☐ MAUDLIN YEARS, THE
379112 / Sep '96 / Koch International

Allison, Ben

☐ SEVEN ARROWS
378322 / Nov '96 / Koch Jazz

Allison, Bernard

☐ BORN WITH THE BLUES
Baby chile / Tell me why / Walkin' / Young boy's blues / In the open / You gave me the blues / Home goin' / When I'm lonely / Change must come / Rocket 88 / Garbage man
RUF 1017 / 29 Sep '97 / Ruf

☐ NO MERCY
Rock me baby / Don't go to sleep on me / Break 'in up somebody' home / Change your way of living / Driven wheel / Next generation / Boo boo's boogie / Tin pan alley / Help
INAK 9029CD / Nov '97 / In Akustik

Allison, David

☐ ACOUSTIC MOVES
Christmas eve 1950 / Big reach / Lost tribe / Summer rain / Raga / Corrunich / Gathering in rattlesnake country / Spirit of Italy / Street / Connel / Sangita / Japanese garden / Communique / I'm on my way / End credits
SMD 614 / Mar '98 / Smiddy Made

☐ GUITAR GI-TAR
LDL 1211CD / Mar '94 / Lochshore

☐ REPORTING
Birnam oak / Dreamdays / Excuse me / Ceuta / Chinese whispers / Ishka / Spiral / Journey / Something more comfortable / Forgive, forget... / Border / Going home
DUNCD 007 / Feb '92 / Dunkeld

Allison, Luther

☐ BAD LOVE
RUF 1021 / Feb '98 / Ruf

☐ BLUE STREAK
RUF 7712 / Feb '98 / Ruf

☐ HAND ME DOWN MY MOONSHINE
Good morning love / One more / Lightning bolt / I need a friend / Castle / She's fine / Stay with me / Farmer's child / Don't burn my bread / You're the one / Hand me down my moonshine / Meet me in my hometown
INAK 9015CD / Jul '97 / In Akustik

☐ HERE I COME
493332 / Mar '96 / Melodie

☐ LIFE IS A BITCH
493312 / Mar '96 / Melodie

☐ LIVE 1989
RRCD 901309 / Apr '95 / Ruf

☐ LIVE IN MONTREUX 1974-1994
RUF 1008 / Feb '98 / Ruf

☐ LOVE ME MAMA
DE 625 / Nov '96 / Delmark

☐ LOVE ME PAPA
ECD 260152 / Jan '92 / Evidence

☐ RECKLESS
ALCD 4849 / May '97 / Alligator
RUF 1012 / Feb '98 / Ruf

☐ RICH MAN
Chicago / Rich man / Love is free / Cold as ice / Freedom / Fight / Big mistake / Get down / Cry (crying for peace)
TRIP 8001 / Apr '96 / Ruf

☐ SWEET HOME CHICAGO (Charly Blues Masterworks Vol.37)
Dust my broom / I got worries / You don't love me / Goin' down / I'm gonna leave you alone / Sweet home Chicago
CDBM 37 / Jan '93 / Charly

Allison, Mose

☐ AUTUMN SONG
Promenade / Eyesight to the blind / It's crazy / That's alright Mama / Devil in the cane field / Strange / Autumn song / Do nothin' 'til you hear from me / Spires / Groovin' high
OJCCD 894 / Nov '96 / Original Jazz Classics

☐ BEST OF MOSE ALLISON, THE
I don't worry about a thing / Your mind is on vacation / It didn't turn out that way / If you're going to the city / Swingin' machine / I ain't got nothin' but the blues / Stop this world / I'm the wild man / New parchman / Rollin' stone / Don't forget to smile / Seventh son / I love the life I live, I live the life I love / What's with you / That's the stuff you gotta watch / Your molecular structure / Just like livin' / Everybody cryin' mercy / Night club / One of these days
RSACD 814 / Oct '94 / Sequel

☐ DOWN HOME PIANO
Dinner on the ground / Crepuscular air / Mule / Creek bank / Town / Devil in the cane field / Minstrels / Moon and cypress / Carnival / Mojo woman
OJCCD 922 / Jun '97 / Original Jazz Classics

☐ EARTH WANTS YOU, THE
Certified senior citizen / This ain't me / You can't push people around / My ideal / Earth wants you / Cabaret cards / Red wagon / Variation on Dixie / What a shame / Nataral born Malcontent / Who's in, who's out / Children of the future / I don't love you
CDP 8276402 / Dec '95 / Blue Note

☐ GIMCRACKS AND GEWGAWS
Gimcracks and gewgaws / Numbers on paper / Cruise control / St Louis blues / Mockingbird / More you get / Texanna / What will it be / So tired / Somebody gonna have to move / Fires of spring / What's with you / Old man blues
8232112 / 12 Jan '98 / Blue Note

☐ HIGH JINKS (The Mose Allison Trilogy/ 3CD Set)
Transfiguration of Hiram Brown suite / Barefoot, dirt road / City home / Cuttin' out / Gotham day / Gotham night / Ech / River / Finale / How little we know / Baby, please don't go / Make yourself comfortable / Deed I do / Love for sale / Barefoot, dirt road / I love the life I live / News / Fool's paradise / You turned the tables on me / Isobel / You're a sweetheart / Night ride / Path / Mad with you / Hittin' on one / I ain't got nobody / Can't we be friends / Pretty girl is like a melody / Am I blue / V8 Ford blues / Please don't talk about me when I'm gone / Baby, please don't go / Hey, good lookin' / I love the life I live / A ain't got nobody / Back on the corner / Life is suicide / Deed I do / Ask me nice / You're a sweetheart / Mad with you / High jinks / So rare / Hills
J3K 64275 / Feb '97 / Sony Jazz

☐ JAZZ PROFILE
Ever since the world ended / Top forty / Putting up with me / I looked in the mirror / Getting there / What's your movie / Ever since I stole the blues / Was / Getting paid waltz / My backyard / Certified senior citizen / This ain't me / You can't push people around / Earth wants me
CDP 8552302 / May '97 / Blue Note

☐ MOSE ALLISON SAMPLER
Don't get around much anymore / Parchman Farm / Seventh son / I hadn't anyone till you / Mojo woman / Moon and cypress / Blueberry Hill / I'll never be free
OJCX 009 / Jan '98 / Original Jazz Classics

☐ SAGE OF TIPPO
60412320682 / 19 May '98 / Thirty Two

☐ TELL ME SOMETHING (The Songs Of Mose Allison) (Various Artists)
One of these days: *Morrison, Van* / You can count on me (to do my part): *Morrison, Van* / If you live: *Sidran, Ben* / Was: *Fame, Georgie* / Look here: *Sidran, Ben* / City home: *Fame, Georgie* / No trouble living: *Sidran, Ben* / Benediction: *Morrison, Van & Ben Sidran* / *Georgie Fame* / Back on th corner: *Fame, Georgie* / Tell me something: *Morrison, Van* / I don't want much: *Morrison, Van & Mose Allison* / News nightclub: *Morrison, Van* / Perfect moment: *Morrison, Van & Mose Allison*
5332032 / Sep '96 / Verve

Allman Brothers

☐ ALL LIVE
Jessica / Stormy Monday / Statesboro blues / Can't lose what you never had / Ain't wastin' time no more / Done somebody wrong / Ramblin' man / Don't mess up a good thing / Turn on your love light / Will the circle be unbroken / Queen of hearts
5518242 / Nov '96 / PolyGram

☐ ALLMAN BROTHERS BAND, THE
Don't want you no more / It's not my cross to bear / Black hearted woman / Trouble no more / Every hungry woman / Dreams / Whipping post
5312572 / Jun '98 / Capricorn

☐ BEGINNINGS
Black hearted woman / Trouble no more / Every hungry woman / Dreams / Whipping post / Revival / Don't keep me wonderin' / Midnight rider / In memory of Elizabeth Reed / Hoochie coochie man / Please call home / Leave my blues at home / Don't want you no more / It's not my cross to bear
5312592 / Jun '98 / Capricorn

☐ BROTHERS AND SISTERS
Wasted words / Ramblin' man / Come and go blues / Jelly jelly / Southbound / Jessica / Pony boy
5312622 / Jun '98 / Capricorn

☐ BROTHERS OF THE ROAD
Brothers of the road / Leaving / Straight from the heart / Heat is on / Maybe we can go back to yesterday / Judgement / Two rights / Never knew how much I needed you / Things you used to do / I beg of you
RE 2132 / Aug '97 / Razor & Tie

☐ DECADE OF HITS 1969-1979, A
Whipping post / Dreams / In memory of Elizabeth Reed / One way out / Blue sky / Wasted words / Revival / Crazy love / Little Martha / Ain't wastin' time no more / Jessica / Melissa / Southbound / Midnight rider / Ramblin' man / Statesboro blues
5111562 / Mar '92 / Polydor

☐ EAT A PEACH
Ain't wastin' time no more / Le bers in A minor / Melissa / Mountain jam / One way out / Trouble no more / Stand back / Blue sky / Little Martha
5312612 / Jun '98 / Capricorn

☐ ENLIGHTENED ROGUES
Crazy love / Can't take it with you / Pegasus / Need your love so bad / Blind love / Try it one more time / Just ain't easy / Sail away
5312652 / Jun '98 / Capricorn

☐ FILLMORE CONCERTS (2CD Set)
5172942 / Apr '96 / Polydor

☐ HELL & HIGH WATER (The Best Of The Arista Years)
Hell and high water / Mystery woman / From the madness of the west / I got a right to be wrong / Angeline / Famous last words / Brothers of the road / Leavin' / Straight from the heart / Judgement / Never knew how much (I needed you)
07822187242 / Sep '94 / RCA

☐ IDLEWILD SOUTH
Revival / Don't keep me wonderin' / Midnight rider / In memory of Elizabeth Reed / Hoochi coochie / Please call home / Leave my blues at home
5312582 / Jun '98 / Capricorn

☐ LIVE AT FILLMORE EAST (2CD Set)
Statesboro blues / (I) done somebody wrong / They call it stormy Monday / You don't love me / Hot lanta / In memory of Elizabeth Reed / Whipping post
8232732 / Jul '88 / Polydor
5312602 / 15 Jun '98 / Capricorn

☐ MADNESS OF THE WEST
Hell and high water / Mystery woman / From the madness of the West / I got a right to be wrong / Angeline / Famous last words / Keep on keepin' on / So long / Brothers of the road / Leavin' / Straight from the heart / Heat is on / Maybe we can go back to yesterday / Judgement / Two rights / Never knew how much (I needed you) / Things you used to do
743215696124 / 23 Mar '98 / Camden

☐ MYCOLOGY
Good clean fun / Seven turns / End of the line / Get on with your life / Nobody knows / No-one to run with / Back where it all begins / Sailin' 'cross the Devil's sea / Midnight rider / Every hungy woman
4890872 / 8 Jun '98 / Epic

☐ REACH FOR THE SKY
Hell and high water / Mystery woman / From the madness of the West / I got a right to be wrong / Angeline / Famous last words / So long
RE 2131 / Aug '97 / Razor & Tie

☐ WIN, LOSE OR DRAW
Can't lose what you never had / Just another love song / Nevertheless / Win, lose or draw / Louisiana Lou and Three Card Monty John / High falls / Sweet mama
5312632 / Jun '98 / Capricorn

☐ WIPE THE WINDOWS CHECK THE OIL DOLLAR GAS
Wasted words / Southbound / Ramblin' man / In memory of Elizabeth Reed / Ain't wastin' time no more / Come and go blues / Can't lose what you never had / Don't want you no more / It's not my cross to bear / Jessica / Introduction
5312642 / Jun '98 / Capricorn

Allman, Duane

☐ ANTHOLOGY, AN (2CD Set)
8314442 / Apr '89 / Polydor

Allman, Greg

☐ SEARCHING FOR SIMPLICITY
Whippin' post / House of blues / Come back and help me / Silence ain't golden no more / Rendezvous with the blues / Wolf's a howlin' / Love the poison / Don't deny me / Dark end of the street / Neighbour neighbour / I've got news for you / Memphis in the meantime / Startin' over
4816912 / 5 Jan '98 / Epic

Alloy

☐ ALLOY
VROOM 4 / Aug '93 / Engine

Allred, John

☐ IN THE BEGINNING
ARCD 19115 / Nov '94 / Arbors Jazz

Allure

☐ ALLURE
Introduction / Anything you want / You're gonna love me / Head over heels / No question / All cried out / Story / Come into my house / When you need someone / Give you all I got / I'll give you anything / Wanna get with you / Last chance / Mama said
4875242 / May '97 / Crave

Allyn, David

☐ SOFT AS SPRING
ACD 155 / Jan '94 / Audiophile

Allyson, Karrin

☐ AZURE-TE
How high the moon / Ornithology / Gee baby / Bernie's tune / Night and day / Blame it on my youth / Yardbird suite / Good morning heartache / Stompin' at the Savoy / Azure te / Some other time / Samba '88
CCD 4641 / May '95 / Concord Jazz

☐ COLLAGE
It could happen to you / Fried bananas / Autumn leaves (Les fueilles mortes) / Robert Frost / All of you / And so it goes / Joy Spring / Ask me now / Cherokee / Here, there and everywhere / Give it up or let me go / Faltando um pedaco / Live for life
CCD 4709 / Jul '96 / Concord Crossover

☐ DAYDREAM
Daydream / Like someone in love / My foolish heart / So danca samba / Corcovado / Show me / Monk medley / Everything must change/Donna Lee/ Indiana / I ain't got nothin' but the blues / You can't rush spring
CCD 47732 / Sep '97 / Concord Jazz

☐ SWEET HOME COOKIN'
One note samba / I cover the waterfront / Can't we be friends / Yeh yeh / Goodbye Pork Pie Hat / No moon at all / Sweet home cookin' man / You are too beautiful / Social call / Dindi / In a sentimental mood / I love Paris
CCD 4593 / Apr '94 / Concord Jazz

Alma Flamenca

☐ ANDALUCIA VIVA
31064 / Oct '96 / Divusca

Almadraba

☐ CANTOS DEL CAMPO Y DE LA MER
CDH 008 / Dec '94 / Sonifolk

Almanac Singers

☐ JAZZERS AND GROOVERS
CDOK 3010 / Dec '97 / Lochshore

Almanzor

☐ TRIO DE VEUZE BRETAGNE
AVPL 14CD / Apr '95 / Diffusion Breizh

Almario, Justo

☐ INTERLUDE
CDGR 240 / 1 Jun '98 / Charly

Almeida, Laurindo

☐ ARTISTRY IN RHYTHM (Almeida, Laurindo Trio)
Chariots of fire / Astronauta / Andante / Te amo / Artistry in rhythm / Always on my mind / Slaughter on 10th Avenue / Up where we belong / Almost a farewell / Liza / Puka shells in a whirl
CCD 4238 / Mar '94 / Concord Jazz

☐ BRAZILIAN SOUL (Almeida, Laurindo & Charlie Byrd)
Carioca / Naquele tempo / Cochichando / Luperce / Famoso / Choro il / Brazilian soul / Stone flower / For jeff / Don't cry for me argentina
CCD 4150 / Jul '88 / Concord Picante

☐ CHAMBER JAZZ
Dingue li bangue / Unaccustomed Bach / Odeon / Bourree and double / Melissa / You and I / Clair de Lune / Chopin a la breve / Turuna
CCD 4084 / May '91 / Concord Jazz

☐ DANCE THE BOSSA NOVA
Lisbon antigua / Meditation (meditacao) / O barquinho (little boat) / More / Danke schoen / I left my heart in san francisco / Satin doll / Heartaches / I will follow him (chariot) / Recado bossa nova / Hava nagila / Fly me to the moon (in other words) / Rio bonita (beautiful rio) / Till then / Sukiyakl / Say wonderful things / What kind of fool am I / Alley cat song
CD 62055 / May '94 / Saludos Amigos

☐ LATIN ODYSSEY (Almeida, Laurindo & Charlie Byrd)
Memory / Zum and ressurection / El nino / Gitanerias / Adios / El cavilan / Estrellita / Turbilhao / Intermezzo malinconico
CCD 4211 / Jan '90 / Concord Picante

☐ MUSIC OF THE BRAZILIAN MASTERS (Almeida, Laurindo & Charlie Byrd)
Escorregando / Aindo me recordo / Rosa / Baia / Didl / Retratos / Invocation to shango / Veleiro / O boto / Valsa de esquina, no.8 / Modinha / Vou vivendo / Weekend cruise to catalina / Promises
CCD 4389 / Oct '89 / New Note

☐ OUTRA VEZ (ONCE AGAIN)
Outra vez / Jolly crow / Danza five / Blue skies / Goin' home / Samba de break / Beethoven and Monk / Esacdo / Um a zero / Carinhoso / Corcovado / Girl from Ipanema / Desafinado
CCD 4497 / Feb '92 / Concord Jazz

☐ TANGO (Almeida, Laurindo & Charlie Byrd)
Orchids in the moonlight / Blue tango / Jalousie / Los enamorados / La Rosita / Tanog alegre / La cumparsita / Moon was yellow / Hernando's hideaway / Tanguero / Breakin' away: *Laima*
CCD 4290 / Jul '88 / Concord Picante

Almighty

☐ CRANK
Ultraviolet / Wrench / Unreal thing / Jonestown mind / Move right in / Crank and deceit / United state of apathy / Welcome to defiance / Way beyond belief / Crackdown / Sorry for nothing / Cheat / Shitzophrenic
CDCHR 6086 / Sep '94 / Chrysalis

☐ JUST FOR LIFE
RAWCD 118 / May '96 / Raw Power

☐ SOUL DESTRUCTION
Crucify / Free 'n' easy / Joy bang one time / Love religion / Bandaged knees / Praying to the red light / Sin against the light / Little lost sometimes / Devil's toy / What more do you want / Hell to pay / Loaded
8479612 / Mar '96 / Polydor

Almighty Dread

☐ EMERGENCY
SPCD 02 / 8 Jun '98 / Dynamics

Almlof, Kalle

☐ LEJSMELATAR
GCD 30 / Dec '97 / Giga

Almond, Marc

☐ FANTASTIC STAR
Caged / Out there / We need jealousy / Idol (parts 1 and 2 All Gods fall) / Baby night eyes / Adored and explored / Child star / Looking for love (in all the wrong places) / Addicted / Edge of heartbreak / Love to die for / Betrayed / On the prowl / Come in sweet assassin / Brilliant creatures / Shining brightly
5286592 / 15 Sep '97 / Some Bizarre

☐ FLESH VOLCANO/SLUT (Almond, Marc & Foetus)
Flesh volcano/Slut / Universal cesspool / Bruise 'n' chain / Love amongst the ruined / Burning boats / Million manias / Beat out the rhythm on a drum
SBZ 034CD / 10 Nov '97 / Some Bizarre

☐ MOTHER FIST AND HER FIVE DAUGHTERS (CD/Rom)
Mother Fist / There is a bed / Saint Judy / Room below / Angel in her kiss / Hustler / Melancholy rose / Mister Sad / Sea says / Champ / Ruby red / River / Melancholy rose / Ruby red
SBZCD 031 / 3 Nov '97 / Some Bizarre

☐ STORIES OF JOHNNY (CD/Rom)
Traumas, traumas, traumas / Stories of Johnny / House is haunted / Love letters / Flesh is willing / Always / Contempt / I who never / My candle burns / Loves little white lies / Stories of Johnny / House is haunted / Love letters
SBZCD 030 / 27 Oct '97 / Some Bizarre

☐ TENEMENT SYMPHONY
Meet me in my dream / Beautiful brutal thing / I've never seen your face / Vaudeville and burlesque / Champagne / Prelude / Jackie / What is love / Trois chansons de bilitis / Days of Pearly Spencer / My hand over my heart
9031755182 / Feb '95 / Some Bizarre/ WEA

☐ TORMENT AND TOREROS (2CD Set) (Marc & The Mambas)
Intro / Boss cat / Bulls / Catch a fallen star / Animal in you / In my room / First time / (Your love is a) Lesion / My former self / Once was / Untouchable one / Blood wedding / Black heart / Narcissus/Gloomy Sunday/ Vision / Torment / Million manias / My little book of sorrows / Beat out that rhythm on a drum
SBZ 028CD / 10 Nov '97 / Some Bizarre

☐ TWELVE YEARS OF TEARS
Tears run rings / Champagne / Bedsitter / Mr. Sad / There is a bed / Youth / If you go away / Jackie / Desperate hours / Waifs and strays / Something's gotten hold of my heart / What makes a man / Tainted love / Say hello, wave goodbye
4509920332 / Apr '93 / Some Bizarre/ WEA

☐ UNTITLED (CD/Rom) (Marc & The Mambas)
Untitled / Empty eyes / Angels / Big Louise / Caroline says / Margaret / If you go away / Terrapin / Twilights and lowlifes / Sleaze / Sleaze
SBZ 027CD / 10 Nov '97 / Some Bizarre

☐ VERMINE IN ERMINE (CD/Rom)
Shining sinners / Hell was like a city / You have / Split up / Crime sublime / Gutter hearts / Ugly head / Boy who came back / Solo adultos / Joey Demento / Pink slack blues / Tenderness is a weakness / You have / Boy who came back / Tenderness is a weakness
SBZ 029CD / 10 Nov '97 / Some Bizarre

☐ VIOLENT SILENCE (Almond, Marc & Foetus)
Universal cess pool / Bruise 'n' chain / Flesh volcano (slut) / Blood tide / Healthy as hate / Things you love me for / Body unknown / Unborn stillborn
SBZCD 022 / 15 Sep '97 / Some Bizarre

☐ VIOLENT SILENCE/A WOMAN'S STORY (CD/Rom)
Indigo blue / Woman's story / Heel / Salty dog / Plague / Little white cloud that cried / For one moment / Just good friends / Oily black limousine / Blood tide / Healthy as hate / Things you love me for / Body unknown / Unborn stillborn / Woman's story
SBZ 035CD / 10 Nov '97 / Some Bizarre

☐ VIRGIN'S TALE VOL.1, A
Stories of Johnny / Love letter / Blond boy / House is Haunted / Broken bracelets / Cara Cara / Heel / Salty dog / Plague / Little white cloud that cried / For one moment / Just good friends
SBZ 032CD / 17 Nov '97 / Some Bizarre

☐ VIRGIN'S TALE VOL.2, A
Gyp of the blood / World full of people / Black lullabye / Pirate Jenny / Surabaya Johnny / Two sailors on the beach / Anarcoma / Jackal jackal / Broken hearted and beautiful / I'm sick of you tasting of somebody else
SBZ 033CD / 10 Nov '97 / Some Bizarre

Almqvist, Peter

☐ PETER ALMQVIST TRIO & HORACE PARLAN (Almqvist, Peter Trio & Horace Parlan)
STCD 4205 / Aug '97 / Storyville

Almqvist, Thomas

☐ REWIND
Intro / Traces of pangaea / Voice of the moth / No sense / Borders / Hot fingers / Quebec / Sun signs / Michael's butterfly / Conscious dreams / Shadow of a black crow / Changing winds / Sortie
RESCD 513 / Jul '97 / Resource

Alonso, Tom

☐ INDIAN SUMMER
Indian summer / Pearl / Mashed potato valley breakdown / Blue hearts / Don't forget to dream / Rain / Cold coffee suite / Screenscape
CCD 711 / Nov '96 / Clean Cuts

Alonson, Pachito

☐ UNA SALSA EN PARIS
74321433542 / Feb '97 / Milan

Aloof

☐ COVER THE CRIME
Favelas / Circumstances / Society / Too high / Victim (version) / Excursion / Mind / Cover the crime / Religion
0630102322 / May '95 / East West

☐ SEEKING PLEASURE
Morning spangle / What I miss the most / Going home / I find fun / N89 / All I want is you / Lies / Wasting away / Personality / Alone
3984240542 / 24 Aug '98 / East West

☐ SINKIN'
Stuck on the shelf / Bitter sweet / One night stand / Sinking / Last stand / Losing it / Hot knives at lunchtime / Space dust / Sunk / Wish you were here / Abuse
0630145842 / Jun '96 / East West

☐ SINKING
One night stand / Bittersweet / Stuck on the shelf / Abuse / Wish you were here / Sinking / One night stand / Hot knives at lunchtime / Losing it / Sunk / Last stand
0630177392 / Mar '97 / East West

Alpamayo

☐ FOLKLORE DE PERU Y ECUADOR
EUCD 1220 / Sep '93 / ARC

☐ MUSIC FROM PERU AND ECUADOR
EUCD 1184 / Apr '92 / ARC

Alperin, Mikhail

☐ WAVE OF SORROW (Alperin, Mikhail & Arkady Shilkloper)
Song / Poem / Wave of sorrow / Toccata / Unisons / Introduction and dance / Short storey / Prelude in B minor / Miniature / Epilogue
8396212 / Jan '90 / ECM

Alperin, Misha

☐ NORTH STORY
Morning / Psalm No.1 / Ironical evening / Alone / Afternoon / Psalm No.2 / North story / Etude / Kristi blodsdraper (Fucsia)
5310222 / May '97 / ECM

Alpert, Herb

☐ SECOND WIND
ALMCD 010 / Jul '96 / Almo Sounds

Alpert, Pauline

☐ KEYBOARD WIZARDS OF THE GERSHWIN ERA VOL.1
Rain on the roof / Glow worm / Fascinatin' rhythm / Song of india / Girl friend / Dream of a doll / Church mouse on a spree / Whistle while you work / Louise / Magnolia / Hallelujah / Doll dance / Continental / Say it with music / Mountain greenery / American patrol / Piccolino / Lover / Between the devil / Carioca / Piano poker / Merry minnow / Hooray for what / Hungarian rhapsody / Sweet sue / Toy trumpet / Where or when
GEMMCD 9201 / Dec '95 / Pearl

Alpha & Omega

☐ ALMIGHTY JAH (Alpha & Omega & Dub Judah)
AOCD 77 / Oct '92 / Alpha & Omega

☐ DANIEL/KING & QUEEN
AOCD 1 / Nov '93 / Alpha & Omega

☐ DUB PLATE SELECTION VOL.1
AOCD 95 / Apr '95 / Alpha & Omega

☐ DUB PLATE SELECTION VOL.2
Promised land / Dub signs / Shashamani / Ancient wisdom / Jerusalem / Jah is calling / Warrior / King and queen / Stepping up / Firmament / No man's land / Africa Ethiopia
AOCD 98 / Apr '97 / Alpha & Omega

☐ EVERYDAY LIFE
AOCD 93 / Jun '93 / Alpha & Omega

☐ FAITH IN THE DARK
AOCD 94 / Mar '94 / Alpha & Omega

☐ OVERSTANDING/WATCH & PRAY
AOCD 27 / Sep '93 / Alpha & Omega

☐ SIGNS, THE
BTT 0292 / Aug '94 / Buback

☐ SOUND SYSTEM DUB
RUSCD 8216 / Oct '95 / ROIR

☐ TREE OF LIFE
AOCD 96 / Nov '95 / Alpha & Omega

☐ VOICE IN THE WILDERNESS
Words of thy mouth / Rastafari / Firmament / Voice in the wilderness / Seven seas / Rightful ruler / Dub prophet / This judgement / Ancient of days / Shashamani / Break every chain / Words
AOCD 97 / Oct '96 / Alpha & Omega

Alpha

☐ COME FROM HEAVEN
My things / Rain / Sometime later / Delaney / Hazledub / Slim / Come from heaven / Back / Nyquil / Apple orange / With / Herb / Somewhere
CDSAD 2 / 15 Sep '97 / Melankolic

Alpha Band

☐ INTERVIEWS (Alpha Band & T-Bone Burnett)
Interviews / Cheap perfume / Ten figures / Dogs / Last chance to dance / East of East / You angel you / Spark in the dark / Rich man / Mighty man / Back in my baby's arms again
EDCD 272 / Jul '91 / Edsel

Alpha Blondy

☐ BEST OF ALPHA BLONDY, THE
SHANCD 43075 / Oct '90 / Shanachie
CDRRS 034 / Oct '96 / Jayrem

☐ BEST OF ALPHA BLONDY, THE
Cocody rock / Apartheid is Nazism / Come back Jesus / Jerusalem / Politiqui / Sweet Fanta Diallo / Banana / Cafe Cacao / Masada / Rendezvous / Yeye / Fulgence kassy / Amour papier / Longeur
CDEMC 3746 / Mar '96 / Premier/EMI

☐ COCODY ROCK
Cocody rock / Tere / Super powers / Interplanetary revolution / Fangandan kameleba / Bory samory
SH 64011 / Dec '94 / Shanachie

☐ JERUSALEM (Alpha Blondy & The Wailers)
Jerusalem / Politique / Bloodshed in Africa / I love Paris / Kalachnikov love / Travailler c'est trop dur / Miwa / Poultevard de la mort / Dji
SHCD 43054 / Mar '98 / Shanachie

☐ RASTA POUE
387262 / Nov '92 / Syllart

Alpha Jerk

☐ ALPHA JERK
TBX 010 / 17 Aug '98 / Toybox

Alpha Seven

☐ GREAT LIFT JOURNEYS OF NORWICH & OTHER STORIES
AFOS 2 / Jan '97 / Sofacom

Alpha Stone

☐ ELASTICATED WAVEBAND
RAPTCD 18 / 3 Aug '98 / Enraptured

Alphastone

☐ STEREOPHONIC POP ART MUSIC
BCD 4054 / Sep '96 / Bomp

Alphaville

☐ FOREVER YOUNG
Victory of love / Summer in Berlin / Big in Japan / To Germany with love / Fallen angel / Forever young / In the mood / Sounds like a melody / Jet set / Lies
2404812 / Nov '84 / WEA

Alquimia

☐ SEPARATE REALITY, A
AMPCD 037 / 29 Jun '98 / AMP

Altamont

☐ ALTAMONT/ACID KING (Altamont/ Acid King)
MR 088CD / Sep '97 / Man's Ruin

Altan

☐ ALTAN
Cat that ate the candle/Over the water to Bessie / An tSeanchaileach Ghallda/Dermot Byrne's / Lass of Glenshee / Tommy Peoples/Loch Altan/Danny Meehan's / Ta mo Chleamhnas a Dheanamh / Come ye by Atholl/Kitty O'Connor / An FeochanWedding jig/Huddai Galagher's march / A Bhean Udai Thall / Con Cassidy's Highland/Neilly O'Boyle's Highland and reel / An Feochan / Moll Dubh a Ghleanna / Tommy Bhetty's waltz / Brenda Stubberts/Breen's/ The red box / Paddy's trip to Scotland/Dinky's/ Shetland fiddler
KCD 440 / Jan '97 / Celtic Collections

☐ BEST OF ALTAN, THE
Tommy Peoples/Windmill/Finton McManus's / Moll Dubh a' Ghleanna / Jimmy Lyon's/The teelin/The red crow/The broken bridge / Sunset / Glory reel/ Heathery Cruach / Flower of Magherally / Mazurka / A Bhean Udai Thall / King of the pipers / 'Si do Mhaimeo I / Jug of punch / Emyvale/Ril gan ainm/ Three merry sisters of fate / An Mhaighdean Mhara / Dulaman / Drowsy Maggie/Rakish Paddy/Harvest storm / An Feochan
GLCD 1177 / Feb '97 / Green Linnet

☐ BLACKWATER
Johnny Boyle's / King of the pipers / Dark haired lass / Biddy from Muckross / Sean Maguire's 'stor a stor a ghra / Strathspey / Con McGinley's / Newfoundland reel ta me 'mo shui / An gasur mor / Bunker hill / Among the bushes / Molly na gcuach ni chilleanain / Jenny picking cockles / Farewell to Leitrim / John Doherty's ar bhruach na carraige baine / Dance of the honeybees / Blackwaterside / Tune for Frankie
CDV 2796 / Mar '96 / Virgin

☐ ESSENTIAL ALTAN
REMCD 500 / Feb '98 / Reactive

☐ FIRST TEN YEARS, THE (1986-1995)
GLCD 1153 / May '95 / Green Linnet

☐ HARVEST STORM
Pretty Peg/New ships a-sailing/Bird's nest/Man from Bundoran / Donal Agus Morag / King of the pipers / Seamus O'Shanahan's/Walking in Liffey Street / Mo choill / Snowy path / Drowsy Maggie/ Rakish Paddy/Harvest storm / Si do Mhaimeo / Marley's/Mill na maidi / Rosses highlands / Nobleman's wedding / Bog an Lochain/Margaree reel/Humours of Westport / Dobbin's flowery vale
GLCD 1117 / '92 / Green Linnet

☐ HORSE WITH A HEART
Curlew/McDermott's reel/Three scones of Boxty / Lass of Glenshee / Con Cassidy's and Neil Gow's highlands/Moll and Tiarna / McSweeney's reels / Road to Durham / An t-Oilean Ur / An grianan/Horse with a heart / Bhean udai thall / Welcome home grainne/Con McGinley's / Tuirse mo chroi / Come ye bey atholl/Kitty O'Connor / An feochan / Paddy's trip to Scotland/Dinky's/Shetland fiddlers
GLCD 1095 / Aug '89 / Green Linnet

☐ ISLAND ANGEL
Tommy Peoples/The windmill/Fintan McManus / Brid og ni Mhaille / Fernanagh highland/Donegal highland/John Doherty's / King George IV / An Mhaighdean Mhara / Andy De Jarlis/Ingonish/Mrs. McGhee / Humours of Andytown/Kylebrack rambler/Gladstone / Dulaman / Mazurka / Jug of punch / Glory reel/Heathery cruach / An cailin Gaelach / Drumnagarry/Pirrie wirrie/Big John's / Island angel / Preety Peg/New ships a-sailing/Birds nest/Man from Bundoran
GLCD 1137 / Oct '93 / Green Linnet

☐ RED CROW, THE
GLCD 1109 / Mar '92 / Green Linnet

☐ RUNAWAY SUNDAY
Suil Ghorm / John Doherty's reels / Caide sin don te sin / Germans / Clan Ronald's/JB's reel / Paddy Mac's reel/Kitty Sheain / I wish my love was a red red rose / Mazurka / Australian waters / Moment in time / Ciaran's capers / Citi ni Eoahra / Flood in the holm/ Scots Mary/The dancer's denial / Gleanntain Ghlas Ghaoth Dobhair / Time has past
CDV 2836 / 28 Jul '97 / Virgin

Altar

☐ PROVOKE
D 00055CD / 17 Aug '98 / Displeased

☐ YOUTH AGAINST CHRIST
D 00033CD / 3 Nov '97 / Displeased

Altena, Maarten

☐ CITIES AND STREETS
ARTCD 6082 / Aug '91 / Hat Art

☐ CODE (Altena, Maarten Ensemble)
ARTCD 6094 / Jan '92 / Hat Art

☐ RIF (Altena, Maarten Octet)
ARTCD 6056 / Nov '90 / Hat Art

Altenberg, Steve

☐ DIG DEEP (Altenberg, Steve Quartet)
Whatever you want / It's easy to remember / Dig deep / Hackensack / Long way from home / Constellation / Coleen / Steve's blues / Very thought of you / Driftwood / Old devil moon
9920202 / 27 Apr '98 / Via Jazz

Alter Ego

☐ MEMOIRES D'OUTREMER
GL 4035CD / Nov '95 / Green Linnet

☐ MEMORIES FROM OVERSEAS
XENO 4035CD / Sep '95 / Xenophile

Alter, Myriam

☐ SILENT WALK (Alter, Myriam Quintet)
CHR 70035 / Sep '96 / Challenge

Altered Images

☐ REFLECTED IMAGES (The Best Of Altered Images)
Intro - Happy Birthday / Dead pop stars / Happy birthday / Love and kisses / Real toys / I could be happy / See those eyes / Pinky blue / Forgotten / See you later / Don't talk to me about love / Bring me closer / Love to stay / Change of heart / Thinking about you / Happy birthday (12" mix) / Don't talk to me about love (12" mix) / Love to stay (12" mix) / Bring me closer (12" mix) / Last goodbye (don't talk to me about love) / Outro - Happy birthday
4843392 / Jul '96 / Epic

Altered States

☐ CAFE 9.15 (Altered States & Ned Rothenberg)
PP 001 / Jan '97 / Phenotype

Alternative Radio

☐ JUST COOK WILL YER (Theme From Hotel)
OCDS 003 / 9 Feb '98 / Ocean Deep

☐ WOOD, WIRE & SKIN
PULCD 3 / Jul '95 / Pulse

Alternative TV

☐ IMAGE HAS CRACKED, THE (Alternative TV Collection)
Alternatives / Action time vision / Why don't you do me right / Good times / Still life / Viva la rock 'n' roll / Nasty little lonely / Red / Splitting in two / Love lies limp / Life / How much longer / You bastard / Another coke / Life after life / Life after dub / Force is blind / Lost in a room / How much longer / You bastard
CDPUNK 24 / Oct '96 / Anagram

☐ INDUSTRIAL SESSIONS, THE
OVER 49CD / Apr '96 / Overground

☐ MY LIFE AS A CHILD STAR
OVER 39CD / Oct '94 / Overground

☐ PEEP SHOW
Chrissie's dream / Let's sleep now / River / Tumbletime / My baby's laughing / Scandal / White walls / Animal
OVER 54CD / Oct '96 / Overground

☐ PUNK LIFE
OVER 70CD / 12 Jan '98 / Overground

☐ RADIO SESSIONS, THE
OVER 44CD / Sep '95 / Overground

☐ VIBING UP THE SENILE MAN/WHAT YOU SEE IS WHAT YOU ARE
CDMGRAM 102 / Mar '96 / Anagram

Alternatives

☐ BUZZ
Pudgy / Sex face / Black hole / Half cheek sneek / Nubbing
SST 245CD / Oct '89 / SST

Alto Summit

☐ ALTO SUMMIT
Blue minor / Summer knows / Minority / Stars fell on Alabama / Autumn in New York / All the things you are / Song for Sass / God bless the child
MCD 92652 / Jan '98 / Milestone

Alton, Roy

☐ BEST OF ROY ALTON, THE
WEMCD 001 / 1 Dec '97 / World Sound

Altrincham Choral Society

☐ SEASON'S GREETINGS
AVC 613 / 1 Dec '97 / Avid

Alva

☐ FAIR-HAIRED GUILLOTINE
AVANT 72 / May '97 / Avant

Alvarez, Adalberto

☐ A BAILAR EL TOCA TOCA
74321401362 / Sep '96 / Milan

☐ MAGISTRAL
Bailala / Como gozan los Cubanos / A la hora de la telenovela / Soy yo no busques mas / Uno nunca sabe / La vi caminando: Alvarez, Adalberto & Michel Camilo / Las puertas del corazon / Por esto te llaman Gil / Mi veneracion / Aun no es tarde
74321491372 / Jul '97 / Milan

Alvarez, Javier

☐ PAPALOTL - TRANSFORMACIONES EXOTICAS
Acuerdos por diferencia / Temazcal / Papaloti / Mannam / Asi el acero
CDSDL 390 / Nov '92 / Saydisc

Alvin & The Chipmunks

☐ CHIPMUNK CHRISTMAS
It's beginning to look like Christmas / Chipmunk jingle bells / Chipmunk song / Spirit of Christmas / Have yourself a merry little Christmas / Crashup's Christmas / Here comes Santa Claus / Silent night / Sleigh ride / Deck the halls with boughs of holly / We wish you a merry Christmas
4727402 / 3 Nov '97 / Columbia

Alvin, Dave

☐ BLACKJACK DAVID
HCD 8091 / 20 Jul '98 / Hightone

☐ BLUE BLVD
DFGCD 8424 / Jun '94 / New Rose

☐ EVERY NIGHT ABOUT THIS TIME
Every night about this time / 4th of July / Long white Cadillac / Romeo's escape / Brother (on the line) / Jubilee train / Border radio / Fire away / New tattoo / You got me / I wish it were Saturday night
DIAB 835 / 26 Jan '98 / Diablo

☐ INTERSTATE CITY (Alvin, Dave & The Guilty Men)
HCD 8074 / Aug '96 / Hightone

☐ KING OF CALIFORNIA
HCD 8054 / Oct '94 / Hightone

☐ MUSEUM OF HEART
HCD 8049 / Jul '94 / Hightone

☐ ROMEO'S ESCAPE
RE 2074 / Jun '96 / Razor & Tie

Alvin, Phil

☐ COUNTRY FAIR 2000
HCD 8056 / Nov '94 / Hightone

Always August

☐ LARGENESS WITH (W)HOLES
Mass man / Watton's bluff / Alien nation / In the dark / Krypto / About time / Rahsaan rollin' cat / It's a wheel
SST 135CD / May '93 / SST

Alzir, Bud

☐ BUD ALZIR
HANCD 2 / Oct '95 / Hansome

AM 4

☐ AND SHE ANSWERED
8396202 / Nov '89 / ECM

Am I Blood

☐ AGITATION
Negative / Examination / Day will be executed / Segregated holocaust / Suicidal solution / Sorrow / Scarr in the head / Final scream / Stains / Suffocated love / Eternal you
NB 3052 / 6 Apr '98 / Nuclear Blast

AM5

☐ THIS IS AM5
MR 5501 / Feb '98 / Moroccanroll

Ama, Shola

☐ MUCH LOVE
You're the one I love / Much love / You might need somebody / Who's loving my baby / Celebrate / I love your ways / We got a vibe / Summer love / (I don't know) Interlude / I can show you / All mine / One love
3984200202 / Sep '97 / WEA

Amalgama

☐ ENCUENTRO
NUBA 7702 / 1 Jun '98 / Nuba

Amalgamation Of Soundz

☐ AMALGAMATION OF SOUNDZ
Tears for Yazd / Maternal blues / Eric / Hut / Fiesta de Castellon / 63rd suite / Cat in the rain / Orchid
FILT 020CD / Jun '97 / Filter

Amant

☐ BEST OF AMANT, THE (If There's Love)
HTCD 90 / 20 Apr '98 / Hot Productions

Amaro Del

☐ WORLD OF GYPSY MUSIC (Amaro Del & Big String Orchestra)
323055 / Feb '94 / Koch

Amarok

☐ CANCIONES DE LOS MUNDOS PERDIDOS
21066CD / Nov '95 / Sonifolk

☐ ELS NOSTRES PETITS AMICS
BCD 001 / May '96 / SBD

Amartichitt, Ooleya Mint

☐ MAURITANIA
3018642 / 24 Feb '98 / Long Distance

Amayon

☐ PURULENCE SPLIT
CDAR 016 / Feb '94 / Adipocre

Amaze Me

☐ AMAZE ME
ZR 1997008 / Jun '98 / Z

☐ DREAM ON
NTHEN 035CD / 16 Feb '98 / Now & Then

Amazing Band

☐ ROAR
FMRCD 40 / Aug '97 / Future

Amazing Blondel

☐ AMAZING BLONDEL/A FEW FACES
Saxon lady / Bethel town mission / Season of the year / Canaan / Shepherd's song / You don't want my love / Love sonnet / Spanish lace / Minstrel's song / Bastard love
EDCD 421 / Mar '95 / Edsel

☐ ENGLAND
Paintings / Seascape / Landscape / Afterglow / Spring air / Cantus firmus to counterpoint / Sinfonia for guitar and strings / Dolor dulcis / Lament to the Earl of Bottesford Beck
EDCD 501 / Nov '96 / Edsel

☐ EVENSONG
Pavan / St. crispin's day / Spring season 3.39 / Willowood / Evensong / Queen of scots / Ploughman / Old moot hall / Lady marion's galliard / Under the greenwood tree / Anthem
EDCD 458 / Feb '96 / Edsel

☐ FANTASIA LINDUM
EDCD 459 / Apr '96 / Edsel

☐ LIVE ABROAD
HTDCD 56 / Apr '96 / HTD

☐ RESTORATION
Benedictus / Praeludium in D / Highwayman / Fugue / Cawdor and widdershins / Aubaird / Love lies bleeding / Edagio / Sir John in love again / Interlude / Road to Sedgemoor / Cawdor revisited
HTDCD 70 / Mar '97 / HTD

Amazing Rhythm Aces

☐ OUT OF THE BLUE
ARA 2 / Oct '97 / Ara

☐ RIDE AGAIN
ARA 1 / 15 Jun '98 / Ara

Amazing Royal Crowns

☐ AMAZING ROYAL CROWNS, THE
Shiverin' in the corner / Do the devil / Fireball stomp / Scene of the crime / Minute with the maker / Gretschy / Mr. Lucky / Rollercoaster / 1965 GTO / King of the joint / Wreckin' machine / If he can't / Harem caravan / Swimming in drinks
VEL 797162 / 15 Jun '98 / Velvel

Amazone

☐ DEMONS
NZ 019CD / Nov '94 / Nova Zembla

Amazulu

☐ AMAZULU
Too good to be forgotten / Excitable / After tonight / All over the world / Things the lonely do / Montego bay / Don't you just know it / Cairo / Moonlight romance / Upright, forward
5521062 / Mar '96 / Spectrum

Ambassadeurs

☐ AMBASSADEURS FEATURING SALIF KEITA (Ambassadeurs & Salif Keita)
Kolangoman / Seidou bahkili / Moussou gnaleden / Super koulou / Sali
ROUCD 5053 / May '94 / Rounder

Ambassadors Of Funk

☐ MONSTER JAM
NOMIS 1CD / Feb '89 / Living Beat

Ambelique

☐ AMBELIQUE SINGS THE CLASSICS
VPCD 1498 / Jun '97 / VP

Amber Asylum

☐ FROZEN IN AMBER
SAG 001CD / Nov '96 / Misanthropy

☐ NATURAL PHILOSOPHY OF LOVE, THE
Cupid / Looking glass / Song of the spider war / Jorinda and Joringel / Poppies
RR 69552 / Jun '97 / Relapse

Ambersunshower

☐ WALTER T. SMITH
GEE 1000572 / 13 Apr '98 / Gee Street

Ambient Disciples

☐ ENTER THE DREAMZONE
Insomnia / Dreaming in the rain / 7 Days and one week / Dreamscape / Last inferno / Fable / Easy dreams / Exception / Pitfall / Dreamchild / Diablo / Driven by you / Distant dreams / Puke
DC 881022 / Jul '97 / Disky

Ambisonic

☐ ECOHERO
Intro / I'm a dead man / Mobilized / Wake up ya sleepy head / Cyber cowboy / Green onozone / Helicopter kinda girl / Blue / Meanwhile downunder / Kaleidescope / Heinrich the psychoanalytic haddock / Orb of x ite / Harley to Hollywood / Outro
NRCD 1036 / 27 Oct '97 / Nation

Ambition Company

☐ MONSTA MASH
Monsta mash / Abracadabra / Okey cokey / Octopus garden / Rockula shaking all over / Time warp / Werewolf of London / Black magic London / Creepy night monster blues / Spirit in the sky / Devil went down to Georgia
CDMFP 6398 / 15 Sep '97 / Music For Pleasure

Ambrose

☐ AMBROSE (Ambrose & His Orchestra)
Don't let that moon get away / Says my heart / Love bug will bite you / Two sleepy people / Rhythm's OK in Harlem / Blue skies are round the corner / Goodnight to you all / I've got a pocketful of dreams / Sailor, where art thou / While a cigarette was burning / Lord and Lady Whoozis / Moon or no moon / Lambeth Walk / Chestnut tree / I may be poor but I'm honest / Oh they're tough, mighty tough, in the West / Ten pretty girls / Organ, the monkey and me / In a little French casino / Fifty million robins can't be wrong / Smile when you say goodbye / Sympathy
CDAJA 5066 / Feb '90 / Living Era

☐ AT THE MAYFAIR HOTEL 1927-1935 (Ambrose & His Orchestra)
Dance little lady / I'm more than satisfied / My heart stood still / My dream memory / Nicolette / Didn't I tell you / Little dream nest / Song of the sea / Somewhere / Then I'll be tired of you / Punch and Judy show / Ambrose's jubilee cavalcade / Humming to myself / For you / Lovable and sweet / 'S wonderful / Me and the man in the moon / Take your finger out of your mouth / Whispering pines of Nevada / Birth of the blues / Adoree' / Chirp chirp / Roll away clouds
PASTCD 9713 / '90 / Flapper

☐ CAN'T HELP SINGING (Ambrose & His Orchestra)
Can't help singing / Oh what it seemed to be / Let's take the long way home / I'd rather be me / In the land of beginning again / Chickery chick / Strange music / Homesick / That's all / Ac-cen-tchu-ate the positive / Kiss me (besame mucho) / Pony express / Nightingale / China moon / On the atchison / Topeka and the Santa Fe / Oasis / It's you that I love / Long ago and far away / Fool with a dream / Nocturne of the oasis / At the crossroads / Symphony / My serenade
RAJCD 892 / 2 Feb '98 / Empress

☐ CONTINENTAL, THE
Continental / Way you look tonight / Fine romance / You and the night and the music / Easter parade / I travel alone / Beautiful lady in blue / My kid's a crooner / I'll be tired of you / Maracas / Carmba / Snowman / Little boy blue / Night was yellow / Lost my man / I'm all in / Keep me in your dreams / Red sails in the sunset / It looks like rain in Cherry Blossom Lane / Too marvellous for words / Stars fell out of Heaven / Until the real thing comes along / Life begins / Lost in a fog / When day is done
CDEA 6002 / Aug '97 / Vocalion

☐ GLAMOUR OF THE THIRTIES (Ambrose & His Orchestra)
You are my lucky star / Piccolino / Cheek to cheek / Stay as sweet as you are / Who's been polishing the sun / Just a wearyin' for you / Man about town / I'll step out of the picture / Wotcha got a trombone for / Why was I born / One-way street / Knock knock, who's there / Squibs / La cuchuracha / I'm gonna wash my hands of you / Yip neddy / College rhythm / Home james and don't spare the horses / Wood and ivory / Dames / I only have eyes for you / Then I'll be tired of you
PASTCD 7055 / Nov '94 / Flapper

Ambrosetti, Flavio

☐ FLAVIO AMBROSETTI ANNIVERSARY 1949-1976 (2CD Set)
Perdido / Dancing on the ceiling / Just one of those things / Out of bush / Flavio's blues / It don't mean a thing / Anthropology / Junior's idea / Gentilino's serenade / Straight no chaser / Our suite dig / Atisiul / Age of prominence / Darn that dream / Blues for Ursula / Moon dreams / Alpen honky tonk
ENJ 90272 / Jul '96 / Enja

Ambrosetti, Franco

☐ LIGHT BREEZE
Versace / Silli's nest / Deborah / Culture and sensitivity / Contempo latinsky / Elegia / My foolish heart / Virtusismo / One for the kids / Percussion dreams / Giant steps / Still in the sky
ENJ 93312 / 26 May '98 / Enja

Ambush

☐ LACH
CC 008CD / May '95 / Common Cause

☐ PIGS
EFA 124062 / Dec '95 / Common Cause

Amduscias

☐ AMDUSCIAS
BLACK 011MCD / 6 Apr '98 / Blackend

Amebix

☐ ARISE
VIRUS 46CD / Jul '94 / Alternative Tentacles

☐ MONOLITH
Monolith / Nobody's driving / Power remains / Time bomb / Last will and testament / ICBM / Chain reaction / Fallen from grace / Coming home
HMRXD 99 / Aug '87 / Heavy Metal

Amen

☐ GRIND THE BASTARDS DOWN
DISTCD 46 / 13 Apr '98 / Distortion

Amen Corner

☐ NATIONAL WELSH COAST LIVE EXPLOSION COMPANY
MacArthur Park / Baby, do the Philly dog / You're my girl (I don't want to discuss it) / Shake a tail feather / So fine / (Our love) Is in the pocket / Penny Lane / High in the sky / Gin house / Bend me, shape me / (If paradise is) half as nice
CDIMM 016 / Feb '94 / Charly

☐ VERY BEST OF AMEN CORNER
(If paradise is) half as nice / Get back / Hello susie / Proud mary / Recess / When we make love / Lady riga / At last I've found someone to love / Welcome to the club / Things ain't what they used to be / Sanitation / Mr. nonchalant / Weight / Scream and scream again / Run run run / High in the sky
12360 / Aug '94 / Laserlight

America

☐ ALIBI
176572 / 23 Mar '98 / Magic

☐ AMERICA
Riverside / Sandman / Three roses / Children / Here / I need you / Rainy day / Never found the time / Clarice / Donkey jaw / Pigeon song
7599272572 / Jan '93 / WEA

☐ AMERICA IN CONCERT
Tin man / I need you / Border / Sister golden hair / Company / You can do magic / Ventura Highway / Daisy Jane / Horse with no name / Survival
CDGOLD 1072 / Oct '96 / EMI Gold

☐ BEST OF AMERICA, THE (Centenary Collection)
You can do magic / Border / Last unicorn / All my life / Survival / Tall treasures / One morning / Honey / My dear / One in a million / Right before your eyes / We got all night / Lady with a bluebird / Only game in town / Ventura highway / Daisy Jane / I need you / Tin man / Sister golden hair / Horse with no name
CTMCD 307 / Feb '97 / EMI

☐ HEARTS
Daisy Jane / Half a man / Midnight / Bell Tree / Old Virginia / People in the valley / Company / Woman tonight / Story of a teenager / Sister golden hair / Tomorrow / Seasons
9362459862 / Jun '95 / WEA

☐ HISTORY (America's Greatest Hits)
Horse with no name / I need you / Ventura highway / Don't cross the river / Only in your heart / Muskrat love / Tin man / Lonely people / Sister golden hair / Daisy Jane / Woman tonight / Sandman
256169 / Jan '87 / WEA

☐ KING BISCUIT PRESENTS...
KBFHCD 012 / 6 Jul '98 / King Biscuit

☐ PERSPECTIVE
176592 / Oct '97 / Magic

☐ VIEW FROM THE GROUND
You can do magic / Never be lonely / You girl / Inspector Mills / Love on the vine / Desperate love / Right before your eyes / Jody / Sometimes lovers / Even the score
NSPCD 509 / Mar '95 / Connoisseur Collection

☐ YOU CAN DO MAGIC
DC 864352 / Mar '96 / Disky

☐ YOUR MOVE
My kinda woman / She's a runaway / Cast the spirit / Loves worn out again / Border / Your move / Honey / My dear / Tonight is for dreamers / Don't let me be lonely / Someday woman
176582 / 24 Mar '98 / Magic

American Analogue Set

☐ FROM OUR LIVING ROOM TO YOURS
EJ 14CD / 17 Nov '97 / Emperor Jones

American Blues Exchange

☐ BLUEPRINTS
FLASH 55 / 1 Jun '98 / Flash

American Boys' Choir

☐ ON CHRISTMAS DAY
First Noel / Personent hodie / Sussex carol / Once in Royal David's City / Deck the halls with boughs of holly / Jesus Christ the apple tree / Twelve days of Christmas / O come all ye faithful (Adeste Fidelis) / God rest ye merry gentlemen / I sing of a maiden / Hark the herald angels sing / Salvator mundi
RCD 30129 / Dec '92 / Rykodisc

American Breed

☐ BEND ME SHAPE ME (The Best Of American Breed)
VSD 5493 / Oct '94 / Varese Sarabande

American Jazz Orchestra

☐ PLAYS THE MUSIC OF JIMMIE LUNCEFORD
MM 65072 / Oct '94 / Music Masters

American Jazz Quintet

☐ FROM BAD TO BADDER
1201142 / Mar '92 / Black Saint

American Music Club

☐ MERCURY
Gratitude walks / If I had a hammer / Challenger / I've been a mess / Hollywood 4-5-92 / What Godzilla said to God when his name wasn't... / Keep me around / Dallas, airports, bodybags / Apology for an accident / Over and done / Johnny Mathis' feet / Hopes and dreams of heaven's 10,000 whores / More hopes and dreams / Will you find me / Book of life
CDV 2708 / Mar '93 / Virgin

☐ SAN FRANCISCO
Fearless / It's your birthday / Can you help me / Love doesn't belong to anyone / Wish the world away / How many six packs does it take to screw in a light / Cape Canaveral / Hello Amsterdam / Revolving door / In the shadow of the valley / What holds the world together / I broke my promise / Thorn in my side is gone / I'll be gone / Fearless reprise / I just took my two sleeping pills and now I'm like a...
CDV 2752 / Sep '94 / Virgin

American Patrol Orchestra

☐ SOUNDS OF THE BIG BANDS VOL.1
PRCDSP 207 / Jul '95 / Prestige

American Poijat

☐ FINISH BRASS IN USA
GVCD 810 / Mar '95 / Global Village

American Standard

☐ WONDERLAND
LF 177CD / Jul '95 / Lost & Found

Amestigon

☐ HOLLENTANZ
NPR 045CD / 8 Jun '98 / Napalm

Amisi, Reddy

☐ PRUDENCE
503802 / Apr '95 / Declic

☐ ZIGGY
GP 9710 / Jan '97 / Galaxie

AMM

☐ AMMUSIC 1966
Later during a flaming Riviera sunset / Later during a flaming Riviera sunset / Ailantus glandulosa / In the realm of nothing whatever / After rapidly circling the Plaza / After rapidly circling the Plaza / What is there in uselessness to cause you distress / Silence
RERAMMCD / Feb '96 / ReR/ Recommended

☐ FROM A STRANGE PLACE
PSFD 80 / Oct '96 / PSF

☐ GENERATIVE THEMES
MRCD 6 / Oct '95 / Matchless

☐ INEXHAUSTIBLE DOCUMENT, THE
MRCD 13 / Oct '95 / Matchless

☐ LAMINAL (3CD Set)
MRCD 31 / Jun '97 / Matchless

☐ LIVE AT THE CRYPT
MRCD 5 / Oct '95 / Matchless

☐ NAMELESS UNCARVED BLOCK
MRCD 20 / Oct '95 / Matchless

☐ NEWFOUNDLAND
MRCD 23 / Oct '95 / Matchless

☐ TO HEAR AND BACK AGAIN
MRCD 3 / Oct '95 / Matchless

AMM

☐ BEFORE DRIVING TO THE CHAPEL... (We Took Coffee With Rick & Jennifer Reed)
MRCD 35 / Oct '97 / Matchless

☐ IT HAD BEEN AN ORDINARY ENOUGH DAY IN PUEBLO, COLORADO.
Radioactivity / Convergence / Kline / Spittlefields' Slide / For A
8432062 / May '91 / ECM

Ammer Einheit

☐ DEUTSCHE KRIEGER
INV 098CD / Oct '97 / Invisible

Ammerians Octet

☐ NOORDERZON
BVHAASTCD 9306 / Oct '93 / Bvhaast

Ammons, Albert

☐ ALTERNATE TAKES 1936-1946
DOCD 1008 / 28 Oct '97 / Document

☐ BACK BEAT VOL.2 (The Rhythm Of The Blues) (Ammons, Albert & His Rhythm Kings)
Ammons stomp / Suitcase blues / Doin' the boogie woogie / Oh baby boogie / Why I'm leaving you / Red sails in the sunset / Deep in the heart of Texas boogie / Hiroshima / Roses of Picardy / In a little Spanish town / Margie tuxedo boogie / Rhythm boogie / Baltimore breakdown / Clipper
5102862 / Jan '95 / Mercury

☐ BOOGIE WOOGIE KING 1936-1947, THE
159142 / 24 Apr '98 / Jazz Archives

☐ BOOGIE WOOGIE MAN
TPZ 1067 / Aug '97 / Topaz Jazz

☐ BOOGIE WOOGIE VOL.1 (Ammons, Albert & Pete Johnson/Meade 'Lux' Lewis)
STCD 8025 / Jul '96 / Storyville

☐ BOOGIE WOOGIE VOL.2 (Ammons, Albert & Pete Johnson/Meade 'Lux' Lewis)
STCD 8026 / May '97 / Storyville

☐ CLASSICS 1939
CLASSICS 715 / Jul '93 / Classics

☐ CLASSICS 1939-1940
CLASSICS 927 / Apr '97 / Classics

Ammons, Gene

☐ BLUE GENE
Blue gene / Scamperin' / Blue greens and beans / Hip tip
OJCCD 192 / Aug '94 / Original Jazz Classics

☐ BOSS IS BACK, THE
Tastin' the jug / I wonder / Ger-ru / Here's that rainy day / Madame queen / Jungle boss / Jungle strut / Didn't we / He's a real gone guy / Feeling good / Blue velvet / Son of a preacher man
PCD 24129 / Dec '95 / Prestige

☐ BOSS TENOR
Hittin' the jug / Close your eyes / My romance / Canadian sunset / Blue Ammons / Confirmation / Savoy
OJCCD 297 / Feb '93 / Original Jazz Classics

☐ GROOVE BLUES
Ammon joy / Groove blues / Jug handle / It might as well be spring
OJCCD 723 / Nov '95 / Original Jazz Classics

☐ JAMMIN' WITH GENE (Ammons, Gene All Stars)
Jammin' with Gene / We'll be together again / Not really the blues
OJCCD 211 / Jun '96 / Original Jazz Classics

☐ LATE HOUR SPECIAL
Party's over / Soft winds. / Lullaby of the leaves / Things ain't what they used to be / I want to be loved / Lascivious / Makin' whoopee
OJCCD 942 / Jul '98 / Original Jazz Classics

☐ PREACHIN'
Sweet house / Yield not / Abide with me / Prayer / Blessed assurance / You'll never walk alone / I believe / Precious memories / What a friend / Holy holy / Light
OJCCD 792 / Nov '95 / Original Jazz Classics

☐ RED TOP (The Savoy Sessions)
El sino / Ineta / Wild Leo / Just chips / Street of dreams / Good time blues / Travellin' light / Red top / Fuzzy / Stairway to the stars / Jim Dawg / Big slam / Big slam
SV 0242 / Oct '97 / Savoy Jazz

Amon Amarth

☐ ONCE SENT FROM THE GOLDEN HALL
398414133CD / 2 Mar '98 / Metal Blade

Amon Duul

☐ AIRS ON A SHOESTRING
Hymn for the hardcore / Pioneer / One moment of anger is two pints of blood / Marcus Lied / Olaf
CDTB 043 / Jul '87 / Thunderbolt
14515 / Apr '97 / Spalax

☐ BEST OF AMON DUUL II 1969-1974, THE (Amon Duul II)
CLP 0922 / Jan '97 / Cleopatra

☐ CARNIVAL IN BABYLON (Amon Duul II)
MANTRA 063 / 1 Jun '98 / Mantra

☐ COLLAPSING
14949 / Jun '98 / Spalax

☐ DANCE OF THE LEMMINGS (Amon Duul II)
MANTRA 014 / Sep '97 / Mantra

☐ DIE LOESUNG (Amon Duul & Bob Calvert)
Big wheel / Urban Indian / Adrenalin Rush / Visions of fire / Drawn to the flame / They call it home / Die Losung / Drawn to the flame (part 2)
CDTB 115 / 26 Jun '98 / Thunderbolt

☐ DISASTER
14948 / 23 Mar '98 / Spalax

☐ EXPERIMENTE
14842 / Oct '96 / Spalax

☐ FLAWLESS (Amon Duul II)
Nada Cairo / Surrounded by the stars / Castaneda da dream / Wie der wind am ende einer strasse / Kiss ma eee / Cerberus / Speed inside my shoes / La paloma / Nada moonshine union / Dancing on fire / Jam '71 / What you gonna do / Jim hai jam UK '96
MYSCD 113 / Aug '97 / Mystic

☐ FOOL MOON
Who who / Tribe / Tik tok song / Haupmotor / Hymn for the hardcore
CDTB 117 / Mar '95 / Thunderbolt
14516 / Jun '97 / Spalax

☐ HAWK MEETS PENGUIN
One moment of anger is two pints of blood / Hawk meets penguin
CDTB 102 / Jun '92 / Thunderbolt
14848 / Apr '97 / Spalax

☐ KOBE (RECONSTRUCTIONS) (Amon Duul II)
CTCD 039 / Jul '97 / Captain Trip

☐ LIVE IN TOKYO (Amon Duul II)
MYSCD 107 / Nov '96 / Mystic

☐ MEETINGS WITH MENMACHINES (Unremarkable Heroes Of The Past)
Pioneer / Old one / Marcus lied / Song / Things aren't always what they seem / Burundi drummer's nightmare
CDTB 107 / Mar '93 / Thunderbolt
14820 / Jun '97 / Spalax

☐ NADA MOONSHINE (Amon Duul II)
Casteneda da dream / Nada moonshine / Speed inside my shoes / Sirens in Germanistan / Ca va / Kiss ma eee / Carpetride in velvet night / Black pearl of wisdom / Lilac lillies / Guadalquivir / Surrounded by stars / Dancing on fire / Casteneda da dream
MYSCD 106 / Aug '96 / Mystic

☐ PARADIESWARTS DUUL
Love is peace / Snow your first and sun your open mouth / Paramechanische welt / Eternal flow / Paramechanical world
REP 4678 / Dec '97 / Repertoire

☐ PHALLUS DEI (Amon Duul II)
MANTRA 012 / 1 Jun '98 / Mantra

☐ PSYCHEDELIC UNDERGROUND
14947 / Oct '96 / Spalax
REP 4616 / Jun '97 / Repertoire

☐ VIVE LA TRANCE (Amon Duul II)
MANTRA 062 / 1 Jun '98 / Mantra

☐ WOLF CITY (Amon Duul II)
MANTRA 013 / 1 Jun '98 / Mantra

☐ YETI (Amon Duul II)
MANTRA 010 / 1 Jun '98 / Mantra

Amon Tobin

☐ BRICOLAGE
Easy muffin / Yasawas / Dream sequence / New York editor / Defocus / Nasty / Bitter and twisted / Mission / Wires and snakes / Creatures / Stoney Street / One small step / One day in my garden / Chomp samba
ZENCD 029 / May '97 / Ninja Tune

Amorphis

☐ BLACK WINTER DAY
NB 1172 / Mar '95 / Nuclear Blast

☐ ELEGY
NB 141CD / May '96 / Nuclear Blast

☐ KARELIAN ISTHMUS
Karelia / Gathering / Grail's mysteries / Warrior's trail / Black embrace / Exil of the sons of Uisliu / Lost name of God / Pilgrimage / Misery path / Sign from the north side / Vulgar necrolatry
NB 072CD / Oct '95 / Nuclear Blast
RR 60452 / Jun '97 / Relapse

☐ MY KANTELE
My kantele / Brother slayer / Lost son (the brother slayer part 2) / Leviation / I hear you call
RR 69562 / Jun '97 / Relapse

☐ PRIVILEGE OF EVIL
Pilgrimage from darkness / Black embrace / Privilege of evil / Misery path / Vulgar necrolatry / Excursing from existence
RR 60242 / Jun '97 / Relapse

☐ TALES FROM 1000 LAKES
NB 097CD / Jul '96 / Nuclear Blast

Amorphous Androgynous

☐ TALES OF EPHEDRINA
Swab / Mountain goat / In mind / Ephidrena / Auto-pimp / Pod room / Fat cat
ASW 6101 / Sep '97 / Astralwerks
CDEBV 1 / 19 Jan '98 / EBV

Amos, Tori

☐ BOYS FOR PELE
Beauty queen / Horses / Blood roses / Father Lucifer / Professional widow / Mr. Zebra / Marianne / Caught a lite sneeze / Muhammad my friend / Hey Jupiter / Way down / Little Amsterdam / Talula / Not the Red Baron / Agent Orange / Doughnut song / In the springtime of his voodoo / Putting the damage on / Twinkle
7567806962 / Jan '97 / East West

☐ FROM THE CHOIRGIRL HOTEL
Spark / Cruel / Black dove / Raspberry swirl / Jackie's strength / Ieee / Liquid diamonds / She's your cocaine / Northern lad / Hotel / Playboy mommy / Pandora's aquarium
7567830952 / 4 May '98 / East West

☐ INTERVIEW DISC
UFOMWW 12CD / Nov '96 / UFO

☐ INTERVIEW DISC
SAM 7017 / Nov '96 / Sound & Media

☐ INTERVIEW SESSIONS
CHAT 9 / 2 Feb '98 / Chatback

☐ LITTLE EARTHQUAKES
Crucify / Girl / Silent all these years / Precious things / Winter / Happy phantom / China / Leather / Mother / Tear in your hand / Me and a gun / Little earthquakes
7567803582 / Jan '92 / East West

☐ UNDER THE PINK
Pretty good year / God / Bells for her / Past the mission / Baker baker / Wrong band / Waitress / Cornflake girl / Icicle / Cloud on my tongue / Space dog / Yes, Anastasia
7567825672 / Jan '94 / East West

AMP

☐ ASTRALMOONBEAMPROJECTIONS
KRANK 17CD / May '97 / Kranky

☐ PASSE PRESENT
RAPTCD 16 / 11 May '98 / Enraptured

☐ SIRENES
WJ 9 / Jun '97 / Wurlitzer Jukebox

AMP Studio

☐ SYZYGY
AAR 001CD / 18 May '98 / AAR

Ampersand

☐ MUG OF MISCHIEF
CDHOLE 007 / Jun '96 / Golf

Amps

☐ PACER
Pacer / Tipp city / I am decided / Mom's drunk / Bragging party / Hoverin' / First revival / Full on idle / Breaking the split screen barrier / Empty glasses / She's a girl / Dedicated
GAD 5016CD / 6 Jul '98 / 4AD

Amps For Christ

☐ AMPS FOR CHRIST
VMFM 35CD / Jun '97 / Vermiform

☐ BEGGARS GARDEN
SHR 87 / Jun '97 / Shrimper

Amram, David

☐ AT HOME/AROUND THE WORLD
Travelling blues / Birds of Montparnasse / Splendour in the grass / Sioux rabbit song / Home on the range / Kwahare / Pascua / Homenaje a Guatemala / From the Khyber pass / Aya zehn
CDFF 094 / Oct '96 / Flying Fish

☐ NO MORE WALLS
Waltz from After The Fall / Wind from the Indies / Pull my daisy / Brazilian memories / Sao Paulo / Going North / Tompkins Square Park consciousness expander
CDFF 752 / Jun '97 / Flying Fish

☐ TRIPLE CONCERTO
Allegro con brio / Blues / Rondo a la turca / Elegy for violin and orchestra
CDFF 751 / 16 Mar '98 / Flying Fish

Amsallem, Franck

☐ ANOTHER TIME
Out a day / For the record / How deep is the ocean / And keep this place in mind a better one is heart to find / Running after eternity / Dee / On your own / Affreusement votre / A time for love
AL 73117 / Jun '98 / A

☐ IS THAT SO
SSC 171D / Apr '96 / Sunnyside

☐ REGARDS (Amsallem, Franck & Tim Ries Quartet)
FRLCD 020 / Nov '93 / Freelance

Amsterdam Jazz Quintet

☐ PICTURES OF AMSTERDAM
Sailing / Windows / Market / Homecoming / Stress / Traces / Listen to the wind / Omar's bakery
AL 73042 / Nov '96 / A

Amsvartner

☐ TROLLISH MIRROR
BLACK 005CD / 13 Oct '97 / Blackend

Amuedo, Leonardo

☐ DOLPHIN DANCE
CHR 70008 / Aug '95 / Challenge

Amundson, Monti

☐ I SEE TROUBLE
I see trouble / Oh Johnny why / Looking back / What I was thinking / King bee / You win, I lose / Broke down car / Continental breakfast / Cornbread blues / Lesson or two / I'm good / Worried about my life / I live a good life
MMBCD 2 / Nov '96 / Me & My

☐ MEAN 18, THE
TRACD 9914 / Jul '93 / Tramp

☐ MONTI AMUNDSON & THE BLUBINOS (Amundson, Monti & The Blubinos)
Man on the floor / Would I lie / All I wanna do / Sweet talk / Easy way out / Four in the morning / Better to be lonely / Cream in my heart / Hat back blues / Your turn to be the fool / Killing time
MMBCD 3 / May '97 / Me & My Blues

Amy, Curtis

☐ KATANGA (Amy, Curtis & Dupree Bolton)
Katanga / Lonely woman / Native land / Amyable / You don't know what love is / Shade of brown / Soulful bee a soulful rose / 24 hour blues / Lisa
4948502 / 20 Jul '98 / Pacific Jazz

Amygdala

☐ MEMENTO MORI
Bridge of death / Waters of intuition / Practicing dying / Adoration of the Earth / Moment of death / Decent to the afterworld / Fire of the Holy Spirit
HYP 3910181CD / 13 Apr '98 / Hyperium

An Garda Siochana

☐ MUSICAL CELEBRATION
TOLCD 2 / 15 Dec '97 / Dara

An Teallach Ceilidh Band

☐ SHIP IN FULL SAIL, A
Reels / Marches / Jigs / Song / Slip jig / Waltz / Slow air and reel / Polkas
LCOM 5237 / Aug '94 / Lismor

Ana D

☐ SATELITE
ERCD 1045 / 16 Feb '98 / Elefant

Anacrusis

☐ REASON
Stop me / Not forgotten / Silent crime / Afraid to feel / Vital / Terrified / Wrong / Misshapen intent / Child inside / Quick to doubt
CDATV 9 / Feb '90 / Active

Analogue

☐ AAD
GUM 027CD / Oct '96 / Sonic Bubblegum

Anam

☐ ANAM
CACD 001CD / Apr '95 / CACD

☐ FIRST FOOTING
Mylie's revenge/Pipers wedding / Take this moment / Siul a ruin / Last pint/Trimthe velvet / Next market day/The market square / Planxty Joe Burke / Lovely Joan / Dan Amhairgin / Stellagg / Sally free and easy / Sweet flowers of Milltown/Paddy's trip to Lake Arthur / Liberty
JVC 90112 / May '97 / JVC World Library

☐ SAOIRSE
CACD 002CD / Apr '95 / CACD

Anao Atao

☐ ESOTERIC STONES (Celtic Music From Cornwall & Beyond)
Esoteric stones / Ros Keltek's favourite / Other side of Carna / Forest cry / International waters / Tinner's puzzle / An Gernyas / Quadrilles / Marvor / Mai Soazig / Dr. Syntax's head / Yntra Deu Dyr
KESCD 001 / Jul '94 / Kesson

Anathema

☐ ALTERNATIVE 4
Shroud of false / Fragile dreams / Empty / Lost control / Re-connect / Silence / Reality / Regret / Feel / Destiny
CDVILE 73 / 15 Jun '98 / Peaceville

☐ ETERNITY
CDXVILE 64 / Nov '96 / Peaceville

☐ PENTECOST 3
CDMVILE 51 / Mar '95 / Peaceville

22

☐ SILENT ENIGMA, THE
Restless oblivion / Sunset of age / Silent enigma / Shroud of frost / Nocturnal emission / Dying wish / Alone / Cerulean twilight / Black orchid
CDVILE 52 / Oct '95 / Peaceville

Anatomy

☐ WHERE ANGELS LIE
DSTK 7662CD / Dec '96 / Destruktive Kommndoh

Anche Passe

☐ ENTRE TARENTELLE
Y 225032CD / Dec '93 / Silex

Ancient

☐ CAINIAN CHRONICLE, THE
398414110CD / Jul '96 / Metal Blade

☐ MAD GRANDIOSE BLOODFIENDS
398414143CD / 10 Nov '97 / Metal Blade

Ancient Beatbox

☐ ANCIENT BEATBOX
Laride / Raining / Wooden box / I'll wait for you / Bouree a pichon / Diamond / Many lives of Diana / All we live for
COOKCD 021 / Jul '96 / Cooking Vinyl

Ancient Future

☐ ASIAN FUSION
Prelude / Bookenka (the adventurer) / Trader / Mezgoof / Empress / Ja nam / Sunda straits / Morning sung / Sumbatico / Dusk song of the fisherman / Ladakh / Garuda
ND 63023 / Jun '93 / Narada

☐ NATURAL RHYTHMS
PH 9006CD / Feb '94 / Philo

Ancient Rites

☐ BLASFEMIA ETERNAL
M 7017CD / Feb '96 / Osmose

☐ FATHERLAND
M 7035CD / 3 Aug '98 / Mascot

Ancients Rebirth

☐ DAMNATED HELL'S ARRIVAL
NR 023CD / 25 May '98 / Necropolis

And Also The Trees

☐ AND ALSO THE TREES
So this is silence / Talk without words / Midnight garden / Tease the tear / Impulse of man / Shrine / Twilights pool / Out of the moving life of circles
NORMAL 85CD / Mar '94 / Normal

☐ ANGELFISH
MEZCD 1 / Aug '96 / China

☐ FAREWELL TO THE SHADE
Prince Rupert / Nobody Inn / Lady D'Arbanville / Pear tree / Horse fair / MacBeth's head / Belief in the rose / Misfortunes / Ill omen
NORMAL 114CD / Mar '94 / Normal

☐ FROM HORIZON TO HORIZON
NORMAL 154CD / Mar '94 / Normal

☐ GREEN IS THE SEA
NORMAL 134CD / Mar '94 / Normal

☐ KLAXON, THE
NORMAL 164CD / Mar '94 / Normal

☐ MILLPOND YEARS, THE
Suffering of the stream / Simple tom and the ghost of jenny bailey / House of the heart / This ship in trouble / Count jefferey / Shaletown / Sandstone man / From the silver frost / Millpond years / Needle street / L'unica strada
NORMAL 100CD / Mar '94 / Normal

☐ RETROSPECTIVE 1983-1986, A
Shantell / Talk without words / Shrine / Midnight garden / Impulse of man / Twilights pool / Room lives in Lucy / Scarlet arch / Slow pulse boy / Maps in her wrists and arms / Dwelling place / Vincent Crane / Gone like the swallows / Virus meadow
422010 / May '94 / New Rose

☐ VIRUS MEADOW
Slow pulse boy / Maps in her wrists and arms / Dwelling place / Vincent Crane / Jack / Headless clay woman / Gone like the swallows / Virus meadow
NORMAL 90CD / Mar '94 / Normal

And Did Those Feet

☐ SPIRIT OF THE AGE, THE
Things in the world (money can't buy) / It's the quiet life / Spirit of the age / Never waste a good bit / Surprisingly most unsurprising / Come the day / Green place / Almost Elizabeth / Element waltz / Who are you / Living fire
TERRCD 005 / Feb '97 / Terra Nova

And Oceans

☐ DYNAMIC GALLERY OF THOUGHTS
SOM 008CD / 13 Apr '98 / Seasons Of Mist

And One

☐ BEST OF AND ONE, THE
MA 00692 / Dec '97 / Noise

☐ IST
MA 612 / Nov '94 / Machinery

☐ SPOT
MA 342 / Nov '93 / Machinery

And You Will Know Us By The Trail Of The Dead

☐ AND YOU WILL KNOW US BY THE TRAIL OF THE DEAD
TRCD 66 / 26 Jan '98 / Trance Syndicate

Andarta

☐ ABRED
KMCD 61 / Feb '96 / Keltia Musique

Anders, Christian

☐ SEINE GROSSEN ERFOLGE
Das Schiff der grossen Illusionen / Wer liebt hat keine Wahl / Das schonste madchen / Am strand von Las Chapas / Verliebt in den lehrer / Wenn die liebe dich vergisst / Denn ich liebe dich so sehr / Ich leb' nur fur dich allein / In den augen der andern / Maria Lorena / In Chicago (In the ghetto) / Nur mit dir will ich leben / Love dreamer / Tu's nicht Jenny / Der letzte tanz / Einsamkeit hat viele namen
DC 875402 / Mar '97 / Disky

Anders, Lezlie

☐ WITH LOVE LEZLIE
Here's to life / Fever / Cry me a river / Guess who I saw today / Our love is here to stay / Lover man / Very thought of you / Miracles / On the Southside of Chicago / Perfect / More than you know / Fine and mellow / At the same time / What a difference a day makes / My buddy
CYCD 74801 / Feb '97 / Celebrity

Anders, Robin Adnan

☐ OMAIYO
Omaiyo / Umbasa / Desert wild / Bimbale / Rana / Abdul / Tourra / Kadar / Tuva
RCD 10442 / 3 Aug '98 / Rykodisc

Andersen, Arild

☐ HYPERBOREAN
Patch of light / Hyperborean / Patch of light II / Duke Vinaccia / Infinite distance / Vanishing waltz / Island / Invisible sideman / Rambler / Dragon dance / Stillness / Too late for a picture
5373422 / Sep '97 / ECM

☐ IF YOU LOOK FAR ENOUGH
If you look / Svev / For all we know / Backe / Voice / Woman / Place / Drink / Main man / Song I used to play / Far enough / Jonah
5139022 / '90 / ECM

☐ SAGN
Sagn / Gardsjenta / Eisemo / Toll / Draum / Laurdagskveld / Tjovane / Sorgmild / Svarm / Gamlestev / Reven / Nystev / Lussi / Rysen / Belare / Sagn
8496472 / Oct '91 / ECM

Andersen, Ronald

☐ JAZZ GOES CRAZY (Live At The Femo Jazz Festival 1996) (Andersen, Ronald Special Edition Band)
MECCACD 2024 / Oct '97 / Music Mecca

Anderson, Al

☐ PAY BEFORE YOU PUMP
CURCD 034 / Feb '97 / Curb

Anderson, Alistair

☐ GRAND CHAIN, THE
CROCD 216 / Jun '88 / Black Crow

Anderson, Angry

☐ BEATS FROM A SINGLE DRUM
Calling / Frightened kid / Suddenly / Runaway / Winnie mandela / Get it right / Say goodbye / Failing / Clear and simple / Born to be wild
CDGRUB 11 / Apr '89 / Food For Thought

Anderson, Carleen

☐ BLESSED BURDEN
Until I see you again / Woman in me / Leopards in the temple / Shifting times / Fortune's drive / Redemption / Who was that masked man / Interlude highlands part I / Interlude highlands part II / I'm gonna miss you / Maybe I'm amazed / Peace in the valley / Piece of clay / Burning bridges
CIRCD 35 / 20 Apr '98 / Circa

☐ TRUE SPIRIT (Remix Album 2CD Set)
True spirit / Morning loving / Mama said / Ain't givin' up on you / Only one for me / Nervous breakdown / Secrets / Let it last / Feet wet up / Welcome to changes / Ian Green's groove conclusion / Mama said / True spirit / Apparently nothin' / Nervous breakdown / Let it last
CIRCDD 30 / Feb '95 / Circa

☐ TRUE SPIRIT
True spirit / Morning loving / Mama said / Ain't givin' up on you / Only one for me / Nervous breakdown / Secrets / Let it last / Feet wet up / Welcome to changes / Ian Green's groove conclusion
CIRCD 30 / Jan '95 / Circa

Anderson, Cat

☐ PLAYS W.C. HANDY
Yellow dog blues / Ole miss / Careless love (loveless love) / Beale street blues / St. louis blues / Hesitating blues / Aunt hagar's blues / Harlem blues / Memphis blues / Baby won't you please come home / Just squeeze me
BB 886 / Nov '97 / Black & Blue

Anderson, Clifton

☐ LANDMARKS
PC / Mommy / Landmarks along the way / Princess Neh Neh / I've never been in love before / My one and only love / I thought it was understood / Thanks
MCD 92662 / Jan '98 / Milestone

Anderson, Clive

☐ BLUES ONE (Anderson, Clive Trio)
DIW 607 / Nov '91 / DIW

Anderson, Eric

☐ AVALANCHE
7599267792 / Jan '96 / WEA

☐ ERIC ANDERSON
7599267782 / Jan '96 / WEA

☐ GHOSTS UPON THE ROAD
Belgian bar / Spanish steps / It starts with a lie / Trouble in Paris / Listen to the rain / Ghosts upon the road / Too many times (I will try) / Carry me away / Six senses of darkness / Irish lace
PLUCD 003 / Apr '96 / Plump

Anderson, Ernestine

☐ GREAT MOMENTS WITH ERNESTINE ANDERSON
I love being here with you / Day by day / Ain't nobody's business if I do / As long as I live / Don't get around much anymore / Please send me someone to love / Skylark / In a mellow tone / Someone else is steppin' in / Time after time / Body and soul / Never make your move too soon
CCD 4582 / Nov '93 / Concord Jazz

☐ ISN'T IT ROMANTIC
369062 / 1 Sep '98 / Koch Jazz

☐ LIVE AT THE 1990 CONCORD JAZZ FESTIVAL
Blues in the closet / I let a song go out of my heart / I should care / There is no greater love / Skylark / On my own / Never make your move too soon
CCD 4454 / May '91 / Concord Jazz

☐ SUNSHINE
Love / Summertime / Time after time / God bless the child / I've got the world on a string / I'm walkin' / I want a little boy / You are my sunshine / Satin doll / Sunny
CCD 4109 / Jan '92 / Concord Jazz

☐ WHEN THE SUN GOES DOWN
Someone else is steppin' in / In the evening / I love being here with you / Down home blues / I'm just a lucky so and so / Alone on my own / Mercy mercy mercy / Goin' to Chicago blues
CCD 4263 / '88 / Concord Jazz

Anderson, Fred

☐ FRED ANDERSON & THE DKV TRIO (Anderson, Fred & The DKV Trio)
OD 12014 / Jan '98 / Okka Disk

☐ MISSING LINK
NCD 23 / Jun '97 / Nessa

Anderson, Ian

☐ WALK INTO LIGHT
Fly by night / Made in England / Walk into light / Trains / End game / Black and white television / Toad in the hole / Looking for Eden / User friendly / Different Germany
BGOCD 350 / Jun '97 / Beat Goes On

Anderson, Ian A.

☐ UNRULY (English Country Blues Band)
CDFMS 27 / Apr '93 / Rogue

Anderson, Ivie

☐ INTRODUCTION TO IVIE ANDERSON 1932-1942, AN
4020 / May '95 / Best Of Jazz

☐ IVIE ANDERSON (Anderson, Ivie & Duke Ellington)
CD 14561 / May '95 / Jazz Portraits

Anderson, John

☐ TAKIN' THE COUNTRY BACK
Somebody slap me / South moon under / Sara / Brown eyed girl / Small town / Takin' the country back / Who's who / Fall / I used to love her / Jump on it / It's a long way back
5360042 / 6 Oct '97 / Mercury

Anderson, John

☐ I'M IN THE MOOD FOR SWING VOL.1
LPCD 1021 / Apr '94 / Disky

☐ I'M IN THE MOOD FOR SWING VOL.2
LPCD 1022 / Apr '94 / Disky

☐ SWING THE MOOD
American patrol / Tequila / In the mood / Hawaii 5-0 / Moonlight melody / At the sign of the swinging / String of pearls / Pretty blue eyes / Little brown jug / Tuxedo medley / Chattanooga medley / Midnight in Moscow / Manhattan spiritual / Cherry pink / Stranger on the shore / 12 bar thingy / Stripper / Peanut vendor / March of the mods / Glenn Miller medley
MCVD 30005 / Nov '96 / Emerald Gem

Anderson, Jon

☐ ANGEL'S EMBRACE
Naturemusic / Myo maya / Midnight cello / New Eire land / Cloudsinging / Angel's embrace / Prayersong
VHOCD 10 / 25 May '98 / Higher Octave

☐ CHANGE WE MUST
State of independence / Shaker loops / Hearts / Alive and well / Kiss / Chagall duet / Run on, Jon / Candle song / View from the coppice / Hurry home / Under the sun / Change we must
CDC 5550882 / Oct '94 / EMI

☐ DESEO
Amor real / A-de-o / Bridges / Seasons / Floresta / Cafe / This child / Danca do ouro / Midnight dancing / Deseo / Latino / Bless this
01934111402 / May '94 / Windham Hill

☐ DESEO REMIXES, THE
Deep Floresta / Intercity 125 / Speed deep / Master Mute vs The Tone-E / FSOL Deseo reconstruction / Amor real / Master Mute / Bless this
72902103382 / Jul '95 / High Street

☐ EARTH MOTHER EARTH
4160 / Sep '97 / Ell

☐ MORE YOU KNOW, THE
Magic love / Maybe / Say / More you know / Heaven's love / Faithfully / Take take take / Come 'n' gimme love / Dancing fool / Sad / Ever / Free (some would say) / Some TV / Youth / Advertising / 10 million
EAGCD 018 / 2 Mar '98 / Eagle

☐ OLIAS OF SUNHILLOW
Ocean song / Meeting / Sound out the galleon / Dance of Ranyart Olias / Qoquaq en transic / Solid space / Moon ra chords song of search / To the runner / Naon / Transic to
7567802732 / Jan '96 / Atlantic

☐ SONG OF SEVEN
For you, for me / Some are born / Don't forget / Heart of the matter / Hear it / Everybody loves you / Take your time / Days / Song of seven
7567814752 / May '96 / Atlantic

☐ TOLTEC
Part 1 / Part 2 / Part 3
72902103462 / Jun '96 / High Street

Anderson, Krister

☐ SKANDIA SKIES
LICD 3166 / Jan '97 / Liphone

Anderson, Laurie

☐ BIG SCIENCE
From the air / Big science / Sweaters / Walking and falling / Born never asked / O superman / Example 22 / Let X=X / It tango
257002 / Apr '82 / WEA

☐ BRIGHT RED
Speechless / Bright red / Puppet motel / Speak my language / World without end / Freefall / Muddy river / Beautiful pea green boat / Love among the sailors / Poison / In our sleep / Night in Baghdad / Tightrope / Same time tomorrow
9362455342 / Dec '96 / WEA

☐ MISTER HEARTBREAK
Sharkey's day / Langue d'armour / Gravity's angel / Blue lagoon / Excellent birds / Sharkey's night
9250772 / Feb '84 / WEA

☐ STRANGE ANGELS
Strange angels / Monkey's paw / Coolsville / Ramon / Baby doll / Beautiful red dress / Day the devil comes to getcha / Dream before / My eyes / Hiawatha
9259002 / Mar '94 / WEA

☐ UGLY ONE WITH THE JEWELS
White lily / Salesman / Night flight from houston / End of the world / Same time tomorrow / Word of mouth / Ouija board / Soul is a bird / Cultural ambassador / Mysterious / Someone else's dream / Maria teresa teresa maria / Hollywood strangler / On the way to jerusalem / Rotowhirl / John lilly / Geographic north pole / Ugly one with the jewels
9362458472 / Mar '95 / WEA

Anderson, Leif

☐ LEIF 'SMOKE RINGS' ANDERSON PRESENTS... (Various Artists)
ANC 9096 / Aug '94 / Ancha

☐ SWING SESSIONS VOL.1 (Anderson, Leif 'Smoke Rings')
ANC 9093 / Sep '94 / Ancha

Anderson, Little Willie

☐ SWINGING THE BLUES
CD 4930 / Feb '95 / Earwig

Anderson, Lynn

☐ LATEST AND GREATEST
1509592982 / 31 Mar '98 / Intersound

☐ ROSE GARDEN
Rose garden / What a man my man is / How can I unlove you / Keep me in mind / Listen to a country song / Top of the world / You're my man / You don't have to say you love me / Cry / Close to you / Midnight train to Georgia / Silver threads and golden needles / Ride ride / We've only just begun
101492 / May '97 / A-Play Collection

Anderson, Marc

☐ NATURE'S DRUMS (Anderson, Marc & Jai Bunito Aeo)
2666 / Aug '96 / NorthSound

Anderson, Marian

☐ GREAT VOICES OF THE CENTURY
CDMOIR 432 / Apr '96 / Memoir

☐ SPIRITUALS (He's Got The Whole World In His Hands)
He's got the whole world in his hands / Dere's no hidin' place / I want Jesus to walk with me / Oh, didn't it rain / I am bound for de kingdom / Oh wasn't dat a wide ribber / My soul's been anchored in de lord / Lord I can't stay away / Sometimes I feel like a Motherless child / Hold on / Scandalise my name / Great gittin' up mornin' / Done foun' my los' sheep / I stood on de ribber ob Jerdon / Behold that star / Heav'n Heav'n / Oh Peter, go ring dem bells / Trampin' / Hard trials / Oh heaven is one beautiful place / I know / Lord how come me here / Prayer is de key / He'll bring it to pass / You go / Jus' keep on singin' / Ain't got time to die / I been in de storm so long / I've been 'buked / Let's have a union / Jus' keep on singin'/Ride on King Jesus
09026619602 / Jun '95 / RCA Victor

☐ SPIRITUALS
PASTCD 7073 / Aug '95 / Flapper

Anderson, Mildred

☐ NO MORE IN LIFE
Everybody's got somebody but me / I ain't mad at you / Hard times / No more in life / Roll 'em Pete / What more can a woman do / That ole devil called love / Mistreater / I'm lost
OBCCD 579 / Jun '96 / Original Blues Classics

Anderson, Moira

☐ 20 SCOTTISH FAVOURITES
Dark island / Farewell my love / Soft lowland tongue o' the borders / Loch Lomond / Always Argyll / John Anderson, my Jo / Rowan tree / O Waly Waly / Isle of Mull / Sleeps the noon / O lovely land of Canada / Eriskay love lilt / Way old friends do / Ye banks and braes o' bonnie Doon / Durisdeer / Glencoe / Ae fond kiss / My ain folk / Calling me home / Amazing grace
LCOM 9033 / Nov '90 / Lismor

☐ LAND FOR ALL SEASONS, A
Uist tramping song / Mull of Kintyre / Mairi's wedding / D'ye mind lang lang syne / Loch Maree / These are my mountains / Land for all seasons / Come by the hills / Dancing in Kyle / Skye boat song / Wild mountain thyme / Flowers of the forest / Leaving Lismore / Road to the Isles
LCOM 6022 / Aug '96 / Lismor

☐ MOIRA - IN LOVE
Time after time / Love is the sweetest thing / You light up my life / Shadow of your smile / Here's that rainy day / And I love you so / More I see you / Until it's time for you to go / Nearness of you / I won't last a day without you / I just fall in love again / Sometimes when we touch / If / I'll walk alone / You needed me / Somewhere my love
DLCD 104 / Oct '87 / Dulcima

Anderson, Paul

☐ JOURNEY HOME
CDGR 162 / Feb '98 / Ross

Anderson, Pink

☐ BALLAD & FOLKSINGER
OBCCD 577 / Jan '96 / Original Blues Classics

☐ CAROLINA BLUES MAN
My baby left me this morning / Baby, please don't go / Mama where did you stay last night / Big house blues / Meet me in the bottom / Weeping willow blues / Baby I'm going away / I had my fun / Every day in the week / Thousand woman blues
OBCCD 504 / Nov '92 / Original Blues Classics

Anderson, Ray

☐ BLUES BRED IN THE BONE
ENJA 50812 / 17 Nov '97 / Enja

☐ CHEER UP (Anderson, Ray & Hans Bennink/Christy Doran)
ARTCD 6175 / Dec '95 / Hat Art

☐ DON'T MOW YOUR LAWN
Don't mow your lawn / Diddleybop / Damaged but good / Alligatory peccadillo / What'cha gonna do with that / Airwaves / Blow your own horn / Disguise the limit
ENJACD 80702 / Aug '94 / Enja

☐ FUNKORIFIC (Anderson, Ray Lapis Lazuli Band)
Pherominical / Runnin' around / Mirror mirror / Damaged but good / Hammond eggs / Monkey talk / I'm not a spy / Funkorific / Willie and Muddy
ENJ 93402 / 24 Aug '98 / Enja

☐ HEADS AND TALES
Hunting and gathering / Heads and tales / Matters of the heart / Unsung songs / Cheek to cheek / Tapajack / Tough guy / Road song / Drink and blather
ENJ 90552 / Nov '95 / Enja

☐ RIGHT DOWN YOUR ALLEY
SNCD 1087 / Dec '86 / Soul Note

☐ SLIDERIDE (Anderson, Ray & Craig Harris/George Lewis/Gary Valente)
ARTCD 6165 / Mar '96 / Hat Art

☐ WISHBONE
Gahtooze / Ah soca / Duke Ellington's sound of love / Comes love / Cape Horn / Cheek to cheek / Wishbone suite
GV 794542 / Mar '91 / Gramavision

Anderson, Reid

☐ DIRTY SHOW TUNES (Anderson, Reid Quartet)
FSNT 030 / 24 Apr '98 / Fresh Sound New Talent

Anderson, Roshell

☐ ROLLING OVER
ICH 1142CD / Feb '94 / Ichiban

Anderson, Stuart

☐ ACTS NATURALLY
Act naturally / Act naturally / Nessie (the loch ness monster) / Muckin o' geordie's byre / Do you want your old lobby washed down con shine / I've never kissed a bonnie lass before / Let the four winds blow / Gypsy rover / Mockingbird hill / You are my sunshine / Midgies / Casey jones / Mull of kintyre
CDITV 559 / Oct '92 / Scotdisc

☐ SCOTLAND OUR HOME (Anderson, Stuart Jnr. & Snr.)
MMCD 9602 / Sep '96 / Mariner Music

☐ STUART ANDERSON'S PARTY
Doon in the wee room / Bonnie Wee Jeannie McCall / Donald, where's yer troosers / Stuart's song / Marriage / Coulter's candy / Ghostie / Catch me if you can / Wee Kirkcudbright centipede / Come to the Ceilidh
CDITV 502 / Nov '89 / Scotdisc

Anderson, Tom

☐ SILVER BOW: SHETLAND FOLK FIDDLING (Anderson, Tom & Aly Bain)
Jack broke da prison door/Donald Blue/Sleep soond / Lasses trust in Providence/Bonnie Isle o'Whalsay / Da day dawn/Da cross reel / Shive her up/Ahint da deakes o'Voe / Da silver bow / Auld Foula reel/Wynadepla / Da slockit light/Smith o'Couster/Da grocer / Da auld resting chair/ Hamnavoe polka/Maggie's reel / Bridal march/Da bride's a bonnie ting / Jack is yet alive/Auld clettenroe / Da mill/Doon da Rooth / Pit hame da borrowed Claes/Wha'll dance wi' Wattie / Bush below da gairden / Soldier's joy / Shetland moods / Dean brig/Banks / Ferrie reel/Lay Dee at Dee/ Spencie's reel / Up an'doon the harbour/Lucky can you link ony / Silvery voe/Pottinger's reel / If I get a bonnie lass/Jeannie shoke da bairn / Auld swaara / Faroe rum/Aandowin' at da Bow / Mrs. Jamieson's favourite/Lady Mary Ramsay / All da ships ir sailin'/ Sheldor Geo/Mak a kishie needle dye / Freddie's tune/Da blue yow / Full rigged ship/New rigged ship / Naanie an' Betty/A yow cam to wir door yarmin / Maggie O'Ham/Da Foula shaalds / Come agen ye're welcome/Da corbie an' da craw / Ian S Robertson/ Madam Vanoni
TSCD 469 / Sep '93 / Topic

Anderson, Wayne

☐ BACK TO THE GROOVE
CPCD 8142 / Nov '95 / Charly

Andersson, Krister

☐ ABOUT TIME
FLCD 1 / Feb '94 / Flash Music

☐ CONCORD AND TIME (Andersson, Krister Quartet)
FLCD 2 / May '97 / Flash Music

Anderza, Earl

☐ OUTA SIGHT
All the things you are / Blues baroque / You'd be so nice to come home to / Freeway / Outa sight / What's new / Benign / Lonesome road / I'll be around / Freeway / Benign
4948492 / 20 Jul '98 / Pacific Jazz

Andes

☐ LES GUARANIS
339353 / Dec '86 / Musidisc

Andras

☐ DIE RUCKKEHR DER DUNKLEN KREIGER
LEP 012CD / 22 Sep '97 / Last Epitaph

Andre, Peter

☐ NATURAL
Flava / Natural / Mysterious girl / I feel you / You are (part 2) / All I ever wanted / Show U somethin' / To the top / Tell me when / Only one / Message to my girl / Turn it up / PS Get down on it
7432145945
D 2005 / Sep '96 / Mushroom

☐ TIME
MUSH 18CD / 17 Nov '97 / Mushroom

Andreone, Leah

☐ VEILED
It's alright, it's ok / Happy birthday / Mother tongue / You make me remember / Who are they to say / Problem child / Come sunday morning / Kiss me goodbye / Hell to pay / Will you still love me / Imagining you
07863668972 / Mar '97 / RCA

Andrews Sisters

☐ 36 UNFORGETTABLE MEMORIES (2CD Set)
Bei mir bist du schon / Sing sing sing / Shoo shoo baby / In the mood / Woodpecker song / Beer barrel polka / Chico's love song / Don't sit under the apple tree / House of blue lights / I'll be with you in apple blossom time / Nice work if you can get it / Rhumboogie / Three little sisters / Ti pi tin / Daddy / Hit the road / Oh Johnny oh Johnny oh / South American way / Rum and coca cola / Don't be that way / Hold tight, hold tight (Seafood Mama) / Say Si Si / Beat me Daddy eight to the bar / Boogie woogie bugle boy / Tu-Li tulip time / Straighten up and fly right / Well all right / Strip polka / Corns for my country / Down by the Ohio / Joseph Joseph / Says my heart / Elmer's time / Oh Mama / Jitterbug lullaby / Sonny boy
TNC 96208 / Aug '96 / Natural Collection

☐ ANDREWS SISTERS 1937-1943
394672 / Mar '94 / Music Memoria

☐ ART VOCAL 1937-1944
700172 / Sep '96 / Art Vocal

☐ BEAT ME DADDY, EIGHT TO THE BAR (1937-1940)
Beat me Daddy, eight to the bar / Beer barrel polka / Bei mir bist du schon / Ciribiribin: *Andrews Sisters & Bing Crosby* / Cock-eyed mayor of Kaunakakai / Ferryboat serenade / From the land of the sky blue water / Hold tight, hold tight / I love you too much / I want my mama / Let's have another one / Long time no see / Nice work if you can get it / 1-2-3 O'Leary / Oo-oo-oo-oh boom / Pagan love song / Pennsylvania 6-5000 / Rumboogie / Shortnin' bread / Well alright / Why talk about love / You don't know how much you can suffer
CDAJA 5096 / Dec '95 / Living Era

☐ BEST OF THE ANDREWS SISTERS, THE
MCCD 199 / May '95 / Music Club

☐ BEST OF THE ANDREWS SISTERS, THE
PLSCD 222 / Jul '97 / Pulse

☐ BEST OF THE ANDREWS SISTERS, THE (2CD Set)
Bei mir bist du schon / Beat me daddy eight to the bar / Hold tight / Ferry boat serenade / (I'll be with you) in apple blossom time / Nice work if you can get it / Says my heart / Tu-li-tulip time / Beer barrel polka (Roll out the barrel) / Well all right / Yodellin' jive / Say si si / Woodpecker song / Rhumboogie / Scrub me mama with a boogie beat / Aurora / Boogie woogie bugle boy / Three little sisters / Strip polka / Pistol packin' Mama / Shoo-Shoo baby / Straighten up and fly right / Why talk about love / Just a simple melody / South American way / Don't fence me in / Rum and coca-cola / South America, take it away / Begin the beguine / Rock, rock, rock-a-bye baby / Hit the road / Bounce me brother with a solid four / Yes my darling daughter / Elmer's tune / Booglie-wooglie piggy / Sleepy serenade / Don't sit under the apple tree / That's the moon my son / Pennsylvania polka / Tico Tico / Three caballeros / One meat ball / Accentuate the positive / There's a fella waitin' in Poughkeepsie / Put that ring on my finger / Johnny Fedora and Alice Blue-Bonnet / Patience and fortitude / Her bathing suit never got wet / House of blue lights / Coffee song
CPCD 83142 / Nov '97 / Charly

☐ BOOGIE WOOGIE BUGLE BOY
Bei mir bist du schon / Joseph Joseph / Oh ma-ma / Sha-sha / When a Prince of a fella meets a Cinderella / Begin the beguine / Beer Barrel Polka / Jumpin' jive / Oh Johnny oh Johnny oh / South America Way / Let's have another one / Say si si / Rumboogie / Beat me Daddy, eight to the bar / Pennsylvania 6-5000 / Boogie woogie bugle boy
HADCD 173 / May '94 / Javelin

☐ COLLECTION, THE
Rum and coca cola / Rum and coca cola / In the mood / Sing, sing, sing / Shoo shoo baby / Don't be that way / Hold tight (sea food mama) / Say "si si" / Don't sit under the apple tree / Beer barrel polka / I'll be with you in apple blossom time / Boogie woogie bugle boy / Woodpecker song / Beat me daddy, eight to the bar / Tu-li-tulip time / Straighten up and fly right / Well all right (tonight's the night) / Strip polka / Down by the ohio / Chico's love song / House of blue lights / Nice work if you can get it / Rhumboogie / Three little sisters / Ti-pi-tin
COL 052 / Jan '95 / Collection

☐ CREAM OF THE ANDREWS SISTERS, THE
Beat me Daddy, eight to the bar / Joseph Joseph / Pennsylvania 6-5000 / Oh Johnny oh Johnny, oh / Bei mir bist du schon / Hold tight, hold tight / Rumboogie / Say "si, si" / South American way / Jumpin' jive / Where have we met before / Pagan love song / Oh, ma-ma / Sha-sha / Begin the beguine / Billy boy / When a Prince of a fella meets a Cinderella / Just a simple melody / Love is where you find it / Why talk about love / Let's have another one
PASTCD 9766 / Oct '91 / Flapper

☐ HOLD TIGHT...IT'S THE ANDREWS SISTERS (20 Greatest Hits)
Don't sit under the apple tree / Sabre dance / Rum and coca cola / Put that ring on my finger / Twenty four hours of sunshine / I can dream, can't I / That lucky old sun / Coca roca / Pussy cat song / Lulaby of Broadway / Is you is or is you ain't my baby / Three caballeros / Accentuate the positive / Hold tight, hold tight / Beer barrel polka / Boogie woogie bugle boy / Pennsylvania polka / Victory polka
DBCD 12 / Oct '87 / Dance Band Days

☐ JAZZ AND BLUES (36 Outstanding Jazz Tracks/2CD Set)
Bei mir bist du schon / Sing sing sing / Shoo shoo baby / In the mood / Woodpecker song / Beer barrel polka / Chico's love song / Don't sit under the apple tree / House of blue lights / I'll be with you in apple blossom time / Nice work if you can get it / Rhumboogie / Three little sisters / Ti pi tin / Daddy / Hit the road / Oh Johnny oh Johnny oh / South American way / Rum and Coca Cola / Don't be that way / Hold tight hold tight (seafood mama) / Say si si / Beat me daddy eight to the bar / Boogie woogie bugle boy / Tu-li tulip time / Straighten up and fly right / Well alright / Strip polka / Corns for my country / Down by the Ohio / Joseph Joseph / Says my heart / Elmer's tune / Oh mama / Jitterbug lullaby / Sonny boy
BN 214 / Aug '98 / Blue Nite

☐ LEGENDARY CHESTERFIELD SESSIONS VOL.1, THE (Andrews Sisters & Glenn Miller Orchestra)
09026631132 / 6 Apr '98 / RCA Victor

☐ MAGIC OF THE ANDREWS SISTERS, THE
Well all right / Beat me Daddy, eight to the bar / Bei mir bist du schon / Pennsylvania 6-5000 / I'll be with you in apple blossom time / Ferryboat serenade / Rhumboogie / Long time, no see / Short'nin bread / Say "Si Si" / Oh, Johnny, oh Johnny, oh / Hold tight hold tight / Sonny boy / Don't sit under the apple tree / Let's have another one / Ti-pi-tin / Yes my darling daughter / Boogie woogie bugle boy / South America way / Nice work if you can get it / Beer barrel polka / Jospeh Joseph / Strip polka / Oh Ma Ma (The Butcher's boy)
PAR 2063 / Jul '96 / Parade

☐ MAXENE: AN ANDREWS SISTER (Andrews, Maxene)
Bel mir bist du schoen / Don't sit under the apple tree / Remember / Fascinating rhythm / I'll be with you in apple blossom time
CDSL 5218 / May '92 / DRG

☐ MISTER FIVE BY FIVE
Mister five by five / Strip polka / What to do / That's the moon my son / One meat ball / Sing a tropical song / Lonesome Mamma / I've got a guy in Kalamazoo / Massachusetts / Straighten up and fly right / Well alright / Begin the beguine / Long time no see / Little jitterbug / I love you too much / Beat me Daddy eight to a bar / Cock-eyed Mayor of Kaunakakai / Pennsylvania 65000 / Say si si / Beer barrel polka / Pross Tchai / Ferryboat serenade / Rhumboogie
RAJCD 869 / Mar '96 / Empress

☐ PORTRAIT OF THE ANDREWS SISTERS, A
GALE 401 / May '97 / Gallerie

☐ RUM AND COCA COLA
Rum and coca cola / Rum and coca cola / Don't sit under the apple tree / Hold tight (wanna some seafood, mama) / Joseph joseph / Ti-pi-tin / Shortnin' bread / Is you is or is you ain't my baby / Put that ring on my finger / Sonny boy / Beer barrel polka / Lullaby of broadway / Alexander's ragtime band / Strip polka / Pennsylvania polka / When the midnight choo choo leaves for alabam / Jumpin' jive (jive) / Sing a tropical / Rhumboogie / Say "si si" / Carmen's boogie / I remember mama / Beat me daddy, eight to the bar
RMB 75018 / Nov '93 / Remember
GO 3815 / 1 Dec '97 / Golden Options

☐ TICO TICO
DAWE 49 / Apr '97 / Magic

☐ VERY BEST OF THE ANDREWS SISTERS, THE
Boogie woogie bugle boy / Sonny boy / Hit the road / Beer barrel polka / Rhumboogie / Say si si / Well alright / Lullaby to a jitterbug / I'll be with you in apple blossom time / Beat me Daddy / South American way / Bei mir bist du schoen / Joseph Joseph / Ti-pi-tin / Long time no see / Yes my darling daughter
SUMCD 4047 / Nov '96 / Summit

☐ VERY BEST OF THE ANDREWS SISTERS, THE
HMNCD 039 / 22 Jun '98 / Half Moon

Andrews, Chris

☐ HIT SINGLE COLLECTABLES
DISK 4508 / Apr '94 / Disky

☐ SIMPLY THE BEST
WMCD 5707 / Oct '94 / Disky

Andrews, Ernie

☐ GREAT CITY, THE
Great city / Time after time / Jug and I got up this morning / Skylark / Fire and rain / If I loved you / Come back little girl / If I had your love
MCD 5543 / Dec '95 / Muse

☐ NO REGRETS
When they ask about you / Don't you know I care (or don't you care to) / I'll never be free / You call it madness / Hunt is on / Until the real thing comes along / When did you leave Heaven / Sweet Lorraine / Sweet slumber
MCD 5484 / Nov '93 / Muse

☐ REGRETS
60412320722 / 14 Jul '98 / Thirty Two

Andrews, Harvey

☐ 25 YEARS ON THE ROAD
HYCD 200105 / Feb '95 / Hypertension

☐ JOURNEY, THE
Manet and Monet / It's a wonderful day / Never noticed / Press ganged / Life / Downshifting / On my way / I'm here / Leaving home / Waiting room / Centurion / Journey
HYCD 297173 / Dec '97 / Hypertension

☐ MARGERITA COLLECTION, THE
HASKA 001CD / Nov '96 / Haska

☐ SNAPS
HYCD 295159 / Dec '95 / Hypertension

☐ SOMEDAY FANTASY
LBEECD 006 / Jan '95 / Beeswing

☐ WRITER OF SONGS
LBEE 002CD / Jan '94 / Beeswing

Andrews, Inez

☐ TWO SIDES OF INEZ ANDREWS, THE
SH 6019 / Mar '96 / Shanachie

Andrews, Julie

☐ CHRISTMAS WITH JULIE ANDREWS
Away in a manger / Hark the herald angels sing / I wonder as I wander / In the bleak midwinter / It came upon a midnight clear / O come all ye faithful (adeste fidelis) / O little town of Bethlehem / Patapan / Rocking / See amid the winter snow / Silent night / Holy boy / Secret of Christmas / What child is this
4891862 / 10 Nov '97 / Columbia

Andreyev Balalaika Ensemble

☐ BALALAIKA
MCD 61713 / Jul '94 / Monitor

Andromeda

☐ ANDROMEDA
SB 042 / Jun '97 / Second Battle

☐ RETURN TO SANITY
HBG 122/5 / Apr '94 / Background

Andromeda

☐ ANTHOLOGY 1966-1969
KSCD 9492 / Jun '97 / Kissing Spell

Andromeda

☐ SEE INTO THE STARS
SARCD 003 / Mar '93 / Saraja

Andwella's Dream

☐ LOVE AND POETRY
SPACD 1961 / Jun '97 / Fingerprint

Andy, Bob

☐ BOB ANDY'S SONG BOOK
SOCD 1121 / Feb '96 / Studio One

☐ FIRE BURNING
CDTRL 343 / Feb '95 / Trojan

☐ FRIENDS
AV 001CD / Apr '96 / I-Anka

☐ HANGING TOUGH
VPCD 1484 / Mar '97 / VP

☐ SONGS OF BOB ANDY, THE (Various Artists)
JOVECD 1 / Sep '93 / Jove Music

☐ YOUNG, GIFTED AND BLACK
CDTRL 343 / Nov '94 / Trojan

Andy, Horace

☐ ELEMENTARY (Andy, Horace & The Rhythm Queen)
Hanging on to jah / Hanging on to jah / Love is a treasure / You're so fine / Roll away / Be my queen / Elementary / Baby don't go / Hold them / Eating mess / Place I want to be / Ooh e baby
RNCD 2016 / Jul '93 / Rhino

☐ GOOD VIBES 1975-1979 (Originals And Versions)
Reggae rhythm / Serious thing / Skylarking / Youth of today / Problems / Mr. Bassie discomix / Pure ranking discomix / Good vibes / Control youself / Ital vital
BAFCD 019 / Jul '97 / Blood & Fire

☐ HITS FROM STUDIO ONE AND MORE
RNCD 2116 / Sep '95 / Rhino

☐ IN THE LIGHT (Dub/Vocal)
Do you love my music / Hey there woman / Government land / Leave Rasta / Fever / In the light / Problems / If I / Collie herb / Rome / Music dub / Dub there / Government dub / Rasta dub / Fever dub / Dub the light / Problems dub / I and I / Collie dub / Dub down Rome
BAFCD 6 / May '95 / Blood & Fire

☐ LIFE IS FOR LIVING
ARICD 106 / Mar '95 / Ariwa Sounds

☐ MR. BASSIE
Fever / Mr. Bassie / Mother and child reunion / Conscious dreadlocks / Oh Lord why Lord / Child of the ghetto / Ain't no sunshine / New broom / Come into my life / I may never see my baby / See a man's face / Slacky tidy / Just don't want to be lonely / Funny man
CDHB 88 / Jun '98 / Heartbeat

☐ PRIME OF HORACE ANDY, THE (20 Classic Cuts From The 1970's)
Skylarking / Love of a woman / Zion gate / Just say who / Something on my mind / You are my angel / Money money / Rain from the sky / My guiding star / Bless you / Don't try to use me / Nice and easy / True love shines bright / Collie weed / Ain't no sunshine / Sea of love / Love you to want me / Natural mystic / Better collie / Riding for a fall
MCCD 302 / Jun '97 / Music Club

☐ ROOTS AND BRANCHES
ARICD 125 / Mar '97 / Ariwa Sounds

☐ RUDE BOY
Kuff dem / That's how I feel: *Andy, Horace & Bunny Rugs* / Noisy street / Done with it / All for love / Midnight hour / Don't take your guns to town / All night / Just my imagination / Live in love / Rude boy / That's how I feel: *Andy, Horace & Ricky General/ Bunny Rugs*
SHANCD 45010 / May '98 / Shanachie

☐ SEEK AND YOU WILL FIND
BLKCD 15 / Nov '95 / Blakamix

☐ SKYLARKING (The Best Of Horace Andy)
Spying glass / Natty Dread a weh she want / Rock to sleep / One love / Problems / Fever / Children of Israel / Money money / Girl I love you / Elementary / Every tongue shall tell / Skylarking / Do you love my music / Spying glass
CSAD 1 / Sep '96 / Melankolic

☐ SKYLARKING
SOCD 1116 / May '97 / Studio One

☐ YOU ARE MY ANGEL
Thank you Lord / I'll forgive you / You are my angel / I'm not a know it all / Keep on trying / Ain't no sunshine / Can I change your mind / Don't break your promise / Dream lover / John saw them coming / Riding for a fall / Rain from the skies
CDTBL 197 / Nov '96 / Trojan

Andy, Kendrick

☐ ANOTHER NIGHT IN THE GHETTO
FBKCD 1 / Mar '95 / Fence Beater

Anekdoten

☐ NUCLEUS
Nucleus / This far from the sky / Here / Harvest / Untitled / Rubankh / Pendylum swing / Book
VIRTA 002 / Sep '97 / Virta

☐ VEMOD
VIRTA 001 / Sep '97 / Virta

Aneke, Aster

☐ ASTER
TRECD 107 / Jul '98 / Triple Earth

Anesthesia

☐ PVC
BR 043CD / 24 Nov '97 / Blue Room Released

Anesthesy

☐ EXALTATION OF THE ECLIPSE
BMCD 54 / May '94 / Black Mark

Ange

☐ A DIEU
992005 / Jul '96 / Wotre Music

Angel Cage

☐ SOPHIE MAGIC
ORGAN 016CD / Jul '95 / Org

Angel Corpse

☐ EXTERMINATE
OPCD 066 / 2 Mar '98 / Osmose

☐ HAMMER OF GODS
OPCD 047 / Nov '96 / Osmose

Angel, Dave

☐ 39 FLAVOURS OF TECH FUNK (2CD Set) (Various Artists)
Move your body: *Dj Dainskin* / Funk music: *Angel, Dave* / Gimme sound: *Pooley, Ian* / Help: *Modman* / Enlite: *Pooley, Ian* / D tuned: *Peace Division* / Stomp: *Slater, Luke* / Past silence: *DJ Restyle* / Water: *Basoski, Olav* / Don't let me down: *Mark Seven* / Bring the bass: *Basoski, Olav* / Gonz gets F U: *Mark Seven* / Filter: *Driver, Jan* / Don't stop: *Mark NRG* / Discontamination: *Nasty, Billy* / Gold rush: *Smith, Christian* / High naturally: *Wared 69* / First few steps: *Spirit Guide* / Police: *Mulder* / Drum tumbler: *Mackerel, Jack* / Triangular funk: *Velocity Boy* / Foothought: *Bushflange* / Wanna go bang: *Protein Boy* / Prize: *Basoski, Olav* / Beats u up: *Basoski, Olav* / Keep on dancin': *Basoski, Olav* / On guard: *Pooley, Ian* / This is disco: *Angel, Dave* / Jimmis' technique: *Lekebusch, Cari & Alexi Delano* / Laydown: *2 B Continued* / Tremmer: *Subjective* / B2: *Mark Seven* / High: *Mark Seven* / Jumping jupiter: *Awtsventin, Nico* / Formulas: *Awtsventin, Nico* / Poison: *Green, Marc* / 4.50: *Beyer, Adam*
REACTCD 130 / 7 Sep '98 / React

☐ CLASSICS
Bounce back / Sighting / Jungle love / Trip to darkness / Free flow / Fallen destiny / Endless motions / Brother from jazz / Down deep / Lust / Dimension of drums / Great Daine
RS 96089CD / 16 Feb '98 / R&S

☐ GLOBETROTTING
Coming on / Philly bluntz / Funk music / Club hell / Sensor Zurich / K road NZ / This is disco / Tokyo stealth fighter / Liquid rooms / Chicago emerald city
GLOBECD 1
BRCD 625 / 1 Sep '97 / 4th & Broadway

☐ TRANCE LUNAR PARADISE
SDIMCD 1 / Dec '94 / Sound Dimension

Angel Dust

☐ BORDER OF REALITY
CM 77220CD / 8 Jun '98 / Century Media

Angel Witch

☐ '82 REVISITED (Live At The East Anglia Rock Festival)
Gorgon / Nowhere to run / They wouldn't dare / Sorceress / Evil games / White witch / Angel of death / Angel witch / Evil games / They wouldn't dare / Nowhere to run
CDTB 173 / May '97 / Thunderbolt

☐ ANGEL WITCH PLUS
Angel witch / Atlantis / White witch / Confused / Sorcerers / Gorgon / Sweet danger / Free man / Angel of death / Devil's tower / Loser / Suffer / Dr. Phibes / Flight nineteen / Baphonet
ESMCD 598 / 31 Aug '98 / Essential

☐ SCREAMIN' ASSAULT
She don't lie / Frontal assault / Something wrong / Straight from hell / Reawakening / Screamin' n' bleedin' / Waltz the night / Rendezvous with the blade / Goodbye / Take to the wing / Fatal kiss / Undergods / UXV
KILCD 1001 / Dec '88 / Killerwatt

Angelic Gospel Singers

☐ BEST OF THE ANGELIC GOSPEL SINGERS, THE
NASH 4509 / Feb '96 / Nashboro

Angelic Upstarts

☐ ANGEL DUST (The Collected Highs)
Murder of Liddle Towers / Police oppression / I'm an upstart / Teenage warning / Never 'ad nothin' / Last night another soldier / Two million voices / Kids on the street / England / Hearts lament / Shotgun solution / Never say die / Woman in disguise / Solidarity / Lust for glory / Never give up / Waiting, hating / Reason why / Nobody was saved / Geordie's wife / Loneliness of the long distance runner / 42nd Street / Burglar / Five flew over the cuckoo's nest / As the passion / Young punk / Where we started
CDMGRAM 7 / Aug '93 / Anagram

☐ BLOOD ON THE TERRACES/LOST AND FOUND
Pride of our passion / Everyday / I wanna knighthood / Heart attack in Paris / Four grey walls / I don't wanna fight the soviet / Our day will come / Blood on the tereraces / Heroin is good for you / It's your life / I won't pay for liberty / Solidarity / Never return to hell / When will they learn / Tut shuffle / Box on / Living in exile / No nukes / Calypso / Never ad nothing / Leave me alone / Teenage warning / Last night another soldier / Guns for the Afghan rebels
LOMACD 11 / Feb '94 / Loma

☐ BOMBED OUT
DOJOCD 198 / Aug '94 / Dojo

☐ INDEPENDENT SINGLES COLLECTION
Murder of the Liddle Towers / Police oppression / Woman in disguise / Lust for glory / Solidarity / 42nd Street / Five flew over the cuckoo's nest / Dollars and pounds / Don't stop / Not just a name / Leech / Leave me alone / White riot / Machine gun Kelly / Young ones / We're gonna take the world / England / Soldier / Thin red line / Brighton bomb / There's a drink in it
CDPUNK 59 / May '95 / Anagram

☐ LAST TANGO IN MOSCOW
One more day / Machine Gun Kelly / Progress / Blackleg miner / Who's got the money / Last tango in Moscow / I think it should be free / Never return / Rude boy / No news / Jarrow woman / Nowhere to run / Paint it in red / There's a drink in it / Listen to the silence / She don't cry anymore / I won't pay for liberty / Never return to hell / When will they learn / No nukes
AHOYCD 087 / 11 May '98 / Captain Oi

☐ RARITIES
Victory for Poland / Action man / Cry wolf / Soldier / Gonna be a star / Different strokes / Spirit of St.George / Good boy / Too long gone / Are you ready / Give us a clue / I won't pay for liberty / Never return to hell / When will they learn / Solidarity / Tut shuffle / Living in exile / Box on / No nukes / Calypso
AHOYCD 080 / 1 Dec '97 / Captain Oi

☐ REASON WHY
Woman in disguise / Never give up / Waiting, hating / Reason why / Nobody was saved / Geordie's wife / Loneliness of the long distance runner / 42nd Street / Burglar / Solidarity / As the passion / Young punk / Where we started / Lust for glory / Five flew over the cuckoo's nest / Dollars and pounds / Don't stop / Not just a name / Leech / Leave me alone / Murder of Liddle Towers / White riot
SUMCD 4086 / Jan '97 / Summit

☐ TWO MILLION VOICES
Two million voices / Ghost town / You're nicked / England / Heath's lament / Guns for the Afghan rebels / I understand / Mensi's marauders / Mr. Politician / Kids on the street / Jimmy / We're gonna take the world / Last night another soldier / I wish
DOJOCD 81 / May '93 / Dojo

Angelopoulos, Lycourgos

☐ BYZANTINE MASS - AKATHISTOS HYMN (Angelopoulos, Lycourgos & The Greek Byzantine Choir)
PS 65118/9 / Nov '93 / PlayaSound

Angelou

☐ AUTOMIRACLES
HAVENCD 10 / 18 May '98 / Haven

Angelou, Maya

☐ MISS CALYPSO
SCP 9705 / Nov '97 / Scamp

Angels

☐ BEST OF THE ANGELS, THE
My boyfriend's back / He's so fine / 'Till / He's the kissing kind / Little Beatle boy / I adore him / Thank you and goodnight / Guy with the black eye / Why don't the boy leave me alone / World without love / Wow wow wee (he's the boy for me) / Dream boy / Boy from Crosstown / Snowflakes and teardrops / Has anybody seen my boyfriend / Guess the boy don't love me anymore / You can't take my boyfriend's Woody / Cry baby cry / (Love me) now / Jamaica Joe / My boyfriend's back
5527602 / Feb '97 / Spectrum

Angels

☐ DARK ROOM
ANGELS 123 / 15 Jun '98 / Shock

☐ WATCH THE RED
ANGELS 345 / 15 Jun '98 / Shock

Angels Ov Light

☐ PSYCHICK YOUTH RALLY
CSR 8CD / Aug '95 / Cold Spring

Anger

☐ MIAMI, FLORIDA
SPV 08436212 / Nov '94 / SPV

Angina Pectoris

☐ ANGUISH
SPV 08445612 / Oct '94 / SPV

☐ INSOMNIA
SPV 08445802 / Apr '96 / SPV

Angkor Wat

☐ CORPUS CHRISTI
CDZORRO 5 / May '90 / Metal Blade

☐ WHEN OBSCENITY BECOMES THE NORM...AWAKE
398414088CD / Jun '97 / Metal Blade

Anglaspel

☐ JAZZ IN SWEDEN 1982
1270 / Jan '89 / Caprice

Anglim, Carlene

☐ MELLOW FRENZY (Anglim, Carlene & Allister Gittens)
Mason's apron / Golden castle / Paddy gets drunk in Paris/Reel Beatrice/Unknown / Beauty spot/ Dunboyne straw platters/Fermoy lasses / Vrchar/ Saucers / Monaghan jig / Knocknagow jig / Crowley's reel/Farewell to Erin/Julia Delaney's / Canadian waltz / Lads of Laois / Strop the razor/ Foxhunters / Begrudgers/Jenny's chickens / Taimse un choladh
CDLDL 1276 / May '98 / Lochshore

Angra

☐ ANGELS CRY
DCD 9412 / Feb '97 / Dream Circle

☐ FIREWORKS
SPV 08518482 / 1 Sep '98 / SPV

Angrum, Steve

☐ STEVE ANGRUM & GEORGE LEWIS/ KID SHEIK (Angrum, Steve & George Lewis/Kid Sheik)
AMCD 56 / Dec '97 / American Music

Angry Samoans

☐ RETURN TO SAMOA
YUPPY 008CD / Jun '97 / Vermiform

Angstrom, Kenneth

☐ KENNETH ANGSTROM
NCD 8855 / Jul '98 / Phontastic

Anibaldi, Leo

☐ VIRTUAL LANGUAGE, THE
PWD 7448 / May '94 / Pow Wow

☐ VOID
CAT 031CD / Sep '96 / Rephlex

Anima

☐ STURMISCHER HIMMEL
14278 / 16 Feb '98 / Spalax

Animals

☐ ANIMALS
Story of Bo Diddley / Bury my body / Dimples / I've been around / I'm in love again / Girl can't help it / I'm mad again / She said yeh / Right time / Memphis / Boom boom / Around and around
DORIG 125 / 6 Oct '97 / EMI

☐ ANIMALS LIVE IN NEWCASTLE 1963/ YARDBIRDS LIVE AT THE MARQUEE (Animals/Yardbirds)
14550 / Jun '97 / Spalax

☐ ANIMALS, THE
House of the rising sun / We've gotta get out of this place / Roadrunner / Let the good times roll / Hallelujah I love her so / I'm going to change the world / Bring it on home to me / Worried life blues / Baby let me take you home / For miss caulker / I believe to my soul / How you've changed / Don't let me be misunderstood / It's my life
16137 / Jul '95 / Laserlight

☐ ANIMALS, THE
House of the rising sun / Howlin' / Night fighter / San Franciscan nights / Bist immer / Roadbuster / We gotta get out of this place / Don't let me be misunderstood / To love somebody / Frisco queen / When I was young / Love fire / Paymaster / Stand up
302492 / Feb '98 / Hallmark

☐ ARK
Loose change / Love is for all time / My favourite enemy / Prisoner of the light / Being there / Hard times / Night / Trying to get to you / Just can't get enough / Melt down / Gotta get back to you / Crystal nights
CLACD 412 / Nov '96 / Castle

☐ GREATEST HITS LIVE
It's too late / House of the rising sun / It's my life / Don't bring me down / Don't let me be misunderstood / I'm crying / Bring it on home to me / O lucky man / Boom boom / We gotta get out of this place / When I was young
CLACD 424 / Nov '96 / Castle

☐ INSIDE LOOKING OUT (1965-1966 Decca Sessions)
Inside looking out / Outcast / Don't bring me down / Cheating / Help me girl / CC rider / One monkey don't stop now show / Maudie / Sweet little sixteen / You're on my mind / Clapping / Gin house blues / Squeeze her, tease her / What am I living for / I put a spell on you / That's all I am to you / She'll return it / Mama told me not to come / I just want to make love to you / Boom boom / Big boss man / Pretty thing
NEXCD 153 / Feb '91 / Sequel

☐ LIVE AT THE CLUB A-GO-GO, NEWCASTLE
Let it rock / Gotta find my baby / Bo Diddley / Almost grown / Dimples / Boom boom / C jam blues
308142 / 13 Oct '97 / Hallmark

☐ LOVE IS
OW 30338 / Sep '94 / One Way

☐ MOST OF THE ANIMALS
RVCD 05 / May '91 / Raven

☐ RARITIES
PRCDSP 500 / Aug '92 / Prestige

☐ ROADRUNNERS (1966-1968 Live)
Heartbreak hotel / Work song / Corrina corrina / Jailhouse rock / Roadrunner / Gin house blues / Hey gyp (dig the slowness) / Shake, rattle and roll / When I was young / CC rider / Rock me baby / Tobacco road / So long / Inside looking out / Maudie / Yes I'm experienced / San franciscan nights / Monterey / Paint it black
RVCD 11 / Oct '92 / Raven

☐ SINGLES PLUS
Baby let me take you home / Gonna send you back to Walker / House of the rising sun / Talkin' 'bout you / I'm crying / Take it easy / Don't let me be misunderstood / Club a gogo / Bring it on home to me / For Miss Caulker / We gotta get out of this place / I can't believe it / It's my life / I'm going to change the world / Bury my body / Dimples / She said yeah / Right time / Bright lights big city / Let the good times roll
CZ 10 / Aug '88 / EMI

Animals On Wheels

☐ DESIGNS AND MISTAKES
Palid / Toasted bot bop / Soluble ducks / Nodding dogs / Family / Scene for Ash / Fall like dandruff / Shoddy kicks / Flush fit fanatic / Loath / Clay pot / Eggshell / Stans soluble fish / Invert and click / Break some off son
ZENCD 32 / 12 Jan '98 / Ninja Tune

Animals That Swim

☐ WORKSHY
ELM 24CD / Sep '94 / Elemental

Animated Egg

☐ ANIMATED EGG
FLASH 67 / 1 Jun '98 / Flash

Anitas Livs

☐ WILD WORLD WEB
SLACD 014CD / Nov '95 / Slask

Anka, Paul

☐ BEST OF PAUL ANKA, THE
472106 / Apr '96 / Flarenasch

☐ GOLDEN HOUR OF PAUL ANKA
You and me today / My way / She's a lady / Let me be the one / Jubilation / We make it happen / Everything's been changed / Yesterday my life was more of just the same / Les filles de Paris / Do I love you / Something good is coming / Double life / Love is / Some kind of friend / Life song / Pretty good / Kathum
12844 / Sep '96 / Laserlight

☐ GREATEST HITS
Diana / You are my destiny / (All of a sudden) my heart sings / Lonely boy / Put your head on my shoulder / Time to cry / Puppy love / (You're) Having my baby / Times of your life / I don't wanna run your life / Hold me till the morning comes / Freedom from the world
PWKS 4260 / '95 / Carlton

☐ HAVING MY BABY
16122 / May '95 / Laserlight

☐ HIS GERMAN RECORDINGS
BCD 15613 / Feb '92 / Bear Family

☐ MASTERS, THE
EABCD 037 / 24 Nov '97 / Eagle

☐ TOUCH OF CLASS, A
Anytime (I'll be there) / I don't like to sleep alone / Out of my mind in love / It's sad to see the old hometown again / There's nothing stronger than our love / Wake up / Today I became a fool / Girl, you turn me on / Walk away / Water runs deep / Bring the wine / One man woman, one woman man / Something about you / (You're) Having my baby / Let me get to know you / Love is a lonely song / How can anything be beautiful / I gave a little and lost a lot / Papa / It doesn't matter anymore
TC 861882 / 2 Feb '98 / Disky

☐ VERY BEST OF PAUL ANKA, THE
Diana / Love me warm and tender / Can't get used to losing you / Eso beso / Moon river / My way / He'll have to go / Ramblin' rose / All I have to do is dream / Memories are made of this / Who's sorry now / You always hurt the one you love / I can't stop loving you / Save the last dance for me / Oh lonesome me / Crazy love / End of the world / Steel guitar and a glass of wine / Goodnight my love / Put your head on my shoulder
74321511902 / 25 Aug '97 / Camden

Ann Can Be

☐ 27 ON AND OFF
TOODAMNHY 62 / Jan '95 / Too Damn Hype

Annabouboula

☐ GREEK FIRE
SHCD 64027 / Jul '91 / Shanachie

Anne Marie

☐ BE TOUGH
EBSC 004 / Oct '96 / Echo Beach

Annie Anxiety

☐ JAKOMO
EB 003 / 20 Apr '98 / Echo Beach

Annihilator

☐ ALICE IN HELL (Remastered)
Crystal Ann / Alison hell / WTYD / Wicked mystic / Burns like a buzzsaw blade / Word salad / Schizos (are never alone) / Ligeia / Human insecticide / Powerdrain / Schizos (are never alone) (demo) / Ligeia (demo)
RR 87232 / 15 Jun '98 / Roadrunner

☐ BAG OF TRICKS
Alison Hell / Phantasmagoria / Back to the crypt / Gallery / Human insecticide / Fun Palace / WTYD / Word salad / Live wire / Knight jumps Queen / Fantastic things / Bats in the belfry / Evil appetite / Gallery / Alison Hell / Phantasmagoria
RR 89972 / Sep '96 / Roadrunner

☐ IN COMMAND LIVE 1989
RR 88522 / Nov '96 / Roadrunner

☐ KING OF THE KILL
Box / King of the kill / Hell is a war / Bliss / Second to none / Annihilator / Twenty one / In the blood / Fiasco (slate) / Fiasco / Catch the wind / Speed / Bad child
CDMFN 171 / Oct '94 / Music For Nations

☐ NEVER NEVER LAND (Remastered)
Fun palace / Road to ruin / Sixes and sevens / Stonewall / Never never land / Imperilled eyes / Kraf dinner / Phantasmagoria / Reduced to ash / I am in command / Kraf dinner (demo) / Mayhem (demo) / Freed from the pit
RR 87222 / 15 Jun '98 / Roadrunner

☐ REFRESH THE DEMON
CDMFN 197 / Mar '96 / Music For Nations

☐ REMAINS
Murder / Dead wrong / Bastiage / Never / Human remains / I want / No love / Tricks and traps / Wind / Sexecution / REaction
CDMFN 228 / Jul '97 / Music For Nations

☐ SET THE WORLD ON FIRE
Set the world on fire / No zone / Bats in the belfry / Snake in the grass / Phoenix rising / Knight jumps queen / Sounds good to me / Edge / Don't bother me / Brain dance
RR 92002 / Mar '96 / Roadrunner

Anomoanon

☐ MOTHER GOOSE
PRI 9CD / 24 Aug '98 / Palace

Anonymous 4

☐ LOVE'S ILLUSION
HMU 907109 / Oct '94 / Harmonia Mundi

Anorexia Nervosa

☐ EXILE
SOM 004CD / 13 Oct '97 / Seasons Of Mist

Another Fine Day

☐ LIFE BEFORE LAND
Life before land / Lazy daisy / Green thought (in green shade) / Ammonite spiral / So blue / Buckets and spades / Esperanto
RBADCD 7 / Jun '94 / Beyond

Another Green World

☐ INVISIBLE LANDSCAPE
MEYCD 16 / Sep '96 / Magick Eye

Another Man's Poison

☐ HOWSA 'BOUT THAT
WWRCD 021 / 6 Apr '98 / Walzwerk

Anouk

☐ TOGETHER ALONE
DNCD 1571 / 16 Feb '98 / Dino

Anschell, Bill

☐ DIFFERENT NOTE ALTOGETHER
743431503022 / 5 May '98 / Accurate

Ansill, Jay

☐ ORIGAMI
FF 530CD / '92 / Flying Fish

Ant & Dec

☐ CULT OF ANT & DEC, THE
Cult of Ant and Dec / When I fall in love / Shout / Falling / Crazy / Cloud 9 / Just a little love / Better watch out / Game of love / Bound / Masterplan / Universal sun / Apology
TCD 2887 / May '97 / Telstar

Ant Bee

☐ LUNAR MUZIK
DIVINE 020CD / 29 Sep '97 / Taste/ Divine

☐ WITH MY FAVOURITE MOTHERS AND OTHER BIZARRE MUZIK
Lunar eggs - clips run amuck / Girl with the stars in her hair / Motorhead snorks - Motorhead speaks / Live jam / Jimmy Carl Black speakin' at ya / In a star / Do you like worms / Bunk speaks / Another gardner variation / Pachuco falsetto laughs / Here we go round the lemon tree / Who slew the beast / Dom Dewild speaks / Dom Dewild transforms (Before your very ears) / Dom Dewild speaks again
DIVINE 003CD / 7 Oct '97 / Taste/Divine

Ant Trip Ceremony

☐ 24 HOURS
ANT 23 / Jul '97 / Anthology

Antediluvian Rocking Horse

☐ MUSIC FOR THE ODD OCCASION
SEELAND 505 / Mar '97 / Seeland

Antena, Isabelle

☐ CAMINO DEL SOL
TWI 1142 / Oct '96 / Les Disques Du Crepuscule

☐ EN CAVALE
TWI 6102 / Oct '96 / Les Disques Du Crepuscule

☐ HOPING FOR LOVE
Des Calins, Des Caresses / Laying on the sofa / Naughty, naughty / Sweet boy / La tete contre les murs / Le poisson des mers du sud / Quand le jazz entre en lice melodie / L'ideal / Musique de 4 a 6 / Toutes les etoiles de tunisie / Otra bebera
TWI 7592 / Oct '96 / Les Disques Du Crepuscule

☐ TOUS MES CAPRICES
TWI 842CD / Oct '96 / Les Disques Du Crepuscule

Antenna

☐ HIDEOUT
Shine / Wallpaper / Stillife / Rust / Dreamy / Don't be late / Fade / Easy listening / Danger buggy / Second skin / Hallelujah / Grey St.
MR 00462 / Apr '93 / Mammoth

Anthea

☐ WORDS AND BEATS
ULTR 1001 / 23 Mar '98 / Thin Air Music

Anthem

☐ NO SMOKE WITHOUT FIRE
Shadow walk / Blinded pain / Love on the edge / Power and blood / Night we stand / Hungry soul / Do you understand / Voice of thunderstorm / Fever eyes
CDMFN 101 / Aug '90 / Music For Nations

Anthony B

☐ REAL REVOLUTIONARY
GRELCD 230 / Aug '96 / Greensleeves

☐ UNIVERSAL STRUGGLE
Storm winds / Heavy load / Universal struggle / Gangstas think twice / Waan back / Seek Jah first / Nah vote again / Damage / Splifftail / Zinc fence jungle / Mockingbird / Jerusalem / Money worries / Rastaman school / Sunburnt faces / Marley memories / Storm sax
CRCD 78 / 22 Dec '97 / Charm

Anthony, Mike

☐ SHORT MORNING
GPCD 005 / Dec '92 / Gussie P

Anthony, Pad

☐ X-RATED LADIES
PMCD 0001 / 20 Apr '98 / Sir Peter

Anthony, Ray

☐ 22 ORIGINAL BIG BAND RECORDINGS
I get a kick out of you / Loaded with love / What is this thing called love / They didn't believe me (foxtrot) / Blacksmith blues / Sometimes I'm happy / Kiss of fire / For dancers only / Trumpet boogie / Margie / House party hop / Sentimental journey / Busman's holiday / My marilyn / Mr. anthony's boogie / I'm yours / My blue heaven / Blue tango / Scatterbrain / Delicado / Blue moon / Honeydripper
HCD 412 / Sep '92 / Hindsight

☐ ALL THAT JAZZ (Anthony, Ray Orchestra)
AERO 1030 / Jul '96 / Aerospace

☐ BOOGIE, BLUES AND BALLADS (Anthony, Ray Orchestra)
Boogie blues / Birth of the blues / Swingin' shepherd blues / Beat me Daddy eight to the bar / Lil' darlin' / Our love is here to stay / Kansas City / Girl talk / Fly me to the moon / Memories of you / Cow cow boogie / I left my heart in San Francisco / Bad bad Leroy Brown / Night train
RACD 1041 / Jun '97 / Aerospace

☐ CHESTERFIELD SHOWS 1953 (Anthony, Ray Orchestra)
DAWE 83 / May '98 / Magic

☐ DANCE PARTY (Dances From Waltz To Tango) (Anthony, Ray & Arthur Murray)
Swing / Shuffle my boogie / Guantanamera / Bunny hop cha cha / New York, New York / Last cheater's waltz / Don't cry for me Argentina / Coffee song / Riviera rumba / Tango, anyone
AERO 1009 / Jul '96 / Aerospace

☐ DANCING IN THE DARK
Dancing in the dark / True blue Lou / Begin the beguine / Cheek to cheek / Dancing on the ceiling / I wonder what's become of Sally / Continental / You and the night and the music / Taking a chance on love / You're the cream in my coffee / It's de-lovely / I get a kick out of you
AERO 995 / May '96 / Aerospace

☐ DIRTY TRUMPET FOR A SWINGIN' PARTY/HAPPY TRUMPETS (Anthony, Ray Orchestra)
Let me entertain you / Some of these days / St. Louis blues / Harlem nocturne / Sugar blues / Booby trap / Walkin' the Sunset Strip / Big stomp / Skoklaan / Candy wrapper / Mr. Anthony's blues / Shoutin' truth / Inka dinka doo / String of pearls / Elmer's tune / Happiness is / Popcorn / Bill Bailey / Tijuana taxi / Taste of honey / What now my love / Spanish flea / Zorba the Greek / Mame
RACD 1027 / Jun '97 / Aerospace

☐ DREAM DANCING IN HAWAII/DREAM DANCING MEMORIES (Anthony, Ray Orchestra)
Hawaiian sunset / Beyond the reef / Harbour lights / Hawaiian nights / Tiny bubbles / Now is the hour / Paradise / Hawaiian wedding song / Blue Hawaii / Blue moon / Sweet Leilani / Aloha / Still wind / Evening sun / World belongs to me / Why should we wonder / Misty night / Goodnight ladies / Moonlight madness / Heaven only knows / Reverie / Raindrops and moonbeams / Londonderry air / Summer breezes
RACD 1026 / Jun '97 / Aerospace

☐ DREAM DANCING IN THE LATIN MOOD (Anthony, Ray Orchestra)
Yesterday I heard the rain / What a difference a day made / Amapola / Perfida / Besame mucho / Green eyes / Poinciana / Adios / Frenesi / Jungle drums / Yellow days / Sabor a mi / You belong to my heart / Maria Elena / Always in my heart / Yours
RACD 1042 / 6 Jul '98 / Aerospace

☐ DREAM GIRL/MOMENTS TOGETHER
Love is here to stay / Careless / Everything I have is yours / Many faces / Goodnight waltz / No other love / Please Mr.Sun / Things I love / With you in mind / Oh what it seems to be / In time / If I ever love again / Dream girl / Bewitched / Nearness of you / When I fall in love / My foolish heart / You'll never know / Pretend / I fell in love / Darn that dream / I didn't know what time it was / My private melody / It's the talk of the town
CTMCD 119 / Jun '97 / EMI

☐ EARLY YEARS, THE (Anthony, Ray US Navy Band/Orchestra)
Chloe: *Anthony, Ray US Navy Band* / East of the sun: *Anthony, Ray US Navy Band* / How many hearts have you broken: *Anthony, Ray US Navy Band* / Candy: *Anthony, Ray US Navy Band* / Coquette: *Anthony, Ray US Navy Band* / My postwar years with you: *Anthony, Ray US Navy Band* / I'm beginning to see the light: *Anthony, Ray US Navy Band* / Trees: *Anthony, Ray US Navy Band* / Accentuate the positive: *Anthony, Ray US Navy Band* / Ten o'clock curfew: *Anthony, Ray US Navy Band* / Night and day: *Anthony, Ray Orchestra* / I can't give you anything but love: *Anthony, Ray Orchestra* / Embraceable you: *Anthony, Ray Orchestra* / My melancholy baby: *Anthony, Ray Orchestra* / Let's fall in love: *Anthony, Ray Orchestra* / Summertime: *Anthony, Ray Orchestra* / Carioca: *Anthony, Ray Orchestra* / Darktown strutters ball: *Anthony, Ray Orchestra*
MONTCD 005 / 9 May '98 / Montpellier

☐ HITS OF RAY ANTHONY, THE
Slaughter on 10th Avenue / Man with the horn / Mr. Anthony's boogie / Oh mein papa / Bunny hop / Thunderbird / Dragnet / At last / Harlem nocturne / Stardust / Peter Gunn / Tenderly / When the saints go marching in
AERO 999 / May '96 / Aerospace

☐ HOOKED ON BIG BANDS (Live)
AERO 1012 / Jul '96 / Aerospace

☐ I REMEMBER GLENN MILLER
Tuxedo Junction / Chattanooga choo choo / Serenade in blue / Elmer's tune / Sunrise serenade / Song of the Volga boatmen / In the mood / I know why / Sweet as apple cider / At last / Little Brown jug / Moonlight serenade
AERO 1011 / Jul '96 / Aerospace

☐ MUSIC OF YOUR MEMORIES
What's new / Here's that rainy day / Like someone in love / My funny valentine / To love and be loved / All the way / Misty / I should care / I'm through with love / Guess I'll hang my tears out to dry / Alone together / Party's over
AERO 1019 / Jul '96 / Aerospace

☐ NAVY SHOW BROADCASTS 1952, THE (Anthony, Ray Orchestra)
Young man with a horn / Lullaby of Broadway / Sentimental journey / Wheel of fortune / Continental / As time goes by / You're driving me crazy / Bermuda / Begin the beguine / I'll walk alone / They didn't believe me / Deep night / Rhapsody / Dinah / I get a kick out of you / That old black magic / Delicado / Perdido / I'll remember April / Blacksmith blues / Sometimes I'm happy / Trumpet boogie / I let a song go out of my heart / For dancers only
MONTCD 006 / 9 May '98 / Montpellier

☐ SWEET AND SWINGIN' 1949-1953
CCD 96 / May '95 / Circle

☐ SWING'S THE THING
Baby but you did / Roll 'em around / South Dakota / This may be the time / Every dog has his day / Why should I worry / Why don't you want to come home / You gotta get lucky sometime / Mr. Moon / Indubitably / You're the one for me / Lavender mood
AERO 998 / May '96 / Aerospace

☐ SWINGIN' AT THE TOWER
Flying home / Night train / How high the moon / Perdido / One o'clock jump / Swingin' at the Tower
AERO 996 / May '96 / Aerospace

☐ TENDERLY
AERO 1029 / Jul '96 / Aerospace

☐ TRIP THROUGH 50 YEARS OF MUSIC, A (Live From The Royal Hawaiian Hotel) (Anthony, Ray Orchestra)
Vehicle / Hold on I'm coming / Get ready / It's impossible / Aquarius/Let the sun shine in / Everything is beautiful / Everybody's talkin' / Sing sing sing / Toot toot tootsie goodbye / I wanna be loved by you / Black bottom / Varsity drag / Charleston / Tuxedo junction / In the mood / Jukebox Saturday night / Flat foot floogie / Bei mir bist du shoen / Opus no.1 / Take the 'A' train / Spanish flea / Tijuana taxi / Spinning wheel / Lucretia MacEvil / Smiling phases / Free / Love story / Oh happy day
RACD 1025 / Jun '97 / Aerospace

Anthrax

☐ AMONG THE LIVING
Among the living / Caught in a mosh / I am the law / Efilnikufesin (NFL) / Skeleton in the closet / Indians / One world / ADI Horror of it all / Imitation of life
IMCD 186 / Mar '94 / Island

☐ ATTACK OF THE KILLER B'S
IMCD 179 / Mar '94 / Island

☐ MOSHERS 1986-1991
VSOPCD 252 / 9 Mar '98 / Connoisseur Collection

☐ PERSISTENCE OF TIME
Time / Blood / Keep it in the family / In my world / Gridlock / Intro to reality / Belly of the beast / Got the time / H8 red / One man stands / Discharge
IMCD 178 / Mar '94 / Island

☐ SOUND OF WHITE NOISE, THE
Potter's field / Only / Room for one more / Packaged rebellion / Hy pro glo / Invisible / 1000 points of hate / Black lodge / C11 H17... / Burst / This is not an exit
7559614302 / May '93 / Elektra

☐ SOUND OF WHITE NOISE, THE (Japanese Issue)
VICP 60320 / 27 Apr '98 / Victor

☐ SPREADING THE DISEASE
Gung ho / Armed and dangerous / Afters / Enemy / SSC / Stand or fall / Mad house / Lone justice / AIR
IMCD 136 / Aug '91 / Island

☐ STATE OF EUPHORIA
Be all, end all / Out of sight out of mind / Make me laugh / Anti-social / Who cares wins / Now it's dark / Schism / Misery loves company / Thirteen / Finale
IMCD 187 / Mar '94 / Island

☐ STOMP 442
Fueled / Nothing / Bare / Random acts of senseless violence / Tester / Drop the ball / American pompeii / In a zone / Perpetual motion / Riding shotgun / King size
7559618562 / Dec '95 / Elektra

☐ VOLUME 8: THE THREAT IS REAL
IGN 740343 / 20 Jul '98 / Ignition

Anti Cimex

☐ MADE IN SWEDEN (Live)
DISTC 53 / Sep '93 / Distortion

☐ RAPED ASS
DISTCD 9 / Feb '95 / Distortion

☐ SCANDINAVIAN JAWBREAKER
DISTCD 7 / Jul '93 / Distortion

Anti Establishment

☐ OI COLLECTION
1980's / Mechanical man / No trust / Future girl / Anti men / Misunderstood / Life is a ripoff / Mary is dead / Front page news / Future girl / It's killing you / Step outside / House of the rising sun / Savage city / Confusion / I feel hate / War monger / Sid's song
AHOYCD 078 / 3 Nov '97 / Captain Oi

Anti Flag

☐ DIE FOR THE GOVERNMENT
NRA 70CD / 15 Apr '97 / New Red Archives

☐ THEIR SYSTEM DOESN'T WORK FOR YOU
AF 0001CD / 15 Jun '98 / AF

Anti Gravity

☐ BOOGIE FOR HANUMAN
Boogie for hanuman / Mobius man / This melody no verb / Dark house midday / Weaving time / G mu nu / Ishmael
AC 5018 / Oct '97 / Accurate

Anti Heroes

☐ AMERICAN PIE
TAANG 125CD / 11 Aug '97 / Taang

Anti Nowhere League

☐ ANTI NOWHERE LEAGUE PUNK SINGLES COLLECTION
Streets of London / So what / I hate people / Let's break the law / Woman / Rocker / World War III / For you / Ballard of JJ Decay / Out on the wasteland / We will survive / Queen and country / So what (live) / I hate people (live) / Snowman / Fuck around the clock
CDPUNK 44 / Jan '95 / Anagram

☐ BEST OF ANTI NOWHERE LEAGUE, THE
SMMCD 514 / 27 Apr '98 / Snapper

☐ BEST OF THE ANTI NOWHERE LEAGUE, THE
CLEO 07279CD / Jan '94 / Cleopatra

☐ HORSE IS DEAD, THE (The Anti Nowhere League Live)
RRCD 219 / May '96 / Receiver

☐ PERFECT CRIME/ LIVE IN YUGOSLAVIA
Crime / Atomic harvest / On the waterfront / Branded / (I don't believe) This is my England / Johannesburg / Shining / Working for the company / System / Curtain / Let's break the law / Streets of London / We will survive / I hate people / For you / Woman / Can't stand rock 'n' roll / Wreck a nowhere / Paint it black / We are the league
LOMACD 9 / Nov '92 / Loma

☐ RETURN TO YUGOSLAVIA
IRRCD 076 / 20 Jul '98 / Knock Out

☐ SCUM
SPV 08453012 / Nov '97 / SPV

☐ SO WHAT (A Tribute To The Anti-Nowhere League) (Various Artists)
SPV 08453982 / Jul '97 / SPV

☐ WE ARE THE LEAGUE
We are the league / Animal / Woman / Can't stand rock 'n' roll / (We will not) rememeber you / Snowman / Streets of London / I hate people / Reck-a-nowhere / World War III / Nowhere man / Let's break the law / Rocker / So what
SMMCD 515 / 29 Sep '97 / Snapper

Anti Pasti

☐ BEST OF ANTI PASTI, THE
DOJOCD 230 / Mar '96 / Dojo

☐ CAUTION IN THE WIND
Caution in the wind / One Friday night / X affair / Get out now / Mr. Mystery / East to the West / See how they run / Hate circulation / Agent ABC / Best of us / Guinea pigs / Beyond belief
CDPUNK 53 / May '95 / Anagram

☐ LAST CALL, THE
No government / Brew your own / Another dead soldier / Call the army (I'm alive) / City below / Twenty four hours / Night of the war cry / Freedom row / St. George (get's his gun) / Last call / Ain't got me / Truth and justice / Hell / I wanna be your dog
CDPUNK 48 / Mar '95 / Anagram

☐ PUNK SINGLES COLLECTION
No government / 1980 / Two years too late / Something new / Let them free / Another dead soldier / Hell / Six guns / Now's the time / Call the army (I'm alive) / Ain't got me / Another dead soldier / East to the West / Burn in your own flames / Caution in the wind / Last train to nowhere / Blind faith
CDPUNK 106 / 29 Jun '98 / Cherry Red

Anti Social

☐ BATTLE SCARRED SKINHEADS
Too many people / Let's have some fun / Backstreet boys / Your choice / New punks / Screw u / Battle scarred skinheads / Official hooligan / Sewer rat / What have we got / Bollocks / Can't even dream / Anti war / New punks / Union Jack / Live and let live / Brick wall
AHOYCD 044 / 8 Jun '98 / Captain Oi

Antidote NYC

☐ VIVA PENDEJOS
Newtro-no, no, no / Caught up / Choice / Git wit it (naked live) / Haunted by your memory / Don't care / We're comin afta you / Rageman / Intro-return 2 burn / Be true 2 yourself / Positively negative / No no no / Something must be done / Road warrior / Another day / Stick it out / Foreign job lot (live) / Road warrior (live) / Rise above (live)
CDATV 24 / Apr '92 / Active

Antique Six

☐ CAUGHT AT THE TROUT INN
JCD 001 / Nov '96 / Trout

Antisect

☐ IN DARKNESS THERE IS NO CHOICE
18524 2 / Sep '94 / Southern

Antiseen

☐ HELL
BSR 011CD / Nov '95 / Tear It Up

☐ HERE TO RUIN YOUR GROOVE
SPV 08545882 / Dec '96 / SPV

Antoine Rencontre Les Problems

☐ 1960'S FRENCH EP COLLECTION, THE
519372 / Jul '97 / Magic

Antoine, Marc

☐ CLASSICAL SOUL
Smart but casual / French dream / P C H (Pacific coast highway) / Unity / Universal language / Timeless line / Follow your bliss / New boundaries / Classical soul
NYC 60102 / Dec '94 / NYC

☐ MADRID
Sunland / Masdrid / Dreamsicle / Sarava / Plaza Mayor / Jazzenco / Concache / Amour Hispanic / Cabrillo / Rebecca's waltz
GRP 99262 / 13 Jul '98 / GRP

Antolini, Charly

☐ COOKIN' (Antolini, Charly Jazz Power)
After you've gone / My romance / Jumpin' at the woodside / My ship / Yesterdays / Dick blues / Soon / Tickle toe / Like someone in love / Perdido / Oh lady be good
CDLR 45024 / Feb '91 / L&R

☐ CRASH
BLR 84 002 / May '91 / L&R

☐ IN THE GROOVE
Jesus christ superstar / Handicraft / Punching ball / Gringo domingo / Scratches / Y Luego / Skinny / Gemma ham
INAK 806CD / Nov '97 / In Akustik

Anton, Paul

☐ LIVIN' IT UP
SIAMCD 111 / Dec '96 / Siam

☐ PAUL ANTON
I know a man / Just don't matter / Forgive me / What's a guy supposed to do / I know a man (Smooth vibe) / We had it going on / Just say / Looking at you / In my life
SIAMCD 108 / Feb '95 / Siam

Antones Women

☐ BRINGING THE BEST IN BLUES
Something's got a hold on me / Hurtback / Big town / Playboy / Neighour neighbour / Down South in New Orleans / You'll lose a good thing / I'm a good woman / Queen Bee / But I forgive you / Cuban getaway / Twelve bar blues / Richest one / Wrapping up our love
ANTCD 9902 / Jan '93 / Antones

Antonov, Yuri

☐ MIRROR
MK 437052 / Jul '92 / Mezhdunarodnaya Kniga

Antonym

☐ TONANYSM
RM 1 / Jun '97 / Radiator

Anuna

☐ ANUNA
Media vita / Invocation / Pater noster / Suantrai / Cormacus / Jerusalem / Crist and St.Marie / Fionnghuala / Si do mhaimeo / Blue bird / Silent O'Moyle / Bean phaidin an poc ar buile / Sanctus / Raid / First day / Faigh an gleas
7567827332 / Apr '95 / Atlantic

☐ BEHIND THE CLOSED EYE (Anuna & The Ulster Orchestra)
August / Aisling / Great wood / From nowhere to nowhere / Annaghdown / Ceann dubh dilis / Ave Maria / Gathering mushrooms / Behind the closed eye / Midnight / Coming of winter / Where all roses go / 1901
DANUCD 009 / Nov '97 / Anuna Teo

☐ DEEP DEAD BLUE
DANU 007CD / Feb '97 / Danu

☐ OMNIS
DANU 005CD / Oct '95 / Danu

☐ OMNIS (Rerecorded Version)
DANU 008CD / Jun '97 / Danu

☐ OMNIS
UND 53098 / 29 Sep '97 / Universal

Anvil

☐ ABSOLUTELY NO ALTERNATIVE
MASSCD 134 / 8 Dec '97 / Massacre

☐ FORGED IN FIRE
Forged in fire / Shadow zone / Free as the wind / Never deceive me / Butter-bust jerky / Future wars / Hard times-fast ladies / Make it up to you / Motormount / Winged assassins
3023342 / 11 May '98 / Axe Killer

☐ PLUGGED IN PERMAMENT
MASSDP 098 / Jun '96 / Massacre

☐ POUND FOR POUND
MASSCD 097 / Jun '96 / Massacre

Any Old Time

☐ PHOENIX (Traditional Music From Cork & Beyond)
DARA 025CD / Jun '96 / Dara

Any Old Time String Band

☐ I BID YOU GOODNIGHT
ARHCD 433 / Apr '96 / Arhoolie

Any Trouble

☐ WHERE ARE ALL THE NICE GIRLS
Second choice / Playing Bogart / No idea / Foolish pride / Nice girls / Turning up the heat / Romance / Hurt / Girls are always right / Growing up / Honolulu / (Get you off) the hook
742462 / 16 Mar '98 / Charly

☐ WRONG END OF THE RACE
Open fire / Old before your time / Lover's moon / Lucky day / Coming of age / Baby, now that I've found you / All the time in the world / Wheels in motion / Turning up the heat / Yesterday's love / Playing Bogart / Eleventh hour / Cheating kind / Snapshot / Between the black and the grey / Kid gloves / Like a man / Learning the game / Wrong end of the race
BGOCD 295 / Nov '95 / Beat Goes On

Anyways

☐ LOVE LIES
PAXCD 011 / Apr '92 / Pax

Anywhen

☐ ANYWHEN
CS 005 / 6 Apr '98 / Clear Spot

AOS 3

☐ DIVERSIONARY TACTICS
ANOK 1CD / Oct '95 / Inna State

☐ GOD'S SECRET AGENT
WOWCD 28 / Mar '94 / Words Of Warning

Apache Indian

☐ MAKE WAY FOR THE INDIAN
Make way for the Indian / Armagideon time / Boba / Raggamuffin girl / I pray / Born for a purpose / Back up / Right time / Who say / Boom shak-a-lak / Ansa dat
CID 8016 / Mar '95 / Island

☐ NO RESERVATIONS
Don raja (prelude) / Chok there / Fe real / Fix up / AIDS warning / Guru / Wan' know me / Come follow me / Don't touch / Arranged marriage / Drink problems / Movie over India / Magic carpet / Badd Indian / Don raja
IMCD 215 / Mar '96 / Island

☐ REAL PEOPLE
3984204562 / 13 Oct '97 / Coalition

Aparis

☐ DESPITE THE FIRE-FIGHTERS EFFORTS
Sunrise / Waveforms / Welcome / Fire / Green piece / Orange / Hannibal
5177172 / May '93 / ECM

Apartment 3-G

☐ SHIT NOBODY WANTS TO LISTEN
CDR 021 / Feb '97 / Cravedog

Apartments

☐ APART
Doll hospital / No hurry / Breakdown in Vera Cruz / To live for / Welcome to Walsh world / Your ambulance rides / Friday rich/Saturday poor / World of liars / Place of bones / Cheerleader / Everything is given to be taken away
HOT 1063CD / Jul '97 / Hot

☐ DRIFT
HOT 1060CD / Jul '98 / Hot

☐ EVENING VISITS, THE
Mr. Somewhere / What's the morning for / All the birthdays / Great fool / Speechless with Tuesday / Cannot tell the days apart / Lazarus Lazarus / Black road shines
HOT 1059CD / Jul '98 / Hot

☐ FETE FORAINE
What's the morning for / Knowing you were loved / Not every clown can be in the circus / On every corner / Sunset hotel / End of some fear / Thankyou for making me beg / Things you'll keep / Paint the days white
HOT 1068CD / Jul '98 / Hot

☐ LIFE FULL OF FAREWELLS, A
Things you'll keep / Failure of love is a brick wall / You became my big excuse / End of some fear / Not every clown can be in the circus / Thank you for making me / All the time in the world
HOT 1050CD / Mar '95 / Hot

Apaza, L.

☐ PERUVIAN HARP & MANDOLIN
CDT 105CD / Nov '95 / Music Of The World

Apazie, Don

☐ DON APAZIE (Apazie, Don & His Havana Casino Orchestra)
HQCD 10 / '91 / Harlequin

APE

☐ STRIP LIGHT
DOR 41CD / Jun '95 / Dorado

Apemen

☐ APEMEN
NITR 004 / Jan '97 / Demolition Derby

☐ PHANTACITY
Phantacity / Get it right / Someone like me / Love train / Remember Thomas A-Beckett / Mrs. Applegate / Tell the truth / She's a girl / Let the good times surround you / Love in / Creation / Mary Anne / Fire
DRCD 011 / Sep '96 / Detour

Aperghis, George

☐ PARCOURS
TE 008 / Jan '97 / BUDA

☐ TRIPTYQUE
TEO 14 / 24 Feb '98 / EPM

Apes, Pigs & Spacemen

☐ SNAPSHOT
Unknown territories / Beanman / Monster / Blood simple / Ice cream / Virtual / Hollow / Chair / Mother Courage / Nine lives / Humiliation / Trouble / Suits
CDMFNX 219

☐ CDMFN 219 / Jun '97 / Music For Nations

☐ TRANSFUSION
Great place / Fragments / Do I need this / Come round the world / Safety net / Twice the man / Regurgitate / PVS / Take our sorrow's swimming / Seep / Open season
CDMFN 192

☐ CDMFN 192 / Oct '95 / Music For Nations

Apex

☐ BARRICADE
PD 008CD / Apr '97 / E-Bon

Apex Jazz Band Of Northern Ireland

☐ UPTOWN BUMP
PKCD 089 / Jan '98 / PEK

Aphasia

☐ MESOPHERIC BREAKS
NM 023 / 10 Aug '98 / Noise Museum

Aphex Twin

☐ ANALOGUE BUBBLEBATH VOL.1
TVT 4810CD / 2 Feb '98 / TVT

☐ ANALOGUE BUBBLEBATH VOL.3 (AFX)
CAT 008CD / 10 Nov '97 / Rephlex

☐ CLASSICS
Digeridoo / Flaphead / Phloam / Isoprophlex / Polynomial - C / Tamphex (head fhug mix) / Phima place / Dodecahedron / Analogue bubblebath / En trange to exit / Afx 2 / Metapharstic / We have arrived
RS 95035CD / 16 Feb '98 / R&S

☐ I CARE BECAUSE YOU DO
WARPCD 30 / Apr '95 / Warp

☐ RICHARD D. JAMES
WARPCD 43 / Nov '96 / Warp

☐ SELECTED AMBIENT WORKS VOL.1 1985-1992
Xtal / Tha / Pulsewidth / Ageispolis / Greencalx / Heliospan / We are the music makers / Schotkey / Ptolemy / Hedphelym / Delphium / Actium
AMB 3922CD / 16 Feb '98 / Apollo

☐ SELECTED AMBIENT WORKS VOL.2
WARPCD 21 / Feb '94 / Warp

Aphrodite

☐ APHRODITE PRESENTS FULL FORCE (2CD Set) (Various Artists)
Shadow: Rob & Goldie / After Dark: A-Sides & Cool Hand Flex / Dark coast: DJ Creation / Hypnosis: Smith, Simon 'Bassline' / Believe: E-Z Rollers / Cut Throat Flow: Optical / Moments in space: Nookie / Covert: Austin M / Atmosphere: DJ Phantasy / Funk: D'Cruze / Acoustic vibes: Level Vibes / Oh gosh: Heavyweight / Spiral of jazz: Ricochet / Baretter: Sling Ting / Punks: A-Sides / Bad ass: Aphrodite & DJ Creation / Zanzibar: Smith, Simon 'Bassline' / Knowledge and wisdom: DJ Phantasy / Ghetto: System X / Style from the dark side: Aphrodite / This song: Mental Power / Beauty and the beast: Level Vibes / Destroy: Austin M / Psycho: Ricochet / Bring dat beat: Yarn & KO
DBM 30344 / Aug '97 / Death Becomes Me

☐ APHRODITE RECORDINGS
Aphromoods / King of the beats / Woman that rolls / Spice / Summer breeze / Music's hypnotising / Listen to the rhythm / Dub moods / Style from the dark side / Tower bass / I wanted it more and more / Sweet mind
APHCD 1 / 23 Feb '98 / Aphrodite

Aphrodite's Child

☐ 666 (2CD Set)
Aegean sea / All the seats were occupied / Altomont / Babylon / Battle of the beast / Beast / Break / Capture of the beast / Do it / Four horsemen / Hic-et-nunc / Infinity / Lamb / Lament / Loud loud / Marching beast / Ofis / Seven trumpets / Seventh seal / System / Tribulation / Wakening beast / Wedding of the lamb
8384302 / Aug '98 / Mercury

Apocalypse Hoboken

☐ HOUSE OF THE RISING SON OF A BITCH
787662 / 29 Jun '98 / Kung Fu

Apocalypse Theatre

☐ CAIN OR AN OPEN VEIN
Live at the scene / Silver nails / Waiting for the end / Cain or an open vein / Slaughterhaus X / Pour Paris / Dead quiet / Monsters / Time after time / Speaking tongues / Elijah / Needles dreams / Anthem
TX 60013CD / 17 Aug '98 / Triple XXX

Apollo 440

☐ ELECTRO GLIDE IN BLUE
Stealth overture / Ain't talkin' 'bout dub / Altamont super highway revisited / Electro glide in blue / Vanishing point / Tears of the the gods / Carrera rapida / Krupa / White man's throat / Pain in any language / Stealth mass in F sharp minor / Raw power
SSX 2440CDR / Jul '97 / Stealth Sonic
SSX 2440CD / Mar '97 / Stealth Sonic

☐ MILLENNIUM FEVER
Rumble/Spirit of America / Liquid cool / Film me and finish me off / I need something stronger / Pain is a close up / Omega point / (Don't fear) the reaper / Astral America / Millenium fever / Stealth requiem
SSX 440 CD / Nov '94 / Epic

Apollon, Dave

☐ MAN WITH THE MANDOLIN, THE (2CD Set)
ACD 27 / 3 Aug '98 / Acoustic Disc

Apollyon Sun

☐ GOD LEAVES
God leaves / Reefer boy / Cane / Concrete Satan / Bedlam and blind
MYNCD 1 / 22 Jun '98 / Mayhem

Appellation Controllee

☐ APPELLATION CONTROLLEE
MWCD 1001 / Jun '92 / Music & Words

☐ TIZ
DIGIT 5679142 / Dec '95 / Dig It

Appendix Out

☐ RYE BEARS A POISON
DC 126CD / 13 Oct '97 / Drag City

Appice, Carmine

☐ CARMINE APPICE'S GUITAR ZEUS (Guitar Zeus)
342622 / Dec '95 / No Bull

Apple, Fiona

☐ TIDAL
Sleep to dream / Sullen girl / Shadowboxer / Criminal / Slow like honey / First taste / Never is a promise / Child is gone / Pale September / Carrion
4837502 / Sep '96 / Columbia

Appleorchard

☐ TACET
RSTR 007D / Nov '96 / Rumblestrip

Apples In Stereo

☐ FUN TRICK NOISEMAKER
SPART 42CD / 20 Apr '98 / Spin Art

☐ SCIENCE FAIRE
SPART 48CD / 5 Jan '98 / Spin Art

☐ TONE SOUL EVOLUTION
Seems so / What's the # / About your fame / Shine a light / Get there fine / Silvery light of a dream / Silvery light of a dream / We'll come to be / Tin pan alley / You said that last night / Try to remember / Find our way / Coda
SPART 57
4344310132 / 4 May '98 / Sire

Appleseed

☐ KICK IT TILL IT BREAKS
KSRCD 4 / 8 Jun '98 / Kingsize

Appleseed Cast

☐ END OF THE RING WARS, THE
DER 370CD / 17 Aug '98 / Deep Elm

Appleton, Jon

☐ CONTES DE LA MEMOIRE
IMED 9635 / Jun '97 / Diffunzioni Musicali

Appleyard, Peter

☐ BARBADOS COOL
Tangerine / Stompin' at the Savoy / Airmail special / Passion flower / Django / Prelude to a kiss / Memories of you / Fascinating rhythm / Broadway / Cherokee
CCD 4475 / Aug '91 / Concord Jazz

☐ BARBADOS HEAT
You stepped out of a dream / Body and soul / Take the 'A' train / Satin doll / Caravan nuages / Here's that rainy day / Sing sing sing
CCD 4436 / Nov '90 / Concord Jazz

April March

☐ APRIL MARCH AND LOS CINCOS (April March & Los Cincos)
SFTRI 491CD / 22 May '98 / Sympathy For The Record Industry

☐ PARIS IN APRIL
SFTRI 456CD / Oct '96 / Sympathy For The Record Industry

☐ SINGS ALONG
SFTRI 434CD / Apr '97 / Sympathy For The Record Industry

April Wine

☐ ELECTRIC JEWELS
RR 4212 / Jul '93 / Repertoire

☐ ON RECORD
REP 4213 / Aug '91 / Repertoire
RR 4213 / Jul '93 / Repertoire

Aqua

☐ AQUARIUM
UMD 85020 / 3 Nov '97 / Universal

Aqua Velvets

☐ NOMAD
Nomad / Surf nouveau / Smoking panatelas on the blue / Mediterranean Sea / Holly tiki / Snorkel mask replica / Return to Paia / Ho'okipa / In a Spanish mood / Nervous on Neptune / Summer at dreampoint / Shakahoochie / Shrunken head
74321408292 / Sep '96 / Milan

Aquabats

☐ AQUABATS
HOR 001CD / 6 Oct '97 / Fearless

Aquarhythms

☐ GREETINGS FROM DEEPEST AMERICA
ASW 6209 / 6 Oct '97 / Astralwerks

Aquarius

☐ AQUARIUS DUB
AQCD 001 / 19 Jan '98 / Aquarius

Aquartet

☐ ROUE LIBRE
DPCD 96014 / Feb '96 / Mustradem

Aquasky

☐ ORANGE DUST
Opaque / Orange dust / Universe / Plane invaders / Rough / Raw skillz
5378362 / Aug '97 / Passenger

Aquaturbia
□ PSYCHEDELIC DRUGSTORE
HBG 122/15 / Apr '93 / Background

Aquaviva, John
□ TRANSMISSIONS (Various Artists)
Salacious: Gianelli / Relations: Pooley, Ian / Seven 2 mix: Seven / Vision 3: Mario J / Hardphunk: Hardtrax / Always did always will: Tralopscinor / Manik sax: Phulasole, Chuck / Bang the box: Basement Trax / Son: Sun Children / Getn house: Calisto / Gasoline: Barada / Rescue: Omegaman / Loop: LFO & Fuse / Logan's run: LA Williams / Spaz: Plastikman / Track for O.J. Simpson: Parker, Terrence / Phreakin': DJ HMC
CDTIVA 1017 / 25 Aug '97 / Additive

Aqueos
□ TALL CLOUDTREES
HERM 2222 / Oct '96 / Hermetic

Ar Braz, Dan
□ ACOUSTIC
GLCD 3035 / Oct '93 / Green Linnet

□ MUSIQUE POUR LES SILENCES A VENIR/SEPTEMBRE BLEU/BORDERS OF (L'Essentiel Dan Ar Braz/3CD Set)
KM 022338 / Jul '96 / Keltia Musique

□ MUSIQUES POUR LES SILENCES A VENIR
KMCD 02 / Aug '89 / Keltia Musique

□ SONGS
KMCD 14 / '91 / Red Sky

Ar C'hoarezed Goadec
□ LES VOIX LEGENDAIRES DE BRETAGNE
KMCD 11 / '91 / Keltia Musique

AR Kane
□ NEW CLEAR CHILD
Deep blue breath / Grace / Tiny little drop of perfumed time / Surf motel / Gather / Honey be (For Stella) / Cool as moons / Snow White's world / Pearl / Sea like a child
STONE 011CD / 30 Mar '98 / 3rd Stone

Ar Menez, Dialouled
□ DIAOULED AR MENEZ
CD 318 / May '93 / Diffusion Breizh

Ar Re Yaouank
□ BREIZH POSITIVE
STSC 02CD / Apr '95 / Diffusion Breizh

Ar-Log
□ AR-LOG VOL.4 & 5
SAIN 9068CD / Aug '94 / Sain

□ AR-LOG VOL.6
SCD 2119 / Aug '96 / Sain

Arab Strap
□ PHILOPHOBIA
Packs of three / Soaps / Here we go / New birds / One day after school / Islands / Night before the funeral / Not quite a yes / Piglet / Afterwards / My favourite muse / I would've liked me a lot last night / First time you're unfaithful
CHEM 021CD / 20 Apr '98 / Chemikal Underground

Arabesque
□ NIKRIZ (Arabesque & Hassan Erraji)
TUGCD 1001 / 6 Oct '97 / Riverboat

□ TRADITIONAL ARABIC MUSIC (Arabesque & Hassan Erraji)
Longa / Taksim hisayun / Ansam (Breezes) / Reddle guelbi / Hiwar (dialogue) / Sama'i thaqil / Sidi blal / Cerga / Alway mizan / Bab arraja (The door of hope)
CDSDL 387 / Mar '94 / Saydisc

Aragon, Louis
□ CHANSONS DE POETES
984262 / Nov '97 / EPM

Aranbee Symphony Orchestra
□ ARANBEE POP SYMPHONY ORCHESTRA, THE (Under the Direction of Keith Richard)
There's a place / Rag doll / I got you babe / We can work it out / Play with fire / Mother's little helper / In the midnight hour / Take it or leave it / Sittin' on a fence / I don't want to go on without you
C5CD522 / Sep '90 / See For Miles

Ararso, Shimelis
□ ETHIOPIAN WEDDING SONGS
RPM 0052 / 9 Mar '98 / Rags Productions

Arawi
□ DOCTRINE OF CYCLES, THE
NA 029 / Oct '90 / New Albion

ARBAT
□ DROM
829552 / 24 Feb '98 / BUDA

Arbete & Fritid
□ DEEP WOODS
Ganglat efter lejsme Per Larsson/Malung / Finsk sorgmarsch / Gabergsbrudens dodsmarsch / Arbete and Fritid / Tva springare / Tva springare / Vals / Dorisk drone / Thuicandra / Harmageddon boogie / Jag ar inte som andra / European way / Smavarmt / Maklins brudmarsch/Orsa / Hin hales halling / Franska valsen
RESCD 501 / Jul '97 / Resource

Arbuckle, Les
□ BUSH CREW, THE
AQ 1032 / Apr '95 / Audioquest

ARC
□ 12K
RA 011 / Jun '96 / Radikal Ambience

ARC
□ OUT OF AMBER
Early reflection / Distant window / Circadian rhythms / Snare in the woods / At the air's edge / Out of amber / Expecting to land / Radio pills / Snow dance / Goodbye dry land
SLAMCD 205 / Oct '96 / Slam

Arcadia
□ SO RED THE ROSE
Election day / Keep me in the dark / Goodbye is forever / Flame / Missing / Rose arcana / Promise / El diablo / Lady Ice
CDPRG 1010 / 6 Jul '98 / EMI Gold

Arcadia Reach
□ BLUE DELTA
TERRCD 009 / Jan '98 / Terra Nova

Arcady
□ AFTER THE BALL
Hennessey's / River / Barn dances / Field behind the plow / Heaven's gate / Lullybye / Jackie Daly's reels / Breton reels / Trios matelots du Port - De - Bere / I'd cross the wild Atlantic / Tripping down the stairs / After the ball / Spinsters waltz
DARACD 037 / Sep '93 / Dara

□ MANY HAPPY RETURNS
SHCD 79095 / Aug '95 / Shanachie
DARACD 080 / Aug '96 / Dara

Arcane
□ CASCADE
ARC 179CD / 10 Nov '97 / Displeased

Arcane Device
□ FETISH
SR 9009 / Jul '94 / Silent

Arcara
□ ARCARA
ESM 010 / 2 Mar '98 / Escape

□ MATTER OF TIME, A
Gunshy / Lost in time / Eternal affair / Never tell your dreams goodbye / Walk away / Fight isn't over / Matter of time / Blonde and blue / Fears cry from you / Let it ride / Love in the first degree / Believe
ESM 020 / 1 Nov '97 / Escape

Arceneaux, Fernest
□ ZYDECO STOMP (Arceneaux, Fernest & Thunders)
Got you on my mind / Bernadette / Bye bye lucille / Done got over you / I can't live happy / Big mamou / Sweet little angel / Zydeco stomp / Back to louisiana / Night time / Mother's love / Last night / It's alright / I don't want nobody / Mean woman / London zydeco / Chains of love / Reconsider baby
JSPCD 258 / Jul '95 / JSP

Arch Enemy
□ BLACK EARTH
WAR 011CD / Nov '96 / Wrong Again

□ STIGMATA
CM 77212CD / 25 May '98 / Century Media

Arch Rival
□ IN THE FACE OF DANGER
In the face of danger / Time won't wait / Me against the world / Rock the night away / Fortune hunter / God bless America / Revolution / Shotgun at Midnight / Siren's song / Can you tell me why
KILCD 1005 / Oct '93 / Killerwatt

Archer, Tasmin
□ GREAT EXPECTATIONS
Sleeping satellite / Arienne / Lords of the new church / When it comes down to it / Steeltown / Higher you climb / In your care / Somebody's daughter / Hero / Ripped inside / Halfway to heaven
CDEMC 3624 / Sep '92 / EMI

Archers Of Loaf
□ VEE VEE
Step into the light / Harnessed in slums / Nevermind the enemy / Greatest of all time / Underdogs / Nipomo / Floating friends / 1985 / Fabroch nostalgia / Let the loser melt / Death in the park / Worst has yet to come / Undercacheivers march and fight song
A064 D / Mar '95 / Alias

Archetype
□ ARCHETYPE
CD 831 / May '93 / Diffusion Breizh

Archey, Jimmy
□ DOCTOR JAZZ VOL.4 (1951-1952)
STCD 6044 / May '96 / Storyville

□ JIMMY ARCHEY
BCD 310 / Jun '94 / GHB

□ LIVE IN NEW YORK 1951-1952 (Archey, Jimmy Band)
STCD 6058 / Oct '97 / Storyville

Archibald, Red
□ WEST COAST SOUL STEW (Archibald, Red & The Internationals)
BTR 19972 / 20 Apr '98 / Bluetone

Archies
□ SUGAR SUGAR
Sugar sugar / Jingle jangle / Bang shang a lang / Feelin' so good / Melody Hill / Over and over / You little angel you / Everything's alright / Sugar and spice / Bicycles, rollerskates and you / Kissin' hot dog
CDSGP 0225 / Sep '97 / Prestige

Architex
□ ALTITUDE PRESENTS ARCHITEX
ARXCD 01 / 22 Jun '98 / Vinyl

Archive
□ LONDINIUM
Old artist / All time / So few words / Headspace / Darkroom / Londinium / Man made / Nothing else / Skyscraper / Parvaneh / Beautiful love / Organ song / Last live / Untitled
ARKCD 1001 / Jan '97 / Island

Arckanum
□ KAMPEN
NR 024CD / 11 May '98 / Necropolis

□ KOSTOGHER
NR 011CD / May '97 / Necropolis

Arcturus
□ ASPERA HIEMS SYMFONIA
ALC 002CD / Apr '96 / Misanthropy

□ LA MASQUERADE INFERNALE
Master of disguise / Ad astra / Chaos path / La masquerade / Alone / Of nails and sinners / Throne of tradegy / Painting my honor
CDMFN 230 / 3 Nov '97 / Music For Nations

Arcwelder
□ ENTROPY
TG 158CD / May '96 / Touch & Go

□ PULL
TG 108CD / Feb '93 / Touch & Go

□ XERXES
TG 126CD / Apr '94 / Touch & Go

Arden, Jann
□ HAPPY
5407892 / 8 Jun '98 / A&M

□ LIVING UNDER JUNE
Could I be your girl / Demolition love / Looking for it (finding heaven) / Insensitive / Gasoline / Wonderdrug / Living under June / Unloved / Good mother / It looks like rain / I would live for you
5403362 / 15 Sep '97 / A&M

Arden, Victor
□ KEYBOARD WIZARDS OF THE GERSHWIN ERA VOL.3 (Arden, Victor & Phil Ohman)
GEMMCD 9203 / Dec '95 / Pearl

Arditti String Quartet
□ FERNEYHOUGH VOL.2 (Arditti String Quartet & Asko Ensemble/Magnus Andersson)
MO 782029 / Dec '96 / Montaigne

Ardley, Neil
□ KALEIDOSCOPE OF RAINBOWS
Prologue / Rainbow one / Rainbow two / Rainbow three / Rainbow four / Rainbow five / Rainbow six / Rainbow seven / Epilogue
AMPCD 029 / Apr '97 / AMP

Ardoin, Amade
□ I'M NEVER COMIN' BACK
ARHCD 7007 / Jan '96 / Arhoolie

Ardoin, Boisec
□ LA MUSIQUE CREOLE (Ardoin, Boisec & Canray Fontenot)
ARHCD 445 / Apr '96 / Arhoolie

Ardoin, Chris
□ GON' BE JUS' FINE (Ardoin, Chris & Double Clutchin')
Lake Charles connection / Beauty in your eyes / When I'm dead and gone / Cowboy / Ardoin two step / Gon' be jus' fine / I believe in you / We are the boys / I don't want what I can't keep / Dimanche apres midi / Angel / Back door man / When the morning comes / We are the boys
ROUCD 2127 / Jul '97 / Rounder

Area
□ AGATE LINES
TMCD 59 / Nov '90 / Third Mind

Arecibo
□ TRANS PLUTONIAN TRANSMISSIONS
AT 02CD / Mar '95 / Atmosphere

Arena
□ CRY
Theme / Cry / Offering / Problem line / Isolation / Fallen idols / Guidance / Only child / Stolen promise / Healer
VGCD 005 / Apr '97 / Verglas Music

□ PRIDE
Welcome to the cage / Crying for help V / Empire of a thousand days / Crying for help VI / Medusa / Crying for help VII / Fool's gold / Crying for help VIII / Sirens
VGCD 004 / Sep '96 / Verglas Music

□ SONGS FROM THE LIONS CAGE
Solomon / Crying for help IV / Midas vision / Jericho / Crying for help I / Out of the wilderness / Crying for help / Valley of the kings
VGCD 001 / Feb '95 / Verglas Music

□ VISITOR
Crack in the ice / Pins and needles / Double vision / Elea / Hanging tree / Blister of grace / Blood red room / In the blink of an eye / (Don't forget to) breathe / Serenity / Tears in the rain / Enemy without / Running from Damascus / Visitor
VGCD 012 / 20 Apr '98 / Verglas Music

□ WELCOME TO THE STAGE
VGCD 009 / 17 Nov '97 / Verglas Music

Arena, Tina
□ DON'T ASK
Chains / Heaven help my heart / Sorento moon (I remember) / Wasn't it good / Message / Love is the answer / Greatest gift / That's the way a woman feels / Baby be a man / Standing up / Show me heaven
4778869 / Aug '96 / Columbia

Argent
□ ALL TOGETHER NOW
Hold your head up / Keep on rolling / Tragedy / I am the dance of ages / Be my lover, be my friend / He's a dynamo / Pure love / Fantasia / Prelude / Finale
4773772 / Aug '94 / Epic
379412 / Jun '97 / Koch International

□ COMPLETE BBC SESSIONS, THE
Where are we going wrong / Rejoice / Uranus / Hold your head up / Keep on rolling / Rejoice / Tragedy / Keep on rolling / Liar / It's only money part 1 / It's only money part 2 / And give rock 'n' roll to you
SFRSCD 039 / 29 Sep '97 / Strange Fruit

□ IN DEEP
God gave rock 'n' roll to you / It's only money part 1 / It's only money part 2 / Losing hold / Be glad / Christmas for the free / Candles on the river / Rosie
4805292 / May '95 / Columbia

□ NEXUS
Coming of Kohoutek / Once around the sun / Infinite wanderer / Love / Music from the spheres / Thunder and lightning / Keeper of the flame / Man for all reasons / Gonna meet my maker
4894422 / 26 Jan '98 / Epic

Argentina, Imperio

☐ RECORDAR
BMCD 7601 / Nov '97 / Blue Moon

☐ YO SIEMPRE TE ESPERE VOL.2
BMCD 7605 / Jan '98 / Blue Moon

Arguelles, Julian

☐ HOME TRUTHS
BDV 9503 / Oct '95 / Babel

☐ PHAEDRUS
Phaedrus / Invisible thread / Duet / Forests / Maxine / Red rag / Wild rice / Everything I love / Hi Steve
AHUM 010 / Oct '91 / Ah-Um

☐ SCAPES (Arguelles, Julian & Steve)
BDV 9614 / Oct '96 / Babel

☐ SKULL VIEW (Arguelles, Julian Quartet)
BVD 9719 / Dec '97 / Babel

Arguelles, Steve

☐ ARGUELLES
Redman / Don't tell me now / Lucky star / Dis at ease / Cherry waltz / Blessed light / Elderberries / My heart belongs to Daddy / Guara / Hermana guapa / Tin tin / Trimmings
AHUM 007 / Aug '90 / Ah-Um

Argyle Park

☐ MISGUIDED
REX 460132 / Nov '95 / Rex

Aria

☐ ARIA
Willow / Un bel di / Secret tear / Dido / Pacê pace / Pamina blue / Habanera / Home
TCD 4009 / 24 Aug '98 / Astor Place

Arita, Yoshihiro

☐ WHALE DANCE
SCR 28 / Aug '96 / Strictly Country

Arizona Smoke Revue

☐ BEST OF BLUEGRASS
Duelling banjos / Old Joe Clark / Earl's breakdown / Communications breakdown / Reuben's train / Foggy mountain breakdown / Old groundhog / Auld Lang Syne / Columbus George / Battle of New Orleans / Cannonball line / Black mountain rag / Teetotallers reel / Sailor's hornpipe / Orange blossom special
3036300022 / Feb '96 / Carlton

Ark

☐ VOYAGE OF TRANQUILITY, A
Ark / Dawn of tranquility / Heavenly stars / Eternal skies / With a rhythm from the deep / Castaway / In earth's shadow / To sail through the universe / Drifting to love / Peace...your reality / In the garden of your mind / Through the forests of time / You are forever
CDMFP 6390 / Jun '97 / Music For Pleasure

Arkarna

☐ FRESH MEAT
House on fire / Eat me / Futures overrated / So little time / Block capital / Born yesterday part 1 / Born yesterday part 2 / Peace of mind / Direct dubit / R U ready
3984200512 / Aug '97 / WEA

Arkenstone, David

☐ ANOTHER STAR IN THE SKY
Pool of radiance / Far far away / Light in the east / Under the canopy / Voices of the night / Another star in the sky / Taken by the wind / Canyon of the moon / Naked in the wind / Ride into midnight
ND 62012 / May '94 / Narada

☐ CHRONICLES
Papillon (on the wings of the butterfly) / Southern cross / Rug merchant / Firedance / Borderlands / From the forge to the field / Passage / Ballet / Desert ride / Hindu holiday / Ancient legend / Valley in the clouds / Stepping stars / Out of the forest and into the trees / Voices of the anasazl / North wind
ND 64007 / Jun '93 / Narada

☐ CONVERGENCE (Arkenstone, David & David Lanz)
Madre de la tierra / Yosemite / Madrona / North wind / Dragon's daughter / Long way from home / Thousand small gold bells / Oaks / Cello's song / Love on the beach / Keeper of the flame
ND 64012 / Feb '97 / Narada

☐ ENCHANTMENT (A Magical Christmas)
We three Kings / Do you hear what I hear / Angels we have heard on high / Overture / Masters in this hall / Silver bells / March / O come, O come Emmanuel / I saw three ships / Waltz of the snowflakes / Coventry carol / Children's galop
ND 62016 / 17 Nov '97 / Narada

☐ ETERNAL CHAMPION
NDA 45448 / 9 Mar '98 / Narada

☐ QUEST OF THE DREAM WARRIOR
Prelude: Tallis the messenger / Rhythms of vision / Journey begins: Kyla's ride / Voice / Dance of the maidens / Magic forest / Road to the sea / Temple of vaal / Wings of the shadow / Homecoming
ND 64008 / Jun '95 / Narada

☐ RETURN OF THE GUARDIANS
Border journey / Trail of tears / Chosen voices / Winds of change / Forgotten lands / Two hearts / City in the clouds / Musk / Water of life - out of darkness transformation / Reunion
ND 64011 / Feb '97 / Narada

☐ SPIRIT OF OLYMPIA, THE (Arkenstone, David & Kostia/David Lanz)
Prelude: Let the games begin / Savannah runner / Memories of gold / Keeper of the flame / From the forge to the field / Heartfire / Celebration / Close without touching / Glory / Night in the village / Walk with the stars / Marathon man / Spirit of Olympia
CD 4006 / May '92 / Narada

Arkkon

☐ ARKKON
TK 01CD / Oct '96 / Tonus Kozmetica

Arlen, Harold

☐ COME RAIN OR COME SHINE (The Harold Arlen Songbook) (McNair, Sylvia & Andre Previn/David Finck)
Over the rainbow / Stormy weather / Between the devil and the deep blue sea / It was written in the stars / As long as I live / That old black magic / Morning after / Sleepin' bee / Accentuate the positive / Goose never be a peacock / I wonder what becomes of me / It's only a paper moon / In the shade of the banana tree / Coconut sweet / Right as the rain / I've got the world on a string / Come rain or come shine / This time the dream's on me / Let's take a walk around the block / Last night when we were young
4468182 / Jun '96 / Philips

☐ MUSIC OF HAROLD ARLEN, THE
3243315052 / 17 Mar '98 / Harb

☐ SONGWRITER SERIES VOL.4 (Over The Rainbow) (Various Artists)
Devil and the deep blue sea / I've got the world on a string / I gotta a right to sing the blues / Public melody no.1 / When the sun comes out / Hittin' the bottle / Let's fall in love / Let's put our heads together / Now I know / As long as I live / Raisin' the rent / Blues in the night / Down with love / Over the rainbow / It's only a paper moon / Buds won't bud / One for my baby / One for the way / Stormy weather / Kickin' the gong around / Two blind loves / That old black magic / Ac cent tchu ate the positive / Ill wind / Get happy
PASTCD 7095 / 27 Oct '97 / Flapper

☐ THAT OLD BLACK MAGIC (The Harold Arlen Songbook) (Various Artists)
5375732 / Jul '97 / Verve

Armacost, Tim

☐ FIRE
Norwegian wood / Old familiar faces / Long haired girl / Pennies from heaven / Table master / Maconde / There's a lull in my life / Voyage / Imprint / Bailey's blues
CCD 4697 / Jun '96 / Concord Crossover

Armageddon

☐ ARMAGEDDON
Buzzard / Silver tightrope / Paths and planes and future gains / Last stand before / Basking in the white of the midnight sun / Warnin' comin' on / Basking in the white of the midnight sun / Brother ego / Basking in the white of the midnight sun
RR 7089 / 20 Apr '98 / Repertoire

☐ CROSSING THE RUBICON
WAR 970304CD / 24 Nov '97 / War

Armagh Piper's Club

☐ SONGS OF THE CHANTER
PTICD 3007 / Aug '96 / Pure Traditional Irish

Armagideon

☐ EASE THE TENSION
ASCD 001 / Jun '95 / Armagideon Sounds

☐ STEPPIN' FORWARD
ASCD 003 / Mar '95 / Armagideon Sounds

☐ THROUGH THE HAZE
Grow more dub / Outer limits / Changes / Itoju / Take heed / Spiral galaxy / Flowers / Dubutainment / Comets tail / Super nova / Edutainment / Peace and harmony / Hydro dub / Spiral galaxy / Edutainment
DBHD 006CD / 2 Mar '98 / Dubhead

Armand

☐ EVERYTHING I NEED (Armand & Bluesology)
NMC 9718 / 19 Mar '98 / New Moon

Armani, Robert

☐ BLOW IT OUT
ACVCD 013 / Nov '95 / ACV

☐ DANCE MANIA
MM 00052 / 17 Aug '98 / Urban Substance

☐ MADMAN STANDS
ACVCD 007 / Apr '95 / ACV

☐ NEXT START
ACVCD 4 / Nov '93 / ACV

☐ RIGHT TO SILENCE
ACVCD 6 / Jul '94 / ACV

☐ SPECTACULAR
ACVCD 19 / Sep '96 / ACV

☐ VII CHAPTER
CSCD 002 / Mar '97 / ACV

Armatrading, Joan

☐ JOAN ARMATRADING
Down to zero / Help yourself / Water with the wine / Love and affection / Save me / Join the boys / People / Somebody who loves you / Like fire / Tall in the saddle
CDMID 104 / Oct '92 / A&M

☐ LOVE AND AFFECTION (Anthology/ 2CD Set)
Down to zero / True love / Talking to the wall / Show some emotion / I'm lucky / One more chance / Did I make you up / All a woman needs / Square the circle / Somebody who loves you / It could have been better / Alice / No love / Tall in the saddle (live) / Turn out the light / Shouting stage / One night / Save me / My family / City girl / Warm love / Power of dreams / Love by you / Weakness / More than one kind of love / Love and affection / Rosie / Bottom to the top / Drop the pilot / Me myself / Cool blue stole my heart / Water with the wine / Flight of the wild geese / Dry land / Always / Promise land / Can't get over (how I broke your heart)
5404052 / Feb '97 / A&M

☐ SHOW SOME EMOTION
Won'cha come on home / Show some emotion / Warm love / Never is too late / Peace in mind / Opportunity / Mama mercy / Get in the sun / Willow / Kissin' and a hugging
CDMID 105 / Oct '92 / A&M

☐ VERY BEST OF JOAN ARMATRADING
Love and affection / Down to zero / Drop the pilot / Show some emotion / Shouting stage / Willow / Rosie / I'm lucky / Me, myself and I / (I love it when you) call me names / Bottom to the top / More than one kind of love / Weakness in me / All the way from America
3971222 / Apr '91 / A&M

☐ WHAT'S INSIDE
In your eyes / Everyday boy / Merchant of love / Shapes and sizes / Back on the road / Trouble / Shape of a pony / Can't stop loving you / Beyond the blue / Recommend my love / Would you like to dance / Songs / Lost the love
74321272692 / May '95 / RCA

Armchair Martian

☐ ARMCHAIR MARTIAN
HEDCD 062 / Feb '97 / Headhunter

Armitage Shanks

☐ CACOPHONY NOW
DAMGOOD 141CD / 12 Jan '98 / Damaged Goods

☐ SHANK'S PONY
DAMGOOD 94CD / Jul '96 / Damaged Goods

Armored Saint

☐ SAINTS WILL CONQUER
Raising fear / Nervous man / Book of blood / Can U deliver / Mad house / No reason to live
398414055CD / May '96 / Metal Blade

☐ SYMBOL OF SALVATION
Reign of fire / Dropping like flies / Last train home / Tribal dance / Truth always hurts / Half drawn bridge / Another day / Symbool of salvation / Hanging judge / Warzone / Burning question / Tainted past / Spineless
398417014CD / May '96 / Metal Blade

Armoured Angel

☐ MYSTERIUM
ID 000312CD / May '95 / Modern Invasion

☐ STIGMARTYR
NF 100012 / Apr '95 / Modern Invasion

Armstrong Family

☐ WHEEL OF THE YEAR, THE
FF 594CD / Feb '93 / Flying Fish

Armstrong, Christopher

☐ NOTES IN MA HEID
Biggar / Orlando tango / Jig set / Saney Mackenzie / Dodds / Chrysler / Cone tango / Burns / Barbour roar / Slow air / Bonanza breakfast / Dreams of a child
CDLDL 1271 / Dec '97 / Lochshore

Armstrong, Craig

☐ SPACE BETWEEN US
Weather storm / This love / Sly / After the storm / Laura's theme / My father / Balcony scene / Rise / Glasgow / Let's go out tonight / Childhood / Hymn
CDSADX 3 / 2 Feb '98 / Melankolic

Armstrong, Frankie

☐ FAIR MOON REJOICES, THE
Voices / London song / Earth, air, fire and water / Invitation / Flying high, feeling free/Canaries in the mine / Still is the memory / Speech to Apollo / Out of the darkness / I feel that all the stars shine in me / Ballad of Marie Sanders / Whore and the holy one / Mourn not the dead/Song of Augustina Ruiz / Farewell my friends / Let the slave
HARCD 027 / Mar '97 / Harbour Town

☐ I HEARD A WOMAN SINGING
Cattle call / Mr Fox / Come Georgie hold the bairn / My daughter my son / Nothing between us now / New boots / Millworker / Lady Margaret / Tam lin / Taken by surprise / Ballad of Erica Levine / I don't want your red red roses
CDFF 332 / 16 Mar '98 / Flying Fish

☐ TILL THE GRASS O'ERGREW THE CORN
Broomfield Hill / Lady Diamond / Hares on the mountain / Fair Lizzie / Young Orphy / Proud girl / Lover's ghost / Wife of Usher's well / John Blunt / Child waters / Well below the valley / Clerk Colven
FECD 116 / Mar '97 / Fellside

☐ WAYS OF SEEING
Ways of seeing / Meeting / Girl in a garden / Zaspo janko / Soothing croon / Low ground / Dead leaves / Message from Mother Earth / Bread and roses / I only believe in miracles / Seven gates / We are women / Trial / Pearl / Weave and mend / Shall there be womanly times
HARCD 009 / Nov '96 / Harbour Town

Armstrong, James

☐ SLEEPING WITH A STRANGER
HCD 8068 / Dec '95 / Hightone

Armstrong, Lil

☐ CLASSICS 1936-1940
CLASSICS 564 / Oct '91 / Classics

Armstrong, Louis

☐ 1924-1930 (6CD Set) (Armstrong, Louis & The Blues Singers)
CC rider / Jelly bean blues / Countin' the blues / Early in the morning / You've got the right key but the wrong keyhole / Of all the wrong you've done to me / Everybody loves my baby / Texas moaner blues / Papa, mama's all alone / Changeable daddy of mine / Baby, I can't use you no more / Trouble everywhere I roam / Poor house blues / Anybody here want to try my cabbage / Thunderstorm blues / If I lose, let me lose / Screamin' the blues / Good time flat blues / Mandy, make up your mind / I'm a little blackbird looking for a bluebird / Nobody knows the way I feel this morning / Early every morn' / Cake walkin' babies from home / Broken busted blues / Pickin' on your baby / St. Louis blues / Reckless blues / Sobbin' hearted blues / Cold in hand blues / You've been a good ole wagon / You've got to beat me to keep me / Mining camp blues / Cast away / Papa de da da / World's jazz crazy (and so am I) / Railroad blues / Shipwrecked blues / Court house blues / My John blues / Nashville woman's blues / Careless love blues / JC Holmes blues / I ain't gonna play no second fiddle / I miss my Swiss / You dirty mistreater / Come on coot do that thing / Have your chill, I'll be here when your fever rises / Find me at the greasy spoon / Just wait 'til you see my baby do the Charleston / Livin' high / Coal cart blues / Santa Claus blues / Squeeze me / You can't shush Katie (the grabbiest girl in town) / Lucy long / Low land blues / Kid man blues / Lazy woman blues / Lonesome lovesick blues / Gambler's dream / Sunshine baby / Adam and Eve had the blues / Put it where I can get it / Washwoman blues / I've stopped my man / Lonesome all alone blues / Trouble in mind / Georgia man / You've got to go home on time / What kind o' man is that / Deep water blues / G'man, I told you / Listen to ma / Lonesome hours / Jealous woman like me / Special delivery blues / Jack O'diamonds / Mail train blues / I feel good / Man for every day in the week / Bridwell blues / St. Peter blues / He likes it slow / Pleadin' for the blues / Pratt city blues / Mess, Katie, mess / Lovesick blues / Lonesome weary blues / Dead drunk blues / Have you ever been down / Lazy man blues / Flood blues / You're a real sweetheart / Too busy / Was it a dream / Last night I dreamed you kissed me / I can't give you anything but love / Baby / Sweetheart on parade / I must have that man / S'posin' / To be in love / Funny feathers / How do you do it that way / Ain't misbehavin' / Blue yodel no. 9 (Standing on the corner)
CDAFS 10186 / Sep '91 / Affinity

☐ 2 FACETS OF LOUIS
4737542 / Jan '95 / Sony Jazz

☐ 20 BLUES CLASSICS
Black and blue / Muskrat ramble / Dear old southland / Hobo you can't ride this train / I gotta right to sing the blues / I can't give you anything but love / Body and soul / Someday you'll be sorry / Heebie jeebies / Royal Garden blues / Tiger rag / Jeepers creepers / Baby won't you please come home / Harlem stomp / Wolverine blues / St. James infirmary / Do you know what it means to miss New Orleans / That lucky old sun / Brother Bill / Old rocking chair
SUMCD 4080 / Nov '96 / Summit

☐ 2ND ALLSTAR JAZZ FESTIVAL (Armstrong, Louis Allstars)
CD 09 / Jul '93 / Krazy Kat

☐ ALL OF ME
GO 3818 / 1 Dec '97 / Golden Options

☐ AMBASSADOR SATCH
4718712 / Jan '95 / Sony Jazz

☐ AT HIS BEST
High society / I've got the world on a string / St. James infirmary / You rascal you / Sweet Sue just you / I gotta right to sing the blues / Ain't misbehavin' / St. Louis blues / Mahogany hall stomp / Savoy blues / Lazy river / Rockin' chair / Sweethearts on parade / Swing that music / That's my home / Basin street blues
309112 / 13 Jul '98 / Hallmark

☐ AUDIO ARCHIVE
Jeepers creepers / Mame / On the sunny side of the street / Hello Dolly / Ain't misbehavin' / Basin Street blues / Cabaret / When the saints go marching in / Fly me to the moon / Tiger rag / Kiss to build a dream on / (Back home again in) Indiana / Please don't talk about me when I'm gone / St. Louis blues / Someday you'll be sorry / Back o' town blues / That's my desire / Jelly roll blues / Mack the knife / Blueberry Hill
CDAA 015 / Jan '93 / Tring

☐ BACK O'TOWN
158732 / Apr '97 / Blues Archives

☐ BASIN STREET BLUES
BLCD 760128 / Jun '88 / Black Lion

☐ BEST OF LOUIS ARMSTRONG VOL.2
Bye 'n' bye / Cabaret / I want a big butter and egg man / Chimes blues / Tin roof blues / Mame / Honeysuckle rose / Dippermouth blues / Someday you'll be sorry / Indianna / Snake rag / Blueberry hill / Sweethearts on parade / So long dearie / Cheese cake / Royal garden blues
CDSGP 055 / Apr '93 / Prestige

☐ BEST OF LOUIS ARMSTRONG, THE
When the saints go marching in / On the sunny side of the street / Ain't misbehavin' / Tiger rag / Muskrat ramble / Jelly roll blues / C'est si bon (it's so good) / Hello dolly-mame / Mack the knife / Kiss to build a dream on / Tyrees blues / Pretty little missy / Dear old southland / Panama / St. james infirmary / New orleans stomp
CDSGP 038 / Jan '93 / Prestige

☐ BEST OF SATCHMO, THE
Struttin' with some barbecue / Confessin' / When the saints go marching in / Stardust / St. Louis blues / Basin Street blues / Mahogany Hall stomp / Georgia on my mind / Black and blue / All of me / Chinatown my Chinatown / Just you, just me
399231 / May '97 / Koch Presents

☐ BIG BANDS VOL.1 1930-1931
My sweet / Dinah / Tiger rag / Confessin' (that I love you) / Body and soul / Just a gigolo / Shine / I can't believe that you're in love with me / Indian cradle song / Exactly like you / I'm a ding dong daddy from dumas / I'm in the market for you / If I could be with you one hour tonight / Memories of you / You're lucky to me / Sweethearts on parade / You're driving me crazy / Peanut vendor / Walkin' my baby back home / I surrender dear / When it's sleepy time down south
JSPCD 305 / Oct '88 / JSP

☐ BIG BANDS, THE
PDSCD 534 / Aug '96 / Pulse

☐ C'EST SI BON
Mame / When the saints go marching in / Ain't misbehavin' / Cabaret / Kiss to build a dream on / Please don't talk about me when I'm gone / Blueberry Hill / Hello Dolly / St. Louis blues / That's my desire / Mack the knife / Back o' town blues / Fly me to the moon / (Back home again in) Indiana / Tiger rag / Black and blue / C'est si bon / St. James infirmary / Someday you'll be sorry / Sweethearts on parade / Jelly roll blues
GRF 036 / '93 / Tring

☐ CARNEGIE HALL 1947 (Armstrong, Louis Orchestra & Edmond Hall Orchestra)
CLA 1919 / May '98 / Ambassador

☐ CARNEGIE HALL CONCERT 1947
CLACD 1919 / Feb '98 / Ambassador

☐ CHICAGO CONCERT 1956
Memphis blues / Frankie and Johnny / Tiger rag / Do you know what it means to miss New Orleans / Basin Street blues / Black and blue / West End blues / On the sunny side of the street / Struttin' with some barbecue / Manhattan / When it's sleepy time down South / (Back home again in) Indiana / Gypsy / Faithful hussar / Rockin' chair / Bucket's got a hole in it / Perdido / Clarinet marmalade / Mack the knife / Tenderly / You'll never walk alone / Stompin' at the Savoy / Margie / Mama's back in town / That's my desire / Kokomo / I love you so
4718702 / Nov '93 / Columbia

☐ CLASSICS 1925-1926 (Armstrong, Louis Hot Five)
CLASSICS 600 / Sep '91 / Classics

☐ CLASSICS 1926-1927
CLASSICS 585 / Aug '91 / Classics

☐ CLASSICS 1928-1929
CLASSICS 570 / Oct '91 / Classics

☐ CLASSICS 1929-1930
CLASSICS 557 / Dec '90 / Classics

☐ CLASSICS 1930-1931
CLASSICS 547 / Dec '90 / Classics

☐ CLASSICS 1931-1932
CLASSICS 536 / Dec '90 / Classics

☐ CLASSICS 1932-1933
CLASSICS 529 / Dec '90 / Classics

☐ CLASSICS 1934-1936
CLASSICS 509 / Apr '90 / Classics

☐ CLASSICS 1936-1937
CLASSICS 512 / Apr '90 / Classics

☐ CLASSICS 1937-1938
CLASSICS 515 / Apr '90 / Classics

☐ CLASSICS 1938-1939
CLASSICS 523 / Apr '90 / Classics

☐ CLASSICS 1940-1942 (Armstrong, Louis Orchestra)
CLASSICS 685 / Mar '93 / Classics

☐ CLASSICS 1944-1946
CLASSICS 928 / Apr '97 / Classics

☐ CLASSICS 1946-1947
CLASSICS 992 / 24 Apr '98 / Classics

☐ COLLECTION, THE
What a wonderful world / Hello dolly / Mack the knife / Jeepers creepers / St. james infirmary / When the saints go marching in / Royal garden blues / Jelly roll blues / Chimes blues / Someday you'll be sorry / Tiger rag / When you're smiling / New orleans stomp / Back ole town blues / When it's sleepy time down south / Dippermouth blues / Snake rag / Dinah / Stompin' at the savoy / C'est si bon (it's so good) / Ain't misbehavin' / Pretty little missy / La vie en rose / On the sunny side of the street / Stardust
COL 001 / Jan '95 / Collection

☐ COMPLETE CHICAGO CONCERT 1958, THE (2CD Set)
Flee as a bird to the mountain/Oh didn't he ramble / Memphis blues/Frankie and Johnny/Tiger rag / Do you know what it means to miss New Orleans / Basin Street blues / Black and blue / West End blues / On the sunny side of the street / Struttin' with some barbecue / When it's sleepy time down South / Manhattan/When it's sleepy time down South / Indiana / Gypsy / Faithful Hussar / Rockin' chair / Bucket's got a hole in it / Perdido / Clarinet marmalade / Mack the knife / Tenderly/You'll never walk alone / Stompin' at the Savoy / Margie / Big Mama's back in town / That's my desire / Ko ko mo (I love you so) / When the saints go marching in / Star spangled banner
C2K 65119 / Jun '97 / Sony Jazz

☐ COMPLETE RCA VICTOR RECORDINGS, THE (4CD Set)
That's my home / Hobo / I hate to leave you now / You'll wish you'd never been born / (I'll be glad when you're dead) you rascal you / When it's sleepy time down South / Nobody's sweetheart / When you're smiling / St. James Infirmary / Dinah / I've got the world on a string / I gotta right to sing the blues / Hustlin' and bustlin' for baby / Sittin' in the dark / High Society / He's a son of the South / Some sweet day / Basin Street blues / Honey do / Snowball / Mahogany Hall stomp / Swing you cats / Honey don't you love me anymore / Mississippi Basin / Laughin' Louie / Tomorrow night / Dusky stevedore / There's a cabin in the pines / Mighty river / Sweet Sue, just you / I wonder who / St. Louis blues / Don't play me cheap / That's my home / Hobo, you can't ride this train / I hate to leave you now / You'll wish you'd never been born / When you're smiling / St. James Infirmary / Dinah / Mississippi Basin / Laughin' Louis / Tomorrow night / Blue yodel no.9 / Long, long journey / Snafu / Linger in my arms a little longer / Whatta ya gonna do / No variety blues / Joseph 'n' his brudders / Back o' town blues / I want a little girl / Sugar / Blues for yesterday / Blues in the South / Endie / Blues are brewin' / Do you know what it means to miss New Orleans / Where the blues were born in New Orleans / Mahogany Hall stomp / I wonder, I wonder, I wonder / I believe / Why doubt my love / It takes time / You don't learn that in school / Ain't misbehavin' / Rockin' chair / Back o' town blues / Pennies from heaven / Save it pretty Mama / St. James Infirmary / Jack Armstrong blues / Rockin' chair / Some day you'll be sorry / Fifty fifty blues / Song was born / Please stop playin' those blues boy / Before long / Lovely weather we're having / Rain, rain / Never saw a better day / When Joanna loves me / That old feeling / Polka dots and moonbeams / Here's that rainy day / I've grown accustomed to her face / Bewitched / Blues for fun / Rude old man / Polka dots and moonbeams / Bewitched
07863666822 / Apr '97 / RCA Victor

☐ COMPLETE RECORDINGS 1924-1925 (2CD Set) (Armstrong, Louis & Fletcher Henderson Orchestra)
F 38001/2/3 / May '97 / Forte

☐ COMPLETE TOWN HALL CONCERT, THE
Cornet chop suey / Our Monday date / Dear old Southland / Big butter and egg man / Tiger rag / Struttin' with some barbecue / Sweethearts on parade / St. Louis blues / Pennies from Heaven / On the sunny side of the street / I can't give you anything but love / Back o' town blues / Ain't misbehavin' / Rockin' chair / Muskrat ramble / Save it pretty Mama / St. James Infirmary / Royal Garden blues / Do you know what it means to miss New Orleans / Jack Armstrong blues
ND 897462 / Jun '94 / Jazz Tribune

☐ CREOLE JAZZ (Armstrong, Louis & King Oliver's Jazzband)
TCD 1069 / 23 Mar '98 / Tradition

☐ DO YOU KNOW WHAT IT MEANS TO MISS NEW ORLEANS (Live)
Do you know what it means to miss New Orleans / Mahogany Hall stomp / Someday you'll be sorry / That's my desire / When the saints go marching in / Bucket's got a hole in it / Struttin' with some barbecue / Kiss to build a dream on / Baby it's cold outside
8379192 / Mar '94 / Verve

☐ DOCTOR JAZZ
BMCD 3067 / 5 Jan '98 / Blue Moon

☐ ESSENCE OF ARMSTRONG
PHONTCD 9308 / Dec '94 / Phontastic

☐ ESSENTIAL LOUIS ARMSTRONG, THE
4618702 / Jan '95 / Sony Jazz

☐ ESSENTIAL RECORDINGS 1925-1940 (4CD Set)
CDDIG 17 / Jun '95 / Charly

☐ ESSENTIAL SATCHMO, THE
What a wonderful world / Blueberry Hill / Hello Dolly / La vie en rose / Cabaret / Lazy river / Whiffenpoof song / On the sunny side of the street / Georgia on my mind / When you're smiling / That lucky old sun / Home fire / Dream a little dream of me / Give me your kisses (I'll give you my heart) / Fantastic, that's you / Hellzapoppin' / Hello brother / Sunshine of love
MCCD 088 / Dec '92 / Music Club

☐ FLETCHER HENDERSON & LOUIS ARMSTRONG 1924-1925 (Armstrong, Louis & Fletcher Henderson Orchestra)
Money blues / Why couldn't it be poor little me / I'll see you in my dreams / Tell me, dreamy eyes / My Rose Marie / Poplar Street blues / Shanghai shuffle / Mandy, make up your mind / Go 'long mule / Memphis bound / How come you do me like you do / Alabamy bound / Copenhagen / Meanest kind of blues / I miss my Swiss / Alone at last / Shanghai shuffle / When you do what you do / Words / Carolina stomp / Bye and bye / Naughty man / Play me slow / TNT / One of these days / Sugarfoot stomp
CBC 1003 / Jan '92 / Timeless Historical

☐ GENIUS OF LOUIS ARMSTRONG (40 Jazz Classics From The Legendary Satchmo/2CD Set)
All of me / Chinatown, my Chinatown / I'm in the mood for love / Sweethearts on parade / You can depend on me / Jeepers creepers / West End blues / Melancholy baby / Struttin' with some barbecue / SOL blues / Wild man blues / St. James infirmary / Potato head blues / Squeeze me / Ain't misbehavin' / (What did I do to be so) black and blue / That rhythm man / Sweet Savannah Sue / Blue, turning grey over you / I hate to leave you now / Pennies from heaven: *Armstrong, Louis & Bing Crosby* / Flat foot floogie: *Armstrong, Louis & Mills Brothers* / You won't be satisfied (until you break my heart): *Armstrong, Louis & Ella Fitzgerald* / Coal cart blues: *Armstrong, Louis & Sidney Bechet* / Swing that music / Blue yodel No.9 / My sweet lovin' man / Sugar / Do you know what it means to miss New Orleans / Stardust / Memories of you / Shoe shine boy / When it's sleepy time down south / Shanghai shuffle / St. Louis blues: *Armstrong, Louis & Bessie Smith* / CC rider: *Armstrong, Louis & Ma Rainey* / Dead drunk blues / How do you do it that way / Pleadin' for the blues / Careless love blues: *Armstrong, Louis & Bessie Smith*
330342 / Mar '97 / Hallmark

☐ GEORGIA ON MY MIND
Old rockin' chair / (I'll be glad when you're dead) you rascal you / Wild man blues / Confessin' / Lazy river / Dinah / I ain't got nobody / Georgia bo bo / You're lucky to me / Monday date / St. James infirmary / Georgia on my mind / West End blues / Ain't misbehavin' / Knocking a jug / I can't believe that you're in love with me / St. Louis blues / Chinatown, my Chinatown / Drop that sack / My sweet
DBCD 17 / Jun '88 / Dance Band Days

☐ GOLD COLLECTION, THE
D2CD 04 / Dec '92 / Deja Vu

☐ GREAT CONCERT, THE
401542CD / Jul '94 / Musidisc

☐ GREAT LOUIS ARMSTRONG 1937 - 1941, THE
Yes suh / Wolverine blues / Cut off my legs and call me shorty / Cain and Abel / When it's sleepy time down South / Hep cats' ball / Do you call that a buddy / Down in honky tonk town / You run your mouth, I'll run my business / Save it pretty Mama / Perdido street blues / Me and brother blues / Struttin' with some barbecue / 2.19 Blues / (I'll be glad when you're dead) you rascal you / Lazy 'Sippi steamers / I'll get mine bye and bye / Harlem stomp / Hey lawdy mama / I double dare you / Public melody number one / Yours and mine
PASTCD 7002 / Jan '93 / Flapper

☐ GREATEST HITS
Theme from three penny opera / Back o' town blues / Black and blue / Ain't misbehavin' / Basin street blues / Cabaret / When it's sleepy time down south / All of me / West End blues / Struttin' with some barbecue / Indiana
CK 65420 / 26 Jan '98 / Sony Jazz

☐ GUVNOR, THE
Mahogany hall stomp / St. Louis blues / I'm confessin' that I love you / Dinah / Chinatown, my Chinatown / Georgia on my mind / Lazy river / Rockin' chair / I hope Gabriel likes my music / Struttin' with some barbecue / I double dare you / Hear me talkin' to ya / Save it pretty Mama / Shoe shine boy / Red nose / West End blues / St. James infirmary / (I'll be glad when you're dead) you rascal you / You're luky to me / Wild man blues
PAR 2015 / Apr '95 / Parade

☐ HAPPY FIFTIES, THE (3CD Set)
CLA 19203 / Jan '97 / Ambassador

☐ HEAR ME TALKIN' TO YA
MACCD 167 / Aug '96 / Autograph

☐ HELLO DOLLY
Mame / When the saints go marching in / Ain't misbehavin' / Cabaret / Kiss to build a dream on / Blueberry hill / Hello dolly / St. Louis blues / That's my desire / Mack the knife / Back o' town blues / Big butter and egg man / Black and blue / C'est si bon / St. James Infirmary / Someday you'll be sorry / Sweethearts on parade
101632 / May '97 / A-Play Collection

☐ HIGH SOCIETY
Someday you'll be sorry / Dippermouth blues / Do you know what it means to miss New Orleans / Honeysuckle rose / Panama / Save it pretty Mama / High society / Rockin' chair / Back o' town blues / Tin roof blues / You can depend on me
TCD 1046 / May '97 / Tradition

☐ HOT FIVE TO ALL-STARS (1925-56)
Alligator crawl / Wild man blues / Melancholy blues / Willie the weeper / Ory's creole trombone / Struttin' with some barbecue / Hotter than that / West End blues / Potato head blues / Keyhole blues / Gully low blues / Basin Street blues / SOL blues / 12th Street rag / Savoy blues / Muskrat ramble / Cornet chop suey / Skid-dat-de-dat / Come back sweet Papa / Yes, I'm in the barrel / Weary blues / Put 'em down / Monday date / Rockin' chair / Jack / Armstrong blues / Mahogany hall stomp / Do you know what it means to miss New Orleans / Where the blues was born in New Orleans / Blues for yesterday / Sugar / Long long journey / (I'll be glad when you're dead) you rascal you / Perdido street blues / 2.19 blues / Down in honky tonk town / Coal cart blues / Wolverine blues / Cut off my legs and call me shorty / Satchel mouth swing / Loved walked in / On the sunny side of the street / Swing that music / Dusky stevedore / That's my home / I surrender dear / Blue turning grey over you / That rhythm man / What did I do to be so black and blue / Struttin' with some barbecue / All that meat and no potatoes / Ole Miss / Back o' town blues / (Back home again in) Indiana / That's my desire / Ain't misbehavin' / Aunt Hagar's blues / Tin roof blues / Panama / My bucket's got a hole in it / New Orleans function / Free as a bird / Didn't he ramble / When it's sleepy time down South
CDB 1205 / '92 / Giants Of Jazz

☐ HOT FIVES AND HOT SEVENS
My heart / I'm in the barrel / Gut bucket blues / Come back sweet Papa / Georgia grind / Heebie jeebies / Cornet chop suey / Oriental strut / You're next / Muskrat ramble / Don't forget to mess around / I'm gonna gitcha / Droppin' shucks / Whosit / King of the Zulus / Big fat Ma and skinny Pa
4608212 / May '90 / CBS

☐ HOT FIVES AND HOT SEVENS
West end blues / Alligator crawl / Melancholy blues / Willie the weeper / Ory's creole trombone / Struttin' with some barbecue / Hotter than that / Potato head blues / Keyhole blues / Savoy blues / Basin street blues / Weary blues / Wild man blues / S.o.l. blues / Skid-dat-de-dat / Muskrat ramble / Cornet shop suey / A monday date
CD 56010 / Aug '94 / Jazz Roots

☐ HOT FIVES AND HOT SEVENS VOL 3
JSPCD 314 / Jun '98 / JSP

☐ HOT FIVES AND HOT SEVENS VOL.1 1925-1926
My heart / Yes I'm in the barrel / Gut bucket blues / Come back sweet papa / Georgia grind / Heebie Jeebies / Comet chop suey / Oriental strut / You're next / Muskrat ramble / Don't forget to mess around / I'm gonna gitcha / Dropping shucks / Who' sit / He likes it slow / King of the zulus / Big fat ma and skinny pa / Lonesome blues / Sweet little papa / Jazz lips / Skid-dat-de-dat / Big butter and egg man from the west / Sunset cafe stomp / You made me love you / Irish black bottom
JSPCD 312 / May '98 / JSP

☐ HOT FIVES AND HOT SEVENS VOL.2
Willie the weeper / Wild man blues / Chicago breakdown / Alligator crawl / Potato head blues / Melancholy blues / Weary blues / 12th Street rag / Keyhole blues / SOL blues / Gully low blues / That's when I'll come back to you / Put 'em down blues / Ory's creole trombone / Last time / Struttin' with some barbecue / Got no blues / Once in a while / I'm not rough / Hotter than that / Savoy blues
JSPCD 313 / Apr '98 / JSP

☐ HOT FIVES AND HOT SEVENS VOL.2
4630522 / Apr '89 / Sony Jazz

☐ HOT FIVES AND HOT SEVENS VOL.2 1926-1927
7810842 / Aug '93 / Jazztime

☐ HOT FIVES AND HOT SEVENS VOL.3
Fireworks: *Armstrong, Louis & His Hot Five* / Skip the gutter: *Armstrong, Louis & His Hot Five* / Monday date: *Armstrong, Louis & His Hot Five* / Don't jive me: *Armstrong, Louis & His Hot Five* / West end blues: *Armstrong, Louis & His Hot Five* / Sugar foot strut: *Armstrong, Louis & His Hot Five* / Two deuces: *Armstrong, Louis & His Hot Five* / Squeeze me: *Armstrong, Louis & His Hot Five* / Knee drops: *Armstrong, Louis & His Hot Five* / Symphonic raps: *Dickerson, Carroll Savoyagers* / Savoyagers stomp: *Dickerson, Carroll Savoyagers* / No (no papa no): *Armstrong, Louis Orchestra* / Basin street blues: *Armstrong, Louis Orchestra* / Muggles: *Armstrong, Louis Orchestra* / Knockin a jug: *Armstrong, Louis Orchestra* / No one else but you: *Armstrong, Louis & His Savoy Ballroom Five* / Beau Koo Jack: *Armstrong, Louis & His Savoy Ballroom Five* / Save it pretty mama: *Armstrong, Louis & His Savoy Ballroom Five* / Weather bird: *Armstrong, Louis & His Savoy Ballroom Five* / Hear me talkin' to ya: *Armstrong, Louis & His Savoy Ballroom Five* / St. James infirmary: *Armstrong, Louis & His Savoy Ballroom Five* / Tight like this: *Armstrong, Louis & His Savoy Ballroom Five*
JSPCD 314 / Jun '98 / JSP

☐ HOT FIVES AND HOT SEVENS VOL.3
S.o.l. blues / Gully low blues / When I'll come back to you / Put 'em down blues / Ory's creole trombone / Last time / Struttin' with some barbecue / Got no blues / Once in a white / I'm not rough / Hotter than that / Savoy blues / Fireworks / Skip the gutter / A monday date / Don't jive me
4651892 / Jul '88 / CBS

☐ HOT FIVES AND HOT SEVENS VOL.4
I can't give you anything but love / Mahogany hall stomp / Ain't misbehavin' / (what did I do to be so) black and blue / That rhythm man / Sweet savannah sue / Some of these days / Some of these days / When you're smiling / When you're smiling / After you've gone / I ain't got nobody / Dallas blues / Louis' blues / Rockin' chair / Song of the islands / Bessie couldn't help it / Blue turning grey over you / Dear old southland / Rockin' chair / I can't give you anything but love
JSPCD 315 / Jun '98 / JSP

☐ **I GOT RHYTHM**
I got rhythm / Honeysuckle rose / Jeepers creepers / Tiger rag / Muskrat ramble / Way down yonder in New Orleans / When the saints go marching in / Body and soul / Sweet hearts on parade / You're driving me crazy / Just a gigolo / Ain't misbehavin' / Back o' town blues / C'est si bon / Stompin' at the Savoy / Shine / On the sunny side of the street / La vie en rose / Hucklebuck / Memories of you
PWK 137 / May '90 / Carlton

☐ **I WISH YOU WERE DEAD YOU RASCAL YOU**
St Louis blues / West End blues / I've got the world on a string / Cornet chop suey / Save it pretty mama / Potato head blues / Heebie Jeebies / Knockin' a jug / Mahogany hall stomp / (I'll be glad when you're dead) you rascal you / When it's sleepy time down south / Hobo, you can't ride this train / Weather bird / I gotta right to sing the blues / Dear old southland / Lonesome road / I'm confessin' / Stardust
CWNCD 2028 / Jul '96 / Javelin

☐ **INTRODUCTION TO LOUIS ARMSTRONG 1924-1938, AN**
4004 / Dec '93 / Best Of Jazz

☐ **JAZZ AND BLUES (36 Outstanding Jazz Tracks/2CD Set)**
St. James infirmary / Blueberry Hill / Someday you'll be sorry / New Orleans stomp / Back ole town blues / Chimes blues / Jelly roll blues / I can't believe that you're in love with me / Do you know what it means to miss New Orleans / That rhythm man / Struttin's with some barbeque / La vie en rose / Stompin' at the Savoy / Tiger rag / When it's sleepy time down south / I love the guy / Baby it's cold outside / Muskrat ramble / Jeepers creepers / A kiss to build a dream on / When the saints go marchin' in / Mack the knife / C'est si bon / St. Louis blues / Black and blue / Dippermouth blues / Bye and bye / Rockin' chair / C. jam blues / Stardust / Royal garden blues / Indiana / I used to love you / Where did you stay last night / If I could be with you (tonight) / Way down yonder in New Orleans
BN 201 / Aug '98 / Blue Nite

☐ **JAZZ CLASSICS MASTERWORKS (Armstrong, Louis & Sidney Bechet)**
Yes, I'm in the barrel / Struttin' with some barbecue / Cornet shop suey / Wild man blues / SOL blues / Weary blues / Basin Street blues / Monday date / West End blues / Mahogany Hall stomp / On the sunny side of the street / Baby, won't you please come home / C jam blues / Kansas City man blues / Jazz me blues / Honeysuckle Rose
17051 / Nov '95 / Laserlight

☐ **JAZZ COLLECTION (2CD Set)**
Mahogany hall stomp / Black and blue / Royal garden blues / Muskrat ramble / On the sunny side of the street / High society / Down by the river side / Swing low sweet chariot / When the saints go marchin' in / What a wonderful world / Georgia on my mind / C'est si bon / Mack the knife / Blueberry hill / Cabaret / Kiss to build a dream on / Hello Dolly / That's my desire / Panama / Blue skies / Lover / Whispering / Song was born / Jack Armstrong blues / La vie en rose / Sweet Georgia Brown
24 366 / Nov '97 / Laserlight

☐ **JAZZ GREATS**
Sugar / Do you know what it means to miss New Orleans / St. Louis blues / Basin Street blues / Everybody's talkin' / I gotta right to sing the blues / Medley / Ain't misbehavin' / Rockin' chair / Mood indigo / My one and only love / Someday you'll be sorry / What a wonderful world
74321499662 / 6 Oct '97 / RCA Victor

☐ **JAZZ MASTERS**
Just one of those things / That old feeling / I gotta right to sing the blues / Learnin' the blues / Let's do it / There's a boat that's leavin' soon for New York / Blues in the night / You're the top / Body and soul / When your lover has gone / Fine romance / Home / I've got the world on a string / I was dancing alright / When the saints go marchin' in
5198182 / 5 May '98 / Verve

☐ **JAZZ PORTRAITS**
Can anyone explain / My sweet hunk o'trash / You won't be satisfied (until you break my heart) / Fifty fifty blues / You can't lose a broken heart / Frim fram sauce / (I'll be glad when you're dead) you rascal you / Oops / Life is so peculiar / Dream a little dream of me / Struttin' with some barbecue / Necessary evil / Lazybones / Long gone / Now you has jazz / Who walks in when I walk out / Boog it / Honeysuckle rose
CD 14513 / May '94 / Jazz Portraits

☐ **LEGENDARY LOUIS ARMSTRONG, THE (4CD Set)**
Jeepers creepers / Stompin' at the savoy / I got rhythm / On the sunny side of the street / Tea for two / New orleans stomp / Snake rag / Lover / Dippermouth blues / Just a gigolo / Muskrat ramble / Way down yonder in New Orleans / I used to love you / Body and soul / Back o' town blues / Shine / Mame / When the saints go marching in / Ain't misbehavin' / Cabaret / Kiss to build a dream on / Blueberry hill / Hello dolly / St. Louis blues / That's my desire / Mack the knife / Big butter and egg man / Black and blue / C'est si bon / St. James's infirmary / Someday you'll be sorry / Sweethearts on parade / Heebie jeebies / Cornet chop suey / Muskrat ramble / Keyhole blues / Potato head blues / Hotter than that / Struttin' with some / Barbeque / West End blues / My monday date / Muggles / I can't give you anything but love / Dinah / I'm a ding dong daddy / I'm confessin' that I love you / Memories of you / You're lucky to me / Stardust / Sleepy time down south / Between the devil and the deep blue sea / Lawd you made the night too long / Hobo you can't ride this train / That's my home / I gotta right to sing the blues / I'm in the mood for love / I hope Gabriel likes my music / Basin street blues / Coal cart blues / Perdido street blues / Some sweet day / Mahogany hall blues stomp / Ev'ntide / Swing that music
QUAD 006 / Nov '96 / Tring

☐ **LEGENDARY LOUIS ARMSTRONG, THE**
Jeepers creepers / Basin Street blues / Stompin' at the Savoy / I got rhythm / On the sunny side of the street / Tea for two / New Orleans stomp / Lover / Dippermouth blues / Just a gigolo / Muskrat ramble / Way down yonder in New Orleans / Royal garden blues / La vie en rose / I used to love you / Body and soul / Back ole town blues / Shine
QED 127 / Nov '96 / Tring

☐ **LIVE 1938-1940 (Armstrong, Louis & Fats Waller)**
MM 31056 / Aug '93 / Music Memoria

☐ **LIVE AT THE WINTER GARDEN, NEW YORK 1947/BLUE NOTE, CHICAGO (Armstrong, Louis Allstars)**
STCD 8242 / May '97 / Storyville

☐ **LOUIS & LUIS (Original recordings 1929-1940) (Armstrong, Louis & Luis Russell)**
Baby, won't you please come home / Bessie couldn't help it / Blue turning grey over you / 2.19 blues / Bye and bye / Confessin' / Dallas blues / Mahogany hall stomp / On the sunny side of the street / Our Monday date / Perdido Street blues / Public Melody Number One / Rockin' chair / St. Louis blues / Savoy blues / Struttin' with some barbecue / Sweethearts on parade / Swing that music / Thanks a million / West End blues / When it's sleepy time down South / When the saints go marching in / Wolverine blues / You run your mouth, I'll run my business / You're a lucky guy
CDAJA 5094 / Sep '92 / Living Era

☐ **LOUIS AND THE ANGELS/LOUIS AND THE GOOD BOOK**
When did you leave heaven / You're a heavenly thing / I married an angel / Sinner kissed an angel / Angela Mia / Angel child / And the angels did sing / Fools rush in / I'll string along with you / Angel / Prisoner's song / Goodnight angel / Nobody knows the trouble I've seen / Shadrack / Go down Moses / Rock my soul / Esekial saw de wheel / On my way / Down by the riverside / Swing low sweet chariot / Sometimes I feel like a motherless child / Jonah and the whale / Didn't it rain / This train
MCLD 19379 / 22 Jun '98 / MCA

☐ **LOUIS ARMSTRONG**
LECD 050 / May '94 / Dynamite

☐ **LOUIS ARMSTRONG**
Savoy blues / Ory's creole trombone / Weary blues / Muskrat ramble / On the sunny side of the street / Mahogany hall stomp / Tea for two / C jam blue / High society / Wild man blues / S.o.l. blues / West end blues / Put 'em down blues / Melancholy blues / Back o' town blues
22701 / Nov '95 / Music

☐ **LOUIS ARMSTRONG (2CD Set)**
R2CD 4004 / 13 Apr '98 / Deja Vu

☐ **LOUIS ARMSTRONG (CD/CD Rom Set)**
What a wonderful world / Hello dolly / Jeepers creepers / Foggy day: *Armstrong, Louis & Ella Fitzgerald* / Sweethearts on parade: *Armstrong, Louis & Frank Sinatra* / St. James Infirmary / Kiss to build a dream on / Blueberry Hill / Cabaret / Chimes blues / Jelly Roll blues / Mack The Knife / New Orleans stomp / Pretty little missy / Snake rag / When the Saints go marchin' in / Someday you'll be sorry
WWCDR 002 / Apr '97 / Weton-Wesgram

☐ **LOUIS ARMSTRONG**
Hello Dolly / When the Saints go marchin' in / Alligator crawl / Gipsy / New Orleans function / I've got a feeling I'm falling / Struttin' with some barbecue / C'est si bon / La vie en rose / Someday / When it's sleepy time down South / Black and blue / High society / Kiss to build a dream on / On the sunny side of the street / Only you
399527 / Jun '97 / Koch Presents

☐ **LOUIS ARMSTRONG**
UAE 30032 / Jan '98 / Members Edition

☐ **LOUIS ARMSTRONG & EARL HINES (Armstrong, Louis & Earl Hines)**
Chicago breakdown / Symphonic raps / Savoyager's stomp / West end blues / Sugar foot strut / Two deuces / Squeeze me in / Knee drops / No, papa, no / Basin street blues / No one else but you / Beau koo jack / Save it, pretty mama / Weather bird rag / Muggles / Hear me talkin' to ya / St. james infirmary / Tight like this
4663082 / Jan '95 / Sony Jazz

☐ **LOUIS ARMSTRONG & HIS ALL STARS (Armstrong, Louis Allstars)**
High society / Back o' town blues / C jam blues / Boogie woogie on st. louis blues / Panama / Fine and dandy / Blue skies / Don't fence me in / Lover / Whispering / Song was born / Mahogany hall stomp / Ain't misbehavin' / Jack armstrong blues
15773 / Jul '92 / Laserlight

☐ **LOUIS ARMSTRONG & HIS ALL STARS**
CD 14550 / Jul '94 / Jazz Portraits

☐ **LOUIS ARMSTRONG & HIS ALL STARS (Armstrong, Louis Allstars)**
When it's sleepy time down South / Hello Dolly / Blueberry Hill / Volare / St. James infirmary / Girl from Ipanema / (Back home again in) Indiana / Muskrat ramble / Mack the knife / I love Paris / Time after time / Cabaret / Tiger rag / When the saints go marching in / This could be the start of something big / Please don't talk about me when I'm gone / Stompin' at the Savoy / That's my desire / Closer walk with thee / Them there eyes / Avalon / Kiss to build a dream on / Ole miss
STCD 4095 / Feb '89 / Storyville

☐ **LOUIS ARMSTRONG 1925-1928**
Wild man blues / S.o.l. blues / Basin street blues / Alligator crawl / Ory's creole trombone / A monday date / West end blues / Skid-dat-de-dat / Muskrat ramble / Savoy blues / Yes I'm in the barrel / Come back sweet papa / Put 'em down blues / Struttin' with some barbecue / Twelfth street rag (one step) / Cornet shop suey / Weary blues / Melancholy blues
15721 / Apr '94 / Laserlight

☐ **LOUIS ARMSTRONG 1928-1931**
HRM 6002 / Sep '88 / Hermes

☐ **LOUIS ARMSTRONG 1931-1947 (Armstrong, Louis Orchestra/Hot Seven/Dixieland Seven)**
CD 14563 / May '95 / Jazz Portraits

☐ **LOUIS ARMSTRONG 1946-1951 (When You & I Were Young Maggie)**
CLA 1915 / Mar '94 / Ambassador

☐ **LOUIS ARMSTRONG 1949-1957 (Heavenly Music)**
CLA 1916 / Mar '94 / Ambassador

☐ **LOUIS ARMSTRONG 1952-1956 (Moments To Remember)**
CLA 1917 / Aug '95 / Ambassador

☐ **LOUIS ARMSTRONG AND HIS ALL STARS (1961-1962)**
STCD 4012 / Feb '89 / Storyville

☐ **LOUIS ARMSTRONG AND HIS GREAT BIG BAND**
JCD 19 / Feb '91 / Jass

☐ **LOUIS ARMSTRONG AND KING OLIVER**
Just gone / Canal Street blues / Mandy Lee blues / I'm going to wear you off my mind / Chimes blues / Weatherbird rag / Dippermouth blues / Froggie Moore / Snake rag / Alligator hop / Zulu's ball / Workin' man blues / Krooked blues / Mabel's dream / Southern stomps (take 1) / Southern stomps (take 2) / Riverside blues / King Oliver / Jelly roll morton / Tom cat blues / Terrible blues / Santa Claus blues / Texas moaner blues / Of all the wrongs you've done to me / Nobody knows the way I feel this morning / Early every morn' / Cake walkin' babies from home
MCD 47017 2 / Jun '93 / Milestone

☐ **LOUIS ARMSTRONG AND THE ALL STARS**
Mahogany hall stomp / Tea for two / Black and blue / Royal garden blues / That's my desire / I cried for you / Muskrat ramble / C jam blues / High society / Boff boff (final)
15728 / Apr '94 / Laserlight

☐ **LOUIS ARMSTRONG COLLECTION, THE**
Mame / Stompin' at the Savoy / I got rhythm / Honeysuckle rose / When the saints go marching in / Muskrat ramble / Way down yonder in New Orleans / Ain't misbehavin' / Royal garden blues / La vie en rose / Cabaret / Hucklebuck / I used to love you / Kis to build a dream on / Hello Dolly / Please don't talk about me when I'm gone / Just a gigolo / I'm your ding dong daddy from Dumas / Blueberry hill / I'm in the market for you / Peanut vendor / Mahogany hall stomp / St. Louis blues / You're lucky to me / That's my desire / I'm confessin' that I love you / Mack the knife / If I could be with you one hour tonight / Jeepers creepers / Basin Street blues / Body and soul / Back o' town blues / Memories of you / You're driving me crazy / I want a big butter and egg man / Shine / On the sunny side of the street / (Back home again in) Indiana / Dear old southland / Tiger rag / Bye and bye / Black and blue / Tea for two / Jelly Roll blues / Chimes blues / Dippermouth blues / C'est si bon / Savoy stomp / I can't give you anything but love / St. James Infirmary / That rhythm man / Lover / Someday you'll be sorry / Snake rag / New Orleans stomp / Sweethearts on parade
TFP 011 / Nov '92 / Tring

☐ **LOUIS ARMSTRONG COLLECTORS' EDITION**
DVX 812 / Apr '95 / Deja Vu

☐ **LOUIS ARMSTRONG GOLD (2CD Set)**
D2CD 4004 / Jun '95 / Deja Vu

☐ **LOUIS ARMSTRONG IN CONCERT**
RTE 10012CD / Apr '95 / RTE/Europe 1

☐ **LOUIS ARMSTRONG LIVE IN PARIS**
ACDCH 553 / Jun '90 / Milan

☐ **LOUIS ARMSTRONG MEETS OSCAR PETERSON (The Silver Collection) (Armstrong, Louis & Oscar Peterson)**
That old feeling / I'll never be the same / How long has this been going on / I was doing all right / Moon song / There's no you / Sweet Lorraine / Let's fall in love / Blues in the night / What's new / Just one of those things / You go to my head / I get a kick out of you / Makin' whoopee / Willow weep for me / Let's do it
8257132 / Mar '92 / Verve

☐ **LOUIS ARMSTRONG MEETS OSCAR PETERSON (Remastered) (Armstrong, Louis & Oscar Peterson)**
5390602 / Oct '97 / Verve Master Edition

☐ **LOUIS ARMSTRONG PLAYS W.C. HANDY**
St. Louis blues / Yellow dog blues / Loveless love / Aunt Hagar's blues / Louis Armstrong monologue / Long gone / Memphis blues (or, Mister Crump) / Beale Street blues / Ole Miss / Chantez les bas (sing 'em low) / Hesitating blues / Atlanta blues (make me one pallet on your foot) / Interview with WC Handy / Loveless love / Hesitating blues / Louis Armstrong's alligator story / Long gone
CK 64925 / Apr '97 / Sony Jazz

☐ **LOUIS ARMSTRONG VOL.1 (Bourbon Street Parade)**
BMCD 3071 / 5 Jan '98 / Blue Moon

☐ **LOUIS ARMSTRONG VOL.1 1935 (Armstrong, Louis & Luis Russell/Victor Young)**
Sunny side of the street / Ain't misbehavin' / I'm in the mood for love / You are my lucky star / I hope Gabriel likes my music / Solitude thanks a million / Shoe shine boy / Red sails in the sunset / On treasure island / Got a bran' new suit
CLA 1901 / Mar '94 / Ambassador

☐ **LOUIS ARMSTRONG VOL.2 (Limehouse Blues)**
BMCD 3073 / 5 Jan '98 / Blue Moon

☐ **LOUIS ARMSTRONG VOL.2 1936**
Music goes 'round and around / Rhythm saved the world / I'm putting all my eggs in one basket / Yes yes, my my / Somebody stole my break / I come from a musical family / If we never meet again / Lyin' to myself / Eventide / Swing that music / Dinah
CLA 1902 / Mar '94 / Ambassador

☐ **LOUIS ARMSTRONG VOL.3 1936-1937**
CLA 1903 / Jul '96 / Ambassador

☐ **LOUIS ARMSTRONG VOL.4 1938**
CLA 1904 / Jun '96 / Ambassador

☐ **LOUIS ARMSTRONG VOL.5 1938-1939**
Naturally / I've got a pocketful of dreams / I can't give you anything but love / Ain't misbehavin' / 12th street rag / Swing that music / Flat foot floogie / Elder Eatmore's sermon on throwing stones / Elder Eatmore's sermon on generosity / Tiger rag / Jeepers creepers / I got rhythm / On the sunny side of the street / Blues / Honeysuckle rose / Shadrack / Nobody knows the trouble I've seen / Jeepers creepers / What is this thing called swing / Rockin' chair / Lazybones
CLA 1905 / Jun '94 / Ambassador

☐ **LOUIS ARMSTRONG VOL.6 1939-1940**
CLA 1906 / Mar '94 / Ambassador

☐ **LOUIS ARMSTRONG VOL.7 1940-1941**
CLA 1907 / Jun '95 / Ambassador

☐ **LOUIS ARMSTRONG VOL.8 1941-1942**
CLA 1908 / Dec '97 / Ambassador

☐ **MACK THE KNIFE**
When it's sleepy time down South / (Back home again in) Indiana / Now you has jazz / High society calypso / Mahogany hall stomp / Blue moon / Sweet Georgia Brown / Riff blues / Mack the knife / Lazy river / Stompin' at the Savoy
CD 2310 941 / Jun '93 / Pablo

☐ **MACK THE KNIFE**
Mame / When the saints go marching in / Ain't misbehavin' / Cabaret / Kiss to build a dream on / Blueberry hill / Hello Dolly / St. Louis blues / That's my desire / Mack The Knife / Back o' town blues / Big butter and egg man / Black and blue / C'est si bon / St. James infirmary / Someday you'll be sorry / Sweethearts on parade
QED 033 / Nov '96 / Tring

☐ **MACK THE KNIFE**
Jeepers creepers / Kiss to build a dream on / When the saints go marchin' in / Mack the knife / C'est si bon / St. Louis blues / Black and blue / Dippermouth blues / Bye and bye / Rockin' chair / C jam blues / Stardust / Royal Garden blues / Indiana / I used to love her / Where did you stay last night / If I could be with you tonight / Way down yonder in New Orleans
BN 004 / Apr '98 / Blue Nite

☐ **MAHOGANY HALL STOMP (Original Recordings 1927-36)**
Mahogany Hall stomp / Rockin' chair / Savoy blues / Sweethearts on parade / Swing that music / Lyin' to myself / Thankful / I come from a musical family / Eventide / Red nose / If we never meet again / Peanut vendor / You're lucky to me / St. James Infirmary / (I'll be glad when you're dead) you rascal you / Lazy river / I ain't got nobody / Ain't misbehavin'
CDAJA 5049 / Nov '87 / Living Era

☐ **MASTERPIECES (Hot Five and Hot Seven 1925-28)**
Alligator crawl / Wild man blues / Melancholy blues / Willie the weeper / Ory's creole trombone / Struttin' with some barbecue / Hotter than that / West end blues / Potato head blues / Keyhole blues / Gully low blues / Basin street blues / S.o.l. blues / Twelfth street rag (one step) / Savoy blues / Muskrat ramble / Cornet shop suey / Skid-dat-de-dat / Come back sweet papa / Yes I'm in the barrel / Weary blues / Put 'em down blues / A monday date
CD 53001 / Mar '92 / Giants Of Jazz

☐ **MASTERPIECES 1926-41**
158132 / Mar '94 / Masterpieces

☐ **MASTERPIECES 1927-42**
158142 / Mar '94 / Masterpieces

☐ **MASTERS OF JAZZ (2CD Set)**
R2CD 8001 / 13 Apr '98 / Deja Vu

☐ **MASTERS, THE (2CD Set)**
EDMCD 012 / 24 Nov '97 / Eagle

☐ **MEMORIAL ALBUM, THE**
UAE 34122 / 27 Apr '98 / Memorial Album

☐ **MIDNIGHTS AT V-DISC (Armstrong, Louis & Jack Teagarden/Woody Herman)**
Jack Armstrong blues: *Armstrong, Louis & Jack Teagarden* / Jack Armstrong blues: *Armstrong, Louis & Jack Teagarden* / Rosetta: *Armstrong, Louis & Jack Teagarden* / Rosetta: *Armstrong, Louis & Jack Teagarden* / Miss Martingale: *Armstrong, Louis*

& Jack Teagarden / Miss Martingale: *Armstrong, Louis & Jack Teagarden* / Can't we talk it over: *Armstrong, Louis & Jack Teagarden* / Sheik of Araby: *Armstrong, Louis & Jack Teagarden* / If I could be with you: *Armstrong, Louis & Jack Teagarden* / If I could be with you: *Armstrong, Louis & Jack Teagarden* / Confessin': *Armstrong, Louis & Jack Teagarden* / Confessin': *Armstrong, Louis & Jack Teagarden* / Jeep is jumpin': *Herman, Woody & The Vanderbilt All Stars* / Northwest passage: *Herman, Woody & The Vanderbilt All Stars* / Somebody loves me: *Herman, Woody & The Vanderbilt All Stars* / John Hardy's wife: *Herman, Woody & The Vanderbilt All Stars* / Just you just me: *Herman, Woody & The Vanderbilt All Stars* / Billy Bauers tune: *Herman, Woody & The Vanderbilt All Stars*
JUCD 2048 / Jun '98 / Jazz Unlimited

☐ MORE LOUIS ARMSTRONG
Boy from New Orleans / I've got the world on a string / High society / Back o'town blues / Mahogany hall stomp / Sweet Sue just you / Medley / Snafu / Jack Armstrong blues / Save it pretty mama / I want a little girl / Where the blues were born in New Orleans / Honey do / Song was born / Pennies from heaven / Blues for yesterday / There's a cabin in the pines / Please stop playin' those blues boy
74321584782 / Jun '98 / RCA Victor

☐ NEW ORLEANS JAZZ
BN 003 / Apr '98 / Blue Nite

☐ ON THE ROAD
I love jazz / High society / Ole miss blues / Blue moon / Sweet georgia brown / Blues / Mack the knife / Tenderly / You'll never walk alone / Baby it's cold outside / When it's sleepy time down south / Mahogany hall stomp / C'est si bon (it's so good) / La vie en rose
15798 / Jan '93 / Laserlight

☐ ON THE SUNNY SIDE OF THE STREET
JASSCD 19 / Aug '90 / Jass

☐ PLATINUM COLLECTION, THE
I got rhythm / Stardust / Between the devil and the deep blue sea / Ain't misbehavin' / I can't give you anything but love / Knockin' a jug / Lawd, you made the night too long / That's my home / Hobo, you can ride this train / I gotta right to sing the blues / Black and blue / That rhythm man / I ain't got nobody / Rockin' chair / Bessie couldn't help it / Dallas blues / Dear old Southland / Sugar foot strut / Basin Street blues / Once in a while / Sweet little Papa / You made me love you / Chicago breakdown / Coal cart blues / Down in Honky Tonk town / 2.19 blues / Perdido Street blues / Jeepers creepers / Dippermouth blues / Eventide / Swing that music / I'm in the mood for love / I can't believe that you're in love with me / I'm a ding dong Daddy (from Dumas) / I'm in the market for you / If I could be with you one hour tonight / Body and soul / Memories of you / You're lucky to me / Sweethearts on parade
PC 613 / Jul '97 / Platinum Collection

☐ PLAYS AND SINGS THE GREAT STANDARDS (1928-1932)
Basin street blues / St. james infirmary / I can't give you anything but love / Mahogany hall stomp / Ain't misbehavin' / Black and blue / After you've gone / St. louis blues / Dear old southland / My sweet / I can't believe that you're in love with me / Dinah / Confessin' / If I could be with you one hour tonight / Shine / When it's sleepy time down south / Lazy river / Stardust / Georgia on my mind / All of me
BLE 592262 / Nov '92 / Black & Blue

☐ PORGY AND BESS (Armstrong, Louis & Ella Fitzgerald)
Summertime / I got plenty o' nuttin' / My man's gone now / Bess you is my woman now / It ain't necessarily so / There's a boat that's leavin' soon for New York / Bess, oh where's my Bess / I'm on my way / I loves you Porgy / Woman is a sometime thing
8274752 / Feb '93 / Verve

☐ PORTRAIT OF LOUIS ARMSTRONG, A
GALE 402 / May '97 / Gallerie

☐ QUINTESSENCE VOL.2, THE (2CD Set)
Chimes blues / Tears / Texas moaner blues / Mandy, make up your mind / Cake walkin' babies / Cold in hand blues / You've been a good ole wagon / Skid-dat-de-dat / Big butter and egg man / Wild man blues / Chicago breakdown / Alligatoe crawl / Twelfth street rag / Keyhole blues / SOL blues / Gully low blues / Got no blues / Once in a while / Fireworks (a rhythmic explosion) / Skip the gutter / Two dueces / Knee drops / Symphonic raps / Hear me talkin' to ya / Some of these days / Dear old Southland / Body and soul / Hobo, you can't ride this train / I gotta right to sing the blues / Basin Street blues / Shoe shine boy / Ev'ntide / Thankful / I double dare you / You won't be satisfied / Do you know what it means to miss New Orleans
FA 221 / Apr '97 / Fremeaux

☐ QUINTESSENCE, THE (The Vocalist/ 2CD Set)
FA 230 / Apr '96 / Fremeaux

☐ QUINTESSENCE, THE (1925-1940/2CD Set)
FA 201 / Oct '96 / Fremeaux

☐ RADIO DAYS
MCD 0562 / Apr '94 / Moon

☐ RARE BATCH OF SATCHMO, A
PLSCD 136 / Apr '96 / Pulse

☐ SATCH PLAYS FATS
Honeysuckle rose / Blue turning grey over you / I'm crazy 'bout my baby / I've got a feeling I'm falling in love / Keepin' out of mischief now / All that meat and no potatoes / Squeeze me / Black and blue / Ain't misbehavin'
4509802 / Feb '88 / CBS

☐ SATCHMO - WHAT A WONDERFUL WORLD
What a wonderful world / Nobody knows the trouble I've seen / Baby it's cold outside / Sweet Lorraine / Summertime / It ain't necessarily so / On the sunny side of the street / Tyree's blues / Cheek to cheek / Top hat, white tie and tails / Can't we be friends / Tin roof blues / Circle of your arms / Uncle Satchmo's lullaby / When the saints go marching in
8377862 / Jan '90 / Verve

☐ SATCHMO 1931-1947
Do you know what it means to miss new orleans / Where the blues were born in new orleans / Rockin' chair / Jack armstrong blues / Blues for yesterday / Sugar / Long long journey / Mahogany hall stomp / Perdido street blues / 2;19 blues / Down in honky tonk town / Coal cart blues / Wolverine blues / Cut off my legs and call me "shorty" / Satchel mouth swing / Swing that music / I surrender dear / Dusky stevedore
CD 56030 / Nov '94 / Jazz Roots

☐ SATCHMO AT THE CINEMA
Hello dolly / Basin street blues / Jubilee / Up a lazy river / I'm shooting high / Thanks a million / La vie en rose / Baby it's cold outside / Jeepers creepers / Moon river / I'm putting all my eggs in one basket / I believe / Sugar / Ain't misbehavin' / Pennies from heaven / Someday you'll be sorry / Do you know what it means to miss new orleans / Song was born / Rockin' chair / St. louis blues
3035900062 / '95 / Carlton

☐ SATCHMO THE GREAT
BN 002 / Apr '98 / Blue Nite

☐ SATCHMO'S IMMORTAL PERFORMANCES 1929-1947
CD 53088 / Mar '90 / Giants Of Jazz

☐ SATCHMO: A MUSICAL AUTOBIOGRAPHY VOL.1
JUCD 2003 / Jul '89 / Jazz Unlimited

☐ SATCHMO: A MUSICAL AUTOBIOGRAPHY VOL.2
JUCD 2004 / Jun '89 / Jazz Unlimited

☐ SATCHMO: A MUSICAL AUTOBIOGRAPHY VOL.3
JUCD 2005 / Dec '90 / Jazz Unlimited

☐ SOMEDAY
MCD 080 / Dec '95 / Moon

☐ SPOTLIGHT ON LOUIS ARMSTRONG
Mack the knife / I got rhythm / Just a gigolo / When the saints go marching in / That's my desire / Heebie jeebies / Ain't misbehavin' / On the sunny side of the street / Cabaret / Blueberry hill / Hello Dolly / I can't give you anything but love / Sweethearts on parade / Jeepers creepers / You're driving me crazy / Way down yonder in New Orleans
HADCD 140 / Feb '94 / Javelin

☐ ST. LOUIS BLUES
Mahogany hall stomp / St. Louis blues / I'm confessin' that I love you / Dinah / Chinatown, my chinatown / Georgia on my mind / Lazy river / Rockin' chair / Wild man blues / You're lucky to me / (I'll be glad when you're dead) you rascal you / St. James infirmary / West End blues / Red nose / Shoe shine boy / Save it pretty Mama / Hear me talkin' to ya / I double dare you / Struttin' with some barbecue / I hope Gabriel likes my music
MUCD 9028 / Apr '95 / Musketeer

☐ THANKS A MILLION
AMSC 574 / Jun '96 / Avid

☐ THIS IS JAZZ
Cornet chop suey / Heebie jeebies / Potato head blues / West End blues / Memories of you / Starbust / When you're smiling / Dinah / Tiger rag / Lazy river / Basin street blues / Big butter and egg man / Ain't misbehavin' / When it's sleepy time down south / I've got the world on a string / Between the devil and the deep blue sea
CK 64613 / May '96 / Sony Jazz

☐ THIS IS JAZZ
I'm not rough / St Louis blues / On the sunnyside of the street / I surrender dear / Rockin' chair / All of me / Body and soul / Mack the knife / Love you funny thing / Just a gigolo / (What did I do to be so) Black and blue / Sweethearts on the parade / When your lover has gone / Memories of you / Summer song / When it's sleepy down south
CK 65039 / May '97 / Sony Jazz

☐ THIS IS LOUIS
What a wonderful world / Basin Street blues / Ain't misbehavin' / Sugar / St. Louis blues / Swing, you cats / Rockin' chair / Pennies from heaven / Do you know what it means to miss New Orleans / St. James Infirmary / High society / Tiger rag / Jack Armstrong blues / Where the blues were born in New Orleans / Mahogany Hall stomp / Back o' town blues / Song was born / Hobo, can't you ride this train / Long long journey / SNAFU
74321523742 / 29 Sep '97 / Camden

☐ TRIBUTE TO THE LOUIS ARMSTRONG HOT FIVE, THE (Various Artists)
My heart / Yes I'm the barrel / Gutbucket blues / Come back sweet Papa / Georgia grind / Heebie jeebies / Cornet chop suey / Oriental strut / You're next / Muskrat ramble / Don't forget to mess around / I'm gonna gitcha / Dropping shucks / Who's it / King of the Zulus / Big fat Ma and skinny Pa / Lonesome blues / Sweet little Papa / 19 jazz lips / Skid-dat-de-dat
QED 225 / Nov '96 / Tring

☐ ULTIMATE COLLECTION, THE
Blueberry hill / C'est si bon / Dream a little dream of me / Georgia on my mind / Hello Dolly / Jeepers creepers / Moon river / Only you / Up a lazy river / What a wonderful world / Basin Street blues / Rockin' chair / Someday you'll be sorry / Pennies from heaven / On the sunny side of the street / Tiger rag / Ain't misbehavin' / High society rag / St. Louis blues / What a wonderful world (II) / Do you know what it means to miss New Orleans / Faithful hussar / Mack the knife
74321197062 / May '94 / Bluebird

☐ UNRELEASED MASTERS (Cornell University: Second Set)
Manhattan murals / Hy'a Sue / Fantazm / Tootin' through the roof / Brown Betty / Humouresque / How high the moon / Don't be so mean to baby / Lover come back to me / It's Monday everyday / Limehouse blues
MM 65162 / Feb '97 / Music Masters

☐ VINTAGE MELLOW JAZZ (3CD Set) (Armstrong, Louis & Lionel Hampton/ Duke Ellington)
When the saints go marching in / I'm confessin' / Our Monday date / You are my lucky star / As long as you live you'll be dead if you die / On the sunny side of the street / Lyin' to myself / Solitude / Shoe shine boy / So little time / I double dare you / Love walked in / Public melody number one / True confession / Thankful / Red sails in the sunset / Falling in love with you / Yours and mine / Hear me talkin' to ya / Save it pretty Mama / (I'll be glad when you're dead) you rascal you / When it's sleepy time down south / Hot mallets / Shufflin' at the Hollywood / Central Avenue breakdown / Dinah / Four or five times / Twelfth street rag / Chasin' with chase / Rythm, rhythm / China stomp / Blue / Pig boot sonata / Three quarter boogie / Bouncing at the beacon / Ain't cha comin' home / Munson street breakdown / When the lights are low / Shoe shiners drag / Ring dem bells / I've found a new baby / Singin' the blues / Flying home / Take the 'A' train / Perdido / Five O'clock whistle / Sidewalks of New York / At a Dixie roadside diner / Sophisticated lady / Harlem air shaft / Me and you / Concerto for cootie / My greatest mistake / Johnny come lately / Sepia panorama / Cotton tail / Don't get around much anymore / Blue goose / C Jam blues / Pitter panther patter / Raincheck / Hayfoot, strawfoot / Moon mist / Morning glory / Saratoga swing
EMPRESS 1003 / Jul '96 / Empress

☐ WE HAVE ALL THE TIME IN THE WORLD (The Pure Genius Of Louis Armstrong)
What a wonderful world / C'est si bon / Blueberry hill / It don't mean a thing if it ain't got that swing / Mack the knife / Cabaret / Tiger rag / I'm just a lucky so and so / Hello Dolly / Georgia on my mind / Moon river / Nobody knows the trouble I've seen / Back o' town blues / Faithful hussar / Mood indigo / Jeepers creepers / Go down Moses / Only you (and you alone) / When the saints go marching in / We have all the time in the world
CDEMTV 89 / Nov '94 / EMI

☐ WEST END BLUES (Armstrong, Louis Hot Five)
West end blues / Alligator crawl / Melancholy blues / Willie the weeper / Ory's creole trombone / Struttin' with some barbecue / Hotter than that / Potato head blues / Keyhole blues / Savoy blues / Basin street blues / Weary blues / Wild man blues / S.o.l. blues / Skid-dat-de-dat / Muskrat ramble / Cornet shop suey / A monday date
CD 14530 / Jan '94 / Jazz Portraits

☐ WEST END BLUES (1926-1933)
Static strut / Cornet chop suey / Heebie jeebies / Sweet little papa / I want a big butter and egg man / Potato head blues / Struttin' with some barbecue / I'm not rough / Hotter than that / Savoy blues / West end blues / Skip the gutter / Beau koo jack / Weather bird / Muggles / Mahogany hall stomp / I'm a ding dong daddy / Confessin' / If I could be with you one hour tonight / You're lucky to me / Stardust / Lawd, you made the night too long / Basin street blues / Mahogany hall stomp
IGOCD 2035 / Dec '95 / Indigo

☐ WEST END BLUES 1926-1933
158722 / Apr '97 / Archives

☐ WHAT A WONDERFUL WORLD
What a wonderful world / Everybody's talkin' (echoes) / Boy from New Orleans / We shall overcome / Creator has a master plan / Mood indigo / This black cat has nine lives / My one and only love / His father wore long hair / Give peace a chance
ND 88310 / Nov '88 / Bluebird

☐ WHAT A WONDERFUL WORLD
What a wonderful world / Jeepers creepers / Georgia on my mind / On the sunny side of the street / Cabaret / Hello Dolly / Lazy river / When you're smiling / Whiffenpoof song / Blueberry Hill / La vie en rose / I can't give you anything but love / When it's sleepy time down South / Surrender dear / Some of these days / Exactly like you
PLATCD 304 / Apr '88 / Platinum

☐ WHAT A WONDERFUL WORLD
Down by the riverside / Swing low, sweet chariot / What a wonderful world / Georgia on my mind / Moon river / Hello Dolly / C'est si bon / Cabaret / Mack the knife / Blueberry Hill / Basin Street blues / When the saints go marching in
12723 / Apr '96 / Laserlight

☐ YOU RASCAL YOU
When the saints go marching in / I'm confessin' that I love you / Our Monday date / You are my lucky star / As long as you'll be dead if you die / Red nose / Lyin' to myself / Solitude / Shoe shine boy / So little time / I double dare you / Love walked in / Public melody number one / True confession / I'm thankful / Red sails in the sunset / Eventide / Yours and mine / Hear me talkin' to ya / Save it pretty Mama / (I'll be glad when you're dead) you rascal you / When it's sleepy time down South
RAJCD 821 / Mar '97 / Empress
HMNCD 016 / 3 Nov '97 / Half Moon

Army Air Forces Overseas Orchestra

☐ FAREWELL PERFORMANCES
I sustain the wings / Tail end charlie / In the gloaming / Homesick, that's all / I can't give you anything but love / Rhapsody in blue / Tuxedo junction / Oranges and lemons / American patrol / Swing low, sweet chariot / Sun valley jump / Have you got any gum, chum / Autumn serenade / I sustain the wings / In the mood / Stardust / My buddy / In the middle of may / Moonlight serenade / My blue heaven / Symphony / Air corps song / Moonlight serenade
HCD 248 / May '94 / Hindsight

Arnaz, Desi

☐ BIG BANDS OF HOLLYWOOD (Arnaz, Desi Orchestra & Chico Marx Orchestra)
Chiu chiu (vocal by desi arnaz) / Begin the beguine / Easy street (vocal by amanda lane) / Cachita (vocal by desi arnaz) / Till we meet again (vocal by desi arnaz) / Speak low / Rico pulpa / Abraham (vocal by mel torme) / Velvet moon (vocal by skip nelson) / Pagliacci / Swing stuff / Beer barrel polka (chico marx, piano) / Mr. five by five (vocal kim kimberly) / Chicago strut
15767 / Jul '92 / Laserlight

☐ DESI ARNAZ 1937-1947
Echa un pie / Ah viene la conga / Vereda tropical / Union triste / Vira y vira / Conga conga / Africa canta / South America way / Le conga en Nueva York / Tabu / Cachita / El Marimbulero / Alegre conga / Piensa en mi / Un poquito de tu amor / Siboney / Green eyes / Babalu / Peanut vendor / La borrichita / In Santiago Chile / Tico tico / Carnival in Rio
HQCD 106 / Jan '98 / Harlequin

Arnaz, Lucie

☐ JUST IN TIME
Lover / 'S Wonderful / Slow dancing / Sorry 'bout the whole darn thing / I love to dance/I got lost in his arms / Things we did last summer / View from here / I'm beginning to see the light/Moonglow / My foolish heart / Just in time / Recipe for love / Another you / Witchcraft / Quiereme mucho / Make someone happy / Blue skies
CCD 4573 / Nov '93 / Concord Jazz

Arnez, Chico

☐ ESSENTIAL SALSA (Arnez, Chico & His Cubana Brass)
Rhythm is gonna get you / Mama you can't go / Do the salsa / Get on your feet / Girl from Brazil / Jezebel / 1-2-3 / Live for loving you / That's my desire / Oye mi canto (hear my voice) / Cheeky Chico / What goes around / 18th Century salsa / Specialization / Real wild house / Go away / Conga
CDMFP 6174 / Sep '95 / Music For Pleasure

Arnheim, Gus

☐ ECHOES FROM THE COCONUT GROVE 1931
TT 410 / May '98 / Take Two

Arnold

☐ BARN TAPES, THE
Float my boat / Calling Ira Jones / Face / Dog on the stairs / Windsor park / Sun / 2 Chairs / Medication time
CRECD 218 / May '97 / Creation

☐ HILLSIDE
CRECD 231 / 13 Jul '98 / Creation

Arnold, Billy Boy

☐ BACK WHERE I BELONG
ALCD 4815 / Nov '93 / Alligator

☐ BLOWIN' THE BLUES AWAY
BB 1004 / 25 May '98 / Rhino

☐ CHECKIN' IT OUT (The 1977 London Sessions)
Dirty mother fucker / Don't stay out all night / 1-2-99 / Riding the el / Just to know / Christmas time / I wish you would / Ah'w baby / Sweet Miss Bea / Blue and lonesome / Eldorado Cadillac / Mary Bernice / It's great to be rich / Just a dream / Catfish
NEBCD 850 / Aug '96 / Sequel

☐ ELDORADO CADILLAC
ALCD 4836 / Nov '95 / Alligator

☐ GOING TO CHICAGO
TCD 5018 / Jul '95 / Testament

Arnold, David

☐ SHAKEN AND STIRRED (The David Arnold 007 Project)
Diamonds are forever: *Arnold, David & David McAlmont* / 007 theme: *Arnold, David & LTJ Bukem* / Spy who loved me: *Arnold, David & Aimee Mann* / All time high: *Arnold, David & Pulp* / Space march: *Arnold, David & Leftfield* / Live and let die: *Arnold, David & Chrissie Hynde* / Moonraker: *Arnold, David & Shara Nelson* / Thunderball: *Arnold, David & ABC* / From Russia with love: *Arnold, David & Natacha Atlas* / You only live twice: *Arnold, David & Candi Staton* / On her majesty's secret service: *Arnold, David & Propellerheads* / All the time in the world: *Arnold, David & Iggy Pop* / Diamonds are forever / Nobody does it better / Spacemarch / James Bond theme
3984207382 / 20 Oct '97 / East West

Arnold, Eddy

☐ CATTLE CALL/THEREBY HANGS A TALE
Streets of Laredo / Cool water / Cattle call / Leanin' on the old top rail / Ole faithful / Cowboy's dream / Wayward wind / Tumbling tumbleweeds / Cowpoke / Where the mountains meet the sky / Sierra Sue / Carry me back to the Lone Prairie / Jim I wore a tie today / Tom Dooley / Nellie sits a waitin' / Tennessee stud / Battle of Little Big Horn / Wreck of ol' 97 / Red headed stranger / Johnny Reb / Riders in the sky / Boot Hill / Ballad of Davy Crockett / Partners / Jesse James
BCD 15441 / Apr '90 / Bear Family

☐ ESSENTIAL EDDY ARNOLD, THE
It's a sin / I'll hold you my heart (till I can hold you in my arms) / Don't rob another man's castle / Eddy's song / I really don't want to know / Make the world go away / Molly darling / Just call me lonesome / Tip of my fingers / Cattle call / What's he doing in my world / Anytime / I want to go with you / Somebody like me / Take me in your arms and hold me / Lonely again / Turn the world around / Then you tell me goodbye / That's what I get for loving you / You don't miss a thing
07863668542 / Aug '96 / RCA Nashville

☐ MASTERS, THE
EABCD 109 / 30 Mar '98 / Eagle

☐ TENNESSEE PLOWBOY AND HIS GUITAR 1944-1950, THE (5CD Set)
Mother's prayer / Mommy please stay home with me / Cattle call / Each minute seems a million years / Did you see my daddy over there / Many tears ago / I walk alone / You must walk the line / I'll have to live and learn / Be sure there's no mistake / I couldn't belive it was true / I talk to myself about you / All alone in this world without you / Can't win can't place can't show / What is life without love / That's how much I love you / Why didn't you take that too / Chained to a memory / Easy rockin' chair / To my sorrow / It's a sin / I'm somebody nobody loves / That little boy of mine / Don't bother to cry / Me too / I'll hold you in my heart / Bouquet of roses / What a fool I was / Little angel with the dirty face / Wondering what to do / Prisoner's song / Rockin' alone in an old rockin' chair / It makes no difference now / Will the circle be unbroken / Seven years with the wrong woman / Molly darling / I'm thinking tonight of my blue eyes / Who at the door is standing / Then I turned and walked slowly away / Texarkana baby / In the hills of tomorrow / My daddy is only a picture / Say you'll be mine / There's not a thing I wouldn't do for you / I've got a lifetime to forget / Anytime / Heart full of love / My heart cries for you / I've got other fish to fry / This is the thanks I get for loving you / You know how talk gets around / Just a little lovin' / Till the end of the world / Save a little corner in your heart / MOTHER / I would'nt trade the silver in my mother's hair / That wonderful mother of mine / Bring your roses to her now / I wish I had a girl like you mother / My mother's sweet voice / There's no wings on my angel / Echo of your footsteps / Don't rob another man's castle / Show me the way back to your heart / Homesick lonesome and sorry / One kiss too many / I was foolish when I fell in love with you / Something old something new something borrowed something blu / I tied a little string around my finger / I'm throwing rice / Shepherd of my heart / Why should I cry / CHRISTMAS / To the last beat of my heart / Take me in your arms and hold me / Evil tempt me not / When Jesus beckons me home / Will santy come to shanty town / Beautiful Isle of somewhere / Lily of the valley / Softly and tenderly / Mama and daddy broke my heart / You touched me / Nearest thing to heaven / Prison without walls / Cuddle buggin' baby / Enclosed one broken heart / Tie me to your apron strings again / Behind the clouds / Million miles from you heart / At the close of a long long day / If I never go to heaven / Lovebug itch / White Christmas / Santa Claus is comin' to town / There's been a change in me / Precious little baby / Through a strnger's eyes / Open thy merciful arms / Jesus and the athiest / Kentucky waltz / May the lord bless and keep you / I'm writing a letter to the lord
BCD 15726 / Jul '98 / Bear Family

Arnold, Harry

☐ HARRY ARNOLD
ANC 9097 / Aug '94 / Ancha

☐ PREMIARI - HARRY ARNOLD & HIS SWEDISH RADIO BAND
ANC 9501 / Dec '94 / Ancha

Arnold, Kokomo

☐ KING OF THE BOTTLENECK GUITAR 1934-1937
Milk cow blues / Old original kokomo blues / Back to the woods / Sagefield woman blues / Old black cat blues (jinx blues) / Sissy man blues / Front door blues (32 20 blues) / Back door blues / Twelves (dirty dozens) / Biscuit roller blues / Chain gang blues / How long, how long blues / Bo weevil / Busy bootin' / Policy wheel blues / Milk cow blues no. 4 / Model "t" woman blues / I'll be up some day / Mr. charlie / Back fence picket blues / Wild water blues / Red beans and rice / Buddie brown blues (rolling time)
BLE 592502 / Nov '92 / Black & Blue

☐ OLD ORIGINAL KOKOMO BLUES
Mister charlie / Sagefield woman blues / Mean old twister / Monday morning blues / Twelves (dirty dozen) / Salty dog / Policy wheel blues / Travelin' rambler blues / Honeydripper / Front door blues / Lonesome southern blues / I'll be up someday / Sissyman blues / Backdoor blues / Milkcow blues / Paddlin' madeline blues / Long and tall / Old original kokomo blues / How long how long blues / You should not a' done it / Big leg mama / Cause you're dirty / Foolman blues
KATCD 102 / 29 Sep '97 / Catfish

Arnold, P.P.

☐ BEST OF P.P. ARNOLD, THE (Kafunta/ First Lady Of Immediate)
(If you think) you're groovy / Something beautiful happened / Born to be together / Am I still dreaming / First cut is the deepest / Everything's gonna be alright / Treat me like a lady / Would you believe / Speak to me / God only knows / Eleanor Rigby / Yesterday / Angel of the morning / It'll never happen again / As tears go by / To love somebody / Dreamin' / If you see what I mean / Though it hurts me badly / Welcome home / Life is but nothing / Time has come
SEECD 235 / Oct '88 / See For Miles

☐ FIRST CUT, THE
(If you think you're) Groovy / Something beautiful happened / Born to be together / Am I still dreaming / Though it hurts me badly / First cut is the deepest / Everything is gonna be alright / Treat me like a lady / Would you believe / Life is but nothing / Speak to me / Time has come / Letter to Bill / Kafunta one / God only knows / Elanor Rigby / Yesterday / Angel of the morning / It'll never happen again / As tears go by / To love somebody / Dreamin' / Welcome home
CCSCD 819 / 2 Mar '98 / Castle

Arnold, Wayne

☐ TOUGH LIFE
She makes me feel good / Keep giving your love / Ready when you are / Just take me back / Lucky tough life / You got what I need / Love is on your side / Everything reminds me / Love storm / You're the reason / All or nothing / Right back into love / Closer / How long does it take
CD 013 / Sep '92 / ATR

Arnoux, Viviane

☐ CHEVAL ROUGE (Arnoux, Viviane & F. Michaud)
829062 / Jul '95 / BUDA

Arnstrom, Kenneth

☐ HITTIN' THE ROOTS (Arnstrom, Kenneth New Orleans Band)
NCD 8849 / Aug '97 / Phontastic

☐ SAXCESS
NCD 8836 / Dec '95 / Phontastic

Arpeggio

☐ BEST OF ARPEGGIO, THE (Love And Desire)
HTCD 82 / 20 Apr '98 / Hot Productions

Arpin, John

☐ TWO PIANO RAGS (Arpin, John & Catherine Wilson)
3036801282 / Jun '98 / Hallmark

Arranmore

☐ BY REQUEST
FE 1418 / Dec '94 / Folk Era

☐ LIVE
FE 1405 / Nov '94 / Folk Era

Arrested Development

☐ 3 YEARS, 5 MONTHS AND 2 DAYS IN THE LIFE OF...
Man's final frontier / Mama's always on stage / People everyday / Blues happy / Mr. Wendal / Children play with earth / Raining revolution / Fishin' for religion / Give a man a fish / U / Eave of reality / Natural / Dawn of the dreads / Tennessee / Washed away
CCD 1929 / May '92 / Cooltempo

☐ BEST OF ARRESTED DEVELOPMENT, THE
People everyday / Mr. Wendal / Raining revolution / Tennessee / Africa's inside me / Revolution / Give a man a fish / Ease my mind / Fishing 4 religion / Natural / Pride / Shell / Mama's always on stage / Ease my mind / Mr. Wendal / People everyday
4947452 / 25 May '98 / EMI

Arriale, Lynne

☐ LONG ROAD HOME (Arriale, Lynne Trio)
Bye-ya / Will o' the wisp / Night in Tunisia / Wouldn't it be lovely / Letters from Mike O'Brien / Con Alma / I wished on the moon / Dove / Long road home
TCB 7952 / 27 Oct '97 / TCB

Arrow

☐ BEST OF ARROW, THE
Slouch hat / Memories of Norway / Memories of Jaren / Evening breakfast / Kirsi
100121 CD / Sep '88 / Red Bullet

☐ CARRIBEAN PARTY, A (The Best Of Arrow)
AHLCD 45 / 25 May '97 / Hit

☐ OUTRAGEOUS
040 CD / Jan '94 / Arrow

☐ PHAT
ARROW 0043CD / Dec '95 / Arrow

☐ RIDE DE RIDDIM
ARROW 0045CD / Jan '97 / Arrow

Arroyo, Joe

☐ LA NOCHE (Arroyo, Joe Y La Verdad)
La noche / Pal bailodor / Somos series / El caminante / Yo soy el punto cubano / A mi dios todo le debo / Fuego en mi mente / El arbol / El palo / Te quiero mas / El son del caballo / Suave bruta / El gailan pollero / Simula timula / La rumbera / Las cajas / La concha / Mis zapatos blancos
TUGCD 1015 / 18 May '98 / World Music Network

☐ REBELLION (Arroyo, Joe Y La Verdad)
Yamulemao / Rebellion / Bam bam / Mary / La vuelta / Musa original / El coquero / El maletero / Son apretao / Echao pa'lante / Tumbatecho / En horabuena / Pan de arroz / De clavel / El barbero / Rosa Angelina
WCD 012 / Jul '89 / World Circuit

Ars Moriendi

☐ MEMORANDUM
ACT 61 / 3 Nov '97 / Ant Zen

Ars Nova

☐ FEAR AND ANXIETY
AMPCD 038 / 31 Jul '98 / AMP

Arsenal FC

☐ FOREVER (Arsene's Army)
KICD 003 / 15 Jun '98 / KI

☐ GOOD OLD ARSENAL (Various Artists)
Good old Arsenal / Boys from Highbury / Come on you gunners / Arsenal / Arsenal we're on your side / Here we go again / Arsenal rap / Highbury sunshine / Gooneroonie / Ooh ooh Tony Adams / Charlie George Calypso / Fever pitch / Arriverdici Liam / Gus Caesar rap / One night at Anfield / Roll out the red carpet / Kings of London / Victory song 1993 / Highbury heartbeat / Ian Wright Wright Wright / I wish I could play like Charlie George
CDGAFFER 1 / Nov '95 / Cherry Red

Arson Garden

☐ WISTERIA
ASKD 66013 / Nov '92 / Vertebrae

Art Connection

☐ STOLEN MOMENTS
BEST 1035CD / Nov '93 / Acoustic Music

Art Ensemble Of Chicago

☐ ART ENSEMBLE OF CHICAGO (Art Ensemble Of Chicago & Fontella Bass)
How strange (part one) / Ole jed (part two) / Horn web
500172 / Nov '93 / Musidisc

☐ DREAMING OF THE MASTERS SUITE
DIW 854 / Mar '92 / DIW

☐ EDA WOBU
JMY 10082 / Aug '91 / JMY

☐ FULL FORCE
Magg zelma / Care free / Charlie m / Old time southside street dance / Full force
8291972 / Oct '86 / ECM

☐ SPIRITUAL, THE
BLCD 760219 / May '97 / Black Lion

☐ THIRD DECADE
Prayer for jimbo kwesl / Funky aeco / Walking in the moonlight / Bell piece / Zero / Third decade
8232132 / Feb '85 / ECM

☐ TUTANKHAMUN
BLCD 760199 / Apr '95 / Black Lion

☐ URBAN BUSHMEN
8293942 / Jul '85 / ECM

Art Ensemble Of Soweto

☐ AMERICA-SOUTH AFRICA
DIW 848 / Aug '91 / DIW

Art In America

☐ ART IN AMERICA
RMED 0103CD / 19 Jan '98 / Renaissance

Art Lande

☐ RUBISA PATROL
Celestial guests / Many chinas / Jaimi's birthday song / Romany / Corinthian melodies / For Nancy / Monk in his simple room
5198752 / Mar '94 / ECM

Art Of Noise

☐ AMBIENT COLLECTION, THE
Opus 4 / Nothing was going to stop them / Island / Ode to Don Jose / Roundabout 727/Ransom in the sand / Robinson Crusoe / Art of love / Opus for 4 / Crusoe / Camilla / Counterpoint / Eye of a needle / Nation rejects
WOLCD 1012 / Apr '91 / China

☐ BEST OF THE ART OF NOISE, THE
Beat box / Moments in love / Close (to the edit) / Peter Gunn / Paranoimia / Legacy / Dragnet '88 / Kiss / Something always happens / Opus 4
WOLCD 1027 / Aug '92 / China

☐ DRUM 'N' BASS COLLECTION
WOLCD 1072 / Oct '96 / China

☐ FON MIXES
Instruments of darkness (all of us are one people) / Instruments of darkness (all of us are one people) / Roller 10 / Back to backbeat / Shades of paranoimia / Ode to a.d.j. (interlude 2) / Catwalk / Legs / L.e.f. / I of the needled / Crusoe / Art of slow love (youth) (slow concept by phil barber) / No sun
WOLCD 1023 / Nov '91 / China

☐ IN NO SENSE I NONSENSE
Galleons of stone / Dragnet / Fin du temps / How rapid / Opus for four / Debut / EFL / Ode to Don Jose / Day at the races / Counterpoint / Roundabout 727 / Ransom on the sand / Roller 1 / Nothing was going to stop them then, anyway / Crusoe / One earth
WOLCD 1017 / Jul '91 / China

☐ IN VISIBLE SILENCE
Opus for four / Paranoimia / Eye of a needle / Legs / Slip of the tongue / Backbeat / Instruments of darkness / Peter Gunn: *Art Of Noise & Duane Eddy* / Camilla / Chameleon's dish
WOLCD 1016 / Jul '91 / China

☐ STATE OF THE ART (3CD Set)
Opus / OPus for 4 / Nothing was going to stop / Crusoe / Island / Camilla / Ode to Don Jose / Counterpoint / Roundabout 727 / Eye of a neddle / Robinson Crusoe / Nation rejects / Art of love / Instruments of darkness / Yebo (interlude 1) / Roller 10 / Back to back beat / Shades of paranoimia / Ode to a DJ / Catwalk / Dragnet and Peter Gunn / Legs / LEF / I of the needle / Art of slow love / No sun / Something always happens / Ode to Don Jose / Art Of Love / Yebo / Opus 4 / Island / Camilla the old old story / Kiss / Eye of the needle / Peter Gunn / Crusoe
WOLCD 1075 / Aug '97 / China

Art Of Trance

☐ WILDLIFE ON ONE
PLAT 25CD / Nov '96 / Platipus

Artaek, Lagun

☐ SONGS FROM THE BASQUE COUNTRY (Artaek, Lagun Groupe)
ARN 64223 / Jun '93 / Arion

Artango

☐ DOUBLES JEUX
ARN 62304 / Jul '95 / Arion

☐ PIANO - BANDONEON
ARN 62245 / Aug '93 / Arion

Artch

☐ ANOTHER RETURN
ACTCD 5 / Jul '91 / Active

Artefakto

☐ DES CONSTRUCTION
CDZOT 113 / Oct '94 / Zoth Ommog

Artension

☐ PHOENIX RISING
SH 1112 / Nov '97 / Shrapnel

Artharwan

☐ ADVENTURES OF EVOLUTION
DC 881902 / Oct '97 / Disky

Arthea

☐ PASSAGES
SM 106550 / Apr '97 / Wergo

Arthur, Dave

☐ MORNING STANDS ON TIPTOE/THE LARK IN THE MORNING (Arthur, Dave & Toni)
Maiden came from London town / Morning stands on tiptoe / Female rambling sailor / Padstow drinking song / Guilty sea captain / Eynsham poaching song / Green grass / Barley grain for me / Jolly ploughboy / Blackburn poachers / John Peel / Bold Robinson / Green broom / Bendigo champion of England / Football match / All frolicking I'll give over / Death of Queen Jane / Creeping Jane / Merchant's daughter of Bristol / Bold dragoon / Cold blows the winter's wind / Lark in the morning / Poor old horse / Hey John Barleycorn / Bedlam / Admiral Benbow / Father father build me a boat / Press gang / Six jolly miners
HILLCD 18 / May '97 / Wooded Hill

Arthur, Davey

☐ CELTIC SIDE SADDLE
Celtic side saddle / Hail Mary full of grace / Galway farmer / Fair city set / Emigrant / Over the ocean / Slip 'n' slides / Euston station / Mad lady and me / Walk / Sit you down / Ness pipers / Sister Marcella
PRKCD 26 / Aug '94 / Park

☐ CUT TO THE CHASE
Blue stack set / When another domino falls / New York miracle / Small drop on the side / Cut to the chase / Song for yesterday / Girls / Singing tap set / Nobleman's wedding / Seamus Alfonsus set / She loves to dance / Girls
BLUE 31 / 20 Oct '97 / Blue Bowl

Arthur, Joseph

☐ BIG CITY SECRETS
Big city secret / Mercedes / Mikel K / Good about me / Daddy's on prozac / Marina / Birthday card / Crying like a man / Porcupine / Dessert / Haunted eyes / Bottle of you
CDRW 64 / Jun '97 / Realworld

Arthur, Neil

☐ SUITCASE
Breaking my heart / I love, I hate / Suitcase / Jumping like a kangaroo / I know these things about you / Heaven / That's what love is like / One day, one time / Jukebox theory / Beach
CDCHR 6065 / Feb '94 / Chrysalis

Artifacts

☐ THAT'S THEM
Art of scratch / Arts of facts / 31 bumrush / To ya chest / Where yo skillz at / Collaboration of mics / Ultimate / It's a perfect hit / This is da way / Interview / Break it down / Skwad training / Ingredients to time travel / Return to da wrongside / Who's this / Ultimate
7567927532 / Apr '97 / Atlantic

Artificial Joy Club

☐ MELT
IND 90125 / 11 May '98 / Interscope

Artillery

☐ FEAR OF TOMORROW
Time has come / Almighty / Show you hate / King thy name is slayer / Out of the sky / Into the universe / Eternal war / Deed of darkness
3038632 / 1 Jun '98 / Axe Killer

Artisan

☐ BREATHING SPACE
FESTIVAL 9CD / Oct '93 / Festival

☐ BYGONE CHRISTMAS
BF 112CD / Nov '96 / Bygone Films

☐ OUR BACKYARD
BOING 9604CD / Nov '96 / Bedspring

☐ ROCKING AT THE END OF TIME
FESTIVAL 7CD / '92 / Festival

☐ WINGS
What's the use of wings / Talk to me / Curupay freijo / Feel the rhyme / Mabel / Trivia / Under the misteltoe / Mad old Mike / Buy and buy / One minute song
TERRCD 006 / Feb '97 / Terra Nova

Artwoods

☐ 100 OXFORD STREET
Sweet Mary / If I ever get my hands on you / Goodbye sisters / Oh my love / I take what I want / Big city / She knows what to do / I'm looking for a saxophonist / Keep looking / I keep forgettin' / I feel good / One more heartache / Down in the valley / Be my lady / Stop and think it over / Don't cry no more
EDCD 107 / 25 Nov '97 / Edsel

☐ ART GALLERY
REP 4533 / Nov '97 / Repertoire

Arundel, Jeff

☐ RIDE THE RIDE
Ride the ride / Garden / Down on blue / Magdalena / Left at last / My last trend / Allison / Voice of storm / Harmon killebrew / Only gone / Slow train / Elmwood Avenue
FIENDCD 799 / 6 Oct '97 / Demon

Arvanitas, George

☐ MY FAVOURITE PIANO SONGS
BB 649 / 24 Apr '98 / Black & Blue

☐ RENCONTRE
Footprints / Dear old Stockholm / Very early / Fables of faubus / Off minor / Come Sunday / Bolivia / East of the sun / Goodbye pork pie hat / Dug's blues / Nuages / In a sentimental mood
4912322 / 13 Jul '98 / Sony Jazz

Arzachel

☐ ARZACHEL
Garden of earthly delights / Azathoth / Queen st. gang / Leg / Clean innocent fun / Metempsychosis
DOCD 1983 / 28 Oct '96 / Drop Out

As Friends Rust

☐ FISTS OF TIME, THE
ED 025CD / 13 Jul '98 / Good Life

As One

☐ ART OF PROPHECY
Eclectricity / Relentless / Tomorrow people / Glow / Hideout / Space party ethics / Destination other / Theme from Op-Art / You who never arrived / Freefall / Hustler / Splendor solis / Return of the Kingpin / Farewell
SHLD 102CD / Mar '97 / Shield

☐ CELESTIAL SOUL
Celestial soul / Ikiru / Interstellar / Dhyana / Laetoli / Hybrid / We no longer understand / Renaissance / Ariois / Return to Talimakan / What might have beeen
CDOVD 463 / Jan '96 / Virgin

☐ IN WITH THEIR ARPS AND MOOGS...
Epic / Chiaro / Last of the almoravids / Electric hymn / Kiss / Sphere of the fixed stars / Triumphant / Queen constance / Message in Herbie's shirts / Short track about love / Hyeres
CLR 430CD / May '97 / Clear

☐ PLANETARY FOLKLORE
Another modal morning / Soul soul soul / Libran legacy / Freedom waltz / Planetary folklore / Away from all of this / Amalia's mode / Path of most resistance / Brown blue brown on blue / Mind filter
MW 083CD / 27 Oct '97 / Mo Wax

☐ REFLECTIONS
Mihara / Meridian / Orchila / Shamballa / Dance of the uighurs / Majik jar / Star gaze / Soleil levant / Lunate / Asa nisi masa / Moon over the moab
ELEC 5CD / Apr '96 / New Electronica

As Serenity Fades

☐ EARTHBORN
CDAR 018 / May '94 / Adipocre

Asalah

☐ AL MUSHTAKA
3108512 / 23 Mar '98 / Odeon

Asana

☐ TRIKUTI
NH 005 / Jun '97 / Neu Harmony

Asante

☐ ASANTE MODE
Intro...Asante mode / Look what you've done / All about you / Don't push me away / Why / Don't say goodnight / People get ready / Prelude...what goes on / What's the plan / Dopest Ethiopian / Interlude...the phone call / Cathin' feelins
4811342 / Nov '95 / Columbia

Ascension

☐ ABOMINATION
TBX 019CD / 17 Aug '98 / Toybox

☐ BROADCAST (2CD Set)
SX 030CD / Oct '96 / Shock

Ascione, Joe

☐ MY BUDDY (Ascione, Joe Octet)
Cottontail / My Buddy / J and B's bag / Here's that rainy day / Limehouse blues / Hi fly / Nica's dream / Straight no chaser / Soft winds / I want to be happy / Love for sale / Blues no.5
CD 036 / Aug '97 / Nagel Heyer

Asgard

☐ SONGS OF G
BEST 1042CD / Nov '93 / Acoustic Music

Ash

☐ 1977
Lose control / Goldfinger / Girl from Mars / I'd give you anything / Gone the dream / Kung fu / Let it flow / Innocent smile / Angel interceptor / Lost in you / Dark side light side
INFECT 40CD / May '96 / Infectious

☐ LIVE AT THE WIRELESS
Darkside lightside / Girl from Mars / Oh yeah / T Rex / I'd give you anything / Kung fu / What Deaner was talking about / Goldfinger / Petrol / Clear invitation to the dance
DEATH 3 / Feb '97 / Death Star

☐ TRAILOR
INFECT 14CD / Oct '94 / Infectious

Ash Ra Tempel

☐ BEST OF THE PRIVATE TAPES, THE (2CD Set)
CLP 299 / 29 Jun '98 / Cleopatra

☐ JOIN INN/STARRING ROSI
CLP 309 / 20 Jul '98 / Cleopatra

☐ LE BERCEAU DE CRISTAL
14275 / 23 Mar '98 / Spalax

☐ NEW AGE OF EARTH (Ashra)
Sunrain / Ocean of tenderness / Deep distance / Nightloat
CDV 2080 / Jun '90 / Virgin
14505 / Feb '97 / Spalax

☐ SEVEN UP (Ash Ra Tempel & Timothy Leary)
14249 / Oct '96 / Spalax

☐ STARRING ROSI
14247 / Jan '97 / Spalax

☐ SUNRAIN (Ashra)
Sunrain / Midnight on mars / Morgana da capo / Oasis / Cyrille / Screamer / Mistral / 77
Slightly delayed / Ice train / Deep distance / Ocean of tenderness / Phantasus / Blackouts
CDOVD 463 / Jan '96 / Virgin

☐ TROPICAL HEAT (Ashra)
Mosquito dance / Tropical heat / Pretty papaya / Nights in sweat / Don't stop the fan / Monsoon
CDBT 138 / Feb '91 / Thunderbolt

☐ WALKIN' THE DESERT (Ashra)
First movement / Second movement / Third movement / Fourth movement / Desert
CDTB 086 / Apr '90 / Thunderbolt

Ash, Vic

☐ EYES HAVE IT, THE (Ash, Vic Quartet)
Touch of your lips / Bernie's tune / I thought about you / November rose / Between the devil and the deep blue sea / Silver minor / Namely you / Soon / Carnaval samba / Nancy with the laughing face / Eyes have it
ABCD 3 / Oct '96 / AB

Asha

☐ CELESTINE
CD 407 / 6 Jul '98 / New World

☐ CONCERT OF ANGELS
CD 239 / 6 Jul '98 / New World

☐ LOVE IS THE ONLY PRAYER
CD 436 / 6 Jul '98 / New World

Asha, Ras Imru

☐ SPIRITUAL WARRIOR
ROTCD 010 / Jun '96 / Reggae On Top

Asha Vida

☐ AS ONE OF ONE
IC 128CD / Jul '97 / Icon

☐ NATURE'S CLUMSY HAND
BUR 16 / 27 Apr '98 / Burnt Hair

Ashbrook, Karen

☐ HILLS OF ERIN
MMCD 207 / Dec '94 / Maggie's Music

Ashby, Dorothy

☐ JAZZ HARPIST
Thou swell / Stella by starlight / Dancing on the ceiling / Aeolian groove / Quietude / Spicy / Lamenation
SV 0194 / Oct '97 / Savoy Jazz

Ashby, Harold

☐ I'M OLD FASHIONED
STCD 545 / '92 / Stash

☐ ON THE SUNNY SIDE OF THE STREET
Out of nowhere / There is no greater love / Honeysuckle rose / Pennies from heaven / It's the talk of the town / Satin doll / These foolish things / On the sunny side of the street / Scuffin' / In my solitude / Just squeeze me
CDSJP 385 / Oct '92 / Timeless Jazz

☐ VIKING, THE
GEMCD 160 / '87 / Gemini

☐ WHAT AM I HERE FOR (Ashby, Harold Quartet)
I can't get started / What am I here for / Mood indigo / Frankie and Johnny / Once in a while / Poinciana / C jam blues / Prelude to a kiss / September in the rain / Perdido
CRISS 1054CD / 20 Oct '97 / Criss Cross

Asher, Meira

☐ DISSECTED
Sida / Fear and ruddy / Give peace / Psalm 19 / Dissect me / Maligora the sand child / Daddy came / Taht a' shams
CRAM 094 / Mar '97 / Crammed Discs

Ashes

☐ DEATH HAS MADE IT'S CALL
NFR 015CD / 13 Oct '97 / Nuclear Blast

Ashford & Simpson

☐ BEEN FOUND (Ashford & Simpson/ Maya Angelou)
HOP 45122 / Nov '96 / Ichiban

☐ SOLID
Solid / Jungle / Honey I love you / Babies / Closest to love / Cherish forever more / Tonight we escape (we make love) / Outta the world
MUSCD 501 / Sep '94 / MCI Original Masters

Ashkaru

☐ MOTHER TONGUE
Maray-Wollelaye / Tigel / Ring my faith / Bellema / Sigh like you do / Labour of love / Must give back / Enat / If I chose / Know joy
3202142 / Dec '95 / Triloka

Ashley, Steve

☐ FAMILY ALBUM, THE
RGFCD 002 / Nov '91 / Road Goes On Forever

Ashley, Tyrone

☐ BEST OF TYRONE ASHLEY, THE (Looks Like Love Is Here To Stay)
HTCD 68 / 20 Apr '98 / Hot Productions

Ashman, Micky

☐ THROUGH DARKEST ASHMAN (Ashman, Micky & His Jazzband)
Wedding of the painted doll / In the shade of the old apple tree / Who were you with last night / If those lips could only speak / Jungle nights in Harlem / Ostrich walk / Darkness on the delta / Listen to the mocking bird / Under the bamboo tree / Hummingbird / Brownskin Mama / Snake rag / Pagan love song / Green cockatoo / Zambesi
LACD 86 / Oct '97 / Lake

Ashtabula

☐ RIVER OF MANY DEAD FISH, THE
SB 73CD / Jun '97 / Siltbreeze

Ashton, Dean

☐ MAGIC GUITAR OF DEAN ASHTON, THE
MACCD 371 / 30 Mar '98 / Autograph

Ashton, Gwyn

☐ BEG, BORROW AND STEEL
Sun don't shine / Ain't got time for that stuff / I can't be satisfied / Leaving in the morning / Double crossin' Mama / Wastin' my time / Ulura sunset / Train time shuffle / Can't get my way around you / Stop holding out / Sweet love
RGFGACD 036 / Aug '97 / Road Goes On Forever

☐ FEEL THE HEAT
Trouble knockin' at your door / Ain't got time for that stuff / Just a little bit / We'll find the way / Too late / Wanted man / Bad luck blues / Someone like you / Loaded six shooter / Wastin' my time / Take me back home
RGFGACD 037 / Nov '97 / Road Goes On Forever

Ashton, Susan

☐ WAKENED BY THE WIND
Down on my knees / No one knows / My heart / Benediction / Ball and chain / I hear you / Land of nod / In my father's hands / In amazing grace land / Suffer in silence / Beyond justice to mercy
SPD 1259 / Aug '95 / Alliance Music

Ashtray Boy

☐ EVERYMAN'S 4TH DIMENSION, THE
AJAX 057CD / Dec '96 / Ajax

☐ HONEYMOON SUITE, THE
Ananda marga / Shirley MacLaine / Observatory Hill / There is a fountain / Time for a baby / How Charles destroyed the inland sea / Infidel / Little nature child / Hit / Love in a bakery / Honeymoon suite
SR 1003 / Jan '96 / Scout

Ashtray Navigations

☐ ASHTRAY NAVIGATIONS/UNIVERSAL INDIANS (Ashtray Navigations/ Universal Indians)
ASH 1 / 1 Dec '97 / Bentley Welcomes Careful Drivers

☐ FOUR RAGA MOODS
AN 001 / 29 Sep '97 / Bentley Welcomes Careful Drivers

Asia

☐ ALPHA
Don't cry / Smile has left your eyes / Never in a million years / My own time (I'll do what I want) / Heat goes on / Eye to eye / Last to know / True colours / Midnight sun / Open your eyes
GED 04008 / Nov '96 / Geffen

☐ AQUA
Aqua part 1 / Who will stop the rain / Back in town / Love under fire / Someday / Little rich boy / Voice of reason / Lay down your arms / Crime of the heart / Far cry / Don't call me / Heaven on earth / Aqua part 2
SMMCD 521 / 23 Feb '98 / Snapper

☐ ARCHIVA VOL.1
Heart of gold / Tears / Fight against the tide / We fall apart / Mariner's dream / Boys from diamond city / ALO / Reality / I can't wait a lifetime / Dusty road / I believe / Ginger
LV 104CD / 29 Jun '98 / Resurgence

35

☐ ARCHIVA VOL.2
Obsession / Moon under the water / Love like the video / Don't come to me / Smoke that thunders / Satellite blues / Showdown / This season / Can't tell these walls / Higher you climb / Right to cry / Armenia
LV 105CD / 29 Jun '98 / Resurgence

☐ ARENA
Into the arena / Arena / Heaven / Two sides of the moon / Day before the war / Never / Failings / Words / U bring me down / Tell me why / Turn it around / Bella nova
SMMCD 522 / 23 Feb '98 / Snapper

☐ ARIA
Anytime / Anytime / Are you big enough / Are you big enough / Desire / Desire / Summer / Summer / Sad situation / Sad situation / Don't cut the wire / Don't cut the wire (brother) / Feels like love / Feels like Love / Remembrance day / Remembrance day / Enough's enough / Enough's enough / Military man / Military man / Aria / Aria
SMMCD 523 / 23 Feb '98 / Snapper

☐ ASIA NOW (Live In Nottingham 1990)
Wildest dreams / Sole survivor / Don't cry / Voice of America / Time again / Prayin' 4 a miracle / Smile has left your eyes / Only time will tell / Days like these / Heat goes on / Go / Heat of the moment / Open your eyes
BP 253CD / Mar '97 / Blueprint

☐ LIVE IN KOLN
Go / Back in town / Sad situation / Rememberance day / Someday / Heat goes on / Anytime / Sole survivor / Summer / Feels like love / Little rich boy / Desire / Who will stop the rain / Military man / Only time will tell / Heat of the moment
BP 254CD / Jul '97 / Blueprint

☐ LIVE IN MOSCOW
Time again / Sole survivor / Don't cry / Only time will tell / Rock 'n' roll dream / Starless / Book of Saturday / Kari-Anne / Open your eyes / Heat of the moment / Heat goes on / Go / Smile has left your eyes (parts I and II)
EAMCD 037 / 30 Mar '98 / Eagle

☐ LIVE IN OSAKA 1992 (2CD Set)
Go / Band intro / Lay down your arms / Love under fire / Rock 'n' roll dreams / Geoff Downes solo / Video kills radio star / Little rich boy / Voice of America / Aqua / Who will stop the rain / Wildest dreams / Back in town / Don't cry / Someday / Steve Howe solo / Voice of reason / Only time will tell / Heat goes on / Far cry
BP 252CD / May '97 / Blueprint

☐ LIVE IN PHILADELPHIA (2CD Set)
Go / Lay down your arms / Rock and roll dreams / Love under fire / Little rich boy / Aqua / Heat goes on / Don't cry / Someday / Steve Howe guitar solo / Wildest dreams / Back in town / Open your eyes / Who will stop the rain / Only time will tell / Sole survivor / Heat of the moment
BP 255CD / 3 Nov '97 / Blueprint

Asiabeat

☐ DRUMUSIQUE
Dancing out of Bali / Enter the dragon / Code of the Ninja warrior / Rhythm harvest / Joy / North of no place / West of somewhere / River of gems / Temple of dreams
DOMO 710162 / 20 Oct '97 / Domo

Asian Dub Foundation

☐ FACTS AND FICTIONS (Asian Dub Foundation Sound System)
NATCD 58 / Oct '95 / Nation

☐ RAFI'S REVENGE
5560062 / 11 May '98 / FFRR

Askey, Arthur

☐ BAND WAGGON (Askey, Arthur & Tommy Trinder & Richard Murdoch)
Adolf / (We're gonna hang out the) washing on the Siegfried Line / Big and stinkers moment musical / Worm / Big and stinkers parlour games / Chirrup / Seagull song / Proposal / Kiss me goodnight, Sergeant Major / How ashamed I was / Bee song
PASTCD 9729 / Jan '91 / Flapper

☐ BUSY BEE, THE
Bee song / Have a bit of pity on the crooner / Knitting / Chirrup / Two little doodlebugs / Worm / C'est la guerre / Guest / I pulled myself together / Ding dong bell / Ballad / She was very shy / Sarah Sarah / Follow the white line / FDR Jones / Seagull song / Minding the baby / Thingy mumm bob / Bandwagon
RAJCD 885 / May '97 / Empress

☐ HELLO PLAYMATES
CDMFP 6376 / May '97 / EMI

Askill, Michael

☐ FREE RADICALS
150272 / Aug '97 / Black Sun

Asleep At The Wheel

☐ VERY BEST OF ASLEEP AT THE WHEEL, THE
Cherokee boogie / I'll never get out of this world alive / Space buggy / Letter that Johnny Walker read / Let me go home whiskey / Trouble in mind / Runnin' after fools / Miles and miles of Texas / Route 66 / My baby thinks she's a train / Am I high / Ragtime Annie / Somebody stole his body / When love goes wrong / Louisiana 1927 / Ain't nobody here but us chickens / One o'clock jump
SEECD 81 / 3 Nov '97 / See For Miles

Asmund & Sturla

☐ ASMUND & STURLA
H 7129CD / Aug '97 / Heilo

Asmussen, Svend

☐ MUSICAL MIRACLE VOL.1 1935-1940
PHONTCD 9306 / Dec '94 / Phontastic

☐ PHENOMENAL FIDDLER
PHONTCD 9310 / Jul '96 / Phontastic

☐ SLUKAFTER IN THE TIVOLI-COPENHAGEN 1984
Believe it, beloved / Nadja / Exactly like you / Hot house / Body and soul / Coconut calypso / Someone to watch over me / Barney goin' / Out of nowhere / Pent-up house / Things ain't what they used to be
PHONT CD 8804 / Apr '90 / Phontastic

☐ SVEND ASMUSSEN 1942 VOL.7
THORANR 7 / Oct '94 / Hep

☐ TWO OF A KIND (Asmussen, Svend & Stephane Grappelli)
STCD 4088 / Feb '89 / Storyville

Asocial

☐ TOTAL ASOCIAL
FINNREC 011CD / Jun '96 / Finn

Asoj

☐ SPIRIT OF KLEZMER
341052 / May '96 / Koch International

Asphalt

☐ 257 KNOCK OUT
DARK 0082 / Feb '95 / Dark Empire

Asphyx

☐ ASPHYX
CM 770632 / May '94 / Century Media

☐ CRUSH THE CENOTAPH
CM 97232 / Sep '94 / Century Media

☐ GOD CRIES
CM 77117CD / Mar '96 / Century Media

☐ LAST ONE ON EARTH
8497342 / Nov '92 / Century Media

☐ RACK, THE
CM 97162 / Sep '94 / Century Media

Asphyxiator

☐ TRAPPED BETWEEN TWO WORLDS
Bestow the children of dark water / Night stalker / Serial killer / True fucking hate / Struggling / Day that I die / Lizzie Borden / At last there's peace / Futile / Trapped between two worlds
ASP 001 / 23 Feb '98 / Holier Than Thou

Ass Ponys

☐ ELECTRIC ROCK MUSIC
5402702 / 15 Sep '97 / A&M

Assad, Badi

☐ CHAMELEON
5398892 / 16 Mar '98 / IE

☐ ECHOES OF BRAZIL
JD 154 / May '97 / Chesky

Assad, Sergio & Odair

☐ LATIN AMERICAN MUSIC FOR TWO GUITARS
7559792652 / Jan '94 / Nonesuch

☐ SAGA DOS MIGRANTES (Music Of The Americas)
7559793652 / Aug '96 / Nonesuch

Assassin

☐ UPCOMING TERROR
3036562 / 11 May '98 / Axe Killer

Asseccoires

☐ VENDETTA
EFA 063282 / Nov '95 / Ausfahrt

Assert

☐ MORE THAN A WITNESS
HAUS 015CD / 13 Jul '98 / Household Name

Assfort

☐ EJACULATION
DISCCD 012 / Sep '95 / Discipline

Asshole

☐ ASSHOLE
SMUT 002 / Oct '97 / Yeehaw

Assia, Lys

☐ SCHWEIZER MADEL
Ganz leis' erklingt musik / Ich habe mir fur heute nacht / Schweizer madel / Sowas tun die Herrn doch / Seit heut' bin ich verliebt / Marchen von Tahiti / Sing, kleiner Kolibri / Von gestern abend bis heute morgen / Tanz' diesen Walzer, Madeleine / Nachts in Paris / Erst kommt musik / Was kostet das Hundchen dort im Fenster / Holland madel / Heute klopft mein herz / Als der schnitter durch das korn ging / Bella Notte / Monsieur Taxi-Chauffeur / Wenn der Pierre tanz mit Madeleine / Refrain / Du bist musik / Die weissen bluten von Tahni / Traumkonzert / Dino / Der erste kuss / Die Welt war nie so schon fur mich / Nach vielen Jahren der Reise / Die Sterne von Venezia / I'll be waiting
BCD 16108 / Nov '96 / Bear Family

Associates

☐ POPERA
Party fears two / Club country / Eighteen Carat love affair / Love hangover / Those first impressions / Waiting for the loveboat / Breakfast / Take me to the girl / Heart of glass / Country boy / Rhythm divine / Tell me Easter's on Friday / Q Quarters / Kitchen person / Message oblique speech / White car in Germany
9031724142 / Jan '91 / WEA

☐ SULK
It's better this way / Party fears two / Club country / Love hangover / Eighteen carat love affair / Arrogance gave him up / No / Skipping / White car in Germany / Gloomy Sunday / Associate
K 2400052 / Jul '88 / WEA

Association

☐ 1960'S FRENCH EP COLLECTION, THE
175042 / 23 Feb '98 / Magic

☐ DON'T LOOK BACK
60562 / Nov '90 / Enja

Assorted Jelly Beans

☐ ASSORTED JELLYBEANS
787602 / 15 Jun '98 / Kung Fu

Assuck

☐ ANTI CAPITAL
POLLUTE 17 / Aug '97 / Sound Pollution

☐ ANTICAPITAL
CC 005CD / Jun '94 / Common Cause

☐ MISERY INDEX
POLLUTE 34 / Aug '97 / Sound Pollution

Assumpaco, Itamar

☐ INTERCONTINENTAL
Sutil / Sutil / Adeus pantanal / Adeus pantanal / Pesquisa de mercado I / Pesquisa de mercado I / Oferenda / Oferenda / Sexto sentido / Sexto sentido / Pesquisa de mercado il / Pesquisa de mercado il / Ouca-me / Ouca-me / Maremoto / Maremoto / Nao ha saidas / Nao ha saidas / Mal menor / Mal menor / Ze pelintra / Ze pelintra / Perdidos nas estrelas / Perdidos nas estrelas / Parece que foi ontem / Parece que foi ontem / Homen-mulher / Homen-mulher / Ausencia / Ausencia / Filho de santa maria / Filho de santa maria / Pesquisa de mercado iii / Pesquisa de mercado iii / Espirito que canta / Espirito que canta
MES 159912 / Apr '93 / Messidor

☐ SAMPA MIDNIGHT
Prezadissimos ouyintes / Ideia fixa / Navalha na liga / Movido a agua / Desapareca eunice / Tete tentel / Vamos nessa / Eldorado / Sampa midnight / Isso nao vai ficar assim / Z da questao meu amor / Totalmente a revelia / Cade ines / Chavao abre porta grande / E o quico
MES 158022 / Feb '93 / Messidor

Astaire, Fred

☐ ASTAIRABLE FRED
Evening with fred astaire (first medley) / Another evening with fred astaire (second medley) / Astaire time (third medley) / Hello baby / There's no time like the present / Sweet sorrow / Just like taking candy from a baby / Calypso hooray / Notorious landlady / Martini / It happens every spring / You worry me / That face / Something's gotta give / Slue foot / 's wonderful
CDMRS 911 / '88 / DRG

☐ ASTAIRE SINGS
AVC 537 / May '94 / Avid

☐ CRAZY FEET
Night and day / My one and only / Fascinating rhythm / New sun in the sky / Louisiana / Swiss miss / I'd rather Charleston / High hat / Whichness of the whatness / I've got you on my mind / Puttin' on the Ritz / White heat / Dancing in the dark / Hang on to me / Oh gee, oh gosh / Not my girl / Half of it dearie blues / Babbitt and the bromide / I love Louisa / Funny face / Crazy feet
CDAJA 5021 / Oct '88 / Living Era

☐ CRAZY FEET
Crazy feet / I used to be colour blind / Fine romance / Yam / I'd rather lead a band / Let's call the whole thing off / Nice work if you can get it / Foggy day / We saw the sea / Let's face the music and dance / Let yourself go / Cheek to cheek / Yam step / They can't take that away from me / I'm putting all my eggs in one basket / Way you look tonight / I'm building up to a awful let down / Pick yourself up / Night and day / Wedding in the spring / You were never lovelier / Shorty George / I'm old fashioned / Dearly beloved
RAJCD 856 / May '98 / Empress

☐ CREAM OF FRED ASTAIRE, THE
We saw the sea / I'm putting all my eggs in one basket / Puttin' on the Ritz / Way you look tonight / Let's call the whole thing off / Hoops / Hang on to me / I'd rather charleston / Night and day / Crazy feet / Shall we dance / Fine romance / Top hat, white tie and tails / Wedding cake walk / Dig it / Just like taking candy from a baby / I've got you on my mind / Let's face the music and dance / So near and yet so far / Who cares / They all laughed / Isn't this a lovely day (to be caught in the rain) / Slap that bass / Cheek to cheek / I'd rather lead a band
PASTCD 7013 / Aug '93 / Flapper

☐ FASCINATING RHYTHM
Shall we dance / Fascinating rhythm / Night and day / Crazy feet / Puttin' on the ritz / My one and only / Babbitt and the bromide / I've got you on my mind / Foggy day / Let's call the whole thing off / New sun in the sky / High hat / Hang on to me / Funny face / They can't take that away from me / Nice work if you can get it
HADCD 163 / May '94 / Javelin

☐ FINE ROMANCE
GO 3819 / 1 Dec '97 / Golden Options

☐ FINE ROMANCE, A
CDD 548 / May '91 / Progressive

☐ FRED ASTAIRE COLLECTOR'S EDITION
DVGH 7022 / Apr '95 / Deja Vu

☐ FRED ASTAIRE IN HOLLYWOOD
AMSC 570 / Jun '96 / Avid

☐ LET'S FACE THE MUSIC
Let's face the music and dance / Things are looking up / Way you look tonight / Nice work if you can get it / Poor Mr. Chisolm / Let's call the whole thing off / They all laughed / Shall we dance / My one and only / I'm putting all my eggs in one basket / Piccolino / Pick yourself up / They can't take that away from me / Isn't this a lovely day / No strings I'm fancy free / Fascinating rhythm
SUMCD 4049 / Nov '96 / Summit

☐ LET'S FACE THE MUSIC AND DANCE
Change partners / Cheek to cheek / I used to be colour blind / I'm putting all my eggs in one basket / Let's face the music and dance / No strings / Top hat, white tie and tails / Yam / Foggy day / I can't be bothered now / I've got beginner's luck / Let's call the whole thing off / Nice work if you can get it / Shall we dance / Slap that bass / They all laughed / They can't take that away from me / Things are looking up / Poor Mr. Chisholm / Dearly Beloved / Fine romance / I'm old fashioned / Never gonna dance / Pick yourself up / Way you look tonight / You were never lovelier / Since I kissed my baby goodbye
CDAJA 5123 / Mar '94 / Living Era

☐ LET'S FACE THE MUSIC AND DANCE (All His Greatest Hits)
They can't take that away from me / Isn't this a lovely day / I'm putting all my eggs in one basket / They all laughed / Let's call the whole thing off / Shall we dance / Way you look tonight / Nice work if you can get it / Poor Mr. Chisholm / Let's face the music and dance / Piccolino / I used to be colour blind / Foggy day / My one and only / Pick yourself up / Yam / Let yourself go / Things are looking up / No strings (I am fancy free) / Fascinating rhythm
305512 / Oct '96 / Hallmark

☐ LET'S FACE THE MUSIC AND DANCE (A Tribute To Fred Astaire Live) (BBC Concert Orchestra)
Top hat selection / I'm putting all my eggs in one basket / Smoke gets in your eyes / I won't dance / Fine romance / Continental / Night and day / I love a piano / Couple of swells / I've got my eyes on you / Overture / S'Wonderful / Be careful it's my heart / Nice work if you can get it / Theme from Finians Rainbow / Puttin' on the ritz / Way you look tonight / Change partners / Let's call the whole thing off / That's entertainment
11212 / Oct '97 / BBC Concert Orchestra

☐ LOVE OF MY LIFE
DHDL 124 / Sep '93 / Halcyon

☐ PORTRAIT OF FRED ASTAIRE, A (2CD Set)
Fascinating rhythm / Hang on to me / I'd rather Charleston / Half of it dearie blues / Swiss Miss / Funny face / Rabbit and the bromide / High hat / My one and only / Louisiana / Not my girl / Crazy feet / Puttin' on the ritz / I love Louisa / New sun in the sky / I've got you on my mind / Night and day / After you, who / Flying down to Rio / Music makes me / Cheek to cheek / No strings / Isn't this a lovely day / Top hat, white tie and tails / Piccolino / I'd rather lead a band / I'm building up to an awful let down / I'm putting all my eggs in one basket / Let yourself go / Let's face the music and dance / We saw the sea / Never gonna dance / Pick yourself up / Way you look tonight / Fine romance / Bojangles of Harlem / They can't take that away from me / They all laughed / (I've got) beginner's luck / Let's call the whole thing off / Shall we dance / Slap that bass / Foggy day / Things are looking up / I can't be bothered now / Nice work if you can get it / I used to be colour blind / Yam
GALE 414 / 6 Oct '97 / Gallerie

☐ PUTTIN' ON THE RITZ
Fascinating rhythm / Hang on to me / Half of it dearie blues / I'd rather charleston / Swiss miss / Funny face / Babbitt and the bromide / High hat / My one and only / Not my girl / Louisiana / Puttin' on the ritz / Crazy feet / I love louisa / New sun in the sky / White heat (dancing in the dark) / Night and day / I've got you on my mind / Cheek to cheek / Fine romance / I can't be bothered now
RMB 75010 / Nov '93 / Remember

☐ PUTTIN' ON THE RITZ
MCCD 204 / May '95 / Music Club

☐ SONGS FROM THE MOVIES
No strings / Isn't this a lovely day (to be caught in the rain) / Top hat, white tie and tails / Cheek to cheek / Piccolino / We saw the sea / Let yourself go / I'd rather lead a band / I'm putting all my eggs in one basket / Let's face the music and dance / Pick yourself up / Way you look tonight / Fine romance / Bojangles of Harlem / Never gonna dance / I've got beginner's luck / Slap that bass / They all laughed / Let's call the whole thing off / They can't take that away from me / Shall we dance / I can't be bothered now / Things are looking up / Foggy day / Nice work if you can get it
PPCD 78115 / Feb '95 / Past Perfect

☐ STEPPIN' OUT - ASTAIRE SINGS
Steppin' out with my baby / Let's call the whole thing off / Top hat, white tie and tails / They can't take that away from me / Dancing in the dark / 'S wonderful / Way you look tonight / They all laughed / I concentrate on you / Night and day / Fine romance / Nice work if you can get it / Continental / I won't dance / You're easy to dance with / Change partners / Cheek to cheek
5230062 / Aug '94 / Verve

Asteroid 4

☐ INTRODUCING...
LOUNGE 11CD / 11 May '98 / Lounge

Asteroid B-612

☐ ALL NEW HITS
LRR 027 / Jun '97 / Lance Rock

☐ NOT MEANT FOR THIS WORLD
ANDA 209 / Jul '97 / Au-Go-Go

Astle, Jeff

☐ SINGS
Back home / Sugar sugar / Lovey dovey / Lily the pink / You're in my arms / Puppet on a string / Congratulations / Ob-la-di ob-la-da / Glory O / Make me an island / Cinnamon stick / There'll always be an England / Sweet water / Summer sadness
RETRO 805 / Nov '95 / RPM

Astley, Rick

☐ HOLD ME IN YOUR ARMS
She wants to dance with me / Take me to your heart / I don't want to lose her / Giving up on love / Ain't too proud to beg / Put yourself in my place / Till then / Dial my number / I'll never let you down / I don't want to be your lover / Hold me in your arms
74321369122 / Jun '96 / RCA

☐ WHENEVER YOU NEED SOMEBODY
Never gonna give you up / Whenever you need somebody / Together forever / It would take a strong, strong man / Love has gone / Don't say goodbye / Slippin' away / No more looking for love / You move me / When I fall in love
ND 75150 / Jan '92 / RCA

Astley, Virginia

☐ ALL SHALL BE WELL
My smallest friend / All shall be well / You take me away / I live for the day / Love's eloquence / Although I know / Martin / Blue sky white sky / How I miss you
RBXCD 1002 / Nov '97 / Rosebud

☐ FROM THE GARDENS WHERE WE FEEL SECURE
RBXCD 1001 / Nov '97 / Rosebud

☐ HAD I THE HEAVENS
RBXCD 1003 / Nov '97 / Rosebud

Aston, Jay

☐ UNPOPULAR SONGS
PGCD 2 / 9 Feb '98 / Pink Gun

Aston Villa FC

☐ COME ON YOU VILLA (Various Artists)
CDGAFFER 9 / Nov '96 / Cherry Red

Astor, Peter

☐ GOD AND OTHER STORIES
DAN 9304CD / Feb '95 / Danceteria

☐ SUBMARINE
CRELPCD 065 / May '94 / Creation

Astral Engineering

☐ CHRONOGLIDE
WI 01 / Feb '95 / Worm Interface

Astral Navigations

☐ HOLYGROUND
HBG 122/1 / Jun '97 / Background

Astral Project

☐ ELEVADO
742492 / 17 Mar '98 / Compass

Astral Projection

☐ ASTRAL FILES (2CD Set)
Ionized / Zero / Enlightened evolution / Free Tibet / Maian dream / Kabalah dream / Time began with the universe / Utopia / Electronic / Ambience
TRANR 607CD / Feb '97 / Transient

☐ DANCING GALAXY
Dancing galaxy / Sound form / Flying into a star / No one ever dream / Cosmic ascension / Life on mars / Liquid sunrise / Ambient galaxy
TRANR 612CD / 20 Oct '97 / Transient

Astralasia

☐ ASTRALOGY
MEYCD 10 / Nov '95 / Magick Eye

☐ AXIS MUNDI
MEYCD 9 / May '95 / Magick Eye

☐ PITCHED UP AT THE EDGE OF REALITY
EYELPCD 4 / Oct '93 / Magick Eye

☐ SEVEN POINTED STAR, THE
MEYCD 18 / Nov '96 / Magick Eye

☐ SPACE BETWEEN, THE
MEYCD 014 / May '96 / Magick Eye

☐ WHATEVER HAPPENED TO UTOPIA
EYECDLP 5 / May '94 / Magick Eye

☐ WHITE BIRD
MEYCD 22 / 1 Jun '98 / Magick Eye

Astream

☐ WOODFISH
BTR 009CD / Sep '96 / Bad Taste

Astrid

☐ BOY FOR YOU
NUDE 10CD / 10 Aug '98 / Nude

Astro Zombies

☐ ASTRO ZOMBIES
AZ 001 / Apr '98 / Bananajuice

Astrocat

☐ REALMS
BINARY 0110101 / Jul '97 / TEQ

Astronauts

☐ COMPETITION COUPE/ORBIT CAMPUS
COLCD 2708 / 24 Nov '97 / Collectables

☐ DOWN THE LINE/TRAVELLIN' MEN
COLCD 2710 / 24 Nov '97 / Collectables

☐ EVERYTHING'S A-OK/ASTRONAUTS ORBIT CAMPUS
Bo Diddley / If I had a hammer / It's so easy / Dream lover / Wine, wine, wine / Money / Big boss man / Stormy Monday blues / Shortnin' bread / I need you / What'd I say / Johnny B Goode / Be bop a lula / Good golly Miss Molly / Let the good times roll / Linda Lou / Bony Moronie / Shout wah diddy / Roll over Beethoven / Shop around / Greenback dollar / Summertime / Sticks and stones
BCD 15443 / Jul '89 / Bear Family

☐ GO GO GO FOR YOU FROM US
COLCD 2709 / 24 Nov '97 / Collectables

☐ SURFIN' WITH THE ASTRONAUTS/ COMPETION COUPE
Baja / Surfin' USA / Miserlou / Surfer's stomp / Suzie Q / Pipeline / Kuk / Banzai pipeline / Movin' / Baby let's play house / Let's go trippin' / Batman / Little ford ragtop / Competition coupe / Hearse / Fifty five bird / Devil driver's theme / Happy ho Daddy / Our car club / Devil driver / Chevy scarfer / 4.56 Stingray / Aguila / 650 Scrambler
BCD 15442 / Jul '89 / Bear Family

☐ SURFIN' WITH THE ASTRONAUTS/ EVERYTHING'S A-OK
COLCD 2707 / 24 Nov '97 / Collectables

AstroPuppees

☐ YOU WIN THE BRIDE
Underdog / She can't say no / Lower the line / Little weekend / Dear John / Amanda / Stuck in the middle with you / Don't be / It's not me, it's her / You win the bride
HCD 8076 / Dec '96 / Hightone

Aswad

☐ ANOTHER CHAPTER OF DUB VOL.2
BUBBCD 3 / Jun '95 / Gut

☐ ASWAD
Concrete slaves / Ire woman / Red up / Back to Africa / Natural progression / Ethiopian rhapsody / Can't stand the pressure / Rebel soul
IMCD 58 / May '88 / Island

☐ BBC SESSIONS, THE
SFRSCD 002 / Feb '97 / Strange Fruit

☐ BEST OF ASWAD, THE
BUBBCD 4 / 6 Oct '97 / Bubblin'

☐ BIG UP
One shot chilla / Danger in your eyes / Runaway / Roxanne / Lay this on you / If I was / Push / Ring it / Babe / Get a grip / Hurry love / What I know / Without you / Golden bbay
GUTCD 3 / 15 Sep '97 / Gut

☐ DISTANT THUNDER
Message / Don't turn around / Set them free / Smoky blues / I can't get over you / Give a little love / Tradition / Feelings / International melody / Bittersweet / Justice
RRCD 27 / Sep '91 / Reggae Refreshers

☐ HULET
Behold / Sons of criminals / Judgement day / Not guilty / Can't walk the street / Corruption / Playing games / Hulet
IMCD 56 / May '88 / Island

☐ LIVE AND DIRECT
Not guilty / Not satisfied / Your recipe / Roots rocking drum and bass line / African children / Soca rumba / Rockers medley / Love fire
IMCD 54 / May '88 / Island

☐ NEW CHAPTER
African children / Natural progression / Ways of the Lord / I will keep on loving you / He gave the sun to shine / Tuff we tuff / Didn't know at the time / Zion / In a your rights / Candles / Love fire
IMCD 55 / Jul '90 / Island

☐ REGGAE GREATS
Don't turn around / Woman / Justice / Give a little love / Message / Gave you my love / Babylon / Chasing for the breeze / Sons of criminals / 54-46 (was my number) / Hulet / Behold / Smoky blues / Bubbling
5500662 / Jul '97 / Spectrum

☐ RISE AND SHINE AGAIN
BUBBCD 2 / Mar '95 / Gut

☐ ROOTS ROCKIN' (The Island Anthology/2CD Set)
I a rebel soul / Can't stand the pressure / Back to Africa / Sons of criminals / Judgement day / Not guilty / Warrior charge / Three Babylon / It's not our wish / Rainbow culture / Dub fire / Tuff we tuff / Not satisfied / Roots rockin' / Drum and bass line / African children / 5446 was my number / Just a little herb / Need your love / Java / Bubbling / Gimme the dub / Need rub / Message / Don't turn around / Feelings / Don't get weary / Smokey blues / On and on / Dancing on my own / Smile / Fire / Old fire stick / Gotta find a way
5243202 / 25 Aug '97 / Island Jamaica

☐ SHOWCASE
Warrior charge / Babylon / Rainbow culture / It's not our wish / Three babylon / Back to Africa
IMCD 57 / May '88 / Island

☐ TO THE TOP
Pull up / Wrapped up / Bubbling / Noh bada wid it / Gimme the dub / Nuclear soldier / Kool noh / Star of my show / Hooked on you
IMCD 59 / Oct '89 / Island

Asylum Street Spankers

☐ SPANKS FOR THE MEMORIES
Introduction / If I had possession over judgement day / Superchief / Song with no words / Introduction / Lee Harvey / I'll see you in my dreams / Hesitation blues / Startin' to hate Country / Walkin' and whistlin' blues / Shave 'em dry / Brazil / Tradewinds / Introduction / Funny cigarette / Hometown boy
WWCD 1060 / Feb '97 / Watermelon

Async Sense

☐ ASYNC SENSE
EFA 127132 / Apr '95 / Imbalance

At The Gates

☐ GARDENS OF GRIEF
BS 04CD / Aug '95 / Dolores

☐ RED IN THE SKY IS OURS/WITH FEAR I KISS THE BURNING DARKNESS
CDVILE 59 / May '95 / Peaceville

☐ SLAUGHTER OF THE SOUL
Blinded by fear / Slaughter of the soul / Cold / Under the serpent sun / Into the dead sky / Suicide nation / World of lies / Unto others / Nausea / Need / Flames of the end
MOSH 143CD / 1 Sep '97 / Earache

☐ TERMINAL SPIRIT DISEASE
Swarm / Terminal spirit disease / World returned / Forever blind / Fevered circle / Beautiful wound / All life ends / Burning darkness / Kingdom gone
CDVILE 47 / Jun '94 / Peaceville

Atabal

☐ MUSICA MORENA
ATABAL 93 / Jan '98 / Fresh Sound

Ataraixa

☐ MOON SANG, THE
EFA 121622 / Dec '95 / Apollyon

Atari Teenage Riot

☐ 1995
Start the riot / Into the death / Raver bashing / Speed / Sex / Midi junkies / Delete yourself you got no chance to wine / Helzajagd auf nazis / Cyberpunks are dead / Atari teenage riot / Kids are united / Riot 1995
DHRCD 001 / Apr '95 / Digital Hardcore

☐ BURN BERLIN BURN
GR 042CD / 5 Jan '98 / Grand Royal

☐ FUTURE OF WAR, THE
Get up while you can / Fuck all / Sick to death / PRESS / Deutschland (has gotta die) / Destroy 2000 years of culture / Not your business / You can't hold us back / Heatwave / Redefine the enemy / Deathstar / Future of war
DHRCD 006 / Mar '97 / Digital Hardcore

Ataris

☐ ANYWHERE BUT HERE
Four chord wonder / Are we there yet / Bite my tongue / Perfectly happy / Hey kid / Ray / As we speak / Sleepy / Lately / Let it go / Neilhouse / Make it last / Alone in Santa Cruz / Angry nerd rock / Take me back / Blind and unkind / Clara
787632 / 15 Jun '98 / Kung Fu

Atcha Acoustic

☐ FROM LHASA TO LEWISHAM
Pretty little thing / Lazy days / If you love her / Bar / Blue drag / Tibet blues / Manyatela / Another me / Night alone / Uncle in Harlem / Wintertime blues / Angel by my side
TALENT 2001 / Jun '97 / Latent Talent

Athamay

☐ PLEASURE OF SIN
NIGHT 011CD / Sep '96 / Nightbreed

Atharwan

☐ NATURAL HEALING
DC 881892 / Oct '97 / Disky

Atheist

☐ ELEMENTS
Green / Water / Samba Briza / Air / Displacement / Animal / Mineral / Fire / Fractal point / Earth / See you again / Elements
CDMFN 150 / Jul '93 / Music For Nations

☐ PIECE OF TIME
Piece of time / Unholy war / Room with a view / On they slay / Beyond / I deny / Why brother / Life / No truth
CDATV 8 / Jan '90 / Active

☐ UNQUESTIONABLE PRESENCE
Mother man / Unquestionable presence / Your life's retribution / Enthralled in essence / An incarnation's dream / Formative years / Brains / And the psychic saw
CDATV 20 / Oct '91 / Active

Athena

☐ GREEK PARTY/SYRTAKI DANCE
CDSGP 0117 / Apr '95 / Prestige

Athena

☐ NEW RELIGION, A
RS 0072992CD / 17 Aug '98 / Rising Sun

Athenians

☐ 12 OF THE MOST POPULAR SYRTAKIS
EUCD 1058 / '89 / ARC

☐ ALEXIS SORBAS
EUCD 1057 / '89 / ARC

☐ ATHENIANS LIFE
EUCD 1036 / '89 / ARC

☐ BEST OF GREECE, THE
EUCD 1091 / '89 / ARC

☐ GREEK POPULAR MUSIC
EUCD 1024 / '89 / ARC

☐ REMBETIKO
EUCD 1063 / '89 / ARC

Atherton, Michael

☐ AUSTRALIAN MADE, AUSTRALIAN PLAYED
OZM 1008CD / Nov '95 / Sounds Australian

Atila

☐ BEGINNING OF THE END
LV 001 / Dec '97 / Lost Vinyl

37

Atkin, Pete

☐ BEWARE OF THE BEAUTIFUL STRANGER (Driving Through Mythical Amercica)
Master of the revels / Sunrise / Have you got a biro I can borrow / Frangipanni was her flower / Touch has a memory / Rider to the world's end / Luck of the draw / Original honky tonk night train blues / Girl on a train / Tonight your love is over / You can't be expected to remember / Laughing boy / Beware of the beautiful stranger / All I ever did / Sunlight gate / Pearl driller / No dice / Flowers and the wine / Where have they all gone / Prince of aquitaine / Thief in the night / Driving through mythical America / Faded mansion on the hill / Practical man / Lady of a day / Be carefull when they offer you the moon
C5HCD 664 / 6 Oct '97 / See For Miles

Atkins, Chet

☐ ALMOST ALONE
Big foot / Waiting for Susie B / Little Mark musik / Jam man / I still write your name in the snow / Pu, uana hulu (Remembering Gabby) / Happy again / Sweet Alla Lee / Maybelle / Mr. Bo Jangles / Cheek to cheek / You do something to me / Ave Maria
4835242 / 13 Jul '98 / Sony Music

☐ CHRISTMAS WITH CHET ATKINS
RE 21552 / Nov '97 / Razor & Tie

☐ COLLECTION, THE
On the road again / Tenderly / Orange blossom special / Rodrigo's guitar concerto de Aranjuez / Take five / Caravan / Vincent / Mostly Mozart / Storms never last / Limehouse blues / Over the waves / It don't mean a thing if it ain't got that swing / Brandenburg / Struttin' / I'll see you in my dreams / Heart of glass / Black and white/Ragtime Annie/Hot Toddy
74321140942 / Jul '93 / RCA

☐ ESSENTIAL CHET ATKINS, THE
Mr. Sandman / Poor people of Paris / Boo boo stick beat / Alley cat / Travelin' / Yakety axe / Yesterday / Blue angel / Theme from Zorba the Greek / Snowbird / Steeplechase lane / Jerry's breakdown / Black mountain rag / Fiddlin' around / Somewhere my love / Entertainer / Londonderry air / On my way to Canaan's land / Tennessee rag/Beaumont rag / Chet's medley
07863668552 / Aug '96 / RCA Nashville

☐ GALLOPIN' GUITAR
Guitar blues / Brown eyes cryin' in the rain / Ain'tcha tired of makin' me blue / I'm gonna get tight / Canned heat / Standing room only / Don't hand me that line / Bug dance / I know my baby loves me / Nashville jump / My guitar is my sweetheart / I'm pickin' the blues / Gone gone gone / Barnyard shuffle / Save your money / (I may be colour blind but) I know when... / I've been working on the guitar / Dizzy strings / Money, marbles and chalk / Wednesday night waltz / Guitar waltz / Telling my troubles to my old guitar / Dance of the goldenrod / Gallopin' guitar / Barber shop rag / Centipede boogie / Under the Hickory nut tree / I was bitten by the same bug twice / One more chance / Old buck dance / Boogie man boogie / Main street breakdown / Confusin' / Music in my heart / Indian love call / Birth of the blues / Mountain melody / You're always brand new / My crazy heart / Hybrid corn / Jitterbug waltz / One man boogie / Crazy rhythm (instrumental) / Crazy rhythm / Rustic dance / Rainbow / In the mood / Spanish fandango / Midnight / Goodbye blues / Your mean little heart / Sweet bunch of daisies / Blue gypsy / Third man theme / One man boogie (take D) / St. Louis blues / Listed knot / Lover come back to me / Stephen Foster medley / Hangover blues / Imagination / Black mountain rag / Guitar polka / Dream train / Meet Mr. Callaghan / Chinatown, my Chinatown / High rockin' swing / Pig leaf rag / Oh by jingo / Hello ma baby / Bells of St. Mary's / Country gentlemen / Memphis blues / Alice blue gown / 12th street rag / Peeping Tom / Three o'clock in the morning / Georgia camp meeting / City slicker / Dill pickle rag / Rubber doll rag / Beautiful Ohio / Kentucky derby / Wildwood flower / Guitars on parade / Simple Simon / Rubber doll rag (alternate version) / Get up and go / Pagan love song / Beautiful Ohio / Downhill drag / Avalon / Sunrise serenade / San Antonio rose / Set a spell / Mr. Misery / Get up and go / South / Alabama jubilee / Corine Corina / (Back home again in) Indiana / Red wing / Frankie and Johnny / Gay Ranchero / Ballin' the Jack / Honeysuckle rose / At the Darktown strutter's ball / Old spinning wheel / Silver bells / Under the double eagle / Have you ever been lonely / Caravan / Ol' man river / Mr. Sandman / New Spanish two-step
BCD 15714 / Oct '93 / Bear Family

☐ MASTERS, THE
EABCD 107 / 30 Mar '98 / Eagle

☐ NECK AND NECK (Atkins, Chet & Mark Knopfler)
Poor boy blues / Sweet dreams / There'll be some changes made / Just one time / So soft / Your goodbye / Yakety axe / Tears / Tahitian skys / I'll see you in my dreams / Next time I'm in town
4674352 / Nov '90 / CBS

☐ READ MY LICKS
Young thing / Mountains of Illinois / After you're gone / Every now and then / Somebody loves me now / Norway (Norweigan mountain song) / Read my licks / Take a look at her now / Around the bend / Dream / Vincent
4746282 / 13 Jul '98 / Sony Music

Atkins, Flynn Adam

☐ LOUDER
Night after night / Trudgin' / Miss Pioneer / Care to dance / Plasmic plight / Spanish Harlem / Promise / Honeymoon / Miss Pioneer / Directions / Turn your eyes / Louder
ELD 0002 / 27 Oct '97 / Eartube Empire

Atkins, Juan

☐ INFINITI COLLECTION
EFA 017942 / Jun '96 / Tresor

Atkins, Mark

☐ DIDGERIDOO CONCERTO
LRF 338 / Aug '96 / Larrikin

Atlan, Francoise

☐ SEPHARDIC SONGS
926842 / 5 Jan '98 / BUDA

Atlanta

☐ DISCO SUCKAS
TKCD 35 / Apr '97 / 2 Kool

Atlantic Starr

☐ SECRET LOVERS (The Best Of Atlantic Starr)
Circles / Silver shadow / Send for me / Secret lovers / Love me down / Stand up / When love calls / Am I dreaming / Touch for a four leaf clover / One love / Gimme your lovin' / If your heart isn't in it / One love / Freak-a-Ristic
5525412 / Sep '96 / Spectrum

Atlantic Wave Band

☐ SERIOUS HITS
SPINCD 156 / Dec '97 / Spindrift

Atlantik

☐ 360 DEGREES SOCA
JW 144CD / 9 Feb '98 / JW

Atlantis

☐ ATLANTIS
REP 4145 / Aug '91 / Repertoire

☐ IT'S GETTING BETTER
REP 4232 / Aug '91 / Repertoire

Atlantis Five

☐ DANS L'OMBRE DES SHADOWS
176862 / 1 Dec '97 / Magic

Atlas, Natacha

☐ DIASPORA
NATCD 47 / Jun '95 / Nation

☐ HALIM
Marifnaash / Moustahil / Amulet / Leyli / Kidda / Sweeter than any sweets / Ya weledi / Enogoom wil amar / Andeel / Gafsa / Ya alibi ehda / Agib
NATCD 1087 / May '97 / Nation

Atmosfear

☐ JANGALA SPIRITS
Theme from higher communication / Hot sulpher boogie / Klatter klatter / Jangala spirits / Money / Dub to scratch / Return to whatever / Optical delusion / Galactic lifeboat
META 49701 / Apr '97 / Meta 4

Atom Bomb Yoga

☐ IN PAST TIMES
She said tomorrow / Enough shame / Hubble / In past times / America / Lazy for you / London / Honey / Last night / 1000 Paths / Lifeguard / Lonely hearted / Final hour
MYSCD 116 / 29 Sep '97 / Mystic

Atom Heart

☐ BINARY AMPLIFIED SUPER STEREO
RI 032CD / Nov '95 / Rather Interesting

Atom Heart Mother

☐ SKIN 'EM UP, CHOP 'EM OUT RAWHIDE
Human / Life is dangerous / Lost in space / Tortuga / Hypermellow / Double white line / Dreamtown / Re-animator / Mouheva
ABT 095 CD / Oct '92 / Abstract

Atom Seed

☐ GET IN LINE
What you say / What you say / Rebel / Shake that thing / Shot down / Forget it joe / Better day / What was the matter with rachmaninov / Castle in the sky / Bitchin'
HMRXD 163 / Nov '92 / Heavy Metal

Atomic 61

☐ PURITY OF ESSENCE
CSR 21CD / Oct '95 / Cavity Search

☐ TINNITUS IN EXTREMIS
CSR 106CD / Oct '95 / Cavity Search

Atomic Rooster

☐ ATOMIC ROOSTER
They took control of you / She's my woman / He did it again / Where's the show / In the shadows / Do you know who's looking for you / Don't lose your mind / Watch out I can't stand it / Lost in space
REP 4135 / Aug '91 / Repertoire

☐ BEST OF ATOMIC ROOSTER, THE
Devil's answer / Oh she, oh she's my woman / Tomorrow night / Play it again / Death walks behind you / Lose your mind / I don't need you anymore / He did it again / Who's looking for you / Show / No change by me / Hold it through the night
12666 / Apr '96 / Laserlight

☐ DEATH WALKS BEHIND YOU
Death walks behind you / Vug / Tomorrow night / Seven streets / Sleeping for years / I can't take no more / Nobody else / Gershatzer
REP 4069 / Aug '91 / Repertoire

☐ DEVIL HITS BACK, THE
Devil's answer / When do I start to live / Play it again / Control of you / Lost in space / Tomorrow night / Living underground / End of the day / Lose your mind / Hiding in the shadows / Looking for you / Watch out
DMCD 1023 / Nov '89 / Demi-Monde

☐ DEVIL'S ANSWER (2CD Set)
Banstead / And so to bed / Friday 13th / Broken wings / Tomorrow night / Play the game / Vug / Sleeping for years / Death walks behind you / Devil's answer / Rock / Breakthrough / Break the ice / Spoonful of bromide / Stand by me / Never to lose / Don't know what went wrong / Space cowboy / People you can't trust / All in Satan's name / Close your eyes / Save me / Can't find a reason / All across the country / Voodoo in you / Goodbye planet earth / Satan's wheel
SMDCD 128 / May '97 / Snapper

☐ DEVIL'S ANSWER
Friday the 13th / Seven lonely streets / Tomorrow night / Shabooloo / Death walks behind / Stand by me / Breakthrough / Save me / Close your eyes / Play it again / In the shadows / Devil's answer / People you can't trust / Spoonful of bromide helps the medicine go down / All in Satan's name
HUX 005 / 25 May '98 / Hux

☐ HEADLINE NEWS
Hold your fire / Headline news / Taking a chance / Metal minds / Land of freedom / Machine / Dance of death / Carnival / Time / Future shock / Watch out/ Reaching out
BP 171CD / Jul '97 / Blueprint

☐ IN HEARING OF ATOMIC ROOSTER
Breakthrough / Break the ice / Decision/Indecision / Spoonful of bromide / Helps the pulse rate go down / Devil's answer / Black snake / Head in the sky / Rock / Price
REP 4068 / Aug '91 / Repertoire

Atomic Spuds

☐ GARBAGE SURFERS
AS 007 / Jan '96 / Bananajuice

Atrocity

☐ BLUT
MASSCD 033 / Nov '94 / Massacre

☐ CALLING THE RAIN
MASSCD 071 / Aug '95 / Massacre

☐ DIE LIEBE (Atrocity & Das Ich)
MASSCD 069 / Nov '95 / Massacre

☐ HALLUCINATIONS
NB 038CD / Jan '91 / Nuclear Blast

☐ HUNT, THE
MASSCD 112 / Jan '97 / Massacre

☐ WERK 80
Shout / Rage hard / Wild boys / Great commandment / Send me an angel / Tainted love / Der mussolini / Being boiled / Don't go / Let's dance / Maid of Orleans
MASSDP 138
MASSCD 138 / 27 Oct '97 / Massacre

☐ WILLENSKRAFT
MASS 099CD / Sep '96 / Massacre

Atrox

☐ MESMERISED
HNF 031CD / 10 Nov '97 / Head Not Found

Attack

☐ MAGIC IN THE AIR
AFT 1001 / 2 Mar '98 / Aftermath

Attack

☐ ZOMBIES
AHOY 22 / Nov '94 / Captain Oi

Attar, Bachir

☐ IN NEW YORK (Attar, Bachir & Elliot Sharp)
EMY 1142 / Sep '97 / Enemy

Attention Deficit

☐ ATTENTION DEFICIT
MAX 9022CD / 20 Jul '98 / Mascot

Attia, Adolphe

☐ JEWISH LITURGICAL FEASTS
LDX 2741033 / Sep '96 / Le Chant Du Monde

☐ JEWISH LITURGICAL MUSIC
CMT 274993 / Oct '94 / La Chant Du Monde

Attica Blues

☐ ATTICA BLUES
Intro / Blueprint / Atlanta / It's alright / Impulse / Medieval / 3ree (a means to be) / Tender (the final story) / 808 song / Pendulum being / Gone too far / REAL expense / Vybra / Questions / Enter
MW 080CD / 22 Sep '97 / Mo Wax

Attika

☐ WHEN HEROES FALL
MASSCD 023 / Feb '94 / Massacre

Attila The Stockbroker

☐ SIEGE OF SHOREHAM
HELMETCD 1 / Aug '96 / Demi-Monde

Attractions

☐ MAD ABOUT THE WRONG BOY
Arms race / Damage / Little Miss Understanding / Straight jacket / Mad about the wrong boy / Motorworld / On the third stroke / Slow patience / La la la la loved you / Single girl / Lonesome little town / Taste of poison / High rise housewife / Talk about me / Sad about girls / Camera camera
FIENDCD 25 / Jul '91 / Demon

Attrition

☐ HIDDEN AGENDA, THE
HY 39100812 / Dec '93 / Hyperium

Atwood, Eden

☐ CAT ON A HOT TIN ROOF
For every man there's a woman / Twilight world / Silent movie / Cat on a hot tin roof / You've changed / My ship / Every time we say goodbye / Right as the rain / I'm glad there is you / Never let me go / Not while I'm around
CCD 4599 / Jun '94 / Concord Jazz

☐ NIGHT IN THE LIFE
When the sun comes out / I've grown accustomed to his face / Willow weep for me / Folks who live on the hill / If I love again / I could have told you / Spring can really hang you up the most / Lost in the stars/So many stars / You taught my heart to sing / Why did I choose you / Moon river
CCD 4730 / Dec '96 / Concord Jazz

☐ NO ONE EVER TELLS YOU
I didn't know what time it was / I was the last one to know / Is you is or is you ain't my baby / Ballad of the sad young men / Old devil moon / Cow cow boogie / No one ever tells you / Too late now / Gentle rain / Nothing's changed / Them there eyes
CCD 4560 / Jul '93 / Concord Jazz

☐ THERE AGAIN
It never entered my mind / You're my thrill / Nearness of you / In love in vain / Music that makes me dance / I'm always drunk in San Francisco / Sonny boy / Everything I've got belongs to you / In the days of our love / Only you (and you alone) / You don't know what love is / Auld lang syne
CCD 4645 / Jun '95 / Concord Jazz

Au Pairs

☐ EQUAL BUT DIFFERENT
Pretty boys / Ideal woman / Come again / Monogamy / It's obvious / Love song / Repetition / Dear John / Set up / Headache / We're so cool / Armagh / Steppin' out / America / Sex without stress / Intact / Shakedown / Slider / Unfinished business
RPM 139CD / Jun '94 / RPM

☐ LIVE IN BERLIN
Diet / Headache for Michelle / Dear John / Love song / Set up / Inconvenience / Armagh / Repetition / We're so cool / Cum again / Piece of my heart
ESMCD 452 / Oct '96 / Essential

☐ PLAYING WITH A DIFFERENT SEX
We're so cool / Love song / Set up / Repetition / Headache for michelle / Come again / Armagh / Unfinished business / Dear john / It's obvious / You / Domestic departure / Kerb crawler / Diet / It's obvious / Inconvenience / Pretty boys / Headache for michelle
RPM 107 / Nov '92 / RPM

☐ SENSE AND SENSUALITY
RPM 111 / Aug '93 / RPM

Aube

☐ AUBE/KNURL (Aube/Knurl)
ALIENCD 6 / 13 Oct '97 / Alien8

☐ CARDIAC STRAIN
ALIENCD 2 / Mar '97 / Alien8

☐ EVOCATION
AATP 03 / 2 Mar '98 / Auf Abwegen

☐ MASCHINENWERK (Aube & Cock ESP)
CHCD 18 / Jun '97 / Charnel House

☐ PAGES FROM THE BOOK
E&J 006 / 27 Apr '98 / Elsie & Jack

☐ SUBSTRUCTURAL PENETRATION 1991-1995 (4CD Set)
ILIGHT 008CD / 11 May '98 / Iris Light

Auberon
☐ TALE OF BLACK
BMCD 103 / 6 Apr '98 / Black Mark

Aubert, Carmelita
☐ AY CARMELA
BMCD 7602 / Nov '97 / Blue Moon

Aubrey, Rene
☐ SIGNES
3024002 / Nov '97 / Arcade

Audience
☐ AUDIENCE
Banquet / Waverley stage coach / River boat Queen / Harlequin / Heaven was an island / Too late I'm gone / Maidens cry / Troubles / Going song / Paper round / House on the hill / Man on box / Leave it unsaid / Pleasant conversation
RPM 148 / Oct '95 / RPM

☐ HOUSE ON THE HILL, THE
Jackdaw / You're not smiling / I had a dream / Raviole / Eye to eye / I put a spell on you / House on the hill / Nancy
CASCD 1032 / Oct '90 / Charisma

☐ LUNCH
Stand by the door / Seven sore bruises / Hula girl / Ain't the man you need / In accord / Barracuda Dan / Thunder and lightning / Party games / Trombone gulch / Buy me an island
CASCD 1054 / Feb '91 / Charisma

Audio Active
☐ APOLLO CHOCO
186942 / 8 Dec '97 / On-U Sound

☐ APOLLO CHOCO (Remixed)
ONUCD 0095 / 15 Jun '98 / On-U Sound

☐ HAPPY HAPPER
ONUCD 77 / Jun '95 / On-U Sound

☐ HAPPY SHOPPING IN EUROPE
EFA 186352 / Nov '95 / On-U Sound

☐ WAY OUT IS THE WAY IN, THE (Audio Active & Laraaji)
New laughter mode (the way in) / Music and cosmic (feel yourself) / Throw inhibition / How time flies / Laaraajingle / Space visitors for tea - tat lump on your head / Hither and zither / Blooper's dance floor / New laugher mode (the way out)
ASCD 026 / Nov '95 / All Saints

☐ WE ARE AUDIO ACTIVE
ONUCD 73 / Sep '94 / On-U Sound

Audio Assault Squad
☐ COMIN' UP OUTTA THIS BITCH
TED 41742CD / May '94 / Ichiban

Audioweb
☐ AUDIOWEB
Sleeper / Yeah / Into my world / Faker / Who's to blame / Time / Jah love / Bank robba sensi / Lover / Drip feed
MUMXD 9604
MUMCD 9604 / Feb '97 / Mother

Auerbach, Loren
☐ AFTER THE LONG NIGHT/PLAYING THE GAME (Auerbach, Loren & Bert Jansch)
Rainbow man / Frozen beauty / Christabel / So lonely / Journey of the moon through sorrow / Carousel / Weeping willow blues / Give me love / I can't go back / Smiling faces / Yarrow / Playing the game / Is it real / Sorrow / Days and nights
CDLA 001 / Nov '96 / Christabel

Auffret, Anne
☐ ROUE GRALON NI HO SALUD (Auffret, Anne & Yann Fanch Kemener)
KM 42CD / Feb '94 / Keltia Musique

Aufray, Hughes
☐ AU CASINO DE PARIS (2CD Set)
3032272 / Jan '98 / Arcade

Auger, Brian
☐ DEFINITELY WHAT (Auger, Brian & The Trinity)
OW 30012 / Sep '94 / One Way

Augscholl, Charly
☐ BUS STOP
322 424 / Oct '91 / Koch

August, Lynn
☐ SAUCE PIQUANTE
BT 1092CD / Jul '93 / Black Top

Auld, Georgie
☐ CANYON PASSAGE (Auld, Georgie & His Orchestra)
MVSCD 57 / '88 / Musicraft

☐ JUMP GEORGIE JUMP
Short circuit / Mandrake root / Poinciana / Jivin with the jug / Yesterdays / I'll always be in love with you / Stompin' at the Savoy / Sentimental journey / Jump Georgie jump / I'm always chasing rainbows / I can't get started (with you) / Taps Miller / Concerto for tenor
HEPCD 27 / Jul '96 / Hep

Auld Reekie Dance Band
☐ CAPITAL REELS
Dashing white sergeant / Dashing white sergeant (encore) / Eightsome reel / Foursome reel / Scottish waltz / Hamilton House (jig) / Hamilton House (encore) / Duke of Perth / Duke of Perth (encore) / Strip the willow (Jig) / Strip the willow / Duke and Duchess of Edinburgh / Duke and Duchess of Edinburgh (Encore) / Gay Gordons / Scottish reform (jig) / Scottish reform / Reel of the 51st division (Reel of the 51st division (encore)
LCOM 5190 / May '95 / Lismor

Auldridge, Mike
☐ EIGHT STRING SWING
Little rock getaway / Redskin rag / Bethesada / Swing scene / Caravan / Almost to Tulsa / Bluegrass boogie / Pete's place / Crazy red top / Stompin' at the Savoy
SHCD 3725 / '92 / Sugar Hill

☐ HIGH TIME (Auldridge, Mike & Lou Reid/T. Michael Coleman)
SHCD 3776 / Jan '90 / Sugar Hill

☐ MIKE AULDRIDGE
Southern rain / Tennessee traveller / Mountain slide / Blues for Barbara / Last train to Clarksville / California dreamin' / Dreaming my dreams / Indian summer / Carolina sunshine girl / All thumbs / Spanish grass / Lloyd's of Nashville / Georgia on my mind
FF 70029 / May '97 / Flying Fish

☐ TREASURES UNTOLD
SH 3780 / Jan '97 / Sugar Hill

Auletta, Ted
☐ ALL THE THINGS YOU ARE (The Music Of Jerome Kern) (Auletta, Ted Orchestra & Reid Shelton)
ACD 45 / May '98 / Audiophile

Auntie Christ
☐ LIFE COULD BE A DREAM
LOOKOUT 176CD / May '97 / Lookout

Aura
☐ BUTTERFLY CHRYSALIS CATERPILLAR
INFECT 19CD / May '95 / Infectious

☐ ORANGES ARE BLUE
INFECT 26CD / Jul '96 / Infectious

☐ SHATTERED DAWNBREAK
HHR 005CD / Nov '96 / Hammerheart

Aura Noir
☐ BLACK THRASH ATTACK
MR 009CD / 22 Sep '97 / Malicious

☐ DREAMS LIKE DESERTS
HR 002CD / Feb '96 / Hot

Aural Expansion
☐ REMIXED SHEEP
SSR 159 / Jan '96 / SSR

☐ SURREAL SHEEP
SSR 143 / Aug '95 / SSR

Aurelia Saxophone Quartet
☐ TANGO NUEVO
Escuelo / Adios nonino / Caliente / Contrabajeando / Cuatro estaciones portenas / Vayamos al diablo / Four for tango / Milonga del angel / Contrabajissimo / Michelangelo 70 / Fuga y misterio / Variaciones de la fuga / Astor que estas en los cielos
KTC 1186 / May '98 / Etcetera

Aurora
☐ PSYCHEDELIC TRANCE (2CD Set)
DBCD 201 / Nov '96 / Dancebeat

Aurora Borealis
☐ HARPA
GR 4132CD / Dec '97 / Grappa

Aurora Project
☐ BALANCE OF RISK
CENCD 011 / Feb '96 / Centaur

Aurra
☐ BEST OF AURRA, THE
CDGR 158 / Aug '97 / Charly

Austin, Claire
☐ MEMORIES OF YOU (Austin, Claire & Don Ewell)
ACD 143 / Apr '93 / Audiophile

Austin, Gene
☐ GENE AUSTIN - THE VOICE OF THE SOUTHLAND (25 Vintage Hits)
Voice of the Southland / My blue heaven / When my sugar walks down the street / My bundle of love / Sweet child, I'm wild about you / Ya gotta know how to love / Ev'rything's made for love / Ain't she sweet / Lonesome road / Sweetheart of sigma chi / All of my dreams / Just like a melody from out of the sky / Carolina moon / I've got a feeling I'm falling / How am I to know / Rollin' down the river / When your lover has gone / Please don't talk about me when I'm gone / Without that gal / Love letters in the sand / I don't stand a ghost of a chance with you / Everything I have is yours / I love for you / When I'm with you / Ramona
CDAJA 5217 / Dec '96 / Living Era

☐ TIME TO RELAX 1925-1936, A
TT 414 / May '98 / Take Two

Austin Lounge Lizards
☐ CREATURES FROM THE BLACK SALOON
Golden triangle / Hot tubs of tears / Pflugerville / Car Hank died in / Swingin' from your crystal chandeliers / Kool whip / We are in control / Didn't go to college / Saquaro / Keeping up with the Joneses / War between the States / Old fat and drunk / Chester Woolah / Anahuac
WM 1000 / Jun '93 / Watermelon

☐ EMPLOYEE OF THE MONTH
Stupid Texas song / Hey little minivan / Dogs they really miss you / Rocky byways / Last words / Monkey on my back / Flatnose the tree-climbing dog / Love in a refrigerator box / La cacahuate / Trailways of tears / Leonard Cohen's day job / Momma don't allow medley / Other shore
SHCD 3874 / 9 Mar '98 / Sugar Hill

☐ HIGHWAY CAFE OF THE DAMNED
Highway Cafe of the Damned / Cornhusker refugee / Industrial strength tranquilizer / Wendell, the uncola man / Acid rain / I'll just have one beer / Dallas, Texas / Ballad of Ronald Reagan / When drunks go bad / Jalapeno Maria / Get a haircut Dad / Chester Ninitiz oriental garden waltz
WM 1001 / Jun '93 / Watermelon

☐ SMALL MINDS
WM 1034 / Nov '95 / Watermelon

Austin, Lovie
☐ CLASSICS 1924-1926
CLASSICS 756 / Aug '94 / Classics

Austin, Patti
☐ CARRY ON
Carry on / Givin' in to love / I will remember you / How can I be sure / Why did she come in with you / I just can't let go / Monday, Monday / More I thing about it / Nobody to dance with / I'll be waiting for you / (Don't know) Whether to laugh or cry
GRP 96602 / 25 May '98 / GRP

☐ HAVANA CANDY
Havana candy / That's enough for me / Little baby / I just want to know / Golden oldies / I need somebody / We're in love / Lost in the stars
ZK 65124 / 8 Sep '97 / Sony Jazz

Austin, Sherrie
☐ WORDS
Lucky in love / Innocent man / One solitary tear / Trouble in paradise / That's no way to break a heart / I want to fall in love (so hard it hurts) / Words / Tenderly / Put your heart into it / You keep on lovin' me
78221884322 / 15 Sep '97 / RCA

Australian Marching Band
☐ MARCHING DOWN BROADWAY
MBPCD 7005 / 11 May '98 / Quantum Mobius

Autechre
☐ AMBER
WARPCD 25 / Nov '94 / Warp

☐ AUTECHRE
Acroyear / 777 / Rae / Melve / Vose in / Fold4wrap5 / Under Boac / Corc / Caliper remote / Arch carrier / Drane2
WARPCD 066 / 22 Jun '98 / Warp

☐ CHIASTIC SLIDE
WARPCD 49 / Feb '97 / Warp

☐ INCUNABULA
WARPCD 17 / Apr '96 / Warp

☐ TRI REPETAE
WARPCD 38 / Nov '95 / Warp

Auteurs
☐ AFTER MURDER PARK
Light aircraft on fire / Child brides / Land lovers / New brat in town / Everything you say will destroy you / Unsolved child murder / Married to a lazy lover / Buddha / Tombstone / Fear of flying / Dead sea navigators / After murder park
DGHUT 33 / Mar '96 / Hut

☐ AUTEURS VS. U-ZIQ
Lenny Valentino 3 / Daughter of a child / Chinese bakery / Lenny Valentino 1 / Lenny Valentino 2 / Underground movies
DGHUTM 20 / Oct '94 / Hut

☐ NEW WAVE
Show girl / Bailed out / American guitars / Junk shop clothes / Don't trust the stars / Starstruck / How could I be so wrong / Housebreaker / Valet parking / Idiot brother / Early years / Home again
CDHUT 7 / Mar '93 / Hut

☐ NOW I'M A COWBOY
Modern history (Accoustic version) / Lenny Valentino / Brain child / I'm a rich man's toy / New French partner / Upper classes / Chinese bakery / Sister like you / Underground movies / Life classes / Modern history / Daughter of a child
CDHUT 16 / May '94 / Hut

Authority
☐ WHO KNOWS
GMM 113 / Jul '97 / Gimmie My Money

Autoclave
☐ AUTOCLAVE
DIS 108CD / Aug '97 / Dischord

Autograph
☐ MISSING PIECES
USG 37651422 / Apr '97 / USG

Autohaze
☐ COUNTER CLOCKWISE
SHINEUS 22 / 30 Mar '98 / Summershine

Automatic Head Detonator
☐ LIVE OUTSIDE THE HOLLYWOOD PALLADIUM SONIC YOUTH GIG
LS 02 / Jun '96 / Lo-Fi Recordings

☐ WHAT THE FUCK DO YOU KNOW
LF 001 / Mar '95 / Lo-Fi Recordings

Automator
☐ BETTER TOMORROW, A
URCD 016 / Jul '96 / Ubiquity

Autonomex
☐ EARLYMAN MEETS AUTONOMEX
WOWCD 38 / Oct '95 / Words Of Warning

Autopop
☐ SELECTION BOX
Unhand me brother / Diamond / Crisis girl / Still hanging around / Bootboy remembers / Being seen / Wasted / Tristan
MASKCD 069 / Apr '97 / Vinyl Japan

Autopsia
☐ MYSTERY SCIENCE
34502 / Mar '97 / Hypnobeat

☐ REQUIM POUR UN EMPIRE
HYCD 185000 / Nov '92 / Hypertension

Autopsy
☐ ACTS OF THE UNSPEAKABLE
Meat / Necrocannibalistic vomitorium / Your rotting face / Blackness within / Act of the unspeakable / Frozen with fear / Spinal extractions / Death twitch / Sculptures / Pus / Rot / Lobotomised / Funereality / Tortured moans of agony / Ugliness and secretions / Orgy in excrements / Voices / Walls of the coffin
CDVILE 33 / Apr '97 / Peaceville

☐ MENTAL FUNERAL
Twisted mass of burnt decay / In the grip of winter / Fleshcrawl / Torn from the womb / Slaughterday / Dead / Robbing the grave / Hole in the head / Destined to fester / Bonesaw / Dark crusade / Mental funeral
CDMVILE 25 / Jun '96 / Peaceville

☐ MENTAL FUNERAL/SEVERED SURVIVAL
CDVILE 25 / Aug '95 / Peaceville

☐ SEVERED SURVIVAL
Charred remains / Service for a vacant coffin / Disembowel / Gasping for air / Ridden with disease / Pagan saviour / Impending dread / Severed survival / Critical madness / Embalmed / Stillborn
CDMVILE 12 / Jun '96 / Peaceville

☐ SHITFUN
CDVILE 49 / Jul '95 / Peaceville

Autour De Lucie

☐ AUTOUR DE LUCIE
067003010429 / Oct '96 / Nettwerk

☐ IMMOBILE
301212 / 23 Mar '98 / Nettwerk

Autry, Gene

☐ BACK IN THE SADDLE AGAIN
CTS 55430 / Aug '94 / Country Stars

☐ BACK IN THE SADDLE AGAIN (25 Cowboy Classics)
Back in the saddle again / Blue yodel no.5 / Any old time / High steppin' Mama / Silver haired Daddy of mine / Tumbling tumbleweeds / Ridin' down the canyon / Mexicali Rose / Blue Hawaii / Dust / Old trail / Paradise in the moonlight / Rhythm of the hoofbeats / South of the border (Down Mexico way) / Blueberry Hill / Be honest with me / When swallows come back to Capistrano / You are my sunshine / Year ago tonight / I'll never let you go / I'll wait for you / After tomorrow / Lonely river / Have I told you lately that I love you / Goodbye little darlin' goodbye
CDAJA 5188 / Apr '96 / Living Era

☐ BEST OF GENE AUTRY, THE
MACCD 219 / Aug '96 / Autograph

☐ LAST ROUND-UP, THE (Cowboy Classics 1933-1947)
Last round up / Someday in Wyoming / Dear old western skies / Old covered wagon / Texas plains / Mother here's a bouquet for you / Guns and guitars / When golden leaves are falling / Down in the land of Zulu / It's round up time in Reno / I want a pardon for daddy / If today were the end of the world / When I first laid eyes on you / If it wasn't for the rain / Little old band of gold / Mary dear / Sycamore lane / Cowboy's trademarks / Last letter / I wish all my children were babies again / Take me back to your heart / Ages and ages ago / Last mile / Pretty Mary / Little big dry
CDAJA 5264 / Jun '98 / Living Era

☐ LEGENDARY SINGING GROUPS OF THE WEST
Silent rails / Wild and wooley west / Yours / That's my home / Rancho pillow / Martins and the coys / Cowboy / Dude ranch / Somebody else is taking my place / Great grand dad / Old home place / Shame on you / Cowboy blues / Roll wagon roll / Nobody's darlin' but mine
VSD 5841 / 9 Feb '98 / Varese Sarabande

☐ SINGING COWBOY
Tumbling tumbleweeds / Guns and guitars / Ride ranger ride / Take em back to my roots / Colorado saddle / Gaucho serenade / Ride tenderfoot ride / Melody ranch / Back in the saddle again / Down Mexico way / Call of the canyon / In old capistrano / Sioux city Sue / Trail to San Antone / Loaded pistols / Ghost riders in the sky
VSD 5840 / 9 Feb '98 / Varese Sarabande

Autumn Leaves

☐ AUTUMN LEAVES
Building bridges / Light of your love / Right on / Keeping it cool / Vera cruz / Eye of the hurricane / Lies and alibis / Ten minutes romance / Thythm of the road / Together we're strong / Swing across Texas / Steppin' out on me / Thank you for the time / Blue water / Don't it make ya wanna dance
BCD 15734 / May '93 / Bear Family

Autumn Leaves

☐ TREATS & TREASURES
GRIMSEY 009 / 10 Aug '98 / Grimsey

Auzet, Roland

☐ LA VIE C'EST MARRANT COMME CA CHANGE
IMP 946 / Jan '97 / IMP

Avail

☐ 4AM FRIDAY
LOOKOUT 138CD / Jun '96 / Lookout

☐ LIVE IN SAN FRANCISCO
LK 192CD / 9 Feb '98 / Lookout

☐ OVER THE JAMES
LK 195CD / 27 Apr '98 / Lookout

Available Jelly

☐ HAPPY CAMP
RAMBOY 10 / Aug '97 / Ramboy

☐ MONUMENT
RAMBOY 7 / Oct '94 / Ramboy

Avalanche

☐ HANGOVER SQUARE
CDCOR 198 / 30 Mar '98 / Corrida

Avalanches

☐ EL PRODUCTO
001 GRAM / 27 Apr '98 / Epigram

Avalon

☐ HIGHER GROUND
Lion of the north / Sons of the sea / Into the mists / Soldier's dream / Palais de danse / Stretch the bowl / Wild cherry tree / Ellis isle
IRCD 017 / Aug '92 / Lismor

Avalon, Frankie

☐ FABULOUS FRANKIE AVALON, THE
Venus / Why / Dede Dinah / Gingerbread / Bobby Sox to stockings / Boy without a girl / Just ask your heart / I'll wait for you / Don't throw away all those teardrops / Where are you / Togetherness / You are mine
CDFAB 007 / Sep '91 / Ace

☐ FRANKIE AVALON
REP 4158 / Aug '91 / Repertoire

☐ HIT SINGLE COLLECTABLES
DISK 4501 / Apr '94 / Disky

Avatar

☐ DEEP ARCHITECTURE
SUB 32D / Apr '97 / Subversive

☐ MEMORIAN DRACONIS
WSR 002CD / Jul '96 / Shiver

Avaton

☐ AVATON
ML 4831 / 11 May '98 / Musurgia Graeca

Avec Cholesterol

☐ LU REVE DU DIABLE
R2D2 105CD / Apr '96 / R2D2

Avenue Vendome

☐ SATURN CHATEAUX
FCP 104 / Dec '97 / Full Court

Average White Band

☐ ABOVE AVERAGE
Pick up the pieces / Cut the cake / Queen of my soul / Person to person / You got it / Work to do / Walk on by / When will you be mine / Let's go round again / For you, for love / If I ever lose this Heaven / Schoolboy crush / Your love is a miracle / Love of your own / Cloudy / I heard it through the grapevine / Atlantic Avenue / Got the love
CCSCD 438 / Oct '96 / Castle

☐ AVERAGE WHITE BAND (2CD Set)
Catch me before I have to testify / Let's go round again / Watcha gonna do for me / Help is on the way / Shine / For you for love / Into the night / Our time has come / If love only lasts for one night / Pick up the pieces / Person to person / Cut the cake / If I ever lose this heaven / Cloudy / TLC / I'm the one / Love your life / Schoolboy crush / I heard it through the grapevine
SMDCD 173 / May '97 / Snapper

☐ CUT THE CAKE
Cut the cake / School boy crush / It's a mystery / Groovin' the night away / If I ever lose this heaven / Why / High flyin' woman / Cloudy / How sweet can you get / When they bring down the curtain
SMMCD 508 / 29 Sep '97 / Snapper

☐ LET'S GO ROUND AGAIN - BEST OF THE AVERAGE WHITE BAND
AHLCD 15 / Mar '94 / Hit

☐ SOUL TATTOO
ARTFULCD 7 / Feb '97 / Artful

☐ VERY BEST OF AVERAGE WHITE BAND, THE
Pick up the pieces / Put it where you want it / Schoolboy crush / Queen of my soul / It's a mysterie / Work to do / Cut the cake / Groovin' the night away / How sweet can you get / Big city lights / She's a dream / Your love is a miracle / Into the night / You got it / When will you be mine / Person to person
12891 / Feb '97 / Laserlight

☐ WHITE ALBUM, THE
You got it / Got the love / Pick up the pieces / Person to person / Work to do / Nothing you can do / Just wanna love you tonight / Keepin' it to myself / Just can't give you up / There's always someone waiting
ESMCD 439 / Oct '96 / Essential

Avery, Teodross

☐ MY GENERATION
Addis abeba / Mode for my father / Theme for Malcolm / Lover man / To the east / Mr. Wonsey / Salome / Sphere / My generation / Anytime, anyplace / It's about that time
IMP 11812 / Jan '96 / Impulse Jazz

Avia

☐ AVIA
Wake up and sing out / Spring song of the masses / Russian lesson part 1 (goodbye) / Night watch / I don't love you / Russian lesson part 2 (home) / Celebration / Aviavial / Semaphore
HNCD 1358 / Jul '90 / Hannibal

Aviator

☐ AVIATOR
Front line / Back on the street / Don't turn away / Wrong place, wrong time / Never let the rock stop / Come back / Magic / Can't stop / Too young / Every schoolboy knows / Through the night
ESM 017 / 2 Mar '98 / Escape

Awankana

☐ FLAMBOYAN
SM 18042 / Nov '93 / Wergo

☐ GENTLE RIVER
SM 18022 / Feb '92 / Wergo

☐ KINGDOM IS NOT AFAR, THE
SM 18012 / Aug '92 / Wergo

☐ RINGSEL
SM 18052 / Nov '93 / Wergo

Aweke, Aster

☐ EBO
22222 / Jul '98 / Barkhanns

☐ KABU
TRECD 110 / Jul '98 / Triple Earth

☐ LIVE IN LONDON
BARKCD 102 / Jul '98 / Barkhanns

Awful Truth

☐ AWFUL TRUTH
It takes so long / I should have known all along / Ghost of heaven / Drowning man / Circle of pain / Higher / No good reason / Mary
CDZORRO 3 / Aug '90 / Metal Blade

AWOL

☐ WHAT IT BE LIKE
BRY 4175CD / Apr '94 / Ichiban

AX

☐ ASTRONOMY
FRR 027 / 29 Jun '98 / Freek

Axe

☐ 25 YEARS FROM HOME
Running the gauntlet / Rock 'n' roll party / Burn the city down / Heat in the street / Now or never / Life's just an illusion / Eagle flies alone / Living on the edge / All through the night / First time last time / Forever / Back on the streets / Heroes and legends / Sting of the rain
199633 / Sep '97 / Made To Measure

☐ FIVE
Intro / Magic (in our eyes) / Heroes and legends / Sting of the rain / Life in the furnace / Burn me once (burn me twice) / Where there's smoke (there's fire) / Holding onto the night / Anyplace on this highway (is home) / Battles
MTM 199617 / Feb '97 / Made To Measure

Axton, Hoyt

☐ A&M YEARS, THE (2CD Set)
Sweet misery / Less than the song / Sweet fantasy / Days are short / Mary makes magic / Peacemaker / Nothin' to lose / Oklahoma song / Mexico City hangover / Hungry man / Somebody turned on the light / Blue prelude / Maybellene / Life machine / That's alright / Geronimo's Cadillac / When the morning comes / Good lookin' child / I dream of highways / Pet parade / Telephone booth / Boney fingers / Billy's theme / I love to sing / Southbound / Lion in the winter / Blind fiddler / Pride of man / Greensleeves / No no song / Nashville / Speed trap (out of state cars) / Roll your own / Whiskey / In a young girl's mind / Sometimes it's easy / Idol of the band / Evangelina / Flash of fire / Lay lady lay / Jealous man / Paid in advance / Old greyhound / Stone and a feather / Gypsy moth / Beyond these walls / Penny whistle song / Devil
5409572 / Jul '98 / A&M

☐ FREE SAILIN'
Bluebird / Honky tonk music / Way of the world / Heart you break may be your own / Jive man / Free sailing / Them downers / Left my gal in the mountains / Darrell and judy / Endless road
EDCD 471 / Apr '96 / Edsel

☐ MY GRIFFIN IS GONE
On the natural / Way before the time of towns / Beelzebub's laughter / Sunshine fields of love / It's alright now / Gypsy will / Revelations / Snow blind friend / Childhood's end / Sunrise / Kingswood manor
EDCD 553 / 6 Apr '98 / Edsel

☐ SNOWBLIND FRIEND
You're the hangnail in my life / Little white moon / Water for my horse / Funeral of the king / I light this candle / Never been to Spain / You taught me how to cry / Snowblind friend / Pancho and Lefty / Seven come eleven / I don't know why I love you
EDCD 426 / May '95 / Edsel

Aydin, Aliev

☐ GARMON OF AYDIN ALIEV, THE
927012 / 24 Apr '98 / BUDA

Ayers, Kevin

☐ BANANA FOLLIES
Introduction / (Don't sing no more) Sad songs / Pretty little girl / Two little pigeons / Murder in the air / 'Orrible orange / Whatevershebringswesing / Take me to Tahiti / O wot a dream / Ball bearing blues / Fake Mexican tourist blues / Interview / You say you like my hat / Falling in love again / End
HUX 007 / 27 Jul '98 / Hux

☐ BANANAMOUR
Don't let it get you down / Shouting in a bucket blues / When your parents go to sleep / Interview / International anthem / Decadence / Oh wot a dream / Hymn / Beware of the dog
BGOCD 142 / Jun '92 / Beat Goes On

☐ CONFESSIONS OF DR DREAM
Day by day / See you later / Didn't feel lonely till I thought of you / Everybody's sometime and some people's all the time blues / It begins with a blessing / Once I awakened / But it ends with a curse / Ballbearing blues / Confessions of Dr. Dream / Irreversible neural damage / Invitation / One chance dance / Dr. Dream / Two goes into four
BGOCD 86 / Oct '90 / Beat Goes On

☐ GARDEN OF LOVE, THE
Garden of love
VP 180CD / 1 Jun '98 / Voiceprint

☐ JOY OF A TOY
Joy of a toy continued / Clarietta rag / Song for insane times / Eleanor's cake which ate her / Oleh oleh bandu bandong / Town feeling / Girl on a swing / Stop this train / Lady Rachel / All this crazy gift of time
BGOCD 78 / '89 / Beat Goes On

☐ KEVIN AYERS COLLECTION
Lady Rachel / May I / Puis-je / Stranger in blue suede shoes / Caribbean moon / Shouting in a bucket blues / After the show / Didn't feel lonely till I thought of you / Once upon an ocean / City waltz / Blue star / Blaming it all on love / Strange song / Miss Hanaga / Money, money, money
SEECD 117 / Jun '97 / See For Miles

☐ RAINBOW TAKEAWAY
Blaming it all on love / Ballad of a salesman who sold himself / View from the mountain / Rainbow takeaway / Waltz for you / Beware of the dog / Strange song / Goodnight, goodnight / Hat song
BGOCD 189 / Apr '93 / Beat Goes On

☐ SHOOTING AT THE MOON (Ayers, Kevin & The Whole World)
May I / Colores para Dolores / Lunatics lament / Underwater / Red, green and blue you / Rheinhardt and Geraldine / Pisser dans un violon / Oyster and the flying fish / Clarence in Wonderland / Shooting at the moon
BGOCD 13 / Apr '90 / Beat Goes On

☐ SINGING THE BRUISE (Live At The BBC)
Why are we sleeping / You say you like my hat / Gemini chile / Lady Rachel / Derby day / Interview / We did it again / Oyster and the flying fish / Butterfly dance / Whatevershebringswesing / Falling in love again / Queen thing
BOJCD 019 / Aug '96 / Band Of Joy

☐ SOPORIFICS (June 1 1974) (Ayers, Kevin & John Cale/Nico/Brian Eno)
Driving me backwards / Baby's on fire / Heartbreak hotel / End / May I / Shouting in a bucket blues / Stranger in blue suede shoes / Everybody's sometime and some people's all the time blues / Two goes into four
IMCD 92 / Feb '90 / Island

☐ STILL LIFE WITH GUITAR
INDELCD 2 / 27 Mar '98 / Indelible

☐ SWEET DECEIVER
Observations / Guru banana / City waltz / Toujours la voyage / Sweet deceiver / Diminished but not finished / Circular letter / Once upon an ocean / Farewell again
BGOCD 98 / Aug '92 / Beat Goes On

☐ THAT'S WHAT YOU GET BABE
That's what you get / Where do I go from here / You never outrun your love / Given and taken / Idiots / Super salesman / Money, money, money / Miss Hanaga / I'm so tired / Where do the stars end
BGOCD 190 / Jun '93 / Beat Goes On

☐ TOO OLD TO DIE YOUNG (2CD Set)
Lady Rachel / May I / Clarence in Wonderland / Whatevershebringswesing / There is loving / Margaret / Colores para Dolores / Crazy gift of time / Why are we sleeping / Didn't feel lonely / Observations / Stranger in blue suede shoes / Interview / Farewell again / Shouting in a bucket blues / If you want to be a star / Love's gonna turn you around / Mr. Cool / Blue
HUX 006 / 29 Jun '98 / Hux

☐ WHATEVER SHE BRINGS WE SING
There is loving / Among us / Margaret oh my / Song from the bottom of a well / Whatever she brings we sing / Stranger in blue suede shoes / Champagne cowboy blues / Lullaby
BGOCD 11 / Apr '88 / Beat Goes On

☐ YES WE HAVE NO MANANAS
Star / Mr. Cool / Owl / Love's gonna turn you round / Falling in love again / Help me / Ballad of Mr. Snake / Everyone knows the song / Yes I do / Blue
BGOCD 143 / Apr '93 / Beat Goes On

Ayers, Roy

☐ DRIVE
Black family / Fast money / Lots of love / Everybody / D.c. city / Drive / And then we were one / Chicago
ICH 1028CD / Mar '94 / Ichiban

☐ ESSENTIAL GROOVE - LIVE
Everybody loves the sunshine / Hot / Red, black and green / Searchin' / Love will bring us back together / Don't wait for love / We live in London baby / Long time ago / Poo poo la la
JHCD 035 / '88 / Ronnie Scott's Jazz House

☐ EVERYBODY LOVES THE SUNSHINE
Hey u / Golden rod / Keep on walking / You and me my love / Third eye / It ain't your sign / People and the world / Everybody loves the sunshine / Tongue power / Lonesome cowboy
8338442 / Sep '93 / Polydor

☐ GOOD VIBRATIONS
Everybody loves the sunshine / Easy to move / Mission / Wrapped up in your love / X marks the spot / Poo poo la la / Ivory tower
JHCD 028 / Jan '94 / Ronnie Scott's Jazz House

☐ HOT
Can't you see me / Running away / Love will bring us together / Lots of love / Everyone loves the sunshine / Hot / Pete King / Sweet tears / Philadelphia mambo / We live in London baby
JHCD 021 / Jan '94 / Ronnie Scott's Jazz House

☐ LIVE AT MONTREUX 1972 (Ayers, Roy Ubiquity)
5316412 / Jul '96 / Verve

☐ LOTS OF LOVE
CDGR 239 / 1 Jun '98 / Charly

☐ SEARCHIN'
Searchin' / Yes / You send me / Mystic voyage / Love will bring us together / Spirit of the Do Do / Long time ago / Can you see me
JHCD 013 / Jan '94 / Ronnie Scott's Jazz House

☐ SHINING SYMBOL, A (The Ultimate Collection)
Running away / Love will bring us back together / Searching / Everybody loves the sunshine / Mystic voyage / Time and space / Evolution / He's a superstar / 2000 black / Red, black and green / We live in Brooklyn baby / He's coming / I wanna touch you baby / Can't you see me / Fire weaver / Shining symbol
5193782 / May '93 / Polydor

☐ VIBESMAN (Live At Ronnie Scott's)
MCCD 215 / Oct '95 / Music Club

☐ VIBRANT
In the dark / Poo poo la la / Hot / Programmed for love / Nite flyte / Let me love you / I really wanna be with you / Marlon / Can't you just see me / Running away / Love will bring us back together / Everybody / Black family
VSOPCD 179 / Feb '93 / Connoisseur Collection

☐ WAKE UP
Midnight after dark / Suave / Sweet talk / Spirit of dodo '89 / Crack is in the mirror (wake up) / You've got the power / Mystic vibrations
ICH 1040CD / Oct '93 / Ichiban

Ayibobo
☐ FREESTYLE
DIW 877 / Jan '94 / DIW

Ayler, Albert
☐ FONDATION MAEGHT NIGHTS
COD 004 / Mar '92 / Jazz View

☐ GOIN' HOME
BLCD 760197 / Nov '94 / Koch

☐ LIVE IN EUROPE
Mothers / Children / Holy spirits / Our prayer / Ghosts - bells / Truth is marching in / Omega
LS 2902 / Mar '93 / Lagoon

☐ MY NAME IS ALBERT AYLER
BLCD 760211 / Mar '96 / Black Lion

☐ TRUTH IS MARCHING IN (Ayler, Albert Quintet)
30003 / Sep '92 / Giants Of Jazz

☐ VIBRATIONS (Ayler, Albert & Don Cherry)
Ghosts / Children / Holy spirit / Vibrations / Mothers
FCD 41000 / Sep '87 / Freedom

☐ WITCHES AND DEVILS
FCD 41018 / Jan '87 / Freedom

Ayreon
☐ ACTUAL FANTASY
TM 008 / 11 May '98 / Transmission

☐ FINAL EXPERIMENT, THE
TM 001 / 11 May '98 / Transmission

Ayres, Mitchell
☐ ON GUARD WITH CONNIE FRANCIS (Ayres, Mitchell Orchestra & Bob Crosby Bobcats)
EBCD 2133 / Sep '97 / Jazzband

Aytekin, Ziya
☐ ZIYA
SJE 8CD / Aug '96 / Sjelvar

Ayuo
☐ SONGS FROM A EURASIAN JOURNEY
VICG 60011 / 24 Nov '97 / Victor

AZ
☐ DOE OR DIE
Uncut raw / Gimme your's / Ho happy Jackie / Rather unique / I feel for you / Sugarhill / Mo money / Mo murder (homicide) / Doe or die / We can't win / Your world don't stop / Sugarhill (remix)
CTCD 51 / Sep '97 / Cooltempo

☐ PIECES OF A MAN
New life / I'm known / How ya livin' / Trading places / Just because / SOSA / It's a boy thing / Pieces of a black man / Last dayz / Whatever happened: AZ & RZA / Trial of the century: AZ & RZA / Betcha don't know: AZ & RZA
8467152 / 20 Apr '98 / Cooltempo

AZ
☐ MUSIC FOR SCATTERED BRAINS
ALP 81CD / Feb '97 / Atavistic

Az Yet
☐ AZ YET
Last night / Saved for someone else / Care for me / Every little bit / Hard to say I'm sorry / That's all I want / Secrets / Through my heart (the arrow) / I don't want to be lonely / Sadder than blue / Inseparable lovers / Time to end this story
73008260342 / Jun '97 / LaFace

Azala
☐ MARIGAIZTO
KD 205CD / Aug '97 / Elkar

Azalia Snail
☐ DEEP MOTIF
CF 013 / Nov '96 / Candy Floss

☐ FUMAROLE RISING
CAT 007 / May '97 / Catapult

Azar
☐ SALAM KABYL DANCE
AAA 144 / Aug '97 / Club Du Disque Arabe

Azevedo, Geraldo
☐ BEREKEKE
925632 / Jun '93 / BUDA

Aznavour, Charles
☐ 20 CHANSONS D'OR
Je m'voyais deja / Trousse - chemise / Les plaisirs demodes / Qui / Les comediens / La mamma / For me... formidable / Non, je n'ai rien oublie / Le temps / Que c'est triste venise / Tu t'laisses aller / Et pourtant / La Boheme / Les deux guitares / Desormais / Il faut savoir / Comme Ils Disent / Hier encore / L'amour c'est comme un jour / Emmenez - moi
CDEMC 3716 / Jul '95 / EMI

☐ LES COMEDIENS
CD 352072 / May '93 / Duchesse

☐ SHE (The Best Of Charles Aznavour)
She / Yesterday when I was young / Happy days / La Boheme / How sad Venice can be / No, I could never forget / Happy Anniversary / You've got to learn / I didn't see the time go by / And in my chair / Three is a time / You've let yourself go / Old fashioned way / Take me along / To my daughter / Sound of your name / It will be my day / Ave Maria / What makes a man / They fell
PRMTVCD 4 / Nov '96 / Premier/EMI

☐ WE WERE HAPPY THEN
Then / Let's turn out the light / I will warm your heart / It's heaven / Take me along / Happy days / You make me hungry for loving / Until tomorrow comes / Pretty shitty days / We had it all
CDSL 5189 / '88 / DRG

Azreal
☐ THERE SHALL BE NO ANSWER
NBAZ 001CD / Nov '95 / Nuclear Blast

Azrie, Abed
☐ AROMATES
7559792412 / Jan '95 / Nonesuch

Aztec Camera
☐ FRESTONIA
Sun / On the avenue / Rainy season / Crazy / Imperfectly / Beautiful girl / Debutante / Sunset / Method of love / Phenomenal world
0630119292 / Oct '95 / WEA

☐ HIGH LAND, HARD RAIN
Oblivious / Boy wonders / Walk out to winter / Bugle sounds again / We could send letters / Pillar to post / Release / Lost outside the tunnel / Back on board / Down the dip / Haywire / Orchid girl / Queen's tattoos
4509928492 / Sep '93 / WEA

☐ KNIFE
Just like the USA / Head is happy (heart's insane) / Backdoor to heaven / All I need is everything / Backwards and forwards / Birth of the true / Knife / Still on fire
K 2404832 / Sep '93 / WEA

☐ LOVE
Deep and wide and tall / How men are / Everybody is a number one / More than a law / Somewhere in my heart / Working in a goldmine / One and one / Paradise / Killermont street
K 2422022 / Sep '93 / WEA

☐ STRAY
Stray / Crying scene / Get outta London / Over my head / Good morning Britain / How it is / Gentle kind / Notting Hill blues / Song for a friend
9031716942 / Sep '93 / WEA

Aztec Productions
☐ NOCTURNAL FLAVOURS
Shifty's waltz / Shadows fall / Organism / Jazz always / Breeze / Live and direct / Phantom phone phreak / Peace of mind / Questions for Icarus / Mind talk / Springtime on Venus / Shifty's rolecall
XEN 007CD / 23 Mar '98 / Funky Xen

Azukx
☐ EVERYTHING IS EVERYTHING
MNTCD 1 / Oct '95 / Mantra

Azuquita
☐ LOS ORIGINALES
FA 407 / Jul '96 / Fremeaux

Azusa Plane
☐ AMERICA IS DREAMING OF US (2CD Set)
DBC 016/017 / 27 Apr '98 / Dark Beloved Cloud

☐ TYCHO-MAGNETIC ANOMALY AND THE FULL CONSCIOUSNESS OF HIDDEN
CAM 002CD / 5 Jan '98 / Camera Obscura

Azymuth
☐ AZYMUTH
5230102 / Jul '94 / ECM

☐ AZYMUTH '85
Adios Iony / Dream - lost song / Who are you / Breathtaking / Potion 1 / February daze / Till bakeblikk / Potion 2
8275202 / Dec '85 / ECM

☐ BEST OF AZYMUTH, THE
Club Morrocco / Cascades of the seven waterfalls / Textile factory / Right on / Somewhere in Brazil / Outubro / 500 miles high / Dear Limmertz / Song of the jet / Areiras / All the carnaval / Maracana
MCD 91602 / Apr '94 / Milestone

☐ CARIOCA
Love beat / Valsas de uma cidade / Beyond the door / Bom tempo / Labaredas / O bloco do eu sozinho / Toque de cuica / Guaratiba / Love beat prelude
MCD 9169 / Oct '93 / Milestone

☐ CARNIVAL
Jazz carnival / Wuiema Roupa / Faca de conta / Esperando minha vez / Calma / Tudo que voce podia ser / Prefacio / Tempos atraz / Ausgang / Quem com quem
FARO 011CD / Oct '96 / Far Out

☐ CRAZY RHYTHM
Bossa nova usa / Toc de bola / Too much time / Tropical horizon / Hobalala / O pescador / Theme for tiago / Diza
MCD 9156 / Oct '93 / Milestone

☐ HOW IT WAS THEN...NEVER AGAIN
How it was then / Looking on / Whirlpool / Full circle / How deep is the ocean / Stango / Mindiatyr / Wintersweet
4238202 / Apr '95 / ECM

☐ JAZZ CARNIVAL - BEST OF AZYMUTH
Jazz carnival / Dear Limmertz / Estreito de taruma / Cascade of the seven waterfalls / Missing doto / Maracana / Samba da barra / Textile factory / Turma do samba / Papaia: Malheiros, Alex / Partido alto: Bertrami, Jose Roberto / Pantanal Il swamp: Conti, Ivan
CDBGP 1007 / Mar '88 / Beat Goes Public

Azzola, Marcel
☐ L'ACCORDEONISTE (Homage A Edith Piaf)
L'accordeoniste / La vie en rose / L'Etranger / Les trois cloches / La goualante du pavre Jean / Mon legionnaire / Jezebel / Padam...padam / Milord / C'est un gars / Hymne a l'amour
5215002 / Jun '94 / Verve

Azzolini, Giorgio
☐ SCICLUNA STREET, THE
RTCL 804CD / Jul '96 / Right Tempo

B-Bumble & The Stingers

☐ NUT ROCKER AND ALL THE CLASSICS
Nut rocker / Bumble boogie / School day blues / Boogie woogie / Near you / Bee hive / Caravan / Nautilus / Nola / Rockin' on 'n' off / Mashed / Apple knocker / Moon and the sea / All of me / Dawn cracker / Scales / 12th Street rag / Canadian sunset / Baby mash / Night time madness / In the mood / Chicken chow mein / Bumble bossa nova / Canadian sunset (Alt.)
CDCHD 577 / Jul '95 / Ace

B-Girls

☐ WHO SAYS THAT GIRLS CAN'T ROCK
OPM 2111CD / Feb '97 / Other People's Music

B So Global

☐ WORLD IS COVERED IN WINDOWS, THE
CHILLUM 002 / Jan '96 / Chill Um

B-12

☐ ELECTRO-SOMA
Soundtrack of space / Hall of mirrors / Mondrin / Obsessed / Bio dimension / Basic emotion / Metropolis / Obtuse / Debrise / Telefone / Satorl / Static emotion
WARPCD 9 / Apr '96 / Warp

B-52's

☐ B-52'S
Planet Claire / Fifty two Girls / Dance this mess around / Rock lobster / Lava / There's a Moon in the sky (called Moon) / Hero worship / 6060 842 / Downtown
IMCD 1 / May '90 / Island

☐ BOUNCING OFF THE SATELLITES
Summer of love / Girl from Ipanema goes to Greenland / Housework / Detour thru your mind / Wig / Theme for a nude beach / Juicy jungle / Communicate / She brakes for rainbows
IMCD 105 / May '90 / Island

☐ COSMIC THING
Cosmic thing / Dead beat club / Junebug / Bush fire / Topaz / Dry county / Love shack / Roam / Channel Z / Follow your bliss
K 9258542 / Dec '96 / WEA

☐ DANCE THIS MESS AROUND (The Best Of The B-52's)
Party out of bounds / Dirty back road / Wig / Rock lobster / Give me back my man / Planet Claire / Devil in my car / 6060 842 / Dance this mess around / Strobelight / Song for a future generation
IMCD 238 / Mar '97 / Island

☐ GOOD STUFF
Tell it like it is / Hot pants explosion / Good stuff / Revolution earth / Dreamland / Is that you mo-dean / World's green laughter / Vision of a kiss / Breezin' / Bad influence
7599269432 / Jun '92 / WEA

☐ MESOPOTAMIA
Loveland / Mesopotamia / Throw that beat in the garbage can / Deep sleep / Cake / Nip it in the bud
IMCD 107 / May '90 / Island

☐ PARTY MIX
Party out of bounds / Private Idaho / Give me back my man / Lava / Dance this mess around / Fifty two girls
IMCD 106 / May '90 / Island

☐ PLANET CLAIRE
Planet Claire / Rock lobster / Lava / Downtown / 6060-842 / 52 Girls / Give me back my man / Strobe light / Dirty back road / Loveland / Nip it in the bud / Song for a future generation / Wig / Girl from Ipanema goes to Greenland
5512102 / Aug '95 / Spectrum

☐ TIME CAPSULE (Songs For A Future Generation)
Planet Claire / Rock lobster / Private Idaho / Quiche Lorraine / Mesopotamia / Summer of love / Channel Z / Deadbeat club / Love shack / Roam / Good stuff / Is that you mo.Dean / Meet the Flinstones / Debbie / Hallucinating Pluto
9362469592 / 6 Jul '98 / Reprise

☐ WHAMMY
Legal tender / Whammy kiss / Song for a future generation / Butterbean / Trism / Queen of Las Vegas / Don't worry / Big bird / Work that skirt
IMCD 109 / May '90 / Island

☐ WILD PLANET
Party out of bounds / Dirty back road / Running around / Give me back my man / Private Idaho / Quiche Lorraine / Strobelight / Fifty three miles West of Venus / Devils in my car
IMCD 108 / May '90 / Island

B-Movie

☐ REMEMBRANCE DAY
Man on a threshold / Refugee / Drowning man / Soundtrack / Nowhere girl / Institution walls / This still life / Left out in the cold / Remembrance day / Aeroplanes and mountains / Remembrance day / Remembrance day
CDMRED 137 / Mar '97 / Cherry Red

B-Movie Rats

☐ KILLER WOMAN
DB 19CD / 12 Jan '98 / Deadbeat

B-Thong

☐ FROM STRENGTH TO STRENGTH
M 7028CD / 1 Sep '97 / Mascot

B-Tribe

☐ SUAVE SUAVE
Suave suave / Que mala vida / Sensual / Ahoy / Hablando / Interlude / Albatros / Te siento / Nanita / Poesia / Yo quiero todo / Manha de carneval
0630175182 / Feb '97 / East West

B12

☐ TIME TOURIST
WARPCD 37 / Feb '96 / Warp

Baader Meinhof

☐ BAADER MEINHOF
Baader Meinhof / Meet me at the airport / There's gonna be an accident / Mogadishu / Theme from Burn Warehouse Burn / GSG 29 / ...it's a moral issue / Back on the farm / Kill Ramirez / Baader Meinhof / I've been a bad boy
CDHUT 36 / Oct '96 / Hut

Baba Jam Band

☐ KAYADA
BEST 1036CD / Nov '93 / Acoustic Music

Babacar

☐ BABACAR
BCAR 1CD / 31 Aug '98 / Mesmer

Babata

☐ JJY MUSIC
122120 / Jul '96 / Long Distance

Babe Ruth

☐ FIRST BASE/AMAR CABALLERO
BGOCD 382 / 27 Apr '98 / Beat Goes On

Babe The Blue Ox

☐ (BOX)
Home / Honey do / Chicken head bone sucker / Gymkhana / Spatula / Waiting for water to boil / Booty / Born again / National Geographic / Tongue tied / Snicker
RTD 15715752 / Jun '93 / World Service

Babes In Toyland

☐ FONTANELLE
Bruise violet / Right now / Blue bell / Handsome and gretel / Blood / Magick flute / Won't tell / Quiet room / Spun / Short song / Jungle train / Pearl / Real eyes / Mother / Gone
185012 / '92 / Southern

☐ PAINKILLERS
185122 / Jun '93 / Southern

Babs, Alice

☐ ALICE BABS & DUKE ELLINGTON/NILS LINDBERG 1973 (Babs, Alice & Duke Ellington/Nils Lindberg)
ABCD 005 / Oct '96 / Bluebell

☐ ALICE BABS, RED MITCHELL, ARNE DOMNERUS & NILS LINDBERG
ABC 052 / Mar '94 / Bluebell

☐ FAR AWAY STAR (Babs, Alice & Duke Ellington/Nils Lindberg Orchestras)
Far away star / Serenade to Sweden / Spaceman / Jeep's blues / Daydream / Is God a three-letter word for love / Jump for joy / Warm valley / Blues for the maestro
ABC 000005 / Oct '90 / Bluebell

☐ SWING IT (1939-1953)
PHONTCD 9302 / Jun '94 / Phontastic

Baby Animals

☐ BABY ANIMALS
Rush you / Early warning / Painless / Make it end / Big time friends / Working for the enemy / One word / Break my heart / Waste of time / One too many / Ain't gonna get
72787230102 / Jul '98 / Imago

Baby Bird

☐ BAD SHAVE
KW Jesus TV roof appeal / Bad jazz / Too handsome / Steam train / Bad shave / O my God, you're a king / Restaurant is guilty / Valerie / Shop girl / WBT / Hate song / 45 + Fat / Sha na na / Bug in a breeze / It's OK / Happy bus / Swinging from tree to tree
BABYBIRDCD 002 / Oct '95 / Baby Bird

☐ FATHERHOOD
No children / Cooling towers / Cool and crazy thing to do / Bad blood / Neil Armstrong / May be / But love / Good weather / Not about a girl / Dustbin liner / Fatherhood / Failed old singer / Daisies / Godamn it, you're a kid / Aluminium beach / Iceberg / I didn't want to wake you up / Good night
BABYBIRDCD 003 / Dec '95 / Baby Bird

☐ HAPPIEST MAN ALIVE, THE
Razor blade shower / Sundial in a tunnel / Little white man / Halfway up the hill / Horse sugar / Please don't / He furious / Louse / Copper feel / Sea gullaby / Dead in love / Candy girl / Gunfingers / M-Word / Married / In the country / Plane crash xmas / Beautiful disease / You'll get a slap / In the morning
BABYBIRDCD 004 / Apr '96 / Baby Bird

☐ I WAS BORN A MAN
Blow it to the moon / Man's tight vest / Lemonade baby / CFC / Corner shop / Kiss your country / Hong Kong blues / Dead bird sings / Baby bird / Farmer / Invisible tune / Alison / Love love love
BABYBIRD 001 / Jul '95 / Baby Bird

☐ THERE'S SOMETHING GOING ON
Bad old man / If you'll be mine / Back together / I was never here / First man on the sun / You will always love me / Life / All men are evil / Take me back / It's not funny anymore / There's something going on
ECHCD 024 / 24 Aug '98 / Echo

Baby D

☐ DELIVERANCE (2CD Set)
Got to believe / So pure / Destiny / Come into my world / Casanova / Winds of love / I need your loving / Daydreaming / Euphoria / Nature's warning / Take me to heaven / Let me be your fantasy / Have it all / Daydreaming - Acenhallucination / So pure
82286832 / 17 Aug '98 / Systematic

Baby Doc

☐ IN WORSHIP OF FALSE IDOLS (Baby Doc & The Dentist)
TECLP 23CD / Jul '95 / Truelove

Baby Ford

☐ HEADPHONEASYRIDER
BMI 1035CD / Apr '97 / Black Market International

Baby Fox

☐ DUM DUM BABY
Dum dum baby / Heaven's gate / Rookery / Nearly beautiful / Zodiac / Bad girl love / Bluebird / Fury to forgiveness / Rainy London Sunday / Halloween / Still point / That's the way it is / Line's cleared / Naked hour
RR 87332 / 23 Mar '98 / Roadrunner

☐ NORMAL FAMILY, A
COB 58992 / Jul '96 / Deep Blue

Baby Gobal

☐ BABY GOBAL
VR 046CD / 27 Apr '98 / Victory

Baby Mammoth

☐ 10,000 YEARS UNDER THE STREET
PORK 035 / Aug '96 / Pork

☐ ANOTHER DAY AT THE ORIFICE
I'm not joking / Blessing the meek / Narrow / Delta's young champion / Frank furtive / 100% Polyester / Three wheeler / Thighwig / Hair breaks / Zingari's pet hoax / Divine milk shower / Ignore the fix
PORK 051 / 13 Apr '98 / Pork

☐ BRIDGING TWO WORLDS
PORK 042 / Feb '97 / Pork

☐ ONE, TWO, FREAK
PORK 044 / Jul '97 / Pork

Baby Wayne

☐ RAM DJ
HBCD 147 / Jan '94 / Heartbeat

Babyface

☐ CLOSER LOOK, A
Mary Mack / Two occasions / I love you babe / Chivalry / Lovers / It's no crime / Love saw it: Babyface & Karyn White / Love makes things happen: Babyface & Pebbles / My kinda girl / Whip appeal / Lovers
4693482 / Feb '97 / Epic

☐ DAY, THE
Every time I close my eyes / Talk to me / I said I love you / When your body gets weak / Simple days / All day thinkin' / Seven seas / Day (that you gave me a son) / How come, how long / This is for the lover in you
4853682 / Nov '96 / Epic

☐ FOR THE COOL IN YOU
For the cool in you / Lady lady / Never keeping secrets / Rock bottom / And our feelings / Saturday / When can I see you / Illusions / Bit old fashioned / You are so beautiful / I'll always love you / Well alright
4739492 / Jan '94 / Epic

☐ LOVERS
You make me feel brand new / Lovers / Chivalry / I love you / Mary Mack / Faithful / If we try / Take your time / I love you babe
4879282 / Jul '97 / Epic

☐ UNPLUGGED
Change the world / Talk to me / Whip appeal / Breathe again / Exhale / I'll make love to you / End of the road / I'll make love to you / End of the road / End of the road / Day that you gave me a son / Gone too soon / How come how long
4890692 / 17 Nov '97 / Epic

Babylon Dance Band

☐ BABYLON DANCE BAND
When I'm home / Bold beginnings / Reckoning / Shively spleen / Roger / Leave / Resources / See that girl / Jacob's chain / ABC / Golden days / Someday / All a radical / Shake
OLE 0332 / May '94 / Matador

Babylon Sad

☐ KYRIE
MASSCD 026 / Feb '94 / Massacre

Babylon Whores

☐ COLD HEAVEN
Deviltry / Omega therion / Beyond the sun / Metatron / Enchirdion / In arcadia / Babylon astronaut / Flesh of a swine / Cold heaven
CDMFN 226 / Aug '97 / Music For Nations

Babylon Zoo

☐ BOY WITH THE X-RAY EYES, THE
Animal army / Spaceman / Zodiac sign / Paris green / Confused art / Caffeine / Boy with the x-ray eyes / Don't feed the animals / Fire guided light / Is your soul for sale / I'm cracking up I need a pill
CDEMC 3742 / Sep '97 / EMI

Babys

☐ ISN'T IT TIME
Isn't it time / Everytime I think of you / Golden mile / Please don't leave me here / Wrong or right / Piece of the action / Broken heart / California / Love don't prove I'm right / I was one / White lightning / Looking for love / Dying man / You (got it)
DC 881882 / 2 Jan '98 / Disky

Baca, Susana

☐ SUSANA BACA
Negra presentuosa / Molino molero / Heces / Tu mirada y mi voz / Zamba malato / Luna lena / Caras lindas / Se mi van los pies / Inciente candela / Senor de los milagros
9362466272 / 16 Feb '98 / WEA

☐ VESTIDA DE VIDA
KAR 074 / Nov '97 / IMP

Bacan

☐ CARA (Bacan & Lilian Vieira)
CHR 70036 / Sep '96 / Challenge

Bacan, Pedro

☐ EN PUBLIC A BOBIGNY (Bacan, Pedro & Les Clan Des Pinini)
Sabeis ustedes Senores / Que quiere que tenga / Pobresito de aquel / Tu querer y mi querer / Gitania / Lo mucho que te quiero
PW 011 / Jul '97 / Pee Wee

Baccara

☐ DIE HIGHLIGHTS
Yes sir I can boogie / Set me free / Fantasy love / Say a little prayer / We need / Without you / FUN / Touch me / Call me up / Are u alone tonite / I lose control / I want u / Never gonna give up
12962 / Sep '97 / Laserlight

Bach Choir

☐ FAMILY CAROLS
CHAN 8973 / Nov '97 / Chandos

☐ IN DULCI JUBILO (Bach Choir & Philip Jones Brass Ensemble)
Fanfare / O come all ye faithful (adeste fidelis) / Gabriel's message / Angelus ad virginem / Ding dong merrily on high / Virgin most pure / God rest ye merry gentlemen / In dulci jubilo / Unto us is born a son / Nun seid ihr wohl gerochen / Lord Jesus hath a garden / Come all ye shepherds / Wassail song / We three Kings / Il est ne / Jingle bells / Deck the hall / Holly and the ivy / We wish you a merry Christmas / Ach mein herzliebes Jesulein / Once in Royal David's city / Hush my dear, lie still and slumber / Shepherd's pipe carol / Away in a manger / Stille nacht / Sussex carol / Star carol / Hark the herald angels sing / Fanfare
4489802 / Nov '96 / Decca

☐ UNFORGETTABLE CHRISTMAS CAROLS VOL.2
Hark the herald angels sing / I saw three ships / We've been awhile a-wandering / Up good Christen folk and listen / I sing of a maiden / God rest ye merry gentlemen / Away in amnager / O little one sweet / Unto us is born a son / Wassail / When Christ was born / Infant holy infant lowly / When an angel host entuned / Born in a manger / Patapan / Carol with lullaby / Christmas carol / Masters in this hall / Gabriel's message / See amid the winter's snow / Child is born / Rocking / Coventry carol / Past three o'clock
724357251723 / 17 Nov '97 / EMI Classics

Bach, Johnny

☐ BACH ON THE BOTTLE AGAIN (Bach, Johnny & The Moonshine Boozers)
Lost John / Down the road / Move it / Wanted man / I don't wanna go home / Ice cold baby / Dissatisfied / Black rat swing / Hot lips baby / De bop / It ain't my job to tell you / Rock around the town / Jailhouse rock / I wanna bop / Move it / Hot lips baby
JRCD 30 / Sep '97 / Jappin' & Rockin'

Bacharach, Burt

☐ BACHARACH MOODS (20 Easy Listening Classics) (Various Artists)
Do you know the way to San Jose / There's always something there to remind me / Message to Michael / Maybe / Arthur's theme / Raindrops keep falling on my head / Look of love / Windows of the world / Stronger than before / Close to you / Walk on by / Anyone who had a heart / I'll never fall in love again / Magic moments / This guy's in love with you / Trains and boats and planes / Alfie / I say a little prayer / What the world needs now is love / That's what friends are for
308782 / 11 May '98 / Hallmark

☐ BEST OF BURT BACHARACH, THE
5404522 / Apr '96 / A&M

☐ BEST OF BURT BACHARACH, THE (RTE Concert Orchestra/Richard Hayman)
8990051 / May '96 / Naxos

☐ BLUE BACHARACH (A Cooler Shaker) (Various Artists)
This guy's in love with you: *Turrentine, Stanley* / Wives and lovers: *Wilson, Nancy* / Say a little prayer: *Wilson, Reuben* / Look of love: *Three Sounds* / What the world needs now is love: *Turrentine, Stanley* / They don't give medals (to yesterday's heroes): *Rawls, Lou* / Do you know the way to San Jose: *Holmes, Richard 'Groove'* / Walk on by: *Turrentine, Stanley* / Promises, promises: *Jazz Crusaders* / Knowing when to leave: *Watts, Ernie Quintet* / Always something there to remind me: *Turrentine, Stanley* / Wives and lovers: *Green, Grant* / Alfie: *Wilson, Nancy*
CDP 8577492 / 1 Oct '97 / Blue Note

☐ BURT BACHARACH ALBUM, THE (Broadway Sings The Best Of Bacharach) (Various Artists)
What's new pussycat: *Graae, Jason* / Are you there: *Alvin, Farah* / I'll never fall in love again: *Haines, Guy* / My little red book: *Joyce, Melba* / One less bell to answer: *Noll, Christine* / Bacharach at the movies: *Plaids* / Alfie: *Nicastro, Michelle* / Look of love: *Krakowski, Jane* / Anyone who had a heart: *La Chanze* / Whoever you are I love you: *Egan, Susan* / House is not a home: *Purl, Linda* / Bachcarach love story: *Hicks, Shauna* / That's what friends are for: *Reddy, Helen*
VSD 5889 / 29 Jun '98 / Varese Sarabande

☐ BURT BACHARACH/HAL DAVID SONGBOOK, THE (Various Artists)
I say a little prayer: *Warwick, Dionne* / What the world needs now is love: *De Shannon, Jackie* / Alfie: *Black, Cilla* / Message to Michael: *Warwick, Dionne* / I just don't know what to do with myself: *Springfield, Dusty* / Do you know the way to San Jose: *Warwick, Dionne* / Twenty four hours from Tulsa: *Pitney, Gene* / Close to you: *Monro, Matt* / You'll never get to heaven (If you break my heart): *Warwick, Dionne* / Anyone who had a heart: *Black, Cilla* / I'll never fall in love again: *Gentry, Bobbie* / Walk on by: *Van Dyke, Leroy* / Story of my life: *Holliday, Michael* / What's new pussycat: *Jones, Tom* / This guy's in love with you: *Distel, Sacha* / Trains and boats and planes: *Kramer, Billy J.* / Make it easy on yourself: *Walker Brothers* / House is not a home: *Bassey, Shirley* / Always something there to remind me: *Shaw, Sandie* / Look of love: *Warwick, Dionne* / Raindrops keep falling on my head: *Distel, Sacha* / Wishin' and hopin': *Merseybeats* / Only love can break a heart: *Yuro, Timi* / Promises, promises: *Warwick, Dionne*
VSOPCD 128 / Jan '89 / Connoisseur Collection

☐ CLOSE TO YOU
MACCD 277 / Aug '96 / Autograph

☐ EASY LISTENING BACHARACH (Various Artists)
Promises, promises: *Faith, Percy* / Send me no flowers: *Day, Doris* / Alfie: *Bennett, Tony* / Wives and lovers: *Williams, Andy* / I'll never fall in love again: *Page, Patti* / Walk on by: *Torme, Mel* / Close to you: *Mathis, Johnny* / Trains and boats and planes: *Harris, Anita* / Do you know the way to San Jose: *Goulet, Robert* / House is not a home: *Fame, Georgie* / This girl's in love with you: *Jones, Salena* / Make it easy on yourself: *Bennett, Tony* / Blue on blue: *Vinton, Bobby* / Raindrops keep falling on my head: *Nero, Peter* / My little red book: *Torme, Mel* / I say a little prayer: *Harris, Anita* / Look of love: *Mathis, Johnny* / Story of my life: *Robbins, Marty* / If I could go back: *Williams, Andy* / What the world needs now is love: *Bennett, Tony*
4851252 / Aug '96 / Columbia

☐ FOREVER BURT BACHARACH (Various Artists)
Walk on by: *Shapiro, Helen* / I say a little prayer: *Goodwin, Ron & His Orchestra* / Close to you: *Monro, Matt* / Alfie: *Cher* / Do you know the way to San Jose: *Manuel* / What the world needs now is love: *De Shannon, Jackie* / Raindrops keep falling on my head: *Gentry, Bobbie* / Trains and boats and planes: *Kramer, Billy J. & The Dakotas* / Magic moments: *Hilton, Ronnie* / Look of love: *Tarmey, Bill* / I'll never fall in love again: *Gentry, Bobbie* / House is not a home: *Bassey, Shirley* / This guy's in love with you: *O'Connor, Des* / Message to Martha: *Faith, Adam* / Once in a blue moon: *Cole, Nat 'King'* / Keep away from other girls: *Shapiro, Helen* / Make it easy on yourself: *Black, Cilla* / Anyone who had a heart: *Carr, Vikki* / Keep me in my mind: *Cogan, Alma*
CDMFP 6264 / Nov '96 / Music For Pleasure

☐ HIT MAKER (Bacharach, Burt & His Orchestra)
Don't make me over / Walk on by / Don't go breaking my heart / Blue on blue / Last one to be loved / Always something there to remind me / Twenty four hours from Tulsa / Trains and boats and planes / Wives and lovers / Saturday sunshine / House is not a home / Anyone who had a heart
UMD 80389 / 8 Sep '97 / Universal

☐ MAGIC MOMENTS (The Classic Songs Of Burt Bacharach) (Various Artists)
Magic moments: *Como, Perry* / Raindrops keep fallin' on my head: *Como, Perry* / (They long to be) close to you: *Como, Perry* / House is not a home: *Como, Perry* / Look of love: *Simone, Nina* / Alfie: *Warwick, Dionne* / Sunny weather lover: *Warwick, Dionne* / Anyone who had a heart: *McGovern, Maureen* / There's always something there to remind me: *Feliciano, Jose* / I say a little prayer: *Davis, Skeeter* / Do you know the way to San Jose: *Ames, Ed* / Make it easy on yourself: *Ames, Ed* / What the world needs now is love: *Ames, Ed* / Wives and lovers: *Ames, Ed* / What's new pussycat: *Cramer, Floyd* / I just don't know what to do with myself: *Cramer, Floyd* / Any day now: *Milsap, Ronnie* / I'll never fall in love again: *Atkins, Chet* / This guy's in love with you: *Stuckey, Nat* / Blue on blue: *Anka, Paul* / Promises promises: *Hirt, Al*
74321447232 / Feb '97 / Camden

☐ MAGIC MUSIC OF BURT BACHARACH (Various Artists)
GRF 195 / Jan '93 / Tring

☐ MAGIC OF BURT BACHARACH, THE (Various Artists)
CPCD 8227 / Aug '96 / Charly

☐ MAN AND HIS MUSIC, A
Do you know the way to San Jose / I say a little prayer / I'll never fall in love again / No one remembers my name / This guy's in love with you / Time and tenderness / Wives and lovers / Raindrops keep fallin' on my head / (They long to be) close to you / Look of love / Alfie / Where are you / Us / Another Spring will rise / Message to Michael / Reach out for me / Bond Street / Young grow younger every day
5542392 / Oct '97 / Spectrum

☐ MUSIC OF BURT BACHARACH, THE (Various Artists)
24 hours from Tulsa: *Pitney, Gene* / Arthur's theme: *Bilk, Acker* / Raindrops keep fallin' on my head: *Thomas, B.J.* / Do you know the way to San Jose: *Coombe Music* / I say a little prayer: *Coombe Music* / I'll never fall in love again: *Coombe Music* / Make it easy on yourself: *Butler, Jerry* / Love that really counts: *Merseybeats* / Magic moments: *Coombe Music* / Alfie: *Coombe Music* / House is not a home: *Coombe Music* / Any day now: *Drifters* / Look of love: *Coombe Music* / Answer to everything: *Shannon, Del* / Only love can break your heart: *Pitney, Gene* / There's always something there to remind me: *Coombe Music* / What the world needs now is love: *Coombe Music* / This guy's in love with you: *Coombe Music* / Close to you: *Coombe Music* / Baby it's you: *Shirelles* / Walk on by: *Coombe Music* / Man who shot Liberty Valance: *Pitney, Gene* / Trains and boats and planes: *Kramer, Billy J.* / Wishin' and hopin': *Merseybeats*
QED 183 / Nov '96 / Tring

☐ MUSIC OF BURT BACHARACH, THE (Various Artists)
Raindrops keep falling on my head / I'll never fall in love again / What's new pussycat / Close to you / I say a little prayer / Walk on by / Man who shot Liberty Valance / Wives and lovers / On my own / Do you know the way to San Jose / Promises promises / Casino Royale / Arthur's theme / Magic moments / That's what friends are for / Alfie / What the world needs now is love / Wishin' and hopin'
CD 6115 / Jan '98 / Music

☐ REACH OUT
Reach out for me / Alfie / Bond street / Are you there / What the world needs now is love / Look of love / House is not a home / I say a little prayer / Windows of the world / Lisa / Message to Michael
3941312 / Sep '95 / A&M

Bachelors

☐ BEST OF THE BACHELORS, THE
Diane / I wouldn't trade you for the world / Whispering / Rose of Tralee / Marie / Sound of silence / Maggie / Unicorn / You'll never walk alone / Love me with all your heart / Ramona / Key to my heart / Danny Boy / Charmaine / No arms can ever hold you / Marta / Stay / He ain't heavy, he's my brother / I need love / I believe
CD 6041 / Oct '96 / Music

☐ CLASSIC ARTISTS
JHD 049 / Jun '92 / Tring

☐ DIANE
I wouldn't trade you for the world / Sound of silence / Rose of Tralee / Ramona / Key to my heart / I believe / Whispering / Charmaine / Danny boy / No arms can ever hold you / Diane / Marta / Love me with all your heart / Marie
302342 / Feb '98 / Hallmark

☐ GOLDEN HITS & PRECIOUS MEMORIES
Diane / No arms can ever hold you / Charmaine / He's got the whole world in his hands / Whispering / Put your arms around me, honey / Moonlight and roses / Little white cloud that cried / Ramona / Only you / Pennies from heaven / Dream / Whispering grass / Saints (when the saints go marching in) / I wouldn't trade you for the world / Ten pretty girls / With all my heart / Whistle down the wind / Marie / Old Bill / Pagan love song / Faraway places / If / Always / True love for evermore / Skip to my Lou / Melody of love / I'm yours / I believe
8444862 / Jan '96 / Deram

☐ I BELIEVE
I believe / Charmaine / I wouldn't trade you for the world / Ramona / No arms can ever hold you / Marie / Walk with faith in your heart / Stay / Rose of Tralee / I need love / Unicorn / Danny Boy / Diane / Whispering / Love me with all of your heart / Sound of silence / In the chapel in the moonlight / Maggie / Key to my heart / He ain't heavy, he's my brother
3036001252 / 13 Oct '97 / Carlton

☐ WORLD OF THE BACHELORS, THE
I believe / Diane / I wouldn't trade you for the world / Whispering / I'll be with you in apple blossom time / Marie / He's got the whole world in his hands / No arms can ever hold you / Angel and the stranger / Ramona / With these hands / I'll see you in my dreams / Faraway places / Jailer, bring me water / When the saints go marching in / Stars will remember / True love for evermore / Whispering grass / Charmaine / You'll never walk alone
5520172 / May '96 / Spectrum

Bachicha, Bianco

☐ ORIGINAL TANGOS
995302 / Jun '93 / EPM

Bachir, Munir

☐ MEDITATIONS
W 260071 / Sep '96 / Inedit

Bachman

☐ ANY ROAD
341082 / Sep '93 / Koch

Bachman, Randy

☐ MERGE
TNSD 0117 / Sep '97 / True North

Bachman-Turner Overdrive

☐ ANTHOLOGY (2CD Set)
5149022 / Jan '94 / Phonogram

☐ GREATEST HITS
Lookin' out for no.1 / Hey you / Taking care of business / You ain't seen nothin' yet / Flat broke love / Rock 'n' roll nights / Roll on down the highway / Freeways / Down down / Let it ride / Can we all come together / Jamaica
8300392 / Jan '86 / Phonogram

☐ KING BISCUIT PRESENTS...
Let it ride / Give it time / Roll on down the highway / Welcome home / Takin' care of business / Slow down boogie / You ain't seen nothing yet / Interview
KBFHCD 013 / 24 Aug '98 / King Biscuit

☐ NOT FRAGILE
Not fragile / Roll down the highway / You ain't seen nothin' yet / Free wheelin' / Sledgehammer / Blue moanin' / Second hand / Givin' it all away / Rock is my life, and this is my song
8301782 / '92 / Phonogram

☐ ROLL ON DOWN THE HIGHWAY
You ain't seen nothin' yet / Roll on down the highway / Lookin' out for no.1 / Heartaches / Stayed awake all night / Just for you / Down and out man / Blue collar / Hey you / My wheel's won't turn / Takin' care of business / Stonegates / Not fragile / Away from home / Life still goes on (I'm lonely) / Take it like a man \ / Shotgun rider / Sledgehammer
5504212 / Aug '94 / Spectrum

☐ VERY BEST OF BACHMAN-TURNER OVERDRIVE, THE
Hey you / Roll on down the highway / Not fragile / Hold back the water / Blue collar / You ain't seen nothing yet / Take it like a man / Four wheel drive and free wheelin' medley / Gimme your money please
10312 / Oct '97 / Go On Deluxe

Bachs

☐ OUT OF THE BACHS
FLASH 43 / 1 Jun '98 / Flash

Bachue Cafe

☐ BACHUE CAFE
HRM 001CD / Mar '96 / Highlander

Back Bay Ramblers

☐ BACK BAY RAMBLERS
SOSCD 1262 / Dec '94 / Stomp Off

☐ MY MAMA'S IN TOWN (Back Bay Ramblers & Jimmy Mazzy)
SOSCD 1279 / Dec '94 / Stomp Off

Back Porch Blues

☐ BACK TO BASICS
BCD 00082 / Jul '96 / Burnside

Back To Base

☐ ELECTRIC EYE
Mission / Dr. Base / Electric eye / Untouchables / Free the drum / Wasi
SPICD 004 / 9 Feb '98 / MPR

Back To The Future

☐ PROGRESSIVELY FUNKY
HDHCD 502 / Jul '91 / HDH

Backbeats

☐ BACKBEATS
NERCD 088 / Nov '96 / Nervous

Backhouse, Miriam

☐ GYPSY WITHOUT A ROAD
Far away Tom / Widow / Farmers have gone East / Long lankin / Nasty spider / Dark side of the moon / John Riley / Keys of Canterbury / Gypsy without a road
CDDORIS 001 / 2 Feb '98 / Vinyl Tap

Backsters

☐ BACKSTERS LIVE, THE
63301440122 / 3 Aug '98 / Zebra

Backstreet Boys

☐ BACKSTREET'S BACK
CHIP 186 / Aug '97 / Jive

☐ INTERVIEW SESSIONS
CHAT 3 / 8 Dec '97 / Chatback

Backstrom, Ola

☐ OLA BACKSTROM
GCD 21CD / Apr '95 / Grappa

Backtrack Blues Band

☐ KILLIN' TIME
Killin' time / Heavy built woman / Cruesin' for a bluesin' / Like it or not / Work to do / Babe oh babe / Come on to me mama / Don't need nobody / I make my home in Florida / You'll come back someday
ICH 9005CD / Jun '94 / Ichiban

Backus, Gus

☐ DIE SINGLES 1959-1961
BCD 15482 / '88 / Bear Family

☐ HILLBILLY GASTHAUS
Saginaw Michigan / Terribly pretty / Tennessee waltz / Oh Susanna / Laughin' and singin' / House I call my home / Don't fence me in / Home on the range / San Antonio rose / Long is the road / Reach for me / Paint and glue / On top of Old Smokey / I'm coming home / Deshalb ich nach Alaska / Das gross stadt m'dchen / Tennesse waltz (German) / Oh Susanna (German) / Nur in Tennessee / Der letzte trapper / Oh Cathrin / Heim will ich gehn / San Antonio rose (German) / Lang, lang, lang ist das her / He Alter John / Ese alles halb so schwer / Ein haus auf der Sierra / Es ist schon, Mutter
BCD 15765 / May '94 / Bear Family

☐ MY CHICK IS FINE
My chick is fine / You can't got it alone / Big Willie broke jail tonight / Short on love / Linda / Little kiss / Whisper / Queen of the stars / Listen / Priscilla / Happy end in Switzerland / Vaya con dios / For stealing her away / Just say goodbye (and you can go) / I'm coming home / Lost and found / Something you've got / Guess you'll have to do without / It feels so good / Blind man in our town / Need you all the time / Autumn breeze / Turn around / For I smile 'cause I think of you / Touch on your heart / My scrapbook / Memories of Ofheidelberg / Wonderful rainbow
BCD 15769 / Nov '95 / Bear Family

Backwater

☐ ANGELS ARE COOL
CHE 57CD / Oct '96 / Che

Backworld

☐ HOLY FIRE
Revolution 12 / Holy fire / Flowers of deceit / Angels of ashes / Winter flies / Twisted circle / Darkness of his smile / Winter flies / Come with joy / Wisdom of the flesh / Wine that flows
HCD 001 / Oct '97 / Harbringer House

Backyard Babies

☐ DIESEL AND POWER
MRRCD 008 / 8 Jun '98 / Megarock

☐ TOTAL 13
3984227462 / 13 Apr '98 / Coalition

Bacon, Max

☐ HIGHER YOU CLIMB (Bacon, Max & His Orchestra)
NTHEN 023CD / Jan '96 / Now & Then

Bacon, Paul

☐ PAUL BACON & HIS HOT COMBINATION (Bacon, Paul & His Hot Combination)
JCD 273 / Mar '97 / Jazzology

Bacoum Bibey Graham & Haley

☐ BACOUM BIBEY GRAHAM & HALEY
You're the one / Black eyed Susie / Lantern / I'm going to make it after all / I'll live again / Ready for the times / On a high high mountain / Lead me on and on / Our last goodbye / I'm country / How country girls can love / Hitch hiking to California / Feast from the father's supply / Waves of sorrow
REBCD 1743 / 9 Mar '98 / Rebel

Bad Boys

☐ BAD BOYS
BAD 001 / Nov '96 / Bad Boys

Bad Boys Inc.

☐ BAD BOYS INC.
Change your mind / Love here I come / I would give you forver / More to this world / Whenever you need someone / Falling for you girl / Take me away (I'll follow you) / Walking on air / You're my destiny / Honestly / Dream along with me tonight / Don't talk about love
5402872 / Oct '94 / A&M

☐ TAKE ME HOME
You're my destiny / Falling for you girl / Whenever you need someone / Walking on air / I would give you forever / I'm gonna miss you / Don't talk about love / Honestly / Take me home / Ain't nothing gonna keep me from you / Dream along with me tonight / Second chance / Heaven knows / Hearts of fire
5402002 / Jan '94 / A&M

Bad Brains

☐ BAD BRAINS
RUDCD 8223 / May '96 / ROIR

☐ BLACK DOTS
Don't need it / At the Atlantis / Pay to cum / Supertouch/Shitfit / Regulator / You're a migraine / Don't bother me / Banned in DC / Why'd you have to go / Man won't annoy ya / Redbone in the city / Black dots / How low can a punk get / Just another damn song / Attitude / Send you no flowers
CAROL 005CD / Sep '96 / Caroline

☐ FIRST ALBUM
RUSCD 8223 / 22 Sep '97 / ROIR

☐ GOD OF LOVE
Cool mountainer / Justice keepers / Long time / God of love / Tongue tee tie / To the heavens / Big fun / Thank jah / How I love thee / Darling I need you / Overs the water / Rights of a child
9362458822 / May '95 / Warner Bros.

☐ I AGAINST I
Intro / I against I / House of suffering / Re-ignition / Secret 77 / Let me help / She's calling you / Sacred love / Hired gun / Return to heaven
SST 065CD / May '93 / SST

☐ LIVE
I cried / At the movies / Regulator / Right brigade / I against I / I and I survive / House of suffering / Re-ignition / Sacred love / She's calling you / Coptic times / F.v.k. (fearless vampire killers) / Secret 77 / Day tripper
SST 160CD / May '93 / SST

☐ QUICKNESS
Soul craft / Voyage into infinity / Messengers / With the quickness / Gene machine / Don't bother me / Don't blow bubbles / Sheba / Yout juice / No conditions / Silent tears / Prophet's eye / Endtro
CAROLCD 1375 / Jun '97 / Caroline

☐ ROCK FOR LIGHT
Big takeover / Attitude / Right brigade / Joshua's song / I and I survive / Banned in DC / Supertouch / Destroy Babylon / FVK / Meek / I / Coptic times / Sailin' on / Rock for light / Rally round jah throne / At the movies / Riot squad / How low can a punk get / We will not / Jam
CAROLCD 1613 / Jun '97 / Caroline

☐ YOUTH ARE GETTING RESTLESS, THE (Live At The Paradiso Amsterdam 1987)
I / Rock for light / Right brigade / House of suffering / Day tripper / She's a rainbow / Coptic times / Sacred love / Re-ignition / Let me help / Youth are getting restless / Banned in DC / Sailin' on / Fearless vampire killer / At the movies / Revolution (dub) / Pay to cum / Big takeover
CAROLCD 1617 / Jun '97 / Caroline

Bad Company

☐ 10 FROM 6
Can't get enough / Feel like makin' love / Run with the pack / Shooting star / Movin' on / Bad company / Rock 'n' roll fantasy / Electric land / Ready for love / Live for the music
7816252 / Jan '86 / Atlantic

☐ BAD COMPANY
Can't get enough / Rock steady / Ready for love / Don't let me down / Bad company / Way I choose / Movin' on / Seagull
7567924412 / Sep '94 / Atlantic

☐ BURNIN' SKY
Burnin' sky / Leaving you / Like water / Morning sun / Knapsack / Heartbeat / Passing time / Man needs woman / Too bad / Master of ceremony / Peace of mind / Everything I need
7567924502 / Sep '94 / Atlantic

☐ COMPANY OF STRANGERS
Company of strangers / Clearwater highway / Judas my brother / Gimme gimme / Down down down / Down and dirty / You're the only reason / Loving you out loud / Dance with the devil / Pretty woman / Abandoned and alone / Where I belong / Little Martha
7559618082 / Aug '95 / Atlantic

☐ DESOLATION ANGELS
Rock 'n' roll fantasy / Crazy circles / Gone gone gone / Evil wind / Early in the morning / Lonely for your love / Oh, Atlanta / Take the time / Rhythm machine / She brings me love
7567924512 / Sep '94 / Atlantic

☐ HERE COMES TROUBLE
How about that / Stranger than fiction / Here comes the trouble / This could be the one / Both feet in the water / Take this town / What about you / Little angel / Hold on to my heart / Broken hearted / My only one
7567917592 / Oct '92 / Atlantic

☐ HOLY WATER
Holy water / Walk through fire / Stranger stranger / If you needed somebody / Fearless / Lay your love on me / Boys cry tough / With you in a heartbeat / I don't care / Never too late / Dead of the night / I can't live without you / Hundred miles
7567913712 / Jun '90 / Atlantic

☐ RUN WITH THE PACK
Live for the music / Simple man / Honeychild / Love me somebody / Run with the pack / Silver blue and gold / Young blood / Do right by your woman / Sweet lil' sister / Fade away
7567924352 / Jul '94 / Atlantic

☐ STORIES TOLD AND UNTOLD
7559619762 / 5 Jan '98 / Warner Bros.

☐ STRAIGHT SHOOTER
Good lovin' gone bad / Feel like makin' love / Weep no more / Shooting star / Deal with the preacher / Wild fire women / Anna / Call on me
7567826372 / Jun '94 / Atlantic

☐ WHAT YOU HEAR IS WHAT YOU GET (The Best Of Bad Company - Live)
How about that / Holy water / Rock 'n' roll fantasy / If you needed somebody / Here comes trouble / Ready for love / Shooting star / No smoke without a fire / Feel like makin' love / Take this town / Movin' on / Good lovin' gone bad / Fist full of blisters / Can't get enough / Bad company
7567923072 / Dec '93 / Atlantic

Bad Examples

☐ SLOW MUSIC
EFA 037652 / Nov '95 / Atatak

☐ TEMPTATION AND YOU
EFA 037702 / 6 Oct '97 / Atatak

Bad Habits

☐ WHAT DO YOU REALLY NEED FOR
LF 287CD / 6 Oct '97 / Lost & Found

Bad Influence

☐ NEW AGE WITCH HUNT
SKULD 007 / Jan '97 / Skuld

Bad Livers

☐ DELUSIONS OF BANJER
Uncle lucius / Ghost train / If it runs / How dark my shadow's grown / Better times / Git them pretty girls / Shit creek / Six feet down / Adventures of pee pee the sailor / Country blues / Crow black chicken / I know you're married / Pretty daughter / Precious time
QS 14CD / Sep '92 / Quarter Stick

☐ HOGS ON THE HIGHWAY
Hogs on the highway / Lathe crick / Counting the crossties / Shufflin' to Memphis / Dallas Texas / Corn liqour made a fool out of me / Saludamas a tejas / National blues / Mr. Modal / My old man / Cluck old hen / News not the weather / Falling down the stairs
SHCD 3862 / Mar '98 / Sugar Hill

☐ HORSES IN THE MINES
QS 20CD / May '94 / Quarter Stick

Bad Manners

☐ BEST OF BAD MANNERS, THE
Lip up fatty / Special brew / Lorraine / Just a feeling / Can can / My girl lollipop / Walking in the sunshine / Skaville UK / This is ska / Midnight rider / You fat ... / Christmas time again / Gonna get along without you now
BBSCD 010 / Sep '90 / Blue Beat

☐ CAN CAN
Can can / My girl lollipop / Walking in the sunshine / Special brew / Runaway / Echo / El pussy cat / Here comes the major / Lip up fatty / Lorraine / Under sea adventures of Ivor the Engine / Tequila / Never will change / Fatty fatty / This is ska / Non shrewd / Rosemary / Feel like jumpin' / Buffalo ska / Hey little girl / Return of the ugly / Skinhead girl / Sally brown / Skaville UK / Skinhead love affair / Walking in sunshine
CANCAN 001CD / 3 Nov '97 / Can Can

☐ DON'T KNOCK THE BALDHEAD (Live)
Echo 4+2 / This is ska / My girl lollipop / Fatty fatty / Lorraine / Feel like jumping / Skaville UK / Walking on sunshine / King ska / Samson and delilah / Wet dream / Just a feeling / El pussy cat / Ne-ne-na-na-na-nu-nu / Sally brown / Don't be angry / Wooly bully / Inner London violence / Special brew / Don't knock the baldhead / Lip up fatty / Can can
RRCD 249 / 22 Sep '97 / Receiver

☐ DON'T KNOCK THE BALDHEAD
EFA 056062 / 22 Sep '97 / Pork Pie

☐ EAT THE BEAT
Since you've gone away / Return of the ugly / Stampede / Rosemary / Bonanza ska / Sally Brown / Skinhead girl / Non shrewd / Mafia / Pipeline / Big five / Viv la ska revolution / Dume batty / Gonna get along without you now / Johnny's knee / How big do you love me / Oh Jamaica / Gonna get along without you now
DOJOCD 248 / May '96 / Dojo

☐ FATTY FATTY
Ni ni nananana nu nu / Here comes the major / Fatty fatty / King skarfa / Monster mash / Caledonia (what makes your big head hard) / Magnificent seven / Wooly bully / Lip up fatty / Special brew / Inner london violence / Scruffy was a huffy chuffu tugboat
LG 21005 / Jun '93 / Lagoon

☐ INNER LONDON VIOLENCE
Echo 4 + 2 / Just a feeling / Wooly bully / Only funking / Lollipop / Ivor the engine / Lorraine / Romeo, sampson and delilah / Walking in sunshine / Inner london violence / Special brew / Magnificent / Lip up fatty / Can can
LG 21094 / Apr '94 / Lagoon

☐ RARE
TLCD 298 / 13 Apr '98 / Tea Leaf

☐ RETURN OF THE UGLY
Skaville UK / Sally Brown / Since you've gone away / Rosemary / Bonanza ska / Return of the ugly / Hey little girl / Buffalo ska / Memory train / This is ska / Gonna get along without you now
DOJOCD 242 / Jul '95 / Dojo

☐ SKINHEAD
Pipeline / Skinhead girl / Stampede / Non shrewd / Johnny's knee / Skinhead love affair / How big do you love me / Baby elephant walk / Big five / Rock steady breakfast / Mafia / Viva la ska revolution / Skinhead girl / You fat bastard
LG 21026 / Jul '93 / Lagoon

☐ THIS IS SKA
DOJOCD 245 / Jan '96 / Dojo

☐ VIVE LA SKA REVOLUTION (2CD Set)
Skaville UK / Sally Brown / Bonanza ska / Return of the ugly / Skinhead love affair / Non shrewd / Big 5 / Stampede / Skinhead girl / Mafia / Pipeline / Viva la ska revolution / Gonna get along without you / How big do you love / Johnny Knee / This is ska / Oh Jamaica / Fatty fatty / Lip up fatty / Special brew / Walking in the sunshine / That'll do nicely / Since you've gone away / Can can / Samson and Delilah / Lorraine / My girl lollipop / Inner London violence / Wooly bully / Just a feeling
SMDCD 140 / May '97 / Snapper

Bad Moon Rising

☐ BAD MOON RISING
Hands on / If it ain't dirty / Without your love / Full moon / Lie down / Old flames / Built for speed / Dark side of babylon / Sunset after midnight / Wayward son
CDFLAG 78 / Jan '93 / Under One Flag

☐ BLOOD
Dangerous game / Servants of the sun / Devil's son (Where our children die) / Blood on the streets / Tears in the dark / Heart of darkness / Chains / Till the morning comes / Time will tell / Remember me
CDFLAG 79 / Apr '93 / Under One Flag

Bad News

☐ CASH IN COMPILATION, THE
Hey hey bad news / Bad dreams / Warriors of Ghengis Khan / AGM / Bohemian rhapsody / Pretty woman / O levels / Life with Brian / Bad news / Masturbike / Double entendre / Drink till I die / Cashing in on Christmas
DOJOCD 152 / Sep '93 / Dojo

Bad Religion

☐ AGAINST THE GRAIN
864092 / Dec '90 / Epitaph

☐ ALL AGES
864432 / Nov '95 / Epitaph

☐ BAD RELIGION 1980-1985
864072X / Nov '91 / Epitaph

☐ FUCK ARMAGEDDON, THIS IS A BAD RELIGION TRIBUTE (Various Artists)
TR 003CD / Dec '96 / Tribute

☐ GENERATOR
864162 / Mar '92 / Epitaph

☐ NO CONTROL
864062 / Jun '93 / Epitaph

☐ NO SUBSTANCE
Hear it / Shades of truth / All fantastic images / Biggest killer in American history / No substance / Raise your voice / Sowing the seeds of Utopia / Hippy killers / State of the end of the Millennium / Vocacious march of Godlines / Mediocre / Victims of the revolution / Strange denial / At the mercy of the imbeciles / Same person / In so many ways
4895702 / 6 Apr '98 / Columbia

☐ STRANGER THAN FICTION
Incomplete / Leave mine to me / Stranger than fiction / Tiny voices / Handshake / Better off dead / Infected / Television / Individual / Hooray for me / Slumber / Marked / Inner logic / What it is / 21st Century (digital boy)
4773432 / Sep '94 / Columbia

Bad Seeds

☐ BAD SEEDS/LIBERTY BELL (Bad Seeds/Liberty Bell)
642440 / Apr '97 / Arcade

Bad Yodellers

☐ I WONDER
SR 30190CD / Jan '92 / Semaphore

☐ WINDOW
SR 330591CD / '91 / Semaphore

Badawi

☐ JERUSALEM UNDER FIRE
RUSCD 8234 / 3 Nov '97 / ROIR

Badfinger

☐ ASS
Apple of my eye / Get away / Icicles / Winner / Blind owl / Constitution / When I say / Cowboy / Can I love you / Timeless / Do you mind
CDSAPCOR 27 / Feb '97 / Apple

☐ BBC LIVE IN CONCERT
Come and get it / No matter what / Better days / Only you and I know / We're for the dark / Sweet Tuesday morning / Feelin' alright / Take it all / Suitcase / Love is easy / Blind owl / Constitution / Icicles / Mattered spam / I can't take it
SFRSCD 031 / Jul '97 / Strange Fruit

☐ COME AND GET IT (A Tribute To Badfinger) (Various Artists)
CPR 2181 / Feb '97 / Copper

☐ COME AND GET IT - BEST OF BADFINGER
Come and get it / Maybe tomorrow / Rock of all ages / Dear Angie / Carry on till tomorrow / No matter what / Believe me / Midnight caller / Better days / Without you / Take it all / Money / Flying / Name of the game / Suitcase / Day after day / Baby blue / When I say / Icicles / I can love you / Apple of my eye
CDSAPCOR 28 / Apr '95 / Apple

Badgewearer

☐ THANK YOU FOR YOUR CUSTOM
GUIDE 7CD / Aug '96 / Guided Missile

Badie, Bernard

☐ SOUND TRAXX
SUB 48772 / 27 Apr '98 / Distance

Badjie, Saikouba

☐ BOUGARABOU (Solo Drumming Of Casamance)
VPU 1005CD / May '97 / Village Pulse

Badland

☐ BADLAND
BF 14 / Sep '96 / Bruce's Fingers

Badloves

☐ GET ON BOARD
D 24025 / Mar '94 / Mushroom

Badmarsh

☐ DANCING DRUMS (Badmarsh & Shri)
CASTE 5CD / 16 Mar '98 / OutCaste

Badu, Erykah

☐ BADUIZM
Rimshot (Intro) / On and on / Appletree / Otherside of the game / Sometimes / Certainly (Flipped it) / No love / 4 Leaf clover / Certainly
UND 53027 / Mar '97 / MCA/Kedar

☐ LIVE
UND 53109 / 17 Nov '97 / MCA/Kedar

Baez, Joan

☐ BAPTISM
Old welsh song / I saw the vision of armies / Minister of war / Song in the blood / Casida of the lament / Of the dark past / London / In Guernica / Who murdered the minutes / Oh little child / No man is an island / From portrait of the artist as a young man / All the pretty little horses / Childhood / Magic wood / Poems from the Japanese / Colours / All in green went my love riding / Gacela of the dark death / Parable of the old man and the young / Epitaph for a poet / Evil / Old Welsh song
VMD 79275 / Jun '98 / Vanguard

☐ BEST OF JOAN BAEZ, THE
Diamonds and rust / Forever young / Prison trilogy / Simpel twist of fate / Never dreamed you'd leave in summer / Love song to a stranger / Please come to Boston / Children and all that jazz / Sweeter for me / Imagine / Gracias a la vida (heres to life) / Night they drove old Dixie down
CDMID 108 / Oct '92 / A&M

☐ BLESSED ARE... (2CD Set)
Blessed are / Night they drove old Dixie down / Salt of the Earth / Three horses / Brand new Tennessee waltz / Lost, lonely and wretched / Lincoln freed me today / Outside the Nashville city limits / San Francisco Mabel Joy / When time is stolen / Heaven help us all / Angeline / Help me make it through the night / Let it be / Put your hand in the hand / Gabriel and me / Milanese waltz/Marie Flore / Hitchhikers song / 33rd of August / Fifteen months / Plane wreck at Los Gatos (Deportee) / Maria Delores
VCD2 6570 / Jan '97 / Vanguard

☐ DIAMONDS (A Joan Baez Anthology/ 2CD Set)
Prison trilogy (Billy Rose) / Rainbow Road / Love song to a stranger / Myths / In the quiet morning / To Bobby / Son of Bangladesh / Tumbleweed / Imagine / Diamonds and rust / Fountain of sorrow / Never dreamed you'd leave in summer / Children and all that jazz / Simple twist of fate / Blue sky / Hello in there / Jesse / (Ain't gonna let nobody) Turn me around / Suzanne / I shall be released / Blowin' in the wind / Stewball / Ballad of Sacco and Vanzetti / Joe Hill / Love is just a four letter word / Forever young / Boulder to Birmingham / Swing low, sweet chariot / Oh happy day / Please come to Boston / Lily, Rosemary and the Jack of Hearts / Night they drove old Dixie down / Amazing Grace
5405002 / Mar '96 / A&M

☐ DIAMONDS AND RUST IN THE BULLRING
Diamonds and rust / No woman, no cry / Swing low, sweet chariot / El preso numero nuevo / Txoria txori / Gracias a la vida (Here's to life) / Ain't gonna let nobody turn me round / Famous blue raincoat / Let it be / Llego con tres heridas / Ellas danzan solas (cueca sola) / No nos moveran
CDVIP 174 / Apr '97 / Virgin VIP

☐ FAREWELL ANGELINA
Farewell Angelina / Daddy, you've been on my mind / It's all over now baby blue / Baby blue / Wild mountain thyme / Rangers command / Colours / Satisfied mind / River in the pines / Pauvre rutebeuf / Sagt mir wo die blumen sind / Hard rain's gonna fall
VMD 79200 / Oct '95 / Vanguard

☐ GONE FROM THE DANGER
GRACD 223 / 22 Sep '97 / Grapevine

☐ GREATEST HITS AND OTHERS
Night they drove old Dixie down / Dangling conversation / Help me make it through the night / Blessed are / Eleanor Rigby / Let it be / There but for fortune / Brand new Tennessee waltz / I pity the poor immigrant / Love is just a four letter word / Heaven help us all
VMD 79332 / Oct '96 / Vanguard

☐ HONEST LULLABY
Let your love flow / No woman, no cry / Light a light / She sings at the end of the movie / Before the deluge / Honest lullaby / Michael / For Sasha / For all we know / Free at last
4736952 / Feb '97 / Columbia

☐ IMAGINE
Diamonds and rust / Night they drove old Dixie down / Simple twist of fate / Imagine / In the quiet morning / Best of friends / Forever young / Prison trilogy / Jesse / Children and all that jazz / Please come to Boston / Never dreamed you'd leave in summer / Gracias a la vida (here's to life) / Sweeter for me / Love song to a stranger / Dida / Amazing grace
CDMID 180 / Mar '93 / A&M

☐ JOAN
Be not too hard / Eleanor Rigby / Turquoise / La colombe / Dangling conversation / Lady came from Baltimore / North / Children of darkness / Greenwood side / If you were a carpenter / Annabel Lee / Saigon bride
VMD 79240 / Apr '97 / Vanguard

☐ JOAN BAEZ
Silver dagger / East Virginia / Ten thousand miles / House of the rising sun / All my trials / Wildwood flower / Donna Donna / John Riley / Rake and the rambling boy / Little Moses / Mary Hamilton / Henry Martin / El preso numero nuevo
VMD 2077 / Oct '95 / Vanguard

☐ JOAN BAEZ IN CONCERT
Babe I'm gonna leave you / Geordie / Copper kettle / Kumbaya / What have they done to the rain / Black is the colour of my true love's hair / Danger waters / Gospel ship / House carpenter / Pretty boy floyd / Lady mary / Ate amanha / Matty groves
VMD 2122 / Jan '96 / Vanguard

☐ JOAN BAEZ IN CONCERT VOL.2
Once I had a sweetheart / Jackaroe / Don't think twice, it's alright / We shall overcome / Portland Town / Queen of hearts / Manha de carnaval / Te ador / Long black veil / Fennario / Ne belle cardillo / With God on our side / Three fishers / Hush little baby / Battle hymn of the Republic
VMD 2123 / Jan '96 / Vanguard

☐ JOAN BAEZ VOL.2
Wagoner's lad / Trees they do grow high / Lily of the West / Silkie / Engine 143 / Once I knew a pretty girl / Lonesome radio / Banks of the Ohio / Pal of mine / Barbara Allen / Cherry tree carol / Old blue / Railroad boy / Plaisir d'amour
VMD 2097 / Oct '95 / Vanguard

☐ JOAN BAEZ VOL.5
There but for fortune / Stewball / It ain't me babe / Death of Queen Jane / Child No.170 / Bachianas Brasileires No.5 / Go 'way from my window / I still miss someone / When you hear them cuckoos hollerin' / Birmingham Sunday / So we'll go no more a-roving / O'Cangaceiro / Unquiet grave / Child no.78
VMD 79160 / Apr '97 / Vanguard

☐ NOEL
O come, o come Emmanuel / Coventry carol / Good king Wencelas / Little drummer boy / Wonder as I wander, bring a torch Jeanette, Isabella / Down in yon forest / Carol of the birds / Angels we have heard on high / Ave maria / Mary's wandering / Away in a manger / Cantique de nord / What child is this / Silent night
VCD 792330 / Oct '96 / Vanguard

☐ ONE DAY AT A TIME
Sweet Sir Galahad / No expectations / Long black veil / Ghetto / Carry it on / Take me back to the sweet sunny south / Seven Bridges Road / Jolie blon / Joe Hill / Song for David / One day at a time
VMD 79310 / Oct '96 / Vanguard

☐ PLAY ME BACKWARDS
Play me backwards / Amsterdam / Isaac and Abraham / Stones in the road / Steal across the border / I'm with you / I'm with you (reprise) / Strange rivers / Through your hands / Dream song / Edge of glory
CDVIP 164 / Oct '96 / Virgin VIP

☐ PLAY ME BACKWARDS
VI 874842 / Nov '96 / Disky

☐ RARE, LIVE & CLASSIC 1958-1989 (3CD Set)
Scarlet ribbons / Jimmy Brown / Careless love / Auctioneer / Black is the colour of my true love's hair / John Hardy / We are crossing River Jordan / John Riley / Silver dagger / House of the rising sun / Low down chariot / Wagoner's lad / Last night I had the strangest dream / Geordie / What have they done to the rain / Troubled and I don't know why / With God on our side / We shall overcome / Go 'way from my window / Mama, you've been on my mind / There but for fortune / Colours / River in the pines / Pack up your sorrows / Swallow song / Legend of a girl child Linda / Children of darkness / Catch the wind / I am a poor wayfaring stranger / Sweet Sir Galahad / Donna Donna / Long black veil / Mama tried / Sing me back home / Joe Hill / Night they drove old Dixie down / Blessed are... / Hello in there / Love song to a stranger / In the quiet morning / Angel band / Johnny, I hardly knew ya / Gracias a la vida / Diamonds and rust / Children and all that jazz / Blowin' in the wind / Swing low, sweet chariot / Jesse / Honest lullaby / Jackaroe / Marriott USA / Amazing grace / Forever young / Farewell Angelina / Hard rain's a-gonna fall / Here's to you / Blues improv / Ring them bells / El preso numero nueve / Speaking of dreams
VCD 3125 / Apr '96 / Vanguard

☐ RING THEM BELLS
GRACD 208 / Sep '95 / Grapevine

☐ SPEAKING OF DREAMS
China / Warriors of the sun / Carrickfergus / Hand to mouth / Speaking of dreams / El Salvador / Rambler gambler / Whispering bells / Fairfax county / A mi manera (Comme d'habitude)
CDVGC 12 / '90 / Goldcastle

Bag

☐ OF FEAR
LOST 011 / May '97 / Lost

Bagad Bleimor

☐ SONEREZH GELTIEK
KMCD 12 / '91 / Keltia Musique

Bagad Brieg

☐ DELC'H DA NOZ
433CD / Jul '95 / Diffusion Breizh

Bagad De Lann Bihoue

☐ 30TH ANNIVERSARY 1952-1982
KMCD 86 / 1 Jun '98 / Keltia Musique

☐ BAGAD DE LANN BIHOUE
KMCD 09 / '91 / Keltia Musique

Bagad Kemper

☐ BAGAD KEMPER
KMCD 05 / Jul '90 / Keltia Musique

☐ LIP AR MAOUT (Battering Rams)
KMCD 50 / Apr '95 / Keltia Musique

Bagad Ronsed-Mor

☐ AG AN DOUAR D'AR MOR
CD 426 / Apr '94 / Diffusion Breizh

☐ COEFF 116
CD 441 / Aug '97 / Arfolk

Baghdaddies

☐ LAST TANGO IN BABYLON
GAZCD 016 / 27 Apr '98 / Gaz's Rockin' Records

Bagley, Bob

☐ COVERING ALL THE BASS (Bagley, Bob & Friends)
SBCD 3014 / Jun '96 / Sea Breeze

Baha Men

☐ KALIK
7567923942 / Sep '94 / Warner Bros.

Bailey, Admiral

☐ REGGAE DANCEHALL SENSATION
RRTGCD 7759 / Mar '90 / Rohit

☐ UNDISPUTED CHAMPION
Right foot out / Kill them with it / Me head a hurt me / Try some hustling / Big belly man / Don't want no kiss / Me a the danger / Don't be lazy / X rated country / Oil a bawl forward / Man and woman / Don't have me up / Winey winey / Come pon top / Rock and roll chat / Cater for woman / Jump up / Old time something / Ha fi ina it / Laugh after them
RNCD 2014 / Aug '93 / Rhino

Bailey, Benny

☐ BENNY BAILY & THE CZECH-NORWEGIAN QUARTET (Bailey, Benny & The Norwegian Quartet)
GEMCD 69 / Dec '87 / Gemini

☐ BIG BRASS
Hard sock dance / Alison / Tipsy / Please say yes / Kiss to build a dream on / Maud's mood
CCD 79011 / Feb '97 / Candid

☐ FOR HEAVEN'S SAKE (Bailey, Benny Quintet)
Little jazz / Blues East / Peruvian nights / Mood indigo / For heaven's sake / One for Wilton / No mo blues
HHCD 1006 / May '95 / Hot House

☐ PERUVIAN NIGHTS
Deep south / Reflectory / Caballeros / Hot house / No mo blues / Neptune / Peruvian nights / Blues easr / Set call
TCB 96102 / Jun '96 / TCB

Bailey, Buster

☐ BUSTER BAILEY STORY 1926-1945, THE
159022 / 5 Jan '98 / Jazz Archives

☐ CLASSICS 1925-1940
CLASSICS 904 / Nov '96 / Classics

☐ INTRODUCTION TO BUSTER BAILEY 1924-1942, AN
4038 / Nov '96 / Best Of Jazz

Bailey, Chris

☐ 54 DAYS AT SEA
DB 1145 / Mar '94 / Mushroom

☐ ENCORE
422009 / Oct '95 / Last Call

☐ WHAT WE DID ON OUR HOLIDAYS
ROSE 30 CD / Aug '90 / New Rose

Bailey, Craig

☐ NEW JOURNEY, A
CB no.1 / What would I do without you / Laura / Bells / Cherokee / Soul flower / Casanova / Li'l darlin' / No hip hop / Love dreams / New journey
CCD 79725 / May '97 / Candid

Bailey, Deford

☐ LEGENDARY DEFORD BAILEY, THE (Country Music's First Black Superstar)
630814020828 / 19 May '98 / Revenant

Bailey, Derek

☐ AIDA
DEX 5 / Apr '97 / Dexter's Cigar

☐ CYRO
INCUSCD 01 / '90 / Incus

☐ DEREK BAILEY & HAN BENNINK (Bailey, Derek & Han Bennink)
CORTI 09 / Jul '97 / Cortical

☐ FIGURING (Bailey, Derek & Barre Phillips)
INCUSCD 05 / '90 / Incus

☐ GUITAR, DRUMS 'N' BASS (Bailey, Derek & DJ Ninj)
AVAN 060 / Oct '96 / Avant

☐ HAN (Bailey, Derek & Han Bennink)
INCUSCD 02 / '90 / Incus

☐ INCUS TAPES
CORTI 010 / Jul '97 / Cortical

☐ LACE
EM 4013 / Dec '96 / Emanem

☐ MUSIC AND DANCE (Bailey, Derek & Min Tanaka)
REV 201 / 3 Nov '97 / Revenant

☐ NO WAITING (Bailey, Derek & Joelle Leandre)
P 198 / May '98 / Potlatch

☐ SOHO SUITES VOL.1 & 2 (2CD Set) (Bailey, Derek & Tony Oxley)
INCUS 29/30 / Aug '97 / Incus

☐ TOHJINBO (Derek & The Ruins)
PLE 11012 / Jun '98 / Paratactile

☐ TRIO PLAYING (Bailey, Derek & John Butcher/Oren Marshall)
INCUSCD 28 / Sep '97 / Incus

☐ VIPER (Bailey, Derek & Min Xiao-Fen)
AVANT 050 / Jul '98 / Avant

Bailey, Mildred

☐ FORGOTTEN LADY, A
158602 / Sep '96 / Jazz Archives

☐ HARLEM LULLABY
Georgia on my mind / Concentratin' / Harlem lullaby / Junk man / Ol' Pappy / Squeeze me / Downhearted blues / Porter's love song / Smoke dreams / Rockin' chair / Moon got in my eyes / It's the natural thing to do / Worried over you / Thanks for the memory / More than ever / Please be kind / I let a song go out of my heart / Rock it for me / My melancholy baby / Lonesome road
CDAJA 5065 / Dec '89 / Living Era

☐ LA SELECTION 1931-1939
700092 / Nov '92 / Art Vocal

☐ ME AND THE BLUES
In love in vain / It's a womans perogative / I'll close my eyes / Me and the blues / At sundown / Lover come back to me / Born to be blue / You started something / Can't we be friends / All that glitters is not gold
SV 0200 / Oct '97 / Savoy Jazz

☐ THANKS FOR THE MEMORY (1935-1944)
Lover come back to me / It had to be you / I never knew / Please don't talk about me when I'm gone / I didn't know about you / I'll get by / St. Louis blues / Evaline / Thanks for the memory / Don't be that way / Gulf coast blues / 'Tain't what you do / Barrelhouse music / Rock it for me / Arkansas blues / Darn that dream / I don't stand a ghost of a chance with you / Peace brother / I've got my love to keep me warm / There'll be some changes made / When day is done / Rockin' chair
CD 53282 / Feb '97 / Giants Of Jazz

☐ THAT ROCKIN' CHAIR LADY
TPZ 1007 / Oct '94 / Topaz Jazz

Bailey, Pearl

☐ BEST OF PEARL BAILEY
ATJCD 8007 / Jul '94 / Disky

☐ SOME OF THE BEST
As long as I live / Tired / I've got you under my skin / Easy street / Personality / Alla en el Rancho Grande / World weary / Hit the road to dreamland / I love my argentine / When the world was young / Supper time / In Spain they say si, si
12643 / May '97 / Laserlight

Bailey, Philip

☐ LIFE AND LOVE
How can I rely on you / Anything is possible / Tonight / Weightless / Someway somehow / Down / Talking to myself / Caution to the wind / Steppin' through time / Life and love / Feining for your love / All night waiting / Bailes' song / How can I rely on you
EAGCD 027 / 29 Jun '98 / Eagle

Bailey, Roy

☐ BUSINESS AS USUAL
CFCD 400 / Jul '94 / Fuse

☐ GENTLE MEN (2CD Set) (Bailey, Roy & Robb Johnson/Vera Coomi)
Grandfathers / Gentleman always wants horses / Three brothers / And then the trumpet sounded / Deeper than dugouts / R.S.M. Schofield is my shepherd / I played for Kitchener / At the mercy of the guns / Garden / Bloody medals / Soldier on / Empty chair / Noni and his golden serenaders / Boy of my dreams / When Harry took me to see Ypres / Sweet dreams / Silence of the salient / Whistle / Music from between the wars / Nobody's enemy / German exchange / Hindsight / Dead man's pennies / Candles in the rain / Making the gardens grow
IRR 030 / Dec '97 / Irregular

☐ NEVER LEAVE A SONG UNSUNG
CFCD 398 / Feb '88 / Fuse

☐ NEW DIRECTIONS IN THE OLD
Poison train / Blackwaters / Migrant's lullaby / This old town / Brass band music / Language of the land / Calling Joe Hill / Here's to the juggler/Katherine / Lass of Lochroyan / Do you remember / Last house in our street / Light years away / Do you think that I do not know / Ballad maker's apprentice
CFCD 402 / May '97 / Fuse

☐ PAST MASTERS
Streets of London / Punch and Judy man / Malvinas / Curtains of old Joe's house / Rain forest falls / Gracias a la vida / Two good arms / In these hard times / Song of the leaders / Roses of eyam / War without bangs / Green peace really green / All used up / Ghost story / Sleep well/gravity / Maria Diaz / Years grow tall / Daughters of the revolution
CFCD 403 / Feb '98 / Fuse

☐ WHAT YOU DO WITH WHAT YOU'VE GOT
What you do with what you've got / Ugly ones / Let your hair hang down / Patience Kershaw / See it come down / Send me back to Georgia / Rose of York / Day before the war / If they come in the morning / Song of the exile / Hard times of old England / Burning times / New Year's Eve / Everything possible / Rollin' home
CFCD 399 / Feb '89 / Fuse

☐ WHY DOES IT HAVE TO BE ME
CFCD 396 / Jul '95 / Fuse

Bailiff, Jessica

☐ EVEN IN SILENCE
KRANK 026 / 1 Jun '98 / Kranky

Bailongo

☐ TANGOLEANDA
SYNCD 166 / Jun '94 / Syncoop

Bailter Space

☐ CAPSUL
TB 005CD / 27 Oct '97 / Turnbuckle

☐ PHOTON EP
TB 012 / 17 Aug '98 / Turnbuckle

☐ WAMMO
Untied / Splat / At five we drive / Zapped / Colours / Retro / Glimmer / Voltage / D thing / Wammo
OLE 1422 / Jul '95 / Matador

Bain, Aly

☐ ALY BAIN AND FRIENDS (Bain, Aly & Various Artists)
Waiting for the federals: *Bain, Aly & Phil Cunningham* / Donald MacLean's farewell to Oban: *Bain, Aly & Phil Cunningham* / Sands of Burness: *Bain, Aly & Phil Cunningham* / Miller's reel: *Bain, Aly & Phil Cunningham* / Dean Cadalan Samhach: *Capercaillie* / Kerryman's daughter: *Boys Of The Lough* / O'Keefe's plough: *Boys Of The Lough* / Sligo maid: *Boys Of The Lough* / Humours of Ballinahinch: *Boys Of The Lough* / Gravel walk: *Boys Of The Lough* / Out by East Da Vong: *Boys Of The Lough* / Maiden's prayer: *Junior Daugherty* / Jimmy Mann's reel: *Hunter, William* / Aly's sound: *Hunter, William* / It's all just talk: *Gregson & Collister* / Pearl: *Cunningham, Phil* / Floggin': *Bain, Aly & Violet Tulloch* / Chimes at midnight: *Bain, Aly* / Humours of Tulla: *O'Connor, Martin* / Fox Hunter's reel: *O'Connor, Martin* / St. Anne's reel: *O'Connor, Martin* / New road under my wheels: *Junior Daugherty* / Anne's tune: *Moore, Hamish & Dick Lee* / Love of the islands: *Hunter, William* / Compliments to Dan R MacDonald: *Hunter, William* / Marie MacLennan's reel: *Hunter, William* / Bonjour Tristesse: *Queen Ida & The Bon Temps Zydeco Band*
CDTRAX 026 / Mar '89 / Greentrax

☐ ALY BAIN WITH YOUNG CHAMPIONS
Dr. Donaldson/The anvil: *Bain, Aly & Violet Tulloch* / Ross Memorial Hospital: *Bain, ALy & Scott Williams* / Buain an Rainich/Brochan Lom/Cockle gatherers: *Ross, Gail & Vicki Ferguson* / Balkan Hills/Duke of Gordon/Deil and the dirk: *Lindsay, Bruce* / Pear tree: *Gardiner, Scott* / Mr. Michie/J.F. Dickie's delight/ J.F. Dickie's reel: *Kostulin, Russell* / An Ataireachd Ard: *Ferguson, Vicki* / Aspen bank: *Williams, Scott* / Ardgualich/High road to Linton: *Thoumire, Simon* / Heaven's gate/Le Grande Chaine/Waiting for the Federals: *Bain, Aly & Russel Kostulin* / Conundrum/ Mrs. Stewart of Grantully: *Bennett, Martyn* / Morning dew/Blarney pilgrim/Langstrom's pony: *Bennett, Martyn* / Helen Robertson: *Smith, Angie* / Humble tattie: *Gardiner, Scott* / Ballachulish Glen: *Ross, Gail* / Leaving Lismor/Heights of Dargai/Kilt is my delight: *Lindsay, Bruce* / Wee burr stuck tae ma apron: *Robertson, Nicole* / Midnight on the water/ Bonaparte's retreat / Music of Spey / Sixereen/ Barrowburn reel/Fairy dance: *Bain, Aly & Violet Tulloch* / Margaret's waltz/Laird o'Drumblair/Deil among the tailors: *Bain, Aly & Young Champions*
SPRCD 1032 / May '90 / Springthyme

☐ ALY MEETS THE CAJUNS (Bain, Aly & Various Artists)
Midland two step: *Bain, Aly & Doucet Cajun Band* / My friend: *Bain, Aly & Wayne Toups* / Mazuka: *Bain, Aly & Queen Ida* / Jongle a moi: *Bain, Aly & Doucet Cajun Band* / Sassy on step: *Bain, Aly & Boozoo Chavis* / Jolie blon: *Bain, Aly & Dewey Balfa* / La contre danse a perepere: *Bain, Aly & Harry LaFleur* / Water pump: *Bain, Aly & D.L. Menard* / J'ai ete au bal: *Bain, Aly & Wayne Toups* / Paper in my shoe: *Bain, Aly & Boozoo Chavis* / La vie est pas donne: *Bain, Aly & Harry LaFleur* / Back door: *Bain, Aly & D.L. Menard* / Chere toute toute: *Bain, Aly & Doucet Cajun Band* / Rosa majeur: *Bain, Aly & Queen Ida* / Devant ta porte: *Bain, Aly & D.L. Menard* / When I was poor: *Bain, Aly & Dewey Balfa*
LCOM 9009 / Oct '92 / Lismor

☐ DOWN HOME
LCOM 9027 / '90 / Lismor

☐ FIRST ALBUM
Peter Davidson/Jessica's tune/Barrowburn reel / Louis' waltz/Le grande chaine/The newly weds' reel / Waiting for the Federals / Dr. James Donaldson/ The anvil reel / Auld noost / Barmaid/The carpenter/ The reconcilliation / Hangman's reel / Calum Donaldson/The scholar/Maid in a box / Kevin MacCann's/Munster grass/Barclays / Margaret's waltz / Blaydon flats/Alamootie/Dodd's farewell to Shetland / Da braaken baa/Violet Tulloch's hornpipe / Shack's farewell to the Workman's Club/Glen Farquhar/Reested
WHIRLIE 001CD / Dec '93 / Whirlie

☐ FOLLOW THE MOONSTONE
WHIRLIECD 4 / Oct '95 / Whirlie

☐ LONELY BIRD
Gillan's reel/Charles Sutherland/Donald Stewart the piper / Mrs. Jamieson's favourite / Rosemary Brown / Spey in spate/Pottinger's reel/Dowd's reel / Beauty of the North/Pirates hornpipe / Midnight on the water/Bonaparte's retreat / Herr Roloff's farewell / Aly's waltz / Annalese Bain/Phil Cunningham's reel/ Andy Brown's reel / Lonely bird / Weindia little/Da fashion o da delting lasses/Da black hat / Junior's waltz / Captain Campbell/Earl Grey/Largo's fairy dance
WHIRLIE 2CD / Oct '88 / Whirlie

☐ NORTH SEA MUSIC
HCD 7121 / May '97 / Helio

☐ PEARL, THE (Bain, Aly & Phil Cunningham)
Megan's wedding/The Herra Boys/The Barrowburn reel / Bonnie Nancy / Devant ta porte/Mamou two step / Jig runrig/The Swedish jig / Queendale Bay / Waltz of the little girls / Shores of Loch Bee/ Headlands/Floggin' reel / Music of Spey / Seud nan ceud bliadhna/Memories of Father Angus MacDonell/Br / Belle mere's waltz / Auld fiddler/B flat tune / Pearl
WHIRLIE 3CD / Oct '94 / Whirlie

☐ PIOBAIREACHD
ABCD 003 / May '98 / Alan Bain

☐ RUBY (Bain, Aly & Phil Cunningham)
Estonian waltz/La vie est pas Donne/La bastringue / Violet Tulloch, Queen of Lerwick / Flett from Flotta/ Sabhal lain ic Uisdean/The drampipe / Aly's soond/ Logan water / Wee bells of Tak-Ma-Doon road/ Glencoe Village Hall / Lady Mary Ramsay's reel / Sarah's song / Bonaparte's retreat / Sunset over Foula/Isles of Gletness/Starry night in Shetland / La Ronfleuse Gobel/La grande Chaine/Gallop de Malbaie / Ruby
WHIRLIECD 5 / Sep '97 / Whirlie

Bainbridge, Harvey

☐ INTERSTELLA CHAOS
TASTE 40CD / Jan '95 / Taste

☐ RED SHIFT
TASTE 65CD / May '97 / Taste/Divine

Bair, Gerald

☐ WE ALL FALL DOWN
Where I come from / Hangin' out with Elvis / I feel like / Come to me / We all fall down / Driving out of rockway / Bleeker / I don't want to talk about that / Little left / Love is a strange thing / Janey / Dreaming
MAIM 11142 / 18 May '98 / Mayhem

Baird, Dan

☐ BUFFALO NICKEL
Younger face / Cumberland river / I want you bad / On my way / Lil bit / Hell to pay / Woke up Jake / Birthday / Hush / Trivial as the truth / Hit me like a train / Frozen head state park
74321295172 / Jan '96 / American

☐ LOVE SONGS FOR THE HEARING IMPAIRED
One I am / Julie and lucky / I love you period / Look what you started / Look at what you started / Seriously gone / Pick up the knife / Knocked up / Baby talk / Lost highway / Dixie beauxderaunt
74321287582 / Jun '95 / American

Baiza, Joe

☐ PROSPEROUS AND QUALIFIED (Baiza, Joe & The Universal Congress)
SST 180CD / May '93 / SST

Bajourou

☐ BIG STRING THEORY
Hakilma / Mansa / Mankan / Fanta barana / I ka di nye / Sora / Bastan toure / Nkani / Jodoo
CDORBD 078 / Mar '93 / Globestyle

Baka Beyond

☐ JOURNEY BETWEEN
MBE / Flight of the swallow / Mountain song / Konti / Cotu / Land's End / Soiridh lies / Queen of Ngorongoro
HNCD 1415 / 27 Apr '98 / Hannibal

☐ MEETING POOL, THE
Woosi / Ancestor's vice / Lupe / Ohureo / Lost dance of Atlantis / Journey / Ndaweh's dream / Booma lena
HNCD 1388 / Oct '95 / Hannibal

☐ SPIRIT OF THE FOREST, THE (Baka Beyond & Martin Cradick)
Spirit of the forest / Man who danced too slowly / Canya jam / Ngombi / Baka play baka / Nahwia / Elephant song / Bounaka
HNCD 1377 / Oct '93 / Hannibal

Baka Pygmies

☐ HEART OF THE FOREST
Yelli 1 / Yelli 2 / Yelli 3 / Water drums 1 / Water drums 2 / Nursery rhyme / Venolouma / Ieta / Ngombi na peke 1 / Limbindi and voices / Earth bow / Limbindi / Water drums 3 / Welcome song / Banja's song / Ngombi na peke 2 / Ngombi na peke 3 / Acapella / Toji / Forest party / Distant yelli
HNCD 1378 / Oct '93 / Hannibal

Bakardy, Vell

☐ GENUINE LIQUA HITS
Drink wit me / Playa shit / Drunk bitches / Fantasy (it's reality) / Up in the hood / Deep sheet / Forever / FATHA / Liqua ndustry / Daddy's lil andgel / Typical day / Little kids / Life's so hard / Came up
74321312652 / Jan '96 / RCA

Bakdhi, Javed Salamat

☐ QAWWALI - MUSIQUES DU PENDJAB VOL.3
ARN 64323 / Nov '96 / Arion

Baked Beans

☐ BAKED BEANS
Bake daga / Desert bean / Heinz 1 / Has been
4509953462 / Mar '94 / Warner Bros.

☐ I WANT I CAN'T
LF 272CD / May '97 / Lost & Found

Baker, Anita

☐ COMPOSITIONS
Talk to me / Whatever it takes / Lonely / More than you know / Fairy tales / Perfect love affair / Soul inspiration / No one to blame / Love you to the letter
7559609222 / Jul '90 / Elektra

☐ GIVING YOU THE BEST THAT I GOT
Priceless / Lead me into love / Giving you the best that I got / Good love / Rules / Good enough / Just because I love you / You belong to me
9608272 / Oct '88 / Elektra

☐ RAPTURE
Sweet love / You bring me joy / Caught up in the rapture / Been so long / Mystery / No one in the world / Same ole love / Watch your step
9604442 / Apr '86 / Elektra

☐ RHYTHM OF LOVE
Rhythm of love / Look of love / Body and soul / Baby / I apologise / Plenty of room / It's been you / You belong to me / Wrong man / Only for a while / Sometimes I wonder why / My funny valentine
7559615552 / Sep '94 / Elektra

☐ SONGSTRESS
Angel / You're the best thing yet / Feel the need / Squeeze me / No more tears / Sometimes / Will you be mine / Do you believe me
7559611162 / Nov '91 / Elektra

Baker Boys

☐ FACING OUR TIME
SITCD 9221 / Nov '95 / Sittel

Baker, Chet

☐ ALBERTS HOUSE
REP 4167 / Aug '91 / Repertoire

☐ ART OF THE BALLAD, THE
Polka dots and moonbeams / Autumn in New York / My old flame / Alone together / I should care / When lights are low / Stairway to the stars / Indian summer / Almost like being in love / I've grown accustomed to her face / Lament for the living / I'm old fashioned / My heart stood still
PRCD 110112 / Sep '98 / Prestige

☐ AT THE FORUM THEATRE
FSRCD 9004 / 23 Feb '98 / Fresh Sound

☐ BALLADS FOR TWO (Baker, Chet & Wolfgang Lackerschmid)
Blue bossa / Five years ago / Why shouldn't you cry / Dessert / Softly as in the morning sunrise / You don't know what love is / Waltz for Susan
INAK 856CD / Jul '97 / In Akustik

☐ BEST OF CHET BAKER PLAYS, THE
Carson city stage / Imagination / All the things you are / Bea's flat / Happy little sunbeam / Pro defunctus / Moonlight becomes you / Stella by starlight / Darn the dream / Sweet Lorraine / Minor yours / CTA / To Mickey's memory / Jumpin' off a clef
CDP 7971612 / Feb '92 / Blue Note

☐ BEST OF CHET BAKER SINGS, THE
Thrill is gone / But not for me / Time after time / I get along without you very well / There will never be another you / Look for the silver lining / My funny valentine / I fall in love too easily / Daybreak / Just friends / I remember you / Let's get lost / Long ago (and far away) / You don't know what love is / That old feeling / It's always you / I've never been in love before / My buddy / Like someone in love / My ideal
CDP 7929322 / Jan '90 / Blue Note

☐ BOSTON 1954
UPCD 2735 / Apr '97 / Uptown

☐ BUT NOT FOR ME
STCD 584 / Jun '94 / Stash

☐ CHET
Alone together / How high the moon / It never entered my mind / 'Tis Autumn / If you could see me now / September song / You'd be so nice to come home to / Time on my hands / You, the night, and the music
OJCCD 87 / Feb '92 / Original Jazz Classics
OJC20 0872 / Sep '98 / Original Jazz Classics

☐ CHET BAKER AND STRINGS (Baker, Chet & Zoot Sims)
You don't know what love is / I'm through with love / Love walked in / You better go now / I married an angel / Love / I love you / What a difference a day makes / Why shouldn't I / Little duet / Wind / Trickledidlier
CK 65562 / 8 Jun '98 / Sony Jazz

☐ CHET BAKER IN CONCERT (Baker, Chet & Lee Konitz)
IN 1052CD / Jan '97 / India Navigation

☐ CHET BAKER IN MILAN
Lady bird / Cheryl blues / Tune up / Line for lyons / Pent up house / Look for the silver lining / Indian summer / My old flame
OJCCD 370 / Feb '92 / Original Jazz Classics

☐ CHET BAKER IN TOKYO
K 32Y6281 / Jul '89 / Concord Jazz

☐ CHET BAKER QUARTET AND RUSS FREEMAN, THE (Baker, Chet & Russ Freeman)
Isn't it romantic / Lamp is low / This time the dream's on me / Maid in Mexico / Russ job / Imagination / Long ago and far away / Long ago and far way / Carson City stage / Easy to love / Batter up / No ties / No ties / All the things you are / Thrill is gone / Thrill is gone / Band aid / Bea's flat / Moon love / Moon love / Happy little sunbeam / Happy little sunbeam / I fall in love too easily / Winter wonderland / Winter wonderland
4931642 / 18 May '98 / Pacific Jazz

☐ CHET BAKER SAMPLER
Almost like being in love / How high the moon / You'd be so nice to come home to / My old flame / When lights are low / I talk to the trees / Soft winds
OJCX 001 / Jan '98 / Original Jazz Classics

☐ CHET BAKER SINGS AGAIN
CDSJP 238 / '89 / Timeless Jazz

☐ CHET IN PARIS (The Barclay Years 1955-1956)
FSR CD 1/2 / May '88 / Fresh Sound

☐ COOL CAT
Swift shifting / 'Round midnight / Caravelle / For all we know / Blue moon / My foolish heart
CDSJP 262 / Mar '90 / Timeless Jazz

☐ COOLS OUT (Baker, Chet Quintet)
Extra mild / Halema / Jumpin' off a cliff / Route / Lucius lou / Pawnee junction
CDBOP 013 / Feb '89 / Boplicity

☐ DIANE (Baker, Chet & Paul Bley)
SCCD 31207 / Jul '88 / Steeplechase

☐ EMBRACEABLE YOU
Night we called it a day / Little girl blue (instrumental) / Embraceable you / They all laughed / There's a lull in my life / What is there to say / While my lady sleeps / Forgetful / How long has this been going on / Come rain or come shine / On Green Dolphin Street / Little girl blue / Travellin' light
CDP 8316762 / Jun '95 / Pacific Jazz

☐ ENSEMBLE AND SEXTET
FSRCD 9001 / 23 Feb '98 / Fresh Sound

☐ GREAT MOMENTS WITH CHET BAKER
Ray's ideas / In a sentimental mood / They'll never be another you / My melancholy baby / Father X-mas / How deep is the ocean / For all we know / Sea breeze / Round midnight / Beatrice / My funny Valentine
WWJ 3001 / 27 Apr '98 / World Wide Jazz

☐ HAIG '53 - THE OTHER PIANO-LESS QUARTET (Baker, Chet & Stan Getz)
CD 214W982 / Mar '92 / Philology

☐ HEART OF THE BALLAD (Baker, Chet & Enrico Pieranunzi)
W 202 / Aug '92 / Philology

☐ I REMEMBER YOU (The Legacy Vol.2)
But not for me / Broken wing / Nardis / You go to my head / Just friends
ENJ 90772 / Dec '96 / Enja

☐ IN A SOULFUL MOOD
On green Dolphin Street / 'Round Midnight / Milestones / Lucius Lu / Mr. B / Night bird / I'm old fashioned / Airegin
MCCD 269 / Nov '96 / Music Club

☐ IN EUROPE - 1955
214 W422 / Aug '91 / Philology

☐ IN ITALY (Unissued 1975-1988)
W 812 / Apr '95 / Philology

☐ IN NEW YORK
Fair weather / Polka dots and moonbeams / Hotel 49 / Solar / Blue thoughts / When lights are low / Soft winds
OJCCD 207 / Feb '92 / Original Jazz Classics

☐ **INTRODUCES JOHNNY**
All or nothing at all / Crazy she calls me / Way you look tonight / This is always / When the sun comes out / What is there to say / Everything I've got belongs to you / We could make such beautiful music / It might as well be spring / Yesterdays
OJCCD 433 / Feb '92 / Original Jazz Classics

☐ **ISN'T IT ROMANTIC**
Porgy and Bess suite / Isn't it romantic / Time after time / You don't know what love is / Donna Lee / Lover man / Look for the silver lining / There will never be another you / Autumn in New York / Marilyn
JHR 73573 / Nov '93 / Jazz Hour

☐ **IT COULD HAPPEN TO YOU**
Do it the hard way / I'm old fashioned / You're driving me crazy / It could happen to you / My heart stood still / More I see you / Everything happens to me / Dancing on the ceiling / How long has this been going on / Old devil moon / While my lady sleeps (take 10) / You make me feel so young (take 5)
OJCCD 303 / Feb '92 / Original Jazz Classics
OJC20 3032 / Sep '98 / Original Jazz Classics

☐ **ITALIAN SESSIONS, THE**
Well you needn't / These foolish things / Barbados / Star eyes / Somewhere over the rainbow / Pent-up house / Ballata in forma di blues / Blues in the closet
09026685902 / Oct '96 / RCA Victor

☐ **JAZZ MASTERS**
5169392 / 5 May '98 / Verve

☐ **JAZZ MASTERS**
Thrill is gone / Time after time / I get along without you very well (except sometimes) / My funny valentine / I fall in love too easily / You don't know what love is / It's always you / I've never been in love before / My buddy / Like someone in love
CDMFP 6306 / Mar '97 / Music For Pleasure

☐ **JAZZ PORTRAITS**
Line for Lyons / Cherry / Thrill is gone / But not for me / My funny valentine / There will never be another you / Time after time / Daybreak / You don't know what love is / Let's get lost / Love / I fall in love too easily / Just friends / I remember you / Long ago and far away / That old feeling / My ideal / Everything happens to me
CD 14511 / May '94 / Jazz Portraits

☐ **JAZZ PROFILE**
Bockbanal / That old feeling / Dot's groovy / Route / I get along without you very well / Russ Job / But not for me / Picture of health / I fall in love too easily / Lucius Lu / Halena
CDP 8549022 / May '97 / Blue Note

☐ **LAST CONCERT VOL.1 & 2**
ENJA 60742 / Nov '91 / Enja

☐ **LEGACY, THE**
Here's that rainy day / How deep is the ocean / Mr. B / In your own sweet way / All of you / Dolphin dance / Look for the silver lining / Django / All blues
ENJ 90212 / Jun '95 / Enja

☐ **LIVE AT FAT TUESDAY'S**
FSRCD 131 / Sep '91 / Fresh Sound

☐ **LIVE AT NICK'S**
CRISSCD 1027 / Mar '90 / Criss Cross

☐ **LIVE AT ROSENHEIMER**
CDSJP 233 / May '89 / Timeless Jazz

☐ **LIVE IN EUROPE 1956**
556622 / Apr '94 / Accord

☐ **LIVE IN EUROPE 1956 VOL.2**
COD 034 / Aug '92 / Jazz View

☐ **LIVE IN ROSENHEIM/SINGS AGAIN/ HEARTBREAK (3CD Set)**
Funk in deep freeze / I'm a fool to want you / Portrait in black and white / In a sentimental mood / If I should lose you / Arbor way / All of you / Body and soul / Look for the silver lining / I can't get started / My funny valentine / Alone together / Someone to watch over me / How deep is the ocean / Everything happens to me / Angel eyes / All of you / My funny valentine / Blue moon / I'm a fool to want you / You and the night and the music / As time goes by / 'Round midnight / My melancholy baby / My foolish heart
CDSJP 007 / Dec '96 / Timeless

☐ **LIVE IN SWEDEN**
Lament / My ideal / Beatrice / You can't go home again / But not for me / Ray's idea / Milestones
DRCD 178 / Sep '89 / Dragon

☐ **LONELY STAR (The Prestige Sessions)**
Grade 'a' gravy / Serenity / Fine and dandy / Have you met miss Jones / Rearin' back / So easy / Madison avenue / Lonely star / Wee, too / Tan gaugin
PRCD 241722 / Jan '97 / Prestige

☐ **MISTER B/AS TIME GOES BY/COOL CAT (3CD Set)**
Dolphin dance / Ellen and David / Strollin' / In your own sweet way / Mister B / Beatrice / White blues / Father X-mas / You and the night and the music / As time goes by / My melancholy baby / I am a fool to want you / When she smiles / Sea breeze / You have been here all along / Angel eyes / You'd be so nice to come home to / 'Round midnight / Swift shifting / Round midnight / Caravelle / For all we know / Blue moon / My foolish heart
CDSJP 006 / Dec '96 / Timeless

☐ **MY FAVOURITE SONGS**
ENJA 50972 / 17 Nov '97 / Enja

☐ **MY FUNNY VALENTINE**
My funny valentine / Someone to watch over me / Moonlight becomes you / This is always / I'm glad there is you / Time after time / Sweet Lorraine / It's always you / Let's get lost / Moon love / Like someone in love / I've never been in love before / Isn't it romantic / I fall in love too easily
CDP 8282622 / Jan '94 / Pacific Jazz

☐ **NAIMA (Unusual Chet Vol.1)**
214 W522 / Aug '91 / Philology

☐ **NEWPORT YEARS VOL.1, THE**
214 W512 / Aug '91 / Philology

☐ **NIGHT AT THE SHALIMAR CLUB, A**
214 W592 / Sep '91 / Philology

☐ **NO PROBLEM (Baker, Chet Quartet)**
SCCD 31131 / '88 / Steeplechase

☐ **ON A MISTY NIGHT (The Prestige Sessions)**
Cut plug / Boudoir / Etude in three / Sleeping Susan / Go-go / Lament for the living / Pot luck / Bud's blues / Romas / On a misty night / Hurry
PRCD 241742 / Jan '97 / Prestige

☐ **ONCE UPON SUMMERTIME**
Tidal breeze / Shifting down / E.s.p. / Song is you / Once upon a summertime (la valse des lilas)
OJCCD 405 / Feb '92 / Original Jazz Classics

☐ **OUT OF NOWHERE**
Fine and dandy / There will never be another you / Oh lady be good / Au privave / All the things you are / Out of nowhere / There is no greater love / Theme
MCD 91912 / Apr '94 / Milestone

☐ **PICTURE OF HEALTH (Baker, Chet & Art Pepper)**
Picture of health / For miles and miles / CTA / For minors only / Minor yours / Resonant emotions / Tynan time
4941062 / 22 Jun '98 / Pacific Jazz

☐ **QUARTET (Baker, Chet & Russ Freeman)**
Love nest / Fan Tan / Summer sketch / An afternoon at home / Say when / Lush life / Amblin' / Hugo Hurwhey
CDP 8554532 / Mar '97 / Pacific Jazz

☐ **RISING SUN COLLECTION, THE**
Milestones / Oh you crazy moon / There will never be another you / Snowbound / Love for sale
RSCD 0010 / May '96 / Just A Memory

☐ **ROUND MIDNIGHT**
Round midnight / Secret love / What's new / All blues / Darn that dream / Phil's bossa / My funny valentine / Straight no chaser / Round midnight / Blues for Inge
CHR 70052 / Jun '98 / Challenge

☐ **SHE WAS GOOD TO ME**
4509542 / Jan '95 / Sony Jazz

☐ **SILENT NIGHTS**
DCCD 04 / Nov '96 / Dinemec Jazz

☐ **SILENT NIGHTS/CHRISTMAS JAZZ ALBUM (Baker, Chet & Christopher Mason)**
CDVR 032 / '88 / Varrick

☐ **SINGS**
That old feeling / It's always you / Like someone in love / My ideal / I've never been in love before / My buddy / But not for me / Time after time / I get along without you very well / My funny Valentine / There will never be another you / Thrill is gone / I fall in love too easily / Look for the silver lining
8232342 / 19 Jan '98 / Pacific Jazz

☐ **SINGS THE GREAT BALLADS**
Time after time / I fall in love too easily / It's always you / I've never been in love before / My funny valentine / Thrill is gone / I get along without you very well / Like someone in love / My buddy / You don't know what love is
JD 1262 / 15 Jun '98 / Jazz Door

☐ **SONGS FOR LOVERS**
Come rain or shine / My old flame / That old feeling / Lullaby of the leaves / There's a lull in my life / Moonlight in Vermont / Darn that dream / My ideal / Theres a lull in my life / Imagination / Embraceable you / Lush life / Goodbye
CDP 8571582 / Jul '97 / Pacific Jazz

☐ **SPECIAL GUESTS (Baker, Chet & Wolfgang Lackerschmid)**
Mr. Biko / Balzwaltz / Latin one / Rue Gregoire Du Tour / Here's that rainy day / Toku du
INAK 857CD / Jul '97 / In Akustik

☐ **STAIRWAY TO THE STARS (The Prestige Sessions)**
Cherokee / Bevan beeps / Comin' on / Stairway to the stars / No fair lady / When you're gone / Choose now / Chabootie / Carpsie's groove / I waited for you / 490
PRCD 241732 / Jan '97 / Prestige

☐ **STELLA BY STARLIGHT**
BS 18006 / Jul '96 / Bandstand

☐ **STROLLIN'**
ENJA 50052 / 17 Nov '97 / Enja

☐ **THERE'LL NEVER BE ANOTHER YOU (Baker, Chet & Philip Catherine)**
Beatrice / There'll never be another you / Leaving / My foolish heart
CDSJP 437 / Aug '97 / Timeless

☐ **THIS IS JAZZ**
Little duet / Love walked in / You don't know what love is / I'm through with love / You'd better go now / Wind / Autumn leaves / She was too good to me / Tangerine / What'll I do
CK 64779 / May '96 / Sony Jazz

☐ **TOGETHER - THE COMPLETE STUDIO RECORDINGS (Baker, Chet & Paul Desmond)**
Tangerine / You can't go home again / How deep is the ocean / You'd be so nice to come home to / I'm getting sentimental over you/You've changed / Autumn leaves / Concierto de aranjuez
4729842 / Jan '93 / Epic

☐ **WEST COAST LIVE (2CD Set) (Baker, Chet & Stan Getz)**
My funny valentine / Strike up the band / Way you look tonight / Yardbird suite / Yesterday's / Winter wonderland / Come out wherever you are / Move / What's new / Half nelson / Little Willie leaps / Soft shoe / Whispering / Bernie's tune / All the things you are / Winter wonderland / Gone with the wind / All the things you are / Darn that dream / Crazy rhythm
CDP 8356342 / Apr '97 / Parlophone

☐ **WHEN SUNNY GETS BLUE**
SCCD 31221 / Jul '88 / Steeplechase

☐ **WHITE BLUES**
Well you needn't / These foolish things / Star eyes / Somewhere over the rainbow / Blues in the closet / My one and only love / Almost blue / White blues / 'Round midnight / Swift shifting / Caravelle / Dolphin dance / Ellen and David
74321451892 / May '97 / Camden

☐ **WITCH DOCTOR (Baker, Chet & Lighthouse All Stars)**
Loaded / I'll remember April / Winter wonderland / Pirouette / Witch doctor
OJCCD 609 / Feb '92 / Original Jazz Classics

☐ **WITH FIFTY ITALIAN STRINGS**
I should care / Violets for your furs / Song is you / When I fall in love / Goodbye / Autumn in new york / Angel eyes / Street of dreams / Forgetful / Deep in a dream
OJCCD 492 / Feb '92 / Original Jazz Classics

☐ **WITH STRINGS**
You don't know what love is / I'm through with love / Love walked in / You'd better go now / I married an angel / Love / I love you / What a difference a day makes / Why shouldn't I / Little duet / Wind / Trickleydidlier
4669682 / Apr '92 / Columbia

☐ **YOUNG CHET**
Look for the silver lining / But not for me / Time after time / My funny valentine / There will never be another you / Extra mild / Night on Bop Mountain / Down / Taboo / I can't get started / It's only a paper moon / Autumn in New York
CDP 8361942 / Feb '96 / Pacific Jazz

Baker, Duck

☐ **AMERICAN TRADITIONAL (Baker, Duck & Molly Andrews)**
DBMA 1CD / Jul '93 / Dayjob

☐ **CLEAR BLUE SKY**
BEST 1065CD / Apr '95 / Acoustic Music

☐ **MOVING BUSINESS, THE (Baker, Duck & Molly Andrews)**
DBMA 2CD / Oct '94 / Dayjob

☐ **OPENING THE EYES OF LOVE**
SHAN 97025CD / May '93 / Shanachie

☐ **SPINNING SONG (The Music of Herbie Nichols)**
AVAN 040 / Jan '97 / Avant

☐ **THOUSAND WORDS, A (Baker, Duck & John Renbourn)**
BEST 1021CD / Nov '93 / Acoustic Music

Baker, Etta

☐ **ONE DIME BLUES**
Never let your deal go down / One dime blues / Knoxville rag / Broken hearted blues / Lost john / Dew drop / Going down the road feeling bad / Near the cross I watch and pray / Spanish fandango / Round my back door selling coal / But on the other hand baby / Crow jane / John henry / Alabama wagonwheel / Bully of the town / Going to the racetrack / Police dog blues / Marching jaybird / Railroad bill / Carolina breakdown
ROUCD 2112 / Sep '91 / Rounder

Baker, George

☐ **STAR PORTRAITS (Baker, George Selection)**
Paloma blanca / Morning sky / Wild bird / Little green bag / Baby blue / Love me like I love you / Dear ann / Dreamboat / All my love / You don't love me anymore / Superstar / Sing for the day
16029 / '93 / Laserlight

Baker, Ginger

☐ **AFRICAN FORCE**
ITM 1417 / '89 / ITM

☐ **HORSES AND TREES**
Interlock / Dust to dust / Satou / Uncut / Mountain time / Makuta
MPG 74046 / Jul '97 / Movieplay Gold
CDGR 193 / Nov '97 / Charly
TRS 41232 / Jul '98 / Terrascape

☐ **PALANQUIN'S POLE (Baker, Ginger & African Force)**
ITM 1433 / Apr '90 / ITM

Baker, Josephine

☐ **BONSOIR MY LOVE**
J'ai deux amours / La petite tonkinoise / Voulez vous de la canne a sucre / Dis moi Josephine / Ram pam pam / Si j'etais blanche / Madiana / Les mots d'amour / C'est luiHaiti / Sous le ciel d'afrique / Espabilate / Partir sur un bateau blanc / Nuit d'alger / Doudou / Nuits de Miami / Mayari / La conga blicoti / Vous faites partie de moi / C'est si facile de vous aimer / C'est un nid charmant / Comme une banque / J'ai un message pour toi / Bonsoir my love
DRGCD 5573 / 26 May '98 / DRG

☐ **DIS MOI JOSEPHINE BAKER (24 Hits 1926-1944)**
Dis moi Josephine / J'ai deux amours / La petite Tonkinoise / Sleepy time gal / Then I'll be happy / Pretty little baby / Voulez vous de la canne a sucre / Aux Iles Hawaii / Love is a dreamer / My fate is in your hands / You're driving me crazy / Mon reve c'etait vous / Sans amour / Les mots d'amour / Ram-pam-pam / Si j'etais blanche / Madiana / Sous le ciel d'afrique / La conga Blicoti / C'est si facile de vous aimer (easy to love) / Mon couer est un oiseau des iles / De temps en temps / Sur deux notes / Brazil
CDAJA 5239 / Dec '97 / Living Era

☐ **EXOTIQUE**
PASTCD 7059 / Apr '95 / Flapper

☐ **FABULOUS JOSEPHINE BAKER, THE**
Paris ses amours / Le marchand de bonheur / Mo 'lo' / J'attendrai / Donnez moi la man / Je voudrais / La Seine / Sonny boy / Sous les toits de Paris / Mon p'tit bonhomme / En Avril a Paris / Sag beim Abschied leise 'Servus' / Don't touch my tomatoes
09026616682 / Jun '95 / RCA Victor

☐ **J'AI DEUX AMOURS**
AC 75103 / 27 Apr '98 / Arkadia

☐ **JOSEPHINE BAKER GOLD COLLECTION, THE (2CD Set)**
R2CD 4060 / 9 Mar '98 / Deja Vu

☐ **JOSEPHINE BAKER STORY, THE**
La petite tonkinoise / J'ai deux amours / I wonder where my baby is tonight / Pretty little baby / Voulez-vous de la canne au sucre / Bye bye blackbird / Dis-moi josephine / Suppose / Si j'etais blanche / La conga bucott / Confessin' (that I love you) / Madiana / King for a day live) / You're driving me crazy / Haitl / My fate is in your hands / I've got you under my skin / Ram pam pam
CDD 3401 / Jul '92 / Concord Jazz

☐ **PORTRAIT OF JOSEPHINE BAKER, A (2CD Set)**
La petit Tonkinoise / Voulez-vous de la canne a sucre / Pardon si je t'importune / Dis moi Josephine / Aux Iles Hawaii / Madiana / Mon reve c'etait vous / Si j'etais blanche / Les mots d'amour / Ram pam pam / Sans amour / C'etait lui / Haiti / Sous le ciel d'afrique / Partir sur un baeeau blanc / Doudou / Mayari / La conga blicoti / Mon couer est un oiseau des iles / Comme une banque / C'est un nid charmant / \Sur deaux notes / Bonsoir my love / J'ai deux amours / Who / That certain feeling / Dinah / Sleepy time gal / I love my baby / Everybody loves my baby / PrettAlways / Y little babay / Afraid to dream / If you were the only girl in the world / After I say I'm sorry / Then I'll be happy / Bye bye blackbird / Lonesome lovesick blues / Breezin' along with the breeze / Hello bluebird / Blue skies / I'm leaving for Alybamy / Suppose / Love is a dreamer / King for a day / My fate is in your hands / Confessin' / You're drivin me crazy
GALE 420 / 6 Oct '97 / Gallerie

Baker, Kenny

☐ **BIRTH OF A LEGEND 1941-1946, THE**
Tea for two / Red duster rag / King Porter stomp / Ain't cha got music / Stevedore stomp / Ain't misbehavin' / One o'clock jump / Cymbal Simon / Riff up them stairs / Five flat flurry / Trunk call / All is not gold that jitters / How am I to know / I wish I were twins / Soft winds / Sequence / Needlenose / First edition / Drop me off at Harlem / Merely A-minor / 1234 jump / Up / No script / Bakerloo non stop
HEPCD 58 / 15 Jun '98 / Hep

☐ **HALF DOZEN (After Hours)**
How's this / Love me or leave me / If I could be you / Keepin' out of mischief now / How can you face me / Puttin' on the ritz / Doo dee / St. Louis blues / Honolulu blues / Minute to midnight / Blues in thirds / Apex blues / I'm a ding dong daddy / Studio B boogie / West wind / Oh baby
LACD 88 / Dec '97 / Lake

☐ **TRIBUTE TO THE GREAT TRUMPETERS**
I can't get started (with you) / And the angels sing / Tenderly / You made me love you / Satchmo / Morning glory / How long has this been going on / Georgia / Memories of you / Little jazz / Music goes 'round and around / Carnival time / Won't you come home, Bill Bailey / What's new / Sugar blues / Davenport blues / Echoes of Harlem / Our love is here to stay
CDSIV 1124 / Jul '95 / Horatio Nelson

Baker, LaVern

☐ BLUES BALLADS
I cried a tear / If you love me / You're teasing me / Love me right / Dix-a-billy / So high so love / I waited too long / Why baby why / Humpty Dumpty heart / It's so fine / Whipper snapper / St. Louis blues / How often / Hurting inside / I didn't know I was crying / Help each other romance / You're the boss / I'll never be free
RSACD 911 / Mar '97 / Sequel

☐ LAVERN
Lots and lots of love / Of course I do / You'll be crying / Miracles / I'm in a crying mood / Mine all mine / Harbour lights / I'll never be free / Romance in the dark / Everybody is somebody's fool / How long will it be / Fool that I am / Living my life for you / I can't hold out any longer / Fee fi fo fum / I'll still do the same for you / Game of love
RSACD 909 / Mar '97 / Sequel

☐ LAVERN BAKER SINGS BESSIE SMITH
Gimme a pigfoot / Baby doll / On revival day / Money blues / I ain't gonna play no second fiddle / Backwater blues / Empty bed blues / There'll be a hot time in the old town tonight / Nobody knows you when you're down and out / After you've gone / Young woman's blues / Preaching the blues
RSACD 914 / Mar '97 / Sequel

☐ PRECIOUS MEMORIES
Precious memories / Carrying the cross for my boss / Just a little closer walk with thee / Touch me Lord Jesus / Didn't it rain / Precious Lord / Somebody touched me / In the other room / Journey to the sky / Everytime I feel the spirit / Too close / Without a God
RSACD 915 / Mar '97 / Sequel

☐ ROCK 'N' ROLL WITH LAVERN BAKER
Jim Dandy / Tra la la / I can't love you enough / Get up get up (you sleepy head) / That's all I need / Bop ting-a-ling / Tweedle dee / Still / Play it fair / Tomorrow night / That lucky old sun / Soul on fire / My happiness for ever / How can you leave a man like this / Learning to love / Jim Dandy got married / Substitute / Voodoo voodoo / Tiny Tim / If you love me
RSACD 910 / Mar '97 / Sequel

☐ SAVED
Saved / For love of you / Manana / My time will come / Shadows of love / Must I cry again / Bumble bee / Shake a hand / Don Juan / Wheel of fortune / Itty bitty girl / Eager beaver / You don't tell me / Loads of love / Hey Memphis / No love so true / Eternally / Senor big and fine
RSACD 912 / Mar '97 / Sequel

☐ SEE SEE RIDER
CC rider / You better stop / He's a real gone guy / Story of my love / You said / I'm leaving you / Don't let the stars get in your eyes / Trying / Half of your love / Little bird told me so / Endless love / All the time / Trouble in mind / Oh Johnny oh Johnny / Fly me to the moon / Go away / You better find yourself another fool / Ain't gonna cry no more
RSACD 913 / Mar '97 / Sequel

☐ SOUL ON FIRE
Soul on fire / Tomorrow night / Tweedlee dee / That's all I need / Bop-ting-a-ling / Play it fair / Jim Dandy / My happiness forever / Get up, get up (you sleepy head) / Sill / I can't love you enough / Jim Dandy got married / I cried a tear / Whippersnapper / I waited to long / Shake a hand / How often / You said / Saved / CC rider
7567823112 / Mar '93 / WEA

Baker, Lee

☐ FRESH OIL (Baker, Lee & The Agitators)
BLW 5503CD / May '97 / Blues Works

Baker, Marilyn

☐ FACE TO FACE
Face to face / He is the rock / I know where you're coming from / Constantly amazed / Brand new heart / Lord I love you / He knows your sorrows / Don't deceive yourselves / When I think / Lord's my shepherd / O Lord you are so mighty / Open your ears / My God how great you are / I love to talk with Jesus
WSTCD 9722 / Apr '92 / Word

Baker, McHouston 'Mickey'

☐ MISSISSIPPI DELTA BLUES
Good advice / High sheriff blues / Blues before sunrise / Terraplane blues / Animal farm / Alabama march / Spoonful / Sun is going down / Sweet home Chicago / My black woman / Can't find my baby / Trouble is / A woman / Lazy daisy / Drucilla
5197282 / Mar '94 / Verve

☐ ROCK WITH A SOCK
Guitar mambo / Riverboat / Love me baby / Oh happy day / Where is my honey / I'm tired / Stranger blues / I wish I knew / Down to the bottom / You better heed my warning / Midnight hours / Please tell me / Shake walkin' / Greasy spoon / Bandstand stomp / Rock with a sock / Old devil moon / Guitarambo / Spinnin' rock boogie / I don't stand a ghost of a chance with you / Chloe / Man I love / Bobi, Mickey and Silvia / Hello stranger / My love / Woe woe is me / Can't get you on the phone / I'll always want you near
BCD 15654 / Aug '93 / Bear Family

Baker, Tom

☐ MAN FROM THE SOUTH, THE (Baker, Tom & Bob Banard)
LB 9701 / Feb '98 / La Brava

☐ TOM BAKER & FRIENDS 1982-1994
LB 0003 / Jul '98 / La Brava

Baker-Baldwin Radiogram Washboards

☐ OZARK BLUES
SOSCD 1243 / Jul '93 / Stomp Off

Baker-Gurvitz Army

☐ BAKER-GURVITZ ARMY
REP 4163 / Aug '91 / Repertoire

Bal Sagoth

☐ BATTLE MAGIC
Battle magic / Naked steel / Tale from the deep woods / Return to the praesidium of woods / Crystal shards / Dark leige of chaos / When rides the scion of storms / Blood slakes the sand at circus maximus / Thwarted by the dark (blade of the vampire hunter) / Atlantis falls
NIHIL 029CD / 30 Mar '98 / Cacophonous

☐ BLACK MOON BROODS OVER LEMURIA, A
Dreaming of Utlantean spires / Spellcraft and moonfire / Black moon broods over Lemuria / Enthroned in the Temple of the Serpent Kings / Shadows 'neath the black pyramid / Witch-storm / Ravening / Into the silent chambers of the Sapphirean Throne / Valley of silent paths
NIHIL 4CD / Jun '97 / Cacophonous

☐ STARFIRE BURNING
NIHIL 18CD / Nov '96 / Cacophonous

Balaam & The Angel

☐ PRIME TIME
Shame on you / Prime time / Next to me / What love is / Gathering dust / Eagle / She's not you / Mr. Business / Like a train / Burnin' / Just no good
CDBLEED 1 / Apr '93 / Bleeding Hearts
DARK 003CD / 2 Feb '98 / Darkend

Balaban, Red

☐ RED BALABAN & THE EDDIE CONDON ALL STARS VOL.1 (Balaban, Red & Eddie Condon All Stars)
JCD 291 / May '98 / Jazzology

☐ RED BALABAN & THE EDDIE CONDON ALL STARS VOL.2 (Balaban, Red & Eddie Condon All Stars)
JCD 292 / May '98 / Jazzology

Balachander, S.

☐ MUSIC OF THE VEENA VOL.1
VICG 50362 / Mar '96 / JVC World Library

Balafon Marimba Ensemble

☐ BALAFON MARIMBA ENSEMBLE, THE
I already have a husband / Nhamo / Caderas / Taireva / Temerina / Amatoto / Nhimutimu / Mashamba nzou
SHCD 67002 / Feb '93 / Shanachie

☐ HARARE TO KISINGANI
SHCD 67004 / Mar '94 / Shanachie

Balalaika Ensemble Wolga

☐ KALAKOLTSCHIK
EUCD 1064 / '89 / ARC

☐ KALINKA
EUCD 1054 / '89 / ARC

☐ POPULAR FOLK SONGS FROM RUSSIA
Cossack's dance / Bandura / Oriental dance / Legend of the 12 brigands / Katjusche / Ej uchnjem / Wass duli / Bajuschki baju / White acacia / Uri balki / Tears fall out of clouds / Roaring volga
EUCD 1126 / '91 / ARC

☐ SONGS FROM THE TAIGA
EUCD 1050 / '89 / ARC

☐ WOLGA (The Best Of Russian Folk Songs)
EUCD 1146 / Jan '92 / ARC

Balalaikas Of Moscow

☐ BALALAIKAS OF MOSCOW, THE
Pedlars / Shall we go to the river / Melody of Saratov / Song of the Volga boatmen / Bells / My joy is alive / Elegie / When I met you / Moon is shining / Tritsch-tratsch polka / Little comrade come and see me / Girl comes to see me in the evening / Russian ditties / Dark eyes / Long road / Kalinka / Lara's theme / Gypsy dance / O birch tree / Flight of the bumble bee / Katiusha
PS 65185 / Jun '97 / PlayaSound

Balance

☐ BALANCE/IN FOR THE COUNT
RME 0104CD / 19 Jan '98 / Renaissance

Balanco

☐ BOSSA AND BALANCO
SCC 305 / 19 Jan '98 / Schema

Balanescu Quartet

☐ LUMINITZA
East / East / Democracy / Still with me / Link / Revolution / Link again / Luminitza / Mother
CDSTUMM 124 / Jan '94 / Mute

☐ POSSESSED
Robots / Robots / Autobahn / Computer love / Pocket calculator / Possessed / Want me / No time before time / Hanging upside down
CDSTUMM 111 / Sep '92 / Mute

Bald

☐ BALD
132161 / Feb '97 / XIII Bis

Baldan, Bebo

☐ EARTHBEAT (Baldan, Bebo & David Torn)
Desire / Earthbeat / Diving into the world / Niceday / San Isidro / Shakti no Brasil / Asoka's / On Namah Shivaya / Santoor / Ralph
MASOCD 90082 / Oct '95 / Materiali Sonori

Baldan-Bembo, Alberto

☐ IO E MARA
Ore 18 / Ore 20 / Ore 22 / Ore 24 / Ore 4 / Ore 6 / Ore 10 / Ore 16 / Ore 18
ET 910CD / 12 May '98 / Timewarp

Baldry, Long John

☐ IT AIN'T EASY
Conditional discharge / Don't try to lay no Boogie-Woogie / Black girl / It ain't easy / Morning morning / I'm ready / Let's burn down the cornfield / Mr. Rubin / Rock me when he's gone / Flying
LICD 901235 / Nov '96 / Line

☐ IT STILL AIN'T EASY
It still ain't easy / Midnight in New Orleans / One step ahead / I never loved nobody / Get it while the gettin's good / What've I been drinking / Insane asylum / You wanna dance / Shake that thang / Like you promised / Busker / Can't keep from crying / No more / Soft and furry
SP 1163CD / Sep '96 / Stony Plain

☐ LET THE HEARTACHES BEGIN/WAIT FOR ME
Long and lonely nights / Stay with me baby / Every time we say goodbye / For all we know / Better by far / Let the heartaches begin / Wise to the ways of the world / Since I lost you baby / Smile / Annabella / We're together / I can't stop loving you / Sunshine of your love / Spanish Harlem / Henry Hannah's 42nd St. parking lot / Man without a dream / Cry like a baby / River deep, mountain high / How sweet it is (to be loved by you) / MacArthur Park / Brigadier McKenzie / Ligts of Cincinatti / Spinning wheel / Wait for me / Mexico / When the sun comes shining through
BGOCD 272 / May '95 / Beat Goes On

☐ LONG JOHN'S BLUES/LOOKING AT LONG JOHN
You've lost that lovin' feelin' / Only a fool breaks his own heart / Make it easy on yourself / Let him go / Drifter / Cry me a river / Stop her on sight (SOS) / Turn on your love light / I love Paris / Keep on runnin' / Ain't nothin' you can do / Bad luck soul / Got my mojo working / Gee baby ain't I good to you / Rool 'em Pete / You're breaking my heart / Hoochie coochie / Everyday (I got the blues) / Dimples / Five long years / My babe / Times are getting tougher / Goin' down slow / Rock the joint
BGODCD 2 / Dec '90 / Beat Goes On

☐ MEXICO
Let the heartaches begin / Every time we say goodbye / Lights of Cincinatti / Since I lost you baby / Spinning wheel / Annabella (Who flies to me when she's lonely) / Stay with me baby / Sunshine of your love / It's too late now / When the sun comes shining through / For all we know / Spanish Harlem / Cry like a baby / How sweet it is (to be loved by you) / MacArthur Park / Smile / River deep, mountain high / Mexico (Underneath the sun in)
5507572 / Feb '95 / Spectrum

☐ RIGHT TO SING THE BLUES
HYCD 2917167 / Feb '97 / Hypertension

☐ ROCK WITH THE BEST
Midnight show / When you're ugly like me / Bad attitude / Twenty five years of pain / Rock with the best / Too late for crying / Love is where you find it / Stay the way you are / Passing glances / Let the heartaches stop / Iko iko / Hand jive / Got rhythm / Black girl
HYCD 296164 / Nov '96 / Hypertension

☐ VERY BEST OF LONG JOHN BALDRY, THE
Let the heartaches begin / Spinning wheel / It's too late now / Spanish Harlem / When the sun comes shining through / Mexico / River deep mountain high / Man without a dream / Cry like a baby / Lights of Cincinnati / Sunshine of your love / Wise to the ways of the world / Stay with me baby / Hold back the daybreak / Hey Lord you made the night too long / Macarthur Park / How sweet it is / For all we know / I can't stop loving you / Every time we say goodbye
MCCD 306 / Jun '97 / Music Club

Baldwin, Bob

☐ COLD BREEZE
SH 5035 / Jul '97 / Shanachie

Baldwin, Gary

☐ SPYCATCHER (Baldwin, Gary & Mick Hanson)
Camp Freddie / What was that / Today I sing the blues / One for Carlos / Good news blues / Looking for / Old grand dad / Don't eat me alive / September sun / Spycatcher / Who can I turn to
LZDCD 111 / Jun '98 / Loose Tie

Balfa Brothers

☐ NEW YORK CONCERTS PLUS, THE
Jolie blon / Les flames d'enfer / Les bars de la prison / Two step de lacassine / I don't want you anymore / La valse de grand bois / J'ai passe devant ta porte / Hippy ti yo / Madame Sostan / La valse criminel / You had some but you won't have anymore / Tee yeaux noir / Chanson de les mardi gras / Dying in misery / In my old wagon / Cowboy waltz / Texas two step / Coeur criminel / Les traces de mon bogue / J'etais au balle / Valse de kaplan
CDCHD 338 / Oct '91 / Ace

☐ TRADITIONAL CAJUN MUSIC VOL.1 & 2
Drunkard's sorrow waltz / Lacassine special / My true love / La valse de Grand Bois / Family waltz / Newport waltz / Indian on a stomp / T'ai petite et t'ai meon / Two step a Hadley / Valse de Balfa / Parlez-nous a boire / Les blues de cajun / 'Tit galop pour mamou / Je suis Orphelin / T'en as eu mais t'en n'auras plus / Two step de l'anse a paille / La danse de Mardi Gras / Je me suis Marillie / Enterre moi pas / Chere joules roses / Chere bassette / J'ai passe devant ta porte / Les flames d'enfer / Madeleine / Drunkards sorrow waltz
CDCHD 955 / Nov '90 / Ace

Balfa, Dewey

☐ SOUVENIRS/FAIT A LA MAIN (Balfa, Dewey & Friends)
Equand j'etais pauvre / La valse du Canada / La valse de deux familles / 1755 / Bienvenue au paradis / Fiddlesticks / J'ai pleure / Don't stop the music / La reel de joie / La mauvaise nouvelle / Watermelon reel / Grand mamou / Pauvre hobo / La jolie blonde / Back door / Valse de balfa / Blues a Leo Soileau / Two step a Nathan Abshire / Chere toute toute / J'ai passe devant ta porte / Les veuves de la coulee / Les flames d'enfer / T'ai petite et t'ai meon / Perrodin two step
CDCHD 328 / Jul '91 / Ace

Balfa Toujours

☐ A VIELLE TERRE HAUTRE
SW 6121CD / Jul '95 / Swallow

☐ DEUX VOYAGES
Allons a Tepatate / Deux voyages / J'ai vu le loup, le Renard et le Belette / Chicot two-step / La Valse a Canray / Bee de la Manche / 73 special / Le Canard a Bois Sec / Le falcon gris / La Valse a Grandpere / Jeunes filles de la campagne / Galop a Wade Fruge / Cher petit monde / Octa's two-step / La musique de ma jeunesse / Le Reel de Nonc Will
ROUCD 6071 / Oct '96 / Rounder

☐ NEW CAJUN TRADITION
La vielle terre haute / True love waltz / Madam boso / Apres nous esperer / J'ai perdu mes lunettes / Reel de deshotels / Old fashioned two step / Les fleurs du Printemps / Rodair special / La marraine / Petite fille de la campagne / La valse de vieux vacher / Texas two step / Arrete pas la musique / Reel du melon d'eau / Pop, tu me parles toujours / L'anse aux pailles / La valse des Balfa / C'est tout perdu / Dans le coeur de basile / Two-step a tina / Tow truck blues
CDCHD 613 / Jun '95 / Ace

Balham Alligators

☐ CAJUN DANCE PARTY (17 Sizzlers From The Swamp)
Cuvee cajun / Bayou pom pom / Guerre civille / Grand Texas / Wet and swampy / Rosie cheeks / Cher Mama / Colinda / Jole blon / Lacassine / Diggy liggy lo / Last waltz / Balham two step / Lache pas mes patats / Big Mamou / Hobo blues / Goodnight Irene
EMPRCD 719 / Jun '97 / Emporio

☐ GATEWAY TO THE SOUTH
Allons rock'n'roll / Hot rod / Bayou teche / Big bad dog / Malhereuse / You gotta have money / Cash on the barrelhead / Secret love / Too much / Honky tonk song / Last waltz / Johnny B Goode
PRPCD 001 / Nov '97 / Proper

☐ PO' BOY 'N' MAKE IT SNAPPY, A
PRPCD 5 / Feb '98 / Proper

Balia, Alberto

☐ ARGIA (Music From Sardinia)
KAR 995 / Nov '97 / IMP

Balin, Marty

☐ FREEDOM FLIGHT
SLD 70052 / Nov '97 / Trove

Balistic Brothers

☐ BALISTIC BROTHERS VS. THE ECCENTRIC AFROS VOL.1
NYX 2 / Gangstalene / Uschis groove / And it goes like this / MCF 287 / Blacker / Valley of the Afro Temple / Grover's return
DSTCD 001 / 29 Sep '97 / Cooking Vinyl

☐ BALISTIC BROTHERS VS. THE ECCENTRIC AFROS VOL.2
Delancey Street...the theme / Unhooked and lost / Save the children / Jam Jah / Divine Fact blacker 2 / Good vibes...goodnight / Anti-gun movement / Blacker 94 eq / Blacker
DST 005CD / 29 Sep '97 / Cooking Vinyl

☐ RUDE SYSTEM
Tuning up / Soul catcher / Marching on / Shiva's prelusion / Shiva's waltz / Conversation / Future James (Jack) / Streets are real / Blacker (4 the good times) / Rule of the bone / Love supreme / Silent runnings
SBCD 001 / Jul '97 / Soundboy

Balkana

☐ MUSIC OF BULGARIA, THE
Trio bulgarka / Trakiiskata troika, kostadin varimezov, jimmy vassiliev / Yanka rupkina trakiiskata troika / Roumen rodopski georgi mussorliev / Trakiiskataa troika, kostadin varimezov, jimmy vassiliev / Trio bulgarka / Kostadin varimezov, jimmy vassiliev / Yanka rupkina trakiiskata troika / Yanka rupkina, trakiiskata troika, kostadin varimezov / Roumen rodopski, trakiiskata troika / Trio bulgarka / Georgi mussorliev / Yanka rupkina / Trakkiiskata troika / Trio bulgarka / Stoyan velichkov / Kostatin varimezov
HNCD 1335 / Oct '87 / Hannibal

Balke, Jon

☐ FURTHER (Balke, Jon & The Magnetic North Orchestra)
Departure / Step one / Horizontal song / Flying thing / Shaded place / Taraf / Moving carpet / Eastern forest / Changing forest / Wooden voices / Arrival
5217202 / May '94 / ECM

☐ NONSENTRATION (Balke, Jon & Oslo 13)
Stealing space / Stealing space II / Stop / Blic / Constructing stop / Laws of freedom / Disappear here / Nord / Circling the square / Art of being
8496532 / Feb '92 / ECM

Ball, E.C.

☐ E.C. BALL
COPP 0141CD / Mar '98 / Copper Creek

☐ E.C. BALL WITH ORMA BALL (Ball, E.C./Orma Ball/Friendly Gospel Singers)
ROUCD 11577 / Mar '96 / Rounder

☐ MOUNTAIN MUSIC
ROU 11577 / May '96 / Rounder

Ball, Ed

☐ CATHOLIC GUILT
Mill Hill self hate club / Love is blue / Docklands blues / Controversial girlfriend / Hampstead therapist / Tilt / Trailblaze / Never live to love again / This is the story of my love / This is real
CRECD 200 / May '97 / Creation

☐ IF A MAN EVER LOVED A WOMAN
CRECD 195 / Jul '95 / Creation

☐ WONDERFUL WORLD OF ED BALL
CRECD 183 / Feb '95 / Creation

Ball, Kenny

☐ BEST OF KENNY BALL, THE (Hits & Requests) (Ball, Kenny & His Jazzmen)
March of the Siamese children / Muskrat ramble / I wanna be like you / Rondo / Sukiyaki / T'ain't what you do (it's the way that you do it) / Kansas City stomps / Music goes 'round and around / Green leaves of summer / Acapulco 1922 / So do I / Midnight in Moscow / Samantha / Casablanca / Chimes blues / Hello Dolly / Original Dixieland one-step / Wild man blues / Basin Street blues / Ory's creole trombourne / When I'm sixty four / At the jazz band ball
TRTCD 147 / 16 Feb '98 / TrueTrax

☐ DIXIELAND CHRISTMAS, A
PWKS 4219 / Oct '95 / Carlton

☐ GREAT MOMENTS WITH KENNY BALL
Midnight in Moscow / Samantha / Them there eyes / Teddy bear's picnic / Fur elise / I've got rhythm / I shall not be moved / St.Louis blues / So do I / BP boogie / Riverside blues / Snag it / Pay off / Sweet Georgia brown / Stevedore stomp
WWJ 3004 / 27 Apr '98 / World Wide Jazz

☐ GREATEST HITS
I love you Samantha / I still love you all / Someday (you'll be sorry) / Midnight in Moscow / My mother's eyes / March of the Siamese children / Green leaves of summer / So do I / Pay off / Sukiyaki / Casablanca / Rondo / Acapulco 1922 / Hello Dolly / When I'm 64 / Heartaches / Margie / Caterina / Nina never knew / I wanna be like you
PLSCD 255 / 27 Oct '97 / Pulse

☐ GREENSLEEVES (Ball, Kenny & His Jazzmen)
Flow gently sweet Afton / Nobody knows you (when you're down and out) / I got rhythm / Ostrich walk / I shall not be moved / St. Louis blues / Greensleeves / My mother's eyes / I wanna be like you / Mood indigo / Them there eyes / Old folks / Sweet Georgia Brown
CDTTD 505 / Jul '94 / Timeless Traditional

☐ HELLO DOLLY
Midnight in Moscow / March of the Siamese children / Sukiyaki / Maple Leaf rag / Swing low, sweet chariot / Down by the riverside / When I'm sixty four / Puttin' on the Ritz / At the jazz band ball / American patrol / Hello Dolly / Cabaret / Green leaves of Summer / I got plenty o' nuttin' / Big noise from Winnetka / Acapulco 1922 / I love you Samantha / Washington Square / Lazy river / Alexander's ragtime band
5507582 / Feb '95 / Spectrum

☐ IN DISNEYLAND
PLSCD 153 / Feb '97 / Pulse

☐ KENNY BALL & HIS JAZZMEN 1960-1961 (Ball, Kenny & His Jazzmen)
Hawaiian war chant / Them there eyes / Georgia swing / Riverside blues / Sorry / Original Dixieland one-step / Teddy bear's picnic / I got plenty of nuthin' / Dinah / Lazy river / 1919 / South Rampart Street Parade / Savoy blues / Ostrich walk / Blue turning grey over you / Fingerbuster / Big noise from Winnetka / Potato head blues
LACD 76 / Mar '97 / Lake

☐ LIGHTING UP THE TOWN (Ball, Kenny & His Jazzmen)
ISCD 113 / Jul '93 / Intersound

☐ LIVE AT THE BP STUDIENHAUS (Ball, Kenny & His Jazzmen)
CDTTD 605 / May '98 / Timeless Traditional

☐ STRICTLY JAZZ (Ball, Kenny & His Jazzmen)
At the jazz band ball / Dark eyes / Basin street blues / Kansas city stomp / Entertainer / Blue turning grey over you / Someday you'll be sorry / High society / Tin roof blues / Maple leaf rag / Down by the riverside / Savoy blues / Steamboat stomp / Louisiania / Livery stable blues (barnyard blues) / Dinah / Milenberg joys / Jazz me blues / Them there eyes / Georgia swing / Lazy river / CC rider / Memphis blues / Temptation rag
KAZCD 19 / Jul '92 / Kaz

☐ VERY BEST OF KENNY BALL, THE (Ball, Kenny & His Jazzmen)
I got plenty o'nuttin' / Pennies from heaven / Teddy bear's picnic / Your feet's too big / Preacher / Stevedore stomp / Pay off / I still love you all / Royal garden blues / Ol' man river / I want a big butter and egg man / Flying high / You are the sunshine of my life / I can't get started / Midnight in Moscow / Samantha
CDTTD 598 / Dec '95 / Timeless Jazz

Ball, Marcia

☐ BLUE HOUSE
ROUCD 3131 / Oct '94 / Rounder

☐ GATORHYTHMS
How you carry on / La ti da / Power of love / Mobile / Find another fool / Mama's cooking / What's a girl to do / Daddy said / You'll come around / Red hot
ROUCD 3101 / Oct '88 / Rounder

☐ HOT TAMALE BABY
Never like this before / I'm gonna forget about you / Love's spell / I don't know / Hot tamale baby / That's enough of that stuff / Don't you know I love you / Another man's woman / If I ever needed love / Uh uh baby
ROUCD 3095 / '88 / Rounder

☐ LET ME PLAY WITH YOUR POODLE
Let me play with your poodle / Why women cry / Crawfishin' / How big a fool / Right tool for the job / I'm just a prisoner / I still love you / Can't trust my heart / Story of my life / Something I can't do / For the love of a man / American dream / Louisiana 1927
ROUCD 3151 / Jul '97 / Rounder

☐ SING IT (Ball, Marcia & Irma Thomas/ Tracy Nelson)
ROUCD 2152 / 19 Jan '98 / Rounder

☐ SOULFUL DRESS
Soulful dress / Made your move too soon / I'd rather go blind / Jailbird / Eugene / My mind's made up / Thousand times / That's why I love you / Soul on fire / Don't want no man
ROUCD 3078 / '88 / Rounder

Ball, Michael

☐ COLLECTION, THE
Love changes everything / One step out of time / House is not a home / Cry me a river / You don't have to say you love me / Someone to watch over me / Stormy weather / As dreams go by / On Broadway / You made me love you / Secret of love / You'll never know (How much I love you) / Beautiful heartache / It's still you / Who needs to know / No one cries anymore / Holland Park / Simple affair of the heart / First man you remember
5517712 / Nov '95 / Spectrum

☐ FIRST LOVE
Rose / Let the river run / Somewhere / If you could read my mind / (Something inside) So strong / How can I be sure / If you go away (Ne me quitte pas) / I'm gonna be strong / I'm so sorry / All by myself / Walk away / When you believe in love
4835992 / Jan '96 / Columbia

☐ MICHAEL BALL
One step out of time / It's still you / Holland park / Secret of love / As dreams go by / Who needs to know / Simple affair of the heart / If you need another love / Beautiful heartache / No one cries anymore / Love changes everything
5113302 / Mar '96 / Polydor

☐ MUSICALS
All I ask of you / Something's coming / Losing my mind / Memory / Don't rain on my parade / With one look / Show me / I dreamed a dream / You'll never walk alone / Easy terms / Last night of the world / Loving you / Anthem / Love changes everything / One more look (outro)
5338922 / Nov '96 / PolyGram TV

☐ VERY BEST OF MICHAEL BALL, THE
Song for you / Sunset Boulevard / Holland Park / Love changes everything / No one cries anymore / One step out of time / We break our own hearts / Call on me / As dreams go by / Everyday everynight / No more steps to climb / House is not a home / Maria / Beautiful heartache / It's still you / If I can dream / Empty chairs at empty tables / Always on my mind / Simple affair of the heart / On Broadway
5238912 / Nov '94 / Polydor

Ball, Tom

☐ BLOODSHOT EYES (Ball, Tom & Kenny Sultan)
FF 386CD / Feb '93 / Flying Fish

☐ DOUBLE VISION (Ball, Tom & Kenny Sultan)
Perfect woman / Your shoes don't fit my feet / No money, no honey / Automobile mechanic / I feel alright now / Sweet Georgia Brown/Bill Bailey / Sweet temptation / Sloppy Joe / Television / Roll of the tumblin' dice / Wing and a prayer / Ride that train / Back to California / Who drank my beer
CDFF 656 / Sep '96 / Flying Fish

☐ GUITAR MUSIC
Estudio sin luz / Variation on forlorn hope fancy / Sweet Papa Lowdown / Fantasia no.30 / Joseph Spence medley / Cane break blues / Heigh ho holiday / Variation on a barrios prelude / Morley's pavan / Mirabella / Volt no.6 / Old time medley / Sarabande / Needed time / Lejania
CDKM 3906 / Jan '97 / Kicking Mule

☐ TOO MUCH FUN (Ball, Tom & Kenny Sultan)
FF 532CD / '92 / Flying Fish

Balla Et Ses Balladins

☐ AFRICAN DANCE FLOOR CLASSICS
ADC 302 / Feb '94 / PAM

Ballantine, David

☐ PAINT
DTAB 16CD / Nov '95 / Dtab

Ballard, Hank

☐ 20 HITS (Ballard, Hank & The Midnighters)
KCD 5003 / Apr '97 / King

☐ SING 24 SONGS (Ballard, Hank & The Midnighters)
KCD 950 / Mar '90 / King

Ballard, Russ

☐ RUSS BALLARD/THE FIRE STILL BURNS
RME 0105CD / Oct '97 / Renaissance

☐ WINNING/BARNET DOGS
RMED 0122CD / 9 Mar '98 / Renaissance

Ballas, Corky

☐ PASSION VOL.2 (Ballas, Corky & Shirley)
DLD 1061 / Dec '95 / Dance & Listen

Ballbusters

☐ NO HANG UPS
0090674DDX / Oct '95 / Deep Distraxion/Profile

Baller, Bla

☐ HER ER VI
CFF 01CD / Dec '97 / CFF

Ballero, Jimmy

☐ JIMMY BALLERO AND THE RENEGADE BAND (Ballero, Jimmy & The Renegade Band)
Shine them buckles / Shine them buckles / Pit bulls and chain saws / Blue rodeo / Twang town / She's awesome / Old hippie (the sequel) / Native american / Feel free / Too much fun / We dared the lightning / Elvis, marilyn and james dean / Gotta get a little crazy / Jesus is coming
SCD 27 / Feb '93 / Southland

Ballew, Michael

☐ I LOVE TEXAS
Music is sweet / Greatest Texas song / Glenda Pearl / Ain't no future / I love Texas / Blue water / Country music / Rodeo cool / Hot spot / Lovin' me / Cheatin' / Take it slow / My family / Your daddy don't live in heaven / Pretending fool / Seminole County Jail / Crazy dreams / Dark side of the dancefloor / As precious as you are / Women love, love out there / Hazelwood Avenue
BCD 15669 / Jun '92 / Bear Family

☐ LIVE AT GRUENE HALL
Hot spot / Damned ol' beer / Whiskey's fine / I can't drive home / I can't do that (anymore) / Leavin' these honky tonks / I love to ride / Texas gal / Top of the world / Heavy on the blues / Where are the rangers / Sixteen tons / Music is sweet / Darkside on the dancefloor / Old cowboy / Cowboy and the preacher / Texas blue water / I love Texas
BCD 16167 / May '97 / Bear Family

☐ YOU BETTER HOLD ON
Blue to the bone / Livin' in limbo / Nothin' on me / Tiny fingers, tiny toes / Texas gal / Blue water / Boot scootin' / Your memory is better than mine / You better hold on / Hill country wine / For the honey / Dig in, get tough / Today will never end
BCD 15896 / Jun '95 / Bear Family

Ballin, Chris

☐ DO IT RIGHT
EMH 3CD / Jun '96 / Intimate

Balliu, Rudy

☐ RUDY BALLIU NEW ORLEANS TRIO (Balliu, Rudy New Orleans Trio)
BCD 383 / Dec '97 / GHB

☐ RUDY BALLIU'S SOCIETY SERENADERS (Balliu, Rudy & His Society Serenaders)
BCD 343 / Jul '96 / GHB

Ballochmyle Ceilidh Band

☐ FOR OUR FRIENDS
Take me back / My world's come down / Greem holm / Mcdonald's awa' to the wars / Ness bothan / Alistdair mcleod of tobermory / One day at a time / Let me be there / Katie martin's waltz / Marjory waltz / She's not you / I'm gonna be a country boy again / Mary lou / Boy's of killybegs / Miss alison smith / Hurlock's reel / Lovat's reel / Dancing the baby / It keeps right on a hurtin' / Summertime in ireland / Boswell castle / Skye crofters / Veil of white lace / Bad moon rising
CDLOC 1071 / Dec '91 / Lochshore

☐ TOUCH OF COUNTRY, A
CDSLP 622 / Aug '94 / Klub

Ballou, Dave

☐ AMONGST OURSELVES
SCCD 31436 / 1 Jun '98 / Steeplechase

Ballroom Dance Orchestra

☐ COME DANCING RHUMBA
Have I told you lately / Another day in Paradise / And I love her / Spanish eyes / Europe / Feelings / Endless love / Most beautiful girl in the world / La isla bonita / I have a dream / It's too late / He ain't heavy he's my brother / I heard it through the grapevine / How deep is your love / Killingly me softly / All out of love
306092 / Jan '97 / Hallmark

Ballyclare Male Voice Choir

☐ MARVELLOUS AND WONDERFUL
CDPOL 906 / Jan '95 / Outlet

☐ WALKING WITH GOD
CDPOL 901 / Jan '95 / Outlet

Balogh, Kalman

☐ GIPSY CIMBALOM, THE
EUCD 1102 / '91 / ARC

☐ ROMA VANDOR
MWCD 4009 / Apr '95 / Music & Words

Balogh, Meta

☐ GYPSY MUSIC FROM THE HUNGARIAN VILLAGES (Balogh, Meta & Kalman)
EUCD 1373 / Nov '96 / ARC

Balthaus, Dirk

☐ TALES OF THE FROG
BEST 1082CD / Mar '96 / Acoustic Music

Baltic Quartet

☐ BALTIC QUARTET
SITCD 9222 / Aug '95 / Sittel

Baltimore

☐ THOUGHT FOR FOOD
SPV 08496112 / Jul '94 / SPV

Baltimores

☐ BOOZE, BATTLE AND WOMEN
PEPCD 116 / Oct '96 / Pollytone

Bam Bam

☐ BEST OF WESTBROOK CLASSICS
EFAO 17822 / Mar '95 / Tresor

Bamba, Amadu

☐ DRUMS OF THE FIRDU FULA
VPU 1004CD / May '97 / Village Pulse

Bambaataa, Afrika

☐ HIP HOP FUNK DANCE CLASSICS VOL.1
SPOCK 3CD / Jul '91 / Music Of Life

☐ WARLOCKS, WITCHES, COMPUTERCHIPS
FILECD 464 / Feb '96 / Profile

☐ ZULU GROOVE
World destruction / Shango message / Wild style / Zulu groove / Thank you / Let's party down / Soca fever / World destruction
HVD 5103 / Jan '98 / Hudson Vandam/ Subharmonic

Bambaraka

☐ AUTOMATIC ORIGINAL
SM 0002 / Sep '97 / Sakti

Bambi

☐ WARNING
DAMGOOD 118CD / Mar '97 / Damaged Goods

Bamboleo

☐ TE GUSTO O TE CALGO BIEN
1611710032 / 17 Mar '98 / Ahi Nama

☐ YO NO ME PAREZCO A NADIE
1611710132 / 17 Mar '98 / Ahi Nama

Bana Maquis

☐ LEILA
2002968 / Jan '97 / Dakar Sound

Banabila, Michel

☐ DESERT DREAMFIELDS
DC 881942 / Oct '97 / Disky

Banana Slug String Band

☐ PENGUIN PARADE
9425892 / Aug '96 / Music For Little People

Bananarama

☐ BUNCH OF HITS
Love in the first degree / Bad for me / I heard a rumour / Ain't no cure / I can't let you go / Hooked on love / Young at heart / Robert De Niro's waiting / Hotline to heaven / Dance with a stranger / Scarlett / Ghost / Rough justice / Cheers then
5500122 / May '93 / Spectrum

☐ GREATEST HITS
Venus / I heard a rumour / Love in the first degree / I can't help it / I want you back / Love, truth and honesty / Nathan Jones / Really saying something / Shy boy / Robert De Niro's waiting / Cruel summer / T'ain't what you do (it's the way that you do it) / Na na hey hey kiss him goodbye / Rough justice / Trick of the night / Aie a mwana / Venus (Mix) / Love in the first degree (mix)
8281062 / Jan '93 / London

Banane Metalik

☐ REQUIEM DE LA DEPRAVATION
BM 666 / Jun '98 / Bananajuice

Banchory Strathspey & Reel Society

☐ GEOL NA FIDHLE
CDTIV 605 / Aug '95 / Scotdisc

☐ TRIBUTE TO SCOTT SKINNER, A
March, strathspey and reel / Slow air / Jig / Slow air strathspey reel / Hornpipe / Reel / Waltz / March, strathspey and reel / March, strathspey and reel / Hornpipe / Patrol strathspey hornpipe / 68 march / Slow air march / 68 march reel / Slow air / March, strathspey and reel / Reel
CDITV 578 / Nov '94 / Scotdisc

Banco De Gaia

☐ BIG MEN CRY
Drippy / Celestine / Drunk as a monk / Big men cry / Gates does Windows / One billion miles out / Starstation Earth
BARKCD 025 / Jul '97 / Planet Dog

☐ LAST TRAIN TO LHASA
BARKCD 011 / May '95 / Planet Dog

☐ LIVE AT GLASTONBURY
BARKCD 021 / Jul '96 / Ultimate

☐ MAYA
BARKCD 3 / Feb '94 / Ultimate

Band

☐ ACROSS THE GREAT DIVIDE (3CD Set)
Tears of rage / Weight / I shall be released / Chest fever / In a station / To kingdom come / Lonesome Suzie / Rag mama rag / Night they drove old dixie down / King Harvest (has surely come) / Rockin' chair / Whispering pines / Up on cripple creek / Across the great divide / Unfaithful servant / Shape I'm in / Daniel and the sacred harp / All la glory / Stage fright / When I paint my masterpiece / Moon struck one / Life is a carnival / River hymn / Don't do it / Calsonia mission / WS Walcott medicine show / Medicine show / Get up Jake / This wheel's on fire / Share your love with me / Mystery train / Acadian driftwood / Ophelia / It makes no difference / Living in a dream / Saga of Pepote Rouge / Right as rain / Who do you love / Do the honky tonk / He don't love you / Katie's been gone / Bessie Smith / Orange juice blues / Ain't no cane on the brazos / Slippin' and slidin' / Twilight / Back to Memphis / Too wet to work / Loving you is sweeter than ever / Don't ya tell Henry / Endless highway / She knows / Evangeline / Out of the blue / Last waltz (refrain) / Last waltz
CDBAND 1 / Nov '94 / Capitol

☐ BAND, THE
Across the great divide / Rag mama rag / Night they drove old Dixie down / When you awake / Up on Cripple Creek / Whispering pines / Jemima surrender / Rockin' chair / Look out Cleveland / Jawbone / Unfaithful servant / King harvest (Has surely come)
CDP 7464932 / 18 Aug '97 / Capitol

☐ CAHOOTS
Life is a carnival / When I paint my masterpiece / Last of the blacksmiths / Where do we go from here / 4% pantomime / Shoot out in Chinatown / Moon struck one / Thinkin' out loud / Smoke signal / Volcano / River hymn
7484202 / 1 Jun '98 / Capitol

☐ COLLECTION, THE
Weight / Night they drove old Dixie down / Ain't got no home / I shall be released / Change is gonna come / Third man theme / Don't do it / Stage fright / King Harvest has surely come / Long black veil / River hymn / Georgia on my mind / Great pretender / 4% Pantomime
CDGOLD 1075 / Feb '97 / EMI Gold

☐ HIGH ON THE HOG
TRACD 228 / Apr '96 / Transatlantic

☐ ISLANDS
Right as rain / Street walker / Let the night fall / Ain't that a lot of love / Christmas must be tonight / Islands / Saga of Pepote Rouge / Georgia on my mind / Living in a dream / Knockin' lost John
7935912 / 1 Jun '98 / Capitol

☐ JERICHO
Remedy / Blind Willie McTell / Caves of Jericho / Atlantic city / Too soon gone / Country boy / Move to Japan / Amazon (river of dreams) / Stuff you gotta watch / Same thing / Shine a light / Blues stay away from me
ESMCD 393 / Feb '97 / Essential

☐ LAST WALTZ, THE
Last waltz / Up on Cripple Creek / Who do you love / Helpless / Stage fright / Coyote / Dry your eyes / It makes no difference / Such a night / Night they drove old Dixie down / Mystery train / Mannish boy / Further on up the road / Shape I'm in / Down South in New Orleans / Ophelia / Tura lura larai (That's an Irish lullaby) / Caravan / Life is a carnival / Baby let me follow you down / I don't believe you (she acts like we never have met) / Forever young / I shall be released / Last waltz suite / Well / Evangeline / Out of the blue / Weight
K 266076 / Mar '88 / WEA

☐ LIVE AT WATKINS GLEN
Back to Memphis / Endless highway / I shall be released / Loving you is sweeter than ever / Too wet to work / Don't ya tell Henry / Rumour / Time to kill / Jam / Up on cripple creek
8317422 / 1 Jun '98 / Capitol

☐ MOONDOG MATINEE
7935922 / 1 Jun '98 / Capitol

☐ MUSIC FROM BIG PINK
Tears of rage / To Kingdom come / In a station / Caledonia mission / Weight / We can talk / Long black veil / Chest fever / Lonesome Suzie / This wheel's on fire / I shall be released
7460692 / 1 Jun '98 / Capitol

☐ SHAPE I'M IN, THE (The Very Best Of The Band)
Shape I'm in / Across the great divide / Night they drove old dixie down / Stage fright / Rag mama rag / Ophelia / Up on cripple creek / Twilight / King harvest / Life is a carnival / I shall be released / Tears of rage / Acadian driftwood / Weight / It makes no difference / Chest fever / Share your love with me / Don't do it
4950512 / 3 Aug '98 / Capitol

☐ STAGE FRIGHT
Strawberry wine / Sleeping / Just another whistle stop / All la glory / Shape I'm in / WS Walcott medicine show / Daniel and the sacred harp / Stage fright / Rumour / Time to kill
7935932 / 1 Jun '98 / Capitol

☐ TO KINGDOM COME (2CD Set)
Back to Memphis / Tears of rage / To kingdom come / Long black veil / Chest fever / Weight / I shall be released / Up on Cripple Creek / Loving you is sweeter than ever / Rag mama rag / Night they drove old Dixie down / Unfaithful servant / King harvest (has surely come) / Shape I'm in / WS Walcott medicine show / Daniel and the sacred harp / Stage fright / Don't do it (baby don't you do it) / Life is a carnival / When I paint my masterpiece / 4% pantomime / River hymn / Mystery train / Endless highway / Get up Jake / It makes no difference / Ophelia / Acadian driftwood / Christmas must be tonight / Saga of Pepote Rouge / Knockin' lost John
CDS 7921692 / Sep '89 / Capitol

☐ WEIGHT, THE
Weight / Night they drove all dixie down / Ain't got no home / I shall be released / Change is gonna come / Third man theme / Don't do it (baby don't you do it) / Stage fright / King harvest (has surely come) / Long black veil / Rhythm hymn / Georgia on my mind / Great pretender / 4% pantomine
DC 867162 / Nov '96 / Disky

Band Ar Jazz

☐ ZERO UN
CD 859 / Aug '96 / Escalibur

Band Of Holy Joy

☐ TRACKSUIT VENDETTA, A (Holy Joy)
EQCD 004 / Jun '92 / Ecuador

Band Of Hope

☐ RHYTHMS AND REDS
MFCD 512 / Aug '94 / Musikfolk

Band Of Outsiders

☐ NO REFLECTION
EFA 15658CD / Oct '92 / Repulsion

Band Of Pain

☐ RECULVER
ILIGHT 011CD / 10 Aug '98 / Iris Light

Band Of Susans

☐ HERE COMES SUCCESS
BFFP 114CD / Apr '95 / Blast First

☐ LOVE AGENDA
BFFP 43CD / Jan '89 / Blast First

☐ NOW
Pearls of wisdom / Following my heart / Trash train / Paint it black / Now is now (Remix) / Paint it black (instrumental)
RTD 15914912 / Apr '93 / World Service

☐ VEIL
Mood swing / Not in this life / Red and the black / Following my heart / Stained glass / Last temptation of Susan / Truce / Trouble spot / Out of the question / Pearls of wisdom / Trollbinder's theme / Blind
RTD 15715612 / Jun '93 / World Service

☐ WIRED FOR SOUND
BFFP 111CD / Jan '95 / Blast First

Band Of The Rising Sun

☐ SETTING IT RIGHT
Grand hornpipe / Slip jigs / Charlesworth Hornpipe / Hard times / Dutch skipper / Wounded hussar / Oldham white hare / Berwick jockey / Northern lass / Lancaster lassses / Morpeth rants / Chesire rolling hornpipe / Go George
FSCD 37 / Jun '97 / Folksound

Banda Black Rio

☐ BEST OF BANDA BLACK RIO, THE
Gafieira universal / Vidigal / Expresso madureira / Leblon via vaz lobo / Cravo e canela / Maria fumaca / Miss Sheryl / Mr. Funky Samba / Samboreando / Rio de fevereiro / Casta forte / Chega mais
USCD 3 / May '96 / Universal Sound

Banda De Gaites Mieres Del Camin

☐ EL TREBOLE DE SAN XUAN
FA 8759CD / Nov '96 / Fono Astur

Banda Machos

☐ 30 DE COLECCION (3CD Set)
5330807312 / 5 May '98 / Fonovisa

Banda Maguey

☐ 30 DE COLECCION (3CD Set)
5330807302 / 5 May '98 / Fonovisa

Banda Mantiquiera

☐ ALDEIA
Linha de passe / Procura / Seis no choro / Carinhoso / Insensatez / Cubango / Aldeia
ACT 50082 / Sep '97 / Act

Banda Olodum

☐ O MOVIEMENTO
Alegria geral / Rosa / Amor de eva / Mul mulher / Literatura faraonica / Luz celeste / Requebra / Papa furado / O falo da dala / Suenos lejos / Jazz E blues / Te amo / Cara preta / Tropicum / Ideologia / Bahia viva
4509949122 / Feb '91 / East West

Bandit Queen

☐ HORMONE HOTEL
Scorch / Back in the belljar / Miss Dandys / Nailbiter / Give it to the dog / Petals and razorblades / Overture for beginners / Big sugar emotional thing / Essence vanilla / Oestrogen / Frida Kahlo / Hormone hotel / Blue black
AMUSE 26CD / Feb '95 / Playtime

Bandoni, Mike

☐ MIKE BANDONI
NOZACD 9 / Sep '97 / Ninebar

☐ STAR CHILDREN
NOZACD 008 / 22 Jun '98 / Ninebar

Bands Of The British Army

☐ MARCHING TO GLORY
MU 5009 / Oct '92 / Musketeer

Bandulu

☐ GUIDANCE
INF 003CD / Jun '93 / Infonet

Bandy, Moe

☐ HONKY TONK AMNESIA
RAZCD 2096 / Apr '96 / Razor & Tie

Bang Bang Machine

☐ AMPHIBIAN
Breathless / Love and things / Tough Delilah / Fantasia / Slide / Show me your pain / Love it bleeds / When love comes down / Requiem of silence
TOPPCD 036 / Mar '96 / Ultimate

☐ ETERNAL HAPPINESS
TOPPCD 009 / Jun '94 / Ultimate

Bang, Billy

☐ BANG ON
Bama swing / Sweet Georgia Brown / Peaceful dreams / Spirits entering / They plan / Three faces of Eve / Yesterdays / Don's dream / Willow weep for me / Mr. Simms
JUST 1052 / 17 Nov '97 / Justin Time

☐ BANGCEPTION (Bang, Billy & Dennis Charles)
HATOLOGY 517 / Jul '98 / Hatology

☐ LIVE AT CARLOS
1211362 / '88 / Soul Note

☐ OUTLINE NO.12
CDGR 256 / 29 Jun '98 / Charly

☐ RAINBOW GLADIATOR (Bang, Billy Quartet)
1210162 / Nov '92 / Soul Note

☐ TRIBUTE TO STUFF SMITH
1212162 / Nov '93 / Soul Note

☐ VALVE NO.10 (Bang, Billy Quartet)
1211862 / Nov '91 / Soul Note

Bang On A Can

☐ CHEATING, LYING, STEALING
SK 62254 / Aug '96 / Sony Classical

☐ INDUSTRY
SK 66483 / Jan '95 / Sony Classical

☐ MUSIC FOR AIRPORTS (Brian Eno's Defining Classic Reinterpreted)
1/1 / 1/2 / 2/1 / 2/2
5368472 / 5 May '98 / Point Music

Bang Tango

☐ LOVE AFTER DEATH
CDMFN 174 / Feb '95 / Music For Nations

Bang The Party

☐ BACK TO PRISON
WAFCD 4 / Sep '90 / Warriors Dance

Bangash, Aman Ali

☐ RAGA PURIYA KALYAN
Alap, jor and jhala / Gat composition
NRCD 0078 / Jul '97 / Navras

Bangham, Kid

☐ PRESSURE COOKER (Bangham, Kid & Amyl Justin)
Danger zone / Shoot me / Face down in the blues / I wouldn't treat a dog / Big man around town / My turn to talk / No justice / Hurricane Jane / Lonely one / Kid stuff / Let's do it over / I go crazy / Rocket in my pocket
CDTC 1162 / Oct '97 / Tonecool

Banging Rush

☐ HOLIDAY IN EDEN
199631 / 2 Mar '98 / Psychoactive

Bangles

☐ ALL OVER THE PLACE
Hero takes a fall / Live / James / All about you / Dover beach / Tell me / Restless / Going down to Liverpool / He's got a secret / Silent treatment / More than meets the eye
4879292 / Jul '97 / Columbia

☐ DEFINITIVE COLLECTION, THE
Walk like an Egyptian / Walking down your street / Manic Monday / Eternal flame / My side of the bed / If she knew what she wants / Be with you / Following / In a different light / Unconditional love / Hazy shade of winter / In your room / I'll set you free / No kind of love / Everything I wanted / Going down to Liverpool / Some dreams come true / Wishing on a telstar / Waiting for you / Hero takes a fall / All about you
4805442 / 13 Jul '98 / Columbia

☐ DIFFERENT LIGHT
Manic Monday / In a different light / Walking down your street / Walk like an Egyptian / Standing in the hallway / Return post / If she knew what she wants / Let it go / September gurls / Angels don't fall in love / Following / Not like you
4844532 / Aug '96 / CBS

☐ GREATEST HITS
Hero takes a fall / Going down to Liverpool / Manic monday / If she knew what she wants / Walk like an Egyptian / Walking down your street / Following / Hazy shade of winter / In your room / Eternal flame / Be with you / I'll set you free / Everything I wanted / Where were you when I needed you
4667692 / Apr '95 / CBS

Bangs

☐ TIGER BEAT
KRS 294CD / 23 Mar '98 / Kill Rock Stars

Banjo Express

☐ OLD TIME COUNTRY MUSIC
PV 710 781 / '88 / Disques Pierre Verany

Banks, Billy

☐ CLASSICS 1932
CLASSICS 969 / 5 Jan '98 / Classics

Banks, Buddy

☐ COMPLETE 1945-1949
BMCD 6015 / 1 Jun '98 / Blue Moon

Banks, Chico

☐ CANDY LICKIN' MAN
Red dress / Candy lickin' man / Down the road I go / It must be love / Angel of mercy / Soul serenade / All your love / Careless things we do / Got to be some changes made / You're fine / Groove me / Sky is crying / Truck load of lovin' / Call my job
ECD 26090 / 14 Oct '97 / Evidence

Banks, Darrell

☐ LOST SOUL OF DARRELL BANKS, THE
Open the door to your heart / Angel baby / You better go / Here comes the tears / I've got that feeling / I'm gonna hang my head and cry / Look into the eyes of a fool / Our love is in the pocket / Love of my woman / I'm knocking at your door / I wanna go home / Harder you love / I could never hate her / Don't know what to do / Only the strong survive / I'm the one who loves you / My love is strictly reserved / I will fear no evil / Baby whatcha got for me / Somebody somewhere needs you / Just because your love is gone / Forgive me / Beautiful feeling / Never alone / No one blinder / When a man loves a woman / We'll get over
GSCD 109 / Mar '97 / Goldmine

Banks, Peter

☐ INSTINCT
No place home / All points south / Fogbound / Sticky wicket / Shortcomings / Code blue / Angels / Anima mundi / Swamp report / Instinctive behaviour / Dominating factor / Never the same
HTDCD 11 / Feb '93 / HTD

☐ LIVE
Small beginnings / Room with a view / Children of the universe / Dreams of heaven / Dead again / Pysco synch
BP 235CD / Jun '97 / Blueprint

☐ REDUCTION
Fade to blue / Dirty little secret / As night falls / Pirate's pleasure / Rosa nova / Fathat / Age of distortion / Sleep on it / Knuckledust / No strings / 2000 lies
HTDCD 76 / 15 Sep '97 / HTD

☐ TWO SIDES OF PETER BANKS
OW S2118009 / Sep '94 / One Way

Banks, R.C.

☐ CHANKY CHANK MAN
Chanky chank man / I'm the one / Let's celebrate / That's my crowd / Hello raindrops / Bon amis / Hello big city / This town / I wish that you were mine / One and only / Jump / Grand promenade
MRCD 0596 / Feb '97 / Club De Musique

Banks, Tony

☐ CURIOUS FEELING, A
From the undertow / Lucky me / Lie / After the lie / Curious feeling / Forever morning / You / Somebody else's dream / Waters of Lethe / For a while / In the dark
CASCD 1148 / May '88 / Charisma

☐ SOUNDTRACKS
Shortcut to somewhere / Smilin' Jack Casey / Quicksilver suite / You call this victory / Lion of symmetry / Red wing suite
CASCD 1173 / Jul '87 / Charisma

☐ STILL
Red day on blue street / Angel face / Gift / Still it takes me by suprise / Hero for an hour / I wanna change the score / Water out of wine / Another murder of a day / Back to back / Final curtain
CDV 2658 / Jun '91 / Virgin

Bann, Stan

☐ GOOD INTENTIONS (Bann, Stan Big Band)
SB 2087 / Sep '97 / Sea Breeze

Bannal

☐ WAULKING SONGS
Bhean ud thall / Gu de th' orr' Aire / 'S muladach mi's air aineol / 'S I tir mo ruin sa ghaidhealiacha / He mandu / Latha dhomh's mi 'm beinn a' Cheathaich / Dh'eirich moch maduinn cheitein / Beir soiridh soiridh bhuam / Thug mi 'n oidhche ge b'fhad I / Chan eil mi gun mhulad orm / Clo mhicllemhicheil / Gura mi tha trom duilich / Chunnaic mise 'n t-og uasal / Mile marbhphaisg air a' ghaol / Mhurchaidh bhig / He mo leannan ho mo leannan / Mo nighean donn ho gu / Chaidh mi 'na ghleannan as t-foghar / An long Eireannach
CDTRAX 099 / Feb '96 / Greentrax

Bannerjee, Nikhil

☐ RAGA AHIR
DSAV 1054 / Dec '95 / Multitone

Bannlust

☐ DIGITAL TENSIONS
CRAFT 27 / 26 Jan '98 / Sabotage

Bantam Rooster

☐ DEAL ME IN
EFACD 12889 / Apr '97 / Crypt

Banyumas Bamboo Gamelan

☐ TRADITIONAL MUSIC FROM CENTRAL JAVA
NI 5550 / 9 Mar '98 / Nimbus

Baphomet

☐ LATEST JESUS
MASSCD 007 / Apr '97 / Massacre

☐ TRUST
MASSCD 027 / Apr '97 / Massacre

Baptista, Cyro

☐ VIRA LOUCOS (The Music Of Villa Lobos)
AVAN 061 / Oct '97 / Avant

Bar Feeders

☐ SCOTTO EL BLOTTO
DILL 018 / 16 Mar '98 / Dill

Bar-Kays

☐ SOUL FINGER
Knucklehead / Soul finger / With a child's heart / Bar-kays boogaloo / Hell's Angels / You can't sit down / House shoes / Pearl high / I want someone / Hole in the wall / Don't do that
8122702982 / Jul '93 / Atco

Baraban

☐ IL VALZER DEI DISERTORI
ACB 01 / Jan '94 / Robi Droli

Barabas, Tom

☐ CLASSICA NOUVEAU
SP 7152CD / Jul '96 / Soundings Of The Planet

☐ SEDONA SUITE
SP 7142CD / Jul '96 / Soundings Of The Planet

Barachois

☐ ACADIAN MUSIC FROM PRINCE EDWARD ISLAND
Pot pourri / Bartarache la rigondaine / Reel du pendu / La vieux soldat / Mon tour va venir un jour / Reel des Narcisse / Reel du barachois / J'aurais quelque chose a dire / Je mari jaloux / Les deux John / Envoyez d'l'avant / Le voyager / Marie Blanche / Le p'tit moine/La reel des acadiens
IRCD 048 / May '97 / Iona

Barazaz

☐ ECHOUNDER
CD 828 / May '93 / Diffusion Breizh

Barbarin, Paul

☐ OXFORD SERIES VOL.15
AMCD 35 / Jan '94 / American Music

☐ OXFORD SERIES VOL.16 (Barbarin, Paul Jazzband)
AMCD 36 / Jul '96 / American Music

☐ SOUNDS OF NEW ORLEANS VOL.1 (Barbarin, Paul Band/Percy Humphrey)
STCD 6008 / Mar '97 / Storyville

☐ STREETS OF THE CITY (Barbarin, Paul & His New Orleans Band)
Just a little while to stay here / Who's sorry now / Smiles / Fidgety feet / Just a closer walk with thee / High society / Panama / Way down yonder in New Orleans / When I was a little child / Weary blues / Sweet Georgia Brown / Tin roof blues / Just a closer walk with thee / Big bad bully
504CD 9 / Mar '98 / 504

Barber, Chris

☐ 40 YEARS JUBILEE (Vol.1 1954-1955/ Vol.2 1955-1956 2CD Set)
Hiawatha rag / Jeep's blues / If I ever cease to love / Merrydown blues / Goin' to town / Lord, Lord, Lord / Someday sweetheart / When I move to the sky / On a Monday / Shout 'em Aunt Tillie / Spanish Mama / Please get him off my mind / CC rider / Black cat on the fence / In the evening / Midnight special / Papa de da da / Keystone blues / Jailhouse blues / High society / Bye and bye / Magnolia's wedding day / Jelly bean blues / Everywhere you go / Goin' down the road feelin' bad / Long gone lost John / Tiger rag / Can't afford to do it / Original tuxedo rag / Bogalousa strut / How long blues / Railroad Bill / Whistling Rufus / Reckell blues / Panama / Back water blues / Big house blues / Royal telephone
CDTTD 589 / Jul '95 / Timeless Traditional

☐ 40 YEARS JUBILEE AT THE OPERAHOUSE NURNBERG
Isle of capri / We sure do need him now / It's tight like that / Old rugged cross / Hush-a-bye / Worried man blues / Down by the riverside / Ice cream / Workin' man blues / Petite fleur / Sweet Georgia Brown / Brown / Slap 'n' slide / Tiger rag / Mile end stomp / Wild cat blues
CDTTD 590 / Dec '94 / Timeless Traditional

☐ ACKER, KENNY AND CHRIS (Barber, Chris & Kenny Ball/Acker Bilk)
PLSCD 209 / Apr '97 / Pulse

☐ ALL THAT JAZZ (Barber, Chris & Acker Bilk/Kenny Ball)
Hello dolly-mame / Hello dolly-mame / Bare necessities / Green leaves of summer / So do I / When somebody thinks you're wonderful / Lady madonna / Sukiyakl / April showers / I can't give you anything but love / Lonesome road / One sweet letter from you / You rascal you / Brown skinned mama / Papa de da da / Mean mistreater / Dardanella / Mercy, mercy, mercy / Stompin' at the savoy / At sundown / Gee baby, ain't I good to you / There'll be some changes made / Time's a wastin' / Someday you'll be sorry
KAZCD 18 / Jan '92 / Kaz

☐ BARBER, BALL & BILK (Barber, Chris & Acker Bilk/Kenny Ball)
Big noise from Winnetka / Sweet Sue, just you / Livery stable blues / Careless love / Willie the weeper / 1919 March / Sweet Georgia Brown / Bourbon street parade / Dinah / Burgundy St. Blues / Marching through Georgia / Petite fleur / Temptation rag / Chelsea cakewalk / Yama yama man / South Rampart Street Parade / Bill Bailey, won't you please come home / Dardanella / Bugle boy march / Milenberg joys
TRTCD 130 / 19 Dec '97 / TrueTrax

☐ BARBER, BALL & BILK (Barber, Chris & Acker Bilk/Kenny Ball)
SSLCD 205 / Jun '95 / Savanna

☐ BEST OF BARBER AND BILK, THE (Barber, Chris Jazzband/Acker Bilk Paramount Jazzband)
April showers: *Barber, Chris Jazzband* / Doin' the crazy walk: *Barber, Chris Jazzband* / Hushabye: *Barber, Chris Jazzband* / Everybody loves my baby: *Barber, Chris Jazzband* / I can't give you anything but love: *Barber, Chris Jazzband* / Whistling Rufus: *Barber, Chris Jazzband* / Bugle call rag: *Barber, Chris Jazzband* / Beale Street blues: *Barber, Chris Jazzband* / Magnolia's wedding day: *Barber, Chris Jazzband* / Petite fleur: *Barber, Chris Jazzband* / Bye and bye: *Barber, Chris Jazzband* / Cre march: *Bilk, Acker & His Paramount Jazz Band* / Dardanella: *Bilk, Acker & His Paramount Jazz Band* / Franklin Street blues: *Bilk, Acker & His Paramount Jazz Band* / Blaze away: *Bilk, Acker & His Paramount Jazz Band* / Easter parade: *Bilk, Acker & His Paramount Jazz Band* / Marching through Georgia: *Bilk, Acker & His Paramount Jazz Band* / Louisian-i-ay: *Bilk, Acker & His Paramount Jazz Band* / El abanico: *Bilk, Acker & His Paramount Jazz Band* / Carry me back: *Bilk, Acker & His Paramount Jazz Band* / Travelling blues: *Bilk, Acker & His Paramount Jazz Band* / Delia gone: *Bilk, Acker & His Paramount Jazz Band* / Under the double eagle: *Bilk, Acker & His Paramount Jazz Band*
LACD 73 / Oct '96 / Lake

☐ BEST OF CHRIS BARBER & HIS JAZZ BAND, THE (Barber, Chris & His Jazz Band)
Petite fleur / When the saints go marching in / Bourbon Street parade / Bill Bailey won't you please come home / I wish I could shimmy like my sister Kate / Sweet Georgia Brown / Everybody loves my baby / Majorca / High society / April showers / Brown skin mama / Wild cat blues / Sweet Sue, just you / Jailhouse blues / Sheikh of Araby / New St. Louis blues
21022 / Jul '97 / Laserlight

☐ BEST SELLERS
STCD 200 / Oct '87 / Storyville

☐ CHRIS BARBER (Barber, Chris & The Zenith Hot Stompers)
Ole Miss rag / Riverside blues / Just a little while to stay here / Bugle boy march / Saratoga swing / Precious Lord, take my hand / Sweet Georgia Brown / Goin' home / Panama rag / Sweet Sue, just you / Creole love call / Bye and bye
CDTTD 582 / Feb '94 / Timeless Traditional

☐ CHRIS BARBER & HIS NEW ORLEANS FRIENDS
Birth of the blues / Coquette / Ma, she's making eyes at me / Over in the glory land / Sentimental journey / Yes sir that's my baby / Eyes of Texas are upon you / Mood indigo / My blue heaven / Let me call you sweetheart / Nobody's sweetheart / I ain't got nobody / Lord, lord, lord / Panama
CDTTD 573 / Oct '93 / Timeless Jazz

☐ CHRIS BARBER CONCERTS, THE (2CD Set)
Bourbon street parade / New blues / Willy the weeper / Mean mistreater / Yama yama man / Old man mose / Mood indigo / Bearcat crawl / Lowland blues / Panama / Savoy blues / Lonesome road / Sheik or araby / Bill Bailey, won't you please come home / You took advantage of me / Sweet Sue, just you / Moonshine / (I'll be glad when you're dead) you rascal you / Bugle boy march / Pretty baby / Majorca / Indiana / Georgia grind / Rock in rhythm / My old kentucky home / Rent party blues / Careless love / Strange things happen everyday / Mama don't allow
LACDD 55/56 / Nov '95 / Lake

☐ CHRIS BARBER'S BLUES BOOK VOL.1 (Good Mornin' Blues)
BGOCD 380 / 12 Jan '98 / Beat Goes On

☐ COLLABORATION (Barber, Chris & Barry Martin)
BCD 40 / Mar '93 / GHB

☐ COPENHAGEN CONCERT 1954
STCD 5527 / Jul '96 / Storyville

☐ DIXIE FROM THE ISLAND VOL.1 (Barber, Chris & Max Collie/Pete Allen/ Terry Lightfoot)
Texas moaner blues / Stevedore stomp / Immigration blues / Gospel train / Nobody knows you when you're down and out / After you've gone / Jazz me blues / That's a plenty / Mayfair blues / West End blues / Drum boogie / Honky tonk train blues
8747022 / Jul '96 / DA Music

☐ ECHOES OF ELLINGTON VOL.1 (Barber, Chris Jazz & Blues Band)
Stevedore stomp / Jeep's blues / I'm slapping Seventh Avenue with the sole of my shoe / In a mellow tone / Prelude to a kiss / Second line / Perdido / Moon indigo / Shout 'em Aunt Tillie
CDTTD 555 / Jun '91 / Timeless Traditional

☐ ECHOES OF ELLINGTON VOL.2 (Barber, Chris Jazz & Blues Band)
Squatty roo / Blues for Duke / Take the 'A' train / Warm valley / Caravan / Sophisticated lady / It don't mean a thing if it ain't got that swing / Just squeeze me / Mooche / Jeep is jumpin'
CDTTD 556 / May '91 / Timeless Traditional

☐ ECHOES OF HARLEM
Doin' the crazy walk / Baby / Magnolia's wedding day / Dixie Cinderella / New St. Louis blues / Here comes my blackbird / Can't we get together / I can't give you anything but love / Sweet Savannah Sue / Porgy / Diga diga doo / Custard pie / Betty and Dupree / This little light of mine / Key to the highway / If I could only hear mother pray again / No worries on my mind / Glory
LACD 87 / 1 Nov '97 / Lake

☐ ELITE SYNCOPATIONS (Great British Traditional Jazzbands Vol. 2)
Swipsey cakewalk / Bohemia rag / Elite syncopations / Cole's moan / Peach / St. George's rag / Favourite / Reindeer ragtime two step / Entertainer / Georgia cake walk / Thriller rag / Whistling Rufus / Tuxedo rag / Bugle call rag
LACD 43 / Feb '95 / Lake

☐ ENTERTAINER, THE (Barber, Chris Jazzband)
Down home rag / Baby, won't you please come home / Entertainer / New St. Louis blues / Ory's creole trombone / Bourbon Street parade / High society / Stevedore stomp / Sheik of Araby / Georgia cakewalk / Lil' Liza Jane / Burgundy Street blues / On the sunny side of the street / When the saints go marching in
8325932 / Mar '94 / Philips

☐ ESSENTIAL CHRIS BARBER (Featuring Ottilie Patterson & Monty Sunshine)
Panama rag / Petite fleur / Savoy blues / I wish I could shimmy like my sister Kate / Sweet Georgia Brown / Thriller rag / Beale Street blues / Bill Bailey, won't you please come home / Bourbon Street parade / New blues / Trombone cholly / Texas moaner / Willie the weeper / Careless love / Everybody loves my baby / High society / Jailhouse blues / Make me a pallet on the floor / One sweet letter from you / Tishomingo blues / Trouble in mind / When you and I were young / Whistling Rufus / Wildcat blues
KAZCD 13 / Oct '90 / Kaz

☐ GREAT MOMENTS WITH CHRIS BARBER
I wish I could shimmy like my sister Kate / Volga boatman's song / Perdido street blues / Jazz holiday / Do what ory say / Bei mir bist du schon / Bourbon street parade / Stevedor stomp / Oh lady be good / Alligator hop / Over in the gloryland / We sure do need him now / When the saints go marching in / Take me back to New Orleans / Down by the riverside / That's my home
WWJ 3002 / 27 Apr '98 / World Wide Jazz

☐ **GREAT REUNION CONCERT, THE**
Bourbon Street parade / Saturday night function / Martinique / Isle of Capri / Hush-a-bye / It's tight like that / Fairfield reunion / Bobby Shaftoe / On a Monday / Bury my body / Long gone lost John / Jenny's ball / Chimes blues / Whistling Rufus / Jazz me blues / Just a sittin' and a rockin' / Stevedore stomp
CDTTD 553 / Jul '91 / Timeless Traditional

☐ **HE'S GOT THE WHOLE WORLD IN HIS HANDS**
He's got the whole world in his hands / Topsy / When the saints go marching in / Mr. Sun / My old Kentucky home / Stormy Sunday / Just a little while to stay here / In come the blues / Mabel's dream / We shall walk through the streets of the city / Mama don't you think I know / Money blues / Fine time / Swanee River / 42nd Street / Down by the riverside / Morning order blues / Dippermouth blues
CDTTD 599 / Mar '96 / Timeless Jazz

☐ **HOT GOSPEL 1963-1967 (Barber, Chris Jazzband)**
LACD 39 / Sep '94 / Lake

☐ **IN CONCERT (Barber, Chris Jazz & Blues Band)**
Take the 'A' train / Just a sittin' and a rockin' / Blues for yesterday / Summertime / Oh Lady be good / When you're smiling / Just a closer walk with thee / Lord, lord, you've sure been good to me / Shady green pastures / They kicked him out of heaven / Precious Lord, take my hand
CDTTD 557 / Feb '91 / Timeless Traditional

☐ **IN HIS ELEMENT**
Sheik of Araby / Battersea rain dance-crocker's eleven / Working man blues / Royal garden blues / Stardust / Sweet Sue / Going up the river / Oh, didn't he ramble / New orleans overture / Creole moods / Basieland / Blues colours / New Orleans celebration / Alligator hop / Basin street blues / Ice cream
CDTTD 572 / Jul '92 / Timeless Traditional

☐ **IN THE BEGINNING**
BLC 760520 / Nov '97 / Black Lion

☐ **JAZZ BAND FAVOURITES (Barber, Chris Jazzband)**
Petite fleur / Whistling Rufus / When the saints go marching in (part 1) / When the saints go marching in (part 2) / Sweet Georgia Brown / High society / Bugle call rag / Mack the knife / Hamp's blues / Bill Bailey, won't you please come home / I shall not be moved / O Sole Mio / Wini Wini (let's do the Tamoure) / Bonsoir Mes souvenirs / Good morning blues / Bad luck blues / Morning train / Frankie and Johnny / If I had a ticket / Great bear / Jeeps blues / Sweetest little baby
CC 273 / Oct '91 / Music For Pleasure

☐ **JAZZ HOLIDAY (Barber, Chris & Rod Mason's Hot Five)**
CDTTD 524 / Sep '96 / Timeless Traditional

☐ **JAZZ JAMBOREE (Barber, Chris & Acker Bilk/Kenny Ball)**
PDSCD 514 / Sep '97 / Pulse

☐ **LIVE AT THE BP STUDIENHAUS (2CD Set)**
Bourbon Street Parade / All the girls go crazy about the way I walk / Take me back to New Orleans / That's a plenty / High society / Isle of Capri / Can't you line 'em / Midnight special / Over in the new burying ground / Worried man blues / Ice cream blues / BP march / Hiawatha rag / Chimes blues / Just a closer walk thee / Old rugged cross / Won't you come home Bill Bailey / St. Philip Street breakdown / We shall walk through the streets of the city / Wabash blues / On the sunny side of the street / Big noise from Winnetka/Pitt's extract / Sweet Georgia Brown/Slap 'n' slide / When the saints go marching in / Down by the riverside
CDTTD 615 / 23 Feb '98 / Timeless Traditional

☐ **LIVE IN '85 (Barber, Chris Jazz & Blues Band)**
CDTTD 527 / Jul '94 / Timeless Traditional

☐ **LIVE IN EAST BERLIN**
BLCD 760502 / Oct '90 / Black Lion

☐ **LIVE IN MUNICH**
Bourbon Street parade / All the girls go crazy about the way I walk / Tin roof blues / That's a plenty / Honeysuckle rose / Big noise from Winetka/Pitt's extract / Magnolia's wedding day / Take me back to New Orleans / Double check stomp / Stevedore stomp / Goin' to town / St. Louis blues / Harmonica harper
CDTTD 600 / Mar '96 / Timeless Jazz

☐ **MARDI GRAS AT THE MARQUEE (Barber, Chris & Dr. John)**
Bourbon street parade / Darktown strutters' ball / New strack-a-lee / Life / Oh eliza / Down in san anton / Right place, wrong time / Such a night / Iko iko / Wicked shall cease / Big brass drum / Mac's boogie woogie / You lie too much / Memories of smiley
CDTTD 546 / May '89 / Timeless Traditional

☐ **NEW ORLEANS SYMPHONY (2CD Set)**
New Orleans overture / Bourbon street parade / Lead me on / Announcement / South Rampart Street Parade / Music from the land of dreams / Announcement/Mood Indigo / Harlem rag / Announcement/Wild cat blues / Announcement/ Ragtime / Blues / Stomp / Reprise stomp / Announcement: Introduction of the band / Announcement/Take me back to New Orleans / Under the bamboo tree / Das gibt's nur einmal / Immigration blues / Announcement/Down by the riverside / Announcement/Ice Cream/Ice Cream
CDTTD 610 / Sep '96 / Timeless Traditional

☐ **PANAMA (Barber, Chris & Wendell Brunious)**
I wish I could shimmy like my sister Kate / Just a little while to stay here / Georgia on my mind / My blue heaven / Oh lady be good / Careless love / Anytime / That's my desire / Panama
CDTTD 568 / Oct '91 / Timeless Traditional

☐ **PETITE FLEUR**
Petite fleur / When the saints go marching in / Wild cat blues / April showers / Sweet Georgia Brown / Majorca / High society / Whistling Rufus / Bourbon street parade / Trouble in mind / Everybody loves my baby / Jailhouse blues / When you and I were young Maggie / Bill Bailey, won't you please come home / Beals Street blues / Mood indigo / (I'll be glad when you're dead) you rascal you / Bye and bye / Savoy blues
5507442 / Feb '95 / Spectrum

☐ **SOUTH RAMPART STREET PARADE**
BLR 84 016 / ' / L&R

☐ **STARDUST (Barber, Chris Jazz & Blues Band)**
Man I love / Stardust / All of me / On the sunny side of the street / Bei mir bist du schoen (part 1) / St. louis blues / Georgia on my mind / After you've gone / Over the rainbow / Lover come back to me
CDTTD 537 / May '89 / Timeless Traditional

☐ **SWING IS HERE (European Concert Tour) (Barber, Chris & John Lewis/ Trummy Young)**
Home folks / Time / Mood indigo / T'ain't what you do (it's the way that you do it) / Georgia / Someday you'll be sorry / Muskrat ramble / When the saints go marching in
BLCD 760517 / Apr '96 / Black Lion

☐ **TAKE ME BACK TO NEW ORLEANS (Barber, Chris & Dr. John)**
Take me back to New Orleans / Ti-pi-ti-na / Perdido street blues / New Orleans, Louisiana / Decatur drive / New Orleans / Meet me on the Levee / Harlem rag / Ride on / Big bass drum (on a mardi gras day) / At the cemetery / Concert on Canal Street / Bourbon Street scene / Basin Street / Just a little while to stay here / Oration by Dr. John / What a friend we have in Jesus / When the saints go marching in / Concert in Canal Street / Buddy Bolden's blues / South Rampart Street Parade / Burgandy Street Blues / Canal Street Blues / Bourbon Street Parade / Do you know what it means to miss New Orleans / Professor Longhair's tip / Brass band blues / Basin Street blues
BLC 760163 / '92 / Black Lion

☐ **THAT'S IT THEM (Barber, Chris & Acker Bilk)**
Just a closer walk with thee / Stranger on the shore / Bugle boy march / Wabash blues / On the sunny side of the street / South / Lou-easy-an-I-a / Panama / Poor butterfly / That's my home / High society
CDTTD 619 / Jul '97 / Timeless Jazz

☐ **ULTIMATE, THE (Barber, Chris & Acker Bilk/Kenny Ball)**
(I love you) Samantha: *Ball, Kenny* / Panama rag: *Ball, Kenny* / Midnight in Moscow: *Ball, Kenny* / Nobody knows you: *Ball, Kenny* / Avalon: *Ball, Kenny* / I wan'na be like you: *Ball, Kenny* / Christopher Columbus: *Bilk, Acker* / Spanish harlem: *Bilk, Acker* / That da da strain: *Bilk, Acker* / Them there eyes: *Bilk, Acker* / Stranger on the shore: *Bilk, Acker* / That's my home: *Bilk, Acker* / Good Queen Bess: *Barber, Chris* / Perdido St blues: *Barber, Chris* / Harlem rag: *Barber, Chris* / Mary had a little lamb: *Barber, Chris* / Muskrat ramble
CND 1012 / 27 Jul '98 / Camden

☐ **WHO'S BLUES**
BLR 84 009 / May '91 / L&R

Barber, Damien

☐ **BOXED**
NOF 002 / May '96 / Nof

Barber, Patricia

☐ **CAFE BLUE**
AIM 1058 / Jun '96 / Aim

☐ **MODERN COOL**
PREM 741 / 31 Aug '98 / Premonition

Barberis, Takis

☐ **EPISODES**
ML 0177 / 11 May '98 / Musurgia Graeca

Barbieri, Gato

☐ **CALIENTE**
Fireflies / Fiesta / Europa (Earth's cry, Heaven's smile) / Don't cry / Rochelle / Adios / I want you / Behind the rain / Adios
3945972 / Mar '94 / A&M

☐ **CHAPTER THREE: VIVA EMILIANO ZAPATA**
Milongo triste / Lluvia azul / El sublime / La podrida / Cuando vuelva a tu lado / Viva Emiliano Zapata
GRP 1112 / Jan '92 / GRP

☐ **GATO BARBIERI IN NEW YORK CITY**
In search of the mystery / Michelle / Obsession no.2 / Cinematique
30019 / Sep '92 / Giants Of Jazz

☐ **GATO...PARA LOS AMIGOS**
Llamerito tango / Carnavalito / Brazil / Viva Emiliano Zapata / Encuentros / Latino America / El arriero / Bolivia / Finale (medley)
4880012 / Aug '97 / Sony Jazz

☐ **LATINO AMERICA (2CD Set)**
Encuentros / India / La China Leoncia Arreo / Nunca mas / La China Leoncia Arreo / Nunca mas / Gato gato / To be continued / Encontros / Latino America / Marissea / Para Nosotros / Juana Azurduy / Latino America / Mate
IMP 22362 / 10 Nov '97 / Impulse Jazz

☐ **QUE PASA**
Straight into the sunshine / Blue gala / Mystica / Dancing with dolphins / Circulos / Guadeloupe / Cause we've ended as lovers / Indonesia / Woman I remember / Granada / Adentro
CK 67855 / Apr '97 / Sony Jazz

Barbieri, Richard

☐ **FLAME (Barbieri, Richard & Tim Bowness)**
Night in heaven / Song of love and everything (parts 1 and 2) / Brightest blue / Flame / Trash talk / Time flown / Torch dance / Feel
TPLP 58CD / Sep '94 / One Little Indian

☐ **INDIGO FALLS**
Only forward / World's end / Feed the fire / Falling into years / Wilderness / Towards the light / Sky fall
MPCD 005 / 24 Nov '97 / Medium

Barbosa, Beto

☐ **GIRANDO NO SALAO**
ATR 31050 / 12 May '98 / Atracao

Barbosa, Zelia

☐ **SERTAO E FAVELAS**
LDX 2741002 / Aug '95 / La Chant Du Monde

Barbosa-Lima, Carlos

☐ **CHANTS FOR THE CHIEF**
A chamada dos ventos/Cancao naturna / Uirapuru do Amazonas / Cuhna-tan do Andira / Varando furos / Canto dos esquecidos/Yara levou o meu amor / Canto do missionario / Ventos do sertao / Canto da alvorada / Canto do verde-amado / Canoa furada/ Cancao noturna/A chamada / Dos ventos - epilogo / Cajija de musica / Impressao de rua / Sonha yaya / Teotecacinte / Fantasy on an Hawaiian lullaby / Batucada / Entre olas / Panaderos / Cubanita / Corrion / De totana / Patio gitano / Alaiceria / Luna y clavel / Romance flamenco / Bailando
CCD 4489 / Jan '92 / Concord Picante

☐ **FROM YESTERDAY TO PENNY LANE**
Two ladies, one old, one new / Cumberland Road / Clio / Eleanor Rigby / She's leaving home / Yesterday / Ticket to ride / Got to get you into my life / Here, there and everywhere / Penny Lane / Etude in a menuet form / El colivri / Confession / Blue clouds / Embers / Rhapsody in blue
CCD 42041 / Nov '96 / Concord Concerto

☐ **MUSIC OF THE AMERICAS (Barbosa-Lima, Carlos & Sharon Isbin)**
Sambo Chorado / Chants for the chief No. 3 / Chants for the chief No. 7 / Carioquinha / Mazurka No. 3 / Caminho dos estados unidos / Brazil / Grande valsa / Lamento / Cochichando / Um a zero / Lullaby for Janine / Playful squirrels / Interlude dance / Vera cruz / Always / I got rhythm / Kathy's waltz / In your own sweet way / Duke / Timothy 'O'
CCD 4461 / May '91 / Concord Jazz

☐ **O BOTO**
Concerto in A major / Tonadilla / Capriccio diabolico / Adios / Piccola arietta no.2 / O boto / Nana para una negrita / Concierto Antillano
CCD 420482 / 16 Feb '98 / Concord Concerto

☐ **TWILIGHT IN RIO**
Twilight in Rio / Mi bossa blue (my blue bossa) / En la playa (at the beach) / Puerta de tierra / Etude on a theme by Mendelssohn / La alborada (dawn) / La mariposa (the butterfly) / Choro da saudade (choro of longing) / Danza paraguaya / Junto a tu corazon / Pais de abanico / El sueno de la munequita / Dinora / Um amor de valsa / Emerald / Sardius
CCD 42017 / Mar '95 / Concord Concerto

Barbour, Freeland

☐ **KILLIEKRANKIE**
Glorious revolution / White rose / House of Stewart / Bluidy clavers / Cameronians march / Lands beyond forth / Tremble false Whigs / Band at distance / Dudhope / Green field of Dalcomera / Blair Castle / Braes of Glen Roy / Murray's siege / Mackay's advance / Men from Lochaber / Am feasgair samhraidh (the summer evening) / Allt Girnaig / Thickets of Raon Ruaraidh / Battle of Killiecrankie / MacBean's Chase / Flight and Pursuit / Urrard House / South to Dunkeld / Fiery cross / Battle of Dunkeld / Thanksgiving / There is no enemy in sight / Old Blair / Killiecrankie
LAPCD 126 / '89 / Lapwing

Barboza, Raul

☐ **LA TIERRA SIN MAL**
CDLLL 257 / Mar '96 / La Lichere

☐ **MUSIC AFTER THE GUARANI INDIANS**
CDLLL 167 / Aug '93 / La Lichere

☐ **MUSIC FROM THE BORDER**
Chamame parisien / Paseando por et rhin / El cimarron del estribo / Isla saca / Bailanta en la campana / El estibador / La pulseada / Chamigo claude / Musicos del metro / Corrientes / Improvisando en la mayor / Melodia para oskar / Ferviente ilusion / Atardecer en gordes
12453 / Jul '95 / Laserlight

Barchem Big Band

☐ **MAGNIFYING GLASS**
Love walked in / Magnifying glass / Threesome / Tangerine / Centre of gravity / Egalitarian / You and the night and the music / Grey eminence / Way you look tonight
AL 73133 / Jun '98 / A

Barclay James Harvest

☐ **BARCLAY JAMES HARVEST LIVE**
Summer soldier / Medicine man / Crazy city / After the day / Great 1974 mining disaster / Galadriel / Negative earth / She said / Paper wings / For no one / Mockingbird
VSOPCD 164 / Jun '91 / Connoisseur Collection

☐ **BEST OF BARCLAY JAMES HARVEST, THE (Centenary Collection)**
Taking some time on / Mother dear / Mocking bird / Vanessa Simmons / Early morning / Brother thrush / Medicine man / Someone there you know / Harry's song / Ursula (the swansea song) / Song with no meaning / Crazy over you / Delph town morn / Song for dying / Galadriel / I'm over you / Child of man / Child of the universe / Rock and roll woman / Thank you
CTMCD 309 / Feb '97 / EMI

☐ **BJH & OTHER SHORT STORIES**
Medicine man / Someone there you know / Harry's song / Ursula (the Swansea song) / Little lapwing / Song with no meaning / Blue John blues / Poet / After the day / Crazy (over you) / Delph Town morn / Summer soldier / Thank you / Hundred thousand smiles out / Moonwater
BGOCD 160 / Nov '92 / Beat Goes On

☐ **CAUGHT IN THE LIGHT**
5193032 / Jun '93 / Polydor

☐ **ENDLESS DREAM**
VSOPCD 228 / Aug '96 / Connoisseur Collection

☐ **EVERYONE IS EVERYBODY ELSE**
8334482 / Feb '92 / Polydor

☐ **GONE TO EARTH**
Hymn / Love is like a violin / Friend of mine / Poor man's moody blues / Hard hearted woman / Sea of Tranquility / Spirit on the water / Leper's song / Taking me higher
8000922 / Jan '89 / Polydor

☐ **HARVEST YEARS, THE**
Early morning / Mr. Sunshine / Pools of blue / I can't go on without you / Eden unobtainable / Brother thrush / Poor wages / Taking some time on / When the world was woken / Good love child / Iron maiden / Dark now my sky / She said / Song for dying / Galadriel / Mocking bird / Vanessa Simmons / Happy old world (quad mix) / Ball and chain / Medicine man / Ursula (The Swansea song) / Someone there you know / Poet/After the day / I'm over you / Child of man / Breathless / When the city sleeps / Summer soldier / Hundred thousand smiles out / Moonwater / Joker / Good times
CDEN 5014 / May '91 / Harvest

☐ **MOCKINGBIRD**
Mocking bird / I can't go without you / Early morning / Ball and chain / Medicine man / Someone there you know / Joker / Summer soldier / When the city sleeps / Brother trush / Good love child / Iron maiden / Moonwater
DC 867212 / Mar '97 / Disky

☐ **OCTOBERON**
World goes on / May day / Ra / Rock 'n' roll / Star / Polk street rag / Believe in me / Suicide
8219302 / Oct '91 / Polydor

☐ **ONCE AGAIN**
She said / Happy old world / Song for dying / Galadriel / Mockingbird / Vanessa Simmons / Ball and chain / Lady loves
BGOCD 152 / Nov '92 / Beat Goes On

☐ **RING OF CHANGES**
Fifties child / Looking from the outside / Teenage heart / Highwire / Midnight drug / Waiting for the right time / Just a day away / Paraiso des cavalos / Ring of changes
8116382 / Oct '88 / Polydor

Barde, Jerome

☐ **FELIZ**
Marc / Dad's delight / No words / La Nina Cecile / Citrons / Barde bleue / Ombrage / Feliz / Lefru / I'll be seeing you
SSC 1042D / Oct '91 / Sunnyside

Bardens, Pete

☐ **BIG SKY**
China blue / Puerto Rico / Big sky / Gunblasters / On the air tonight / You got it / Brave new world / On a roll / Last waltz / For old time's sake
HTDCD 22 / Sep '96 / HTD

Bardo Pond

☐ HIGH FREQUENCIES
Limerick / Sentence / Tantric porno / Wank / High frequency / Sometimes words / Yellow turbin / Rumination / Be a fish / Tapir song / RM
OLE 1802 / Apr '96 / Matador

☐ LAPSED
Tommy gun angel / Pick your brain / Flux / Anandamide / Green man / Straw dog / Aldrin
OLE 2102
OLE 2101 / 3 Nov '97 / Matador

Bardot, Brigitte

☐ LES PLUS BELLES (The Best Of Brigitte Bardot)
5323502 / Nov '96 / Mercury

Bardots

☐ EYE-BABY
Pretty O / Chained up / Cruelty blonde / Sister Richard / Slow asleep / Sunsetted / My cute thought / Obscenity thing / Gloriole / Caterina / A / Shallow
CHEREE 031 CD / Sep '92 / Cheree

☐ V-NECK
CHE 44CD / May '96 / Che

Bare, Bobby

☐ ALL AMERICAN BOY
All american boy / Shame on me / Detroit city / 500 miles away from home / Miller's cave / Four strong winds / Streets of baltimore / Game of triangles / (margie's at) the lincoln park inn / Come sundown / Please don't tell me how the story ends / Ride me down easy / Marie laveau / Drop kick me, jesus / Numbers / Tequila sheila / He was a friend of mine / When I'm gone / To whom it may concern / I don't believe I'll fall in love today / Bye bye love
CTS 55428 / Nov '94 / Country Stars

☐ ALL AMERICAN BOY, THE (4CD Set)
Darlin' don't / Another love has ended / Down on the corner of love / Life of a fool / Beggar / Livin' end / Vampira / Tender years / When the one you love / All American boy / What you gonna do now / I'm hanging up my rifle / That's where I want to be / Lynching party / Sweet singin' Sam / More than a poor boy could give / No letter from my baby / Book of love / Can can ladies / Lorena / Zig zag twist / Island of love / Sailor man / These tender years / Lovesick / Great big car / Brooklyn bridge / That mean old clock / Day my rainbow fell / Above and beyond / Shame on me / To whom it may concern / Wallflower / I don't believe I'll fall in love today / Dear waste basket / Baby, don't believe him / I'm gettin' lonely / Heart of ice / Candy coated kisses / Gods were angry with me / I'd fight the world / Is it wrong (for loving you) / Dear waste basket / Detroit city / Lonely town / She called me baby / 500 miles away from home / It all depends on Linda / Worried man blues / Homestead on the farm / Abilene / Gotta travel on / Noah's ark / I wonder where you are tonight / Let me tell you about Mary / What kind of bird is that / Jeannie's last kiss / Miller's cave / Sittin' and thinkin' / Have I stayed away too long / Long way back to Tennessee / Long black limousine / Down in Mexico / I was coming home to you / Another bridge to burn / I've lived a lot in my time / He was a friend of mine / Take me home / When I'm gone / Sweeter than the flowers / Four strong winds / When the wind blows in Chicago / Just to satisfy you / Let it be me / In the misty moonlight / I love you / Too used to being with you / Together again / We'll sing in the sunshine / Out of our minds / I don't care / That's all I want from you / Invisible tears / Dear John letter / True love / Rosalie / Alle glauben dass ich gluckli ch bin / Times are gettin' hard / I'm a long way from home / Deepening snow / I'm a man of constant sorrow / She picked a perfect day / One day at a time / So soon / Countin' the hours - countin' the days / Don't think twice, it's alright / Blowin' in the wind / Delia's gone / Lemon tree / It's alright / Salt Lake City / Changing my mind / Good old Tennessee / Das haus auf der sierra / Sixteen / Wilder wolfund brauner bar / Molly Brown / Little bit later on down the line / Got leavin' on her mind / Try to remember / All the good times are past and gone / Memories / Heaven help my soul / We helped each other out / In the same old way / Talk me some sense / You can't stop the wild wind from blowing / It ain't me babe / Long black veil / Passin' through / What color (is a man)
BCD 15663 / Jan '94 / Bear Family

☐ BOBBY BARE SINGS LULLABYS, LEGENDS & LIES
Lullabys, legends and lies / Paul / Marie Lavaau / Daddy what if / Wonderful soup stones / Winner / In the hills of Shiloh / She's my ever lovin' machine / Mermaid / Rest awhile / Bottomless well / True story / Sure hit songwriters pen / Rosalie's good eat's cafe
BCD 15683 / Apr '93 / Bear Family

☐ ESSENTIAL BOBBY BARE, THE
All American boy / Shame on me / Detroit City / 500 miles away from home / Miller's cave / Four strong winds / Dear John letter: *Bare, Bobby & Skeeter Davis* / It's alright / Streets of Baltimore / Game of triangles: *Bare, Bobby & Norma Jean/Liz Anderson* / Charleston railway tavern / Margie's at the Lincoln Park Inn / Bless America again / Your husband, my wife: *Bare, Bobby & Skeeter Davis* / Ride me down easy / Daddy what if / Marie Laveau / Winner / Dropkick me Jesus / Vegas: *Bare, Bobby & Jeanne*
7863674052 / May '97 / RCA

☐ FOR THE GOOD TIMES
MACCD 220 / Aug '96 / Autograph

☐ GREATEST HITS
WMCD 5681 / Nov '93 / Disky

☐ HARD TIME HUNGRYS
Hard time hungrys / Farmer feeds us all / Able bodied man / Warm and free / $100,000 in pennies / Unemployment line / Back home in Huntsville again / Bottles and boxes / Truck driver truck driver / Alimony / Two for dollar / Daddy's been around the house too long
EDCD 551 / 2 Mar '98 / Edsel

☐ MASTERS, THE
EABCD 110 / 30 Mar '98 / Eagle

☐ MERCURY YEARS 1970-1972, THE (3CD Set)
That's how I got to Memphis / Come sundown / I took a memory to lunch / I'm her hoss if I never win a race / Woman you've been a friend to me / It's freezing in El Paso / Mrs. Jones your daughter cried all night / Don't it make you wanna go home / Mary Ann regrets / Leaving on a jet plane / Fool / Waitress in the Main Street cafe / Please don't tell me how the story ends / How about you / Help me make it through the night / Rosalie / Dropping out of sight / Where have all the flowers gone / Travelling minstrel man / For the good times / Hello darlin' / Alabama rose / World is weighing heavy on my mind / Mama bake a pie (papa kill a chicken) / Coal river / Christian soldier / Don't you ever get tired of hurting me / West Virginia woman / New York City snow / Jesus is the only one that loves us / Loving her was easier (than anything I'll ever do again) / I need some good news bad / Me and Bobby McGee / Million miles to the city / Just the other side of nowhere / City boy country born / Short and sweet / Puppet and the parakeet / Great society talking blues / Year that Clayton Delaney died / Roses are red / Lonely street / Crazy arms / Jesus Christ what a man / Fallen star / That's alright / Pamela Brown / When I want to love a lady / Love forever / Darby's castle / Lot of soul / Just in case / What am I gonna do / When love is gone / Lorena / Don't ask me, ask Marie / Laying here lying in bed / Take some and give some / Sylvia's mother / Footprints in the snow / Lord let a lie come true / Under it all / Are you sincere / Even the bad times are good / High and dry / She gave her heart to Jethro / Music City USA
BCD 15417 / Dec '87 / Bear Family

Bare Minimum

☐ BARE MINIMUM
RXR 004CD / Oct '96 / RX Remedy

☐ CAN'T CURE THE NAILBITERS
RXR 13CD / 18 May '98 / RX Remedy

☐ NIGHT WE STREAK
RXR 008 / Nov '96 / RX Remedy

Bare Necessities

☐ TAKE A DANCE
FF 564CD / Apr '94 / Flying Fish

Barefoot Contessa

☐ BAREFOOT CONTESSA
LOLACD 1 / Jun '95 / Backs

☐ YOU CAN'T GO HOME AGAIN
LOLA 3CD / Apr '97 / Indie 500

Barefoot Jerry

☐ KEYS TO THE COUNTRY/ BAREFOOTIN'
Battle of New Orleans / Summit ridge drive / Woes of the road / Wilma Lou / Appalachian fever / You can't say it all / Tonite's the nite I do / Georgia on my mind / Uncle Pen / My God (is alright with me) / Barefootin' / I ain't gettin' no touchin' / Keep on funkin' / Sentimental man / Dixie dancer / Hiroshima hole / Diana / Tokin' ticket / Headin' for the hills / Highland grass
SEECD 467 / Jan '97 / See For Miles

☐ SOUTHERN DELIGHT/BAREFOOT JERRY
Hospitality song / I'm proud to be a redneck / Smokies / Quit while you're ahead (song of sensible compromise) / Blood is not the answer / Come to me tonight / Finishing touches / Minstrel is free at last / Nobody knows / That's OK, he'll be your brother someday / Castle rock / One woman / In god we trust / Message / Friends / Snuff queen / Little Maggie / Warm / Fish 'n' tits / Ain't it nice here / Ebeneezer
SEECD 485 / Jul '97 / See For Miles

☐ WATCHING TV/YOU CAN'T GET OFF WITH YOUR SHOES ON
Watching TV / Funny lookin' eyes / Pig snoots and nehi red / Hay Queen / Two mile pike / Faded love / There must be a better way / If there were only time for love / Violets and daffodils / Mother Nature's way of saying high / Ali Baba / Boogie woogie / Slowin' down / You can't get off with your shoes on / West side of Mississippi / Measure of your worth / Lucille / Hero Frodo / Sinkin' in the sea / Cades cove
SEECD 466 / Jan '97 / See For Miles

Barely Pink

☐ NUMBERONEFAN
BD 9040 / Nov '97 / Big Deal

Barely Works

☐ BEST OF BARELY WORKS
Byker hill / As a thoiseach / This fire / Liberty / Blackberry blossom / Cuckoo's nest / Big river / Bread and water / Maybe I'm a fool / June / Back to the mountains / Moving cloud / Cliff / Treen beach / Pull me up / Old Joe Clarke / Riddle me wry / Stand together
COOKCD 079 / Feb '95 / Cooking Vinyl

Baren, Gasslin

☐ OCCULT SONGS
1C 567 1999 48 / '88 / Harmonia Mundi

Barenaked Ladies

☐ GORDON
Hello city / Enid / Grade 9 / Brian Wilson / Be my Yoko Ono / Wrap your arms around me / What a good boy / King of bedside manor / Box set / I love you / New kid (on the block) / Blame it on me / Flag / If I had one hundred thousand dollars / Crazy
7599269562 / Aug '92 / East West

☐ MAYBE YOU SHOULD DRIVE
Jane / These apples / Great provider / Intermittently / You will be waiting / Everything old is new again / A / Wrong man was convicted / Life in a nutshell / Little tiny song / Am I the only one / Alternative girlfriend
9362457092 / Aug '94 / Warner Bros.

Barenberg, Russ

☐ HALLOWEEN REHEARSAL
ROUCD 11534 / '88 / Rounder

☐ MOVING PICTURES
Our time / Through the gates / Talking / Return to the brandywine / Magic foot / Open arms / Keep it up-prince charlie / Edge of the atlantic / Les veuves de la coulee (widows of the creek)
ROUCD 0249 / Aug '88 / Rounder

Barenboim, Daniel

☐ MI BUENOS AIRES QUERIDO (Barenboim, Daniel & Rodolfo Mederos/Hector Console)
0630134742 / Sep '96 / Teldec Classics

Baresi, Michelle

☐ BERLIN & POGO
EFA 800402 / Sep '95 / Twah

Bargad, Rob

☐ BETTER TIMES (Bargad, Rob Sextet)
CRISS 1086CD / May '94 / Criss Cross

Barge, Gene

☐ DANCE WITH DADDY G...PLUS (Classic R&B Sax)
I feel fine / Shake / Fine twine / Jerk / Way you do the things you do / In crowd / Twine time / Come see about me / Voice your choice / Monkey time / It's all over now / How sweet it is to be loved by you / Ain't too proud to beg / Chippie the hippie from Mississippi / Green tambourine / Little bit o' soul / Little boy blue / Quick getaway / Blowing in the wind
SEECD 442 / Jul '98 / See For Miles

Bariu, Laver

☐ SONGS FROM THE CITY
CDORBD 091 / Jan '96 / Globestyle

Bark Psychosis

☐ GAME OVER
Blue / Three girl rhumba / I know / All different things / Manman / Bloodrush / Street scene / Murder city / Scum / Pendulum man
STONE 031CD / 16 Mar '98 / 3rd Stone

☐ HEX
Loom / Street scene / Absent friend / Big shot / Fingerspit / Eyes and smiles / Pendulum man
CIRCD 29 / Apr '94 / Circa

☐ INDEPENDENCY
I know / Nothing feels / All different things / By-blow / Manman / Blood rush / Tooled up / Scum
STONE 010CD / 30 Mar '98 / 3rd Stone

Barker, 'Blue' Lu

☐ CLASSICS 1938-1939
CLASSICS 704 / Jun '93 / Classics

Barker, Dave

☐ DOUBLE BARREL (Barker, Dave & Ansell Collins)
RASCD 3225 / Jan '96 / Ras

☐ MONKEY SPANNER
Lucky boy / Lockjaw / Funky reggae / Sweeter she is / I've got to get a message to you / Follow your heart / Just my imagination / I got to get away / Girl in my dreams / Sex machine / Don't turn your back on me (blessed are the meek) / I feel alive / Double barrel / Lonely man / Heart of a man / Love love love / You ain't got a heart at all / Your love's a game / Baby I need your love / Monkey spanner / It's summer / Travelling man / Love is what I bring (I'm the one love forgot) / Only the strong survive / What a confusion
CDTRL 382 / Jun '97 / Trojan

☐ PRISONER OF LOVE
CDTBL 127 / Apr '96 / Trojan

Barker, Guy

☐ INTO THE BLUE
Into the blue / JJ swing / Oh Mr. Rex / Low down lullaby / Did it 'n' did it / Sphinx / Enigma / Ill wind / This is the life / Weatherbird rag
5276562 / Jun '95 / Verve

☐ ISN'T IT
Sheldon the cat / Isn't it / In a mist / I get along without you very well / All or nothing / Amandanita / Good speed / Day and night / Lament for the black tower
SPJCD 545 / Jul '93 / Spotlite

☐ TIMESWING
Timeswing / Cat strut / Duke Ellington's sound of love / Whole bit / Sleeping in iridium / As and when / O subjectivo objectivo / Sometime soon / And all of that / Isn't it romantic
5330292 / Oct '96 / Verve

☐ WHAT LOVE IS
Peacocks / Change partners / You don't know what love is / Mona Lisa / Crazy she calls me / Close your eyes / Star crossed lovers / I got it bad and that ain't good / Monk's mood / Ornette in New York / Things we did last summer / Angel eyes
5583312 / 5 May '98 / EmArCy

Barker, Hamish

☐ NATURAL CULTURE
Dawn awakening / White dove / Indian elephant / Pilot whale / Barn owl / Canadian beaver / Ocean / Arabian camel / Oriental peacock / Australian wallaby / Peruvian llama
DJC 004 / 9 Feb '98 / Blueprint

Barker, Les

☐ CARDI AND A BLOKE, A
DOG 011 / Dec '95 / Mrs. Ackroyd

☐ EARWIGO
DOG 004CD / Apr '95 / Mrs. Ackroyd

☐ GNUS & ROSES (Mrs. Ackroyd Band)
DOG 10CD / Jun '94 / Mrs. Ackroyd

☐ INFINITE NUMBER OF OCCASIONAL TABLES, AN
DOG 008CD / Sep '94 / Mrs. Ackroyd

☐ ORANGES AND LEMMINGS (Mrs. Ackroyd Band)
DOG 007CD / Sep '94 / Mrs. Ackroyd

☐ PROBABLY THE BEST ALBUM EVER MADE BY ANYBODY IN OUR STREET
Cosmo revisited / Dachshunds with erections / Jason and the arguments / Weddell waddle penguin / Hard cheese of old England / King Harold was a ventriloquist / Everything glows / Stay go and fetch / Earwigo
TERRCD 007 / Jul '97 / Terra Nova

☐ UP THE CREEK WITHOUT A POODLE
DOG 012 / Feb '97 / Mrs. Ackroyd

Barker, Sally

☐ FAVOURITE DISH
Moses / Favourite dish / Blue moon / Landing light / Honeymoon is over / Hold on / Good woman / I know what I like (in your wardrobe) / Sleepy eyes / Wind, she carries
HYCD 296165 / Feb '97 / Hypertension

☐ IN THE SPOTLIGHT
PUP 1 CD / Aug '89 / Old Dog

☐ TANGO/MONEY'S TALKING
HYCD 200149 / Mar '95 / Hypertension

☐ THIS RHYTHM IS MINE
Money's talking / This rhythm is mine / Angry women / Lay your body down / While you sleep / Big world / Chinese whispers / Or did you jump / Married man / Simple life / Chains / Another train
HYCD 200106 / Sep '93 / Hypertension

Barkmarket

☐ EASY LISTENING
OUT 1012 / Aug '96 / Brake Out

Barkus, Juke Boy

☐ SHAKE IT IN THE DARK (Barkus, Juke Boy & Baldie McGhee/The Roof Top Playboys)
WIGCD 015 / 18 Aug '97 / Alopecia

Barley Bree

☐ ANTHEM FOR THE CHILDREN
SH 52020 CD / '90 / Shanachie

☐ BEST OF BARLEY BREE, THE
SHCD 52039 / Mar '95 / Shanachie

Barleycorn

☐ GREEN & GOLD
DOCDK 108 / May '94 / Dolphin

☐ MY LAST FAREWELL
DOCDX 9010 / Sep '96 / Dolphin

☐ SONG FOR IRELAND, A
Song for Ireland / Cavan Ireland / Portland Town / Dublin in my tears / Roseville fair / Long before your time / Over my mountains / Charlie on the MTA / Mary's song / Lakes of Coolfin
DOCDX 9004 / Jul '96 / Dolphin

☐ WALTZING FOR DREAMERS
Waltzing's for dreamers / West country lady / Rose of allendale / Star of the county down / Forty five years from now / Instrumental medley / Bluenose / Lark in the morning / Song of the mira / All he ever saw was you / Banks of the roses / Hearts on fire
DOCDK 104 / May '94 / Dolphin

Barleyshakes

☐ GACH EAN
SNS 007 / Aug '97 / SNS

Barlow, Charles

☐ BEST OF THE DANSAN YEARS VOL.9, THE (Barlow, Charles Orchestra & Irven Tidswell Orchestra)
Play fiddle play (waltz) / Thorn birds (love theme) (waltz) / Seal it with a kiss-the kiss waltz (waltz) / Blue tango (tango) / Annientamento (tango) / Don't tell a soul (slow foxtrot) / Hold me (slow foxtrot) / You're nobody till somebody loves you (slow foxtrot) / 's wonderful (quickstep) / Too close for comfort (quickstep) / Call me irresponsible-green eyes (cha cha cha) / Isn't this a lovely day (cha cha cha) / Perdido (cha cha cha) / Sam baba (rhum baba) (samba) / Samba de orfeu (orpheus) (samba) / Woman in love (rhumba) / How wonderful to know-come prima-o sole mio (rhumba) / Amapola-when I fall in love (rhumba) / Lady of spain (paso doble) / Take the 'a' train (jive)
DACD 009 / Mar '95 / Dansan

Barlow, Eric

☐ BALLROOM FAVOURITES
Moonlight and roses / Tonight you belong to me / Avalon / Romany rose / Wyoming / Blue eyes / I've never been in love before / I left my heart in San Francisco / Sweetest song in the world / Mistakes / Dancing with tears in my eyes / Moonlight saunter / Underneath the stars / Mayfair quickstep / You're dancing on my heart / It's foolish but it's fun / First time I saw you / Luna rossa / Rosanna / You're still the only girl in the world / Girl of my dreams / In a shanty in old shanty town / Waltzing Matilda / Heart of my heart / Old mother Kelly's doorstep / Lily of laguna / Me and my shadow / If you knew Susie / Ma he's making eyes at me / Spanish eyes / Strangers in the night / Military two step / Hello hello who's your lady friend / Take me back to dear old blighty
EMPRCD 636 / Jun '96 / Emporio

Barlow, Gary

☐ OPEN ROAD
Love won't wait / So help me girl / My commitment / Hang on in there baby / Are you ready now / Everything I ever wanted / I fall so deep / Lay down for love / Forever love / Never knew / Open road / Always
74321417202 / 1 May '97 / RCA

☐ YOUTHOLOGY VOL.1 (2CD Set/ Documentary and Music)
OTR 1100036 / Jun '97 / Metro Independent

☐ YOUTHOLOGY VOL.2 (2CD Set/ Documentary and Music)
OTR 1100037 / Jun '97 / Metro Independent

☐ YOUTHOLOGY VOL.3 (2CD Set/ Documentary and Music)
OTR 1100038 / Jun '97 / Metro Independent

Barmy Army

☐ ENGLISH DISEASE
ONUCD 8 / Jun '94 / On-U Sound

☐ ENGLISH DISEASE, THE
ONUCD 0048 / 1 Jun '98 / On-U Sound

Barnard, Bob

☐ BOB BARNARD & THE AUSTRALIAN JAZZ ALLSTARS 1977
LB 9511 / Jun '96 / La Brava

☐ CORNET CHOP SUEY
OPUS3CD 19503 / Jul '96 / Opus 3

☐ NEW YORK NOTES 1995 (Barnard, Bob & Keith Ingham)
SKCD 23061 / Jan '97 / Sackville

☐ PARTNERS IN CRIME (Barnard, Bob & Ralph Sutton)
SKCD 2023 / Dec '97 / Sackville

☐ STARDUST
LB 9711 / Feb '98 / La Brava

Barnard, Tony

☐ LONDON SESSIONS, THE (Barnard, Tony Trio)
Foggy day / Ornithology / St Thomas / Seven come eleven / All the things you are / Once removed / My romance / Undecided / Nisty / Bluesology
WAVE 33 / 2 Mar '98 / Wave

Barnbrack

☐ 22 IRISH FOLK PUB SONGS
CDHRL 199 / Feb '95 / Outlet

☐ IRISH PUB FOLK SINGALONG
CDPUB 024 / May '96 / Outlet

☐ OTHER IRELAND
You never learned to dance / Hannigan's hooley/ Bold O'Donoghue/If you're Irish / Mother's love/ Goodbye Johnny/Gentle Mother / Old refrain / Lough Ree/Cottage in ivy/Homes of Donegal / Danny boy / Cavan girl / Fields of Athenry / Postman Pat/My forever friend / 40 shades of green / Punch and Judy man / Lovely Rose of Clare / Nancy Spain/ Leavin' of Liverpool/Murshin durkin / Irish rover/ Goodbye Mick/Buy me a banana
CHCD 2810 / Jun '98 / Outlet

☐ SLICE OF HOME, A
Belfast / Fields of Athenry / Whiskey in the jar/ Coutin' in the kitchen/I'll tell me ma / My lagan softly flowing / If we only had one Ireland over here / I'll take you home again Kathleen / Galway boy / Mickey Marley's roundabout / Ringsend rose / Limerick you're a lady / Belfast mill / When I was a lad / Cockles and mussels/When Irish eyes are smiling/ Galway shawl / Town I loved so well / Molly, my Irish Molly / Rose of Tralee / Carrickfergus / Rathlin island / Inn of Innisfree / Danny boy
MCVD 30004 / Nov '96 / Emerald Gem

☐ THREE OF THE BEST
Hannaghan's hooley / Boul O'Donaghue / If you're Irish / Lovely rose of Clare / Daisy a day / Two loves / Delaney's donkey / McNamara's band / My forever friend / Dublin in the rare oul times / You never learned to dance / Forty shades of green / Lannigan's ball / Cavan girl / Old rugged cross / Danny boy
CHCD 2008 / Mar '97 / Outlet

Barnes, Alan

☐ BELOW ZERO (Barnes, Alan & David Newton Trio)
Woodville / Song for Strayhorn / Below zero / Estate / College groove / Flower is a lovesome thing / K-4 Pacific / Lady's vanity / Waltz for Debbie / Blessed land / Mambo koyama
CCDEU 48422 / 17 Aug '98 / Concord Jazz

☐ HERE COMES TROUBLE
Here comes trouble / SOS / Never let me go / Little Nemo / Clare's cares / Hushed tones / Quasimodo / East of the village / Arriving soon
FJCD 110 / Jun '96 / Fret

☐ LIKE MINDS (Barnes, Alan & David Newton)
'Round midnight / Blues in thirds / Batida differente / Poor butterfly / I'm just a lucky so and so / Lament for Javanette / Lull at dawn / Waltz for Sonny Criss / Walkin' shoes / Peacocks / Nobody else but me / Cotton tail
FJCD 105 / Nov '94 / Fret

☐ PLAY HAROLD ARLEN (Barnes, Alan & Brian Lemon)
ZECD 7 / May '96 / Zephyr

☐ THIRSTY WORK
Ecaroh / Stars fell on Alabama / Groovy samba / Sweet and lovely / Stay as sweet as you are / Double take and fade away / Go home / Solitude / Autumn in New York / Thirsty work
FJCD 106 / Mar '95 / Fret

☐ YESTERDAYS (Barnes, Alan & Brian Lemon)
I told every little star / Yesterday / Bill / Folks who live on the hill / All things you are / They didn't believe me / Dearly beloved / Look for the silver lining / Smoke gets in your eyes / Pick yourself up / I'm old fashioned / Long ago and far away
ZECD 11 / 6 Oct '97 / Zephyr

☐ YOUNG MINDS - OLD HANDS (Barnes, Alan & Brian Lemon Octet)
Moonglow / Boar jibu / Everything happens to me / Very thought of you / Wabash / From this moment on / Honeysuckle rose / Intimacy of the blues
ZECD 13 / 6 Oct '97 / Zephyr

Barnes, Emile

☐ EMILE BARNES & LOUISIANA JOYMAKERS
AMCD 13 / Aug '95 / American Music

Barnes, George

☐ 2 GUITARS & A HORN (Barnes, George & Carl Kress)
Mountain greenery / 's wonderful / I don't stand a ghost of a chance (with you) / Thou swell / Foggy day / Someone to watch over me / Gone with the wind / How high the moon / Blue moon / Three little words / Original / Liebesfreud / Golden retriever puppy dog blues (no.1) / Love is just around the corner / Snowfall / Keepin' out of mischief now / This can't be love / Mood indigo / Satin doll / At sundown / Disenchanted trout / Please / Something tender / Eel's nephew / Golden retriever puppy dog blues (no.2)
JCD 636 / Jan '93 / Jass

☐ PLAYS SO GOOD
Night and day / I'm coming Virginia / Days of wine and roses / Don't get around much anymore / On a clear day (You can see forever) / I've found a new baby / Honeysuckle rose / St. Louis blues / At sundown
CCD 4067 / Apr '94 / Concord Jazz

Barnes, J.J.

☐ BORN AGAIN, AGAIN
Can't see me leaving you / Time is love / Good men don't grow on trees / You are just a living doll / Wishful thinking / You owe it to yourself / No if's, and's or but's / (I just make believe I'm) touching you
NEMCD 936 / Jul '97 / Sequel

☐ GROOVESVILLE MASTERS, THE (2CD Set)
Baby, please come back home / Your love is gone / Chains of love / I need a change / To an early grave / Time has come / Now I got you back / Sweet sherry / Help me / Welcome to the club / Cloudy days
GSCD 108 / 20 Apr '98 / Goldmine

☐ KING OF NORTHERN SOUL
Whatever happend to our melody / On top of the world / Talk of the grapevine / Our love is in the pocket / Try it one more time / In and out of my life / Say it / Build a foundation / Sweet as a honey bee / Eternity / Happy road / That's just never enough / Please let me in / I've seen the light / Real humdinger / You can bet your love / Open the door to your heart / Sweet sherry
3035990112 / Feb '96 / Motor City

Barnes, Jimmy

☐ BARNSTORMING
D 245212 / May '94 / Mushroom

☐ BEST OF JIMMY BARNES, THE (2CD Set)
TVD 93465 / Aug '97 / Mushroom

☐ FLESH & WOOD
TVD 93390 / Dec '94 / Mushroom

☐ HEAT
TVD 93372 / Jun '93 / Mushroom

☐ PSYCLONE
TVD 93433 / Jun '95 / Mushroom

☐ SOUL DEEP
TVD 93344 / Aug '94 / Mushroom

☐ TWO FIRES
Lay down your guns / Let's make it last all night / Little darlin' / Love is enough / Hardline / One of a kind / Sister mercy / When your love is gone / Between two fires / Fade to black / Hold on
TVD 93318 / May '94 / Mushroom

Barnes, Johnny

☐ FANCY OUR MEETING
Samba rossi / Blue horizon / Boko's bounce / Hawk / Moonlight becomes you / Fascinating rhythm / Falling in love with you
CLGCD 019 / Feb '89 / Calligraph

☐ LIKE WE DO (Barnes, Johnny & Roy Williams/Digby Fairweather)
But not for me / Nightingale sang in Berkeley Square / Serenade to a jobsworth / Fascinating rhythm / Kiss to build a dream on / Like we do / Once in a while / Wrap your troubles in dreams / Southern comfort / Struttin' with some barbecue / Please don't talk about me when I'm gone / One two button my shoe / I'm sorry I made you cry
LACD 69 / Oct '96 / Lake

Barnes, Paul

☐ PAUL BARNES & HIS POLO PLAYERS
AMCD 55 / Aug '95 / American Music

Barnes, Ricky

☐ WELCOME TO HILLTOP USA (Barnes, Ricky & The Hootowls)
OK 33025CD / Feb '95 / Okra

Barnes, Roosevelt

☐ HEARTBROKEN MAN, THE (Barnes, Roosevelt 'Booba' & The Playboys)
How long this must go on / Don't cry no more / Ain't going to worry about tomorrow / Tell me what I've done-my last affair / Heartbroken man / Blind man-i pity the fool / Rocking daddy / Tin pan alley / Baby scratch my back / Louise, louise blues / No place to go
R 2623 / Jul '95 / Rooster

Barnes, Will

☐ TEXAS IN MY BLOOD
Texas music in my blood / My old truck / First show boat / Don't make me sing redneck mother again / Port Arkansas / Whiskyta / Speed of the race / Tupelo county jail / Sunshine lady / Rock 'n' roll roadie / My bike / She ran off with buck / Second fiddle in one man band / I always die in Dallas / Standing on the rock / Naked with the girl next door / Clap for me (But don't give me the claps) / Granpa was a farmer / Desperados waiting for a train / Marajuana polka
BCD 15991 / Jul '96 / Bear Family

Barnet, Charlie

☐ CAPITOL BIG BAND SESSION, THE
Redskin rhumba / Eugipelliv / Lonely street / Cuba / Charlie's other aunt / Easy living / Charlie's other aunt / Overtime / O'Henry / Portrait of Edward Kennedy / Kennedy Ellington / Bebop spoken here / Gloomy Sunday / OOver the rainbow / All the things you are / Pan Americana / Ill wind / Claude reigns / Really / Spain / My crime / Theme for Cynthia / (I'm a dreamer) Aren't we all
8212582 / 10 Aug '98 / Capitol Jazz

☐ CHARLIE BARNET & RHYTHM MAKERS 1938
TAXCD 3715 / Mar '94 / Tax

☐ CHARLIE BARNET AND HIS ORCHESTRA 1935-1939 (Make Believe Ballroom) (Barnet, Charlie & His Orchestra)
Make believe ballroom / Prelude in c sharp minor / I let a song go out of my heart / You go to my head / Stop look and listen / Harmony in Harlem / Blue turning grey over you / In-a-jam / Chatterbox / Rock it for me / Lullaby in rhythm / Prelude to a kiss / Jump jump's here / Undecided / You got me / Gal from Joe's / Jump session / Knocking at the famous door / Tin roof blues / I'm praying humble / Always / On a holiday / Nagasaki / Growlin'
CD 53274 / Nov '97 / Giants Of Jazz

☐ CHEROKEE
Cherokee/Redskin rhumba / Serenade to May / Moten swing / Pompton turnpike / East side, west side / Charleston Alley / Skyliner / Blue juice / Wild mab of the fish pond / Southern fried / Smiles
ECD 220652 / Nov '93 / Evidence

☐ CHEROKEE
Cherokee / Duke's idea / Count's idea / Right idea / Wrong idea / Ogoun Badagris (voodoo war God) / Oh what you said (We are burnt up) / Night clow / Ebony rhapsody / I never knew / Lament for a lost love (Solace) / All night record man (Stay up Stan) / Last jump (A jump to end all jumps) / Miss Annabelle Lee / Lazy bug / Echoes of Harlem / Afternoon of a moax (Shake, rattle, 'n roll) / Leapin' at the Lincoln / Swing street strut / Clap hands, here comes Charlie / Between 18th and 19th on Chestnutt Street / Only a rose / Scotch and soda
CD 53277 / Jun '96 / Giants Of Jazz

☐ INTRODUCTION TO CHARLIE BARNET 1935-1944, AN
4039 / Nov '96 / Best Of Jazz

☐ LIVE 1957-1959 (Barnet, Charlie Orchestra)
JH 3005 / Mar '97 / Jazz Hour

☐ MAKE BELIEVE BALLROOM 1936-1941 (Barnet, Charlie Orchestra)
RACD 7123 / May '96 / Aerospace

☐ MORE (Barnet, Charlie Orchestra)
Evergreens / Stardust / Take the 'A' train / Goodbye / Early autumn / Flying home / I can't get started (with you) / Begin the beguine / Darn that dream / Midnight sun / One o'clock jump / Harlem nocturne
ECD 22112 / Jan '95 / Evidence

☐ SKYLINER (Barnet, Charlie Orchestra)
Gal from Joe's / Night song / Echoes of Harlem / Lazy bug / Midweek function / Lament for a lost love / Cherokee / That all night record man / Last jump / Duke's idea / Count's idea / Wrong idea / Right idea / Things ain't what they used to be / Washing whirligig / Strollin' / Moose / Pow-wow / Great lie / Drop me off in Harlem / Gulf coast blues / Skyliner / Xango
TPZ 1041 / Mar '96 / Topaz Jazz

☐ THOSE SWINGING YEARS
Redskin rhumba / Jeep is jumpin' / In a mellow tone / Into each life some rain must fall / Yalta / Great lie / Blue moon / E-bob-o-lee-bob / Mellow mood / In there / You always hurt the one you love / Xango / Gulf coast blues / I like to riff / Bakiff / Drop me off in Harlem
HCD 264 / Jun '97 / Hindsight

☐ TRANSCRIPTION PERFORMANCES 1941, THE (Barnet, Charlie Orchestra)
Swing low, sweet chariot / Nowhere / It's a haunted town / Charleston alley / Lumby / Conga del moaxo / Redskin rhumba / Fantasia / Blue juice / Phyllysse / Wings over Manhattan / Little John ordinary / Little dip / Wild mab of the fish pond / Dutch kitchen stomp / Plowin' / Consider yourself kissed / Spanish kick (Habanera) / Barcarolle / Song of the Volga Boatmen / Reflections / Bar is now open / Ponce de Leon
HEPCD 53 / Apr '97 / Hep

☐ WINGS OVER MANHATTAN 1941 (Barnet, Charlie Orchestra)
Swing low, sweet chariot / Afraid to say hello / Haunted town / Harmony haven / Nowhere / Blue juice / Buffy boy / Fantasia / Phylysee / Wings over Manhattan / Little dip / Little John ordinary / Why / Wild mab of the fish pond / Consider yourself kissed / Dutch kitchen stomp / Plowin' / Spanish kick / Herat you stole from me / Bar is open / Barcarolle / Ponce de Leon / Song of the Volga boatmen / Reflections
VN 1002 / Nov '96 / Viper's Nest

Barnett, Bobby

☐ AMERICAN HEROES AND WESTERN LEGENDS
Oklahoma's OK / Hanging of Judge Parker / Ballad of Belle Starr / Cherokee Bill / Bill Doolin / Ballad of pretty boy Floyd / Sequoyah / Captain David L Paine / Iron horse / Gunfight at the OK Corral / Wyatt Earp / Ballad of Doc Holiday / Bat Masterson / Story of the Dalton gang / Three guardsmen / Run of '89 / Ballad of Geronimo / Chief Crazy Horse / Pawnee Bill / Bill Pickett of the 101 / Lost Dutchman mine / Tombstone Arizona / Tom Mix / Salute to Will Rogers / Jim Thorpe / Cowboy hall of fame / Tribute to Woody Guthrie
BCD 16121 / Apr '97 / Bear Family

Barneys

☐ HAPPY CHRISTMAS LOVE BARNEY
5396982 / 17 Nov '97 / PolyGram TV

Barnshakers

☐ HONKY TONK SESSION, A
GRCD 6048 / Nov '96 / Goofin'

☐ STRING-O-RAMA
GRCD 6068 / Sep '96 / Goofin'

Barnyard Ballers

☐ PUNKABILLY INVASION
HB 8003 / 13 Apr '98 / Hairball 8

Baron, Christy

☐ I THOUGHT ABOUT YOU
JD 152 / May '97 / Chesky

Baron, Jean

☐ BRITTANY
ARN 64302 / Jul '95 / Arion

☐ DANSAL E BREIZ (Baron, Jean & Christian Anneix)
KMCD 41 / Aug '93 / Keltia Musique

☐ DANSE DE BRETAGNE (Baron, Jean & Christian Anneix)
KMCD 07 / Jul '90 / Keltia Musique

☐ E BRO ROUE MORVAN (Baron, Jean & Christian Anneix)
KMCD 68 / Sep '96 / Keltia Musique

☐ SACRED MUSIC AND BRETON AIRS (Baron, Jean & Michel Ghesquiere)
KMCD 69 / Nov '96 / Keltia Musique

Baron, Joey

☐ CRACKSHOT (Baron, Joey & Barondown)
AVAN 059 / Feb '96 / Avant

☐ DOWN HOME
Mighty fine / Little boy / Wide load / Crock pot / What / Listen to the women / Aren't we all / Supposing
INT 35032 / 17 Nov '97 / Intuition

☐ RAISED PLEASURE DOT
804492 / Apr '94 / New World

Baroques

☐ PURPLE DAY
B 1005 / 16 Feb '98 / Distortions

Baroudi, Hamid

☐ CITY NO MAD
EFA 042232 / Aug '94 / Vielklang

☐ MAD CT MIX
BARBARITY 014 / Jan '97 / Barbarity

Barr, John

☐ IN WHATEVER TIME WE HAVE
Cockeyed optimist / Does the moment ever come / Johnny one note / One hand one heart/Not while I'm around / Multitudes of armys / If I really wanted you / Marking time / Care for clowns / I love a piano / In whatever time we have / If I ever say I'm over you / There won't be trumpets / When I see you / Grateful / Quiet thing / Corner of the sky
MBJBTDM 2 / 3 Feb '98 / Dress Circle

Barra MacNeils

☐ TIMESPAN
Row row row / Flower basket medley / Lone harper / My heart's in the highlands / Glenpark medley / Song for peace / Coaltown road / Highland exchange medley / Standing by the subway / Playhouse medley / One for Jeffy / Beautiful Point Aconi
IRCD 043 / Mar '97 / Iona

☐ TRADITIONAL ALBUM, THE
Clumsy lover set / Celtic harp / Tribute to Robert Stubbert / Visit medley / Maids of Arrochar / Brolum set / Twice a year fiddler / March/Strathspeys/Reels / Memories of Mary Ann MacKenzie / Wedding party medley / Toonik tyme / Twin fiddles / Neil Gow's lament for the death of his second wife
IRCD 047 / Mar '97 / Iona

Barracudas

☐ COMPLETE BARRACUDAS
Barracuda wavers / Surfers are back / Rendezvous / I can't pretend / We're living in violent times / Don't let go / This ain't my time / I saw my death in a dream last night / Somewhere outside / On the strip / Chevy baby / Summer fun / His last summer / (I wish it could be) 1965 Again / Somebody / KGB (Made a man out of me) / Campus tramp / California lament / Codeine / My little red book / Neighbourhood girls / Tokyo rose
DOJOCD 99 / May '93 / Dojo

☐ DROP OUT WITH THE BARRACUDAS
I can't pretend / We're living in violent times / Don't let go / Codine / This ain't my time / I saw my death in a dream last night / Somewhere outside / Summer fun / His last summer / Somebody / Campus tramp / On the strip / California lament / (I wish it could be) 1965 again
VOXXCD 2009 / Jul '94 / Voxx

☐ SURF AND DESTROY
899027 / May '94 / New Rose

☐ TWO SIDES OF A COIN
I want my woody back / Subway surfin' / Inside mind / Hour of degradation / Next time round / Take what he wants / Dead skin / Two sides of coin / Kingdom of pain / Twentieth Century myth / Very last day / Wastin time / Daggers of justice / There's a world out there / Seven and seven is / Codeine / Song for Lorraine / Fortunate son
CDMGRAM 62 / May '95 / Anagram

Barratt, Sigurd

☐ SIGURD BARRATT & THE CIGARS (Barratt, Sigurd & The Cigars)
MECCACD 2041 / Oct '97 / Music Mecca

Barre, Martin

☐ MEETING, THE
Meeting / Potion / Outer circle / I know your face / Misere / Time after time / Spanner / Running free / Tom's / Dreamer / Audition
IMACD 23016 / 18 May '98 / Imago

☐ TRICK OF MEMORY, A
Bug / Way before your time / Bug bee / Empty cafe / Suspicion / I be thank you / Blues for all reasons / Trick of memory / Steal / Another view / Cold heart / Bug c / Morris minus / In the shade of the shadow
TT 5008 / Apr '94 / XYZ

Barrelhouse Jazz Band

☐ DRIVING HOT JAZZ FROM THE 20'S
BCD 49 / Apr '94 / GHB

Barreto, Don

☐ DON BARRETO ET SON ORCHESTRE CUBAIN 1932-1934 (Barreto, Don Et Son Orchestre Cubain)
La belle Creole / El beso / Negro bachatera / Chi chi biguine / Runidera / Biguine d'amour / Mi amor esta en el valle / A si pare / Lacrimas negras / Lamento esclavo / Marta / Negra consentida / Belle Melanie / Serenata Cubana / Nuestro cantar / La biguine qu'a pas fini / Mujer sonadora / Amor Cubano / Se acaba el mundo / Vengo por la Conga
HQCD 06 / Oct '91 / Harlequin

Barrett Sisters

☐ HE'S GOT THE WHOLE WORLD IN HIS HANDS
BB 1982 / May '96 / Black & Blue

Barrett, 'Sweet' Emma

☐ LAST RECORDINGS 1974 & 1978 (Barrett, Sweet Emma)
MG 9001 / Feb '95 / Mardi Gras

☐ MARDI GRAS PARTY 1960 (Barrett, 'Sweet' Emma & Her Bellboys)
Just a closer walk with thee / Ice cream / Alice blue gown / All of me / Shine / Ting-a-ling / Mack the knife / Panama / I'm gonna sit right down and right myself a letter / Bill Bailey / If I ever cease to love / Sister Kate / St. Louis blues / Happy birthday / Who's sorry know / When the saints go marching in / Indiana / Basin street blues
504CD 67 / Mar '98 / 504

☐ SWEET EMMA
OJCCD 183 / Nov '95 / Original Jazz Classics

Barrett, 'Wild' Willy

☐ OPEN TOED AND FLAPPING
Jack o' diamonds / Crow that chicken / Open toed and flapping / HT blues / Hair across the frets / Father Jim / Chinatown / MK special / Notting Hill / Hot clubbing / Cowboy / Judge and the devil / Blacksmith's rope
PRKCD 29 / Apr '95 / Park

Barrett, Dan

☐ IN AUSTRALIA (Barrett, Dan & Tom Baker)
ARCD 19143 / Oct '97 / Arbors Jazz

☐ JUBILESTA
ARCD 19107 / Nov '94 / Arbors Jazz

Barrett, Greg

☐ MEMPHIS HEAT
Into the mystic / Same old blues / Your love keeps me satisfied / Rainy night in Georgia / Worth her weight in gold / Since you've been gone / Standing next to rainbows / Until you come back to me (that's what I'm gonna do) / Before the light goes out tonight / That's all I want from you / Spanish Harlem / Goosebumps
INAK 9043CD / Jul '97 / In Akustik

Barrett, Larry

☐ BEYOND THE MISSISSIPPI
GRCD 342 / May '97 / Glitterhouse

☐ FLOWERS
GRCD 298 / 17 Nov '97 / Glitterhouse

Barrett, Syd

☐ BARRETT
Baby lemonade / Love song / Dominoes / It is obvious / Rats / Maisie / Gigolo aunt / Waving my arms in the air / Wined and dined / Wolfpack / Effervescing elephant / I never lied to you
CDGO 2054 / May '94 / Harvest

☐ CRAZY DIAMOND (The Complete Syd Barrett - 3CD Set)
Terrapin / No good trying / Love you / No man's land / Dark globe / Here I go / Octopus / Golden hair / Long gone / She took a long cold look / Feel / If it's in you / Late night / Octopus (Take 1 and 2) / It's no use trying / Love you (Take 1) / Love you (Take 3) / She took a long cold look (Take 4) / Golden hair (Take 5) / Baby lemonade / Love songs / Dominoes / It is obvious / Rats / Maisie / Gigolo aunt / Waving my arms in the air / I never lied to you / Wined and dined / Wolfpack / Effervescing elephant / Baby lemonade / Waving my arms in the air (takes) / I never lied to you / Love song (Take 1) / Dominoes (take 1) / Dominoes (Take 2) / It is obvious (alt. takes) / Opel / Clowns and jugglers / Rats / Golden hair (vocal) / Dolly rocker / Word song / Wined and dined / Swan Lee (Silas Lang) / Birdie hop / Let's split / Lanky (Part 1) / Wouldn't you miss me / Milky way / Golden hair (Inst.) / Gigolo aunt (Take 9) / Clowns and jugglers (Octopus) / Late night (Take 2) / Effervescing elephant (Take 2)
SYDBOX 1 / Apr '93 / Harvest

☐ MADCAP LAUGHS, THE
Terrapin / No good trying / Love you / No man's land / Here I go / Dark globe / Octopus / Golden hair / Long gone / She took a long cold look / Feel / If it's in you / Late night
CDGO 2053 / May '94 / Harvest

☐ OPEL
Opel / Clowns and jugglers / Rats / Golden hair / Dolly rocker / Word song / Wined and dined / Swan Lee (Silas Lang) / Birdie hop / Let's split / Lanky (part 1) / Wouldn't you miss me / Milky way / Golden hair (Inst.)
CDGO 2055 / May '94 / Harvest

Barretto, Ray

☐ ANCESTRAL MESSAGES
New world spirit / Song for Chano / Freedom jazz dance / On a sunday afternoon / Beautiful love / Killer Joe / Aquablue / Gabriela / My Latin New York / Ancestral messages
CCD 4549 / May '93 / Concord Picante

☐ BEYOND THE BARRIO
Nadie se salva la rumba / Tu proprio dolor / Lucretia the cat / Aguadilla / Vive y vacila / Canto abacua / Cancion para el nino / Lo tuyo lo mio / Aguardiente d cana / Ya no puede ser / Tin tin deo / Prestame tu mujer / Eras
CDHOT 518 / Apr '95 / Charly

☐ CARNAVAL
Manha de carnaval / Sugar's delight / Exodus / Descarga la moderna / Summertime / El negro y Ray / Mira que Linda / Concinando suave / Pachango oriental / Barretto en la tumbadora / Cumbamba / El Paso / Linda Mulata / Oye heck / Los Cueros / Pachanga suavecito / Ponte dura / Pachango para bailar
FCD 24713 / Oct '93 / Fantasy

☐ LA CUNA
La cuna / Dolorosa / Mambotango / Old castle / Pastime paradise / Cocinado
ZK 66126 / Feb '96 / Sony Jazz

☐ LIVE AT THE BEACON THEATRE NEW YORK 1976
Intro / Vaya / Ahora si que vamo a gozar / Bab ban quere / Guarare / Night Flowers (flores de noche) / Slo flo / Cocinando / Que viva la misica
MES 159502 / Feb '93 / Messidor

☐ MY SUMMERTIME
8358302 / Apr '96 / Owl

☐ RAY BARRETTO 1939-1943
HQCD 36 / Feb '94 / Harlequin

☐ TABOO (Barretto, Ray & New World Spirit)
Taboo / Bomba-Riquen / Work song / Cancion de'l yunque (Song for the rain forest) / Guaji-Rita / 99 MacDougal St / Montuno blue / Brother Tom / Lazy afternoon / Effendi
CCD 4601 / Jul '94 / Concord Picante

Barrie, J.J.

☐ NO CHARGE
Beunas dias senorita / My son / Where's the reason / I just fall in love again / While the feeling's good / It's too soon to know / Lady singer with a country music band / I love you / No charge / Lucille I got a honey of a deal / Husbands and wives / Sunday morning blues / Rainbows in my mind / I can't sing our love song / At my age / Very thought of you
SCD 28 / Feb '97 / Start

Barriere, Alain

☐ 30 ANNEES EN CHANSONS (2CD Set)
3032562 / Jan '98 / Arcade

Barrister

☐ NEW FUJI GARBAGE (& Africa's International Music Ambassadors) (Barrister, Chief Dr. Sikiru Ayinde)
Refined Fuji garbage / Fuji worldwide
CDORBD 067 / Feb '91 / Globestyle

Barriteau, Carl

☐ MAN AND HIS MUSIC, THE (Barriteau, Carl Orchestra)
Hut-sut song: *Stone, Lew & His Band* / Tuxedo junction: *Johnson, Ken 'Snakehips' & his West Indian Orchestra* / Mirage: *Winstone, Eric & His Band* / Lovers lullaby: *Winstone, Eric & His Band* / I said no: *Hatchett's Swingtette* / Watch the birdie: *Hatchett's Swingtette* / Three little sisters: *Loss, Joe & His Orchestra* / Pennsylvania polka: *Loss, Joe & His Orchestra* / Oasis: *Ambrose & His Orchestra* / Pony express: *Ambrose & His Orchestra* / Tea for two / Tea for two / Am I blue / I wished on the moon / Somebody loves me / Minor mood / I'll get by / Is you is or is you ain't ma baby / Primrose Hill / Sultan goes to Harlem / Into each life some rain must fall / Ol' man rose / Concerto for clarinet
RAJCD 896 / 29 Jun '98 / Empress

Barron, Bill

☐ NEXT PLATEAU, THE
MCD 5368 / Sep '92 / Muse

Barron Knights

☐ BEST OF THE BARRON KNIGHTS, THE
California girls / DIY / Mr. Bronski meets Mr. Evans / Air hostess song / All through the night / Street rhymes / Bohemian Rhapsody / Space oddity / Have you seen her / Wally song / Loan arranger / Superglue / Sister Josephine / Then he kicked me / Nellie the courier / Money for nothing / Stick to selling onions / Club erotica / Franksie / Don't let the Germans pinch your sunbeds / Little darling / Gas board bill / I'm anti biotics / Big bad bond / Ozone friendly
QED 103 / Nov '96 / Tring

☐ BEST OF THE BARRON KNIGHTS, THE
How about us / Olympic record / I've got you under my skin / Sunday shopping / Merry gentle pops / Can can / Traces / Chapel lead is missing / Cilla Black's hat / Under new management / Green knickers / Pop go the workers / Cold in my nose / Call up the groups '64 / Battle of Agincourt / All shock up
306362 / Jan '97 / Hallmark

☐ BEST OF THE BARRON KNIGHTS, THE
Cilla Black's hat / Can can / Chapel lead is missing / Bottle of Agincourt / Sunday shopping / Call up the groups / Call up the groups / Pop go the workers / Merry gentle pops / Under new management / Olympic record / Traces / I've got you under my skin / Come to the dance
CDSGP 0338 / Apr '97 / Prestige

☐ TWO SIDES OF THE SENSATIONAL BARRON KNIGHTS, THE
You are all I need / Before you leave / Bottle on the shelf / Lonely / You know what I mean / Don't let it die / Turning my back on you / Oh little girl / To the woods / Hey ho Europe / Beetroot song / I couldn't spell / You know what / Green knickers / With her head tucked underneath her arm / Three finger picker / What is a pop star / Cold in my nose / Peaceful life / Ballad of Frank Spencer / Nothin' doin' / Pardon me / I'm gonna give my love to you / I'm a nut
C5CD 572 / Jun '97 / See For Miles

Barron, Kenny

☐ ARTISTRY OF KENNY BARRON, THE
Morning of the carnival / Like someone in love / Body and soul / Rhythm-a-ning / Lover man / Well you didn't
WAVE 34CD / 20 Jul '98 / Wave

☐ INVITATION
CRISS 1044CD / Apr '91 / Criss Cross

☐ KENNY BARRON AT THE PIANO
60170400032 / 14 Apr '98 / PREV

☐ LEMURIA-SEASCAPE (Barron, Kenny Trio)
Ask me now / Sweet Lorraine / Fungii mama / Slow grind / Have you met Miss Jones / Maria Isabel / You go to my head / Magical look in your eyes / Seascape
CCD 79508 / Feb '97 / Candid

☐ LIVE AT MAYBECK RECITAL HALL VOL.10
I'm getting sentimental over you / Witchcraft / Bud-like / Spring is here / Well you needn't / Skylark / And then again / Sunshower
CCD 4466 / Jun '91 / Concord Jazz

☐ MOMENT, THE
RSRCD 121 / Nov '94 / Reservoir

☐ ONLY ONE, THE
RSRCD 115 / Nov '94 / Reservoir

☐ OTHER PLACES
Anywhere / Other places / Mythology / For Heaven's sake / Ambrosia / Wildlife / I should care / Nikara's song / Hey, it's me you're talkin' to
5196992 / Mar '94 / Verve

☐ RED BARRON DUO, THE (Barron, Kenny & Red Mitchell Trio)
STCD 4137 / Feb '90 / Storyville

☐ RHYTHM-A-NING (Barron, Kenny & John Hicks Quartet)
Sunshower / Naima's love song / Blue monk / After the morning / Ghost of yesterday / Rhythm-a-ning
CCD 79044 / Feb '97 / Candid

☐ SAMBAO
Sambao / Yalele / Bacchanal / Belem encounter / Ritual / Gardenia / On the other side
5127362 / Mar '94 / EmArCy

☐ WANTON SPIRIT
5223642 / Dec '94 / Verve

☐ WHAT IF
ENJA 50132 / 17 Nov '97 / Enja

Barron, Ronnie

☐ MY NEW ORLEANS SOUL
AIM 1038 / Apr '95 / Aim

Barros, Alberto

☐ TITAN DE LA SALSA
RMD 815232 / 7 Apr '98 / RMM

Barrow, Arthur

☐ EYEBROW RAZOR
EFA 034192 / Aug '95 / Muffin

Barrowside

☐ HIDDEN CORNER, THE
RTMCD 73 / Feb '96 / Round Tower

☐ WISH & THE WAY, THE
RTMCD 66 / Dec '94 / Round Tower

Barrueco, Manuel

☐ CANTOS Y DANZAS
CDC 5565782 / 6 Apr '98 / EMI Classics

Barry Boom

☐ LIVING BOOM, THE
FADCD 016 / Nov '90 / Fashion

☐ TRUST ME
MERCD 010 / Jan '93 / Merger

Barry, Claudja

☐ BEST OF CLAUDJA BARRY, THE (Dancin' Fever)
Boogie woogie dancing shoes / Dancin' fever / Work me over / Sweet dynamite / Down and counting / I will follow him / Radio action / Two of us / Love for the sake of love / Feel the fire / Take it easy / If I do it to you / Johnny Johnny please come home
HTCD 13 / 20 Apr '98 / Hot Productions

Barry, Ged

☐ SHOWBIZ WILDERNESS
RMCD 004 / 3 Nov '97 / Ready Made

Barry, John

☐ BEYONDNESS OF THINGS, THE
4600092 / 14 Apr '98 / Decca

☐ HIT AND MISS
Hideaway / When the saints go marching in / Long John / Twelfth street rag / Hit and miss / Beat for beatniks / Blueberry hill / Never let go / WalkHit and miss / Walk don't run / Black stockings / Mgnificent seven / It doesn't matter anymore / Spanish Harlem / James Bond Theme / Cutty sark / Cherry pink and apple blossom white / Unchained melody / I'll be with you in apple blossom time / Voaire / That fatal kiss
CDMFP 6392 / Jul '97 / Music For Pleasure

☐ HITS AND THE MISSES, THE (2CD Set) (Various Artists)
PLAY 007 / 6 Apr '98 / Play It Again

☐ SOUNDSCAPE (The Best Of John Barry)
Persuaders / Midnight cowboy / Ipcress file / Knack / Wednesday's child / Space march (capsule in space) / Girl with the sun in her hair / Vendetta / Danny Scipio / James Bond / Goldfinger / Diamonds are forever / From Russia with love / You only live twice / Thunderball / On her majesty's secret service / 007 / Walk don't run / Beat for beatniks / Hit and miss / Born free
4885822 / 22 Sep '97 / Columbia

Barry, John

☐ NASHVILLE STYLE
(Tonight we just might) fall in love again / Summer's comin' / Hey baby / Don't take the girl / Bobbie Ann Mason / Indian outlaw / If the world had a front porch / Gone country / One boy, one girl / You got it / Sold (the Grundy County auction incident) / I like it, I love it
HBCD 9501 / Feb '96 / Brewhouse

Barry, Margaret

☐ HER MANTLE SO GREEN (Barry, Margaret & Michael Gorman)
TSCD 474 / Aug '94 / Topic

☐ IRELAND'S OWN
PTICD 1029 / Aug '96 / Pure Traditional Irish

Barta, Steve

☐ BLUE RIVER
Wish upon a canvas / Blue river / In another life / Like an old piano / Rossport / Carinho (dearest one) / High road / Asleep in the sweet light / Umtradah / On the edge
KOKO 1303 / Mar '96 / Kokopelli

Barthelemy, Claude

☐ MONSIEUR CLAUDE
ZZ 84124 / Feb '97 / Deux Z

☐ SOLIDE (Barthelemy, Claude & Pierre Ledic/Charles Biddle)
EVCD 316 / Feb '94 / Evidence

Bartholomew, Dave

☐ BASIN STREET BREAKDOWN
Basin street breakdown / Golden rule / Bad habit / In the alley / Twins / Lawdy Lawdy Lord (part 1) / Lawdy Lawdy Lord (part 2) / Country boy / Pyramid / Messy bessy / I'll never be the same / Mr. Fool / Stormy weather / Nickel wine / Sweet home blues / Mother knows best / High flying woman / My ding a ling
CDCHARLY 273 / Jan '93 / Charly

Barton, Lou Ann

☐ DREAMS COME TRUE (Barton, Lou Ann/Marcia Ball/Angela Strehli)
Fool in love / Good rockin' daddy / It hurts to be in love / Love sweet love / Gonna make it / You can if you think you can / I idolize you / Dreams come true / Bad thing / Turn the lock on love / Something's got a hold on me / Snake dance
ANTCD 0014 / Mar '91 / Antones

☐ OLD ENOUGH
ANTCD 0021 / Oct '95 / Antones

Bartos, Alexandre

☐ ART OF THE DIDJERIDOO, THE
ARN 60391 / Aug '97 / Arion

Bartram & Holloway

☐ FOUR RED FEET
WGSCD 268 / Feb '96 / Wild Goose

Bartz, Gary

☐ ALTO MEMORIES (Bartz, Gary & Sonny Fortune)
5232682 / Dec '94 / Verve

☐ EPISODE ONE - CHILDREN OF HARLEM
CHR 70001 / May '96 / Challenge

☐ HARLEM BUSH MUSIC - TAIFA/ UHURU (Bartz, Gary NTU Troop)
Rise / People dance / Du (rain) / Drinking song / Taifa / Parted / Warrior's song / Blue (a folk tale) / Uhuru sasa / Vietcong / Celestial blues / Planets
CDBGPD 108 / Jan '97 / Beat Goes Public

☐ JUJU STREET SONGS (Bartz, Gary NTU Troop)
I wanna be where you are / Black maybe / Betha baptist / Africans unite / Teheran / Sifa zote / Whasaname / Betcha by golly wow / Dr. Follows dance / Standin' on the corner / Sing me a song today
PRCD 24181 / Aug '97 / Prestige

☐ THERE GOES THE NEIGHBORHOOD (Bartz, Gary Candid All Stars)
Racism (blues in double Bb minor) / On a misty night / Laura / Tadd's delight / Impressions / I've never been in love before / Flight path
CCD 79506 / Feb '97 / Candid

☐ WEST 42ND STREET (Live At Birdland 1990) (Bartz, Gary Quintet)
West 42nd Street / Speak low / It's easy to remember / Cousins / Night has a thousand eyes
CCD 79049 / Feb '97 / Candid

Bartz, Richard

☐ ESCAPE
EFA 125462 / Aug '96 / Kurbel

Bascomb, Paul

☐ BAD BASCOMB
Blues and the beat / More blues-more beat / Black out / Pink cadillac / Soul and body / Coquette / Love's an old story / Nona / Mumble's blues / Indiana / Got cool too soon / Liza's blues / I know just how you feel / Soul and body / Blues and the beat / More blues-more beat / Pink cadillac
DD 431 / Mar '97 / Delmark

Baseball Annie

☐ BASEBALL ANNIE
LF 213CD / May '96 / Lost & Found

☐ EP COLLECTION
LF 298CD / 27 Oct '97 / Lost & Found

Baseline

☐ RETURNS
Though dreamers die / Avenger / Che cha / Northsea night / Strike again / Loudly at night / Magic kingdom / Returns / Wheeling
CHR 70047 / Mar '97 / Challenge

☐ STANDARDS
CHR 70023 / Feb '96 / Challenge

Basement 5

☐ 1965-1980/BASEMENT 5 IN DUB
Riot / No ball games / Hard work / Immigration / Last white christmas / Heavy traffic / Union games / Too soon / Omega man / Paranoiaclaustrophobia (dub) / Work (dub) / Games (dub) / Immigration (dub) / Holocaust (dub)
IMCD 145 / Jul '92 / Island

Basement Jaxx

☐ ATLANTIC JAXX - A COMPILATION (Various Artists)
Intro: *Basement Jaxx* / Be free: *Basement Jaxx* / Smaba magic: *Basement Jaxx* / Live your life: *Joseph, Corrina* / Fly life: *Basement Jaxx* / Ennao: *Basement Jaxx* / Belo horizonti: *Heartists* / Lonely: *Joseph, Corrina* / Set yo body free: *Joseph, Corrina* / Daluma: *Joseph, Corrina* / Grapesoda: *Ratcliffe* / Missing you: *Richards, Ronnie* / Undaground: *Basement Jaxx*
JAXXCD 001 / 28 Oct '97 / Atlantic Jaxx

☐ MIXMAG LIVE VOL.25 (Various Artists)
MMLCD 025 / 5 May '98 / Mixmag Live

Bashful Brother Oswald

☐ BROTHER OSWALD
ROUCD 0013 / Jun '95 / Rounder

Bashir, Munir

☐ UD DUET (Bashir, Munir & Omar)
Fog el-Nakhel / Pasta Baghdadiyya / Hanan / Dabka / Ishtar / Al-amira al Andaluciyya
B 6874 / May '98 / Auvidis/Ethnic

Basho, Robbie

☐ GUITAR SOLI
Seal of the blue lotus / Mountain man's farewell / Dravidian Sunday / Grail and the lotus / Dharma prince / Oriental love song / Sansara in sweetness after sandstorm / Salangadou / Golden shamrock / Street dakini / Chung mei - the Chinese orchid
CDTAK 8902 / Jan '97 / Takoma

☐ SEAL OF THE BLUE LOTUS, THE
Seal of the blue lotus / Mountain man's farewell / Dravidian Sunday / Bardo blues / Sansara in sweetness after sandstorm / Black lotus - hymn to fugen
CDTAK 1005 / Apr '96 / Takoma

Basie Alumni

☐ SWINGING FOR THE COUNT
Red bank shuffle / Snapper / Jive at five / Swinging for the count / Blue and sentimental / Kansas City Kitty / Basie like / Slow boat / Jumpin' at the Woodside
CCD 79724 / Jan '97 / Candid

Basie, Count

☐ AIN'T MISBEHAVIN' (Basie, Count Orchestra)
Blues in my heart / I don't stand a ghost of a chance (with you) / Idaho / Red roses for a blue lady / Moonglow / Ma, he's making eyes at me / Ain't misbehavin' / Sweet lorraine / M squad / Don't worry 'bout me / As long as I live / I've got the world on a string / Flight of the foo birds
15778 / Jan '93 / Laserlight

☐ AMERICANS IN SWEDEN VOL.1 (Stockholm 1954) (Basie, Count Orchestra)
TAX 37012 / Aug '94 / Tax

☐ AMERICANS IN SWEDEN VOL.2 (Stockholm 1954) (Basie, Count Orchestra)
TAX 37022 / Aug '94 / Tax

☐ ANTHOLOGY
EN 517 / Sep '95 / Encyclopaedia

☐ APRIL IN PARIS
Jumpin' at the woodside / I guess I'll have to change my plan / 9.20 special / Jeepers creepers / Swingin' the blues / With plenty of money and you / Shorty George / Chicago / Broadway / I've grown accustomed to her face / Out the window / Poor little rich girl / Lester leaps in / Anything goes / Are you having any fun / Dickie's dream / Growing pains / Jive at five / Life is a song / April in Paris
TRTCD 171 / Dec '94 / TrueTrax

☐ APRIL IN PARIS
PLSCD 146 / Apr '97 / Pulse

☐ APRIL IN PARIS (Remastered)
5214022 / Oct '97 / Verve Master Edition

☐ AT NEWPORT
Swingin' at Newport / Polka dots and moonbeams / Lester leaps in / Sent for you yesterday and here you come today / Boogie woogie I may be wrong / Evenin' / Blee blop blues / Alright, OK you win / Comeback / Roll 'em Pete / Smack dab in the middle / One o'clock jump
8337762 / Mar '94 / Verve

☐ ATOMIC BAND LIVE IN EUROPE
BS 18010 / Jul '96 / Bandstand

☐ ATOMIC MR. BASIE, THE (Basie, Count Orchestra)
Kid from Red Bank / Duet / After supper / Flight of the Foo birds / Double O / Teddy the toad / Whirly bird / Midnite blue / Splanky / Fantail / Li'l darlin'
CDP 8286352 / Mar '95 / Blue Note

☐ ATOMIC MR. BASIE, THE (The Complete Atomic Basie) (Basie, Count Orchestra)
Kid from Red Bank / Duet / After supper / Flight of the Foo Birds / Double O / Teddy the toad / Whirly bird / Midnite blue / Splanky / Fantail / Li'l darlin' / Silks and satins / Sleepwalker's serenade / Sleepwalker's serenade / Late late show / Late late show
CDROU 1055 / Feb '94 / Roulette

☐ AUDIO ARCHIVE
Lester leaps in / Going to Chicago / All of me / Platterbrains / I struck a match in the dark / Dance of the gremlins / Feather merchant / Everyday I have the blues / Stormy Monday blues / Swingin' the blues / Jumpin' at the woodside / One O'clock jump / Every tub / John's idea / Tom thumb / April in Paris / Fiesta in blue / Blues and sentimental / Down for double / Something new
CDAA 013 / Oct '92 / Tring

☐ AUTUMN IN PARIS (Basie, Count Orchestra)
Whirly bird / Little pony / Corner pocket / Lovely baby / Blee blop blues / Nails / Kid from Red Bank / Spring is here / Why not / Well, alright, OK, you win / Roll 'em / Ol' man river / Duet / Gee baby ain't I good to you / One o'clock jump
DAWE 13 / Nov '93 / Magic

☐ BASIC BASIE (Basie, Count Orchestra)
Idaho / Blues in my heart / I don't stand a ghost of a chance with you / Red roses for a blue lady / Moonglow / Ma, he's making eyes at me / M Squad / Sweet Lorraine / Ain't misbehavin' / Don't worry 'bout me / As long as I live / I've got the world on a string
8212912 / Mar '94 / MPS Jazz

☐ BASIE AND FRIENDS
Easy does it / Zoot / Love me or leave me / NHOP / She's funny that way / Turnaround / Madame Fitz / Royal garden blues
CD 2310925 / Apr '94 / Pablo

☐ BASIE AND ZOOT (Basie, Count & Zoot Sims)
I never knew / It's only a paper moon / Blues for Nat Cole / Captain Bligh / Honeysuckle rose / Hardav / Mean to me / Surrender dear
OJCCD 822 / Jun '95 / Original Jazz Classics

☐ BASIE BOOGIE (Basie, Count Orchestra)
In a mellotone / Midgets / Whirly bird / Basie boogie / Deacon / Cute / Ol' man river / Kid from red bank / Spring is here / Why not / Corner pocket / Little pony / Blee bop blues
JHR 73502 / May '93 / Jazz Hour

☐ BASIE IN LONDON (Basie, Count Orchestra)
Jumpin' at the Woodside / Shiny stockings / How high the moon / Nails / Flute juice / One o'clock jump / Alright, OK you win / Roll 'em Pete / Comeback / Blues backstage / Corner pocket / Blee blop blues / Yesterdays / Untitled / Sixteen men / Swinging / Plymouth rock
8338052 / Jan '94 / Verve

☐ BASIE JAM VOL.1
Doubling blues / Hanging out / Red bank blues / One nighter / Freeport blues
CD 2310 718 / May '94 / Pablo

☐ BASIE JAM VOL.2
Mama don't wear no drawers / Doggin' around / Kansas City line / Jump
OJCCD 631 / Feb '92 / Original Jazz Classics

☐ BASIE RHYTHM (Basie, Count & Harry James)
Shoe shine boy / Evening / Boogie woogie / Oh lady be good / Jubilee / When we're alone / I can dream, can't I / Life goes to a party / Texas chatter / Song of the wanderer / Dreamer in me / One o'clock jump / My heart belongs to daddy / Sing for your supper / You can depend on me / Cherokee (part I) / Cherokee (part II) / Blame it on my last affair / Jive at five / Thursday / Evil blues / Oh lady be good
HEPCD 1032 / Jan '92 / Hep

☐ BASIE'S BAG (Basie, Count Orchestra)
Firm roots / Three in one / Hampton strut / For my lady / Way out Basie / Clarks / Basie's bag / Here's that rainy day / Count Basie rememberance suite
CD 83358 / Jan '94 / Telarc

☐ BEST OF COUNT BASIE
Kid from Red Bank / Secret love / Cute / I cried for you / Blue and sentimental / Jumpin' at the woodside / Meet BB / Teach me tonight / Moten swing / One o'clock jump / Whirly bird / Hallelujah, I love her so / Makin' whoopee / Lullaby of Birdland / If I were a bell / Jackson County Jubilee / Sunset glow / Tickle toe / Ol' man river / Li'l darlin'
CDMFP 6133 / Sep '94 / Music For Pleasure

☐ BEST OF COUNT BASIE, THE
Tree frog / Sweet pea / Ticker / Flirt / Blues for Alfy / Billie's bounce / Festival blues / Jumpin' at the Woodside / Blue and sentimental / Red bank boogie / Shorty George / Rock-a-bye Basie / Every tub / Swingin' the blues / Sent for you yesterday / Boogie woogie / Broadway / Texas shuffle / Tickle toe / Doggin' around / Dickie's dream / Topsy / Lester leaps in / Out the window
CD 2405408 / Apr '94 / Pablo

☐ BEST OF THE BASIE BIG BAND, THE
Blues for Alfy / Heat's on / CB express / Sweet pea / Way out Basie / Featherweight / Katy / Prime time / Mr. Softie
CD 24054222 / Apr '94 / Pablo

☐ BIG BAND MONTREUX 1977
Heat's on / Freckle face / Splanky / More I see you / Night in tunisia / Hittin' 12 / Bags of dreams / Things ain't what they used to be / It's need to be bee'd with / Li'l darlin' / Jumpin' a the woodside / One o'clock jump
OJCCD 377 / Feb '92 / Original Jazz Classics

☐ BIRDLAND 1956
JUCD 2028 / May '98 / Jazz Unlimited

☐ BLUES ALLEY
All heart / Blues alley / Cherokee / Night in Tunisia / Goin' to chicago blues / Kid from red bank / Shiny stockings / Shadow of your smile / Splanky / Basie's thought / Blues in Hoss's flat / Magic flea / One o'clock jump
CDC 9060 / Apr '95 / LRC

☐ BLUES AND BOOGIE WOOGIE 1937-1947
159122 / 24 Apr '98 / Jazz Archives

☐ BROADCAST TRANSCRIPTIONS 1944-1945
CD 884 / Sep '95 / Music & Arts

☐ CLASS OF 1954
In case you didn't know / These foolish things / Peter pan / Ain't it the truth / Ingin' the ooh / Confessin' / These foolish things (alt. take) / In case you didn't know (alt. take) / One o'clock jump (intro) / You for me / Bubbles / You're not the kind / Jonesy / Two for the blues / Blee blop blues / Yesterdays / Perdido
BLC 760924 / Oct '94 / Black Lion

☐ CLASSIC YEARS, THE
CDSGP 0172 / Mar '96 / Prestige

☐ CLASSICS 1936-1938 (Basie, Count Orchestra)
Shoe shine boy / Evening / Boogie woogie / Oh lady be good / Honeysuckle rose / Pennies from Heaven / Swingin' at the daisy chain / Roseland shuffle / Exactly like you / Boo-hoo / Glory of love / Smarty / One o'clock jump / Listen my children / John's idea / Good morning blues / Our love was meant to be / Time out / Topsy / I keep remembering / Out the window / Don't you miss your baby / Let me dream / Georgianna
CLASSICS 503 / Apr '90 / Classics

☐ CLASSICS 1938-1939 (Basie, Count Orchestra)
Blues in the dark / Sent for you yesterday / Every tub / Now will you be good / Swingin' the blues / Mama don't want no peas, no rice, no coconut oil / Blue and sentimental / Doggin' around / Stop beatin' around the mulberry bush / London Bridge is falling down / Texas shuffle / Jumpin' at the woodside / How long blues / Dirty dozen / Hey lawdy mama / Fives / Boogie woogie / Dark rapture / Shorty George / Blues I like to hear / Do you wanna jump children / Pansie stomp / My heart belongs to daddy / Sing for your supper / Old red
CLASSICS 504 / Apr '90 / Classics

☐ CLASSICS 1939 VOL.1
CLASSICS 513 / Apr '90 / Classics

☐ CLASSICS 1939 VOL.2
CLASSICS 533 / Dec '90 / Classics

☐ CLASSICS 1939-1940
CLASSICS 563 / Oct '91 / Classics

☐ CLASSICS 1940-1941 (Basie, Count Orchestra)
CLASSICS 623 / Sep '92 / Classics

☐ CLASSICS 1941
CLASSICS 652 / Nov '92 / Classics

☐ CLASSICS 1942
CLASSICS 684 / Mar '93 / Classics

☐ CLASSICS 1943-1944
CLASSICS 801 / Mar '95 / Classics

☐ CLASSICS 1945-1946
CLASSICS 934 / Apr '97 / Classics

☐ CLASSICS 1946-1947
CLASSICS 988 / 24 Apr '98 / Black & Blue

☐ CORNER POCKET (Basie, Count Orchestra)
Spring is here / Fantail / Teddy the toad / Pensive miss / Corner pocket / Scoot / Sweety cake / Cute / Li'l darlin' / Low life
15789 / Aug '92 / Laserlight

☐ COUNT BASIE (2CD Set)
R2CD 4012 / 13 Apr '98 / Deja Vu

☐ COUNT BASIE
22704 / Feb '96 / Music

☐ COUNT BASIE
One o'clock jump / Dance of the gremlins / Jazz me blues / Blee blop blues / Bubbles / You for me / Basie goes wess / Straight live / Let's jump / Ska-di-de-dee-doo / Slow but sure / Two for the blues / Basie talk
15704 / Apr '94 / Laserlight

☐ COUNT BASIE & HIS GREAT VOCALISTS
I can't believe that you're in love with me / Don't worry 'bout me / If I can't be here with you (one hour tonight) / Goin' to Chicago blues / I want a little girl / My old flame / If I didn't care / Moon nocturne / Somebody stole my gal / All of me / Angels sing / Between the devil and the deep blue sea / Blue shadows and white gardenias / That old feeling / Jivin' with Joe Jackson / Blue skies
CK 66374 / Jul '95 / Sony Jazz

☐ COUNT BASIE & SARAH VAUGHAN (Basie, Count & Sarah Vaughan)
Perdido / Lover man / I cried for you / Alone / There are such things / Mean to me / Gentleman is a dope / You go to my head / Until I met you / You turned the tables on me / Little man (you've had a busy day) / Teach me tonight / If I were a bell / Until I met you
CDP 8372412 / Apr '96 / Roulette

☐ COUNT BASIE 1937-1943 (Basie, Count & His Orchestra)
Jumpin' at the woodside / One o'clock jump / Swingin' the blues / Topsy / Every tub / Boogie woogie / Dickie's dream / Twelfth street rag (one step) / Red wagon / Oh lady be good / Jive at five / Fives / Texas shuffle / Clap hands here comes charlie / Oh red / Tickle toe / I never knew / Sugar blues / Love jumped out / Super chief / Lester leaps in / Red bank boogie / Rhythm man / Fiesta in blue / Yeah man
CD 53072 / Mar '92 / Giants Of Jazz

☐ COUNT BASIE 1944 (Basie, Count Orchestra)
One o'clock jump / Gee baby, ain't I good to you / Untitled stomp / Lady be good / Jumpin' at the woodside / Do nothing till you hear from me / Basie boogie / Avenue c / Baby won't you please come home / Dinah / Bird calls / Call me darling / Rock-a-bye basie / Every tub
HCD 224 / Jul '94 / Hindsight

☐ COUNT BASIE AND THE KANSAS CITY SEVEN (Basie, Count & The Kansas City Seven)
I'll always be in love with you / Snooky / Blues for Charlie Christian / Jaws / I'm confessin' that I love you / I want a little girl / Blues in C / Brio
MCAD 5656 / '88 / Impulse Jazz

☐ COUNT BASIE AND THE KANSAS CITY SEVEN (Basie, Count & The Kansas City Seven)
Trey of hearts / Oh lady be good / Secrets / I want a little girl / Shoe shine boy / Count's place / Senator Whitehead / Tally-ho, Mr Basie / What'cha talkin'
IMP 12022 / May '97 / Impulse Jazz

☐ COUNT BASIE COMPLETELY LIVE
Little pony / One o'clock jump / Blues / Indian summer / Who me / Jumpin' at the woodside / Spring is here / Teddy the toad / Pensive Miss / Corner pocket / Sweety cake / Cute / Lil darling / Dance of the gremlins / Let's jump / Slow but sure / Jazz me blues / Five o'clock in the morning blues / Flight of the foo birds / Chestnut street ramble / Dinah / Basie boogie / Rock a bye basie
24368 / Nov '97 / Laserlight

☐ COUNT BASIE GOLD (2CD Set)
D2CD 4012 / Jun '95 / Deja Vu

☐ COUNT BASIE ORCHESTRA 1944-1956 (Basie, Count Orchestra)
What am I here for / April in paris / Jive at five / There's a small hotel / Hob nail boogie / Blee blop blues / Basie talks / Paradise squat / Softly, with feeling / Beaver junction / Nails / Did you ever see jackie robinson hit that ball / Seventh avenue express / Mr. roberts' roost / Mad boogie / King / Mutton leg / Patience and fortitude / Wild bill's boogie / Stay cool / High tide / Jimmy's boogie woogie / Taps miller
CD 53094 / Apr '94 / Giants Of Jazz

☐ COUNT BASIE SWINGS - JOE WILLIAMS SINGS (Basie, Count & Joe Williams)
Everyday I have the blues / Comeback / Alright, OK you win / In the evening / Roll 'em Pete / Teach me tonight / My baby upsets me / Please send me someone to love / Ev'ry day (I fall in love) / As I love you / Stop, don't / Too close for comfort
5198522 / Dec '93 / Verve

☐ COUNT BASIE, ARTIE SHAW & TOMMY DORSEY (3CD Set) (Basie, Count/Artie Shaw/Tommy Dorsey)
MAK 102 / Dec '93 / Avid

☐ COUNT ON THE COAST VOL.1 (Basie, Count & Joe Williams)
PHONTCD 7555 / '88 / Phontastic

☐ COUNT ON THE COAST VOL.2
PHONTCD 7575 / Oct '92 / Phontastic

☐ CREAM OF COUNT BASIE VOL.1, THE
Oh lady be good / Panassie stomp / Blame it on my last affair / My heart belongs to daddy / Thursday / Jive at five / Sing for your supper / Smarty (you know it all) / Our love was meant to be / Let me dream / One o'clock jump / Honeysuckle rose / Dark rapture / Roseland shuffle / Fives / Boo-hoo / Boogie woogie / Glory of love / Cherokee / Dirty dozens / Stop beatin' around the Mulberry bush
PASTCD 9774 / Feb '92 / Flapper

☐ CREAM OF COUNT BASIE VOL.2, THE (Basie, Count Orchestra)
Clap hands, here comes Charlie / Riff interlude / I left my baby / Don't worry 'bout me / What goes up must come down / Pound cake / Lester leaps in / Dickie's dream / How long blues / Red wagon / Exactly like you / Pennies from heaven / Swinging at the Daisy Chain / Listen my children / Our love was meant to be / Now will you be good / Swingin' the blues / You can depend on me / Georgianna / Blues I like to hear / Oh Red / Good morning blues
PASTCD 9793 / Jun '92 / Flapper

☐ DO YOU WANNA JUMP
Georgianna / Sent for you yesterday / Panassie stomp / Blues I like to hear / Stop beatin' around the mulberry bush / Swingin' the blues / Texas shuffle / Shorty George / Blue in the dark / Every tub / Nor will you be good / Mama don't want no peas, no rice, no coconut oil / Blue and sentimental / Doggin' around / London Bridge is falling down / Jumpin' at the woodside / Dark rapture / Do you wanna jump children
HEPCD 1027 / Oct '89 / Hep

☐ ESSENTIAL COUNT BASIE VOL.1
Oh lady be good / Goin' to Chicago blues / Live and love tonight / Love me or leave me / Rock-a-bye Basie / Baby don't tell on me / If I could be with you one hour tonight / Taxi war dance / Jump for me / Twelfth street rag / Miss Thing (part 1) / Miss Thing (part 2) / Lonesome Miss Pretty / Nobody knows / Pound cake / How long blues
4600612 / Jan '95 / Sony Jazz

☐ ESSENTIAL COUNT BASIE, THE
Clap hands, here comes Charlie / Tickle toe / Broadway / Jump the blues away / It's sand man / Ain't it the truth / For the good of your country / High tide / Queer street / Rambo / Stay cool / Stay on it / Golden bullet / Song of the Islands / One o'clock jump / Tootsie
4671432 / Jul '93 / Columbia

☐ FAMOUS JAZZ SESSIONS
BN 005 / Apr '98 / Blue Nite

☐ FANCY PANTS (Basie, Count Orchestra)
Put it right there / By my side / Blue chip / Fancy pants / Hi five / Time stream / Samantha / Strike up the band
CD 2310920 / Apr '94 / Pablo

☐ FARMERS MARKET BARBEQUE
Way out Basie / St. Louis blues / Beaver Junction / Lester leaps in / Blues for the barbeque / I don't know yet / Ain't that something / Jumpin' at the Woodside
J33J 20056 / Apr '86 / Pablo

☐ FIVES 1936-1942, THE
How long blues / Bugle blues / Cafe society blues / Royal Garden blues / Sugar blues / Farewell blues / Way back blues / St. Louis blues / Boogie woogie / Dirty dozen / Fives / Oh Red / Hey lawdy Mama / Love me or leave me / Live and love tonight / I ain't got nobody / Shoe shine boy / Evenin' / Boogie woogie / Oh lady be good / Red wagon / Fare thee honey, fare thee well / Dupree blues / When the sun goes down
CD 53296 / Feb '97 / Giants Of Jazz

☐ FOR THE SECOND TIME (Basie, Count & Kansas City 3)
Sandman / If I could be with you one hour tonight / Draw / On the sunny side of the street / One I love (belongs to somebody else) / Blues for Eric / I surrender dear / Race horse
OJCCD 600 / Feb '92 / Original Jazz Classics

☐ FOUR TO A BAR (Basie, Count Orchestra)
Jive at five / Easy does it / Miss Thing / Love jumped out / If I could be with you one hour tonight / Between the devil and the deep blue sea / Don't worry 'bout me / You can depend on me / Clap hands, here comes Charlie / I left my baby / Swingin' the blues / Rock-a-bye Basie / Pound cake / Twelfth street rag / How long blues / Riff interlude / It's the same old south / One o'clock jump
PAR 2030 / Sep '94 / Parade

☐ FRANKLY BASIE (Count Basie Plays The Hits Of Frank Sinatra)
Second time around / Hey jealous lover / I'll never smile again / Saturday night is the loneliest night of the week / This love of mine / I thought about you / In the wee small hours of the morning / Come fly with me / On the road to Mandalay / Only the lonely / South of the border (Down Mexico way) / All of me / My kind of town (Chicago is) / Come rain or come shine / Hey jealous lover
5198492 / Mar '94 / Verve

☐ FUN TIME (Basie, Count Orchestra)
Fun time / Why not / Li'l darlin' / In a mellow tone / Body and soul / Good time blues / I hate you baby / Lonesome blues / Whirly bird / One o'clock jump
CD 2310945 / Apr '94 / Pablo

☐ GET TOGETHER
Ode to pres / Basies bag / Like it used to be / Swinging on the cusp / My main men / I can't get started (with you) / What will i tell my heart / Talk of the town / I can't give you anything but love / I'm confessin' that I love you
CD 2310924 / Apr '87 / Pablo

☐ GOLD COLLECTION, THE
D2CD 12 / Dec '92 / Deja Vu

☐ GOLDEN YEARS, THE (4CD Set)
Basie power / Meetin' / Blues in Hoss's flat / Why not / Good time blues / Festival blues / Splanky / More I see you / I needs to be bee'd with / Bookie blues / All of me / Shiny stockings / Basie / There will never be another you / Doubling blues / Baby Lawrence / Burning / Captain Bligh / Honeysuckle rose / Blues for Eric / I surrender dear / One o'clock jump / Memories of you / You got it / Ode to Pres / Honi coles / Opus six / Blues in C / Heat's on / Orange sherbert / Ticker / Swee' pea / Prime time / Corner pocket / Every tub / How sweet it is / CB express / Beaver junction / Way out Basie / Moten swing / Me and you / Time stream / Katy / Blues machine / I'm getting sentimental over you / My kind of trouble is you / Don't worry 'bout me / Lena and Lenny / Honeydripper / Blues around the clock / Flip, flop and fly / My jug and I / Cherry red / Wee baby / Blues for Joe Turner / Everyday I have the blues / Stormy Monday / I hate you baby / Lonesome blues / TV Momma / Corrine Corrina
4PACD 4419 / Feb '97 / Pablo

☐ I TOLD YOU SO
Tree frog / Flirt / Blues for Alfy / Something to live for / Plain brown wrapper / Sweet pea / Too close for comfort / Told you so / Git
OJCCD 824 / Jun '95 / Original Jazz Classics

☐ IN CONCERT (2CD Set) (Basie, Count Orchestra)
RTE 15042 / 7 Apr '98 / RTE/Europe 1

☐ INDISPENSABLE COUNT BASIE, THE
Bill's mill / Brand new wagon / One o'clock boogie / Futuile frustration / Swingin' the blues / St. Louis boogie / Basie's basement / Backstage at Stuff's / My buddy / Shine on harvest moon / Lopin' / I never knew / Sugar / Jungle king / I ain't mad at you / After you've gone / House rent boogie / South / Don't you want a man like me / Seventh Avenue express / Sophisticated swing / Guest in a nest / Your red wagon / Money is honey / Just a minute / Robbin's nest / Hey pretty baby / Bye bye baby / Just an old manuscript / She's a wine-o / Shoutin' blues / Wonderful thing / Mine too / Walking slow behind you / Normania / Rat race / Sweets
ND 89758 / Mar '94 / RCA

☐ INTRODUCTION TO COUNT BASIE 1936-1944, AN
4026 / Nov '95 / Best Of Jazz

☐ JAM SESSION AT MONTREUX 1975
Billie's bounce / Festival blues / Lester leaps in
CD 2310 750 / May '94 / Pablo
OJCCD 9332 / Nov '97 / Original Jazz Classics

☐ JAZZ GREATS
Bill's mill / One o'clock boogie / Brand new wagon: *Rushing, Jimmy Group* / Bye bye baby / After you've gone / Seventh Avenue express / If you see my baby / Mr. Roberts' roost / Just a minute / Shine on harvest moon / Hey pretty baby / Sweets sugar / Basie's basement / Swingin' the blues
74321499702 / 6 Oct '97 / RCA Victor

☐ JAZZ MASTERS
Big red / April in Paris / Two Franks / Shiny stockings / Royal Garden blues / Stereophonic / Blue and sentimental / Everyday / Paradise squat / Kansas City / Wrinkels / Midgets / KC organ blues / Every tub / Polka dots and moonbeams / Sent for you yesterday / One o'clock jump
5198192 / 5 May '98 / Verve

☐ JAZZ MASTERS
CDMFP 6296 / Mar '97 / Music For Pleasure

☐ JAZZ PORTRAITS (Basie, Count Orchestra)
Jumpin' at the woodside / One o'clock jump / Swingin' the blues / Tops / Every tub / Texas shuffle / Jive at five / Oh Lady be good / Twelfth street rag / Clap hands, here comes Charlie / Dickie's dream / Lester leaps in / Tickle toe / I never knew / Love jumped out / Super chief / Red bank boogie / Rhythm man
CD 14506 / May '94 / Jazz Portraits

☐ JAZZ PROFILE
Little tempo / Corner pocket / I needs to be be'd with / Segue in c / Back to the apple / Deacon / Easin' it / No moon at all / Everyday I have the blues / Whirly-bird / One o' clock jump
CDP 8332732 / 6 Oct '97 / Blue Note

☐ JIVE AT FIVE
Blame it on my last affair / Blue and sentimental / Cherokee / Honeysuckle rose / How long blues / Jive at five / John's idea / Jumpin' at the woodside / Oh lady be good / Moten swing / One o'clock jump / Panassie stomp / Roseland shuffle / Shoe shine boy / Swingin' at the daisy chain / Texas shuffle / Time out / You can depend on me
CDAJA 5089 / '92 / Living Era

☐ JUBILEE ALTERNATIVES (Basie, Count Orchestra)
Jumpin' at the woodside / I'm gonna move to the outskirts of town / I've found a new baby / Andy's blues / Avenue C / Basie's bag (Basie boogie) / More than you know / Let's jump / Harvard blues / One o'clock jump / Dinah / Baby, won't you please come home / Rock-a-bye Basie / Swing shift / Gee baby ain't I good to you / Beaver Junction / My what a fry
HEPCD 38 / Mar '90 / Hep

☐ JUMPIN' AT THE WOODSIDE (Basie, Count Orchestra)
Jumpin' at the woodside / One o'clock jump / Swingin' the blues / Topsy / Every tub / Texas shuffle / Jive at five / Oh lady be good / Twelfth street rag / Clap hands / Here comes Charley / Dickie's dream / Lester leaps in / Tickle toe / I never knew / Love jumped out / Super Chief / Red bank boogie / Rhythm man
CD 56015 / Aug '94 / Jazz Roots

☐ KANSAS CITY 6
Walking the blues / Blues for little jazz / Vegas drag / Wee baby / Scooter / St. Louis blues / Opus six
OJCCD 449 / Nov '95 / Original Jazz Classics

☐ KANSAS CITY 7
Jaylock / Exactly like you / I'll always be in love with you / If I could be with you for one hour tonight / Honi coles / Blues for Norman / Count me in
CD 2310908 / Nov '95 / Pablo

☐ KANSAS CITY SHOUT (Basie, Count/ Joe Turner/Eddie Vinson)
My jug and I / Cherry red / Apollo daze / Standing on the corner / Stormy Monday / Signifying / Just a dream on my mind / Blues for Joe Turner / Blues for Joel / Everyday I have the blues / Blues au four
CD 2310859 / May '94 / Pablo

☐ LIVE AT MANCHESTER CRAFTSMEN'S GUILD (Basie, Count Orchestra & New York Voices)
Down for the count / Whirly bird / Cotton tail / In a mellow tone / Basie / Please send me someone to love / Bug out / Love makes the world go round / Farmer's market / Basie power
JAZZMCG 1002 / Mar '97 / Blue Jackel

☐ LIVE AT THE EL MOROCCO (Basie, Count Orchestra)
Gone an' git it y'all / Night at El Morocco / Right on, right on / That's the kind of love I'm talking about / Corner pocket / Little Chicago fire / Shiny stockings / Angel eyes / Major Butts / Vignola express / Basie / One o'clock jump
CD 83312 / Jul '92 / Scorpio

☐ LIVE AT THE FAMOUS DOOR 1938
JH 3003 / Mar '97 / Jazz Hour

☐ LIVE IN JAPAN 1978
Heat's on / Freckle face / Ja da / Things ain't what they used to be / Bit of this and a bit of that / All of me / Shiny stockings / Left hand funk / John the III / Basie / Black velvet / Jumpin' at the Woodside
CD 2308246 / May '94 / Pablo

☐ LOOSE WALK (Basie, Count & Roy Eldridge)
Loose walk / In a mellow tone / Makin' whoopee / If I had you / I surrender dear / 5400 North
CD 2310928 / Aug '94 / Pablo

☐ **MAKIN' WHOOPEE**
Ain't misbehavin' / Makin' whoopee / Shake rattle and roll / One o'clock jump / Summertime / Lester leaps in young / Jumpin' at the Woodside / These foolish things / I got it bad and that ain't good / Dance of the gremlins / Two for T blues / Ska-di-de-dee-doo / Jazz me blues / Let's jump / Lullaby of Birdland / April in Paris
CDMT 026 / Oct '96 / Meteor

☐ **MASTERS OF JAZZ (2CD Set)**
R2CD 8002 / 13 Apr '98 / Deja Vu

☐ **ME AND YOU**
CD 2310891 / May '86 / Pablo

☐ **MOSTLY BLUES AND SOME OTHERS (Basie, Count & The Kansas City Seven)**
I'll always be in love with you / Snooky / Blues for Charlie Christian / Jaws / I'm confessin' that I love you / I want a little girl / Blues in C / Brio
CD 2310919 / Feb '87 / Pablo

☐ **ON THE ROAD (Basie, Count Orchestra)**
Wind machine / Blues for Stephanie / John the III / There'll never be another you / Bootie's blues / Splanky / Basie / Watch what happens / Work song / In a mellow tone
OJCCD 854 / Nov '95 / Original Jazz Classics

☐ **ON THE ROAD '79**
CD 31121 / May '86 / Pablo

☐ **ON THE WEST COAST 1958 (Basie, Count Orchestra & Joe Williams)**
NCD 8839 / Jul '96 / Phontastic

☐ **ONE O'CLOCK JUMP (Live) (Basie, Count Orchestra)**
Blues / Indian summer / Who, me / Jumpin' at the woodside / Baby all the time / Little pony / Ol' man river / One o'clock jump / Untitled
15797 / Jan '93 / Laserlight

☐ **ONE O'CLOCK JUMP**
Swingin' the blues / Oh lady be good / Topsy / One o'clock jump / Jumpin' at the woodside / Love jumped out / Dickie's dream / I never knew / Twelfth street rag / Lester leaps in / Super chief / Every tub / Tickle toe / Texas shuffle / Jive at five / Clap hands, here comes Charlie
HADCD 175 / May '94 / Javelin

☐ **PLATINUM COLLECTION, THE (40 Great Tracks/2CD Set) (Basie, Count & Tony Bennett)**
Chicago: *Bennett, Tony* / Jive at five: *Basie, Count* / Easy does it: *Basie, Count* / Miss thing: *Basie, Count* / Love jumped out: *Basie, Count* / I guess I'll have to change my plan: *Bennett, Tony* / If I could be with you one hour tonight: *Basie, Count* / Between the devil and the deep blue sea: *Basie, Count* / Don't worry 'bout me: *Basie, Count* / You can depend on me: *Basie, Count* / Jeepers creepers: *Bennett, Tony* / Clap hands here comes Charlie: *Basie, Count* / I left my baby: *Basie, Count* / Swinging the blues: *Basie, Count* / Rock-a-bye Basie: *Basie, Count* / With plenty of money and you: *Bennett, Tony* / Pound cake: *Basie, Count* / Twelfth Street rag: *Basie, Count* / How long blues: *Basie, Count* / I've grown accustomed to her face: *Bennett, Tony* / Poor little rich girl: *Bennett, Tony* / Riff interlude: *Basie, Count* / It's the same old South: *Basie, Count* / One o'clock jump: *Basie, Count* / Jumpin' at the Woodside: *Basie, Count* / Anything goes: *Bennett, Tony* / Lester leaps in: *Basie, Count* / Count steps in: *Basie, Count* / Bugle blues: *Basie, Count* / I want a little girl: *Basie, Count* / Are you havin' any fun: *Bennett, Tony* / Shout and feel it: *Basie, Count* / Basie's boogie: *Basie, Count* / Everyday I have the blues: *Basie, Count* / Goin' to Chicago: *Basie, Count* / Growing pains: *Bennett, Tony* / John's idea: *Basie, Count* / I'll always be in love with you: *Basie, Count* / Red bank boogie: *Basie, Count* / Life is a song: *Bennett, Tony*
PC 624 / 29 Jun '98 / Start

☐ **PORTRAIT OF COUNT BASIE, A (2CD Set)**
One o'clock jump / Topsy / Every tub / Swingin' the blues / Jumpin' at the Woodside / Texas shuffle / Boogie woogie / Fives / Oh Red / Red wagon / Jive at five / Oh lady be good / Goin' to Chicago blues / Rock-a-bye-Basie / Don't worry 'bout me / And the angels sing / If I didn't care / Twelfth Street rag / How long, how long blues / Clap hands here comes Charlie / Dickie's dream / Lester leaps in / I never knew / Let's make hey, while the sun shines / Louisiana / Blues (I still think of her) / Easy does it / Taxi wardance / Tickle toe / Somebody stole my gal / Gone with what wind / Super chief / Blow top / Moten swing / Evenin' / All or nothing at all / Draftin' blues / Moon fell in the river / What's your number / Broadway / Love jumped out / Fiesta in blue / All of me / Sugar blues / Rhythm man / Yeah man / Red bank boogie / That old feeling / Blue skies / Jivin' Joe Jackson
GALE 413 / 6 Oct '97 / Gallerie

☐ **QUINTESSENCE, THE (1937-1941/2CD Set)**
FA 202 / Oct '96 / Fremeaux

☐ **ROUND TRIP**
Ain't misbehavin' / Shake, rattle and roll / Jumpin' at the woodside / Makin' whoopee / Summertime / These foolish things / Lester leaps in / One o'clock jump / I got it bad and that ain't good / Ska-di-de-dee-doo / Two for the blues / Dance of the gremlins / Let's jump / Jazz me blues / April in Paris / Lullaby of Birdland
SUMCD 4045 / Nov '96 / Summit

☐ **SONNY LESTER COLLECTION**
CDC 9065 / Nov '93 / LRC

☐ **SOPHISTICATED SWING**
Sophisticated swing / Cheek to cheek / Hey pretty baby / Your red wagon / One o'clock boogie / Money is honey / Don't you want a man like me / Shoutin' blues / After you've gone / Jungle King South / Swinging the blues / Walking slowly behind you / Bye bye baby
74321451902 / Feb '97 / Camden

☐ **STRAIGHT AHEAD**
Straight ahead / It's oh so nice / Lonely Street / Fun time / Magic flea / Switch in time / Hay burner / That warm feeling / Queen Bee
GRP 18222 / 27 Jul '98 / Chess Mates

☐ **SWING MACHINE, THE (1937-1962) (Basie, Count Orchestra)**
One o'clock jump / Swingin' the blues / Topsy / Every tub / Boogie woogie / Dickie's dream / 12th Street rag / Red wagon / Oh lady be good / Jive at five / Fives / Texas shuffle / Clap hands, here comes Charlie / Oh red / Tickle toe / I never knew / Sugar blues / Love jumped out / Super chief / Lester leaps in / Red bank boogie / Rhythm man / Fiesta in blue / Yeah man / What am I here for / April in Paris / There's a small hotel / Hob nail boogie / Blee blop blues / Basie talks / Paradise squat / Softly, with feeling / Beaver Junction / Nails / Did you see Jackie Robinson hit that ball / Seventh Avenue express / Mr. Roberts' roost / Mad boogie / King / Mutton leg / Patience and fortitude / Wild Bill's boogie / Stay cool / High tide / Jimmy's boogie woogie / Taps miller / Jumpin' at the woodside / Moten swing / Blue and sentimental / Sent for you yesterday / Blues in hoss's flat / Who me / Little pony / Legend / Goin' to Chicago blues / One o'clock junp / Shorty George / Duet / Double O / Splanky / Miss Missouri / Meetin' time / Stompin and jumpin'
CDB 1210 / '92 / Giants Of Jazz

☐ **SWINGIN' MACHINE LIVE, THE (Basie, Count Orchestra)**
LEJAZZCD 17 / Jun '93 / Le Jazz

☐ **SWINGSATION**
Honeysuckle rose / Swinging at the Daisy chain / Roseland shuffle / Boogie woogie (I may be wrong) / One o' clock jump / John's idea / Time out / Topsy / Sent for you yesterday / Every tub / Swingin' the blues / Blue and sentimental / Doggin' around / Texas shuffle / Jumpin' at the woodside / Shorty George / Jive at five / Oh lady be good
GRP 99202 / 24 Aug '98 / GRP

☐ **THIS IS JAZZ**
One o'clock jump / Lester leaps in / 9:20 special / Oh lady be good / Goin' to Chicago blues / Red bank boogie / Dickie's dream / Miss thing / Tickle toe / How long blues / Broadway / Rock-a-bye Basie / Blow top / Let me see / Taxi war-dance / Moten swing / Jumpin' at the Woodside
CK 64966 / Oct '96 / Sony Jazz

☐ **TOPEKA, KANSAS 1955**
JASSCD 17 / '88 / Jass

☐ **YESSIR THAT'S MY BABY (Basie, Count & Oscar Peterson)**
Blues for Roy / Teach me tonight / Joe Turner blues / Blues for cat / Yes sir that's my baby / After you've gone / Tea for two / Poor butterfly
CD 2310923 / Dec '86 / Pablo

Basil, Toni

☐ **MICKEY (The Best Of Toni Basil)**
Mickey / Over my head / Street beat / Time after time / Spacewalkin' the dog / Do you wanna dance / Go for the burn / Nobody / You gotta problem / Space girls / Hanging around / Little in red book
301642 / Jun '97 / Hallmark

☐ **VERY BEST OF TONI BASIL, THE**
Mickey / Nobody / Hanging around / Time after time / Over my head / Do you wanna dance / Spacewalkin' the dog / Shopping A to Z / Space girls / You gotta problem / Little red book / Thief on the loose / Street beat / Go for the burn / Be stiff / Easy for you to say / Mickey
EMPRCD 752 / 8 Sep '97 / Emporio

Basin Brothers

☐ **LET'S GET CAJUN**
FF 539CD / Jul '92 / Flying Fish

Basin Street Six

☐ **COMPLETE CIRCLE RECORDINGS, THE**
BCD 103 / Aug '94 / GHB

Baskett, Larry

☐ **CHALICE (Baskett, Larry Trio)**
ESP / I've never been in love before / Estate / Born to be blue / Lament / Blue gardenia / Black Nile / Spring can really hang you up the most / Indian summer / Nancy with the laughing face
AL 73047 / Nov '96 / A

☐ **POOR BOY BLUE**
Beatrice / Haunted heart / Milestones / So in love / Theme for Denise / Poor boy blue / Northern lights / Child / Love letters / There's no you / Paradizer adieu / If you should leave me
AL 73086 / Jul '97 / A

Bass Communion

☐ **BASS COMMUNION**
STONE 036CD / 27 Apr '98 / 3rd Stone

Bass Dance

☐ **LOUD**
Caiou baby / Starbright / Brother man / Autotomic / Blue africans / Whar / Don't kick / Who's that girl
REVXD 161 / Oct '90 / FM

Bass, Fontella

☐ **NO WAYS TIRED**
Jesus, the light of the world / You don't know what the lord told me / No ways tired / Everlasting arms / What the world needs now / All my burdens / I surrender all / Lean on me / This place I call home / This little light of mine / I must tell jesus
7559793572 / Feb '95 / Nonesuch

☐ **RESCUED (The Best Of Fontella Bass)**
Rescue me / You'll never know / Don't you mess up a good thing / Soul of a man / You're gonna miss me / I surrender / Free at last / Baby what you want me to do / Joy of love / I can't rest / Oh no not my baby / Don't jump / Leave it in the hands of love
MCD 09335 / Apr '97 / Chess/MCA

Bass Junkie

☐ **IN BASS NO-ONE CAN HEAR YOU SCREAM**
BRK 9CD / 27 Apr '98 / Breakin'

Bass Odyssey

☐ **CLIPPING THE WINGS (OF THE IMAGINATION)**
Fifty Foot intro / Power of dub / Pythian / E-space / Brain machine / Monkey sanctuary / Patient 29 / Jonquil / Sebaceous overflow / Seraphim / PG Trips / Birth / Clipping the wings (Of the imagination) / End oddity
DIVINE 002CD / 7 Oct '97 / Taste/Divine

Bass X

☐ **HAPPY TO BE HARDCORE**
EVCD 6 / Jul '97 / Evolution

Bass-O-Matic

☐ **SET THE CONTROLS FOR THE HEART OF THE BASS**
In the realm of the senses / Set the controls for the heart of the bass / Fascinating rhythm / Rat cut a bottle / Love catalogue / Zombie mantra / Freaky angel / Wicked love / Ease on by / My tears have gone
CDVIP 188 / Apr '97 / Virgin VIP

Bassdrumbone

☐ **HENCE THE REASON**
Hence the real reason / For Don C / Fictionary / Sambali / Moto proto / Speak again brother / Disappearing afternoon / Lips apart / When zweeble walked by
ENJ 93222 / 27 Oct '97 / Enja

Bassett, Johnny

☐ **BASSETT HOUND**
Bassett hound / Walk my blues away / Ningyo mambo / Sweet potato pie / You little doll / Still can boogie / Years gone by / Mellow side / Pick up the pieces / Cold winter mourning / Bouncing with bassett
FCD 6004 / Jan '98 / Fedora

☐ **I GAVE MY LIFE TO THE BLUES**
I'll get over you / Mean feeling / Drink muddy water / Blowing the horn / I love a good woman (but I like the bad ones too) / If the shoe is on the other foot / Too hot to trot / They call me lucky / Weed head woman / Same ol' blues / Tired of waiting / Mercedes woman / Double dealing / I gave my life to the blues
BM 9034 / Dec '96 / Black Magic

Bassey, Shirley

☐ **20 GREAT LOVE SONGS**
I (who have nothing) / As long as he needs me / You'll never know / It could happen to you / More / House is not a home / In other words / Once in a lifetime / Moon river / Who can I turn to / Fools rush in / I'll get by / With these hands / There will never be another you / Memory / People / What kind of fool am I / No regrets / What now my love
LS 886352 / 2 Feb '98 / Disky

☐ **20 OF THE BEST**
As long as he needs me / You'll never know / Reach for the stars / Climb ev'ry mountain / I'll get by (as long as I have you) / Tonight / What now my love / What kind of fool am I / I (who have nothing) / My special dream / Gone / Goldfinger / No regrets / Big spender / Something / Fool on the hill / Where do I begin / For all we know / Diamonds are forever / Never never never
CDMFP 6252 / Aug '96 / Music For Pleasure

☐ **60TH ANNIVERSARY CONCERT, THE**
ARTFULCD 10 / 27 Apr '98 / Artful

☐ **ALL BY MYSELF**
All by myself / This masquerade / If and when / He's out of my life / New York state of mind / Can you read my mind / Only when I laugh / Solitaire / New York medley / We don't cry out loud / That's what friends are for / Sorry seems to be the hardest word / Greatest love of all / Dio come ti amo
MOCD 001 / Feb '95 / More Music

☐ **BASSEY - THE EMI/UA YEARS 1959-1979 (5CD Set)**
'S Wonderful / As long as he needs me / You'll never know / So in love / Reach for the stars / Who are we / I'll get by / Tonight / What now my love / Above all others / It could happen to you / It all depends on you / I who have nothing / Gone / How do you believe / Goldfinger / My child / Seesaw of dreams / It's yourself / Secrets / Stay on the island / Once in a lifetime / Liquidator / Mr. Kiss Kiss Bang Bang / Boy from Ipanema / More / House is not a home / Don't take the lovers from the world / Take away / I've got a song for you / Shirley / Give him your love / We were lovers / Who could love me / Do I look like a fool / Big spender / Dangerous game / La vita / I must know / This is my life / Without a word / If he walked into my life / To give / My love has two faces / Clown town / Does anybody miss me / I'll never fall in love again / (You are) My way of life / Bus that never comes / Fa fa fa (live for today) / Something / Spinning wheel / Yesterday I heard the rain / Sea and sand / What about today / You and I / Light my fire / Yesterday when I was young / Fool on the hill / Where do I begin / Till love touches your life / For the love of him / Vehicle / Diamonds are forever / Way a woman loves / For all we know / Greatest performance of my life / Lost and lonely / Way of love / Day by day / Ballad of the sad young men / If I should love again / Let me be the one / Never never never / Somehow / Going going gone / Make the world a little younger / Everything I own / All that went to waste / I'm not anyone / Jesse / Living / Natalie / If I never sing another song / Can't take my eyes off you / You take my heart away / Come in from the rain / Tomorrow morning / Razzle dazzle / You made me love you / My man / Nature boy / Greatest love of all / Moonraker / Just one of those things / Burn my candle (at both ends) / All the things you are / If I were a bell / Lovely way to spend the evening / Lot of livin' to do / No regrets / Typically English / Fly me to the moon / Please Mr. Brown / I'm a fool to want you / You / Johnny one note / I could have danced all night / Lovely way to spend an evening
BASSEY 1 / Nov '94 / Premier/EMI

☐ **BORN TO SING**
As I love you / Stormy weather / Love for sale / Birth of the blues / Hands across the sea / There's never been a night / Night and day / My funny valentine / Kiss me honey, honey kiss me / Gypsy in my soul / Crazy rhythm / How about you / Wayward wind / Born to sing the blues
5501852 / Mar '94 / Spectrum

☐ **CLASSIC TRACKS**
5143472 / Jan '94 / Phonogram

☐ **COLLECTION, THE**
Does anybody miss me / I'll never fall in love again / Never never no / Picture puzzle / I only miss him / As I love you / This is my life / Who am I / Funny girl / Sunny / I've been loved / Where is tomorrow / Think of me (You are) / My way of life / We / Give me you / It's always 4 am / Hold me, thrill me, kiss me / Now you want to be loved / Medley: Goin' out of my head/ You go to my head / Softly as I leave you / Time for us / Joker / I must know / You're gonna hear from me / If you go away / Burn my candle (at both ends) / Shadow of your smile / Kiss me honey, honey kiss me / Impossible dream / Johnny one note / Summer wind / Walking happy / Strangers in the night / Look for me tomorrow (I'll be gone) / Let me sing and I'm happy / On a clear day (you can see forever) / It must be him / All or nothing at all / Dangerous games / I'm glad there is you / That's life / (You are) My way of life / You can have him / Lady is a tramp / You and I / Big spender / Sweet charity
CDDL 1239 / Apr '93 / Music For Pleasure

☐ **DIAMONDS (The Best Of Shirley Bassey)**
Diamonds are forever / Something / Big spender / I who have nothing / For all we know / Where do I begin / Who can I turn to / Far away / Reach for the stars / Climb every mountain / Goldfinger / Never never never / If you go away / As long as he needs me / With these hands / What now my love / What kind of fool am I / I'll get by / You'll never know / This is my life
CDP 7904692 / May '88 / Premier/EMI

☐ **DIAMONDS ARE FOREVER**
Diamonds are forever / Killing me softly / Easy to love / If you go away / New york state of mind / Moon river / People / It's impossible / Can you read my mind / I get a kick out of you / We don't cry out loud / You are the sunshine of my life / Lady is a tramp / He's out of my life / Only when I laugh / Cry me a river / Moonraker / In other words (fly me to the moon) / Let there be love / Ev'ry time we say goodbye
PRS 23011 / Aug '93 / Personality

☐ **DIAMONDS ARE FOREVER (3CD Set)**
Diamonds are forever / Fly me to the moon / In other words / Nearness of you / You'll never know / Fool on the hill / Domage, domage(Too bad, too bad) / For all we know / Yesterday when I was young / Just one of those things / Fools rush in (Where angels fear to tread) / Moon river / Don't rain my parade / Sing / Send in the clowns / I don't know how to love him / Ave Maria / Killing me softly with his sing / Where do I begin (Love story) / Never never never / Party's over / Let there be love / Gone / As long as he needs me / Everything's coming up roses / Day by day / Easy to love / I've got you under my skin / Jesse / Somewhere / Ev'ry time we say goodbye / You'll never walk alone / I get a kick out of you / (I) who have nothing / No regrets / What now my love / Tonight / Something / Light my fire / With these hands / Feel like making love / Lady is a tramp / Alone again (naturally) / There will never be another you / People / On a wonderful day like today / Nobody does it like me / This is my life / Big spender
HR 883252 / Oct '97 / Disky

☐ **GOLDFINGER**
Goldfinger / Send in the clowns / I (who have nothing) / Climb ev'ry mountain / All by myself / On a wonderful day like today / Somewhere / Once in a lifetime / Shadow of your smile / This masquerade / And I love you so / Way we were / If and when / I've got you under my skin / As long as he needs me / New York, New York / Bridge over troubled water / Just one of those things / Solitaire / Party's over
PRS 23010 / Aug '93 / Personality

☐ **GREATEST HITS COLLECTION**
As I love you / Kiss me honey honey / What now my love / I (who have nothing) / Goldfinger / Big spender / Something / For all we know / Never never never / I am what I am / This is my life / All by myself / This masquerade / He's out of my life / Solitaire / I want to know what love is / Dio come ti amo / That's what friends are for / All I ask of you / Wind beneath my wings
ST 5006 / Nov '93 / Star Collection

☐ **HER GOLDEN VOICE**
DC 862012 / Mar '96 / Disky

☐ I AM WHAT I AM
Big spender / Goldfinger / Kiss me honey, honey kiss me / What now my love / Something / As long as he needs me / As I love you / Send in the clowns / I am what I am / I (who have nothing) / Natalie / And I love you so / Never never never / For all we know / This is my life / If you don't understand
ANT 003 / Nov '96 / Tring
100132 / May '97 / A-Play Collection

☐ I'M IN THE MOOD FOR LOVE
What now my love / Moon river / Fools rush in / No regrets / I wish you love / Liquidator / Nearness of you / This love of mine / Where are you / If love were all / There will never be another you / Days of wine and roses / People / Second time around / Tonight / Strange how love can be / I'm in the mood for love / I get a kick out of you / Angel eyes / To be loved by a man / Hold me tight / I believe in you / Let's start all over again / I'm a fool to want you
4932812 / 12 Jan '98 / EMI Gold

☐ LET ME SING AND I'M HAPPY
Send in the clowns / Don't cry for me Argentina / Can't help falling in love / Spinning wheel / That's life / Until it's time for you to go / On a clear day (You can see forever) / Something / Feel like makin' love / Shadow of your smile / Let me sing and I'm happy / Diamonds are forever / Alone again (naturally) / Killing me softly / Fool on the hill / Yesterday when I was young
CZ 98 / 3 Aug '98 / Music For Pleasure

☐ LIVE
Goldfinger / Where am I going / I Capricorn / Let me sing and I'm happy / Johnny One Note / For all we know / I'd like to hate myself in the morning / I who have nothing / Day by day / And I love you so / Diamonds are forever / Narration / Big spender / Never never never / You and I / Something / This is my life / Lovely way to spend an evening / Party's over / Lovely way to spend an evening / On a wonderful day like today / I get a kick out of you / Who can I turn to / You'd better love me / Other woman / He loves me / With these hands / Lot of livin' to do / I who have nothing / La Bamba / You can have him / Second time around / Lady is a tramp / Somewhere / Lovely way to spend an evening
CDDL 1221 / Apr '92 / Music For Pleasure

☐ LOVE ALBUM, THE
Something / What now my love / Where do I begin / Tonight / As long as he needs me / Time after time / As time goes by / With these hands / You'll never know / It must be him / Look of love / You made me love you / Softly as I leave you / I wish you love / Who can I turn to / Party's over / I'll never fall in love again / If you go away / I get a kick out of you / Nearness of you
CDMFP 5879 / Jan '92 / Music For Pleasure

☐ POWER OF LOVE, THE
3036400172 / May '97 / Carlton
CP 1007 / 6 Apr '98 / Rhino

☐ SHIRLEY
In the still of the night / Let there be love / All at once (deja) / For every man there's a woman / I'm in the mood for love / So in love / If I were a bell / There will never be another you / Hooray for love / Too late now / I'm shooting high / Every time we say goodbye
DORIG 101 / Jul '97 / EMI

☐ SHIRLEY BASSEY
Love is a many splendored thing / Nearness of you / Fools rush in / Who are we / Angel eyes / Till / Lovely way to spend an evening / This love of mine / You're nearer / Goodbye lover, hello friend / Where or when / Where are you / Climb ev'ry mountain
DORIG 100 / 1 Sep '97 / EMI

☐ SHIRLEY BASSEY - 40 GREAT SONGS
Goldfinger / Send in the clowns / I (who have nothing) / Climb ev'ry mountain / All by myself / On a wonderful day like today / Somewhere / Once in a lifetime / Shadow of your smile / This masquerade / And I love you so / Way we were / If and when / I've got you under my skin / As long as he needs me / New York, New York / Bridge over troubled water / Just one of those things / Solitaire / Party's over / Diamonds are forever / Killing me softly / Easy to love / If you go away / New york state of mind / Moon river / People / It's impossible / Can you read my mind / I get a kick out of you / We don't cry out loud / You are the sunshine of my life / Lady is a tramp / He's out of my life / Only when I laugh / Cry me a river / Moonraker / In other words (fly me to the moon) / Let there be love / Ev'ry time we say goodbye
DBP 102002 / Nov '93 / Double Platinum

☐ SHIRLEY BASSEY SINGS ANDREW LLOYD WEBBER
Memory / All I ask of you / Starlight Express / Last man in my life / Chanson d'enfance / I don't know how to love him / With one look / Macavity / Don't cry for me Argentina / Tell me on a Sunday / Wishing you were somehow here again / As if we never said goodbye / Memory reprise
CDDPR 114 / Nov '93 / Premier/MFP

☐ SHIRLEY BASSEY: THE SINGLES
Something / Where do I begin / Diamonds are forever / Fool on the hill / Make the world a little younger / Big spender / Never never never / When you smile / If you go away / And I love you so / Does anybody miss me / For all we know / Goldfinger / No regrets / I who have nothing / What kind of fool am I
CDMFP 6004 / Aug '88 / Music For Pleasure

☐ SHOW MUST GO ON, THE
Slave to the rhythm / You'll see / Every breath you take / Can I touch you there / I'll stand by you / When I need you / All woman / He kills everything / Where is the love / We've got tonight / One day I'll fly away / Hello / Baby come home to / Show must go on
5337122 / Oct '96 / PolyGram TV

☐ SINGS THE MOVIES
5293992 / Oct '95 / PolyGram TV

☐ SINGS THE MOVIES
Goldfinger / Where do I begin / Tonight / Big spender / Diamonds are forever / As long as he needs me / Lady is a tramp / As time goes by / You'll never walk alone / Climb every mountain / Moon river / Funny girl / Just one of those things / S'Wonderful / You'll never know / More / Liquidator / I don't know how to love him
CDMFP 6205 / Nov '95 / Music For Pleasure

☐ SOMETHING
Goldfinger / What now my love / Something / As long as he needs me / Kiss me honey honey kiss me / As I love you / Big spender / Send in the clowns / I am what I am / I (who have nothing) / Natalie / And I love you so / Never never never / For all we know / This is my life / If you don't understand
RMB 75079 / Apr '95 / Remember

☐ SOMETHING
Diamonds are forever / Something / Strange how love can be / This love of mine / There will never be another you / Hold me tight / Make the world a little younger / When you smile / Does anybody miss me / Fools rush in / People / It must be him / Party's over / Liquidator
16150 / Apr '96 / Laserlight

☐ SONGS FROM THE SHOWS
Moon river / People / Tonight / If love were all / Days of wine and roses / I believe in you / I've never been in love before / Far away / Lady is a tramp / Somewhere / It might as well be Spring / Don't rain on my parade / I get a kick out of you / Just one of those things / As long as he needs me / Where or when / 'S Wonderful / Everything's coming up roses / He loves me / Something wonderful / If ever I would leave you / You'll never walk alone
CC 272 / Oct '91 / Music For Pleasure

☐ THIS IS MY LIFE
What now my love / Something / As long as he needs me / Kiss me honey honey / As I love you / Big spender / Send in the clowns / I am what I am / Goldfinger / I (who have nothing) / Natalie / And I love you so / Never never never / For all we know / This is my life
MCCD 038 / Sep '91 / Music Club

☐ THIS IS SHIRLEY BASSEY
When you smile / Something / I get a kick out of you / Fly me to the moon / Sing / Lady is a tramp / Don't rain on my parade / Other side of me / I've got you under my skin / On a wonderful day like today / Somewhere / Lot of livin' to do / Once in a lifetime / Nobody does it like me / Goldfinger / As long as he needs me / Just one of those things / I who have nothing / Easy to love / Climb every mountain / Send in the clowns / Every time we say goodbye / Let there be love / What kind of fool am I / Everything's coming up roses / With these hands / Party's over / Tonight / Where do I begin / What now my love / No regrets / Big spender / Diamonds are forever
CDDL 1140 / Oct '88 / Music For Pleasure

☐ TOUCH OF CLASS, A
Something / As time goes by / With these hands / As long as he needs me / You'll never know / Party's over / Who can I turn to / I wish you love / Softly as I leave you / Tonight / What now my love / It must be him / I'll never fall in love again / If you go away / I get a kick out of you / Nearness of you / (Where do I begin) Love story / Look of love / You made me love you / Time after time
TC 865452 / 2 Feb '98 / Disky

Bassholes

☐ BLUE ROOTS
REV 204 / 17 Nov '97 / Revenant

☐ DEAF MIX VOL.3
ITR 49CD / Jun '97 / In The Red

☐ LONG WAY BLUES
Big carnival overture / Or was it just a dream / She shimmy wobble / Long way blues / Hail bop / Lightswitch / Cabooseman blues / Afrodite / Knocked out on my lawn / Joan Dark / Ass welt boogie / Angel of death / Turpentine
OLE 3052 / 8 Jun '98 / Matador

Bassline Generation

☐ JUNGLE EXPLORERS
EFA 127192 / Apr '95 / Mask

Basso, Jose

☐ CLAVELES BLANCO
BMT 015 / Jan '98 / Blue Moon

Bastaldua, Papi

☐ SONGS OF PARAGUAY
VICG 53412 / Mar '96 / JVC World Library

Bastard

☐ ZING BOOM
EFA 610542 / Mar '96 / Platten Meister

Bastards

☐ WORLD BURNS TO DEATH
LF 110CD / Nov '94 / Lost & Found

Bataan, Joe

☐ AFRO FILIPINO
Chico and the man / La bottle / X Rated symphony / Laughing and crying / Hey girl / When you're down / Women don't want to love me / Ordinary guy / What good is a castle
CDGR 185 / Sep '97 / Charly

☐ BEST OF JOE BATAAN, THE
CDGR 178 / Aug '97 / Charly

☐ SALSOUL
Mi nube / Muchacho ordinario / When sunny gets blue / Mujer mia / Fin / Latin strut / Johnny / Peace friendship and solidarity / Aftershow funk / Continental square dance
CDGR 184 / Sep '97 / Charly

Bates

☐ PSYCHO JUNIOR
SPV 08480702 / Apr '96 / SPV

Bates, Barney

☐ LADY LOVES THE BLUES, THE
AECD 3579 / Sep '97 / Animated Expressions

Bates, Django

☐ AUTUMN FIRES (Green Shoots)
Autumn leaves / Sweetie / Jetty / Ralf's trip / Is there anyone up there / Hollyhocks / Solitude / Loneliness of being right / Rat king / Dufy / Giant steps / Calm farm (for Paddy) / Infinity in a twinkling
5140142 / Mar '94 / jMT

☐ GOOD EVENING...HERE IS THE NEWS (Bates, Django & London Sinfonietta)
4520992 / May '96 / Argo

☐ LIKE LIFE
Tightrope / Once a penguin always a penguin / Loneliness of being right / Like life / New York New York / Misplaced swans / Strange voyage of Donald Crowhurst / Importance of boiling water / Peculiar terms of physical intimacy / Armchair march / Nights at the circus
STCD 4221 / Jun '98 / Storyville

☐ SUMMER FRUITS (And Unrest)
Tightrope / Armchair march / Food for plankton (in detail) / Sad Afrika / Three architects called Gabrielle/Just what I expected / Queen of puddings / Hyphen / Nights at the circus / Discovering metal / Little Petherick / March hare dance
5140082 / Jan '94 / jMT

Bates, Martyn

☐ IMAGINATION FEELS LIKE POISON
Mock sun / I can't look for you / Bones of your face / Years of salt / I forget you / God on the tree / Full sail / Flanaghan / Fully bright / Mystery seas / This wayward love / Fantacinni playground / Ellen Massey / Letters to a scattered family / Silvery images / No-one spoke / Mountain tomb
ASR 022 / Apr '97 / Ambivalent Scale

☐ LETTERS WRITTEN/RETURN OF THE QUIET
CDMRED 134 / Oct '96 / Cherry Red

☐ LOVE SMASHED ON A ROCK
IR 002CD / Jan '90 / Integrity

Bates, Phil

☐ NAKED
World's gone crazy / Port in a storm / Fine time / Ordinary man / Writing on the wall / Naked / My decline and fall / Celtic dawn / World without pain / Invisible again / Soul prelude/Secret place in my soul / Life in the slow lane / Don't wanna lie anymore / Showdown / Way the river flows
HYCD 297172 / 20 Oct '97 / Hypertension

Bathers

☐ KELVINGROVE BABY
MA 22 / Feb '97 / Marina

☐ LAGOON BLUES
MAMCD 33962 / Apr '94 / Marina

☐ SUNPOWDER
MA 12 / May '95 / Marina

Bathory

☐ BLOOD FIRE DEATH
Odens ride over Nordland / Golden wall of heaven / Pace 'til death / Dies irae / Fine day to die / Holocaust / For all those who died / Blood fire death
BMCD 6664 / Oct '94 / Black Mark

☐ HAMMERHEART
Baptised in fire and ice / Father to son / Song to haul up high / Home of the brave / One rode to asa bay / Shores in flames / Valhalla / Rider at the gates of dawn
BMCD 6665 / Oct '94 / Black Mark

☐ IN CONSPIRACY WITH SATAN (A Tribute To Bathory) (Various Artists)
NFR 029CD / 6 Jul '98 / No Fashion

☐ JUBILEUM VOL.1
Rider at the gate of dawn / Crawl to your cross / Sacrifice / Dies irae / Through blood by thunder / You don't move me (I don't give a fuck) / Odens ride over Nordland / Fine day to die / War / Enter the eternal fire / Song to hall up high / Sadist / Under the runes / Equimanthorn / Blood fire death
BMCD 6667 / Nov '92 / Black Mark

☐ JUBILEUM VOL.2
BMCD 66616 / 20 Jul '98 / Black Mark

☐ OCTAGON
BMCD 66611 / May '95 / Black Mark

☐ REQUIEM
BMCD 666 / Nov '94 / Black Mark

☐ RETURN, THE
Revelation of doom / Total destruction / Born for burning / Wind of mayhem / Bestial lust / Possessed / Rite of darkness / Reap of evil / Son of the damned / Sadist / Return of the darkness and evil
BMCD 6662 / May '92 / Black Mark

☐ TWILIGHT OF THE GODS
BMCD 6666 / '92 / Black Mark

Batimbos

☐ MAITRES-TAMBOURS DU BURUNDI
Arrivee et salut a l'assistance / Offrande / Appel / Suite de danses rituelles / Suite de danses et d'appels rituels
ARN 64016 / '87 / Arion

Batin, Abdul Zahir

☐ LIVE AT THE JAZZ CULTURAL
CJR 1029CD / Sep '95 / Cadence

Batiste, Alvin

☐ BAYOU MAGIC
IN 1069CD / Jan '97 / India Navigation

Batiste, Milton

☐ MILTON BATISTE
BCD 324 / Aug '94 / GHB

☐ MILTON BATISTE & RUE CONTI JAZZ BAND
LA 031CD / Jan '94 / Lake

Batmen

☐ WEIRD SCIENCE
SPYC 0001 / 27 Apr '98 / Aquarius

Batmobile

☐ BAIL IS SET AT SIX MILLION DOLLARS
Kiss me now / Magic word called love / Can't find my way back home / Mystery Street / Calamity man / Shoot shoot / Gorilla rock / Gates of heaven / Girls, girls, girls / Hang on / 100 pounds of trouble / Ace of spades
NERCD 035 / '90 / Nervous

Batoh, Masaki

☐ COLLECTED WORKS (Ghost From The Darkened Sea/Kikaokubeshi)
NS 011 / Feb '97 / Now Sound

Baton Rouge

☐ BATON ROUGE
Didn't I / Ghost of you / You can jump alone / Shelter / Victims of the night / Hands of time / Love by the numbers / Not in the mood for a heartache / I know better than you do / Love's a loaded gun / Love takes / Back under fire
199632 / Sep '97 / Made To Measure

Bators, Stiv

☐ DEAD BOYS, THE
642002 / May '94 / New Rose

☐ DISCONNECTED
BCD 4043 / Feb '94 / Bomp

☐ LAST RACE
BRCD 96129 / 20 Apr '98 / Bond Age

Bats

☐ FEAR OF GOD
R 2832 / Mar '92 / Rough Trade

Battalion Of Saints

☐ CUTS
TAANG 116CD / Sep '97 / Taang

☐ DEATH
TAANG 103CD / Sep '97 / Taang

☐ DEATH R US
T 103CD / Dec '96 / Taang

Batten, Jennifer

☐ MOMENTUM (Batten, Jennifer Tribal Rage)
MCR 0123 / Aug '97 / Mondo Congo

Battering Ram

☐ IRISH REBEL SONGS
Take it down from the mast / Sean South / Man from the Daily Mail / Dungannon '57 / General Munro / Swallow's tail reel/The Sligo maid / Henry Joy / Come out and fight / Wind that shakes the barley / Foggy dew / Who dares to say / Reels / British army / James Larkin / Broad black brimmer
EDCD 9012 / Jun '98 / Easydisc

Battery

☐ EP COLLECTION
LF 299CD / 27 Oct '97 / Lost & Found

☐ ONLY THE DIEHARD REMAIN
LF 089CD / May '94 / Lost & Found

☐ TILL THE END
LF 216CD / Mar '96 / Lost & Found

☐ WE WON'T FALL
LF 055 / Aug '93 / Lost & Found

☐ WHATEVER IT TAKES
REV 065CD / 16 Feb '98 / Revelation

Battiato, Franco

☐ SHADOW, LIGHT
L'ombra della luce / Messa arcaica - Kyrie, Gloria, Credo, Sanctus, Agnus Dei / Haiku / Povera patria / Ricerca sul Terzo / Sacre sinfonie del tiemp
CDHEMI 3 / Feb '96 / Hemisphere

Battlefield Band

☐ ACROSS THE BORDERS
Miss Sarah MacManus / Appropriate dipstick / Cafe Breton fiddlers welcome to Shetland / Tramps and hawkers / Snow on the hills / Xesus and Felisa / Concert reel / Green mountains / Arran convict / My home town / Kalabakan / Turieadh lain ruaidh / Trimdon grange explosion / Simon Thoumire's jig / Shake a leg / Ril gan ainm / Miss Kate Rusby / Green and the blue / Donnie McGregor / Clumsy lover / Woe be gone / Bubba's reel / Frank's reel / Six days on the road / In and out the harbour / Top tier / Sleepy maggie / Molly Rankin'
COMD 2065 / Jan '97 / Temple

☐ AFTER HOURS
After hours-the green gates-the ship in full sail / Frideray / A chance as good as any-reid's rant / Anthem / Dear green place / Look across the water-mrs garden of troup-the keelman ower / Green plaid / Mary cassidy / I am the common man / St. kilda girl's lament-the st. kilda wedding march / Lads o' the fair / Sauchiehall street salsa / Boar and the fox / Battle of waterloo-kilcoy's march-the quaker / Snows of france and holland / Bad moon rising-the rising moon reel
COMD 2001 / Feb '94 / Temple

☐ ANTHEM FOR THE COMMON MAN
Old changing way / Hook of holland-dominic macgowan / Snows of france and holland / Anthem / Yew tree / Port of call / Miners' wives / I am the common man / Mchugh's other foot-the man with two women (sauciehall str
COMD 2008 / Feb '94 / Temple

☐ AT THE FRONT
Lady Carmichael / South of the Grampians / Mickie Ainsworth / Bachelor / Ge do theid mi do m'leabradh / Battle of Harlaw / Jenny Nettles / Grays of tongside / Tae the beggin' / Tamosher / Blackbird and the thrush / Moray club / Lang Johnnie More / Brown milkmaid / Dunnottar castle / Maid of Glengarrysdale / Disused railways / Lady Leroy / Stirling castle / Earl of Mansfield
TP 56CD / Aug '94 / Temple

☐ BATTLEFIELD BAND
Silver spear / Humours of Tulla / Shipyard apprentice / Crossing the Minch / Minnie Hynd / Glasgow gaelic club / Brisk young lad / Birnie bouzie / Compliments of the band / AA Cameron's strathspey / Scott Skinner's compliments to Dr MacDonald / Bonnie Jean / Paddy Fahey's / Joseph's fancy / Hog's reel / It was a' for our rightful king / Inverness gathering / Marquis of Huntly's strathspey / John MacNeil's reel / Miss Margaret Brown's favourite / Deserts of Tulloch / Cruel brother
TP 55CD / Aug '94 / Temple

☐ CELTIC HOTEL
Conway's farewell / Andy Renwick's Ferrett / Short coated Mary / Seacoalers / Return To Kashmagiro / Cuddly with the wooden leg / Jack the can / Rovin' dies hard / Muineira sul sacrato della chiesa / Hyoy Frwynen / E kostez an hebont / Celtic Hotel / Left handed fiddler / Floating crowbar / Ships are sailing / Lucy Campbell / June apple / We work the black seam / Tail o' the bank / Cran Tara / Madadh Ruadh
COMD 2002 / Feb '94 / Temple

☐ FAREWELL TO NOVA SCOTIA
CD 802 / May '96 / Escalibur

☐ HOME GROUND
COMD 034 / Feb '94 / Temple

☐ HOME IS WHERE THE VAN IS
Major malley's march and reel-malcolm currie / Bonny barbry-o / Braw lads of galla water / Up and waur them a', willie / Boar and the fox / Blackhall rocks / Mary cassidy
COMD 2006 / Feb '94 / Temple

☐ LIVE CELTIC FOLK MUSIC
Medley / Gallant Grahams / Medley / Blackhall rocks / Athole Highlanders / Medley / Lads o' the fair / Medley / Medley
MRCD 188 / Feb '98 / Munich

☐ NEW SPRING
Green and the blue / Seann bhriogais aig uilleam-lady margaret stewart / Working away-the toastie jig / Darien / Devil uisge beatha / Farewell to ravenscraig- my night out with big iain / I feel like going home
COMD 2045 / Feb '94 / Temple

☐ ON THE RISE
John mackenzie's fancy-the train jouney north / Montrose / She's late but she's timely / Bad moon rising-the rising moon reel / Dear green place / Island earth no more-flight of the eaglets
COMD 2009 / Feb '94 / Temple

☐ OPENING MOVES
Silver spear/Humours of Tulla / Shipyard apprentice / Cruel brother / Ge do theid mi do m'leabradh / Battle of Harlaw / Jenny Nettles/Grays of tongside / Tae the beggin / Tamosher / Blackbird and the thrush/Moray club / Lang Johnnie More / Brown milkmaid/Dunnottar castle / Maid of Glengarrysdale / Disused railway / Lady Leroy / Miss Drummond of Perth/Fiddler's joy / Traditional reel/Shetland fiddler / My last farewell to stirling/Cuidich'n right / I hae laid a herrin' in salt/My wife's a wanton wee thing / Banks of the allan / Battler of Falkirk Muir / Joe McGann's fiddle/Centre's bonnet
TSCD 468 / Sep '93 / Topic

☐ QUIET DAYS
River / Dalnabreac-the bishop's son-miss sharon mccusker / Captain campbell-stranger at the gate-john keith laing / Hold back the tide / Curstaidh's farewell / Hoodie craw / Colonel maclean of ardgour-pipe major jimmy macgregor-rocki / How will I ever be simple again-dawn song
COMD 2050 / Feb '94 / Temple

☐ RAIN HAIL OR SHINE
Bodachan a gharaidh/General MacDonald/Craig an fhithich / Heave ya ho / Magaret Ann/Manor park/ Trip to the Bronx / Jenny o'the braes / Magheracloone/Norland wind/Gardez loo/Donald Maclean / Beaches of St.Valery / Wee Michael's march/Oot b'est da vong / Lass o'Glencoe / Canongate twitch/Steamboat to Detroit/Twenty pounds of gin/B
COMD 2074 / Apr '98 / Temple

☐ STAND EASY/PREVIEW
COMD 2052 / Feb '94 / Temple

☐ THERE'S A BUZZ
Shining clear / Sir sidney smith's march / A chance as good as any-reid's rant / Lord haddo's favourite / One miner's life-the image of god / Green plaid
COMD 2007 / Feb '94 / Temple

Batucada

☐ ESPECIAL FUTEBOL
IRS 800 / Jan '98 / IMP

Bauer, Konrad

☐ THREE WHEELS FOUR DIRECTIONS (Bauer, Konrad Trio)
VICTOCD 023 / Nov '94 / Victo

☐ TORONTO TONE
VICTOCD 017 / Nov '94 / Victo

Bauer, Uschi

☐ YODEL HITS FROM USCHI BAUER
399382 / Sep '92 / Koch

Bauge, Andre

☐ L'INOUBLIABLE
La rose rouge / J'ai toujours cru qu'un basier / Heure exquise / La valse improvisee / Qui, c'est une valse de vienne / O ma rose-marie / Marche de nina rosa / Ah combien perfides sont les femmes / On croit toujours aux mots d'amour / Partir c'est mourir un peu / Dans une ronde eternelle / Lorsque dans ton berceau tout blanc / Plaisir d'amour / L'anneau d'argent / Les vieilles de chez nous / J'ai fait trois fois le tour du monde / Vive la paresse / Les envoyes du paradis / Duo politique / Dans le sommeli / Le barbier de seville (air de figaro)
UCD 19022 / Jun '95 / Forlane

Bauhaus

☐ BELA (A Tribute To Bauhaus) (Various Artists)
DOP 51 / 1 Jun '98 / Doppelganger

☐ BURNING FROM THE INSIDE
She's in parties / Antonin artaud / Wasp / King volcano / Who killed Mr. Moonlight / Slice of life / Honeymoon croon / Kingdom's coming / Burning from the inside / Hope / Lagartija Nick / Here's the dub / Departure / Sanity assassin
BBL 45 CD / Sep '88 / Beggars Banquet

☐ CRACKLE
BEGL 2018CD / 17 Aug '98 / Beggars Banquet

☐ IN THE FLAT FIELD
Dark entries / Double dare / In the flat field / God in an alcove / Dive / Spy in the cab / Small talk stinks / St. Vitus dance / Stigmata martyr / Nerves / Telegram Sam / Rose garden funeral of sores / Terror couple kill colonel / Scopes / Untitled
GAD 013CD / 6 Jul '98 / 4AD

☐ MASK
Hair of the dog / Passion of lovers / Of lilies and remains / Hollow hills / Dancing / Kick in the eye / Muscle in plastic / In fear of fear / Man with the X-ray eyes / Mask
BBL 29CD / Oct '88 / Beggars Banquet

☐ PRESS THE EJECT AND GIVE ME THE TAPE
In the flat field / Rosegarden funeral of sores / Dancing / Man with the X-ray eyes / Bela Lugosi's dead / Spy in the cab / Kick in the eye / In fear of fear / Hollow hills / Stigmata martyr / Dark entries
BBL 38CD / '89 / Beggars Banquet

☐ SINGLES 1981-1983
Passion of lovers / Kick in the eye / Spirit / Ziggy Stardust / Lagartija Nick / She's in parties
BBP 4CD / Dec '88 / Beggars Banquet

☐ TRIBUTE TO BAUHAUS (Various Artists)
CLEO 9681CD / Mar '96 / Cleopatra

Bauls Of Bengal

☐ MAN OF HEART, A (Music From India)
ARNR 0596 / Sep '97 / Amiata

Baumann, Agnenta

☐ TIME FOR LOVE, A
TMCD 006 / May '97 / Touche

Baumann, Peter

☐ PHASE BY PHASE
Repeat repeat / Daytime logic / This day / Meridian moorland / Meadow of infinity (Part 1) / Meadow of infinity (part 2) / Romance / Home sweet home / MAN Series two / Bicentennial presentation / Phase by phase / White bench and black bench / Biking up the strand / Dance at dawn
CDOVD 464 / Jan '96 / Virgin

Bauza, Mario

☐ 944 COLUMBUS (Bauza, Mario & His Afro-Cuban Jazz Orchestra)
MES 158282 / Apr '94 / Messidor

☐ MY TIME IS NOW (Bauza, Mario & His Afro-Cuban Jazz Orchestra)
MES 158252 / Jun '93 / Messidor

☐ TANGA
MES 158192 / Apr '96 / Messidor

Bavarian Oktoberfest Band

☐ MUSIC OF OKTOBERFEST
1509589162 / 27 Apr '98 / Intersound

Bawl

☐ YEAR ZERO
Approaching zero / Older and older / My spine hurts / Beyond safe ways / Mistake / Shallow / Sticky rock / Fake it / Ex-boyfriend / Mechanic from Rhyll / Girls=songs / Unfinished / Some people need others / He's all that's great about pop
DEPAD 005 / Sep '96 / Dependent

Baxter, Blake

☐ H FACTOR, THE
EFA 122952 / Jun '97 / Disko B

☐ VAULT, THE
EFA 122762 / Oct '95 / Tresor

Baxter, Bruce

☐ GUITAR ALBUM, THE (Baxter, Bruce Orchestra)
New kid in town / Summer of my life / Mississippi / Isn't she lovely / Stand by your man / Fernando / Hey Baby / Fallen angel / Save your kisses for me / Tie a yellow ribbon round the old oak tree / Don't give up on us / You just might see me cry / Don't cry for me Argentina / Solitaire / (Do the) Spanish Hustle / Little bit more / Alone again (naturally) / I love to love / You'll never find another love like mine / Yesterday / Let it be / Summer of '42 / Sailing
306832 / Aug '97 / Hallmark

Baxter, Les

☐ BY POPULAR REQUEST
BA 0014 / Dec '96 / Bacchus Archives

☐ COLOURS OF BRAZIL/AFRICAN BLUE
Felicidade / Canta de ossanha / Balan samba / Day of the roses / Man and a woman / Who will buy / Somewhere in the hills / Goin' out of my head / Tristeza / Berimbau / Laia ladaia / Banda / Born free / Yellow sun / Flame tree / Zebra / Dark river / Topaz / Tree of life / Girl of Uganda / Magenta mountain / Johannesburg blues / Jalaba / Azure sands Kalahari
GNPD 2036 / Oct '95 / GNP Crescendo

☐ QUE MANGO
SCP 9718 / Nov '97 / Scamp

Baxter, Phil

☐ HOT AND RARE
DCP 203D / Jul '98 / Diamond Cut

Bay B Kane

☐ GUARDIAN OF RUFF, THE
WHSCD 1 / Jan '95 / Whitehouse

☐ HAVE A BREAK
WHSCD 3 / Nov '95 / Whitehouse

Bay City Rollers

☐ ABSOLUTE ROLLERS
(Dancing) on a Saturday night / Shang-a-lang / Remember (sha la la) / Bye bye baby / I only want to be with you / All of me love all of you / Give a little love / Summer love sensation / Rebel rebel / Money honey / Keep on dancing / Love me like I love you / Once upon a star / Be my baby / You made me believe in magic / Way I feel tonight / Another rainy day in New York City / It's a game / There goes my baby / Rock 'n' roll love letter / Bay City Rollers megamix
74321265752 / Aug '95 / Arista

☐ BAY CITY ROLLERS
I only want to be with you / Give a little love / Dance dance dance / Saturday night / Back on the street / Shang-a-lang / You made me believe in magic / Rebel rebel / Be my baby / It's a game / Money honey / Let's pretend / Another rainy day in new york city / Strangers in the wind / Way I feel tonight / Marlena
295588 / Dec '92 / Ariola Express

☐ BYE BYE BABY
Keep on dancing / Remember / Shang a lang / Summerlove sensation / Bye bye baby / Give a little love / Money honey / Love me like I love you / I only wanna be with you / You made me believe in magic / Rock 'n' roll love letter
QED 106 / Nov '96 / Tring

☐ GREATEST HITS
JHD 025 / Jun '92 / Tring

☐ GREATEST HITS
Remember (sha la la) / Give a little love / Shang a lang / Yesterday's hero / I only wanna be with you / Summerlove sensation / Bye bye baby / It's a game / Saturday night / Rock 'n' roll love letter / You made me believe in magic
RM 1551 / Apr '97 / BR Music

☐ SHANG-A-LANG
I only want to be with you / Give a little love / Dance dance dance / Saturday night / Back on the street / Shang-a-lang / You made me believe in magic / Rebel rebel / Be my baby / It's a game / Money honey / Let's pretend / Another rainy day in New York City / Strangers in the wind / Way I feel tonight / Marlena
743215696025 / 23 Mar '98 / Camden

☐ VERY BEST OF THE BAY CITY ROLLERS, THE
Remember (sha la la la) / Give a little love / Shang-a-lang / Yesterday's hero / I only wanna be with you / Summer love sensation / Bye bye baby / It's a crime / Saturday night / Rock 'n' roll letter / You made me believe in magic / Megamix
100602 / May '97 / A-Play Collection

☐ VERY BEST OF THE BAY CITY ROLLERS, THE
Shang-a-lang / Bye bye baby / Remember (sha la la) / Saturday night / I only wanna be with you / Give a little love / Rock 'n' roll love letter / It's a game / You made me believe in magic / MONEY / Summerlove sensation / Yesterday's hero / Dedication / Holding on / Heart's on fire / Be my baby / Mega-mix / Give a little love
309062 / 13 Jul '98 / Hallmark

Bay Laurel

☐ BITTER INTOXINS
NOX 009CD / 16 Mar '98 / Noxious

☐ UNDER A CLOUDED SKY
NOX 003CD / May '95 / Noxious

Bayer Sager, Carole

☐ CAROLE BAYER SAGER
Come in from the rain / Until the next time / Don't wish too hard / Sweet alibis / Aces / I'd rather leave while I'm in love / Steal away again / You're moving out today / Shy as a violet / Home to myself
7559606172 / Jan '96 / Elektra

Bayete

☐ AFRICA UNITE
Mmalo-we / Africa unite / Amasoka / Ungayingeni / Mmangwane / Inkinobho / Umkhaya-lo / Umbugwala / Amadlozi / Jabula time
CIDM 1119 / Mar '97 / Mango

Baylor, Helen

☐ LOOK A LITTLE
DAYCD 4215 / May '93 / Word

Bayou Gumbo

☐ BALD ON THE BAYOU
BEANDOG 47CD / May '93 / Beandog

Bazooka

☐ BLOWHOLE
SST 308CD / Oct '94 / SST

☐ CIGARS, OYSTERS AND BOOZE
SST 325CD / Jan '96 / SST

☐ PERFECTLY SQUARE
SST 296CD / May '93 / SST

☐ SONIC BUSINESS ENVIROMENT
Homemade money / Snakes alive / Calling all kittens / Big big dinner / So much for gladhand / Casual day / Fishing returns / On the lam / USS Meltdown / Later
SST 356CD / 20 Oct '97 / SST

Bazzle, Germaine

☐ NEW NEW ORLEANS MUSIC VOL.3 (Bazzle, Germaine & Friends)
ROUCD 2067 / '88 / Rounder

BB & The Blues Shacks

☐ FEELIN' FINE TODAY
CDST 01 / Nov '95 / Stumble

BBC Big Band

☐ AGE OF SWING VOL.1, THE
Begin the beguine / Let's dance / Cherokee / American patrol / Very thought of you / Little brown jug / I'm getting sentimental over you / You made me love you / Moonlight sonata / Chattanooga choo choo / St. Louis blues / Mood indigo / Sweet Georgia Brown / I get a kick out of you / 'S wonderful / After you've gone / On the sunny side of the street / Take the 'A' train / Swannee river / Sophisticated lady
EMPRBX 003 / Sep '94 / Empress

☐ AGE OF SWING VOL.2, THE
Moonlight sonata / South Rampart Street Parade / King Porter stomp / Little brown jug / Solitude / Eager beaver / Serenade in blue / I know why / On the Alamo / Hornet / Listen to my music / Wrappin' it up the lindy / Chattanooga choo choo / Caravan / Apple honey / I'm getting sentimental over you / Harlem nocturne / Leave us leap / You made me love you / Boogie woogie Maxine
EMPRCD 534 / Sep '94 / Emporio

☐ AGE OF SWING VOL.3, THE
Down south camp meeting / Don't be that way / Anvil chorus / St. Louis blues march / Mood indigo / Intermission riff / Jersey bounce / Hot toddy / 'S wonderful / Oh lady be good / Chloe / Leap frog / Pennsylvania 6-5000 / Opus no.1 / I got it bad and that ain't good / String of pearls / Sweet Georgia Brown / I'll never smile again / Stardreams / I get a kick out of you / Long John Silver
EMPRCD 535 / Sep '94 / Emporio

☐ AGE OF SWING VOL.4, THE
Moonlight serenade / After you've gone / Pompton turnpike / On the sunny side of the street / Do nothin' 'til you hear from me / At last / Flying home / Cotton tail / Body soul / Painted rhythm / Tuxedo junction / Take the 'A' train / Swanee river / Don't sit under the apple tree / Sophisticated lady / Swingin' the blues / Memories of you / I can't get started / Poor Butterfly / Song of the Volga boatmen / Woodchoppers ball
EMPRCD 536 / Sep '94 / Emporio

☐ AGE OF SWING, THE
In the mood / Very thought of you / Let's dance / American patrol / Artistry in rhythm / Begin the beguine / Big john special / Skyliner / What is this thing called love / Hamp's boogie woogie / I've got a gal in kalamazoo / Cherokee / Opus in pastels / Boogie woogie / Snowfall / One o'clock jump / Song of india / Perdido / Sing, sing, sing
EMPRCD 507 / Apr '94 / Emporio

☐ BBC BIG BAND
Don't count / Song of the Volga boatmen / Street scene / King Porter stomp / Camptown races / Ol' man river / Herman's habit / Crescendo in blue / Alfresco / Say it isn't so / Opus in pastel / Magic time
RBBCD 001 / Feb '95 / Radio Big Band

☐ SHOWSTOPPERS
Battle royal / Fanfare / Porgy and bess suite / Sing sing sing / Threshold / Bugle call rag / Concerto for clarinet / Embraceable you / West side story suite
BBB 004 / Nov '96 / BBC Big Band

BBC Concert Orchestra

☐ LOVE AND ROMANCE (Great Love Songs)
Waltzing with love / Love is meant to make us glad / I've never been in love before / I won't send roses / Portrait of a flirt / I don't know how to love him / Love is the sweetest thing / Clair de lune / Love is here to stay / Secret love / Charlie girl / St. Valentine's day chorus / West side story medley
10722 / Oct '97 / BBC Concert Orchestra

BBE

☐ EARLY WORKS
ZYX 204342 / May '97 / ZYX

☐ GAMES
Tales of history / New romantic / Symphonic paradise / Bar / Audience and the bird / Le grande theme / Seven days and one week / Univeral flash / Flash / First level / Cosmos / Desire / Aquatic nebular / Freetime / Le noveau monde / Rock in the sky / Second level / Exit
4934932 / 2 Feb '98 / Positiva

BBM

☐ AROUND THE NEXT DREAM
Waiting in the wings / City of gold / Where in the world / Can't fool the blues / High cost of living / Glory days / Why does love (Have to go wrong) / Naked flame / I wonder (Why are you so mean to me) / Wrong side of town
CDV 2745 / Jun '94 / Virgin

BC Kid

☐ STOP THOSE MF'S
EFA 008772 / Jun '96 / Shockwave

BDF

☐ SUSTRAIDUM ROOTS DUB
MSR 001 / 9 Feb '98 / Massive Sounds

Be Bops

☐ LET'S KEEP THINGS MOVIN'
PT 622003 / Oct '97 / Part

Be Sharp

☐ NIGHT BY NIGHT
RMCCD 0186 / Aug '96 / Red Steel

☐ PIER PRESSURE
RMCCD 0184 / Sep '96 / Red Steel

☐ PLAY THIS
RMCCD 0185 / Aug '96 / Red Steel

Be-Bop Deluxe

☐ AIR AGE (Be-Bop Deluxe Anthology/ 2CD Set)
Axe victim / Love with the madman / Sister seagull / Heavenly homes / Ships in the night / Twilight capers / Kiss of light / Crying to the sky / Sleep that burns / Life in the air age / Electrical language / Panic in the world / Maid in heaven / Between the worlds / Blazing apostles / Lovers are mortal / Down on terminal street / Darkness (l'immoraliste) / Adventures in a Yorkshire landscape / Night creatures / Music in dreamland / Jean Cocteau / Beauty secrets / Life in the air age / Speed of the wind / Modern music / Dancing in the moonlight / Honeymoon on mars / Lost in the neon world / Dance of the Uncle Sam humanoids / Modern music (reprise) / Fair exchange / Autosexual / New mysteries / Surreal estate / Islands of the dead / Visions of endless hopes / Bird charmers destiny / Gold at the end of my rainbow
CDEM 1602 / Feb '97 / Premier/EMI

☐ AXE VICTIM
Axe victim / Love is swift arrows / Jet silver and the dolls of venus / Third floor heaven / Night creature / Rocket cathedrals / Adventures in a Yorkshire landscape / Jets at dawn / No trains to heaven / Darkness (L'immoraliste) / Piece of mine (live) / Mill Street junction / Adventures in a Yorkshire landscape (live)
CDP 7947262 / Feb '91 / Premier/EMI

☐ DRASTIC PLASTIC
Electrical language / New precision / New mysteries / Surreal estate / Love in flames / Panic in the world / Dangerous stranger / Superenigmatix / Visions of endless hopes / Possession / Islands of the dead / Blimps / Lovers are mortal / Lights
7947332 / 1 Jun '98 / EMI

☐ FUTURAMA
Stage whispers / Love with the madman / Maid in heaven / Sister seagull / Sound track / Music in dreamland / Jean Cocteau / Between the worlds / Swansong / Between the worlds (single version) / Maid in heaven (live) / Speed of the wind
7920742 / 1 Jun '98 / EMI

☐ LIVE - IN THE AIR-AGE
Life in the air age / Ships in the night / Piece of mind / Fair exchange / Mill Street junction / Adventures in a Yorkshire landscape / Blazing apostles / Shine / Sister seagull / Maid in heaven
CDP 7947322 / Feb '91 / Premier/EMI

☐ MODERN MUSIC
Orphans of Babylon / Twilight capers / Kiss of light / Bird charmer's destiny / Gold at the end of my rainbow / Bring back the spark / Modern music / Dancing in the moonlight / Honeymoon on Mars / Lost in the neon world / Dance of the Uncle Sam humanoids / Modern music (reprise) / Forbidden lovers / Down on terminal street / Make the music magic / Futurist manifesto / Quest for the harvest of the stars / Autosexual
7947312 / 1 Jun '98 / EMI

☐ RAIDING THE DIVINE ARCHIVES (Best Of Be-Bop Deluxe)
Jet Silver and the Dolls of Venus / Adventures in a Yorkshire landscape / Maid in Heaven / Ships in the night / Life in the air age / Kiss of light / Sister Seagull / Modern music / Japan / Panic in the world / Bring back the spark / Forbidden lovers / Electrical Language / Fair exchange / Sleep that burns / Between the worlds / Music in dreamland
CDP 7941582 / Apr '90 / Premier/EMI

☐ SUNBURST FINISH
Fair exchange / Heavenly homes / Ships in the night / Crying to the sky / Sleep that burns / Beauty secrets / Life in the air age / Like an old blues / Crystal gazing / Blazing apostles / Shine / Speed of the wind / Blue as a jewel
CDP 7947272 / Feb '91 / Premier/EMI

☐ TRAMCAR TO TOMORROW
HUX 009 / 31 Aug '98 / Hux

☐ VERY BEST OF BE-BOP DELUXE, THE
9043127182 / 7 Apr '98 / Collectables

Beach Boys

☐ 20 GOLDEN GREATS: BEACH BOYS
Surfin' USA / Fun, fun, fun / I get around / Don't worry baby / Little deuce coupe / When I grow up (to be a man) / Help me Rhonda / California girls / Barbara Ann / Sloop John B / You're so good to me / God only knows / Wouldn't it be nice / Good vibrations / Then I kissed her / Heroes and villains / Darlin' / Do it again / I can hear music / I break away
CDP 7467382 / Nov '87 / Capitol

☐ 20 GREAT LOVE SONGS
Good vibrations / Then I kissed her / God only knows / Darlin' / Help me Rhonda / All summer long / Wendy / Don't worry baby / You're so good to me / Why do fools fall in love / I can hear music / Wouldn't it be nice / Surfer girl / Devoted to you / I'm so young / There's no other (like my baby) / She knows me too well / Good to my baby / Please let me wonder / I was made to love her
LS 863072 / 2 Feb '98 / Disky

☐ ALL SUMMER LONG
Good vibrations / Help me Rhonda / Surfin' USA / California girls / I get around / Surfin' safari / Surfer girl / Catch a wave / Warmth of the sun / Be true to your school / Little deuce coupe / In my room / Shut down fun, fun, fun / Girls on the beach / Wendy / Let him run wild / Don't worry baby / Girl don't tell me / You're so good to me / All summer long
DC 878682 / Mar '97 / Disky

☐ BEACH BOYS TODAY/SUMMER DAYS AND SUMMER NIGHTS
Do you wanna dance / Don't hurt my little sister / Help me Rhonda / Please let me wonder / Kiss me baby / In the back of my mind / Girl from New York City / Then I kissed her / Girl don't tell me / Let him run wild / Summer means new love / And your dreams come true / I'm so young (alt. take) / Graduation day / Good to my baby / When I grow up (to be a man) / Dance, dance, dance / I'm so young / She knows me too well / Bull session with Big Daddy / Amusement Parks USA / Salt Lake City / California girls / You're so good to me / I'm bugged at my ole man / Little girl I once knew / Let him run wild (alternate take) / Help me Rhonda (LP version) / Dance, dance, dance (alt. take)
CDP 7936942 / Jul '90 / Capitol

☐ BEACH BOYS/JAN & DEAN (Beach Boys/Jan & Dean)
CD 115 / Oct '94 / Timeless Treasures

☐ BEST OF THE BEACH BOYS, THE (2CD Set)
California girls / Surfin' USA / Little deuce coupe / Fun, fun, fun / Surfer girl / I get around / Girls on the beach / Don't worry baby / When I grow up (to be a man) / All summer long / Wendy / Do you wanna dance / Dance, dance, dance / In my room / Help me Rhonda / Then I kissed her / Little girl I once knew / Barbara Ann / Sloop John B / You're so good to me / Caroline no / God only knows / Wouldn't it be nice / Heroes and villains / Good vibrations / Darlin' / Wild honey / Friends / Do it again / Blue birds over the mountain / I can hear music / Break away / Cotton fields / Forever / Tears in the morning / Disney girls / Surf's up / Sail on sailor / Rock 'n' roll music / Here comes the night / Lady Lynda / Sumahama / California dreamin' / Kokomo
CDESTVD 3 / Jun '95 / Capitol

☐ CHRISTMAS ALBUM
Little Saint Nick / Man with all the toys / Santa's beard / Merry Christmas baby / Christmas day / Frosty the snowman / We three kings of Orient are / Blue Christmas / Santa Claus is coming to town / White Christmas / I'll be home for Christmas / Auld Lang Syne
CDMFP 6150 / Oct '94 / Music For Pleasure

☐ EARLY YEARS, THE
Balboa blue / Barbi / Karate / Luau / Surfer girl / Surfer's shoes / Surfin' / Surfin' safari / What is a young girl made of / Wipe out
SUMCD 4172 / 23 Feb '98 / Summit

☐ ENDLESS HARMONY
Soulful old man sunshine / Soulful old man sunshine / Radio concert promo / Medley / Surfer girl / Help me Ronda / Kiss me baby / California girls / Good vibrations / Heroes and villains / Heroes and villains / God only knows / Radio concert promos / Wonderful/Don't worry Bill / Do it again / Loop de loop / Barbara / Till I die / Long promised road / All alone / Brian's back / Endless harmony
4963912 / 17 Aug '98 / Capitol

☐ ENDLESS SUMMER
Surfin' safari / Surfer girl / Catch a wave / Warmth of the sun / Surfin' USA / Be true to your school / Little deuce coupe / In my room / Shut down / Fun, fun, fun / I get around / Girls on the beach / Wendy / Let him run wild / Don't worry baby / California girls / Girl don't tell me / Help me Rhonda / You're so good to me / All summer long / Good vibrations
CDMFP 50528 / Jul '91 / Music For Pleasure

☐ FRIENDS/20-20
Meant for you / Friends / Wake the world / Be here in the morning / When a man needs a woman / Passing by / Anna Lee, the healer / Little bird / Be still / Busy doing nothing / Diamond head / Transcendental meditation / Do it again / I can hear music / Bluebirds over the mountain / Be with me / All I want to do / Nearest faraway place / Cotton fields / I went to sleep / Time to get alone / Never learn not to love / Our prayer / Cabinessence / Breakaway / Celebrate the news / We're together again / Walk on by / Old folks at home/Ol' man river
CDP 7936972 / Sep '90 / Capitol

☐ GOOD VIBRATIONS - 30 YEARS OF THE BEACH BOYS (5CD Set)
Surfin' USA (demo) / Little surfer girl / Surfin' (rehearsal) / Surfin' / Their hearts were full of spring (demo) / Surfin' safari / 409 / Punchline (instrumental) / Surfin' USA / Shut down / Surfer girl / Little deuce coupe / In my room / Catch a wave / Surfer moon / Be true to your school / Spirit of America / Little saint Nick (45RPM) / Things we did last summer / Fun, fun, fun / Don't worry baby / Why do fools fall in love / Warmth of the sun / I get around / All summer long / Little Honda / Wendy / Don't back down / Do you wanna dance / When I grow up to be a man / Dance, dance, dance / Please let me wonder / She knows me too well / Radio station jingles/Honda 55 / Concert promo/hushabye (live) / California girls / Help me Rhonda / Then I kissed her / And your dreams come true / Little girl I once knew (45 version) / Barbara Ann (45 version) / Ruby baby (party outtake) / Koma (radio promo spot) / Sloop John B / Wouldn't it be nice / You still believe in me / God only knows / Hang on to your ego (alternative version) / I just wasn't made for these times / Pet sounds / Caroline no / Good vibrations (45 version) / Our prayer / Heroes and villains / Heroes and villains (sections) / Wonderful / Cabinessence / Wind chimes / Heroes and villains (intro) / Do you like worms / Vegetables / I love to say da da / Surf's up / With me tonight / Heroes and villains (45 version) / Darlin' / Wild honey / Let the wind blow / Can't wait too long / Cool cool water / Meant for you / Friends / Little bird / Busy doin' nothin' / Do it again / I can hear music / I went to sleep / Time to get alone / Breakaway / Cotton fields / San Miguel / Games two can play / I just got my pay / This whole world / Add some music / Forever / Our sweet love / HELP is on the way / 4th of July / Long promised road / Disney girls / Till I die / Sail on sailor / California / Trader / Funky pretty / Fairy tale music / You need a mess of help to stand alone / Marcella / All this is that / Rock 'n' roll music / It's over now / It's OK / Had to phone ya / That same song / Still I dream of it / Let us go on this way / Night was so young / I'll bet he's nice / Airplane / Come go with me / Our team / Baby blue / Good timin' / Goin' on / Getcha back / Kokomo / In my room (demo) / Radio spot / I get around (track) / Radio spot / Dance, dance, dance (track) / Hang on to your ego (tracking session) / God only knows (training session) / Good vibrations (sessions) / Heroes and villains (track) / Cabinessence (track) / Surf's up (track) / Radio spot / All summer long (vocals) / Wendy (vocals) / Hush-a-bye / When I grow up to be a man (vocals) / Wouldn't it be nice (vocals) / California girls (vocals) / Radio spot / Concert intro/ surfin' USA (live 1964) / Surfer girl (live 1964) / Be true to your school (live 1964) / Good vibrations (live 1966) / Surfer girl (live in Hawaii rehearsals 1967) / Blue birds over the mountain / Tears in the morning / Here comes the night / Lady Lynda / Sumahama
CDS 7812942 / Oct '93 / Capitol

☐ GREATEST HITS
Good vibrations / I get around / California girls / Surfin' safari / Little deuce coupe / God only knows / Barbara Ann / Surfin' USA / When I grow up (to be a man) / Wouldn't it be nice / Sloop John B / Surfer girl / Do it again / Break away / You're so good to me / I can hear music / Caroline no / Heroes and villains / Disney girls / Lady Lynda / Then I kissed her / Darlin' / Friends / Wild honey / In my room / Cotton fields (the cotton song)
4956962 / 29 Jun '98 / EMI

☐ I LOVE YOU
Good vibrations / Then I kissed her / God only knows / Darlin' / Help me Rhonda / All summer long / Wendy / Don't worry baby / You're so good to me / Why do fools fall in love / I can hear music / Wouldn't it be nice / Surfer girl / Devoted to you / I'm so young / There's no other (like my baby) / She knows me too well / Good to be my baby / Please let me wonder / I was made to love her
CDMFP 5988 / Jun '93 / Music For Pleasure

☐ PET SOUNDS
Caroline no / Wouldn't it be nice / You still believe in me / That's not me / Don't talk / I'm waiting for the day / Let's go away for awhile / Sloop John B / God only knows / I know there's an answer / Here today / I just wasn't made for these times / Pet sounds / Hang on to your ego / Trombone dixie
CDFA 3298 / Nov '93 / Fame

☐ PET SOUNDS SESSIONS, THE (4CD Set)
Wouldn't it be nice / You still believe in me / That's not me / Don't talk / I'm waiting for the day / Let's go away for a while / Sloop John B / God only knows / I know there's an answer / Here today / I just wasn't made for these times / Pet sounds / Caroline no / Sloop John B / Sloop John B / Trombone Dixie / Trombone dixie / Pet sounds / Pet sounds / Let's go away for awhile / Let's go away for awhile / Wouln't it be nice / Wouldn't it be nice / Wouldn't it be nice / You still believe in me / You still believe in me / You still believe in me / You still believe in me / Caroline no / Caroline no / HAng on to your ego / Hang on to your ego / Don't talk (put your head on my shoulder) / Don't talk (put your head on my shoulder) / I just wasn't made for these times / That's not me / Good vibrations / Good vibrations / I'm waiting for the day / I'm waiting for the day / God only knows / God only knows / Here today / Here today / Wouldn't it be nice / You still believe in me / Thats not me / Don't talk / I'm waiting for the day / Sloop John B / God only knows / Hang on to your ego / Here today / I just wasn't made for these times / Caroline no / Caroline no / Caroline no / Wouldn't it be nice / You still believe in me / Don't talk / I'm waiting for the day / Sloop John B / God only knows / Hang on to your ego / Here today / I just wasn't made for these times / Banana and Louie / Caroline no / Dog barking sessions / Caroline no (10) / God only knows (10) / Wouldn't it be nice / Sloop John B / God only knows (10) / Wouldn't it be nice / You still believe in me / That's not me / Don't talk (put your head on my shoulder) / I'm waiting for the day (10) / Let's go away for awhile (10) / Sloop John B (11) / God only knows / I know there's an answer / Here today (11) / Pet sounds / Caroline no (11)
CDS 8376622 / 27 Oct '97 / Capitol

☐ SMILEY SMILE/WILD HONEY
Heroes and villains / Vegetables / Fall breaks and back to winter / She's goin' bald / Little pad / Good vibrations / With me tonight / Wind chimes / Gettin' hungry / Wonderful / Whistle in / Wild honey / Aren't you glad / I was made to love her / Country air / Thing or two / Darlin' / I'd love just once to see you / Here comes the night / Let the wind blow / How she boogalooed it / Mama says / Heroes and villains (alt. take) / Good vibrations (various sessions) / Good vibrations (early take) / You're welcome / Their hearts were full of spring / Can't wait too long
CDP 7936962 / Jul '90 / Capitol

☐ SUMMER DREAMS
I get around / Surfin' USA / In my room / Fun, fun, fun / Little deuce coupe / Warmth of the sun / Surfin' safari / Help me Rhonda / Good vibrations / Sloop John B / You're so good to me / God only knows / Then I kissed her / Wouldn't it be nice / Heroes and villains / Wild honey / California girls / Don't worry baby / All summer long / Wendy / When I grow up (to be a man) / Dance, dance, dance / Little girl I once knew / Barbara Ann / Do it again / Friends / Darlin' / Bluebirds over the mountain / I can hear music / Breakaway / Cotton fields / California dreamin'
CDP 7946202 / Jun '90 / Capitol

☐ SUMMER IN PARADISE
Hot fun in the summertime / Surfin' / Summer of love / Island fever / Still surfin' / Slow summer dancin' (One summer night) / Strange things happen / Remember / Walking in the sand / Lahaina Aloha / Under the boardwalk / Summer in paradise / Forever
CDFA 3321 / Apr '95 / Fame

☐ SURF SENSATION (Beach Boys/Jan & Dean)
Surfin' safari: *Beach Boys* / Fun fun fun: *Jan & Dean* / Surfin': *Beach Boys* / Ride the wild surf: *Jan & Dean* / Judy: *Beach Boys* / Baby talk: *Jan & Dean* / Surfer girl: *Beach Boys* / Help me Rhonda: *Jan & Dean* / Beach boy stomp: *Beach Boys* / I get around: *Jan & Dean* / Barbie: *Beach Boys* / Surf city: *Jan & Dean* / Luau: *Beach Boys* / Sidewalk surfin': *Jan & Dean* / What is a young girl made of: *Beach Boys* / Cindy: *Jan & Dean*
SUMCD 4170 / 26 Jan '98 / Summit

☐ SURFIN' BACK TO BACK (Beach Boys/ Jan & Dean)
Surfin' safari: *Beach Boys* / Surfin': *Beach Boys* / Judy: *Beach Boys* / Surfer girl: *Beach Boys* / Beach boy stomp: *Beach Boys* / Barbie: *Beach Boys* / Luau: *Beach Boys* / What is a young girl made of: *Beach Boys* / Surf city: *Jan & Dean* / Ride the wild surf: *Jan & Dean* / Baby talk: *Jan & Dean* / Help me Rhonda: *Jan & Dean* / I get around: *Jan & Dean* / Fun fun fun: *Jan & Dean* / Sidewalk surfin': *Jan & Dean* / Cindy: *Jan & Dean*
ECD 3214 / Mar '95 / K-Tel

☐ TODAY/SUMMER DAYS AND SUMMER NIGHTS/SMILEY SMILE (The Originals/3CD Set)
Do you wanna dance / Good to my baby / Don't hurt my little sister / When I grow up (to be a man) / Help me Rhonda / Dance, dance, dance / Please let me wonder / I'm so young / Kiss me baby / She knows me too well / In the back of my mind / She knew me too well / Girl from New York City / Amusement parks USA / Then I kissed her / Salt Lake City / Girl don't tell me / Help me Rhonda / California girls / Let him run wild / You're so good to me / Summer means new love / I'm bugged at my ol' man / Your dream comes true / Heroes and villains / Vegetables / Fall breaks and back to winter (W Woodpecker symphony) / She's goin' bald / Little pad / Good vibrations / With me tonight / Wind chimes / Gettin' hungry / Wonderful / Whistle in
CDOMB 018 / 27 Jul '98 / Capitol

Beach Buddha

☐ GILDING THE LILY
AQUACD 3 / Feb '97 / Aquarius

Beachcombers

☐ SIZE 10 (Beachcombers & Kenny Baker)
RSCD 677 / Jul '98 / Raymer

Beacon Street Union

☐ EYES OF THE BEACON ST. UNION/ THE CLOWN DIED IN MARVIN GARDEN
Recitation / My love is / Beautiful Delilah / Sportin' life / Four hundred and five / Mystic mourning / Sadie said no / Speed kills / Blue avenue / South end incident / Green destroys the gold / Prophet / Clown died in Marvin Gardens / Clown's overture / Angus of Aberdeen / Blue suede shoes / Not very August afternoon / Now I taste the years / King of the jungle / May I light your cigarette / Baby please don't go
3497 / Jun '97 / Head
SEECD 495 / 10 Aug '98 / See For Miles

Beadle, 'Sax' Gordon

☐ HAVE HORN WILL TRAVEL
CDBB 9589 / 19 Jan '98 / Bullseye Blues

Beaker, Norman

☐ INTO THE BLUES (Beaker, Norman Band)
Cross me off your list / Modern days, lonely nights / Doctor doctor / No feeling in this love anymore / Break it down / Time will tell / No reason to believe in me / New home / That's unnatural / Ain't the truth bad enough / Loaded for bears / Treat your woman right / Into the blues / Cry to me / Poor wages
JSPCD 230 / Oct '89 / JSP

☐ OLDER I GET THE BETTER I WAS, THE
Little Hollywood / Give it a try / Lies like a river / Too much too soon / New version of you / Let it be me / Two people / Let the world take the blame / Standing on shaky ground / Make her feel a woman again / Wrong man / Heading for the ghetto / Gourmet dinner in a takeaway
CIT 5CD / Jun '98 / Out Of Time

Beal, Jeff

☐ RED SHIFT
369042 / 3 Aug '98 / Koch Jazz

Beamer, Kapono

☐ PARADISE FOUND
ISCD 117 / Oct '91 / Intersound

Beamer, Keola

☐ WOODEN BOAT
DCT 38024CD / Mar '96 / Dancing Cat

Beanfield

☐ BEANFIELD
COMP 033CD / 29 Sep '97 / Compost

Bear

☐ SCHADENFREUDE
VES 006 / 18 May '98 / Vespertine

Bear, Keith

☐ ECHOES OF THE UPPER MISSOURI
SPALAX 14962 / Oct '96 / Spalax

Beard, Chris

☐ BAR WALKIN'
You ain't all that / Barwalkin' / Everything man / I'm your man / All night long / Caught up / I had a dream / Get yo self a life / Delivery man / It's about time / Playing the blues for a living / I need it all
JSPCD 288 / Jul '97 / JSP

Beard, Jim

☐ TRULY
Big pants / Tandoori taxi / Gone was, gone will be / In all her finery / Social climate / Side two / Hand to hand / Gonna tell on you / Major Darlings' impossible halftime show
ESC 036522 / Apr '97 / Escapade

Beard, Joe

☐ FOR REAL (Beard, Joe & Duke Robillard)
9259210492 / 24 Mar '98 / AQ

Beasley, Walter

☐ TONIGHT WE LOVE
Slowly but surely / Let's stay together / My oasis / What's my name / Killing me softly / Sweetness / People make the world go round / Never can say goodbye / My girl / Tonight we love
SHCD 5032 / Mar '98 / Shanachie

Beastie Boys

☐ AGLIO E OLIO
Brand new / Deal with me / Believe me / Nervous assistant / Square wave in unison / You catch a bad one / I can't think straight / I want some
GR 026 / 16 Mar '98 / Grand Royal

☐ CHECK YOUR HEAD
Jimmy James / Funky boss / Pass the mic / Gratitude / Lighten up / Finger lickin' good / So what'cha want / Biz Vs. the nuge / Time for livin' / Something's got to give / Blue nun / Stand together / Pow / Maestro / Groove Holmes / Live at PJ's / Mark on the bus / Professor Booty / In 3's / Mamaste
CDP 7989382 / Apr '92 / Grand Royal

☐ DEF AND DUMB (Interview)
DIST 005 / Mar '96 / Disturbed

☐ HELLO NASTY
Super disco breakin / Move / Remote control / Song for the man / Just a test / Body movin / Intergalatic / Sneakin' out the hospital / Putting shame in your game / Flowin' prose / And me / Three MC's and one DJ / Can't won't / Song for junior / I don't know / Negotiation limerick file / Electrify / Picture this / Unite / Dedication / Dr. Lee PhD / Instant death
4957232 / 6 Jul '98 / Grand Royal

☐ ILL COMMUNICATION
Sure shot / Tough guy / B boys makin' with the freak freak / Bobo on the corner / Root down / Sabotage / Get it together / Sabrosa / Update / Futterman's rule / Alright hear this / Eugene's lament / Flute loop / Do it / Ricky's theme / Heart attack man / Scoop / Shamballa / Bodhisattva vow / Transitions
CDEST 2229 / May '94 / Grand Royal

☐ IN SOUND FROM WAY OUT, THE
Groove Holmes / Sabrosa / Namaste / Pow / Son of Neckbone / In 3's / Eugene's lament / Bobo on the corner / Shambala / Lighten up / Ricky's theme / Transition / Drinkin' wine
CDEST 2281 / Apr '96 / Grand Royal

☐ LICENSED TO ILL
Rhymin and stealin' / New style / She's crafty / Posse in effect / Slow ride / Girls / (You gotta) Fight for your right (to party) / No sleep till Brooklyn / Paul Revere / Hold it, now hit it / Brass monkey / Slow and low / Time to get ill
5273512 / Jul '95 / Def Jam

☐ PAUL'S BOUTIQUE
To all the girls / Shake your rump / Johnny Ryall / Egg man / High plains drifter / Sounds of science / Three minute rule / Hey ladies / Five piece chicken dinner / Looking down the barrel of a gun / Car thief / What comes around / Shadrach / Ask for Janice / B boy bouillabaisse
CDP 7917432 / May '92 / Grand Royal

☐ ROOT DOWN
Root down / Root down / Root down / Time to get ill / Heart attackman / Maestro / Sabrosa / Fluteloop / Time for livin' / Something's got to give
CDEST 2262 / May '95 / Grand Royal

☐ SOME OLD BULLSHIT
Egg raid on mojo (demo) / Beastie Boys / Transit cop / Jimi / Holy snappers / Riot fight / Ode to... / Michelle's farm / Egg raid on mojo / Transit cop (demo) / Cooky puss / Bonus batter / Beastie revolution / Cooky puss (censored version)
CDEST 2225 / Mar '94 / Grand Royal

Beasts Of Bourbon

☐ AXEMAN'S JAZZ
REDCD 4 / Mar '94 / Red Eye

☐ BLACK MILK
REDCD 12 / Mar '94 / Red Eye

☐ FROM THE BELLY OF THE BEASTS
REDCD 30 / Mar '94 / Red Eye

☐ GONE
Saturated / Fake / Makem cry / Mullett / Get on / I s'pose / What a way to live / That sinking feeling again / So long / Is that love / This day is over / Unfolded
REDCD 58 / Feb '97 / Red Eye

☐ JUST RIGHT
REDCD 20 / Mar '94 / Red Eye

☐ LOW ROAD, THE
REDCD 26 / Mar '94 / Red Eye

☐ SOUR MASH
REDCD 5 / Mar '94 / Red Eye

Beat

☐ BPM (The Very Best Of The Beat)
Mirror in the bathroom / Hands off...she's mine / Twist and crawl / Jackpot / Tears of a clown / Ranking fullstop / Rough rider / Best friend / Stand down Margaret / Too nice to talk to / All out to get you / Door of your heart / Drowning / Can't get used to losing you / I confess / Save it for later
74321231952 / Jan '96 / Arista

☐ CLASSIC SESSIONS (International Beat)
Yeah yeah yeah / Ska beat boogie / Ride a white swan / Rocksteady / Making plans / Head man's plans / I fought the law / Sign of the times / Fitz / Rudy / Stand and be counted / What are you / Yesterday's clown / Step it up / Magical feeling / Hard world / Firing line / Taking the pills
CDBM 127 / 29 May '98 / Blue Moon

☐ DANCEHALL ROCKERS (International Beat)
CDBM 109 / Jan '96 / Blue Moon

☐ GANGSTERS (Special Beat)
CLP 0180 / 2 Feb '98 / Cleopatra

☐ LIVE IN JAPAN (Special Beat)
Concrete jungle / Monkey man / Tears of a clown / Rough rider / Too much too young / Get a job / Rat race / Spar wid me / Too nice to talk to / Too hot / Do nothing / Nite club / Noise in this world / Gangsters / Ranking full stop / Mirror in the bathroom / Doesn't make it alright / Enjoy yourself / Jackpot / Message to you Rudy / Save it for later / You're wondering now
DOJOCD 146 / Jun '94 / Dojo

Beat Angels

☐ RED BADGE OF DISCOURAGE
EP 1820 / Jun '97 / Epiphany

Beat Brothers

☐ LEGEND (Documentray/Live)
OTR 1100011 / Apr '97 / Metro Independent

Beat Farmers

☐ MANIFOLD
SECT2 10019 / Oct '95 / Sector 2

☐ TALES OF THE NEW WEST
Bigger stones / There she goes again / Reason to believe / Lost weekend / California kid / Never goin' back / Goldmine / Showbiz / Lonesome hound / Where do they go / Selfish heart
FIENDCD 39 / Sep '90 / Demon

☐ VIKING LULLABYS
SECT2 10013 / Apr '95 / Sector 2

Beat Happening

☐ JAMBOREE
SP 62B / Mar '94 / Sub Pop

Beatles

☐ 1962-1966 (2CD Set)
Love me do / Please please me / From me to you / She loves you / I want to hold your hand / All my loving / Can't buy me love / Hard day's night / And I love her / Eight days a week / I feel fine / Ticket to ride / Yesterday / Help / You've got to hide your love away / We can work it out / Day tripper / Drive my car / Norwegian wood / Nowhere man / Michelle / In my life / Girl / Paperback writer / Eleanor Rigby / Yellow submarine
CDPCSP 717 / Feb '94 / Apple

☐ 1967-1970 (2CD Set)
Strawberry Fields forever / Penny Lane / Sergeant Pepper's lonely hearts club band / With a little help from my friends / Lucy in the sky with diamonds / Day in the life / All you need is love / I am the walrus / Hello goodbye / Fool on the hill / Magical mystery tour / Lady Madonna / Hey Jude / Revolution / Back in the USSR / While my guitar gently weeps / Ob-la-di ob-la-da / Get back / Don't let me down / Ballad of John and Yoko / Old brown shoe / Here comes the sun / Come together / Something / Octopus's garden / Let it be / Across the universe / Long and winding road
CDPCSP 718 / Feb '94 / Apple

☐ ABBEY ROAD
Come together / Something / Maxwell's silver hammer / Oh darling / Octopus's garden / I want you (she's so heavy) / Here comes the sun / Because / You never give me your money / Sun king / Mean Mr Mustard / Polythene Pam / She came in through the bathroom window / Golden slumbers / Carry that weight / End Her Majesty
CDP 7464462 / Nov '88 / Apple

☐ AND YOUR BIRD CAN SING (36 Classic Interpretations Of Beatles Standards/ 2CD Set) (Various Artists)
Ob-la-di ob-la-da: *Marmalade* / Good day sunshine: *Tremeloes* / Michelle: *Overlanders* / You've got to hide your love away: *Silkie* / Bad to me: *Kramer, Billy J.* / Nowhere man: *Three Good Reasons* / Things we said today: *Sandpipers* / Fool on the hill: *Mendes, Sergio* / Girl: *St. Louis Union* / Norwegian wood: *London Jazz Four* / World without love: *Peter & Gordon* / Got to get you into my life: *Bennett, Cliff* / I call your name: *Mamas & The Papas* / Drive my car: *Campbell, Junior* / Rocky racoon: *Fairweather-Low, Andy* / I'll cry instead: *Cocker, Joe* / Something: *Bassey, Shirley* / Here comes the sun: *Harley, Steve* / Lucy in the sky with diamonds: *John, Elton* / Get back: *Stewart, Rod* / Yesterday: *Charles, Ray* / Hey Jude: *Pickett, Wilson* / Come together: *Ross, Diana* / Let it be: *Knight, Gladys* / Imagine: *Baez, Joan* / And I love her: *Robinson, Smokey* / Can't buy me love: *Fitzgerald, Ella* / Eleanor Rigby: *Havens, Richie* / Here, there and everywhere: *Harris, Emmylou* / I'm a loser: *Faithfull, Marianne* / She's leaving home: *Ferry, Bryan* / Do you want to know a secret: *Fairground Attraction* / Tomorrow never knows: *Monsoon* / Revolution: *Thompson Twins* / Dear Prudence: *Siouxsie & The Banshees* / Getting better: *Status Quo*
5531102 / Jul '98 / Debutante

☐ ASK YOU ONCE AGAIN (Interview)
3D 002 / Nov '96 / Network

☐ BEATLES ANTHOLOGY VOL.1, THE (2CD Set)
Free as a bird / That'll be the day / In spite of all the danger / Hallelujah / I love her so / You'll be mine / Cayenne / My bonnie / Ain't she sweet / Cry for a shadow / Searchin' / Three cool cats / Sheik of Araby / Like dreamers do / Hello little girl / Besame mucho / Love me do / How do you do it / Please please me / One after 909 (sequence) / One after 909 (complete) / Lend me your comb / I'll get you / I saw her standing there / From me to you / Money (that's what I want) / You really got a hold on me / Roll over Beethoven / She loves you / Till there was you / Twist and shout / This boy / I want to hold your hand / Moonlight bay / Can't buy me love / All my loving / You can't do that / I love her / Hard's day night / I wanna be your man / Long tall Sally / Boys / Shout / I'll be back (take 2) / I'll be back (take 3) / You know what to do / No reply (demo) / Mr. Moonlight / Leave my kitten alone / No reply / Eight days a week / Hey hey hey / Kansas City / Eight days a week (complete)
CDPCSP 727 / Nov '95 / Apple

☐ BEATLES ANTHOLOGY VOL.2, THE (2CD Set)
Real love / Yes it is / You've got to hide your love away / If you've got trouble / That means a lot / I'm down / Yesterday / It's only love / I feel fine / Ticket to ride / Yesterday / Help / Everybody's trying to be my baby / Norwegian wood / I'm looking through you / 12-bar original / Tomorrow never knows / Got to get you into my life / And your bird can sing / Taxman / Eleanor Rigby / I'm only sleeping (rehearsal) / I'm only sleeping / Rock 'n' roll music / She's a woman / Strawberry Fields forever (demo) / Strawberry Fields forever (take 1) / Strawberry Fields forever / Penny Lane / Day in the life / Good morning, good morning / Only a northern song / Being for the benefit of Mr. Kite / Being for the benefit of Mr. Kite / Lucy in the sky with diamonds / Witihin you without you / Sgt. Pepper's Lonely Hearts Club Band (reprise) / You know my name (look up the number) / I am the walrus / Fool on the hill / Your mother should know / Fool on the hill (Take 4) / Hello goodbye / Lady Madonna / Across the universe
CDPCSP 728 / Mar '96 / Apple

☐ BEATLES ANTHOLOGY VOL.3, THE (2CD Set)
Beginning / Happiness is a warm gun / Helter skelter / Mean Mr. Mustard / Polythene Pam / Glass onion / Junk / Piggies / Honey pie / Don't pass me by / Ob-la-di ob-la-da / Good night / Cry baby cry / Blackbird / Sexy Sadie / While my guitar gently weeps / Hey Jude / Not guilty / Mother nature's son / Glass onion / Rocky Raccoon / What's the new Mary Jane / Step inside love / I'm so tired / I will / Why don't we do it in the road / Julia / I've got a feeling / She came in through the bathroom window / Dig a pony / Two of us / For you blue / Teddy boy / Medley / Long and winding road / Oh darling / All things must pass / Mailman, bring me no more blues / Get back / Old brown shoe / Octopus's garden / Maxwell's silver hammer / Something / Come together / Come and get it / Ain't she sweet / Because / Let it be / I me mine / End
CDPCSP 729 / Nov '96 / Apple

☐ BEATLES BOX SET, THE (From Please Please Me To Past Masters 2 - 16CD Set)
I saw her standing there / Misery / Anna (go to him) / Chains / Ask me why / Please please me / Love me do / PS I love you / Baby it's you / Do you want to know a secret / Taste of honey / There's a place / Twist and shout / It won't be long / All I've got to do / All my loving / Don't bother me / Little child / Till there was you (The music man) / Please Mr. Postman / Roll over Beethoven / Hold me tight / You really got a hold on me / I wanna be your man / Devil in her heart / Not a second time / Money (that's what I want) / Hard day's night / I should have known better / If I fell / I'm happy just to dance with you / And I love her / Tell me why / Can't buy me love / Any time at all / I'll cry instead / Things we said today / When I get home / You can't do that / I'll be back / No reply / I'm a loser / Baby's in black / Rock 'n' roll music / I'll follow the sun / Mr. Moonlight / Kansas City / Eight days a week / Words of love / Honey don't / Every little thing / I don't want to spoil the party / What you're doing / Everybody's trying to be my baby / Help / Night before / You've got to hide your love away / I need you / Another girl / You're going to lose that girl / Ticket to ride / Act naturally / It's only love / You like me too much / Tell me what you see / I've just seen a face / Yesterday / Dizzy Miss Lizzy / Drive my car / Norwegian wood / You won't see me / Nowhere man / Think for yourself / Word / Michelle / What goes on / Girl / I'm looking through you / In my life / Wait / If I needed someone / Run for your life / Taxman / Eleanor Rigby / I'm only sleeping / Love you to / Here there and everywhere / Yellow submarine / She said she said / Good day sunshine / And your bird can sing / For no one / Doctor Robert / I want to tell you / Got to get you into my life / Tomorrow never knows / Sgt. Pepper's Lonely Hearts Club Band / With a little help from my friends / Lucy in the sky with diamonds / Getting better / Fixing a hole / She's leaving home / Being for the benefit of Mr. Kite / Within you without you / When I'm sixty four / Lovely Rita / Good morning good morning / Sgt. Pepper's Lonely Hearts Club Band / Day in the life / Back in the USSR / Dear Prudence / Glass onion / Ob-la-di ob-la-da / Wild honey pie / Continuing story of Bungalow Bill / While my guitar gently weeps / Happiness is a warm gun / Martha my dear / I'm so tired / Blackbird / Piggies / Rocky Raccoon / Don't pass me by / Why don't we do it in the road / I will / Julia / Birthday / Yer blues / Mother nature's son / Everybody's got something to hide except me and my monkey / Sexy Sadie / Helter skelter / Long long long / Revolution 1 / Honey pie /

Savoy truffle / Cry baby cry / Revolution 9 / Goodnight / Yellow submarine / Only a northern song / All together now / Hey bulldog / It's all too much / All you need is love / Pepperland / Sea of time / Sea of holes / Sea of monsters / March of the meanies / Pepperland laid waste / Yellow submarine in Pepperland / Magical mystery tour / Fool on the hill / Flying / Blue Jay way / Your mother should know / I am the walrus / Hello goodbye / Strawberry fields forever / Penny Lane / Baby you're a rich man / All you need is love / Come together / Something / Maxwell's silver hammer / Oh darling / Octopus's garden / I want you (she's so heavy) / Here comes the sun / Because / You never give me your money / Sun King / Mean Mr. Mustard / Polythene Pam / She came in through the bathroom window / Golden slumbers / Carry that weight / End / Her Majesty / Two of us / Dig a pony / Across the universe / I me mine / Dig it / Let it be / Maggie Mae / I've got a feeling / One after 909 / Long and winding road / For you blue / Get back / Love me do / From me to you / Thank you girl / She loves you / I'll get you / I want to hold your hand / This boy / Komm gib mir deine hand / Sie liebt dich / Long tall Sally / I call your name / Slow down / Matchbox / I feel fine / She's a woman / Bad boy / Yes it is / I'm down / Day tripper / We can work it out / Paperback writer / Rain / Lady Madonna / Inner light / Hey Jude / Revolution / Get back / Don't let me down / Ballad of John and Yoko / Old brown shoe / Across the universe / Let it be / You know my name (look up the number)

CDS 7913022 / Dec '88 / Apple

☐ **BEATLES CLASSICS PERFORMED ON PAN PIPES, THE (Various Artists)**

Free as a bird / Lucy in the sky with diamonds / Michelle / Blackbird / And I love her / Yesterday / Eleanor Rigby / Strawberry Fields forever / Penny Lane / Hey Jude / Something / All my loving / Norwegian wood / She loves you / With a little help from my friends / If I fell / Long and winding road / Here, there and everywhere / Let it be

SUMCD 4060 / Nov '96 / Summit

☐ **BEATLES EP COLLECTION, THE (14EP Set)**

From me to you / Thank you girl / Please please me / Love me do / Twist and shout / A taste of honey / Do you want to know a secret / There's a place / K saw her standing there / Misery / Anna (go to him) / Chains / All my loving / Ask me why / Money (that's what I want) / P.s. / I love you / Long tall sally / I call your name / Slow down / Matchbox / I should have known better / If I fell / Tell me why / And I love her / Anytime at all / I'll cry instead / Things we said today / When I get home / No reply / I'm a loser / Rock and roll music / Eight days a week / I'll follow the sun / Baby's in black / Words of love / I don't want to spoil the party / She loves you / I want to hold your hand / Can't buy me love / I feel fine / Yesterday / Act naturally / You like me too much / It's only love / Nowhere man / Drive my car / Michelle / You won't see me / Magical mystery tour / Your mother should know / I am the walrus / Fool on the hill / Flying (instrumental) / Blue jay way / Magical mystery tour / Your mother should know / I am the walrus / Fool on the hill / Flying (instrumental) / Blue jay way / Inner light / Baby you're a rich man / She's a woman / This boy

CDBEP 14 / Apr '92 / Apple

☐ **BEATLES FOR SALE**

No reply / I'm a loser / Baby's in black / Rock 'n' roll music / I'll follow the sun / Mr. Moonlight / Kansas City / Eight days a week / Words of love / Honey don't / Don't want to spoil the party / What you're doing / Everybody's tryin' to be my baby

CDP 7464382 / Nov '88 / Apple

☐ **BEATLES INTERVIEW PICTURE DISC, THE (Beatles Conquer The USA)**

CBAK 4001 / Feb '88 / Baktabak

☐ **BEATLES KARAOKE PARTY, THE (Various Artists)**

MACCD 375 / 30 Mar '98 / Autograph

☐ **BEATLES SAX MOODS, THE (Evolution)**

Something / Free as a bird / Michelle / If I fell / My love / You've got to hide your love away / Let it be / Long and winding road / Lady Madonna / Strawberry fields forever / In my life / Across the universe / I will / For no one / Yesterday / Here, there and everywhere / Real love / Eleanor Rigby / Hey Jude

3036000422 / May '96 / Carlton

☐ **BEATLES TALK DOWNUNDER VOL.1, THE (Australia 1964)**

CBAK 4024 / Jun '91 / Baktabak

☐ **BEATLES TALK DOWNUNDER VOL.1, THE**

12679 / Mar '96 / Laserlight

☐ **BEATLES TALK DOWNUNDER VOL.2, THE**

CBAK 4034 / Jun '91 / Baktabak

☐ **BEATLES TALK DOWNUNDER VOL.2, THE**

12680 / Mar '96 / Laserlight

☐ **BEATLES TAPES, THE (David Wigg Interviews 1969-1973)**

Interview (part 1) June 1969: *Lennon, John & Yoko Ono* / Give peace a chance: *Lennon, John & Yoko Ono* / Interview (Part 2) June 1969: *Lennon, John & Yoko Ono* / Imagine: *Lennon, John* / Interview (Part 3) June 1969: *Lennon, John & Yoko Ono* / Come together: *Lennon, John & Yoko Ono* / Interview October 1971: *Lennon, John & Yoko Ono* / Interview (Part 1) March 1970: *McCartney, Paul* / Because: *McCartney, Paul* / Interview (Part 2) March 1970: *McCartney, Paul* / Hey Jude: *McCartney, Paul* / Interview (Part 1) March 1969: *Harrison, George* / Here comes the sun: *Harrison, George* / Interview (Part 2) March 1969: *Harrison, George* / Something: *Harrison, George* / Interview December 1968: *Starr, Ringo* / Interview July 1970: *Starr, Ringo* / Interview (Part 1) December 1973: *Starr, Ringo* / Octopus's Garden: *Starr, Ringo* / Interview (Part 2) December 1973: *Starr, Ringo* / Yellow submarine: *Starr, Ringo*

8471852 / Oct '90 / Polydor

☐ **BEATLES, THE (The White Album) (2CD Set)**

Back in the USSR / Dear Prudence / Glass onion / Ob-la-di ob-la-da / Wild honey pie / Continuing story of bungalow Bill / While my guitar gently weeps / Happiness is a warm gun / Martha my dear / I'm so tired / Blackbird / Piggies / Rocky raccoon / Don't pass me by / Why don't we do it in the road / I will / Julia / Yer blues / Mother nature's son / Everybody's got something to hide except me and my monkey / Sexy Sadie / Helter skelter / Long long long / Revolution 1 / Honey pie / Savoy truffle / Cry baby cry / Revolution 9 / Goodnight

CDS 7464438 / Nov '88 / Apple

☐ **BIOGRAPHY SERIES**

10026 / 3 Nov '97 / Metro Independent

☐ **CLASSIC BEATLES (Symphonic Rock Orchestra)**

322879 / Mar '93 / Koch

☐ **COME TOGETHER VOL.2 (Various Artists)**

Tomorrow never knows: *Krantz, Wayne* / Strawberry fields: *De Gruy, Philip* / Drive my car: *Hunter, Charlie* / I am the walrus: *Rogers, Adam* / Not a second time: *Rypdal, Terje* / Yes it is: *Quine, Robert* / Because: *Tronzo, David* / Golden slumbers: *Ford, Robben* / If I needed someone: *Hedges, Michael*

NYC 60142 / Apr '95 / NYC

☐ **DOWNTOWN DOES THE BEATLES (Various Artists)**

KFWCD 113 / Nov '94 / Knitting Factory

☐ **FAB FOUR (Interview/4CD Set)**

8016 / 17 Aug '98 / Point

☐ **FOREVER LENNON & MCCARTNEY (Various Artists)**

Can't buy me love: *Martin, George Orchestra* / All my loving: *Monro, Matt* / Ticket to ride: *Cogan, Alma* / Eleanor Rigby: *Strings For Pleasure* / Do you want to know a secret: *Kramer, Billy J. & The Dakotas* / I want to hold your hand: *Martin, George Orchestra* / Hey Jude: *Loss, Joe Orchestra* / Michelle: *David & Jonathan* / World without love: *Peter & Gordon* / I feel fine: *Cogan, Alma* / Get back: *Shadows* / Yesterday: *Seekers* / Sgt. Peppers Lonely Hearts Club Band: *Palmer, David & The London Symphony Orchestra* / Got to get you into my life: *Bennett, Cliff* / With a little help from my friends: *Young Idea* / Day tripper: *Lulu* / Fool on the hill: *Bassey, Shirley* / Paperback writer: *Shadows* / Back in the USSR: *Bennett, Cliff*

CDMFP 6276 / Nov '96 / Music For Pleasure

☐ **GEORGE HARRISON INTERVIEW**

GEORGE 1 / Jun '96 / UFO

☐ **HARD DAY'S NIGHT, A**

I should have known better / If I fell / I'm happy just to dance with you / And I love her / Tell me why / Can't buy me love / Hard day's night / Anytime at all / I'll cry instead / Things we said today / When I get home / You can't do that / I'll be back

CDP 7464372 / Nov '88 / Apple

☐ **HELP (Film Soundtrack)**

Help / Night before / You've got to hide your love away / I need you / Another girl / You're going to lose that girl / Ticket to ride / Act naturally / It's only love / You like me too much / Tell me what you see / I've just seen a face / Yesterday / Dizzy Miss Lizzy

CDP 7464392 / Nov '88 / Apple

☐ **HITS OF THE BEATLES (Various Artists)**

DCD 5276 / Aug '92 / Disky

☐ **IN WORDS AND MUSIC (2CD Set) (McCartney, Paul)**

OTR 110029 / Apr '97 / Metro Independent

☐ **INSIDE INTERVIEWS**

15981 / Mar '96 / Laserlight

☐ **INTERVIEW DISC**

SAM 7001 / Nov '96 / Sound & Media

☐ **INTERVIEWS VOL.2**

CBAK 4009 / Apr '88 / Baktabak

☐ **INTERVIEWS: ALL TOGETHER NOW**

12677 / Mar '96 / Laserlight

☐ **INTERVIEWS: BEATLEMANIA**

12678 / Mar '96 / Laserlight

☐ **INTERVIEWS: IN MY LIFE**

12676 / Mar '96 / Laserlight

☐ **INTROSPECTIVE**

Twist and shout / I saw her standing there / Till there was you / Interview part one / Roll over Beethoven / Hippy hippy shake / Taste of honey / Interview part two

CINT 5004 / Jun '91 / Baktabak

☐ **LEGEND BEGINS, THE (Sheridan, Tony & The Beatles)**

Sweet Georgia Brown / Let's dance / Take out some insurance / Why (can't you love me again) / Cry for a shadow / Ya ya / Ruby baby / What'd I say

305492 / Oct '96 / Hallmark

☐ **LET IT BE**

Two of us / Dig a pony / Across the universe / I me mine / Dig it / Let it be / Maggie Mae / I've got a feeling / One after 909 / Long and winding road / Get back

CDP 7464472 / Nov '88 / Apple

☐ **LIVE RECORDINGS 1962**

CDTAB 5001 / '88 / Baktabak

☐ **MAGICAL AND MYSTICAL WORDS - LATE SIXTIES (Spoken Word Collection)**

OZITCD 0033 / Aug '98 / Ozit

☐ **MAGICAL MYSTERY TOUR**

Magical mystery tour / Fool on the hill / Flying / Blue jay way / Your mother should know / I am the walrus / Hello goodbye / Strawberry fields forever / Penny Lane / Baby, you're a rich man / All you need is love

CDP 7480622 / Nov '88 / Apple

☐ **MARCHING WITH THE BEATLES (Band Of The Irish Guards)**

BNA 5144 / 15 Jun '98 / Bandleader

☐ **ORCHESTRAL SGT. PEPPER (Arranged/Conducted By David Palmer) (Royal Academy Symphony Orchestra)**

Sergeant Pepper's lonely hearts club band / With a little help from my friends / Lucy in the sky with diamonds / Getting better / Fixing a hole / She's leaving home / Being for the benefit of Mr. Kite / When I'm sixty four / Lovely Rita / Sergeant Pepper's lonely hearts club band (reprise) / Day in the life

CDDPR 125 / Jun '97 / Premier/MFP

☐ **PAN PIPES PLAY LOVE SONGS FROM THE BEATLES (Various Artists)**

Free as a bird / Something / I will / Across the universe / If I fell / Michelle / For no one / Fool on the hill / Strawberry fields forever / You've got to hide your love away / Imagine / In my life / Blackbird / And I love her / My love / Here there and everywhere / Mother Nature's son / Yesterday / Long and winding road / Real love

309052 / 13 Jul '98 / Hallmark

☐ **PAST MASTERS VOL.1**

Love me do / From me to you / Thank you girl / She loves you / I'll get you / I want to hold your hand / This boy / Komm gib mir deine hand / Sie liebt dich / Long tall Sally / I call your name / Slow down / Matchbox / I feel fine / She's a woman / Bad boy / Yes it is / I'm down

CDP 7900432 / Aug '88 / Apple

☐ **PAST MASTERS VOL.2**

Day tripper / We can work it out / Paperback writer / Rain / Lady Madonna / Inner light / Hey Jude / Revolution / Get back / Don't let me down / Ballad of John and Yoko / Old brown shoe / Across the universe / Let it be / You know my name (look up the number)

CDP 7900442 / Aug '88 / Apple

☐ **PAUL MCCARTNEY INTERVIEW**

PAUL 1 / Jun '96 / UFO

☐ **PLAY THE BEATLES BALLADS (Various Artists)**

For no one / Michelle / Strawberry fields forever / Here, there and everywhere / In my life / And I love her / If I fell / Long and winding road / Something / Fool on the hill / Free as a bird / Real love / You've got to hide your love away / Imagine / My love / Blackbird / Mother nature's son / Across the universe / Yesterday / I will

3036000262 / Jan '96 / Carlton

☐ **PLEASE PLEASE ME**

Taste of honey / I saw her standing there / Misery / Anna / Chains / Boys / Ask me why / Please please me / Love me do / I love you / Baby it's you / Do you want to know a secret / There's a place / Twist and shout

CDP 7464352 / Nov '88 / Apple

☐ **QUOTE UNQUOTE VOL.1 (The Sixties Interviews)**

MM 002 / 27 Mar '98 / MagMid

☐ **QUOTE UNQUOTE VOL.2 (Sixties Interviews)**

MM 009 / 31 Jul '98 / MagMid

☐ **RARE PHOTOS AND INTERVIEWS VOL.1**

JG 0012 / 17 Aug '98 / Point

☐ **RARE PHOTOS AND INTERVIEWS VOL.2**

JG 0022 / 17 Aug '98 / Point

☐ **RARE PHOTOS AND INTERVIEWS VOL.3**

JG 0032 / 17 Aug '98 / Point

☐ **REGGAE TRIBUTE TO THE BEATLES VOL.1, A (Various Artists)**

Yesterday: *Livingstone, Dandy* / Hey Jude: *Holt, John* / Come together: *Israelites* / Something: *Dillon, Phyllis* / Let it be: *Thomas, Nicky* / Get back: *Anonymously Yours* / My Jude: *Joe's All Stars* / My sweet Lord: *Lynn, Keith, Brendon Lee & The Dragonaires* / World without love: *Davis, Del* / Give peace a chance: *Maytals* / Lady Madoona: *Crystalites* / Isn't it a pity: *Thomas, Nicky* / Don't let me down: *Harry J All Stars* / Blackbirds singing: *Sweet, Roslyn & The Paragons* / Eleanor Rigby: *Seaton, B.B.* / World without love: *Arthey, Johnny Orchestra*

EMPRCD 584 / Oct '95 / Emporio

☐ **REGGAE TRIBUTE TO THE BEATLES VOL.2, A (Various Artists)**

Ob-la-di ob-la-da: *Heptones* / Hard day's night: *Minott, Sugar* / Yesterday: *Taylor, Tyrone* / My love: *Boothe, Ken* / You won't see me: *Smith, Ernie* / And I love her: *Mohawks* / Norwegian wood: *Williams, Marshall* / My sweet Lord: *Sterling, Fitzroy* / Don't let me down: *Griffiths, Marcia* / Here comes the sun: *Penn, Dawn* / In my life: *Robinson, Jackie* / Imagine: *Cadogan, Susan* / Hey Jude: *Dynamites* / Let it be: *Soulettes* / Carry that weight: *Dobson, Dobby* / Happy Xmas (war is over): *Holt, John*

EMPRCD 718 / Jun '97 / Emporio

☐ **RELOADER (A Tribute To The Beatles/ 4CD Set) (Various Artists)**

DOP 54 / 23 Mar '98 / Dressed To Kill

☐ **REVOLVER**

Taxman / Eleanor Rigby / I'm only sleeping / Love you to / Here, there and everywhere / Yellow submarine / She said she said / Good day sunshine / And your bird can sing / For no one / Dr. Robert / I want to tell you / Got to get you into my life / Tomorrow never knows

CDP 7464412 / Nov '88 / Apple

☐ **RINGO STARR INTERVIEW**

RINGO 1 / Jun '96 / UFO

☐ **ROCKUMENTARY - IN THEIR OWN WORDS (5CD Set)**

15968 / Dec '95 / Laserlight

☐ **ROCKUMENTARY NO.1 - THE LOST BEATLES INTERVIEWS**

12591 / Dec '95 / Laserlight

☐ **ROCKUMENTARY NO.2 - THINGS WE SAID TODAY (Talking With The Beatles)**

12592 / Dec '95 / Laserlight

☐ **ROCKUMENTARY NO.3 - JOHN LENNON FOREVER**

12593 / Dec '95 / Laserlight

☐ **ROCKUMENTARY NO.4 - PAUL MCCARTNEY: BEYOND THE MYTH**

12594 / Dec '95 / Laserlight

☐ **ROCKUMENTARY NO.5 - THE SECRET LIFE OF GEORGE HARRISON**

12595 / Dec '95 / Laserlight

☐ **RUBBER SOUL**

Drive my car / Norwegian wood / You won't see me / Nowhere man / Think for yourself / Word / Michelle / What goes on / Girl / I'm looking through you / In my life / Wait / If I needed someone / Run for your life

CDP 7464402 / Nov '88 / Apple

☐ **SGT. PEPPER'S LONELY HEARTS CLUB BAND**

Sergeant Pepper's lonely hearts club band / With a little help from my friends / Lucy in the sky with diamonds / Getting better / Fixing a hole / She's leaving home / Being for the benefit of Mr. Kite / Within you without you / When I'm sixty four / Lovely Rita / Good morning good morning / Day in the life

CDP 7464422 / Jun '92 / Apple

☐ **SGT. PEPPER'S LONELY HEARTS CLUB BAND (Various Artists)**

Got to get you into my life: *Earth, Wind & Fire* / Strawberry Fields forever: *Farina, Sandy* / When I'm sixty four: *Howerd, Frankie & Sandy Farina* / Mean Mr. Mustard: *Howerd, Frankie* / Fixing a hole: *Burns, George* / Because: *Cooper, Alice & Bee Gees* / Golden slumbers: *Frampton, Peter*

5570762 / 6 Apr '98 / Polydor

☐ **SIE LIEBT DICH (Beatles Lieder Vol.2) (Various Artists)**

Sag nie mehr 'I love you': *Schumann, Theo Combo* / Komm gibt mir deine hand: *Amigos* / So soll es immer sein: *Electra Combo* / Liebe: *Tornadoes* / Ich bin dein fan: *Bonnies* / Ich bin froh: *Gerry & His Comets* / Manchmal wenn ich traume: *Loving Hearts* / Wenn du vor mir gehst: *Bonnies* / Eine welt ohne liebe: *Bottcher, Gerd & Detlef Engel* / Maxwells silberhammer: *Lee, Teddy* / Ja das hatt ich wissem Mussen: *Quick, Benny* / Michelle: *Tielman Brothers* / Fur unes beide: *Roos, Mary* / Eleonore Rigby: *March, 'Little' Peggy* / Manchmal: *Lavi, Daliah* / Gestern noch: *Van Hoog, Grit* / Jeder braucht einen freund: *Schmidt, Helmut* / Das tragst du lange mit dir: *Gott, Karel* / Hey Jude: *Sommer, Mark* / Goodnight: *Fritsch, Thomas* / Hoopla-di hoppla da: *Travellers* / Nur keine Beatles Frisur: *Bottcher, Gerd* / Mein boyfreund hat 'nen Beatle-haarschnitt: *Bottcher, Gerd* / Die vier aus Liverpool: *Landin, Mara*

BCD 16173 / Aug '97 / Bear Family

☐ **SINGLES COLLECTION (22CD Singles Set)**

Love me do / PS I love you / From me to you / Thank you girl / Please please me / Ask me why / She loves you / I'll get you / I want to hold your hand / This boy / Can't buy me love / You can't do that / Hard day's night / Things we said today / I feel fine / She's a woman / Ticket to ride / Yes it is / Help / I'm down / We can work it out / Day tripper / Paperback writer / Rain / Yellow submarine / Eleanor Rigby / Strawberry fields forever / Penny Lane / All you need is love / Baby, you're a rich man / Hello goodbye / I am the walrus / Lady Madonna / Inner light / Hey Jude / Revolution / Get back / Don't let me down / Ballad of John and Yoko / Old brown shoe / Something / Come together / Let it be / You know my name (look up the number)

CDBSCP 1 / Nov '92 / Apple

☐ **SONGS OF THE BEATLES, THE (Various Artists)**

Love me do / Please please me / From me to you / She loves you / Twist and shout / I want to hold your hand / Can't buy me love / Hard day's night / I feel fine / Eight days a week / Ticket to ride / Help / We can work it out / Day tripper / Paperback writer / Yellow submarine / Yesterday

SUMCD 4205 / 11 May '98 / Summit

☐ **SPIRIT OF LENNON & MCCARTNEY, THE (Instrumental Versions) (Various Artists)**

Strawberry fields forever / Fool on the hill / Here there and everywhere / Dear Prudence / Let it be / Because / Nowhere man / Yesterday / In my life / She's leaving home / If I fell / For no one / This boy / Michelle / Across the universe / And I love her / Julia / Mother Nature's son

RECD 508 / Dec '97 / REL

☐ TRIBUTE TO THE BEATLES, A (Various Artists)
Sgt. Pepper's lonely hearts club band: *Exit* / If you need someone: *Smart Riddle* / Love me do: *Space Cakes* / Things we said today: *Revengers* / Love away flow: *Revengers* / Come together: *Revengers* / Taxman: *Skainsmate* / Something in the way: *Disgraceland* / Tomorrow never knows: *Persuaders* / Wait: *Dilemmas* / Rain: *Hipster* / You got to hide your love away: *In Between Days* / Across the universe: *Lighthouse* / Day tripper: *Mourning After*
TR 014CD / 13 Apr '98 / Tribute

☐ WITH THE BEATLES
It won't be long / All I've got to do / All my loving / Don't bother me / Little child / Till there was you / Please Mr. Postman / Roll over Beethoven / Hold me tight / You really got a hold on me / I wanna be your man / Devil in her heart / Not a second time / Money
CDP 7464362 / Nov '88 / Apple

☐ WITHOUT THE BEATLES (Various Artists)
JAR 015CD / Jul '97 / Jar Music

☐ WITHOUT THE BEATLES (A Tribute To The Beatles) (Various Artists)
RG 003 / 16 Feb '98 / Orgone Company

☐ YELLOW SUBMARINE
Yellow submarine / Only a northern song / All you need is love / Hey bulldog / It's all too much / All together now / Pepperland / Sea of time / Sea of holes / Sea of monsters / March of the meanies / Pepperland laid to waste / Yellow submarine in Pepperland
CDP 7464452 / Nov '88 / Apple

☐ YESTERDAY VOL.1 (16 Fab Beatle Reggae Classics) (Various Artists)
CDTRL 294 / Mar '94 / Trojan

☐ YESTERDAY VOL.2 (The Black Album) (Various Artists)
CDTRL 338 / Apr '94 / Trojan

☐ YESTERDAY VOL.3 (Various Artists)
CDTRL 365 / Oct '96 / Trojan

Beatnigs

☐ BEATNIGS
VIRUSUK 065CD / 10 Nov '97 / Alternative Tentacles

Beatnik Filmstars

☐ ALL POPSTARS ARE TALENTLESS SLAGS
SCRATCH 27 / Jun '97 / Scratch

☐ BOSS DISQUE
NOLCD 45 / 7 Sep '98 / Noise-O-Lution

☐ IN HOSPITALABLE
MRG 125CD / Sep '97 / Merge

☐ LAID BACK & ENGLISH
LADIDA 027CD / Jul '94 / La-Di-Da

☐ PHASE 3
MOBSTAR 008CD / Jan '97 / Mobstar

Beatnuts

☐ BEATNUTS
No equal / Let off a couple II / Psycho dwarf II / Off tha books / Props over here / Treats / RU / Ready II / Get funky
4895952 / 9 Feb '98 / Epic

Beaton, Alex

☐ 20 HITS OF SCOTLAND
Scots wha hae / Dumbarton's drums / These are my mountains / Annie Laurie / Wee castanettes / Man's a man for a' that / Ae fond kiss / Killiecrankie / Skye boat song / Hey Johnny Cope / Amazing grace / Stoutest man in the forty twa / Glencoe / Scottish soldier / Flowers of the forest / Loch Lomond / Big Nellie May / Rowan tree / Fower of Scotland / Bonnie Galloway / Scotland the brave
LCOM 9031 / Aug '90 / Lismor

Beats

☐ UP UNTIL NOW
CDCOT 102 / Oct '94 / Cottage

Beats The Hell Out Of Me

☐ ROLLING THUNDER MUSIC
148072 / Oct '95 / Metal Blade

Beatsystem

☐ BEATSYSTEM
Invade areas where nothing's definite / No more / For Pierre / No jumping up and down/Spooky action at a distance / There are 23 million... / Drone number one / Tibet / Closely tuned drone
EMIT 2297 / 27 Oct '97 / Emit

Beau

☐ BEAU/CREATION
Welcome / 1917 Revolution / Fising song / Pillar of economy / Sundancer / Morning sun / Ways of winter / Nine minutes / Spider / Is this your day / Blind faith / Release / Silence returns / Imagination / Soldier of the willow / Painted vase / Nations pride / Rain / Summer has gone / Welcome tag piece / There was once a time / April meteor / Creation / Ferris street / Reason to be
SEECD 421 / May '95 / See For Miles

Beau Brummels

☐ AUTUMN OF THEIR YEARS
She sends me / Tomorrow is another day / She loves me / Woman / Dream on / Cry some / I grow old / No lonelier man / This is love / She's my girl / I'll tell you / Let me in / Love is just a game / Till the day / I will go / Stay with me awhile / I'm alone again / Down on me / Can't be so / Fine with me / Coming home / That's all that matter / Laugh laugh / Still in love with you baby / Just a little / When it comes to your love
CDWIKD 127 / Feb '94 / Big Beat

☐ SIXTIES GEMS
Just a little / Don't talk to strangers / When it comes to your love / In good time / Fine with me / Sad little girl / Still in love with you baby / You tell me why / They'll make you cry / Good time music / Laugh laugh / Woman / She loves me
HADCD 213 / Jun '97 / Spotlight On

Beau Hunks

☐ CELEBRATION ON THE PLANET MARS, A (A Tribute To Raymond Scott) (Beau Hunks Sextette)
Raymond Scott speaks / War dance for the wooden Indians / Toy trumpet / Powerhouse / Celebration on planet Mars / Boy scout in Switzerland / Dinner music for a pack of hungry cannibals / Bird life in the Bronx / Square dance for eight Egyptian mummies / Girl at the typewriter / Penguin / Bumpy weather over Newark / Ectoplasm / Peter Tambourine / Twilight in Turkey / Street corner in Paris / Reckless night on board an ocean liner / Egyptian barn dance / Snake woman / Dedicated piece
379092 / Nov '95 / Koch International
BASTA 3090562 / Sep '97 / Basta

☐ EDWARD MACDOWELL'S WOODLAND SKETCHES, OPUS 51
To a wild rose / Will o' the wisp / At an old trysting place / In Autumn / From an Indian lodge / To a water lily / From Uncle Remus / Deserted farm / By a meadow brook / Told at sunset
BASTA 3090382 / Sep '97 / Basta

☐ FINGERBUSTIN' (Beau Hunks & R. Hansen Heijtmajer)
Fingerbustin' / Saxarella / Copenhagen / Krazy kapers / Supplication (valse caprice) / Beebe / Nola / Manhattan serenade / Saxophobia / Rudy's fingers / Wolverine blues / Mood Hollywood / Poor buttermilk / Trumbology / High society (march) / Kitten on the keys / Milneburg joys / Deep purple / Weary blues / Greenwich witch / Dardanella / Waddlin' at the Waldorf / Oodles of noodles / Feelin' no pain
BASTA 3090582 / Sep '97 / Basta

☐ MANHATTAN MINUET (The Works Of Raymond Scott) (Beau Hunks Sextette)
Manhattan minuet / Oil gusher / Christmas night in Harlem / Curley cue / Devil drums / Little bit of rigoletto / Tobacco auctioneer / Sleepwalker / Moment musical / Happy farmer / Quintette plays Carmen / Steeplechase / Siberian sleighride / New Years's eve in a haunted house
BASTA 3090362 / Sep '97 / Basta

Beaumont Hannant

☐ BASIC DATA MANIPULATION
GPRCD 2 / Nov '93 / GPR

☐ SCULPTURED
GPRCD 9 / Oct '94 / GPR

☐ TEXTUROLOGY
GPR 4CD / Apr '94 / GPR

Beaumont, Howard

☐ SHALL WE DANCE
Take the 'A' train / Dancing in the dark / Deep in my heart / Perhaps, perhaps, perhaps / Once in a while / Makin' whoopee / La Rosita / Blue skies / Hey good lookin' / Bye bye blues
CDGRS 1295 / May '97 / Grosvenor

Beauregarde

☐ BEAUREGARDE
GRC 010 / 5 Jan '98 / GRC

Beausoleil

☐ ALLONS A LAFAYETTE
ARHCD 308 / Apr '95 / Arhoolie

☐ ARC DE TRIOMPHE TWO STEP
Arc de triomph two step / Love bridge / Bosco Moscow stomp / Euen fille a la campagne / Bayou tech / Johnny can't dance / Travailler c'est trop dur / CIA / Take it to me / Ti Maurice / Valse de grand chemin / Just because
HEMIMDCD 105 / 6 Oct '97 / Hemisphere

☐ BAYOU BOOGIE
Zydeco gris gris / Fais pas ca / It's you I love / Dimanche apres-midi / Madame Bozo / Kolinda / Maman Rosin Boudreaux / Chez Seychelles / Jongle a moi / Flame will never die / La vaise de malchanceaux / Beausoleil boogie
ROUCD 6015 / '88 / Rounder

☐ BAYOU CADILLAC
Bon temps rouler / Rolling pin / Valse bebe / Hey baby, quoi ca dit / Couchon de lait / Flammes d'enfer / Bunk's blues / Le sud de la louisianne / Baby please don't go / Macaque sur mon dos / Island zydeco / Not fade away-bo diddley-iko iko (bayou cadillac)
ROUCD 6025 / May '88 / Rounder

☐ BEST OF BEAUSOLEIL, THE
Parlez-nous a boire / Tous le deux por la meme / J'ai ete au Zydeco / Voyage au mariage / Cortableau / La valse des jonglemonts / Mecredi soire passe / Grand mallet / Bee's blues / Shoo, black / Leger's chase / Je veux me marier / Valse de grand meche / Joe Pitre's so bad / Creole french blues / Chanson D'Acadie / Le Bozo two-step / Si j'aurais de ailes / Chez Varise Connor / La chanson de cinquante sous / La valse du vacher / Hot chili Mama
ARHCD 458 / Sep '97 / Arhoolie

☐ HOT CHILI MAMA (Beausoleil & Michael Doucet)
ARHCD 5040 / Apr '95 / Arhoolie

☐ L'ECHO
Chez denouse mcgee / O bebe waltz / Freeman's zydeco / La ville des manteau / Quel espoir / Hip et ti-yeaux / Angelas' waltz / Cajun crawl / Chere petite blond / La cravate a ziggy zag / Joe falcon's waltz / One iota / Evangeline waltz / La belle de bayou teche / Lizzette la douce
8122718082 / Nov '94 / Warner Bros.

☐ LA DANSE DE LA VIE
La danse de la vie / Dans le Grand Brouillard / L'ouragon / Dis-moi pas / Jeunes filles de la campagne / Quelle belle vie / RD special / Chanson pour Ezra / Menage a trois reels / Zydeco X / Je tombe aux Genoux / Attrape mes larmes / La fille de quatorze ans
8122712212 / Jun '93 / Atlantic

☐ LIVE FROM THE LEFT COAST
Les veuves de la coulee / La chanson de mardi gras / Plus tu tournes / Pine grove blues / Les filles a nonc helaire (the daughters of uncle helaire) / La valse de kfly / La chanson du cafe / La betaille / Cajun groove (scott playboy special) / Chez seychelles / Maman rosin au zydeco bal / Two-step a will bolfa / Reel de dennis mcgee
ROUCD 6035 / May '88 / Rounder

☐ PARLEZ-NOUS A BOIRE
Le jig francais (french jig) / Voyage au mariage (my true love) / Courtableu / La rue canal (canal street) / Paquet d'epingles (packet of pins) / Valse de grand meche / Mercredi soir passe / Sue / Reels cadien / Chanson d'acadie / Pierrot grouilletee et mamselle josette / Ma douce amie (my sweet love) / Parlez-nous a boire (speak to us of drinking) / Your mama threw me out / Robin's two step / Acadian blues / Midland two step / Le bozo two step
ARHCD 322 / Apr '95 / Arhoolie

☐ THEIR SWALLOW RECORDINGS
J'ai vu le loup / Valse a Beausoleil / Two-step des freres Mathieu / Travailler c'est trop dur / Potpourri cadjin / He, Mom / Valse des Balfa / Zydeco gris gris / Les barres de la prison / Hommage aux freres Balfa / Chanson / Love bridge waltz / Tu peux cognai / Contredanse de mamou / Reel de Dennis McGee / Blues a bebe / Talle du ronces / Blues de morse / Fi fi a Poncho / J'ai fait la tour de grand bois / Je m'endors, je m'endors / La valse de grand bois / Trinquez, trinquez
CDCHD 379 / Sep '92 / Ace

☐ VERY BEST OF BEAUSOLEIL, THE
Zydeco gris gris / Cajun telephone stomp / Evangeline waltz / Cajun crawl / La nuit de Clifton Chenier / Menage a trois reels / Conja / Le jig Francais / L'Ouragon / Joe Falcon's waltz / Tasso/ McGee's reel / Chanson pour Ezra / Freeman's zydeco / Sur le Pont de Lyon / Quelle belle vie / Hip et ti-yeaux / RD Special / Zydeco X
NSCD 024 / 11 May '98 / Nascente

Beautiful South

☐ 0898 BEAUTIFUL SOUTH
Old red eyes is back / We are each other / Rocking chair / We'll deal with you later / Domino man / 36D / Here it is again / Something that you said / I'm your No.1 fan / Bell-bottomed tear / You play glockenspiel, I'll play drums / When I'm 84
8283102 / Apr '92 / Go Discs

☐ BLUE IS THE COLOUR
Don't marry her / Little blue / Mirror / Blackbird on the wire / Sound of north America / Have fun / Liars bar / Rotterdam (or anywhere) / Foundations / Artificial flowers / One god / Alone
8288452 / Oct '96 / Go Discs

☐ CARRY ON UP THE CHARTS (The Best Of The Beautiful South)
Song for whoever / You keep it all in / I'll sail this ship alone / Little time / My book / Let love speak up for itself / Old red eyes is back / We are each other / Bell bottomed tear / 36D / Good as gold (stupid as mud) / Everybody's talkin' / Prettiest eyes / One last love song / Dream a little dream
8285722 / Nov '94 / Go Discs

☐ CHOKE
Tonight I fancy myself / Let love speak up itself / I've come for my award / I think the answer's yes / Mother's pride / Rising of Grafton Street / My book / Should've kept my eyes shut / Lips / Little time / I hate you (but you're interesting)
8282332 / Oct '90 / Go Discs

☐ MIAOW
Hold on to what / Good as gold / Especially for you / Everybody's talkin' / Prettiest eyes / Worthless lie / Hooligans don't fall in love / Hidden jukebox / Hold me close / Tattoo / Mini correct / Poppy
8285072 / 15 Sep '97 / A&M

☐ WELCOME TO THE BEAUTIFUL SOUTH
Song for whoever / Have you ever been away / From under the covers / I'll sail this ship alone / Girlfriend / Straight in at 37 / You keep it all in / Woman in the wall / Oh Blackpool / Love is / I love you (but you're boring)
AGOCD 16 / Oct '89 / Go Discs

Beautiful World

☐ IN EXISTENCE
In the beginning / In existence / Evolution / Magicien du bonheur / I know / Silk road / Love song / Journey of the ancestors / Revolution of the heart / Coming of age / Spoken word / Wonderful world / Final emotion
4509951202 / Mar '94 / WEA

Beauvoir, Jean

☐ ROCKIN' IN THE STREET
Jacknifed / Feel the heat / Rockin' in the street / Standing on my own two feet / Dyin' at your door / Same song plays on and on / Sorry I missed your wedding day / If love could only / Spend your life with me / Find my way home / Never went down / Alone again / Searching for a light / Drive you home / If I was me / Missing the young days / Gamblin' man / Nina
CDOVD 465 / Jan '96 / Virgin

Beaven, Nancy

☐ WILD GARDEN, THE
SCD 195 / Mar '96 / Starc

Becaud, Gilbert

☐ ET MAINTENANT
CD 352127 / Jul '93 / Duchesse

Because

☐ MAD SCARED DUMB AND GORGEOUS
Orientation / Her rhythm and her blues / A glass room / Song of all things / Archaeology / Love is coming / Stolen / Feast of stephen / You don't forget / Mad scared dumb and gorgeous
HAVENCD 1 / May '92 / Haven

Bechegas, Carlos

☐ FLUTE SOLOS/MOVEMENT SOUNDS (Bechegas, Carlos Trio)
LEOLABCD 032 / May '97 / Leo Lab

Bechet, Leonard

☐ LEONARD BECHET & ALTON PURNELL 1973 (Bechet, Leonard & Alton Purnell)
BCD 236 / Apr '97 / GHB

Bechet, Sidney

☐ AMERICAN FRIENDS
VGCD 655623 / Jan '93 / Vogue

☐ AT STORYVILLE
C jam blues / Crazy rhythm / Jazz me blues / Basin street blues / Indiana / Bugle blues / Honeysuckle rose / On the sunny side of the street / Oh lady be good
BLC 760902 / Apr '91 / Black Lion

☐ BECHET
Kansas City man blues / Old fashioned love / Texas moaner blues / Mandy, make up your mind / Papa de da da / Wild cat blues / Coal cart blues / Sweetie dear / I want you tonight / Ja da / Really the blues / I've found a new baby / When you and I were young Maggie / Shake it and break it / Old man blues / Wild man blues / Nobody knows the way I feel this morning / Blues in thirds / Blues for you Johnny / Ain't misbehavin' / Save it pretty Mama / Stompy Jones
PASTCD 9772 / Jan '92 / Flapper

☐ BECHET-MEZZROW QUINTET
401172CD / Jul '94 / Musidisc

☐ BLUES IN THIRDS
LEJAZZCD 30 / Aug '94 / Le Jazz

☐ BLUES IN THIRDS 1940-1941
Blues in thirds / Ain't misbehavin' / Save it, pretty mama / Stompy Jones / You're the limit / Perdido Street blues / Down in honky-tonk town / Old man blues / Shake it and break it / Strange fruit / Wild man blues / Mooche / I ain't gonna give nobody / Blues in the air / China boy / Dear old southland / Egyptian fantasy / Baby, won't you please come home / Slippin' and slidin' / I know that you know / I'm comin' Virginia / Georgia cabin / Limehouse blues / Texas moaner blues
CD 53105 / May '97 / Giants Of Jazz

☐ BORN TO SWING
JC 98003 / 26 May '98 / Jazz Classix

☐ CENTENARY CELEBRATION 1997 (Great Original Performances 1924-1946)
Indian summer: *Bechet, Sidney & His New Orleans Feetwarmers* / Sweetie Dear: *Bechet, Sidney & His New Orleans Feetwarmers* / I've found a new baby: *Bechet, Sidney & His New Orleans Feetwarmers* / Maple leaf rag: *Bechet, Sidney & His New Orleans Feetwarmers* / Shag: *Bechet, Sidney & His New Orleans Feetwarmers* / One o'clock jump: *Bechet, Sidney & His New Orleans Feetwarmers* / Old man blues: *Bechet, Sidney & His New Orleans Feetwarmers* / Swing parade: *Bechet, Sidney & His New Orleans Feetwarmers* / Blues in the air: *Bechet, Sidney & His New Orleans Feetwarmers* / Bugle call rag - ole Miss: *Bechet, Sidney & His New Orleans Feetwarmers* / Make up your mind: *Williams,*

Clarence Blue Five / Early every morning: *Red Onion Jazzband* / Okey doke: *Sissle, Noble* / Characteristic blues: *Sissle, Noble* / Viper mad: *Sissle, Noble* / Blackstick: *Sissle, Noble* / When the sun sets down south: *Sissle, Noble* / Sweet papootie: *Sissle, Noble* / Really the blues: *Ladnier, Tommy* / Weary blues: *Ladnier, Tommy* / Blues in thirds: *Bechet, Sidney Trio* / Muskrat ramble: *Levine, Henry* / Blues of Bechet
RPCD 632 / Apr '97 / Robert Parker Jazz

☐ **CLASSICS 1923-1936**
CLASSICS 583 / Oct '91 / Classics

☐ **CLASSICS 1937-1938**
CLASSICS 593 / Sep '91 / Classics

☐ **CLASSICS 1938-1940**
CLASSICS 608 / Oct '92 / Classics

☐ **CLASSICS 1940**
CLASSICS 619 / Sep '92 / Classics

☐ **CLASSICS 1940-1941**
CLASSICS 638 / Nov '92 / Classics

☐ **CLASSICS 1941-1944**
CLASSICS 860 / Mar '96 / Classics

☐ **CLASSICS 1945-1946**
CLASSICS 954 / Nov '97 / Classics

☐ **COMPLETE SIDNEY BECHET VOL.1 & 2 1932-1941, THE**
One o'clock jump / Preachin' blues / Old man blues / Blues in thirds / Ain't misbehavin' / Save it pretty Mama / Stompy Jones / Muskrat ramble / Coal black shine / Sweetie dear / Lay your racket / Maple leaf rag / Ja da / Really the blues / Weary blues / Indian summer / I want you tonight / I've found a new baby / When you and I were young Maggie / Maggie / Sidney's blues / Shake it and break it / Wild man blues / Nobody knows the way I feel this morning / Make a pallet on the floor / St. Louis blues / Blues for you / Johnny / Eygptian fantasy
ND 89760 / May '94 / Jazz Tribune

☐ **COMPLETE SIDNEY BECHET VOL.3 & 4 1941, THE**
I'm coming Virginia / Limehouse blues / Georgia cabin / Texas moaner / Strange fruit / You're the limit / Rip up the joint / Suey / Blues in the air / Mooche / Laughin' in rhythm / 12th Street rag / I know that you know / Egyptian fantasy / Baby, won't you please come home / Slippin' and slidin' / Sheikh of Araby / Blues of Bechet / Swing parade / When it's sleepy time down South / I ain't gonna give nobody none o' this jelly roll
ND 89759 / Jun '94 / Jazz Tribune

☐ **COMPLETE SIDNEY BECHET VOL.5, THE**
Mood indigo / Oh lady be good / What's this thing called love / After you've gone / Bugle call rag/Ole Miss rag / St. Louis blues / Revolutionary blues / Comin' on with the come on / Careless love / Royal Garden blues / Everybody loves my baby / I ain't gonna give nobody none o' this Jelly Roll / If you see me comin' / Gettin' together / Rosetta / Minor jive / World is waiting for the sunrise / Who / Blues my baby gave to me / Rompin'
74321155192 / Jun '94 / Jazz Tribune

☐ **FREIGHT TRAIN BLUES**
Sweetie dear / I want you tonight / I've found a new baby / Lay your racket / Maple leaf rag / Shag / Okey doke / Characteristic blues / Viper mad / Blackstick / When the sun sets down south (Southern sunset) / Sweet patootie / Freight train blues / Trixie blues / My Daddy rocks me (Part I) / My Daddy rocks me (Part II) / What a dream / Hold tight / Jungle drums / Chant in the night / Ja da / Really the blues / When you and I were young Maggie / Weary blues
GRF 100 / '93 / Tring

☐ **GENIUS OF SIDNEY BECHET, THE**
JCD 35 / Aug '95 / Jazzology

☐ **INTRODUCTION TO SIDNEY BECHET 1923-1941, AN**
4017 / Mar '95 / Best Of Jazz

☐ **JAZZ AT STORYVILLE**
C jam blues / Crazy rhythm / Jazz me blues / Basin street blues / Indiana / Bugle blues / Honeysuckle rose / On the sunny side of the street / Oh lady be good
BLCD 760902 / Jun '88 / Black Lion

☐ **JAZZ GREATS**
Les oignons: *Bechet, Sidney & Claude Luter Orchestra* / Mon homme: *Bechet, Sidney & Claude Luter Orchestra* / Maryland: *Bechet, Sidney & Claude Luter Orchestra* / Royal garden blues: *Bechet, Sidney & Claude Luter Orchestra* / Le marchand de poisson: *Bechet, Sidney & Claude Luter Orchestra* / Dans les rues d'antides: *Bechet, Sidney & Claude Luter Orchestra* / As-tu le cafard: *Bechet, Sidney & Claude Luter Orchestra* / Si tu vois ma mere: *Bechet, Sidney & Claude Luter Orchestra* / Rockin' chair / Summertime / St. Louis blues / Souvenirs de la nouvelle Orleans: *Bechet, Sidney & Teddy Buckner* / When the saints go marchin' in: *Bechet, Sidney & Claude Luter*
74321556922 / Feb '98 / RCA Victor

☐ **JAZZ PORTRAITS**
Shag / Maple leaf rag / Sweetie dear / I've found a new baby / Lay your racket / I want you tonight / Polka dot rag / T'ain't a fit night out for man or beast / When the sun sets down south (southern sunset) / Freight train blues / Chant in the night / Characteristic blues / Black stick blues / Jungle drums / Really the blues / Weary blues / When you and I were young Maggie / Ja da
CD 14517 / May '94 / Jazz Portraits

☐ **LEGENDARY SIDNEY BECHET, THE**
Maple leaf rag / I've found a new baby / Weary blues / Really the blues / High society / Indian summer / Sidney's blues / Shake it and break it / Wild man blues / Save it pretty Mama / Stompy Jones / Muskrat ramble / Baby, won't you please come home / Sheikh of Araby / When it's sleepy time down South / I'm coming Virginia / Strange fruit / Blues in the air / Mooche / Twelfth St. rag / Mood indigo / What is this thing called love
ND 86590 / Apr '89 / Bluebird

☐ **MASTERS OF JAZZ (2CD Set)**
R2CD 8003 / 13 Apr '98 / Deja Vu

☐ **MASTERS OF JAZZ VOL.4**
STCD 4104 / May '93 / Storyville

☐ **OLYMPIA CONCERT 1954**
VGCD 655625 / Jan '93 / Vogue

☐ **QUINTESSENCE, THE (1932-1943/2CD Set)**
FA 206 / Oct '96 / Fremeaux

☐ **RARE RECORDINGS 1947-1953**
Polka dot stomp / Kansas city man blues / Jazz me blues / Sugar / Dear old southland / Blues in my heart / Indiana / Basin street blues / Honeysuckle rose / C jam blues / On the sunny side of the street
15709 / Apr '94 / Laserlight

☐ **REALLY THE BLUES (Original Recordings 1932-1941)**
Baby, won't you please come home / 2.19 blues / Blues in thirds / China boy / Egyptian fantasy / Four or five times / High society / I ain't gonna give nobody none o' this jelly roll / I thought I heard Buddy Bolden say / Indian summer / Lay your racket / Maple leaf rag / Mooche / Muskrat ramble / Nobody knows the way I feel this morning / Perdido Street blues / Preachin' blues / Really the blues / Sheikh of araby / When it's sleepy time down South / Stompy Jones / Strange fruit / Texas moaner / When you and I were young Maggie / Wild man blues
CDAJA 5107 / Jul '93 / Living Era

☐ **SIDNEY BECHET & HIS NEW ORLEANS FEETWARMERS 1940-1941**
882442 / Aug '93 / Music Memoria

☐ **SIDNEY BECHET & HIS NEW ORLEANS FEETWARMERS 1941-1943**
882452 / Aug '93 / Music Memoria

☐ **SIDNEY BECHET & MUGGSY SPANIER/DON EWELL/DOC EVANS VOL.1**
DD 226 / Feb '95 / Delmark

☐ **SIDNEY BECHET & PEE WEE RUSSELL (Bechet, Sidney & Pee Wee Russell)**
Crazy rhythm / Jazz me blues / Indiana / Bugle blues / On the sunny side of the street / Missy / Sugar / Sweet Georgia Brown / If I had you / I want a little girl
8747142 / Jul '96 / DA Music

☐ **SIDNEY BECHET 1932-1951**
I've found a new baby / Sweetie dear / Shag / Maple leaf rag / Really the blues / Weary blues / Lay your racket / I want you tonight / Ja-da / When you and I were young / Oh, didn't he ramble / I thought I heard buddy bolden say / High society / Winin' boy blues / Tain't a fit night out for man or beast / Black stick blues / When the sun sets down south / Indian summer / Preachin' blues (up jumped the devil) / Characteristic blues / Jungle drums / Chant in the night / Polka dot rag / Summertime / Blues in thirds / Ain't misbehavin' / Save it, pretty mama / Stompy jones / You're the limit / Perdido street blues / Down in honky tonk town / Old man blues / Shake it and break it / Strange fruit / Wild man blues / Mooche / I ain't gonna give nobody none of my jelly-roll / Blues in the air / China boy / Dear old southland / Egyptian fantasy / Baby won't you please come home / Slippin' and slidin' / I know that you know / I'm coming virginia / Georgia cabin / Limehouse blues / Texas moaner blues / At a georgia camp meeting / Shim-me-sha-wabble / Sister kate / Fidgety feet / Groovin' the minor / I had it but it's all gone now / Old stack o'lee blues / Darktown strutters' ball / Revolutionary blues / Out of the gallion / Jelly roll blues / Laura / Changes made / Blame it on the blues / Mood indigo / St. louis blues / Blue horizon / Rose room / Love for sal / Oh lady be good / What is this thing called love / Bugle call rag-ole miss blues
CDB 1214 / Jul '92 / Giants Of Jazz

☐ **SIDNEY BECHET 1944-1945 (2CD Set)**
414682 / Mar '96 / Music Memoria

☐ **SIDNEY BECHET IN CONCERT**
710440 / Apr '95 / RTE/Europe 1

☐ **SIDNEY DE PARIS 1943-1944**
409392 / Nov '95 / Music Memoria

☐ **SLIPPIN' AND SLIDIN' (The Bluebird Sessions)**
Slippin' and slidin' / 12th St. rag / Shake it and break it / Old man blues / Ain't misbehavin' / Stompy Jones / Muskrat ramble / Coal black shine / Baby won't you please come home / Sweetie dear / Weary blues / One o'clock jump / Swing parade / I ain't gonna give nobody none of this jelly roll / Limehouse blues / Texas moaner blues / Blues in the air / I'm coming, Virginia / You're the limit / Rose bloom / Bugle call rag/Ole Miss Blues / St. Louis blues
74321487302 / May '97 / Camden

☐ **SUMMERTIME 1932-1940**
I've found a new baby / Sweetie dear / Shag / Maple leaf rag / Really the blues / Weary blues / Lay your racket / I want you tonight / Ja-da / When you and I were young, Maggie / Oh, didn't he ramble / I thought, I heard Buddy Bolden say / High society / Winnin' boy blues / Tain't a fit night out for man or beast / Black stick blues / When the sun sets down south / Indian summer / Preachin' blues / Characteristic blues / Jungle drums / Chant in the night / Polka dot rag / Summertime
CD 53104 / May '97 / Giants Of Jazz

☐ **WEARY BLUES**
Shag / Maple leaf rag / Sweetie dear / I've found a new baby / Lay your racket / I want you tonight / Polka dot rag / Tain't a fit night out for man or beast / When the sun sets down south (southern sunset) / Freight train blues / Chant in the night / Characteristic blues / Black stick blues / Jungle drums / Really the blues / Weary blues / When you and I were young maggie / Ja-da
CD 56052 / Mar '95 / Jazz Roots

☐ **WEARY BLUES**
Black stick / Viper mad / When the sun sets down south / Sweet patootie / Chant in the night / Jungle drums / Hold tight (want some sea food mama) / What a dream / Weary blues / Really the blues / Summertime / High society / Indian summer / Sidney's blues / One o'clock jump / Preaching blues / Dear old scotland / Perdido street blues / Shake it and break it / Wilman blues
JHR 73553 / Jan '93 / Jazz Hour

☐ **YOUNG SIDNEY BECHET 1923-1925**
Wild cat blues / Blind man blues / 'Taint nobody's business if I do / Down on the levee blues / If I let you get away with it once more you'll do it all the / Shreveport blues / House rent blues / Texas moaner blues / You've got the right key, but the wrong key hole / Cake walking babies from home / Pickin' on your baby / Cake walking babies
CBC 1028 / 24 Aug '98 / Timeless Historical

Beck

☐ **INTERVIEW SESSIONS**
CHAT 6 / 6 Nov '97 / Chatback

☐ **MELLOW GOLD**
Loser / Pay no mind (snoozer) / Fuckin' with my head (Mountain dew rock) / Whiskeyclone / Hotel City 1997 / Soul suckin' jerk / Truckdrivin' neighbours downstairs / Sweet sunshine / Beercan / Steal my body home / Nightmare hippy girl / Motherfucker / Blackhole
GED 24634 / Mar '94 / Geffen

☐ **ODELAY**
Devils haircut / Hotwax / Lord only knows / New pollution / Derelict / Novacane / Jack-ass / Where it's at / Minus / Sissyneck / Readymade / High 5 (rock the Catskills) / Ramshackle / Diskobox
GED 24926
GED 24908 / Jun '96 / Geffen

☐ **ONE FOOT IN THE GRAVE**
KLP 28CD / Jun '97 / K

☐ **STEREOPATHETIC SOULMANURE**
FLIP 060CD / 25 May '98 / Flipside

Beck, Elder Charles

☐ **ELDER BECK & ELDER CURRY 1930-1939**
BDCD 6035 / Apr '93 / Blues Document

☐ **ELDER CHARLES BECK VOL.2 1946-1956**
DOCD 5524 / Apr '97 / Document

Beck, Gordon

☐ **ONCE IS NEVER ENOUGH**
FMRCD 20 / Sep '96 / Future

☐ **ONE FOR THE ROAD**
Good times, sometimes / Out of the shadows into the sun / Thoughts / Long, lean and lethal / What's this / Beautiful, but / One for the road / Shhhh / Pay now, live later
JMS 186752 / Nov '95 / JMS

Beck, Jeff

☐ **BECKOLOGY (3CD Set)**
Trouble in mind: *Tridents* / Nursery rhyme: *Tridents* / Wandering man blues: *Tridents* / Steeled blues: *Yardbirds* / Heart full of soul: *Yardbirds* / I'm not talking: *Yardbirds* / I ain't done wrong: *Yardbirds* / I'm a man: *Yardbirds* / Shapes of things: *Yardbirds* / Over under sideways down: *Yardbirds* / Happenings ten years time ago: *Yardbirds* / Hot house of Omagararshid: *Yardbirds* / Lost women: *Yardbirds* / Rack myh mind: *Yardbirds* / Nazz are blue: *Yardbirds* / Psycho daisies: *Yardbirds* / Jeff's boogie: *Yardbirds* / Too much monkey business: *Yardbirds* / Sun is shining: *Yardbirds* / You're a better man than I: *Yardbirds* / Love me like I love you: *Yardbirds* / Hi ho silver lining / Tallyman / Beck's bolero / I ain't superstitious: *Beck, Jeff Group* / Rock my plimsoul: *Beck, Jeff Group* / Jailhouse rock: *Beck, Jeff Group* / Plynth (water down the drain): *Beck, Jeff Group* / I've been drinking: *Beck, Jeff Group* / Definitely maybe: *Beck, Jeff Group* / New ways/train train: *Beck, Jeff Group* / Going down: *Beck, Jeff Group* / I can't give back the love I feel for you: *Beck, Jeff Group* / Superstition: *Beck Bogert Appice* / Black cat moan: *Beck Bogert Appice* / Blues deluxe BBA boogie: *Beck Bogert Appice* / Jizz whizz: *Beck Bogert Appice* / 'Cause we've ended as lovers / Goodbye Pork Pie Hat / Love is green / Diamond dust / Freeway jam: *Beck, Jeff & Jan Hammer Group* / Pump / People get ready: *Beck, Jeff & Rod Stewart* / Escape / Gets us all in the end / Back on the street / Wild thing / Train kept a rollin' / Sleepwalk / Stumble / Big block: *Beck, Jeff/Terry Bozzio/Tony Hymas* / Where were you: *Beck, Jeff/Terry Bozzio/Tony Hymas*
4893192 / 6 Apr '98 / Legacy

☐ **BEST OF JEFF BECK, THE**
Shapes of things / Morning dew / You shook me / I ain't superstitious / All shook up / Jailhouse rock / Plynth (water down the drain) / Hi ho silver lining / Tallyman / Love is blue / I've been drinking / Rock my plimsoul / Beck's bolero / Rice pudding / Greensleeves / Spanish boots
CDMFP 6202 / Nov '95 / Music For Pleasure

☐ **BEST OF JEFF BECK, THE**
Hi-ho silver lining / Beck's Bolero / Greensleeves / You shook me / Tallyman / Rock my plimsoul / Jailhouse rock / Shapes of things / All shook up / I ain't superstitious / Plynth (water down the drain) / Love is blue / Morning dew / Spanish boots / Rice pudding / I've been drinking
CDGOLD 1060 / Oct '96 / EMI Gold

☐ **BLOW BY BLOW**
It doesn't really matter / She's a woman / Constipated duck / Air blower / Scatterbrain / 'Cause we've ended as lovers / Thelonious / Freeway jam / Diamond dust
4690122 / Apr '94 / Epic

☐ **FLASH**
Ambitious / Gets us all in the end / Escape / People get ready / Stop, look and listen / Get workin' / Ecstacy / Night after night / You know, we know / Get us all in the end / Ecstasy
4688672 / Feb '97 / Epic

☐ **GUITAR LEGEND**
Heart full of soul / What do you want / I'm not talking / Steeled blues / I'm a man / Stroll on / I ain't done nothing wrong / Like Jimmy Reed again / Mister you're a better man than I / Jeff's blues / Down in the boots / Chuckles / Steelin' / LA breakdown
308582 / 20 Apr '98 / Hallmark

☐ **THERE AND BACK**
Star cycle / Too much to lose / You never knew / Pump / El Becko / Golden road / Space boogie / Final peace
4777812 / Feb '97 / Epic

☐ **TRUTH/BECK-OLA (Beck, Jeff Group)**
Shapes of things / Let me love you / Morning dew / You shook me / Ol' man river / Greensleeves / Rock my plimsoul / Beck's bolero / Blues deluxe / I ain't superstitious / All shook up / Spanish boots / Girl from Mill Valley / Jailhouse rock / Plynth (water down the drain) / Hangman's knee / Rice pudding
CDP 7954692 / Feb '91 / Premier/EMI

Beck, Joe

☐ **BECK AND SANBORN**
ZK 40805 / Aug '97 / Sony Jazz

☐ **FINGER PAINTING**
EFA 034532 / Nov '95 / Wavetone

Becker, Jason

☐ **PERPETUAL BURN**
Altitudes / Perpetual blues / Mabel's fatal fable / Temple of the absurd / Eleven blue Egyptians / Dweller in the cellar / Opus pocus
RR 95282 / Sep '88 / Roadrunner

Becker, Walter

☐ **COLLECTION, THE (Becker, Walter & Donald Fagen)**
Brain tap shuffle: *Becker, Walter* / Brooklyn: *Becker, Walter* / Mock turtle song: *Becker, Walter* / Yellow peril: *Becker, Walter* / Soul ram: *Becker, Walter* / Ida Lee: *Becker, Walter* / Any world (that I'm welcome to): *Becker, Walter* / You go where I go: *Becker, Walter* / This seat's been taken: *Becker, Walter* / Berry Town: *Becker, Walter* / More to come: *Fagen, Donald* / Little with sugar: *Fagen, Donald* / Take it out on me: *Fagen, Donald* / Android warehouse: *Fagen, Donald* / Roaring of the lamb: *Fagen, Donald* / Charlie Free: *Fagen, Donald* / Sun mountain: *Fagen, Donald* / Horse in town: *Fagen, Donald* / Stone piano: *Fagen, Donald* / Parker's band: *Fagen, Donald* / Oh wow, it's you: *Fagen, Donald*
CLACD 365 / Aug '93 / Castle

☐ **ELEVEN TRACKS OF WHACK**
Down in the bottom / Junkie girl / Surf and or die / Book of liars / Lucky Henry / Hard up case / Cringemaker / Girlfriend / My Waterloo / This moody bastard / Hat too flat
74321226092 / Nov '94 / Giant

☐ **FOUNDERS OF STEELY DAN (Becker, Walter & Donald Fagen)**
Android warehouse / A horse in town / More to come / Parker's band / Oh wow it's you again / Stone piano / Yellow peril / Take it out on me / Brain tap shuffle / Mock turtle song / Charlie freak / Roaring of the lamb / Soul ram / Brooklyn / Little with sugar / You go where I go / Ida lee / Any world (that I'm welcome to) / This seat's been taken / Berrytown / Sun mountain
RMB 75004 / Nov '93 / Remember

☐ **ROOT OF STEELY DAN, THE (Becker, Walter & Donald Fagen)**
Android warehouse / Parker's band / You go where I go / Little with sugar / Stone piano / Roaring of the lamb / Charlie freak / This seal's been taken / More to come / Oh wow it's you / Take it out on me / Ida lee / Barrytown / Any world / Caves of Altamira / Horse in town / Sun mountain
306152 / Jan '97 / Hallmark

☐ **YOU GOTTA WALK IT LIKE YOU TALK IT (Or You'll Loose That Beat/Original Soundtrack) (Becker, Walter & Donald Fagen)**
You gotta walk it like you talk it / Flotsam and jetsam / War and peace / Roll back the meaning / You gotta walk it like you talk it (reprise) / Dog eat dog / Red giant/white dwarf / If it rains
SEECD 357 / Jun '97 / See For Miles

Beckerman, Sid

☐ **KLEZMER PLUS**
In Odess'/Yas / Tish nigun / Freylekhs in D / Yiddish theater medley / Shloymke and nifty / Ot azoy / Sydney's eygene Bulgars / Freylekhs in D minor / Doina / Shiroh / Husid'l medley / Waltz medley / Dave Tarras' B-flat Bulgars
FF 70488 / 15 Dec '97 / Flying Fish

Beckett, Harry

☐ ALL FOUR ONE
White sky / Time of day / One for all / Enchanted / Shadowy light / Happy 96 / Images of clarity / Better git it in your soul
SPJCD 547 / May '93 / Spotlite

☐ COMPARED 2 WHAT (Beckett, Harry Quintet)
BASIC 50008 / Apr '96 / ITM

☐ IMAGES OF CLARITY (Beckett, Harry & Didier Levallet/Tony Marsh)
EVCD 315 / Feb '94 / Evidence

Beckingham, Keith

☐ HAMMOND SHOWCASE REVISITED
There's no business like show business / Medley / Medley / Medley / Medley / Smile to smile / This heart of mine / This is my lovely day / Smoke gets in your eyes / Medley / Donkey serenade / Stormy weather / I have dreamed / Serenade in the night / My Fair Lady selection / Medley / Michael Legrand medley / Medley / Green cockatoo / Twilight time / Jerry Allen tribute / Branch line / Medley
OS 220 / May '96 / OS Digital

Becton, William

☐ BROKEN (Becton, William & Friends)
Broken / Still in love with you / Fall afresh / Sure won't forget / No turning back / In your arms of love / 'Til the end / Joy / Be encouraged / Closer to you / Courage to journey on / 'Til you take the pain away / Let the healing again / Since the Lord changed my life / 'Til the end (jazz version)
CDK 9145 / Oct '95 / Alliance Music

Bede, Arran

☐ GOSSAMER MANSION
CDLCDL 1221 / Nov '94 / Lochshore

Bedford, David

☐ GREAT EQUATORIAL
Great equatorial (Part 1 to part 6)
VP 156CD / Oct '94 / Voiceprint

☐ INSTRUCTIONS FOR ANGELS
Theme / Wanderers of the pale wood / Dazzling burden / Be music, night / First came the lion rider / Instructions for angels / Alleujah tympanis
CDV 2090 / Jun '97 / Virgin

☐ NURSES SONG WITH ELEPHANTS
It's easier than it looks / Nurses song with elephants / Some bright stars from Queens College / Trona / Sad and lonely faces
BP 116CD / Aug '96 / Blueprint

☐ ODYSSEY, THE
Penelope's shroud / King Aeolus / Penelope's shroud / Phaeacian games / Penelope's shroud / Sirens / Scylla and Charybdis / Penelope's shroud / Circe's island / Penelope's shroud completed / Battle in the hall
CDOVD 444 / Apr '94 / Virgin

☐ RIGEL 9
Forest / Anders' capture / City / Anders and the red one / Kapper and Lee in the forest / Death of the orange one / Funeral procession / Anders alone in the city / Ritual song / Anders flight through the forest / At the ship: countdown and lift-off / Finale
CDOVD 484 / Jun '97 / Charisma

☐ RIME OF THE ANCIENT MARINER, THE
Rime of the ancient mariner
CDOVD 443 / Apr '94 / Virgin

☐ SONG OF THE WHITE HORSE, THE
Prelude: Wayland's Smithy / White horse / Blowing stone / Song of the white horse / Postlude / Text / Choir 1 / Choir 2
VP 110 CD / Feb '93 / Voiceprint

☐ STAR'S END
Side one / Side two
CDV 2020 / Jun '97 / Virgin

☐ VARIATIONS ON A RHYTHM
Variations on a rhythm of Mike Oldfield / Superman / Day of the percherons / Have mercy on my eyes
BP 191CD / 6 Oct '97 / Blueprint

Bedhead

☐ BEHEADED
R 4052 / Oct '96 / Rough Trade

☐ TRANSACTION DE NOVO
Exhume / More than ever / Parade / Half thought / Extramundane / Forgetting / Lepidoptera / Psychodomatica / Present
TR 67CD / 2 Feb '98 / Trance Syndicate

☐ WHAT FUN LIFE WAS
TR 21CD / Apr '94 / Trance

Bedlam A Go Go

☐ ESTATE STYLE ENTERTAINMENT
Northern lights / Aimy / Paranoid / Flat 29 / Demons / Heroin / Asylum / Season no.5 / When the penny drops / Meeting of the minds / My so called life
BDLM 4CD / 13 Jul '98 / Sony Soho2

Bedlam Rovers

☐ FROTHING GREEN
NORM 171CD / Mar '94 / Normal

☐ LAND OF NO SURPRISE
NORMAL 191CD / Aug '95 / Normal

☐ SQUEEZE YOUR INNER CHILD
RTS 16 / Apr '95 / Return To Sender

☐ WALLOW
NORMAL 151CD / Mar '94 / Normal

Bee, Celi

☐ BEST OF CELI BEE AND THE BUZZY BUNCH, THE (For The Love Of My Man) (Bee, Celi & Buzzy Bunch)
Superman / Hurt me hurt me / One love / Closer closer / Macho (a real one) / Together / Comin' up strong / Lost in love / Fly me on the wings of love suite / Can't let you go thing / For the love of my man / Blow my mind / It's love / Boomerangs
HTCD 34 / 20 Apr '98 / Hot Productions

Bee Gees

☐ CHILDREN OF THE WORLD
You should be dancing / You stepped into my life / Love so right / Lovers / Can't keep a good man down / Boogie child / Love me / Subway / Way it was / Children of the world
8236582 / Nov '89 / Polydor

☐ CLAUSTROPHOBIA
Three kisses of love / Could it be / Claustrophobia / Every day I have to cry some / Wine and woman / Second hand people / You wouldn't know / Glasshouse / Turn around look at me / Spicks and specks / Monday's rain / I am the world / Big chance / How many birds / Battle of the blue and the grey / Follow the wind
CDSGP 0307 / 27 Oct '97 / Prestige

☐ CUCUMBER CASTLE
If I only had my mind on something else / Then you left me / I was the child / Sweetheart / My thing / Turning tide / IOIO / Lord / I lay down and die / Bury me down by the river / Chance of love / Don't forget to remember
8337832 / Nov '89 / Polydor

☐ ESP
ESP / You win again / Live or die / Giving up the ghost / Longest night / This is your life / Angela / Overnight / Crazy for your love / Backtafunk
9255412 / Feb '95 / WEA

☐ EVER INCREASING CIRCLES
Three kisses of love / Battle of the blue and grey / Take hold of that star / Claustrophobia / Could it be / Turn around and look at me / Theme from Jamie McPheeters / You wouldn't know / How many birds / Big chance / I don't think it's funny / How love was true / Glasshouse
MM 001 / 27 Mar '98 / MagMid

☐ FOREVER YOUNG
Spicks and specks / Wine and woman / Turn around, look at me / I am the world / Follow the wind / Three kisses of love / Could it be (I'm in love) / To be or not to be / I don't think it's funny / Claustraphobia / Every day I have to cry / Take hold of that star
322691 / Nov '93 / Koch

☐ HORIZONTAL
World / And the sun will shine / Lemons never forget / Really and sincerely / Birdie told me / With the sun in my eyes / Massachusetts / Harry Braff / Daytime girl / Earnest of being George / Change is made / Horizontal
8336592 / Mar '90 / Polydor

☐ IDEA
Let there be love / In the Summer of his years / Down to earth / I've gotta get a message to you / When the swallows fly / I started a joke / Swansong / Kitty can / Indian gin and whisky dry / Such a shame / Idea / I have decided to join the airforce / Kilburn towers
8336602 / Nov '89 / Polydor

☐ INSTRUMENTAL MEMORIES (Various Artists)
You win again / Massachusets / Words / I've gotta get a message to you / Secret love / For whom the bell tolls / Love so right / First of May / Too much heaven / Spirits having flown / Run to me / Paying the price of love / Saved by the bell / Don't forget to remember / To love somebody / New York mining disaster 1941 / Alone / How deep is your love
308212 / Sep '97 / Hallmark

☐ LEGEND BEGINS, THE
Spicks and specks / You wouldn't know / I was a lover, a leader of men / How love was true / To be or not to be / Theme from Jamie McPhetter's / I want home / I am the world / Could it be I'm in love / I don't think it's funny / Every day I have to cry / Wine and women / Claustrophobia / Turn around, look at me
307662 / Jul '97 / Hallmark

☐ LIFE IN A TIN CAN
Saw a new morning / I don't wanna be the one / South Dakota morning / Livin in Chicago / While I play / My life has been a song / Come home Johnny Bridie / Method in my madness
8337882 / Jul '92 / Polydor

☐ MELODY FAIR (A Bee Gees Tribute) (Various Artists)
ER 80012CD / Nov '97 / Eggbert

☐ ONE
Ordinary lives / Bodyguard / Tears / Flesh and blood / House of shame / One / It's my neighbourhood / Tokyo nights / Wish you were here / Will you ever let him
9258872 / Feb '95 / WEA

☐ SIZE ISN'T EVERYTHING
Paying the price of love / Kiss of life / How to fall in love Pt 1 / Omega man / Haunted house / Heart like mine / Anything for you / Blue island / Above and beyond / For whom the bell tolls / Fallen angel / Decadance
5199452 / Sep '93 / Polydor

☐ SPICKS AND SPECKS
In the morning / Like nobody else / All by myself / Storm / Butterfly / Exit stage right / Coalman / I am the world / Cherry red / I want home / Monday's rain / How many birds / Second hand people / Born a man / Spicks and specks / I was a lover, a leader of men / Timber / Claustrophobia / Could it be / I don't think it's funny / Three kisses of love / Turn around, look at me / Every day I have to cry / How love was true / You won't see me / Lonely winter
RMB 75068 / Aug '93 / Remember

☐ SPICKS AND SPECKS (The Early Years)
Spicks and specks / Guess I don't know why I bother with myself / I don't think it's funny / Glass house / Wine and women / Monday's rain / I am the world / Turn around, look at me / How love was true / Peace of mind / Second hand people / Timber / Where are you / I was a lover, a leader of men / I want home / They play high and I play down
SPCD 354 / Feb '94 / Disky

☐ SPIRITS HAVING FLOWN
Tragedy / Too much heaven / Love you inside out / Reaching out / Spirits (having flown) / Living together / I'm satisfied / Until
8273352 / Nov '89 / Polydor

☐ SPOTLIGHT ON BEE GEES
Wine and women / Turn around, look at me / How many birds / Claustrophobia / Three kisses of love / To be or not to be / I don't think it's funny / Spicks and specks / How love was true / Follow the wind / Take hold of that star / I was a lover, a leader of men / I am the world / Second hand people / Every day I have to cry / Monday's rain
HADCD 105 / Feb '94 / Javelin

☐ STILL WATERS
Alone / I surrender / I could not love you more / Still waters run deep / My lover's prayer / With my eyes closed / Irresistible force / Closer than close / I will / Obsessions / Miracles happen / Smoke and mirrors
5373022 / Mar '97 / Polydor

☐ TO BE OR NOT TO BE (2CD Set)
Three kings of love / Battle of the blue and grey / Take hold of that star / Claustrophobia / Could it be / Turn around look at me / Theme from Jamie McPheeters / You wouldn't know / How many birds / Big chance / I don't think it's funny / How love was true / Glasshouse / Everyday I have to cry / Wine and women / Follow the wind / I was a lover / Children laughing / I want home / Spicks and specks / I am the world / Playdown / I don't know why I bother myself / Monday's rain / To be or not to be / Second hand people
CDTB 170 / 24 Oct '97 / Thunderbolt

☐ TRAFALGAR
How can you mend a broken heart / Israel / Greatest man in the world / It's just the way / Remembering / Somebody / Stop the music / Trafalgar / Don't wanna live inside myself / When do I / Dearest / Lion in winter / Walking back to Waterloo
8337862 / Mar '90 / Polydor

☐ TWO YEARS ON
Two years on / Portrait of Louise / Man for all seasons / Sincere relation / Back home / First mistake I made / Lonely days / Alone again / Tell me why / Lay it on me / Every second, every minute / I'm weeping
8337852 / Mar '90 / Polydor

☐ VERY BEST OF THE BEE GEES
You win again / How deep is your love / Night fever / Tragedy / Massachusetts / I've gotta get a message to you / You should be dancing / New York mining disaster 1941 / World / First of May / Don't forget to remember / Saved by the bell / Run to me / Jive talkin' / More than a woman / Stayin' alive / Too much heaven / Ordinary lives / To love somebody / Nights on Broadway
8473392 / Nov '90 / Polydor

☐ YOU WOULDN'T KNOW
JHD 006 / Jun '92 / Tring

Beebe, Jim

☐ SULTRY SERENADE, A (Beebe, Jim Chicago Jazz)
Chicago / Canal St. blues / Blue prelude / This joint is jumpin' / Sultry serenade / Travellin' light / Bye and bye / Drummin' man / Buddy Bolden's blues / Just a closer walk with thee / Night train
DE 230 / Jun '97 / Delmark

Beechman, Laurie

☐ NO ONE IS ALONE
VSD 5623 / Nov '96 / Varese Sarabande

☐ TIME BETWEEN THE TIME
Another hundred people / It might be you / Look at that face / Very precious love / Long before I knew you / Look of love / House is not a home / I'll never stop loving you / Shining sea/Shadow of your smile / Soon it's gonna rain/Rain sometimes / Music that makes me dance / Time between the time / Never never land / Home
DRGCD 5230 / Nov '93 / DRG

Beekeepers

☐ THIRD PARTY FEAR AND THEFT
Eyeballed / Killer cure / Inheritance / Second skin / Do you behave like that at home / I only want to see you suffer / Beau peepshow / Elsewhere / Catgut
BBQCD 199 / 2 Mar '98 / Beggars Banquet

Beenie Man

☐ BEENIE MAN GOLD
CRCD 32 / May '94 / Charm

☐ BEENIE MAN MEETS MAD COBRA (Beenie Man & Mad Cobra)
VPCD 1413 / Aug '95 / VP

☐ DEFEND IT
SVCD 3 / Feb '94 / Shocking Vibes

☐ MAESTRO
Intro / Heights of great man / Nuff gal / Yaw yaw / Be my lady / Maestro / Old dog / Jerusalem / Blackboard / Any Mr. man / Slowly: *Beenie Man & Little Kirk* / Man royal / Oh Jah Jah: *Beenie Man & Silver Cat* / His-story / Africans / Girl's way / Nuh lock: *Beenie Man & Little Kirk* / One big road / Si mi ya / Never been down / Outro/Special thanks
GRELCD 234 / Jan '97 / Greensleeves

☐ MANY MOODS OF MOSES
SVCD 7 / Mar '98 / Shocking Vibes

☐ REGGAE MAX
JSRNCD 14 / Mar '97 / Jet Star

☐ RUFF & RUGGED STRICTLY RAGGA
RNCD 2041 / Jan '94 / Rhino

Beer, Phil

☐ ALLANZA (Beer, Phil & Incantation)
RGFCD 012 / Nov '90 / Road Goes On Forever

☐ HARD HATS
Fireman's song / Chance / This far / Blinded by love / More / Blind fiddler / This year / Hard hats / She could laugh / Think it over
HTDCD 24 / Sep '96 / HTD

☐ SHOW OF HANDS
RGFCD 010 / Nov '91 / Road Goes On Forever

☐ WORKS, THE
OCOCD 1 / Feb '96 / Old Court

Beergut 100

☐ FIST FULL OF COPPER
BFRCD 008 / 8 Jun '98 / Step 1

Beers Family

☐ SEASONS OF PEACE
Run like a deer / Seasons of peace / Song of the virgin / Blue spring rain / Three little drummers from Africa / I got a bird that whistles / Ladybug song / Simple gifts / Fiddler's green / Two foxes / Kitty alone / Dumbarton's drums / Green gravel / Peace carol / Blackhawk waltz
BCD 146 / Jun '97 / Biograph

Bees, Andrew

☐ MILITANT
ML 818112 / Sep '95 / Music

Beesley, John

☐ ORCHESTRALLY ORGANISED
Cabaret / All the things you are / Take five / Yellow submarine / Caravan / Gigue fugue / Whiter shade of pale / Waterloo march / Henry Mancini medley / I dreamed a dream / Bohemian rhapdosy / Power of love / Olympic flame / Morning / Blue rondo a la Turk / Summertime / Stars and stripes forever
OS 204 / Mar '94 / OS Digital

Beeston Pipe Band

☐ AMAZING GRACE
EUCD 1189 / Apr '92 / ARC

Beevar, Brian

☐ ONCE IN A LIFE
RM 2222 / Aug '96 / Real

BEF

☐ MUSIC FOR LISTENING TO (British Electric Foundation)
Groove thang / Optimum chant / Uptown apocalypse / BEF ident / Baby called Billy / Rise of the east / Music to kill your parents by
11242 / Sep '97 / Caroline

Beger, Albert

☐ THIS LIFE (Beger, Albert Quartet)
Passengers / Fishermen / Winds / Hassidute / Purple house / Love / Dao / This life
4891922 / 9 Feb '98 / Sony Jazz

Beggar's Opera

☐ ACT ONE
Poet and peasant / Passacaglia / Memory / Raymond's road / Light cavalry / Sarabande / Think
REP 7041 / 15 Dec '97 / Repertoire

☐ FINAL CURTAIN, THE
SCRCD 015 / Sep '96 / Scratch

Beggars & Thieves

☐ LOOK WHAT YOU CREATE
MTMCD 199619 / Apr '97 / Made To Measure

Beggars Thieves & Madmen

☐ BEGGARS THIEVES & MADMEN
Many things before / Just one chance / Don't turn away / No way out / Somebody help me / Free at last
HTT 0952 / 27 Oct '97 / Holier Than Thou

Begley, Brendan

☐ WE WON'T GO HOME 'TIL MORNING
KMCD 9510 / Dec '97 / Kells

Begley, Philomena

☐ COUNTRY QUEEN FOR 30 YEARS
Every second / Look at us / Walkin', talkin', cryin', barely beatin' broken heart / Picture of me (without you) / Bright lights and country music / Start living again / Bed you made for me / Home I'll be / Our wedding day / Just one time / If my heart had windows / Family tree / Last rose of summer / Life is not always a rainbow / Gold and silver days / Bing bang boom
RZRCD 522 / Nov '92 / Ritz

☐ IN HARMONY (Begley, Philomena & Mick Flavin)
No love left / Just between you and me / I'm wasting your time you're wasting mine / Till a tear becomes a rose / Always, always / We're strangers again / We'll get ahead someday / All you've got to do is dream / Daisy chain / Don't believe me I'm lying / You can't break the chains of love / Let's pretend we're not married tonight / How can I (help you forgive me) / Somewhere between
RZCD 0061 / Apr '91 / Ritz

☐ SILVER ANNIVERSARY ALBUM
Key is in the mailbox / Here today and gone tomorrow / Rose of my heart / Behind the footlights / Jeannie's afraid of the dark / Red is the rose / Dark island / Leavin' on your mind / Queen of the silver dollar / Blanket on the ground / Truck drivin' woman / One is one too many / Galway Bay / Old arboe
RZCD 505 / '90 / Ritz

☐ SIMPLY DIVINE (Begley, Philomena & Ray Lynam)
You don't know love / Simply divine / Together alone / Near you / Don't cross over an old love / Making plans / Sweetest of all / I'll never need another you / She sang the melody / As long as we're dreaming / Hold on / Fire of two old flames
RZSCD 425 / Apr '93 / Ritz

Begley, Seamus

☐ MEITHEAL (Begley, Seamus & Stephen Cooney)
HBCD 0004 / Jul '93 / Hummingbird

Begnagrad

☐ BROKEN DANCE, A
AAYACDT 1190 / Apr '91 / Ayaa Disques

Beguiled

☐ BLUE DIRGE
EFA 115742 / Apr '94 / Crypt

Behemoth

☐ GROM
SOL 005CD / 28 Jul '97 / Solistium

Beherit

☐ DRAWING DOWN THE MOON
SP 1014CD / May '96 / Spinefarm

☐ ELECTRIC DOOM
SPI 028CD / Mar '96 / Spinefarm

☐ H4180V21C
SP 119CD / Jun '94 / Spinefarm

Beiderbecke, Bix

☐ 20 CLASSIC TRACKS
Jazz me blues / Somebody stole my gal / Ol man river / Wringin' and twistin' / Clarinet marmalade / Ostrich walk / Mississippi mud / Baby, won't you please come home / Goose pimples / Margie / Louisiana / Rhythm king / Three blind mice / Krazy cat / Good man is hard to find / Thou swell / Wa-da-da / Louise / Japanese sandman / Dusky stevedore
CDMFP 6163 / May '95 / Music For Pleasure

☐ AT THE JAZZ BAND BALL (1924-1928)
Fidgety feet / Tiger rag / Flock o'blues / I'm glad / Toddlin' blues / Davenport blues / In a mist / Riverboat shuffle / Ostrich walk / At the jazz band ball / Clementine / Deep down South / For no reason at all / From Monday on / I'm coming Virginia / Jazz me blues / Krazy kat / Mississippi mud / San / Since my best gal turned me down / Singin' the blues / Way down yonder in New Orleans
CDAJA 5080 / Apr '91 / Living Era

☐ BEIDERBECKE AFFAIR, THE
Riverboat shuffle / Tiger rag / Davenport blues / I'm looking over a four leaf clover / Trumbology / Clarinet marmalade / Ostrich walk / Way down yonder in New Orleans / Three blind mice / Clementine / Royal garden blues / Coquette / When / Lovable / Is it gonna be long / Oh you have no idea / Felix the cat / T'ain't so honey, t'ain't so / I'd rather cry over you / Louisiana / Futuristic rhythm / Raisin' the roof / Rockin' chair / Strut Miss Lizzie / Georgia on my mind
GRF 079 / '93 / Tring

☐ BEIDERBECKE COLLECTION, THE (20 Classics From The Jazz Genius)
I'm coming Virginia / Rhythm king / At the jazz band ball / Ostrich walk / Somebody stole my gal / Goose pimples / Royal garden blues / Cryin' all day / Good man is hard to find / Trumbology / Singing the blues / Since my best gal turned me down / Louisianna / Clarinet marmalade / Sorry / Riverboat shuffle / Thou swell / Ol' man river / Wa-da-da (Everybody's doin' it now) / Jazz me blues
306302 / Jan '97 / Hallmark

☐ BIX
Singin' the blues / Jazz me blues / At the jazz band ball / Royal garden blues / Sorry / I'm coming virginia / Trumbology / Goose pimples / Riverboat shuffle / For no reason at all in 'c' / Fidgety feet / Thou swell / Margie / Clementine / Ol' man river / Louisiana / In a mist (bixology) / I'll be a friend with pleasure
CD 14532 / Jan '94 / Jazz Portraits

☐ BIX 'N' BING (Recordings From 1927-1929) (Beiderbecke, Bix/Bing Crosby/ Paul Whiteman Orchestra)
Changes / Mary / There ain't no sweet man that's worth the salt of my tears / Sunshine / Mississippi mud / High water / From Monday on / Loveable / My pet / Louisiana / Do I hear you saying I love you / You took advantage of me / That's my weakness now / Because my baby don't mean maybe now / I'm in seventh heaven / Reaching for someone (and not finding anyone there) / Oh Miss Hannah / Your mother and mine / Waiting at the end of the road / T'ain't so honey, t'ain't so
CDAJA 5005 / Oct '88 / Living Era

☐ BIX BEIDERBECKE
DVX 08062 / May '95 / Deja Vu

☐ BIX BEIDERBECKE (2CD Set)
R2CD 4023 / 13 Apr '98 / Deja Vu

☐ BIX BEIDERBECKE & THE WOLVERINES
CBC 10013 / Feb '94 / Timeless Jazz

☐ BIX BEIDERBECKE 1924
CBC 1013 / Jun '93 / Bellaphon

☐ BIX BEIDERBECKE AND THE CHICAGO CORNETS
Fidgety feet / Jazz me blues / Oh baby / Copenhagen / Riverboat shuffle / Susie / Royal garden blues / Tiger rag / I need some pettin' / Sensation / Lazy daddy / Tia Juana / Big boy / I'm glad / Flovk o' blues / Toddlin' blues / Davenport blues / Prince of Wails / When my sugar walks down the street / Steady roll blues / Mobile blues / Really a pain / Chicago blues / Hot mittens / Buddy's habit
MCD 47019 2 / Jun '93 / Milestone

☐ BIX BEIDERBECKE BAND, THE (Beiderbecke, Bix Band)
Jazz me blues / Royal garden blues / At the jazz band ball / Since my best gal turned me down / Sorry / Somebody stole my girl / Goose pimples / Ol' man river / Thou swell / Rhythm king / Wa da da / Singin' the blues / Louisiana / Ostrich walk / Clarinet marmalade / I'm coming Virginia / River boat shuffle / Way down yonder in New Orleans
SUMCD 4176 / 23 Feb '98 / Summit

☐ BIX BEIDERBECKE GOLD (2CD Set)
D2CD 4023 / Jun '95 / Deja Vu

☐ BIXOLOGY
Jazz me blues / At the jazz band ball / Royal garden blues / Sorry / Singin' the blues / I'm coming Virginia / Way down yonder in New Orleans / For no reason at all in C / Goose pimples / Trumbology / Ostrich walk / Riverboat shuffle / Davenport blues / Copenhagen / Fidgety feet / Tiger rag / In a mist / Clementine / Thou swell / Ol' man river / Wa-da-da / Louisiana / Margie / I'll be a friend with pleasure / Bessie couldn't help it
CD 53017 / Jun '88 / Giants Of Jazz

☐ CLASSIC YEARS, THE
CDSGP 0178 / Nov '95 / Prestige

☐ CLASSICS 1924-1927
CLASSICS 778 / Mar '95 / Classics

☐ CLASSICS 1927-1930
CLASSICS 788 / Nov '94 / Classics

☐ GENIUS OF BIX BEIDERBECKE
Jazz me blues / Thou swell / Royal garden blues / At the jazz band ball / Mississippi mud / Riverboat shuffle / T'ain't so honey, t'ain't so / Clementine / Lonely melody / There ain't no sweet man that's worth the salt of my tears / Dardanella / Sugar / Since my best gal turned me down / Wa-da-da / Rhythm king / Clarinet marmalade / I'm coming Virginia / Crying all day / Deep down South / I'll be a friend with pleasure
PASTCD 9765 / Oct '91 / Flapper

☐ INDISPENSABLE BIX BEIDERBECKE 1924-1930, THE
I didn't know / Idolizing / Sunday / I'm proud of a baby like you / I'm looking over a four leaf clover / I'm gonna meet my sweetie now / Hoosier sweetheart / My pretty girl / Slow river / In my merry Oldsmobile / Clementine / Washboard blues / Changes / Mary / Lonely melody / San / Back in your own backyard / There ain't no sweet man that's worth the salt of my tears / Dardanella / From Monday on / Mississippi mud / Sugar / Coquette / When / Lovable / My pet / Forget me not / Louisiana / You took advantage of me / Rockin' chair / Barnacle Bill the sailor / Deep down south / I don't mind walking in the rain / I'll be a friend with pleasure / Georgia on my mind / Bessie couldn't help it
ND 89572 / Mar '94 / RCA

☐ INTRODUCTION TO BIX BEIDERBECKE 1924-1930, AN
4012 / Aug '94 / Best Of Jazz

☐ JAZZ MASTERS
Jazz me blues / Somebody stole my gal / Ol' man river / Wringing and twisting / Clarinet marmalade / Ostrich walk / Mississippi mud / Baby won't you please come home / Goose pimples / Margie / Louisiana / Rhythm king / Three blind mice / Krazy kat / Good man is hard to find / Thou swell / Dusky stevedore / Japanese sandman / Louise / Wa-da-da
CDMFP 6297 / Mar '97 / Music For Pleasure

☐ JAZZ ME BLUES
Trumbology / Singin' the blues (till my daddy comes home) / Ostrich walk / Riverboat shuffle / For no reason at all in 'c' / I'm coming Virginia / Way down yonder in New Orleans / In a mist (bixology) / Clementine / Jazz me blues / At the jazz band ball / Royal garden blues / Goose pimples / Sorry / Since my best girl turned me down / There'll come a time / Mississippi mud / Thou swell / Wa-da-da (ev'rybody's doin' it now) / Ol' man river
JHR 73517 / '91 / Jazz Hour

☐ JAZZ ME BLUES
CDD 490 / Jul '91 / Progressive

☐ LEON BISMARCK 'BIX' BEIDERBECKE
Singin' the blues / Jazz me blues / All the jazz band hall / Royal garden blues / Sorry / I'm coming Virginia / Trumbology / Goose pimples / Riverboat shuffle / For no reason at all in C / Fidgety feet / Thou swell / Margie / Clementine / Ol' man river / Louisiana / In a mist / I'll be a friend with pleasure
CD 56016 / Aug '94 / Jazz Roots

☐ QUINTESSENCE, THE (1924-1930/2CD Set)
FA 215 / Oct '96 / Fremeaux

☐ SINGIN' THE BLUES
Trumbology / Clarinet marmalade / Singin' the blues / Ostrich walk / Riverboat shuffle / I'm going Virginia / Way down yonder in New Orleans / For no reason at all / Three blind mice / Blue river / There's a cradle in Caroline / In a mist / Wringin' and twistin' / Humpty and dumpty / Krazy kat / Baltimore / There ain't no land like Dixieland to me / Just an hour of love / I'm wondering who
4663092 / '91 / Sony Jazz

☐ TIGER RAG
TKCD 020 / Nov '96 / Magnum America

Beil, Peter

☐ CORINNA CORINNA
Corinna Corinna / Komm zuruck schone Nina / Sophia / Dreizehn girls / Ich geh allein / Das bist du / Kleid aus seide / Lass den lippenstift zu haus / Dir hat der mond den kopf verdreht / Carolin / Carolina / Weine nie / Und dein zug fahrt in die nacht / Kleine nervensage Monika / Vor deinem fenster / Nummer eins in meinem herzen / Go on Billy / Sweet Rosalie / Viel zu schon / Weil ich dich liebe / Muss das sein / My sunny baby / Veronika / Eine blond eine braun / Ich bin verliebt in deinen mund / Mein sohn sei schlau / Einsam geh ich durch die dunkel nacht / Wenn du auch einen andern kusst / Das glaub ich nie von dir / Wann wird es wieder so sein
BCD 16170 / Aug '97 / Bear Family

Being

☐ SELECTED TRANSMISSIONS (2CD Set)
Mune / McLaren / Fotts / Mavebeep / Flee / Ayemooth / Foamy / Ryam / Toobit / Aquapan / Eeeshab / Toyled / Quickie
SE 006CD / Feb '96 / Special Emissions

☐ TIDES
EFA 290092 / Nov '95 / Spacefrog

Beins, Burkhard

☐ YARBLES
HATOLOGY 510 / May '98 / Hatology

Beirach, Richie

☐ ANTARCTICA
Ice shelf / Neptune's bellows / Penguins on parade / Deception island / Mirage / Water lilies (The cloud) / Empress
ECD 220862 / Jun '94 / Evidence

☐ DOUBLE EDGE (Beirach, Richie & David Liebman)
STCD 4091 / Feb '89 / Storyville

☐ ELEGY FOR BILL EVANS
STCD 4151 / Feb '90 / Storyville

☐ LEAVING
STCD 4149 / Feb '90 / Storyville

☐ LIVE AT MAYBECK RECITAL HALL
Introductory annoucement / All the things you are / On green dolpin street / Some other time / You don't know what love is / Spring is here / All blues / 'round midnight / Remember / Elm
CCD 4518 / Aug '92 / Concord Jazz

☐ OMERTA
STCD 4154 / Feb '90 / Storyville

☐ TRUST (Beirach, Richie Trio)
What are the rules / Trust / Moor / Jamala / Boston Harry / Gargoyles / Nefertiti / Johnny B / Rectilinear
ECD 221432 / Mar '96 / Evidence

Beken, Munir Nurettin

☐ ART OF THE TURKISH UD, THE
Karce / Fihrist taksimi / Pesrev / Taksim / Pesrev / Taksim / Saz semaisi / Kocekeler / Cecen kizi / Son pesrev/Son yuruk semaii / Kapris / Ege de yagmur sevinci / Susamurunun aski / Dugun evinde / Fantaisie / Konser etudu / Kervan
ROUCD 1135 / May '97 / Rounder

Bekka & Billy

☐ BEKKA & BILLY
ALMCD 18 / 22 Sep '97 / Almo Sounds

Bel Canto

☐ BIRDS OF PASSAGE
CRAM 065 / '88 / Crammed Discs

☐ MAGIC BOX
Kiss of Spring / Bombay / Rumour / Magic box / Freelaunch in the jungle / Sleepwalker / Big belly butterfly / Magic box
7567926172 / May '96 / Atlantic

☐ SHIMMERING, WARM AND BRIGHT
CRAM 077 / Apr '92 / Crammed Discs

☐ WHITE OUT CONDITION
CRAM 57 / Aug '93 / Crammed Discs

Bel, M'Bilia

☐ BAMELI SOY
Faux pas / Lizanga bambanda / Bameli soy / Nazali mwasi
SHCD 43025 / Jul '91 / Shanachie

Belafonte, Harry

☐ CALYPSO FROM JAMAICA
Man smart, woman smarter / Kingston market / Come back Liza / Calypso war / Island in the sun / I do adore her / Belinda / Not me / Hosanna / Jackass song / Kitch cavalcade / Mahalia, I want back my dollar / Brown skin girl / Dolly dawn / Donkey city / Coconut woman
CD 62072 / Apr '95 / Saludos Amigos

☐ FOLK SONGS FROM THE WORLD
One more dance / Hene ma tov / A hole in the bucket / I know where I'm going / Click song / La bamba / Chickens / Old king cole / I've been driving on bald mountain-water boy / Vaichazkem / Suzanne / Didn't it rain / Red rosy bush (american mountain love song) / A little lyric of great importance
CD 12518 / Feb '95 / Music Of The World

☐ HARRY BELAFONTE
Mama look a boo boo / Day-O (Banana boat song) / Angelina / Matilda, Matilda / Coconut woman / John Henry / Jamaica farewell / Scarlet ribbons / Jump in the line / Jump down, spin around / Hava Nagila / Danny boy / Kingston market / Manha de carnival / Island in the sun / Shenandoah / When the saints go marching in
399544 / Jun '97 / Koch Presents

☐ HARRY BELAFONTE RETURNS TO CARNEGIE HALL
Jump down, spin around / Suzanne / Little lyric of great importance / Chickens / Vaichazkem / I do adore her / Ballad of Sigmund Freud / I've been driving on bald mountain / Waterboy / Hole in the bucket / Click song / One more dance / Ox drivers / Red rosy bush / Didn't it rain / Hene ma tov / I know where / I'm going / Old King Cole / La bamba
09026626902 / Jun '95 / RCA Victor

☐ ISLAND IN THE SUN
Coconut woman / Jamaica farewell / Man smart (woman smarter) / Matilda / Island in the sun / Jump in the line / Banana boat song (day-o) / Manha de carnaval / Angelina / Danny boy / Jump down, spin around / Mama look a boo boo / Kingston market / Hava naglia / Scarlet ribbons (for her hair) / When the saints go marching in
WMCD 5643 / May '94 / Disky

☐ MASTERS, THE
EABCD 036 / 24 Nov '97 / Eagle

☐ STATIONEN
Wave / Kwela / Island in the sun / Skin to skin / Paradise in gazankulu / Jamaica farewell / Try to remember / Sing for the song
16092 / Jul '94 / Laserlight

☐ VERY BEST OF HARRY BELAFONTE, THE
Banana boat song (day-o) / Island in the sun / Scarlet ribbons (for her hair) / Mary's boy child / Coconut woman / Mama look a boo-boo (shut your mouth go away) / Michael row the boat ashore / Jamaica farewell / Danny boy / Matilda matilda / Shenandoah / Unchained melody / Abraham, Martin and John / Brown skin girl / This land is your land / By the time I get to Phoenix
MCCD 059 / '92 / Music Club

Belanger, Jean-Francois

☐ CAP-AUX-SORCIERS
JFB 01CD / Apr '96 / JFB

Belasco, Pete

☐ GET IT TOGETHER
5339672 / 15 Sep '97 / Verve Forecast

Belden, Bob

☐ TAPESTRY
I feel the earth move / So far away / It's too late / Home again / Beautiful / Way over wonder / Where you lead / You've got a friend / Will you still love me tomorrow / Smackwater Jack / Tapestry / You make me feel like a woman
8578912 / 2 Feb '98 / Blue Note

Belew, Adrian

☐ EXPERIMENTAL GUITAR SERIES VOL.1
DGM 9611 / Feb '97 / Discipline

☐ OP ZOP TOO WAH
DGM 9609 / Dec '96 / Discipline

Belisha Beacon

☐ GOODBYE
LF 245CD / Jul '96 / Lost & Found

Bell, Alan

☐ WITH BREAD & FISHES
DRGNCD 942 / Apr '94 / Dragon

Bell, Archie

☐ ARCHIE BELL
MCCD 342 / 20 Apr '98 / Music Club

Bell, Carey

☐ BROUGHT UP THE HARD WAY (A Retrospective)
Strange woman / Gladys shuffle / It's alright in the dark / It's so easy to love you / 85 percent / Locked up so long / Second hand man
JSPCD 802 / Feb '98 / JSP

☐ CAREY BELL'S BLUES HARP
DE 622 / Dec '95 / Delmark

☐ DEEP DOWN
I got to let go / Let me stir in your pot / When I get drunk / Low down dirty shame / Borrow your love / Lonesome stranger / After you / I got a rich man's woman / Jawbreaker / Must I holler / Tired of giving you my love
ALCD 4828 / Feb '95 / Alligator

☐ DYNASTY (Bell, Carey & Lurrie)
Brought up the hard way / (I shoulda did) What my mama told me / Sail on / I'll be your 44 / Gladys shuffle / I need you so bad / 1215 W. Belmont / Second hand man / New harp in town / Going back to Louisiana / No picks / I don't need no woman
JSPCD 276 / Jan '97 / JSP

☐ GOOD LUCK MAN
My love strikes like lightning / Love her don't shove her / Sleeping with the devil / Hard working woman / Bell hop / Bad habits / Good luck man / Hard hearted woman / Going back to Mississippi / I'm a business man / Brand new deal / Good lover / Double cross
ALCD 4854 / Oct '97 / Alligator

☐ HARPSLINGER
What my Mama told me / Pretty baby / Blues with a feeling / 85% / Sweet little woman / It's so easy to love you / Strange woman / Last night
JSPCD 264 / Nov '95 / JSP

☐ HEARTACHES AND PAIN
Carey bell rocks / Heartaches and pain / One day your gonna get lucky / Black-eyed peas / So hard to leave you alone / Stop that train conductor / Everything's gonna be alright / Capri crash
DD 666 / Mar '97 / Delmark

Bell, Chris

☐ I AM THE COSMOS
RCD 10222 / Mar '97 / Rykodisc

Bell, Clive

☐ EATING
SLCD 0005 / Feb '98 / Sound Language

☐ SHAKUHACHI
EUCD 1135 / '91 / ARC

Bell, Delia

☐ DREAMING (Bell, Delia & Bill Grant)
Dreaming / Beggin' to you / Foggy mountain home / Sad situation / Heartbreak express / Silver tongue and gold plated lies / It'll be me / Flame in my heart / Wall / Don't worry about me / Louisa / Night flyer / Won't you come and sing for me / Jack and Lucy
ROUCD 0427 / Nov '97 / Rounder

Bell, Derek

☐ ANCIENT MUSIC FOR THE IRISH HARP
Reminiscences of Sean O Riada / Colonel O'Hara / Little Molly O / Love in secret / Soft mild morning / Wexford bells / Lady Blaney / Within a mile of Edinburgh town / An buachaill Caol Dubh / Lady Iveagh/Black rose bud / Dawning of the day/Green woods of truagh/Captivating youth / Carolan's devotion / Lonesome/An paistin fionn / Churchyard of Creagan/Brown sloe bush/Benevolent father Dona / Untitled air/Thomas a Burca / Lulaby/Bardic hornpipe / Harp serenade/Paraguayan dance in G / Dances from the Quechua Indians
CC 59CD / Feb '93 / Claddagh

☐ CAROLAN'S FAVOURITE (Music of Carolan, Vol 2)
Carolan's favourite jig/Carolan's fancy / Squire Wood's lamentation on ye refusal of his halfpence / Sean Jones / Lady St. John / David Poer/Seamus Plunkett / Lament for Terence O'Connor / Lady Dillon / Michael O'Connor / Carolan's welcome/ Madam Keel / Right Reverend Lord bishop MacMahon of Clogher / Carolan's variations on cock up your beaver
CC 28CD / Jan '90 / Claddagh

☐ CAROLAN'S RECEIPT
Sidh Beag / Carolan's receipt for drinking / Lady Athenry / Fanny Poer / Blind Mary / Sir Festus Burke / Carolan's quarrel with the landlady / Carolan's ramble to Cashel / Mrs. Poer / John O'Connor / Ode to Whiskey / George Brabazon / Mable Kelly / Madam Maxwell/Carolan's nightcap/Lady Gethin / Brighid Cruis / John O'Reilly / Carolan's farewell to music
CC 18CD / Nov '90 / Claddagh

☐ CELTIC EVENING, A
CSL 12 / Feb '98 / Clarity Sound & Light

☐ DEREK BELL'S MUSICAL IRELAND
She moved through the fair / Boys of Bluehill/ Hillsborough Castle/Greencastle hornpipe / Carrickfergus / Little white cat / Gartan mothers lullaby / Im aonar seal / Down by the Sally Gardens / Eileen my secret love / Piper through the meadow straying / Limerick's lamentation / Christ the seed / I wish the shepherd's pet were mine
CC 35CD / Nov '90 / Claddagh

Bell, Ed

☐ ED BELL 1927-1930
DOCD 5090 / '92 / Document

Bell, Eric

☐ LIVE TONITE
Songs / Stumble / Oh pretty woman / Things I used to do / Madame George / Walk on water / Three o'clock blues / Hold that plane / Whiskey in the jar / Rocker / Baby please don't go
BMAC 0315 / 29 Sep '97 / BMA

Bell, Freddy

☐ ROCKIN' IS OUR BUSINESS (Bell, Freddy & The Bellboys)
Hound dog / Move me baby / Five-ten fifteen hours / Old town hall / Big bad wolf / I said it and I'm glad / Rockin' the polonaise / Giddy up and ding dong / Alright, OK you win / Hucklebuck / Rompin' and stompin' / Stay loose, Mother goose / Hey there you / Take the first train out of town / Voo doo / Teach you to rock / I'm advertising / You're gonna be sorry / Variety / Rockin' is my business
BCD 15901 / Mar '96 / Bear Family

Bell, Graeme

☐ GRAEME BELL & FRISCO JOE'S GOODTIME BOYS (Bell, Graeme & Frisco Joe's Goodtime Boys)
BAC 062 / Dec '97 / Bilarm

Bell, Lurrie

☐ 700 BLUES
I've got papers on you baby / How many more years / All over again / 700 blues / She walks right in / Honey bee / You got to stop this mess / Found love / Million miles from nowhere / You got me dizzy / I'll be your 44 / Sadie / Baby take it easy
DE 700 / Jun '97 / Delmark

☐ EVERYBODY WANTS TO WIN
Everybody wants to win / Going back to louisiana / I feel so bad / 1215w. belmont avenue / Second hand man / Train I ride / Teenie weenie bit / No picks / Cadillac assembly line
JSPCD 227 / May '93 / JSP

☐ MERCURIAL SON
DE 679 / Dec '95 / Delmark

☐ YOUNG MAN'S BLUES
Everybody wants to win / Smokin' dynamite / Second hand man / Crosscut saw / Teenie weenie bit / Cadillac assembly line / Lurrie's shuffle / Reconsider baby / Ghetto woman / 1215 W.Belmont / I'm your 44 / Going back to Louisiana
JSPCD 2102 / 20 Oct '97 / JSP

Bell, Madeline

☐ BEAT OUT THAT RHYTHM ON A DRUM (Bell, Madeline & Netherlands Metropole Orchestra)
369102 / 3 Aug '98 / Koch

Bell, Maggie

☐ QUEEN OF THE NIGHT
Caddo queen / Woman left lonely / Souvenirs / Queen of the night / Oh my my / As years go passing by / Yesterday's music / We had it all / Other side / Trade winds
REP 4661 / Sep '97 / Repertoire

☐ SUICIDE SAL
Wishing well / Suicide Sal / I was in chains / If you don't know / What you got / In my life / Comin' on strong / Hold on / I saw him standing there / It's been so long
REP 4663 / Sep '97 / Repertoire

Bell, Paddie

☐ MAKE ME WANT TO STAY
ALACD 102 / Mar '97 / Alauda

Bell, Rico

☐ RETURN OF RICO BELL, THE
BS 012 / 19 Jan '98 / Bloodshot

Bell, T.D.

☐ IT'S ABOUT TIME (Bell, T.D. & Erbie Bowser)
BMCD 9019 / Apr '93 / Black Magic

Bell Tower

☐ POP DROPPER
TOPPCD 002 / Jul '94 / Ultimate

Bell, Vince

☐ PHOENIX
CD 1027 / Sep '94 / Watermelon

Bell, William

☐ BEST OF WILLIAM BELL, THE
I forgot to be your lover / Private number / Born under a bad sign / My kind of girl / Lonely soldier / Save us / Penny for your thoughts / My baby specializes / My whole world is falling down / All for the love of a woman / 'Til my back ain't got no bone / I'll be home / Smile can't hide (a broken heart) / Gettin' what you want (losin' what you got)
CDSXE 113 / Jul '97 / Stax

☐ BOUND TO HAPPEN/WOW
I forgot to be your lover / Hey Western union man / My whole world is falling down / Everyday people / Johnny I love you / All God's children got soul / Happy / By the time I get to Phoenix / Bring the curtain down / Smile can't hide a broken heart / Born under a bad sign / I got a sure thing / I can't make it (all by myself) / Till my back ain't got no bone / All for the love of a woman / My door is always open / Penny for your thoughts / You'll want diamonds / Winding winding road / Somebody's gonna get hurt / I'll be home
CDSXD 970 / Apr '91 / Stax

☐ LITTLE SOMETHING EXTRA, A
She won't be like you / All that I am / Let's do something together / Forever wouldn't be too long / You got me where you want me / Quittin' time / That's my love / You need a little something extra / There's a love / Never let me go / We got something good / Will you still love me tomorrow / Love will find a way / What did I do wrong / Sacrifice / Love is after me / Life I live / Wait / You're never too old
CDSXD 037 / Sep '91 / Stax

☐ PHASES OF REALITY
Save us / True love don't come easy / Fifty dollar habit / What I don't know won't hurt me / Phases of reality / If you really love him / Lonely for your love / Man in the street
CDSXE 058 / Jul '92 / Stax

☐ SOUL OF A BELL, THE
Everybody loves a winner / You don't miss your water / Do right woman, do right man / I've been loving you too long / Nothing takes the place of you / Then you can tell me goodbye / Eloise (hang on in there) / Any other way / It's happening all over / Never like this before / You're such a sweet thing
7567822522 / Apr '95 / Atlantic

Bell-Armstrong, Vanessa

☐ DESIRE OF MY HEART
1241431142 / 27 Apr '98 / Verity

Bella Bella

☐ PLUS GRANDS SUCCES VOL.1 1971-1975 (Bella Bella & Freres Soki)
NG 029 / Jan '97 / Ngoyarto

☐ PLUS GRANDS SUCCES VOL.2 1971-1975 (Bella Bella & Freres Soki)
NG 030 / Jan '97 / Ngoyarto

Bellamy Brothers

☐ BEST OF THE BEST
Let your love flow / If I said you had a beautiful body (would you hold it agains / Old hippie / You ain't just whistlin' Dixie / Dancin' cowboys / Sugar daddy / Lovers live longer / Crazy from the heart / Feelin' the feelin' / Do you love as good as you look / For all the wrong reasons / Redneck girls / When I'm away from you / I'd lie to you for your love / You'll never be sorry / Santa Fe / I need more of you / Big love / Kids of the baby boom / Get into reggae cowboy / Cowboy beat
SCD 22 / Feb '97 / Start

☐ CRAZY FROM THE HEART/REBELS WITHOUT A CLUE
Crazy from the heart / I'll give you all my love tonight / Santa Fe / It's rainin' girls / Ying yang / Melt down / Ramblin' again / We don't wanna got for it / Your name / White trash / Rebels without a clue / I'll help you hurt him / Fountain of middle age / Stayin' in love / Get your priorities in line / Big love / When the music meant everything / Courthouse / Andy Griffith Show / Little naive
SCD 24 / Feb '97 / Start

☐ DANCIN'
Redneck girl / Reggae cowboy / Shine them buckles / Cowboy beat / Rip off the knob / Hard way to make an easy livin' / Big hair / Twang town / Get a little crazy / We dared the lightning / If I said you had a beautiful body
SCD 29 / Feb '97 / Start

☐ HEARTBREAK OVERLOAD
Rip off the knob / Not / Heartbreak overload / Blame it on the fire in my heart / On a summer night / Sweet nostalgia / Bubba / Stayin' in love / D-D-D-D-Divorce / Can I come on home to you / Hemingway hideaway / Andy Griffith Show / Hard on a heart / Nobody's perfect
SCD 23 / Feb '97 / Start

☐ LET YOUR LOVE FLOW
Let's fall in love again / I could be persuaded / Big love / Let your love flow / Sweet nostalgia / Do you love as good as you look / Crazy from the heart / If I said you had a beautiful body / Strength of the weaker sex / Lovers live longer / I'll give you all my love tonight / Stayin' in love / I'd lie to you for your love / Everybody's somebody's darlin' / Center of my universe / Tough love / We don't wanna go for it / Save your love
SCD 32 / 30 Mar '98 / Start

☐ OVER THE LINE
Over the line / Slow hurry / Afterglow / Guilty of the crime / Catahoula / Passions thunder / Tough love / Mama likes to reggae / Hurricane Alley / Wonderful mistake / Hanging in / My wife left me for my girlfriend
SCD 30 / Jul '97 / Start

☐ REALITY CHECK/ROLLIN' THUNDER
Too late / I could be persuaded / Have a little compassion / Was there life before this love / Makin' promises / What's this world coming to / Forever ain't long enough / How can you be everywhere at the same time / I don't wanna lose you / Reality check / All in the name of love / Down to you / She don't know that she's perfect / Strength of the weaker sex / Anyway I can / Rollin' thunder / What's the dang deal / Our love / Lonely eyes / I make her laugh
SCD 25 / Feb '97 / Start

☐ REGGAE COWBOYS, THE
Almost Jamaica / I'll be your baby tonight / Let your love flow / Get into reggae cowboy / Some broken hearts / I'll fly away / I make her laugh / Bye bye love / Mama likes to reggae / Having too much fun / I love her mind / Strong weakness
SCD 33 / 29 Jun '98 / Start

☐ SONS OF BEACHES
Shine them buckles / Big hair / Pit bulls and chain saws / Blue rodeo / Twang town / She's awesome / Old hippie (the sequel) / Native American / Feel free / Too much fun / We dared the lightening / Elvis, Marilyn and James Dean / Gotta get a little crazy / Jesus is coming
SCD 27 / Feb '97 / Start

☐ TROPICAL CHRISTMAS
Merry christmas and a happy new year / Tropical christmas / Jingle bells / White Christmas / We all get lazy at christmas / Light up the candles / Rudolph the red nosed raindeer / Old hippie christmas / Our love is like christmas / Rockin' around the Christmas tree / It's so close to christmas / Silent night
SCD 31 / 13 Oct '97 / Start

☐ VERY BEST OF THE BELLAMY BROTHERS, THE
Let your love flow / If I said you had a beautiful body / Dancin' cowboys / Redneck girl / Lovers live longer / Do you love as good as you look / Big love / Crazy from the heart / Our love / Old hippie / Sugar daddy / I don't wanna lose you
10252 / Oct '97 / Go On Deluxe

Bellamy, Peter

☐ TRANSPORTS, THE
Overture / Ballad of Henry and Susannah: *Bellamy, Peter & Dave Swarbrick* / Us poor fellows: *Jones, Nic* / Robber's song: *Jones, Nic* / Ballad of Henry and Susannah (part 2): *Jones, Nic* / I once lived in service: *Waterson, Norma* / Norwich gaol: *Winsor, Martin* / Sweet loving friendship: *Winsor, Martin* / Black and bitter night: *Waterson, Mike* / Humane turnkey: *Carthy, Martin* / Plymouth mail: *Legg, Vic* / Green fields of England: *Watersons* / Roll down: *Tawney, Cyril* / Still and silent ocean: *Waterson, Mike & Norma* / Ballad of Henry and susannah (parts 3,4and5): *Bellamy, Peter & Dave Swarbrick* / Convict's wedding dance: *Bellamy, Peter & Dave Swarbrick*
TSCD 459 / Aug '92 / Topic

Belle & Sebastian

☐ IF YOU'RE FEELING SINISTER
Stars of track and field / Seeing other people / Me and the Major / Like Dylan in the movies / Fox in the snow / Get me away from here / If you're feeling sinister / Mayfly / Boy done wrong again / Judy and the dream of horses
JPRCD 001 / Nov '96 / Jeepster

Belle, Regina

☐ BEST OF REGINA BELLE, THE
Didn't I (blow your mind this time) / Baby come to me / Quiet time / So many times / What goes around / How could you do it to me / Love TKO / Show me the way / Someday we'll all be free / Save the children / All I want is forever / This is love / If I could / Make it like it was / Whole new world
4890352 / 2 Feb '98 / Columbia

☐ REACHIN' BACK
Reachin' back / Could it be I'm falling in love / Love TKO / You make me feel brand new / Hurry up this way again / Whole town's laughing / You are everything / Let me make love to you / I'll be around / Just don't want to be lonely / Didn't I blow your mind this time
4807622 / Sep '95 / Columbia

Belle Stars

☐ HIT SINGLE COLLECTABLES
DISK 4514 / Apr '94 / Disky

☐ SIGN OF THE TIMES
Sign of the times / Sweet memory / Iko iko / Clapping song / Mockingbird / Hiawatha / Indian summer / Take another look / Slick trick / Another latin love song / Reason / Entertainer / Having a good time / 80's romance / Burning / Harlem shuffle
12365 / May '94 / Laserlight

☐ VERY BEST OF THE BELLE STARS, THE
STIFFCD 5 / Apr '94 / Disky

Belleville A Capella Choir

☐ SOUTHERN JOURNEY VOL.11 (Honor The Lamb)
Gospel train / Kee me as n apple of thine eye / David wa a sheperh boy / What a time / Lord is my strength and song / None but the righteous / Come on Israel / Medley of Spirituals / House of the Lord / Honor honor / On the battle field for my Lord / Creation / Honor the lamb
ROUCD 1711 / Feb '98 / Rounder

Bellita

☐ Y JAZZTUMBATA
RWCD 9705 / Jan '98 / Fresh Sound

Bellou, Sotiria

☐ REBETIKO
ML 0142 / 11 May '98 / Musurgia Graeca

Bells Of

☐ 4 YOUR LISTENING PLEASURE
MIGUEL 3 / 11 May '98 / Miguel

Bellson, Louie

☐ AIR BELLSON (Bellson, Louie Magic 7)
Air Jordan / Lou's blues / Tito / Tempo de carlo / Ballade / Groove blues / 150 pounds of bones / Bassiano / Mele Kalikimaka / Smooth and mellow / Another shade of the blues / Waltz a-way / PMH
CCD 47422 / Feb '97 / Concord Jazz

☐ ART OF CHART
1343148002 / 27 Apr '98 / Concord Jazz

☐ ART OF THE CHART, THE (Bellson, Louie & Big Band)
Berne baby Berne / Intimacy of the blues / To CP with love / Summer love / Who brings you the good news / Your wake up call / Conte / With bells on / Quiet riot / Admiral / Ike, Mike and Spike / 3x5+16
CCD 48002 / 8 Jun '98 / Concord Jazz

☐ AT THE FLAMINGO HOTEL 1959 (Bellson, Louie & Big Band)
JH 1026 / Feb '93 / Jazz Hour

☐ DUKE ELLINGTON - BLACK, BROWN AND BEIGE (Bellson, Louie & His All Star Orchestra)
Hawk talks / Skin deep / Work song / Come Sunday / West Indian dance / Emancipation proclamation / Ellington-Strayhorn suite / European skallyhoppin' / Portrait of Billy Strayhorn / Sketches
5224292 / Mar '94 / Limelight

☐ EAST SIDE SUITE (Bellson, Louie & His Jazz Orchestra)
Tenor time / What makes Moses run
MM 5009 / Oct '94 / Music Masters

☐ HOT
MM 5008 / Oct '94 / Music Masters

☐ LIVE AT JAZZ SHOWCASE (Bellson, Louie Four)
Sonny side / Duke's blues / 3 p.m. / I hear a rhapsody / Jam for your bread / Warm alley / Cherokee
CCD 4350 / Jul '88 / Concord Jazz

☐ LIVE AT THE CONCORD SUMMER FESTIVAL
Now and then / Here's that rainy day / My old flame / It might as well be spring / These foolish things / Body and soul / True blue / Roto blues / Starship concord / Dig
CCD 4025 / May '95 / Concord Jazz

☐ LIVE FROM NEW YORK (Bellson, Louie & Big Band)
Soar like an eagle / Louie shuffle / Blow your horn / LA suite / Louie and Clark expedition / Francine / Santos
CD 83334 / Jul '94 / Telarc

☐ LOUIE BELLSON & HIS BIG BAND
CCD 4036 / Nov '96 / Concord Jazz

☐ LOUIE IN LONDON
Carnaby Street / Proud Thames / London suite / Kings Road boogaloo / Hyde Park 2am / Limehouse blues / Sketches from the National Gallery
DRGCD 8471 / Jul '96 / DRG

☐ ORIGINALS, THE
STBCD 2509 / Mar '96 / Stash

☐ PEACEFUL THUNDER
MM 65074 / Oct '94 / Music Masters

☐ PRIME TIME
Step lighty / Space ship 2 / I remember Clifford / With you in mind / What's new / Cotton tail / Let me dream / Thrash in / And then she stopped / Collaborations
CCD 40642 / May '97 / Concord Jazz

☐ RAINCHECK
Raincheck / Alone together / I thought about you / Blue moon / Body and soul / Oleo / Song is you / Tristamente / Funky blues / More I see you
CCD 4073 / Nov '95 / Concord Jazz

☐ SALUTE (Bellson, Louie Quintet)
CRD 329 / Nov '95 / Chiaroscuro

☐ THEIR TIME WAS THE GREATEST
Hallelujah / Liza / 24th Day / Brush taps / Well alright then / Y-not / Stix and bones / Zig zag / It's those magical drums in you / Acetnam / Our Manne Shelly / All about Steve
CCD 4683 / Apr '96 / Concord Jazz

Belly

☐ KING
Puberty / Seal my fate / Red / Silverfish / Super connected / Bees / King / Now they'll sleep / Untitled and unsung / Li'l Ennio / Judas my heart
GAD 5004CD / 6 Jul '98 / 4AD

☐ STAR
Someone to die for / Angel / Dusted / Every word / Gepetto / Witch / Slow dog / Low red moon / Feed the tree / Full moon, empty heart / White belly / Untogether / Star / Sad dress / Stay
GAD 3002CD / 6 Jul '98 / 4AD

Belmez

☐ BESERKER
SPV 08407952 / Apr '95 / Candlelight

Belmonde, Pierre

☐ 101% PAN PIPES (4CD Set)
Love changes everything / Riverdance / Windmills of your mind / We have all the time in the world / I believe / From a distance / Greensleeves / Bunch of thyme / Waterfalls / It must have been love / Annie's song / Lady in red / Without you / Unchained melody / Sky boat song / Fernando / Danny boy / Scarlet ribbons / Beautiful dreamer / Theme from Love Story / Up where we belong / Dirty old town / Bless this house / Ave Maria / Amazing grace / Change the world / I will always love you / Holding back the years / Love is all around / Wonderful tonight / Perfect year / Constant craving / Summer in the city / Caribbean blue / Summer of '42 / Summer love / All I have to do is dream / Good day sunshine / El condor pasa / Harry's Game / Someday / Beauty and the beast / House of the rising sun / Sunshine after the rain / I never dreamed you'd leave in summer / Wonderful world / You are the sunshine of my life / All by myself / You are my sunshine / Unforgettable / When I fall in love / Orinoco flow / Back for good / Wind of change / Fields of gold / Sailing / Morning has broken / I can't stop loving you / You don't bring me flowers / Bright eyes / Don't cry for me Argentina / Whiter shade of pale / Time after time / Careless whisper / When you and I were young, Maggie / Green leaves of summer / Mull of Kintyre / Colours of the wind / Forbidden colours / Aria / Miss you nights / Feelings / Stranger on the shore / Concerto de aranjuez / Forever autumn / Nights in white satin / Free as a bird / Think twice / Sacrifice / No more "I love yous" / I swear / Power of love / I'm not in love / Show me heaven / Eternal flame / Local hero / Happy ever after / Love hurts / Stay another day / Streets of Philadelphia / Wonderwall / Kiss from a rose / Get here / Take my breath away / Don't give up / Sadness (Part 1) / Road / Up on the roof / Heaven for everyone / Anywhere is / Jealous guy
ECD 3320 / Mar '97 / K-Tel

☐ CHANGE THE WORLD
Change the world / I will always love you / Holding back the years / Love is all around / Wonderful tonight / Perfect year / Constant craving / Summer in the city / Carribean blue / Summer of '42 / Summer love / All I have to do is dream / Good day sunshine / El condor pasa / Harry's Game / Someday / Beauty and the beast / House of the rising sun / Sunshine after the rain / I never dreamed you'd leave in summer / Wonderful world / You are the sunshine of my life / When I fall in love / Unforgettable / You are my sunshine / All by myself
ECD 3324 / Mar '97 / K-Tel

☐ FREE AS A BIRD
Free as a bird / Think twice / Sacrifice / No more "I love yous" / I swear / Power of love / I'm not in love / Stay another day / Love hurts / Happy ever after / Local hero / Eternal flame / Show me heaven / Streets of Philadelphia / Wonderwall / Kiss from a rose / Get here / Jealous guy / Anywhere is / Heaven for everyone / Up on the roof / Road / Sadness (Part 1) / Don't give up / Take my breath away
ECD 3322 / Mar '97 / K-Tel

☐ FROM A DISTANCE
Love changes everything / Riverdance / Windmills of your mind / We have all the time in the world / I believe / From a distance / Greensleeves / Bunch of thyme / Waterfalls / It must have been love / Annie's song / Lady in red / Without you / Unchained melody / Sky boat song / Fernando / Danny boy / Scarlet ribbons / Beautiful dreamer / Theme from Love story / Up where we belong / Dirty old town / Bless this house / Ave Maria / Amazing grace
ECD 3321 / Mar '97 / K-Tel

☐ HALCYON DAYS (The Sound Of The Pan Pipes)
Bunch of thyme / From a distance / Skye boat song / Mull of Kintyre / Danny boy / Beautiful dreamer / Maggie / Scarlet ribbons / Dirty old town / Bless this house / Isle of Innisfree / Those endearing young charms / Greensleeves / Morning has broken / Green leaves of summer / Lord's my shepherd / Ave Maria / Amazing grace
ECD 3298 / Feb '97 / K-Tel

☐ MISS YOU NIGHTS
Orinoco flow / Back for good / Wind of change / Fields of gold / Careless whisper / Time after time / Whiter shade of pale / Don't cry for me Argentina / Bright eyes / You don't bring me flowers / I can't stop loving you / Morning has broken / Sailing / When you and I were young Maggie / Green leaves of summer / Aria / Miss you nights / Feelings / Stranger on the shore / Concerto de aranjuez / Forever autumn / Nights in white satin / Forbidden colours / Colours of the wind / Mull of Kintyre
ECD 3323 / Mar '97 / K-Tel

☐ NO.1 PAN PIPE LOVE ALBUM VOL.2, THE
ECD 3429 / 6 Jul '98 / K-Tel

☐ PAN-PIPE DREAMS
We have all the time in the world / Think twice / Sacrifice / No more I love you's / I swear / Power of love / I'm not in love / Stay another day / Love changes everything / Love hurts / Windmills of your mind / Happy ever after / Local hero / Fernando / Eternal flame / Show me heaven / Without you / Lady in red
ECD 3206 / Mar '95 / K-Tel

Belmondo Quintet

☐ FOR ALL FRIENDS
CHR 70016 / Aug '95 / Challenge

Belmont, Sarah

☐ DREAMLAND MAGIC FLUTE
If you leave me now / I will always love you / Wind of change / Tears in heaven / (Everything I do) I do it for you / All I have to do is dream / Massachussetts / Fly away / Air that I breathe / When a man loves a woman / California dreamin' / One moment in time / I just called to say I love you / San Francisco / All that she wants / Half a minute / Dreamland / Tenderness / It's no longer just a dream / Air
12708 / Feb '96 / Laserlight

Beloved

☐ BLISSED OUT
Up, up and away (happy sexy mix) / Wake up soon / Pablo (special K dub) / It's alright now (back to basics) / Hell (honky tonk) / Time after time (muffin mix) / Sun rising / Your love takes me higher
9031729072 / Nov '90 / East West

☐ CONSCIENCE
Spirit / Sweet harmony / Outerspace girl / Lose yourself in me / Paradise found / You've got me thinking / Celebrate your life / Rock to the rhythm of love / Let the music take you / 1000 Years from today / Dream on
4509914832 / Dec '96 / East West

☐ HAPPINESS
Hello / Your love takes me higher / Time after time / Don't you worry / Scarlet beautiful / Sun rising / I love you more / Wake up soon / Up, up and away / Found
2292462532 / Feb '95 / East West

☐ SINGLE FILE (The Best Of The Beloved)
Sun rising / Sweet harmony / Your love takes me / Satellite / Outerspace girl / Time after time / Hello / Ease the pressure / It's alright now / You've got me thinking / Deliver me / Mark's deep house
0630199322 / Aug '97 / East West

☐ X
Crystal wave / Deliver me / Satellite / Dream within a dream / Ease the pressure / Spacemen / Three steps to heaven / Missing you / Physical love / For your love
0630133162 / Mar '96 / East West

Belphegor

☐ BLUTSABBETH
LEP 010CD / 27 Oct '97 / Last Epitaph

Belton, Richard

☐ MODERN SOUNDS IN CAJUN MUSIC
Cajun stripper / I'll have to forget you / Just a dream / Un autre soir d'ennui (Another sleepless night) / Cajun waltz / San Antonio rose / Madamme Sostan / Chrokee waltz / Who-diggie / Oh yea yi-yi / La jolie blonde / For the last time / Musician's paradise / Laisser les cajun danser / Give me another chance / J'ai pleurer pour toi / Oh lucille / I'm not a fool anymore / Cajun Fugitive / Won't be satisfied / Chere toute toute / Cette la j'aime / Roll on wagon wheel / She didn't know I was married / Heartbroken waltz / Cajun streak
CDCHD 378 / Jan '93 / Ace

Beltram, Joey

☐ BIG APPLE BITES BACK, THE (Mixed By Joey Beltram/Steve Stoll/Frankie Bones - 2CD Set) (Various Artists)
3027392 / 2 Mar '98 / Mirakkle/Trax

☐ CLASSICS
Energy flash / Jazz 303 / Subsonic trance / Psychobase / My sound / Melody / Sub-bass experience / Reflex / Mind to mind / Mentasm / Fuck you all MF / Get into life / She ain't coming home
RS 96100CD / 16 Feb '98 / R&S

☐ MIXMAG LIVE VOL.6 (Joey Beltram/E-Lustrious)) (Various Artists)
MMLCD 006 / Jul '96 / Mixmag Live

☐ PLACES (2CD Set)
EFA 292782 / Aug '97 / Tresor

Beltran, John

☐ EARTH & NIGHTFALL
Blue world / Pluvial interlude / Synaptic transmission / Sub surface / Earth and nightfall / Mutualism / Dawn / Anticipation / Nitric / Fragile interlude / Aquatic / Vienna
RS95072CD / Jun '95 / R&S

☐ MOVING THROUGH HERE
AMB 7947CD / 24 Nov '97 / R&S

☐ TEN DAYS OF BLUE
Flex / Collage of dreams / Guitaris breeze / Ten days of blue / Venim and wonder / Deluge / Decembers tragedy / Soft summer / Collage of dreams (Outro)
PF 049CD / Aug '96 / Peacefrog

Belvin, Jesse

☐ BLUES BALLADEER, THE
Daddy loves baby / My love comes tumbling down / Dream girl / Confusin' blues / Baby don't go / Blues has got me / Hang your tears out to dry / Don't stop / Love me / Puddin' 'n' tane / Open up your heart / What's the matter / Ding dong baby / One little blessing / Gone / Love love of my life / Where's my girl / Let's try romance / Come back / Love of my life
CDCHD 305 / Nov '93 / Ace

☐ GOODNIGHT MY LOVE
Goodnight my love / (I love you) for sentimental reasons / I'll mess you up medley / Don't close the door / Senorita / Let me love you tonight / I need you so / My satellite / Just to say hello / Dream house / I'm not free / You send me / By my side / Let's make up / Summertime / I want you with me Christmas / Goodnight my love (alt take) / Sad and lonesome / Beware / What can I do without you / I'll make a bet
CDCHD 336 / Nov '93 / Ace

Beme Seed

☐ FUTURE IS ATTACKING
BFFP 50 CD / Jul '89 / Blast First

Ben

☐ BEN
REP 4195 / Aug '91 / Repertoire

Ben, Jorge

☐ HOOKED ON SAMBA VOL.2 (2CD Set)
1919382 / 24 Apr '98 / EPM

☐ PAIS TROPICAL - FILHO MARAVILHA
1917482 / Apr '97 / EPM

Ben, Kaira

☐ SINGA
ST 1072 / May '96 / Stern's

Benachally Ceilidh Band

☐ HAPPY FEET
Gay Gordons / Dashing white Sergeant / Old time waltz / Strip the willow / Slow foxtrot / St. Bernard's waltz / Highland Scottische / Cumberland square eight / Eva three step / Duke of Perth / Pride of Erin waltz / Virginia reel / Military two step / Canadian barn dance / Orcadian strip the willow / Last dance
SMD 610 / Dec '97 / Smiddy Made

Benaiah

☐ CHILDREN OF ISRAEL
CAPS 002CD / May '96 / Sphinx

☐ WE NAH GIVE UP
CAPS 001CD / May '96 / Sphinx

Benani, Hamdi

☐ MULAF OF ANNABA
AAA 154 / Sep '97 / Club Du Disque Arabe

Benatar, Pat

☐ BEST SHOTS
Hit me with your best shot / Love is a battlefield / We belong / We live for love / Sex as a weapon / Invincible / Shadows of the night / Heartbreaker / Fire and ice / Treat me right / If you think you know how to love me / You better run
CCD 1538 / Sep '97 / Chrysalis

☐ CONCERT CLASSICS
If you think you know how to love me / So sincere / I need a lover / My clone sleeps alone / In the heat of the night / We live for love / No you don't / Just like me / Heartbreaker / You better run / Come on let's go / Come on lets go
CRANCH 6 / 13 Jul '98 / Ranch Life

☐ INNAMORATA
Only you / River of love / I don't want to be your friend / Strawberry wine / Purgatory / Papa's roses / At this time / Dirty little secrets / Angry / In these times / Innamorata
060768621626 / 8 Sep '97 / CMC

☐ VERY BEST OF PAT BENATAR
Heartbreaker / We live for love / Promises in the dark / Fire and ice / Ooh ooh song / Hit me with your best shot / Shadows of the night / Anxiety (get nervous) / I want out / Lipstick lies / Love is a battlefield / We belong / All fired up / Hell is for children / Invincible / Somebody's baby / Everybody lay down / True love
CDCHR 6070 / Apr '94 / Chrysalis

Bender

☐ JEHOVAH'S ALLSTARS
WOWCD 48 / Jun '96 / Words Of Warning

☐ LOST CITY OF DALSTON
WOWCD 43 / Jun '95 / Words Of Warning

Benediction

☐ DARK IS THE SEA
NB 059CD / Apr '92 / Nuclear Blast

☐ DREAMS YOU DREAD, THE
NB 120CD / Jun '95 / Nuclear Blast

☐ GRAND LEVELLER
Vision in the shroud / Graveworm / Jumping at shadows / Opulence of the absolute / Child of sin / Undirected aggression / Born in a fever / Grand leveller / Senile dementia / Return to the eve
NB 241CD / Apr '97 / Nuclear Blast

☐ GRIND BASTARD
Deadfall / Agonised / West of hell / Magnificat / Nervebomb / Electric eye / Grind bastard / Shadows world / Bodiless / Carcinoma angel / We the freed / Destroyer
NB 2462 / 30 Mar '98 / Nuclear Blast

☐ GROTESQUE ASHEN EPITAPH, THE
NB 0882 / May '94 / Nuclear Blast

☐ SUBCONSCIOUS TERROR
Intro-portal to your phobias / Subconscious terror / Artefacted irreligion / Grizzled finale / Eternal eclipse / Experimental stage / Suspended animation / Divine ultimatum / Spit forth the dead / Confess all goodness
NB 165CD / Jun '96 / Nuclear Blast

☐ TRANSCEND THE RUBICON
NB 073CD / Jun '93 / Nuclear Blast

Benediction Moon

☐ PIA
CD 445 / 6 Jul '98 / New World

Beneke, Tex

☐ DANCERS DELIGHT
DAWE 79 / Mar '97 / Magic

☐ PALLADIUM PATROL
AERO 1031 / Jul '96 / Aerospace

☐ TEX BENEKE DIRECTS THE GLENN MILLER ORCHESTRA 1946-1947
DHDL 134 / Jul '98 / Halcyon

Benet, Eric

☐ TRUE TO MYSELF
True to myself / I'll be there / If you want me to stay / Let's stay together / Just friends / Femininity / While you where here / Spiritual thang / Chains / All in the game / More than just a girlfriend / What if we was cool / Let's stay together
9362462702 / Apr '97 / Warner Bros.

Benford, Mac

☐ WILLOW
ROUCD 0371 / Feb '96 / Rounder

Benito, Oscar

☐ FOLKLORE DE PARAGUAY
EUCD 1221 / Sep '93 / ARC

Benjamin, Sathima Bea

☐ MORNING IN PARIS
Dam that dream / I got it bad and that ain't good / I could write a book / I should care / Spring will be a little late this year / Solitude / Man I love / Your love has faded / I'm glad there is you / Soon / Lover man / Nightingale sang in Berkeley Square
ENJ 93092 / Mar '97 / Enja

Bennet

☐ STREETS VS SCIENCE
RR 87612 / 3 Nov '97 / Roadrunner

☐ SUPER NATURAL
RR 88662
RR 88662N / Sep '96 / Roadrunner

Bennett, Billy

☐ ALMOST A GENTLEMAN
Nell / My mother doesn't know I'm on the stage / Mandalay / I'll be thinking of you / Ogul mogul - a kanakanese love lyric / No power on earth / She was poor but she was honest / Family secrets / Please let me sleep on your doorstep tonight / Christmas day in the cookhouse / Club raid / Mottoes / Green tie on the little yellow dog
TSCD 780 / Jul '97 / Topic

Bennett, Brian

☐ CHANGE OF DIRECTION/ ILLUSTRATED LONDON NOISE
Slippery Jim De Grize / Canvas / Whisper not / Memphis / Tricycle / Sunshine superman / On Broadway / Sunny afternoon / Little old lady / 98.6 / Con Alma / Change of direction / Love and occasional rain / I heard it through the grapevine / Chameleon / Just lookin' / Rocky raccoon / Ticket to ride
SEECD 205 / Nov '87 / See For Miles

☐ MISTY
Wave / Laura / Misty / Close to you / Madrid / Love for sale / Who can I turn to / Shadow of your smile / What are you doing the rest of your life / Blue hankerchief
C5CD 610 / Sep '95 / See For Miles

☐ ROCK DREAMS/VOYAGE...PLUS
Rock dreams / Rock and rock dreamer / Banja booja / Rave on / Milwaukee massacre / C'mon everybody / Thunderbolt / Saturday / Girls back home / Wallop / Jonty jump / Farewell to friend / Drum odyssey / Voyage / Solstice / Chail reaction / Pendulum force / Air quake / Ocean glide / Clearing skies
C5HCD 661 / 6 Oct '97 / See For Miles

Bennett, Cliff

☐ 25 GREATEST HITS (Bennett, Cliff & The Rebel Rousers)
You've got what I like / I'm in love with you / That's what I said / When I get paid / Poor Joe / Hurtin' inside / Everybody loves a lover / My old stand by / Love is a swinging thing / Got my mojo working / Beautiful dreamer / One way love / I'll take you home / Something you've got / It's alright / Three rooms with running water / Need your loving tonight / Got to get you into my life / Ain't love good ain't love proud / 6345-789 / I'm not tired / CC Rider blues / I'll take good care of you / Good times / Back in the USSR
4954852 / 6 Jul '98 / EMI Gold

☐ CLIFF BENNETT & THE REBEL ROUSERS (Bennett, Cliff & The Rebel Rousers)
I can't stand it / Sweet and lovley / Make yourself at home / You've really got a hold on me / Ain't that lovin' you baby / Sha la la / One way love / Steal your heart away / It's all right / Beautiful dreamer / Mercy mercy / Talking about my baby / Pick up
DORIG 118 / 3 Nov '97 / EMI

Bennett, Don

☐ CHICAGO CALLING (Bennett, Don Sextet)
About time / Sleeping child / Love found me / Makin' whoopee / Dance of the night child / Au privave / Prayer for Sean / Steven's song / All the things you are
CCD 79713 / Feb '97 / Candid

☐ SOLAR (Bennett, Don Trio)
Blues for Nikki / Since I fell for you / Solar / You don't know what love is / If I should lose you / Tune up / Afternoon in Paris / In search of... / It's you or no one / Blue moon / Night in Tunisia
CCD 79723 / Feb '97 / Candid

Bennett, Duster

☐ JUMPIN' AT SHADOWS
IGOCD 2010 / Nov '94 / Indigo

☐ OUT IN THE BLUE
IGOCD 2018 / Apr '95 / Indigo

Bennett, Elinor

☐ TELYNAU A CHAN/FOLK SONGS & HARPS
Clychau Aberdyfi / Ar lan y mor / Paid a deud / Merch y melinydd / Meillionen / Morfa Rhuddlan / Syr Harri Ddu / Codiad yr ehedydd / Ar hyd y nos / Gwyr Harlech / Dafydd y Garreg Wen / Y bore glas / Gwcw fach / Ei di'r deryn du / Y deryn pur / Cainc Dafydd broffwyd / Annhawdd ymadael / Pant corlan yr wyn / Hen benillion / Marwnad Sion Eos / Bugeilio'r gwenith gwyn / Huna blentyn / Y gwydd / Migildi magildi
SCD 4041 / Feb '95 / Sain

Bennett, Gordon

☐ ENGLISH PUBSONGS (Bennett, Gordon & The Good Times)
CNCD 5980 / Apr '94 / Disky

Bennett, Lou

☐ NOW HEAR MY MEANING
MASCD 001 / 5 Jan '98 / Mas I Mas

Bennett, Martyn

☐ BOTHY CULTURE
Tongues of Kali / Aye / Shputnik in Glenshiel / Hallaig / Ud the doudouk / 4 notes / Joik / Yer man from Athlone
RCD 10381 / 13 Oct '97 / Rykodisc

☐ MARTYN BENNETT
ECLCD 9614 / Mar '96 / Eclectic

Bennett, Pinto

☐ PURE QUILL (Bennett, Pinto & The Motel Cowboys)
You cared enough to lie / Livin' and dyin' for love / Peaceful woman / I ain't in it for the money / True lovin' daddy / No sweat / Stranger in the mirror / Prarie blues / Ballad of Hai-Sing / Different ways to sing the blues / Pure quill
336322 / Nov '97 / Koch International

Bennett, Richard

☐ WALKING DOWN THE LINE
Sounds of winter / Greensleeves / Banks of the Ohio / Walking down the line / Pallet on the floor / If I could go back home again / True love is hard to find / Roan mountain rag / Johnstown flood / Rain pours down
REBCD 1738 / Jul '97 / Rebel

Bennett, Richard Rodney

☐ HAROLD ARLEN'S SONGS
ACD 168 / Oct '93 / Audiophile

☐ SPECIAL OCCASIONS
Civil war ballet / Hero ballet / Within the quota / Ghost town
DRGCD 6102 / Apr '94 / DRG

☐ SURE THING, A (A Tribute To Jerome Kern) (Bennett, Richard Rodney & Barry Tuckwell/Neil Richardson)
CDEMX 2270 / Apr '96 / Eminence

Bennett, Samm

☐ BIG OFF, THE
KFWCD 126 / Nov '94 / Knitting Factory

☐ HISTORY OF THE LAST FIVE MINUTES
KFWCD 166 / Oct '96 / Knitting Factory

☐ LIFE OF CRIME (Bennett, Samm & Chunk)
KFWCD 110 / Nov '94 / Knitting Factory

Bennett, Steve

☐ STEVE BENNETT'S BLUESBUSTERS (Bennett, Steve Bluesbusters)
SMV 002CD / May '97 / Smallville

Bennett, Tony

☐ 16 MOST REQUESTED SONGS
Because of you / Stranger in paradise / Rags to riches / Boulevard of broken dreams / Cold cold heart / Just in time / I left my heart in San Francisco / I wanna be around / Who can I turn to / For once in my life / This is all I ask / Smile / Tender is the night / Shadow of your smile / Love story
4724182 / Nov '92 / Columbia

☐ ALL TIME GREATEST HITS
Something / Love story / Maybe this time / Just in time / For once in my life / I left my heart in San Francisco / Because of you / Boulevard of broken dreams / Stranger in paradise / I wanna be around / Time for love / Who can I turn to / This is all I ask / Smile / Sing you sinners / Firefly / Put on a happy face / Love look away / Rags to riches / Where do I begin / Shadow of your smile
4688432 / Sep '91 / Columbia

☐ AS TIME GOES BY (3CD Set)
As time goes by / Manhattan / Blue moon / There's a small hotel / Reflections / There'll be some changes made / Lucky to be me / You must believe in Spring / This funny world / I used to be colourblind / Spring is here / I could write a book / Make someone happy / Bad and the beautiful / Lady is a tramp / I've got five dollars / Lost in the stars / Life is beautiful / Wait till you see her / You took advantage of me / Who can I turn to / My romance / Two lonely people / You're nearer / Mountain greenery / Maybe September / Experiment / Isn't it romantic / One / I wish I were in love again / You don't know what love is / Lonely girl / This can't be love / Mr. Magic / Lover / Have you met Miss Jones / All mine / Bridges / Thou swell / My heart stood still / Most beautiful girl in the world / Cole Porter medley
HR 883602 / Oct '97 / Disky

☐ AS TIME GOES BY
As time goes by / Chicago / Anything goes / Have you met Miss Jones / You don't know what love is / I wish I were in love again / My romance / Lady is a tramp / Manhattan / There's a small hotel / You're nearer / My heart stood still / You took advantage of me / Make somebody happy / I could write a book / Isn't it romantic / Maybe September / Lover / Spring is here / Most beautiful girl in the world
4939042 / 16 Mar '98 / EMI

☐ BEAT OF MY HEART, THE
Let's begin / Lullaby of broadway / Let there be love / Love for sale / Crazy rhythm / Beat of my heart / So beats my heart for you / Blues in the night / Lazy afternoon / Let's face the music and dance / Just one of those things / It's so peaceful in the country / In Sandy's eyes / I get a kick out of you / You go to my head / I only have eyes for you / Begin the beguine
4882802 / 29 Sep '97 / Columbia

☐ BLUE VELVET
BMCD 3013 / Apr '97 / Blue Moon

☐ CHICAGO (Bennett, Tony & Count Basie Orchestra)
With plenty of money and you / I guess I'll have to change my plans / Growing pains / Life is a song / Anything goes / Are you havin' any fun / Jeepers creepers / Poor little rich girl / Chicago (that toodling town) / I've grown accustomed to her face
CDSGP 0220 / Aug '97 / Prestige

☐ FORTY YEARS (The Artistry Of Tony Bennett/4CD Set)
Boulevard of broken dreams / Because of you / Cold cold heart / Blue velvet / Rags to riches / Stranger in Paradise / While the music plays on / May I ever love again / Sing the sinners / Just in time / Lazy afternoon / Ca, c'est l'amour / I get a kick out of you / It amazes me / Penthouse serenade (When we're alone) / Lost in the stars / Lullaby of Broadway / Firefly / Sleepin' bee / Man that got away / Sky lark / September song / Till / Begin the beguine / Put on a happy face / Best is yet to come / This time dream's on me / Close your eyes / Toot toot tootsie / Goo'bye / Dancing in the dark / Stella by starlight / Tender is the night / Once upon a time / I left my heart in San Francisco / Until I met you / If I love again / I wanna be around / Good life / It was me / Spring in Manhattan / Moment of truth / This is all I ask / Taste of honey / When Joanna loved me / I'll be around / Nobody else but me / It had to be you / I've got just about everything / Who can I turn to / Waltz for Debby / I walk a little faster / Wrap your troubles in dreams (And dream your troubles away) / If I ruled the world / Fly me to the moon / Love scene / Sweet lorraine / Shadow of your smile / I'll only miss her when I think of her / Baby, dream your dream / Smile / Maybe September (song from Oscar) / Emily / Very thought of you / Time for love / Country girl / Days of love / Keep smiling at trouble (trouble's a bubble) / For once in my life / Who cares (as long as you care for me) / Hi-ho / Baby don't quit now / Something / I do not know a day I did not love you / Old devil moon / Remind me / Maybe this time / Some other time / My foolish heart / But beautiful / How do you keep the music playing / What are you afraid of / Why do people fall in love / I got lost in her arms / When I lost you / Shakin' the blues away / Antonia / When do the bells ring for me
4893242 / 6 Apr '98 / Legacy

☐ HERE'S TO THE LADIES
People / I'm so in love again / Somewhere over the rainbow / My love went to London / Poor butterfly / Sentimental journey / Cloudy morning / Tenderly / Down in the depths / Moonlight in Vermont / Tangerine / God bless the child / Day break / You showed me the way / Honeysuckle Rose / Maybe this time / I got rhythm / My ideal
4812662 / Nov '95 / Columbia

☐ HOLLYWOOD AND BROADWAY
CDSIV 6145 / Jul '95 / Horatio Nelson

☐ I LEFT MY HEART IN SAN FRANCISCO/ I WANNA BE AROUND
I left my heart in San Francisco / Once upon a time / Tender is the night / Smile / Love for sale / Taking a chance on love / Candy kisses / Have I told you lately that I love you / Rules of the road / Marry young / I'm always chasing rainbows / Best is yet to come / Good life / If I love again / I wanna be around / Love look away / Let's face the music and dance / Once upon a summertime / If you were mine / I will live my life for you / Someone to love / It was me / Quiet nights
4775922 / Oct '94 / Columbia

☐ IF I RULED THE WORLD (Songs For The Jet Set)
Song of the jet set / Fly me to the moon / How insensitive / If I ruled the world / Love scene / Take the moment / That was then this is now / Sweet Lorraine / Right to love / Watch what happens / All my tomorrows / Two by two / Falling in love with love
4882822 / 29 Sep '97 / Columbia

☐ IN PERSON (Bennett, Tony & Count Basie)
Just in time / When I fall in love / Taking a chance on love / Without a song / Fascinating rhythm / Solitude / Pennies from Heaven / Lost in the stars / Firefly / There will never be another you / Lullaby of Broadway / Ol' man river
CK 642763 / Jan '96 / Mastersound

☐ MOVIE SONG ALBUM, THE
Maybe September / Girl talk / Gentle rain / Emily / Pawnbroker / Samba de orfeu / Shadow of your smile / Smile / Second time around / Days of wine and roses / Never too late / Trolley song
4879472 / Jul '97 / Columbia

☐ ON HOLIDAY
Solitude / All of me / When a woman loves a man / Me myself and I (Are all in love with you) / She's funny that way (I got a woman, crazy for me) / If I could be with you (One hour tonight) / Willow weep for me / Laughing at life / I wished on the moon / What a little moonlight can do / My old flame / That olde devil called love / Ill wind (you're blowin' me no good) / These foolish things (remind me of you) / Some other spring / Crazy she calls me / Good morning, heartache / Trav'lin light / God bless the child
4872632 / May '97 / Columbia

☐ PERFECTLY FRANK
Time after time / I fall in love too easily / East of the sun and west of the moon / Nancy / I thought about you / Night and day / I've got the world on a string / I'm glad there is you / Nightingale sang in Berkeley Square / I wished on the moon / You go to my head / Lady is a tramp / I see your face before me / Day in, day out / Indian summer / Call me irresponsible / Here's that rainy day / Last night when we were young / I wanna be in love again / Foggy day / Don't worry 'bout me / One for my baby (and one more for the road) / Angel eyes / I'll be seeing you
4722222 / Aug '94 / Columbia

☐ RODGERS & HART SONGBOOK, THE (Bennett, Tony & Ruby Braff/George Barnes Quartet)
This can't be love / Blue moon / Lady is a tramp / Lover / Manhattan / Spring is here / Have you met Miss Jones / Isn't it romantic / Wait till you see her / I could write a book / Thou swell / Most beautiful girl in the world / There's a small hotel / I've got five dollars / You took advantage of me / I wish I were in love again / This funny world / My heart stood still / My romance / Mountain greenery
CDSIV 1129 / Jul '95 / Horatio Nelson

☐ SINGING AND SWINGING (Bennett, Tony & Count Basie)
HADCD 184 / Nov '95 / Javelin

☐ SNOWFALL (The Tony Bennett Christmas Album)
Snowfall / My favourite things / Christmas song / Santa Claus is coming to town / We wish you a merry Christmas / Silent night / O come all ye faithful (Adeste Fidelis) / Jingle bells / Where is love / Christmasland / I love the winter weather / I've got my love to keep me warm / White Christmas / Winter wonderland / Have yourself a merry little Christmas / I'll be home for Christmas
4775972 / 3 Nov '97 / Columbia

☐ SONGS FROM THE HEART
MCCD 238 / Mar '96 / Music Club

☐ SPECIAL MAGIC OF TONY BENNETT
What is this thing called love / Love for sale / I'm in love again / You'd be so nice to come home to / Easy to love / It's all right with me / Night and day / Dream dancing / I've got you under my skin / Get out of town / Experiment / One / This funny world / Lost in the stars / As time goes by / I used to be colour blind / Mr. Magic
JHD 053 / Mar '93 / Tring

☐ THIS IS JAZZ
Dancing in the dark / When lights are low / Out of this world / Let's face the music and dance / Solitude / Crazy rhythm / Close your eyes / Judy / Love scene / Have you met Miss Jones / While the music plays on / Just one of those things / Sweet Lorraine / Danny boy
CK 65049 / 4 May '98 / Sony Jazz

☐ TOGETHER AGAIN (Bennett, Tony & Bill Evans)
Child is born / Make someone happy / Bad and the beautiful / Lucky to be me / You're near me / Two lonely people / You don't know what love is / Maybe September / Lonely girl / You must believe in spring
CDMRS 901 / '88 / DRG
CDSIV 1122 / Jul '95 / Horatio Nelson

☐ TONY BENNETT AT CARNEGIE HALL (2CD Set)
Lullaby of broadway / Just in time / All the things that you are / Fascinating rhythm / Stranger in paradise / Our love is here to stay / Love look away / Climb every mountain / Put on a happy face / Comes once in a lifetime / My ship / Speak low / Lost in the stars / Always / Anything goes / Ol' man river / Lazy afternoon / Sometimes I'm happy / Have I told you lately that I love you / That old black magic / Sleepin' bee / I've got the world on a string / What good does it do / One for my baby / This could be the start of something big / Without a song / Toot toot tootsie / It amazes me / Rules of the road / Firefly / Best is yet to come / I left my heart in San Francisco / How about you / April in Paris / Chicago / Solitude / I'm just a lucky so and so / Taking a chance on life / My heart tells me / Pennies from heaven / Rags to riches / Blue velvet / Smile / Because of you / Sing you sinners / De glory road
4882812 / 29 Sep '97 / Columbia

☐ TONY BENNETT SWINGS (Bennett, Tony & Count Basie Orchestra)
Jumpin' at the Woodside / I guess I'll have to change my plans / 9.20 special / Jeepers creepers / Swingin' the blues / Poor little rich girl / Shorty George / Chicago / Broadway / I've grown accustomed to her face / Out the window / With plenty of money and you / Lester leaps in / Anything goes / Are you havin' any fun / Dickie's dream / Growing pains / Jive at five / Life is a song / April in Paris
CD 6097 / Aug '97 / Music

☐ TONY BENNETT/BILL EVANS ALBUM, THE (Bennett, Tony & Bill Evans)
Young and foolish / Touch of your lips / Some other time / When in Rome / We'll be together again / My foolish heart / Waltz for debby / But beautiful / Days of wine and roses
OJCCD 439 / Feb '92 / Original Jazz Classics

☐ TOUCH OF CLASS, A
Isn't it romantic / I wish I were in love again / This can't be love / Reflections / As time goes by / Lucky to be me / Mr.Magic / Lady is a tramp / There'll be some changes made / You took advantage of me / Thou swell / Spring is here / My romance / Bridges / Lover / I could write a book / You're nearer / This funny world / I've got five dollars / There's a small hotel
TC 886792 / 2 Feb '98 / Disky

☐ UNPLUGGED
Old devil moon / Speak low / It had to be you / I love a piano / It amazes me / Girl I love / Fly me to the moon / You're the world to me / Rags to riches / When Joanna love me / Good life/I wanna be around / I left my heart in San Francisco / Steppin' out with my baby / Moonglow: *Bennett, Tony & k.d. Lang* / They can't take that away from me: *Bennett, Tony & Elvis Costello* / Foggy day / All of you / Body and soul / It don't mean a thing if it ain't got that swing / Autumn leaves
4771702 / Aug '94 / Columbia

Bennett, Winston

☐ PRISONER OF YOUR LOVE (Bennett, Winston & Merger)
Prisoner of your love / You to me are as love / Shine on / Young generation / On the road again / If I was a baby / Ain't gonna do it / Ask them / Jenny / Andria / Lost a friend / Glad to be alive / Happiness
PRCD 604 / May '96 / President

Benoit, Bernard

☐ GUITARE AND BOMBARDE - BARZAZ BREIZH
GRI 190832 / Sep '96 / Griffe

Benoit, Blue Boy

☐ PARLEZ-VOUS FRANCAIS
CDLLL 87 / Aug '93 / La Lichere

☐ PLUS TARD DANS LA SOIREE
CDLLL 187 / Aug '93 / La Lichere

Benoit, David

☐ BENOIT/FREEMAN PROJECT (Benoit, David & Russ Freeman)
Reunion / When she believed in me / Mediterranean nights / Swept away / End of our season / After the love has gone / Smartypants / It's the thought that counts / Mirage / That's all I could say
GRP 97392 / Feb '94 / GRP

☐ FREEDOM AT MIDNIGHT
Freedom at midnight / Along the Milky Way / Kei's song / Man with the panama hat / Pieces of time / Morning sojourn / Tropical breeze / Passion walk / Del sasser / Last goodbye
GRP 95452 / 25 May '98 / GRP

Benoit, Emile

☐ VIVE LA ROSE
AMBER 9014CD / Mar '98 / Amber

Benoit, Tab

☐ NICE AND WARM
JR 12012 / Apr '93 / Justice

☐ WHAT I LIVE FOR
Blues come walkin' in / Who's been talkin' / Cross the line / Time and time again / Cherry tree blues / Somehow / She's my number one / Too many drivers at the wheel / Night life / Don't cut off your hair / Wide open / What I live for
JR 12022 / Oct '94 / Justice

Benson, Brendan

☐ ONE MISSISSIPPI
Tea / Bird's eye view / Sittin' pretty / I'm blessed / Crosseyed / Me just purely / Got no secrets / How 'bout you / Emma J / Insects rule / Imaginary girl / House in Virginia / Cherries / Strawbearry rhubard pie
CDVUS 117 / May '97 / Virgin

Benson, George

☐ 20/20
No one emotion / Please don't walk away / I just wanna hang around you / Nothing's gonna change my love for you / La mer / New day / You are the love of my life / Hold me / Stand up / 20/20 / Shark bite
9251782 / Feb '92 / WEA

☐ BEST OF GEORGE BENSON, THE
California dreamin' / Gentle rain / One rock don't make no boulder / Take five / Summertime / Theme from good king bad / Body talk / Summer of '42 / My latin brothers / Ode to a Kudu / I remember Wes / From now on
4654052 / Oct '92 / Columbia

☐ BEST OF GEORGE BENSON, THE
9548362292 / 13 Apr '98 / WEA

☐ BEST, THE
Shape of things to come / My woman's good to me / Here comes the sun / Water brother / Tell it like it is / Oh darling / My cherie amour / Golden slumbers / You never give me your money / Footin' it / Don't let me lose this dream
3932032 / Mar '94 / A&M

☐ BEYOND THE BLUE HORIZON
So what / Gentle rain / All clear / Ode to a kudu / Somewhere in the east / All clear / Ode to a kudu / Somewhere in the east
ZK 65130 / 8 Sep '97 / Sony Jazz

☐ BODY TALK
239206 / Dec '86 / Musidisc

☐ BREEZIN'
This masquerade / Six to four / Breezin' / So this is love / Lady / Affirmation
256199 / Jun '89 / WEA

☐ COLLABORATION (Benson, George & Earl Klugh)
Mount Airey groove / Mimosa / Brazilian stomp / Dreamin' / Since you're gone / Collaboration / Jamaica / Romeo and Juliet
9255802 / Feb '95 / WEA

☐ GEORGE BENSON COLLECTION, THE
Turn your love around / Love all the hurt away / Give me the night / Cast your fate to the wind / Love ballad / Nature boy / Last train to Clarksville / Livin' inside your love / Never give up on a good thing / On Broadway / White rabbit / This masquerade / Here comes the sun / Breezin' / Moody's mood / We got the love / Greatest love of all
K 266107 / Jul '88 / WEA

☐ GEORGE BENSON COOKBOOK, THE
Cooker / Benny's back / Bossa rocka / All of me / Big fat lady / Benson's rider / Ready and able / Borgia stick / Return of the prodigal son / Jumpin' with symphony Sid
4769032 / Sep '94 / Columbia

☐ GIVE ME THE NIGHT
What's on your mind / Dinorah, Dinorah / Love dance / Star of the story / Midnight love affair / Turn out the lamplight / Love x love / Off Broadway / Moody's mood / Give me the night
256823 / Apr '84 / WEA

☐ GUITAR GENIUS OF GEORGE BENSON, THE
Love for sale / This masquerade is over / Witchcraft / There will never be another you / All blues / Blue bossa / Oleo / Li'l darlin'
QED 075 / Nov '96 / Tring

☐ IN FLIGHT
Nature boy / Wind and I / World is a ghetto / Gonna love you more / Valdez in the country / Everything must change
256327 / '86 / WEA

☐ IN YOUR EYES
Feel like makin' love / Inside love (so personal) / Lady love me (one more time) / Love will come again / In your eyes / Never too far to fall / Being with you / Use me / Late at night / In search of a dream
9237442 / Jul '88 / WEA

☐ IT'S UPTOWN WITH THE GEORGE BENSON QUARTET (Benson, George Quartet)
Clockwise / Summertime / Ain't that peculiar / Jaguar / Willow weep for me / Foggy day / Hello birdie / Bullfight / Stormy weather / Eternally / Myna bird blues
4769022 / Sep '94 / Columbia

☐ JAZZ MASTERS
Thunder walk / Sack o' woe / Tuxedo junction / Billie's bounce / Something/Octopus's garden / What's new / Shape of things to come / Low down and dirty / I remember Wes / Boss
5218612 / 5 May '98 / Verve

☐ LIL' DARLIN'
Witchcraft / Blue bossa / Oleo / Li'l darlin'
CDTB 078 / Sep '90 / Thunderbolt

☐ LIVE AT CASA CARIBE (Benson, George Quartet)
COD 011 / Mar '92 / Jazz View

☐ LIVE AT CASA CARIBE VOL.2 (Benson, George Quartet)
COD 035 / Jun '92 / Jazz View

☐ LIVE AT CASA CARIBE VOL.3 (Benson, George Quartet)
COD 036 / Aug '92 / Jazz View

☐ LOVE FOR SALE
Love for sale / L'il darlin' / There will never be another you / Blue bossa / All blues / Oleo
100722 / May '97 / A-Play Collection

☐ LOVE REMEMBERS
I'll be good to you / Got to be there / My heart is dancing / Love of my life / Kiss and make up / Come into my world / Love remembers / Willing to fight / Somewhere Island / Lovin' on borrowed time / Lost in love / Calling you
7599266852 / Dec '96 / WEA

☐ LOVE WALKED IN
All the things you are / Invitation / Love walked in / Dahlin's delight
CDTB 088 / Dec '90 / Thunderbolt

☐ MASQUERADE
Love for sale / This masquerade / There will never be another you / All blues
CDTB 072 / Oct '89 / Thunderbolt

☐ NEW BOSS GUITAR OF GEORGE BENSON, THE (Benson, George & 'Brother' Jack McDuff Quartet)
Shadow dancers / Sweet Alice blues / I don't know / Just another Sunday / Will you still be mine / Easy living / Rock-a-bye / My three sons
OJCCD 461 / Apr '92 / Original Jazz Classics

☐ QUARTET ALL BLUES
Love walked in / Dahlin's delight / Love for sal / (I'm afraid) the masquerade is over / There will never be another you / All blues
CDSGP 034 / Jul '92 / Prestige

☐ QUARTET BLUE BOSSA
Witchcraft / Blue bossa / Oleo / Ll'l darlin' / All the things you are / Invitations
CDSGP 035 / Jul '92 / Prestige

☐ SHAPE OF THINGS TO COME
Footin' it / Face it boy it's over / Shape of things that are and were / Chattanooga choo choo / Don't let me lose this dream / Last train to Clarksville / Shape of things to come
3969952 / Mar '94 / A&M

☐ SILVER COLLECTION, THE
Billie's bounce / Low down and dirty / Thunder walk / Doobie doobie blues / What's new / I remember Wes / Windmills of your mind / Song for my Father / Carnival joys / Giblet gravy / Walk on by / Sack o' woe / Groovin'
8234502 / Sep '92 / Verve

☐ SPOTLIGHT ON GEORGE BENSON
Witchcraft / Love for sale / There will never be another you / All blues / Li'l darlin' / Oleo
HADCD 102 / Feb '94 / Javelin

☐ STANDING TOGETHER
C-Smooth / Standing together / All I know / Cruise control / Poquito Spanish, Poquito funk / Still waters / Fly by night / Back to love / Keep rollin' / You can do it baby
GRP 99252 / 1 Jun '98 / GRP

☐ TELL IT LIKE IT IS
Soul limbo / Are you happy / Tell it like it is / Land of 1000 dances / Jackie all / Don't cha hear me callin' to ya / Water brother / My woman's good to me / Jama Joe / My cherie amour / Out in the cold again
3930202 / Mar '94 / A&M

☐ THAT'S RIGHT
That's right / Thinker / Marvin said / True blue / Hold'n on / Song for my brother / Johnnie Lee / Summer love / P Park / Footprints in the sand / When love comes calling / Where are you now
GRP 98242 / Jun '96 / GRP

☐ THIS IS JAZZ
Clockwise / Myna bird blues / Willow weep for me / Stormy weather / Cooker / Borgia stick / Ode to a kudu / Take five / I remember Wes / Good King Bad / Summertime / From now on
CK 64631 / May '96 / Sony Jazz

☐ TWICE THE LOVE
Twice the love / Starting all over / Good habit / Everybody does it / Living on borrowed love / Let's do it again / Stephanie / Tender love / You're still my baby / Until you believe
K 9257052 / Dec '96 / WEA

☐ WHILE THE CITY SLEEPS
Shiver / Love is here tonight / Teaser / Secrets in the night / Too many times / Did you hear the thunder / While the city sleeps / Kisses in the moonlight
9254752 / Feb '95 / WEA

☐ WITCHCRAFT
All blues / Witchcraft / Love for sale / Ll'l darlin' / There will never be another you / Oleo
JHR 73523 / Sep '93 / Jazz Hour

Benson, Jeffrey

☐ WHEN LIGHTS ARE LOW (Benson, Jeffrey & Charles Alexander)
DEEP 001 / Sep '97 / Deep River

Benson, Vicki

☐ BEST OF VICKI BENSON, THE (Easy Love)
HTCD 78 / 20 Apr '98 / Hot Productions

Bensusan, Pierre

☐ BAMBOULE
BEST 1040CD / Nov '93 / Acoustic Music

☐ LIVE AU NEW MORNING (Bensusan, Pierre & Didier Malherbe)
176652 / 5 Jan '98 / XIII Bis

☐ LIVE IN PARIS (Bensusan, Pierre & Didier Malherbe)
63301444012 / 21 Apr '98 / Zebra

☐ MUSIQUES
ROUCD 3038 / Mar '96 / Rounder

☐ PIERRE BENSUSAN VOL.2
ROUCD 3037 / Mar '96 / Rounder

☐ PRES DE PARIS
ROUCD 3023 / Mar '96 / Rounder

☐ PRES DE PARIS/PIERRE BENSUSAN VOL.2
DADGADCD 1 / Dec '97 / Dadgad

☐ SOLILAI
Nice feeling / Bamboule / Au jardin d'amour / Santa Monica / Suite flamande aux pommes / Milton / Solilai / Doa tea
CMA 945CD / Jan '95 / La Chant Du Monde
ROUCD 3068 / Mar '96 / Rounder

☐ SPICES
Femme cambree / Mille vallees / Le bateau fiction / Shi big, shi mhor / Agadiramadan / La cour interieure / Last pint / Les voiles catalanes / Montsegur / Four am
CMA 944CD / Jan '95 / Danceteria
ROUCD 3128 / Mar '96 / Rounder
DADGADCD 3 / Dec '97 / Dadgad

☐ WU WEI
CMA 942 / Oct '94 / Danceteria
ROUCD 3138 / Mar '96 / Rounder

Bente's Gammaldansorkester

☐ I GODLYNT LAG
B 1011CD / Dec '94 / Musikk Distribujson

Bentley Rhythm Ace

☐ BENTLEY RHYTHM ACE
Let there be flutes / Midlander (There can only be one) / Why is a frog too / Mind that gap / Run on the spot / Bentley's gonna sort you out / Ragtopskodacarchaser / Whoosh / Who put the bom in the bom bom diddleye bom / Spacehopper / Return of the harbour carbootechodisco roadshow
CDPCS 7391 / 8 Sep '97 / Parlophone

☐ BENTLEY RHYTHM ACE (US Version)
ASW 6223 / 6 Oct '97 / Astralwerks

Bentley, Alison

☐ ALISON BENTLEY QUARTET (Bentley, Alison Quartet & Mornington Lockett)
Fairly normal / Bit of a risk / Harlequin cat / Maybe / Rabbits / Angels on a pin / Mink / Making time / Pigs / Sonnet blues
SLAMCD 211 / Oct '96 / Slam

☐ WOMEN WITH STANDARDS (Bentley, Alison & Mandy Fox/Anita Wardell/ Shirley Kent)
SLAMCD 403 / Nov '97 / Slam

Bentley, Earlene

☐ BEST OF EARLENE BENTLEY, THE (I'm Living My Own Life)
Boys come to town / I'm living my own life / Caught in the act / Stargazing / Point of no return / Don't delay / I got you covered / Conviction / YMCA / Stop that man / Freedom
HTCD 56 / 20 Apr '98 / Hot Productions

Bentley, Ed

☐ BOLLA KEYBOARD BLUES
CDSGP 003 / Jan '94 / Prestige

☐ METROPOLIS
CDSGP 0137 / Sep '95 / Prestige

Benton, Brook

☐ 20 GREATEST HITS
It's just a matter of time / So close / Thank you pretty baby / So many ways / Ties that bind / Kiddio / Same one / Fools rush in / Think twice / For my baby / Boll weevil song / Frankie and johnny / It's just a house without you / Revenge / Shadrack / Lie to me / Hotel happiness / I got what I wanted / My true confession / Rainy night in georgia
RMB 75041 / Nov '93 / Remember

☐ BEST OF BROOK BENTON, THE
Boll weevil song / It's just a matter of time / So many ways / Kiddio / Hotel happiness / Think twice / Endlessly / Thank you pretty baby / Same one / Frankie & Johnny / Lie to me / House is not a home / Another cup of coffee / Fools rush in (where angels fear to tread)
5527892 / 3 Aug '98 / Spectrum

☐ COLLECTION, THE
Beautiful memories / I got what I wanted / Rainy night in georgia / Boll weevil song / Kiddio / Hotel happiness / So many ways / Frankie and johnny / It's just a matter of time / Think twice / Fools rush in / Lie to me / Revenge / Thank you pretty baby / My true confession / For my baby / It's just a house without you / Ties that bind / So close / Door that is open / Lover's question / Crazy in love with you / I wanna do everything for you / If only I had known / Only your love
COL 047 / Jan '95 / Collection

☐ RAINY NIGHT IN GEORGIA
Rainy night in Georgia / Think twice / Same one / Hotel happiness / So many ways / Endlessly / Revenge / Thank you pretty baby / Lied to me / Kiddio / Boll weevil song / Baby (you've got what it takes) / My true confession / It's just a matter of time / Rockin' good way / Frankie and Johnny / It's just a house without you / I got what I wanted / For my baby / So close
CD 6103 / Oct '97 / Music

☐ RAINY NIGHT IN GEORGIA, A
Rainy night in Georgia / It's just a matter of time / Boll weevil song / Baby, you got what it takes / Rockin' good way / Lie to me / So many ways / Hotel happiness / Kiddio / Endlessly / Revenge / Same one / Think twice
CDSGP 033 / Sep '92 / Prestige

☐ THAT OLD FEELING
That old feeling / Second time around / Nightingale sang in Berkeley Square / Impossible, incredible, but true / Moon river / Love is a many splendoured thing / Hawaiian wedding song / There I've said it again / Once in love with Amy / Try a little tenderness / More / Just as much as ever / Hey there / Peg o' my heart / I only have eyes for you / Goodnight my love / Call me irresponsible / Blue moon / There goes my heart / Unforgettable
74321432542 / Feb '97 / Camden

Benton, Buster

☐ BLUES AT THE TOP
You're my lady / Blues and trouble / It's good in my neighbourhood / Lonesome for a dime / I wish't I knew / From Missouri / Dangerous woman / That's your thing / Can't wait to see my baby's face / In the ghetto / Honey bee / Hawk is coming / I must have a hole in my head / Cold man ain't no good / Money's the name of the game
ECD 260302 / Feb '93 / Evidence

Benumb

☐ SOUL OF THE MARTYR
Driven on / No regret / LNF / Nothing personal / Sick / Monetary gain / Oblivious / Stood up and sold out / CTOA / IHMUST / Blind / Struggle on / Purpose / Crawl stagger fall / Self-righteous / Stuck pig / Self inflicted / TPU / TYG / Agony 1 / Agony 2 / Consumed / No hope / AAD / Of my own / Deprivation / Beyond fucked / Reoccurrence / Lost perception / Perseverence / Overwhelmed overcome / Nothing from nothing / ADS / Choke
RR 69862 / 13 Jul '98 / Relapse

Benzie, Ian F.

☐ SO FAR
CDLDL 1228 / May '95 / Lochshore

BEP

☐ RIPPER
KI 57CD / Jan '95 / Konkurrel

Beraki, Ghidion

☐ TEWOFAYNETNA
RPM 0102 / 9 Mar '98 / Rags Productions

Berard, Al

☐ DANSE LA LOUISIANE (Berard, Al & The Basin Brothers)
ROUCD 6065 / Aug '96 / Rounder

Berendsen, Ben

☐ AMONG THE TREES (Berendsen, Ben & Marcel Van Der Heyden)
322801 / Mar '93 / Koch

Beresford, Steve

☐ CUE SHEETS
TZ 7501 / Oct '96 / Tzadik

☐ SHORT IN THE UK
INCUSCD 27 / Mar '97 / Incus

☐ SIGNALS FOR TEA
AVAN 039 / Apr '95 / Avant

Berezan, Jennifer

☐ BORDERLINES
FF 615CD / Apr '94 / Flying Fish

Berg, Bob

☐ ANOTHER STANDARD
You and the night and the music / Summer wind / Michelle / Just in time / My man's gone now / All the way / No trouble / It was a very good year / I could write a book
SCD 90132 / 6 Oct '97 / Stretch

☐ ENTER THE SPIRIT
Second sight / Snapshot / Promise / Nature of the beast / Sometime ago / No moe / Night moves / Blues for Bella / I loves you Porgy / Angles
SCD 90042 / Mar '97 / Stretch

☐ GAMES (Berg, Bob & Mike Stern)
JD 1275 / 12 Jan '98 / Jazz Door

☐ RIDDLES
Morning star (A primeira estrela) / Something in the way she moves / Ramiro's dream / Children of the night / Riddle me this / Ebony eyes / Ahmed-6 / Coaster / For little Mia
SCD 90082 / Mar '97 / Stretch

Berg, Matraca

☐ MASTERS, THE
Things you left undone / I got it bad / Lying to the moon / I must have been crazy / You are the storm / Calico plains / Appalachian rain / Baby walk on / Alice in the looking glass / Dancin' on the wire / Slow poison / Tall drink of water / Let's pace it baby / I won't let go / Jolene / Guns in my head / Waiting for the sky to fall / Come to momma / River of no return
EABCD 112 / 30 Mar '98 / Eagle

☐ SPEED OF GRACE, THE
Slow poison / Tall drink of water / Let's face it, baby / I won't let go / Jolene / Guns in my head / Waiting for the sky to fall / Lying on the moon / Come on momma / River of no return
74321192302 / Mar '94 / RCA

☐ SUNDAY MORNING TO SATURDAY NIGHT
Alone for the ride / That train don't run / Back in the saddle / Here you come raining on me / Some people fall some people fly / Back when we were beautiful / Sunday morning to Saturday night / Good ol' girl / Give me tonight / If I were an angel / Resurrection
RTD 53047 / 3 Oct '97 / Radioactive

Berg, Rene

☐ LEATHER, THE LONELINESS
CMG 005CD / Nov '92 / Communique

Bergalli, Gustavo

☐ ON THE WAY
DRCD 212 / Oct '93 / Dragon

☐ TANGO IN JAZZ (Bergalli, Gustavo & Facundo)
TMCD 007 / Oct '97 / Touche

Bergcrantz, Anders

☐ LIVE 1996 (Bergcrantz, Anders Quartet)
DRCD 293 / Feb '98 / Dragon

Bergen Military Band

☐ BERGENSIANA
Fanfare og koral / I himmelen / Bruremarsj / Norsk kunstnerkarnaval / Hordarapsodi / Sommer aften idyll / Bivuakk-minner marsj / Springdans / Romanse / Bergensiana
DOYCD 070 / Apr '98 / Doyen

Bergens, Sodra

☐ KAMARINSKAYA (Bergens, Sodra Balalaika Orchestra)
Skomorosina / Pod dugoj kolokolclk pojot / Slbirskaja polka / Ja krolla rubasku / U zari, u zorenki / U vorot, vorot / Korobejniki / Kak na gorke / Trava moja travuska / Russkaja vesiolaja / Vspomni, vspomni / Ocesxvel / Na otdyche / Zaigraj moja volynka / Kamarinskaya / Ty poduj / Ech da uz vy noci / Valenki
XOUCD 103 / May '97 / Xource

Berger, Bengt

☐ BITTER FUNERAL BEER BAND
In a Balinese bar / Two ewe songs / Upper region / Twisted pattern / Ammasu / Pire for Palme / Dar-Kpen: Gan da Yina / Praise drumming for ANC
8393082 / '89 / ECM

Berger, Boy

☐ KANSAS CITY
In unser'm stadtchen / Wie du / Zu jung / Nimm dir zeit / Sag nicht goodbye / Keine kusst wie du / Kansas city / Komm mein Madel (tanz mit mir) / Mehr und mehr / Jup jup jumbo / Warum liebe ich gerade dich / Sie hat grune Augen rote haare / Bitte drei vanille / Das ist klasse: *Berger, Boy & Regine* / Du bist meine ganze welt / Ich trau' dir: *Berger, Boy & Regine* / Wir sind das Stadtgesprach / Du lachst mir ins gesicht / Kusse von Babette / Wulle wulle / Ti ja ja ho / Twist in Acapulco / Vertrau auf mich / Das sag ich dir wenn / Speil nicht katz und maus / Honolulu lady / Die veilchen bluh'n im mai: *Berger, Boy & Regine* / Hey boy hey girl: *Berger, Boy & Regine* / Schlud daran / Memphis Tennessee / Keep smiling / Sugar baby / Kitty kat
BCD 16182 / Nov '97 / Bear Family

Berger, Karl

☐ AROUND (Berger, Karl & Friends)
1201122 / May '91 / Black Saint

Bergeron, Chuck

☐ COMPOSITIONS
AL 73107 / Dec '97 / A

Bergeron, Shirley

☐ FRENCH ROCKING BOOGIE
French rocking boogie / J'ai fait mon idee / Old home waltz / Quel etoile / New country waltz / Perrodin two step / Chez Tanie / Mama and papa / Since that first time / True love waltz / J'ai passe devant ta porte / Poor hobo / La valse a August breaux / Eunice two step / La valse de cherokee / Bosco blues / Madam Sostan / La crepe a nazare / Chere bassette / Vermillion two step / La valse de grand bois / Chere toute toute
CDCHD 353 / Apr '92 / Ace

Bergh, Totti

☐ MAJOR BLUES (Bergh, Totti Quintet)
GMCD 68 / Apr '98 / Gemini

☐ WARM VALLEY
GMCD 91 / May '97 / Gemini

Bergheim 34

☐ BERGHEIM 34
FILO 002 / 6 Jul '98 / First Love

Bergheim, Dordi

☐ VAKN OPP OG SLA...
BK 16CD / Aug '97 / Buen

Bergin, Johnny

☐ COME DANCING
Everything's in rhythm with my heart / Please don't talk about me when I'm gone / Dream of me/Dreamy melody/Dream lover / Where the blue of the night/ Sailing by / You brought a new kind of love to me/ Undecided/A sky blue sh / Alexander's ragtime band / September in the rain/I'll string along with you / In a shady nook/Love letters in the sand / 'Deed I do / Goodbye blues / Blueberry hill/Goodnight sweetheart / We'll meet again/I don't want to walk without you / Breezin' along with the breeze / I saw stars/Auf weidersehn, sweetheart / Deep purple/ Moonlight bay / Here's that rainy day / More I see you, The/Red sails in the sunset / Play to me gipsy / Ecstasy / When the red red robin/Glory of love / You're driving me crazy/Makin' whoopee/Roamin' in the Glomin
SAV 173CD / Jun '92 / Savoy

☐ COME DANCING VOL.2
Ma, he's making eyes at me/Moonstruck / You always hurt the one you love / Five foot two, eyes of blue / Some of these days/My blue heaven / If I had a talking picture of you / If I had my way/Pennies from heaven / Dancing with my shadow/Everything stops for tea / There's a land of begin again / Let us be sweethearts over again / I'll always be in love with you / Tennessee waltz/Far away places / Tell me I'm forgiven / Golden tango / Till there was you / I hear a rhapsody/Come back to Sorrento / All I do is dream of you/Ukelele lady/Soldiers of the Queen / Elmer's tune/Battle of New Orleans/Davy Crockett / You made me love you/A slow boat to China / Me and my shadow / Carolina in the morning / Maybe it's because I'm a Londoner/Lambeth walk / Japanese sandman/Old father Thames / Seven lonely days/ Exactly like you/Glad rag doll / Lida rose/You are my everything/Spread a little happiness / Black hills of Dakota / Bye bye blues / 'S Wonderful
SAV 192CD / Jun '93 / Savoy

Bergin, Mary

☐ FEADOGA STAIN
Ril gan ainm/Cinnie le dia ah surely/The union reel / Inion mhic sheain Miss Johnson's/Mike Russell's / Tom Billy's portanna/Langshern pony / Sean Reid's/ The drunken landlady / Liam O'Raghallaigh / Bian ui Croidheain/Gearoid O Comain/An la baish / Port Sean Seosamh/Sean Tiobrad Arann / Rothal an Tsaoil / Beath na smeire duibhe/Maude Miller / Mo thrua go beaca me ariamh/Chuig na gluine I ngaineamh thu / Garra na bhfeileoig/Miss Galvin / Lady on the island/The concert reel / An bothan sa photach / Mo mhuirnin ban / Mick Hand's/Reel of Mullinavat / Port Mhuineachain/Nora Crionna / Kitty gone a milking/Last night's fun / Wind that shakes the barley
CEFCD 071 / '89 / Gael Linn
SHANCD 79006 / 22 Apr '98 / Shanachie

☐ FEADOGA STAIN VOL.2
CEFCD 149 / Feb '93 / Gael Linn

Bergin, Sean

☐ LIVE AT THE BIMHUIS
BVHAASTCD 9202 / Oct '93 / Bvhaast

Bergman, Borah

☐ BERGMAN/BRAXTON/BOTZMANN (Bergman, Borah & Anthony Braxton/ Peter Brotzmann)
M 00001 / Aug '97 / Mixtery

☐ HUMAN FACTOR, THE (Bergman, Borah & Andrew Cyrille)
1212122 / Apr '93 / Soul Note

☐ NEW FRONTIER, A
1210302 / May '94 / Soul Note

☐ REFLECTIONS ON ORNETTE COLEMAN & THE STONE HOUSE (Bergman, Borah & Hamid Drake)
1212802 / Jan '96 / Soul Note

Bergmann Brothers

☐ FINE ARTISTE
BERGCD 02 / Mar '98 / Blue Heron

Bergonzi, Jerry

☐ FAST COMPANY (Bergonzi, Jerry & Joey Calderazzo)
Lag / Loud-zee / Echoes / Not afraid of... / Implication / Suite / Fast company / Conjunction
BJAC 50222 / 29 Jun '98 / Blue Jackel

☐ LINEAGE
1232372 / Mar '91 / Red

☐ SIGNED BY... (Bergonzi, Jerry & Joachim Kuhn)
ZZ 84104 / Feb '94 / Deux Z

☐ TILT (Bergonzi, Jerry Quartet)
1232452 / Mar '92 / Red

☐ VERTICAL REALITY
500642 / 21 Aug '97 / Musidisc

Bergstrom, Totte

☐ TOTTE BERGSTROM
FE 1433 / Aug '96 / Folk Era

Berigan, Bunny

☐ 1936-1938
Take my word / Rendezvous with a dream / On a coconut island / On the beach at Bali-Bali / But definitely / Sing sing sing / I'm an old cowhand / Empty saddles / On your toes / Did I remember / San Francisco / I can't escape from you / I can't pull a rabbit out of my hat / When I'm with you / Dardanella / When did you leave heaven / You're not the kind / You've got to eat your spinach baby / Sweet misery of love / That's a plenty / Now it can be told / My walking stick / Wacky dust / A sky of blue and so forth / Flat foot floogie / Shanghai shuffle / I got a guy / Tonight will live / Cowboy from Brooklyn / Devil's holiday / Easy to find and hard to lose / Wearing of the green / Pied piper / Sunday / Frankie and johnny / Don't wake up my heart / I'll always be in love with you / I never knew I could love anybody / How to make love in 10 easy lessons / Black bottom / There's a brand new picture in my picture frame / There's something about an old love / Small fry / Sing you sinners / Meet the beat of my heart / T'aint so honey t'aint so / Where in the world / Peg o' my herat / Hi-yo silver / Mahogany hall stomp
JASSCD 627 / Oct '92 / Jass

☐ 1938 BROADCASTS-PARADISE RESTAURANT
JH 1022 / Feb '93 / Jazz Hour

☐ BUNNY BERIGAN & HIS RHYTHM MAKERS 1936-1938 (2CD Set) (Berigan, Bunny & His Rhythm Makers)
Take my word / Rendevous with a dream / On a coconut island / On the beach at Bali Bali / But definitely / Sing sing sing / I'm old cowhand / Empty saddles / On your toes / Did I remember / San Francisco / I can't escape from you / I can't pull a rabbit out of a hat / When I'm with you / Dardanella / When did you leave heaven / You're not the kind / You've gotta eat your spinach baby / Sweet misery of love / That's a plenty / Now it can be told / My walking stick / Wacky dust / (A sky of blue) and so forth / Flat foogie Shanghai shuffle / I got a guy / Tonight will live / Cowboy from Brooklyn / Devil's holiday / Easy to find hard to lose / Wearing of the green / Pied piper / Sunday / Frankie and Johnny / Don't wake up my heart / I'll always be in love with you / I never knew (I could love anybody) / (How to make love)in 10 easy lessons / Black bottom / There's a brand new picture in my picture frame / There's something about an old love / Small fry / Sing you sinners / Will you remember tonight tomorrow / So help me / Meet the beat of my heart / T'aint so honey ain't so / Where in the world / Peg o' my heart / Hi-ho silver / Mahogany hall stomp
CDJZCL 5016 / Aug '97 / Jazz Classics

☐ BUNNY BERIGAN 1936-38
JCD 627 / Feb '91 / Jass

☐ BUNNY BERIGAN AND HIS RHYTHM MAKERS 1936 (Berigan, Bunny & His Rhythm Makers)
TAX 37102 / Aug '94 / Tax

☐ BUNNY BERIGAN AND HIS RHYTHM MAKERS VOL.2 - 1938 (Berigan, Bunny & His Rhythm Makers)
JASSCD 638 / May '94 / Jass

☐ CLASSICS 1935-1936
CLASSICS 734 / Jan '94 / Classics

☐ CLASSICS 1936-1937
CLASSICS 749 / Aug '94 / Classics

☐ CLASSICS 1937
CLASSICS 766 / Aug '94 / Classics

☐ CLASSICS 1937-1938
CLASSICS 785 / Nov '94 / Classics

☐ CLASSICS 1938
CLASSICS 815 / May '95 / Classics

☐ CLASSICS 1938-1942
CLASSICS 844 / Nov '95 / Classics

☐ DEVIL'S HOLIDAY
Shanghai shuffle / I got a guy / Tonight will live / Cowboy from brooklyn / Devil's holiday / Easy to find, hard to lose / Wearing of the green / Pied piper / Sunday / Frankie and johnny / Don't wake up my heart / I'll always be in love with you / I never knew / (how to make love in) ten easy lessons / Black bottom / There's a brand new picture in my picture frame / There's something about an old love / Small fry / Sing you sinners / Will you remember tonight tomorrow / So help me / Meet the beat of my heart / Tain't so, honey, tain't so / Where in the world / Peg o' my heart / Hi-yo silver / Mahogany hall stomp
JCD 638 / Jan '93 / Jass

☐ GANG BUSTERS 1938-1939
When a prince / Livery stable blues / Let this be a warning / Why doesn't somebody / High society / Father dear father / Button, button / Rockin' rollers / Jubilee / Sobbin' blues / I cried for you / 'Deed I do / In a mist / Flashes / Davenport blues / Candlelights / In the dark / Walking the dog / Patty cake / Jazz me blues / You had it comin' to you / There'll be some changes made / Little gate's special / Gangbuster's holiday
HEPCD 1036 / May '92 / Hep

☐ INTRODUCTION TO BUNNY BERIGAN 1935-1939, AN
4021 / May '95 / Best Of Jazz

☐ PORTRAIT OF BUNNY BERIGAN
Me minus you / She reminds me of you / Troubled / Plantation moods / In a little Spanish town / Solo hop / Nothin' but the blues / Squareface / King Porter stomp / Buzzard / Tillie's downtown now / You took advantage of me / Chicken and waffles / I'm coming Virginia / Blues / Swing Mister Charlie / Blue Lou / Marie / Black bottom / Prisoner's song / I can't get started (with you)
CDAJA 5060 / Apr '89 / Living Era

☐ SWINGIN' HIGH
TPZ 1013 / Feb '95 / Topaz Jazz

Berio, Luciano

☐ ACOUSMATRIX 7, ELECTRONIC WORKS (Berio, Luciano & Bruno Maderna)
BVHAASTCD 9109 / Oct '94 / Bvhaast

Berk, Dick

☐ EAST COAST STROLL
RSRCD 128 / Nov '94 / Reservoir

☐ LET'S COOL ONE
RSRCD 122 / Nov '94 / Reservoir

Berki, Lazlo

☐ GYPSY VIOLIN
VICG 52702 / Mar '96 / JVC World Library

Berking, Willy

☐ DENN ICH BIN ZUM TANZEN GEBOREN
BCD 16269 / Jul '98 / Bear Family

☐ EIN LEBEN VOLL MUSIK
BCD 16265 / Jul '98 / Bear Family

☐ SOLISTENPARADE
BCD 16267 / Jul '98 / Bear Family

☐ TROPICAL NIGHT
BCD 16268 / Jul '98 / Bear Family

☐ WITH A SONG IN MY HEART
BCD 16266 / Jul '98 / Bear Family

Berkovi, Justin

☐ CHARM HOSTEL
EFA 044262 / 5 May '98 / Force Inc.

Berlin

☐ COUNT THREE AND PRAY
Will I ever understand you / You don't know / Like flames / Heartstrings / Take my breath away / Trash / When love goes to war / Hideaway / Sex me, talk me / Pink and velvet
5509012 / Jan '95 / Spectrum

Berlin Contemporary Jazz Orchestra

☐ BERLIN CONTEMPORARY JAZZ ORCHESTRA
Ana / Salz / Reef und kneebus
8417772 / Oct '90 / ECM

☐ LIVE IN JAPAN '96
DIW 922 / Feb '97 / DIW

Berlin, Irving

☐ BERLIN, GERSHWIN AND PORTER (2CD Set) (Various Artists)
R2CD 4024 / 13 Apr '98 / Deja Vu

☐ BLUE SKIES (The Irving Berlin Songbook) (Various Artists)
Let yourself go: *Fitzgerald, Ella* / You're just in love: *Vaughan, Sarah & Billy Eckstine* / Say it isn't so: *Holiday, Billie* / Remember: *Hartman, Johnny & Errol Garner* / No strings (I'm fancy free): *Astaire, Fred* / I used to be colour blind: *O'Day, Anita* / How deep is the ocean: *Williams, Joe* / This year's kisses: *Fitzgerald, Ella* / Supper time: *Waters, Ethel* / Blue skies: *Washington, Dinah* / Always: *Vaughan, Sarah & Billy Eckstine* / Top hat, white tie and tails: *Astaire, Fred* / Isn't this a lovely day: *Fitzgerald, Ella & Louis Armstrong* / Let's face the music and dance: *O'Day, Anita* / Waiting at the end of the road: *Laine, Frankie* / All by myself: *Fitzgerald, Ella*
5316362 / Jul '96 / Verve

☐ COMPLETE IRVING BERLIN SONGBOOKS, THE (Cheek To Cheek/ Blue Skies/How Deep Is The Ocean - 3CD Set) (Various Artists)
5394422 / 10 Nov '97 / Verve

☐ FOREVER IRVING BERLIN (Various Artists)
Let's face the music and dance: *Cole, Nat 'King'* / I've got my love to keep me warm: *Martin, Dean* / All by myself: *Darin, Bobby* / Easter paradise: *Garland, Judy* / I've got the sun in the morning: *Riddle, Nelson & Orchestra* / Cheek to cheek: *Monro, Matt* / If I had you: *Vaughan, Sarah* / Say it isn't so: *Washington, Dinah* / Blue skies: *Cogan, Alma* / Change partners: *Crosby, Bing* / Happy birthday: *Lee, Peggy* / Isn't this a lovely day: *Haymes, Dick* / Late, late show: *Cole, Nat 'King'* / Let me sing a happy song: *Monro, Matt* / Puttin' on the ritz: *Garland, Judy* / Supper time: *Wilson, Nancy* / There's no business like show business: *Wilson, Nancy* / Maybe it's because (I love you too much): *Lee, Peggy* / Always: *Darin, Bobby* / White Christmas: *Martin, Dean*
CDMFP 6262 / Nov '96 / Music For Pleasure

☐ HOW DEEP IS THE OCEAN (The Irving Berlin Songbook) (Various Artists)
5377012 / Aug '97 / Verve

☐ MELODY LINGERS ON, THE (25 Songs Of Irving Berlin) (Various Artists)
Alexander's ragtime band: *Smith, Bessie Band* / What'll I do: *Pidgeon, Walter* / Always: *Layton & Johnstone* / Song is ended but the melody lingers on: *Ellis, Segar* / Puttin' on the ritz: *Astaire, Fred* / Me: *Etting, Ruth* / Say it isn't so: *Keller, Greta* / Heat wave: *Waters, Ethel* / I never had a chance: *Keller, Greta* / Cheek to cheek: *Astaire, Fred* / Isn't it a lovely day: *Hildegarde* / Let's face the music and dance: *Astaire, Fred* / Pretty girl is like a melody: *O'Connor, Cavan* / This year's kisses: *Holiday, Billie* / Marie: *Dorsey, Tommy & His Orchestra* / I've got my love to keep me warm: *Powell, Dick* / You forgot to remember: *Boswell, Connee* / It's a lovely day tomorrow: *Lynn, Vera* / All alone: *Shore, Dinah* / Blue skies: *Sinatra, Frank* / How deep is the ocean: *Lee, Peggy* / Girl that I marry: *Sinatra, Frank* / They say it's wonderful: *Como, Perry* / Easter parade: *Crosby, Bing* / White Christmas: *Crosby, Bing*
CDAJA 5245 / Oct '97 / Living Era

☐ TOP HAT, WHITE TIE AND TAILS (Various Artists)
MACCD 192 / Aug '96 / Autograph

☐ UNSUNG IRVING BERLIN
VSD 5770 / Apr '97 / Varese Sarabande

Berline, Byron

☐ DAD'S FAVORITES
Coming down from Denver / New broom / Grey eagle / B and B rag / Redbird / Ragtime Annie / Lime rock / Stones rag / Miller's reel / Arkansas traveller / Sweet memories waltz / Birmingham fling
ROUCD 0100 / Jul '97 / Rounder

☐ DOUBLE TROUBLE (Berline, Byron & John Hickman)
SHCD 3750 / Aug '95 / Sugar Hill

☐ FIDDLE AND A SONG
Sally goodin / Rose of old Kentucky / My dixie darling / Roly poly / Faded love / Skippin' along on top / Sweet memory waltz / Fiddle faddle / Second fiddle / Fiddle's dream / Were you there / Cajun medley
SHCD 3838 / Sep '96 / Sugar Hill

☐ JUMPIN' THE STRINGS
SHCD 3787 / Jan '97 / Sugar Hill

☐ NOW THEY ARE FOUR (Berline, Byron & Dan Crary/John Hickman)
Big dog / Train of memory / Weary blues from waiting / Moonlight motor inn / They don't play George Jones on MTV / Speak softly you're talking to my heart / Santa Anna / Leave me the way I am / Kodak 1955 / Hallelujah Harry
SHCD 3773 / Jul '90 / Sugar Hill

☐ OUTRAGEOUS
Barndance / Fall creek / Passin' by / Don't put it away / Coming home / Jack rabbit / Stampede / Byron's barn / Outrageous / Skippin' around / Oklahoma stomp / Funky deer
FF 70227 / Sep '96 / Flying Fish

Bermejo, Mili

☐ CASA CORAZON (Bermejo, Mili Quartet)
GLCD 4016 / May '94 / Green Linnet

☐ IDENTIDAD
XENO 4020CD / Apr '96 / Xenophile

Bernard, Alison

☐ FUNKIFINO
Fantasy / Live together / Slippin' and slidin' / Feel my groove / Looking for an answer / If / I'm beginning to wonder / Waiting for the bass to come / Ain't no fun to me / Family affair / Too many women / If I should
RUF 7716 / Feb '98 / Ruf

Bernard, Rod

☐ SWAMP ROCK 'N' ROLLER
Pardon Mr Gordon / Recorded in England / Memphis / Gimme back my cadillac / Who's gonna rock my baby / Forgive / My old mother in law / I might as well / Boss man's son / Fais do do / Loneliness / Colinda / I want somebody / Diggy liggy lo / Lawdy Miss Clawdy / Prisoner's song / Thirty days / That's alright mama / Lover's blues / Maybellene / Midnight special / My babe / Jambalaya / Big mamou / New Orleans / Give me love / Shake, rattle and roll / This should go on forever
CDCHD 488 / May '94 / Ace

Bernard, Will

☐ MEDICINE HAT
5393252 / 9 Feb '98 / Antilles/Verve

Bernard-Smith, Simon

☐ PRAISE HIM ON THE PANPIPES
SOPD 2050 / May '92 / Spirit Of Praise

Berne, Tim

☐ ANCESTORS, THE (Berne, Tim Sextet)
Sirius b / Shirley's song / San Antonio / Ancestors
1210612 / Oct '90 / Soul Note

☐ BIG SATAN
9100052 / Oct '97 / Winter & Winter

☐ BLOODCOUNT UNWOUND (3CD Set)
Bro' ball / No Ma'am / Yes Dear / Loose ends / Bloodcount / Mr. Johnson's blues / Other / What are the odds
SCREWU 70001 / Apr '97 / ScrewGun

☐ FRACTURED FAIRY TALES
Now then / SEP / Hong Kong sad song/More coffee / Evolution of a pearl / Lightnin' bug boute / Telex blues
8344312 / Jan '91 / jMT

☐ FULTON STREET MAUL
378262 / Nov '96 / Koch Jazz

☐ MEMORY SELECT (Berne, Tim & Bloodcount)
5140292 / Apr '96 / jMT

☐ NICE VIEW (Berne, Tim Caos Totale)
It could have been a lot worse / Third rail / Impacted wisdom
5140132 / Jul '93 / jMT

☐ SANCTIFIED DREAMS
Velcho man / Hip doctor / Elastic lad / Blue alpha (for alpha) / Mag's groove / Terre haute
378252 / Jun '97 / Koch Jazz

☐ VISITATION RITES
Poetic Licence / Piano justice / I can't wait till tomorrow
SCREWU 70002 / 17 Nov '97 / ScrewGun

Bernie

☐ I SAW THE LIGHT
I saw the light / This world is not my home / Me and Jesus / One day at a time / Morning has broken / Tramp on the streets / Precious memories / Fly away / Daddy sang bass / Why me Lord / Old rugged cross / Amazing grace / Rivers of Babylon / Swing low, sweet Chariot / He's got the whole world in his hands / Old country church / Safe in the arms of Jesus / Go tell it on the mountain / Will the circle be unbroken / When the saints go marching in / Count your blessings / Family bible / Rock of ages / How great thou art
PLATCD 339 / Mar '93 / Platinum

Bernstein, Peter

☐ BRAIN DANCE (Bernstein, Peter Quintet)
Brain dance / Chant / Means and ends / Dual nature / While we're young / You leave me breathlesss / Lady bug / Danger zone
CRISS 1130CD / Jul '97 / Criss Cross

☐ SIGNS
CRISS 1095 / Apr '95 / Criss Cross

☐ SOMETHIN'S BURNIN' (Bernstein, Peter Quartet)
CRISS 1079CD / Nov '93 / Criss Cross

Bernstein, Steven Jesse

☐ PRISON
SPCD 37195 / Jul '92 / Sub Pop

Beron, Paul

☐ TRASNOCHANDO
BMT 009 / Jul '97 / Blue Moon

Berrios, Steve

☐ AND THEN SOME (Berrios, Steve & Son Bacheche)
Son bacheche / Leri eyo / Al mundo de los recuerdos / Bemsha swing / Chamalongo / Blues for sarka / Un ecobio / With the sweetness / Fire and brimstone / Mojiganga / Hominaje a un trovador / Uncle Toms
MCD 92552 / Sep '96 / Milestone

Berroguetto

☐ NAVICULARIA
DF 002CD / Aug '97 / Do Fol

Berry, Bill

☐ HELLO REV (Berry, Bill LA Big Band)
Hello rev / Star crossed lovers / Bink / And how / Earl / Little song for Mex / Be your own best friend / Tulip or turnip / Boy meets horn / Cotton tail
CCD 4027 / Aug '90 / Concord Jazz

☐ SHORTCAKE
Avalon / Betty / Bloose / I didn't know about you / Royal Garden blues / Moon song / I'm getting sentimental over you / I hadn't anyone till you
CCD 4075 / Feb '95 / Concord Jazz

Berry, Chuck

☐ 20 GREAT TRACKS
Maybellene / Roll over Beethoven / Reelin' and rockin' / Rock 'n' roll music / Sweet little sixteen / Johnny B Goode / No particular place to go / Memphis Tennessee / Wee wee hours / You never can tell / Go go go / Downbound train / No money down / Havana moon / House of blue lights / Crying steel / I'm just a lucky so and so / Promised land / My Mustang Ford / Drifting heart
CDMFP 5936 / Apr '92 / Music For Pleasure

☐ BEST OF CHUCK BERRY, THE
Roll over Beethoven / No particular place to go / Memphis Tennessee / Havana moon / Wee wee hours / Nadine / Let it rock / Sweet little sixteen / Maybellene / Back in the USA / Little queenie / Almost grown / Johnny B Goode / School day / Oh baby doll / Sweet little rock 'n' roller / Reelin' and rockin' / Promised land / Rock 'n' roll music / Downbound train / Brown eyed handsome man / Merry Christmas baby / Bye bye Johnny / Around and around / No money down
MCCD 019 / May '91 / Music Club

☐ BEST OF CHUCK BERRY, THE (2CD Set)
Roll over Beethoven / Sweet little sixteen / Johnny B Goode / You never can tell / You can't catch me / Downbound train / Too much monkey business / Havana moon / School day / Oh baby doll / Beautiful Delilah / Sweet little rock'n'roller / Antony boy / Little Queenie / Almost grown / Let it rock / Back in the USA / Reelin' and rockin' / Around and around / Brown eyed handsome man / Maybellene / No particular place to go / Rock 'n' roll / Run Randolph run / Jo Jo Gunne / Carol / Confessin' the blues / Jaguar and thunderbird / Down the road apiece / Thirty days / Merry Christmas baby / My ding-a-ling / I'm talking about you / Too pooped to pop / Bye bye Johnny / Promised land / Tulane / Come on / Nadine (is it you) / Memphis Tennessee
MCD 11560 / 16 Feb '98 / MCA

☐ CHUCK BERRY
Rock and roll music / Johnny B. Goode / Maybellene / Rellin' and rockin' / You never can tell / Sweet little sixteen / Let it rock / Roll over Beethoven / Back in the USA / Little Queenie / No particular place to go / No money down / Memphis Tennessee / Nadine / I got to find my baby / School days / Wee wee hours / Too much monkey business
CD 111 / Oct '94 / Timeless Treasures

☐ CHUCK BERRY
Rock 'n' roll music / Johnny B Goode / Maybellene / Reelin' and rockin' / You never can tell / Sweet little sixteen / Let it rock / Roll over Beethoven / Back in the USA / Little Queenie / No particular place to go / No money down / Memphis Tennessee / Nadine / I got to find my baby / School days / Wee wee hours / Too much monkey business
399537 / May '97 / Koch Presents

☐ CHUCK BERRY
UAE 30022 / Jan '98 / Members Edition

☐ CHUCK BERRY & BO DIDDLEY (Berry, Chuck/Bo Diddley)
Memphis Tennessee: *Berry, Chuck* / Brown eyed handsome man: *Berry, Chuck* / Too much monkey business: *Berry, Chuck* / No particular place to go: *Berry, Chuck* / Rock 'n' roll music: *Berry, Chuck* / Around and around: *Berry, Chuck* / Carol: *Berry, Chuck* / You can never tell: *Berry, Chuck* / Nadine: *Berry, Chuck* / You can't catch me: *Berry, Chuck* / Mona: *Diddley, Bo* / I'm a man: *Diddley, Bo* / Pills: *Diddley, Bo* / You can't judge a book by it's cover: *Diddley, Bo* / Who do you love: *Diddley, Bo* / Say man: *Diddley, Bo* / Pretty thing: *Diddley, Bo* / Hey bo diddley: *Diddley, Bo* / Road runner: *Diddley, Bo* / Say boss man: *Diddley, Bo*
ASTCD 4009 / Oct '97 / Go On Deluxe

☐ CHUCK BERRY IN CONCERT
CDSGP 0155 / Mar '95 / Prestige

☐ CHUCK BERRY IN LONDON/FRESH BERRIES
BGOCD 395 / 15 Jun '98 / Beat Goes On

☐ **EP COLLECTION, THE**
Reelin' and rockin' / Johnny b. goode / Nadine / Don't you lie to me / Round and round / No particular place to go / Childhood sweetheart / My little love light / Maybellene / I'm talking about you / Roll over beethoven / Sweet little sixteen / You can't catch me / Memphis, tennessee / I got a booking / You never can tell / Things I used to do / Jamaica farewell / Thirty days / Oh baby doll / School days / Bye bye johnny / Back in the u.s.a. / Rock and roll music
SEECD 320 / Jul '91 / See For Miles

☐ **GREAT 28 HITS, THE**
Maybellene / Thirty days / You can't catch me / Too much monkey business / Brown eyed handsome man / Roll over beetoven / Havana moon / School days / Rock and roll music / Oh baby doll / Reelin' and rockin' / Sweet little sixteen / Johnny b. goode / Around and around / Carol / Beautiful delilah / Memphis, tennessee / Sweet little rock and roller / Little queenie / Almost grown / Back in the u.s.a. / Let it rock / Bye bye johnny / I'm talking about you / Come on / Nadine / No particular place to go / I want to be your driver
CHLD 19116 / Jan '94 / Chess/MCA

☐ **HAIL HAIL ROCK 'N' ROLL (Live In Toronto)**
School days / Rock 'n' roll music / Nadine / Memphis Tennessee / Reelin' and rockin' / Bonsoir cherie / Sweet little sixteen / Maybellene / In the wee hours / Carol / My ding-a-ling / Johnny B. Goode
AIM 0009CD / 20 Oct '97 / Aim

☐ **HIS BEST VOL.1**
MCD 09371 / Aug '97 / Chess/MCA

☐ **LIVE ON STAGE**
Schooldays / Sweet little sixteen / Roll over Beethoven / Everyday I have the blues / Bio / Maybellene/Mountain dew / Let it rock / Carol/Little Queenie / Keys to the highway / Got my mojo working / Reelin' and rockin' / Johnny B Goode
CDMF 092 / Mar '95 / Magnum Force

☐ **MORE CHUCK BERRY/CHUCK BERRY**
BGOCD 394 / 24 Nov '97 / Beat Goes On

☐ **ON THE BLUES SIDE**
Confessin' the blues / Runaround / Worried life blues / Things that I used to do / Blues for Hawaiians / Wee wee hours / I still got the blues / Down the road apiece / No money down / Stop and listen / Blue on blue / Sweet sixteen / I got to find my baby / I just want to make love to you / Merry Christmas baby / Deep feeling / Wee hour blues / Don't you lie to me / Ain't that just like a woman / Driftin' blues / Blue feeling
CDCH 397 / Sep '93 / Ace

☐ **SWEET LITTLE ROCK 'N' ROLLER**
Carol / Back in the USA / Sweet little rock 'n' roller / Little queenie / School days / Promised land / Maybeline / Nadine / Blues for Hawaiians / No money down / Fraulein / Roll over Beethoven / Memphis Tennessee / Sweet little sixteen / Johnny B Goode / No particular place to go / Down the road a piece / Let it rock / You never can tell / My ding-a-ling
MCD 80245 / Apr '97 / Chess/MCA

☐ **TWO GREAT GUITARS/SUPER SUPER BLUES BAND (Berry, Chuck & Bo Diddley/Howlin' Wolf/Muddy Waters)**
Liverpool drive / Chuck's beat / When the Saints go marching in / Bo's beat / Long distance call / Medley / Sweet little angel / Spoonful / Diddley daddy / Little red rooster / Going down slow
BGOCD 334 / Feb '97 / Beat Goes On

☐ **VERY BEST OF CHUCK BERRY, THE**
MCBD 19536 / Apr '97 / MCA

☐ **VERY BEST OF CHUCK BERRY, THE**
Johnny B Goode / Sweet little sixteen / Hail, hail rock 'n' roll / Hoochie coochie man / Reelin' 'n' rockin' / My ding a ling / Johnny B Goode (reprise) / Nadine (is it you) / Maybelline / In the wee, wee hours / Bon soire Cherie / Memphis / Rock 'n' roll music / Carol
100362 / May '97 / A-Play Collection

Berry, Dave

☐ **VERY BEST OF DAVE BERRY, THE**
Memphis Tennessee / My baby left me / Baby it's you / Crying game / One heart between two / Little things / This strange effect / Mama / Can I get it from you / I'm gonna take you there / If you wait for love / Stranger / Heartbeat / Change our minds / Suspicions (in your mind) / I got the feeling / Girl from the Fair Isle / Sticks and stones / I love you babe / Coffee song
5520192 / Jan '97 / Spectrum

Berry, Erica

☐ **LIFE AND LOVE**
XECD 13 / 25 May '98 / Expansion

Berry, Heidi

☐ **BELOW THE WAVES**
Ribbons / Below the waves / Little tragedy / Legacy / Northshore train / Gather all the hours / River song / All for you / Living memory / Dancer / Out of my hands / Firefly / Nobody tells on you / Will it all change / Houses made of wood / Hasten the buds to bloom
CRECD 048 / May '94 / Creation

☐ **HEIDI BERRY**
Mercury / Little fox / Moon and the sun / One-string violin / Darling companion / Distant thunder / Heart like a wheel / For the rose / Follow / Ariel / Dawn
GAD 3009CD / 6 Jul '98 / 4AD

☐ **LOVE**
GAD 1012CD / 6 Jul '98 / 4AD

☐ **MIRACLE**
Mountain / Time / Holy grail / Darkness / Miracle / Californian / Queen / Only human / Northern country
GAD 6011CD / 6 Jul '98 / 4AD

Berry, Jan

☐ **SECOND WAVE**
OW 34524 / Jun '97 / One Way

Berry, John

☐ **FACES**
She's taken a shine / Change my mind / I will if you will / He doesn't even know her / Faithfully / Livin' on love / Time to be a man / Forty again / Love is everything / I give my heart
PRMDCD 14 / Sep '96 / Premier/EMI

☐ **FAITHFULLY**
Your love amazes me / You and only you / Fire / Faithfully / Standing on the edge of goodbye / If I had any pride at all / Kiss me in the car / I give my heart
PRMCD 7 / Jun '96 / Premier/EMI

☐ **STANDING ON THE EDGE**
Every time my heart calls your name / Standing on the edge of goodbye / Prove me wrong / I think about it all the time / If I had any pride left at all / Desperate measures / What are we fighting for / There's no cross that love won't bear / Ninety miles an hour / I never lost you / You and only you
CDEST 2265 / Jun '95 / Capitol

Berry, Leon 'Chu'

☐ **BLOWING UP A BREEZE**
TPZ 1024 / Jul '95 / Topaz Jazz

☐ **CLASSICS 1937-1941**
CLASSICS 784 / Nov '94 / Classics

Berry, Mike

☐ **ROCK 'N' ROLL BOOGIE... PLUS**
I'm a rocker / Don't fight it / Love rocket / Don't ever change / Stay close to me / Hard times / Take me high / It's a hard hard world / Tribute to Buddy Holly / Boogaloo does / Midnight train / Hey Joe / One by one / Rebel without a cause / Take a heart / Dial my number / New Orleans / Wake up Suzy / Baby boy / Low country woman / Hey baby / Think it over / Don't be cruel
C5CD 541 / Oct '92 / See For Miles

☐ **TRIBUTE TO BUDDY HOLLY, A**
Tribute to Buddy Holly / Only rock 'n' roll / Heaven out of hell / Peggy Sue got married / Dreams can come true / Think it over / Raining in my heart / That'll be the day / Peggy Sue / Rave on / Stay close to me / Fool's paradise / I'm gonna love you too / Holly
302512 / Jul '97 / Hallmark

Berry, Richard

☐ **GET OUT OF THE CAR**
Mad about you / Angel of my life / Yama yama pretty mama / Next time / Rockin' man / Oh oh, get out of the car / Crazy lover / I'm still in love with you / Jelly roll / Big John / One little prayer / Big break
CDCH 355 / Mar '92 / Ace

Berry, Robert

☐ **PILGRIMAGE TO A POINT**
No one else to blame / You've changed / Shelter / Another man / Love we share / Blame / Otherside / Freedom / Last ride into the sun
CYCL 019 / Apr '95 / Cyclops

Berryhill, Cyndi Lee

☐ **GARAGE ORCHESTRA**
Father of the seventh son / I wonder why / Radio astronomy / Song for Brian / UFO suite / I want stuff / Every someone tonight / Scariest thing in the world / Etude for ph machine
UGCD 5502 / 27 Apr '98 / Unique Gravity

☐ **NAKED MOVIE STAR**
Me, Steve, Kirk and Keith / Me, Steve, Kirk and Keith / Supernatural fact / Indirectly yours / Trump / 12 dollar motel / Turn off the century / What's wrong with me / Yipee / Baby (should I have the baby)
AWCD 1016 / Jul '89 / Awareness

Bert & His Lobster Band

☐ **LAKE OF DREAMS**
Lake of dreams / Longest day
CDRPM 0023 / Oct '97 / RP Media

Bert, Eddie

☐ **ENCORE**
Bert tram / One for Tubby / It's only sunshine / Opicana / Conversation / Crosstown / Manhattan suite
SV 0229 / Oct '97 / Savoy Jazz

☐ **HUMAN FACTOR, THE (Bert, Eddie Sextet)**
FSR 5005CD / Nov '95 / Fresh Sound

☐ **LIVE AT BIRDLAND (Bert, Eddie & J.R. Monterose)**
FSRCD 198 / Dec '92 / Fresh Sound

Bertoncini, Gene

☐ **BOSSA NOVA COLLECTION, A (Bertoncini, Gene & Michael Moore)**
Once I loved / No more blues / Zingaro / Rio Pindare / O grand amor / Quiet nights of quiet stars / Let go / Pensativa
VN 1004 / Nov '96 / Viper's Nest

☐ **JOBIM - SOMEONE TO LIGHT UP MY LIFE**
CRD 343 / Jan '97 / Chiaroscuro

☐ **TWO IN TIME (Bertoncini, Gene & Michael Moore)**
CRD 308 / Mar '96 / Chiaroscuro

Bertone, Bruno

☐ **LA MUSICA FROM ITALY (Bertone, Bruno Mandoline Orchestra)**
15209 / '91 / Laserlight

☐ **NIGHTS IN WHITE SATIN**
Love story (where do I begin) / Strangers in the night / Something / Bright eyes / Woman / You are the sunshine of my life / Michelle / Lara's theme (somewhere my love) / To all the girls I've loved before / Spanish eyes / Don't it make my brown eyes blue / Tara's theme / Feelings / Annie's song / Love is blue / If you leave me now / Unchained melody / Memory / Nights in white satin
CD 6005 / Apr '96 / Music

☐ **SONG SUNG BLUE**
Song sung blue / Don't cry for me Argentina / Oh happy day / Fool on the hill / Septemberwind / Yesterday / Bilitis / Last farewell / Sailing / Greensleeves / Eleanor Rigby / House of the rising sun / Banks of the Ohio / Around the world / Cast your face to the wind / Whiter shade of pale / My way
CD 6008 / Apr '96 / Music

☐ **STRICTLY DANCING: FOX-TROT (Bertone, Bruno Ballroom Orchestra)**
15337 / Jun '92 / Laserlight

Bertram, Rainer

☐ **GIB MEIN HERZ MIR WEIDER**
Gib mein herz mir wieder / Dir mocht ich treu sein / Itsy bitsy teenie weenie Honolulu Strand bikini / Es brauch ja nicht Hawaii zusein / All deine Wunsche / Verzeih' mir / Du kannst alles haben / Darling good night / Lass die Andern alle wandern / Sei wieder gut / Hoch in den Bergen / In Valencia / Reich mir die Hande / So schon war noch nie eine party / Nie mehr lass ich von Mary / Jeden Tag ein bisschen mehr / Ihr herz gehort schon einem anderen / Oho, comme-ci, comme-ca / Brigitte Bardot / Warum siehst du mich heute so verliebt an / Old Shatter / Siehst du den Stern / Happy end in Switzerland / Sie hatte schwarzes haar / Barfuss / Meine traume gehen so gern spazieren / Haziendero / Ja, das war Joe / Karina Lu / Shon ist's verliebt zu sein / Seite an Seite
BCD 16209 / Nov '97 / Bear Family

Beseech

☐ **FROM A BLEEDING HEART**
398414162 CD / 25 May '98 / Metal Blade

Besses O' The Barn

☐ **HYMNS AND THINGS**
Praise my soul the King of heaven / Eventide / Dem bones / Ave Maria / Simple gifts / Nun's chorus / Deep harmony / Jerusalem / Hymn tune medley / Aurelia / O, for the wings of a dove / God be in my head / Dear Lord and the father of mankind / Sandon / Thanks be to God
CHAN 4529 / Aug '93 / Chandos

☐ **SHOWCASE FOR BRASS**
Three figures / In memoriam RK / Summer scherzo / Belmont variations / Northwest passage
CHAN 4525 / May '93 / Chandos

Best, Anita

☐ **CROSSHANDED**
AMBER 98042CD / Mar '98 / Amber

Best, Barbara

☐ **SWING LOW (Best, Barbara Singers)**
BB 1992 / May '96 / Black & Blue

Best, Pete

☐ **BACK TO THE BEAT (Best, Pete Band)**
My Bonnie / Roll over Beethoven / Dancing in the streets / Dizzie Miss Lizzie / Money / Love me do / Stand by me / Long tall Sally / I saw her standing there / Twist and shout / Hippy hippy shake / Johnny B Goode / C'mon everybody
PBSCD 2000 / Apr '96 / Splash

☐ **BEYOND THE BEATLES 1963-1968 (Best, Pete Combo)**
All aboard / Why did you leave me baby / Shimmy like my sister Kate / I need your lovin' / I can't do without you now / I don't know why I do / I'll try anyway / I'm checking out now baby / Keys to my heart / She's alright / I'm blue / Castin' my spell / Off the hook / Pete's theme / Everybody / I wanna be there / Rock 'n' roll music / Don't play with me / Way I feel about you / I'll have everything too / How do you get to know her name / She's not the only girl in town / If you can't get her / More than I need myself
CDMRED 124 / Feb '96 / Cherry Red

☐ **LIVE AT THE ADELPHI/INTERVIEW (Best, Pete Band)**
CDMRED 136 / Sep '96 / Cherry Red

Bestial Warlust

☐ **BLOOD AND VALOUR**
MIM 7321CD / Jul '96 / Modern Invasion

☐ **VENGEANCE WAR TIL DEATH**
MIN 73162 / Feb '95 / Modern Invasion

Bethania, Maria

☐ **CANCOES E MOMENTOS**
ML 51014 / 14 Apr '98 / Musica Latina

☐ **CANTO DO PALE**
Abertura/Texto/O canto do paje / Tocando em frente / Maria/Linda flor logrador / Quase / Pronta pra cantar tomara / Flor de ir embora / Awo/Inhansa / Palavra
8480222 / Jan '94 / Philips

☐ **DEZEMBROS**
Anos dourados / Doce espera / Errie sim / Tranchan / Quero ficar com voce / Gostoso demais / Sei de cor / Estrela do meu ceu / Yorubahia / Cancoes e momentos
CDGR 169 / Sep '97 / Charly

☐ **LAS CANCIONES QUE HICISTE PARA MI**
Las canciones que hiciste para mi / Olha / Fiera herida / Palabras / Costumes / Detalhes / Tu no sabes / Necesito de tu amor / Seu corpo / Tu / Emocione
5187872 / Jan '95 / Verve

☐ **MEL**
Mel / Ela e eu / Cherio de amor / Da cor Brasileira / Loucura / Gota de sangua / Grito de sangua / Grito de alerta / Labios del Mel / Amando sobre os jornais / Nenhum verao / Infinito desejo / Queda d'agua
8382872 / Jan '95 / Verve

☐ **MEMORIA DA PELE**
Reconvexo / Tenha calma / Confesso / Junho / Morena / Salve as folhas / Memoria da pele / A mais bonita / Guerra no mar / Vinganca / Paiol do ouro vinheta
8389282 / Mar '94 / Verve

☐ **OLHO D'AGUA**
Sodade meu bem sodade / Vida va / Invisivel / Ilumina / Medalha de sao Jorge / O tempo e a cancao / Bilhete de despedida / Olho d'agua / Louvacao a oxum / Rainha negra buzio / Modinha / Alem da ultima estrela / Sodade meu bem sodade
5120522 / Jan '94 / Philips

Bethlehem

☐ **DARK METAL**
CDAR 022 / Jul '94 / Adipocre

Betjeman, Sir John

☐ **WORDS AND MUSIC (Betjeman, Sir John & Mike Read)**
November night: *Richard, Cliff* / Narcissus: *Almond, Marc* / Greenaway: *Young, Paul* / Youth and age: *Anderson, Jon* / Pershore Station: *Sharp, Richard* / Peggy: *Blunstone, Colin* / Myfanwy at Oxford: *Pitney, Gene* / Indoor games: *Sayer, Leo* / Moira MacCavendish: *Donovan* / Distant view: *Read, Mike* / In memory: *Blunstone, Colin* / Sunday morning Kings Cambridge: *Rodolfus Choir* / Myfanwy: *Essex, David*
EAGCD 029 / 22 Jun '98 / Eagle

Beto & The Fairlanes

☐ **SALSAFIED**
DOS 7009 / Sep '94 / Dos

Betrayer

☐ **CALAMITY**
MNO 2CD / Nov '94 / Nuclear Blast

Betsy

☐ **ROUGH AROUND THE EDGES**
All over my heart / If I don't stay the night / Love me like you mean it / Draggin' it back / Bits and pieces / Hard to believe / You can look (but you can't touch) / Southern wind / Passage / This house
7567924282 / Nov '94 / Warner Bros.

Bettencourt, Nuno

☐ **SCHIZOPHONIC**
Gravity / Swollen princess / Crave / What you want / Fallen angels / 2 weeks in dizkneelande / Pursuit of happiness / Fine by me / Karmalaa / Confrontation / Note on the screen door / I wonder / Got to have you / You / Severed
5405932 / Feb '97 / A&M

Better Daze

☐ **ONE STREET OVER**
URCD 017 / Jul '96 / Ubiquity

Better Than A Thousand

☐ **JUST ONE**
REV 060CD / Sep '97 / Revelation

☐ **VALUE DRIVEN**
Demand independance / Born to give / Self worth / Poison in your brain / I'll not resist / Crisis of man / Once again / Like the wind / Power within / Transformation / We must believe / Twelve
GOW 06CD / 3 Aug '98 / Grapes Of Wrath

Bettie Serveert

☐ **DUST BUNNIES**
Geek / Link / Musher / Dust bunnies / What friends / Misery galore / Story in a nutshell / Sugar the pill / Rudder / Pork and beans / Fallen foster / Co-coward / Heaven
BBQCD 189 / Mar '97 / Beggars Banquet

□ LAMPREY
BBQCD 169 / Jan '95 / Beggars Banquet

□ PALOMINE
GU 3CD / 6 Jul '98 / Guernica

□ PLAYS VENUS IN FURS
BKMN 74 / 10 Aug '98 / Brinkman

□ SOMETHING SO WILD
BBQ 58CD / Jun '95 / Beggars Banquet

Betts, Dickey

□ ATLANTA'S BURNING DOWN (Betts, Dickey & Great Southern)
Good time feeling / Atlanta's burning down / Leaving me again / Back on the road again / Dealin' with the devil / Shady streets / You can have her (I don't want her) / Mr. Blues Man
RE 2142 / Aug '97 / Razor & Tie

□ DICKEY BETTS & GREAT SOUTHERN (Betts, Dickey & Great Southern)
Out to get me / Run gypsy run / Sweet Virginia / Way love goes / Nothing you can do / California blues / Bougainville
RE 2141 / Aug '97 / Razor & Tie

Betty & The Bops

□ BETTY & THE BOPS
622592 / Apr '97 / Skydog

Beuf, Sylvian

□ IMPRO PRIMO (Beuf, Sylvian Quartet)
BBRC 9311 / Jan '94 / Big Blue

Beulah

□ HANDSOME WESTERN STATES
E 6014CD / 13 Oct '97 / Elephant 6

Bevan, Tony

□ ORIGINAL GRAVITY (Bevan, Tony & Greg Kingston & Matt Lewis)
INCUSCD 03 / '90 / Incus

□ TWISTERS (Bevan, Tony & Steve Noble)
06CD / May '97 / Scatter

Beverley Sisters

□ GREEN FIELDS
Together wherever we go / Hold me / English muffins and Irish stew / We have to be so careful / Green fields / Skye boat song / Oh wishing star / Water or the wine / Sultan / Sphinx won't tell / I was never loved by anyone else / Undecided / Teasin' / Yell for your Mama / String along / I wish I wuz / Wheel of fortune / Poor Whip poor Will (move over, move over) / For you / In the wee small hours of the morning / Once in a while / When the boys talk about the girls / I'm always chasing rainbows / No one but you
CDMFP 6220 / Apr '96 / Music For Pleasure

□ SING AND SWING (Beverley Sisters & Syd Lawrence Orchestra)
Roll out the barrel: *Beverley Sisters* / Army, the Navy and the Air Force: *Beverley Sisters* / St. Louis blues: *Lawrence, Syd Orchestra* / I know why and so do you: *Foxes* / I'll be seeing you: *Wright, Babette* / Woodchopper's ball: *Lawrence, Syd Orchestra* / Alexander's ragtime band: *Foxes* / In the mood: *Lawrence, Syd Orchestra* / Yankee doodle boy: *Beverley Sisters* / Guam: *Beverley Sisters* / I'll be with you in apple blossom time: *Beverley Sisters* / Oh what a lovely war: *Beverley Sisters* / Skyliner: *Lawrence, Syd Orchestra* / Keep the home fires burning: *Beverley Sisters*
3036001112 / Jul '97 / Carlton

□ SISTERS, SISTERS
QPRM 601D / Aug '93 / Polyphonic

□ VERY BEST OF THE BEVERLEY SISTERS, THE
Willie can / I dreamed / Little drummer boy / Little donkey / Have you ever been lonely / Sisters / Left right out of your heart / Mr. Wonderful / Long black nylons / Strawberry fair / Morning has broken / It's illegal, it's immoral, or it makes you fat / If anybody finds this, I love you / Greensleeves / I saw Mommy kissing Santa Claus / Naughty lady of shady lane / Little things mean a lot / Somebody bad stole de wedding bell / We like to do things like that / Mama doll song / Triplets / Changing partners
5523692 / Jan '97 / Spectrum

Beverly & Duane

□ BEVERLY AND DUANE
EXCDM 3 / 13 Oct '97 / Expansion

Bevinda

□ PESSOA EM PESSOAS
669972 / Jan '98 / Melodie

Bevis Frond

□ ANY GAS FASTER
Lord Plentiful reflects / Rejection day (am) / Ear song (olde world) / This corner of England / Legendary / When you wanted me / Lost rivers / Somewhere else / These dark days / Head on a pole / Your mind's gone grey / Old sea dog / Rejection day (pm) / Good old fashioned pain / Olde worlde
CDRECK 18 / Jan '90 / Reckless

□ AUNTIE WINNIE ALBUM, THE
Malvolios dream-journey to pikes / Foreign laugh / Down again / Will to lose / Repressor / Winters blues / Miz-maze / Close / Without mind / City of the sun / Die is cast / Miskatonic variations
CDRECK 17 / Jul '89 / Reckless

□ GATHERING OF FRONDS, A
CDRECK 25 / Mar '92 / Reckless

□ INNER MARSHLAND
Cries from the inner marshland / Termination station grey / Window eye / Once more / Defoliation part one / Reflections in a tall mirror / Hey mr. undecided / I've got eyes in the back of my head / Minsmere sphagnum / Medieval sienese acid blues / Defoliation part two / I can't get into your scene / Song for the sky / Shrine
CDRECK 14 / Jul '89 / Reckless

□ IT JUST IS
WO 21CD / Oct '93 / Woronzow

□ MIASMA
Garden gate / She's in love with time / Wild mind / Wild afterthought / Splendid isolation / Earl of walthamstowe / Newgate wind / Release yourself / Maybe / Ride the train of thought / Confusion days / Rat in a waistcoat / In another year / Mudman / Now you know / 1970 home improvements
CDRECK 13 / Jul '89 / Reckless

□ NEW RIVER HEAD
WO 16CD / Sep '91 / Woronzow

□ NORTH CIRCULAR (2CD Set)
W 406CD / 10 Nov '97 / Woronzow

□ SON OF WALTER
W 028CD / Oct '96 / Woronzow

□ SPRAWL
WO 22CD / Oct '94 / Woronzow

□ SUPERSEEDER
WO 26CD / Oct '95 / Woronzow

□ TRIPTYCH
Into the cryptic mist / Debbie's new song for drums / Lights are changing / Gemini machine / Phil exorcises the daemons / Old man blank / Daily round / Hurt goes on / Corinthian / Nowhere fast / Tangerine infringement beak / Hey joe / Purtle sline / Soot / Long journey into light
CDRECK 15 / Mar '89 / Reckless

Bevoir, Paul

□ DUMB ANGEL
Dumb intro / Changing places / What the butler saw / Jimmy webb / Equestrian / Maybe not / One in the window / I might fly away / Sunday school / Somewhere for matilda / Forgive me / One angel's tears
TANGCD 8 / May '94 / Tangerine

□ HAPPIEST DAYS OF YOUR LIFE, THE
It's a wonderful place / Lion tamer's story / Every night at seven / It's gotta stop somewhere / Trapeze artist's story / Vale row / Living in a different world / Small town parade / Mad professor / Happiest days of your life
TANGCD 2 / Aug '92 / Tangerine

Bevort, Pernille

□ ALIVE
MECCACD 2038 / Oct '97 / Music Mecca

Bewitched

□ DIABOLICAL DESECRATION
OPCD 034 / May '96 / Osmose

□ ENCYCLOPEDIA OF EVIL
OPCD 041 / Jul '96 / Osmose

□ PENTAGRAM PRAYER
OPCD 057 / 24 Nov '97 / Osmose

Bex, Emmanuel

□ ENFANCE (Bex, Emmanuel Quintet)
540252 / 1 Jun '98 / Musidisc

Bey, Andy

□ BALLADS, BLUES & BEY
Someone to watch over me / You'd be so nice to come home to / I let a song go out of my heart / In a sentimental mood / Willow weep for me / Yesterdays / If you could see me now / I'm just a lucky so and so / Daydream / Embraceable you
ECD 221622 / Oct '96 / Evidence

Bey, Ronnell

□ NEARNESS OF YOU, THE (Bey, Ronnell & Eartha Kitt/Clark Terry)
BASIC 50017 / Apr '96 / ITM

Beyer, Adam

□ RECODED
PRRUKCD 002 / 22 Sep '97 / Planet Rhythm UK

Beyond

□ NO LONGER AT EASE
SOME 04CD / 13 Apr '98 / Some

Beyond Dawn

□ LONGING FOR SCARLET DAYS
CDAR 019 / May '94 / Adipocre

□ PITY LOVE
CANDLE 012CD / Nov '95 / Candlelight

□ REVELRY
AMAONO 14CD / 13 Apr '98 / Misanthropy

Beytelman, Gustavo

□ TANGO - PEDACITO DE CIELO (Beytelman, Gustavo & Ciro Perez/ Roberto Tormo)
X 55523 / Oct '97 / Aspic

BF

□ ALL BETS ARE OFF
All bets are off / We're still around / Depend on me / It's coming back / Diggin' up the past / Stay true / God of nothing / Fight or run / Truth / Justice will prevail / We're only watching / It's not our fault / Through bitter eyes / Can't tell no one
CM 77177CD / 13 Oct '97 / Century Media

□ CHOOSE MY PATH
CM 77221CD / 22 Jun '98 / Century Media

BF Trike

□ BF TRIKE
BFT 1001 / May '97 / Rockadelic

BFM

□ CITY OF DOPE
City of dope / Go amazen' (do yo' thang) / Can't slow down / Am I black enough / Let yourself go / Why ya *p* ain't tight / Gimme a bottle / Larceny / Give it up / Pass the joint
ICH 1118CD / Sep '91 / Ichiban

Bhatt, Krishna

□ KIRWANI (Bhatt, Krishna & Zakir Hussain)
ARNR 0495 / Aug '97 / Amiata

Bhatt, Vishnwa Mohan

□ BOURBON AND ROSEWATER
WLACS 47CD / Nov '95 / Waterlily Acoustics

□ GATHERING RAINCLOUDS
WLAES 22CD / Nov '95 / Waterlily Acoustics

□ JUGALBANDI
CDA 92059CD / Jan '95 / Music Today

□ SANGEET TRIO IN CONCERT (Sangeet Trio)
C 560091 / Dec '96 / Ocora

□ SARADAMANI
WLAES 23CD / Feb '96 / Waterlily Acoustics

Bhattacharya, Pandit Amit

□ CLASSIC MUSIC FROM NORTH INDIA
KMCD 54 / Jul '95 / Keltia Musique

Bhawalker, Uday

□ RAGAS PURIYA AND JOG
NRCD 0058 / May '96 / Navras

Bhundu Boys

□ FRIENDS ON THE ROAD
Radio Africa / Pombi / Ring of fire / Gonzo nachin'ai / Bitter to the south / Foolish harp/Waerara / Anna / Church on fire / Don't forget Africa / Anyway / My best friend / Lizzie
COOKCD 053 / Feb '93 / Cooking Vinyl

□ MUCHIYEDZA (OUT OF THE DARK)
Kachembere / Hazvisekanwe / Satan ngaaparadzwe / Tamba wega / Misodzi pamatama / Pafunge / Dorica / Mumhanzi we jit / Mhunza musha
COOKCD 118 / Feb '97 / Cooking Vinyl

□ TRUE JIT
Jit jive / My foolish heart / Chemedzevana / Rugare / Vana / Wonderful world / Ndoitasei / Susan / African woman / Happy birthday / Jekesa / I don't think that man should sleep alone / Over you / Loving you / You shoulda kept a spare / Past / You make my nature dance / Perfect lovers / After midnite / I love your daughter / After dark
2422032 / Sep '87 / WEA

Bi Kyo Ran

□ PARALLAX (2CD Set)
BELLE 95186 / Jun '97 / Belle Antique

Biafra

□ ICARO
76302 / 19 May '98 / RGE

Biafra, Jello

□ SKY IS FALLING, THE (Biafra, Jello & No Means No)
VIRUS 85CD / Feb '91 / Alternative Tentacles

Bianchi, Maurico

□ AKTIVITAT
DVLR 002CD / Jan '94 / Dark Vinyl

Bianco Bachicha

□ TANGOS IN PARIS 1926-1941
HQCD 66 / Jun '96 / Harlequin

Bias

□ MODEL CITIZEN
Model city / Offensive motion / Jury with no peers / Jack's knife / Smitten with extremism / Pain conduit / Rising tide of ignorance / Dictating morals / Evil snippet
SST 352CD / 29 Sep '97 / SST

Bibb, Eric

□ GOOD STUFF
OPUS3CD 19603 / Mar '97 / Opus 3

□ ME TO YOU
Keep my cool / Sing your song: *Bibb, Eric & Taj Mahal* / Catch up to your heart / Between a woman an'a man / Talk to me / You're the one / Something much greater: *Bibb, Eric & Pops Staples* / Strong love / Looking through the window / Gonna walk this road / Better man / I need a vacation / I'll be your car / Me to you
3984204442 / 6 Oct '97 / Code Blue

□ SPIRIT AND THE BLUES (Bibb, Eric & Needed Time)
Lonesome valley / In my father's house / Needed time / I am blessed / Just keep goin' on / Where shall I be / Woke up this mornin' / I want Jesus to walk with me / You're gonna need somebody on your bond / Braggin' / Water under the bridge / Tell ol' Bill / Satisfied mind / Meetin' at the buildin'
OPUS3CD 19401 / Nov '96 / Opus 3

Bible

□ EUREKA
Skywriting / Honey be good / Skeleton crew / November brides / Cigarette girls / Crystal Palace / Wishing game / Red Hollywood / Tiny lights / Blue shoes stepping
HAVENCD 5 / Nov '95 / Haven

□ RANDOM ACTS OF KINDNESS
HAVENCD 8 / Nov '95 / Haven

□ WALKING THE GHOST BACK HOME
Graceland / Mahalia / Walking the ghost back home / Kid galahad and the chrome kinema / King chicago / Sweetness / Spend, spend, spend / (talk to me like) jackie kennedy / She's my bible / High, wide and handsome
HAVENCD 4 / Nov '95 / Haven

Bick-Clark, Nancy

□ CROSSING TO IRELAND (Bick-Clark, Nancy & Sara Johnson)
RS 00113CD / May '96 / Rising Star

Bickley

□ POGO AU GO GO
F 032CD / 27 Apr '98 / Fearless

Biddleville Quintette

□ BIDDLEVILLE QUINTETTE VOL.1 1926-1929
DOCD 5361 / Jun '95 / Document

□ BIDDLEVILLE QUINTETTE VOL.2 1929
DOCD 5362 / Jun '95 / Document

Biddu Orchestra

□ BEST OF BIDDU ORCHESTRA, THE (Blue Eyed Soul)
Summer of '42 / Blue eyed soul / Exodus / Black magic man / Aranjuez mon amor / Couldn't we be friends / Rain forest / Jump for joy / Laura / I could have danced all night / Trippin' on a soul cloud / Girl you'll be a woman soon / Nirvana / Lover's serenade / Chic chica chic chica chic / Blacker the berry (sweeter the juice) / Eastern journey / Stud / Disco dewanee
HTCD 49 / 20 Apr '98 / Hot Productions

□ SUMMER OF '42
Summer of '42 / Blue eyed soul / Exodus / Black magic woman / Concierto de Aranjuez / Couldn't we be friends / Rain forest / Jump for joy / Laura / I could have danced all night / Trippin' on a soul cloud / Girl you'll be a woman soon / Nirvana / Love's serenade
QED 130 / Nov '96 / Tring

Biddulph, Rick

□ SECOND NATURE
VP 178CD / Jan '95 / Voiceprint

Biff Bang Pow

☐ ACID HOUSE ALBUM, THE
CRECD 046 / May '94 / Creation

☐ DEBASEMENT TAPES
Long live neil young and all who sail in him / In bed with paul weller / It makes you scared / It happens all the time / Death of england / In the afternoon / Sleep / Back to the start / Inside the mushroom / Everybody wants to divorce her
CRECD 125 / Jun '93 / Creation

☐ L'AMOUR, DEMURE, STENHOUSEMUIR
She haunts / Someone to share my life with / Startripper / There must be a better life / She paints / Ice cream machine / Hug me honey / Miss you / She kills me / I'm waiting for my time / Someone stole my wheels / Song for a nail / Love's going out of fashion / Girl from well lane / Baby you just don't care / Chocolate elephant man / Tell laura I love her / Searching for the pavement
CRECD 099 / May '94 / Creation

☐ ME
My first friend / Miss you / I'm burned / Song for a nail / She saved me / You just can't buy satisfaction / Sad eyes in velvet / Guilt ridden / Lovers / Baby you just make me strong
CRECD 071 / May '94 / Creation

☐ SONGS FOR THE SAD EYED GIRL
CRECD 058 / Jan '90 / Creation

Big 5

☐ IN YER FACE
TX 51210CD / 17 Nov '97 / Triple XXX

☐ IN YER FACE (2CD Set)
SKANKDCD 011 / Jan '95 / Skank

☐ LIVE JIVE
TX 51228CD / 8 Dec '97 / Triple XXX

Big 6

☐ READY TO ROCK
Let's hang out tonight / All of me / Sombrero / Out tonight / At last / Jump Al jump / Mama weer all crazee now / Lady of Nagoya / Happy baby / Sincerely / Tiger feet / Twentieth century boy / Stop it I like it / Groovey geezer / She walk right in / Fire / New Orleans / Long tall Sally / Are you ready to rock / All night long
JRCD 18 / Jun '95 / Jappin' & Rockin'

Big Al

☐ DA BUDDAH KLAN
TWCTFW / Texas niggas / Zoota bang / Breaking fools down / You too near me / Neighborhood drug dealer / Tony montana / Walk with me / Fenna grab the AK / Strictly conversation / Kickin' it like big players / Clockhound AKA gorilla pimpin / Hard dick no conscious / Exit the dragon / Texas G's
PCD 1468 / Mar '97 / Profile

Big Allanbik

☐ BATQUE Y BLUES
Gully low blues / My babe / I just wanna make love to you / Let it loose / Jessica / Fare / Let the good times roll / Blues for Douglaston / Seventh son / Evil / Stormy Monday
BLU 10312 / 24 Aug '98 / Blues Beacon

Big Ass Truck

☐ BIG ASS TRUCK
UPSTART 024 / Nov '95 / Upstart

☐ KENT
UPSTART 027 / Mar '96 / Upstart

Big Audio Dynamite

☐ F-PUNK
RAD 11280 / Jun '95 / Radioactive

☐ THIS IS BIG AUDIO DYNAMITE
Medicine show / Sony / E=MC2 / Bottom line / Sudden impact / Stone Thames / BAD / Party
4629992 / Nov '88 / CBS

☐ TIGHTEN UP VOL.88
Rock non stop (all night long) / Other 99 / Funny names / Applecart / Esquerita / Champagne / Mr. Walker said / Battle of All Saints Road / Battle of New Orleans / Duellin' banjos / Hip neck and thigh / Two thousand shoes / Tighten up vol. 88 / Just play music
4611992 / Sep '94 / CBS

Big Bad Smitty

☐ COLD BLOOD
HMG 1003 / Dec '97 / Hightone

☐ MEAN DISPOSITION
How many more years / Long ol' lonesome day / You don't know me / Feel like love / Still a fool / You don't love nobody / Cairo / Angel of mercy / Smitty's boogie / Sweet feelin' / I didn't marry your family / Walk the back streets cryin' / Mean disposition / Lonely man
AIM 1037 / Sep '97 / Aim

Big Bad Wolf

☐ BIG BAD WOLF
199652 / 25 May '98 / Made To Measure

Big Band All Stars

☐ SWITCHED ON SWING
PLSCD 197 / Apr '97 / Pulse

Big Ben Banjo Band

☐ BIG BEN BANJO PARTY
PLSCD 224 / Jul '97 / Pulse

Big Berta

☐ LAKA TONG (Big Bertha & The Bulldozers)
GRCD 6075 / 24 Oct '97 / Goofin'

Big Big Train

☐ ENGLISH BOY WONDERS
GEPCD 1020 / 1 Dec '97 / Giant Electric Pea

☐ GOODBYE TO THE AGE OF STEAM
Wind distorted pioneers / Head hit the pillow / Edge of the known world / Landfall / Dragon bone hill / Blow the house down / Expecting snow / Blue silver red / Losing your way
GEPCD 1007 / May '94 / Giant Electric Pea

Big Black

☐ BIG BLACK: LIVE
BFFP 49CD / Oct '89 / Blast First

☐ PIGPILE
TG 81CD / Nov '92 / Touch & Go

☐ RICH MAN'S EIGHT TRACK
BFFP 23CD / Jun '88 / Blast First

☐ SONGS ABOUT FUCKING
Power of independent trucking / Model / Bad penny / L dopa / Precious thing / Columbian necktie / Kitty empire / Ergot / Kasimir S Pulaski Day / Fish fry / Tiny, King of the Jews / Bombastic intro / He's a whore
TG 24CD / '94 / Touch & Go

Big Boy Bloater

☐ JUMPIN' RHYTHM AND BLUES
SPIN 001 / Jun '98 / Spindrift

Big Brutha Soul

☐ VOYAGE TO BRUTHALAND
Big Brutha Soul is up in here / Uh oh oh (the freak show) / It's goin' down / Never did like you / It's all good / Kickin' wi da hos / Thinking 'bout you / Soldiers of the night / Respect to... / Voyage to bruthaland / It's all good
AIM 4003CD / 20 Oct '97 / Aim

Big Chief

☐ BIG CHIEF BRAND PRODUCT
SPCD 89260 / Apr '93 / Sub Pop

☐ MACK AVENUE SKULL GAME
SP 109/285CD / Sep '93 / Sub Pop

☐ SHOUT OUT (Big Chief & Thornett)
SPCD 135322 / Sep '94 / Sub Pop

Big Chief

☐ IT DON'T MAKE SENSE
TPCD 001 / 22 Sep '97 / Teepee

Big Country

☐ BBC RADIO 1 SESSIONS, THE
Heart and soul / Harvest home / Angle park / Inwards / 1000 stars / Porroh man / Close action
SFRSCD 065 / 29 Jun '98 / Strange Fruit

☐ BRIGHTON ROCK
SRECD 703 / 22 Sep '97 / Snapper

☐ CROSSING, THE
In a big country / Inwards / Chance / Thousand stars / Storm / Harvest home / Lost patrol / Close action / Fields of fire / Porroh man
5323232 / Mar '96 / Mercury

☐ ECLECTIC
River of hope / King of emotion / Big yellow taxi / Buffalo skinners / Summertime / Dixie / Eleanor Rigby / Winter sky / Sing it / I'm on fire / Where the rose is sown / Come back to me / Ruby Tuesday
TRACD 234 / Aug '96 / Transatlantic

☐ GREATEST HITS LIVE, THE
Harvest home / Peace in our time / Just a shadow / Broken hearts (13 valleys) / Storm / Chance / Look away / What are you working for / Steeltown / Ships / Wonderland / Long way home / In a big country / Lost patrol
DC 878632 / Mar '97 / Disky

☐ IN A BIG COUNTRY
In a big country / Thousand stars / Tracks of my tears / Giant / One great thing / Hold the heart / Look away / Honky tonk woman / Restless natives / Longest day / Everything I need / Black skinned blue eyed boys / Fly like an eagle / Kiss the girl goodbye / Keep on dreaming / Freedom song
5508792 / Jul '95 / Spectrum

☐ KINGS OF EMOTION (2CD Set)
SMDCD 101 / 27 Apr '98 / Snapper

☐ NO PLACE LIKE HOME
We're not in Kansas / Republican party reptile / Dynamite lady / Keep on dreaming / Beautiful people / Hostage speaks / Beat the devil / Leap of faith / Ships / Into the fire
5323272 / Mar '96 / Mercury

☐ PEACE IN OUR TIME
King of emotion / Broken hearts / Thousand yard stare / From here to eternity / Everything I need / Peace in our time / Time for leaving / River of hope / In this place
5323262 / Mar '96 / Mercury

☐ RESTLESS NATIVES AND RARITIES
All fall together / Over the border / Made in heaven / Not waving but drowning / On the shore / Balcony / Dead on arrival / Pass me by / Promised land / Return of the two headed King / When a drum beats / World on fire / Winter sky / I'm only waiting / Flag of nations / Kiss the girl goodbye / Song of the South / Blue on a green planet / Normal / God's great mistake / Restless natives / Longest day
5584112 / 1 Jun '98 / Mercury

☐ SEER, THE
Eiledon / Hold the heart / Look away / One great thing / Remembrance day / Red fox / Sailor / Seer / Teacher / I walk the hill
5323252 / Mar '96 / Mercury

☐ SEER, THE/THE CROSSING (2CD Set)
Look away / Seer / Teacher / I walk the hill / Eiledon / One great thing / Hold the heart / Remembrance day / Red fox / Sailor / In a big country / Inwards / Chance / Thousand stars / Storm / Harvest home / Lost patrol / Close action / Fields of fire / Porroh man
5286072 / Aug '95 / Mercury

☐ STEELTOWN
Flame of the west / East of Eden / Steeltown / Where the rose is sown / Come back to me / Tall ships go / Girl with grey eyes / Raindance / Great divide / Just a shadow
5323242 / Mar '96 / Mercury

☐ THROUGH A BIG COUNTRY (Greatest Hits)
In a big country / Fields of fire / Chance / Wonderland / Where the rose is sown / Just a shadow / Look away / King of emotion / East of Eden / One great thing / Teacher / Broken heart (thirteen valleys) / Peace in our time / Eiledon / Seer / Harvest home
5323282 / Mar '96 / Mercury

☐ WHY THE LONG FACE
TRACD 109 / Apr '96 / Transatlantic

☐ WITHOUT THE AID OF A SAFETY NET
Harvest home / Just a shadow / Thirteen valleys / Storm / Chance / Look away / Steeltown / Ships / Wonderland / In a big country / Peace in our time / What are you working for / Long way home / Lost patrol
CDGOLD 1082 / Feb '97 / EMI Gold

Big Dish

☐ RICH MAN'S WARDROBE
Christina's world / Wishing time / Swimmer / Life / Big new beginning / Jealous / Faith healer / Jean / Where do you live / Waiting for the parade / European rain / Loneliest man in the world / Voodoo baby / Slide / Prospect street
VI 874882 / Nov '96 / Disky

Big Dogs

☐ LIVE AT THE BIRCHMERE
SCR 24 / Jul '95 / Strictly Country

Big Drill Car

☐ ALBUM/TAPE/CD TYPE THING
16 lines / Clamato 11 / No need / Brody / In green fields / Diamond earrings / Reform before / Head on / Swanson / About us
CRZ 008CD / Jan '90 / Cruz

☐ SMALL BLOCK
Five year itch / Glory / Let me walk / Mag wheel / Annie's needle / Les cochons sans poils
CRZ 014CD / May '93 / Cruz

Big E The Black

☐ LIVIN' BIG E
50533 / Jun '97 / Raging Bull

Big Elastic Band

☐ WHEN BIG ROY SANG ON ANNIE MCGREGOR'S JUKE BOX
Jimmy Shand's on the wireless / Old folk / Frontiersong / Meet me on the landing / On golden streets / Along came rock 'n' roll / When Big Roy sang on Annie McGregor's juke box / Blue lagoon / All stood up / Here we go again / Sunday morning - Saturday night / Accordion under the bed
LCOM 5254 / Nov '96 / Lismor

Big Eye

☐ HIDDEN CORE, THE
DUKE 027 / Nov '95 / Hydrogen Dukebox

Big Fat Love

☐ HELL HOUSE
GR 041CD / May '97 / Grand Royal

Big Flame

☐ RIGOUR
DC 19 / Dec '96 / Drag City

Big Foot Chester

☐ TABERNACALIN
SFTRI 520CD / 23 Mar '98 / Sympathy For The Record Industry

Big George

☐ LEGEND SO FAR, THE (Big George & The Business)
So many roads / Raglan road / All fool's day / When the gypsy cast her spell / Victoria / Jesus gonna make it alright / Tower Hill road / Ain't nothing left / Let my love / Tonight the bottle let me down / You can't always get what you want
OZITCD 0034 / Aug '98 / Ozit

Big Head Todd

☐ BEAUTIFUL WORLD (Big Head Todd & The Monsters)
Resignation superman / Caroline / Crazy Mary / Helpless / Tower / Please don't tell her / Beautiful world / True lady / Heart of wilderness / If you can't slow down / Boom boom: *Big Head Todd & The Monsters/John Lee Hooker* / These days without you
74321441092 / May '97 / Revolution

☐ SISTER SWEETLY
Broken hearted saviour / Sister sweetly / Turn the light out / Tomorrow never comes / It's alright / Groove thing / Soul for every cowboy / Ellis island / Bittersweet / Circle / Brother John
74321147992 / Jun '94 / Giant

☐ STRATAGEM (Big Head Todd & The Monsters)
Kensington line / Stratagem / Wearing only flowers / Neckbreaker / Magdalena / Angel leads me on / In the morning / Candle / Ninety nine / Greyhound / Poor miss / Shadowlands
74321229042 / Oct '94 / Giant

Big Hello

☐ APPLE ALBUM
PARCD 039 / 26 May '98 / Parasol

Big House

☐ BIG HOUSE
Dollar in my pocket (pretty things) / All nite / Refuse 2 run / Baby doll / Can't cry anymore / Devil's road / Nothing comes 4 free / Happiness / LA / Angel on my arm
MCD 11446 / Apr '97 / MCA

Big Iron

☐ TIERRA DEL DIABLO
50592 / 6 Oct '97 / Semaphore

Big Joe

☐ COOL DYNAFLOW (Big Joe & The Dynaflows)
Cool dynaflow / Trouble walkin' down the road / Black cadillac / Tough act to follow / Mambo mama / I lost my true love / Let's rock (one more time) / Livin' with the blues / I'd rather drink muddy water / Alberta's kitchen / All this and gravy too
TRCD 9915 / Apr '93 / Tramp

☐ LAYIN' IN THE ALLEY (Big Joe & The Dynaflows)
BT 1098CD / Feb '94 / Black Top

Big Maceo

☐ BLUEBIRD RECORDINGS 1941-1942, THE
Worried life blues / Ramblin' mind blues / County jail blues / Can't you read / So long baby / Texas blues / Tuff luck blues / I got the blues / It's all up to you / Bye bye, baby / Why should I hang around / Poor Kelly blues / Some sweet day / Anytime for you / My last go around / Since you been gone
07863667152 / Feb '97 / Bluebird

Big Maybelle

☐ BLUES, CANDY & BIG MAYBELLE
Candy / Ring dang dilly / Blues early, early / Little bird told me / So long / That's a pretty good love / Tell me who / Ramblin' blues / Rock house / I don't want to cry / Pitiful / Good man is hard to find / How it lies / Goin' home baby / Say it isn't so / If I could be with you one hour tonight / Goodnight wherever you are / White Christmas / Silent night / I ain't got nobody / I understand / I got it bad and that ain't good / Some of these days / Until the real thing comes along
SV 0262 / Oct '97 / Savoy Jazz

☐ MAYBELLE SINGS THE BLUES
Oh lord what are you doing to me / Same old story / I don't want to cry / Yesterday's kisses / Don't let the sun catch you cryin' / That's all / Put yourself in my place / I will never turn my back on you / I cried for you / Only you / I won't cry anymore / I know love / I just don't know what to do with myself / In the still of night / Let me go / No better for you / It's a man's man's man's world / Maybelle sings the blues / Don't pass me by / It's been raining
CDRB 14 / Nov '94 / Charly

Big Miller

☐ LAST OF THE BLUES SHOUTERS, THE
SCD 42 / Feb '93 / Southland

Big Mountain

☐ FREE UP
All kinds of people / Dream weaver / Them' a say free up the pressure / Friction / Real thing / Let's stay together / Monkey see monkey do / Fe real / Tell me where the people go / Calling you out / Billion bleeding hearts
743214411421 / 8 Sep '97 / Giant

☐ RESISTANCE
Hooligans / Resistance / Rise Rasta rise / Get together / Caribbean blue / Sweet and deadly / Troddin' / Know your culture / Soul teacher / Where do the children play / Retire / Inner city youth / Wante wante / Love is the only way / Bobbin' and weavin' / Hooligans dub
74321299882 / Oct '95 / RCA

Big Punisher

☐ CAPITAL PUNISHMENT
Twinz / I'm not a player / Punish me / Beware / Glamour life / Wishful thinking / I ain't a killer / Toe 2 toe / Parental discretion / Boomerang / Still not a player
74321560932 / 20 Apr '98 / Loud

Big Red Goad

☐ TRUCK DRIVIN' PSYCHO
Tiger in my tank / Diesel smoke / Dangerous curves / Thunder on the road / Tombstone every mile / Payload Daddy / I got lost / My bucket's got a hole in it / Movin' on / Understand your man / Big big rollin' man / Truck drivin' son of a gun / Freightiner fever / Jacknife / Poor white trash
H 3309CD / Oct '97 / Hierarchy

Big Red Kite

☐ SHORT STORIES
SR 1010 / May '96 / Scout

Big Rhythm Combo

☐ TOO SMALL TO DANCE
BM 9025CD / Aug '94 / Black Magic

Big Road Breaker

☐ DISINTERPRETITIONED
MUZA 09CD / Jun '97 / Muzamuza

Big Sandy

☐ ON THE GO (Big Sandy & The Flyrite Trio)
NOHITCD 006 / Jan '94 / No Hit

☐ SWINGIN' WEST (Big Sandy & The Flyrite Trio)
Some mother's son / Seabird / Strikers stand firm / Roisin dubh / Kathleen joins up / Bobby calls the strike / Prison mass / Alice's theme / Kiss / Some mother's son (oganaigh oig) / Seabird / I had to do it / Kathleen's decision / Watching annie's house / Escape and capture / At the police station / No slop out / Meeting bobby sands / Seabird / Bridge attack
HCD 8064 / Oct '95 / Hightone

Big Six

☐ WE THE BOY'S WILL ROCK YA
We the boys will rock ya / West coast jive / Blue moon / Tell me baby / Come back baby / Master blaster / Hup de bop / No way out / Hey pretty mama / Sh boom / Eight ball / Hey hey we're gonna rock you / Cold feet / Giving my love to you / Brookshire drive / Mama / She can really move / Magic roundabout / Rock 'n' roll nightmare / Hammer it down
JRCD 25 / 20 Oct '97 / Jappin' & Rockin'

Big Star

☐ BIG STAR LIVE
RCD 10221 / Mar '97 / Rykodisc

☐ NO.1 RECORD/RADIO CITY
Feel / Ballad of El Goodo / In the street / Thirteen / Don't lie to me / India song / When my baby's beside me / My life is right / Give me another chance / Try again / Watch the sunrise / O my soul / Life is white / Way out west / What's goin' ahn / You get what you deserve / Mod lang / Back of a car / Daisy glaze / She's a mover / September gurls / Morpha too / I'm in love with a girl
CDWIK 910 / Jan '90 / Big Beat

☐ NO.1 RECORD/RADIO CITY/THE THIRD ALBUM/SISTER LOVERS (2CD Set)
Feel / Ballad of El Goodo / In the street / Thirteen / Don't lie to me / India song / When my baby's beside me / My life is right / Give me another chance / Try again / Watch the sunrise / ST 100/6 / O my soul / Life is white / Way out West / What's goin' on / You get what you deserve / Mod lang / Back of a car / Daisy glaze / She's a mover / September gurls / Morpha too / I'm in love with a girl / Kizza me / You can't have me / Jesus Christ / Downs / Whole lotta shakin' goin' on / Thank you friends / O Dana / Femme fatale / Stroke it Noel / Holocaust / Night time / Kanga roo / For you / Take care / Blue moon / Dream lover / Big black car
LICD 921172 / Sep '97 / Line

☐ THIRD ALBUM, THE/SISTER LOVERS
Kizza me / You can't have me / Jesus Christ / Downs / Whole lotta shakin' goin' on / Thank you friends / O'Dana / Femme fatale / Stroke it, Noel / Holocaust / Nightime / Kangaroo / For you / Take care / Blue mood / Dream lover / Big black car
RCD 10220 / Mar '97 / Rykodisc

Big Stick

☐ CRACK 'N' DRAG
Crack attack / Crack attack / Billy jack paddy wack / Friends and cars / Shoot the president / Drag racing / Hell on earth / Jesus was born (on an indian reservation)
BFFP 25CD / Nov '93 / Blast First

Big Tent Revival

☐ AMPLIFIER
2438251862 / 24 Mar '98 / FFRT

Big Three

☐ CAVERN STOMP
Some other guy / I'm with you / Let true love begin / By the way / Cavern stomp / Peanut butter / Bring it on home to me / What'd I say / Don't start running away / Zip a dee doo dah / Reelin' and rockin' / You've got to keep her under hand / High School confidential
8440062 / Jan '96 / Mercury

Big Three

☐ BIG THREE FEATURING MAMA CASS, THE
I may be right / Anna Fia / Tony and Delia / Grandfather's clock / Silkie / Ringo / Down in the valley / Wild women / All the pretty little horses / Glory glory / Come away Melinda / Young girl's lament / Banjo song / Winken blinken and nod / Ho honey ho / Nora's dove (Dink's song) / Come along / Rider / It makes a long time man feel bad / Sing hallelujah / Dark as a dungeon
NEMCD 755 / Oct '95 / Sequel

Big Time Sarah

☐ BLUES IN THE YEAR 1D1
Blues in the year 1D1 / Hound dog / Ain't nobody's business / Woke up this morning / Long tall daddy / You don't love me baby / Cadillac assembly line / Steal away / Chicken heads / Down home blues / Bouncin' and breakin' / Little red rooster / I don't want no man
DE 692 / Jun '97 / Delmark

☐ LAY IT ON 'EM GIRLS
DD 659 / Jul '93 / Delmark

Big Tom

☐ 25 GOLDEN GREATS (Big Tom & The Mainliners)
Back in my baby's arms / Gentle mother / Old rustic bridge / I'll settle for old Ireland / Wheels fell off the wagon / Isle of Innishfree / My own washing / Kentucky waltz / Be careful of stones that you throw / Bunch of violet blues / From summer to winter / Sing me back home / Carroll county accident / Blue eyes crying in the rain / Sunset years of my life / Wedding bells / Flowers for mama / My world's come down / Old log cabin for sale / Please mama please / Before I met you / Tears on a bridal bouquet / They covered the old swimming hole / Cold hard facts of life / Give my love to rose
MCVD 30006 / Nov '96 / Emerald Gem

☐ BIG TOM AND THE MAINLINERS
ARCD 003 / May '98 / Ainm

Big Town Playboys

☐ HIP JOINT
Ain't no big deal on you / When it rains it pours / Shake your hips / Glamour girl / I don't care who knows / Kiddio / Forever true / Rock me again / Girls all over the world / My heart is mended / No place to go
CDBLUH 017 / Jun '96 / Blue Horizon

☐ OFF THE CLOCK (Big Town Playboys Live)
EDGCD 007 / 27 Apr '98 / Eagle

☐ PLAYBOY BOOGIE
Hurry baby / Chicken shack boogie / Happy payday / Walkin' / She walked right in / What more do you want me to do / Playboy boogie / Come on / Down the road apiece / I done it / Shake your hips / Roomin' house boogie / Driftin'
SPINCD 203 / Aug '96 / Spindrift

Big Twist

☐ BIGGER THAN LIFE (Live From Chicago) (Big Twist & The Mellow Fellows)
ALCD 4755 / May '93 / Alligator

☐ PLAYING FOR KEEPS (Big Twist & The Mellow Fellows)
300 pounds of heavenly joy / Flip flop / I want your love / Polk salad Annie / Pouring water on a drowning man / I've got a problem / I brought the blues on myself / We're gonna make it / Just one woman
ALCD 4732 / Jun '91 / Alligator

Big Wheel

☐ SLOWTOWN
You shine, And / Down / Lied / Vicious cirle / Pete Rose / Birthday / Down the line / Daddy's at the wheel / Storm / Tuff skins / Bug bites / Lazy days
MR 00472 / Apr '93 / Mammoth

Big Wheeler

☐ BONE ORCHARD (Big Wheeler & The Ice Cream Men)
Bad bacon baby / I got a feeling I got the blues / Bone orchard / You got me messed up / Hell bound man / She loves another man / Evil woman / Down in Virginia / Katie Blues / Damn good mojo / Everybody needs somebody / Man or mouse / Chains of love / Bad bacon baby
DE 661 / Mar '97 / Delmark

Big Youth

☐ A LUTA CONTINUA
Survival plan / Sing another song / Feel it / Weatherman / Rock johnny roll / K.k.k. / Bush mama / Action / A luta continua / Song of praise
HBCD 28 / Sep '85 / Heartbeat

☐ DJ ORIGINATORS (Big Youth & Dillinger)
RGCD 020 / Dec '95 / Rocky One

☐ DREADLOCKS DREAD
Train to Rhodesia / House of dreadlocks / Lightning flash / Weak heart / Natty dread she want / Some like it dread / Marcus Garvey / Big Youth special / Dread organ / Blackman message / You don't care / Moving away
CDFL 9006 / Sep '90 / Frontline

☐ HIGHER GROUND
VPCD 1440 / Oct '95 / VP

☐ HIT THE ROAD JACK
What's going on / Hit the road Jack / Wake up everybody / Get up stand up / Jah man of Syreen / Ten against one / Hotter fire / Way of the light / Dread high ranking / Dread is the best
CDTRL 137 / Sep '95 / Trojan

☐ JAMMING IN THE HOUSE OF DREAD
DANCD 112 / Jun '97 / Danceteria

☐ MANIFESTATION
No nukes / Love fighting so / Turn me on / Mr. Right / Like it like that / Conqueror / Spiderman meet the Hulk / No way to treat a lady
HBCD 46 / Apr '88 / Heartbeat

☐ REGGAE PHENOMENON
Give praises / Plead I cause / I am your man / Hip-ki-do / Rivrton city / It's not unusual / Papa was a rolling stone / Love and happiness / Weeping in the night (joy in the morning) / Reggae phenomenon / Get up, stand up / Notty no jester / Johnny reggae / Hit the road jack / Phil pratt thing / Wolf in sheep's clothing / Facts of life / Tell it black / Mammy hot daddy cool / Dread in a babylon
CDTRD 411 / Mar '94 / Trojan

☐ SAVE THE WORLD
504002 / Nov '95 / Declic

☐ SCREAMING TARGET
Screaming target / Pride and joy rock / Be careful / Tippertone rock / One of these fine days / Screaming target / Killer / Solomon A Gunday / Honesty / I am alright / Lee a low / Concrete jungle
CDTRL 61 / Mar '94 / Trojan

☐ SOME GREAT BIG YOUTH
World War III / Living / Roots foundation / Get on up / Dancing mood / Time alone will tell / Suffering / Love Jah with all of my heart / Green bay killing / We can work it out
CDBM 015 / Jul '92 / Blue Moon

Bigard, Barney

☐ BARNEY BIGARD & THE PELICAN TRIO
JCD 228 / Oct '93 / Jazzology

☐ BARNEY BIGARD AND THE LEGENDS OF JAZZ
BCD 338 / Jun '95 / GHB

☐ BARNEY BIGARD STORY 1929-1945, THE
158502 / Jul '96 / Jazz Archives

☐ CLARINET LAMENT
Saturday night function / Turtle twist / Clarinet lament / Clouds in my heart / Pigeons and peppers / Barney going easy / Just another dream / Early mornin' / Honey hush / Watch the birdie / Solid rock / Diga diga doo / Lament for Javanette / Lull at dawn / Ready Eddy / World is waiting for the sunrise / Big eight blues / Moonglow / Tea for two / Step steps up, steps step down / Rose room / Coquette
TPZ 1055 / Oct '96 / Topaz Jazz

☐ CLASSICS 1944
CLASSICS 896 / Oct '96 / Classics

☐ CLASSICS 1944-1945
CLASSICS 930 / Apr '97 / Classics

☐ INTRODUCTION TO BARNEY BIGARD 1928-1941, AN
4028 / Feb '96 / Best Of Jazz

Bigazzi, Arlo

☐ 2
MASO 90076 / 25 May '98 / Materiali Sonori

Bigband Orchestra

☐ LEGEND OF GLENN MILLER, THE
500582 / Jan '94 / Musidisc

Bigeneric

☐ MYRIADES
EFA 698262 / Jul '95 / Spacefrog

Bigeou, Esther

☐ ESTHER BIGEOU 1921-1923
DOCD 5489 / Nov '96 / Document

Biggie Tembo

☐ OUT OF AFRICA
Punza / Mushonga / Harare jit / Ngaraire / Mozambique / Out of africa / Jinga / Nherra
COOKCD 039 / Feb '92 / Cooking Vinyl

Biggs, Barry

☐ SIDESHOW
JMC 200117 / Jun '95 / Jamaican Gold

Bigjig

☐ FEET TO THE FLOOR
SMALLCD 9404 / Apr '94 / Smallworld

Biglight

☐ NOWHERE
SPV 08544422 / Nov '96 / SPV

Big'N

☐ DISCIPLINE THROUGH SOUND
GR 23CD / Aug '96 / Skingraft

Bigod 20

☐ SUPERCUTE
CDZOT 122 / Nov '94 / Zoth Ommog

Bijma, Greetje

☐ BAREFOOT
Barefoot / Bosnia / Painter at work / As I drive by / Glazed frost / Lonely walk / Katsjima / Sings with strings / Duck pond / Guess where it's coming from / Vortex
ENJ 80382 / Oct '93 / Enja

Bikaye, Bony

☐ COMPUTER'S DREAMS
926602 / Oct '96 / BUDA

Bikini Beach Band

☐ BIKINI BEACH BAND LEAVE HOME, THE
Mission impossible / Gimme gimme gimme/Smells like teen spirit / Love will tear us apart again / Motorcade / Secret agent man / Lounge wetsuit / Surburbia / Anarchy in the UK / Popcorn / Music to watch girls by / Fever / Some might say / Design for life
STIM 9CD / 3 Aug '98 / Stim

Bikini Kill

☐ PUSSY WHIPPED
Blood one / Alien she / Magnet / Speed heart / L'il red / Tell me so / Sugar / Starbellied boy / Hamster baby / Rebel girl / Starfish / For Tammy Rae
WIJ 028CD / Oct '93 / Wiiija

☐ REJECTS ALL AMERICAN
KRS 260CD / Apr '96 / Kill Rock Stars

☐ SINGLES, THE
KRS 298 / 22 Jun '98 / Kill Rock Stars

☐ YEAH YEAH YEAH YEAH
Double dare ya / Liar / Carnival / Suck my left one / Feels blind / Thurston hearts the who / White boy / This is not a test / Don't need you / Jigsaw youth / Resist psychic death / Rebel girl / Outta me
KRS 204CD / Mar '94 / Kill Rock Stars

Bila, Vera

☐ KALE KALORE
3037302 / 24 Apr '98 / Last Call

☐ ROM POP
7422510 / Jan '97 / Last Call

Bile

☐ TEKNO WHORE
0086822CTR / Jul '97 / Edel

Bilezikjian, John

☐ MUSIC FROM THE ARMENIAN DIASPORA PLAYED ON THE OUD
GV 809CD / May '94 / Global Village

Bilk, Acker

☐ ACKER BILK AND HIS PARAMOUNT JAZZ BAND (Bilk, Acker & His Paramount Jazz Band)
LACD 36 / Oct '94 / Lake

☐ ACKER BILK IN HOLLAND
I can't believe that you're in love with me / Clarinet marmalade / Mood indigo / Them there eyes / Take the 'A' train / World is waiting for the sunrise / Just a closer walk with thee / Jeepers creepers / Lover man / Watermelon man / I don't want to set the world on fire / St. Thomas / Georgia / Senora Signora / Blues walk / Stranger on the shore / Nobody's sweetheart / Once in a while / Old music master
CDTTD 506/7 / Aug '94 / Timeless Traditional

☐ ACKER BILK SONGBOOK
Just when I needed you most / I want to know what love is / I just called to say I love you / Longfellow serenade / Truly / Hundred ways / Still / Always on my mind / Memory / Ships / Arthur's tree / Do that to me one more time / This masquerade / Stuck on you / If ever you're in my arms again / Could I have this dance / To all the girls I've loved before / Three times a lady / Hello / Just once
QED 112 / Nov '96 / Tring

☐ AFTER MIDNIGHT
Stranger on the shore / Right here waiting / Room in your heart / Smack a Latin / Another day in paradise / Don't know much / After midnight / Don't wanna lose you / How am I supposed to live without you / I'm not in love / Best of me / Anything for you / Disney girls / If leaving is easy / When summer comes / Traces of dreams
PWKM 4019 / Feb '96 / Carlton

☐ ALL THE HITS PLUS MORE
Rainy night in Georgia / Taste of honey / You've got a friend / Aria / Whiter shade of pale / Lonely / Yesterday / Stranger on the shore / Nights in white satin / White cliffs of Dover / Lay lady lay / Buona sera / Bridge over troubled water / Summer set / (Everything I do) I do it for you
CDSGP 0371 / 24 Nov '97 / Prestige

☐ AT SUNDOWN (Bilk, Acker & Humphrey Lyttelton)
At Sundown / When you and I were young Maggie / You're exceptional to me / Lower than low / Just a little while to stay here / You're a lucky guy / Red beans and rice / Wabash blues / Carry me back to old Virginny / Summertime / I used to love you / Lonesome blues / Jazz me blues / Southern sunset
CLGCD 027 / May '92 / Calligraph

☐ BLAZE AWAY (Bilk, Acker & His Paramount Jazz Band)
Riverboat shuffle / I'm gonna sit right down and write myself a letter / Black and tan fantasy / Spain / Blaze away / Wabash blues / Way down yonder in New Orleans / Aria / Keepin' out of mischief now / Jazz me blues / Memphis blues / Exactly like you / Is you is or is you ain't my baby / Singin' the blues / Please don't talk to me... / Stranger on the shore
CDTTD 543 / Mar '90 / Timeless Traditional

☐ BRIDGE OVER TROUBLED WATER
Bridge over troubled water / Stranger on the shore / Touch me in the morning / Evergreen / She / When I need you / You're my best friend / Way we were / Raindrops keep falling on my head / Amazing Grace / Raining in my heart / September song / Don't cry for me Argentina / Aria / Talking in your sleep / Misty / Without you / This guy's in love with you / Forever autumn / Ebony and ivory
5507322 / Mar '95 / Spectrum

☐ CAN'T SMILE WITHOUT YOU (Bilk, Acker, His Clarinet & Strings)
TRTCD 129 / Oct '94 / TrueTrax

☐ CHRISTMAS ALBUM
White Christmas / Have yourself a merry little christmas / Silent night holy night / When a child is born / Mary's boy child / I'll be home for Christmas / O little town of Bethlehem / Mistletoe and wine / Christmas song / Little drummer boy / Away in a manger / First Noel / It came upon a midnight clear / I'm walking in the air / In the bleak midwinter / Once in royal David's city
120312 / Oct '97 / Jingle

☐ CLARINET MOODS
Stranger on the shore / Summertime / Night and day / I wonder who's kissing her now / Long ago and far away / Fly me to the moon / Body and soul / Embraceable you / I'll get by / That ole buttermilk sky / Pennies from heaven / South of the border / Try a little tenderness
CDMFP 6394 / Jul '97 / Music For Pleasure

☐ COLLECTION, THE
Stranger on the shore / Do that to me one more time / Hello / I just called to say I love you / I want to know what love is / Longfellow serenade / To all the girls I've loved before / Arthur's theme / Three times a lady / Could I have this dance / If ever you're in my arms again / Just when I needed you most / Still / This masquerade / Memory / One hundred ways / Ships / Stuck on you / Just once / Truly / Always on my mind
COL 070 / Mar '95 / Collection

☐ FEELINGS (4CD Set)
PBXCD 409 / 20 Apr '98 / Pulse

☐ GREAT MOMENTS WITH ACKER BILK
Jeepers creepers / Just a closer walk with thee / Watermelon man / Blaze away / I don't want to set the world on fire / Aria / Jazz me blues / St.Thomas / Is you is or is you ain't my baby / Senora/Signora / Stranger on the shore / Blues walk / High society / South / Please don't talk about me when I'm gone
WWJ 3003 / 27 Apr '98 / World Wide Jazz

☐ HEARTBEATS
Get here / Unchained melody / Somerset skies / Crazy for you / Close to you / When I'm back on my feet again / Rio nights / I've got you under my skin / Sacrifice / Walk on by / Cuts both ways / It's easy now / Here we are / On Takapuna Beach / You've lost that lovin' feelin' / Heartbeats
PWKS 4084 / Feb '96 / Carlton

☐ HITS, BLUES AND CLASSICS (Bilk, Acker & His Paramount Jazz Band)
Louisian-i-ay / Black and tan fantasy / My baby just cares for me / Papa dip / That's my home / Semper fidelis / Basin Street blues / White cliffs of Dover / Blaze away / Nairobi / When it's sleepy time down South / Savoy blues / Just a closer walk with thee / South / Mood indigo / Buona sera / Ain't misbehavin' / Aria / Beale Street blues / Stranger on the shore
KAZ CD 10 / Aug '88 / Kaz

☐ IMAGINE
Mull of Kintyre / Norwegian wood / Sailing / Send in the clowns / Stranger on the shore / Yesterday / Windmills of your mind / You are the sunshine of my life / Aranjuez mon amour / Aria / Ebony and ivory / Feelings / Fool on the hill / Imagine / Michelle / Missing you
PLS CD 511 / Jun '95 / Pulse

☐ IN A MELLOW MOOD
PLSCD 163 / Apr '97 / Pulse

☐ JAZZ TODAY COLLECTION
Travelling blues / Delia gone / Gladiolus rag / Willie the weeper / Dardanella / Franklin street blues / Easter parade / Marching through georgia / Blaze away / Under the double eagle / El abanico / Cre march / Carry me back to old virginny / Jump in the line / Higher ground / Louisian-i-ay
LACD 48 / Jun '95 / Lake

☐ LOVE ALBUM, THE
When I fall in love / Groovy kind of love / Silvery nights / Could've been / My love / He ain't heavy, he's my brother / Good times / One moment in time / Till I loved you / Candle in the wind / Tune for melody / Take my breath away / Love changes everything / Sweet crystal / Lady in red / Every time we say goodbye
PWKS 534 / Feb '96 / Carlton

☐ MAGIC CLARINET OF ACKER BILK
Jean / We've only just begun / Rose / Eres tu (touch the wind) / Morning has broken / You're the best thing that ever happened to me / I left my heart in san francisco / I can't stop loving you / Hey jude / First time I ever saw your face / Ramblin' rose / If I give my heart to you / Never my love / Stranger on the shore / Let it be me / My way
EMPRCD 513 / Jul '94 / Emporio

☐ MELLOW MOODS
MACCD 162 / Aug '96 / Autograph

☐ NEW ORLEANS DAYS
LA 36CD / Jun '94 / Lake

☐ OSCAR WINNERS
When you wish upon a star / For all we know / Three coins in the fountain / Love story / Last time I saw Paris / Swinging on a star / Mona Lisa / Love is a many splendoured thing / Can you feel the love tonight / Up where we belong / All the way / You'll never know / Days of wine and roses / It might as well be spring / Hello Dolly / Over the rainbow
3036000022 / Oct '95 / Carlton

☐ REFLECTIONS
Stranger on the shore / Petit fleur / Georgia on my mind / Ain't misbehavin' / I left my heart in San Francisco / La paloma / Greensleeves / Sentimental journey / Moon river / I'm in the mood for love / Creole love call / Dinah / Shenandoah / Only you
5500462 / Jun '93 / Spectrum

☐ STRANGER ON THE SHORE (Bilk, Acker & Leon Young String Chorale)
Stranger on the shore / It had to be you / Petite fleur / Ain't misbehavin' / Greensleeves / Only you / Sentimental journey / I'm in the mood for love / La mer / Moon river / Shenandoah / I left my heart in San Francisco
8307792 / Mar '94 / Philips

☐ STRANGER ON THE SHORE (The Best Of Acker Bilk)
Stranger on the shore / Windmills of your mind / Cavatina / Magnificent Mog / If / Bilitis / Amazing Grace / For the good times / Lazy serenade / Shepherd's song / When I need you / Pescadores / Aria / As time goes by / Love letters / Pacelbel Canon / Skylark / Autumn leaves / Love said goodbye / First of Spring / Colours of my life / Clair / She's leaving home
PLSCD 202 / Feb '97 / Pulse

☐ STRANGER ON THE SHORE
Sweet Georgia brown / Riverboat shuffle / Black and tan fantasy / Don't roll those bloodshot eyes at me / Blaze away / Mood indigo / White cliffs of Dover / Stranger on the shore / That's my home
307902 / Sep '97 / Hallmark

☐ TOGETHER AGAIN (Bilk, Acker & Ken Colyers Jazzmen)
Down among the sheltering palms / Down among the sheltering palms / It looks like a big time tonight / Sweet substitute (take 2) / If I ever cease to love / Clarinet mamalade / Carolina moon / Mabel's dream / Liza / Lily of the valley / Corrine, corrina (take 1) / Sweet substitute (take 1)
LACD 53 / Oct '95 / Lake

☐ UNCHAINED MELODY (32 Great Love Songs From The King Of Clarinet/2CD Set)
Unchained melody / Traces of dreams/Wind beneath my wings / He ain't heavy he's my brother / Close to you / Love story / Over the rainbow / Disney girls / You've lost that loving feeling / Up where we belong / Don't wanna lose you / Cuts both ways / When I fall in love / I'm not in love / Lady in red / Sacrifice / My love / Can you feel the love tonight / Love changes everything / Another day in paradise / Groovy kind of love / If leaving me is easy / Take my breath away / Candle in the wind / I've got you under my skin / Every time we say goodbye / Crazy for you / Heartbeats / Right here waiting / Best of me / Walk on by / Room in your heart / It might as well be Spring
330382 / Mar '97 / Hallmark

Bill & Ben
☐ SOUTH OF THE RIVER
Jaz club / Sawn off / Rod's groove / Country man dub / Rip it up / Come before / Magnetic funk / 10" of funk / Red tracksuit / 8 hand version / H.V. FILL / On the sly / C'mon y'all / Mr. Sequin's encore / Unknown thing / Until the next time
HHUKCD 004 / 13 Oct '97 / Harthouse

Bill Ding
☐ AND THE SOUND OF...
HEFTY 003 / May '97 / Hefty

☐ TRUST IN GOD, BUT TIE UP YOUR CAMEL
HEFTY 05 / Apr '97 / Hefty

Bill, Jason
☐ VIA ST. LOUIS (Bill, Jason & Jack Rose)
DFR 36 / 22 Jun '98 / Drunken Fish

Billet, Cuff
☐ AT ALGIERS POINT, LOUSIANNA (Billet, Cuff & Sam Rimington/ International All Star Band)
Nothing blue but the sky / You're the one I care for / Blue and broken hearted / I need thee every hour / Linda / West Indies blues / Try a little tenderness / Some sweet day / I apologise / Red wing / No moon at all / Cuban Pete / Magic is the moonlight / Does Jesus care / I don't see me in your eyes anymore / Alice blue gown / Spanish shawl
504CDS 68 / Jul '98 / 504

Billy & The Lucky Boys
☐ ROBBER
PT 605002 / Jun '96 / Part

☐ WILD TRAIN
PT 605001 / Jun '96 / Part

Billy Bacon & Forbidden Pigs
☐ 13 YEARS OF BAD ROAD
TX 51252CD / 8 Jun '98 / Triple XXX

Billy Bunter
☐ FUTURE OF HARD DANCE VOL.1, THE (2CD Set) (Bunter, Billy 'Daniel')
Ready to fly / Ready to fly / This beat kicks / Freedom / Mortal combat / Time for change / Raise the titanic / Let the rhythm unwind / New generation / Welcome to the future / In control / Forever and a day / Global sounds / Let yourself go / 20mm / Time to start pumpin'
ALPHACD 1 / Jun '97 / Alpha Projects

Billy Tipton's Memorial Saxophone Quartet
☐ SAXHOUSE
KFWCD 143 / Feb '95 / Knitting Factory

Billys
☐ ROCKABILLY REBELS
Boppin' the blues: *Billys & Carl Perkins/The Jordanaires* / Matchbox: *Billys & Carl Perkins* / Honey don't: *Billys & Carl Perkins* / Blue suede shoes: *Billys & Carl Perkins/The Jordanaires* / Blue jean bop: *Billys & Carl Perkins/The Jordanaires* / So glad you're mine / Baby what you want me to do / Drinking wine spo-dee-o-dee / Dream girl / Warm beer in the morning: *Billys & The Jordanaires* / No longer no more / That's why I know: *Billys & The Jordanaires* / Cadillac queen / I just wonder why / Sweet little baby: *Billys & The Jordanaires*
303902 / Jun '97 / Hallmark

Bim Skala Bim
☐ AMERICAN PLAYHOUSE
DOJOCD 209 / Jul '96 / Dojo

☐ BOSTON SKA VOL.1 (2CD Set)
SKANKDCD 101 / Jan '95 / Skank

☐ BOSTON SKA VOL.2 (2CD Set)
SKANKCD 102 / Oct '92 / Skank

Bina, Sima
☐ MUSIC OF NORTH KHORASSAN, IRAN
926362 / Feb '96 / BUDA

☐ PERSIAN CLASSICAL MUSIC
NI 5391 / Apr '95 / Nimbus

Bindstouw, Af
☐ LIVE AT THE FEMO JAZZ 1995 (Bindstouw, Af Jazz Men)
MECCACD 1084 / May '97 / Music Mecca

Binelli, Daniel
☐ TANGO
150202 / Aug '97 / Black Sun

Bingert, Hector
☐ CANDOMBE
ADCD 7 / May '97 / ADCD

Bingham, Mark
☐ I PASSED FOR HUMAN
DOG 006CD / Sep '94 / Wild Dog

Bingham, Terry
☐ TERRY BINGHAM
OSS 108CD / Aug '97 / Ossian

Bingo Trappers
☐ SIERRA
SHR 91CD / Mar '97 / Shrimper

Bingy Bunny
☐ KINGSTON 12 TOUGHIE (A Tribute To Bingy Bunny)
RASCD 3189 / Sep '96 / Ras

Binney, David
☐ LUXURY OF GUESSING, THE
AQ 1030 / Apr '95 / Audioquest

Bio-Com
☐ COMING UP FOR AIR
Five fathoms deep / Gridiron / Jacob's reef / Dollarsworth / Veering Northwesterly / Sub marine / Dexter / Van der belt / Coming up for air / Pas de deux
ADDSCD 001 / 1 Jun '98 / Deepstar

Bio-Tek
☐ DARKNESS MY NAME IS
ZOT 187CD / 29 Sep '97 / Zoth Ommog

☐ TEST TUBE LOGIC
Wu jung / Tazer / Slipstream / Needle point / Filter / Test tube logic / Biorhythm / Levent / Nexus / Agent orange / Ice zone
KINXCD 10 / 20 Oct '97 / Kinetix

Biochip C
☐ INSIDE VOL.2
EFA 008302 / Jul '95 / Anodyne

Biohazard
☐ BIOHAZARD
MCD 1067 / Aug '94 / MCA
SPV 07646502 / Dec '96 / SPV
7646502 / 23 Feb '98 / Magnetic

☐ MATELEAO
Authority / Stigmatized / Cleansing / Modern democracy / Competition / In vain / Thorn / True strengths / Way / Waiting to die / Lot to learn / Gravity / Better days / Control / These eyes (have seen)
9362462082 / May '96 / Warner Bros.

☐ NO HOLDS BARRED (Live)
Shades of grey / What makes us tick / Authority / Urban discipline / Modern democracy / Business / Tales from the hardside / Better days / Victory / Lot to learn / How it is / After forever / Tears of blood / Chamber spins three / Wrong side of the tracks / Waiting to die / These eyes / Punishment / Hold my own
RR 88032 / Aug '97 / Roadrunner

☐ STATE OF THE WORLD ADDRESS
State of the world address / Down for life / What makes us tick / Tales from the hard side / How it is / Remember / Five blocks to the subway / Each day / Failed territory / Lack there of / Pride / Human animal / Cornered / Love denied
9362455952 / May '94 / WEA

☐ URBAN DISCIPLINE (Remastered)
Chamber spins three / Punishment / Shades of grey / Business / Black and white and red all over / Man with a promise / Disease / Urban discipline / Loss / Wrong side of the tracks / Mistaken identity / We're only gonna die (from our own arrogance) / Tears of blood / Fallen / Sad man / Business (demo) / Urban discipline (demo)
RR 87472 / 8 Jun '98 / Roadrunner

Biomuse
☐ WRONG
4 Rubber feet / Race / Sine God / Very approximately / Convolvotron / Medral / Anaural / Ursonate / Ba-Umf / Wrong / X
WORDD 002 / Nov '95 / Language

Biosinites
☐ FIRST TAKE
FMPCD 80 / May '97 / Full Moon

Biosphere
☐ MICROGRAVITY
Microgravity / Baby satellite / Tranquillizer / Fairy tale / Cloudwalker 11 / Chromosphere / Cygnus-A / Baby interphase / Biosphere
AMBCD 3921 / Jun '93 / Apollo

☐ PATASHNIK
Phantasm / Startoucher / Decryption / Novelty waves / Patashnik / Mir / Shield / Seti project / Trance / Mestigoth / Botanical dimensions / Caboose / Entrance
AMB 3927CD / 16 Feb '98 / Apollo

☐ SUBSTRATA
As the sun kissed the horizon / Poa alpina / Chukhung / Things I tell you / Times when I know you'll be sad / Hyperborea / Kobresia / Antennaria / Uva-ursi / Sphere of no-form / Silene
ASCD 033 / May '97 / All Saints

Biota

☐ ALMOST NEVER
RERBCD 3 / Oct '96 / ReR/ Recommended

☐ BELLOWING ROOM/TINCT
RERBCD 2 / Apr '90 / ReR/ Recommended

☐ TUMBLE
RERBCD / Apr '90 / ReR/ Recommended

Bird, Ted

☐ MADE IN AMERICA
Dirty little town / Land o' plenty / Drivin' in Rhode Island / Still in your power / Hurricane / Sadness in my eyes / Daddy's diamonds / Philadelphia kid / Southern Ohio / Lady crystal / That far to fall / When she gets drinkin' whiskey / On the radio / Dollar bill / Allyson's waltz
CDSL 5219 / Aug '92 / DRG

Bird, Tony

☐ SORRY AFRICA
CDPH 1135 / Dec '90 / Philo

Birdland W

☐ BIRDLAND W AND LESTER BANGS (Birdland W & Lester Bangs)
BA 118CD / 15 Jan '98 / Bacchus Archives

Birds

☐ BIRDS
PALSLCD 1 / 30 Mar '98 / Pal-SI

Birdsong Mesozoic

☐ SONIC ECOLOGY
RCD 20073 / Apr '92 / Rykodisc

Birkin, Jane

☐ BEST OF JANE BIRKIN, THE
Je t'aime moi non plus / Ex fan des sixties / Ballade de Johnny Jane / La gadoue / Yesterday yes a day / Di doo dah / Fuir le bonheur de peur qu'il ne se sauve / Baby alone in Babylon / Les dessous chics / Quoi / These foolish things / Avec le temps / Et quand bien meme / Baby Lou / Les yeux fermes / Je suis venu te dire que je m'en vais / La javanaise
5346912 / Mar '97 / Mercury

Birkin Tree

☐ CONTINENTAL REEL
NT 6753CD / Aug '96 / New Tone

Birmingham 6

☐ ERROR OF JUDGEMENT
CLP 9748 / Oct '96 / Cleopatra

☐ YOU CANNOT WALK HERE
CLP 9887 / Jun '97 / Cleopatra

Birmingham City FC

☐ HAPPY COS I'M BLUE (Birmingham City FC & Supporters)
Keep right on: Lauder, Harry / Happy cos I'm blue: Hockey, Trevor / Home and away: Andrews, Harvey / Lads from the Tilton: Phillips, Colin Combo / Keep right on: Blues Players 1968 / Birmingham blues: Phillips, Colin Combo / Beau brummie: Green, Roy / Bobby Latchford: Saint, Andrew / Louie Louie: Rockin' Berries / Davey boy: Holmes, John / Blue nose: Kop Dis / Trevor's blues: Saint, Andrew / My colour is blue: Small Heath Alliance / Keep right on: Team Of '91 / Barry Fry Song: Austin, Steve / You'll never walk alone: Francis, Trevor & Viv Anderson / Keep right on: Small Heath Alliance / When the blues win the cup: Andrews, Harvey
CDGAFFER 10 / Aug '97 / Cherry Red

Birmingham Jubilee Singers

☐ 1926-1927 VOL.1
DOCD 5345 / May '95 / Document

Birmingham Sunlights

☐ FOR OLD TIME'S SAKE
FF 588CD / Nov '94 / Flying Fish

Biro, Daniel

☐ COMPARATIVE ANATOMY OF ANGELS
SCD 28022 / Sep '96 / Sargasso

Birth Control

☐ BACKDOOR POSSIBILITIES
RR 7054 / Jun '97 / Repertoire

☐ BANG
PMS 7068 / 24 Nov '97 / Repertoire

☐ BIRTH CONTROL
No drugs / Recollection / Deep inside / Foolish action / Sundown / Change of mind / Light my fire / No drugs / All I want is you / October / Freedom
PMS 7064 / Oct '97 / Repertoire

☐ CONDOMIUM
74861 / 5 Jan '98 / Affengeil

☐ OPERATION
RR 7072 / 24 Nov '97 / Repertoire

Birtha

☐ BIRTHA/CAN'T STOP THE MADNESS
Free spirit / Fine talking man / Tuesday / Feeling lonely / She was good to me / Work on a dream / Too much woman (for a hen pecked man) / Judgement day / Forgotten soul / Can't stop the madness / My pants are too short / Freedom / Let us sing / Don't let it get you down / (When will ya) understand / Rock me / All this love / Sun / My man told me
SEECD 474 / Feb '97 / See For Miles

Birthday Party

☐ HEE HAW
Release the bats / Blast off / Friend catcher / Mr. Clarinet / Happy birthday
GAD 307CD / 6 Jul '98 / 4AD

☐ HITS
Friend catcher / Happy birthday / Mr. Clarinet / Nick the stripper / Zoo music girl / King Ink / Release the bats / Blast off / She's hit / Gold blade / Hamlet (pow pow pow) / Dead Joe / Junkyard / Big Jesus trash can / Wild world / Sonny's burning / Deep in the woods / Swampland / Jennifer's veil / Mutiny in Heaven
GAD 2016CD / 6 Jul '98 / 4AD

☐ IT'S STILL LIVING LIVE
LINKCD 028 / 16 Feb '98 / Missing Link

☐ JUNKYARD
She's hit / Dead Joe / Dim locator / Hamlet pow pow pow / Several sins / Big Jesus trash can / Kiss me black / Six inch gold blade / Kewpie doll / Junkyard
GAD 207CD / 6 Jul '98 / 4AD

☐ MUTINY/BAD SEED
CAD 301CD / Jul '89 / 4AD
GAD 301CD / 6 Jul '98 / 4AD

☐ PRAYERS ON FIRE
Zoo music girl / Zoo music girl / Capers / Nick the stripper / Ho ho / Figure of fun / King ink / Dead song / Yard / Dull day / Just you and me / Blundertown / Kathy's kisses
GAD 104CD / 6 Jul '98 / 4AD

Birtwistle, Harrison

☐ PANIC/EARTH DANCES
Panic: Birtwistle, Harrison & John Harle/Paul Clavis/ BBC SO / Earth dances: Birtwistle, Harrison & The Cleveland Orchestra
4521042 / Oct '96 / Argo

Biry, Daniel

☐ FEATHERED SNAKE, THE
AMPCD 009 / Feb '95 / AMP

Bis

☐ NEW TRANSISTER HEROES
Tell it to the kids / Sweet shop avengers / Starbright boy / Popstar kill / Mr. important / Antiseptic poetry / Popyura / Skinny tie sensurround / Poster parent / Monstarr / Everybody thinks they're going to get theirs / Rebel soul / Photo shop / X-Defect / Lie detector test / Dinosaur germs / Troubled land: King Loser
WIJCD 1064 / Apr '97 / Wiiija

Biscuit, Karl

☐ AKTUALISMUS
MTM 28 / Dec '92 / Made To Measure

Bishop, Duffy

☐ BACK TO THE BONE (Bishop, Duffy Band)
BCD 00232 / Aug '96 / Burnside

☐ BOTTLED ODDITIES (Bishop, Duffy Band)
BCD 00182 / May '96 / Burnside

Bishop, Elvin

☐ ACE IN THE HOLE
Another mule kickin' in your stall / Driving wheel / Give me some of that money / Ace in the hole / Party 'til the cows come home / Think / Home of the blues / Pigmeat on the line / Ain't that love / Fishin' / Blue flame / Talkin' mood / Fooled around and fell in love
ALCD 4833 / Aug '95 / Alligator

☐ BIG FUN
Don't you lie to me / Beer drinking woman / Oklahoma country girl / My dog / Midnight hour blues / No more broken hearts / Right string but the wrong yo-yo / She puts me in the mood / Country boy / Honest I do / Fishin' again
ALCD 4767 / Aug '92 / Alligator

☐ DON'T LET THE BOSSMAN GET YOU DOWN
Fannie Mae / Don't let the bossman get you down / Murder in the first degree / Kissing in the dark / My whiskey head buddies / Stepping up in class / You got to rock 'em / Come on in this house / Soul food / Rollin' with my blues / Devil's slide / Just your fool
ALCD 4791 / Apr '91 / Alligator

Bishop, Joni

☐ ENDLESS CHRISTMAS (Bishop, Joni & Electra Reed)
Endless Christmas / Toys / Drummer boy / Oh how joyfully / Noel / (Christmas day) all over again / God rest ye merry gentlemen / Low how a rose/Es skaistu rozit zinu / Coventry carol / Christmas song / What child is this / Silent night/Klusa nakts
CDSGP 0213 / 24 Nov '97 / Prestige

☐ EVERYDAY MIRACLES
When God made you / I'd hardly noticed you were gone / Majove rose / Everyday miracles / Rest assured / Money tree / Art of flying / Sequoia / Thief of hearts / Living love
CDSGP 0134 / Nov '95 / Prestige
BWE 91CD / Nov '96 / BWE

☐ THREADS
BWE 0094CD / May '97 / BWE

Bishop, Rick

☐ SALVADOR KALI
REV 102 / 26 May '98 / Revenant

Bishop, Stephen

☐ INTRODUCTION TO STEPHEN BISHOP, AN
HMNCD 011 / Jun '97 / Half Moon

Bishop, Walter Jr.

☐ MILESTONES
BLCD 760109 / Feb '89 / Black Lion

Bishops

☐ BEST OF THE BISHOPS, THE
Train train / Baby you're wrong / Stay free / I want candy / I take what I want / Mr. Jones / I need you / Down in the bottom / You're in my way / Talk to you / Taste and try / Someone's got my number / Good times / Your Daddy won't mind / What's your number / Till the end of the day / These arms of mine / Rolling man / Paul's blues / No lies / Too much, too soon / Sometimes good guys don't wear white / Don't start me talkin' / Somebody's gonna get their head kicked in tonight / I don't like it / Route 66 / Train, train
CDWIKD 150 / Aug '95 / Chiswick

Bisi, Martin

☐ SEE YA IN TIAJUANA
NAR 123CD / Jul '95 / New Alliance

Bisiker, Mick

☐ HOME AGAIN
Home again / Don't you go / Jigs / Katy Jane / Si beag si mor / Rose of Allendale / Maid from the shore / Mossy green banks of the lea / Jigs and reels / Downhills of life / Rainbows end
FE 083CD / Feb '88 / Fellside

Bisk

☐ STRANGE OR FUNNY HA HA
SR 118 / Jun '97 / Sub Rosa

☐ TIME
SR 112 / Sep '96 / Sub Rosa

Bismillah

☐ ETERNAL SPIRIT
Alap / Vilambit / Gat composition
NRCD 0080 / Jul '97 / Navras

Bison, Fred

☐ BEATROOTS
Girl guitar / I'm on edge / Psychedelic garden / Psychedelic garden / Tell me something / Quagmirehand / Here to cry / Be ready / Orient time / Fried slice / Quagmirehead / Confused / Theme from action inc. / Prowler / Quagmirehead / Blowin' smoke / Fuse blews / Soul destruction / Can't seem to figure it out
WO 19CD / Apr '94 / Woronzow

Bisserov Sisters

☐ PIRIN WEDDING AND RITUAL SONGS
PAN 7005CD / Nov '95 / Pan

Bissonette, Gregg

☐ GREGG BISSONETTE
M 7038CD / 13 Apr '98 / Mascot

Bissonnette, Sarah

☐ HERE COMES SARAH
JCCD 3027 / Oct '97 / Jazz Crusade

Bitch

☐ BITCH IS BACK
Do you wanna rock / Hot and heavy / Me and the boys / Storm raging up / Bitch is back / Head banger / Fist to face / Turns me on / Skullcrusher
398414218CD / Jan '97 / Metal Blade

☐ DAMNATION
398414213CD / Jan '97 / Metal Blade

☐ ROSE BY ANY OTHER
398414214CD / Jan '97 / Metal Blade

Bitch Magnet

☐ BEN HUR
COMM 21CD / Dec '96 / Communion

☐ UMBER
COMM 12CD / Dec '96 / Communion

Bitchcraft

☐ DON'T COUNT ON IT
IT 0062 / Feb '95 / Iteration

Bitches Brue

☐ WE MIGHT NOT BE AMERICAN BUT STILL WE F**K
Let the boys / Jack back into rock / We might not be american (but still we ...ck) / Money makes money / Kick it, kiss it / Little mr. lonely heart / Raise the risk / Knocked for six / Bring out the worst / Runnin' away from hollywood
HMRXD 131 / Aug '89 / Heavy Metal

Bitter Grin

☐ DESTINATION
WWRCD 024 / Nov '96 / Walzwerk

Bitter Springs

☐ FROM THE PARISH OF ARTHRITIS
DISHY 27CD / 15 Sep '97 / Dishy Recordings

Bittersweets

☐ LESSON ONE
THEN 029CD / Nov '96 / Thats Entertainment

Bizarre Inc.

☐ SURPRISE
Keep the music strong / Feel is real / Surprise / Get up (Sunshine Street) / Never give you up / Love groove / Soul fire / Porcelain cafe / Breakaway / Miracle / Take a look / Shout it out
5148192 / 15 Sep '97 / Some Bizarre/ Mercury

Bjerkestrand, Kjetil

☐ PRIMA LUNA
FX 186CD / Dec '97 / Kirkelig Kulturverksted

Bjork

☐ BACHALORETTE
TPLP 91CD / 11 May '98 / One Little Indian

☐ BEST MIXES FROM THE ALBUM DEBUT (For All The People Who Don't Buy White Labels)
Human behaviour / One day / Come to me / Anchor song
MUMCD 59 / Oct '94 / Mother

☐ DEBUT
Human behaviour / Crying / Venus as a boy / There's more to life than this / Like someone in love / Big time sensuality / One day / Aeroplane / Come to me / Violently happy / Anchor song / Play dead: Bjork & David Arnold
TPLP 31CDX / Nov '93 / One Little Indian

☐ GLING GLO
TPLP 61CD / Mar '97 / One Little Indian
SM 27 / 19 Jan '98 / Smekkleysa

79

☐ HOMOGENIC
Hunter / Joga / Unravel / Bertolucci / All neon like / 5 years / Immature / Jacko / Pluto / All is full of love
TPLP 71CD
TPLP 71CDL / 22 Sep '97 / One Little Indian

☐ JOGA
TPLP 81CD / 27 Apr '98 / One Little Indian

☐ POST
Army of me / Hyperballad / Modern things / It's oh so quiet / Enjoy / You've been flirting again / Isobel / Possibly maybe / I miss you / Cover me / Headphones
TPLP 51CD / Jun '95 / One Little Indian

☐ TELEGRAM
TPLP 51CDT / Nov '96 / One Little Indian

Bjorkenheim, Raoul

☐ RITUAL (Bjorkenheim, Raoul & Krakatu)
RUNE 86 / Jun '97 / Cuneiform

Bjorkman, Erik

☐ SVARDSJO SPELMANSLAG
GCD 33 / May '97 / Giga

Bjornstad, Ketil

☐ RIVER, THE (Bjornstad, Ketil & David Darling)
River
5311702 / Feb '97 / ECM

☐ SEA VOL.1, THE
5217182 / Sep '95 / ECM

☐ SEA VOL.2, THE (Bjormstag & Darling/ Christensen/Rypdal)
Laila / Outward bound / Brand / Mother / Song for a planet / Consequences / Agnes / Mime / December / South
5373412 / 2 Mar '98 / ECM

☐ WATER STORIES
Glacial reconstruction / Levels and degrees / Surface movements / View (part one) / Between memory and presentiment / Ten thousand years later / Waterfall / Flotation and surroundings / Riverscape / Approaching the sea / View (part two) / History
5190762 / Sep '93 / ECM

BKA

☐ CLEVER
FILERCD 405 / Jun '91 / Profile

Blab Happy

☐ SMOTHERED
XXCD 22 / 27 Oct '97 / Demon

Black & Farrell

☐ CATARACT JUMP
FR 9520141 / Dec '96 / Blueprint

Black & White Gospel Singers

☐ LOOK TO GOD
FA 405 / Nov '95 / Fremeaux

Black & White Minstrels

☐ 30 GOLDEN GREATS (Black & White Minstrels & The Joe Loss Orchestra)
Baby face / Ain't she sweet / Good ole mammy song / Nostalgia, Home town, Strollin', Underneath the arches / Y viva Espana / Happy feet/I want to be happy/Happy days are here again / Consider yourself / Mame / Tzena, tzena, tzena / Hava Nagila / Bring me sunshine / Paloma blanca / Old fashioned way / You are my sunshine / Laugh a happy laugh / Continental / Piccolino / When the red, red robin comes bob, bob, bobbin' along / Hopscotch / Mexican shuffle / Tijuana Taxi / La Bamba / (We're gonna) rock around the clock
CDMFP 5720 / Mar '93 / EMI

Black

☐ TURN LOOSE THE IDIOTS
NORMAL 196CD / Jan '96 / Normal

☐ WONDERFUL LIFE
Ravel in the rain / Sixteens / Leave yourself alone / It's not you Lady Jane / Hardly star crossed lovers / Wonderful life / Everything's coming up roses / Sometimes for the asking / Finder / Paradise / I'm not afraid / I just grew tired / Blue / Just making memories / Sweetest smile
CDMID 166 / Aug '91 / A&M

Black

☐ BLACK BLOOD
NR 012CD / Sep '96 / Necropolis

Black Ace

☐ I'M THE BOSS CARD IN YOUR HAND
ARHCD 374 / Apr '95 / Arhoolie

Black, Alastair

☐ BALANDA DANCING (Black, Alastair & Stephen Richter)
LARRCD 317 / Nov '94 / Larrikin

Black, Andrea

☐ JUMPING FROM THE WALL
AKRCDA 38 / Mar '95 / AKR

Black Banjo Songsters

☐ BLACK BANJO SONGSTERS OF NORTH CAROLINA AND VIRGINIA, THE
SFWCD 40079 / 6 Apr '98 / Smithsonian Folkways

Black, Bill

☐ GOES WEST AND PLAYS (Black, Bill Combo)
San antonio rose / Tumbling tumbleweeds / Deep in the heart of texas / There's a gold mine in the sky / Yellow rose of texas / El rancho grande / Home on the range / Red river valley / Down in the valley / Cool water / Riding down the canyon / Cattle call / I'll never be free / Birth of the blues / Blues in the night / Basin street blues / Comin' on / St. louis blues / Got you on my mind / Wabash blues / Peter gunn / Weary blues / Midnight / Blues in my heart
HIUKCD 124 / Jun '93 / Hi

☐ GREATEST HITS (Black, Bill Combo)
Do it rat / Josephine / Rollin' / Hearts of stone / Yogi / White silver sands / Blue tango / Willie / Ole buttermilk sky / Royal blue / Don't be cruel / Smokie part 2 / School days / Sweet little sixteen / Roll over Beethoven / Maybellene / Carol / Little queenie / Brown eyed handsome man / Nadine / Thirty days / Johnny B Goode / Reelin' and rockin' / Memphis Tennessee
HIUKCD 115 / 28 May '91 / Hi

☐ HI MASTERS, THE (Black, Bill Combo)
White silver sands / Movin' / Smokie / Monkey shine / Don't be cruel / Little queenie / Josephine / Willie / You win again / Memphis Tennessee / Hearts of stone / Twist her / Honky train / Mack the knife / Do it rat now
HEX 31 / 4 Aug '98 / Hi

☐ LET'S TWIST HER/THE UNTOUCHABLE SOUND (Black, Bill Combo)
Twist-her / Night train / Corrine, corrina / Hucklebuck / Royal twist / Yogi / My girl josephine / Twisteroo / Johnny b. goode / Slippin' and slidin' / Twist with me baby / Smokie (pt. 2) / Joey's song / Castle rock / Red top / Tippin' in / Skokian / Woodchopper's ball / So what / Night train (slow version) / Your cheatin' heart / Ain't that a shame / Little brown jug / I can't stop loving you
HIUKCD 131 / Jun '92 / Hi

☐ SOLID AND RAUNCHY AND MOVIN' (Black, Bill Combo)
Don't be cruel / Singin' the blues / Blueberry Hill / I almost lost my mind / Cherry pink / Mona Lisa / Honky Tonk / Tequila / Raunchy / You win again / Bo Diddley / Mack the knife / Movin' / What'd I say / Hey Bo Diddley / Witchcraft / Work with me Annie / Be bop a lula / My babe / Forty miles of bad road / Ain't that lovin' you baby / Honky train / Walk / Torquay
HIUKCD 112 / 28 May '91 / Hi

☐ THAT WONDERFUL FEELING (Black, Bill Combo)
Nobody knows / This ole house / When the saints go marching in / This is no secret / Swing low, sweet chariot / Just a closer walk with thee / When the roll is called up yonder / He's got the whole world in his hands / Do lord / Down by the riverside / Old time religion / Dry bones / T.d.'s boogie woogie / Near you / Sentimental journey / Tuxedo junction / Canadian sunset / Leap frog / In the mood / Java / Two o'clock jump / So rare / Oh / Stranger on the shore
HIUKCD 145 / Aug '94 / Hi

☐ WONDERFUL WORLD OF BILL BLACK, THE
Blueberry hill / Hey bo diddley / My girl josephine / Don't be cruel / Tequila / Mack the knife / Be bop a lula / Roll over beethoven / Johnny b. goode / Slippin' and slidin' / Ain't that a shame / Cool water / Yellow rose of texas / This ole house / Swing low, sweet chariot / Old time religion / He's got the whole world in his hands / Stranger on the shore
HILOCD 22 / Aug '96 / Hi

Black, Bill

☐ DAWNING, THE (Black, Bill & His Scottish Dance Band)
SPRCD 1037 / May '96 / Springthyme

Black Box

☐ DREAMLAND
Everybody everybody / I don't know anybody else / Open your eyes / Fantasy / Dreamland / Ride on time / Hold on / Ghost box / Strike it up
74321158672 / Sep '93 / De-Construction

☐ HITS AND MIXES (The Best Of Black Box)
Ride on time / Ghost box / Everybody everybody / Fantasy / I don't know anyone else / Strike it up / Open your eyes / Hold on / Get down / Strike it up / Bright on time / Everybody everybody / Fantasy / Ride on time / Everybody everybody / I don't know anyone else / Fantasy
74321431542 / 22 Nov '97 / Camden

Black Box Recorder

☐ ENGLAND MADE ME
Girl singing in the wreckage / England made me / New baby boom / It's only the end of the world / Ideal home / Child psychology / I c one female / Uptown top ranking / Swinging / Kidnapping an heiress / Hated Sunday
4939072 / 20 Jul '98 / Chrysalis

Black Brothers

☐ WHAT A TIME (Black, Shay/Michael/ Martin)
DART 3192 / 15 Jun '98 / Dara

Black, Bud

☐ WANTED (Black, Bud & Les Muscutt)
Outside / Love nest / Chattanooga choo choo / Hello Montreal / When I lost you / I'm just wild about animal crackers / Tuck me to sleep in my old Kentucky home / I like bananas / Please / Alabamy bound / On the way to Cape May / White sport coat / My cutie's due at two to two / Nobody's baby / Bye bye blues / Kansas city kitty / Way down yonder in New Orleans / Yearning
AGGRO 101 / Jun '98 / Aggro

Black Cat Bones

☐ BARBED WIRE SANDWICH
Chauffeur / Death Valley blues / Feelin' good / Please tell me baby / Coming back / Save my love / Four women / Sylvester's blues / Good lookin' woman
SEECD 405 / May '96 / See For Miles

☐ TAYLORMADE
MMCD 99006 / Sep '97 / Music Maniac

Black, Cilla

☐ 35TH ANNIVERSARY COLLECTION
You're my world / Anyone who had a heart / I can't go on living without you / It's for you / You've lost that loving feeling / From both sides now / Alfie / Gypsies tramps and thieves / Bridge over troubled water / Conversations / Yesterday / Make it easy on yourself / Aqaurius / For once in my life / Step inside love / Love letters / Something tells me (somethings gonna happen tonight) / Liverpool lullaby / Your song / Don't answer me
4961812 / 3 Aug '98 / Music For Pleasure

☐ BEST OF THE EMI YEARS, THE
You're my world / Anyone who had a heart / Love of the loved / It's for you / You've lost that lovin' feelin' / I've been wrong before / Goin' out of my head / Love's just a broken heart / Alfie / Fool am I / Sing a rainbow / Don't answer me / When I fall in love / Yesterday / Make it easy on yourself / What good am I / I only live to love you / Step inside love / Where is tomorrow / What the world needs now is love / Conversatikons / Surround yourself with sorrow / If I thought you'd ever change your mind / Something tells me (something's gonna happen tonight) / Liverpool lullaby / Baby we can't go wrong
CDEMS 1410 / Jun '91 / EMI

☐ CILLA BLACK 1963-1973 (The Abbey Road Decade/3CD Set)
Love of the loved / Shy of love / Anyone who had a heart / Just for you / You're my world / Suffer now I must / It's for you / He won't ask me / You've lost that loving feeling / Is it love / I've been wrong before / I don't want to know / Love's just a broken heart / Yesterday / Alfie / Night time is here / Don't answer me / Right one is left / Fool am I / For no one / What good am I / Over my head / I only live to love you / From now on / Step inside love / I couldn't take my eyes off you / Where is tomorrow / Work is a four letter word / Surround yourself with sorrow / London bridge / Conversations / Liverpool lullaby / If I thought you'd ever change your mind / It feels so good / Child of mine / That's why I love you / Something tells me (Something's gonna happen tonight) / La la la lu / World I wish for you / Down in the city / You you you / Silly wasn't I / Abyssinian secret / Trees and lonliness / There I go / Time / M'Innamoro / Mon C'e Domani / Fever / Shot of rhythm and blues / (Love is like a) heatwave / Some things you never get used to / Poor boy / Shotgun / Cherry song / Please don't teach me to love you / Any time you need me / Only you can free my mind / All my love / Step inside love / Work is a four letter word / Step inside love / Your heart is free (just like the wind) / On a street called hope / Changes / Surround yourself with sorrow
CILLA 1 / 15 Sep '97 / EMI

Black, Clint

☐ GREATEST HITS
Like the rain / Summer's comin' / Good run of bad luck / State of mind / Bad goodbye: *Black, Clint & Wynonna* / Better man / Killin' time / We tell ourselves / Half way up / Burn one down / Cadillac Jack favor / Put yourself in my shoes / Wherever you go / Life get's away / No time to kill / Desperado
07863666712 / Oct '96 / RCA Nashville

☐ NO TIME TO KILL
No time to kill / Thinking again / Good run of bad luck / State of mind / Bad goodbye / Back to back / Half the man / I'll take Texas / Happiness alone / Tuckered out
07863662392 / Jul '93 / RCA

☐ NOTHIN' BUT THE TAILIGHTS
Nothin' but the tailights / That something in my life / Our kind of love / Loosen up my strings / Still holding on / Something that we do / Shoes that you're wearing / You don't need me now / What I feel inside / You know it all / Ode to chet / Bitter side of sweet
7863675152 / 1 Sep '97 / RCA

☐ ONE EMOTION
You walked by / Life gets away / One emotion / Summer's comin' / Untanglin' my mind / Hey hot rod / Change in the air / I can get by wherever you go / You made me feel / Good run of bad luck / Bad goodbye
74321229572 / Oct '94 / RCA

☐ PUT YOURSELF IN MY SHOES
Put yourself in my shoes / Gulf of Mexico / One more payment / Where are you now / Old man / This nightlife / Loving blind / Heart like mine / Good night loving
PD 90544 / Jan '90 / RCA

Black Crowes

☐ AMORICA
Gone / Conspiracy / High head blues / Cursed diamond / Non-fiction / She gave good / Sunflower / P25 London / Ballad in urgency / Wiser time / Downtown money waster / Descending / Tied up and swallowed
74321236822 / Oct '94 / American

☐ SHAKE YOUR MONEY MAKER
Twice as hard / Jealous again / Sister luck / Could I've been so blind / Seeing things / Hard to handle / Thick 'n' thin / She talks to angels / Struttin' blues / Stare it cold
74321248392 / Dec '94 / American

☐ SOUTHERN HARMONY AND MUSICAL COMPANION, THE
Sting me / Remedy / Thorn in my pride / Bad luck blue eyes goodbye / Sometimes salvation / Hotel illness / Black moon creepin' / No speak, no slave / My morning song / Time will tell
74321248402 / Dec '94 / American

☐ THREE SNAKES AND ONE CHARM
Under a mountain / Good Friday / Nebakanezer / One mirror too many / Blackberry / Girl from a pawnshop / (Only) Halfway to everywhere / Bring on, bring on / How much for your wings / Let me share the ride
74321384842 / Jul '96 / American

Black, Dick

☐ KEEP THE MUSIC GOING (Black, Dick Scottish Dance Band)
CDKBP 517 / Mar '95 / Klub

☐ STILL IN SEQUENCE (Black, Dick Scottish Dance Band)
CDKBP 518 / 24 Oct '97 / Klub

Black Dog

☐ BYTES
Object orient / Object orient / Carceres ex novum / Phil / Focus mel / Phil / Olivine / Phil / Clan (mongol nordes) / Phil / Yamenn / Phil / Fight the hits / Phil / Merck / Phil / Jauqq / 34 heart
WARPCD 8 / Apr '96 / Warp

☐ MUSIC FOR ADVERTS
PUPCD 2 / Jul '96 / Warp

☐ SPANNERS
PUPCD 1 / Jan '95 / Warp

☐ TEMPLE OF TRANSPARENT BALLS
GPRCD 1 / Jul '93 / GPR

Black, Donald

☐ WESTWIND (Scottish Mouth Organ Music)
Pipe jigs / J Scott Skinner slow airs / Cape Breton set / Slow airs / Welcome Christmas morning / Shetland reels / Pipe slow air and marches / Hebridean duet / Shores of Loch Linnhe / Slow air and pipe marches / Touch of the Irish / Lewis danns a rathad
CDTRAX 091 / Jul '95 / Greentrax

Black Dyke Mills Band

☐ BEST OF BRASS, THE
Napoli / Grandfather's clock / Crown Imperial / Grand march / Tone poem / Finlandia / Be still my soul / David of the white rock / Merry wives of Windsor / Iolanth / Hungarian march / Cornet carillon / Londonderry air / Messiah overture / Hallelujah chorus
PLSCD 251 / 27 Oct '97 / Pulse

☐ BLITZ
Blitz / Pageantry / Journey into freedom / Tam O'Shanter's ride
CHAN 8370 / Aug '85 / Chandos

☐ CATHEDRAL BRASS
Praise my soul / Cavalleria rusticana / Share my yoke / Alleluiah sing to Jesus / Procession to the minister / Day thou gavest / Trumpet Voluntary / Lost chord / Love divine / Abide with me / Morning has broken / Thine be the glory / Panis Angelicus
DOYCD 060 / Sep '97 / Doyen

☐ COMPLETE CHAMPIONS
Contest music / Royal parks / Salute to youth / Cloudcatcher fells
CHAN 4509 / Apr '92 / Chandos

☐ ESSENCE OF TIME, THE
Pondashers (march) / Circius (wind of the north) / Hinode / Maytime in madrid / Essence of time / Meiso / Toccata (oh the blessed lord) / Sweet shepherdess / Carnival of venice / A london overture
QPRL 047D / Oct '97 / Polyphonic

☐ ESSENTIAL DYKE
Queensbury / Le roi d'ts / Pandora / Deep harmony / Galop / Macushla / Capriccio Italien / Knight templar / Cornet carillon / Rule Britannia / Abide with me / Angels guard thee / Hungarian rhapsody No. 1
DOYCD 034 / Oct '94 / Doyen

☐ GREAT BRITISH MARCHES
Queensbury / Roll away Bet / Battle Abbey / ORB / Senator / Invincible / Pompous main / Cossack / Imperioso / Raby / Captain / Olympus / Knight templar
DOYCD 039 / May '95 / Doyen

☐ GREAT BRITISH TRADITION, THE
Endeavour / West country fantasy / North country fantasy / Sir Roger De Coverley / Sally in our alley / On Ilkley Moor baht'at / Fifth of August / Lincolnshire poacher / Carnival of the animals suite / Carmen fantasy
CHAN 4524 / May '93 / Chandos

☐ GREGSON - BRASS MUSIC VOL.2
Prelude for an occasion / Plantagenets / Essay / Laudate dominum / Prelude and capriccio / Concerto grosso / Partita
DOYCD 044 / Nov '95 / Doyen

☐ LION AND THE EAGLE, THE
Yeoman of the guard / Phil the fluter's ball / Land of my fathers (Hen wlad fy nhadau) / Fantasia on the dargason / Scottish lament / Will ye no' come back again / Auld lang syne / Pomp and circumstance march No.4 / Stars and stripes forever / Rhapsody on negro spirituals / Go down Moses / Peter, go ring dem bells / Every time I feel de spirit / I'm a rollin' through an unfriendly world / Stephen Foster fantasy / Camptown races / My old Kentucky home / Beautiful dreamer / Jeanie with the light brown hair / Old folks at home (Swanee river) / Oh Susanna / Old black Joe / Strike up the band / Embraceable you / They can't take that away from me / Someone to watch over me / Oh lady be good / Rhapsody in blue / Man I love
CHAN 4528 / Aug '93 / Chandos

☐ MORE OF THE WORLD'S MOST BEAUTIFUL MELODIES
Your tiny hand is frozen / Celeste Aida / Skye boat song / Bruch and Mendelssohn violin concerto themes / Flower song / Holy city / I hear you calling me / Ave Maria
CHAN 8513 / '87 / Chandos

☐ PLANETS, THE/THE MOORSIDE SUITE (Black Dyke Mills Band & The Halle Chorus)
DOYCD 050 / Dec '96 / Doyen

☐ REVELATIONS
Toccata / Revelation / Symphony for brass on a theme of Purcell / Paragon / Amparito roca / Ted Heath Big Band Set / Impromptu for tuba / Ave Maria / Carnival of Venice / March
DOYCD 046 / Jun '96 / Doyen

☐ RHAPSODY IN BRASS
Frogs / Academic festival overture / Rhapsody in brass / Prometheus unbound / Symphonic suite / Resurgam
QPRL 061D / Oct '97 / Polyphonic

☐ SACRED SYMPHONIES (Black Dyke Mills Band & Fresno Wind Ensemble)
Dawnflight / Lowry sketchbook / Toccata brillante / Revelation / Concert gallop / Symphonia sacra
DOYCD 053 / Jun '96 / Doyen

☐ SLAVONIC BRASS
Overture/The bartered bride / Polovtsian dances / Les preludes / Slavonic dance no.1 / Andante/ Symphony no.6 / Finale/Symphony no.5 / Capriccio Espagnol / Rusalka's song to the moon / Process of the sirdar / Slavonic dance no.8 / Andantino and finale/Symphony no.4 / Baba Yaga and the great gate of Kiev
QPRL 053D / Oct '97 / Polyphonic

Black Eagle Jazz Band

☐ BLACK EAGLE JAZZ BAND VOL.7
SOSCD 1224 / Oct '92 / Stomp Off

☐ BLACK EAGLE JAZZ BAND VOL.9
SOSCD 1303 / Jul '96 / Stomp Off

☐ DON'T MONKEY WITH IT
SOSCD 1147 / Oct '92 / Stomp Off

☐ SOME SWEET DAY
In the sweet bye and bye / Careless love / Perfect rag / Perdido Street blues / Ponchartrain blues / Martha / Purple rose of Cairo / Love song of the Nile / Some sweet day / Misty morning / Dreaming the hours away / Baby o' mine / Lina blues
LACD 65 / Aug '96 / Lake

Black Eg

☐ BLACK EG
Just Vincent / British gas makes it alright / Good, the bad and the ugly / Get a job / My radio / Mi-lai hotel / African disease / Drugs / Monster man / Jesus right now / Twilight zone / So easy (no new york)
CRECD 086 / May '94 / Creation

Black Family

☐ BLACK FAMILY, THE
Broom o'the Cowdenknowes / Colannon / Motorway song / Tomorrow is a long time / Donkey riding / Will ye gang, love / Bramble and the rose / Ploughboy lad / Warlike lads of Russia / Dark and roving eye / James Connolly / Wheel the perambulator
DARACD 023 / 23 Mar '98 / Dara

☐ TIME FOR TOUCHING HOME
Alabama John Cherokee / Rough ride / Old bones / Farewell to the gold / Sweet liberty / Peat bog soldiers / Weave and mend / Time alone / Song of the diggers / Since Maggie went away / First Christmas / Eliza Lee / This love will carry
DARACD 035 / Jan '94 / Dara

Black Flag

☐ DAMAGED
Rise above / Spray paint / Six pack / What I see / Tv party / Thirsty and miserable / Police story / Gimmie gimme gimme / Depression / Room 13 / Damaged il / No moe / Padded cell / Life of pain / Damaged I / Jealous again / Revenge / White minority / No values / You bet we've got / Something against you
SST 007CD / May '93 / SST

☐ EVERYTHING WENT BLACK
Gimmie gimmie gimmie / I don't care / White minority / No values / Revenge / Depression / Clocked in / Police story / Wasted / Gimmie gimmie gimmie / Depression / Police story / Clocked in / My rules / Jealous again / Police story / Damaged I / Louie louie / No moe / Room 13 / Depression / Damaged il / Padded cell / Gimmie gimmie gimmie
SST 015CD / May '93 / SST

☐ FAMILY MAN
Family man / Salt on a slug / Hollywood diary / Let your fingers do the walking / Shed reading (rattus norvegicus) / No deposit, no return / Armageddon man / Long lost dog of it / I won't stick any of you unless and until I can stick all / Account for what / Pups are doggin' it
SST 026CD / May '93 / SST

☐ FIRST FOUR YEARS, THE
Nervous breakdown / Fix me / I've had it / Wasted / Jealous again / Revenge / White minority / No values / You bet we've got something personal against you / Clocked in / Six pack / I've heard it before / American waste / Machine / Louie louie / Damaged I
SST 021CD / May '93 / SST

☐ IN MY HEAD
SST 045CD / May '93 / SST

☐ LIVE '84
Process of weeding out / Nervous breakdown / I can't decide / Slip it in / My ghetto / Black coffee / I won't stick / Forever time / Fix me / Six pack / My war / Jealous again / I love you / Swinging man / Three nights / Nothing left inside / Wound up / Rat's eyes / Bars
SST 030CD / 26 Jan '98 / SST

☐ LOOSE NUT
SST 035CD / May '93 / SST

☐ MY WAR
My war / Can't decide / Beat my head against the wall / I love you, goodbye / Forever time / Swinging man / Nothing left inside / Three nights / Scream
SST 023CD / May '93 / SST

☐ PROCESS OF WEEDING OUT
Your last affront / Screw the law / Process of weeding out / Southern rise
SST 037CD / May '93 / SST

☐ SLIP IT IN
Slip it in / Black coffee / Wound up / Rat's eyes / Obliteration / Bars / My ghetto / You're not evil
SST 029CD / May '93 / SST

☐ WASTED...AGAIN
Wasted / TV party / Six pack / I don't care / I've had it / Jealous again / Slip it in / Annihilate this week / Loose nut / Gimmie gimmie / Louie Louie / Drinking and driving
SST 166CD / May '93 / SST

☐ WHO'S GOT THE 10%
Loose nut / I'm the one / Annihilate / Wasted / Bastard in love / Modern man / This is good / Sinking / Jam / Best one yet / My war / Slip it in-gimmie, gimmie, gimmie / Drinking and driving / Louie louie
SST 060CD / May '93 / SST

Black Fork

☐ ROCK FOR LOOT
LOOKOUT 172CD / Aug '97 / Lookout

Black, Frances

☐ FRANCES BLACK & KIERAN GOSS (Black, Frances & Kieran Goss)
Wall of tears / Everybody loves a lover / Weakness in me / Cast the stone / Losin' sleep / Heard it all before / Isabelle / Forever lovin' you / Time has come / Love at a distance / Shadowing you / Time / Fallin' (I've just seen a face)
TRACD 112 / Apr '96 / Transatlantic

☐ SKY ROAD, THE
DARA 068CD / Aug '97 / Dara

☐ SMILE ON YOUR FACE, THE
TORCD 084 / Jul '97 / Dara

☐ TALK TO ME
All the lies that you have told me / Don't be a stranger / On Grafton Street / Soldiers of destiny / Talk to me while I'm listening / Intuition / Colder than Winter / Always will / Time of inconvenience / World of our own / If love had wings
7567827362 / Apr '95 / Warner Bros.
DARA 056CD / Aug '97 / Dara

Black, Frank

☐ BLACK SESSIONS, THE (Live In Paris)
ANANCD 7 / 15 Oct '97 / Anoise Annoys

☐ CULT OF RAY, THE
Marsist / Men in black / Punk rock city / You ain't me / Jesus was right / I don't want to hurt you (every single time) / Mosh, don't pass the guy / Kicked in the taco / Creature crawling / Adventure and the resolution / Dance war / Cult of Ray / Last stand of Shazeb Andleeb
4816479 / Jan '96 / Dragnet

☐ FRANK BLACK
Los angeles / I heard ramona sing / Hang on to your ego / Fu manchu / Places named after numbers / Czar / Old black dawning / Ten percenter / Brackish boy / Two spaces / Tossed (instrumental version) / Parry the wind high, lew / Adda lee / Every time I go around here / Don't ya rite 'em
GAD 3004CD / 6 Jul '98 / 4AD

☐ FRANK BLACK & THE CATHOLICS (Black, Frank & The Catholics)
All my ghosts / Back to Rome / Do you feel bad about it / Dog gone / I gotta move / I need peace / King and Queen of Siam / Six sixty six / Solid gold / Steak 'n' sabre / Suffering / Man who was too loud / All my ghosts / Living on soul / Humboldt county massacre / Changing of the guards
BIAS 370CD
BIAS 370CDX / 4 Apr '98 / Play It Again Sam

☐ PEEL SESSIONS, THE (Black, Frank & Teenage Fanclub)
Handyman / Man who was too loud / Jacques Tati / Sister Isobel
SFRSCD 042 / 8 Dec '97 / Strange Fruit

☐ TEENAGER OF THE YEAR
Whatever happened to pong / Thalassocracy / (i want to live on an) abstract plain / Calistan / Vanishing spies / Speedy marie / Headache / Sir rockaby / Freedom rock / Two reelers / Fiddle riddle / Ole mulholland / Fazer eyes / I could stay here forever / Hostess with the mostest / Superabound / Big red / Space is gonna do me good / White noise maker / Pure denizen of the citizens band / Bad, wicked world / Pie in the sky
GAD 4009CD / 6 Jul '98 / 4AD

Black Grape

☐ IT'S GREAT WHEN YOU'RE STRAIGHT... YEAH
Reverend Black Grape / In the name of the father / Tramazi parti / Kelly's heroes / Yeah yeah brother / Big day in the North / Shake well before opening / Submarine / Shake your money / Little Bob
RAD 11224 / Aug '95 / Radioactive

☐ STUPID STUPID STUPID
Get higher / Squeaky / Marbles / Dadi was a badi / Rubber band / Spotlight / Tell me something / Money back guaranteed / Lonely / Words
RARD 11716 / 10 Nov '97 / Radioactive

Black Harmony

☐ BLACK HARMONY
Party with Jesus / La cite / Aurore / Les elans du coeur / Nous tous / Esprit divin / Loue ton dieu / When the saints go marching in / Meci / La cite (dance in heaven mix)
FA 413 / Oct '96 / Fremeaux

Black Hole

☐ TIME STOPS HERE
MEYCD 13 / 2 Feb '98 / Magick Eye

Black, Ika

☐ SPECIAL LOVE
Special love / What you gonna do / Every bit of my heart / Human life / Loving vibration / Nothing but heartaches / Together now / Goodbye little man
KMCD 004 / Oct '88 / Keyman

Black Ivory

☐ BATTLE OF THE BANDS (Black Ivory/ Odds & Ends)
Don't turn around: *Black Ivory* / Surrender: *Black Ivory* / I'll find a way: *Black Ivory* / Got to be there: *Black Ivory* / Spinning around: *Black Ivory* / I keep asking you questions: *Black Ivory* / Time is love: *Black Ivory* / Find the one who loves you: *Black Ivory* / Our future: *Black Ivory* / We made it: *Black Ivory* / Just leave me some: *Black Ivory* / You and I (see today): *Black Ivory* / Foot track: *Odds & Ends* / Who could doubt my love: *Odds & Ends* / Apples, peaches, pumpkin pie: *Odds & Ends* / Let me try: *Odds & Ends* / Give me something: *Odds & Ends* / Talk that talk: *Odds & Ends* / Love makes the world go round: *Odds & Ends* / Yesterday my love: *Odds & Ends*
NEMCD 731 / Jul '97 / Sequel

Black Jack

☐ BLACK JACK
ES 1241CD / Nov '97 / Estrus

Black Jazz Chronicles

☐ FUTURE JUJU
Up and down / If the creator came today / Ancient future / Sun of my suns / Dope stuff / Snooky's spirit / Future Juju / Alien waters / World will rock / New Orleans / All Allah / One bad morning / Promises and lies
NUX 121CD / 16 Feb '98 / Nuphonic

Black Jester

☐ DIVINE COMEDY
Enigma overture / Towards the black theatre / Behind the gate / On the neon crucifixes road / Abyss / Another childhood's stake / Falling in the nightwhirl / Room after room / Requiem for an endless jigsaw / Final stage / Angel and the fisherman / Harbour of sinners / Detatching march / Tears of dew / One more time / Towards the light / Sailing in the window's life / Flying ship / Lost in the open skies / Divine parade / Epilogue for a white rose
ERO 1001 / 23 Feb '98 / Cyclops

Black, Jimmy Carl

☐ WHEN DO WE GET PAID
DIVINE 050CD / 29 Sep '97 / Taste/ Divine

Black Knights

☐ LOST KNIGHTS RETURN
BZCD 101 / Jul '98 / Booze

Black Lace

☐ 20 ALL TIME PARTY FAVOURITES
Agadoo / Hands up / Atmosphere / DISCO / We danced we danced / Wig wam bam / I just called to say I love you / Viva Espana / I am the music man / Dancing in the street / Superman / Simon says / Birdie song / Brown girl in the ring / Soaking up the sun / Let's twist again / Sailing/You'll never walk alone / Hokey cokey / Do the conga / YMCA/In the navy
BLPFCD 1 / Nov '89 / Connoisseur Collection

☐ ACTION PARTY
Agadoo / I am the music man / Wig wam bam / Hi ho silver lining / Penny arcade / Superman / Do the conga / Locomation / Hippy hippy shake / Good golly Miss Molly / Twist and shout / Do you love me / Bump / Come on Eileen / Let's dance / Do wah diddy diddy / Mandolin jivin' / Dancin' party / (We're gonna) Rock around the clock / This ole house / Birdie song / Teardrops / Knock three times / We danced we danced / Time warp
PLATCD 3915 / Apr '93 / Platinum

☐ GREATEST HITS
WAGCD 258 / 3 Aug '98 / Flair

☐ SATURDAY NIGHT
LACECD 2 / 3 Aug '98 / Flair

☐ VERY BEST OF BLACK LACE, THE
Agadoo / Superman / I am the music man / Wig wam bam / Do the conga / YMCA/In the navy / Bump / Penny arcade / Achy breaky heart / Locomotion / Hi ho silver lining / Do the bump / Clapping song / Come on Eileen
10122 / Oct '97 / Go On Deluxe

Black Lodge

☐ COVET
HNF 010CD / Mar '95 / Head Not Found

Black Lodge Singers

☐ POW WOW WOW
SPA 14286 / Nov '94 / Spalax

Black Lung

☐ DEPOPULATION BOMB, THE
NZ 036CD / May '95 / Nova Zembla

☐ EXTRAORDINARY POPULAR DELUSIONS
NZ 096 / 27 Apr '98 / Nova Zembla

☐ PSYCHOCIVILIZED SOCIETY, THE
NZ 092 / 13 Oct '97 / Nova Zembla

Black, Mary

☐ BABES IN THE WOOD
GRACD 008 / Jan '95 / Grapevine

☐ BY THE TIME IT GETS DARK
By the time it gets dark / Schoolday's over / Once in a very blue moon / Farewell farewell / Sparks might fly / Katy / Leaving the land / There is a time / Jamie / Leaboy's lassie / Trying to get the balance right
GRACD 004 / Jan '95 / Grapevine

☐ CIRCUS
GRACD 014 / Sep '95 / Grapevine

☐ COLLECTED
Mo Ghile Mear / Fare thee well my own / True love / Men o' worth / She moved through the fair / Love's endless war / Both sides of the Tweed / My youngest son came / Home today / Isle of St. Helena / Don't explain / Everything that touches me
GRACD 002 / Jan '95 / Grapevine

☐ COLLECTION, THE
Moon and St. Christopher / No frontiers / Babes in the wood / Carolina rua / Katie / Columbus / Adam at the window / Ellis island / Bright blue rose / Vanities / Only a woman's heart / Song for Ireland / Tearing up the town / There's a train that leaves tonight
GRACD 10 / Jan '95 / Grapevine

☐ HOLY GROUND, THE
GRACD 011 / Jan '95 / Grapevine

☐ MARY BLACK
Rose of Allendale / Loving you / Loving Hannah / My Donald / Crusader / Anachie Gordon / Home / God bless the child / Rare's hill
GRACD 001 / Jan '95 / Grapevine

☐ NO FRONTIERS
No frontiers / Past the point of rescue / Shadow / Carolina rua / Shuffle of the buckled / Columbus / Another day / Fat valley of pain / I say a little prayer / Vanities / Fog in the monterey
GRACD 009 / Jan '95 / Grapevine

☐ SHINE
GRACD 015 / Mar '97 / Grapevine

☐ WITHOUT THE FANFARE
There's a train that leaves tonight / State of heart / Night time / Crow on the cradle / Greatest dream / Water is wild / Ellis island / Strange thing / Without the fanfare / As I leave behind Neidin / Diamond days / Going gone
GRACD 003 / Jan '95 / Grapevine

Black Nasty

☐ TALKING TO THE PEOPLE
Talking to the people / I must be in love / Nasty soul / Getting funky round here / Black nasty boogie / We're doin' our thing / I have no choice / It's not the world / Rushin' sea / Booger the hooker
CDSXE 091 / Nov '93 / Stax

Black, Neal

☐ BLACK POWER (Black, Neal & The Healers)
DFGCD 8435 / Jun '96 / Dixie Frog

Black Oak Arkansas

☐ AIN'T LIFE GRAND
Taxman / Fancy Nancy / Keep on / Good stuff / Rebel / Back door man / Love can be found / Diggin' for gold / Crying shame / Let life be good to you
RSACD 830 / Jun '95 / Sequel

☐ EARLY TIMES
Someone something / When I'm gone / Let us pray / Sly fox / Mean woman / No one and the sun / Theatre / Collective thinking / Older than grandpa
CDSXE 067 / Nov '92 / Stax

☐ HIGH ON THE HOG
Swimmin' in quicksand / Back to the band / Movin' / Happy hooker / Red hot lovin' / Jim Dandy / Moonshine sonata / Why shouldn't I smile / High 'n' dry / Madman
RSACD 832 / Jun '95 / Sequel

☐ HOT & NASTY
Mean woman (if you ever blues) / Uncle Lijah / Hot and nasty / Lord have mercy on my soul / When electricity came to Arkansas / Keep the faith / Fever in my mind / Hot rod / Gravel roads / Mutants of the monster / Jim Dandy / Happy hooker / Son of a gunn / Dixie / Everybody wants to see heaven / Diggin' for gold / Taxman / So you want to be a rock 'n' roll star
8122711462 / Mar '93 / WEA

☐ IF AN ANGEL CAME
Gravel roads / Fertile woman / Spring vacation / We help each other / Full moon ride / Our mind's eye / To make us what we are / Our eyes are on you / Mutants of the monster
RSACD 831 / Jun '95 / Sequel

☐ KEEP THE FAITH
Keep the faith / Revolutionary all American boys / Feet on earth, head in sky / Fever in my mind / Big one's still coming / White headed woman / We live on day to day / Short life line / Don't confuse what you don't know
RSACD 828 / Jun '95 / Sequel

☐ KING BISCUIT PRESENTS...
Hot rod / Rock 'n' roll / Great balls of fire / Jim Dandy (to the rescue) / Hot and nasty / Fist full / Maybe I'm amazed / Love on ice / When the band was shakin' all over / Lord have mercy / Keep the faith / I love you more than you ever know
KBFHCD 022 / 24 Aug '98 / King Biscuit

☐ STREET PARTY
Dancing in the street / Sting me / Good good woman / Jailbait / Sure been working hard / Son of a gun / Brink of creation / I'm a man / Goin' home / Dixie / Everybody wants to see heaven / Hey y'all
RSACD 829 / Jun '95 / Sequel

Black Ocean Drowning

☐ BLACK OCEAN DROWNING
EFA 08439CD / Oct '92 / Dossier

Black Rhino

☐ PAPER ROUTE
61130708812 / 19 May '98 / RIDB

Black Rock Coalition

☐ HISTORY OF OUR FUTURE
Son talkin' (intro) / HOPE / Make it my world / Bluestime in America / Tough times / M.L.K...check / It will all / Think twice / Didn't live long / Hustler man / Son talkin' / Dadahdoodahda / Royal pain / Good guys / Michael Hill's Bluesband / Jupiter / Blue print / JJ Jumpers / Blackasaurus mex / PBR Streetgang / Shock counsel
RCD 20211 / Sep '91 / Rykodisc

Black, Roy

☐ GRAFIN MARIZA/DIE BLUME VON HAWAII
Zardas / Schwesterlein / Komm mit nach varasdin / Komm czigan / Wo wohnt die liebe / Ich mochte traumen / Gruss mir mein Wien / Braunes madel von der pussta / Sag ja mein lieb / Juliska Rosika / Eh ein kurzer mond / Einmal mocht ich wieder tanzen / Ein paradies am meeresstrand / My little boy / Blum von Hawaii / Wir singen zur jazzband / Will dir die welt zu fussen legen / Ich muss madel seh'n / My golden baby / Kann nicht kussen ohne liebe / Heute' hab' ich ein schwipserl / Ich hab' ein diwnapuppchen / Traumschone perle de Sudsee / Bin nur ein Jonny
BCD 15829 / Jan '97 / Bear Family

Black Sabbath

☐ BLACK SABBATH
Black Sabbath / Wizard / Behind the wall of sleep / NIB / Evil woman / Sleeping village / Warning
ESMCD 301 / Oct '96 / Essential

☐ BLACK SABBATH VOL.4
Wheels of confusion / Tomorrow's dream / Changes / FX / Supernaut / Snowblind / Cornucopia / Laguna sunrise / St. Vitus dance / Under the sun
ESMCD 304 / Feb '96 / Essential

☐ BORN AGAIN
Trashed / Stonehenge / Disturbing the priest / Park / Hot line / Zero the hero / Digital bitch / Born again / Keep it warm
ESMCD 334 / Apr '96 / Essential

☐ COLLECTION, THE
Paranoid / Behind the wall of sleep / Sleeping village / Warning / War pigs / Hand of doom / Planet caravan / Electric funeral / Rat salad / Iron man / After forever / Supernaut / St. Vitus dance / Wheels of confusion / Snowblind / Killing yourself to live / Sabbra cadabra / Writ
CCSCD 109 / Nov '85 / Castle

☐ CROSS PURPOSES
I witness / Cross of thorns / Psychophobia / Virtual death / Immaculate deception / Dying for love / Back to Eden / Hand that rocks the cradle / Cardinal sin / Evil eye
EIRSCD 1067 / Jan '94 / IRS/EMI

☐ ETERNAL IDOL, THE
Shining / Ancient warrior / Hard life to love / Glory ride / Born to lose / Scarlet Pimpernel / Lost forever / Eternal idol
ESMCD 336 / Apr '96 / Essential

☐ HEADLESS CROSS/TYR/DEHUMANIZER (3CD Set)
Gates of hell / Headless cross / Devil and daughter / When death calls / Kill in the spirit world / Call of the world / Black moon / Rightwing / Anno mundi / Law maker / Jerusalem / Sabbath stones / Battle of Tyr / Odin's court / Valhalla / Feels good to me / Heaven in black / Computer God / After all / TV crimes / Letters from Earth / Master of insanity / Time machine / Sins of the father / Too late / I / Buried alive
CDOMB 014 / 27 Jul '98 / IRS/EMI

☐ HEAVEN AND HELL
Neon knights / Children of the sea / Lady evil / Heaven and hell / Wishing well / Die young / Walk away / Lonely is the word
RAWCD 104 / Apr '96 / Raw Power

☐ HEAVEN AND HELL
Neon knights / Children of the sea / Lady evil / Heaven and hell / Lonely is the word / Wishing well / Die young / Walk away
ESMCD 330 / Jan '96 / Essential

☐ INTERVIEW, THE
CBAK 4071 / Feb '94 / Baktabak

☐ IRON MAN
Sabbath bloody Sabbath / Wizard / Sweet leaf / Electric funeral / Into the void / Wheels of confusion / Paranoid / Iron man / Am I going insane (Radio) / Killing yourself to live / Snowblind / Hole in the sky / Laguna sunrise / War pigs
5507202 / Sep '94 / Spectrum

☐ LEGACY (A Tribute To Black Sabbath) (Various Artists)
Warpigs: *Webstrana* / Iron man: *Mobile Whorehouse* / Supernault: *On Target* / Zonk: *Sweetleaf* / Planet caravan: *Union Carbide Productions* / Black sabbath: *Sort Sol* / Symptom of the universe: *Omnicron* / Who are you: *New Clear Family* / Paranoid: *Oven & Stone* / Tomorrow's dream: *ELD* / Sabbath bloody sabbath: *In The Colonnades* / NIB: *White Stains* / Changes: *K9 Corps* / Evil woman: *All Steel Coaches* / Into the void: *Raw Animal* / FX: *Omala*
TR 007CD / 6 Apr '98 / Tribute

☐ LIVE AT LAST
Tomorrow's dream / Sweet leaf / Killing yourself to live / Cornucopia / War pigs / Laguna sunrise / Paranoid / Wicked world
ESMCD 331 / Aug '96 / Essential

☐ LIVE EVIL
E 5150 / Neon knights / NIB / Children of the sea / Voodoo / Black Sabbath / War pigs / Iron man / Mob rules / Heaven and hell / Sign of the Southern cross / Paranoid / Children of the grave / Fluff
ESMCD 333 / Apr '96 / Essential

☐ MASTER OF REALITY
Sweet leaf / After forever / Embryo / Children of the grave / Lord of this world / Solitude / Into the void / Orchid
ESMCD 303 / Oct '96 / Essential

☐ MASTERS OF MISERY (A Black Sabbath Tribute) (Various Artists)
Shock wave: *Cathedral* / Snowblind: *Sleep* / Zero the hero: *Godflesh* / Hole in the sky: *Confessor* / Changes: *Fudge Tunnel* / Who are you: *Old* / Lord of this world: *Brutal Truth* / NIB: *Pitch Shifter* / Wizard: *Scorn* / Sweet leaf: *Cadaver* / Solitude: *Cathedral*
TFCK 88607 / Jan '95 / Toys Factory

☐ MASTERS OF MISERY (Black Sabbath Tribute Album) (Various Artists)
Wheels of confusion: *Cathedral* / Snowblind: *Sleep* / Zero the hero: *Godflesh* / Hole in the sky: *Confessor* / Killing yourself to live: *AC* / Changes: *Fudge Tunnel* / Who are you: *Old* / Lord of this world: *Brutal Truth* / Paranoid: *Ultraviolence* / NIB: *Pitch Shifter* / Wizard: *Scorn* / Cornucopia: *Iron Monkey* / Solitude: *Cathedral*
MOSH 189CD / 8 Dec '97 / Earache

☐ MOB RULES
Turn up the night / Voodoo / Sign of the Southern Cross / E5150 / Mob rules / Country girl / Slippin' away / Falling off the edge of the world / Over and over
ESMCD 332 / Jan '96 / Essential

☐ NATIVITY IN BLACK (A Tribute To Black Sabbath) (Various Artists)
After forever: *Biohazard* / Children of the grave: *White Zombie* / Paranoid: *Megadeth* / Supernaut: *1000 Homo DJ's* / Iron man: *Osbourne, Ozzy* / Lord of this world: *Corrosion Of Conformity* / Solitude: *Cathedral* / Symptom of the universe: *Sepultura* / Wizard: *Bullring Brummies* / Sabbath bloody Sabbath: *Dickinson, Bruce* / NIB: *Ugly Kid Joe* / War pigs: *Faith No More* / Black Sabbath: *Type O Negative*
4776712 / 15 Jun '98 / Epic

☐ NEVER SAY DIE
Never say die / Johnny Blade / Junior's eyes / Hard road / Shock wave / Air dance / Over to you / Breakout / Swinging the chain
ESMCD 329 / Jan '96 / Essential

☐ PARANOID
War pigs / Planet caravan / Iron man / Electric funeral / Hand of doom / Rat salad / Fairies wear boots / Wicked world / Paranoid
ESMCD 302 / Oct '96 / Essential

☐ SABBATH BLOODY SABBATH
Sabbath bloody Sabbath / National acrobat / Fluff / Sabbra cadabra / Killing yourself to live / Who are you / Looking for today / Spiral architect
ESMCD 305 / Feb '96 / Essential

☐ SABBATH STONES, THE (The IRS Years)
Headless cross / When death calls / Devil and daughter / Sabbath stones / Battle of Tyr / Odin's court / Valhalla / TV crimes / Virtual death / Evil eyes / Kiss of death / Guilty as hell / Loser gets it all / Disturbing the priest / Heart like a wheel / Shining
EIRSCD 1076 / Apr '96 / IRS/EMI

☐ SABOTAGE
Hole in the sky / Don't start (too late) / Symptom of the universe / Megalomania / Thrill of it all / Supertzar / Am I going insane (Radio) / Writ
ESMCD 306 / Feb '96 / Essential

☐ SEVENTH STAR
In for the kill / No stranger to love / Turn to stone / Sphinx (The guardian) / Seventh star / Danger zone / Heart like a wheel / Angry heart / In memory
ESMCD 335 / Apr '96 / Essential

☐ TECHNICAL ECSTASY
All moving parts (stand still) / Backstreet kids / Dirty women / Gypsy / It's alright / Rock 'n' roll doctor / She's gone / You won't change me
ESMCD 328 / Jan '96 / Essential

☐ UNDER THE WHEELS OF CONFUSION (Black Sabbath 1970-1987/4CD Set)
Black Sabbath / Wizard / Nib / Evil woman / Wicked world / War pigs / Paranoid / Iron man / Planet caravan / Hand of doom / Sweet leaf / After forever / Children of the grave / Into the void / Lord of this world / Orchid / Supernaut / Tomorrow's dream / Wheels of confusion / Am I going insane / Changes / Snowblind / Laguna surprise / Cornucopia / Sabbath bloody Sabbath / Kill yourself to live / Hole in the sky / Writ / Symptom of the universe / Dirty woman / Backstreet kids / Rock 'n' roll doctor / She's gone / Hard road / Never say die / Neon knights / Heaven and hell / Die young / Lonely is the word / Digital bitch / Trashed / Hotline / Mob rules / Voodoo / Turn up the night / Sign of the cross / Falling off the edge of the world / In for the kill / Seventh star / Heart like a wheel / Shining / Eternal idol
ESFCD 419 / Nov '96 / Essential

☐ WE SOLD OUR SOULS FOR ROCK 'N' ROLL (2CD Set)
Black Sabbath / Wizard / Warning / Paranoid / Wicked world / Tomorrow's dream / Fairies wear boots / Changes / Sweet leaf / Children of the grave / Sabbath bloody Sabbath / Am I going insane / Laguna sunrise / Snowblind / War pigs / Iron man
ESDCD 605 / 26 Jan '98 / Essential

Black Scorpio

☐ BLACK SCORPIO ALL STARS (Various Artists)
794522 / Dec '95 / Melodie

Black Sheep

☐ WOLF IN SHEEPS CLOTHING, A
Intro / U mean I'm not / Butt in the meantime / Have UNE pull / Strobelite honey / Are U mad / Choice is yours / To whom it may concern / Similak child / Try counting sheep / Flavor of the month / La menage / LASM / Gimme the finga / Hoes we knows / Go to hail / Black with NV / Pass the 40 / Blunted / For Doz that slept
8483682 / Oct '91 / Mercury

Black Slate

☐ AMIGO (The Best Of Black Slate)
Amigo / Boom boom / Sticks man '80 / Freedom time (black star liner) / Rocker's palace / Live a life / Losing game / Mind your motion / Thin line between love and hate / Sirens in the city / Legalise collie herb / Reggae everytime / Reggae music / Amigo
CDRRS 036 / Oct '96 / Jayrem

☐ GET UP AND DANCE
EXRCD 002 / Nov '95 / Elixir

Black Sorrows

☐ BETTER TIMES
Better times / Better times / Ain't love the strangest thing / A night like this / Too long gone / Stella / Steps of time / Bitter cup / Sweet inspiration / Stormwind / Resurrection
TIMBCD 601 / Aug '93 / Timbuktu

☐ LUCKY CHARM
TIMBCD 603 / Mar '95 / Timbuktu

Black, Stanley

☐ TOUCH OF LATIN, A (18 Lush & Lovely Latin American Favourites) (Black, Stanley & His Orchestra)
Granada / La macarenas / Carmen fantasy / Cancion del mar / Mexican hat dance / Siboney / Estrelita / Tropical / Cherry pink and apple blossom white / Malaguena / Cavaquinho / Solamente una vez / La bamba / Samba de orfeo / Valencia / Ay ay ay / Nostalgia / Breeze and I
306222 / Jan '97 / Hallmark

Black Sun Ensemble

☐ LAMBENT FLAME
CDRECK 11 / Oct '89 / Reckless

Black Swan Network

☐ LATE MUSIC VOL.1, THE
CAM 003CD / Jul '97 / Camera Obscura

Black Symphony

☐ BLACK SYMPHONY
RS 0072872CD / 17 Aug '98 / Rising Sun

Black Syndrome

☐ ZARATHUSTRA
MIN 05CD / Jul '96 / Minority/One

Black Tape For A Blue Girl

☐ TEARDROP
HY 39100262 / Nov '92 / Hyperium

Black Train Jack

☐ YOU'RE NOT ALONE
Handouts / Not alone / Joker / What's the deal / Struggle / Alright then / Lottery / Regrets / Back up / Reason / Mr. Walsh blues / That reminds me
RR 90172 / Sep '96 / Roadrunner

Black Uhuru

☐ ANTHEM
What is life / Party next door / Try it / Black Uhuru anthem / Botanical roots / Somebody's watching you / Bull in the pen / Elements
RRCD 41 / Jul '92 / Reggae Refreshers

☐ BLACK SOUNDS OF FREEDOM
I love King Selassie / Satan Army Band / Time to unite / Natural mystic / Edan out deh / Love crisis / African love / Hard ground / Willow tree / Sorry for the man
GRELCD 23 / Feb '97 / Greensleeves

☐ BLACK UHURU
Shine eye girl / Leaving to Zion / General penitentiary / Guess who's coming to dinner / Abortion / Natural reggae beat / Plastic smile
CDVX 1004 / Jun '89 / Virgin

☐ BRUTAL
Let us pray / Dread in the mountain / Brutal / City vibes / Great train robbery / Uptown girl / Vision / Reggae with you / Conviction or fine / Fit you haffe fit
RASCD 3015 / Jun '95 / Ras

☐ BRUTAL DUB
Let us dub / Dub in the mountain / Brutalize me with dub / City dub / Dub you haffe dub / Robbery dub / Uptown dub / Visions of dub / Dub it with you / Conviction or a dub
RASCD 3020 / Nov '92 / Ras

☐ CHILL OUT
Chill out / Darkness / Eye market / Right stuff / Mondays / Fleety foot / Wicked act / Moya (Queen of I jungle) / Emotional slaughter
RRCD 43 / Jun '88 / Reggae Refreshers

☐ DUB FACTOR, THE
Ion storm / Youth / Big spliff / Boof n baff b biff / Puffed out / Android rebellion / Apocalypse back breaker / Sodom / Slaughter
RRCD 28 / Sep '91 / Reggae Refreshers

☐ GUESS WHO'S COMING TO DINNER
Shine eye gal / Leaving to zion / General penitentiary / Guess who's coming to dinner / Abortion / Natural reggae beat / Plastic smile
HBCD 18 / Apr '88 / Heartbeat

☐ IRON STORM
Bloodshed / Colourblind affair / Dance hall vibes / Statement / Tip of the iceberg / Iron storm / Breakout / Trouble / Colourblind affair
R 279035 / Mar '94 / Mesa

☐ LIBERATION: THE ISLAND ANTHOLOGY
Chill out / Party next door / Black Uhuru anthem / Guess who's coming to dinner / Shine eye gal (live) / Sponji reggae / Wicked act / Botanical roots / Somebody's watching you / Utterance / Slaughter / I love King Selassie / Darkness-dubness / Elements / What is life / Youth of Eglington / Youth right stuff / World is Africa / Happiness (live) / Mondays-killer / Tuesday / Solidarity / Ion storm / Try it / Bull in the pen / Sinsemilla / Puff she puff / Party in session
CRNCD 1 / Feb '94 / Mango

☐ LIVE
SONCD 0080 / Nov '95 / Sonic Sounds

☐ LIVE IN NEW YORK
Brutal / Great train robbery / Sheck-a-lack - babylon release the chain / Foreign mind - many a sorrow / Fit / Let us pray / Anthem / Emotional slaughter / Solidarity
RBUCD 88000 / Aug '88 / Rohit

☐ POSITIVE DUB
Cowboy town / Firecity / Positive / My concept / Space within my heart / Dry weather house / Pain / Create
RE 159CD / Nov '94 / ROIR

☐ RAS PORTRAITS
Brutal / Fire city / Great train robbery / Dub in the mountain / Positive / Fit you haffe fit / Cowboy town / Dread in the mountain / Robbery dub / Space within your heart / Dub it with you / Painfully dub
RAS 3312 / Jul '97 / Ras

☐ RED
Youth of Eglington / Sponji reggae / Sistren / Journey / Utterance / Puff she puff / Rock stone / Carbine
RRCD 18 / Nov '90 / Reggae Refreshers

☐ REGGAE GREATS
Happiness / World is Africa / Sponji reggae / Youth of Eglington / Darkness / What is life / Bull in the pen / Elements / Push push / Right stuff
5525822 / Jul '97 / Spectrum

☐ SINSEMILLA
Happiness / World is Africa / Push push / There is fire / No loafing / Sinsemilla / Every dreadlocks / Vampire
RRCD 12 / Sep '90 / Reggae Refreshers

Black Umfolosi

☐ FESTIVAL - UMDLALO
Bazali bethu jazz song / Phetsheya kwezilwandle over the seas / Ingoma yakwethu catch our song / Inobembela njiba / Emthimbeni wedding / When shall wars / Sawelu umfula ushangane / Salu 'randela / Gumboot dance / Helele mama Afrika / Side of the city / Take me home
WCD 037 / Sep '93 / World Circuit

☐ UNITY
Umangivuka / Unity / Sizohlabelela / Sanqamula mazwe / Hour / Ngenani endelinl / Hlalanathl / Ukuthandana / Children of the frontline states / Baby noora / Umalanl / 10th anniversary / Take me home / Masiyenl / Ngiyamaz'upaba / Ngiyamvuma / Vukawendoda / I remember / Asigwabi lamadimonl / Ubankwa wezigodo
WCD 020 / Oct '91 / World Circuit

Black Voices

☐ SPACE TO BREATHE
T&M 005 / Dec '95 / Tradition & Moderne

☐ WOMEN IN (E)MOTION FESTIVAL
T&M 103 / Nov '94 / Tradition & Moderne

Black Watch Band

☐ SCOTCH ON THE ROCKS
Scotch on the rocks / Sands of time / Hundred pipers / Caller herrin' / Ye banks and braes / Will ye no' come back again / Song on the wind / Charlie is my darling / Afton water / Robin Adair / Skye boat song / Dream of peace / Papa's got a brand new bagpipe
SUMCD 4055 / Nov '96 / Summit

☐ SCOTCH ON THE ROCKS
Scotch on the rocks / Una paloma Blanca / Hoots mon / Pennsylvania 6-5000 / Y viva espania / Slaves' chorus / Patricia / Birmingham brass band / Scot in New York / SSTT (Supersonic tartan tonic) / Sons of the thistle / Dance of the cuckoo's / Lass of fyve / Pipers waltz / Do the spanish hustle / Let's go to Jersey / Windmills / Highland safari / Strike up the band / Caribbean honeymoon / Purple heather / Bump / Marines hymn
307442 / Aug '97 / Hallmark

☐ ST. ANDREW'S BALL VOL.2
SAB 220 / May '98 / St. Andrew's Ball

Black Widow

☐ BLACK WIDOW VOL.1
REP 4031 / Aug '91 / Repertoire

☐ BLACK WIDOW VOL.3
REP 4241 / Dec '97 / Repertoire

☐ BLACK WIDOW VOL.4
Sleighride / More than a day / You're so wrong / Waves / Part of a new day / When will you know / Floating / Pictures in my head / I see you
MYSCD 117 / 20 Oct '97 / Mystic

☐ SACRIFICE
In ancient days / Way to power / Come to the Sabbat / Conjuration / Seduction / Attack of the demon / Sacrifice
CLACD 262 / '91 / Castle
REP 4067 / Aug '91 / Repertoire

Blackalicious

☐ MELODICA
Swan lake / Lyric fathom / Attica black / Forty ounce / Rhymes for the deaf / Deep in the jungle
MWSSCD 001 / Apr '96 / Mo Wax

Blackbyrds

☐ ACTION/BETTER DAYS
Supernatural feeling / Lookin' ahead / Mysterious vibes / Something special / Street games / Soft and easy / Dreaming about you / Dancin' dancin' / Loneliness for your love / Better days / Do it girl / Without your love / Do you wanna dance / Love don't strike twice / What's on your mind / Don't know what to say / What we have is right
CDBGPD 090 / Nov '94 / Beat Goes Public

☐ BEST OF THE BLACKBYRDS, THE
Blackbyrds' theme / Rock creek park / Time is movin' / Don't know what to say / Love don't strike twice / Supernatural feeling / Soft and easy / Do it fluid / Walking in rhythm / Happy music / Something special / Baby / Gut level / Dreaming about you / Mysterious vibes
CDBGP 918 / Jun '88 / Beat Goes Public

☐ BLACKBYRDS/FLYING START
Do it fluid / Gut level / Reggins / Runaway / Funkie junkie / Summer love / Life styles / Hot day today / I need you / Baby / Love is love / Blackbyrds' theme / Walking in rhythm / Future children, future hopes / April showers / Spaced out
CDBGPD 86 / Jul '94 / Beat Goes Public

☐ CITY LIFE/UNFINISHED BUSINESS
Rock creek park / Thankful 'bout yourself / City life / All I ask / Happy music / Love so fine / Flying high / Hash and eggs / Time is movin' / In life / Enter in / You've got that somwthing / Party land / Lady / Unfinished business
CDBGPD 089 / Sep '94 / Beat Goes Public

Blackeyed Biddy

☐ HIGH SPIRITS
Jim mcallister's jig / Paraead nicoll of drumossle / Temple house / Ballad of sawney bean / Come by the hills / Slow air-reels / C.m. barbour / Fiddlin' around / Cobbler / Christine mcritchie / Santiano / Man's man / Winding up the piper
DUNCD 014 / Jun '88 / Dunkeld

☐ PEACE, ENJOYMENT & PLEASURE
Rolling hills of the borders / Too small a word / Silent majority / Monday morning / Ailsa ann anderson / Bonnie ship the diamond / Right to be free / Swedish waltz- the lonesome boatman / Ae fond kiss / Farewell tae the haven / Little cascade-keir's tune
CDTRAX 056 / May '93 / Greentrax

Blackfeather

☐ AT MOUNTAINS OF MADNESS
D 19716 / Oct '97 / Festival

☐ BOPPIN' THE BLUES
D 19717 / 16 Mar '98 / Festival

Blackfoot

☐ AFTER THE REIGN
CDVEST 15 / Jun '94 / Bulletproof

☐ FLYING HIGH
HF 9547 / 5 Jan '98 / Germanofon

☐ KING BISCUIT PRESENTS...
Rattlesnake rock 'n' roller / Wishing well / Teenage idol / Train train / Easy livin' / Highway song / On the run / Fly away / Livin' in the city
KBFHCD 023 / 24 Aug '98 / King Biscuit

☐ MEDICINE MAN
Doin' my job / Stealer / Sleazy world / Not gonna cry any more / Runnin' runnin' / Chilled to d'bone / Guitar slingers song and dance
CDMFN 106 / Oct '90 / Music For Nations

☐ NO RESERVATIONS
HF 9530 / 5 Jan '98 / Germanofon

Blackfoot Sue

☐ BEST OF BLACKFOOT SUE, THE
CSAPCD 123 / Jul '96 / Connoisseur Collection

Blackfoot, J.D.

☐ OHIO DREAM
59482 / 27 Apr '98 / Sisapa

☐ SONG OF CRAZY HORSE
59452 / 27 Apr '98 / Sisapa

☐ TOKALA
59442 / 27 Apr '98 / Tokala

☐ ULTIMATE PROPHECY
59472 / 27 Apr '98 / Tokala

Blackgirl

☐ TREAT U RIGHT
Krazy / Treat U right / Can U feel it / Where did we go wrong / Chains / Ooh yeh (Smooth) / 90's Girl / Nubian prince / Things we used to do / Can't live without U / Let's do it again / Home
07863663592 / Jul '94 / Arista

Blackhawk

☐ BLACKHAWK
07822187082 / Sep '94 / Arista

☐ LOVE AND GRAVITY
Love and gravity / Stepping stones / Postmarked Birmingham / Will you be there / It ain't about love anymore / Nobody's fool / If that was a lie / Hole in my heart / Hold me harmless / She dances with her shadow / Lonely boy
7822188372 / Aug '97 / Arista

☐ STRONG ENOUGH
Big guitar / Like there ain't no yesterday / Cast iron heart / I'm not strong enough to say no / Almost a memory now / King of the world / Bad love gone good / Any man with a heartbeat / Kiss is worth a thousand words / Hook, line and sinker
07822187922 / Sep '95 / Arista

Blackhouse

☐ 5 MINUTES AFTER I DIE
BHCD 5 / Aug '93 / Nuclear Blast

☐ HOPE LIKE A CANDLE
DV 12 / Aug '93 / Nuclear Blast

☐ SHOCK THIS NATION
DISC 028 / Oct '96 / Discordia

Blackmail

☐ BLACKMAIL
EFA 152212 / 1 Dec '97 / Blu Noise

Blackman, Cindy

☐ ARCANE
MCD 5341 / Sep '92 / Muse

☐ IN THE NOW
In the now / Banana for Ron / Passage / King among man / Sophia / Prince of darkness / Happy house / Strawberry for Cindy / Let love rule
HCD 7024 / Jun '98 / Highnote

☐ TRIO (Blackman, Cindy/Santi Debriano/Dave Fiuczynski)
FRLCD 015 / Oct '92 / Freelance

Blackmore, Ritchie

☐ ROCK PROFILE VOL.1 (Various Artists)
Return of the outlaws: *Outlaws* / Texan spiritual: *Outlaws* / If you gotta pick a baby: *Collins, Glenda* / Big fat spider: *Heinz* / Doo dah day: *Outlaws* / Thou shalt not steal: *Collins, Glenda* / I'm not a bad guy: *Heinz* / Ritchie Blackmore interview: *Blackmore, Ritchie* / Been invited to a party: *Collins, Glenda* / Shake with me: *Outlaws* / Movin' in: *Heinz* / Keep a knockin': *Outlaws* / I shall be released: *Boz* / Playground: *Deep Purple* / Wring that neck: *Deep Purple* / Why didn't Rosemary: *Deep Purple* / Living wreck: *Deep Purple* / Guitar job: *Blackmore, Ritchie* / No, no, no: *Deep Purple* / Highway star: *Deep Purple* / A200: *Deep Purple* / Gypsy: *Deep Purple* / Hold on: *Deep Purple* / Show me the way to go home: *Blackmore, Ritchie*
RPVSOPCD 143 / Oct '89 / Connoisseur Collection

☐ ROCK PROFILE VOL.2 (Various Artists)
Getaway: *Blackmore, Ritchie* / Little brown jug: *Blackmore, Ritchie* / Honey hush: *Sutch, Screaming Lord* / Train kept a rollin': *Sutch, Screaming Lord* / Gemini suite: guitar movement: *Lord, Jon* / Bullfrog: *Green Bullfrog* / Good golly Miss Molly: *Sutch, Screaming Lord* / Great balls of fire: *Sutch, Screaming Lord* / Hurry to the city: *Pie, Randy & Family* / Still I'm sad: *Rainbow* / Man on the silver mountain: *Rainbow* / Lady of the lake: *Rainbow* / Sixteenth century greensleeves: *Rainbow* / I call, no answer: *Green, Jack* / Son of Alerik: *Deep Purple*
RPVSOPCD 157 / Apr '91 / Connoisseur Collection

☐ SESSION MAN
RPM 120 / Oct '93 / RPM

☐ SHADOW OF THE MOON (Blackmore's Night)
Shadow of the moon / Clock ticks on / Be mine tonight / Play minstrel play / Ocean gypsy / Minstrel hall / Magical world / Writing on the wall / Renaissance faire / Memmingen / No second chance / Mond tanz / Spirit of the sea / Greensleeves / Wish you were here
0099022WHE / 6 Oct '97 / Edel
HTDCD 84 / 25 May '98 / HTD

Blacknote

☐ NOTHIN' BUT THE SWING
Core / Mahonisms / Double indemnity / Saturday night / For someone so beautiful / An open letter (to Vanessa) / J'ai beaucoup de chance (I'm so lucky) / Getting your trane on / West coastings / Two souls coalesce / I saw her first / Allergic reaction / Early morning (before dawn)
IMP 11772 / Jun '96 / Impulse Jazz

Blackout

☐ BLACKOUT
SHCD 6017 / Jul '95 / Sky High

Blackshine

☐ OUR PAIN IS YOUR PLEASURE
GUN 145CD / 6 Oct '97 / Gun

Blackstar

☐ BARBED WIRE SOUL
Game over / Smile / Sound of silence / Rock'n'roll circus / New song / Give up the ghost / Revolution of the heart / Waste of space / Deep wound / Better the Devil / Instrumental
CDVILE 69 / 29 Sep '97 / Peaceville

Blackstone

☐ BLACKSTONE
ESM 021 / 2 Mar '98 / Escape

Blackstone Edge

☐ GYPSY
GRACD 001 / Feb '96 / Granite

Blackstones

☐ OUTBURST
CDSGP 0219 / Nov '95 / Prestige

☐ RIDIN' HIGH
CDSGP 0274 / Sep '96 / Prestige

☐ SOMEBODY OUGHT TO WRITE ABOUT IT
CDSGP 0334 / Mar '97 / Prestige

Blackstreet

☐ ANOTHER LEVEL
Black and Street intro / This is how we roll / No diggity: *Blackstreet & Dr. Dre* / Fix / Good lovin' / Let's stay in love / We gonna take you back/Don't leave me / Never gonna let you go / I wanna be your man / Taja's lude / My paradise / Deja's poem / (Money can't) Buy me love / Blackstreet on the radio / I can't get you (out of my mind) / I'll give it to you / Happy song (tonite) / Motherlude / Lord is real (time will reveal)
IND 90071 / Oct '96 / Interscope

☐ BLACKSTREET
Intro (Blackstreet philosophy) / Baby be mine / U blow my mind / Hey love (keep it real) / I like the way you work / Good life / Physical thing / Make U wet / Booti call / Love's in need / Joy / Before I let you go / Confession (interlude) / Tonight's the night / Happy home / Wanna make love / Once in a lifetime / Givin' you all my lovin' / Falling in love again / Candlelight night
IND 92351 / Aug '96 / Interscope

Blackthorne

☐ AFTERLIFE
Cradle of the grave / Afterlife / We won't be forgotten / Breaking the chains / Over and over / Hard feelings / Baby you're the blood / Sex crime / Love from the ashes / All night long
DERCD 089 / 2 Mar '98 / Derock

☐ VERY BEST OF IRISH TRADITIONAL FOLK MUSIC, THE
CDBALLAD 007 / Mar '97 / Outlet

Blacktop

☐ I GOT A BAAD FEELIN
ITR 027CD / Dec '96 / In The Red

Blacktop Rockets

☐ MAKE MINE A DOUBLE
BR 002 / May '98 / Straight 8

☐ WHAT'LL YA HAVE
BR 001 / Apr '97 / Straight 8

Blackwell

☐ TRIBUTE TO BLACKWELL (Various Artists)
1201132 / Nov '90 / Black Saint

Blackwell, Ed

☐ WALLS-BRIDGES (Blackwell, Ed Trio)
1201532 / Mar '97 / Black Saint

☐ WHAT IT BE LIKE
Nebula / Grandma's shoes / Pentahouve / First love / Lito (Part 1,2,3,)
ENJ 80542 / Jul '94 / Enja

Blackwell, Otis

☐ BRACE YOURSELF (A Tribute To Otis Blackwell) (Various Artists)
SHCD 5705 / Apr '94 / Shanachie

☐ OTIS BLACKWELL 1953-1955 (The Complete Joe Davis Sessions)
FLYCD 26 / Feb '91 / Flyright

Blackwell, Scrapper

☐ VIRTUOSO GUITAR
Kokomo blues / Kokomo blues / Good woman blues / My dream blues / Hard time blues / Penal farm blues / Down in black bottom / Pack up her trunk blues / Back door blues / Blue day blues / Whiskey man blues / Trouble blues (part 1) / Trouble blues (part 2) / Barrelhouse woman no. 2
YAZCD 1019 / Apr '91 / Yazoo

Blackwood Singers

☐ GREATEST GOSPEL
I believe / Spirit of the living God / Glory glory clear the road / First day in heaven / House of God / This olde house / When the saints go marching in / Jonah / Amazing grace / I'll fly away / Yesterday / No further than your knees
HADCD 171 / May '94 / Javelin

Blad, Nikolai

☐ NIKOLAI BLAD
EICD 4 / Mar '96 / Eino

Blade

☐ ALWAYS
Always / Time / Psycho killers / Slow horse / Drug city / I still want you / Honey love / Life in the city / Hard to find / Life
IYFCD 11 / 15 Sep '97 / In Yer Face

☐ PLANNED AND EXECUTED
BLADE 1208CD / Jan '96 / Move/691 Influential

Blade, Brian

☐ BRIAN BLADE FELLOWSHIP, THE
Red river / Undertow / Folklore / In spite of everything / Life line / Mohavi / Lura / Loving without asking
8594172 / 4 May '98 / Blue Note

Blade Fetish

☐ ABSINTHE
EFA 064802 / Mar '94 / Tess

Blades, Ruben

☐ AGUA DE LUNA
Isobel / No te Duermas / Blackaman / Ojos de Perro Azul / Claro Oscuro / Laura Farina / La cita / Agua de luna
15964 / Sep '89 / Messidor

☐ ANTECEDENTE (Blades, Ruben Y Son Del Solar)
Juana mayo / 'Tas caliente / La marea / Contrabando / Patria / Noches del ayer / Nuestro adios / Nacer de ti / Plaza herrera
15993 / Aug '89 / Messidor

☐ ESCENAS
Cuentas del alma / Tierra dura / La cancion del final del mundo / La sorpresa / Caina / Silencois / Muevete
1115939 / Jan '87 / Messidor

Blaenavon Male Voice Choir

☐ NEW DAY, A
Sailor's chorus / You are the new day / Diolch i'r Ior / Oh Isis and Osiris / There is nothing like a dame / Sometimes / A ca / Pan fo'r nos yn hir / George Jones / Myfanwy / Rhythm of life / Sanctus / Men of Harlech / Softly as I leave you / Migildi magildi / Tydi a roddaist / When the saints go marching in / Nidaros
OS 222 / Jul '96 / OS Digital

Blaggers ITA

☐ FUCK FASCISM
KONCD 002 / Mar '97 / Knock Out

☐ ON YER TOEZ (Blaggers)
On yer toez / Crazy / Bronco bullfrog / Nice one blaggers / Britain's dreams / Young blaggers / Weekend warriors / Save your hate / Jailhouse doors
MBC 001CD / 22 Jun '98 / M-Butcher

☐ UNITED COLOURS
WOWCD 27 / '94 / Words Of Warning

Blahzay Blahzay

☐ BLAH BLAH BLAH
5329672 / Sep '96 / Mercury Black Vinyl

Blaine, Terry

☐ IN CONCERT (Blaine, Terry & Mark Shane Quintet)
JJZ 9502 / Nov '96 / Jukebox

☐ WHOSE HONEY ARE YOU
JJZ 9201 / Nov '96 / Jukebox

Blair 1523

☐ BEAUTIFUL DEBRIS
VOXXCD 2060 / Mar '93 / Voxx

Blair, Ric

☐ ALWAYS BY MY SIDE
SCD 0619 / Oct '97 / FMG

Blak, Kristian

☐ KINGOLOG
HJF 16CD / Aug '97 / Tutl

☐ SHALDER GEO/TJALDURSGJOGV
HJF 44CD / Dec '97 / Tutl

Blak Twang

☐ 19 LONGTIME
BJAM 0003 / 8 Jun '98 / Black Jam

☐ DETTWORK SOUTH EAST
ANTICDLP 3 / Jan '97 / Anti-Static

Blake & Brian

☐ ANOTHER PERFECT DAY
CURCD 057 / 15 Jun '98 / Curb

Blake, Al 'Big'

☐ MR. BLAKE'S BLUES (Blake, Big Al & The Hollywood Fats Band)
BCM 7108 / Dec '97 / Blue Collar

Blake, Arthur 'Blind'

☐ BLIND BLAKE VOL.1
DOCD 5024 / Nov '93 / Document

☐ MASTER OF RAGTIME GUITAR, THE
IGOCD 2046 / Aug '96 / Indigo

Blake, Eubie

☐ MEMORIES OF YOU
Charleston rag / Chevy chase / Mirandy / Fizz water / Crazy blues / Memphis blues / Dangerous blues / Arkansas blues / Down home blues / Good fellow blues / Don't tell your monkey man / Boll weevil blues / If you don't want me blues / I'm just wild about Harry / Memories of you
BCD 112 / Jul '91 / Biograph

Blake, Karl

☐ MANDIBLES
SHP 616131/01CD / Oct '96 / Swordex Hieroglyph Proper

☐ PAPER THIN RELIGION
USEO 13102CD / Oct '96 / Pro-Evil Pro-Devil

Blake, Kenny

☐ INTERIOR DESIGN
Hey mister / Take five / What can I say / Irene / Little stars / Harlem nocturne / Alladin / Babylon sisters / Soulmates / Oasis
101S 71342 / Jun '93 / 101 South
INAK 30112CD / Nov '97 / In Akustik

☐ INTIMATE AFFAIR, AN
Intimate affair / Sunday serenade / European underground / Stand a little closer / ABC / Contemplation swing / Heartland to soulville / Every time I think of u / Constantinople strut / Shady side / Steeltown
INAK 30372CD / Jul '97 / In Akustik

☐ RUMOUR HAS IT
INAK 30142CD / Nov '97 / In Akustik

☐ SINCE YOU ASKED
Kiss / Large and in charge / Amy / Once not once / Windfall / La Puerta (The door) / Next with me / Alice's song / Best of my love / One to another / What's new / Little sunflower
INAK 30232CD / Nov '97 / In Akustik

Blake, Michael

☐ KINGDOM OF CHAMPA
Champa theme / Dislocated in Natran / Folksong / Purple city / Mekong / Hue is hue / Perfume river
INT 31892 / Jun '97 / Intuition

Blake, Norman

☐ BACK HOME IN SULPHUR SPRINGS
ROUCD 0012 / Nov '95 / Rounder

☐ BLAKE AND RICE (Blake, Norman & Tony Rice)
ROUCD 0233 / Aug '88 / Rounder

☐ BLIND DOG (Blake, Norman & Nancy)
Little stream of whiskey / Grand coulee dam / Prettiest little girl in the country / Billy gray / Otto wood the bandit / Blind dog / Everybody works but father / Fifty miles of elbow room / Shellegra / Old time farmer / Wreck of the old '97 / Black mountain rag
ROUCD 0254 / '90 / Rounder

☐ CHATTANOOGA SUGAR BABE
Rescue from Moose river golmine / Weathered old caboose behind the train / Ol' Bill Miner (the gentleman bandit) / Poor old dad / Chattanooga sugar babe / Platonia the pride of the plains / Dr. Edmundo's favorite Portugese waltz / Founding of the famous GPR / Paramount rag / Keep smiling old pal / Bulmullo house/Broke down gambler / Ragtime Texas / Chattanooga rag / Dixie flyer blues
SHANCD 6027 / May '98 / Shanachie

☐ FIELDS OF NOVEMBER/OLD & NEW
FF 004CD / May '93 / Flying Fish

☐ HOBO'S LAST RIDE, THE (Blake, Norman & Nancy)
SHCD 6020 / Sep '96 / Shanachie

☐ JUST GIMME SOMETHIN' I'M USED TO (Blake, Norman & Nancy)
SHCD 6001 / Apr '92 / Shanachie

☐ NATASHA'S WALTZ (Blake, Norman & Nancy)
New brick road / Dusty rose / Walnut river / Pig on the engine / Third street gypsy rag / Georgia home / Peezlewhister / Old fiddler's roll call / Pueblo / Tonealty / Natasha's waltz / Blake's march / Texola waltz / Diamonds in the rough / Jeff davis / Nancy's hornpipe / Three ravens / Sleepy-eyed joe / Cairo waltz / Davenport march / Obc no.3
ROUCD 11530 / '88 / Rounder

☐ NORMAN & NANCY BLAKE COMPACT DISC
Hello stranger / New bicycle hornpipe / Marquis Huntley / Florida rag / Jordan am a hard road to travel / Belize / Elzic's farewell / Lighthouse on the shore / Grand junction / Butterfly weed / President Garfield's hornpipe / In Russia (we have parking lots too) / Wroxall / If I lose I don't care / Chrysanthemum / Lima road jig / Boston boy / Last night's joy / My love is like a red rose / Wildwood flower / Tennessee mountain fox chase
ROUCD 11505 / '88 / Rounder

☐ NORMAN BLAKE & TONY RICE VOL.2 (Blake, Norman & Tony Rice)
It's raining here this morning / Lost Indian / Georgie / Father's hall / Two soldiers / Blackberry blossom / Eight more miles to Louisville / Lincoln's funeral train (The sad journey to Springfield) / Molly Bloom / D-18 Song (Thank you, Mr. Martin) / Back in yonder's world / Bright days / Salt creek
ROUCD 0266 / Jul '90 / Rounder

☐ SLOW TRAIN THROUGH GEORGIA
Fiddler's dram-whiskey before breakfast / Slow train through georgia / Old grey mare / Down home summertime blues / Spanish fandango / Randall collins / Church street blues / Done gone / Bully of the town / Nashville blues / Ginseng sullivan / Macon rag / Nobody's business / Streamline cannonball / Cattle in the cane / Little joe / Weave and way / Six white horses / Richland avenue (front porch wood pile) rag / Banks of good hope-the green fields of america / Columbus stockade blues / Down at milow's house
ROUCD 11526 / '88 / Rounder

☐ WHILE PASSING ALONG THIS WAY (Blake, Norman & Nancy)
SHAN 6012CD / Apr '95 / Shanachie

☐ WHISKEY BEFORE BREAKFAST
Hand me down my walking cane / Under the double eagle / Six white horses / Salt river / Old grey mare / Down at Mylow's house / Sleepy eyed Joe / Indian creek / Arkansas traveller / Girl I left in Sunny Tennessee / Mistrel boy to war has gone / Ash grove / Church Street blues / Macon rag / Fiddler's dream / Whiskey before breakfast / Slow train through Georgia
ROUCD 0063 / Aug '93 / Rounder

Blake, Perry

☐ PERRY BLAKE
Little boys and little girls / Hunchback of San Francisco / 1971 / Anouska (I want to come home) / Broken statue / Genevieve (the pilot of your thighs) / So long / Naked man / Widows by the radio / Weeping tree / House in the clouds
5376092 / 11 May '98 / Polydor

Blake, Peter

☐ PRIVATE DAWN
WCL 110082 / May '95 / White Cloud

Blake, Ran

☐ DUKE DREAMS
RN 1210272 / Oct '94 / Soul Note

☐ EPISTROPHY
1211772 / Sep '92 / Soul Note

☐ THAT CERTAIN FEELING
ARTCD 6077 / Jul '91 / Hat Art

☐ UNMARKED VAN (A Tribute To Sarah Vaughan)
Sarah / My reverie / Sometimes I feel like a Motherless child / Tenderly / Make yourself comfortable / Tenderly / Solitary Sunday / My man's gone now / Old devil moon / Homage to Roy Haynes / Whatever Lola wants / Wallflower waltz / Tenderly / April / April / Call me / Moonlight on the Ganges / Girl from Ipanema / Stompin' at the Savoy / Little tear / Septembro / Unmarked man / Tenderly
1212272 / May '97 / Soul Note

Blake, Seamus

☐ CALL, THE
1088CD / Jan '95 / Criss Cross

Blake, Tim

☐ BLAKE'S NEW JERUSALEM
MANTRA 068 / 1 Jun '98 / Mantra

☐ CRYSTAL MACHINE
MANTRA 067 / 1 Jun '98 / Mantra

☐ MAGICK
MANTRA 069 / 1 Jun '98 / Mantra

Blake, Tomcat

☐ I'VE BEEN WONDERING
DTCD 3037 / Jan '97 / Double Trouble

Blakey, Art

☐ 1958: PARIS OLYMPIA (Blakey, Art & The Jazz Messengers)
Just by myself / I remember Clifford / Are you real / Moanin' / Justice / Blues march / Whisper not
8326592 / Feb '92 / Fontana

☐ ART BLAKEY & THE JAZZ MESSENGERS (Blakey, Art & The Jazz Messengers)
Alamode / Invitation / Circus / You don't know what love is / I hear a rhapsody / Gee baby ain't I good to you
IMP 11752 / Feb '96 / Impulse Jazz

☐ ART BLAKEY IN CONCERT
RTE 15022 / Apr '95 / RTE/Europe 1

☐ ART COLLECTION (The Best Of Art Blakey)
Fuller love / Oh, by the way / Webb City / Second thoughts / In walked Bud / Dark side, light side / Jody
CCD 4495 / Jan '92 / Concord Jazz

☐ BEST OF ART BLAKEY & THE JAZZ MESSENGERS, THE (Blakey, Art & The Jazz Messengers)
Moanin' / Blues march / Lester's left town / Night in Tunisia / Dat dere / Mosaic / Free for all
CDP 7932052 / Dec '95 / Blue Note

☐ BEST OF ART BLAKEY, THE
Generique / No problem / Moanin' / I remember Clifford / Whisper not / Night in Tunisia / My romance / Blues march
8482452 / Jun '91 / EmArCy

☐ BIG BAND
BET 6002 / Jan '95 / Bethlehem

☐ BIG BEAT, THE (Blakey, Art & Max Roach/Elvin Jones/Philly Joe Jones)
Caravan / High priest / Theme / Conversation / Jody's cha-cha / Larry-Larue / Lady luck / Buzz-at / Pretty Brown / Six and four / Stablemates / Carioca ("El Tambores") / Battery blues / Gone gone gone / Tribal message
MCD 47016 2 / Apr '94 / Milestone

☐ BLAKEY 60 (The Best Of Art Blakey & The Jazz Messengers) (Blakey, Art & The Jazz Messengers)
It's only a paper moon / Dat dere / Night in Tunisia / So tired / Ping pong / Witch doctor / Freedom rider / Afrique / Little busy / Giantis
4930722 / 11 May '98 / Blue Note

☐ BLUES MARCH (Blakey, Art & The Jazz Messengers)
Summit / Along came Betty / Lester left town / Blues march / Nellie Bly / It's only a paper moon
JHR 73539 / May '93 / Jazz Hour

☐ BUHAINA (Blakey, Art & The Jazz Messengers)
Moanin' / Chant for Bu / One for Trane / Mission eternal / Along came Betty / Gertrude's bounce
BGPD 1114 / 24 Nov '97 / Beat Goes Public

☐ DAY WITH ART BLAKEY VOL.1
Summit / Breeze and I / Blues march / Moanin' / It's only a paper moon
PRCDSP 201 / Aug '93 / Prestige

☐ DRUM KING (Modern Classics From A Jazz Legend)
Right down front / Sweet sakeena / Late spring / Pristine / For miles and miles / For minors only / Deox / Krafty / Tippin'
308112 / 13 Oct '97 / Hallmark

☐ DRUM KINGS (Blakey, Art & Max Roach)
Transfiguration / Exhibit A / Scotch blues / Rhapsody in blue / Summertime / Someone to watch over me / Man I love / Flight to Jordan / That old devil called love again / Four x / Crackle hut / CM / Speculate / Audio blues
306292 / Jan '97 / Hallmark

☐ DRUM SUITE
Sacrifice / Cubano chant / Oscarlypso / Nica's tempo / D's dilemma / Just for Marty
809882 / Mar '96 / Columbia

☐ FREEDOM RIDER
Tell it like it is / Freedom rider / El toro / Petty Larceny / Blue lace / Uptight / Pisces / Blue ching
8212872 / 19 Jan '98 / Blue Note

☐ HARD DRIVE, THE (Out Of This World...And The Next World Too) (Blakey, Art & The Jazz Messengers)
BET 6001 / Jan '95 / Bethlehem

☐ I GET A KICK OUT OF BU (Blakey, Art & The Jazz Messengers)
1211552 / Nov '90 / Soul Note

☐ IN SWEDEN (Blakey, Art & The Jazz Messengers)
Webb City / How deep is the ocean / Skylark / Gypsy folk tales
ECD 22044 / Mar '93 / Evidence

☐ **JAZZ GREATS (Blakey, Art & The Jazz Messengers)**
On the street where you live / Night in Tunisia / Theory of Art / Moanin' / Lester left town
74321556862 / Feb '98 / RCA Victor

☐ **JAZZ MASTERS (Blakey, Art & The Jazz Messengers)**
Dat dere / Blues march / Lester left town / Night in Tunisia / Moanin'
4934672 / 16 Feb '98 / EMI Jazz

☐ **JAZZ MESSENGERS (Blakey, Art & The Jazz Messengers)**
Sacrifice / Cubano chant / Oscalypso / Nica's tempo / D's dilemma / Just for Marty
4809882 / Dec '95 / Sony Jazz

☐ **JAZZ MESSENGERS, THE**
Infra-rae / Nica's dream / It's you or no one / Ecaroh / Carol's interlude / End of a love affair / Hank's symphony / Weird-o / Ill wind / Late show / Deciphering the message / Carol's interlude
CK 65265 / 1 Sep '97 / Sony Jazz

☐ **KYOTO**
High priest / Never never land / Wellington's blues / Nihon bash / Kyoto
OJCCD 145 / Feb '92 / Original Jazz Classics

☐ **LAUSANNE 1960 VOL.1 (Blakey, Art & The Jazz Messengers)**
Now's the time / Announcement / Lester left town / Noise in the attic / Dat dere / Kozo's waltz
TCB 02022 / Jul '95 / TCB

☐ **LAUSANNE 1960 VOL.2 (Blakey, Art & The Jazz Messengers)**
Announcement / It's only a paper moon / 'Round midnight / Summit / Night in Tunisia / This here
TCB 02062 / Jul '96 / TCB

☐ **LEGACY OF ART BLAKEY, THE (Jazz Messengers)**
One by one / A la mode / Whisper not / Oh by the way / Plexus / Blues march
CD 83407 / May '98 / Telarc

☐ **LIVE AT BUBBA'S**
Moanin' / My funny valentine / Soulful Mister Timmons / Au privave / Free for all
CDGATE 7003 / Oct '90 / Kingdom Jazz

☐ **LIVE AT MONTREUX AND NORTHSEA/ IN MY PRIME I/CHIPPIN' IN (3CD Set)**
Minor thesis / Wheel within a wheel / Bit a bitadose / Stairway to heaven / Linwood / Jodie / 1978 / To see her face / Life every voice and sing / Hawkman / People who laugh / Time will tell / Reflections in blue / ETA / Brainin' stormin' / Byrdflight / Hammerhead / Aquarius rising / Kay pea / Chippin' in / Raincheck / Chandek's den / Kenji's walk / Love walked in
SJP 011 / 26 May '98 / Timeless

☐ **LIVE IN STOCKHOLM 1959**
DRGCD 182 / Oct '88 / Dragon

☐ **MELLOW BLUES (Blakey, Art & The Jazz Messengers)**
MCD 0322 / Jan '92 / Moon

☐ **MIDNIGHT SESSION (Blakey, Art & The Jazz Messengers)**
Casino / Biddie griddies / Potpourri / Ugh / Mirage / Reflections of Buhainia
SV 0145 / Oct '97 / Savoy Jazz
CY 18059 / 13 Apr '98 / Savoy Jazz

☐ **MOANIN' (Blakey, Art & The Jazz Messengers)**
Moanin' / Moanin' / Are you real / Along came Betty / Drum thunder suite / Blues march / Come rain or come shine / Slide's delight / You don't know what love is / Blues for Eros / Blue moon / Theme song
CDP 7465162 / Mar '95 / Blue Note

☐ **MOANIN'**
Slide's delight / You don't know what love is / Blues for Eros / Moanin' / Blue moon / Theme
17127 / May '97 / Laserlight

☐ **NIGHT IN TUNISIA, A (Blakey, Art & The Jazz Messengers)**
Night in Tunisia / Moanin' / Blues march
8000642 / Jul '88 / Philips

☐ **OH BY THE WAY (Blakey, Art & The Jazz Messengers)**
Oh by the way / Duck soup / Tropical breeze / One by one / Sudan blue / My funny valentine / Alicia
CDSJP 165 / Feb '92 / Timeless Jazz

☐ **ONE FOR ALL (Blakey, Art & The Jazz Messengers)**
Here we go / One for all (and all for one) / Theme for Penny / You've changed / Accidentally yours / Medley / Green is mean / I'll wait and pray / Logarhythms / Bunyip / Polka dots and moonbeams / Nica's tempo
3953292 / Mar '94 / A&M

☐ **ORGY IN RHYTHM**
Buhaina chant / Ya ya / Toffi / Split skins / Amuck / Elephant walk / Abdullah's delight
CDP 8565862 / Jun '97 / Blue Note

☐ **RUCERDO (Blakey, Art & The Jazz Messengers)**
CDSGP 0108 / May '96 / Prestige

☐ **STRAIGHT AHEAD**
Falling in love with love / My romance / Webb City / How deep is the ocean / ETA / Theme
CCD 4168 / Oct '90 / Concord Jazz

☐ **THEORY OF ART (Blakey, Art & The Jazz Messengers)**
Night in Tunisia / Off the wall / Couldn't it be you / Theory of Art / Evans / Night at Tony's / Social call
09026687302 / Mar '97 / RCA Victor

☐ **THIS IS JAZZ**
Moanin / Nica's dream / Little Melonae / Hank's symphony / Nica's tempo / I remember Clifford
CK 65044 / May '97 / Sony Jazz

☐ **UGETSU**
One by one / Ugetsu / Time off / Ping pong / I didn't know what time it was / On the ginza
OJCCD 90 / Feb '92 / Original Jazz Classics

Blakey, Rev. Johnny

☐ **1927-1929 (Blakey, Rev. Johnny & Rev. M.L. Gipson)**
DOCD 5363 / Jul '95 / Document

Blakulla

☐ **BLAKULLA**
APM 9717 / 15 Dec '97 / APM

Blame

☐ **LOGICAL PROGRESSION SESSIONS VOL.2 (Various Artists)**
Sunstars: *Artemis* / Object: *Odyssey* / Centuries: *Blame* / Algebra: *Total Science* / Beneath the surface: *PHD* / Butterflies and moths: *Blu Mar Ten* / Orbiting probes: *KMC* / Ritual: *Odyssey* / Between worlds: *Blame*
GLRPS 002 / 27 Jul '98 / Good Looking

☐ **LOGICAL PROGRESSION VOL.2 (Mixed/Compiled By Blame - 2CD Set) (Various Artists)**
Visions of Mars: *Blame* / Expressions: *Odyssey* / Seafarer: *Artemis* / Solitude: *Blame* / West side blues: *Intense* / Dreams: *Tayla* / Breeze: *Nookie* / Global access: *Blu Mar Ten* / Cuban Lynx: *Blame* / Close your eyes: *Chameleon* / Love and happiness: *PFM* / Positive notions: *Intense* / Universal music: *Seba* / In the area: *Ils & Solo* / Atlantis (I need you): *LTJ Bukem* / 360 Click: *Blame* / Complexities: *Source Direct* / Dark skies: *Intense*
GLRCD 002 / Apr '97 / Good Looking
GLRCDX 002 / 27 Apr '98 / Good Looking

Blanc Estoc

☐ **MISTUCK**
WB 1164CD / Jun '97 / We Bite

Blanca, Peres

☐ **STRICTLY DANCING: RHUMBA (Blanca, Peres Band)**
15338 / Jun '92 / Laserlight

Blanchard, Terence

☐ **HEART SPEAKS, THE**
Aparecida / Antes que seja tarde / Meu pais (my country) / Valse Mineira / Heart speaks / Congada blues / Nocturna / Just for Nana / Orizimba and Rosicler / Choros das aguas / Love dance/Comecar de novo / Menino / Aparecida reprise
4836382 / 26 Jan '98 / Sony Jazz

☐ **NEW YORK SECOND LINE (Blanchard, Terence & Donald Harrison)**
New York second line / Oliver Twist / I can't get started (with you) / Duck steps / Dr. Drums / Isn't it so / Subterfuge
CCD 43002 / '88 / Concord Jazz

☐ **ROMANTIC DEFIANCE**
Premise / Unconditional / Betrayal of my soul / Divine order / Romantic defiance / Focus / Romantic processional / Morning after / Celebration
4804892 / Jun '95 / Sony Jazz

Blancmange

☐ **BEST OF BLANCMANGE, THE**
VSOPCD 226 / Jun '96 / Connoisseur Collection

☐ **MANGE TOUT**
Don't tell me / Game above my head / Blind vision / Time became the tide / That's love that it is / Murder / See the train / All things are nice / My baby / Day before you came
5521082 / Mar '96 / Spectrum

☐ **SECOND HELPINGS (Best Of Blancmange)**
God's kitchen / I've seen the world / Feel me / Living on the ceiling / Waves / Game above my head / Blind vision / That's love that it is / Don't tell me / Day before you came / What's your problem
8280432 / Jun '90 / London

☐ **THIRD COURSE, THE**
Feel me / I've seen the world / God's kitchen / I can't explain / Waves / Lose your love / No wonder they never made it back / Day before you came / All things are nice / Running thin / Game above my head / Wasted / Get out of that / Lorraine's my nurse
5501942 / Mar '94 / Spectrum

Bland, Bobby

☐ **BLUES IN THE NIGHT**
Blue moon / If I hadn't called you back / Ask me 'bout nothin' (but the blues) / Jelly jelly / When you put me down / Blind man / Chains of love / Fever / Blues in the night / Loneliness hurts / Feeling is gone / I'm too far gone (to turn around) / Black night / Share your love with me
CD 14531 / Jan '94 / Jazz Portraits

☐ **CALIFORNIA ALBUM**
This time I'm gone for good / Up and down world / It's not the spotlight / (If loving you is wrong) I don't want to be right / Going down slow / Right place at the right time / Help me through the day / Where baby went / Friday the 13th child / I've got to use my imagination
BGOCD 64 / Jan '89 / Beat Goes On

☐ **DREAMER**
Ain't no love in the heart of the city / I wouldn't treat a dog (the way you treated me) / Lovin' on borrowed time / End of the road / I ain't gonna be the first to cry / Dreamer / Yolanda / Twenty four hour blues / Cold day in hell / Who's foolin' who
BGOCD 63 / Oct '89 / Beat Goes On

☐ **LIVE AT LONG BEACH**
Mel's groove (instrumental) / Ain't that lovin' you / I'll take care of you / Soul of a man / I intend to take your place / Soon as the weather breaks / Today I started loving you again / Share your love with me / Recess in heaven / That's the way love is-ain't nothin' you can do (medley) / Feeling is gone-stormy monday blues (medley) / Farther up the road
CDBL 750 / Nov '94 / Charly

☐ **TOGETHER AGAIN - LIVE (Bland, Bobby & B.B. King)**
Let the good times roll / Strange things happen / Feel so bad / Mother in law blues / Mean ol' world / Everyday I have the blues / Thrill is gone / I ain't gonna be the first to cry
BGOCD 162 / Feb '93 / Beat Goes On

☐ **TWO STEPS FROM THE BLUES**
Cry cry cry / Two steps from the blues / I pity the fool / I'll take care of you / I'm not ashamed / Don't cry no more / Lead me on / I've just got to forget you / Little boy blue / St. James infirmary
BGOCD 163 / Feb '93 / Beat Goes On

☐ **VOICE, THE (Duke Recordings 1959-1969)**
Who will the next fool be / I pity the fool / Don't cry no more / Ain't that lovin' you / I'm not ashamed / Cry cry cry / I'll take care of you / Call on me / Blue moon / Turn on your love light / Stormy Monday blues / Two steps from the blues / Ain't nothin' you can do / Ain't doing too bad Part 1 / Sometimes you gotta cry a little / Ain't no tellin' / Yield not to temptation / I'm too far gone (to turn around) / These hands / Good time Charlie Part 1 / Ask me 'bout nothin' (but the blues) / Share your love with me / That did it / Shoes / Back in the same old bag again / Chains of love
CHCD 323 / Nov '93 / Ace

Blanks 77

☐ **KILLER BLANKS**
700122 / Mar '97 / Radical

☐ **TANKED AND POGOED**
RAD 700152 / Jul '97 / Radical

Blanston, Gern

☐ **GERN BLANSTON**
CSR 014CD / Oct '95 / Cavity Search

Blarney Lads

☐ **SEVEN DRUNKEN NIGHTS**
Bold O'Donaghue / Paddle me own canoe / Molly Malone / Doherty's reel / Paddy Ryan's dream / McGinnelly's reel / Ferryman / Cod liver oil / Coolies / Home boys home / Father O'Flynn / Irish washerwoman / Blackberry blossom / Lannigan's ball / All for me grog / Wild rover / Galway races / An dearig dun / Welcoming / Mursheen durkin / Paddy Cathy's reel / Dinny's fancy / Spanish lady / Maid behind the bar / Gravel walk / Holy ground / Finnegan's wake / Irish Rover / Rakes of mallow / Seven drunken nights
CD 6023 / Jun '96 / Music

Blas, Johnny

☐ **MAMBO 2000**
Mucho chops / Mambo to the max / Feels so right / Grab a hold of yourself / Mambo 2000 / Es la verdad / We're partners in love / Mambone / Como asi / Picadillo (a lo blas)
CBCD 012 / 24 Aug '98 / Cubop

Blasnost

☐ **BLASNOST**
BEST 1023CD / Nov '93 / Acoustic Music

Blast

☐ **POWER OF EXPRESSION, THE**
Time to think / Surf and destroy / Fn' with my head / E.i.b. / Our explanation / Future / Break it down / Time waits for no one / I don't need it / It's alive / Look into myself / Nightmare / Something beyond
SST 148CD / May '93 / SST

☐ **TAKE THE MANIC RIDE**
SST 225CD / May '93 / SST

Blast Off

☐ **ROCKIN' TO THE MUSIC**
PEPCD 120 / Oct '97 / Pollytone

Blast Off Country Style

☐ **C'MON AND ...**
TEENBEAT 131CD / Mar '94 / Teenbeat

Blasters

☐ **AMERICAN MUSIC**
HCD 8086 / Oct '97 / Hightone

Blastula

☐ **BLASTULA**
ALP 40CD / Mar '97 / Atavistic

Blatz

☐ **SHIT SPLIT (2CD Set) (Blatz/Filth)**
LOOKOUT 43CD / May '97 / Lookout

Blaze

☐ **BASIC BLAZE**
SLIPCD 61 / 18 Aug '97 / Slip 'n' Slide

Blazers

☐ **EAST SIDE SOUL**
ROUCD 9053 / Jul '95 / Rounder

☐ **GOING UP THE COUNTRY**
CRCDM 3 / Jun '96 / CRS

☐ **JUST FOR YOU**
ROUCD 9063 / Aug '97 / Rounder

☐ **SHORT FUSE**
ROUCD 9043 / Apr '94 / Rounder

Blazing Rains

☐ **BLAZING RAINS**
SF 002CD / Mar '97 / Sugar Free

Blazing Redheads

☐ **BLAZING REDHEADS**
Paradise drive / Cienega / Sea level / In search of... / Cha cha slippers / February song / Santa Fe / Get down (and stay down) / Final segment / Mozambo / Street dreamin' / My Picasso
RR 26CD / May '96 / Reference Recordings

☐ **CRAZED WOMEN**
RR 41CD / May '96 / Reference Recordings

Bleed

☐ **ACTION MAN**
BLEED 7CD / Jun '97 / Bleed

Bleedin' Hearts

☐ **SECONDS TO GO**
CSCCD 1003 / Sep '95 / CRS

Bleep & Booster

☐ **WORLD OF BLEEP & BOOSTER**
Technotropolis / Sexy / Electro city / Genk / Find the light / Boosterdrome / Glock / Amber to atoms / Wonder of the world / Piano 1
8285112 / Sep '94 / London

Blegvad, Peter

☐ **DOWNTIME**
RERPBCD / Jul '88 / ReR/ Recommended

☐ **KEW RHONE (Blegvad, Peter & John Greaves)**
Good evening / Twenty two proverbs / Exhuming the first American / Kew Rhone / Pipeline / Catalogue of fifteen objects and their titles / One footnote (to Kew Rhone) / Three tenses onanism / Nine mineral emblems / Apricot / Gegenstand
VP 200CD / 20 Apr '98 / Voiceprint

☐ **NAKED SHAKESPEARE, THE**
How beautiful you are / Karen / Lonely too / First blow struck / Weird monkeys / Naked Shakespeare / Irma / Like a baby / Powers in the air / You can't miss it / Vermont / Blue eyed William
CDV 2284 / Jun '91 / Virgin

Bleiming, Christian

☐ **JIVIN' TIME**
BEST 1010CD / Nov '93 / Acoustic Music

Bleizi Ruz

☐ **CELTIC TRIP**
SHAMCD 1039 / Mar '98 / Shamrock

☐ **MUSIQUES & DANSES DE BRETAGNE**
PL 3355/65CD / Jun '94 / Diffusion Breizh

Blender

☐ RETURN OF THE BLENDER
XBR 001CD / Jun '96 / Dolores

Blenner, Serge

☐ VISION ET POESIE
SKYCD 3053 / Sep '95 / Sky

Blessed End

☐ MOVIN' ON
GF 112 / 22 May '98 / Gear Fab

Blessed Ethel

☐ WELCOME TO THE RODEO
2DMCD 012 / Nov '95 / 2 Damn Loud

Blessed Rain

☐ BRING IT HOME AGAIN
0200501 / 25 May '98 / Carrera

Bley, Carla

☐ BIG BAND THEORY
On the stage in cages / Birds of paradise / Goodbye Pork Pie Hat / Fresh impression
5199662 / Oct '93 / Watt

☐ DINNER MUSIC
8258152 / Jan '94 / ECM

☐ DUETS (Bley, Carla & Steve Swallow/ Andy Sheppard)
Baby baby / Walking batteriewoman / Utviklingssang / Ladies in Mercedes / Romantic notions / Remember / Ups and downs / Reactionary tango parts 1/2/3 / Soon I will be done with the troubles of this world
8373452 / Nov '88 / ECM

☐ ESCALATOR OVER THE HILL
8393102 / 13 Jul '98 / ECM

☐ FANCY CHAMBER MUSIC
Wolfgang tango / Romantic notion no.4 / End of Vienna / Tigers in training / Romantic notion no.6 / Jon Benet
5399372 / 13 Jul '98 / Watt

☐ FLEUR CARNIVORE
Fleur carnivore / Song of the eternal waiting of canute / Ups and downs / Girl who cried champagne (parts 1, 2 and 3) / Healing power
8396622 / Nov '89 / Watt

☐ GO TOGETHER (Bley, Carla & Steve Swallow/Andy Sheppard)
Sing me softly of the blues / Mother of the dead man / Masquerade / Ad infinitum / Copyright royalties / Peau douce / Doctor / Fleur carnivor
5176732 / May '93 / Watt

☐ GOES TO CHURCH (Bley, Carla Big Band)
Setting Calvin's waltz / Exaltaion/Religious experience/Major / One way / Beads / Permanent wave / Who will rescue you
5336822 / Nov '96 / Watt

☐ HEAVY HEART
Light or dark / Talking hearts / Joyful noise / Ending it / Starting again / Heavy heart
8178642 / Jan '94 / ECM

☐ I HATE TO SING
Internationale / Murder / Very very simple / I hate to sing / Piano lesson / Lone arranger / Battleship
8238652 / Jul '96 / Watt

☐ LIVE
Blunt object / Lord is listenin' to ya, hallelujah / Time and us / Still in the room / Real life hits / Song sung long
8157302 / Feb '86 / ECM

☐ MUSIQUE MECANIQUE
440 / Jesus maria and other spanish strains / Musique mecanique I / Musique mecanique ii (at midnight) / Musique mecanique iii
8393132 / Sep '89 / ECM

☐ NIGHT-GLO
Pretend you're in love / Night-glo / Rut / Crazy with you / Wildlife
8276402 / Dec '85 / ECM

☐ SEXTET
More Brahms / Houses and people / Girl who cried champagne / Brooklyn Bridge / Lawns / Healing power
8316972 / Apr '87 / ECM

☐ SOCIAL STUDIES
8318312 / Jul '87 / ECM

☐ SONGS WITH LEGS (Bley, Carla & Steve Swallow/Andy Sheppard)
Real life hits / Lord is listenin' to ya, hallelujah / Chicken / Misterioso / Wrong key donkey / Crazy with you
5270692 / Feb '95 / Watt

☐ TROPIC APPETITES
What will be between us and the moon tonight / In India / Enormous tots / Caucasian bird rifles / Funnybird song / Indonesian dock sucking supreme / Song of the jungle stream / Nothing
5574802 / 13 Jul '98 / Watt

Bley, Paul

☐ ANNETTE (Bley, Paul/Various Artists)
ARTCD 6118 / Nov '92 / Hat Art

☐ BLUES FOR RED
1232382 / Mar '91 / Red

☐ CHANGING HANDS
JUST 402 / Jul '92 / Justin Time

☐ FABULOUS PAUL BLEY QUINTET, THE (Bley, Paul Quintet)
500542 / Sep '96 / Musidisc

☐ FOOTLOOSE
When will the blues leave / Floater / Turns / Around again / Syndrome / Cousins / King korn / Vashikar
SV 0140 / Oct '97 / Savoy Jazz

☐ FRAGMENTS
Memories / Monica jane / Line down / Seven / Closer / Once around the park / Hand dance / For the love of sarah / Nothing ever was, anyway
8292802 / Sep '86 / ECM

☐ HANDS ON
Remembering / Points / Ram dance / Three fifth / Hands on / If / Cowhand
ECD 221842 / Jul '97 / Evidence

☐ IN A ROW
ARTCD 6081 / Aug '91 / Hat Art

☐ IN THE EVENINGS OUT THERE
Afterthoughts / Portrait of a silence / Soft touch / Speak easy / Interface / Allignment / Fair share / Tomorrow today / Note police
5174692 / Sep '93 / ECM

☐ LIVE AT SWEET BASIL (Bley, Paul Group)
1212352 / Jun '91 / Soul Note

☐ MEMOIRS (Bley, Paul, Charlie Haden & Paul Motian)
1212402 / May '92 / Soul Note

☐ MINDSET (Bley, Paul & Gary Peacock)
1212132 / Dec '97 / Soul Note

☐ NOTES ON ORNETTE
SCCD 31437 / 1 Jun '98 / Steeplechase

☐ OUTSIDE IN (Bley, Paul & Sonny Greenwich)
JUST 692 / Apr '95 / Justin Time

☐ PAUL BLEY QUARTET (Bley, Paul Quartet)
8352402 / May '88 / ECM

☐ PAUL BLEY WITH GARY PEACOCK (Bley, Paul Trio)
Blues / Getting started / When will the blues leave / Long ago and far away / Moor / Gary / Big Foot / Albert's love theme
8431622 / Oct '90 / ECM

☐ PAUL BLEY, NIELS HENNING, ORSTED PEDERSON (Bley, Paul, Niels Henning & Orsted Pederson)
SCCD 31005 / Nov '90 / Steeplechase

☐ RAMBLIN'
1231172 / Feb '96 / Red

☐ SWEET TIME
JUST 56 / Oct '94 / Justin Time

☐ TIME WILL TELL (Bley, Paul, Evan Parker & Barre Philips)
Poetic justice / Time will tell / Above the treeline / You will, Oscar, you will / Sprung / No questions / Vine laces / Clawback / Marsh tides / Instance / Burlesque
5238192 / Feb '95 / ECM

☐ TOUCHING
BLCD 760195 / Jun '94 / Black Lion

Blige, Mary J.

☐ LIVE
MCD 11848 / 27 Jul '98 / MCA

☐ MY LIFE
Intro / Mary Jane / You bring me joy / Marvin interlude / I'm the only woman / K Murray interlude / My life / You gotta believe / I never wanna live without you / I'm going down / My life interlude / Be with you / Mary's joint / Don't go / I love you / No one else / Be happy / (You make me feel like) a natural woman
MCD 11398 / Jan '96 / MCA

☐ SHARE MY WORLD
Intro / I love you / Love is all we need / Round and round / Share my world / Share my world (interlude) / Seven days / It's on / Thank you Lord (interlude) / Missing you / Everything / Keep your head / Can't get you off my mind / Get to know you better / Everything / Our love / Not gon' cry / (You make me feel like a) Natural woman
MCD 11619 / Apr '97 / MCA

☐ WHAT'S THE 411
Leave a message / Reminisce / Real love / You remind me / Intro' talk / Sweet thing / Love no limit / I don't want to do anything / Slow down / My love / Changes I've been going through / What's the 411
MCLD 19315 / Jul '96 / MCA

☐ WHAT'S THE 411 (Remix)
Leave a message / You don't have to worry / My love / Real love / What's the 411 / Reminisce / Mary and Andre / Sweet thing / Love no limit / You remind me / Changes I've been going through / I don't want to do anything
MCLD 19338 / Oct '96 / MCA

Blind Faith

☐ BLIND FAITH
Had to cry today / Can't find my way home / Well alright / Presence of the Lord / Sea of joy / Do what you like
8250942 / Nov '90 / Polydor

Blind Guardian

☐ BATTALIONS OF FEAR
859810 / Sep '89 / SPV

Blind Idiot God

☐ BLIND IDIOT GOD
SST 104CD / May '93 / SST

☐ UNDERTOW
EMY 1072 / Sep '97 / Enemy

Blind Illusion

☐ SANE ASYLUM, THE
Sane asylum / Vengeance is mine / Kamikaze / Vicious vision / Bloodshower / Death noise / Smash / Metamorphosis of a monster
CDFLAG 18 / Mar '88 / Under One Flag

Blind Light

☐ ABSENCE OF TIME, THE
EFA 275012 / Feb '97 / Alda

Blind Melon

☐ BLIND MELON
Soak the sin / Tones of home / Ronettes / Paper scratcher / Dear ol' dad / Change / No rain / Deserted / Sleepyhouse / Holy man / Seed to a tree / Drive / Time
CDEST 2188 / Mar '93 / Capitol

☐ NICO
Pusher / Hell / Soup / No rain / Soul one / John Sinclair / All that I need / Glitch / Life ain't so shitty / Swallowed / Pull / St. Andrew's hall / Letters from a porcupine
CDEST 2291 / Feb '97 / EMI

☐ SOUP
Galaxie / Two times four / Vernie / Skinned / Toes across the floor / Walk / Dumptruck / Car seat (God's presents) / Wilt / Duke / St. Andrew's fall / New life / Mouthful of cavities / Lemonade
CDEST 2261 / Apr '97 / Capitol

Blind Mr. Jones

☐ STEREO MUSICALE
Sisters / Spooky Vibes / Regular Disease / Small caravan / Flying With Lux / Henna And Swayed / Lonesome Boatman / Unforgettable Waltz / Going on cold / Spook Easy / One Watt Above darkness / Dolores / Against The Glass
CDBRED 100 / Oct '92 / Cherry Red

☐ TATOOINE
Hey / Disneyworld / Viva fisher / See you again / Big plane / Drop for days / Surfer baby / Please me / What's going on / Mesa
CDBRED 113 / May '94 / Cherry Red

Blind Passengers

☐ DESTROYKA
CD 08561292 / Apr '96 / SPV

Blink 182

☐ BUDDHA
787652 / 20 Oct '97 / Kung Fu

☐ CHESHIRE CAT
GRL 001CD / Oct '96 / Grilled Cheese

☐ DUDE RANCH
MCD 11624 / 3 Nov '97 / MCA

Blink Twice

☐ OTHER LOCATIONS
EFA 129662 / Apr '97 / Glasnost

Bliss

☐ SIN TO SKIN
MASSCD 152 / 19 Jan '98 / Massacre

Blitz

☐ BEST OF BLITZ, THE
Attack / Fight to live / Forty five revolutions / Someone's gonna die / Time bomb / 4Q / Never surrender / Razors in the night / Voice of a generation / Nation / Fatigue / Suffragette city / Overdrive / Those days / Killing dream / Walkaway
DOJOCD 123 / Mar '93 / Dojo

☐ BLITZED ON ALL OUT ATTACK
Warriors / 4Q / Time bomb / Criminal damage / Razors in the night / Attack / Escape / Never surrender / Nation on fire / Warriors (Live) / Someone's gonna die / Forty five revolutions / Fight to live / Youth / I don't need you / Propaganda / Closedown / Your revolution / New age / Bleed / Caberet / Vicious / Escape (demo) / Youth (demo) / Bleed (demo) / Crimianl damage
DOJOCD 93 / Apr '93 / Dojo

☐ COMPLETE BLITZ SINGLES COLLECTION
Someone's gonna die / Attack / Fight to live / Forty five revolutions / Never surrender / Razors in the night / Voice of a generation / Warriors / Youth / New age / Fatigue / Bleed / Telecommunication / Teletron / Solar / Husk
CDPUNK 25 / Dec '93 / Anagram

☐ KILLING DREAM, THE/RARE INTERVIEWS
STEPCD 111 / 24 Nov '97 / Step 1

☐ VERY BEST OF BLITZ, THE
Attack / Fight to live / 45 Revolutions / Someone's gonna die / Time bomb / 4Q / Never surrender / Razor's in the night / Voice of a generation / Nation on fire / Youth / Warriors / Bleed / New age / Fatigue / Suffragette city / Overdrive / Those days / Killing dream / Walkaway
CDPUNK 104 / 1 Jun '98 / Anagram

Blitz Babiez

☐ THOUGHT SPAWN
35520162 / Oct '96 / Onefoot

Blitzkrieg

☐ FUTURE MUST BE OURS
RRCD 010 / Oct '96 / Retch

☐ MISTS OF AVALON
NM 032 / 13 Jul '98 / Neat Metal

☐ TEN
NM 010CD / Oct '97 / Neat Metal

☐ UNHOLY TRINITY
NM 002CD / Oct '97 / Neat Metal

Blitzkrieg Bop

☐ TOP OF THE BOPS
OVER 69CD / 16 Feb '98 / Overground

Blizard, Ralph

☐ SOUTHERN RAMBLE
ROUCD 0352 / Aug '95 / Rounder

Block

☐ LEAD ME NOT INTO PENN STATION
INDIGO 58532 / Dec '96 / Zensor

☐ MEAN MACHINE
CDZOT 101 / Nov '93 / Zoth Ommog

Block, Brandon

☐ BRANDON BLOCK LIVE VOL.1
QPM 7 / Nov '96 / QPM

☐ THUMPIN' SCORCHERS VOL.1 (Various Artists)
BASHCD 001 / 9 Feb '98 / Thumpin'

Block, Rory

☐ AIN'T I A WOMAN
Silver wings / Faithless world / Sisters / Ain't I a woman / Come on in my kitchen / Rolling log / Maggie Campbell / Never call your name / Road to Mexico / Cool drink of water / Walk in Jerusalem / Never called your name
NETCD 0038 / Nov '92 / Network

☐ ANGEL OF MERCY
NET 47CD / Apr '94 / Network

☐ BEST BLUES AND ORIGINALS VOL.1
MRCD 137 / Jun '93 / Munich

☐ BEST BLUES AND ORIGINALS VOL.2
Uncloudy day / Devil got my man / Down in the dumps / Since you been gone / Achin' heart / Hilarity rag / Kind hearted man / Love my blues away / Elder green is gone / Just like a man / Swing low, sweet chariot / Ecstasy / Feel just like going on / Frankie and Albert / No place like home / Midnight light / I might find a way / Dr. Make it right / No way for me to get along / Back to the woods / I've got a rock in my sock / Highland overture (for Wendy) / Long journey
NETCD 43 / Jul '93 / Network

☐ GONE WOMAN BLUES (The Country Blues Collection)
Big road blues / Preaching blues / Joliet bound / Maggie Campbell / Hellhound on my trail / Bye bye blues / Gone woman blues / Pea vine blues / Rolling log / I let my Daddy do that / Tallahatchie blues / Tain't long to day / Terraplane blues / Come on in my kitchen / Be ready when he comes / Cypress grove / Railroadin' some / Heavenly blues / Cool drink of water / Do your duty / Rowdy blues / On the wall / Devil got my man / Take my heart again
ROUCD 11575 / Mar '97 / Rounder

☐ HIGH HEELED BLUES
Walkin' blues / Travelin' blues / Got to have you be my man / Devil got my man / Down in the dumps / Water is wide / Since you been gone / Cross road blues / Achin' heart / Hilarity rag / Kind hearted man / Uncloudy day
ROUCD 3061 / '88 / Rounder

☐ HOUSE OF HEARTS
Farewell young man / Heavenly bird / Do you love me / Morning bells / Gentle kindness / Misty glen / On the water / Bonnie boy / Krye / House of hearts
ROUCD 3104 / '88 / Rounder

☐ I'VE GOT A ROCK IN MY SOCK
Send the man back home / Moon's goin' down / Gypsie boy / I've got a rock in my sock / Foreign lander / Goin' back to the country / M and o blues / Lovin' whiskey / Highland overture (for wendy)
ROUCD 3097 / '88 / Rounder

☐ MAMA'S BLUES
Terraplane blues / Bye bye blues / Big road blues / Do your duty / Spirit returns / Got to shine / Mama's blues / Ain't no shame / Hawkins blues / Weepin' willow blues / Sing good news
ROUCD 3117 / Mar '97 / Rounder

☐ RHINESTONE AND STEEL STRINGS
Future blues / I might find a way / El vuelo del alma / Lovin' fool / Golden vanity / Dr. make it right / No way for me to get along / Back to the woods / God's gift to woman / Sit down on the banks
ROUCD 3085 / Aug '88 / Rounder

☐ TORNADO
ROUCD 314 / May '96 / Rounder

☐ TURNING POINT
Turning point / Holdin' on / Far away / All of my life / Spiderboy / Gedachentrein / All as one / Heather's song / Old times are gone / Leavin' here / Down the highway / Tomorrow
MRCD 145 / Aug '94 / Munich

☐ WHEN A WOMAN GETS THE BLUES
ROUCD 3139 / Apr '95 / Rounder

☐ WOMEN IN (E)MOTION FESTIVAL
T&M 107 / Jan '95 / Tradition & Moderne

Blockhead

☐ TRIAL OF TEARS
HOS 7021CD / 27 Apr '98 / Hall Of Sermon

Blodwyn Pig

☐ AHEAD RINGS OUT
It's only love / Sing me a song that I know / Up and coming / Change song / Dear Jill / Modern alchemist / Leave it with me / Ain't ya coming home, babe
BGOCD 54 / Aug '94 / Beat Goes On

☐ FULL PORKY, THE (Live In London 1991)
ANDCD 20 / Jun '98 / A New Day

☐ GETTING TO THIS
Drive me / Variations on Nainos / See my way / Long lamb blues / Squirreling must go on / San Francisco sketches / Beach scape / Fisherman's wharf / Telegraph hill / Close the door, I'm falling out of the room / Worry / Toys / To Rassman / Send your son to die
BGOCD 81 / Aug '94 / Beat Goes On

☐ LIVE AT THE LAFAYETTE
Dunstable truck driver man's blues / See my way / Oh no / Baby girl / Cosmogrification / Cat squirrel / It's only love / Dharma for six / Six days on the road / Boogie train/slow down
IGOCD 2067 / Feb '98 / Indigo

☐ MODERN ALCHEMIST, THE
It's only love / Modern alchemist / Change song / Summers day / Cat squirrel / Dear Jill / See my way / Drive me / Slow down / Ain't you coming home babe
IGOXCD 507 / May '97 / Indigo

Bloedow, Oren

☐ LUCKIEST BOY IN THE WORLD
In the clinch / Endless tears / Living room / Do I have to take you outside / Prayer no.2 / Like an arch / Foot of the wall / Babyland / 100% live / I need a fire / In the clinch
KFWCD 120 / 20 Apr '98 / Knitting Factory

☐ OREN BLOEDOW
KFWCD 115 / Nov '94 / Knitting Factory

Blond, Leigh

☐ SEE ME THRU
See me thru / One more day / Too many people / You can't always keep the ones you love / Love is a dream / Dylan & Derek / Good head for business / Lay it all down / Backs to the wall / Isabelle
RM 52 / Jul '98 / RM

Blonde On Blonde

☐ CONTRASTS
Ride with Captain Max / Spinning wheel / No sleep blues / Goodbye / I need my friend / Mother Earth / All day and all night / Eleanor Rigby / Conversationally making the grade / Regency / Island on an island / Don't be too long / Jeanette Isabella / Country life
SEECD 406 / Jul '94 / See For Miles

☐ REFLECTIONS ON A LIFE
14526 / Feb '97 / Spalax

Blonde Redhead

☐ FAKE CAN BE JUST AS GOOD
TG 169CD / Apr '97 / Touch & Go

Blondie

☐ ATOMIC
Atomic / Heart of glass / Sunday girl / Call me / Tide is high / Denis / Dreaming / Rapture / Hanging on the telephone / (I'm always touched by your) presence dear / Island of lost souls / Picture this / Union city blue / War child / Ripe her to shreds / One way or another / X offender / I'm gonna love you too / Fade away and radiate / Atomic / Atomic
4949962 / 13 Jul '98 / EMI

☐ AUTOAMERICAN
Europa / Live it up / Here's looking at you / Tide is high / Angels on the balcony / Go through it / Do the dark / Rapture / Faces / T-Birds / Walk like me / Follow me
CDCHR 6084 / Sep '94 / Chrysalis

☐ BEAUTIFUL (The Remix Album)
Union city blue / Dreaming / Rapture / Heart of glass / Sunday girl / Call me / Atomic / Tide is high / Hanging on the telephone / Fade away and radiate
CDCHR 6105 / Jul '95 / Chrysalis

☐ BEST OF BLONDIE, THE
Denis / Tide is high / In the flesh / Sunday girl / (I'm always touched by your) presence dear / Dreaming / Hanging on the telephone / Rapture / Picture this / Union city blue / Call me / Atomic / Rip her to shreds / Heart of glass
CCD 1371 / Jan '88 / Chrysalis

☐ BLONDIE
X offender / Rifle range / Look good in blue / In the sun / Shark in Jet's clothing / Man overboard / Rip her to shreds / Little girl lies / In the flesh / Kung fu girls / Attack of the giant ants
CDCHR 6081 / Sep '94 / Chrysalis

☐ BLONDIE AND BEYOND
Underground girl / English boys / Sunday girl (French version) / Susie and Jeffrey / Shayla / Denis / X offender / Poets problem / Scenery / Picture this / Angels on the balcony / Once I had a love / I'm gonna love you too / Island of lost souls / Call me (Spanish version) / Heart of glass / Ring of fire / Bang a gong (get it on) / Heroes
CDCCHR 6063 / Jan '94 / Chrysalis

☐ COMPLETE PICTURE, THE (The Best Of Deborah Harry & Blondie)
Heart of glass / I want that man: *Harry, Deborah* / Call me / Sunday girl / French kissin' in the USA: *Harry, Deborah* / Denis / Rapture / Brite side: *Harry, Deborah* / (I'm always touched by your) presence dear / Well did you evah: *Harry, Deborah & Iggy Pop* / Tide is high / In love with love: *Harry, Deborah* / Hanging on the telephone / Island of lost souls / Picture this / Dreaming / Sweet and low: *Harry, Deborah* / Union City Blue / Atomic / Rip her to shreds
CCD 1817 / Mar '91 / Chrysalis

☐ DENIS
Denis / Tide is high / Hanging on the telephone / Rip her to shreds / Picture this / X Offender / Rifle range / For your eyes only / Susie and Jeffrey / Die young stay pretty / Island of lost souls / Platinum blonde / War child / In the flesh
DC 867192 / Nov '96 / Disky

☐ EAT TO THE BEAT
Dreaming / Hardest part / Union city blue / Shayla / Eat to the beat / Accidents never happen / Die young stay pretty / Slow motion / Atomic / Sound asleep / Victor / Living in the real world
CPCD 1225 / Nov '92 / Chrysalis

☐ ESSENTIAL COLLECTION, THE
Denis / Tide is high / Hanging on the telephone / Rip her to shreds / Picture this / X Offender / Rifle range / For your eyes only / Susie and Jeffrey / Die young stay pretty / Island of lost souls / Platinum blonde / War child / In the flesh
CDGOLD 1091 / Feb '97 / EMI Gold

☐ HUNTER, THE
Orchid club / Island of lost souls / Dragonfly / For your eyes only / Beast / War child / Little Caesar / Danceway / Can I find the right words (to say) / English boys / Hunter gets captured by the game
CDCHR 6083 / Sep '94 / Chrysalis

☐ PARALLEL LINES
Fade away / Hanging on the telephone / One way or another / Picture this / Pretty baby / I know but I don't know / 11.59 / Will anything happen / Sunday girl / Heart of glass / I'm gonna love you too / Just go away
CCD 1192 / Jul '94 / Chrysalis

☐ PLASTIC LETTERS
Fan mail / Denis / Bermuda triangle / Youth nabbed as sniper / Contact in Red Square / (I'm always touched by your) presence dear / I'm on E / I didn't have the nerve to say no / Love at the pier / No imagination / Kidnapper / Detroit 442 / Cautious lip
CDCHR 6085 / Sep '94 / Chrysalis

☐ PLATINUM COLLECTION, THE (2CD Set)
X offender / In the flesh / Man overboard / Rip her to shreds / Denis / Contact in red square / Kung fu girls / I'm on E / (I'm always touched by your) presence dear / Poets problem / Detroit 442 / Picture this / Fade away and radiate / I'm gonna love you too / Just go away / Hanging on the telephone / Will anything happen / Heart of glass / Rifle range / 11.59 / Sunday girl / I know but I don't know / One way or another / Dreaming / Sound asleep / Living in the real world / Union city blue / Hardest part / Atomic / Die young stay pretty / Slow motion / Call me / Tide is high / Susie and Jeffrey / Rapture / Walk like me / Island of lost souls / Dragon fly / War child / Little Caesar / Out in the streets / Platinum blonde / Thin line / Puerto Rico / Once I had a love / Atomic (remix) / Rapture (remix)
CDCHR 6089 / Oct '94 / Chrysalis

☐ PROUD TO BE BLONDIE (A Tribute To Blondie) (Various Artists)
41289 / 29 Jun '98 / V&V

Blood

☐ FALSE GESTURES FOR A DEVIOUS PUBLIC
Done some brain cells last night / Degenerate / Gestapo khazi / Well sick / Sewer brain / Sucker / Mesrine / Rule 43 / Joys of noise / Waste of flesh and bones / Throttle you blue
MOGCD 008 / 2 Mar '98 / Mog

☐ METAL CONFLICTS
SPV 08412412 / Apr '95 / SPV

Blood Divine

☐ MYSTICA
Mystica / As rapture fades / Visions in blue / Passion reigns / Leaving me helpless / Enhanced by your touch / Visions / I believe / Sensual ecstasy / Fear of a lonely world / Prayer
CDVILE 70 / 13 Sep '97 / Peaceville

Blood Duster

☐ STR8 OUTTA NORTHCOTE
Givin' stiff to the stiff / Hippie kill team / Metal as fuck / I hate girls and crusty punx / Chop chop / Tittie / Motherload / Meat song (stiffy at McDonalds) / Deathsquad / Instrumental 1 / Simple life / Where does all the money go when releasing a full length alb / It's just not metal / Celebrating 35% / Pig fat / FSS / Ohahh / Derek 2 / Rollcall / Shoved up your pisshole / Ballad of Hoyt / Pure digital silence
RR 69802 / 13 Apr '98 / Relapse

☐ YEEST
Albert / Northcote / Motherfuckin' / Chuck / Showered with affection / Strop / Nasty chicks / Intro / Mortician / Vulgar taste / Kill kill kill / Intro / Sadomasifuck / Rectal spawn / Intro / Grossman the meatman / Bloodfart / Knee deep in menstrual blood / Intro / Chunky bit / Intro / Simultaneous pleasure pinch / Intro / Theatre of the macabre / Gimmie some lovin' / Raping the elderly / Intro / Anal feast / Fisting the dead / Intro / Derek
RR 69322 / 26 Jan '98 / Relapse

Blood Farmers

☐ BLOOD FARMERS
H 00372 / Apr '95 / Hellhound

Blood For Blood

☐ REVENGE ON SOCIETY
VR 087CD / 27 Apr '98 / Victory

Blood On The Saddle

☐ NEW BLOOD
422062 / Feb '97 / Last Call

Blood Or Whiskey

☐ BLOOD OR WHISKEY
SUNCD 24 / May '97 / Sound

Blood Shanti

☐ PURE SPIRIT
ABACD 002 / Aug '96 / Aba Shanti

Blood, Sweat & Tears

☐ WHAT GOES UP (The Best Of Blood, Sweat & Tears/2CD Set)
Refugee from Yuhupitz / I can't quit her / House in the country / I love you more than you'll ever know / You've made me so very happy / More and more / And when I die / Sometimes in winter / Smiling phases / Spinning wheel / God bless the child / Children of the wind / Hi de ho / Lucretia / Mac evil / He's a runner / Something's coming on / 40,000 headmen / Go down gamblin' / Mama gets high / Lisa, listen to me / Valentine's day / John the baptist (Holy John) / So long Dixie / Snow queen / Maiden voyage / I can't move to the mountains / Time remembered / Roller coaster / Tell me that I'm wrong / Got to get you into my life / You're the one / Mean ole world
4810192 / Jan '96 / Columbia

Bloodbath

☐ LIVE
PP 002 / Jan '97 / Phenotype

Bloodcount

☐ DISCRETION
Is that a gap / Opener / Talk dirty to me / Eye are us / Byram's world
SCREWU 70003 / 2 Mar '98 / ScrewGun

Bloodfire Posse

☐ PRIMO
RASCD 3108 / Nov '92 / Ras

Bloodgood

☐ ALL STAND TOGETHER
SOS / All stand together / Escape from the fire / Say goodbye / Out of love / Kingdom come / Fear no evil / Help me / Rounded are the rocks / Lies in the dark / Streetlight dance / I want to live in your heart
CD 08793 / Jan '92 / Broken

Bloodhound Gang

☐ ONE FIERCE BEER COASTER
GED 25124 / 1 Sep '97 / Geffen

Bloodlet

☐ ELETIC
VR 031CD / Jan '96 / Victory Europe

☐ SERAPHIM FALL
VR 072CD / 16 Mar '98 / Victory

Bloodthron

☐ IN THE SHADOW OF YOUR BLACK WINGS
SOM 006CD / 13 Oct '97 / Seasons Of Mist

Bloody Sods

☐ UP 'N' RUNNIN'
STEPCD 110 / 24 Nov '97 / Step 1

Bloom, Jane Ira

☐ ART & AVIATION
Gateway to progress / Further into the night / Hawkin's parallel universe / Straight no chaser/Miro / Oshumare / Art and aviation / Most distant galaxy / I believe Anita / Lost in the stars
AJ 0107 / Jun '93 / Arabesque

☐ MODERN DRAMA
378282 / Nov '96 / Koch Jazz

☐ NEARNESS, THE
Nearly summertime / Midnight round / 'Round midnight / B6 Bop / Middnight's measure / In the wee small hours of the morning / Painting over Paris / Wing dining / Panosonic / White tower / It's a corrugated world / Monk's tale / Nearness of you / Lonely house / All diesel kitchen of tomorrow / Yonder
AJ 0120 / Apr '96 / Arabesque

☐ SLALOM
378272 / Jun '97 / Koch Jazz

Bloom, Luka

☐ ACOUSTIC MOTORBIKE, THE
Can't help falling in love / You / Exploring the blue / Acoustic motorbike / This is your country / Be well / Listen to the hoofbeat / Bridge of sorrow / Bones / I believe in you / Mary watches everything / I need love
7599266702 / Dec '96 / Reprise

☐ RIVERSIDE
Delerious / Dreams in America / Gone to pablo / Man is alive / Irishman in Chinatown / Rescue mission / One / Hudson lady / This is your life / You couldn't have come at a better time / Hill of Allen
7599260922 / Dec '96 / Reprise

☐ TURF
Cold comfort / True blue / Diamond mountain / Right here, right now / Sunny sailor boy / Black is the colour of my true love's hair / To begin to / Freedom song / Holding back the river / Background noise / Fertile rock / I did time / Sanctuary
9362456082 / Jun '94 / Reprise

Bloomfield, Mike

☐ AMERICAN HERO
Hully gully / Wings of an angel / Walking the floor / Don't you lie to me / Junko partner / Knockin' myself out / Women lovin' each other / Cherry red / RX for the blues / You must have Jesus
MM 005 / 1 Jun '98 / MagMid

☐ BEST OF MIKE BLOOMFIELD, THE
Michigan water blues / Frankie and Johnny / Mr. Johnson and Mr. Dunn / Your friends / Hitch-hike on the possum trot line / Between the hard place and the ground / Pleading blues / Papa-Mama-rompah-stompah / Effinonna rag / Orphan's rag / Gospel truth / See that my grave is kept clean
CDTAK 8905 / 27 Oct '97 / Takoma

☐ BETWEEN A HARD PLACE AND THE GROUND
Eyesight to the blind / Linda Lou / Kansas City blues / At the Darktown strutter's ball / Mop mop / Call me a dog / I'm glad I'm jewish / Great gifts from heaven / Lo though I am with thee / Jockey blues / Between a hard place and the ground / Uncle Bon's barrelhouse blues / Wee wee hours / Vamp in C / One of these days
CDTB 076 / Sep '90 / Thunderbolt

☐ BLUES GUITAR AND RAGTIME GUITAR
When I need you / Memphis radio blues / Blake's rag / Just a closer walk with thee / At the cross / Hawaiian guitar waltz / Gonna need somebody on my bond / Blues for Norman / Wheelchair rag / Farther along / Mood indigo
SHCD 99007 / Mar '98 / Shanachie

☐ GOSPEL TRUTH
Cruisin' for a bruisin' / Linda Lu / Papa mama / Rompha stompin' / Junker's blues / Midnight / It'll be me / Motorised blues / Mathilda / Winter moon / Snow blind / Lights out / Your friend / Orphan blues / Juke joint / Knockin' myself out
CDTB 179 / Oct '96 / Thunderbolt

☐ KNOCKIN' MYSELF OUT
CDSGP 0216 / Mar '96 / Prestige

☐ LIVE ADVENTURES OF MIKE BLOOMFIELD AND AL COOPER (2CD Set) (Bloomfield, Mike & Al Kooper)
Opening speech / 59th Street Bridge song / I wonder why / Her holy modal highness / Weight / Mary Ann / Together / That's alright / Green onions
4851512 / Mar '97 / Columbia

☐ TRUE SOUL BROTHER, A
8400892 / May '96 / Affinity

Bloss, Rainer

☐ AMPSY
Oracle / From long ago / Energy / Adoring multitudes / Psyche / I'm the heat / He's an angel / Who the hell is she / Lights out baby / Love is a beginning
CDTB 032 / May '87 / Thunderbolt

☐ DRIVE INN VOL.3
Archimedes plaza / Dawn patrol / Love 15 / Eternal restroom / Ford galaxy / Mysterion / Astrodome / Nebula / Enter space / Space driver / Gagarin lighthouse / Endless / Metamorphis
CDTB 181 / 31 Jul '98 / Thunderbolt

Blount

☐ TRAUMA
F 018CD / Apr '97 / Fearless

Blount, Chris

☐ BEAUTIFUL OHIO (Blount, Chris New Orleans Jazz Band)
CBCD 03 / Feb '98 / Chris Blount

☐ NEW ORLEANS IMPRESSIONS (Blount, Chris & The Delta Four)
PKCD 042 / May '96 / PEK

☐ NEW ORLEANS JAZZ BAND
PKCD 031 / Oct '94 / PEK

☐ NIGHT AT THE CASINO, A (Blount, Chris New Orleans Jazz Band)
RSCD 675 / Jul '98 / Raymer

☐ OLD RUGGED CROSS, THE (Blount, Chris New Orleans Jazz Band)
Mary wore a golden chain / Amazing grace / Lord, Lord, Lord / Only a look / Royal telephone / Old rugged cross / In the sweet bye and bye / Hands of God / Lead me saviour / It is no secret / Walking with the King / Evening prayer / Yes Lord I'm crippled / His eye is on the sparrow / End of a perfect day
LACD 16 / Nov '93 / Lake

☐ THANK YOU MR. MOON (Blount, Chris New Orleans Jazz Band)
RSCD 673 / Jul '98 / Raymer

BLOW

☐ FLESHMACHINE
PA 004CD / Mar '95 / Paragoric

☐ KISS LIKE CONCRETE
COTINDCD 8 / May '96 / Cottage Industry

☐ MAN AND GOAT ALIKE
COTINDCD 1 / Mar '95 / Cottage Industry

☐ PIGS
COTINDCD 10 / Aug '96 / Cottage Industry

Blow Monkeys

☐ CHOICES (The Singles Connection)
Wait: Howard, Robert & Kym Mazelle / Choice / Slaves no more / Celebrate the day (after you) / Wicked ways / Diggin' your scene / It doesn't have to be this way / Out with her / This is your life / It pays to belong / Wait / Choice / Man from Russia / Atomic lullaby / Wildflower / Forbidden fruit
74321137072 / Apr '93 / RCA

☐ FOR THE RECORD (The Best Of The Blow Monkeys)
Digging your scene / Springtime for the world / Out with her / Wicked ways / Wait / No woman is an island / Squaresville / Some kind of wonderful / It doesn't have to be this way / (Celebrate) The day after you / It pays to belong / Atomic lullaby / Choice / This is the way it has to be / This is your life / Digging your scene / Celebrate
74321393342 / Jun '96 / Camden

Blow Pipes

☐ ZENORIA
BPCD 01 / Nov '97 / Babel

Blowpipe

☐ FIRST CIRCLE
Conc / Kucou / Chixalub / Toba / Trench / First circle / Prop / Unkindness
STITCH 6CD / Jul '97 / Needlework

☐ PENDULUM
ROB 001 / 11 May '98 / Robot

Blowzabella

☐ BEST OF BLOWZABELLA, THE
Blowzabella/Marriage marches / L'enfant de dieu/ Faerie dance / Jenny pluck pears/Half hannikin / Polka piquee / Bourees three and four / Shave the monkey/Boys of the mill / Eglantine/Man in the brown hat/Schottishe fran havero/Minah / Eight step waltz/Lisa/Stukka gruppa / Glass island / Newbury jig/Moll in the wood/Sword dance/Old wife of Coverda / New jigs / Death in a Fen/Bruton town/Our Captain cried / Spaghetti panic / Jan mijne man/Go mauve / Horizonto
OSMOCD 001 / Oct '95 / Osmosys

☐ BOBBITYSHOOTY
Shave the monkey/Boys of the mill / Presbyterian hornpipe/Red lyon / La ronde des milloraines / Branle de borgogne/Horse branle / Bobbityshooty / Carl wark / Eglantine/Man in the brown hat/ Schottische fran havero/Minah / Topman and the afterguard / Medley / Scaramouche/Kathryn Arwen's march / Blowzabella/Jon's jig
OSMOCD 015 / Mar '98 / Osmosys

☐ RICHER DUST, A
Wars of the roses / Death in a fen/Bruton Town/Our Captain cried / Moth / Man in the brown hat / Diamond / New hornpipes / All things are quite silent
OSMOCD 010 / Jan '97 / Osmosys

☐ VANILLA
Spaghetti panic / La belle c'est endormir-famous wolf / Jan mijne man-go mauve / Fulmine / Beanfield-monster cafe / I wish, I wish / Down side-solvieg's songs-doctor feg / Horizonto / In continental mood-the old queen-flatworld / Lover's ghost / R.s.b. and the hobb / Spaghetti panic (live)
GLCD 3050 / Feb '95 / Green Linnet

☐ WALL OF SOUND
Kopenitsa / Eight step waltz/Lisa/Stukka gruppa / Hallowed ground / Newbury jig/Moll in the wood/ Sword dance (ghost tune)/Old wi / Sideways glance / Roger De Coverley/Trip o'er Tweed / Finnish Scottish / Last chance bouree / Glass island / Sinfonia
OSMOCD 005 / Jul '96 / Osmosys

Blue

☐ MEXICAN CHURCH
Small bones / Gorgon / Dark blue / Mass / Simononian / Cut me free / She's machine / Lower / Metal / Slow wave / Sand stone / Staff announcement
SOP 008CD / Jun '96 / Sabres Of Paradise

☐ NIGHTWORK
ILIGHT 009CD / 13 Apr '98 / Iris Light

☐ RESISTANCE
Diamandra / Doctor / External / Black stone / Circle line / Division dub / Still moving / Golden / Prisoner
SOP 004CD / Apr '95 / Sabres Of Paradise

Blue 101

☐ FROZENLAND
OOR 19CD / Jun '95 / Out Of Romford

Blue Aeroplanes

☐ BEST OF WARHOL'S 15, THE
REMCD 526 / 1 Jun '98 / Reactive

☐ FRIENDLOVERPLANE
Veils of colour / Veils of colour / Weird heart / Le petit cadeau de don juan / Severn beach / Police (36 divinity) / Action painting / Who built this station in the midwest / Old men sleeping on the bowery / 88 out / Ashtrays from mt. etna / Gunning the works / King of the soap box / Tolerance / Etiquette / Continually torn apart / Days of 49 / I wanna be your lover / Warhol's fifteen / Shame / Couple in the next room / Stripped
FIRE 33015 / Oct '91 / Fire

☐ FRUIT
FIRECD 057 / Jun '96 / Fire

☐ HUH (The Best Of The Blue Aeroplanes)
Jacket hangs / Huh / Colour me / Razor walk / Growing up, growing down / Fun / Weightless / ...And stones / You (are loved) Jack leaves and back spring / Anti-pretty / Disney head / Your own world / What it is / Lovething/Higherthing / Sixth continent
CDCHRM 101 / Feb '97 / Chrysalis

☐ LIFE MODEL
BBQCD 143 / Feb '94 / Beggars Banquet

☐ ROUGH MUSIC
BBQCD 167 / Jan '95 / Beggars Banquet

☐ SPITTING OUT MIRACLES
FIRE 33010 / Oct '91 / Fire

☐ TOLERANCE
FIRE 33003 / Oct '91 / Fire

Blue Amazon

☐ JAVELIN, THE
Intro/Never forget / Searchin' / Runner / Javelin / Paradise regime / No other love / And then the rain falls
BALP 1A / 20 Oct '97 / Sony Soho2

Blue, Barry

☐ GREATEST HITS
(Dancing) on a Saturday night / If I show you I can dance / Heads I win, tails you lose / Hot shot / Problem child / Behind my eyes / Miss hit and run / Do you wanna dance / New day / Girl next door / Hobo man / Life jacket round my heart / Back to the wall / School love
305782 / Oct '96 / Hallmark

☐ VERY BEST OF BARRY BLUE, THE
Dancin' on a saturday night / Miss, hit and run / Don't wanna be blue / Ooh I do / Kalamazoo / Pay at the gate / Queen of hearts / One way ticket (to the blues) / School love / Do you wanna dance / Tip of my tongue / Don't put your money on my horse / Rosetta stone / When winter kept us warm / Back to the wall / A trick of the light / Run into your daddy's arms / Hotshot
MCCD 103 / May '93 / Music Club

Blue Blood

☐ BIG NOISE, THE
One more night / Running back / Don't turn out the light / Love grows wild / Never rains in england / Secret lover / My idea of heaven / I can't wait / Night time city / Road to ruin
CDMFN 93 / Oct '89 / Music For Nations

Blue Brass Connection

☐ COOL AFFAIRS
Endless flight / Vine City / Va ja jo / Mama Laura / Impulse / Latine Lee / Rhythm-a-ning / For Loui
5132772 / Jan '92 / Amadeo

Blue By Nature

☐ BLUE TO THE BONE
SHA 0092 / Nov '96 / Shattered

Blue Caps

☐ HEP TO THE BEAT
PEPCD 119 / Jan '97 / Pollytone

☐ LEGENDARY BLUE CAPS, THE
Wrapped up in rockabilly / Baby blue / Yes I love you baby / I got a baby / Blue cap man / I lost an angel / Silly song / Lotta lovin' / Say Mama / Down at the in den / Dance to the bop / Johnny's boogie / Be bop a Lula / Rap / Unchained melody / Jealous heart / September in the rain / Am I that easy to forget / Jezebel / I dreamed of an old love affair
CDMF 089 / Jun '93 / Magnum Force

Blue Cats

☐ TUNNEL, THE
NERCD 069 / Sep '92 / Nervous

Blue Cheer

☐ HIGHLIGHTS AND LOWLIVES
Urban soldiers / Hunter of love / Girl from London / Blues steel dues / Big trouble in paradise / Flight of the enola gray / Hoochie coochie man / Down and dirty
CDTB 125 / Jun '91 / Thunderbolt

☐ LIVE AND UNRELEASED 1968-1974
CTCD 023 / Jul '97 / Captain Trip

☐ LIVE AND UNRELEASED VOL.2
CTCD 026 / Jul '97 / Captain Trip

Blue Crystal

☐ EROTIQUE
Essence of love / Gentle touch / Body harmony / Passion dance / Anticipation / Basic instinct / Gift of love / Hearts of fire / Ryhthmic energy / Ambience
BC 012CD / 12 Feb '98 / Blue Crystal

☐ SPIRIT DANCER
BCCD 004 / Feb '96 / Blue Crystal

Blue Devils

☐ BETTY'S MAD DASH
FCD 3041 / May '98 / Fury

Blue Dog

☐ WHAT IS ANYTHING
KFWCD 152 / Feb '95 / Knitting Factory

Blue Environment

☐ ECHOSPACE
AQDCD 002 / Jul '95 / Aquadar

☐ SEA, SPACE, OCEAN
AQUADAR 1CD / Sep '94 / Aquadar

Blue For Two

☐ SEARCH AND ENJOY
RA 91392 / Sep '92 / Roadrunner

Blue Hearts

☐ HEART'S ABOUT TO BREAK
3 BC / Nov '95 / Big Cactus

Blue Highway

☐ IT'S A LONG, LONG ROAD
REB 1719CD / Apr '96 / Rebel

☐ MIDNIGHT STORM
I'd rather be a lonesome pine / Preville flood / Some day / Midnight storm / Keen mountain prison / Getting over you / Last dollar blues / He walked all the way home / Cold frosty morn / Find me out on a mountain top / Whither thou go / May your life be sweet and simple
REBCD 1746 / 9 Mar '98 / Rebel

☐ WIND TO THE WEST
REB 1731CD / Aug '96 / Rebel

Blue Horses

☐ CRACKING LEATHER SKIN AND BONE
Helen / Sitting pretty / Pill/Farmers daughter / Under the leaves / Farewell to JK / Wiccaman / Into the woods / Screaming crying / All went away / Cabbage train / Big white telephone
NSBHCD 001 / Jan '98 / Native Spirit

Blue Humans

☐ CLEAR TO HIGHER TIME (Blue Humans & Rudolph Grey)
Lightning / Movement / Finally / Under power / Clear to higher time
NAR 077CD / May '93 / New Alliance

Blue Jam

☐ RAPPER'S PARADISE (Blue Jam & The Ghetto Street Fighters)
Gangsta's paradise / Tonite's the night / I got 5 on it / Hey lover / Big poppa / Player's anthem / Ain't nuthin' but a 'she' thing / 1st Of the month / Too hot / Ice cream / Craziest / Danger / Keep their heads ringin' / Sugar hill / Dear Mama / How high
12839 / May '96 / Laserlight

Blue Jays

☐ BLUE JAYS, THE
60 BRR / Jan '98 / BRR

Blue Law

☐ GONNA GETCHA
HNRCD 02 / Apr '96 / Hengest

Blue Lazer

☐ BEST OF BLUE LAZER, THE
HTCD 114 / 20 Apr '98 / Hot Productions

Blue Magic

☐ BLUE MAGIC
Sideshow / Look me up / What's come over me / Just don't want to be lonely / Stop to start / Welcome to the club / Spell / Answer to my prayer / Tear it down
7567804132 / Jan '96 / Atlantic

Blue Meanies

☐ FULL THROTTLE
THK 048CD / Jun '97 / Thick

Blue Mink

☐ BLUE MINK ARCHIVE
Melting pot / Randy / I wanna be around (with you) / Good morning freedom / Yesterday's gone / By the devil I was tempted / Our world / Stop us / Let him stay / Stay with me / Banner man / Song for Madeline / Non commercial blues / Morning glory / Mind your business / Mary Jane / Country chick / But not forever / Chopin up stix / Over the top
RMCD 210 / Nov '97 / Rialto

☐ VERY BEST OF BLUE MINK
Melting pot / We have all been saved / Stay with me / By the devil (i was tempted) / Good morning freedom / Can you feel it baby / Gimme reggae / World (you're closing in on me) / Randy / Banner man / Cat house / Jubilation / Bang bang, johnny's gang is after me / Get up / Gasoline alley bred / Our world / You are the sunshine of my life / Gap
MCCD 117 / Aug '93 / Music Club

Blue Mountain

☐ HOMEGROWN
Bloody 98 / Myrna Lee / Pretty please / Black dog / Generic America / Last words of Midnight Clyde / Babe / It ain't easy to love a liar / Ira Magee / Town clown / Dead end street / Rain
RR 88302 / Sep '97 / Roadrunner

Blue Mountain Panpipe Ensemble

☐ CHRISTMAS PANPIPE FAVOURITES
Little drummer boy / Christmas song / We three kings / Stop the cavalry / I saw three ships / Jingle bells / Mistletoe and wine / Sleigh ride / Have yourself a merry little Christmas / Good King Wenceslas / Silent night / When a child is born / Deck the halls with boughs of holly / Little donkey / Winter wonderland / Silver bells / Jolly old St. Nicholas / Let it snow, let it snow, let it snow / Happy holiday / White Christmas
CDMFP 6179 / Oct '96 / Music For Pleasure

☐ PAN PIPE LOVE SONGS
Without you / To much love will kill you / Sometimes when we touch / Lady in red / When I fall in love / Whole new world / I'm not in love / Get here / Love us all around / You need me / Always on my mind / Wind beneath my wings / Love lifted me / Power of love / On the wings of love / It must have been love / Greatest love of all / (Everything I do) I do it for you / Secret love
CDMFP 6169 / Jun '95 / Music For Pleasure

Blue Nile

☐ HATS
Downtown lights / Over the hillside / Let's go out tonight / Headlights on the parade / From a late night train / Seven am / Saturday night
LKHCD 2 / Apr '92 / Linn/Virgin

☐ PEACE AT LAST
Happiness / Sentimental man / Holy love / War is love / Soon / God bless you kid / Body and soul / Love came down / Tomorrow morning / Family life
9362458482 / Jun '96 / Warner Bros.

☐ WALK ACROSS THE ROOFTOPS, A
Walk across the rooftops / Tinsel Town in the rain / From rags to riches / Stay / Easter parade / Heatwave / Automobile noise
LKHCD 1 / Sep '88 / Linn/Virgin

Blue Noise

☐ 11 SONGS
Wicked messenger / If not you / Solitary heart / Good morning heartache / She wails / Mission / Leave the fear / Solitary heart / Rise and fall / Tomorrow people / Flag
CDMI 7002 / 13 Oct '97 / GMG

Blue Note Six

☐ FROM VIENNA WITH SWING
JCD 243 / Jun '95 / Jazzology

Blue Notes

☐ LEGACY (Live In South Africa 1964)
OGCD 007 / Feb '98 / Ogun

Blue Oyster Cult

☐ AGENTS OF FORTUNE
This ain't the summer of love / True confessions / (Don't fear) the reaper / ETI (Extra Terrestrial Intelligence) / Revenge of Vera Gemini / Sinful love / Tattoo vampire / Morning final / Tenderloin / Debbie Denise
4680192 / Apr '95 / Columbia

☐ BAD CHANNELS
IRSCD 993018 / Nov '96 / Intercord

☐ BLUE OYSTER CULT
Transmission MC / I'm the lamb but I ain't no sheep / Then came the last days of May / Stairway to the stars / Before the kiss / Redcap / Screams / She's as beautiful as a foot / Cities on flame / Workshop of the telescopes / Redeemed
4688742 / Feb '97 / Epic

☐ CLUB NINJA
White flags / Dancin' in the ruins / Rock not war / Perfect water / Spy in the house of the night / Beat 'em up / When the war comes / Shadow warrior / Madness to the method
379432 / Jun '97 / Koch International

☐ HEAVEN FORBID
CD 08518932 / 6 Apr '98 / SPV
6076862412 / 24 Mar '98 / CMC

☐ LIVE 1976
Stairway to the stars / Harvester of eyes / Cities on flame / ME262 / Dominance and submission / Astronomy / ETI (Extra Terrestrial Intelligence) / Buck's boogie / This ain't the summer of love / (Don't fear) the reaper
CLACD 269 / Oct '91 / Castle

☐ SOME ENCHANTED EVENING
R U ready 2 rock / ETI (Extra Terrestrial Intellegence) / Astronomy / Kick out the jams / Godzilla / (Don't fear) the reaper / We gotta get out of this place
4879312 / Jul '97 / Columbia

☐ WORKSHOP OF THE TELESCOPES (2CD Set)
Cities on flame with rock and roll / Transmaniacon MC / Before the kiss / Redcap / Stairway to the stars / Buck's boogie / Workshop of the telescopes / Red and the black / 7 screaming diz-busters / Career of evil / Flaming telepaths / Astronomy / Subhuman / Harvester of eyes / ME 262 / Born to be wild / (Don't fear) the reaper / This ain't the summer of love / ETI (Extra Terrestrial Intelligence) / Godzilla / Goin' through the motions / Golden age of leather / Kick out the james / We gotta get out of this place / In thee / Marshall plan / Veteran of the psychic wars / Burnin' for you / Dominance and submission / Take me away / Shooting shark / Dancin' in the ruins / Perfect water
4809492 / Jan '96 / Columbia

Blue People

☐ BLUE
JVC 90012 / Feb '96 / JVC

Blue Phantom

☐ DISTORTIONS
GRC 013 / 5 Jan '98 / GCR

Blue Pillar Organ

☐ STREET ORGAN FAVOURITES
SOW 90135 / Jan '95 / Sounds Of The World

Blue Planet

☐ PEACE FOR KABUL
39850002 / 21 Aug '97 / Blue Flame

Blue Rags

☐ RAG 'N' ROLL
SPCD 407 / 1 Sep '97 / Sub Pop

Blue Rhythm Boys

☐ AT LAST
That's the stuff you gotta watch / I'll go crazy / Person to person / I'm walkin' / It isn't right / Cajun love affair / Trace of you / Crazy mixed up world / Ride 'n' roll / Babie's comin' home / Mother earth / I'll try / Hoochie coochie man / Come on back / Wang dang doodle / Breathless / Blue rhythm boogie / Go on ahead / Catfish
CDWIK 105 / Apr '92 / Big Beat

☐ THAT OL' BLUE MAGIC
NITCD 006 / Apr '98 / Rockout

Blue Rose

☐ BLUE ROSE
SHCD 3768 / Jan '97 / Sugar Hill

Blue Sky Boys

☐ IN CONCERT 1964
Are you from dixie / Quit that ticklin' me / I'm just here to get my baby out of jail / Worried man blues / After the ball / Behind these prison walls of love / Last letter / Fox / Sweetest gift / Only one step more / Uncle josh comedy skit / Don't trade / Kentucky / If I could hear my mother pray again / Sweetheart mountain rose / It was midnight on the stormy deep / Beautiful / In the hills of roane county / I'm saved
ROUCD 11536 / ' / Rounder

Blue Stingrays

☐ SURF 'N' BURN
Monsoon / Echo park / Goldfinger / Brave new world / Russian roulette / Moon over Catalina / Malibu babylon / Blue venus / Land of the unknown / Surfer's life / Stingray stomp / Zuma sunset / Ju ju beads / Green sea
60012 / 15 Sep '97 / Epitaph

Blue Tip

☐ DISCHORD NO.101
DIS 101CD / Jun '96 / Dischord

Blue Whale

☐ CONGREGATION
SHMCD 5093 / 10 Aug '98 / Shimmy Disc

Blue Wisp Big Band

☐ ROLLIN'
SB 2077 / Jan '97 / Sea Breeze

Bluebells

☐ BEST OF THE BLUEBELLS, THE
82840522 / Apr '93 / London

Blueberry Hill

☐ 50 HOMEGROWN FAVOURITES
Medley / Medley / Medley / Medley / Medley / Medley / Medley / Medley / Medley / Medley (10) / Medley (11) / Wild mountain thyme (will ye go lassie go)
SOW 530 / Sep '97 / Sound Waves

☐ D-DAY FAVOURITES 1944
SOW 510 / May '94 / Sound Waves

☐ IT'S PARTY TIME
SOW 520 / May '95 / Sound Waves

☐ IT'S PARTY TIME AGAIN
It's party time again / I do like to be beside the seaside/Yellow submarine / Bladen races/I do like to be beside the seaside / Love grows where my Rosemary goes/American pie / I can see clearly now/Living next door to Alice / Summer holiday / Hard day's night/I should have known better/ Heartbeat / From me to you/Three steps to heaven / JCB song / I believe/What a wonderful world/It's only make believe / Unchained melody/The answer to everything / I'll never find another you/Halfway to paradise / I only wanna be with you/Will you still love me tomorrow / Freedom come freedom go / Do you want to know a secret/Nowhere man / Me and you and a dog named Boo/Everyday / Atmosphere / Answer me/Another Saturday night/Wonderful world / Cockles and mussels/Daisy Daisy/Home on the range / My Bonnie lies over the ocean / Johnny's so long at the fair/She's a lassie from Lancashire / Down at the old Bull and Bush/I'm forever blowing bubbles
SOWCD 526 / 15 Sep '97 / Sound Waves

☐ ONE STEP FORWARD (Blueberry Hill & Sheila G. White)
My baby loves me / Dream baby / One more last chance / On the road / Mercury blues / Wild one / Achy breaky heart / Live till I die / Honey (Won't you open that door) / You make me feel like a man / Chattahoochee / One step forward / Blue roses / Bootscootin boogie / Ancient history / Cotton Eye Joe / When will I be loved / Loves gotta hold on you / I swear / Guitars and cadillacs
3036300162 / Jun '98 / Carlton

☐ OUR KINDA COUNTRY (Blueberry Hill & Sheila G. White)
Ghost riders in the sky / Blue moon over Kentucky / Do what you do do well / Good hearted woman / Folsom prison / Truck driving man / Wild side of life / Peaceful easy feeling / Take it easy / When I was yours / Six days on the road / Walk on by / I love you because / Take these chains from my heart / Ramblin' rose / Walking after midnight / From a Jack to a King / Tonight the bottle let me down / Running bear / Delta dawn / I really had a ball last night / Jambalaya / Me and Bobby McGee / Your cheating heart / Paper roses / Don't fence me in / Hello Mary Lou / I'm gonna be a country girl again / Walk tall / On top of the world / San Quentin / Sea of heartbreak / Blanket on the ground / Gypsy woman / Okie from Muskogee / Take me home country roads / Together again / Sweet dreams / You're my best friend / Today I started loving you again / Oh lonesome me / I walk the line / Turn out the light / Let's think about living / Leaving on a jet plane / What I've got in mind / Single girl / If I said you had a beautiful body / Harper valley PTA / Sloop John B
SOW 523 / Aug '96 / Sound Waves

Bluebird

☐ BLUEBIRD
REV 061CD / 29 Sep '97 / Revelation

Bluebird Society Orchestra

☐ MUSIC OF HIGH SOCIETY
ST 583 / Jul '94 / Stash

Bluebirds

☐ SOUTH FROM MEMPHIS
ICD 9420 / Oct '96 / Icehouse

☐ SWAMP STOMP
ICD 9407
TX 1012CD / Jul '95 / Taxim

Blueboy

☐ BANK OF ENGLAND, THE
SHINKANSEN 12CD / 6 Jul '98 / Shinkansen

☐ IF WISHES WERE HORSES
SARAH 612CD / Mar '95 / Sarah

Bluegills

☐ BLUEGILLS, THE
Real gone / Waiting for the big one / Don't gimme that gimme / Tell tale signs / Don't tell me that / Bluegills / We hang on / Soul full of blues / Rock bottom / My funky valentine / I'm a little mixed up / In a funk in a phone booth
ATM 123 / Nov '96 / Atomic Theory

Bluegrass Album Band

☐ BLUEGRASS INSTRUMENTALS VOL.6
ROUCD 0330 / Aug '96 / Rounder

☐ SONGS OF BILL MONROE, THE
On my way back to the old home / I believe in you darling / Cheyenne / Letter from my darlin' / Lonesome moonlight waltz / When you are lonely / Sitting alone in the moonlight / Molly and Tenbrooks / On the old Kentucky shore / Brown County breakdown / Toy heart / River of death
EDCD 7003 / Oct '96 / Easydisc

☐ SONGS OF FLATT & SCRUGGS, THE
I'll never shed another tear / Down that road / Don't this road look rough and rocky / Is it too late now / Your love is like a flower / Old home town / Come back darling / I'm waiting to hear you call me darling / Somehow tonight / I'd rather be alone / Head over heals / So happy I'll be
EDCD 7002 / Aug '96 / Easydisc

Bluejean

☐ TRY MY LOVIN'
EBCD 28 / Jan '95 / Eightball

Bluerunners

☐ CHATEAU CHUCK, THE
MON 6118CD / Mar '94 / Ichiban

☐ TO THE COUNTRY
Longest day / Au bout du chemin / Landslide / Rhode Island / Stringbean / Au boro du bayou / Curb service / Sound of love / Au festival / Doorway / Ossun 2 step / Quand la nuit coule du ciel / To the country / Made up my mind / Blueco
ROUCD 6073 / Feb '98 / Rounder

Blues Band

☐ HOMAGE
Let the good times roll / I go crazy / Temperature/ Fever / Rolling and tumbling / CC rider / How can such a poor man stand such times and live / Work song / Sweet home Chicago / Wang dang doodle / You shook me / I can tell / Fine brown frame / I ain't got you / That same thing / Rainin' in my heart / Send me some lovin' / Honest I do
ESMCD 202 / 29 Sep '97 / Essential

Blues Boy Willie

☐ BE WHO VOL.1
Why are you cheatin' on me / Same ol' fishing hole / Crack up / Stealing your love tonight / Let me funk with you / Can we talk before we separate / Highway blues / Be who
ICH 1064CD / Oct '93 / Ichiban

☐ BE WHO VOL.2
Party all night / I still care / Break away / Rest of my life / Where is Leroy / Love darling love / Let's get closer / Be who, two
ICH 1119CD / Jun '94 / Ichiban

Blues Brothers

☐ BEST OF THE BLUES BROTHERS
Expressway / Everybody needs somebody to love / I don't know / She caught the Katy / Soul man / Rubber biscuit / Goin' back to Miami / Gimme some lovin' / B Movie / Boxcar blues / Flip flop fly
7815862 / Jun '89 / Atlantic

☐ BLUES BROTHERS - MUSIC FROM THE FILM (Original Soundtrack)
Minnie the moocher / Jailhouse rock / Sweet home chicago / Theme from rawhide / Peter Gunn / Gimme some lovin' / She caught the Katy / Old landmark / Shake a tail feather / Everybody needs somebody to love / Think
7567827872 / Nov '95 / Atlantic

☐ BRIEFCASE FULL OF BLUES
I can't turn you loose / Hey bartender / Messin' with the kid / I got everything I need / Shot gun blues / Rubber biscuit / Groove me / Soul man / Flip flop and fly / B Movie / Boxcar blues
250556 / Mar '87 / Atlantic

☐ LIVE FROM CHICAGO HOUSE OF BLUES
Intro / Chicken shack / I wish you would / All my money back / Blues why you worry me / 634-5789 / Flip flop fly / Viva Las Vegas / Green onions / Sweet home Chicago / Messin' with the kid / Born in Chicago / Groove with me tonight / All she wants to do is rock / Money that's all I want
0099172WHE / 6 Oct '97 / Edel

☐ LIVE IN MONTREUX (Blues Brothers Band)
Hold on I'm comin' / In the midnight hour / She caught the katy / Thrill is gone / I can't turn you loose / Sweet home Chicago / Knock on wood / Rasie your hand / Peter Gunn / Soul finger / Hey bartender / Soul man / Everybody needs somebody to love / Green onions
9031716142 / Feb '95 / Atlantic

☐ MADE IN AMERICA
Soul finger / Funky Broadway / Who's making love / Do you love me / Guilty / Perry Mason / Riot in cell block 9 / Green onions / I ain't got you / From the bottom / Going to Miami
7567814782 / Jun '89 / Atlantic

Blues Busters

☐ IN MEMORY OF THE BLUES BUSTERS
How sweet it is (to be loved by you) / Wings of a dove / I don't know / Donna / Behold / Soon you'll be gone / Wide awake in a dream / Baby what you want me to do / You're no good / Oh baby / My girl / Amen / That's heaven to me / Shame and scandal / From russia with love / Pretty girls / Love me forever
JMC 200114 / Sep '93 / Jamaican Gold

Blues Company

☐ PUBLIC RELATIONS
Public relations / Red blood / Dance all night / Midnight train / Just can't keep from crying / She's gone / I've got the blues / Rhythm of Zydeco / Cry for me / Big bad wolf / Gambler / Blow Jay blow / Change / Crippled mind
INAK 9018 / Aug '95 / In Akustik

☐ SO WHAT
What's wrong / Cold blue moon / Stay with me / Downhome blues / Mean woman blues / Rattlesnake blues / Pension blues / Look here baby / Good times boogie / Teeny weeny bit / Drinkin' blues / Mr. TNT / Black nite
INAK 8803CD / Jul '97 / In Akustik

☐ VINTAGE
INAK 9036 / Nov '95 / In Akustik

Blues Factory

☐ TAKE A STROLL
Stollin' with bone / Smoke / Just one more time / Six-pack woman / Too much tequila / I don't believe / You had your chance / Look at the moon / Hot little mama / I'm gonna hit that highway / Huckle boogie / Next time you see me
CBHCD 2003 / Feb '98 / CRS

Blues Magoos

☐ PSYCHEDELIC LOLLIPOP
REP 4194 / Aug '91 / Repertoire

Blues Mobile Band

☐ NEW DAY YESTERDAY, A
PRD 70772 / May '95 / Provogue

☐ OUT IN THE BLUE
What I do / She's gone / I'm going home / I can't stand it / Try hard / Leave this town / I've got dreams to remember / Leave me alone / Tell me why / Helpless without you / Too late
PRD 70852 / Nov '95 / Provogue

Blues 'n' Trouble

☐ FIRST TROUBLE/NO MINOR KEYS (2CD Set)
Born in Chicago / Natural born lover / CT / Downtown saturday night / Blues 'n' trouble / Sloppy drunk / Tearstains on my pillow / Mystery train / Wake up mama / Deep blue feeling / Spank the plank / Texas / What's the matter / Red hot / Wake up mama / Fine fine fine / All my love in vain / Clock on the wall / Honey pot / Tight 'n' juicy / Free to ride / You can run / Madison blues / Double trouble / Beautiful city / Let it rock / Slow down / Cadillac / Double trouble
RGFBNTDCD 010 / Jun '98 / Road Goes On Forever

☐ HAT TRICK
I got your number / Why / Cherry peaches / Travelling light / When the lights go down / Comin' home / What's the matter / Be mine tonight / Rockin' with you Jimmy / TNT / See my baby shake it / I don't need no doctor
CDBLUH 001 / Feb '92 / Blue Horizon

Blues Project

☐ ANTHOLOGY (2CD Set)
5297852 / Jun '97 / Polydor

☐ LIVE AT TOWN HALL
OW 30010 / Jul '94 / One Way

Blues Section

☐ BLUES SECTION
LRCD 3 / Dec '94 / Love

☐ BLUES SECTION VOL.2
LXCD 604 / Aug '95 / Love

Blues Traveller

☐ FOUR
Runaround / Stand / Look around / Fallible / Mountains win again / Freedom / Crash burn / Price to pay / Hook / Good, the bad and the ugly / Just wait / Brother John
5402652 / Nov '94 / Polydor

☐ STRAIGHT ON 'TILL MORNING
Carolina blues / Felicia / Justify the thrill / Canadian rose / Business as usual / Yours / Psycho JOe / Great big world / Battle of someone / Most precarious / Gunfighter / Last night I dreamed / Make my way
5407502 / Jun '97 / A&M

Bluesix

☐ LOOKING AT THE COVER
TRCD 9931 / 7 Apr '98 / Tramp

Bluestars

☐ BLUESTARS
ZERO 0011 / 5 Jan '98 / Zero

Bluetile Lounge

☐ HALF-CUT
SLR 024 / 8 Jun '98 / Smells Like

Bluetones

☐ EXPECTING TO FLY
Talking to Clarry / Bluetonic / Cut some rug / Things change / Fountainhead / Carnt be trusted / Slight return / Putting out fires / Vampire / Parting gesture / Time and again
BLUE 004CD / Feb '96 / Superior Quality

☐ RETURN TO THE LAST CHANCE SALOON
Tone blooze / Unpainted Arizona / Solomon bites the worm / UTA / Four day weekend / Sleazy bed track / IF / Jub jub bird / Sky will fall / Ames / Down at the reservoir / Heard you were dead / Broken starr / Woman done gone left me
BLUED 008 / 9 Mar '98 / Superior Quality

Bluezeum

☐ PORTRAIT OF A GROOVE
Portrait of a groove / Can I get that funk / Luv uncondishunal / Dreamtyme / Every day and every night / Just anotha day / Swing / Strange love last night / Soundscape
CD 83331 / Nov '96 / Telarc Jazz

Bluiett, Hamiet

☐ BALLADS AND BLUES
1212882 / Dec '97 / Soul Note

☐ BIRTHRIGHT
IN 1030CD / Jan '97 / India Navigation

☐ EBU
SNCD 1088 / Jan '86 / Soul Note

☐ IM/POSSIBLE TO KEEP
IN 1072CD / Jan '97 / India Navigation

☐ LIVE AT CARLOS I (Bluiett, Hamiet & Concept)
Mighty denn / Full, deep and mellow / Nalikoal / Oleo / Night in Tunisia
JAM 9129 / Jun '97 / Just A Memory

☐ LIVE AT CARLOS I - ANOTHER NIGHT (Bluiett, Hamiet & Concept)
I'll never close my eyes / Wide open / Autumn leaves / John / Sobra una nube
JAM 91362 / 17 Nov '97 / Justin Time

☐ LIVE AT THE KNITTING FACTORY (Bluiett Baritone Saxophone Group)
Opening statement / Settagast strut / A's song / KMA/QB / Pit stop / Discusion among friends / Lowdown blues / Blunita / Revival / Neck bones / JB's groove
KFWCD 217 / 18 May '98 / Knitting Factory

☐ SAME SPACE (Bluiett, Hamiet & DD Jackson/Mor Thiam)
Aseeko / Closing melody / Titled-Un / Can't help it / Peace song / Jamm'd / Gnu tune / Kasima / Spirit / Moment / A/B original / Mon diue / Conversation
JUST 1092 / 29 Jun '98 / Justin Time

☐ SANKOFA/REAR GARDE
1212382 / Sep '93 / Soul Note

Blum, Eberhard

☐ ALEA
ARTCD 6180 / Feb '96 / Hat Art

Blumfeld

☐ LETAT AT MOI
ABB 73CD / Feb '95 / Big Cat

Blunstone, Colin

☐ ECHO BRIDGE
INDELCD 4 / 27 Apr '98 / Indelible

☐ GREATEST HITS
Say you don't mind / Old and wise / Caroline goodbye / Andorra / I don't believe in miracles / She's not there / Tell her no / Time of the season / What becomes of the broken hearted / Tracks of my tears / Still burning bright / Don't feel no pain
CLACD 351 / Aug '93 / Castle

☐ LIGHT INSIDE, THE
Your love is like the sun / Seventh heaven / Love's a stranger / Slow burn / You make love so good / Walking in the rain / Till we try again / Send me your broken hearts / Don't let the darkness touch you / Knowing you / Hearts that turn / Losing you
MYSCD 125 / 1 Jun '98 / Mystic

☐ SOME YEARS IT'S THE TIME OF
She loves the way they love her / Misty roses / Caroline goodbye / Though you are far away / Mary won't you warm my bed / Let me come closer to you / Say you don't mind / I don't believe in miracles / How wrong can one man be / Andorra / How could we dare to be wrong / Wonderful / Beginning / Keep the curtains closed today / You who are lonely / It's magical / This is your captain calling
EK 66449 / Jul '95 / Columbia

Blur

☐ BIOGRAPHY SERIES
10016 / 3 Nov '97 / Metro Independent

☐ BLUR
Beetlebum / Song 2 / Country sad ballad man / MOR / On your own / Theme from retro / You're so great / Death of a party / Chinese bombs / I'm just a killer for your love / Look inside America / Strange news from another star / Movin' on / Essex dogs
FOODCD 19 / Jun '97 / Food

☐ BUSTIN' AND DRONIN' (2CD Set)
Movin' on / Death of a party / On your own / Essex dogs / Death of a party / Theme from retro / Death of a party / On your own / Popscene / Song 2 / On your own / Chinese bombs / Moving on / MOR
TOCP 504445 / 9 Mar '98 / Food

☐ GREAT ESCAPE, THE
Stereotypes / Country house / Best days / Charmless man / Fade away / Top man / Universal / Mr. Robinson's quango / He thought of cars / It could be you / Ernold Same / Globe alone / Dan Abnormal / Entertain me / Yoko and Hiro
FOODCD 14 / Sep '95 / Food

☐ LEISURE
She's so high / Bang / Slow down / Reptition / Bad day / Sing / There's no other way / Fool / Come together / High cool / Birthday / War me down
FOODCD 6 / Aug '91 / Food

☐ MODERN LIFE IS RUBBISH
For tomorrow / Advert / Colin Zeal / Pressure on Julian / Star shaped / Blue jeans / Chemical world / Intermission / Sunday Sunday / Oily water / Miss America / Villa Rosie / Coping / Turn it up / Resigned / Commercial break
FOODCD 9 / May '93 / Food

☐ PARKLIFE
Girls and boys / Tracy Jacks / End of a century / Parklife / Bank holiday / Debt collector / Far out / To the end / London loves / Trouble in the message centre / Clover over Dover / Magic America / Jubilee / This is a low
FOODCD 10 / Apr '94 / Food

Blurt

☐ PAGAN STRINGS
14988 / Feb '97 / Spalax

Blyth Power

☐ OUT FROM UNDER THE KING
DR 004CD / Sep '96 / Downwarde Spiral

☐ PARADISE RAZED
DR 003CD / Feb '95 / Downwarde Spiral

☐ PASTOR SKULL
Pastor skull / Man who came in third / Gabriel the angel / In the lines of graves / Breitenfeld / General Winter / Sunne in splendour / Stonehaven / Vane tempest / Pandora's people / Stitching in time
DR 002CD / Sep '96 / Downwarde Spiral

Blythe, Arthur

☐ CALLING CARD
As of yet / Blue blues / Naima's love song / Hip dripper / Odessa / Elaborations / Jitterbug waltz / Break tune
ENJ 90512 / Feb '96 / Enja

☐ METAMORPHOSIS/THE GRIP
IN 1029CD / Jan '97 / India Navigation

☐ NIGHT SONG
CCD 1016 / Jul '98 / Clarity

☐ RETROFLECTION
Jana's delight / JB blues / Peacemaker / Light blue / Lenox avenue breakdown / Faceless woman / Break tune
ENJ 80462 / Mar '94 / Enja

Blyton, Carey

☐ FOLKSONG ARRANGEMENTS, THE
Anti-confederation song / Lukey's boat / Great big sea hove in Long Beach / Bonny banks of Virgie-o / Blooming bright star of Belle isle / Anti-confederation song / Badger drive / I'se the b'y that builds the beat/We'll rant and roar/Kellig / Squid jiggin' ground/Squarin' up time / Jack was every inch a sailor / Donkey riding / Auction block / Pull on the oars / Eskimo lullaby / Kelligrew's soiree / Lukey's boat / Sherpardess' carol / Cherry-tree carol / Huron carol / Lullaby / Plea of the miller / David of the white rock / Lullaby / Robin redbreast / Blue Christmas / Pianoman / Maiden deceived / Early one morning / Bobby Shafto / O waly waly / Early one morning / What shall we do with the drunken sailor / There's a tavern in the town
URCD 131 / Oct '97 / Upbeat

BMX Bandits

☐ C-86 AND MORE
ER 1048 / Jul '97 / Elefant

☐ GETTING DIRTY
CRECD 174 / May '95 / Creation

☐ LIFE GOES ON
CRECD 133 / Sep '93 / Creation

☐ STAR WARS
ASK 007CD / '92 / Vinyl Japan

☐ THEME PARK
CRECD 202 / Oct '96 / Creation

☐ THEME PARK
BD 9048 / Nov '97 / Big Deal

BNFL Band

☐ BY REQUEST (BNFL Band/Richard Evans)
Toccata / Revelation / Paragon / Amparito roca / Ted Heath big band set / Impromptu for tuba / Ave Maria / Carnival of Venice / March
QPRL 078D / Oct '97 / Polyphonic

☐ MUSIC OF PHILIP SPARKE VOL.1, THE (Cambridge Variations) (BNFL Band/ Richard Evans)
Jubilee overture / Music for a festival / Serenade for horns / Malvern suite / Concerto grosso / Mountains song / Cambridge variations
QPRL 081D / Aug '96 / Polyphonic

☐ PARTITE
Sinfonia for brass op 85 'maoriana / Sinfonia for brass op 85 'maoriana
QPRL 062D / Sep '93 / Polyphonic

☐ ROMANCE IN BRASS VOL.2
Kiss me again / Spread a little happiness / Just the way you are / Somewhere out there / Serenade for Toni / Annie Laurie / Girl with the flaxen hair / Meditation from thais / Li'l darlin' / Indian summer / Aubade / Love on the rocks / Romance de l'amour / Passing by / Myfanwy / Sweet shepherdess / Georgia on my mind / Folks who live on the hill / Memory
QPRL 063D / Apr '94 / Polyphonic

☐ TRAVELLIN' LIGHT (BNFL Band & Russel Gray/Intrada Brass/Waitakere Brass)
Charivari / Apres un reve / Napoli / Solveig's song / Jubilance / Hornpipe of the seashore / Songs of Erin / Higgin's hornpipe/The Kildare fancy / David of the white rock / Grand Russian fantasia / Dark haired Marie / Zelda / My love is like a red, red rose / Phantasy
QPRL 079D / Oct '97 / Polyphonic

☐ UN VIE DE MATELOT
Un vie de matelot / Snowdon fantasy / Little suite for brass / Rococo variations / Land of the long white cloud
QPRL 069D / Oct '94 / Polyphonic

Bo, Eddie

☐ BEST OF EDDIE BO, THE
Hook and sling / If it's good to you (it's good for you) / Getting to the middle / Check your bucket / Getting to the middle / Don't turn me loose / We're doing it / Disco party
HUBCD 16 / Apr '97 / Hubbub

☐ CHECK MR POPEYE
Check Mr. Popeye / Now let's Popeye / It must be love / Dinky doo / I'll do anything for you / Warm daddy / Roamin-itis / Hey there baby / I need someone / Tell it like it is / You got your mojo working / Ain't you ashamed / Baby I'm wise / Every dog has his day
ROUCD 2077 / '88 / Rounder

Boa

☐ WRONG ROAD
GF 113 / 22 Jun '98 / Gear Fab

Boards Of Canada

☐ MUSIC HAS THE RIGHT TO CHILDREN
Wildlife analysis / Eagle in your mind / Colour of fire / Telephasic workshop / Triangles and rhombuses / Sixtyten / Turquoise hexagon sun / Kaini industries / Bocuma / Roygbiv / Rue the whirl / Aquarius / Olson / Pete standing alone / Smokes quantity / Open the light / One very important thought
WARPCD 055 / 20 Apr '98 / Warp

Boat Band

☐ BURNING THE WATER
HARCD 030 / Apr '95 / Harbour Town

Boatman, James

☐ MAIN STREET USA
CCS 9896 / Nov '96 / Channel Classics

Boatman, Tooter

☐ ROCKIN' TOOTER BOATMAN
CLCD 4408 / Jan '97 / Collector/White Label

Bob & Earl

☐ DANCETIME USA (Bob & Earl/The Olympics)
Baby, your time is my time: *Bob & Earl* / Big brother: *Bob & Earl* / Land of 1000 dances: *Bob & Earl* / I can't get away: *Bob & Earl* / My little girl: *Bob & Earl* / I'll keep running back: *Bob & Earl* / Dancin' everywhere: *Bob & Earl* / Send for me I'll be there: *Bob & Earl* / Ooh honey babe: *Bob & Earl* / Harlem shuffle: *Bob & Earl* / Bounce: *Olympics* / Mine exclusively: *Olympics* / Baby, do the philly dog: *Olympics* / Duck: *Olympics* / Same old thing: *Olympics* / I'll do a little bit more: *Olympics* / We go together: *Olympics* / Secret agent: *Olympics*
GSCD054 / Jul '95 / Goldmine

Bob & Ray

☐ STEREO SPECTACULAR, A (Various Artists)
Bob and Ray visit Dr Ahkbar at the castle: *Bob & Ray* / Bob and Ray in the round room: *Bob & Ray* / Thing: *Bob & Ray* / Bob and Ray in the laboratory: *Bob & Ray* / End: *Bob & Ray* / Riders in the sky: *Melachrino, George* / Minute on the rocks: *Henderson, Skitch* / Buck dance: *Schory, Dick* / New fangled tango: *Horne, Lena* / Second Hungarian rhapsody: *Guckenheimer Sour Kraut Band* / First Noel: *Lieber, Richard* / We'll gather lilacs in the spring: *Andrews, Julie* / Song of the Volga boatmen: *Sauter-Finegan Orchestra* / Whatever Lola wants: *Lane, Abbe* / Ox drivers: *Belafonte Singers*
743212574929 / Jul '96 / RCA

Bob & The Bearcats

☐ HIGH HEELS AND HOMICIDE
PEPCD 115 / Sep '96 / Pollytone

Bob Delyn

☐ GEDON
Gortoz pell zo gortoz gwell / Poeni dim / Llys Ifor Haul / Ffair y Bala / Corsydd Fyrjinia / Mil harddach wyt / Beaj iskis / Seance Watcyn Wynn / Y swn / Tren bach y sgwarnogod / Blodau haearn blodau glo / Y clewr olaf / Llewg zotrog oz llep zotrog (Kig ejen c'hoazh)
CRAICD 021 / Aug '94 / Crai

☐ GWBADE BACH COCHLYD
CRAICD 049 / Oct '96 / Crai

Bobbejaan

☐ ICH STEH AN DER BAR UND HABE KEIN GELD
Ich steh on der bar und habe kein geld / Roy old boy / Ich weine in mein bier / Ein hauschen auf der heide / Vie biitre tranen / Marina / Kili watch / Die letzte rose / Ich muss ein cowboy sein / Spiel gitarre spiel / Ach war ich nur / Wie ne kneipe ohne bier / Und das hat mir g'rad noch gefenlt / O-la-la Luise / Dein herz kommt mir vor wie ein wanderpokal / Was kohn ich denn dafur / Zwischen Tennessee und Oklahoma / Schon langsam und nur nicht zu schnell / Die katz kam wieder / Ein voles glas und ein volles pomemon /

Naie / Was meine frau alles wissen will / Der weg nach Winnepeg / Texas rangers abschied / Ich hab kein geld fur ein orchester / Das treibt den Mann an die Theke / Der verliebte pfeifer / Der pfeifer und sein schatten
BCD 15921 / Jul '96 / Bear Family

Bobby & Steve

☐ BREAKBEAT SESSIONS VOL.2 (Black Trax)
Black trax / Night grooves / Fantasy / Benji / Midnight / Everybody / Hustle / I wanna / Soul / Groove on / Don't you / Tell me / Tribe
343712 / May '96 / Koch Dance Force

Bobby & The Midnites

☐ WHERE THE BEAT MEETS THE STREET
(I want to live in) America / Where the beat meets the street / She's gonna win your heart / Ain't that peculiar / Lifeguard / Rock in the 80's / Lifeline / Falling / Thunder and lightning / Gloria Monday
RE 821772 / 1 Jun '98 / Razor & Tie

Bobby O

☐ BEST OF BOBBY O, THE (How To Pick Up Girls)
I'm so hot for you / She has a way / Beat by beat / How to pick up girls / Lonely too long / Give it up / Man like me / Confusion / Pump it up / Whisper to a scream / Mixed-up world / Suspicious minds / I'll never find another girl like you / Reputation / Hangin' on
HTCD 15 / 20 Apr '98 / Hot Productions

Bobo Dread

☐ HEART OF STONE
PCD 0923 / 5 May '98 / Forward

Bobo, Willie

☐ JUICY
Knock on wood / Mating call / Mercy mercy mercy / Felicidad / La desccarga sel bobo / Juicy / Ain't too proud to beg / Music to watch girls by / Dreams / Dis-advantages / Roots / Shing a ling baby / Untitled / Juicy (3 takes) / Ain't too proud to beg / Music to watch girls (3 takes) / Dis-advantage (2 takes) / Shing a ling baby (2 takes)
5198572 / 3 Aug '98 / Verve

☐ TALKIN' VERVE
5375752 / Jul '97 / Verve

☐ UNO DOS TRES
5216642 / Feb '95 / Verve

Bobs

☐ COVER THE SONGS OF...
ROUCD 9049 / Nov '94 / Rounder

☐ I BROW CLUB
Ambient one / Hey coach don't call me a queer / Why not try right now / Swingers / Late model love / Crow / Change of heart / Bongwater day / Is it something that I said / Waiting song / Vapor carioca / There's a nose ring in my soup / Bumps in the baseline / Leisure suit / Like a parrot / Gate
ROUCD 9062 / Dec '97 / Rounder

☐ PLUGGED
ROUCD 9059 / Oct '95 / Rounder

☐ SHUT UP AND SING
ROUCD 9039 / Jan '94 / Rounder

☐ TOO MANY SANTA'S
ROUCD 9060 / Sep '96 / Rounder

Bobvan

☐ WATER DRAGON
Ay triste / Eyebrow and curved hair / Water dragon / Branle poitevin / Serendipity / Careful with that fax Eugene / Labbra Rosse / Shrinking of the gigantic / Perky Pat's lament / Memory
SSR 127 / Jan '94 / SSR

Bocage, Peter

☐ PETER BOCAGE & HIS CREOLE SERENADERS
AMCD 93 / Nov '96 / American Music

Bocelli, Andrea

☐ ARIA (The Opera Album)
4620332 / 27 Apr '98 / Philips

☐ ROMANZA
Con te partiro / Vivere: *Bocelli, Andrea & Gerardina Trovato* / Per amore / Il mare calmo della sera / Caruso / Macchine da guerra / La tue parole / Vivo per lei / Romanza / La luna che non c'e / Rapsodia / Voglio restare cosi / E chiove / Miserere: *Bocelli, Andrea & John Miles* / Time to say goodbye: *Bocelli, Andrea & Sarah Brightman*
4564562 / May '97 / Philips

Bock, Wolfgang

☐ BISCAYA SUNSET
SKYCD 3054 / Sep '95 / Sky

Bocle, Gildas

☐ CELTIC TALES (Bocle, Gildas/Jean Baptiste & Le Mars/Pellitteri)
Ker maria / Celtic tale no.4 / Pipelines / Seascape / Half / Celtic tale no.1 / One's way / Voiles / Beeline / Celtic tale no.2 / Neuf / Virages / Celtic tale no.3
4873082 / 1 Sep '97 / Sony Jazz

Boddy, Ian

☐ CLIMB
SER 005 / Jun '96 / Something Else

☐ CONTINUUM (2CD Set)
SER 011 / Apr '97 / Something Else

☐ DEEP, THE
Standing at the edge / Dark descent / Deep / In the realm of poseidon / Leviathan / Flow current flow / Sirens call / Aquanaut / Re-emergence / Surface flight / Sub aquiem
SER 006 / Sep '94 / Something Else

☐ PHOENIX
SER 009 / Jun '96 / Something Else

☐ SPIRITS
SER 007 / Jun '96 / Something Else

☐ UNCERTAINTY PRINCIPLE, THE
Times arrow / Virtual journey / Chromazone / Space cadet / Interstellar interlude No.1 / Cassiopeia's dream / Interstellar interlude No.2 / Sopernova / Uncertainty principle 1 / Uncertainty principle 2 / Uncertainty principle 3 / Beyond the event horizon / Times end
SER 004 / Sep '94 / Something Else

Bodner, Phil

☐ FINE AND DANDY
JHR 73511 / May '93 / Jazz Hour

☐ NEW YORK JAM
STB 2505 / Sep '95 / Stash

Body

☐ BODY ALBUM PLUS
OZITCD 0032 / 6 Apr '98 / Ozit

Body Count

☐ BODYCOUNT
Smoked pork / Body Count's in the house / Now sports / Body Count / Statistic / Bowels of the devil / Real problem / KKK Bitch / Note / Voodoo / Winner loses / There goes the neighborhood / Oprah / Evil dick / Body Count anthem / Momma's gotta die tonight / Ice T/Freedom of speech
9362451392 / Mar '94 / WEA

☐ BORN DEAD
Body m/f count / Masters of revenge / Killin' floor / Necessary evil / Drive-by / Last breath / Hey Joe / Shallow graves / Who are you / Street lobotomy / Born dead
RSYND 2 / Sep '94 / Rhyme Syndicate

☐ VIOLENT DEMISE - THE LAST DAYS
Interview / My way: *Body Count & Raw Breed* / Strippers intro / Strippers / Truth or death / Violent demise / Bring it to pain / Music business / I used to love her / Root of all evil / Dead man walking / Interview end / You're fuckin' with BC / Ernie's intro / Dr. K / Last days
CDV 2813 / Mar '97 / Virgin

Body Lovers

☐ NUMBER ONE OF THREE
YG 05 / 20 Apr '98 / Young God

Bodyjar

☐ NO TOUCH RED
BHR 078CD / 27 Apr '98 / Burning Heart

☐ TAKE A LOOK INSIDE
BHR 035CD / Feb '96 / Burning Heart

☐ TIME TO GROW UP
BHR 036CD / Jul '96 / Burning Heart

Boe, Knut Ivar

☐ FERDAMANN
HCD 7100 / Dec '94 / Musikk Distribujson

Boehmer, Conrad

☐ ACOIUSMATRIX VOL.5
BVHAASTCD 9011 / Oct '93 / Bvhaast

☐ IN ILO TEMPORE
BVHAASTCD 9008 / Oct '93 / Bvhaast

☐ WOUTERJE PIETERSE
BVHAASTCD 9401/2 / Oct '94 / Bvhaast

Boeren, Eric

☐ CROSS BREEDING (Boeren, Eric Go Dutch With Ornette)
BIMHUIS 005 / Aug '97 / Bvhaast

Bofill, Angela

☐ LOVE IN SLOW MOTION
All she wants is love / Love in slow motion / Real love / Galaxy of my love / Guess you didn't know / Sail away / Are you leaving me now / Let them talk / Soul of mine / Love changes / Black angel
XECD 8 / Jun '96 / Expansion

Bogan, Lucille

☐ LUCILLE BOGAN
SOB 32352 / Dec '92 / Story Of The Blues

☐ LUCILLE BOGAN VOL.1 1923-1930
BDCD 6036 / Apr '93 / Blues Document

☐ LUCILLE BOGAN VOL.3 1934-1935
BDCD 6038 / Apr '93 / Blues Document

Bogart, Deanna

☐ CROSSING BORDERS
FF 601CD / Feb '93 / Flying Fish

☐ GREAT UNKNOWN, THE
Sittin' on a mountain / Love funk / Wrong side of love / Won't be long / Lovin' me / OK I'll play the blues / Life of the party / But you know / Great unknown / Peephole / Adam bomb boogie
SHANCD 9011 / Jun '98 / Shanachie

Boggs, Dock

☐ COUNTRY BLUES (Complete Early Recordings 1927-1929)
REV 205 / 17 Nov '97 / Revenant

Bogguss, Suzy

☐ ACES
Outbound plane / Aces / Someday soon / Let goodbye hurt like it should / Save yourself / Yellow river road / Part of me / Letting go / Music on the wind / Still hold on
CDP 7985472 / Feb '92 / Capitol

☐ COUNTRY CLASSICS
Under the gun / My side of the story / Moment of truth / All things made new again / Wild horses / Fear of flying / As if I didn't know / Blue days / Burning down / Friend of mine
CDMFP 6330 / Apr '97 / Music For Pleasure

☐ NOBODY LOVE NOBODY GETS HURT
Just enough rope / When I run / Wish hearts would break / Nobody love nobody gets heart / Family tree / Somebody to love / Moonlight and roses / Take me back / From where I stand / Surrender / Train of thought
8573102 / 27 Jul '98 / Chrysalis

☐ SOMETHING UP MY SLEEVE
Diamonds and tears / Just like the weather / Just keep comin' back to you / You never will / You'd be the one / Take it to the limit / Hey Cinderella / Souvenirs / You wouldn't say that to a stranger / Take it like a man / No green eyes / Something up my sleeve: *Bogguss, Suzy & Billy Dean*
CDEST 2211 / Sep '93 / Capitol

☐ VOICES IN THE WIND
Heartache / Drive south / Don't wanna / How come you go to her / Other side of the hill / In the day / Love goes without saying / Eat at Joe's / Lovin' a hurricane / Letting go / Cold day in July
CDP 7985852 / Oct '92 / Liberty

Boghall & Bathgate Caledonia Pipe Band

☐ INTERCONTINENTAL DRUMMERS FANFARE, THE
LCOM 9042 / Jul '91 / Lismor

☐ RUBIC CUBE, THE
2/4 marches / Hornpipes / March, strathspey and reel / Slow air and 9/8 jigs / Selection / Reels / Hornpipe and jig / March and strathspey and reel / Slow air and 6/8 jigs / Strathspeys and reels / 6/8 marches / Jigs
LCOM 5181 / Aug '96 / Lismor

Bogle, Eric

☐ EMIGRANT AND THE EXILE, THE (Bogle, Eric & John Munro)
Poacher's moon / Were you there / Strangers / World cup fever / Ballard of Charles Devenport / Progress / Marking time / Campbell's daughter / One small star / Listen to the old ones / End of an auld song / Cuddy river reverie / Old and in the way / Kissing English arses talking blues / Standing in the light
CDTRAX 121 / Feb '97 / Greentrax

☐ ERIC BOGLE SONGBOOK VOL.1
Reason for it all / Nobody's moggy now / Hard hard times / Scraps of paper / If wishes were fishes / Front row cowboy / And the band played waltzing Matilda / Little Gomez / Aussie Bar-b-q / When the wind blows
CDTRAX 028 / Aug '89 / Greentrax

☐ ERIC BOGLE SONGBOOK VOL.2
Now I'm easy / Glasgow lullaby / No man's land / Do you know any Bob Dylan / My youngest son came home today / Belle of Broughton / Leaving Nancy / Singing the spirit home / Wee china pig / Leaving the land / Rosie / All the fine young men / Across the hills of home
CDTRAX 051 / Apr '92 / Greentrax

☐ HARD, HARD TIMES
TUT 72162 / Jan '94 / Wundertute

☐ I WROTE THIS WEE SONG (Live - 2CD Set)
Sound of singing / Leaving the land / Silly slang song / Mirrors / Reason for it all / Flying finger filler / Vanya / Don't you worry about that / Somewhere in America / Them old song writing blues / Rosie / Feed the children / Singing the spirit home / Leaving Nancy / Now I'm easy / Plastic Paddy / No man's land / Never again- remember / Short white blues / Welcome home / Daniel smiling / Eric and the informers / Shelter / Gift of years
CDTRAX 082D / Jan '95 / Greentrax

☐ MIRRORS
Refugee / One small life / Plastic Paddy / Welcome home / Flat stony broke waltz / Vanya / Don't you worry about that / Mirrors / Song / Big (in a small way) / At risk / Never again - remember / Somewhere in America / Wouldn't be dead for quids / Wishing is free
CDTRAX 068 / Nov '93 / Greentrax

☐ NOW I'M EASY
LRF 041CD / Mar '89 / Larrikin
CMCD 004 / Dec '97 / Celtic Music

☐ PLAIN AND SIMPLE
Lady from Bendigo / Dan / Aussie bar-b-q / Glasgow lullaby / Belle of Broughton / Mary and me / No man's land / Queensland whalers / No use for him / Bloody rotten audience / Gentle Annie
CDTRAX 147 / 1 Nov '97 / Greentrax

☐ SCRAPS OF PAPER
LARRCD 104 / Jun '94 / Larrikin
FF 70311 / Mar '97 / Flying Fish

☐ SINGING THE SPIRIT HOME
Old song / Lifeline / Singing the spirit home / Twenty years ago / All the fine young men / Leaving the land / Australian through and through / Lancelot and Guinevere / Silo / Shelter
LRF 186CD / '88 / Larrikin

☐ SMALL MIRACLES
Small miracles / Digger's legacy / Dedication day / Ekka's silver jubilee song / Always back to you / Blessing / Here in the green / Sayonara Australia / Golden city / Somebody's daughter / Keeper of the flame / Romeo and juliet in Sarajevo / Red heart / Troy's song / Unsung hero / Heart of the land / One small star
CDTRAX 130 / Jun '97 / Greentrax

☐ VOICES IN THE WILDERNESS
Peace has broken out / Lily and the poppy / Blues for Alex / What kind of man / Wilderness / Feed the children / Amazon / Silly slang song / Fences and walls / It's only Tuesday / Gift of years
CDTRAX 040 / Apr '91 / Greentrax

☐ WHEN THE WIND BLOWS
LARRCD 144 / Jun '94 / Larrikin

Bohannon, Hamilton

☐ ESSENTIAL DANCEFLOOR ARTISTS VOL.4
Truck stop (original full album version) / South african man (original full album version) / Red bone (original full album version) / Bohannon's beat (original full album version) / Disco stomp (original full album version) / Keep on dancing (original full album version) / Pimp walk (original full album version) / Fat man (original full album version) / Stop and go (original full album version) / Foot stompin' music (original full album version) / Dance your ass off (original full album version) / Let's start the dance (original 12" club remix)
DGPCD 699 / Jun '94 / Deep Beats

Bohinta

☐ SESSIONS
AMCD 001 / May '97 / Aarde

☐ WISHES
NORA 001CD / Aug '96 / Nora

Bohren, Spencer

☐ DIRT ROADS
3024452 / Nov '97 / Last Call

Boiarsky, Andrew

☐ INTO THE LIGHT
RSRCD 149 / Feb '98 / Reservoir

Boiled In Lead

☐ ALLOY
OMM 2017CD / 17 Mar '98 / Omnium

☐ ANTLER DANCE
OMM 2007CD / Dec '94 / Omnium

☐ OLD LEAD
OMM 2001CD / Dec '94 / Omnium

☐ SONGS FROM THE GYPSY
OMM 2013CD / Jul '95 / Omnium

Boiler NYC

☐ NEW PROFESSIONALS
Superseed / Stegosaurus / Defleshed / Frontin' / Vice grip / Lungbutter rising / Bingo / Feed / Roswall / Tapeworm / Hollow point
MAIM 111222 / 15 Jun '98 / Mayhem

Boilermaker Jazz Band

☐ BURGUNDY STREET BLUES
BCD 140 / Apr '96 / Biograph

☐ DON'T GIVE UP THE SHIP
BCD 133 / May '98 / Biograph

☐ HONKY TONK TOWN
Meet you there / Coquette / Over in Glory land / Trust in me / When we danced at the Mardi Gras / Lonesome blues / Honky Tonk town / My sweeet southern belle / You always hurt the one you love / Whinin' boy blues
BCD 148 / Jun '97 / Biograph

Boine, Mari

☐ EALLIN (Mari Boine Live)
5337992 / Nov '96 / Antilles/New Directions

☐ GOASKINVIELLJA/EAGLE BROTHER
Cuvges vuovttat / Duodalas calbmi / Sami eatnan duoddarat / Modjas Katrin / Das aiggun cuozzut / Dolgesuorbmageziiguin / Skadja / Goaskinviellja / Rahkesvuodain / Mu ahkku / Ale ale don
5213882 / Jan '94 / Verve

☐ LIEHKASTIN
MB 94CD / Dec '94 / Lean

☐ SALMER PA VEIEN HJEM (Paus, Boine Persen, Bremmnes)
FXC 105 / Jul '93 / Kirkelig Kultuverksted

Boingo

☐ BOINGO
Insanity / Hey / Mary / Can't see (useless) / Pedestrian wolves / Lost like this / Spider / War again / I am the walrus / Tender lumplings / Change / Helpless
74321189712 / Oct '94 / Giant

Bojan Z

☐ BOJAN Z QUARTET (Bojan Z Quartet)
No name valse / Play ball / Zilbra / Mashala / Ginger pickles / Les instants / Grand od bora / Nishka bania / Spirito
LBLC 6565 / Nov '95 / Label Bleu

☐ YOPLA
Yopla / Beyond the frame / Un demi-porc et deaux caisses de bierre / Zajdi, Zajdi / Night thing / Multi don kulti / Ingenuity / Post it / Dugan evinde / She-dance
LBLC 6590 / Jun '96 / Label Bleu

Bojsen-Moller, Cai

☐ SUPER SONIC JAZZY SESSION
APR 033CD / 20 Apr '98 / April

Boksch

☐ OCKER 1-8
EFA 610522 / Jun '96 / Platten Meister

Bolan, Marc

☐ BBC SESSIONS, THE (T-Rex)
PILOT 016 / 1 Jun '98 / Burning Airlines

☐ BEST OF MARC BOLAN & T-REX 1972-1977, THE (2CD Set) (Bolan, Marc & T-Rex)
Telegram Sam / Jet tambourine / Mystic lady / Metal guru / Baby strange / Slider blues / Children of the revolution / Lady / Children of the world / Jitterbug love / Solid gold easy action / Born to boogie / 20th century boy / Mister Mister / Street and babe shadow / Midnight / You move like a dog / Sitting here / Left hand Luke / Free angel / Mad Donna / Groover / Saturday night / Metropolis incarnate / Truck on / Satisfaction pony / I wanna go / Untitled poem / Teenage dream / Interview / Are you ready / Light of love / Children of Ram / Precious star / Venus Loon / Sound pit / Galaxy / Dock of the bay / Till dawn / New York city / London boys / Crimson moon / Soul of my suit / Celebrate summer
MEDCD 536 / 29 Sep '97 / Demon

☐ BOLAN'S ZIP GUN (T-Rex)
Light of love / Solid baby / Precious star / Spaceboss / Token of my love / Think zinc / Till dawn / Girl in the thunderbolt suit / Golden belt / I really love you babe / Zip gun boogie / Do you wanna dance / Dock of the bay
EDCD 393 / May '94 / Edsel

☐ CAT BLACK
CLP 9803 / Oct '96 / Cleopatra

☐ COMPLETE BBC SESSIONS, THE (2CD Set) (T-Rex)
PILOT 017 / 2 Feb '98 / Burning Airlines

☐ DANDY IN THE UNDERWORLD (T-Rex)
Dandy in the underworld / Crimson moon / Universe / I'm a fool for you girl / I love to boogie / Visions of domino / Jason B Sad / Groove a little / Soul of my suit / Hang ups / Pain and love / Teen riot structure / To know him is to love him / City port / Dandy in the underworld / Tame my tiger / Celebrate Summer
EDCD 395 / May '94 / Edsel

☐ DAZZLING RAIMENT (The Alternate 'Futuristic Dragon') (T-Rex)
Futuristic dragon / Chrome star / All alone / New York City / My little baby / Sensation Boulevard / Dreamy lady / Dawn storm / Casual agent / London boys / Life's an elevator / Futuristic dragon / Dreamy lady / Casual agent / All alone / All alone / Dreamy lady / London boys / Life's an elevator
EDCD 522 / Jun '97 / Edsel

☐ DEFINITIVE TYRANNOSAURUS REX, THE (Tyrannosaurus Rex)
Deborah / Weilder of words / Mustang Ford / One inch rock / Conesuela / Friends / Juniper suction / Warlord of the royal crocodiles / Chariots of silk / Iscariot / King of the rumbling spires / Once upon the seas of Abyssinia / By the light of the magical moon / Day laye / Great horse / Elemental child / Child star / Chateau in Virginia Waters / Salamanda paraganda / Stacey Grove / Eastern spell / Pewter suitor / Cat black (the wizards hat) / Seal of seasons / Misty coast of Albany / Do you remember / Blessed wild apple girl / Find a little wood / Pavilions of the sun / Lofty skies
NEXCD 250 / Nov '93 / Sequel

☐ DIRTYSWEET VOL.1 (T-Rex)
Metal guru / Buick Mackane / Rabbit finger / Spaceball ricochet / Mad Donna / Electric slim and the factory hen / Broken hearted blues / Shock rock / Tenement lady / Venus loon / Change / Liquid gang / Interstellar soul / Girl in the thunderbolt suit / Solid baby / Zip gun boogie / New York city / Sensation boogie / Dreamy lady / Crimson moon / Dandy in the underworld / I love to boogie / Soul of my suit
FELD 1 / 1 Sep '97 / Demon

☐ DIRTYSWEET VOL.2 (T-Rex)
Groover / 20th century boy / Mystic lady / Rock on / Solid gold / Easy action / Children of the revolution / Sitting here / Midnight / Think zinc / Carsmile Smith and the old one / London boys / Ride my wheels / Dawn storm / Jason B. Sad / Groove a little / Spaceball richochet / Over the flats / This is my life / Shy boy
FELD 2 / Aug '97 / Demon

☐ EARLY RECORDINGS
Your scare me to death / You've got the power / Eastern spell / Charlie / I'm weird / Hippy gumbo / Mustang Ford / Observations / Jasmine '49 / Cat black / Black and white incident / Perfumed garden of Gulliver Smith
EMPRCD 545 / Nov '94 / Emporio

☐ ELECTRIC BOOGIE (2CD Set) (T-Rex)
Cadillac / Beltane Walk / One inch rock / Debora / Ride a white swan / Girl / Cosmic dancer / Hot love / Get it on / Jewel / Elemental child / Jam session
PILOT 013 / Aug '97 / Burning Airlines

☐ ELECTRIC WARRIOR SESSIONS, THE (T-Rex)
Get it on / Monolith / Cosmic dancer / Life's a gas / Honey don't / Woodland rock / Monolith / Summertime blues / Jeepster / Baby strange / Jewel / Get it on
PILOT 004 / Jan '97 / Burning Airlines

☐ ESSENTIAL COLLECTION, THE (Bolan, Marc & T-Rex)
5259612 / Sep '95 / PolyGram TV

☐ FUTURISTIC DRAGON (T-Rex)
Futuristic dragon / Jupiter liar / Chrome sitar / All alone / New York City / My little baby / Calling all destroyers / Theme for a dragon / Sensation boulevard / Ride my wheels / Dreamy lady / Dawn storm / Casual agent / London boys / Laser love / Life's an elevator
EDCD 394 / May '94 / Edsel

☐ GET IT ON
MASQCD 1010 / Jul '97 / Masquerade

☐ GREAT HITS 1972-1977 (The A-Sides) (T-Rex)
Telegram Sam / Metal guru / Children of the revolution / Solid gold easy action / 20th century boy / Groover / Truck on / Teenage dream / Light of love / Zip gun boogie / New York City / Dreamy lady / London boys / I love to boogie / Laser love / To know you is to love you / Soul of my suit / Dandy in the underworld / Celebrate Summer
REXLUX 1013 / 1 Sep '97 / Demon

☐ GREAT HITS 1972-1977 (The B-Sides) (T-Rex)
Cadillac / Baby strange / Thunderwing / Lady / Jitterbug love / Sunken rags / Xmas riff / Born to boogie / Free angel / Midnight / Sitting here / Satisfaction pony / Explosive mouth / Space boss / Chrome sitar / Do you wanna dance / Dock of the bay / Solid baby / Baby boomerang / Life's an elevator / City port / All alone / Groove a little / Tame my tiger / Ride my wheels
EDCD 402 / Oct '94 / Edsel

☐ LEFT HAND LUKE (The Alternate Tanx) (T-Rex)
Tenement lady darling / Rapids / Mister mister / Broken hearted blues / Country honey / Mad Donna / Born to boogie / Life is strange / Street and the babe shadow / Highway knees / Left hand Luke / Children of the revolution / Solid gold easy action / Free angel / Mister mister / Broken hearted blues / Street and the babe shadow / Tenement lady / Tenement lady / Broken hearted blues / Mad Donna / Street and the babe shadow / Left hand Luke
EDCD 410 / May '95 / Edsel

☐ LEGEND LIVES, THE (Various Artists)
Children of the revolution / Telegram sam / Ride a white swan / Debora / 20th century boy / Salamanda palaganda / Child star / Metal guru / Get it on / Solid gold easy action / By the light of the magical moon / Jeepster / Life's an elevator / Hot love / Ain't no square with crowscrew hair
305482 / Oct '96 / Hallmark

☐ LIGHT OF LOVE (T-Rex)
Light of love / Solid baby / Precious star / Token of my love / Space boss / Think zinc / Till dawn / Teenage dream / Girl in the thunderbolt suit / Explosive mouth / Venus moon
EDCD 413 / May '95 / Edsel

☐ LIVE (2CD Set) (T-Rex)
Jeepster / Visions of domino / New York City / Soul of my suit / Groove a little / Telegram Sam / Hang ups / Debora / I love to boogie / Teen riot structure / Dandy in the underworld / Hot love / Get it on: *T-Rex & The Damned* / Jeepster / Telegram Sam / Token of my love / Teenage dream / Zip gun boogie
EDCD 530 / Jun '97 / Edsel

☐ LIVE AT THE BBC (T-Rex)
BOJCD 016 / May '96 / Band Of Joy

☐ LIVE AT THE LYCEUM (2CD Set) (T-Rex)
Unicorn/Hot rod mama / Afghan woman / Mustang ford / Stacy grove / Salamanda palaganda / Wind quartets / One inch rock / Chariots of silk / Seal of seasons / Conesuala / Nijinksky hind / Once upon the seas of abyssinia / Do you remember / Wizard / Eastern spell / Strange orchestras / Interview with Marc Bolan
PILOT 028 / 10 Aug '98 / Burning Airlines

☐ LOVE AND DEATH
You scare me to death / You've got the power / Eastern spell / Charlie / I'm weird / Hippy gumbo / Mustang Ford / Observations / Jasmine '49 / Cat black (the wizard's hat) / Black and white incident / Perfumed garden of Gulliver Smith / Wizard / Beyond the rising sun / Rings of fortune
CDMRED 70 / 24 Aug '98 / Cherry Red

☐ MARC (Songs From The Granada TV Series) (Bolan, Marc & T-Rex)
Sing me a song / I love to boogie / Jeepster / Celebrate summer / New York city / Ride a white swan / Endless sleep / Groove a little / Let's dance / Hot love / Dandy in the underworld / Get it on / Debora / Laser love / Dandy in the underworld
EDCD 545 / 6 Jul '98 / Edsel

☐ MARC BOLAN ARCHIVE
Jasper C. Debussy / Lunacy's back / Beyond the rising sun / Black and white incident / Observations / Eastern spell / You got the power / Hippy gumbo / Sarah crazy child / Rings of fortune / Hot rod Mama / Beginning of doves / Mustang Ford / Pictures of the purple people / One inch rock / Jasmine '49 / Charlie / Misty mist / Cat black / Sally was an angel
RMCD 229 / Apr '98 / Rialto

☐ MESSING WITH THE MYSTIC (Unissued Songs 1972-1977) (T-Rex)
Is it true / Over the flats / Jet tambourine / Children of the world / Mr. Motion / Hope you enjoy the show / All of my love / Saturday night / Down home lady / Sky church music / Plateau skull / Bolan's zip gun / Magical moon / Bust my ball / Savage Beethoven / Reelin' an' a rockin' an' a boppin' an' a Bolan / Christmas bop / Funky London childhood / Love drunk / Foxy boy / 20th century boy / Sing me a song / Endless sleep / Messing with the mystic
EDCD 404 / Oct '94 / Edsel

☐ METAL GURU (7CD Set) (Bolan, Marc & T-Rex)
BBOX 1609 / 29 Sep '97 / Demon

☐ MISSING LINK TO T-REX, THE (Peregrine-Took, Steve)
95282 / May '97 / Cleopatra

☐ PRECIOUS STAR (T-Rex)
EDCD 443 / Jun '96 / Edsel

☐ PREHISTORIC
Jasper C Debussy / Beyond the rising sun / Eastern sun / Mustang Ford / One inch rock / Cat black / Hot rod mama / Rings of fortune / Black and white incident / You got the power / Jasmine '49 / Sarah crazy child / Sally was an angel / Charlie / Pictures of purple people
EMPRCD 589 / Oct '95 / Emporio

☐ PRINCE OF PLAYERS (Alternate Dandy In The Underworld) (T-Rex)
Dandy in the underworld / Crimson moon / I'ma fool for you girl / I love to boogie / Funky London childhood / Jason B. Sad / Groove a little / Soul of my suit / Hang ups / Pain and love / Teen riot structure / To know you is to love you (to know him is to love him) / City port / Tame my tiger / Celebrate summer / I love to boogie / Soul of my suit / Pain of love / Pain of love / Teen riot structure / City port / Celebrate summer / Weird strings
EDCD 523 / 6 Jul '98 / Edsel

☐ PROPHETS, SEERS & SAGES (T-Rex)
CUCD 10 / Oct '94 / Disky

☐ SLIDER, THE (T-Rex)
Metal guru / Mystic lady / Rock on / Slider / Baby boomerang / Spaceball ricochet / Buick McKane / Telegram Sam / Rabbit fighter / Baby strange / Ballrooms of Mars / Chariot choogle / Main man / Cadillac / Thunderwing / Lady
EDCD 390 / May '94 / Edsel

☐ SPACEBALL (US Radio Tours 1971-1972/2CD Set) (T-Rex)
Spaceball ricochet / Jeepster / Cosmic dancer / Main man / Ballrooms of Mars / Mystic lady / Girl / Baby strange / Left hand Luke / Slider / Spaceball ricochet / Cosmic dancer / Planet Queen / Elemental child / Jewel / Hot love / Cosmic dancer / Honey don't / Planet Queen / Get it on blues
PILOT 021 / 3 Nov '97 / Burning Airlines

☐ TANX (Bolan, Marc & T-Rex)
Tenement lady / Rapids / Mister mister / Broken hearted blues / Shock rock / Country honey / Electric slim and the factory hen / Mad Donna / Born to boogie / Life is strange / Street and babe shadow / Highway knees / Left hand Luke and the beggar boys / Children of the revolution / Jitterbug love / Sunken rags / Solid gold easy action / Xmas message / 20th century boy / Free angel
EDCD 391 / May '94 / Edsel

☐ TRIBUTE TO MARC BOLAN AND T-REX, A (Various Artists)
Slider: *Smithereens* / Light of love: *Molotov Combo* / Ride a white swan: *Scornclouds* / Cosmic dancer: *New* / Ballroom of Mars: *Cruxshadows* / Get it on: *Friendly Ghost* / 20th century boy: *Three Johns* / Groover: *Shrunken Heads* / Raw ramp: *Dramarama* / Catblack: *Futuristic Dragon* / Jeepster: *Alone On The Red* / Telegram Sam: *Jump The Gun* / Metal guru: *Jump The Gun*
32271CD / 15 Feb '98 / Pavement

☐ UNCHAINED: THE BEST OF THE UNRELEASED RECORDINGS (Bolan, Marc & T-Rex)
NESTCD 907 / 29 Sep '97 / Demon

☐ UNCHAINED: UNRELEASED RECORDINGS VOL.1 (1972 - Part 1) (Bolan, Marc & T-Rex)
Over the flats / Sugar baby / Children of the world / Did you ever / Alligator man / Shame on you / Guitar blues / Shadow blues / Cry baby (Acoustic/Electric) / Rollin' stone / What do I see / Shame on you little girl / Always / Auto machine / Unicorn horn (A thousand Mark Field charms) / Jam / Sailors of the highway (wah wah)
EDCD 411 / May '95 / Edsel

☐ UNCHAINED: UNRELEASED RECORDINGS VOL.2 (1972 - Part 2) (Bolan, Marc & T-Rex)
Wouldn't I be the one / Meadows of the sea / Mr. Motion (Versions 1 and 2) / City port / Just like me / Is it true / Zinc rider / Canyon / Fast blues - easy action / Bolan's blues / Shake it wind one / Work with me baby / Spaceball boot / Electric lips / Slider blues / Ellie May / My baby's new Porsche / Dark-lipped woman
EDCD 412 / May '95 / Edsel

☐ UNCHAINED: UNRELEASED RECORDINGS VOL.5 (Bolan, Marc & T-Rex)
EDCD 444 / Jun '96 / Edsel

☐ UNCHAINED: UNRELEASED RECORDINGS VOL.6 (Bolan, Marc & T-Rex)
EDCD 445 / Jun '96 / Edsel

☐ UNCHAINED: UNRELEASED RECORDINGS VOL.7 (Bolan, Marc & T-Rex)
Riff / Freeway / I'm a voodoo man / Decadent priestess / Midnight creeps across your window / Demon grave / Memphis highway / Bombs out of London / Funky London childhood / London boys / Savage deception of love / Angel when I'm mad / Over you babe / Mellow love / 20th century baby / Shy boy / Love drunk / Foxy boy / 20th century baby / Hot George / Write me a song / Mellow love / Endless sleep / Sing me a song / Riff
EDCD 524 / Jun '97 / Edsel

☐ UNCHAINED: UNRELEASED RECORDINGS VOL.8 (Bolan, Marc & T-Rex)
EDCD 525 / 29 Sep '97 / Edsel

☐ UNICORN (T-Rex)
Unicorn / Chariots of silk / 'Pon a hill / Seal of seasons / Throat of winter / Cat black (the wizard's hat) / Stones for Avalon / She was born to be my unicorn / Like a white star, tangled and far / Tulip, that's what you are / Warlord of the royal crocodiles / Evenings of Damask / Sea beasts / Iscariot / Nijinsky hind / Pilgrim's tale / Misty coast of Albany / Romany soup
CUCD 11 / Oct '94 / Disky

☐ VERY BEST OF MARC BOLAN & T-REX, THE (T-Rex)
Telegram Sam / Metal guru / Children of the revolution / Solid gold easy action / Twentieth century boy / Truck on (tyke) / Teenage dream / Light of love / New York City / London boys / I love to boogie / Laser love / Lady / Born to boogie / Dandy in the underworld / Life's an elevator / All alone / Celebrate summer / Buick Mckane / Chariot choogle
MCCD 030 / May '91 / Music Club

☐ WIZARD, A TRUE STAR, A (3CD Set) (Bolan, Marc & T-Rex)
Interview / Telegram Sam / Spaceball ricochet / Cadillac / Metal guru / Baby strange / Over the flats / Thunderwing / Is it true / Interview / Rabbit fighter / Jingle/Pepsi ad / Sunken rags / Slider / Buick MacKane / Would I be the one / Rock on / Children of the revolution / Painted pony / Solid gold easy action / 20th century boy / Street and the babe shadow / I wanna go / Interview / You got the look / Electric slim / Groover / Sure enough / Interview / Highway knees / Midnight poem / Left hand Luke / Interview / Change / Delanie / Interview / Venus loon / All my love / Leopards / Interstellar soul / Carsmile Smith / Interview / Saturation syncopation / Down home lady / Sky church music / Teenage dream / Till dawn / Jitterbug love / Are you ready Steve / Light of love / Satisfied / Think zinc / Solid baby / Bust my ball / Token of my love / Children of Rarn / Interview / Interview / Brain police / Futuristic dragon / New York City / Reelin' and a wheelin' / Dreamy lady / Christmas bop / Rip it up / Teenager in love / Capital Radio jingle / Jupiter liar / Pale horse riding / Chrome sitar / Piccadilly radio jingle / Jeepster rap / Funky London childhood / Dawn storm / Casual agent / 20th century baby / I love to boogie / Interview (10) / London boys / Life's an elevator / Funky riff / Pain and love / Dandy in the underworld / Hang ups / Teen riot structure / Hot George / 21st century stance / Interview (11) / Celebrate summer / Interview (12)
FBOOK 17 / Feb '97 / Demon

☐ ZINC ALLOY AND THE HIDDEN RIDERS OF TOMORROW (Bolan, Marc & T-Rex)
Venus loon / Sound pit / Explosive mouth / Galaxy / Change / Nameless wildness / Teenage dream / Liquid gang / Carsmile Smith and the old one / You got to live to stay alive / Interstellar soul / Painless persuasion v the meathawk imm / Avengers / Leopards featuring gardenia and the mighty slug / Groover / Midnight / Truck on (tyke) / Sitting here / Satisfaction pony
EDCD 392 / May '94 / Edsel

Boland, Francy

☐ TWO ORIGINALS (Boland, Francy & Kenny Clarke)
5235252 / Jan '95 / PolyGram Jazz

Bolek

☐ MEMORIES OF POLAND
MCD 71409 / Jun '93 / Monitor

Bolin, Tommy

☐ FROM THE ARCHIVES VOL.1
RPM 158 / Jan '96 / RPM

☐ FROM THE ARCHIVES VOL.2
63301443012 / 3 Aug '98 / Zebra

☐ TEASER
Grind / Homeward / Strut / Dreamer savannah woman / Teaser / People, people / Marching powder / Wild dogs / Lotus
4680162 / May '94 / Epic

Bolivar, Michael

☐ HANGIN' OUT
CCD 1009 / Jul '98 / Clarity

Boll Weevil Jass Band

☐ MUSIC TO STOMP YOUR FEET BY
BCD 31 / May '98 / GHB

Boll Weevils

☐ HEAVYWEIGHT
DSRCD 35 / Sep '95 / Dr. Strange

☐ WEEVIL LIVE
DSR 048CD / Oct '96 / Dr. Strange

Bolland, C.J.

☐ 4TH SIGN, THE
Mantra / Nightbreed / Thrust / Aquadrive / Pendulum / Spring yard / Camargue / Inside out / Jungle man
RS 92024CD / 2 Mar '98 / R&S

☐ ANALOGUE THEATRE, THE
Obsidion / Pesticide / Analogue theatre / On line / Prophet / People of the universe / There can be only one / Kung kung ka / Sugar is sweeter
TRUCD 13 / Oct '96 / Internal

☐ ANALOGUE THEATRE, THE (New Version)
Obsidion / Pesticide / Analogue theatre / On line / Prophet / People of the universe / There can be only one / Kung kung ka / Counterpoint / Sugar is sweeter / Electro power / Sugar is sweeter
8289092 / May '97 / FFRR

☐ DJ KICKS (Various Artists)
K7 038CD / Sep '95 / Studio K7

☐ ELECTRONIC HIGHWAY
Tower of Naphtali / Drum tower / Neural paradox / Spoof / Con Spirito / Bones / Zenith / Nec plus ultra / Catharsis
RS 95011CD / 16 Feb '98 / R&S

Bollenback, Paul

☐ DOUBLE GEMINI
Breaking the girl / After the love has gone / Double gemini / Reflections of jaco / Let her cry / So many stars / Open hand / Field of gold / I am singin' / Cat's eye
CHR 70046 / Dec '97 / Challenge

Bollin, Zuzu

☐ TEXAS BLUES MAN
Big legs / Hey little girl / Blues in the dark / Kidney stew / Cold cold feeling / Why don't you eat where you slept last night / Headlight blues / How do you want your rollin' done / Leary blues / Rebecca / Zu's blues
ANTCD 0018 / Feb '92 / Antones

Bolling, Claude

☐ BLACK, BROWN AND BEIGE
74321162782 / May '96 / Milan

☐ CINEMADREAMS
74321355012 / Jul '96 / Milan

☐ RAGTIME BOOGIE-WOOGIE JAZZ CLASSICS
3-4 6-8 boogie / Mississippi rag / Death ray boogie / On the Mississippi / Louisiana glide / Maple leaf rag / Tiger rag / Man that got away / Yesterdays / Begin the beguine / Tea for two / Dardanella / Honky tonk train blues / Harlem strut / Pinetop's boogie woogie / Entertainer's rag / Waiting for the Robert E Lee / Perfect rag
8225062 / Jan '93 / Philips

☐ VICTORY CONCERT, THE
887971 / Aug '94 / Milan

☐ VINTAGE BOLLING
Baroque and blue / Sentimentale / Fugace / Hispanic dance / Mexicaine / Romance / Gavotte / Slavonic dance / Cross over the USA / Way down yonder in New Orleans / Do you know what it means to miss New Orleans / Back home again in Indiana
74321331202 / Apr '96 / Milan

☐ WARM UP THE BAND
4684132 / Jan '95 / Sony Jazz

Bollock Brothers

☐ BEST OF THE BOLLOCKS, THE
CDCRM 1011 / Jul '93 / Charly

☐ FOUR HORSEMEN OF THE APOCALYPSE, THE
Legend of the snake / Woke up this morning and found myself dead / Mistress of the macabre / Faith healer / King Rat / Four horsemen of the Apocalypse / Return to the garden of Eden / Loud, loud, loud / Seventh seal
CDCRH 109 / Feb '97 / Charly

☐ LAST SUPPER, THE
Horror movies / Enchantment / Reincarnation of Bollock Brothers / Save our souls / Face in the mirror / Last supper / Act became real / Gift
CDCRH 103 / Feb '97 / Charly

☐ LIVE - IN PUBLIC IN PRIVATE
Woke up this morning and found myself dead / Drac's back / Four horsemen of the Apocalypse / Count Dracula where's yar troosers / King Rat / Midnight Moses / Faith healer / Rock 'n' roll
CDCRH 105 / Feb '97 / Charly

☐ LIVE PERFORMANCES (Official Bootleg)
Slow removal of Vincent Van Gogh's left ear / Loose / Horror movies / Bunker / Last supper / Reincarnation of Bollock Brothers / New York / Holidays in the sun / Problems / Vincent: Fagan, Michael / Pretty vacant: Fagan, Michael / God save the queen: Fagan, Michael
CDCRH 102 / Feb '97 / Charly

☐ NEVER MIND THE BOLLOCKS 1983
Holidays in the sun / Problems / No feelings / God save the queen / Pretty vacant / Submission / New York / Seventeen / Anarchy in the UK / Liar / Bodies / EMI
CDCRH 104 / Feb '97 / Charly

Bollocks

☐ TOTAL FUCKIN' BOLLOCKS
KOCD 067 / 20 Jul '98 / Knock Out

Bolovaristiboum

☐ IVRY PORT
3001806 / 24 Apr '98 / IMP

Bolshoi

☐ BIGGER GIANTS
Fly / Sliding seagulls / Hail Mary / Giants / Happy boy / By the river / Sob story / Boxes / Holiday by the sea / Amsterdam / Crosstown traffic / Happy boy (long version)
SITL 15CD / '88 / Situation 2

Bolthrower

☐ 4TH CRUSADE
MOSH 070CD / 1 Sep '97 / Earache

☐ FOR VICTORY
War / Remembrance / When glory beckons / For victory / Graven image / Lest we forget / Silent demise / Forever fallen / Tank (MK1) / Armageddon bound
MOSH 120CD / 1 Sep '97 / Earache

☐ REALM OF CHAOS
Eternal war / Through the eye of terror / Dark millenium / All that remains / Lost souls domaine / Plague bearer / World eater / Drowned in torment / Realm of chaos
MOSH 013CD / 1 Sep '97 / Earache

☐ WAR MASTER
MOSH 029CD / 1 Sep '97 / Earache

Bolton, Michael

☐ ALL THAT MATTERS
Safe place from the storm / Best of love / Let's make a long story longer / A heart can only be so strong / Fallin' / Forever's just a matter of time / Whenever I remember loving you / Show her the way / Why me / Can't get close enough to you / Let there be love / Pleasure or pain / Go the distance when there are no words
4885312 / 10 Nov '97 / Columbia

☐ EARLY YEARS, THE (Bolotin, Michael)
Lost in the city / Everybody needs a reason / Your love / It's just a feelin' / Dream while you can / Take me as I am / These eyes / You mean more to me / If I had your love / Give me a reason / Tell me how you feel / Time is on my side
ND 90593 / Feb '97 / RCA

☐ EVERYBODY'S CRAZY
Everybody's crazy / Save our love / Can't turn it off / Call my name / Everytime / Desperate heart / Start breaking my heart / You don't want me bad enough / Don't tell me it's over
4666622 / May '91 / Columbia

☐ GREATEST HITS 1985-1995
Soul provider / (Sittin' on the) dock of the bay / How am I supposed to live without you / How can we be lovers / When I'm back on my feet again / Georgia on my mind / Time, love and tendernes / When a man loves a woman / Missing you now / Steel bars / Said I loved you but I lied / Lean on me / Can I touch you there / I promise you I found someone / Love so beautiful / This river
4810022 / Sep '95 / Columbia

☐ HUNGER, THE
Hot love / Wait on love / (Sittin' on the) dock of the bay / Gina / That's what love is all about / Hunger / You're all I need / Take a look at my face / Walk away
4844682 / Aug '96 / Columbia

☐ MERRY CHRISTMAS IN VIENNA, A
Fanfare / I wonder as I wonder / Ave Maria / Marin Wiegenlied / Silent night / Children of Christmas / Geso bambino / In the bleak midwinter / Villancico yaucano / White Christmas / Aleuya fum fum fum / Corramos corramos / Dormi dormi / Spolu do betlema / Widemann / Jingle bell / Joy to the world / Silent night
SK 62970 / 24 Nov '97 / Sony Classical

☐ MICHAEL BOLTON
Fool's game / She did the same thing / Home town hero / Can't hold on, can't let go / Fighting for my life / Paradise / Back in my arms again / Carrie / I almost believed you
4667422 / 11 May '98 / Columbia

☐ MICHAEL BOLTON/EVERYBODY'S CRAZY/THE HUNGER (3CD Set)
4683272 / Jul '93 / Columbia

☐ ONE THING, THE
Said I loved you but I lied / I'm not made of steel / One thing / Soul of my soul / Completely / Lean on me / Ain't got nothing if you ain't got love / Time for letting go / Never get enough of your love / In the arms of love / Voice of my heart
4743552 / Nov '93 / Columbia

☐ SOUL PROVIDER
Soul provider / Georgia on my mind / It's only my heart / How am I supposed to live without you / How can we be lovers / You wouldn't know love / When I'm back on my feet again / From now on: *Bolton, Michael & Suzie Benson* / Love cuts deep / Stand up for love
4635432 / 8 Sep '97 / Columbia

☐ THIS IS THE TIME - THE CHRISTMAS COLLECTION
Silent night / Santa claus is coming to town / Have yourself a merry little Christmas / Joy to the world / Ave maria: *Bolton, Michael & Placido Domingo* / Christmas song / O holy night / White Christmas / This is the time: *Bolton, Michael & Wynonna* / Love is the power: *Bolton, Michael & Wynonna*
4850192 / Nov '96 / Columbia

☐ TIME, LOVE AND TENDERNESS
Love is a wonderful thing / Time, love and tenderness / Missing you now / Forever isn't long enough / Now that I found you / When a man loves a woman / We're not makin' love anymore / New love / Save me / Steel bars
4678122 / Apr '91 / Columbia

☐ TIMELESS (The Classics)
Since I fell for you / To love somebody / Reach out, I'll be there / You send me / Yesterday / Hold on I'm coming / Bring it on home to me / Knock on wood / Drift away / White Christmas
4723022 / 27 Jul '98 / Columbia

Bolton, Polly

☐ LOVELIEST OF TREES (Bolton, Polly Band & Nigel Hawthorne)
SHEPCD 1 / Aug '96 / Shepherd Music

☐ NO GOING BACK
SPINCD 134 / May '90 / Spindrift

☐ SONGS FROM A COLD OPEN FIELD
PBBCD 02 / May '93 / PBB

☐ VIEW ACROSS THE BAY
PBB 003CD / Mar '98 / PBB

Boltz, Ray

☐ BETHLEHEM STAR
Bethlehem star / Gift / Glad tidings / Go tell it on the mountain / Her eyes are on the child / I believe in Bethlehem / Perfect tree / Sent by the Father / Still her little child / What a beautiful name
7019957609 / Dec '97 / Word

Bom

☐ BOM BOM SHEVAYA
OCH 2CD / Aug '96 / Ochre

Bomb 20

☐ FIELD MANUAL
Fall / Burn the shit down / Don't you know / Ultimate supremecy / You killed me first / Anyday / We can fuck / Donutz and blood / Innocent bystanders / Lory vs. Bomb 20 / No left / If I go down / Round 2 / Made of shit / La belle / Just came close / Edutainment break / Dumb / Hoover boogie / Wonda what it takes
DHRCD 015 / 8 Jun '98 / DHR

Bomb Bassets

☐ TAKE A TRIP WITH...
LK 165CD / Aug '97 / Lookout

Bomb Everything

☐ ALL POWERFUL FLUID, THE
Hoeda hoeda / All powerful fluid / Who cares / Monochrome man / Offer me your mouth / One act / Liquid cosh / Stay sweet / Baby's on fire / Deeper / Fountainhead
CDDVN 10 / Jul '92 / Devotion

Bomb Party

☐ FISH
NORMAL 103CD / May '89 / Normal

Bomb The Bass

☐ CLEAR
Bug powder dust / Sleepyhead / One to one religion / Dark heart / If you reach the border / Brain dead / 5ml Barrel / Somewhere / Sandcastles / Tidal wave / Empire
IMCD 239 / Mar '97 / Island

Bomboras

☐ IT CAME FROM PIER 13
ID 123345CD / Feb '97 / Dionysus

☐ ORGAN GRINDER
ID 123354 / 15 Dec '97 / Dionysus

Bombshell Rocks

☐ UNDERGROUND RADIO
JABSC 0015CD / 3 Aug '98 / Sidekicks

Bon

☐ FULL CIRCLE COMING HOME
EFA 130022 / Oct '94 / Ozone

Bon Jovi

☐ 7800 DEGREES FAHRENHEIT
In and out of love / Price of love / Only lonely / King of the mountain / Silent night / Tokyo road / Hardest part is the night / Always run to you / To the fire / Secret dreams
8245092 / Jan '90 / Vertigo
5380262 / 7 Sep '98 / Jambco

☐ BON JOVI
Runaway / She didn't know me / Shot through the heart / Love lies / Burning for love / Breakout / Come back / Get ready
8149822 / Apr '84 / Vertigo
5380232 / 7 Sep '98 / Jambco

☐ BON JOVI: INTERVIEW PICTURE DISC
CBAK 4004 / Apr '88 / Baktabak

☐ CROSS ROAD
5229362 / 7 Sep '98 / Jambco

☐ INTERVIEW DISC
SAM 7004 / Nov '96 / Sound & Media

☐ INTERVIEWS VOL.2, THE
CBAK 4070 / Feb '94 / Baktabak

☐ KEEP THE FAITH
I believe / Keep the faith / I'll sleep when I'm dead / In these arms / Bed of roses / If I was your mother / Dry county / Woman in love / Fear / I want you / Blame it on the love of rock and roll / Little bit of soul / Save a prayer
5141972 / Nov '92 / Jambco
5380342 / 7 Sep '98 / Jambco

☐ NEW JERSEY
Lay your hands on me / Bad medicine / Born to be my baby / Living in sin / Blood on blood / Stick to your guns / Homebound train / I'll be there for you / Ninety nine in the shade / Love for sale / Wild is the wind / Ride cowboy ride
8363452 / Sep '88 / Vertigo
5380242 / 7 Sep '98 / Jambco

☐ SLIPPERY WHEN WET
Let it rock / You give love a bad name / Livin' on a prayer / Social disease / Wanted dead or alive / Raise your hands / Without love / I'd die for you / Never say goodbye / Wild in the streets
8302642 / Sep '90 / Vertigo
5380252 / 7 Sep '98 / Jambco

☐ THESE DAYS
Hey God / Something for the pain / This ain't a love song / These days / Lie to me / Damned / My guitar lies bleeding in my arms / (It's hard) Letting you go / Hearts breaking even / Something to believe in / If that's what it takes / Diamond ring / All I want is everything / Bitter wine
5282482 / Jun '95 / Jambco
5380362 / 7 Sep '98 / Jambco

☐ THESE DAYS (2CD Tour Pack Set)
Hey God / Something for the pain / This ain't a love song / These days / Lie to me / Damned / My guitar lies bleeding in my arms / (It's hard) Letting you go / Hearts breaking even / Something to believe in / If that's what it takes / Diamond ring / All I want is everything / Bitter wine / Fields of fire / I thank you / Mrs. Robinson / Let's make it baby / I don't like Mondays / Crazy / Tumblin' dice / Heaven help us
5326442 / Jun '96 / Jambco

Bon Jovi, Jon

☐ BLAZE OF GLORY - YOUNG GUNS II
Billy get your guns / Blaze of glory / Santa Fe / Never say die / Bang a drum / Guano City / Miracle / Blood money / Justice in the barrel / You really got me now / Dyin' ain't much of a livin'
8464732 / Aug '90 / Vertigo

☐ DESTINATION ANYWHERE
5360112 / Jun '97 / Mercury

☐ DESTINATION ANYWHERE (Special Edition/2CD Set)
Queen of New Orleans / Janie don't take your love to town / Midnight in Chelsea / Ugly / Staring at your window with a suitcase in my hand / Every word was a piece of my heart / It's just me / Destination anywhere / Learning how to fall / Naked / Little city /

August 7 4:15 / Cold hard heart / Queen of New Orleans / Midnight in Chelsea / Destination anywhere / Ugly / It's just me / August 7 4:15 / Jailbreak / Not fade away / Janie don't take your love to town
5367582 / 17 Nov '97 / Mercury

☐ POWER STATION YEARS 1980-1983, THE (Bongiovi, John)
Who said it would last forever / Open your heart / Stringin' a line / Don't leave me tonight / More than we bargained for / For you / Hollywood dreams / All talk no action / Don't keep me wondering / Head over heels / No one does it like you / What you want / Don't you believe him / Talkin' in your sleep
MASQCD 1011 / Jul '97 / Masquerade

Bonano, Sharkey

☐ SHARKEY & HIS KINGS OF DIXIELAND (Bonano, Sharkey & His Kings Of Dixieland)
BCD 124 / Jul '96 / Biograph

☐ SHARKEY BONANO 1928-1937
Panama / Dippermouth blues / Sizzling the blues / High society / Git wit it / Ideas / Everybdoy loves my baby / Yes she do - no she don't / I'm satisfied with my gal / High society / Mudhole blues / Swing in, swing out / Blowin' off steam / Mr. Brown goes to town / Wash it clean / When you're smiling / Swingin' on the Swanee shore / Old fashioned swing / Big boy blue / Swing like a rusty gate / Doodlebug / Magnolia blues / I never knew what a gal could do / Never had a reason to believe in you
CBC 1001 / Jan '92 / Timeless Historical

Boncana

☐ BEST OF SALSA, THE
089672 / 24 Feb '98 / Melodie

Bond, Eddie

☐ ROCKIN' DADDY (2CD Set)
Double duty lovin' / Talking off the wall / Love makes a fool (Everyday) / Your eyes / I got a woman / Rockin' Daddy / Slip, slip slippin in / Baby, baby, baby (What am I gonna do) / Flip flop Mama / Boppin' Bonnie / You're part of me / King on your throne / They say we're too young / Backslidin / Love love love / Lovin' you, lovin' you / Hershey bar / One step close to you / Show me (Without sax) / Broke my guitar / This old heart of mine / Show me / One more memory / I can't quit / My bucket's got a hole in it / (Back home again in) Indiana / They'll never take her love from me / Day I found you / Standing in the window / Back street affair / Our secret rendezvous / I'd just be fool enough / You nearly lose your mind / I thought I heard you calling my name / Big boss man / In my solitude / Most of all I want to see Jesus / Where could I go but to the Lord / Satisfied / When they ring those golden bells / If we never meet again / Will I be lost or will I be saved / Just a closer walk with thee / Pass me not, o gentle saviour / I saw the light / Letter to God / Precious memories / Hallelujah way
BCD 15708 / May '93 / Bear Family

☐ ROCKIN' DADDY
Rockin' daddy / Big boss man / Can't win for losing / When the jukebox plays / Hey Joe / Monkey and the baboon / Blues got me / Standing in your window / Look like a monkey / I'll step aside / Memphis Tennessee / My bucket's got a hole in it / Winners circle / Juke joint Johnny / You'll never be a stranger to me / Boo bop da caa caa / Heart full of heartaches / Here comes the train / Someday I'll sober up / Double duty lovin' / Let's make the parting sweet / Tomorrow I'll be gone / One more memory / Country shindig / When the jukebox plays / Raunchy / Cold dark waters / Your eyes / It's been so long darling / Your old standby / This old heart of mine
STCD 1 / '92 / Stomper Time

Bond, Graham

☐ HOLY MAGIC
REP 4106 / Aug '91 / Repertoire

☐ LIVE AT KLOOKS KLEEK (Bond, Graham Organisation)
Wade in the water / Big boss man / Early in the morning / Person to person blues / Spanish blues / Introduction by Dick Jordan / First time I met the blues / Stormy Monday / Train time / What'd I say
CDGR 195 / Dec '97 / Charly

☐ ROCK GENERATION (Bond, Graham/ Animals)
14553 / 16 Feb '98 / Spalax

☐ TWO HEADS ARE BETTER THAN ONE...PLUS (Bond & Brown)
Lost tribe / Ig the pig / Oobati / Amazing grass / Scunthorpe crabmeat train sideways boogie shuffle stomp / CFDT (Colonel Fright's Dancing Terrapins) / Mass debate / Looking for time / Milk is turning sour in my shoes / Macumbe / Beginning / Aeroplane drinking man / Italian song / Spend my nights in armour / Fury of war / Magpie man / Drum roll / Swing song / Sailor's song / Ending
SEECD 345 / Apr '92 / See For Miles

☐ WE PUT OUR MAGICK ON YOU
REP 4107 / Aug '91 / Repertoire

Bond, Joyce

☐ CALL ME
OCD 33 / Jan '90 / Orbitone

☐ NICE TO HAVE YOU BACK AGAIN
Nice to have you back again / Nothing ever comes easy / Love me and leave me / Lonesome Road / You've been gone too long / If I ever fall in love again / No other one is sweeter than you
SPCD 06 / Dec '95 / Spindle

☐ YOU TOUCH MY HEART
You touch my heart / My mother's eyes / I wanna be true / Lovely paradise / Do the teasy / Do right man do right woman / Dreaming of a little island / Roving eyes / How sweet it is (to be loved by you)
SPCD 04 / Dec '95 / Spindle

Bondi Cigars

☐ BAD WEATHER BLUES
LRF 258 / Oct '93 / Larrikin

Bonds, Gary 'US'

☐ BEST OF GARY 'US' BONDS, THE
New orleans / Quarter to three / Dear lady twist / Do the bumpsie / Copy cat / No more homework / Seven day weekend / Not me / School is out / School is in / Lover's moon / I wanta holler (but the town's too small) / Soul food / Havin' so much fun / Perdido (parts 1 and 2) / Where did the naughty little girl go / Twist twist senora / Take me back to new orleans
MCCD 111 / Jun '93 / Music Club

☐ CLUB SOUL CITY
This little girl / Hold on (to what you got) / From a Buick 6 / Jole Blon / Club soul city / It's only love / Rendezvous / Soul deep / Way back when / Turn the music down / Just like a child / Angelyne / Dedication / All I need / Pretender / Out of work / Bring her back / Last time / Daddy's come home / Love is on the line
DC 881852 / 2 Feb '98 / Disky

☐ GREATEST HITS
TRLGCD 100 / Sep '90 / Timeless Jazz

☐ TAKE ME BACK TO NEW ORLEANS
Take me back to New Orleans / Send her to me / Shine on lover's moon / Please forgive me / Workin' for my baby / Give me one more chance / My little room / What a dream / Don't go to strangers / Food of love / Girl next door / What a crazy world / I'm that kind of guy / Call me for Christmas / Guida's Romeo and Juliet / Million tears / Time ol' story / My sweet Ruby Rose / I know why dreamers cry / I walk the line / Oh yeah oh yeah / Nearness of you / I love you so / I don't wanna wait (why wait 'til Saturday night)
CDCHD 549 / Aug '94 / Ace

Bone Machine

☐ DISAPPEARING INC.
BM 004 / Oct '96 / Big Disc

☐ SEARCH AND DESTROY
NTHEN 022CD / Jan '96 / Now & Then

Bone Structure

☐ BONE STRUCTURE
On Green Dolphin Street / Vatican roulette / Modal T / Lush life / Doodlin' / Bone idle rich / Latin line / Shades of blue and green / Last minute waltz / Spanish white
CLGCD 020 / Jun '92 / Calligraph

Bone Thugs n' Harmony

☐ ART OF WAR, THE
Retaliation / Handle the vibe / Look into my eyes / Body rott / It's all mo'thug / Ready 4 war / Ain't nothin' changed / Clog up yo mind / Thug in me / Hardtimes / Mind of a Souljah / If I could teach the world / Family tree / Mo thug / Thug luv / Hatin' nation / 7 sign / Wasteland warriors / Neighbourhood slang / U ain't Bone / Get cha thug on / All original / Blaze it / Let the law end / Whom die they lie / Friends / Evil paradise / Mo thug family tree
4880802 / Jul '97 / Ruthless

☐ E1999 ETERNAL
Da introduction / East 1999 / Eternal / Crept and we came down '71 (the getaway) / Mr. Bill Collector / Budsmokers only / Crossroads / Me killa / Land of the heartless / No shorts, no losses / First of the month / Budds lovaz / Die die die / Mr. Ouija 2 / Mo murda / Shots to the double glock
4810382 / Jul '95 / Ruthless
4810386 / Aug '96 / Ruthless

Bonesaw

☐ ABANDONED
LF 099CD / Jun '94 / Lost & Found

☐ SHADOW OF DOUBT
LF 189CD / Jan '96 / Lost & Found

☐ WRITTEN IN STONE
LF 140CD / May '95 / Lost & Found

Boneshakers

☐ BOOK OF SPELLS
VPBCD 40 / Apr '97 / Virgin

Bonewire

☐ THROWN INTO MOTION
NIHIL 3CD / Mar '95 / Cacophonous

Boney M

☐ 20 GREATEST CHRISTMAS SONGS
Christmas medley / Oh Christmas tree / Hark the herald angels sing / Zion's daughter / First Noel / O come all ye faithful (adeste fidelis) / Petit Papa Noel / Darkness is falling / Joy to the world / White Christmas / Jingle bells / Feliz Navidad / When a child is born / Little drummer boy / Medley / Auld lang syne
258116 / Nov '96 / Hansa

☐ BEST OF BONEY M, THE
Rivers of babylon / Ma Baker / Rasputin / He was a steppenwolf / Daddy cool / Motherless child / Brown girl in the ring / Sunny / No woman, no cry / Mary's boy child / Hooray hooray it's a holi-holiday / Never change lovers in the middle of the night / Voodoonight / Still I'm sad / Nightflight to Venus / Heart of gold / Gotta go home
74321476812 / Apr '97 / Camden

☐ DADDY COOL (Greatest Hits)
290 799 / Jun '92 / Ariola Express

☐ GREATEST HITS
JHD 032 / Jun '92 / Tring

☐ GREATEST HITS
Brown girl in the ring / Rivers of babylon / Ma baker / Hooray hooray it's a holi-holiday / Daddy cool / Sunny / Mary's boy child / Rasputin / Belfast / Painter man / No woman no cry / Gotta go home / Megamix
TCD 2656 / Mar '93 / Telstar

☐ NIGHT FLIGHT TO VENUS
Night flight to venus / Rasputin / Painter man / He was a steppenwolf / King of the road / Rivers of Babylon / Voodoo night / Brown girl in the ring / Never change lovers in the middle of the night / Heart of gold
74321212692 / Jun '94 / Arista

Bonfa, Luiz

☐ SAMBOLERO - GUITARRA DO BRASIL
BMCD 3059 / Apr '97 / Blue Moon

Bonfanti, Paolo

☐ TRYIN' TO KEEP THE WHOLE THING ROCKIN'
On my best behaviour / Blues don't pay / Dead end / Look ka py py / Two steps from the blues / Changes I'm goin' thru / Route one / Stream of your love / I'm just tryin' / You were right
MRCD 1096 / Feb '97 / Club De Musique

Bonfire Madigan

☐ FROM THE BURNPILE
KRS 299CD / 15 Jun '98 / Kill Rock Stars

Bonga, Ntshuk

☐ URBAN RITUAL (Bonga, Ntshuk Tsisha)
Burning myths / City escapes / Ancient whispers / Urban precipice / Ritual reality / Rites of speech / Mzangwa mzangwa / Song unsung / Before the snow
SLAMCD 213 / Oct '96 / Slam

Bongo Logic

☐ TIPI QUEROS
RLCD 1003 / 29 Jun '98 / Ryko Latin

Bongshang

☐ CRUDE
Le introducement / Things to come / Floggin set / If and when / Lee highway blues / Phosphene / Tamlinn / Hangmans reel / Dig a hole / Scotland / Frosty morning / AKA Crude / Wedding row / Reprise
DOOVFCD 1 / Oct '94 / Doovf
IRCD 032 / Nov '95 / Iona

☐ HURRICANE JUNGLE
DOOVFCD 2 / May '97 / Doovf

Bongwater

☐ BIG SELL OUT, THE
SHIMMY 050CD / Nov '97 / Shimmy Disc

☐ DOUBLE BUMMER (2CD Set)
SHIMMY 011CD / Nov '97 / Shimmy Disc

☐ POWER OF PUSSY, THE
SHIMMY 040CD / 16 Mar '98 / Shimmy Disc

Bongzilla

☐ METHODS FOR ATTAINING EXTREME ALTITUDES
Melovespot / High like a dog / Smoke / I love Maryjane
RR 69932 / 9 Mar '98 / Relapse

Bonham, Jason

☐ WHEN YOU SEE THE SUN (Bonham, Jason Band)
When you see the sun / Drown in me / Out on the prey / Searching / Ordinary black and white / Kiss the world goodbye / Your day will come / Rain / Can't go on / Turning back the time / Unknown / Shagkabob
4892652 / 5 Jan '98 / Epic

Bonham, Tracy

☐ BURDEN OF BEING UPRIGHT, THE
5241872 / Jun '96 / Island Red

Bonilla, Luis

☐ PASOS GIGANTES (Bonilla, Luis Latin Jazz All Stars)
Pasos gigantes (giant steps) / Deluge / Panama / Caravan / Dolphin / If you could see me now / Irazu / Eva / Mambo Barbara
CCD 79507 / Feb '97 / Candid

Bonilla, Marc

☐ EE TICKET
Entrance / White noise / Mannequin highway / Commotion / Lycanthrope / Hit and run / Afterburner / Hurling blues skyward / Antonio's love jungle / Razor back / Slaughter on Memory Lane / Exit
7599267252 / Apr '92 / Reprise

Bonn, Issy

☐ LET BYGONES BE BYGONES
Every night about this time / Shrine of Saint Cellia / Greetings from you / When the lights go on again / Soon it will be Sunday / My heart is dancing with you / Let bygones be bygones / Before you break my heart / There I've said it again / Across the bridge of gold / Someday you'll want me to want you / Goodnight till tomorrow / Waiting / Till then / My little sailor man / Don't believe everything you dream / My yiddishe momme / There's a land of begin again / Just a little fond affection / That lovely weekend
SWNCD 021 / Nov '97 / Sound Waves

Bonner, Cathy

☐ SAME BLOOD
Something I said / Lipstick heart / Miss Pretty Face / California / Hand on your heart / Same blood / Driving rain / Hurtings like falling / Real me / My best dress
RDEPR 100 / Oct '97 / Rideout

Bonner, Joe

☐ IMPRESSIONS OF COPENHAGEN
ECD 220242 / Aug '92 / Evidence

☐ TWO AND ONE (2CD Set)
SCCD 37033 / 5 Jan '98 / Steeplechase

Bonner, Juke Boy

☐ JUKE BOY BONNER 1960-1967 (Bonner, Weldon 'Juke Boy')
Look out Lightning / Jumpin' with Juke Boy / Dust my broom / That a while ago / Three ring circus / Look out your window / True love darling / Jumpin' at the studio / I'm going up / Life is a dirty deal / Nine below zero
FLYCD 38 / Oct '91 / Flyright

☐ LIFE GAVE ME A DIRTY DEAL (Bonner, Weldon 'Juke Boy')
ARHCD 375 / Apr '95 / Arhoolie

Bonnet, Graham

☐ HERE COMES THE NIGHT
Something about you / Here comes the night / Long time gone / Only one woman / Please call me / Change is gonna come / I'll go crazy / I go to sleep / Look don't touch / Eyes of a child / Don't talk just kiss / What she says, you hear it means
PCOM 1114 / Jul '91 / President

Bonnet, Guy

☐ CANTE (Bonnet Sings Trenet)
A la porte du garage / Mes jeunes annees / Y'a-d'la joie / La mer / Route N7 / Je chante / La java du Diable / Une noix / Le soleil et la lune / Que reste-t-il de nos amours / La jolie Sardane / Longtemps / Boum / Pour finir
UCD 19112 / Nov '95 / Forlane

Bonney, Simon

☐ EVERYMAN
CDSTUMM 114 / Mar '96 / Mute

☐ FOREVER
Ravenswood / Forever / Part of you / Like caesar needs a brutus / Saw you falling / Someone loves you / There can only be one / Now that she's gone / Sun don't shine / Ravenswood (reprise)
CDSTUMM 99 / May '92 / Mute

Bonniwell Music Machine

☐ BEYOND THE GARAGE
SC 11030 / 20 Jul '98 / Sundazed

Bonzo Dog Band

☐ BESTIALITY OF BONZO DOG BAND
Intro and the outro / Canyons of your mind / Trouser press / Postcard / Mickey's son and daughter / Sport (the odd boy) / Tent / I'm the urban spaceman / Mr. Apollo / Shirt / Bad blood / Readymades / Rhinocratic oaths / Can blue men sing the whites / Mr. Slater's parrot / Strain / We are normal / My pink half of the drainpipe / Jazz, delicious hot, disgusting cold / Big shot / Jollity farm / Humanoid boogie
CDP 7926752 / Apr '90 / Premier/EMI

☐ CORNOLOGY (The Intro/The Outro/ Dog Ends) (3CD Set)
CDS 7995952 / Jun '92 / Premier/EMI

☐ **FOUR BONZO ORIGINALS (Gorilla/ Doughnut/Tadpoles/Keynsham) (4CD Set)**
Cool Britannia / Equestrian statue / Jollity Farm / (I left my heart) in San Francisco / Look out, there's a monster coming / Jazz, delicious hot, disgusting cold / Death cab for cutie / Narcisaus / Intro and the outro / Mickey's son and daughter / Big shot / Music for the head ballet / Piggy bank love / I'm bored / Sound of music / We are normal / Postcard / Beautiful Zelda / Can blue men sing the whites / Hello Mabel / Kama Sutra / Humanoid boogie / Trouser press / My pink half of the drainpipe / Rockaliser baby / Rhinocratic oaths / Eleven mustachioed daughters / Hunting tigers out in "Indiah" / Shirt / Tubas in the moonlight / Dr. Jazz / Monster mash / I'm the urban spaceman / Ali Baba's camel / Laughing blues / By a waterfall / Mr. Apollo / Canyons of your mind / You done my brain in / Keynsham / Quiet talks and summer walks / Tent / We were wrong / Joke shop man / Bride stripped bare by Bachelors / Look at me I'm wonderful / What do you do / Mr. Slater's parrot / Sport (The odd boy) / I want to be with you / Noises for the leg / Busted
CDBONZO 1 / Feb '96 / Premier/EMI

☐ **GORILLA**
Cool Britannia / Equestrian statue / Jollity farm / I left my heart in San Francisco / Look out, there's a monster coming / Jazz, delicious hot, disgusting cold / Death cab for a cutie / Narcissus / Intro and the outro / Mickey's son and daughter / Big shot / Music for head ballet / Piggy bank love / I'm bored / Sound of music
BGOCD 82 / Jul '95 / Beat Goes On

☐ **HISTORY OF THE BONZOS, THE**
BGOCD 376 / 12 Jan '98 / Beat Goes On

☐ **INTRO, THE (Gorilla/Doughnut)**
Cool Britannia / Equestrian statue / Jollity farm / I left my heart in San Francisco / Look out there's a monster coming / Jazz, delicious hot, disgusting cold / Death cab for cutie / Narcissus / Intro and the outro / Mickey's son and daughter / Big shot / Music for the head ballet / Piggy bank love / I'm bored / Sound of music / We are normal / Postcard / Beautiful Zelda / Can blue men sing the whites / Hello Mabel / Kama Sutra / Humanoid boogie / Trouser press / Pink half of the drainpipe / Rockaliser baby / Rhinocratic oaths / Mustachioed daughters
CDP 7995962 / Jun '92 / Premier/EMI

☐ **OUTRO, THE (Tadpoles/Keynsham)**
Hunting tigers out in Indiah / Shirt / Tubas in the moonlight / Dr. Jazz / Monster mash / I'm the urban spaceman / Ali Baba's camel / By a waterfall / Mr. Apollo / Canyons of your mind / You done my brain in / Keynsham / Quiet talks and summer walks / Tent / We were wrong / Joke shop man / Bride stripped bare by 'bachelors' / Look at me I'm wonderful / What do you do / Mr. Slater's parrot / Sport (the odd boy) / I want to be with you / Noises for the leg / Busted
CDP 7995972 / Jun '92 / Premier/EMI

Bonzos

☐ **341 BROOME ST.**
RT 024 / Sep '97 / Roto

Boo Radleys

☐ **C'MON KIDS**
C'mon kids / Meltin's worm / Melodies for the deaf (colours for the blind) / Get on the bus / Everything is sorrow / Bullfrog green / What's in the box (see watcha got) / 4 saints / New Brighton promenade / Fortunate sons / Shelter / Ride the tiger / One last hurrah
CRECD 194 / Sep '96 / Creation

☐ **EVERYTHING'S ALRIGHT FOREVER**
Spaniard / Towards the light / Losing it (song for abigail) / Memory babe / Skyscraper / I feel nothing / Room at the top / Does this hurt / Sparrow / Smile fades fast / Firesky / Song for the morning to sing / Lazy day / Paradise
CRECD 120 / Mar '92 / Creation

☐ **GIANT STEPS**
I hang suspended / Upon 9th and fairchild / Wish I was skinny / Leaves and sand / Butterfly McQueen / Rodney King / Thinking of ways / Barney (and me) / Spun around / If you want it, take it / Best lose the fear / Take the time around / Lazarus / One is for / Run my way runway / I've lost the reason
CRECD 149 / Aug '93 / Creation

☐ **LEARNING TO WALK**
R 3012 / Nov '93 / Rough Trade

☐ **WAKE UP**
CRECD 179 / Mar '95 / Creation

Boo-YaaTRIBE

☐ **ANGRY SAMOANS**
Skarred for life / Breakin life sykos / Buried alive / Full metal Jack / Kill for the family / Retaliate / Boogie man / Where U want I / Gang bangin' / Mr Mister Redeyes / Angry Samoans / No free ride
CDVEST 81 / May '97 / Bulletproof

☐ **DOOMSDAY**
CDVEST 20 / Jul '94 / Bulletproof

☐ **METALLY DISTURBED**
CDMVEST 76 / Aug '96 / Bulletproof

Boogalusa

☐ **BOOGALUSA**
Goodnight Bob / Hunger / Dead man sing / To the water / Recondie on the radio / Shakedown zydeco / Silent phrases / Big lights / Heart jump / Way you say
CDLDL 1223 / Feb '97 / Lochshore

☐ **CARELESS ANGELS & CRAZY CAJUNS**
LDLCD 1208 / Oct '93 / Lochshore

Boogie Down Productions

☐ **CRIMINAL MINDED**
MIL 47872 / Jun '97 / MIL Multimedia

☐ **CRIMINAL MINDED (Hot Club Version)**
MIL 57852 / 15 Sep '97 / B-Boy/MIL Multimedia

☐ **MAN AND HIS MUSIC, A (Criminal Minded Remix)**
MIL 20002 / 20 Oct '97 / B-Boy/MIL Multimedia

Boogiemen

☐ **BOOGIE TIME**
BLRCD 033 / May '97 / Blue Loon

Book Of Wisdom

☐ **CATACOMBS**
NACD 201 / Oct '95 / Nature & Art

Bookbinder, Roy

☐ **LIVE BOOK - DON'T START ME TALKIN'**
ROUCD 3130 / May '94 / Rounder

☐ **POLK CITY RAMBLE**
ROUCD 3153 / 19 Jan '98 / Rounder

☐ **ROY BOOKBINDER**
Friend like me / Gonna get myself a motorhome / Something different / Mississippi blues / Gin done done it / I'm going home / Good gal / Nobody knows / I'm hurtin' / Waiting for a train / Cigarette blues / My road is rough and rocky / Tell me how do you feel
ROUCD 3107 / '88 / Rounder

☐ **TRAVELIN' MAN**
GCD 1017 / Jan '98 / Genes

Booker, Chuckii

☐ **NIICE 'N' WIILD**
Spinnin / Love is medicine / Out of the dark / You don't know / With all my heart / I git around / Games / Deep c diiver / Soul triilogy 1 / Soul triilogy 11 / Soul triilogy 111 / Niice n wiild / I should have loved you
7567824102 / Nov '92 / WEA

Booker, James

☐ **JUNCO PARTNER**
Black minute waltz / Goodnight Irene / Pixie / On the sunny side of the street / Make a better world / Junco partner / Put out the light / Medley / Pop's dilemma / I'll be seeing you
HNCD 1359 / Feb '93 / Hannibal

☐ **KING OF THE NEW ORLEANS KEYBOARD**
How do you feel / Going down slow / Classified / One hell of a nerve / Blues rhapsody / Rockin' pneumonia and the boogie woogie flu / Please send me someone to love / All by myself / Ain't nobody's business if I do / Something you got / Harlem in Hamburg
CDJP 1 / Apr '92 / JSP

☐ **NEW ORLEANS PIANO WIZARD (Live)**
On the sunny side of the street / Black night / Keep on gwine / Come rain or come shine / Something stupid / Please send me someone to love / Tell me how do you feel / Let them talk / Come in my house
ROUCD 2027 / '88 / Rounder

☐ **RESSURECTION OF THE BAYOU MAHARAJAH**
Tico tico-papa was a rascal (medley) / Lawdy miss clawdy-ballad at the maple leaf (medley) / Minute waltz (chopin) / All by myself / Save your love for me / Classic partner / St. james infirmary / Gitanarias / Pop's dilemma-irene goodnight
ROUCD 2118 / Aug '93 / Rounder

☐ **SPIDERS ON THE KEYS**
Papa was a rascal / Sunny side of the street / So swell when you're well / Taste of honey / He's got the whole world in his hands / Gonzo's blue dream / Eleanor rigby / Malaguena / Piano salad / Little coquette / Besame mucho / Tico tico / Over the rainbow
ROUCD 2119 / Oct '93 / Rounder

Booker, Steve

☐ **FAR CRY FROM HERE, A**
RMRCD 1 / Aug '96 / JVO

Booker T

☐ **BOOKER T (The Prize Collection - 2CD Set)**
AZCD 03 / 25 May '98 / Azuli

☐ **GO TELL IT ON THE MOUNTAIN (Booker T Trio)**
SHCD 114 / Oct '92 / Silkheart

Booker T & The MG's

☐ **AND NOW**
My sweet potato / Jericho / No matter what shape / One mint julep / In the midnight hour / Summertime / Working in the coal mine / Don't mess up a good thing / Think / Taboo / Soul jam / Sentimental journey
8122702972 / Jul '93 / Atlantic

☐ **BEST OF BOOKER T AND THE MG'S, THE**
Green onions / Slim Jenkins' place / Hip hug-her / Soul dressing / Summertime / Bootleg / Jelly bread / Tic-tac-toe / Can't be still / Groovin' / Mo' onions / Red beans and rice / Terrible thing / My sweet potato / Be my lady / Booker-loo
7567812812 / Jan '93 / Atlantic

☐ **BEST OF BOOKER T AND THE MG'S, THE**
Time is tight / Soul limbo / Heads or tails / Over easy / Hip hug-her / Hang 'em high / Johnny I love you / Slum baby / Fiver / Soul clap '69 / Sunday sermon / Born under a bad sign / Mrs. Robinson / Something / Light my fire / It's your thing / Fuquawi / Kinda easy like / Meditation / Melting pot
CDSX 46 / Apr '93 / Stax

☐ **DOIN' OUR THING**
I can dig it / Expressway to your heart / Doin' our thing / You don't love me / Never my love / Exodus song / Beat goes on / Ode to Billie Joe / Blue rondo / You keep me hangin' on / Let's go get stoned
8122710142 / Jul '93 / Atlantic

☐ **GREEN ONIONS**
Green onions / Rinky dink / I got a woman / Mo' onions / Twist and shout / Behave yourself / Stranger on the shore / Lonely avenue / One who really loves you / You can't sit down / Woman, a lover, a friend / Comin' home baby
7567822552 / Oct '94 / Atlantic

☐ **HIP HUG HER**
Hip hug-her / Slim Jenkin's place / Soul sanction / Get ready / More / Double or nothing / Carnaby street / Slim Jenkins' joint / Pigmy / Groovin' / Booker's notion / Sunny
8122710132 / Jul '93 / Atlantic

☐ **IN THE CHRISTMAS SPIRIT**
Jingle bells / Santa Claus is coming to town / Winter wonderland / White Christmas / Christmas song / Silver bells / Merry Christmas baby / Blue Christmas / Sweet little Jesus boy / Silent night / We three kings / We wish you a merry Christmas
7567823382 / Jul '93 / Atlantic

☐ **MCLEMORE AVENUE**
Golden slumbers / Here comes the sun / Come together / Because / Mean Mr Mustard / She came in through the bathroom window / Carry that weight / End / Something / You never give me your money / Polythene Pam / Sun king / I want you
CDSXE 016 / Nov '88 / Stax

☐ **MELTING POT**
Melting pot / Back home / Chicken pox / Fuquawi / Kinda easy like / Hi ride / LA jazz song / Sunny Monday
CDSXE 055 / Sep '92 / Stax

☐ **PLAY THE HIP HITS**
Baby scratch my back / Harlem shuffle / Hi-heel sneakers / Downtown / I was made to love her / Georgia on my mind / Boot-leg / Hole in the wall / Fannie Mae / Day tripper / You left the water running / Every beat of my heart / Ain't that peculiar / You can't do that / Wang dang doodle / On a Saturday night / Carmen / You're so fine / Raunchy / You are my sunshine / Soul man / Gimme some lovin' / When something is wrong with my baby
CDSXD 065 / Apr '95 / Stax

☐ **SOUL DRESSING**
Soul dressing / Tic-tac-toe / Big train / Jelly bread / Aw 'mercy / Outrage / Night owl walk / Chinese checkers / Home grown / Mercy mercy / Plum Nellie / Can't be still
7567823372 / Feb '95 / Atlantic

Boom

☐ **MOVIN' OUT**
SLOWDIME 12CD / 6 Apr '98 / Slowdime

Boom Boyz

☐ **BOTTOM, THE**
BRY 4185CD / Mar '94 / Ichiban

Boomtown Rats

☐ **TONIC FOR THE TROOPS**
Like clockwork / Blind date / I never loved Eva Braun / Living in an island / Don't believe what you read / She's so modern / Me and Howard Hughes / Can't stop / Watch out for the normal people / Rat trap
5140532 / Jul '93 / Mercury

Boon Man

☐ **TIN MAN**
Tin man / Don't walk away / Kick or the kiss / Baby I know / Ever the way / Sleepy people / Every day / One from the heart / How deep (is your heart) / Growing wild in the desert / Tears me down / Knight
RES 106CD / Apr '97 / Resurgence

Boondocks

☐ **STRAIGHT FROM NOWHERE**
50572 / Jun '97 / Raging Bull

Boone Creek

☐ **ONE WAY TRACK**
One way rider / Head over heels / Little community church / Mississippi Queen / In the pines / Can't you hear me callin' / No Mother / God / Blue and lonesome / Daniel prayed / Sally Goodun
SHCD 3701 / Jan '97 / Sugar Hill

Boone, Daniel

☐ **BEAUTIFUL SUNDAY**
Beautiful sunday / Sunshine lover / Skydriver / Annabelle / Sweet joanna / Daddy don't you walk so fast / Mamma (bixio) / Crying / In ohio / Who turned the lights out of my life / In love again / Funny little things / Taste the wine / One day / Sad and lonely lady / Rock and roll bum
12550 / Jun '95 / Laserlight

☐ **VERY BEST OF DANIEL BOONE, THE**
MCCD 247 / Jun '96 / Music Club

Boone, Pat

☐ **APRIL LOVE**
Love letters in the sand / I love you more and more / I almost lost my head / Friendly persuasion / Mr. Blue / April love / Speedy Gonzales / Ain't that a shame / Tutti frutti / Don't forbid me / Wonderful time up there / I believe in music / I'll be home / Moody River / She fights that lovin' feelin' / Jambalaya / You so easy on my mind / Bernadine / Where there's a heartache / Poetry in motion
HADCD 162 / May '94 / Javelin

☐ **APRIL LOVE**
Ain't that a shame / I'll be home / Tutti frutti / I almost lost my mind / Friendly persuasion (thee I love) / Don't forbid me / Why baby why / Love letters in the sand / Bernadine / Remember you're mine / April love / Wonderful time up there / Moody river / Johnny will / Speedy gonzales / Mr. blue / Wanted / I believe in music / Golden rocket / Jambalaya (on the bayou) / I love you more and more everyday / You lay so easy on my mind
RMB 75070 / Apr '94 / Remember

☐ **BABY OH BABY**
Baby, oh baby / Rose Marie / Baby sonnenschein / Wie eine lady / Ein goldener stern / Komm zu mir wenn du einsam bist / Oh lady / Nein nein valentina / Mary Lou / Wo find ich meine traume / Die casanova siempre / Amor al reves / En cualquier lugar / Cartas en la arena / Tu che non hai amato mai / E furtvol la pioggia cade / Se tu non fossi qui
BCD 15645 / Jun '92 / Bear Family

☐ **COLLECTION, THE**
Love letters in the sand / April love / Speedy gonzales / Bernadine / Ain't that a shame / Don't forbid me / I almost lost my mind / Moody river / Wonderful time up there / I'll be home / Friendly persuasion (thee I love) / Don't want to fall away from you april / I believe in music / Poetry in motion / Indiana girl / Tutti frutti / Jambalaya / Johnny comes a shining / Mr. blue / Oklahoma sunshine / She fights that lovin' feeling / Texas woman / You lay so easy on my mind / Where there's a heartache / Won't be home
COL 036 / Jan '95 / Collection

☐ **EP COLLECTION, THE**
Main attraction / BINGO / That lucky old sun / Begin the beguine / Friendly persuasion / Peace in the valley / Love letters in the sand / Rock around the clock / Say it with music / April love / Pretty girl is like a melody / Bernadine / Girl that I marry / Count your blessings instead of sheep / I'll build a stairway to paradise / Johnny Will / Jingle bells / Stardust / Autumn leaves / Don't forbid me / St Louis blues / That's my desire / All I do is dream of you / I'll be home / Always you and me
SEECD 487 / 6 Oct '97 / See For Miles

☐ **FAMILY CHRISTMAS**
12289 / Nov '95 / Laserlight

☐ **FIFTIES, THE - COMPLETE (12CD Set)**
Until you tell me so / (I'll never be free) my heart belongs to you / Remember to be mine / Halfway chance / I need someone / Loving you madly / Two hearts / Tra-la-la / Ain't that a shame / Angel eyes / Tennessee Saturday night / Take the time / Now I know / No arms can ever hold you (no other arms) / Rich in love / You're gonna be sorry / At my front door / Gee Whittakers / Tutti frutti / I'll be home / Hoboken baby / Just as long as I'm with you / I almost lost my mind / Long tall Sally / Am I seeing angels / Bingo / Money honey / Treasure of love / I'm in love with your / Friendly persuasion (thee I love) / King for a day / When you help a friend in need / All I do is dream of you / Ev'ry little thing / Would you like to take a walk / Chains of love / Harbour lights / Sunday / Hummin' the blues / I'm waiting just for you / Bug your pardon / Chattanooga shoe shine boy / With you / Forgive me / Begin the beguine / Mocking bird / Indiana holiday / Coax me a little / Marry me, marry me / That lucky old sun / Scattered toys / Old fashioned Christmas / Why did I choose you / Honey hush / Tomorrow night / Rock me baby / Anastasia / Poem / Gold / Don't forbid me / Flip, flop and fly / Pledging my love / Ain't nobody here but us chickens / Shake a hand / Please send me someone to love / I'm in love again / Rock around the clock / Shot gun boogie / Five, ten, fifteen hours / Too soon to know / And I'm scared / Fat man / When I write my song / Great googa mooga / Why, baby why / Peace in the valley / He'll understand and say well done / Technique / Bernadine / Talking to myself about you / Just a closer walk with thee / Steal away / Louella / Without my love / Louella / There's a goldmine in the sky / Sweet hour of prayer / Old rugged cross / In the garden / Now the day is over / Too soon to know / Love letters in the sand / Beyond the sunset / It is no secret / My God is real / Softly and tenderly / Will the circle be unbroken / Have thine own way Lord / Yield not temptation / Whispering hope / There's a goldmine in the sky / Cathedral in the pines / From a Jack to a King / Remember you're mine / How deep is the ocean / Pretty girl is like a melody / Tom tom / Cheek to cheek / Always / They say it's wonderful / All alone / What'll I do / All by myself / Remember / Soft lights and sweet music / Be careful, it's my heart / Girl that I marry / Say it with music / Count your blessings / Clover in the meadow / April love / Wonderful time up there / My little red book / I've got you on my mind / Call it stormy Monday / Keep your chin / Therefore, I love you / Peace on Earth / Have faith / It dreams come true / Baby has gone bye bye / If dreams come true / That's

how much I love you / If dreams come true / That's how much I love you / September song / Ebb tide / I'll walk alone / To each his own / Autumn leaves / Anniversary song / Stardust / Cold, cold heart / Solitude / Deep purple / Blueberry hill / St. Louis blues / Heartaches / Her hand in mine / He / I believe / Ave Maria / Lord's prayer / They can't take that away from me / Yes indeed / Don't worry 'bout me / Lazy river / Lonesome road / American beauty / Rose / Little white lies / Sweet Sue, just you / It's a pity to say goodnight / Sweet Georgia Brown / Gone fishin' / My baby just cares for me / I'll build a stairway to paradise / Robins and roses / I've heard that song before / Frenesi / Sweet Georgia Brown / Two little kisses / Gee, but it's lonely / For my good fortune / Gee, but it's lonely / Wait for me Mary / Havin' fun spo-dee-o-dee / I'll remember tonight / Mardi Gras march / Bourbon Street blues / Fiddle, a rifle, an axe and a bible / Bigger than Texas / Loyalty / Yes indeed / For my good fortune / Jingle bells / Here comes Santa Claus / My happiness / You can't be true, dear / Side by side / Midnight / Silver bells / I'll be home for Christmas / It came upon a midnight clear / Rudolph the red-nosed reindeer / Santa Claus is coming to town / O little town of Bethlehem / O come all ye faithful (adeste fidelis) / Joy to the world / Hark, the herald angels sing / First Noel / Wait for me Mary / Bewildered / Good rockin' tonight / How soon / With the wind and rain in your hair / Shake a hand / Money honey / 'Tis sweet to be remembered / Rock boll weevil / Brightest wishing star / Beulah / Rock boll weevil / Anytime / True love / I'm in the mood for love / Fascination / Secret love / How soon / Because of you / Maybe you'll be there / Tenderly / You belong to me / Why don't you believe me / Nearness of you / More than you know / You're my girl / You just can't plan these things / Goodnight, sleep tight / Do I worry / Wang dang taffy apple tango / Bewildered / For a penny / Alone / Walking the floor over you / Oh what a felling / Last night was the end of the world / Drifting and dreaming / Tumbling tumblweeds / Beside me / I'll never be free / Sentimental me / Let the rest of the world go by / Melody of love / Let me call you sweetheart / Vaya con dios / Twixt, twelve and twenty / All at once / Brightest wishing star / Why don't you haul off and love me / It's a sin / Didn't it rain / No middle ground / (Remember me) I'm the one who loves you / Fools hall of fame / This girl is mine / I've got a dream on my mind / God be with you / Take the name of Jesus / I love to tell a story / Blessed assurance / Saviour, like a shepherd lead us / He leadeth me / God will take care of thee / I'll be home for Christmas / White Christmas / Joy to the world / Silent night / O little town of Bethlehem / It came upon a midnight clear / First Noel / Adeste fidelis / O holy night / God rest ye merry gentlemen / Hark, the herald angels sing / Santa's coming in a whirly bird / That's all / I want to be there / To the centre of the Earth / Many dreams ago / Wait for me Mary / Faithful heart / Boone's rock'n'roll / Too marvellous for words / My love is like a red, red rose / Twice as tall / Come Spring / What a friend we have in Jesus / I am thine, O Lord / Let the lower lights be burning / Nearer my God to thee / Rock of ages / Loving you madly / Money honey / Friendly persuasion (thee I love) / Ev'ry little thing / Love letters in the sand / Pledging my love / I'm waiting just for you / Walking the floor over you / Love letters in the sand / Beyond the sunset / Louella / Baby has gone, bye bye / St. Louis blues / Two little kisses / For my good fortune / Bigger than Texas / Wait for me Mary / How soon / It's a sin / Didn't it rain / I almost lost my mind / Don't forbid me / Love letters in the sand / Why baby why / Bernadine / There's a goldmine in the sky / I'm in love with you / Chains of love / Remember you're mine / Anastasia / I'm waiting just for you / Friendly persuasion (thee I love) / Wonderful time up there / Too soon to know / That's how much I love you
BCD 15884 / Jun '97 / Bear Family

☐ INSPIRATIONAL COLLECTION
VSD 5903 / 7 Apr '98 / Varese Sarabande

☐ LOVE LETTERS (20 Classics)
Love letters in the sand / I love you more and more / I almost lost my head / Friendly persuasion / Mr. Blue / April love / Speedy Gonzalez / Ain't that a shame / Tutti frutti / Don't forbid me / Wonderful time up there / I believe in music / I'll be home / Moody river / She fights that lovin' feelin' / Jambalaya / You lay so easy on my mind / Bernadine / Where there's a heartache / Poetry in motion
SUMCD 4081 / Nov '96 / Summit

☐ LOVE LETTERS IN THE SAND (Pat Boone At His Best)
PLSCD 211 / Apr '97 / Pulse

☐ VERY BEST OF PAT BOONE, THE
Ain't that a shame / Bernadine / Don't forbid me / Friendly persuasion / I almost lost my mind / Jambalaya (on the bayou) / Moody river / Remember your mine / Speedy Gonzales / Love letters in the sand / Tutti frutti / Hey good lookin' / I believe in music / I love you more and more every day / Oh boy / Poetry in motion / Three bells / April love
12999 / Jul '97 / Laserlight

Boone, Richard

☐ MAKE SOMEONE HAPPY (Boone, Richard & Bent Jaedig Quintet)
STCD 8282 / May '97 / Storyville

Boot Camp Clik

☐ FOR THE PEOPLE
1-900 get da boot / Down by law / Night riders / Headz are reddee / Watch your step / Illa noyz / Rag time / Blackout / Ohkeedoke / Rugged terrain / Dugout / Go for yours / Likkle youth man dem / Last time
CDPTY 145 / 30 Jun '97 / Priority/Virgin

Booth, Tim

☐ BOOTH & THE BAD ANGEL (Booth, Tim & Angelo Badalamenti)
I believe / Dance of the bad angels / Hit parade / Fall in love with me / Old ways / Life gets better / Heart / Rising / Butterfly's dream / Stranger / Hands in the rain
5268522 / Jul '96 / Fontana

Booth, Webster

☐ THREE GREAT TENORS (Booth, Webster & Josef Locke/Richard Tauber)
Lovely maid in the moonlight: *Booth, Webster & Joan Cross* / My heart and I: *Tauber, Richard* / Soldier's dream: *Locke, Josef* / English rose: *Booth, Webster* / Hear my song: *Locke, Josef* / Take a pair of sparkling eyes: *Booth, Webster* / Song of songs: *Tauber, Richard* / When the stars are brightly shining: *Booth, Webster* / Serenade: *Tauber, Richard* / March of the grenadiers: *Locke, Josef* / Wandering minstrel: *Booth, Webster* / Break of day: *Tauber, Richard* / One alone: *Tauber, Richard* / If I can help somebody: *Locke, Josef* / Faery song: *Booth, Webster & John T. Cockerill* / You are my heart's delight: *Tauber, Richard* / I'll walk beside you: *Locke, Josef* / Love is my reason: *Tauber, Richard* / Goodbye: *Locke, Josef* / Lost chord: *Booth, Webster*
CDSL 8248 / Jul '95 / EMI

Boothe, Ken

☐ ACCLAIMED
UPCD 004 / May '97 / Upstairs

☐ ACCLAIMED
UPSCD 01 / 22 Jun '98 / Upstairs

☐ BLOOD BROTHERS
PKCD 080896 / 23 Mar '98 / K&K

☐ COLLECTION, THE
RNCD 2124 / Nov '95 / Rhino

☐ EVERYTHING I OWN
One that I love / You left the water running / Say you / Can't see you / Lady with the starlight / Somewhere / Live good / Old fashion way / Can't fight me down / I'm not for sale / Why baby why / Freedom street / It's gonna take a miracle / Now I know / Artibella / Stop your crying / I wish it would be peaceful again / Your feeling and mine / Make me feel alright / So nice / Rasta never fail / Second chance / Silver words / Is it because I'm black / Everything I own / Crying over you
CDTRL 381 / Jun '97 / Trojan

☐ FREEDOM ST.
0444052 / Mar '97 / Rhino

☐ I AM JUST A MAN
LG 21101 / Mar '95 / Lagoon

☐ KEN BOOTHE COLLECTION
CDTRL 249 / Mar '94 / Trojan

☐ MR. ROCKSTEADY
SOCD 1112 / 2 Feb '98 / Studio One

☐ SAY YOU
Old fashion way / Redemption song / Lady with the starlight / Say you / Let me tell you / Give me your love / Hard to confess / Mellow mood / Money in my pocket / Black rose / Ali Baba / Love is overdue / Everything I own / Rivers of Babylon / Many rivers to cross / Kingston town / Sweet sensation / Stay a little bit longer
RN 7028 / 8 Sep '97 / Rhino

☐ SINGS HITS FROM STUDIO ONE AND MORE
I'm in a dancing mood / I'm in a dancing mood dub / My heart is gone / My heart is gone dub / Take my hands / Take my hands dub / When I fall in love / When I fall in love dub / Do you love me / Do you love me dub / Got to tell you goodbye / Got to tell you goodbye dub / Without love / Without love dub / Train is coming / Train is coming dub / Moving away / Moving away dub / Puppet on a string / Puppet on a string dub / You are no good / You are no good dub / Now you come running / Now you come running dub
RN 7012 / 20 Apr '98 / Rhino

Boots

☐ HERE ARE THE BOOTS
216032 / 22 Jun '98 / Tis

Boots & His Buddies

☐ CLASSICS 1935-1937
CLASSICS 723 / Dec '93 / Classics

☐ CLASSICS 1937-1938
CLASSICS 738 / Feb '94 / Classics

Bootstrappers

☐ BOOTSTRAPPERS
NAR 046CD / May '93 / New Alliance

Booty, Charlie

☐ AFTER HOURS
SACD 108 / Mar '95 / Solo Art

Booze & Blues

☐ MOTORWAY LIGHTS
BOO 003 / Nov '94 / B&B

Booze Brothers

☐ BREWERS DROOP
CLACD 428 / Mar '97 / Castle

Bop Brothers

☐ STRANGE NEWS
Thrill me / Cruisin' and coastin' / One mint julep / Big bad beautiful blues / Strange news / Money is getting cheaper / Long slow ride down / Little finger / Georgia on my mind / Chicken and the hawk
ABACACD 1 / Jul '95 / Abacabe

Bop City

☐ BOP CITY - HIP STRUT
No problem / Hip strut / New rhumba / Funk in deep freeze / Duid deed / Another kind of soul / Squirrel / Bop city / Ahmad's blues / Squirrel
HIBD 8013 / Oct '96 / Hip Bop

Bop Fathers

☐ BOP FATHERS VOL.2
COD 027 / Jul '92 / Jazz View

Boqus

☐ BOQUS
SD 016 / 13 Apr '98 / Stereo Deluxe

Bordas

☐ LES CHANTS DE MARINS
ARN 64398 / 21 Aug '97 / Arion

Borderlands

☐ FROM CONJUNTO TO CHICKEN SCRATCH
SFWCD 40418 / Oct '94 / Smithsonian Folkways

Bore, Sergio

☐ INTUICAO DE TUPA
EX 3582 / Jun '97 / Instinct

☐ TAMBORES URBANOS
Adivinhacao / Voices of percussion / Rumbata / Tambores urbanos / El cogollo / Chama criolla / Stop killing the Amazon / El poliangito / Lamento Africano / Pingentes / Luz de lua / Marimba / Suite Brasila part 1
ME 000342 / Oct '95 / Soulciety

Boredoms

☐ ONANIE BOMB MEETS THE SEX PISTOLS
Wipe out shock / Shoppers / Boredom Vs.SDI / We never sleep / Bite my bollocks / Young assouls / Call me God / No core punk / Lick'n cock boatpeople / Melt down boogie / Feedbackfuck / Anal eater / God from anal / Born to anal
EN 001 / Sep '94 / Earthnoise

☐ SOUL DISCHARGE '99
Your name is limitless / Bubblebop shot / Fifty two boredom / Sun, gun, run / Z and U and T and A / TV Scorpion / Pow wow now / JB Dick and Tina Turner pussy / GIL '77 / Jup-na-keeeeel / Catastro mix '99 / Milky way / Songs without electric guitars / Hamaiin disco bollocks / Hamaiin disco without bollocks
EN 002 / Sep '94 / Earthnoise

☐ WOW VOL.2
AVANT 026 / Nov '93 / Avant

Borenius, Louis

☐ LAST OF THE AZTECS (Borenius, Louis Coup D'Etat)
LOTCD 4304 / May '97 / Loose Tie

Borgat, Stephane

☐ DIATONICOEUR
CNAI 55388 / Mar '96 / Le Cire Jaune

Borge, Victor

☐ COMEDY IN MUSIC
Comedy in music / Comedy in music / Requests / Tea for two / Malagena / Stardust / Nola / Trees / One fine day / Tales from the vienna woods / Third man theme / Nocturne / Blue Danube waltz / Mozart opera by Borge / Danube waltz / Three Borge favourites / Family background / Phonetic punctuation
4840422 / May '96 / Columbia

Borghetti, Renato

☐ CARONA PRO NORTE
ML 51021 / 14 Apr '98 / Musica Latina

Borghi, Emmanuel

☐ ANECDOTES
A 22 / Oct '96 / Seventh

Boris & His Bolshie Balalaika

☐ PSYCHIC REVOLUTION
Toadstool soup / Onward christian soldiers / Purple haze / Burnin' with the fire / Blacklisted blues / Voodoo chile / Moonsong / Goin' nowhere / Psychic revolution (sunsong)
DELECCD 014 / Nov '94 / Delerium

Boris The Sprinkler

☐ END OF THE CENTURY
CRVW 42 / 22 May '98 / Clearview

Borknagar

☐ BORKNAGAR
MR 012CD / Oct '96 / Malicious

☐ OLDEN DOMAIN
CM 77175CD / 1 Sep '97 / Century Media

Borland, Adrian

☐ 5.00 AM
EAR 001CD / 29 Sep '97 / Earth

☐ CINEMATIC
Dreamfuel / Bright white light / When can I be me / Cinematic / Night cascade / Neon and stone / Long dark train / Antartica / Western veil / We are the night / Dreamfuel 2 / I can't stop the world / Heading emotional / South / Spanish hotel / March
RES 002 / Mar '96 / Resolve

☐ OVER THE UNDER
EAR 002CD / 29 Sep '97 / Earth

Born Against

☐ PATRIOTIC BATTLE HYMNS
VMFM 612 / Nov '94 / Vermiform

Born Jamericans

☐ KIDS FROM FOREIGN
Instant death interlude / Warning sign / So ladies / Sweet honey / Informa fe dead / Cease and seckle / Ain't no stoppin' / Why do girls / Oh gosh / Nobody knows / Boom shak-a-tack
7567923492 / Jun '94 / Warner Bros.

Bornkamp, Arno

☐ REED MY MIND
BVHAASTCD 9304 / Oct '94 / Bvhaast

Borrfors, Monica

☐ SECOND TIME AROUND
1397 / Jun '85 / Caprice

☐ YOUR TOUCH
1350 / Oct '90 / Caprice

Borstlap, Michiel

☐ MICHIEL BORSTLAP LIVE
CHR 70030 / Nov '95 / Challenge

☐ RESIDENCE (Borstlap, Michiel Trio)
Song for B / In your own sweet way / Residence / I love you / Damascus / Dream of the elders / Columbo / Memory of enchantment
CD 9920152 / 17 Nov '97 / Via Jazz

Bosch, Jimmy

☐ SONEANDO TROMBON
Descargarana / Otra oportunidad / Crisis de identidad / Muy joven para mi / Gaviota / La soledad / Padre soy / Cha cha gabriel / Erbin on the phone / Jimmy bop
RLCD 1004 / 6 Mar '98 / Ryko Latin

Bosco, Joao

☐ AFRO CANTO GUITAR
68909 / Apr '97 / Tropical

☐ CORACAO TROPICAL
68969 / Apr '97 / Tropical

☐ DA LICENCA MEU SENHOR
Pagodespell / Forro em limoeiro / Se voca juras / Pai grande / Peixe vivo/O verto / Tico tico no fuba / Desafinado / Espinha de bacalhau / Expresso 2222 / No tabuleiro da baiana / Um gago apaixonado / Melodia sentimental / Rio De Janeiro / Herois da liberdade
4792132 / Jul '96 / Sony Jazz

Bose, Miguel

☐ SIGN OF CAIN, THE
One touch / Fire and forgiveness / They're only words / Home / Sign of cain / Hunter and the prey / Wako-shamen / I hold only you / Mayo / Nada particular
4509950532 / Feb '95 / East West

Boske, Joe

☐ AMARA - ISLAND CURRENTS
QPCD 001 / Dec '97 / Quay

Boson, Higgs

☐ HIGGS BOSON
FHPCD 1 / Sep '96 / FHP

Boss

☐ BORN GANGSTAZ
Call from mom / Deeper / Comin' to getcha / Mai sister is a bitch / Thelma and Louise / Drive-by / Progress of elimination / Livin' loc'd / Recipe of a hoe / Blind date with Boss / Catch a bad one / Born gansta / 1800 body bags / Diary of a mad bitch / 2 to da head / I don't give a fuck / Call from dad
4740742 / Aug '93 / Columbia

Boss Martians

☐ 13 EVIL TALES
ID 123344CD / Jan '97 / Dionysus

☐ INVASION OF THE BOSS MARTIANS LIVE
VR 1963 / 24 Nov '97 / Vagrant

☐ JETAWAY SOUNDS OF...
HILLS 1 / Jun '97 / Hillsdale

Boss Quartet

☐ BOSS QUARTET, THE
LICD 23171 / Aug '97 / Liphone

Bostic, Earl

☐ 14 HITS
KCD 5010 / Apr '97 / King

☐ BEST OF BOSTIC, THE
Flamingo / Always / Deep purple / Smoke rings / What, no pearls / Jungle drums / Serenade / I can't give you anything but love / Seven steps / I'm gettin' sentimental over you / Don't you do it / Steamwhistle jump
KCD 500 / Mar '90 / King

☐ BLOWS A FUSE
Night train / 8.45 stomp / That's the groovy thing / Special delivery stomp / Moonglow / Mambostic / Earl blows a fuse / Harlem nocturne / Who snuck the wine in the gravy / Don't you do it / Disc jockey's nightmare / Flamingo / Steam whistle jump / What, no pearls / Tuxedo Junction
CDCHARLY 241 / Oct '90 / Charly

☐ BLOWS A FUSE
KCD 6001 / 17 Nov '97 / King

☐ BOSTIC FOR YOU
Sleep / Moonglow / Velvet sunset / For you / Very thought of you / Linger awhile / Cherokee / Smoke gets in your eyes / Memories / Embraceable you / Wrap your troubles in dreams (and dream your troubles away) / Night and day
KCD 503 / Mar '90 / King

☐ FLAMINGO (Charly R&B Masters Vol.16)
Flamingo / Sleep / Always / Moonglow / Ain't misbehavin' / You go to my head / Cherokee / Streamwhistle jump / What, no pearls / Deep purple / Mambostic / Sweet Lorraine / Where or when / Harlem nocturne / 720 in the books / Tuxedo junction / Night train / Special delivery stomp / Song of the Islands / Liebestraum / Liszt
CDRB 16 / Mar '95 / Charly

☐ JAZZ TIME
LEJAZZCD 52 / Jan '96 / Le Jazz

Boston

☐ BOSTON
More than a feeling / Peace of mind / Foreplay (long time) / Rock 'n' roll band / Smokin' / Hitch a ride / Something about you / Let me take you home tonight
CD 81611 / Mar '87 / Epic
4894122 / 2 Feb '98 / Columbia

☐ DON'T LOOK BACK
Journey / It's easy / Man I'll never be / Feeling satisfied / Part / Used to bad news / Don't be afraid
CD 86057 / Mar '87 / Epic

☐ FOR REAL
I need your love / Surrender to me / Livin' for you / Walk on (some more) / What's your name / Magdalene / We can make it
MCD 10973 / May '94 / MCA

☐ GREATEST HITS
Tell me / Higher power / More than a feeling / Peace of mind / Don't look back / Cool the engines / Livin' for you / Feelin' satisfied / Party / Foreplay long time / Amanda / Rock 'n' roll band / Smokin' / Man I'll never be / Star spangled banner/4th of July reprise / Higher power
4843332 / Jun '97 / Epic

☐ THIRD STAGE
Amanda / We're ready / Launch / Cool the engines / My destination / New world / To be a man / I think I like it / Can'tcha say / Still in love / Hollyann
MCLD 19066 / Oct '92 / MCA

Boston, Rick

☐ NUMB
WD 00402 / Oct '96 / World Domination

Bostonian Friends

☐ PEACE FROM AFRICA
151472 / Nov '92 / EPM

Boswell Sisters

☐ AIRSHOTS AND RARITIES 1930-1935
Here comes the sun / Liza Lee / Down the river of golden dreams / Rarin' to go / There's a wah wah girl in Agua Caliente / Let me sing and I'm happy/Crazy rhythm/Farewell blues/Mammy / My mad moment / Gee but I'd like to make you happy / I'm in training for you / When the little red roses get the blues for you / Does my baby love / Song of the dawn / Liza Lee / Rainy days / At the Darktown strutter's ball / Sleep come on and take me / Heebie jeebies / Why don't you practice what you preach / Fare the well Annabelle / Lullaby of Broadway
RTR 79009 / Feb '97 / Retrieval

☐ ANTHOLOGY 1930-1940
EN 518 / Sep '95 / Encyclopaedia

☐ BOSWELL SISTERS 1931-1935
Sing a little jingle / Down among the sheltering palms / Dinah / Washboard blues / Put that sun back in the sky / Was that the human thing to do / Stardust / Sleep, come on and take me / Lawd, you made the night too long / We just couldn't say goodbye / Darktown strutters' ball / Fare thee well annabelle / If I had a million dollars / 42nd street / Old man of the mountain / It's the girl / Strange as it seems / Lullaby of broadway
CD 56082 / Mar '95 / Jazz Roots

☐ BOSWELL SISTERS COLLECTION VOL.1 (1931-1932)
COCD 21 / Mar '95 / Collector's Classics

☐ IT'S THE GIRLS (Boswell Sisters & Connee Boswell)
It's the girls / That's what I like about you / Heebie jeebies / Concentratin' on you / Wha'd ja do to me / I'm all dressed up with a broken heart / When I take my sugar to tea / Don't tell him what happened to me / Roll on Mississippi roll on / I'm gonna cry (cryin' blues) / This is the missus / That's love / Life is just a bowl of cherries / My future just passed / What is it / Shine on harvest moon / Gee but I'd like to make you happy / We're on the highway to Heaven / Time on my hands / Nights when I'm lonely / Shout, sister, shout / It's you
CDAJA 5014 / Jun '88 / Living Era

☐ IT'S YOU
PASTCD 7087 / May '96 / Flapper

☐ OBJECT OF MY AFFECTION
GO 3810 / 1 Dec '97 / Golden Options

☐ SYNCOPATED HARMONISTS FROM NEW ORLEANS
TT 406 / May '98 / Take Two

Boswell, Connee

☐ DEEP IN A DREAM
HQCD 80 / Sep '96 / Harlequin

☐ HEART AND SOUL (25 Hits 1932-1942)
All I do is dream of you / Amapola / Basin Street blues: *Boswell, Connee & Bing Crosby* / Bob White: *Boswell, Connee & Bing Crosby* / Carioca / Deep in a dream / Gipsy love song / Heart and soul / I cover the waterfront / I hear a rhapsody / I let a song go out of my heart / In the middle of a kiss / It's the talk of the town / Little man you've had a busy day / Me minus you / On the isle of May / One dozen roses / Sand in my shoes / Stormy weather / Sunrise serenade / That old feeling / They can't take that away from me / Under a blanket of blue / You forgot to remember / You grow sweeter as the years go by
CDAJA 5221 / Aug '97 / Living Era

Boswell, Eve

☐ EMI PRESENTS THE MAGIC OF EVE BOSWELL
Pickin' a chicken / I believe / True love / Heatwave / Dear hearts and gentle people / All my love / If / Transatlantic lullaby / Hi-Lili, Hi-Lo / Sugar bush / Here in my heart / Moon above Malaya / I'm yours / Bridge of Sighs / If you love me / Bewitched / Little shoemaker / More than ever / Skokiaan / On the waterfront / These are the things we'll share / Ready, willing and able / Blue star / Young and foolish / Gypsy in my soul
CDMFP 6370 / May '97 / Music For Pleasure

Both Worlds

☐ MEMORY RENDERED VISIBLE
Cornered / Hate mantra / Spiritual flu / Space junkies / Free speech (will cost you) / Mode of ignorance / Karma inc / Over the edge / Inner outlet / Not of this body / Militant / When innocence was
VR 065CD / 17 Nov '97 / Victory
RR 87502 / 4 May '98 / Roadrunner

Bothwell, Johnny

☐ STREET OF DREAMS (Bothwell, Johnny & His Orchestra)
HEPCD 54 / 29 Sep '97 / Hep

Bothy Band

☐ AFTER HOURS (Live In Paris)
Kesh jig / Butterfly / Casadh an tsugain / Farewell to Erin / Heathery hills of Yarrow / Queen Jane / Pipe on the hob / Mary Willies / How can I live at the top of a mountain / Rosie Finn's favourite / Green groves of Erin
GL 3016CD / Jul '94 / Green Linnet
LUNCD 030 / Dec '97 / Mulligan

☐ BBC LIVE IN CONCERT
Martin Wynne's / Longford tinker / Two jigs / Kid in the mountain / Patsy Geary's / Coleman cross / Sixteen come next Saturday / Road to Lisdoonvarna / Lucy Campbell / Laurel tree / Fionnghuala / Farewell to Erin / Kesh gig / Give us a drink of water / Flower of the flock / Famous Ballymote / Tar road to Sligo / Maids of Mitchelstown / I wish my love was a red red rose / Bucks of Oranmore / Morning star / Fisherman's lilt / Drunken landlady / Do you love an apple / Jig and five reels
SFRSCD 063 / 18 May '98 / Strange Fruit

☐ BEST OF THE BOTHY BAND, THE
Salamanca / Banshee / Sailor's bonnet / Petty peg / Craig's pipes / Blackbird / Maids of Mitchelstown / Casadh an tsugain / Music in the glen / Fionnghuala / Old hag you have killed me / Do you love an apple / Rip the calico / Death of Queen Jane / Green groves of Erin / Flowers of Red Hill
LUNCD 041 / Aug '86 / Mulligan
GL 3001CD / Jul '94 / Green Linnet

☐ BOTHY BAND
Kesh jig / Give us a drink of water / Flowers of the flock / Famous Ballymote / Green groves of Erin / Flowers of Red Hill / Do you love an apple / Julia Delaney / Patsy Geary's / Coleman's cross / Is trua nack bhfuil me in Eirinn / Navvy on the line / Rainy day / Tar road to Sligo / Paddy Clancy's jig / Martin Wynn's / Lonford tinker / Pretty peg / Craig's pipes / Hector the hero / Laird of Drumblair / Traveller / Humors of Lissade / Butterfly / Salamanca / Banshee / Sailor's bonnet
LUNCD 002 / Jan '92 / Mulligan
GL 3011CD / Jul '94 / Green Linnet

☐ OLD HAG YOU HAVE KILLED ME
Music in the Glen / Fionnghuala / Kid on the mountain / Farewell to Erin / Summer will come / Laurel tree / Sixteen come next Sunday / Old hag you have killed me / Calum Sgaire / Ballintore fancy / Maid of Coolmore / Michael Gorman's reel
GL 3005CD / Jul '94 / Green Linnet
LUNCD 007 / Dec '97 / Mulligan

☐ OUT OF THE WIND INTO THE SUN
Morning star / Maids of Mitchelstown / Rip the Calico / Streets of Derry / Pipe on the hob / Sailor boy / Blackbird / Strayaway child / Factory girl / Slides
LUNCD 013 / Oct '88 / Mulligan
GL 3013CD / Jul '94 / Green Linnet

Bottcher, Gerd

☐ FUR GABI TU' ICH ALLES
Fur gabi tu ich alles / Du schaust mich an / Deine roten lippen / Adieu lebewohl goodbye (Tonight is so right for love) / Goodbye rock a hula baby / Wine nicht um mich / Geld wie heu / Man geht so leicht am gluck vorbei Tina Lou / Jambalaya / Ein dutzend and're manner / Oh Billy Billy Black / Sing / Sing denn mein zuhause das bist du / Susanna ich kenn' die / Strassen der weiten / Ay ay ay ay oh / Signorina / Ich such' dich auf allen Wegen / Ich komme wieder / Du heut nacht / Carolin, Carolin / Meine braut, die kann das besser / Bing bang bungalow / Lady Lou / Ich finde nichts dabei
BCD 15402 / Dec '87 / Bear Family

☐ PRETTY WOMAN
Pretty woman / Wer wird der nachste sein / Weil du meine grosse liebe bist: *Bottcher, Gerd & Detlef Engel* / Aber du darling dear / In der twist spelunke von McMiller: *Bottcher, Gerd & Detlef Engel* / Oh Katherin / So wie ein Indianer / Heim heim mocht ich ziehn: *Bottcher, Gerd & Detlef Engel* / Blue lady / Mach nicht nochzeit ohne mich / Sailor boy: *Bottcher, Gerd & Detlef Engel* / Weil du himmelblaue augen hast / Wo ist mein baby heut nacht / Lorelei / Uber die prarie: *Bottcher, Gerd & Detlef Engel* / Schenk mir dein vertauen / Nur keine Beatle-frisur / Nur Anne-Marie kommt in frage / Zwei caballeros: *Bottcher, Gerd & Detlef Engel* / Ich stehe zu dir / Madchen gibt's wie sand am meer / Stern von Samoa: *Bottcher, Gerd & Detlef Engel* / Niemals darfst du mich verlassen / Eine gefiel mir am allerbesten / Crazy little bluebird / Eine welte ohne liebe: *Bottcher, Gerd & Detlef Engel* / Tschau / Auf wiedersehn
BCD 16107 / Dec '96 / Bear Family

Botti, Chris

☐ MIDNIGHT WITHOUT YOU
5371322 / May '97 / Verve Forecast

Bottle Of Smoke

☐ WRENCH IN THE MONKEY
SFTRI 479CD / Aug '97 / Sympathy For The Record Industry

Bottle Rockets

☐ BOTTLE ROCKETS
Early in the morning / Gas girl / Trailer Mama / Wave that flag / Kerosene / Every kinda everything / Got what I wanted / Manhattan countryside / Rural route / Bud Nanney theme / Lonely cowboy
ESD 80772 / Mar '96 / East Side Digital

☐ BROOKLYN SIDE, THE
Welfare music / Gravity falls / I'll be comin' around / Radar gun / Sunday sports / Pot of gold / 1000 dollar car / Idiots revenge / Young lovers in town / Take me to the bank / Stuck in a rut / I wanna come home now / Queen of the world
ESD 81002 / Mar '96 / East Side Digital

Bottom 12

☐ DANCE OR BE SHOT (Remixes)
EFA 032592 / Aug '97 / Noise-O-Lution

☐ SONGS FOR THE DISGRUNTLED POSTMAN
EFA 032502 / Dec '95 / Noise-O-Lution

Bottom Feeders

☐ BIG SIX
Big six / Wrecked / Can't stand you / Here come squeenie / 69 drags pack / Better of dead / I love you / Strange muscle / Out of it / Potty mouth / Five forty one / Giant gurl / Iatlaians are pretty fucking cool / Beer song
PO 15CD / Oct '96 / Scooch Pooch
206152 / Jul '97 / Epitaph

Bouchard, Dominic

☐ HEOL DOUR (Bouchard, Dominic & Cyrille Colas)
KMCD 40 / Aug '93 / Keltia Musique

☐ VIBRATIONS
KMCD 03 / Jul '90 / Keltia Musique

Boucher, Judy

☐ CAN'T BE WITH YOU TONIGHT
Can't be with you tonight / That night we met / You close the door / Mr. dream maker / Dreaming of a little island / Turn back the time / I was such a fool / Loving me / Lovely paradise / You caught my eye
OCD 024 / Sep '86 / Orbitone

☐ DEVOTED TO YOU
KU 106CD / Apr '94 / Kufe

☐ JUST THE 2 OF US (Boucher, Judy & Tim Chandell)
CRCD 79 / 22 Dec '97 / Charm

☐ TAKE ME AS I AM
KUCD 113 / Mar '96 / Kufe

☐ TAKE YOUR MEMORY WITH YOU...
KUCD 118 / 12 Jan '98 / Kufe

☐ TEARS ON MY PILLOW
KUCD 100 / Jul '92 / Kufe

Boud Deun

☐ ASTRONOMY MADE EASY
RUNE 91 / Jun '97 / Cuneiform

Boudreaux, Helene

☐ UNE DEUXIEME (Boudreaux, Helene & Pete Bergeron)
SW 6120CD / Jul '95 / Swallow

Bouffard, Patrick

☐ MUSIC FOR HURDY GURDY FROM AUVERGNE
C 560007 / Nov '90 / Ocora

☐ REVENANT DE PARIS
49502CD / Apr '96 / Acousteak

Boukan Ginen

☐ JOU A RIVE
XENO 4024 / Feb '95 / Xenophile

☐ REV AN NOU
Salouwe / Afrika / Zanfan nago / Se yo ki lakoz / Kouman napfe / Neg yo danjere / Timounyo / Je'n la nape gade / Ma doute / Rev an nou / Move fanmi
XENO 4027CD / Oct '96 / Xenophile

Boulevard Of Broken Dreams

☐ BROKEN DREAMS BOX (3CD Set)
Boulevard of broken dreams / Hummin' to myself / Detour ahead / In other words, we're through / Clouds / I cover the waterfront / I get along without you very well / Cottage for sale / It's the talk of the town / Chloe / You broke the only heart that ever loved you / Travelin' light / Street of dreams / Trav'lin' all alone / Walkin' by the river / Who walks in when I walk out / Who needs you / Beguine des reves Brisees / Voz de Cabo Verde / You let me down / I'm painting the town red / More than you know / Dark side of the road / Lonely avenue / Only the lonely / Ouverture / Goodbye / So long / It's a lonesome old town / Remember / It's too soon to know / Just for a thrill / You don't know what love is / Night and day / Ten cents a dance / End of a love affair / Got the South in my soul / All night long / Love for sale
BASTA 3090372 / Sep '97 / Basta

☐ DANCING WITH TEARS IN MY EYES
Ouverture / Goodbye / So long / It's a lonesome old town / Remember / It's too soon to know / Just for a thrill / You don't know what love is / Night and day / Ten cents a dance / End of a love affair / Got the South in my soul / All night long / Love for sale
BASTA 3090352 / Sep '97 / Basta

☐ IT'S THE TALK OF THE TOWN
Boulevard of broken dreams / Hummin' to myself / Detour ahead / In other words, we're through / Clouds / I cover the waterfront / I get along without you very well / Cottage for sale / It's the talk of the town / Chloe / You broke the only heart that ever loved you / Travelin' light
BASTA 3090332 / Sep '97 / Basta

☐ LONELY AVENUE
Street of dreams / Trav'lin' all alone / Walkin' by the river / Who walks in when I walk out / Who needs you / Beguine des Reves Brisees / Voz de Cabo Verde / You let me down / I'm painting the town red / More than you know / Dark side of the road / Lonely Avenue / Only the lonely
BASTA 3090342 / Sep '97 / Basta

Boulton, Laura

☐ NAVAJO SONGS
SFWCD 40403 / Dec '94 / Smithsonian Folkways

Bouncing Souls

☐ BOUNCING SOULS
Cracked / Kate is great / Low life / Chunk song / East side mags / Toilet / Successful guy / Whatever / Serenity / Party / Holiday / Screamer / ECFU / Eyes / Shark attack
65102 / 20 Oct '97 / Epitaph

☐ GOOD, THE BAD...
BYO 031CD / Jan '97 / Better Youth Organisation

☐ MANIACAL LAUGHTER
BYO 037CD / Jan '97 / Better Youth Organisation

Bounty Killer

☐ DOWN IN THE GHETTO
Down in the ghetto / See you no more (2004) / How the west was won / Prophecy fulfil / If a war / Go away / Dead this time / Inspired by god / Trespass / Defend the poor / Can't beat we / Gal
GRELCD 210 / Jan '97 / Greensleeves

☐ GHETTO GRAMMA
Ancient day killing / Convince / Smoke the herb / Fat and sexy / Book book book / Gal fi get wock / No no no (world a respect): *Bounty Killer & Dawn Penn* / Report you missing / Fear no evil / Mi heart beat / Runaround girl: *Bounty Killer & Chuck Turner* / Down grade mi gun / I'll be back: *Bounty Killer & Colin Roach* / Income / Wedding done arrange / You've got me waiting: *Bounty Killer & Nitty Kutchie/Angel Doolas* / War is not a nice thing / Mangoose / This world's too haunted: *Bounty Killer & Junior Reid* / Time to realize: *Bounty Killer & Dirtsman*
GRELCD 238 / Aug '97 / Greensleeves

☐ GUNS OUT
GRELCD 206 / Jan '97 / Greensleeves

☐ JAMAICA'S MOST WANTED
GRELCD 195 / Jan '97 / Greensleeves

☐ MY XPERIENCE VOL.1
Fed up / Lord is my light and salvation / Hip-hopera ("Mr Punk") / Guns and roses / Mama / Change like the weather / War beyond the stars / Living dangerously / War face (ask fi war) / Marathon ("To Chicago") / Revolution III / Gun down / Mi nature / Virgin Island / Who send dem / Seek God / Maniac / Suicide or murder / Benz and the Bimma / My experience
CDV 2823 / Dec '96 / Virgin

☐ NO ARGUMENT
Cellular phone / Scare him / Seek god / More gal / Mama / Miss ivy last son / Oh please / No argument / Action speak louder than words / Woman a run mi down / Searching / Celluar number
GRELCD 222 / Jan '97 / Greensleeves

Bouquet

☐ CORAL KINGDOM
POPCD 1 / 20 Apr '98 / Popstar

Bourbonese Qualk

☐ FEEDING THE HUNGRY GHOST
FUNFUNDVIERZ 69 / Jun '94 / Funfundvierz

☐ MY GOVERNMENT
CD 34 / Feb '90 / Funfundvierz

Bourbons

☐ HOUSE PARTY 1964-1966
AA 058 / Jul '97 / Arf Arf

Bourelly, Jean-Paul

☐ ROCK THE CATHARTIC SPIRITS (Vibe Music & The Blues)
DIW 911 / Oct '96 / DIW

☐ TRIPPIN'
EMY 1272 / Sep '97 / Enemy

Bournet, P.

☐ PLAY JOHN MCLAUGHLIN AND ASTOR PIAZZOLLA (Bournet, P. & Enrique Alberti)
IMP 948 / Jan '97 / IMP

Boutouk, Ian

☐ GIPSY CLASSICS (The Soul Of The Gipsy Violin) (Boutouk, Ian & Batalonia Gipsy Orchestra)
995552 / Jul '95 / EPM

Boutte, Lillian

☐ JAZZ BOOK, THE
Now baby or never / Comes love / On revival day / Don't worry 'bout me / Lover come back to me / Muddy water / Tennessee waltz / That old feeling / Embraceable you / Barefootin'
BLU 10202 / Dec '94 / Blues Beacon

☐ LILLIAN BOUTTE
Teardrops from my eyes / 'Tis autumn / Meet me at the station / My one and only love / You hit the spot / Funghi Mama / Who can I turn to / Almost like being in love / Meet me at no special place / Hold it / When you wish upon a star
FJCD 111 / Jul '96 / Fret

☐ LILLIAN BOUTTE WITH HUMPHREY LYTTLETON AND BAND (Boutte, Lillian/Humphrey Lyttelton & His Band)
Back in your own backyard / Miss Otis regrets / Squiggles / I double dare you / Lillian
CLGCD 018 / Oct '88 / Calligraph

☐ LIVE IN TIVOLI (Boutte, Lillian & Her American Band)
MECCACD 1030 / Jun '93 / Music Mecca

Bouzouki Ensemble

☐ SONGS OF GREECE
SOW 90131 / Sep '94 / Sounds Of The World

Bovell, Dennis

☐ DUB DEM SILLY
ARKCD 107 / Oct '95 / Arawak

☐ DUB OF AGES
LKJCD 015 / Apr '97 / LKJ

☐ DUBMASTER
JMC 200210 / Jan '94 / Jamaican Gold

☐ STRICTLY DUBWISE (Bovell, Dennis Dub Band)
14808 / Jun '97 / Spalax

☐ TACTICS
LKJCD 010 / Mar '95 / LKJ

Bover, Albert

☐ DUO (Bover, Albert & Fumero)
FSNT 025 / 5 Jan '98 / Fresh Sound New Talent

Bow Wow Wow

☐ APHRODISIAC (The Best Of Bow Bow Wow)
I want candy / Roustabout / Cowboy / Baby oh no / Lonesome tonight / Joy of eating raw flesh / See jungle (jungle boy) / Louis Quatorze / Mario (your own way to Paradise) / Prince of darkness / Quiver (arrows in my) / Rikki Dee / (I'm a) TV savage / Do you wanna hold me / What's the time (hey buddy) / Elimination dancing / El boss dicho / Love, peace and harmony / Chihuahua / Aphrodisiac / Go wild in the country
74321419672 / Oct '96 / Camden

☐ LIVE IN JAPAN
(I'm a) TV savage / Golly golly go buddy / Mickey put it down / Orang-outang / See jungle / Go wild in the country / Baby, oh no / Elimination dancing / Louis quatorze / I want candy / C30 C60 C90 go / Prince of darkness / GSBT / Sun, sea and piracy
RRCD 233 / Feb '97 / Receiver

☐ SEE JUNGLE SEE JUNGLE GO JOIN YOUR GANG YEAH...
Jungle boy / Chihuahua / Sinner sinner sinner / Mickey put it down / TV savage / Elimination dancing / Golly golly / Go buddy / King Kong / Go wild in the country / I am not a know it all / Why are babies so wise / Orang-utan / Hello hello daddy
OW 34502 / Jun '97 / One Way

☐ WHEN THE GOING GETS TOUGH, THE TOUGH GET GOING
Aphrodisiac / Do you wanna hold me / Roustabout / Lonesome tonight / Love me / What's the time / Mario (your own way to paradise) / (Arrows in my) quiver / Man mountain / Rikki Dee / Tommy Tucker / Love peace and harmony
OW 34503 / Jun '97 / One Way

Bowden, Chris

☐ TIME CAPSULE
Epsilon / Time capsule / Telescopic / Epsilon transmission / Mothers and daughters now Mothers / Retrospective / Sane
SJRCD 031 / Jun '96 / Soul Jazz

Bowdler, John

☐ LET'S FACE THE MUSIC AND DANCE
JB 001CD / Oct '94 / Key

Bowen, Ralph

☐ MOVIN' ON (Bowen, Ralph Quintet)
CRISS 1066CD / Oct '92 / Criss Cross

Bowen, Robin Huw

☐ HARP MUSIC OF WALES
All through the night (ar hyd y nos) / Smith's hornpipe-the policeman (pibdawns y gof-dyn y geg) / Ash grove (llwyn onn) / Saiforella polka (polca saiforella) / David of the white rock (dafydd y garreg wen) / Gypsy hornpipe (pwt-ar-y-bys, meillionen o feirionnydd) / Clover of meirionnydd / Snowdon's bald summit-new year's eve (moel yr wyddfa-nos / Sailing home (hwylio adref) / March of the men of harlech (gorymdaith gwyr harlech) / Thread of life (y llinyn arian) / Lambs' fold vale (pant corlan yr wyn) / Megan's daughter-megan' grand-daughter (merch megan-wyres
CDSDL 412 / Oct '95 / Saydisc

☐ HUNTING THE HEDGEHOG
RHB 002CD / Jun '94 / Teires

Bowers, Bryan

☐ VIEW FROM HOME, THE
FF 70037 / Mar '89 / Flying Fish

Bowery Electric

☐ BEAT
Beat / Empty words / Without stopping / Under the sun / Fear of flying / Looped / Black light / Inside out / Coming out / Post script / Low density
BBQCD 188 / Feb '97 / Warp

☐ BOWERY ELECTRIC
KRANK 007CD / Mar '97 / Kranky

☐ VERTIGO
Fear of flying / Fear of flying / Black light / Without stopping / Coming down / Black light / Empty words / Fear of flying / Elementary particles
BBQ 315CDD / 25 Aug '97 / Beggars Banquet

Bowie, David

☐ 1966
I'm not losing sleep / I dig everything / Can't help thinking about me / Do anything you say / Good morning girl / And I say to myself
CLACD 154 / Dec '89 / Castle

☐ ALADDIN SANE
Watch that man / Aladdin Sane / Drive-in Saturday / Panic in Detroit / Cracked actor / Time / Prettiest star / Let's spend the night together / Jean Genie / Lady grinning soul
CDP 7947682 / 1 Sep '97 / Premier/EMI

☐ ASHES TO ASHES (A Tribute To David Bowie/2CD Set) (Various Artists)
DOP 53 / 25 May '98 / Dressed To Kill

☐ BEST OF DAVID BOWIE 1969-1974, THE
Jean Genie / Space oddity / Starman / Ziggy Stardust / John / I'm only dancing / Rebel rebel / Lets spend the night together / Suffragette city / Oh you pretty thing / Velvet goldmine / Wheels / Nobody told me / Borrowed time / Working class hero / Happy Xmas / Give peace a chance
8218492 / 27 Oct '97 / EMI

☐ BEST OF DAVID BOWIE 1974-1979, THE
Sound and vision / Golden years / Fame / Young Americans / John I'm only dancing / Can you hear me / Wild is the wind / Knock on wood / TVC 15 / 1984 / It's hard to be a saint in the city / Look back in anger / Secret life of Arabia / DJ / Beauty and the beast / Breaking glass / Boys keep swinging / Heroes
4943002 / 20 Apr '98 / EMI

☐ BIOGRAPHY SERIES
10025 / 3 Nov '97 / Metro Independent

☐ BLACK TIE, WHITE NOISE
Wedding / You've been around / I feel free / Black tie, white noise / Jump they say / Nite flights / Pallas Athena / Miracle goodnight / Don't let me down / Looking for Lester / I know it's gonna happen someday / Wedding song / Lucy can't dance
74321136972 / Jul '96 / Arista

☐ CHANGESBOWIE
Space oddity / John I'm only dancing / Changes / Ziggy Stardust / Suffragette City / Jean Genie / Diamond dogs / Rebel rebel / Young Americans / Fame '90 / Golden years / Heroes / Ashes to ashes / Fashion / Let's dance / China girl / Modern love / Blue Jean / Starman / Life on Mars / Sound and vision
CDP 7941802 / Apr '90 / Premier/EMI

☐ DARK SIDE OF DAVID BOWIE, THE (A Tribute To David Bowie) (Various Artists)
Space oddity: *Crimson Joy* / Motel: *Syria* / Outside: *Dreadful Shadows* / Blue Jean: *Gallery Of Fear* / Time will crawl: *Burning Gates* / Scary monsters: *Sepulcrum Mentis* / Big brother: *Cream VIII* / Be my wife: *Exedra* / Five years: *Endless* / Girls: *Kill The Audience* / Holy holy: *Marquee Moon* / Look back in anger: *Swans Of Avon* / Station to station: *Merry Thoughts* / Ziggy Stardust: *Nuit D'Octobre*
SPV 08452932 / 1 Jun '98 / SPV

☐ DAVID BOWIE
Uncle Arthur / Sell me a coat / Rubber band / Love you till Tuesday / There is a happy land / We are hungry men / When I live my dream / Little bombardier / Silly boy blue / Come and buy my toys / Join the gang / She's got medals / Maid of Bond street / Please Mr. Gravedigger
8000872 / Apr '91 / Deram

☐ DAVID BOWIE SONGBOOK, THE (Various Artists)
VSOPCD 236 / Apr '97 / Connoisseur Collection

☐ DERAM ANTHOLOGY 1966-1968, THE
8447842 / Aug '97 / Deram

☐ EARTHLING
Little wonder / Looking for satellites / Battle for Britain / Seven years in Tibet / Dead man walking / Telling lies / Last think you should do / I'm afraid of Americans / Law (earthlings on fire)
74321449442 / Feb '97 / RCA

☐ HEROES
Beauty and the beast / Joe the lion / Sons of the silent age / Blackout / V2 Schneider / Sense of doubt / Moss garden / Neukoln / Secret life of Arabia / Heroes / Abdulmajid / Joe the lion ('91 Mix)
CDP 7977202 / Aug '91 / Premier/EMI

☐ HUNKY DORY
Changes / Oh you pretty things / Eight line poem / Life on Mars / Kooks / Quicksand / Fill your heart / Andy Warhol / Song for Bob Dylan / Queen bitch / Bewlay Brothers / Bombers / Supermen / Quicksand (demo version) / Bewlay brothers (alternative mix)
CDP 7918432 / 1 Sep '97 / Premier/EMI

☐ INTERVIEW COMPACT DISC: DAVID BOWIE
CBAK 4040 / Sep '90 / Baktabak

☐ INTERVIEW DISC
TELL 03 / Dec '96 / Network

☐ INTROSPECTIVE
I'm not losing sleep / I dig everything / Can't help thinking about me / Interview part one / Do anything you say / Good morning girl / And I say to myself / Interview part two
CINT 5001 / Nov '90 / Baktabak

☐ LET'S DANCE
Modern love / China girl / Let's dance / Without you / Ricochet / Criminal world / Cat people (putting out fires) / Shake it / Under pressure: *Queen & David Bowie*
CDVUS 96 / Nov '95 / Virgin

☐ LET'S DANCE
Modern love / China girl / Let's dance / Without you / Ricochet / Criminal world / Cat people / Shake it
4930942 / 19 Jan '98 / EMI

☐ LODGER
Fantastic voyage / African night flight / Move on / Yassassin / Red sails / DJ / Look back in anger / Boys keep swinging / Repetition / Red money / I pray ole / Look back in anger (1988 version)
CDP 7977242 / Aug '91 / Premier/EMI

☐ LONDON BOY
Space oddity (original version) / Did you ever have a dream / There is a happy land / Rubber band / Let me sleep beside you / Maid of Bond Street / We are hungry men / When I live my dream / Karma man / Laughing knome / She's got medals / Little bombardier / Please Mr. Grave Digger / Gospel according to Tony Day / Sell me a coat / Join the gang / Love you til Tuesday / London boys
5517062 / Mar '96 / Spectrum

☐ LOW
Speed of life / Breaking glass / What in the world / Sound and vision / Always crashing in the same car / Be my wife / New career in a new town / Warszawa / Art decade / Weeping wall / Subterraneans / Some are / All saints / Sound and vision (1991 remix)
CDP 7977192 / Aug '90 / Premier/EMI

☐ MAN WHO SOLD THE WORLD, THE
Width of a circle / All the madmen / Black country rock / After all / Running gun blues / Saviour machine / She shook me cold / Man who sold the world / Supermen / Lightning frightening / Holy holy / Moonage daydream / Hang on to yourself
CDP 7918372 / 1 Sep '97 / Premier/EMI

☐ NEVER LET ME DOWN
Day in day out / Time will crawl / Beat of your drum / Never let me down / Zeroes / Glass spider / Shining star (makin' my love) / New York's in love / '87 and cry / Bang bang
4930972 / 19 Jan '98 / EMI

☐ OUTSIDE
Leon take us outside / Outside / Heart's filthy lesson / Small plot of land / Baby Grace (a horrid cassette) / Hallo spaceboy / Motel / I have not been to Oxford town / No control / Algeria touchshriek / Voyeur of utter destruction / Ramona A Stone/I am with name / Wishful beginnings / We prick you / Nathan Adler / I'm deranged / Thru' these architects eyes / Strangers when we meet
74321307022 / Sep '95 / RCA

☐ RARESTONEBOWIE
All the young dudes / Queen bitch / Sound and vision / Time / Be my wife / Footstompin' / Ziggy Stardust / My death / I feel free
GY 014 / May '95 / NMC

☐ RISE AND FALL OF ZIGGY STARDUST & THE SPIDERS FROM MARS, THE
Five years / Soul love / Moonage daydream / Starman / It ain't easy / Lady Stardust / Star / Hang on to yourself / Ziggy Stardust / Suffragette city / Rock 'n' roll suicide / John I'm only dancing / Velvet goldmine / Sweet head / Ziggy Stardust / Lady Stardust
CDP 7944002 / Jun '90 / Premier/EMI

☐ SANTA MONICA '72
Ziggy Stardust / Changes / Superman / Life on mars / Five years / Space oddity / Andy Warhol / My death / Width of a circle / Queen bitch / Moonage daydream / John I'm only dancing / Waiting for the man / Jean genie / Suffragette city / Rock 'n' roll suicide
GY 002 / Mar '94 / NMC

☐ SCARY MONSTERS
It's no game / Up the hill backwards / Scary monsters (and super creeps) / Ashes to ashes / Fashion / Teenage wildlife / Scream like a baby / Kingdom come / Because you're young / It's no game (part 2) / Space oddity / Panic in Detroit / Crystal Japan / Alabama song
CDP 7993312 / May '92 / Premier/EMI

☐ SINGLES COLLECTION, THE (2CD Set)
Space oddity / Changes / Starman / Ziggy Stardust / Suffragette city / John I'm only dancing / Jean genie / Drive-in Saturday / Life on Mars / Sorrow / Rebel rebel / Rock 'n' roll suicide / Diamond dogs / Knock on wood / Young Americans / Fame / Golden years / TVC 15 / Sound and vision / Heroes / Beauty and the beast / Boys keep swinging / DJ / Alabama song /

Ashes to ashes / Fashion / Scary monsters (and super creeps) / Under pressure: *Queen & David Bowie* / Wild is the wind / Let's dance / China girl / Modern love / Blue jean / This is not America / Dancing in the street: *Bowie, David & Mick Jagger* / Absolute beginners / Day in, day out
CDEM 1512 / Nov '95 / Premier/EMI

☐ SPACE ODDITY
Space oddity / Unwashed and somewhat slightly dazed / Don't sit down / Letter to Hermione / Cygnet committee / Janine / Occasional dream / Wild eyed boy from Freecloud / God knows I'm good / Memory of a free festival / Conversation piece / Memory of a free festival / Memory of a free festival
CDP 7918352 / 1 Sep '97 / Premier/EMI

☐ STAGE (2CD Set)
Hang on to yourself / Ziggy Stardust / Five years / Soul love / Star / Station to station / Fame / TVC 15 / Warszawa / Speed of life / Art decade / Sense of doubt / Breaking glass / Heroes / What in the world / Blackout / Beauty and the beast / Alabama song
CDS 7986172 / Feb '92 / Premier/EMI

☐ STATION TO STATION
Station to station / Golden years / Word on a wing / TVC 15 / Stay / Wild is the wind / Word on a wing (live) / Stay (live)
CDP 7964352 / Apr '91 / Premier/EMI

☐ TONIGHT
Loving the alien / Don't look down / God only knows / Tonight / Neighborhood threat / Blue jean / Tumble and twirl / I keep forgetting / Dancing with the big boys
4931022 / 19 Jan '98 / EMI

☐ ZIGGY STARDUST THE MOTION PICTURE
Watch that man / Moonage daydream / Suffragette city / Changes / Time / All the young dudes / Space oddity / White light, white heat / My death / Wild eyed boy from Freecloud / Oh you pretty things / Hang on to yourself / Ziggy Stardust / Cracked actor / Width of a circle / Let's spend the night together / Rock 'n' roll suicide
CDP 7804112 / Sep '92 / Premier/EMI

Bowie, Lester

☐ ALL THE MAGIC
For Louie / Spacehead / Ghosts / Trans traditional suite / Let the good times roll / Organic echo / Dunce dance / Charlie M (part II) / Thirsty / Almost Christmas / Down home / Okra influence / Miles Davis meets Donald Duck / Deb Deb's face / Monkey waltz / Fraudulent fanfare / Organic echo (part II)
8106252 / Nov '91 / ECM

☐ AVANT POP (Bowie, Lester Brass Fantasy)
Emperor / Saving all my love for you / B funk / Blueberry hill / Crazy / Macho / No shit / O, what a night
8295632 / Sep '86 / ECM

☐ FUNKY T COOL T (Bowie, Lester New York Organ Ensemble)
DIW 853 / Feb '92 / DIW

☐ GREAT PRETENDER
Great pretender / It's howdy doody time / When the doom (moon) comes over the mountain / Rios negroes / Rose drop / Oh how the ghost sings
8293692 / '90 / ECM

☐ I ONLY HAVE EYES FOR YOU
I only have eyes for you / Think / Lament / Coming back Jamaica / Nonet / When the spirit returns
8259022 / '90 / ECM

☐ ORGANIZER, THE (Bowie, Lester New York Organ Ensemble)
DIW 821 / Mar '91 / DIW

☐ WORKS
Charlie M / Rose drop / B funk / When the spirit returns / Let the good times roll
8372742 / Jun '89 / ECM

Bowles, Paul

☐ BLACK STAR AT THE POINT OF DARKNESS
SUBCD 01437 / Jul '91 / Sub Rosa

Bowling Green

☐ ONE POUND NOTE
PLAN 15CD / 22 Jun '98 / Blue Planet

Bowlly, Al

☐ AL BOWLLY
Love is the sweetest thing / Dark eyes / Careless / Goodnight sweetheart / Over the rainbow / Moon love / Close your eyes / When you wear your Sunday blue / Man and his dream / What do you know about love / Marie / You're as pretty as a picture / Romany / Small town / Dreaming / Little rain must fall / Give me my ranch / I'm madly in love with you / I miss you in the morning / It was a lover and his lass / Blow blow thou winter wind / Au revoir but not goodbye / South of the border / Bella bambina / Ridin' home
CDMFP 6355 / Jun '97 / Music For Pleasure

☐ AL BOWLLY AND THE GREAT BRITISH BANDS
Actions speak louder than words / To be worthy of you / Thanks / Is I in love I is / Looking on the bright side of life / Night on the desert / Hurt / Linda / Dinah / When Mother Nature sings her lullaby / Good evening / What do you know about love / Proud of you / Heart and soul / Is that the way to treat a sweetheart / Smile when you say goodbye / Small town / My own / Home town / Bei mir bist du schon / Girl in the Alice blue gown / My Capri serenade
PASTCD 7088 / Aug '97 / Flapper

☐ DANCE BAND YEARS, THE (2CD Set) (Bowlly, Al & Ray Noble Orchestra)
Very thought of you / Over my shoulder / By the fireside / When you've got a little springtime in your heart / Hold my hand / Close your eyes / Lazy day / Lying in the hay / We've got the moon and sixpence / Time on my hands / You ought to see Sally on Sunday / One morning in May / Maybe I love you too much / I'll do my best to make you happy / I'll string along with you / How could we be wrong / Sailin' on the Robert E. Lee / Roll up the carpet / Love locked out / Dreaming a dream / After all, you're all I'm after / There's something in your eyes / Hang out the stars in Indiana / Got a date with an angel / Guilty / I was true / One little quarrel / All I do is dream of you / Remember me / I never had a chance / Little valley in the mountains / Freckle face, you're beautiful / Isle of Capri / Weep no more my baby / Goodnight sweetheart / Thanks / Me on the side of my head / This is romance / Song without words / Love is the sweetest thing / On a steamer coming over / Oceans of time / Yours truly is truly yours / Dinner for one please James / Where am I / Down by the river / Touch of your lips / Why dream / Where the lazy river goes / With all my heart
PDSCD 557 / 13 Oct '97 / Pulse

☐ GOODNIGHT SWEETHEART
Romany Bixio / I miss you in the morning / Give me my ranch / Man and his dream / Make love with a guitar/When I dream of home / Lonely / Moon love / Hey gypsy, play gypsy / What do you know about love / Make-Believe Island/The woodpecker song / Dark eyes / Au revoir but not goodbye / Somewhere in France with you / Don't say goodbye / I'm stepping out with a memory tonight / I haven't time to be a millionaire / I'm madly in love with you / Small town / Turn your money in your pocket/I'll never smile again / We'll go smiling along / Thanks for everything / Could be Donaldson / Ferry boat serenade / Goodnight sweetheart
SWNCD 011 / 15 Sep '97 / Sound Waves

☐ JUST A BOWL OF CHERRIES
Lady of Spain / Smile, darn ya, smile / Adeline / Save the last dance for me / Goodnight Vienna / All of me / My sweet Virginia / Auf wiedersehen my dear / Rain on the roof / Can't we talk it over / Just humming along / One more kiss / By the fireside / Weep no more my baby / Dinner at eight / This is romance / And so, goodbye / Wagon wheels / I idolize my baby's eyes / Falling in love / Life is just a bowl of cherries / You call it madness / Was that the human thing to do / Now that you're gone / You ought to see Sally on Sunday / Pied piper of Hamlin
PASTCD 7003 / Feb '93 / Flapper

☐ LOVE IS THE SWEETEST THING
Love is the sweetest thing / When you wear your Sunday blue / You're a sweetheart / Dreaming / Bi mir bist du schoen / Man and his dream / Over the rainbow / Have you ever been lonely / Marie / It was a lover and his lass / What do you know about love / Something to sing about / Moon love / Little rain must fall / Bella bambina / Au revoir (but not goodbye) / I'll string along with you / In my little red book / Blow, blow thou winter wind / Goodnight sweetheart
PAR 2024 / Jul '94 / Parade

☐ PROUD OF YOU
Marie / Sweet someone / Colorado sunset / Is that the way to treat a sweetheart / When Mother Nature sings her lullaby / Two sleepy people / Sweet as a song / Goodnight angel / Any broken hearts to mend / Al Bowlly remembers (medley) / Very thought of you / You're as pretty as a picture / Proud of you / True / Summer's end / There's rain in my eyes / Bei mir bist du schon / When the organ played 'O promise me' / While the cigarette was burning / Penny serenade
CDAJA 5064 / Sep '89 / Living Era

☐ SWEET SOMEONE
What do you know about love / Small town / Sweet is the word for you / Love, you funny thing / On a little dream ranch / Sweet someone / Romany / Everything's been done before / Basin street blues / Dark eyes / Judy / Madonna mine / Music maestro please / My melancholy baby / You opened my eyes / Dark clouds / If I had a million dollars / Looking for a little bit of blue / Little white gardenia / Little lady make believe
CDMOIR 307 / Apr '94 / Memoir

☐ TWO SLEEPY PEOPLE
Two sleepy people / Goodnight angel / Any broken hearts to mend / Sweet as a song / When Mother Nature sings her lullaby / Is that the way to treat a sweetheart / Marie / Sweet someone / Colorado sunset / Al Bowlly remembers (Medley) / Very thought of you / You're as pretty as a picture / Proud of you / True / Penny serenade / While the cigarette was burning / When the organ played 'O promise me' / Bei mir bist du schon / There's rain in my eyes / Summer's end
GRF 097 / '93 / Tring

☐ VERY THOUGHT OF YOU, THE
Whispering / Faded summer love / Tell me (you love me) / You didn't know the music / Dinah / Time alone will tell / Foolish facts / Eleven more months and ten more days / If I have to go on without you / My sweet Virginia / Out of nowhere / I'm so used to you now / Hurt / Leave the rest to nature / From me to you / Just another dream of you / In London on a night like this / Night and day / Night on the Desert / Judy / Madonna mine / Very thought of you
RAJCD 837 / 1 Jun '98 / Empress

☐ VERY THOUGHT OF YOU, THE
Time on my hands / Goodnight sweetheart / Sweet and lovely / Pied Piper of Hamlin / By the fireside / Love is the sweetest thing / How could we be wrong / Weep no more my baby / Love locked out / You ought to see Sally on Sunday / One morning in May / Very thought of you / Isle of Capri / Blue Hawaii / In my little red book / Penny serenade / They say / South of the border (Down Mexico way) / Over the rainbow / Somewhere in France with you / When you wish upon a star / Who's taking you home tonight / Blow, blow thou winter wind / It was a lover and his lass
CDP 7943412 / May '90 / Premier/EMI

☐ VERY THOUGHT OF YOU, THE
Top hat, white tie and tails / Lover come back to me / Where the lazy river goes by / Be still my heart / I've got you under my skin / Maria, my own / Soon / Carelessly / Touch of your lips / Eadie was a lady / Very thought of you / Why dream / My canary has circles under it's eyes / True / Dinner for one please James / Little Dutch mill / On a little dream ranch / Blue Hawaii / Down by the river / Goodnight sweetheart
PLCD 540 / Jul '95 / President

Bowman, Gill

☐ CITY LOVE
Your average woman / Very good year / Verses / Ballad of the four Mary's / Make it good / City love / Psychics in America / Story today / Lang-a-growing / Different game / If I didn't love you
FE 080CD / Feb '91 / Fellside

☐ PERFECT LOVER
Take me home / Walking away / Rantin' dog / Dear friend / Comin' thro' the rye / This time / To be like you / Ae fond kiss / Dream Angus / Making friends / Somebody's baby
CDTRAX 081 / Sep '94 / Greentrax

☐ TOASTING THE LASSIES
Green grow the rashes / Now westlin' winds / Banks o'Doon / Sweet Tibbie Dunbar / Rantin' dog / Sweet afton / Auld lang syne / This in no my ain lassie / Rosebud by my early walk / Lea rig / De'il's awa' wi' tha exciseman / Ae fond kiss / Comin' thro' the rye
CDTRAX 085 / Feb '95 / Greentrax

Bown, Alan

☐ LISTEN/STRETCHING OUT
Wanted man / Crash landing / Loosen up / Pyramid / Forever / Curfew / Make us all believe / Make up your mind / Get myself straight / Messenger / Find a melody / Up above my hobby horse's head / Turning point / Build me a stage / Stretching out
EDCD 362 / Jan '93 / Edsel

☐ OUTWARD BOWN
Toyland / Magic handkerchief / Mutiny / Little Lesley / Sally Green / Story boook / Technicolour dream / We can help you / Love is a beautiful thing / Violin shop / You're not in my class / My girl the month of May
SEECD 490 / 27 Apr '98 / See For Miles

Bowne, Dougie

☐ ONE WAY ELEVATOR
DIW 920 / Jan '97 / DIW

Bows, Jim

☐ FOLLOW ME
Going nowhere / There's no future without love / Name / Big mountain blues / Living hell / Nothing to say / What they're asking / Over the wall / Follow me / Heaven or hell / I wanna be you
23151822 / 6 Oct '97 / Wise Owl

Bowyer, Brendan

☐ IRELAND'S BRENDAN BOWYER
DOCX 9012 / Jul '96 / Dolphin

Box & Banjo Band

☐ DANCING PARTY
Hello Dolly / Margie / When you wore a tulip / Bye bye love / Heart of myself / I'm gonna sit right down and write myself a letter / Singin' the blues / Bless 'em all / After the ball was over / Oh dear what can the matter be / Locomotion / How do you do it / Roll out the barrel / Pack up your troubles / Who were you with last night / Happy wanderer / Yankee doodle boy / Dixie / She'll be coming round the mountains / Please help me, I'm falling / Crystal chandeliers / I can't stop loving you / Laughing samba / Wedding samba / Bluebell polka / You're free to go / Anna Marie / He'll have to go / Can Can / Nightingale sang in Berkeley Square / Birth of the blues / Once in a while / Peggy O'Neil / Garden where the praties grow / Teddy O'Neil / Wild rover / Loch Lomond / Bluebells of Scotland / Bonnie lass o'Fyvie / Mormond Braes / New York, New York
LCOM 5209 / May '92 / Lismor

☐ GO DANCING
Bye bye blackbird / At the Darktown strutter's ball / Alexander's ragtime band / You made me love you / Oh you beautiful doll / On the sunny side of the street / When Irish eyes are smiling / Lily McNally McNair / Too-ra-loo-ra-loo-ra / Let's twist again / Birdie dance / I love a lassie / Roamin' in the gloamin' / Stop your ticklin' Jock / Just a wee deoch an' Doris / Anniversary song / Bicycle built for two / I'll be your sweetheart / Alley cat / El Cumbanchero / Charleston / I wonder where my baby is tonight / Yes sir that's my baby / Side by side / Lily of Laguna / Carolina in the morning / Me and my gal / Isle of Capri / Jealousy / O sole mio / Camptown races / Steamboat Bill / Oh Susanna / Beautiful Sunday / Una paloma blanca / Amarillo / California here I come / Waiting for the Robert E Lee / Baby face / Swanee / Come back to Sorrento / Edelweiss / Lara's theme / Quickstep / Breakaway blues / Pride of Erin / Twist and tweet / Gay Gordons / Old time waltz / Samba / Madison / Foxtrot / Tango / Barn dance / Slosh / Mississippi dip / Modern waltz
LCOM 9020 / Sep '95 / Lismor

☐ SINGALONGA SCOTLAND
Hundred thousand welcomes / Northern lights / Wee Cooper o' Fife / Skye boat song / Come in, come in / Strip the willow / Scottish soldier / Sailing up the Clyde / Annie Laurie / Star of Rabbie Burns / Dark island / Lassie come and dance with me / Auld hoose / Roses of Prince Charlie / Gay Gordons / Song of the Clyde / Wachlin' hame / Bonnie Dundee / Auld lang syne
LCOM 9017 / Sep '95 / Lismor

Box Of Frogs

☐ BOX OF FROGS/STRANGELAND
RME 0106CD / 15 Dec '97 / Renaissance

Box Office Poison

☐ BEYOND THE TWILIGHT ZONE
Think for yourself / Checkmate / Mysteries / Magic / Love on the phone / Cry out the pain / Sad world / 1995 / Backstreet Boulevard / 16 year old / We're all insane / Alien / We are the future
FLEGCD 4 / Jun '97 / Future Legend

☐ HEAVY BREATHING DECADE
Come with me / I want to sleep with you / Don't sleep with him / Take me to heaven and back / Strip show / All the young girls love Alice / I want you all the time / Making love to the general vibe / Is it sex you seek / For the video / All I want is a baby / Penicillin passion / Teenage sex / Sex on the internet / Come with me
FLEG 11CD / 26 May '98 / Future Legend

Box Tops

☐ SOUL DEEP (The Best Of The Box Tops)
Letter / Neon rainbow / Happy times / Cry like a baby / Fields of clover / Choo choo train / She shot a hole in my soul / People gonna talk / I met her in church / Sweet cream ladies forward march / Together / I must be the devil / Soul deep / I shall be released / Happy song / Turn on a dream / I see only sunshine / You keep tightening up on me
7822189372 / 2 Feb '98 / RCA

☐ TEAR OFF
3027412 / 23 Mar '98 / Last Call

Boxcar

☐ ALGORHYTHM
PULSE 24CD / Sep '96 / Pulse 8

☐ VERTIGO
Gas stop (who do you think you are) / Insect / Vertigo / Freemason (you broke the promise) / Comet / Hit and run / 900 hours / Lelore / Cruel to you / This is the town / Index
VOLTCD 024 / Mar '92 / Volition

Boxcar Willie

☐ ACHY BREAKY HEART
Rockin' bones / Sally let your bangs hang down / Train of love / Maybellene / That's alright Mama / Sixteen chickens and a tamborine / Mystery train / Pipeliner blues / No help wanted / Haunted house / Hank you're like your Daddy / Caribbean / Boney Maronie / Memphis / Achy breaky heart
5501342 / Oct '93 / Spectrum

☐ AMERICAN SONGS (2CD Set)
R2CD 4056 / 13 Apr '98 / Deja Vu

☐ BEST OF BOXCAR WILLIE, THE
Waiting for a train / From a Rolls to the rails / Lord made a hobo out of me / Take me home / I wake up every morning with a smile on my face / I came so close to calling you last night / I'm so lonesome I could cry / (I heard that) Lonesome whistle / Daddy was a railroad man / Hot box blues / I can't help it (if I'm still in love with you) / Day Elvis died / Hank, you still make me cry / Train medley
307862 / Jul '97 / Hallmark

☐ BEST OF BOXCAR WILLIE, THE
CD 6111 / Jan '98 / Music

☐ BOXCAR WILLIE & SPECIAL GUESTS
MU 5061 / Oct '92 / Musketeer

☐ COUNTRY FAVOURITES
King of the road / Wabash cannonball / You are my sunshine / Boxcar blues / Don't let the stars get in your eyes / Your cheatin' heart / I saw the light / Wreck of the old '97 / Hank and the hobo / Peace in the valley / Mule train / Hey good lookin' / Kaw-Liga / Move it on over / London leaves / Rollin' in my sweet babies arms / Divorce me COD / Red river valley / Heaven / San Antonio Rose / Train melody
RM 1540 / Apr '97 / BR Music

☐ COUNTRY GREATS
Freightline fever / Truck driving man / Phantom 309 / Truck drivin' son-of-a-gun / Six days on the road / Teddy bear / White line fever / Girl on the billboard / How fast them trucks will go / Trucker's prayer / Give me 40 acres (to turn this rig around) / Convoy / Spirit of America / Old Kentucky home / Dixie / Thank you old flag of mine / America / North to Alaska / Play the star spangled / Battle hymn of the republic / There's a star-spangled banner waving somewhere / Yankee doodle / Battle of New Orleans
QED 035 / Nov '96 / Tring

☐ HEART BREAKIN' HILLBILLY SONGS
Only in my mind / Lonesome old town / Long black veil around my heart / Forty nine nights / Why do you want me / Long black limousine / I don't feel like doing anything / Danny boy / Reflections of an old man / Cody, Wyoming / Nothing but memories / Long long train / If I didn't love you / Old King Cole
RZRCD 536 / Oct '93 / Ritz

☐ KING OF THE RAILROAD
CTS 55431 / Sep '94 / Country Stars

☐ KING OF THE ROAD
King of the road / Wabash cannonball / You are my sunshine / Boxcar blues / Don't let the stars get in your eyes / Your cheatin' heart / I saw the light / Wreck of ol' 97 / Hank and the hobo / Peace in the valley / Mule train / Hey good lookin' / Kaw-liga / Move it on over / London leaves / Rollin' in my sweet baby's arms / Divorce me COD / Red river valley / Heaven / San Antonio rose
PLATCD 23 / Apr '88 / Platinum

☐ KING OF THE ROAD
King of the road / Wabash cannonball / You are my sunshine / Boxcar blues / Don't let the stars get in your eyes / Your cheatin' heart / I saw the light / Wreck of the old '97 / Hank and the hobo / Peace in the valley / Mule train / Hey good lookin' / Kaw-Liga / Move it on over / London leaves / Rollin' in my sweet baby's arms / Divorce me COD / Red river valley / Heaven / San Antonio rose
WB 870962 / Mar '97 / Disky

☐ TWO SIDES OF BOXCAR
Freightline fever / Truck drivin' man / Phantom 309 / Truck drivin' son of a gun / Six days on the road / Teddy bear / Whiteline fever / Girl on a billboard / How fast them trucks will go / Truckers' prayer / Forty acres / Convoy / Spirit of America / Old Kentucky home / Dixie / Thank you old flag of mine / America / North to Alaska / Play the star spangled banner over me / Battle hymn of the Republic / Star spangled banner waving somewhere / Yankee doodle / America the beautiful / Battle of New Orleans
GRF 151 / Feb '93 / Tring

Boxer

☐ BELOW THE BELT
Shooting star / All the time in the world / California calling / Hip kiss / More than meets the eye / Waiting for a miracle / Loony Ali / Save me / Gonna work out fine / Town drunk
CDV 2049 / Jun '97 / Virgin

☐ BLOODLETTING
Hey bulldog / Blizzard / Rich man's daughter / Big city fever / Loner / Why pick on me / Love has got me / Dinah-low / Teachers
CDV 2073 / Jun '97 / Virgin

Boxer

☐ HURT PROCESS
VR 333 / 4 May '98 / Vagrant

Boy George

☐ AT WORST... THE BEST OF BOY GEORGE AND CULTURE CLUB
Do you really want to hurt me: *Culture Club* / Time (clock of the heart): *Culture Club* / Church of the poison mind: *Culture Club* / Karma chameleon: *Culture Club* / Victims: *Culture Club* / I'll tumble 4 ya: *Culture Club* / It's a miracle: *Culture Club* / Miss me blind: *Culture Club* / Move away: *Culture Club* / Love is love / Love hurts / Everything I own / Don't cry / After the love / More than likely / Crying game / Generations of love / Bow down mister / Sweet toxic love
VTCD 19 / Oct '93 / Virgin

☐ CHEAPNESS AND BEAUTY
Fun time / Blindman / Genocide peroxide / Sad / Satan's butterfly ball / Same thing in reverse / Cheapness and beauty / If I could fly / God don't hold a grudge / Evil is so civilised / Your love is what I am / Unfinished business / Il adore
CDVIP 203 / 3 Aug '98 / Virgin VIP

☐ EVERYTHING I OWN
Everything I own / Sold / To be reborn / Keep me in mind / What becomes of the brokenhearted / Whisper / Where are you now when I need you / I'll adore / Something strange called love / If I could fly / Don't cry / Freedom / I love you / Cheapness and beauty
VI 867222 / Nov '96 / Disky

☐ SOLD
Sold / I asked for love / Keep me in mind / Everything I own / Freedom / Just ain't enough / Where are you now / Little ghost / Next time / We've got the right / To be reborn
CDVIP 204 / 3 Aug '98 / Virgin VIP

Boy Sets Fire

☐ DAY THE SUN WENT OUT, THE
IR 19CD / Oct '97 / Initial

Boyack, Pat

☐ BREAKIN' IN (Boyack, Pat & The Prowlers)
BBCD 9557 / Dec '94 / Bullseye Blues

☐ SUPER BLUE AND FUNKY (Boyack, Pat & The Prowlers)
For you my love / I'll be the joker / Longwallin' / Why must I suffer / Mexican vodka / Louisiana love shack / Can't you see / Sweet redemption / Think (before you do) / Ol' blondie swings again / Way you do / Righteous love / Poppa stoppa / Look at me look at you
CDBB 9587 / Jul '97 / Bullseye Blues

Boyce, Max

☐ LIVE AT TREORCHY
9-3 / Scottish trip / Ballad of Morgan the moon / Outside-half factory / Asso asso yagoshi / Duw it's hard / Ten thousand instant Christians / Did you understand / Hymns and arias
CDSL 8251 / Jul '95 / EMI

Boyd, Eddie

☐ 7936 SOUTH RHODES
You got to reap / Just the blues / She is real / I'll never stop (I can't stop loving you) / She's gone / Thank you baby / Third degree / You are my love / Blues is here to stay / Ten to one / Be careful / Blackslap
BGOCD 195 / May '95 / Beat Goes On

☐ EDDIE BOYD & HIS BLUES BAND (Boyd, Eddie Blues Band)
Too bad / Dust my broom / Unfair lovers / Key to the highway / Vacation from the blues / Steakhouse rock / Letter missin' blues / Ain't doing too bad / Blue coat man / Save her doctor / Rack 'em back / Too bad (part 2) / Big bell / Pinetop's boogie woogie / Night time is the right time / Train is coming
8440122 / Jan '94 / Deram

☐ FIVE LONG YEARS
Five long years / Hello stranger / Where you belong / I'm comin' home / My idea / Big question / Come on home / Blue Monday blues / Eddie's blues / All the way / Twenty four hours of fear / Rock the rock / Rosa Lee / Hound dog
ECD 260512 / Sep '94 / Evidence

☐ LIVE IN SWITZERLAND
I'm coming home to you / Early in the morning / I ain't doing too bad at all / Mr. Highwayman / Little red rooster / I'm sitting here waiting / Third degree / Hotel blues / I got a woman / Cool kind treatment / Five long years / She's the one / It's miserable to be alone / Save her doctor / Rattlin' and runnin' around / Reel good feeling / Her picture in the frame
STCD 8022 / Mar '95 / Storyville

Boyer, Jacqueline

☐ MITSOU
Tom Pilibi / Gruss mir die liebe / Mademoiselle de Paris in Tirol / Ich sag: oui, oui, oui / Liebe-liebelei: *Boyer, Jacqueline & Lucienne* / Frederick / Du bist das grosse los: *Boyer, Jacqueline & Francois Lubiana* / In der kleinen bar auf dem Grand Boulevard: *Boyer, Jacqueline & Francois Lubiana* / Mitsou / Mon cher Robert / Happy sing-song: *Boyer, Jacqueline & Dany Mann/Peter Weck* / Regenschirm song: *Boyer, Jacqueline & Paul Kuhn* / Hongkong madchen / Wenn du sie liebst, dann sag es ihr / Ganz in der nah' von den Champs-Elysees / Suleika / Jacques mit dem frack / Butterfly / Hor das signal, korporal / Ein weekend in Paris / Mademoiselle / Little, little china girl / Urlaub an der Cote D'Azur / C'est la vie / Comme au premier jour / Il bat mon coeur / Loin (greensleeves) / Melodie
BCD 16147 / Apr '97 / Bear Family

Boyer, Jean Pierre

☐ GRILLER PISTACHE
PS 65146CD / Jul '95 / PlayaSound

Boyer, Lucienne

☐ CHANSOPHONE 1926-1931
701262 / Jun '93 / Chansophone

☐ LADY IN BLUE, THE
995722 / 21 Aug '97 / EPM

☐ PARLEZ-MOI D'AMOUR
Parlez-moi d'amour / Prenez mes roses / Dans la fumee / Gigolette / C'est un chagrin de femme / La barque d'Yves / Quand tu seras dans mes bras / Ne dis pas toujours / Moi, j'crache dans l'eau / Si petite / Sans toi / Parle-moi d'autre chose / L'etoile d'amour / C'est ma faute / Comme une femme / Ta main / En se regardant / Estampe Marocaine / Parle-moi de toi / Mon rendez-vous / Je t'aime / Embrasse-moi / Mon p'tit kaki
CDAJA 5226 / May '97 / Living Era

Boyes, Jim

☐ OUT OF THE BLUE
NMV 1CD / Feb '93 / No Master's Voice

Boyfriend

☐ HAIRY BANJO
Hey big star / Summerthing / Kojak / Guitarist nipple / Rockwieller / Searching / Leathered / Two / Don't even try / Girl on my mind / Why should I pretend / Air you breathe / Sunburnt
RUST 003CD / Mar '93 / Creation

☐ RUBBER EAR
RUST 006CD / Jun '94 / Creation

Boyle, Gary

☐ ELECTRIC GLIDE
Snap crackle / Electric glide / Gaz / Hayabusa / Grumble / Morning father joys / Brat No.2 / It's almost light again
NAIMCD 002 / Apr '97 / Naim Audio

Boymerang

☐ BALANCE OF THE FORCE
Soul beat runna / Mind control / River (VIP) / You like it like that / ACID / Where it's at / Secret life / Still / Lazarus
REG 13CD / May '97 / Regal

Boyoyo Boys

☐ BACK IN TOWN
Back in town / Maraba start 500 / Dayeyton special / Duba duba / Mapetla / Pulukwani centre / Brakpan no.2 / Dube station / Arcie special / Vezunyawo
ROUCD 5026 / Jan '88 / Rounder

Boyracer

☐ WE ARE MADE OF THE
SLR 048 / Dec '96 / Slumberland

Boys

☐ BEST OF THE BOYS, THE
I don't care / First time / Sick on you / Tumble with me / Cop cars keep running / Brickfield nights / U.s.i. / Heroine / Classified susie / T.c.p. / Terminal love / Kamikaze / Waiting for the lady / Independent girl / You'd better move on / Weekend / Let it rain
DOJOCD 137 / Mar '95 / Dojo

☐ BOYS/ALTERNATIVE CHARTBUSTERS, THE
Sick on you / I call your name / Tumble with me / Tonight / I don't care / Soda pressing / No money / Turning grey / First time / Box number / Kiss like a nun / Cop cars / Keep running / Tenement kids / Living in the city / What'cha gonna do / Brickfield nights / USI / Taking on the world / Sway (Quien sera) / Do the contract / Heroine / Not ready / Teacher's pet / Classified Susie / TCP / Neighbourhood brats / Stop stop stop / Talking / Backstage pass / Cast of thousands / School days
LOMACD 12 / Feb '94 / Loma

☐ COMPLETE PUNK SINGLES COLLECTION
CDPUNK 85 / Nov '96 / Anagram

☐ LIVE AT THE ROXY
Kamikaze / Soda pressing / Brickfield nights / Terminal love / Living in the city / Sabre dance / Sick on you / You'd better move on / T.c.p. / Independent girl / New guitar in town / Cop cars / See you later / You can't hurt a memory
RRCD 135 / Nov '90 / Receiver

☐ TO HELL WITH THE BOYS/BOYS ONLY
LOMACD 20 / Nov '94 / Loma

Boys Life

☐ BOYS LIFE
CRC 04CD / 23 Feb '98 / Crank

☐ DEPARTURES AND LANDFALLS
HED 063CD / Oct '96 / Headhunter

Boys Next Door

☐ DOOR, DOOR
Nightwatchman / Nightwatchman / Friends of my world / Voice / Roman roman / Somebody's watching / After a fashion / Dive position / I mistake myself / Shivers
DOORCD 1 / Mar '93 / Grey Area

Boys Of The Lough

☐ DAY DAWN
LOUGH 006CD / Dec '94 / Lough

☐ FAIR HILLS OF IRELAND
Bonnie labouring boy / Mickey Doherty's highland/ Banks of the Allan/Maurice O'Keeff / Ban chnoic erin o / Wandering minstrel/Fasten the leg in her/ Coleman's cross / Ook pick waltz / Midsummer's night/Tinker's daughter/Over the moor to Maggie / Father Brian MacDermott Roe / Boys of the lough/ Lucky in love/Sleep sound in the morning / Pinch of snuff / Erin gra mo chroi / Ross memorial hospital / Lancers/Petronella/Ger the rigger / Wind that shakes the barley / Hunt
LOUGHCD 005 / Oct '89 / Lough

☐ FAREWELL AND REMEMBER ME
Sean Bui/Tommy Peoples/The lark in the morning / Leitrim queen / Lucky can du link ony/Pottinger's/ Billy Nicholson / Farewell and remember me / Angus polka No.1/Angus polka No.2/Donegal barn dance / An spailpin fanach/The one-horned buck / Valencia harbour/The jug of punch/MacArthur Road / Lovely Ann / Holly bush/The new ships are sailing / Waterford waltz/The stronsay waltz
LOUGHCD 002 / Oct '90 / Lough

☐ GOOD FRIENDS GOOD MUSIC
Crook of gold / Midsummer's night / Tinker's daughter / Flail / Paddy Doory's / Pride of Leinster / Kitty's gone a milking / Master McDemott's / Roll her in the rye grass / First house in Connaught / Humours of ennistymon / Leather britches / Dennis Murphy's hornpipe / Hop high ladies / Canadain waltz / New riggit ship / Kitchen girl / Newlyweds reel / La grand chaine / Bretton wedding march / Wild irishman / Scholar / Down the broom / Gatehouse maid / Gaelic mouth music / Farewell to Gibaltar / Captain Horne / High road to Linton / Far from home / Da road to Houll / Robertson's reel / Bonnie lass of Bonne Accord
CDPH 1051 / Mar '97 / Philo

☐ IN THE TRADITION
Out on the ocean / Padeen O'Rafferty / Isabelle Blackley / Kiss her under the coverlet / Lads of Alnwick / Road to Cashel / Paddy Kelly's brew / Lord Gregory / Dark woman of the glen / LO Forbes Esq of Corse / Hawk / Charles Sutherland / Eddie Kelly's jigs / Green fields of Glentown / Eclipse / Tailor's twist / Biddy from Sligo / Sunset / Peoples / Padraig O'Keefe's / Con Cassidy's highland reel / Sea apprentice / Miss McDonald / For Ireland I'd not tell her name
OSSCD 70 / Apr '93 / Ossian

☐ LIVE AT CARNEGIE HALL
Garrison Keillor / Maho snaps/Charlie Hunter/The mouse in the cupboard/The rose / I'll buy boots for Maggie/Brendan Begley's polka/O'Connor's / Leaving Glasgow/The Killarney boys of pleasure / Forest flower/James Byrne's reel/Jenny dang the weaver / Margaert's waltz/Captain Caswell/The jig of slurs / Flower of Magherally / Glencoe bridge march/Stirling castle/O'Keefe's polkas / On Raglan Road / Donegal jig No.1/Donegal jig No.2 / Hanged man's reel / Kerryman's daughter/O'Keefe's plough/The sligo maid
LOUGHCD 004 / Oct '89 / Lough
SA 001 CD / Jul '90 / Sagem

☐ LIVE IN PASSIM
CDPH 1026 / Feb '97 / Philo

☐ SWEET RURAL SHADE
Out on the ocean/Mooney's jig/Isabelle Blackley / Forest flower/Kitty the hare/Jenny Dang the weaver / Maro snaps/Charlie Hunter/The mouse in the cupboard/Rosewood / Hills of Donegal / Todd's sweet rural shade / Once I loved / Tim O'Leary's waltz / Captain Carswell/Green hills of Tyrol/Trip to Windsor / Humours of Flinn
LOUGH 003CD / Nov '96 / Lough

☐ WELCOMING PADDY HOME
When sick is it tea you want / Cape Breton wedding reel no 1 / Teelin march / Welcoming Paddy home / Miss Rowan Davies / Eugene Stratton / Antrim rose / Alexander's / Rose of Ardee / Tonbigbee waltz / Irish washerwoman
LOUGHCD 001 / Dec '94 / Lough

Boystown Gang

☐ BEST OF BOYSTOWN GANG, THE (Disco Kicks)
I can't take my eyes off you / Come and get your love / Signed sealed delivered (I'm yours) / Disco kicks / You're the one / Remember me/Ain't no mountain high enough / Cruisin' the streets / I just can't help believing/Keep on holding on / Dance trance medley / When will I see you again / You do it for me
HTCD 44 / 20 Apr '98 / Hot Productions

☐ CRUISIN' THE STREETS/DISCHARGE
Remember me/Ain't no mountain high enough suite / Cruisin' the streets / Can't take my eyes off you / Come and get your love / Signed, sealed, delivered (I'm yours) / You're the one / Disco kicks / Can't take my eyes off you (reprise)
MOCD 3004 / Feb '95 / More Music

Boyz II Men

☐ CHRISTMAS INTERPRETATIONS
5302572 / 15 Sep '97 / Motown

☐ COOLEYHIGHHARMONY
Please don't go / Lonely heart / This is my heart / Uhh ahh / It's so hard to say goodbye to yesterday / Motownphilly / Under pressure / Sympin' / Little things / Your love / End of the road
5300892 / 15 Sep '97 / Motown

☐ EVOLUTION
Doin' just fine / Never / 4 seasons of loneliness / Girl in the life magazine / Song for mama / Can you stand the rain / Can't let her go / Baby c'mon / Come on / All night long / Human II (don't turn your back on me) / To the limit / Dear god / Just hold on
5308222 / 22 Sep '97 / Motown

☐ REMIX COLLECTION, THE
Under pressure / Vibin' / I remember / Water runs dry / U know / I'll make love to you / Uhh ahh / Motownphilly / On bended knee / Brokenhearted / Thank you / Sympin'
5305982 / Oct '95 / Motown

Boyz Next Door

☐ RADIO HONOLULU
1+2CD 109 / 1 Jun '98 / 1+2

Boyzone

☐ DIFFERENT BEAT, A
Paradise / Different beat / Melting pot / Ben / Don't stop looking for love / Isn't it a wonder / Words / It's time / Games of love / Strong enough / Heaven knows / Crying in the night / Give a little / She moves through the fair
5337422
5338762 / Dec '96 / Polydor

☐ SAID AND DONE
5278012 / Aug '95 / Polydor

☐ WHERE WE BELONG
Picture of you / Baby can I hold you / All that I need / Must have been high / And I / That's how love goes / Where did you go / I'm learning / One kiss at a time / While the world is going crazy / This is where I belong / Will be yours / Good conversation / You flew away / I'm learning
5573982
5575572 / 25 May '98 / Polydor

☐ WHERE WE BELONG
5592002 / 24 Aug '98 / Polydor

Boze, Calvin

☐ COMPLETE CALVIN BOZE 1945-1952, THE
BMCD 6014 / 1 Jun '98 / Blue Moon

Bozzio, Terry

☐ BLACK LIGHT SYNDROME (Bozzio Levin & Stevens)
380901920 CD / 23 Mar '98 / Mascot

BR5-49

☐ BIG BACKYARD BEAT SHOW
There goes my love / Wild one / Hurtin' song / Out of habit / Storybook endings (if you stop believin') / 18 wheels and a crowbar / Pain pain go away / You are never nice to me / Goodbye Maria / Seven nights to rock / My name is Mudd / You flew the coop / Change the way I look / Georgia on a fast train
07822188622 / 20 Jul '98 / Arista

☐ BR5-49
Even if it's wrong / Cherokee boogie / Honk tonk song / Lifetime to prove / Little Ramona / Crazy arms / I ain't never / Chains of this town / Are you getting tired of me / Hickory wind / One long Saturday night
07822188182 / Sep '96 / Arista

☐ LIVE FROM ROBERT'S
Hillbilly thang / 18 wheels and a crowbar / Bettie Bettie / Me 'n' Opie (down by the duckpond) / Knoxville girl / Ole Stewfoot
0782210800 / Jun '96 / Arista

Braam, Bentje

☐ BENTJE BRAAM (Braam, Bentje & Michiel)
BVHAASTCD 9007 / Oct '93 / Bvhaast

Brackeen, Charles

☐ ATTAINMENT (Brackeen, Charles Quartet)
SHCD 110 / May '89 / Silkheart

Brackeen, Jo Anne

☐ FI-FI GOES TO HEAVEN
Estilo magnifico / Stardust / Fi Fi goes to heaven / Zingaro / I hear a rhapsody / Cosmonaut / Dr. Chang
CCD 4316 / Jul '87 / Concord Jazz

☐ INVITATION
BLCD 760218 / May '96 / Black Lion

☐ LIVE AT MAYBECK RECITAL HALL VOL.1
Thou swell / Dr. Chu Chow / Yesterdays / Curved space / My foolish heart / Calling Carl / I'm old fashioned / Strike up the band / Most beautiful girl in the world / It could happen to you / African Aztec
CCD 4409 / Mar '90 / Concord Jazz

☐ NEW TRUE ILLUSION (Brackeen, Jo Anne & Clint Houston)
Steps what was / Search for peace / New true illusion / My romance / Freedent / Solar
CDSJP 103 / Jun '91 / Timeless Jazz

☐ SIX ATE
Six ate / Circle / Old devil moon / C-sri / Nefertiti / Snooze / I didn't know what time it was / Zulu
CHCD 71009 / Mar '97 / Candid

☐ TAKE A CHANCE
Recado bossa nova / Children's games / Estate / Cancao do sal / Frevo / Mountain flight / Island / Take a chance / Ponta de areia / Duduka / Mist on a rainbow
CCD 4602 / Jul '94 / Concord Picante

☐ TURNAROUND
There is no greater love / Rubies and diamonds / Picasso / Bewitched, bothered and bewildered / Turnaround / Tricks of the trade
ECD 221232 / Sep '95 / Evidence

Bracken, Mark

☐ CELTIC DAWN
MCD 1752 / Aug '96 / Midsummer

Bracket

☐ 4 WHEEL VIBE
Circus act / Cool aid / Happy to be sad / John Wilkes isolation booth / Tractor / Green apples / Closed caption / Trailer park / Fresh air / PC / G vibe / Warren's song part 4 / Two hotdogs for 99c / Metal one / Pessimist / Lazy / My stepson
CAROLCD 1787 / Jun '97 / Caroline

☐ 924 FORESTVILLE STREET
Get it rite / Dodge ball / Missing link / Sleep / Huge balloon / Stalking stuffer / Why should eye / Warren's song / Can't make me / Skanky love song / J Weed / Rod's post
CAROLCD 1754 / Jun '97 / Caroline

☐ E IS FOR EVERYTHING
FAT 548CD / Nov '96 / Fatwreck Chords

Brad

☐ INTERIORS
Secret girl / Day brings / Lift / I don't know / Upon my shoulders / Sweet Al George / Funeral song / Circle and line / Some never come home / Candles / Those three words
4879212 / Jun '97 / Epic

Braden, Don

☐ AFTER DARK (Braden, Don Septet)
CRISS 1081CD / May '94 / Criss Cross

☐ ORGANIC
Moonglow / Saving all my love / Walking / Brighter days / Cousin Esan / Twister / Belief / It might as well be spring / Plain ol' blues
4812582 / Oct '95 / Sony Jazz

☐ TIME IS NOW, THE (Braden, Don Quintet)
CRISS 1051CD / Nov '91 / Criss Cross

☐ VOICE OF THE SAXOPHONE, A
Soul station / Speak no evil / Winelight / After the rain / Dust kicker / Monk's hat / Cozy / Face I love / Point of many returns / Voice of the saxophone
09026687972 / 8 Sep '97 / RCA Victor

Bradford

☐ SHOUTING QUIETLY
FOUND 001CD / Feb '90 / Foundation 2000

Bradford, Alex

☐ RAINBOW IN THE SKY
Packing up / Rainbow in the sky / Too close to heaven / I've found someone / Take the Lord along with you / Bells keep on ringing / I won't sell out / Oh my loving mother / Oh Lord, save me / Holy ghost / Let Jesus lead you / Captain Jesus / Life's candlelight / Feel like I'm running for the Lord / Dinner, Mr Rupe / It all belongs to him / Steal away / Over in Beulah land / I've got a job / Man is wonderful / Great consolation / What makes a man turn his back on God / Don't you want Jesus / See if I care
CDCHD 413 / Nov '93 / Ace

☐ TOO CLOSE
Too close to heaven / Lord, Lord, Lord / He lifted me / I don't care what the world may do / He leads me safely through / God is all / Just the name of Jesus / Right now / Don't let Satan turn you 'round / Life's candlelight / He'll wash you whiter than snow / Oh Lord, save me / Holy ghost / Crossing over Jordan / If mother knew / I dare you / I can't tarry / Without a God / Safe in Jesus' arms / Meeting ground / What did John do / There's only one way (to get to heaven) / What folks say about me / Truth will set you free / God searched the world / Lifeboat / Man is wonderful / Move upstairs / This may be the last time
CDCHD 480 / Jul '93 / Ace

☐ TOO CLOSE TO HEAVEN
One step / Walk through the streets / Just in time / Left my sins behind me / Let the Lord be seen in you / Climbing up the mountain / I wasn't gonna tell nobody / What about you / Lord looks out for me / Oh my Lord / Too close / Angel on vacation / When you pray / He always keeps his promises / They came out shouting / Let your conscience be your guide / Nothing but the holy ghost / Daniel is a prayin' man / Just to know / I made it in / I made God a promise
CPCD 8114 / Jul '95 / Charly

Bradford, Carmen

☐ FINALLY YOURS
Destiny (prelude) / Destiny / Maybe September / Rough ridin' / Right to love / I believe to my soul / I love you more than you'll ever know / Chicago hello / You must believe in spring / More than a trial
ECD 22186 / May '97 / Evidence

☐ WITH RESPECT
Even Steven / Mr. Paganini / Look who's mine / High wire / Finally / Maybe now / Little Esther / Ain't no use / Was I in love alone / He comes to me in comfort / Nature boy
ECD 22115 / Jun '95 / Evidence

Bradford, Geoff

☐ RETURN OF A GUITAR LEGEND, THE
Going down slow / Broke and hungry / Dark side / Pontiac / Keys to the highway / Paris strut / Alimony / Red's piece / Hallelujah, I love her so / Blind Blake's rag / Blues jumped the devil / Auto-mechanics blues
RNCD 001 / Jun '95 / Beat Goes On

Bradford, Perry

☐ PERRY BRADFORD & THE BLUES SINGERS 1923-1927
DOCD 5353 / Jun '95 / Document

Bradford, Terry

☐ HANDS ACROSS THE OCEAN
RZRCD 556 / Mar '96 / Ritz

Bradley, Josephine

☐ FIRST LADY OF THE BALLROOM (Bradley, Josephine & Her Ballroom Orchestra)
PASTCD 7092 / Aug '96 / Flapper

Bradley, Paul

☐ ATLANTIC ROAR (Traditional Irish Fiddle)
Munster grass / Gooseberry bush / Cead moladh don mhaighdean / Tommy People's / Mrs. Crotty's / Bracken's / Farewell to Connaught / Lord Mayo / Atlantic roar / Old Killeavy / The boul' red O'Hanlon / Brigid of Knock / The locomotive / Old bush / Toss the feathers / Piping jig / Strathspey and reels
PTICD 1090 / Jun '98 / Outlet

Bradley, Tommie

☐ TOMMIE BRADLEY & JAMES COLE
DOCD 5189 / Oct '93 / Document

Bradley, Will

☐ BASIN STREET BOOGIE (1941-1942) (Bradley, Will & Orchestra)
RACD 7110 / May '96 / Aerospace

☐ FAMOUS DOOR BROADCASTS 1940 (Bradley, Will & Ray McKinley)
Fatal fascination / Flying home / All the things you are / When you wish upon a star / Old Doc Yak / In a little Spanish town / It's a blue world / Starlit hour
TAX 37132 / Aug '94 / Tax

☐ FIVE O'CLOCK WHISTLE (1939-1941) (Bradley, Will & Orchestra)
RACD 7101 / May '96 / Aerospace

☐ ROCK-A-BYE THE BOOGIE (1940-1941) (Bradley, Will & Orchestra)
RACD 7112 / May '96 / Aerospace

Brady, Paul

☐ BACK TO THE CENTRE
Back to the centre / Walk the white line / Wheel of heartbreak / Deep in your heart / To be the one / Follow on / Soul beat / Airwaves / Island / Homes of donegal
8268092 / Apr '86 / Mercury

☐ GREEN CROW CAWS, THE (A Musical Celebration Of The Works Of Sean O'Casey)
Down where the bees are humming / As I wait in the boreen for Maggy / Eros / Eros / Sour soul'd cleric / Lament for Thomas Ashe / Nora / My bodice neat and modest / White legg'd Mary / Since Maggy went away / Niall / I tuck'd up my sleeves / Rare time for death in Ireland / All round me hat
SEECD 376 / 3 Nov '97 / See For Miles

☐ MOLLOY, BRADY, PEOPLES (Brady, Paul/Matt Molloy/Tommy Peoples)
Creel of turf / Tom Billys / Crosses of Annagh / McFadden's handsome daughter / Newport lass / Rambling pitchfork / Shamrock shore / Munster buttermilk / Connaught man's rambles / Speed the plough / Toss the feathers / Limerick lasses / Foxhunters / Mick Finns / Blackthorn / Fergal O'Gara / Cloon / Mulqueeney's / Out in the ocean / Rainy day / Grand canal / Scotsman over the border / Killavil / John Brennans / Drag her round the road / Graf spee
LUNCD 017 / Aug '86 / Mulligan

☐ PRIMITIVE DANCE
Steal your heart away / Soul commotion / Paradise is here / It's gonna work out fine / Awakening / Eat the peach / Don't start knocking / Just in case of accidents / Game of love: Brady, Paul & Mark Knopfler
8321332 / Apr '87 / Mercury

☐ TRICK OR TREAT
Soul child / Blue world / Nobody knows / Can't stop wanting you / You and I / Trick or treat / Don't keep pretending / Solid love / Love goes on / Dreams will come
8484542 / Apr '91 / Mercury

☐ TRUE FOR YOU
Great pretender / Let it happen / Helpless heart / Dance the romance / Steel claw / Take me away / Not the only one / Interlude / Trouble round the bend
8108932 / May '89 / Mercury

☐ WELCOME HERE KIND STRANGER
LUNCD 024 / Aug '94 / Mulligan

Brady, Shane

☐ LIVING ROOM, THE
HYCD 200120 / Feb '95 / Hypertension

Brady, Tim

☐ IMAGINARY GUITARS
JTR 84402 / Nov '92 / Justin Time

☐ INVENTIONS
JTR 84332 / Apr '92 / Justin Time

☐ SCENARIO
JTR 84452 / Apr '94 / Justin Time

Braff, Ruby

☐ AS TIME GOES BY
Shoe shine boy / Lonely moments / This is all I ask / Love me or leave me / Liza / As long as I live / Jeepers creepers / My shining hour / Sugar / As time goes by / You're sensational / I love you, Samantha / True love / Basin street blues / Linger awhile
CCD 79741 / Jul '97 / Candid

☐ BRAFF PLAYS WIMBLEDON (Second Set)
Rockin' chair / When a woman loves a man / I cried for you / Pennies from heaven / I'm pullin' through / I know that you know / Save it pretty mama
ZECD 16 / 9 Mar '98 / Zephyr

☐ BRAVURA ELOQUENCE (Braff, Ruby Trio)
Ol' man river / Smile (who'll buy my violets) / Lonely moments / Here's Cari / God bless the child / It's bad for me / I've grown accustomed to her face / Make sense / I'm shooting high / Orange / Persian rug / Travellin' light / Royal Garden blues / Judy medley
CCD 4423 / Aug '90 / Concord Jazz

☐ CALLING BERLIN VOL.2 (Braff, Ruby & Ellis Larkins)
ARCD 19140 / May '97 / Arbors Jazz

☐ CORNET CHOP SUEY
Cornet chop suey / Nancy with the laughing face / Ooh, that kiss / Do it again / Love me or leave me / It's the same old South / It had to be you / I must have that man / Sweet and slow / Shoe shine boy / You're sensational / I love you Samantha / True love / Lover come back to me
CCD 4606 / Aug '94 / Concord Jazz

☐ EASY NOW
My walking stick / Willow weep for me / When my sugar walks down the street / Song is ended (but the melody lingers on) / Give my regards to broadway / This is my lucky day / Someday you'll be sorry / Yesterdays / For now / I just couldn't take it baby / Little man you've had a busy day / Swinging on a star / Old folks / Did you ever see a dream walking / Pocket full of dreams / Moonlight becomes you / Pennies from Heaven / Go fly a kite / Please / All alone / You're sensational / Too-ra-loo-ra-loo-ra / White Christmas
74321185222 / Jul '94 / RCA

☐ FIRST, A (Braff, Ruby & Scott Hamilton)
Romance in the dark / When a woman loves a man / Rockin' chair / Dinah / All my life / Shine / If you were mine-i wished on the moon (medley) / Bugle blues
CCD 4274 / Jan '89 / Concord Jazz

☐ HEAR ME TALKIN'
You've changed / Hear me talkin' to ya / Don't blame me / No one else but you / Nobody knows you (when you're down and out) / Buddy Bolden's blues / Mean to me / Where's Freddy
BLC 760161 / Apr '92 / Black Lion

☐ HUSTLIN' AND BUSTLIN'
Hustlin' and bustlin' / There's a small hotel / What's the reason / 'S wonderful / When it's sleepy time down South / Flaky / Fine and mellow / Ad lib blues
BLCD 760908 / Sep '88 / Black Lion

☐ INSIDE AND OUT (Braff, Ruby & Roger Kellaway)
Love walked in / Yesterdays / Memories of you / I want to be happy / I got rhythm / Always / Between the devil and the deep blue sea / Basin Street blues / Exactly like you
CCD 4691 / Apr '96 / Concord Jazz

☐ LIVE AT THE NEW SCHOOL (Braff, Ruby & George Barnes)
CRD 126 / Aug '94 / Chiaroscuro

☐ LIVE AT THE REGATTABAR
Persian rug / 'S wonderful / Louisiana / Sweet Sue, just you / Do it again / No one else but you / Crazy rhythm / Where are you / Between the devil and the deep blue sea / Orange / Give my regards to Broadway
ARCD 19131 / Nov '94 / Arbors Jazz

☐ ME, MYSELF AND I (Braff, Ruby Trio)
Muskrat ramble / You've changed / Honey / Me, myself and I / When I fall in love / That's my home / Let me sing and I'm happy / You're a lucky guy / No one else but you / When you're smiling / Swan lake / Jubilee
CCD 4381 / Jul '89 / Concord Jazz

☐ MR. BRAFF TO YOU (Braff, Ruby Quintet)
PHONT CD 7568 / Apr '88 / Phontastic

☐ MUSIC FROM MY FAIR LADY (Braff, Ruby & Dick Hyman)
Wouldn't it be loverly / With a little bit of luck / I'm just an ordinary man / Rain in Spain / I could have danced all night / Ascot gavotte / On the street where you live / Show me / Get me to the church on time / Without you / I've grown accustomed to her face
CCD 4393 / '89 / Concord Jazz

☐ MUSIC FROM SOUTH PACIFIC (Braff, Ruby & Dick Hyman)
Bali Ha'i / Some enchanted evening / Cock-eyed optimist / Wonderful guy / Happy talk / Dites moi / This nearly was mine / There is nothin' like a dame / Honeybun / Younger than Springtime / Bali Ha'i (final version)
CCD 4445 / Feb '91 / Concord Jazz

☐ PLAY NICE TUNES (Braff, Ruby & Dick Hyman)
ARCD 19141 / May '98 / Arbors Jazz

☐ PLAYS GERSHWIN (Braff, Ruby & George Barnes)
'S wonderful / I got rhythm / They can't take that away from me / Nice work if you can get it / Somebody loves me / But not for me / Summertime / Bidin' my time / Love walked in / Embraceable you / Liza
CCD 6005 / Jul '88 / Concord Jazz

☐ PLAYS WIMBLEDON - THE FIRST SET
Someday sweetheart / Very thought of you / Wouldn't it be loverly / I've got a feeling I'm falling / Take the 'A' train / This is all I ask / It's the same Old South / When I fall in love / China boy
ZECD 15 / Apr '97 / Zephyr

☐ REMEMBERS LOUIS ARMSTRONG
ARCD 19163 / Sep '97 / Arbors Jazz

☐ RODGERS & HART (Braff, Ruby & George Barnes)
Mountain greenery / Isn't it romantic / Blue room / There's a small hotel / Thou swell / I wish I were in love again / Lover / You took advantage of me / Spring is here / Lady is a tramp
CCD 6007 / Jul '88 / Concord Jazz

☐ RUBY BRAFF & BUDDY TATE WITH THE NEWPORT ALLSTARS (Braff, Ruby & Buddy Tate & Newport Allstars)
Mean to me / Body and soul / I surrender dear / Lullaby of the leaves / Take the 'A' train / Don't blame me
BLC 760138 / Oct '90 / Black Lion

☐ RUBY BRAFF VOL.1 (Braff, Ruby & His New England Songhounds)
I'm crazy about my baby / Blue and sentimental / This can't be love / Thankful / Sho-time / My shining hour / Days of wine and roses / Down on honky tonk town / Tell me more / These foolish things / More than you know / Ev'ry time we say goodbye
CCD 4478 / Sep '91 / Concord Jazz

☐ RUBY BRAFF VOL.2 (Braff, Ruby & His New England Songhounds)
Indian summer / Thousand Islands / What's new / Heartaches / Cabin in the sky / You're a sweetheart / Please / All alone / Lullaby of birdland / Nice work if you can get it / As time goes by / Keepin' out of mischief now
CCD 4504 / May '92 / Concord Jazz

☐ RUBY GOT RHYTHM
There's a small hotel / 'S wonderful / I wish I could shimmey like my sister Kate / Flaky / Shoe shine boy / Fine and mellow / Hear me talkin' to ya / Ruby got rhythm / When my sugar walks down the street / Smart Alex blues / Between the devil and the deep blue sea
8747162 / Jul '96 / DA Music

☐ SAILBOAT IN THE MOONLIGHT (Braff, Ruby & Scott Hamilton)
Lover come back to me / Where are you / 'Deed I do / When lights are low / Jeepers creepers / Milkman's matinee / Sweethearts on parade / Sailboat in the moonlight
CCD 4296 / Apr '86 / Concord Jazz

Bragg, Billy

☐ BACK TO BASICS
Milkman of human kindness / To have and have not / Richard / Lover's town revisited / New England / Man in the iron mask / Busy girl buys beauty / It says here / Love gets dangerous / From a Vauxhall Velox / Myth of trust / Saturday boy / Island of no return / This guitar says sorry / Like soldiers do / St. Swithins day / Strange things happen / Lover sings / Between the wars / World turned upside down / Which side are you on
COOKCD 060 / 20 Apr '98 / Cooking Vinyl

☐ BREWING UP WITH BILLY BRAGG
It says here / Love gets dangerous / Myth of trust / From a Vauxhall Velox / Saturday boy / Island of no return / St. Swithin's day / Like soldiers do / This guitar says sorry / Strange things happen / Lover sings
COOKCD 107 / Sep '96 / Cooking Vinyl

☐ DON'T TRY THIS AT HOME
Accident waiting to happen / Moving the goalposts / Everywhere / Cindy of a thousand lives / You woke up my neighbourhood / Trust / God's footballer / Few / Mother of the bride / Tank park salute / Dolphins / North Sea bubble / Rumours of war / Wish you were her / Body of water / Sexuality
COOKCD 062 / 20 Apr '98 / Cooking Vinyl

☐ LIFE'S A RIOT WITH SPY VS. SPY/ BETWEEN THE WARS
Milkman of human kindness / To have and to have not / Richard / New England / Man in the iron mask / Busy girl buys beauty / Lovers town revisited / Between the wars / Which side are you on / World time upside down / It says here
COOKCD 106 / Sep '96 / Cooking Vinyl

☐ MERMAID AVENUE (Bragg, Billy & Wilco)
Walt Whitman's niece / California stars / Way over yonder in the minor key / Birds and ships / Hoodoo voodoo / She came along to me / At my window sad and lonely / Ingrid Bergman / Christ for president / I guess I planted / One by one / Eisler on the go / Hesitating beauty / Another man's done gone / Unwelcome guest
7559622042 / 29 Jun '98 / Elektra

☐ TALKING WITH THE TAXMAN ABOUT POETRY
Greetings to the new brunette / Train train / Marriage / Ideology / Levi Stubbs' tears / Honey I'm a big boy now / There is power in a union / Help save the youth of America / Wishing the days away / Passion / Warmest room / Home front
COOKCD 108 / Sep '96 / Cooking Vinyl

☐ VICTIM OF GEOGRAPHY
Greetings to the new brunette / Train train / Marriage / Ideology / Levi Stubbs' tears / Honey I'm a big boy now / There is power in a union / Help save the youth of America / Wishing the days away / Passion / Warmest room / Home front / She's got a new spell / Must I paint you a picture / Tender Comrade / Price I pay / Little time bomb / Rotting on remand / Valentine's day is over / Life with the lions / Only one / Short answer / Waiting for the great leap forwards
COOKCD 061 / 20 Apr '98 / Cooking Vinyl

☐ WILLIAM BLOKE VOL.2
Boy done good / Just one victory / Qualifications / Sugardaddy / Never had no one ever / Run out of reasons / Rule nor reason / Thatcherites
COOKCD 127 / Jun '97 / Cooking Vinyl

☐ WORKERS PLAYTIME
She's got a new spell / Must I paint you a picture / Tender comrade / Price I pay / Little time bomb / Rotting on remand / Valentine's day is over / Life with the lions / Only one / Short answer / Waiting for the great leap forwards
COOKCD 109 / Sep '96 / Cooking Vinyl

Brahaspati, Sulochana

☐ RAG BIULASKHANI TODI/RAGA MISHRA BHAIRAVI
NI 5305 / Sep '94 / Nimbus

Brahem, Anouar

☐ BARZAKH
Raf raf / Barzakh / Sadir / Ronda / Hou / Sarandib / Souga / Parfum de Gitane / Bou naouara / Kerkenah / La nuit des yeux / Le belvedera assiege / Oaf
8475402 / May '91 / ECM

☐ CONTE DE L'INCROYABLE AMOUR
Etincelles / Le chien sur les genoux de la devineresse / L'oiseau de bois / Lumiere du silence / Conte de l'incroyable amour / Peshrev Hidjaz Homayoun / Diversion / Nayzak / Battements / En souvenir d'Iram retrouvee / Epilogue
5119592 / Jun '92 / ECM

☐ KHOMSA
Comme un depart / L'infini jour / Souffle en vent de sable / Regard de mouette / Sur l' infini blue / Claquet les voiles / Vague / E la nave va / Ain ghazel / Khomsa / Suele / Nouvelle vague / En robe d'olivier / Des rayons et des ombres / Un sentier d'alliance / Comme un absence
5270932 / Feb '95 / ECM

☐ THIMAR (Brahem, Anouar & John Surman/Dave Holland)
Badhra / Kashf / Houdouth / Talwin / Waqt / Uns / Al Hizam Al Dhahbi / Qurb / Mazad / Kernow / Hulmu Rabia
5398882 / 15 Jun '98 / ECM

Brahmachari, Prahlad

☐ SONGS OF THE BAULS (Brahmachari, Prahlad & Kumkum)
VICG 50312 / Mar '96 / JVC World Library

Brahms 'n' Liszt

☐ CLASSICAL COCKNEY
Set sail / This is the 90's / Madame Belle Fruit / Music / Going nowhere / Miss Tu Tu / Flash the plastic / Daddy wouldn't buy me a pit bull / Henry VIII / China ship / Strollin' / Far too many love songs / Dagenham dustbins / Bill Bailey, Won't you please come home / Mabely Street / Pulling on a rope / Breezing along / All things bright and beautiful
URCD 109 / Jun '93 / Upbeat

Braid

☐ FRAME AND CANVAS
PRC 018CD / 30 Mar '98 / Polyvinyl

Brain Bats

☐ BRAIN BATS, THE
CYCD 101 / Jul '96 / Cyclone

Brain Pilot

☐ BRAIN PILOT
N 20072 / Apr '94 / Nova Zembla

☐ ILLEGAL ENTRY
NZ 043 / Oct '96 / Nova Zembla

☐ MIND FUEL
NZ 037 / Jul '95 / Nova Zembla

Brainbox

☐ PRIMORDIA
W 230069 / Jun '95 / Nettwerk

Brainbox

☐ BRAINBOX (Brainbox & Jan Akkerman)
CDP 1033DD / Jun '97 / Pseudonym

Braindance

☐ BRAINIAC
HOO 20CD / Mar '97 / Helen Of Oi

Braindead Sound Machine

☐ BRAINDEAD VOL.2
EFA 007602 / Apr '95 / Shockwave

Brainiac

☐ BONSAI SUPERSTAR
GROW 462 / Jan '95 / Grass

☐ HISSING PRIGS IN STATIC COUTURE
TG 155CD / Apr '97 / Touch & Go

Brainiac 5

☐ WORLD INSIDE, THE
CDRECK 1 / Jun '88 / Reckless

Brainless

☐ SUPERPUNKTUESDAY
CDHOLE 005 / Oct '95 / Golf

Brainstorm

☐ SEMI-DETACHED HOUSE MUSIC
TBCD 06 / Apr '97 / T&B

Brainstorm

☐ SMILE AWHILE
FGBG 4215 / Jun '97 / Musea

Brainticket

☐ ADVENTURE
CLP 0076 / 6 Oct '97 / Cleopatra

☐ CELESTIAL OCEAN
CLP 9935 / Mar '97 / Cleopatra

☐ COTTONWOODHILL
P 81120 / 23 Mar '98 / Phonag

☐ VOYAGE
CLP 0075 / 6 Oct '97 / Cleopatra

Bram Stoker

☐ SCHIZO POLTERGEIST
AACD 023 / Aug '97 / Audio Archive

Bramhall, Doyle

☐ BIRD NEST ON THE GROUND
ANT 0027CD / Oct '95 / Antones

Bran Van 3000

☐ GLEE
Gimme Sheldon / Couch surfer / Drinking in LA / Problems / Highway to Heck / Forest / Rainshine / Carry on / Afrodiziak / Luck now / Cum on feel the noize / Exactly like me / Everywhere / Une chanson / Old school / Willard / Supermodel / Oblonging / Mama don't smoke
8236042 / 15 Jun '98 / Parlophone

Branagan, Geraldine

☐ GOLD AND SILVER DAYS
Gold and silver days / Candle / Sonny / Ain't that a shame / Tonight as we dance / What's another year / Troubled times / Water is wide / Woman's heart / Stay with me / Will ye go, lassie go / Love me tender / Don't fly too high / Take me back
KCD 460 / Mar '97 / Irish

Branca, Glenn

☐ SELECTION FROM THE SYMPHONIES
ALP 35CD / 8 Dec '97 / Atavistic

☐ SYMPHONIES NO.8 AND 10
BFFP 106CD / Oct '96 / Blast First

☐ SYMPHONY NO.1
RE 125CD / Nov '94 / ROIR

Branch, Billy

☐ MISSISSIPPI FLASHBACK (Branch, Billy & The Sons Of Blues)
GBWCD 005 / Sep '92 / GBW

☐ WHERE'S MY MONEY (Branch, Billy & The Sons Of Blues)
Where's my money / You want it all / Third degree / Small town baby / Son of Juke / Sons of blues / Tell me what's on your mind / (Get up I feel like being a) sex machine / Eyesight to the blind / Take out the time
ECD 26069 / Jul '95 / Evidence

Branch Manager

☐ ANYTHING TRIBAL
DIS 107CD / Jul '97 / Dischord

Branco, Walter

☐ MEU BALANEO
MRBCD 002 / May '95 / Mr. Bongo

Brand, Kelly

☐ DREAM IN STONE, A (Brand, Kelly Sextet)
378182 / Sep '96 / Koch Jazz

Brand New Heavies

☐ BEST OF THE ACID JAZZ YEARS, THE
MCCD 331 / 16 Mar '98 / Music Club

☐ BRAND NEW HEAVIES, THE
Dream come true / Stay this way / People get ready / Never stop / Put the funk back in it / Ride in the sky / Brand new heavies / Gimme one of those / Got to give / Sphynx / Dream come true (Mix)
JAZIDCD 023 / Feb '95 / Acid Jazz

☐ BROTHER SISTER
Back to love / Ten ton take / Mind trips / Spend some time / Keep together / Snake hips / Fake / People giving love / World keeps spinning / Forever / Daybreak / Midnight at the Oasis / Dream on dreamer / Have a good time / Brother sister
8285572 / Apr '94 / Acid Jazz/FFRR

☐ HEAVY RHYME EXPERIENCE VOL.1
Bona fied funk / It's getting hectic / Who makes the loot / Wake me when I'm dead / Jump 'n' move / Death threat / State of yo / Do what I gotta do / Whatgabothat / Soul Flower
8283352 / Jul '92 / Acid Jazz/FFRR

☐ SHELTER
I like it / Sometimes / Shelter / You are the universe / Crying water / Day by day / Feels like right / Highest high / Stay gone / You've got a friend / Once is twice enough / After forevver / Last to know
8288872
8288902 / Apr '97 / FFRR

☐ SHELTER (Version II)
I like it / Sometimes / Shelter / You are the universe / Crying water / Day by day / Feels like right / Highest high / Stay gone / You've got a friend / Once is twice enough / After forever / Last to know
8289752 / 13 Oct '97 / FFRR

Brand New Unit

☐ DIDDLY SQUAT
CMD 045 / 1 Jun '98 / Creative Man

☐ LOOKING BACK AGAIN
BYO 43 / Jun '97 / Better Youth Organisation

☐ UNDER THE BIG TOP
EXC 0102 / May '94 / Excursion

Brand Nubian

☐ ONE FOR ONE
All for one / Concerto in X minor / Ragtime / To the right / Dance to my ministry / Drop the bomb / Wake up / Step to the rear / Slow down / Try to do me / Who can get busy like this man / Grand puba / Positive and LG dedication / Feels so good / Brand nubian
7559609462 / Feb '91 / WEA

Brand, Oscar

☐ PIE IN THE SKY
TCD 1021 / Aug '96 / Tradition

Brand X

☐ BRAND-X
Nuclear burn / Touch wood / Hate zone / Euthanasia waltz / Running of three / Sun in the night / Born ugly / Why should I lend you mine / Unorthodox behaviour / Malaga virgen / Smacks of euphoric hysteria / Macrocosm
VI 867242 / Nov '96 / Disky

☐ DO THEY HURT
Noddy goes to Sweden / Voidarama / Act of will / Fragile / Cambodia / Triumphant limp / DMZ
CASCD 1151 / May '89 / Charisma

☐ LIVESTOCK
Nightmare patrol / Ish / Euthanasia waltz / Isis mourning / Malaga virgen
CLACD 5 / May '89 / Virgin

☐ MANIFEST DESTINY
True to the Clik / Stellerator / Virus / XXL / Worst man / Manifest destiny / Five drops / Drum dbu / Operation hearts and minds / Mr. Bubble goes to Hollywood
OM 1002CD / 13 Oct '97 / Outer Music

☐ MASQUES
Poke / Masques / Black moon / Deadly nightshade / Earth dance / Access to data / Ghost of Mayfield Lodge
CASCD 1138 / May '89 / Charisma

☐ MISSING PERIOD
Dead pretty / Kugleblitz / Modern mysteries / Why don't you lend me yours / Miserable virgin / Tito's leg
OM 1004CD / 17 Nov '97 / Outer Music

☐ MOROCCAN ROLL
Sun in the night / Why should I lend you mine / Maybe I'll lend you mine after all / Hate zone / Collapsar / Disco suicide / Orbits / Malaga virgen / Machocosm
CASCD 1126 / May '89 / Charisma

☐ PLOT THINS, THE (A History Of Brand X)
Nuclear burns / Born ugly / Why should I lend you mine / Disco suicide / Malaga virgen / Isis mourning / Poke / Ghost of Mayfield lodge / Dance of the illegal aliens / Algon / Cambodia / Triumphant limp
CDVM 9005 / Oct '92 / Virgin

☐ PRODUCT
Don't make waves / Dance of the illegal aliens / Soho / Not good enough - see me / Algon / Rhesus perplexus / Wal to wal / And so to F / April
CASCD 1147 / May '89 / Charisma

☐ UNORTHODOX BEHAVIOUR
Nuclear burn / Euthanasia waltz / Born ugly / Smacks of euphoric hysteria / Unorthodox behaviour / Running on three / Touch wood
CASCD 1117 / May '89 / Charisma

Brandon, Kirk

☐ STONE IN THE RAIN
Stone in the rain / Communication / How long / Satellite / Children of the damned / Europa / Psycho woman / Revolver / Propaganda / Heroes / Future world / Spirit tribe
CDGRAM 92 / Mar '95 / Anagram

Brandon, Mary-Ann

☐ EVERYTHING I TOUCH
APCD 091 / Jun '92 / Appaloosa

☐ SELF APPOINTED HOMECOMING QUEEN
APCD 070 / '92 / Appaloosa

Brandos

☐ PASS THE HAT
SPV 08544202 / Sep '96 / SPV

Brandtson

☐ LETTERBOX
DER 366CD / 6 Jul '98 / Deep Elm

Brandwein, Naftule

☐ KING OF THE KLEZMER CLARINET
Heiser Bulgar / Freit sich, Yiddelach / Der Turkisher-Bulgar tanz / Kolomeika / Naftule spielt far dem Rebin / Nifty's freilach / Oi Tate, S'is gut / Der Terk in America / Wie bist die Gewesen vor prohibition / Das Teureste in Bukowina / Der Heisser / A Hora mit tzibeles / Fun tashlach / Leben zol Palastina / Dem

Rabin's Chusid / Der Yid in Jerusalem / Bulgar ala Naftule / Kleine Princessin / Turkishe Yale Vey Uve / Naftule, shpiel es noch amol / Araber tanz / Nifty's eigene / Fufzehn yahr fon der heim awek / Vie tsvie is Naftule der driter / Freilicher yontov
ROUCD 1127 / Feb '97 / Rounder

Brandy

☐ BRANDY
I wanna be down / I dedicate / I'm yours / As long as you're here / Sunny day / I dedicate / Give me you / Love is on my side / I dedicate / Always on my mind / Brokenhearted / Best friend / Movin' on / Baby
7567826102 / Nov '94 / Atlantic

☐ NEVER SAY NEVER
Intro / Angel / Boy is mine: Brandy & Monica / Learn the hard way / Almost doesn't count / On top of the world / You don't know me / Never say never / Truthfully / Have you ever / Put that on everything / Boy is mine / In the car / Happy / One voice / Tomorrow / Everything I do
7567830392 / 8 Jun '98 / Atlantic

Brandywine Bridge

☐ AND SO TO THE FAIR (Brandywine Bridge Play The Music Of Warwick Castle)
Horses brawl / Lavender blue / Ballad of Moll Bloxham / Jaunty John / English meadow / Dancing boy/Donkey riding/Bobby Shaftoe / Weekend in Warwick / Bernard of Clairvaux / Salisbury Plain / Beggar's song / When a knight won his spurs / Over the hills and far away / Boar's head carol / Rose of Allendale / Lorna of Wychwood / Unto the fair / Hi ho bendigo / Billy the budgie
SAMLSCD 503 / Nov '96 / Soundalive

Brandywine Singers

☐ WORLD CLASS FOLK
FE 1402 / Nov '94 / Folk Era

Branigan, Laura

☐ SELF CONTROL
Lucky one / Self control / Ti amo / Heart / Will you still love me tomorrow / Satisfaction / Silent partners / Breaking out / Take me / With every beat of my heart
7801472 / '87 / Atlantic

Brann, Chris

☐ DEEPFALL (2CD Set)
Deep fall / Eyes / Calling 610 / Journey to the centre / All about the music / Soul star / Grey souls / Young po nee / Out
PF 071CD / 2 Feb '98 / Peacefrog

Brannigan, Owen

☐ SINGS SCOTTISH AND NEWCASTLE
MWMCDSP 22 / Mar '98 / Mawson & Wareham

Brasilia

☐ RIVER WIDE
A chamada do Rio / Angel voices / River wide / Tudo joia / Sanctuary / Seeds of joy / With open arms / Voce ja foi a Bahia / Samba em preludio / Song of praise
KOKO 1304 / Mar '96 / Kokopelli

Brass Construction

☐ BRASS CONSTRUCTION
Movin' / Peekin' / Changin' / Love / Talkin' / Dance
MUSCD 510 / May '95 / MCI Original Masters

☐ GET UP TO GET DOWN
Get up to get down / Can you see the light / L-o-v-e u / What's on your mind / Talkin' / Dancin' / Right place / Walkin' the line / We can work it out / Startin' all over again / Watch out / Partyline / Renegades
CTMCD 325 / Jul '97 / EMI

☐ MOVIN' AND CHANGIN' (The Best Of Brass Construction)
Goodnews / Changing / What's on your mind (expression) / Love / Ha cha cha (funktion) / Movin' / Wake up / Message (inspiration) / LOVEU / Help yourself / Perceptions (what's the right direction) / Get up to get down / Can you see the light / Walkin' the line / Give and take
CZ 525 / Feb '98 / EMI

Brass Monkey

☐ COMPLETE BRASS MONKEY, THE
TSCD 467 / Sep '93 / Topic

Brass Pennies

☐ PRIDE OF ENGLAND
Rule Britannia / Rose of England / Oh I do like to be beside the seaside / All the nice girls love a sailor / Man who broke the bank at Monte Carlo / We'll meet again / White cliffs of Dover / Over the sticks / Sing as we go / Wish me luck as you wave me goodbye / Sally / Knees up Mother Brown / Bless them all / English country garden / John Peel / Robin Hood / Billy Boy / British grenadiers / There's a tavern in the town
CDITV 581 / Aug '94 / Scotdisc

Brass Tracks Jazz Orchestra

☐ FIRST TRACK
SB 2083 / Jan '97 / Sea Breeze

Brasshoppers

☐ VA VA VOOM
Froogie doogie / Big bottom / Dan's samba / Last night / Top boiler / Maria of my soul / Diver's boot / Carmen Miranda's hat / Afro trip / Mo' better blues / Bop bee oo / Va va voom / Weird moment
33WM 102 / Aug '96 / 33 Jazz

Brassil

☐ BRASSIL PLAYS BRAZIL (Brass Music From NE Brazil)
NI 5462 / Feb '96 / Nimbus

Bratland/Opheim

☐ DAM (Bratland/Opheim & The Oslo Chamber Choir)
FX 147CD / Apr '95 / Musikk Distribujson

Bratmobile

☐ REAL JANELLE, THE
Real Janelle / Brat girl / Yeah, huh / Die / I live in a town where the boys amputate their hearts / Where eagles dare
KRS 219CD / Aug '94 / Kill Rock Stars

Brauer, Timna

☐ JEWISH SPIRITUALS
39850132 / 24 Feb '98 / IMP

Braun, Grace

☐ IT WON'T HURT
Do right / Mermaid and the sailor / It won't hurt / O my ladies / Bittersweet / Lover's dream / What wondrous love is this / Stand by me / Carter's lullaby / Hopeless / Liftin' up me / Jenny Wren
SRRCD 026 / Jul '97 / Slow River

Brave Boys

☐ NEW ENGLAND TRADITIONS IN FOLK MUSIC
802392 / Sep '95 / New World

Brave Combo

☐ BRAVE COMBO
Money can't buy everything (american polish polka) / Cabti a la salsa (salsa) / Besame mucho (latin stroll) / Our imagined image (foxtrot) / Viva la reina (tex mex polka) / Chem-oo-chem (armenian folk song) / Poor people of paris (muzak swing) / La negra (mariachi huapango) / Night (rhumba) / Can can (fast cabaret polka) / Move (frustration pack ska) / Tick tock polka (czech polka) / Ay, me duele (mexican cha cha) / Oh, what a beautiful morning (twist) / Tubular jugs (schottische)
ROUCD 9019 / '88 / Rounder

☐ GROUP DANCE EPIDEMIC
Hokey pokey / Mexican hat dance / Never on Sunday / Limbo rock/Hand jive / Hustle / Chicken dance / Mana vu / Jeffrey / Peanut vendor / Jeopardy / Hokey pokey / Bunny hop
ROUCD 9055 / Jun '97 / Rounder

☐ KISS OF FIRE
Kiss of fire / I get ideas / Way to say goodbye / Burn slow / I could have danced all night / J'ai faim, toujours / Eyes of Santa Lucia / Candles / Serendipity / Take a deep breath / Day in the life of a fool / Under Paris skies
WMCD 1058 / Feb '97 / Watermelon

☐ MOOD SWING MUSIC
Three ducks waltz / Little bit of soul / Conmigo no quires nada / Skin / Volare / Three ducks polka / Come back to Sorrento / Sombras nada mas / Walking stick / Pirate Captain's quickstep / Burn slow / Three ducks ondo / Besos Besitos / Herrgard's polka / Girl / Tales from the Vienna Woods / Mas tequila / Three ducks cha cha / Always Vienna (the last words of Sigmund Freud) / Polka overture
ROUCD 11574 / Nov '96 / Rounder

☐ MUSICAL VARIETIES
Anna / People are strange / Forozinho aperreado / Lorianna / Gigl / Ice machine in the desert / El cumbanchero / O holy night cha cha cha / Julida / Rosemary's baby / Viva seguin / Skokiaan / La turbina / Clarinet polka / Watermelon heart / Habanera rock / Let's trim twist again / Sixteen tons / La cumparsita / Come back to me / Speak up mambo / Oaxaca / Perfidia / Beer barrel polka
ROUCD 11546 / '88 / Rounder

☐ NO NO NO CHA CHA CHA
Charanga y mambo (charanga) / Way of love (salsa) / No, no, no, cha cha cha (cha cha) / Por eso (me olvido de ti) / Cumbia sabanera (cumbia) / Recuerdos (bolero) / Nothing is permanent (samba) / Cumbia veracruzana (cumbia) / Cha cha for two (cha cha) / Hernanado's hideaway (tango) / Busy office rhumba (muzak rhumba) / Siren song (huapango) / Robertin, roberton (cumbia) / Fly me to the moon (bossa nova) / Cielito lindo (merengue)
ROUCD 9035 / Apr '93 / Rounder

☐ POLKA PARTY
Pretty dancing girl / Hosa dyna / Turkish march / Pop goes the weasel / Three weeks / Cuando escuches este vas / Don't get married / Peanut polka / Do something different / Polka medley / Come back to me / High bounce polka
EDCD 7052 / May '98 / Easydisc

☐ POLKAS FOR A GLOOMY WORLD
ROUCD 9045 / Jul '95 / Rounder

☐ POLKATHARSIS
Happy wanderer / Crazy Serbian butchers dance / Old country polka / Anniversary song / Who stole the kishka / La Rufalina / Lovesick / Atotonilco / New mind polka / Jeusita en chihuahua / Westphalia waltz / Pretty dancing girl / Hey ba ba re bop
ROUCD 9009 / '88 / Rounder

Brave Old World

☐ BEYOND THE PALE
ROUCD 3135 / Jul '94 / Rounder

Bravo, Soledad

☐ VOLANDO VOY
Clara vena / Volando voy / Juglar / Milonga triste / La ultima curda / Yo vivo enamorado / Deja / Tonadas de ordeno / Clara vena
MES 159662 / Apr '93 / Messidor

Braxton, Anthony

☐ 11 COMPOSITIONS (Braxton, Anthony & Brett Larner)
CDLR 244 / May '97 / Leo

☐ 2 COMPOSITIONS (ENSEMBLE) 1989/1991
ARTCD 606 / Apr '92 / Hat Art

☐ 4 COMPOSITIONS 1992
1201242 / Nov '93 / Black Saint

☐ 5 COMPOSITIONS 1986
1201062 / Nov '92 / Black Saint

☐ 6 COMPOSITIONS 1984
BSR 0086 / Jan '86 / Black Saint

☐ 6 MONK COMPOSITIONS
1201162 / Aug '88 / Black Saint

☐ 8 DUETS, HAMBURG 1991
CD 710 / Jun '92 / Music & Arts

☐ ANTHONY BRAXTON: TOWN HALL 1972
ARTCD 6119 / Nov '92 / Hat Art

☐ COMPOSITION NO.165
NA 050 / Nov '92 / New Albion

☐ COMPOSITION NO.174
CDLR 217 / May '95 / Leo

☐ COMPOSITION NO.192 (Braxton, Anthony & Lauren Newton)
CDLR 251 / 1 Jun '98 / Leo

☐ COMPOSITION NO.96
CDLR 169 / Mar '94 / Leo

☐ COMPOSITIONS NO.10 & 16
HATN 108 / Jul '98 / Hat Now

☐ CREATIVE ORCHESTRA (Koln 1978)
ARTCD 26171 / Apr '95 / Hat Art

☐ DORTMUND 1976
ARTCD 6075 / Jul '91 / Hat Art

☐ DUET - MERKIN HALL, NEW YORK (Braxton, Anthony & Richard Teitelbaum)
CD 949 / Oct '96 / Music & Arts

☐ DUETS (Braxton, Anthony & Mario Pavone)
CD 786 / Nov '93 / Music & Arts

☐ DUETS 1987 (Braxton, Anthony & Gino Robair)
CD 1026 / Aug '98 / Music & Arts

☐ DUO (Braxton, Anthony & Evan Parker)
CDLR 193 / Mar '94 / Leo

☐ DUO 1976 (Braxton, Anthony & George Lewis)
ART 6150CD / Jul '94 / Hat Art

☐ DUO 1991 (Amsterdam) (Braxton, Anthony & George Grawe)
OD 12018 / Feb '98 / Okka Disk

☐ EIGHT (3): TRISTANO COMPOSITIONS 1989
ARTCD 6052 / Nov '90 / Hat Art

☐ ENSEMBLE - VICTORIAVILLE 1988
VICTOCD 07 / Nov '94 / Victo

☐ EUGENE (1989) (Braxton, Anthony & Northwest Creative Orchestra)
1201372 / Jan '92 / Black Saint

☐ KNITTING FACTORY 1994 VOL.1 (2CD Set)
CDLR 222/3 / Oct '95 / Leo

☐ LEIPZIG 1993 (Braxton, Anthony & Ted Reichman)
CD 848 / Feb '96 / Music & Arts

☐ MEMORY OF VIENNA, A (Braxton, Anthony & Ran Blake)
HATOLOGY 505 / Oct '97 / Hatology

☐ MOMENT PRECLEUX (Braxton, Anthony & Derek Bailey)
VICTOCD 02 / Nov '94 / Victo

☐ OPEN ASPECTS
ARTCD 6106 / Nov '93 / Hat Art

☐ PIANO MUSIC 1968-1988
ARTCD 4619414 / Jan '97 / Hat Art

☐ QUARTET (LONDON) 1985 (Braxton, Anthony Quartet)
CDLR 200/201 / '90 / Leo

☐ SANTA CRUZ 1993 (Braxton, Anthony Quartet)
ARTCD 6190 / Jul '97 / Hat Art

☐ SILENCE/TIME ZONES (Braxton, Anthony & Richard Teitelbaum)
BLCD 760221 / May '97 / Black Lion

☐ TOGETHER ALONE (Braxton, Anthony & Joseph Jarman)
DD 428 / Dec '94 / Delmark

☐ TRIO (Braxton, Anthony & Evan Parker/ Paul Rutherford)
CDLR 197 / Nov '94 / Leo

☐ VICTORIAVILLE 1992 (Braxton, Anthony Quartet)
VICTOCD 021 / Nov '94 / Victo

☐ WESLEYAN
ARTCD 6128 / Sep '93 / Hat Art

☐ WILLISAU 1991
ARTCD 46100 / Jul '92 / Hat Art

Braxton, Toni

☐ SECRETS
Come on over here / You're making me high / There's no me without you / Unbreak my heart / Talking in my sleep / How could an angel break my heart / Find me a man / Let it flow / Why should I care / I don't want to / I love me some time / In the late of night / Toni's secrets / You're making me high / Unbreak my heart / I don't want to
74321460122 / 1 Nov '97 / Arista

☐ TONI BRAXTON
Another sad song / Breathe again / Seven whole days / Love affair / Candlelight / Spending my time with you / Love shoulda brought you home / I belong to you / How many ways / You mean the world to me / Best friend / Breathe again (Reprise)
74321162682 / Feb '97 / Arista

Braxtons

☐ BRAXTONS, THE
So many ways / Where's the good in goodbye / Slow flow / Girl on the side / I'd still say yes / LADI / Never say goodbye / Take me home to Momma / Boss
7567828752 / Sep '96 / Atlantic

Brazen Abbot

☐ BAD RELIGION
USG 10172 / 20 Apr '98 / USG

☐ EYE OF THE STORM
USG 37437422 / Apr '97 / USG

☐ LIVE AND LEARN
USG 400042 / 20 Apr '98 / USG

Brazil, Noel

☐ LAND OF LOVE, THE
TORCD 090 / Jul '97 / Dara

Breach

☐ FRICTION
BHR 026CD / Oct '95 / Burning Heart

☐ IT'S ME GOD
BHR 057CD / Jun '97 / Burning Heart

☐ OUTLINES
BHR 014CD / Oct '94 / Burning Heart

Breach, Joyce

☐ CONFESSIONS
ACD 269 / Apr '93 / Audiophile

☐ JOYCE BREACH & JERRY MELAGI TRIO (Breach, Joyce & Jerry Melagi)
ACD 199 / Aug '95 / Audiophile

☐ LOVERS AFTER ALL
ACD 282 / Oct '93 / Audiophile

☐ NOTHIN' BUT BLUE SKIES (Breach, Joyce & Hal Smith)
ACD 302 / 27 Apr '98 / Audiophile

☐ THIS MOMENT (Breach, Joyce & William Roy)
ACD 293 / Mar '97 / Audiophile

Bread

☐ BREAD
Dismal day / London bridge / Could i / Any way you want me / Last time / Look at me / Move over / You can't measure the cost / It don't matter to me / Family doctor / Friends and lovers / Don't shut me out
0349735022 / Jan '96 / Elektra

☐ DAVID GATES & BREAD ESSENTIALS
Dismal day / Goodbye girl / She's the only one / Lost without your love / Sweet surrender / Never let her go / He's a good lad / Aubrey / Guitar man / Ann / Soap (I use the) / Let your love go / Too much love / If / Diary / Everything I own / Down on my knees / Make it with you / Look what you've done / I want you with me / Baby I'm a want you / Mother freedom / It don't matter to me / Any way you want me
7559619612 / Sep '96 / Elektra

☐ LET YOUR LOVE GO
Make it with you / It don't matter to me / Let your love go / If / Baby I'm a want you / Everything I own / Diary / Guitar man / Sweet surrender / Aubrey / Lost without your love / Hooked on you / Make it by yourself / Dismal day
RMB 75063 / Aug '92 / Remember

☐ MANNA
Let your love go / Take comfort / Too much love / If / Be kind to me / He's a good lad / She was my lady / Live in your love / What a change / I say again / Come again / Truckin'
0349735042 / Jan '96 / Elektra

☐ ON THE WATERS
Why do you keep me waiting / Make it with you / Blue satin pillow / Look what you've done / I am that I am / Been too long on the road / I want you with me / Coming apart / Easy love / In the afterglow / Call on me / Other side of love
0349735032 / Jan '96 / Elektra

Bread & Butter

☐ ADVENTURES OF BREAD AND BUTTER VOL. 1, THE
Dana in the booth: *Bread & Butter/Dana Bryant* / Swing with this / rescue me / Sunrise morn moon / Keep it going dontchastop / Box that beat / Mean street: *Bread & Butter/Dana Bryant* / Fat beats: *Bread & Butter/Dizzy Gillespie* / Intro to meditation: *Bread & Butter/Dizzy Gillespie* / Sands of time / I'm yours: *Bread & Butter/Latasha Latasha* / Smashing / Shedding: *Bread & Butter/Kenny Garret* / Dramatic dialect: *Bread & Butter/Latasha Latasha* / Burn baby burn / Come back home / 24/7: *Bread & Butter/Ialah Hathway/Roy Hargrove* / Soul of the people: *Bread & Butter/Dana Bryant*
JAZ 202992 / 27 Jul '98 / Jazzateria

Breadmakers

☐ COOL
CORD 024CD / Apr '97 / Corduroy

Breag

☐ CAN JAH
Zion / Faistine / Goltrai / Elrigh Suas / An bothar mor / Baint an Fheir / Rasta no lay down / Cuir e le cheile / Jah sa jungal / La jah / Ceol na gcrann
CHCD 2011 / Jun '98 / Outlet

Breakaways

☐ STEP BACK
LF 296CD / 27 Oct '97 / Lost & Found

Breakdown

☐ BLACKLISTED
EB 007CD / 29 Sep '97 / Eyeball

Breakstone, Joshua

☐ WALK DON'T RUN (Breakstone, Joshua Quartet)
Lullaby of the leaves / Telstar / Ram-bunk-shush / Perfidia / Walk don't run / Taste of honey / Apache / Caravan / Slaughter on 10th Avenue / Blue star
ECD 22058 / Oct '93 / Evidence

Breath Of Life

☐ LOST CHILDREN
HOS 7043CD / 27 Apr '98 / Hall Of Sermon

☐ SWEET PARTY
HOS 7044CD / 27 Apr '98 / Hall Of Sermon

☐ TASTE OF SORROW
HOS 7041CD / 27 Apr '98 / Hall Of Sermon

Breathin' Canyon Band

☐ HARMONY OF A COUPLE, THE
642085MAN85 / Nov '94 / Mantra

☐ MOTHER AND CHILD
642086MAN86 / Nov '94 / Mantra

Breathless

☐ BETWEEN HAPPINESS AND HEARTACHE
I never know where you are / Over and over / Wave after wave / You can call it yours / All that matters now / Clearer than daylight / Flowers die / Help me get over it
BREATHCD 10 / Oct '91 / Tenor Vosa

☐ HEARTBURST
SAT 70012 / Feb '94 / Tenor Vosa

Breathnach, Maire

☐ ANGEL'S CANDLES
Mystic's slipjigs / Eist / Angel's candles / Carillion's / Moling / West ocean waltz / Swans at Coole / Beta / Carnival / Breatnaigh abu / Roundabout/Parallel / Goban/Halloween jig / Dreamer / Cuimhne / Aisling Samhna / Hop, skip, jump
SCD 593 / Jul '93 / Starc

☐ CELTIC LOVERS
SC 696 / Aug '96 / Starc
HBCD 0013 / 16 Jun '98 / Hummingbird

☐ VOYAGE OF BRAN
Inis sui / Bran / Branohm / Imhewin / Tir na mban / Piobaireachd / Lament for nechtan / Maarein / Ohm ripples / Argatnel / An tiolar firean / Manannan mac lir
7567827342 / Apr '95 / Warner Bros.

Breathnach, Siobhan

☐ CELTIC HARP
OSS 33CD / Mar '94 / Ossian

Breaux, Zachary

☐ GROOVIN'
Coming home baby / Impressions / Picadillo / Alice / Where is the love / Red, black and green / Lagos / Thinking of Alexis
JHCD 023 / Jan '94 / Ronnie Scott's Jazz House

☐ LAIDBACK
Small town in Texas / Laid back / West side worry / Find a place / Going out of my head / Intro / Remember the sixties / Ten days before / Midnight cowboy / In the midst of it all / On 6th street
NYC 60092 / Oct '94 / NYC

Brechin, Sandy

☐ OUT OF HIS BOX
CDBAR 6001 / Apr '96 / Brechin All

Brecker Brothers

☐ COLLECTION, THE
Skunk funk / Sponge / Squids / Funky sea, funky dew / Bathsheba / Dream theme / Straphangin' / East river
ND 90442 / Apr '90 / RCA

☐ COST OF LIVING, THE (Brecker, Michael Group)
JD 1260 / 12 Jan '98 / Jazz Door

☐ HEAVY METAL BE BOP
OW 31447 / Jun '97 / One Way

☐ LIVE (Brecker, Michael Band)
JD 1230 / 12 Jan '98 / Jazz Door

☐ LIVE AT SWEET BASIL (Brecker, Randy)
Sleaze factor / Thrifty man / Ting chang / Incidentally / Hurdy gurdy / Moontide / Mojoe
GNPD 2210 / Jun '95 / GNP Crescendo

☐ LIVE IN NEW YORK 1992
Some skunk funk / Common ground / Spunch / Song for barry / Spherical / N. y. special
JD 1248 / 12 Jan '98 / Jazz Door

☐ NOW YOU SEE IT (NOW YOU DON'T) (Brecker, Michael)
Escher sketch / Minsk / Ode to the doo da day / Never alone / Peep / Dogs in the wine shop / Quiet city / Meaning of the blues
GRP 96222 / 25 May '98 / GRP

☐ OUT OF THE LOOP
Slang / Ecovation / Scrunch / Secret heart / African skies / When it was / Harpoon / Night crawler / Then she wept
GRP 97842 / Sep '94 / GRP

☐ RETURN OF THE BRECKER BROTHERS
Above and below / That's all there is to it / On the backside / Big idea / Bikutsi / Funk / Good gracious / New Guinea / Roppongi / Sozinho (alone) / Sperical
GRP 96842 / 25 May '98 / GRP

☐ SNEAKING UP BEHIND YOU (The Very Best Of The Brecker Brothers)
East river / Skunk funk / Inside out / Funky sea / Straphangin' / Threesome / Rocks / Baffled / Jacknife / Tee'd off / Not Ethiopia / Sneaking up behind you
74321511992 / Sep '97 / RCA

☐ TALES FROM THE HUDSON (Brecker, Michael)
Slings and arrows / Midnight voyage / Song for Bilbao / Beau rivage / African skies / Introdduction to naked soul / Naked soul / Willie T / Cabin fever
IMP 11912 / Jun '96 / Impulse Jazz

☐ TWO BLOCKS FROM THE EDGE (Brecker, Michael)
Madam Toulouse / Two blocks from the edge / Bye George / El nino / Cat's cradle / Impaler / How long 'til the sun / Delta city blues
IMP 12612 / 27 Apr '98 / Impulse Jazz

Brecker, Randy

☐ INTO THE SUN
Village dawn / Just between us / Sleaze factor / Into the sun / After love / Gray area / Tijuca / Buds / Four worlds / Hottest man in town
CCD 47612 / 13 Jul '98 / Concord Vista

Breeders

☐ LAST SPLASH
New year / Cannon ball / Invisible man / No aloha / Roi / Do you love me now / Flipside / I just wanna get along / Mad lucas / Divine hammer / S.o.s. / Hag / Saints / Drivin' on 9 / Roi (reprise)
CAD 3014CD / Jun '93 / 4AD

☐ POD
Glorious / Happiness is a warm gun / Hellbound / Fortunately gone / Opened / Limehouse / Doe / Oh / When I was a painter / Iris / Only in 3's / Metal man
CAD 0006CD / May '90 / 4AD

Breeding Fear

☐ CHASE IS ON, THE
SPV 08487092 / Dec '96 / SPV

Breen, Ann

☐ BEST OF FRIENDS
Blue forever / Silver threads among the gold / Killarney / Runaround angel / May the good lord / You'll never get to heaven / Sonny / Close to you
PLAYCD 1038 / Mar '96 / Play

☐ EVENING WITH ANN BREEN, AN
PLACD 100 / Oct '94 / Play

☐ SAVE THE LAST DANCE
DHCD 725 / Nov '96 / Homespun

☐ SINCERELY
APLCD 1040 / Dec '96 / Avid

☐ SPECIALLY FOR YOU MOTHER
Pal of my cradle days / Too-ra-loo-ra-loo-ral (that's an irish lullaby) / Gentle mother / Two loves / What a friend we have in mother / Bunch of violets blue / Spinning wheel / Medals for mothers / Boy of mine / Skye boat song / Qua sera sera (whatever will be will be) / Among my souvenirs / You always hurt the one you love / I'll be your sweetheart / When you and I were young maggie / If I had my life to live over
PHCD 509 / Jan '95 / Outlet

☐ VERY BEST OF ANN BREEN, THE
DHCD 724 / Nov '96 / Homespun

Breeze

☐ INTIMATE MOMENTS
TJCD 001 / Nov '92 / TJ

Bregovic, Goran

☐ EDERLEZI
La nuit / Ederlezi / Mescina/Moonlight / Tv screen: *Bregovic, Goran & Iggy Pop* / 7/8 7 11/8 / Auscencia: *Bregovic, Goran & Cesaria Evora* / Cajesukarije cocec / Talijanska / Elo Hi: *Bregovic, Goran & Ofra Haza* / Death / Man from Reno: *Bregovic, Goran & Scott Walker* / Ederlezi / Lullaby / American dreamers: *Bregovic, Goran & Johnny Depp*
5583502 / 27 Apr '98 / Mercury

Brel, Jacques

☐ GREATEST HITS
CD 352111 / Jul '93 / Duchesse

☐ JACQUES BREL ALBUM, THE (Various Artists)
ITM 1455 / Apr '92 / ITM

☐ NE ME QUITTE PAS
Ne me quitte pas / Marieke / On n'oublie rien / Les flamandes / Les prenoms de Paris / Quand on n'a l'amour / Les biches / Le prochain amour / Le moribond / La valise a mille temps / Je ne sais pas pourquoi
8130092 / Jul '90 / ECM

Bremnes, Kari

☐ GATE VED GATE
FXCD 143 / Jan '95 / Musikk Distribujson

Brennan, Dave

☐ TAKE ME TO THE MARDI GRAS (Brennan, Dave Jubilee Jazzband)
Don't go 'way nobody / Dauphine Street blues / Bright star blues / Move the body over / Ride red ride / Roses of Picardy
LACD 20 / Nov '93 / Lake

Brennan, Dennis

☐ IODINE IN THE WINE
Familiar surroundings / Mighty long time / Blue sky red road / Lies / Pill of love / Iodine in the wine / Youngstown / Ones and fours / Worried man / Call your rider / River rise up / Lemmy go down
UPST 036 / Feb '97 / Upstart

☐ JACK IN THE PULPIT
UPSTART 016 / May '95 / Upstart

Brennan, John

☐ THROUGH THE EAR OF A TEARDROP (Brennan, John 'Wolf' Hextet)
CDLR 254 / 1 Jun '98 / Leo

Brennan, Maire

☐ MAIRE
Ce leis / Against the wind / Oro / Voices of the land / Jealous heart / Land of youth / I believe (deep within) / Beating heart / No easy way / Atlantic shore
74321228212 / Sep '94 / RCA

☐ MISTY EYED ADVENTURE
Days of dancing / Place among the stones / Watchman / An fharraige / Big yellow taxi / Pilgrim's way / Mighty one / Heroes / Misty eyed adventures / Dream on / Eirgh suas a stoirin
74321233552 / 1 Sep '97 / RCA Victor

☐ PERFECT TIME
MCD 60052 / 20 Apr '98 / MCA

☐ VOICE OF CLANNAD, THE
7019965601 / Mar '98 / Word

Brennan, Max

☐ ALIEN TO WHOM
1300 milliseconds of brass / Fusion spot / Blue book / Banging the bass / F1 culture / Narita Express / Alien to whom / Mind the gap / Venusian shuffle / We have been tweeked
SBLCD 5025 / 1 Jun '98 / Sublime

Brennan, Paul

☐ FIRE IN THE SOUL (Brennan, Paul Band)
FE 090CD / Apr '93 / Fellside

Breton Clarinet Quintet

☐ BRETON CLARINET QUINTET (2CD Set)
Bazh du soaz / Kamm ha diskamm / Hola bonbon / Ton toke hast / Un petit canon / Marecage / Ottomar / Senir Domingo / Lannhellen / Lein kerr / La marche du grand conseil / Ar riboterezz / 3 temps pour une melodie tres douce / Lann benn davad / Musique tetue / C'est la gavotte / Le chien aboie et la clarinette basee et la treujenn-goal / Toutrakansko / Volte valse / Rond / Le claire / Fisel / Au rendez-vous des petits matins clames... / La casquette / Boked eured / Pour toujours cette musique obsedante / Ton arsene
Y 225064 / Feb '98 / Silex

Brett, Seamus

☐ CELTIC RHAPSODY, A (Piano Classics From Ireland)
DOCDK 112 / 15 Dec '97 / Dara

Breuer, Carolyn

☐ ACQUAINTANCE
Let's face the music and dance / I got it bad and that ain't good / Zest for life / Simply be / Where can I go without you / I'm old fashioned / I know you / Murphy's law / Aspire / Hale bop
AL 73073 / Jul '97 / A

☐ SIMPLY BE (Breuer, Carolyn & Fee Claassen Quintet)
CHR 70017 / Sep '95 / Challenge

Breuker, Willem

☐ BAAL/BRECHT/BREUKER
BVHAASTCD 9006 / Oct '93 / Bvhaast

☐ BOB'S GALLERY
BVHAASTCD 8801 / Oct '93 / Bvhaast

☐ BUSY DRONE, THE (Music For Han Bennink) (Breuker, Willem & Misha Mengelberg/Louis Andriessen)
BVHAASTCD 9603 / Apr '98 / Bvhaast

☐ DEZE KANT OP DAMES
BVHAASTCD 9301 / Oct '93 / Bvhaast

☐ HEIBEL
BVHAASTCD 9102 / Oct '93 / Bvhaast

☐ KOLLEKTIEF - TO REMAIN
BVHAASTCD 8904 / Oct '93 / Bvhaast

☐ METROPOLIS
BVHAASTCD 8903 / Oct '93 / Bvhaast

☐ MONDRIAAN STRINGS- PARADE
BVHAASTCD 9101 / Oct '93 / Bvhaast

☐ MUSIC FOR FILMS OF FREAK DE JONGE
BVHAASTCD 9205 / Oct '93 / Bvhaast

☐ MUSIC FOR THE FILMS OF JOHAN VAN DER KEUKEN 1967-1994, THE (2CD Set)
BVHAASTCD 9709/10 / Apr '98 / Bvhaast

☐ TWICE A WOMAN (Original Soundtrack)
BVHAASTCD 9708 / Apr '98 / Bvhaast

☐ VERA BETHS & MONDRIAAN STRINGS
BVHAASTCD 8802 / Oct '93 / Bvhaast

Brewer & Shipley

☐ ARCHIVE ALIVE
80006 / Jun '97 / Archive

Brewer, Gary

☐ LIVE IN EUROPE
COPP 0144CD / Dec '96 / Copper Creek

Brewer, Jack

☐ EYSIAN INTERVALS (Brewer, Jack & Bazooka)
For poetress relieved / Reggie's plateau / Wilmington / Going to New Orleans / Remarkable citizens / Amerika I'm your poet / Elysium / Changing schools / Child gargoyle / Second mate / Chore / Last punk anthem / World cried... / Pallbearer dreams
NAR 125CD / 29 Sep '97 / New Alliance

Brewer, Teresa

☐ TEENAGE DANCE PARTY
Hula hoop song / Ricky ticky song / Why baby why / Teardrops in my heart / Tweedle dee / After school / Rock love / Pledging my love / Lula rock a hula / On Treasure Island / If were a train / Gone / Empty arms / Since you went away / Dark moon / So shy / It's the same old jazz / Bobby / Jingle bell rock / Born to love
BCD 15440 / Apr '89 / Bear Family

☐ VERY BEST OF TERESA BREWER
Mexicali rose / Music music music (put another nickel in) / When I leave the world behind / Till I waltz again with you / Hula hoop song / Ricochet / Anymore / Last night on the back porch / Fools rush in (where angels fear to tread) / Your cheatin' heart / Have you ever been lonely / Jealous heart / San antonio rose / Jambalaya / Half as much / My happiness / Let me go lover / A tear fell / You send me / Bell bottom blues / Hawaiian wedding song / By the light of the silvery moon / Ma, he's making eyes at me / Shine on harvest moon
SOW 710 / Jun '93 / Sound Waves

Brian Jonestown Massacre

☐ GIVE IT BACK
BCD 4068 / 29 Sep '97 / Bomp

☐ METHODRONE
BCD 4050 / Aug '95 / Bomp

☐ STRUNG OUT IN HEAVEN
TVT 57802 / 3 Aug '98 / TVT

☐ TAKE IT FROM THE MAN
BCD 4055 / Jan '97 / Bomp

☐ THANK GOD FOR MENTAL ILLNESS
BCD 4061 / Nov '96 / Bomp

Briar, Celia

☐ DARK ROSE
WCL 11005 / May '94 / White Cloud

Brick

☐ VOLVOLAND
DOL 051CD / 23 Feb '98 / Dolores

Brick Layer Cake

☐ TRAGEDY - TRAGEDY
TG 127D / Oct '94 / Touch & Go

Brickell, Edie

☐ GHOST OF A DOG (Brickell, Edie & New Bohemians)
Mama help me / Black and blue / Carmelito / He said / Times like this / 10,000 angels / Ghost of a dog / Strings of love / Woyaho / Oak cliff bra / Stwisted / This eye / Forgiven / Me by the sea
GFLD 19269 / Feb '95 / Geffen

☐ PICTURE PERFECT MORNING
Tomorrow comes / Green / When the lights go down / Good times / Another woman's dream / Stay awhile / Hard times / Olivia / In the bath / Picture perfect morning / Lost in the moment
GFLD 19332 / Sep '96 / Geffen

☐ SHOOTING RUBBERBANDS AT THE STARS (Brickell, Edie & New Bohemians)
What I am / Little Miss S / Air of December / Wheel / Love like we do / Circle / Beat the time / She / Nothing / Now / Keep coming back
GFLD 19268 / Feb '95 / Geffen

Brickman, Jim

☐ PICTURE THIS
Dream come true / Sun, moon and stars / Sound of your voice / Picture this / Edgewater / You never know / Coming home / Frere Jacques / Secret love / First step / Valentine: *Brickman, Jim & Martina McBride* / Sweet dreams: *Brickman, Jim & Martina McBride* / Hero's dreams: *Brickman, Jim & Martina McBride*
01934112112 / Mar '97 / Windham Hill

Bricktop's Jazz Babes

☐ STOMPIN' AT THE JAZZ CAFE
BCD 326 / Jan '94 / GHB

Bride

☐ JESUS EXPERIENCE, THE
ORCD 9703 / Oct '97 / Pamplin

☐ SILENCE IS MADNESS
Fool me once / Hot down south tonight / Silence is madness / Until the end we rock / Evil dreams / Under the influence / All hallow's eve / No more nightmares / Rock those blues away
CMGCD 002 / Nov '90 / Communique

Brides Of Funkenstein

☐ BRIDES OF FUNKENSTEIN - LIVE
Introduction / War ship touchante / Birdie / Ride on / Bridesmaids / Vanish in our sleep / Together / Disco to go / James Wesley Jackson comedy spot: *Jackson, James Wesley*
NEMCD 719 / Nov '94 / Sequel

Bridewells

☐ CAGE
Cage / Cage / Way of the world / Girl / Juggler / Smile I still care / Snake eyes / Clear as the day / Paris / Inner city blues / Rachel / Sail the wind
EXPALCD 14 / Oct '92 / Expression

Bridges, Eugene

☐ BORN TO BE BLUE (Bridges, Eugene 'Hideaway')
If you don't wanna love me / Little boy blue / Tears of a fool / Born to be blue / Learn how to let you go / Aching heart / Good times / (My only reason for working) ain't no reason no more / Doctor can you tell me / Somebody loves me / Good thang / Change is gonna come
WESF 105 / 15 Jun '98 / Blueside

Bridget

☐ BRIDGET OF CALIFORNIA
GROW 0402 / Feb '95 / Grass

Bridgewater, Cecil

☐ MEAN WHAT YOU SAY
8357298002 / 27 Apr '98 / Brownstone

Bridgewater, Dee Dee

☐ DEAR ELLA
A-tisket a-tasket / Undecided / Midnight sun / Let's do it (let's fall in love) / How high the moon / If you can't sing it you'll have to swing it / Cotton tail / My heart belongs to daddy / (I'd like to get you on a) slow boat to China / Oh lady be good / Stairway to the stars / Dear Ella / Das moritat von Mackie Messer
5378962 / 15 Sep '97 / Verve

☐ IN MONTREUX
All of me / How insensitive / Just friends / Child is born / Strange fruit / Night in Tunisia / Sister Sadie/ Next time I fall in love/Senor Blues
8479132 / Jan '92 / Polydor

☐ IN MONTREUX
CDCRH 121 / Sep '97 / Charly

☐ KEEPING TRADITION
Just one of those things / Fascinating rhythm / Island / Angel eyes / What is this thing called love / Les feuilles mortes/Autumn leaves / I'm a fool to want you/I fall in love too easily / Lullaby of Birdland / What a little moonlight can do / Love vibrations / Polka dots and moonbeams / Sister Sadie
5196072 / Mar '93 / Verve

☐ PRECIOUS THINGS (Featuring Ray Charles)
CDSGP 053 / Aug '92 / Prestige

☐ VICTIM OF LOVE
Heartache caravan / Till the next somewhere / Wall of love / Love takes chances / I go my way / Mr. Guitar Man / Can't we try love again / Sunset and blue
CDCRH 122 / Nov '97 / Charly

Brien, Steve

☐ TOKEN ENTRY
LB 9612 / Jul '98 / La Brava

Brier

☐ BALLADS AND CRAIC
Fairy tale of New York / First of May / Dingle bay / Primrose polka / Black is the colour / Finnegan's wake / Home boys home / Peace song / Town I loved so well / Flight of the earls / Liberty boy (Home again in Dublin) / Dreams of tomorrow / Waltz medley / Dirty old town / Streets of New York / Lotto song / Lonesome boatman / Dear little town in old county down
PHCD 540 / Mar '97 / Outlet

☐ BEST OF IRISH FOLK, THE
CHCD 1038 / Aug '94 / Chyme

Brier, Tom

☐ RISING STAR
SDSCD 1274 / Jun '94 / Stomp Off

Brigades

☐ TILL LIFE US DO PART
DANCD 011 / Apr '90 / Danceteria

Brigadier Jerry

☐ HAIL HIM
CDTZ 014 / Aug '93 / Tappa

☐ ON THE ROAD
RAS 3071CD / Feb '91 / Ras

Briggs, Anne

☐ SING A SONG FOR YOU
Hills of Greenmoor / Sing a song for you / Sovay / I thought I saw you again / Summer's in / Travelling's easy / Bonambuie / Tongue in cheek / Bird in the bush / Sullivan's John
FLED 3008 / Feb '97 / Fledg'ling

Briggs, Arthur

☐ HOT TRUMPET IN EUROPE 1927-1933
158472 / Feb '96 / Jazz Archives

Briggs, Tim

☐ TIM BRIGGS
1509592972 / 31 Mar '98 / Intersound

Brighouse & Rastrick Band

☐ BANDSMAN'S CHOICE
Cleopatra / Meeting of the waters / Poeme / Trumpeter's lullaby / Napoli / Morning has broken / Fee des eaux / Carrickfergus / I'll take you home again Kathleeen / Miss Blue Bonnet / David of the white rock / Londonderry air / Flower duet / Silver threads among the gold / Una furtiva lagrima / St. Clement / Carnival of Venice
QPRL 086D / Oct '97 / Polyphonic

☐ EVENING WITH BRIGHOUSE & RASTRICK BAND, AN
Floral dance / Overture to Mack and Mabel / Amazing grace / Great little army / Because / Le carnaval Romain (The Roman carnival) / Marching through Georgia / Nimrod / Army of the nile / Lento from Eurphoria concerto (1972) / Eriskay love lilt / Poet and peasant
CDMFP 6151 / Feb '95 / EMI

☐ FLORAL DANCE, THE
295941 / Oct '94 / Ariola

☐ MARCHES & WALTZES
King cotton / Waltz of the flowers / Radetzky march / Westminster waltz / Espana / French military march / Waltz (Symphonie Fantastique) / Old comrades / West riding / Gold and silver / Cornish cavalier / Morning papers / BB and CF / Waltz from Sleeping Beauty / Colonel Bogey
DOYCD 032 / Oct '94 / Doyen

Bright

☐ ALBATROSS GUEST HOUSE
DRL 044 / Sep '97 / Darla

Bright, Larry

☐ SHAKE THAT THING
DFCD 71253 / May '97 / Del-Fi

Brightman, Sarah

☐ ANDREW LLOYD WEBBER COLLECTION, THE
Phanton of the opera: *Brightman, Sarah & Michael Crawford* / Unexpected song / Chanson d'enfance / All I ask of you: *Brightman, Sarah & Cliff Richard* / Don't cry for me Argentina: *Brightman, Sarah & Cliff Richard* / Another suitcase in another hall: *Brightman, Sarah & Cliff Richard* / Love changes everything: *Brightman, Sarah & Cliff Richard* / Amigos para siempre: *Brightman, Sarah & Jose Carreras* / Memory / Gus the theatre cat / Anything but lonely / Macavity the mystery cat / Tell me on a Sunday / Wishing you were somehow here again / Pie Jesu: *Brightman, Sarah & Paul Miles Kingston* / Music of the night
5393302 / 1 Dec '97 / Polydor

☐ AS I CAME OF AGE
River cried / As I came of age / Some girls / Love changes everything / Alone again or / Bowling green / Something to believe in / Take my life / Brown eyes / Good morning starshine / Yesterday / It must be tough to be that cool
8435632 / May '90 / Polydor

☐ DIVE
Dive / Captain Nemo / Second element / Ship of fools / Once in a lifetime / Cape horn / Salty dog / Siren / Seven seas / Johnny wanna live / By now / Island / When it rains in America / La mer
5400832 / Apr '93 / A&M

Brightside

☐ BULLET PROOF
LF 304CD / 25 May '98 / Lost & Found

☐ FACE THE TRUTH
LF 127 / Mar '95 / Lost & Found

☐ PUNCHLINE
LF 185CD / Apr '96 / Lost & Found

Brignola, Nick

☐ IT'S TIME
RSRCD 123 / Nov '94 / Reservoir

☐ LIVE AT SWEET BASIL
RSRCD 125 / Nov '94 / Reservoir

☐ ON A DIFFERENT LEVEL
RSRCD 112 / Nov '94 / Reservoir

☐ POINCIANA
RSRCD 151 / Apr '98 / Reservoir

☐ RAINCHECK
Raincheck / Tenderly / Hurricane Connie / My ship / I wish I knew / Hesitation blues / Jo Spring / Jitterbug waltz / Darn that dream / North Star
RSRCD 108 / '89 / Reservoir

☐ SPRING IS HERE (Brignola, Nick & Netherlands Metropole Orchestra)
369052 / 3 Aug '98 / Koch Jazz

☐ TRIBUTE TO GERRY MULLIGAN (Brignola, Nick & Sal Salvador)
STCD 574 / Feb '94 / Stash

☐ WHAT IT TAKES
RSRCD 117 / Nov '94 / Reservoir

Brim, John

☐ ICE CREAM MAN, THE
CDTC 1150 / May '94 / Tonecool

Brinkmann, Thomas

☐ CONCEPT 1.96 VR VARIATIONS
MNS 4001 / 29 Jul '98 / Minus

Brinsley Schwarz

☐ BRINSLEY SCHWARZ
REP 4421 / Feb '94 / Repertoire

☐ BRINSLEY SCHWARZ/DESPITE IT ALL
Hymn to me / Shining brightly / Rock 'n' roll women / Lady Constant / What do you suggest / Mayfly / Ballad of a has been Beauty Queen / Country girl / Slow one / Funk angel / Piece of home / Love song / Starship / Edbury Down / Old Jarrow
BGOCD 239 / Jun '94 / Beat Goes On

☐ HEN'S TEETH
Shy boy / Lady on a bicycle / Rumours / And she cried / Tell me a story / Understand a woman / Tomorrow today / Turn out the light / In my life / I can see her face / Hypocrite / Version / I've cried my last tear / (It's gonna be a) bringdown / Everybody / I like you I don't love you / Daytripper / Slow down / I should have known better / Tell me why / There's a cloud in my heart / I got the real thing
EDCD 546 / 6 Apr '98 / Edsel

☐ NERVOUS ON THE ROAD
Nervous on the road / It's been so long / Happy doing what we're doing / Surrender to the rhythm / Feel a little funky / I like it like that / Brand new you, brand new me / Home in my hand / Why why why
BGOCD 289 / Oct '95 / Beat Goes On

☐ PLEASE DON'T EVER CHANGE
Hooked on love / I worry / Home in my hand / I won't make it without you / Speedoo / Why do we hurt the one we love / Don't ever change / Play that fast thing / Down in Mexico / Version
EDCD 237 / Sep '90 / Edsel

☐ SILVER PISTOL
Dry land / Merry go round / One more day / Nightingales / Silver pistol / Last time I was fooled / Unknown number / Range war / Egypt / Niki Hoeke speedway / Ju ju man / Rockin' chair
EDCD 190 / Sep '90 / Edsel

Brise Glace

☐ WHEN IN VANITAS
GR 17CD / Sep '94 / Skingraft

Brisker, Gordon

☐ GIFT, THE (Brisker, Gordon Quartet)
860012 / Jun '97 / Naxos Jazz

Brislin, Kate

☐ OUR TOWN (Stecher, Jody & Kate Brislin)
Going to the west / Home / Old country stomp / In between dreams / Showerbread reel/The twisted arm / Too late, too late / Bramble and the rose / Our town / Twilight is stealing / Curtains of the night / Queen of the Earth and child of the stars / Roving on last winter's night / Henry the true machine / Won't you come and sing for me
ROUCD 0304 / Jul '93 / Rounder

☐ SLEEPLESS NIGHTS
ROUCD 0374 / Feb '96 / Rounder

Brissett, Annette

☐ ANNETTE (Brissett, Annette & The Taxi Gang)
RASCD 3088 / Apr '92 / Ras

Bristol Citadel Choir

☐ MIGHTY TO SAVE (Salvation Army Hymns) (Bristol Citadel Choir/Bristol Easton Songsters Choirs)
Why are you doubting and fearing / I bring my heart to Jesus / My life must be Christ's broken bread / I know thee who thou art saviour / Hear me while before thy feet / Yet once again / By God's abundant mercy / With my heart shone bright in Heavenly light / Life is a journey, long is the road / Once on a day / Was Christ led forth to die / Let me love thee / Thou art claiming / In the secret of my presence / Blessed Lord, in thee is refuge
KMCD 865 / May '96 / Kingsway

Britannia Building Society Foden Band

☐ ANTHOLOGY
White knuckle ride / Here's that rainy day / Four pieces for four trombones / Consecration / Blue John / Whisper a prayer / Scarborough Fair / Street fair / Elegy for Mippy / Nightingale sang in Berkeley Square / Concert piece for trombone / Bluesleeves / Londonderry air / Adagio / Every time we say goodbye / Eternal quest
QPRL 076D / Oct '97 / Polyphonic

☐ BAND OF THE YEAR
Spanish dance / Winter / You'll never walk alone / Tea for two / Solvejg's song / Eighteenth variation from a rhapsody on a theme of Paganini / American in Paris / Postcard from Mexico / Pretty girl is like a melody / Puttin' on the ritz / Sweet and low / In the wood / Bolero
GRCD 33 / Oct '88 / Grasmere

☐ BEST OF BRASS AND VOICES, THE (Britannia Building Society Foden Band/Halifax Choral Society)
Hallelujah chorus / Praise my soul / Swing low, sweet chariot / Oh God our help in ages past / Fantasy on North Country tunes / Onward, Christian soldiers / Chorus of the Hebrew slaves / Crimond / Grand march from Aida / Day thou gavest Lord is ended / Jerusalem / Pomp and circumstance
DOYCD 041 / Aug '95 / Doyen

☐ FESTIVAL OF BRASS 1992, A
DOYCD 019 / Jan '93 / Doyen

☐ MUSIC OF JOHN MCCABE
Salamander / Cloudcatcher fells / Desert 11 horizons / Images / Northern lights
DOYCD 030 / May '95 / Doyen

☐ PINES OF ROME (Britannia Building Society Foden Band/Howard Snell)
Pines of the Villa Borghese / Pines close to a catacomb / Pines of the Gianicolo / Pines of the Appian Way / Dawn / Chloe's dance / Bacchanale / Circuses / Jubilee / October festival / La befana - the Epiphany festival
DOYCD 045 / Aug '96 / Doyen

☐ YEAR OF THE DRAGON
Midwest / Midwest / I hear you calling me / Blues march / Yesterday / Devil's gallop / Greensleeves / Entry of the gods into valhalla / Praise / Impresario (overture) / Softly as I leave you / Galop / Badinerie / Fantasy on 'moto perpetuo' / Way we were / Year of the dragon
DOYCD 021 / May '93 / Doyen

British Airways Band

☐ TICKET TO RIDE
BNA 5138 / 13 Apr '98 / Bandleader

British Modbeats

☐ MOD IS...
FLASH 70 / 20 Jul '98 / Flash

British North American Act

☐ IN THE BEGINNING
AFT 005 / Jun '97 / Afterglow

British Saxophone Quartet

☐ EARLY OCTOBER
Early October / Neologie musicale / Time to go now
SLAMCD 216 / Oct '96 / Slam

British Tuba Quartet

☐ ELITE SYNCOPATIONS
Russian and Ludmila / La danza / Minute waltz / Fantasy / King's hunt / Canzona / La spiritata / Trepak / Chit chat polka / Fascinating Gershwin / Nightingale sang on Berkeley Square / 42nd Street / On my own / Elite syncopations / Rumpole of the bailey / Puttin' on the Ritz / Three movements from Quatre Chansons
QPRZ 012D / Oct '97 / Polyphonic

☐ EUPHONIC SOUNDS
Celestial suite / Il ritorno / They didn't believe me / Quartet for brass / Mon coeur se recommende a vous / John come kiss me now / Bocoxe / Favourite rag / Spiritual jazz suite / Greensleeves / Get me to the church on time / Air / Pink panther / Euphonis sounds / You made me love you / William Tell overture
QPRZ 009D / Oct '97 / Polyphonic

☐ FIREWORKS
Fanfare no.1 / Overture/The merry wives of Windsor / Flower duet / Now hear this / Overture/Distressed innocence / Flander's cauldron / Overture/The force of destiny / Pigs / Westminster intrada / Kierkegaard / Fireworks / Petite caprice / Montagues and capulets / Perpetuum mobile / Cool suite / Strollin' lazin' hangin' cruisin' / Bavarian polka
QPRZ 020D / Oct '97 / Polyphonic

☐ MARCH TO THE SCAFFOLD
Thunderer / Hava nagila / Dance of the sugar plum fairy / On the sunny side of the street / Glyder landscape / Sortie in E flat / Triplet for four tubas / Fugue / Battle royal / Dido's lament / Minitures for four valve instruments / Turkish march / In memoriam / April is in my mistress' face / Sonatina for tuba quartet / March to the scaffold
QPRZ 013D / Oct '97 / Polyphonic

Britton, Dan

☐ RIDING THE RED WHITE AND BLACK HORSES
Easier to see / Really loved me / Lonely eyes / Save it for the judge / Magical time / Bite back / Haunted / Year of the horse / Big world / Thought you were gone / Easy / Last time I saw you
RDEPR 099 / 27 Apr '98 / Rideout

Broadbent, Alan

☐ CONCORD DUO SERIES (Broadbent, Alan & Gary Foster)
Ode to the road / Speak low / Wonder why / Lady in the lake / 317 East 32nd / What is this thing - hot house / If you could see me now / In your own sweet way / One morning in May / Relaxin' at Camarillo
CCD 4562 / Jul '93 / Concord Jazz

☐ LIVE AT MAYBECK RECITAL HALL VOL.14
I hear a rhapsody / Oleo / You've changed / Lennie's pennies / Nardis / Sweet and lovely / Don't ask why / Parisian thoroughfare
CCD 4488 / Dec '91 / Concord Jazz

☐ PACIFIC STANDARD TIME
Summer night / This one's for Bud / Easy living / Easy to love / I should care / Django / Beautiful love / In love in vain / Someday my prince will come / I've never been in love before / Reets and I
CCD 4664 / Sep '95 / Concord Jazz

☐ PERSONAL STANDARDS
Consolation / Ballad impromptu / Long goodbye / Everytime I think of you / Song of home / North / Chris craft / Idyll / Uncertain terms
CCD 47572 / May '97 / Concord Jazz

Broadcast

☐ WORK AND NON WORK
Accidentals / Book lovers / Message from home / Phantom / We've got time / Living room / According to no plan / World backwards / Lights out
WARPCD 52 / Jun '97 / Warp

Broadside Band

☐ ENGLISH COUNTRY DANCES
Cuckolds all in a row / Shepherd's Holyday or Labour in Vaine / Newcastle / Beggar boy / Picking of sticks / Faine I would if I could or Parthenia / Gathering peascods / Night-peece or The shaking of the sheets / Chelsey Reach or Buckingham-House / Jameko / Epping Forest / Well-Hall / Fits come on me now or Bishop of Chester's jig / Mad robin / Red house / Mr. Beveridge's magot / Geud man of Ballangigh / To a new Scotch jigg / Childgrove / Wooly and Georgey / Portsmouth / Whitehall minuet / Bloomsberry market
CDSDL 393 / Mar '94 / Saydisc

☐ ENGLISH NATIONAL SONGS (Broadside Band & John Potter/Lucie Skeaping)
Greensleeves / Gather ye rosebuds while ye may / When the King enjoys his own again / Northern lass / Harvest home / Sally in our alley / Roast beef of old England / Vicar of Bray / Rule Britannia / God save the King / Nancy Dawson / Miller of the Dee / British Grenadiers / Hunting we will go / Drink to me only with thine eyes / Chapter of Kings / Lass of Richmond Hill / Begone dull care / Tom Bowling / Early one morning / Home sweet home
CDSDL 400 / Mar '94 / Saydisc

☐ JOHN PLAYFORD'S POPULAR TUNES
Greenwood / Heart's ease / Excuse me / Lady Catherine Ogle / Scotchman's dance / In the Northern lass / Never love thee more / Miller's jig / Granadees march / Saraband by Mr.Simon Ives / Lady Hatton's almaine / Prins Robbert Masco / Prince Rupert's march / Daphne / Lilliburlero / Parthenia / La chabott / Jocobella / Paul's steeple / Lady Nevils delight / Whisk / New rigaudon / Italian rant / Bouzar castle / Childgrove / Mr. Lane's minuet / Up with aily / Cheshire rounds / Hunt the squirrel
CDSAR 28 / Jul '94 / Amon Ra

☐ OLD ENGLISH NURSERY RHYMES (Broadside Band & Tim Laycock/Vivien Ellis)
Girls and boys come out to play / Polly put the kettle on/Lucy Locket / Jack and Jill went up the hill / Tom, he as the piper's son / Little boy blue come blow your horn / Little Miss Muffet, she sat on a tuffet / Oh dear what can the matter be / Here we go round the mulberry bush / Oranges and lemons / Oats and beans and barley grow / Farmer's in the den / Dance to your Daddy / Ring o'roses / Hey diddle diddle / Humpty Dumpty / I had four brothers over the sea / I saw a ship a-sailing / There was a man who lived in the moon / If all the world were paper / Lavender's blue / Sing a song of sixpence / I had a little nut tree / Oliver Cromwell lay buried and dead / Old King Cole was a merry old soul / Grand old Duke of York/Lion and the unicorn / Ding dong bell, pussy's in the well / Hickery dickery dock / Three blind mice / There were three little kittens / I love little pussy / Pussy cat, pussy cat, where have you been / Three mice went into a hole to spin / My Daddy is dead, but I can't tell you how / Jolly fat frog lived in the river / North wind doth blow / Who killed cock robin / Frog he would a wooing go / Mary had a little lamb / Baa baa black sheep / Litle Bo Peep / Hot cross buns / Little Jack Horner / Dame get up and bake your pies / Pat a cake, pat a cake, baker's man / Oh what have you got for dinner Mrs. Bond / Hush a bye baby on the tree top / Dance a baby diddy / Hey diddle dumpling, my son John / Twinkle twinkle little star / Sleep, baby, sleep / Boys and girls come out to play
CDSDL 419 / Sep '96 / Saydisc

☐ POPULAR 17TH CENTURY DANCE TUNES
HMA 1901039CD / Oct '94 / Musique D'Abord

☐ SONGS & DANCES FROM SHAKESPEARE (Broadside Band & Deborah Roberts/John Potter)
Full fathom five thy Father lies / Where the bee sucks / O Mistress mine where are you roaming / Poor soul sat sighing / It was a lover and his lass / Sellengers round / Scottish jigge / Hoboken brawl / Staines morris / How should I your true love know / Tomorrow is St. Valentine's day / And will he not come again / In youth when I did love / Woosell cock, so black of hue / O sweet Oliver / When daffodils begin to peer / Jog on, jog on, the footpath way / Kemp's jig / Passamezzo pavan / Bargamasca / Queen Mary's dumpe / As you came from that holy land / I loathe that I did love / Bonny sweet robin / Come live with me / There dwelt a man / Farewell dear love / Fortune my foe / Earl of Essex measure / La volta / Sinkapace galliard / Coranto / Take , o take those lips away / Sigh no more ladies / Hark, hark, the lark / Lawn as white as driven snow / Get ye hence / When that I was and a little tiny boy
CDSDL 409 / Feb '95 / Saydisc

Broadways

☐ BROKEN STAR
AM 021CD / 26 Jan '98 / Asian Man

Broberg, Bosse

☐ SWEDE IN COPENHAGEN, A
MECCACD 2033 / Jan '98 / Music Mecca

☐ WEST OF THE MOON (Broberg, Bosse & Red Mitchell)
DRCD 235 / Oct '94 / Dragon

Broccoli

☐ BROCCOLI
SEEP 19CD / Nov '96 / Rugger Bugger

☐ HOME
SEEP 23CD / 5 May '98 / Rugger Bugger

Brock, Dave

☐ AGENT OF CHAOS (Brock, Dave & The Agents Of Chaos)
SHARP 042CD / Apr '88 / Flicknife

☐ STRANGE DREAMS
EBSCD 116 / Dec '96 / Emergency Broadcast System

☐ STRANGE TRIPS AND PIPE DREAMS
Hearing aid test / White zone / UFO Line / Space / Pipe dream / Self / Something going on / Bosnia / Parasites are here on earth / Gateway / It's never too late / La forge / Encounter
EBSSCD 116 / 24 Nov '97 / Emergency Broadcast System

Brock, Jim

☐ LETTERS FROM THE EQUATOR
RR 56CD / May '96 / Reference Recordings

☐ TROPIC AFFAIR
Pass-a-grill / Ladies of the calabash / Tropic affair / Anya / Quo qui's groove / Sidewalk / Palm-palm girls / O vazio
RR 31CD / May '96 / Reference Recordings

Brock, Paul

☐ MO CHAIRDIN
CEFCD 155 / Jan '94 / Gael Linn

Brodie, Mark

☐ SHORES OF HELL, THE (Brodie, Mark & Beaver Patrol)
SH 031CD / Nov '95 / Shreder

Brodsky Quartet

☐ BRODSKY QUARTET
Chromatic fantasy / Concertino / String quartet no.1 Op.8 (1923)
SILKD 6014 / Jun '97 / Silva Classics

Brodsky, Chuck

☐ LETTERS IN THE DIRT
RHRCD 87 / Oct '96 / Red House

☐ RADIO
RHRCD 119 / 1 Sep '98 / Red House

Broggs, Peter

☐ RAS PORTRAITS
Rastafari liveth / You've got to be wise / Jah Jah voice is calling / Cheer up / Rastaman chant Nyahbingi / Just can't stop praising Jah / Cease the war / Military man / Don't let the children cry / Just because I'm a Rastaman / International farmer / Leggo me hand / 400 years
RAS 3304 / Jun '97 / Ras

☐ RASTAFARI LIVETH
RASCD 3001 / Nov '92 / Ras

☐ REASONING
RASCD 3051 / Jul '90 / Ras

☐ REJOICE
Jah voice is calling / Rejoice / Africa is waiting / Jah almighty / Rastafari liveth / World peace treaty / Jah run things / True rastaman / Thank you Jah / Praise Jah / Survival / Cornerstone / International farmer
RASCD 3178 / Sep '97 / Ras

☐ RISE AND SHINE
You got to be wise / Rise and shine / I admire you / International farmer / Leggo mi hand / Bloodstain / Fuss and fight / I love to play reggae / Jah is the ruler / Rastaman chant Nyahbingi
RASCD 3011 / Sep '93 / Ras

Broken Arrow

☐ BROKEN ARROW
74321348652 / Apr '96 / RCA

Broken Bones

☐ BRAIN DEAD
Killing fields / Last breath / Losing control / Jump / Going down / Shutdown / Brain dead / Life's too fast / Bitching / Mercy / Maniac / Lesson / Money, pleasure and pain / Who cares about the cost / Stabbed in the back (still bleeding) / Booze for free / Crack attack / Trader in death / Blue life / Religion is responsible / Madness / Last breath (live)
CDJUST 19 / Oct '92 / Rough Justice

☐ COMPLETE SINGLES
CLP 96872 / Jan '97 / Cleopatra

☐ LOSING CONTROL
Killing fields / Nowhere to run / Jump / Going down / Shutdown / Brain dead / Life's to fast / Bitching / Mercy / Maniac / Lesson
HMRXD 133 / Aug '89 / Heavy Metal

☐ STITCHED UP
Stitched up / Fix / Propaganda / Wasted nation / Forget it / In fear / Gotta get away / Bring 'em down / Limited greed / Sick world
CDJUST 18 / Oct '91 / Rough Justice

☐ TRADER IN DEATH
Traders in death / Money, pleasure and pain / Who cares about the cost / Stabbed in the back (still bleeding) / Booze for free / Crack attack / Trader in death / Blue lie blue life
HMRCD 141 / Mar '90 / Heavy Metal

Broken Dog

☐ BROKEN DOG
ABB 122CD / Mar '97 / Big Cat

☐ ZERO
ABB 163CD / 10 Aug '98 / Big Cat

Broken Hearts Are Blue

☐ TRUTH ABOUT LOVE
CR 025CD / May '97 / Caulfield

Broken Hope

☐ LOATHING
398414120CD / Mar '97 / Metal Blade

☐ SWAMPED IN GORE
140962 / Nov '95 / Metal Blade

Broken Pledge

☐ MUSIQUE IRLANDAISE
BCD 6801 / Jan '95 / Auvidis/Ethnic

Brokesch, Susanne

☐ SHARING THE SUNHAT
EFA 123002 / Apr '97 / Disko B

Brokken, Corry

☐ LA MAMMA
La Mamma / Das gluck kam zu mir wie ein Traum / La boheme / Nimm meine hand / Alle meine Traume / Heiss ist der kaffee in San Jose / Kind nummer zehn / Und doch / Van deinen Traumen kannst du nict leben / Spiel Zigeuner / Menschen / Was wird aus mir / Vorbei / Ich bin glucklich obwohl ich weine / Und sie trug eine Rose im Haar / Was weisst du von mi / Ouzo / Femde strassen / Da ist die Andere / Warum machst du dir das so leicht / Mylady / Der mann, den ich will / Deine Mutter ist da / Meine Leibesmelodie / Die letzten sieben Tage
BCD 15883 / Dec '96 / Bear Family

☐ MILORD
Damals war alles so schon / Seit wir uns seh'n / Milord / Bonjour Paris / Er sah aus wie ein lord / Du bist durchschaut / Maurice, der altecharmeur / Er macht musik am montparnasse / Wie der traum meiner schlaflosen nachte / Es war im fruhling, cherie / Wenn ich nur wusst / Gluck und glas / Flomarkt melodie / Moro / Gib mir die hand / Doch

nur dann hab'ich weh getan / Venedig in grau / So ist die liebe, mon ami / Don Juan / Es kann si viel gesch'n / 14 April / Ich traum so gern von San Francisco / Ich bin girl und du bist boy / Ein haus ist kein / Zuhaus / Sag lieber nein / Ohne mich wird morgen hochezeit zein / Gut nacht, mein schatz, gut nacht
BCD 15877 / Jul '96 / Bear Family

☐ **NANA - DIE RONNEX AUFNAHMEN**
Nana / Unter den tausend laternen / Rio De Janeiro / Sing nachtigall sing / Schon war die nacht / Mein guter stern / Ganz leis erklingt musik / Graue schleier / Ein tag mir dir / Nun weiss ich den weg zu deinem herzen / Rio De Janeiro / Nana / Autoscooter's boogie / Begin the beguine / Net als toen / Hier in die stille laan / Wees mar niet boos / Als de bomen bloeien op het plein / Wacht op mij / Autoscooter's boogie / Naar Hawaii / Hoe zaou het zijn / Hier in de vrieje natuur
BCD 16120 / Aug '97 / Bear Family

Bromberg, Brian

☐ **BASSICALLY SPEAKING**
NOVA 9031 / Jan '93 / Nova

☐ **IT'S ABOUT TIME**
NOVA 9146 / Jan '93 / Nova

Bromide

☐ **ISCARIOT HEART**
SR 61652 / Feb '97 / Scratchy

Bronco Bullfrog

☐ **BRONCO BULLFROG**
TWISBIG 13 / 29 Jun '98 / Twist

Bronski Beat

☐ **AGE OF CONSENT, THE**
Why / It ain't necessarily so / Screaming / No more war / Love and money / Smalltown boy / Heatwave / Junk / Need a man blues / I feel love / I feel love/ Medley: *Bronski Beat & Marc Almond* / Run from love / Hard rain / Memories / Puit d'amour / Heatwave
8288242 / Jul '96 / London

☐ **HUNDREDS AND THOUSANDS**
Cadillac car / Heatwave / Why / Run from love / Hard rain / Smalltown boy / Junk / Infatuation / Close to the edge / I feel love
5500432 / Jun '93 / Spectrum

Bronx Horns

☐ **SILVER IN THE BRONX**
Sister Sadie / Home cookin' / Senor blues / Preacher / Peace / Sayonara blues / Que pasa / Mexican hip dance / Silver's serenade / Filthy McNasty
CDSJP 445 / 27 Jul '98 / Timeless

Bronzemen

☐ **RADIO TRANSCRIPTIONS 1939**
DOCD 5501 / Nov '96 / Document

Brood

☐ **HITSVILLE**
IDI 2330CD / Sep '95 / Dionysus

Brook Brothers

☐ **BROOK BROTHERS, THE**
REP 4096 / Aug '91 / Repertoire

Brook, Michael

☐ **ALBINO ALLIGATOR**
Arrival / Doggie dog / Slow town / Preparation / Miscalculation / Aftermath / Tunnel / Albo gator / Promise / City / Kicker / Exit / Ill wind (you're blowing me no good)
GAD 7003CD / 6 Jul '98 / 4AD

☐ **COBALT BLUE**
Shona bridge / Breakdown / Red shift / Skip wave / Slipstream / Andean / Slow breakdown / Ultramarine / Urbana / Lakbossa / Ten / Hawaii
GAD 2007CD / 6 Jul '98 / 4AD

☐ **SHONA**
SINE 002 / Sep '95 / Sine

Brooker, Gary

☐ **NO MORE FEAR OF FLYING**
No more fear of flying / Say it ain't so Joe / Pilot / Savannah / Angelina / Give me something to remember you by / Let me in / Old Manhattan melodies / Get up and dance / Fat cats / SS (self sufficient) blues / Switchboard Susan
REP 4659 / Sep '97 / Repertoire

☐ **WITHIN OUR HOUSE (Brooker, Gary Ensemble)**
REP 4660 / Sep '97 / Repertoire

Brooklyn Allstars

☐ **BEST OF THE BROOKLYN ALLSTARS, THE**
NASH 4504 / Feb '96 / Nashboro

Brooklyn Bounce

☐ **BEGINNING**
8212437782 / 17 Mar '98 / Edeltone

Brooklyn Funk Essentials

☐ **COOL, STEADY & EASY**
Take the L train (to Brooklyn) / Creator has a master plan / Revolution was postponed because of rain / Brooklyn recycles / Madame Zzaj / Headnaddas journey to the planet Addiskizm / Big apple boogaloo / Blow your brains out / Stickman crossing the Broklyn bridge / Dilly dally / Take the L train (to 8 ave)
DOR 22CD / Jun '94 / Dorado

Brookmeyer, Bob

☐ **BOB BROOKMEYER & FRIENDS (Brookmeyer, Bob & Stan Getz)**
Jive hoot / Misty / Wrinkle / Bracket / Skylark / Sometime ago / I've grown accustomed to her face / Who cares
468413 2 / Nov '93 / Columbia

☐ **BOB BROOKMEYER WITH STOCKHOLM JAZZ ORCHESTRA (Brookmeyer, Bob & Stockholm Jazz Orchestra)**
Cats / Lies / Tick tock / Dreams / Missing work / Ceremony
DRCD 169 / Sep '89 / Dragon

☐ **OLD FRIENDS (Brookmeyer, Bob Quartet)**
Stella by starlight / Polka dots and moonbeams / Who cares / All blues
STCD 8292 / Jun '98 / Storyville

☐ **OUT OF THIS WORLD (Brookmeyer, Bob & Netherlands Metropole Orchestra)**
369132 / 3 Aug '98 / Koch

☐ **PARIS SUITE (Brookmeyer, Bob New Quartet)**
CHR 70026 / Sep '95 / Challenge

☐ **TRADITIONALISM REVISITED**
Louisiana / Santa Claus blues / Truckin' / Some sweet day / Sweet like this / Jada / Don't be that way / Honeysuckle rose / Slow freight / Sheik of Araby
4948472 / 20 Jul '98 / Pacific Jazz

Brooks & Dunn

☐ **BORDERLINE**
My Maria / Man this lonely / Why would I say goodbye / Mama don't get dressed up for nothing / I am that man / More than a Margarita / Redneck / Rhythm and blues / My love will follow you / One heartache at a time / Tequila town / White line Casanova
07822188102 / Apr '96 / Arista

☐ **GREATEST HITS COLLECTION**
My Maria / Honky tonk truth / You're gonna miss me when I'm gone / Boot scootin' boogie / He's got you / Hard workin' man / That ain't no way to go / Rock my world (little country girl) / Neon moon / Lost and found / She's not the cheatin' kind / Brand new man / Days of thunder / We'll burn that bridge / She used to be mine / Mama don't get dressed up for nothing / My next broken heart / Whiskey under the bridge / Little Miss Honky Tonk
7822188522 / 6 Oct '97 / Arista

☐ **IF YOU SEE HER**
How long gone / I can't get over you / South of Santa Fe / If you see him / If you see her / Brand new whiskey / Born and raised in black and white / Your love don't take a back seat to nothing / Husbands and wives / Way gone / When love dies / You're my angel
07822188652 / 8 Jun '98 / Arista

☐ **WAITIN' ON SUNDOWN**
Little Miss Honky Tonk / She's not the cheatin' kind / Silver and gold / I'll never forgive my heart / You're gonna miss me when I'm gone / My kind of crazy / Whiskey under the bridge / If that's the way you want it / She's the kind of trouble / Good few rides away
7822187652 / Jun '97 / RCA

Brooks, Bernard

☐ **CHEERS**
Away in a manger/The miner's dream of home / Does Santa Claus sleep with his whiskers/Jingle bells / Little boy that Santa Claus forgot/I saw mommy kissing / I'll be home for christmas-white christmas (foxtrot) / Winter wonderland-a broken doll (cha cha) / Blame it on the bossa nova / Fly me to the moon-blame it on the bossanova (reprise)(boss
DLD 1017 / Jul '93 / Dance & Listen

☐ **MOVING ON**
DLD 1060 / Dec '95 / Dance & Listen

☐ **SWING AND SWAY VOL.1**
Little old lady-'a' your adorable (blues) / Oh, donna clara-strangers in the night (tango) / Alone-echo of a serenade (tango) / My own-I'll take you home again kathleen (rumba) / Memories of you-I'm getting sentimental over you (rumba) / In a little spanish town-stars fell on alabama (cha cha) / Red roses for a blue lady-dream (cha cha) / Rose in a garden of weeds-mem'ries live longer than drea / Last waltz of the evening-who's taking you home tonight (w / Amy-wheezy anna (quickstep) / Goodbye blues-harlem (quickstep) / Without you-yours (rumba) / Only forever-amapola (rumba) / Harbour lights-tell me I'm forgiven (tango) / Tangerine-marta (tango) / Oh buddy I'm in love-just an echo in the valley (blues) / If I knew you were comin' I'd baked a cake-ja-da (blues) / Johnson rag (swing) / Deep in the heart of texas-ilkley moor baht'at (swing)
DLD 1005 / '92 / Dance & Listen

☐ **SWING AND SWAY VOL.10**
King's horses-it's a hap hap happy day (swing) / Apple for the teacher-that's my weakness now (s / I'll walk alone-blueberry hill (foxtrot) / I'll string along with you-if you could care (foxt / Walkin' my baby back home-please don't talk about / Honey (I'm in love with you)-'ida' (sweet as apple / Remember me-sleepy time gal (saunter) / Moonlight and roses-it had to be you (saunter) / From rags to riches-you always hurt the one you lo / Into each life some rain must fall-arrivederci rom / Where the blue of the night meets the gold of the day / I'll always be in love with you-falling in love ag / It's a lovely day tomorrow-jealous (quickstep) / Cuddle up a little closer lovey mine-orange colour
DLD 1024 / '92 / Dance & Listen

☐ **SWING AND SWAY VOL.11**
All of me / Some of these days / Beautiful dreamer / Ramona / Love letters in the sand / 'Deed I do
DLD 1026 / May '92 / Dance & Listen

☐ **SWING AND SWAY VOL.12**
That certain party/When you're smiling / If I had a talking picture of you/Clementine / King of the road/ The man who comes around / On mother Kelly's doorstep/Underneath the arches / Babette/ Charmaine / Dancing with tears in my eyes/I love you truly / Stars will remember / Hernando's hideaway / My melancholy baby/Taking a chance on love / Just walking in the rain/On a slow boat to China / There's a boy coming home on leave/Blue skies/Playmates / Rose Rose I love you/Nursie nursie / Always in my hair/There will never be another you / Stranger on the shore/More than ever / It's the talk of the town/ Dance of the hours / Just walking in the rain/Singin' in the rain / Jingle jangle jingle/Who's been polishing the sun / I wonder where my baby is tonight / Silver wings/You always hurt the one you love / You, you, you/Too young / Snowbird/Don't sweetheart me / I'm thinking tonight of my blue eyes / Beautiful Ohio/ The shadow waltz / Just for a while/Santa Lucia
DLCD 1029 / Jul '92 / Dance & Listen

☐ **SWING AND SWAY VOL.16**
My foolish heart-embraceable you (rumba) / Love letters (straight from the heart)-you call it madness / Pennsylvania polka-over there (swing) / She's too fat for me-yes my darling daughter (swing) / My buddy-until tomorrow (saunter) / Stage door canteen (i left my heart at the..)-whispering gr / Just for fun-I'm forever blowing bubbles (cha cha) / Beautiful ohio-kiss me honey honey kiss me (cha cha) / Dear hearts and gentle people-mountain greenery (quickstep) / One alone / Riding down the sunset trail-roll along covered wagon roll / Down every street-why do I love you (blues) / Sleepy lagoon-where the waters are blue (waltz) / Softly, softly (come to me)-you are everywhere (waltz) / If I had you (foxtrot) / I know why and so do you-dearly beloved (foxtrot) / Best things in life are free-who (stole my heart away) / Sometimes I'm happy-sarawaki (quickstep) / Dreamy melody-home on the range (waltz) / Blue tahitian moon-it's time to say goodnight (waltz)
DLD 1039 / Jul '93 / Dance & Listen

☐ **SWING AND SWAY VOL.2**
DLD 1007 / '92 / Dance & Listen

☐ **SWING AND SWAY VOL.3**
Rose Marie / Only a rose / At the Balalaika / Blue tango / Don't get around much anymore / Makin' whoopee / Sunny side of the street / It's magic / Maybe / Sierra Sue / Marie Elena / I'm in the mood for love / Just one more chance / Carolina in the morning / You're driving me crazy / So what's new / 12th Street rag / Charleston / Are you lonesome tonight / Wonderful one / When you and I were seventeen / I wonder who's kissing her now / Carolina moon / Alice blue gown / You are my sunshine / Baby face / My blue heaven / Yes sir that's my baby / Sugartime / I'm looking over a four leaf clover / Oh what it seemed to be / Where are you / Please be kind / Music maestro please / Oh my papa / I wish you love / My special angel / Moving south
DLD 1008 / '92 / Dance & Listen

☐ **SWING AND SWAY VOL.4**
DLD 1011 / '92 / Dance & Listen

☐ **SWING AND SWAY VOL.5**
Sally-tenderley (waltz) / Sally-tenderly (waltz) / Object of my affection-seems like old times (foxtrot) / Object of my affection-seems like old times (f / Wishing (will make it so)-the lady is a tramp (quickstep) / Wishing (will make it so)-the lady is a tramp (quickstep) (2 / Shy serenade-coronation street (theme) (gavotte) / Woman in love-the very thought of you (tango) / Does your heart beat for me-yesterday (rumba) / La cumparsita (tango) / Does your heart belong to me-yesterday (rumba) / There's a kind of hush (rumba) / Let's do it-show me the way to go home (cha cha) / There's a kind of hush (rumba) / Shy serenade-coronation street (theme) (gavotte) / Oh carol-blue moon (cha cha) / Spanish eyes-jealousy (tango) / September song-september in the rain (tango) / Moonglow-love is here to stay (rumba) / Crazy rhythm-pistol packin' mama (swing) / Mack the knife-scotland the brave (swing)
DLD 1012 / Dec '92 / Dance & Listen

☐ **SWING AND SWAY VOL.6**
Bless you, make believe-when day is done (saunter) / I can't begin to tell you-you're my everything (foxtrot) / Let's do it-show me the way to go home (cha cha) / Oh carol-blue moon (cha cha) / Spanish eyes-jealousy (tango) / September song-september in the rain (tango) / Moonglow-our love is here to stay (rumba) / Crazy rhythm-pistol packin' mama (swing) / Mack the knife-scotland the brave (swing)
DLD 1015 / '92 / Dance & Listen

☐ **SWING AND SWAY VOL.7**
Red sails in the sunset-you belong to me / It's now or never / When you wore a tulip and I wore a red red rose-you are my / Whiffenpoof song-it happened in monterey / Yellow bird-time on my hands / How wonderful to know-i just called to say I love you / P.s. I love you-sunday morning / Don't bring lulu-chinatown, my chinatown / Whistling rufus-I've got sixpence / At the jazz band ball-tiger rag / Tropical magic-and I love you so / Perhaps, perhaps, perhaps-once in a while / Wouldn't it be lovely-yes we have no bananas / Tea for two-i was kaiser bill's batman / We just couldn't say goodbye-i won't tell a soul / Gypsy-goodnight sweetheart
DLD 1018 / '92 / Dance & Listen

☐ **SWING AND SWAY VOL.8**
Ain't she sweet-bye bye blues (quickstep) / Sweet georgia brown-when the saints go marching in (quickst / I don't want to set the world on fire-georgia on my mind / In the chapel in the moonlight-shoe-shine boy (cha cha) / Little lady make believe-lights out (foxtrot) / I found a million dollar baby-near you (foxtrot) / Oh what it seemed to be-where are you (foxtrot) / Woman in love-the very thought of you (tango) / La cumparsita (tango) / Play to me gypsy-isle of capri (tango) / Green eyes-lady of spain (tango) / Please be kind-music maestro please (foxtrot) / I can't begin to tell you-you're my everything (foxtrot) / Sunny side of the street-it's magic (cha cha) / Don't get around much anymore-makin' whoopee (cha cha) / Scatter brain-winter wonderland (blues)
DLD 1021 / '92 / Dance & Listen

☐ **SWING AND SWAY VOL.9**
DLD 1022 / '92 / Dance & Listen

Brooks, Big Leon

☐ **LET'S GO TO TOWN**
CD 4931 / Feb '95 / Earwig

Brooks, David 'Bubba'

☐ **BIG SOUND OF BUBBA BROOKS, THE**
Blues for Tina / Mood indigo / Robin's nest / Willow weep for me / Harvard blues / Pocket corner / Body and soul / I let a song out of my heart / Moon river
501395 / Jun '96 / Claves

☐ **SMOOTH SAILING**
Cotton tail / Stella by starlight / Pennies from heaven / Old folks / Prelude to a kiss / In a mellow tone / Billies bounce / Stardust / Smooth sailing
TCB 97702 / 23 Mar '98 / TCB

Brooks, E.

☐ **TWIN TOWERS (Brooks, E. & E. Brooks Jr.)**
GSCD 2411 / 9 Feb '98 / Strakers

Brooks, Elkie

☐ **AMAZING (Brooks, Elkie & The Royal Philharmonic Orchestra)**
Nights in white satin / One more heartache / Our love / Lilac wine / From the heart / Paint your pretty picture / Gasoline alley / Minutes / Will you write me a song / Don't cry out loud / Growing tired / 'Round midnight / It all comes back on you / We've got tonight / Off the beaten track / No more the fool / Only women bleed
3036000282 / Apr '96 / Carlton

☐ **BEST OF ELKIE BROOKS, THE**
Pearl's a singer / Sunshine after the rain / Don't cry out loud / Nights in white satin / Gasoline alley / I guess that's why they call it the blues / Growing tired / Ain't misbehavin' / Goin' back / Fool if you think it's over / Our love / Only love can break your heart / Runaway / Money / If you leave me now / Blue moon / Minutes / Lilac wine
5513292 / Aug '98 / Spectrum

☐ **BOOKBINDER'S KID**
Sail on / Stairway to heaven / You ain't leavin' / Keep it a secret / When the hero walks alone / What's the matter baby / Can't wait all night / Kiss me for the last time / Love is love / Foolish games / Only love will set you free / I can dream, can't I
CLACD 327 / May '93 / Castle

☐ **CIRCLES**
INDELCD 5 / 27 Apr '98 / Indelible

☐ **EVENING WITH ELKIE BROOKS, AN**
ARTFULCD 8 / 18 Aug '97 / Artful

☐ **GOLD AND BLUES**
No more the fool / Only women bleed / We've got tonight / Only love will set you free / I ain't got nothing but the blues / I'd rather go blind / Trouble in mind / Please send me someone to love / Stairway to heaven / Blues for mama / Tell me more and more and then some / Nobody but you / Baby what you want me to do / Can't wait all night / I can dream can't I / Break the chain
SELCD 507 / Mar '98 / Castle Select

☐ **NO MORE THE FOOL**
No more the fool / Only women bleed / Blue jay / Break the chain / We've got tonight
CLACD 326 / May '93 / Castle

☐ **NOTHIN' BUT THE BLUES**
I ain't got nothin' but the blues / Baby get lost / Blues for Mama / Baby what do you want me to do / Tell me more then some / I'd rather go blind / I wonder who / Ain't no use / Nobody but you / I love your lovin' ways / Bad bad whiskey / Fine and mellow / Me and my gin / Mean and evil / Trouble in mind / Please send me someone to love
ESMCD 402 / Jan '97 / Essential

☐ **PEARLS**
Superstar / Fool (if you think it's over) / Giving it up for your love / Sunshine after the rain / Warm and tender love / Lilac wine / Pearl's a singer / Don't cry out loud / Too busy thinking about my baby / If you leave me now / Paint your pretty picture / Dance away
CDA 20116 / Apr '84 / A&M

☐ **PEARLS VOL.2**
Goin' back / Our love / Gasoline Alley / I just can't go on / Too much between us / Giving us hope / Money / Nights in white satin / Loving arms / Will you write me a song
5500602 / Jun '93 / Spectrum

☐ **PEARLS VOL.3**
MER 007 / Mar '93 / Tring

☐ **PEARLS/TWO DAYS AWAY (2CD Set)**
CDA 24122 / Jan '92 / A&M

☐ **ROUND MIDNIGHT**
'Round midnight / Cry me a river / Just for a thrill / Travelling light / Don't explain / Rainy day / All night long / What kind of man are you
CLACD 403 / '95 / Castle

☐ VERY BEST OF ELKIE BROOKS, THE
Pearl's a singer / No more the fool / Don't cry out loud / Fool if you think it's over / I just can't go on / Sunshine after the rain / I guess that's why they call it the blues / Nights in white satin / Only love can break your heart / Ain't misbehavin' / Lilac wine / Blue moon / If you leave me now / Goin' back / Gassoline alley / We've got tonight / Our love / Loving arms / Runaway / Growing tired
5407122 / 6 Apr '98 / PolyGram TV

☐ WE'VE GOT TONIGHT
TRTCD 200 / Jun '95 / TrueTrax

☐ WE'VE GOT TONIGHT
PLSCD 159 / Apr '97 / Pulse

Brooks, Ernie

☐ FALLING, THEY GET YOU
422501 / Nov '94 / New Rose

Brooks, Garth

☐ BEYOND THE SEASON
Go tell it on the mountain / God rest ye merry gentlemen / Old man's back in town / Gift / Unto you this night / White Christmas / Friendly beasts / Santa looks a lot like Daddy / Silent night / Mary's dream / What child is this
CDP 7987422 / Nov '97 / Liberty

☐ CHASE, THE
That summer / Somewhere other than the night / Face to face / Every now and then / Mr. Right / Learning to live again / Walkin' after midnight / Dixie chicken / Night rider's lament
CDESTU 2184 / Sep '92 / Liberty

☐ FRESH HORSES
Old stuff / Cowboys and angels / Fever / That ol' wind / Rollin' / Change / Beaches of Cheyenne / It's midnight Cinderella / She's every woman / Ireland
CDGB 1 / Nov '95 / Capitol

☐ HITS
Ain't going down (til the sun comes up) / Friends in low places / Burning bridges / Callin' Baton Rouge / River / Much too young (to feel this damn old) / Thunder rolls / American Honky-Tonk Bar Association / If tomorrow never comes / Unanswered prayers / Standing outside the fire / Rodeo / What she's doing now / We shall be free / Papa loved Mama / Shameless / Two of a kind, workin' on a full house / That summer / Red strokes / Dance
CDEST 2247 / Dec '94 / EMI

☐ IN PIECES
Standing outside / Night I called the old man out / American honky-tonk bar association / One night a day / Kickin' and screamin' / Ain't going down (til the sun comes up) / Red strokes / Callin' baton rouge / Night will only know / Cowboy song / Fire
CDEST 2212 / Aug '93 / Liberty

☐ NO FENCES
If tomorrow never comes / Not counting you / Much too young (to feel this damn old) / Dance / Thunder rolls / New way to fly / Two of a kind, workin' on a full house / Victim of the game / Friends in low places / Wild horses / Unanswered prayers / Same old story / Mr. Blue / Wolves
CDEST 2136 / Nov '90 / Capitol

☐ ROPIN' THE WIND
Against the grain / Rodeo / What she's doing now / Burning bridges / Papa loved Mama / Shameless / Cold shoulder / We bury the hatchet / In lonesome dove / River / Alabama clay / Everytime that it rains / Nobody gets off in this town / Cowboy Bill
CDESTU 2162 / Jan '92 / Capitol

☐ SEVENS
Longneck bottle / How you ever gonna know / She's gonna make it / I don't have to wonder / Two pina coladas / Cowboy cadillac / Fit for a king / Do what you gotta do / You move me / In another's eyes / When there's no one around / Friend to me / Take the keys to my heart / Belleau wood
8565992 / 1 Dec '97 / Capitol

Brooks, Hadda

☐ ANYTIME, ANYPLACE, ANYWHERE
Anytime anyplace anywhere / That's my desire / Don't go to strangers / Don't you think I ought to know / Man with the horn / But not for me / Rain sometime / Heart of a clown / Ol' man river / Dream / Foggy day / Trust in me / Please be kind/I'm blue / Stolen love / All of me
DRGCD 91423 / Sep '94 / DRG

☐ ROMANCE IN THE DARK
Variety bounce / That's my desire / Romance in the dark / Bully wully boogie / Out of the blue / Honey, honey, honey / Keep your hand on your heart / Bewildered / Jukebox boogie / Trust in me / Don't take your love from me / Schubert's serenade in boogie / Tough on my heart / When a woman cries / Say it with a kiss / I've got my love to keep me warm / I feel so good / It all depends on you / Don't call it love / Honky tonk boogie / Don't you think I ought to know / You won't let me go / Tootsie timesie
CDCHD 453 / Jun '93 / Ace

☐ TIME WAS WHEN
Time was when / My romance / You won't let me go / I must have that man / I'm a fool to want you / I feel so good / Miss Brown to you / Can you look me in the eye / You go your way and I'll go crazy / Close your eyes (and I'll be there) / Thrill is gone / Mama's blues / How do you speak to an angel / I hadn't anyone till you / I need a little sugar in my bowl
VPBCD 30 / Feb '96 / Pointblank

Brooks, Lonnie

☐ BAYOU LIGHTNING
Voodoo daddy / Figure head / Watchdog / Breakfast in bed / Worked up woman / Alimony / Watch what you got / I ain't superstitious / You know what my body needs / In the dark
ALCD 4717 / May '93 / Alligator

☐ DELUXE EDITION
Jealous man / Something you got / Temporary insanity / End of the rope / Don't take advantage of me / You know what my body needs / In the dark / Hoodoo she do / Figurehead / One more shot / Cold lonely nights / Zydeco / Family rules / Roll of the tumbling dice / Like father, like son
ALCD 5602 / 6 Oct '97 / Alligator

☐ HOT SHOT
Don't take advantage of me / Wrong number / Messed up again / Family rules / Back trail / I want all my money back / Mr. hot shot / One more shot
ALCD 4731 / May '93 / Alligator

☐ LET'S TALK IT OVER
DD 660 / Jan '94 / Delmark

☐ LIVE FROM CHICAGO
Two headed man / Trading post / In the dark / Got me by the tail / One more shot / Born with the blues / Eyeballin' / Cold lonely nights / Hideaway
ALCD 4759 / May '93 / Alligator

☐ ROADHOUSE BLUES
ALCD 4843 / Aug '96 / Alligator

☐ SATISFACTION GUARANTEED
Temporary insanity / Man's gotta do / Feast or famine / Lyin' time / Little RR and CB / Wife for tonight / Family curse / Horoscope / Like Father, like son / Holding on to the memories / Accident / Price is right
ALCD 4799 / May '93 / Alligator

☐ SWEET HOME CHICAGO
BLE 595542 / Apr '91 / Black & Blue

☐ TURN ON THE NIGHT
Eyeballin' / Inflation / Teenage boogie man / Heavy traffic / I'll take care of you / TV mama / Mother nature / Don't go to sleep on me / Something you got / Zydeco
ALCD 4721 / May '93 / Alligator

☐ WOUND UP TIGHT
Got lucky last night / Jealous man / Belly rubbin' music / Bewitched, bothered and bewildered / End of the rope / Wound up tight / Boomerang / Musta' been dreaming / Skid row / Hush mouth money
ALCD 4751 / May '93 / Alligator

Brooks, Meredith

☐ BLURRING THE EDGES
I need / Bitch / Watched you fall / Pollyanne / Shatter / My little town / What would happen / It don't get better / Birthday / Stop / Wash my hands
CDEST 2298 / Aug '97 / Parlophone

Brooks, Paul

☐ HOOKED ON CHRISTMAS
Walking in the air / Frosty the snowman / Blue Christmas / Silver bells / Go tell it on the mountain / Do they know it's Christmas / Sleigh ride / Jingle bells / Away in a manger / O come all ye faithful (adeste fidelis) / We three Kings / Holly and the ivy / While shepherds watched their flocks / Little drummer boy / Christmas song / I wish it could be Christmas every day / Jingle bell rock / Last Christmas / I believe in Father Christmas / Have yourself a merry little Christmas / Silent night / White Christmas / We wish you a merry Christmas / Deck the halls / God rest ye merry gentlemen / Merry Christmas everyone / Hark the herald angels sing / Twelve days of Christmas / Good King Wenceslas / Ding dong merrily on high / First Noel / Winter wonderland / Mary's boy child / Do you hear what I hear / Rudolf the red nosed reindeer / O little town of Bethlehem / Scarlet ribbons / Rockin' around the Christmas tree / Rock 'n' roll Christmas / Christmas alphabet / Santa Claus is coming to town / Mistletoe and wine / When a child is born / I saw three ships
ECD 3235 / Jun '97 / K-Tel

☐ HOOKED ON THE 20TH CENTURY
ECD 3427 / 6 Jul '98 / K-Tel

☐ HOOKED ON THE USA
Tara's theme / Oh Susannah / Swanee River / When Johnny comes marching home / Shenandoah / Camptown races / Beautiful dreamer / Dixie / Some folks / Battle hymn of the republic / Swing low, sweet chariot
ECD 3312 / Mar '97 / K-Tel

☐ PIANO MOODS (18 Romantic Instrumentals)
How deep is your love / Free as a bird / Jesus to a child / Living years / Exhale / Lifted / Take a bow / Heaven for everyone / My old piano / Earth song / Piano in the dark / Jealous guy / Smoke gets in your eyes / Fever / Don't give up / I am blessed / If you don't know me by now / Search for a hero
ECD 3280 / Jan '97 / K-Tel

☐ SAX SEDUCTION (18 Sensual Instrumentals)
Killing me softly with his song / Je t'aime / Move closer / Lovin' you / Sexual healing / Love letters / Have I told you lately / One more night / How deep is your love / Fever / Private dancer / First time ever I saw your face / When a man loves a woman / Touch me in the morning / Summer (the first time) / Way you look tonight / Where is the love / Make it with you
ECD 3303 / Feb '97 / K-Tel

☐ SOUL OF SPAIN, THE
La paloma / Spanish Harlem / Chiquitita / Spanish eyes / In a little Spanish town / Man without love / Spanish flea / Maria Elena / Quando, quando, quando / Lady of Spain / Boy from nowhere / Guantanamera / Fernando / Concierto de Aranjuez / Spanish romance / Una paloma blanca / La isla bonita / Granada
ECD 3372 / Jun '97 / K-Tel

Brooks, Randy

☐ RANDY BROOKS 1945-1947 (Brooks, Randy & His Orchestra)
CCD 35 / Mar '95 / Circle

☐ RANDY BROOKS 1945-1947
JH 1049 / Jul '96 / Jazz Hour

Brooks, Terry

☐ RAW POWER (Brooks, Terry & Strange)
AK 004CD / 12 May '98 / Akarma

☐ ROCK THE WORLD
AK 006 / 15 Jun '98 / Akarma

☐ TRANSLUCENT WORLD
AK 001CD / 12 May '98 / Akarma

Brooks, Tina

☐ BACK TO THE TRACKS
Back to the tracks / Street singer / Blues and I / For heaven's sake / Ruby and the pearl
8217372 / 2 Feb '98 / Blue Note

Broom, Bobby

☐ NO HYPE BLUES
CRISS 1109 / Dec '95 / Criss Cross

☐ WAITIN' AND WAITIN'
Without a song / Hot house / Always / End of a love affair / Burt's blues / Speedball / Waitin' and waitin' / Mo'
CRISS 1135CD / Sep '97 / Criss Cross

Broom, Mark

☐ ANGIE IS A SHOPLIFTER
PP 08CD / Oct '96 / Pure Plastic

Broonzy, 'Big' Bill

☐ ALL TIME BLUES CLASSICS
8420292 / Oct '96 / Music Memoria

☐ BIG BILL BROONZY 1935-1940
Southern blues / These ants keep biting me / Married life is a pain / Pneumonia blues (I keep on aching) / Detroit special / Falling rain / Horny frog / Hattie blues / Somebody's got to go / It's your time now / Living on easy street / Baby I done got wise / Just a dream (on my mind) / That's alright baby / IC blues / Cotton choppin' blues / My last goodbye to you / Don't you be no fool / Just a dream / Oh yes / Jivin' Mr. Fuller blues / What is that she got
BLE 592532 / Dec '92 / Black & Blue

☐ BIG BILL BROONZY 1955 LONDON SESSIONS, THE
When do I get to be called a man / Partnership woman / Southbound train / St. Louis blues / Minding my own business / It feels so good / Saturday evening / Glory of love / Southern saga inc Joe Turner blues / In the evening / Going down this road feeling bad
NEXCD 119 / Apr '90 / Sequel

☐ BIG BILL BROONZY VOL.10 (1940)
DOCD 5132 / Oct '92 / Document

☐ BIG BILL BROONZY VOL.12 (1945-1947)
BDCD 6047 / Sep '94 / Blues Document

☐ BIG BILL BROONZY VOL.4 (1935-1936)
DOCD 5126 / Oct '92 / Document

☐ BIG BILL BROONZY VOL.5 (1936-1937)
DOCD 5127 / Oct '92 / Document

☐ BIG BILL BROONZY VOL.6 (1937)
DOCD 5128 / Oct '92 / Document

☐ BIG BILL BROONZY VOL.7 (1937-1938)
DOCD 5129 / Oct '92 / Document

☐ BIG BILL BROONZY VOL.8 (1938-1939)
DOCD 5130 / Oct '92 / Document

☐ BIG BILL BROONZY VOL.9 (1939)
DOCD 5131 / Oct '92 / Document

☐ BIG BILL'S BLUES
Too too train blues / Mistreatin' mama blues / Bull cow blues / Long tall mama / I'll be back home again / Keep your hands off her / Big Bill blues / I'm a Southern man / Southern flood blues / You do me any old way / New shake 'em on down / Let me dig it / Baby I done got wise / Just a dream / Just got to hold you tight / Oh yes / Looking up at down / You better cut that out / Lonesome road blues / When I had been drinking / All by myself / Night watchman blues / Tell me baby / I'm gonna move to the outskirts of the town
TPZ 1038 / Feb '96 / Topaz Jazz

☐ BLUES, THE (Chicago 1937-1945)(2CD Set)
FA 252 / Feb '96 / Fremeaux

☐ EVENING WITH BIG BILL BROONZY VOL.1 (Club Montmartre, Copenhagen 1956)
STCD 8016 / May '95 / Storyville

☐ EVENING WITH BIG BILL BROONZY VOL.2
STCD 8017 / May '95 / Storyville

☐ HISTORICAL RECORDINGS 1932-1937
157422 / Feb '93 / Blues Collection

☐ HOUSE RENT STOMP
Big Bill blues / Little city woman / Back water blues / Guitar shuffle / Romance without finance / Jacqueline / Lonesome / House rent stomp / Willie Mae blues / Saturday evening blues / Louise Louise blues / Key to the highway / Swing low, sweet chariot / Stump blues / Makin' my getaway / Boogie woogie / CC rider / Going down the road feelin' bad / Plowhand blues / I'm gonna move to the outskirts of town / How long blues
CD 52007 / '92 / Blues Encore

☐ I CAN'T BE SATISFIED
I can't be satisfied / Bull cow blues / Long tall mama / Worrying you off my mind / How you want it done / Too too train blues / Good jelly / Rising sun shine on / Good liquor gonna carry me down / Hattie blues / Horny frog / Friendless blues / Mississippi river blues / Come home early / Big bully blues / It's your time now / Southern flood blues / WPA rag
CBCD 005 / 24 Aug '98 / Collector's Blues

☐ I FEEL SO GOOD
IGOCD 2006 / Nov '94 / Indigo

☐ REMEMBERING BIG BILL BROONZY (The Greatest Minstrel Of The Authentic Blues)
John Henry / Bill Bailey, won't you please come home / Blue tail fly / Leroy Carr / Trouble in mind blues / Stump blues / Get back / Willie Mae / Hey hey / Tomorrow / Walkin' down a lonesome road
BGOCD 91 / Dec '90 / Beat Goes On

☐ SINGS FOLK SONGS
SFWCD 40023 / Mar '95 / Smithsonian Folkways

☐ SOUTHERN BLUES (Charly Blues Masterworks Vol.49)
Southern blues / These ants keep biting me / Pneumonia blues (i keep on aching) / Detroit special / Horny frog / Hattie blues / Somebody's got to go / It's your time now / Living on easy street / Baby I done got wise / Just a dream (on my mind) / It's alright baby / I.c. blues / Cotton choppin' blues / My last goodbye to you / Midnight steppers / Hit the right lick / That number of mine / Rocking chair blues / Bad acting women
CDBM 49 / Jun '93 / Charly

☐ STAYIN' HOME WITH THE BLUES
I love my whiskey / You've been mistreating me / Five feet seven / I wonder / Keep your hands off her / Hey hey / Stump blues / Get back (black brown and white) / Willie Mae / Mopper's blues / I know she will / Hollerin' the blues / Southbound train / Tomorrow / You changed / John Henry / Make me getaway / In the evening
5379452 / Oct '97 / Spectrum

☐ TREAT ME RIGHT
TCD 1005 / Feb '96 / Tradition

☐ WARM WITTY AND WISE
I can't be satisfied / Long tall mama / Worrying you off my mind / Too too train blues / How do you want it done / C & A blues / Southern flood / It's a low down dirty shame / Trucking little woman / Night time is the right time / New shake 'em on down / Baby I done got wise / Just a dream / Whiskey & good time blues / Too many drivers / Horny frog / Spreaden' snakes blues / Messed up in love / Getting older every day / All by myself / In the army now
4898932 / 20 Jul '98 / Sony Blues

☐ YOUNG BIG BILL BROONZY 1928-1935
YAZCD 1011 / Jun '91 / Yazoo

Bros

☐ INTERVIEW COMPACT DISC: BROS
CBAK 4017 / Nov '89 / Baktabak

Brosnan, John

☐ COOK IN THE KITCHEN, THE
JB 01CD / Nov '96 / JB

Brostrom, Hakan

☐ CELESTIAL NIGHTS
DRCD 257 / Oct '94 / Dragon

☐ DARK LIGHT
DRAGON 190 / May '89 / Dragon

Brother Boys

☐ BROTHERS BOYS
Wanna wanna wanna / Blue from now on / Diamond stream / Majestic / Loose talk / First time / (you've got the look of a) perfect diamond / Tango till you're sore / Two men / Blue days black nights / Town that never sleeps / My shoes keep walking back to you / Black fifty ford / Nickel plate road / I'm no longer in your heart / Jordan am a hard road to travel / Small southern town / Everybody wants to go to heaven
NHD 1101 / Aug '90 / Zu Zazz

☐ PLOW
Gonna row my boat / I got over the blues / Kiss the dream girl / Alone with you / Twist you up / Then and only then / Hoping that you're hoping / I see love / Blue guitar / Little box / Darkest day / Satellite shack / What will be in the fields tomorrow
SHCD 3805 / Jul '92 / Sugar Hill

☐ PRESLEY'S GROCERY
SHCD 3844 / Oct '95 / Sugar Hill

Brother Cane

☐ SEEDS
Horses and needles / Hung on a rope / Fools shine on / Kerosene / Breadmaker / Rise on water / 20/20 Faith / Bad seeds / Stain / Intempted / Voice of Eujena / High speed freezin'
CDVUS 95 / Mar '96 / Virgin

Brother Desmond

☐ ME AND MI BIBLE
RDRCD 4001 / 15 Dec '97 / Record Factory

Brother JT

☐ COME ON DOWN
DFR 35 / 20 Oct '97 / Drunken Fish

☐ DOOMSDAY ROCK (Brother JT & Vibrolux)
SB 65CD / May '97 / Siltbreeze

☐ MUSIC FOR THE OTHER HEAD (Brother JT & Vibrolux)
Comet / Music for the other head / Blur / Mind (Rot)
SB 41 / Feb '97 / Siltbreeze

☐ RAINY DAY FUN
DFR 030 / Dec '96 / Drunken Fish

Brother Love

☐ ROCK 'N' ROLL CRIMINAL
SGCD 12 / Sep '97 / September Gurls

Brother Most

☐ MOOD & INTENSITY
Red rover parts 1 and 2 / Dead man walking / Dreamscape / Wasn't in the plan / Ready / Bunga nattural
GRS 45012 / May '96 / Ichiban

Brother Orchid

☐ WINTERSHADOW
NIGHTCD 022 / 17 Aug '98 / Nightbreed

Brother Russell

☐ FILLED
V 132 / 20 Apr '98 / Vinyl Communication

☐ PRESENTS MELBA COMES ALIVE
VC 123CD / Oct '97 / Vinyl Communication

Brother Weasel

☐ SWINGIN' N GROOVIN'
SST 365CD / 3 Aug '98 / SST

Brotherhood

☐ ELEMENTALZ
One 3 / Alphabetical response / Nothing in particular / Mad headz / On the move / Goin' undaground / Punk funk / You gotta life / One shot / Incredible / Clunk click / Nominate / Dark stalkers / British accent / Pride (revisited)
CDBHOOD 1 / Feb '96 / Bite It

☐ XXIII
CDBITE 7 / Aug '93 / Bite It

Brotherhood Of Breath

☐ LIVE AT WILLISAU
OGCD 001 / Sep '94 / Ogun

Brotherhood Of Man

☐ 20 GREAT HITS
Save you kisses for me / United we stand / Angelo / My sweet rosalie / When will I see you again / We don't talk anymore / Chanson d'amour / Bright eyes / Together we are beautiful / Dancing queen / Figaro (mozart) / Oh boy (the mood I'm in) / Middle of the night / Where are you going to my love / Beautiful lover / How deep is your love / When I need you / Sailing / Without you / Don't go breaking my heart
CDPT 817 / May '96 / Prestige

☐ BEST OF BROTHERHOOD OF MAN (16 Super Hits)
Save your kisses for me / United we stand / Angelo / Where are you going / How deep is your love / Dancing queen / Together we're beautiful / When will I see you again / Singing in the rain / Catch me catch me if you can / My sweet rosalie / Bright eyes / Blame it on the boogie / Ring my bell / Use it up and wear it out / Tragedy
12210 / May '94 / Laserlight

☐ UNITED WE STAND
8206232 / Jan '96 / Deram

☐ VERY BEST OF THE BROTHERHOOD OF MAN
Save your kisses for me / United we stand / Angelo / My sweet Rosalie / When will I see you again / We don't talk anymore / Cahnson d'amour / Bright eyes / Together we are beautiful / Dancing queen / Figaro / Oh boy (the mood I'm in) / Middle of the night / Where are you going to my love / Beautiful lover / How deep is your love / When I need you / Sailing / Without you / Don't go breaking my heart
EMPRCD 654 / Jun '96 / Emporio

Brother's Keeper

☐ CONTINUUM
WN 1147CD / Sep '96 / We Bite

Brothers Brooks

☐ BROTHERS BROOKS, THE
DOS 7011 / Dec '94 / Dos

Brothers Creeggan

☐ BROTHERS CREEGGAN VOL.1
77752113222 / 21 Apr '98 / FTCH

☐ BROTHERS CREEGGAN VOL.2
77752111872 / 21 Apr '98 / FTCH

Brothers Johnson

☐ AIN'T WE FUNKIN' NOW
VSOPCD 229 / Jun '96 / Connoisseur Collection

☐ BEST OF BROTHERS JOHNSON, THE
I'll be good to you / Free and single / Land of ladies / Get the funk out ma face / Tomorrow / Runnin' for your lovin' / Strawberry letter 23 / Right on time / Q / Blam / Ain't we funkin' now / Light up the night / Stomp / Treasure / Real thing / You keep me comin' back / I'm giving you all my love / Kick it to the curb
5543632 / 4 May '98 / Spectrum

Brotzmann, Caspar

☐ HOME
BFFP 110CD / Jan '95 / Blast First

☐ KOKSOFEN
ABBCD 052 / Aug '95 / Big Cat

☐ TRIBE, THE
ZSCM 08 / Jul '92 / Special Delivery

☐ ZULU TIME
BFFP 129CD / Jul '96 / Blast First

Brotzmann, Peter

☐ DARE DEVIL
DIW 857 / May '92 / DIW

☐ EXHILARATION (Brotzmann, Peter & Borah Bergman/Andrew Cyrille)
1213302 / Sep '97 / Soul Note

☐ LOW LIFE (Brotzmann, Peter & Bill Laswell)
Death rattle / Low life / Disengage / Locomotive / Barrier / Wheeling vultures / Curved dog / Abasement / Land one / Tingle hairs / Last detective
CDGR 209 / 2 Feb '98 / Charly

☐ SPREADING BLUSHES OR ACCELERATING ORIGINAL SIN (Brotzmann, Peter & Keiji Haino)
PSFD 79 / Oct '96 / PSF

☐ WELS CONCERT, THE (Brotzmann, Peter & Hamid Drake/Mahmoud Gania)
OD 12013 / Jan '98 / Okka Disk

Brou, Roland

☐ CHANTS AND COMPLAINTS DE HAUTE BRETAGNE
RS 220 / May '96 / Keltia Musique

☐ TROIS GARCONS DU LION D'OR
RSCD 220 / Jul '96 / Keltia Musique

Broughton, Ben

☐ CONTINUING ADVENTURES OF... (Broughton, Ben & Joe)
101REC 5CD / Dec '96 / 101

Broughton, Edgar

☐ BANDAGES (Broughton, Edgar Band)
REP 4201 / Aug '91 / Repertoire
CLACD 261 / Jun '92 / Castle

☐ EDGAR BROUGHTON BAND/IN SIDE OUT (Broughton, Edgar Band)
Evening over rooftops / Birth / Piece of my mind / Poppy / Don't even know what day it is / House of turnabout / Madhatter / Getting hard / What is a woman for / Thinking of you / For Dr Spock (part one) / For Dr Spock (Part two) / Get out of bed / There's nobody there / Side by side / Sister Angela / I got mad / They took it away / Homes fit for heroes / Gone blue / Chilly morning mamma / Rake / Totin this guitar / Double agent / It's not you / Rock 'n' roll
BGOCD 179 / Mar '93 / Beat Goes On

☐ LIVE HITS HARDER (Broughton, Edgar Band)
0884948906 / Dec '95 / CTE

☐ OORAH (Broughton, Edgar Band)
Hurricane man-rock 'n' roller / Roccocococooler / Eviction / Oh you crazy boy / Things on my mind / Exhibits from a new museum-green lights / Capers
BGOCD 114 / Sep '91 / Beat Goes On

☐ SING BROTHER SING (Broughton, Edgar Band)
There's no vibrations but wait / Moth / People / Peter (nelson) / Momma's reward (keep them freaks a-rollin') / Refugee / Office dan / Old gopher / Aphrodite / Granma / Psychopath the psychopath, is for butterflies / It's falling away
BGOCD 7 / Feb '92 / Beat Goes On

☐ SUPERCHIP...PLUS (Broughton, Edgar Band)
Metal Sunday / Superchip / Who only fade away / Curtain / Outrageous behaviour / Not so funny farm / Night hogs / Pratfall / Overdose / Do you wanna be immortal / Subway information / Last electioneer / Ancient homeland / Innocent bystanders / Fourteen the virus
SEECD 464 / Oct '96 / See For Miles

☐ WASA WASA (Broughton, Edgar Band)
Death of an electric citizen / American boy soldier / Why can't somebody love me / Neptune / Evil / Crying / Love in the rain / Dawn crept away
BGOCD 129 / Feb '92 / Beat Goes On

Broussard, Donny

☐ UNDER THE LOUISIANA MOON
Under the Louisianna moon / Raised like a cajun / Mom and Pop spoke only in French / With her heart / Open the door / Mom, the prettiest rose / Waltz of poor parents / House dance / Music in French / Bayou vermilion / Tears fall like rain
SOC 90252 / Jul '96 / Cajun Sound

Brown & Black

☐ BROWN, BLACK AND BLUE
VP 162CD / Nov '96 / Voiceprint

Brown

☐ BROWN
RI 036 / May '96 / Rather Interesting

Brown, Alison

☐ OUT OF THE BLUE (Brown, Alison Quartet)
742482 / 16 Mar '98 / Charly

Brown, Angela

☐ ANGELA BROWN LIVE
BEST 1038CD / Nov '93 / Acoustic Music

☐ BREATH TAKING BOOGIE SHAKING (Brown, Angela & A. Humphrey/C. Christl)
BEST 1004CD / Nov '93 / Acoustic Music

☐ WILD TURKEY (Brown, Angela & C. Christl)
BEST 1017CD / Nov '93 / Acoustic Music

Brown, Ari

☐ ULTIMATE FRONTIER
Big V / Lester Bowie's gumbo stew / One for Luba / Meeting time / Ultimate frontier / Sincerity / Motherless child
DE 486 / Jun '97 / Delmark

Brown, Arthur

☐ CHISHOLM IN MY BOSOM/DANCE
Need to know / Money walk / Let a little sunshine (into your life) / I put a spell on you / She's on my mind / Lord is my saviour / Chisholm in my bosom / We gotta get out of this place / Helen with the sun / Take a chance / Crazy / Hearts and minds / Dance / Out of time / Quietely with tact / Soul garden / Lord will find a way / Is there nothing beyond God
SEECD 431 / Aug '95 / See For Miles

☐ CRAZY WORLD OF ARTHUR BROWN, THE
Nightmare / Fanfare - fire poem / Fire / Come and buy / Time / I put a spell on you / Spontaneous apple creation / Rest cure / I've got money / Child of my kingdom
8337362 / Feb '91 / Polydor

☐ CRAZY WORLD OF ARTHUR BROWN, THE
TWCD 2012 / Nov '97 / Touch Wood

☐ GALACTIC ZOO DOSSIER (Kingdom Come)
Internal messenger / Space plucks / Galactic zoo / Metal monster / Simple man / Night of the pigs / Sunrise / Trouble / Brains / Galactic zoo / Space plucks / Galactic zoo / Creep / Creation / Gypsy escape / No time
BP 135CD / Nov '96 / Blueprint

☐ JAM (Kingdom Come)
BP 163CD / Jun '97 / Blueprint

☐ JOURNEY (Kingdom Come)
Time captives / Triangles / Gypsy / Superficial roadblocks / Conception / Spirit of joy / Come alive
BP 137CD / Mar '97 / Blueprint

☐ KINGDOM COME (Kingdom Come)
Teacher / Scientific experiment / Whirl pool / Hymn / Water / City melody / Traffic light song
BP 136CD / Aug '96 / Blueprint

☐ ORDER FROM CHAOS
When you open the door / When you open the door / King of England / Juices of love / Nightmare / Fire poem / Fire / Come and buy / Pick it up y'all / Mandela / Time captains / I put a spell on you
BP 144CD / Sep '96 / Blueprint

☐ REQUIEM
Chant / Shades / Animal people / Spirits take flight / Gabriel / Requiem / Machanicla masseur / Busha-busha / Fire ant and the cockroaches / Tear down the wall / Santa put a spell on me / Pale stars / Chromatic alley / Falling up
VP 125 CD / Feb '93 / Voiceprint

☐ SPEAK NO TECH
King of England / Conversations / Strange romance / Not fade away / Morning was cold / Speak no tech / Names are names / Love lady / Big guns don't die / Take a picture / You don't know / Old friend my colleage / Lost my soul in London / Joined forever / Mandala / Desert floor
VPCD 124 CD / Feb '93 / Voiceprint

☐ STRANGELANDS, THE
CDRECK 2 / Jun '88 / Reckless

Brown, Arthur

☐ MARYLAND TO MOSCOW (Brown, Arthur Jazz Band)
RSCD 653 / Sep '96 / Raymer

Brown, Barry

☐ FAR EAST
JJCD 30 / 17 Aug '98 / Channel One

☐ LOVE AND PROTECTION
CDSGP 0182 / Sep '96 / Prestige

Brown, Bessie

☐ BESSIE BROWN 1925-1929/LIZA BROWN 1929 (Brown, Bessie & Liza Brown)
DOCD 5456 / Jun '96 / Document

Brown, Bobby

☐ BOBBY
Humpin' around / Humpin' around / Two can play that game / Get away / Till the end of time / Good enough / Pretty little girl / Lovin' you down / One more night / Something in common / That's the way love is / College girl / Storm away / I'm your friend / Humpin' around / Humpin' around
MCLD 19300 / 22 Sep '97 / MCA

☐ DON'T BE CRUEL
Don't be cruel / My prerogative / Roni / Rock wit'cha / Every little step / I'll be good to you / All day, all night / Take it slow
MCLD 19212 / Aug '93 / MCA

☐ DON'T BE CRUEL/BOBBY (2CD Set)
Don't be cruel / My perogative / Roni / Rock witcha / Every little step / I'll be good to you / All day, all night / Take it slow / Humpin' around / Two can play that game / Get away / Til the end of time / Good enough / Pretty little girl / Lovin' you down / One more night / Something in common / That's the way love is / College girl / Storm away / I'm your friend
MCD 33730 / Jul '96 / MCA

☐ FOREVER
MCD 11691 / 27 Oct '97 / MCA

Brown, Bobby

☐ CAPE BRETON FIDDLE COMPANY (Brown, Bobby & Cape Breton Fiddlers)
Selection of reels / Selection of jigs / Clog strathspey and reel / Hornpipe medley / Pastoral strathspey / Polk medley no.2 / March and reel medley / Slow air / Strathspey and reel medley / Clog and hornpipe medley
LCOM 5251 / Feb '96 / Lismor

☐ FOR OLD TYME'S SAKE
BRG 019 / 2 Apr '98 / Bobby Brown

Brown, Bundy

☐ DIRECTIONS IN MUSIC (Brown, Bundy & Doug Scharin/James Warden)
THRILL 033CD / Jul '97 / Thrill Jockey

Brown, Charles

☐ CHARLES BROWN LIVE
Quicksand / Saving my love for you / Seven days long / Just the way you are / Black night / So long / Cottage for sale / Brown's boogie
CDCBL 757 / Oct '95 / Charly

☐ CLASSICS 1944-1945
CLASSICS 894 / Sep '96 / Classics

☐ CLASSICS 1946
CLASSICS 971 / 5 Jan '98 / Classics

☐ COOL CHRISTMAS BLUES
BBCD 9561 / Nov '94 / Bullseye Blues

☐ DRIFTING AND DREAMING (Brown, Charles & Johnny Moore's Three Blazers)
Travellin' blues / I'll get along somehow / Copyright on your love / If you should ever leave / When your lover has gone / Blues because of you / Sail on blues / More than you know / You should show me the way / It had to be you / You are my first love / You won't let me go / Make believe land / So long / Warsaw concerto (part 1) / Warsaw concerto (part 2) / You left me forsaken / How deep is the ocean / Nutmeg / It's the talk of the town / What do you know about love
CDCHD 589 / Jan '96 / Ace

☐ HONEYDRIPPER, THE
5298482 / Apr '96 / Verve

☐ I'M GONNA PUSH ON (Live At Nosebacke) (Brown, Charles & Hjartslag)
Teardrops from my eyes / Black night / Please don't drive me away / Trouble blues / Please come home for Christmas / Just the way you are / Bad bad whiskey / I'm gonna push on / I wanna go back home to Gothenburg / I'll do my best
RBD 200 / Jan '91 / Stockholm

☐ JUST A LUCKY SO 'N' SO
BB 9521CD / Feb '94 / Bullseye Blues

☐ SO GOES LOVE
New Orleans blues / My heart is mended / (Oh oh) what do you know about love / Money's gettin' cheaper / She's gone again / I'll get along somehow / So goes love / Stormy Monday / Sometimes I feel like a motherless child / Ain't no use / You'll never know / Blue because of you
5399672 / 20 Apr '98 / Verve

☐ THESE BLUES
These blues / Honey / May I never love again / I got it bad and that ain't good / Is you is or is you ain't my baby / Hundred years from today / Save your love for me / I did my best for you / Sunday kind of love
5230222 / Oct '94 / Verve

Brown, Clarence

☐ GATE SWINGS (Brown, Clarence 'Gatemouth')
5376172 / Jul '97 / Verve

☐ GATE'S ON THE HEAT (Brown, Clarence 'Gatemouth')
Gate's on the heat / Man and his environment / Funky Mama / Please Mr. Nixon / St. Louis blues / Jelly jelly / Drifter / One mint julep / Dollar got the blues / River's invitation / Never ending love for you / Louisiana breakdown
5197302 / Feb '94 / Verve

☐ LIVE (Brown, Clarence 'Gatemouth')
Pressure cooker / Frosty / Gate's tune / When my blue moon turns to gold again / Louisianne / Up jumped the devil / Dark end of the hallway / Chicken shift / 'a' train / Honeyboy / Boogie woogie on st. louis blues
CDCBL 753 / Jan '95 / Charly

☐ LONG WAY HOME (Brown, Clarence 'Gatemouth')
5294652 / Mar '96 / Verve

☐ MAN, THE (Brown, Clarence 'Gatemouth')
5237612 / Feb '95 / PolyGram Jazz

☐ NO LOOKING BACK (Brown, Clarence 'Gatemouth')
Better off with the blues / Digging new ground / Dope / My own prison / Stop time / C jam blues / Straighten up and fly right / Peeper / Blue gummed catahoula (alligator eating boy) / I will be your friend / We're outta here
ALCD 4804 / May '93 / Alligator

☐ ONE MORE MILE (Brown, Clarence 'Gatemouth')
Information blues / Song for Renee / Stranded / Sunrise cajun style / Big yard / Ain't that dandy / One more mile / Ronettes / Flippin' out / Neat baku
ROUCD 2034 / '88 / Rounder

☐ ORIGINAL PEACOCK RECORDINGS (Brown, Clarence 'Gatemouth')
Midnight hour / Sad hour / Ain't that dandy / That's your daddy yaddy yo / Dirty work at the crossroads / Hurry back good news / Okie dokie stomp / Good looking woman / Gate's salty blues / Just before dawn / Depression blues / For now so long
ROUCD 2039 / '88 / Rounder

☐ PRESSURE COOKER (Brown, Clarence 'Gatemouth')
ALCD 4745 / May '93 / Alligator

☐ REAL LIFE (Brown, Clarence 'Gatemouth')
Real Life / Okie Dokie stomp / Frankie and Johnny / Next time you see me / Take the 'A' train / Please send me someone to love / Catfish / St. Louis blues / What a shame what a shame
ROUCD 2054 / '88 / Rounder

☐ STANDING MY GROUND (Brown, Clarence 'Gatemouth')
Got my mojo working / Born in louisiana / Cool jazz / I hate these doggone blues / She walks right in / Leftover blues / Louisiana zydeco / What am I living for / Never unpack your suitcase
ALCD 4779 / May '93 / Alligator

☐ TEXAS SWING (Brown, Clarence 'Gatemouth')
ROUCD 11527 / '88 / Rounder

Brown, Cleo

☐ LEGENDARY CLEO BROWN, THE
(Lookie lookie) here comes Cookie / You're a heavenly thing / (You take the East, take the West, take the North) I'll take / Stuff is here and it's mellow / Pinetop's boogie woogie / Pelican stomp / Never too tired for love / Give a broken heart a break / Mama don't want no peas an' rice an' coconut oil / Me and my wonderful one / When Hollywood goes black and tan / When / You're my fever / Breakin' in a pair of shoes / Latch on / Love in the first degree / My gal Mezzanine
PLCD 548 / Nov '96 / President

☐ LIVING IN THE AFTERGLOW (Brown, Cleo & Marian McPartland)
ACD 216 / Jun '96 / Audiophile

Brown, Clifford

☐ BEGINNING AND THE END, THE
I come from Jamaica / Ida red / Walkin' / Night in Tunisia / Donna Lee
4777372 / Oct '94 / Columbia

☐ BEST OF CLIFFORD BROWN, THE
Brownie speaks / You go to my head / Get happy / Brownie eyes / Cherokee / Easy living / Hymn of the orient / Joy spring / Daahound / Tiny capers / Weed dot / Once in a while / Night in Tunisia
8233732 / 2 Mar '98 / Blue Note

☐ COMPLETE PARIS SESSIONS VOL.1, THE (Original Vogue Masters)
Brown skins / Deltitnu / Keeping up with Joneses / Conception / All the things you are / I cover the waterfront / Goofin' with me
74321457282 / May '97 / Vogue

☐ COMPLETE PARIS SESSIONS VOL.2, THE
Minority / Salute to the band box / Strictly romantic / Baby / Quick step / Bum's rush / No start, no end
74321457292 / 19 Jan '98 / Vogue

☐ COMPLETE PARIS SESSIONS VOL.3, THE
(Venez donc) Chez moi / All weird / Blue and brown / I can dream, can't I / Song is you / Come rain or come shine / It might as well be spring / You're a lucky guy
74321457302 / 5 May '98 / Vogue

☐ JAZZ MASTERS (Brown, Clifford & Max Roach)
5281092 / 5 May '98 / Verve

☐ ULTIMATE CLIFFORD BROWN, THE
5397762 / 16 Mar '98 / Verve

☐ WITH STRINGS (Remastered)
Yesterdays / Laura / Blue moon / Can't help lovin' dat man / Embraceable you / Willow weep for me / Memories of you / Smoke gets in your eyes / Portrait of Jennie / Where or when / Stardust
5580782 / 26 May '98 / Verve Master Edition

Brown, D.R.

☐ LIVE IN THE MIND'S EYE
BEARD 005CD / Oct '92 / Beard

Brown, Damon

☐ RHYTHM INDICATIVE (Brown, Damon Quintet)
Judy's goat / Minnie the minx / Web / Monkey's dream / Love untold / Blues for JW / Swing features / Don / Rhythm indicative / It hasn't moved / Bye bye blackbird
ZZCD 9806 / 29 Jun '98 / Zah Zah

Brown, Dennis

☐ 20 GOLDEN GREATS
CDSGP 0104 / Oct '94 / Prestige

☐ 20 MAGNIFICENT HITS
DBP 1CD / Jul '93 / Dennis Brown Productions

☐ ANOTHER DAY IN PARADISE
(Sittin' on the) dock of the bay / Last thing on my mind / Just a guy / My girl / Everybody needs love / Ain't that lovin' you / Another day in paradise / Queen Majesty / I'm still waiting / Conversation / Green green grass of home / Girl I got a date
CDTRL 310 / Mar '94 / Trojan

☐ AT THE PENTHOUSE (Brown, Dennis & Leroy Smart)
RN 7024 / Jun '97 / Rhino

☐ BEAUTIFUL MORNING
Beautiful morning / True true true / Waiting for you / My my / Love me tender / Rebel with a cause / Can you dig it / Token for two / Give it up now / Hip hip hooray / Too late / Beautiful dub / True dub / Waiting dub / My dub / Rebel with a dub / Dig it dub / Token for dub / Give it up dub / Hip hip hooray dub
WRCD 002 / Nov '97 / World

☐ BEST OF DENNIS BROWN VOL.1, THE
60042 / Nov '95 / Declic

☐ BEST OF DENNIS BROWN VOL.2, THE
60052 / Nov '95 / Declic

☐ BEST OF DENNIS BROWN, THE
JMGL 6048 / Jan '94 / Joe Gibbs

☐ BLAZING
Moving on / Here we go again / My heart cries for you / Fever / Moonlight / Your mamma / Not another minute / Hello / Never gonna give you up / Those lies / It's impossible / Shepherd be careful / Sherry baby / Hypocrite corner / Warning
GRELCD 171 / May '92 / Greensleeves

☐ BROWN SUGAR
RASCD 3207 / '88 / Ras

☐ CLASSIC HITS
SONCD 0022 / Apr '92 / Sonic Sounds

☐ COSMIC FORCE
HBCD 135 / Apr '93 / Heartbeat

☐ COULD IT BE
VPCD 1478 / May '96 / VP

☐ CROWN PRINCE OF REGGAE
Westbound train / Wolf and leopards / Cassandra / Silhouettes / No more will I roam / Tribulation / Let me down easy / Without you / Rock with me Deborah / Rolling down / Black magic woman / Go now / Melting pot / Song my Mother used to sing / You're no good / How could I let you get away / Love you madly / I didn't know / Only a smile / Africa
CPCD 8187 / Oct '96 / Charly

☐ CROWN PRINCE, THE
Have a heart / Candy girl / Have you ever been in love / Cheri amour / Sunshine of my life / Call me fire / Take me there / Overjoyed / Ababa jahni / See and blind-hear and deaf / Beautiful world / Have a dub / Candy dub / Have you ever been in dub / Cheri dub / Sunshine dub / Fire dub / Take me dub / Over dub / Ababa dub
WRCD 015 / Nov '97 / World

☐ DENNIS BROWN LIVE AT MONTREUX
So jah say / Wolves and leopards / Ain't that lovin' you / Words of wisdom / Drifter / Milk and honey / Yabby you / Don't feel no way / Whip them Jah / Money in my pocket
CDBM 016 / Apr '91 / Blue Moon

☐ FOUL PLAY
JGMLCD 4850 / Jan '94 / Joe Gibbs

☐ FRIENDS FOR LIFE
SHCD 45004 / Jun '93 / Shanachie

☐ GIVE PRAISES
CDTZ 012 / Aug '93 / Tappa

☐ GOOD TONIGHT
If you want me / Without your love / Orders to shoot / This is your night / Take me home / No more walls / Where is the love / Freedom fires / Bubbling sweet tonight / Night like this / Poison
GRELCD 152 / Aug '90 / Greensleeves

☐ GREATEST HITS
Show us the way / Cassandra / Run too tuff / Westbound train / Africa / Love jah / No more will I roam / Some like it hot / Too much information / Here I come again / Silver words / Whip them jah jah / Hot like a melting pot / You and your smiling face
RRTGCD 7709 / '88 / Rohit

☐ HEAVEN
8412952 / May '96 / Declic

☐ HIT AFTER HIT
RGCD 027 / Feb '95 / Rocky One

☐ HOTTER FLAMES (Brown, Dennis & Frankie Paul)
VPCD 1310 / Aug '93 / VP

☐ I DON'T KNOW
DGVCD 1600 / Oct '95 / Dynamite & Grapevine

☐ IF I DIDN'T LOVE
If I didn't love you / Birds have their nest / Long and winding road / Blood sun / Run too late / Only a smile / Silver words / Go now / Home sweet home
JMC 200202 / Dec '92 / Jamaican Gold

☐ IT'S THE RIGHT TIME
Feeling is right / It's all over now / Please love me as do / Good vibrations / Play it everystyle / Be true to yourself / Let me prove myself true / Oh girl / I feel to shout / I need some good loving / You are no good / I have no fear / Give a helping hand / God bless our souls / Stand up for your rights / It's the right time / Travelling man / Joy in the morning
RNCD 2021 / Sep '93 / Rhino

☐ JOSEPH'S COAT OF MANY COLOURS
Slave driver / Open your eyes / Creator / Cup of tea / Together brothers / Oh what a day / Well without water / Three meals a day / Home sweet home / Man next door
CDBM 010 / Nov '88 / Blue Moon

☐ JOY IN THE MORNING
LG 21106 / Mar '95 / Lagoon

☐ JUDGE NOT (Brown, Dennis/Gregory Isaacs)
Crazy list: *Brown, Dennis* / Judge not: *Brown, Dennis* / Deceiving girl: *Brown, Dennis* / Live and love: *Isaacs, Gregory* / Street walker: *Isaacs, Gregory* / Inner city lady: *Isaacs, Gregory*
GRELCD 72 / Sep '88 / Greensleeves

☐ LIGHT MY FIRE
CDHB 154 / May '94 / Heartbeat

☐ LIMITED EDITION
GRELCD 177 / Nov '92 / Greensleeves

☐ LIVE IN MONTEGO BAY
SONCD 0039 / Jan '93 / Sonic Sounds

☐ LIVE IN MONTREUX
SUMCD 4159 / Jan '98 / Summit

☐ LOVE LIGHT
Little bit more / Tribulation / Rocking time / Caress me girl / Love light / Hold on to what you've got / Little village / Have you ever been in love
CDBM 102 / Apr '95 / Blue Moon

☐ LOVER'S PARADISE
CDSGP 068 / Oct '93 / Prestige

☐ MILK AND HONEY
RASCD 3193 / Feb '96 / Ras

☐ MONEY IN MY POCKET
Money in my pocket / Ah so we stay / Changing times / Silhouettes / Africa / Yagga yagga (you'll suffer) / I am the conqueror / Show us the way / Cassandra / No more will I roam
CDTRL 197 / Mar '94 / Trojan

☐ MONEY IN MY POCKET
Money in my pocket / God bless my soul / Hot like a melting pot / If you're rich / My time / No more will I roam / Oh girl / Run too tuff / Some like it hot / Travelling man / Truth and rights / When I am down / Why do fools / You're no good
CD 6105 / Oct '97 / Music

☐ MUSICAL HEATWAVE
Baby don't do it / What about the half / Don't you cry / Cheater / Let love in / Concentration / Silhouettes / He can't spell / Musical heatwave / I don't know / How could I let you get away / Lips of wine / Let me down easy / Changing times / Black magic woman / Money in my pocket / It's too late / Song my mother used to sing / Westbound train / Cassandra / I am the conqueror / No more will I roam / Why seek more / Moving away
CDTRL 327 / Mar '94 / Trojan

☐ MY TIME
Hot like a melting pot / Open the gate / Go now / My time / Traveling man / You're no good / Have no fear / If your rich / God bless my soul / Fight for truths and rights
RRTGCD 7713 / Jan '89 / Rohit

☐ NO CONTEST (Brown, Dennis & Gregory Isaacs)
Easy life / Jealousy / Why cry / Big all around / No camouflage / Neon lights flashing / I'll make it up to you / Love me or leave me / Open up
GRELCD 133 / Jul '89 / Greensleeves

☐ NOTHING LIKE THIS
There's nothing like this / Have you ever been in love / Rock 'n' roll lady / Dance nah keep / Come home / Slave driver / Come let me love you / Street kid / Give love a chance / People of the world / It's not a one man thing
GRELCD 199 / Feb '94 / Greensleeves

☐ ONE OF A KIND
111912 / Mar '94 / Musidisc

☐ OPEN THE GATE (Greatest Hits Vol.2)
Words: *Davis, Anthony 'Sangie' & Lee 'Scratch' Perry* / Vampire: *Irons, Devon & Dr. Alimantado* / Babylon falling: *Heptones* / Babylon falling version: *Upsetters* / Mistry Babylon: *Heptones* / Mistry Babylon version: *Upsetters* / Garden of life: *Sibbles, Leroy* / History: *Jackson, Carlton* / Sons of slaves: *Delgado, Junior* / Open the gate: *Burnett, Watty* / Talk about it: *Diamonds* / Yama-ky: *Upsetters* / Cherry oh baby: *Donaldson, Eric* / Rainy night in Portland: *Burnett, Watty* / Ruffer ruff: *Smart, Horace* / Ruffer dub: *Upsetters* / Neckodeemus: *Congos* / Know love: *Twin Roots* / City too hot: *Perry, Lee 'Scratch'* / Bionic rats: *Perry, Lee 'Scratch'* / Bad weed: *Murvin, Junior*
CDHB 177 / Apr '95 / Heartbeat

☐ OVERPROOF
SHCD 43086 / Jun '91 / Shanachie

☐ PRIME OF DENNIS BROWN, THE
Equal rights / Money in my pocket (12" mix with deejay trinity) / Wolves and leopards / Ain't that lovin' you / Here I come / So jah say / Words of wisdom / Cassandra / Slave driver / Man next door / Concrete castle king / Drifter / Boasting / Jah can do it / Should I / Love me always / Oh mother / Malcolm x
MCCD 118 / Aug '93 / Music Club

☐ RAS PORTRAITS
Milk and honey / Sitting and watching / Should I / Give thanks to the Father / Revolution / Your love / Easy / Sea of love / Victory is mine / Wisdom / Hold on to what you've got
RAS 3322 / Jul '97 / Ras

☐ REGGAE MAX
JSRNCD 11 / Mar '97 / Jet Star

☐ SARGE
JASCD 4 / Mar '97 / Sarge

☐ SATISFACTION FEELING
TRDCD 111586 / 13 Oct '97 / Joe Frazier

☐ SLOW DOWN
Slow down / Woman / Joy in the morning / They fight / Let's build our dreams / Love by the score / Can't keep a good man down / Icy road / Now and forever / Come on over / Africa we want to go
GRELCD 80 / Feb '87 / Greensleeves

☐ SMILE LIKE AN ANGEL
Let me live / Pretend you're happy / Westbound train / Don't expect me to be your friend / Play girl / Smile like an angel / Poorer side of town / We will be free / Summertime / Silver words / My kind / Golden streets
CDBM 034 / Jun '95 / Blue Moon

☐ SO AMAZING (Brown, Dennis & Janet Kay)
CDTRL 315 / Mar '94 / Trojan

☐ SOME LIKE IT HOT
HBCD 107 / Nov '92 / Heartbeat

☐ SONGS OF EMANUEL
SONCD 0082 / Apr '96 / Sonic Sounds

☐ TEMPERATURE RISING
CDTRL 353 / Jun '95 / Trojan

☐ TOGETHER AS ONE
RGCD 043 / Apr '97 / Rocky One

☐ TRACKS OF MY LIFE (2CD Set)
SMDCD 224 / 10 Aug '98 / Snapper

☐ UNCHALLENGED
Let there be light / First impression / Lust for money / One way affair / Those lies / Great kings of africa / Lover's holiday / Price of war / Formula / Mama's love / Why cry / Mend a broken heart
GRELCD 138 / Oct '89 / Greensleeves

☐ UNFORGETTABLE
CRCD 24 / Sep '93 / Charm

☐ VICTORY IS MINE
Victory is mine / Call me / We are in love / Don't give up / Everyday people / Sea of love / Just because / Should I / Jah can do it / Sad news
CDBM 084 / Apr '91 / Blue Moon

☐ VISION OF THE REGGAE KING
GOLDCD 001 / Jun '94 / Goldmine

☐ VISIONS
Deliverance will come / Oh mother / Love me always / Concrete castle king / Malcolm X / Repatriation / Jah can do it / Milk and honey / Stay at home / Say what you say
SHANCD 44002 / Mar '98 / Shanachie

☐ WOLVES AND LEOPARDS
Wolves and leopards / Emanuel / Here I come / Whip them Jah / Created by the Father / Party time / Rolling down / Boasting / Children of Israel / Lately girl
CDBM 046 / Apr '87 / Blue Moon
DBPCD 2 / 27 Oct '97 / Dennis Ting

☐ YOU GOT THE BEST OF ME
SAXCD 004 / Oct '95 / Saxon Studio

Brown, Earl

☐ SYNERGY
ARTCD 6177 / Dec '95 / Hat Art

☐ TWENTY FIVE PAGES
WER 66122 / Jul '97 / Wergo

Brown, Florie

☐ IRISH FIDDLE TUNES
EUCD 1308 / Jul '95 / ARC

Brown, Foxy

☐ ILL NA NA
Intro chicken coop / (Hol matrimony) Letter to the firm / Foxy's bell / Get me home / Promise / Interlude the set up / If I / Chase / Ill na na / No on'es / Fox boogie / I'll be / Outro
5365352 / 29 Sep '97 / Def Jam

Brown, Gabriel

☐ MEAN OLD BLUES 1943-1949
FLYCD 59 / Jun '96 / Flyright

Brown, Gerry

☐ LIVE AT THE EXCISE HOUSE (Brown, Gerry Mission Hall Jazzband)
RSCD 656 / Mar '97 / Raymer

Brown, Gina

☐ IN HIS TIME
Don't think you've arrived / I've fallen in love / You're not my husband / Centred in your love / In his time / Come to Jesus / We need to pray / Seek his face / Forgive / Make up your mind / Choose life / I surrender all
GTD 014127 / 24 Nov '97 / Grapetree

Brown, Glen

☐ CHECK THE WINNER
GRELCD 603 / May '90 / Greensleeves

☐ SENSI DUB VOL.6 (Brown, Glen & Roots Radics)
OMCD 26 / Feb '93 / Original Music

☐ TERMINATION DUB (Glen Brown 1973-1979) (Brown, Glen & King Tubby)
BAFCD 15 / Mar '97 / Blood & Fire

☐ WAY TO MOUNT ZION, THE
RUSCD 8215 / Oct '95 / ROIR

Brown, Greg

☐ 44 AND 66
RHRCD 02 / Oct '96 / Red House

☐ BATH TUB BLUES
RHRCD 42 / Oct '96 / Red House

☐ DOWN IN THERE
RHRCD 35 / Oct '96 / Red House

☐ FURTHER IN
RHRCD 88 / Oct '96 / Red House
8425802 / Apr '97 / Sky Ranch

☐ IN THE DARK WITH YOU
RHRCD 08 / Oct '96 / Red House

☐ IOWA WALTZ, THE
RHRCD 01 / Oct '95 / Red House

☐ LIVE ONE, THE
RHRCD 78 / Dec '95 / Red House

☐ ONE BIG TOWN
RHRCD 28 / Oct '96 / Red House

☐ ONE MORE GOODNIGHT KISS
RHRCD 23 / Oct '96 / Red House

☐ POET GAME, THE
RHRCD 68 / May '95 / Red House
8401422 / Sep '96 / Sky Ranch

☐ SLANT 6 MIND
RCHD 98 / Nov '97 / Red House

☐ SONGS OF INNOCENCE AND EXPERIENCE
RHRCD 14 / Oct '96 / Red House

Brown, Herschel

☐ COMPLETE HERSCHEL BROWN 1928-1929, THE
DOCD 8001 / Jan '97 / Document

Brown, Horace

☐ HORACE BROWN
Why why why / How can we stop: *Brown, Horace & Faith Evans* / Things we do for love / I want your baby / One for the money / Taste your love / Trippin' / I like / Just let me know / Gotta find a way / You need a man / Enjoy
5306942 / Jun '96 / Motown

Brown, Hylo

☐ HYLO BROWN 1954-1960 (2CD Set) (Brown, Hylo & The Timberliners)
Flower blooming in the wildwood / Put my little shoes away / Blue eyed darling / Will the angels play their harps for me / Old home town / Love and wealth / I'll be all smiles tonight / Gathering flowers from the hillside / Little Joe / Darling Nellie across the sea / When it's lamplighting time in the valley / Why do you weep dear willow / Test of love / Dark as a dungeon / Lost to a stranger / Sweethearts or strangers / In the clay beneath the tomb / Wrong kind of life / I'll be broken hearted / Let's stop fooling our hearts / Lovesick and sorrow / Get lost, you wolf / One sided love affair / Only one / Prisoner's song / Nobody's darlin' but mine / One way train / Foolish pride / John Henry / There's more pretty girls than one / Stone wall (around my heart) / Shuffle of my feet / Your crazy heart / You can't relive the past / I've waited as long as i can / It's all over but the crying / Thunder clouds of love / Just any old love / Darlin' how can you forget so soon / Sweethearts and strangers: *Brown, Hylo & The Jordanaires*
BCD 15572 / Mar '92 / Bear Family

Brown, Ian

☐ UNFINISHED MONKEY BUSINESS
Under the paving stones:The beach / My star / Can't see me / Ice cold cube / Sunshine / Lions / Corpses in their mouth / What happened to ya / Nah nah / Deep pile dreams / Unfinished monkey business
5395652 / 2 Feb '98 / Polydor

Brown, James

☐ 40TH ANNIVERSARY COLLECTION, THE (2CD Set)
5358882 / Aug '98 / Polydor

☐ BEST OF JAMES BROWN, THE
MACCD 228 / Aug '96 / Autograph

☐ COLD SWEAT
Give it up or turn it loose / Too funky in here / Gonna have a funky good time / Try me / Get on the good foot / Get up offa that thing / Georgia on my mind / Hot pants / I got the feelin' / It's a man's man's man's world / Cold sweat / I can't stand it / Papa's got a brand new bag / I feel good / Please please please / Jam
HADCD 164 / May '94 / Javelin

☐ COLD SWEAT (The Best Of James Brown Live)
Introduction/Give it up or turn it loose / It's too funky here / Doing it to death / Try me / Get on the good foot / Get up offa that thing / Georgia on my mind / Hot pants / I got the feelin' / It's a man's man's man's world / Cold sweat / I can't stand myself (when you touch me) / Papa's got a brand new bag / I got you (I feel good) / Please, please, please / Jam
305802 / Oct '96 / Hallmark

☐ COLLECTION, THE
Sex machine / Hot pants / I got the feeling / It's a man's man's man's world / Cold sweat / I can't stand it / Papa's got a brand new bag / I feel good (i got you) / Please please please / Jam (1980) / Give it up, turn it loose / It's too funky in here / Gonna have a funky good time / Try me / Get on the good foot / Get up offa that thing / Georgia on my mind / Right time (the night time is the right time) / For your precious love / Tennesse waltz
COL 003 / Mar '95 / Collection

☐ EARLY STUDIO HITS (2CD Set)
Bells / I don't mind / Just you and me darling / Lost someone / I love you yes I do / Come over here / Dancin' little thing / I do just what I want / So long / Tell me what you're gonna do / Love don't love nobody / You don't have to go / Papa's got a brand new pig bag / Sex machine / Bodyheat / Gonna have a funky good time / Give it up, or turn it loose / It's too funky in here / Doing it to death / Try me / Get on the good foot / Get up offa that thing / Georgia on my mind / Hot pants / I got the feelin / It's a man's man's man's world / Cold sweat / I can't stand myself (when you touch me) / I got you (I feel good) / Please please please / I am
DBG 53045 / May '96 / Double Gold

☐ FUNKY GOODTIME (Live In Atlanta 1984)
It's a man's man's man's world / Super bad / Disco rap / Turn it loose (Give it up) / It's too funky in here / Gonna have a funky good time / Try me / I got the feeling / Get on the good foot / Prisoner of love / Get up offa that thing / Georgia on my mind / Cold sweat / When you touch me (I can't stand myself) / Papa's got a brand new bag / I got you (I feel good)
PLATCD 153 / Mar '96 / Platinum

☐ FUNKY MEN
Rapp payback (Where iz Moses) / Honky tonk / Rock groove machine / Way to get down / Mashed potatoes / Funky men / Smokin' and drinkin' / Bessie / JB's wedge / Just wanna make you dance / Headquarters / Back from the dead / JB's internationals / Stay with me / Rapp payback (Where iz Moses)
DC 882832 / 2 Feb '98 / Disky

☐ FUNKY PRESIDENT (The Very Best Of James Brown Vol.2)
Funky President / Try me / My thang / Body heat / Talkin' loud and sayin' nothing / There was a time / Doing it to death / Payback / Soul power / I got the feeling / Honky tonk / Get up, get into it and get involved / I got ants in my pants / Funky drummer / It's a new day
5198542 / Mar '96 / Polydor

☐ GODFATHER OF SOUL, THE
It's a man's man's man's world / Papa's got a brand new bag / Nature boy / Think / Signed, sealed, delivered (I'm yours) / Please please please / How do you stop / Call me super bad / Spinning wheel / Mona Lisa / This old heart / Good good lovin' / Bewildered / (Get up I feel like being a) sex machine
5500402 / May '93 / Spectrum

☐ GODFATHER OF SOUL, THE
It's a man's man's man's world / Super bad / Disco rap / Turn it loose (give it up) / It's too funky in here / Gonna have a funky good time / Try me / I got the feelin' / Get on the good foot / Prisoner of love / Get up offa that thing / Georgia on my mind
MUCD 9009 / Apr '95 / Musketeer

☐ GODFATHER RETURNS, THE
Get up offa that thing / Hey America / Stormy Monday / Body heat / For once in my life / What the world needs now is love / Back stabbin' / Hot pants / Stagger Lee / Need your love so bad / Woman / Never can say goodbye / Time after time / Georgia on my mind
5501992 / Sep '94 / Spectrum

☐ GOLD COLLECTION, THE (2CD Set)
R2CD 4055 / 13 Apr '98 / Deja Vu

☐ I FEEL GOOD
It's a man's man's man's world / Papa's got a brand new bag / Nature boy / Think / Signed sealed and delivered / Please please please / How do you stop / Super bad / Spinning wheel / Mona Lisa / This old heart / Good good lovin' / Bewildered / Sex machine / Need your love so bad / Time after time / I got you / Hold it
5521032 / Apr '97 / Spectrum

☐ IN THE JUNGLE GROOVE
It's a new day / Funky drummer / Give it up or turn it loose(remix) / I got to move / Talking loud and saying nothing(remix) / Get up, get into it and get involved / Soul power (re-edit) / Hot pants
8296242 / May '88 / Urban

☐ JAMES BROWN AT STUDIO 54
Gonna have a funky good time / Get up offa that thing / Body heat / (Get on up I feel like being a) Sex machine / Try me / Papa's got a brand new bag / Get on the good foot / Medley / Medley
CPCD 8031 / Jan '95 / Charly

☐ JAMES BROWN LIVE
Give it up or turn it loose / It's a man's man's man's world / I got the feelin' / I can't stand it / Hot pants / Try me / I feel good today / Get up offa that thing / Please please please / Jam / Cold sweat / Georgia on my mind / It's too funky in here / Gonna have a funky good time / Get on the good foot / (Get up I feel like being a) sex machine
15136 / Jun '93 / Laserlight

☐ JAMES BROWN LIVE (The Godfather Of Soul & Funk)
IMT 100099 / Sep '96 / Scratch

☐ JAMES BROWN LIVE
Give it up, turn it loose / Too funky in here / Gonna have a funky good time / Try me / Get on the good foot / Get up offa that thing / Hot pants / I got the feeling / It's a man's man's man's world / Cold sweat / I can't stand it / Papa's got a brand new bag / I feel good / Please please please / Jam
SUMCD 4027 / Nov '96 / Summit

☐ LIVE AT THE APOLLO VOL.1
Intro/Opening fanfare / Try me / I don't mind / Lost someone / Night train / I'll go crazy / Think / Medley / Outro/Closing fanfare
8434792 / Jul '90 / Polydor

☐ LIVE IN CONCERT
Give it up or turn it loose / It's too funky in here / Doing it to death (gonna have a funky good time) / Try me / Get on the good foot / Prisoner of love / Get up offa that thing / Georgia on my mind / I got the feelin' / It's a man's man's man's world / Super bad / Disco rap / Cold sweat / I can't stand myself (when you touch me) / Papa's got a brand new bag / I got you (I feel good)
QED 028 / Nov '96 / Tring

☐ MASTER SERIES
Get up (I feel like being a) sex machine / Papa's got a brand new bag / Get up offa that thing / Honky tonk / Keep keepin' / I'll go crazy / It's a man's man's man's world / Hot pants (she got to use what she got to get what she wants / Brother rapp / Eyesight / I can't help it (I just do-do-do) / I never never never will forget / She's the one / Bodyheat / Regrets / I don't want nobody to give me nothing (open up the door I'll get it myself) / Stone cold drag / Mother Popcorn (you got to have a mother for me)
5551432 / 23 Mar '98 / Polydor

☐ MASTERS, THE (2CD Set)
EDMCD 017 / 24 Nov '97 / Eagle

☐ ON STAGE (2CD Set)
Gonna have a funky good time (doing it to death) / Get up offa that thing / Body heat / Sex machine / Try me / Papa's got a brand new bag / Get on the good foot / Medley / I got the feeling / Cold sweat / Please, please, please / Jam / Medley / Introduction/Give it up or turn it loose / It's too funky in here / Doing it to death / Try me / Get on the good foot / Get up offa that thing / Georgia on my mind / Hot pants / I got the feelin' / It's a man's man's man's world / Cold sweat / I can't stand myself (when you touch me) / Papa's got a brand new bag / I got you (I feel good) / Please, please, please / Jam
CPCD 82562 / Nov '96 / Charly

☐ SEX MACHINE (The Very Best Of James Brown Vol.1)
Please please please / Think / Night train / Out of sight / Papa's got a brand new bag (part 1) / I got you (I feel good) / It's a man's man's man's world / Cold sweat / Say it loud, I'm black and I'm proud / Hey America / Make it funky / (Get up I feel like being a) sex machine / I'm a greedy man / Get on the good foot / Get up offa that thing / It's too funky in here / Livin' in America / I'm real / Hot pants / Soul power
8458282 / Nov '91 / Polydor

☐ SLAUGHTER'S BIG RIP OFF (Original Soundtrack)
Slaughter theme / Tryin' to get over / Transmografication / Happy for the poor / Brother rap / Big strong / Really really really / Sexy sexy sexy / To my brother / How long can I keep it up / Peole get up and drive your funky soul / King slaughter / Straight ahead
3145171362 / Aug '96 / Polydor

☐ SOUL JUBILEE (Live At Chastain Park/ 25th Anniversary Concert) (Brown, James & The Soul G's)
Give it up or turn it loose / It's too funky in here / Try me / Get on the good foot / Get up offa that thing / Georgia on my mind / Hot pants / I got the feelin' / It's a man's man's world / Cold sweat / I can't stand myself (when you touch me) / Papa's got a brand new bag / I got you (I feel good) / Please please please / Jam
CDBM 081 / Apr '90 / Blue Moon

☐ SUPER BAD AT 65 (A Tribute To James Brown) (Various Artists)
Mother Popcorn (you gotta have a mother for me): *Black, Frank* / I can't stand myself (when you touch me): *Whitley, Chris* / It's a man's man's man's world: *Mercury Rev* / In the middle: *Taylor, James Quartet* / I'll go crazy: *World Famous Blue Jays* / People wake up and live: *Fleming, Don* / Get up (I feel like being a) sex machine: *Q-Burns Abstract Message* / Ain't that a groove: *Shear, Jules* / Hot pants: *Scarnella* / Don't be a dropout: *Fleshtones* / Whole world needs liberation: *McDermott, Chris* / Please please please: *Sex Mob* / King Heroin: *Doublespeak* / Call me super bad: *Little Sammy D* / Shhhhhhh (for a little while): *Broke Dick Dog*
ZERCD 1220 / 8 Jun '98 / Zero Hour

☐ TELL ME WHAT YOU'RE GONNA DO (Brown, James & The Famous Flames)
Just you and me darling / I love you, yes I do / I don't mind / Come over here / Bells / Love don't love nobody / Dancin' little thing / Lost someone / And I do just what I want / So long / You don't have to go / Tell me what you're gonna do
CPCD 8053 / Mar '95 / Charly
EMBCD 3357 / 2 Feb '98 / Ember

Brown, Jeri

☐ APRIL IN PARIS
Gentle piece / Once upon a summertime / Twelfth of never / When April comes again / Who can I turn to / Morning lovely / I could have loved you / Summertime / Poem - as the mist leaves no scar / Greensleeves / Windmills of your mind
JUST 922 / Feb '97 / Justin Time

☐ FRESH START
Come, come play with me / Wandering love / Nothing else but you / Fresh start / Moment I look at you / Bohemia after dark / Moonray / You're a joy / Vision is the key / Orange sky / Shall we gather at the river / Fresh start (reprise)
JUST 782 / May '96 / Justin Time

☐ UNFOLDING - THE PEACOCKS
JUST 452 / Apr '93 / Justin Time

☐ ZAIUS
Oo-shoo-be-doo-be / Creator has a master plan / Be natural / Sun song / Ungle from Ghana / Be mine / Zaius / Medley
JUST 1172 / 27 Jul '98 / Justin Time

Brown, Jim

☐ BACK TO THE COUNTRY (Brown, Jimmy & Willy Lee Harris)
TCD 5013 / Dec '94 / Testament

Brown, Jocelyn

☐ ABSOLUTELY
Mindbuster / Freedom / Somebody else's guy / Absolutely / Reach out / I want to know what love is / Turn out the lights / This love is true / Everyday / Feel like makin' love / Many rivers to cross / No excuse
BR 1402 / Mar '95 / BR Music

Brown, Joe

☐ JOE BROWN STORY, THE (Brown, Joe & The Bruvvers)
People gotta talk / Comes the day / Savage / At the Darktown strutter's ball / Swagger / Jellied eels / Shine / Switch / Crazy mixed up kid / I'm Henery the Eighth (I am) / Good luck and goodbye / Popcorn / Picture of you / Layabout's lament / Talking guitar / Lonely Island pearl / Your tender look / Other side of town / It only took a minute / All things bright and beautiful / That's what love will do / What's the name of the game / Casting my spell / What a crazy world we're living in / Hava Nagila / You can't lie to a liar / Sweet little sixteen / Nature's time for love / Spanish bit / Sally Ann / There's only one of you / Walkin' tall / Hercules unchained / You do things to me / Everybody calls me Joe / Don't / Just like that / Teardrops in the rain / Lonely Circus / Sicilian tarantella / Sea of heartbreak / Mrs. O's theme / Little ray of sunshine / Your loving touch / Satisfied mind / Th' wife / Rich man's son and the poor man's daughter / With a little help from my friends / Show me around
NEDCD 235 / Oct '93 / Sequel

☐ LIVE AND IN THE STUDIO
Hallelujah I love her so / Some of these days / Girls, girls, girls / El relicario / Old apache squaw / Castin' my spell / What a crazy world / Alley oop / Have nagila (the hora) / Sheik of araby / You can't lie to a liar / Sweet little sixteen / All things bright and beautiful / That's what love will do / Spanish bit / Nature's time for love / It only took a minute / A picture of you / A lay about's lament / Other side of town / Sally ann / Sea of heartbreak / Charlie girl / I'm henry the eigth I am / Everybody calls me joe
C5MCD 612 / Jun '94 / See For Miles

☐ ON STAGE
It'll be me / Shine / That's what love will do / All things bright and beautiful / Get rhythm / Is a bluebird blue / Sea of heartbreak / Dragonfly / You can't lie to a liar / Henry VIII / Picture of you / That'l be the day / Hava nagila / Battle of New Orleans
JETCD 1002 / Feb '98 / Jet

☐ PICTURE OF YOU, A
Picture of you / That's what love will do / It only took a minute / Sea of heartbreak / English country garden / Shine / With a little help from my friends / Alley oops (live) / Little ray of sunshine / What a crazy world we're livin' in (live) / Sweet little sixteen (live) / Hallelujah I love her so (live) / I'm Henry the eighth I am / Just like that / My favourite occupation / Hava nagila (the hora) / All things bright and beautiful / Nature's time for love
5507592 / Apr '95 / Spectrum

Brown, Junior

☐ SEMI-CRAZY
CURCD 025 / May '96 / Curb

Brown, Kevin

☐ ROAD DREAMS
Diamond ring / Harder you love / Five seconds to go / I still love you / Put a smile on your face / Just a valley away / Some people / I should have known better / Talk to me / Farther along / Juke box queen / I wish the world
HNCD 1340 / May '88 / Hannibal

☐ RUST
Don't quit / Hey Joe Louis / Write a bible of your own / Telephone tears / We'll be with you / If I had my way / You don't have to tell me / Southern Streets / Meltdown / Sunny side up
HNCD 1344 / May '89 / Hannibal

Brown, Lee

☐ LEE BROWN 1937-1940 (Piano Blues Rarities)
DOCD 5344 / May '95 / Document

Brown, Les

☐ 22 ORIGINAL BIG BAND RECORDINGS
Picolino / Frenesl / September song / I've got my love to keep me warm / Where are you / How about you / Ridin' high / Pink coats / Love me or leave me / Swingin' at the met / Harlem nocturne / Sentimental journey / Speak low / Countin' the blues / Boy next door / Moonglow / I never knew / Whatever lola wants / At sundown / Begin the beguine / Back in your own backyard / Rain
HCD 408 / Sep '92 / Hindsight

☐ BIG BAND CLASSICS (Brown, Les & Billy May)
ISCD 129 / Jul '93 / Intersound

☐ DIGITAL SWING (Brown, Les & His Band Of Renown)
How high the moon / I can't get started (with you) / Blue skies / For all we know / What is this thing called love / Just friends / Perky / One more blues / St. Louis blues / Come rain or come shine / Misty / You're nobody 'til somebody loves you / Yo Henry
FCD 9650 / Apr '94 / Fantasy

☐ ELITCH GARDENS, DENVER 1959 VOL.1
DSTS 1002 / ' / Status

☐ ELITCH GARDENS, DENVER 1959 VOL.2 (Brown, Les & His Band Of Renown)
DSTS 1006 / Feb '95 / Status

☐ GREAT LES BROWN, THE
Piccolino / I've got my love to keep me warm / How about you / Ridin' high / Frenesl / September song / Harlem nocturne / Love me or leave me / Moonglow / Speak low / Begin the beguine / Sentimenal journey
HCD 330 / May '95 / Hindsight

☐ HEATWAVE (Brown, Les & His Band Of Renown)
DAWE 54 / Nov '93 / Magic

☐ LES BROWN & JOHNNY MERCER/ MARGARET WHITING
DAWE 68 / Apr '94 / Magic

☐ LES BROWN AND HIS BAND OF RENOWN (Brown, Les & His Band Of Renown)
Opening theme / Sunday blues / This October / September in the rain / Tall boy / My baby just cares for me / September song / Love me or leave me / Sentimental journey / Oh baby / I'll remember April / Midnight sun / Lullaby in rhythm / Willow weep for me / I'll take romance / It don't mean a thing (if it ain't got that swing) / This year's crop of kisses / Don't take your love from me / Closing theme
HCD 252 / May '94 / Hindsight

☐ LES BROWN AND HIS GREAT VOCALISTS
Robin Hood / Lament to love / I guess I'll have to dream the rest / Good man is hard to find / I got it bad and that ain't good / 'Tis autumn / Sentimental journey / Sleigh ride in July / My dreams are getting better all the time / Day by day / I guess I'll get the papers and go home / OH how I miss you tonight / Comes the sandman (a lullaby) / Just a gigolo / Crosstown trolley / Rock me to sleep
CK 66373 / Jul '95 / Columbia

☐ LES BROWN AND THE DUKE (Brown, Les & Duke Ellington)
House hop / There's frost on the moon / Dancing with a debutante / Wang wang blues / Go feather your nest / I'm coming virginia / Rigamarole / Big apple / Let 'er go / Alligator crawl / Dance of the blue devils / Swanee river / 52nd street fever
15760 / Apr '94 / Laserlight

☐ RIDIN' HIGH
BMCD 3058 / Apr '97 / Blue Moon

Brown, Lloyd

☐ STRAIGHT NO CHASER
CRDCD 002 / Jul '96 / Groove & A Quarter

Brown, Marion

☐ AFTERNOON OF A GEORGIA FAUN
5277102 / Jul '96 / ECM

☐ BACK TO PARIS
FRLCD 002 / Oct '92 / Freelance

☐ PORTO NOVO
Similar limits / Sound and structure / Improvisation / Qbic / Porto novo / And then they danced / Rhythmus
BLCD 760200 / Apr '95 / Black Lion

Brown, Marty

☐ HERE'S TO THE HONKY TONKS
HCD 8075 / Oct '96 / Hightone

Brown, Maxine

☐ OH NO NOT MY BABY
Since I found you / Gotta find a way / I wonder what my baby's doing tonight / Let me give you my lovin' / It's torture / One in a million / Oh no not my baby / You're in love / Anything for a laugh / Coming back to you / Yesterday's kisses / Ask me / All in my mind / Little girl lost / I want a guarantee / Secret of livin' / Baby cakes / One step at a time / I've got a lot of love left in me / I don't need anything / Oh Lord what are you doing to me / I cry alone / Funny / Misty morning eyes / Love that man / Losing my touch / Put yourself in my place / It's gonna be alright
CDKEND 949 / Oct '90 / Kent

Brown, Nappy

☐ AW, SHUCKS
You know it ain't right / Let love take care (of the rest) / Aw shucks baby / Still holding on / It's not what you do / Mind your own business / True love / Chickadee / Night time (live jam version)
ICH 9006CD / Jun '94 / Ichiban

☐ BEST OF BOTH WORLDS, THE (All New Rockin' Blues) (Brown, Nappy & Kip Anderson)
Rocket 88 / Drinkin' wine spo-dee-o-dee / It should've been me / (Night time) is the right time / Down in the bottom / Knife and a fork / Big foot man / Don't be angry / When you're ugly like me / Who threw the whiskey in the well / Hit the road Jack / You never had it so good
WESF 104 / 19 Jan '98 / Westside

☐ BLACK TOP BLUES-A-RAMA VOL.2 (Live At Tipitina's)
CD 1045 / '88 / Black Top

☐ DON'T BE ANGRY
Is it true / That man / Ronettes / Two faced woman / Just a little love / It's really you / Don't be angry / Land I love / I'm in the mood / Open up that door / I want to live / Skiddy woe / I'm getting lonesome / I cried like a baby / Little by little
SV 0259 / Oct '97 / Savoy Jazz

☐ JUST FOR ME
Night time / Bye bye baby / Things have changed / Just for me / We need to love one another / What more can I say / You must be crazy woman / Deep sea diver
JSPCD 274 / Jan '97 / JSP

☐ SOMETHING'S GONNA JUMP OUT THE BUSHES
CD 1039 / '88 / Black Top

☐ TORE UP (Brown, Nappy & The Heartfixers)
Who / Lemon squeezin' daddy / Heartbreak / Losing hand / Tore up over you / Hard luck blues / Hidden charms / I ain't my cross to bear / Tonight I'll be staying here with you / Jack the rabbit / You can make it if you try
ALCD 4792 / May '93 / Alligator

Brown, Norman

☐ AFTER THE STORM
Take me there / After the storm / That's the way love goes / Any love / Lydian / For the love of you / Trashman / It costs to love / Let's come together / Acoustic time / El dulce sol / Family
5303012 / Mar '94 / MoJazz

☐ BETTER DAYS AHEAD
5306642 / Jul '96 / MoJazz

☐ JUST BETWEEN US
Stormin' / Just between us / East meets West / Love's holiday / It's a feelin' / Too high / Something just for you / Here to stay / Moonlight tonight / Sweet taste / Inside
5300912 / Feb '93 / MoJazz

Brown, Oscar Jr.

☐ MR. OSCAR BROWN JR. GOES TO WASHINGTON
One life / Beautiful girl / Maxine / Maggie / Living double in a world of trouble / Glorious tired feeling / Tower of time / Muffled drums / Brother where are you / Forty acres and a mule / Call of the city / Summer in the city / Brother where are you
5574522 / 3 Aug '98 / Verve

☐ SIN AND SOUL...AND THEN SOME
Work song / But I was cool / Bid 'em in / Signifyin' monkey / Watermelon man / Somebody buy me a drink / Rags and old iron / Dat dere / Brown baby / Humdrum blues / Sleepy / Afro blue / Mr. Kicks / Hazel's hips / World of grey / Forbidden fruit / Straighten up and fly right
CK 64994 / Nov '96 / Sony Jazz

Brown, Peggy

☐ DENN SIE FAHREN HINAUS AUF DAS MEER
Denn sie fahren hinaus auf das Meer / Honeymoon mit dir allein / Sag, ist das die liebe / Gegen liebe gibt es keine medizin / Jeden Sonntag eine Rose von dir / Melodie aus Germany / Meine reklame boy / Schiffe ohne Hafen# / Wenn es abend wird / Ein tango in der Hafenbar / Zahlen jeden Stunde / Spiel nicht mit der liebe / Eine trane fiel ins Meer / Lieber Jonny, komm doch wieder / Gondola d'amore / Lass mich nie wieder weinen / Das lexicon d'amour / Die Berge von Dakota / Ein mann wie du / Du bist meine Welt / Silberweisse Wogen / Don Carlos / Keiner weiss ob sie sich wiedersehn / Ein wiedersehn mit Jacky / Jedes gluck auf der Welt / Komm doch wieder / Das kann nur liebe sein / Bitte sag's nicht weiter / Gehn am Kai die lichter aus / Alone on the shore
BCD 16110 / Nov '96 / Bear Family

Brown, Pete

☐ THOUSANDS ON A RAFT (Brown, Pete & Piblokto)
REP 4408 / 15 Jun '98 / Repertoire

Brown, Peter

☐ GET FUNKY WITH ME (The Best Of The TK Years)
Do you wanna get funky with me / Dance with me / Crank it up / Can't be love do it to me anyway / Love in our hearts / You should do it / Without love / Fantasy love affair / Stargazer
WESM 553 / 16 Feb '98 / Westside

Brown, Phil

☐ WHISTLING FOR THE MOON
Bowland air / Teddy O'Neill / Women of Ireland / Old man Quinn/Alexander's hornpipe / Lonesome boatman / Danny boy / Dark island / Copy nook / Endearing young charms / King of the fairies / Terminal love song / As I roved out / Leaboy's lassie / Down by the Sally Gardens / Whalley roundabout
FSCD 34 / Oct '95 / Folksound

Brown, Phil

☐ DISCOVERY
At the sign of the swinging cymbal / Romance for violin and orchestra no.2 in F / Vienna is Vienna / Girl from Corsica / Up to the races / So eine liebe gibt es einmal nur / Carmen medley / Missing / London kid / At the woodchopper's ball / Eine kleine nachtmusik / Dizzy fingers / Mornings at seven / Taste of honey / Rare auld times / Abba medley / Discovery / Who cares
CDRS 1284 / Nov '95 / Grosvenor

Brown, Polly

☐ BEWITCHED - THE POLLY BROWN STORY
That same old feeling: *Pickettywitch* / (It's like a) sad old kinda movie: *Pickettywitch* / All those days: *Pickettywitch* / Baby I won't let you down: *Pickettywitch* / To love somebody / Crazy love / Wild night / Amoreuse / Honey honey / Best of everything: *Sweet Dreams* / That's the way love grows: *Sweet Dreams* / Up in a puff of smoke / Special delivery / SOS / You're my number one / One girl too late / Short down in flames / I need another song / Do you believe in love at first sight / Bewitched, bothered and bewildered / Believe in me / Angel / It's me you're leaving / Writing you a letter / Precious to me
RPM 143 / Apr '95 / RPM

Brown, Pud

☐ PUD BROWN & NEW ORLEANS JAZZMEN
JCD 216 / Apr '94 / Jazzology

☐ PUD BROWN & THE SPIRIT OF NEW ORLEANS JAZZ BAND (Brown, Pud & The Spirit Of New Orleans Jazz Band)
BCD 247 / Aug '94 / GHB

☐ PUD BROWN PLAYS CLARINET
JCD 166 / Apr '94 / Jazzology

Brown, Ray

☐ BASS FACE (Brown, Ray Trio)
Milestones / Bass face / In the wee small hours of the morning / Tin Tin Deo CRS - CRAFT / Takin' a chance on love / Remember / Makin' whoopee / Phineas can be
CD 83340 / Oct '93 / Telarc

☐ BLACK ORPHEUS
Days of wine and roses / I thought about you / Balck Orpheus / How insensitive / My foolish heart / Please send me someone to love / Ain't misbehavin' / When you wish upon a star / Things ain't what they used to be
ECD 220762 / Feb '94 / Evidence

☐ BROWN'S BAG
Blues for Eddie Lee / Keep on pumpin' / You are my sunshine / Time for love / Surrey with the fringe on top / Emily
CCD 6019 / Aug '91 / Concord Jazz

☐ DON'T GET SASSY (Brown, Ray Trio)
Tanga / Con alma / Brown's new blues / Don't get sassy / Good life / Everything I love / Kelly's blues / When you go / Raincheck / In a sentimental mood / Squatty roo
CD 83368 / Sep '94 / Telarc

☐ LIVE AT SCULLERS (Brown, Ray Trio)
Freddie Freeloader / You're my everything / But not for me / Bye bye blackbird / If you only knew / Whirlybird
CD 83405 / Feb '98 / Telarc Jazz

☐ LIVE AT THE CONCORD JAZZ FESTIVAL - 1979 (Brown, Ray Trio)
Blue bossa / Bossa nova do marilla / Manha de carnaval / St. Louis blues / Fly me to the moon / Georgia on my mind / Here's that rainy day / Please send me someone to love / Honeysuckle rose
CCD 4102 / Mar '90 / Concord Jazz

☐ MOORE MAKES 4 (Brown, Ray Trio)
S.o.s. / Bye bye blackbird / Stars fell on alabama / Ralph's boogie / Quasimodo / Like someone in love / Polka dots and moonbeams / Squatty roo / Everything I love / My romance / Champ
CCD 4477 / Oct '91 / Concord Jazz

☐ MUCH IN COMMON (2CD Set) (Brown, Ray & Milt Jackson)
5332592 / Jan '97 / Verve

☐ RAY BROWN THREE, A (Brown, Ray & Monty Alexander/Sam Most)
I wish you love / I can't stop loving you / Jamento / Blue monk / Candy man / Too late now / You're my everything / There is no greater love
CCD 42132 / May '97 / Concord Jazz

☐ SEVEN STEPS TO HEAVEN (Brown, Ray Trio)
Two RB's / Seven steps to heaven / Dejection blues / Thumb / My romance / Cotton tail / Samba de orfeu / There is no greater love / In a sentimental mood / Stella by starlight / Things ain't what they used to be
CD 83384 / Feb '96 / Telarc

☐ SOLAR ENERGY
Exactly like you / Cry me a river / Teach me tonight / Take the 'A' train / Mistreated but undefeated blues / That's all / Easy does it / Sweet Georgia Brown
CCD 4268 / Jul '89 / Concord Jazz

☐ SOME OF MY BEST FRIENDS ARE...
Lover / Ray of light / Just a gigolo / St. Louis blues / Bag's groove / Love walked in / Nearness of you / Close your eyes / Giant steps / My romance / How come you do me like you do / If I love again / St Tropez
CD 83373 / Apr '95 / Telarc

☐ SOME OF MY BEST FRIENDS ARE...THE SAX PLAYERS (Brown, Ray Trio)
How high the moon / Love walked in / Polka dots and moonbeams / Crazeology / Port of Rico / Moose the mooche / Easy living / Just you, just me / Fly me to the moon / When it's sleepy time down South / These foolish things / God bless the child
CD 83388 / Jun '96 / Telarc

☐ SOMETHING FOR LESTER
Ojos de rojo / Slippery / Something in common / Love walked in / Georgia on my mind / Little girl blue / Sister sadie
OJCCD 412 / Feb '93 / Original Jazz Classics

☐ SUMMERTIME (Brown, Ray Trio & Ulf Wakenius)
West Coast blues / Summertime / Topsy / Yours is my heart alone / It's only a paper moon / My one and only / Reunion blues / Watch what happens / More I see you / Honeysuckle rose / Cakes' blues
CD 83430 / May '98 / Telarc

☐ SUPERBASS (Recorded Live At Sculler's) (Brown, Ray & John Clayton/ Christian McBride)
SuperBass theme / Blue Monk / Bye bye blackbird / Lullaby of birdland / Who cares / Mack The Knife / Centrepiece / Sculler blues / Brown funk / SuperBass theme
CD 83393 / Aug '97 / Telarc Jazz

☐ TASTY (Brown, Ray & Jimmy Rowles)
Sleepin' bee / I'm gonna sit right down and write myself a letter / Night is young and you're so beautiful / My ideal / Come Sunday / Close your eyes / Nancy with the laughing face / Smile
CCD 4122 / Jul '95 / Concord Jazz

☐ THREE DIMENSIONAL (Brown, Ray Trio)
Ja da / Paradise / You are my sunshine / Nancy / Gumbo hump / Classical in G / My romance / Take me out to the ball game / Ellington medley / Equinox / Time after time
CCD 4520 / Sep '92 / Concord Jazz

Brown, Reuben

☐ ICE SCAPE
SCCD 31423 / Nov '97 / Steeplechase

Brown, Rob

☐ BLINK OF AN EYE (Brown, Rob & Matthew Shipp)
NMR 3 / 16 Feb '98 / No More

Brown, Robert

☐ MASTERS OF PIOBAIREACHD VOL.1 (Brown, Robert & Robert Nicol)
Patrick Og MacCrimmon's lament / Battle of the pass of crieff / I got a kiss of the King's hand / Earl of seaforths salute / In praise of Morag / Unjust incarceration
CDTRAX 153 / 2 Feb '98 / Greentrax

Brown, Roy

☐ BLUES DELUXE
Cadillac baby / Hard luck blues / New Rebecca / Sweet peach / Love don't love nobody / Dreaming blues / Good man blues / Too much lovin' ain't no good / Teenage jamboree / Train time blues / Bar room blues / Long about sundown / Beautician blues / Drum boogie / Double crossin' woman / Swingin' with Johnny / Wrong woman blues / Good rockin' man / I've got the last laugh now / Big town / Brown angel / Rock-a-bye baby / Lonesome lover / Answer to Big Town
CDCHARLY 289 / Nov '93 / Charly

☐ GOOD ROCKIN' BROWN'S BACK IN TOWN (Roy Brown Live)
Travellin' blues / Let the four winds blow / Love for sale / Boogie woogie blues / Good rockin' tonight / Boogie at midnight/Love don't love nobody / Losing hand/Tin Pan Alley
AIM 0008CD / 20 Oct '97 / Aim

☐ MIGHTY, MIGHTY MAN
Mr. Hound Dog's in town / Bootleggin' baby / Trouble at midnight / Everything's alright / This is my last goodbye / Don't let it rain / Up jumped the devil / No love at all / Ain't it a shame / Ain't no rockin' no more / Queen of diamonds / Gal from Kokomo / Fannie Brown got married / Worried life blues / Black diamond / Letter to baby / Shake 'em up baby / Rinky dinku doo / Adorable one / School bell rock / Ain't got no blues today / Good looking and foxy too
CDCHD 459 / Sep '93 / Ace

Brown, Roy 'Chubby'

☐ FAT OUT OF HELL
Rockin' good Christmas / It's a condom / Protect your bum de de bum / Play your funky horn / Stunt / Awful / Toss me off / Play your funky horn / Santa, where's me fucking bike / Rockin' good Christmas
5370602 / Nov '96 / PolyGram TV

☐ TAKE FAT AND PARTY
5297482 / Nov '95 / PolyGram TV

Brown, Rula

☐ RULA
BCR 1002 / Nov '95 / Bee Cat

Brown, Ruth

☐ BEST OF THE REST OF RUTH BROWN, THE
Hello little boy / Please don't freeze / Bye bye young men / I still love you / When I get you baby / Show me / New love / I hope we meet / Look me up / Just too much / Book of lies / I'll step aside / Mama he treats your daughter mean / 5-10-15 hours / Papa Daddy / Jack O' Diamonds / What I wouldn't give / Door is still open / I burned your letter / Honey boy / It tears me all to pieces / Sure nuff / Here he comes / Mama he treats your daughter mean / Oh what a dream
RSACD 864 / Mar '97 / Sequel

☐ BLUES ON BROADWAY
Nobody knows you (When you're down and out) / Good morning heartache / If I can't sell it I'll keep sittin' on it / Ain't nobody's business if I do / St. Louis blues / Am I blue / I'm just a lucky so and so / I don't break dance / Come Sunday
FCD 9662 / Mar '94 / Fantasy

☐ HAVE A GOOD TIME
Gee baby, ain't I good to you / You won't let me go / 5-10-15 hours / Have a good time / Teardrops from my eyes / Always on my mind / Yes sir, that's my baby / When I fall in love / Mama he treats your daughter mean / What a wonderful world
FCD 9661 / Nov '95 / Fantasy

☐ LIVE IN LONDON
I've got the world on a string / I'm a lucky so and so / Have a good time / Fine and mellow / Lover man / Good morning heartache / Secret love / Fine Brown frame / It could happen to you / 5-10-15 Hours / Be anything (but be mine) / Since I fell for you / He's a real gone guy
JHCD 042 / Sep '95 / Ronnie Scott's Jazz House

☐ MISS RHYTHM (The Greatest Hits/2CD Set)
So long / Hey pretty baby / I'll get along somehow (part 1) / I'll come back someday / Sentimental journey / Rb blues / Teardrops from my eyes / Standing on the corner / I'll wait for you / I know / Don't cry / Shrine of st. cecilia / It's all for you / Shine on / Be anything / 5-10-15 hours / Have a good time / Daddy daddy / Mama he treats your daughter mean / Wild wild young men / Ever since my baby's been gone / Love contest / Oh what a dream / Ol' man river / Somebody touched me
RSDCD 816 / Oct '94 / Sequel

☐ R+B=RUTH BROWN
That train don't stop here / In another world / I'm gonna move to the outskirts of town / Destination heartbreak / Too little too late / Sold my heart to the junkman / Go on fool / False friend blues / Break it to me gently / I don't know / Bite my tongue / Love letters / Can't get excited
CDBB 9583 / Sep '97 / Bullseye Blues

☐ SONGS OF MY LIFE
Songs of my life / I've got the world on a string / While we're young / God bless the child / It could happen to you / Tears in heaven / Stormy weather / They say / I wonder where our love has gone / I know why / Can't help lovin' dat man / I'll be seeing you
FCD 9665 / Jun '94 / Fantasy

☐ YOU DON'T KNOW ME/TOUCH ME IN THE MORNING
If I were a bell / Skylark / Gee baby ain't I good to you / Miss Brown's blues / Smile / Secret love / You don't know me / Almost like being in love / Willow weep for me / I'll never fall in love again / What'll I do / Everybody's talking / Touch me in the morning / After the lovin' / Way you look tonight / Best thing that ever happened
IGOCD 2074 / Oct '97 / Indigo

Brown, Sam

☐ STOP
Walking back to me / Your love is all / It makes me wonder / This feeling / Tea / Piece of my luck / Ball and chain / Wrap me up / I'll be in love / Merry go round / Sometimes / Can I get a witness / High as a kite / Nutbush City Limits
CDMID 181 / Jul '93 / A&M

Brown, Sandy

☐ HISTORIC USHER HALL CONCERT 1952, THE
I ain't gonna tell nobody / Keyhole blues / Gatemouth / Room rent blues / Entertainer / If I had a talking picture of you / Ory's creole trombone / Squeeze me / High society / Commercial break / Everybody loves my baby / Savoy blues / Just a closer walk with thee / Buddy's habits
LACD 94 / Apr '98 / Lake

☐ IN THE EVENING (Brown, Sandy & Brian Lemon Trio)
Ole Miss / Oxford Brown / In the evening / Ebun / Eight / Legal Pete / Badger / True love's heart / Lucky Schiz and the big dealer / Minstrel song / Louis / Strike up the band / I'm coming Virginia / Sandy's blues / Gentlemen of the bar
HEPCD 2017 / 5 Jan '98 / Hep

☐ MCJAZZ & FRIENDS
LACD 58 / Feb '96 / Lake

Brown, Sarah

☐ SAYIN' WHAT I'M THINKIN'
BPCD 5030 / Apr '96 / Blind Pig

Brown, Sawyer

☐ GREATEST HITS
CURCD 013 / Jan '95 / Curb

☐ OUTSKIRTS OF TOWN
Boys and me / Farmer tan / Outskirts of town / Thank God for you / Listenin' for you / Eyes of love / Hard to say / Drive away / Heartbreak highway / Love to be wanted / Hold on
CURCD 006 / Mar '94 / Curb

☐ SIX DAYS ON THE ROAD
CURCD 44 / May '97 / Curb

☐ WANTIN' AND HAVIN' IT ALL
CURCD 17 / Sep '95 / Curb

Brown, Scott

☐ THEORY OF EVOLUTION, THE
EVCD 5 / Nov '96 / Evolution

Brown, Shirley

☐ DIVA OF SOUL
You ain't got to hide your man / If you're weak enough / Good loving man / One more time / You ain't woman enough to take my man / Put your monet where your mouth is / Talk to me / Sprung on his love / Better you go your way / Leftover love / Ain't nothing like the lovin' we got / Anticipation / A two way thang / Long on lovin'
DOMECD 7 / Oct '95 / Dome

☐ FOR THE REAL FEELING
When, where, what time / Crowding in on my mind / After a night like this / Dirty feelin' / Hang on Louie / Eyes can't see / Move me, move me / Love starved
CDSXE 082 / Nov '92 / Stax

☐ WOMAN TO WOMAN
Woman to woman / Yes sir brother / It ain't no fun / As long as you love me / Stay with me baby / I've got to go on without you / It's worth a whipping / So glad to have you / Passion / I can't give you up / I need you tonight / Between you and me
CDSXE 002 / Aug '87 / Stax

Brown, Steven

☐ DAY IS GONE, THE
SUBCD 00921 / '89 / Sub Rosa

Brown, Sue

☐ CALL AND CRY (Brown, Sue & Lorraine Irwing)
WGS 284CD / Dec '97 / Wild Goose

Brown, Teacher Ras Sam

☐ HISTORY PAST AND PRESENT
RASCD 3199 / Feb '97 / Ras

Brown, Terry Lee Jr.

☐ CHOCOLATE CHORDS
PLACCD 08 / 26 Jan '98 / Plastic City UK

Brown, Tom

☐ TOM BROWN & HIS NEW ORLEANS JAZZ BAND (Brown, Tom & His New Orleans Jazz Band)
BCD 3 / Aug '94 / GHB

Brown/Crane

☐ FASTER THAN THE SPEED OF LIGHT
BP 228CD / Oct '96 / Blueprint

Browne, Duncan

☐ TRAVELLING MAN, THE (Browne, Duncan & Sebastian Graham Jones)
CDSGP 0114 / Sep '95 / Prestige

Browne, Jackson

☐ BEST OF JACKSON BROWNE, THE
Doctor my eyes / These days / Fountain of sorrow / Late for the sky / Pretender / Running on empty / Call it a loan / Sombody's baby / Tender is the night / In the shape of a heart / Lives in the balance / Sky blue and black / Barricades of heaven / Rebel Jesus / Next voice you hear
7559621112 / 22 Sep '97 / Elektra

☐ FOR EVERYMAN
Take it easy / Our Lady of the Well / Colours of the sun / I thought I was a child / These days / Redneck friend / Times you come / Ready or not / Sing my songs to me / For everyman
243003 / Jan '87 / Asylum

☐ HOLD OUT
Disco apocalypse / Hold on, hold out / Of missing persons / Call it a loan / That girl could sing / Hold out / Boulevard
2522262 / Jan '87 / Asylum

☐ I'M ALIVE
I'm alive / My problem is you / Everywhere I go / I'll do anything / Miles away / Too many angels / Take this rain / Two of me, two of you / Sky blue and black / All good things
7559615242 / Oct '93 / Asylum

☐ JACKSON BROWNE
Jamaica say you will / Child in these hills / Song for Adam / Doctor my eyes / From silver lake / Something fine / Under the falling sky / Looking into you / Rock me on the water / My opening farewell
253022 / Dec '86 / Asylum

☐ LATE FOR THE SKY
Late for the sky / Fountain of sorrow / Farther on / Late show / Road and the sky / For a dancer / Walking slow / Before the deluge
243007 / Jan '87 / Asylum

☐ LAWYERS IN LOVE
For a rocker / Lawyers in love / On the day / Cut it away / Downtown / Tender is the night / Knock on any door / Say it isn't true
9602682 / Jul '87 / Asylum

☐ LIVES IN THE BALANCE
For America / Soldier of plenty / In the shape of a heart / Candy / Lawless Avenue / Lives in the balance / Till I go down / Black and white
K 9604572 / Dec '96 / Asylum

☐ LOOKING EAST
Looking east / Barricades of heaven / Some bridges / Information wars / Culver moon / Nino / Baby how long / It is one / Alive in the world / I'm the cat
7559618672 / Feb '96 / Asylum

☐ PRETENDER, THE
Fuse / Your bright baby blues / Linda Paloma / Here come those tears again / Only child / Daddy's time / Sleep's dark and silent gate / Pretender
253048 / Dec '86 / Asylum

☐ RUNNING ON EMPTY
Running on empty / Road / Rosie / You love the thunder / Cocaine / Shaky town / Love needs a heart / Nothing but time / Load-out / Stay
253070 / Jan '87 / Asylum

☐ WORLD IN MOTION
World in motion / Enough of the night / Chasing you into the night / How long / Anything can happen / When the stone begins to turn / Word justice / My personal revenge / I am a patriot / Lights and virtues
9608322 / Feb '95 / Asylum

Browne, Ronan

☐ SOUTH WEST WIND, THE (Browne, Ronan & Peter O'Loughlin)
Jenny picking cockles/Colliers' reel / Frieze breeches jig / Shaskeen/Five mile chase / Banks of Lough Gowna/Willie Clancy's Paidin O Raifeartaigh / Paidin O Raifeartaigh jig / Connaught heifers/Corney is coming / Bold trainer O / Dublin reel/Steampacket/ Hand me down the tackle / An ghaoth aniar aneas/ Petticoat loose / Spike Island lassies/Farewell to Connaught / Drunken gauger / Queen of the rushes/ Chorus / Byrne's and Alfie's rambles / Bridie's joy/ The spinner's delight / Thrush in the morning/ Crooked road
CC 47CD / Feb '93 / Claddagh

Browne, Ronnie

☐ SCOTTISH LOVE SONGS
Dumarton's drums / My love is like a red red rose / Come all ye fair and tender maidens / Touch and the go / Bonnie lass o'Fyvie / Loch Lomond / Bonnie Earl o'Moray / Canvas of my life / Kate Dalrymple / Massacre of Glencoe / Mary Hamilton / Queen's Maries / Leezie Lindsay / Gin I were a Baron's heir / Willie's gan tae Melville Castle / Parting glass
CDITV 602 / Oct '95 / Scotdisc

Browne, Tom

☐ ANOTHER SHADE OF BROWNE
Bluesanova / Philly twist / Sleepy lagoon / Pove / Bee Tee's / Minor plea / In a sentimental mood / Eighty one
HIBD 8011 / Sep '96 / Hip Bop

☐ FUNKIN' FOR JAMAICA
Funkin' for Jamaica / Thighs high / Byegones / Never my love / Brighter tomorrow / Lazy bird / Rockin' radio / Mr. Business / Martha / Charisma / I never was a cowboy / Secret fantasy / Turn it up / Fungi mama
743215696520 / 23 Mar '98 / Camden

Browns

☐ THREE BELLS, THE (8CD Set)
Rio de Janeiro / Looking back to see / Itsy witsy bitsy me / Why am I fallin' / Draggin' Main Street / You're love is as wild as the west wind / Cool green / Do memories haunt me / It's love I guess / I'm your man, I'm your gal / Set the dawgs on 'em / Jungle magic / You thought, I thought / Here today and gone tomorrow / Grass is green / Lookin' on / I take the chance / I can't see for lookin' / I'm in heaven / Goo goo dada / Just as long as you love me / Getting used to being lonely / Man with a plan / Sweet talk / Don't tell me your troubles / Last thing that I want / Preview of the blues / My Isle of golden dreams / I'm in heaven / Guess I'm crazy / Sky princess / I'll hold you in my heart / How can it be imagination / I heard the bluebirds sing / It takes a long, long train with a red caboose / Don't use the word lightly / Waltz of the angels / Table next to me / Money / You'll always be in my heart / Behave yourself, Jose / Just in time / Man in the moon / Ain't no way in this world / Crazy dreams / True love goes far beyond / Only one way to love you / Be my love / Land of golden dreams / Love is in season / Would you care / Trot / Beyond the shadow / This time I would know / Three bells / Wake up Jonah / Be my love / Heaven fell last night / Your pretty blue eyes / Unchained melody / Indian love call / Blues stay away from me / Dream on / Where did the sunshine go / We should be together / Bye bye love / I still do / Only the lonely / Hi de ank tum / Love me tender / Put on an old pair of shoes / Blue bells ring / Scarlet ribbons / Red sails in the sunset / That's my desire / That little boy of mine / Halfway to heaven / Teen-ex / Oh my Papa / Margo / Cool water / True love / Enchanted sea / Old lamplighter / Billy McCoy / Am I that easy to forget / Whiffenpoof song / Streamlined cannonball / My adobe hacienda / Pledge of love / Wabash blues / Who's gonna buy you ribbons / Margo / Chandelier of stars / Eternally / Brighten the corner where you are / Blue skirt waltz / Have you ever been lonely / Lonely little robin / Wayward wind / Old village choir / High noon / Lavender blue / Blues in my heart / Chandelier of stars / Whiffenpoof song / Blue Christmas / This land is your land / In the pines / Brighten the corner where you are / Greenwillow christmas / Remember me / Twelfth of never / Nevada / Where I was (when we became strangers) / You're so much a part of me / Revenge / Bandit / Send me the pillow that you dream on / Down in the valley / Shenandoah / Columbus Stockade blues / Clementine / Poor wayfaring stranger / Ground hog / Poor wildwood flower / Who's gonna shoe your pretty little feet / John B Sails / My pretty quadroon / Down on the old plantation / My baby's gone / Alpha and omega / Foolish pride / Angel's dolly / Alpha and omega / My baby's gone / Whispering wine / Remember me / Lord I'm coming home / How great thou art / Child of the King / Just as I am / Church in the wildwood / Evening prayer / In the garden / Whispering hope / When they ring those golden bells / Where no one stands alone / My latest sun is sinking fast / Faith unlocks the door / It's just a little heartache / No love at all / Buttons and bows / Old master painter / They call the wind Maria / Forty shades of green / Is it make believe / Everlasting / Twelfth rose / Watching my

world fall apart / Oh no / Dear Teresa / Rumba boogie / Great speckled bird / Don't let the stars get in your eyes / Sugarfoot rag / Fair and tender ladies / Tragic romance / Four walls / You nearly lose your mind / Mansion on the hill / Wondering / Mommy please stay home with me / Anna / Pirogue / Happy fool / Grass is red / Circuit ridin' preacher / Half breed / Young land / Gun, the gold, the girl / Mister and Mississippi / Blowin' in the wind / Tobacco road / Then I'll stop loving you / You're easy to remember / I know my place / My baby doesn't love me anymore / Love didn't pass me by / Outskirts of town / Tangled web / My destiny / Johnny I hardly knew you / Three hearts in a tangle / Everybody's darlin' plus mine / Meadow green / One take away one / No sad songs for me / I feel like crying / Big blizzard / Watch the roses grow / Little too much to dream / Little boy blue / Maybe tomorrow / I can stand it (as long as you can) / Gone / This heart of mine / I'm so lonesome I could cry / Yesterday's gone / You can't grow peaches on a cherry tree / Two of a kind / Spring time / When I stop dreaming / Too soon to know / Now I can live again / I will bring you water / June is as cold as Decmeber / I'd just be fool enough / Maker of raindrops and roses / Making plans / Born to be with you / Million miles from nowhere / Big daddy / Where does a little tear come from / Coming back to you / Do not ask for love / Gigawackem / Rhythm of the rain / Greener pastures / After losing you / Tip of my fingers / Four strong winds / Sorry I never knew you / Old country church / They tore the old country church down / Though your sins be as scarlet / He will set your fields on fire / Night watch / When I lift up my head / Taller than trees / Mocking bird / Jezebel / Rusty old halo / Weapon of prayer / I hear it now / Ride ride ride / Country boy's dream / All of me belongs to you / Where does the good times go / I'm a lonesome fugitive / Once / Walk through this world with me / Happy tracks / Misty blue / If the whole world stops lovin'
BCD 15665 / Dec '93 / Bear Family

Brownside

☐ **EASTSIDE DRAMA**
TX 51242CD / 24 Nov '97 / Triple XXX

Brownstone

☐ **FROM THE BOTTOM UP**
Party wit me / Grapevyne / If you love me / Sometimes dancin' / I can't tell you why / Don't cry for me / Pass the lovin' / Fruit of life / True to me / Wipe it up / Deeper feelings / Half of you
4773622 / 27 Jul '98 / MJJ Music

☐ **STILL CLIMBING**
Let's get it started / 5 Miles to empty / Love me like you do / In the game of love / Foolish pride / Kiss and tell / Baby love / Around you / Revenge / All I do / If you play your cards right / You give good love
4853882 / May '97 / MJJ Music

Brozman, Bob

☐ **BLUE HULA STOMP**
C stomp blues / Body and soul / Hilo march / Ukelele spaghetti / Do you call that a buddy / Chili blues / Paauau waltz / Short man's vindication / Wasting my love on you / Hano hano hanlei / Blue hula stomp / Hilo hula / Agogostein's lament
CDKM 3905 / Jan '97 / Kicking Mule

☐ **BLUES 'ROUND THE BEND**
847162 / Apr '96 / Sky Ranch

☐ **DEVIL'S SLIDE**
ROUCD 11557 / '88 / Rounder

☐ **GOLDEN SLIDE**
8441862 / Jun '97 / Sky Ranch

☐ **KIKA KILA MEETS KI HOALU (Brozman, Bob & Ledward Kaapana)**
8448452 / Nov '97 / Sky Ranch

Brubeck, Darius

☐ **GATHERING FORCES VOL.1 (Brubeck, Darius & Dan)**
Earthrise / Three mile island / Kearsage strut / Just think about what happens / Tugela rail / Parrot / I say there's hope
BW 022 / Sep '93 / B&W

☐ **GATHERING FORCES VOL.2**
Kitu / Friendship ragga and boogie / Hariji / Mamazala / Amaselesele emvuleni (frogs) / October / Gathering forces
BW 046 / Feb '95 / B&W

☐ **LIVE AT THE NEW ORLEANS & HERITAGE FESTIVAL 1990 (Afro Cool Concept) (Brubeck, Darius & Victor Ntoni)**
Kwela mama / Lakutshon ilanga / Daveyton special / Mokotedi / Kilamanjaro
BW 024 / Oct '93 / B&W

Brubeck, Dave

☐ **24 CLASSIC RECORDINGS (Brubeck, Dave Trio)**
You stepped out of a dream / Lullaby in rhythm / Singin' in the rain / I'll remember april / Body and soul / Let's fall in love-she's a friend / Laura / Indiana / Blue moon / Tea for two / Undecided / That old black magic / September song / Sweet georgia brown / Spring is here / 's wonderful / Perfidia / Avalon / I didn't know what time it was / Always / How high the moon / Squeeze me in / Heart and soul / Too marvellous for words (vocal george melachrino)
CDJZD 005 / Jan '91 / Fantasy

☐ **25TH ANNIVERSARY REUNION (Brubeck, Dave Quartet)**
St. Louis blues / Three to get ready / African times suite / First movement (African theme) / Second movement (African breeze) / Third movement / Salute to Stephen Foster / Take five / Don't worry 'bout me
3969982 / Mar '94 / A&M

☐ **75TH BIRTHDAY CELEBRATION**
83349CD / Nov '95 / Telarc

☐ **ALL THE THINGS WE ARE**
Like someone in love / In your own sweet way / All the things you are / Deep in a dream / Here's that rainy day / Polka dots and moonbeams / It could happen to you / Don't get around much anymore
7567813992 / Mar '93 / Atlantic

☐ **BACK HOME**
Cassandra / (I'm afraid) the masquerade is over / Hometown blues / Two-part contention / Caravan
CCD 4103 / Jul '94 / Concord Jazz

☐ **BLUE RONDO (Brubeck, Dave Quartet)**
How does your garden grow / Festival hall / Easy as you go / Blue rondo a la Turk / Dizzy's dream / I see, Satie / Swing bells / Strange meadowlark / Elana Joy
CCD 4317 / Aug '90 / Concord Jazz

☐ **CONCORD ON A SUMMER NIGHT (Brubeck, Dave Quartet)**
Benjamin / Koto Song / Black And Blue / Take five / Softly, William, softly
CCD 4198 / Nov '86 / Concord Jazz

☐ **DAVE BRUBECK & PAUL DESMOND (Brubeck, Dave Octet & Paul Desmond)**
Jeepers creepers / On a little street in Singapore / Trolley song / I may be wrong, but I think you're wonderful / Blue moon / My heart stood still / Let's fall in love / Over the rainbow / You go to my head / Crazy Chris / Give a little whistle / Oh lady be good / Tea for two / This can't be love
OJCCD 101 / Nov '95 / Original Jazz Classics

☐ **DAVE BRUBECK CHRISTMAS, A**
'Homecoming' jingle bells / Santa Claus is coming to town / Joy to the world / Away in a manger / Winter wonderland / O little town of Bethlehem / What child is this (Greensleeves) / To us is given / O tannenbaum / Silent night / Cantos para pedir las posadas / Run, run, run to Bethlehem / 'Farewell' jingle bells / Christmas song
CD 83410 / Nov '96 / Telarc Jazz

☐ **DAVE BRUBECK IN CONCERT (Brubeck, Dave Quartet)**
Perdido / These foolish things / Stardust / Way you look tonight / I'll never smile again / I remember you / For all we know / All the things you are / Lullaby in rhythm
FCD 60013 / Mar '94 / Fantasy

☐ **DAVE DIGS DISNEY (Brubeck, Dave Quartet)**
Alice in Wonderland / Give a little whistle / Heigh ho / When you wish upon a star / Someday my Prince will come / One song
4712502 / Jan '95 / Sony Jazz

☐ **ESSENTIAL DAVE BRUBECK QUARTET, THE (Brubeck, Dave Quartet)**
4737342 / Jan '95 / Sony Jazz

☐ **GONE WITH THE WIND**
Swanee river / Lonesome road / Georgia on my mind / Camptown races / Sort'nin' bread / Basin Street blues / Ol' man river / Gone with the wind
4509842 / May '93 / Columbia

☐ **GREAT CONCERTS, THE**
Pennies from Heaven / Blue rondo a la Turk / Take the 'A' train / Wonderful Copenhagen / Tangerine / For all we know / Take five / Real ambassador / Like someone in love
4624032 / May '90 / CBS

☐ **GREATEST HITS**
Take five / I'm in a dancing mood / In your own sweet way / Camptown races / Duke / It's a raggy waltz / Bossa nova USA / Trolley song / Unsquare dance / Blue rondo a la Turk / Mr. Broadway
CD 32046 / Jun '89 / CBS

☐ **IN THEIR OWN SWEET WAY (Brubeck, Dave & Chris/Dan/Darius/Matthew)**
In your own sweet way / Bifocal blues / Sermon on the mount / Michael my second son / Ode to a cowboy / Dave 'n' Darius / We will all remember Paul / Sixth sense / My one bad habit / Sweet Georgia Brown
CD 83355 / Jun '97 / Telarc Jazz

☐ **JAZZ AT COLLEGE OF THE PACIFIC (Brubeck, Dave Quartet)**
All the things you are / Laura / Lullaby in rhythm / I'll never smile again / I remember you / For all we know
OJCCD 47 / Feb '92 / Original Jazz Classics

☐ **JAZZ AT OBERLIN (Brubeck, Dave Quartet)**
These foolish things / Perdido / Stardust / Way you look tonight / How high the moon
OJCCD 46 / Sep '93 / Original Jazz Classics

☐ **JAZZ COLLECTION (2CD Set)**
Le souk / Stompin' for Mili / In your own sweet way / History of a boy scout / Home at last / Someday my Prince will come / Tangerine / Golden horn / Georgia on my mind / Three to get ready / Blue rondo a la Turk / Take five / Darktown strutters ball / There'll be some changes made / Somewhere / Weep no more / Unsquare dance / Summer song / Non-sectarian blues / Bossa nova USA / It's a raggy waltz / World's fair / Fujiyama / Upstage rumba / My favourite things / La paloma azul / Recuerdo / St. Louis Blues
4804632 / Jul '95 / Columbia

☐ **JAZZ GOES TO COLLEGE**
Balcony rock / Out of nowhere / Le souk / Take the 'A' train / Song is you / Don't worry 'bout me / I want to be happy
4656822 / Feb '93 / CBS

☐ **JAZZ IMPRESSIONS OF EURASIA**
Nomad / Brandenburg Gate / Golden horn / Thank you / Marble arch / Calcutta blues
4712492 / Apr '92 / Columbia

☐ **JAZZ IMPRESSIONS OF NEW YORK**
4669712 / Jan '95 / Sony Jazz

☐ **JUST YOU, JUST ME**
Just you, just me / Strange meadowlark / It's the talk of the town / Brother can you spare a dime / Lullaby / Tribute / I married an angel / Music maestro please / Briar bush / Newport waltz / I understand / More than you know
CD 83363 / Sep '94 / Telarc

☐ **LAST SET AT NEWPORT**
Introduction / Blues for Newport / Take five / Open the gates
7567813822 / Mar '93 / Atlantic

☐ **LATE NIGHT BRUBECK (Live From Blue Note)**
These foolish things / Here's that rainy day / Theme for June / Duke / Thing's ain't what they used to be / C Jam blues / Don't get around much anymore / Who will take care of me / Koto song / So wistfully sad / Mean to me
CD 83345 / Mar '94 / Telarc

☐ **LIVE (Brubeck, Dave Quartet)**
BS 18009 / Jul '96 / Bandstand

☐ **LIVE AT MONTREUX 1982 (Brubeck, Dave Quartet)**
DM 15015 / Jul '96 / DMA Jazz

☐ **LIVE AT THE BERLIN PHILHARMONIC (Brubeck, Dave & Gerry Mulligan)**
Things ain't what they used to be / Blessed are the poor / Duke of New Orleans / Indian song / Limehouse blues / Lullaby de Mexico / St. Louis blues / Out of the way of the people / Basin street blues / Take five / Out of nowhere / Mexican jumpin' bean
4814152 / Nov '95 / Sony Jazz

☐ **MOSCOW NIGHT**
Three to get ready / Theme for june / Give me a hit / Unsquare dance / St. louis blues
CCD 4353 / Jul '88 / Concord Jazz

☐ **NIGHTSHIFT**
Yesterdays / I can't give you anything but love / Travellin' blues / Thank you you go to my head / Blues for Newport / Ain't misbehavin' / Knives / River stay 'way from my door
CD 83351 / May '95 / Telarc

☐ **PAPER MOON**
Music maestro please / I hear a rhapsody / Symphony / I thought about you / It's only a paper moon / Long ago and far away / St. Louis blues / Music, Maestro, Please
CCD 4178 / Aug '92 / Concord Jazz

☐ **PLAYS AND PLAYS AND PLAYS**
OJCCD 716 / Nov '95 / Original Jazz Classics

☐ **PLAYS MUSIC FROM WEST SIDE STORY (Brubeck, Dave Quartet)**
Maria, my own / I feel pretty / Somewhere / A quiet girl / Tonight / What is this thing called love / Most beautiful girl in the world / Night and day / My romance
4504102 / Jan '95 / Sony Jazz

☐ **QUARTET, THE**
Castillian drums / Three to get ready / St. Louis Blues / Forty days / Summer song / Someday my Prince will come / Brandenburg Gate / In your own sweet way
17080 / Jan '97 / Laserlight

☐ **SOMEDAY MY PRINCE WILL COME (Brubeck, Dave Quartet)**
Someday my prine will come / One moment / Joe's blues / Take the 'a' train / Mexican fire dance / Three to get ready / Forty days / Summer song / These foolish things (remind me of you)
JHR 73572 / Nov '93 / Jazz Hour

☐ **STARDUST**
Mam'selle / Stardust / Frenesi / Me and my shadow / At a perfum counter / Crazy Chris / Foggy day / Somebody loves me / Lyons busy / Look for the silver lining / Alice in wonderland / All the things you are / Lulu's back in town / My romance / Just one of those things
FCD 24728 / Jun '94 / Fantasy

☐ **TAKE FIVE**
Take five / Bossa nova USA / Unsquare dance / Someday my Prince will come / I'm in a dancing mood / It's a raggy waltz / Blue rondo a la Turk / Kathy's waltz / My favourite things / Castillian drums / Duke / Trolley song
VN 160 / May '95 / Viper's Nest

☐ **TAKE FIVE**
Take five / Unsquare dance / Bossa nova USA / Duke / Ain't misbehavin' / All by myself / Blues in the dark / Evenin' / I never know / My melancholy baby / River stay away from my door / There'll be some changes made / You can depend on me / Flamingo / C jam blues / Am I blue
BN 006 / Apr '98 / Blue Nite

☐ **TAKE THE "FIVE" TRAIN**
MCD 0522 / Apr '94 / Moon

☐ **THIS IS JAZZ**
Take five / Gone with the wind / Someday my prince will come / Blue rondo a la Turk / Pennies from heaven / When you wish upon a star / Jeepers creepers / For all we know
CK 64615 / May '96 / Sony Jazz

☐ **THIS IS JAZZ (Dave Brubeck Plays Standards)**
St. Louis blues / I feel pretty / Things ain't what they used to be / Sometimes I'm happy / Like someone in love / What is this thing called love / Georgia on my mind / Someday my Prince will come
CK 65450 / 4 May '98 / Sony Jazz

☐ **TIME FURTHER OUT (Brubeck, Dave Quartet)**
It's a raggy waltz / Bluesette / Charles Matthew hallelujah / Far more blues / Far more drums / Maori blues / Unsquare dance / Bru's boogie woogie / Blue shadows in the street / Slow and easy / It's a raggy waltz (live)
CK 64668 / Nov '96 / Sony Jazz

☐ **TIME IN**
4746352 / Jan '95 / Sony Jazz

☐ **TIME OUT (Brubeck, Dave Quartet)**
Blue rondo a la Turk / Strange meadowlark / Take five / Three to get ready / Kathy's waltz / Everybody's jumpin' / Pick up sticks
CK 65122 / Apr '97 / Sony Jazz

☐ **TIME OUT/TIME FURTHER OUT/TIME IN (2CD Set)**
It's a raggy waltz / Bluesette / Charles Matthew Hallel / Far more blues / Far more drums / Maori blues / Unsquare dance / Bru's boogie woogie / Blue shadows in... / Slow and easy / It's a raggy waltz / Blue rondo a la turk / Strange meadowlark / Take five / Three to get ready / Kathy's waltz / Everybody's jumpin' / Pick up sticks
4893472 / 1 Dec '97 / Sony Jazz

☐ **TO HOPE - A CELEBRATION (Recorded Live At The Washington National Cathedral) (Brubeck, Dave Quartet & Cathedral Choral Society Chorus)**
To hope - a celebration / Lord have mercy / Desert and the parched land / Peace of Jerusalem / Alleluia / Father all powerful / Holy holy holy while he was at supper / When we eat this bread / Through him, with him / Great Amen / Our Father / Lamb of God / All my hope / Gloria
CD 80430 / Sep '96 / Telarc

☐ **TRITONIS**
Brother can you spare a dime / Like someone in love / Theme for June / Lord, Lord / Mr. Fats / Tritonis
CCD 4129 / Jul '95 / Concord Jazz

☐ **WE'RE ALL TOGETHER AGAIN FOR THE FIRST TIME (Brubeck, Dave & Friends)**
Truth / Unfinished woman / Koto song / Take five / Rotterdam blues / Sweet Georgia Brown
7567813902 / Mar '93 / Atlantic

Brubeck, Matthew

☐ **REALLY (Brubeck, Matthew & David Widelock)**
CDJP 1030 / Nov '91 / Jazz Point

Bruce & Terry

☐ **BEST OF BRUCE & TERRY, THE**
SC 11052 / 13 Jul '98 / Sundazed

Bruce, Ed

☐ **PUZZLES**
Puzzles / Blue denim eyes / By route of New Orleans / Shadows of her mind / Lonesome is me / Tiny golden locket / If I could just go home / Walker's woods / Give me more than you take / I'm getting better / Painted girls and wine / Price I pay to stay / Something else to mess your mind / I know better / Memphis morning / Blue bayou / Why can't I come home / Last train to Clarksville / Her sweet love and the baby / I'll take you away / Ninety seven more to go / I'd be best leaving you / Ballad of the drummer boy / Best be leaving you
BCD 15830 / Mar '95 / Bear Family

Bruce, Ian

☐ **BLODWEN'S DREAM**
John / Factory life / Eldorado / Classical music / Ghost of the chair / Farewell deep blue / No noise / This peaceful evening / I can play you anything / Black fog / Blodwen's dream
FE 076CD / Nov '95 / Fellside

☐ **FREE AGENT**
Scarborough settlers lament / Bizzie Lizzie / Hearts of Ohio / Find out who your friends are / Please be here / Out of sight (Rolling Stones) / Corners / No satisfaction / Bad bet / Anchor line / Dawn of a brand new day / Free agents / Ladies left behind / Find out who your friends are (reprise)
IRCD 026 / Jul '94 / Iona

☐ **HODDEN GREY**
Stoutest man in the forty TWA / Trumpet sounds / Jute mill song / Will ye go tae Flanders / She was a rum one / Diamond ship / List bonnie laddie / Johnny Gallacher / Gi'e me a lass wi' a lump o'land / Kiss the children for me Mary / Tatties an' herrin' / Yella haired laddie / Forfar sodger / Bleacher lassie o' Kelvinhaugh / Slippy stane
CDTRAX 156 / 2 Mar '98 / Greentrax

☐ **KIND AND GENTLE NATURE**
WGS 277CD / Nov '96 / Wild Goose

☐ OUT OF OFFICE
FE 085CD / Jul '92 / Fellside

Bruce, Jack

☐ BBC LIVE IN CONCERT
You burned the tables on me / Folk song / Letter of thanks / Smiles and grins / We're going wrong / Clear out / Have you ever loved a woman / Powerhouse sod / You sure look good to me
SFRSCD 067 / 20 Jul '98 / Strange Fruit

☐ CITIES OF THE HEART (2CD Set)
Can you follow / Running thro' our hands / Over the cliff / Statues / First time I met the blues / Smiles and grins / Bird alone / Neighbor, neighbor / Born under a bad sign / Ships in the night / Never tell your Mother she's out of tune / Theme from an imaginary western / Golden days / Life on earth / NSU / Sittin' on top of the world / Politician / Spoonful / Sunshine of your love
CMPCD 1005 / 6 Apr '98 / CMP

☐ COLLECTOR'S EDITION, THE
CMPCD 1013 / May '98 / CMP

☐ LIVE ON THE TEST
Can you follow / Morning story / Keep it down / Peaces of mind / One / Spirit / Without a word / Smiles and grins / White room / Hit and room / Slow blues / Livin' without ja / Dancing on the air / In this way / Theme for an imaginary western / Politician
WHISCD 010 / 16 Mar '98 / Strange Fruit

☐ MONKJACK
Third degree / Boy / Shouldn't we / David's harp / Know one blues / Time repairs / Laughing on music / Street / Folksong / Weird of Hermiston / Tightrope / Food / Immoral ninth
CMPCD 1010 / Sep '95 / CMP

☐ SOMETHIN' ELSE
CMPCD 1001 / 30 Mar '98 / CMP

☐ TRUCE (Bruce, Jack & Robin Trower)
Gonna shut you down / Gone too far / Thin ice / Last train to the stars / Take good care of yourself / Falling in love / Fat gut / Shadows touching / Little boy lost
S21 17609 / May '94 / One Way

Bruce Lee Band

☐ BRUCE LEE BAND
AM 004CD / Feb '97 / Asian Man

Bruce, Michael

☐ IN MY OWN WAY
OW 34486 / Jun '97 / One Way

Bruce, Vin

☐ CAJUNS OF THE BAYOU, THE
Les cadjins du bayou / He' jolie / La valse de la belle riviere / La cle'de mon coeur / Le del aisse / Troler / Appelle-moi sur le telephone / Ma vie da musicien / C'est malheur reux / Ma belle du bayou / Prends ces chaines de mon coeur / Si j'aurais des ailes
SOC 90251 / Jul '96 / Cajun Sound

Bruford, Bill

☐ EARTHWORKS
Thud / Making a song and dance / Up North / Pressure / My heart declares a holiday / Emotional shirt / It needn't end in tears / Shepherd is eternal / Bridge Of Inhibition
EEGCD 48 / Mar '87 / EG

☐ EARTHWORKS LIVE
Nerve / Up north / Stone's throw / Pilgrim's way / Emotional shirt / It needn't end in tears / All heaven broke loose / Psalm / Old song / Candles still flicker in Romania's dark / Brige of inhibition
CDVE 922 / Apr '94 / Virgin

☐ HEAVENLY BODIES (A Collection) (Bruford, Bill Earthworks)
Stromboli kicks / Making a song and dance / Up north / Candles still flicker in Romania's darkness / Pigalle / My heart declares a holiday / Temple of the winds / Nerve / Gentle persuasion / It needn't end in tears / Libreville / Dancing on Frith street / Bridge of inhibition
CDVE 934 / Jul '97 / Venture

☐ IF SUMMER HAD ITS GHOSTS
DGM 9705 / 29 Sep '97 / Discipline

☐ MASTER STROKES 1978-85
Hell's bells / Gothic 17 / Travels with myself / And someone else / Fainting in coils / Beelzebub / One of a kind / Drum also waltzes / Joe Frazier / Sahara of snow / Palewell park / If you can't stand the heat / Five G / Living space / Split seconds
EGCD 67 / Dec '88 / EG

☐ STAMPING GROUND
72438394762 / Aug '94 / Venture

☐ UPPER EXTREMITIES (Bruford, Bill & Tony Levin)
Cerulean sea / Original sin / Etude revisited / Palace of pearls / Fin de siecle / Drumbass / Cracking the midnight glass / Torn drumbass / Thick with thin air / Cobalt canyons / Deeper blue / President's day
DGM 9805 / 29 Jun '98 / Discipline

Bruijnje, Joep

☐ VITAMINS/MEDICINE
Trois sur quatre / Ghetto boy / Back to the border / Caroline / Twice a year / Just another day / Billy / Painting and drawing / Last one / Oh oh oh / She is in love / Little things / Remember this / Muscle of love / People / Sentimental mood / I'm living again / Make up / Let's close our eyes
BASTA 3090532 / Oct '97 / Basta

Bruisers

☐ ANYTHING YOU WANT...IT'S ALL RIGHT HERE
CYCD 107 / 2 Mar '98 / Cyclone

☐ BRUISERS BOX SET (4CD Set)
LF 999 / 16 Mar '98 / Lost & Found

☐ CRUISIN' FOR A BRUISIN'
LP 095 / Jul '94 / Lost & Found

☐ SOCIETY'S FOOLS
LF 142CD / May '95 / Lost & Found

☐ STILL STANDING UP
LF 280CD / May '97 / Lost & Found

☐ UP IN FLAMES
LF 215CD / Apr '96 / Lost & Found

Brujeria

☐ MATANDO GUEROS
Para de Venta / Leyes narcos / Sacrificio / Santa Lucia / Matando Gueros / Seis seis seis / Cruza la Frontera / Grenudos Locos / Chingo de Mecos / Narcos-Satanicos / Desperado / Culeros / Misas Negras (sacrificio III) / Chinga tu Madre / Verga del Brujo/Estan Chingados / Molestando Ninos Muertos / Machetazos / Castigo del Brujo / Christa de la Roca
RR 90612 / Sep '96 / Roadrunner

☐ RAZA ODIADA
RR 89232 / Sep '96 / Roadrunner

Bruneau, Jimmy

☐ DRUM DANCE OF THE DOGRIB
72933762602 / 19 May '98 / CYN

Brunel, Bunny

☐ DEDICATION
500362 / Nov '93 / Musidisc

Bruner, Cliff

☐ CLIFF BRUNER & HIS TEXAS WANDERERS 1937-1950 (5CD Set) (Bruner, Cliff Texas Wanderers)
So tired / Milk cow blues / Right key / You got to hi de hi / Shine / Can't nobody truck like me / Bringin' home the bacon / Under the silvery moon / Corrine Corrina / Four or five times / In the blue of the night / Oh you pretty woman / I ain't gonna give nobody none o' this jelly / Old fashioned love / Oh how I miss you tonight / One sweet letter from you / Dream train / Sun bonnet Sue / Tonight you belong to me / By a window at the end of the lane / Girl of my dreams / I saw your face in the moon / Red lips kiss my blues away / You can depend on me / In the blue of the night / Shine / Can't nobody truck like me / Sugar / My Daddy, my Mother and me / Truckin' on down / River stay away from my door / Baby won't you please come home / Beaumont rag / Annie Laurie / Bring it on home to Grandma / Ease my wearied mind / Remember / It makes no difference now / My bonnie lies over the ocean / Over moonlit waters / Draggin' the bow / Yearning just for you / Old Joe Turner blues / When you're smiling / Sister Kate / Sittin' on the moon / Kangaroo blues / I'll keep on loving you / I hate to lose you / Jessie / Over the hill / I'll keep on smiling / Truck driver's blues / I'm tired of you / Because / I'll forgive you / I'm still in love with you / Stardust / Other way / Peggy Lou / Singin' the low down blues down low / It's all over now / Tell me why little girl tell me why / Girl that you loved long ago / Little white lies / Kelly swing / San Antonio rose / Take me back again / You don't love me but I'll always care / I'm heading for that ranch in the sky / Over the trail / Ten pretty girls / Sorry / Sparkling blue eyes / New falling rain blues / I'll keep thinking of you / 'Neath the purple on the hills / 'Neath the purple on the hills / Draft board blues / I'll be faithful / Jesse's sister / Let me smile my last smile at you / Tequila rag / Red river rose / My time will come someday / Sun has gone down on our love / If it's wrong to love you / Born to be blue / Baby won't you tell me what you're doing to... / Snowflakes / That's what I like about the South / You took everything / My pretty blonde / You always hurt the one you love / Don't make me blue / Mother gave a son / I'll try not to cry / Won't you mend my aching heart / Roadhouse rag / Too wet to plow / Jessie / Lucille from mobile / You were all the world to me / You took advantage of a lonely heart / Honey what you doing to me / Santa Fe waltz / Rio Grande polka / Unfaithful one / San Antonio blues / Out of business / Mr. Postman / Ouch / You took advantage of a lonely heart / You better do better baby / Hard luck blues / Sweetest little Danny / I was a gambler in Texas / You've got to give me what's mine / I'm dying by pieces dear
BCD 15932 / Apr '97 / Bear Family

Brunet, Alain

☐ ROMINUS
LBLC 6541 / Jan '92 / Label Bleu

Bruninghaus, Ranier

☐ CONTINUUM
Strahlenspur / Stille / Continuum / Raga rag / Schattenfrei / Innerfern
8156792 / '90 / ECM

☐ FREIGEWEHT
Stufen / Spielraum / Radspuren / Die flusse hinauf / Freigeweht
8473292 / Feb '96 / ECM

Brunning Sunflower Blues Band

☐ TRACKSIDE BLUES
APCD 031 / Jun '94 / Appaloosa

Bruno, Francisco

☐ EL LUGAR (THE PLACE) (Bruno, Francisco & Richie Havens)
Sibo teaches the people to dance / El lugar (the place) / Yatagan / Alvorada / Night of magruna / World is so small / Three friends of winter / Baires / El lugar (the place) (instrumental)
CDSGP 063 / Aug '92 / Prestige

Bruno, Jimmy

☐ BURNIN
Eternal triangle / Pastel / One for Amos / Our love is here to stay / Burnin' / Moonlight in Vermont / Central Park West / Giant steps / Witchcraft / On the sunny side of the street / Rose for a peg / That's all
CCD 4612 / Sep '94 / Concord Jazz

☐ LIKE THAT
EV / Raezer's edge / Waltz for Nancy / There is no greater love / Uguana's uncle / Pat's house / Night dreamer / Way you look / Tonight / Like that / Stars fell on Alabama / Unit seven
CCD 4698 / Jun '96 / Concord Jazz

☐ LIVE AT BIRDLAND
F8 / Move / Groove yard / Valse hot / Segment / Au privava / These foolish things remind me of you / For JT / Anthropology / My one and only love
CCD 47682 / Jul '97 / Concord Jazz

☐ SLEIGHT OF HAND (Bruno, Jimmy Trio)
Egg plant pizza / Stompin' at the Savoy / Body and soul / Wheat thins / Night mist / Big shoes / Mandha de carnaval / Tenderly / Song for Jimmy and Susanna / All the things you are / Lionel's hat / Here's that rainy day
CCD 4532 / Nov '92 / Concord Jazz

Bruno's Salon Band

☐ LUCKY DAY
SOSCD 1251 / May '93 / Stomp Off

Brunsden, Martin

☐ OUT OF THE WOOD
IS 01CD / Apr '94 / Isis

Bruntnell, Peter

☐ CAMELOT IN SMITHEREENS
Panelbeater / Camelot in smithereens / Have you seen that girl again / I'm after you / Bewitched / 25 Reasons / Saturday Sam / Vera / Shake / Ellison
ALMCD 14 / 8 Sep '97 / Almost

Brus Trio

☐ AIM
DRCD 214 / Nov '87 / Dragon

Brutal Juice

☐ I LOVE THE WAY THEY SCREAM WHEN THEY DIE
VIRUS 157CD / Nov '94 / Alternative Tentacles

☐ I LOVE THE WAY...
VIRUSUK 157CD / 10 Nov '97 / Alternative Tentacles

Brutal Truth

☐ EXTREME CONDITIONS...
MOSH 069CD / 1 Sep '97 / Earache

☐ KILL TREND SUICIDE
RR 69482 / Feb '97 / Relapse

☐ NEED TO CONTROL
Collapse / Black door mine / Turn face / God player / I see red / Iron lung / Bite the hand / Ordinary madness / Media blitz / Judgement / Brain trust / Choice of a new generation / Mainliner / Displacement / Crawlspace
MOSH 11OCD / 1 Sep '97 / Earache

☐ SOUNDS OF THE ANIMAL KINGDOM
Dimentia / KAP / Vision / Fuck toy / Jiminez Cricket / Soft mind / Average people / Blue world / Callous / Fisting / Die laughing / Dead smart / Sympathy kiss / Pork farm / Promise / Foolish bastard / Postulate then liberate / Machine parts / In the words of Sun Ra / Unbaptise / Cybergod
RR 69682 / 27 Oct '97 / Relapse

Brutality

☐ SCREAMS OF ANGUISH
NB 075CD / Jul '93 / Nuclear Blast

☐ WHEN THE SKY TURNS BLACK
NB 1152 / Jan '95 / Nuclear Blast

Bruton, Stephen

☐ RIGHT ON TIME
DOS 7013 / Jul '95 / Dos

☐ WHAT IT IS
DOSCD 7002 / Sep '94 / Dos

Bruynel, Ton

☐ LOOKING EARS
BVHAASTCD 9214 / Oct '93 / Bvhaast

Bryan, Morgan

☐ ASLEEP WHILE THE RAIN FALLS
Sudan / Run / In the deepest reflection / Hunting / Lost this boy / Indian mist / Homecoming / In my eyes / You must have been waiting / Tides / Greatest truth / Gulf dancer / Flight of hyperion
DCD 01 / Oct '93 / Dox Music

☐ THORN
DT 11 / '94 / Dox Music

☐ UNDER EVERY SKY
DCD 02 / '94 / Dox Music

Bryant, Dana

☐ WISHING FROM THE TOP
Wishing from the top / Food / Dominican girdles / Margaret second cousin / Ode to chaka khan canis rufus / Heat (slight return) / Electric skies / Religion / Heavy mellow (too many) / Cat daddy at the sugah shack / Bone simple / Heat
9362456422 / Jul '96 / Warner Bros.

Bryant, Don

☐ COMIN' ON STRONG
Don't turn your back on me / Star of love / I'll do the rest / Lonely soldier / Call of distress / Is that asking too much / I'll go crazy / It's so lonely being me / Been so long / I will be true / I like it like that / My baby / Everything is gonna be alright / Glory of love / Comin' on strong / Can't hide the hurt / There is something on your mind (parts 1 and 2) / Shop around / What are you doing to my world
HIUKCD 133 / Aug '92 / Hi

☐ HI MASTERS, THE
I like it like that / Lonely soldier / Call of distress / Is that asking too much / There is something on your mind / I'll go crazy / Doing the mustang / What are you doing to my world / Clear days and stormy nights / Comin' on strong / Can't hide the hurt / Slip away / Every time I think of you I get the blues / My baby / Love's gonna live here again
HEX 32 / 4 Aug '98 / Hi

Bryant, Freddie

☐ BRAZILIAN ROSEWOOD
FSNT 035 / 1 Jun '98 / Fresh Sound New Talent

Bryant, Jimmy

☐ SUNTIDE DESERT JAM (Bryant, Jimmy & Jody Reynolds & Les Paul)
Out of nowhere / Jammin' the blues / Caravan / (Back home again in) Indiana / Rose of desert view / Speedo / I can't get started (with you) / Yakety axe / Undecided / Market street blues / Rose room / How high the moon
C5CD 611 / Feb '94 / See For Miles

Bryant, Leon

☐ FINDERS KEEPERS/MIGHTY BODY (HOTSY TOTSY)
Finders keepers / Your kind of loving / I'm gonna put a spell on you / Are you ready (until tonight) / You're my everything / Honey / I can see me loving you / Never / Mighty body (hotsy totsy) / Come and get it / Just the way you like it / Something more / You can depend on me / Can I / I promise / In the heat of the night
DEEPM 011 / Jan '97 / Deep Beats

Bryant, Ray

☐ HOT TURKEY
BB 881 / Apr '97 / Black & Blue

☐ MONTREUX 1977
Take the 'a' train / Georgia on my mind / Jungle town jubilee / If I could just make it to heaven / Django / Blues no. 6 / Satin doll / Sometimes I feel like a motherless child / St. louis blues / Things ain't what they used to be
OJCCD 371 / Nov '95 / Original Jazz Classics

☐ PLAYS BASIE AND ELLINGTON
Jive at five / Swingin' the blues / 9.20 special / Teddy the toad / Blues for Basie / I let a song go out of my heart / It don't mean a thing if it ain't got that swing / Things ain't what they used to be
8322352 / Mar '88 / ECM

☐ POT POURRI (Bryant, Ray Trio)
DB blues / One o'clock jump / Milestones / Undecided / In walked Bud / In a mellow tone / My one and only love / Night in Tunisia
OJCCD 936 / Jul '98 / Original Jazz Classics

☐ RAY BRYANT TRIO
Golden earrings / Angel eyes / Blues changes / Splittin' / Django / Thrill is gone / Daahoud / Sonar
OJCCD 793 / Nov '95 / Original Jazz Classics

☐ TRIBUTE TO HIS JAZZ PIANO FRIENDS, A (Bryant, Ray Trio)
C jam blues / In crowd / Duke / Doodlin' / Cast your fate to the wind / Cute / 'Round midnight / Moanin' / Sunshower / Hi-fly / Birdland
JVC 90312 / Feb '98 / JVC

Bryant, Rusty

☐ FIRE EATER
Fire eater / Free at last / Hooker / Mister S
PCD 10014 / Jun '96 / Prestige

□ FRIDAY NIGHT FUNK FOR SATURDAY NIGHT BROTHERS
Friday night funk for Saturday night brothers / Down by the Cuyahoga / Have you seen her / Mercy mercy mercy / Blues for a brother
PCD 10054 / Jun '96 / Prestige

□ LEGENDS OF ACID JAZZ, THE
Cootie boogaloo / Funky Mama / Funky rabbits / Night train / With these hands / Home fries / Cold duck time / Ballad of Oren Bliss / Lou Lou / Soul liberation / Freeze-dried soul
PRCD 24168 / Oct '96 / Prestige

Bryant, Willie

□ BLUE AROUND THE CLOCK
DEL 685CD / Feb '96 / Delmark

□ BLUES AROUND THE CLOCK
Amateur night in Harlem / Blues around the country / Blues around the country / Naggin' wife blues: *Pomus, Doc* / Blues without booze: *Pomus, Doc* / Sneaky Pete / Because your baby is on your mind / Honey in a hurry: *Watson, Laurel* / Blues around the clock / Blues around the clock / Alley alley blues: *Pomus, Doc* / Blues in the red: *Pomus, Doc* / Reboppin' for red: *Smith, Ben* / I found out: *Range, Bob* / Tell me: *Range, Bob* / Algiers blues / Phungie phungie an' stchew / Kangaroo blues: *Watson, Laurel* / I can't sleep: *Range, Bob* / You'll never miss the water 'til the well runs dry: *Range, Bob* / It's over because we're through: *Range, Bob*
DE 685 / Jun '97 / Delmark

□ CLASSICS 1935-1936
CLASSICS 768 / Aug '94 / Classics

Bryant's Jubilee Quartet

□ BRYANT'S JUBILEE QUARTET/ QUINTET 1928-1931
DOCD 5437 / May '96 / Document

Bryars, Gavin

□ FAREWELL TO PHILOSOPHY (Bryars, Gavin & English Chamber Orchestra/ James Judd)
Farewell to philosophy / One last bar, then Joe can sing / By the vaar
4541262 / Sep '96 / Point Music

□ HOMMAGES
My first hommage / English mail coach / Vespertine park / Hi-tremelo
TWI 0272 / Oct '93 / Les Disques Du Crepuscule

□ MAN IN A ROOM
4565142 / 15 Sep '97 / Point Music

□ SINKING OF THE TITANIC
TWI 9222 / Oct '93 / Les Disques Du Crepuscule
CDVE 938 / 15 Jun '98 / Venture

Bryden, Beryl

□ BERYL BYRDEN 1975 & 1984
ACD 113 / Aug '94 / Audiophile

□ I'VE GOT WHAT IT TAKES (A BBC Radio Celebration Of The Music Of Bessie Smith) (Bryden, Beryl & The Blue Boys)
Sunset Cafe stomp / Beale Street blues / Downhearted blues / I've got what it takes / St. Louis blues / Hotter than that / Trombone cholly / Nobody knows you when you're down and out / Cakewalking babies / Froggie more / Wild man blues / There'll be a hot time in the old town tonight / Gimme a pigfoot and a bottle of beer / Kitchen man / Forty and tight / Good man is hard to find / Young woman's blues / Alexander's ragtime band
LACD 71 / Oct '96 / Lake

Bryson, Jeanie

□ I LOVE BEING HERE WITH YOU
Cheek to cheek / Squeeze me in / Bittersweet / Sleeping bee / Love dance / I feel so smoochie / Cloudy morning / Sunshower / You've changed / Change partners / I love being here with you
CD 83336 / May '93 / Telarc

Bryson, Peabo

□ I'M SO INTO YOU (Bryson, Peabo & Natalie Cole)
Feel the fire / Reaching for the sky / Love walked out on me / Crosswinds / I'm so into you / Don't touch me / Let's fall in love / You send me / Love will find you / I love the way you love me / Turn the hands of time / Let the feeling flow / Give me your love / I believe in you / Tonight I celebrate my love
CTMCD 326 / Jul '97 / EMI

Brythoniaid Male Voice Choir

□ 20 OF THE BEST
Cymru'n un / Cymru'n un / Nant y mynydd / Santa lucia / Myfanwy / Jacob's ladder / Castilla / La vergine / Cytgan y morwyr / Lord's prayer / Ar hyd y nos / Llanfair / Pse wfary of waiting / Salm 23 / Mawr yw jehofa / Battle hymn of the republic / Ti a dy ddoniau / Rew-di-rano / Dry bones / Tros y garreg
SCD 2018 / Feb '93 / Sain

BSG

□ WARM INSIDE
XM 031CD / Apr '92 / X-Mist

BT

□ ESCM
Firewater / Orbitus teranium / Flaming June / Road to Lostwithiel / Memories in a sea of forgetfullness / Solar plexus / Nectar / Remember / Love peace and grease / Content
3984200652 / 22 Sep '97 / Perfecto/ East West

□ IMA
Quark / Nocturnal transmission / Sasha's voyage of ima / Tripping the light fantastic / Divinity
0630123452 / Oct '95 / Perfecto/East West

Buarque, Chico

□ SONHO DE UM CARNAVAL (2CD Set)
1917492 / Apr '97 / EPM

Bubble Puppy

□ GATHERING OF PROMISES, A
Hot smoke and sasafrass / Todds tune / I've got to reach you / Lonely / Gathering of promises / Hurry sundown / Elizabeth / It's safe to say / Road to St Stephens / Beginning
642038 / 1 Jun '98 / EVA

Buccaneer

□ CLASSIC
Intro - Moonlight Sonata / Bad man sonata / Gal skin fi bore: *Buccaneer & Red Rat* / Hold on pon him / Brick wall: *Buccaneer & Richie Stephens/Dennis Brown* / Nowadays woman / Poverty: *Buccaneer & Papa San* / Vintage old bruk: *Buccaneer & Papa San* / Skettel concerto / Hotter this year / Good director / Second place / Punky brewster / Stop light / Buccaneer medley / Real ganja man / Man tief sonata / Outro - Blue danube waltz
GRELCD 235 / Mar '97 / Greensleeves

□ THERE GOES THE NEIGHBOURHOOD
MAINCD 1 / Dec '94 / Main Street

Buchanan, Brian

□ AVENUES
Swampbird / First snow / Pettiford bridge / Old country / Getting sentimental over you / My foolish heart / Pumpkinhead / Buddy's tune / All of you / Samba de like you / What it is
JFCD 002 / Dec '94 / Jazz Focus

Buchanan, Isobel

□ SONGS OF SCOTLAND
John Anderson, My Jo / I'm owre young tae marry yet / Ye banks and braes o' bonnie Doon / Aye waukin' o / Comin' thro' the rye / Queen's mairies / My heart is sair / Deirdre's farewell to Scotland / Durisdeer / Rowan tree / Oor ain fireside / Mairi's wedding / Bonnie Earl O'Moray / Charlie is my darling / My ain folk
LCOM 6038 / Sep '95 / Lismor

□ WHITE CLIFFS OF DOVER, THE (Songs and Music of the 40's) (Buchanan, Isobel & English Chamber Orchestra)
Calling all workers / Dambusters march / Knightsbridge march / Spitfire prelude and fugue / There'll always be an England / We'll meet again / White cliffs of Dover / Nightingale sang in Berkeley square / When I grow too old to dream / Would you please oblige us with a Bren Gun / It's a lovely day tomorrow / I'll be seeing you / Love is the sweetest thing / All the things you are / Long ago and far away / So in love / Every time we say goodbye / I only have eyes for you / Always
CDDCA 598 / Nov '87 / ASV

Buchanan, Jack

□ ELEGANCE
Night time / Living in clover / Fancy our meeting / Oceans of time / Like Monday follows Sunday / When we get our divorce / Not bad / Dancing honeymoon / And her mother came too / Who / Now that I've found you / You forgot your gloves / One I'm looking for / Sweet so an so / I think I can / Dapper Dan / Alone with my dreams / Two little bluebirds / Goodnight Vienna / It's not you / There's always tomorrow
CDAJA 5033 / Apr '91 / Living Era

□ JACK BUCHANAN
Fancy our meeting / You forgot your gloves / I've looked for trouble / This year, next year / Goodnight Vienna / Chirp chirp / Leave a little for me / Dapper Dan / One good tune deserves another / Let's say goodnight till the morning / Stand up and sing / Alone with my dreams / Weep no more baby / Who / Take a step / I think I can / Now that I've found you / Yes Mr. Brown / Don't love you / Living in clover / Jack Buchanan medley
PASTCD 9763 / Nov '91 / Flapper

□ THIS'LL MAKE YOU WHISTLE
Leave a little for me / Like Monday follows Sunday / Everything stops for tea / From one minute to another / I'm still dreaming / I'm in a dancing mood / Now that I've found you / This'll make you whistle / Stand up and sing / I would if I could / Night time / It's not you / There's always tomorrow / Take it or leave it / Let's say goodnight till the morning / Help a lame dog / Oceans of time / Sun is round the corner / What a pleasant surprise / I'm simply wild about horses / Weep no more, my baby / Who do you think you are / Oceans of time
CMSCD 010 / Oct '91 / Movie Stars

Buchanan, Jim

□ SYSTEM AT WORK
AMI 9701CD / Mar '98 / AMI

Buchanan, Roy

□ BUCH AND THE SNAKE STRETCHERS
GCD 7519 / Jan '98 / Genes

□ DANCING ON THE EDGE
Peter Gunn / Chokin' kind / Jungle gym / Drowning on dry land / Petal to the metal / You can't judge a book by the cover / Cream of the crop / Beer drinking woman / Whiplash / Baby, baby, baby / Matthew
ALCD 4747 / May '93 / Alligator

□ HOT WIRES
High wire / That did it / Goose grease / Sunset over broadway / Ain't no business / Flash Gordon / 25 miles / These arms of mine / Country boogie / Blues lover
ALCD 4756 / May '93 / Alligator

□ MALAGUENA
11132 / Jul '97 / Annecillo

□ ROY BUCHANAN LIVE
Short fuse / Green onions / Strange kind of feeling / Pressure / Peter Gunn / Chicago smoke shop / Blues in E / Hey Joe / Foxy lady / Fantasia
CDCBL 758 / May '95 / Charly

□ SWEET DREAMS (The Roy Buchanan Anthology/2CD Set)
5170862 / Apr '96 / Polydor

□ WHEN A GUITAR PLAYS THE BLUES
When a guitar plays the blues / Mrs. Pressure / Nickel and a nail / Short fuse / Why don't you want me / Country boy / Sneaking Godzilla through the alley / Hawaiian punch / Chicago smokeshop
ALCD 4741 / Aug '92 / Alligator

□ YOU'RE NOT ALONE
SB 050 / 13 Jul '98 / Second Battle

Buchman, Rachel

□ JEWISH HOLIDAY SONGS FOR CHILDREN
ROUCD 8028 / Jan '94 / Rounder

□ SING A SONG OF SEASONS
ROUCD 8042 / May '97 / Rounder

Buck Naked

□ BAREBOTTOM BOYS, THE
HEYCD 0332 / Mar '98 / Heyday

Buck O Nine

□ PASS THE DUTCHIE
TVT 57652 / 18 May '98 / TVT

□ TWENTY EIGHT TEETH
TVT 57602 / Apr '97 / TVT

Buck Pets

□ TO THE QUICK
Living is the biggest thing / Shave / Walk it to the payphone / To the quick / Nothing's ever gonna be alright again / Smiler with a knife / C'mon baby / Crutch / Rocket to you / Car chase / Worldwide smile / Manatee / Bargain
727262 / Nov '93 / Restless

Buck Wild

□ BEAT ME SILLY
LOBSTER 1003CD / Jul '96 / Lobster/ Fat Wreck Chords

Buckethead

□ COLMA
Watching the boats with my dad / Wondering / Sanctum / Wishing well / Big sur moon / For mom / Hills of eternity / Whitewash / Lone sal bug / Ghost / Machete / Colma
VHOCD 9 / 25 May '98 / Higher Octave

Buckethead & Brain

□ PIECES
AVAN 054 / Jan '98 / Avant

Buckfunk 3000

□ FIRST CLASS TICKET TO TELOS
Intro / Fried funk and microchips / Planet shock future rock / March of the cybermen / Panic button / 3000 / Goodbye / Funkbwithu / Art of cybernetics / For funk's sake / I can't stop / First class ticket to Telos / Feedback
WORDD 007 / 23 Feb '98 / Language

Buckingham Banjos

□ BANJO SPECTACULAR (Buckingham Banjos & Fred Hartley)
4524942 / Mar '97 / Decca

Buckle, Jason

□ FLYING LO-FI
Cribbins (that howl) / Royal court / Let's get sectioned / Hobnobbin / Loose lumps on the forcourt / All 4's / Flex / Send him in Mistress Whip / Batty rhymer / Sod it till hometime / Kiss me quick / Get in that bloody house / Kengy the coalman / Cover me in tranzparent tatoos please / One for da laydeez / Don't force it baby girl / Fire when ready r kid / Cheap aftershave lingers longer / Heavy soil / Boz off / Pence fuck / Droppin off / Nowt to do wi'me / Riffy dips / Life in the Arndale Centre / Depressed mode / Fierce ogly / Pub grub for tea-time
CAT 064CD / 29 Jun '98 / Rephlex

Buckley, Jeff

□ GRACE
Mojo Pin / Grace / Last Goodbye / Lilac Wine / So real / Hallelujah / Lover you should've come over / Corpus christi carol / Eternal life / Dream brother
4759282 / Aug '94 / Columbia

□ LIVE AT SIN-E
Mojo pin / Eternal life / Je n'en connais pas la fin / Way young lovers do
ABB 61CD / Mar '94 / Big Cat

□ SKETCHES FOR MY SWEETHEART THE DRUNK (2CD Set)
Sky is a landfill / Everybody here wants you / Witches' rave / Morning theft / New year's prayer / Yard of blonde girls / Opened once / Vancouver nightmares by the sea / You and I / Nightmares by the sea / New year's prayer / Haven't you heard / I know I could be so happy baby (if we wanted to be) / Murder suicide / Meteor slave / Back in New York city / Gunshot glitter / Demon John / Your flesh is so nice / Jewel box / Satisfied mind
4886612 / 11 May '98 / Columbia

Buckley, Jimmy

□ COUNTRY FAVOURITES
RZCD 557 / Apr '96 / Ritz

Buckley, Tim

□ DREAM LETTER LIVE IN LONDON 1968 (2CD Set)
PT 340703CD / 11 May '98 / Manifesto

□ GREETINGS FROM LA
Move with me / Get on top / Sweet surrender / Night hawkin' / Devil eyes / Hong Kong bar / Make it right
7599272612 / Jan '96 / Elektra

□ HAPPY SAD
Strange feeling / Buzzin' fly / Love from room 109 at the islander / Dream letter / Gypsy woman / Sing a song for you
7559740452 / Feb '92 / WEA

□ HONEY MAN
ED 450CD / Nov '95 / Edsel

Buckner, Milt

□ GREEN ONIONS
Green onions / Sleep / Since I feel for you / Milt's boogie woogie / Sweet Georgia Brown / After you've gone / Pour toutes mes soeurs / Hard socks dance / That's all
BLE 590872 / Oct '94 / Black & Blue

□ MILT BUCKNER & ILLINOIS JACQUET (Buckner, Milt & Illinois Jacquet)
PCD 7017 / Aug '94 / Progressive

Buckner, Richard

□ BLOOMED
GRCD 340 / May '97 / Glitterhouse

Bucks Fizz

□ BEST AND THE REST, THE
MER 010 / Mar '93 / Tring

□ BEST OF BUCKS FIZZ
Land of make believe / Making your mind up / Piece of the action / I hear talk / Run for your life / Talking in your sleep / Now those days are gone / My camera never lies / If you can't stand the heat / Heart of stone / Magical / London town / One of those nights / Golden days
74321183272 / Feb '94 / Ariola Express

□ BEST OF BUCKS FIZZ
74321292792 / Jul '95 / RCA

□ BEST OF BUCKS FIZZ, THE
Land of make believe / My camera never lies / If you can't stand the heat / Piece of the action / Now those days are gone / Run for your life / Golden days / I hear talk / When we were young / Talking in your sleep / Heart of stone / One of those nights / Rules of the game / London town / Thief in the night / Making your mind up
74321446722 / Feb '97 / Camden

□ MAKING YOUR MIND UP (The Very Best Of Bucks Fizz)
Making your mind up / Land of make believe / I hear talk / My camera never lies / Now those days are gone / When we were young / Lazy with your love / Talking in your sleep / Piece of the action / If you can't stand the heat / Run for your life / One of those nights / London town / (Gimmie one more) chance / Let's party all night / New beginning
309102 / 13 Jul '98 / Hallmark

Buckshot Lefonque

□ MUSIC EVOLUTION
Here we go again / Music evolution / Wasineveritis / James Brown / Another day / Try these on / Buckshot rebuttal / My way (doin' it) / Better than I am / Paris is burning / Jungle grove / Weary with oil / Black Monday / Phoenix / Samba hop / ...And we out / One block past it
4841952 / May '97 / Columbia

Buckwheat Zydeco

☐ 100% FORTIFIED ZYDECO
CD 1024 / '88 / Black Top

☐ BUCKWHEAT ZYDECO & THE 11'S SONT PARTIS BAND (Buckwheat Zydeco & The 11's Sont Partis Band)
Hot tamale baby / Ya ya / Someone else is steppin' in / Lache pas la patate / Turning point / Walkin' to new orleans / Zydeco boogaloo / Your man is home tonight / Buck's boogie / Madame pitre / Help me understand you / Tutti fruttl / This must be love / Zydeco la louisianne / My feet can't fail me now / Tee nah nah / Warm and tender love
ROUCD 11528 / '88 / Rounder

☐ TURNING POINT
Turning point / Buck's boogie / Madame pitre / Zydeco boogaloo / Mon papa / Zydeco la louisianne / Help me understand you / I'm just so tired / Tutti fruttl / This must be love
ROUCD 2045 / '88 / Rounder

☐ WAITIN' FOR MY YA-YA
ROUCD 251 / '88 / Rounder

Bucky

☐ LIVE AT THE VINEYARD THEATRE (Bucky & John Pizzarelli)
CHR 70025 / Feb '96 / Challenge

Budapest Gypsy Orchestra

☐ BUDAPEST GYPSY ORCHESTRA
CDODE 1310 / Feb '90 / ODE

Budapest Klezmer Band

☐ YIDDISH FOLKLORE
HMA 1903070CD / Aug '94 / Musique D'Abord

Budapest Ragtime Band

☐ ELITE SYNCOPATIONS
CDPAN 122 / Apr '93 / Pan

Budd, Harold

☐ AGUA
SINE 003 / Sep '95 / Sine

☐ GLYPH
MTM 37 / Jul '96 / Made To Measure

☐ LOVELY THUNDER
Gunfighter / Sandtreader / Ice floes in Eden / Olancha farewell / Flowered knife shadows (for Simon Raymonde) / Gypsy violin
EEGCD 46 / Oct '86 / EG

☐ LUXA
Sidelong glance from my round neggertiti / Agnes Martin / Anish Kapoor / Paul McCarthy / Serge Poliakoff / Djion / Porphyry / How dark the response to our slipping away / Nove Alberi / Chet / Mandan / Ferai / Grace Marion Brown (sweet earth flying) / Steven Brown (pleasure)
ASCD 030 / Sep '96 / All Saints

☐ MOON AND THE MELODIES, THE (Budd, Harold & The Cocteau Twins)
Sea, swallow me / Memory gongs / Why do you love me / Eyes are mosaics / She will destroy you / Ghost has no home / Bloody and blunt / Ooze out and away, one how
CAD 611CD / Nov '86 / 4AD

☐ MUSIC FOR 3 PIANOS (Budd, Harold & Ruben Garcia & Daniel Lentz)
Pulse, pause, repeat / La muchacha de los suenos dorados / Iris / Somos tres / Messenger / La casa bruja
ASCD 014 / Dec '92 / All Saints

☐ PAVILION OF DREAMS, THE
Bismallahi'rrahmani'rrahim / Let us go into the House of The Lord / Butterfly Sunday / Madrigals of the rose ange / Juno
CDOVD 482 / Jun '97 / EG

☐ PEARL, THE (Budd, Harold & Brian Eno)
Late October / Stream with bright fish / Silver ball / Against the sky / Lost in the humming air / Dark eyed sister / Their memories / Pearl / Foreshadowed / Echo of night / Still return
EEGCD 37 / Jan '87 / EG

☐ SERPENT IN QUICKSILVER/ ABANDONED CITIES
Afar / Wanderer / Rub with ashes / Children on the Hill / Widows charm / Serpent in quicksilver / Dark star / Abandoned cities
ASCD 08 / Jun '92 / All Saints

☐ WHITE ARCADES, THE
White arcades / Balthus bemused by colour / Child with a lion / Real dream of sails / Algebra of darkness / Totems of the red sleeved warrior / Room / Coyote / Kiss
ASCD 03 / Jun '92 / All Saints

Budd, Roy

☐ REBIRTH OF THE BUDD
Fear is the key / Birth of the Budd / Get Carter / Soldier blue / Theme to Mr. Rose / Aranjeuz mon amour / Jesus Christ superstar / Whizz ball / In my hole / Too much attention / Lead on / Zeppelin / Carey treatment / Envy, greed and gluttony / Girl talk / Pavanne / Call me / Play thing / Little boat / So nice / Wonderful life is / Fields of green, skies of blue / Lust / Hurry to me / This hostage escapes
NEMCD 927 / Apr '97 / Sequel

Buddah On The Moon

☐ STRATOSPHERIC
DRIVE 12 / Jun '97 / Drive-In

Buddhist Monks Of Maitri Vihar Monastry

☐ TIBETAN MANTRAS AND CHANTS
IN 5730 / Nov '97 / Interra

Buddy & Ghost Riders

☐ FOR FOOLS ONLY
BRAM 1992322 / Nov '93 / Brambus

Budget Girls

☐ ON A TIGHT BUDGET
DAMGOOD 129CD / 9 Mar '98 / Damaged Goods

Budgie

☐ BANDOLIER
REP 4100 / Aug '91 / Repertoire

☐ BBC SESSIONS, THE
PILOT 042 / 1 Jun '98 / Burning Airlines

☐ BEST OF BUDGIE, THE
Breadfan / I ain't no mountain / I can't see my feelings / Baby, please don't go / Zoom club / Breaking all the house rules / Parents / In for the kill / In the grip of a tyre-fitter's hand
HMNCD 017 / 3 Nov '97 / Half Moon

☐ BUDGIE
REP 4012 / Aug '91 / Repertoire

☐ ECSTASY OF FUMBLING BOX (2CD Set)
REP 4435WO / 6 Jul '98 / Repertoire

☐ HEAVIER THAN AIR (2CD Set)
Rape of the locks / Rocking man / Young is a world / Sky high percentage / In the grip of a tyrefitters hand / I turned to stone / You're a superstar / She used me up / Hot as docker's armpit / Author / Whiskey river / Nude disentegrating parachutist woman / Breadfan / You're the biggest thing since powdered milk / Melt the ice away / In the grip of a tyrefitter's hand / Smile boy smile / In for the kill/You're the biggest thing since powdered milk / Love for you and me / Parents / Who do you want for your love / Don't dilute the water / Breakin' all the house rules / Breadfan
PILOT 42 / 17 Aug '98 / Burning Airlines

☐ IN FOR THE KILL
REP 4027 / Aug '91 / Repertoire

☐ NEVER TURN YOUR BACK ON A FRIEND
REP 4013 / Aug '91 / Repertoire

☐ ORNITHOLOGY VOL.1 (Six Ton Budgie)
Southern girl / Three legged race / Say it like it is / In the grip of a tyrefitter's hand / You know I will return / Martin John shuffle / Pink cadillac / Oh so far / Our life / Motorbiking / Young is a world / Dead to rights
AXEL/VINTAP 2 / Jul '97 / Axel/Vinyl Tap

☐ SQUAWK
Whiskey river / Rocking man / Rolling home again / Make me happy / Hot as a docker's armpit / Drug store woman / Bottled / Young is a world / Stranded
REP 4026 / Aug '91 / Repertoire

☐ UNPLUCKED (Six Ton Budgie)
VINTAP 001CD / 2 Feb '98 / Axel/Vinyl Tap

☐ WE CAME WE SAW (Live At The Reading Festival 1980/1982/2CD Set)
Breaking all the house rules / Crime against the world / Napoleon Bona / Forearm smash / Panzer division destroyed / Wildfire / I turned to stone / You're a superstar / She used me up / Breadfan / Forearm smash / Crime against the world / I turned to stone / Truth drug / You're a superstar / She used me up / Panzer division destroyed / In the grip of a tyrefitters hand / I turned to stone / You're a superstar / She used me up
PILOT 014 / 3 Nov '97 / Burning Airlines

Budha Building

☐ SOUNDS FROM THE ABNORMAL HEART
DSCD 001 / Jul '97 / TEQ

Bue, Papa

☐ 40 YEARS JUBILEE CONCERT (Bue, Papa Viking Jazz Band)
MECCACD 2010 / May '97 / Music Mecca

☐ COLLECTION, THE (2CD Set) (Bue, Papa Viking Jazz Band)
MECCACD 2101 / May '97 / Music Mecca

☐ DOWN BY THE RIVERSIDE 1969-1971 (Bue, Papa Viking Jazz Band)
STCD 5503 / May '97 / Storyville

☐ EVERYBODY LOVES SATURDAY NIGHT (Bue, Papa Viking Jazz Band)
Everybody loves Saturday night / Yellow dog blues / Blueberry Hill / Song was born / Weary blues / Tin roof blues / New Orleans / Mack the knife / Oh baby / I'm confessin' that I love you / Basin Street blues / Big butter and egg man / Maple leaf rag
CDTTD 590 / Nov '93 / Timeless Traditional

☐ ICE CREAM (Bue, Papa Viking Jazz Band)
MECCAVCD 1000 / Jul '93 / Music Mecca

☐ LIVE AT SLUKEFTER (Bue, Papa Viking Jazz Band)
MECCACD 1028 / Jun '93 / Music Mecca

☐ ON STAGE (Bue, Papa Viking Jazz Band)
CDTTD 511 / Sep '86 / Timeless Traditional

☐ TIVOLI BLUES (Bue, Papa Viking Jazz Band)
MECCACD 1001 / Aug '90 / Music Mecca

Buen, Knut

☐ AS QUICK AS FIRE
HSR 0002 / Mar '96 / Henry Street

☐ FJELLTRAMPEN
BK 20CD / Dec '97 / Buen

☐ HULDREJENTA
BK 17CD / Aug '97 / Buen

☐ LANGT INN I HUGHEIMEN
BK 19CD / Aug '97 / Buen

☐ MYLLARFYKEN
BK 18CD / Aug '97 / Buen

☐ SAMSPEL
BK 12CD / Mar '96 / Buen

☐ STEV OG SLATT (Buen, Knut & Agnes Buen Garnas)
BK 15CD / Aug '97 / Buen

Buffalo

☐ DEAD FOREVER
REP 4141 / Aug '91 / Repertoire

Buffalo Daughters

☐ CAPTIN VAPOUR ATHLETES
Counter parrot / Cold summer / Vampeee / Silver turkey / California blues / Dr. Moog / Brush your teeth / Kelly / Big Wednesday / Baby amoebae goes South / LI303VE / Vapour action fever / Designs and mistakes
GR 030CD / 10 Nov '97 / Grand Royal

☐ NEW ROCK
New rock / Rhythm and basement / Great five lakes / What's the trouble with my silver turkey / Autobacs / Socks drugs and rock and roll / Airport rock / Super blooper / Sad guitar / No Tokyo / No new rock / Sky high / Down sea / Jellyfish blues
GR 053 / 27 Apr '98 / Grand Royal

☐ SOCKS, DRUGS AND ROCK 'N' ROLL EP
GR 043CD / Jun '97 / Grand Royal

Buffalo Road

☐ HOTEL INCIDENT
OLKCD 002 / Apr '95 / Backwater

Buffalo Springfield

☐ AGAIN
Mr. Soul / Child's claim to fame / Everydays / Expecting to fly / Bluebird / Hung upside down / Sad memory / Good time boy / Rock 'n' roll woman / Broken arrow
7903912 / '88 / Atlantic

☐ BUFFALO SPRINGFIELD
For what its worth / Sit down I think I love you / Nowadays Clancy can't even sing / Go and say goodbye / Pay the price / Burned / Out of my mind / Mr. Soul / Bluebird / Broken arrow / Rock 'n' roll woman / Expecting to fly / Hung upside down / Child's claim to fame / Kind woman / On the way home / I am a child / Pretty girl why / Special care / Uno mundo / In the hour of not quite rain / Four days gone / Questions
756903892 / Feb '92 / Atlantic

☐ LAST TIME AROUND
On the way home / It's so hard to wait / Pretty girl why / Four days gone / Carefree country day / Special care / Hour of not quite rain / Questions / I am a child / Merry go round / Uno mundo / Kind woman
7567903932 / Mar '94 / Atlantic

☐ RETROSPECTIVE (The Best Of Buffalo Springfield)
For what it's worth / Hello Mr. Soul / Sit down I think I love you / Kind woman / Bluebird / On the way home / Nowadays Clancy can't even sing / Broken arrow / Rock 'n' roll woman / I am a child / Go and say goodbye / Expecting to fly
K 7904172 / Mar '88 / Atlantic

Buffalo Tom

☐ BIG RED LETTER DAY
Sodajerk / I'm allowed / Tree house / Would not be denied / Latest monkey / My responsibility / Dry land / Torch singer / Late at night / Suppose / Anything that way
BBL 142CD / 10 Nov '97 / Beggars Banquet

☐ BIRD BRAIN
Bird brain / Caress / Enemy / Fortune teller / Directive / Skeleton key / Guy who is me / Crawl / Baby / Bleeding heart
BBL 31CD / 10 Nov '97 / Beggars Banquet

☐ BUFFALO TOM
Sunflower suit / Plank / Impossible / 500,000 warnings / Bus / Racine / In the attic / Flushing stars / Walk away / Reason why
BBL 126CD / 10 Nov '97 / Beggars Banquet

☐ LET ME COME OVER
Staples / Taillights fade / Mountains of your head / Mineral / Dare / Larry / Velvet roof / I'm not there / Stymied / Porchlight / Frozen lake / Saving grace / Crutch
BBL 36CD / 10 Nov '97 / Beggars Banquet

☐ SLEEPY EYED
Tangerine / Summer / Kitchen door / Rules / It's you / When you discover / Sunday night / Your stripes / Sparklers / Clobbered / Sundress / Twenty points / Souvenir / Crueler
BBL 177CD / 10 Nov '97 / Beggars Banquet

Buffalo, Norton

☐ LOVIN' IN THE VALLEY OF THE MOON/ DESERT HORIZON
Lovin' in the valley of the moon / One kiss to say goodbye / Ghetto hotel / Nobody wants me / Puerto de azul / Hangin' tree / Another day / Rosalie / Jig is up / Eighteen wheels / Sea of key / Echoes of the last stampede / Desert horizon / Age old puppet / Wasn't it bad enough / Thinkin' 'bout you babe / Hopin' you'll come back / High tide in wingo / Walkin' down to Suzy's / Cold, cold city nights / Where has she gone / Sun comes in the morning / Anni in the morning
EDCD 431 / Jul '95 / Edsel

Buffett, Jimmy

☐ ALL TIME GREAT HITS
Margaritaville / Fins / Come Monday / Volcano / Changes in latitudes / Cheeseburger in paradise / Son of a son of a sailor / Stars fell on Alabama / Miss you so badly / Why don't we all get drunk / Pirate looks at forty / We went to Paris / Grapefruit - juicy fruit / Pencil thin mustace / Boat drinks / Chanson pour les petits enfants / Banana republic / Lat mango in Paris
PLATCD 4903 / Sep '94 / Platinum

☐ DON'T STOP THE CARNIVAL
Intro / Public relations / Caraloo / Island fever / Sheila says / Just an old truth teller / Henny's song / Kinja rules / Thousand steps to nowhere / It's all about the water / Champagne si, Agua no / Public relations / Handiest Frenchman in the Caribbean / Hippolyte's habitat / Who are you trying to fool / Fat person man / Up on the hill / Domicile / Funeral dance / Time to go home
5244852 / 18 May '98 / Island

Bufford, Mojo

☐ STATE OF THE (BLUES) HARP
Picking / Groundhog blues / Mo's stroll / Jealous of my baby / I'm a blueman / I wanna know why / Jack potato boogie / Come home baby / Big leg woman
JSPCD 233 / Mar '90 / JSP

Buford, Mojo

☐ HOME IS WHERE MY HARP IS
BLN 032CD / 15 Jun '98 / Blue Loon

☐ STATE OF THE BLUES HARP
Picking rags / Groundhog blues / Mo's stroll / Jealous of my baby / I'm a blues man / I wanna know / Jack potato boogie / Come home baby / Big leg woman / Watch dog / Jealous of my baby / Mo's stroll / Deep sea diver / Picking rags
JSPCD 2108 / Jun '98 / JSP

Bug

☐ TAPING THE CONVERSATION
WSCD 018 / Jun '97 / Word Sound Recordings

Bug Guts

☐ BIG BOWL OF WARM FUR
VC 102 / Nov '96 / Vinyl Communication

Bug, Steve

☐ RELEASED TRACKS
RAW 610CD / Dec '96 / Raw Elements

Bugbear

☐ PLAN FOR THE ASSASINATION OF
THE BUGBEAR
Theme from the bugbear / (I got a) New crush / Ride roughshod / Punkist / Mystic boy / Marlin / Damaged III / Dando motherfucker / Fucking through / Triple-brrr / Panik / I love the girl with the money shot face / Teen city intrigue / I like violence / 22 Boy whore / I hate my band
MASKCD 049 / Jun '95 / Vinyl Japan

Bugnon, Cyrille

☐ SOUTHERN PERSPECTIVE (Bugnon,
Cyrille Quartet)
Jook joint blues / Black Nile / Tribulations of a cat in
Dog City / Spring can really hang you up the most / Southern perspective / Upper Manhattan medical group / Magnetic fields
TCB 98302 / 27 Jul '98 / TCB

Bugs

☐ INFINITE SYNDROME
UR 027 / 16 Dec '97 / Ubiquity

Bugskull

☐ CROCK
DRL 028 / Jan '97 / Darla

☐ DISTRACTED SNOWFLAKE VOL.1
DRL 031 / Jun '97 / Darla

☐ SNAKLAND
SCR 020 / Dec '96 / Scratch

Buhaina

☐ SWALLOWS AND AFRICANS
IRO 9601CD / 16 Jul '97 / Iroko

Buhalis, Chris

☐ KENAI DREAMS
Kenai dreams / Footprints in the snow / Time / Employee 1209 / Clay pigeons / Plant me I will grow / Where I lead me / Mary's song / How to be alone / Highway shoes / Small disguise
OMC 0008 / 20 Apr '98 / One Man Clapping

Buhlan, Bully

☐ DIE LICHTER VON BERLIN
BCD 16188 / May '98 / Bear Family

☐ LINKS EIN MADCHEN, RECHTS EIN
MADCHEN
Rauber rock / Links ein madchen, rechts ein madchen / Du wirst niemals ein cowboy sein / Mir ist so dideldadeldum / Eine frau muss man kussen / Leo, Leo, Leo / Irgendwann, irgendwie, irgendwo / So schon ist Melanie / Signorina aus Messina / Sowas wie dich / Wie lange das noch gut geht / Heute abend ball (im alten ballhaus) / Ich schreibe meiner frau heut' einen liebsb / Kannst du das vergessen / Einmal blond, einmal braun / Fragen sie den fachmann / Ja, der Tobby (choo choo eisenbahn) / Du bist ja viel zu schade / Das war der sch.hinderhannes / Eine marchenweise / Wenn der regen nicht wer / Damals waren wir sechzehn / Dieser tag / Uber leierlastenmann / Ich hab' mich so an dich gewohnt / Ich hab' noch einen koffer in Berlin / Das war sein milljoh / Lass mich dein primaner auf der 'prima' sein
BCD 16136 / Apr '97 / Bear Family

Buick 6

☐ CYPRESS GROVE
TX 1003CD / Jan '94 / Taxim

☐ JUICE MACHINE
TX 1014CD / Apr '96 / Taxim

Buick MacKane

☐ PAWN SHOP YEARS, THE
End / Falling down again / Black shiny beast / Edith / Queen Anne / Say goodnight / Big shoe head / John Conquest, you've got enough dandruff on / Wandering eye / Loose
RCD 10361 / Feb '97 / Rykodisc

Built To Spill

☐ NORMAL YEARS, THE
KLP 52CD / May '96 / K

☐ PERFECT FROM NOW ON
Randy described eternity / I would hurt a fly / Stop the show / Made up dreams / Velvet waltz / Out of site / Kicked it in the sun / Untrustable/Part 2
EFA 0499226 / Feb '97 / City Slang

☐ THERE'S NOTHING WRONG WITH
LOVE
EFA 049632 / Oct '95 / City Slang

Buju Banton

☐ BUJU BANTON MEETS GARNETT SILK
AND TONY REBEL (Buju Banton &
Friends)
RNCD 2033 / Oct '93 / Rhino

☐ INNA HEIGHTS
PHCD 2068 / 17 Nov '97 / Penthouse

☐ MR. MENTION
Batty rider / Love how the gal dem flex / Long black woman / Love how you sweet / Woman no fret / Have to get you tonight / Dickie / Love me brownin' / Buju movin' / Who say / How the world a run / Bona fide love
5220222 / Jan '94 / Mercury

☐ TIL SHILOH
Shiloh / Till I'm glad to rest / Murderer / Champion / Untold stories / Not an easy road / Only man / Complaint / Chuck it so / How could you / Wanna be loved / It's all over / Hush baby hush / What you're gonna do / Rampage
5241352 / Jul '95 / Island

☐ VOICE OF JAMAICA
Searching / Red rose / Commitment / Deportees / No respect / If loving was a crime / Good body / Wicked act / Tribal war / Little more time / Him take off / Willy (don't be silly) / Gone a lead / Make my day / Operation ardent
5180132 / Aug '93 / Mercury

Bulag, Ci

☐ MORIN HUUR
VICG 52122 / Feb '96 / JVC World
Library

Bulgarian National Folk Ensemble

☐ PIRIN FOLK
Bulgarian folk medley (excerpt) / Pirin horo / Mori ezh / Oi, dano, dano / Raiki v grandina / Vila se gora / Mladezhiko horo / Koito me chue / Mori aresah si / Oplakva se ptichka / Doidi ludo / Sbor se sbira / Zvonche dranka / Bre ovcharche / Pesen and tanz / Tragna moma za voda / Aide horo / Kavali svirat / Yuzhni pesni / Altun maro / Proletni pesni / Na megdana
CDPT 827 / Jun '94 / Prestige

Bulgarka Junior Quartet

☐ FETES TRADITIONNELLES
BULGARES
D 2550 / Nov '96 / Studio SM

☐ LEGEND OF THE BULGARIAN VOICES
EUCD 1331 / Nov '95 / ARC

Bull City Red

☐ COMPLETE RECORDINGS 1935-1939
SOB 035272 / Dec '92 / Story Of The
Blues

Bull, Geoff

☐ GEOFF BULL
LB 9791 / Jul '98 / La Brava

☐ VINTAGE GEOFF BULL
BCD 356 / Nov '96 / GHB

Bull, Sandy

☐ INVENTIONS
TRS 60042 / 2 Feb '98 / Timeless

Bulldog Breed

☐ MADE IN ENGLAND
SPMWRCD 0052 / Jun '97 / Worldwide

Bullet In The Head

☐ JAWBONE OF AN ASS
ORGAN 0112 / May '94 / Lungcast

Bullet LaVolta

☐ GIFT, THE
TAANG 29CD / Nov '92 / Taang

Bullhead, Earl

☐ LAKOTA SONGS, THE
SPALAX 14871 / Oct '96 / Spalax

Bullitnuts

☐ 1ST OF THE DAY
PORK 036 / Sep '96 / Pork

☐ DIFFERENT BALL GAME
PORK 054 / 27 Jul '98 / Pork

☐ NUT ROAST
PORK 046 / 29 Sep '97 / Pork

Bullock, Hiram

☐ CARRASCO
What you want / It do for love / Carrasco / We're gonna get it right / Can't hide love / Montevideo / And the melody lingers on / Bean burrito / Don't you worry 'bout a thing / Amazonas / Backdoor man
FCD 96792 / Nov '97 / Ace

Bullyrag

☐ SONGS OF PRAISE
Jump up in a fashion / Learn to live / You can have me / This / Summer daze / Plague / Frantic / It makes me laff / Wishing / I will learn
5683292 / 1 Jun '98 / Vertigo

Bumble Bee Slim

☐ UNISSUED TEST PRESSINGS AND
ALTERNATE TAKES 1934-1937
DOCD 5570 / 21 Sep '97 / Document

Bumble Bees

☐ BUMBLE BEES
HBCD 0012 / 17 Nov '97 / Hummingbird

Bum's Rush

☐ BUM'S RUSH
Kitchen sync / Who's Jud / Bummin' around / Full metal boob toob / Unpickin' the fishnet / Hyper tresco / You say potato / In the pocket / Sniff the g-lover / Hail bobber / Mr Phixit
MACD 011 / 23 Feb '98 / M

Bunch, John

☐ JOHN BUNCH PLAYS KURT WEILL
CRD 144 / Mar '96 / Chiaroscuro

☐ SOLO PIANO
ARCD 19184 / Sep '97 / Arbors Jazz

☐ STRUTTIN' (Bunch, John & Phil
Flanagan)
ARCD 19157 / May '97 / Arbors Jazz

Bundrick, John 'Rabbit'

☐ DREAM JUNGLE
RMCCD 0199 / May '96 / Red Steel

☐ RUN FOR COVER
RMCCD 0198 / Jul '96 / Red Steel

☐ SAME OLD STORY
RMCCD 0182 / Aug '96 / Red Steel

☐ TOUR GUIDE
RMCCD 0204 / Jul '96 / Red Steel

Bunka, Roman

☐ COLOUR ME CAIRO
ENJACD 90832 / Dec '95 / Enja

Bunn, Teddy

☐ SPIRITS OF RHYTHM
JSPCD 307 / Apr '89 / JSP

Bunnett, Jane

☐ RENDEZ VOUS BRAZIL/CUBA
Baiao do porao / Pam Pam / Ritos de angola / Choro de pere / Barreto / For you / Forro na vovo / Um a zero / Rendez-vous / Sweet melody
JUST 742 / Aug '96 / Justin Time

☐ WATER IS WIDE, THE
Elements of freedom / Time again / Real truth / Serenade to a cuckoo / You must believe in spring / Influence peddling / Pannonica / Brakes' sake / Burning tear / Lucky strike / Water is wide / Rockin' in rhythm
ECD 220912 / Jul '94 / Evidence

Bunny & Ricky

☐ FREEDOM FIGHTER
ART 06 / 1 Dec '97 / Black Art

Bunny Melody

☐ TRUE TO YOU
Never love this way again / Everybody bawling / Still missing you / Before the next teardrop falls / True to you / Four seasons / Rumour / You're a lady / Think it over / Impossible love / Lonely girl / Miss you tonight / Money / Ettie (sweet and dandy) / Victors cup
CDSGP 0399 / Jun '98 / Prestige

Bunny Rugs

☐ TALKING TO YOU
GRELCD 215 / May '95 / Greensleeves

Burach

☐ BORN TIRED
How on Earth / Funky fat challenge / Nothing left to say / Highfield set / Drop my body / Born tired / Ring around the moon / Antidote / Sleep of the dead / Smuggler's skull and cross bones / You're not the only one / Destitution / Lullaby
CDTRAX 136 / Jul '97 / Greentrax

☐ WEIRD SET, THE
All I ask / Boiling black kettle / Curve / Post-conscious modernisation of outer space / Candlelight reel / Jar o'lentils / Zombie song / Return to Milltown / Tarbolton lodge / Oni bucharesti / Green Loch / Vincent black lightening 1952 / Rest of your life / January the 8th / Concertina / Dick Gossips / Earl's Wallfray round / Walking the line / What shall we drink to tonight
CDTRAX 093 / Jul '95 / Greentrax

Burbank, Albert

☐ CREOLE CLARINETS (Burbank, Albert
& Raymond Burke)
MG 9005 / Feb '95 / Mardi Gras

Burch, Elder J.E.

☐ COMPLETE RECORDED WORKS
1927-29 (Burch, Elder J.E. & Rev.
Beaumont)
DOCD 5329 / Mar '95 / Document

Burch, Paul

☐ PAN-AMERICAN FLASH
Big "g" / Big "g" / Ballad for trombone / All creatures great and small / Ticket to ride / La belle americaine / Simoraine / Holiday for strings / Blaythorne suite / Mozart rondo / Dunlapps creek / Simple girls / Superman
CPR 004 / 16 Feb '98 / Checkered

Burdett, Phil

☐ PATCHOULI ELECTRIC
CDSGP 0291 / Jul '96 / Prestige

Burdon, Eric

☐ BEAST OF BURDON
Dey won't / Wall of silence / Street walker / Lights out / It hurts me too / Bird on the beach / Take it easy / Crawling king snake / No more elmore / Road
RTD 39700162CD / 1 Dec '97 / Institute
Of Art

☐ BIG HITS (2CD Set)
CPCD 82882 / Jul '97 / Charly

☐ ERIC BURDON DECLARES WAR
Vision of Rassan / Dedication / Roll on Kirk / Tobacco Road / I have a dream / Blues for the Memphis Slim / Birth / Mother Earth / Mr. Charlie / Danish pastry / You're no stranger
74321305262 / Sep '95 / Avenue

☐ ERIC BURDON LIVE
RRCD 220 / Jul '96 / Receiver

☐ GREATEST HITS
House of the rising sun / Spill the wine / San Franciscan nights / Help me girl / Bring it on home to me / We gotta get out of this place / Don't let me be misunderstood / White houses / Anything / Monterey / When I was young / CC rider / Boom boom / I'm crying / It's my life / Don't bring me down
RM 1542 / Apr '97 / BR Music

☐ HOUSE OF THE RISING SUN
House of the rising sun / Spill the wine / San Franciscan nights / Help me girl / Bring it on home to me / We've gotta get out of this place / Don't bring me down / It's my life / I'm crying / Boom boom / CC rider / When I was young / Monterey / Anything / White houses / Night / Gonna send you back to Walker / Inside looking out / Don't let me be misunderstood
WB 885942 / 2 Feb '98 / Disky

☐ LIVE AT THE ROXY
CDTB 184 / 28 Nov '97 / Thunderbolt

☐ LOST WITHIN THE HALLS OF FAME
I used to be an animal / When we were a gang / American dreams / Rock and roll shoes / Memories of Anna / New Orleans rap / I will be with you again / Brand new day / Nightrider / Going back to Memphis / Leo's place / Woman's touch / Is there another world / Don't shoot me
JETCD 1011 / Feb '98 / Jet

☐ MASTERS, THE
EABCD 073 / 24 Nov '97 / Eagle

☐ MISUNDERSTOOD
AIM 1054 / Oct '95 / Aim

☐ NIGHTWINDS DIE
RTD 39700873CD / 22 Jun '98 / Institute
Of Art

☐ RARE MASTERS VOL.1
SPV 08589992 / Mar '96 / SPV

☐ RARE MASTERS VOL.2
SPV 08544232 / Aug '96 / SPV

☐ SOLDIER OF FORTUNE
Heart attack / Power company / Highway mover / Wicked man / Ghetto child / Portrait of a soldier / Devil's daughter / Comeback / You can't kill my spirit / Yes indeed, yeah / House of the rising sun / Ghetto child (reprise)
CDTB 180 / Feb '97 / Thunderbolt

☐ THAT'S LIVE (Burdon, Eric & The Band)
INAK 854 CD / '88 / In Akustik

Burgess, John

☐ KING OF THE HIGHLAND PIPERS
TSCD 466 / May '93 / Topic

☐ PIPING CENTRE 1996 RECITAL
SERIES VOL.2, THE (Burgess, John/
Donald MacPherson)
Delvinside/Highland lassie going to the fair/Pretty apron: Bugpes, John / Taken from hell/The Lewis soldier/Thick lies the mist: Burgess, John / Roes among the heather/Hiro hirum/Lewis wedding: Burgess, John / Mundo MacLeod/Colonel Davidson/ Jeannie Carruthers/Achany Gle: Burgess, John / 74th's farewell to Edinburgh: Burgess, John / Swallow-tailed coat/Turf lodge: Burgess, John /

Lord Alexander Kennedy/Delvinside/Pretty Marion: *Burgess, John / Tom Bigbee* waltz/Bobby Cuthbertson/Ballachulish walkabout: *Burgess, John* / March of the Cameron men: *Burgess, John* / Captain E.B.B. Tawse, V.C.: *MacPherson, Donald* / Marion's hornpipe/Alan MacPherson of Mosspark: *MacPherson, Donald* / Hugh Kennedy MA, BSc/ Trevisans' march: *MacPherson, Donald* / Caber feidh/The shepherd's crook/Alick C. MacGregor: *MacPherson, Donald* / Smith of Chillichassie/Too long in this condition: *MacPherson, Donald* / Duchess of Edinburgh/Arniston Castle/John MacKechnie: *MacPherson, Donald* / Knightswood ceilidh/Major D. Manson at Clachantrushal: *MacPherson, Donald* / Calum Beag/Donnie MacGregor/Donald Cameron's powder horn: *MacPherson, Donald* / Curlew: *MacPherson, Donald*
COMD 2067 / Aug '97 / Temple

Burgess, Mark

☐ **PARADYNING (Burgess, Mark & Yves Altana)**
GOODCD 8 / Oct '95 / Dead Dead Good

☐ **SPRING BLOOMS TRA LA LA (2CD Set)**
INDIGO 11742 / Oct '96 / Indigo

Burgess, Sally

☐ **OTHER ME, THE**
DMHCD 7 / Oct '96 / Timbre

Burgess, Sonny

☐ **1956 - 1959**
We wanna boogie / Red headed woman / Prisoner's song / All night long / Life's too short to live / Restless / Ain't got a thing / Daddy blues / Fannie Brown / Ain't gonna do it / You / Hand me down my walking cane / Please listen to me / Gone / My babe / My bucket's got a hole in it / Sweet misery / What'cha gonna do / Oh mama / Truckin' down the avenue / Feelin' good / So glad you're mine / One night / Always will / Little town baby / You're not mine / Mr. Blues / Find my baby for me / Tomorrow night / Tomorrow never comes / Skinny Ginny / So soon / Mama Loochie / Mama Loochie / Itchy / Thunderbird / Kiss goodnight / Sadie's back in town / Smoochin' Jill / My baby loves me / One broken heart
BCD 15525 / Jul '91 / Bear Family

☐ **ARKANSAS WILD MAN, THE**
We wanna boogie / Red headed woman / Prisoner's song / Restless / Ain't got a thing / Daddy blues / Hand me down my walking cane / Fannie Brown / One broken heart / Gone / Please listen to me / My babe / Sweet misery / Oh mama / Truckin' / Down tha avenue / What'cha gonna do / So glad you're mine / One night / My little town baby / Mr. Blues / Find my baby for me / Tomorrow night / Skinny Ginny / Mama Loochie / Sadie's back in town
CPCD 8103 / Jun '95 / Charly

☐ **RAZORBACK TAPES, THE (Burgess, Sonny & The Pacers/Bobby Crafford)**
CLCD 4405 / Oct '96 / Collector/White Label

☐ **SONNY BURGESS**
ROUCD 3144 / Jun '96 / Rounder

Burgin, 'Rockin' Johnny

☐ **STRAIGHT OUT OF CHICAGO (Burgin, 'Rockin' Johnny Band)**
House band blues / Undercover lover / Got my eyes on you / If you got money / Sweet thing / Stranger blues / Cut you a loose / Stompin' at the fishmarket / My woman is gone / Tend to your business / Sugar mama / I wanna boogie / Tribute to fast fingers
DE 720 / Jul '98 / Delmark

Burgos, 'Wild' Bob

☐ **HOMETOWN ROCKIN'**
PT 606001 / Jun '96 / Part

☐ **REBEL KEEPS ROCKIN', THE**
Right behind you / White lightning / Salt Box Hill / Hypnotised / Dreamland boogie / Long live rock'n'roll / Emma / Reedin' the blues / It's been a long time / Whatever will be will be (que sera sera) / Back seat driver / Beware of the hound / Ride on rebels / Forever rockin' / Taste of wild berries / Mumbo jumbo / Beat the clock / I'm telling you now
RAUCD 024 / Jun '97 / Raucous

Burke, Alan

☐ **ON THE OTHER HAND**
APB 001CD / Aug '97 / Gurug

Burke, Joe

☐ **BUCKS OF ORANMORE, THE (Burke, Joe & Charlie Lennon)**
Yellow tinker/The Sally Gardens / Connachtman's rambles/The cat in the corner / Dillon's fancy/Toss the feathers / Frieze breeches / Beeswing/Tailor's twist / Paddy Kelly's reels / Rambles of Kitty/Sacko's jig / High level/Western / Master Crowley's/Jug of punch / Golden eagle/Fiddler's contest / Trim the velvet / PJ Moloneys/Paddy Fahy's / Mullingar Lea/ Crooked road to Dublin / Job of Journeywork/The blackbird / Humours of Ennistymon/Larry O'Gaff / Wonder/Liverpool hornpipe / Willie Coleman's/ Dinny O'Brien's / Bucks of Oranmore
GLCD 1165 / Feb '97 / Green Linnet

☐ **HAPPY TO MEET, SORRY TO PART**
Dowd's no.9/The Galway rambler / Dowd's no.9/ The Galway rambler / Bonaparte's retreat / Captain Kelly's/Jennie's wedding / Maid on the mountain / Bells of Tipperary/Miss Galvin's reel / Father O'Flynn/Haste to the wedding / Rogaire dubh/Split the whisker / Boyne hunt/Come West along the road / High reel/Geoghegan's reel / Cherish the ladies / Dunlavin green / Star of Munster/The blackberry blossom / Happy to meet and sorry to part/Paddy in London / Aggie Whyte's/Miss Thornton (reels)
GLCD 1069 / Feb '93 / Green Linnet

☐ **PURE IRISH TRADITIONAL MUSIC ON THE ACCORDION**
Lambert's jig / Knockagow / Richard Dwyer's / Paddy Kelly's / Morrison's / Molly's / Jackson's jig / Ivy leaf / Ginley's fancy / Last night's fun / Hut in the bog / Music in the glen / Green fields of America / Paddy Fahy's / Pigeon on the gate / Bunch of key's / Ballinasloe fair / Drunken tinker / Fahy's / Port padraig na carra / Frost is all over / Spike island lassies / Farewell to Leitrim / Return from Camden Town / Ton Moyland's frolic / Limestone rock / Boyne hunt
PTICD 1015 / Mar '97 / Pure Traditional Irish

☐ **TAILOR'S CHOICE, THE**
Dark woman of the Glen / Mills are grinding/Paddy Doorhy's reel / Green blanket / Dean Brig of Edinburgh / Jack Coughlan's fancy / Coolin' / Sean Reid's fancy/Kerry reel / Mama's pet/Tailor's choice / Blind Mary / Humours of Quarry Cross/Jackson's bottle of brandy / Roisin Dubh / Fort of Kincora/ Caroline O'Neill's hornpipe / Were you at the Rock / Limestone rock/Banshee reel / O'Rahilly's grave
GLCD 1045 / Aug '93 / Green Linnet

☐ **TRADITIONAL MUSIC OF IRELAND**
Bucks of Oranmore/Wind that shakes the barley / Dogs among the bushes/Gorman's / Trip to the cottage/Tatter Jack Walsh / Minny Foster/The banks / Sporting Nell/Boyne hunt / Murray's fancy/Smell of the bog / Patsy Tuohey's/Molly Ban / College groves/Flogging reel / Jackson's reel / Grey goose/ Sixpenny money / Bonnie Kate/Jenny's chickens / Galway bay/Contradiction / Pat burke's jigs/ Fraher's jigs / Longford spinster/Paddy Lynn's delight
GLCD 1048 / Jun '93 / Green Linnet

Burke, Keni

☐ **NOTHIN' BUT LOVE**
XECD 12 / 30 Mar '98 / Expansion

Burke, Kevin

☐ **CELTIC FIDDLE FESTIVAL (Burke, Kevin & Johnny Cunningham/Christian Lemaitre)**
Melodie/Rondes de Loudeac / Melodie/Rondes de Loudeac / Dionne reel/Mouth of the Tobique / Larides de pontivy et de josselin / Mist covered mountains of home / Pigeon on the gate/Lafferty's/ Morning dew / Suite de Loudeac / Canyon moonrise
GLCD 1133 / Oct '93 / Green Linnet

☐ **CELTIC FIDDLE FESTIVAL ENCORE (Burke, Kevin & Johnny Cunningham/ Christian Lemaitre)**
Ward's favourite/Morning star / La jolie bataliere/ Rondes de loudiac / Hector the hero / Medley / Up in the air/Across the black river/All in good time / Marches et gavottes pourlet / Johnny's big set / Teolena/Marche de Roskonval/Sandizan / Ton bale pier baudouin/Dans fisel / Farewell to Ireland/ Foxhunter's reel / Two andros/Andros psg / Dark island
GLCD 1189 / May '98 / Green Linnet

☐ **EAVESDROPPER (Burke, Kevin & Jackie Daly)**
LUNCD 039 / Aug '94 / Mulligan

☐ **HOOF AND MOUTH (Burke, Kevin & Open House)**
Tour de taille / Drag her round the road / Sporting Paddy / Connemara stockings / Jame's Keanes / Okarina / Tattoo / Hoof and mouth / Oedipus rex / Split rock / Pipe on the hob / Blue adder / When I die / Paddy the caffler / Glen cottage polka / Tolka polka / Dueino kolo / Tour de traille / Kivatasaluevalssie / Bright sunny south
GLCD 1169 / Mar '97 / Green Linnet

☐ **IF THE CAP FITS**
Kerry reel/Michael Coleman's reel/Wheels of the world / Dinney Delaney's/Yellow wattle / Mason's apron/Laington's reel / Paddy Fahy's jigs/Cliffs of Moher / Star of Munster / Biddy Martin's and Bill Sullivan's polkas/Ger the Rigger / Bobby Casey's hornpipe / Toss the feathers / College groves/Pinch of snuff/Earl's chair / Woman of the house/Girl that broke my heart/Drunken tinker / Paddy Cronin/ McFadden's handsome daughter / Hunter's purse/ Toss the feathers
GLCD 3009 / Aug '92 / Green Linnet
LUNCD 021 / Dec '97 / Mulligan

☐ **IN GOOD COMPANY (The Very Best Of Kevin Burke)**
REMCD 512 / Feb '98 / Reactive

☐ **OPEN HOUSE**
Bus stop reel-miss mccloud's reel-lost indian / Fraílich / Open house-two to the bar-porter for three / Bourrees / Crawley's reel-the house of hammill-the mullingar races / Humours of ennistyman-old as the hills / Untitled reel-queen of the may-the congress / Glory in the meeting house / La partida / Long acre-clyde's banks / Mickey the moulder-stan chapman's
GLCD 1122 / Jun '92 / Green Linnet

☐ **PORTLAND (Burke, Kevin & Michael O'Dohmnhaill)**
Maudabawn chapel/Wild Irishman/Moher reel / Eirigh a shiuir / Breton Gavottes / Rolling waves/ Market town/Scatter the mud / Aird ui chumhaing / Paddy's return/Willy Coleman's/Up in the air / Lucy's fling/S'iomadh rud a chunnaic mi/Some say the Devil i / Is fada Liom Uaim I / Tom Morrison's/ Beare Island reel/George White's favourite / Dipping the sheep
GLCD 1041 / Oct '88 / Green Linnet

☐ **PROMENADE**
LUNCD 028 / Aug '94 / Mulligan

☐ **SWEENEY'S DREAM**
OSS 18CD / Mar '94 / Ossian

☐ **UP CLOSE**
Lord Gordon's reel / Finnish polka/Jessica's polka / Thrush in the straw/Health to the ladies/Boys of the town / Tuttle's reel/Bunch of green rushes/Maids of Mitchelstown / Shepherd's daughter/Jerusalem ridge / Michael Kennedy's reel / Bloom of youth/ Molloy's favourite/Cabin hunter / Boys of Ballycastle/Stack of barley / Raheen medley / Rambler/Chapel bell / Peeler's jacket/Flax in bloom/ Eileen curran / Orphan/Mist on the mountain/Stolen purse
GLCD 1052 / Feb '90 / Green Linnet

Burke, Malena

☐ **SALSEANDO**
Homenaje a matamoros / Longina / Chencha la gamba / Comprension / Me voy p'al pueblo / Bruca manigua / Capullito de aleli / De noche / Realidad y fantasia / Que bella es Cuba / El madrugador / Seguire sin sonar
PSCCD 1006 / Feb '95 / Pure Sounds From Cuba

Burke, Raymond

☐ **IN NEW ORLEANS (Burke, Raymond & Cie Frazier)**
Gypsy love song / Hindustan / Dead bug blues / Wonderful one / I want somebody to love / At sundown / Oh daddy / All that I ask is love / I surrender dear / Sweet little you / Honky tonk town / Maybe you're mine / Blues in A flat / Dirty rag / All by myself
504CDS 27 / Mar '98 / 504

☐ **RAYMOND BURKE & HIS SPEAKEASY BOYS**
AMCD 47 / Jan '94 / American Music

Burke, Solomon

☐ **DEFINITION OF SOUL, THE**
VPBCD 38 / Jan '97 / Virgin

☐ **GREATEST HITS**
Down in the valley / Just out of reach / How many times / Baby (I wanna be loved) / Gotta travel on / Looking for my baby / I'm hanging up my heart for you / Cry to me / I almost lost my mind / Tear fell / Be bop Grandma / Keep the magic working
RSACD 859 / Jan '97 / Sequel

☐ **HOME IN YOUR HEART (The Best Of Solomon Burke)**
Home in your heart / Down in the valley / Looking for my baby / I'm hanging up my heart for you / Cry to me / Just out of reach / Goodbye baby (baby goodbye) / Words / Stupidity / Send me some lovin' / Go on back to him / Baby (I wanna be loved) / Can't nobody love you / Got to get you off my mind / Someone to love me / You're good for me / Dance, dance, dance / Everybody needs somebody to love / Tonight's the night / Baby, come on home / If you need me / Price / Get out of my life woman / Save it / Take me (just as I am) / When she touches me / I wish I knew (how it would feel to be free) / Party people / Keep a light in the window / I feel a sin coming on / Meet me in the church / Someone is watching / Detroit city / Shame on me / I stayed away too long / It's just a matter of time / Since I met you baby / Time is a thief / Woman how do you make me love you like I do / It's been a change / What'd I say
8122702842 / Jul '93 / Atlantic

☐ **I WISH I KNEW**
I wish I knew (How it would feel to be free) / Get out of my life woman / Meet me in church / By the time I get to Phoenix / Then you can tell me goodbye / What'd I say / Since I met you baby / Save it / Shame on me / Why, why, why / I feel a sin coming on / Lawdy Miss Clawdy / Mountain of pride / Suddenly / Keep lookin' / I stayed away too long / I need your love so bad
RSACD 863 / Mar '97 / Sequel

☐ **IF YOU NEED ME**
If you need me / Words / Stupidity / Go on back to him / I said I was sorry / It's alright / Home in your heart / I really don't want to know / You can make it if you try / Send me some lovin' / This little ring / Tonight my heart she is crying
RSACD 860 / Jan '97 / Sequel

☐ **KING OF ROCK 'N' SOUL, THE**
Good rockin' tonight / My babe / Lonesome highway / Letter from my darling / Sweet walkin' woman / Everybody needs somebody to love / If you need me/ Tonight's the night/I almost lost my mind / Down in the valley / Got to get you off my mind
CDBTEL 7006 / May '97 / Black Top

☐ **KING OF SOUL**
Boo hoo hoo / Hold on I'm comin' / Sweeter than sweetness / Sidewalks, fences and walls / Let the love flow / More / Lucky / Please come back home to me
CPCD 8014 / Feb '94 / Charly

☐ **KING SOLOMON (The Soul Sounds Of Solomon Burke)**
It's been a change / Take me as I am / Time is a thief / Keep a light in the window / Baby, come on home / Detroit city / Someone is watching / Party people / When she touches me / Woman how do you make me / It's just a matter of time / Presents for Christmas / Only love can save me now / I don't want you anymore / Can't stop loving you now
RSACD 862 / Mar '97 / Sequel

☐ **LIVE AT HOUSE OF BLUES**
BT 1108CD / Dec '94 / Black Top

☐ **ROCK 'N' SOUL**
Goodbye baby goodbye / Cry to me / Won't you give him (one more) / If you need me / Hard, ain't it hard / Can't nobody love you / Just out of reach / You're too good for me / You can't love them all / Someone to love me / Beautiful brown eyes / He'll have to go / Everybody needs somebody / Yes I do / Price / Got to get you off my mind / Peepin' / Little girl that loves me / Dance dance dance / Maggie's farm
RSACD 861 / Mar '97 / Sequel

☐ **SOUL ALIVE**
Everybody needs somebody to love / I almost lost my mind / Just out of reach / If you need me / Tonight's the night / You're good for me / What am I living for / Monologue / Take me (just as I am) / Down in the valley / Proud Mary / Tonight's the night (reprise) / Beautiful brown eyes / Just a matter of time / Hold what you've got / He'll have to go / Cry to me / Gotta get you off my mind / Meet me in the church / Price / Words / Send me some lovin' / Having a party / Amen
ROUCD 11521 / Oct '96 / Rounder

☐ **SOUL OF THE BLUES**
BT 1095CD / Jan '94 / Black Top

☐ **VERY BEST OF SOLOMON BURKE, THE**
Just out of my reach / Cry to me / Down in the valley / I'm hanging up my heart for you / If you need me / Can't nobody love you / You're good for me / Goodbye baby / Everybody needs somebody to love / Price / Got to get you of my mind / Tonight's the night / Someone is watching / Take me just as I am / I wish I knew (how it would feel to be free) / Soul meeting (the soul clan)
8122729722 / 4 May '98 / Rhino

Burland, Dave

☐ **BENCHMARK**
FC 004CD / Jul '94 / Fat Cat

☐ **HIS MASTERS CHOICE**
RGFCD 009 / '92 / Road Goes On Forever

☐ **ROLLIN'**
BURL 01CD / Aug '97 / Burl

Burman, Karin & Peter

☐ **GROWING GREEN**
GIM 003 / May '97 / Gimli

Burn, Chris

☐ **HENRY COWELL CONCERT, A**
ACTA 7 / Oct '94 / Acta

☐ **MUSIC FOR THREE RIVERS**
VICTOCD 050 / Nov '97 / Victo

☐ **NAVIGATIONS (Burn, Chris Ensemble)**
ACTACD 12 / Jun '98 / Acta

Burnel, Jean-Jacques

☐ **EUROMAN COMETH**
Euroman / Jellyfish / Freddie Laker (Concorde and Eurobus) / Euromess / Do the European / Tout comprendre / Triumph (of the good city) / Pretty face / Crabs / Eurospeed (your own speed) / Deutschland nicht uber alles
EW 002CD / 11 May '98 / Eastworld

Burnell, Kenny

☐ **MOON AND SAND**
Moon and sand / My ship / For once in my life / UMMG / Blue bossa / Stolen moments / Love for sale / Lost in the stars
CCD 4121 / Jun '92 / Concord Jazz

Burnett, John

☐ **OH BABY (Burnett, John Jazz Bandits)**
PKCD 099 / May '98 / PEK

Burnett, Neil

☐ **INTO THE GREEN**
Sutil / Pomegranate / Away in Killarney/Planxty Racher / Orion's belt / Snowball fight / Lethe/ Reunion / Into the green/Race to 5 bolts bridge / Luna increscens/Sol invictus / Moira / Midsummer storm / Journey of the Magi / Audience of birds / Into the green
RECD 524 / Apr '98 / REL

Burnett, Rev. J.C.

☐ **REV. J.C. BURNETT VOL.1 1926-1927**
DOCD 5557 / 21 Sep '97 / Document

☐ **REV. J.C. BURNETT VOL.2 1927-1945**
DOCD 5558 / 21 Sep '97 / Document

Burnett, Richard D.

☐ **RICHARD D. BURNETT 1926-1930**
DOCD 8025 / May '98 / Document

Burnett, T-Bone

☐ **B52 BAND & THE FABULOUS SKYLARKS**
We have all got a past / Bring me back again / Now I don't mind no light sermon / Wouldn't you think I'd know by now / You been away for so long / Sliding by / Hot rod banjo / Mama please don't you lie / Clarification blues / Money changer / I don't wanna hear you cry no more / Linda Lu
EDCD 568 / 6 Jul '98 / Edsel

☐ BEHIND THE TRAP DOOR
Strange combination / Amnesia and jealousy (oh Lana) / Having a wonderful time wish you were here / Law of average / My life and the women who lived it / Welcome home, Mr.Lewis
VEXCD 3 / Aug '92 / Demon

☐ TRUTH DECAY
Quicksand / Talk talk talk talk talk / Boomerang / Love at first sight / Madison Avenue / Drivin' wheel / Come home / Power of love / House of mirrors / Tears, tears, tears / Pretty girls / I'm coming home
FIENDCD 71 / Jun '97 / Demon

Burnette, Dorsey

☐ GREAT SHAKIN' FEVER
Great shakin' fever / Don't let go / Dying ember / Raining in my heart / Sad boy / He gave me my hands / Good good lovin' / Full house / Feminine touch / It's no sin / Creator / Biggest lover in town / Buckeye road / That's me without you / No one but him / Cry for your love / Rains came down / Country boy in the army / Somebody nobody wants / It could've been different / Little child / With all your heart / Look what you've missed / Gypsy magic / I would do anything
BCD 15545 / '93 / Bear Family

Burnette, Johnny

☐ 25 GREATEST HITS
Dreamin' / You're sixteen / Little boy sad / Clown shoes / Big big world / Girl of my best friend / Moody river / Mona Lisa / Dream lover / Fool / You're the reason / Lovers question / Let's think about living / Settin' the woods on fire / Cincinnati fireball / Sweet Suzie / Cryin' in the chapel / It's only make believe / Walk on by / (I wish it was Saturday night) All week long / Love me / That's the way I feel / Don't do it / Opposite / Girls
4954822 / 6 Jul '98 / EMI Gold

☐ BURNETTE BROTHERS, THE (Burnette, Johnny & Dorsey)
RSRCD 005 / Dec '94 / Rockstar

☐ DREAMIN'/JOHNNY BURNETTE
Dreamin' / Lovesick blues / Please help me, I'm falling / Haul off and love me one more time / Love me / Kaw-Liga / Settin' the woods on fire / I want to be with you always / Cincinnati fireball / My special angel / Finders keepers / I really don't want to know / You're sixteen / Crying in the chapel / Dream lover / Oh lonesome me / I beg your pardon / I love you baby / Little boy sad / It's only make believe / Singin' the blues / You're so fine / I go down to the river / Let's think about living
BGOCD 329 / Dec '96 / Beat Goes On

☐ HITS AND OTHER FAVOURITES/ ROSES ARE RED
You're the reason / Dreamin' / Just out of reach / Moody river / Girl of my best friend / You're sixteen / Little boy sad / Walk on by / Little bitty tear / God country and my baby / Hello walls / Big big world / Girls / Red sails in the sunset / Ballad of the one eyed jacks / Treasure of love / Blue blue morning / Memories are made of this / Pledge of love / I'm still dreamin' / Roses are red / Lonesome waters / Clown shoes / Fool of the year / Poorest boy in town / I've got a lot of things to do / Girls / Honestly I do / Choo choo train / Angry at the big oak tree / When today is a long time ago / Way I am
BGOCD 406 / 3 Aug '98 / Beat Goes On

☐ ORIGINAL, THE
You're sixteen / Dreamin' / Little boy sad / Big big world / God country and my baby / Cincinnati fireball / Girls / Settin' the woods on fire / Clown shoes / Damn the defiant / Opposite / Sweet Suzie / I beg your pardon / (I go) down to the river / I've got a lot of things to do / Fool of the year
TO 886262 / 2 Feb '98 / Disky

☐ ROCK 'N' ROLL TRIO/TEAR IT UP (Burnette, Johnny Rock 'N' Roll Trio)
Honey hush / Lonesome train (on a lonesome track) / Sweet love on my mind / Rockabilly boogie / Lonesome tears in my eyes / All by myself / Train kept a rollin' / I just found out / Your baby blue eyes / Chains of love / I love you so / Drinkin' wine spo-dee-o-dee / Tear it up / You're undecided / Oh baby babe / Eager beaver baby / Touch me / Midnight train / If you want it enough / Blues stay away from me / Shattered dreams / My love, you're a stranger / Rock therapy / Please don't leave me
BGOCD 177 / Jun '93 / Beat Goes On

☐ ROCKABILLY BOOGIE (The Complete Recordings) (Burnette, Johnny Rock 'N' Roll Trio)
Rockabilly boogie / Please don't leave me / Rock therapy / Lonesome train (on a lonesome track) / Sweet love on my mind / My love, you're a stranger / Your baby blue eyes / I love you so / Train kept a rollin' / All by myself / Drinkin' wine spo-dee-o-dee / Blues stay away from me / Honey hush / Lonesome tears in my eyes / I just found out / Chains of love / Lonesome train (on a lonesome track) / I love you so (master) / If you want it enough / Butterfingers / Eager beaver baby / Touch me / Tear it up / Oh baby babe / You're undecided / Midnight train / Shattered dreams
BCD 15474 / '88 / Bear Family

☐ THAT'S THE WAY I FEEL
RSRCD 006 / Dec '94 / Rockstar

Burnin' Chicago Blues Machine

☐ BOOGIE BLUES
GBW 003 / Mar '92 / GBW

Burnin' Rain

☐ RITUAL MEDICINE SHOW
ME 1001 / May '97 / Mind Eye

Burning Flames

☐ FAN DE FLAMES
BF 015 / Jul '97 / JW

☐ WORKEY WORKEY (Highlights From The 9th Cartagena Festival)
CPCD 8134 / Jan '96 / Charly

Burning Heads

☐ BE ONE WITH THE FLAMES
Time's up / Gigi pirate / Wise guy / Groundtown / Gray / Wrong / Draw your breaks / No reply / Make believe / Time to split / Nothing / PFK / Fuck Ip / Shoes / All's fine
65332 / 11 May '98 / Epitaph

Burning Red Ivanhoe

☐ BURNING RED IVANHOE
REP 4209 / Aug '91 / Repertoire

Burning Sky

☐ CREATION
CR 7027CD / Nov '96 / Canyon

Burning Spear

☐ ALIVE IN CONCERT (2CD Set)
122252 / 20 Jul '98 / Musidisc

☐ APPOINTMENT WITH HIS MAJESTY
Appointment with His Majesty / Play Jerry / Reggae physician / Music / African Jamaican / Loving you / My island / Don't sell out / Commercial development / Glory be to Jah / Clean it up / Come in peace
HBCD 20605 / Jun '97 / Heartbeat

☐ BURNING SPEAR
Far over / Burning spear / Greetings / Image / Rock / Education / She's mine / Message / Oh jah / Jah is my driver
SOCD 0150 / 15 Jun '98 / Studio One

☐ CHANT DOWN BABYLON (The Island Anthology/2CD Set)
Marcus Garvey / Slavery days / I and I survive / Old Marcus Garvey / Tradition / Invasion / Door peep / No more war / Black soul / Man in the hills / Cultivation / Sun / Throw down your arms / It's a long way round / Dry and heavy / Black disciples / Lion / Jordan river / Jah no dead / Marcus children suffer / Social living / Marcus say Jah no dead / Nyah Keith / Civilize reggae / Mek we dweet / My roots / Recall some great men / Great men's dub / One people / African woman / Jah kingdom / Praise him / Should I / Estimated prophet / Thank you
5241902 / Jul '96 / Island Jamaica

☐ DRY AND HEAVY
Any river / Sun / It's a long way around / IWIN / Throw down your arms / Dry and heavy / Wailing / Disciples / Shout it out
RRCD 40 / Jul '93 / Reggae Refreshers

☐ FAR OVER
HBCD 11 / '88 / Heartbeat

☐ FITTEST OF THE FITTEST, THE
Fittest of the fittest / Fireman / Bad to worst / Repatriation / Old Boy Garvey / 2000 years / For you / In Africa / Vision
HBCD 22 / '88 / Heartbeat

☐ HAIL HIM
African teacher / African postman / Cry blood Africa / Hail HIM / Jah a go raid / Columbus / Road foggy / Follow Marcus Garvey / Jah see and know
HBCD 145 / Jun '94 / Heartbeat

☐ LIVE 1993
503582 / Sep '94 / Declic

☐ LIVING DUB VOL.1
HBCD 131 / Jun '93 / Heartbeat

☐ LIVING DUB VOL.2
HBCD 132 / Jan '94 / Greensleeves

☐ LIVING DUB VOL.3
8425392 / 5 May '98 / Declic

☐ LOVE AND PEACE (Live)
CDHB 175 / Jan '95 / Heartbeat

☐ MEK WI DWEET
Mek wi dweet / Garvey / Civilization / Elephants / My roots / Great man / African woman / Take a look / One people / Mek we dweet in dub
CIDM 1045 / Jun '90 / Mango

☐ ORIGINAL BURNING SPEAR, THE
SONCD 0023 / Apr '92 / Sonic Sounds

☐ RASTA BUSINESS
406042 / Nov '95 / Declic

☐ REGGAE GREATS
Door peep / Slavery days / Lion / Black disciples / Man in the hills / Tradition / Throw down your arms / Social living / Marcus Garvey / Dry and heavy / Black wa-da-da (Invasion) / Sun
5525852 / Jul '97 / Spectrum

☐ RESISTANCE
Resistance / Mek we yadd / Holy foundation / Queen of the mountain / Force / Jah say / We been there / Jah feeling / Love to you
HBCD 33 / '88 / Heartbeat

☐ ROCKING TIME
SOCD 1123 / 2 Feb '98 / Studio One

☐ SOCIAL LIVING
Marcus children suffer / Social living / Nayah Keith / Institution / Marcus senior / Civilised reggae / Mr. Garvey / Come / Marcus say Jah no dead
BAFCD 4 / Oct '94 / Blood & Fire

☐ WORLD SHOULD KNOW, THE
HBCD 119 / Feb '93 / Greensleeves
8412122 / May '96 / Declic

Burning Star

☐ BURNING STAR
ABS 207 / 1 Sep '98 / ABS

Burns, Eddie

☐ DETROIT (Burns, Eddie Band)
Orange driver / When I get drunk / Kidman / Bottle up and go / Inflation blues / Detroit / Butterfly / Boom boom / Time out / New highway 61 / Blue jay
ECD 260242 / Feb '92 / Evidence

Burns, Hugh

☐ DEDICATION
BRGCD 15 / Nov '95 / Bridge

Burns, Jerry

☐ JERRY BURNS
Pale red / Casually unkind / Hardly me / Fall for lovers / Sometimes I'm wild / Crossing over / Simple heart / Completely my dear / Safe in the rain / Stepping out slowly
4716452 / Jun '92 / Columbia

Burns, Jimmy

☐ LEAVING HERE WALKING
Leaving here walking / Twelve year old boy / Miss Annie Lou / Whiskey headed woman / One room country shack / Shake your boogie / Better know what you're doing / Rollin' and tumblin' / Gypsy woman / How many times / Mean mistreating mama / Notoriety woman / Talk to me / Catfish blues
DE 694 / Jun '97 / Delmark

Burns, Kenneth Jethro

☐ BYE BYE BLUES
ACD 26 / 3 Aug '98 / Acoustic Disc

Burns, Robert

☐ COMPLETE SONGS OF ROBERT BURNS VOL.1, THE (Various Artists)
When rosy May comes in wi' flowers / O, that I had ne'er been married / Wee Willie Gray / O wha'll mow me now / Brose and butter / Wintry West extends his blast / Sweet Afton / Duncan Gray cam here to woo / Winter it is past / Guide 'en to you kimmer / Kellyburn braes / Slave's lament / Of a the airts the wind can blaw / What can a young lassie / Ay waulkin O / O steer her up, an huad her gaun / Cooper o' Cuddy / O rattlin roarin Willie / To the weavers gin ye go / Lady Mary Ann / Montgomerie's Peggy / Lea rig / Yestreen I had a pint o' wine
CKD 047 / Mar '96 / Linn

☐ COMPLETE SONGS OF ROBERT BURNS VOL.2, THE (Various Artists)
Soldier's return / Reel O' Stumpie / I hae a wife o'ma ain / My Nanie O / Ye Jacobites by name / Rantin, rovin Robin / O let me in this ae night / Auld man's mare's dead / How cruel are the parents / Leezie Lindsay / My wife's a wanton wee thing / To Daunton me / Hey ca' thro / De'il's awa' wi' tha exciseman / Silver tassie / Kissin my Katie / Scots wha hae / O were I on Parnassus Hill / O an ye were dead gudeman / Willie Wastle / Beware o' bonnie Ann / Willie brew'd a peck o' maut / Rosebud by my early walk / Whistle o'er the lave o't / Jumpin John / Dusty miller / My collier laddie / Weary pund o' tow / Now westlin winds
CKD 051 / May '96 / Linn

☐ COMPLETE SONGS OF ROBERT BURNS VOL.3, THE (Various Artists)
CKD 062 / Aug '97 / Linn

☐ COMPLETE SONGS OF ROBERT BURNS VOL.4, THE (Various Artists)
CKD 083 / 26 Jan '98 / Linn

☐ PRIDE AND PASSION (The Songs Of Robert Burns) (Various Artists)
John Anderson / Whistle o'er the lave o't / O wert thou in the cauld blast / Green grow the rashes / Rosebud / Parcel o' rogues / Ca' the Yowes / Rantin' dog / Eppie McNab / Ae fond kiss / Man's a man for a' that / Duncan Gray / Auld lang syne / Rattlin', roarin' Willie / Rantin', rovin' Robin
RECD 503 / Jan '98 / REL

Burns Sisters

☐ CLOSE TO HOME
CDPH 1178 / Aug '95 / Philo

☐ IN THIS WORLD
Dance upon this Earth / I won't turn my back / Old friend / My father's blue eyes / Far from my home / Working girl blues / Can I walk away tonight / Heavenly blue / In this world / Stay away from me / Owl / Johnny's got a gun / No more silence
CDPH 1198 / Feb '97 / Philo

☐ TRADITION (Holiday Songs Old & New)
Songs we love / O come O come Emmanuel / Golden cradle / Little drummer boy / Children go where I send thee / Silent night / Come come / What child is this / Shaloo shalom / This Christmas / Tibetan prayer for peace
CDPH 1208 / Dec '97 / Philo

Burnside, R.L.

☐ ACOUSTIC STORIES
When my first wife left me / Death bell blues / Skinny woman / Monkey in the pool room / Hobo blues / Walking blues / Long haired doney / Poor black mattie / Meet me in the bottom / Miss glory B / Kind-hearted woman blues
MC 0034 / Nov '97 / MC

☐ ASS POCKET 'O' WHISKEY
Goin' down south / Boogie chillen / Poor boy / 2 Brothers / Snake drive / Shame'n on down / Criminal inside me / Walkin' blues / Tojo told Hitler / Have you ever been lonely
OLE 2142 / Jun '96 / Matador

☐ MISSISSIPPI BLUES (Le Blues Dans Sa Tradition La Plus Pure)
Jumper hanging out on the line / Sweet little angel / Long haired donkey / Nightmare blues / Poor black Mattie / Catfish blues / Death bells / Dust my broom / Bad luck and trouble / Rollin' and tumblin' / When my first wife quit me
ARN 60397 / 21 Aug '97 / Arion

☐ MR. WIZARD
Going over the hill / Alice May / Georgia woman / Snake drive / Rolling tumbling / Out on the road / Highway 7 / Tribute to Fred / You gotta' move
03012 / Mar '97 / Epitaph

☐ SOUND MACHINE GROOVE
HMG 6501 / Aug '97 / Hightone

☐ TOO BADD JIM
03072 / 17 Nov '97 / Fat Possum

Burnweed

☐ MASTERPIECE
SLVN 002 / 30 Mar '98 / Recognition

Burrage, Ronnie

☐ SHUTTLE
SSCD 8052 / Apr '94 / Sound Hills

Burrell, Dave

☐ HIGH WON - HIGH TWO
BLCD 760206 / Nov '95 / Black Lion

☐ IN CONCERT (Burrell, Dave & David Murray)
VICTOCD 016 / Nov '94 / Victo

☐ WINDWARD PASSAGES
ARTCD 6138 / Feb '94 / Hat Art

Burrell, Kenny

☐ BEST OF KENNY BURRELL, THE
Now see how you are / Cheetah / DB Blues / Phinupi / Chitlins con carne / Midnight blue / Love your spell is everywhere / Loie / Daydream / Togethering / Summertime / Jumpin' blues / Jeannine
CDP 8304932 / Apr '95 / Blue Note

☐ BLUE LIGHTS (2CD Set)
Phinupi / Yes baby / Scotch blues / Man I love / I never knew / Caravan / Chuckin' / Rock salt / Autumn in New York
CDP 8571842 / Aug '97 / Blue Note

☐ BLUESY BURRELL (Burrell, Kenny & Coleman Hawkins)
Tres palabras / No more / Guilty / Monotono blues / I thought about you / Out of this world / It's getting dark / I never knew
OJCCD 926 / Jun '97 / Original Jazz Classics

☐ ELLINGTON A LA CARTE
Take the 'A' train / Sultry serenade / Flamingo / In a mellow tone / Don't worry 'bout me / Azure / I ain't got nothin' but the blues / Do nothin' 'til you hear from me / Mood indigo
MCD 5435 / Jul '95 / Muse

☐ GUITAR FORMS (Remastered) (Burrell, Kenny & Gil Evans)
5214032 / Oct '97 / Verve Master Edition

☐ JAZZ MASTERS
5276522 / 5 May '98 / Verve

☐ JAZZMEN DETROIT
Afternoon in Paris / You turned the tables on me / Apothegh / Your host / Cotton tail / Tom's thumb
SV 0176 / Oct '97 / Savoy Jazz

☐ KENNY BURRELL AND JOHN COLTRANE (Burrell, Kenny & John Coltrane)
911900482 / 7 Apr '98 / JVC

☐ LAID BACK
60412320642 / 27 Apr '98 / Thirty Two

☐ LIVE AT THE BLUE NOTE
Tones for Joan's bones / Entertainer / Embraceable you / Quasi Modo / Dear Ella / Birk's works / I've got a crush on you / Take the 'A' train / All blues / Groove merchant
CCD 4731 / Nov '96 / Concord Jazz

☐ LIVE AT THE VILLAGE VANGUARD (Burrell, Kenny Trio)
All night long / Will you still be in my mind / I'm a fool to want you / Trio / Broadway / Soft winds / Just a sittin' and a rockin' / Well you needn't / Second balcony jump / Willow weep for me / Work song / Woody 'n' you / In the still of the night / Don't you know I care (or don't you care to) / Love you madly / It's getting dark
LEJAZZCD 22 / Feb '94 / Le Jazz

☐ LOTUS BLOSSOM
Warm valley / I don't stand a ghost of a chance with you / If you could see me now / Lotus blossom / Once upon a summertime / For once in in my life / Minha saudade / Young and foolish / Old folks / They can't take that away from me / There will never be another you / Night has a thousand eyes / I'm falling for you / Satin doll
CCD 4668 / Oct '95 / Concord Jazz

☐ LOVE IS THE ANSWER
13431420532 / 27 Apr '98 / Concord Jazz

☐ MIDNIGHT BLUE
Chitlins con carne / Mule / Soul lament / Midnight blue / Wavy gravy / Gee baby ain't I good to you / Saturday night blues
CDP 7463992 / Sep '92 / Blue Note

☐ MONDAY STROLL (Burrell, Kenny & Frank Wess)
Monday stroll / East wind / Wess side / Southern exposure / Woolafunt's lament / Over the rainbow / Kansas city side
SV 0246 / Oct '97 / Savoy Jazz

☐ ODE TO 52ND STREET
So little time / Growing / Round and round we go / Recapitulation / I want my baby back / Con alma / Soulero / Wild is the wind / Blues fuse
GRP 18242 / 27 Jul '98 / Chess Mates

☐ PRESTIGE 7088
Don't cry baby / Drum boogie / Strictly confidential / All of you / Perception
OJCCD 19 / Jun '96 / Original Jazz Classics

☐ SOULERO
Hot bossa / Mother in law / People / Sabella / Girl talk / Suzy / Tender gender / La petite mambo / If someone had told me / I'm confessin' that I love you / My favourite things / I want my baby back / Con alma / Soulero / Wild is the wind / Blues fuse
GRP 18082 / Oct '95 / GRP

☐ TIN TIN DEO
Tin Tin Deo / Old folks / Have you met Miss Jones / I remember you / Common ground / If you could see me now / I hadn't anyone till you / La petite mambo
CCD 4045 / Jul '94 / Concord Jazz

☐ WHEN LIGHTS ARE LOW
CCD 4083 / Jul '96 / Concord Jazz

Burri, Jessica

☐ WEIHNACHTSLIEDER AUS DEUTSCHLAND, ENGLAND UND AMERIKA
Maria durch ein Dornwald ging / Es flog ein voglen leise / O komm Emmanuel / Oh Heiland, reiss die Himmel auf / Sunny bank / Nowel syng we bothe al and som / Coventry carol / What child is this / First Noel / Holly and the ivy / Twelve days of Christmas / Ich steh' an deine Krippen hier / O Jesuslein suss / Nun singet und seid froh / Es ist ein ros' entsprungen / O du frohliche / Stille nacht / Mary wrote three links of chain / O Mary / Mary had a baby / Sweet little Jesus boy / Little drummer boy / Go tell it on the mountain
BCD 16012 / Nov '96 / Bear Family

Burroughs, Chris

☐ WEST OF TEXAS
ROSE 203 CD / Jul '90 / New Rose

Burroughs, William S.

☐ ELVIS OF LETTERS (Burroughs, William S. & Gus Van Sant)
Burroughs break / Word is virus / Millions of images / Hipster be-bop junkie
TK91CD 001 / Jun '94 / T/K

☐ SPARE ASS ANNIE AND OTHER TALES (Burroughs, William S. & Disposable Heroes Of Hiphoprisy)
Wrinkled earlobes are a sign of impending heart attacks / Spare ass Annie / This is insane (interlude 2) / Last words of Dutch Schultz / Vultures are gone and will never come back / Mildred Pierce reporting 2 (Old Sarge) / Dr. Benway operates / Warning to young couples (huntsmen's hounds) / Did I ever tell you about the man who taught his ass to talk / Last words / One God universe / Fletch is here (interlude 4) / Junky's christmas / Words of advice for young people / Last words
IMCD 240 / Mar '97 / Island

Burrows, Stuart

☐ FAVOURITE SONGS OF WALES
Baner ein gwald / Yr hen gerddor / Cartref / O fe fydd yn haf o hyd / Gwlad y delyn (country of the harp) / Yr eos (the nightingale) / Y bugail (the shepherd) / Galwad y tywsog (the prince's call) / Myfanwy / Unwaith eto'n nghymru annwyl / Llwybr yr wyddfa (the snowdon pathway) / Sul y blodau (palm sunday) / Arafa, don (be still, o wave)
SCD 2032 / Dec '94 / Sain

Burt, Matt

☐ GRUMPY GROOVY
PSYBAB 010 / 20 Oct '97 / Stickman

Burtnick, Glenn

☐ RETROSPECTACLE
MTM 199613 / Nov '96 / Made To Measure

Burton, Abraham

☐ MAGICIAN, THE
I can't get started (with you) / Little Melonae / Addition to the family / It's to you / Mari's soul / Gnossienne no.1 / Magician
ENJ 90372 / Nov '95 / Enja

Burton, Aron

☐ PAST, PRESENT AND FUTURE
EARWIGCD 4927 / Oct '93 / Earwig

Burton, Gary

☐ DUSTER (Burton, Gary Quartet)
CD 378462 / Nov '97 / Black Lion

☐ GENUINE TONG FUNERAL
OW 34510 / Sep '97 / One Way

☐ TANGO EXCURSION, A (Burton, Gary & Astor Piazolla Reunion)
Biyuya / Allegro tangabile / Caliente / Tanguedia / Triunfal / Soledad / Lunfardo / Revirado / La muerte del angel / Decarigimo / Concierto para quiento / Mi refugio
CCD 47932 / 16 Mar '98 / Concord Jazz

Burton, Gary

☐ COUNTRY ROADS AND OTHER PLACES (Burton, Gary Quartet)
Country roads / Green mountains / True or false / Gone, but forgotten / Ravel prelude / And on the third day / Singing song / Whichita breakdown / My foolish heart / Family joy
378542 / May '98 / Koch Jazz

☐ CRYSTAL SILENCE (Burton, Gary & Chick Corea)
Senor Mouse / Arise, her eyes / I'm your pal / Desert air / Crystal silence / Falling grace / Feelings and things / Children's song / What game shall we play today
8313312 / Mar '88 / ECM

☐ DEPARTURE (Burton, Gary & Friends)
September song / Poinciana / Depk / Tenderly / If I were a bell / For all we know / Japanese waltz / Tossed salads and scrambled eggs / Born to be blue / Ecaroh
CCD 47492 / Apr '97 / Concord Jazz

☐ DREAMS SO REAL (The Music Of Carla Bley) (Burton, Gary Quintet)
Dreams so real / Ictus / Syndrome / Jesus maria / Vox humana / Doctor / Intermission music
8333292 / Jul '88 / ECM

☐ DUET (Burton, Gary & Chick Corea)
Duet suite / Children's song no. 15, no. 2, no. 5, no. 6 / Radio / Song to gayle / Never / La fiesto
8299412 / Oct '88 / ECM

☐ GARY BURTON & THE BERKLEE ALL STARS (Burton, Gary & The Berklee All Stars)
Fat lady / Fat lady / Firm roots / Coral / Why'd you do it / Inner voyage / First memory / Blues walk / Crystal silence
JD 3301 / Jul '88 / JVC

☐ HOTEL HELLO (Burton, Gary & Steve Swallow)
Chelsea bells (for hern) / Hotel overture + vamp / Hotel hello / Inside in / Domino biscuit / Vashkar / Sweet henry / Impromptu / Sweeping up
8355862 / '90 / ECM

☐ LIVE IN CANNES
My foolsih heart / One / No more blues / Night has a 1000 eyes / Autumn leaves / African flower / Bogota
JWD 102214 / Apr '95 / JWD

☐ NEW QUARTET, THE
Open your eyes you can fly / Coral / Tying up loose ends / Brownout / Olhos de gato / Mallet man / Four or less / Nonsequence
8350022 / Sep '88 / ECM

☐ NEW VIBE MAN IN TOWN
Joy spring / Over the rainbow / Like someone in love / Minor blues / Our waltz / So many things / Sir John / You stepped out of a dream
74321218282 / Jan '95 / RCA

☐ PASSENGERS (Burton, Gary Quartet & Eberhard Weber)
Sea journey / Nocada / Whopper / B and g (midwestern nights dream) / Yellow fields / Claude and betty
8350162 / Oct '88 / ECM

☐ REAL LIFE HITS (Burton, Gary Quartet)
Syndrome / Beatle / Fleurette Africaine (the African flower) / Ladies in Mercedes / Real life hits / I need you here / Ivanushka Durachok
8252352 / '88 / ECM

☐ RING (Burton, Gary Quintet & Eberhard Weber)
Mevlevia / Unfinished sympathy / Tunnel of love / Intrude / Silent spring / Colours of chloe
8291912 / Oct '86 / ECM

☐ THROB (Burton, Gary & Keith Jarrett)
Grow your own / Moonchild / In your quiet place / Como en Vietnam / Fortune smiles / Raven speaks
8122715942 / Mar '94 / Atlantic

☐ TIMES SQUARE
5219822 / Jul '94 / ECM

☐ WHIZ KIDS (Burton, Gary Quintet)
Last clown / Yellow fever / Soulful Bill / La divetta / Cool train / Loop
8311102 / Feb '87 / ECM

☐ WORKS
Olhos de gato / Desert air / Tunnel of love / Vox humana / Three / Brotherhood / Chelsea bells / Coral / Domino biscuit
8232672 / Jun '89 / ECM

Burton, Gary

☐ TENNESSEE FIREBIRD (Burton, Gary & Friends)
Gone / Tennessee firebird / Just like a woman / Black is the colour of my true love's hair / Faded love / Panhandle rag / I can't help it / I want you / Alone and forsaken / Walter L / Born to lose / Beauty contest / Epilogue
BCD 15458 / Jun '89 / Bear Family

Burton, James

☐ CORN PICKIN' AND SLICK SLIDIN' (Burton, James & Ralph Mooney)
Columbus Stockade blues / Texas waltz / It's such a pretty world today / Moonshine / Laura / There goes my everything / I'm a lonesome fugitive / My elusive dreams / Corn pickin' / Your cheatin' heart / Spanish eyes / Sneaky strings
SEECD 377 / Aug '97 / See For Miles

☐ GUITAR SOUNDS OF JAMES BURTON, THE
Polk salad Annie / Susie-Q / Fire and rain / Fools rush in / Johnny B Goode / I know (you don't want me no more) / Delta lady / Mystery train / Rock and raunch / Hound dog / Hi-heel sneakers / Long reach
5405532 / Jun '97 / A&M

Burton, Joe

☐ ST. LOUIS BLUES
PS 012CD / Sep '95 / P&S

☐ SUBTLE SOUND
PS 006CD / Sep '95 / P&S

☐ TASTY TOUCH OF JOE BURTON, THE
PS 013CD / Sep '95 / P&S

Burton, Larry

☐ HUSTLER'S PARADISE
BRAM 1992332 / Nov '93 / Brambus

Burton, Rahn

☐ POEM, THE (Burton, Rahn Trio)
DIW 610 / Nov '92 / DIW

Burton, W.E.'Buddy'

☐ BUDDY BURTON & ED 'FATS' HUDSON 1928-1936 (Burton, W.E. 'Buddy' & Ed 'Fats' Hudson)
JPCD 1511 / Dec '94 / Jazz Perspectives

Bury Lawn School Pupils

☐ CHILDREN'S CHRISTMAS CAROLS
We wish you a merry Christmas / Little donkey / Holly and the ivy / Ding dong merrily on high / We three kings / Scarlet ribbons for her hair / First Noel / Twelve days of Christmas / Rocking / Away in a manger / Little drummer boy / Torches / O little town of Bethlehem / Jingle bells / Rudoplh the red nosed reindeer / Silent night
CDMFP 6399 / 6 Oct '97 / Music For Pleasure

Burzum

☐ BALDER'S DOD
AMAZON 013CD / 1 Sep '97 / Misanthropy

☐ BURZUM/ASKE
AMAZON 003CD / 3 Nov '97 / Misanthropy

☐ DET SOMEGAG VAR
AMAZON 002CD / 3 Nov '97 / Misanthropy

☐ FILOSOFEM (CD/Book Set)
AMAZON 009BK / 3 Nov '97 / Misanthropy

☐ HVIS LYSET TAR OSS
AMAZON 001CD / 3 Nov '97 / Misanthropy

Busaras, David

☐ SMEGMA 'STRUCTIONS DON'T RHYME
SR 1008 / Jan '96 / Scout

Busby, Colin

☐ BIG SWING BAND FAVOURITE (Busby, Colin Big Swing Band)
At the woodchoppers' ball / Sing sing sing / April in Paris / Take the 'A' train / String of pearls / Begin the beguine / One o'clock jump / Skyliner / In the mood / St. Louis blues march / Satin doll / Little brown jug
CDSIV 1117 / Jul '95 / Horatio Nelson

Busby, Sid

☐ PORTRAITS (Busby, Sid & The Berkeley Orchestra)
Portrait of my love / With a song in my heart / Days of wine and roses / I can't get started (with you) / My son, my son / Serenade in blue / Java / Stardust / As time goes by / Serenata / And this is my beloved / Love changes everything / Violino tzigano / When a love affair has ended
PCOM 1105 / Aug '90 / President

Buscemi

☐ MOCHA SUPREME
Mocha supreme / Big bugs in Brazil / Yves eaux / It might as well be quiet / Soap girl Nina / Fingersnappin' after dark / Desole / What the funk is happening / Gloomy business / Delores del sorte
DSL 008CD / 15 Jun '98 / Downsall Plastics

Bush

☐ DECONSTRUCTED
IND 90161 / 17 Nov '97 / Interscope

☐ INTERVIEW SESSIONS
CHAT 8 / 2 Feb '98 / Chatback

☐ RAZORBLADE SUITCASE
Personal Holloway / Greedy fly / Swallowed / Insect kin / Cold contagious / Tendency to start fires / Mouth / Straight no chaser / History / Synapse / Communicator / Bonedriven / Distant voices
IND 90091 / Feb '97 / Interscope

☐ SIXTEEN STONE
Everything zen / Swim / Bomb / Little things / Comedown / Body / Machinehead / Testosterone / Monkey / Glycerine / Alien / X-girlfriend
IND 90001 / Aug '96 / Interscope

Bush Chemists

☐ DUB CONVENTION (Bush Chemists & The Dub Organiser)
FDCD 001 / Aug '96 / Fashion

☐ DUBS FROM ZION VALLEY (Bush Chemists & Jonah Dan)
JKPD 001CD / Apr '97 / JKP

☐ LIGHT UP YOUR SPLIFF
DNCD 005 / Jan '96 / Conscious Sounds

☐ MONEY RUN TINGS (Bush Chemists & King General)
DNCD 006 / Jun '96 / Conscious Sounds

☐ STRICTLY DUBWISE
WWCD 6 / Jul '94 / Wibbly Wobbly

Bush, Johnny

☐ TALK TO MY HEART
Please talk to my heart / Moment isn't very long / Any fool could see / This house has no doors / Neon nightmare / Least I can do is try / Cheatin' line / It sure feels good / Winds of change / Bottle, your memory and me / Sound a breaking heart makes / Deep in love and buried in the blues / As long as theres women like you
WMCD 1069 / Apr '98 / Watermelon

Bush, Kate

☐ DREAMING, THE
Sat in your lap / There goes a tenner / Pull out the pin / Suspended in Gaffa / Leave it open / Dreaming / Night of the swallow / All the love / Houdini / Get out of my house
CDP 7463612 / Mar '91 / EMI

☐ HOUNDS OF LOVE
Running up that hill / Hounds of love / Big sky / Mother stands for comfort / Cloudbusting / And dream of sheep / Under ice / Waking the witch / Watching you without me / Jig of life / Hello earth / Morning fog / Big sky / Running up that hill / Be kind to my mistakes / Under the ivy / Burning bridge / My lagan love
CDCNTAV 3 / Jun '97 / EMI

☐ KATE BUSH: INTERVIEW DISC
CBAK 4011 / Apr '88 / Baktabak

☐ KICK INSIDE, THE
Moving / Saxophone song / Strange phenomena / Kite / Man with the child in his eyes / Wuthering Heights / James and the cold gun / Feel it / Oh to be in love / L'amour looks something like you / Them heavy people / Room for the life / Kick inside
CDEMS 1522 / Sep '94 / EMI

☐ LIONHEART
Symphony in blue / In search of Peter Pan / Wow / Don't push your foot on the heartbrake / Oh England my lionheart / Full house / In the warm room / Kashka from Baghdad / Coffee homeground / Hammer horror
CDEMS 1523 / Sep '94 / EMI

☐ NEVER FOR EVER
Babooshka / Delius / Blow away / All we ever look for / Egypt / Wedding list / Violin / Infant kiss / Night scented stock / Army dreamers / Breathing
CDP 7463602 / Oct '90 / EMI

☐ NEVER FOR EVER
KB 2 / Oct '92 / UFO

☐ RED SHOES, THE
Rubber band girl / And so is love / Eat the music / Moments of pleasure / Song of Solomon / Lily / Red shoes / Top of the city / Constellation of the heart / Big stripey lie / Why should I love you / You're the one
CDEMD 1047 / Nov '93 / EMI

☐ SENSUAL WORLD, THE
Sensual world / Love and anger / Fog / Reaching out / Heads we're dancing / Deeper understanding / Between a man and a woman / Never be mine / Rocket's tail / This woman's work / Walk straight down the middle
CDP 7930782 / Oct '89 / EMI

☐ WHOLE STORY, THE
Wuthering Heights / Cloudbusting / Man with the child in his eyes / Breathing / Wow / Hounds of love / Running up that hill / Army dreamers / Sat in your lap / Experiment IV / Dreaming / Babooshka / Big sky
CDP 7464142 / Nov '86 / EMI

Bush League Allstars

☐ OLD NUMBERS
GRCD 401 / Apr '97 / Glitterhouse

Bush, Sam

☐ GLAMOUR AND GRITS
Whayasay / Same ol' river / All night radio / Stingray / Ballad of Spider John / Watson Allman / Is this love / Brilliancy / Spooky Lane / Ol' Joe Clark / Lord came under me / (One night in old) Galway
SHCD 3849 / Mar '98 / Sugar Hill

☐ HOWLIN' AT THE MOON
Ozzie and Max / Howlin' at the moon / Big rabbit / Face tomorrow / Funk 42 / Hold on / Cloverleaf rag / Beaver Creek mansion / Crossing the Transippi / Go with the flow / Harbor docks / Mr. Freddie / Song for Roy / Take me out to the ball game
SHCD 3876 / 20 Apr '98 / Sugar Hill

☐ LATE AS USUAL
Big mon / Last letter home / Norman and nancy / Russian rag / Leather britches / Diadem / Sailin' shoes / Crooked smile / Broadway / Samanda lynn / Funk 55
ROUCD 0195 / Aug '88 / Rounder

Bushfire

☐ DIDGERIDOO MUSIC OF THE AUSTRALIAN ABORIGINEES
EUCD 1224 / Sep '93 / ARC

Bushgiants

☐ NEWLANDING
BUSH 96001 / Apr '97 / Knock On Wood

Bushkin, Joe

☐ ROAD TO OSLO/PLAY IT AGAIN, JOE
Now you has jazz / Hallelujah / Bess, you is my woman now / How long has this been going on / Man I love / Yesterday / Ain't been the same since the Beatles / There'll be a hot time in the town of Berlin / Oh look at me now / I love a piano / Phone call to the past / I've grown accustomed to her face / Someday I'll be sorry / Sunday of the Shepherdess / Sail away from Norway / I can't get started (with you) / Someday you'll be sorry / Man that got away / One for my baby (and one more for the road) / It had to be you / Learnin' the blues / There's always the blues / Our love is here to stay / What's new
DRGCD 8490 / Feb '95 / DRG

Bushman

☐ NYAH MAN CHANT
Nayh man chant / Cannabis / Man a lion / Rude boy life / Remember the days / Black starliner / She's gone / Grow your natty / My day / Anything for your love / Call the hearse / Poor people power
GRELCD 239 / Aug '97 / Greensleeves

Bushwick Bill

☐ PHANTOM OF THE RAPRA
Phantom's theme / Wha cha gonna do / Times is hard / Who's the biggest / Ex-girlfriend / Only God knows / Already dead / Bushwicken / Subliminal criminal / Inhale exhale / Mr. President / Phantom's reprise
CDVUS 91 / Jun '95 / Virgin

Business

☐ BEST OF THE BUSINESS, THE
Out in the cold / Streets where you live / Harry May / NJ Blacklist / Suburban rebels / Product / Smash the disco / Disco girls / H-Bomb / Blind justice / Get out while you can / Guttersnipe / Real enemy / Loud, proud and punk / Get out of my house / Outlaw / Saturday's heroes / Front line / Spanish jails / Freedom / Coventry / No emotions / Do a runner / Welcome to the real world / Fear in your heart / Never say never / Look at him now / Drinking and driving
DOJOCD 124 / Apr '93 / Dojo

☐ BEST OF THE BUSINESS, THE
SMMCD 539 / 27 Apr '98 / Snapper

☐ COMPLETE SINGLES COLLECTION
Harry May / National insurance blacklist / Step into Christmas / Dayo / Disco girls / Smash the discos / Loud, proud and punk / H-bomb / Last train to Clapham Junction / Law and order / Do they owe us a living / Tell us the truth / Get out of my house / All out tonight / Foreign girl / Out law / Drinking and driving / Hurry up Harry / H-bomb (live) / Do a runner / Coventry / Welcome to the real world / No emotions / Anywhere but here / All out / (You're) Going down in history
CDPUNK 57 / Jun '95 / Anagram

☐ IN AND OUT OF BUSINESS
MOGCD 001 / 2 Mar '98 / Mog

☐ KEEP THE FAITH
CM 770832 / Oct '94 / Century Media

☐ OFFICIAL BOOTLEG, THE
MOGCD 002 / 2 Mar '98 / Mog

☐ SATURDAY'S HEROES
Spanish jails / All out tonight / Never been taken / Shout it out / Harder life / Freedom / Frontline / Foreign girl / Nothing can stop us / Saturday's heroes / Drinking and driving / Hurry up Harry / Get out of my house / Outlaw / Coventry
AHOYCD 013 / 3 Nov '97 / Captain Oi

☐ SMASH THE DISCOS/LOUD PROUD AND PUNK
STEPCD 024 / 4 May '98 / Step 1

☐ SUBURBAN REBELS
AHOYCD 7 / Oct '93 / Captain Oi

☐ SUBURBAN REBELS/WELCOME TO THE REAL WORLD
LOMACD 32 / Aug '94 / Loma

☐ TRUTH THE WHOLE AND NOTHING BUT THE TRUTH
BHR 067CD / 22 Sep '97 / Burning Heart

☐ WELCOME TO THE REAL WORLD
Mouth an' trousers / Do a runner / Ten years / We'll take 'em on / Fear in your heart / Welcome to the real world / Never say never / Hand ball / Living in day dreams / Look at him now / We gotta go / Never say never (reprise) / Coventry / No emotions / Tina Turner / Welcome to the real world
AHOYCD 2 / 9 Mar '98 / Captain Oi

Buskirk, Paul

☐ NACOGDOCHES WALTZ
JR 17012 / Apr '94 / Justice

Busstra, Marnix

☐ ON THE FACE OF IT (Busstra, Marnix Quartet)
Strega / Brandon head / That's a fact / Snake and the hammer / On the face of it / Little Big Mama / Searching for silence
9920072 / Oct '96 / Via Jazz

Busta Rhymes

☐ COMING, THE
Coming / Do my thing / Abandon ship / Everything remains raw / Hot fudge/Interlude / Flipmode squad meets def squad / Keep it movin' / End of the world / Finish line / Still shining / Ill vibe / It's a party / Woo hah got you all in check
7559617422 / Mar '96 / WEA

☐ FLIPMODE REMIXES
Woo hah got you all in check / It's a party / Do my thing / Abandon ship
7559639922 / Jul '97 / Elektra

☐ WHEN DISASTER STRIKES
Intro / Whole world lookin' at me / Survival hungry / When disaster strikes / So hardcore / Get high tonight / Turn it up / Put your hands where my eyes can see / It's all good / There's not a problem my squad can't fix / We can take it outside / Rhymes galore / Thing we be doin' for money / One / Dangerous / Body rock / Get off my block / Outro
7559620642 / 22 Sep '97 / Elektra

Bustan Abraham

☐ PICTURES THROUGH THE PAINTED WINDOW
Gipsy soul / Jazz kar-kurd / Fountain head / Here comes (Muwashah) / Longa / Walls of Jerico / Samai nahawand / Wallah / Pictures through the painted window
CRAW 17 / May '97 / Cramworld

Buster Bloodvessel

☐ SKINHEAD LOVE AFFAIR (Buster's All Stars)
Pipeline / Skinhead girl / Stampede / Non shrewd / Johnnie's knee / Baby elephant walk / Big five / Rock steady breakfast / Mafia / Viva la ska revolution / Skinhead love affair / Pipeline / Skinhead boy / Baby elephant walk / Skinhead love affair / Christmas time again
SKACD 102 / 4 May '98 / House Of Ska

Busters

☐ RUDER THAN YOU
PHZCD 27 / Sep '93 / Unicorn

Butanes Soul Revue

☐ ONE NIGHT
ATR 1139 / 19 Jan '98 / Atomic Theory

Butcher, John

☐ BEST OF JOHN BUTCHER, THE
RE 82172E / 30 Jun '98 / Razor & Tie

Butera, Sam

☐ BY REQUEST (Butera, Sam & The Wildest)
When you're smiling / Just a gigolo/I ain't got nobody / For once in my life / Up a lazy river / Ol' man mose / Night train / Lover is a 5 letter word / Alexander's ragtime band / Margie / Come to the cabaret / Mari-yootch / St. Louis blues / Your rascall you / French poodle / My first, my last / Closer to the bone / Greenback dollar bill
JASCD 314 / Aug '95 / Jasmine

☐ HOT NIGHTS IN NEW ORLEANS
Shine the buckle / Chicken scratch / Sam's clan / Easy rocking / Wailin' walk / Screw driver / Things I love / Do you care / I don't want to set the world on fire / Tout / Long ago / Giddyap baby / Sweep up / Sam's reverie / Who's got the key / Ooh / Linda / Tout / Ooh
BCD 15449 / Apr '89 / Bear Family

☐ SHEER ENERGY (Butera, Sam & The Wildest)
Let the good times roll / For you / I can't get started (with you) / Jump, jive and wail / Glow worm / Closer to the bone / Hard hearted Hannah / Body and soul / Night train / Rosetta / You ain't no ordinary woman / Pennies from heaven / Kansas City / Why not / Ol' man river
JASCD 313 / Jul '95 / Jasmine

☐ TRIBUTE TO LOUIS PRIMA
Josephine / Please no lean on the bell / That old black magic / Please no squeeza da banana / Medley: Robin Hood / Buona sera / White cliffs of Dover / I got you under my skin / Angelina / Oh Marie / Felicia / No capicia / Medley / Tiger rag / Just the way you are / Romance without finance / Exodus / Che-la-luna
JASCD 319 / Mar '95 / Jasmine

☐ TRIBUTE TO LOUIS PRIMA VOL.2, A
Oh babe / Exactly like you / I'm confessin' (that I love you) / Ol' man river / Dog / One mint julip / Sheik of araby / Sunny side of the street / I want a sunday kind of love / Music goes round and round / Pump song / Medley / Chantilly lace / Last dance / Three handed woman / Mala femina / Way down in new orleans
JASCD 320 / Apr '95 / Jasmine

Butler, Bernard

☐ PEOPLE MOVE ON
CRECD 221 / 6 Apr '98 / Creation

Butler, Carl

☐ CRYING MY HEART OUT OVER YOU (Butler, Carl & Pearl)
Crying my heart out over you / Fools like me / Garden of shame / Dog eat dog / If teardrops were pennies / Holding on with open arms / Take me back to Jackson / Don't let me cross over / Blue eyes and waltzes / My joy / Precious memories / I hope we walk the last mile together
BCD 15739 / Jul '93 / Bear Family

Butler, Freddy

☐ WITH A DAB OF SOUL
There was a time / That's when I need you / I like your style / I fell in love / Never let love go / They say I'm afraid / This thing / Just because you've been hurt / You'd better get hip girl / Give me lots of lovin' / She's foolin' you / Deserted
SSCD 003 / Feb '97 / Goldmine

Butler, George

☐ KEEP ON DOING WHAT YOU'RE DOING (Butler, George 'Wild Child')
BMCD 9015 / Nov '93 / Black Magic

☐ STRANGER
BB 9539CD / Aug '94 / Bullseye Blues

Butler, Henry

☐ BLUES AFTER SUNSET
I've got my eyes on you / Baby let me hold your hand / I really love you / Butler's boogie / Relaxing blues / Blue moments / Marriage song / Tee na na / Bourbon street blues / Death has no mercy / Tetherball / CC rider
CDBT 1144 / Jun '98 / Black Top

Butler, Jerry

☐ ICE MAN
CDRB 30 / Nov '95 / Charly

☐ NOTHING SAYS I LOVE YOU LIKE I LOVE YOU/THE BEST LOVE
(I'm just thinking about) cooling out / Let's make love / Sad eyes / Mighty good people / I'm glad to be back / Nothing says I love you like I love you / Dream world / Are you lonely tonight / Best love I ever had / Would you mind / Don't be an island / Tell me girl (why it has to end) / Reach out for me / We've got this feeling again / Angel face / Best love I ever had
WESM 566 / 16 Mar '98 / Westside

☐ TIME & FAITH
ICH 1151CD / Feb '94 / Ichiban

☐ WHATEVER YOU WANT
Rainbow Valley / Lonely soldier / Thanks to you / When trouble calls / Aware of love / Isle of sirens / It's too late / Moon River / Woman with soul / Let it be whatever it is / I almost lost my mind / Good times / Give it up / Believe in me / Just for you / For your precious love
CDSGP 083 / Sep '93 / Prestige

Butler, John

☐ LOYAL SERPENT, THE
Wings of the morning / Boulevard / All my honey / When it all becomes avaliable / Let go / Bag of bones / Maybe tomorrow / Day's you've made / Monpellier on ice / Yes I do / Billy and the snake charmer / Leave me the sinners
CDCHR 6128 / 3 Nov '97 / Chrysalis

Butler, Jonathan

☐ BEST OF JONATHAN BUTLER, THE
CHIP 133 / Mar '93 / Jive

☐ DO YOU LOVE ME
Song for Elizabeth / Do you love me / Other side of the world / Life after you / New life / Dancing on the shore / You don't belong to me / Way you look tonight / Amen / Kiss / Lost to love / My only joy
N2K 10005 / 13 Oct '97 / N2K

Butler, Ken

☐ VOICES OF ANXIOUS OBJECTS
TZA 7402 / 27 Oct '97 / Tzadik

Butler, Lester

☐ 13
HCD 8078 / Jun '97 / Hightone

Butler, Margie

☐ CELTIC LULLABY
EUCD 1191 / Apr '92 / ARC

☐ MAGIC OF THE CELTIC HARP, THE
EUCD 1316 / Jul '95 / ARC

Butler Twins

☐ NOT GONNA WORRY ABOUT TOMORROW
Finally found me a girl / My Baby's coming home / Not gonna worry about tomorrow / I know you don't love me baby / 1-900 / You don't need me / Going down a long country road / Crackhouse baby / That old devil (crossroads) / Bring it on back to me / Travellin' down south
JSPCD 257 / Apr '95 / JSP

☐ PURSUE YOUR DREAMS
My old Tom cat / I'm talkin' about love / Livin' in paradise / Jack Daniels and me / Pursue your dreams / Hey baby / How long / Blues walked in this morning / Tribute to Little Walter / Inner city blues / What's a poor man's supposed to do / Take a little walk with me / Cold winter nights
JSPCD 268 / May '96 / JSP

Butlers

☐ SKINTIGHT (2CD Set)
BOCD 004 / 20 Jul '98 / Knock Out

Butt, Clara

☐ HEART OF THE EMPIRE
Enchantress / O lovely night / Abide with me / Land of Hope and Glory / Softly and gently / Sweetest flower / Kashmiri song / O rest the Lord / Lost chord / Annie Laurie / Rosary / Home sweet home / Barbara Allen / Trees / Shenandoah / Minstrel boy / Swanee river / Love's old sweet song / Handel's Largo / Keys of Heaven / Softly awakes my heart / Rule Britannia
PASTCD 7012 / Aug '93 / Flapper

Butt Steak

☐ MEN WHO PAUSE
GKCD 017 / 17 Nov '97 / Go-Kart

Butter 08

☐ BUTTER
9MM / Shut up / Butter of '69 / Dick serious / How do I relax / It's the rage / Mono Lisa / What are you wearing / Sex symbol / Degobrah / Hard to hold / Butterfucker
GR 029CD / 10 Nov '97 / Grand Royal

Butterbeans & Susie

☐ BUTTERBEANS & SUSIE VOL.1 (1924-1925)
DOCD 5544 / Jul '97 / Document

☐ BUTTERBEANS & SUSIE VOL.2 (1924-1927)
DOCD 5545 / Jul '97 / Document

☐ VOCAL DUET, THE
CARCD 1501 / Sep '97 / Clifford

Buttercup

☐ GOLD
SO 4 / 16 Mar '98 / Spirit Of Orr

☐ LOVE
SO 11 / 16 Mar '98 / Spirit Of Orr

Butterfield, Paul

☐ **EAST-WEST LIVE (Butterfield Blues Band)**
WINNER 447 / Jun '97 / Winner

☐ **OFFER YOU CAN'T REFUSE, AN (Butterfield, Paul & Walter Horton)**
Easy / Have a good time / Mean mistreater / In the mood / West side blues / Louise / Tin pan alley / Walters boogie / Everything's gonna be alright / Poor boy / Got my mojo working / Last night / Loaded / One room country shack
CLACD 429 / Apr '97 / Castle

☐ **PAUL BUTTERFIELD BLUES BAND (Butterfield Blues Band)**
Born in Chicago / Shake your moneymaker / Blues with a feeling / Thank you Mr. Poobah / I got my mojo working / Mellow down easy / Screamin' / Our love is drifting / Mystery train / Last night / Look over yonder's wall
7559606472 / Nov '94 / WEA

☐ **STRAWBERRY JAM (Butterfield Blues Band)**
WINNER 446 / Jun '97 / Winner

Butterfly Child

☐ **ONOMATOPOEIA**
R 3082 / Aug '93 / Rough Trade

☐ **SOFT EXPLOSIVES**
HIT 24 / 3 Aug '98 / Tommy Boy

Butterglory

☐ **ARE YOU BUILDING A TEMPLE IN HEAVEN**
K 167 / May '96 / Konkurrel

☐ **RAT TAT TAT**
K 179 / 15 Dec '97 / Konkurrent

Butterworth, Mary

☐ **MARY BUTTERWORTH**
PG 21098 / 15 Jun '98 / QCCS

Butthole Surfers

☐ **ELECTRICLARRYLAND**
Birds / Cough syrup / Pepper / Thermador / Ulcer breakout / Jingle of a dog's collar / TV star / My brother's wife / Ah ha / Lord is a monkey / Let's talk about cars / LA / Space
CDEST 2285 / May '96 / Capitol

☐ **HAIRWAY TO STEVEN**
Hairway (part 1) / Hairway (part 2) / Hairway (part 3) / Hairway (part 4) / Hairway (part 5) / Hairway (part 6) / Hairway (part 7) / Hairway (part 8) / Hairway (part 9)
BFFP 29CD / Feb '88 / Blast First

☐ **HOLE TRUTH AND NOTHING BUTT, THE**
TR 35CD / Mar '95 / Trance

☐ **INDEPENDENT WORM SALOON**
Who was in my room last night / Wooden song / Tongue / Chewin' George Lucas' chocolate / Goofy's concern / Alcohol / Dog inside your body / Strawberry / Some dispute over T-shirt sales / Dancing fool / You don't know me / Annoying song / Dust devil / Leave me alone / Edgar / Ballad of naked men / Clean it up
CDP 7987982 / Mar '93 / Capitol

☐ **LOCUST ABORTION TECHNICIAN**
Sweat loaf / Graveyard / Graveyard / Pittsburgh to Lebanon / Weber / Hay / Human cannonball / USSA / O-men / Kuntz / Twenty two going on twenty three
BFFP 15CD / Jun '87 / Blast First

☐ **PIOUHGD**
Revolution part 1 / Revolution part 2 / Lonesome bulldog / Lonesome bulldog / Hurdy gurdy man / Golden showers / Lonesome bulldog / Blindman / No, I'm iron man / Something / PSY / Lonesome bulldog / Barking dogs
DAN 069CD / Dec '94 / Danceteria

Buttons & Bows

☐ **FIRST MONTH OF SUMMER, THE**
John D McGurk's / I les de la Madeleine / First month of summer / Fitmaurice's polka / Sir Sidney Smith / Man from Bundoran / Humours of Kinvara / Green garters / Inisheer / Gypsy hornpipe / Margaret's waltz / Four courts / Joyous waltz / Piper's despair
GLCD 1079 / Feb '92 / Green Linnet

☐ **GRACE NOTES**
CEFCD 151 / Jan '94 / Gael Linn

Buzzcocks

☐ **ANOTHER MUSIC IN A DIFFERENT KITCHEN**
Fast cars / No reply / You tear me up / Get on our own / Love battery / Sixteen / I don't mind / Fiction romance / Autonomy / I need / Moving away from the pulsebeat
PRDFCD 3 / Jul '96 / Premier/EMI

☐ **CHRONOLOGY**
Boredom / Sixteen / Fast cars / No reply / Whatever happened to / Oh shit / I need / Fiction romance / Autonomy / Just lust / ESP / Lipstick / Promises / Mother of turds / You say you don't love me / I don't know what to do with my life / I don't know / Runaway from home / Drive system / Jesus made me feel guilty / You know you can't help it / I believe / No friend of mine
CDGO 2073 / Jun '97 / EMI Gold

☐ **ENTERTAINING FRIENDS (Live At The Hammersmith Odeon - March 1979)**
Ever fallen in love / I don't mind / Harmony in my head / Promises / Orgasm addict / Breakdown / What do I get / Fiction romance / Fast cars / Oh shit / Autonomy
CDGOLD 1029 / May '96 / EMI Gold

☐ **FRENCH**
DOJOCD 237 / Sep '95 / Dojo

☐ **FRENCH**
SMMCD 541 / 27 Apr '98 / Snapper

☐ **I DON'T MIND**
CDGOLD 1093 / 15 Sep '97 / EMI Gold

☐ **LEST WE FORGET**
RE 158CD / Nov '94 / ROIR

☐ **LIVE AT THE ROXY 2ND APRIL 1977**
Orgasm addict / Get on your own / What do I get / Sixteen / Oh shit / No reply / Fast cars / Friends of mine / Time's up / Boredom
RRCD 131 / Jul '93 / Receiver

☐ **LOVE BITES**
Real world / Ever fallen in love / Operator's manual / Nostalgia / Just lust / Sixteen again / Walking distance / Love is lies / Nothing left / ESP / Late for the train
PRDFCD 4 / Jul '96 / Premier/EMI

☐ **OPERATORS MANUAL (Buzzcocks Best)**
Orgasm addict / What do I get / I don't mind / Autonomy / Fast cars / Get on our own / Sixteen / Fiction romance / Love you more / Noise annoys / Ever fallen in love / Operators manual / Nostalgia / Walking distance / Nothing left / ESP / Promises / Lipstick / Everybody's happy nowadays / Harmony in my head / You say you don't love me / I don't know what to do with my life / I believe / Are everything / Radio nine
CDP 7975342 / Mar '96 / Premier/EMI

☐ **PRODUCT (3CD Set)**
Fast cars / No reply / You tear me up / Get on your own / Love battery / Sixteen / I don't mind / Fiction romance / Autonomy / I need / Moving away from the pulsebeat / Real world / Ever fallen in love / Operator's manual / Nostalgia / Just lust / Walking distance / Love is lies / Nothing left / ESP / Late for the train / Paradise / Sitting 'round at home / You say you don't love me / You know you can't help it / Mad mad Judy / Raison D'etre / I don't know what to do with my life / Money / Hollow inside / Different kind of tension / I believe / Radio nine / Orgasm addict / Love you more / Promises / Everybody's happy nowadays / Harmony in my head / Whatever happened to / Oh shit / Noise annoys / Lipstick / Why can't I touch it / Something's gone wrong again / Breakdown / What do I get / Times up / Are everything / Strange thing / What do you know / Why she's a girl from the chainstore / Airwaves dream / Running free / I look alone
PRODUCT 1 / May '95 / Premier/EMI

☐ **SINGLES GOING STEADY**
Orgasm addict / What do I get / I don't mind / Love you more / Ever fallen in love / Promises / Everybody's happy nowadays / Harmony in my head / Whatever happened to / Oh shit / Autonomy / Noise annoys / Just lust / Lipstick / Why can't I touch it / Something's gone wrong again
CDFA 3241 / Oct '90 / Fame

Buzzkill

☐ **UP**
VIRUS 188CD / Dec '96 / Alternative Tentacles

Buzzoven

☐ **AT A LOSS**
OFFREC 003 / 26 May '98 / Off The Record

☐ **CHOKEHOLD**
ALLIED 84 / Mar '97 / Allied

☐ **GOSPEL ACCORDING, THE**
ALLIED 84CD / Mar '97 / Allied

By The Grace Of God

☐ **BY THE GRACE OF GOD**
VR 057CD / 28 Jul '97 / Victory

Byard, Jaki

☐ **BLUES FOR SMOKE**
Excerpts from European episode / Aluminum baby / Pete and Thomas / Spanish tinge no.1 / Flight of the fly / Blues for smoke / Jaki's blues next / Diane's melody / One two five
CCD 9018 / Feb '97 / Candid

☐ **EMPIRICAL**
MCD 6010 / Sep '92 / Muse

☐ **PHANTASIES (Byard, Jaki & The Apollo Stompers)**
SNCD 1075 / Dec '86 / Soul Note

☐ **PHANTASIES VOL.2 (Byard, Jaki & The Apollo Stompers)**
1211752 / Jun '91 / Soul Note

Byas, Don

☐ **ALL THE THINGS YOU ARE**
Walkin' / Don't blame me / Lady bird / All the things you are / There'll never be another you / Billie's bounce / Moonlight in vermont / Night in tunisia
JHR 73541 / Sep '93 / Jazz Hour

☐ **AUTUMN LEAVES**
Ronnie's intro / Autumn leaves / I remember Clifford / Bags' groove / All the things you are / Ladybird / Moonlight in Vermont / Walkin'
JHAS 613 / 23 Feb '98 / Ronnie Scott's Jazz House

☐ **CLASSICS 1944-1945**
CLASSICS 882 / Jul '96 / Classics

☐ **CLASSICS 1945 VOL.1**
CLASSICS 910 / Jan '97 / Classics

☐ **CLASSICS 1945 VOL.2**
CLASSICS 959 / Nov '97 / Classics

☐ **INTRODUCTION TO DON BYAS 1935-1945, AN**
4044 / Apr '97 / Best Of Jazz

☐ **INTRODUCTION TO DON BYAS, AN**
4045 / Jun '97 / Best Of Jazz

☐ **LIVING MY LIFE**
VGCD 650122 / Jan '93 / Vogue

☐ **LOVER MAN**
If I had you / Lover man / I can't give you anything but love / Remember my forgotten man / GDB / Time on my hands / Blues for Don Carlos / Sweet Lorraine / April in Paris / Don't blame me / Unknown original / No one but you / Darling je vous aime beaucoup / Le musicien / Lover come back to me / I can't get started (with you) / Athena / Sincerely / Minor encamp / Cerisier rose et pommier blanc / Hold my hand / Un jour tu verras / Just one of those things / Anatole
74321154702 / Oct '93 / Vogue

☐ **NIGHT IN TUNISIA, A**
BLCD 760136 / Oct '90 / Black Lion

☐ **ORIGINAL 1945 RECORDINGS**
TAXS 82 / Mar '97 / Tax

☐ **SAVOY JAM PARTY**
Riffin' and jivin' / Free and easy / Worried and blue / Don's idea / Savoy jam party / 1944 stomp / What do you want with my heart / Sweet and lovely / White rose kick / My deep blue dream / Byas'd opinion / Candy / How high the moon / Donby / Byas a drink / I don't know why / Old folks / Cherokee / September in the rain / Living my life / To each his own / They say it's wonderful / Cynthia's in love / September song / St. Louis blues
SV 0268 / Oct '97 / Savoy Jazz

☐ **THOSE BARCELONA DAYS**
FSR 3001CD / 5 Jan '98 / Fresh Sound

☐ **THREE TENORS, THE (Byas, Don & Paul Gonsalves/Ben Webster)**
I'll remember April / Lady Bird / Yesterdays / Just a-sittin' and a-rockin' / Hi ya Sue / I'm in the market for you / Tea for two / Stardust / What's new / Autumn leaves / Easy to love
8747062 / Jul '96 / DA Music

☐ **WALKIN'**
BLCD 760167 / Oct '93 / Black Lion

Bygraves, Max

☐ **CHEERS**
It had to be you / I'll string along with you / I'll be seeing you / Sit right down and write myself a letter / My very good friend the milkman / When somebody thinks you're wonderful / He's got the whole world / Michael row the boat ashore / Amen amen / Who's sorry now / You made me love you / For me and my gal / We'll meet again / Hometown / In old shanty town / Underneath the arches / (My) Mammy / Sonny boy / Rockabye your baby / Mistakes / Dancing with tears in my eyes / Are you lonesome tonight / When I grow to old to dream / It's a long way to Tipperary / Pack up your troubles / Kiss me goodnight Sgt. Major / Run rabbit run / We're gonna hang out the washing / Bless 'em all / She loves you / All my loving / Hard day's night / Can't buy me love / I love a lassie / Just a wee doech and Doris / Keep right on to the end of the road / Knees up Mother Brown / Robert E Lee / Australia / Shuddaup your face / Maybe it's because I'm a Londoner / When the saints go marching in / John Brown's body / D'ye ken John Peel / Grand old Duke of York / She'll be coming round the mountain / Comrades / Two lovely black eyes / Lassie from Lancashire / Let's all sing like the birdies / Down at the old bull and bush / Swanee river / Poor old Joe / My Bonnie lies over the ocean / If you knew Susie
CDSIV 1143 / Jul '95 / Horatio Nelson

☐ **GOLDEN MEDLEYS**
I don't know why I love you / You made me love you / Me and my shadow / Moonlight and roses / You were meant for me / You are my sunshine / Let the rest of the world go by / Let me call you sweetheart / Girl of my dreams / Where the blue of the night meets the gold of the day / Everybody loves somebody / Just one more chance / What a wonderful world / Nightingale sang in Berkeley Square / I left my heart in San Francisco / One of those songs / Baby face / Toot toot tootsie goodbye / Swanee / Happy days are here again / Powder your face with sunshine / I'm looking over a four leaf clover / When you're smiling / Put your arms around me honey / Wyoming Lullaby / What'll I do / When your hair has turned to silver / Till we meet again / It had to be you / I'll get by / I'll string along with you / I'll be seeing you / You'd be so nice to come home to / I love you because / True love / Charmaine / I'll be your sweetheart / When I grow too old to dream / Who's taking you home tonight / You need hands / Au revoir / Auf wiedersehen sweetheart / Arrivederci Roma / Goodbye blues
5507602 / Mar '95 / Spectrum

☐ **I WANNA SING YOU A SONG**
MACCD 172 / Aug '96 / Autograph

☐ **I WANNA SING YOU A SONG**
PLSCD 196 / Apr '97 / Pulse

☐ **SINGALONG YEARS, THE**
Don't bring Lulu / Ma, he's making eyes at me / Yes sir that's my baby / I wonder where my baby is tonight / Who's sorry now / Amy, wonderful Amy / Underneath the arches / Home town / South of the border (Down Mexico way) / Is it true what they say about Dixie / Baby face / California here I come / I've got a lovely bunch of coconuts / You're a pink toothbrush / Who wants to be a millionaire / Beatles medley / What a wonderful world / Tie a yellow ribbon round the ole oak tree / Dance in the old-fashioned way / Neighbours / It's bad / Repeats
74321183232 / Sep '96 / Ariola Express

☐ **SINGALONGACHRISTMAS PARTY**
We wish you a merry Christmas / Oh come all ye faithful / Once in royal David's city / While shepherds watched their flocks / First Noel / Good King Wenceslas / Hark the herald angels sing / Christmas island / I saw Mummy kissing Santa Claus / Rudolph the red nosed reindeer / Little drummer boy / Have yourself a merry little Christmas / Jingle bells / Sleigh ride / Deck of cards / Jingle bell rock / White Christmas / Winter wonderland / Mary's boy child / Christmas song / I love Lassie / Wee Doc and Doris / Keep right on to the end of the road / Auld lange syne
TOTCD 5 / 10 Nov '97 / Total

☐ **SINGALONGAMAX**
PLSCD 228 / Jul '97 / Pulse

☐ **SINGALONGAMAXMAS**
PLSCD 259 / 29 Sep '97 / Pulse

☐ **SINGALONGAWARYEARS**
MCCD 102 / May '93 / Music Club

☐ **SINGALONGAWARYEARS VOL.2**
This is the army Mr. Jones / Fleet's in port again / Army, Navy and Airforce / Roll out the barrel / I'm gonna get lit up (when the lights go on in London) / Chattanoga choo choo / Jeepers creepers / I've got a gal in Kalamazoo / Three little fishes / You'd be so nice to come home to / If I should fall in love again / You don't have to tell me / One day when we were young / I remember you / Don't sit under the apple tree / Yes my darling daughter / Woodpecker song / Put your arms around me honey / That lovely weekend / It's been a long, long time / You must have been a beautiful baby / Blueberry hill / Sentimental journey / Pennies from heaven / Hokey cokey / Horsey horsey / Under the spreading chestnut tree / Lambeth walk / White Christmas
MCCD 159 / May '94 / Music Club

Byles, Junior

☐ **BEAT DOWN BABYLON (The Upsetter Years)**
Beat down Babylon / Da-da / I've got a feeling / Don't know why / Demonstration / Coming home / Joshua's desire / Place called Africa / Poor chubby / Matter of time / Fun and games (motion dub) / Pretty fe true (pretty dub) / King of Babylon / Pharaoh hiding
CDTRL 253 / 24 Nov '97 / Trojan

☐ **CURLY LOCKS**
Da da / Come da da / Fever / Lick the pipe Peter: *Byles, Junior & Jah-T/Errol Thompson* / Place called Africa / Africa stand: *Byles, Junior & Dennis Alcapone* / Long way / When will better come / Informer man / Curly locks / Curly locks / Curly locks / Fun and games / Education rock / Got the tip / What is this world coming to / Demonstration / Cutting razor: *Byles, Junior & The Versatiles* / Now generation / Thanks we get / Matter of time / Are you leading me on
CDHB 208 / Feb '97 / Heartbeat

☐ **JORDAN**
CDHB 45 / Oct '95 / Heartbeat

BYOB

☐ **BYOB**
Too good to let go / Ramifications of shaking one's ass / Change it / Distances / Go jazz go / Outerspacegethithang / Ramblifications of getting and saying high / Rackett / Day off in the life / Where ya going to
RCD 10310 / Oct '94 / Rykodisc

Byrd, Charlie

☐ **AQUARELLE**
Concerto grosso / Canta mais / In a mist / 'S wonderful / Man I love / I got rhythm / Quintet (Mozart K 581) / Los Angeles aquarelle suite / In the dark / Modinha / Candlelights
CCD 42016 / Apr '94 / Concord Concerto

☐ **AU COURANT (Byrd, Charlie Trio)**
This can't be love / My romance / St. Louis blues / On a clear day (you can see forever) / There'll be some changes made / If you never came to me / I didn't know what time it was / Avalon / Emily / There's a small hotel / Blue room / Have you met Miss Jones / Willow weep for me / Days of wine and roses
CCD 47792 / 16 Feb '98 / Concord Jazz

☐ **BLUEBYRD**
It don't mean a thing if it ain't got that swing / Vou vivendo / Nice work if you can get it / Jitterbug waltz / Soft light and sweet music / Ain't got nothing but the blues / This can't be love / Carinhoso / Mama I'll be home someday / Isn't it a lovely day / Saturday night fish fry
CCD 4082 / Oct '91 / Concord Jazz

☐ **BOSSA NOVA - GUITAR JUBILEE (Byrd, Charlie & Joao Gilberto)**
CD 62006 / Oct '93 / Jasmine

☐ **BOSSA NOVA YEARS, THE (Byrd, Charlie Trio)**
Meditation / One note samba / Corcovado / Triste / Dindi / O pato / Girl from Ipanema / Samba d'Orpheus / How insensitive / Wave / P'ra dizer adeus / O nosso amor
CCD 4468 / Jul '91 / Concord Jazz

☐ **DU HOT CLUB DE CONCORD**
Swing '59 / Golden earrings / Lamentos / Carinhoso / Till the clouds roll by / Jubilee / Frenesi / At the seaside (na praia) / Gypsy boots (sapatos novos) / Old New Orleans Blues / Cotton tail / Perfidia / Moon river / Besame mucho / They didn't believe me
CCD 4674 / Nov '95 / Concord Jazz

☐ **GREAT GUITARS VOL.2 (Byrd, Charlie & Barney Kessel)**
Lover / Makin' whoopee / Body and soul / Outer drive / On green dolphin street / Nuages: Going out of my head
CCD 4023 / Mar '95 / Concord Jazz

☐ **GUITAR ARTISTRY OF CHARLIE BIRD, THE**
Taking a chance on love / Moonlight in Vermont / Speak low / Nuages / Everything I've got (belongs to you) / Makin' whoopee / Django / Nice work if you can get it / House of the rising sun / Ring them harmonics / Taboo / To Ginny
OJCCD 9452 / Aug '98 / Original Jazz Classics

☐ **I'VE GOT THE WORLD ON A STRING**
I'm gonna sit right down and write myself a letter / Blue skies / How deep is the ocean / Gee baby ain't I good to you / I've got the world on a string / Goody goody / They can't take that away from me / Avalon / Just you, just me / One to nothing / Don't get around much anymore / Satin doll / Travellin' on / Someone to light up my life / So danco samba / Imagination / Straight no chaser
CDSJP 427 / May '95 / Timeless Jazz

☐ **ISN'T IT ROMANTIC (Byrd, Charlie Trio)**
Isn't it romantic / I could write a book / Cheek to cheek / Very thought of you / Thou swell / One morning in May / I didn't know what time it was / There's a small hotel / Someone to watch over me / Thought about me / Last night when we were young
CCD 4252 / Aug '92 / Concord Jazz

☐ **IT'S A WONDERFUL WORLD (Byrd, Charlie Trio & Scott Hamilton)**
It's a wonderful world / Between the devil and the deep blue sea / My shining hour / I got it bad and that ain't good / Caravan / Fine and dandy / Mood indigo / Bernie's tune / Don't you know I care / Let's fall in love/She's a friend / Street of dreams
CCD 4374 / May '89 / Concord Jazz

☐ **JAZZ 'N' SAMBA**
Limehouse blues / Take care of yourself / Jazz 'n' samba / Man and a woman / Sweet georgia brown / Chung king / Blusette / When your lover has gone / Someone to light up my life / Willow weep for me / Danza no. 5 / Carolina in the morning / One note samba / Things ain't what they used to be / Oh, lady be good / It don't mean a thing (if it ain't got that swing)
HCD 606 / Aug '95 / Hindsight

☐ **JAZZ RECITAL**
Prelude / My funny valentine / Little girl blue / My heart stood still / Blue interlude / Spring is here / Foggy day / Spanish guitar blues / Chuck a tuck / Homage to Charlie Chrittian
SV 0192 / Oct '97 / Savoy Jazz

☐ **LATIN BYRD**
Duck / Amor flamengo / Azul tiple / Cancion di Argentina / Manha de carnaval / Homage a villa Lobos / Bogota / Mexican song / Mexican song / Galopera / Vals / Outra vez / Presente de Natal / Insensatez / Three note samba / Samba da minha terra / Limehouse blues / Saudade da Bahia / Anna / Socegadamente / Chega de saudade / Cancao de ninar para Carol
MCD 470052 / Aug '96 / Milestone

☐ **MIDNIGHT GUITAR**
Blues from night people / First show / 2 a.m. / Four o'clock funk / Blues my naughty sweetie gives to me / Blue prelude / This can't be love / Jive at five
SV 0247 / Oct '97 / Savoy Jazz

☐ **MOMENTS LIKE THIS**
Little girls at play / Si tu vois ma mere / My ideal / Rose of the Rio Grande / Too late now / Rosetta / Russian lullaby / As long as I live / Wang wang blues / Prelude to a kiss / Soon / Polka dots and moonbeams / Moments like this / Don't explain
CCD 4627 / Jan '95 / Concord Jazz

Byrd, Donald

☐ **AT THE HALF NOTE CAFE (2CD Set)**
My girl Shirl / Child's play / Chan / Portrait of Jennie / Cecile / Jeannine / Between the devil and the deep blue sea / Theme from Mr. Lucky / Kinyas / When Sunny gets blue
CDP 8571872 / Aug '97 / Blue Note

☐ **BEST OF DONALD BYRD, THE**
Change (makes you want to hustle) / You and music / Black Byrd / Think twice / Onward 'til morning / Lanasana's priestess / Street lady / Flight time / Places and spaces / Wind parade / Dominoes / Steppin' into tomorrow / Just my imagination / Love's so far away / Dominoes (Live)
CDP 7986382 / Feb '92 / Blue Note

☐ **BLACKJACK**
Blackjack / West of Pecos / Loki / Eldorado / Beale street / Pentatonic / All members
8212862 / 19 Jan '98 / Blue Note

☐ **BLUE BREAKBEATS**
Dance band / Lansana's priestess / Wind parade / Miss Kane / Jelly roll / You and music / Love's so far away
4947082 / 13 Jul '98 / Blue Note

☐ **BYRD'S WORD**
Winterset / Gotcha goin' n' comin' / Long green / Stareyes / Someone to watch over me
SV 0132 / Oct '97 / Savoy Jazz

☐ **BYRD'S WORLD**
Winterset / Gotcha goin' and comin' / Long green / Stareyes / Someone to watch over me
CY 18061 / Jun '98 / Savoy Jazz

☐ **EARLY BYRD - THE BEST OF THE JAZZ SOUL YEARS**
Slow drag / West of Pecos / Books Bossa / Jelly roll / Mustang / Blackjack / Weasil / Dude / Emperor / Little rasti
CDP 7896062 / Jun '93 / Blue Note

☐ **ETHIOPIAN KNIGHTS**
8543282 / 13 Apr '98 / Blue Note

☐ **FIRST FLIGHT**
DELMARK 407 / Feb '87 / Delmark

☐ **GROOVIN' FOR NAT**
Hush / Child's play / Angel eyes / Smoothie / Suede / Friday's child / Out of this world / Groovin' for Nat
BLCD 760134 / '88 / Black Lion

☐ **MOTOR CITY SCENE (Original Bethlehem Classics) (Byrd, Donald & Pepper Adams)**
CDGR 167 / Aug '97 / Charly

☐ **MUSTANG**
Mustang / Fly little bird fly / I got it bad and that ain't good / Dixie Lee / On the trail / I'm so excited by you / Gingerbread boy / I'm so excited by you
8599632 / 10 Nov '97 / Blue Note

☐ **PLACES AND SPACES**
Change (makes you want to hustle) / Wind parade / (Fallin' like) dominoes / Places and spaces / You and the music / Night whistler / Just my imagination
CDP 8543262 / Feb '97 / Blue Note

☐ **STREET LADY**
Lansana's priestess / Miss Kane / Sister love / Street lady / Witch hunt / Woman of the world
CDP 8539232 / Jan '97 / Blue Note

Byrd, James

☐ **CRIMES OF VIRTUOSITY**
M 7037CD / 20 Jul '98 / Mascot

Byrd, Joe

☐ **AMERICAN METAPHYSICAL CIRCUS (Byrd, Joe & The Field Hippies)**
OW 26792 / Jun '97 / One Way

Byrd, John

☐ **COMPLETE RECORDINGS 1929-1931 (Byrd, John & Walter Taylor)**
SOB 035172 / Dec '92 / Story Of The Blues

Byrd, Tracy

☐ **BIG LOVE**
Big love / Cowgirl / Good ol' fashioned love / Don't take her she's all I got / If I stay / Don't love make a diamond shine / Tucson too soon / I don't believe that's how you feel / Driving me out of your mind / I love you that's all / Lifestyles of the not so rich and famous / Keeper of the star
MCD 11546 / Oct '96 / MCA

☐ **TRACY BYRD**
That's the thing about a memory / Back in the swing of things / Someone to give my love to / Holdin' heaven / Why / Out of control raging fire / Hat trick / Why don't that telephone ring / Edge of a memory / Talk to me Texas
MCAD 10649 / Mar '94 / MCA

Byrds

☐ **20 ESSENTIAL TRACKS FROM THE BOXED SET**
Mr. Tambourine Man / I'll feel a whole lot better / All I really want to do / Turn turn turn / 5-D / Eight miles high / Mr. Spaceman / So you want to be a rock 'n' roll star / Have you seen her face / Lady friend / My back pages / Goin' back / Ballad of Easy Rider / Jesus is just alright / Chestnut mare / I wanna grow up to be a politician / He was a friend of mine / Paths of victory / From a distance / Love that never dies
4716652 / Jul '91 / Columbia

☐ **BALLAD OF EASY RIDER (Remastered)**
Ballad of Easy Rider / Fido / Oil in my lamp / Tulsa County / Jack Tarr the sailor / Jesus is just alright / It's all over now, baby blue / There must be someone (I can talk to) / Deportee (Plane wreck at Los Gatos) / Armstrong, Aldrin and Collins / Way beyond the sun / Mae Jean goes to Hollywood / Oil in my lamp / Tulsa County / Fiddler a dram (Moog experiment) / Ballad of Easy Rider / Build it up
4867542 / Mar '97 / Columbia

☐ **BEST OF THE BYRDS, THE**
Eight miles high / Turn turn turn / All I really want to do / Outta sight / Quit this / Chestnut mare / You ain't goin' nowhere / Do you remember / He was a friend of mine / It won't be wrong / Time and place / Sarah Jane / Home again
SUMCD 4158 / 26 Jan '98 / Summit

☐ **BYRDMANIAX**
Glory glory / Pale blue / I trust / Tunnel of love / Citizen Kane / I wanna grow up to be a politician / Absolute happiness / Green apple quick step / My destiny / Kathleen's song / Jamaica say you will
CLCD 900930 / 12 Jan '98 / Line

☐ **BYRDS PLAY DYLAN, THE**
Mr. Tambourine man / All I really want to do / Chimes of freedom / Spanish Harlem incident / Time they are a changin' / Lay down your weary tune / My back pages / You ain't goin' nowhere / Nothing was delivered / This wheel's on fire / It's all over now baby blue / Baby blue / Lay lady lay / Positively 4th street
4767572 / Feb '96 / Columbia

☐ **BYRDS, THE**
Full circle / Sweet Mary / Changing heart / For free / Born to rock 'n' roll / Things will be better / Cowgirl in the sand / Long live the King / Borrowing time / Laughing / See the sky about to rain
7559609552 / Jan '93 / WEA

☐ **BYRDS, THE**
GFS 077 / Jul '97 / Going For A Song

☐ **DEFINITIVE COLLECTION, THE**
Mr. Tambourine man / Chimes of freedom / Bells of Rhymney / I'll feel a whole lot better / All I really want to do / Turn turn turn / Set you free this time / Eight miles high / 5D (fifth dimension) / Mr. Spaceman / So you want to be a rock 'n' roll star / My back pages / Have you seen her face / Goin' back wasn't born to follow / Lady friend / You ain't going nowhere / Lay lady lay / Ballad of easy rider / Jesus is just alright / Chestnut mare / I trust / I wanna grow up to be a politician / Glory glory / America's great national pastime
4805482 / 13 Jul '98 / Columbia

☐ **DR. BYRDS AND MR. HYDE (Remastered)**
This wheel's on fire / Old Blue / Your gentle way of loving me / Child of the universe / Nashville West / Drug store truck drivin' man / King Apathy III / Candy / Bad night at the whisley / Medley / Stanley's song / Lay lady lay / This wheel's on fire / Medley
4867532 / Mar '97 / Columbia

☐ **FIFTH DIMENSION**
5D (fifth dimension) / Wild mountain thyme / Mr. Spaceman / I see you / What's happening / I come and stand at every door / Eight miles high / Hey Joe (where you gonna go) / Captain soul / John Riley / 2-4-2 fox trot (The lear jet song) / Why / I know my rider / Psychodrama City / Eight miles high / Why / John Riley
4837072 / May '96 / Columbia

☐ **GREATEST HITS**
Mr. Tambourine man / I'll feel a whole lot better / Bells of Rhymney / Turn turn turn / All I really want to do / Chimes of freedom / Eight miles high / Mr. Spaceman / 5-D (fifth dimension) / So you want to be a rock 'n' roll star / My back pages
4678432 / Feb '91 / Columbia

☐ **MR. TAMBOURINE MAN**
Mr. Tambourine Man / I'll feel a whole lot better / Spanish Harlem incident / You won't have to cry / Here without you / Bells of Rhymney / All I really want to do / I knew I'd want you / It's no use / Don't doubt yourself babe / Chimes of freedom / We'll meet again / She has a way / I'll feel a whole lot better / It's no use / You won't have to cry / All I really want to do / You and me
4837052 / May '96 / Columbia

☐ **NOTORIOUS BYRD BROTHERS, THE (Remastered)**
Artificial energy / Goin' back / Natural harmony / Draft morning / Wasn't born to follow / Get to you / Change is now / Old John Robertson / Tribal gathering / Dolphin's smile / Space odyssey / Moog raga / Bound to fall / Triad / Goin' back / Universal mind decoder / Draft morning
4867512 / Mar '97 / Columbia

☐ **SWEETHEART OF THE RODEO (Remastered)**
You ain't going nowhere / I am a pilgrim / Christian life / You don't miss your water / You're still on my mind / Pretty Boy Floyd / Hickory wind / One hundred years from now / Blue Canadian Rockies / Life in prison / Nothing was delivered / You got a reputation / Lazy days / Pretty Polly / Christian life / Life in prison / You're still on my mind / One hundred years from now / All I have is memories
4867522 / Mar '97 / Columbia

☐ **TURN TURN TURN**
Turn turn turn / It won't be long / Set you free this time / Lay down your weary tune / He was a friend of mine / World turns all around her / Satisfied mind / If you're gone / Times they are a changin' / Wait and see / Oh Susannah / She don't care about time / Times they are a changin' / It's all over now baby blue / Day walk (never before) / World turns all around her / Stranger in a strange land
4837062 / May '96 / Columbia

☐ **ULTIMATE BYRDS, THE (4CD Set)**
Mr. Tambourine man / I'll feel a whole lot better / Chimes of freedom / She has a way / All I really want to do / Spainish harlem incident / Bells of Rhymney / It's all over now baby blue / She don't care about time / Turn, turn, turn / It won't be wrong / Lay down your weary tune / He was a friend of mind / World turns all around her / Day walk (never before) / Times are a a-changing / 5-D (Fifth dimension) / I know my rider / Eight miles high / Why / Psychodrama City / I see you / Hey Joe (where you gonna go) / Mr. Spaceman / John Riley / Roll over Beethoven / So you want to be a rock 'n' roll star / Have you seen her face / My back pages / Time between / It happens each day / Renaissance Fair / Everybody's been burned / Girl with no name / Triad / Lady friend / Old John Robertson / Goin' back / Draft morning / Wasn't born to follow / Dolphin's smile / Reputation / You ain't goin' nowhere / Christian life / I am a pilgrim / Pretty boy Floyd / You don't miss your water / Hickory wind / Nothing was delivered / Hundred years from now / Pretty Polly / Lazy days / This wheel's on fire / Nashville West / Old blue / Drug store truck drivin' man / Bad night at the whiskey / Lay lady lay / Mae Jean goes to Hollywood / Easy rider theme / Oil in my lamp / Jesus is just alright / Way beyond the sun / Tulsa county / Deportee / Lover of the Bayou / Willin' / Black mountain rag / Positively 4th Street / Chestnut mare / Just a season / Kathleen's song / Truck stop girl / Just like a woman / Stanley's song / Glory glory / I trust / I wanna grow up to be a politician / Green apple quick step / Tiffany Queen / Bugler / Lazy waters / Farther along / White's lightning / He was a friend of mine / Paths of victory / From a distance / Love that never dies
4676112 / 1 Dec '97 / Columbia

☐ **VERY BEST OF THE BYRDS, THE**
Mr. Tambourine man / All I really want to do / Chimes of freedom / I'll feel a whole lot better / Turn turn turn / Times they are a-changin' / World turns all around her / It won't be wrong / He was a friend of mine / Eight miles high / 5D / Mr. Spaceman / So you want to be a rock 'n' roll star / My back pages / Renaissance Fair / Goin' back / Wasn't born to follow / Dolphin's smile / You ain't goin' nowhere / One hundred years from now / You're still on my mind / Hickory wind / Ballad of Easy Rider / Jesus is just alright / It's all over now baby blue / Lay lady lay / Chesnut Mare
4879952 / Jun '97 / Columbia
4879959 / 13 Jul '98 / Columbia

☐ **YOUNGER THAN YESTERDAY (Remastered)**
So you want to be a rock 'n' roll star / Have you seen her face / CTA - 102 / Renaissance fair / Time between / Everybody's been burned / Thoughts and words / Mind gardens / My back pages / Girl with no name / Why / It happens each day / Don't make waves / My back pages / Lady friend / Old John Robertson / Mind gardens
4837082 / May '96 / Columbia

Byrne, David

☐ **DAVID BYRNE**
Long time ago / Angels / Crash / Self made man / Back in the box / Sad song / Nothing at all / My love is you / Lillies of the valley / You and eye / Strange ritual / Buck naked
9362455582 / May '94 / Sire

☐ **FEELINGS**
Fuzzy freaky / Miss America / Soft seduction / Dance on vaseline / Gates of paradise / Amnesia / You don't know me / Daddy go down / Finite alright / Wicked little doll / Burnt by the sun / Civil wars / They are in love
9362466052 / May '97 / Sire

☐ **FOREST, THE**
Ur / Kish / Dura europus / Nineveh / Ava / Machu picchu / Teotihuacan / Asuka / Samara / Tula
7599265842 / Jun '91 / Sire

☐ **REI MOMO**
Independence day / Make believe mambo / Call of the wild / Dirty old town / Rose tattoo / Dream police / Don't want to be part of your world / Marching through the wilderness / Lie to me / Women vs. men / Carnival eyes / I know sometimes a man is a wrong / Loco de amor / Good and evil / Office cowboy
9259902 / Feb '95 / Sire

☐ **UH-OH**
Now I'm your mom / Girls on my mind / Something ain't right / She's mad / Hanging upside down / Twistin' in the wind / Walk in the dark / Cowboy's mambo / Tiny town / Somebody
7599267992 / Feb '95 / Sire

Byrne, Dermot

☐ **DERMOT BYRNE**
HBCD 0007 / Mar '96 / Hummingbird

☐ **RAW WHISKEY BLUES (Byrne, Dermot & Blues Combo)**
Line 'em/Rollin' and tumblin' / Slow train / Preachin' blues / Raw whiskey blues / Walking blues / Low down blues / Fortune teller / Catfish to kingbee / Borrow love and go / Old Riley / Death letter blues / M&O blues / Going down to Clarksdale / John Henry
MMBCD 5 / Jun '98 / Me & My Blues

Byrne, Donna

☐ **LET'S FACE THE MUSIC AND DANCE**
ST 579 / Jun '94 / Stash

Byrne, James

☐ **ROAD TO GLENLOUGH, THE**
Con McGinley's reel / Paddy Hiudai's jigs / An londubb (the blackbird) / Fickle lad / Wild Irishman / Muineal a bhardail (the drake's neck) / Road to Glenlough / Devil's dream / McConnell's barndance / John byrne's jig / Glory reel / Jig na mire (the mad jig) / Jimmy Lyons's highlands / Johnny Boyle's jig / Mick Carr's barndances / Tripping upstairs / Sean Parnell's reel / Maidin fhombair (one harvest morning) / Mick Carr's highlands / Heather breeze / Sportin' ballee / Dulaman na binne buidhe (the seaweed at the yellow cliff) / Ril ne drithuieog (the reel of sparks)
CC 52CD / Nov '95 / Claddagh

Byrne, Jeanette

☐ **ELERGY**
74321574472 / 18 May '98 / RCA

Byrnes, Martin

☐ **MASTERS OF IRISH MUSIC, THE**
LEACD 2004 / Oct '97 / Leader

Byron

☐ **BYRON**
WKFMXD 173 / Mar '92 / FM Coast To Coast

Byron, Don

☐ **BUG MUSIC**
7559794382 / Mar '97 / Nonesuch

☐ MUSIC FOR SIX MUSICIANS

Uh-oh changewhite history month / Shelby Steele would be mowing your lawn / Press made Rodney King (responsible for the LA riots) / I'll chill on the Marley tapes / Sexwork (clarenceanita) / That sucking sound (for Ross Perot) / Crown heights / Allure of entanglement / Importance of being Sharpton

7559793542 / '95 / Nonesuch

☐ NO VIBE ZONE (Byron, Don Quintet)

KFWCD 191 / Oct '96 / Knitting Factory

☐ NU BLAXPLOITATION

Alien / Domino theories / Blinky / Mango meat / Interview / Schizo jam / Dodi / I'm stuck / I cannot commit / Fencewalk / Hagalo / Domino theories / If 6 was 9 / Furman

4937112 / 15 Jun '98 / Blue Note

Bystanders

☐ BIRTH OF MAN

That's the end / (You're gonna) hurt yourself / My love - come home / 98.6 / Royal blue summer sunshine day / Make up your mind / Green grass / Cave of clear light / Painting the time / This time / Have I offended the girl / If you walk away / Stubborn kind of fellow / Pattern people / When jezamine goes / This world is my world

SEECD 301 / '90 / See For Miles

Byzar

☐ GAIATRONYK

ASP 0973CD / 22 Jun '98 / Asphodel

C

C&C Music Factory

☐ GONNA MAKE YOU SWEAT
Gonna make you sweat / Here we go / Things that make you go hmmmm / Just a touch of love (everyday) / Groove of love (what's this world called love) / Live happy / Ooh baby / Let's get funkee / Givin' it to you / Bang that beat
4678142 / Apr '94 / Columbia

C&MA Gospel Singers

☐ C&MA GOSPEL SINGERS/QUINTETTE 1924
DOCD 5569 / 21 Sep '97 / Document

C. Gibbs Review

☐ SINCERITY'S GROUND
CDEAR 016 / Jan '97 / Earth Music

CA Quintet

☐ TRIP THRU HELL
852126 / May '94 / EVA

Caballe, Monserrat

☐ OUR CHRISTMAS SONGS (Caballe, Monserrat & Marti)
74321416872 / 24 Nov '97 / RCA Victor

Caballero, Don

☐ FOR RESPECT
EFA 049292 / Oct '93 / City Slang

☐ WHAT BURNS NEVER RETURN
TG 185CD / 8 Jun '98 / Touch & Go

Cabaret Voltaire

☐ 2 X 45
CABS 9CD / Oct '90 / Mute

☐ 8 CREPUSCULE TRACKS
Sluggin for Jesus (part 1) / Sluggin for Jesus (part 2) / Fools game-sluggin for Jesus (part 3) / Yashar / Your agent man / Gut level / Invocation / Shaft
TWI 7492 / Mar '96 / Les Disques Du Crepuscule

☐ CABARET VOLTAIRE 1974-1976
CABS 15CD / Mar '92 / Mute

☐ CONVERSATION, THE
Exterminating angel / Brutal but clean / Message / Let's start / Night rider / I think / Heat / Harmonic parallel / Project 80 / Exterminating angel (Outro)
AMB 4934CD / Jul '94 / Apollo

☐ COVENANT, THE SWORD AND THE ARM OF THE LORD, THE
L 21st / I want you / Hell's home / Kick back / Arm of the Lord / Warm / Golden halos / Motion rotation / Whip blow / Web
CVCD 3 / Sep '91 / Some Bizarre/Virgin

☐ CRACKDOWN, THE
24-24 / In the shadows / Talking time / Animation / Over and over / Just fascination / Why kill time (when you can kill yourself) / Haiti / Crackdown / Diskono / Double vision / Badge of evil / Moscow
CVCD 1 / Apr '86 / Some Bizarre/Virgin

☐ JOHNNY YES NO
CABSCD 10 / Oct '90 / Mute

☐ LISTEN UP WITH CABARET VOLTAIRE
Baader meinhof / Sex in secret / Raising the count / This is our religion / Loosen the clamp / Automotivation / Dead man's shoes / Time in minutes / Trust in the lord / Over and over / Playing the time / Mercy man / Why / Don't drive fast / Enough's enough / That's the way it works
CABS 5CD / Jun '90 / Mute

☐ LIVE AT THE LYCEUM
CABS 13CD / '88 / Mute

☐ LIVE AT THE YMCA
Untitled / On every other street / Nag, nag, nag / Set up / Expect nothing / Havoc / Here she comes now / No escape / Baader meinhof
CABS 4CD / Jun '90 / Mute

☐ LIVING LEGENDS
Do the mussolini (headkick) / Talkover / Here she comes now / Set up / Nag, nag, nag / Silent command / Jazz the glass / Walls of jerico / Seconds too late / Eddies out / Burnt to the ground-chance versus causality (extract) / Control addict / Is that me (finding someone at the door again)
CABS 6CD / Jun '90 / Mute

☐ MICROPHONIES
Do right / Operative / Digital rasta / Spies in the wires / Earthshaker / James Brown / Slammer / Blue heat / Sensoria
CVCD 2 / Sep '91 / Some Bizarre/Virgin

☐ MIX UP
Kurlian photograph / No escape / 4th shot / Heaven and hell / Eyeless sight (live) / Photophobia / On every other street / Expect nothing / Capsules / Untitled / On every other street / Nag, nag, nag / Set up / Expect nothing / Havoc / No escape / Baader meinhof
CABS 8CD / Oct '90 / Mute

☐ PLASTICITY
TWI 9752 / Mar '96 / Les Disques Du Crepuscule

☐ RADIATION
Sensoria / Digital rasta / Kind / Ruthless / Sleep walking / Big funk / Operative / You like to torment me / Hey hey / We've got heart / Sex money freaks / I want you / Zoom zoom
PILOT 039 / 13 Jul '98 / Burning Airlines

☐ RED MECCA
CABS 3CD / Jun '90 / Mute

☐ THREE MANTRAS
Eastern mantra / Western mantra
CABS 7CD / Jun '90 / Mute

☐ VOICE OF AMERICA
Voice of america-damage is done / Partially submerged / Kneel to the boss / Premonition / This is entertainment / If the shadows could march-1974 / Stay out of it / Obsession / News from nowhere / Messages received
CABS 2CD / Jun '90 / Mute

Cabazz

☐ FAR AWAY
DRCD 194 / Jan '89 / Dragon

☐ KAOTIKA
DRCD 241 / Oct '94 / Dragon

Cabestan

☐ FEMMES DE MARINS
KMCD 81 / 24 Apr '98 / Keltia Musique

Cabildo's 3

☐ YUXTAPOSICION
SCEB 902CD / 16 Dec '97 / Schema

Cable

☐ DOWN-LIFT THE UP-TRODDEN
INFECT 32CD / Mar '96 / Infectious

☐ WHEN ANIMALS ATTACK
Souvenir / Bluebirds are blue / Signature tune / Freeze the atlantic / Ultra violet / I'm always right / Colder climate / Whisper firing line / God gave me gravity / From here you can see yourself / Do the tube
INFECT 35CD
INFECT 35CDX / May '97 / Infectious

Cables, George

☐ BLUESOLOGY
SCCD 31434 / 1 Jun '98 / Steeplechase

☐ BY GEORGE
Bess you is my woman now / My man's gone now / I got rhythm / Embraceable you / Someone to watch over me / Foggy day / Summertime
CCD 14030 / Apr '94 / Contemporary

☐ DARK SIDE, LIGHT SIDE (Cables, George Trio)
SCCD 31405 / Apr '97 / Steeplechase

☐ INTRODUCING JEFF JEROLAMON
CCD 79522 / Feb '97 / Candid

☐ LIVE AT MAYBECK RECITAL HALL VOL.35
Over the rainbow / Helen's song / Bess you is my woman now / Someone to watch over me / You don't know what love is / Lullaby / Everything happens to me / Goin' home / Little B's poem
CCD 4630 / Jan '95 / Concord Jazz

☐ NIGHT AND DAY (Cables, George Trio)
DIW 606 / Sep '91 / DIW

☐ PERSON TO PERSON
SCCD 31369 / Feb '96 / Steeplechase

Cabo Verde Show

☐ SANTO CATARINA
012331 / Jan '97 / Sun

Cabrette

☐ CORNEMUSE D'AUVERGNEL 1895-1976
Y 225104 / Aug '93 / Silex

Cacavas, Chris

☐ CHRIS CACAVAS AND JUNKYARD LOVE (Remastered) (Cacavas, Chris & Junkyard Love)
Driving misery / Truth / Wrecking yard / I didn't mean that / Angel on a mattress spring / Load of me / Blue river / Honeymoon / Four corners USA / Jukebox lullabye / Driving misery / Truth / Load off me / Four corners / Can you hear
NORMAL 180CD / Dec '97 / Normal

☐ DWARF STAR
RTS 14 / Dec '94 / Return To Sender

☐ GOOD TIMES
Just do something / Saint / Good times / Chain of roses / Did you hear what she said / Empty bottle trail / Trouble mountain / Over you / Rocking chair / Many splintered thing / What makes a man
NORMAL 140CD / Sep '93 / Normal

☐ NEW IMPROVED PAIN (Cacavas, Chris & Junkyard Love)
NORMAL 200CD / Oct '95 / Normal

☐ PALE BLONDE HELL
NORMAL 170CD / Mar '94 / Normal

Cactus

☐ CACTOLOGY
Evil / Parchman farm / You can't judge a book by the cover / One way or another / Alaska / Long tall Sally / Let me swim / Bro Bill / Rock 'n' roll children / Song for Aries / Restrictions / Oleo / Feel so good / Rumblin' man / Bad stuff / Parchman farm
8122724112 / Jul '96 / Atlantic

☐ CACTUS
You can't judge a book by the cover / Parchman farm / My lady from south of Detroit / Let me swim / Oleo / No need to worry / Feel so good / Bro Bill
7567802902 / Jan '96 / Atlantic

Cadaver

☐ HALLUCINATING ANXIETY
NECRO 4 CD / Dec '90 / Necrosis

Cadaverous Condition

☐ TRYST (Cadaverous Condition/Todd Dillingham)
SQD 002CD / 18 Aug '97 / Serpent Qui Danse

Caddick, Bill

☐ WINTER WITH FLOWERS
FLED 3004 / Jul '95 / Fledg'ling

Cadets

☐ STRANDED IN THE JUNGLE (The Legendary Modern Recordings)
Let's rock 'n' roll / Fools rush in / My clumsy heart / Annie met Henry / Rollin' stone / Don't be angry / Hands across the table / Smack dab in the middle / Pretty Evey / Love can do most anything / Baby ya know / Love bandit / Why did I fall in love / Church bells may ring / Car jumped / Ring chimes / Heartbreak hotel / Dancin' Dan / Rum Jamaica rum / Don't / I got loaded / I'll be spinning / Sugar baby / Stranded in the jungle
CDCHD 534 / Sep '94 / Ace

Cadicamo, Enrique

☐ HOMENAJE A LOS POETAS DEL TANGO
EBCD 74 / Jul '96 / El Bandoneon

☐ LITTO NEBIA QUINTETO
KAR 980 / Sep '96 / IMP

Cadillac Angels

☐ CADILLAC ANGELS
RR 102 / 10 Nov '97 / Radar

Cadillac Blues Band

☐ LIVE 1996
INAK 9042 / Feb '97 / In Akustik

Cadillacs

☐ BEST OF THE CADILLACS, THE
Gloria / No chance / Down the road / Window lady / Speedoo / Zoom / You are / Woe is me / Betty my love / Girl I love / Sugar sugar / My girl friend / Speedo is back / Peek-a-boo / Zoom boom zing / Please Mr. Johnson / Romeo / Tell me today
NEMCD 604 / Aug '90 / Sequel

☐ COMPLETE JOSIE SESSIONS, THE
Gloria / I wonder why / Wishing well / Carelessly / I want to know about love / No chance (alt) / Sympathy / Party for two / Party for two (alt) / Corn whiskey / Down the road / Window lady / Speedoo / Zoom boom zing / Let me explain (alt) / Let me explain / You are (version 1) / Zoon (version 3) / Oh wahtcha do / Shock-a-doo /

You are / Why / (That's) All I need / Baby's coming home to me baby / Girl I love / Betty my love / Woe is me / Rudolph the red nosed reindeer / Don't take your love from me / If you want to be a woman of mine / About that girl named Lou / Sugar sugar / Broken heart / C'mon home baby / Hurry home / Lucy / From this day on / My girlfriend / Don't be mad with my heart / Buzz buzz buzz / Yeah yeah baby / Holy smoke baby / I want to know / Ain't you gonna / It's spring / Speedoo is back / Look-a-here / Great googly moo / Copy cat / Oh oh Lolita / Peek-a-boo / Jelly bean / Please Mr. Johnson / Your heart is so blind / Cool it fool / Jay Walker / Who ya gonna kiss / Vow / Naggity nag / You're not in love with me / Bad Dan McGoon / Romeo Romeo / Always my darling / Dumbell / Still you left me baby / Dum dee dum dum / Frankenstein / I want to be loved / I'm in love / Tell me today / Let me down easy / It's love / That's why / Louise / Rock 'n' roll is here to stay / Boogie man / I'll never let you go / Wayward wanderer
BCD 15648 / Mar '95 / Bear Family

Cadogan, Susan

☐ HURT SO GOOD
CDTRL 122 / Jun '95 / Trojan

Caducity

☐ WEILIAON WIELDER
SHR 012CD / Nov '95 / Shiva

Caedmon

☐ CAEDMON
KSCD 9450 / Jun '97 / Kissing Spell

Caesar

☐ LIVE AT CAESAR'S PALACE
E 12251CD / Sep '93 / Disko B

☐ NO REST FOR THE LONELY
Before my head explodes / Life support / Situations complications / Stains / Horrorscope / Simon the ghost / My loss / Visions of Mars / I took it home / Man with a plan / Slavesong
WOLCD 1085 / 13 Jul '98 / China

Caesars Palace

☐ ROCK DU MUTA
DOL 036CD / Jun '96 / Dolores

Caetano, Gal, Gil & Bethania

☐ COLLECTION, THE
883720 / May '97 / Milan

Cafe Jacques

☐ ROUND THE BACK
Meaningless / Ain't no love in the heart of the city / Sands of Singapore / Farewell my lovely / Eberehtel / Dark eyed Johnny / Sandra's a phoenix / None of your business / Crime passionelle / Lifeline
4872362 / Mar '97 / Columbia

Cafe Orchestra

☐ AFTER HOURS
GRACD 229 / Sep '97 / Grapevine

☐ TOPAZ
GRACD 221 / Jun '97 / Grapevine

☐ TRES CAFE
GRACD 228 / Sep '97 / Grapevine

Cage, John

☐ LITANY FOR THE WHALE
HMU 907187 / Jul '98 / Harmonia Mundi

☐ LOST WORKS, THE
City wears a slouch hat / Fads and fancies in the academy / Chant with claps
MODE 55 / Jan '98 / Mode

☐ SIXTY EIGHT/QUARTETS I-VIII
ARTCD 6168 / Dec '95 / Hat Art

☐ SIXTY-TWO MESOSTICS RE MERCE CUNNINGHAM
ARTCD 26095 / Jan '92 / Hat Art

☐ SONATAS AND INTERLUDES (Plus Composition In Retrospect/2CD Set)
BRIDGE 9081A/B / 1 Sep '98 / Bridge

☐ SONATAS AND PRELUDES
MODE 50 / Jun '97 / Mode

☐ TWO, FIVE AND SEVEN (2CD Set)
CD 6192 / Feb '97 / Hat Hut

☐ WORKS FOR CELLO/LECTURE ON NOTHING
KTC 2016 / May '98 / Etcetera

126

Cagney & Lacee

☐ SIX FEET OF CHAIN
KAR 041 / May '97 / No.6

Caillier, Jackie

☐ FRONT PORCH CAJUN MUSIC
ZNCD 1011 / Oct '96 / Zane

Cain & Abel

☐ CAIN AND ABEL
35699 / Nov '96 / Sphinx Ministry

Cain, Chris

☐ SOMEWHERE ALONG THE WAY
BPCD 5024 / Dec '95 / Blind Pig

☐ UNSCHEDULED FLIGHT
Drinking straight tequila / Helping hand / Good ole days / Do you call that a buddy / Blues for Curtis J / Good news / Change my luck / I still want to believe / Living on a fault line / Something's got to give / Bad situation / Day your good luck goes away / You give me the strength / Three nights without my baby / Unscheduled flight
CCD 11056 / May '98 / Crosscut

Cain, Jackie

☐ JACKIE & ROY FOREVER (Cain, Jackie & Roy Kral)
01612651282 / Dec '95 / Music Masters

Cain, Jonathan

☐ BODY LANGUAGE
HOMCD 7104 / 10 Nov '97 / Higher Octave

☐ FOR A LIFETIME
Wish for christmas / Day to remember / One look / Bridal march / For a lifetime / Open arms / Just to love you / Blue nocturne / China moon / Precious moments / Waves and dreams / Olema Waltz
VHOCD 11 / 25 May '98 / Higher Octave

Cain, Michael

☐ CIRCA (Cain, Michael & Ralph Alessi/ Peter Epstein)
Siegfried and Roy / Social drones / Ped cruc / Miss M / Circa / Egg / Top o' the dunes / ...And their white tigers / Red rock rain / Suchness of Dory Philpott / Marche
5370472 / Feb '97 / ECM

☐ STRANGE OMEN
Emanations / Strange omen / Follow through / Bestido al cielo de noche / Piano sketch no.1 / Piano sketch no.2 / Piano sketch no.3 / Piano sketch no.4 / Way things work / Heroine's serenity / Facing North
CCD 790505 / Feb '97 / Candid

☐ WHAT MEANS THIS
As I gazed / What means this / Meander / Two Kims / How so / Clearly / Figure of speech / Ginnette
CCD 79529 / Feb '97 / Candid

Caine, Jackie

☐ ALEC WILDER COLLECTION (Caine, Jackie & Roy Kral)
ACD 257 / Oct '92 / Audiophile

☐ TRIBUTE TO ALAN J. LERNER, A (Caine, Jackie & Roy Kral)
ACD 230 / Oct '92 / Audiophile

Caine, Marti

☐ MARTI
Still crazy after all these years / Not like this / Waters of March / Guess who I saw today / When the sun comes out / Why did I choose you / Send in the clowns / Looking for the right one / It never entered my mind / What does a woman see in a man / Some cats know / Everything must change / Evert time we say goodbye / Goodbye / I'll be around / Les boys / I've loved these days / Thank song
1731070042 / Aug '96 / Carlton

Caine, Uri

☐ BLUE WAIL (Caine, Uri Trio)
9100342 / Aug '98 / Winter & Winter

☐ PRIMAL LIGHT
9100042 / Oct '97 / Winter & Winter

☐ SPHERE MUSIC
Mr. BC / This is a thing called love / When the world is given / 'Round midnight / Let me count the ways / Jelly / Just in time / We see / Jan fan
5140072 / May '94 / jMT

☐ TOYS
5140222 / May '96 / jMT

☐ WAGNER E VENEZIA (Caine, Uri Ensemble)
9100132 / Feb '98 / Winter & Winter

Caiora, Al

☐ DEEP IN A DREAM
Love letters / There'll never be another you / I got it bad and that ain't good / Everything happens to me / Deep in a dream / You are too beautiful / I got a crush on you / Thunderbird
SV 0205 / Oct '97 / Savoy Jazz

☐ SERENADE IN BLUE
Serenade in blue / Don't worry 'bout me / Moments like this / Early Autumn / Black and blue / Indian summer / Blue the night / Dram-buie
SV 0232 / Oct '97 / Savoy Jazz

Cairney, John

☐ ROBERT BURNS STORY, THE
Man's a man for a' that / Ye banks and braes / My love is like a red, red rose / Ae fond kiss / Flow gently sweet Afton / Auld lang syne / To a mouse / Holy Willie's prayer / Tam o' Shanter
RECD 448 / Jan '98 / REL

Cairo

☐ CONFLICT AND DREAMS
Angels and rage / Corridors / Western desert / Image / Then you were gone / Valley of the shadow
RR 87492 / 23 Feb '98 / Roadrunner

Caja De Pandora

☐ PANDORA'S BOX
CDSD 01 / 19 Jan '98 / Sol

Cajun, Richard

☐ CAJUN TRACKS (Cajun, Richard & The Zydeco Brothers)
BCAT 04CD / Jun '94 / Bearcat

☐ NO KNOWN CURE (Cajun, Richard & The Zydeco Brothers)
BCAT 03CD / Jun '93 / Bearcat

☐ THAT CAJUN THING (Cajun, Richard & The Zydeco Brothers)
BCAT 05CD / Aug '94 / Bearcat

Cajuns Denbo

☐ STOMPIO
Yr uffern hon / Llond fy mol / Jole blon / Ffwl fel fi / Sut fath o foi / Elen / Deugam acadien / Y drws cefn / Walts hefo fi / Puntan yn fy llaw / Diggy diggy lo / Dawnsia nawr / Cajun cwins / Tit galop
SCD 2155 / Feb '97 / Sain

Cake

☐ FASHION NUGGET
Frank Sinatra / Distance / Friend is a four letter word / Open book / Daria / Race car ya ya's / I will survive / Stickshifts and safety belts / Perhaps, perhaps, perhaps / It's coming down / Nugget / She'll come back to me / Italian leather sofa / Sad songs and waltzes
5328672 / Mar '97 / Capricorn

☐ MOTORCADE OF GENEROSITY
Comanche / Up so close / Jolene / You part the waters / Jesus wrote a blank cheque / I bombed Korea / Ain't no good / Ruby sees all / Pentagram / Haze of love / Is this love / Rock 'n' roll lifestyle / Mr. Mastodon Farm
5325062 / Jul '97 / Capricorn

Calabash Case

☐ CALABASH CASE
WR 011CD / 29 Jul '98 / Wrenched

☐ PARADING CONSTANTLY
WR 8 / Jan '97 / Wrenched

Calazans, Teca

☐ FIROLIU
829302 / Oct '96 / BUDA

Caldwell, Randy

☐ FRONT
5399332482 / 7 Apr '98 / HTL

Cale, J.J.

☐ CLOSER TO YOU
Long way home / Sho-biz blues / Slower baby / Devil's nurse / Like you used to / Borrowed time / Rose in the garden / Brown dirt / Hard love / Ain't love funny / Closer to you / Steve's song
CDV 2746 / Jun '94 / Virgin

☐ EIGHT
Money talks / Losers / Hard times / Reality / Takin' care of business / People lie / Unemployment / Trouble in the city / Teardrops in my tequila / Livin' here too
8111522 / Sep '89 / Mercury

☐ FIVE
Thirteen days / Boilin' pot / I'll make love to you anytime / Don't cry sister / Too much for me / Sensitive kind / Friday / Lou easy Ann / Let's go to Tahiti / Katy Kool lady / Fate of a fool / Mona
8103132 / Jul '93 / Mercury

☐ GRASSHOPPER
City girls / Devil in disguise / One step ahead of the blues / You keep me hangin' on / Downtown LA / Can't live here / Grasshopper / Drifter's wife / Thing going on / Nobody but you / Mississippi river / Does your mama like to reggae / Dr. Jive
8000382 / Nov '84 / Mercury

☐ GUITAR MAN
Death in the wilderness / It's hard to tell / Day's go by / Low down / This town / Guitar man / If I had a rocket / Perfect woman / Old blue / Doctor told me / Miss Ol St.Louie / Nobody knows
CDVIR 48 / Apr '96 / Virgin

☐ NATURALLY
Call me the breeze / Call the doctor / Don't go to strangers / Woman I love / Magnolia / Clyde / Crazy mama / Nowhere to run / After midnight / River runs deep / Bringing it back / Crying eyes
8300422 / Jan '87 / Mercury

☐ OKIE
Crying / I'll be there (if you ever want me) / Starbound / Rock 'n' roll records / Old man and me / Ever lovin' woman / Cajun moon / I'd like to love you baby / Anyway the wind blows / Precious memories / Okie / I got the same old blues
8421022 / May '90 / Mercury

☐ REALLY
Lies / Everything will be alright / I'll kiss the world goodbye / Changes / Right down here / If you're ever in Oklahoma / Riding home / Going down / Soulin' / Playin' in the streets / Mo Jo / Louisiana woman
8103142 / Aug '89 / Mercury

☐ SHADES
Carry on / Deep dark dungeon / Wish I had not said that / Pack my jack / If you leave her / Mama don't / What do you expect / Cloudy day / Love has been and gone
8001052 / Aug '89 / Mercury

☐ TEN
Lonesome train / Digital blues / Feeling in love / Artificial paradise / Passion / Take dirt some insurance / Jailer / Low rides / Texas / She's in love / Shady grove / Roll on mama
ORECD 523 / Sep '92 / Silvertone

☐ WHEN THE WIND BLOWS (The Anthology/2CD Set)
5329012 / Jun '97 / Mercury

Cale, John

☐ 23 SOLO PIECES
Paris s'eveille / Sanctus / Animals at night / Cowboy laughs at the round-up / Primary motive / Booker T / Velvet underground / Antarctica starts here
YMCD 007 / Nov '95 / Yellow Moon

☐ ARTIFICIAL INTELLIGENCE
Every time the dogs bark / Dying on the vine / Sleeper / Vigilante lover / Chinese takeaway / Song of the valley / Fade away tomorrow / Black rose / Satellite walk
BBL 68CD / Mar '96 / Beggars Banquet

☐ FEAR
Fear is a man's best friend / Buffalo ballet / Barracuda Emily / Ship of fools / Gun / Man who couln't afford to orgy / You know we more than I know / Momma scuba
IMCD 140 / Aug '91 / Island

☐ FRAGMENTS OF A RAINY SEASON
HNCD 1372 / Oct '92 / Hannibal

☐ GUTS
Guts / Mary Lou / Helen of Troy / Pablo Picasso / Leaving it up to you / Fear is a man's best friend / Gun / Dirty-ass rock and roll / Rock 'n' roll / Heartbreak hotel
IMCD 203 / Jul '94 / Island

☐ HELEN OF TROY
My Maria / Helen of Troy / China Sea / Engine / Save us / Cable hogue / I keep a close watch / Pablo Picasso / Coral moon / Baby, what you want me to do / Sudden death / Leaving it up to you / Sylvia said
IMCD 177 / Mar '94 / Island

☐ HONI SOIT
Honi soit / Dead or alive / Strange times in Casablanca / Fighter pilot / Wilson Joliet / Streets of Laredo / River bank / Russian roulette / Magic and lies
CDMID 1936 / Jul '94 / A&M

☐ ISLAND YEARS ANTHOLOGY, THE (2CD Set)
Fear is a man's best friend / Buffalo ballet / Barracuda / Emily / Ship of fools / Gun / Man couldn't afford to orgy / You know me more than I know / Momma scuba / Sylvia said / All I want is you / Bamboo floor / Mr. Wilson / Talking it all away / Dirty-ass rock 'n' roll / Darling I need you / Rollaroll / Heartbreak hotel / Ski patrol / I'm not the loving kind / Guts / Jeweller / My Maria / Helen Of Troy / China Sea / Engine / Save us / Cable hogue / I keep a close watch / Pablo Picasso / Leaving it up to you / Baby, what you want me to do / Sudden death / You and me / Coral moon / Mary Lou
5242352 / Sep '96 / Island

☐ LA NAISSANCE DE L'AMOUR
La naissance de l'amour / If you love me no more / And if I love you still / Judith / Converging themes / Opposites attract / I will do it, I will keep it / Keep it to yourself / Walk towards the sea / Unquiet heart / Waking up to love / Mysterious relief / Never been so happy / Beyond expectations / Conversations in the garden / La naissance de l'amour III / Secret dialogue / Roma / On the dark side / La naissance de l'amour II / Eye to eye / Maria's car crash and hotel rooms / La naissance de l'amour IV
TWI 9542 / Nov '93 / Les Disques Du Crepuscule

☐ MUSIC FOR A NEW SOCIETY
Taking your life / Thoughtless kind / Sanities / If you were still around / Close watch / Broken bird / Chinese envoy / Changes made / Damn life / Rise Sam and Rimsky Korsakov / Library of force
YMCD 003 / Mar '96 / Yellow Moon

☐ PARIS 1919
Child's Christmas in Wales / Hanky panky no how / Endless plain of fortune / Andalucia / MacBeth / Paris 1919 / Graham Greene / Half past France / Antarctica starts here
7599259262 / Oct '93 / WEA

☐ SLOW DAZZLE
Mr. Wilson / Taking it all away / Dirty-ass rock and roll / Darling I need you / Rollaroll / Heartbreak Hotel / Ski patrol / I'm not the loving kind / Guts / Jeweller
IMCD 202 / Jul '94 / Island

☐ WALKING ON LOCUSTS
Dancing undercover / Set me free / So what / Crazy Egypt / So much for love / Tell me why / Indistinct notion of cool / Secret corrida / Circus / Gatorville and points east / Some friends / Entre nous
HNCD 1395 / Sep '96 / Hannibal

☐ WORDS FOR THE DYING
Introduction / There was a saviour / On a wedding anniversary / Interlude II / Lie still, sleep becalmed / Do not go gentle into that good night / Songs without words I / Songs without words II / Soul of Carmen Miranda
ASCD 009 / Oct '95 / All Saints

Caledon

☐ NOBLE TROUSERS, THE
HYCD 297169 / Feb '97 / Hypertension

Calennig

☐ TRADE WINDS
Tommy's gone away / Y bore glas-ilo man / Llydaw / Nothing but a humbug-hoffder y dyn ifanc-machynlleth / Lowlands / Tiger bay / Ffarwel I aberystwyth-swansea gals / Farewell to the sail-walk along you saucy anna / Suo gan-y gelynnen-llantony abbey
SCD 2091 / Jun '95 / Sain

Calexico

☐ BLACK LIGHT, THE
Gypsy's curse / Fake fur / Ride (part II) / Where water flows / Black light / Sideshow / Chach / Missing / Minas de cobre (For better metal) / Over your shoulder / Vinegaroon / Trigger / Sprawl / Stray / Old man waltz / Bloodflow / Frontera
087072 / 18 May '98 / City Slang

☐ SPOKE
QS 51CD / Sep '97 / Quarter Stick

Calglia

☐ MUSIC OF THE BALKANS & ANATOLIA VOL.2
Aide mor' milia / Guvercin / Da li znaes, pomnis II / Krivo horo / Daglar, daglar / Potamia / Derde derman / Razlozko kalajdzijsko horo / Te kam dashte dhe te du / To aidhonI / Turnalar / Ispaice / Acem kizl / Naz bar / Bas bar / Alexandra / Suite of armenian dance tunes / Beratce / Koskum var / Posednica
PANCD 2007 / May '93 / Pan

Caliche

☐ MUSIC OF THE ANDES
Festival of the flowers / Andean dawn / Memories of the lake / Flight of the Condor / Bell bird / Returning to a new time / Winds from the South / Silver paper / She left my crying
CDSDL 388 / Mar '94 / Saydisc

Calico

☐ CALICO
177012 / 1 Dec '97 / Magic

☐ CELANOVA SQUARE
Covering ground / Breizh trilogy / Two days to go / Waterbed / Mattay shuffle / Between the strings / Hidden note / Celanova aquare / Above and beyond / King John
OSS 100CD / Mar '98 / Ossian

California

☐ TRAVELER
Rocker arm reel / Walk in the Irish rain / Scissors, paper and stone / My sweet blue eyed darling / Spurs / Farmers son / California traveler / I'll dry every tear that falls / Whiplash / Sasquatch / Uncle Pen / Band of angels
SHCD 3803 / Oct '92 / Sugar Hill

California Cajun Orchestra

☐ NONC ADAM TWO-STEP
ARHCD 436 / Sep '95 / Arhoolie

☐ NOT LONESOME ANYMORE
Hix wagon wheel special / Valse criminelle / Monsieur leonard / Sugar bee / Lake charles two-step / Not lonesome anymore / Jolie bassette / Mon coeur fait p'us mal / L'anse aux pailles / Tell me pretty mama / Veuve de basile / Shamrock two-step / Louisiana waltz / Midland two step / Hathaway two-step / Valse du mariage / Lake arthur stomp
ARHCD 356 / Apr '95 / Arhoolie

California Guitar Trio

☐ PATHWAYS
Allegro con brio symphony no.5 / Arroyo / Pathways / Leap / Adagio opus 11 / Great divide / Scramble / Classical gas / Kaleidoscope / Ananda / Adagio sostenuto moonlight sonata / Presto agitato moonlight sonata / Jesu joy of man's desiring / Misirlou
DGM 9803 / 22 Jun '98 / Discipline

California Guitar Trio

☐ INVITATION
Train to lamy suite / Punta patri / Toccata and fugue in d minor / Fratres / Train to Lamy / Apache / Above the clouds / Prelude circulation / Good, the bad and the ugly
DGM 9501 / Apr '95 / Discipline

☐ YAMANASHI BLUES
Yamanashi blues / Melrose Avenue / Corrente / Walk don't run / Ricercar / Pipeline / Beeline / Chromatic fugue in D minor / Tenor madness / Sleepwalk / Carnival / Prelude in C minor / Ciaccona / Blockhead / Kan-non power
DGM 9301 / Aug '94 / Discipline

California Ramblers

☐ EDISON LATERALS VOL.2, THE
DCP 301D / Jul '98 / Diamond Cut

California Sunshine

☐ IMPERIA
20752 / 12 Jan '98 / Phonokol

☐ NASHA
21052 / 30 Mar '98 / Phonokol

California, Randy

☐ KAPT. KOPTER AND THE (FABULOUS) TWIRLY BIRDS
Downer / Devil / Day tripper / Mother and child reunion / Things yet to come / Rain / Rainbow / I don't want nobody
EDCD 164 / May '97 / Edsel

☐ KAPT. KOPTER AND THE (FABULOUS) TWIRLY BIRDS
Downer / Devil / I don't want nobody / Day tripper / Mother and child reunion / Things yet to come / Rain / Rainbow / Live for the day / Walkin' the dog / Rebel
4875792 / Jun '97 / Epic

Calle, Ed

☐ DOUBLE TALK (2CD Set)
Mr. Slick / Hot sauce / You're the one / Island girl / Mowtown melody / Double talk / Autumn / Antes que seja tarde (Before it's too late) / Blocks / Me and Mrs Jones
4697992 / Jun '96 / Sony Jazz

Callender, Bobby

☐ RAINBOW
Rainbow / Nature / Sade masoch / Purple / Mother superior / Autumn / Man / I'm just high on life / Symphonic pictures / Raga man / Story of Rahsa and D'Hara
CDWIKD 179 / 23 Mar '98 / Big Beat

Callier, Terry

☐ ESSENTIAL (The Very Best Of Terry Callier)
MCD 11781 / 27 Apr '98 / MCA

☐ FIRST LIGHT
Ordinary Joe / If I could make you mine / Can't catch the train / Golden circle / Lean on me / Gravy waltz / Alley wind song / Naomi / Trick all your time away / Blues ofor Marcus / 900 miles / Occasional rain
76691787402 / 27 Apr '98 / Premonition

☐ I JUST CAN'T HELP MYSELF
I don't want anybody else / Brown eyed lady / Gotta get closer to you / Satin doll / Until tomorrow / Alley wind song / Can't catch the trane / Bowlin' green
UMD 80511 / 15 Jun '98 / Universal

☐ NEW FOLK SOUND OF TERRY CALLIER, THE
900 Miles / Oh dear, what can the matter be / Johnny be gay if you can / Cotton eyed Joe / It's about time / Promenade in green / Spin spin spin / I'm a drifter
CDBGPM 101 / Nov '95 / Beat Goes Public

☐ OCCASIONAL RAIN
Segue go head on / Ordinary Joe / Golden circle / Segue go head on / Trance on Sedgewick street / Do you finally need a friend / Segue go head on / Sweet Edie D / Occasional rain / Segue go head on / Blues for Marcus / Lean on me / Last segue go head on
UMD 80512 / 15 Jun '98 / Universal

☐ TIME PEACE
Ride suite ride / Lazarus man / Keep your heart right / Java sparrow / People get ready/Brotherly love / Love theme from Spartacus / No more blues / Time peace / Following your footprints / C'est la vie / Coyote moon / AKA New York AI / Traitor to the race
5392492 / 2 Feb '98 / Talkin' Loud

☐ VERY BEST OF TERRY CALLIER
Dancing girl / What colour is love / You goin' miss your candyman / Just as long as we're in love / Ho tsing mee / I'd rather be with you / You don't care
CDARC 514 / Apr '94 / Charly

☐ WHAT COLOR IS LOVE
Dancing girl / What color is love / You goin' to miss your candyman / Just as long as we're in love / Ho tsing mee (a song of the sun) / I'd rather be with you / You don't care
UMD 80510 / 15 Jun '98 / Universal

Calliope

☐ I CAN SEE YOU WITH MY EYES CLOSED
THK 0312 / May '97 / Thick

Calloway, Blanche

☐ CLASSICS 1925-1935
CLASSICS 783 / Nov '94 / Classics

Calloway, Cab

☐ BEST OF CAB CALLOWAY, THE
Aw you dog / Ghost of Smokey Joe / Tarzan of Harlem / Reefer man / I ain't gettin' nowhere fast / I gotta right to sing the blues / FDR Jones / Queen Isabella / Swing swing swing / Black rhythm / Jiveinformation please / Mister Paganini swing for Minnie / Pickin' the cabbage / Beale Street Mama / Do you wanna jump children / Kicking the gong around / Minnie the moocher / Jumpin' jive / Eadie was a lady / Hi-de-ho Romeo
306522 / May '97 / Hallmark

☐ CAB CALLOWAY & HIS ORCHESTRA 1939-1942 (Calloway, Cab Orchestra)
CD 14567 / May '95 / Jazz Portraits

☐ CAB CALLOWAY ON FILM 1934-1950
FLYCD 944 / Feb '95 / Flyright

☐ CLASSICS 1930-1931
CLASSICS 516 / Apr '90 / Classics

☐ CLASSICS 1931-1932
CLASSICS 526 / Apr '90 / Classics

☐ CLASSICS 1932
CLASSICS 537 / Dec '90 / Classics

☐ CLASSICS 1932-1934
CLASSICS 544 / Dec '90 / Classics

☐ CLASSICS 1934-1937
CLASSICS 554 / Dec '90 / Classics

☐ CLASSICS 1937-1938
CLASSICS 568 / Oct '91 / Classics

☐ CLASSICS 1938-1939
CLASSICS 576 / Oct '91 / Classics

☐ CLASSICS 1939-1940
CLASSICS 595 / Sep '91 / Classics

☐ CLASSICS 1940 (Calloway, Cab Orchestra)
CLASSICS 614 / Feb '92 / Classics

☐ CLASSICS 1940-1941 (Calloway, Cab Orchestra)
CLASSICS 629 / Nov '92 / Classics

☐ CLASSICS 1940-1942
CLASSICS 682 / Mar '93 / Classics

☐ CLASSICS 1942-1947
CLASSICS 996 / 1 Jun '98 / Classics

☐ CRUISIN' WITH CAB (Calloway, Cab Orchestra)
Get with it / That old black magic / Airmail stomp / Jealous / I've got a girl named Netty / Bassically blue / You got it / Blue Serge suit / One o'clock jump / This is always / All by myself in the moonlight / Jumpin' jive / Everybody eats when they come to my house / I don't want to love you / Yesterdays / Cruisin' with Cab / Stormy weather / Duck trot
TPZ 1010 / Oct '94 / Topaz Jazz

☐ FRANTIC IN THE ATLANTIC
I got a girl named Netty / This is always / Jealous / Blue serge suit / One o'clock jump / Frantic in the Atlantic / Jumpin' jive / Airmail stomp / Cruisin' with cab / You got it / That old black magic / Everybody eats when they come to my house / Duck trot
DBCD 10 / Dec '88 / Dance Band Days

☐ GET WITH CAB
WWCD 2403 / Apr '92 / West Wind

☐ HI DE HO MAN, THE
Minnie the moocher / Smooth one / Miss Hallelujah Brown / There's a sunny side to everything / Some of these days / Jumpin' jive / Man from Harlem / Pluckin' the bass / St. James infirmary / St. Louis blues / Boogie woogie / Viper's drag / Ain't that something / I've got you under my skin / Ratamacue / Come on with the come on
74321267292 / Aug '97 / Milan

☐ HI-DE-HI-DE-HO
Hi de ho man / I'll be around / Summertime / It ain't necessarily so / Kicking the gong around / (I'll be glad when you're dead) You rascal you / Minnie the Moocher / I see a million people / St. James Infirmary / Stormy weather / Jumpin' jive
74321185242 / Oct '94 / RCA Victor

☐ HI-DE-HO (Calloway, Cab Orchestra)
Minnie the moocher / Long about midnight / Moonglow / Margie / Scar song / (I'll be glad when you're dead) you rascal you / Harlem camp meeting / There's a cabin in the cotton / Father's got his glasses on / Nobody's sweetheart / Between the devil and the deep blue sea / Kicking the gong around / Hotcha razz ma tazz / Jitterbug / Harlem hospitality / Lady with the fan / Zaz zuh zaz
PAR 2008 / Apr '95 / Parade

☐ HI-DE-HO MAN, THE
St. Louis blues / Minnie the moocher / St. James infirmary / Nobody's sweetheart / Six or seven times / (I'll be glad when you're dead) you rascal you / Kicking the gong around / Between the devil and the deep blue sea / Minnie the moocher's wedding day / Seat song / Bugle call rag / Blues in my heart / Sweet Georgia Brown / Mood Indigo / Dinah / Aw you dawg
HADCD 174 / May '94 / Javelin

☐ HIS BEST SIDE
Minnie the moocher / Scat song / Reefer man / Calling all bars / Doin' the new low down / Bugle call rag / Margie / Wedding of Mr. and Mrs. Swing / Six or seven times / Jonah joins the Cab / Corinne Corrina / Hey Doc / Keep that hi-de-hi in your soul / St. James infirmary / Man from Harlem / Jumpin' jive
SUMCD 4034 / Nov '96 / Summit

☐ INTRODUCTION TO CAB CALLOWAY 1930-1942, AN
4011 / Aug '94 / Best Of Jazz

☐ JUMPIN' JIVE
Jumpin' jive / Minnie the moocher / Hi de ho man / Kickin' the gong around / (I'll be glad when you're dead) You rascal you / St. James infirmary / Harlem hospitality / Zaz zuh zaz / Father's got his glasses on / Scat song / Little town gal / Summertime / Stormy weather / There's a cabin in the cotton / Emaline / Ol' Joe Louis / Rooming house boogie / I beeped when I should have bopped / Just a crazy song (hi-hi-hi) / It looks like Susie / Growlin' Dan / Last dollar / Oh you sweet thing / I'll be around
743215358220 / 23 Mar '98 / Camden

☐ KICKING THE GONG AROUND
Minnie the moocher / Without rhythm / Aw you dog / Bugle call rag / Downhearted blues / Nightmare / Black rhythm / Yaller / Between the Devil and the deep blue sea / Nobody's sweetheart / Trickeration / St. Louis blues / Mood indigo / Farewell blues / (I'll be glad when you're dead) you rascal you / My honey's lovin' arms / Some of these days / Six or seven times / Somebody stole my gal / Kicking the gong around
CDAJA 5013 / Sep '90 / Living Era

☐ KING OF HI-DE-HO (Calloway, Cab Orchestra)
Minnie the moocher / Man from Harlem / Chinese rhythm / Jumpin' jive / Scat song / Trickeration / Kicking the gong around / Lonesome nights / Run little rabbit / Bye bye blues / Ad-de-day
CDHD 260 / Feb '97 / Happy Days

☐ KING OF HI-DE-HO 1934-1947, THE
Minnie the moocher / Honey dripper / Hi de ho man / St. james infirmary / Hey now, hey now / Calloway boogie / San francisco fan / Ghost of a chance / Jungle king / Oh grandpa / Two blocks down, turn to the left / A chicken ain't nothing but a bird / Pluckin' the bass / Hoy hoy / (hep-hep) the jumpin' jive / Abi gezunt / Fifteen minute intermission / Everybody eats when they come to my house / I want to rock / My gal / I ain't got nobody / I'll be around / Nagasakl / Weakness
CD 53096 / Mar '92 / Giants Of Jazz

☐ KINGS OF THE COTTON CLUB, THE (Calloway, Cab & Scatman Crothers)
You've got your troubles / If I were a rich man / I will wait for you / Sway / You're nobody till somebody loves you / Mame / Hello dolly / Sunshine / September song / Cabaret / I'm gonna sit right down and write myself a letter / I got rhythm / Baby won't you please come home / Best things in life are free / Gal looks good / Please don't talk about me when I'm gone
15378 / Jan '93 / Laserlight

☐ MINNIE THE MOOCHER
Nagaski / Hoy hoy / Jumpin' jive / Give baby give / I want to rock / Minnie the moocher / Honey dripper / Hi de ho man / Jungle king / Calloway boogie / Two blocks down town to the left / Chicken ain't nothin' but a bird / I can't give you anything but love / Stormy weather / You got it / Everybody eats when they come to my house / Afternoon moon / This is always / Duck trot / That old black magic / How big can you get / Hey now hey now / Birth of the blues / We the cats shall help you / Foo a little ballyhoo
CD 56073 / Mar '95 / Jazz Roots

☐ MINNIE THE MOOCHER
GRF 077 / '93 / Tring

☐ MINNIE THE MOOCHER
Nagasaki / Hoy hoy (Hep-hep) the jumpin' jive / Give, baby, give / I want to rock / Minnie the moocher / Honeydripper / Hi-de-ho man / Jungle swing / Calloway boogie / Two blocks down turn left / Chicken ain't nothin' but a bird / Stormy weather / Evreybody eats when they come to my house / Afternoon moon / This is always / Duck trot / That old black magic / How big can you get / Birth of the blues / We the cats / Foo a little ballyhoo
QED 043 / Nov '96 / Tring

☐ RADIO YEARS 1940-1945, THE
JUCD 2027 / May '97 / Jazz Unlimited

Calo, Miguel

☐ LES ESTRELLAS
EBCD 92 / 24 Apr '98 / El Bandoneon

☐ LOCO TURBION
BMT 017 / Jan '98 / Blue Moon

Calua

☐ DOWN THE LINE
CAL 001CD / Dec '97 / Ceol Calua

Calva Y Nada

☐ SCHLAF
HYP 39101852CD / 8 Jun '98 / Hyperium

Calvary

☐ ACROSS THE RIVER OF LIFE
DREAM 001MCD / Jul '96 / Polyphemus

Calvert, Eddie

☐ EMI YEARS, THE
Oh mein papa / Poor people of Paris / Stranger in paradise / April in Portugal / On a slow boat to China / Love is a many splendoured thing / I'm getting sentimental over you / Sucu sucu / My son, my son / Malaguena / Cherry pink and apple blossom white / Mandy (the pansy) / Around the world / Forgotten dreams / My Yiddishe Momme / Summertime / John and Julie / Little serenade (Piccolossima serenata) / I love Paris / Zambesi
CDP 7801372 / Aug '92 / Premier/EMI

☐ GOLDEN SOUNDS OF EDDIE CALVERT, THE
GS 863572 / Mar '96 / Disky

☐ OH MEIN PAPA
Oh mein Papa / Love is a many splendored thing / April in Portugal / Forgotten dreams / What is this thing called love / Why do I love you / Free and easy / Love is the sweetest thing / And the angels sing / My son, my son / Zambesi / Georgia on my mind / Holiday night / Cherry pink and apple blossom white / Whispering / Taking a chance on love / Carnival of Venice / John and Julie / Roses of Picardy / They didn't believe me
CDMFP 6210 / Feb '96 / Music For Pleasure

Calvert, Robert

☐ CAPTAIN LOCKHEAD AND THE STARFIGHTERS
Aerospaceage inferno / Aircraftsman (a door in the foot) / Widow maker / Two test pilots discuss the starfighter's performance / Right stuff / Board meeting (seen through a contact lense) / Song of the gremlin (part 1) / Ground crew (last minute reassembly before take off) / Hero with a wing / Ground control to pilot / Ejection / Song of the gremlin (part 2) / Bier garten / Catch a falling star fighter
BGOCD 5 / Oct '88 / Beat Goes On

☐ FREQ REVISITED
Ned ludd / Talk one / Acid rain / Talk two / All the machines are quiet / Talk three / Picket line / Talk four / Cool courage of the bomb / Squad / Talk five / Work song / Lord of the Hornets / Greenfly and the rose
CDMGRAM 55 / Jun '92 / Anagram

☐ HYPE
Over my head / Ambitious / It's the same / Hanging out on the seafront / Sensitive / Evil rock / We like to be frightened / Teen ballad of Deano / Flight 105 / Luminous green glow of the dashboard / Greenfly and the rose / Lord of the hornets
SEECD 278 / '89 / See For Miles

☐ LIVE AT THE QUEEN ELIZABETH HALL
Evil rock / Catch a falling starfighter / Gremlins / Aerospace age inferno / Test tube conceived / Working down a diamond mine / All the machines are quiet / Work song / Telekinesis / Acid rain / Lord of the hornets
BGOCD 187 / Apr '93 / Beat Goes On

☐ TEST TUBE CONCEIVED
Telekinesis / I hear voices / Fanfare for the perfect race / On line / Save them from the scientists / Fly on the wall / Thanks to the scientists / Test tube conceived / In vitro breed / Rah rah man
CDTB 113 / '91 / Thunderbolt

Calvin Krime

☐ YOU'RE FEELING SO ATTRACTIVE
AMREP 071CD / 3 Aug '98 / Amphetamine Reptile

Calvin Party

☐ LIES, LIES & GOVERNMENT
Tell me about poverty / Lies, lies and government 1 / Lies, lies and government 2 / Caspers ballroom / Flowers / Looking at me for / Life and other sex tragedies / Repetition no.2 / Pomo Gothic / Heart and soul / First thing / Celebration / Sweetest dream
PROBE 043CD / Feb '96 / Probe Plus

☐ LIFE AND OTHER SEX TRAGEDIE, THE
All messed up / Monster / Song from England / Messalina / Gun / Alphabet song / Look back in angst uh / Taxi man / None the less / Less is more / Mass
PROBE 038CD / Sep '94 / Probe Plus

Camacho, Wichy

☐ LA ROMANCE
Desilucionado / Todo por amor / Dime carino / Me das libertad / Me pides que te ame / Amor de fantasia / Dosis del amor / Solicito un amor
66058079 / Nov '95 / RMM

Camara, Ladsi

☐ AFRICA, NEW YORK (Master Drummer)
LYRCD 7345 / Jul '94 / Lyrichord

Camber

☐ BEAUTIFUL CHARADE
DER 359 / 6 Jul '98 / Deep Elm

Cambridge Singers

☐ CHRISTMAS STAR (Carols For The Christmas Season)
CSCD 503 / Nov '97 / Collegium

Camel

☐ BREATHLESS
Breathless / Echoes / Wing and a prayer / Down on the farm / Starlight ride / Summer lightning / You make me smile / Sleeper / Rainbow's end
8207262 / Jun '92 / Deram

☐ CAMEL
Slow yourself down / Mystic queen / Six ate / Separation / Never let go / Curiosity / Arubaluba
CP 002CD / Jul '93 / Camel Productions

☐ COMING OF AGE (2CD Set)
Lunar sea / Hymn to her / Rhayader / Rhayader goes to town / Preparation / Dunkirk / Drafted / Docks / Beached / Spirit of the water / Ice / Sasquatch / Milk 'n' honey / Mother road / Needles / Rose of Sharon / Irish air / Irish air / Harbour of tears / Cobh / Send home the slates / Under the moon / Watching the bobbins / Eyes of Ireland / Running from paradise / End of the day / Coming of age / Hour candle
CP 008CD / 6 Apr '98 / Camel Productions

☐ DUST & DREAMS
CP 001CD / Jul '93 / Camel Productions

☐ HARBOUR OF TEARS
CP 006CD / Jan '96 / Camel Productions

☐ NEVER LET GO
CP 004CD / Oct '93 / Camel Productions

☐ ON THE ROAD 1972
Lady fantasy / Six ate / White rider / God of light
CP 003CD / Jul '93 / Camel Productions

☐ ON THE ROAD 1981
CP 007CD / Mar '97 / Camel Productions

☐ ON THE ROAD 1982
Sasquatch / Highways of the sun / Hymn of her / Neon magic / You are the one / Drafted / Lies / Captured / Heart's desire / Heroes / Who we are / Manic / Wait and never let go
CP 005CD / Jan '95 / Camel Productions

☐ RAIN DANCES
First light / Metrognome / Tell me / Highways of the sun / Unevensong / One of these days I'll get an early night / Skylines / Elke / Rain dances
8207252 / Jan '93 / Deram

☐ SNOW GOOSE
Great marsh / Rhayader / Rhayader goes to town / Sanctuary / Fritha / Snow goose / Friendship / Rhayader alone / Flight of the snow goose / Preparation / Dunkirk / Epitaph / Fritha alone / La princesse perdue / Pressure points / Refugee / Stationary traveller
8000802 / Jul '93 / Deram

Camelia Jazz Band

☐ THAT'S MY HOME
JCD 249 / Aug '95 / Jazzology

Cameo

☐ BEST OF CAMEO, THE
Word up / Single life / Candy / Shake your pants / Rigor mortis / Attack me with your love / Talkin' out the side of your neck / Sparkle / Back and forth / Flirt / She's strange / I just want to be / Skin I'm in / It's over / She's mine
5149292 / Jun '93 / Club

☐ BEST OF CAMEO, THE
Word up / She's strange / Candy / Rigor mortis / Attack me with your love / Sparkle / She's mine / Be yourself / Freaky dancin' / Goodbye / Post mortem / Keep it hot / I just want to be / Flirt / You make me work / Shake your pants / Single life / Back and forth
5580122 / 20 Apr '98 / Spectrum

☐ NASTY
Intro / Flirt / She's strange / Back and forth / Skin I'm in / Why have I lost you / Sparkle / Candy / Shake your pants / I just want to be / Keep it hot / Word up / Come fly with me / Nasty / Mega-mix
ESMCD 445 / Oct '96 / Essential

☐ WORD UP
Word up / Urban warrior / Candy / Back and forth / Don't be lonely / She's mine / Fast, fierce and funny / You can have the world
8302652 / Sep '86 / Club

Cameron Highlanders Of Ottawa

☐ ADVANCE
68 marches / 68 marches / 34 marches / Solo pipes / 24 marches / 24 marches / Medley / 68 marches / Solo pipes / 34 marches / MSR / 44 marches / 44 slow march / Ottawa valley set / Regimental tunes
BNA 5108 / Jan '95 / Bandleader

Cameron, Jimmie

☐ SONG PAINTERS (Cameron, Jimmie & Vella)
KAR 619290 / Jan '98 / Melodie

Cameron, John Allan

☐ GLENCOE STATION
Getting dark again / Parlour sessions / Saban the woodfitter / Cape Bretton shore / Emigrant eyes / Islanders / Miners song / Roving gyspy song / Heading for Halifax / Evangeline / Kitchen session
IRCD 051 / May '97 / Iona

Camilla's Little Secret

☐ STEPS, THE
SNRCD 944 / May '95 / S&R

Camilo, Aramis

☐ PUNTO
RMD 804782 / 7 Apr '98 / RMM

☐ REALIDAD
RMD 80739 / 7 Apr '98 / RMM

Camilo, Michel

☐ MICHEL CAMILO
Suite sandrine / Nostalgia / Dreamlight / Crossroads / Sunset (Interlude/Suite sandrine) / Yarey / Pra voce / Blue brossa / Caribe
4633302 / Dec '90 / Sony Jazz

☐ ON FIRE
4658802 / Jan '95 / Sony Jazz

☐ ONE MORE ONCE
One more once / Why not / Resolution / Suite sandrine / Dreamlight / Just kidding / Caribe / Suntan / On the other hand / Not yet
4777532 / Oct '94 / Columbia

☐ RENDEZVOUS
4737722 / Jan '95 / Sony Jazz

Camire, William

☐ FOURTEEN YEARS
Preface / Premonition / Fourteen years / Patchouli / From a distant shore / Girl who makes you cry is always love / Bokhara / Aries under Autumn sky / Monument beach
ALCD 1013 / 24 Aug '98 / Alchemy

Camp Creek Boys

☐ OLD TIME STRING BAND
Firtune / Let me fall / Old Joe Calrk / Fall on ym knees / Honeysuckle / Suzanna Gal / June apple / Cider mill / Fire in the mountain / Cotton eyed Joe / Breakig up Christmas / Pretty little girl
COCD 2719 / 9 Mar '98 / County

Camp Lo

☐ UPTOWN SATURDAY NIGHT
FILECD 470 / Feb '97 / Profile

Camp, Manuel

☐ ROSEBUD (Camp, Manuel & M. Simon)
FSNT 011CD / Sep '96 / Fresh Sound New Talent

Campbell Brothers

☐ SACRED STEEL GUITARS VOL.2 (Pass Me Not) (Campbell Brothers & Katie Jackson)
Pass me not oh gentle saviour / I feel good / Walk with me / Jump for joy / Mary don't you weep / None but the righteous / What a friend we have in Jesus / Morning train / There is no failure in God / I've got a felling / What's his name...Jesus / It won't be very long / Medley of offertory tune / End of my journey
ARHCD 461 / Nov '97 / Arhoolie

Campbell Family

☐ SINGING CAMPBELLS, THE
Fur does bonnie lorna lie / Sleep till yer mammy / Nicky tams / Road and the miles to Dundee / Drumdelgie / I ken faur I'm gaun / My wee man's a miner / Fa, fa, fa wid be a bobby / Foul Friday / Me an' mi mither / We three kings of Orient are / Bogie's bonnie belle / Cruel mother / Lang-a-growing / Lady Eliza / Will ye gang love / I wish I wish / McGinty's meal and ale
OSS 97CD / Aug '94 / Ossian

Campbell, Al

☐ RASTA TIME
Rasta time / Can't get not peace / Free man / Ain't that lovin' you / You must get a beating / No more running / Hit me with music / I can't hide / Tribal war / When the grass is green / Feeling of love / It's true / If you don't love jah / Soul sister
LG 21056 / Feb '93 / Lagoon

☐ REVIVAL SELECTION
KICKCD 55 / 9 Mar '98 / Kickin'

☐ ROAD BLOCK
EXTCD 5 / May '97 / Exterminator

☐ SOULFUL, THE
RNCD 2067 / Jul '94 / Rhino

Campbell, Ali

☐ BIG LOVE
Big love (intro) / Happiness / That look in your eyes / Let your yeah be yeah / You can cry on my shoulder / Somethin' stupid / Big love / You could meet somebody / Talking blackbird / Pay the rent / Drive it home / Stop the guns
CDV 2783 / Jun '95 / Kuff

Campbell, Anthony

☐ YOUR SPECIAL GIFT
CAMCD 3 / Oct '95 / Stringbean

Campbell, Blind James

☐ BLIND JAMES CAMPBELL
ARHCD 438 / Jun '95 / Arhoolie

Campbell, Chris

☐ MEETINGS WITH REMARKABLE ALLOYS
JHR 2021 / Feb '95 / Larrikin

☐ RINGS OF FIRE
JHR 2022 / Nov '94 / Larrikin

Campbell, Cornell

☐ NATTY DREAD IN A GREENWICH FARM
Why did you leave me to cry / I am just a country boy / Somebody has stolen my girl / King's heart / I wonder why / Lost in a dream / Duke of earl / Natural facts / Sun / Girl of my dreams / Dance in a greenwich farm / Natty dread in a greenwich farm
TSL 104CD / Jul '95 / Striker Lee

☐ SILVER JUBILEE
Queen of the minstrel / I'll never let it go / Boxing / Duke of earl / Investigator / Trick in the book / Love trap / Drifter / Rope in / 100lbs of collie / I'll mash you down / Stars / Undying love / Minstrel / You don't care for me / Natty dread in a greenwich farm / Gorgan / My confession / My only lover / Once ago / Have mercy on jah / I need to belong to someone / They can't get me out / Jah jah a go rest the wicked / Will you always be sincere
RNCD 2024 / Sep '93 / Rhino

☐ SINGS HITS FROM STUDIO ONE
RN 7039 / 25 May '98 / Rhino

☐ TELL THE PEOPLE
CDSGP 072 / May '94 / Prestige

Campbell, Don

☐ ALBUM, THE
JGLGCD 01 / May '94 / Juggling

Campbell, Eddie C.

☐ KING OF THE JUNGLE
R 2602 / Feb '96 / Rooster

☐ LET'S PICK IT
Messin' with my pride / Don't throw your love on me so strong / All my whole life / All of my life / Double dutch / Red light / Cold and hungry / Love me with a feeling / Dream / Let's pick it / Big leg mama / That will never do
ECD 260372 / Sep '93 / Evidence

☐ THAT'S WHEN I KNOW
BPCD 5014 / Dec '94 / Blind Pig

Campbell, Gary

☐ INTERSECTION
MCD 9236 / Apr '96 / Milestone

Campbell, Gene

☐ GENE CAMPBELL & WILLIE REED 1928-1935 (Campbell, Gene & Willie Reed)
BDCD 6043 / May '93 / Blues Document

Campbell, Glen

☐ 20 GOLDEN GREATS
Rhinestone cowboy / Both sides now / By the time I get to Phoenix / Too many mornings / Wichita lineman / One last time / Don't pull your love, then tell me goodbye / Reason to believe / It's only make believe / Honey come back / Give me back that old familiar feeling / Galveston / Dreams of an everyday housewife / Last thing on my mind / Where's the playground / Try a little kindness / Country boy / All I have to do is dream / Amazing grace
CDP 7486132 / Oct '90 / Liberty

☐ 20 GREATEST HITS (The Concert Collection)
Rhinestone cowboy / Gentle on my mind / Wichita lineman / Galveston / Country boy / By the time I get to Phoenix / Dreams of the everyday housewife / Heartache number three / Please come to Boston / Trials and tribulation / It's only make believe / Crying / Bluegrass medley / Milk cow blues / Rollin' (in my sweet baby's arms) / I'm so lonesome I could cry / Southern nights / Amazing grace / Try a little tenderness / In your loving arms / It's your world (boys and girls) / Mull of Kintyre
PLATCD 139 / Feb '97 / Platinum

☐ BEST OF GLEN CAMPBELL, THE
MACCD 266 / Aug '96 / Autograph

☐ BOY IN ME, THE
Boy in me / Living the legacy / Where time stands still / Call it even / Come harvest time / Best is yet to come / Something to die for / Mercy's eyes / All I need is you / Amazing grace
8441875372 / May '95 / Alliance Music

☐ COUNTRY CLASSICS
Honey come back / By the time I get to Phoenix / Country girl / Gentle on my mind / Reason to believe / One last time / (I'm getting used) to the crying / It's only make believe / How high did we go / If this is love / Love is not a game / For my woman's love / Last thing on my mind / Everything a man could ever need / Dream baby / Hey little one / Your cheatin' heart / This is Sarah's song / Let go / God only knows
CDMFP 6321 / Apr '97 / Music For Pleasure

☐ GLEN CAMPBELL COLLECTION, THE (2CD Set)
RE 2129 / Mar '97 / Razor & Tie

☐ GLEN CAMPBELL IN CONCERT
Rhinestone cowboy / Gentle on my mind / Medley / By the time I get to Phoenix / Dreams of an everyday housewife / Heartache number three / Please come to Boston / It's only make believe / Crying / Bluegrass medley / Milk cow blues / Rollin' in my sweet baby's arms / I'm so lonesome I could cry / Southern nights / Amazing grace / Try a little kindness / Mull of Kintyre
TRTCD 163 / Dec '94 / TrueTrax

☐ GLEN CAMPBELL IN CONCERT
15346 / Aug '91 / Laserlight

☐ GLEN CAMPBELL LIVE
Rhinestone cowboy / Gentle on my mind / Wichita lineman / Galveston / Country boy / By the time I get to Phoenix / Dreams of the everyday housewife / Heartache no.3 / Please come to Boston / It's only make believe / Crying / Bluegrass medley / Milk cow blues / Rollin' (in my sweet baby's arms) / I'm so lonesome I could cry / Southern nights / Amazing grace / Try a little kindness / Mull of Kintyre / In your loving arms again / It's your world boys and girls / Trials and tribulations
EMPRCD 523 / Sep '94 / Emporio

☐ GLEN CAMPBELL LIVE 1994
Gentle on my mind / By the time I get to Phoenix / Galveston / Kentucky means paradise / Wichita lineman / Mansion in branson / Here in the real world / Classical gas / Rhinestone cowboy / Let it be me / No more nights / Southern nights
12437 / Mar '95 / Laserlight

☐ GREATEST HITS LIVE
Rhinestone cowboy / Gentle on my mind / Medley / By the time I get to Phoenix / Dreams of an everyday housewife / Heartache number two / Please come to Boston / It's only make believe / Crying / Bluegrass medley / Milk cow blues / Rollin' in my sweet baby's arms / I'm so lonesome I could cry / Southern nights / Amazing grace / Try a little kindness / Mull of Kintyre / In your loving arms again / It's your world girls and boys / Trials and tribulations
GRF 182 / Feb '93 / Tring

☐ GREATEST HITS LIVE
Rhinestone cowboy / Gentle on my mind / Medley / By the time I get to Phoenix / Dreams of the everyday housewife / Heartache number three / Please come to Boston / It's only make believe / Crying / Medley / Milk cow blues / Rollin' in my sweet baby's arms / I'm so lonesome I could cry / Southern nights / Amazing Grace / Try a little kindness / Mull Of Kintyre
CDSD 081 / Nov '96 / Sundown

☐ GREATEST HITS LIVE
Rhinestone cowboy / Gentle on my mind / Medley / By the time I get to Phoenix / Dreams of the everyday housewife / Heartache number three / Please come to Boston / It's only make believe / Crying / Bluegrass medley / Milk cow blues / Rollin' (in my sweet baby's arms) / I'm so lonesome I could cry / Southern nights / Amazing grace / Try a little kindness / Mull of Kintyre / In your loving arms again / It's your world girls and boys / Trials and tribulations
QED 185 / Nov '96 / Tring

☐ IN CONCERT
Rhinestone cowboy / Gentle on my mind / Wichita lineman / Galveston / Country boy / By the time I get to Phoenix / Dreams of an everyday housewife / Heartache number three / Please come to Boston / Trials and tribulations / Crying/Blue grass medley / Milk cow blues / Rollin' in my sweet baby's arms / I'm so lonesome I could cry / Southern nights / Amazing grace / Try a little kindness / In your loving arms again / It's your world girls and boys / Mull of Kintyre
CPCD 8003 / Oct '93 / Charly

☐ MASTERS, THE
Rhinestone cowboy / Gentle on my mind / Medley / By the time I get to Phoenix / Dreams of the everyday housewife / Heartache number three / Please come to Boston / It's only make believe / Crying / Medley / Milk cow blues / Rollin' in my sweet baby's arms / I'm so lonesome I could cry / Southern nights / Amazing grace / Try a little kindness / Mull of Kintyre
EABCD 090 / 30 Mar '98 / Eagle

☐ RHINESTONE COWBOY
WMCD 5666 / Oct '94 / Disky

☐ RHINESTONE COWBOY
MU 5027 / Oct '92 / Musketeer

☐ RHINESTONE COWBOY (Live In Concert)
Rhinestone cowboy / Gentle on my mind / Wichita lineman/Galveston/Country boy / By the time I get to Phoenix / Dreams of the everyday housewife / Heartache number three / Please come home to Boston / Crying / It's only make believe / Bluegrass medley / Milk cow blues / Rollin' (in my sweet baby's arms) / I'm so lonely I could cry / Southern nights / Amazing grace / Try a little kindness / Mull of Kintyre
SUMCD 4021 / Nov '96 / Summit

☐ RHINESTONE COWBOY (Greatest Hits Live)
Gentle on my mind / By the time I get to Phoenix / Galveston / Kentucky means paradise / Wichita lineman / Mansion in Branson / Here in the real world / Classical gas / Rhinestone cowboy / Medley / Dreams of the everyday housewife/Sunflower / Let it be me / No more nights / Southern nights
CTS 55444 / Feb '97 / Country Stars

☐ THAT CHRISTMAS FEELING
Christmas is for children / Old toy trains / Little altar boy / It must be getting close to Christmas / Have yourself a merry little Christmas / Blue Christmas / Christmas song / Pretty paper / There's no place like home / I'll be home for Christmas / Christmas day
CDMFP 6243 / Oct '96 / Music For Pleasure

☐ WITCHITA LINEMAN
PLSCD 210 / Apr '97 / Pulse

Campbell, Ian

☐ AND ANOTHER THING
CMCD 070 / Dec '97 / Celtic Music

☐ CONTEMPORARY CAMPBELLS/NEW IMPRESSIONS (Campbell, Ian Folk Group)
Marilyn Monroe / Dirty old town / Thirty foot trailer / My Donal / Battle of the Somme / Hard life on the cut / Net hauling song / Death come easy / Rights of man / Liverpool lullaby / Four pounds a day / Dove / Bloody Orkney / D-Day dodgers / Lord of the dance / Berwick Brose / Snow is falling / Bold Benjamin / New York gals / Shoemaker / Baron o'Brackley / Aye waulkin o' / Lover let me in / Greensleeves / Can ye sew cushions / Farewell to Tarwathy / Gulls o' Invergordon / Laird o' Windy Wa's / Card song
ESMCD 523 / 24 Nov '97 / Essential

☐ SOMETHING TO SING ABOUT (Campbell, Ian Folk Group)
Apprentice song / Ox-plough song / Haymakers / Greasy wheel / Iron horse / Durham lockout / Sheffield grinder / Testimony of Patience Kershaw / Medley of children's street songs / Flash frigate / Ask a p'liceman / Rigs of London town / No courage in him / Girl I left behind me / Cutty Wren / Leave them a flower / Signature tune
HILLCD 21 / 6 Oct '97 / Wooded Hill

☐ THIS IS THE IAN CAMPBELL FOLK GROUP/ACROSS THE HILLS (Campbell, Ian Folk Group)
TWA recruiting sergeants / Keel row / Unquiet grave / To hear the nightingale sing / Drover's dream / Traditional medley / Rocking the cradle / Jute Mill song / Johnny lad / Blow boys blow / Down in the coal mine / Garton mother's lullaby / Bells of Rhymney / Apprentice's song / Rocky road to Dublin/Drops of brandy / Homeward bound / Waters of Tyne / Wee cooper of Fife / Across the hills / Come kiss me love / Blind man, he could see / I know my love / Derby ram / Mary Mild / Remember me / Cockfight / Gypsy rover / Chocho Losa / Keeper / Collier laddie / We're nae awa' to bide awa'
ESMCD 357 / Jan '96 / Essential

Campbell, Jo Ann

☐ THAT REAL GONE GAL (The Complete Gone & Roulette Recordings)
Wait a minute / It's true / I really really love you / I'm nobody's baby / Mama (can I go out tonight) / Beachcomber / You're driving me mad / I ain't got no steady date / Wassa matta with you baby / Rock 'n' roll love / You-ooh / Nervous / Happy New Year baby / How about that / Tall boy / Let me do my twist / It's true / Mama (can I go out tonight) / Wait a minute
WESM 508 / 22 Sep '97 / Westside

Campbell, John

☐ LIVE AT MAYBECK RECITAL HALL VOL.29
Just friends / You and the night and the music / Invitation / Easy to love / Emily / I wish I knew / Darn that dream / Touch of your lips
CCD 4581 / Nov '93 / Concord Jazz

☐ ONE BELIEVER
Devil in my closet / Angel of sorrow / Wild streak / Couldn't do nothin' / Tiny coffin / World of trouble / Voodoo edge / Person to person / Take me down / One believer
7559610862 / Oct '91 / Elektra

Campbell, Kate

☐ MOONPIE DREAMS
When panthers roamed in Arkansas / Moonpie dreams / See Rock City / Bud's See-Mint boat / Bascom's blues / Tupelo's too far / Older angel / Delmus Jackson / Signs following / Galaxie 500 / Waiting for the weather to break / Wrought iron fences
FIENDCD 791 / Feb '97 / Demon

☐ SONGS FROM THE LEVEE
Mississippi and me / Lanterns on the levee / Wild iris / Like a buffalo / Locust years / A cotton field away / Jerusalem inn / Trains don't run from nashville / South of everything / Bury me in bluegrass
FIENDCD 780 / Apr '96 / Demon

☐ VISIONS OF PLENTY
Visions of plenty / Bowl-a-rama / Jesus and tomatoes / Crazy in Alabama / This side of heaven / Suit yourself / Bus 109 / Deep tang / Funeral food / Perfect world / Sing me out
FIENDCD 943 / 4 May '98 / Demon

Campbell, Kenna

☐ CURAIDH SINTE
WHFP 0001 / Dec '96 / WHFP

Campbell, Martin

☐ ROOTSMAN THE REAL THING (Campbell, Martin & Hi Tech Roots Dynamics)
TBXCD 010 / 23 Mar '98 / Top Beat

Campbell, Mike

☐ LOVING FRIENDS
ACD 279 / May '95 / Audiophile

☐ MY ROMANCE
ACD 287 / Sep '97 / Audiophile

☐ ONE ON ONE
ACD 259 / Jun '93 / Audiophile

Campbell, Mont

☐ MUSIC FROM A ROUND TOWER
Shen Nong's miracle herbs / In pursuit of a gazelle / Eunuch's song / Tarak Totoosh / Driftwood biographies / Kua Fu races with the sun / When the rain comes, roses dance on gold / Makoma / Ernest Scott pursues a theory / Anyphylaxis / Mwamburi dies manfully at the hands of a thousand Thracians / Travels over a black Earth / Ikhwan el Safa / What the rose said to the cypress / Dede Korkut at the Boma / Moment to listen to the audience / Wise King Konuzion / Evening over Hickling Broad / Serenitsa / Enormous colony of peewits takes flight from Brickett's Poin
RES 120CD / Jan '97 / Resurgence

Campbell, Pete

☐ FROM JAMAICA WITH LOVE
WSRCD 108 / 15 Sep '97 / World Sound

Campbell, Phil

☐ DREAMING
SCD 1036 / Nov '96 / Spring

Campbell, Rocky

☐ VALLEY OF TEARS
ANGELLA 001CD / May '95 / Angella

Campbell, Rory

☐ MAGAID A PHIPIR (The Piper's Whim)
Lachie and the tractor / Careau Llaniscu / Cutting down the privet hedge / Donachd head / An Islay melody / Medley / Barlinnie highlander / Medley / Medley / Shepherd's crook / Mirren's pyjamas / Calum fighader agus Calum taillear (Malcolm the weaver and M / Mo shuiridhach, bi suigartach (My woer, be merry) / Trad reel / Medley / Breton andro (nouvelle suite d'an dros pour pipes) / Medley / I hae a wife o' my ain / Tending the cattle with a heavy heart / Medley / Medley / Magaid a phipir (piper's whim) / Trad jig / Medley / Oiseanbeag reel / Sloe jig / Clementina / Medley / Medley (10)
CDLDL 1250 / Mar '97 / Lochshore

Campbell, Roy

☐ NEW KINGDOM
Jahne's waltz / Booker's lament / Straight on up straight on down / Charmaine / La tierra del fuego suite / Losaida / Sermon
DE 469 / Mar '97 / Delmark

Campbell, Royce

☐ PITAPAT
A sharp blues / I should care / You stepped out of a dream / I fall in love too easily / Yesterdays / It could happen to you / Pitapat / I'm glad there is you / How deep is the ocean / No big deal / Nardis
AL 73126 / Jun '98 / A

Campbell, Sarah Elizabeth

☐ LITTLE TENDERNESS, A
Mexico / I never meant to fall / Part of a story / Waltz with you / Geraldine and Ruthie Mae / Heartache / Tell me baby / To remember / My heart can't seem to forget / I could use a little tenderness
DJD 3220 / Nov '95 / Dejadisc

☐ RUNNING WITH YOU
DJD 3210 / May '94 / Dejadisc

Campbell, Tevin

☐ BACK TO THE WORLD
Back to the world / Break of dawn / Could you learn to love / Beautiful thing / We can work it out / I got it bad / Tell me where / Could it be / I'll be there / I need you / You don't have to worry / Dry your eyes
9362460032 / Jul '96 / Qwest

☐ I'M READY
Can we talk / Don't say goodbye girl / Interlude / Halls of desire / I'm ready / What do I say / Uncle sam / Paris 1798430 / Always in my heart / Shhh / Brown eyed girl / Infant child
9362453882 / Dec '96 / Qwest

☐ TEVIN
Interlude/over the rainbow and on to the sun / Tell me what you want me to do / Li'l brother / Strawberry letter 23 / One song / Round and round / Just ask me to / Perfect world / Look what we'd have (if you were mine) / She's all that
7599262912 / Apr '92 / Qwest

Campbells

☐ POWER & HONESTY
IRVCD 562 / Apr '93 / Scotdisc

Campi, Ray

☐ EAGER BEAVER BOY
Hot dog / All the time / Boogie boogie boo / Rock it / Thought of losing / Waffle stompin' mama / Blue ranger / Ballin' keen / Let 'er roll / Dobro daddio from Del Rio / Born to be wild / How low can you feel / Where my sweet baby goes / Tribute to 'You know who' / Eager beaver boy / Pretty mama / One part stops where the other begins / Pinball millionaire / When two ends meet / Good time woman / It ain't me / Chug-a-lug / Parts unknown / Wicked wicked woman / Shelby county penal farm / Don't give your heart to a rambler / Play anything / Major label blues
BCD 15501 / Sep '90 / Bear Family

☐ HOLLYWOOD CATS
PT 613001 / Jun '96 / Part

☐ ORIGINAL ROCKABILLY ALBUM, THE
Caterpillar / It ain't me / Let go of Louise / Livin' on love / My screamin' screamin' Mimi / Long tall Sally / Johnny's jive / Play it cool / Give that love to me / You can't catch me / I didn't mean to be mean / Crossing / Loretta
CDMF 063 / Jul '90 / Magnum Force

☐ PERPETUAL STOMP (The Ray Campi Anthology 1957-1996)
BA 12CD / Nov '96 / Bacchus Archives

☐ ROCKABILLY REBELLION (The Best Of Ray Campi Vol.1)
HMG 6003 / Nov '97 / Hightone

☐ ROCKABILLY ROCKET
Second story man / Don't get pushy / Cravin' / Separate ways / Gonna bid my blues goodbye / How can I get on top / Little young girl / Chew tobacco rag / You don't rock and roll at all / Ruby Ann / I don't know why you still come around / Runnin' after fools / Jimmie skins the blues
CDMF 046 / May '94 / Magnum Force

☐ TAYLOR, TEXAS 1988
Curtain of tears / Haunted hungry heart / Woods are full of them now / Dessau waltz / When they operated on papa / Butterball bounce / Wild side of live / That's that / Million tears / Honk your horn / Love for sale / Honky tonk women / Bermuda grass waltz
BCD 15486 / Nov '89 / Bear Family

☐ TRAIN RHYTHM BLUE
MOUP 6018 / 19 Jan '98 / Mouthpiece

Campoli, Alfredo

☐ ALDREDO CAMPOLI AND HIS SALON ORCHESTRA (Campoli, Alfredo & His Salon Orchestra)
Mosquitoes' parade / Shadow waltz / Elgar's serenade / Little valley in the mountains / Snowman / Czardas / Liszt, Chopin and Mendelssohn / Mouse in the clock / Simonetta / Musical box / Wild violets / Parade of the pirates / Cavatina / Moths around the candle flame / Waltzing to Archibald Joyce / Serenade / Love in idleness / Knave of diamonds / Fairy tale / In old Vienna / La petite tonkinoise / Garden of roses
PASTCD 9707 / '90 / Flapper

☐ CAMPOLI'S CHOICE
PASTCD 7744 / Jun '91 / Flapper

☐ SALON MUSIC OF THE THIRTIES
Ah sweet mystery of life / Butterfly / Canary / Czardas / Daddy long legs / Goodnight waltz: *Campoli, Alfredo & Cavan O'Connor* / Grasshoppers dance: *Campoli, Alfredo & Cavan O'Connor* / Gypsy love song: *Campoli, Alfredo & Cavan O'Connor* / Her first dance / Hiawatha / Moths around the candle flame / Old Spanish tango / Old spinning wheel: *Campoli, Alfredo & Cavan O'Connor* / Old violin: *Campoli, Alfredo & Olive Groves* / Only my song: *Campoli, Alfredo & Olive Groves* / Pale Volga moon: *Campoli, Alfredo & Cavan O'Connor* / La petite tonkinoise / Popular Viennese waltzes / Softly awakes my heart / Song of paradise / Tell me tonight / Waltzing to Irving Berlin
CDAJA 5135 / Jul '94 / Living Era

Campus Tramps

☐ TFFT
1+2CD 101 / 1 Jun '98 / 1+2

Cam'ron

☐ CONFESSIONS OF FIRE
Intro / Glory / 357 / Rockin' and rollin' / Wrong ones / Death / Horse & carraige: *Cam'ron & Mase* / Me my moms & Jimmy: *Cam'ron & Kenny Greene* / Prophecy / We got it: *Cam'ron & Mase* / D rugs: *Cam'ron & Brotha* / Feels good: *Cam'ron & Usher* / Phone interlude / Pimps a pimp: *Cam'ron & Jermaine Dupri* / Confessions / Me & my boo: *Cam'ron & Charli Baltimore* / Shanghai / Who's nice
4912152 / 20 Jul '98 / Epic

Can

☐ ANTHOLOGY
SPOONCD 30/31 / Oct '94 / Grey Area

☐ CAN
All gates open / Safe / Sunday jam / Sodom / Spectacle / E.F.S. No.99 / Ping pong / Can be
SPOONCD 28 / Jan '95 / Grey Area

☐ CAN DELAY 1968
Butterfly / Pnoom / Nineteen century man / Thief / Man named Joe / Uphill / Little star of Bethlehem
SPOONCD 12 / Jul '89 / Grey Area

☐ CANNIBALISM VOL.1
Father cannot yell / Soup / Mother Sky / She brings the rain / Mushroom / One more night / Outside my door / Spoon / Hallelujah / Aumgn / Dizzy dizzy / Yoo doo right
SPOONCD 1/2 / Jul '89 / Grey Area

☐ CANNIBALISM VOL.2
Uphill / Pnoom / Connection / Mother upduff / Little star / T.v. spot / Doko e. / Turtles have short legs / Shikaku maru ten / Gomorrha / Blue bag / Red hot indians / Half past one / Flow motion / Smoke / I want more and ..... / Laugh till you cry / A spectacle / Animal waves / Sunshine day and night / E.p.s. no. 7 / Melting away
SPOONCD 21 / Jan '95 / Grey Area

☐ CANNIBALISM VOL.3
SPOONCD 22 / Jan '95 / Grey Area

☐ EGE BAMYASI
Pinch / Sing swan song / One more night / Vitamin C / Soup / I'm so green / Spoon
SPOONCD 8 / Jul '89 / Grey Area

☐ FLOW MOTION
I want more / Cascade waltz / Laugh till you cry... live till you die / And more / Babylonian pearl / Smoke (E.F.S. No.59) / Flow motion
SPOONCD 26 / Jan '95 / Grey Area

☐ FUTURE DAYS
Future days / Spray / Moonshake / Bel-air
SPOONCD 9 / Jul '89 / Grey Area

☐ INNER SPACE
All gates open / Safe / Subday jam / Sodom / Spectacle / Can can / Ping pong / Can be
CDTB 020 / '88 / Thunderbolt

☐ INNER SPACE
All gates open / Safe / Subday jam / Sodom / Aspectable / Ping pong / Can can / Can be
MM 010 / 31 Jul '98 / MagMid

☐ INNER SPACE/OUT OF REACH
All gates open / Safe / Sunday jam / Sodom / Aspectable / Ping pong / EFS no.99 Can-Can / Can be / Serpentine / Pauper's daughter and I / November / Seven days awake / Give me no roses / Like Inobe God / One more day
CDTB 186 / 2 Mar '98 / Thunderbolt

☐ LANDED
Full moon on the highway / Half past one / Hunters and collectors / Vernal equinox / Red hot Indians / Unfinished
SPOONCD 25 / Jan '95 / Grey Area

☐ MONSTER MOVIE
Father cannot yell / Mary Mary so contrary / Outside my door / Yoo doo right
SPOONCD 4 / Jul '89 / Grey Area

☐ OUT OF REACH
Surpentine / Pauper's daughter and I / November / Seven days awake / Give me no 'roses' / Like inobe God / One more day
CDTB 025 / Nov '88 / Thunderbolt

☐ RADIO WAVES
ECHO 01 / 20 Jul '98 / Sonic Platter

☐ RITE TIME
SPOONCD 29 / Oct '94 / Grey Area

☐ SACRILEGE (2CD Set)
Pnoom / Blue bag (inside paper) / Tango whiskey man / TV Spot / Vitamin C / Hallelujah / Oh yeah / Unfinished / Future days / More / Father cannot yell / Dizzy spoon / Yoo doo right / Flow motion
SPOONCD 39/40 / May '97 / Grey Area

☐ SAW DELIGHT
Don't say no / Sunshine day and night / Call me / Animal waves / Fly by night
SPOONCD 27 / Jan '95 / Grey Area

☐ SOON OVER BABALUMA
Dizzy dizzy / Come sta, la luna / Splash / Chain reaction / Quantom physics
SPOONCD 10 / Jul '89 / Grey Area

☐ SOUNDTRACKS
Deadlock / Tango whiskeyman / Don't turn the light on, leave me alone / Soul desert / Mother sky / She brings the rain
SPOONCD 5 / Jul '89 / Grey Area

☐ TAGO MAGO
Paperhouse / Mushroom / Oh yeah / Hallelujah / Aumgn / Peking O / Bring me coffee or tea
SPOONCD 6/7 / Jul '89 / Grey Area

☐ UNLIMITED EDITION
Gommorha / Ooko e / Lh 7o2 / I'm too leise / Musette / Blue bag (inside paper) / E.f.s. no. 27 / T.v. spot / E.f.s. no. 7 / Empress and the ukraine king / E.f.s. no. 10 / Mother upduff / E.f.s. no. 36 / Cutaway / Connection / Fall of another year / E.f.s. no. 8 / Transcendental express / Ibis
SPOONCD 23/24 / Jan '95 / Grey Area

Canadian All Stars

☐ EUROPEAN CONCERT
SKCD 23055 / Oct '94 / Sackville

Canadian Brass

☐ RENAISSANCE MEN
09026681082 / Nov '95 / RCA Victor

☐ SWINGTIME
Artistry in rhythm / Blue rondo a la Turk: *Bernhardt, Warren & Gordon Gottlieb* / Back home in Indiana: *Sims, Zoot Quartet* / 'Round midnight: *Stoltzman, Richard & Canadian Brass* / AT the Woodchopper's ball: *Stoltzman, Richard & Canadian Brass* / Lady is a tramp: *Mulligan, Gerry Quartet* / Sugar blues: *Eldridge, Roy* / Man I love: *Eldridge, Roy* / Whatever happened to the dream / Concierto de Aranjuez / I found love / Ellington medley / One o'clock jump: *Taylor, Joe & Canadian Brass* / Night and day: *Sims, Zoot Quartet*
09026683152 / Oct '95 / RCA Victor

Canambu

☐ SON CUBANO: THE RHYTHM STICKS
CORA 123 / Apr '95 / Corason

Cananes

☐ ARTY BARBEQUE
AJAX 054 / 23 Mar '98 / Ajax

Canaro, Francisco

☐ FRANCISCO CANARO 1924-1940
Don Juan / Mi Buenos Aires querido / La cumparsita / Esta noche me emborracho / Yira yira / El pescante / La cancion de la ribera / La maleva / Nada mas / Recuerdos de Paris / Pura parada / La Morocha / Malandrin / Un tropezon / Yo tambien era dichoso / Talan talan / La mina del Ford / Nelly / Departamento se alquila / Pecado mortal / La muchachada del centro / Sueno tus besos / Melodia oriental
HQCD 117 / May '98 / Harlequin

☐ NOBLEZA DE ARRABAL 1937-1941
EBCD 90 / Jan '98 / El Bandoneon

☐ TIEMPOS VIEJOS
BMT 018 / Jan '98 / Blue Moon

Canavan, Josie

☐ O AIRD GO HAIRD (Canavan, Josie & Tommy)
CICD 044 / Dec '94 / Clo Iar-Chonnachta

Candid Jazz Masters

☐ FOR MILES
Milestones / All blues / Nardis / My funny valentine / Walkin' / So what / If I were a bell / Milestrane
CCD 79710 / Mar '97 / Candid

Candida, Ana

☐ NOCTURNOS BRASILEIROS
ATR 32056 / 17 Aug '98 / Atracao

Candido

☐ DANCIN' AND PRANCIN'
Dancin' and prancin' / Jingo / Thousand finger man / Rock and shuffle
CPCD 8074 / Mar '95 / Charly

Candiria

☐ BEYOND REASONABLE DOUBT
TDH 0022 / Jun '97 / Too Damn Hype

Candlebox

☐ CANDLEBOX
Don't you / Change / You / No sense / Far behind / Blossom / Arrow / Rain / Mothers dream / Cover me / He calls home
9362453132 / Jul '93 / Maverick

☐ WIDELUX
Simple lessons / Drowned / Butterfly / Lucy / Become (to tell) / Crooked halo / It's amazing / Butterfly (reprise) / Vulgar before me / Bothered / Understanding / Best friend
9362459622 / Aug '95 / Maverick

Candlemass

☐ ANCIENT DREAMS
A cry from the crypt / Darkness in paradise / Incarnation of evil / Bearer of pain / Ancient dreams / Bells of acheron / Epistle no. 81 / Black sabbath medley / Mirror, mirror
CDATV 7 / Feb '90 / Active

☐ AS IT IS, AS IT WAS (The Best Of Candlemass) (2CD Set)
Solitude / Bewitched / Dying illusion / Demon's gate / Mirror mirror / Samaritan / Into the unfathomed tower / Bearer of pain / Where the runes still speak / At the gallows end / Mourner's lament / Tale of creation / Ebony throne / Under the oak / Well of souls / Dark are the veils of death / Darkness in paradise / End of pain / Sorcerer's pledge / Solitude '87 / Crystal ball '87 / Bullfest '93
CDMFN 166 / Oct '94 / Music For Nations

☐ CANDLEMASS LIVE IN STOCKHOLM 9TH JUNE 1990
Well of souls / Bewitched / Dark reflections / Demon's gate / Through the infinitive halls of death / Mirror mirror / Sorceror's pledge / Dark are the veils / Solitude / Under the oak / Bells of Acheron / Samaritan / Gallows end
CDMFN 109 / Nov '90 / Music For Nations

☐ CHAPTER SIX
Dying illusion / Julie laughs no more / Where the runes still speak / Ebony throne / Temple of the dead / Aftermath / Black eyes / End of pain
CDMFN 128 / May '92 / Music For Nations

☐ DACTYLIS GLOMERATA
Wiz / I still see the black / Dust flow / Cylinder / Karthago / Abstract sun / Apathy / Lidcain god / Molotov
CDMFN 237 / 13 Apr '98 / Music For Nations

☐ EPICUS DOOMICUS METALLICA
BD 013 / Apr '95 / Black Dragon

☐ NIGHTFALL
CDATV 3 / Jun '88 / Active

☐ TALES OF CREATION
Prophecy / Dark reflections / Voices in the wind / Under the oak / Tears / Into the unfathomed tower / At the edge of heaven / Somewhere in nowhere / Through the infinitive halls of death / Dawn / Tale of creation
CDMFN 95 / Sep '89 / Music For Nations

Candler, Norman

☐ DANCE AND DREAM
ISCD 128 / May '98 / Intersound

☐ MAGIC DREAMS (Candler, Norman Strings)
ISCD 116 / Oct '91 / Intersound

☐ MAGIC STRINGS VOL.1
ISCD 001 / Jul '93 / Intersound

☐ MAGIC STRINGS VOL.2
ISCD 002 / Jul '93 / Intersound

☐ SOFT MAGIC, THE (Candler, Norman & The Magic Strings)
ISCD 101 / Oct '89 / Intersound

Candy Snatchers

☐ CANDY SNATCHERS
SH 21272 / Dec '96 / Safe House

☐ PISSED OFF RIPPED OFF
GK 025 / Oct '97 / Go-Kart

Candyskins

☐ SUNDAY MORNING FEVER
Mrs. Hoover / 24 hours / Car crash / Monday morning / Get on / Europe and Japan / Hang myself on you / Disco hell / Circles / Face the day / DRUNK / No no no / Help me / In my hair
TOPPCD 054 / Mar '97 / Ultimate

Cane 141

☐ SCENE FROM 6AM
Summerlong / Set up / Easter in West / Down Angel road / Whither I roam / Carnival song / When you ride away / We should get together / Super 8
SECCD 22 / 13 Jul '98 / Secret

Canibus

☐ CAN-I-BUS
UND 53136 / 10 Aug '98 / Universal

Cannabis

☐ JOINT EFFORT
GF 114 / 13 Jul '98 / Gear Fab

Cannach

☐ MOONS OF GLENLOY, THE
O'Neils / Sleeping loon / Twa caroies / Broken dreams / Norry highwayman / Pink bog / Kathleen MacDonald / Horse thief / Mountains of kintail / Black bog jig / Travellers / Audry's last trip
CDLDL 1263 / Dec '97 / Lochshore

Canned Heat

☐ BEST OF CANNED HEAT, THE
On the road again / Amphetamine Annie / My crime / Time was / Goin' up the country / Sugar bee / Whiskey headed woman / Bullfrog blues / Let's work together / World in a jug / Fried hockey boogie / Rollin' and tumblin' / I'm her man / Parthenogenesis
DC 878652 / Mar '97 / Disky

☐ BIG ROAD BLUES
CDSGP 079 / Feb '96 / Prestige

☐ BLUES BAND
Stranger / Quiet woman / Iron horse / Junior's shuffle / Creole Queen / Keep it to yourself / Boogie music / Goin' up the country / See these tears / One kind favour / Oh baby / Gorgo boogie
MYSCD 120 / 24 Nov '97 / Mystic

☐ BOOGIE UP THE COUNTRY
Ansage / Mercury blues / Take me to the river / Rollin' and tumblin' / Amphetamine Annie / Bullfrog blues / Sweet home Chicago / Kidman blues / Going up the country / Let's work together / Trouble no more / Younderswall / Boogie / Absage
INAK 8804CD / Jul '97 / In Akustik

☐ BURNIN' LIVE
AIM 1033CD / Oct '93 / Aim

☐ CANNED HEAT '70 CONCERT (Live In Europe)
That's all right (mama) / Bring it on home / Pulling hair blues / Back out on the road-on the road again (medley) / London blues / Let's work together / Goodbye for now
BGOCD 12 / Sep '89 / Beat Goes On

☐ FUTURE BLUES
Sugar bee / Shake it and break it / That's all right (mama) / My time ain't long / Skat / Let's work together / London blues / So sad (the world's in a tangle) / Future blues
BGOCD 49 / Sep '89 / Beat Goes On

☐ HISTORICAL FIGURES AND ANCIENT HEADS
Sneakin' around / Rockin' with the king / Long way from LA / That's alright Mama / Hill's stomp / I don't care what you tell me / Cherokee dance / Utah
BGOCD 83 / Aug '90 / Beat Goes On

☐ INTERNAL COMBUSTION
AIM 1044 / Apr '95 / Aim

☐ KING BISCUIT PRESENTS...
Intro / On the road again / Bullfrog blues / Chicken shack / Stand up (for what you are) / Goin' up the country / Don't know where she went (she split) / Human condition / Shake 'n' boogie
KBFHCD 014 / 27 Jul '98 / King Biscuit

☐ LET'S WORK TOGETHER (The Best Of Canned Heat)
On the road again / Bullfrog blues / Rollin' and tumblin' / Amphetamine Annie / Fried hockey boogie / Sic 'em pigs / Poor moon / Let's work together / Going up the country / Boogie music / Same all over / Time was / Sugar bee / Rockin' with the king / That's alright mama / My time ain't long / Future blues / Pony blues / So sad (the world's in a tangle) / Chipmunk song
CDP 7931142 / Sep '89 / Liberty

☐ LIVE AT THE TOPANGA CORRAL/ VINTAGE
AK 003/5 / 12 May '98 / Akarma

☐ LIVE IN AUSTRALIA
AIM 1003CD / Oct '93 / Aim

☐ MASTERS, THE
Big road blues / I've got my mojo working / Pretty thing / Louise / Dimples / Talk to me baby / Straight ahead / Rollin' and tumblin' / I'd rather be a devil / It hurts me too / Bullfrog blues / Sweet sixteen / Dust my broom
EABCD 098 / 30 Mar '98 / Eagle

☐ NEW AGE, THE
Keep it clean / Harley Davidson blues / Don't deceive me / You can run but you sure can't hide / Lookin' for my rainbow / Rock 'n' roll music / Framed / Election blues / So long wrong
BGOCD 85 / Dec '90 / Beat Goes On

☐ ON THE ROAD AGAIN
On the road again / Amphetamine Annie / My crime / Time was / Going up the country / Sugar bee / Whiskey headed woman / Bullfrog blues / Let's work together / World in a jug / Fried hockey boogie / Rollin' and tumblin' / I'm her man / Dust by broom / Parthenogenesis
CDGOLD 1076 / Feb '97 / EMI Gold

☐ RE-HEATED
SPV 858805 / Mar '96 / SPV

☐ STRAIGHT AHEAD
Big road blues / Got my mojo working / Pretty thing / Louise / Dimples / Talk to me baby / Straight ahead / Rollin' and tumblin' / I'd rather be a devil / It hurts me too / Bullfrog blues / Sweet sixteen / Dust my broom
CDTB 130 / Apr '97 / Thunderbolt

☐ TIES THAT BIND
ACH 80002 / Jul '97 / Archive

☐ UNCANNED (The Best Of Canned Heat) (2CD Set)
On the road again (Alternate take) / Nine below zero / TV Mama / Rollin' and tumblin' / Bullfrog blues / Evil is going on / Goin' down slow / Dust my broom / Help me / Story of my life / Hunter / Whiskey and wimmen / Shake, rattle and roll / Mean ol' world / Fannie Mae / Gotta boogie (The world boogie) / My crime / On the road again / Evil woman / Amphetamine Annie / Old owl song / Christmas blues / Going up the country / Time was / Low down (and high up) / Same all over / Big fat (The fat man) / It's alright / Poor moon / Sugar bee / Shake it and break it / Future blues / Let's work together / Wooly bully / Human condition / Long way from LA / Hill's stomp / Rockin' with the king / Harley Davidson blues / Rock 'n' roll music
CDEM 1543 / Aug '94 / Liberty

Cannibal Corpse

☐ BLEEDING
Staring through the eyes of the dead / Fucked with a knife / Stripped, raped and strangled / Pulverized / Return to flesh / Pick-axe murders / She was asking for it / Bleeding / Force fed broken glass / Experiment in homicide
398414137CD / Feb '97 / Metal Blade

☐ BUTCHERED AT BIRTH
Meat hook sodomy / Gutted / Living dissection / Under the rotted flesh / Covered with sores / Vomit the soul / Butchered at birth / Rancid amputation / Innards decay
398414072CD / Mar '96 / Metal Blade

☐ EATEN BACK TO LIFE
Shredded humans / Put them to death / Scattered remains, splattered brains / Rotting head / Bloody chunks / Buried in the backyard / Edible autopsy / Mangled / Born in a casket / Undead will feast / Skull full of maggots
398414024CD / Mar '96 / Metal Blade

☐ GALLERY OF SUICIDE
398414151CDD
398414151CD / 27 Apr '98 / Metal Blade

☐ TOMB OF THE MUTILATED
Hammer smashed face / I cum blood / Addicted to vaginal skin / Split wide open / Necrodedophile / Cryptic stench / Post mortem ejaculation / Beyond the cemetry / Entrails ripped from a virgin's cunt
398414010CD / Mar '96 / Metal Blade

☐ VILE
398414104CD / Apr '96 / Metal Blade

Canning, Francis

☐ MY DREAMS OF LONG AGO
After all these years / Let the rest of the world go by / Village where I went to school / Old rugged cross / If those lips could only speak / If I had my life to live over / Fool such as I / True love / Mother's love's a blessing / I will love you all my life / When I grow too old to dream / Old rustic bridge by the mill / My dreams of long ago / Maggie / Sunshine of your smile / Pal of my cradle days / Silver threads among the gold / I'll be your sweetheart
LCOM 3006 / Sep '95 / Lismor

Cannon, Ace

☐ HI MASTERS, THE
Tuff sax / St.Louis blues / Kansas city / Prisoner of love / You don't know me / Heartbreak hotel / Willow weep for me / Moon river / Stranger in paradise / Wonderland by night / As time goes by / Yesterday / Woolly bully / Green onions / White silver sands
HEX 33 / 4 Aug '98 / Hi

☐ ROCKIN' ROBIN
HADCD 198 / Nov '95 / Javelin

Cannon, Gus

☐ COMPLETE (Cannon, Gus & His Jug Stompers)
YAZCD 1082 / Apr '91 / Yazoo

☐ GUS CANNON VOL.1 (1927-1928)
DOCD 5032 / Feb '92 / Document

☐ GUS CANNON VOL.2 (1929-1930) (Cannon, Gus & Noah Lewis)
DOCD 5033 / Feb '92 / Document

Canny, Paddy

☐ LEGANDARY CLARE FIDDLER, THE
CICD 129 / Dec '97 / Clo Iar-Chonnachta

Cano, Nacho

☐ FEMININE SIDE, THE
Together forever / Two hearts / Affairs of the heart / Loaded gun / El patio / Search of the soul / Payer for the world / Same old story / Feminine side / Dance teacher / De las riunas el dolor
CDVIR 64 / 29 Sep '97 / Virgin

☐ WORLD SPLIT BY THE SAME GOD, A
Patio / Dance instructor / Waltz of the mad / Land of cement / Piano (Piano) / World split by the same God / Wounded water / Piano violin and guitar / Battle / Vaikuntha / Battle (Piano) / Battle (Orchestra) / World split by the same God (End)
CDVIR 40 / Jun '96 / Virgin

Canon, Sean

☐ GEM OF THE SEA
CMCD 068 / Dec '97 / Celtic Music

Canorous Quintet

☐ ONLY PURE HATE
NFR 028CD / 6 Jul '98 / No Fashion

☐ SILENCE OF THE WORLD BEYOND
NFR 019CD / Jan '97 / No Fashion

Cantairi Oga Atha Cliath Choir

☐ FIVE CENTURIES OF SONG
AC 6456 / Dec '96 / Chorus

Cantelon, Paul

☐ MODERN DAY MOZART, A
Time to go / Sunrise on Lac Leman / A watch spring / Angel / Azuza / GMT / Vallejo street / Juarez / Castletown / Battle won / Minnis bay / Carrick a rede / Dance of the blessed spirits / La paloma / Monk meets Poulenc
CDSGP 9013 / Apr '98 / Prestige

Canter, Robin

☐ OBOE COLLECTION
CDSAR 22 / '88 / Amon Ra

Canterbury Cathedral Choir

☐ CANTERBURY CAROLS
O come, all ye faithful / Sussex carol / Stille nacht (Silent night) / Once in Royal David's City / Ding dong merrily on high / Candlelight carol / God rest ye merry Gentlemen / Three kings / O little town of Bethlehem / Gaudete, Christus natus est / In the bleak midwinter / While shepherds watched their flocks by night / Away in a manger / Hark the herald angels sing / Toccata for organ
YORKCD 109 / Nov '97 / York Ambisonic

Canticle

☐ COLLECTION, THE
If you're Irish / Holy ground / Green glens of Antrim / Mick McGilligan's ball / I'll take you home again Kathleen / Courtin' in the kitchen / Come back Paddy Reilly / Let him go let him tarry / I know where I'm goin' / Rose of Tralee
EMPRCD 720 / Jun '97 / Emporio

Cantovivo

☐ ANTOLOGIA
BRAM 1991202 / Nov '93 / Brambus

Cantrell, Jerry

☐ BOGGY DEPOT
Dickeye / Cut you in / My song / Settling down / Breaks my back / Jesus hands / Devil by his side / Keep the light on / Satisfy / Hurt a long time / Between / Cold piece
4887052 / 6 Apr '98 / Columbia

Cao, Emilio

☐ CARTAS MARINAS
F 1021CD / Jun '94 / Sonifolk

☐ SINBAD EN GALICIA
DF 004CD / Aug '97 / Do Fol

Capability Green

☐ 53310761
CDHOLE 011 / Jun '96 / Golf

Capaldi, Jim

☐ LET THE THUNDER CRY
Let the thunder cry / Favella music / Child in the storm / Only love / Louie louie / Warm / Dreams do come true / Old photographs / We don't need / Anxiety
JETCD 1003 / Feb '98 / Jet

☐ OH HOW WE DANCED
Eve / Big thirst / Love is all you can try / Last day of dawn / Don't be a hero / Open your heart / How much can a man really take / Oh how we danced
EDCD 502 / Nov '96 / Edsel

☐ SHORT CUT DRAW BLOOD
Goodbye love / It's all up to you / Love hurts / Johnny too bad / Short cut draw blood / Living on a marble / Boy with a problem / Keep on trying / Seagull
EDCD 504 / Nov '96 / Edsel

☐ WHALE MEAT AGAIN
It's all right / Whale meat again / Yellow sun / I've got so much lovin' / Low rider / My brother / Summer is fading
EDCD 503 / Nov '96 / Edsel

Capart, Louis

☐ MARIE-JEANNE GABRIELLE
KMCD 06 / '91 / Keltia Musique

☐ PATIENCE
KMCD 13 / '91 / Keltia Musique

☐ RIVES GAUCHES DE BRETAGNE ET D'AILLEURS
KMCD 80 / Nov '97 / Keltia Musique

Capella Cordina

☐ MISSA L'HOMME ARME
LEMS 8009 / Aug '94 / Lyrichord

☐ TWO THREE VOICE MASSES, THE
LEMS 8010 / Aug '94 / Lyrichord

Capercaillie

☐ BEAUTIFUL WASTELAND
Beautiful wasteland / M'ionam / Ille dhiunn / Shelter / Finlay's / Am mur gorm / Tree / Keppehall / Co nimire rium / Thuy thu / Sardinia / Hebridean halle bopp
SURCD 021 / Aug '97 / Survival

☐ BLOOD IS STRONG, THE
Aignish / Arrival / Iona / Calum's road / Fear / Dean Cadalan samhach / Grandfather mountain / An atairreachd ard / 'S fhada leam an oidhche gheamhraidh / Hebrides / Lordship of the isles / Arrival reprise / Columcille / Downtown Toronto
SURCD 014 / May '98 / Survival

☐ CAPERCAILLIE
Miracle of being / When you return / Grace and pride / Tobermory / Take the floor / Stinging rain / Aladsair / Crime and passion / Bonaparte / When you return
SURCD 018 / May '98 / Survival

☐ CROSSWINDS
Puirt-a-beul / Soraidh bhuam gu barraidh / Glenorchy / Am buachaille ban / Haggis / Brenda Stubbert's set / Ma theid mise tuilleagh / David Glen's / Urnaigh a 'bhan-thigreach / My laggan love / Fox on the town / An ribhinn donn
GLCD 1077 / May '92 / Green Linnet

☐ DELIRIUM
Rann na mona / Waiting for the wheel to turn / Aodann Strathbain / Cape Breton song / You will rise again / Kenny MacDonald's jigs / Dean saor an spiorad / Coisich a ruin (walk my beloved) / Dr. MacPhail's reel / Heart of the highland / Breisleach / Islay Ranter's reels / Servant to the slave
SURCD 015 / May '98 / Survival

☐ GET OUT
Waiting for the wheel to turn / Pige ruadh / Silver spear reels / Outlaws / Coisich a ruin (walk my beloved) / Fear a'bhata / Dr. MacPhail's trance
SURCD 016 / May '95 / Survival

☐ SECRET PEOPLE
Bonaparte / Grace and pride / Tobar Mhoire (Tobermory) / Miracle of being / Crime of passion / Whinney hills jigs / An eala bhan (the white swan) / Selce Ruairidh (Roddy's drum) / Stinging rain / Hi rim bo / Four stone walls / Harley ashtray / Oran / Black fields
SURCD 017 / May '98 / Survival

☐ SIDEWAULK
Alasdair Mhic Cholla Ghasda / Balindore / Fisherman's dream / Sidewaulk reels / Iain Ghlinn'Cuaich / Fosgail an Dorus / Turnpike / Both sides of the tweed / Weasel / Oh mo Dhuthaich
CDGL 1094 / Feb '89 / Green Linnet

☐ TO THE MOON
To the moon / Claire in heaven / Wanderer / Price of fire / Rob Roy reels / Ailein Duinn / Nil si / Crooked mountain / God's alabi / Collector's daughter / Only you
SURCD 019 / May '98 / Survival

Capital Letters

☐ HEADLINE NEWS
Fire / Daddy was no murderer / President Amin / Smoking my ganja / Unemployed / Rejoice / Buzzrock / Run run run / Out of Africa
GRELCD 7 / Nov '92 / Greensleeves

Capitalist Casualties

☐ COLLECTION, THE
SAH 35 / May '97 / Slap A Ham

Capitol Punishment

☐ FIRST LINE-UP, THE
WB 078166CD / Sep '93 / We Bite

☐ MESSIAH COMPLEX
WB 2102CD / Apr '94 / We Bite

Capleton

☐ ALMS HOUSE
GRELCD 182 / Mar '93 / Greensleeves

☐ CAPLETON AND FRIENDS (Capleton & Friends)
KPCRCD 59 / Jan '97 / Charm

☐ I TESTAMENT
Divide and rule / East coast to the west coast / Old and the young / Hurts my heart / Original man / Escape the judgement / Nah bow (do now) / Steep mountain / Mark of the beast / No man can save no man / Movin' on / Ready to shout / Death row / Stop the coming / Love the one you're with / Free our minds / Raggy road / Babylon a use dem brain
5363802 / 13 Apr '98 / Mercury

☐ PROPHECY
Tour / Big time / Obstacle / Leave Babylon / Heathen reign / Don't dis the trinity / No competetion / Wings of the morning / See from afar
5292642 / Oct '95 / RAL

Cap'n Jazz

☐ ANALPHABETAPOLOTHOLOGY (2CD Set)
JT 1036CD / 19 Jan '98 / Jade Tree

☐ KITES, KUNG FU AND TROPHIES
MWG 002CD / Apr '97 / Man With Gun

Capone, Eddie

☐ EXPERIENCE
TR 12CD / Jul '96 / Treatment

Capp, Frank

☐ CAPP-PIERCE JUGGERNAUT (Capp-Pierce Juggernaut)
Avenue C / All heart / Moten swing / Basie / Mr. Softie / It's sand man / Dickie's dream / Take the 'A' train / Wee baby blues / Roll 'em Pete
CCD 4040 / Jul '91 / Concord Jazz

☐ FRANK CAPP TRIO PRESENTS RICKEY WOODWARD (Capp, Frank Trio)
Oleo / Au privave / If I should lose you / Speak low / Sweet Lorraine / Polka dots and moonbeams / Doxy / Three bears / You tell me
CCD 4469 / Jul '91 / Concord Jazz

☐ IN A HEFTI BAG (Capp, Frank Juggernaut)
I'm shoutin' again / Cherry point / Flight of the Foo birds / Kid from Red Bank / Splanky / Fantail / Li'l darlin' / Duet / Whirly bird / Cute / Awful nice to be with you / Bag a' bones / Midnight blue / Dinner with my friends / Teddy the toad / Scoot / Late date
CCD 4655 / Jul '95 / Concord Jazz

☐ JUGGERNAUT STRIKES AGAIN (Capp-Pierce Juggernaut)
One for Marshall / I remember Clifford / New York shuffle / Chops, fingers and sticks / You are so beautiful / Parker's mood / Word from Bird / Charade / Things ain't what they used to be / Little Pony
CCD 4183 / Aug '90 / Concord Jazz

☐ PLAY IT AGAIN SAM (Capp, Frank Juggernaut)
Heat's on / Warm breeze / Ja da / Sweet Georgia Brown / Katy / Wind machine / Soft as velvet / Ya gotta try / Freckle face / Satin 'n' glass / 88 Basie Street / Night flight
CCD 47472 / Mar '97 / Concord Jazz

☐ QUALITY TIME
Dip stick / Back to Brea / I've never been in love before / Daahoud / There you have it / Tadd's delight / 9:20 Special / Sophisticated lady / Things ain't what they used to be
CCD 4677 / Dec '95 / Concord Jazz

Cappadonna

☐ PILLAGE, THE
Slang editorial / Pillage / Run / Blood on blood war / Supa ninjaz / MCF / Splish splash / Oh Donna / Milk the cow / South of the border / Check for a nigga / Dart throwing / Young hearts / Everything is everything / Pump up your fist / Black boy
4888502 / 16 Mar '98 / Razor Sharp/ Epic

Cappelletti, Arrigo

☐ TRANSFORMATION (Cappelletti, Arrigo Quartet)
Y225024 / Jun '93 / Silex

Capricorn

☐ LOST IN JELLYWOOD
SPERM 1003 / 1 Jun '98 / Sperm

Capris

☐ CAPRIS 1954-1958
FLYCD 56 / Oct '93 / Flyright

Captain Barkey

☐ GO GO WINE
KPSTONECD 1 / Jan '97 / Stone Love

Captain Beefheart

☐ BLUE JEANS AND MOONBEAMS
Captain's holiday / Pompadour swamp / Party of special things to do / Blue jeans and moonbeams / Twist ah luck / Further than we've gone / Rock 'n' roll's evil doll / Observatory quest / Same old blues
CDV 2023 / Jun '88 / Virgin

☐ CARROT IS AS CLOSE AS A RABBIT GETS TO A DIAMOND
Sugar bowl / Past sure is tense / Happy love song / Floppy boot stomp / Blue jeans and moonbeams / Run paint run run / This is the day / Tropical hot dog night / Observatory crest / Host the ghost the most holy O / Harry Irene / I got love on my mind / Pompadour swamp / Love lies / Sheriff of Hong Kong / Further than we've been / Candle mambo / Light reflected off the oceans of the moon / Carrot is as close as a rabbit gets to a diamond
CDVM 9028 / Jul '93 / Virgin

☐ DOC AT THE RADAR STATION
Hothead / Ashtray heart / Carrot is as close as a rabbit gets to a diamond / Run paint run run / Sue Egypt / Brickbats / Dirty blue gene / Best batch yet / Telephone / Flavour bud living / Sheriff of Hong Kong / Making love to a vampire with a monkey on my knee
CDV 2172 / Jun '88 / Virgin

☐ ELECTRICITY
Sure 'nuff 'n yes I do / Zig zag wanderer / Dropout boogie / I'm glad / Electricity / Yellow brick road / Abba zaba / Plastic factory / Trust us / Beatle bones 'n smokin' stones / Moody Liz / Big black baby shoes / Gimme dat harp boy / Dirty blue gene / Tarotplane / Kandy korn
74321558462 / 26 Jan '98 / Camden

☐ ICE CREAM FOR CROW
Ice cream for crow / Host the ghost the most holy O / Semi-multicoloured caucasian / Hey Garland, I dig your tweed coat / Evening bells / Cardboard cut-out sundown / Past sure is tense / Ink mathematics / Witch doctor love / 81 poop hatch / Thousanth and tenth day of the human totem pole / Skeleton makes good
CDV 2237 / Apr '88 / Virgin

☐ LEGENDARY A&M SESSIONS, THE
Diddy wah diddy / Who do you think you're fooling / Moonchild / Frying pan / Here I am I always am
BLIMPCD 902 / Mar '92 / Edsel

☐ LONDON 1974
Mirror man / Upon the me oh my / Full moon hot sun / Sugar bowl / Crazy little thing / This is the day / New electric ride / Abba zabba / Peaches
MPG 74025 / Nov '93 / Movieplay Gold

☐ PEARLS BEFORE SWINE (Poems, Paintings, Aphorisms & Discography-CD/Book Set)
SB 1 / 23 Feb '98 / Sonic Book

☐ SHINY BEAST (BAT CHAIN PULLER)
Floppy boot stomp / Tropical hot dog night / Ice rose / Harru Irene / You know you're a man / Bat chain puller / When I see mummy I feel like a mummy / Owed I Alex / Candle mambo / Love lies / Suction prints / Apes-ma
CDV 2149 / Jul '87 / Virgin

☐ SPOTLIGHT KID/CLEAR SPOT (Captain Beefheart & His Magic Band)
I'm gonna booglariza you baby / White jam / Blabber 'n smoke / When it blows it's stacks / Alic in blunderland / Spotlight kid / Click clack / Grow fins / There ain't no Santa Claus / Glider / Low yo yo stuff / Nowadays a woman's gotta hit a man / Too much time / Circumstances / My head is my only house unless it rains / Sum zoom spark / Clear spot / Crazy little thing / Long neck bottles / Her eyes are a blue million miles / Big eyes beans from Venus / Goldne birdies
7599262492 / Aug '90 / Warner Bros.

☐ STRICTLY PERSONAL
Ah feel like acid / Safe as milk / Trust us / Son of mirror man-mere man / On tomorrow / Beatle bones n' smokin' stones / Gimme dat harp boy / Kandy korn
CZ 529 / Jul '94 / Premier/EMI

☐ TROUT MASK REPLICA
Hair pie: Bake II / Pena / Well / When Big Joan sets up / Fallin' ditch / Sugar 'n' spikes / Ant man bee / Orange claw hammer / Wild life / She's too much for my mirror / Hobo chang ba / Blimp (mousetrapreplica) / Steal softly thru snow / Old fart at play / Veteran's day poppy
7599271962 / Sep '94 / Warner Bros.

☐ UNCONDITIONALLY GUARANTEED
Upon the my-o-my / Sugar bowl / New electric ride / Magic be / Happy love song / Full moon hot sun / I got love on my mind / This is the day / Lazy music / Peaches
CDV 2015 / Jun '88 / Virgin

☐ ZIG ZAG WANDERER (The Best Of The Buddah Years)
Sure nuff 'n' yes I do / Zig zag wanderer / Dropout boogie / I'm glad / Electricity / Yellow brick road / Abba zabba / Plastic factory / Tarot plane / Kandy korn / Trust us / Beatle bones 'n' smokin' stones / Safe as milk / Gimme dat harp boy
HILLCD 6 / Nov '96 / Wooded Hill

Captain Gumbo

☐ BACK A LA MAISON
MWCD 2006 / Apr '93 / Music & Words

☐ CHANK-A-CHANK
MWCD 2012 / Aug '94 / Music & Words

☐ ONE MORE TWO STEP
MWCD 2001 / Jun '92 / Music & Words

Captain Hollywood

☐ ANIMALS & HUMANS
PULSE 20CD / Apr '95 / Pulse 8

Captain Howdy

☐ MONEY FEEDS MY MUSIC MACHINE
SHMCD 5135 / Apr '98 / Shimmy Disc

Captain Kowatchi

☐ CONFERENCE OF THE BIRDS, THE
BKA 0004 / 6 Oct '97 / Baraka Foundation

Captain Rizz

☐ MANIFESTO
Voodoo Rizz / Rizz's radio song / Rizz's anthem / City of angels / St. Cecelia / Rizz's radio song (instrumental) / Voodoo Rizz (instrumental)
EBSCD 112 / Nov '96 / Emergency Broadcast System

Captain Sensible

☐ BEST OF CAPTAIN SENSIBLE, THE
CLP 0041 / Aug '97 / Cleopatra

☐ CAPTAIN'S BOX (2CD Set)
BAH 32 / Jun '97 / Humbug

☐ LIVE AT THE MILKY WAY
Interstella overcoat / Jet boy jet girl / Smash it up / Back to school / Come on Geoffrey Brown / Happy talk / Kamikaze millionaire / Exploding heads and teapots / Love song / Neat neat neat / New rose / Wot / Looking at you / Hey Joe / Glad it's all over
BAH 12 / Aug '94 / Humbug

☐ MASTERS, THE
While wrecking the car / Bob's brown nose / Neverland / Stately homes of England / Smashing the chains / Mr. Browns exploding wallet / Monty's revenge / Mr. Farmer / Lottery love rat / One hit wonder / World of Matilda Free / Cigarette Sandy / Happy talk / Wot 1
EABCD 101 / 30 Mar '98 / Eagle

☐ MEATHEAD
BAH 14 / Aug '95 / Humbug

☐ REVOLUTION NOW
Missing the boat / Smash it up (part 4) / Toys take over / S.2 / A riot on eastbourne pier / Wake up (you're only dreaming) / Green light / Lib 23 / Revolution now / Phone in / I get so excited / Vosene / Kamikaze millionaire / Exploding heads and teapots (past their prime) / Coward of treason cove
BAH 3 / Jul '96 / Humbug

☐ SLICE OF CAPTAIN SENSIBLE, A
BAH 30 / Jun '97 / Humbug

☐ UNIVERSE OF GEOFFREY BROWN, THE
Holiday in my head / Come on Geoffrey Brown / Getting to me / Street of shame / Geoff loosens his tie / Home / Government Dirty Tricks Dept. WC1 / Life up in the stars / Message / Trip to Cornwall / Universe of Geoffrey Brown
BP 294CD / 10 Aug '98 / Blueprint

Captive Heart

☐ ONLY THE BRAVE
MTM 199614 / Nov '96 / Made To Measure

Captor

☐ DOGFACE
PCD 042 / 16 Mar '98 / Diehard

☐ DROWNED
PCD 034 / Jul '96 / Progress

Carabelli, Adolfo

☐ CUATRO PALABRAS
EBCD 87 / Apr '97 / El Bandoneon

Caramia, Tony

☐ PIANO
SOSCD 1313 / Jul '96 / Stomp Off

Caramuru, Fabio

☐ TOM JOBIM PIANO SOLO
MC 003 / 14 Apr '98 / MP

Caravan

☐ ALBUM, THE
Heartbreaker / Corner of me eye / What'cha gonna tell me / Piano player / Make yourself at home / Golden mile / Bright shiny day / Clear blue sky / Keepin' up de fences
CDKVL 9003 / Jan '87 / Kingdom

☐ ALL OVER YOU (Re-Recorded Special Edit)
If I could do it all over again, I'd do it all over you / Place of my own / Love in your eye/To catch me a brother / In the land of grey and pink / Golf girl / Disassociation (nine feet underground) / Hello hello / Astorteri 25 / For Richard / Memory Iain Hugh / Headless / Be alright/Chance of a lifetime / If I could do it all over again, I'd do it all over you
HTDCD 57L / Apr '97 / HTD

☐ BACK TO FRONT
Back to Herne Bay front / Bet you wanna take it all / Hold on hold on / Videos of Hollywood / Sally don't change it / Take my breath away / Proper job / Back to front / All aboard / AA man
CDKVS 5011 / Jan '87 / Kingdom

☐ BATTLE OF HASTINGS
HTDCD 41 / Oct '95 / HTD

☐ BLIND DOG AT ST. DUNSTAN'S
Here I am / Chiefs and indians / Very smelly, grubby little oik / Bobbing wide / Come on back / Very smelly, grubby little oik, A (reprise) / Jack and Jill / Can you hear me / All the way
HTDCD 60 / May '96 / HTD

☐ CANTERBURY COLLECTION, THE
It's never too late / What'cha gonna tell me / All aboard / Piano player / Sally don't change it / Bright shiny day / Clear blue sky / Bet you wanna take it all / Hold on hold on / Corner of me eye / Take my breath away
CDKVL 9028 / Jan '87 / Kingdom

☐ CARAVAN
Place of my own / Ride / Policeman / Love song with flute / Cecil runs / Magic man / Grandma's lawn / Where but for Caravan would I be
HTDCD 65 / Sep '96 / HTD

☐ COOL WATER
Cool water / Just the way you are / Tuesday is rock 'n' roll night / Crack of the willow / Ansaphone / Cold fright / Side by side / You won't get me up in one of those / To the land of my fathers / Poor Molly / Send reinforcements
HTDCD 18 / 2 Mar '98 / HTD

☐ CUNNING STUNTS
Show of our lives / Stuck in a hole / Lover / No backstage pass / Dabsong conshirtoe / Fear and loathing in Tollington Park rag
HTDCD 52 / Jan '96 / HTD

☐ IN THE LAND OF GREY AND PINK
Golf girl / Winter wine / Love to love you / In the land of grey and pink / Nine feet underground: Nigel blows a tune / Love's a friend / Make it 76 / Dance of the seven paper hankies- hold granded by the nose / Honest I did - disassociation / 100% proof
8205202 / Apr '89 / Deram

☐ LIVE AT THE ASTORIA
HTDCD 79 / 17 Nov '97 / HTD

☐ LIVE IN CONCERT
Love in your eye / For Richard / Dab song concerto / Hoedown
SFRSCD 058 / 27 Apr '98 / Strange Fruit

☐ SONGS FOR OBLIVION FISHERMEN
Hello hello / If I could do it all over again I'd do it all over you / As I feel I die / Love song with flute / Love to love you / In the land of grey and pink / Memory Iain Hugh / Hunting we shall go / Love in your eye / Mirror for the day / For Richard / Virgin on the ridiculous
HUX 002 / 23 Feb '98 / Hux

☐ TRAVELLING MAN
In the land of grey and pink / Crack of the willow / Cold as ice / Liar / If I could do it all over do it over you / Cool water / Travelling ways / Place of my own / Somewhere in your heart / Wendy wants another 6' mole / Side by side / I know my place / You're laughing / If it wasn't for your ego / It's a sad sad affair
CRESTCD 029 / Feb '98 / Mooncrest

Caravans

☐ ACTION OR SLANDER
(I'm gonna) mainline baby / Mobile Alabama / Killer boogie / Ballad of Lucy Jordan / All messed up / Nothin' 'bout nothin'
RAUCD 028 / May '97 / Raucous

Caravans

☐ AMAZING GRACE
Amazing grace / Just like him / Nobody knows like the Lord / Sacred Lord / Lord stay with me / To whom shall I turn / I'm ready to serve the Lord / No coward soldier / Till I meet the Lord / Jesus will save / Till you come / Lord don't leave us now / Jesus and me / One of these old days / Everything you need / What will tomorrow bring / I don't mind / It must not suffer loss / I'm going thru' / Place like that
CPCD 8088 / Apr '95 / Charly

Caravensari

☐ PIG
SZDATCD 02 / Jul '93 / Samizdat

☐ SHOCK HORO
SAMIZDAT 03CD / Apr '95 / Samizdat

Carawan Family

☐ HOMEBREW
FF 609CD / Apr '94 / Flying Fish

Carawan, Guy

☐ TREE OF LIFE
FF 525CD / '92 / Flying Fish

Carbo, Gladys

☐ STREET CRIES
1211972 / Oct '90 / Soul Note

Carbon

☐ LARYNX
SST 194CD / May '93 / SST

Carbon, Lisa

☐ POLYESTER
CAT 026CD / Jan '96 / Rephlex

☐ TRIO
RI 043CD / Mar '97 / Rather Interesting

Carbonell, Augustin

☐ AUGUSTIN 'BOLA' CARBONELL
MES 158142 / Apr '93 / Messidor

☐ BOLA
NUBA 7701 / 1 Jun '98 / Nuba

☐ BOLA-VUELO FLAMENCO
NUBA 7705 / 1 Jun '98 / Nuba

☐ CARMEN
Alegrias de cascorro / Travesia la comadre / Minerico / Gina / Esencia jonda / Galicia / Coral / Alchacon / Carmen / Improvisation
158142 / Aug '90 / Messidor

Carbonized

☐ DISHARMONIZATION
FDN 2006CD / Sep '93 / Foundation 2000

☐ SCREAMING MACHINES
FDN 2013CD / Sep '96 / Foundation 2000

Carcamo, Pablo

☐ 20 BEST OF CARIBBEAN TROPICAL MUSIC (Carcamo, Pablo & Jaime Mella)
EUCD 1112 / '91 / ARC

☐ BEST OF CARIBBEAN TROPICAL MUSIC
EUCD 1322 / Nov '95 / ARC

☐ CARIBBEAN TROPICAL MUSIC VOL.2
EUCD 1162 / '91 / ARC

☐ CARIBBEAN TROPICAL MUSIC VOL.3
EUCD 1201 / Sep '93 / ARC

☐ CUMBIA DANCE PARTY (Carcamo, Pablo & Enrique Ugarte)
EUCD 1234 / Nov '93 / ARC

☐ FLY AWAY HOME
EUCD 1128 / '91 / ARC

☐ IT'S TIME FOR MAMBO (Carcamo, Pablo & Vanessa Lawicki/Miguel Castro)
EUCD 1225 / Sep '93 / ARC

☐ MAGIC OF THE PARAGUAYAN AND THE INDIAN FLUTES (Carcamo, Pablo & Oscar Benito)
EUCD 1245 / Nov '93 / ARC

☐ MI CHILOE
EUCD 1095 / '91 / ARC

☐ MOST POPULAR SONGS FROM CHILE, THE
EUCD 1217 / Sep '93 / ARC

☐ MY INSPIRATION
EUCD 1181 / Apr '92 / ARC

☐ SAMBA BOSSA (Carcamo, Pablo, Hossam Ramzy & Ulrick Stiegler)
EUCD 1142 / '91 / ARC

Carcass

☐ HEARTWORK
Buried dreams / Carnal fudge / No love lost / Heartwork / Embodiment / This mortal coil / Albeit macht fleisch / Blind bleeding the blind / Doctrinal expletives / Death certificate
MOSH 097CD / 1 Sep '97 / Earache

☐ NECROTICISM - DESCANTING THE INSALUBRIOUS
Inpropagation / Corporeal jigsore quandary / Symposium of sickness / Pedigree butchery / Incarnated solvent abuse / Carneous cacoffin / Lavaging expectorate of Lysergide composition / Forensic clinicism - The Sanguine article
MOSH 042CD / 1 Sep '97 / Earache

☐ REEK OF PUTRIFICATION
Genital grinder / Regurgitation of giblets / Pyosisified (still rotten to the gore) / Carbonized eye-sockets / Frenzied detruncation / Vomited anal tract / Yesterday / Fermenting innards / Excreted alive / Suppuration / Foeticide / Microwaved utergestation / Splattered cavities / Psychopathologist / Burnt to a crisp / Pungent excruciation / Manifestation of verrucose urethra / Oxidised razor masticator / Malignant defecation
MOSH 006CD / 1 Sep '97 / Earache

☐ SWANSONG
Keep on rotting in the free world / Tomorrow belongs to nobody / Black star / Cross my heart / Child's play / Room 101 / Polarized / Generation hexed / Firm hand / Go to hell / Don't believe a word / Rock the vote
MOSH 160CD / 1 Sep '97 / Earache

☐ SYMPHONIES OF SICKNESS
MOSH 018CD / 1 Sep '97 / Earache

☐ WAKE UP AND SMELL THE CARCASS
Edge of darkness / Emotional flatline / Ever increasing circles / Blood splattered banner / I told you S (corporate rock really does suck) / Buried dreams / No love lost / Rot 'n' roll / Edge of darkness / This is your life / Rot 'n' roll / Pyosisified (still rotten to the core) / Hepatic tissue fermentation / Genital grinder II / Hepatic tissue fermentation / Exhume to consume
MOSH 161CD / Oct '96 / Earache

Carcasses, Bobby

☐ JAZZ TIMBERO
TUMICD 068 / 29 Jun '98 / Tumi

Carcrash International

☐ FRAGMENTS OF A JOURNEY IN HELL
CLEO 94612 / Apr '94 / City Slang

Cardiacs

☐ ALL THAT GLITTERS IS A MARE'S NEST
ALPHCD 018 / May '95 / Alphabet Business Concern

☐ ARCHIVE CARDIACS
ALPHCD 000 / May '95 / Alphabet Business Concern

☐ BELLEYE
ORGAN 011CD / Apr '95 / Org

☐ CARDIACS LIVE
Icing on the world / In a city lining / Tarred and feathered / Loosefish scapegrace / Is this the life / To go off and things / Gina Lollibrigida / Goosegash / Cameras / Big ship
ALPHCD 010 / May '95 / Alphabet Business Concern

☐ LITTLE MAN AND A HOUSE AND THE WHOLE WORLD WINDOW, A
Back to the cave / Little man and a house / In a city lining / Is this the life / Interlude / Dive / Icing on the world / Breakfast line / Victor / RES / Whole world window / I'm eating in bed
ALPHCD 007 / May '95 / Alphabet Business Concern

☐ ON LAND AND IN THE SEA
Two bites of cherry / Baby heart dirt / Leader of the starry skys / I hold my own / Arnald / Horsehead / Fast robert / More's nest / Stench of honey / Buds and spawn / Safety bowl / Ever so closely guarded line
ALPHCD 012 / May '95 / Alphabet Business Concern

☐ RUDE BOOTLEG
ALPHCD 005 / May '95 / Alphabet Business Concern

☐ SAMPLER
ALPHCD 019 / May '95 / Alphabet Business Concern

☐ SEASIDE
Jibber and twitch / Gena Lollabrigida / Hello Mr. Sparrow, / It's a lovely day / Wooden fish on wheels / Hope day / To go off and things / Ice a spot and a dot on the dog / R.e.s. / To go off and things
ALPHCD 013 / May '95 / Alphabet Business Concern

☐ SING FOR GOD (2CD Set)
ALPHCD 022 / Jun '96 / Alphabet Business Concern

☐ SING FOR GOD VOL.1
ALPHCD 023 / Jun '96 / Alphabet Business Concern

☐ SING FOR GOD VOL.2
ALPHCD 024 / Jun '96 / Alphabet Business Concern

☐ SONGS FOR SHIPS AND IRONS
ALPHCD 014 / May '95 / Alphabet Business Concern

Cardigans

☐ COMPLETE SINGLES COLLECTION (10CD Single Box Set)
CARDSIN 1 / May '97 / Border

☐ EMMERDALE
5232152 / Jan '97 / Stockholm

☐ FIRST BAND ON THE MOON
Your new cuckoo / Been it / Heartbreaker / Happy meal II / Never recover / Step on me / Love fool / Loser / Iron man / Great divide / Choke
5331172 / Sep '96 / Stockholm

☐ LIFE
Carnival / Gordon's garden party / Daddy's car / Sick and tired / Tomorrow / Rise and shine / Beautiful one / Travelling with Charley / Fine / Celia inside / Hey, get out of my way / After all / Sabbath bloody Sabbath
5235562 / Jun '95 / Stockholm

☐ TRIBUTE TO THE CARDIGANS (Various Artists)
Losers: Anywhen / After all: Red Sleeping Beauty / Hey, get out of my way: Mobyletters / Gordon's garden party: Groove Tunnel / Daddy's car: Lonos / Been it: Inbetweendays / Sick and tired: Dilemmas / Step on me: Elvis Ellington / Fire and shine: Sulky / Tomorrow: Flow
TR 012CD / Jun '97 / Tribute

Cardinal Sin

☐ SPITEFUL INTENTS
WAR 010CD / Jan '97 / Wrong Again

Cardona, Milton

☐ BEMBE
Salute to Eleuga / Eleuga / Ogun / Ochosi / Ebioso / Babalu aye / Obatala / Chango / Ochun / Yemaya
AMCL 10042 / Jun '96 / American Clave

Cardosa, Elizeth

☐ CANCAO DO AMOR DEMAIS
FT 1801 / 12 May '98 / Festa

☐ ELIZETH CARDOSA
60972 / 12 May '98 / RGE

Cards In The Spokes

☐ REACT
ALLIED 089CD / 10 Nov '97 / Allied

Cardwell, Joi

☐ JUMP FOR JOI
EBCD 51 / Jan '95 / Eightball

☐ TROUBLE (The Remix Compilation)
EBCD 58 / Jan '95 / Eightball

Cardy, Wes

☐ WES CARDY COLLECTION
CDRPM 0009 / 8 Sep '97 / RP Media

Care

☐ DIAMONDS AND EMERALDS
Diamonds and emeralds / Evening in the ray / Chandeliers / Flaming sword / Cymophone / Love crowns and crucifies / Temper temper / White cloud / Caretaking / My boyish days / Sad day for England / Soldiers and sailors / Whatever possesed you / Such is life / What kind of world / Nature prayed upon / Misericorde / Besides 1 and 2
74321500232 / Jun '97 / Camden

Care, Simon

☐ TWO'S UP (Care, Simon & Gareth Turner)
OC 02CD / May '97 / Old Court

Carey, Mariah

☐ BIOGRAPHY SERIES
10019 / 3 Nov '97 / Metro Independent

☐ BUTTERFLY
Honey / Butterfly / My all / Roof / Fourth of July / Breakdown / Babydoll / Close my eyes / Whenever you call / Fly away / Beautiful ones / Outside / Honey / Honey
4885372 / 8 Sep '97 / Columbia

☐ DAYDREAM
Fantasy / Underneath the stars / One sweet day: *Carey, Mariah & Boyz II Men* / Open arms / Always be my baby / I am free / When I saw you / Long ago / Melt away / Forever / Daydream interlude / Looking in
4813672 / Sep '95 / Columbia

☐ EMOTIONS
Emotions / And you don't remember / Can't let go / Make it happen / If it's over / You're so cold / So blessed / To be around you / Till the end of time / Wind / Vanishing
4688512 / Oct '91 / Columbia

☐ MARIAH CAREY
Vision of love / There's got to be a way / I don't wanna cry / Someday / Vanishing / All in your mind / Alone in love / You need me / Sent from up above / Prisoner / Love takes time
4668152 / Aug '90 / Columbia

☐ MARIAH CAREY UNPLUGGED
Emotions / If it's over / Someday / Vision of love / Make it happen / I'll be there / Can't let go
4718692 / Jul '92 / Columbia

☐ MERRY CHRISTMAS
Silent night / All I want for Christmas is you / O holy night / Christmas (Baby please come home) / Miss you most (at Christmas time) / Joy to the world / Jesus born on this day / Santa Claus is coming to town / Hark the herald angels sing/Gloria (In Excelsis Deo) / Jesus oh what a wonderful child / God rest ye merry gentlemen
4773422 / Nov '96 / Columbia

☐ MUSIC BOX
Dream lover / Hero / Anytime you need a friend / Music box / Now that I know / Never forget you / Without you / Just to hold you once again / I've been thinking about you / All I've ever wanted / Everything fades away
4742702 / Sep '93 / Columbia

Carey, Mutt

☐ MUTT CAREY & LEE COLLINS (Carey, Mutt & Lee Collins)
AMCD 72 / Jan '94 / American Music

Caribbean Clan

☐ ULTIMATE IN REGGAE
HADCD 176 / Nov '95 / Javelin

Caribbean Jazz Project

☐ ISLAND STORIES
Bluellespie / Sadie's dance / Calabash / Tjader motion / Zigzag / Shadowplay / Libertango / Lost voice / Grass roots
INAK 30392 / Jul '97 / In Akustik

Caribbean Steel Orchestra

☐ STEEL BAND CARNIVAL
303122 / Jun '98 / Hallmark

Carioca

☐ CARIOCA
Revoada / Pitanga / Alvorada / Briza / Branca / Despertar / Brilho / Caminho do sol / Bemtev / Revoada final
5177092 / Jul '93 / Carmo

Carisma

☐ 1825
HGDSRRR 3 / Nov '96 / Escape

Carl Crack

☐ BLACK ARK
Fu man chu / What's going on / Khoi san / Darling / Mein geist ist dein geist / Dogon / Sonnenfreunde / If you mess with me / Gangsta / KR 6200 / Headcase / Tin tin / Indaba / Herbstlaub / Shit / Times like these / Fucking day / Drunken style / Plasma / Radio tachernobyl / Durban poison
DHRLTDMCD 005 / 4 May '98 / Digital Hardcore

Carl, Rudiger

☐ SOLO (Live Frankfurt/Bonn 1993-1995)
FMPCD 86 / Sep '97 / Full Moon

Carle, Frankie

☐ 1946 BROADCASTS (Carle, Frankie & His Orchestra)
JH 1008 / '91 / Jazz Hour

☐ FRANKIE CARLE 1944-1946 (Carle, Frankie & His Orchestra)
CCD 43 / Jul '93 / Circle

☐ FRANKIE CARLE 1944-1949 (Carle, Frankie & His Orchestra)
CCD 146 / Jul '93 / Circle

☐ GOLDEN TOUCH, THE (Frankie Carle At The Piano)
CCD 138 / Mar '97 / Circle

Carles, Maggie

☐ CANTO AMO SUENO
1107771072 / 17 Mar '98 / FRV

Carless, Dorothy

☐ THAT LOVELY WEEKEND
Daddy / It can't be wrong / My sister and I / Room 504 / That lovely weekend / You too can have a lovely romance / Love stay in my heart / We three / Until you fall in love / Where's my love / I want to be in Dixie / This is no laughing matter / When the sun comes out / Our love affair / I can't love you anymore / I'll always love you / I'd know you anywhere / I guess I'll have to dream the rest / I'm sending my blessing / Ragtime cowboy Joe / Never a day goes by / Walkin' by the river
RAJCD 849 / Jan '97 / Empress

Carless, Ray

☐ BODY MOVES
Afrordckin / Masai St Louis / Events in a Thai bath house / My mama told me so / Jake's Blues / Children / Messiah
TRIOCD 302 / Jul '98 / Triple Earth

Carlin, Bob

☐ BANGING AND SAWING
Too young to marry / Walk along John / Ninety degrees / Ora Lee / Far in the mountain / Geese honking / Old sledge / Ten yards of calico / Paddy on the turnpike / Indian on a stump / Hosses in the canebreak / Cuttin' at the Point / Grasshopper sitting on a sweet potato vine / Chinese breakdown / Cider / Back step Cindy / Farewell Trion / Black snake bit me on the toe / Little boy, little boy / Big footed man in the sandy lot / Pretty Polly Ann / Spring creek gal / Old bunch of keys / Cherokee shuffle
ROUCD 0197 / Oct '96 / Rounder

☐ FUN OF OPEN DISCUSSION (Carlin, Bob & John Hartford)
ROUCD 0320 / Apr '95 / Rounder

Carlisle, Belinda

☐ BEST OF BELINDA VOL.1, THE
Heaven is a place on Earth / Same thing / Circle in the sand / Leave a light on for me / Little black book / Summer rain / Vision of you / I get weak / La luna / I plead insanity / World without you / Do you feel like I feel / Half the world / Runaway horses
BELCD 1 / Sep '92 / Offside

☐ HEAVEN ON EARTH
Heaven is a place on Earth / Circle in the sand / I feel free / Should I let you in / World without you / I get weak / We can change / Fool for love / Nobody owns me / Love never dies
CDV 2496 / Dec '87 / Virgin

☐ LIVE YOUR LIFE BE FREE
Live your life be free / Do you feel like I feel / Half the world / You came out of nowhere / You're nothing without me / I plead insanity / Emotional highway / Little black book / Love revolution / World of love / Loneliness game
CDV 2680 / Oct '91 / Virgin

☐ REAL
Goodbye day / It's too real (big scary animal) / Too much water / Lay down your arms / Where love hides / One with you / Wrap my arms / Tell me / Windows of the world / Here comes my baby
CDVIP 165 / Oct '96 / Virgin VIP

☐ RUNAWAY HORSES
Leave a light on for me / Runaway horses / Vision of you / Summer rain / La luna / Same thing / Deep deep ocean / Valentine / Whatever it takes / Shades of Michaelangelo
CDV 2599 / Oct '89 / Virgin

☐ WOMAN AND A MAN, A
In too deep / California / Remember September / Listen to love / Always breaking my heart / Love doesn't live here / He goes on / Kneel at your feet / Love in the key of C / My heart goes out to you
CDCHR 6115 / Sep '96 / Chrysalis

Carlisle, Bob

☐ BUTTERFLY KISSES
CHIP 187 / 8 Sep '97 / Jive

Carlisle, Cliff

☐ BLUES YODELER AND STEEL GUITAR WIZARD
Memphis yodel / No Daddy blues / Hobo blues / Columbus stockade blues / Shanghai rooster yodel / I don't mind / High steppin' Mama / It ain't no fault of mine / That nasty swing / Get her by the tail on the down hill grade / My lovin' Kathleen / Wild cat woman and a tom cat man / You'll miss me when I'm gone / Rambling yodeler / When the evening sun goes down / Handsome blues / My rockin' Mama / Payday flight / My travellin' night / Trouble minded blues / Pan-American blues / I'm saving Saturday night for you / Footprints in the snow / Black Jack David
ARHCD 7039 / Nov '96 / Arhoolie

Carlisle, Una Mae

☐ UNA MAE CARLISLE & SAVANNAH CHURCHILL 1944 (Carlisle, Una Mae & Savannah Churchill)
T'ain't yours / Without you baby / I'm a good good woman / Ain't nothin' much / I like it 'cause I love it / You gotta take your time / He's the best little Yankee to me / I speak so much about you / Teasin' me / You and your heart of stone / You're gonna change your mind / Rest of my life: *Carlisle, Una Mae* / He's commander in chief of my heart / Two faced man / Tell me your blues / Fat meat is good meat: *Churchill, Savannah* / That glory day: *Carlisle, Una Mae* / Crying need for you: *Carlisle, Una Mae* / I carry the torch for you: *Carlisle, Una Mae* / Behavin' myself for you: *Carlisle, Una Mae*
HQCD 19 / Jun '94 / Harlequin

Carlo & The Belmonts

☐ CARLO & THE BELMONTS
We belong together / Such a long way / Santa Margherita / My foolish heart / Teenage Clementine / Little orphan girl / Five minutes more / Write me a letter / Brenda the great pretender / Ring-a-ling / Baby doll / Mairzy doats and dozy doats / Story of love / Kansas City
CHCHD 251 / 30 Mar '98 / Ace

Carlos

☐ BIGGER TEETH
HEDCD 072 / 27 Oct '97 / Headhunter

Carlotti, Jean-Marie

☐ PACHIQUELI VEN DE NEUCH (PROVENCE)
Y225034 / Jun '93 / Silex

Carlton, Larry

☐ GIFT, THE
Ridin' the treasure / Things we said today / Goin' nowhere / Gift / Shop 'til you drop / Pammie dear / Osaka cool / My old town / Mourning dove / Buddy
GRP 98542 / Oct '96 / GRP

☐ KID GLOVES
Kid gloves / Preacher / Michele's whistle / Oui oui si / Heart to heart / Just my imagination / Where be Mosada / Farm jazz / Terry T / If I could I would
GRP 96832 / Aug '92 / GRP

☐ RENEGADE GENTLEMAN
Crazy Mama / RCM / Sleep medicine / Cold day in hell / Anthem / Amen AC / Never say naw / Farm jazz / Nothin' comes / Bogner / Red hot poker / I gotta right
GRP 97442 / Aug '93 / GRP

☐ SINGING/PLAYING
EDCD 439 / Oct '95 / Edsel

☐ SLEEPWALK
Last nite / Blues bird / Song for Katie / Frenchman's flat / Upper kern / 10 p.m. / You gotta get it while you can / Sleepwalk
GRP 01262 / Aug '92 / GRP

☐ WITH A LITTLE HELP FROM MY FRIENDS
EDCD 480 / Jun '96 / Edsel

Carman, Jenks Tex

☐ CHIPPEHA (The Essential Dixie Cowboy 1947-1957)
REV 207 / 26 May '98 / Revenant

☐ HILLBILLY HULA
Hillbilly hula / Another good dream gone wrong / Hilo march / Gosh I miss you all the time / Locust hill rag / Calssons go rolling along / Samoa stomp / Dixie cannonball / Sweet Luwanna / My lonely heart and I / Indian polka / I'm a poor lonesome fellow / Don't feel sorry for me / My trusting heart / Gonna stay right here / (I've recieved) a penny postcard / Ten thousand miles (Away from home) / I could love you darling / You tell her, I s-t-u-t-t-e-r / Blue memories
BCD 15574 / Mar '92 / Bear Family

Carmel

☐ COLLECTED (A Collection Of Work 1983-1990)
And I take it for granted / Sally / It's all in the game / I'm not afraid of you / Every little bit / I have fallen in love (Je suis tombee amoureuse) / More, more, more / You can have him / Bad day / J'oublierai ton nom / I'm over you
8282192 / May '92 / London

☐ LIVE IN PARIS
Bad day / I'm not afraid / Stand together / Sticks and stones / Sugar you're sweet / It's all in the game / More more more / Lullaby / Rekindle your youth / If birds can fly / Sally / Tracks of my tears
120752 / Mar '97 / Musidisc UK

Carmello, Janusz

☐ PORTRAIT
When the saints go marching in / Some time ago / Fun run / Song for Babyshka / Tiny capers / Li'l darlin' / Joy spring / Daydream / Lover man
HEPCD 2044 / Sep '90 / Hep

Carmen, Eric

☐ GREATEST HITS
All by myself / Never gonna fall in love again / That's rock'n'roll / Hey Deanie / Hungry eyes / Make me lose control / Change of heart / She did it / It hurts too much / No hard feelings / Boats against the current
258999 / Jun '96 / Arista

Carmen, Phil

☐ BACK FROM LA LIVE
HYCD 200148 / Mar '95 / Hypertension

Carmichael's Ceilidh

☐ CARMICHAEL'S CEILIDH
CDLOC 1081 / Jul '94 / Lochshore

Carmichael, Anita

☐ COME WITH ME
SAXCD 004 / May '94 / Saxology

Carmichael, Hoagy

☐ ART VOCAL 1927-1942
700182 / Sep '96 / Art Vocal

☐ HOAGY CARMICHAEL 1927-1944
Washboard blues / Stardust / Rockin' chair / Georgia / Lazy river / Lazybones / Moon country / Two sleepy people / Little old lady
CBC 1011 / Jun '93 / Timeless Jazz

☐ HOAGY CARMICHAEL 1951
FLYCD 912 / Oct '92 / Flyright

☐ HOAGY CARMICHAEL SONGBOOK (Various Artists)
Stardust: *Cole, Nat 'King'* / Washboard blues: *Dorsey, Tommy* / Rockin' chair: *Armstrong, Louis* / Little old lady: *Hutchinson, Leslie 'Hutch'* / Lamplighter's serenade: *Miller, Glenn Orchestra* / Lazybones: *Carmichael, Hoagy* / Georgia on my mind: *Jones, Tom* / Skylark: *Shore, Dinah* / Old music master: *Mercer, Johnny* / Nearness of you: *Fitzgerald, Ella* / Old buttermilk sky: *Four Freshmen* / I should have known you years ago: *Davis, Beryl* / One morning in May: *Monro, Matt* / Blue orchids: *Vaughan, Sarah* / I get along without you very well: *Newley, Anthony* / In the cool, cool, cool of the evening: *Mancini, Henry* / Doctor, lawyer, indian chief: *Hutton, Betty* / Judy: *Laine, Frankie* / My resistance is low: *Sarstedt, Robin* / When love goes wrong: *Whiting, Margaret & Jimmy Wakely* / Memphis in June: *Skellern, Peter* / Ivy: *Stafford, Jo* / How little it matters, how little we know: *Monro, Matt*
VSOPCD 123 / Oct '88 / Connoisseur Collection

☐ JAZZ PORTRAIT
CD 14585 / Nov '95 / Complete

☐ MR. MUSIC MASTER
Mr. Music Master / Stardust / Rockin' chair / Moon country / Riverboat shuffle / Two sleepy people / Judy / Skylark / Moonburn / Hong Kong blues / One morning in May / Lazy river / I get along without you very well / Blue orchids / Little old lady / Georgia on my mind / Sing me a swing song / Lazybones / Washboard blues / Snowball / Small fry / Sing it way down low
PASTCD 7004 / Mar '93 / Flapper

☐ OLD MUSIC MASTER, THE
CDMOIR 527 / 26 May '98 / Memoir

☐ STARDUST
Darktown strutters ball / Hong kong blues / Old music master / Casanova cricket / Rockin' chair / I may be wrong (but I think you're wonderful) / Memphis in June / Who killed 'er (who killed the black widder) / Georgia on my mind / Huggin' and chakin' / Don't forget to say no baby / Old piano roll blues / Doctor, lawyer, indian, chief / For every man there's a woman / Old buttermilk sky / Shh the old man's sleeping / Riverboat shuffle / Put yourself in my place baby / Old man Harlem / Tune for humming / My resistance is low / Monkey song / Stardust
3035900052 / Apr '96 / Essential Gold

Carmichael, John

☐ MORE CARMICHAEL'S CEILIDH
CDLOC 1095 / Aug '96 / Lochshore

Carmina

☐ WEATHER IN THE HEART
Bird of paradise / Carolan / Leaving wakes / Down to land/Garrett Barry's / Five lakes / Red river valley girl / Mountains of prayer
RHYD 5014 / Jun '98 / Rhiannon

Carmona, Juan

☐ BORBOREO
ED 13055 / May '96 / L'Empreinte Digitale

☐ FALLA LORCA (Carmona, Juan & Francoise Atlan)
Anda laleo / El pano moruno / Asturiana / Nana del caballo grande / Los cuatro muleros / La Tarara / Nana del carino / Zorongo / Las tres hojas / Romance de Don Boyso / Los mozos de Monleon / El Vito / Los pelegrinitos / Nana / Sevillana del siglo XVIII / Los reyes de la baraja / Las morillas de Jaen / El cafe de Chinitas / Nana de Sevilla
ED 13062 / May '97 / L'Empreinte Digitale

Carn, Doug

☐ INFANT EYES
Welcome / Little D's poem / Moon child / Infant eyes / Passion dance / Acknowledgement / Peace
BLACKJAZZ 3CD / Apr '98 / Black Jazz

Carnage

☐ DARK RECOLLECTIONS
NECRO 3 CD / Dec '90 / Necrosis

Carnahan, Danny

☐ CUT & RUN (Carnahan, Danny & Robin Petrie)
FLE 1006CD / Jun '94 / Fledg'ling

Carne, Jean

☐ JEAN CARNE/HAPPY TO BE WITH YOU
Free love / No laughing matter / I'm in love once again / Don't you know love when you see it / Where did you ever go / You are all I need / If you wanna go back / You got a problem / Time waits for no one / There's a shortage of good men / Together once again / (No no) you can't come back now / Revelation/Infant eyes / Happy to be with you / Don't let it go yo your head / I bet she won't love you like I do / You light up my life
WESM 567 / Feb '98 / Westside

☐ LOVE LESSONS
Don't stop doin' whatcha doin' / Make love / Good thing goin' on / So I can love you / Have I told you that I love you / No one does it better / Fallin' for you / It's not for me to say / Misty / Someone to watch over me
XECD 6 / Dec '95 / Expansion

☐ WHEN I FIND YOU LOVE/SWEET AND WONDERFUL
When I find you love / Intro/My love don't come easy / Start the fire / All I really need is you / Lonely girl in a cold cold world / What's on your mind / Give it up / Was that all is was / Bet your lucky star / Don't say no (to love) / Sweet and wonderful / Don't love nobody / We got some catchin' up to do / Mystic stranger / I just thought of a way / Love (makes me do foolish things)
WESM 574 / 20 Apr '98 / Westside

Carneiro, Nando

☐ CATAVENTO
MPCD 3035 / Jul '98 / Mariposa

☐ VIOLAO
Violao / Charada / Poromim / Juliana / As gralhas / GRES luxo artezanal / O compones / Liza
8492122 / May '91 / Carmo

Carnes, Kim

☐ BETTE DAVIS EYES
Bette Davis eyes / Divided hearts / Invisible hands / Mistaken identity / Abadabadango / More love / Bon voyage / You make my heart beat faster / Cry like a baby / Does it make you remember / I pretend / Young love / Invitation to dance / Crazy in the night
DC 867252 / Nov '96 / Disky

☐ MISTAKEN IDENTITY
Bette Davis eyes / Hit and run / Mistaken identity / When I'm away from you / Draw of the cards / Break the rules tonite / Still hold on / Don't call it love / Miss you tonite / My old pals
MUSCD 507 / Nov '94 / MCI Original Masters

☐ SWEET LOVE SONG OF MY SOUL
Sweet love song of my soul / Everything has got to be free / Do you want to dance / I won't call you back / To love / To love somebody / Fell in love with a poet / One more river to cross / You can do it to me anytime / Rest on me
CDTB 084 / '89 / Thunderbolt

Carol, Rene

☐ HAFENMARIE
Hafenmarie / Ein vagabundenherz / Gruss mir die sterne von Montana / Solang es liebe gibt / Solang du freunde hast / Der rote Wien / Auf der insel bell'amore / Das macht der sonnenschein / Jonny komm wieder / Strassenmusikant / Ich hab nur dich / Prinzessin Sonnenschein / Im hafen von San Remo / Carina / Bianca rosa / Ich mocht' mit dir mal ein Marchen erleben / Die schonen marchen / Sieben meere und kein kuss / Tief in deinen augen / Unter Palmen und Cypressen / Du darfst nicht weinen / Schones madchen lass' das weinen / Schenk' mir deine freundschaft / Sonne, wind und sterne / Wo meine sterne Bundeswehr parodie / Bildzeitungs parodie
BCD 16137 / Jan '97 / Bear Family

☐ KEIN LAND KANN SCHONER SEIN
Kein land kann schoner sein / Ich hab' ein herz gefunden / Ich muss dich wiedersehn / Nicoletta / Das lied der Geigen / Der goldschmied von Toledo / Lass mich nicht zu lang allein / Wann kommst du wieder nach hause / Marchenland Hawaii / Serenata di Napoli / Sieben nachte blieb der Jos, in Santa Fe / Ich mochte stundenlang in deine augen sehn / Am blauen Gardasee (Angeli) / Die Mondscheinserenade / Ich will immer an dich denken / Romanita / Meine Heimat ist die liebe / Vergiss nicht, dass ich bei dir bin / Schau zu den sternen der liebe / An wen denkst du / Verlieb dich in mich / Leb' wohl, Marie / Viola-Violetta / Musikant / Chicita May / Du braune Madonna der Sudsee / Das schiff deine Sehnsucht / Mitten im Meer / Wo ist mein Zuhause
BCD 15985 / May '96 / Bear Family

☐ LIEBE UND WEIN
BCD 16140 / May '98 / Bear Family

Carole, Jill

☐ EASTER BUNNY SEX AND SANTA CLAUS, THE
Red fire truck / Every now and then / Animal dreams / Heart of Oaxaca / Ground zero / Sunday best / I'll try the time machine / Walk the plank / Heart of Dixie / Wish you were here / Road atlas
MYSCD 124 / 1 Jun '98 / Mystic

Caron, Alain

☐ PLAY
Pac man / In and out / D-Code / Ton Jardin / Pole position / Grand cafe / Impressions / Apres la pluie / B12 / Trouble
JMS 186942 / 17 Nov '97 / JMS

☐ RHYTHM 'N' JAZZ
Bump / Fat cat / District 6 / Slam the clown / Little Miss March / I C U / Cherokee drive / Flight of the bebop bee / Donna Lee / Intuitions
JMS 186782 / Nov '95 / JMS

Carousel

☐ ABCDEFGHIJKLMNOPQRSTUVWXYZ
MASK 050CD / Feb '95 / Vinyl Japan

Carpathian Full Moon

☐ SERENADES IN BLOOD
AV 006 / Sep '94 / Avantgarde

Carpe Tembrum

☐ MAJESTIC NOTHINGNESS
HNF 036CD / 10 Nov '97 / Head Not Found

Carpendale, Howard

☐ HELLO AGAIN
Hello again / Du lachst nicht mehr / Schade / (Sittin' on the) dock of the bay / Liebe von gestern / Bitte nenn' mich immer daddy / Ghandi / Sandy river / Augen wie asphalt / Joshua fit the battle of Jericho / Hello how are you / Wie du es willst / Happy birthday rock 'n' roll / Verloscht dann das licht
DC 875422 / Mar '97 / Disky

Carpenter, Bob

☐ SILENT PASSAGE
CMCD 027 / Dec '97 / Celtic Music

Carpenter, Mary-Chapin

☐ COME ON, COME ON
Hard way / He thinks he'll keep her / Rhythm of the blues / I feel lucky / Bug / Not too much to ask / Passionate kisses / Only a dream / I am a town / Walking through fire / I take my chances / Come on come on
4718982 / Feb '97 / Columbia

☐ HOMETOWN GIRL
Lot like me / Other streets and other towns / Hometown girl / Downtown train / Family hands / Road is just a road / Come on home / Waltz / Just because / Heroes and heroines
4879322 / Jul '97 / Columbia

☐ PLACE IN THE WORLD, A
Keeping the faith / Hero in your own hometown / I can see it now / I want to be your girlfriend / Let me into your heart / What if we went to Italy / That's real / Ideas are like stars / Naked to the eye / Sudden gift of fate / Better to dream of you / Place in the world
4851822 / Oct '96 / Columbia

☐ SHOOTING STRAIGHT IN THE DARK
Going out tonight / Right now / More things change / When she's gone / Middle ground / Can't take love for granted / Down at the twist and shout / When Halley came to Jackson / What you didn't say / You win again / Moon and St Christopher
4674682 / Sep '96 / Columbia

☐ STATE OF THE HEART
How do / Something of a dreamer / Never had it so good / Read my lips / This shirt / Quittin' time / Down in Mary's land / Goodbye again / Too tired / Slow country dance / It don't bring you
4666912 / Apr '90 / Columbia

☐ STONES IN THE ROAD
Why walk when you can fly / House of cards / Stones in the road / Keeper for every flame / Tender when I want to be / Shut up and kiss me / Last word / End of my private days / John Doe No.24 / Jubilee / Outside looking in / Where time stands still / This is love
4776792 / 13 Jul '98 / Columbia

Carpenter, Richard

☐ PIANIST ARRANGER COMPOSER CONDUCTOR
Prelude / Yesterday once more / Medley / I need to be in love / Sandy / Time / For all we know / One love / Bless the beasts and children / Flat baroque / All those years ago / Top of the world / We've only just begun / Karen's theme
5407032 / 22 Sep '97 / A&M

Carpenter, Thelma

☐ SOUVENIR, A
ACD 111 / 27 Apr '98 / Audiophile

Carpenters

☐ CARPENTERS
Rainy days and Mondays / Saturday / Let me be the one / (A place to) hideaway / For all we know / Superstar / Druscilla penny / One love / Bacharach and David medley / Sometimes
5500632 / May '93 / Spectrum

☐ CARPENTERS PERFORMED ON PANPIPES, THE (Various Artists)
We've only just begun / For all we know / Rainy days and mondays / Those good old dreams / Look to your dreams / I need to be in love / Please Mr Postman / Top of the world / Only yesterday / Sing / Superstar / Now / I just fell in love again / Yesterday once more / Close to you
SUMCD 4083 / Nov '96 / Summit

☐ CHRISTMAS COLLECTION (2CD Set)
O come o come Emmanuel / Overture / Christmas waltz / Sleigh ride / It's Christmas time/Sleep well little children / Have yourself a merry Christmas / Santa Claus is coming to town / Christmas song / Silent night / Jingle bells / First snowfall/Let it snow / Carol of the bells / Merry Christmas darling / I'll be home for Christmas / Christ is born / Winter wonderland/Silver bells/White Christmas / Ave Maria / It came upon a Midnight clear / Overture / Old fashioned Christmas / O Holy night / (There's no place like) home for the holidays / Medley / Little altar boy / Do you hear what I hear / My favourite things / He came here for me / Santa Claus is comin' to town / What are you doin' New Year's eve / Nutcracker / I heard the bells on Christmas day
5406032 / Nov '96 / A&M

☐ CLOSE TO YOU
We've only just begun / Love is surrender / Maybe it's you / Reason to believe / Help / Close to you / Baby it's you / I'll never fall in love again / Crescent moon / Mr. Guder / I kept on loving you / Another song
CDMID 138 / Oct '92 / A&M

☐ HORIZON
Aurora / Only yesterday / Desperado / Please Mr. Postman / I can dream, can't I / Solitaire / Happy / Goodbye and I love you (I'm caught between) / Love me for what I am / Eventide
CDMID 141 / Oct '92 / A&M

☐ IF I WERE A CARPENTER (A Tribute To The Carpenters) (Various Artists)
Goodbye to love: *American Music Club* / Top of the world: *Shonen Knife* / Superstar: *Sonic Youth* / Close to you: *Cranberries* / For all we know: *Bettie Serveert* / It's going to take some time: *Dishwalla* / Solitaire: *Crow, Sheryl* / Hurting each other: *Napolitano, Johnette & Marc Moreland* / Yesterday once more: *Redd Kross* / Calling occupants of interplanetary craft: *Babes In Toyland* / Rainy days and Mondays: *Cracker* / Let me be the one: *Sweet, Matthew* / Bless the beasts and children: *4 Non Blondes* / We've only just begun: *Grant Lee Buffalo*
5402582 / Sep '94 / A&M

☐ INTERPRETATIONS (A 25th Anniversary Celebration)
Without a song / Sing / Bless the beasts and children / When I fall in love / From this moment on / Tryin' to get the feeling again / When it's gone / Where do I go from here / Desperado / Superstar / Rainy days and Mondays / Ticket to ride / If I had you / Please Mr. Postman / We've only just begun / Calling occupants of interplanetary craft / Little girl blue / You're the one / Close to you
5402512 / Oct '94 / A&M

☐ KAREN CARPENTER (Carpenter, Karen)
Lovelines / All because of you / If I had you / Making love in the afternoon / If we try / Remember when lovin' took all night / Still in love with you / My body keeps changing my mind / Make believe it's your first time / Guess I just lost my head / Still crazy after all these years / Last one singin' the blues
5405882 / Nov '96 / A&M

☐ LOVE SONGS
I need to be in love / Solitaire / We've only just begun / This masquerade / You're the one / Can't smile without you / Superstar / Rainy days and mondays / Top of the world / Make believe it's your first time / I just fall in love again / (They long to be) close to you / For all we know / Where do I go from here / Only yesterday / All you get from love is a love song / When I fall in love / Hurting each other / I won't last a day without you / Song for you / Goodbye to love
5408382 / 10 Nov '97 / A&M

☐ NOW AND THEN
Sing / This masquerade / Heather / Jambalaya / I can't make music / Yesterday once more / Fun, fun, fun / End of the world / Da doo ron ron / Dead man's curve / Johnny angel / Night has a thousand eyes / Our day will come / One fine day
CDMID 140 / Oct '92 / A&M

☐ PASSAGE
B'wana she no home / All you get from love is a love song / I just fell in love again / On the balcony of the Casa Rosada / Don't cry for me Argentina / Sweet sweet smile / Two sides / Man smart, woman smarter / Calling occupants of interplanetary craft
CDMID 143 / Oct '92 / A&M

☐ REFLECTIONS
I need to be in love / I just fall in love again / Baby it's you / Can't smile without you / Beechwood 45789 / Eve / All of my life / Reason to believe / Your baby doesn't love you anymore / Maybe it's you / Ticket to ride / Sweet sweet smile / Song for you / Because we are in love (The wedding song)
5515932 / 3 Aug '98 / Spectrum

☐ SINGLES 1969-73, THE
We've only just begun / Top of the world / Ticket to ride / Superstar / Rainy days and Mondays / Goodbye to love / Yesterday once more / It's going to take some time / Sing / For all we know / Hurting each other / Close to you
CDA 63601 / Jun '84 / A&M

☐ SINGLES 1974-1978, THE
Sweet sweet smile / Jambalaya / Can't smile without you / I won't last a day without you / All you get from love is a love song / Only yesterday / Solitaire / Please Mr. Postman / I need to be in love / Happy / There's a kind of hush / Calling occupants of interplanetary craft
CDA 19748 / '88 / A&M

☐ SONG FOR YOU, A
Song for you / Top of the world / Hurting each other / It's going to take some time / Goodbye to love / Intermission / Bless the beasts and children / Flat baroque / Piano picker / I won't last a day without you / Crystal lullaby / Road ode
CDMID 139 / Oct '92 / A&M

Carpetbaggers

☐ SIN NOW...PRAY LATER
HCD 8071 / May '96 / Hightone

Carpettes

☐ BEST OF THE CARPETTES, THE
CDPUNK 80 / Jun '96 / Anagram

☐ EARLY YEARS, THE
OVER 68CD / 15 Sep '97 / Overground

Carr, Ian

☐ SOUNDS AND SWEET AIRS (Carr, Ian & John Taylor)
130642 / May '96 / Celestial Harmonies

Carr, James

☐ ESSENTIAL JAMES CARR, THE
RE 2060 / Sep '96 / Razor & Tie

☐ SOUL SURVIVOR
Soul survivor / Man worth knowing / Put love first / I can't leave your love alone / Things a woman need / Daydreaming / All because of your love / I'm into something / Memphis after midnight / That's how strong a woman's love is
CDCH 487 / Oct '93 / Ace

☐ TAKE ME TO THE LIMIT
Take me to the limit / Sugar shock / Love attack / You gotta love your woman / High on your love / She's already gone / Our garden of Eden / I can't leave your love alone / What's a little love between friends / Lack of attention
CDCH 310 / Jan '91 / Ace

Carr, Leroy

☐ AMERICAN BLUES LEGEND
CPCD 8333 / 27 May '98 / Charly

☐ BLACK BOY SHINE 1934-1937
DOCD 5465 / Jul '96 / Document

☐ DON'T CRY WHEN I'M GONE
Barrelhouse woman / Alabama women blues / You left me crying / 11.29 blues / How long has that evening train been gone / Suicide blues / Sloppy drunk blues / 'Fore day rider / Rocks in my bed
PYCD 07 / Apr '90 / Magpie

☐ HOW LONG BLUES
159062 / Jan '98 / Blues Collection

☐ HURRY DOWN SUNSHINE
IGOCD 2016 / Mar '95 / Indigo

☐ PIANO BLUES 1929-1935
PYCD 17 / Nov '92 / Magpie

☐ REMAINING TITLES, THE (Carr, Leroy & Scrapper Blackwell)
SOB 035382 / Oct '92 / Story Of The Blues

☐ SLOPPY DRUNK (2CD Set)
How long how long blues / Tennessee blues / You got to reap what you sow / Low down dirty blues / Box car blues / How long how long blues / Baby don't you love me no more / Tired of your low down ways / Prison bound blues / Straight alky blues / Naptown blues / Gettin' all wet / Just worryin' blues / Christmas in jail ain't it a pain / Prison cell blues / Papa wants a cookie / Memphis town / Dirty dozen / Sloppy drunk blues / Long road blues / Four day rider / Alabama women blue / Papa's on the house top / Papa's got your water on / New how long how long blues / Gone mother blues / Midnight hour blue / Blues before sunrise / I ain't got no money now / Southbound blues / Barrel house woman / I believe I'll make a change / Bo bo stomp / Hustlers blues / It's too short / Rocks in my bed / When the sun goes down / Bad luck all the time / Big four blues / Just a rag / Ain't it a shame / Going back home / Six cold feet in the ground
KATCD 108 / 1 Sep '98 / Catfish

Carr, Richard

☐ STRING THING (Carr, Richard & Bucky Pizzarelli)
Boulevard of broken dreams / Willow weep for me / We've got the moon and sixpence / Star crossed lovers / Srtrictly business / St Elsewhere / Blloodcount / Fair rosemary / Hit the road to dreamland / Crazy rhythm / Send in the clowns
SAVCD 2010 / 16 Mar '98 / Savant

Carr, Romey

☐ BLISS
What'll I do / Midnight sun / Lil darlin' / Nearness of you / Windmills of your mind / Summer knows / I've got a crush on you / My funny Valentine / I don't want to play in your yard / My foolish heart / Out of this world / More than you know / First time ever I saw your face / Remind me / If ever I would leave you / One voice
ALBACD 03 / 9 Feb '98 / Alba

☐ ROBERT BURNS, A WOMAN'S MAN
ALBACD 02 / Jul '96 / Alba

☐ WOMAN KNOWS, A
Bonny banks of Loch Lomond / Nae luck about the house / Ae fond kiss / Wee willie winkie / My love is like a red red rose / Eriskay love lilt / Whistle and I'll come to you my lad / Queen's Marines / Charlie is my darling / Amazing grace (the lord is my shepherd) / Ca' the yowes / Ye banks and brae's o' bonnie doon / In praise of Islay / Cockle gatherer / Hush-a-bye-baby / Bonnie wee thing / Wee Cooper o' Fife / I left my dearie lying here / Peat-fire flame / Auld lang syne
ALBACD 01 / Sep '95 / Alba

Carr, Sister Wynona

☐ DRAGNET FOR JESUS
Each day / Lord Jesus / I want to go to heaven and rest / I'm a pilgrim traveller / I heard the news (Jesus is coming again) / Our father / He said he would / I see Jesus / Don't miss that train / I heard mother pray one day / Good old way / See his blessed face / Did he die in vain / I know someday God's gonna call me / Conversation with Jesus / Ball game / Letter to heaven / In a little while / Untitled instrumental / Operator, operator / Dragnet for Jesus / Fifteen rounds for Jesus / Nobody but Jesus / Just a few more days
CDCHD 411 / Nov '93 / Ace

☐ JUMP JACK JUMP
Jump Jack jump / Till the well runs dry / Boppity bop (boogity boog) / Should I ever love again / I'm mad at you / Old fashioned love / Hurt me / It's raining outside / Nursery rhyme rock / Ding dong daddy / Someday, somewhere, somehow / Act right / What do you know about love / Now that I'm free / Heartbreak melody / Please Mr. Jailer / Weatherman / If these walls could speak / Touch and go / If I pray / Finders keepers / Things you do to me / How many times / Give me your hand to hold
CDCHD 513 / Jan '94 / Ace

Carr, Vikki

☐ IT MUST BE HIM/THE WAY OF TODAY
It must be him / None but the lonely heart / Her little heart went to loveland / Laila Ladala (Reza) / Look again / Cuana caliente el sol / Hoe does the wine taste / Should I follow / May I come in / Toys / San Francisco / Can I trust you (Lot Ti Daro Di Piu) / Anyone who had a heart / My prayer / My heart reminds me / You don't have to say you love me / Nowhere man / If you love me, really love me / Strangers in the night / I will wait for you / My world is empty without you / I hear a rhapsody
CTMCD 102 / Nov '96 / EMI

☐ UNFORGETTABLE, THE
He's a rebel / Mirror / Only love can break a heart / Bye bye blackbird / How does the wine taste / Unforgettable / It must be him / With pen in hand / Alfie / Can't take my eyes off you / By the time I get to Phoenix / Never my love / All my love / Singing my song / Sunday morning coming down / Yesterday when I was young / Walk away / If you love me (I won't care) / Poor butterfly / Everything I touch turns to tears
CDSL 8255 / Sep '95 / Music For Pleasure

Carrack, Paul

☐ 21 GOOD REASONS
How long / Real feeling / No future in your eyes / You're all that I need / Tempted / Do me lover / Oh how happy / Rumour / I need you / Always better with you / Little unkind / One good reason / Don't shed a tear / Button off my shirt / When you walk in the room / I live by the groove / Only my heart can tell / Battlefield / Loveless / Silent running / Living years
CDCHR 6067 / Feb '94 / Chrysalis

☐ BEAUTIFUL WORLD
Way I'm feeling tonight / Time to let go / Beautiful world / Perfect love / You give me something / Satisfied / Close to me / It goes without saying / If you'd ever needed someone / Some kinda love
ARKCD 001 / May '98 / EMI

☐ BLUE VIEWS
Eyes of blue / For once in our lives / No easy way out / Oh oh oh my my my / Only a breath away / Nothing more than a memory / Somewhere in your heart / Love will keep us alive / Always have always will / Don't walk over me / How long
EIRSCD 1075 / Jan '96 / IRS/EMI
ARKK 10007 / May '97 / ARKK

Carrasco, Joe 'King'

☐ BANDIDO ROCK
Juarez and zapata / Pachuco hop / Bandido rock / Arriba sandino / Hey gringo no pasaran / Banana / Chicano town / Dame tu nook nook / Kry tuff / Fuera yanqui
ROUCD 9012 / '88 / Rounder

☐ BORDER TOWN (Carrasco, Joe 'King' & The Crowns)
Escondido / Hola coca cola / Who bought the guns / Are you Amigo / Put me in jail / Mr. Bogota / Walk it like you talk it / Current events (are making me tense) / Cucaraca taco / Baby let's go to Mexico / Vamos a bailar / Tamale baby
ROSE 40CD / '88 / New Rose

Carreg Lafar

☐ YSBRYD Y WERIN
SCD 2102 / Jan '96 / Sain

Carreras, Jose

☐ BEST OF JOSE CARRERAS, THE
TRTCD 187 / Jul '96 / TrueTrax

☐ BEST OF JOSE CARRERAS, THE
I have a dream / With a song in my heart / Be my love / Musica proibta / Tristesse / Per Silvia / Panis angelicus / Amore perduto / En Aranjuez con tu amor / Beloved / All the things you are / If I loved you / All I ask of you: *Carreras, Jose & Barbara Dickson* / Lippen schweigen / E lucevan le stelle / Che gelida manina / Vieni sul mar / Marechiare / Torna a surriento / Granada / Amigos para siempre: *Carreras, Jose & Sarah Brightman*
3984216672 / 8 Jun '98 / Erato

☐ BRILLIANT VOICE, THE
MU 5042 / Oct '92 / Musketeer

☐ CELEBRATION OF CHRISTMAS, A (Carreras, Jose & Natalie Cole/Placido Domingo)
I walked today where Jesus walked / Panis angelicus: *Carreras, Jose* / O joyful children: *Domingo, Placido* / Christmas song: *Cole, Natalie* / Ay para navidad / Holly and the ivy: *Cole, Natalie & Jose Carreras* / I'll be home for Christmas / Agnus Dei: *Domingo, Placido* / Lord's prayer: *Carreras, Jose* / Winter wonderland: *Cole, Natalie* / Navidad: *Carreras, Jose & Placido Domingo* / White Christmas / What child is this / Pero mira como beben los peces en el rio / May each day / Cantique de noel / Amazing grace / Oh, du frochliche / Sleigh ride
0630146402 / Nov '96 / Erato

☐ JOSE CARRERAS SINGS ANDREW LLOYD WEBBER
Memory / Phantom of the opera / Music of the night / You / Pie Jesu / Tell me on a Sunday / Half a moment / There's me / Starlight express / Unexpected song / Love changes everything
2569242 / Nov '89 / WEA

☐ MY ROMANCE
All the things you are / Drinking song / Lippen schweigen / This nearly was mine / Rose Marie / If I loved you / Lover come back to me / Indian love call / Wolgalied / Softly as in a morning sunrise / Deep in your heart dear / Cancion del gitano / Dein ist mein ganzes herz
0630177892 / 8 Sep '97 / Erato

☐ ROMANTICA
PLSCD 117 / Apr '96 / Pulse

☐ WHITE CHRISTMAS
White Christmas / O come all ye faithful (Adeste fidelis) / Agnus dei / Caro mio ben / Maria / Pieta, Signore / What child is this / Mille cherubini / Pregaria / Panis angelicus / El romanc / Andantino / Silent night
DSHCD 7010 / Nov '95 / D-Sharp

Carrere, Tia

☐ DREAM
State of grace / I wanna come home with you tonight / Innocent side / I never even told you / Gift of perfect love / Surrender / Love is a cannibal / We need to belong / Our love / Dream a perfect dream
9362453002 / Oct '93 / WEA

Carrick, Brian

☐ 1995 BUDE FESTIVAL (Carrick, Brian & The New City Stompers)
PKCD 054 / Jul '96 / PEK

☐ BRIAN CARRICK & HIS HERITAGE STOMPERS
BCD 345 / Jun '96 / GHB

☐ JAZZ IN NEW ORLEANS (Carrick, Brian & Waldren Joseph)
Streets of the city / Washington and Lee swing / Careless love blues / Bugle boy march / Swanee river / Old rugged cross / Let me call you sweetheart / Lady be good / St. Louis blues / Darktown strutter's ball / I ain't got nobody / Ting-a-ling / I'm confessin' / Anytime
504CDS 65 / Jun '98 / 504

☐ SPIRIT OF NEW ORLEANS, THE (Carrick, Brian Heritage Hall Stompers)
PKCD 050 / May '96 / PEK

Carrier, Chubby

☐ DANCE ALL NIGHT (Carrier, Chubby & Bayou Swamp Band)
BP 5007CD / Mar '94 / Blind Pig

☐ WHO STOLE THE HOT SAUCE
BLPCD 5032 / Sep '96 / Blind Pig

Carrier, Roy

☐ AT HIS BEST
ZNCD 1010 / Nov '95 / Zane

☐ SOULFUL SIDE OF ZYDECO (Carrier, Roy & Joe Walker)
ZNCD 1003 / Oct '95 / Zane

Carroll, Baikida

☐ DOOR OF THE CAGE
1211232 / Apr '95 / Soul Note

Carroll, Barbara

☐ EVERYTHING I LOVE
You'd be so nice to come home to / Ace in the hole / I wish I could forget you / As long as I live / Song for Griffin / Hundred years from today / Now's the time / Everything I love / Heavenly / That face / Chelsea bridge
DRGCD 91438 / Dec '95 / DRG

☐ OLD FRIENDS
ACD 254 / Feb '91 / Audiophile

☐ THIS HEART OF MINE
Way you look tonight / I wanna be yours / Sweet lilacs / On second thought/Why can't I / Lester leaps in / Some other time / Rain sometimes / Whenever a soft rain falls / It's like reaching for the moon / Never let me go / In some other world / This heart of mine
91416 / Jul '94 / DRG

Carroll, Dina

☐ ONLY HUMAN
Escaping / Only human / Give me the right / World come between us / Love will always bring you back to me / I didn't mean to hurt you / Living for the weekend / Mind, body and soul / Run to you / Do you think I'm in love / I don't want to talk about it / Perfect year
5340962 / Oct '96 / Mercury

☐ SO CLOSE
Special kind of love / Hold on / This time / Falling / So close / Ain't no man / Express / Heaven sent / You'll never know / Don't be a stranger / Why did I let you go / If I knew you then
5400342 / Jan '93 / A&M

Carroll, Jeanne

☐ TRIBUTE TO WILLIE DIXON (Carroll, Jeanne & C. Christi/Willie Dixon)
BEST 1014CD / Nov '93 / Acoustic Music

Carroll, Johnny

☐ ROCK BABY, ROCK IT
Hearts of stone / Why cry / Love is a merry go round / Stingy thing / Crazy little Mama / Sexy ways / Cut out / You two timed me two times too often / You made me love you / Hot rock / Rock'n'roll Ruby / Wild wild women / Corrina, Corrina / Crazy, crazy lovin' / Tryin' to get to you / That's the way I love / I'll wait / Rock baby, rock it / Swing / Bandstand doll / Sugar / Lost without you / Rag mop / Little Otis / Trudy / Run come see / Sally Ann / Run come see / Crazy, crazy lovin' / Wild wild women / You made me love you / Rockin' Maybelle / Sugar baby
BCD 15928 / May '96 / Bear Family

☐ TEXABILLY
Two timin' / Lonesome boy / Who's to say / My bucket's got a hole in it / 16 tons rockabilly / Her throbbin' lips
HMG 6602 / Sep '97 / Hightone

Carroll, Karen

☐ GOSPEL
Glory glory since I laid my burdens down / I want to be a christian / He's got the whole world in his hands / Peace, be still / Amazing grace / Oh happy day / Walk with me / Jesus is on the mainline / Doxology / When the saints go marching in
HFCD 002 / Jun '93 / Hot Fox

☐ HAD MY FUN
DE 680 / Dec '95 / Delmark

☐ TALK TO THE HAND
DE 707 / Jan '98 / Delmark

Carroll, Kevin

☐ REDEMPTION DAY (Carroll, Kevin & The Sleestacks)
MRCD 0995 / Jun '96 / Club De Musique

Carroll, Liane

☐ CLEARLY
BRGCD 19 / Oct '95 / Bridge

☐ DOLLY BIRD
Don't try to live your life in one day / Bird chase bird / Do it again / Briar and the rose / Yatra Ta / Suzanne / Natural woman / Fairytale in New York / Perfect day / And when I die
JHCD 051 / 24 Oct '97 / Ronnie Scott's Jazz House

Carroll, Liz

☐ FRIEND INDEED, A
SHCD 34013 / Aug '95 / Shanachie

☐ KISS ME KATE (Carroll, Liz & Tommy McGuire)
SHCD 34012 / Dec '95 / Shanachie

☐ LIZ CARROLL
Reel Beatrice/Abbey reel / Out on the road/Princess Nancy / For Eugene/Gravity hill / Clarke's favourite/Pigeon on the gate / Tune for Mairead and Anna Ni Mhaonaigh / Sock in the hole/Hole in the sock / Mrs. Carroll's Strathspey/Chapter 16 / Helicopters/Crossing the Delaware / Sister's reel/Wynding the hay / Lacey's jig/Tune for Charles/Geese in the bog / Par cark/Baiting the hook/Jumping the white nut eater / Greenleaf Strathspey/Setting sun / Wee dollop/Houseboat / G reel/Merle's tune / Western reel/Road to recovery
GLCD 1092 / Feb '91 / Green Linnet

☐ TRION
FF 70586 / Jul '92 / Flying Fish

Carroll, Ronnie

☐ ROSES ARE RED (The Ronnie Carroll Story)
Last love / Walk hand in hand / Wisdom of a fool / Around the world / April love / To be loved / Wonder of you / Footsteps / Chain gang / (You've got to) move two mountains / Ring a ding girl / Roses are red (my love) / If only tomorrow (could be like today) / Say wonderful things / Mary Rose / Let's fall in love: *Carroll, Ronnie & Millicent Martin* / Love is a ball: *Carroll, Ronnie & Millicent Martin* / Twelfth of never / Tears and roses / Clinging vine / Dear heart / Without love / Endlessly / House is not a home / My heart cries for you / I'll never fall in love again: *Carroll, Ronnie & Aimi McDonald*
GEMCD 004 / Nov '96 / Diamond

Carroll, Toni

☐ CELEBRITY
ACD 122 / Nov '96 / Audiophile

Carry Nation

☐ PROTECT AND SURVIVE
LF 211CD / Apr '96 / Lost & Found

Cars

☐ CARS, THE
Good times roll / My best friend's girl / Just what I needed / I'm in touch with your world / Don't cha stop / You're all I've got tonight / Bye bye love / Moving in stereo / All mixed up
K 252088 / Jan '84 / Elektra

☐ DOOR TO DOOR
Leave or stay / You are the girl / Double trouble / Fine line / Everything you say / Ta ta wayo wayo / Strap me in / Coming up you / Wound up on you / Go away / Door to door
MCD 09322 / 23 Feb '98 / Chess/MCA

☐ GREATEST HITS
Just what I needed / Since you're gone / You might think / Good time roll / Touch and go / Drive / Tonight she comes / My best friend's girl / Heartbeat city / Let's go / Magic / Shake it up
9604642 / Nov '85 / Elektra

☐ HEARTBEAT CITY
Looking for love / Jackie / Not the night / Drive / Shooting for you / Why can't I / Magic / You might think / I do refuse / Stranger eyes / Hello again
9602962 / Jul '84 / Elektra

☐ JUST WHAT I NEEDED - ANTHOLOGY (2CD Set)
My best friend's girl / Moving in stereo / Good times roll / Let's go / Double life / Nightspots / Dangerous type / Panorama / That's it / Magic / Why can't I have you / Cruiser / I'm not the one / Shake it up / Since you're gone / Don't tell me no / Gimme some slack / Funtime / Don't go to pieces / Slipaway / Cool fool / Take me now / Little black egg / Door to door / Strap me in / Ta ta wayo wayo / You are the girl / Leave or stay / Breakaway / Tonight she comes / Hello again / You might think / Drive / Touch and go / Got a lot on my head / Candy-o / It's all I can do / You're all I've got tonight / Don't cha stop / Just what I needed
0349735062 / Jan '96 / Elektra

Carson, Ernie

☐ ERNIE CARSON & GOOSE HOLLOW GANG
BCD 297 / Apr '94 / GHB

☐ OLD BONES (Carson, Ernie & Castle Jazz Band)
SOSCD 1283 / Mar '95 / Stomp Off

☐ WHER'M I GONNA LIVE (Carson, Ernie & Castle Jazz Band)
SOSCD 1277 / Dec '94 / Stomp Off

Carson, 'Fiddlin' John

☐ 'FIDDLIN' JOHN CARSON VOL.1 1923-1924
DOCD 8014 / 28 Oct '97 / Document

☐ 'FIDDLIN' JOHN CARSON VOL.2 1924-1925
DOCD 8015 / 28 Oct '97 / Document

☐ 'FIDDLIN' JOHN CARSON VOL.3 1925-1926
DOCD 8016 / 28 Oct '97 / Document

☐ 'FIDDLIN' JOHN CARSON VOL.4 1926-1927
DOCD 8017 / 28 Oct '97 / Document

☐ 'FIDDLIN' JOHN CARSON VOL.5 1927-1929
DOCD 8018 / Dec '97 / Document

☐ 'FIDDLIN' JOHN CARSON VOL.6 1929-1930
DOCD 8019 / Dec '97 / Document

☐ 'FIDDLIN' JOHN CARSON VOL.7 1930-1934
DOCD 8020 / 5 Feb '98 / Document

Carson, Sam

☐ **NO SURRENDER (14 Great Loyalist Songs)**
Derry's walls / No surrender / Auld orange flute / Green grassy slopes of the Boyne / Lily O / Dolly's brae / Protestant boys / Sash / Battle of Garvagh / Orange and blue / Aghalee heroes / Blackman's dream / Boyne water / Sprigs of Kilrea
CDUCD 3 / Apr '97 / Ulster Music

Carsten, Mannie

☐ **JUST A KISS (Mannie Carsten's Hot Jazz Syndicate)**
CD 1201 / Oct '94 / Hep

Carstensen, Dee

☐ **MAP, THE**
BTR 70152 / 24 Aug '98 / Blue Thumb

☐ **REGARDING THE SOUL**
Time / Before you / Underneath my skin / Love thing / Angel / What a little love can do / To you from me / Hemingway's shotgun / Stay / This time around / Light
120252 / Jun '97 / Musidisc UK

Carter, Anita

☐ **RING OF FIRE**
Ring of fire / Fair and tender ladies / Satan's child / Fly pretty swallow / As the sparrow goes / All my trials / Voice of the bayou / Sour grapes / Johnny I hardly knew you / My love / Kentuckian song / Five short years ago / No my love, no farewell / Running back / Take me home / John John John / John Hardy / I never will marry / In the highways / Bury me beneath the willow / Beautiful isle o'er the sea / Wildwood flower
BCD 15434 / '88 / Bear Family

Carter, Benny

☐ **3-4-5 (The Verve Small Group Sessions)**
Little girl blue / June in January / Jeepers creepers / Rosetta / Birth of the blues / When your lover has gone / Moon is low / This love of mine / Moonglow / My one and only love / Our love is here to stay / This can't be love / Tenderly / Unforgettable / Ruby / Moon song / Don't you think / Will you still be mine / We'll be together again
8493952 / Mar '91 / Verve

☐ **BENNY CARTER IN EUROPE 1936-1937**
Black bottom / Mighty like the blues / Pardon me pretty baby / Just a mood / Royal garden blues / Rambler's rhythm / Lazy afternoon / I ain't got nobody / Waltzin' the blues / When day is done / Bugle call rag / There'll be some changes made / If only I could read your mind / Gin and jive / New street swing / I'll never give in / Skip it / Somebody loves me / Blues in my heart / My buddy / Nightfall / I've got two lips
PASTCD 7023 / Sep '93 / Flapper

☐ **BENNY CARTER SONGBOOK VOL.1, THE (Various Artists)**
Only trust your heart / All that jazz / I was wrong / Rain / Cow-cow boogie / Fresh out of love / Speak now / Kiss from you / I see you / We were in love / Key largo / Lonely woman / When lights are low / My kind of trouble is you / You bring out
MM 65172 / 2 Apr '98 / Music Masters

☐ **BENNY CARTER SONGBOOK VOL.2, THE (Various Artists)**
My mind is still on you: Williams, Joe / I'm the caring kind: *Whitfield, Weslia* / Rock me to sleep: *Brown, Ruth* / Stop me before I fall in love again/Nevermore: *Strick, Billy* / He doesn't need me now/Slow carousel: Marano, Nancy / Doozy: Hendricks, Joe / Malibu: *Kazan, Lainie* / Blue moonlight: *Shaw, Marlena* / Evening star: *Rankin, Kenny* / Whisper to one: *Lea, Barbara* / Echo of my dream: *Krall, Diana* / When Hilma smiles: *Carter, Benny*
MM 65155 / Nov '97 / Music Masters

☐ **CLASSICS 1929-1933**
CLASSICS 522 / Apr '90 / Classics

☐ **CLASSICS 1933-1936**
CLASSICS 530 / Dec '90 / Classics

☐ **CLASSICS 1936**
CLASSICS 541 / Dec '90 / Classics

☐ **CLASSICS 1937-1939**
CLASSICS 552 / Dec '90 / Classics

☐ **CLASSICS 1939-1940**
CLASSICS 579 / Oct '91 / Classics

☐ **CLASSICS 1940-1941**
CLASSICS 631 / Mar '92 / Classics

☐ **CLASSICS 1943-1946**
CLASSICS 923 / Apr '97 / Classics

☐ **COMPLETE RECORDINGS VOL.1 (3CD Set)**
Goodbye blues / Cloudy skies / Got another sweetie now / Bugle call rag / Dee blues / Do you believe in love at first sight / Wrap your troubles in dreams (and dream your troubles away) / Tell all your daydreams to me / Swing it / Synthetic love / Six bells stampede / Love you're not the one for me / Blue interlude / I never knew / Once upon a time / Krazy kapers / Devil's holiday / Lonesome nights / Symphony in riffs / Blue Lou / Shoot the works / Dream lullaby / Everybody shuffle / Swingin' at Maida vale / Night fall / Big Ben blues / These foolish things / When day is done / I've got two lips / Swingin' the blues / Scandal in flat / Accent on swing / You understand / If I could only read your mind / I gotta go / When lights are low / Waltzing the blues / Tiger rag / Blue / Some of these days / Gloaming / Poor butterfly / Drop in next time your passing / Man I love / That's how the first song was born / There'll be some changes made / Jingle bells / Royal garden blues / Carry me back to old Virginny / Gin and jive / Nagasaki / There's a small hotel / I'm in the mood for swing / Rambling in C / Black bottom / Rambler's rhythm / New street swing / I'll never give in
CDAFS 10223 / Oct '92 / Affinity

☐ **COOKIN' AT CARLOS VOL.1**
You'd be so nice to come home to / All the things you are / Key Largo / Just friends / My romance / 'S Wonderful / Time for the blues
MM 5033 / Oct '94 / Music Masters

☐ **COSMOPOLITE (The Oscar Peterson Verve Sessions)**
Gone with the wind / I got it bad and that ain't good / Long ago (and far away) / I've got the world on a string / Street scene / Imagination / Pick yourself up / I get a kick out of you / Laura / That old black magic / Angel eyes / Song is you / Foggy day / You took advantage of me / Poinciana / Prisoner of love / Frenesi / Gone with the wind / I got it bad and that ain't good / Long ago (and far away) / I've got the world on a string
5216732 / Oct '94 / Verve

☐ **FURTHER DEFINITIONS**
Honeysuckle rose / Midnight sun will never set / Crazy rhythm / Blue star / Cotton tail / Body and soul / Cherry / Doozy / Fantastic that's you / Come on back / We were in love / If dreams come true / Prohibido / Rock bottom / Titmouse
IMP 12292 / Apr '97 / Impulse Jazz

☐ **GENTLEMAN AND HIS MUSIC, A**
Sometimes I'm happy / Blues for George / Things ain't what they used to be / Lover man / Idaho / Kiss from you
CCD 4285 / Jan '87 / Concord Jazz

☐ **GROOVIN' IN LA 1946**
Bugle call rag / Night and day / Every time I think of you / Baranco boogie / Love for sal / Patience and fortitude / Without a song / Oofdah / I can't get started / Jump call / Back bay boogie / Air mail special / Hello, goodbye, forget it / Fiesta in blue / Fiesta in brass / I don't know what it is / Crusin' with cab / Come sunday / Grovin' high
HEPCD 15 / Nov '92 / Hep

☐ **IN RIFFS 1930-1937**
Bugle call rag / Everybody shuffle / Shoot the works / Dee blues / Swing it / Nightfall / Bream lullaby / Pardon me pretty baby / Lazy afternoon
CDAJA 5704 / Jan '91 / Living Era

☐ **INTRODUCTION TO BENNY CARTER 1929-1940, AN**
4001 / Dec '93 / Best Of Jazz

☐ **JAZZ GIANT**
Old fashioned love / I'm coming Virginia / Walkin' thing / Blue Lou / Ain't she sweet / How can you lose / Blues my naughty sweetie gives to me
OJCCD 167 / Oct '92 / Original Jazz Classics

☐ **JAZZ PROFILE**
Love for sale / I can't escape from you / I can't get started / I surrender dear / Riffamarole / Malibu / Cuttin' time / Hollyridge drive / I didn't like it the first time / And the angels sing / Moon of Manarkoora / Far away places / Anything goes / March wind / September song / June is bustin' out
CDP 8331462 / 6 Oct '97 / Blue Note

☐ **KING, THE**
Walkin' thing / My kind of trouble is you / Easy money / Blue star / I still love him so / Green wine / Malibu / Blues in D flat
CD 2310768 / Mar '94 / Pablo

☐ **LIVE BROADCASTS 1939-1941 (Carter, Benny & His Orchestra)**
JH 1005 / Oct '91 / Jazz Hour

☐ **LOVE SONGS IN A SWINGIN' AFFAIR**
BMCD 3079 / 24 Apr '98 / Blue Moon

☐ **MASTERPIECES ARCHIVES**
158672 / Jan '97 / Jazz Archives

☐ **MONTREUX 1977 (Carter, Benny Quartet)**
Three little words / In a mellow tone / Wave / Undecided / Body and soul / On green dolphin street / Here's that rainy day
OJCCD 374 / Nov '95 / Original Jazz Classics

☐ **NEW JAZZ SOUNDS (2CD Set)**
5316372 / Jul '96 / Verve

☐ **NEW YORK NIGHTS**
What is this thing called love / Easy money / But beautiful / Just in time / Shadow of your smile / Secret love / When lights are low / Perdido / Green Dolphin Street
MM 65154 / Mar '97 / Music Masters

☐ **SKYLAND DRIVE & TOWARDS**
PHONTCD 9305 / Apr '94 / Phontastic

☐ **SYMPHONY IN RIFFS**
Blue interlude / Blues in my heart / Bugle call rag / Dee blues / Devil's holiday / Dream lullaby / Everybody shuffle / Just a mood / Lazy afternoon / Lonesome nights / Nightfall / Once upon a time / Pardon me pretty baby / Pastoral / Shoot the works / Skip it / Swing it / Swingin' with Mezz / Symphony in riffs / Waltzing the blues / When lights are low / You understand
CDAJA 5075 / '91 / Living Era

☐ **TAKE THE 'A' TRAIN**
FSRCD 306 / 5 Jan '98 / Fresh Sound

☐ **THESE FOOLISH THINGS**
Blue interlude / How come you like me like you do / Once upon a time / Devil's holiday / Lonesome nights / Shoot the works / Dream lullaby / Blue Lou / Krazy kapers / Symphony in riffs / I never knew / Music at sunrise / Firebird / Everybody shuffle / Synthetic love / Swingin' at Maida Vale / These foolish things / When day is done / I've got two lips / Swingin' the blues / Just a mood / Big Ben blues / Nightfall
GRF 087 / '93 / Tring

Carter, Betty

☐ **DROPPIN' THINGS**
30 years / Stardust/Memories of you / What's the use / Open the door / Droppin' things / I love music / Why music / Dull day (In Chicago)
8439912 / Mar '91 / Verve

☐ **FEED THE FIRE**
5236002 / Oct '94 / Verve

☐ **I'M YOURS, YOU'RE MINE**
5331822 / Nov '96 / Verve

☐ **IT'S NOT ABOUT THE MELODY**
Naima's love song / Stays as sweet as you are / Make him believe / I should care / Once upon a summertime / You go to my head / In the still of the night / When it's sleepy time down South / Love we had yesterday / Dip bag / You're mine you
5138702 / Apr '92 / Verve

☐ **MEET BETTY CARTER & RAY BRYANT (Carter, Betty & Ray Bryant)**
Let's fall in love / Social call / Run away / Frenesi / Moonlight in Vermont / Thou swell / I could write a book / Gone with the wind / Way you look tonight / Tell him I said hello / Can't we be friends / Sneaking around / Old devil moon / Willow weep for me / What is this thing called love / Threesome / No moon at all / Bryant's folly / Get happy
4850992 / Sep '96 / Sony Jazz

Carter, Bo

☐ **BANANA IN YOUR FRUIT BASKET**
Pig meat is what I crave / What kind of scent is this / Mashing that thing / Blue runner blues / Howling tom cat blues / Don't mash my digger so deep / Pin in your cushion / Ram rod daddy / All around man / Pussy cat blues / My pencil won't write no more / Ants in my pants / Banana in your fruit basket / Cigarette blues
YAZCD 1064 / Apr '91 / Yazoo

☐ **BO CARTER VOL.2 (1931-1934)**
DOCD 5079 / Mar '95 / Document

☐ **BO CARTER VOL.3 (1934-1936)**
DOCD 5080 / Mar '95 / Document

☐ **BO CARTER VOL.4 (1936-1938)**
DOCD 5081 / Mar '95 / Document

☐ **BO CARTER VOL.5 (1938-1940)**
DOCD 5082 / Mar '95 / Document

☐ **RAREST BO CARTER VOL.1 (1928-1931)**
DOCD 5078 / Mar '95 / Document

Carter, Carlene

☐ **ACTS OF TREASON**
Love like this / Lucky ones / Little acts of treason / He will be mine / Come here you / Change / Hurricane / Go wild / You'll be the one / All night long / Come here you (reprise)
74321294872 / Aug '95 / Giant

☐ **HINDSIGHT 20/20**
Sweet meant to be / I fell in love / Every little thing / Unbreakable heart / Come on back / Me and Wildwood Rose / Never together but close sometimes / Cry / Sweetest thing / Baby ride easy / I love you cause I want to / I'm so cool / He will be mine / Hurricane / Change / Trust yourself / One tender night / It's no wonder / Love like this / Do it in a heartbeat
74321360122 / Sep '96 / Giant

☐ **I FELL IN LOVE**
I fell in love / Come on back / Sweetest thing / My Dixie darling / Goodnight Dallas / One love / Leaving side / Guardian angel / Me and the wildwood rose / You are the one / Easy from now on
7599261392 / Jan '96 / Reprise

☐ **LITTLE ACTS OF TREASON**
Love like this / Lucky ones / Little acts of treason / He will be mine / Come here you / Change / Hurricane / Go wild / You'll be the one / All night long / Come here you (reprise)
74321259892 / 9 Feb '98 / Giant

☐ **LITTLE LOVE LETTERS**
Little love letter / Every little thing / Wastin' time with you / Unbreakable heart / Sweet meant to be / Nowhere train / Long hard fall / Little love letter / I love you 'cause I want to / World of miracles / First kiss / Hallelujah in my heart / Rain / Heart is right
74321156062 / Sep '96 / Giant

☐ **MUSICAL SHAPES/BLUE NUN**
Cry / Madness / Baby ride easy / Bandit of love / I'm so cool / Appalachian eyes / Ring of fire / Too bad about Sandy / That very first kiss / Foggy mountain top / Too drunk / Oh how happy / Love is a four-letter verb / That boy / 300 pounds of hungry / Tougher stuff / I need a hit / Rock-a-baby / Me and my 38 / Do me lover / Too many teardrops / Billy / C'mon feets / Think dirty / If the shoe fits / Home run hitter / When you comin' back
FIENDCD 703 / Sep '91 / Demon

Carter, Clarence

☐ **BEST OF CLARENCE CARTER, THE**
RSACD 801 / Oct '94 / Sequel

☐ **DOCTOR CC**
Dr. CC / I stayed away too long / If you let me take you home / Leftover love / You been cheatin' on me / Try me / Let's funk / Strokin'
ICH 1003CD / Oct '93 / Ichiban

☐ **DOCTOR'S GREATEST PRESCRIPTIONS, THE (The Best Of Clarence Carter)**
Strokin' / Trying to sleep tonight / Messin' with my mind / I was in the neighbourhood / Dr. C.C. / Love me with a feeling / I'm not just good, I'm the best / I'm the best / Slip away / Grandpa can't fly his kite / Kiss you all over / I've got a thing for you baby / I'm between a rock and a hard place
ICH 1116CD / Feb '94 / Ichiban

☐ **DYNAMIC CLARENCE CARTER, THE**
I'd rather go blind / Think about it / Road of love / You've been a long time comin' / Light my fire / That old time feeling / Steal away / Let me comfort you / Look what I got / Too weak to fight / Harper Valley PTA / Weekend love
7567803772 / Jan '96 / Atlantic

☐ **DYNAMIC CLARENCE CARTER, THE**
I'd rather go blind / Think about it / Road of love / You've been a long time comin' / Light my fire / That old time feeling / Steal away / Let me comfort you / Look what I got / Too weak to fight / Haper Valley PTA / Weekend love / Don't make my baby cry / Take if off him (and put it on me) / Few troubles I've had
RSACD 904 / Jan '97 / Sequel

☐ **HAVE YOU MET CLARENCE CARTER...YET**
ICH 1141CD / Nov '92 / Ichiban

☐ **HOOKED ON LOVE**
Trying to sleep tonight / Grandpa can't fly his kite / I can't see myself / While you were loving him / I feel it / Slip away / Let me be the other man / What'd I say
ICH 1016CD / Mar '94 / Ichiban

☐ **PATCHES**
Willie and Laura Mae Jones / Say man / I'm just a prisoner (of your good lovin') / Let it be / I can't leave your love alone / Your love lifted me / Till I can't take it anymore / Patches / It's all in your mind / Changes / CC blues / Getting the bills (but no merchandise) / Scratch my back / I'm the one / If you can't beat 'em / Lonesomest lonesome
RSACD 906 / Mar '97 / Sequel

☐ **PATCHES (The Best Of Clarence Carter)**
CDSGP 0131 / Dec '94 / Prestige

☐ **PATCHES (The Best Of Clarence Carter)**
Patches / Slip away / You talk too much / Brick house / Starting all over again / Too weak to fight / Back stabbers / Everybody play the fool / Got a thing about you baby / You don't have to say you love me / I'm easy / Drift away / Woman don't go astray / Lovely day
AIM 2011CD / 20 Oct '97 / Aim

☐ **TESTIFYIN'**
Bad news / Snatching it back / Soul deep / I smell a rat / Doin' our thing / You can't miss what you can't measure / Instant reaction / Making love / Feeling is right / Back door Santa / I can't do without you / Devil woman / Court room / Slipped, tripped and fell in love / I hate to love and run
RSACD 905 / Mar '97 / Sequel

☐ **THIS IS CLARENCE CARTER**
Do what you gotta do / Looking for a fox / Slippin' around / I'm qualified / I can't see myself / Wind it up / Part time love / Thread the needle / Slip away / Funky fever / She ain't gonna do right / Set me free / Step by step / Rooster knees and rice / I stayed away too long / Tell Daddy
RSACD 903 / Jan '97 / Sequel

☐ **TOUCH OF THE BLUES**
I'm not just good, I'm the best / Rock me baby / Why do I stay here / It's a man down there / All night, all day / Kiss you all over / Stormy Monday blues / Dance to the blues
ICH 1032CD / Oct '93 / Ichiban

Carter, Deana

☐ **DID I SHAVE MY LEGS FOR THIS**
Angel without a prayer / Rita Valentine / I've loved enough to know / I can't shake you / Are you coming home today / Did I shave my legs for this / Turn those wheels around / Graffiti Bridge / Before we ever heard goodbye / We share a wall / Don't let go / Just what you need
CDEST 2249 / Mar '95 / Capitol

Carter, Derrick

☐ **PAGAN OFFERING (Various Artists)**
Lo9ve: *Swayzak* / Solid space business: *Attaboy* / Wired: *Dino & Terry* / Mr. Roachclip: *Freaks* / Better day: *Presence* / Three point five: *Francis, Terry* / I want to talk: *Fulton, Maurice* / Wormhole: *Soul Edge* / Pagan thing: *Salt City Orchestra* / After hours: *Hester, Paul* / Future luv: *Presence* / Main event: *House Of 909*
PAGANCD 1007 / 24 Aug '98 / Pagan

Carter Family

☐ **ANCHORED IN LOVE**
ROUCD 1064 / Jan '94 / Rounder

☐ **HISTORIC REUNION, AN**
379252 / Jun '97 / Koch International

☐ MY CLINCH FAMILY HOME
Foggy mountain top / Sweet fern / Bring back my blue eyed boy / God gave Noah the rainbow sign / Cyclone of rye cove / My clinch mountain home / Forsaken love / Grave on the green hillside / I'm thinking tonight of my blue eyes / Diamonds in the rough / Lulu walls / I have no one to love me / Little Moses / Engine 143 / Don't forget this song / Homestead on the farm
ROUCD 1065 / Jan '94 / Rounder

☐ ON BORDER RADIO VOL.1
ARHCD 411 / Jan '96 / Arhoolie

☐ ON BORDER RADIO VOL.2
Why there is a tear in my eyes / Sleep baby sleep / Just another broken heart / I can not be your sweetheart / Red wing / Broken down saint / Weeping willow / You are my flower / Gathering flowers from the hillside / Last letter / I wouldn't mind dying / Who's that knocking at my window / Diamonds in the rough / Fatal wedding / It's hard to please your mind / Death is only a dream / Theme / Xet station break / Church in the wildwood / Are you tired of me darling / Sourwood mountain / Bury me not on the lone prairie / My bonnie blue eyes / Yankee doodle / Storms on the ocean / Sugar hill / Hello stranger / Cowboy Jack / Nobody's darling / Funny when you fell that way / Dixie darling / Shrtning bread / Soldier and his sweetheart / Polly wolly doodle all day / My gold chain watch and chain / River of Jordan / I will never marry / God gave Noah the rainbow sign / Theme out and xet station break
ARHCD 412 / 16 Mar '98 / Arhoolie

☐ WHEN THE ROSES BLOOM IN DIXIELAND
ROUCD 1066 / Nov '95 / Rounder

☐ WORRIED MAN BLUES
ROUCD 1067 / Nov '95 / Rounder

Carter, James

☐ CONVERSIN' WITH THE ELDERS
Naima / Freereggaehibop / Lester leaps in / Centerpiece / Atitled valse / Composition #40q (and symbol) / Blue creek / Parker's mood / Moten swing
7567829082 / Jan '96 / Atlantic

☐ JURASSIC CLASSICS
Take the 'A' train / Out of nowhere / Epistrophy / Ask me now / Equinox / Sansu / Oleo
4786122 / Jun '95 / Sony Jazz

☐ ON THE SET
DIW 875 / Nov '93 / DIW

Carter, Jason

☐ ON THE MOVE
ROUCD 0387 / Aug '97 / Rounder

Carter, Joe

☐ DUETS
ST 578 / Jul '94 / Stash

Carter, John

☐ SEEKING (Carter, John & Bobby Bradford)
ARTCD 6085 / Aug '91 / Hat Art

☐ TANDEM VOL.1 (Carter, John & Bobby Bradford)
Tandem / Petals / Angels / Portrait of JBG / Circle / Woodman's Hall blues / Woman / Echoes from Rudolph's
EM 4011 / Oct '96 / Emanem

☐ TANDEM VOL.2 (Carter, John & Bobby Bradford)
EM 4012 / Jan '97 / Emanem

Carter, John

☐ SPIRIT FLYING FREE (Carter, John & Martin Barre)
Student / Winter setting / No easy way / Spirit flying free / Melody of words / Laugh it off / Don't mess around with me / I can't forget / Exciting eyes / I'll make a stand this time / Your dry land
ANDCD 16 / May '97 / A New Day

Carter, John

☐ AS YOU LIKE IT VOL.1 (The Denmark Street Demos 1963-1967)
Am I losing you / Try just a little bit harder / Thank you for loving me / La la la (baby do it) / I can't let you go / When I dance with you / Come to the party / I don't love you anymore / Don't put the blame on me / What a wonderful feelin' / It's your turn to cry / Can't you hear my heartbeat / She won't show up tonight / Mad / Head to toe / Vicar's daughter / Brown and Porter's (meat exporters) / I told you so / How can I turn away / Is it true / Til I met you / Sunday for tea / Baby what can I do now / Crying all night / Everybody tries / Waiting here for someone
WESM 523 / Feb '98 / Westside

Carter, Lisa

☐ COUNTRY ROADS
Blue bayou-crying / Talkin in your sleep-so sad to watch good love go bad / Sweet dreams-together again / That'll be the day-when will I be loved
SOV 017CD / Jan '93 / Sovereign

Carter, Mabel

☐ WILDWOOD PICKIN'
VCD 77021 / May '97 / Vanguard

Carter, Ron

☐ AD IDEM
Stellarator / Hip no twist / Away / Force 10 / Midnight sun / Save the best till last / Terraformimg / Stealth rider / Ad idem / Ready to rise / Blasted funk
QFM 007 / Jun '97 / Steady On

☐ NEW YORK SLICK
Slight smile / Tierra Espanola / Aromatic / Alternate route / NY slick
OJCCD 916 / May '97 / Original Jazz Classics

☐ PASTELS
Woolaphant / Ballad / One bass rag / Pastels / Twelve plus twelve
OJCCD 665 / Sep '93 / Original Jazz Classics

☐ PEG LEG
Peg leg / Sheila's song / Hasta luego, mi amiga / Chapter xl / Epistrophy / My ship / Patchoull
OJCCD 621 / Oct '95 / Original Jazz Classics

☐ RON CARTER PLAYS BACH
8308902 / Mar '88 / ECM

☐ THIRD PLANE (Carter, Ron, Tony Williams & Herbie Hancock)
Third plane / Quiet times / Lawra / Stella by starlight / United blues / Dolphin dance
OJCCD 754 / Apr '94 / Original Jazz Classics

☐ UPTOWN CONVERSATION
Einbahnstrasse / Einbahnstrasse / Uptown conversation / Half a row / Ten strings / Little waltz / R j / Doom / Doom
7567819552 / Apr '95 / Atlantic

☐ WHERE (Carter, Ron & Eric Dolphy/Mal Waldron)
Rally / Bass duet / Softly as in a morning sunrise / Where / Yes indeed / Saucer eyes
OJCCD 432 / May '93 / Original Jazz Classics

Carter, Sara

☐ SARA & MAYBELLE (Carter, Sara & Maybelle)
Lonesome pine special / Hand that rocked the cradle / Goin' home / Ship that never returned / Three little strangers / Sun of the soul / Weary prodigal son / While the band is playing Dixie / Farther on / No more goodbyes / Happiest day of all / Charlie Brooks / I told them what you're fighting for / We all miss you Joe / San Antonio rose / Mama's Irish jig / Black mountain rag / Let's be lover's again / Give me your love and I'll give mine / Letter from home / There's a mother always waiting / Tom cat's kitten / Kitty Puss
BCD 15471 / Jul '93 / Bear Family

Carter, Sydney

☐ LOVELY IN THE DANCES (The Songs Of Sydney Carter) (Various Artists)
George Fox / Julian of Norwich / Carol of the creatures / Holy horses / Like the snow / Friday morning / Lord of the dance / Cocks are crowing / John Ball / First of my lovers / Bitter was the night / Come love carolling / I used to dance / I come like a beggar
OSMOCD 008 / Dec '97 / Osmosys

Carter Twins

☐ NUMBER ONE
74321534112 / 15 Nov '97 / RCA

Carter USM

☐ 101 DAMNATIONS
Road to domestos / Every time a church bell rings / Twenty four minutes from Tulse Hill / All American national sport / Sheriff Fatman / Taking of Peckham 123 / Crimestoppers A go-go / Good grief Charlie Brown / Midnight on the murder mile / Perfect day to drop the bomb / GI blues
ABBCD 101 / Aug '95 / Big Cat

☐ 1992 - THE LOVE ALBUM
1993 / Is wrestling fixed / Only living boy in New Cross / Suppose you gave a funeral and nobody came / England / Do re me, so far so good / Look mum, no hands / While you were out / Skywest and crooked / Impossible dream
CCD 1946 / May '92 / Chrysalis

☐ 30 SOMETHING
My second to last will and testament / Anytime anyplace anywhere / Prince in a pauper's grave / Shoppers' paradise / Billy's smart circus / Bloodsport for all / Sealed with a Glasgow kiss / Say it with flowers / Falling on a bruise / Final comedown
CCD 1897 / Feb '92 / Chrysalis

☐ I BLAME THE GOVERNMENT
Wrong place at the wrong time / 23:59 End of the world / Sunshine / Undertaker and the hippy protest singer / Sweetheart sugar baby / Growing old disgracefully / Man who bought the world / Winning the war / I blame the government / Citizens band radio / Psycho Bill / Closedown / Girls can keep a secret
COOKCD 136 / 12 Jan '98 / Cooking Vinyl

☐ STRAW DONKEY (The Singles)
Sheltered life / Sherrif Fatman / Rubbish / Anytime, anyplace, anywhere / Bloodsport for all / After the watershed / Only living boy in New Cross / Do re me, so far so good / Impossible dream / Lean on me I won't fall over / Lenny and Terence / Glam rock cops / Let's get tattoos / Young offender's mum / Born on the 5th of November
CDCHR 6110 / Sep '97 / Chrysalis

☐ WORLD WITHOUT DAVE, A
Broken down in broken town / World without Dave / Before the war / Nowhere fast / Johnny cash / And God created Brixton
COOKCD 120 / Mar '97 / Cooking Vinyl

☐ WORRY BOMB
Cheap 'n' cheesy / Airplane food/Airplane fast food / Young offender's mum / Gas (man) / Life and soul of party dies / My defeatist attitude / Worry bomb / Senile delinquent / Me and Mr. Jones / Let's get tattoos / Going straight / God, Saint Peter and the Guardian Angel / Only looney left in town / Ceasefire / Alternative Alf Garnet / Do re me, so far so good / Bachelor for Baden Powell / Re-educating Rita / Only living boy in New Cross / Lean on me I won't fall over / Granny farming in the UK / Travis / Sing fat lady sing / Lenny and Terence / Commercial fucking suicide (part 1)
CDCHR 6096 / Feb '95 / Chrysalis

Carter, Wilf

☐ COWBOY SONGS (8CD Set)
My Swiss moonlight lullaby / Capture of Albert Johnson / Hobo's blues / Twilight on the prairie / Roundup in the fall / Cowboy's best friend is his pony / He rode the strawberry roan / Little silver haired sweetheart of mine / Take me back to old Montana / Sway back Pinto Pete / Yodelling trailrider / Cowboy, don't forget your Mother / Cowboy blues / Smoke went up the chimney just the same / Moonlight prison blues / Prairie blues / Down the old cattle trail / I miss my Swiss / Cowboy's high toned dance / Hobo's dream of heaven / My little Swiss and me / Lover's lullaby yodel / Awaiting the chair / Life and death of John Dillinger / Cowhand's guiding star / Hobo's song of the Mounties / By the silvery moonlight trail / Dying mother's prayer / I long for old Wyoming / How my yodelling days began / I'm hittin' the trail / Lonesome for my baby tonight / I'm gonna ride to heaven on a streamlined train / Sundown blues / Cowboy lullaby / Yodelling hillbilly / Two-gun cowboy / Hillbilly valley / Returning to my old prairie home / Pete Knight, the King of the cowboys / Cowboy's mother / Calgary roundup / Trail to home sweet home / My blues have turned to sunshine / Dear old Daddy of mine / My little grey haired Mother in the West / Little log shack I can always call home / Rescue from the Moose River goldmine / Keep smiling old pal / Don't let me down old pal / Won't you be the same old pal / Last ride down Lariat Trail / Rose of my heart / Memories of my grey haired Mother in the West / Broken down cowboy / That tumbledown shack by the trail / Covered wagon headed west / Midnight, the unconquered outlaw / Fate of old Strawberry Road / Cowboy's wedding in May / Sweetheart of my childhood days / Ridin' a maverick / There'll be no blues up yonder / Goodbye little pal of my dreams / I loved her till she done me wrong / Under the light of the Texas moon / I'm still waiting for you / Longing for my Mississippi home / Old Alberta plains / Cowboy's heavenly dream / My old Montana home (my old Montana blues) / Why did I ever start roaming/Roaming my whole life away / Hobo's yodel / Yodelling cowgirl / Fate of Sunset Trail / Prairie sunset / I just can't forget you old pal / Roundup time in heaven / Put my little shoes away / When the bright prairie moon is rolling by / Roll on dreamy Texas moon / Old barn dance / Dreamy prairie moon / Roundup time in sunny old Alberta / Roll along moonlight yodel / My faithfull Pinto pal / Preacher and the cowboy / When the sun says goodnight to the prairie / Where is my boy tonight / There's a loveknot in my lariat / My little Yoho lady / Answer to my Swiss moonlight lullaby / Hindenburg disaster / Pete Knight's last ride / I wish I had never seen sunshine / Everybody's been some mother's darlin' / You'll always be mine in my dreams / Dusty trails / By the grave of nobody's darlin' / What a friend we have in mother / Martins and McCoys / Nobody's darling but mine / Little red patch on the seat of my trousers / Golden memories of Mother and Dad / My Honeymoon Bridge brokedown / Down the yodelling trail at twilight / I'm only a dude in cowboy clothes / My Lulu / Rootin' tootin' cowboy / Little red patch on the seat of my trousers / We'll meet again in Peaceful Valley / My brown eyed prairie rose / I'll meet you at the roundup in the Spring / Down on the prairie / My yodelling sweetheart / Yodelling memories / Cowboy's airplane ride / Memories of my little old log shack / My last old yodel song / My yodelling days are through / Headin' for that land of gold / Wilf Carter blues / Golden lariat / Cowboy who never returned / When it's twilight over Texas / My only memories of you / When I say hello to the Rockies / When I bid the prairie goodbye / My dreams come true / You left your brand on my heart / Yodelling love call / It makes no difference now / What difference does it make / Answer to it makes no difference now / Roll along Kentucky moon / Blue Ridge Mountain blues/Birmingham Jail / Red River Valley blues / When the white azales start blooming / My ramblin' days are through / I still think of you, sweet Nellie Dean / He left the one who loved him for another / When it's roll call in the Bunk-house / My true and earnest prayer / Beautiful girl of the prairie / It's all over now / Rattlin' cannonball / My old Canadian home / I'll get mine by and by / Dad's little Texas lad / Thinking what a wonderful Mother of mine / You are my sunshine / My Texas sweetheart / Echoing hills yodel back to me / You were with me in the waltz of my dreams / When that somebody else were you / My Missoula Valley moon / Old chuck wagon days / It's a cowboy's night to howl / Back ridin' trails again / Let's go back to the Bible / Why should I feel sorry for you now / I bought a rock for a Rocky Mountain gal / It's great to be back in the saddle again / If you don't really care / Why did we ever part / La Verne my brown eyed rose / Last letter / Ride for the open range / Call of the range / Streamlined yodel song / My old lasso is headed straight for you / Memories that never die / I'm thinking tonight of my blue eyes / Prisoner's song / I may be wrong / Old buddies / Sweetheart's farewell / Sittin' by the old Corral / I'll always keep smilin' for you / First love of mine / Waiting for a train / West of Rainbow Trail / Yodelling my babies to sleep / Just one more ride / Rescue from the Moose River goldmine
BCD 15939 / Jun '97 / Bear Family

☐ DYNAMITE TRAIL - THE DECCA YEARS 1954-1958
One golden curl / My mountain high yodel song / I'm gonna tear down the mailbox / Maple leaf waltz / There's a tree on every road / I bought a rock for a rocky mountain gal / Shoo shoo sh'lala / Sunshine bird / Kissing on the sly / Alpine milkman / Dynamite trail / Strawberry road / Ragged but right / There's a padlock on your heart / Yodelin' song / On a little two acre farm / Strawberry road / My little lady / Silver bell yodel / Away out on the mountain / Blind boy's prayer / X's from down in Texas / Let a little sunshine in your heart / There's a bluebird on your windowsill / My French Canadian girl / Sick, sober and sorry / Sinner's prayer / My prairie rose / Yodeling my babies to sleep / Born to lose
BCD 15507 / Jul '90 / Bear Family

☐ PRAIRIE LEGEND, A (4CD Set)
Farewell, sweetheart, farewell / Old Shep / I've hung up my chaps and saddle / You'll get used to it / I ain't gonna hobo no more / Don't be mean, I wasn't mean to you / Sinner's prayer / Plant some flowers by my graveside / There's a goldstar in her window / My blue skies / Put me in your pocket / Smilin' through tears / Born to lose / No letter today / Our Canadian flag / So hard to start all over again / I'll never die of a broken heart / Dreaming of my blue eyes / Memories bring heartaches to me / My Queen of the prairies / Rye whiskey / One golden curl / Hang the key on the bunkhouse door / I'm a fool for foolin' around / There's a loveknot in my lariat / It's later than you think / Too many blues / Singing on borrowed time / Just an old forgotten letter / She lost her cowboy pal / Ol' lonely / If we can't be sweethearts, why can't we be... / Don't cry over me / Sharing your love with somebody new / Don't wait till Judgement Day / Cowboy days ain't ramblin' days no more / 'Neath a blanket of stars / I never knew that I could be so blue / It's just a wild rose I'm sending / Where the sleepy Rio's flowing / You'll be sorry you turned me down / Dream lullaby yodel / It's hard to forget you / Tramp's mother / Take away those blues around my heart / Midnight train / I'm gonna tear down the mailbox / It can't be done / All I need is some more lovin' / (There's a) Bluebird on your windowsill / When the iceworms nest again / Shackles and chains / No, no, don't ring those bells / Give a little, take a little / Unfaithful one / Little shirt my mother made for me / Guilty conscience / Take it easy blues / My heart's closed for repairs / My wife is on a diet / Let's go back to the bible / She'll be there / I wish there were only three days in the year / When that love bug bites you / Just a woman's smile / Rudolph the red nosed reindeer / Apple, cherry, mince and choc'late cream / Jolly old St. Nicholas / KP blues / Blue Canadian Rockies / Dear Evalina / My Oklahoma rose / What cigarette is best / Sick, sober and sorry / Teardrops don't always mean a broken heart / Wha hoppen / Punkinhead (The little bear) / Night before Christmas in Texas that is / Goodbye Maris (I'm off to Korea) / Driftwood on the river / Manhunt / (All you gave me) Mockingbird love / Square dance boogie / Sweet little lover / Huggin', squeezin', kissin', teasin' / Sleep one little sleep / Alabama Saturday night / Hot foot boogie / I remember the rodeo / Pete Knight, the King of the cowboys / When the iceworms nest again / My little grey haired Mother in the west / He rode the strawberry roan / Rattlin' cannonball / Calgary roundup / That silver haired daddy of mine / Smoke went up the chimney just the same / Capture of Albert Johnson / Beautiful girl of the prairie / Singing in my last roundup
BCD 15754 / Nov '93 / Bear Family

Carthy, Eliza

☐ ELIZA CARTHY & NANCY KERR (Carthy, Eliza & Nancy Kerr)
Waterloo fair/Speed the plow / Lucy's waltz/Liza's favourite / Alistair's / Unquiet grave / March of the Kings of Laiose / Old man came courting / Swedish wedding march / Whittingham Fair/For Whittingham Fair / Bushes and briars / Tune / Wrong favour / Prague/Polly Bishop's slip jig/The storyteller / Black and white rag
MCR 3991CD / Nov '93 / Mrs. Casey

☐ ELIZA CARTHY & THE KINGS OF CALICUTT (Carthy, Eliza & The Kings Of Calicutt)
Trip / Whirly / Bonaparte's / Tractor / Mother / Mr. Walker / Sea / Sheffield / Fisher / Storyteller
TSCD 489 / Jul '97 / Topic

☐ HEAT LIGHT AND SOUND
TSCD 482 / Feb '96 / Topic

☐ RED RICE (2CD Set)
Accordian song / 10,000 miles / Billy boy/The widow's wedding / Time in the son / Stumbling on / Stingo/The stacking reel / Greenwood laddie/Mrs. Capron's reel tune / Walk away / Adieu adieu / Russia / Red rice / Blow the winds/The game of draughts / Snow it melts the soonest / Medley / Miller and the lass / Herring song / Mons meg / Tuesday morning / Haddock and chips / Americans have stolen my true love away / Medley / Medley / Benjamin Bowmaneer / Medley
TSDCD 2001 / May '98 / Topic

☐ SHAPE OF SCRAPE (Carthy, Eliza & Nancy Kerr)
Edward Corcoran/Black joke / I know my love / Low down in the broom/The sukebind / Downfall of Paris / Keek (or ride) in the creel / Mary custy air / Growling (The trees they do grow high) / Poor and young single sailor / Balter Svens Parapolkett / Bonny light horseman/Michael Turner's waltz / Wanton wife of Castlegate/Princess Royal / Gypsy hornpipe/The hawk/Indian Queen
MCR 5992CD / Jul '95 / Mrs. Casey

Carthy, Martin

☐ BECAUSE IT'S THERE
Nothing rhymed / May song / Swaggering Boney / Lord Randal / Long John, old John and Jackie North / Jolly tinker / Lovely Joan / Three cripples / Siege of Delhi / Death of young Andrew
TSCD 389 / May '95 / Topic

☐ BUT TWO CAME BY (Carthy, Martin & Dave Swarbrick)
Ship in distress / Banks of the sweet primroses / Long lankin / Brass band music
TSCD 343 / May '94 / Topic

☐ **COLLECTION, THE**
GLCD 1136 / Jan '94 / Green Linnet

☐ **CROWN OF HORN**
Bedmaking / Locks and bolts / King Knapperty / Geordie / Willie's lady / Virginny / Worcestershire wedding / Bonnie lass o'Anglesey / William Taylor the poacher / Old Tom of Oxford / Palaces of gold
TSCD 300 / Oct '95 / Topic

☐ **LANDFALL**
Here's adieu to all judges and juries / Brown Adam / O'er the hills / Cruel mother / Cold haily windy night / His name is Andrew / Bold poachers / Dust to dust / Broomfield hill / January man
TSCD 345 / Apr '96 / Topic

☐ **MARTIN CARTHY**
High Germany / Trees they do grow high / Sovay / Ye mariners all / Queen of hearts / Broomfield hill / Springhill mine disaster / Scarborough Fair / Lovely Joan / Barley and the rye / Wind that shakes the barley / Two magicians / Handsome cabin boy / And a begging I will go
TSCD 340 / May '93 / Topic

☐ **OUT OF THE CUT**
Devil and the feathery wife / Reynard the fox / Song of the lower classes / Rufford Park poachers / Molly Oxford / Rigs of the time / I sowed some seeds / Frair in the well / Jack Rowland / Old horse
TSCD 426 / Aug '94 / Topic

☐ **PRINCE HEATHEN (Carthy, Martin & Dave Swarbrick)**
Arthur McBride / Salisbury Plain / Polly on the shore / Rainbow / Died for love / Staines Morris / Reynardine / Seven yellow gypsies / Little Musgrave / Wren
TSCD 344 / Jun '94 / Topic

☐ **RIGHT OF PASSAGE**
Ant and the grasshopper / Eggs in her basket / Stitch in time / McVeagh / Hommage a roche proulx / All in green / Company policy / Banks of the Nile / La carde use / Bill Norrie / Sleepwalker / Cornish young man / Dominion of the sword
TSCD 452 / Dec '88 / Topic

☐ **RIGS OF THE TIMES (The Best Of Martin Carthy)**
Skewball / Ant and the grasshopper / Foxhunt / Devil and the feathery wife / Sheepstealer / Begging song / Geordie / Billy boy / Lovely Joan / Sovay / Bill Norrie / Question of sport / Old horse / All of a row / Work life out to keep life in / Rigs of the time / Such a war has never been / Dominion of the sword / Byker hill
MCCD 145 / Dec '93 / Music Club

☐ **SECOND ALBUM**
Two butchers / Ball o'yarn / Farewell Nancy / Lord Franklin / Rambling sailor / Lowlands of Holland / Fair maid on the shore / Bruton town / Box on her head / Newlyn town / Brave Wolfe / Peggy and the soldier / Sailor's life
TSCD 341 / Sep '93 / Topic

☐ **SWEET WIVELSFIELD**
Shepherd O shepherd / Billy boy / Three jolly sneaksmen / Trimdon grange / All of a row / Skewball / Mary Neal / King Henry / John Barleycorn / Cottage in the wood
TSCD 418 / Apr '96 / Topic

Cartland, Barbara

☐ **GREAT ROMANTIC SONGS**
Nightingale sang in Berkeley Square / White cliffs of Dover / Moment I saw you / Our love affair / I can't give you anything but love / Lovely to look at / You are my heart's delight / All I do is dream of you / Goodnight sweetheart / Nearness of you / Too marvellous for words / Cheek to cheek / Stately homes of England / On the sunny side of the street / With a song in my heart / That lovely weekend / Goodnight sweet dreams goodnight / At last / Wrap your troubles in dreams / Moonlight becomes you / As time goes by / Duel of hearts theme
CDSIV 6132 / Jul '95 / Horatio Nelson

Cartwright, Deirdre

☐ **DEBUT (Cartwright, Deirdre Group)**
Spartia / Slipper 15s 8d / I thought of you / Trap / When pushing comes to shoving / Grand loup / Pisces moon / One more / Walk with me
BTF 9401 / Oct '94 / Blow The Fuse

☐ **PLAY**
Got my modem working / Some folks tune / Strange but true / Flamengo / Warm front / View from a mountain / Voluble / You wish
BTF 9703 / 9 Feb '98 / Blow The Fuse

Carty, John

☐ **AT THE RACKET (Carty, John & Brain McGrath)**
RAR 001CD / Mar '98 / Racket

☐ **CAT THAT ATE THE CRADLE (Carty, John & Brain McGrath)**
CICD 099 / Aug '94 / Clo Iar-Chonnachta

☐ **LAST NIGHT'S FUN**
Tansey's favourite/Heather breeze / Devaney's goat/Whistling postman / Old grey goose/Pathway to the well / Bunch of keys/Jackson's / Champion hornpipe/Last night's fun / Glen of Aherlow / McGovern's favourite/Tom Ward's downfall / Home ruler/Boys of Bluehill / Anderson's/Miss Thornton's / Farewell to Ireland/Farewell to Erin / Luck penny/ Maid on the green / Drunken landlady/Tom Steele / Siver spear/Over the moor to Peggy / Shandon bells/ Brian Rooney's / Jimmy Duffy's / George White's favourite/Lass of Carracastle / Danny Meehan's/ Teetotaller's fancy
SH 79098 / Mar '98 / Shanachie

Carty, Paddy

☐ **TRADITIONAL IRISH MUSIC**
SHCD 34017 / Apr '97 / Shanachie

Caruso, Enrico

☐ **GREAT CARUSO, THE**
Vesti la giubba / Una furtiva lagrima / Chiudo e mar / M'appari tutt'amor / Solenne in quest'ora / Che gelida manina / O soave fanciulla / Del tempio al limitar / Celeste aida / Se m'ami ancor ai nostri monti ritorneremo / Recondita armonia / La fleur que tu m'avais jetee / Mamma que vino e generoso / Oh monstruosa colpa si pel ciel / Libiamo ne'lieti calici / O figli ah la paterna mano / Mia piccirella / Pimpinella / For you alone / Trusting eyes / Luna d'estate / O sole mio
CDAJA 5228 / Oct '97 / Living Era

Carvalho, Beth

☐ **LIVE AT OLYMPIA**
1919852 / 24 Apr '98 / EPM

Carvenius, Rolf

☐ **ROLF CARVENIUS & HIS SINGING CLARINET**
CCCD 2 / Feb '95 / Cloetta

Carvin, Michael

☐ **EACH ONE TEACH ONE**
Surrey with the fringe on top/Eternal triangle / Waltz for Gina / Nails (to Michael Carvin) / Smoke gets in your eyes / Recife's blues / I don't stand a ghost of a chance with you / One by one
MCD 5485 / Feb '95 / Muse

Cary, Marc

☐ **CARY ON**
Vibe / Afterthought / When I think of you / So gracefully / We learn as we go / Trial / Melody in C / He who hops around
ENJ 90232 / May '95 / Enja

Casa Loma Orchestra

☐ **BONEYARD SHUFFLE**
Chant of the jungle / Zig zag / Swing low sweet chariot / Casa loma stomp / Riverboat shuffle / Boneyard shuffle / Rockin' chair / Lazy bones / Washboard blues / Lazy river / Stardust / In the still of the night / Georgia on my mind
HEPCD 1056 / Apr '98 / Hep

☐ **CASA LOMA STOMP**
Love is a dreamer / Lucky me, loveable you / Happy days are here again / Sweeping the clouds away / Anytime's the time to fall in love / China girl / San Sue strut / When the little red roses (Get the blues for you) / Exactly like you / Dust / Leave it that way / On the sunny side of the street / Alexander's ragtime band / Casa Loma stomp / Overnight / Put on your grey bonnet / Little did I know / Royal garden blues
HEPCD 1010 / Mar '97 / Hep

☐ **MANIACS BALL**
Alexander's ragtime band / Put on your old grey bonnet / I wanna be around my baby all the time / I'm crazy 'bout my baby / White jazz / Black jazz / Maniac's ball / Clarinet marmalade / I never knew / Indiana / Blue jazz / Thanksgivin' / Lady from St Paul / Dame of the lame duck / Rhythm man / New Orleans / Wild goose chase / Moon country / Milenberg joys / Out of space / Copenhagen / Royal garden blues / Rose of the Rio Grande / Jungle jitters / Bugle call rag / Study in Brown
HEPCD 1051 / Jul '96 / Hep

Casadei, Raoul

☐ **GOLDEN YEARS**
74321455752 / Nov '97 / Ricordi

Casal, Neal

☐ **RAIN WIND AND SPEED**
GRCD 409 / 8 Sep '97 / Glitterhouse

☐ **SUN RISES HERE, THE**
GRCD 430 / 11 May '98 / Glitterhouse

Cascade

☐ **LET IT BE ME**
CDOK 3007 / Nov '88 / OK

Cascathina & Inhana

☐ **A SUADADE E DEMAIS**
RVCD 120 / 19 May '98 / Revivendo

☐ **DESPERTAR DO SERTAO**
RVCD 121 / 19 May '98 / Revivendo

☐ **FLOR SERRANO**
RVCD 122 / 19 May '98 / Revivendo

Case

☐ **CASE**
5331342 / Aug '96 / Def Jam

Case, Neko

☐ **VIRGINIAN, THE (Case, Neko & Her Boyfriends)**
Last to know / Slip / Pissed of 2am / Sway / One more time / She doesn't live here anymore / Broken bottle / I wanna be your dog / She towers above / Five hearts breaking / Garvity/Falling down again/Street hassle
BS 028 / 23 Feb '98 / Bloodshot

Case, Peter

☐ **FULL SERVICE NO WAITING**
VCD 79504 / 30 Mar '98 / Vanguard

☐ **SINGS LIKE HELL**
GRCD 351 / Nov '96 / Glitterhouse
VMD 79476 / Apr '97 / Vanguard

Casey, Al

☐ **JIVIN' AROUND**
Surfin' hootenanny / El aguila / Thunder beach / Baja / Surfin' blues / Lonely surfer / Guitars, guitars, guitars / Hearse / Ramrod / Caravan / Surfin' blues part II / Surfs you right / Cookin' / Hot food / Indian love call / Jivin' around / Doin' the shotish / Doin' it / Hucklebuck / Full house / Laughin' / Monte carlo / Huckleberry hound / Chicken feathers / Easy pickin' / What are we gonna do in '64
CDCHD 612 / Aug '95 / Ace

☐ **JUMPIN' WITH AL**
BB 8732 / Jan '97 / Black & Blue

☐ **SIDEWINDER**
Undecided / You come a long way from St. Louis / Sidewinder / Ashokan farewell / Endless sleep / Limeshouse blues / Saguaro sunrise / Route 1 / Plectrum banjo medley / Fool
BCD 15889 / Aug '95 / Bear Family

☐ **TRIBUTE TO FATS, A**
1044 / Jan '95 / Jazz Point

Casey Jones

☐ **CASEY JONES & THE GOVERNERS (Casey Jones & The Governers)**
REP 4675 / Sep '97 / Repertoire

☐ **DON'T HA HA (Casey Jones & The Governers)**
REP 4674 / Sep '97 / Repertoire

Casey, Karan

☐ **SONGLINES**
SHANCD 87007 / May '97 / Shanachie

Casey, Nollaig

☐ **CAUSEWAY (Casey, Nollaig & Arty McGlynn)**
Causeway / Cabbage and cale / Sel Le Thoil / Jack Palance's reel / Tra an phearla / Rainy summer / Stor mo chiroi / Comanche moon / Trip to Tokyo / Dun na sead / Murals / Lois na banrfona
TARA 3035 / Aug '95 / Tara

Cash Crew

☐ **FROM AN AFROPEAN PERSPECTIVE**
Introlude - my resume (peep it) / Bounce back / Afropean prelude / Play 4 U / Notting 'ill shit / Who's to blame / Turn it out / Ruffie / Original freaky Flo / Time is now / 2 da start prelude / Back 2 da start / Codes of honour / Nothing is impossible / Turn it out / Turn it out / Conclusion
74321380202 / Nov '96 / RCA

Cash, Johnny

☐ **AMERICAN RECORDINGS**
Delia's gone / Let the rain blow the whistle / Beast in me / Drive on / Why me Lord / Thirteen / Oh bury me not / Bird on the wire / Tennessee stud / Down there by the train / Redemption / Like a soldier / Man who couldn't cry
74321236852 / Oct '94 / American

☐ **AT FOLSOM PRISON/JOHNNY CASH AT SAN QUENTIN**
Folsom Prison blues / Dark as the dungeon / I still miss someone / Cocaine blues / 25 minutes to go / Orange blossom special / Long black veil / Send a picture of Mother / Wall / Dirty old egg-sucking dog / Flushed from the bathroom of your heart / Jackson / Give my love to rose / I got stripes / Green green grass of home / Greystone chapel / Wanted man / Wreck of the old '97 / I walk the line / Darlin' companion / Starkville City / San Quentin / Boy named Sue / There'll be peace in the valley / Folsom Prison blues
4814002 / Jan '95 / Columbia

☐ **BEST OF JOHNNY CASH, THE**
Boy named Sue / Thing called love / Busted / Daddy sang bass / Don't take your guns to town / Folsom Prison blues / Ghost riders in the sky / Hey porter / I'm so lonely I could cry / I walk the line / It ain't me babe / Jackson / One piece at a time / Orange blossom special / Ring of fire / Ballad of Ira Hayes
4837252 / Feb '96 / Columbia

☐ **BEST OF JOHNNY CASH, THE**
PLSCD 132 / Apr '96 / Pulse

☐ **BEST OF JOHNNY CASH, THE**
MACCD 145 / Aug '96 / Autograph

☐ **BEST OF JOHNNY CASH, THE**
Ring of fire / I walk the line / Thing called love / Sunday morning coming down / Folsom Prison blues / Home of the blues / Guess things happen that way / Way of a woman in love / Ballad of Ira Hayes / Tennessee flat top box / I got stripes / Get rhythm / Cry cry cry / Hey Porter / Ballad of a teenage Queen / Five feet high and rising / Long black veil / I still miss someone / Blue train / (There'll be) peace in the valley (for me) / Night Hank Williams came to town / Family bible
5543832 / 6 Apr '98 / Spectrum

☐ **BEST OF THE SUN YEARS 1955-1961**
Cry cry cry / I'm so doggone lonesome / Folsom Prison blues / I walk the line / There you go / Train of love / Next in line / Wreck of the old '97 / Home of the blues / Give my love to rose / Ballad of a teenage queen / Big river / Guess things happen that way / Come in stranger / You're the nearest thing to heaven / Luther played the boogie / Katy too / Straight a's in love / Oh lonesome me / Get rhythm
MCCD 082 / Sep '92 / Music Club

☐ **BIGGEST HITS**
Don't take your guns to town / Ring of fire / Understand your man / One on the right is on the left / Rosanna's going wild / Folsom Prison blues / Baddy sand bass / Boy named Sue / Sunday morning coming down / Flesh and blood / Thing called love / One piece at a time / There ain't no good chain gang / Riders in the sky / Baron
CD 32304 / Jun '91 / Columbia

☐ **CLASSIC CASH**
Get rhythm / Long black veil / I still miss someone / Blue train / Five feet high and rising / Don't take your guns to town / Guess things happen that way / I walk the line / Ballad of Ira Hayes / Folsom Prison blues / Tennessee flat top box / Thing called love / Cry cry cry / Sunday morning coming down / Peace in the valley / Home of the blues / I got stripes / Ring of fire / Ways of a woman in love / Suppertime
8345262 / Mar '89 / Mercury

☐ **COLLECTION, THE**
Wide open road / Cry cry cry / Folsom Prison blues / So doggone lonesome / Mean eyed cat / New Mexico / I walk the line / I love you because / Straight A's in love / Home of the blues / Rock Island line / Country boy / Doin' my time / Big river / Ballad of a teenage queen / Oh lonesome me / You're the nearest thing to heaven / Always alone / You win again / Hey good lookin' / Blue train / Katy too / Fools hall of fame / Ways of a woman in love / Down the street to 301
CCSCD 146 / Feb '93 / Castle

☐ **COLLECTION, THE**
I walk the line / Folsom Prison blues / Rock island line / Ballad of a teenage queen / Hey porter / I forgot to remember to forget / I love you because / Straight a's in love / Train of love / Big river / Cold cold heart / Ways of a woman in love / Guess things happen that way / Two timin' woman / Get rhythm / Goodbye little darling / Hey good lookin' / I could never be ashamed of you / You're the nearest thing to heaven / Just about time / Sugartime / Thanks a lot / Next in line / Port of lonely hearts / Country boy
COL 004 / Jan '95 / Collection

☐ **COME ALONG AND RIDE THIS TRAIN (4CD Set)**
Come along and ride this train / Loading coal / Slow rider / Lumberjack / Dorraine of ponchartrain / Going to Memphis / When papa played the dobro / Boss Jack / Old Doc Brown / Legend of John Henry's hammer / Tell him I'm gone / Another man done gone / Casey Jones / Nine pound hammer / Chain gang / Busted / Waiting for a train / Roughneck / Pick a bale of cotton / Cotton pickin' hands / Hiawatha's vision / Hammer and nails / Shifting whispering sands / Ballad of Boot Hill / I ride an old paint / Hardin wouldn't run / Mr. Garfield / Streets of Laredo / Johnny Reb / Letter from home / Bury me not on the lone prairie / Mean as hell / Sam Hall / Twenty five minutes to go / Blizzard / Sweet Betsy from Pike / Green grow the lilacs / Rodeo hand / Stampede / Remember the Alamo / Reflections / Big foot / As long as the grass shall grow / Apache tears / Custer / Talking leaves / Ballard of Ira Hayes / Drums / White girl / Old apache squaw / Vanishing race / Paul Revere / Road to Kaintuck / Battle of New Orleans / Lorena / Gettysburg address / Big battle / Come and take a trip in my airship / These are my people / From the sea to shining sea / Whirl and the suck / Call daddy from the mine / Frozen four hundred pound to middin' cotton picker / Walls of a prison / Masterpiece / You and Tennesse / She came from the mountains / Another song to sing / Flint arrowhead / Cisco Clifton's fillin' station / Shrimpin' sailin' / From sea to shining sea / Hit the road and go / If it wasn't for the Wabash river / Lady / After the ball / No earthly good / Wednesday car / My cowboy's last ride
BCD 15563 / May '91 / Bear Family

☐ **COUNTRY CHRISTMAS**
15417 / Nov '95 / Laserlight

☐ **COUNTRY CLASSICS (2CD Set)**
I walk the line / Country boy / Get rhythm / Oh lonesome me / Train of love / Give my love to Rose / Ballad of a teenage queen / Blue train / You win again / Hey porter / Wide open road / There you go / Cry cry cry / So doggone lonesome / Mean eyed cat / Rock Island line / Two timin' woman / Big river / Folsom Prison blues / Doin' my time / I was there when it happened / Luther played the boogie / Home of the blues / I just thought you'd like to know / Remember me / Come in stranger / Thr ways of a woman in love / Guess things happen that way / You're the nearest thing to heaven / Straight 'A's in love / I heard that lonesome whistle blow / Goodbye little darling / Story of a broken heart / Down the street to 301 / Next in line / It's just about time
330232 / Jul '96 / Hallmark

☐ **FOLSOM PRISON BLUES (Original Sun Hits)**
Cry cry cry / Folsom Prison blues / So doggone lonesome / I walk the line / Get rhythm / There you go / Train of love / Next in line / Don't make me go / Home of the blues / Give my love to Rose / Ballad of a teenage queen / Big river / Guess things happen that way / Come in stranger / Ways of a woman in love /

You're the nearest thing to heaven / It's just about time / Luther played the boogie / Thanks a lot / Katy too / Goodbye little darling / Straight A's in love / I love you because / Mean eyed cat / Oh lonesome me / Rock Island line / Down the street to 301
CPCD 8101 / Jun '95 / Charly

☐ **GOLDEN YEARS, THE**
I walk the line / Guess things happen that way / Ballad of a teenage Queen / Folsom Prison blues / Hey good lookin' / I can't help it / I forgot to remember to forget / You're the nearest thing to Heaven / Big river / Born to lose / You win again / Get rhythm / Rock Island line / Thanks a lot / Next in line / There you go / Oh lonesome me / Ways of a woman in love
REMCD 506 / Feb '98 / Reactive

☐ **GREATEST HITS**
I walk the line / Big river / Don't take your guns to town / I got stripes / Five feet high and rising / Tennessee flat top box / Bonanza / Ring of fire / Understand your man / It ain't me babe / Orange blossom special / One on the right is on the left / (Ghost) Riders in the sky / Jackson: *Cash, Johnny & June Carter* / Boy named Sue / Daddy sang bass / If I were a carpenter / What is truth / Flesh and blood / Wanted man / Man in black / Thing called love / Kate / One piece at a time / Highway patrolman / Johnny 99
4805492 / 13 Jul '98 / Columbia

☐ **HEROES (Cash, Johnny & Waylon Jennings)**
Folks out on the road / I'm never gonna roam again / American by birth / Field of diamonds / Heroes / Even cowgirls get the blues / Love is the way / Ballad of forty dollars / I'll always love you - in my own crazy way / One too many mornings
RE 2078 / Aug '96 / Razor & Tie

☐ **ITCHY FEET (20 Foot-Tappin' Greats)**
Folsom Prison blues / I walk the line / Ring of fire / Forty shades of green / I still miss someone / There ain't no good chain gang / Busted / Twenty five minutes to go / Orange blossom special / It ain't me babe / Boy named Sue / San Quentin / Don't take your guns to town / One on the right is on the left / Jackson / Hey porter / Daddy sang bass / I got stripes / Thing called love / One piece at a time
4681162 / 27 Jul '98 / Columbia

☐ **JOHNNY CASH**
I walk the line / Oh lonesome me / Folsom Prison blues / Guess things happen this way / Born to loose / Thanks a lot / Country boy / Hey good lookin' / Big river / Luther's boogie / Train of love / I love you because / I forget to remember to forget / Sugartime / Blue train / Wreck of the old '97
12373 / Oct '95 / Laserlight

☐ **JOHNNY CASH**
Cry cry cry / I'm so doggone lonesome / Next in line / There you go / Home of the blues / Give my love to Rose / Ballad of a teenage Queen / Come in stranger / Katy too / You are the nearest thing to Heaven / Straight A's in love / Get rhythm / Rock Island line / Hey Porter / Way of a woman in love / Mean eyed cat
12786 / Feb '97 / Laserlight

☐ **JOHNNY CASH (CD/CD Rom Set)**
Going by the book / Ballad of a teenage queen / Guess things happen that way / Folsom Prison blues / I walk the line / Ways of a woman in love / Rock Island line / You're the nearest thing to heaven / Next in line / I just thought you'd like to know / Straight A's in love / Hey porter / Get rhythm / Big river / Born to lose / Sugartime / I love you because / Thanks a lot
WWCDR 001 / Apr '97 / Weton-Wesgram

☐ **JOHNNY CASH 1958-1986 (The CBS Years)**
Oh what a dream / I still miss someone / Pickin' time / Don't take your guns to town / Five feet high and rising / Seasons of my heart / Legend of John Henry's hammer / Ring of fire / Ballad of Ira Hayes / Orange Blossom special / Folsom Prison blues / San Quentin / Boy named Sue / Sunday morning coming down / Man in black / One piece at a time / Riders in the sky / Without love / Baron / Highway patrolman
4504662 / Apr '87 / CBS

☐ **JOHNNY CASH IN CONCERT**
TRTCD 188 / Jun '95 / TrueTrax

☐ **JOHNNY CASH LIVE**
Get rhythm / Ring of fire / Rock island line / Peace in the valley / Sunday morning coming down / Boy named Sue / Folsom Prison blues / Highwayman / Big river / Sixteen tons / Wall / I still miss someone / I got stripes / City of New Orleans / Jackson / If I were a carpenter / Orange blossom special / Casey Jones / I walk the line
12888 / May '97 / Laserlight

☐ **JOHNNY CASH LIVE (His Greatest Hits Old And New)**
Folsom Prison blues / Big river / Get rhythm / Sunday morning coming down / Boy named Sue / Rock island line / Peace in the valley / Long black veil / Ring of fire / I got stripes / City of New Orleans / Sixteen tons / I still miss someone / These hands / Jackson / If I were a carpenter / Highwayman / Help me / Wall / Orange blossom special
300032 / Jun '98 / Hallmark

☐ **LIVE - IN THE RING OF FIRE**
Folsom Prison blues / These hands / Peace in the valley / Rock Island line / Wall / I still miss someone / Ring of fire / Sunday morning coming down / Highwayman / Big river / Sixteen tons / Boy named Sue / Help me / City of New Orleans / If I were a carpenter / Orange blossom special
SUMCD 4020 / Nov '96 / Summit

☐ **MAN IN BLACK VOL.1, THE (5CD Set)**
Wide open road / You're my baby / My treasure / Hey porter / Folsom Prison blues / My two timin' woman / Cry cry cry / Port of lonely hearts / I couldn't keep from crying / New Mexico / So doggone lonesome / Mean eyed cat / Luther played the boogie / Rock 'n' roll Ruby / I walk the line / Brakeman's blues / Get rhythm / Train of love / There you go / One more ride / I love you because / Goodbye little darling / Straight A's in love / Don't make me go / Next in line / Home of the blues / Give my love to Rose / Rock Island line / Wreck of ol' '97 / Belshazar / Country boy / Leave that junk alone / Doin' my time / If the good Lord's willing / (I heard that) lonesome whistle / I was there when it happened / Remember me / Big river / Ballad of a teenage queen / Goodnight Irene / Come in stranger / Guess things happen that way / Sugartime / Born to lose / You're the nearest thing to heaven / Story of a broken heart / Always alone / Story of a broken heart (false starts) / You tell me / Life goes on / You win again / I could never be ashamed of you / Hey good lookin' / I can't help it / Cold cold heart / Blue train / Katy too / Ways of a woman in love / Fools hall of fame / Thanks a lot / It's just about time / I forgot to remember to forget / I just thought you'd like to know / Down the street to 301 / Oh what a dream / I'll remember you / Drink to me / What do I care / Suppertime / It was Jesus / Mama's baby / Troubador / Run softly blue river / All over again / That's all over / Frankie's man / Johnnie / Walking the blues / Lead me father / That's enough / I still miss someone / Pickin' time / Don't take your guns to town / I'd rather die young / Shepherd of my heart / Cold shoulder
BCD 15517 / Sep '90 / Bear Family

☐ **MAN IN BLACK VOL.2, THE (1959-1962/5CD Set)**
Snow in his hair / I saw a man / Lead me gently home / Are all the children in / Swing low, sweet chariot / I call him / Old account / He'll be a friend / These things shall pass / It could be you / God will / Great speckled bird / Were you there / He'll understand and say well done / God has my fortune laid away / When I've learned / I got shoes / Let the lower lights be burning / If we never meet again / When I take my vacation in heaven / When he reached down his hand for me / Taller than trees / I won't have to cross Jordan alone / My god is real / These hands / Peace in the valley / Day in the Grand Canyon / I'll remember you / I got stripes / You dreamer you / Five feet high and rising / Rebel Johnny Yuma / Lorena / Second honeymoon / Fable of Willie Brown / Smiling Bill McCall / Johnny Yuma / Man on the hill / Hank and Joe and me / Caretaker / Clementine / I want to go home / Old Apache squaw / Don't step on mother's roses / My grandfather's clock / I couldn't keep from crying / My shoes keep walking back to you / I will miss you when you go / I feel better all over / Bandana / Wabash blues / Viel zu spat / Woistzuhause, mama / Heartbeat / Hello again / Tall man / Girl in Saskatoon / Locomotive man / Losing kind / Five minutes to live / Forty shades of green / Big battle / Blues for two / Jeri and Nina's melody / Why do you punish me / Just one more / Seasons of my heart / Honky tonk girl / I'm so lonesome I could cry / Time changes everything / I'd just be fool enough / Transfusion blues / Lovin' locomotive man / Mr. Lonesome / Folsom Prison blues / I walk the line / Hey porter / I forgot more than you'll ever know / There's a mother always waiting / Tennessee flat top box / Sing it pretty Sue / Little at a time / So do I / Bonanza / Shamrock doesn't grow in California / I'm free from the chain gang now / Delia's gone / Lost on the desert / Accidentally on purpose / You remember me / In the jailhouse now / Let me down easy / In them cottonfields back home / You won't have to go far / No one will ever know / Danger zone / I'll be all smiles tonight / Send a picture of Mother / Hardin wouldn't run / Blue bandana / So doggone lonesome / Johnny Reb
BCD 15562 / Aug '91 / Bear Family

☐ **MAN IN BLACK VOL.3, THE (1963-1969/6CD Set)**
Ring of fire / Matador / I'd still be there / Still in town / El matador (spanish) / Fuego d'amour (spanish) / My old faded rose / It ain't me babe / Don't think twice it's alright / One too many mornings / Mama, you've been on my mind / Long black veil / Wall / Orange blossom special / Troublesome waters / I walk the line / Folsom Prison blues / Wreck of the old '97 / Hey porter / Big river / All God's children ain't free / Amen / When it's springtime in Alaska / You wild Colorado / Danny Boy / I still miss someone / Give my love to Rose / Goodbye little darlin' goodbye / Dark as a dungeon / Bottom of the mountain / Understand your man / Time and time again / Hardin wouln't run / Certain kinda hurtin / How did you get away from me / Bad news / Cup of coffee / Dirty old egg sucking hound / One on the right is one on the left / Concerning your new song / Bug that tried to crawl around the world / Flushed from the bathroom of your heart / Dirty old egg sucking dog / Take me home / Song of the coward / Please don't play red river valley / Foolish questions / Singing stars queen / Austin prison / Boa constrictor / Everybody loves a nut / Sound of laughter / Joe Bean / Frozen lagger / Baby is mine / Happy to with you / For lovin' me / You'll be alright / Fast boat to Sidney / Long legged guitar pickin' man / Pack up your sorrows / Jackson / Is this my destiny / Wound time can't erase / You comb her hair / Ancient history / Happiness is you / Guess things happen that way / I got a woman / What I'd say / Oh, what a good thing we had / No, no, no / Shanty town / What'd I say / Matador (original) / Wer kennt den weg / In Virginia / Kleine Rosmarie / Besser so, Jenny Jo / Thunderball / Sons of Katie Elder / Put the sugar to bed / Red velvet / Rosanna's going wild / Wind changes / On the line / Roll call / You beat all I ever saw / I tremble for you / Cattle call / Bill's theme / Spanish Harlem / Folk singer / Southwind / Devil to pay / 'Cause I love you / See Ruby fall / Rout # 1 / Box 144 / Sing a travelling song / If I were a carpenter / To beat the devil / Blisterd / Wrinkled, crinkled, wadded dollar bill / I've got a thing about trains / Six white horses / Jesus was a carpenter / Man in black / Christmas spirit / I heard the bells on Christmas day / Blue Christmas / Gifts they gave / Here was a man / Christmas as I knew it / Silent night / Little drummer boy / It came upon a midnight clear / Ringing the bells for jim / We are the shepherds / Who kept the sheep / Ballad of the harpweavers / Wildwood flowers / Engine 143 / Keep on the sunnyside / Single girl, married girl / Banks of the Ohio / My clinch mountain home / Lonesome valley / Worried man blues / Brown hearted lover / Brown eyes / I'm working on a building / Gathering flowers from the hillside / When the roses bloom again / I taught the weeping willow / Rock Island line / Ballad of Ira Hayes
BCD 15588 / Nov '95 / Bear Family

☐ **MAN IN BLACK, THE**
Ring of fire / I walk the line / Get rhythm / It Ain't Me Babe / I still miss someone / Ghost riders in the sky / Baron / Sunday morning coming down / Daddy sang bass / Jackson / One piece at a time / Orange blossom special / Folsom Prison blues / San Quentin / Boy named Sue / Thing called love / Don't take your guns to town / Wanted man / Big river / Without love / No expectations / Highway patrolman / Singin' in
MOODCD 35 / Aug '94 / Columbia

☐ **MASTERS, THE**
EABCD 059 / 24 Nov '97 / Eagle

☐ **MASTERS, THE (2CD Set)**
EDMCD 021 / 24 Nov '97 / Eagle

☐ **PERSONAL CHRISTMAS COLLECTION**
Christmas spirit / I heard the bells on Christmas day / Blue Christmas / Christmas as I knew it / Little drummer boy / Christmas with you / Silent night / Joy to the world / Away in a manger / O little town of Bethlehem / Hark the herald angels sing / O come all ye faithful (Adeste Fidelis)
4777692 / 3 Nov '97 / Columbia

☐ **RING OF FIRE**
Ring of fire / Thing called love / I walk the line / Long black veil / Cats in the cradle / Goin' by the book / As long as I live / Ways of a woman in love / Night Hank Williams came to town / Folsom Prison blues / Five feet high and rising / Mystery of life / That's one you owe me / Suppertime / Family bible / Big light / Sixteen tons / Peace in the valley
5509322 / Mar '95 / Spectrum

☐ **SINGS THE COUNTRY CLASSICS**
EABCD 058 / 24 Nov '97 / Eagle

☐ **SUN YEARS, THE (3CD Set)**
Wide open road / You're my baby / Folsom Prison blues / Two timin' woman / Goodnight Irene / Port of lonely hearts / My treasure / Cry cry cry / Hey porter / Luther played the boogie / So doggone lonesome / Mean eyed cat / I couldn't keep from crying / New Mexico / Rock 'n' roll Ruby / Get rhythm / I walk the line / Train of love / There you go / One more ride / Goodbye little darling / I love you because / Straight A's in love / Don't make me go / Next in line / Give my love to Rose / Home of the blues / Wreck of ol' 97 / Rock Island line / Belshazar / Leave that junk alone / Country boy / Doin' my time / If the good Lord's willing / (I heard that) lonesome whistle / Remember me / I was there when it happened / Come in stranger / Big river / Ballad of a teenage queen / Oh lonesome me / Guess things happen that way / You're the nearest thing to Heaven / Sugartime / Born to lose / Always alone / Story of a broken heart / You tell me / Life goes on / You win again / I could never be ashamed of you / Cold cold heart / Hey good lookin' / I can't help it / Blue train / Katy too / Ways of a woman in love / Thanks a lot / It's just about time / I just thought you'd like to know / I forgot to remember to forget / Down the street to 301
CDSUNBOX 5 / Oct '95 / Charly

☐ **TENNESSEE TOPCAT**
CTJCD 1 / Apr '95 / Cotton Town Jubilee

☐ **UNCHAINED**
Rowboat / Sea of heartbreak / Rusty cage / One rose / Country boy / Memories are made of this / Spiritual / Kneeling drunkards plea / Southern accents / Mean eyed cat / Meet me in heaven / I never picked cotton / Unchained / I've been everywhere
74321397422 / Nov '96 / American

☐ **UP THROUGH THE YEARS 1955-1957**
Cry cry cry / Hey Porter / Folsom Prison blues / Luther played the boogie / So doggone lonesome / I walk the line / Get rhythm / Train of love / There you go / Goodbye little darling / I love you because / Straight A's in love / Next in line / Don't make me go / Home of the blues / Give my love to Rose / Rock Island line / Wreck of ol' 97 / Ballad of a teenage queen / Big river / Guess things happen that way / Come in stranger / You're the nearest thing to heaven / Blue train
BCD 15247 / Nov '86 / Bear Family

☐ **VERY BEST OF JOHNNY CASH, THE (2CD Set)**
Cry, cry, cry / So doggone lonesome / Folsom Prison blues / I walk the line / Get rhythm / There you go / Train of love / Next in line / Don't make me go / Home of the blues / Give my love to Rose / Ballad of a teenage queen / Big river / Guess things happen that way / Come in stranger / Ways of a woman in love / You're the nearest thing to heaven / It's just about time / Luther played the boogie / Thanks a lot / Katy too / Goodbye little darlin' / I love you because / Straight A's in love / Mean-eyed cat / Oh, lonesome me / Rock Island line / Two timin' woman / Wide open road / Hey porter / Wreck of the old '97 / Belshazar / Country boy / Doin' my time / If the good Lord's willing / I heard that lonesome whistle cry / Remember me (I'm the one who loves you) / I was there when it happened / Born to lose / Life goes on / Blue train / Goodnight Irene / Fool's hall of fame / I forgot to remember to forget / I can't help it (if I'm still in love with you) / Always alone / I could never be ashamed of you / Story of a broken heart / You win again / I thought you'd like to know
CPCD 82412 / Oct '96 / Charly

☐ **VH1 STORYTELLERS (Cash, Johnny & Willie Nelson)**
(Ghost) riders in the sky / Worried man / Family bible / Don't take your guns to town / Funny how time slips away / Flesh and blood / Crazy / Unchained / Night life / Drive on / Me and Paul / I still miss someone / Always on my mind / Folsom Prison blues / On the road again
4915312 / 29 Jun '98 / Columbia

Cash Money

☐ **BLACK HEARTS AND BROKEN WILLS**
TG 177CD / Apr '97 / Touch & Go

☐ **HALOS OF SMOKE AND FIRE**
TG 187CD / 16 Mar '98 / Touch & Go

Cash, Rosanne

☐ **RETROSPECTIVE**
Our little angel / On the surface / All come true / Wheel / Sleeping in Paris / 707 / Runaway train / I'm only sleeping / It hasn't happened yet / On the inside / What we really want / I count the tears / Pink bedroom / Seventh Avenue / Lover is forever
4816132 / Nov '95 / Columbia

Cashmere

☐ **BEST OF CASHMERE, THE**
HTCD 102 / 20 Apr '98 / Hot Productions

Casino Steel

☐ **CASINO STEEL & HOLLYWOOD BRATS/THE BOYS/GARY HOLTON (Various Artists)**
Little ole wine drinker me: *Hollywood Brats* / You can't hurt a memory: *Boys* / Ruby: *Holton, Gary & Casino Steel* / Cajun invitation: *Claudia/Big Hand/Casino* / Strange brew: *CCCP* / Ballad of the sad cafe: *Scott & Steel* / Dust of the angels wings: *Casino Steel & The Bandits* / Waiting for the lady: *Boys* / Candy: *Holton, Gary & Casino Steel* / Suckin' on Suzie: *Hollywood Brats* / Independent girl: *Boys* / Ghost riders in the sky: *Holton, Gary & Casino Steel* / Honky tonk night: *Claudia/Big Hand/Casino* / Chez Maximes: *Hollywood Brats* / This ain't America: *Scott & Steel* / Little rebel: *Casino Steel & The Bandits* / Gotta serve somebody: *Claudia/Big Hand/Casino*
MISSCD 1993 / Apr '97 / Mission Discs

Casiopea

☐ **WORLD LIVE 1988 (Brazil/Australia/Japan/Mexico/USA)**
Doo loo doo / Bayside express / Taiyo fu / Red zone / Princess Moon / Inshie / Sold swing / Magnetic vibration / Mei mu / Supersonic / Movement / Access
8378292 / Mar '94 / Polydor

Cassandra Complex

☐ **SEX AND DEATH**
Kneel (to the Boss) / Mouth of heaven / War against sleep / Come out / Satisfy me / Give me what I need / Devil's advocate / You make me sick / Voices / Realm of the senseless / Frankie teardrop / In memoriam JC / You still make me sick
BIAS 255CD / Nov '93 / Play It Again Sam

Cassiber

☐ **FACE WE ALL KNOW, A**
This was the way it was / Remember / Old Gods / Two o'clock in the morning / Philosophy / Gut / Start the show / Screaming comes across the sky / They go in under archways / They have begun to move / Time gets faster / It's never quiet / Philosophy / Screaming holds / Philosophy / I was old / Way it was / To move
RERCCD / Jun '97 / ReR/Recommended

☐ **MAN OR MONKEY**
RERCCD 2 / Oct '96 / ReR/Recommended

☐ **PERFECT WORLDS**
RERB 0000CD / Oct '96 / ReR/Recommended

Cassidy

☐ **LONG HARD ROAD**
ARCD 007 / May '98 / Ainm

Cassidy, David

☐ **CLASSIC SONGS**
778352 / 3 Aug '98 / Curb

☐ **DAYDREAMER**
Could it be forever / Tenderly / Darlin' / Thin ice / Someone / She knows all about boys / I'll meet you halfway / I am a clown / Daydreamer / Get it up for love / How can I be sure
ST 5004 / Nov '93 / Star Collection

☐ **WHEN I'M A ROCK 'N' ROLL STAR (The David Cassidy Collection)**
RE 21172 / Dec '96 / Razor & Tie

Cassidy, Eva

☐ **SONGBIRD**
Fields of gold / Wade in the water / Autumn leaves / Wayfaring stranger / Songbird / Time is a healer / I know you by heart / People get ready / Oh had I a golden thread / Over the rainbow
G 210045 / Jul '98 / Blix Street

Cassidy, Jane

☐ **MARY ANN MCCRACKEN (Cassidy, Jane & Maurice Leyden)**
ASH 004CD / Apr '95 / Ash

Cassidy, Patrick

☐ **CHILDREN OF LIR, THE**
Grave / Ceileabhradh dhuit a bhuidhbh dheirg / Croidhe lir 'na chrotal cro / Eistigh re clog an chleirigh / Iongnadh liom an baile seo / Go rinn iorrais iartharaigh / Marcradh shiodha (the fairy cavalcade) / Olc an bheatha seo (evil is this existence) / Tuath de danann / Amach daoibh a chlann an righ / Mairseail righ lir / Mochean do mharcshluaigh na n-each
7567827442 / Apr '95 / Warner Bros.

☐ **CRUIT**
CEFCD 130 / Jan '94 / Gael Linn

☐ **DEIRDRE OF THE SORROW**
01934112472 / 21 Mar '98 / Windham Hill

Casswells

☐ CASSWELLS, THE
X39 / Speeding / Easy / Around the bend / You'll never leave Cirencester / Cloths / Minehead / Thugs / Tonight / Her final wish / Life after Elvis / Walter Mattheau / Fighting man / Wanker / That's the least of our worries
ASKCD 078 / Aug '98 / Vinyl Japan

Cast

☐ COLOURS OF LICHEN
CUL 109CD / Jul '96 / Culburnie

☐ WINNOWING
CUL 104CD / Oct '95 / Culburnie

Cast

☐ ALL CHANGE
Alright / Promised land / Sandstorm / Mankind / Tell it like it is / Four walls / Fine time / Back of my mind / Walkaway / Reflections / History / Two of a kind
5293122 / Sep '95 / Polydor

☐ INTERVIEW, THE
SPEEK 001 / 16 Mar '98 / Talking Music

☐ MOTHER NATURE CALLS
Free me / On the run / Live the dream / Soul tied / She sun shines / I'm so lonely / Mad hatter / Mirror me / Guiding star / Never gonna tell you what to do (revolution) / Dance of the stars
5375672 / Apr '97 / Polydor

☐ MOTHER NATURE CALLS (Special Edition/2CD Set)
Free me / On the run / Live the dream / Soul tied / She sun shines / I'm so lonely / Mad hatter / Mirror me / Guiding star / Never gonna tell you what to do / Dance of the stars / Flying / Fine time / Walk away
5396812 / 10 Nov '97 / Polydor

Cast Iron Hike

☐ WATCH IT BURN
VR 052CD / Jun '97 / Victory

Cast Of Thousands

☐ PASSION
This is love / Passion / September / Tear me down / Girl / Immaculate deception / Colour fields / This experience / Thin line / Nothing is forever
CDAFTER 6 / Jun '88 / Fun After All

Castillo, Alberto

☐ CANTOR DE LOS 100 BARRIOS PORTENOS
BMT 005 / Jan '98 / Blue Moon

Castle, Ben

☐ BIG CELEBRATION (Castle, Ben & Roy)
KMCD 735 / Jun '94 / Kingsway

Castle, Geoff

☐ EXPANDED
FORT 1 / Mar '96 / Turret

Castle, Joey

☐ ROCK 'N' ROLL DADDY-O
Don't knock it / Cathy / Please love me / That ain't nothing but right / That ain't nothing but right / Cathy / Lucy ann / Don't knock it / That's my secret / Phantom lover (I'm the) / Marsha / True lips / Rock and roll daddy-o / Wild love / Please love me / Shake hands with a fool / Come a little closer baby / That ain't nothing but right
BCD 15560 / Apr '92 / Bear Family

Castle, Pete

☐ FALSE WATERS
MATS 012CD / Nov '95 / Steel Carpet

Castro, Miguel

☐ EXOTIC RHYTHMS OF LATIN AMERICA
EUCD 1214 / Sep '93 / ARC

Castro, Tommy

☐ CAN'T KEEP A GOOD MAN DOWN
Can't keep a good man down / You knew the job was dangerous / Suitcase full of blues / You gotta do what you gotta do / I want to show you / My time after awhile / Take the highway down / High on the hog / You only go around once / Nobody loves me like my baby / Hycodan / Can't you see what you're doing to me
BPCD 5041 / May '97 / Blind Pig

☐ EXCEPTION TO THE RULE
BPCD 5029 / Feb '96 / Blind Pig

Castro-Neves, Oscar

☐ MARACUJA
Maracuja / Love in the afternoon / Scandal No.2 / El groove del segundo de mayo / Caiu no samba / Seresta / Buzios / Must it be now / Wiggle / Vea LA / Water circles / Ballad rocks and snow
JVC 20192 / Aug '96 / JVC

☐ MORE THAN YESTERDAY
Playful lovers / Felicia and Bianca / My heart knows / More than yesterday / Te gosto tanto / Unconditional love / Lady in purple / Impossible goodbye / Always new / My sweet sweetie pie / Ponto de encontro / Just hold on / Oh what a sight
JVC 20032 / Nov '97 / JVC

☐ TROPICAL HEART
Holding with an open hand / You are my romance / New hope / If the dance is over / Envelope / I still do / My heart surrenders / Maya's gift / I have seen tomorrow / Jasmina's perfume / Souvenirs / Tropical heart / Lullaby for a magical child
JVC 20262 / Dec '93 / JVC

Casual

☐ FEAR ITSELF
CHIP 148 / Feb '94 / Jive

Casuals

☐ VERY BEST OF THE CASUALS, THE
Jesamine / Toy / Fool's paradise / Hey hey hey / Hello it's me / Sunflower eyes / Now you can be / Daddy's song / Love me tonight / Someday man / Seven times seven / Weather vane / Never my love / My name is love / Adios amour / I've got something too / Caroline / Someday rock 'n' roll lady / Naughty boy
5520882 / Jan '97 / Spectrum

Casus Belli

☐ TAILGUNNRANGELES
ARRCD 64007 / Aug '95 / Amphetamine Reptile

Cat Power

☐ WHAT WOULD THE COMMUNITY THINK
In this hole / Good clean fun / What would the community think / Nude as the news / They tell me / Taking people / Fate of the human carbine / King rides by / Bathosphere / Water and air / Enough / Coat is always on
OLE 2020 / Sep '96 / Matador

Cat Rapes Dog

☐ GOD, GUNS AND GASOLINE
KK 034CD / Sep '90 / KK

☐ MAXIMUM OVERDRIVE
KK 031 / Nov '89 / KK

☐ RARITIES (Best Of Cat Rapes Dog - 2CD Set)
KK 134DCD / Jul '95 / KK

Cat Scratch Fever

☐ BIG BANG
RAUCD 034 / 23 Mar '98 / Raucous

☐ DEATH WESTERN
1000 miles / 12 bars / Louise / Hot dog / Ballad of Claudia / When payday rolls around / Dead man's hand / Miss Sally / Ace of spades / Gunslinger / Krystal phoenix / I never knew what hit me
WOWCD 03 / Feb '97 / Words Of Warning

Cat Sun Flower

☐ CHILDISH
EFA 127752 / Oct '95 / Freak Scene

Catalano, Frank

☐ CUT IT OUT
Confirmation / Love vibrations / Those wacky ways / Willow weep for me / Cut it out / I mean you / God made it ebautiful / Party time / 502 blues / Tenor madness
DE 501 / 9 Mar '98 / Delmark

Catalogue

☐ PENETRATION
QRTCD 6187 / Oct '96 / Hat Art

Catamenia

☐ HALLS OF FROZEN NORTH
MASSCD 153 / 26 Jan '98 / Massacre

Catatonia

☐ CATATONIA
CRAI 039CDS / Dec '93 / Crai

☐ INTERNATIONAL VELVET
Mulder and Scully / Game on / I am the mob / Road rage / Johnny come lately / Goldfish and paracetamol / International velvet / Why I can't stand one night stands / Part of the furniture / Don't need the sunshine / Strange glue / My selfish gene
3984208342 / 2 Feb '98 / Blanco Y Negro

☐ WAY BEYOND BLUE
Sweet catatonia / You've got a lot to answer for / Infantile / Dream on / This boy can't swim / Bleed / Gyda gwen / For tinkerbell / Painful / Way beyond blue / Some half-baked ideal called wonderful / Whale / Lost cat
0630163052 / Sep '96 / Blanco Y Negro

Catch 22

☐ KEASBEY NIGHTS
VR 073CD / 30 Mar '98 / Victory

Cate Bros.

☐ STRUCK A VEIN
BIGBURGER 1245 / 15 Jun '98 / Icehouse

Cater, Pete

☐ PLAYING WITH FIRE (Cater, Pete Big Band)
Youbetchalife / New arrival / Way I feel / Springtime / Time for love / Suspect / Nightingale sang in Berkeley Square / Some other time / Caravan / Regulator
JITCD 9812 / 12 Apr '98 / Jazzizit

Caterpillar

☐ THOUSAND MILLION MICRONAUGHTS
CPS 021CD / Jun '94 / Compulsive

Catfish Hodge Band

☐ ADVENTURES AT CATFISH POND
9425872 / Aug '96 / Music For Little People

Catfish Keith

☐ CHERRY BALL
Mr. Catfish's advice / Cool can of beer / Your head's too big / By and by I'm going see the King / Cherry ball / Rabbits in your drawers / Swim deep, pretty mama / Hawaiian cowboy / Deep sea moan / Goin' up north to get my hambone boiled / Ramblin' blues / Leave my wife alone / Mama don't you sell it, papa don't you give it away / That ain't no way for me to get along
FTRCD 003 / Sep '93 / Fish Tail

☐ JITTERBUG SWING
Jitterbug swing / Slap a suit on you / Come back old devil / Blues at midnight / 12th street rag / Move to Louisiana / Gonna give that life / Preachin' the blues / Goin' down to Memphis / Texas tea party / Oh, captain / Fistful of riffs / Police and a sergeant / Tell everybody / Takin' my time
FTRCD 002 / Nov '93 / Fish Tail

☐ PEPPER IN MY SHOE
Jealous hearted see / Knockin' myself out / Saturday night stroll / Oh Mr Catfish / Daddy, where you been / Pepper in my shoe / You got to move / Tell me, baby / Nineteen bird dogs / Howling tom cat
FTRCD 001 / Nov '93 / Fish Tail

☐ TWIST IT BABE
FTRCD 005 / 3 Sep '97 / Fish Tail

Catharsis

☐ ET S'AIMER...ET MOURIR
SPA 14280 / Nov '94 / Spalax

Cathedral

☐ CARNIVAL BIZARRE, THE
Vampire sun / Hopkins (witchfinder general) / Utopian blaster / Night of the seagulls / Carnival bizarre / Electric grave / Palace of the fallen majesty / Blue light / Fangalactic supergoria / Interias cave
MOSH 130CD / 1 Sep '97 / Earache

☐ ETHEREAL MIRROR, THE
Violet vortex / Ride / Enter the worms / Midnight mountain / Fountain of innocence / Grim luxuria / Jaded entity / Ashes you leave / Phantasmagoria / Imprisoned in flesh
MOSH 077CD / 1 Sep '97 / Earache

☐ FOREST OF EQUILIBRIUM
Picture of beauty and innocence (intro) / Comiserating the celebration / Ebony tears / Serpent eve / Soul sacrifice / A funeral request / Equilibrium / Reaching happiness, touching pain
MOSH 043CD / 1 Sep '97 / Earache

☐ SUPERNATURAL BIRTH MACHINE
Cybertron 71/Eternal countdown / Urko's conquest / Stained glass horizon / Cyclops revolution / Birth machine 2000 / Nightmare castle / Fireball demon / Phaser quest / Suicide asteroid / Dragon ryder / Magnetic hole
MOSH 156CD / Oct '96 / Earache

Catherine Wheel

☐ ADAM AND EVE
Future boy / Delicious / Broken nose / Phantom of the American mother / Ma solitude / Satellite / Thunderbird / Here comes the fat controller / Goodbye / For dreaming
4930992 / 4 May '98 / Chrysalis

☐ FERMENT
Texture / I wanna touch you / Black metallic / Indigo is blue / She's my friend / Shallow / Ferment / Flower to hide / Tumble down / Bill and Ben / Salt
5109032 / Feb '92 / Fontana

☐ HAPPY DAYS
God inside my head / Way down / Little muscle / Heal / Empty head / Receive / My exhibition / Eat my dust you insensitive fuck / Shocking / Love tips up / Judy staring at the sun / Hole / Fizzy love / Kill my soul / Glitter
5147172 / 15 Sep '97 / Fontana

☐ LIKE CATS AND DOGS
5324562 / Sep '96 / Fontana

Catherine's Cathedral

☐ EQUILIBRIUM
NOX 004CD / Sep '95 / Noxious

☐ INTOXICATION
NOX 001CD / Oct '94 / Noxious

Catherine, Philip

☐ I REMEMBER YOU (Catherine, Philip Trio)
CRISS 1048CD / Nov '91 / Criss Cross

☐ LIVE
Piano groove / Dance for Victor / I fall in love too easily / Rene Thomas / Wondering why / Nem um talvez / Mingus in the sky / Freddie Freeloader / Stella by starlight / December 26th
FDM 365872 / 27 Oct '97 / Dreyfus

☐ MOODS VOL.1 (Catherine, Philip Trio)
CRISS 1060CD / Oct '92 / Criss Cross

☐ MOODS VOL.2
CRISS 1061CD / Nov '93 / Criss Cross

☐ TRANSPARENCE
Transparence / Dance for victor / Nem um talvez / L'eternel desir / Father Christmas / Rene Thomas / Galerie St. Hubert / Ozone / Goodbye / April blue
INAK 8701CD / Jul '97 / In Akustik

☐ TWIN HOUSE (Catherine, Philip & Larry Coryell)
Ms. Julie / Homecoming / Airpower / Twin house / Mortgage on your soul / Gloryell / Nuages / Twice a week
92022 / Apr '94 / Act

Catlett, Sid

☐ CLASSICS 1944-1946
CLASSICS 974 / 5 Jan '98 / Classics

Catley, Marc

☐ FINE DIFFERENCE (Catley, Marc & Geoff Mann)
We are one / One of the green things / Keep on / Calling / Love is the only way / This time / Freedom / Closer to you / True riches / War is won / Growth / All along the way / Weep for the city / Theospeak / Somewhere here / Hosea / Hello
PCDN 133 / Apr '92 / Plankton

☐ MAKE THE TEA
Make the tea / Jesus stops traffic / Ethnic praise / All glory to the wealthy / Newpraise / This is the day after yesterday / Times seven / P-r-r-raise the-e-e Lord / Jesus was so nice / Jesus you really are just God / Come to the quiet / Come and fill me with your power holy spirit / Lying in the spirit / Shepherding song / Lord I still just want to praise you / Now Lord in the outgoing faith situation / Lord / Hard livin' guy / If I had a rhyming dictionary / Gonna rock you tonite / Legend of ham 'n' egg / Hundred miraculous things before breakfast
PCDN 135 / May '92 / Plankton

☐ OFF THE END OF THE PIER SHOW, THE (Catley, Marc & Geoff Mann)
Over the edge / River - blue water / River - white water / River - delta / Twittering machine / Terence the termite stares down his underpants in growing am / In the wilderness / Europe after the rain
PCDN 130 / Aug '91 / Plankton

Catney, Dave

☐ FIRST FLIGHT
JR 004012 / Sep '92 / Justice

☐ JADE VISIONS
JR 004022 / Nov '92 / Justice

☐ REALITY ROAD
JR 04032 / Jun '94 / Justice

Cato, Pauline

☐ BY LAND AND SEA (Cato, Pauline & Tom McConville)
TCCD 01 / Sep '96 / Tomcat

☐ CHANGING TIDES (Cato, Pauline & Tom McConville)
Go to Berwick Johnny/High road to Linton / Omnibus/Beeswing / Gypsy's lullaby/Billy Pigg's hornpipe / Gardebylaten/Rejnlaender/ Trettondagsmarschen / Keel row / South shore/De'il amang the tailors / Hector the hero/Iron man / Willafjord/Miss McLeods/Sleep soond in da mornin' / Ned of the hill / I'll get wedded in my auld claes/ Coffee bridge / Golden eagle/Alexander's hornpipe / Roslin Castle/Jump at the sun / Forth bridge/Easy club reel / Peacock follows the hen/(Another) peacock follows the hen / Peacock's revenge
PCCD 02 / Jul '94 / Cato

☐ WANSBECK PIPER, THE
Calliope house/Tripping upstairs / Captain Ross/ Cuckold come out of the amrey (Variations) / Piper's weird / Carrick hornpipe/Happy hours / Lament for Ian Dickson / Acrobat / Wild hills o' Wannies / Town green polka/Bluebell polka / Exhibition/The hawk / Neil Gow's lament for the death of his second wife / Rowley burn/Remember me / Lady's well/Random (Variations) / Wallington Hall/Locomotive / Moving cloud/New high level (Whinham)/Mason's apron
PCCD 01 / Aug '92 / Cato

Cat's Cradle
☐ CATS CRADLE
Invisible man / Time and again / Scribbling / Cold comfort / D(S)ribbling / Raining down / Niagra / Sense of ourselves / One move ahead / Dynamite dream / Music is the magic / Gift of our time / Your rules
33WM 104 / Sep '97 / 33 Jazz

Cat's Miaow
☐ KISS AND A CUDDLE, A
BUS 10152 / Mar '97 / Bus Stop

☐ SONGS FOR GIRLS TO SING
DRIVE 14 / 10 Nov '97 / Drive-In

Cattanach, Dave
☐ DANCING IN THE SHADOWS
Every day / Been and gone / Prince of the winding road / Do you need me / Chameleon man / Lady angel / Black eyed smoke / Man made / I mean you / Cold heart / Who needs / Closing eyes
CDLDL 1252 / Sep '97 / Lochshore

Cattle Company
☐ HERO
JHS 003 / Dec '94 / Bunny

Caudel, Stephen
☐ EARTH IN TURQUOISE
Earth in turquoise / Call of destiny / Coronation / Gargantuan / Forbidden love / Dark of night / Eve of battle/dawn / Legend is born
DSR 1CD / 22 Jun '98 / CDS

☐ IMPROMPTU ROMANCE
CDSGP 9023 / Apr '95 / Prestige

Caught In The Act
☐ RELAPSE OF REASON
NTHEN 025CD / Jan '96 / Now & Then

☐ VIBE
ZYX 204504 / Jun '97 / ZYX

Caught On The Hop
☐ NATION OF HOPKEEPERS
HARCD 024 / Oct '93 / Harbour Town

Cauld Blast Orchestra
☐ DURGA'S FEAST
Mixed blood / Black rock / March of the undecided / Belvedere / Tango for a drowning man / Last gift / Silver silber / Sleep of the innocent / Symphony of mammon
ECLCD 9410 / Jan '96 / Eclectic

☐ SAVAGE DANCE
Reels within wheels / Tower of babel stomp / Cauld blast / Savage dance / Oyster wives' rant / Tarbolton lodge / Railyard band / Rantin' reel / Green shutters / Bottle hymn of the republic / Quaich
ECLCD 9002 / Jan '96 / Eclectic

Caulfields
☐ WHIRLIGIG
5403312 / 15 Sep '97 / A&M

Cause For Alarm
☐ CAUSE FOR ALARM
VE 19CD / Mar '95 / Victory

☐ CAUSE FOR ALARM/WARZONE (Cause For Alarm/Warzone)
VR 0126 / Jan '96 / Victory

☐ CHEATERS AND THE CHEATED
VR 049CD / Apr '97 / Victory

Causing Much Pain
☐ SOUTHERN POINT OF VIEW, A
THT 4211CD / Aug '95 / Ichiban

Caustic Resin
☐ MEDICINE IS ALL GONE
A 1260 / 10 Aug '98 / Alias

Cavallaro, Carmen
☐ UNCOLLECTED 1946, THE (Cavallaro, Carmen & His Orchestra)
My sentimental heart / Zing went the strings of my heart / I didn't know what time it was / I'll follow my secret heart / It's de-lovely / (When the moonlight fell) on the waterfall / I've got you under my skin / Souvenir / Rose room / Lover / I want to be happy / By the waters of Minnetonka / Carefree / Sweet Lorraine / To a wild rose / Kiss me again / Just one of those things / My sentimental heart
HCD 112 / Nov '94 / Hindsight

Cavatina
☐ SOUND OF CHRISTMAS, THE
Sleigh ride / Ding dong merrily on high / Good King Wenceslas / First Noel / Ave Maria / What child is this / God rest ye merry gentlemen / Little drummer boy / Holly and the ivy / Golden bells / Past three o'clock / O little town of Bethlehem / Christmas song / Walking in the air / Little shepherd boy / In the bleak midwinter / Trio from l'enfance du Christ, Opus 25 / Coventry carol / We three kings of Orient are / Holy boys / Interlude from Ceremony Of Carols, Opus 28 / Amid the roses Mary sits / Rudolph the red nosed reindeer / White Christmas / Silent night
PWK 123 / Oct '95 / Carlton

Cave, Nick
☐ BEST OF NICK CAVE AND THE BAD SEEDS, THE (Cave, Nick & The Bad Seeds)
Deanna / Red right hand / Straight to you / Tupelo / Nobody's baby now / Stranger than kindness / Into my arms / (Are you) The one I've been waiting for / Carny / Do you love me / Mercy seat / Henry Lee / Weeping song / Ship song / Where the wild roses grow / From here to eternity
CDMUTEL 004 / 11 May '98 / Mute

☐ BEST OF NICK CAVE AND THE BAD SEEDS, THE (& Ltd. Edition Live At The Royal Albert Hall/2CD Set) (Cave, Nick & The Bad Seeds)
Stranger than kindness / Ship song / Let love in / Brompton oratory / Red right hand / Lime tree arbour / Weeping song / Henry Lee / Where the wild roses grow / Deanna / Straight to you / Tupelo / Nobody's baby now / Into my arms / (Are you) the one that I've been waiting for / Carny / Do you love me / Mercy seat / From her to eternity
LCDMUTEL 004 / 11 May '98 / Mute

☐ BOATMAN'S CALL (Cave, Nick & The Bad Seeds)
Into my arms / Time tree arbour / People ain't no good / Brompton oratory / There is a kingdom / (Are you) The one I've been waiting for / Where do we go now but nowhere / West country girl / Black hair / Idiot prayer / Far from me / Green eyes
CDSTUMM 142 / Mar '97 / Mute

☐ FIRST BORN IS DEAD, THE (Cave, Nick & The Bad Seeds)
CDSTUMM 21 / Apr '88 / Mute

☐ FROM HER TO ETERNITY (Cave, Nick & The Bad Seeds)
Avalanche / Cabin fever / Well of misery / From here to eternity / In the ghetto / Moon in the ghetto / St. Huck / Wings off flies / Box for black Paul / From here to eternity (1987)
CDSTUMM 17 / '87 / Mute

☐ GOOD SON, THE (Cave, Nick & The Bad Seeds)
Foi na cruz / Good son / Sorrow's child / Weeping song / Ship song / Hammer song / Lament / Witness song / Lucy
CDSTUMM 76 / Apr '90 / Mute

☐ HENRY'S DREAM (Cave, Nick & The Bad Seeds)
Papa won't leave you Henry / I had a dream Joe / Straight to you / Brother my cup is empty / Christina the astonishing / When I first came to town / John Finns' wife / Loom of the land / Jack the ripper
CDSTUMM 92 / Apr '92 / Mute

☐ KICKING AGAINST THE PRICKS (Cave, Nick & The Bad Seeds)
Muddy water / By the time I get to Phoenix / I'm gonna kill that woman / Sleeping anleah / Long black veil / Hey joe / Singer / All tomorrow's parties / Hammer song / Something's gotten hold of my heart / Jesus met the woman at the well / Carnival is over
CDSTUMM 28 / Aug '86 / Mute

☐ LET LOVE IN (Cave, Nick & The Bad Seeds)
Do you love me / Nobody's baby now / Lover man / Jangling Jack / Red right hand / I let love in / Thirsty dog / Ain't gonna rain anymore / Lay me low / Do you love me part 2
CDSTUMM 123 / Apr '94 / Mute

☐ LIVE SEEDS (Cave, Nick & The Bad Seeds)
CDSTUMM 122 / Sep '93 / Mute
LCDSTUMM 122 / Aug '96 / Mute

☐ MURDER BALLADS (Cave, Nick & The Bad Seeds)
Song of joy / Stagger Lee / Henry Lee / Lovely creature / Where the wild roses grow / Curse of Millhaven / Kindness of strangers / Crow Jane / O'Malley's bar / Death is not the end
LCDSTUMM 138 / Jan '96 / Mute

☐ TENDER PREY (Cave, Nick & The Bad Seeds)
Mercy seat / Up jumped the devil / Deanna / Watching alice / Mercy / City of refuge / Slowly goes the night / Sunday's slave / Sugar sugar sugar / New morning
CDSTUMM 52 / Sep '88 / Mute

☐ YOUR FUNERAL, MY TRIAL (Cave, Nick & The Bad Seeds)
Sad waters / Carny / Your funeral and my trial / Stranger than kindness / Jack's shadow / Hard on for love / She fell away / Long time man / Scum
CDSTUMM 34 / Feb '87 / Mute

Caveman
☐ POSITIVE REACTION
FILERCD 406 / Apr '91 / Profile

☐ WHOLE 9 YARDS
FILERCD 429 / May '92 / Profile

Caveman Shoestore
☐ FLUX
Knife edge / Pond at night / Actualize / Four year old / Ticket to obscurity / Kurtain / All this air / Lightning / Henzyme / Underneath the water / Underneath the city / Cold
TK 93CD056 / Jun '94 / T/K

Cavendish Dance Band
☐ ST. ANDREW'S BALL VOL.1
SAB 200 / May '94 / St. Andrew's Ball

Cavour, Ernesto
☐ EL VUELO DEL PICAFLOR
Padre viento / Rosario de uvas / Danza agraria / Matraca de quena y charango / Carnaval de san luis / Leyenda de la kantuta / Las mamalitas / El vuelo del picaflor / La yegua y el arroyo / La cueca destrozada / Hailon en chiceria / Tres pastores / Chulupi / Ida y vuelta / Rio choqueyapu / Bailecitos desairados / Te amare despues te muerto
68953 / Apr '97 / Tropical

Caymmi, Nana
☐ BEIJO PARTIDO
3001802 / 24 Feb '98 / IMP

Cazazza, Monte
☐ WORST OF MONTE
Psychiatric review / To mom on mother's day / Candy man / Rabid rats (vietnam) / Distress / Mary bell / Kick that habit man / Firstlast / Tiny tears / Stairway to hell / Sex is no emergency / A snitch is a snitch / A is for atom / If thoughts could kill / Mark of the devil / Six eyes from hell / Liars (feed those christians to the lions) / Climax
MONTE 1CD / Jun '92 / Grey Area

CBQ
☐ CIRCLES AND TRIPLETS
DRCD 230 / May '87 / Dragon

Cecil
☐ BOMBAR DIDDLAH
Dream awake / Plastics keep coming / Spirit level / Upside down smile / Fishes / My neck / No excuses / Poshinalagweedy
CDPCS 7384 / Oct '96 / Parlophone

☐ SUBTITLES
Larger than a mountain to the ant / Zips for lips / Most tiring day / Red wine at dead time / Fullstop / Acres / Hostage in a frock / Measured / Lovetooth 14 / Charm wrestling / In this day and aged
8598212 / 30 Mar '98 / Parlophone

Ceddo
☐ UNCHAINED
ITMP 970052 / Jan '91 / ITM

Cedron
☐ ET GUITARES
088762 / Nov '97 / Melodie

Cee Bee Beaumont
☐ NO INTRODUCTION NECESSARY
DAMGOOD 114CD / 23 Feb '98 / Damaged Goods

☐ PRE-STRESSED
Micro-cycle offensive / Wormhole / Deadshot / After the slide / Gumkick / Swamp drag / Weeny roast / York Way rumble / Continental cooler / Led pedal / Scooter Joe / Zero agenda / N19 mudslide / Roscoe monstertruck / Mad dog glove compartment / Mansize / Dumpsterville patrol vehicle / Slap dunk / Offord Road divide / Zippo raid
DAMGOOD 66CD / Jul '95 / Damaged Goods

Cee Mix
☐ HOME IS WHERE THE BASS IS
INCCD 3311 / Jul '96 / Incoming

☐ LOW FLYING FRAGMENTS
Safe slip / Drive by / Square walk / Mindfunk / Cocobong / What's real / Interlude no.1 / Edge of real / Slippin' / X-es / Paraguru
INCCD 3316 / 13 Oct '97 / Incoming

Ceile
☐ MANCUNION WAY
Donal de barras/Cock o' the north / Kitty come over/ Flowers of spring/Maguires / Home to me / Wild Irishman set / What can I say / Heading home/ Foxhunter / I feel fine / Trip to Miriams/Homestead reel/Golden stud / Wash over me / Chapel hat pegs/ Blind cobblers thumbs/Ceiler reel
SLIPCD 001 / Jun '98 / Slip Discs

Celea
☐ WORLD VIEW (Celea & Liebman/ Reisinger)
Acid birds / Nadir / Witches groove / Village / Jungle / City / Desert / Sky / Unity / Sixteen tones / Piano trio / Dirgis
LBLC 6592 / Jun '97 / Label Bleu

Celestial Season
☐ FOREVER SCARLET
CDAR 015 / Feb '94 / Adipocre

☐ ORANGE
IS 779990CD / Jun '97 / I Scream Music

☐ SONIC ORD
D 00054CD / 10 Nov '97 / Displeased

Celestin, Oscar 'Papa'
☐ 1950'S RADIO BROADCASTS, THE
Sheik of Araby / Eh la bas / Lil' Liza Jane / Just a closer walk with thee / Bill Bailey / Mama don't allow / Jazz it blues / It don't mean a thing if it ain't got that swing / Panama / San / Sister Kate / Dippermouth blues / Tiger rag / Maryland my Maryland / Milenburg joys / War cloud / Woodchopper's ball / High society / Fidgety feet / Ballin' the jack / Oh didn't he ramble / When the saints go marching in
ARHCD 7024 / Nov '96 / Arhoolie

☐ NEW ORLEANS CLASSICS (Celestin, Oscar 'Papa' & Sam Morgan)
Original tuxedo rag: *Celestin, Oscar 'Papa' Original Tuxedo Orchestra* / Careless love / Black rag / I'm satisfied you love me / My Josephine / Station calls / Give me some more / Dear Almanzoer / Papa's got the jim-jams / As you like it / Just for you dear, I'm crying / When I'm with you / It's jam up / Sweetheart of TKO / Ta ta daddy / Steppin' on the gas / Everybody's talking about Sammy / Mobile stomp / Sing on / Short dress gal / Bogalousa strut / Down by the riverside / Over in the glory land
AZCD 12 / Nov '92 / Azure

Celetia
☐ CELETIA
Are U ready / Missing your love / Work me over / All my loving / This feelings killing me / Be my honey / It rains in my heart / Candelight / Way U make me feel / Up and down / Excited / Gonna get down
DESCD 03 / Jan '96 / Diesel

☐ RUNAWAY SKIES
BLRCD 32 / 10 Nov '97 / Big Life

Celias, Elyane
☐ ETOILES DE LA CHANSON
414722 / Mar '96 / Music Memoria

Celibate Rifles
☐ BLIND EAR
Johnny / Worlds keep turning / Electravision mantra / Dial om / Wonderful life '88 / Sean O'Farell / Belfast / Cycle / They're killing us all (to make the world safe) / O salvation / El Salvador / Fish and trees
HOT 1046CD / Oct '94 / Hot

☐ CELIBATE RIFLES, THE
HOT 1007CD / Nov '92 / Hot

☐ HEAVEN ON A STICK
Light of life / Light of life / Happy house / Excommunication / S and m t.v. / Contemplating r.d. laing (and the bird of paradise) / G.d. absolutely / Dream of night / Groovin' in the land of love / Electric flowers / Compared to what / Outside my window / Wild child
HOT 1038CD / May '97 / Hot

☐ KISS KISS BANG BANG
Back in the red / Temper, temper / JNS / Pretty colours / Nether world / Some kinda feeling / New mistakes / Carmine vattelly (NYNYC) / City of fun / Conflict of instinct / Sometimes / Burn my eye / SOS
HOT 1029CD / Nov '92 / Hot

☐ ON THE QUIET
Netherworld / Back on the corner / Sentinel / Electric flowers / This gift / No sign / Electric snake river / Jesus on TV / Boys (what did the detectives say) / Astra wally / Hot generation / Hindu gods of love
HOT 1067CD / Jul '98 / Hot

☐ PLATTERS DU JOUR
Kent's theme / Let's get married / Twenty four hours / Tubular greens / Pretty pictures / Out in the west again / Summer holiday blues / Merry Christmas blues / Wild desire / I'm waiting for the man / Sometimes / E=MC2 / Six days on the road / Groupie girl / Eddie / Ice blue / Thank you America / Back in the red / Rainforest / Dancing barefoot / Jesus on TV / More things change / Junk
HOT 103334CD / Oct '94 / Hot

☐ ROMAN BEACH PARTY
HOT 1030CD / Nov '92 / Hot

☐ SIDEROXYLON
HOT 1001CD / Mar '93 / Hot

☐ SOFA
Killing time / Wild desire / Sometimes / Bill Bonney regrets / Jesus on TV / Johnny / Electravision mantra / Wonderful life / More things change / Oceanshore / New mistakes / Back in the red / Ice blue / This week / Nether world / Glasshouse / Frank Hyde (slight return) / Darlinghurst confidential / Pretty pictures / Gonna cry
HOT 1043CD / Jul '95 / Hot

☐ SPACEMAN IN A SATIN SUIT, A
Spirits / Kev the Head / Brickin' around / Living what I dream / City of hope / Seams / Big world / Whatever you want / Kathy says / Diamond sky / Cuttin' it fine / This gift / Let's do it again / Spaceman in a satin suit
HOT 1047CD / Apr '96 / Hot

☐ TURGID MIASMA OF EXISTENCE, THE
HOT 1024CD / Nov '92 / Hot

☐ YIZGARNNOFF
Brickin' around / Word about Jones / Cycle / Downtown / Johnny / Happy house / Dream of night / Groovin' in the land of love / S and MTV / Electravision mantra / 2000 light years from home / More things change / Tubular greens / Invisible man / Glasshouse / O salvation / Oceanshore / Baby, please don't go
HOT 1041CD / Jul '95 / Hot

Cell
☐ LIVING ROOM
Milky / China latina / Sad and beautiful / Goodbye / Chained / Come around / Living room / Fly / Halo / Soft ground / Camera / Blue star
EFA 049332 / Feb '94 / City Slang

☐ SLO-BLO
EO 4909CD / Nov '92 / City Slang

Celluloid Mata
☐ FANCY BINARIES
NM 014CD / 17 Nov '97 / Noise Museum

Celtarabia
☐ ANCIENT FORCES
Ride / Oro / Corvus / Lark / Ancient forces / Armenian / Eight step trance / She moved through the fair/ Wedding day
OSMOCD 011 / Mar '97 / Osmosys

Celtic Frost
☐ IN MEMORY OF CELTIC FROST (Various Artists)
DWELL 1006CD / Jul '96 / Dwell

☐ MORBID TALES/EMPERORS RETURN
NCD 3 / '88 / Noise

☐ PARCHED WITH THIRST AM I, AND DYING (1984-1992)
Idols of Chagrin / A... descent to Babylon / Return to the Eve / Juices like wine / Inevitable factor / Heart beneath / Cherry orchards / Tristesses de la lune / Wings of solitude / Usurper / Journey into fear / Downtown Hanoi / Circle of the tyrants / In the chapel in the moonlight / I won't dance / Name of my bride / Mexican radio / Under Appolyon's sun
N 01912 / Mar '92 / Noise

☐ TO MEGA THERION
N 00313 / Jul '92 / Noise

☐ VANITY/NEMESIS
Heart beneath / Wine in my hand (third from the sun) / Wings of solitude / Name of my bride / This island earth / Restless seas / Phallic tantrum / Kiss or a whisper / Vanity / Nemesis / Heroes
N 01992 / Jul '92 / Noise

Celtic Orchestra
☐ CELTIC REFLECTIONS (Instrumental Airs & Melodies Of Ireland)
Carrickfergus / My Lagan love / Spancil Hill / Go lassie go / Sally Garden / Water is wide / Buachail on Eirne / Ag Chriost an Siol / West's awake / Bruach na carraige baine / Mo ghealе mear / Believe me if all those endearing young charms / Clare to here
DOCDK 109 / 24 Mar '98 / Dolphin

Celtic Spirit
☐ CELTIC SPIRIT
MCCD 243 / Jun '96 / Music Club

Celtic Thunder
☐ HARD NEW YORK DAYS
KMCD 9503 / Dec '97 / Kells

☐ LIGHT OF OTHER DAYS, THE
When new york was irish / Bachelor's warning / Streets of belfast / Oft in the stilly night / Carracanada reel-mulhaire's no.3 / Maid of black curls / Galway ghost
GLCD 1086 / Jan '90 / Green Linnet

Celtus
☐ MOONCHILD
Strange day in the country / Moonchild / Every step of the way / Some kind of wonder / Brother's lament / Beyond the dark / Love turns to dust / Rosa-ree / Pilgrim / Trikuti / We two are one
4877152 / Jun '97 / Sony Soho2

Cement
☐ CEMENT
Living sound delay / Shout / I feel / Four / Prison love / Six / Blue / Too beat / Take it easy / Old days / Reputation shot / Chip away / KCMT
RTD 15715732 / Jun '93 / World Service

Cemetary
☐ BLACK VANITY
BMCD 59 / Oct '94 / Black Mark

☐ EVIL SHADE OF GREY, AN
Dead red / Where the rivers of madness stream / Dark illusions / Evil shade of grey / Sidereal passing / Scars / Nightmare lake / Souldrain
BMCD 020 / Jun '92 / Black Mark

☐ SWEETEST TRAGEDIES
BMCD 136 / 6 Jul '98 / Black Mark

Cenotaph
☐ RIDING OUR BLACK OCEANS
CYBERCD 13 / Feb '95 / Cyber

Centinex
☐ REFLECTIONS
RRS 954CD / Mar '97 / Centinex

Central Nervous System
☐ 6 DEGREES
WB 1158CD / Apr '97 / We Bite

☐ REALITY CHECK
WB 1122CD / Jul '95 / We Bite

Centry In Dub
☐ THUNDER MOUNTAIN
WWCD 10 / Mar '95 / Wibbly Wobbly

Centurian
☐ OF PUREST FIRE
FMP 018CD / 6 Jul '98 / Full Moon

Century
☐ RELEASE THE CHAINS
DNCCD 4 / May '95 / Conscious Sounds

Ceolbeg
☐ FIVE
Mother Farquhar / Skate in the hand / Gillie's favourite / Willie Wastle / Chow man / Catriona Og / Cadal Cha / Cockerel in the creel / Duncan Finlay / Black cocks of Berriedale / Presence / Old Maid's dream / Borderline / Les freres Denis / India / Nodding song / Gude'en tae ye kimmer / Skye Bridge dance / Duncan Cla's / Gaberlunzie man
CDTRAX 100 / Apr '96 / Greentrax

☐ NOT THE BUNNY HOP
Big parcel / Not the bunny hop / Queen of Argyll / Tam Billy's jig / Archie Beag and Calum Mor / Miss Donella Beaton / High and mighty / Arthur Gillies / Farewell tae the haven / It was long ago / Three wheeled rabbit / My lass has a lovely red schleppack / De'il's awa' wi' tha exciseman / Seagull / Soft horse reel / Pumpkin's fancy / Snug in the blanket / Otago River / Iain Ghlinn Cuaich / Shores of Loch Bea
CDTRAX 053 / Feb '93 / Greentrax

☐ SEEDS TO THE WIND
Mazurka set / Senorita Ana Rocio / Seeds to the wind / Coupit yowe set / Glenlivet / A the airts / Here's a health tae the sauters / Cajun two-step / Johnny Cope / See the people run / Lord Galloway's lamentation
CDTRAX 048 / Dec '91 / Greentrax

☐ UNFAIR DANCE, AN
Zito the bubbleman / Galicia revisited / Jolly beggar / Gale warning / Collier's way / Stand together / Wild west waltz / Ceol beag / Seton's lassie / Train journey north / My love is like a red red rose / Sleeping tune
CDTRAX 058 / Jul '93 / Greentrax

Ceoltoiri
☐ CELTIC LACE
MMCD 203 / Dec '94 / Maggie's Music

☐ SILVER APPLES OF MOON
MMCD 202 / Dec '94 / Maggie's Music

Cephas, John
☐ COOL DOWN (Cephas, John 'Bowling Green' & Phil Wiggins)
ALCD 4838 / Feb '96 / Alligator

☐ DOG DAYS OF AUGUST
FF 394CD / May '93 / Flying Fish

☐ FLIP, FLOP AND FLY (Cephas, John 'Bowling Green' & Phil Wiggins)
FF 58CD / May '93 / Flying Fish

☐ GUITAR MAN (Cephas, John 'Bowling Green' & Phil Wiggins)
Black cat on the line / Richmond blues / Weeping willow / Guitar man / Police dog blues / Corrine / Careless love / Brownsville
FF 70470 / Oct '96 / Flying Fish

☐ SWEET BITTER BLUES (Cephas, John 'Bowling Green' & Phil Wiggins)
Bittersweet blues / St. James infirmary / I saw the light / Sickbed blues / Piedmont rag / Dog days of August / Roberta-a-thousand miles from home / Highway 301 / Hoodoo woman / Louisiana chase / Bowling green rag / Bye bye baby / Last fair deal gone down / Big boss man / Burn your bridges / Running and hiding
ECD 260502 / Sep '94 / Evidence

Cerberus Shoal
☐ AND FAREWELL TO HIGHTIDE
TREE 03CD / 16 Mar '98 / Tree Roots

Cerbone, Lisa
☐ CLOSE YOUR EYES
Amber / Blue frog / Asbury Park / My little sister and me / Manic depressive jubilation / Close your eyes / Tears / Three boys in the schoolyard / Painful smile (New Year's Day) / Dead end street
INDIGO 12102 / Jul '97 / Strange Ways

Cerebral Fix
☐ DEATH EROTICA
Death erotica / World machine / Clarissa / Haunted eyes / Mind within mine / Splintered wings / Creator of outcasts / Angel's kiss / Still in mind / Raft of Medusa / Never again / Too drunk to funk / Burning / Living after midnight
CDFLAG 75 / Nov '92 / Under One Flag

Cerebros Exprimidos
☐ DEMENCIA
GRITA 33994CD / Jun '96 / Grita

Ceremonial Oath
☐ CARPET
BS 002CD / Apr '95 / Black Sun

Cerrone
☐ BEST OF THE REMIXES, THE
3020712 / Jul '97 / Arcade

Certain Ratio
☐ CHANGE THE STATION
CDROB 50 / Nov '96 / Rob's Records

☐ FORCE
Only together / Bootsy / Fever 103 degrees / Naked and white / Mickey way / And then she smiled / Take me down / Anthem / Si fermi o gredo
CREV 027CD / Oct '94 / Rev-Ola

☐ GRAVEYARD AND THE BALLROOM, THE
CREV 022CD / Oct '94 / Rev-Ola

☐ I'D LIKE TO SEE YOU AGAIN
Touch / Saturn / Hot knights / I'd like to see you again / Show case / Sesamo apriti - corco vada / Axis / Guess who
CREV 025CD / Oct '94 / Rev-Ola

☐ LOOKING FOR A CERTAIN RATIO - REMIX
CRECD 159 / Jun '94 / Creation

☐ OLD AND THE NEW, THE
CREV 026CD / Oct '94 / Rev-Ola

☐ SEXTET
CREV 024CD / Oct '94 / Rev-Ola

☐ TO EACH
CREV 023CD / Oct '94 / Rev-Ola

Cervenka, Exene
☐ SURFACE TO AIR SERPENTS
213CD 004 / Jun '96 / 2.13.61

Cesar, Silvio
☐ BRAZILIAN MUSIC
Aquarelo do Brasil/Rio De Janeiro/Isto Aqui O Que E / Garota de Ipanema / Tristeza / Amigo ze / Boi de Cara Preta / Batacuda Brasileira / Bananeira / Prefixo de Verao / O Negocio e Amar/Est amos al / Anos Dourados / Gafieira flor de liz / Brasiliana / Na Gloria / Cidade Mara Vilhosa / Reticencias / Inutil Paisagem / Cariinhoso
12612 / 22 Sep '97 / Laserlight

Cetera, Peter
☐ SOLITUDE/SOLITAIRE
Big mistake / They don't make 'em like they used to / Glory of love / Queen of the masquerade ball / Daddy's girl / Next time I fall / Wake up love / Solitude/Solitaire / Only love knows why
92547422 / Aug '90 / WEA

☐ WORLD FALLING DOWN
Restless heart / Even a fool can see / Feels like heaven / Wild ways / World falling down / Man in me / Where there's no tomorrow / Last place God made / Dip your wings / Have you ever been in love
7599268942 / Jun '92 / WEA

☐ YOU'RE THE INSPIRATION
After all: *Cetera, Peter & Cher* / Next time I fall in love: *Cetera, Peter & Amy Grant* / Feels like heaven: *Cetera, Peter & Chaka Khan* / Forever tonight: *Cetera, Peter & Crystal Bernard* / SOS: *Cetera, Peter & Ronna Reeves* / I wasn't the one: *Cetera, Peter & Agnetha Faltskog* / If you leave me now / Baby what a big surprise / You're the inspiration / Do you love me that much / She doesn't need me anymore
0037122EDL / 24 Nov '97 / Edel

Ceyleib People
☐ TANYET
Aton 1: Leyshem / Zendan / Ceyladd beyta / Becal / Ddom / Toadda BB / Aton 11: Dyl / Ralin / Tygstyl / Pendyl / Jacayl / Menyatt dyl com
DOCD 1991 / Jan '92 / Drop Out

Chabenat, Giles
☐ DE L'EAU ET DES AMANDES (Chabenat, Giles & Frederic paris)
Y 225060CD / Nov '95 / Silex

Chabez, Carlos Hernandez
☐ SONGS OF MEXICO (Chabez, Carlos Hernandez & Los Trovadores)
VICG 53352 / Mar '96 / JVC World Library

Chacksfield, Frank
☐ INCOMPARABLE JEROME KERN, THE (Chacksfield, Frank Orchestra/Chorus)
Last time I saw Paris / All the things you are / Folks who live on the hill / Look for the silver lining / She didn't say yes / Smoke gets in your eyes / I won't dance / Long ago (and far away) / Who / Yesterdays / Showboat medley
4551532 / Aug '97 / Decca

☐ MUSIC OF COLE PORTER, THE (Chacksfield, Frank Orchestra)
Night and day / Begin the beguine / I love Paris / My heart belongs to Daddy / Every time we say goodbye / Wunderbar / Just one of those things / You'd be so nice to come home to / Friendship / In the still of the night / Blow, Gabriel, blow
4524912 / Mar '97 / Decca

Chacon, Don Antonio
☐ DON ANTONIO CHACON 1913-1927
20093CD / Aug '97 / Sonifolk

Chad & Jeremy
☐ CHAD AND JEREMY SING FOR YOU
14524 / Jan '97 / Spalax

Chadbourne, Eugene
☐ CAMPER VAN CHABOURNE (Chadbourne, Eugene & Camper Van Beethoven)
Reason to believe / I talk to the wind / Fayettenam / Evil filthy preacher / Games people play / Zappa medley / Ba-lue bolivar ba-lues are / Boy with the coins / Psychedelic basement / Hum-allah hum-allah / Careful with that axe, Eugene / They can make it rain bombs
HYMN 7 / Aug '97 / Fundamental

☐ END TO SLAVERY
INTAKTCD 047 / May '97 / Intakt

☐ LOCKED IN A DUTCH COFFEE SHOP (Chadbourne, Eugene & Jimmy Carl Black)
HYMN 2 / Aug '97 / Fundamental

☐ PATRIZIO (Chadbourne, Eugene & Paul Lovens)
VICTOCD 046 / Mar '97 / Victo

☐ TERROR HAS SOME STRANGE KINFOLK (Chadbourne, Eugene & Evan Johns)
VIRUS 119CD / Jun '93 / Alternative Tentacles

Chadima, Mikolas
☐ PSEUDODEMOKRITUS
P 00982 / Jun '97 / Black Point

Chadwick, Guy
☐ LAZY SOFT AND SLOW
Soft and slow / You've really got a hold on me / One of these days / In her heart / Song for Gala / Mirrored in her mind / Wasted in song / Fall in love with me / This strength / Crystal love song / Close your eyes
SETCD 053 / 16 Feb '98 / Setanta

Chain
☐ TOWARD THE BLUES
D 19718 / Oct '97 / Festival

Chain Gang
☐ PERFUMED
Dead at the Meadowlands / Metallands / Kill for you / Beijing / Cut of the drug Czar's head / Satanic rockers / Pal / Kill the bouncers at the Ritz / Nam / Brother and sister / That's how strong my love is / Rockland / Born in Brazil / Prostitute / Guts boss / My fly / Cannibal him / Piss your pants / Son of Sam / Murder for the millions / Wrestler / OTB / Label this
OLE 0192 / Mar '94 / Matador

Chain Of Strength
☐ ONE THING, THE
REV 010CD / Apr '96 / Revelation

Chain, Paul
☐ ALKAHEST
GOD 013CD / Feb '96 / Rise Above

Chaino
☐ KIRBY ALLAN PRESENTS...
BA 1122 / 20 Apr '98 / Bacchus Archives

Chainsaw Kittens

☐ POP HEIRESS
Sore on the floor / Pop heiress dies / Dive into the sea / I ride free / Media star hymn / Silver millionaire / We're like / Justine find heaven / Soldier on my shoulder / Burn you down / Closet song / Loneliest China place
7567923182 / Feb '95 / Atlantic

Chainsaw Sisters

☐ HOT SAUCE
NM 7CD / Apr '95 / No Master's Voice

Chairmen Of The Board

☐ BEST OF CHAIRMEN OF THE BOARD, THE
CCSCD 810 / Mar '97 / Renaissance Collector Series

Chaix, Henri

☐ JIVE AT FIVE
SKCD 22035 / Jun '94 / Sackville

☐ JUMPIN' PUNKINS (Chaix, Henri Trio)
SKCD 22020 / Jun '93 / Sackville

Chaka Demus

☐ BAD BAD CHAKA
792112 / Jan '94 / Jammy's

☐ CHAKA DEMUS & PLIERS GOLD (Chaka Demus & Pliers)
Bogle dance / Thief / Nuh me / World a girls / Winning machine / You send come call me / Blood in a eyes / Sweet Jamaica / Love up de gal / Terror girl wine / Pretty face
CRCD 11 / Apr '92 / Charm

☐ CHAKA DEMUS MEETS SHABBA RANKS
RNCD 2101 / Apr '95 / Rhino

☐ CONSCIOUSNESS A LICK (Chaka Demus & Pliers)
080902 / Jun '96 / Melodie

☐ EPONYMOUS (Chaka Demus & Pliers)
RN 7040 / 9 Feb '98 / Rhino

☐ FOR EVERY KINDA PEOPLE (Chaka Demus & Pliers)
Every kinda people / We pray / Boom smilin' / Witness stand / Posse come jump around / In the mood / What's the move / Searching / Man smart, woman smarter / Hurry up and come / Comin' home / War a gwaan (down the lane)
IJCD 3008 / Jan '97 / Island Jamaica

☐ GAL WINE (Chaka Demus & Pliers)
VYDCD 7 / Sep '95 / Vine Yard

☐ GAL WINE (Chaka Demus & Pliers)
Gal wine / Monkey skank / Shock out / Take long fe come / Can't test me / Duty character / Baby I won't stop you / Champion girl / Come on home / Don't hang it on the line / Everyman want a slice / Just a lick / Lively me up / Me no in a it / Mi bad but mi good / Run the city / Step up / Them a say one / We gonna rock / When I get your love
CD 6106 / Oct '97 / Music

☐ GAL WINE WINE (Chaka Demus & Pliers)
GRELCD 173 / Jul '92 / Greensleeves

☐ RUFF THIS YEAR (Chaka Demus & Pliers)
RASCD 3112 / Apr '93 / Ras

☐ TEASE ME (Chaka Demus & Pliers)
Tease me / She don't let nobody / Nuh betta nuh deh / Bam bam / Friday evening / Let's make it tonight / One nation under a groove / Tracy / Sunshine day / Murder she wrote / Roadrunner / I wanna be your man / Twist and shout / Gal wine
CIDMX 1102 / Jan '94 / Mango

☐ WORLD ENTERPRISE (Chaka Demus & Pliers)
RNCD 2028 / Nov '93 / Rhino

Chako

☐ EBB & FLOW
DDE 3931 / May '96 / Scout

Chalice

☐ CHALICE DUB
Break on through / Uptown / Planet trash / Information libertaire / Caroline's suitcase / Feel it / King kong drinks coca-cola / Saturdays and strangeways / Breeding dinosaurs / Wild and wonderful
ROTCD 006 / Feb '95 / Reggae On Top

Chalkdust

☐ GONE MODERN
GSCD 2410 / 9 Feb '98 / Strakers

Chalkias, Tassos

☐ GREEK MUSIC TRADITION
MM 216 / 11 May '98 / Musurgia Graeca

Challis, Bill

☐ BILL CHALLIS AND HIS ORCHESTRA 1936 (Challis, Bill & Orchestra)
CCD 71 / Jun '95 / Circle

Chaloff, Serge

☐ FABLE OF MABEL, THE
You brought a new kind of love to me / Fable of Mabel / Let's jump / Zdot / On baby / Salute to tiny / Sherry / Easy Street / All I do is dream of you
BLCD 760923 / Oct '90 / Black Lion

Chamber Jazz Sextet

☐ PLAYS PAL JOEY
I could write a book / My funny valentine / I didn't know what time it was / Zip / Lady is a tramp / Bewitched / There's a small hotel / Terrific rainbow
CCD 79030 / Feb '97 / Candid

Chamber Strings

☐ GOSPEL MORNING
ISM 1005CD / 23 Mar '98 / Idiot Savant Music

Chambers, Joe

☐ PHANTOM OF THE CITY
Phantom of the city / Fun / For miles / Nuevo mundo / El Gaucho / You've changed / In and out
CCD 79517 / Feb '97 / Candid

Chambers, Ken

☐ ABOVE YOU
TAANG 83 / Aug '94 / Taang

Chambers, Paul

☐ FIRST BASSMAN
VJ 004 / 23 Feb '98 / Vee Jay

☐ GO (2CD Set)
VJ 017 / 23 Feb '98 / Vee Jay

☐ JUST FRIENDS (Chambers, Paul & Cannonball Adderley)
Ease it / Just friends / I got rhythm / Julie Ann / Awful mean / There is no greater love
LEJAZZCD 24 / Feb '94 / Le Jazz

Chamblee, Eddie

☐ BLOWING IN PARIS
BB 891 / 24 Apr '98 / Black & Blue

☐ CHAMBLEE, EDDIE & JULIAN DASH/ JOE THOMAS 1951-1955 (Chamblee, Eddie & Julian Dash/Joe Thomas)
BMCD 1052 / Apr '97 / Blue Moon

☐ EDDIE CHAMBLEE 1947-1952
BMCD 1049 / Apr '97 / Blue Moon

Chameleons

☐ FAN AND THE BELLOWS, THE
Fan and the bellows / Nostalgia (long and short versions) / Less than human / In shreds / Prisoner of the sun / Turn to the vices / Love is / Everyday I'm crucified / Endlessly falling / Nathan's phase / Singing rule britannia / Pleasure and pain
GOODCD 9 / Sep '96 / Dead Dead Good

☐ LIVE AT THE GALLERY CLUB
VICD 007 / Jun '96 / Visionary/ Jettisoundz

☐ RADIO 1 EVENING SHOW SESSIONS
CDNT 1 / Jan '93 / Night Tracks

☐ RETURN OF THE ROUGHNECKS, THE (The Best Of The Chameleons/2CD Set)
GOODCD 12
GOODCD 12X / May '97 / Dead Dead Good

☐ SCRIPT OF THE BRIDGE
Don't fall / Here today / Monkeyland / Seal skin / Up the down escalator / Less than human / Pleasure and pain / Thursday's child / As high as you can go / Person isn't safe anywhere these days / Paper tiger / View from a hill / Nostalgia / In shreds
GOODCD 6 / Sep '96 / Dead Dead Good

☐ STRANGE TIMES
Mad Jack / Caution / Soul in isolation / Swamp thing / Time / End of time / Seriocity / In answer / Childhood / I'll remember / Tears / Paradiso / Inside out / Ever after / John I'm only dancing / Tomorrow never knows
GFLDD 19207 / Jun '93 / Geffen

☐ WHAT DOES ANYTHING MEAN BASICALLY
Silence, sea and sky / On the beach (eine gefahrliche affare) / One flesh / P.s. goodbye / Perfume garden / Intrigue in tangiers / Return of the roughnecks / Singing rule britannia (while the walls close in) / Looking inwardy / Home is where the heart is
GOODCD 7 / Sep '96 / Dead Dead Good

Champion, Simon

☐ CAMPFIRES AND DREAMTIME
Campfires / Echoes / Turu-etya / Storyteller / Valley of the kings / Set sail / Far away
EUCD 1218 / Sep '93 / ARC

Champs

☐ EARLY SINGLES, THE (30 Great A & B Sides)
Tequila / Train to nowhere / El rancho rock / Midnighter / Chariot rock / Subway / Turnpike / Rockin' Mary / Gone train / Beatnik / Caramba / Moonlight bay / Night train / Rattler / Sky high / Double eagle rock / Too much tequila / Twenty thousand leagues / Red eye / Little Matador / Alley cat / Coconut drive / Tough train / Face / Hokey pokey / Jumping bean / Sombrero / Shoddy shoddy / Cantina / Panic button
CDCHD 525 / Jun '96 / Ace

☐ GO CHAMPS GO/EVERYBODY'S ROCKIN'
Go champs go / El rancho rock / I'll be there / Sky high / What's up buttercup / Lollipop / Tequila / Train to nowhere / Midnighter / Robot walk / Just walking in the rain / Night beat / Everybody's rockin' / Chariot rock / Caterpillar / Turnpike / Lavenia / Mau mau stomp / Rockin' Mary / Subway / Toast / Bandido / Ali baba / Foggy river
CDCHD 451 / Jun '93 / Ace

☐ LATER SINGLES, THE
Tequila twist / Limbo rock / Experiment in terror / La cucuracha / Limbo dance / Latin limbo / Varsity rock / That did it / Mr. Cool / 3/4 mash / Nik nak / Shades / Cactus juice / Roots / San Juan / Jalisco / Only the young / Switzerland / Kahlua / Fraternity waltz / Bright lights, big city / French 75 / Man from Durango / Red pepper / Anna / Buckaroo
CDCHD 631 / Feb '97 / Ace

☐ TEQUILA
Tequila / Train to nowhere / Sombrero / Experiment in terror / La cucaracha / Too much tequila / Turn pike / Beatnik / El rancho rock / Midnighter / Chariot rock / Subway / Limbo rock / Red eye / Gone train / Caramba
CDCH 227 / Jan '94 / Ace

☐ TEQUILA
MCCD 283 / Dec '96 / Music Club

☐ WING DING
Wing ding / TNT / Percolator / Swanee river blues / Baja / Roughneck / Istanbul / Stampede / Shiverin' and shakin' / Lowdown / Siesta / Volkswagen / Suicide / Cherokee stomp / Shiver / Rockin' crickets / Fireball / Hot line / You are my sunshine / Wildwood flower / Clubhouse / Eternal love / Rattler / 20,000 leagues / Double eagle rock / Jumping bean / Man from Durango / Roots
CDCHD 460 / Oct '93 / Ace

Chan, Johnny

☐ SO YOU WANT ACTION
ID 123357CD / 27 Apr '98 / Dionysus

Chance, James

☐ LIVE IN NEW YORK (Chance, James & the Contortions)
DANCD 082 / Nov '94 / Danceteria

☐ LOST CHANCE
RUSCD 8214 / Oct '95 / ROIR

☐ MOLOTOV COCKTAIL LOUNGE
EMY 1572 / Sep '97 / Enemy

☐ SOUL EXORCISM
RE 191CD / Nov '94 / ROIR

Chancey, Vincent

☐ NEXT MODE
DIW 914 / Jan '97 / DIW

Chandell, Tim

☐ COLLECTION, THE
ANGCD 021 / 13 Oct '97 / Angella

☐ LOVE LETTERS
PILPCD 115 / May '93 / Pioneer

Chandler, Gene

☐ NOTHING CAN STOP ME (Greatest Hits)
VSD 5515 / Apr '95 / Varese Sarabande

Chandler, Kerri

☐ KAOZ THEORY
HURTCD 010 / 11 May '98 / Harmless

☐ SHAKE YOUR ASS
BB 042142CD / Jan '96 / Broken Beat

Chandler, Omar

☐ PIECES OF MY HEART
I know what's on your mind / Ecstasy / Later tonite / Buckwild / Let's settle down / Show me / Tell me what you're feeling / Guess who's back / For the love of you
XECD 10 / Feb '97 / Expansion

Chandra, Sheila

☐ ABONECRONEDRONE
CDRW 56 / Sep '96 / Realworld

☐ WEAVING MY ANCESTORS' VOICES
Speaking in tongues / Dhyana and donalogue / Ever so lonely/Eyes/Ocean / Enchantment / Call / Bhajan / Speaking in tongues II / Sacred stones / Om namaha shiva
CDRW 24 / May '92 / Realworld

☐ ZEN KISS, THE
La sagesse (Women, I'm calling you) / Speaking in tongues III / Waiting / Shehnai song / Love it is a killing thing / Speaking in tongues IV / Woman and child / En mireal del penal / Sailor's life / Abbess Hildegard / Kafi noir
CDRW 45 / May '94 / Realworld

Change

☐ GLOW OF LOVE, THE
Lover's holiday / It's a girl's affair / Angel in my pocket / Glow of love / Searching / End
7599234382 / Jan '96 / WEA

Changelings

☐ CHANGELINGS, THE
Pomegranate / Season of mist / Earthquake at Versailles / Sony of the Sephardim / Pranam / Into this divide / Incantation / Solitude / Awakening / Seraphim / 11:59 / October 30 / Sunday morning
WSCD 015 / Jan '97 / World Serpent

Changing Faces

☐ ALL DAY, ALL NIGHT
Intro / GHETTOUT / My lovely / Thinkin' about you / I apologize / Time after time / All of my days: *Changing Faces & Jay-Z* / All day, all night / GHETTOUT part 2 / My heart can't take much more / I got somebody else / Goin' nowhere / No stoppin' this groove / All that / Baby tonight
7567927202 / Jun '97 / Big Beat/ Atlantic

☐ CHANGING FACES
Stroke you up / Foolin' around / Lovin' ya boy / One of those things / Keep it right there / Am I wasting my time / Feeling all this love / Thoughts of you / Come closer / Baby your love / Movin' on / Good thing / All is not gone
7567923692 / Oct '94 / Warner Bros.

Changui

☐ AHORA SI - HERE COMES CHANGUI
CORACD 121 / Feb '95 / Corason

Channel 3

☐ I'VE GOT A GUN/AFTER THE LIGHTS GO OUT
Fear of life / Out of control / I've got a gun / Wetspots / Accident / You make me feel cheap / You lie / Catholic boy / Waiting in the wings / Strength in numbers / Double standard boys / Life goes on / What about me / Separate peace / No love / After the lights go out / Truth and trust / I'll take my chances / All my dreams / Can't afford it / I didn't know / Manzanar / Mannequin
CDPUNK 2 / Jun '94 / Anagram

Channel Light Vessel

☐ AUTOMATIC
Testify / Train travelling north / Dog day afternoon / Ballyboots / Place we pray for / Bubbling blue / Duende / Flaming creatures / Bill's last waltz / Thunderous accordions / Fish owl moon / Little luminaries
ASCD 019 / Apr '97 / All Saints

☐ EXCELLENT SPIRITS
Invisible spectator / Footsteps / Haiku detour / Birdie / Loose connections / Eternal lightbulbs / Slow jig and whirligig / Stone in your palm / Accordian night / Offering / Same shape different meaning / Everything everywhere / Century that dared to dream
ASCD 027 / Jun '96 / All Saints

Channel Zero

☐ BLACK FUEL
Black fuel / Mastermind / Call on me / Fool's parade / Self control / Misery / Hill / Love/Hate satellite / Caveman / Put it in / Wasted / Outro
BIAS 350CD / May '97 / Play It Again Sam

☐ STIGMATIZED FOR LIFE
Chrome dome / Repetition / Stigmatized for life / America / Play a little / Gold / Testimony / Unleash the dog / Big now / Last gasp
BIAS 259CD / Jun '94 / Play It Again Sam

☐ UNSAFE
Suck my energy / Heroin / Bad to the bone / Help / Lonely / Run WTT / Why / No more / Unsafe / Dashboard devils / As a boy / Man on the edge
BIAS 290CD / Feb '95 / Play It Again Sam

Channelsurfers

☐ TUNNEL VISION
ORCD 9736 / Oct '97 / Pamplin

Channing, Carol

☐ JAZZ BABY
Jazz baby / Thoroughly modern Millie / Join us in a cup of tea / Doin' the old yahoo step / Little game of tennis / Teeny little weeny nest of two / Ain't misbehavin' / You've got to see Mama ev'ry night / Ma, he's making eyes at me / You're the cream in my

coffee / Baby, won't you please come home / Good man is hard to find / Button up your overcoat / Wouldn't you like to lay your head upon my pillow / Little girl from Little Rock / Bye bye baby / Homesick blues / Diamonds are a girl's best friend
DRGCD 13112 / Apr '94 / DRG

Chantan

☐ PRIMARY COLOURS
Gloomy winter's noo awa / John Anderson my Jo / Slaves lament / Darn that dream / Collier laddie / Donal og / Witches reel / Dowie dens o'Yarrow / Ribbonbow / Wha'll mow me noo / Braes O'Killiecrankie / Boser girls / Hishey bah / Down in the jungle
CUL 108CD / Jan '97 / Culburnie

Chantays

☐ PIPELINE
VSD 5491 / Oct '94 / Varese Sarabande

☐ TWO SIDES OF.../PIPELINE
REP 4114 / Aug '91 / Repertoire

Chantel

☐ CLUB GUERILLA
SDW 0212 / Feb '97 / Shadow

Chantels

☐ BEST OF THE CHANTELS
He's gone / Plea / Maybe / I've lied: *Wilson, Willie & The Chantels* / So real / Every night (I pray) / Whoever you are / I love you so / How could you call it off / Prayee / Sure of love / Memories / If you try / I can't take it (there's our song again) / Goodbye to love: *Barrett, Richard & The Sevilles* / Look in my eyes / Well I told you
NEMCD 605 / Oct '90 / Sequel

☐ WE ARE THE CHANTELS/THERE'S OUR SONG AGAIN
Maybe / Plea / Come my little baby / Congratulations / Prayee / He's gone / I love you so / Every night (I pray) / Whoever you are / How could you call it off / Sure of love / I can't take it / Never let go / Believe me (my angel) / C'est si bon / Ific / My darlin' / I'm the girl / My memories of you / I'll walk alone / I'm confessin' / Goodbye to love
WESM 564 / Feb '98 / Westside

Chanteurs Du Pays De Vilaine

☐ DANSES EN ROND, DANSES EN CHENE
RSCD 215 / Feb '96 / Keltia Musique

Chanticleer

☐ REFLECTIONS (An Anniversary Celebration)
0630184432 / 20 Oct '97 / Teldec Classics

☐ WONDROUS LOVE
Dulaman / Fengyang ge / Nelly bly / Oy polna, polna korobushka / Brigg Fair / El Manisero / Molihua / Die vogelhochzeit / Wondrous love / Na bahia tem / La Villanella / Loch Lomond / Domaredansen / Arirang / La vasija de barro / South Australia / La petenera / Sakura / Or'cha BaMidbar / Diu, diu deng / L'amour de moy / Sohran bushi / American folk medley
0630166762 / Mar '97 / Teldec Classics

Chantre, Teofilo

☐ TERRA & CRETCHEU
086722 / Jul '95 / Melodie

Chaos

☐ COLOURS
1998 / 2 Feb '98 / Blue House

Chaos AD

☐ BUZZ CANER
Thin life / Mess head / Bioslate / Generation shit / Dreaded pestilence / Mind war electro / Friend track / Psultan (part 1) / Theme from cumberland wrestling / Male pill (part 6) / Up the Gary / Davey's safety lamp
CAT 059CD / 11 May '98 / Rephlex

Chaos UK

☐ ENOUGH TO MAKE YOU SICK/THE CHIPPING SODBURY TAPES
Head on a pole / Vicious cabaret / Kettlehead / Midas touch / Loser / Drink thudd / 2010 (The day they made contact) / Urban nightmare / Cider I up landlord / Down on the farm / C-rap / Intro / World stock market / Indecision / Kill / Uniform choice / No taxi / Think / Rises from the rubble / Brain bomb / Too cool for school, too stupid for the real world / Courier / Farmyard
CDPUNK 12 / May '93 / Anagram

☐ FLOGGIN THE CORPSE
Intro / Maggie / Hate / Police protection / No security / Kill your baby / Selfish few / False prophets / End is nigh / Parental love / Victimised / Four minute warning / Farmyard / Victimised part 2
CDPUNK 65 / Oct '95 / Anagram

☐ HEARD IT SEEN IT DONE IT
Gob on you / You bastard / Public image / Butcher baby / Pump it up / Don't talk to me / New religion / Sick of you / Fuck all y'all / Handle with care / Witch hunt / Plaistow Patricia / Blackmail man / Belsen was a gas
DISCCD 14 / 26 Jan '98 / Discipline

☐ LIVE IN JAPAN
Kill your baby / Indecision / Four Minute warning / Too cool for school, too stupid for the real world / Head on a pole / Farmyard boogie / Vicious / Lawless Britain / Detention centre / Mid touch / 2010 (The day they made contact) / Crap song / Cider I up landlord / Down on the farm / Police story / Speed (Encore)
DOJOCD 114 / Feb '94 / Dojo

☐ MORNING AFTER THE NIGHT BEFORE
CDMGRAM 109 / Jan '97 / Anagram
CLP 9982 / Jun '97 / Cleopatra

☐ RADIOACTIVE EARSLAUGHTER/ 100% 2 FINGERS IN THE AIR PUNK ROCK
Month of Sundays / Red sky at night / Used and abused / Political dreaming / Skate song / Back to school / Depression / Hope you got a fucking headache / Happy spastik / Swindle / Wall street crash / Ronnie 1 / Ronnie 2 / Alcoholic / More songs about cider / Bitch bitch bitch
CDPUNK 103 / 16 Feb '98 / Anagram

☐ SHORT SHARP SHOCK (Lawless Britain)
Lawless Britain / Living in fear / Detention centre / Suport / Control / People at the top / Global domination / No one seems to really care / Farmyard stomp (again)
CDPUNK 71 / Feb '96 / Anagram

☐ TOTAL CHAOS
Selfish few / Fashion change / You'll never own me / End is nigh / Victimised / Parental love / Leech / Chaos / Mentally insane / Urban guerilla / Farmyard boogie / Four minute warning / Kill your baby / Army / No security / What about a future / Hypocrite / Senseless conflict
CDPUNK 26 / Feb '94 / Anagram

Chaotic Dischord

☐ FUCK RELIGION, FUCK POLITICS.../ DON'T THROW IT ALL AWAY
Rock 'n' roll swindle / Don't throw it all away / Stab your back / Sausage, beans and chips / Who killed ET (I killed the fucker) / 22 Hole Doc Martens / Anarthy in Woolworths / Batcave benders meet / Alien durex machine / City claustraphobia / Boy Bill / Wild mohicans (for wattie) / SOAHC / Sound of music / Cider 'n' dogs / Destroy peace 'n' freedom / Boring bastards / Shadow / Anti christ / 77 in 82 (What's it got to do with you) / There woz cows / Alternative culture / Loud, tuneless 'n thick (Ugly's too good for you)
CDPUNK 72 / Feb '96 / Anagram

☐ GOAT FUCKING VIRGIN KILLERZ FROM HELL
CDPUNK 84 / Oct '96 / Anagram

☐ THEIR GREATEST FUCKIN' HITS
Fuck religion, fuck politics, fuck the lot of you / Fuck the world / Fuck off and die / Loud, tuneless and thick / Are students safe / Anarchy in woolworths / You bastards can't fuck us around / Psycho hippy skateboard punx / Destroy peace and freedom / Sausage beans and chips / Anti-christ / Life of Brian / Never trust a friend / City claustrophobia / Who killed ET (I killed the fucker) / I am the sturgeon / There was cows / Get off my fuckin' allotment / Me and my girl (seal clubbing) / Goat fuckin' virgin killerz from hell / Sound of music / Pop stars / Twenty two hole Doc Martens / Boy Bill / Sold out to the GPO / Soach / Glue accident / Great rock 'n' roll swindle / Don't throw it all away / Stab your back
CDPUNK 27 / Mar '94 / Anagram

Chaouqi, Si Mohamed

☐ TIKTOU
Takadoum / Casamance blues / Feast of tranquility / Naar O Lilla day and night / Tiktou / Hajouj locura / Gnawa sarewa / Tbel trance / Lala Mary-Am chlha
SMGNA 1 / Jun '96 / Sakti

Chaperals

☐ ANOTHER SHOW
Hello everybody / Lucky guy / Falling leaves / Lover's question / Sh-boom / White cliffs of Dover / Motorbiene / Angels listened / Jitterbug Mary / Sitting in my room / Zoom, zoom, zoom / So allein / In gee-home is where the heart is
BCD 15573 / Jul '91 / Bear Family

Chapin, Harry

☐ BOTTOM LINE (Encore Collection/2CD Set)
Taxi / Story of a life / I Miss America / Mercenaries / Better place / I want to learn a love song / Mr. Tanner / WOLD / Cat's in the cradle / Mismatch / Old folkie / Let time go lightly / Remember when the music / Thirty thousand pounds of bananas / Sequel
VEL 47401 / 18 May '98 / Velvel

☐ GREATEST STORIES-LIVE
Dreams go by / WOLD / Saturday morning / I wanna learn a love song / Mr. Tanner / Better place to be / Let time go lightly / Cats in the cradle / Taxi / Circle / 30,000 pounds of bananas / She is always seventeen / Love is just another world / Shortest story
9606302 / '89 / Elektra

Chapin, Thomas

☐ ANIMA (Chapin, Thomas Trio)
KFWCD 121 / Nov '94 / Knitting Factory

☐ HAYWIRE (Chapin, Thomas Trio)
KFWCD 176 / Oct '96 / Knitting Factory

☐ I'VE GOT YOUR NUMBER
I've got your number / Drinkin' / Time waits / Moon ray / Don't look now / Present / Walking wounded / Rhino
AJ 0110 / Nov '93 / Arabesque

☐ INSOMNIA (Chapin, Thomas Trio)
KFWCD 132 / Feb '95 / Knitting Factory

☐ MENAGERIE DREAMS (Chapin, Thomas Trio & John Zorn)
KFWCD 167 / Oct '96 / Knitting Factory

☐ SKY PIECE (Chapin, Thomas Trio)
Sky piece / Bypass / Just now / Alphaville / Night bird song / Triptych / Ask me now / Don't mind if you do / Changes 2 tyres / Essaouira / And...
KFWCD 208 / 20 Apr '98 / Knitting Factory

☐ THIRD FORCE (Chapin, Thomas Trio)
KFWCD 103 / Nov '94 / Knitting Factory

☐ YOU DON'T KNOW ME
Izzit / Kaokoland / Kunene / Opuwo / Namibian sunset / Kura kura / Goodbye / You don't know me
AJ 0115 / Jun '95 / Arabesque

Chapman, Gary

☐ THIS GIFT
Rockin' around the Christmas tree / Rudolph the red nose reindeer / Santa Claus is coming to town / I'll be home for Christmas / Christmas song / This gift / Silent night / Mary did you know / Holy night / Part of Heaven / Hark the herald angels
CD 10013 / Nov '97 / Reunion

Chapman, Michael

☐ BBC SESSIONS 1969-1975, THE
Naked ladies in electric ragtime you say / Postcards of Scarboro' / Rabbit hills / Trinkets and rings / Hero returns / Firewater dreams / Dawning of the day / Time enough to spare / Waiting for a train / Deal gone down / Party pieces / Among the trees
SFRSCD 060 / 18 May '98 / Strange Fruit

☐ BEST OF MICHAEL CHAPMAN 1969-1971, THE
Naked ladies and electric ragtime / Rainmaker / You say / In the valley / Kodak ghosts / Postcards of Scarborough / It didn't work out / Last lady song / Wrecked again / First leaf of autumn / Soulful lady / Polar bear fandango / All in all / Fennario / Shuffle boat river farewell / Small stones
SEECD 230 / 8 Jun '98 / See For Miles

☐ DREAMING OUT LOUD
Overture from strange places / Cowboy phase / Hell to pay / Gamelan 1 / All is pride / Sensimilia / Fool in the night / Gamelan 2 / Only pretend / Overture reprise / For once
FIENDCD 796 / Jun '97 / Demon

☐ FULLY QUALIFIED SURVIVOR
Fishbeard sunset / Soulful lady / Rabbit hills / March rain / Kodak ghosts / Andru's easy rider / Trinkets and rings / Aviator / Naked ladies and electric ragtime / Stranger in the room / Postcards of Scarborough
C5CD 527 / Apr '96 / See For Miles
REP 4687 / 24 Nov '97 / Repertoire

☐ NAVIGATION
PLANCD 07 / Mar '96 / Planet

☐ RAINMAKER
REP 4670 / 24 Nov '97 / Repertoire

☐ STILL MAKING RAIN
SPINCD 143 / Dec '97 / Spindrift

Chapman, Owen 'Snake'

☐ UP IN CHAPMAN'S HOLLOW
ROUCD 0378 / Aug '96 / Rounder

Chapman, Philip

☐ DREAM MAKER
CD 435 / 6 Jul '98 / New World

☐ KEEPER OF DREAMS
CD 164 / 6 Jun '98 / New World

☐ MUSIC FOR RELAXATION (Chapman, Philip & Stephen Rhodes/Anthony Miles)
CD 262 / 6 Jul '98 / New World

Chapman, Roger

☐ HE WAS SHE WAS YOU WAS WE WAS
Higher round / Ducking down / Making the same mistake / Blood and sand / King bee / That same thing / Face of stone / Hyenas only laugh for fun
CLACD 373 / Apr '94 / Castle

☐ HYENAS ONLY LAUGH FOR FUN
CLACD 305 / Jun '92 / Castle

☐ KICK IT BACK
Walking the cat / Cops in shades / House behind the sun / Chicken fingers / Kick it back / Son of Red Moon / Someone else's clothes / Hideaway / Toys / Do you / Hot night to rhumba / Stranger than strange / Just a step away (let's go) / Jesus and the Devil
ESMCD 175 / Aug '96 / Essential

☐ KISS MY SOUL
ESMCD 382 / May '96 / Essential

☐ LIVE IN BERLIN
Shadow on the wall / How how how / Let me down / Mango crazy
CLACD 313 / Nov '92 / Castle

☐ LIVE IN HAMBURG
Moth to a flame / Keep forgettin' / Midnite child / Who pulled the nite down / Talking about you / Going down / Short list / Can't get in / Keep a knockin' / Hoochie coochie man / Let's spend the night together
CLACD 320 / Nov '92 / Castle

☐ MANGO CRAZY
CLACD 304 / Jun '92 / Castle

☐ SHADOW KNOWS, THE
Busted loose / Leader of man / Ready to roll / I think of you now / Sitting up pretty / How how how / Only love is in the red / Sweet vanilla / I'm a good boy now
CLACD 370 / Mar '94 / Castle

☐ TECHNO PRISONERS
Drum / Wild again / Techno prisoners / Black forest / We will touch again / Run for your love / Slap bang in the middle / Who's been sleeping in my bed / Ball of confusion
CLACD 371 / Mar '94 / Castle

☐ TURN UNSTONED, A
SPV 08518952 / May '98 / SPV

☐ WALKING THE CAT
Kick it back / Son of Red Moon / Stranger than strange / Just a step away (let's go) / Fool / Walking the cat / J and D / Come the dark night / Hands off / Jivin' / Saturday night kick back
CLACD 372 / '94 / Castle

Chapman, Steven Curtis

☐ HEAVEN IN THE REAL WORLD
Heaven in the real world / King of the jungle / Dancing with the dinosaur / Mountain / Treasure of you / Love and learn / Burn the ships / Remember your chains / Heartbeat of heaven / Still listening / Facts are facts / Miracle of mercy
SPD 1408 / Jul '95 / Alliance Music

☐ SIGNS OF LIFE
Lord of the dance / Children of the burning heart / Signs of life / Walk / Let us pray / Free / Only natural / Rubber meets the road / What could I say / Celebrate you / Land of opportunity / Hold on to Jesus
SPD 1554 / Oct '96 / Alliance Music

Chapman, Topsy

☐ TOPSY CHAPMAN & MAGNOLIA JAZZBAND
BCD 320 / Apr '94 / GHB

Chapman, Tracy

☐ CROSSROADS
Crossroads / Freedom now / Be careful of my heart / Born to fight / This time / Bridges / Material world / Sub city / Hundred years / All that you have is your soul
K 960 8882 / Sep '89 / Elektra

☐ MATTERS OF THE HEART
Bang bang bang / So / I used to be a sailor / Love that you had / Woman's work / If these are the things / Short supply
7559612152 / Jun '92 / Elektra

☐ NEW BEGINNINGS
Heaven's here on earth / Cold feet / New beginning / Smoke and ashes / At this point in my life / Rape of the world / Promise / I'm ready / Remember the tinman / Give me one reason / Tell it like it is
7559618502 / Nov '95 / Elektra

☐ TRACY CHAPMAN
Talkin' bout a revolution / Fast car / Across the lines / Behind the wall / Baby can I hold you / Mountains O' things / She's got her ticket / Why / For my lover / If not now... / For you
9607742 / Apr '88 / Elektra

Chaquico, Craig

☐ ONCE IN A BLUE UNIVERSE
Oceans apart / Feelin' alright / Dipsea trail / Blue universe (Kimberley's eyes) / Dreamcatcher / Indian spring / Midnight swim / Trade winds / Lights out San Francisco / Holding back the years
VHOCD 4 / 25 May '98 / Higher Octave

Chardiet, Simon

☐ BUG BITE DADDY
Gerbil on the wheel of love / Bug bite Daddy / Different way to live / Surf octopus / Taking up space / What's new pussycat / Lesson in love / All by myself / Truth hearts / No soul / Have love, will travel / Rik-a-tik (ikety pikety) / I'd be grateful / Left wing fascist / Broke, bored and lonesome / Rock my blues away / Bop-a-lena / Panic button / Run chicken run / Goldfinger / Surf 2000 / Dr. No / Attack of the little ones / Good, the bad and the ugly
UPSTART 037 / Mar '97 / Upstart

Charge

☐ CHARGE
KSCD 9419 / Jun '97 / Kissing Spell

Charge 69

☐ APPARENCE JUGEE
KOCD 070 / 27 Apr '98 / Knock Out

Charivari Trio

☐ ROMANCE DE BARRIO
MWIC 8000CD / Nov '96 / 1Cub4t

Charlap, Bill

☐ ALONG WITH ME
CRD 326 / Mar '96 / Chiaroscuro

☐ DISTANT STAR (Charlap, Bill Trio)
Along the way / While we're young / Last night when we were young / Here I'll stay / Distant star / Bon ami / '39 Worlds fair / Starlight / Heather on the hill
CRISS 1131CD / Jul '97 / Criss Cross

☐ MULLIGAN
CRD 349 / May '97 / Chiaroscuro

☐ PIANO & BASS (Charlap, Bill & Sean Smith)
PCD 7092 / Jan '94 / Progressive

☐ SOUVENIR (Charlap, Bill Trio)
Turnaround / Half step / Souvenir / Waltz new / Confirmation / Godchild / Alone together / Goodbye Mr. Evans
CRISS1108CD / 20 Oct '97 / Criss Cross

Charlatans

☐ BETWEEN 10TH AND 11TH
SITU 37CD / Mar '92 / Situation 2

☐ CHARLATANS, THE
BBQCD 174 / Aug '95 / Beggars Banquet

☐ MELTING POT (The Best Of The Charlatans)
Only one I know / Then / Opportunity / Over rising / Sproston green / Weirdo / Theme from wish / Patrol / Can't get out of bad / I never want an easy life if me and he were ever to get ther / Jesus Hairdo / Crashin' in / Just lookin' / Here comes a soul saver / Just when you're thinking things over / One to another / North Country Boy
BBQCD 198 / 23 Feb '98 / Beggars Banquet

☐ SOME FRIENDLY
You're not very well / White shirt / Only one I know / Opportunity / Then / 109 / Polar bear / Believe you me / Flower / Sonic / Sproston green
BBL 30CD / Sep '95 / Beggars Banquet

☐ TELLIN' STORIES
With no shoes / North country boy / Tellin' stories / One to another / You're a big girl now / How can you leave us / Area 51 / How high / Only teethin' / Get on it / Rob's theme
BBQCD 190 / Apr '97 / Beggars Banquet

☐ UP TO OUR HIPS
Come in number 21 / I never want an easy life if me and he were ever to get ther / Can't get out of bed / Feel flows / Autograph / Jesus Hairdo / Up to our hips / Patrol / Another rider up in flames / Inside looking out
BBQCD 147 / Mar '94 / Beggars Banquet

Charlatans

☐ AMAZING CHARLATANS, THE
Baby won't you tell me / Number one / Blues ain't nothin' / Jack of diamonds / Codeine blues / I saw her / 32-20 / Shadow knows / Alabama bound / 'Long come a viper / Sidetrack / By hook or by crook / Devil got my man / Alabama bound / I always wanted a girl like you / How can I miss you when you won't go away / Walkin' / We're not on the same trip / Sweet Sue just you / East Virginia / Steppin' in society / I got mine / Groom 'n' clean ad
CDWIKD 138 / Aug '96 / Big Beat

☐ FIRST ALBUM/ALABAMA BOUND
842020 / Jun '94 / EVA

Charles & Eddie

☐ CHOCOLATE MIX
Keep on smilin' / Jealousy / 24-7-365 / Wounded bird / Peace of mind / Sunshine and happiness / Smile my way / She's so shy / I can't find the words / Little piece of heaven / Dear God / To someone else / Zarah / Your love / Best place in the world / Goodbye song
CDEST 2256 / May '95 / Capitol

☐ DUOPHONIC
House is not a home / NYC / Would I lie to you / Hurt no more / I understand / Unconditional / Love is a beautiful thing / Where do we go from here / Father to son / December 2nd / Be a little easy on me / Vowel song / Shine / Bonus cut
CDESTU 2186 / May '95 / Capitol

Charles River Valley Boys

☐ BEATLE COUNTRY
ROUCDSS 41 / Apr '95 / Rounder

Charles, Bobby

☐ LOUISIANA RHYTHM & BLUES MAN
CDRB 31 / Nov '95 / Charly

☐ SMALL TOWN TALK
Street people / Long face / I must be in a good place now / Save me Jesus / He's got all the whisky / Let yourself go / Grow too old / I'm that way / Tennessee blues
SEECD 218 / Mar '88 / See For Miles

☐ WISH YOU WERE HERE RIGHT NOW
SPCD 1203 / May '95 / Stony Plain

Charles, Christophe

☐ UNDIRECTED 1986-1996
EFA 006832 / Feb '97 / Mille Plateau

Charles, Ray

☐ ALONE IN THE CITY
RMB 75009 / Nov '93 / Remember

☐ AUDIO ARCHIVE
I wonder who's kissing her now / Let's have a ball / Goin' down slow / Sittin' on top of the world / Alone in the city / Blues is my middle name / This love of mine / Now she's gone / Can anyone ask for more / CC rider / Rockin' chair blues / Hey now / Sentimental blues / Can't you see darling / Tell me baby / Baby, let me hold your hand / I won't let you go / I'm gonna drown myself / Snow is fallin' / If I give you my love
CDAA 003 / Jan '92 / Tring

☐ BERLIN 1962 (Jazz At The Philharmonic)
Band intro / Strike up the band / One mint julep / I got a woman / Georgia on my mind / Margie / Danger zone / Hallelujah I love her so / Come rain or come shine / Hide nor hair / Alexander's ragtime band / I believe my soul / Hit the road Jack / Right time / Bye bye love / Unchain my heart / What'd I say
PACD 5301 / Jun '96 / Pablo

☐ BEST OF RAY CHARLES - THE ATLANTIC YEARS
It should've been me / Don't you know / Blackjack / I've got a woman / What would I do without you / Greenbacks / Come back / Fool for you / This little girl of mine / Hallelujah, I love her so / Lonely avenue / It's alright / Ain't that love / Swanee river rock / That's enough / What I'd say / (Night time) is the right time / Drown in my own tears / Tell the truth / Just for a thrill
8122717222 / Aug '94 / Atlantic

☐ BEST OF RAY CHARLES, THE
Hard times / Rock house / Sweet sixteen bars / Doodlin' / How long blues / Blues waltz
7567813682 / Mar '93 / Atlantic

☐ BLUES & JAZZ ANTHOLOGY
Someday / Sun's gonna shine again / Midnight hour / Worried life blues / Low society / Losing hand / Sinner's prayer / Funny (but I still love you) / Feelin' sad / I wonder who / Nobody cares / Ray's blues / Mr. Charles blues / Black jack / Come back / Fool for you / Hard times (no one knows better than I) / Drown in my own tears / What would I without you / I want a little girl / Early in the morning / Night time is the right time / Two years of torchure / I believe to my soul / Man I love / Music music music / I surrender dear / Hornful soul / Ain't misbehavin' / Doodlin' / Sweet sixteen bars / Undecided / Rock house / X-ray blues / Love on my mind / Fathead / Bill for Bennie / Hard times / Willow weep for me / Spirit feel
8122716072 / Mar '94 / Atlantic

☐ BLUES AND SOUL GREATS
301482 / Apr '98 / Hallmark

☐ BLUES BEFORE SUNRISE
Blues / I've had my fun / CC rider / Walkin' and talkin' / Baby let me hold your hand / Why did you go / Blues before sunrise / Ain't that fine / Don't put all your dreams in one basket / This love of mine / All to myself / If I give you my love / Late in the evening blues / Sittin' on top of the world / Back home / Kiss me baby
SUMCD 4044 / Nov '96 / Summit

☐ BLUES IS MY MIDDLE NAME
Goin' down slow / Alone in the city / Now she's gone / Rockin' chair blues / Sentimental blues / Can anyone ask for more / Let's have a ball / This love of mine / Can't you see darling / If I give you my love / Sittin' on top of the world / Kiss me baby / I'm gonna drown myself / Snow is fallin' / Blues is my middle name / I wonder who's kissing her now / CC rider / Hey now / Tell me baby / All to myself alone / Baby, let me hold your hand / I won't let you go / I'm glad for your sake / Walkin' and talkin' / I'm wonderin' and wonderin' / I found my baby there
GRF 033 / '93 / Tring

☐ BLUES IS MY MIDDLE NAME
Baby won't you please come home / She's on the ball / Hallelujah I love her so / Margie / Ego song / I believe to my soul / If I give you my love / You always miss the water (when the well runs dry) / What'd I say / Come rain or come shine / I've had my fun (going down slow) / CC rider / I love you, I love you (I will never let you go) / Baby let me hold your hand / This love of mine / Ain't that fine / Let the good times roll / Blues is my middle name
ECD 3341 / May '97 / K-Tel

☐ BLUES IS MY MIDDLE NAME
Blues is my middle name / Walkin' and talkin' / Hey now / Going away blues / CC Rider / Alone in the city / Sitting on top of the world / Rocking chair blues / How long / You won't let me go / Sentimental blues / Can anyone ask for more / Kiss me baby / I wonder who's kissing her now / I'm going down to the river / Tell me baby / Easy riding gal / All the girls in town
CWNCD 2039 / Jun '97 / Crown

☐ BLUES IS MY MIDDLE NAME
Baby tell me what have I done / I'm glad for your sake / Baby won't you please come home / I'm going down to the river / Snow is falling / Blues is my middle name / Going down slow / She's on the ball / Hey now / Honey honey / I will not let you go / Can't you see darling / Can't see you darling / Sentimental blues / CC rider (easy riding gal) / How long
CDB 6101 / Sep '97 / Music

☐ CLASSIC YEARS, THE
Sticks and stones / Georgia on my mind / Ruby / Hard hearted Hannah / Theme that got / One mint julep / I've got news for you / Hit the road Jack / Unchain my heart / Hide nor hair / At the club / I can't stop loving you / Born to lose / You don't know me / You are my sunshine / Your cheatin' heart / Don't set me free / Take these chains from my heart / No one / Without love (there is nothing) / Busted / That lucky old sun / Baby don't you cry / My heart cries for you / My baby don't dig me / No one to cry to / Smack dab in the middle / Makin' whoopee / Cry / Crying time / Together again / Let's go get stoned / Please say you're fooling / I don't need no doctor / In the heat of the night / Yesterday / Eleanor Rigby / Understanding and nine more
ESBCD 144 / Jul '91 / Essential

☐ CLASSIC YEARS, THE
CDSGP 0121 / Jun '94 / Prestige

☐ COLLECTION, THE
What'd I say / CC rider / Tell me how so you feel / Sentimental blues / Heartbreaker / I'm wonderin' and wonderin' / I wonder who's kissing her now / This love of mine / I love you, I love you (I won't let you go) / Can't you see darling / Goin' down slow / Let's have a ball / Hey now / I found my baby there / You be my baby / Kiss me baby / Oh baby / Rockin' chair blues / Sittin' on top of the world / Walkin' and talkin' / I'm glad for your sake / If I give you my love / I'm movin' on / Talkin' bout you / Leave my woman alone
COL 005 / Jul '96 / Collection

☐ EARLY YEARS, THE
KCD 5011 / Apr '97 / King

☐ GENIUS OF RAY CHARLES, THE
Am I blue / Deed I do / When your lover has gone / Two years of torture / It had to be you / Alexanders ragtime band / You won't let me go / Tell me you'll wait for me / Just for a thrill / Don't let the sun catch you cryin' / Let the good times roll / Come rain or come shine
7567813382 / Jun '93 / Atlantic

☐ GENIUS OF RAY CHARLES, THE
Blues is my middle name / Rocking chair blues / Sentimental blues / Can anyone ask for more / Let's have a ball / This love of mine / Can't you see darling / If I give you my love / Sitting on top of the world / Kiss me baby / I'm going to drown myself / Snow is falling / I wonder who's kissing her now / CC rider / Hey now / Tell me baby / All to myself / Baby let me hold your hand / I'm glad for your sake
QED 017 / Nov '96 / Tring

☐ GOING DOWN SLOW
Goin' down slow / Honey honey / Can anyone ask for more / Can't see you darling / Let's have a ball / Ain't that fine / Rocking chair blues / Sentimental blues / How long / Tell me baby / Misery in my heart / Alone in the city / She's on the ball / Don't put all your dreams in one basket / You always miss the water / Baby won't you please come home
CDBM 120 / Sep '96 / Blue Moon

☐ GOLD COLLECTION, THE
D2CD 05 / Dec '92 / Deja Vu

☐ GREAT RAY CHARLES, THE
Ray / Melancholy baby / Black coffee / There's no you / Doodlin' / Sweet sixteen bars / I surrender dear / Undecided
7567817312 / Jun '93 / Atlantic

☐ GREATEST COUNTRY AND WESTERN HITS
Your cheating heart / Hey good lookin' / Take these chains from my heart / Don't tell me your troubles / I can't stop loving you / Just a little lovin' (will go a long way) / It makes no difference now / You don't know me / You are my sunshine / I'll never stand in your way / Someday (you'll want me to want you) / I love you so much it hurts / Careless love / Oh, lonesome me / Hang your head in shame / Midnight / No letter today / Crying time / Together again / Don't let her know
PRS 23002 / Jun '95 / Personality

☐ GREATEST HITS (2CD Set)
Hit the road Jack / Georgia on my mind / Unchain my heart / I can't stop loving you / Sticks and stones / Ruby / You are my sunshine / You don't know me / Baby it's cold outside / Your cheatin' heart / Hide nor hair / Born to lose / One mint julep / I've got news for you / At the club / But on the other hand baby / No one / Without love / That lucky old sun / Don't set me free / Take these chains from my heart / Busted / Crying time / Let's go get stoned / My heart cries for you / Here we go again / I don't need no doctor / Smack dab in the middle / Ol' man river / Baby don't you cry / Makin' whoopee / Together again / I choose to sing the blues / In the heat of the night / Yesterday / Eleanor Rigby / Them that got / If you were mine / Don't change on me / Look what they've done to my song
CPCD 83162 / Sep '97 / Charly

☐ LIVE
Hot rod / Blues waltz / In a little Spanish town / Sherry / Right time / Fool for you / I got a woman / Talkin' 'bout you / Swanee river rock / Yes indeed / Frenesi / Spirit feel / Tell the truth / Drown in my own tears / What'd I say
7567817322 / Jun '93 / Atlantic

☐ MY WORLD
My world / Song for you / None of us are free / So help me God / Let me take over / One drop of love / If I could / Love has a mind of its own / I'll be there / Still crazy after all these years
7599267352 / Mar '93 / WEA

☐ PLATINUM COLLECTION, THE (2CD Set)
Baby won't you please come home / She's on the ball / Honey honey / Ain't that fine / How long / I found my baby there / You never miss the water / Snow is falling / Tell me baby / Blues before sunrise / Some day / Baby let me hold your ahnd / Kissa me baby / CC rider / Sentimental blues / Don't put all your dreams in one basket / Why did you go / Can't you see me darling / This love of mine / Goin' down slow / Confession blues / I love you / What have I done / Alone in this city / Thego song / Late in the evening / Sitting on top of the world / If I give you my love / Rockin' chair blues / Let's have a ball / Can anyone ask for more / Back home / Guitar blues / Walkin' and talkin' / I'm wondering and wondering / Let me hear you call / Misery in my heart / Lonely boy / Hey now / I wonder who's kissing her now
PC 616 / 10 Nov '97 / Platinum Collection

☐ RAY CHARLES
LECD 049 / May '94 / Dynamite

☐ RAY CHARLES (2CD Set)
R2CD 4005 / 13 Apr '98 / Deja Vu

☐ RAY CHARLES
I can't stop loving you / I've got a woman / What'd I say / Makin' believe / Makin' whoopee / Unchain my heart / Ruby / Crying time / Together again / Mess around / Georgia on my mind / Born to lose / Busted / Take these chains from my heart / Yesterday / Hit the road Jack / Eleanor Rigby
399526 / Jun '97 / Koch Presents

☐ RAY CHARLES
UAE 30082 / Jan '98 / Members Edition

☐ RAY CHARLES GOLD (2CD Set)
D2CD 4005 / Jun '95 / Deja Vu

☐ ROCK + SOUL = GENIUS
JMY 10092 / Aug '91 / JMY

☐ ROCKIN' CHAIR BLUES
MACCD 227 / Aug '96 / Autograph

☐ SEE SEE RIDER
CC rider / Sentimental blues / She's on the ball / This love of mine / How long blues / You never miss the water / Someday / Baby, let me hold your hand / Baby, won't you please come home / Ain't that fine / Don't put all your dreams in one basket / Why did you go / Let me hear you call my name / Sittin' on top of the world / Going down slow (I've had my fun) / Can't you see darling / What have I done / Money honey / Blues before sunrise / Snow is fallin' / Baby, won't you please come home
MUCD 9011 / Apr '95 / Musketeer

☐ SITTIN' ON TOP OF THE WORLD
BMCD 3033 / Nov '97 / Blue Moon

☐ SOUL MEETING (Charles, Ray & Milt Jackson)
Hallelujah, I love her so / Blue genius / X-ray blues / Soul meeting / Love on my mind / Bags of blues
7567819512 / Mar '93 / Atlantic

☐ STRONG LOVE AFFAIR
All she wants to do is love me / Angelina / Tell me what you want me to do / Everybody's handsome child / Fever / I need a good woman bad / If you give me your heart / Separate ways / Out of my life / Strong love affair / Say no more / No time to waste time
9362461072 / Feb '96 / Qwest

☐ TWO IN ONE (Charles, Ray & Nat 'King' Cole)
I wonder who's kissing her now / Kiss me baby / Hey now / Snow is falling / Misery in my heart / Let me hear you call my name / Why did you go / Walkin' and talkin' / Baby let me hold your hand / CC rider / Nature boy / Sweet lorraine / Route 66 / Little girl / Frim fram sauce / That ain't right / Gone with the draft / This will make you laugh / I like to riff / Hit that jive jack
CDTT 8 / Apr '94 / Charly

Charles, Teddy

☐ JAZZ AT THE MUSEUM OF MODERN ART
FSRCD 212 / Oct '96 / Fresh Sound

☐ ON CAMPUS (Charles, Teddy & Zoot Sims)
FSCD 43 / Oct '90 / Fresh Sound

Charles, Tina

☐ BEST OF TINA CHARLES, THE (I Love To Love)
I love to love / Rendezvous / Dance little lady dance / Fire down below / Halfway to paradise / Falling in love / When you got love / Take all of me / Dr. Love / You set my heart on fire / Love me like a lover / Disco fever / I'll go where your music takes me / Hold me / Love bug/Sweets for my sweet / Why / Fallin' in love in summertime
HTCD 48 / 20 Apr '98 / Hot Productions

☐ I LOVE TO LOVE
I love to love (but my baby loves to dance) / You set my heart on fire (part 1) / Hey boy / Take all of me / Love me like a lover / Why / Hold me / Disco fever / Disco love
4895182 / 2 Feb '98 / Columbia

☐ VERY BEST OF TINA CHARLES, THE
I love to love (but my baby loves to dance) / Dr. Love / I'll go where your music takes me / Dance little lady dance / You set my heart on fire / Love bug / World of emotion / This is the moment / Foundation of love / Time for a change / You can do magic / Smarty pants / Band of gold / You're so vain / Don't play that song (you lied) / Stoney end / River deep, mountain high / Tina's medley
SUMCD 4052 / Nov '96 / Summit
10222 / Oct '97 / Go On Deluxe

Charleston Chasers

☐ CHARLESTON CHASERS, THE
CBC 1040 / Dec '97 / Timeless Historical

☐ PLEASURE MAD
SOSCD 1287 / Aug '95 / Stomp Off

Charlesworth, Bob

☐ MUSIC FOR THE 3RD EAR
WWCD 12 / Sep '95 / Wibbly Wobbly

Charlesworth, Dick

☐ DICK CHARLESWORTH & HIS CITY GENTS
BCD 272 / Aug '95 / GHB

Charley

☐ SLUGGER
ER 80024CD / Nov '97 / Eggbert

Charlie

☐ FIGHT DIRTY/GOOD MORNING
RME 0154CD / 15 Dec '97 / Renaissance

☐ NO SECOND CHANCE/LINES (2CD Set)
RME 0153CD / Oct '97 / Renaissance

Charlie & His Orchestra

☐ GERMAN PROPAGANDA SWING VOL.1 1941-1943
You're driving me crazy / You can't stop me from dreaming / St. Louis blues / Slumming on Park Avenue / Dinah / Daisy / FDR Jones / Who'll buy my bublitchky / I'm putting all my eggs in one basket / King's horses / I've got a pocketful of dreams / Three little fishes / Why'd ya make me fall in love with you / Miss Annabelle Lee / South of the border / Hold tight / Man with the big cigar / I'm sending you the Siegfried Line / Bye bye blackbird / Japanese sandman / Who's afraid of the big bad wolf / Unter'n linden
HQCD 03 / Oct '91 / Harlequin

☐ GERMAN PROPAGANDA SWING VOL.2 1941-1944
Nice people / Thanks for the memory / Indian love call / Sheik of Araby / Let's put out the lights / Bei mr bist du schon / Lili Marlene / Elmer's tune / Picture me without you / I double dare you / MacPherson is rehearsin' / I can't give you anything but love / Daisy stardust / United air man / I got rhythm / And so another lovely day is over / Roll on the blue funnel / Under an umbrella in the evening / Calling invasion forces / Atlantic wall / Submarine
HQCD 09 / Oct '91 / Harlequin

Charlie Chaplin

☐ 20 SUPER HITS
SONCD 0003 / Oct '90 / Sonic Sounds

☐ CHARLIE CHAPLIN MEETS PAPA SAN (Charlie Chaplin & Papa San)
RNCD 2068 / Aug '94 / Rhino

☐ LIVE AT CLARENDON (Charlie Chaplin & King Sturgav Sounds)
DHV 1CD / Nov '95 / Tamoki Wambesi

☐ OLD AND NEW TESTAMENT
RASCD 3090 / Apr '92 / Ras

☐ QUENCHIE
TWCD 1028 / Jun '92 / Tamoki Wambesi

☐ RAS PORTRAITS
Ruffian / License to kill / DJ roll call / Send Ninjaman home / Rappin' Chaplin / Don't touch crack / Charlie in the party / Not a bag of locks / Chalice contest / From a distance / Through some corn / Promise land / Obeah business
RAS 3318 / Jun '97 / Ras

☐ RED POND/CHAPLIN CHANT
TWCD 1014 / Apr '94 / Tamoki Wambesi

☐ TAKE TWO
RASCD 3060 / Jul '90 / Ras

Charlottes

☐ THINGS COME APART
Liar / Prayer song / See me, feel me / By my side / Mad girls love song / Beautify / Love in the emptiness / We're going wrong / Blue / Venus
CDBRED 92 / Jan '91 / Cherry Red

Charmers, Lloyd

☐ OH ME OH MY
JASCD 14 / 20 Apr '98 / Sarge

☐ SWEET MEMORIES VOL.7
JASCD 16 / 8 Jun '98 / Sarge

Charming Prophets

☐ ALIENS AND ME
SISSY 005 / Jun '97 / Sticksister

Charon

☐ SORROWBURN
RRS 962CD / 3 Aug '98 / Diehard

Chartbusters

☐ MATING CALL
Kirk's works / Mambo bounce / 245 / Minor march / Mating call / Jugsville / Oleo / Don't go to strangers / Back on the farm / Doxy
PRCD 110022 / Jun '96 / Prestige

Chas & Dave

☐ AIN'T NO PLEASING YOU
Ain't no pleasing you / That's what I like / My melancholy baby / Sunday / One o' them days / Poor old Mr. Woogie / Bored stiff / Turn that noise down / Behave yourself / Rabbit / Wish I could write a love song / That old piano / Nobody / Miss you all the time / Flying / Stop dreaming / London girls / There in your eyes / I miss ya gel / Mustn't grumble
TRTCD 149 / Oct '94 / TrueTrax

☐ AIN'T NO PLEASING YOU
PLSCD 157 / Apr '97 / Pulse

☐ ALL TIME JAMBOREE
PDSCD 518 / Sep '97 / Pulse

☐ GIVE IT SOME STICK (2CD Set)
SMDCD 193 / 22 Sep '97 / Snapper

☐ ONE FING 'N' ANUVVER
What a stupid day / Another useless day / Lazy cow / I can make it / Gambler / If I could only play like that / Mama and papa jazz / Clive of India / Ponder's End allotment club / Better get your shoes on / Dry party / Ballad of the rich / Deceived / One fing 'n' anuvver / It's so very hard / Woortcha / I am a rocker / Old time song / Old dog and me / Scruffy old cow
GEMCD 020 / 2 Feb '98 / Diamond

☐ WHALLOP (It's Party Time)
I'm a rocker/Lovin' up a storm/Reelin' and rockin' / Jailhouse rock/Peggy Sue/Don't be cruel / My babe/ What'd I say/Sweet little sixteen / Pretend/Shake rattle and roll/Just a little too much / Whole lotta shakin' goin' on/Down the line/Rave on / Say mama/ I'm comin' home/All shook up / Good golly miss Molly/Bony Maronie/Too much monkey business / Twenty flight rock/I'm ready / I wonder in whose arms/Bye bye Johnny / Feel so fine/I'm a rocker / Wallop / Rabbit / That's what I like / Beer belly / Margate / London girls / Wish I could write a love song / Ain't no pleasing you / Stars over 45/When I'm cleaning windows/Any old iron / Run rabbit run/ Laughing policeman/What a rotten song / Give it to the girl next door/Too fat polka / Cinderella/Rolling round the world/Good ol' boys/Ask old Bro / Chinese laundry blues/Margie/Big fat fly/Not me / Hair hair hair/Little bit of cucumber/Where did you get that / Ferry boat inn/Beer barrel polka/Down the road / Baby face/Who were you with last night / Somebody stole my gal/Fall in and follow me / Swanee/Are you from Dixie
SELCD 512 / 30 Mar '98 / Castle Select

Chase

☐ ENNEA/PURE MUSIC
A 28726 / Nov '97 / One Way

Chase, Allan

☐ DARK CLOUDS WITH SILVER LININGS (Chase, Allan Quartet)
Dark clouds with silver linings / Poinciana / Comin' up / How little we know / Borderick / Close your eyes / East of the sun / Routine / Of thee I sing / Dismal / Yeah / Clamdiggers
AC 5013 / Jul '97 / Accurate

Chassagnite, Francois

☐ SAMYA CYNTHIA
CDLLL 97 / Aug '93 / La Lichere

Chastain

☐ IN DEMENTIA
MASSCD 122 / May '97 / Massacre

☐ SICK SOCIETY
MASSCD 076 / Nov '95 / Massacre

Chastain, David T.

☐ 7TH OF NEVER, THE
MASSCD 077 / Oct '95 / Massacre

☐ MOVEMENTS THROUGH TIME
Thunder and lightning / 827 / Fortunate and happenstance / Citizen of hell / Blitzkrieg / Oracle within / New York rush / We must carry on / Capriccio / In E minor / No man's land / Seven Hills groove / Now or never / Trapped in the wind / Zoned in danger / Bargin
KILCD 1002 / Oct '93 / Killerwatt

Chastain, Paul

☐ HEY WIMPUS (Chastain, Paul & Ric Menck)
AMCD 100 / 16 Mar '98 / Action

Chateau Neuf Spelemannslag

☐ SPELL
HCD 7104CD / Apr '95 / Helio

☐ TJUVGODS
GR 4124CD / Dec '97 / Grappa

Chattaway, Jay

☐ SPACE AGE
ND 66003 / Nov '92 / Narada

Chatuye

☐ HEARTBEAT IN THE MUSIC
Irarra hayanh gurigiya (that's how people are) / Heartbeat in the music / Gumagarugu / Wagiribuduba (we'll come back) / Dusumaba (take it easy) / Poppy pea / Geebei tubanh ounli (you've got too many houses) / Play, darling, play / Sidiheiguagudala (he's frightened by his debts) / I know what I know-play, darling, play
ARHCD 383 / Apr '95 / Arhoolie

Chatwell, J.R.

☐ JAMMIN' WITH JR
Never slept a wink last night / Little coquette / Jammin' with JR / Ragged but right / Right or wrong / Pipedreams / Corrine Corrina / Pipeliner's blues / John The Baptist / You can count on me / Worried over you
EDCD 560 / 1 Jun '98 / Edsel

Chaurand, Anne

☐ CELTIA
ECLCD 9613 / Feb '96 / Eclectic

Chaurasia, Hariprasad

☐ ABOVE AND BEYOND
IMUT 1064 / Jul '96 / Multitone

☐ RAG AHIR BHAIRAV
NI 5111 / Sep '94 / Nimbus

☐ RAG BHIMPALASI
NI 5298 / Sep '94 / Nimbus

☐ RAG KAUNSI KANHRA
NI 5182 / Sep '94 / Nimbus

☐ RAG LALIT
NI 5152 / Sep '94 / Nimbus

☐ RAGA DARBARI KANADA/DHUN IN RAGA
NI 5638 / Sep '94 / Nimbus

☐ RAGA PATDIP/PAHADI DHUN (Chaurasia, Hariprasad & Shib Sankar Ray)
NI 5469 / Aug '96 / Nimbus

☐ RAGAS DURGAWATI & MISHRA SHIVARANJANI
Alaap / Drut gat composition / Gat composition / Alaap / Dhun 6 beat dadra taal
NRCD 0090 / Feb '98 / Navras

Chavela

☐ CHAVELA VARGAS
68983 / Jul '97 / Tropical

Chaves, Guillermo

☐ EL SUSPIRO DEL MORO (Chaves, Guillermo & Marc Loopuyt/Adel Shamseddin)
AUB 006777 / Apr '93 / Auvidis/Ethnic

Chavez

☐ GONE GLIMMERING
Nailed to the blank / Spot / Break up your band / Ghost by the sea / Relaxed fit / Wakeman's air / Flaming gong / In our pools / Pentagram ring / Laugh track
OLE 1332 / Jul '95 / Matador

☐ RIDE THE FADER
Top pocket man / Guard attacks / Unreal is here / New room / Tight around the jaws / Lions / Our boys will shine / Tonight / Memorize this face / Cold joys / Flight '96 / Ever overpsyched / You must be stopped
OLE 2002 / Nov '96 / Matador

Chavis, Boozoo

☐ BOOZOO, THAT'S WHO
ROUCD 2126 / Jan '94 / Rounder

☐ LEGENDS OF ZYDECO: SWAMP MUSIC VOL.7
US 0203 / Apr '95 / Trikont

☐ LIVE AT RICHARD'S ZYDECO DANCE HALL VOL.1 (Chavis, Boozoo & The Majic Sounds)
ROUCD 2069 / '88 / Rounder

☐ LIVE AT THE HABIBI TEMPLE
ROUCD 2130 / Sep '94 / Rounder

Che Shizu

☐ SUISHO
PSFD 89 / Dec '97 / PSF

Cheap 'n' Nasty

☐ BEAUTIFUL DISASTER
WOLCD 1002 / May '91 / China

Cheap Seats

☐ CALL IT WHAT YOU WILL
Something in the water / It's just love / Sometimes they do / Drop me gently / I'll get over you / From where I stand / Can't stop my heart / Water into wine / She wears the clown / If I lose you (I lose you) / Broken heart attack / After the rain / Rambling man
GEMINI 02 / Jul '97 / JVO

☐ LITTLE LESS TALK AND A LOT MORE ACTION, A
Cheap seats / Beer, whisky, women / Mr. Blue / I need somebody / Little rock / Devil comes back to Georgia / Theme from 'Two's Country' / Case / Take good care (of my little girl) / Make the world go away / It doesn't matter anymore / My home town / Tulsa time / Highways and heartaches / In pictures / Lipstick promises / Little less talk...and a lot more action
GEMINI 01 / 17 Nov '97 / JVO

☐ NOT THAT DIFFERENT
GR 04 / 20 Apr '98 / Gemini

Cheap Trick

☐ AT THE BUDOKAN (The Complete Concert/2CD Set)
Hello there / Come on come on / ELO kiddies / Speak now / Big eyes / Look out / Downed / Can't hold on / Caroline / Surrender / Auf wiedersehen / Need your love / High roller / Southern girls / I want me to want you / California man / Goodnight man / Ain't that a shame / Clock strikes ten
4896502 / 4 May '98 / Columbia

☐ CHEAP TRICK
Hot love / Speak now or forever hold your peace / He's a whore / Mandocello / Ballad of TV violence / Ello kiddies / Daddy should have stayed in High School / Taxman / Mr. Thief / Cry cry / Oh Candy / Surrender / California / High roller / Auf wiedersehen / Takin' me back / On the radio / Heaven tonight / Stiff competition / How are you
4879332 / Jul '97 / Epic

☐ CHEAP TRICK
Anytime / Hard to tell / Carnival game / Shelter / You let a lotta people down / Baby no more / Yeah yeah / Say goodbye / Wrong all along / Eight miles low / It all comes back to you
RAACD 002 / Jun '97 / Red Ant

☐ GREATEST HITS
Magical mystery tour / Dream police / Don't be cruel / Tonight it's you / She's tight / I want you to want me / If you want my love / Ain't that a shame (live) / Surrender / Flame / I can't take it / Can't stop fallin' into love / Voices
4690862 / Apr '94 / Epic

☐ SEX, AMERICA, CHEAP TRICK
Hello there / ELO kiddies / Hot love / Oh, Candy / Mandocello / Lovin' money / I want you to want me / Southern girls / So good to see you / Down on the bay / Mrs. Henry / Violins / Ballad of TV violence / You're all talk / Fan club / Surrender / High roller / On top of the world / Auf Wiedersehen / I want you to want me / Clock strikes ten / Dream police / Way of the world / Gonna raise hell / Voices / Stop this game / Just got back / Baby loves to rock / Everything works if you let it / World's greatest lover / Waitin' for the man/ Heroin / Daytripper / I need love / World's greatest lover / I'm the man / Born to raise hell / Ohm sweet ohm / She's tight / Love's got a hold on me / If you want my love / Lookin' out for / Don't make our love a crime / All I really want / I can't take it / Twisted heart / Invaders of the heart / Y O Y O Y / Tonight it's you / Cover girl / This time around / Place in France / Funk / Take me to the top / Money is the route of all fun / Fortune cookie / You want it / Flame / Through the night / Stop that thief / I know what I want / Had to make you mine / I can't understand it / Can't stop falling into love / Come on Christmas
E4K 649384 / Aug '96 / Columbia

☐ WOKE UP WITH A MONSTER
My gang / Woke up with a monster / You're all I wanna do / Never runout of love / Didn't know I had it / Ride the pony / Girlfriends / Let her go / Tell me everything / Cry baby / Love me for a minute
9362454252 / Mar '94 / WEA

Cheater Slicks

☐ DON'T LIKE YOU
ITR 030CD / Dec '96 / In The Red

☐ FORGIVE THEE (2CD Set)
ITR 054 / 13 Oct '97 / In The Red

☐ SKIDMARKS
EFACD 12898 / 30 Mar '98 / Crypt

Cheatham, Doc

☐ AT THE BERNE JAZZ FESTIVAL (Cheatham, Doc & Jim Galloway)
SKCD 23045 / Jun '93 / Sackville

☐ DUETS AND SOLOS (2CD Set) (Cheatham, Doc & Sammy Price)
SK2CD 5002 / Mar '97 / Sackville

☐ HEY DOC
BB 887 / Nov '97 / Black & Blue

☐ LIVE AT THE SWEET BASIL
JCD 283 / Dec '97 / Jazzology

☐ SWINGING DOWN IN NEW ORLEANS
JCD 233 / Dec '95 / Jazzology

☐ YOU'RE A SWEETHEART
SKCD 2038 / Jul '96 / Sackville

Cheatham, Jeannie

☐ **BASKET FULL OF BLUES (Cheatham, Jeannie & Jimmy)**
Blues like Jay McShann / Heaven or hell blues / Buddy Bolden's blues / Song of the wanderer / Basket full of blues / All the time / Baby, where have you been / Band rat blues / Little girl blue/Am I blue / Bye 'n' bye blues / Ballad of the wannabes / Don't cha boogie with your black drawers off
CCD 4501 / Mar '92 / Concord Jazz

☐ **BLUES AND THE BOOGIE MASTERS**
What we do for fun / Lead dog blues / Little bitty bluebird blues / Don't let me wake up / Blues and the boogie masters / Lonesome road / Line in the sand / Too many goodbyes / Up in Rickey's room / Leave that woman blues / Please send me someone to love
CCD 4579 / Nov '93 / Concord Jazz

☐ **GUD NUZ BLUZ (Cheatham, Jeannie & Jimmy)**
Mr. CP / Low lines blues / Shop-o-holic / Careless love / That ain't right / What a fool I was / Few good men / Coal yard and ice house blues / Fine and mellow / Go down go down / Gud nuz bluz
CCD 4690 / Apr '96 / Concord Jazz

☐ **MIDNIGHT MAMA**
Wrong direction blues / CC rider / Worried life blues / Big fat daddy blues / Midnight mama / Piney Brown / Finance company / How long blues / Reel ya' deel ya dee dee dee
CCD 4297 / Nov '96 / Concord Jazz

Checker, Chubby

☐ **LET'S TWIST AGAIN**
Twist / Limbo rock / Let's twist again / Hucklebuck / Pony time / Mary ann limbo / Popeye the hitchhiker / Dance the mess around / Twist it up / Fly / Let's limbo some more / Hooka tooka / Hey bobba needle / Loddy lo / Rosie / Dancin' party / Slow twistin' / Twenty miles / Birdland / Let's do the freddie
RMB 75058 / Nov '93 / Remember

☐ **LET'S TWIST AGAIN**
Let's twist again / Limbo rock / Twenty miles / Pony time / Slow twistin' / Let's limbo some more / Popeye the hitchhiker / Loddy lo / Hey bobba needle / Birdland / Hucklebuck / Dance the mess around / Twist / Hooka tooka / Fly / Let's do the Freddie / Twist it up / Dancin' party
308622 / 20 Apr '98 / Hallmark

☐ **ULTIMATE COLLECTION, THE (16 All Time Classics)**
Twist / Limbo rock / Dancin' party / Hey babba needle / Loddy lo / Slow twistin' / Fly / Party time / Let's twist again / Let's limbo some more / Birdland / Dance the mess around / Popeye (The hitchiker) / Twenty miles / Twist it up / Hucklebuck
ECD 3045 / Jan '95 / K-Tel

☐ **VERY BEST OF CHUBBY CHECKER, THE**
Limbo rock / Twist / Hey Bobba Needle / Dancin' party / Slow twistin' / Loddy lo / Pony time / Fly / Let's limbo some more / Let's twist again / Dance the mess around / Birdland / Twenty miles / Popeye / Hucklebuck / Twist it up
SUMCD 4181 / 23 Feb '98 / Summit

Checkists

☐ **NEVER MIND THE ELECTRODES**
WSCD 009 / Oct '96 / World Serpent

Cheech & Chong

☐ **GREATEST HIT**
Earache my eye / Dave / Let's make a dope deal / Basketball Jones / Blin melon chitlin' / Sister Mary elephant / Sergeant Stadanko / Dave / Cruisin' / Continuing adventures of Pedro De Pacas / Pedro and man at the drivein / Trippin' in court
7599236142 / Jan '93 / WEA

Cheek, Chris

☐ **GIRL NAMED JOE, A**
FSNT 032 / 1 Jun '98 / Fresh Sound New Talent

☐ **I WISH I KNEW (Cheek, Chris Quartet)**
FSNT 022 / 5 Jan '98 / Fresh Sound New Talent

Cheeky Monkey

☐ **FOUR ARMS TO HOLD YOU**
SHOECD 002 / 30 Mar '98 / Shoeshine

Cheer Accident

☐ **DUMB ASK**
NM 001CD / Oct '97 / Neat Metal

Chelon, Georges

☐ **MA COMPILATION**
984322 / Nov '97 / EPM

Chelsea

☐ **FOOLS AND SOLDIERS**
I'm on fire / Come on / No flowers / Urban kids / 12 men / Trouble is the day / Your toy / Decide / Curfew / Look at the outside / Don't get me wrong / Fools and soldiers / Bring it on home / No admission / Loner / Route 66 / Right to work
RRCD 242 / Jul '97 / Receiver

☐ **LIVE AT THE MUSIC MACHINE 1978**
REM 016 CD / Mar '92 / Released Emotions

☐ **UNRELEASED STUFF**
I'm on fire / Come on / No flowers / Urban kids / Twelve men / Trouble is the day / Young toy / Decide / Curfew / Look at the outside / Don't get me wrong / Fools and soldiers / Comeon
CLAYCD 101 / Jul '94 / Clay

Chelsea FC

☐ **BLUE FLAG (A Tribute To Chelsea Football Club) (Various Artists)**
Blue is the colour: *Chelsea FC 1972* / Liquidator: *Billy Bluebeat* / Back on the ball: *Chelsea FC 1984* / We'll keep the blue flag flying high: *Boys From The Shed* / London medley: *Chelsea FC 1972* / Flying high 94: *True Blue Crew* / Chelsea heaven Chelsea hell: *True Blue Crew* / Ruudy's rock steady crew: *Turtle, Henry* / Chelsea: *Stamford Bridge* / We'll keep the blue flag flying high: *Turtle, Henry* / Chelsea of blue: *Chelsea FC* / No one can stop us now: *Chelsea FC 1994* / Blue days of Chelsea: *Pensioners* / Chelsea we love you: *Chelsea FC 1987* / Chelsea wonderland: *Billy Bluebeat* / 1 Minute to Matthew: *Billy Bluebeat* / Pride of London: *Billy Bluebeat*
CDGAFFER 20 / 17 Nov '97 / Cherry Red

☐ **BLUE IS THE COLOUR**
Blue is the colour / Chirpy chirpy cheep cheep / Football is / Give me back my soccer boots / Maybe it's because I'm a Londoner / Let's all go down the Strand / On mother Kelly's doorstep / Strollin' / Let's all sing together / Song sung blue / Stop and take a look / Son of my father / Alouette
MONDE 19CD / Oct '94 / Cherry Red

Chemical Brothers

☐ **DIG YOUR OWN HOLE**
Block rockin' beats / Dig your own hole / Elektrobank / Piku / Setting sun / It doesn't matter / Don't stop the rock / Get up on it like this / Lost in the K-hole / Where do I begin / Private psychedelic reel
XDUSTCD 2 / Apr '97 / Freestyle Dust

☐ **EXIT PLANET DUST**
Leave home / In dust we trust / Song to the siren / Three little birdies down beats / Fuck up beats / Chemical beats / Life is sweet / Playground for a wedgeless firm / Chico's groove / One too many mornings / Alive: alone
XDUSTCD 1 / Jun '95 / Freestyle Dust

☐ **LIFE IS SWEET**
ASW 6162 / 20 Apr '98 / Astralwerks

Chemical Dance Culture

☐ **PHUTURISTIC TRANCE (Test 1)**
TJAM 0001 / 25 May '98 / Tecnojam

Chemical People

☐ **ANGELS 'N' DEVILS**
CRZ 019CD / May '93 / Cruz

☐ **APREGGIO MOTORCADE**
Counting days / Last one / I hope you're there / Can't see your face / Tables turn / No reason why / No hope / Waiting / It's up to you / Forgot about
CRZ 040CD / 13 Oct '97 / Cruz

☐ **CHEMICAL PEOPLE**
CRZ 023CD / May '93 / Cruz

☐ **LET IT GO**
CRZ 025CD / May '93 / Cruz

☐ **RIGHT THING, THE**
Captain / Right thing / A pornography / Duck song / Different scene / Some other time / Unanswered question / Aqua il / Overdosed / Nutro / Cheri love affair / Jam
CRZ 013CD / Aug '90 / Cruz

☐ **SO SEXIST**
CRZ 002CD / Jan '90 / Cruz

☐ **SOUNDTRACKS**
CRZ 020CD / May '93 / Cruz

☐ **TEN-FOLD HATE**
New food / Aquaman / Old habits / Strange tastes / She's got a bad case / Ed intro / Cherry / Intro / All the best things / Nudist camp / Metallica / Cop a feel / Moodchanger / Vacation / Outrage / Black throat
CRZ 007CD / Jan '90 / Cruz

Chemirani, Djamchid

☐ **TRADITION CLASSIQUE DE L'IRAN VOL.1 (Le Zarb)**
HMA 190388 / Nov '93 / Musique D'Abord

Chemlab

☐ **EAST SIDE MILITIA**
398414115CD / Oct '96 / Metal Blade

Chen, Sisi

☐ **TIDES AND SAND**
HSR 0001 / Mar '96 / Henry Street

Cheneour, Paul

☐ **DANCE IN THE FIRE (Cheneour, Paul & Dilly Meah)**
RGM 289CD / Apr '98 / Red Gold Music

☐ **REIKI HEALING SYMBOLS IN SOUND**
RGM 197CD / Apr '98 / Red Gold Music

☐ **TIME HAS COME, THE**
Med mig sjalv / Time has come / First find an angel / Glass bead game / Who will cry / Rain / Moontide / Village / Sowena / Shroud / Fantasie I / Fantasie II / Fantasie III / Knots / Rain / Nasrudin
RGM 294CD / Feb '95 / Red Gold Music

Cheng, Shui Cheng

☐ **ART OF THE CHINESE PIPER, THE**
ARN 60377 / 21 Aug '97 / Arion

Chenier, C.J.

☐ **BIG SQUEEZE, THE**
ALCD 4844 / Sep '96 / Alligator

Chenier, Clifton

☐ **60 MINUTES WITH THE KING OF ZYDECO**
ARCD 301 / Apr '95 / Arhoolie

☐ **BOGALUSA BOOGIE**
One step at a time / M'appel fou (they call me crazy) / Quelque chose sur mon idee (there's something on my mind) / Ride 'em cowboy / Ma mama ma dit (my mama told me) / Je me reveiller le matin (i woke up this morning) / I may be wrong / Take off your dress / Allons a grand coteau (let's go to grand coteau) / Je suis en recolteur (I'm a farmer) / Ti na na / Come go along with me / Bogalusa boogie
ARHCD 347 / Apr '95 / Arhoolie

☐ **BON TON ROULET**
Bon ton roulet / Froglegs / If I ever get lucky / Black gal / Long toes / Baby please don't go / Houston boogie / Blues de ma negresse / Sweet little doll (cher catin) / Jole blonde / Ay ay ay / French town waltz / Keep on scratching / Black snake blues / Let's talk it over / Walking to louisiana / Key to the highway / Things ain't like they used to be / I got a little girl / I'm on the wonder / Jump the boogie
ARHCD 345 / Apr '95 / Arhoolie

☐ **CAJUN SWAMP MUSIC LIVE**
CPCD 8237 / Aug '97 / Charly

☐ **CLIFTON CHENIER IN NEW ORLEANS**
Boogie Louisiana / Cotton picker blues / J'aime pain de mais / Pousse cafe waltz / Hello Rosa-Lee / Jusque parce que je t'aime / Boogie in Orleans / Rumblin' on the bayou / I'm gonna take you home tonite / Mon vieux buggy / Crying my heart out to you / Tous les jours / Mardi gras boogie
GNPD 2119 / Sep '95 / GNP Crescendo

☐ **CLIFTON CHENIER SINGS THE BLUES (Home Cookin' & Prophesy Sides From 1969)**
Ain't no need of crying (every day is the same) / Rosemary / Brown skinned woman / Done got over / Gone a la maison / Be my chauffeur / My little angel / Paper in my shoe / Blues after hours / Trouble in mind / In the mood / Worried life blues / Grand prix / Hungry man blues / Falksy girl / Easy easy baby / Tante na na / Do right sometime / Highway blues
ARHCD 351 / Apr '95 / Arhoolie

☐ **KING OF THE BAYOUS**
Tu le ton son ton (every now and then) / Hard to love someone / Who can your good man be (brown skin woman) / Zodico two-step (french two-step) / Going la maison / I believe I'll go back home / Release me / Grand mamou (big mamou) / Ton na na (aunt na na) / I'm coming home / Josephine par se ma femme (josephine is not my wife) / It's christmas time / Coming home tomorrow / Me and my chauffeur / Mo veux connaitre (where she slept) / Tired of crying over you / Clifton's blues / Let's rock a while
ARHCD 339 / Apr '95 / Arhoolie

☐ **KING OF ZYDECO LIVE AT MONTREUX**
Intro and jambalaya / You're fussin' too much / Clifton's boogie woogie / Hey, tite fille / Cher catin / Zydeco sont pas sale / Je marche le plancher / Release me / I'm a hog for you / Louisiana two step / Black gal / Money / I'm on the wonder / Woo woo / Hush hush / Calinda
ARHCD 355 / Apr '95 / Arhoolie

☐ **LIVE AT LONG BEACH & SAN FRANCISCO BLUES FESTIVAL**
Introduction and theme / I've had my fun (going down slow) / Zydeco two step / Calinda / What'd I say / Party down / I'm coming home / Pinetop's boogie woogie / They call me crazy / Zydeco cha cha / You gonna miss me / Caledonia / New orleans beat / Clifton's zydeco / Let the good times roll / Rock me / Louisiana two step / Cher catin / I'm the zydeco man
ARHCD 404 / Apr '95 / Arhoolie

☐ **LIVE AT ST. MARK'S**
ARHCD 313 / Apr '95 / Arhoolie

☐ **LOUISIANA BLUES AND ZYDECO**
Zydeco sont pas sale / Lafayette waltz / Louisiana two step / Clifton's waltz / Louisiana blues / Why did you go last night / Eh, 'tite fille / Banana man / Hot rod / It's hard / I can look down at your woman / I can't stand / Monifique / Johnny can't dance / I lost my baby (in french) / Pepper in my shoe / Can't go home no more / Wrap it up zydeco
ARHCD 329 / Apr '95 / Arhoolie

☐ **MY BABY DON'T WEAR NO SHOES**
My baby don't wear no shoes / My baby don't wear no shoes / She's my woman / Blue flame blues / Check out the zydeco / Harry's big mama blues / Let me in your heart / Bow-legged woman / Banana man / I'm all shook up / Used and abused / I'll be long gone
ARHCD 1098 / Apr '95 / Arhoolie

☐ **ON TOUR**
157722 / Feb '93 / Blues Collection

☐ **OUT WEST**
I'm on the wonder / Hucklebuck / Je marche le plancher (you know it ain't fair) / Calinda / You're the one for me / You're fussin' too much / Just like a woman / All your love / C. c. special (take no. 2) / I'm a hog for you / C. c. special (take no. 1) / Ti na na / Zydeco cha cha / Crawfish jambalaya / Ma negresse est gone / Breaux bridge waltz / Louisiana two step
ARHCD 350 / Apr '95 / Arhoolie

☐ **TOO MUCH FUN (Chenier, Clifton & His Red Hot Louisiana Band)**
ALCD 4830 / Apr '95 / Alligator

☐ **ZODICO BLUES & BOOGIE**
Boppin' the rock / Ay tet fee / Cat's dreamin' / Squeeze box boogie / Things I did for you / Think it over / Zodico stomp / Yesterday (I lost my best friend) / Chenier's boogie / I'm on my way (back home to you) / All night long / Opelousas hop / Wherever you go I'll go / Clifton's dreamin'
CDCHD 389 / May '92 / Ace

☐ **ZYDECO SONT PAS SALE**
Zydeco sont pas sale / Blues de ma negresse / Cher Catin / Going la Maison / J'ai conet, c'est pas ma femme / Jole blonde / Mo veux connaitre / Je suis en recolteur / Je me reveiller le martin / Je marche le plancher / Louisiana two step / Weetee ta robe / Zydeco two-step / Breau Bridge waltz / Tu le ton son ton
ARHCD 9001 / Sep '97 / Arhoolie

Chenille Sisters

☐ **HAUTE CHENILLE (A Retrospective)**
RHRCD 81 / Jan '96 / Red House

☐ **TRUE TO LIFE**
RHRCD 67 / May '95 / Red House

Chenut, Regis

☐ **ART OF THE CELTIC HARP, THE**
ARN 60357 / Nov '97 / Arion

Cher

☐ **ALL I REALLY WANT TO DO/SONNY SIDE OF CHER/CHER (3CD Set)**
All I really want to do / I go to sleep / Needles and pins / Don't think twice / She thinks I still care / Dream baby / Bells of Rhymney / Girl don't come / CC rider / Come and stay with me / Cry myself to sleep / Blowin' in the wind / Bang bang (my baby shot me down) / Young girl (une entante) / Where do you go / Our day will come / Elusive butterfly / Like a rolling stone / Ol' man river / Come to your window / Girl from Ipanema / It's not unusual / Time / Milord / Twelfth of never / You don't have to say you love me / I feel something in the air / Will you love me tomorrow / Until it's time for you to go / Cruel war / Catch the wind / Pied piper / Homeward bound / I want you / Alfie
CDOMB 005 / 27 Jul '98 / EMI

☐ **BANG BANG (MY BABY SHOT ME DOWN)**
Dream baby / All I really want to do / I go to sleep / Come and stay with me / Where do you go / See see blues / Bang bang (my baby shot me down) / Needles and pins / Come to your window / Alfie / She's no better than me / Behind the door / Magic in the air (I feel something in the air) / Mama (when my dollies have babies) / You better sit down kids / Click song number one / But I can't love you any more / It all adds up now / I wasn't ready / Take me for a little while / Song called children / Reason to believe
CDP 7927732 / Sep '96 / EMI

☐ **CHER**
I found someone / We all sleep alone / Bang bang (my baby shot me down) / Main man / Give our love a fightin' chance / Perfection / Dangerous times / Skin deep / Working girl / Hard enough getting over you
GED 24164 / Nov '96 / Geffen

☐ **CHER'S GREATEST HITS 1965-1992**
Oh no not my baby / Whenever you're near / Many rivers to cross / Love and understanding / Save up all your tears / It's in his kiss (The shoop shoop song) / If I could turn back time / Just like Jesse James / Heart of stone / I found someone / We all sleep alone / Bang bang (my baby shot me down) / Dead ringer for love / Dark lady / Gypsies, tramps and thieves / I got you babe
GED 24439 / Nov '92 / Geffen

☐ **HEART OF STONE**
If I could turn back time / Just like Jesse James / You wouldn't know love / Heart of stone / Still in love with you / Love on a rooftop / Emotional fire / All because of you / Does anybody really fall in love anymore / Starting over / Kiss to kiss / After all
GEFD 24239 / Jan '91 / Geffen

☐ **HOLDIN' OUT FOR LOVE**
JHD 021 / Jun '92 / Tring

☐ **IT'S A MAN'S WORLD**
Don't come around tonite / What about the moonlight / Same mistake / Gunman / Sun ain't gonna shine anymore / Shape of things to come / It's a man's man's man's world / Walking in Memphis / Not enough love in the world / One by one / I wouldn't treat a dog (the way you treated me) / Angels running / Paradise is here / I'm blowin' away
0630126702 / Nov '95 / WEA

☐ **LOVE HURTS**
Save up all your tears / Love hurts / Love and understanding / Fires of Eden / I'll never stop loving you / One small step / World without heroes / Could've been you / When love calls your name / When lovers become strangers / Who you gonna believe / It's in his kiss (The shoop shoop song)
GFLD 19266 / Feb '95 / Geffen

☐ TAKE ME HOME/PRISONER
Take me home / Wasn't it good / Say the word / Happy was the day we met / Git down / Love and pain / Let this be a lesson to you / It's too late to love me now / My song (too far gone) / Prisoner / Holdin' out for love / Shoppin' / Boys and girls / Mirror image / Hell on wheels / Holy smoke / Outrageous
5500382 / May '93 / Spectrum

Cherish The Ladies

☐ BACK DOOR, THE
Character's Polka/The Warlock/The Volunteer/The Donegal Trav / Back door / Redican's/Sean Ryan's/ Take the bull by the horns / Galway Hornpipe/Dessie O'Connor/Mother reel / Coal Quay market/Happy days/Rabbit in the field / Maire Mhor / If ever you were mine / Paddy O'Brien's/Toss the feathers/ Jenny Dang the weaver / My own native land / Pepin Arsenault/The Shepherd's daughter/A bunch in the dark / Three weeks we were wed / Jessica's polka / Tear the Calico/I have no money / Carrigdhoun / Redican's mother / Humours of Westport/The morning dew/The glass of beer/Yougha
GLCD 1119 / Nov '92 / Green Linnet

☐ CHERISH THE LADIES
Callan lassies / Flowing bowl / Donegal jig / Cherish the ladies / Scully Casey's / O'Bryne's / Boys of the 25 / Farrel O'Gerbhaigh / Dark slender boy / Bonnie Prince Charlie / Dairy maid / Heathery breeze / Dublin reel / Trip to Athlone / Gold ring / Murphy's / O'Rourke's / Pinch of snuff / Hewlett / Sonny Mazurka / Churn of buttermilk / O'Kennedy's / Tom Ward's down fall
PTICD 1043 / Aug '96 / Pure Traditional Irish

☐ IRISH WOMEN MUSICIANS IN AMERICA
SHCD 79053 / Mar '95 / Shanachie

☐ NEW DAY DAWNING
Highway to Kilkenny / Green grow the rushes oh / Barrel Rafferty's jigs / A Neansai mhile gra / Crowley's reels/Tom Ward's downfall / Green cottage polkas / Lord Mayo / Galway rover / Joe Ryan's barn dance set / Ned of the hill / Broken wings / Rayleen's reel / Keg of brandy
GLCD 1175 / Oct '96 / Green Linnet

☐ ONE AND ALL (The Best Of Cherish The Ladies)
Cat rambles to the child's saucepan: O'Keefe, Maire & Harry Bradshaw / Cameronian set / Green cottege polka / Jer O'Connell's / Tom's tavern / Broken wings / Declan's waltz / Waltz duhamel / Neansai mhile gra / Highway to Kilkenny / Boys of Portaferry / Abbey reel / Ashmaleen house / Three weeks we were wed / O'keefes / Shepherds lamb / John O'Leary's / Green grow the rushes oh / Jessica's polka / Tear the calico / I have no money / Back door / Crowley's reels / Tom Ward's downfall / My own native land / Joe Ryan's barn dance set
GLCD 1187 / Mar '98 / Green Linnet

☐ OUT & ABOUT
Old favourite/Flogging reel/Leave my way/The Kerryman/Spoon river/Ladies of Carrick/Kinnegad slashers/Old man Dillon / Declan's waltz/Waltz Duhamel / Cameronian set / Inisheer / O'Keefe's/ Shepherd's lamb/Johnny O'Leary / Roisin dubh / Le voyage de Camouret/House of Hamill / Cat rambles to the child's saucepan/Maire O'Keefe/Harry Brad / Missing piece / Out and about set
GLCD 1134 / Oct '93 / Green Linnet

☐ THREADS OF TIME
Medley / High Germany / Medley / Ballad of Aughrim/ Star above the garter / Lake side of Innisfree/Tip toe home/Paddy Kelly's / Bergen / Anascaul olka/Pat Enright's/Joe Wilson's / Medley
09026631312 / 6 Apr '98 / RCA Victor

Cherry, Don

☐ ART DECO
Art deco / Body and soul / Maffy / Blessing / I've grown accustomed to her face / When will the blues leave / Bemsha swing / Folk medley / Passing / Compute
3952582 / Jul '94 / A&M

☐ BROTHERHOOD SUITE
FLCD 4 / Feb '98 / Flash Music

☐ DONA NOSTRA
In memoriam / Fort cherry / Arrows / M'bizo / Race face / Prayer / What reason could O give / Vienna / Ahaye-da
5217272 / Apr '94 / ECM

☐ IN ANKARA/THE ETERNAL NOW (The Sonet Recordings/2CD Set)
Gandalf's travels / Ornette's concert / Ornette's tune / St. John and the dragon / Efeler / Anadolu havasi / Discovery of bhupala / Waterboy / Yaz geldi / Tamzara / Kara deniz / Kocekce / Man on the moon / Creator has a master plan / Two flutes / Gamla stan / Old town by night / Love train / Piano piece for two pianos and three piano players / Moving pictures for the ear
5330492 / Dec '96 / Verve

☐ MU (The Complete Session)
Brilliant action / Amejelo / Total vibrations / Sun of the east / Terrestrial beings / Mystics of my sound / Dollar brand / Spontaneous composing / Exert / Man on the moon / Bamboo night / Teo-teo can / Smiling faces / Going places / Psycho drama / Theme albert heath / Theme dollar brand / Babyrest / Time for
LEJAZZCD 56 / Aug '96 / Le Jazz

☐ OLD AND NEW DREAMS (Cherry, Don & Dewey Redman/Eddie Blackwell/ Charlie Haden)
Handwoven / Dewey's tune / Chairman Mao / Next to the quiet stream / Augmented / Old and new dreams
BSR 0013CD / Oct '86 / Black Saint

☐ SYMPHONY FOR IMPROVISERS
CDP 8289762 / Sep '94 / Blue Note

Cherry, Eagle Eye

☐ DESIRELESS
5372262 / 20 Jul '98 / Polydor

Cherry, Ed

☐ FIRST TAKE
Jean Pauline / Little sunflower / Lorenzo's wings / Third stone from the sun / Serious / In a sentimental mood / Inner circle / Rachel's step / Blue interrogation
5199422 / Jun '94 / Groovin' High

Cherry, Neneh

☐ HOMEBREW
Sassy / Money love / Move with me / I ain't gone under yet / Twisted / Buddy X / Somedays / Trout: *Cherry, Neneh & Michael Stipe* / Peace in mind / Red paint
CIRCD 25 / Oct '92 / Circa

☐ MAN
Woman / Feel it / Hornbeam / Trouble man / Golden ring / 7 seconds: *Cherry, Neneh & Youssou N'Dour* / Kootchi / Beastiality / Carry me / Together now / Everything
CDHUT 38 / Sep '96 / Hut

☐ RAW LIKE SUSHI
Buffalo stance / Manchild / Kisses on the wind / Inna city mamma / Next generation / Love ghetto / Heart / Phoney ladies / Outre risque locomotive / So here I come / My bitch / Heart (it's a demo) / Buffalo stance (sukka mix) / Manchild (Mix)
CIRCD 8 / Apr '92 / Circa

Cherry People

☐ CHERRY PEOPLE, THE
And suddenly / Girl on the subway / On to something new / Imagination / Mr. Hyde / Do something to me / Ask the children / I'm the one who loves you / Don't hang me up girl / Light of love
NEMCD 723 / May '95 / Sequel

Chertock, Michael

☐ PALACE OF THE WIND
CD 80477 / 8 Sep '97 / Telarc

Cherub

☐ SARC ART
MASSCD 045 / Jan '95 / Massacre

Cherubs

☐ HEROIN MAN
TR 24CD / Jun '94 / Trance

☐ SHORT FOR POPULAR
TR 48CD / Aug '96 / Trance Syndicate

Chesapeake

☐ FULL SAIL
SHCD 3941 / Dec '95 / Sugar Hill

☐ PIER PRESSURE
Once a day / Full force gale / Bed of roses / Nothing ain't a lot / Carolina star / Sleepwalk(ing) at the drive-in / Baby blue eyes / White pilgrim / Guilty / Rockin' hillbilly / Don't lay down / Working on a building
SHCD 3872 / 9 Mar '98 / Sugar Hill

☐ RISING TIDE
SHCD 3827 / May '95 / Sugar Hill

Chescoe, Laurie

☐ LAURIE CHESCOE'S GOOD TIME JAZZ
I wanna girl / Dans les rues D'Antibes / Is you is or is you ain't my baby / My blue heaven / Limehouse blues / I want a little girl / Bloodshot eyes
JCD 002 / Oct '90 / Jazzology

☐ LONDON PRIDE 1994 (Chescoe, Laurie Good Time Jazz Band)
JCD 244 / Jan '97 / Jazzology

Chesney, Kenny

☐ ME AND YOU
07863669082 / Jun '96 / RCA

Chesnutt, Mark

☐ ALMOST GOODBYE
It sure is Monday / Woman, sensuous woman / Almost goodbye / I just wanted you to know / April's fools / Texas is bigger than it used to be / My heart's too broke (To pay attention) / Vickie Vance gotta dance / Till a better memory comes along / Will
MCAD 10851 / Mar '94 / MCA

☐ GREATEST HITS
Bubba shot the jukebox / Too cold at home / Blame it on Texas / Almost goodbye / It's a little too late / Ol' country / Brother jukebox / Gonna get a life / Let it rain / It sure is Monday / Goin' through the big D / I'll think of something
MCD 11529 / Feb '97 / MCA

Chesnutt, Vic

☐ ABOUT TO CHOKE
PLR 0052
PLR 0055 / Nov '96 / Texas Hotel

☐ DRUNK
Sleeping man / Bourgeois and biblical / One of many / When I ran off and left her / Dodge / Gluefoot / Drunk / Naughty fatalist / Super Tuesday / Kick my ass
TXH 0222 / Jul '96 / Texas Hotel

☐ IS THE ACTOR HAPPY
Gravity of the situation / Sad Peter Pan / Strange language / Onion soup / Doubting woman / Wrong piano / Free of hope / Betty lonely / Thumbtack / Thailand / Guilty by association
TXH 0232 / Jul '96 / Texas Hotel

☐ LITTLE
Isadora Duncan / Danny Carlisle / Giupetto / Bakersfield / Mr. Riely / Rabbit box / Speed racer / Soft Picasso / Independence Day / Stevie Smith
TXH 0202 / Jul '96 / Texas Hotel

☐ SAMPLER
TXH 0213 / Jul '94 / Texas Hotel

☐ WEST OF ROME
Latent blatant / Withering away / Sponge / Where were you / Lucinda Williams / Florida / Stupid pre-occupation / Panic / Miss Mary / Steve Willougby / West of Rome / Big huge valley / Soggy tongues / Fuge
TXH 0212 / Jul '96 / Texas Hotel

Chessa, Totore

☐ OGANITTOS
NT 6743CD / Mar '96 / Newtone

Chest

☐ MYSTERY SUPERETTE
NONG 03CD / 22 Sep '97 / Fierce Panda

Chester, Bob

☐ BOB CHESTER & HIS ORCHESTRA 1940-41
CCD 44 / Jan '94 / Circle

☐ OCTAVE JUMP 1939-1942 (Chester, Bob & His Orchestra)
RACD 7103 / May '96 / Aerospace

Chester, Paul Vernon

☐ SUITE DJANGO
Naissence / Valse des enfants / Flame of destiny / Redemption / Nin nin / Broad-brimmed hat / Baro and matelo / Hotel claridge / Selmer swing / American dream / Naguine's tears
FJCD 112 / Jan '97 / Fret

Chesterfield Kings

☐ LET'S GET STONED
MIRROR 19CD / 24 Nov '97 / Mirror

☐ NIGHT OF THE LIVING EYES
MIRROR 13CD / 24 Nov '97 / Mirror

☐ SURFIN' RAMPAGE
MIRROR 23CD / 5 Jan '98 / Mirror

Chesterfields

☐ KETTLE
Nose out of joint / Ask Johnny Dee / Two girls and a treehouse / Shame about the rain / Everything a boy could ever need / Kiss me stupid / Thumb / Storm Nelson / Holiday hymn / Oh Mr. Wilson / Boy who sold his suitcase / Completely and utterly
ASKCD 030 / Sep '93 / Vinyl Japan

Chesterman, Charlie

☐ DYNAMITE MUSIC MACHINE
Goodbye to you / Everybody's baby / Go go lil' Fairlane / Love song / Big hairy eyeball / Talahassee lassie / Wants to be Bob Dylan singing electric guitar blues / Bread and butter / Jaguar tan / Where'd ya go / Ready willing and able / Fireball
SRRCD 028 / 8 Sep '97 / Slow River

☐ HIT THIS AND KICK THAT
Sexy Rickenbacker / Lonesome cowboy's lament / Mister Blue / Hello Judy / So long now / New lease on life (parts 1 and 2) / Short brown hair brown eyes / Mona's prayer / Jackhammers / Trash / Theo's El Camino / I've got time / Got you bad
RCD 10367 / Sep '96 / Rykodisc

Chevalier, Maurice

☐ CHARMER, THE
Paris sera toujours Paris / You took the words right out of my mouth / Appelez ca comme vous voulez / Hello beautiful / Ma pomme / Walkin' my baby back home / Notre espoir / Oh, come on, be sociable / Mimi / On top of the world alone / Toi et moi / Mama Inez / Nouveau bonheur / Sweepin' the clouds away / La chanson du macon / March de menilmontant
HADCD 158 / May '94 / Javelin

☐ ENCORE MAURICE
Hello beautiful / Up on top of a rainbow (sweepin' the clouds away) / Ca m'est egal / On top of the world alone / Mais ou est ma Zou-Zou / It's a great life / Mama Inez / Toi et moi / Savez-vous / Bon soir / Goodnight Cherie / Paris je t'aime d'amour / Walkin' my baby back home / Mon coeur / Nobody's using it now / Vous etes mon nouveau bonheur / Right now / Les ananas / O come on be sociable / Lovin' in the moonlight / Paris stay the same / You brought a new kind of love to me / Mon cocktail d'amour / Dites moi ma mere
CDAJA 5016 / Feb '87 / Living Era

☐ FLEUR DE PARIS
Ma pomme / Paris sera toujourd Paris / Fleur de Paris / Le chanson de Macon / Ca s'est passe un Dimanche / Ca sent si bon la France / Prosper / Appelez ca comme vous le voulez / Partout c'est l'amour / Le chapeau do zozo / Donnez-moi la main / Y A d'la joie / Mimile / Dites-moi ma mere / Ca fait d'excellents Francais / Quand un viconte / Notre Espoir / Mon vieux Paris
306272 / Jan '97 / Hallmark

☐ FRENCH MONUMENT, A
995692 / Jul '96 / EPM

☐ IMMORTAL MAURICE CHEVALIER, THE
CD 118 / May '95 / Timeless Treasures

☐ LE ROI DU MUSIC HALL
Valentine / Paris, je t'aime d'amour / La romance de la plune / Mimi / Quand un vicomte / Donnez-moi la Main Mam'zelle / Prosper / Le chapeau de Zozo / L'amour est passe pres de vous / Un p'tit air / Ah si vous connaissiez ma poule / Ca s'est passe un dimanche / Il pleurait / Ca fait d'excellents Francais / Ma pomme / Appelez-ca comme vous voulez / Paris ser toujours Paris / On est comme on est / Y a du bonheur pour tout le monde
UCD 19055 / Mar '96 / Forlane

☐ LOUISE (The Great French Stars - 25 Hits)
Louise / Oh Maurice / Quand on est tout seul / Dites moi ma mere / Oui papa / Wait till you see 'ma cherie' / Valentine / My love parade / Paris stay the same / All I want is just one girl / You bought a new kind of love to me / Livin' in the sunlight lovin' in the moonlight / My ideal / Moonlight saving time / Oh that Mitzi / Mimi / Rhythm of the rain / I was lucky / You took the words right out of my mouth / Prosper / Ma pomme / Ah si vous connaissiez ma poule / La choupetta / Place pigalle
CDAJA 5233 / Oct '97 / Living Era

☐ MAURICE CHEVALIER GOLD COLLECTION, THE (2CD Set)
R2CD 4061 / 9 Mar '98 / Deja Vu

☐ MAURICE CHEVALIER'S PARIS
What would you do / You brought a new kind of love to me / Le chapeau de Zozo (Zozo's new hat) / Livin' in the sunlight, livin' in the moonlight / Rhythm of the rain / Ma pomme (my apple) / You've got that thing / You look so sweet, Madame / Oh cette mitzi (oh that mitzi) / Singing a happy song / Paris, je t'aime d'amour (Paris, stay the same) / Valentine / Tzinga-doodle-day / Wait 'til you see ma cherie / Donnez-moi la main, Mam'zelle / Mimi / Quand un vicompte / My love parade / Les mots qu'on voudrait dire / All I want is just one girl / Personne ne s'en sert maintenant (nobody's using it now) / Louise
QED 061 / Nov '96 / Tring

☐ ON TOP OF THE WORLD
Valentine / It's a habit of mine / Wait till you see Ma cherie / On top of the world alone / Sweepin' the clouds away / All I want is just one girl / Mama Inez / Toi et moi / You brought a new kind of love / Living in the sunlight / Paris stay the same / My love parade / Dites moi ma mere / Quand on est tout seul / Walkin' my baby back home / Oh, come on, be sociable / You took the words right out of my mouth / Hello beautiful / Mimi / Ma pomme / Ah Si vous connaissiez ma poule / Singing a happy song / Rhythm of the rain
PASTCD 9711 / '90 / Flapper

☐ PARIS SERA TOUJOURS PARIS
Paris, Je t'Aime d'Amour / Mais ou est ma Zou-Zou / Toi et moi / Ca m'est Egal / Louise / Mon Coeur / Vous etes mon Nouveau Bonheur / Les Ananas / Ma Pomme / Paris sera toujours Paris / Ca Fait d'excellents Francais / Fleur de Paris / Mimi / La Marche de Menilmontant / Ca c'est passe un dimanche / Bon soir / Savez-vous / Valentine / Hello beautiful / La Choupetta
MDF 102608 / Nov '96 / Mudisque

☐ PORTRAIT OF MAURICE CHEVALIER, A (2CD Set)
Valentine / Mon coeur / Si vous etes / Mais ou est ma zou zou / Moi j'fais mes coups en dessous / Marguerite / Moi-z-et elle / Sans avoir l'air d'y toucher / Ma reguliere / Quand on revient / Dites moi ma mere / Ma Louise / J'ai peur de coucher tout seul / Mon veux Paris / Une brune une blonde / Le petit dame de l'expo / Mon cocktail d'amour / Le chapeau de zozo / Mimi / Paris je taime d'amour / Quand un vicomte / Donnez moi la main mamzell / Les mirlitons / Prosper / Y'a d'la joie / Ma pomme / L'amour est passe pres de vous / Un p'tit air / On est comme on est / Ca s'est passe un dimanche / Ah si vous connaissiez ma poule / Appelez ca comme vous voulez / Partout ca'est amour / Arthue Fox a poils durs / Mimile / Ca fait excellents Francais / Il pleurait / Paris sera toujours Paris / La choupetta / Notre espoir / La chanson du Macon / Ca sent la bon la France / La marche de mentillmontant / La polka de barbus / La fete a neu neu / Quai de bercy / Fleur de Paris
GALE 416 / 6 Oct '97 / Gallerie

☐ SUCCES ET RARETES 1920-1928
701552 / Sep '96 / Chansophone

☐ VALENTINE
AC 75102 / 27 Apr '98 / Arkadia

Chevelles

☐ AT SECOND GLANCE
NLL 001 / 29 Jun '98 / Not Lame

Chewy Marble

☐ CHEWY MARBLE
52706 / 8 Jun '98 / Permanent

Chi

☐ SINCERITY IS A BOY CALLED DEL
FECK 002 / 23 Mar '98 / Simpleton

Chi-Ad

☐ **VIRTUAL SPIRIT**
Healing magic / Ocean also dreams / Astral warrior / State of mind / Serpent's fire / Inner energy / Paranormal activity (spooky) / Organic forms / Sacred vision
9100718 / 26 Jan '98 / Nova Tekk

Chi-Lites

☐ **BEST OF THE CHI-LITES**
Give it away / Let me be the man my daddy was / Twenty four hours of sadness / I like your lovin' / Are you my woman (tell me so) / For god's sake give more power to the people / Have you seen her / Oh girl / Coldest day of my life / We need order / Letter to myself / Stoned out of my mind / I found sunshine / Homely girl / Too good to be forgotten / There will never be any peace (until God is seated at the... / Toby / It's time for love / You don't have to go
CDKEN 911 / Jun '87 / Kent

☐ **BEST OF THE HITS, THE**
Homely girl / Toby / For god's sake give more power to the people / I want to pay you back (For loving me) / Too good to be forgotten / Twenty four hours of sadness / Lonely man / Coldest day of my life / You don't have to go / There will never be any peace (Until God is seated at the co / I found sunshine / It's time for love / Give it away / Oh girl / Stoned out of my mind / Have you seen her / Letter to myself / Let me be the man my Daddy was / We are neighbours
CPCD 8051 / Mar '95 / Charly

☐ **CHI-LITES COLLECTION, THE**
Have you seen her / Oh girl / Heavenly body / Strung out / Round and round / All I wanna do is make love to you / Give me a dream / Super mad / Men and you / Tell me where it hurts / Whole lot of good good loving / Get down with me / Try my side / Hot on a thing / Never speak to a stranger
SUMCD 4116 / May '97 / Summit

☐ **GREATEST HITS**
KWEST 5402 / Mar '93 / Kenwest

☐ **HAVE YOU SEEN HER (The Very Best Of The Chi-Lites)**
PWKS 4240 / Feb '95 / Carlton

☐ **JUST SAY YOU LOVE ME**
Happy music / Solid love affair / Just you and I tonite / Just say you love me / Inner city blues / There's a change / Eternity / Only you
ICH 1057CD / Mar '94 / Ichiban

☐ **SWEET SOUL MUSIC**
Have you seen her / Heavenly body / Strung out / Round and round / Give me a dream / Super mad / All I wanna do is make love to you / Love shock / Me and you / Tell me where it hurts / Oh girl / Get down with me / Hot on a thing (called love) / Never speak to a stranger / Whole lot of good loving / Try my side (of love)
CPCD 8019 / Feb '94 / Charly

☐ **VERY BEST OF THE CHI-LITES, THE**
Have you seen her / For god's sake give more power to the people / Oh girl / Coldest day of my life / Homely girl / Are you my woman (tell me so) / Let me be the man my daddy was / There will never be any peace (until god is se / I found sunshine / Too good to be forgotten / It's time for love / You don't have to go / I like your lovin' / Stoned out of my mind / Give it away / Letter to myself
MCCD 029 / May '91 / Music Club

Chiarelli, Rita

☐ **JUST GETTING STARTED**
HYCD 200151 / Jul '95 / Hypertension

Chiasson, Warren

☐ **GOOD VIBES FOR KURT WEILL**
ACD 236 / Jun '93 / Audiophile

Chiavola, Kathy

☐ **HARVEST**
It won't be long / Baby blue eyes / Shenandoah valley waltz / Will you love me still / Stay away from me / Big picture / Thirty years of tears / No end of love / Dance / One hundred miles / I am a pilgrim / Pilgrims on the way / Harvest
FIENDCD 779 / Apr '96 / Demon

Chiba, Setsuko

☐ **MANGO MAN GO**
14896 / Aug '97 / Spalax

Chic

☐ **BEST OF CHIC VOL.2, THE**
Rebels are we / What about me / Twenty six / Will you cry (when you hear this song) / Stage fright / Real people / Hangin' / Give me the lovin' / At last I am free / Just out of reach / When you love someone / Your love is cancelled / Believer / You are beautiful / Flash back / You can't do it alone / Tavern on the green
8122710862 / Mar '93 / Atlantic

☐ **C'EST CHIC**
Le freak / Chic cheer / I want your love / Happy man / Dance, dance, dance / Savoir faire / At last I am free / Sometimes you win / Funny bone / Everybody dance
7567815522 / Feb '93 / Atlantic

☐ **CHIC**
Dance, dance, dance / Sao Paulo / You can get by / Everybody dance / Est-ce que c'est chic / Falling in love with you / Strike up the band
7567804072 / Feb '92 / Atlantic

☐ **MEGACHIC (The Best Of Chic Vol. 1)**
Megachic (medley) / Chic cheer / My feet keep dancing / Good times / I want your love / Everybody dance / Le freak / Dance, dance, dance
2292417502 / Aug '90 / Atlantic

Chicago

☐ **25 OR 6 TO 4**
CDSGP 0126 / Oct '94 / Prestige

☐ **CHICAGO 17**
Stay the night / We can stop the hurtin' / Hard habit to break / Only you / Remember the feeling / Along comes a woman / You're the inspiration / Please hold on / Prima donna / Once in a lifetime
9250602 / Apr '84 / WEA

☐ **CHICAGO 20**
Explain it to my heart / If it were you / You come to my senses / Somebody / Somewhere / What does it take / One from the heart / Chasin' the wind / God save the queen / Man to woman / Only time can heal the wounded / Who do you love / Holdin' on
7599263912 / Dec '96 / WEA

☐ **CHICAGO TRANSIT AUTHORITY, THE (Chicago Transit Authority)**
Does anybody really know what time it is / Beginnings / Questions 67 and 68 / Listen / Poem 58 / Free form guitar / South California purples / I'm a man / Proloque, August 29 / Someday / Liberation / Introduction
4747882 / May '94 / Columbia

☐ **GROUP PORTRAIT**
4692092 / May '94 / Legacy

☐ **HEART OF CHICAGO, THE**
If you leave me now / Baby what a big surprise / Take me back to Chicago / Hard to say I'm sorry / Love me tomorrow / Hard habit to break / You're the inspiration / Along comes a woman / Remember the feeling / If she would have been faithful / What kind of man would I be / Look away / Where did the loving go / Only you / Will you still love me
WX 328CD / Feb '94 / WEA

☐ **I'M A MAN**
25 or 6 to 4 / I'm a man / Purple song / Beginnings / Liberation / Questions / Does anybody know what time it is
305652 / Jul '97 / Hallmark

☐ **IN CONCERT**
Beginnings / Purples / I'm a man / Questions 67 and 68 / Does anybody really know what time it is / 25 or 6 to 4 / Liberation
HADCD 172 / May '94 / Javelin

☐ **LIVE IN TORONTO**
Beginnings / Purples / 25 or 6 to 4 / Does anybody really know what time it is / I'm a man / Questions 67 and 68 / Liberation
CDTB 103 / Jul '95 / Thunderbolt

☐ **MASTERS, THE**
Beginnings / South California purples / 25 or 6 to 4 / Does anybody know what time it is / I'm a man / Questions 67 and 68 / Liberation
EABCD 088 / 30 Mar '98 / Eagle

☐ **NIGHT AND DAY**
Moonlight serenade / Night and day / Chicago / Blues in the night / In the mood / Caravan / Take the 'A' train / String of pearls / Don't get around much anymore / Sophisticated lady / Goody goody / Dream a little dream
74321267672 / 1 Sep '97 / Giant

Chicago Beau

☐ **CHICAGO BEAU & FRIENDS**
GBW 009 / Feb '94 / GBW

☐ **MY ANCESTORS**
GBW 004 / Mar '92 / GBW

Chicago Jazz Ensemble

☐ **CHICAGO JAZZ ENSEMBLE, THE (Chicago Jazz Ensemble & William Russo)**
Chicago suite no.1 / Horn blower / Artistry in percussion / Soothe me / Goin' to Chicago blues / Second line / Mauve the blues / It don't mean a thing if it ain't got that swing / Transblucency / Ready go
CMD 8052 / 8 Nov '97 / CMG

Chicago String Band

☐ **CHICAGO STRING BAND**
TCD 5006 / Oct '94 / Testament

Chicane

☐ **FAR FROM THE MADDENING CROWDS**
0091372EXT / 13 Oct '97 / Xtravaganza

Chicken Bones

☐ **HARDROCK IN CONCERT**
SB 023 / Jul '97 / Second Battle

Chicken Chest

☐ **ACTION PACKED (Chicken Chest & Leslie Thunder)**
RE 174CD / Jun '97 / ROIR

Chickenpox

☐ **DINNER DANCE AND LATE NIGHT MUSIC**
BHR 025CD / Jul '95 / Burning Heart

☐ **STAY AWAY FROM THE WINDOWS**
BHR 074CD / 16 Mar '98 / Burning Heart

Chickweed

☐ **TODAY IS A GOOD DAY**
HCCD 004 / 27 Apr '98 / Human Condition

Chicory Tip

☐ **CHICORY TIP**
12377 / May '95 / Laserlight

☐ **VERY BEST OF CHICORY TIP, THE (20 Original Recordings)**
Son of my father / What's your name / Cigarettes, women and wine / I see you / Future is past / Big wheels rolling / Join our gang / Me and Stan Foley / Good grief Christina / Move on / IOU / Take your time Caroline / Sweat, dust and red wine / Lodi / Pride comes before a fall / Excuse me baby / Friend of mine / Whta she thinks about / I can here you calling / Memory
SUMCD 4099 / Mar '97 / Summit

Chiefs

☐ **HOLLYWEST CRISIS**
FLIP 92 / Oct '97 / Flipside

Chieftains

☐ **ANOTHER COUNTRY**
Wabash cannonball / Morning dew/Father Kelly's reels / I can't stop loving you / Heartbreak hotel / Heartbreak hotel/Cliffs of Moher / Cotton eyed Joe / Nobody's darlin' but mine / Goodnight Irene
09026609392 / Nov '92 / RCA

☐ **BEST OF THE CHIEFTAINS, THE**
Up against the Buachalawns / Boil the breakfast early / Friel's kitchen / No.6 the Coombe / O'Sullivan's march / Sea image / Speic seoigheach / Dogs among the bushes / Job of journeywork / Oh the breeches full of stitches / Chase around the windmill / Toss the feathers / Ballinasloe Fair / Cailleach an airgid / Cuil addha slide / Pretty girl / Wind that shakes the barley / Reel with the Beryle
4716662 / 27 Jul '98 / Columbia

☐ **CHIEFTAINS LIVE**
Morning dew / George Brabazon / Kerry slides / Carrickfergus / Carolan's concerto / Foxhunt / Round the house and mind the dresser / Caitlin trial / For the sakes of old decency / Carolan's farewell to music / Banish misfortune / Tarbolton/The pinch of snuff / Star of munster/Flogging reel / Limerick's lamentation / O'Neill's march / Ril mhor
CC 21CD / Apr '89 / Claddagh

☐ **CHIEFTAINS VOL.1**
Se fath mo Bhuartha / Lark on the Strand / An fhallaingin mhuimhneagh / Trim the velvet / An combra Donn/Murphy's hornpipe / Cailin na Gruaige Doinne / Comb your hair or curl it/Boys of Ballisodare / Musical priest/Queen of May / Walls of Liscarroll jig / Dhruimfhion donn dilis / Connemara stocking/ Limestone rock/Dan Breen's reel / Casadh an tSugain / Boy in the Gap / St. Mary's / Church Street polka / Garrett Barry/The battering ram / Kitty goes milking/Rakish Paddy
CC 2CD / Nov '90 / Claddagh

☐ **CHIEFTAINS VOL.10**
Christmas reel / Salut a la Compagnie / My love is in America / Manx music / Master Crowley's reels / Pride of Pimlico / An Faire / Turtle dove / Sir Arthur Shaen/Madam Cole / Garech's wedding / Cotton eyed Joe
CC 33CD / Nov '90 / Claddagh

☐ **CHIEFTAINS VOL.2**
Banish misfortune / Gillian's apples / Planxty George Brabazon / Bean an fhir rua / O'Farrell's welcome to Limerick / An paistin Fionn/Mountain top / Foxhunt / An mhaighdean mhara / Tie the bonnet/O'Rourke's reel / Callaghan's and Byrne's hornpipes / Pigtown/ Tie the ribbons/Bag of potatoes / Humours of whiskey/Hardiman the fiddler / Donald Og / Brian Boru's march / Sweeney's polka/Denis Murphy's polka / Scartagien polka
CC 7CD / Aug '92 / Claddagh

☐ **CHIEFTAINS VOL.3**
Strike the gay harp / Lord Mayo / Lady on the island / Sailor on the rock / Sonny's mazurka / Tommy Hunt's jig / Eibi gheal chiuin ni chearbhaill / Defahunty's hornpipe / Hunter's purse / March of the King of Laois / Carolan's concerto / Tom Billy's / Road to Lisdoonvarna / Merry sisters / An ghaoth aneas / Lord Inchiquin / Trip to Sligo / An raibh tu ag an Gcarraig / John Kelly's / Merrily kiss the Quaker / Dennis Murphy's
CC 10CD / Jan '93 / Claddagh

☐ **CHIEFTAINS VOL.4**
Drowsy Maggie / Morgan Magan / Tip of the whistle / Bucks of Oranmore / Battle of Aughrium / Morning dew / Carrickfergus / Hewlett / Cherish the ladies / Lord Mayo / Mna ban / Star above the garter / Weavers
CC 14CD / Oct '88 / Claddagh

☐ **CHIEFTAINS VOL.5**
Timpan reel / Tabhair dom do lamh / Three Kerry polkas / Ceol Bhriotanach / Chieftains knock on the door / Robber's glen / An ghe agus an gra geal / Humours of Carolan / Sambradh Sambradh (Summertime Summertime) / Kerry slides
CC 16CD / '88 / Claddagh

☐ **CHIEFTAINS VOL.6**
Chattering magpie / First Tuesday of Autumn/Green grow the rushes O / Bonaparte's retreat / Away with ye / Caledonia / Princess Royal/Blind Mary/John Drury / Rights of man / Round the house and mind the dresser
CC 20CD / Nov '90 / Claddagh

☐ **CHIEFTAINS VOL.8**
Session / Dr. John Hart / Sean sa cheo / Fairies' hornpipe / Sea image / If I had Maggie in the wood / An speic seogheach / Dogs among the bushes / Miss Hamilton the job of journeywork / Wind that shakes the barley / Reel with the Beryle
CC 29CD / Dec '93 / Claddagh

☐ **CHIEFTAINS VOL.9**
Boil the breakfast early / Mrs. Judge / March: Oscar and Malvina / When a man's in love / Path through the wood / Travelling through Blarney / Carolan's welcome / Up against the Buachalawns / Gol na mBan san Ar / Chase around the windmill
CC 30CD / '88 / Claddagh

☐ **FILM CUTS**
O'Sullivan's march / Dublin / You're the one / Treasure island / Barry Lyndon love theme / Tristan and Isolde / Grey fox / Fighting for dough / Ireland moving
09026684382 / Jul '96 / RCA

☐ **GREATEST HITS**
Millenium celtic suite / Wexford carol / Iron man / Stray away child / Here's a health to the company / Coolin' medley / Boffyflow and Spike / O'Mahoney's frolics / Dan tros fisel / Heulliadenn tonniou breizh-izel
74321339452 / Jan '96 / Camden

☐ **IRISH EVENING, AN**
North americay / Lilly Bolero/The white cockade / Little love affairs / Red is the rose / Mason's apron / Stone (a special dance for when two lovers meet) / Raglan road / Behind blue eyes / Damhsa
RD 60916 / Jun '92 / RCA

☐ **LIVE IN CHINA**
Full of joy / In a suzhow garden / If I had Maggie in the wood / Reason for my sorrow / Chieftains in China / Planxty irwin / Off the great wall / Tribute to O'Carolan / Wind from the south / China to Hong kong
CC 42CD / Aug '85 / Claddagh

☐ **LONG BLACK VEIL, THE**
Mo ghile mear / Long black veil / Foggy dew / Have I told you lately that I love you / Changing your demeanor / Lily of the west / Coast of Malabar / Dunmore lassies / Ferny Hill / Tennessee waltz / Tenessee mazurka / Rocky road to Dublin
74321251672 / Jan '95 / RCA

☐ **MAGIC OF THE CHIEFTAINS**
O'Mahoney's frolics / Coolin' medley / Wexford carol / Marches / Boffyflow and Spike / Celtic wedding / Here's a health to the company / Strayaway child / Iron man / Millennium celtic suite / Dans tro fisel / Heuliadenn toniou breizh-izel
MCCD 048 / Jan '92 / Music Club

☐ **SANTIAGO (Chieftains & Linda Ronstadt/Los Lobos/Ry Cooder/ Carlos Nunez)**
Txalaparta / Arku-Dantza/Arin-Arin / El besu (the kiss) / Nao vas ao mar, Toino (don't go to sea, Toino) / Dum paterfamilias/Ad honorem / Dueling chanters (sixpenny money/Polka de Vilagarcia) / Galician Overture / Guadalupe / Minho Waltz / Setting sail/ Muineira de frexido / Maneo / Santiago de Cuba / Galleguita/Tutankhamen / Tears of stone / Duublin in Vigo / Alboreda gallega / Miudino / Lola / Jackson's morning brush / Muineira de Cabana / Muineira de Chantada
09026686022 / Nov '96 / RCA Victor

Chiffons

☐ **BEST OF THE CHIFFONS**
Sweet talking guy / One fine day / He's so fine / Tonight I'm gonna dream / Out of this world / I have a boyfriend / Nobody knows what's going on / When the boy's happy (the girl's happy too) / Tonight I met an angel / Love so fine / Open your eyes / Sailor boy / Stop, look and listen / My block / Oh my lover / Just for tonight / My boyfriend's back / Why am I so shy / I'm gonna dry my eyes / Did you ever go steady
CDMFP 6219 / Apr '96 / Music For Pleasure

☐ **ONE FINE DAY**
He's so fine / One fine day / My block / A love so fine / When the boy's happy (the girl's happy too) / I have a boyfriend / Sailor boy / Nobody knows what's going on (in my mind but me) / Sweet talkin' guy / Out of this world / Stop, look and listen / My boyfriend's back / Oh my lover / Mystic voice / Up on the bridge / Did you ever go steady / March / Keep the boy happy / Real thing / I'm gonna dry my eyes / Open your eyes (i will be there) / Heavenly place / Teach me how / If I knew then what I know now / Lucky me / Tonight I met an angel
RMB 75071 / Apr '94 / Remember

Chihabi, Abou

☐ **FOLKOMOR OCEAN**
PS 65188 / Jul '97 / PlayaSound

Child, Jane

☐ **HERE NOT THERE**
Mona Lisa smiles / Do whatcha do / Monument / All I do / Sshhh / Perfect love / I do not feel as good as you / Heavy smile / Calling / Step out of time / Sarasvati / Here not there
9362452962 / Sep '93 / Warner Bros.

Childe Rolande

☐ FOREIGN LAND
Walk a lonely road / Fair wind / Aranmor / Just landed / Out of the dream / Living in a game of chance / More fool you / Time and the tide / Dead reckoning / Poison pen / Ghost / Foreign land
CDLDL 1251 / Mar '97 / Lochshore

Childers, Buddy

☐ ARTISTRY IN JAZZ (Childers, Buddy & The Russ Garcia Strings)
Come home again / Shadow of your smile / Stardust / You are too beautiful / Body and soul / 'Round midnight / My Diane / Lush life / Stars fell on Alabama / Sophisticated lady / Angel eyes / Din di (jin je)
CCD 79735 / Jan '97 / Candid

☐ IT'S WHAT'S HAPPENING NOW (Childers, Buddy Big Band)
Killer Joe / Polka dots and moonbeams / Time on my hands / Someone to watch over me / Dearly beloved / Come home again / Boy from Ipanema / Star eyes / Out of nowhere / Bernie's tune / Goodbye old friend / Bone zone
CCD 79749 / Jun '98 / Candid

☐ WEST COAST QUINTET
Straight no chaser / My funny valentine / Buffy / Street of dreams / Scam / What's new / All the things you are / Lament / Cotton tail
CCD 79722 / May '97 / Candid

Childish, Billy

☐ AT THE BRIDGE (Childish, Billy & The Singing Loins)
DAM 22CD / Apr '94 / Damaged Goods

☐ CAPTAIN CALYPSO'S HOODOO PARTY/LIVE IN THE NETHERLANDS (Childish, Billy & The Black Hands)
SCRAG 3UP / Sep '94 / Hangman's Daughter

Children

☐ EVERY SINGLE DAY
SKYCD 2015 / Sep '94 / Sky

Children Of Bodom

☐ SOMETHING WILD
Deadnight warrior / In the shadows / Red light in my eyes / Red light in my eyes part II / Lake bodom / Nail / Touch like angel of death
NB 308CD
SPI 49CD / 30 Mar '98 / Spinefarm

Children Of Dub

☐ ANALOG MEDITATION
CLP 0092 / 6 Oct '97 / Cleopatra

☐ CHAMELEON
MEYCD 15 / Aug '96 / Magick Eye

Children Of Judah

☐ WAITING BY THE GATES OF EDEN
TRIBE 001CD / Jun '95 / Wall Of Sound

Children Of Selma

☐ WHO WILL SPEAK FOR THE CHILDREN
Unite children / We grow up young / Black is beautiful / I just want to be me / Someone died for me / Vote for me / Who will speak for the children / Hello friends / Shoo child / Try looking up / I think of you / If children rule the world
ROUCD 8008 / '88 / Rounder

Children Of The Bong

☐ SIRIUS SOUNDS
Polyphase / Ionosperic state / Interface reality / Veil / Underwater / Life of plant earth / Squigglasonica / Visitor
BARKCD 012 / Jul '95 / Planet Dog

Children On Stun

☐ MONDO WEIRD
MACDL 953 / Apr '97 / Resurrection

Children's Choir

☐ CHRISTMAS CAROLS
Star carol / O little town of Bethlehem / Infant holy infant lowly / Candlelight carol / Once in Royal David's city / In the winter darkness / Silent night / Carol of the children / Here comes Christmas / Silver sleigh / Christmas cheer / Away in a manger / Nativity carol / I saw three ships / In the bleak mid-winter / Mary had a baby / Sussex carol / Little Jesus sweetly slept / While shepherds watched / Child in the manger / Unto us is born a son / Cowboy carol
XMAS 003 / Nov '96 / Tring

Children's Company

☐ POLLY POCKET - POLLY'S DISCO PARTY
Dancing queen / Dance of the little swans / Polly's party song / Summer days
LFPK 2006 / Jul '96 / Listen For Pleasure

Childs Brothers

☐ EUPHONIUM MUSIC
DOYCD 002 / Nov '92 / Doyen

☐ WELSH WIZARDS (Childs Brothers & The Tredegar Town Band)
Fascinating euphs. / Fascinating euphs. / Fantastic fast fingered fandango / Elfriede / Salut d'amour (elgar) / Duo for euphoniums / Song of the seashore / Pantomime / Flight of the bumble bee / Only love / A piece of cake / Largo al factotum / Calon lan / Czardas / Aka tonbl / Two part invention
DOYCD 022 / May '93 / Doyen

Childs, Billy

☐ CHILD WITHIN, THE
SHCD 5023 / Sep '96 / Shanachie

☐ I'VE KNOWN RIVERS
I've known rivers / Starry night / Lament / Way of the new world / This moment / Realism / Somewhere I have never travelled / Siren serenade
SCD 90102 / Mar '97 / Stretch

Childs, Robert

☐ PREMIERE (Childs, Robert & The Black Dyke Band)
Fantasy / Andante and rondo / Arioso and allegro / City in the sea / Concerto for Euphonium
DOYCD 061 / Sep '97 / Doyen

Childs, Toni

☐ UNION
Don't walk away / Walk and talk like angels / Stop you're fussin' / Dreamer / Let the rain come down / Zimbabwe / Hush / Tin drum / Where's the ocean
3951752 / Apr '95 / A&M

☐ WOMAN'S BOAT
Womb / Welcome to the world / Predator / I just want affection / I met a man / Woman's boat / Wild bride / Sacrifice / Lay down your pain / Long time coming / Death
GFLD 19341 / 2 Feb '98 / Geffen

Chillemi, Santos

☐ AVEC L'ACCENT
FA 429 / 24 Apr '98 / Fremeaux

Chilli Willi

☐ I'LL BE HOME (Chilli Willi & Red Hot Peppers)
I'll be home / Goodbye Nashville hello Camden Town / Desert island woman / I wanna love her so bad / Friday song / Don't hurt the one you love / Breathe a little / Choo choo ch'boogle / Walkin' blues / Posing yeah / Midnight blues / Pinball boogie / Jungle song / We get along / Truck drivin' girl / Boppin' the blues / Fire on the mountain / Six days on the road
PRPCD 002 / Dec '97 / Proper

Chillingworth, Sonny

☐ SONNY SOLO
DCT 38005CD / Mar '96 / Dancing Cat

Chillum

☐ CHILLUM
Brain surgeon's intro / Brain strain / Land of 1,000 dreams / Too many bananas / Oh yes we have no pyjamas / Promenade des anglais / Fairy tale / Festival / This is not romance / Incubator / Incubator
SEECD 491 / 18 May '98 / See For Miles

Chilton, Alex

☐ ALEX CHILTON
422051 / May '94 / New Rose

☐ ALEX CHILTON 1970
CREV 044CD / Apr '96 / Rev-Ola

☐ BACH'S BOTTOM
RE 2010 / Mar '97 / Razor & Tie

☐ CLICHES
NR 422481 / Jan '94 / New Rose

☐ FEUDALIST TARTS/NO SEX
RE 2032 / Mar '97 / Razor & Tie

☐ HIGH PRIEST/BLACKLIST
RE 2033 / Mar '97 / Razor & Tie

☐ LIKE FLIES ON SHERBERT
Boogie shoes / My rival / Hey little child / Hook or crook / I've had it / Rock hard / Girl after girl / Waltz across Texas / Alligator man / Like flies on sherbert
COOKCD 095 / Jan '96 / Cooking Vinyl
422445 / Feb '97 / Last Call

☐ LIKE FLIES ON SHERBERT/LIVE IN LONDON
Boogie shoes / My rival / Hey little child / Hook or crook / I've had it / Rock hard / Girl after girl / Waltz across Texas / Alligator man / Like flies on sherbert / Bangkok / No more the moon shines on Lorena / Tramp / In the street / Hey little child / Nighttime / Rock hard / Alligator man / Letter / Train kept a rollin' / Kanga Roo / Stranded on a dateless night / September gurls
C5HCD 666 / 24 Nov '97 / See For Miles

☐ LIVE IN LONDON
Bangkok / Tramp / In the street / Hey little child / Night time / Rock hard / Alligator man / Letter / Train kept a rollin' / Kango roo / My rival / Stranded on a dateless night / September gurls / No more the moon shines on lorena
CREV 015CD / Jun '93 / Rev-Ola

☐ MAN CALLED DESTRUCTION, A
RRCD 901312 / May '95 / Ruf

☐ TOP 30
3021082 / Jun '97 / Arcade

Chimes

☐ CHIMES
Love so tender / Heaven / True love / 1-2-3 / Underestimate / Love comes to mind / I still haven't found what I'm looking for (street mix) / Don't make me wait / Stronger together / Stay / I still haven't found what I'm looking for
4664812 / Jun '90 / CBS

China Crisis

☐ CHINA CRISIS COLLECTION
African and white / No more blue horizons / Christian / Tragedy and mystery / Working with fire and steel / Wishful thinking / Hanna Hanna / Black man ray / King in a catholic style / You did cut me / Arizona sky / Best kept secret / It's everything / St. Saviour square / Scream down at me / Cucumber garden / Golden handshake for every daughter / Some people I know / Instigator / Little Italy / Greenacre Bay / No ordinary lover / Dockland / Forever I and I / Performing seals / This occupation / Watching over burning fields / Animalistic
CDV 2613 / Sep '90 / Virgin

☐ DIFFICULT SHAPES AND PASSIVE RHYTHMS (Some People Think It's Fun To Entertain)
Seven sports for all / No more blues horizons / Feel to be driven away / Some people I know to lead fantastic lives / Christian / African and white / Are we a worker / Red sails / You never see it / Temptations big blue eyes / Jean walks in fresh fields
CDV 2243 / Jul '87 / Virgin

☐ FLAUNT THE IMPERFECTION
Highest high / Strength of character / You did cut me / Black man Ray / Wall of God / Gift of freedom / King in a catholic style / Bigger the punch I'm feeling / World spins, The, I'm part of it / Blue sea
CDV 2342 / Jan '90 / Virgin

☐ WARPED BY SUCCESS
CP 1003 / 20 Apr '98 / Rhino

☐ WHAT PRICE PARADISE
It's everything / Arizona sky / Safe as houses / World's apart / Hampton beach / Understudy / Best kept secret / We do the same / June bride / Days work for the days done / Trading in gold
CDVIP 167 / Dec '96 / Virgin VIP

☐ WISHFUL THINKING (2CD Set)
African and white / No more blue horizons / Wishful thinking / Everyday the same / It's everything / Christian / Good again / Hands on the wheel / Black Man Ray / King in a Catholic style / Thank you / Singing the praises of finer things / Working with fire and steel / Diary of a hollow horse / Hands on wheel / Always / Everyday the same / Without the love / Thank you / Hard to be around / One wish too many / Wishing time / Good again / Real tears / Does it pay / Way we are made / Tell me what it is
SMDCD 117 / May '97 / Snapper

☐ WORKING WITH FIRE AND STEEL-POSSIBLE POP SONGS VOL.2
Working with fire and steel / When the piper calls / Hanna Hanna / Animals in the jungle / Here comes a raincloud / Wishful thinking / Tragedy and mystery / Papua / Gates of door to door / Soulful awakening
CDV 2286 / Sep '84 / Virgin

China Drum

☐ GOOSE FAIR
MNTCD 1002 / Apr '96 / Mantra

☐ SELF MADE MANIAC
One thing / Guilty deafness / Somewhere else / Fiction of life / All I wanna be / Down by the river / Another toy / 60 seconds / Foxhole / Control / Stop it all adding up / Bothered
MNTCD 1009 / 13 Oct '97 / Mantra

Chinafrica

☐ CREATION
CACD 01 / Jul '95 / Graylan

Chinatown

☐ PLAY IT TO DEATH
ETHEL 6 / Mar '97 / Vinyl Tap

Chinchilla

☐ 101 ITALIAN HITS
CRISIS 011CD / Oct '96 / Crisis

Chindamo, Joe

☐ REFLECTED JOURNEY
One world / Fiddle faddle / Goth / Someplace else / Reflected journey / Letter to Cerny / In a space / Gift
AL 73120 / Jun '98 / A

Chinese Millionaires

☐ DETROIT DOUBLE CROSS
RIPOFF 030CD / 23 Mar '98 / Rip Off

Chinkees

☐ CHINKEES ARE COMING, THE
AMO 22CD / 13 Apr '98 / Asian Man

Chino XL

☐ HERE TO SAVE YOU ALL
Here to save you all / Deliver / No complex / Partner to swing / It's all bad / Freestyle rhymes / Riiiot / Waiting to exhale / What am I / Feelin' evil again / Thousands / Kreep / Many different ways / Shabba doo conspiracy / Ghetto vampire / Rise / My hero
74321302782 / Apr '96 / American

Chipmunks

☐ CLUB CHIPMUNK - THE DANCE MIXES
Macarena / Vogue / Stayin alive / Play that funky music / Chipmunk / I'm too sexy / Turn the beat around / Witch doctor / Love shack
4867022 / Dec '96 / Chipmunk/Sony

Chipolata 5

☐ SKINLESS
Intro / Sweet lassi set / Old Joe Clarke / Two men / Three around three / Boa constrictor / Rambling sailor / Lake Arthur / Bacca pipes
HOODCD 001 / May '97 / Hoodlum

Chirag Penchan

☐ RAIL GADDI
DMUT 1039 / Mar '96 / Multitone

Chirgilchin

☐ WOLF AND THE KID, THE
SH 64070 / Oct '96 / Shanachie

Chisholm, Duncan

☐ REDPOINT
CPF 001CD / Mar '98 / Copperfish

Chisholm, George

☐ EARLY DAYS 1935-1944
Jazz me blues / Jazz me blues / Don't try your jive on me / Mazeltov / If you were the only girl in the world / If you were the only girl in the world / Pardon me pretty baby / Oh lady be good / Honeysuckle rose / Let's go / Let's go / No smoking / Archer street drag / Rosetta / You'll always be mine / Penalty / No smoking / Aunt Hagar's blues / At the jazz band ball / Mood for trumpet / All is not gold that jitters / Little Earle / Broadhurst garden blues
CBC 1044 / 20 Apr '98 / Timeless Jazz

Chittison, Herman

☐ CLASSICS 1933-1941
CLASSICS 690 / May '93 / Classics

☐ PS WITH LOVE
IAJRCCD 1006 / Jun '94 / IAJRC

Chiweshe, Stella

☐ AMBUYA/NDIZVOZVO (Chiweshe, Stella & The Earthquake)
Chachimurenga / Nehondo / Njuzu / Mugomba / Chamakuwende / Kasahwa / Chipindura / Ndinogarochema / Sarura Wako
CDORB 029 / May '89 / Globestyle

Chixdiggit

☐ BORN ON THE FIRST OF JULY
DON 015CD / 4 May '98 / Honest Don's

☐ CHIXDIGGIT
SPCD 355 / Jun '96 / Sub Pop

Choates, Harry

☐ FIDDLE KING OF CAJUN SWING
Allons a lafayette / Basile waltz / Cajun hop / Port arthur waltz / Garrt cgiates special / It won't be long / Wrong keyhole / Draggin' the bow / Te petite / Rubber dolly / Louisiana / Poor hobo / Devil in the bayou / Rye whiskey / Fais do do stomp / Lawtell waltz / Bayou pon pon / Chere meon / Harry choates blues / Mari jole blon / Honky tonking days / Grand mamou / Je pase durvan ta port / Hackberry hop / Jole brun / Louisiana boogie
ARHCD 380 / Apr '95 / Arhoolie

☐ FIVE TIME LOSER 1940-1951
Lake Charles shuffle / Old ice man / OST gal / I've grown so lonely for you / Les tete fille lafayette / Gran prairie / La veuve de la coulee / Je pase durvan ta port / Hackberry hop / Poor hobo / I love you I love you / Old cow blues / Nobody cares for me / Sidewalk waltz / Louisianna boogie / She's sweet sweet / What's the use / Do you still love me / I've quit my cattin' around / My pretty brunette / Maggie waltz / Big mamou / Oh meon / Austin special / Saturday night waltz / Five time loser
KKCD 22 / May '98 / Krazy Kat

Chocolate

☐ CALIENTE
CDGR 263 / 3 Aug '98 / Charly

☐ EN SEXTETO
CCD 9001 / Jan '98 / Fresh Sound

Chocolate

☐ HUNG, GIFTED AND SLACK
CDWOOS 1 / Apr '96 / Out Of Step

☐ SUBSTITUTE FOR SEX
Kittredge / S.o.f.t. / Painless / Evening star / Bobby told me / Walking appetites / Bang juice
DPROMCD 15 / Aug '93 / Dirter Promotions

Chocolate Milk

☐ ICE COLD FUNK (The Greatest Grooves Of Chocolate Milk)
RE 21652 / 14 Apr '98 / Razor & Tie

Chocolate Syrup

☐ BATTLE OF THE BANDS VOL.4
(Chocolate Syrup/Jimmy Briscoe & The Little Beavers)
Stop your cryin' / You've got a lot to give / Just in the nick of time / Penguin breakdown / All I ever do is dream about you / What's a matter baby / Who you tryin' to fool girl / We've got to get together / Let one hurt do / Stay with me / My ebony princess / True love / Together together / I only feel this way when I'm with you / Country to city / Where were you / I'll care for you / Forever / You're my love my life my soul / Movin' on
NEMCD 933 / 19 Aug '97 / Sequel

Chocolate Watch Band

☐ 44
Don't need your lovin' / No way out / It's all over now baby blue / I'm not like everybody else / Misty lane / Loose lip sync ship / Are you gonna be there (at the love in) / Gone and passes by / Sitting there standing / She weaves a tender trap / Sweet young thing / I ain't no miracle worker / Blues theme
CDWIK 25 / May '90 / Big Beat

☐ INNER MYSTIQUE
SC 6024 / 22 Jun '98 / Sundazed

☐ INNER MYSTIQUE/NO WAY OUT
842023 / 1 Jun '98 / Revenge

☐ INNER MYSTIQUE/ONE STEP BEYOND
Voyage of the triste / In the past / Inner mystique / I'm not like everybody else / Medication / Let's go, let's go (Aka Thrill on the hill) / It's all over now baby blue / I ain't no miracle worker / Uncle Morris / How ya been / Devil's motorcyle / I don't need no doctor / Flowers / Fireface / And she's lonely
CDWIKD 111 / Apr '93 / Big Beat

☐ NO WAY OUT
SC 6029 / 22 Jun '98 / Sundazed

☐ NO WAY OUT...PLUS
Let's talk about girls / In the midnight hour / Come on / Dark side of the mushroom / Hot dusty road / Are you gonna be there (at the love in) / Gone and passes by / No way out / Expo 2000 / Gossamer wings / Sweet young thing / Baby blue / Misty lane / She weaves a tender trap / Milk cow blues / Don't let the sun catch you crying / Since you broke my heart / Misty lane (Remix)
CDWIKD 118 / Jun '93 / Big Beat

Chocolate Weasels

☐ SPAGHETTIFICATION
Intro / Blue furry plughole / Coda / Zen method / Ramblings / Weasenstein / Way of the weasel / Flying saucers / Reworked from scratch / Music for bodylockers / Jazzman zanussi / Tragic mushrooms / Intervals / 11th hour concept / Banana skins / In continuity / Other side of madness
ZENCD 035 / 30 Mar '98 / Ninja Tune

Chodack, Walter

☐ RAGTIME (The Best Of Scott Joplin)
MAN 4838 / Oct '94 / Mandala

Choeurs D'Enfants

☐ CHANTS DE NOEL (Chants Of Christmas)
74321408322 / Nov '96 / Milan

Choice

☐ SUNDAY SOCCER
HOO 25 / Sep '97 / Helen Of Oi

Choir

☐ CHOIR PRACTICE
I'd rather you leave me / It's cold outside / When you were with me / Don't change your mind (rehersal version) / Dream of one's life / In love's shadow (mod's demo) / I'm slippin' / Leave me be (mod's demo) / I'd rather you leave me (rehearsal version) / Treeberry / Unite / A to F / I only did it 'cause I felt so lonely / Don't change your mind / Anyway I can / Boris' lament / David Watts / These are men
CDSC 11018 / 20 Jul '98 / Sundazed

Choirboys

☐ CHOIRBOYS, THE
REP 4654 / Oct '97 / Repertoire

Chokebore

☐ ANYTHING NEAR WATER
ARRCD 61004 / May '95 / Amphetamine Reptile

☐ BLACK BLACK
BOOMBA 008CD / 13 Apr '98 / Boomba

☐ MOTIONLESS
ARRCD 43/289 / Aug '93 / Amphetamine Reptile

☐ TASTE FOR BITTERS, A
ARRCD 77020 / Dec '96 / Amphetamine Reptile

Chop Shop

☐ RECOVERED PIECES
Intro / Six buckets / Sunny days / Carnival ride / Kick the ballistics / Stoop / Drop da new flavor / X-break / Dab'l do ya / Shaolin shoot out
ME 000362 / Sep '95 / Soulciety

Chopper

☐ CHOPPER
BD 9032 / Dec '97 / Big Deal

☐ DID YOU HEAR THAT
CRACKLE 001 / Aug '97 / Crackle

Chorale Iroise

☐ D'IROISE ET D'AILLEURS
CI 20 / May '96 / Keltia Musique

Chordettes

☐ FABULOUS CHORDETTES, THE
Lollipop / Born to be with you / Eddie my love / Wedding / Mr. Sandman / Teenage goodnight / Just between you and me / Soft sands / Zorro / No other arms, no other lips / Lay down your arms / Never on Sunday
CDFAB 005 / Sep '91 / Ace

☐ MAINLY ROCK'N'ROLL
True love goes on and on / Mr. Sandman / Lonely lips / Hummingbird / Wedding / Eddie my love / Born to be with you / Lay down your arms / Teenage goodbye / Echo of love / Just between you and me / Soft sands / Photographs / Lollipop / Baby come-a-back-a / Zorro / Love is a two way street / No other arms, no other lips / Girl's work is never done / No wheels / Lonely boy / Charlie Brown / I cried a tear / Pink shoelaces / Tall Paul / To know him is to love him / My heart stood still / For me and my gal / Broken vow / Never on Sunday / Faraway star / In the deep blue sea
CDCHD 934 / Jul '90 / Ace

☐ SENTIMENTAL JOURNEY
BMCD 3049 / 5 Jan '98 / Blue Moon

Chords

☐ LIVE AT THE RAINBOW
Something's missing / Happy families / It's no use / Now it's gone / I'm not sure / British way of life / So far away / I'll keep on holding on / Tumbling down / Maybe tomorrow / Breaks my heart / This is what they want
DOJOCD 178 / Jun '94 / Dojo

Chorus Of Disapproval

☐ CHORUS OF DISAPPROVAL
NA 021CD / Jul '96 / New Age

Chosen

☐ SOMETHING FOR THE WEEKEND
Girl called Tuesday / Give it up / Bargain basement lover / Angel / Don't ask me / Slide / Monday Friday man / My medicine / Check out the checkout girl / Old enough to notice / Blue and white / Mr. Weekender
DRCD 009 / Sep '96 / Detour

Chosen Few

☐ IN THE NAME OF THE DJ
What you've been waiting for / All you motherfuckers / In the name of the DJ / Kold dayz / Break / Tranceparent / Freedom / Don't fuck with me / Pump that pussy / Arena / Bassdrum bounce / Chosen paradize / 4 gunz / Zlam (here it comes) / Bring da beat
DB 47762 / 30 Mar '98 / Deep Blue

Chosen Gospel Singers

☐ LIFEBOAT, THE
Before this time another year / Ananais / Don't you know the man / Don't leave me / Family prayer / Leaning on the Lord / 1-2-3 / Lord will make a way somehow / It's getting late in the evening / No room at the hotel / Watch ye therefore / I'm going back with him / I've tried / Lifeboat is coming / What a wonderful sight / Don't worry 'bout me / When I get home / On the main line / Stay with Jesus / Prayer for the doomed
CDCHD 414 / Nov '93 / Ace

Chouteira

☐ CHOUTEIRA
DF 001CD / Aug '97 / Do Fol

☐ GHUAUE
DF 009CD / Dec '97 / Do Fol

Chowdhury, Subroto Roy

☐ BAGESHREE
Raga brageshree / Raga sindhi bhairavi
8888212 / Dec '95 / Tiptoe

☐ MORNING
CDJP 1033 / Feb '93 / Jazz Point

Chozen Ones

☐ CHOZEN ONE, THE
STEPCD 051 / 24 Nov '97 / Step 1

Chraibi, Said

☐ OUD
Souleimane / Awjara / Awjara Ghouzoud / Hitaz kar kurdi / Pensees andalouses / Likaa / Raast danjikah / Ya ommou abaya / Longa nakryse / Nouzha
CP 10196 / May '97 / Cinq Planetes

Chris & Carla

☐ LIFE FULL OF HOLES
GRCD 360 / Feb '95 / Glitterhouse

☐ SHELTER FOR AN EVENING
SPCD 92/264 / Jul '93 / Sub Pop

☐ SWINGER 500
GLOBCD 2 / 23 Mar '98 / Global Warming

Chris & Cosey

☐ CHRONOMANIC
CTI 93002 / Oct '96 / Conspiracy

☐ COLLECTIV VOL.1
CTICD 001 / '89 / Conspiracy

☐ COLLECTIV VOL.2
CTICD 002 / '89 / Conspiracy

☐ COLLECTIV VOL.3
CTICD 007 / '89 / Conspiracy

☐ COLLECTIV VOL.4
CTICD 008 / '89 / Conspiracy

☐ HEARTBEAT (Creative Technology Instite)
CTICD 004 / Aug '88 / Conspiracy

☐ IN CONTINUUM
CTI 95003 / Oct '96 / Conspiracy

☐ METAPHYSICAL (Creative Technology Instite)
CTI 93001 / Oct '96 / Conspiracy

☐ MUZIK FANTASTIQUE
Fantastique / Sound of sound / Masqued / Apocalypso / Afrakira / Hidden man / Visions love / Loves lost immortal / Eternal / Never mind / Melancholia
BIAS 221CD / Oct '92 / Play It Again Sam

☐ POINT SEVEN
Alliz / Pausal / Hipspa / Restless / Repose / Daspooki / Reflux / Azimuth / Cell F
CTICD 005 / Jul '88 / Conspiracy

☐ SKIMBLE SKAMBLE
CC 1096 / Jan '97 / Conspiracy

☐ SONGS OF LOVE AND LUST
CTICD 006 / Jul '88 / Conspiracy

☐ SPACE BETWEEN (Carter, Chris)
ICC 1CD / Jan '92 / Grey Area

☐ TECHNO PRIMITIV
CTICD 003 / Jan '86 / Conspiracy

☐ TRANCE
CTICD 005 / Jul '88 / Conspiracy

Chris & James

☐ DJ'S IN A BOX VOL.5 (Mixed By Chris & James) (Various Artists)
UCCD 005 / Mar '97 / Urban Collective

Chrissos, Theo

☐ WHITE ROSE OF ATHENS, THE
CNCD 5952 / Jul '93 / Disky

Chrissy

☐ SANGRE NUEVE PA LA CALLE
RMD 80957 / 24 Mar '98 / RMM

Christ Agony

☐ DAEMOONSETH ACT II
CDAR 024 / Mar '95 / Fringe

☐ DARKSIDE
HHR 010CD / Jun '97 / Hammerheart

Christ Analogue

☐ IN RADIANT DECAY
No daughter icon / This shall not breathe / Optima / Grain / Cradle and debase / Wear / Rigor / Unclean / Cold magnetic sun
CRGD 84054 / May '97 / Re-Constriction

Christ Denied

☐ ...GOT WHAT HE DESERVED
Banish the vanished / Monk's wetdream / Pay to pray / Deserved no less / Useless sinless life / No salvation / Misery / Angels of death / Body of Christ / Hierarchy of hipocrisy
SPV 08457772 / Feb '97 / SPV

Christ On A Crutch

☐ SHIT EDGE & OTHER SONGS FOR THE YOUNG & SENTIMENTAL
NRA 056CD / 11 Aug '97 / New Red Archives

☐ SPREAD YOUR FILTH (Doughnut And Bourbon Years)
NRA 055CD / 11 Aug '97 / New Red Archives

Christdriver

☐ EVERYTHING BURNS
EXISTSKULD 032CD / Apr '97 / Profane Existence

Christian Death

☐ AMEN (2CD Set)
CM 77107 / Nov '95 / Century Media

☐ ASHES
Ashes / Ashes part ii / When I was bed / Lament - over the shadows / Face / Luxury of tears / Of the wound
NORMAL 15CD / May '94 / Normal

☐ ATROCITIES
NORMAL 18CD / May '94 / Normal

☐ CATASTROPHE BALLET
Awake at the wall / Sleepwalk / Drowning / Blue hour / Evening falls / Androgynous noise hand permeates / Electra descending / Cervix couch / Glass house / Fleeing somnambulist
N 181CD / Jan '96 / Normal

☐ DEATHWISH
NORMAL 84CD / May '94 / Normal

☐ DECOMPOSITION OF VIOLETS, THE
RUSCD 8240 / 27 Apr '98 / ROIR

☐ DOLL'S THEATRE
CLEO 62082 / Jun '94 / Cleopatra

☐ INSANUS, ULTIO, MISERICORDIAQUE
FREUDCD 48 / Jan '95 / Jungle

☐ JESUS POINTS THE BONE
FREUDCD 39 / Mar '92 / Jungle

☐ PORNOGRAPHIC MESSIAH
TRI 006CD / 8 Jun '98 / Trinity

☐ PROPHECIES
FREUDCD 053 / 6 Jul '98 / Jungle

☐ SCRIPTURES
NORMAL 65 / May '94 / Normal

☐ SEX, DRUGS AND JESUS CHRIST
FREUDCD 050 / 26 Jul '98 / Jungle

☐ TALES OF INNOCENCE
CLEO 91092 / Dec '93 / Cleopatra

☐ WIND KISSED PICTURES
NORMAL 76CD / Jan '96 / Normal

Christian Tabernacle Baptist Choir

☐ RIVER OF LIFE (Sound Of Black Gospel In America)
Congregation arrives / Welcome (what a friend we have in Jesus) / Prayer / Victory today is mine / Jesus said / Great change in me / Louie there it is / I'm delivered / Jesus can work it out / I won't leave here like I came / Something about the lord is mighty sweet / Lily of the valley / River of life
VICG 53952 / May '97 / JVC World Library

Christian, Charlie

☐ 1939-1941 (Christian, Charlie & Benny Goodman)
Flying home / Till tom special / Ac-dc current / Seven come eleven / Gone with 'what' wind / Good enough to keep (air mail special) / Breakfast feud / A smoo-o-o-oth one / Six appeal / Royal garden blues / Stardust / I can't give you anything but love / Wholly cats / As long as I live / I never knew / I've found a new baby / Soft winds / Lester's dream
CD 56059 / Mar '95 / Jazz Roots

☐ CHARLIE CHRISTIAN SEXTET 1939-1941
159082 / 5 Jan '98 / Jazz Archives

152

☐ CHARLIE CHRISTIAN WITH BENNY GOODMAN (Christian, Charlie & Benny Goodman)
Flying home / Till tom special / Ac-dc current / Seven come eleven / Gone with 'what' wind / Good enough to keep (air mail special) / Breakfast feud / Smooth one / Six appeal / Royal garden blues / Stardust / I can't give you anything but love / Wholly cats / As long as I live / I never knew / I've found a new baby / Soft winds / Lester's dream
CD 14545 / Jan '94 / Jazz Portraits

☐ GENIUS OF THE ELECTRIC GUITAR
Rose room / Seven come eleven / Till Tom special / Gone with "what" wind / Grand slam / Six appeal / Wholly cats / Royal Garden blues / As long as I live / Benny's bugle / Breakfast feud / I found a new baby / Solo flight / Blue in B / Waiting for Benny / Airmail special
4606122 / Jan '95 / Sony Jazz

☐ GENIUS OF THE ELECTRIC GUITAR
Seven come eleven / Till tom special / Gone with 'what' wind / Good enough to keep (air mail special) / A smoo-o-o-oth one / Six appeal / Royal garden blues / Ac-dc current / Wholly cats / As long as I live / Breakfast feud / Profoundly blue / Solo flight / Soft winds / Honeysuckle rose / I can't give you anything but love / I never knew / Lester's dream / Flying home / Poor butterfly / Benny's bugle / I found a new baby / Stardust
CD 53049 / May '90 / Giants Of Jazz

☐ GUITAR WIZARD
LEJAZZCD 11 / Jun '93 / Le Jazz

☐ IMMORTAL, THE
Swing to bop / Up on teddy's hill / Kerouac / Guy's got to go / Lips flips / Blue 'n' boogie / Hot house / Groovin' high / Dizzy atmosphere / All the things you are
17032 / Jul '94 / Laserlight

☐ INTRODUCTION TO CHARLIE CHRISTIAN 1939-1941, AN
4032 / Jul '96 / Best Of Jazz

☐ JAZZ GUITAR VOL.2, THE
Solo flight / Rose room / Honeysuckle rose / Profoundly blue / I never knew / Sweet georgia brown / Oscar's blues / Bop kick / Buckin' the blues / Floyd's guitar blues / I can't give you anything but love / Somebody loves me / Tiny's boogie / Spotlite / Darn that dream / Jumping for jane / One that got away / Deep in the blues
CD 56027 / Nov '94 / Jazz Roots

☐ LIVE AT MINTONS
DM 15001 / Jul '96 / DMA Jazz

☐ MASTERS OF JAZZ (2CD Set)
R2CD 8004 / 13 Apr '98 / Deja Vu

☐ QUINTESSENCE, THE (1939-1941/2CD Set)
FA 218 / Jul '96 / Fremeaux

☐ SOLO FLIGHT (Christian, Charlie/ Benny Goodman Sextet & Orchestra)
TPZ 1017 / Feb '95 / Topaz Jazz

☐ SOLO FLIGHT (2CD Set)
Flying home / Rose room / Memories of you / AC/DC current no.1 / Dinah / Till tom special / Gone with 'what' wind / Sheik of Araby / Soft winds / Six appeal (my daddy rocks me) / AC/DC current / Ad-lib blues / I never knew / Charlie's dream / Wholly cats no.1 / Lester's dream / Benny's bugle no.1 / Wholly cats no.2 / Honeysucle rose / Flying home / Air mail special / Ida, sweet as apple cider / Benny's bugle / Solo flight / Swing to bop / Stompin' at the savoy / Up on Teddy's hill / Star dust no.1 / Kerouac / Star dust no.2 / Guy's got to go / Lips flips
JZCL 5005 / Nov '96 / Jazz Classics

Christian, Emma

☐ BENEATH THE TWILIGHT
EM 001CD / Oct '94 / Manx Productions

Christian, Frank

☐ FROM MY HANDS
PM 2011 / Nov '95 / Palmetto

Christian, Garry

☐ YOUR COOL MYSTERY
0630189162 / May '97 / Coalition

Christian, Jodie

☐ EXPERIENCE
Bluesing around / Mood indigo / Faith / End of a love affair / They can't take that away from me / If I could let you go / Reminiscing / Blues holiday / All the things you are / Goodbye
DD 454 / Nov '92 / Delmark

☐ FRONT LINE
In a mellow tone / Willow weep for me / Lester left town / Front line / Don't get around much anymore / Chelsea Bridge / Mood indigo / All blues / Faith / Splanky
DE 490 / Jun '97 / Delmark

☐ RAIN OR SHINE
Let's try / Song for Atala / Ballad medley / Yardbird suite / Coltrane's view / Mr. Freddie / Chromatically speaking / Come rain or come shine / Cherokee
DE 467 / Mar '97 / Delmark

☐ SOUL FOUNTAIN
DE 498 / Jan '98 / Delmark

Christian, Neil

☐ NEIL CHRISTIAN & THE CRUSADERS 1962-1973 (With Jimmy Page, Ritchie Blackmore and Nicky Hopkins) (Christian, Neil & The Crusaders)
Road to love / Little bit of something else / Honey hush / She's got the action / Wanna lover / She said yeah / Count down / You're all things bright and beautiful / My baby left me / I remember / Feel in the mood / What would your mamma say / I like it / All last night / One for the money / Get a load of this / Give the game away / Two at a time / Oops / Bit by bit / Bad girl / Gonna love you baby / Yakety yak / Crusading / That's nice / Dedicated follower of fashion / Let me in / Big beat in
SEECD 342 / Feb '97 / See For Miles

Christiana Jazzband

☐ NICE WORK
GMCD 64 / Apr '98 / Gemini

Christians

☐ BEST OF THE CHRISTIANS, THE
Forgotton town / Harvest for the world / Perfect moment / What's in a word / Born again / Words / Ideal world / Bottle / When the fingers point / Father / Greenbank drive / Hooverville (and they promised us the world) / Small axe
CIDTV 6 / Nov '93 / Island

☐ CHRISTIANS, THE
Forgotten town / When the fingers point / Born again / Ideal world / Save a soul in every town / And that's why / Hooverville / One in a million / Sad songs
IMCD 162 / Mar '93 / Island

☐ COLOUR
Man don't cry / I found out / Greenbank Drive / All talk / Words / Community of spirit / There you go again / One more baby in black / In my hour of need
IMCD 181 / Mar '94 / Island

☐ HAPPY IN HELL
What's in a word / Uninvited guest / Garden of love / Say it isn't so (part 2) / Father / Bottle / Storms / Slip away / Learn to love / Still small voice / Happy in hell (acappella)
IMCD 182 / Mar '94 / Island

Christianson, Denny

☐ SUITE MINGUS (Christianson, Denny Big Band)
JUST 152 / Jun '92 / Justin Time

Christie Brothers

☐ CHRISTIE BROTHERS STOMPERS (Christie Brothers Stompers)
SGC/MELCD 20/1 / Jan '94 / Cadillac

Christie Front Drive

☐ CHRISTIE FRONT DRIVE
CR 024CD / Apr '97 / Caulfield

Christie, David

☐ BEST OF DAVID CHRISTIE, THE (Saddle Up)
Saddle up / Our time has come / Lazy love / Stress / Living it up / Strut your funky stuff / Don't stop me I like it / Look / Heart beat to heart beat / Stop (don't do this to me) / I love you / Fame / If you want it (do it yourself) / Jay walk
HTCD 36 / 20 Apr '98 / Hot Productions

Christie, Lou

☐ GLORY RIVERS (Buddah Years)
Genesis and the third verse / Rake up the leaves / Johnstown kite / Canterbury road / I'm gonna make you mine / I'm gonna get married / Are you getting any sunshine / She sold me magic / Life is what you make it / I got love / Boys lazed on the veranda / Tell her / Indian lady / Glory river / Wood child / Paper song / Chuckie wagon / Campus rest / Lighthouse / Look out the window / Paint America love / Shuffle on down to Pittsburgh
NEX CD 187 / Jul '92 / Sequel

☐ GONNA MAKE YOU MINE
Genesis and the third verse / Rake up the leaves / Johnson kite / Canterbury Road / Campus rest / I'm gonna make you mine / I'm gonna get married / Are you getting any sunshine / She sold me magic / Life is what you make it / I got love / Boys lazed on the veranda / Tell her / Indian lady / Glory river / Love is over / Wood child / Paper song / Chuckie wagon / Lighthouse / Paint America love / Shuffle on down to the Pittsburgh
74321558472 / 26 Jan '98 / Camden

☐ HIT SONGS AND MORE
HADCD 204 / Jul '96 / Javelin

☐ LIGHTNING STRIKES
RMB 75048 / Nov '93 / Remember

Christie, Steve

☐ BEACHES AND BALLADS
NC 005CD / Dec '97 / New Country

Christie, Tony

☐ BEST OF TONY CHRISTIE
(is this the way to) amarillo / Home lovin' man / Queen of the mardis gras / I did what I did for maria / Most beautiful girl / Happy birthday baby / Avenues and alleyways / I'm not in love / Solitaire / Don't go down to reno / You've lost that lovin' feelin' / Words (are impossible) / On this night of a thousand stars / Way we were / Didn't we / Las vegas / So deep is the night / Daddy don't you walk so fast / First love, best love / Drive safely darlin'
MCCD 185 / Nov '94 / Music Club

☐ SUMMER IN THE SUN
Sweet September / Can't get the feeling / I will remember / Mexico city / Train to yesterday / What a little love can do / Summer in the sun / I'm not chained to you / Summer wine / Ladies man / Tobago / No one in the world but you tonight / Paradise / Another lonely day / Long gone
21073 / Nov '97 / Laserlight

Christion

☐ GHETTO CYRANO
5362812 / 10 Nov '97 / Mercury

Christlieb, Pete

☐ CONVERSATIONS WITH WARNE (Christlieb, Pete & Warne Marsh)
CRISS 1103 / Oct '95 / Criss Cross

Christmas, Keith

☐ LOVE BEYOND DEALS
HTDCD 61 / 9 Mar '98 / HTD

☐ WEATHERMAN ONE
RRACD 0016 / Jul '92 / Run River

Christopher

☐ CHRISTOPHER
GF 108 / 19 Jan '98 / Gear Fab

Christ's Hospital Choir

☐ CHRISTMAS CAROLS
Break forth, o beautious heavenly light / O come all ye faithful (adeste fidelis) / Tommow shall be my dancing day / Nativity carol / Hymn to the virgin / Of the fathers heart begotten / Von himmel hoch / Maiden most gentle / Noel nouvelet / Eastern monarchs / Puer nayus in Bethlehem / God rest ye merry gentlemen / In dulci jubilo / O little town of Bethlehem / Ding dong merrily on high / Once in Royal David's City / No small wonder / Out of your sleep / Lo he comes with clouds / Descending / Hark the herald angels sing
3037600012 / Oct '95 / Carlton

☐ CHRISTMAS CAROLS FROM CHRIST'S HOSPITAL (Christ's Hospital Choir & Peter Allwood/Mark Wardell)
Break forth O beauteous Heavenly light / O come all ye faithful (adeste fidelis) / Tomorrow shall be my dancing day / Eastern monarchs / Noel nouvelat / Maiden most gentle / Choral preludes / Peur natus in Bethlehem / In dulci jubilo / O come o come Emmanuel final descant / In the bleak midwinter / Of the Father's heart begotten / Hymn to the virgin / Nativity carol / God rest ye merry gentlemen / O little town of Bethlehem / Ding dong merrily on high / Once in Royal David's city / No small wonder / Out of your sleep / Lo he comes with clouds ascending / Hark the herald angels sing
3036700012 / Nov '96 / Carlton

Christy, June

☐ DAY DREAMS
I let a song go out of my heart / If I should lose you / Daydream / Little grass skirt / Skip rope / I'll bet you do / Way you look tonight / Everything happens to me / I'll remember April / Get happy / Somewhere (if not in heaven) / Mile down the highway (there's a toll bridge) / Do it again / He can come back anytime he wants to / Body and soul / You're blase
CDP 8320832 / Aug '95 / Capitol Jazz

☐ FRIENDLY SESSION VOL.1, A (Christy, June & Johnny Guarnieri Quintet)
JASCD 341 / 6 Apr '98 / Jasmine

☐ IMPROMPTU (Christy, June & Lou Levy Sextet)
My shining hour / Once upon a summertime / Show me / Everything must change / Willow weep for me / I'll remember April / Trouble with hello is goodbye / Autumn serenade / Sometime ago / Angel eyes
DSCD 836 / Jun '93 / Discovery

☐ JAZZ SESSIONS, THE (The Best Of June Christy)
Something cool / I want to be happy / Remind me / Looking for a boy / My ship / Rock me to sleep / Day dream / Baby all the time / It's a most unusual day / Midnight sun / Fly me to the moon / Get happy / When sunny gets blue / Willow weep for me / Make someone happy / How high the moon / Spring really can hang you up the most / It don't mean a thing
CDP 8539222 / Jan '97 / Capitol Jazz

☐ SONG IS JUNE, THE
Spring can really hang you up the most / One I love (belongs to somebody else) / Nobody's heart / My shining hour / I remember you / Night time was my mother / I wished on the moon / Song is you / As long as I live / Saturday's children / Remind me / Out of this world / You wear love so well / Off beat / Bad and the beautiful / Who cares about April / You care you say / Out of the shadows / Sleepin' bee / Somewhere if not in heaven
CDP 8554552 / Mar '97 / Capitol Jazz

☐ TAMPICO (Christy, June & Stan Kenton Orchestra)
Tampico / It's been a long long time / Just a sittin' and a rockin' / Shoo fly pie and apple pan dowdy / I been down to Texas / Easy street / On the sunny side of the street / Rika jika Jack / I got the sun in the morning / He's funny that way / Come rain or come shine / Ain't no misery in me / Willow weep for me / Four months three weeks two days one hour blues / It's a pity to say goodnight / His feet's too big for de bed / Don't want that man around / Across the alley from the Alamo / Spider and the fly / Please be kind / I got it bad and that ain't good / Soothe me / Curiosity / I told ya I love ya now get out / He was a good man as good men go
CDMOIR 526 / Apr '98 / Memoir

☐ THROUGH THE YEARS
I can't give you anything but love / I've got a guy / Supper time / Make love to me / I'm thrilled / You're blase / How high the moon / Something cool / Too marvellous for words / It could happen to you / From this moment on / I want to be happy / Do I hear a waltz / You came a long way from st. louis / An occasional man / Get me to the church on time
HCD 260 / Aug '95 / Hindsight

☐ UNCOLLECTED JUNE CHRISTY & THE KEYTONES VOL.1 1946
Don't worry 'bout me / Mean to me / Lover man / One I love belongs to somebody else / Lullaby in rhythm / Sweet lorraine / September in the rain / Moonglow / Wrap your troubles in dreams / This is romance / June's blues / I can't believe that you're in love with me / How long has this been going on / Get happy
HCD 219 / Jun '94 / Hindsight

☐ UNCOLLECTED JUNE CHRISTY & THE KEYTONES VOL.2 1957
HCD 235 / Sep '94 / Hindsight

Chrome

☐ 3RD FROM THE SUN/INTO THE EYES OF THE ZOMBIE KING
CLEO 95332 / 22 May '98 / Cleopatra

☐ BLOOD ON THE MOON/ETERNITY
EFA 7490 CD / Jun '89 / Dossier

☐ CHROME BOX 1978-1983 (3CD Set)
CLP 97702 / 19 Jan '98 / Cleopatra

☐ CHROME SAMPLER VOL.1
EFA 084612 / Feb '95 / Dossier

☐ CHRONICLES VOL.1 & 2
EFA 7499 / Jun '89 / Dossier

☐ CLAIRAUDIENT SYNDROME, THE
EFA 084562 / Jul '94 / Dossier

☐ HALF MACHINE LIP MOVES
TV as eyes / Zombie warfare (can't let you down) / March of the chrome police (a cold clamey bombing) / You've been duplicated / Mondo anthem / Half machine lip moves / Abstract nympho / Turned around / Zero time / Creature eternal / Critical mass
DCD 9009 / '85 / Dossier

☐ HAVING A WONDERFUL TIME IN THE JUICE DOME
EFA 084622 / Mar '95 / Dossier

☐ INTO THE EYES OF THE ZOMBIE KINGS (Chrome & Damon Edge)
DCD 9004 / Aug '88 / Dossier

☐ LYON CONCERT, THE/ANOTHER WORLD
If you come around / I found out today / Our good dreams / Stranger from another world / Moon glow / Sky said / Loving lovely lover / We are connected / Saniby / As we stand here in time / March of the rubber people / Ghosts of the long forgotten future / Version two (raining milk) / Source improves / Frankenstein's party
EFA 7709CD / Jun '89 / Dossier

☐ RETRO TRANSMISSION
CLP 00802 / 5 Jan '98 / Cleopatra

☐ THIRD FROM THE SUN
DCD 9012 / Mar '89 / Dossier

☐ TIDAL FORCES
MR 061CD / 9 Feb '98 / Man's Ruin

Chrome Cranks

☐ DEAD COOL
Dead cool / Desperate friend / Shine it on / Nightmare in pink / Burn baby burn / Bloodshot eye / Down so low / Way out lover
EFA 115902 / May '95 / Crypt

☐ HOT BLONDE COCKTAIL
K 178 / 13 Oct '97 / Konkurrent

☐ LIVE IN EXILE
K 181CD / 15 Dec '97 / Konkurrent

☐ LOVE IN EXILE
K 172CD / Dec '96 / Konkurrent

☐ OILY CRANKS
ALP 11CD / Nov '97 / Atavistic

Chron Gen

☐ BEST OF CHRON GEN
AHOY 18 / Nov '94 / Captain Oi

Chrysanthemums

☐ BABY'S HEAD
RG 001 / 10 Nov '97 / Orgone Company

☐ GO GERMANY/INSEKT INSEKT
JAR 007 / 13 Oct '97 / Jar Music

Chubb Rock

☐ MIND, THE
08516672 / Aug '97 / Black Jam

Chubbies

☐ TRES FLORES
SFTRI 472CD / May '97 / Sympathy For
The Record Industry

Chuchuk, Raymond

☐ LET'S DANCE
SAV 190CD / Jun '93 / Savoy

Chuck

☐ WESTWARD HO
F 029CD / 13 Oct '97 / Fearless

Chuck D

☐ AUTOBIOGRAPHY OF MISTACHUCK
MistaChuck / Free Big Willie / No / Generation
wrekked / Niggativity...do I dare disturb the universe
/ Talk show created the fool / But can you kill the
nigger in you / Underdog / Paid / Endonesia / Pride /
Horizontal heron
5329442 / Oct '96 / Mercury

Chukki Starr

☐ GHETTO YOUTH LIVITY
ARICD 143 / 6 Jul '98 / Ariwa Sounds

Chul, Kim Suk

☐ SHAMANISTIC CEREMONIES OF THE
EASTERN SEABOARD (Chul, Kim Suk
Ensemble)
VICG 52612 / Mar '96 / JVC World
Library

Chum

☐ DEAD TO THE WORLD
CM 77113CD / Jun '96 / Century Media

Chumbawamba

☐ ANARCHY
Give the anarchist a cigarette / Timebomb /
Homophobia / On being pushed / Heaven/Hell / Love
me / Georgina / Doh / Blackpool rock / This years
thing / Mouthful of shit / Never do what you are told /
Bad dog / Enough is enough / Rage
TPLP 46CD / Apr '94 / One Little Indian

☐ ENGLISH REBEL SONGS 1381-1914
Cutty wren / Digger's song / Collier's march /
Triumph of General Ludd / Chartist anthem / Song on
the times / Smashing of the van / World turned
upside down / Poverty knock / Idris strike song /
Hanging on the old barbed wire
TPLP 64CD / Feb '95 / One Little Indian

☐ LOVE/HATE
TPLP 66CD / Oct '95 / One Little Indian

☐ PICTURES OF STARVING CHILDREN/
NEVER MIND THE BALLOTS
How to get your band on the television / British
colonialism and the BBC / Commercial break /
Unilever / More whitewashing / Interlude: Beginning
to take it back / Dutiful servants and political masters
/ Coca-colonisation / In a nutshell invasion / Always
tell the voter what the voter wants to hear / Come on
baby (let's do the revolution) / Wasteland / Today's
sermon / Ah-men / Mr. Heseltine meets his public /
Candidates find common ground
TPLP 56CD / Oct '95 / One Little Indian

☐ SHHH
185152 / 15 Sep '97 / Southern

☐ SHOWBUSINESS
Never do what you are told / Rappoport / Give the
anarchist a cigarette / Heaven/Hell / Hungary /
Homophobia / Morality / Bad dog / Stitch that /
Mouthful of shit / Nazi / Jimbomb / Slad aid
TPLP 56CD / Oct '95 / One Little Indian

☐ SLAP
Ulrike / Tiananmen square / Cartrouble / Chase PC'd
flee attack by own dog / Rubber's has been shot /
Rappoport's testament: I never gave up / Slap /
That's how grateful we are / Meinhof
TPLP 65CD / Feb '95 / One Little Indian

☐ TUBTHUMPER
Tubthumping / Amnesia / Drip drip drip / Big issue /
Good ship lifestyle / One by one / Outsider / Creepy
crawling / Mary Mary / Small town / I want more /
Scapegoat / Top of the world (Ole ole ole)
4952382 / 15 Jun '98 / EMI

☐ UNFAIRYTALE, THE (Dambert
Nobacon)
SEEP 16CD / 9 Mar '98 / Rugger Bugger

Church

☐ ALMOST YESTERDAY 1981-1990
RVCD 43 / Dec '94 / Raven

☐ HEYDAY
Myrrh / Tristesse / Already yesterday / Columbus /
Happy hunting ground / Tantalized / Disenchanted /
Night of light / Youth worshipper / Roman / As you
will / View
7462562 / Oct '97 / Axis

☐ HOLOGRAM OF BAAL (2CD Set)
D 31886 / 24 Aug '98 / Festival

☐ MAGICIAN AMONG THE SPIRITS
D 31562 / Feb '97 / Roadrunner

Church Of God

☐ IN HIM I LIVE (Church Of God & Saints
Of Christ)
LYRCD 7423 / Dec '94 / Lyrichord

Churchills

☐ CHURCHILLS, THE
15591 / 12 Jan '98 / Ban

☐ PRESENT: MANIFIQUE 400
71510TS / 1 Dec '97 / Timsims

CIA

☐ GOD GUTS GUNS
LF 295CD / 27 Oct '97 / Lost & Found

Cibo Matto

☐ VIVA LA WOMAN
Apple / Beef jerky / Theme / Birthday cake / White
pepper ice cream / Sugar water / Know your chicken
/ Le pain perdu / Candy man / Jive / Artichoke
9362459892 / Mar '96 / WEA

Ciccu, Bianca

☐ GUSCH, THE (Ciccu, Bianca & Randy
Brecker)
ITM 1440 CD / Apr '90 / ITM

Cicek, Ali Ekbar

☐ BEKTACHI MUSIC
D 8069 / Nov '96 / Unesco

Cicero, Eugene

☐ EASY LISTENING LOUNGE (Cicero,
Eugene & Dieter Reith)
ISCD 171 / May '98 / Intersound

Cicion Tropical Orchestra
La Colegiala

☐ CYCLONE TROPICAL
Corpino colorado / Corpino colorado / Corazon
rebelde / La colegiala / Micabana / Atrevete a
mirarme de frente / Garzas negras / La gorda en
guarare / La mota / Casita pobre / Cumbia del
clarinete / La carta-tres
UCD 19108 / Jul '95 / Forlane

Ciel, Red

☐ JUMP TO THE MOON
RCL 1 / Mar '96 / RCL

Cierzo, Petisme

☐ CANCIONES Y POEMAS
LCD 10 / 1 Jun '98 / Karonte

Cigar Store Indians

☐ EL BAILE DE LA COBRA
DSR 0798 / 27 Jul '98 / Deep South

Cimarons

☐ BEST OF CIMARONS
CC2 703 / Nov '92 / Crocodisc

☐ MAKA
So free (best things in life) / So free (best things in life)
/ Mother earth / Word / Civilization / Loosening out /
Willin (rock against racism) (maxi version) / Give
thanks and praise / Natty time / Reggae rockin / Truly
/ Willin'
CC 2704 / Jun '93 / Crocodisc

☐ PEOPLE SAY
Ship ahoy / Ship ahoy / Rock reggae rhapsody /
People say / Proud / Paul bogle / Greedy man / Wake
up jah-man-can / I wanna please you / Hear talk of
inflation / Rooting for a cause / Zion / He who hides /
Dim the light / Free as life
LG 21006 / Jun '93 / Lagoon

Cinderella

☐ BAD ATTITUDE 1986-1994
VSOPCD 251 / 9 Mar '98 / Connoisseur
Collection

☐ LONG COLD WINTER
Falling apart at the seams / Gypsy road / Last mile /
Long cold winter / If you don't like it / Coming home /
Fire and ice / Take me back / Bad seamstress blues /
Don't know what you got (til it's gone) / Second wind
8346122 / Jul '88 / Vertigo

Cindytalk

☐ CAMOUFLAGE HEART
TOUCH 3CD / Oct '96 / Touch

☐ IN THIS WORLD
TOUCH 2CD / Oct '96 / Touch

☐ WAPPINSCHAW
TOUCH 1CD / Oct '96 / Touch

Cinerama

☐ VA VA VOOM
Maniac / Comedienne / Hate / Kerry Kerry / Barefoot
in the park / You turn me on / Ears / Me next / Hard
fast and beautiful / Dance girl dance / Honey rider
COOKCD 150 / 27 Jul '98 / Cooking
Vinyl

Cinnamon Smith

☐ CURATE'S HOUSE
MUMCD 9804 / 7 Sep '98 / Mother

Cinorama

☐ GARDEN, THE GARDEN
D 63 / Aug '95 / PSF

Ciotti, Roberto

☐ ROAD 'N' RAIL
Road 'n' rail / Sweet song / New blue truck / Early on
sunday / Reason for the blues / She's mine / City
child / I give myself to love / If you don't love me
CDSGP 039 / 29 Sep '97 / Prestige

Cipher

☐ 360 DEGREES
BOMB 20082 / 17 Nov '97 / Bomb Hip
Hop

Cipolla, Rudy

☐ PORTRAIT OF AN AMERICAN
ORIGINAL
ACD 22 / 30 Mar '98 / Acoustic Disc

Circadian Rhythms

☐ INTERNAL CLOCK
Undercurrents / AEA / Cymbophone / Daily ground /
Belltree / Pure / Timeless / Tumescence / Calumet /
Pure reprise / Clear
WORDD 008 / 23 Mar '98 / Language

Circle

☐ PARIS CONCERT (2CD Set)
Nefertitti / Song for the newborn / Duet / Lookout
farm / Kalvin 73, variation - 3 / Toy room / There is no
greater love
8434632 / Oct '90 / ECM

Circle

☐ HISSI
FDMETCD 1 / Mar '97 / Fourth
Dimension
META 008CD / Oct '97 / Captain Trip

Circle Jerks

☐ GROUP SEX
Deny everything / I just want some skank / Beverly
Hills / Operation / Back against the wall / Wasted /
Behind the door / World up my ass / Paid vacation /
Don't care / Live fast die young / What's your
problem / Group sex / I just
01012 / Jun '97 / Frontier

☐ GROUP SEX/WILD IN THE STREETS
FR 002CD / Apr '97 / Frontier

☐ WILD IN THE STREETS
Wild in the streets / Leave me alone / Stars and
stripes / 86'd (good as gone) / Meet the press /
Trapped / Murder the disturbed / Letter home /
Question authority / Defamation innuendo / Moral
majority / Forced labor / Political Stu / Just like me /
Put a little love in your heart
01052 / Jun '97 / Frontier

Circle Of Dust

☐ CIRCLE OF DUST
REX 460112 / Nov '95 / Rex

Circle Of Soul

☐ ONE MANS POISON
IRS 975558 / 6 Oct '97 / Intercord

Circle Percussion

☐ DRUMS OF THE WORLD
Aly n'diaye rose / Babacar 'ndiaye / Venancio Mbande
/ Timbila / Katsuji kondo
369922 / 3 Aug '98 / Koch World

☐ HARUMI
Midi terranée / Marimba spiritual / Final / Doll's
house story / Miyake
369932 / 3 Aug '98 / Koch World

Circle X

☐ CELESTIAL
Kyoko / Pulley / Crow's ghost / Gothic fragment /
Some things don't grow back / Tell my horse / Big
picture / Cabin 9 / Waxed fruit / Celestial / They come
prancing
OLE 0912 / Jul '94 / Matador

☐ CIRCLE X EP
DEX 3 / Dec '96 / Dexter's Cigar

Circus Lupus

☐ SOLID BRASS
DIS 79D / Jul '93 / Dischord

Cirkus III

☐ PANTOMYNE
AACD 026 / 16 Feb '98 / Audio Archive

Ciro Dammicco

☐ MITTENTE
SRMC 6018 / 5 Jan '98 / Siwan

Cissoko, Sunjul

☐ SONGS OF THE GRIOTS VOL.2
VICG 52272 / Mar '96 / JVC World
Library

CITA

☐ HEAT OF EMOTION
19968 / Oct '96 / Made To Measure

Citania

☐ CITANIA
H 002CD / Jun '94 / Sonifolk

☐ O ASUBIO DO PADRINO
J 101CD / Jun '94 / Sonifolk

Citizen Cain

☐ RAISING THE STONES
Last days of Cain / Bad Karma / First gate / Corcyra /
Dreaming makes the world / Last supper / Ghosts of
Jericho / Silently seeking euridice
CYCL 059 / 23 Feb '98 / Cyclops

☐ SERPENTS IN CAMOUFLAGE
Stab in the back / Liquid kings / Harmless criminal /
Gathering / Dance of the unicorn / Serpents in
camoflauge / Nightwings - As the wheel turns / Stab
in the back
CYCL 064 / 26 May '98 / Cyclops

☐ SOMEWHERE BUT YESTERDAY
Jonny had another face (parallel lines) / Junk and
donuts (an afterthought) / To dance the enamel
faced queen (beyond the boundaries) / Somewhere
but yesterday / Owls / Obsessions / Ballad of Creepy
John / Echoes, the labyrinth penumbra / All the sin's
men / Farewell (a word in your ear) / Strange
barbarians (the mother's child)
CYCL 049 / Feb '97 / Cyclops

Citizen Fish

☐ FREE SOULS IN A TRAPPED
Supermarket song / Break into a run / Rainbows /
Possession / Small scale wars / Home economics /
Paint / Talk is cheap / Face off / Youth / Flesh and
blood / Get off the phone / Experiment earth / How to
write ultimate protest songs / Charity
FISH 24CD / Apr '94 / Bluurg

☐ LIVE FISH
FISH 29CD / Nov '93 / Bluurg

☐ MILLENNIA MADNESS
FISH 34CD / Sep '95 / Bluurg

Citizen's Arrest

☐ CITIZEN ARREST
LF 086CD / Jun '94 / Lost & Found

Citizens' Utilities

☐ LOST AND FOUNDERED
CDSTUMM 135 / Nov '96 / Mute

☐ NO MORE MEDICINE
CDSTUMM 166 / 15 Sep '97 / Mute

Citroen, Soesja

☐ SONGS FOR LOVERS AND LOSERS
CHR 70034 / Sep '96 / Challenge

City Boy

☐ CITY BOY/DINNER AT RITZ (2CD Set)
RMED 00216 / 20 Apr '98 / Renaissance

☐ YOUNG MEN GONE WEST/BOOK
EARLY (2CD Set)
RMED 00217 / 20 Apr '98 / Renaissance

City Waites

☐ **GHOSTS, WITCHES AND DEMONS (From The Castle To The Graveyard)**
Soulcake / Devil's dream / Two daughters of this aged stream / Mermaid / Dead man's moan / Where the bee sucks / Satyr's dance / Widdecombe Fair / Shaking of the sheets / Lunatick lover / But e're we this perform / Gelding of the devil / Miss Bailey's ghost / Full fathom five / Tale of Sir Eglamore and how he slew the wondrous dragon / Witches dance / Finnigan's wake / Song for the sprite Ariel and Ferdinanad / Fairie galliard / Unquiet grave / Wonder of wonders / Witches dance
SAMPPCD 401 / Aug '96 / Soundalive

☐ **LADS & LASSES (The Music Of The English Countryside) (City Waites & The Noise Minstrels)**
Chirping of the lark / Parson's farewell / You lasses and lads / Branles / Newcastle / Country lass / Rufty tufty / Spanish gypsy / Millfield / Argeers / Nonsuch / Great booby / Maiden Lane / Couple of pigeons / Parson in boots / One misty moisty morning / Ward's brae / Merry merry milkmaids / All in a garden green / Bobbing Joan / Sellinger's round / Wilson wilde / Hulichan's jig / Stanes morris / Blue cap / Nine pins / Jenny pluck pears / Half hanekin / Paul's wharf / Grimstock / Heart's ease
SAMPPCD 403 / Aug '96 / Soundalive

☐ **LOW AND LUSTY SONGS (Songs From 17th Century England)**
Brooms for old shoes / Trader's medley / Lavender's green / We be soldiers three / Hey, jolly broom man / Give me my yellow hose again / Oak and the ash / Tobacco is an Indian weed / Lumps of pudding / Farmer's cursed wife / Over the hills and far away / Tomorrow the fox will come to town / My dog and I / Baffled knight / Three ravens / Crossed couple / Back and sides go bare / Broom of the cowdenknowes / Song of the cutpurse
SAMHSCD 202 / Aug '96 / Soundalive

☐ **MADRIGAL FOR ALL SEASONS, A (Songs Of Tudor England)**
To shorten Winter's sadness / Silver swan / Fair Phyllis I saw sitting all alone / Dear love be not unkind / Since my tears and lamenting / On the plains, fairy trains / Bianco fiori / Fine knacks for ladies / April is in my Mistress face / Let us not that young man be / Have you seen the bright lily grow / Little pretty bonny lass / La caccia / Sing we and chant it / Most sacred Queen Elizabeth, her galliard / In going to my naked bed / Aminitas with his Phyllis fair / Say gentle nymphs / Tell me dearest, what is love / Adieu, sweet Amaryllis / Weep you no more sad fountains / Galliard / Say love if ever / Ah, the sighs / Now, oh now / There is a lady sweet and kind / If love be blind
SAMHSCD 201 / Aug '96 / Soundalive

☐ **MUSIC FROM THE TIME OF CHARLES II**
Ayre/Sarabande/Courante/Allemand / Oh my Clarissa / This mossy bank they prest / Broken consort in C major / La chitarra royale / In the merry month of May / King's jig / Among thy fancies / Overture/Gavote / Here's a health unto His Majesty / Armoni concerti / Gather your rosebuds / Mateis suite / Long look't for now may come at last / Overture from Le Bourgeois Gentilhomme / Wanton trick / Matachia/Espanleta/Pavana/Forneo/Canarios / Shepherd well met / Ah Heav'n / What is't I hear / Fine young folly / 29th May / Dialogue between a lover and his friend
SAMFNCD 302 / Aug '96 / Soundalive

☐ **MUSIC FROM THE TIME OF HENRY VIII (City Waites & His Majesty's Sagbutts & Cornets)**
SAMFNCD 301 / Aug '96 / Soundalive

☐ **MUSIC OF THE MIDDLE AGES**
Oh admirabile / Miri it is / Brid on a brier / English dance / Ed'i bi thu / Isle of Rea / Fast stantipes / La rotta / Lamento di Tristan / Dance royale / Angelus and Virginem / Sancta mari gratia / Trotto / Mirth of all this lond / Fors seulement / Tapster, drinker
SAMMTCD 102 / Jun '96 / Soundalive

☐ **MUSIC OF THE STUART AGE**
Trumpet tune / Chirping of the lark / Air / Parson's farewell / Newcastle / Sefauchi's farewell / Tomorrow the fox will come to town / First act tune / Cuckolds all in a row / Fairest isle / Mortlack's ground / Grimstock / Harvest home / Fantasy suite / Heartsease / Jenny pluck pears / How blest are the shepherds / Song tune / Maiden Lane / Lavena / Aire / Martin said to his man
SAMMTCD 105 / Aug '96 / Soundalive

☐ **MUSIC OF THE TUDOR AGE, THE**
Pastime with good company / Galliard / Bransall / Runden / Taundernaken / Pavan / Now is the month of Maying / Galliard / Sing we and chant it / Tourdion / Tree ravens / Thomas Ravenscroft / Honeysuckle / Regina galliard / Oh Mistress mine / Woodycock / Dolent depart / Nightwatch / Galliard Lombardo / Mohrentanz / Heigh ho holiday / Tourdion / Mille regrets / Greensleeves / Daphne / Ballo Lomabardo / Earl of Salisbury's pavan / Now oh now
SAMMTCD 104 / Aug '96 / Soundalive

☐ **MUSICIANS OF GROPE LANE, THE (Music Of Brothels & Bawdy Houses Of Purcell's England)**
Diddle diddle or The kind country lovers: Terry, Clark / Fair maid of Islington / Green stockings / Jovial lass or Dol and Roger / Mundanga Was / Lady of pleasure / Old wife / Beehive / Blue petticoats or green garters / Gelding of the Devil / Maid's complaint for want of a Dil Doul / Oyster Nan / Frolic / Husband who met his match / Jovial broom man / Disappointment / Lusty young Smith / Greensleeves and yellow lace / Jolly brown turd / Two rounds / Tom making a Manteau / When Celia was learning / Lady lie near me / Oh how you protest / Ditty delightful of Mother Watkin's ale / Miss Nelly
070969 / Dec '96 / Musica Oscura

☐ **PILLS TO PURGE MELANCHOLY (City Waites & Richard Wistreich)**
Blowzabella, my bouncing dixie / As oyster nan stood by her tub / There was a lass of Islington / Would ye have a young virgin / With my strings of small wire / Like a ring without a finger / When for air I take my mare / Young Colin cleaving of a beam / Do not rumple my top knot / Come jug my honey let's to bed
CDSDL 382 / Mar '94 / Saydisc

City West Quartet

☐ **CHATTERBOX**
BRAM 1992302 / Nov '93 / Brambus

CIV

☐ **SET YOUR GOALS**
So far so good so what / United kids / Don't got to prove it / Trust slips through your hands / Set your goals / Do something / State of grace / Gang opinion / Solid bond / Marching goals / Soundtrack for violence / Boring summer / All twisted / Choices made / Can't wait one mimute more / Et tu Brute
7567926032 / Nov '95 / Atlantic

☐ **THIRTEEN DAY GETAWAY**
Secondhand superstar / Big girl / Itchycoo park / Haven't been myself in a while / Everyday / Shout it / Owner's manual / Something special / Using something else / It's not your fault / Living life / Ordinary / Little men
7567830732 / 17 Aug '98 / Atlantic

Civil Defiance

☐ **FISHERS FOR SOULS, THE**
CD 2 / Nov '96 / Dream Circle

Ciyo

☐ **SOMEWHERE OUT THERE**
Off the cuff / Somewhere out there / Little sunflower / Sun city / Sincerely yours / Similitude / It don't matter / Thoughts and feelings
DESCD 02 / Aug '96 / Diesel

CJ & Co.

☐ **USA DISCO**
Devil's gun / Big city sidewalk / We got our We got our own thing / Deadeye dick / USA disco / Burning drums of fire / Hear say / Golden touch / Beware the stranger / Sure can't go to the moon
CDSEWD 116 / 26 Jan '98 / Westbound

Clail, Gary

☐ **HUMAN NATURE (The Very Best Of Gary Clail)**
Beef / Human nature / Escape / Who pays the piper / These things are worth fighting for / Emotional hooligan / Temptation / Dreamstealers / Speak no evil / Trouble / Free again / Food clothes and shelter / Rumours / Magic penny
74321511922 / 1 Sep '97 / Camden

Clair Obscur

☐ **ANTIGONE**
AFACD 1567 / Jul '96 / Apocalyptic Vision

☐ **COLLECTION OF ISOLATED TRACKS 1982-1988, A**
EFA 015602 / Oct '95 / Apocalyptic Vision

☐ **IN OUT**
AV 001CD / Oct '93 / Apocalyptic Vision

☐ **PLAY**
EFAO 15542 / Apr '95 / Apocalyptic Vision

☐ **ROCK**
EFA 015502 / Oct '95 / Apocalyptic Vision

☐ **SANS TITRE**
AV 022 / Jun '97 / Apocalyptic Vision

Claire Voyant

☐ **CLAIRE VOYANT**
Heaven knows / Her / Deep / Some day / Aqua / Wanderlust / Land and sea / Morning comes / Fear
HYP 3910189CD / 13 Apr '98 / Hyperium

Clan Sutherland Pipe Band

☐ **CLAN SUTHERLAND PIPE BAND**
EUCD 1311 / Jul '95 / ARC

Clan/Destine

☐ **CLAN/DESTINE**
CR 7037CD / Nov '96 / Canyon

Clancy, Aoife

☐ **IT'S ABOUT TIME**
BM 559CD / Jul '95 / Beaumex

Clancy Brothers

☐ **28 SONGS OF IRELAND (Clancy Brothers & Tommy Makem)**
O'Donnell aboo / Croppy box / Rising of the moon / Foggy dew / Ministrel boy / Wind that shakes the barley / Tipperary far away / Kelly, the boy from Killane / Kevin Barry / Whack for the diddle / Men of the West / Eamonn an chnuic (Ned of the hills) / Nell Flaherty's Drake / Boulavogue / Whisky you're the devil / Maid of the sweet brown knowe / Moonshiner / Bold thady quill / Rosin the beau / Finnegan's wake / Real old mountain dew / Courtin' in the kitchen / Mick McGuire / Jug of punch / Johnny McEldoo / Cruiscin lan / Partlairge / Parting glass
IHCD 10 / Jul '89 / Irish Heritage

☐ **CLANCY BROTHERS & TOMMY MAKEM, THE (Clancy Brothers & Tommy Makem)**
TCD 1022 / Aug '96 / Tradition

☐ **CLANCY BROTHERS CHRISTMAS, THE**
Jingle bells / Sing we the Virgin Mary / Holly tree / Angels we have heard / When Joseph was an old man / Christmas in Carrick / Silent night / Lovely far off city / Christ child lullaby / Curoo curoo / Wren song
4891872 / 10 Nov '97 / Columbia

☐ **CLANCY BROTHERS IN CONCERT (Clancy Brothers & Tommy Makem)**
Isn't it grand boys / Mountain dew / Whistling gypsy rover / Finnegan's wake / Carrickfergus / Haul away Joe / Wild rover / Red haired Mary / Jug of punch / Leaving of Liverpool / Wild colonial boy / Holy ground / Wild mountain thyme
PLATCD 335 / Jul '92 / Platinum

☐ **COME FILL YOUR GLASS WITH US (Clancy Brothers & Tommy Makem)**
TCD 1067 / 9 Feb '98 / Tradition

☐ **FINNEGAN'S WAKE (Clancy Brothers & Tommy Makem)**
Finnegan's wake / Portlairge / Boulavogue / O'Donnell Abu / Tipperary far away / Man of the west / Barnyards of Delgaty / Bard of Armagh / Jug of punch / Bold tenant farmer / Johnny I hardly knew you / Real old mountain dew / Courtin' in the kitchen / Brennan on the moor / Work of the weavers / Stuttering lovers / Paddy Doyle's boots / Maid of Fife-E-O / Roddy McCorley / Castle of Dromore / Ballinderry / Bungle rye / Eileen Aroon
SOW 90168 / Jul '98 / Sounds Of The World

☐ **IRISH DRINKING SONGS (Clancy Brothers & Tommy Makem/Dubliners)**
Whiskey in the jar / Beer, beer, beer / Water is alright in tay / Mountain dew / Jug of this / Pub with no name / Drink it up men / Maloney wants a drink / All for me grog / Galway Bay / Jug of punch / Tim Finnegan's wake / Moonshiner / Juice of the barley / Whiskey, you're the divil / Parting glass
CK 52833 / Mar '97 / Columbia
4872462 / 2 Mar '98 / Columbia

☐ **IRISH FOLK SONGS (Clancy Brothers & David Hammond)**
Wee falorie man / Rockin' the cradle / Gallant forty two / When I was single / B is for Barney / All around the lonely O / Green gravel / Doffin' mistress / Maid of Ballydoo / I love my love / Dark eyed gypsy / Will ye go lassie go / 'Tis pretty to be in Ballinderry / Cruise of the calabar / As I roved out / I'll tell my ma / So early early in the spring / Irish girl / Fan-a-winnow / On the banks of the rose / Bonny boy / Me grandfather died / Maderine rue / Love and porter
SOW 90169 / Jul '98 / Sounds Of The World

☐ **MEN OF THE WEST, THE**
Will ye go lassie go / As I roved out / Cruise of the calabar / Irish girl / B is for blarney / Green gravel / Maid of ballydoo / See saw and others / All around the lonely o / When I was single / I'll tell my Ma / Doffin mistress / I know my love / Dark eyed gypsy / Barnyards of Dalgety / Bard of Armagh / Bold tenant farmer / Johnny I Hardly knew you / Real old mountain dew / O'Donnell aboo / Finnegan's wake / Portlairge / Boulavogue / Courting in the kitchen / Tipperary so far away / Men of the West
SUMCD 4073 / Nov '96 / Summit

☐ **OLDER BUT NO WISER (Clancy Brothers & Robbie O'Connell)**
Ramblin' gamblin' Willie / When the ship comes in / Lily Marlene / Roll on the day / Let no man steal your thyme / Salonika / Flower of Scotland / Curragh of Kildare / Boys of Wexford / Final trawl / Lads of the fair / Those were the days
VCD 79488 / Mar '96 / Vanguard

☐ **REUNION (Clancy Brothers & Tommy Makem)**
Isn't it grand / Mountain dew / Whistling gypsy rover / Finnegan's wake / Carrickfergus / Haul away Joe / Wild rover / Red haired Mary / Jug of punch / Leaving of Liverpool / Wild colonial boy / Holy ground / Wild mountain thyme
CD 5009 / Apr '88 / Ogham

☐ **RISING OF THE MOON (Irish Songs Of The Rebellion) (Clancy Brothers & Tommy Makem)**
TCD 1066 / 9 Feb '98 / Tradition

☐ **TUNES & TALES OF IRELAND LIVE**
FE 2061 / Dec '94 / Folk Era

☐ **TUNES 'N' TALES**
FE 20612 / Dec '96 / Frantic

☐ **WRAP THE GREEN FLAG (Clancy Brothers & Tommy Makem)**
Paddy West / Heave away my Johnny / Bold tenant farmer / Fare thee well Enniskillen / Bold Fentan men / Jennifer Gentle / New South Wales / Wrap the green flag 'round me boys / Johnson's motor car / Valley of Knockanure / Nation once again / Rising of the moon / Leaving of Liverpool / Galway races / Johnny I hardly knew ye / Irish rover
CK 48866 / Mar '97 / Columbia

Clancy Children

☐ **SO EARLY IN THE MORNING**
TCD 1053 / Jul '97 / Tradition

Clancy, Willie

☐ **MINSTREL FROM CLARE, THE**
Langstern pony uilleann pipes / Templehouse / Over the moor to Maggie whistle / Bruachna carraige baine pipes / Erin's lovely lea / Killavil fancy / Dogs among the bushes / Family ointment vocal / Dear Irish boy / Caoineadh an spailpin whistle / Pipe on the hob / Gander vocal / Legacy jig whistle / Flogging reel pipes / Song of the riddles vocal / Spailpin a ruin pipes
GL 3091CD / Sep '94 / Green Linnet

☐ **PIPERING OF WILLIE CLANCY VOL.1, THE**
West wind/Sean Reid's fancy / Rocks of Bawn / Old bush / Will you come down to Limerick / Bold trainer O / Rolling wave / An Ghaoth Aniar-Aneas / Garrett Barry's Mazurka / Jenny picking cockles/My love is in America / Bright lady / Lady's pantaletts/Ravelled Hank of Yarn / Purty Molly Brannigan/Green fields of America / Kitty got a clinking coming from the fair / Bonny bunch of roses / Down the back lane / Paidin O Raifeartaigh / Clancy's jig / Jenny tie the bonnet/ Corney is coming
CC 32CD / Jul '93 / Claddagh

☐ **PIPERING OF WILLIE CLANCY VOL.2, THE**
Sean O Duibhir a Ghleanna / Caislean dhun guaire / McKenna's / Casadh an tSugain / Harvest home / I buried my wife and danced on her grave / Chaillgh, do mhairis me / Fowler on the moor / Bimis as ol s ag pogadh na mban / Milliner's daughter / Trip o'er the mountain / Connaught heifers / Steampacket / Gold ring / Kitty goes milking / Banish misfortune / An buachaill caol dubh / As phis fhliuch / Rakish paddy / Fraher's jig / Garrett Barry's / Dark is the colour of my true love's hair / Chief O'Neill's favourite / Jenny's welcome to Charlie
CC 39CD / Jul '93 / Claddagh

Clandestine

☐ **HAUNTING, THE**
CANCD 0397 / Mar '98 / Candletime

Clannad

☐ **AN AM**
Ri na cruinne / An am (soul) / In fortune's hand / Poison glen / Wilderness / Why worry / Uirchill an chreagain / Love and affection / You're the one / Dobhar
74321330682 / Feb '96 / RCA

☐ **AN DIOLAIM**
Oulaman / Eleanor Plunkett / Two sisters / Fairly shot of her / Siuil a run / Oheanainn sugradh / Galtee hunt / By chance it was / Rince philio a cheoil / Gaoth barra na dtonn / Cumha eoghain rua ui neill / An gabhar ban / Chuaigh me na rosann / Coinleach Ghlas an Fhomair
MCCD 351 / 15 Jun '98 / MCI Music

☐ **ATLANTIC REALM**
Atlantic realm / Predator / Moving thru / Berbers / Signs of life / In flight / Ocean of light / Drifting / Under Neptune's cape / Voyager / Primeval sun / Child of the sea / Kirk pride
74321318672 / Jun '96 / RCA

☐ **BACK2BACK**
74321206932 / Sep '95 / RCA

☐ **BANBA**
Na leatha bhi / Banba oir / There for you / Mystery game / Struggle / I will find you / Soul searcher / Ca de sin don te sin / Other side / Sunset dreams / Gentle place
74321139612 / Aug '96 / RCA

☐ **CLANNAD**
Harry's Game / Closer to your heart / Lady Marian / Newgrange / Mhorag's no Horo Gheallaidh / Nil Sen La / Caislean Oir / In a life time / Now is here / Na Buachailli Alainn / Down by the Sally Gardens / Dulaman / Robin (the hooded man)
KCD 400 / Jan '97 / Celtic Collections

☐ **CLANNAD IN CONCERT**
SHANCD 79030 / Oct '88 / Shanachie

☐ **CLANNAD IN CONCERT**
TFCB 5001 / Oct '94 / Third Floor

☐ **CLANNAD VOL.2**
An gabhar ban / Eleanor Plunkett / Coinleach glas an fhomhair / Rince Philib a Cheoil / By chance it was / Rince Briotanach / Dheanainn sugradh / Gaoth barra na d'tonn / Teidhm abhaile riu / Fairly shot of her / Chuaigh me 'na rosann
CEFCD 041 / Jan '94 / Gael Linn

☐ **CRANN ULL**
Ar a ghabhail 'n a 'chuain damh / Last rose of Summer / Cruscin lan / Bacach Shile Andai / La coimhthioch fan dtuath / Crann ull / Gathering mushrooms / Bunan bui / Planxty Browne
TARACD 3007 / Nov '90 / Tara

☐ **DULAMAN**
CEFCD 058 / Jan '94 / Gael Linn

☐ **FUAIM**
Na Buachailli Alainn / Mheall Si Lena Glorthai Me / Bruachna carraige baine pipes / La Brea Fan Dtuath / An tull / Strayed away / Ni La Na Gaoithe La Na Scoib / Lish young buy a broom / Mhorag's Na Horo Ghealladh / Green fields of Gaothdobhair / Buaireadh / An Phosta
COOKCD 035 / Apr '90 / Cooking Vinyl

☐ **LANDMARKS**
An gleann / Fado / A mhuirnin O / Of this land / Court to love / Golden ball / Bridge of tears / Autumn leaves are falling / Let me see / Loch na Caill
74321560072 / 30 Mar '98 / RCA

☐ **LEGEND**
Robin (the hooded man) / Now is here / Herne / Together we / Darkmere / Strange land / Scarlet inside / Lady Marian / Battles / Ancient forest
ND 71703 / Aug '88 / RCA

☐ **LORE**
Croi croga / Seanchas / Bridge (that carries us over) / From your heart / Alasdair Maccolla / Broken pieces / Trathnona beag areir / Trail of tears / Dealramh go Deo / Farewell love / Fonn mharta / Harry's Game / Robin (the hooded man) / In a lifetime / I will find you / Something to believe in
74321359752 / 2 Feb '98 / RCA

☐ **LORE/THEMES AND DREAMS (2CD Set)**
Croi croga / Seanchas / Bridge (that carries us over) / From your heart / Alasdair Maccolla / Broken pieces / Trathnona beag areir / Trail of tears / Dealramh go Deo / Farewell love / Fonn mharta / Harry's Game / Robin (the hooded man) / In a lifetime / I will find you / Something to believe in / New Grange
74321357952 / Mar '96 / RCA

☐ **MACALLA**
Caislean oir / Wild cry / Closer to your heart / Almost seems (too late to turn) / In a lifetime / Buachaill an Eirne / Blackstairs / Journey's end / Northern skyline
74321160352 / Sep '93 / RCA

☐ **MAGICAL RING**
Harry's Game / Tower hill / Searchran charn tsail / I see red / Passing time / Coinleach glas an fhomair / Ta 'me mo shui / New grange / Fairy queen / Thios fa'n chosta
ND 71473 / Aug '95 / RCA

☐ **PAST PRESENT**
Harry's Game / Closer to your heart / Almost seems (too late to turn) / Hunter / Lady Marian / Sirius / Coinleach glas an fhomair / Second nature / World of difference / In a lifetime / Robin (the hooded man) / Something to believe in / Newgrange / Buachaill an eirne / White fool / Stepping stone
74321289812 / 1 Sep '97 / RCA

☐ **RING OF GOLD**
CMCD 034 / Dec '97 / Celtic Music

☐ **SIRIUS**
In search of a heart / Second nature / Turning tide / Skellig / Stepping stone / White fool / Something to believe in / Live and learn / Many roads / Sirius
ND 75149 / Jan '92 / RCA

☐ **ULTIMATE COLLECTION, THE**
Dulaman / Two sisters / Siuil a run (Irish love song) / Nil sen la / Down by the Sally Gardens / An tull: *Clannad & Enya* / Na buachailli alainn: *Clannad & Enya* / Green fields of Gaothdobhar: *Clannad & Enya* / Mhorag's na horo ghealladh: *Clannad & Enya* / Harry's Game / New Grange / Robin (the hooded man) / In a lifetime: *Clannad & Bono* / Closer to your heart / Something to believe in: *Clannad & Bruce Hornsby* / Hunter / I will find you / Mystery game / Seanchas / Bridge (that carries us over)
74321486742 / May '97 / RCA

Clanton, Jimmy

☐ **GO JIMMY GO (The Very Best Of Jimmy Clanton)**
Just a dream / I trusted you / That's you baby / You aim to please / Letter to an angel / Part of me / Ship on a stormy sea / My love is strong / My own true love / Little boy in love / Go Jimmy go / Another sleepless night / I'm gonna try / Wait / Come back / Down in the aisle: *Clanton, Jimmy & Mary Ann Mobley* / Twist on little girl / I just wanna make love / Just a moment / Venus in blue jeans / Highway bound / What am I looking for / What am I living for / Darkest street in town
WESM 517 / 13 Oct '97 / Westside

Clapton, Eric

☐ **24 NIGHTS (Eric Clapton Live)**
Badge / Running on faith / White room / Sunshine of your love / Watch yourself / Have you ever loved a woman / Worried life blues / Hoodoo man / Pretending / Bad love / Old love / Wonderful tonight / Bell bottom blues / Hard times / Edge of darkness
7599264202 / Nov '90 / Warner Bros.

☐ **ANOTHER TICKET**
Something special / Black rose / Another ticket / I can't stand it / Hold me Lord / Floating bridge / Catch me if you can / Rita Mae / Blow wind blow
5318302 / Sep '96 / Polydor

☐ **AUGUST**
It's in the way that you use it / Run / Tearing us apart: *Clapton, Eric & Tina Turner* / Bad influence / Hung up on your love / I take a chance / Hold on / Miss you / Holy Mother / Behind the mask
9254762 / Feb '95 / Duck/Warner Bros.

☐ **BACKLESS**
Early in the morning / Golden ring / If I don't be there by morning / I'll make love to you anytime / Promises / Roll it / Tell me that you love me / Tulsa time / Walk out in the rain / Watch out for Lucy
5318262 / Sep '96 / Polydor

☐ **BACKTRACKIN' (22 Tracks Spanning The Career Of A Rock Legend - 2CD Set)**
Cocaine / Strange brew / Spoonful / Let it rain / Have you ever loved a woman / Presence of the Lord / Crossroads / Roll it over / Can't find my way home / Blues power / Further on up the road / I shot the Sheriff / Knockin' on Heaven's door / Lay down Sally / Promises / Swing low, sweet chariot / Wonderful tonight / Sunshine of your love / Tales of brave Ulysses / Badge / Little wing / Layla
8219372 / Feb '85 / Polydor

☐ **BEHIND THE SUN**
She's waiting / See what love can do / Same old blues / Knock on wood / Something's happening / Forever man / It all depends / Tangles in love / Never make you cry / Just like a prisoner / Behind the sun
9251662 / Apr '85 / Duck/Warner Bros.

☐ **BLUES POWER**
304002 / Apr '98 / Hallmark

☐ **CREAM OF ERIC CLAPTON, THE**
Layla / Badge / I feel free / Sunshine of your love / Strange brew / White room / Cocaine / I shot the sheriff / Behind the mask / Forever man / Lay down Sally / Knockin' on Heaven's door / Wonderful tonight / Let it grow / Promises / I've got a rock 'n' roll heart / Heart / Crossroads
5218812 / Jan '95 / Polydor

☐ **CROSSROADS (4CD Set)**
Boom boom / Honey in your hips / Baby what's wrong / I wish you would / Certain girl / Good morning little school girl / Ain't got you / For your love / Got to hurry / Lonely years / Bernard Jenkins / Hideaway / All your love / Ramblin' on my mind / Have you ever loved a woman / Wrapping paper / I feel free / Spoonful / Lawdy Mama / Strange brew / Sunshine of your love / Tales of brave Ulysses / Steppin' out / Anyone for tennis / White room / Crossroads / Badge / Presence of the Lord / Can't find my way home / Sleeping in the ground / Comin' home / Tell the truth / Roll it over / Layla / Mean old world / Key to the highway / Crossroads / Got to get better in a little while / Evil / One more chance / Mean old Frisco blues / Snake Lake blues / Blues power / After midnight / Let it rain / Let it grow / Ain't that lovin' you / Motherless children / I shot the sheriff / Better make it through today / Sky is crying / I found a love / (When things go wrong) things hurt me too / Whatcha gonna do / Knockin' on Heaven's door / Someone like you / Hello my old friend / Sign language / Further on up the road / Lay down Sally / Wonderful tonight / Cocaine / Promises / If I don't be there by morning / Double trouble / I can't stand it / Shape you're in / Heaven is one step away / She's waiting / Too bad / Miss you / Wanna make love to you / After midnight
8352612 / Nov '96 / Polydor

☐ **CROSSROADS VOL.2 (Live In The Seventies)**
5293052 / Mar '96 / Polydor

☐ **EC WAS HERE**
Have you ever loved a woman / Presence of the Lord / Driftin' blues / Can't find my way home / Ramblin' on my mind / Further on up the road
5318232 / Sep '96 / Polydor

☐ **ERIC CLAPTON**
Slunky / Bad boy / Lonesome and a long way from home / After midnight / Easy now / Blues power / Bottle of red wine / Lovin' you loving me / I've told you for the last time / I don't know why / Let it rain
5318192 / Sep '96 / Polydor

☐ **ERIC CLAPTON & THE YARDBIRDS (Clapton, Eric & The Yardbirds)**
IMT 100100 / Sep '96 / Scratch

☐ **ERIC CLAPTON AND FRIENDS**
GFS 062 / Jul '97 / Going For A Song

☐ **FROM THE CRADLE**
Blues before sunrise / Third degree / Reconsider baby / Hoochie coochie man / Five long years / I'm tore down / How long blues / Goin' away baby / Blues leave me alone / Sinner's prayer / Motherless child / It hurts me too / Someday after a while / Standing around crying / Driftin' / Groaning the blues
9362457352 / Sep '94 / Warner Bros.

☐ **IN WORDS AND MUSIC (2CD Set)**
OTR 1100028 / Jun '97 / Metro Independent

☐ **INTERVIEW DISC**
SAM 7018 / Nov '96 / Sound & Media

☐ **JOURNEYMAN**
Pretending / Anything for your love / Bad love / Running on faith / Hard times / Hound dog / No alibis / Run so far / Old love / Breaking point / Lead me on / Before you accuse me
92620742 / Oct '89 / Warner Bros.

☐ **JUST ONE NIGHT**
Tulsa time / Early in the morning / Lay down Sally / Wonderful tonight / If I don't be there by morning / All our past times / Worried life blues / Blues power / Knockin' on Heaven's door / Double trouble / Setting me up / After midnight / Ramblin' on my mind / Cocaine / Further on up the road
5318272 / Sep '96 / Polydor

☐ **MONEY AND CIGARETTES**
Everybody oughta make a change / Shape you're in / Ain't going down / I've got a rock 'n' roll heart / Man overboard / Pretty girl / Man in love / Crosscut saw / Slow down Linda / Crazy country hop
9237732 / Feb '95 / Warner Bros.

☐ **NO REASON TO CRY**
Beautiful things / County jail / Carnival / Sign language / Country jail blues / All our past times / Hello old friend / Double trouble / Innocent times / Hungry / Black summer rain
5318242 / Sep '96 / Polydor

☐ **PILGRIM**
My father's eyes / River of tears / Pilgrim / Broken hearted / One chance / Circus / Going down slow / Fall like rain / Born in time / Sick and tired / Needs his woman / She's gone / You were there / Inside of me
9362465774 / 9 Mar '98 / Warner Bros.

☐ **RAINBOW CONCERT**
Badge / Roll it over / Presence of the Lord / Pearly queen / After midnight / Little wing
5274722 / May '95 / Polydor

☐ **RUSH (Original Soundtrack)**
New recruit / Tracks and lines / Realization / Kristen and Jim / Preludin fugue / Cold turkey / Will gaines / Help me up / Don't know which way to go / Tears in heaven
7599267942 / Oct '94 / WEA

☐ **STAGES OF CLAPTON (Various Artists)**
Stepping out: *Mayall, John & The Bluesbreakers* / Ramblin' on my mind: *Mayall, John & The Bluesbreakers* / Hideaway: *Mayall, John & The Bluesbreakers* / Have you heard: *Mayall, John & The Bluesbreakers* / Outside woman blues: *Cream* / Crossroads: *Cream* / They call it stormy Monday: *Mayall, John & The Bluesbreakers* / Well alright: *Blind Faith* / Bell bottom blues: *Derek & The Dominoes* / Blues power: *Derek & The Dominoes* / Driftin' blues: *Clapton, Eric* / Mean ol' Frisco: *Clapton, Eric*
5500282 / May '93 / Spectrum

☐ **STRICTLY THE BLUES**
PLSCD 103 / Aug '96 / Pulse

☐ **SURVIVOR**
I wish you would / For your love / Certain girl / Got to hurry / Too much monkey business / I don't care no more / Bye bye bird / Twenty three hours too long / Baby don't worry / Take it easy baby
CDTB 013 / Mar '95 / Thunderbolt

☐ **THERE'S ONE IN EVERY CROWD**
We've been told (Jesus coming soon) / Swing low, sweet chariot / Little Rachel / Don't blame me / Sky is crying / Singin' the blues / Better make it through the day / Pretty blue eyes / High / Opposite
5318222 / Sep '96 / Polydor

☐ **TIME PIECES VOL.1 (The Best Of Eric Clapton)**
I shot the sheriff / After midnight / Wonderful tonight / Layla / Willie and the hand jive / Knockin' on Heaven's door / Let it grow / Swing low, sweet chariot / Cocaine / Lay down Sally / Promises
8000142 / '83 / RSO

☐ **TIME PIECES VOL.2 (The Best Of Eric Clapton Live In The Seventies)**
Tulsa time / Knockin' on Heaven's door / If I don't be there by morning / Ramblin' on my mind / Presence of the Lord / Can't find my way home / Smile / Blues power
8118352 / Jul '88 / RSO

☐ **UNPLUGGED**
Signe / Before you accuse me / Hey hey / Tears in heaven / Lonely stranger / Nobody knows you (when you're down and out) / Layla / Running on faith / Walkin' blues / Alberta / San Francisco Bay blues / Malted milk / Old love
9362450242 / Aug '92 / Warner Bros.

Clare, Allen

☐ **ALLEN CLARE & LENNY BUSH (Clare, Allen & Lenny Bush)**
CHECD 00108 / Nov '93 / Master Mix

Clarinet Summit

☐ **CLARINET SUMMIT**
IN 1062CD / Jan '97 / India Navigation

Clarinette Quintet

☐ **BAZH DU**
Y 225031CD / Dec '93 / Silex

Clarion

☐ **FROM THE OAK**
BAK 002CD / Jul '95 / Bakkus

Clark, Andy

☐ **A=MH2 (Clark-Hutchinson)**
REP 7081 / Feb '98 / Repertoire

☐ **RETRIBUTION (Clark-Hutchinson)**
RR 7088 / 16 Mar '98 / Repertoire

Clark, Anne

☐ **LAW IS AN ANAGRAM OF WEALTH, THE**
SPV 08492702 / Aug '95 / SPV

☐ **NINETIES, THE (A Fine Collection)**
Abuse / Counter act / Empty me / If I could / Windmills of your mind / Haunted road / Fragility / Seize the vivid sky / Elegy for a lost summer / Echoes remain forever / Dream made real / Letter of thanks to a friend / Our darkness / Sleeper in metropolis
SPV 08544632 / Feb '97 / SPV

☐ **PSYCHOMETRY**
SPV 08489282 / Aug '95 / SPV

☐ **TO LOVE AND BE LOVED**
SPV 08589542 / Mar '96 / SPV

Clark, Buddy

☐ **BAND VOCALS FROM THE 1930'S**
TT 402 / May '98 / Take Two

Clark, David Anthony

☐ **AUSTRALIA BEYOND THE DREAMTIME**
WCL 11013 / May '95 / White Cloud

☐ **TERRA INHABITATA**
WCL 11007 / May '94 / White Cloud

Clark, Dee

☐ **HEY LITTLE GIRL**
I just can't help myself / When I call on you / Just like a fool / Seven nights / Oh little girl / Wondering / Nobody but you / Just keep it up / Hey little girl / How about that / Blues get off my shoulder / At my front door / You're looking good / Your friends / Because I love you / Raindrops / (Don't) walk away from me / I'm going back to school / Shook up over you / I'm a soldier boy
CDRB 19 / Apr '95 / Charly

☐ **RAINDROPS (The Best Of Dee Clark)**
Raindrops / Just a little bit / How about that / Just keep it up / Hey little girl / Dock of the bay / Only you / Twilight time / LeRoy Brown / Little bitty pretty one / Lavender blue / Barefootin' / High heel sneakers / Slip away
CDSGP 0230 / 2 Feb '98 / Prestige

☐ **TAKE CARE OF BUSINESS (The Constellation Masters 1963-1966)**
Crossfire time / It's raining / Come closer / I'm going home / That's my girl / In my apartment / Heartbreak / Warm summer breezes / I ain't gonna be a fool / TCB / I can't run away / I don't need (nobody like you) / She's my baby / It's impossible / Hot potato / Ole fashun love / Nobody but you
WESA 805 / 15 Jun '98 / Westside

Clark, Gary

☐ **TEN SHORT SONGS ABOUT LOVE**
This is why, J / We sail on stormy waters / St. Jude / Short song about love / Make a family / Freefloating / Baby blue No.2 / Nancy / Any Sunday morning / Making people cry / Sail on / Jackson in your kitchen
CIRCD 23 / Apr '93 / Circa

Clark, Gene

☐ **AMERICAN DREAMER 1964-1974**
I'll feel a whole lot better / Set you free this time / She don't care about time / Echoes / So you say you lost your baby / Radio song / With care from someone / Out on the side / Train leaves here this morning / Something's wrong / Through the morning, through the night / She's the kind of girl / One in a hundred / Here tonight / Virgin / With tomorrow / White light / Spanish guitar / American dreamer / Outlaw song / Full circle / From a silver phial / Silver raven
RVCD 21 / Feb '93 / Raven

☐ **ECHOES**
Boston / For me again / I knew I'd love you / Here without you / Set you free this time / If you're gone / Is yours is mine / So you say you lost your baby / Tried so hard / Needing someone / Echoes / Same one / Couldn't, believe her / Keep on pushin' / I found you / Elevator operator / Think I'm gonna feel better / French girl / Only Colombe / So you say you lost your baby
4882242 / 8 Sep '97 / Epic

☐ **FIREBYRD**
SPINCD 122 / Dec '97 / Spindrift

☐ **FIREBYRD**
MPG 74053 / 3 Mar '98 / Movieplay Gold

☐ **FLYING HIGH (2CD Set)**
You showed me / Feel a whole lot better / Set you free this time / She don't care about time / Tried so hard / So you say you lost your baby / French girl / Los Angeles / I pity the poor imigrant / That's alright for me / Trains leaves here this morning / Why not your baby / Radio song / Git it on brother / Something's wrong / Stone must be the wall / No longer a sweetheart of mine / Throught the night through the morning / Kanasa city southern / Polly / Dark hollow / One in a hundred / She's the kind of girl
5407252 / Oct '97 / A&M

☐ **GENE CLARK & THE GOSDIN BROTHERS (Clark, Gene & The Gosdin Brothers)**
Echoes / Think I'm gonna feel better / Tried so hard / Is yours is mine / Keep on pushing / I found you / So you say you lost your baby / Elevator operator / Same one / Couldn't believe her / Needing someone
EDCD 529 / Jun '97 / Edsel

☐ **ROADMASTER**
She's the kind of girl / One in a hundred / Here tonight / Full circle song / In a misty morning / Rough and rocky / Roadmaster / I really don't want to know / I remember the railroad / She don't care about time / Shooting star
ED CD 198 / Jun '90 / Edsel

☐ **SILHOUETTED IN LIGHT (Clark, Gene & Carla Olsen)**
Your fire burning / Number one is to survive / Love wins again / Fair and tender ladies / Photograph / Set you free this time / Last thing on my mind / Gypsy rider / Train leaves here this morning / Almost Saturday night / Del Gato / I'll feel a whole lot better / She don't care about time / Speed of the sound of loneliness / Will the circle be unbroken
FIENDCD 710 / Feb '92 / Demon

☐ **SO REBELLIOUS A LOVER (Clark, Gene & Carla Olsen)**
Drifter / Gypsy rider / Every angel in heaven / Del gato / Deportees / Fair and tender ladies / Almost Saturday night / I'm your toy / Why did you leave me / Don't it make you wanna go home / Are we still making love
FIENDCD 89 / Aug '87 / Demon

☐ **THIS BYRD HAS FLOWN**
Tambourine man / Vanessa / Rainsong / C'est la bonne rue / If you could read my mind / Dixie flyer / Feel a whole lot better / Rodeo rider / All I want / Something about you / Made for love / Blue raven
EDCD 436 / Jul '95 / Edsel

Clark, Glen

☐ **LOOKING FOR A CONNECTION**
DOSCD 7006 / Sep '95 / Dos

Clark, Graham

☐ **ISTHMUS (Clark, Graham & Jon Thorne/Milo Fell)**
Duende / Bang on / System x / Lonestar / Buffalo wings / Dagobert / Isthmus / Ragsville / Second thought / When in Rome... / Secret shortbread
AGASCD 012 / Jul '97 / GAS

Clark, Guy

☐ **BOATS TO BUILD**
Baton Rouge / Picasso's mandolin / How'd you get this number / Boats to build / Too much / Ramblin' Jack and Mahan / I don't love you much do I / Jack of all trades / Madonna w/Child ca 1969 / Must be my baby
7559614422 / Jul '93 / Nonesuch

☐ **CRAFTSMAN**
Fool on the roof / Fools for each other / Shade of all greens / Vila an american dream / One paper kid / In the jailhouse now / Comfort and crazy / Don't you take it too bad / Houston kid / Fool on the roof blues / Who do you think you are / Crystelle / New cut road / Rita Ballou / South coast of Texas / Heartbroke / Partner nobody chose / She's crazy for leaving / Calf rope / Lone star hotel / Blowin' like a bandit / Better days / Home grown tomatoes / Supply and demand / Randall knife / Carpenter / Uncertain Texas / No deal / Tears / Fool in the mirror
CDPH 118485 / Jun '95 / Philo

☐ **ESSENTIAL GUY CLARK, THE**
Texas 1947 / Desperadoes waiting for a train / Like a coat from the cold / Instant coffee blues / Let him roll / Rita Ballou / LA freeway / She ain't going nowhere / Nickel for the fiddler / That old time feelin' Texas cookin' / Anyhow I love you / Virginia's real / Broken hearted people / Black haired boy / Me I'm feeling the same / Ballad of Laverne and Captain Flint / Don't let the sunshine fool you / Last gunfighter ballad / Fools for each other
7863674042 / May '97 / RCA

☐ **KEEPERS (A Live Recording)**
LA freeway / Texas 1947 / Like a coat from the cold / Heartbroke / Last gunfighter ballad / Better days / Homegrown tomatoes / She ain't goin' nowhere / South coast of Texas / That old time feeling / Little of both / Out in the parking lot / Let him roll / Texas cookin' / Desperadoes waiting for a train
SHCD 1055 / Mar '98 / Sugar Hill

☐ **OLD FRIENDS**
SHCD 1025 / Aug '95 / Sugar Hill

☐ **OLD NUMBER ONE**
Rita Ballou / LA freeway / She ain't goin' nowhere / Nickel for the fiddler / That old time feeling / Texas - 1947 / Desperados waiting for the train / Like a coat from the cold / Instant coffee blues / Let him roll
EDCD 285 / Apr '96 / Edsel
SHCD 1030 / Jan '97 / Sugar Hill

☐ **OLD NUMBER ONE/TEXAS COOKIN'**
Rita Ballou / La freeway / She ain't goin' nowhere / Nickel for the fiddler / That old feeling / Desperados waiting for the train / Like a coat from the cold / Instant coffee blues / Let him roll / Texas cookin' / Anyhow I love you / Virginia's real / It's about time / Good to love you lady / Broken hearted people / Black haired boy / Me I'm feeling the same / Ballad of Leverne and Captain Flint / Last gunfighter ballad
74321588132 / 15 Jun '98 / Camden

☐ **TEXAS COOKIN'**
Texas cookin' / Anyhow I love you / Virginia's real / It's about time / Good to love you lady / Broken hearted people / Black haired boy / Me I'm feelin' the same / Ballad of Laverne and Captain Flint / Last gunfighter ballad
EDCD 287 / Apr '96 / Edsel
SHCD 1031 / Oct '97 / Sugar Hill

Clark, Mike

☐ **FUNK STOPS HERE, THE (Clark, Mike, Paul Jackson, Kenny Garrett & Jeff Pittson)**
TIP 8888112 / Jul '92 / Enja

☐ **MASTER DRUMMERS VOL.3**
URCD 011 / Jul '96 / Ubiquity

☐ **MIKE CLARK SEXTET (Clark, Mike Sextet / Ricky Ford & Jack Walrath)**
STCD 22 / Oct '91 / Stash

Clark, Pete

☐ **EVEN NOW (The Music Of Neil Gow)**
SMD 615 / May '98 / Smiddy Made

Clark, Petula

☐ **CLASSIC COLLECTION, THE (4CD Set)**
Downtown / My love / Who am I / I know a place / Don't sleep in the subway / Other man's grass is always greener / Look at mine / Round every corner / Cat in the window (the bird in the sky) / Happy heart / Thank you / You're the one / Don't give up / I will follow him / Baby it's me / You'd better come home / I couldn't live without your love / True love never runs smooth / I want to sing with your band / Valentino / This is my song / Sailor / Romeo / My friend the sea / I'm counting on you / Something missing / Road / Jumble sale / Ya ya twist / American boys / Sign of the times / No one better than you / Kiss me goodbye / Chariot / Cinderella Jones / Let me tell you / In love / Whistlin' for the moon / Welcome home / Colour my world / Groovy kind of love / Days / Black coffee / Homeward bound / Elusive butterfly / Here, there and everywhere / Reach out, I'll be there / Cherish / Every little bit hurts / Nobody I know (partir il nous faut) / Answer me, my love / I want to hold your hand / You belong to me / Dancing in the street / San Francisco (be sure to wear some flowers in your hair) / Well respected gentleman (un jeune homme bien) / Please please me (tu perds ton coeur) / Let it be me / Am I that easy to forget (tu reviendras a ta maison) / Foot tapper (mon bonheur danse) / Call me / Just say goodbye / Heart / Life and soul of the party / There goes my love, there goes my life / Marie De Vere / Close to you / Tiny bubbles (dans mon lit) / Two rivers / Hello Mr Brown / This is goodbye / L'amour viendra / Cranes flying south / Cala di volpe / Crying through a sleepless night / Conversations in the wind / If ever you're lonely / Where did we go wrong / Qu'est ce qui fait courir le monde / Show is over
PBXCD 404 / Jul '97 / Pulse

☐ **COMPLETE GOLDEN HITS COLLECTION, THE**
Little shoemaker / Suddenly there's a valley / With all my heart / Alone / Sailor / My friend the sea / Romeo / Casanova / Downtown / Don't sleep in the subway / My love / This is my song / Other man's grass is always greener / I know a place / You're the one / Round every corner / Sign of the times / I couldn't live without your love / Kiss me goodbye / I don't know how to love him / Downtown '88 / You'd better come home / Who am I / Colour my world / Don't give up
SELCD 508 / Mar '98 / Castle Select

☐ **DOWNTOWN**
Downtown / Sign of the times / This is my song / I couldn't live without your love / You're the one / I know a place / Kiss me goodbye / Colour my world / Mad about you / Don't sleep in the subway / Good life / Other man's grass / My love / Give it a try / Strangers in the night / Call me
15103 / Jun '93 / Laserlight

☐ **DOWNTOWN**
True love never runs smooth / Baby it's mine / Now that you've gone / Tell me (that it's love) / Crying through a sleepless night / In love / Music / Be good to me / This is goodbye / Let me tell you / You belong to me / Downtown / I will follow him / Darling Cheri / You'd better love me
NEBCD 661 / Oct '93 / Sequel

☐ **DOWNTOWN**
Downtown / Don't sleep in the subway / Romeo / I don't know how to love him / If / For all we know / I couldn't live without your love / Where do I go from here / Welcome home / Thank you / This is my song / Sailor / Colour my world / Fly me to the moon / Memories are made of this / I get along without you very well / Night has a thousand eyes / Chariot / Happy heart / My love
5507332 / Mar '95 / Spectrum

☐ **DOWNTOWN**
PDSCD 529 / Aug '96 / Pulse

☐ **EP COLLECTION VOL.2, THE**
I know a place / Tell me / In love / Let me tell you / You'd better love me / Every little bit hurts / Time for love / This is my song / Monday, Monday / I'm begging you / On the path of glory / Resist / Winchester Cathedral / Homeward bound / Jack and John / Music / Forgetting you / Be good to me / My love / Where am I going / 31st of June / Show is over / Colour my world / Here comes the morning / Fancy dancin' man / Bang bang / Groovy kind of love
SEECD 381 / Oct '93 / See For Miles

☐ **EP COLLECTION, THE**
Cinderella Jones / With your love / Who needs you / While the children play / Slumming on Park Avenue / I've grown accustomed to his face / Love me again / Here, there and everywhere / Welcome home / My favourtie things / Sailor / Don't sleep in the subway / Have I the right / Downtown / Gotta tell the world / Everything in the garden / Hold on to what you've got / Life and soul of the party / I couldn't live without your love / Long before I knew you / In a little moment / Baby it's me / True love never runs smooth / Strangers and lovers / We can work it out / Wasn't it you / Come rain or come shine / What would I be
SEECD 306 / Dec '90 / See For Miles

☐ **GOLD**
GOLD 207 / Apr '94 / Disky

☐ **GREATEST HITS**
Downtown / This is my song / Colour my world / My love / I couldn't live without your love / It's a sign of the times / I know a place / Kiss me goodbye / Don't sleep in the subway darling / Other man's grass / You're the one / Give it a try / Mad about you
100522 / May '97 / A-Play Collection

☐ **HELLO PARIS**
3039562 / 13 Jul '98 / Anthology

☐ **HER GREATEST HITS (2CD Set)**
SMDCD 195 / Jul '97 / Snapper

☐ **I COULDN'T LIVE WITHOUT YOUR LOVE/COLOUR MY WORLD**
Strangers in the night / Groovy kind of love / Rain / Wasn't it you / There goes my love, there goes my life / Monday Monday / Bang bang (my baby shot me down) / Homeward bound / Two rivers / Come rain or come shine / Elusive butterfly / I couldn't live without your love / Your way of life / England swings / Cherish / Please don't go / What would I be / While the children play / Who am I / Winchester Cathedral / Las Vegas / Reach out, I'll be there / Special people / Here, there and everywhere / Colour my world / I'm begging you (take me home again) / Love is a long journey / What would I be
RPM 170 / Sep '96 / RPM

☐ **I KNOW A PLACE**
Dancing in the street / Strangers and lovers / Everything in the garden / In crowd / Heart / You're the one / Foggy day / Gotta tell the world / Every little bit hurts / Call me / Goin' out of my head / I know a place / Jack and John / You'd better come home / Sound of love / Round every corner
NEBCD 660 / Jan '95 / Sequel

☐ **I LOVE TO SING**
Madamoiselle de paris / On the atchison, topeka and the Santa Fe / I get along without you very well / Fly me to the moon / Gotta have me go with you / George / There's nothing more to say / Nighty-night / Valentino / Imagination / Thankyou / Saturday sunshine / You'd better love me / Forgetting you / Round about / Never will I / Sound of love / Look at me / Nothing much matters / Make way for love / At the crossroads / Without a song / Only when to love me / Big love sale / Make a time for loving / What I did for love / Downtown / Sailor / Romeo / My friend the sea / I love to sing / I will follow him / I know a place / Things go better with coca-cola / You'd better come home / Round every corner / You're the one / My love / Just say goodbye / Sign of the times / I couldn't live without your love / Who am I / Colour my world / This is my song / Don't sleep in the subway / High / Other man's grass / Kiss me goodnight / Don't give up / Look at mine / You and I / I don't know how to love him / Superstar / Take good care of your heart / Love will find a way / Gotta be better than this / After you / Gotta be love / Theme from a dream / Goodbye Mr. Chips / Things to do / Conversations in the wind / Support your nearest love / Cranes flying south / Melody man / Beautiful sounds / Song is love / I've got to know / I think of you / Lifetime of love / Coming back to you again / On the road / Goin' out of my head / Maybe
NXTCD 265 / Jul '95 / Sequel

☐ **JUMBLE SALE**
Day in, day out / Darn that dream / Mama's talkin' soft / For the very first time / That's how it feels / (where are you) now that I need you / I love a violin / I'm in love again / A doodlin' song / There's a small hotel / Lucky / Too darn hot / Where do I go from here / I love to sing / Be anything (but be mine) / On the atchison, topeka and the santa fe / George / Gotta have me go with you / For every man, there's a woman / Night has a thousand eyes / Fly me to the moon / There's nothing more to say / I get along without you very well / Mademoiselle de paris / Just you, just me / All through the day / When lights are low / Nighty-night / Jumble sale / Too late / Imagination / Ever been in love / You're getting to be a habit with me / With all my love / All over now / Adonis / Suddenly / Watch your heart (aye mon coueur) / If I had my way / My heart (amor) / Tender love / Cinderella jones / No love, no nothin' / Lucky day / Through the livelong day / Whistlin' for the moon / Some other world / Valentino / Isn't this a lovely day / Road / Saturday sunshine / Forgetting you (j'ai tout oublie)
NEDCD 198 / Feb '92 / Sequel

☐ **JUST PET**
Lights of night / Fill the world with love: *Clark, Petula & Jimmy Joyce Singers/Boys Chorus* / Houses / Happy together / Things bright and beautiful / Hey Jude / For those in love / Butterfly / If I only had time / Fool on the hill / No one better than you / Look at mine / You and I / Fill the world with love / Happy together
NEBCD 902 / Sep '96 / Sequel

☐ **LIVE AT THE COPACABANA**
Put on a happy face / I've seen that face before / My love / Our love is here to stay / Come rain or come shine / I know a place / Typically English / I couldn't live without your love / Santa Lucia / Hello Dolly / Call me / M'sieure m'sieure / My name is Petula / (In) a shanty in old Shanty Town / So nice top come home to / Dear hearts
NEBCD 653 / Jun '93 / Sequel

☐ **MERRY CHRISTMAS**
This is christmas / Silent night holy night / Happiest christmas / Il est ne le divin enfant / Marie et son enfant / Cette nuit la / My favourite things / Hark the herald angel sing / List our merry carol / Once in royal david's city / Little Jesus / Holly and the ivy / Away in the manger/Hark the herald angel sing / Minuit chretein / Mon beau sapin / Il est ne le divin enfant / Belle nuit sainte nuit / Le train des neiges / Christmas cards
NEMCD 945 / 29 Sep '97 / Sequel

☐ **MY LOVE**
My love / Hold on to what you've got / We can work it out / Time for love / Just say goodbye / Life and soul of the party / Sign of the times / 31st of June / Where did we go wrong / I can't remember (ever loving you) / Dance with me / If I were a bell / Rain / Love is a long journey / Your way of life
NEBCD 658 / Jun '94 / Sequel

☐ **NIXA YEARS VOL.1, THE**
Suddenly there's a valley / Band of gold / Memories are made of this / Fortune teller / To you, my love / Another door opens / Million stars above / With all my heart / 'Allo mon coeur / Papayer / Tout ce que veut Lola / Histoire D'un amour / Guitare et tambourin / Java pour Petula / Mon couer danse avec la chance / Tango au L'esquimau / Prends mon couer / Lune de miel / Che sbadato / Ne joue pas / Que voulez vous de plus / Je t'aime / Liebe in St. Tropez / Du bist mein anfang und mein schluss / Hark the herald angels sing / List our merry carol / Once in Royal David's City / Little Jesus / Holly and the ivy / Away in a manger
RPM 138 / Aug '94 / RPM

☐ **NIXA YEARS VOL.2, THE**
Gonna find me a bluebird / Alone / Baby lover / Little blue man / Devotion / St. Tropez / Fibbin' / Where do I go from here / Dear Daddy / Through the livelong day / Let's get lost / I love to sing / All through the day / You're a sweetheart / Don't blame me / More I see you / Moi j'prefere l'amour a tout ca / Dis-moi / T es ma pluie et mon beau temps / Grand-mere / Non et non / Garde ta derniere danse pour moi / Sur un tapis volent / Calcutta (ma fete a moi) / Marin / Les gens diront / Calender girl / Ya ya twist / Si c'est oui, c'est oui / Bye bye mon amour
RPM 144 / Nov '94 / RPM

☐ **OTHER MAN'S GRASS IS ALWAYS GREENER, THE/PETULA-KISS ME GOOD**
Smile / Black coffee / Answer me my love / Other man's grass is always greener / Today, tomorrow / I could have danced all night / At the crossroads / Ville de france / Cat in the window (bird in the sky) / For love / Ballad of a sad young man / Don't give up / Have another dream on me / Your love is everywhere / One in a million / Beautiful in the rain / This girl's in love with you / Kiss me goodbye / Sun shines out of your shoes / We're falling in love again / Days / Why can't I cry / Good life
SEECD 435 / Oct '95 / See For Miles

☐ **PETULA CLARK IN MEMPHIS**
I wanna see morning with him / Nothing's as good as it used to be / Goodnight sweet dreams / Right on / Neon rainbow / It don't matter to me / How we gonna live to be a hundred / Years old together / When the world was round / That old time feeling / That's what life is all about / People get ready / When the world was round / Beautiful sounds / Song is love
NEBCD 901 / Sep '96 / Sequel

☐ **POLYGON YEARS VOL.1**
You go to my head / Out of a clear blue sky / Music music music / Blossoms on the bough / Silver dollar / Talky talky talky / Who spilt coffee on the carpet / You are my true love / You're the sweetest in the land / Beloved be faithful / Fly away Peter, fly away Paul / Tennessee waltz / Sleepy eyes / Teasin' / Black note serenade / May kway / Clickety clack / Mariandl / Broken heart / That's how a love song is born / Cold cold heart / Tell me truly / Song of the mermaid / It had to be you / Card / Boy in love / Where did my snowman go / Teasin'
RPM 130 / Jun '94 / RPM

☐ **POLYGON YEARS VOL.2**
Anytime is teatime now / Made in heaven / Temptation rag / My love is a wanderer / Take care of yourself / Christopher Robin at Buckingham Palace / Three little kittens / Poppa Piccolino / Who-is-it song / Little shoemaker / Helpless / Meet me in Battersea Park / Long way to go / Smile / Somebody / Christmas cards / Little Johnny Rainbow / Majorca / Fascinating ryhthm / Get well soon / Romance in Rome / Chee Chee oo chee / Crazy Otto rag / Pendulum song / How are things with you / Tuna puna Trinidad / Chee chee oo chee
RPM 131 / Jun '94 / RPM

☐ **PORTRAIT OF PETULA**
Happy heart / If ever you're lonely (Lontago dagli occhi) / Games people play / Love is the only thing / When I was a child / Ad / My funny valentine / Lovin' things / When I give my heart / Let it be me / Some / Windmills of your mind / When you return / Have another dream on me / One in a million / Your love is everywhere
NEBCD 659 / Jan '95 / Sequel

☐ **PYE YEARS VOL.1 (Don't Sleep In The Subway)**
Never on a Sunday / You can't keep me from loving you / What now my love / Why don't they understand / Have I the right / Volare / One more sunrise / I want to hold your hand / Love me with all your heart / Boy from Ipanema / I who have nothing / Hello Dolly / This is my song / Groovin' / Lover man / San Francisco / Eternally / Resist / Don't sleep in the subway / Imagine / Love is here / How insensitive / I will wait for you / On the path of glory / High / Here comes the morning / Show is over
RPM 146 / Jun '95 / RPM

☐ **PYE YEARS VOL.2**
RPM 159 / Mar '96 / RPM

☐ **RENDEZ-VOUS AVEC/PETULA**
3039572 / 13 Jul '98 / Anthology

☐ **THESE ARE MY SONGS**
Downtown / It's a sign of the times / This is my song / I couldn't live without you / You're the one (un mal pour un bien) / I know a place / Kiss me goodbye / Colour my world / Mad about you / Don't sleep on the subway darling / Good life / Other man's grass is always greener / My love / Give it a try / Call me / Strangers in the night
STFCD 5 / Feb '97 / Start

☐ **TODAY**
I couldn't live without your love / After the hill / Close to you / Spring in September / I've got to know / City lights / Gotta be better than this / After you / Today / Marie de vere / Coming back to you / This is my song / Take good care of your heart / Love will find a way / Look to the sky / I've got love going for me / Everytime I see a rainbow
NEBCD 943 / 29 Sep '97 / Sequel

☐ **VERY BEST OF PETULA CLARK, THE**
PLSCD 156 / Feb '97 / Pulse

☐ **WARM AND TENDER**
Let me be the one / Loss of love / Cry like a baby / Don't say I didn't tell you so / For free / Maybe I'm amazed / Beautiful / Time and love / I've got my eyes on you / Couldn't sleep / I just can't wait to hold you / Song of my life / Song is love / For love / Song of my life / It's so easy
NEBCD 944 / 29 Sep '97 / Sequel

☐ **WHERE THE HEART IS**
I dreamed a dream / Memory / Time after time / Last night of the world / (Everything I do) I do it for you / Tell me it's not true / As if we never said goodbye / With one look / Perfect year / This is my song / Don't sleep in the subway / Home is where the heart is / I couldn't live without your love / Downtown / My love / Romeo
VSOPCD 249 / 26 Jan '98 / Connoisseur Collection

☐ YOU ARE MY LUCKY STAR
It's foolish but it's fun / Sonny boy / Zing went the strings of my heart / Alone / I, yi, yi, yi, yi / Goodnight my love / I wish I knew / Slumming on Park Avenue / As time goes by / It's the natural thing to do / Afraid to dream / You are my lucky star / I yi yi yi yi (I like you very much)
C5CD 551 / Jan '90 / See For Miles

Clark, Roy

☐ MAKIN' MUSIC (Clark, Roy & Clarence 'Gatemouth' Brown)
MCAD 22125 / Jul '94 / One Way

Clark, Sanford

☐ FOOL, THE
Fool / Man who made an angel cry / Love charms / Cheat / Lonesome for a letter / Ooh baby / Darling dear / Modern romance / Travellin' man / Swanee river rock / Lou be doo / Usta be my baby / Nine pound hammer / Glory of love / Don't care / Usta be my baby
BCD 15549 / Jun '92 / Bear Family

☐ SHADES
Better go home (throw that blade away) / Pledging my love / Girl on Death Row / Step aside / (They call me) Country / Shades / Fool / Climbin' the walls / Once upon a time / It's nothing to me / Where's the door / Big lie / Calling all hearts / Black Jack county chain / Big big day tomorrow / Bad case of you / Wind will blow (demo) / Streets of San Francisco / Oh Julie / Kung Fu U / Mother Texas (you've been a mother to me) / Taste of you / Movin' on / Wind will blow / Feathers / Now I know I'm not in Kansas / Nine pound hammer
BCD 15731 / Jul '93 / Bear Family

Clark Sisters

☐ MIRACLE
It's gonna be alright / Miracle / Simply yes / Call me / I don't know why / He's a real friend / Amazing grace / Jesus is the best thing / No doubt about it / Work to do
SPD 1368 / Aug '95 / Alliance Music

Clark, Sonny

☐ COOL STRUTTIN'
Cool struttin' / Blue minor / Sippin' at bells / Deep night / Royal flush / Lover
CDP 7465132 / Mar '95 / Blue Note

☐ DIAL S FOR SONNY
Dial S for Sonny / Bootin' it / It could happen to you / Sonny's mood / Shoutin' on a riff / Love walked in / Bootin' it 5:1
CDP 8565852 / Jun '97 / Blue Note

☐ SONNY CLARK, MAX ROACH, GEORGE DUVIVIER (Clark, Sonny/Max Roach/George Duvivier)
COD 009 / Mar '92 / Jazz View

☐ STANDARDS
Blues in the night / Can't we be friends / Somebody loves me / All of you / Dancing in the dark / I cover the waterfront / Blues in the night / Gee baby / Ain't I good to you / Ain't no use / I can't give you anything but love / Black velvet / I'm just a lucky so and so / Breeze and I / Gee baby ain't I good to you
8212831 / 2 Feb '98 / Blue Note

Clark, Terri

☐ HOW I FEEL
5582112 / 18 May '98 / Mercury

☐ JUST THE SAME
Emotional girl / Poor, poor pitiful me / Just the same / Something in the water / Neon flame / Any woman / Twang thang / You do or you don't / Keeper of the flame / Not what I wanted to hear / Hold your horses
5328792 / Nov '96 / Mercury

☐ TERRI CLARK
5269912 / Feb '96 / Mercury

Clark, Thais

☐ THAIS CLARK & FESSOR'S FUNKY NEW ORLEANIANS (Clark, Thais & Ole 'Fessor' Lindgren)
MECCACD 2011 / May '97 / Music Mecca

Clark, W.C.

☐ HEART OF GOLD
BT 1103CD / May '94 / Black Top

☐ LOVER'S PLEA
Changing my life with your love / Lover's plea / Lonely no more / Someday / Pretty little mama / Are you here / Everywhere I go / Sunshine lady / I'm hooked on you / Why I got the blues / Do you mean it / That's a good idea
CDBT 1145 / Jun '98 / Black Top

Clarke, Alex

☐ SAX
SPLCD 030 / Apr '96 / Sloane

Clarke, Allan

☐ I WASN'T BORN YESTERDAY/THE ONLY ONE
I wasn't born yesterday / Hope / New blood / I'm betting my life on you / Man who manufactures dreams / No prisoner taken / (I will be your) shadow in the street / Light of my smiles / Who's goin' out the back door / Off the record / Only ones / Slipstream / Walls / Baby blue / Brandenburg plaza / Survivor / Driving the doomsday cars / Sanctuary / Imaginations child / Legendary heroes
C5HCD 665 / 24 Nov '97 / See For Miles

Clarke, Ann

☐ UNSTILL LIFE
0888362 / May '91 / SPV

Clarke, Anthony John

☐ SIDEWAYS GLANCE, A
Irish eyes / Tuesday night is always karaoke / Journey home / Seven in Ireland / Ireland's burning / Savin' the best till last / Patrick / Hawk / Irish visit '91 / Turning the corner now / But then I'm Irish / Even at the beat of times
TERRCD 008 / Jul '97 / Terra Nova

Clarke, Buddy

☐ ONCE AND FOR ALWAYS
JZCL 6003 / Feb '97 / Jazz Classics

Clarke, Dave

☐ ARCHIVE ONE
Rhapsody in red / Protective custody / No one's driving / Woki / Southside / Wisdom to the wise / Tales of two cities / Storm / Miles away / Thunder / Splendour
74321361102 / Jun '96 / De-Construction

☐ DJ KICKS (X-Mix Electro Boogie Vol.1/ 2CD Set) (Various Artists)
Phox: *SEM* / We come to dub: *Imperial Brothers* / I am: *Lockstep* / Electronic warfare/The mixes/Aux 88: *Underground Resistance* / Demented spirit: *Octagon Man* / DJ: *Aux 88* / Midnight drive: *Elecktroids* / Future: *Model 500* / Future tone: *Elecktroids* / Subsonic soundscape: *Shiver* / Ignition: *Dynamix II* / We are back: *LFO* / Sole waves: *Detrechno* / Technicolor: *Channel One* / Voice activated: *Dopplereffekt* / I do because I couldn't care less: *I-F* / Primrose path: *Hashim*
K7 050CD / Jan '97 / Studio K7

☐ DJ KICKS (X-Mix Electro Boogie Vol.2 - The Throwdown/2CD Set) (Various Artists)
Sterilization: *Dopplereffekt* / Janitorial bandsaw: *Dodd, Oliver* / Doctor break: *Shiver* / Surgery: *World Class Wrecking Crew* / Face your fate: *KT 19941* / 808 beats: *Unknown DJ* / Space invaders are smoking grass: *I-F* / Crosswalk: *Technasia* / Skin: *Ectomorph* / U can't see me: *DJ Assault* / Describe reality: *Rother, Antony* / Warfare beats: *Transits Of Tone* / Digital system: *Da Sampla* / Boomin': *Web, Will* / Future: *Alien FM* / From scratch: *Like A Tim* / I need to freak: *Aux 88* / Rhythm trax: *DJ Jazzy Jeff & The Fresh Prince* / Fresh mess: *DJ Jazzy Jeff & The Fresh Prince* / B boys breakdance: *High Fidelity Three*
K7 067CD / 13 Apr '98 / Studio K7

Clarke, Gilby

☐ HANGOVER, THE
SPV 08518732 / Aug '97 / SPV

☐ PAWNSHOP GUITARS
Cure me... or kill me / Black / Tijuana jail / Skin and bones / Johanna's chopper / Let's get lost / Pawnshop guitar / Dead flowers / Jail guitar doors / Hunting dogs / Shut up
CDVUS 76 / Jul '94 / Virgin

☐ RUBBER
SPV 08518132 / 29 Jun '98 / SPV

Clarke, Johnny

☐ 20 MASSIVE HITS
3021462 / Jun '97 / Arcade
RN 7020 / 20 Apr '98 / Rhino

☐ AUTHORISED ROCKERS
Rockers time now / It's green and cold / African roots / Be holy my brothers and sisters / Satta a masagana / Stop the tribal war / Declaration of rights / Let's give jah jah praises / Wish it would go on forever / Natty dreadlocks stand up right / Prophesy a fulfilled / Marcus Garvey / Roots, natty roots, natty congo / Wrath of jah / Legalize it / I'm still waiting / Let go violence / Academy award version / Cry tough / Crazy baldheads / Simmer down / Jah jah see them come / Freedom blues
CDFL 9014 / Jun '91 / Frontline

☐ GOLDEN HITS
SONCD 0081 / Nov '95 / Sonic Sounds

☐ LIFT YOURSELF UP
CDSGP 0275 / Sep '96 / Prestige

☐ TRIBUTE TO BOB MARLEY IN A DANCEHALL, A
RN 7038 / 23 Feb '98 / Rhino

Clarke, Kenny

☐ BOHEMIA AFTER DARK
Bohemia after dark / Chasm / Willow weep for me / Hear me talkin' to ya / With apologies to Oscar / We'll be together again / Late entry
SV 0107 / Oct '97 / Savoy Jazz

☐ CALYPSO BLUE (Clarke, Kenny & Francy Boland Sextet)
Ebony samba / Tin tin deo / Please don't leave / Lush life / Man from potter's crossing / Wives and lovers / Ensainado / Lorraine / Love hungry / Balafon / Day by day / Calypso blues / Invitation / Insensatez / Serenata / Con alma / Just give me the time / Born to be blue / Lilemor / Sconsolato
RW 101CD / 24 Apr '98 / Rearward

☐ KENNY CLARKE MEETS THE DETROIT JAZZ MEN
You turned the tables on me / Your host / Cotton tail / Apothegh / Tricrotism / Afternoon in Paris / Tom's thumb
SV 0243 / Oct '97 / Savoy Jazz

Clarke, Mick

☐ ALL THESE BLUES (Clarke, Mick Band)
APCD 058 / '92 / Appaloosa

☐ HAPPY HOME (Clarke, Mick & Lou Martin)
BCD 0026 / Mar '97 / Burnside

☐ LOOKING FOR TROUBLE (Clarke, Mick Band)
APCD 038 / '92 / Appaloosa

☐ NO COMPROMISE (Clarke, Mick Band)
TX 1006CD / Dec '93 / Taxim

☐ TELL THE TRUTH (Clarke, Mick Band)
TX 1001CD / Dec '93 / Taxim

☐ WEST COAST CONNECTION
BRAM 1988012 / Aug '95 / Brambus

Clarke Sisters

☐ TRIBUTE TO THE GREAT SINGING GROUPS, A (The Clarke Sisters Swing Again)
My blue Heaven / Until the real thing comes along / Bei mir bist du schon / Paper doll / I'll get by / I've got a gal in Kalamazoo / Dream / Sugartime / I'm getting sentimental over you / Undecided / I'm forever blowing bubbles / When I take my sugar to tea / St. Louis blues march / Hot toddy / Song of India / I've got my love to keep me warm / I can't get started / Trumpet blues / In the mood / When day is done / Mole
JASCD 603 / Oct '96 / Jasmine

Clarke, Stanley

☐ BASSIC COLLECTION, THE
School days / Wild dogs / We supply / Mothership connection / Journey to love / Hello Jeff / I wanna play for you / Silly putty / Hot fun / Rock 'n' roll jelly / Jamaican boy / Lost in a thought / Between love and magic / Live suite
4851442 / 3 Nov '97 / Sony Jazz

☐ CLARKE/DUKE PROJECT VOL.1 (Clarke, Stanley & George Duke)
4682232 / Jan '95 / Sony Jazz

☐ CLARKE/DUKE PROJECT VOL.2 (Clarke, Stanley & George Duke)
Put it on the line / Atlanta / Trip you in love / You're gonna love it / Good times / Great danes / Every reason to smile / Try me baby / Heroes
EK 38934 / Jul '95 / Sony Jazz

☐ EAST RIVER DRIVE
Justice's groove / Fantasy love / Zabadoobeede (yabadoobeeda) / East river drive / I'm home africa / Funk is its own reward / Theme from boyz n the hood / Christmas in rio / What if I forget the champagne / Never lose your heartthere lies the passion / Illegal / Lords of the low frequencies
4737972 / Jan '95 / Sony Jazz

☐ FIND OUT (Clarke, Stanley Band)
Find out / What if I should fall in love / Born in the USA / Sky's the limit / Don't turn the lights out / Campo Americano / Stereo typica / Psychedelic / My life
EK 40040 / Aug '97 / Sony Jazz

☐ HIDEAWAY
Overjoyed / My love, her inspiration / Where do we go / Boys of Johnson Street / Old friends / When it's cold outside / Listen to the beat of your heart / Basketball / I'm here to stay
EK 40275 / Aug '97 / Sony Jazz

☐ I WANNA PLAY FOR YOU
Rock 'n' roll jelly / All about / Jamaican boy / Christopher Ivanhoe / My greatest hits / Strange weather / I wanna play for you / Just a feeling / Streets of Philadelphia / School days / Quiet afternoon / Together again / Blues for Mingus / Off the planet / Hot fun
4773132 / Jan '95 / Sony Jazz

☐ IF THIS BASS COULD ONLY TALK
If this bass could talk / I wanna play for you / Funny how time flies / Bassically taps / Working man / Come take my hand / Stories to tell / Tradition
4608832 / Jan '92 / Epic

☐ JOURNEY TO LOVE
Silly putty / Journey to love / Hello, Jeff / Song to John / Concerto for jazz-rock orchestra
4682212 / Jan '95 / Sony Jazz

☐ LIVE 1976-1977
4689592 / Jan '95 / Sony Jazz

☐ LIVE AT THE GREEK
Minute by minute / Stratus / Buenos aires / All blues / Goodbye pork pie hat / Her favorite song / School days
4766022 / 26 Jan '98 / Sony Jazz

☐ RITE OF SPRING, THE (Clarke, Stanley & Al Di Meola/Jean-Luc Ponty)
8341672 / Dec '95 / Gai Saber

☐ ROCKS, PEBBLES AND SAND
Danger street / All hell broke loose / Rocks, pebbles and sand / You / Me together / Underestimation / We supply / Story of a man and a woman / She thought I was Stanley Clarke / Fool again / I nearly went crazy (until I realised what had occurred)
4682222 / Jan '95 / Sony Jazz

☐ SCHOOL DAYS
School days / Quiet afternoon / Danger / Desert song / Hot fun / Life is just a game / Dancer
4682192 / Jan '95 / Sony Jazz

☐ STANLEY CLARKE
Vulcan princess / Yesterday Princess / Lopsy lu / Power / Spanish phases for strings and bass / Life suite
4682182 / Jan '95 / Sony Jazz

☐ THIS IS JAZZ
Goodbye pork pie hat / Desert song / Quiet afternoon / Song to John / Christmas in Rio / Spanish phases for strings and bass / What if I forget the champagne / All blues
EK 65452 / 4 May '98 / Sony Jazz

☐ TIME EXPOSURE
Play the bass 103 / Are you ready / Speedball / Heaven sent you / Time exposure / Future shock / Future / Spacerunner / I know just how you feel
EK 38688 / Aug '97 / Sony Jazz

Clarke, Terry

☐ HEART SINGS
Rocks of Ireland / Roll away / Detroit to dingle / Back to the wall / Shelly river / Walk with me / Looking for you / Heart sings / Blue honey / Bruce Channel in this town / Edge of shamrock city / American lipstick / Irish rockabilly blues / Last rhythm
TRACD 226 / May '97 / Transatlantic

Clarke, William

☐ BLOWIN' LIKE HELL
Lollipop mama / Lonesome bedroom blues / Gambling for my bread / Greasy gravy / Trying so hard / Cash money / Must be jelly / Sweet angel's gone / Looking to the future / Drinking by myself / Blowin' like hell
ALCD 4788 / Mar '93 / Alligator

☐ GROOVE TIME
ALCD 4827 / Dec '94 / Alligator

☐ HARD WAY, THE
ALCD 4842 / Aug '96 / Alligator

☐ SERIOUS INTENTIONS
Pawnshop bound / Trying to stretch my money / Educated fool / Going down this highway / I know you're fine / Driving my life away / Chasin' the gator / With a tear in my eye / It's been a long time / Work song / I feel like jumping / Soon forgotten
ALCD 4806 / May '93 / Alligator

Clarvis, Paul

☐ FOR ALL THE SAINTS
MRFD 97123 / Jun '98 / Village Life

Clash

☐ CLASH, THE
Janie Jones / Remote control / I'm so bored with the USA / White riot / Hate and war / What's my name / Deny / London's burning / Career opportunities / Cheat / Protex blue / Police and thieves / 48 hours / Garage land
4687832 / Jun '91 / Columbia

☐ CLASH, THE (American Version)
Clash city rockers / I'm so bored with the USA / Remote control / Complete control / White riot / Hate and war / White man in Hammersmith Palais / London's burning / I fought the law / Janie Jones / Career opportunities / What's my name / Police and thieves / Jail guitar doors / Garageland
CD 32232 / Jan '95 / Columbia

☐ COMBAT ROCK
Inoculated city / Know your rights / Car jamming / Should I stay or should I go / Rock the Casbah / Red angel dragnet / Straight to hell / Overpowered by funk / Atom tan / Sean Flynn / Ghetto defendant / Death is a star
CD 32787 / Jul '92 / Columbia

☐ GIVE 'EM ENOUGH ROPE
Safe European home / English civil war / Tommy gun / Julie's been working for the drug squad / Last gang in town / Guns on the roof / Drug stabbing time / Stay free / Cheapstakes / All the young punks (new boots and contracts)
CD 32444 / '91 / CBS

☐ LONDON CALLING
London calling / Brand new Cadillac / Jimmy Jazz / Hateful / Rudie can't fail / Spanish bombs / Right profile / Lost in the supermarket / Clampdown / Guns of Brixton / Wrong 'em / Boyo / Death or glory / Koka cola / Card cheat / Lover's rock / I'm not down / Revolution rock / Four horsemen
4601142 / '91 / CBS

☐ ON BROADWAY (3CD Set)
Janie Jones / Career opportunities / White riot / 1977 / I'm so bored with the USA / Hate and war / What's my name / Deny / London's burning / Protex blue / Police and thieves / 48 hours / Cheat / Garageland / Capital radio / Complete control / Clash city rockers / City of the dead / Jail guitar doors / Prisoner / White man in Hammersmith Palais / Pressure drop 1-2 / Crush on you / English civil war / I fought the law / Safe European home / Tommy Gun / Julie's been working for the drug squad / Stay free / One emotion / Groovy times / Gates of the West / Armagideon time / London calling / Brand new cadillac / Rudie can't fail / Guns of Brixton / Spanish bombs / Lost in the supermarket / Right profile / Card cheat / Death or glory / Clampdown / Train in vain / Bankrobber / Police on my back / Magnificent seven / Leader / Call up / Somebody got murdered / Washington bullets / Broadway lightning strikes / Every little bit hurts / Stop the world / Midnight to Stevens / This is Radio Clash / Coot confusion / Red angel dragnet / Ghetto defendant / Rock the Casbah / Should I stay or should I go / Straight to hell
4693082 / May '94 / Legacy

☐ SANDINISTA
Hitsville UK / Junco partner / Leader / Rebel waltz / Look here / One more time / Corner soul / Equaliser / Call up / Broadway / Junkie slip / Version city / Crooked beat / Up in heaven / Midnight log / Lose this skin / Kingston advice / Let's go crazy
4633642 / Apr '89 / Columbia

☐ SINGLES, THE
White riot / Remote control / Complete control / Clash city rockers / White man in Hammersmith Palais / Tommy gun / English Civil War / I fought the law / London calling / Train in vain / Bankrobber / Call up / Hitsville UK / Magnificent seven / This is radio clash / Know your rights / Rock the casbah / Should I stay or should I go
4689462 / Nov '91 / Columbia

☐ STORY OF THE CLASH VOL.1, THE (2CD Set)
Magnificent seven / This is Radio Clash / Straight to hell / Train in vain / I fought the law / Somebody got murdered / Bankrobber / Rock the Casbah / Should I stay or should I go / Armagideon time / Guns of Brixton / Clampdown / Lost in the supermarket / White man in Hammersmith Palais / London's burning / Janie Jones / Tommy gun / Complete control / Capital radio / White riot / Career opportunities / Clash city rockers / Safe European home / Stay free / London calling / Spanish bombs / English civil war / Police and thieves
4602442 / Oct '95 / Columbia

☐ SUPER BLACK MARKET CLASH
1977 / Protex blue / Deny / Cheat / 48 Hours / Listen / Jail guitar doors / City of the dead / Prisoner / Pressure drop / One-two crush on you / Groovy times / Gates of the west / Capital radio two / Time is tight / Kick it over / Bankrobber / Stop the world / Cool out / First night back in London / Long time jerk / Cool confusion / Magnificent dance / This is radio clash / Mustapha dance
4745462 / Sep '96 / Columbia

Classen, Martin

☐ STOP AND GO (Classen, Martin Quartet)
BEST 1033CD / Nov '93 / Acoustic Music

Classic Jazz Quartet

☐ COMPLETE RECORDINGS
JCD 138 / Jun '95 / Jazzology

☐ COMPLETE RECORDINGS VOL.2
JCD 139 / Jun '95 / Jazzology

Classix Nouveaux

☐ VERY BEST OF CLASSIX NOUVEAUX, THE
Is it a dream / Inside outside / Robots dance / Every home should have one / Chemin chagrin / Never never comes / 1999 / Never again / Soldier / We don't bite / Forever and a day / Where to go / No sympathy / No violins / No other way / End...or the beginning / Manitou / Guilty / La verite / I will return
CDGOLD 1104 / 15 Sep '97 / EMI Gold

Clastrier, Valentin

☐ HURDY GURDY FROM THE LAND OF THE CATHARS
Comme dans un train pour une etoile / El castel / Endura / Barbacana / Heresie I / Catharsis / Sonnerie glorieuse des armees du pape / Notes de sang / Desordre dans le desordre / Heresie II / Vert / Sine sole nihil / Le bucher / Fin'amors de flamenca / Et la roue de la vie / Anonymuse / O'clast / Pa / Corasol / Autochtone / New delit / Onanie / Ixtaklok / Nemesis / La bondant
Y 225070 / Nov '97 / Silex

☐ PALUDE (Clastrier, Valentin & Michael Riessler/Carlo Rizzo)
WER 8009 / Dec '95 / Wergo

Clatterbox

☐ EAZY DOES IT
CLR 422CD / Apr '96 / Clear

Clau De Lluna

☐ CERCLE DE GAL-LA
H 039CD / Jun '94 / Sonifolk

☐ FICA-LI, NOIA
20049CD / Jun '94 / Sonifolk

Claudia

☐ XQUENDA
74321558802 / 9 Mar '98 / Milan

Clave & Guaguanco

☐ DEJALA EN LA PUNTICA
Para clave y guaguanco / Mamaita / La voz del congo / Iyawo / Avisale a la vecina / Chevere / Capricho de abuela / Para Rita Montaner / La jerigonza / Na Francisca / Dejale en la puntica
8888292 / 27 Oct '97 / Tiptoe

Clawfinger

☐ CLAWFINGER
3984226232 / 2 Mar '98 / Coalition

☐ DEAF, DUMB, BLIND
Nigger / Truth / Rosegrove / Don't get me wrong / I need you / Catch me / Warfair / Wonderful world / Sad to see your sorrow / I don't care
4509933212 / Aug '93 / WEA

☐ USE YOUR BRAIN
Pin me down / Power / Waste my time / It / Die high / Tomorrow / Easy way out / Back to the basics / Undone / Do what I say / Pay the bill / What are you afraid of
4509996312 / Apr '95 / WEA

Clawhammer

☐ PABLUM
E 864252 / Nov '92 / Epitaph

Clay & Scott

☐ STANDING ON THE HIGHWAY
TCD 5030 / 30 Mar '98 / Testament

Clay, Joe

☐ DUCKTAIL
Duck tail / Did you mean jelly bean (what you said cabbage head) / Crackerjack / Goodbye goodbye / Sixteen chicks / Slipping out and sneaking in / Doggone it / Get on the right track baby / You look good to me
BCD 15516 / Jul '90 / Bear Family

Clay, Otis

☐ GOSPEL TRUTH, THE
BP 5005CD / May '94 / Blind Pig

☐ HI MASTERS, THE
Trying to live my life without you / I die a little each day / Holding on to a dying love / I can't make it alone / You can't keep running from my love / Let me be the one / Brand new thing / Precious precious / I didn't know the meaning of pain / That's how it is / Too many hands / I love you I need you / Home is where the heart is / It was jealousy / You did something to me
HEX 34 / 4 Aug '98 / Hi

☐ OTIS CLAY 45'S
Home is where the heart is / Brand new thing / Precious, precious / Too many hands / Trying to live my life without you / Let me be the one / I didn't know the meaning of pain / I can't make it alone / If I could reach out / Woman don't live here no more / I die a little each day / You can't escape the hands of love / You did something to me / It was jealousy
HILOCD 1 / Dec '93 / Hi

☐ THIS TIME AROUND
You're the one I choose / When hearts grow cold / You never miss you water / Soembody help / You want me to do / Help me get over you / Don't you know baby / That's how it is / This time around / It's hard to love / Standing in the rain / City in the sky / I can handle it
CDBB 9590 / 9 Mar '98 / Bullseye Blues

Clay People

☐ STONE TEN STITCHES
CDRED 026 / Jan '97 / Re-Constriction

Clayderman, Richard

☐ ABBA COLLECTION
Gimme gimme gimme / Winner takes it all / Chiquitita / Fernando / Mamma mia / Dancing queen / I have a dream / Super trouper / Name of the game / Lay all your love on me / Knowing me knowing you / One of us / SOS / Money money money
30002 / Oct '97 / Go On Deluxe

☐ ANDREW LLOYD WEBBER COLLECTION, THE
Phantom of the opera / Music of the night / Love changes everything / High flying adored / Seeing is believing / All I ask of you / Don't cry for me Argentina / Another suitcase in another hall / Tell me on Sunday / I don't know how to love him / Memory / Take that look off your face
30012 / Oct '97 / Go On Deluxe

☐ CARPENTERS COLLECTION, THE
Yesterday once more / There's a kind of hush (all over the world) / We've only just begun / Superstar / Top of the world / Rainy days and Mondays / Close to you / Only yesterday / For all we know / Please Mr. Postman / I won't last a day without you / Solitaire / Meldley: For all we know, We've only just begun / Sing
8286882 / Oct '95 / Delphine

☐ CHRISTMAS
White Christmas / Medley / Silent night / Christmas concerto / Little red-nosed reindeer / Little drummer boy / Moonlight sonata / Jingle bells / Snow falls slowly / Largo / Romance / O tannenbaum / Medley / Jesus will always be my joy / Ave Maria
5506442 / Nov '96 / Spectrum

☐ CLASSICAL COLLECTION
Piano concerto no.1 in B flat minor op 23 / Elvira Madigan piano concerto no.21 in C major / Cornish rhapsody / Liebstraum / Concerto no.2 op 18 / La pathetique / Dream of Olwen / Fur Elise / Arabesque / Warsaw concerto / Moonlight sonata / Rhapsody in blue / Clair de lune / Concerto in A minor op 16 / Nocturne / 18th variation op 43 / Gymnopedie 1
30022 / Oct '97 / Go On Deluxe

☐ COLLECTION, THE
Ballade pour Adeline / Yesterday / Moon river / Don't cry for me Argentina / Souvenirs d'enfance / Love is blue / Fur Elise / Only you / Exodus / Rondo pour un tout petit enfant / Moonlight sonata / Bridge over troubled water / Largo / Lettre a ma mere / Woman in love / Lady Di / Liebestraum / Romeo and Julia
AMC 51022 / May '97 / BR Music

☐ COLLECTION, THE (Abba/Classical/ Andrew Lloyd Webber Collections/ 3CD Set)
Gimme gimme gimme / Winner takes it all / Chiquitita / Fernando / Mamma mia / Dancing queen / I have a dream / Super trouper / Name of the game / Lay all your love on me / Knowing me knowing you / One of us / SOS / Money money money / Waterloo / Piano concerto no.1 in B flat minor op 23 / Elvira Madigan piano concerto no.21 in C major / Cornish rhapsody / Liebstraum / Concerto no.2 op 18 / La pathetique / Dream of olwen / Fur Elise / Arabesque / Warsaw concerto / Moonlight sonata / Rhapsody in blue / Clair de lune / Concerto in a minor op 16 / Nocturne / 18th variation op 43 / Gymnopedie 1 / Phantom of the opera / Music of the night / Love changes everything / High flying adored / Seeing is believing / All I ask of you / Don't cry for me Argentina / Another suitcase in another hall / Tell me on a sunday / I don't know how to love him / Memory / Take that look of your face
30152 / Oct '97 / Go On Deluxe

☐ LOVE SONGS
8287382 / Mar '96 / Delphine

☐ MY BOSSA NOVA FAVOURITES
Meditation / Summer samba / Desafinado / One note samba / Jet samba / Girl from Ipanema / O barquinho / A felicidade / Agua de beber / Corvocado / Aguas de Marco / How insensitive / Medley
AHLCD 52 / 6 Oct '97 / Hit

☐ RICHARD CLAYDERMAN & LENA TEIGEN (Clayderman, Richard & Lena Teigen)
29010 / 3 Mar '98 / Music

☐ SONGS OF LOVE
Medley / Nikita / Do you know where you're going to / Lady in red / Take my breath away / You are my world / We are the world / I know him so well / Eleana / Colin Maillard / Eroica / La sorellina / All by myself / I dreamed a dream / All I ask of you
5518202 / May '96 / Spectrum

☐ VERY BEST OF RICHARD CLAYDERMAN, THE
Ballade pour adeline / Dolannes melodie / Yesterday / (Everything I do) I do it for you / Elvira madigan / Guantanamera / Moon river / Serenade / Moonlight sonata / La mer / Liebestraum / Thorn Birds / Plasir D'amour / Pastorale
30032 / Oct '97 / Go On Deluxe

Claypool, Philip

☐ CIRCUS LEAVING TOWN, A
CURCD 18 / Nov '95 / Curb

Clayton, Buck

☐ BADEN-SWITZERLAND
SKCD 22028 / Jul '93 / Sackville

☐ BASEL 1961, SWISS RADIO DAYS JAZZ SERIES VOL.7 (Clayton, Buck All Stars)
Swinging at the coppers' rail / Robbins' nest / Outer drive / Moon glow / Swingin' the blues / Night train / Saint-Louis blues
TCB 02072 / Feb '97 / TCB

☐ BLOW THE BLUES (Clayton, Buck & Buddy Tate)
OJCCD 850 / Nov '95 / Original Jazz Classics

☐ BUCK CLAYTON & BUDDY TATE (Clayton, Buck & Buddy Tate)
OJCCD 757 / Jun '95 / Original Jazz Classics

☐ BUCK CLAYTON ALL STARS 1961 (Clayton, Buck All Stars)
STCD 8231 / May '97 / Storyville

☐ BUCK CLAYTON JAM SESSION, A
CRD 132 / Jul '96 / Chiaroscuro

☐ BUCK CLAYTON LIVE (Clayton, Buck Swing Band)
Scorpio / Swingin' on the state line / Horn o'plenty / Rise 'n' shine / One for me / BC special / Black sheep blues / Sparky / Song for Sarah / Cadillac taxi / What a beautiful yesterday / Bowery bunch
CD 030 / Jan '97 / Nagel Heyer

☐ BUCK CLAYTON STORY 1937-1945, THE
158682 / Jun '97 / Jazz Archives

☐ COPENHAGEN CONCERT (Clayton, Buck All Stars)
SCCD 36006/7 / Nov '90 / Steeplechase

☐ DOCTOR JAZZ VOL.3 (Clayton, Buck Band)
STCD 6043 / Jul '96 / Storyville

☐ ESSENTIAL BUCK CLAYTON, THE
VCD 103/4 / 27 Apr '98 / Vanguard

☐ INTRODUCTION TO BUCK CLAYTON, AN
4046 / Jun '97 / Best Of Jazz

☐ JAM SESSION 1975
CRD 143 / Nov '95 / Chiaroscuro

☐ JAM SESSION VOL.1
BMCD 3044 / 21 Aug '97 / Blue Moon

☐ JAM SESSION VOL.2
BMCD 3045 / 21 Aug '97 / Blue Moon

☐ SWINGIN' DREAM, A (Clayton, Buck Swing Band)
STCD 16 / Oct '92 / Stash

Clayton, Dr. Peter

☐ DOCTOR PETER CLAYTON (1935-1942)
DOCD 5179 / Oct '93 / Document

☐ DR. CLAYTON & HIS BUDDY
SOB 035392 / Apr '93 / Story Of The Blues

Clayton, Jay

☐ JAZZ ALLEY TAPES, THE (Clayton, Jay & Don Lamphere)
You're a weaver of dreams / Nearness of you / Softly as in a morning sunrise / I remember Clifford / New stores / Love for sale / I've grown accustomed to her face / My silent love / Mr. PC / AC
HEPCD 2046 / Sep '92 / Hep

Clayton, Kimber

☐ GOOD GIRLS LOVE BAD BOYS
CURCD 49 / 11 May '98 / Curb

Clayton, Lee

☐ ANOTHER NIGHT
PRLD 700812 / Nov '89 / Provogue

☐ BORDER AFFAIR/NAKED CHILD
Silver stallion / If you can touch her at all / Back home in Tennessee / Border affair / Old number nine / Like a diamond / My woman my love / Tequila is addictive / My true love / Rainbow in the sky / Saturday night special / I ride alone / 10000 alone / Sexual moon / I love you / Jaded virgin / Little cocaine / If I can do it (so can you)
EDCD 434 / Oct '95 / Edsel

☐ LEE CLAYTON
Carnival balloon / Bottle of booze / Henry mccarty / New york city suite / Lord she don't belong in new york city / Don't you think it's time to come home / Mama, spend the night with me / Red dancing / Danger / Lonesome whiskey / Ladies love outlaws
EDCD 475 / Apr '96 / Edsel

☐ SPIRIT OF TWILIGHT
PRD 70652 / Sep '94 / Provogue

Clayton, Paul

☐ WHALING AND SAILING SONGS
TCD 1064 / 12 Jan '98 / Tradition

Clayton, Steve

☐ LOVE IS SAID IN MANY WAYS
Clocks keep ticking-my reverie (medley) / Just a little of your love / You and I - close as pages in a book (medley) / I solemnly swear / Emily / I can't get back to tucson too soon / Love is said in many ways / I met honey at the busy bee / You're mine / When I'm not near the girl I love / Star gazer am I / Standing on the sidelines / Where am I going / Show is over / Pieces of dreams-song from 'the oscar' (maybe september)
STCD 559 / Oct '93 / Stash

Clayton, Vikki

☐ HONOR TOKENED
Slacksmith / Missing you / Birth of Robin Hood / Horncastle fair / Banks of the Nile / Oh your love so vain / Peggy on the sea / Yarmouth town / George Collins / Crazy man Michael / Africa was calling / Beguiled / Girlie press gang / My Donald
ANDCD 18 / 9 Mar '98 / A New Day

☐ IT SUITS ME WELL
HTDCD 83 / 11 May '98 / HTD

☐ MIDSUMMER CUSHION
CDSGP 008 / Jun '94 / Prestige

☐ MOVERS AND SHAKERS
Pilgrim / 10 years / Africa was calling / My Donald / Kisses in the dark / Movers and shakers / Wild nights / Payback / I want something / Girlie press gang / My bonny light horseman / Sir Hugh of Lincoln / Beguiled
ANDCD 15 / May '97 / A New Day

Clayton, Willie

☐ AT HIS BEST
ICH 1503CD / Dec '95 / Ichiban

☐ FEELS LIKE LOVE
ICH 1155CD / Feb '94 / Ichiban

☐ MIDNIGHT DOCTOR (Willie Clayton's Greatest Hits)
Three people (sleeping in my bed) / Walk away from love / In need of a good woman / Dancing with my baby / Equal opportunity: Clayton, Willie & Pat Brown / Young blues man / Meet me tonight / My baby's cheating on me / Let's get together / Looking for a good woman / Lose what you got / Love stealing ain't worth stealing / I love stealing it / Once upon a time / Don't make me pay for his mistakes / Main squeeze / Midnight doctor
WESF 101 / May '98 / Blueside

☐ NO GETTING OVER ME
ICH 1182CD / Aug '95 / Ichiban

Cleaners From Venus

☐ BACK FROM THE CLEANERS
TANGCD 014 / Oct '95 / Tangerine

☐ GOLDEN CLEANERS
TANGCD 3 / Aug '93 / Tangerine

Clear Blue Sky

☐ CLEAR BLUE SKY
REP 4110 / Aug '91 / Repertoire

☐ COSMIC CRUSADER
AFT 1008 / 10 Nov '97 / Aftermath

Clearlight

☐ FOREVER BLOWING BUBBLES
Chanson / Without words / Way / Ergotrip / Et pendent ce temps la / Narcisse et Goldmund / Jungle bubbles
CDV 2039 / Jun '97 / Virgin

☐ SYMPHONY
MANTRA 044 / 1 Jun '98 / Mantra

Clears

☐ CLEARS, THE
SLR 023 / 20 Oct '97 / Smells Like

Clearwater, Eddy

☐ BLUES HANGOUT
ECD 260082 / Jan '92 / Evidence

☐ BOOGIE MY BLUES AWAY
Muddy Waters goin' to run clear / Boogie my blues away / Came up the hard way / Blues at Theresa's / I don't know why / Tore up all the time / Real fine woman / Mayor Daley's blues
DD 678 / Mar '97 / Delmark

☐ CHIEF, THE
Find you a job / Blues for breakfast / Blue blue blue over you / One day at a time / I wouldn't lay my guitar down / Chills / Bad dream / I'm tore up / Lazy woman / Blues for a living
R 2615 / Feb '97 / Rooster

☐ LIVE AT THE KINGSTON MINES, CHICAGO
Last nite / Black night / Just a little bit / Pretty baby / Hoochie coochie man / Everything's gonna be alright / Sweet little sixteen / Reelin' and rockin' / Kansas City / Honky tonk
422213 / Feb '97 / Last Call

☐ MEAN CASE OF THE BLUES
Mean case of the blues / Send for me / Check up on my baby / Love being loved by you / Make it if you try / Hard way to make an easy living / Look whatcha done / Come on down / Party at my house / Don't take my blues
CDBB 9584 / Jul '97 / Bullseye Blues

☐ TWO TIMES NINE
422226 / Feb '97 / Last Call

Cleary, Jon

☐ ALLIGATOR LIPS AND DIRTY RICE
Go ahead baby / Long distance lover / C'mon second line / Groove me / In the mood / Big chief / Let them talk / Pick up the pieces / Burnt mouth boogie
CDCH 377 / Mar '93 / Ace

Cleaver, Robinson

☐ EARFUL OF MUSIC, AN (Wurlitzer Organ Favourites)
Earfull of music / Legend of the glass mountain / Masaniello overture / Things to come / Rondo / To a wild rose / Walk in the Black Forest / Man and a woman / Canadian capers / Alligator crawl / Goldfinger / Black canary hora / Moonlight serenade / Music to watch girls by / Fiddle faddle / Spanish gypsy dance / Skyscraper fantasy / In a persian market / Blaze away / Earful of music
PLCD 544 / Aug '96 / President

Cleaves, Slaid

☐ NO ANGEL KNOWS
Not going down / No angel knows / Dance around the fire / Jennie's alright / Look back at me / Wrecking ball / River runs / Don't tell me / Skunk juice / Last of the V8's / 29 3.32
CDP 1201 / Feb '97 / Philo

Clee-Shays

☐ DYNAMIC GUITAR SOUNDS OF THE CLEE-SHAYS, THE
SC 11049 / 13 Jul '98 / Sundazed

Cleftones

☐ BEST OF THE CLEFTONES
You baby you / Little girl of mine / You're driving me mad / Can't we be sweethearts / Neki-hokey / Happy memories / String around my heart / Why you do me like you do / I like your style of making love / See you next year / She's so fine / Lover boy / Beginners at love / Heart and soul / How do you feel / Please say you want me / (I love you) for sentimental reasons / Lover come back to me
NEMCD 603 / Aug '90 / Sequel

☐ HEART AND SOUL/FOR SENTIMENTAL REASONS
Heart and soul / How do you feel / 100 pounds of clay / Please say you want me / Can't we be sweethearts / Time is running out on our love / Little girl of mine / Heavenly Father / Glory of love / You and I can climb / You baby you / String around my heart / For sentimental reasons / Blues in the night / Red sails in the sunset / She's gone / Vacation in the mountains / My babe she's a rollin' stone / Earth angel / Deed I do / Shadows on the very last row / What did I do that was wrong / Hey babe / Leave my woman alone
WESM 546 / Feb '98 / Westside

Clegg, Johnny

☐ IN MY AFRICAN DREAM
SHAKACD 3 / Aug '94 / Safari

Clement, Giles

☐ WES SIDE STORIES (Clement, Giles Quartet)
500492 / 1 Jun '98 / Musidisc

☐ WOODY (Clement, Giles Trio)
SJRCD 1001 / Sep '97 / String Jazz

Clementine

☐ SOLITA
Don' cha go way mad / These foolish things / Polka dots and moonbeams / Make yourself comfortable / Solita / Always remember you / Sunny / This will make you laugh / Chuck E's in love / You got what it takes / Midnight Tango / Baba cool / Hey hey baby / Sur la route
GOJ 60222 / 24 Aug '98 / Go Jazz

Clements, Vassar

☐ GRASS ROUTES
Beats me / Westport Drive / Come on home / Florida blues / Other end / Rain rain rain / Rambling / Rounder's blues / Fiddlin' will / Non-stop / Flame of love / Turkey in the straw
ROUCD 0287 / Feb '92 / Rounder

☐ HILLBILLY JAZZ
FF 101CD / Jul '92 / Flying Fish

☐ HILLBILLY JAZZ RIDES AGAIN
Hillbilly jazz / Don't hop don't skip / Airmail special / Say goodbye to the blues / Swing street / Woodsheddin' / Be a little discreet / Your mind is on vacation / Caravan / How can I go on without you / Triple stop boogie / Take a break
FF 385CD / May '93 / Flying Fish

Clemons, Clarence

☐ PEACEMAKER
Peace prayer / Into the blue forest / Abraxas / Miracle / Serenity / Spirit dance
72445110322 / Jun '95 / Zoo Entertainment

Cleopatra

☐ COMIN' ATCHA
Cleopatra's theme / Life ain't easy / Don't suffer in silence / Touch of love / Bird song / Thinking about you / What you gonna do boy / World we live in / Dying rose / Two timer / I want you back
3984233562 / 25 May '98 / WEA

Cleveland Fats

☐ OTHER SIDE OF MIDNIGHT, THE
DOG 91132 / 1 Jun '98 / Ichiban

Click

☐ GAME RELATED
Wolf tickets / Hurricane / Out my body / World went crazy / Actin' bad / Get chopped / We don't fk wit' dat / Be about yo' paper / Boss baller / Scandalous / Learn about it / If I took your boyfriend / Rock up my birdie / Hot ones echo thru the ghetto
CHIP 171 / Jul '96 / Jive

Click Click

☐ SHADOWBLACK
More samples than a clinic / Parabellum / Shadowblack / Loss of breath / Memento mori / Hephaestos / Hopi / Stencilhead / Did you get what I want
08543722 / 9 Feb '98 / Westcom

Cliff, Dave

☐ PLAY TADD DAMERON (Cliff, Dave & Geoff Simkins 5)
Ladybird / Squirrel / Blue time / If you could see me now / Flossie Lou / Jahbero / Hot house / Soultrane / Casbah / Good bait / Our delight / Interview
SPJCD 560 / Feb '97 / Spotlite

☐ SIPPIN' AT BELLS (Cliff, Dave & Geoff Simkins)
Back to back / Sal's line / How deep is the ocean / Easy to love / Nobody knows the trouble I've caused / I guess I'll hang my tears out to dry / Nightingale sang in Berkeley Square / Lester's blues / Sippin' at bells / Conception / Once I loved / Touch of your lips / That old feeling / Indian summer
SPJCD 553 / Jul '95 / Spotlite

☐ WHEN THE LIGHTS ARE LOW (Cliff, Dave & Friends)
When the lights are low / Do nothing til you hear from me / Jingles / Purple gazelle / Nearness of you / Falling in love with love / In my solitude / West coast blues / Autumn in New York / I'm getting sentimental over you / Shadow of your smile / You steeped out of a dream
ZECD 18 / 9 Mar '98 / Zephyr

Cliff, Jimmy

☐ 100% PURE REGGAE
Samba reggae / I'm a winner / Breakout / Oneness / Peace / War a Africa / Roll on rolling stone / Be ready / Jimmy Jimmy / Haunted / Baby let me feel it / Stepping out of limbo / True story / Shout for freedom
74321491702 / Jul '97 / Milan

☐ BEST OF JIMMY CLIFF
Hard road to travel / Sooner or later / Sufferin' in the land / Keep your eye on the sparrow / Struggling man / Wild world / Vietnam / Another cycle / Wonderful world, beautiful people / Harder they come / Let your yeah be yeah / Synthetic world / I'm no immigrant / Give and take / Many rivers to cross / Going back west / Sitting in limbo / Come into my life / You can get it if you really want / Goodbye yesterday
RRCD 50 / Mar '96 / Reggae Refreshers

☐ BREAKOUT
I'm a winner / Breakout / Oneness / Peace / Stepping out of limbo / War a Africa / Roll on rolling stone / Be ready / Jimmy Jimmy / Haunted / Baby let me feel it / Samba reggae / True story / Shout for freedom
RIGHT 001 / 5 May '98 / Right Recordings

☐ CLIFF HANGER
Hitting with music / American sweet / Arrival / Brown eyes / Reggae Street / Hotshot / Sunrise / Dead and awake / Now and forever / Nuclear war
4712202 / Feb '97 / Columbia

☐ COOL RUNNER LIVE IN LONDON, THE
Intro (Jimmy Jimmy) / Africa / Yeah ho / Rub-a-dub / Peace / Rock steady / Save the planet / Many rivers to cross / Limbo / Third world people / Harder they come / Samba reggae / Rebel in me / Wonderful world, beautiful people / Justice / Higher and deeper love / Baby let me feel it / True story / Shout for freedom
MOCD 3010 / Feb '95 / More Music

☐ FOLLOW MY MIND
Look at the mountains / News / I'm gonna live, I'm gonna love / Going mad / Dear mother / Who feels it, knows it / Remake the world / No woman, no cry / Wahjahka man / Hypocrite / If I follow my mind / You're the only one
7599263112 / Jan '96 / WEA

☐ FUNDAMENTAL REGGAY
Fundamental reggae / Under the sun, moon and stars / Rip off / On my life / Commercialization / You can't be wrong and get right / Oh Jamaica / No. 1 rip off man / Brother / House of exile / Long time no see / My love is as solid as rock / My people / Actions speak louder than words / Brave warrior
SEECD 83 / Apr '93 / See For Miles

☐ JIMMY CLIFF
Many rivers to cross / Vietnam / My ancestors / Hard road to travel / Wonderful world, beautiful people / Sufferin' in the land / Hello sunshine / Use what I got / That's the way life goes / Come into my life
CDTRL 16 / Mar '94 / Trojan

☐ MANY RIVERS TO CROSS
CDTRL 342 / Jun '94 / Trojan

☐ REGGAE GREATS
Vietnam / Sitting in limbo / Struggling man / Let your yeah be yeah / Bongo man / Harder they come / Sufferin' in the land / Many rivers to cross / Hard road to travel / You can get it if you really want / Sooner or later
5544592 / 1 Jun '98 / Spectrum

☐ SAVE OUR PLANET EARTH
Turning point / Rebel in me / First love / Everliving love / Trapped / Pressure / Image of the beast / Save our planet earth / No justice / Johnny too bad
106552 / Oct '90 / Musidisc

Clifford, Billy

☐ BILLY CLIFFORD
OSS 11CD / Mar '88 / Ossian

Clifford, Linda

☐ BEST OF LINDA CLIFFORD, THE
From now on / Don't give it up / You are you are / Between you baby and me / Love's sweet sensation / It's gonna be a long long winter / March across the lands / Tonight's the night / I had a talk with my man / Shoot your best shot / Red light / Runaway love
DEEPM 008 / 27 Oct '97 / Deep Beats

☐ IF MY FRIENDS COULD SEE ME NOW
If my friends could see me now / You are, you are / Runaway love / Broadway gypsy lady / I feel like falling in love / Please darling, don't say goodbye / Gypsy lady
CPCD 8158 / Jan '96 / Charly

☐ RIGHT COMBINATION (Clifford, Linda & Curtis Mayfield)
Rock you to your socks / Right combination / I'm so proud / Ain't no love lost / It's lovin' time / Love's sweet sensation / Between you baby and me
CPCD 8072 / Jun '94 / Charly

Clifton, Bill

☐ EARLY YEARS 1957-1958, THE
Girl I left in Tennessee / Dixie darlin' / You don't need to think about me ... / I'll be there Mary dear / Paddy on the turnpike / I'll wander back someday / Darling Corey / When you kneel at my mother's grave / Blue ridge mountain blues / Are you alone / Springhill disaster / I'm living the right life now / Lonely heart blues / Cedar Grove / You go to your church / Walking in my sleep / Pal of yesterday / Just another broken heart / Little white washed chimney
ROUCD 1021 / '92 / Rounder

Clifton, Ian

☐ MUSIC FOR LIFE
Dance little lady / 42nd street / London by night / Dragonfly waltz / Love and marriage / Happy heart / Petite fleur / Takes two to tango / I'll never smile again / Try a little tenderness / Up cherry street / So what's new / Friends for life / Amor / Por favor / Cocktails for two / Time was / First man you remember / I'm in a dancing mood
DLD 1033 / Mar '93 / Dance & Listen

☐ MUSIC FOR LIFE VOL.2
Blackpool belle / I've told every little star / Aria / Yellow bird / Friends and neighbours / Put on a happy face
DLD 1041 / Nov '93 / Dance & Listen

Clikatat Ikatowi

☐ LIVE 29-30/8/1995
GRAVITY 26CD / Apr '97 / Gravity

Climax Blues Band

☐ BEST OF THE CLIMAX BLUES BAND, THE
Couldn't get it right / Gotta have more love / I love you / California sunshine / Berlin blues / Briefcase / Like Uncle Charlie / Everyday / Rollin' home / Mighty fire / Mean ol' world / Hey Mama / Little girl / Crazy 'bout my baby / Louisiana blues / Mole on the dole
12540 / Apr '96 / Laserlight

☐ BLUES FROM THE ATTIC
Fool for the bright lights / Chasin change / Don't start me talkin' / Take me back to georgia / So many roads / Seventh son / Last chance saloon / Movie queen / Towards the sun / Couldn't get it right / Evil / Going to new york-money / Let's work together / Let the good times roll
HTDCD 15 / Oct '93 / HTD

☐ CLIMAX CHICAGO BLUES BAND
Mean ol' world / Insurance / Going down this road / You've been drinking / Don't start me talkin' / Wee baby blues / Twenty past one / Stranger in your town / How many more years / Looking for my baby / Lonely, And / Entertainer
C5CD 555 / Oct '92 / See For Miles

☐ COULDN'T GET IT RIGHT...PLUS
Couldn't get it right / Berlin blues / Chasing change / Losin' the humbles / Shopping bag people / Sense of direction / Before you reach the grave / Reaching out / Right now / Cobra / Rollin' home / Sav'ry gravy / Sky high / Loosen up / Running out of time / Mr. Goodtime / I am constant / Mighty fire
SEECD 222 / 16 Mar '98 / See For Miles

☐ DRASTIC STEPS
California sunshine / Lonely avenue / Deceiver / Ordinary people / Winner / Couldn't g... right / Fool for the bright times / Good times / Trouble / American dream / Couldn't get it right (Mix)
C5CD 573 / Sep '91 / See For Miles

☐ FM/LIVE
8255114082 / 7 Apr '98 / Plum

☐ FM/LIVE...PLUS
All the time in the world / Flight / Seventh son / Let's work together / Standing by a river / So many roads, so many trains / You make me sick / Shake your love / Going to New York / I am constant / Mesopopmania / Country hat
SEECD 279 / Sep '89 / See For Miles

☐ GOLD PLATED
Together and free / Mighty fire / Chasing change / Berlin blues / Couldn't get it right / Rollin' home / Sav'ry gravy / Extra
C5CD 670 / 18 May '98 / See For Miles

☐ HARVEST YEARS 1969-1972, THE
Please don't help me / Hey baby everything's gonna be alright / Yeh yeh yeh / Everyday / Towards the sun / You make me sick / Reap what I've sowed / Shake your love / Looking for my baby / Flight / Mole on the dole / That's all / Insurance / Wee baby blues / Crazy about my baby / All right blue / Cut you loose
SEECD 316 / 16 Mar '98 / See For Miles

☐ LOT OF BOTTLE, A
Country hat / Everyday / Reap what I've sowed / Brief case / Alright blue / Seventh son / Please don't help me / Morning, noon and night / Long lovin' man / Louisiana blues / Cut you loose
REP 4046 / Aug '91 / Repertoire
C5CD 548 / Oct '92 / See For Miles

☐ PLAYS ON
Flight / Hey baby's everything gonna be alright yeah yeah yeah / Cubano chant / Little girl / Mum's the word / Twenty past two / Temptation rag / So many roads / City ways / Crazy about my baby
REP 4077 / Aug '91 / Repertoire
C5CD 556 / Oct '92 / See For Miles

☐ RICH MAN
Rich man / Mole on the dole / You make me sick / Standing by a river / Shake your love / All the time in the world / If you wanna know / Don't you mind people grinning in your face
C5CD553 / '90 / See For Miles
REP 4045 / Aug '91 / Repertoire

☐ STAMP ALBUM
Using the power / Mr. Goodtime / I am constant / Running out of time / Sky high / Rusty nail / Devil knows / Loosen up / Spirit returning / Cobra
RR 4719 / Jul '98 / Repertoire
C5CD 669 / 26 May '98 / See For Miles

☐ TIGHTLY KNIT
Hey mam / Shoot her if she runs / Towards the sun / Come on in my kitchen / Who killed McSwiggen / Little link / St. Michael's blues / Bide my time / That's all
C5CD557 / Jun '90 / See For Miles
REP 4079 / Aug '91 / Repertoire

Climax Golden Twins

☐ IMPERIAL HOUSEHOLD ORCHESTRA
SCRATCH 23 / Nov '96 / Scratch

Climax Reunion Jazz Band

☐ RETRO JAZZ DOWN UNDER
CRJS 95 / Jul '96 / Retro Jazz

Cline, Nels

☐ CHEST
LB 006CD / Apr '97 / Little Brother

☐ SAD (Cline, Nels Trio)
SKY 2CD / May '98 / Skycap

Cline, Patsy

☐ BEST OF PATSY CLINE
DCD 5323 / Dec '93 / Disky

☐ COLLECTION, THE
Ain't no wheels on this ship / I can't forget / Fingerprints / Heart you break may be your own / Walkin' after midnight / Life's railway to heaven / Angel / Honky tonk merry go round / I cried all the way to the altar / Try again / I've loved and lost again / I can see an angel / Come on in / I don't wanna / Let the teardrops fall / Hungry for love / Too many secrets / If I could only stay asleep / I love you honey / Pick me up on your way down / In care of the blues / Stop the world (and let me off) / Yes I understand / Hidin' out / Today, tomorrow and forever
COL 007 / Oct '95 / Collection

☐ CRAZY DREAMS
TRTCD 177 / Jun '95 / TrueTrax

☐ CRAZY DREAMS (2CD Set)
I love you honey / Stop, look and listen / Come on in / He will do for you / Walkin' after midnight / Stranger in my arms / I've loved and lost again / Honky tonk merry go round / Turn the cards slowly / Hidin' out / I cried all the way to the altar / Church, a courtroom and then goodbye / Heart you break may be your own / Today, tomorrow and forever / Pick you up on your way down / Too many secrets / Poor man's roses or rich man's gold / Fingerprints / Don't ever leave me / Three cigarettes in an ashtray / Try again / Then you'll know / I can't forget / In care of the blues / Dear God I go to church on a Sunday / Walking dream / Stop the world / I don't wanta / Hungry for love / Cry not for me / Just out of reach / I'm moving along / If I could see the world / Let the teardrops fall / I can see an angel / Lovesick blues / There she goes / I'm blue again / If I could only stay asleep / That wonderful someone / Ain't no wheels on this ship / Never no more / Yes I understand / Just a closer walk with thee / Love me, love me honey do / Gotta lot of rhythm in my soul / Life's railway to Heaven / Crazy dreams / How can I face tomorrow
CPCD 82672 / Dec '96 / Charly

☐ CRAZY DREAMS (2CD Set)
Hidin' out / Turn the cards slowly / Church, a courtroom and then goodbye / Honky tonk merry go round / I love you honey / Come on in / I cried all the way to the altar / Stop, look and listen / I've loved and lost again / Dear god / He will do for you (what he's done for me) / Walkin' after midnight / Heart you break may be your own / Pick me up on your way down / A poor man's roses (or a rich man's gold) / Fingertips / Stranger in my arms / Don't ever leave me again / Try again / Too many secrets / Then you'll know / Three cigarettes in an ashtray / That wonderful someone / In care of the blues / Hungry for love / I can't forget / I don't wanta / Ain't no wheels on this ship / Stop the world (and let me off) / Walking dream / Cry not for me / If I could see the world / Just out of reach / I can see an angel / Come on in (and make yourself at home) / Let the teardrops fall / Never no more / If I could only stay asleep / I'm moving along / I'm blue again / L-o-v-e (love) / Love me love me, honey do / Yes I understand / Gotta lot of rhythm in my soul / Life's railway to heaven / Just a closer walk with thee-beyond the sunset / Lovesick blues / How can I face tomorrow / There she goes / Crazy dreams
CDSD 501 / 28 Nov '97 / Sundown

☐ CRY NOT FOR ME
If I could only stay asleep / Heart you break may be your own / Try again / Three cigarettes in a ashtray / If I could see the world / Cry not for me / Yes I understand / Dear God / I'm blue again / Love, love, love me honey / Stop, look and listen / Don't ever leave me again / Gotta lot of rhythm in my soul / I'm moving along / Honky tonk merry go round / I cried all the way to the alter / Turn the cards slowly / Pick me up on your way down / Come on in / Then you'll know
CDSB 005 / 27 Apr '98 / Starburst

☐ DEFINITIVE PATSY CLINE, THE
Crazy / She's got you / He called me baby / When I get through with you (you'll love me too) / Seven lonely days / Yes I understand / Crazy dreams / Your kinda love / That's how heartache begins / Faded love / Love letters in the sand / Heartaches / Walkin' after midnight / Who can I count on / Three cigarettes in an ashtray / If I could see the world / Come on in (and make yourself at home) / Hidin' out / Just a closer walk with thee-beyond the sunset / I've loved and lost again / Sweet dreams (of you) / Leavin' on your mind / Strange / Your cheatin' heart / Today, tomorrow and forever / I can't forget / Lovesick blues / I don't wanta / Got a lot of rhythm in my soul / Church, a courtroom and then goodbye / I fall to pieces / When you need a laugh / So wrong / Imagine that / Blue moon of kentucky / That wonderful someone / Stop the world (and let me off) / I can see an angel / Dear god / Cry not for me
ARC 94992 / Sep '92 / ARC

☐ DISCOVERY
I don't wanta / Then you'll know / Don't ever leave me again / Two cigarettes in an ashtray / In care of the blues / Your cheatin' heart / Man upstairs / Stop the world (and let me off) / Try again / Walkin' dream / Too many secrets / Down by the riverside / Come on in / Ain't no wheels on this ship / Hungry for love / Walkin' after midnight
PLATCD 5902 / Sep '94 / Platinum

☐ DREAMING
Sweet dreams / I fall to pieces / Crazy / Heartaches / Tra le la le la triangle / Have you ever been lonely / Faded love / Your cheatin' heart / She's got you / Walkin' after midnight / San Antonio rose / Three cigarettes in an ashtray / When I need a laugh / Always
PLATCD 303 / Apr '88 / Platinum

☐ ESSENTIAL COLLECTION, THE
MCAD 410421 / Nov '91 / MCA

☐ HEARTACHE
MCCD 317 / 6 Oct '97 / Music Club

☐ JUST OUT OF REACH
MU 5072 / Oct '92 / Musketeer

☐ LIVE AT THE CIMARRON BALLROOM
MCD 11579 / Aug '97 / MCA

☐ MASTERS, THE (2CD Set)
EDMCD 013 / 24 Nov '97 / Eagle

☐ ONE AND ONLY PATSY CLINE, THE
Stop the world / Walkin' after midnight / Just a closer walk with thee / Just out of reach / I've loved and lost again / Fingerprints / Stranger in my arms / Poor man's roses / I can see an angel / If I could only stay asleep / I'm blue again / Today, tomorrow and forever / I love you honey / Never no more / Love love love me honey / Let the teardrops fall / I'm moving alone / Stop, look and listen
ECD 3086 / Jan '95 / K-Tel

☐ PATSY CLINE
Just a closer walk with thee / Never no more / Ain't no wheels on this ship / He'll do for you / Honky tonk merry go round / Poor man's roses / Pick me up / Turn the cards slowly / Dear God / I love you honey / I can't forget you / Crazy dreams
CD 102 / Oct '94 / Timeless Treasures

☐ PATSY CLINE
DVAD 6072 / May '95 / Deja Vu

☐ PATSY CLINE
GOLD 058 / Jul '96 / Gold

☐ PATSY CLINE (3CD Set)
Walking after midnight / Fingerprints / Honky tonk merry-go-round / Life's railway to heaven / I can see an angel walkin' / Ain't no wheels on this ship / If I could see the world / I don't wanna / Pick me up on the way down / Come on in / Hidin' out / Hungry for love / If I could only stay asleep / Cry not for me / I cried all the way to the altar / Three cigarettes in the ashtray / Heart you break may be your own / I can't forget / Secrets / I love you honey / I've loved and lost again / Try again / Let the teardrops fall / Stop the world and let me off / Too many secrets / Turn the cards slowly / Just out of reach / Today, tomorrow and forever / Crazy dreams / I'm blue again / I'm moving along / Poor man's roses (or a rich man's gold) / Then you'll know / Hungry for love / How can I face tomorrow / Church, a courtroom and then goodbye / Got a lot of rhythm in my soul / Just a closer walk with thee / Stranger in my arms / That wonderful someone / Lovesick blues / Don't ever leave me
KBOX 357 / Nov '96 / Collection

☐ PLATINUM COLLECTION, THE (2CD Set)
Church, a courtroom and then goodbye / Honky tonk merry-go-round / Hidin' out / I cried all the way to the altar / I've loved and lost again / Dear God / Walkin' after midnight / Fingerprints / Stranger in my arms / Try again / Then you'll know / Three cigarettes in an ashtray / He will do for you / Poor man's roses (or a rich man's gold) / Hungry for love / I can't forget you / That wonderful someone / Stop the world / If I could see the world (through the eyes of a child) / Cry not for me / Just out of reach (of my two open arms) / Never no more / Walking dream / In the care of the blues / Turn the cards slowly / Gotta lot of rhthm in my soul / Ain't no wheels on this ship / I don't wanna / I love you, honey / Love me honey do / Too many secrets / Let the teardrops fall / I'm moving along / Stop, look and listen / I can see an angel / If I could only stay asleep / I'm blue again / Yes, I understand / Life's railway to heaven / Today, tomorrow and forever
PC 615 / Jul '97 / Platinum Collection

☐ SPOTLIGHT ON PATSY CLINE
Walkin' after midnight / I cried all the way to the altar / In care of the blues / I can't forget you / I love you honey / Just out of reach / Walking dream / Today, tomorrow and forever / Let the teardrops fall / Hungry for love / Too many secrets / Never no more / Stop the world / I don't wanna / Turn the cards slowly / I've loved and lost again
HADCD 130 / Feb '94 / Javelin

☐ STOP THE WORLD
In care of the blues / Stop the world / Too many secrets / Ain't no wheels on this ship / If I could only stay asleep / Never no more / Love me honey do / Three cigarettes in an ashtray / Honky tonk merry go round / Life's railway to heaven / Try again / Fingerprints / Turn the cards slowly / I cried all the way to the altar / Cry not for me / I love you honey / I'm blue again / Let the teardrops fall / Hidin' out
MUCD 9029 / Apr '95 / Musketeer

☐ THINKING OF YOU
I don't wanna / I can't forget / If I could see the world / Too many secrets / Hidin' out / Let the teardrops fall / Hungry for love / Walkin' dream / Three cigarettes in an ashtray / I cried all the way to the altar / Stop the world (and let me off) / I love you honey / Fingerprints / Just out of reach / Never no more / Pick me up on your way down / Today tomorrow forever / Honky tonk merry go round / Ain't no wheels on this ship
SUMCD 4023 / Nov '96 / Summit

☐ THROUGH THE EYES OF PATSY CLINE (An Anthology/2CD Set)
SMDCD 156 / 9 Feb '98 / Snapper

☐ TODAY, TOMORROW AND FOREVER
Walkin' after midnight / Stop, look and listen / Yes I understand / I can see an angel / Just out of reach / Walking dream / Then you'll know / Don't ever leave me again / I can't forget you / I'm hungry, hungry for your love / I don't wanna / I'm moving along / Gotta lot of rhythm in my soul / Just a closer walk with thee / I've loved and lost again / Todya, tomorrow and forever / If I could see the world / Come on in / Pick me up on your way down / Heart you break may be your own / In care of the blues / Stop the world / Too many secrets / Ain't no wheels on this ship / If only I could stay asleep / Never no more / Love me honey do / Three cigarettes in an ashtray / Honky tonk merry go round / Life's railway to heaven / Try again / Fingerprints / Turn the cards slowly / I cried all the way to the altar / Cry not for me / I love you honey / I'm blue again / Let the teardrops fall / Hidin' out
PAR 2305 / Mar '95 / Parade

☐ TOO MANY SECRETS
Walkin' after midnight / I've loved and lost again / I love you honey / Fingerprints / Never no more / Hidin' out / Walking dream / Let the teardrops fall / Just out of reach / Ain't no wheels on this ship / I can't forget / Too many secrets / In care of the blues / Hungry for love / I don't wanna / If I could see the world / Stop the world (and let me off) / I can see an angel / Today, tomorrow and forever / Life's railway to heaven
CDSB 013 / Jun '96 / Starburst

☐ UNFORGETTABLE
Gotta lot of rhythm in my soul / In care of the blues / Hungry for love / Lovesick blues / Stranger in my arms / Crazy dreams / Honky tonk merry go round / I cried all the way to the altar / Church, a courtroom and then goodbye / I've loved and lost again / Three cigarettes in an ashtray / I can't forget you / Just out of reach / I love you honey / Poor man's roses / Pick me up on your way down / Heart you break may be your own / Turn the cards slowly / That wonderful someone / Don't ever leave me again / Just a closer walk with thee / Dear God / He'll do for you / Never no more
PWK 017 / Feb '96 / Carlton

☐ UNFORGETTABLE CLASSICS VOL.1
MACCD 173 / Aug '96 / Autograph

☐ UNFORGETTABLE CLASSICS VOL.2
MACCD 223 / Aug '96 / Autograph

☐ VERY BEST OF PATSY CLINE, THE
Sweet dreams / Walking after midnight / Crazy / I fall to pieces / Back in baby's arms / He called me baby / She's got you / When you need a laugh / Heartaches / Faded love / So wrong / Strange / Leavin' on your mind / Why can't he be you / You're stronger than me / When I get thru with you (you'll love me too) / Crazy arms / I can't help it (if I'm still in love with you) / I love you so much it hurts / Anytime / Always lonely street / Your cheatin' heart / Just out of reach / Three cigarettes in an ashtray
MCD 11483 / 25 May '98 / MCA

☐ VERY BEST OF PATSY CLINE, THE
PDSCD 507 / Sep '97 / Pulse

☐ WALKIN' AFTER MIDNIGHT (28 Country Classics)
Walkin' after midnight / I've loved and lost again / Poor man's roses / Turn the cards slowly / I cried all the way to the altar / Pick me up on your way down / Stranger in my arms / Honky tonk merry go round / Church a courtroom and then goodbye / Three cigarettes in an ashtray / Never no more / Dear God / Lovesick blues / If I could stay asleep / Just out of reach / Then you'll know / I love honey / Fingerprints / There he goes he'll do for you (what he's done for me) / I can't forget you / Today, tomorrow and forever / Crazy dreams / I can see an angel / If I could see the world
PLATCD 27 / Jul '89 / Platinum

☐ WALKIN' AFTER MIDNIGHT
Church, a courtroom and then goodbye / Honky tonk merry go round / Hidin' out / I cried all the way to the alter / I've loved and lost again / Dear God / Walkin' after midnight / Fingerprints / Stranger in my arms / Try again / Then you'll know / Three cigarettes in an ashtray / He will do for you / Poor man's roses (or a rich man's gold) / Hungry for love / I can't forget / That wonderful someone / Stop the world (and let me off) / If I could see the world (through the eyes of a child) / Cry not for me / Just out of reach (of my two open arms) / Never no more / Walking dream / In care of the blues / Turn the cards slowly
CD 6014 / Apr '96 / Music

☐ WALKIN' AFTER MIDNIGHT
PLSCD 111 / Apr '96 / Pulse

Clint Eastwood

☐ AFRICAN ROOTS
African roots / Some a holler / Rock miss lue / Golden rule / Real clint eastwood / Sit down and wonder / Plain land style / Move your foot / What's the score / Love story / What a wicked act / Hard man fe dead / Shine eye gal / Conscience a bother them
LG 21054 / Mar '93 / Lagoon

☐ STOP THAT TRAIN (Clint Eastwood & General Saint)
Stop Jack / True vegetarian / Everything crash / Monkey man / HAPPY / Stop that train / Vote for me / Nuclear crisis / Rock with me / Shame and scandal
GRELCD 53 / Feb '87 / Greensleeves

☐ TWO BAD DJ'S (Clint Eastwood & General Saint)
Can't take another world war / Another one bites the dust / Talk about run / Sweet sweet Matilda / Special request to all prisoner / Dance have fi nice / Gal pon the front line / Jack Spratt / Tribute to General Echo / Hey Mr. DJ
GRELCD 24 / '89 / Greensleeves

Clinton, Bill

☐ BILL CLINTON JAM SESSION
PRES 001CD / Nov '94 / Pres

Clinton, George

☐ COMPUTER GAMES
Get dressed / Man's best friend / Loopzilla / Pot sharing totts / Computer games / Atomic dog / Free alterations / One fun at a time
7962662 / 1 Jun '98 / EMI

☐ FIFTH OF FUNK
Flatman and Robin / Count Funkula (I didn't know that funk was loaded) / Thumparella (Oh Kay) / Eyes of a dreamer / I found you / Ice melting in your heart / Clone ranger / Who do you love / Up up up and away / Can't get over losing you / Rat kissed the cat / Too tight for light / Every little bit hurts
ESMCD 490 / Apr '97 / Essential

☐ FUNK PERMISSION CARD (Clinton, George & The P-Funk Allstars)
PVCP 8168 / 5 May '98 / P-Vine

☐ GEORGE CLINTON FAMILY SERIES VOL.1 (Various Artists)
Go for yer funk: *Parliament* / Funk it up: *Sterling Silver Starship* / Funkin' for my momma's rent: *Fabulous, Gary & Black Slack* / Send a gram: *Cleaves, Jessica* / Who in the funk do you think you are: *Cleaves, Jessica* / Better days: *Foxxe, Andre* / Chong song: *Collins, Bootsy* / Michelle: *Flastic Brain Flam* / Sunshine of your love: *Blackbyrds* / Interview: *Clinton, George*
ESMCD 383 / Jul '96 / Essential

☐ GEORGE CLINTON FAMILY SERIES VOL.2 (Various Artists)
May Day (SOS): *Funkadelic* / These feet are made for dancin' (footstranger): *Dunbar, Ron* / Booty body ray for the plush funk: *Sterling Silver Starship* / I really envy the sunshine: *Cleaves, Jessica* / Lickety split: *Wesley, Fred & The Horny Horns* / Common law wife: *Flo* / Superspirit: *Morrison, Junie* / Love don't come easy: *Brides Of Funkenstein* / I can't stand it: *Lewis, Tracey & Andre Fox/Flastic Brain Flam* / Monster dance: *Ford, Ron* / We're just funkers: *Hampton, Michael* / Interview: *Clinton, George*
ESMCD 384 / Jul '96 / Essential

☐ GEORGE CLINTON FAMILY SERIES VOL.3 (P Is The Funk) (Various Artists)
Clone communicado / Does disc with dat / Shove on / Rock jam / Love is something / Every booty (get on down) / Personal problems / Bubblegum gangster / She's crazy / Think right / In the cabin of my Uncle Jam (P is the funk) / My love / Interview / Commercials
ESMCD 385 / Jul '96 / Essential

☐ GEORGE CLINTON FAMILY SERIES VOL.4 (Testing Positive For The Funk) (Various Artists)
Live up (to what she thinks of me): *Parliament* / Secrets: *Barnes, Sidney* / She never do's things: *Lewd, Trey* / Take my love: *Brides Of Funkenstein* / Just for play: *Brides Of Funkenstein* / Off the wall: *Cleaves, Jessica* / Get it on: *Jimmy G* / Triune: *Morrison, Junie* / Superstar madness: *Maruga & the Soda Jerks* / One angle: *Funkadelic* / Twenty bucks: *Brides Of Funkenstein* / To care: *Four Tops* / Comin' down from your love: *Savannah, Nick & Dwarf* / Interview: *Clinton, George*
ESMCD 392 / Jul '96 / Essential

☐ GEORGE CLINTON'S BAG 'O' FUNK (Various Artists)
Atomic dog: *Clinton, George* / Hollywood: *Red Hot Chili Peppers* / May the cube be with you: *Dolby's Cube* / Break my heart: *Jimmy G. & The Tackheads* / Last dance: *Clinton, George* / Get lucky: *Well Red* / Work that sucker to death: *Xavier & George Clinton & Bootsy* / Walk the dinasour: *Goombas & George Clinton* / You and your folks: *Day, Otis & The Knights* / Lies: *Jimmy G. & The Tackheads* / Leave my monkey alone: *Zevon, Warren* / Cool Joe: *Clinton, George* / Checkin' you checkin' yourself out: *Hall, Eramus*
DC 880902 / Jul '97 / Disky

☐ GREATEST FUNKIN' HITS, THE
Atomic dog / Flashlight / Booty body ready for the plush funk / Bop gun (one nation) / Break my heart / Mothership connection / Knee deep / Hey good lookin' / Do fries go with that shake / Atomic / Knee deep / Mothership connection starchild
PRMDCD 20 / Mar '97 / Premier/EMI

☐ HARDCORE JOLLIES
Hey good lookin' / Atomic dog / Do fries go with that shake / Thrashin' / One fun at a time / Stingy / Computer games / Bodyguard / Silly millameter / Pot sharing tots / Bangladesh / Free alterations / R and B skeletons in the closet / Man's best friend
DC 881752 / 2 Feb '98 / Disky

☐ HEY MAN, SMELL MY FINGER
Martial law / Paint the white house black / Way up / Dis beat disrupts / Get satisfied / Hollywood / Rhythm and rhyme / Big pump / If true love / High in my hello / Maximumisness / Kick back / Flag was still there / Martial law (Hey man, smell my finger)
NPG 60532 / Mar '95 / New Power Generation

☐ HYDRAULIC FUNK (P-Funk All Stars)
Pump up and down / Pumpin' it up / Copy cat / Hydraulic pump / Throw your hands up in the air / Generator pop / Acupuncture / One of those summers / Catch a keeper / Pumpin' you is so easy / Generator pop (mix)
CDSEWD 097 / Jun '95 / Westbound

Clinton, Larry

☐ 1941 - 1949 (Clinton, Larry & His Orchestra)
CCD 58 / '92 / Circle

☐ FEELING LIKE A DREAM
Feeling like a dream / Jump Joe / I want to rock / Because of you / Nobody knows the trouble I've seen / Taboo / Sahara / Dance of the reed flutes / Arab dance / I may be wrong / Do you call that a buddy / Rockin' chair / Camptown races
HEPCD 1047 / Nov '95 / Hep

☐ SHADES OF HADES (Clinton, Larry & Bea Wain)
Big dipper / Snake charmer / Midnight in the madhouse / I double dare you / I cash clo'es / Two dreams got together / Swing lightly / Military madcaps / I've got my heart set on you / Mr. Jinx stay away from me / True confession / Shades of Hades / Abba dabba / Dr. Rhythm / Campbells are swingin' / Always and always / Jubilee / I was doing all right / One rose (that's left in my heart) / Our love is here to stay / Wolverine blues / Oh Lady be good / Scrapin' the toast
HEPCD 1037 / Oct '93 / Hep

☐ STUDIES IN CLINTON
Martha / Study in blue / Night shades / My reverie / Boogie woogie blues / Milenburg joys / Dippermouth blues / Jitterbug / Over the rainbow / Deep purple
HEPCD 1052 / Nov '96 / Hep

Clive Natural

☐ NATURAL MAN
GRCD 9 / Jul '97 / Graylan

Clivilles & Cole

☐ GREATEST REMIXES VOL.1 (Various Artists)
C and C Music Factory MTV medley: *C&C Music Factory* / Because of you: *Cover Girls* / Don't take your love away: *Love, Lydia Lee* / Two to make it right: *Seduction* / Pride (in the name of love): *Clivilles & Cole* / Let the beat hit 'em: *Lisa Lisa & Cult Jam* / Mind your business: *Clivilles & Cole* / You take my breath away: *Cole, David* / Deeper love: *Clivilles & Cole* / Clouds: *Khan, Chaka* / True love: *Billy* / Notice me: *Sandee* / Do it properly: *Two Puerto Ricans & A Black Man/Dominican*
4879492 / Jul '97 / Columbia

Clock

☐ IT'S ABOUT TIME VOL.2
Oh what a night / It's over / Whoomph (There it is) / Everybody / You give me love (Rap version) / Axel F / Everybody jump around / Fly away / C'mon everybody / Don't go away / September / Finest / On the beach / Holding on 4 U / Gave you my love / Lonely snowman
MCD 60032 / Mar '97 / MCA

☐ IT'S TIME
Axel F / Whoomp (There it is) / Everybody / Holding on in the house / Keep the fires burning / Rythm holding on / Keep pushin' / Clock carnival / Secret / Clock ten to two megamix
MCD 11355 / Sep '95 / MCA

Clock DVA

☐ COLLECTIVE
HY 39100 / Aug '94 / Hyperium

Clockwise

☐ NOSTALGIA
ERCD 1034 / Feb '97 / Empire

Clooney, Rosemary

☐ 70
Secret of life / Oh what a beautiful mornig / I got lost in his arms / Come rain or come shine / One for my baby / I'm beginning to see the light / But beautiful / Just one of those things / Thanks for the memory / It's only a paper moon / (Have) I stayed too long at the fair / Hey there / Long ago and far away / Turn around / Falling in love again / From this moment on / For all we know / Ol' man river / (Our) love is here to stay
CCD 48042 / 13 Jul '98 / Concord Jazz

☐ BEST OF ROSEMARY CLOONEY
Half as much / This ole house / Hey there / Come on a my house / Botch-a-me (ba-ba-baciami piccina) / You're just in love / Mangos / It might as well be spring / In the cool, cool, cool of the evening / Blues in the night / Mambo Italiano / You'll never know / Too old to cut the mustard: *Clooney, Rosemary & Marlene Dietrich* / Beautiful brown eyes / Where will the dimple be / Be my life's companion / Mixed emotions / If teardrops were pennies / I could have danced all night / Tenderly
4840432 / May '96 / Columbia

☐ COME ON-A MY HOUSE (7CD Set)
Everybody has a laughing place / How do you do / Zip a dee doo dah / Uncle Remus said / Sooner or later / Tira lira li / I'm sorry I didn't say I'm sorry / Bread and butter woman / My o'darlin' my o'lovely my O'Brian / Grieving for you / Gonna get a girl / Chowder social / Click song / It's like taking candy from a baby / At a sidewalk penny arcade / I'm my own Grandpaw / Secretary song / Boy from Texas, a girl from Tennessee / Saturday night mood / Who killed'er / There's a man at the door / You started something / Straighten up and fly right / I got rhythm / How high the moon / Dear Mother / Cabaret / When you're in love / It's a cruel cruel world / Busy line / 'A' you're adorable / If I had a million dollars / Cabaret / Bargain day / Lover's gold / Four winds and the seven seas / Don't cry Joe (let her go, let her go) / There's a broken heart for every light / Oh you beautiful doll / Kid's a dreamer / Chicago / Why don't you haul off and love me / Canasta song / I only saw him once / Good time was had by all / On an ordinary morning / Crying myself to sleep / Peach Tree Street / Why fight the feeling / Where do I go / (Remember me) I'm the one who loves you / I whisper your name / Bless this house / Marrying for love / You're just in love / Place where I worship / House of singing bamboo / Love means love / Cherry pies / Ought to be you / When apples grow on cherry trees / Beautiful brown eyes / Shotgun boogie / Mixed emotions / Kentucky waltz / Lady is a tramp / I'll be around / Come on-a my house / Rose of the mountain / If teardrops were pennies / If teardrops were pennies / Find me / I'm waiting just for you / I'm from Texas / Stick with me / I wish I wuz (hi, ho, fiddle dee dee) / Half as much / Be my life's companion / Did anyone call / Tenderly / Why don't you love me / Poor whip, poor will / Botch-a-me / On the first warm day / Too old to cut the mustard / Who kissed me last night / Blues in the night / Good for nothin' / Sweet Leilani / You'll never know / When you wish upon a star / Over the rainbow / On the Atchison, Topeka and the Santa Fe / Continental / In the cool, cool, cool of the evening / It might as well be Spring / If I had a penny / I laughed until I cried / You're after my own heart / Lonely am I / Lonely am I / You're the only one for me / Withered roses / You love me just enough to hurt me / Grapevine swing / Haven't got a worry / I do, I do, I do / What would you do (if you were in my place) / Lovely weather for ducks / Close your eyes / It just happened to happen to me / When I see you / Cheegah choonem (I haven't got it) / Dot's nice, don't fight / It's the same / My baby rocks me / Red garters / Man and woman / Bad news / We'll be together again / When you love someone / You make me feel so young / Woman / Man (uh huh) / Good intentions / What is there to say / Brave man / Tomorrow I'll dream and remember / While we're young / Love is a beautiful stranger / Marry the man / Ay ay (who's the guy) / Bunch of bananas / Younger than springtime / Hello young lovers / While we're young / Love is a beautiful stranger / Crying myself to sleep / Too young / Grieving for you / Love you didn't do right by me / Young at heart / Hey there / This ole house / Besides (he's a man) / Land, sea and air / Blame it on my youth / Young man, young man / Sisters / Touch of the blues / Mr. and Mrs. / My baby sends me / Gee, I wish I was back in the army / Mandy / Count your blessings instead of sheep / Best things happen while you're dancing / Mambo Italiano / Open up your heart / Lord is counting on you / What is a baby / Opening / Feed Fido some rruff / Haven't got a worry / Come on-a my house / I do, I do, I do / Lovely weather for ducks / Haven't got a worry / Opening / Ya got class / When you love someone / Ali baba (be my baby) / Man and a woman / Red garters / Ladykiller / Good intentions / Bad news / Brave man / Santa Claus / White Christmas / Sisters / Snow / I'd rather see a minstrel show / Count your blessings instead of sheep / Love, you didn't do right by me / Choreography / Gee, I wish I was back in the army / Finale / Mr. and Mrs.
BCD 15895 / Nov '97 / Bear Family

☐ DEDICATED TO NELSON
Foggy day / We're in the money / It's so peaceful in the country / Limehouse blues / Do you know what it means to miss New Orleans / I got it bad and that ain't good / Continental / Mean to me / You're in Kentucky / As time goes by / Haven't got a worry / Mangos / At sundown / Nobody likes to be told / What is this thing called love / Come rain or come shine
CCD 4685 / Feb '96 / Concord Jazz

☐ DEMI-CENTENNIAL
Danny boy / Coffee song / I'm confessin' that I love you / I left my heart in San Francisco / Old friends / White Christmas / There will never be another you / Falling in love again / Sophisticated lady / How will I remember you / Mambo italiano / Promise (I'll never say goodbye) / Heart's desire / We'll meet again / Time flies / Dear departed past
CCD 4633 / Mar '95 / Concord Jazz

☐ EVERYTHING'S COMING UP ROSIE (Clooney, Rosemary & Nat Pierce Quintet)
I cried for you / I can't get started (with you) / Do you know what it means to miss New Orleans / I've got such a crush on you / As time goes by / More than you know / Foggy day / Hey there
CCD 4047 / Jun '89 / Concord Jazz

☐ EVERYTHING'S ROSIE
HCD 255 / Nov '94 / Hindsight

☐ FOR THE DURATION
No love, no nothin' / Don't fence me in / I don't want to walk without you / Every time we say goodbye / You'd be so nice to come home to / Sentimental journey / For all we know / September song / These foolish things / They're either too young or too old / More I see you / White cliffs of Dover / Saturday night is the loneliest night of the week / I'll be seeing you
CCD 4444 / Feb '91 / Concord Jazz

☐ GIRL SINGER
Nice 'n' easy / Sweet Kentucky ham / Autumn in New York / Miss Otis regrets / Let there be love / Lovers after all / From this moment on / More than you know / Wave / We fell in love anyway / It don't mean a thing if it ain't got that swing / I'm checkin' out (goodbye) / Of course it's crazy / Straighten up and fly right / Best is yet to come
CCD 4496 / Feb '92 / Concord Jazz

☐ MORE OF THE BEST OF ROSEMARY CLOONEY
It was just one of those things / Someone to watch over me / Imagination / Why shouldn't I / You came a long way from St. Louis / Tenderly / You started something / It never entered my mind / Don't cry Joe / It happened in Monterey / Be my life's companion / If I forget you
12634 / Oct '97 / Laserlight

☐ MOTHERS AND DAUGHTERS
Thank heaven for little girls / Always / Face / Baby mine / Best gift / Maria / God bless the child / Look to the rainbow / Turn around / Hello young lovers / Wrap your troubles in dreams / And I'll be there / Sisters / Child is only a moment / Funny face / Look for the silver lining / Pick yourself up
CCD 47542 / May '97 / Concord Jazz

☐ ROSEMARY CLOONEY SINGS BALLADS
Thanks for the memory / Here's that rainy day / Shadow of your smile / A nightingale sang in berkeley square / Bewitched, bothered and bewildered / Days of wine and roses / Easy living / Spring is here / Why shouldn't I / It never entered my mind
CCD 4282 / Nov '85 / Concord Jazz

☐ ROSEMARY CLOONEY SINGS COLE PORTER
CCD 185 / '89 / Concord Jazz

☐ ROSEMARY CLOONEY SINGS HAROLD ARLEN
Hooray for love / Happiness is a thing called love / One for my baby (and one more for the road) / Get happy / Ding dong the witch is dead / Out of this world / My shining hour / Let's take the long way home / Stormy weather
CCD 4210 / Nov '92 / Concord Jazz

☐ ROSIE AND BING (Clooney, Rosemary & Bing Crosby)
CD 6018 / Apr '96 / Music

☐ ROSIE SINGS BING
CCD 4060 / Jul '96 / Concord Jazz

☐ ROSIE SOLVES THE SWINGIN' RIDDLE
Get me to the church on time / Angry / I get along without you very well / How am I to know / You took advantage of me / April in Paris / I ain't got nobody / Some of these days / By myself / Shine on harvest moon / Cabin in the sky / Limehouse blues
379912 / Dec '97 / Koch

☐ SHOW TUNES
I wish I were in love again / I stayed too long at the fair / How are things in Glocca Morra / When do you start / I'll see you again / Guys and dolls / Manhattan / Everything I've got / Come back to me / Taking a chance on love / All the things you are
CCD 4364 / '91 / Concord Jazz

☐ SINGS RODGERS, HART & HAMMERSTEIN
OH what a beautiful morning / People will say we're in love / Love look away / Gentleman is a dope / It might as well be Spring / Sweetest sounds / I could write a book / You took advantage of me / Lady is a tramp / Little girl blue / My romance / Yours sincerely
CCD 4405 / Mar '90 / Concord Jazz

☐ SINGS THE LYRICS OF IRA GERSHWIN
But not for me / Nice work if you can get it / How long has this been going on / Fascinating rhythm / Our love is here to stay / Strike up the band / Long ago and far away / They all laughed / Man that got away / They can't take that away from me
CCD 4112 / Mar '90 / Concord Jazz

☐ SINGS THE LYRICS OF JOHNNY MERCER
Something's got to give / Laura / Any place I hang my hat is home / I remember you / When october goes / Dream-hit the road to dreamland / G.i. jive / Skylark / Hooray for hollywood
CCD 4333 / Nov '87 / Concord Jazz

☐ SINGS THE MUSIC OF IRVING BERLIN
It's a lovely day today / Be careful it's my heart / Cheek to cheek / How about me / Best thing for you would be me / I got lost in his arms / There's no business like show business / Better luck next time / What'll I do / Let's face the music and dance
CCD 4255 / Jul '88 / Concord Jazz

☐ SINGS THE MUSIC OF JIMMY VAN HEUSEN
Love won't let you get away / I thought about you / My heart is a hobo / Second time around / It could happen to you / Imagination / Like someone in love / Call me irresponsible / Walking happy / Last dance
CCD 4308 / Jan '87 / Concord Jazz

☐ SOME OF THE BEST
All alone / I gotta right to sing the blues / Look to the rainbow / Invitation / I'm glad there is you / On a slow boat to China / Mixed emotions / Man that got away / Rules of the road / How are things in Glocca Morra / Yours sincerely / More than you know
12633 / Aug '97 / Laserlight

☐ SOMETHING TO REMEMBER ME BY
This can't be love / Half as much / Tenderly / Zing a little zong / Who kissed me last night / You'll never know / Merry-go-run-around / Blues in the night / I do I do I do / Chicago style / South Rampart Street / Lovely weather for ducks / Something to remember you by / Haven't got a worry to my name / It's only a paper moon / Only forever / Lonely am I / You're in Kentucky sure as you're born / Medley / It's a most unusual day / You're just in love / Bad news / You make me feel so young / Man and woman / Tomorrow I'll dream and remember
JASCD 335 / May '97 / Jasmine

☐ STILL ON THE ROAD
Take me back to manhattan / Rules of the road / On the road again / Let's get away from it all / Road to Morocco / Let's eat home / Till we meet again / Still crazy after all these years / Ol' man river / Moonlight Mississippi / (Back home again in) Indiana / Corcovado / How deep is the ocean / How are things in Glocca Morra / Still on the road
CCD 4590 / Mar '94 / Concord Jazz

☐ TRIBUTE TO BILLIE HOLIDAY - "HERE'S TO MY LADY"
I cover the waterfront / Good morning heartache / Mean to me / Lover man (oh where can you be) / Don't explain / Comes love / He's funny that way / God bless the child / Them there eyes / Everything happens to me
CCD 4081 / Jul '92 / Concord Jazz

☐ WITH LOVE
Just the way you are / Way we were / Alone at last / Come in from the rain / Meditation / Hello, young lovers / Just in time / Tenderly / Will you still be mine
CCD 4144 / '89 / Concord Jazz

Close Lobsters

☐ HEADACHE RHETORIC
FIRE 33017 / Oct '91 / Fire

Closedown

☐ NEARFIELD
SR 9469CD / Jan '95 / Silent

Clouds

☐ SCRAPBOOK/WATERCOLOUR DAYS
BGOCD 317 / Jul '96 / Beat Goes On

Clout

☐ CLOUT
Save me / Under fire / Best of me / Let it grow / Substitute / You've got all of me / Wish I were loving you / Oowatanite / Since you've been gone / A threat and a promise / Without love / Portable radio / Feel my need / Hot shot / Oh how I long to be with you again / Don't stop
12366 / May '94 / Laserlight

☐ VERY BEST OF CLOUT, THE
Substitute / Save me / Under fire / Portable radio / Oowatanite / You've got it all of me / Wish I was loving you / Since you've been gone / Let it grow / Don't stop / When will you be mine / Without love / Hot shot / Gimme love
10142 / Oct '97 / Go On Deluxe

Cloven Hoof

☐ DOMINATOR
Rising up / Nova battlestar / Reach for the sky / Warrior of the wasteland / Invaders / Fugitive / Dominator / Road of eagles
HMRXD 113 / Jul '88 / FM

☐ SULTAN'S RANSOM, A
Astral rider / Forgotten heroes / DVR / Jekyll and Hyde / 1001 Nights / Silver surfer / Notre dame / Mad mad world / Highlander / Mistress of the forest
HMRXD 129 / Aug '89 / Heavy Metal

Cloverleaf

☐ BORN A RIDER
HYCD 200129 / Mar '95 / Hypertension

Clovers

☐ CLOVERS, THE
Love love love / Lovey dovey / Yes it's you / Ting-a-ling / I played the fool / Hey Miss Fannie / Don't you know I love you / Middle of the night / Blue velvet / Little Mama / Crawlin' / Here goes a fool / I got my eyes on you / Devil or angel / Skylark / Needless / Comin' on / One mint julep / Wonder where my baby's gone / Good lovin' / I confess / Feeling is good / Down in the alley / Your cash ain't nothing but trash
RSACD 857 / Jan '97 / Sequel

☐ DANCE PARTY
Lovebug / All about you / If I could be loved by you / So young / Down in the alley / Nip sip / I, I love you / In the morning time / Your tender love / Fool fool fool / Wishing for your love / There's no tomorrow / Your cash ain't nothing but trash / Alrighty oh sweetie / If you love me (why don't you tell me so) / Love love love / Hey doll baby / Baby baby oh my darling / Bring me love / I'm a lonely fool / From the bottom of my heart / You good lookin' woman / Here comes romance / Bootie green / Drive it home
RSACD 858 / Jan '97 / Sequel

☐ DOWN IN THE ALLEY
One mint julip / Good lovin' / Don't you know I love you / Wonder where my baby's gone / Ting a ling / Crawlin' / Hey Miss Fannie / Lovey dovey / Middle of the night / Fool fool fool / I've got my eyes on you / I confess / Your cash ain't nothin' but trash / Little Mama / Down in the alley / Nip slip / Devil or angel / Blue velvet / In the morning time / Love bug / If I could be loved by you
7567823122 / Mar '93 / Atlantic

☐ **VERY BEST OF THE CLOVERS, THE**
Don't you know I love you / Fool fool fool / One mint julep / Ting a ling / I played the fool / Hey Miss Fannie / Good lovin' / Lovey dovey / Little mama / Your cash ain't nothin' but trash / Blue velvet / Devil or angel / Down in the alley / Pennies from heaven / Love potion no.9 / Lovey
8122729712 / 1 Jun '98 / Rhino

Club 69

☐ **TW STYLE**
TWD 11654 / 15 Sep '97 / Twisted UK

Clusone Trio

☐ **CLUSONE 3**
RAMBOY 5 / Oct '94 / Ramboy

☐ **SOFT LIGHTS AND SWEET MUSIC**
ART 6153CD / Jul '94 / Hat Art

Cluster

☐ **CLUSTER**
SOUL 17 / Feb '97 / Soul Static Sound

☐ **CLUSTER VOL.2**
14864 / Oct '96 / Spalax

☐ **CURIOSUM**
SKYCD 3063 / May '95 / Sky

☐ **ERUPTION**
MT 365 / May '97 / Marginal Talent

☐ **FIRST ENCOUNTER TOUR (2CD Set)**
CLP 9933 / Mar '97 / Cleopatra

☐ **ONE HOUR**
105865 / Dec '96 / Clear Spot

☐ **ZUCKERZEIT**
Hollywood / Caramel / Rote Riki / Rosa / Caramba / Fotschi tong / James / Marzipan / Rotor / Heisse Lippen
14865 / Oct '96 / Spalax

Clutch

☐ **IMPETUS**
Impetus / Pile driver / Passive restraints / Impetus / High calibre consecrator
MOSH 192CD / 15 Dec '97 / Earache

☐ **TRANS NATIONAL SPEEDWAY LEAGUE**
Shogun named Marcus / El Jefe speaks / Binge and purge / Twelve Ounce epilogue / Bacchanal / Milk of human kindness / Rats / Earthworm / Heirloom 13 / Walking in the great shining path of monster trucks / Effigy
7567922812 / Oct '93 / Warner Bros.

Clydesiders

☐ **CROSSING THE BORDERS**
Highland Harry / Tae the beggin' / Surf and the silver fishes / Sonny's dream / Pig set / Land o' the Leal / Band o' shearers / Albion heart / My old man / Kate's wedding / Rowan tree / I once loved a lass / Stay young
RECD 502 / Jan '98 / REL

CMU

☐ **SPACE CABARET/OPEN SPACES**
Space cabaret / Song from the 4th era / Doctor am I normal / Light shine / Voodoo man / Japan / Mystical sounds / Archway 272 / Distand thought, a point of light / Dream / Henry / Slow and lonesome blues / Clown / Open spaces
SEECD 373 / Jun '93 / See For Miles

Coal Chamber

☐ **COAL CHAMBER**
Loco / Oddity / Bradley / Unspoiled / Sway / Big truck / First / Maricon puto / I / Clock / My frustration / Amir of the desert / Dreamtime / Pig
RR 88635 / 1 Dec '97 / Roadrunner

Coal Porters

☐ **EP ROULETTE**
Everything / Emily in ginger / Who'll stop the rain / Help me / Don't fence me in / Me here at your door
SID 008 / 20 Apr '98 / Prima

☐ **LAND OF HOPE & CROSBY**
SID 002 / Sep '94 / Prima

☐ **REBELS WITHOUT APPLAUSE**
RUB 17 / Jul '95 / Rubber

Coasters

☐ **COAST ALONG WITH THE COASTERS**
(Ain't that) just like me / Keep on rollin' / Wait a minute / Stewball / Snake and the bookworm / What about us / Little Egypt / Wake me, shake me / Run run run / My babe / Bad blood / Girls girls girls / Crazy baby / Bell bottom slacks and a chinese kimono / Ladylike / Thumbin' a ride / Ridin' hood / Hongry / Teach me how to shimmy / Bull tick waltz / PTA / Slime / I'm a hog for you / Hey sexy
RSACD 871 / Mar '97 / Sequel

☐ **COASTERS, THE**
One kiss led to another / Brazil / Turtle dovin' / Smokey Joe's cafe / Wrap it up / Riot in cell block no.9 / Loop de loop mambo / One kiss / I must be dreamin' / Lola / Framed / Down in Mexico / Hatchet man / Just like a fool / I love Paris / Whadaya want / If teardrops were kisses / Sweet Georgia Brown / My baby comes to me / Idol with the golden head / What is the secret of your success / Wait a minute / Dance / Gee golly / Three cool cats
RSACD 868 / Mar '97 / Sequel

☐ **GREATEST HITS**
Poison Ivy / Along came Jones / Shadow knows / I'm a hog for you baby / Charlie Brown / Yakety yak / Zing went the strings of my heart / That's rock 'n' roll / Searchin' / Youngblood / She's a yum yum / Saturday night fish fry / What about us / Run red run / Keep on rollin' / Three cool cats / Bad blood / Little Egypt / Girls girls girls / Sorry but I'm gonna have to pass / Besame mucho / Shoppin' for clothes / Bad detective / Lovey dovey
RSACD 869 / Mar '97 / Sequel

☐ **JUST COASTIN'**
I got to boogie / If I had a hammer / Poison ivy / Young blood / Along came Jones / Searchin' / Charlie Brown / Yakety yak / Benjamin and Loretta / Chick is guilty
C5CD 579 / Feb '92 / See For Miles

☐ **ONE BY ONE**
But beautiful / Satin doll / Gee baby ain't I good to you / Autumn leaves / You'd be so nice to come home to / Moonlight in Vermont / Moonglow / Easy living / Way you look tonight / Don't get around much anymore / Willow weep for me / On the sunny side of the street / Girls girls girls / Climb / T'ain't nothing to me / Speedo's back in town / I must be dreamin' / Money money / Let's go get stoned / Along came Jones / Charlie Brown / That is rock and roll / Stewball / Wild one / Riding hood
RSACD 870 / Mar '97 / Sequel

☐ **VERY BEST OF THE COASTERS, THE**
Riot in cell block 9 / Smoky Joe's cafe / Down in mexico / Searchin' / Idol with the golden head / Young blood / Yakety yak / Charlie Brown / Along comes Jones / That is rock and roll / I'm a hog for you / Poison ivy / What about us / Run red run / Little Eygpt / Shoppin' for clothes / Sorry but I'm gonna have to pass
9548326562 / Mar '94 / Atlantic

☐ **YAKETY YAK (The Best Of The Coasters)**
Down in Mexico / Young blood / Searchin' / Yakety yak / Charlie Brown / Along came Jones / Poison ivy / Run Red run / Little Egypt / Love potion no.9 / Deodorant song / One foot draggin' / TV fanatic / It ain't sanitary / As quiet as it's kept / It doesn't take much / Whip it on me baby
AIM 2013CD / 20 Oct '97 / Aim

Coates, Eric

☐ **ERIC COATES**
GEMMCD 9973 / Sep '92 / Pearl

☐ **THREE ELIZABETHS, THE**
Three Elizabeths suite / Music everywhere / Last love / Jester at the wedding / Fanfare no.1 - Salute the soldier / Summer afternoon idyll / Footlights concert waltz / Seven seas / From meadow to Mayfair / Music of the night / Green hills o' Somerset / Stonecracker John / Bird songs at Eventide / Four centuries suite / Impression of a princess / London calling / Moon magic / Joyous youth / Eighth Army march / Mirage / I pitch my lonely caravan at night / Sweet seventeen / Selfish giant / Holborn march / Under the stars / Moresque / Dancing nights / Over to you
75605523902 / Jul '96 / Happy Days

Coates, Gerry

☐ **EVERY PICTURE TELLS A STORY (Coates, Gerry & The Earth Secrets)**
Seven Budweisers in the wind / Let's not forget them / Line dance fever / Who are the bank robbers / Listen to the message / Every picture tells a story / Sun sand and sea / First time I set my eyes on you / Month of Valentine / Sensational lover / Aching with desire / She's like a waterfall / Never too old to fall in love / I'm gonna change my ways / A mother's love / Houston sweet sweet Houston / Teach me to dance / Call of the Highlands / This train is running / If only Christmas could last all year
CDRPM 0031 / 27 Oct '97 / RP Media

Coates, Johnny

☐ **PORTRAIT**
Let's get lost / Ding dong the witch is dead / If I love again / Love is the sweetest thing / Little girl blue / Sha-ga-da-ga-da / Coates oats / Between the devil and the deep blue sea / Skylark / My lucky day / If there is someone lovelier than you
SV 0234 / Oct '97 / Savoy Jazz

Coax

☐ **FEAR OF STANDING STILL**
Orchestra / Turning to gold / Plates / Trophy wife / Rolling thunder / Rebecca in the presence of the enemy / Ring master goes down / Harrison fjord / Colours from the sideshow / Meatball heroes / Joe repairs cars
RQTZ 010 / 4 May '98 / Rainbow Quartz

Cobb, Arnett

☐ **AGAIN WITH MILT BUCKNER (Cobb, Arnett & Milt Buckner)**
BLE 590522 / Apr '91 / Black & Blue

☐ **ARNETT BLOWS FOR 1300**
Arnett blows for 1300 / Go, red go / Walkin' with Sid / Dutch kitchen bounce / Running with Ray / Big league blues / Cobb's idea / When I grow too old to dream / Pay it no mind / Cobb's boogie / Flower garden blues / Cobb's corner / Top flight / Chick she ain't nowhere / Still flying
DD 471 / Mar '97 / Delmark

☐ **BLUE AND SENTIMENTAL (Cobb, Arnett & Red Garland Trio)**
Sweet georgia brown / Black velvet / Blue sermon / Georgia on my mind / Sizzlin' / Way you look tonight / Willow weep for me / Hurry home / P.s. I love you / Blue and sentimental / Darn that dream / Why try to change me now / Your wonderful love
PCD 24122 / Nov '95 / Prestige

☐ **DEEP PURPLE**
BB 8642 / Apr '96 / Black & Blue

☐ **IT'S BACK**
PCD 7037 / '91 / Progressive

☐ **SMOOTH SAILING**
Charmaine / Cobb's mob / I don't stand a ghost of a chance (with you) / Let's split / Blues around dusk / Smooth sailing / Blues in my heart
OJCCD 323 / Dec '95 / Original Jazz Classics

☐ **TENOR TRIBUTE (Cobb, Arnett & Jimmy Heath/Joe Henderson)**
1211842 / Oct '90 / Soul Note

☐ **WILD MAN FROM TEXAS, THE**
BB 892 / 24 Apr '98 / Black & Blue

Cobb, Jimmy

☐ **ENCOUNTER**
PHIL 662 / Oct '94 / Philology

Cobb, Junie C.

☐ **COLLECTION 1926-1929, THE**
COCD 14 / Oct '91 / Collector's Classics

Cobbs, Willie

☐ **DOWN TO EARTH**
R 2628 / Nov '94 / Rooster

Cobham, Billy

☐ **BEST OF BILLY COBHAM, THE**
Quadrant 4 / Snoopy's search / Red baron / Spanish moss / Moon germs / Stratus / Pleasant pheasant / Solo panhandler / Do whatcha wanna
7567815582 / Jan '93 / Atlantic

☐ **FLIGHT TIME (Billy Cobham Live)**
Flight time / Antares / 6 persimmons / Day grace / Whisperer / Princess / Jackhammer
INAK 8616CD / Jul '97 / In Akustik

☐ **MISSISSIPPI NIGHTS**
WEN 001 / 20 Apr '98 / Wenlock

☐ **NORDIC**
RHYTHM 101 / Feb '97 / Rhythm

☐ **SPECTRUM**
Quadrant 4 / Searching for the right door / Spectrum / Anxiety / Taurian matador / Stratus / To the women in my life / Le lis / Snoopy's search / Red Baron
7567814282 / Jan '93 / Atlantic

☐ **STRATUS**
Drum solo intro/Stratus / AC/DC / Kasia / All Hallows Eve / Wrapped in a cloud / Drum solo / Total eclipse / Brooze
INAK 813CD / Jul '97 / In Akustik

☐ **TRAVELLER, THE**
Alfa waves / All that your soul provides / Balancing act / What if / Dipping the biscuits in the soup / Fragolino / Just one step away / Mushu Creole blues / On the inside track / Soul provider
ECD 220982 / Jul '94 / Evidence

Cobolt

☐ **ELEVEN STOREY SOUL DEPARTURE**
ASR 15 / 20 Oct '97 / Ampersand

Cobra

☐ **GOLDMINE (Mad Cobra)**
RASCD 3110 / Apr '93 / Ras

☐ **MAD COBRA**
CSCD 001 / Oct '92 / Graylan

☐ **SEXPERIENCE (Mad Cobra)**
Real men / Sexperience / Never forget / Just party / Sex drive / Change position / Respect / Justice / Wish you were here / Def rock
VERSCD 1 / 5 May '98 / Versatal

☐ **SHOOT TO KILL (Mad Cobra)**
War / Bun till mi fool / Poco jump / Workie workie / Respect woman / Dance cemetary / Me love she / Woman una night / Nah go work / Rod out / Shoot to kill / Ze taurus
RNCD 2020 / Aug '93 / Rhino

☐ **VENOM (Mad Cobra)**
Platinum / Mark 10 / Mr. Pleasure / Wife and darling / RIP / Length and bend / Hotness / To the max / Gal a model / Heartless / Fat and buff / Mate no ready
GRELCD 202 / Mar '94 / Greensleeves

☐ **YOUR WISH**
Your wish / A wash / If a boy dis / Poison gas / Must drop out / Train length / Same way / Rod out / Tight underneath / Nuh tek it
LG 21059 / Nov '92 / Lagoon

Cobra Verde

☐ **EGOMANIA (LOVE SONGS)**
SCAT 67 / Jun '97 / Scat

Cobras

☐ **ONCE BITTEN**
PEPCD 117 / Nov '96 / Pollytone

Cochabamba

☐ **GREATEST HITS**
PV 758 11 / '88 / Disques Pierre Verany

Cochran, Charles

☐ **HAUNTED HEART**
ACD 177 / May '95 / Audiophile

Cochran, Eddie

☐ **BEST OF EDDIE COCHRAN, THE**
Summertime blues / C'mon everybody / Three steps to heaven / Sittin' in the balcony / Drive in show / Jeanie, Jeanie, Jeanie / Teenage heaven / Somethin' else / My way / Cut across Shorty / Twenty flight rock / Weekend / Hallelujah I love her so / Lonely / Sweetie Pie / Three stars / Skinny Jim / Nervous breakdown / Completely sweet / Rock'n'roll blues
CDMFP 6268 / Sep '96 / Music For Pleasure

☐ **CRUISIN' THE DRIVE IN**
RSRCD 009 / Jan '96 / Rockstar

☐ **EARLY YEARS, THE**
Skinny Jim / Half loved / Tired and sleepy / That's what it takes to make a man / Pink pegged slacks / Open the door / Country jam / Don't bye bye baby me / My love to remember / Guybo / Dark lonely street / If I were dying / Jelly bean / Latch on / Slow down / Fool's paradise / Bad baby doll / Itty bitty Betty / Heart of a fool / Instrumental blues
CDCH 237 / Nov '93 / Ace

☐ **EP COLLECTION, THE**
Skinny Jim / Twenty flight rock / Sittin' in the balcony / Blue suede shoes / Pink peg slacks / Mean when I'm mad / Stockin's 'n' shoes / Jeannie Jeannie Jeannie / Pretty girl / Teresa / Sweetie pie / C'mon everybody / Summertime blues / I remember / Rock 'n' roll blues / Milk cow blues / Little angel / Cherished memories / Three steps to heaven
SEECD 271 / Jan '91 / See For Miles

☐ **LA SESSIONS**
Jelly bean / Don't bye bye baby me / Half loved / My love to remember / Dark lonely Street / Guybo / Strollin' guitar / Fourth man theme / Chicken shot blues / Bad baby doll / Lovin' I'm wastin' / Itty bitty Betty / Seriously in love / Fontella / It's Heaven / My baby she loves me / Take my hand / Once more / Bread Fred / Hide and go seek / If I were dying / I wanna know / Uh oh little girl / I can't let you go
RSRCD 003 / Apr '94 / Rockstar

☐ **MIGHTY MEAN**
RSRCD 008 / May '95 / Rockstar

☐ **ONE MINUTE TO ONE**
RSRCD 010 / Oct '96 / Rockstar

☐ **ORIGINAL, THE**
Summertime blues / C'mon everybody / Three steps to heaven / Somethin' else / Sittin' in the balcony / Drive in show / Jeanie Jeanie Jeanie / Teenage heaven / My way / Cut across shorty / Twenty flight rock / Weekend / Hallelujah I love her so / Lonely / Sweetie pie / Three stars / Skinny Jim / Nervous breakdown / Completely sweet / Rock 'n' roll blues
TO 860952 / 2 Feb '98 / Disky

☐ **RARE 'N' ROCKIN' (28 Gems From The Golden Age Of Rock 'n' Roll)**
Jelly bean / Don't bye bye baby me / Guybo / Guitar blues / Meet Mr. Tweedy / Half loved / My love to remember / Mighty mean / Sittin' in the balcony / Twenty flight rock / Chicken shot blues / Somethin' else / Hallelujah I love her so / Skinny Jim / Dark lonely street / Tired and sleepy / Fool's paradise / Slow down / Open the door / One minute to one / Jungle jingle / Little angel / Let's coast awhile / Nervous breakdown / Pink peg slacks / Milk cow blues / Song of New Orleans / Nice 'n' easy
MCCD 318 / 6 Oct '97 / Music Club

☐ **ROCK 'N' ROLL (3CD Set/The Originals) (Cochran, Eddie/Fats Domino/Gene Vincent)**
Singin' to my baby: *Cochran, Eddie* / Sittin' in the balcony: *Cochran, Eddie* / Completely sweet: *Cochran, Eddie* / Undying love: *Cochran, Eddie* / I'm alone: *Cochran, Eddie* / Because I love you: *Cochran, Eddie* / Lovin' time: *Cochran, Eddie* / Proud of you: *Cochran, Eddie* / Am I blue: *Cochran, Eddie* / Twenty flight rockers: *Cochran, Eddie* / Drive in show: *Cochran, Eddie* / Mean when I'm mad: *Cochran, Eddie* / Stockins'n'shoes: *Cochran, Eddie* / Tell me why: *Cochran, Eddie* / Have I told you lately that I love you: *Cochran, Eddie* / Cradle baby: *Cochran, Eddie* / One kiss: *Cochran, Eddie* / My blue heaven: *Domino, Fats* / Swanee river hop: *Domino, Fats* / Second line jump: *Domino, Fats* / Goodbye: *Domino, Fats* / Careless love: *Domino, Fats* / I love her: *Domino, Fats* / I'm in love again: *Domino, Fats* / When my dreamboat comes home: *Domino, Fats* / Are you going my way: *Domino, Fats* / If you need me: *Domino, Fats* / My heart is in your hands: *Domino, Fats* / Fats frenzy: *Domino, Fats* / Blue jean bop: *Vincent, Gene* / Jezebel: *Vincent, Gene* / Who slapped John: *Vincent, Gene* / Ain't she sweet: *Vincent, Gene* / I flipped: *Vincent, Gene* / Waltz of the

wind: Vincent, Gene / Jump back: Vincent, Gene / Wedding bells: Vincent, Gene / Jumps, giggles and shouts: Vincent, Gene / Lazy river: Vincent, Gene / Bop street: Vincent, Gene / Pet o' my heart: Vincent, Gene
CDOMB 006 / 27 Jul '98 / EMI

☐ ROCK 'N' ROLL LEGEND
Pink peg slacks / Latch on (version 1) / My love to remember / Heart of a fool / Yesterday's heartbreak / Latch on (version 2) / Tired and sleepy / Fool's paradise / Slow down / Open the door / Skinny Jim / Half loved / Drownin' all my sorrows / Let's coast awhile / Dark lonely street / Guybo / Take my hand / Jelly bean / Don't bye bye baby me / Chicken shot blues
RSRCD 001 / Apr '94 / Rockstar

☐ ROCK 'N' ROLL TV SHOW
Hallelujah I love her so / C'mon everybody / Somethin' else / Twenty flight rock / Money honey / Have I told you lately / Summertime blues / Milk cow blues / I don't like you anymore / Sweet little sixteen / White lightnin' / Cruisin' the drive / IOU / Bread Fred / Kiss and make up / Borrowed love / Itty bitty Betty / Instrumental blues / Drowning all my sorrows / Pretty little devil / Interview
3036001212 / 13 Oct '97 / Carlton

☐ ROCKIN' IT COUNTRY STYLE (Legendary Chuck Foreman Recordings 1953-1955)
Rockin' it / Gambler's guitar / Jammin' with Jimmy / Tenderly / Steelin' the blues / Stardust / Candy kisses / Chuck and Eddie's boogie / In the mood / I'll see you in my dreams / Hearts of stone / Cannonball rag / Blue gypsy / Poor people of Paris / That's alright mama / She done give her heart to me / Remington ride / Live fast love hard die young / Rockin' and flyin' / Closer closer closer / Healer like time / Water baby blues / Two of a kind / Humerous conservation
RSRCD 011 / 28 Nov '97 / Rockstar

☐ SOMETHIN' ELSE (The Fine Lookin' Hits Of Eddie Cochran)
RE 21622 / 6 Apr '98 / Razor & Tie

☐ SUMMERTIME BLUES
Sittin' in the balcony / Drive in show / Summertime blues / C'mon everybody / Jeannie, jeannie, jeannie / Something else / Hallelujah I love her so / Three steps to heaven / Sweetie pie / Lonely / Weekend / My way / Teenage heaven / One kiss / Tell me why / Have I told you lately that I love you / Blue suede shoes / Twenty flight rock / Three stars / Cotton picker
RMB 75054 / Nov '93 / Remember

☐ SUMMERTIME BLUES
C'mon everybody / Summertime blues / Yesterday's heartbreak / That's my desire / Completely sweet / Mean when I'm mad / Undying love / I'm alone because I love you / Stockin's 'n' shoes / Lovin' time / Never / Nervous breakdown / Rock 'n' roll blues / Fourth man theme
16151 / Sep '96 / Laserlight

☐ VERY BEST OF EDDIE COCHRAN, THE (The Anniversary Album)
C'mon everybody / Three steps to heaven / Weekend / Skinny Jim / Completely sweet / Milk cow blues / Cut across shorty / Hallelujah, I love her so / Something else / Blue suede shoes / Eddie's blues / Sittin' in the balcony / Summertime blues / Twenty flight rock / Three stars / Cherished memories
CDFA 3019 / Mar '90 / Fame

Cochran, Jackie Lee

☐ ROCKABILLY MUSIC
HMG 6604 / Dec '97 / Hightone

Cochrane, Michael

☐ CUTTING EDGE (Cochrane, Michael Quartet)
SCCD 31430 / 5 Jan '98 / Steeplechase

☐ IMPRESSIONS
De ja vu / There will never be another you / Cinco / Impressions / Ballade / Bud Powell / Raindrops / Escape / Blues for Gwen
LCD 15482 / Jun '96 / Landmark

☐ SONG OF CHANGE (Cochrane, Michael Trio)
1212512 / Nov '93 / Soul Note

Cock ESP

☐ MENASHA RED LIGHT DISTRICT
COCK 1 / 1 Dec '97 / Bentley Welcomes Careful Drivers
SUNX 1 / Nov '97 / Sunship

Cock Eyed Ghost

☐ NEVEREST
BD 9046 / Nov '97 / Big Deal

Cock 'n' Bull Band

☐ BELOW THE BELT
C & B 104CD / Dec '93 / Cock & Bull

☐ PUMPED UP AND LOADED
MCRCD 6992 / Jun '96 / Mrs. Casey

Cock Sparrer

☐ BEST OF COCK SPARRER, THE
STEPCD 014 / 8 Jun '98 / Step 1

☐ BLOODY MINDED (The Best Of Cock Sparrer)
DSR 73 / 15 Dec '97 / Dr. Strange

☐ ENGLAND BELONGS TO ME
Runnin' riot / Trouble on the terraces / We love you / Chip on my shoulder / Taken for a ride / Sister suzie / Watcha gonna do about it / Again and again / What's it like to be old / England belongs to me / Working / Riot squad / Where are they now / Argy bargy / Sun says / Price too high to pay / Run with the blind / Closedown / White riot / Out on a island
CANCAN 007CD / 3 Nov '97 / Can Can

☐ LIVE AND LOUD
Riot squad / Watch your back / I got your number / Take 'em all / We love you / Working / Argy bargy / Where are they now / White riot / Running riot / Sun days / Secret army / England belongs to me / Chip on my shoulder
PINCD 103 / 13 Jul '98 / PinHead

☐ LIVE AND LOUD (Cock Sparrer/ Business)
STEPCD 004 / 23 Feb '98 / Step 1

☐ SHOCK TROOPS
Where are they now / Riot squad / Working / Take 'em all / We're coming back / England belongs to me / Watch your back / I got your number / Secret army / Droogs don't run / Out on an island / Argy bargy / Colonel Bogey
AHOYCD 004 / 3 Nov '97 / Captain Oi

☐ SHOCK TROOPS/RUNNIN' RIOT IN '84
STEPCD 028 / 8 Jun '98 / Step 1

☐ TWO MONKEYS
BC 1710CD / 24 Nov '97 / Bitzcore

Cockburn, Bruce

☐ BIG CIRCUMSTANCE
If a tree falls / Shipwrecked at the stable door / Gospel of bondage / Don't feel your touch / Tibetan side of town / Understanding nothing / Where the death squad lives / Radium rain / Pangs of love / Gift / Anything can happen
REVXD 122 / Jan '89 / FM

☐ CHARITY OF THE NIGHT
Night train / Get up Jonah / Pacing the cage / Mistress of storms / Whole night sky / Coming rains / Birmingham shadows / Mines of Mozambique / Live on my mind / Charity of night / Strange waters
RCD 10366 / Feb '97 / Rykodisc

☐ DANCING IN THE DRAGON'S JAWS
Creation dream / Hills of the morning / Badlands flashback / Northern lights / After the rain / Wondering where the lions are / Incandescent blue / No footprints
REVXD 127 / Jul '89 / FM

☐ HUMANS
Grim travellers / Rumours of glory / More not more / You get bigger as you go / What about the bond / How I spent my fall vacation / Guerilla betrayed / Tokyo / Fascist architecture / Rose above the sky
REVXD 124 / Jul '89 / FM

☐ LIVE
Silver wheels / World of wonders / Rumours of glory / See how I miss you / After the rain / Call it democracy / Wondering where the lions are / Nicaragua / Broken wheel / Stolen land / Always look on the bright side of life / Tibetan side of town / To raise the morning star / Maybe the poet
COOKCD 034 / Apr '90 / Cooking Vinyl

☐ STEALING FIRE
REVXD 125 / Jul '89 / FM

☐ TROUBLE WITH NORMAL
Trouble with normal / Candy man's gone / Hoop dancer / Waiting for the moon / Tropic moon / Going up against chaos / Put our hearts together / Civilization and its discontents / Planet of the clowns
REVXD 126 / Jul '89 / FM

☐ WAITING FOR A MIRACLE (Singles 1970-1987)
Mama just wants to barrelhouse all night long / All the diamonds in the world / Burn / Silver wheels / Laughter / Wondering where the lions are / Tokyo / Fascist architecture / Trouble with normal / Rumours of glory / Coldest night of the year / You pay your money and take your chance / Lovers in a dangerous time / If I had a rocket launcher / Peggy's kitchen wall / People see through you / Call it democracy / Stolen land / Waiting for a miracle / One day I walk / It's going down slow
REVXD 90 / May '87 / Revolver

☐ WORLD OF WONDERS
They call it democracy / Lily of the midnight sky / World of wonder / Berlin tonight / People see through you / See how I miss you / Santiago dawn / Dancing in paradise / Down here tonight
REVXD 73 / Mar '87 / Revolver

☐ YOU PAY YOUR MONEY AND YOU TAKE YOUR CHANCE (Live)
Call it democracy / Stolen land / Strange waters / Fascist architecture / You pay your money and you take your chance / Birmingham shadows
RCD 10435 / 12 Jan '98 / Rykodisc

Cocker, Joe

☐ ACROSS FROM MIDNIGHT
Tonight / Could you be loved / That's all I need to know / N'Oubliez jamais / What do I tell my heart / Wayward soul / Loving you tonight / Across from midnight / What do you say / Last one to know / That's the way her love is / Need your love so bad
CDEST 2301 / 8 Sep '97 / Capitol

☐ BEST OF JOE COCKER, THE
Unchain my heart (90's version) / You can leave your hat on / When the night comes / Up where we belong / Now that the magic has gone / Don't you love me anymore / I can hear the river / Sorry seems to be the hardest word / Shelter me / Feels like forever / Night calls / Don't let the sun go down on me / Now that you're gone / Civilised man / When a woman cries / With a little help from my friends
CDESTU 2187 / Oct '92 / Capitol

☐ CIVILISED MAN/COCKER/UNCHAIN MY HEART (The Originals/3CD Set)
Civilzed man / There goes my baby / Come on in / Tempted / Long drag off a cigarette / I love the night / Crazy in love / Girl like you / Hold on (I feel our love is changing) / Even a fool would let go / You can leave your hat on / Heart of the matter / Inner city blues / Love is on a fade / Heaven / Shelter me / A to Z / Don't you love me any more / Livin' without your love / Don't drink the water / Unchain my heart / One / Two wrongs don't make a right / I stand in wonder / River's rising / Isolation / All our tomorrows / Woman loves a man / Trust in me / Satisfied / You can leave your hat on
CDOMB 024 / 27 Jul '98 / Capitol

☐ CIVILIZED MAN
Civilized man / There goes my baby / Come on in / Tempted / Long drag off a cigarette / I love the night / Crazy in love / Girl like you / Hold on (I feel our love is changing) / Even a fool would let go
EJ 2401392 / Apr '92 / Capitol

☐ COCKER
You can leave your hat on / Heart of the matter / Inner city blues / Love is on a fade / Heaven / Shelter me / A to Z / Don't you love me anymore / Livin' without your love / Don't drink the water
CDEST 2009 / Jul '94 / Capitol

☐ COCKER HAPPY
Hitchcock railway / She came in through the bathroom window / Marjorine / She's so good to me / Hello little friend / With a little help from my friends / Delta lady / Darling be home soon / Do I still figure in your life
CUCD 01 / Oct '94 / Disky

☐ ESSENTIAL, THE
Up where we belong / Sweet lil' woman / Easy rider / Threw it away / Ruby Lee / Many rivers to cross / Taking back the night / Honky tonk woman / Sticks and stones / Cry me a river / Please give peace a chance / She came in thru the bathroom window / Letter / Delta lady
5514082 / Nov '95 / Spectrum

☐ HAVE A LITTLE FAITH
Let the healing begin / Have a little faith in me / Simple things / Summer in the city / Great divide / Highway highway / Too cool / Soul time / Out of the blue / Angeline / Hell and high water / Standing knee deep in a river / Take me home
CDEST 2233 / Sep '97 / Capitol

☐ HITCHCOCK RAILWAY
JHD 030 / Jun '92 / Tring

☐ JOE COCKER LIVE
Feeling alright / Shelter me / Hitchcock railway / Up where we belong / Guilty / You can leave your hat on / When the night comes / Unchain my heart / With a little help from my friends / You are so beautiful / Letter / She came in through the bathroom window / High time we went / What are you doing with a fool like me / Living in the promised land
CDESTSP 25 / May '90 / Capitol

☐ LEGEND, THE ESSENTIAL COLLECTION
Up where we belong / With a little help from my friends / Delta lady / Letter / She came in through the bathroom window / Whiter shade of pale / Love the one you're with / You are so beautiful / Let it be / Just like a woman / Many rivers to cross / Talking back to the night / Fun time / I heard it through the grapevine / Please give peace a chance (live) / Don't let me be misunderstood / Honky tonk women / Cry me a river (live)
5154112 / Jun '92 / Polydor

☐ LONG VOYAGE HOME, THE (4CD Set)
With a little help from my friends / I'll cry instead / Those precious words / Marjorine / Bye bye blackbird / Just like a woman / Don't let me be misunderstood / Do I still figure in your life / Feelin' alright / I shall be released / I don't need no doctor / Let it be / Delta lady / She came in through the bathroom window / Hitchcock railway / Dear landlord / Darling be home soon / Something / Wake up little Susie / Letter / Space Captain / Cry me a river / Let's go get stoned / Please give peace a chance / Blue medley / Weight / High time we went / Black-eyed blues / Midnight rider / Woman to woman / Something to say / She don't mind / Pardon me Sir / Put out the light / I can stand a little rain / Moon is a harsh Mistress / You are so beautiful / Guilty / I think it's going to rain today / Jamaica say you will / Jealous kind / Catfish / Song for you / Fun time / I'm so glad I'm standing here today / Ruby Lee / Many rivers to cross / So good so right / Up where we belong / I love the night / Civilized man / Edge of a dream / You can leave your hat on / Unchain my heart / I've got to use my imagination / I'm your man / When the night comes / Can't find my way home / Don't let the sun go down on me / You've got to hide your love away / Love is alive / With a little help from my friends
5402362 / Dec '95 / A&M

☐ MAD DOGS AND ENGLISHMEN
Honky tonk women / Sticks and stones / Cry me a river / Bird on the wire / Feeling alright / Superstar / Let's go get stoned / I'll drown in my own tears / When something is wrong with my baby / I've been loving you too long / Girl from the North Country / Give peace a chance / She came in through the bathroom window / Space captain / Letter / Delta lady
3960022 / Jan '97 / A&M

☐ MIDNIGHT RIDER
WMCD 5701 / Oct '94 / Disky

☐ NIGHT CALLS
Feels like forever / I can hear the river / Now that the magic has gone / Unchain my heart (90's version) / Night calls / There's a storm coming / Can't find my way home / Don't let the sun go down on me / When the night comes / Five women / Love is alive / Please no more / Out of the rain / You've got to hide your love away / When a woman cries
CDESTU 2167 / Feb '92 / Capitol

☐ ON AIR (Cocker, Joe & The Grease Band)
Run shakers life / With a little help from my friends / Majorine / Change in Louise / Can't be so bad / Let's get stoned / That's your business / Delta lady / Hitchcocde highway / Lawdy Miss Clawdy / Darlin' be home soon / Hello little friend
SFRSCD 036 / Jul '97 / Strange Fruit

☐ ONE NIGHT OF SIN
When the night comes / I will live for you / I've got to use my imagination / Letting go / Just to keep from drowning / Unforgiven / Another mind gone / Fever / You know it's gonna hurt / Bad bad sign / I'm your man / One night
CDEST 2098 / Feb '94 / Capitol

☐ ORGANIC
Into the mystic / Bye bye blackbird / Delta lady / Heartful of rain / Don't let me be misunderstood / Many rivers to cross / High lonesome blue / Sail away / You and I / Darlin' be home soon / Dignity / You can leave your hat on / You are so beautiful / Can't find my way home
CDESTD 6 / Oct '96 / Parlophone

☐ SHEFFIELD STEEL
Look what you've done / Shocked / Seven days / Marie / Ruby Lee / Many rivers to cross / Talking back to the night / Just like always / Sweet little woman / So good, so right
IMCD 149 / Jul '92 / Island

☐ SIMPLY THE BEST
WMCD 5705 / Oct '94 / Disky

☐ UNCHAIN MY HEART
Unchain my heart / One / Two wrongs don't make a right / I stand in wonder / River's rising / Isolation / All our tomorrows / Woman loves a man / Trust in me / Satisfied / You can leave your hat on
CDEST 2045 / Aug '92 / Capitol

☐ VERY BEST OF JOE COCKER, THE (The Voice)
With a little help from my friends / Honky tonk women / Delta lady / Marjorine / Don't let me be misunderstood / Something / Pardon me sir / Talking back to the night / Up where we belong / She came in through the bathroom window / Letter / Just like a woman / Jamaica say you will / Cry me a river / Midnight rider / Let it be
BRCD 104 / Jun '94 / BR Music

Cockersdale

☐ BEEN AROUND FOR YEARS
FE 101CD / Jul '94 / Fellside

☐ WIDE OPEN SKIES
Tree song / Fit for heroes / Cuckoo / Poor old horse / Sykehouse Bridge / Ash and oak / Anderson's coast / Barratt's privateers / Auld fisher's farewell to the coquet / Us poor fellows / Long long road / Single handed / Death is not the end / Tortoises always come last / Pilgrim's way
FECD 123 / Sep '97 / Fellside

Cockney Rejects

☐ GREATEST HITS VOL.1
I'm not a fool / Headbanger / Bad man / Fighting in the streets / Shitter / Here they come again / Join the rejects / East End / New song / Police car / Someone like you / They're gonna put me away / Are you ready to ruck / Where the hell is Babylon / I'm forever blowing bubbles / West side boys
DOJOCD 136 / Feb '94 / Dojo

☐ GREATEST HITS VOL.2
War on the terraces / In the underworld / Oi oi oi / Hate of the city / With the boys / Urban guerilla / Rocker / Greatest cockney rip off / Sitting in a cell / On the waterfront / We can do anything / It's alright / Subculture / Blockbuster / Fifteen nights / We are the firm
DOJOCD 138 / Feb '94 / Dojo

☐ GREATEST HITS VOL.3 (Live & Loud)
Rocker / Bad man / I'm not a fool / On the waterfront / On the run / Hate of the city / Easy life / War on the terraces / Fighting in the streets / Greatest cockney rip off / Join the rejects / Police car / East end / Motorhead / Hang 'em high
DOJOCD 168 / Nov '93 / Dojo

☐ LETHAL
NEATCD 1049 / Jan '96 / Neat

☐ OI OI OI
Bad man / I'm not a fool / East end / I'm forever blowing bubbles / West side boys / War on the terraces / Oi oi oi / Rocker / We are the firm / We can do anything / Are you ready to ruck / Hate of the city / Where the hell is babylon / Flares n' slippers / Police car / I wanna be a star / Dead generation / Man's life in the army / Motorhead / Greatest cockney ripoff
CANCAN 005CD / 3 Nov '97 / Can Can

☐ POWER AND THE GLORY
Power and the glory / Because I'm in love / On the run / Lemon / Friends / Van Bollocks / Teenage fantasy / It's over / On the streets again / BYC / Greatest story ever told
DOJOCD 174 / Nov '93 / Dojo

☐ PUNK SINGLES COLLECTION
Flares 'n' slippers / Police car / I wanna be a star / I'm not a fool / East end / Bad man / New song / Greatest cockney rip off / Hate of the city / I'm forever blowing bubbles / West side boys / We can do anything / Nights / We are the firm / On the terraces / Easy life / Motorhead / Hang 'em high / On the streets again / Lomdob / Till the end of the day / Rock 'n' roll dream
CDPUNK 90 / Mar '97 / Anagram

☐ UNHEARD REJECTS/FLARES 'N' SLIPPERS
STEPCD 020 / 8 Jun '98 / Step 1

☐ WILD ONES/LETHAL
LOMACD 38 / Nov '94 / Loma

Coco & The Bean

☐ TALES FROM THE MOUSE HOUSE
Soul tones / Solid gold / Fair play / Poisoned / Weird world / Anytime / All star / Paradise / Versus the 90's / Plain sailing / Drifting
MNTCD 1003 / 27 Jul '98 / Mantra

Coco Steel & Lovebomb

☐ IT
WARPCD 24 / Aug '94 / Warp

☐ NEW WORLD
Great Ocean Road / Park Central / Pacific power / Press zero / On the beach / La Isla / Indurain / This is London / New world / Sun / Last call / Neon Madonna / On the beach / Pianopella
THECD 108 / Jul '97 / Other

Cocoa Brovaz

☐ RUDE AWAKENING
Game of life / Bucktown USA / Still standin' strong / Off the wall / Won on won / Black trump / Money talks / Back 2 life / Cash / Dry snitch / Myah angelow / Spanish Harlem / Memorial / Hold it down / Blown away / What they call him / Live at the garden
CDPTY 150 / 20 Apr '98 / Priority/Virgin

Cocoa T

☐ CAN'T LIVE SO
SHCD 45016 / May '94 / Shanachie

☐ COME LOVE ME
VPCD 1395 / Feb '95 / VP

☐ I AM THE TOUGHEST
JAMCD 10 / 18 May '98 / Jammy's

☐ ISRAEL KING
KPCRCD 61 / Jan '97 / Charm

☐ KINGSTON HOT
GRELCD 174 / Nov '92 / Greensleeves

☐ LOVE ME
DBTXCD 1 / Mar '95 / Digital B

☐ ONE UP
Africa here I come / If it's not you / Yard away home / One up / Stop your nagging / Grow your locks / Virus / Mr. Fisherman / Earthquake / I put my trust in Jah / Grow your locks / Getting closer / Beware
GRELCD 187 / Sep '93 / Greensleeves

☐ ONE WAY
EXCD 11 / 20 Jul '98 / Exterminator

☐ RAS PORTRAITS
Rocking dolly / Bust outta hell / Gotta know rastafari / Jah made them that way / Kingston hot / Dancehall night / I lost my soul / Pose up / I'm going home / Louisiana / No wanted man
RAS 3324 / Jul '97 / Ras

☐ RIKERS ISLAND
One woman show / Fool in love / We must be free / Move up / Bad bwoy / Riker's island / Keep on doing it / Babylon get rude / More than just a lover / Hunting in the ghetto / Me no like rikers island
GRELCD 156 / Dec '90 / Greensleeves

☐ SWEET LOVE
RASCD 3161 / Mar '95 / Ras

☐ TUNE IN
Tune in / Mek dem a gwaan so / Love me truly / Good life / Don't you burn / She loves me now / Over the years / Caan touch dis / Sinner burning / Hot sweet cocoa tea / Criminality / 18 and over / Don't turn it off / Heads of government / Too young
GRELCD 200 / May '94 / Greensleeves

Coctails

☐ COCTAILS, THE
EFA 121182 / Mar '96 / Moll

☐ LIVE AT LOUNGE AX
SAKI 013 / Jul '97 / Carrot Top

☐ PEEL
EFA 121142 / Aug '95 / Moll

Cocteau Twins

☐ BLUE BELL KNOLL
Blue bell knoll / Athol brose / Carolyn's fingers / For Phoebe still a baby / Itchy Glowbo / Cico buff / Suckling The Mender / Spooning good singing gum / Kissed out red floatboat / Ella megalast burls forever
CAD 807CD / Sep '88 / 4AD

☐ FOUR CALENDAR CAFE
Know who you are at every age / Evangeline / Bluebeard / Theft, and wandering around lost / Oil of angels / Squeeze-wax / My truth / Essence / Summerhead / Pur
5182592 / Oct '93 / Fontana

☐ GARLANDS
Blood bitch / Wax and wane / But I'm not / Blind dumb deaf / Gail overfloweth / Shallow than hallow / Hollow men / Garlands
CAD 211 CD / '86 / 4AD

☐ HEAD OVER HEELS
When mama was moth / Sugar hiccup / In our angelhood / Glass candle grenades / Multifoiled / In the gold dust rush / Tinderbox, The (of a heart) / My love paramour / Musette and drums / Five ten fiftyfold
CAD 313 CD / '86 / 4AD

☐ HEAVEN OR LAS VEGAS
Cherry coloured funk / Pitch the baby / Iceblink luck / Fifty fifty clown / Heaven or Las Vegas / I wear your ring / Fotzepolitic / Wolf in the breast / River, road and rail / Frou-frou foxes in the midsummer fires
CAD 0012 CD / Sep '90 / 4AD

☐ MILK AND KISSES
Violaine / Serpentskirt / Tishbite / Half gifts / Calfskin smack / Rilkean heart / Ups / Eperdu / Treasure hiding / Seekers who are lovers
5145012
5323632 / Apr '96 / Fontana

☐ PINK OPAQUE
Spangle maker / Milimilenary / Wax and wane / Hitherto / Pearly dewdrops drops / From the flagstones / Aikea-guinea / Lorelel / Pepper tree / Musette and drums
CAD 513 CD / Jan '86 / 4AD

☐ TINY DYNAMITE/ECHOES IN A SHALLOW BAY
BAD 510/511 CD / Oct '86 / 4AD

☐ TREASURE
Ivo / Lorelei / Beatrix / Persephone / Pandora - for Cindy / Amelia / Aloysius / Cicely / Otterley / Donimo
CAD 412 CD / '86 / 4AD

☐ VICTORIA LAND
Lazy calm / Fluffy tufts / Throughout the dark months of April and May / Whales tales / Oomingmac / Little spacey / Feet-like fins / How to bring a blush to the snow / Thinner the air
CAD 602 CD / '86 / 4AD

Code Indigo

☐ FOR WHOM THE BELL
For whom the bell
AD 16CD / Dec '96 / AD

Codeine

☐ WHITE BIRCH, THE
SPCD 118299 / May '94 / Sub Pop

Codona

☐ CODONA VOL.1
Like that of sky / Codona / Colemanwonder: race face, sortie, Sir Duke / Mumakata / New light
8293712 / '90 / ECM

☐ CODONA VOL.2
Que faser / Godumaduma / Malinye / Drip dry / Walking on eggs / Again and again, again
8333322 / Jul '88 / ECM

☐ CODONA VOL.3
Goshakabuch / Hey da ba doom / Travel by night / Trayra boia / Clicky clacky / Inner organs
8274202 / Feb '86 / ECM

Cody, Robert Tree

☐ WHITE BUFFALO
CRCD 555 / Mar '96 / Canyon

Coe, David Allan

☐ COMPASS POINT/I'VE GOT SOMETHING TO SAY
Heads or tails / Three times loser / Gone (like) / Honey don't / Lost Merle and me / Loving her (will make you lose your mind) / Fish aren't bitin' today / X's and O's (kisses and hugs) / I've got something to say / Back to Atlanta / I could never give you up (for someone else) / Take it easy rider / Great Nashville railroad disaster / Hank Williams Junior Junior / Get a little dirt on my hands / If you hold the ladder (I'll climb to) / This bottle (in my hand) / Take this job and shove it too / Lovin' you comes so natural
BCD 15841 / Mar '95 / Bear Family

☐ HUMAN EMOTIONS/SPECTRUM VII
Would you lay with me (in a field of stone) / If this is just a game / You can count on me / Mississippi river queen / Tomrrow is another day / Human emotions / Love's cheatin' line / Whiskey and women / Jack Daniels if you please / Suicide / Rollin' with the punches / On my feet again / Fall in love with you / What can I do / Sudden death / Fairytale morning / Seven mile bridge / Now's the time / Love is just a porpoise / Please come back to Boston
BCD 15840 / Mar '95 / Bear Family

☐ INVICTUS (MEANS) UNCONQUERED/ TENNESSE WHISKEY
Rose knows / Ain't it funny / Way love can do ya / If you ever think of me / Purple heart / London homesick blues / Stand by your man / As far as this feeling will take us / Someplace to come when it rains / Best game in town / I love robbing banks / Tennessee whiskey / I knew I've given bout all I can take / Pledging my love / I'll always be a fool for you / (Sittin' on the) dock of the bay / Juanita / We've got a bad thing goin' / D-R-U-N-K / Little orphan Annie / Bright morning light
BCD 15842 / Mar '95 / Bear Family

☐ LONGHAIRED REDNECK/ RIDES AGAIN
Long haired redneck / When she's got me (Where she wants me) / Revenge / Texas lullaby / Living on the run / Family reunion / Rock 'n' roll holiday / Free born rambling man / Spotlight / Dakota the dancing bear, Part 2 / Willie, Waylon and me / House we've been calling home / Young Dallas cowboy / Sense of humour / Pumkin certer barn dance / Willie, Waylon and Me (Reprise) / Lately I've been thinking too much lately / Laid back and wasted / Under Rachel's wings / Greener than the grass we laid on / If that ain't country
BCD 15707 / Mar '93 / Bear Family

☐ MYSTERIOUS RHINESTONE COWBOY, THE/ ONCE UPON A RHYME
Sad country song / Crazy Mary / River / 33rd of August / Bossier city / Atlanta song / Old men tell me / Desperados waiting for the train / I still sing the old songs / Old grey goose is dead / Would you lay with me (In a field of stone) / Jody like a melody / Loneliness in Ruby's eyes / Would you be my lady / Sweet vibrations / Another pretty country song / Piece of wood and steel / Fraulein / Shine it on / You never even called me by my name
BCD 15706 / Mar '93 / Bear Family

☐ TATTOO/FAMILY ALBUM
Just to prove my love for you / Face to face / You'll always live inside of me / Play me a sad song / Daddy was a god fearin' man / Canteen of water / Maria is a mystery / Just in time / San Francisco Mabel Joy / Hey gypsy / Family album / Million dollar memories / Divers do it deeper / Guilty footsteps / Take this job and shove it / Houston, Dallas, San Antone / I've got to have you / Whole lot of lonesome / Bad impressions / Heavenly Father, Holy Mother
BCD 15839 / Mar '95 / Bear Family

Coe, Pete

☐ LONG COMPANY
Bring the new year in / Across the Western ocean / Fireman's song / East Boldon/Ann Frazer MacKenzie / PR man from hell / Juniper, gentle and rosemary / What's it worth / William Taylor / As I roved out / Kings and Queens of England / I courted a wee girl / None so steady / Barleycorn / We'll have a May day / Bill Hall's no.1 and no.2
BASHCD 45 / May '97 / Backshift

Coe, Tony

☐ BLUE JERSEY (Live At The 10th Jersey Jazz Festival) (Coe, Tony & Horler/ Ganley/Horler/Creese)
I got rhythm / Three / You stepped out of a dream / Solid silver / What is this thing called love / Blue Jersey / Chrissie / This heart of mine / Royal blues
ABCD 4 / Oct '96 / AB

☐ CANTERBURY SONG
Canterbury song / How beautiful is the night / Light blue / Sometime ago / Re: person I knew / I guess I'll hang my tears out to dry / Lagos / Blue in green
HHCD 1005 / Jun '89 / Hot House

☐ DAYS OF WINE AND ROSES (Coe, Tony & Alan Barnes)
Who cares / Deep in a dream / Oh lady be good / Chilli pepper / Too late now / Flamingo / My old flame / Days of wine and roses / How high the moon / I guess I'll have to change my mind / Blue room / Applecore
ZECD 22 / 5 May '98 / Zephyr

☐ IN CONCERT (Coe, Tony & John Horler/ Malcolm Creese)
Waltz / Blue Rose / Person I knew / Dearly beloved / Body and soul / You stepped out of a dream / Minor dance
ABCD 6 / Jul '98 / ABCD

☐ JAZZPAR 1995 (Coe, Tony & Bob Brookmeyer)
STCD 4206 / May '96 / Storyville

☐ RUBY (Coe, Tony Quartet)
With a song in my heart / My shining hour / Come rain or shine / More than you know / Love walked in / I didn't know what time it was / Prologue / Some other Autumn / Backward tracings / Ruby
ZZCD 9802 / 8 Jun '98 / Zah Zah

☐ SOME OTHER AUTUMN
Aristotle blues / Some other autumn / Line up blues / Body and soul / Reka / Together / Regrets / Perdido / When your lover has gone / In a mellow tone / UMMG
HEPCD 2037 / Jan '96 / Hep

Coen, Jack

☐ BRANCH LINE, THE (Irish Traditional Music From Galway to New York) (Coen, Jack & Charlie)
Scatter the mud / Larry Redigan's jig / Sailor's cravat / Repeal of the union / John Conroy's jig / Peach blossom / Fiddler's contest / Jim Conroy's reel / Pullet / Redican's mother / Humours of Kilkenny / Mike Coen's polka / Branch line / Have a drink with me / Blarney pilgrim / Two woodford flings / Waddling gander / O'Connell's jig on top of Mount Everest / Lads of Laois / Green groves of Erin / Tongs by the fire / Spinning wheel / Whelan's reel / Jenny dang the weaver / Jack Coen's jig / Paddy O'Brien's jig
GLCD 3067 / Oct '93 / Green Linnet

☐ WARMING UP (Coen, Jack/Martin Mulhaire/Seamus Connolly)
GL 1135CD / Mar '94 / Green Linnet

Coex

☐ ASCENTS METEORA
Soul fragments / Interlude / Two figures / Drance / Ascents meteora / Dark
DNDC 010CD / Jul '97 / De Nova Da Capo

☐ SYNAESTHESIA
DNDC 004CD / Oct '96 / De Nova Da Capo

Coffee Sergeants

☐ MOONLIGHT TOWERS
DJD 3204 / May '94 / Dejadisc

Coffin Nails

☐ FISTFUL OF BURGERS
GREYCD 01 / May '96 / Greystone

☐ WRECKERS YARD
GREYCD 02 / Dec '96 / Greystone

Cogan, Alma

☐ ALMA
Let her go / Trains and boats and planes / Ticket to ride / I get a kick out of you / There's a time and a place / Eight days a week / Yesterday / I feel fine / Jolly good company / More / Don't you know Yockomo / Now that I've found you
DORIG 109 / 1 Sep '97 / EMI

☐ EMI PRESENTS THE MAGIC OF ALMA COGAN
Bell bottom blues / This old house / I can't tell a waltz from a tango / Dreamboat / Banjo's back in town / Go on by / Twenty tiny fingers / Never do a tango with an eskimo / Willie can / Birds and the bees / Why do fools fall in love / In the middle of the house / You, me and us / Whatever Lolo wants / Just couldn't resist her with her pocket transistor / Story of my life / Sugartime / Cheek to cheek / Last night on the back porch / We got love / Dream talk / Train of love / Cowboy Jimmie Joe / When I fall in love
CDMFP 6290 / May '97 / Music For Pleasure

☐ EMI YEARS, THE
You, me and us / Bell bottom blues / Mambo Italiano / Got 'n idea / Last night on the back porch / It's all been done before: *Cogan, Alma & Ronnie Hilton* / Lucky lips / Fly away lovers / Little shoemaker / Chiqu chaqui / I can't tell a waltz from a tango / Ricochet / I love you bit: *Cogan, Alma & Lionel Bart* / Never do a tango with an eskimo / Little things mean a lot / Gettin' ready for Freddy / Mama says / Dreamboat / Said the little moment / In the middle of the house
CDEMS 1378 / Jan '91 / EMI

☐ HOUR OF ALMA COGAN, AN
To be worthy of you / Till I waltz again with you / Till they've all gone home / Bell bottom blues / Jilted / Canoodlin / Rag / This ole house / I can't tell a waltz from a tango / (Don't let the) Kiddygeddin / Softly, softly / Dreamboat / Willie can / Lizzie Borden / Birds and the bees / Why do fools fall in love / Whatever Lola wants (Lola gets) / Cahntez, chantez / Fabulous / Party time / Please Mr. Brown / Sugartime / Sorry, sorry, sorry / Pink shoelaces / We got love / Train of love / Just couldn't resist her with her pocket transistor
CC 8240 / Nov '94 / EMI

Cohen, Adam

☐ ADAM COHEN
Tell me everything / Cry ophelia / Don't mean anything / This pain / Quarterback / Sister / Beautiful as you / How the mighty have fallen / Opposites attract / Down she goes / Amazing / It's alright
4887032 / 3 Aug '98 / Columbia

Cohen, Avishai

☐ ADAMA
Ora / Madrid / Bass suite / Reunion of the souls / Dror / No change / Bass and bone fantasy / Adama / Bass suite / Besame mucho / Gadu / Jasonity
SCD 90152 / 6 Apr '98 / Stretch

Cohen, Ben

☐ JAZZ LIPS (Cohen, Ben Hot Five & Hot Seven)
PKCD 057 / Jan '97 / PEK

Cohen, Danny

☐ SELF INDULGENT MUSIC (Cohen, Danny & Mike Boner/Horse Cock Kids)
TZA 7403 / 27 Apr '98 / Tzadik

Cohen, Greg

☐ MOMENT TO MOMENT
DIW 928 / Mar '98 / DIW

☐ WAY LOW
DIW 918 / Jan '97 / DIW

Cohen, Leonard

☐ COHEN LIVE
Dance me to the end of love / Bird on the wire / Everybody knows / Loan of arc / There is a war / Sisters of mercy / Hallelujah / I'm your man / Who by fire / One of us cannot be wrong / If it be your will / Heart with no companion / Suzanne
4771712 / Aug '94 / Columbia

☐ **FUTURE, THE**
Future / Waiting for the miracle / Be for real / Closing time / Anthem / Democracy / Light as the breeze / Always / Tacoma trailer
4724982 / Nov '92 / Columbia

☐ **GREATEST HITS**
Suzanne / Sisters of mercy / So long, Marianne / Bird on the wire / Lady Midnight / Partisan / Hey, that's no way to say goodbye / Famous blue raincoat / Last year's man / Chelsea Hotel no.2 / Who by fire / Take this longing
CD 32644 / 27 Jul '98 / Columbia

☐ **I'M YOUR FAN (The Songs Of Leonard Cohen) (Various Artists)**
Who by fire: *House Of Love* / Hey, that's no way to say goodbye: *McCulloch, Ian* / I can't forget: *Pixies* / Stories of the street: *That Petrol Emotion* / Bird on the wire: *Lilac Time* / Suzanne: *Oryema, Geoffrey* / So long, Marianne: *James* / Avalanche IV: *Murat* / Don't go home with your hard-on: *McComb, David & Adam Peters* / First we take Manhattan: *REM* / Chelsea hotel: *Cole, Lloyd* / Tower of song: *Forster, Robert* / Take this longing: *Astor, Peter* / True love leaves no traces: *Dead Famous People* / I'm your man: *Pritchard, Bill* / Singer must die: *Fatima Mansions* / Hallelujah: *Cale, John* / Tower of song: *Cave, Nick & The Bad Seeds*
9031755982 / Sep '91 / East West

☐ **I'M YOUR MAN**
First we take Manhattan / Ain't no cure for love / Everybody knows / I'm your man / Take this waltz / Jazz police / I can't forget / Tower of song
4606422 / Feb '88 / Columbia

☐ **LIVE SONGS**
Minute prologue / Passing through / You know who I am / Bird on the wire / Nancy / Improvisation / Story of Isaac / Please don't pass me by (a disgrace) / Tonight will be fine / Queen Victoria
4844542 / Feb '97 / Columbia

☐ **MORE BEST OF LEONARD COHEN**
Everybody knows / I'm your man / Take this waltz / Tower of song / Anthem / Democracy / Future / Closing time / Dance me to the end of love / Suzanne / Hallelujah / Never any good / Great event
4882372 / 6 Oct '97 / Columbia

☐ **NEW SKIN FOR OLD CEREMONY**
Is this what you wanted / Chelsea Hotel no.2 / Lover lover lover / Field Commander Cohen / Why don't you try / There is a war / Singer must die / I tried to leave you / Leaving green sleeves / Who by fire / Take this longing
CD 32660 / Mar '96 / Columbia

☐ **RECENT SONGS**
Guests / Humbled in love / Window / Came so far for beauty / Lost Canadian (Un Canadien errant) / Traitor / Our lady of solitude / Gypsy's wife / Smoky life / Ballad of the absent mare
4747502 / Apr '94 / Columbia

☐ **SO LONG, MARIANNE**
Who by fire / So long, Marianne / Chelsea Hotel no.2 / Lady midnight / Sisters of mercy / Bird on the wire / Suzanne / Lover lover lover / Winter lady / Tonight will be fire / Partisan / Diamonds in the mine
4605002 / Oct '95 / Columbia

☐ **SONGS FROM A ROOM**
Bird on the wire / Story of Isaac / Bunch of lonesome heroes / Seems so long ago / Nancy / Old revolution / Butcher / You know who I am / Lady Midnight / Tonight will be fine
32072 / May '90 / Columbia

☐ **SONGS FROM A ROOM/SONGS OF LOVE AND HATE (2CD Set)**
Bird on the wire / Story of Isaac / Bunch of lonesome heroes / Seems so long ago / Nancy / Old revolution / Butcher / You know who I am / Lady Midnight / Tonight will be fine / Avalanche / Last year's man / Dress rehearsal rag / Diamonds in the mine / Love calls you by your name / Famous blue raincoat / Sing another song / Boys / Joan of Arc
4784802 / Mar '95 / Columbia

☐ **SONGS OF LEONARD COHEN, THE**
Suzanne / Master song / Winter lady / Stranger song / Sisters of mercy / So long, Marianne / Hey, that's no way to say goodbye / Stories of the street teachers / One of us cannot be wrong
4686002 / Oct '91 / Columbia

☐ **SONGS OF LOVE AND HATE**
Avalanche / Last year's man / Dress rehearsal rag / Diamonds in the mine / Love calls you by your name / Famous blue raincoat / Sing another song boys / Joan of Arc
4767992 / May '94 / Columbia

☐ **TOWER OF SONG (The Songs Of Leonard Cohen) (Various Artists)**
Everybody knows: *Henley, Don* / Coming back to you: *Yearwood, Trisha* / Sisters of mercy: *Sting & The Chieftains* / Hallelujah: *Bono* / Famous blue raincoat: *Amos, Tori* / Ain't no cure for love: *Neville, Aaron* / I'm your man: *John, Elton* / Bird on a wire: *Nelson, Willie* / Suzanne: *Gabriel, Peter* / Light as the breeze: *Joel, Billy* / If it be your will: *Arden, Jann* / Story of Isaac: *Vega, Suzanne*
5402592 / 15 Sep '97 / A&M

☐ **VARIOUS POSITIONS**
Dance me to the end of love / Coming back to you / Law / Night comes on / Hallelujah / Captain / Hunter's lullaby / Heart with no companion / If it be your will
4655692 / Nov '89 / Columbia

Cohen, Porky

☐ **RHYTHM AND BONES**
CDBB 9572 / Aug '96 / Bullseye Blues

Cohn, Al

☐ **AL AND ZOOT (Cohn, Al Quintet & Zoot Sims)**
It's a wonderful world / Brandy and beer / Two funky people / Chasing the blues / Halley's comet / You're a lucky guy / Wailing boat / Just you, just me
GRP 18272 / 27 Jul '98 / Chess Mates

☐ **BODY AND SOUL (Cohn, Al & Zoot Sims)**
MCD 5356 / Sep '92 / Muse

☐ **COHN'S TONES**
Groovin' with Gus / Infinity / How long has this been going on / Let's get away from it all / Ah Moore / Jane Street / I'm tellin' ya / That's what you think
SV 0187 / Oct '97 / Savoy Jazz

☐ **JAZZ ALIVE (Cohn, Al & Zoot Sims)**
Lover come back / It had to be you / Wee dot / After you've gone
4941052 / 22 Jun '98 / Pacific Jazz

☐ **KEEPER OF THE FLAME (Cohn, Al & The Jazz Seven)**
Bilbo baggins / Mood indigo / Casa 50 / Keeper of the flame / High on you / Feel more like I do now
JHCD 022 / Jan '94 / Ronnie Scott's Jazz House

☐ **NONPAREIL**
Take four / Unless it's you / El Cajon / Raincheck / Mr. George / Girl from Ipanema / This is new / Blue hodge / Expense account
CCD 4155 / Nov '92 / Concord Jazz

☐ **OVERTONES**
P-Town / Woody's lament / High on you / I love you / Vignette / Pensive / I don't want anybody at all / Let's be buddies
CCD 4194 / Nov '96 / Concord Jazz

☐ **PROGRESSIVE AL COHN, THE**
Infinity / Groovin' with Gus / How long has this been going on / Let's get away from it all / That's what you think / I'm tellin' ya / Jane Street / Ah-moore / That's what you think (master)
SV 0249 / Oct '97 / Savoy Jazz

☐ **SKYLARK (2CD Set)**
You stepped out of a dream / Woody's lament / America the beautiful / Lover man / Skylark / What is this thing called love / Tune / I love you / Do nothin' 'til you hear from me / Fred / Sophisticated lady / Danielle / Girl from Ipanema / Tickle toe
JLR 103606 / May '96 / Live At EJ's

☐ **TOUR DE FORCE (Cohn, Al & Scott Hamilton/Buddy Tate)**
Blues up and down / Tickle toe / Let's get away from it all / Soft winds / Stella by starlight / Broadway / Do nothin' 'til you hear from me / Jumpin' at the woodside / Bernie's tune / Rifftide / If
CCD 4172 / Aug '90 / Concord Jazz

Cohn, Marc

☐ **BURNING THE DAZE**
Already home / Girl of mysterious sorrow / Providence / Healing hands / Lost you in the canyon / Saints preserve us / Olana / Turn to me / Valley of the kings / Turn on your radio / Ellis island
7567829092 / 16 Mar '98 / Atlantic

☐ **MARC COHN**
Walking in Memphis / Ghost train / Silver Thunderbird / Dig down deep / Walk on water / Miles away / Saving the best for last / Strangers in a car / Twenty nine ways / Perfect love / True companion
7567821782 / Apr '91 / Atlantic

☐ **RAINY SEASON, THE**
Walk through the world / Rest for the weary / Rainy season / Mama's in the moon / Don't talk to her at night / Paper walls / From the station / Medicine man / Baby king / She's becoming gold / Things we've handed down
7567824912 / Feb '95 / Atlantic

Cohn, Steve

☐ **ITTEKIMASU**
ITM 970059 / Apr '91 / ITM

Coil

☐ **ANGELIC CONVERSATION**
LOCICD 6 / Oct '96 / Threshold House

☐ **BLACK LIGHT DISTRICT**
ESKATON 8 / Oct '96 / Threshold House

☐ **GOLD IS THE METAL**
NORMAL 77 / May '94 / Normal
LOCICD 11 / Oct '96 / Threshold House

☐ **HELLRAISER**
COILCD 001 / Feb '89 / Solar Lodge

☐ **HOW TO DESTROY ANGELS**
LOCICD 5 / Oct '96 / Threshold House

☐ **STOLEN AND CONTAMINATED**
LOCICD 4 / Oct '96 / Threshold House

☐ **TIME MACHINES**
Telepathine / DOET/Hectate / 5 MeO DMT / Dimethylamino / Psilocybin
ESKATON 10 / Jan '98 / Threshold House

☐ **TRANSPARENT (Coil & Zoskia)**
Sicktone / Baptism of fire / Rape / Poisons / Truth / Sewn open / Silence et secrecy / Here to here (double headed secret) / Stealing the words / On balance
LOCICD 13 / Oct '97 / Threshold House

☐ **UNNATURAL HISTORY VOL.1**
LOCICD 2 / Jan '89 / Threshold House

☐ **UNNATURAL HISTORY VOL.2**
LOCICD 10 / Oct '96 / Threshold House

☐ **UNNATURAL HISTORY VOL.3 (Joyful Participation In The Sorrows Of The World)**
First dark ride / Baby food / Music for commercials / Panic / Neither his nor yours / Feeder / Wrong eye / Meaning what exactly / Scope / Lost rivers of London
LOCICD 12 / Jul '97 / Threshold House

☐ **WINDOW PANE/THE SNOW**
LOCICD 7 / Oct '96 / Threshold House

Coila

☐ **GET REEL**
Jigs / Hornpipes / Hoedown / Slow air / Reel / Gaelic waltzes / Jig / Reels / Slow air / Pipe hornpipe and 6/8 marches / Waltzes / Jigs / Pipe reels
LCOM 5258 / May '97 / Lismor

Coinneach

☐ **ICE TREES AND LULLABIES**
CDLDL 1280 / 14 Aug '98 / Lochshore

☐ **LIFE IN A SCOTTISH GREENHOUSE**
How many battles / (Life in a) Scottish greenhouse / Rhythm method / No time to cry / Gloomy summer / Energy rising / Coinneach / Sound of the sound / Animal song / Phantom fiddler
CDLDL 1254 / Mar '97 / Lochshore

Cojazz

☐ **COJAZZ PLUS (Cojazz & Alice Day)**
Sometimes I'm happy / Mr. Ugly / Never make your move too soon / Mascarade is over / Man I love / Harbor bridge / What a wonderful world / Black coffee / Milestones
TCB 96052 / Apr '96 / TCB

Colaiuta, Vinnie

☐ **VINNIE COLAIUTA**
I'm tweeked / Attack of the 20lb pizza / Private earthquake: Error 7 / Chauncey / John's blues / Slink / Darlene's song / Momoska (dub mix) / Bruce Lee / If one was one
SCD 90072 / Mar '97 / Stretch

Colcannon

☐ **LIFE OF RILEY'S BROTHER**
ORP 401CD / Aug '96 / Oxford Road

Colclough, Phil

☐ **PLAYERS FROM A DRAMA (Colclough, Phil & June)**
CMCD 060 / '91 / Celtic Music

Cold

☐ **COLD**
Go away / Give / Ugly / Everyone dies / Strip her down / Insane / Goodbye cruel world / Serial killer / Superstar / Switch / Make her sick
5408292 / 2 Feb '98 / A&M

Cold Cold Hearts

☐ **COLD COLD HEARTS**
KRS 287CD / Apr '97 / Kill Rock Stars

Coldcut

☐ **COLD KRUSH CUTS (Coldcut & DJ Food)**
TFCK 87910 / Jun '97 / Toys Factory

☐ **JOURNEYS BY DJ VOL.8**
JDJCD 8 / Oct '95 / JDJ

☐ **LET US PLAY (CD/CD-ROM Set)**
Return to the margin / Atomic moog / More beats and pieces / Rubaiyat / Pan opticon / Music for no musicians / Noah's toilet / Space journey / Timber / Every home a prison / Cloned again / I'm wild about that thing / Playtime / My little funkit / Coldcut's A-Z / Pic pump / Coldcut infobum videosyncrasy
ZENCD 030 / Sep '97 / Ninja Tune

Coldstream Guards

☐ **LONDON SALUTE**
London salute / State procession / Cockney lover / Bank holiday / Westminster waltz / Birdcage walk / Clarinet on the town / Royal windsor / Covent garden / Knightsbridge march / Nightingale sang in Berkley Square / Cockney cocktail / Foggy day in Camden town / Overture 'Cockaigne (In London town) / March finale / Boys in the old brigade / When the guards are on parade / Coldstream march 'Milanollo
BNA 5119 / 15 Jun '98 / Bandleader

☐ **MUSIC OF ANDREW LLOYD WEBBER (Coldstream Guards Band)**
Phantom of the opera / Think of me / All I ask of you / Music of the night / Pie Jesu / Hosanna / Cats overture / Skimbleshanks the railway cat / Old gumbie cat / Macavity / Memory / I am the starlight / Engine of love / Only you / Race is on / Make up my heart / Light at the end of the tunnel / Starlight express / I'm very you / You're very me / Capped teeth and Caesar salad / Tell me on a Sunday / Take that look off your face / Variations 1-4 / Andrew Lloyd Webber - Symphonic Study
BNA 5025 / '88 / Bandleader

☐ **OUT THE ESCORT (Coldstream Guards Band)**
BNA 5052 / Feb '92 / Bandleader

☐ **TROOPING THE COLOUR (Coldstream Guards Massed Bands)**
Royal salute/God save the Queen / King William IV / Melodies from the North / Les Hugenots / Third battalion / Escort for the colour / Grenadiers march / Medley / Liberton pipe band / Long live Elizabeth / Regimental slow march of the Royal Horse Guards / Regimental slow march of the Life Guards / To your guard / God save the Queen
SUMCD 4072 / Nov '96 / Summit

Cole, B.J.

☐ **HEART OF THE MOMENT**
In at the deep end / Icarus enigma / Eastern cool / Indian willow / Three piece suite / Sands of time / Promenade and arabesque / Kraken wakes / Forever amber / Adagio in blue
RES 107CD / Apr '97 / Resurgence

☐ **TRANSPARENT MUSIC**
Clair de lune / Window on the deep / Satie's gnossienne no 5 / Slight rhapsody / Coventry carol / Sun tear serenade / Ely cathedral / Ravel's pavanne / Satie's gnossien no 3
HNCD 1325 / May '89 / Hannibal

Cole, Bobby

☐ **DANCE-DANCE-DANCE**
Diana / Thorn birds / Look for the silver lining / Music maestro please / Whispering / On Mother Kelly's doorstep / Rock-a-bye your baby with a Dixie melody / Don't bring Lulu / Put your arms around me honey / My blue Heaven / Bring me sunshine / Sheikh of Araby / Powder your face with sunshine / Memories / For ever and ever / I'm always chasing rainbows / Something tells me / All my loving / Hey Jude / I love Paris / Serenata / Melancholy baby / Sleepy time gal
SAV 187CD / May '93 / Savoy

Cole, Cozy

☐ **CLASSICS 1944**
CLASSICS 819 / May '95 / Classics

☐ **CLASSICS 1944-1945**
CLASSICS 865 / Mar '96 / Classics

Cole, Freddy

☐ **CIRCLE OF LOVE, A**
You're nice to be around / Manha de carnaval / They didn't believe me / How little we know / I wonder who my Daddy is / Circle of love / Never let me go / All too soon / If I had you / Angel eyes / Temptation / September morn
FCD 967 / Jun '96 / Fantasy

☐ **I'M NOT MY BROTHER, I'M ME**
SSC 1054D / Jan '92 / Sunnyside

☐ **LIVE AT BIRDLAND WEST**
My hat's the size of my head / I almost lost my mind / Am I blue / Pretend / Walkin' my baby back home / This heart of mine / Send for me / Somewhere along the way / Ballerina / I'm not my brother, I'm me / He was the king / Copacabana triple
17015 / Dec '95 / Laserlight

☐ **LOVE MAKES THE CHANGES**
Love makes the changes / On my way to you / Wonder why / Right to love / Alone with my thoughts of you / Sinner kissed an angel / Brother where are you / Do you know why / Just the way you are / Like a quiet storm
FCD 96812 / Aug '98 / Fantasy

☐ **TO THE ENDS OF THE EARTH**
To the ends of the Earth / I didn't mean to love you / In the still of the night / Candy / For all we know / I'll buy you a star / You don't have to say you're sorry / One at a time / Once you've been in love / Love walked in / Should've been / I'll be seeing you / Two for the road / Close enough for love
FCD 9675 / Jun '97 / Fantasy

Cole, Holly

☐ **BLAME IT ON MY YOUTH (Cole, Holly Trio)**
Trust in me / I'm gonna laugh you right out of my life / If I were a bell / Smile / Purple Avenue / Calling you / God will / On the street where you live / Honeysuckle rose
CDP 7973492 / Feb '97 / Metro Blue

☐ **DARK DEAR HEART**
I've just seen a face / Make it go away / Onion girl / Dark dear heart / You want more / Timbuktu / World seems to come and go / River / Hold on / Brighter lonely day / I told him that my dog wouldn't run / All the pretty little horses
8573652 / 3 Nov '97 / Metro Blue

☐ **DON'T SMOKE IN BED (Cole, Holly Trio)**
I can see clearly now / Don't let the teardrops rust your shining heart / Get out of town / So and so / Tennessee waltz / Everyday will be like a holiday / Blame it on youth / Ev'rything I've got / Je ne t'aime pas / Cry (if you want to) / Whatever will be will be (Que sera sera) / Don't smoke in bed
CDP 7811982 / Feb '97 / Metro Blue

☐ **IT HAPPENED ONE DAY**
Get out of town / Cry (If you want to) / Train song / Losing my mind / Tango til they're sore / Don't let the teardrops rust your shining heart / Whatever will be will be (Que sera sera) / Calling you
CDP 8526990 / Nov '96 / Metro Blue

☐ **TEMPTATION**
Take me home / Train song / Jersey girl / Temptation / Falling down / Invitation to the blues / Cinny's waltz / Frank's theme / Little boy blue / I don't wanna grow up / Tango 'til they're sore / Looking for the heart of Saturday night / Soldier's things / I want you / Good old world / Briar and the rose / Shiver me timbers
CDP 8343482 / Sep '95 / Capitol Jazz

Cole, Lloyd

☐ **BAD VIBES**
Morning is broken / So you'd like to save the world / Holier than thou / Love you so what / Wild mushrooms / My way to you / Too much of a good thing / Fall together / Mr. Wrong / Seen the future / Can't get arrested
5183182 / Oct '93 / Fontana

☐ **DON'T GET WEIRD ON ME BABE**
Butterfly / There for her / Margo's waltz / Half of everything / Man enough / What he doesn't know / Tell your sister / Weeping wine / To the lions / Pay for it / One you never had / She's a girl and I'm a man
5110932 / Mar '96 / Polydor

☐ **EASY PIECES (Cole, Lloyd & The Commotions)**
Rich / Why I love country music / Pretty gone / Grace / Cut me down / Brand new friend / Lost weekend / James / Minor character / Perfect blue / Her last fling / Big world / Nevers end
8276702 / Mar '96 / Polydor

☐ **LOVE STORY**
Trigger happy / Sentimental fool / I didn't know that you cared / Love ruins everything / Baby / Be there / June bride / Like lovers do / Happy for you / Traffic / Let's get lost / For crying out loud
5285292 / 15 Sep '97 / Fontana

☐ **MAINSTREAM (Cole, Lloyd & The Commotions)**
My bag / Twenty nine / Mainstream / Jennifer she said / Mr. Malcontent / Sean Penn blues / Big snake / Hey rusty / These days
8336912 / Oct '87 / Polydor

☐ **RATTLESNAKES (Cole, Lloyd & The Commotions)**
Perfect skin / Speedboat / Rattlesnakes / Down on Mission Street / Forest fire / Charlotte Street / 2 CV / Four flights up / Patience / Are you ready to be heartbroken
8236832 / Jan '92 / Polydor

Cole, Nat 'King'

☐ **20 GOLDEN GREATS: NAT KING COLE**
Sweet Lorraine / Straighten up and fly right / Nature boy / Dance, ballerina, dance / Mona Lisa / Too young / Love letters / Smile / Around the world / For all we know / When I fall in love / Very thought of you / On the street where you live / Unforgettable / It's all in the game / Ramblin' rose / Portrait of Jennie / Let there be love / Somewhere along the way / Those lazy, hazy, crazy days of summer
CDEMTV 9 / Dec '87 / Capitol

☐ **20 GREAT LOVE SONGS**
Unforgettable / Pretend / Tenderly / I could have danced all night / I love you for sentimental reasons / Mona Lisa / Blossom fell / Thses foolish things / More / When I fall in love / It's all in the game / But beautiful / Ain't misbehavin' / Girl from Ipanema / Impossible / For all we know / Stardust / Arrivederci Roma / There goes my heart / Smile
LS 886322 / 2 Feb '98 / Disky

☐ **20 GREATEST LOVE SONGS**
Stardust / Answer me / Autumn leaves / Walkin' my baby back home / These foolish things / There goes my heart / Nightingale sang in Berkeley Square / You made me love you / Blossom fell / More / Love letters / OH how I miss you tonight / Brazilian love song / You're my everything / Love is a many splendoured thing / You'll never know / He'll have to go / Stay as sweet as you are / More I see you / Party's over
CDEMTV 35 / Dec '87 / EMI

☐ **36 UNFORGETTABLE MEMORIES (2CD Set)**
Nature boy / Stardust / You stepped out of a dream / You're the cream in my coffee / Sand and the sea / Too marvellous for words / Darling, je vous aime beaucoup / Don't get around much anymore / Embraceable you / Love is a many splendoured thing / It's crazy but I'm in love / Call the police / Thou swell / Are you fer it / Slow down / Route 66 / Honeysuckle rose / Hit the ramp / Unforgettable / Gee baby ain't I good to you / Mona Lisa / Hit that jive, Jack / For all we know / I like to riff / When you're smiling / End of a beautiful friendship / Scotchin' with the soda / That ain't right / Babs / Coquette / It's only a paper moon / Early American / Cuba / Somebody loves me / To the ends of the Earth / This side up
TNC 96221 / Aug '96 / Natural Collection

☐ **ANATOMY OF A JAM SESSION**
Black market stuff / Laguna leap / I'll never be the same / Swingin' on central / Kicks
BLC 760137 / Oct '90 / Black Lion

☐ **ANY OLD TIME (Cole, Nat 'King' Trio)**
Little joy from Chicago / Sunny side of the street / Candy / Any old time / (Back home again in) Indiana / Man I love / Trio grooves in Brooklyn / That'll just about knock me out / Too marvellous for words / Besame mucho / Wouldn't you like to know
GOJCD 1031 / Mar '95 / Giants Of Jazz

☐ **AUDIO ARCHIVE**
You're the cream in my coffee / Bugle call rag / Sweet Georgia Brown / Too marvellous for words / Sweet Lorraine / Yes sir that's my baby / Frim fram sauce / It's only a paper moon / If you can't smile and say yes / Cole's bop blues / Trouble with me is you / Miss thing / Man on the keys / Satchel mouth baby / On the sunny side of the street / Last but not least / Tea for two / Nat meets June / Don't cry crybaby
CDAA 002 / Jan '93 / Tring

☐ **BEST OF THE NAT KING COLE TRIO, THE (The Vocal Classics 1942-1946) (Cole, Nat 'King' Trio)**
All for you / Straighten up and fly right / Gee baby ain't I good to you / If you can't smile and say yes / Sweet Lorraine / Embraceable you / It's only a paper moon / I realize now / I'm a shy guy / You're nobody 'til somebody loves you / What can I say after I say I'm sorry / I'm thru with love / Come to baby / Do / Frim fram sauce / How does it feel / Route 66 / Baby, baby all the time / But she's my buddy's chick / You call it madness (but I call it love) / Best man / (I love you) for sentimental reasons / You're the cream in my coffee
CDP 8335712 / Nov '95 / Capitol Jazz

☐ **BEST OF THE VOCAL CLASSICS 1947-1950, THE (Cole, Nat 'King' Trio)**
Meet me at no special place (and I'll be there at no particu / Naughty Angeline / I miss you so / That's what / When I take my sugar to tea / What I'll do / This is my night to dream / Makin' whoopee / There I've said it again / I'll string along with you / Too marvellous for words / Love nest / Dream a little dream of me / Little girl / No moon at all / If I had you / For all we know / 'tis autumn / Yes sir, that's my baby / I used to love you (but it's all over now) / Don't let your eyes go shopping (for your heart) / Ooh kickeroonie
CDP 8335722 / Jan '97 / Capitol Jazz

☐ **BODY AND SOUL**
Straighten up and fly right / Gee baby ain't I good to you / Jumpin' at Capitol / If you can't smile and say yes / Sweet Lorraine / Embraceable you / It's only a paper moon / I just can't see for lookin' / Man I love / Body and soul / Prelude in C sharp minor / What is this thing called love / Vom vim veedle / Let's spring one / Beautiful moons ago / Fine sweet tasty / This side up / Babs
SUMCD 4161 / 23 Feb '98 / Summit

☐ **CAPITOL COLLECTORS SERIES: NAT 'KING' COLE**
Straighten up and fly right: *Cole, Nat 'King' & King Cole Trio* / Route 66: *Cole, Nat 'King' & King Cole Trio* / (I love you) for sentimental reasons: *Cole, Nat 'King' & King Cole Trio* / Christmas song: *Cole, Nat 'King' & King Cole Trio* / Nature boy: *Cole, Nat 'King' & Frank Devol Orchestra* / Too young / Walkin' my baby back home: *Cole, Nat 'King' & Billy May Orchestra* / Pretend: *Cole, Nat 'King' & Nelson Riddle Orchestra* / Answer me: *Cole, Nat 'King' & Nelson Riddle Orchestra* / Darling je vous aime beaucoup: *Cole, Nat 'King' & Nelson Riddle Orchestra* / Blossom fell / Send for me: *Cole, Nat 'King' & Billy May Orchestra* / Non dimenticar (Don't forget): *Cole, Nat 'King' & Nelson Riddle Orchestra* / Ramblin' rose: *Cole, Nat 'King' & Belford Hendricks Orchestra* / Dear lonely hearts / All over the world / Those lazy-hazy-crazy days of summer / LOVE / Mona Lisa / Unforgettable
CZ 303 / Apr '90 / Capitol

☐ **CHRISTMAS WITH NAT & DEAN (Cole, Nat 'King' & Dean Martin)**
Christmas song / Let it snow, let it snow, let it snow / White Christmas / Frosty the snowman / Winter wonderland / Happiest Christmas tree / Deck the halls with boughs of holly / O tannenbaum / Silent night / Brahms lullaby / Buon natale / O come all ye faithful (Adeste fidelis) / Rudolph the red nosed reindeer / Little boy that Santa Claus forgot / Cradle in Bethlehem / Christmas blues / Mrs. Santa Claus / Caroling, caroling / O little town of Bethlehem / O holy night / Joy to the world / God rest ye merry gentlemen
CDMFP 5902 / Nov '97 / Music For Pleasure

☐ **CLASSICS 1936-1940**
CLASSICS 757 / Aug '94 / Classics

☐ **CLASSICS 1940-1941**
CLASSICS 773 / Aug '94 / Classics

☐ **CLASSICS 1941-1943**
CLASSICS 786 / Nov '94 / Classics

☐ **CLASSICS 1943-1944**
CLASSICS 804 / Mar '95 / Classics

☐ **CLASSICS 1944-1945**
CLASSICS 861 / Mar '96 / Classics

☐ **CLASSICS 1945**
CLASSICS 893 / Sep '96 / Classics

☐ **CLASSICS 1946**
CLASSICS 938 / Jun '97 / Classics

☐ **COLLECTION, THE**
Embraceable you / Unforgettable / When you're smiling / Route 66 / Mona lisa / You're the cream in my coffee / Honeysuckle rose / Babs / Gone with the draft / This side up / Scotchin' with the soda / Hit that jive jack / Cuba / I like to riff / That ain't right / Call the police / Too marvellous for words / It's only a paper moon / Somebody loves me / Darling, je vous aime beaucoup / Hit the ramp / Are you fer it / It's crazy but I'm in love / Sand and the sea / End of a beautiful friendship
COL 008 / Apr '95 / Collection

☐ **COLLECTION, THE (3CD Set)**
(Get your kicks on) Route 66 / (I love you) For sentimental reasons / This will make you laugh / I'm thru with love / You call it madness (But call it love) / I'm a shy guy / What can I say after I say I'm sorry / Honeysuckle rose / Sweet Lorraine / Embraceable you / Gee, baby, ain't I good to you / Shoo shoo baby / Just you just me / I know that you know / On the sunny side of the street / I realise now / It's only a paper moon / I can't see for looking / You're the cream in my coffee / Christmas song / I'm an errand boy for rhythm / If you can't smile and say yes / Best man / But she's my buddy's chick / I'm in the mood for love / Look what you've done to me / Don't blame me / Bring another drink / I want to thank your folks / I'm lost / It only happens once / Hit that jive, Jack / Easy listening blues / Stop, the red light's on / You don't learn that at school / I don't know why / In the cool of the evening / It is better to be by yourself / Come in out of the rain / I like to riff / Exactly like you: *Cole, Nat 'King' & Frank Sinatra* / If I could be with you (one hour tonight): *Cole, Nat 'King' & Kay Starr* / Baby, won't you please come home: *Cole, Nat King & Jo Stafford* / Baby, baby all the time / I just can't get started / Nat meets June: *Cole, Nat King & June Christy* / I got rhythm / After you get what you want you don't want it / Somebody loves me / Airness a la Nat / Stormy weather: *Cole, Nat King & Kay Starr* / I'd be lost without you / Sweet Lorraine: *Cole, Nat King & Frank Sinatra* / How deep is the ocean / Mean to me / Stompin' at the Panama / Frim fram sauce / Cindy: *Cole, Nat King & Jo Stafford* / Little Joe from Chicago / I've found a new baby: *Cole, Nat 'King' & Frank Sinatra*
390562 / Aug '97 / Hallmark

☐ **DEAR LONELY HEARTS/I DON'T WANT TO BE HURT ANYMORE**
Dear lonely hearts / Miss you / Why should I cry over you / Near you / Yearning (just for you) / My first and only lover / All over the world / Oh how I miss you tonight / Lonesome and sorry / All by myself / Who's next in line / It's a lonesome old town (when you're not around) / I don't want to be hurt anymore / Your crying on my shoulder / Only yesterday / I'm alone because I love you / Don't you remember / You're my everything / I don't want to see tomorrow / Brush those tears from your eyes / Was that the human thing to do / Go if you're going / Road to nowhere / I'm all cried out
4949942 / 8 Jun '98 / EMI

☐ **DESTINATION MOON**
BMCD 3024 / Mar '96 / Blue Moon

☐ **EARLY FORTIES**
FSRCD 139 / Dec '90 / Fresh Sound

☐ **EARLY TRANSCRIPTIONS 1938-1941, THE (2CD Set) (Cole, Nat 'King' Trio)**
Mutiny in the nursery / Swanee river / Don't blame me / Lullaby in rhythm / Flea hop / Chopsticks / Liza / Three blind mice / Caravan / Ta-de-ah / Undecided / T'ain't what you do (it's the way that you do it) / Do you want to jump children / Riffin' in F minor / Blue Lou / Georgie porgie / Limp / Liebestraum / Some like it hot / I like to riff / Moon song / Baby won't you please come home / Sweet Lorraine / Rosetta / Trompin' / Hoy soy / Black spider stomp / Rhythm serenade / Slew foot Joe / Crazy about rhythm / King Cole blues / Vine street jump / B-Flat / You send me / Gone with the draft / Scotchin' with the soda / Windy city boogie woogie / This side up / Ode to a wild clam
JZCL 5013 / Nov '96 / Jazz Classics

☐ **EMBRACEABLE YOU**
Sweet Lorraine / Besame mucho / Too marvellous for words / This will make you laugh / Wouldn't you like to know / That'll just 'bout knock me out / It only happens once / Baby won't you please come home / Baby / Embraceable you / I love you for sentimental reasons / Do nothin' 'til you hear from me / Candy / What can I say after I say I'm sorry / Please consider me / Is you is or is you ain't my baby / Shoo shoo baby / Trouble with me is you / Yes sir that's my baby / If you can't smile and say yes (please don't cry and say no) / Don't cry baby / You call it madness but I call it love / On the sunny side of the street / I love to make love to you / I wanna turn out my light / It's only a paper moon
PASTCD 7816 / Apr '97 / Flapper

☐ **FOR SENTIMENTAL REASONS (25 Early Vocal Classics) (Cole, Nat 'King' Trio)**
(I love you) for sentimental reasons / This will make you laugh / That ain't right / Beautiful moons ago / I'm lost / Straighten up and fly right / Gee baby ain't I good to you / Sweet Lorraine / Embraceable you / It's only a paper moon / Look what you've done to me / I realize now / Don't blame me / I'm thru with love / It only happens once / It is better to be by yourself / I'm in the mood for love / I don't know why I just do / Route 66 / What can I say after I say I'm sorry / But she's my buddy's chick / You call it madness but I call it love / I want to thank you folks / You don't learn that in school / Christmas song (Merry Christmas to you)
CDAJA 5236 / Jun '98 / Living Era

☐ **FOR SENTIMENTAL REASONS (Cole, Nat 'King' Trio)**
I'm in the mood for love / I don't know why (I just do) / Everyone is saying hello again (why must we say goodbye) / Route 66 / I've got the world on a string / Just you, just me / What can I say after I say I'm sorry / To a wild rose / Too marvellous for words / Loan me two till Tuesday / How does it feel / Could-ja / Baby, baby all the time / Rex rhumba (rhumba a la king) / On the sunny side of the street / I'd like to make love to you / How deep is the ocean / You call it madness but I call it love / But she's my buddy's chick / Best man / (I love you) for sentimental reasons / In the cool of the evening / You're the cream in my coffee / Christmas song
PLCD 555 / Feb '97 / President

☐ **GOLD COLLECTION, THE**
D2CD 10 / Dec '92 / Deja Vu

☐ **GOT A PENNY**
I'm lost / Let's spring one / Beautiful moons / Got a penny / All for you / Fine sweet and tasty / My lips remember your kisses / Vom vim veedle / Bugle call rag / Let's pretend / Melancholy Madeline / Pitchin' up the boogie / Honky tonk town
CDSGP 047 / May '93 / Prestige

☐ **GREAT BEGINNINGS**
AMSC 569 / Jun '96 / Avid

☐ **GREAT GENTLEMEN OF SONG - SPOTLIGHT ON NAT KING COLE**
She's funny that way / Sunday, Monday or always / Crazy she calls me / Spring is here / You'll never know / Funny (not much) / I want a little girl / Am I blue / Until the real thing comes along / Embraceable you / Should I / Say it isn't so / Too marvellous for words / Mood indigo / For you / I remember you / That's all / Lights out
CDP 8293932 / Aug '95 / Capitol

☐ **HIT THAT JIVE, JACK (Cole, Nat 'King' Trio)**
Sweet Lorraine / Honeysuckle rose / Scotchin' with soda / Two against one / With plenty of money and you / Stop the red light's on / Call the police / Don't blame me / Hit that jive, Jack / Early morning blues
CWNCD 2032 / Jun '97 / Crown

☐ **IT'S ALMOST LIKE BEING IN LOVE (Cole, Nat 'King' Trio)**
It's almost like being in love / It's only a paper moon / Jumpy jitters / Nothing ever happens / Let's do things / Sentimental blue / What'cha doing to my heart / Love me sooner / I'm through with love / Flo and Joe / Go bongo / Yes sir that's my baby / Tiny's excercise / Gee baby ain't I good to you / Baby I need you / Bop kick
DBCD 15 / Jul '89 / Dance Band Days

☐ **JAZZ AND BLUES (36 Outstanding Jazz Tracks/2CD Set)**
Nature boy / Stardust / You stepped out of dream / You're the cream in my coffee / Sand and the sea / Too marvelous for words / Je vous aime beaucoup / Don't get around much anymore / Embraceable you / Love is a many splendoured you / It's crazy but I'm in love / Call the police / Thou swell / Are you fer it / Slow down / (Get your kicks) on Route 66 / Honeysuckle rose / Hit the ramp / Unforgettable / Gee baby ain't I good to you / Mona Lisa / Hit that jive Jack / For all we know / I like to riff / When you're smiling / End of a beautiful friendship / Scotchin' with the soda / That ain't right / Babs / Coquette / It's only a paper moon / Early American / Cuba / Somebody loves me / To the ends of the Earth / This side up
BN 213 / Aug '98 / Blue Nite

☐ **JAZZMAN, THE**
TPZ 1012 / Feb '95 / Topaz Jazz

☐ **JAZZY - THE BEGINNING (Cole, Nat 'King' Trio)**
Honeysuckle rose / Gone with the draft / This will make you laugh / That ain't right / Trio groove / Blue because of you / All of you / My tips / Sweet Lorraine / Scotchin' with the soda / Call the police / Hit that jive Jack / Sunny side of the street / Tea for two / I'm lost / Got a penny
74321329632 / Aug '97 / Milan

☐ **JUST LOVE SONGS (An Everlasting Collection Of 18 Memorable Tracks)**
(I love you) for sentimental reasons / Embraceable you / It's only a paper moon / I don't know why / Besame mucho / Just you just me / What can I say after I say I'm sorry / If yesterday could only be tomorrow / Too marvellous for words / I'm in the mood for love / That'll just about knock me out / If you can't smile and say yes / Straighten up and fly right / Laura / I realise now / You must be blind / I thought you ought to know / Sweet Lorraine
ECD 3306 / Feb '97 / K-Tel

☐ **LAURA**
BMCD 3040 / Mar '96 / Blue Moon

☐ **LEGEND OF NAT 'KING' COLE, THE (2CD Set)**
Straighten up and fly right / Gee baby ain't I good to you / If you can't smile and say yes / Sweet Lorraine / Embraceable you / It's only a paper moon / I just can't see for lookin' / What is this thing called love / Vom, vim, veedle / Darling, je vous aime beaucoup / It's crazy but I'm in love / Sand and the sea / Crazy rhythm / Thou swell / End of a beautiful friendship / You stepped out of a dream / Somebody loves me / Mona Lisa / (I'll be seeing you) In Cuba / To the ends of the earth / Autumn leaves / Route 66 / When you're smiling / Unforgettable / Frim fram sauce / I'm a shy guy / I'm in the mood for love / Too young / I've grown accustomed to her face / Sweet Sue, just you / House with love in it / Pick yourself up / Take me back to toyland / Just in time / This can't be love / Tea for two / Two different worlds / Early American / Little girl / Night lights
MUCD 9504 / May '96 / Musketeer

☐ **LEGENDARY SONG STYLIST**
MACCD 360 / 26 Jan '98 / Autograph

☐ **LET'S FACE THE MUSIC AND DANCE**
Let's face the music and dance / Let there be love / Route 66 / Something makes me want to dance with you / More I see you / Answer me / These foolish things / Dance, ballerina, dance / Midnight flyer / Sweet Lorraine / Straighten up and fly right / Fly me to the moon / Just one of those things / I'm gonna sit right down and write myself a letter / Ain't misbehavin' / Girl from Ipanema / Papa loves mambo / Baby, won't you please come home / Blue moon / Party's over
CDEST 2228 / Apr '94 / Capitol

☐ **LET'S FALL IN LOVE**
When I fall in love / Stardust around the world / Too young / Very thought of you / On the street where you live / Ramblin' rose / Just one of those things / Let's fall in love / Almost like being in love / Don't get around anymore / Once in a while / These foolish things remind me of you / I'm gonna sit right down and write myself a letter / This can't be love / For all we know / Somewhere along the way
4932832 / 12 Jan '98 / EMI Gold

☐ **LIVE AT THE SANDS**
Ballerina / Funny (not much) / Continental / I wish you love / You leave me breathless / Thou swell / My kind of love / Surrey with the fringe on top / Where or when / Miss Otis regrets / Joe Turner blues
CDEMS 1110 / Mar '91 / Capitol

☐ LOVE IS THE THING
When I fall in love / End of a love affair / Stardust / Stay as sweet as you are / Where can I go without you / Maybe it's because I love you too much / Love letters / Ain't misbehavin' / I thought about Marie / At last / It's all in the game / When Sunny gets blue / Love is the thing
BU 11 / Mar '88 / Capitol

☐ MASTERPIECES (Cole, Nat 'King' Trio)
159172 / 1 Jun '98 / Jazz Archives

☐ MASTERS, THE
EABCD 046 / 24 Nov '97 / Eagle

☐ NAT 'KING' COLE
Sweet Lorraine / It's only a paper moon / Gone with the draft / Route 66 / You're the cream in my coffee / Too marvellous for words / Honeysuckle rose / Sweet Georgia Brown / Easy listening blues / What is this thing called love / This autumn / Babs / Early morning blues / Jumpin' at capitol / Stompin' down broadway / Somebody loves me / Tea for two
22713 / Dec '95 / Music

☐ NAT 'KING' COLE
Sweet Lorraine / It's only a paper moon / Gone with the draft / Route 66 / You're the cream in my coffee / Too marvellous for words / Honeysuckle rose / Sweet Georgia Brown / Easy listening blues / What is this thing called love / This autumn / Babs / Early morning blues / Jumpin' at capitol / Stompin' down Broadway / Somebody loves me / Tea for two
DVX 08092 / May '95 / Deja Vu

☐ NAT 'KING' COLE (2CD Set)
R2CD 4010 / 13 Apr '98 / Deja Vu

☐ NAT 'KING' COLE & OSCAR MOORE/ JOHNNY MILLER 1945-1946 (Cole, Nat 'King' & Oscar Moore/Johnny Miller)
CD 53147 / May '98 / Giants Of Jazz

☐ NAT 'KING' COLE CHRISTMAS ALBUM, THE
Christmas song / Deck the halls with boughs of holly / Frosty the snowman / I saw three ships / Buon Natale (Merry Christmas to you) / O come all ye faithful (Adeste fidelis) / O little town of Bethlehem / Little boy that Santa Claus forgot / O'Tannenbaum / First Noel / Little Christmas / Joy to the world / O holy night / Caroling, caroling / Cradle in Bethlehem / Away in a manger / God rest ye merry gentlemen / Silent night
CDMFP 5976 / Nov '97 / EMI

☐ NAT 'KING' COLE COLLECTION, THE
Straighten up and fly right / Sweet Lorraine / Embraceable you / It's only a paper moon / Mona Lisa / To the end of the Earth / Autumn leaves / Unforgettable / Too young / Just in time / This can't be love / Tea for two / Gee baby ain't I good to you / If you can't smile and say yes / I just can't see for lookin' / Vom, vim, veedle / Crazy rhythm / Thou swell / End of a relationship / Somebody loves me / What is this thing called love
PAR 2069 / Nov '96 / Parade

☐ NAT 'KING' COLE GOLD (2CD Set)
D2CD 4010 / Jun '95 / Deja Vu

☐ NAT 'KING' COLE LIVE (Cole, Nat 'King' & Nelson Riddle Orchestra)
Two different worlds / Thou swell / Mona Lisa / Night lights / Too young / That's my girl / But not for me / Repeat after me / True love / Little girl / Love letters / Just in time / Unforgettable / Love me tender / My foolish heart / Sweet Sue, just you / Somewhere along the way / This can't be love / I'm sitting on top of the world / You are my first love / It's just a little street / Toyland
DATOM 1 / Apr '94 / Touch Of Magic

☐ NAT 'KING' COLE SHOWS VOL.1
Intro / Somebody loves me / I've grown accustomed to her face / Can't you see how happy we will be (piano solo) / Unforgettable / This can't be love / Beautiful friendship / I'll see you in cuba / Mona lisa / Thou swell / Night lights / Two different worlds / It's only a paper moon / Dream I'm building / To the ends of the earth / My foolish heart / Sweet sue, just you / Love letters / I'm shooting high / Autumn leaves / Just one of those things / There goes my heart / Closing theme
OTA 101902 / Mar '95 / On The Air

☐ NAT 'KING' COLE SHOWS VOL.2
Intro / Little girl / Too marvellous for words / Too young / When you're smiling / Night lights / Take me back to toyland / Just in time / Somewhere along the way / Santa claus is coming to town / House with love in it / Mrs. santa claus / Jingle bells / Christmas song / Silent night (instr) / Just in time / Jealous lover / You are my first love / Banana boat song (day-o) / Ballerina / Ro ro rolling along / This can't be love / Namely you / Oh lady be good / September song / Closing theme
OTA 101903 / Mar '95 / On The Air

☐ NAT 'KING' COLE SHOWS VOL.3
Intro / You're the top / But not for me / You are my first love / Just you, just me / There will never be another you / That's my girl / Coquette / True love / Tea for two / My funny valentine / I'm shooting high / Blueberry hill / I've grown accustomed to her face / Ballerina / Pretend / Should I reveal that I love you / It all depends on you / Namely you / This is my night to dream / Unforgettable / Closing theme
OTA 101904 / Mar '95 / On The Air

☐ NAT 'KING' COLE STORY
Straighten up and fly right / Sweet Lorraine / It's only a paper moon / Route 66 / (I love you) for sentimental reasons / Christmas song / Nature boy / Lush life / Calypso blues / Mona Lisa / Orange coloured sky / Too young / Unforgettable / Somewhere along the way / Walkin' my baby back home / Pretend / Blue gardenia / I am in love / Answer me / Smile / Darling je vous aime beaucoup / Sand and the sea / If I may / Blossom fell / To the ends of the earth / Night lights / Ballerina / Stardust / Send for me / St. Louis blues / Looking back / Non dimenticar / Paradise / Oh, Mary, don't you weep
CDS 7951292 / May '91 / Capitol

☐ NAT 'KING' COLE TRIO 1943-1947 (Cole, Nat 'King' & Oscar Moore/ Johnny Miller)
CD 14566 / May '95 / Jazz Portraits

☐ NAT 'KING' COLE TRIO AND OSCAR MOORE/JOHNNY MILLER 1947 (Cole, Nat 'King' Trio & Oscar Moore/Johnny Miller)
When I take my sugar to tea / Three little words / Makin' whoopee / Three blind mice / There I've said it again / Poor butterfly / I'll string along with you / How high the moon / This is my night to dream / I'll never be the same / Too marvellous for words / Moonlight in Vermont / Cole capers / I never had a chance / These foolish things / (It's easy to see) The trouble with me is you / Blues in my shower / Wildroot Charlie / Lament in chords / You've got another heart on your hands / Laguna mood / I think you get what I mean / I'm a little ashamed
CD 53154 / Jan '98 / Giants Of Jazz

☐ NAT 'KING' COLE TRIO WITH OSCAR MOORE & JOHNNY MILLER (1943-1945) (Cole, Nat 'King' Trio & Oscar Moore/Johnny Miller)
Sweet Lorraine / Sweet Georgia Brown / Embraceable you / It's only a paper moon / I just can't see for lookin' / I'm thru with love / Jumpin' at Capitol / Don't blame me / You're nobody 'til somebody loves you / Man I love / Katusha / I realize now / Prelude in C sharp minor / Gee baby ain't I good to you / Bring another drink / I'm a shy guy / Look what you done to me / If you can't smile and say yes / I tho't you ought to know / Barcarolle / It only happens once
CD 53144 / Oct '96 / Giants Of Jazz

☐ NAT 'KING' COLE TRIO, THE (Cole, Nat 'King' Trio)
That's what / Naughty Angeline / On the sunny side of the street / How deep is the ocean / Swingin' the blues
CD 53151 / Dec '97 / Giants Of Jazz

☐ ONE AND ONLY NAT 'KING' COLE, THE
Sweet Lorraine / Our love is here to stay / Autumn leaves / Dance, ballerina, dance / September song / Beautiful friendship / Fly me to the moon / Let there be love / Mona Lisa / Pick yourself up / More I see you / Just one of those things / Let's fall in love / Love is the thing / Stay as sweet as you are / Love letters / Azure te / Serenata / Party's over
CDMFP 6082 / Aug '96 / Music For Pleasure

☐ PLATINUM COLLECTION, THE (2CD Set)
Autumn leaves / Route 66 / Unforgettable / Frim fram sauce / I'm a shy guy / Too young / Two different worlds / Early american / Little girl / Night lights / Straighten up and fly right / Gee baby ain't I good to you / If you can't smile and say yes / Sweet Lorraine / Embraceable you / It's only a paper moon / I just can't see for looking / Blueberry hill / Darling je vous aime beaucoup / It's crazy but I'm in love / Crazy rhythm / You stepped out of a dream / Soembody loves me / Mona lisa / (I'll be seeing you) In Cuba / To the ends of the earth / Pretend / It all depends on you / Jealous love / You are my first love / Banana boat song / Ballerina / Ro ro rolling along / Namely you / Oh lady be good / You're the top / But not for me / Just you just me / My funny valentine
PC 610 / 10 Nov '97 / Platinum Collection

☐ PORTRAIT OF NAT KING COLE TRIO, A (Cole, Nat 'King' Trio)
GALE 428 / 20 Apr '98 / Gallerie

☐ QUINTESSENCE, THE (1936-1944/2CD Set)
FA 208 / Oct '96 / Fremeaux

☐ RAMBLIN' ROSE
When I fall in love / Stardust / Around the world / Too young / Very thought of you / On the street where you live / Ramblin' rose / Just one of those things / Let's fall in love / Almost like being in love / Don't get around much anymore / Once in a while / These foolish things (remind me of you) / I'm gonna sit right down and write myself a letter / This can't be love / For all we know / Somewhere along the way / Cottage for sale / There goes my heart / Ain't misbehavin'
DC 879672 / Mar '97 / Disky

☐ SINCERELY/THE BEAUTIFUL BALLADS
Sweethearts on parade / You are mine / Let me tell you, babe / No other heart / Because you love me / Cappucina / Let true love begin / Baby blue / Silver bird / Nothing in the world / Take a fool's advice / Felicia / Miss me / Marnie / Here's to my lady / Fool was I / Bend a little my way / You'll see / If I knew / Back in my arms / When it's summer / I'll always be remembering (things)
CTMCD 103 / Nov '96 / EMI

☐ SINGLES
Lush life / Jet / Somewhere along the way / Because you're mine / Faith can move mountains / Pretend / Mother Nature and Father Time / Can't I / Tenderly / Smile / Blossom fell / Dreams can tell a lie / Too young to go steady / Love me as though there were no tomorrow / To the ends of the earth / Time and the river / That's you / That Sunday that summer / Look no further / Pretend
CDMFP 5939 / Dec '92 / Music For Pleasure

☐ SUNNY SIDE OF THE STREET, THE (2CD Set) (Cole, Nat 'King' Trio)
Straighten up and fly right / Is you is or is you ain't my baby / Gee baby ain't I good to you / Vom vim veedle / What is this thing called love / I just can't see for looking / Let's spring one / If you can't smile and say yes / Embraceable you / Sweet Lorraine / Prelude in 'c' sharp minor / Beautiful moons ago / It's only a paper moon / Body and soul / FST (fine, sweet and tasty) / Man I love / Jumpin' at capitol / On the sunny side of the street / Lester leaps in / You must be blind / Indiana / Little Joe from Chicago / After you've gone / Mexican Joe / This will make you laugh / Rhythm Sam / Old music master / Wild goose chase / Too marvellous for words / Shoo, shoo baby / I can't give you anything but love / Just another blues / I realise now / I may be wrong / Miss thing / Have fun / Solid potato salad / Do nothin' 'til you hear from me
330062 / Jul '96 / Hallmark

☐ SWEET GEORGIA BROWN
GRF 038 / Jun '92 / Tring

☐ TELL ME ABOUT YOURSELF/THE TOUCH OF YOUR LIPS
Tell me about yourself / Until the real thing comes along / Best thing for you / When you walked by / Crazy she calls me / You've got the Indian sign on me / For you / Dedicated to you / You are my love / This is always / My life / (I would do) anything for you / Touch of your lips / I remember you / Illusion / You're mine, you / Funny (not much) / Poinciana / Sunday, Monday, or always / Not so long ago / Nightingale sung in Berkeley square / Only forever / My need for you / Lights out
CTMCD 106 / Jan '97 / EMI

☐ THIS IS NAT KING COLE (2CD Set)
When I fall in love / On the street where you live / Ramblin' Rose / Gee baby ain't I good to you / I'm an errand boy for rhythm / Honeysuckle rose / End of a love affair / When the world was young / Where can I go without you / Nightingale sang in Berkeley Square / Let's fall in love / Arrivederci Roma / Best thing for you / Tangerine / Late late show / I got it bad and that ain't good / Open up the doghouse / For you my love / Autumn leaves / More I see you / Dance ballerina dance / Mona Lisa / Fly me to the moon / Get out and get under the moon / Miss Otis regrets / Continental / Surrey with the fringe on top / Girl from Ipanema / My kind of girl / Pretend / Smile / Breezin' along with the breeze / Les feuilles mortes / Aqui se hable en Amore / Make believe land / Day isn't long enough / Happy new year / Miss me / Blossom fell / Too young to go steady
CDDL 1305 / Nov '95 / Music For Pleasure

☐ TOUCH OF CLASS, A
When I fall in love / Stardust / Around the world / Too young / Very thought of you / On the street where you live / Ramblin' rose / Just one of those things / Let's fall in love / Almost like being in love / Don't get around much anymore / Ain't misbehavin' / There goes my heart / Cottage for sale / Somewhere along the way / For all we know / This can't be love / I'm gonna sit right down and write myself a letter / These foolsih things / Once in a while
TC 877032 / 2 Feb '98 / Disky

☐ TRIO CLASSICS (2CD Set) (Cole, Nat 'King' Trio)
Sweet Lorraine / Honeysuckle rose / Early morning blues / This will make you laugh / That ain't right / On the sunny side of the street / Back home in Indiana / Too marvellous for words / I may be wrong / Shoo, shoo baby / Miss Thing / Little Joe from Chicago / Do nothin' 'til you hear from me / Old music master / After you've gone / Is you is or is you ain't my baby / Vom, vim, veedle / All for you / Pitchin' up a boogie / Beautiful moons ago / I'm lost / FST (Fine, sweet and tasty) / Straighten up and fly right / Gee baby ain't I good to you / Jumpin' at Capitol / If you can smile and say yes / Embraceable you / It's only a paper moon / I just can't see for lookin' / Man I love / Body and soul / Prelude in C sharp minor / What is this thing called love / Easy listening blues / I'm a shy guy / Barcarolle / Sweet Georgia Brown / I tho't you ought to know / It only happens once / (I call my papa) Fla-ga-la-pa / It's better to be by yourself / Come to baby, do / Frim fram sauce / Homeward bound / I'm an errand boy for rhythm / This way out / I know that you know / But she's my buddy's chick / Oh, but I do / How does it feel
CPCD 82612 / Dec '96 / Charly

☐ TRIO RECORDINGS VOL.3, THE
You must be blind / Too marvelous for words / I may be wrong but I think you're wonderful / I realize now / T'ain't me / Laura / Keep knockin' on wood / If yesterday could only be tomorrow / Blues and swing / Just another blues / Wild goose chase / Mexico joe / Lester leaps in / Wouldn't you like to know / Barcarolle / I thought you ought to know / Bring another drink
15748 / Aug '92 / Laserlight

☐ TRIO RECORDINGS VOL.4, THE
This will make you laugh / Do nothing 'til you hear from me / Old music master / After you've gone / I love to make love to you / Candy / A trio grooves in brooklyn / If you can't smile and say yes / A pile o'cole / Ain't misbehavin' / When we're alone / Lonesome road / I can't give you anything but love / Rosetta
15749 / Aug '92 / Laserlight

☐ TRIO RECORDINGS VOL.5, THE
Gone with the draft / Sweet lorraine / Honeysuckle rose / Babs / Early morning blues / That ain't right / I used to love you / Crazy, but I'm in love / Stompin' down broadway / Somebody loves me / Tea for two / I'm lost / Let's spring one / Beautiful moons ago / Pitchin' up a boogie
15750 / Aug '92 / Laserlight

☐ UNBELIEVABLE
BMCD 3036 / Mar '96 / Blue Moon

☐ UNFORGETTABLE
Unforgettable / Too young / Mona Lisa / (I love you) for sentimental reasons / Pretend / Answer me / Portrait of Jennie / What'll I do / Lost April / Red sails in the sunset / Make her mine / Hajji baba
CDEMS 1100 / Mar '91 / Capitol

☐ UNFORGETTABLE (The Velvet Voice Of Nat King Cole)
Darling Je vous aime beaucoup / It's crazy but I'm in love / Sand and the sea / Crazy rhythm / Thou swell / End of a beautiful relationship / It's only a paper moon / You stepped out of a dream / Somebody loves me / Mona Lisa / Cuba / To the ends of the Earth / Autumn leaves / Route 66 / When you're smiling / Unforgettable / I'm in the mood for love / Embraceable you
PLATCD 154 / Mar '96 / Platinum

☐ UNFORGETTABLE (3CD Set)
Unforgettable / Pretend / Tenderly / Darling je vous aime beaucoup / Fly me to the moon / I could have danced all night / I love you for sentimental reasons / Mona Lisa / Ballerina dance ballerina / When you're smiling / Goodnight Irene goodnight / These foolish things / More / Adelita / Route 66 / Cachito / He'll have to go / When I fall in love / It's all in the game / But beautiful / Ain't misbehavin' / LOVE / Too young / Girl from Ipanema / Let there be love / For all we know / All by myself / Stardust / Arriverderci Roma / Blossom fell / There goes my heart / Quizas quizas quizas / Red sails in the sunset / Smile / Those lazy hazy crazy days of summer / Calypso blues / Love letters / That's all there is (there isn't anymore) / Get me to the church on time / Skip to my Lou / Around the world
HR 883452 / Oct '97 / Disky

☐ UNFORGETTABLE NAT KING COLE, THE
Unforgettable / Dance, ballerina, dance / It's all in the game / Let there be love / St. Louis blues / Beautiful friendship / Let's fall in love / Those lazy hazy crazy days of Summer / Pretend / Mona Lisa / When I fall in love / Nature boy / Ramblin' rose / Smile / Serenata / Tenderly / Love is a many splendoured thing / Stay as sweet as you are / Love letters / Christmas song
CDEMTV 61 / Nov '91 / EMI

☐ UNFORGETTABLE VOICE OF NAT KING COLE, THE
Unforgettable / You stepped out of a dream / I've grown accustomed to her face / It's only a paper moon / Somebody loves me / End of a beautiful friendship / Sand and the sea / When you're smiling / Route 66 / Mona Lisa / Autumn leaves / Cuba / Crazy rhythm / Thou swell / To the ends of the Earth / Darling je vous aime beaucoup / I'm in the mood for love / I'ts crazy (but I'm in love)
300092 / Jun '98 / Hallmark

☐ VOCAL SIDES, THE
15718 / Sep '92 / Laserlight

Cole, Natalie

☐ GOOD TO BE BACK
Safe / As a matter of fact / Rest of the night / Miss you like crazy / I do / Good to be back / Gonna make you mine / Starting over again / Don't mention my heartache / I can't cry / Someone's rocking my dreamboat / Wild women do
7559611152 / Jul '91 / Elektra

☐ HOLLY & IVY
Holly and the ivy / Christmas song / Silent night / Song for christmas / Joy to the world / Christmas medley / Merry Christmas baby / Jingle bells / Caroling caroling / No more blue christmas / First noel / Little boy that santa claus forgot
7559617042 / Nov '94 / Elektra

☐ I'VE GOT LOVE ON MY MIND
JD 1236 / Oct '96 / Jazz Door

☐ SOPHISTICATED LADY
This will be / Good morning heartache / Touch me / Unpredictable you / Sophisticated lady / Joey / I've got love on my mind / Needing you / Your face stays in my mind / Can we get together again / Heaven is with you / Our love / I love you so / Keep smiling / Not like mine / Be thankful / Who will carry on / You / Oh daddy / Stand by
CDMFP 5984 / Jun '93 / Music For Pleasure

☐ STARDUST
Stardust / This morning it was summer / If you could see me now / Ahmad s blues / Where can I go without you / To whom it may concern / If love ain't there / Two for the blues / Dindi / There's a lull in my life / Like a lover / Pick yourself up / What a difference a day made / He was too good to me / Teach me tonight / Let's face the music and dance / Love letters / When I fall in love
7559619902 / Nov '96 / Elektra

☐ TAKE A LOOK
I wish you love / I'm beginning to see the light / Swingin' shepherd blues / Crazy he calls me / Cry me a river / Undecided / Fiesta in blue / I'm gonna laugh you right out of my life / Let there be love / It's sand man / Don't explain / As time goes by / Too close for comfort / Calypso blues / This will make you laugh / Lovers / All about love / Take a look
7559614962 / Jun '93 / Elektra

☐ UNFORGETTABLE
Very thought of you / It's only a paper moon / Route 66 / Mona lisa / LOVE / This can't be love / Smile / Lush life / That Sunday / That summer / Orange coloured sky / (I love you) for sentimental reasons / Straighten up and fly right / Avalon / Don't get around much anymore / Too young / Nature boy / Darling / Je vous aime beaucoup / Almost like being in love / Thou swell / Non dimenticar / Our love is here to stay
7559610492 / Jun '91 / Elektra

Cole, Norris

☐ NORRIS COLE & S. PRIDE (Cole, Norris & S. Pride)
JGMCD 003052 / 22 Dec '97 / Joe Gibbs

Cole, Paddy

☐ CELTIC RENDEZVOUS
ARCD 001 / May '98 / Ainm

Cole, Paula

☐ HARBINGER
Happy home / Saturn girl / Bethlehem / Black boots / Chiaroscuro / Ladder / Garden of eden / She can't feel anything anymore / Hitler's brothers / Dear gertrude / Our revenge / Oh john / Watch the woman's hands / I am so ordinary
9362460412 / Jan '96 / Warner Bros.

☐ THIS FIRE
Tiger / Where have all the cowboys gone / Throwing stones / Carmen / Mississippi / Nietzche's eyes / Road to dead / Me / Feelin' love / Hush hush hush / I don't want to wait
9362464242 / Jul '97 / Reprise

Cole, Richie

☐ ALTO MADNESS
Price is right / Common touch / Last tango in Paris / Island breeze / Big Bo's paradise / Remember your day off... / Moody's mood
MCD 5155 / Sep '92 / Muse

☐ ALTO MADNESS (Starburst) (Cole, Richie & Reuben Brown Trio)
GCD 5001 / Jan '98 / Genes

☐ BOSSA INTERNATIONAL
Confirmation / Confirmation / I can't get started / Fantasy blues / Snowfall / Samba de orfeu (orpheus) / Cherokee
MCD 9180 / Oct '93 / Milestone

☐ HOLLYWOOD MADNESS
Hooray for Hollywood / Hi fly / Tokyo rose sing the Hollywood blues / Relaxin' at Camarillo / Malibu breeze / I love Lucy / Waiting for Waits / Hooray for Hollywood (reprise)
MCD 5207 / Feb '86 / Muse

☐ KUSH (The Music Of Dizzy Gillespie)
Be-bop / You go to my head / Birk's works / I waited for you / Kush / Salt peanuts / Con alma / Night on Tunisia / This is the way / Manteca
INAK 30322CD / Nov '97 / In Akustik

☐ NEW YORK AFTERNOON
Dorothy's den / Waltz for a rainy be-bop evening / Alto madness / New York afternoon / It's the same thing everywhere / Stormy weather / You'll always be my friend
MCD 5119 / Sep '92 / Muse

☐ POPBOP
Overjoyed / Eddie Jefferson / On a misty night / LDorado kaddy / La bamba / When you wish upon a star / Spanish harlem / Star trek 1 / Sonomascope / Saxophobia / Straight no chaser
MCD 91522 / Jan '94 / Milestone

☐ PROFILE
Presidential sax / Paulo / Street of dreams / One for Monterey / Sarah / Volare / We belong together / Festival de samba / Foreign affair / Little darlin' / Park and ride
INAK 30222CD / Nov '97 / In Akustik

☐ RICHIE AND PHIL AND RICHIE (Cole, Richie & Phil Woods)
60412320652 / 27 Apr '98 / Thirty Two

☐ SIGNATURE
Sunday in New York / Trade winds / Doing the jungle walk / Occasional man / Rainbow lady / Take the cole train / If ever I would leave you / Peggy's blue skylight / America the beautiful
MCD 91622 / Jan '94 / Milestone

☐ YAKETY MADNESS (Cole, Richie & Boots Randolph)
Yakety sax / Yakety sax / Good morning heartache / Wabash cannonball / Night train / Jambalaya / Walkin' with mr. lee / Walkin' with mr. boots / Moonglow picnic / Body and soul / Barnyard be-bop
15473 / Jan '94 / Laserlight

Coleman, Anthony

☐ DISCO BY NIGHT
AVAN 011 / Nov '92 / Avant

Coleman, Bill

☐ AN INTRODUCTION TO BILL COLEMAN
4043 / Apr '97 / Best Of Jazz

☐ BILL COLEMAN
JCD 196 / Apr '94 / Jazzology

☐ BILL COLEMAN IN PARIS VOL.2 1936-1938
After you've gone / I'm in the mood for love / Joe Louis stomp / Coquette / Exactly like you / Hangover blues / Rose room / (Back home again in) Indiana / Bill street blues / Merry go round broke down / I ain't got nobody / Baby, won't you please come home / Big boy blues / Swing guitars / Bill Coleman blues / In a little Spanish town / I double dare you / Way down yonder in New Orleans / I wish I could shimmy like my sister Kate
DRGCD 8402 / Sep '93 / DRG

☐ CLASSICS 1936-1938
CLASSICS 764 / Jun '94 / Classics

☐ FONSEQUE/FLEUR
873121 / Aug '92 / Milan

☐ HANGIN' AROUND
Feeling the spirit / Rosetta / Star dust / I'm in the mood for love / After you've gone / Joe Louis stomp / Coquette / Between the devil and the deep blue sea / I got rhythm / Hangin' around Boudon / Ol' man river / Swing time / Indiana / Bill Street blues / Rose room / Merry go round broke down / Way down yonder in New Orleans / (I wish I could shimmy like my) Sister Kate / Wandering man blues / Three o'clock jump / Reunion in Harlem / Hawkins' barrel house / Stumpy
TPZ 1040 / Mar '96 / Topaz Jazz

☐ LIVE AT THE CAVEAU DE LA HUCHETTE (Coleman, Bill & Dany Doriz)
Goody goody / Cave's blues / Bye bye blackbird / Cheek to cheek / Loverman / In a mellotone
590026 / 21 Aug '97 / Musidisc
17155 / Sep '97 / Laserlight

☐ MEETS GUY LAFITTE
BLCD 760182 / Apr '93 / Black Lion

Coleman, Bob

☐ CINCINNATI BLUES 1928-1936 (Coleman, Bob Cincinnati Jug Band)
SOB 035192 / Dec '92 / Story Of The Blues

Coleman, Cy

☐ WHY TRY TO CHANGE ME NOW
PS 003CD / Sep '95 / P&S

Coleman, Deborah

☐ I CAN'T LOSE
BPCD 5038 / Feb '97 / Blind Pig

Coleman, Gary B.B.

☐ BEST OF GARY B.B. COLEMAN, THE
One eyed woman / Baby scratch my back / Cloud 9 / Word of warning / I fell in love on a one night stand / Merry Christmas baby / Watch where you stroke / Think before you act / If you can beat me rockin' / St. James infirmary / I won't be your fool / Christmas blues
ICH 1065CD / Jun '94 / Ichiban

☐ ONE NIGHT STAND
Baby scratch my back / Sitting and waiting / I just can't lose this blues / I'll take care of you / I wrote this song for you / As the years go passing by / I fell in love on a one night stand / Going down
ICH 1034CD / Oct '93 / Ichiban

☐ RETROSPECTIVES
Sky is cryin' / Too much weekend / Welfare Cadillac / Maybe love wasn't meant for me / Blues at sunrise / What's the name of that thing / Romance without finance is a nuisance / Don't give that recipe away / St. James infirmary / If you can beat me rockin' / Fell in love on a one night stand / I just can't lose these blues
ICH 1514 / 29 Jun '98 / Ichiban

☐ ROMANCE WITHOUT FINANCE IS A NUISANCE
She ain't ugly / Don't give away that recipe / If you see my one eyed woman / Dealin' from the bottom of the deck / Romance without finance / Food stamp Annie / Mr. Chicken Stew / Mr. B's frosting
ICH 1107CD / Oct '93 / Ichiban

Coleman, George

☐ AMSTERDAM AFTER DARK
Amsterdam after dark / New arrival / Lo-Joe / Autumn in New York / Apache dance / Blondie's waltz
CDSJP 129 / Mar '91 / Timeless Jazz

☐ AT YOSHI'S
They say it's wonderful / Good morning heartache / Laig gobblin' blues / Ten / Up jumped Spring / Father / Soul eyes
ECD 220212 / Aug '92 / Evidence

☐ BLUES INSIDE OUT (Coleman, George Quintet)
JHCD 046 / Nov '96 / Ronnie Scott's Jazz House

☐ BONGO JOE
I wish I could sing / Science fiction / Innocent little doggie / Cool it right / Listen at that bull / Crazy with love / Great (instrumental) / Transistor radio / Eloise / Dog eat dog
ARHCD 1040 / Apr '95 / Arhoolie

☐ I COULD WRITE A BOOK (Coleman, George Quartet)
Falling in love with love / My funny valentine / Lover bewitched / I didn't know what time it was / My favourite things / Have you met Miss Jones / People will say we're in love / I could write a book / Medley
CD 83439 / Jul '98 / Telarc

☐ MANHATTAN PANORAMA
ECD 220192 / Jun '92 / Evidence

☐ PLAYING CHANGES
Laura / Siorra / Moment's notice
JHCD 002 / Jan '94 / Ronnie Scott's Jazz House

Coleman, Michael

☐ 1891-1945
CEFCD 161 / Jan '94 / Gael Linn

Coleman, Naimee

☐ SILVER WRISTS
Care about you / Control / Better than this / Silver wrists / Still she sings / Ruthless affection / Sometimes / Remind me / True / Hold tight
CDCHR 6119 / Jun '97 / Chrysalis

Coleman, Ornette

☐ ART OF THE IMPROVISERS
Circle with a hole in the middle / Fifth of beethoven / Just for you / Alchemy of scott la faro / Legend of bebop / Music always / Brings goodness / Harlem's manhattan / Moon inhabitants
7567909782 / Apr '95 / Atlantic

☐ AT THE GOLDEN CIRCLE VOL.2
Snowflakes and sunshine / Morning song / Riddle / Antiques
BNZ 181 / Aug '89 / Blue Note

☐ BEAUTY IS A RARE THING (Complete Atlantic Recordings - 6CD Set)
Focus on sanity / Chrology / Peace / Congeniality / Lonely woman / Monk and the nun / Just for you / Eventually / Una muy bonita / Bird food / Change of the century / Music always / Face of the bass / Forerunner / Free / Circle with a hole in the middle / Ramblin' / Little symphony / Tribes of New York / Kaleidoscope / Rise and shine / Mr. and Mrs. People / Blues connotation / I heard it over the radio / P.S Unless one has (Blues connotation No.2) / Revolving doors / Brings goodness / Joy of a toy / To us / Humpty dumpty / Fifth of Beethoven / Motive for its use / Moon inhabitatnts / Legend of bebop / Some other / Embraceable you / All / Folk tale / Poise / Beauty is a rare thing / First take / Free jazz / Proof readers / Wru / Check up / Alchemy of Scott La Faro / Eos / Enfant / Ecars / Cross breeding / Harlem's Manhattan / Mapa / Abstraction / Variants on a theme of Thelonious Monk (criss-cross)
8122714102 / Feb '94 / Atlantic

☐ BEST OF ORNETTE COLEMAN, THE
Broad way blues / Round trip / Dawn / Dee dee / Zig zag / Good old days / Old gospel
8233722 / 2 Mar '98 / Blue Note

☐ BODY META
Voice poetry / Homegrown / Macho woman / Fou amour / European echoes
5319162 / Oct '96 / Harmolodic/Verve

☐ CHANGE OF THE CENTURY
Ramblin' / Free / Face of the bass / Forerunner / Bird food / Una muy bonita / Change of the century
7567813412 / Jun '93 / Atlantic

☐ CHAPPAQUA SUITE (2CD Set)
Part one / Part two / Part three / Part four
4805842 / Dec '95 / Sony Jazz

☐ COLOURS (Coleman, Ornette & Joachim Kuhn)
Faxing / House of stained glass / Refills / Story writing / Three ways to one / Passion cultures / Night plans / Cyber cyber
5377892 / Jul '97 / Harmolodic/Verve

☐ DEDICATION TO POETS AND WRITERS
30010 / Sep '92 / Giants Of Jazz

☐ FREE JAZZ (Deluxe Edition)
Free jazz / First take
8122752082 / 20 Jul '98 / Atlantic

☐ FREE JAZZ - THAT'S JAZZ
Free jazz (part 1) / Free jazz (part 2)
7567813472 / Mar '93 / Atlantic

☐ IN ALL LANGUAGES
Peace warriors / Feet music / Africa is the mirror of all colours / Word for Bird / Space church / Latin genetics / In all mercury / Sound manual / Mothers of the veil / Cloning / Music news / Art of love is happiness / Today, yesterday and tomorrow / Listen up / Feet up / Biosphere / Storytellers
5319152 / Jul '97 / Harmolodic/Verve

☐ ORNETTE FOREVER (Coleman, Ornette & Yochk'o Seffer)
500822 / 23 Feb '98 / Musidisc

☐ ORNETTE ON TENOR
Cross breeding / Mapa / Enfant / Eos / Ecars
8122714552 / Jul '96 / Atlantic

☐ SHAPE OF JAZZ TO COME, THE
Lonely woman / Eventually / Peace / Focus on sanity / Congeniality / Chronology
7567813392 / Jun '93 / Atlantic

☐ SOAPSUDS SOAPSUDS (Coleman, Ornette & Charlie Haden)
Mary Hartman, Mary Hartman / Human being / Soapsuds / Sex spy / Some day
5319172 / Oct '96 / Harmolodic/Verve

☐ SOMETHING ELSE
Invisible / Blessing / Jayne / Chippie / Disguise / Angel voices / Alpha / When will the blues leave / Sphinx
OJCCD 163 / Feb '93 / Original Jazz Classics

☐ SONG X (Coleman, Ornette & Pat Metheny)
Song X / Mob job / Endangered species / Video games / Kathelin Gray / Trigonometry / Song X / Long time no see
GFLD 19195 / Mar '93 / Geffen

☐ SOUND MUSEUM (Hidden Man)
5319142 / Aug '96 / Harmolodic/Verve

☐ SOUND MUSEUM (Three Women)
5316572 / Aug '96 / Verve

☐ TOMORROW IS THE QUESTION
Tomorrow is the question / Tears inside / Mind and time / Compassion / Giggin' / Rejoicing / Lorraine / Turnaround / Endless
OJCCD 342 / Apr '89 / Original Jazz Classics

☐ TONE DIALING (Coleman, Ornette & Prime Time)
Street blues / Search for life / Guadalupe / Bach prelude / Sound is everywhere / Miguel's fortune / La capella / OAC / If I knew as much about you (as you know about me) / When will I see you again / Kathelin Gray / Badal / Tone dialing / Family reunion / Local instinct / Ying yang
5274832 / Mar '96 / Harmolodic/Verve

☐ VIRGIN BEAUTY
Three wishes / Bourgeois boogie / Happy hour / Virgin beauty / Healing the feeling / Singing in the shower / Desert players / Honeymooners / Chanting / Spelling the alphabet
4894332 / 26 Jan '98 / Sony Jazz

Coleman, Steve

☐ CURVES OF LIFE (Coleman, Steve & Five Elements)
Multiplicity of approaches / Country bama / Streets / 'Round midnight / Drop kick live / Gypsy / I'm burning up
74321316932 / Oct '96 / RCA Victor

☐ DEF TRANCE BEAT (Modalities Of Rhythm) (Coleman, Steve & Five Elements)
Flint / Verifiable / Pedagogy / Dogon / Multiplicity of approachs / Khu / Pad thai / Jeannine's sizzling patterns of force / Mantra / Salt peanuts
01241631812 / Apr '95 / Novus

☐ GENESIS/OPENING OF THE WAY (2CD Set)
Day one: Coleman, Steve & Council Of Balance / Day two: Coleman, Steve & Council Of Balance / Day three: Coleman, Steve & Council Of Balance / Day four: Coleman, Steve & Council Of Balance / Day five: Coleman, Steve & Council Of Balance / Day six: Coleman, Steve & Council Of Balance / Day seven: Coleman, Steve & Council Of Balance / Awareness: Coleman, Steve & Council Of Balance / Law of balance: Coleman, Steve & Five Elements / Pi: Coleman, Steve & Five Elements / First cause: Coleman, Steve & Five Elements / Wheel of nature: Coleman, Steve & Five Elements / Rite of passage: Coleman, Steve & Five Elements / Regeneration: Coleman, Steve & Five Elements / Organic movement: Coleman, Steve & Five Elements / Law: Coleman, Steve & Five Elements / Fortitude and chaos: Coleman, Steve & Five Elements / Sati 1: Coleman, Steve & Five Elements / Polar shift: Coleman, Steve & Five Elements / Third dynasty: Coleman, Steve & Five Elements
74321529342 / May '98 / RCA Victor

☐ MYTHS, MODES AND MEANS
Mystic dub / Finger of God / Initiate / Madra / Song of the beginnings / Numerology / Transits
74321316922 / Nov '96 / RCA Victor

☐ PHASE = SPACE (Coleman, Steve & Dave Holland)
DIW 865 / Jan '93 / DIW

☐ SIGN AND THE SEAL, THE (Transmissions Of The Metaphysics Of A Culture) (Coleman, Steve Mystic Rhythm Society & Afro Cuba De Matanzas)
Diurnal Lord (for Agayu) / Seal / Passage of the river / Oya natureza / Secretos del Abacua / Saudade / Metamorphosis of Amalia / Mystery of seven (the guaguanco in progression) / Prologue / Guaguanco / Abacua/Obatala / Son abacua/Obatala / Montuno / Epilogue
74321407272 / Aug '97 / RCA Victor

☐ TALE OF THREE CITIES EP (Coleman, Steve & Metrics)
Be bop / I am who I am / Science / Get open / Slow burn / Left to right
74321247472 / Jul '95 / Novus

☐ WAY OF THE CIPHER, THE
Freestyle / Fast lane / Slow lane / S-ludes / Black Genghis / Chaos (tech jump) / Hyped laxed and warped / Night breed
74321316902 / Nov '96 / RCA Victor

☐ WORLD EXPANSION (BY THE M-BASE NEOPHYTE) (Coleman, Steve & Five Elements)
Desperate move / Stone bone Jr / Mad monkey / Dream state / Tang lung / Yo ho / And they parted ... / In the park / Just a funky old song / Urilai Thrane / To perpetuate the funk / Koshine Koji / Tlydor's bane
8344102 / Jan '94 / jMT

Colenso Abafana

☐ SOUTH AFRICA ZULU POLYPHONY
926832 / 21 Aug '97 / BUDA

Coles, Johnny

☐ NEW MORNING (Coles, Johnny Quartet)
CRISS 1005CD / Oct '92 / Criss Cross

☐ WARM SOUND, THE
378042 / Jan '96 / Koch

Coley, Daryl

☐ LIVE IN OAKLAND - HOME AGAIN (Coley, Daryl & The New Generation Singers)
I will bless your name / Yes Jesus loves me / Jesus saves / Removal of the mask / That's when he's done / I will sing glory / His love / Even me / That special place / I can
01241430242 / Mar '98 / Word

Colianni, John

☐ LIVE AT MAYBECK RECITAL HALL VOL.37
Blue and sentimental / Stardust / What's your story Morning Glory / It never entered my mind / Londonderry air / Don't stop the carnival / When your lover has gone / Ja da / Basin Street blues / I never knew / Baby, won't you please come home / Tea for two / Goodbye / Heart shaped box
CCD 4643 / May '95 / Concord Jazz

Colin, Daniel

☐ PRESTIGE DE L'ACCORDEON VOL.1
242052 / Nov '92 / Wotre Music

Coll, Brian

☐ AT HOME IN IRELAND
CDBC 505 / Jan '95 / Outlet

Collage

☐ GET IN TOUCH/SHINE THE LIGHT
Get in touch with me / Love is for everyone / Simple / Near to me / Young girls / Move in time / Alien Zzz / Kickin' it / Romeo where's Juliet / Winners and losers / Shine the light / In the mix / Step right up / Here and now
DEEPM 034 / Aug '97 / Deep Beats

Collapsed Lung

☐ COOLER
London tonight / Lungs collapse / Ballad night / Sense / Codename: Omega / One foot up the rude ladder / Board game / 25 years / Casino kisschase / TV is life Elvis / Maclife / Connection / Eat my goal / Codename: Omega (instrumental) / Ballad night (instrumental) / Lungs collapse (instrumental) / Casino kisschase (instrumental)
BLUFF 031CD
BLUFF 031CDS / Jun '96 / Deceptive

☐ JACKPOT GOALIE
Maclife intro / Maclife / Down with the plaid fad / Eat my goal / Interactive / I may not know the score but / Something ordinary / Burn rubber soul / Filthy's fix / Dis MX / Begrudgit / Slack agenda
BLUFF 015CD / Apr '95 / Deceptive

Collectif Mu

☐ LIVE AU CRESCENT
A 22 / Jan '97 / Seventh

Collective Quartet

☐ LIVE AT CRESCENT
LEOLABCD 043 / Feb '98 / Leo Lab

☐ ORCA
LEOLABCD 031 / May '97 / Leo Lab

Collective Soul

☐ COLLECTIVE SOUL
Gel / Smashing young man / World I know / Reunion / Bleed / Collection of goods / When the water falls / She gathers rain / Where the river flows / December / Simple / Untitled
7567827452 / Jun '95 / Atlantic

☐ DISCIPLINED BREAKDOWN
Precious declaration / Listen / Maybe / Full circle / Blame / Disciplined breakdown / Forgiveness / Link / Giving / In between / Crowded head / Everything
7559829842 / Mar '97 / Atlantic

☐ HINTS, ALLEGATIONS & THINGS LEFT UNSOLVED
Shine / All / Scream / Breath / Reach / Pretty Donna / Heaven's already here / In a moment / Love lifted me / Burning bridges / Goodnight good guy / Sister don't cry / Wasting time
7567825962 / Aug '94 / Atlantic

Collet, Danny

☐ LOUISIANA SWAMP CATS
FF 628CD / Dec '93 / Flying Fish

Collette

☐ ATTITUDE
No getting over you / Poll tax blues / I don't wanna fall / Rocket-ride to heaven / Count on me / Slow death / Fire / Halfway to paradise / Ruby's gotta heart / Don't trust anyone / No mercy / Work
REVXD 135 / Mar '93 / FM

Collette, Buddy

☐ BUDDY'S BEST (Collette, Buddy Quintet)
Soft touch / Walkin' Willie / Changes / My funny valentine / Cute monster / Orlando blues / Blue sands / It's you
CDBOP 020 / Jul '96 / Boplicity

☐ SOFT TOUCH
FSRCD 214 / Jan '97 / Fresh Sound

☐ TASTY DISH (Collette, Buddy Quartet/ Quintet)
FSRCD 213 / Jan '97 / Fresh Sound

Collide

☐ BENEATH THE SKIN
SPV 08543152 / Sep '96 / SPV

☐ DISTORT
REC 033 / 20 Oct '97 / Re-Constriction

Collie, Max

☐ ACES HIGH (Collie, Max Rhythm Aces)
RCD 114 / Jun '96 / Reality

☐ FRONTLINE BACKLINE (Collie, Max Rhythm Aces)
Royal Garden blues / Kinklets / Down by the river / Gatemouth / Muskrat ramble / St. Louis blues / Isle of Capri / Ory's Creole trombone / Mahogany hall stomp / Lazy river / (I'll be glad when you're dead) you rascal you / Sing on / Oh you beautiful doll / You always hurt the one you love / Sweet Sue, just you
CDTTD 504 / Feb '95 / Timeless Jazz

☐ HIGH SOCIETY SHOW, THE (Collie, Max Rhythm Aces)
RCD 108 / Oct '92 / Reality

☐ MAX COLLIE & FRIENDS PART 2
R 113C / Aug '94 / Reality

☐ MAX COLLIE'S RHYTHM ACES VOL.2 (Collie, Max Rhythm Aces)
BCD 83 / Jun '96 / GHB

☐ MAX COLLIE'S RHYTHM ACES VOL.3 (Collie, Max Rhythm Aces)
BCD 98 / Nov '96 / GHB

☐ SENSATION
CDTTD 530 / Jan '88 / Timeless Traditional

☐ THRILL OF JAZZ, THE (Collie, Max Rhythm Aces)
RCD 111 / Mar '90 / Reality

☐ WORLD CHAMPIONS OF JAZZ (Collie, Max Rhythm Aces)
Too bad / Sweet like this / Salutation march / 'S wonderful / I'm crazy 'bout my baby / Didn't he ramble / Ragtime dance / Dans les rues D'Antibes / Fidgety fingers
BLCD 760512 / Nov '95 / Black Lion

Collier, Graham

☐ CHARLES RIVER FRAGMENTS
Hackney five / Charles river fragments
BHR 004 / Apr '96 / Boathouse

☐ SONGS FOR MY FATHER
Song one / Song two / Song three / Song four / Song five / Song six / Song seven / Song three / Song nine
DNACD 001 / 9 Feb '98 / DNA

Colligan, George

☐ NEWCOMER, THE (Colligan, George Quintet)
SCCD 31414 / 21 Aug '97 / Steeplechase

Collins Kids

☐ HOP, SKIP AND JUMP
Go away don't bother me / Rock 'n' roll polka / Move a little closer / My first love / Hush money / I wish / Cuckoo rock / Beetle bug bop / I'm in my teens / Rockaway rock / They're still in love / Make him behave / Hop, skip and jump / Shortnin' bread rock / Just because / Hoy hoy / Hot rod / Heartbeat / Mama worries / Party / Walking the floor over you / Missouri waltz / You are my sunshine / Soda poppin' around / Young heart / Ain't you ever / What'cha gonna do now / Waitin' and watchin' / Home of the blues / Lonesome road / Early American / Rockin' gypsy / Bye bye / Hurricane / Mercy / Rock boppin' baby / Whistle bait / Sweet talk / Spur of the moment / Rebel / Johnny Yuma / There'll be some changes made / Fireball mail / T-bone / What about tomorrow / Get along home Cindy / You've been gone too long / One step down / There stands the one / Wild and wicked love / Hey mama boom a lacka / More than a friend / Pied piper poodle / Blues in the night / Another man done gone / Sugar plum / Kinda like love / Are you certain / That's your affair
BCD 15537 / Aug '91 / Bear Family

☐ ROCKIN' ON TV 1957-1961
KKCD 14 / Oct '93 / Krazy Kat

☐ ROCKIN'EST, THE
Hop skip and jump / Hoy hoy / Beetle bug bop / Just because / Whistle bait / I'm in my teens / Move a little closer / Hot rod / Rock boppin' baby / Go away don't bother me / Rockaway rock / Rock 'n' roll polka / Cuckoo rock / Sweet talk / Hush money / They're still in love / Make him behave / Shortnin' bread rock / Heartbeat / Lonesome road / Mercy / Party
BCD 16250 / Feb '98 / Bear Family

Collins, Albert

☐ ALBERT COLLINS & BARRELHOUSE LIVE (Collins, Albert & Barrelhouse)
BMCD 225 / '90 / Munich

☐ ALBERT COLLINS LIVE
You're so high / You accuse me / I get the feeling / Angel mercy / Icy blue / Trouble was money / Things I used with my mind / Too many dirty dishes / Things I used to do / Black cat bone
CDCBL 756 / Oct '95 / Charly

☐ COLD SNAP
Cash talkin' / Bending like a willow tree / Good fool is hard to find / Lights are on but nobody's home / I ain't drunk / Hooked on you / Too many dirty dishes / Snatchin' it back / Fake ID
ALCD 4752 / May '93 / Alligator

☐ COLLINS MIX
There's gotta be a change / Honey hush / Master charge / If trouble was money / Don't lose your cool / If you love me like you say / Frosty / Tired man / Moon is full / Collin's mix / Same old thing
VPBCD 17 / Nov '93 / Pointblank

☐ DELUXE EDITION
I ain't drunk / If you love me like you say / Blue Monday hangover / Meltdown / Master charge / Too tired / If trouble was money / T-bone shuffle / Get to gettin' / ...But I was cool / Cold cuts / When the welfare turns its back on you / Good fool is hard to find
ALCD 5601 / 6 Oct '97 / Alligator

☐ DON'T LOSE YOUR COOL
Got togettin' / My mind is trying to leave me / I'm broke / Don't lose your cool / When a guitar plays the blues / But I was cool / Melt down / Ego trip / Quicksand
ALCD 4730 / May '93 / Alligator

☐ FROSTBITE
If you love me like you say / Blue Monday hangover / I got a problem / Highway is like a woman / Brick / Don't go reaching across my plate / Give me my blues / Snowed in
ALCD 4719 / May '93 / Alligator

☐ FROZEN ALIVE
Frosty / Angel of mercy / I got that feeling / Caledonia / Things I used to do / Got a mind to travel / Cold cuts
ALCD 4725 / May '93 / Alligator

☐ ICE PICKIN'
Talking woman blues / When the welfare turns its back on you / Ice pick / Cold cold feeling / Too tired / Master charge / Conversation with Collins / Avalanche
ALCD 4713 / May '93 / Alligator

☐ ICEMAN
Mr. Collins, Mr. Collins / Iceman / Don't mistake kindness for weakness / Travellin' South / Put the shoe on the other foot / I'm beginning to wonder / Head rag / Hawk / Blues for Gabe / Mr. Collins, Mr. Collins (reprise)
VPBCD 3 / Feb '91 / Pointblank

☐ IN CONCERT
CLACD 427 / Mar '97 / Castle

☐ LIVE 1992-1993 (Collins, Albert & The Icebreakers)
Iceman / Lights are on but nobody's home / If you love me (like you say) / Put the shoe on the other foot / Frosty / Travellin' South / Talkin' woman / My woman has a black cat bone / I ain't drunk / T-bone shuffle
VPBCD 27 / Oct '95 / Pointblank

☐ LIVE IN JAPAN (Collins, Albert & The Icebreakers)
Listen here: *Collins, Albert* / Tired man: *Collins, Albert* / If trouble was money: *Collins, Albert* / Jealous man: *Collins, Albert* / Stormy Monday: *Collins, Albert* / Skatin': *Collins, Albert* / All about my girl: *Collins, Albert*
ALCD 4733 / May '93 / Alligator

☐ LOVE CAN BE FOUND ANYWHERE/ TRASH TALKIN'
BGOCD 364 / 26 Sep '97 / Beat Goes On

☐ SHOWDOWN (Collins, Albert/Johnny Copeland/Robert Cray)
T-Bone shuffle / Moon is full / Lion's den / She's into something / Bring your fine self home / Black cat bone / Dream / Albert's alley / Black Jack
ALCD 4743 / May '93 / Alligator

Collins, Bootsy

☐ AHH...THE NAME IS BOOTSY BABY (Bootsy's Rubber Band)
Ahh the name is Bootsy, baby / Pinocchio theory / Rubber dickie / Preview side too / What's a telephone bill / Munchies for your love / Can't stay away / We want Bootsy (reprise)
7599229722 / Jan '96 / WEA

☐ BACK IN THE DAY (The Best Of Bootsy Collins)
Ahh...the name is Bootsy baby / Stretchin' out (in a rubber band) / Pinocchio theory / Hollywood squares / I'd rather be with you / What so never the dance / Can't stay away / Jam fan (hot) / Mug push / Body slam / Scenery / Vanish in our sleep / Psychoticbumpschool
7599265812 / Aug '94 / WEA

☐ BLASTERS OF THE UNIVERSE (Bootsy's New Rubber Band)
Blasters of the universe / JR / Funk express card / Bad girls / Back n the day / Where r the children / Female troubles (The national anthem) / Wide track / Funk me dirty / Blasters of the universe 2 (The sequel) / Goodnight Eddie / Sacred place / Half pass midnight / It's a silly serious world
RCD 9030708 / Aug '94 / Rykodisc

☐ BOOTSY PLAYER OF THE YEAR (Bootsy's Rubber Band)
Bootsy (whats the name)... / As in (I love you) / Roto-rooter / Very yes / Bootzilla / May the force be with you / Hollywood squares
7599263352 / Jan '96 / Warner Bros.

☐ FRESH OUTTA P UNIVERSITY
Off da hook / I'm leavin' you (gotta go gotta go) / Funny ain't broke / Party lick-a-ble's / Ever lost your lover / Pearl drops / Do the freak / Fragile / Holly-wood-if-she-could / Wind mreup / Wind me up / Good-n-nasty / Penetration (in funk we thrust) / Home-of-da-freaks / Fresh outta p university
3984202622 / 17 Nov '97 / WEA

☐ KEEPIN' DAH FUNK ALIVE 4 1995 (Bootsy's New Rubber Band)
Intro / Ahh the name is Bootsy, baby / Bootsy (What's the name of this town) / Psychoticbumpschool / Pinocchio theory / Hollywood squares / Bernie solo / One nation under a groove / P Funk (wants to get funked up) / Cosmic slop / Flash light / Bootzilla / Roto-rooter / I'd rather be with you / Sacred place / Stretchin' out (In a rubber band) / Touch somebody / Night of the thumpasaurus peoples / Keepin' da funk alive 1994-5
RCD 9032324 / Aug '95 / Rykodisc

☐ LORD OF THE HARVEST (Zillatron)
Bugg light / Fuzz face / Exterminate / Smell the secrets / Count zero / Bootsy and the beast / No fly zone the devils playground / Passion continues
RCD 10301 / Jun '94 / Black Arc

☐ ONE GIVETH, THE COUNT TAKETH AWAY, THE
Shine o'Myte (rap popping) / Landshark / Count Dracula / Funkateer, I / Lexicon (of love) / So nice you name him twice / What's wrong radio / Music to smile by / Play on playboy / Take a lickin' and keep on kickin' / Funky funkateer
7599236672 / Jan '96 / WEA

☐ STRETCHIN' OUT (Bootsy's Rubber Band)
Stretchin' out (In a rubber band) / Psychotic bum school / Another point of view / I'd rather be with you / Love vibes / Physical love / Vanish in our sleep
7599263342 / Jan '96 / WEA

☐ THIS BOOT IS MADE FOR FONK-N (Bootsy's Rubber Band)
Under the influence of a groove / Bootsy get live / O boy gorl / Jam fan / Chug-a-lug / Shejam / Reprise
7559232952 / Jan '96 / WEA

☐ ULTRA WAVE
Mug push / Sacred flower / Fat cat / Sound crack / R-encounter / It's a musical / Is that my song
7599263362 / Jan '96 / WEA

Collins, Cal

☐ INTERPLAY (Collins, Cal & Herb Ellis)
Besame mucho / I'll be seeing you / People will say we're in love / That's your head / Tricia's fantasy / I got it bad and that ain't good / Lime house blues
CCD 41372 / May '97 / Concord Jazz

☐ OHIO STYLE (Collins, Cal Quartet)
Falling in love with love / East of the sun and west of the moon / Be anything / Bag's groove / Affair to remember / Skylark / I've got the world on a string / I don't stand a ghost of a chance with you / Tumbling tumbleweeds / Ill wind / Sweet Sue, just you / Until the real thing comes along
CCD 4447 / Feb '91 / Concord Jazz

Collins, Edwyn

☐ GORGEOUS GEORGE
Campaign for real rock / Girl like you / Low expectations / Out of this world / If you could love me / North of heaven / Gorgeous George / It's right in front of you / Make me feel again / You got it all / Subsidence / Occupy your mind
SETCD 014 / Jul '95 / Setanta

☐ HELLBENT ON COMPROMISE
Means to an end / You poor deluded fool / It might as well be you / Take care of yourself / Graciously / Someone else besides / My girl has gone / Now that it's love / Everything and more / What's the big idea / Time of the preacher - long time gone
DIAB 836 / 24 Nov '97 / Diablo

☐ HOPE AND DESPAIR
Coffee table song / Fifty shades of blue / You're better than you know / Pushing it to the back of my mind / Darling they want it all / Wheels of love / Beginning of the end / Measure of the man / Testing time / Let me put your arms around you / Wide eyes child in me / I don't stand a ghost of a chance with you
FIENDCD 144 / Aug '95 / Demon

☐ I'M NOT FOLLOWING YOU
It's a steal / Magic piper / Seventies night / No one waved goodbye / Downer / Keep on burning / Running away with myself / Country rock / For the rest of my life / Superficial cat / Adidas world / I'm not following you
SETCD 039 / Sep '97 / Setanta

Collins, Glenda

☐ BEEN INVITED TO A PARTY (1963-1966)
I lost my heart at the fairground / I feel so good / If you gotta pick a baby / Baby it hurts / Nice wasn't it / Lollipop / Everybody got to fall in love / Johnny loves me / Paradise for two / Thou shalt not steal / Been invited to a party / Something I got to tell you / My heart didn't lie / It's hard to believe it / Don't let it rain on Sunday / In the first place
CSAPCD 108 / Aug '90 / Connoisseur Collection

☐ THIS LITTLE GIRL'S GONE ROCKIN'
Take a chance / Crazy guy / Oh how I miss you tonight / Age for love / Head over heels in love / Find another fool / I lost my heart at the fairground / I feel so good / If you've got to pick a baby / In the first place / Baby it hurts / Nice wasn't it / Lollipop / Everybody's got to fall in love / Johnny love me / Paradise for two / Thou shalt not steal / Been invited to a party / Something I've got to tell you / My heart didn't lie / It's hard to believe it / Don't let it rain on Sunday / Sing c'est la vie / This little girl's gone rockin' / Run to me / You're gonna get your way / Yeah yeah yeah / Self portrait
RPM 182 / 17 Nov '97 / RPM

Collins, Johnny

☐ **SHANTIES AND SONGS OF THE SEA**
Blow the man down (flying fish sailor) / Haul boys haul / Blood red roses / South Australia / Leave her Johnny / Randy Dandy O / Fire marengo / Shallow brown / Eliza Lee / Goodbye fare thee well / Maul / Old Billy Riley / Bold Reilly-O / Down the bay to Julianna / Wild goose / Hard on the beach oar / Roll the wood pile down / Dodger bank / Sailor prayer / Farewell shanty
GRCD 75 / Apr '96 / Grasmere

Collins, Joyce

☐ **SWEET MADNESS**
ACD 262 / Sep '91 / Audiophile

Collins, Judy

☐ **COLORS OF THE DAY - THE BEST OF JUDY COLLINS**
Someday soon / Since you asked / Both sides now / Sons of / Suzanne / Farewell to Tarwathie / Who knows where the time goes / Sunny Goodge Street / My father (always promised) / Albatross / In my life / Amazing grace
9606812 / Feb '92 / Elektra

☐ **FOREVER (An Anthology/2CD Set)**
Someday soon / Who knows where the time goes / Chelsea morning / Suzanne / Born to the breed / Maid of constant sorrow / Since you've asked / Bread and roses / In the hills of Shiloh / City of New Orleans / Fallow way / Grandaddy / My father / La chanson des vieux amants / In my life / Marat sade / Send in the clowns / Both sides now / Desperado / Masters of war / Fisherman song / So early early in the spring / First boy I loved / Albatross / Hard lovin' loser / In the heat of the summer / Pirate Jenny / Turn turn turn / Salt of the earth / Farewell to Tarwathie / Spanish is the loving tongue / Nothing lasts forever / Walls (we are not forgotten) / Bird on a wire / Amazing grace
7559621042 / 8 Dec '97 / Elektra

☐ **JUST LIKE A WOMAN (Judy Collins Sings Bob Dylan)**
Like a rolling stone / It's all over now baby blue / Simple twist of fate / Sweetheart like you / Gotta serve somebody / Dark eyes / Love minus zero / No limit / Just like a woman / I believe in you / With God on our side / Bob Dylan's dream
GED 24612 / 2 Feb '98 / Geffen

☐ **LIVE AT NEWPORT 1959-1966**
Introduction / Greenland whale fisheries / Anathea / Bonny ship The Diamond / Turn turn turn / Blowin' in the wind / Hey Nelly Nelly / Great silkie / Carry it on / Hard lovin' loser / Coming of the roads / Silver dagger / Get together / Bullgine run
VCD 77013 / Oct '95 / Vanguard

☐ **SANITY AND GRACE**
History / Lovin' and leavin' / Sanity and grace / Daughters of time / Born to the breed / Moonfall / Morning has broken / When a child is born / Jerusalem / Life you dream
12701 / Nov '96 / Laserlight

☐ **WIND BENEATH MY WINGS**
When you wish upon a star / Day by day / From a distance / Cats in the cradle / Wind beneath my wings / Pretty polly / Trust your heart / Rose / Amazing grace
15451 / May '94 / Laserlight

Collins, Kathleen

☐ **TRADITIONAL MUSIC OF IRELAND**
SHAN 34010CD / Apr '95 / Shanachie

Collins, Lui

☐ **BAPTISM OF FIRE**
Baptism of fire / Passion / Bring your mind back home / Tinker's coin / Who do you love / Hold the last note out / Wildflower song / January thaw / Sweet goodbye / Second effort / Awaiting the snow / I'm looking for a song / Rooty toot toot for the moon
GLCD 1060 / '92 / Green Linnet

☐ **MADE IN NEW ENGLAND**
GLCD 1056 / Feb '89 / Green Linnet

☐ **THERE'S A LIGHT**
Dance me 'round / All you can do / Ballad of the white seal maid / Leaf in the winter / There's a light / For real / Midwinter night / Enfolding / Ecstasy / Lullabye
GLCD 1061 / Feb '92 / Green Linnet

Collins, Phil

☐ **BOTH SIDES**
Both sides of the story / Can't turn back the years / Everyday / I've forgotten everythin' / We're sons of our fathers / Can't find my way / Survivors / We fly so close / There's a place for us / We want and we wonder / Please come out tonight
CDV 2800 / Oct '93 / Virgin

☐ **BUT SERIOUSLY**
Hang in long enough / That's just the way it is / Do you remember / Something happened on the way to heaven / Colours / I wish it would rain down / Another day in paradise / Heat on the street / All of my life / Saturday night and Sunday morning / Father to son / Find a way to my heart
CDV 2620 / Nov '89 / Virgin

☐ **DANCE INTO THE LIGHT**
Times they are a-changin' / No matter who you are / River so wide / It's in your eyes / Wear my hat / Love police / Just another story / That's what you said / Lorenzo / Same moon / Oughta know by now / Take me down / Dance into the light
0630160002 / Oct '96 / Face Value

☐ **DEEP GREEN (Collins, Phil & Gary Moore/Rod Argent/Friends)**
74321475372 / Aug '97 / Milan

☐ **FACE VALUE**
In the air tonight / This must be love / Behind the lines / Roof is leaking / Droned / Hand in hand / I missed again / You know what I mean / I'm not moving / If leaving me is easy / Tomorrow never knows / Thunder and lightning
CDV 2185 / Jan '84 / Virgin

☐ **HELLO I MUST BE GOING**
I don't care anymore / I cannot believe it's true / Like China / Do you know, do you care / You can't hurry love / It don't matter to me / Thru these walls / Don't let him steal your heart away / West side / Why can't it wait till morning
CDV 2252 / Jun '88 / Virgin

☐ **HITS OF PHIL COLLINS (Various Artists)**
DCD 5260 / Aug '92 / Disky

☐ **NO JACKET REQUIRED**
Sussudio / Only you know and I know / Long long way to go / Don't want to know / One more night / Don't lose my number / Who said I would / Doesn't anybody stay together anymore / Inside out / Take me home / We said hello goodbye
CDV 2345 / Feb '85 / Virgin

☐ **SERIOUS HITS LIVE**
Something happened on the way to heaven / Against all odds / Who said I would / One more night / Don't lose my number / Do you remember / Another day in paradise / Separate lives / In the air tonight / You can't hurry love / Two hearts / Sussudio / Groovy kind of love / Easy lover / Take me home
PCVCD 1 / Nov '90 / Virgin

Collins, Sam

☐ **JAILHOUSE BLUES**
YAZCD 1070 / Apr '91 / Yazoo

Collins, Shirley

☐ **FOR AS MANY AS WILL (Collins, Shirley & Dolly)**
Lancashire lass / Never again / Lord Allenwater / Beggar's opera medley / O Polly you might have toy'd and kist / Oh what pain it is to part / Miser thus a shilling sees / Youth's the season made for joys / Hither dear husband, turn your eyes / Lumps of plum pudding / Gilderoy / Rockley firs / Sweet Jenny Jones / German tune / Moon shines bright / Harvest home medley (Peas, beans, oats and the barley) / Mistress's health / Poor Tom
FLE 1003CD / Jan '94 / Fledg'ling

☐ **FOUNTAIN OF SNOW**
DURTRO 010CD / Jan '92 / Durtro

☐ **SWEET PRIMROSES**
All things are quite silent / Cambridgeshire May Carol / Spencer the rover / Rigs of time / Cruel Mother / Bird in the bush / Streets of Derry/False bride / Locks and bolts rambleaway / Brigg fair / Higher Germaine / George Collins / Babes in the wood / Down in yon forest / Magpie's nest / False true love / Sweet primroses
TSCD 476 / Aug '95 / Topic

Collins, Tommy

☐ **LEONARD (5CD Set)**
Campus boogie / Too beautiful to cry / Smooth sailin' / Fool's gold / You gotta have a license / Let me love you / There'll be no other / I love you more and more each day / Boob-i-lak / You better not do that / I always get a souvenir / High on a hilltop / Untied / What'cha gonna do now / Love-a-me, s'il vous plait / You're for me / I'll be gone / Wait a little longer / Let down / It tickles / It's nobody's fault but yours / I guess I'm crazy / You oughta see pickles now / Those old love letters from you / I wish I had died in my cradle / I'll never, never let you go / I'll always speak well of you / What kind of sweetheart are you / No love have I / All of the monkeys ain't in the zoo / That's the way love is / How do I say goodbye / Man we all ought to know / Are you ready to go / Think it over boys / I think of you yet / Upon this rock / Feet of the traveler / Don't you love me anymore / Retirement in heaven / What have you done / Love is born / I'm nobody's fool but yours / O Mary don't you weep / Did you let your light shine / In the shadow of the cross / When I survey the wondrous cross / Who at my door is standing / My saviour's love / Where could I go but to the Lord / What a friend we have in Jesus / Each step of the way / Softly and tenderly / That's why I love him / Jesus keep me near the cross / Amazing grace / Old rugged cross / Hearts don't break / You belong in my arms / Hundred years from now / Little June / My last chance with you / Sidewalks of New York / Last letter / Oklahoma hills / Great speckled bird / Broken engagement / Wreck of ol' 97 / I'm just here to get my baby out of jail / Have I told you lately that I love you / It makes no difference now / Let's live a little / I'll keep on loving you / I overlooked an orchard / I wonder if you feel the way I do / Juicy fruit / Black cat / We kissed again with tears / Keep dreaming / Don't let me stand in his footsteps / Summer's almost gone / Take me back to the good old days / Oh what a dream / Let her go / When did right become wrong / If I could just go back / I got mine / You'd better be nice / I can do that / I got mine (live) / Shindig in the barn / Million miles / Good goody gumdrop / Clock on the wall / Bee that gets the honey / It's a big jump / It's a pretty good ol' world after all / Take me back to the good old days / Oh what a dream (Without chorus) / Klipps kloppa / If you can't bite, don't growl / Man gotta do what a man gotta do / Man machine / Girl on sugar pie lane / Poor, broke, mixed up mess of a heart / Be serious Ann / Fool's castle / Little time for a little love / I'm not getting anywhere with you / Two sides of life / You're everything to me / Big dummy / There's no girl in my life anymore / Skinny / I'm not looking for an angel / Don't wipe the tears that you cry / Birmingham / Put me irons, lock me up (Throw away the key) / Sam Hill / It's to much like lonesome / Wine take me away / General delivery USA / Roll truck roll / If that's the fashion / Piedras negras / Laura / Branded man / Cincinnati, Ohio / Break my mind / I made a prison band / Best thing I've done in my life / Woman you have been told / Sunny side of life / He's gonna have to catch me first
BCD 15577 / Jan '93 / Bear Family

Collinson, Dean

☐ **LIFE AND TIMES**
Hello hello / Words to that effect / Life and times / This time / Louise / Russian roulette / Game for losers (she is out there) / Runaways / Measure upon measure / Welcome to the club
74321134682 / Sep '93 / Arista

Collinson, Lee

☐ **SLIP THE DRIVER A FIVER**
FLED 3003 / May '95 / Fledg'ling

Collister, Christine

☐ **BLUE ACONITE**
How far to the horizon / Private storm / Can't win / Paper wings / Kicking in my stall / Heart like a wheel / Forever he said / Midnight feast / Blue moon on the rise / Harvest for the world / Broken bicycles
FLED 3010 / Oct '96 / Fledg'ling

☐ **DARK GIFT OF TIME**
Whole night sky / Dirt in the ground / Deeper well / I want to varnish / Black eyed dog / Point scarlett: *Collister, Christine & Helen Watson* / God bless the child / Lowish time / Always there / Free will and testament / Sad and beautiful
FLED 3016 / 16 Mar '98 / Fledg'ling

☐ **HORIZON EP**
How far to the horizon / Harvest for the world / How will I ever be simple again / Guilty / Mirage
CING 4001 / Mar '97 / Fledg'ling

☐ **LIVE**
FLECD 1004 / Sep '94 / Fledg'ling

Colm

☐ **SERUM**
NR 422480 / Jan '94 / New Rose

Colman, Kenny

☐ **DREAMSCAPE**
I won't believe my eyes / Where do you start / You again / When Joanna loved me / Days of wine and roses / So many stars / I wish I'd met you / Autumn leaves / Angel eyes / Let's get away from here / As time goes by / Stardust / We go around only once / I couldn't live without you for a day / Honey come back / Laura / Lost on the wind / As long as there's music
JTR 84662 / 29 Jun '98 / Justin Time

Cologne

☐ **EARLY ELECTRONIC MUSIC**
BVHAASTCD 9106 / Oct '93 / Bvhaast

Cologne Concert Big Band

☐ **LIVE**
Strike up the band / Night on the beach / What is this thing called love / For Heaven's sake / Joe Turner's blues / Unforgettable / Take my breath away / We'll be together again / Cherry point / In a sentimental mood / You've changed / Take the 'A' train
MR 874811 / 8 Apr '98 / Mons

Colombier, Michael

☐ **CAPOT POINTU**
176912 / 1 Dec '97 / Magic

Colombo

☐ **COMPOSITIONS 1924-1942**
FA 009CD / Nov '95 / Fremeaux

Colombo, Lou

☐ **I REMEMBER BOBBY**
It all depends on you / I don't stand a ghost of a chance with you / Octopus rag / Memories of you / (I'm afraid) the masquerade is over / My romance / I remember Bobby / Three little words / Emily / Gypsy / Avalon / Easy living / I let a song go out of my heart
CCD 4435 / Nov '90 / Concord Jazz

Colon, Willie

☐ **CONTRABANDO**
Bailando asi / Manana amor / Contrabando / Che che cole / Barrunto / Te conozco / Calle luna calle sol / Lo que es de juan / Pregunta por ahi / Especial no.5 / Soltera / Quien eres
MES 159592 / Apr '93 / Messidor

☐ **TIEMPO PA'MATAR**
El diablo / Tiempo pa'matar / Noche de lose enmascarados / Callejon sin salido / Volo / Falta de consideracion / Gitana / Serenata
MES 159272 / Feb '93 / Messidor

☐ **TOP SECRETS (Colon, Willie & Legal Alien)**
Asi es la vida / Primera noche de amor / El gran varon / Cuando fuiste mujer / Junto a tl / Nunca se acdada / Asia / Marta
MES 159802 / Jun '93 / Messidor

Color Filter

☐ **SLEEP IN A SYNCHROTON**
DRL 054CD / 9 Mar '98 / Darla

Color Me Badd

☐ **AWAKENING**
All the way (freak style) / Written on your face / Kissing you / Love is stronger than pride / Your touch / I'll never love this way again / Remember when / It's alright / Farmer's daughter / All the way / How could this be / Secret lovers
4898462 / 27 Jul '98 / Epic

☐ **TIME & CHANCE**
Intro / Time and chance / Groovy now / Let me have it all / Roseanna's little sister / How deep / La tremenda (Intro) / In thee / Sunshine choose / Bells / Wildflower / Living without her / Close to heaven / Trust me / Let's start with forever / God is love / God is love (Outro) / C'est la vie / I remember
74321166742 / Nov '93 / RCA

Colorblind James Experience

☐ **SOLID BEHIND THE TIMES**
RHRCD 52 / Oct '95 / Red House

Colorvine

☐ **COLORVINE**
MAR 001 / May '97 / Mark Avenue

Colossamite

☐ **ALL LINGO'S CLAMOUR**
GR 34CDEP / Mar '97 / Skingraft

Colosseum

☐ **BREAD AND CIRCUSES**
Watching your every move / Bread and circuses / Wherever I go / High time / Big deal / Playground / No pleasin' / I could tell you tales / Storms behind the breeze / One that got away / Other side of the sky
CLD 91902 / 17 Nov '97 / Cloud Nine

☐ **DAUGHTER OF TIME (Remastered)**
Three score and ten, Amen / Time lament / Take me back to doomsday / Daughter of time / Theme for an imaginary western / Bring out your dead / Downhill and shadows / Time machine
ESMCD 644 / 3 Aug '98 / Essential

☐ **EPITAPH**
Walking in the park / Bring out your dead / Those about to die / Beware the Ides of March / Daughter of time / Valentine suite
RAWCD 014 / Apr '86 / Raw Power

☐ **IDES OF MARCH, THE**
Those about to die / Beware the ides of March / Machine demands a sacrifice / Elegy / Walking in the park / Backwater blues / Time machine / Bring out your dead / Theme for an imaginary Western / Daughter of time / Rope ladder to the moon / Bolero / Encore... Stormy Monday blues
5507342 / May '95 / Spectrum

☐ **LIVE (Remastered)**
Rope ladder to the moon / Walking in the park / Skelington / I can't live without you / Tanglewood 63 / Encore Stormy Monday blues / Lost angeles
ESMCD 641 / 3 Aug '98 / Essential

☐ **REUNION CONCERT 1994**
Those about to die / Elegy / Valentine suite / January's search / February's valentyne / Grass is always greener / Theme for an imaginary western / Machine demands a sacrifice / Solo colinia / Lost Angeles / Stormy Monday blues
INT 31602 / May '95 / Intuition

☐ **STRANGE NEW FLESH (Colosseum II)**
Dark side of the Moog / Down to you / Gemini and Leo / Secret places / On second thoughts / Winds
CLACD 104 / '86 / Castle

☐ **THOSE WHO ARE ABOUT TO DIE SALUTE YOU (Remastered)**
Walking in the park / Plenty hard luck / Madarin / Debut / Beware the ides of March / Road she walked before / Backwater blues / Those about to die
ESMCD 643 / 3 Aug '98 / Essential

☐ **VALENTYNE SUITE (Remastered)**
Kettle / Elegy / Butty's blues / Machine demands a sacrifice / Valentyne suite
ESMCD 642 / 3 Aug '98 / Essential

Colour Club

☐ **COLOUR CLUB**
Welcome to the Colour Club / Scene / Freedom words / Great issue: Freedom / Trust in me / Consumption / Scene II / On and on / Scene III / Chicago / Cultures of jazz / Scene IV / Howbotsuntinkikdis / Scene V / State of mind / Don't wait too long
JVC 20342 / Aug '94 / JVC

Colour Of Memory

☐ **OLD MAN & THE SEA, THE**
Grace / Rigmarole / Rain parade / Emotional fish / Changed days / Into my own / Always with me / Days on end / Sun fire majestic / Old man and the sea
IRCD 028 / Jan '95 / Iona

Colour Trip

☐ **GROUND LEVEL SEX TYPE THING**
SPV 08436222 / Dec '94 / SPV

☐ GROUNDLEVELSEXTYPE
SPV 8436222 / Dec '96 / SPV

Colourbox

☐ COLOURBOX
Suspicion / Arena / Say you / Just give 'em whiskey / You keep me hangin' on / Moon is blue / Manic / Sleepwalker / Inside informer / Punch
GAD 508CD / 6 Jul '98 / 4AD

☐ COLOURBOX MINI LP
Shotgun / Keep on pushing / Nation / Justice / Official colourbox world cup theme / Baby I love you so / Looks like we're shy one horse / Breakdown
MAD 315 CD / Nov '86 / 4AD

Coltrane, Alice

☐ ASTRAL MEDITATIONS
IMP 12422 / 24 Aug '98 / Impulse Jazz

☐ JOURNEY IN SATCHIDANANDA
Journey in Satchidananda / Shiva-loka / Stover Bombay / Something about John Coltrane / Isis and Osiris
IMP 12282 / Apr '97 / Impulse Jazz

☐ PTAH, THE EL DAOUD
Ptah, the El Daoud / Turiya and Ramakrishna / Blue Nile / Mantra
IMP 12012 / Sep '96 / Impulse Jazz

Coltrane, Joe 'Blue'

☐ MESSING WITH THE BLUES
WCD 120620 / 21 Sep '97 / Wolf

Coltrane, John

☐ AFRICA BRASS VOL.1 & 2
Africa / Blues minor / Greensleeves / Greensleeves / Song of the underground railroad / Africa
MCAD 42001 / Jun '89 / Impulse Jazz

☐ AFRO BLUE IMPRESSIONS
Lonnie's lament / Naima / Chasin' the trane / My favourite things / Afro blue / Cousin Mary / I want to talk about you / Spiritual / Impressions
2620101 / '94 / Pablo

☐ AVANT GARDE, THE (Coltrane, John & Don Cherry)
Focus on sanity / Bemsha swing / Cherryco / Invisible / Blessing
7567900412 / Jul '93 / Atlantic

☐ BAGS AND TRANE (Coltrane, John & Milt Jackson)
Bags and trane / Three little words / Night we called it a day / Be bop / Late late blues
7567813482 / Jun '93 / Atlantic

☐ BAHIA
Bahia / Goldsboro express / My ideal / I'm a dreamer (aren't we all) / Something I dreamed last night
OJCCD 415 / Feb '92 / Original Jazz Classics

☐ BELIEVER, THE
Believer / Nakatini serenade / Do I believe you because you're beautiful / Filidia / Paul's pal
OJCCD 876 / Jun '96 / Original Jazz Classics

☐ BEST OF JOHN COLTRANE, THE
My favourite things / Naima / Giant steps / Equinox / Cousin Mary / Central Park West
7567813662 / Jun '93 / Atlantic

☐ BETHLEHEM YEARS, THE (2CD Set)
Midriff / Ain't life grand / Tippin' / Pristine / El toro valentine / Kiss of no return / Late date / Outer world / Not so sleepy / Love and the weather / If I'm lucky / Turtle walk / Oasis / Midriff / Midriff / Kiss of no return / Kiss of no return / Outer world / Outer world / El torro / Ain't life grand / Ain't life grand / Pristine / Pristine / Pristine / Tippin' / Tippin'
CDGR 2332 / 24 Aug '98 / Charly

☐ BLACK PEARLS
Black pearls / Lover come back to me / Sweet sapphire blues / Believer / Nakatini serenade / Do I love you because you're beautiful
OJCCD 352 / Feb '92 / Original Jazz Classics

☐ BLUE TRAIN
Blue train / Moment's notice / Locomotion / I'm old fashioned / Lazy bird / Blue train / Lazy bird
CDP 8534280 / Mar '97 / Blue Note

☐ BLUE TRANE (John Coltrane Plays The Blues)
Slow trane / Traneing / Billie's bounce / Real McCoy / Big Paul / Sweet sapphire blues
PRCD 11005 / Jun '97 / Prestige

☐ BYE BYE BLACKBIRD
Bye bye blackbird / Traneing in
OJCCD 681 / Feb '92 / Original Jazz Classics

☐ CATTIN' WITH C & Q (Coltrane, John & Paul Quinichette)
OJCCD 460 / Apr '92 / Original Jazz Classics

☐ COAST TO COAST (Coltrane, John Quartet)
MCD 0352 / Jan '92 / Moon

☐ COLTRANE
Bakai / Violets for your furs / Time was / Straight street / While my lady sleeps / Chronic blues
OJCCD 20 / Oct '92 / Original Jazz Classics

☐ COLTRANE JAZZ
Little old lady / Village blues / My shining hour / Fifth house / Harmonique / Like Sonny / I'll wait and pray / Some other blues / Like Sonny / I'll wait and pray
7567813442 / Feb '92 / Atlantic

☐ COLTRANE PLAYS THE BLUES
Blues to Elvin / Blues to Bechet / Blues to you / Mr. Day / Mr. Syms / Mr. Knight / Untitled original
7567813512 / Jun '93 / Atlantic

☐ COLTRANE'S SOUND
Night has a thousand eyes / Central Park West / Liberia / Body and soul / Equinox / Satellite / 26-2 / Body and soul
7567813582 / Mar '93 / Atlantic

☐ COMPLETE 1961 VILLAGE VANGUARD RECORDINGS, THE (4CD Set)
India / Chasin' the train / Impressions / Spiritual / Miles mode / Naima / Braslia / Chasin' another train / India / Spiritual / Softly as in the morning sunrise / Chasin' the train / Greensleeves / Impressions / Spiritual / Naima / Impressions / India / Greensleeves / Miles Mode / India / Spiritual
IMPD 4232 / Sep '97 / Impulse Jazz

☐ COMPLETE 1961 VILLAGE VANGUARD RECORDINGS, THE (The Master Takes)
Spiritual / Softly as in a morning sunrise / Chasin' the Trane / India / Impressions
IMP 12512 / 23 Mar '98 / Impulse Jazz

☐ COMPLETE AFRICA BRASS VOL.1 & 2 (2CD Set)
Greensleeves / Song of the underground railroad / Greensleeves / Damned don't cry / Africa (first version) / Blues minor / Africa (alternate take) / Africa
IMP 21682 / Oct '95 / Impulse Jazz

☐ COMPLETE GRAZ CONCERT, THE (2CD Set)
Bye bye blackbird / Inchworm / Autumn leaves / Everytime we say goodbye / Mr. PC / I want to talk about you / Impressions / My favourite things
CPCD 8262 / Jan '97 / Charly

☐ COUNTDOWN (Coltrane, John & Wilbur Harden)
Wells Fargo / Wells Fargo / EFFPH / Countdown / Rhodomagnetics 1 / Rhodomagnetics 2 / Snuffy / West 42nd street
VGCD 650102 / Oct '93 / Vogue

☐ CRESCENT (Coltrane, John Quartet)
Crescent / Wise one / Bessie's blues / Lonnie's lament / Drum thing
IMP 12002 / Sep '96 / Impulse Jazz

☐ DAKAR
Dakar / Mary's blues / Route 4 / Velvet scene / Witches' pet / Cat walk / CTA / Interplay / Anatomy / Light blue / Soul eyes
OJCCD 393 / Feb '92 / Original Jazz Classics

☐ DIG IT (Coltrane, John & Red Garland Quintet)
Billie's bounce / Crazy rhythm / CTA / Lazy Mae
OJCCD 392 / Apr '93 / Original Jazz Classics

☐ EUROPEAN TOUR, THE
Promise / I want to talk about you / Naima / Mr. PC
CD 23082222 / Jul '94 / Pablo

☐ GIANT STEPS
Giant steps / Cousin Mary / Countdown / Spiral / Syeeda's song flute / Naima / Mr. PC
7813372 / '87 / Atlantic

☐ GIANT STEPS (Deluxe Edition)
Giant Steps / Cousin Mary / Countdown / Spiral / Syeeda's song flute / Naima / Mr. PC / Giant steps (alternative version 1) / Naima (alternative version 1) / Cousin Mary (alternative take) / Countdown (alternative take) / Syeeda's song flute (alternative take) / Giant steps (alternative version 2) / Naima (alternative version 2) / Giant steps (alternative take)
8122752032 / 20 Jul '98 / Atlantic

☐ IN A SOULFUL MOOD
In a sentimental mood / Tunji / Soul eyes / Inchworm / Nancy / Blues minor / After the rain / You don't know what love is / I want to talk about you / Alabama / Naima / Afro blue
MCCD 170 / Sep '94 / Music Club

☐ JAZZ PORTRAITS
Trane's blues / Sweet Sue, just you / Soultrane / Mating call / Monk's mood / Chronic blues / While my lady sleeps / Straight street / Bakay
CD 14507 / May '94 / Jazz Portraits

☐ JOHN COLTRANE & KENNY BURRELL (Coltrane, John & Kenny Burrell)
OJCCD 300 / Oct '92 / Original Jazz Classics

☐ JOHN COLTRANE AND THE JAZZ GIANTS
Airegin / Mating call / Monk's mood / Trinkle tinkle / I love you / Soft lights and sweet music / Billie's bounce / Lover / Russian lullaby / Invitation
FCD 60014 / Oct '93 / Fantasy

☐ JOHN COLTRANE MEETS ERIC DOLPHY (Coltrane, John & Eric Dolphy)
MCD 0692 / Aug '95 / Moon

☐ JOHN COLTRANE QUARTET PLAYS, THE (Coltrane, John Quartet)
Chim chim cheree / Brazilia / Nature boy / Song of praise / Feelin' good
IMP 12142 / Apr '97 / Impulse Jazz

☐ JOHN COLTRANE QUARTET, THE
Out of this world / Soul eyes / Inch worm / Tunji / Miles mode / Big nick / Up against the wall
IMP 12152 / Apr '97 / Impulse Jazz

☐ JOHN COLTRANE SAMPLER
Russian lullaby / I love you / Time was / You leave me breathless / Soft lights and soft music
OJCX 003 / Jan '98 / Original Jazz Classics

☐ LAST TRANE
Lover / Slowtrane / By the numbers / Come rain or come shine
OJCCD 394 / Feb '92 / Original Jazz Classics

☐ LIVE AT BIRDLAND
Mr. PC / Miles mode / My favourite things / Body and soul
CDCHARLY 68 / Jun '87 / Charly
LEJAZZCD 58 / Nov '96 / Le Jazz

☐ LIVE AT BIRDLAND (Coltrane, John Quartet)
Afro blue / I want to talk about you / Promise / Alabama / Your lady
IMP 11982 / Sep '96 / Impulse Jazz

☐ LIVE AT THE VILLAGE VANGUARD AGAIN
Naima / My favourite things
IMP 12132 / Apr '97 / Impulse Jazz

☐ LIVE IN ANTIBES 1965
LEJAZZCD 10 / Jun '93 / Le Jazz

☐ LIVE IN JAPAN (4CD Set)
Afro blue / Peace on Earth / Crescent / Peace on Earth / Leo / My favourite things
GRP 41022 / Jul '91 / GRP

☐ LIVE IN PARIS
Naima / Impressions / Blue valse / Afro blue / Impressions (2nd version)
LEJAZZCD 31 / Sep '94 / Le Jazz

☐ LIVE IN SEATTLE (2CD Set)
Cosmos / Out of this world / Body and soul / Tapestry in sound / Evolution / Afro blue
GRP 21462 / Nov '94 / GRP

☐ LIVE IN STOCKHOLM 1961
My favourite things / Blue train / Naima / Impressions
LEJAZZCD 57 / Sep '96 / Le Jazz

☐ LIVE IN STOCKHOLM 1963
Mr. PC / Traneing in / Spiritual / I want to talk about you
LEJAZZCD 59 / Jan '97 / Le Jazz

☐ LIVING SPACE (Coltrane, John Quartet)
Living space / Untitled 90314 / Dusk dawn / Untitled 90320 / Last blues
IMP 12462 / 23 Mar '98 / Impulse Jazz

☐ LOVE SUPREME, A
Acknowledgement (part 1) / Resolution (part 2) / Pursuance (part 3) / Psalm (part 4)
MCLD 19029 / Apr '92 / MCA

☐ LUSH LIFE
Like someone in love / I love you / Tranes's slow blues / Lush life / I hear a rhapsody
OJC20 1312 / Sep '98 / Original Jazz Classics

☐ MAJOR WORKS OF JOHN COLTRANE, THE (2CD Set)
Ascension I / Ascension II / Om / Kula se mama / Selflessness
GRP 21132 / Jan '92 / Impulse Jazz

☐ MAN MADE MILES
CDSGP 0265 / Jan '97 / Prestige

☐ MASTERS, THE (2CD Set)
EDMCD 018 / 24 Nov '97 / Eagle

☐ MEDITATIONS
Love / Consequences / Serenity / Father and the Son and the Holy Ghost / Compassion
IMP 11992 / Sep '96 / Impulse Jazz

☐ MY FAVOURITE THINGS
My favourite things / Every time we say goodbye / Summertime / But not for me
7567813462 / Mar '93 / Atlantic

☐ MY FAVOURITE THINGS
JHR 73538 / May '93 / Jazz Hour

☐ MY FAVOURITE THINGS
My favourite things / Everytime we say goodbye / Summertime / But not for me / My favourite things part 1 (single version) / My favourite things part 2 (single version)
8122752042 / 20 Jul '98 / Atlantic

☐ NEW WAVE IN JAZZ (Coltrane, John & Archie Shepp)
Nature boy / Ham bone / Brilliant corners / Plight / Blue free / Intellect
GRP 11372 / Mar '94 / GRP

☐ OLE COLTRANE
Ole / Dahomey dance / Aisha / To her ladyship
7813492 / Feb '94 / Atlantic

☐ OM
MCAD 39118 / Jun '89 / Impulse Jazz

☐ ON STAGE 1962
556632 / Mar '96 / Accord

☐ ONCE IN A WHILE
Tanganyika / BJ / Anecdac / Once in a while
CDSGP 0266 / 26 Jan '98 / Prestige

☐ PARIS CONCERT, THE
Mr. PC / Inchworm / Every time we say goodbye
OJCCD 781 / Jun '94 / Original Jazz Classics

☐ PRESTIGE RECORDINGS, THE (16CD Set)
Tenor madness / Weeja / Polka dots and moonbeams / On it / Avalon / Tenor conclave / Hoe deep is the ocean / Just you, just me / Bob's boys / Mating call / Soultrane / Grind / Super jet / On a misty night / Romas / Soul eyes / Anatomy / Interplay / Light blue / CTA / Eclypso / Solacium / Minor mishap / Tommy's time / Dakar / Route 4 / Velvet scene / Witches' pit / Cat walk / Pot pourri / JM's dream doll / Don't explain / Falling in love with love / Blue calypso / Way you look tonight / From this moment on / One by one / Cattin' / Anatomy / Vodka / Sunday / Straight street / While my lady sleeps / Chronic blues / Bakai / Violets for your furs / Time was / I hear a rhapsody / Trane's slo blues / Slowtrane / Like someone in love / I love you / Dealin' / Wheelin' / Robbin's nest / Things ain't what they used to be / You leave me breathless / Bass blues / Soft lights and sweet music / Traneing in / Slow dance / Our delight / They can't take that away from me / Woody 'n' you / I got it bad and that ain't good / Undecided / Soul junction / What is there to say / Birk's works / Hallelujah / All morning long / Billie's bounce / Solitude / Two bass hit / Soft winds / Lazy Mae / Under Paris skies / Two sons / Clifford's kappa / Filide / Paul's pal / Ammon joy / Grove blues / Real McCoy / It might as well be Spring / Lush life / Believer / Nakatini serenade / Come rain or come shine / Lover / Russian lullaby / Theme for Ernie / You say you care / Good bait / I want to talk about you / Lyresto / Why was I born / Freight Trane / I never knew / Big Paul / Rise 'n' shine / I see your face before me / If there is something lovelier than you / Little Melonae / By the number / Black pearls / Lover come back to me / Sweet sapphire blues / Spring is here / Invitation / I'm a dreamer / Aren't we all / Love thy neighbour / Don't take your love from me / Stardust / My ideal / I'll get by / Do I love you because you're beautiful / Then I'll be tired of you / Something I dreamed last night / Bahia / Goldsboro express / Time after time
16PCD 44052 / Nov '96 / Prestige

☐ SAX IMPRESSIONS
Blue train / Naima / Spiritual / Traneing in / My favourite things / Impressions
BN 007 / Apr '98 / Blue Nite

☐ SETTIN' THE PACE
I see your face before me / If there's someone lovelier than you / Little Melonae / Rise and shine
OJCCD 78 / Feb '92 / Original Jazz Classics

☐ SOULTRANE
Good bait / I want to talk about you / You say you care / Theme for Ernie / Russian lullaby
OJCCD 21 / Oct '92 / Original Jazz Classics
OJC20 0212 / Sep '98 / Original Jazz Classics

☐ STANDARD COLTRANE
Don't take your love from me / I'll get by / Spring is here / Invitation
OJCCD 246 / Feb '92 / Original Jazz Classics

☐ STARDUST
Stardust / Time after time / Love thy neighbour / Then I'll be tired of you
OJCCD 920 / Jun '97 / Original Jazz Classics

☐ STELLAR REGIONS
Creation / Sun star / Stellar regions / Iris / Offering / Configuration / Jimmy's mode / Tranesonic / Stellar regions (alternate take) / Sun star (alternate take) / Tranesonic (alternate take)
IMP 11692 / Oct '95 / Impulse Jazz

☐ SUN SHIP
Sun ship / Dearly beloved / Amen / Attending / Ascent
IMP 11672 / Nov '95 / Impulse Jazz

☐ TENOR CONCLAVE (Coltrane, John & Hank Mobley/Al Cohn/Zoot Sims)
Tenor conclave / Tenor conclave / Bob's boy's / How deep is the ocean
OJCCD 127 / Jul '94 / Original Jazz Classics

☐ THANK YOU JOHN COLTRANE (Arkadia Jazz All Stars)
AJ 70002 / 27 Apr '98 / Arkadia

☐ TRANEING IN - WITH THE RED GARLAND TRIO
Traneing in / Slow dance / Bass blues / You leave me breathless / Soft lights and sweet music
OJCCD 189 / Mar '92 / Original Jazz Classics

☐ TRANSCENDENCE
Blue train / Spiritual / Naima / My favourite things / Impressions / Traneing in
SUMCD 4166 / 26 Jan '98 / Summit

☐ TURNING POINT (The Bethlehem Years)
BET 6003 / Jan '95 / Bethlehem

☐ WHEELIN' & DEALIN'
Things ain't what they used to be / Wheelin' / Wheelin' / Robbin's nest / Dealin' / Dealin'
OJCCD 672 / May '93 / Original Jazz Classics

Columbia Corina

☐ DEEP FLITE
DFDCD 7 / Mar '97 / Defender

Columbo, Russ

☐ PRISONER OF LOVE (22 Crooning Hits 1928-1934)
Prisoner of love / Back in your own back yard / Glad rag doll / Peach of a pair / I don't know why / Guilty / You call it madness but I call it love / Sweet and lovely / Time on my hands / You try somebody else / Call me darling / Where the blue of the night / Save the last dance for me / All of me / Just friends / You're my everything / Auf weiderseh'n my dear / Paradise / Living in dreams / When you're in love / Too beautiful for words / I see two lovers / Goodnight sweetheart
CDAJA 5234 / Nov '97 / Living Era

☐ SAVE THE LAST DANCE FOR ME 1928-1934
TT 409 / May '98 / Take Two

Columbus Jazz Orchestra

☐ NIGHT MAGIC
SB 2084 / Sep '97 / Sea Breeze

Column One

☐ FREEDOM IS A SICKNESS
EFA 084892 / 26 Aug '97 / Dossier

Colvin, Shawn

☐ COVER GIRL
Every little thing (he) does is magic / (looking for) the heart of saturday night / One cool remove / Satin sheets / There's a rugged road / Killing the blues / Window to the world / Someday / Twilight / If these walls could speak / This must be the place (naive melody) / You're gonna make me lonesome when you go / 01'55
4772402 / 2 Feb '98 / Columbia

☐ FAT CITY
Polaroids / Tennessee / Tenderness on the block / Round of blues / Monopoly / Orion in the sky / Climb on (a back that's strong) / Set the prairie on fire / Object of my affection / Kill the messenger / I don't know why
4679612 / 13 Jul '98 / Columbia

☐ FEW SMALL REPAIRS, A
Sunny came home / Get out of this house / Facts about Jimmy / You and the Mona Lisa / Trouble / I want it back / If I were brave / Wichita skyline / 84,000 different delusions / Suicide alley / What I get paid for / New thing now / Nothin' on me
4843272 / Oct '96 / Columbia

☐ LIVE 1988
PLUCD 002 / Mar '96 / Plump

☐ STEADY ON
Steady on / Diamonds in the rough / Shotgun down the avalanche / Stranded another long one / Cry like an angel / Something to believe in / Story / Ricochet in time / Dead of the night
4661422 / Aug '95 / Columbia

Colyer, Ken

☐ AT THE DANCING SLIPPER 1969
AZCD 25 / Nov '96 / Azure

☐ BOSTON CHURCH SERVICE
BCD 351 / May '98 / GHB

☐ COLYER'S PLEASURE (Colyer, Ken Jazzmen)
Teasing rag / After you've gone / Highway blues / Dardanella / I can't escape from you / You always hurt the one you love / Creole bo bo / Honeysuckle rose / Barefoot boy / Mahogany Hall stomp / Gettysburg march / La Harpe St. blues / Thriller rag / I'm travelling / Virginia strut
LACD 34 / Nov '94 / Lake

☐ DARKNESS ON THE DELTA (The Hague 1979)
Lord, Lord you've sure been good to me / Darkness on the delta / Yaaka hula hickey dula / Gettysburg march / Deep Bayou blues / Shine / Auf wiedersehen
BLCD 760518 / May '97 / Black Lion

☐ DECCA YEARS 1955-59, THE (Colyer, Ken Jazzmen)
LA 001CD / Jan '94 / Lake

☐ IN HOLLAND (Colyer, Ken & Butch Thompson)
MECCACD 1032 / Nov '94 / Music Mecca

☐ KEN COLYER & CHRIS BLOUNT
KCT 5CD / Oct '92 / Ken Colyer Trust

☐ KEN COLYER & RAYMOND BURKE 1952-1953 (Colyer, Ken & Raymond Burke)
Shine / Just a closer walk with thee / Up a lazy river / Dippermouth blues / Song of the islands / Savoy blues / Silver dollar / Tishomongo blues no.2 / Fidgety feet / In the evening when the sun goes down / Make me a pallet on the floor / Blues no.2 / Willie the weeper / Tishomingo blues no.1 / Panama / Blue no.1 / High society / Indiana / World is waiting for the sunrise
504CD 23 / Mar '98 / 504

☐ KEN COLYER IN CONCERT 1959 (Colyer, Ken Jazzmen)
Sweet fields / When I leave the world behind / Nobody knows the trouble I've seen / Aunt Hagar's blues / Cheek to cheek / Willie the weeper / Muskrat ramble / Peanut vendor / Chimes blues / Don't go 'way nobody
DJCD 001 / Mar '98 / Dine-a-mite

☐ KEN COLYER IN NEW YORK 1953
New Orleans hop scop blues / Climax rag / Black cat on the fence / Thats a plenty / Gravier street blues / How long blues / That's a plenty / Gravier street blues / Frankie and Johnny / Buddy bolden blues / Panama / Winter wonderland / Chiri biri bin
504CD 53 / Mar '98 / 504

☐ KEN COLYER TRUST BAND PLAY NEW ORLEANS JAZZ (Colyer, Ken Trust Band)
Yes Lord I'm crippled / Alexander's ragtime band / Over the waves / Breeze / Salutation march / Panama rag / Lights out / Bogalousa strut / Amazing Grace / Darktown strutters ball / San Jacinto blues / Precious Lord / Silver bell / Sing on / Washington and Lee swing / My life will be sweeter some day
URCD 112 / Aug '94 / Upbeat

☐ LIVE AT THE PIZZA EXPRESS, LONDON, FEBRUARY 1985 (Colyer, Ken Jazz Quartet)
Blame it on the blues / How long blues / Willie the weeper / Dinah / Dallas blues / (Back home again in) Indiana / Scatterbrain, Liza / Sweet Lorraine / Weary blues
AZCD 33 / Jan '95 / Azure

☐ MORE OF KEN COLYER & HIS JAZZMEN 25/1/72 (Colyer, Ken & His Hand Picked Jazzmen)
Pretty baby / Sing on / Snag it / Wabash blues / Louisian-I-Ay / Tishomingo blues / Black cat on the fence / High society
KCT 3CD / Jun '96 / Ken Colyer Trust

☐ ONCE MORE FOR AUNTIE
URCD 137 / Jun '98 / Upbeat

☐ PAINTING THE CLOUDS WITH SUNSHINE
Should I reveal / Painting the clouds with sunshine / When I grow too old to dream / Jungle town / Uptown bumps / Snag it
BLCD 760501 / Oct '90 / Black Lion

☐ SERENADING AUNTIE (BBC Recordings 1955-1960)
Carolina moon / In the evening / Papa dip / Tell me your dreams / My blue heaven / Perdido street blues / Clarinet marmalade / When I leave the world behind / Eccentric rag / Riverside blues / Thriller rag / Hilarity rag / Yancey stomp / Heliotrope bouquet / Creole song / Chrysanthemum rag / You've got to see mama ev'ry night / Ice cream / Dinah / Going home / World is waiting for the sunrise
URCD 111 / Apr '94 / Upbeat

☐ STUDIO 51 REVISITED (Colyer, Ken Jazzmen)
Oh lady be good / Dusty rag / Fidgety feet / Perdido street blues / Ace in the hole / Muskrat ramble / Yes Lord I'm crippled / Riverside blues / In the sweet bye and bye / Wolverine blues
LACD 25 / Jan '95 / Lake

☐ SUNNY SIDE OF KEN COLYER, THE (Colyer, Ken All Stars)
Sunny side of the street / Yaaka hula hickey dula / Canal Street blues (Slow) / Canal street blues (Fast) / Royal garden blues / Bill Bailey, Won't you please come home / Chloe / You always hurt the one you love / Everywhere you go the sunshine follows you
URCD 113 / Oct '94 / Upbeat

☐ TRIBUTE TO THE ORIGINAL CRANE RIVER BAND, A (Colyer, Ken Trust New Orleans Jazz Band & Sonny Morris)
JCCD 3020 / Oct '97 / Jazz Crusade

☐ UP JUMPED THE DEVIL
Sensation rag / Milnburg joys / When you wore a tulip / Mazie (Martha) / Up jumped the devil / Moose march / Breeze / Bourbon street parade / Red sails in the sunset / Dr. Jazz / Tiger rag
URCD 114 / Apr '95 / Upbeat

☐ URGENT REQUEST (Colyer, Ken & Chris Blount Band)
BCD 184 / Nov '96 / GHB

☐ VERY VERY LIVE AT THE 100 CLUB (Colyer, Ken Jazzmen)
Weary blues / Old Kentucky home / Clarinet marmalade / I ain't gonna give nobody none of this jelly roll / St. Philip Street breakdown / When you wore a tulip (and I wore a big red rose) / Careless love / I said I wasn't going to tell nobody / Moose march / Red wing / Till we meet again
URCD 130 / Sep '97 / Upbeat

☐ WANDERING (Crown Hotel Twickenham, July 1965) (Colyer, Ken Skiffle Group)
I'm going to walk and talk with Jesus / No letters today/Colorado trail / Ella speed / Poor Howard / I can't sleep / Muleskinner blues / Wandering / If I could hear my mother pray again / Good morning blues / Drop down mama / Easy ridin' buggy / New York town / Green corn / Casey Jones
LACD 68 / Sep '96 / Lake

☐ WHEN I LEAVE THE WORLD BEHIND (Colyer, Ken & Sammy Rimington)
BCD 152 / Jun '96 / GHB

☐ WRAP YOUR TROUBLES IN DREAMS (Colyer, Ken Quartet)
AZCD 34 / Dec '97 / Azure

Coma Virus

☐ HIDDEN
DFX 027CD / Apr '97 / Side Effects

Combat Shock

☐ WISHFUL DRINKING
BFRCD 003 / 1 Sep '97 / Bomb Factory

Combelle, Alix

☐ CLASSICS 1935-1940
CLASSICS 714 / Jul '93 / Classics

☐ CLASSICS 1940-1941
CLASSICS 751 / May '94 / Classics

☐ CLASSICS 1942-1943
CLASSICS 782 / Nov '94 / Classics

Combustible Edison

☐ I, SWINGER
Cadillac / Millionaire's holiday / Breakfast at Denny's / Intermission / Cry me a river / Impact / Guadaloupe / Carnival of souls / Veldt / Surabaya Johnny / Spy Vs. spy / Theme from The Tiki Wonder Hour
EFA 049342 / Mar '94 / City Slang

☐ SCHIZOPHONIC
RTD 34600022 / Feb '96 / City Slang

Come

☐ DON'T ASK, DON'T TELL
BBQCD 160 / Sep '94 / Beggars Banquet

☐ GENTLY DOWN THE STREAM
One piece / Recidivist / Stomp / Sorry too late / Saints around my neck / Silk city / Middle of nowhere / Fade outs / Jam blues / New coats / Former model / March
WIGCD 043 / 9 Feb '98 / Domino

☐ NEAR LIFE EXPERIENCE
WIGCD 025 / May '96 / Domino

Comecon

☐ CONVERGING CONSPIRACIES
CM 770752 / Jan '94 / Century Media

☐ FABLE FROLIC
CM 77094CD / Sep '95 / Century Media

Comedy Harmonists

☐ AUF WIEDERSEHEN
Das alte spinnrad / Am brunnen vor dem tore / An der schonen blauen donau / Auf wiederseh'n, my dear / Barber of Seville overture / Barcarolle / Ein bisschen leichtsinn kann nicht schaden / Congo lullaby / Creole love call / Hein spielt abends so schon auf dem schifferklavier / Heute nacht oder nie / Holzhackerlied / Humoreske / Ich traum' von eine marchennacht / In stiller nacht / Komm im traum / Liebling mein herz / Muss l' denn zum stadtle hinaus / Night and day / Perpetuum mobile / Puppenhochzeit / Sah ein knab' ein roslein steh'n / Tea for two / Wenn die Sonnja russisch tanzt / Whispering
CDAJA 5204 / Nov '96 / Living Era

☐ COMEDIAN HARMONISTS
Barber of Seville / Must I, then / When Sonia danced in Russian style / Sleep my little Prince / Good moon, you go so gently / Minuet / Creole love call / Little lightness / Blue Danube waltz / Court serenade / Marie Marie / Auf wiedersehen my dear / Liebesleid / Boy saw a rosebush / Woodcutter's song / Village music / Old ship piano / Let's have another beer / In the hayloft / Perpetuum mobile
PASTCD 7000 / Jan '93 / Flapper

Comelade, Pascal

☐ MUSIC FOR FILMS VOL.2
DSA 54042 / Dec '96 / CDSA

Comet, Al

☐ COMET
Saturne / Krishna 88 / Basse pression / L'envol du canard / XTC for you / Platform H / One three seven / L22 / Over the hills
BIAS 349CD / Jul '97 / Play It Again Sam

Comet Gain

☐ CASINO CLASSICS
Footstompers / Million and nine / Turnpike county blue / Last night / Original arrogance / Another girl / Music upstairs / Villain / Stay with me / Charlie / Just seventeen / Ghost of the roman empire / Intergalactic starbed / Chevron action flash
WIJ 042CD / Apr '95 / Wiiija

☐ MAGNETIC POETRY
Strength / Raspberries / Language of the spy / Steps to the sea / These are the dreams of a working girl / Pier Angeli / Final Horses / Tighten up
WIJCD 1054 / 6 Oct '97 / Wiiija

Comite Imaginaire

☐ HOLZ FOR EUROPA
FMPCD 84 / May '97 / Full Moon

Commander Cody

☐ BAR ROOM CLASSICS
AIM 1024CD / Sep '93 / Aim

☐ LET'S ROCK
Let's rock / Rockin' over China / Midnight on the strand / Do you mind / Angel got married / Truckstop at the end of the world / One more ride / Your cash ain't nothin' but trash / Rockabilly funeral / Transfusion / Home of rock 'n' roll
BPCD 72086 / Dec '94 / Blind Pig

☐ TOUR FROM HELL 1973, THE (Commander Cody & His Lost Planet Airmen)
I took three bennies and my semi truck won't start / Smoke smoke smoke / Four five times / What's the matter now / Down to seeds and stems again / Truck stop rock / Goin' back to Tennessee / Mama tried / All I have to offer is me / Git it / Sister Sue / Lost in the ozone again
AIM 1059 / Nov '96 / Aim

☐ VERY BEST OF COMMANDER CODY AND HIS LOST PLANET AIRMEN (Commander Cody & His Lost Planet Airmen)
Back to Tennessee / Wine do yer stuff / Seeds and stems (again) / Daddy's gonna treat you right / Family Bible / Lost in the ozone / Hot rod Lincoln / Beat me Daddy, eight to the bar / Truckstop rock / Truck drivin' man / It should've been me / Watch my 38 / Everybody's doin' it now / Rock that boogie / Smoke, smoke, smoke / Honeysuckle honey / Sunset on the sage (live) / Cryin' time (live)
SEECD 64 / Oct '96 / See For Miles

☐ WORST CASE SCENARIO (Commander Cody & His Lost Planet Airmen)
Big rock / Lights go out / Lose it tonight / Real gone / Green light / Good morning judge / Working mans blues / New radio / They kicked me out of the band / River city / Buddy's cafe / Crash pad blues / Keys to my cadillac / King of the honky tonks / Mansion on the hill / Death ray boogie
AIM 1043 / Apr '95 / Aim

Commander Tom

☐ COMMANDER TOM IN THE MIX (Various Artists)
NOOMCD 0102 / 3 Aug '98 / Noom

☐ EYES
NOOMLP 007 / 2 Mar '98 / Noom

Commando

☐ BATTLE OF THIS WEEK
MNWCD 190 / Mar '90 / MNW

Commercials

☐ BACKSTABBING
SHAG 020 / 1 Jun '98 / Flotsam & Jetsam

Commodores

☐ COMMODORES, THE
Let's get busy / Let's get busy / Shut up and dance / No tricks / Living on the edge / Missing you / Everything reminds me of you / Take my hand / Your smile / Don't rock it
12465 / Oct '95 / Laserlight

☐ RISE UP
Cowboys to girls / Rise up / Losing you / Who's making love / Sing a simple song / Baby this is forever / Love canoe / Come by here / Keep on dancing
CDBM 035 / Apr '87 / Blue Moon

☐ ULTIMATE COLLECTION
5305012 / 10 Aug '98 / Motown

☐ VERY BEST OF THE COMMODORES, THE
Easy / Three times a lady / Nightshift / Brick house / Machine gun / Zoom / Old fashion love / Sail on / Lady (you bring me up) / Oh no / Too hot ta trot / Zoo (the human zoo) / Still / Sweet love / Janet / Flying high / Only you / Animal instinct / Just to be close to you / Wonderland
5305472 / Jul '95 / Motown

Common

☐ ONE DAY IT WILL ALL MAKE SENSE
Introspective / Invocation / Real nigga quotes / Retrospect for life / Gettin' down at the amphitheatre / Food for funk / Gaining one's definition / My city / Hungry / All night long / Stolen moments / 1 2 Many / Stolen moments part 3 / Making a name for ourselves / Reminding me / Pops rap part 2 / Fatherhood
4869062 / 29 Sep '97 / Epic

Common Cause

☐ SAUSALITO
BB 721202 / Mar '97 / Backbeat

Common Language

☐ FLESH IMPACT
Happy (hell) / Mute / Life in the grand hotel / Dead white horse / Such a price / Sharks to blood / 1 / Help us find klaus / Bsh20a / Engel
BFFP 84CD / Sep '93 / Blast First

Communards

☐ COMMUNARDS
Don't leave me this way / La dolarosa / Disenchanted / Reprise / So cold the night / You are my world / Lover man / Don't slip away / Heaven's above / Forbidden love / Breadline Britain / Disenchanted
8288632 / Jan '97 / London

☐ HEAVEN
You are my world / Czardas / So cold the night / Tomorrow / Annie / Hold on tight / If I could tell you / There's more to love (than boy meets girl) / Zing went the strings of my heart / I do it all for love / Sanctified / Judgement day / Heaven's above / Victims (Live)
5500932 / Oct '93 / Spectrum

Como, Perry

☐ 20 GREATEST HITS VOL.1
Magic moments / Caterina / Catch a falling star / I know / When you were sweet sixteen / I believe / Try to remember / Love makes the world go round / Prisoner of love / Don't let the stars get in your eyes / Hot diggity (dog ziggity boom) / Round and round / If I loved you / Hello, young lovers / Delaware / Moonglow / Killing me softly / More / Dear hearts and gentle people / I love you and don't you forget it
ND 89019 / Apr '90 / RCA

☐ 20 GREATEST HITS VOL.2
And I love you so / For the good times / Close to you / Seattle / Tie a yellow ribbon / Walk right back / What kind of fool am I / Days of wine and roses / Where do I begin / Without a song / It's impossible / I think of you / If / We've only just begun / I want to give / Raindrops keep falling on my head / You make me feel so young / Temptation / Way we were / Sing
ND 89020 / Apr '92 / RCA

☐ BEST OF PERRY COMO, THE
Best of times / Days of wine and roses / What's new / Something / For all we know / Very thought of you / I left my heart in San Francisco / It's impossible / Where do I begin / What kind of fool am I / Without a song / Quiet nights of quiet stars / Close to you / You are the sunshine of my life / I think of you / When I need you / If / For the good times / Most beautiful girl in the world / Wind beneath my wings
74321378382 / Jul '96 / RCA

☐ CLASSIC YEARS, THE
I wonder who's kissing her now / Deep in the heart of Texas / Till the end of time / I'm gonna love that girl / Did you get that feeling in the moonlight / May I never love again / I'm always chasing rainbows / I'm confessin' that I love you / Long ago and far away / Have I stayed away too long / Until today / Temptation / Faithful forever / I dream of you / You can't pull the wool over my eyes / Mr. Meadowlark / If I loved you / Fooled by the moon
CDSGP 0314 / 23 Feb '98 / Prestige

☐ INCOMPARABLE, THE (20 Outstanding Classics)
Blue skies / I love you / Goodbye Sue / Aren't you glad you're mine / Here comes Heaven again / All through the day / You won't be satisfied / I can't begin to tell you / I'm always chasing rainbows / Till the end of time / Love letters / Cynthia's in love / It's the talk of the town / You must have been a beautiful baby / It's been a long long time / Te quiero dijiste / Don't blame me / Song of songs / Prisoner of love / So long ago and far away
PLATCD 149 / Mar '96 / Platinum

☐ LOVE COLLECTION, THE
Best of times / Days of wine and roses / What's new / Something / For all we now / Very thought of you / (I left my heart) in San Francisco / It's impossible / Where do I belong / What kind of fool am I / Without a song / (They long to be) close to you / You are the sunshine of my life / I think of you / When I need you / If / For the good times / Most beautiful girl / Wind beneath my wings
74321393422 / Jan '97 / Camden

☐ LOVE LETTERS
Love letters / Blue skies / Cynthia's in love / Long ago and far away / Te quiero dijiste / It's the talk of the town / You won't be satisfied / Aren't you glad your mine / Prisoner of love / Here comes heaven again / Don't blame me / Till the end of time / You must have been a beautiful baby / It's been a long long time / I love you / Song of songs / I can't begin to tell you / Goodbye Sue / All through the day / I'm always chasing rainbows
300112 / Jun '98 / Hallmark

☐ LOVE SONGS
Blue skies / I love you / Goodbye Sue / Aren't you glad you're you / Here comes heaven again / All through the day / You won't be satisfied / I can't begin to tell you / I'm always chasing rainbows / Till the end of time / Love letters / Cynthia's in love / It's the talk of the town / You must have been a beautiful baby / It's been a long long time / Te quiero dijiste / Don't blame me / Song of songs / Prisoner of love / Long ago and far away
CD 6036 / Sep '96 / Music

☐ LOVE SONGS, THE
Love makes the world go round / Very thought of you / World of love / Colours of my love / Mandolins in the moonlight / Where is love / Love / How to handle a woman / Young love / As time goes by / I want to give / Gone is my love / When I fall in love / For the good times / I think I love you / Second time / Island of forgotten lovers / Quiet night of quiet stars
MCCD 125 / Sep '93 / Music Club

☐ PERRY COMO SHOWS 1943 VOL.1, THE
OTA 101905 / Mar '96 / On The Air

☐ PERRY COMO SHOWS 1943 VOL.2, THE
For a little while / Do I know what I'm doing / More than you know / Now we know / My blue heaven / Goodbye Sue / Girl of my dreams / I have faith / I heard you cried last night (and so did I) / Don't get around much anymore / Hit the road to Dreamland / As time goes by / I'm thinking tonight of my blue eyes / Temptation / My ideal / You took advantage of me / It's always you / For me and my gal / Take me in your arms / Johnny Zero / You'd be so nice to come home to
OTA 101906 / Mar '96 / On The Air

☐ PERRY COMO SHOWS 1943 VOL.3, THE
For a little while / Thank your lucky stars / Lazybones / No love, no nothin' / Paper doll / Beard / I've had this feeling before (but never like this) / Put your arms around me honey / It's breaking my heart to keep away from you / 627 South / I'll be home for Christmas / All or nothing at all / Violins were playing / I lost my sugar in Salt Lake City / In an 18th Century drawing room / You'll never know / If that's the way you want it baby / I kiss your hand madame / In the blue of evening / Shine on harvest moon / Secretly
OTA 101907 / Mar '96 / On The Air

☐ PLATINUM COLLECTION, THE
Blue skies / I love you / Goodbye Sue / Aren't you glad you're you / Here comes heaven again / All through the day / You won't be satisfied / I can't begin to tell you / I always chasing rainbows / Til the end of time / Love letters / Cynthia's in love / It's the talk of the town / You must have been a beautiful baby / It's been a long long time / Te quiero dijiste / Don't blame me / Song of songs / Prisoner of love / Long ago and far away / They say it's wonderful / Surrender / Sonata / Dig you later / If I loved you / Deep in the heart of Texas / Did you ever get that feeling in the moonlight / I'm gonna love that gal / I'm confessin' that I love you / Lili Marlene / Have I stayed away too long / May I never love again / Faithful forever / Rainbow on the river / Mr Meadowlark / I dream of you / Garden in the rain / If I'm lucky / More and more / Temptation
PC 607 / 10 Nov '97 / Platinum Collection

☐ TAKE IT EASY
Bridge over troubled water / El condor pasa / Way we were / When I need you / Feelings / Wind beneath my wings / Michelle / Yesterday / For the good times / You are so beautiful / Killing me softly / Most beautiful girl / You are the sunshine of my life / Sunrise sunset / Sing / Close to you / We've only just begun / And I love you so
ND 90490 / Nov '90 / RCA

☐ TILL THE END OF TIME (The Early Hits 1936-1945)
Deep in the heart of Texas / Did you ever get that feeling in the moonlight / Faithful forever / Fooled by the moon / Goodbye Sue / Have I stayed away too long / I dream of you / I wonder who's kissing her now / I'm always chasing rainbows / I'm confessin' that I love you / I'm gonna love that girl / If I loved you / In my little red book / Lili Marlene / Long ago and far away / May I never love again / Mr. Meadowlark / Prisoner of love / Rainbow on the river / Temptation / Till the end of time / Until today / You can't pull the wool over my eyes / You won't be satisfied
CDAJA 5196 / Apr '96 / Living Era

Compagnia Sonadur Di Ponte Caffaro

☐ PAS EN AMUR
ACB 05 / Jan '94 / Robi Droli

Company

☐ COMPANY 91 VOL.1
INCUSCD 16 / Oct '94 / Incus

☐ COMPANY 91 VOL.2
INCUSCD 17 / Oct '94 / Incus

☐ COMPANY 91 VOL.3
INCUSCD 18 / Oct '94 / Incus

☐ ONCE
INCUSCD 04 / '90 / Incus

Company

☐ FROZEN BY HEAT
HGCD 0960 / 15 Jun '98 / High Gain

Company Flow

☐ FUNCRUSHER PLUS
Bad touch example / 7 steps for perfection / Collude-Intrude / Blind / Silence / Legends / Lune Tns / Help wanted / Population control / Definitive / Lenorcism / 89.9 detrimental / Vital nerve / Tragedy of war (in III parts) / Fire in which you burn / Krazy Kings / Last good sleep / Info kill II / Funcrush scratch
RWK 11342 / 29 Sep '97 / Rawkus

Completion

☐ ELECTRONIC MUSIC FOR THE CINEMA
CRECD 233 / 29 Jun '98 / Creation

Complicity

☐ PLAYING GOD
FETISH 016CD / Apr '97 / Grave News

Compostella

☐ WADACHI
TZA 7211 / Feb '97 / Tzadik

Compound Red

☐ ALWAYS A PLEASURE
DESOTO 25 / 3 Aug '98 / Desoto

Compression

☐ COMPRESSION
TOL 9701 / Jun '97 / Tolerance

Compton, Mike

☐ CLIMBING THE WALLS (Compton, Mike & David Grier)
Climbin' the walls / Honky tonk swing / Waters street waltz / Black mountain rag / Bye bye blue / Going up Caney / Huffy / Over the waterfall / Flop eared mule / New five cents / Paul's blues / Fun's all over
ROUCD 0280 / '91 / Rounder

Compulsion

☐ FUTURE IS MEDIUM
TPLP 79CD / May '96 / One Little Indian

Comsat Angels

☐ FICTION
After the rain / Zinger / Now I know / Not a word / Ju ju money / More / Pictures / Birdman / Don't look now / What else / It's history / After the rain / Private party / Mass
RPM 157 / Jan '96 / RPM

☐ SLEEP NO MORE
Eye dance / Sleep no more / Be brave / Gone / Dark parade / Diagram / Restless / Goat of the West / Light years / Our secret / Eye of the lens / Another world / At sea / (Do the) Empty house / Red planet revisited
RPM 156 / Jan '96 / RPM

☐ TIME CONSIDERED (BBC Sessions)
At sea / At sea / Eye of the lens / Total war / Real story / Waiting for a miracle / Ju ju money / Independence day / Eye dance / Gone / Dark parade / Our secret / Now I know / Citadel / High tide / Mr. memory / Island heart / You move me / Narure trails
RPM 106 / Nov '92 / RPM

☐ UNRAVELLED (Dutch Radio Sessions No.1)
After the rain / Always near / Beautiful monster / Cutting edge / Field of tall flowers / SS 100X / Our secret / Storm of change / Citadel / Driving / My mind's eye / Shiva descending
RPM 123 / Jul '94 / RPM

☐ WAITING FOR A MIRACLE
Missing in action / Baby / Independence day / Waiting for a miracle / Total war / On the beach / Monkey pilot / Real story / Map of the world / Postcard / Home is the range / We were
RPM 155 / Jan '96 / RPM

Comstock, Eric

☐ YOUNG MAN OF MANHATTAN
Far away from home / It's after hours / Don't let a good thing get away / Hundred years from today / Lonely town / S'wonderful / Rainy day / About a quarter to nine / Open upon a time / Young and foolish / Way you look tonight / Say young man of Manhattan / Long before I knew you / Beyond the sea / Pillar to post / Every time we say goodbye
HCD 1503 / 23 Mar '98 / Harbinger

Comus

☐ FIRST UTTERANCE
Diana / Herald / Drip drip / Song to Comus / Bite / Bitten / Prisoner
BGOCD 275 / Aug '95 / Beat Goes On

Con Funk Shun

☐ LIVE FOR YA
Ffun / Chase me / Shake and dance with me / Let me put love on your mind / I'm leaving baby / Too tight / Straight from the heart / Baby I'm hooked / By your side / Love's train / Ffun / Throw it up / Head to toe / Mega-mix
ESMCD 444 / Oct '96 / Essential

Concept In Dance

☐ DIGITAL ALCHEMY
DICD 123 / Oct '94 / Beggars Banquet

☐ TRIBAL SCIENCE
DICCD 124 / Aug '95 / Beggars Banquet

Conception

☐ LAST SUNSET
Prevision / Building a force / War of hate / Bowed down with sorrow / Fairy's dance / Another world / Elegy / Last sunset / Live to survive / Among the Gods
N 02322 / Jan '94 / Noise

☐ PARALLEL MINDS
N 02182 / Oct '93 / Noise

Concord Jazz All Stars

☐ AT THE NORTHSEA FESTIVAL VOL.2
Vignette / Emily / That's your red wagon / Sweet Lorraine / Can't we be friends / Out of nowhere / Once in a while / In a mellow tone
CCD 4205 / '83 / Concord Jazz

☐ ON CAPE COD
Man I love / This is always / Recado bossa nova / It never entered my mind / Cherokee / All my tomorrows / Bewitched, bothered and bewildered / As long as I live / Time after time
CCD 4530 / Feb '93 / Concord Jazz

☐ OW
Ow / Fungi mama / My shining hour / I'll close my eyes / Why did I choose you / Blue hodge / I love being here with you / All blues / Down home blues
CCD 4348 / Jul '88 / Concord Jazz

☐ TAKE EIGHT
Dynaflow / Dynaflow / Too late now / Have you met miss jones / Very thought of you / Stella by starlight / Who can I turn to (when nobody needs me) / Lover come back to me
CCD 4347 / Jul '88 / Concord Jazz

Concrete Blonde

☐ RECOLLECTION
God is a bullet / Tomorrow Wendy / Joey / Scene of a perfect crime / Someday / Ghost of a Texas ladies man / Dance along the edge / Bloodletting / Happy birthday / Caroline / Cold part of town / Walking in London / Heal it up / Everybody knows / True / Mexican moon / Still in Hollywood / Mercedez Benz
EIRSCD 1077 / Apr '96 / IRS/EMI

Condell, Sonny

☐ SOMEONE TO DANCE WITH
SCD 295CD / Jan '95 / Starc

Condello, Mike

☐ WALLACE AND LADMO'S GREATEST HITS
W&L 1954 / Dec '97 / W&L

Condemned 84

☐ BOOTS GO MARCHING IN
GMM 111 / Jun '97 / GMM

☐ FACE THE AGGRESSION
GMM 110 / Jun '97 / GMM

Condo, Ray

☐ CONDO COUNTY
DAGCD 8 / Dec '97 / Fury

Condon, Eddie

☐ CHICAGO STYLE (His Greatest Recordings 1927-1940)
Ballin' the jack / Carnegie jump / China boy / Easy to get / Good man is hard to find / Harlem fuss / Home cooking / I ain't gonna give nobody none of my jelly roll / I'm gonna stomp Mr. Henry Lee / I've found a new baby / Indiana / Jazz me blues / Love is just around the corner / Madame Dynamite / Margie / Minor drag / Nobody's sweetheart / Oh baby / Oh Peter you're so nice / Sugar / That's a serious thing / There'll be some changes made / Who's sorry now / Wolverine blues
CDAJA 5192 / Mar '96 / Living Era

☐ CLASSICS 1927-1938
CLASSICS 742 / Feb '94 / Classics

☐ CLASSICS 1938-1940
CLASSICS 759 / Aug '94 / Classics

☐ CLASSICS 1942-1943
CLASSICS 772 / Aug '94 / Classics

☐ CONDON TOWN HALL CONCERT VOL.10
JCD 1019/20 / Jul '96 / Jazzology

☐ DOCTOR JAZZ VOL.5 (Condon, Eddie Band & 'Wild' Bill Davison)
STCD 6045 / May '97 / Storyville

☐ DOCTOR JAZZ VOL.8
STCD 6048 / Jul '96 / Storyville

☐ EDDIE CONDON 1927-1943
Carnegie jump: *Barnet, Charlie & His Orchestra* / Carnegie drag: *Barnet, Charlie & His Orchestra* / Meet me tonight in dreamland: *Barnet, Charlie & His Orchestra* / Diane / (You're some) pretty doll / Dancing fool / Serenade to a shylock / Beat to the socks / Squeeze me / That's a plenty / Home cooking / Madame Dynamite / Tennesee twilight / I'm gonna stomp Mr. Henry lee / That's a serious thing / I'm sorry I made you cry / Makin' friends / Indiana / Oh baby / Nobody's sweetheart / China boy / Sugar / Liza
CD 53292 / Nov '97 / Giants Of Jazz

☐ EDDIE CONDON 1928-1931
One step to heaven / Shimme Sha Wabble / Oh baby (rain or shine) / Indiana / I'm sorry I made you cry / Makin' friends / I'm gonna stomp, Mr Henry Lee / That's a serious thing / Firehouse blues / Tailspin blues / Never had a reason / Hello Lola / One hour / Girls like you were meant for boys like me / Arkansas blues / Georgia on my mind / I can't believe that you're in love with me / Darktown strutters ball / (I'll be glad when you're dead) you rascal you
CBC 1024 / Sep '96 / Timeless

☐ EDDIE CONDON 1930-1944
That's a plenty / Panama / When your lover has gone / Nobody knows you when you're down and out / Rose room / I must have that man / Original dixieland one-step / Baby won't you please come home / Sensation / Fidgety feet / Oh, sister ain't that hot / Georgia grind / Ballin' the jack / I ain't gonna give nobody none of my jelly-roll / Ja-da / Love is just around the corner / Embraceable you / Sunday / California here I come / Eel
CD 53183 / Nov '95 / Giants Of Jazz

☐ EDDIE CONDON 1933-1940
Oh, sister ain't that hot / Georgia grind / Ballin' the jack / I ain't gonna give nobody none of my jelly-roll / Ja-da / Love is just around the corner / It's right here for you / Strut miss lizzie / Sunday / California here I come / (you're some) pretty doll / Dancing foll / Fidgety feet / Sensation / Beat to the socks / Eel / Madame dynamite / Home cooking
CD 56078 / Jul '95 / Jazz Roots

☐ EDDIE CONDON BAND & 'WILD' BILL DAVISON 1951-1952 (Condon, Eddie Band & 'Wild' Bill Davison)
STCD 6056 / Mar '97 / Storyville

☐ EDDIE CONDON LIVE IN 1944 VOL.3 (Condon, Eddie & His All Stars)
JCD 634 / '92 / Jass

☐ HIS JAZZ CONCERT
STCD 530 / Feb '91 / Stash

☐ IN JAPAN
CRD 154 / Dec '95 / Chiaroscuro

☐ LIVE AT THE NEW SCHOOL (Condon, Eddie & Kenny Davern/Gene Krupa)
CRD 110 / Jul '96 / Chiaroscuro

☐ RINGSIDE AT CONDON'S
Dixieland one step / Keepin' out of mischief now / Squeeze me / Memphis blues / Dippermouth blues / Sweet Georgia Brown / Wrap your troubles in dreams (and dream your troubles away) / One I love / Just the blues / Makin' whoopee/You made me love you / I can't give you anything but love / Beale Street blues / Mandy make your mind up / Blues my naughty sweetie gives to me
SV 0231 / Oct '97 / Savoy Jazz

☐ TOWN HALL BLUE (3CD Set)
JCD 1021/22/23 / Nov '96 / Jazzology

☐ TOWN HALL CONCERTS VOL.1 (Condon, Eddie & His All Stars)
Jazz me blues / Cherry / I'm coming Virginia / Love nest / Big butter and egg man / Oh Katharina / Impromptu ensemble / Sugar / It's been so long / Mandy, make up your mind / September in the rain / Song of the wanderer / Walking the dog
JCECD 1001/2 / Oct '92 / Jazzology

☐ TOWN HALL CONCERTS VOL.2
JCECD 1003/4 / ' / Jazzology

☐ TOWN HALL CONCERTS VOL.3
JCECD 1005/6 / Oct '92 / Jazzology

☐ TOWN HALL CONCERTS VOL.4
JCECD 1007/8 / Oct '92 / Jazzology

☐ TOWN HALL CONCERTS VOL.5
JCECD 1009/10 / Oct '91 / Jazzology

☐ TOWN HALL CONCERTS VOL.6
JCECD 1011/12 / Oct '91 / Jazzology

☐ TOWN HALL CONCERTS VOL.8
JCD 1015/16 / Jul '93 / Jazzology

☐ TOWN HALL CONCERTS VOL.9
JCD 1017/18 / Jan '94 / Jazzology

☐ TRANSCRIPTION OF THE TOWN HALL CONCERT (2CD Set) (Condon, Eddie & His All Stars)
Ballin' the jack / That's a plenty / Cherry/alternate take/breakdown take/master take / Sweet Georgia / At the Jazz band ball / When my sugar walks down the street / Uncle Sam's blues / Someone to watch over me / One I love belongs to somebody else / Where ever there's love (there's you and I) / What's new / Ja da / Time on my hands / Royal garden blues / Muskrat ramble / It's been so long / Man I love / 'S wonderful / Just you just me / Old folks / You're lucky to me / At the darktown strutter's ball / Eddie Condon speaks / St. Louis blues / Honeysuckle rose / She's funny that way / It's been so long / Nobody knows (nobody seems to care) / Uncle Sam's Blues / Serenade in thirds / Untitled original / China boy / Impromptu ensemble
JZCL 5008 / Nov '96 / Jazz Classics

☐ WINDY CITY JAZZ
TPZ 1026 / Aug '95 / Topaz Jazz

Conemelt

☐ 24 CARAT CONMELT
Hello customers / Amateur drumatix / Pear shaped funk / Shockin' mess / Shaolin shoes / Dropout bogey / Six string thing / Weeing underwater / Hairy underwater / Hairy knuckle nowhow / Ash fell ill at pinback
ILLCD 004 / 3 Nov '97 / Ill

☐ CONFUSE AND DESTROY
Misty traincrash / Flashermac / Cuckoo clock rock / Joys of surface noises / Big up hte conemelt / Overbite nightmare / Espionage / Big and clever track / Pushbutton twist / Motorskating
SOP 007CD / Jan '96 / Emissions

Conexion Latina

☐ LA CONEXION
Llegue a la cima / Maravilla / La clave / La conexion / Yo quiero tambien / Palmira / Ritmo internacional / Ataconda / Fiesta de despedida
ENJ 90652 / Sep '96 / Enja

Coney Hatch

☐ FRICTION
This ain't love / She's gone / Wrong side of town / Girls from last night's dream / Coming to get you / Fantasy / He's a champion / State love / Burning love
ANK 1070 / 12 Jan '98 / Anthem

Confederate Railroad

☐ WHEN AND WHERE
When and where / Toss a little bone / Bill's laundrymat bar and grill / See ya / All I wanted / My baby's lovin' / Oh no / Sounds of home / When he was my age / Right track wrong train
7567827742 / Jun '94 / Atlantic

Confetti

☐ RETROSPECTIVEL EP
Who's big and clever now / It's kinda funny / Yes please / Tomorrow who knows / Warm / Jenny / Bridge 61 / Diet / Whatever became of Alice and Jane / Here again / River island / Nothing II / Corduroy / Anyone can make a mistake / Once more
ASKCD 039 / Sep '94 / Vinyl Japan

Conflict

☐ AGAINST ALL ODDS
MORTCD 060 / 18 May '98 / Mortarhate

☐ CONCLUSION
To live on in hearts / Right to reply / Someday soon / No more excuses / A declaration of independence / Institute of dreams / Climbing the stairs / A question of priorities / Is never to die
MORTCD 100 / Dec '93 / Mortarhate

☐ DEPLOYING ALL MEANS NECESSARY
CLP 99322 / Apr '97 / Cleopatra

☐ EMPLOYING ALL MEANS NECESSARY
CLEO 1023CD / Jul '94 / Cleopatra

☐ FINAL CONFLICT, THE
You cannot win / Ungovernable farce / Piss in the ocean / Crass / Custom rock / 1986 the struggle continues / Mental mania / Ungovernable force / They said that / Force or service / Arrest / Statement / Day before / This is the ALF / To be continued
MORTCD 50 / Dec '96 / Mortarhate

☐ IN THE VENUE
MORTCD 120 / Feb '97 / Mortarhate

Confrey, Zez

☐ KEYBOARD WIZARDS OF THE GERSHWIN ERA VOL.4
GEMMCD 9204 / Jun '98 / Pearl

Confront

☐ ONE LIFE - DRUG FREE
LF 097CD / Aug '94 / Lost & Found

Confront, James

☐ TEST ONE REALITY
SST 305CD / Mar '95 / SST

Confrontation

☐ CONFRONTATION
LF 139CD / Mar '95 / Lost & Found

Confucius Says

☐ WINDOW
343906 / Dec '97 / Koch

Confuse

☐ COLLECTION, THE
JPC 03 / Nov '96 / Japan Punk Collection

Confusions

☐ BEING YOUNG
EFA 054062 / 22 Sep '97 / Clear Spot

☐ EVERYONES INVITED
EFA 054012 / Feb '97 / Clear Spot

Congaline

☐ DE CONGALINE CARNIVA
CCD 0023 / Apr '96 / CRS

Conglomerate

☐ PRECISELY THE OPPOSITE OF WHAT WE NOW KNOW TO BE TRUE
DIS 004 / Oct '95 / FMR/Dissenter

Congos

☐ HEART OF THE CONGOS
Fisherman / Congo man / Open up the gate / Children crying / La la bam bam / Can't come in / Sodom and Gomorrah / Wrong thing / Ark of covenant / Solid foundation
14805 / Jun '97 / Spalax

☐ HEART OF THE CONGOS (2CD Set)
BAFCD 9 / Jan '96 / Blood & Fire

☐ NATTY DREAD RISE AGAIN
Rock of Gibraltar / Step aside / Music is the key / Seeking a favour / Judgement day / Natty dread rise again / Vibration / This could not be happening / Love is the answer / Apartheid / Sent to Babylon
RASCD 3238 / Feb '97 / Ras

Congregation

☐ EGHAM
FIREMCD 55 / Oct '95 / Fire

Congreso

☐ MEDIA DIA
3001804 / 24 Feb '98 / IMP

Conjunto Alma De Apatzingan

☐ ARRIBA TIERRA CALIENTE
ARHCD 426 / Apr '95 / Arhoolie

Conjunto Bernal

☐ 16 EARLY TEJANO CLASSICS
Voy perdiendo / La ultima palabra / Pensamiento / La margarina / Dios de mi vida / Castigame / Melinda / Si quieres volver / Las texanitas / La coneja / Por la misma senda / La turicata / Para que quiero un amor / Quiereme un poquito / Cosquillitas / Veinte anos
ARHCD 9010 / Nov '97 / Arhoolie

☐ MI UNICO CAMINO
Mi unico camino / Neto's polka / Las palabras del amor / Loretta polka / Sera impossible / Mi borrachera / Ballroom polka / Destino cruel / Al fin mujer / Pa' que me hago ilusiones / Si acaso vuelves / Hoy no es ayer / Despecio / Mujer paseada / Fidel Castro / Melodias mexicanas / Quien te lo dijo / Azul cielo / Caminito de rieles / Connie / Maria bonita / Al regresar / Sentimiento rencor / La chuparrasa
ARHCD 344 / Apr '95 / Arhoolie

Conjunto Casino

☐ MAMBO CON CHA CHA CHA 1953-1955
TCD 080 / Jul '96 / Tumbao Cuban Classics

☐ MOLIENDA CAFE
CCD 507 / Nov '95 / Caney

Conjunto Cespedes

☐ FLORES
Chekere entrance / Flores para tu altar / La misma herencia / Ai deu / Defiende el amor / El tambor tiene magia / Descansa / Son caminos / Genaro / Guira con son / Nosotros / Umelina / Canto a la abuela / Oye mira y calla / Iyesa chekeres
XENO 4043CD / May '98 / Xenophile

☐ UNA SOLA CASA
GLCD 4007 / Jul '93 / Green Linnet

☐ VIVITO Y COLEANDO
XENO 4033CD / Jun '95 / Xenophile

Conjunto Clasico

☐ CLASICO DE NUEVO
Tu mi estrella / Hipocresia / Gracias amor / Se que volvera / Une dia de abril / No te quiero como amiga / Contigo me voy / Me enamore
66058092 / Feb '96 / RMM

Conjunto De Luis Santi

☐ MAMBO INFIERNO
TCD 075 / Feb '97 / Tumbao

Conjunto Explosao Do Samba

☐ BEST OF CARNIVAL IN RIO VOL.3, THE
EUCD 1137 / '91 / ARC

Conjunto Libre

☐ SIEMPRE SERE GUAJIRO
CDGR 154 / May '97 / Charly

Conjunto Matamoros

☐ BAILARE TU SON
TCD 070 / Jul '96 / Tumbao Cuban Classics

Conjunto Niagara

☐ QUE NO SE ACABE EL BONGO 1945-1947
TCD 068 / Jul '96 / Tumbao Cuban Classics

Conklin, Larry

☐ POET'S ORCHESTRA
INAK 9020CD / Jun '93 / In Akustik

☐ SNOW TIGER, THE
INAK 8901 / Jul '95 / In Akustik

Conlan, Bill

☐ VISIONS OF IRELAND
CONCD 001 / 30 Mar '98 / Etude

Conley, Arthur

☐ SOUL DIRECTIONS
Funky Street / Burning fire / Otis sleep on / Hearsay / This love of mine / Love comes and goes / People sure act funny / How to hurt a guy / Get another fool / Put our love together
7567803862 / Jan '96 / Atlantic

☐ SWEET SOUL MUSIC
I can't stop (no no no) / Let nothing separate us / Take me (just as I am) / There's a place for us / Who's foolin' who / Where you lead me / I'm gonna forget about you / I'm a lonely stranger / Wholesale love / Sweet soul music
7567802842 / Jan '96 / Atlantic

Conley, Earl Thomas

☐ PERPETUAL EMOTION
1509592992 / 27 Apr '98 / Intersound

Conlon, Bill

☐ WITH YOU IN MIND
Lucille / I know one / Cowboys don't get lucky all the time / I don't have far to fall / Please please / Chair / Carmen / Not counting you / She's holding her own now / That ain't like your memory / Let's start forever / Streets of Bakersfield
ETCD 189 / Apr '96 / Etude

Conlon, Eddie

☐ 1933-40
CD 14557 / Jul '94 / Jazz Portraits

Conn, Bobby

☐ BOBBY CONN
ALP 302 / May '97 / Atavistic

Connacht Ramblers

☐ CONNACHT RAMBLERS
RR 001CD / Jan '95 / RR

Conneff, Kevin

☐ WEEK BEFORE EASTER, THE
Ellen Brown / Hornpipes / I'm here because I'm here / John Barber / McAuliffe's polkas / Flower of Magherally / Salt / Dark eyed gipsies / Fair maid wont' you call me your Darling / Cape breton reel / Green fields of America / Gathering mushrooms / Estonian waltz / Week before Easter
CCF 23CD / Feb '93 / Claddagh

Connells

☐ RING
Slackjawed / Carry my picture / Doin' you / Find out / Eyes on the ground / Spiral / Hey you / New boy / Disappointed / Burden / Any day now / Running Mary / Logan street / Wonder why / Living in the past
8286602 / Aug '95 / London

Connelly, Chris

☐ WHIPLASH BOYCHILD
Daredevil / Ghost of a saint / This edge of midnight / Last of joy / Amorous humphrey plugg / Stowaway / Hawk, the butcher, the killer of beauties / Game is all yours / Confessions of the highest bidder / Stowaway
CDDVN 14 / Oct '92 / Devotion

Connemara

☐ SIREN SONG
BLX 10031CD / Nov '96 / Blix Street

Conners, Loren Mazzacane

☐ EVANGELINE
ROCO 021CD / 24 Aug '98 / Roadcone

Connick, Harry Jr.

☐ 25
Stardust / Music, maestro, please / On the street where you live / After you've gone / I'm an old cowhand (from the Rio Grande) / Moments notice / Tangerine / Didn't he ramble / Caravan / Lazybones / Muskrat ramble / This time the dream is on me / On the Atchison, Topeka and the Santa Fe
4728092 / Jan '93 / Columbia

☐ BLUE LIGHT, RED LIGHT
Blue light, red light / Blessing and a curse / You didn't know me when / Jill / He is they are / With imagination (I'll get there) / If I could give you more / Last payday / It's time / She belongs to me / Sonny cried / Just kiss me
4690872 / Apr '95 / Columbia

☐ FOREVER FOR NOW
It had to be you / Our love is here to stay / Forever for now / Stardust / Do you know what it means to miss New Orleans / Recipe for love / One last pitch / Heavenly / Blue light, red light / But not for me / Little clown / Where or when / Don't get around much anymore / You don't know me when / It's all right with me / We are in love
4738732 / Jun '93 / Columbia

☐ HARRY CONNICK JR.
Our love is here to stay / Little clown / Zealousy / Sunny side of the street / I mean you / Vocation / On Green Dolphin Street / Little waltz / E / Love is here to stay / Zealou
4879352 / Jul '97 / Columbia

☐ SHE
She / Between us / Here comes the big parade / Trouble / (I could only) whisper your name / Follow the music further / Joe slam and the spaceship / To love the language / Honestly now (safety's just danger out of place) / She blessed be the one / Funky dunky / That party / Booker
4768162 / Aug '94 / Columbia

☐ TO SEE YOU
Let me love tonight / To see you / Let's just kiss / Heart beyond repair / Once / Learn to love / Love me some you / Much love / In love again / Loved by me
488862 / 26 Jan '98 / Columbia

☐ WE ARE IN LOVE
We are in love / Only 'cause I don't have you / Recipe for love / Drifting / Forever for now / Nightingale sang in berkeley square / Heavenly / Just a boy / I've got a great idea / I'll dream of you again / It's all right with me / Buried in blue
4667362 / Apr '94 / Columbia

☐ WHEN MY HEART FINDS CHRISTMAS
Sleigh ride / When my heart finds Christmas / (It must have been ol') Santa Claus / Blessed dawn of Christmas day / Let it snow, let it snow, let it snow / Little drummer boy / Ave Maria / Parade of the wooden soldiers / What child is this / Christmas dreaming / I pray on Christmas / Rudolph the red nosed reindeer / O holy night / What are you doing New Year's Eve
4745512 / 3 Nov '97 / Columbia

Connie & Babe

☐ DOWN THE ROAD TO HOME (Connie & Babe/The Backwoods Boys)
ROUCD 0298 / Nov '95 / Rounder

Conniff, Ray

☐ 'S WONDERFUL/'S MARVELOUS
'S wonderful / Dancing in the dark / Speak low / Wagon wheels / Sentimental journey / Begin the beguine / September song / I get a kick out of you / Stardust / I'm an old cowhand / Sometimes I'm happy / That old black magic / Way you look tonight / I hear rhapsody / They can't take that away from me / Moonlight serenade / I love you / I've told ev'ry little star / You do something to me / As time goes by / In the still of the night / Someone to watch over me / Be my lover / Where or when
4840302 / Jun '96 / Columbia

☐ BEST OF RAY CONNIFF, THE
S'Wonderful / For all we know / Unchained melody / Hi Lili Hi Lo / Look of love / Music to watch girls by / Somewhere my love / Killing me softly with his song / As time goes by / Memories are made of this / Continental / Goin' out of my mind / Up up and away / Smoke gets in your eyes / I'd like to teach the world to sing / Fernando / All by myself / Frost festival / Don't cry for me Argentina / Moonlight sonata
4882492 / 26 Jan '98 / Columbia

☐ CANCION DE AMOR
Brasil / Extrano en el paraiso / Te llevo dentro de mi / Noche y dia / Tentacion / Joven para amar / Gigi / La rueda de la fortuna / Moulin rouge / That old feeling / Di que no es asi / Abril en Paris / Solitario / Los ninos del pireo / Cancion de amor / Purpura real
CD 62094 / Jul '97 / Saludos Amigos

☐ ENCORE - 16 MOST REQUESTED SONGS
Begin the beguine / Besame mucho / Thanks for the memory / Love is a many splendoured thing / It's been a long, long time / Memories are made of this / Midnight lace, part 1 / Hi Lili hi Lo / Invisible tears / Try to remember / This is my song / Red roses for a blue lady / It's impossible / First time I ever saw her face / Seasons in the sun / Memory
4805142 / May '95 / Columbia

☐ FRIENDLY PERSUASION
Tiger rag (hold that tiger) / High noon (do not forsake me) / Ebb tide / So rare / Song of love / April love / June night / Friendly persuasion (thee I love) / Stompin' at the savoy / I understand / Shangri-la / Rose room
CT 9010 / Jan '94 / Columbia

☐ INVISIBLE TEARS
Invisible tears / Honeycomb / Are you lonesome tonight / I walk the line / S'posin' / Oh lonesome me / Everybody loves somebody / Singing the blues / Waitin' for the evening train / Kisses sweeter than wine / Far away places / Marianne
CT 9064 / Jan '94 / Columbia

☐ S'AWFUL NICE/CONTINENTAL
Smoke gets in your eyes / Lullaby of birdland / June in January / I cover the waterfront / Very thought of you / It had to be you / Paradise / April in Paris / That old feeling / Say it isn't so / All the things you are / Lovely to look at / Continental (you kiss while you're dancing) / Whiffen poof song / Beyond the sea / Glow worm / Poor people of Paris / Strange music / Tico tico / White cliffs of Dover / African safri / Morgen / Lisbon Antigua / Green eyes
4898042 / 23 Mar '98 / Columbia

☐ SPEAK TO ME OF LOVE
Lover come back to me / Beyond the sea (la mer) / Don't blame me / Speak to me of love / Sweetest sounds / This nearly was mine / (when your heart's on fire) smoke gets in your eyes / Love has no rules / You'll never walk alone / Under paris skies / Slow poke / Who's sorry now
CT 8950 / Jan '94 / Columbia

☐ TICO TICO
Tico tico / Lisboa Antigua / Aquellos Ojos Verdes / El continental / La mar (la mer) / Extrana musica / La Colina de blueberry / Llorar / RogarParadiso / Todo lo que tu eres / El humo ciega tus ojos / Volare / Rapsodia en blue / Suave como el Amanecer / Una de esas cosas
CD 62090 / Mar '97 / Saludos Amigos

☐ WE WISH YOU A MERRY CHRISTMAS (Conniff, Ray & Singers)
Jolly old St. Nicholas / Little drummer boy / Holy night / We three kings of Orient are / Deck the halls with boughs of holly / Ring Christmas bells / Let it snow, let it snow, let it snow / Count your blessings (instead of sheep) / We wish you a merry Christmas / Twelve days of Christmas / First Noel / Hark the herald angels sing / O come all ye faithful (Adeste Fidelis)
4814372 / 3 Nov '97 / Columbia

Connolly, John

☐ AN TOILEAN AERACH
CICD 063 / Jan '94 / Clo Iar-Chonnachta

☐ BY HUMBER'S BROWN WATER (2CD Set) (Connolly, John & Bill Meek)
MECON 1 / Dec '97 / Mecon

Connolly, Kevin

☐ LITTLE TOWN
RTMCD 74 / Jun '96 / Round Tower

☐ MY MY MY
EFR 103 / Feb '94 / Eastern Front

Connolly, Rita

☐ RITA CONNOLLY
Venezuela / Miracles / Factory girl/Same old man / Alice in Jericho / Fanny Hawke / It's really pouring / Two of us / Amiems / Red dust / Dreams in the morning / Close your eyes
TARACD 3029 / Jul '92 / Tara

☐ VALPARAISO
Ocean floor / Valparaiso / Lizzie Finn / Ripples in the rockpools / Piccadilly / His name is Elvis / Two white horses / Shakin' the blues away / Sun song / Rio / Great guns roar / Quiet land of Erin
TARACD 3033 / Nov '95 / Tara

Connolly, Seamus

☐ HERE AND THERE
Reel le blanc / Pat the budgie / Le reel / Reel of the blindmen / Larry's delight / Dominick McCarthy's Irish barndance/Saunder's fort / I'll always remember you / Dr. Gilbert/Flax in bloom / Sheila Coyle's reel / Bells of congress/Dance for the haymaker/Kitty O'Brien / Marian McCarthy/Jockey to the fair / Thirteen arches/Thoughts of Carignan / Man in the bog/O'Brien from Newtown / Carraigin Ruadh / Earl gray/Mrs. Macinroy of Lude/Spey in spate
GLCD 1098 / Feb '92 / Green Linnet

☐ NOTES FROM MY MIND
Ryan meets Connolly/The new road / Fahy from killybeg house/The bridge at Newton / Sprig of shillelagh/Planxty penny / Munster bacon/The pipers' inn / Larry Redican's bow
GLCD 1087 / Jan '88 / Green Linnet

Connor, Chris

☐ AS TIME GOES BY
Falling in love with love / As time goes by / September in the rain / Gone with the wind / Strike up the band / Lovely way to spend an evening / Foggy day / Goodbye
ENJ 70612 / Nov '92 / Enja

☐ CHRIS (Bethlehem Jazz Classics)
All about Ronnie / Mad miser man / Everything I love / Indian Summer / I hear music / Come back to Sorrento / Out of this world / Lush life / From this moment on / Good man is a seldom thing / Don't wait up for me / In other words
CDGR 136 / Apr '97 / Charly

☐ LONDON CONNECTION
ACD 246 / Jun '93 / Audiophile

☐ SINGS LULLABYS OF BIRDLAND
CDGR 125 / Mar '97 / Charly

☐ SWEET & SWINGING
ACD 208 / Aug '94 / Audiophile

Connor, Joanna

☐ BIG GIRL BLUES
BPCD 5037 / Dec '96 / Blind Pig
RUF 1010 / Feb '98 / Ruf

☐ JOANNA CONNOR BAND, THE (Connor, Joanna Band)
Texas / Walkin' blues / Child from two worlds / No good for me / Heaven / Lost / Read my lips / Your love was never mine / I got love / Fight / Living on the road / Walk away
INAK 9012CD / Nov '97 / In Akustik

☐ LIVING ON THE ROAD
My baby's loving / Good woman gone bad / Sky is crying / Jalapeno mama / Forgotten woman / Midnight sunrise / Wildfire woman / Boogie woogie nighthawk / Dark end of the street / Going back home
INAK 9022CD / Nov '97 / In Akustik

☐ ROCK 'N' ROLL GYPSY
RRCD 901315 / Feb '98 / Ruf

☐ SLIDETIME
Nothin' but the blues / My papa / You don't love me / Got to have you / Slide on in / My man / Free free woman / Money blues / It's not the rock / At the club / Pea vine blues
BPCD 5047 / Jun '98 / Blind Pig

Connors, Bill

☐ OF MIST & MELTING
Melting / Not forgetting / Face in the water / Aubade / Cafe vue / Unending
847324 2 / Jun '93 / ECM

☐ STEP IT
Lydia / Pedal / Step it / Cookies / Brody / Twinkle / Titan / Flickering lights
ECD 220802 / Mar '94 / Evidence

☐ SWIMMING WITH A HOLE IN MY BODY
Feet first / Wade / Sing and swim / Frog stroke / Surrender to the water / Survive / With strings attached / Breath
8490782 / Mar '92 / ECM

Connors, Bob

☐ BRAHMIN BELLHOPS
SOSCD 1305 / Nov '96 / Stomp Off

Connors, Norman

☐ BEST OF NORMAN CONNORS (The Buddah Collection)
Once I've been there / You are my starship / Mother of the future / Captain Connors / Be there in the morning / Kwasi / This is your life / Betcha by golly wow / Valentine love / Stella / Butterfly / Kingston / We both need each other / Romantic journey
NEXCD 118 / Aug '90 / Sequel

☐ SATURDAY NIGHT SPECIAL/YOU ARE MY STARSHIP
Saturday night special / Dindi / Maiden voyage / Valentine love / Akia / Skin diver / Kwasi / We both need each other / Betcha by golly wow / Bubbles / You are my starship / Just imagination / So much love / Creator has a master plan
NEXCD 186 / May '92 / Sequel

☐ THIS IS YOUR LIFE
Stella / This is your life / Wouldn't you like to see / Listen / Say you love me / Captain Connors / You make me feel brand new / Butterfly / Creator / Captain Connors (Mix)
NEMCD 637 / Mar '93 / Sequel

☐ VERY BEST OF NORMAN CONNORS, THE
You are my starship / This is your life / Phoenix / Captain Connors / East 6th Street / Stella / Betcha by golly wow / You make me feel brand new / Valentine love / We both need each other / Say you love me / Look ahead / Treat me like the one you love / Once I've been there / Take it to the limit / Black cow
74321578172 / 27 Apr '98 / Camden

Conrad, Tony

☐ OUTSIDE DREAM SYNDICATE (Conrad, Tony & Faust)
LITHIUM 6 / 6 Apr '98 / Table Of The Elements

☐ SLAPPING PYTHAGORAS
VANADIUM 23 / Jun '97 / Table Of The Elements

Console

☐ PAN OR AMA
PAY 04 / Sep '97 / Payola

Consolers

☐ BEST OF THE CONSOLERS, THE
NASH 4502 / Feb '96 / Nashboro

Consolidated

☐ BUSINESS OF PUNISHMENT
Cutting / Business of punishment / Born of a woman / Das habe ich nicht gewusst / No answer for a dancer / Meat, meat, meat and meat / Dog and pony show / Today is my birthday / Butyric acid / Woman shoots John / Consolidated buries the mammoth / Worthy victim / Recuperation / Empowerless / Emancipate yourself
8285142 / Jun '94 / London

☐ DROPPED
RR 87542 / 17 Nov '97 / Roadrunner

☐ THIS IS FASCISM (2CD Set)
PROCD 14 / May '96 / MC Projects

Conspiracy Of Silence

☐ FACELESS
SHR 013MCD / Nov '95 / Shiva

Constantia Bros.

☐ MUSIC OF GREECE, THE
Zorba's dance / Never on a Sunday / White rose of Athens / Plaka Square dance / Mystic ballerina / Yodelling yiannas / Forever Cyprus green / Serpent's dance / Milisse Mou / Flight of the spirit / Duelling bouzoukis / On wings of love / Waltz in blue / Children of Aphrodite / Mist on the Troodos / Constantia cottage polka
CD 6099 / Aug '97 / Music

Consumed

☐ BREAKFAST AT PAPPA'S
Heavy metal winner / Bye bye fatman / Stand under me / Brutal tooth / Nonsense cone / Bigger shoe
FAT 575CD / 3 Aug '98 / Fatwreck Chords

Contagion

☐ CONTAMINANT PCB
8535100432 / 24 Mar '98 / World Domination

Conte, Paolo

☐ 900
Novecento / Il treno va / Una di queste notti / Pesce veolce del baltico / La Donna della tua vita / Per quel che vale / Inno in re bemolle / Gong oh / I giardini pensil hanno fatto il loro tempo / Schiava del politeama / Chiamami adesso / Brillantina / Do do
4509910332 / Jun '93 / East West

☐ BEST OF PAOLO CONTE, THE
0630194052 / Jul '97 / Warner Bros.

Contemporary Bebop Quintet

☐ ACCEPTANCE
DRCD 299 / Aug '97 / Dragon

Contemporary Piano Ensemble

☐ FOUR PIANOS FOR PHINEAS
Fond times with Junior / While my lady sleeps / Sweet and lovely / Newborn spirit / Moonlight in Vermont / Salt peanuts / Back home / Pass me not / It don't mean a thing if it ain't got that swing
ECD 221562 / Sep '96 / Evidence

☐ KEY PLAYERS, THE
DIW 616 / Feb '94 / DIW

Contempt

☐ SHOUTING THE ODDS
BFRCD 002 / 23 Feb '98 / Bomb Factory

Conti, Ivan

☐ BATIDA DIFERENTE
ITM 94004 / Nov '92 / ITM

Continental Drifters

☐ CONTINENTAL DRIFTERS
MON 6123 / Sep '94 / Monkey Hill

Contours

☐ VERY BEST OF THE CONTOURS, THE
Storm warning / Revenge / I'm coming home to you / Running in circles / When it rains it pours / Face up to the fact / Magic lady / Head over heels / Blinded by the light / One day too late / Look out for the stop sign / Under loves control / Flashback / Rise above it / Gonna win you back / Spread the news around / Ready or not here I come / Heaven sent
3035990052 / Oct '95 / Carlton

Contraband

☐ CONTRABAND
LAPCD 131 / Dec '97 / Lapwing

☐ DE RUYTER SUYTE
BVHAASTCD 9104 / Jun '87 / Bvhaast

☐ LIVE AT THE BIMHUIS
BVHAASTCD 8906 / Jun '88 / Bvhaast

Contrastate

☐ ENGLISH EMBERS
DPROMCD 38 / Oct '96 / Dirter Promotions

Contreras, Orlando

☐ DOS LEYENDAS (Contreras, Orlando & Daniel Santos)
9944132192 / 3 Mar '98 / Orfeon

Control Freak

☐ LOW ANIMAL CUNNING
CSR 021CD / Oct '95 / Cavity Search

Controlled Bleeding

☐ BODY SAMPLES
EFA 5321 D / Mar '93 / Dossier

☐ CURD
EFA 7726 D / Mar '93 / Dossier

☐ GILDED SHADOWS
CLP 0027 / Aug '97 / Hypnotic

☐ KNEES AND BONES
EFA 084842 / May '97 / Dossier

☐ PETS FOR MEAT (Controlled Bleeding & Doc Wor Mirran)
EFA 122052 / Apr '94 / Crypt

☐ SONGS FROM THE DRAIN
EFA 085472 / Jun '94 / Dossier

Conundrum

☐ TOMORROW TRADITION
CDLOC 1085 / Apr '95 / Lochshore

Converge

☐ PETITING THE EMPTY SKY
EVR 040CD / 16 Feb '98 / Equal Vision

☐ WHEN FOREVER COMES CRASHING
EVR 041CD / 13 Apr '98 / Equal Vision

Convoy Crew

☐ TRUCKING GREATS
Convoy / Eighteen wheels / How fast them trucks can go / Movin' on / Me and old CB / Ode to 10-33 / Six days on the road / Teddy bear / Truck drivin' man / Rhythm of the road / Big city / Freightliner fever / Hold everything / I'll have another cup of coffee (then I'll go) / Phantom 309 / Tennessee is home to me / Dixie winds / Trucker's way of life / Wolf creek pass / Trucker's lady / Highway 40 blues
QED 047 / Nov '96 / Tring

Convulse

☐ REFLECTIONS
NB 114CD / Jan '95 / Nuclear Blast

Conway, Francis

☐ WAKE UP
Wake up (introduction) / New York skyline / It's a bedsit / Sweet Carronlaoe / Not even the president / Wake up / Striking it rich / Your drug is Hollywood / Somebody stole my gal / Walking on seashells / Spanish nights / She haunts me / Somewhere in heaven / To the edge of time / One night in Amsterdam
RTMCD 22 / Jan '91 / Round Tower

Conway, Russ

☐ BEST OF RUSS CONWAY
Cabaret / Walk in the black forest / Poor people of paris / Cast your fate to the wind / Ain't misbehavin' / China tea / I want to be happy / Everything's coming up roses / Alligator crawl / A nightingale sang in berkeley square / Oh, babe, what would you say / Tiger rag / It's not goodbye / Old pi-anna rag / Born free / Girl in my soup / Raindrops keep falling on my head / When somebody thinks you're wonderful / Misty / Side saddle / Trudie / Bewitched / My very good friend the milkman / Hello dolly / Sleepy shores / Chopsticks / Satin doll / I'm gonna sit right down and write myself a letter / Alley cat
MATCD 212 / Dec '92 / Castle

☐ CELEBRATION DAY
Celebration day / Matador from Trinidad / Primera / Concerto for dreamers / Mr Happy / Happy Jose / ALone again / Gigolo / Raggity tune / For Pete's sake / Tell me in September / Portugese washerwoman / Nicola / Cuban romance / Gold rush / Bedouin in Baghdhad / Spartans / Casino / Calcutta / Little Leprachaun / Concerto for lovers / Beggars of ROme / I'm shy Mary Ellen I'm shy / Urchinds of Paris / Crunch / Patient heart / Stay a while / Felicity grey / Love is a many splendoured thing / Life is good
CDRUSS 12 / 13 Oct '97 / EMI Gold

☐ EARLY YEARS, THE
Time to celebrate / Roll the carpet up / Westminster waltz / Red cat / Piano pops up / Lantern slide / Harry Lime theme / Jumping for joy / Whistling cat / Toby's walk / Love like ours / Side saddle / Piano pops 8 / Russian rag / Gigi medley / Rustling / Trampolina / Wee boy of Brussels / Rule Britannia / Key to love / Music man selection / Tin pan alley / Parade of the poppets / Lulu / Bingo / Singin bells / Primera / Blitz medley / Angelo / What will they do without us / Late extra
CDRUSS 11 / 13 Oct '97 / EMI Gold

☐ EP COLLECTION, THE
Call of the sea / Side saddle / It's my mother's birthday today / That's a plenty / Soho fair / Darktown strutters ball / Falling tears / Wedgewood blue / Rocking horse cowboy / Empty saddles / Ragtime cowboy Joe / Pixillated penguin / Let the big wheel keep turning / Pal Joey pops (medley) / Musical chairs / Musical chairs (Medley) / Scots pops (Medley) / I'll be seeing you / Twelfth street rag / Temptation rag
SEECD 310 / Feb '91 / See For Miles

☐ GOLDEN SOUNDS OF RUSS CONWAY, THE
GS 863562 / Mar '96 / Disky

☐ GREATEST HITS
Side saddle / Mack the knife / Westminster waltz / Pixillated penguin / Snow coach / Sam's song / Always / Wedding of the painted doll / World outside / China tea / Lesson one / When you're smiling / I'm looking over a four leaf clover / When you wore a tulip / Row row row / For me and my gal / Shine on harvest moon / By the light of the silvery moon / Side by side / Roulette / Toy balloons / Pepe / Royal event / Lucky five / Passing breeze / Got a match / Always you and me / Pablo / Fings ain't wot they used t'be / Polka dots / Where do little birds go / Forgotten dreams / Music music music / If you were the only girl in the world / I'm nobody's sweetheart now / Yes sir that's my baby / Some of these days / Honeysuckle and the bee / Hello hello, who's your lady friend / (In) a shanty in old Shanty Town
CC 203 / May '88 / Music For Pleasure

☐ WALK IN THE BLACK FOREST, A (The Best Of Russ Conway)
PLSCD 162 / Apr '97 / Pulse

Conway, Steve

☐ BEAUTIFUL DREAMER
SWNCD 012 / Sep '97 / Sound Waves

Cooder, Ry

☐ BOOMER'S STORY
Boomer's story / Cherry ball blues / Crow black chicken / Axe sweet Mama / Maria Elena / Dark end of the street / Rally round the flag / Coming in on a wing and a prayer / President Kennedy / Good morning Mr. Railway man
7599263982 / Jan '93 / WEA

☐ BOP TILL YOU DROP
Little sister / Go home girl / Very thing that makes you rich makes me poor / I think it's gonna work out fine / Down in Hollywood / Look at granny run run / Trouble / Don't mess up a good thing / I can't win
256691 / '83 / WEA

☐ BORDERLINE
634 5789 / Speedo is back / Why don't you try me / Down in the boondocks / Johnny Porter / Way we make a broken heart / Crazy about an automobile / Girls from Texas / Borderline / Never make a move too soon
256864 / '88 / WEA

☐ BUENA VISTA SOCIAL CLUB (Cooder, Ry & Ochoa/Compay Segundo/Ibrahim Ferrer)
Chan chan: *Cooder, Ry* / Camino por vereda: *Cooder, Ry* / Veinte anos: *Cooder, Ry* / Pueblo nuevo: *Cooder, Ry* / Dos gardinerias: *Cooder, Ry* / El carretero: *Cooder, Ry* / Candela: *Cooder, Ry* / Amor de loca juventud: *Cooder, Ry* / Orgullecida: *Cooder, Ry* / Murmullo: *Cooder, Ry* / El cuarto de tula: *Cooder, Ry* / Y tu que has hecho: *Cooder, Ry* / Buena vista social club: *Cooder, Ry* / La bayamesa: *Cooder, Ry*
WCD 050 / Jun '97 / World Circuit

☐ CHICKEN SKIN MUSIC
Bourgeois blues / I got mine / Always lift him up / He'll have to go / Smack dab in the middle / Stand by me / Yellow roses / Chloe / Goodnight Irene
254083 / '88 / WEA

☐ GET RHYTHM
Get rhythm / Low commotion / Going back to Okinawa / Thirteen question method / Women will rule the world / All shook up / I can tell by the way you smell / Across the borderline / Let's have a ball
9256392 / Dec '87 / WEA

☐ INTO THE PURPLE VALLEY
How can you keep on moving / Billy the kid / Money honey / FDR in Trinidad / Teardrops will fall / Denomination blues / On a Monday / Hey porter / Great dreams of heaven / Taxes on the farmer feeds us all / Vigilante man
244142 / '88 / WEA

☐ JAZZ
Big bad Bill is sweet William now / Face to face that I shall meet him / Pearls / Tia Juana / Dream / Happy meeting in glory / In a mist / Flashes / Davenport blues / Shine / Nobody / We shall be happy
256488 / '88 / WEA

☐ LAST MAN STANDING (Original Soundtrack)
5334152 / Oct '96 / Verve

☐ MEETING BY THE RIVER, A (Cooder, Ry & V.M. Bhatt)
WLACS 029 / Apr '93 / Waterlily Acoustics

☐ MUSIC BY RY COODER (2CD Set)
Long riders / Archie's funeral (hold to god's unchanging hand) / Jesse james / Greenhouse / See you in hell blind boy / Across the borderline / I can't walk this time / Sunny's tune / Angola / Klan meeting / No quiero / Theme from southern comfort / Highway 23 / Theme from alamo bay / Goose and lucky / East st louis / Cruising with rafe / Cancion mixteca / Canoes upstream / Goyakla is coming / Bound for Canaan / Maria / King of the street / Swamp walk / Bomber bash / Train to Florida / Bound for canaan (the 6th cavalry) / I like your eyes / Johnny Handsome / Feelin' bad blues / Viola lee blues / Nice bike / Houston in two seconds / Paris texas
9362459872 / Jun '95 / WEA

☐ PARADISE AND LUNCH
Tamp 'em up solid / Tattler / Married man's a fool / Jesus on the mainline / It's all over now / Fool about a cigarette / Feeling good / If walls could talk / Mexican divorce / Ditty wa ditty
244260 / Oct '87 / WEA

☐ RY COODER
Alimony / France chance / One meat ball / Do re mi / Old Kentucky home / How can a poor man stand such times and live / And live / Available space / Pig meat / Police dog blues / Goin' to Brownsville / Dark is the night
7599275102 / May '95 / WEA

☐ SHOW TIME
School is out / Alimony / Jesus on the mainline / Dark end of the street / Viva sequin / Do re mi / Volver, volver / How can a poor man stand such times and live / Smack dab in the middle
7599273192 / Aug '92 / WEA

☐ SLIDE AREA, THE
UFO has landed in the ghetto / I need a woman / Gypsy woman / Blue suede shoes / Mama don't treat your daughter mean / I'm drinking again / Which came first / That's the way love turned out for me
K2 56976 / Jul '88 / WEA

☐ WHY DON'T YOU TRY ME TONIGHT
How can a poor man stand such times and live / Available space / Money honey / Tattler / He'll have to go / Smack dab in the middle / Dark end of the street / Down in Hollywood / Little sister / I think it's gonna work out fine / Crazy about an automobile / 634 5789 / Why don't you try me
K 2408642 / '86 / WEA

Cook, Barbara

☐ BARBARA COOK SINGS THE WALT DISNEY SONG BOOK
When you wish upon a star / Give a little whistle / Pink elephants on parade / When I see an elephant fly / With a smile and a song / Lavender blue / Zip a dee doo dah / Dream is a wish your heart makes / Second star to the right / Baby mine / Someone's waiting for you / Sooner or later / I'm late / Someday my Prince will come
PWK 090 / Feb '89 / Carlton

☐ CLOSE AS PAGES IN A BOOK
It's not where you start / Close as pages in a book / I can't give you anything but love / Make the man love me / Exactly like you / April snow / Don't blame me / I'm in the mood for love / On the sunny side of the street / Way you look tonight / Bojangles of Harlem / I must have that man / April fooled me/I'm way ahead
DRGCD 91412 / Nov '93 / DRG

☐ I HAVE DREAMED
DRGCD 91448 / Mar '97 / DRG

☐ LIVE FROM LONDON
Sing a song with me / Let me sing and I'm happy / Beauty and the beast / Never never land / Can you read my mind / Come rain or come shine / Ship in a bottle / Sweet dreams / I see your face before me / Change partners / I'm beginning to see the light / I had myself a true love / Sweet Georgia Brown / Errol Flynn / Love don't need a reason / He was too good to me / Losing my mind / Accentuate the positive / Why did I choose you / In between goodbyes
DRGCD 91430 / Oct '94 / DRG

☐ TILL THERE WAS YOU (Broadway Years)
379052 / Aug '95 / Koch

Cook, Jesse

☐ GRAVITY
Mario takes a walk / Azul / Gravity / Closer to madness / Into the dark / Brio / Falling from grace / Olodum / Rapture / Gipsy / Lluna Llena
ND 63037 / Nov '96 / Narada
VNDCD 4 / 11 May '98 / Virgin

☐ TEMPEST
Tempest / Cascada / Breeze from Saintes Maries / Baghdad / Parasol / Dance of spring / Soledad / Orbit / Fate (parasol reprise) / Jumpstart
ND 63035 / Dec '95 / Narada

Cook, Marty

☐ NIGHT WORK
ENJACD 50332 / May '95 / Enja

Cooke, Sam

☐ IN THE BEGINNING (Cooke, Sam & The Soul Stirrers)
He's my friend / I'm gonna build on that shore / Jesus wash away my troubles / Must Jesus bear the cross alone / Jesus I'll never forget / Nearer to thee / Any day now / Touch the hem of his garment / I don't want to cry / Lovable / Forever / I'll come running back to you / Happy in love / I need you now / That's all I need to know / One more river / He's so wonderful / Jesus gave me water / That's all I need to know / I don't want to cry / Forever / Lovable
CDCHD 280 / Nov '89 / Ace

☐ MAGIC OF SAM COOKE, THE
You send me / Only sixteen / Stealing kisses / Talk of the town / I love you most of all / Comes love / Lover come back to me / Everybody loves to cha cha / Little things you do / Good morning heartache / Win your love for me / Moonlight in Vermont / There, I've said it again / Stealaway / All of my life / That lucky old sun / God bless this child / When I fall in love
MCCD 021 / May '91 / Music Club

☐ MAN AND HIS MUSIC, THE
Meet me at Mary's place / Good times / Shake / Sad mood / Bring it on home to me / That's where it's at / That's heaven to me / Touch the hem of his garment / You send me / I'll come running back to you / Win your love for me / Wonderful world / Cupid / Just for you / Chain gang / Only sixteen / When a boy falls in love / Rome wasn't built in a day / Everybody loves to cha cha / Nothing can change this love / Love will find a way / Another Saturday night / Having a party / Twistin' the night away / Somebody have mercy / Ain't that good news / Soothe me / Change is gonna come
PD 87127 / Apr '86 / RCA

☐ SAM COOKE WITH THE SOUL STIRRERS (Cooke, Sam & The Soul Stirrers)
Peace in the valley / It won't be very long / How far am I from Canaan / Just another day / Come and go to that land / Any day now / He'll make a way / Nearer to thee / Be with me, Jesus / One more river / I'm so glad (trouble don't last always) / Wonderful / Farther along / Touch the hem of his garment / Jesus wash away my troubles / Must Jesus bear the cross alone / That's heaven to me / Were you there / Mean ol' world / Lord remember me / Lovable / Forever / I'll come running back to you / That's all I need to know / I don't want to cry
CDCHD 359 / Nov '91 / Ace

☐ SAM COOKE'S NIGHT BEAT
Lost and lookin' / Mean old world / Nobody knows the trouble I've seen / Please don't drive me away / I lost everything / Get yourself another fool / Little red rooster / Laughin' and clownin' / Trouble blues / You gotta move / Fool's paradise / Shake, rattle and roll
5285672 / Sep '95 / London

☐ TWO ON ONE (Cooke, Sam & Jackie Wilson)
Wonderful world / You send me / Only sixteen / I love you most of all / Everybody likes to cha cha cha / There I've said it again / Win your love for me / When I fall in love / Moonlight in vermont / Ol' man river / Reet petite (the finest girl you ever want to meet) / To be loved / Lonely teardrops / Night / That's why (i love you so) / I'm wanderin' / Talk that talk / Only you, only me / My empty arms / Singing a song
CDTT 1 / Apr '94 / Charly

Cookie & The Cupcakes

☐ KINGS OF SWAMP POP
Got you on my mind / Mathilda / I'm twisted / Great pretender / I've been so lonely / I cried / Breaking up is hard to do / Betty and Dupree / I almost lost my mind / Feel so good / Charged with cheating / Sea of love / Close up the back door / Until then / Even though / Honey hush / Belinda / Trouble in my life / Who would have thought it / I had the blues / Walking down the aisle / Franko-Chinese cha cha cha / Shake 'em up / Mary Lou doin' the Pop-Eye / Just one kiss / Since your love has grown cold / Cindy Lou / Such as love / Married life / Mathilda
CDCHD 142 / Jul '97 / Ace

Cookies

☐ COMPLETE COOKIES
Chains / Don't say nothin' bad about my baby / Girls grow up faster than boys / Will power / Old crowd / Stranger in my arms / Softly in the night / Foolish little girl / I want a boy for my birthday / On Broadway / Only to other people / I never dreamed / I'm into something good / We love and learn / Randy / They're jealous of me
NEMCD 649 / Jun '94 / Sequel

Cool Breeze

☐ ASSIMILATION
DOR 38CD / Apr '95 / Dorado

Cool For August

☐ GRAND WORLD
9362461052 / 4 May '98 / WEA

Coolangubra

☐ SPIRIT TALK
131222 / Aug '97 / Celestial Harmonies

Cooley, Joe

☐ COOLEY
CEFCD 044 / Jan '94 / Gael Linn

Cooley, Spade

☐ SPADE COOLEY
Texas playboy rag/Draggin' the bow / Forgive me one more time / Whispering / Navajo trail / Please forgive me / You can't break my heart / Devil's dream / Blonde fiddle blues / Dill pickle rag / You wuz right baby / Crazy cos' I love you / Texas playboy rag/ Home in San Antone / Mad about him blues / Night train to Memphis / Pins and needles in my heart / Spanish two step / You dont care / There's a new moon/Shame on you / Fort Worth jail / Bury me beneath the willow / If it's wrong to love you / Take me back to Tulsa/Shame on you
RFDCD 18 / Apr '98 / Country Routes

Coolidge, Rita

☐ ALL TIME HIGH
We're all alone / I don't want to talk about it / Loving arms / Closer you get / You're so fine / (Your love has lifted me) Higher and higher / Way you do the things you do / All time high / We've got tonight / Wishin' and hopin' / You / One fine day / I'd rather leave while I'm in love / Words
5500792 / May '93 / Spectrum

☐ COLLECTION, THE
We're all alone / I'd rather leave while I'm in love / (Your love has lifted me) higher and higher / Crazy love / Seven bridges road / I believe in you / Bird on the wire / I'll be your baby tonight / I don't want to talk about it / Words / One fine day / Fool that I am / Tempted / All time high / Walk on in / Wishin' and hopin' / Slow dancer / You / Sweet inspiration / You're so fine
5518162 / Nov '95 / Spectrum

☐ LOVE LESSONS
Heart don't fail me now / Just a kiss away / Nobody but you / If you find it / Love lessons / Ain't no reason / You've got the best of me / Girlfriend / One heartbeat / I want to know what love is / Cherokee
INDELCD 8 / 27 Apr '98 / Indelible

☐ OUT OF THE BLUES
Mean to me / Am I blue / Hallelujah I love him so / Call it stormy Monday / For the good times / Black coffee / Bring it on home to me / Nobody wins / Man I love / When the night rolls in / Out of the blues
MA 1804100 / Jun '97 / Music Avenue

☐ THINKIN' ABOUT YOU
1791721002 / 17 Mar '98 / FMG

☐ WALELA (Coolidge, Rita & Priscilla)
5360492 / 5 Jan '98 / Triloka

Coon, Jackie

☐ BACK IN HIS OWN BACKYARD
ARCD 19109 / Nov '94 / Arbors Jazz

☐ SOFTLY
ARCD 19162 / 1 Jun '98 / Arbors Jazz

Coon-Sanders Orchestra

☐ EVERYTHING IS HOTSY-TOTSY NOW (Coon-Sanders Original Nighthawk Orchestra)
Nighthawk blues / Red-hot Mama / I'm gonna Charleston back to Charleston / Alone at last / Yes, Sir that's my baby / Everything is hotsy-totsy now / Flamin' mamie / Deep Henderson / My baby knows how / Slue foot / Mine, all mine / Wail / Hallucinations / Stay out of the south / Oh you have no idea / Here comes my ball and chain / Little orphan Annie / Rhythm King / We love us / Alone in the rain / After you've gone / Darktown strutters ball / Keepin' out of mischief now
CDAJA 5199 / Sep '96 / Living Era

Cooney, Andy

☐ IRISH INFLUENCE
SHCD 52044 / May '97 / Shanachie

Coope Boyes & Simpson

☐ FALLING SLOWLY
NMCD 9 / Aug '96 / No Master's Cooperative

☐ FUNNY OLD WORLD
NMCD 3 / Feb '96 / No Master's Voice

☐ HERE
NMCDS 1 / Jul '95 / No Master's Voice

☐ HINDSIGHT
Shallow brown / John Barleycorn / Sprig of thyme / Pleasant and delightful / She's like a swallow / Six jolly miners / With my dog and gun / Henry's downfall / Paint said the master to me / Bold princess Royal / Reynardine / Low down in the broom / Wild goose shanty / Coppers' Christmas song / Ten thousand miles
NMCD 11 / Feb '98 / No Master's Cooperative

Cooper

☐ DO YOU NOT KNOW
KIS 6CD / Jan '95 / Konkurrel

☐ NO.2
CDWOOS 3 / Aug '96 / Out Of Step

Cooper, Al

☐ CLASSICS 1938-1941 (Cooper, Al & His Savoy Sultans)
CLASSICS 728 / Dec '93 / Classics

Cooper, Alice

☐ ALICE COOPER
GFS 071 / Jul '97 / Going For A Song

☐ BEAST OF ALICE COOPER, THE
School's out / Under my wheels / Billion dollar babies / Be my lover / Desperado / Is it my body / Only women bleed / Elected / Eighteen / Hello hooray / No more Mr. Nice Guy / Teenage lament '74 / Muscle of love / Department of youth
2417812 / Nov '89 / WEA

☐ BILLION DOLLAR BABIES
Hello hooray / Raped and freezin' / Elected / Unfinished sweet / No more Mr. Nice Guy / Generation landslide / Sick things / Mary Ann / I love the dead / Billion dollar babies
7599272692 / Jan '93 / WEA

☐ CLASSICKS
Poison / Hey stoopid / Feed my Frankenstein / Love's a loaded gun / Stolen prayer / House of fire / Lost in America / It's me / Under my wheels / Billion dollar babies / Eighteen / No more Mr. Nice Guy / Only women bleed / School's out / Fire
4808452 / Oct '95 / Epic

☐ CONSTRICTOR/RAISE YOUR FIST AND YELL (2CD Set)
MCD 33004 / Jul '96 / MCA

☐ FISTFUL OF ALICE, A
School's out / Under my wheels / I'm eighteen / Desperado / Lost in America / Teenage lament '74 / I never cry / Poison / No more Mr. Nice guy / Welcome to my nightmare / Only women bleed / Feed my Frankenstein / Elected / Is elected home
CTMCD 331 / Jun '97 / EMI

☐ FREEDOM FOR FRANKENSTEIN (Hits And Pieces 1984-1994)
He's back (the man behind the mask) / Teenage Frankenstein / Give it up / Freedom / Lock me up / I got a line on you / Poison / House of fire / Bed of nails / Go to hell / Ballad of Dwight Fry / Hey stoopid / It rained all night / Feed my Frankenstein / Fire / Side show / Sick things / Only women bleed/Wind up toy
RVCD 69 / 8 Jun '98 / Raven

☐ GOES TO HELL
Go to hell / You gotta dance / I'm the coolest / Didn't we meet / I never cry / Give the kid a break / Guilty / Wake me gently / Wish you were here / I'm always chasing rainbows / Going home
7599272992 / May '94 / Warner Bros.

☐ HEY STOOPID
Hey stoopid / Love's a loaded gun / Snakebite / Burning our bed / Dangerous tonight / Might as well be on Mars / Feed my Frankenstein / Hurricane years / Little by little / Die for you / Dirty dreams / Wind up toys
4684162 / Mar '96 / Epic

☐ KILLER
Under my wheels / Be my lover / Halo of flies / Desperado / You drive me nervous / Yeah yeah yeah / Dead babies / Killer
K 9272552 / Sep '89 / WEA

☐ LADIES MAN
Freak out / Painting a picture / I've written home to mother / Science fiction / For Alice / Nobody likes me / Going to the river / Ain't that just like a woman
MM 011 / 24 Aug '98 / MagMid

☐ SCHOOL'S OUT
Luney tune / Gutter Cats vs The Jets / Blue turk / My stars / Public animal no. 9 / Alma master / Grand finale / School's out
9272602 / Jun '89 / WEA

☐ SNAKES AND DEAD BABIES
CBAK 4037 / Apr '90 / Baktabak

☐ SNORTING ANTHRAX
DRESS 603 / 25 May '98 / Dressed To Kill

☐ TRASH
Poison / Spark in the dark / House of fire / Why trust you / Only my heart talkin' / Bed of nails / This maniac's in love with you / Trash / Hell is living without you / I'm your gun
4651302 / Aug '89 / Epic

Cooper Clarke, John

☐ DISGUISE IN LOVE
I don't want to be nice / Psyche sluts 1 and 2 / (I've got a brand new) tracksuit / Teenage werewolf / Readers' wives / Post-war glamour girl / (I married) a monster from outerspace / Salome Maloney health fanatic / Strange bedfellows / Valley of the lost women
4805302 / May '95 / Epic

☐ OU EST LA MAISON DE FROMAGE
Serial (part 1) / Letter to Fiesta / Film extra's extra / Majorca / Action man / Kung fu international / Sperm test / Missing persons / Split beans / Dumb row laughs / Bunch of twigs / Trains / Cycle accident / Gimmix / Readers wives / Ten years in an open neck shirt (part 1) / Nothing / (I married a) monster from outer space / Ten years in an open neck shirt (part 2) / Daily Express (you'll never see a nipple in) / Ten years in an open neck shirt (part 3) / Salome Malone / Psycle sluts
RRCD 110 / Nov '96 / Receiver

☐ SNAP CRACKLE AND BOP
Evidently chickentown / Conditional discharge / Sleepwalk / 23rd / Beasley Street / Thirty six hours / Belladonna / It man / Limbo / Distant relation
4773802 / Aug '94 / Epic

Cooper, Dana

☐ MIRACLE MILE
742442 / 30 Mar '98 / Compass

Cooper, Henry

☐ BABY PLEASE
HAR 7001 / 19 Mar '98 / High Action

Cooper, Jim

☐ NUTVILLE
Nutville / Mallethead / Mija / Bemsha swing / Cantor da noite / Sui fumi / Autumn nocturne / Cabbie patch / Tanga
DD 457 / Mar '97 / Delmark

☐ TOUGH TOWN
Cheryl / Waltz for Betty / I waited for you / Tough town / Dolphin / Shades of light / Town sound/She'd be so nice to come home to
DD 446 / Mar '97 / Delmark

Cooper, Lindsay

☐ MUSIC FOR OTHER OCCASIONS
NML 8603CD / Oct '93 / No Man's Land

☐ OH MOSCOW
VICTOCD 015 / Nov '94 / Victo

☐ PIA MATER (Cooper, Lindsay & Charles Gray)
Pia mater
RES 124CD / 15 Sep '97 / Resurgence

☐ RAGS/THE GOLDDIGERS
RERLCD / Apr '91 / ReR/Recommended

Cooper, Mike

☐ CONTINUOUS PREACHING BLUES, THE (Cooper, Mike & Ian A. Anderson)
APCD 037 / Mar '97 / Appaloosa

☐ DO I KNOW YOU/TROUT STEEL
Link / Journey to the East / First song / Theme in C / Thinking back / Think she knows me now / Too late now / Wish she was with me / Do I know you / Start of a journey / Looking back / That's how / Sitting here watching / Goodtimes / I've got mine / Don't talk too fast / Trout steel / In the mourning / Hope you see / Pharoah's march / Weeping rose
BGOCD 276 / Nov '95 / Beat Goes On

☐ PLACES I KNOW/THE MACHINE GUN COMPANY
Country water / Three - Forty Eight / Night journey / Time to time / Paper and smoke / Broken bridges / Now I know / Goodbye blues, goodbye / Places I know / Song for Abigail / Singing tree / Midnight words / So glad (that I found you) / Lady Anne
BGOCD 294 / May '96 / Beat Goes On

Cooper, Pete

☐ WOUNDED HUSSAR, THE
FFS 002CD / Oct '93 / Fiddling From Scratch

Cooper, Roger

☐ GOING BACK TO OLD KENTUCKY
Nine miles out of Louisville / Pine Creek / Cauliflower / New money / Growling old man, fussing old woman / Boatin' up Sandy / Bostony / Warfield / Paddy / Susan's gone / Morris Allen's Brickyard Joe / Weddington's reel / Greek melody / Salt lick / Something sweet to tell / Charleston / Snakewinder / Chillicothe beauty / Portsmouth / Meg Gray / Bumble bee in a jug / Coon dog / Jimmy Arthurs / Going back to old Kentucky / Bear Creek hop
ROUCD 0380 / Oct '96 / Rounder

Cooper, Wilma Lee

☐ WILMA LEE COOPER COLLECTION
REB 1122CD / Apr '96 / Rebel

Cop Shoot Cop

☐ ASK QUESTIONS LATER
Surprise, surprise / Room 429 / Nowhere / Migration / Cut to the chase / $10 bill / Seattle / Purnace / Israeli dig / Cause and effect / Got no soul / Everybody loves you / All the clocks are broken
ABBCD 045 / Apr '93 / Big Cat

☐ CONSUMER REVOLT
ABB 033CD / Apr '92 / Big Cat

☐ RELEASE
ABB 69CD / Aug '95 / Big Cat

☐ WHITE NOISE
White noise / Cop shoot cop / Discount rebellion / Traitormartyr / Coldest day / Feel good / Relief / Empires collapse / Corporate protopop / Heads I win / Chameleon man / Where's the money / If tomorrow / Hung again
ABB 029CD / Oct '91 / Big Cat

Cope, Julian

☐ FLOORED GENIUS VOL.1 (The Best Of Julian Cope)
Reward / Treason / Sleeping gas / Bouncing babies / Passionate friend / Great dominions / Greatness and perfection of love / Elegant chaos / Sunspots / Reynard the fox / World shut your mouth / Trampolene / Spacehopper / Charlotte Anne / China doll
CID 8000 / Aug '92 / Island

☐ FLOORED GENIUS VOL.2
Greatness and perfection of love / Head hang low / Hey high class butcher / Sunspots / Me singing / Hobby / 24A Velocity crescent / Laughing boy / O king of chaos / Reynard the fox / Pulsar / Crazy farm animal / Christmas mourning / Planet rider / You think it's love / Double vegetation
SFRSCD 061 / 18 May '98 / Strange Fruit

☐ FOLLOWERS OF SAINT JULIAN, THE
Transporting / World shut your mouth / I've got levitation / Non-alignment pact / Umpteenth unnatural blues / Trainsporting / Trampolene / Disaster / Mock turtle / Warwick the kingmaker / Almost beautiful child / Eve's volcano (covered in sin)/Vulcano lungo / Pulsar nx / Shot down
IMCD 251 / Jun '97 / Island

☐ FRIED
Reynard the fox / Bill Drummond said / Laughing boy / Me singing / Sunspots / Bloody assizes / Search party / O king of chaos / Holy love / Torpedo / I went on a chourney / Mic mak mok / Land of fear
8228322 / Mar '96 / Mercury

☐ JEHOVAHKILL
Soul desert / No hard shoulder to cry on / Akhenaten / Mystery trend / Upwards at 45 / Cut my friends down / Necropolis / Slow rider / Gimme back my flag / Poet is priest / Julian H Cope / Subtle energies commission / Fa-fa-fa-fine / Fear loves this place / Tower / Peggy Suicide is missing
IMCD 189 / Mar '94 / Island

☐ MY NATION UNDERGROUND
Five o'clock world / Charlotte Anne / China doll / I'm not losing sleep / Vegetation / My nation underground / Someone like me / Great white hoax
IMCD 138 / Aug '91 / Island

☐ PEGGY SUICIDE
Pristeen / Double vegetation / East easy rider / Promised land / Hanging out and hung up on the line / Safesurfer / If you loved me at all / Drive she said / Soldier blue / You... / Not raving but drowning / Head / Leperskin / Beautiful love / Western front 1992 CE / Hung up and hanging out to dry / American lite / Las Vegas basement
IMCD 188 / Mar '94 / Island

☐ ST. JULIAN
Crack in the clouds / Trampoline / Shot down / Eve's volcano (covered in sin) / Space hopper / Planet ride / World shut your mouth / St. Julian / Pulsar / Screaming secrets
IMCD 137 / Aug '91 / Island

☐ WORLD SHUT YOUR MOUTH
Bandy's first jump / Greatness and perfection of love / Elegant chaos / Kolly Kibber's birthday / Head hang low / Metranil vavin / Sunshine playroom / Lunatic and fire pistol / Strasbourg / Quizmaster / Pussyface / Wreck my car / High class butcher / Eat the poor
8183652 / Mar '96 / Mercury

Copeland, Johnny

☐ AIN'T NOTHIN' BUT A PARTY (Live in Houston, Texas)
Ain't nothin' but a party / Johnny gone / Houston / Learned my lessons / Baby please don't go / Big time
ROUCD 2055 / '88 / Rounder

☐ FLYIN' HIGH
Flyin' high / Yesterday / Hooked, hog-tied and collared / Greater man / Jambalaya / San Antone / Thigpen / Promised myself / Love song / Circumstances / Around the world
5175122 / Jan '92 / EmArCy

☐ FURTHER ON UP THE ROAD
AIM 1032CD / Oct '93 / Aim

☐ TEXAS TWISTER
Midnight fantasy / North Caroline / Don't stop by the creek son / Excuses / Jessanne / Houston / When the rain starts fallin' / I de go now / Early in the morning / Twister / Idiom / Easy to love / Media / Morning coffee / Jelly roll / Where or when
ROUCD 11504 / '88 / Rounder

☐ WHEN THE RAIN STARTS FALLIN'
Midnight fantasy / Make my home where I hang my hat / Down on bended knee / Jessanne / Bozalimalamu / Devil's hand / Third party / Conakry / Old man blues / When the rain starts fallin' / Same thing / I wish I was single / Rock 'n' roll lilly / North carolina / Big time / St. louis blues
ROUCD 11515 / '88 / Rounder

Copeland, Keith

☐ POSTCARD FROM VANCOUVER
JFCD 023 / Apr '98 / Jazz Focus

Copeland, Ruth

☐ SELF PORTRAIT/I AM WHAT I AM (Copeland, Ruth & Parliament)
Prologue: child of the North / Thanks for the birthday card / Your love been so good to me / Music box / Silent boatman / To William in the night / No commitment / I got a thing for you Daddy / Gift of me / Medal / Crying has made me stronger / Hare Krishna / Suburban family lament / Play with fire / Don't you wish you had (what you had when you had it) / Gimme shelter
DEEPM 022 / Jun '97 / Deep Beats

Copeland, Shemekia

☐ TURN THE HEAT UP
ALCD 4857 / Jun '98 / Alligator

Copernicus

☐ NO BORDERLINE
MCD 2089 / Jun '94 / Humbug

Coping Saw

☐ OUTSIDE NOW
HBOIS 004CD / Aug '97 / House Of Dubois

Copland, Marc

☐ AT NIGHT
500592 / Nov '92 / Sunnyside

☐ PARADISO (Copland, Marc Trio)
1212832 / Jan '98 / Soul Note

☐ SECOND LOOK (Copland, Marc Quartet)
Second look / Happy stance / Timeless / Snowfall / Au private / Dark territory / Suite sixteen / Amie / If I should lose you
CY 18001 / Oct '97 / Savoy Jazz

☐ **STOMPIN' WITH SAVOY (Copland, Marc Quintet)**
Equinox / I got rhythm / I loves you Porgy / Footprints / Easy to love / Lover man / Woody'n you / Blue in green / One finger snap / All blue
CY 75853 / Oct '97 / Savoy Jazz

Copley, Al

☐ **GOOD UNDERSTANDING (Copley, Al & The Fabulous Thunderbirds)**
SECD 754 / Apr '94 / Suffering Egos

☐ **GOOD UNDERSTANDING (Copley, Al & The Fabulous Thunderbirds)**
Doin' it / Sunshine moonlight / Another woman / Bad bad whiskey / Run riot / What do I do / Man and the blues / Love will heal me too / Good understanding
CDBB 9596 / Dec '97 / Bullseye Blues

☐ **LIVE AT MONTREUX**
OMCD 1201 / Nov '94 / One Mind

☐ **ROYAL BLUE (Copley, Al & Hal Singer)**
BT 1054CD / '92 / Black Top

Copper Family

☐ **COPPERSONGS VOL.2**
COPP 002CD / Nov '95 / Coppersongs

Copper, Monique

☐ **BABAR & DOOS MEL SPEELGOOD**
BVHAASTCD 8907 / Apr '89 / Bvhaast

Copperfield, David

☐ **I GOT VARIETY**
Big enough for me and you / Augusta's song / Buzz / Toys / Medallion man / Like a tune I can't forget / Independent lady / Don't sink your claws into me / I drink to your memory / Big dipper / I got variety
OWNL 60001 / May '96 / Own

Copperpot, Chester

☐ **SHORTCUTS**
DOL 019CD / Apr '95 / Dolores

Coppieters, Francis

☐ **COLOURS IN JAZZ**
ISCD 174 / May '98 / Intersound

Coppin, Johnny

☐ **COUNTRY CHRISTMAS, A**
RSKCD 114 / Jan '96 / Red Sky

☐ **EDGE OF DAY (Music & Poetry) (Coppin, Johnny & Laurie Lee)**
Spring dawn (main theme) / Spring dawn (main theme) / Edge of day / First love / Invasion summer / Milkmaid / Thistle / Landscape / Stork in jerez / Spanish landscape / Day of these days / September evening / Asleep we are divided / Harvest / First taste of cider / Apples / Field of autumn / October sunset / Sunken evening / November / Town owl / Christmas landscape / Wassail / Twelfth night / On Beacon Hill / Boy on ice / Locked in this paradise
RSKCD 108 / May '89 / Red Sky

☐ **FORCE OF THE RIVER**
River song / Reach out for you / Just for you / Shining stars / Full force of the river / All depends on you / May not be far away / Rise with the dawn / Border county road / On a hill in Shropshire / LOng lost love
RSKCD 112 / Oct '93 / Red Sky

☐ **GLOUCESTERSHIRE COLLECTION, THE (Forest & Vale & High Blue Hill/ English Morning)**
In Flanders / Song of Gloucestershire / Piper's wood / Fisherman of Newnham / Cotswold love / Briar roses / Legacy / Warning / High road / Field of Autumn / Cotswold lad / Song of Minsterworth Perry / Have wondered / Cotswold farmers / This night the stars / English morning / Everlasting mercy / Dover's hill / Hill / Tom Long's post / High hill / Holy brook / East wind / Winter / Cotswold tiles / Roads go down
RSKCD 015/107 / Feb '95 / Red Sky

☐ **SONGS AND CAROLS FOR A WEST COUNTRY CHRISTMAS**
Intro: Lord of all this Revelling / Gloucestershire Wassail / Song for loders / My dancing day / Sans Day carol / Come all you worth Christian friends / Sailor's carol / Glastonbury thorn / Oxen / Innocent's song / O little town of Bethlehem / Wiltshire carol / Virgin most pure / Birth / Campden carol / Flowering of the thorn
RSKCD 111 / Nov '90 / Red Sky

Coppola, Imani

☐ **CHUPACABRA**
I'm a tree / Legend of a cowgirl / Naked city (love to see U shine) / It's all about me, me and me / Piece / Karma and the blizzard / One of these days / Pigeon Penelope / Soon (I like it) / Forget myself / La da da
4886602 / 2 Mar '98 / Columbia

Coptic Rain

☐ **11/11**
DY 142 / Jul '95 / Dynamica

☐ **CLARION'S END**
Haunt / Devil in disguise / In to the sun / And all I loved / Rejoice / Selvas / Midgard / Cortex wave / Scanner / Slepnir / Even closer
DY 022CD / Sep '96 / Dynamica

☐ **DIES IREA**
DY 22 / Oct '93 / Dynamica

Cor Godre'r Aran

☐ **EVVIVA**
Evviva beviam / Y blodyn a holltodd y maen / Berwyn / De animals a-comin' / A llawenydd cenwch / Majesty / Ach Fraulein Zart / Creation / Rhythm of life / Mae'r dydd yn cilio / Morte criste / Clychau'r gog / Jerusalem / Ar lan y mor / Gwyr Harlech
SCD 2120 / May '97 / Sain

Cor Meibion Llanelli

☐ **YR YNYS DDIRGEL**
Cragen ddur / Nkosi sikelel'i Afrika / Mae hon yn fyw / Llanfair / Unwaith eto / Yr ynys ddirgel / Draw dros y don / Y Greadigaeth / Ysbryd y nos / Yr anthem geltaidd / Gwawrio mae'r bore / Ffarwel I ddociau lerpwl / Gwawrio geltaidd
SCD 2126 / Nov '96 / Sain

Corbett, Jon

☐ **ANOTHER FINE MESS (Corbett, Jon & Steve Done)**
Commence to dancing / Acrobat / Glove for sale / Millstones / Tapdancer / Waltz for debris / Square midnight / Little weed / ...and there's an end to it
SLAMCD 217 / Oct '96 / Slam

Corbetta, Jerry

☐ **DON'T CALL US (Corbetta, Jerry & Sugarloaf)**
REP 4272WP / 16 Mar '98 / Repertoire

Cordara Orchestra

☐ **BEST OF CORDARA ORCHESTRA, THE (2CD Set)**
Tipsy / Search / Irony / Battuta d'arresto / Perfect / Jet society / Misley / Gad fly / Contrasti / Distensione / Target / Misly / Saguia / Chrisalis / Hypostesis / Trip / Riri
489230CD / 16 Dec '97 / Irma La Douce

Cordas Et Cannas

☐ **PLACE OF WINDS**
Abbas abbadas / Su testamentu / Nanneddu / Tancus serrada / Intr'a duos abbas / Mamma no keret / Tula et pula / Filugnana / Notti d'ea / Procurade 'e moderare / Su falkittu / Abba a bula / Scalmentu / Sos pirates barbarescos / Ninna nanna pizzinnu / In s'abba / Non si poni risisti / Terra de'entos
TERRCD 002 / Nov '96 / Terra Nova

Cordelia's Dad

☐ **COMET**
179CD / Apr '95 / Normal

☐ **CORDELIA'S DAD**
OKRACD 011 / Mar '94 / Okra

☐ **HOW CAN I SLEEP**
OKRACD 33019 / Mar '94 / Okra

☐ **JOY FUN GARDEN, THE**
RTS 3CD / Mar '94 / Normal

☐ **ROADKILL**
SCOF 1004CD / Apr '96 / Scenescof

☐ **SPINE**
APRCD 1023 / May '98 / Appleseed

Cordell, Frank

☐ **SWEET AND DRY/THE MELODY LINGERS ON (Cordell, Frank & His Orchestra)**
Get happy / April in Paris / Pick yourself up / 'Round midnight / Sing for your supper / There's a lull in my life / Summertime / Gone with the wind / Nobody's heart / What is this thing called love / Lover / You stepped out of a dream / Dance little lady / Man I love / Cherokee / You go to my head / Continental / Yesterdays / Just one of those things / Song is ended
CDMFP 6391 / Jul '97 / Music For Pleasure

Cordner, Rodney

☐ **IRELAND - A SENSE OF PLACE**
12513 / Sep '93 / Music Of The World

Cords

☐ **HEAR SEE FEEL TASTE**
CORDS 001 / May '96 / Konkurrent

☐ **NO GURU NO METHOD NO BLEEPER**
AOHEA 11 / 15 Dec '97 / Konkurrent

Corduroy

☐ **DAD MAN CAT/OUT OF HERE (2CD Set)**
SMDCD 172 / 22 Sep '97 / Snapper

☐ **NEW YOU, THE**
Evolver / Joker is wild / Winky wagon / Supercrime / Season of the rich / Designosaur / Hand that rocks the cradle / (I know where the) Good times (have gone) / Data 70 / Crossfire / Fisherman's wharf / New you
ABB 139CD / Apr '97 / Big Cat

Core Foundation

☐ **READY TO FLY (2CD Set)**
Ready to fly / You got it / This beat kicks / Freedom / Mortal combat / Time for change / Raise the Titantic / Let the rhythm unwind / New generation / Welcome to the future / In control / Forever and a day / Global sounds / Let yourself go / 20mm / Time to start pumpin'
ALPHACD 1 / Mar '97 / Alpha Projects

Corea, Chick

☐ **AKOUSTIC BAND, THE**
Autumn leaves / So in love / Morning sprite / Circles / Spain
GRP 95822 / Feb '89 / GRP

☐ **ALIVE (Corea, Chick Akoustic Band)**
On Green Dolphin Street / 'Round midnight / Hackensack / Sophisticated lady / UMMG / Humpty dumpty / How deep is the ocean / Morning sprite
GRP 96272 / Dec '90 / GRP

☐ **ARC (Corea, Chick & Holland & Altschul)**
Nefertiti / Ballad for Tillie / ARC / Vedana / Thanatos / Games
8336782 / Mar '88 / ECM

☐ **BEGINNING, THE**
Drone / Percussion piece / Ballad II / Blues connotation / Balham III
17083 / Jan '97 / Laserlight

☐ **BENEATH THE MASK (Corea, Chick Elektric Band)**
Beneath the mask / Little things that count / One of us is over 40 / Wave goodbye / Lifescape / Jammin' E Cricket / Charged particles / Free step / Ninety nine flavours / Illusions
GRP 96492 / Aug '91 / GRP

☐ **BEST OF RETURN TO FOREVER (Corea, Chick & Return To Forever)**
Musician / Romantic warrior / So long Mickey Mouse / Majestic dance / Music magic / Hello again / Sorceress
4682062 / Jan '95 / Sony Jazz

☐ **CHICK COREA**
Song of wind / Song of wind / What's goin' on / Southern soul / Ole for the gypsies / Sundance
15751 / Apr '94 / Laserlight

☐ **CHICK COREA IN CONCERT (Corea, Chick & Gary Burton)**
Senor Mouse / Bud Powell / Crystal silence / Tweak / Falling grace / Mirror mirror / Song to Gayle / Endless trouble, endless pleasure
8214152 / '84 / ECM

☐ **CHILDREN'S SONGS**
8156802 / Apr '84 / ECM

☐ **EARLY DAYS**
Brain / Converge / Waltz for Bill Evans / Sundance / Dave / Vamp / Jamala
17082 / Mar '97 / Laserlight

☐ **FRIENDS**
One step / Waltse for Dave / Children's song / Samba song / Friends / Sicily / Children's song (15) / Cappucino
8490712 / Jun '92 / Polydor

☐ **GOLD COLLECTION, THE (2CD Set)**
R2CD 4028 / 13 Apr '98 / Deja Vu

☐ **HYMN OF THE SEVENTH GALAXY, THE (Corea, Chick & Return To Forever)**
Hymn of the seventh galaxy / After the cosmic rain / Captain senor mouse / Theme to the mothership / Space circus Part 1-3 / Game maker
8253362 / Apr '92 / Polydor

☐ **JAZZ MASTERS**
You're everything / Lenore / Space circus / Friends / Night streets / Children's song (15) / Spain / Interplay / Nite sprite / Light as a feather / Tweedle dee / Wind dance / My Spanish heart / Captain Marvel
5198202 / 5 May '98 / Verve

☐ **LIGHT AS A FEATHER (Corea, Chick & Return To Forever)**
You're everything / Light as a feather / Captain Marvel / 500 miles high / Children's song / Spain
8271482 / Mar '93 / Polydor

☐ **LIVE IN MONTREUX (Corea, Chick & Joe Henderson)**
Introduction / Hairy canary / Folk song / Psalm / Quintet / Up, up and... / Trinkle, tinkle / So in love / Drum interlude / Slippery when wet
SCD 90092 / Mar '97 / Stretch

☐ **MOZART SESSIONS, THE (Corea, Chick & St. Paul Chamber Orchestra/ Bobby McFerrin)**
Piano concerto no.23/K488 / Piano concerto no.20/ K466 / Song for Amadeus
SK 62601 / Nov '96 / Sony Classical

☐ **MUSIC MAGIC (Return To Forever)**
CK 34682 / Aug '97 / Sony Jazz

☐ **MY SPANISH HEART**
Love castle / Gardens / Day danse / My Spanish heart / Night streets / Hilltop / Wind danse / Armando's rhumba / El Bozo / Spanish fantasy
8256572 / Jan '93 / Polydor

☐ **NATIVE SENSE (The New Duets) (Corea, Chick & Gary Burton)**
Native sense / Love castle / Duende / No mystery / Armando's rhumba / Bagatelle no.6 / POst script / Bagatelle no.2 / Tango '92 / Rhumbata / Four in one
SCD 90142 / 6 Oct '97 / Stretch

☐ **ORIGIN**
Say it again / Double image / Dreamless / Molecules / Soul mates / It could happen to you
SCD 90182 / 13 Jul '98 / Stretch

☐ **PIANO IMPROVISATIONS VOL.1**
Noon Song / Song for Sally / Ballad for Anna / Song of the wind / Sometime ago / Where are you now
8119792 / '88 / ECM

☐ **PIANO IMPROVISATIONS VOL.2**
Afternoon song / Song for lee lee / Song for thad / Trinkle tinkle / Masqualero / Preparation (parts 1 and 2) / Departure from planet earth / Arrival, scenery, imps walk, rest
8291902 / ' / ECM

☐ **REMEMBERING BUD POWELL (Corea, Chick & Friends)**
Bouncin' with Bud / Mediocre / Willow grove / Desk in Sandi / Oblivion / Bud Powell / I'll keep loving you / Glass enclosure / Tempus fugit / Celia
SCD 90122 / Feb '97 / Stretch

☐ **RETURN TO FOREVER**
Return to forever / Crystal silence / What game shall we play today / Sometime ago - la fiesta
8119782 / Mar '88 / ECM

☐ **RETURN TO THE 7TH GALAXY (The Return To Forever Anthology/2CD Set) (Corea, Chick & Return To Forever)**
5331082 / Oct '96 / Verve

☐ **SEPTET**
First movement / Second movement / Third movement / Fourth movement / Fifth Movement / Temple of Isfahan
8272582 / ' / ECM

☐ **SUNDANCE**
Brain / Song of wind / Converge / Sundance
CDGR 150 / Nov '97 / Charly

☐ **TAP STEP**
Samba LA / Embrace / Tap step / Magic carpet / Slide / Grandpa blues / Flamenco
SCD 90062 / Mar '97 / Stretch

☐ **THIS IS JAZZ (Corea, Chick & Return To Forever)**
Romantic warrior / Sorceress / Music magic / So long Mickey Mouse / On Green Dolphin Street
CK 64967 / Oct '96 / Sony Jazz

☐ **THREE QUARTETS**
Quartet / Folk song / Hairy canary / Slippery when wet / Confirmation
SCD 90022 / Mar '97 / Stretch

☐ **TIME WARP**
New life / Wish / Terrain / Day danse / That old feeling / New waltz / 'Round midnight
GRP 98292 / Aug '95 / GRP

☐ **TOUCHSTONE**
Touchstone / Procession / Ceremony / Departure / Yellow nimbus / Duende / Compadres / Estancia / Dance of chance
SCD 90032 / Mar '97 / Stretch

☐ **TRIO MUSIC**
Trio improvisations 1,2,3 / Duet improvisation 1,2,3,4,5 / Slippery when wet / Rhythm-a-ning / 'Round midnight / Eronel / Think of one / Little rootie tootie / Reflections / Hackensack / Music of Thelonious Monk
8277022 / May '87 / ECM

☐ **TRIO MUSIC LIVE IN EUROPE**
Loop / I hear a rhapsody / Night and day / Summer night / Prelude no.2 / Mock up / Hittin' it / Microvisions
8277692 / Dec '86 / ECM

☐ **VOYAGE**
Mallorca / Diversions / Star Island / Free fall / Hong Kong
8234682 / ' / ECM

☐ **WALTZ FOR BILL EVANS**
500782 / Sep '96 / Musidisc

☐ **WORKS**
Where are you now / Noon song / Children's song / Brasilia / Slippery when wet / Duet improvisation / New place / La Fiesta / Return to forever / Song of the wind / 'Round midnight / Rhythm-a-ning / Senor Mouse / Sometime ago / Addendum
8254262 / Jun '89 / ECM

Coria, Enrique

☐ **GUITAR ARTISTRY OF ENRIQUE CORIA, THE (Solos From South America)**
ACD 6 / Jun '97 / Acoustic Disc

☐ **LATIN TOUCH**
ACD 23 / Aug '97 / Acoustic Disc

Cormack, Arthur

☐ **NUAIR BHA MI OG**
COMD 2016 / Feb '94 / Temple

☐ **RUITH NA GAOITH (CHASING THE WIND)**
COMD 2032 / Feb '94 / Temple

Cormann, Enzo

☐ **MINGUS CUERNAVACA (Cormann, Enzo & Jean-Marc Padovani)**
LBLC 6549 / Apr '92 / Label Bleu

Cormier, John Paul

☐ ANOTHER MORNING
IRCD 057 / Feb '98 / Iona

☐ RETURN TO THE CAPE
Haggis/Caber feidh / Cowie's clog/Winston tune / Jerry Sullivan's strathspey/Tammy Sullivan's reel / Flannigan's favourite/Ole French reel/Kelly's reel / Slow air/Moving cloud / Horseshow reel/Winter carnival reel/Pigeon on the gate / Hilda Chasson-Cormier's reel/Temperence reel / Shetland hornpipe/The E flat tune / Holland wedding reel/ Stool of repentance/Sleepy Maggie / Niel Gow's lament/Niel Gow march/Slieveman's clog / Highland dream / Reel made with Hilda/Miss Watson's return to the cape
IRCD 041 / Mar '97 / Iona

Cormier, Joseph

☐ INFORMAL SESSIONS
Mrs. Laura Andrews/Mrs. Ramsey of Rarnton / Mrs. Kennedy of Green/The nine pint Coggie / Jigs in G / Earl Gray/Perthshire volunteers/Miss Margaret Campbell / Reel of Cluny/Milburn / Silver star hornpipe/Karen's reel/Temperance reel / Mrs. Dow/ Bobby's Winston tune/Last night's fun / Farleigh castle/Clear the track/Napoleon hornpipe / Untitled/ Swallow tail/Murray river / Glencoe march/The auld wheel/Jaimie Hardie / Strathern/Miss M'Lean/ Johnny's made a wadding on it / John Roy Stewart/ Fisher's wedding/Saratoga hornpipe / Pottinger's hornpipe/Romp among the whims / Way to Mull river/Traditional tune/Marquis of Tullybardine / Killecrankie / Mr. Barclay/Willie Frazer's/Miss Rattray/Lady Mary Stofford / Unknown/James F. Dickie / Belle of the ball / Moonlight clog/Unnamed hornpipe/Heather Hill / Put me in the big chest / Mrs. Grant of Lagan/Miss Lyle/The red mill / John McNeill highland dancer
ROUCD 7017 / Jun '98 / Rounder

Corn Dollies

☐ EVERYTHING BAG
MC 015CD / Jul '88 / Medium Cool

Cornelius

☐ FANTASMA
Mic check / Micro disneycal world tour / World tour / New music machine / Clash / Count five or six / Magoo opening / Star fruits surf rider / Chapter 8-Seashore and horizon / Free fall / 2010 / God only knows / Thank you for the music / Fantasma
OLE 3002 / 15 Jun '98 / Matador

Cornelius, Gary

☐ FEATHER
OMC 0003 / 20 Apr '98 / One Man Clapping

☐ MENDING FENCES
OMC 0001 / 20 Apr '98 / One Man Clapping

Cornershop

☐ WHEN I WAS BORN FOR THE 7TH TIME
Sleep on the left side / Brimful of Asha / Butter the soul / Chocolat / We're in yr corner / Funky days are back again / What is happening / When the light appears boy / Coming up / Good shit / Good to be on the road back home / It's Indian tabacco my friend / Candyman / State troopers / Norwegian wood
WIJCD 1065 / 8 Sep '97 / Wiiija

☐ WOMAN'S GOTTA HAVE IT
6 a.m. Jullander shere / Honk Kong book of Kung Fu / My dancing days are gone / Call all destroyer / Camp orange / Never leave yourself (vocal overload mix) / Jamsimran King / Wog / Looking for a way in / 7.20 a.m. Jullander shere
WIJ 045CD / Apr '95 / Wiiija

Cornerstone

☐ OUT OF THE VALLEY
FE 1411 / Dec '94 / Folk Era

Cornerstone

☐ BEATING THE MASSES
LF 159CD / Jul '95 / Lost & Found

Cornfield, Klaus

☐ LITTLE TIGERS (Cornfield, Klaus & Lotzi Lapislazuli)
EFA 11312CD / Aug '93 / Musical Tragedies

Cornucopia

☐ FULL HORN
RR 7049 / Jun '97 / Repertoire

Cornwell, Francoise

☐ LE PEUPLE MAGIQUE
860CD / Nov '96 / Escalibur

Cornwell, Hugh

☐ CORNWELL, COOK AND WEST (Cornwell, Cook & West)
UFO 009CD / Jun '92 / UFO

☐ GUILTY
One burning desire / Snapper / Nerves of steel / Black hair, black eyes, black suit / Hot head / Endless day, endless night / Five miles high / Sravandrabellagola / Long dead train / Torture garden / House of sorrow
SMACD 501 / May '97 / Snapper

☐ NOSFERATU (Cornwell, Hugh & Robert Williams)
White room / Losers in a lost land / Nosferatu / Irate caterpillar / Rhythmic itch / Wired / Big bug / Mothra / Wrong way round / Puppets and losers in a lost land
EW 0001CD / 27 Apr '98 / Eastworld

Coro Gabriel

☐ TAXA
APG 001CD / Aug '97 / Robi Droli

Corona

☐ RHYTHM OF THE NIGHT
Baby baby / Try me out / Get up and boogie / I don't wanna be a star / I want your love / In the name of love / I gotta keep dancin' / Rhythm of the night / Baby I need your love / Don't go breaking my heart / When I give my love / Do you want me / You gotta be movin'
0630103322 / May '95 / Eternal

☐ WALKING ON MUSIC
ZYX 204572 / 1 Jun '98 / ZYX

Coronach

☐ REMEMBER ME MY DEAR
CDCMF 008 / Jul '98 / Coronach & Musick Fyne

Coronado, Florencio

☐ ANDEAN HARP
PS 65159 / Feb '96 / PlayaSound

Coronado, Joe

☐ FINAL WARNING (Coronado, Joe & The Texas Beat)
She is fine as wine / Bet you do it real good / Sunrise sorrow / You got to walk on baby / What this woman is doing to me / Final warning / Know who your friends are / Let me tell you about my baby / Wasp / You know and I know
JSPCD 279 / Feb '97 / JSP

Coronados

☐ UN LUSTRE ET PLUS
3019512 / Jan '98 / Last Call

Coroner

☐ CORONER
N 02122 / Apr '95 / Noise

☐ GRIN
Dream path / Lethargic age / Internal conflicts / Cavaet (To the coming) / Serpent moves / Status: Still thinking / Theme for silence / Paralized, mesmerized / Grin (Nails hurt) / Host
N 02102 / May '93 / Noise

☐ MENTAL VORTEX
N 01772 / Aug '91 / Noise

Corpolongo, Rich

☐ JUST FOUND JOY (Corpolongo, Rich Quartet)
Valse / Time impulse / LA blues / Hey, what's happening / Just found joy / Try to, if you can / Time sense / Way it is
DE 489 / Jun '97 / Delmark

☐ SMILES (Corpolongo, Rich Quartet)
Expressivo / Experiemnt / Nancy's blues / Tone row / Margin of space / Different blues / Smiles
DE 502 / 9 Mar '98 / Delmark

Corps Of Drums

☐ BEAT OF BATTLE, THE
Drum and bugle display / Under the double eagle / Salamanca day / Great escape / Flag and empire / La paloma / Yellow bird / Ode to joy / Sheik of Araby / Galanthia / Light of foot / Drum display / Resistance / Seven tears / Drummer's lilt / Marantha / Moray Firth / Trelawny and glo-pri-arg / Wotan's thunder / Vendetta / Victory beatings
303782 / Jun '97 / Hallmark

Corpus

☐ CREATION OF A CHILD
FLASH 45 / 1 Jun '98 / Flash

Corpus Delicti

☐ BEST OF CORPUS DELICITI, THE
CLP 12332 / 17 Aug '98 / Cleopatra

☐ OBSESSIONS
NIGHTCD 013 / Apr '97 / Nightbreed

Corrette, Michel

☐ LE NOUVEAU QUATUOR
CSAR 57 / Nov '92 / Saydisc

Corries

☐ BONNET, BELT AND SWORD
Hot asphalt / Cam ye o'er frae France / Joy of my heart / Jolly beggar / Bring back my granny to me / Glenlyon lament / Johnny Cope / Gaberlunzie king / Haughs o' Cromdale / Banks of Newfoundland / Parcel o' rogues / North sea holes / Katie Bairdie / Oor wee school / I once loved a lass / Blow ye winds in the morning / My brother Bill's a fireman
BGOCD 271 / Mar '95 / Beat Goes On

☐ COMPACT COLLECTION, THE
Flower of Scotland / Dumbarton's drums / Portree kid / Glencoe / Bricklayer's song / Come o'er the stream / MacPherson's rant / Roses of Prince / Lammas tide / Massacre of Glencoe / Ettrick lady / Turn ye tae me / Sherramuir fight / Dark Lochnagar / King fareweel / Man's a man for a' that
LCOM 9006 / Mar '88 / Lismor

☐ FLOWER OF SCOTLAND
Stirling brig / Kelvingrove / Vicar and the frog / Bona line / Loo song / Black Douglas / Bonnie ship the Diamond / Mothers, daughters, wives / Tibbie dunbar / Shenandoah / Castle of Dromore / Food blues / Flower of Scotland
MOICD 002 / Jun '94 / Moidart

☐ IN CONCERT/SCOTTISH LOVE SONGS
Johnny lad / Lord of the dance / Flower of Scotland / Wild mountain thyme / Ca' the yowes / Bonnie lass o'Fyvie / Skye boat song / Wild rover / Kid songs / Hills of Ardmorn / Tiree love song / Annie Laurie / Ae fond kiss / Nut brown maiden / Sally free and easy / Liverpool Judies / Granny's in the cellar / Road to Dundee / Hunting tower / Lowlands of Holland
BGOCD 267 / Feb '95 / Beat Goes On

☐ LIVE FROM SCOTLAND VOL.1
CDPA 002 / Oct '96 / CML

☐ SCOTS WHA'HAE
Stirling Brig / Black Douglas / Scots wha hae / Lammas tide / Battle of Harlaw / Lock the door Lariston / Haughs o' Cromdale / Bonnie Dundee / Braes o'Killiecrankie / Sherramuir fight / News from Moidart / Johnny Cope / King Fareweel
MOICD 009 / Apr '94 / Moidart

☐ SILVER COLLECTION
Killiecrankie / Rise rise / News from Moidart / Johnny Cope / Lock the door Lariston / Scots wha hae / I will go / Loch Lomond / Skye boat song / Welcome Royal Charlie / Parcel o' rogues / Barrett's privateers / Queen's Maries / Jock O'Braidislee / Bonnie lass o'Fyvie / Haughs o' Cromdale / Rose of Allendale / Westering home / Twa recruiting sergeants / Wild mountain thyme
MOICD 005 / Jun '93 / Moidart

☐ SINGING GAMES, THE (The Dawning Of The Day) (Corrie Folk Trio & Paddy Bell)
Singing games / Lock the door, Lariston / Jock o' Braidislee / Doodle let me go / Lass o' Fyvie / Itinerant cobbler / Lord Gregory / McPherson's farewell / Coorie Doon / Greenland fisheries / My love she's but a lassie yet / Shoals o' herrin' / Trooper and the maid / Whistling gypsy / Queen Mary / Leaving of Liverpool / Uist tramping song / Johnnie lad / Roddy McCorly / Verdant braes o' Screen / Around Cape Horn / Fear a' Bhata / Killiecrankie / Jock Hawk's adventure in Glasgow
MOICD 013 / Apr '97 / Moidart

☐ STRINGS AND THINGS/LIVE AT THE ROYAL LYCEUM THEATRE (2CD Set)
Garten mother's lullaby / Heiland Harry / Heidless cross / Rattlin' roarin' Wullie / Jock o' Hazeldean / Flood Garry / Kiss the children for me Mary / I will go / Three Shetland tunes / Dowie dens o' Yarrow / Wha wadna fecht for Charlie / Liberty / Side by side / Tramps and hawkers / Great silkie / Lyceum blues / Ye Jacobites by name / Lowlands away / Abigail / Old triangle / Dream Angus / Maids when you're young / Bonnie Dundee
MOICD 014 / 2 Feb '98 / Moidart

☐ THOSE WILD CORRIES/KISHMUL'S GALLEY
Maid of Amsterdam / There are no pubs in Kirkintilloch / Quiet lands of Erin / Gentleman soldier / Lammas tide / Galway races / Lowlands low / Riever's galley / Kerry recruit / I'm a rover / Cam ye by atholl / Kishmul's galley / Roving journeyman / Lewis bridal song / Spanish shawl / Cruel brother / Gallus bloke / Highland lament / Twa corbies / Night visitor's song / Doran's favourite / Toon o' Kelso / October song / Shamrock and the thistle
BGOCD 326 / Oct '96 / Beat Goes On

☐ VERY BEST OF THE CORRIES, THE
Black Douglas / Wha wadna fecht for Charlie / Isle of Skye / I will go / Sound the pibroch / Derwentwater's farewell / Flood Garry / Bonnie Dundee / Peggy Gordon / Boys of Barehill and Derry hornpipe / Abigail / Tartan mother's lullaby / Maids, when you're young never wed an old man / Rose of Allendale / Kiss the children for me Mary / Westering home
CDSL 8285 / Feb '97 / EMI Gold

Corrigan, Briana

☐ WHEN MY ARMS WRAP AROUND YOU
Love me now / Fool / Come to me / Now you talk / Man is dead / Grounded / Leave taking / Miss america / Back of my hand / Some big big truth / Simply beautiful / I put my arms out for you
0630142712 / Jun '96 / East West

Corringham, Vivienne Dogan

☐ POPULAR TURKISH FOLK SONGS (Corringham, Vivienne Dogan & George Hadjineophytou)
EUCD 1166 / '91 / ARC

Corrosion Of Conformity

☐ ANIMOSITY
Loss for words / Mad world / Consumed / Holier / Positive outlook / Prayer / Intervention / Kill death / Hungry child / Animosity
398414078CD / Apr '96 / Metal Blade

☐ DELIVERANCE
Heaven's not overflowing / Albatross / Clean my wounds / Without wings / Broken man / Senor Limpio / Man de mono / Seven days / 2121313 / My grain / Deliverance / Shake like you / Shelter / Pearls before swine
4776832 / Oct '94 / Columbia

☐ TECHNOCRACY
Technocracy / Hungry child / Happily ever after / Crawling / Ahh blugh / Intervention / Technocracy / Crawling / Happily ever after
398417019CD / May '96 / Metal Blade

☐ WISEBLOOD
King of the rotten / Long whip/Big America / Wiseblood / Goodbye windows / Born again for the last time / Drowning in a daydream / Snake has no head / Door / Man or ash / Redemption city / Wishbone (some tomorrow) / Fuel / Bottom / Feeder (elque come abajo)
4843282
4843289 / Sep '96 / Columbia

Corrs

☐ FORGIVEN NOT FORGOTTEN
Runaway / Leave me alone / Erin shore (traditional intro) / Someday / Minstrel boy / Love to love you / Carraroe jig / Erin shore / Closer / Secret life / Toss the feathers / Right time / Along with the girls / Heaven knows / Forgiven not forgotten
7567926122 / Feb '96 / Atlantic

☐ TALK ON CORNERS
Only when I sleep / When he's not around / What can I do / I never loved you anyway / So young / Don't say you love me / Love gives love takes / Paddy McCarthy / Hopelessly addicted / Intimacy / Queen of Hollywood / No good for me / Little wing
7567830512 / 20 Oct '97 / Lava/Atlantic

Corsini, Ignacio

☐ LA PULPERA DE SANTA LUCIA
EBCD 89 / Jan '98 / El Bandoneon

Cortes, Amparo

☐ ENRIQUE DE MELCHOR
MW 4015CD / Nov '96 / Music & Words

Cortes, Joaquin

☐ PASION GITANA (Gypsy Passion)
Perdidos / Levenda ambiguedad / Naciente / Irradian / Oscura luz
92402 / Jun '96 / Act

Cortes, Jose Luis

☐ EN DIRECTO DESIDE EL PATIO DE MI CASA (Cortes, Jose Luis Y Ng La Banda)
74321401382 / Sep '96 / Milan

Cortes, Mario

☐ CORALES
CMC 0001 / 1 Jun '98 / Karonte

Cortez, Dave 'Baby'

☐ DAVE 'BABY' CORTEZ
Shake / Watermelon man / Boy from New York City / Can't buy me love / How sweet it is (to be loved by you) / Twine time / Stagger Lee / Yeh, yeh / Searchin' / Come see about me / Where did our love go / Paper tiger / Tweetie pie / Things ain't what they used to be / Count down part 1 / Count down part 2 / Belly rub part 1 / Belly rub part 2 / Do any dance / Peg leg / Sticks and stones / My sweet baby parts 1 and 2 / In orbit / Summertime / You talk too much / Hula hoop / Come back
NEMCD 751 / Aug '95 / Sequel

☐ HAPPY ORGANS, WILD GUITARS AND PIANO SHUFFLES
Happy organ / Piano shuffle / Cat nip / Hey hey hey / Mardi gras / Fiesta / Love me as I love you / Whistling organ / Hurricane / Deep in the heart of Texas / Do the slop / You're just right / Red sails in the sunset / Calypso love song / Dave's special / I'm happy / Summertime / Tootsie / It's a sin to tell a lie / Boogie piano / Boogie organ / Shift / Organ bounce / Swinging piano / Riffin'
CDCHD 386 / Jun '93 / Ace

Cortez, Jayne

☐ TAKING THE BLUES BACK HOME
5319182 / Nov '96 / Harmolodic/Verve

☐ WOMEN IN (E)MOTION FESTIVAL (Cortez, Jayne & The Firespitters)
T&M 106 / Nov '94 / Tradition & Moderne

Coryell, Julian

☐ DUALITY
Gay's flight / Seryozha's lament / Deacon blues / Compression / Mr. Compression / Mr.Snike / River / All I really want to do / New duality / Shipbuilding / Darkmen / Truth
N2K 10011 / 13 Oct '97 / N2K

Coryell, Larry

☐ 12 FRETS TO ONE OCTAVE
Allegra's ballerina song / Murali's picture / Flamenco flare-up / Blue monk / Night rain / Dye me blue / Transparence / Blues for Charley the lobster / Light sweet crude / Bartok eleven / Alfonsina del mar / Lotus revelation
SHANCD 97015 / May '98 / Shanachie

☐ BOLERO (Coryell, Larry & Brian Keane)
Improvisation on Bolero / Nothing is forever / Something for Wolfgang Amadeus / Tombeau de couperin (Prelude from) / Elegancia del sol / Fancy frogs / 6 Watch hill road / Blues in Madrid / Motel time / At the airport / Brazilia / Piece for Larry / La pluie / Patty's song
ECD 22046 / Mar '93 / Evidence

☐ COMING HOME
Good citizen swallow / Glorielle / Twelve and twelve / Confirmation / It never entered my mind
MCD 5303 / Jan '86 / Muse

☐ ELEVENTH HOUSE
Birdfingers / Funky waltz / Low-lee-tah / Adam smasher / Joy ride / Yin / Theme for a dream / Gratitude / Ism-ejericico / Right on y'all
VMD 79342 / Oct '95 / Vanguard

☐ EQUIPOISE
Unemployed Floyd / Tender tears / Equipoise / Christina / Joy Spring / First things first
MCD 5319 / Feb '87 / Muse

☐ ESSENTIAL LARRY CORYELL, THE
VCD 75 / Oct '96 / Vanguard

☐ MAJOR JAZZ MINOR BLUES
60412320582 / 7 Apr '98 / Thirty Two

☐ QUIET DAY IN SPRING, A (Coryell, Larry & Urbaniak, Michal)
SCCD 31187 / '88 / Steeplechase

☐ SKETCHES OF CORYELL
SH 5024CD / Oct '96 / Shanachie

☐ SPACES
Spaces / Rene's theme / Gloria's step / Wrong is right / Chris / New year's day in Los Angeles-1968
VMD 79345 / Oct '95 / Vanguard

☐ SPACES REVISITED (Coryell, Larry & Billy Cobham)
Dragon gate / Hong Kong breeze / Spaces revisited / Variations on goodbye pork pie hat / Blues for Django and Stephanie / Morning of the carnival / Oleo / Introduction to Ruby / Ruby my dear
SH 5033 / 9 Mar '98 / Shanachie

☐ TOGETHER (Coryell, Larry & Emily Remler)
Arabian nights / Joy Spring / Ill wind / How my heart sings / Six beats, six strings / Gerri's blues / First things first
CCD 4289 / Nov '86 / Concord Jazz

☐ TOKUDO
MCD 5350 / Sep '92 / Muse

☐ TWELVE FRETS TO ONE OCTAVE
322657 / Jul '97 / Koch International

Coryell, Murall

☐ EYES WIDE OPEN
BIGMO 30232 / Aug '95 / Big Mo

Corytraeth Male Voice Choir

☐ BEST OF CORYTRAETH MALE VOICE CHOIR, THE (1977-1997)
Dashenka / Llawenydd yr Heliwr / Yn ol i fon / Down among the dead men / Orani/Aredig / Ynys Llanddwyn / Arwelfa / Abide with me / Croesi'r anial / Emyn y pasg / Laudamus / Pe cawn i hon / Ym o hyd / I'se weary of waitin' / Star spangled banner / Roll Jordan roll / Y greadigaeth / Nidaros
SCD 2104 / Sep '97 / Sain

Cosa

☐ MAP OF LOVE
INCCD 3309 / May '96 / Incoming

Cosa Nostra

☐ LOVE THE MUSIC
99 2143 / Jul '96 / Ninetynine

☐ MIND SONGS
99 2128 / Jul '96 / Ninetynine

☐ WORLD PEACE
992156CD / Nov '96 / Ninetynine

Cosentino, Saro

☐ ONES AND ZEROS
Days of flaming youth / Bite the bullet / From far away / Defying gravity / Behind the glass / Soul kiss / 9.47 pm Eastern time
RES 129CD / 17 Nov '97 / Resurgence

Cosmetic

☐ SO TRANQUILIZIN
All things must change / Be my girl / Take it to the top / All my love / N-er-gize me / About the money / So tranquilizin / Jet set
1883102 / '85 / Gramavision

Cosmic Baby

☐ THINKING ABOUT MYSELF
Thinking about myself / Treptow / Tag 20000 / Another day in another city / Brooklyn / Au dessous des nuages / Comic greets Florida....in Berlin / Fantasia / Loops of infinity (contemplative) / Movements in love
74321196052 / Apr '94 / RCA

Cosmic Couriers

☐ OTHER PLACES
EFA 035422 / 6 Apr '98 / Think Progressive

Cosmic Invention

☐ HELP YOUR SATORI MIND
NS 132 / Sep '97 / Now Sound

Cosmic Jokers

☐ COSMIC JOKERS
14293 / 23 Mar '98 / Spalax

☐ GALACTIC SUPERMARKET
14292 / 23 Mar '98 / Spalax

☐ LIFE AS ONE
IYFCD 07 / Apr '97 / In Yer Face

☐ PLANETEN SIT IN
14904 / 23 Mar '98 / Spalax

☐ SCI FI PARTY
SPA 14884 / Nov '94 / Spalax

Cosmic Psychos

☐ GO THE HACK
Lost cause / Rip 'n' dig / She's crackin' up / Out of the band / Alright tonite / Pub / Back in town / Elle / Go the hack / You can't come in
SHAGCD 2033 / Oct '97 / Shagpile

☐ OH WHAT A LOVELY PIE
SHAGCD 2037 / Sep '97 / Shagpile

☐ PALOMINO PIZZA
EFA 0492409 / May '93 / City Slang

☐ SELF TOTALLED
ARRCD 63006 / May '95 / Amphetamine Reptile
SHAGCD 2025 / Oct '97 / Shagpile

☐ SLAVE TO THE GRAVE
SHAGCD 2034 / Oct '97 / Shagpile

Cosmic Trigger

☐ SOLAR ECLIPSE
SR 9345 / Jan '94 / Silent

Cosmic Twins

☐ COSMIC TWINS
GRCD 312 / Sep '94 / Glitterhouse

Cosmonauts Hail Satan

☐ CAPE CANNIBAL
FDCD 47/DPROMCD 32 / Nov '96 / 4th Dimension/Dirter

Cosmonks

☐ IN AFTERBURN
L7 001CD / 27 Oct '97 / Lucky Seven

Cosmorama

☐ SPACE ODYSSEY
MI 2006 / 16 Jul '97 / Milano 2000

Cosmosis

☐ COSMOLOGY
TRANR 604CD / Aug '96 / Transient

☐ SYNERGY
TRANR 614CD / 23 Mar '98 / Transient

Cosmotheka

☐ KEEP SMILING THROUGH (Hit Songs Of World War II)
Smiling through / Wish me luck as you wave me goodbye / I love to sit with Sophie in the shelter / I did what I could with my gas mask / Whitehall warriors / Lili Marlene / D-day dodgers / Roll me over / We'll meet again / Follow the white line / I get along without you very well / Hey little hen / Dig dig dig to victory / They're all under the counter / I'm gonna get lit up (when the lights go on in London) / Knees up Mother Brown / Medley
EMPRCD 509 / Apr '94 / Emporio

Cosse, Ike

☐ LOWDOWN THROWDOWN, THE
Bang bang girls / I just wanna rent / Let it happen / Doggy style / Dog dang shoot / Hell to pay / When I get home / She's expensive / My baby's so cynical / Hubba bubba brother / Let it happen
JSPCD 283 / Jul '97 / JSP

Costa, Angela

☐ SOUL DISEASE
Middle of the day / Circus beserk / Stars began to fall / Mothering Sunday / Disillusion / Inside the kiss / Being born / I just don't know / Sisters of mercy / Waiting for my angel / Empty chair / Oh my heart / Soul disease / Wait a minute / Rebirth of wonder
PLAN 010CD / Nov '97 / Planet

Costa, Ercilia

☐ ERCILIA COSTA & ARMANDINHO (Costa, Ercilia & Armandinho)
HTCD 32 / Nov '96 / Heritage

Costa, Johnny

☐ CLASSIC COSTA
CRD 205 / Mar '96 / Chiaroscuro

☐ DREAM (Johnny Costa Plays Johnny Mercer)
CRD 341 / Jan '97 / Chiaroscuro

☐ FLYING FINGERS
CRD 317 / Mar '96 / Chiaroscuro

☐ PORTRAIT OF GERSHWIN, A
CRD 335 / Mar '96 / Chiaroscuro

Costanzo, Sonny

☐ PROMISES TO KEEP (Costanzo, Sonny & Czech Radio Big Band)
CR 00022 / Nov '95 / Czech Radio

Costello, Elvis

☐ ALL THIS USELESS BEAUTY
It's time / Little atoms / Other end of the telescope / Al this useless beauty / Why can't a man stand alone / Shallow grave / Starting to come to me / Poor fractured atlas / I want to vanish / You bowed down / Distorted angel / Complicated shadows
9362461982 / May '96 / Warner Bros.

☐ ALMOST BLUE (Remastered) (Costello, Elvis & The Attractions)
Why don't you love me (like you used to do) / Sweet dreams / Success / I'm your toy / Tonight the bottle let me down / Brown to blue / Good year for the roses / Sittin' and thinkin' / Colour of the blues / Too far gone / Honey hush / How much I lied / He's got you / Cry cry cry / There won't be anymore / Sittin' and thinkin' / Honey hush / Psycho / Your angel steps out of Heaven / Darling you know I wouldn't lie / Shoes keep walking back to you / Tears before bedtime / I'm your toy
DPAM 7 / 17 Nov '97 / Demon

☐ ARMED FORCES (Remastered) (Costello, Elvis & The Attractions)
Accidents will happen / Senior service / Oliver's army / Big boys / Green shirt / Party girl / Goon squad / Busy bodies / Sunday's best / Moods for moderns / Chemistry class / Two little Hitlers / My funny Valentine / Tiny steps / Clean money / Talking in the dark / Wednesday week / Accidents will happen / Alison / Watching the detectives
DPAM 3 / 17 Nov '97 / Demon

☐ BLOOD AND CHOCOLATE (Remastered) (Costello, Elvis & The Attractions)
Uncomplicated / I hope you're happy now / Tokyo storm warning / Home is anywhere you hang your head / I want you / Honey, are you straight or are you blind / Blue chair / Battered old bird / Crimes of Paris / Poor Napoleon / Next time round / Seven day weekend: *Costello, Elvis & The Attractions/Jimmy Cliff* / Forgive her anything / Blue chair / Baby's got a brand new hairdo / American without tears / Town called big nothing
DPAM 12 / 17 Nov '97 / Demon

☐ BRUTAL YOUTH
Pony St. / Kinder murder / Thirteen steps lead down / This is hell / Clown strike / You tripped at every step / Still too soon to know / 20% amnesia / Sulky girl / London's brilliant parade / My science fiction twin / Rocking horse road / Just about glad / All the rage / Favourite hour
9362455352 / Mar '94 / Warner Bros.

☐ EXTREME HONEY (The Very Best Of The Warner Bros. Years)
Bridge I burned / Sulky girl / 13 steps lead down / My dark life / Kinder murder / Hurry down doomsday / Birds will still be singing / Tramp the dirt down / I want to vanish / Veronica / So like candy / All this useless beauty / Other side of summer / Deep dark truthful mirror / Poor fractured atlas / Londons brilliant parade / Couldn't call it unexpected / All the rage
9362468012 / 20 Oct '97 / Warner Bros.

☐ GET HAPPY (Remastered) (Costello, Elvis & The Attractions)
Love for tender / Opportunity / Imposter / Secondary modern / King Horse / Possession / Men called Uncle / Clowntime is over / New Amsterdam / High fidelity / I can't stand up for falling down / Black and white world / Five gears in reverse / B movie / Motel matches / Human touch / Beaten to the punch / Temptation / I stand accused / Riot act / Girls talk / Clowntime is over / Getting mighty crowded / So young / Just a memory / Hoover factory / Ghost train / Dr. Luther's assistant / Black and white world / Riot act
DPAM 5 / 17 Nov '97 / Demon

☐ GIRLS, GIRLS, GIRLS (2CD Set)
Watching the detectives / (I don't want to go to) Chelsea / Alison / Shipbuilding / I want you / Oliver's army / This year's girl / Lover's walk / Pump it up / Strict time / Temptation / High fidelity / Loveable / Mystery dance / Big tears / Uncomplicated / Lipstick vogue / Man out of time / Brilliant mistake / New lace sleeves / Accidents will happen / Beyond belief / Black and white world / Green shirt / Loved ones / New Amsterdam / Angels want to wear my red shoes / King horse / Big sister's clothes / Man called Uncle / Party girl / Shabby doll / Motel matches / Tiny steps / Almost blue / Riot act / Love field / Possession / Poisoned rose / Indoor fireworks / Pills and soap / Sunday's best / Watch your step / Less than zero / Clubland / Tokyo storm warning / Girl's talk / Home is anywhere you hang your head / Honey, are you straight or are you blind / I hope you're happy now / I'll wear it proudly / Poor Napoleon / Sleep of the just / Stranger in the house / Turning the town red
DFIENDCD 160 / Sep '96 / Demon

☐ GOODBYE CRUEL WORLD (Remastered) (Costello, Elvis & The Attractions)
Only flame in town / Home truth / Room with no number / Inch by inch / Worthless thing / Love field / I wanna be loved / Comedians / Joe Porterhouse / Sour milk cow blues / Great unknown / Deportees club / Peace in our time / Turning the town red / Baby it's you: *Costello, Elvis & The Attractions/Nick Lowe* / Get yourself another you / I hope your happy now / Only flame in town / Worthless thing / Motel matches / Sleepless nights / Deportees club
DPAM 10 / 17 Nov '97 / Demon

☐ IMPERIAL BEDROOM (Remastered) (Costello, Elvis & The Attractions)
Beyond belief / Tears before bedtime / Shabby doll / Long honeymoon / Man out of time / Almost blue / And in every home / Loved ones / Human hands / Kid about it / Little savage / Boy with a problem / Pidgin English / You little fool / Town cryer / From head to toe / World of broken hearts / Night time / Really mystified / I turn around / Seconds of pleasure / Stamping ground / Shabby doll / Imperial bedroom
DPAM 8 / 17 Nov '97 / Demon

☐ JULIET LETTERS (Costello, Elvis & Brodsky Quartet)
Jacksons, Monk and Rowe / This sad burlesque / Romeo's seance / I thought I'd write to Juliet / Last post / First to leave / Damnation's cellar / Birds will still be singing / Deliver us / For other eyes / Swine / Expert rites / Dead letter / I almost had a weakness / Why / Who do you think you are / Taking my life in your hands / This offer is unrepeatable / Dear sweet filthy world / Letter home
9362451802 / Dec '96 / WEA

☐ KING OF AMERICA (Remastered) (Costello Show)
Brilliant mistake / Lovable / Our little angel / Don't let me be misunderstood / Glitter gulch / Indoor fireworks / Little palaces / I'll wear it proudly / American without tears / Eisenhower blues / Poisoned rose / Big light / Jack of all parades / Suit of lights / Sleep of the just / People's limousine: *Coward Brothers* / They'll never take her love from me: *Coward Brothers* / Suffering face / Shoes without heels / King of confidence
DPAM 11 / 17 Nov '97 / Demon

☐ KOJAK VARIETY
Strange / Hidden charms / Remove this doubt / I threw it all away / Leave my kitten alone / I've been wrong before / Must you throw dirt in my face / Everybody's cryin' mercy / Bama lama bama loo / Pouring water on a drowning man / Payday / Very thought of you / Please stay / Runnin' out of fools / Days
9362459032 / Dec '96 / Warner Bros.

☐ MIGHTY LIKE A ROSE
Other side of summer / Hurry down doomesday / How to be dumb / All grown up / Invasion hit parade / Harpies bizzare / After the fall / Georgie and her rival / So like Candy / Couldn't call it unexpected No. 2 / Playboy to a man / Sweet pear / Broken / Couldn't call it unexpected No. 4
7599265752 / Feb '95 / Warner Bros.

☐ MY AIM IS TRUE (Remastered) (Costello, Elvis & The Attractions)
Welcome to the working week / Miracle man / No dancing / Blame it on Cain / Alison / Sneaky feelings / (The angels wanna wear my) red shoes / Less than zero / Mystery dance / Pay it back / I'm not angry / Waiting for the end of the world / Radio sweetheart / Stranger in the house / Imagination (is a powerful deceiver) / Mystery dance / Cheap reward / Jump up / Wave a white flag / Blame it on Cain / Poison moon
DPAM 1 / 17 Nov '97 / Demon

☐ OUT OF OUR IDIOT (Costello, Elvis & The Attractions)
Blue chair / Seven day weekend: *Costello, Elvis & The Attractions/Jimmy Cliff* / Turning the town red / Heathrow Town / People's limousine: *Coward Brothers* / So young / American without tears / Get yourself another fool / Walking on thin ice / Baby it's you: *Costello, Elvis & The Attractions/Nick Lowe* / From head to toe / Shoes without heels / Baby's got a brand new hairdo / Flirting kind / Black sails in the sunset / Imperial bedroom / Stampling grams
FIENDCD 67X / Mar '93 / Demon

☐ PUNCH THE CLOCK (Remastered)
Let them all talk / Everyday I write the book / Greatest thing / Element within her / Love went mad / Shipbuilding / TKO (Boxing day) / Charm school / Invisible man / Mouth almighty / King of thieves / Pills and soap / World and his wife / Heathen town / Flirting kind / Walking on thin ice / Town where time stood still / Shatterproof / World and his wife / Everyday I write the book
DPAM 9 / 17 Nov '97 / Demon

☐ SPIKE
This town / Let him dangle / Deep dark truthful mirror / Veronica / God's comic / Chewing gum / Tramp the dirt down / Stalin Malone / Satellite / Pads, paws and claws / Baby plays around / Miss Macbeth / Any king's shilling / Coal train robberies / Last boat leaving
9258482 / Jan '89 / Warner Bros.

☐ **TEN BLOODY MARYS AND TEN HOW'S YOUR FATHERS (Costello, Elvis & The Attractions)**
Clean money / Girls talk / Talking in the dark / Radio sweetheart / Big tears / Crawling to the USA / Just a memory / Watching the detectives / Stranger in the house / Clowntime is over (no.2) / Getting mighty crowded / Hoover factory / Tiny steps / Peace, love and understanding / Dr. Luther's assistant / Radio radio / Black and white world / Wednesday week / My funny valentine / Ghost train
FIENDCD 27 / '86 / Demon

☐ **THIS YEAR'S MODEL (Remastered) (Costello, Elvis & The Attractions)**
No action / This year's girl / Beat / Pump it up / Little triggers / You belong to me / Hand in hand / (I don't want to go to) Chelsea / Lip service / Living in paradise / Lipstick vogue / Night rally / Radio radio / Big tears / Crawling to the USA / Running out of angels / Green shirt / Big boys
DPAM 2 / 17 Nov '97 / Demon

☐ **TRUST (Remastered) (Costello, Elvis & The Attractions)**
Clubland / Lovers' walk / You'll never be a man / Pretty words / Strict time / Luxembourg / Watch your step / New lace sleeves / From a whisper to a scream / Different finger / White knuckles / Shot with his own gun / Fish 'n' chip paper / Big sister's clothes / Black sails in the sunset / Big sister / Sad about girls / Twenty five to twelve / Love for sale / Weeper's dream / Gloomy Sunday / Boy with a problem / Seconds of pleasure
DPAM 6 / 17 Nov '97 / Demon

☐ **TWO AND A HALF YEARS (My Aim Is True/This Year's Model/Armed Forces/ Live/4CD Set)**
Welcome to the working week / Miracle man / No dancing / Blame it on Cain / Alison / Sneaky feelings / (The angels wanna wear my) red shoes / Less than zero / Mystery dance / Pay it back / I'm not angry / Waiting for the end of the world / Watching the detectives / Radio sweetheart / Stranger in the house / Imagination (is a powerful deceiver) / Mystery dance / Cheap reward / Jump up / Wave a white flag / Blame it on Cain / Poison moon / No action / This year's girl / Beat / Pump it up / Little triggers / You belong to me / Hand in hand / (I don't want to go to) Chelsea / Lip service / Living in paradise / Lipstick vogue / Night rally / Radio radio / Big tears / Crawling to the USA / Running out of angels / Green shirt / Big boys / Accidents will happen / Senior service / Oliver's army / Big boys / Green shirt / Party girl / Goon squad / Busy bodies / Sunday's best / Moods for moderns / Chemistry class / Two little Hitlers / (What's so funny 'bout) peace love and understanding / My funny Valentine / Tiny steps / Clean money / Talking in the dark / Wednesday week / Accidents will happen / Alison / Watching the detectives / Mystery dance / Waiting for the end of the world / Welcome to the working week / Less than zero / Beat / Lip service / (I don't want to go to) Chelsea / Little triggers / Radio radio / Lipstick vogue / Watching the detectives / Miracle man / Band introduction / You belong to me / Pump it up
DPAMBOX 1 / 6 Apr '98 / Demon

☐ **VERY BEST OF ELVIS COSTELLO & THE ATTRACTIONS, THE (Costello, Elvis & The Attractions)**
Alison / Watching the detectives / (I don't want to go to) Chelsea / Pump it up / Radio radio / (What's so funny 'bout) peace, love and understanding / Oliver's army / Accidents will happen / I can't stand up for falling down / New Amsterdam / High fidelity / Clubland / Watch your step / Good year for the roses / Beyond belief / Man out of time / Everyday I write the book / Shipbuilding / Love field / Brilliant mistake / Indoor fireworks / I want you
DPAM 13 / Oct '94 / Demon

Costello, Julian

☐ **TEA AND SCANDAL (Costello, Julian Quintet)**
Sitting on the fence / Figment / Mr Palomar / Ermentrude / Pilgrim / Naggar castle / Olives / Merry go round / Apothecary's chest / Fruit and fruition / Gerald the goose
JCQCD 001 / Mar '96 / Avid

Costello, Sean

☐ **CALL THE COPS (Costello, Sean Jivebombers)**
BLUESUN 1017 / May '97 / Blue Sun

Coster, Tom

☐ **FROM THE STREET**
Can't we all just get along / Monk-E Shines / From the street / Dennis the menace / Amazon life / Pharoah's jig / What's the deal / Spankin' / Funky Joe / She said she didn't
JVC 20532 / May '96 / JVC

☐ **GOTCHA**
Keep it to yourself / Latin one / Dreams can come true / Don't look back / Last romance / Gotcha / Calypso dream / Jungle USA / Hope / Please pass the beano / Til we meet again
JVC 20152 / Nov '97 / JVC

☐ **LET'S SET THE RECORD STRAIGHT**
To be or not to be / Slick / Dance of the spirits / Then and now / Thinking of you / Mr. MD / Best of friends / Turkish delight / Blue blues / Welcome to my chambers / Caribbean sunset / For the folks back home
JVC 20252 / Nov '93 / JVC

Coteau

☐ **HIGHLY SEASONED CAJUN MUSIC**
Acadian two step / Bosco/mosco stomp / Travailler c'est trop dur / Arc de triomphe two step / Sweet Suzannah / Basic lady / Quoi faire / Bayou teche / Zydeco gris-gris / Cold-hearted you / Grand mamou / Balfa et grand bois / Mardi gras / Sugarfoot rag
ROUCD 6078 / Nov '97 / Rounder

Cotten, Beverly

☐ **CLOG IN (Cotten, Beverly & The Green Grass Clogs)**
Old Jimmy Sutton / Basic step / Variations / Chugging rhythms / Traditional steps / Smooth style flatfooting / Advanced steps / Hell amongst the yearlings / Coloured aristocracy / Buckdance / Susanana gal / Medley / Miss Liza poor gal / Sandy river belle/Alabama gals
CDFF 237 / Nov '97 / Flying Fish

Cotten, Elizabeth

☐ **FREIGHT TRAIN (North Carolina Folk Songs & Tunes)**
SFWCD 40009 / May '95 / Smithsonian Folkways

Cotter, Eamonn

☐ **TRADITIONAL IRISH MUSIC FROM COUNTY CLARE**
EC 001CD / Apr '96 / EC

Cotton, Billy

☐ **SMILE, DARN YA SMILE**
PASTCD 7085 / Oct '96 / Flapper

☐ **THINGS I LOVE ABOUT THE 40'S, THE (Cotton, Billy & His Band)**
Bottle party / I'm gonna get lit up (when the lights go on in London) / Yeah man / That lovely weekend / You'll be happy little sweetheart in the spring / Shine / Hold tight, hold tight / Toy trumpet / Things I love / Dere's jazz in dem dere horns / Margie / Hut sut song / Man with the mandolin / Lights out / Bon voyage cherie / Aurora / Fifty million robins can't be wrong / Man who comes around / Never took a lesson in my life / Woe is me / Shoe shine boy / Mammy bong
RAJCD 814 / May '97 / Empress

☐ **WAKEE WAKEE (Cotton, Billy & His Band)**
Somebody stole my gal / Bugle call rag / I'm just wild about Harry / Third tiger / Mood indigo / Fancy our meeting / So green / Ooo-la-la / It's only a paper moon / Rhapsody in blue / Skirts / Best wishes / Sweep / Mrs. Bartholomew / You don't understand / Why has a cow got four legs / St. Louis blues / She was only somebody's daughter / Night owl / Young and healthy / You're getting to be a habit with me / Shuffle off to Buffalo / Forty second street / Smile, darn ya, smile
C5CD513 / Aug '90 / See For Miles

Cotton, Brian

☐ **BRIAN COTTON AND THE COTTON CLUB JAZZMEN 1997 (Cotton, Brian Cotton Club Jazzmen)**
COT 001 / Jul '98 / Cotton

Cotton, James

☐ **100% COTTON (Cotton, James Band)**
Boogie thing / One more mile / All walks of life / Creeper creeps again / Rocket 88 / How long can a fool go wrong / I don't know / Burner / Infatuation / Fever
OW 27670 / May '94 / One Way

☐ **CUT YOU LOOSE**
River's invitation / Honest I do / Got to get you off my mind / Coast blues / Next time you see me / Cut you loose / Ain't nobody's business / Set a date / Slippin' and slidin' / Negative 10 4
VMCD 79283 / 27 Apr '98 / Vanguard

☐ **DEALIN' WITH THE DEVIL (The Best Of James Cotton)**
I need you so bad / Don't start me talking / Dealin' with the devil / Creeper / V8 Ford blues / Turn on your lovelight / Southside boogie / There is something on your mind / Knock on wood / So glad you're mine / Diggin' my potatoes / You know it ain't right / Jelly jelly
AIM 2005CD / May '97 / Aim

☐ **DEEP IN THE BLUES**
5298492 / Jun '96 / Verve

☐ **HARP ATTACK (Cotton, James/Junior Wells/Carey Bell/Billy Branch)**
Down home blues / Who / Keep your hand out of my pocket / Little car blues / My eyes keep me in trouble / Broke and hungry / Hit man / Black night / Somebody changed the lock / Second hand man / New kid on the block
ALCD 4790 / May '93 / Alligator

☐ **HIGH COMPRESSION**
Diggin' my potatoes / Ying yang / Twenty three hours too long / No more doggin' / No cuttin' loose / Ain't doing too bad / Sunny road / Superharp / Easy loving / High compression
ALCD 4737 / Oct '93 / Alligator

☐ **HIGH ENERGY (Cotton, James Band)**
Hot and cold / Chicken heads / Hard time blues / I got a feeling / Weather report (the weather man said) / Rock 'n' roll music (ain't nothing new) / Fannie Mae / Caldonia / James theme / Keep cooking mama
OW 27671 / May '94 / One Way

☐ **LIVE AND ON THE MOVE VOL.1 (Cotton, James Band)**
OW 24835 / May '94 / One Way

☐ **LIVE AT ANTONES**
Blow wind / Juke / It ain't right / Gone to main street / Oh baby / Hoochie coochie man / Eyesight to the blind / Midnight creeper
ANTCD 0007 / Jan '93 / Antones

☐ **LIVE FROM CHICAGO (Mr Superharp Himself)**
Here I am / Part time love / Just to be with you / Hard headed / When it rains it really pours / Cross your heart / Come back baby / Born in Chicago / Creeper
ALCD 4746 / May '93 / Alligator

☐ **MIGHTY LONG TIME**
Straighten up baby / Everything gonna be alright / Black nights / Blow wind blow / Sugar sweet / Moanin' at midnight / Baby please / Hold me in your arms / Stormy Monday / 300 pounds of joy / Northside cadillac / Mighty long time
ANTCD 0015 / Mar '91 / Antones

☐ **SEEMS LIKE YESTERDAY**
I got you (I feel good) / There is something on your mind / Money honey / I don't know / Good time Charlie / It ain't right / Stormy Monday / Work song / Knock on wood / Dealing with the devil / Turn on your lovelight/Please please please
JAM 91382 / 27 Jul '98 / Justin Time

☐ **TAKE ME BACK**
CD 72587 / '88 / Blind Pig

Cotton, Joseph

☐ **DANCEHALL DAYS**
EFA 121412 / 29 Jun '98 / Moll Slekta

☐ **STORY TELLER**
JCCD 001 / 27 Jul '98 / Jet Star

Cotton Mather

☐ **KONTIKI**
CPR 2240 / 16 Mar '98 / Copper

Cotton, Mike

☐ **MIKE COTTON SOUND**
BLP 2 / 27 Apr '98 / Beat

Cottone, F.P.

☐ **DREAM IN YOUR HEAD, THE**
INAK 79500 / Jan '97 / In Akustik

Cougars

☐ **COUGARS, THE**
SFTRI 395CD / Apr '96 / Sympathy For The Record Industry

Coughlan, Mary

☐ **AFTER THE FALL**
Woman undone / Sunburn / Still in love / Lucy's dream / John fell off the work-around / Dilmma / Poison words / Run away Teddy / That face / Nobody / Black crow / Saint Judy / When I am laid in earth
ABB 123CD / Mar '97 / Big Cat

☐ **LIVE IN GALWAY**
ABB 116CD / Oct '96 / Big Cat

☐ **LOVE FOR SALE**
Thrills a thrill / Moon over bourbon street / Baby plays around / You go to my head / Love for sale / Fine romance / Damn your eyes / To love a man / Drinking the diamonds / Upon a veil of midnight blue / These boots are made for walking / You send me
DIAB 837 / 3 Nov '97 / Diablo

☐ **LOVE ME OR LEAVE ME**
Ancient rain / Double cross / I'd rather go blind / Invisible to you / Ride on / Leaf from a tree / Delaney's gone back on the wine / Sunday mornings / Red ribbon / Ice cream man / There is a bed / Francis of Assisi / Beach / Man of the world / Seduced / Ain't nobody's business if I do / I get along without you very well / Handbags and gladrags / Whiskey didn't kill the pain
4509940362 / Dec '96 / WEA

☐ **SENTIMENTAL KILLER**
There is a bed / Hearts / Magdalen laundry / Francis of Assisi / Love in a shadow / Ain't no cure for love / Handbags and gladrags / Just a friend of mine / Ballad of a sad young man / Not up to scratch / Sentimental killer
9032771752 / Dec '96 / WEA

☐ **TIRED AND EMOTIONAL**
Double cross / Beach / Meet me where they play the blues / Delaney's gone back on the wind / Sense of silence (SOS) / Nobody's business - the tango / Mama just wants to barrelhouse all night long / Country fair dance (The cowboy song) / Lady in green / Seduced
2420942 / Mar '87 / WEA

☐ **UNCERTAIN PLEASURES**
Man of the world / I can dream, can't I / Whiskey didn't kill the pain / Leaf from a tree / Little death / Invisible to you / I get along without you very well / Heartbreak hotel / Red ribbon / Mother's little helper
9031711002 / Dec '96 / WEA

☐ **UNDER THE INFLUENCE**
Laziest girl / Ice cream van / Parade of clowns / My land is too green / Ride on / Good morning heartache / Fifteen only / AWOL / Dice / Don't smoke in bed / Blue surrender / Sunday morning / Copa
2421852 / Feb '95 / WEA

Couldwell, Adam

☐ **PAINT A BIGGER PICTURE**
Ain't going back / No mountain will stand in his way / Let my tears tell the tale / Rebel at heart / When soul meets soul / Paint a bigger picture / Memory and a memo / Maybe she'll come back / Do miracles really happen / It's more / Born on christmas day
WTCD 297 / Sep '97 / Weeping Tree

Coulibaly Brothers

☐ **ANKA DIA : SONGS & DANCES FROM BURKINA FASO**
AUB 006775 / Apr '93 / Auvidis/Ethnic

Coulter, Phil

☐ **AMERICAN TRANQUILITY**
Shenandoah / Green leaves of summer / Streets of laredo-irene goodnight / Dear sarah (vocal) / Girl I left behind me-the yellow rose of texas / Beautiful dreamer / Nantucket sunrise / Beautiful isle of somewhere / My old kentucky home-i dream of jeannie / Home away from home (vocal) / Banks of the ohio / Pier avenue / Home sweet home-the wabash-carry me back to old virginny / Hoedown
KCD 376 / Jul '95 / Irish

☐ **CELTIC TRANQUILITY**
Planxty Irwin / Tears on the heather / Ar Eirinn ni Nosfhainn ce hi / Battle of Kinsale/The great O'Neill / Before the battle / Valley of tears / Road to Glenaan / Ghost ships of Tory / Year of the French / A thiarna dean trocaire / Wounded hussar / House of the planter / Tune for a found harmonium
KCD 465 / Mar '97 / Irish

☐ **CHRISTMAS COLLECTION (2CD Set)**
White Christmas / Winter wonderland / First Noel / Jingle bells / In the bleak midwinter / Little drummer boy / Walking in the air / When a child is born / All through the night / Song of the shepherd / Oh come all ye faithful / Silent night / Santa is coming to town / Good King Wenceslas / Fairytale of New York / Holy night / Going home for Christmas / Mary's boy child / Morning has broken / We three kings / Angels we have heard on high
KCD 470 / Dec '97 / Irish

☐ **CLASSIC TRANQUILITY**
Derry air / Mary from dungloe / Love thee dearest / Old man / Carrickfergus / Buachaill o'n eirne (come by the hills) / Steal away / Mise eire / My lagan love / Spinning wheel / Maggie / Scorn not his simplicity / Boulavogue / Lake of shadows / Wind in the willows / Town I loved so well
FSCD 001 / Jan '93 / Four Seasons

☐ **ESSENTIAL COLLECTION, THE**
Carrickfergus / Love's old sweet song / Steal away (vocal) / Mise eire / Spinning wheel / Natasha / Scorn not his simplicity (vocal) / Derry air / Cal / Old man (vocal) / Mna na heireann / Nantucket sunrise / Raglan road / Town I loved so well (vocal)
KCD 367 / Jul '95 / Irish

☐ **LOCAL HEROES**
Ride on / Sonny / As I leave behind neiden / Cal / Fairytale of New York / Harry's game / Local hero / Only a woman's heart / Dirty old town / Lady in red / Whiskey in the jar / First time I ever saw your face / I'll tell me ma / Sunday bloody sunday/I still haven't found what I'm looking
RTECD 165 / Jan '95 / Four Seasons

☐ **PEACE AND TRANQUILITY**
If I were a blackbird / Gentle maiden / Dear little town in the old county down / Harry's game / Lament for the wild geese / Old refrain / Lark in the clear air / Hero / Meeting of the waters-the rose of mooncoin / Slievenamon / Water babies / From clare to here / Sally gardens / To hell or to van diemen's land
FSCD 003 / Jan '93 / Four Seasons

☐ **PHIL COULTER'S CHRISTMAS**
Silent night / Mary's boy child / First nowell / In the bleak midwinter / Little drummer boy / Song of the shepherd / Away in a manger / Jingle bells / White christmas / Angels we have heard on high / When a child is born / Good king wenceslas / Walking in the air / Oh holy night / Going home for christmas / O come all ye faithful (adeste fideles)
FSCD 005 / Sep '94 / Four Seasons

☐ **SCOTTISH TRANQUILITY**
Flower of Scotland / Skye boat song / Will ye no' come back again / Loch Lomond / Dark Island / I belong to Glasgow / Ye banks and braes o' bonnie Doon / Wild mountain thyme / Annie Laurie / Rowan tree / Lochnagar / Amazing grace / Eriskay love lilt/ Westering home / Red red rose/Bonnie Mary of Argyll / No awa' tae bid awa'/Scotland the brave / Auld lang syne
MCCD 071 / Jun '92 / Music Club

☐ **SEA OF TRANQUILITY**
Last rose of summer / Cliffs of dooneen / Isle of innisfree / Green glens of antrim / Flight of the earls / Bunch of thyme / Oft in the stilly night / Thorn birds (main theme) / Tranquility / Those endearing young charms / Love's old sweet song / Fields of athenry / She moved through the fair / Take me home / Silver threads among the gold / Emigrants letter-eamon an cnuic
FSCD 002 / Jan '93 / Four Seasons

☐ **SERENITY**
FSCD 004 / Jan '93 / Four Seasons

☐ **ULTIMATE CELTIC JOURNEY, THE**
Derry air (Danny Boy) / Carrickfergus / Meeting of the waters/The rose of Mooncoin / Rose of Tralee / Spancil Hill / Green Glens of Antrim / Raglan Road / Mountains of Mourne / I'll tell me Ma / Anniversary song / Sally Gardens / Water is wide / Spinning wheel / Fields of Athenry / Dear Sarah / One day at a time / Emmigrant's letter/Eamon an Chnuic / Soldier's song
KCD 410 / Jan '97 / Celtic Collections

☐ **WORDS & MUSIC**
Spancil hill / Steal away / Red red rose-bonny mary of argyll / Take me home / John o'dreams / Old man / Will ye go lassie go / West's awake / I loved the ground / Nightingale-galway shawl / Scorn not his simplicity / Beautiful dreamer / Home from the sea / Streets of london / Town I loved so well
FSCD 007 / Sep '94 / Four Seasons

Coulter, William

☐ MUSIC ON THE MOUNTAIN (Coulter, William & Barry Phillips)
GM 123CD / Aug '96 / Gourd Music

Counce, Curtis

☐ EXPLORING THE FUTURE (Counce, Curtis Quintet)
So nice / Angel eyes / Into the orbit / Move / Race for space / Someone to watch over me / Countdown / Exploring the future / Foreplay / Riffin' / Move / Countdown
CDBOP 007 / Jul '96 / Boplicity

Count Bass-D

☐ PRE-LIFE CRISIS
Dozens / Sandwiches (I got a feeling) / T-boz (part 1/2) / Shake / T-boz tried to talk to me / Carmex / I got needs / Broke Thursday / Agriculture / Brown / Hate game / Pink tornado / Sunday school / Baker's dozen
4783732 / Oct '95 / Columbia

Count Bishops

☐ SPEEDBALL + 11
Route 66 / I ain't got you / Beautiful Delilah / Teenage letter / Cry to me / Buzz me babe / Sweet little sixteen / Honey I need / Carol / Don't start crying now / Mercy mercy / Reelin' and rockin' / Down the road apiece / I'm a man / I want candy
CDWIKM 161 / Nov '95 / Chiswick

Count Five

☐ PSYCHOTIC REACTION
Double decker bus / Pretty big mouth / World / Psychotic reaction / Peace of mind / They're gonna get you / Morning after / Can't get your lovin' / You must believe me / Teeny bopper, teeny bopper / Merry go round / Contrast / Revelation in slow motion / Declaration of independence
EDCD 225 / Oct '87 / Edsel

☐ PSYCHOTIC REACTION
REP 4242 / Apr '92 / Repertoire

Count Raven

☐ DESTRUCTION OF THE VOID
Until death do us part / Hippies triumph / Destruction of the void / Let the dead bury the dead / Northern lights / Leaving the warzone / Angel of death / Final journey / On ones hero / Europa
HELL019CD / Apr '94 / Hellhound

☐ HIGH ON INFINITY
Jen / Children's holocaust / In honour / Madman from waco / Masters of all evil / Ode to Rebecca / High on infinity / Ordinary loser / Traitor / Dance / Coming / Lost world / Cosmos
HELL 026 / Apr '94 / Hellhound

☐ STORM WARNING
Intro (Count Raven) / Inam naudemina / True revelation / In the name of rock 'n' roll / Sometimes a great nation / Within the garden of mirrors / Devastating age / How can it be / Social warfare
HELL 009CD / Apr '94 / Hellhound

Count Zero

☐ AFFLUENZA
K 169CD / Aug '96 / Konkurrel

Countdown Dance Band

☐ CHART DANCE MANIA
Gangsta's paradise / Shy guy / Stayin' alive / Love rendezvous / Boombastic / La la la hey hey / Sunshine after the rain / Lick it / Move your ass / Scatman's world / Try me out / Shimmy shake / Another night / Bomb / Boom boom boom / 3 is family
QED 229 / Nov '96 / Tring

Countdowns

☐ RIGHT ON SOUND
Got it goin' on / Crawlin' back / Activate her / On and on and on / County blues / Wray gunn / Lover her so / I got no time for fools like you / Ghetto blaster / Check yourself / You can't win
06302 / 20 Oct '97 / Epitaph

Counterblast

☐ BALANCE OF PAIN
EB 010CD / Oct '96 / Elderberry

Counting Crows

☐ ACROSS THE WIRE (Live From New York/2CD Set)
GED 25226 / 13 Jul '98 / Geffen

☐ AUGUST AND EVERYTHING AFTER
Round here / Omaha / Mr. Jones / Perfect blue buildings / Anna begins / Time and time again / Rain King / Sullivan Street / Ghost train / Raining in Baltimore / Murder of one
GED 24528 / Feb '94 / Geffen

☐ RECOVERING THE SATELLITES
Catapult / Angels of the silences / Daylight fading / I'm not sleeping / Goodnight Elizabeth / Children in bloom / Have you seen me lately / Miller's angels / Another horsedreamers blues / Recovering the satellites / Monkey / Mercury / Long December / Walkaways
GED 24975 / Oct '96 / Geffen

Country All Stars

☐ JAZZ FROM THE HILLS
Stompin' at the Savoy / Tennessee rag / Do something / Indiana march / Sweet Georgia Brown / Midnight train / In a little Spanish town / My little girl / Lady in red / Marie / It goes like this / What's the reason I'm not pleasin' you / When it's darkness on the delta / Vacation train / Fiddle patch / Fiddle sticks
BCD 15728 / Oct '93 / Bear Family

Country Cooking

☐ COUNTRY COOKING (26 Bluegrass Originals)
Big ben / Shot from guns / Cedar hill / Armadillo breakdown / Trouble among the yearlings / Powwow the indian boy / Old old house / Pacific slope / Orange mt. special / Farewell blues / Jaybird-fiddler a dram / Theme time / Huckling the berries / U.s. 40 / Parson's duck / Six mile creek / Tequila mockingbird / Morning glory / Wagons ho / Barrel of fun / Plumber's nightmare / Kentucky bullfight / Silver bell / Babka breakdown / Celebration reel / Western mind
ROUCD 11551 / '88 / Rounder

Country Dance Kings

☐ BEST OF COUNTRY LINE DANCING, THE
ECD 3383 / 18 Aug '97 / K-Tel

☐ COUNTRY DANCE CLUB USA VOL.1
ECD 3378 / 18 Aug '97 / K-Tel

☐ COUNTRY DANCE CLUB: DENIM DANCIN'
He thinks he'll keep her / Standing outside the fire / No doubt about it / My love / If the good die young / I'd like to have that one back / Indian outlaw / Words by heart / Piece of my heart / Who says you can't have it all
33112 / Jun '95 / Irish

☐ COUNTRY DANCE NIGHT (18 Country Line Dancing Favourites)
Rock my world (little country girl) / Chattahoochee / Trashy women / One more last chance / Prop me up beside the jukebox (if I die) / My baby loves me / Blame it on your heart / Live until I die / State of mind / I swear / What's it to you / Fast as you / That's my story / Wild one / Reckless / Mercury blues / Cowboy boogie / Ain't going down (Til the sun comes up)
ECD 3197 / Mar '95 / K-Tel

☐ COUNTRY LINE DANCE JUBILEE VOL.1
ECD 3376 / 18 Aug '97 / K-Tel

☐ COUNTRY LINE DANCE JUBILEE VOL.2
Bubba shot the jukebox / Papa loved Mama / I'm in a hurry (And I don't know why) / What part of no / One more payment / Jukebox with a country song / Whatcha gonna do with a cowboy / I want you bad (And that ain't good) / My next broken heart / Boom it was over
ECD 3377 / 18 Aug '97 / K-Tel

☐ DANCE ALL NIGHT
Good run of bad luck / Before you kill us all / That ain't no way to go / Why haven't I heard from you / Rope the moon / Lovebug / Walking away a winner / Your love amazes me / Addicted to a dollar / Don't take the girl
ECD 3382 / 18 Aug '97 / K-Tel

☐ DANCEHALL DELIGHTS
Rock my world (little country girl) / If bubba can dance / American honky-tonk bar association / My baby loves me / I swear / Live until I die / That's my story / John Deere Green / State of mind / Reckless
ECD 3381 / 18 Aug '97 / K-Tel

☐ DANCIN' LEATHER
ECD 3384 / 18 Aug '97 / K-Tel

☐ DENIM DANCING
ECD 3381 / 18 Aug '97 / K-Tel

☐ KICKIN' IT
ECD 3385 / 18 Aug '97 / K-Tel

Country Gazette

☐ HELLO OPERATOR...THIS IS COUNTRY GAZETTE
Saro Jane / Virginia boys / Love, lost and found / Don't let nobody tie you down / Sweet Allis Chalmers / You can't get the hell out of Texas / Charlotte breakdown / Great Joe Bob (a regional tragedy) / Still feeling blue / Uncle Clooney played the banjo (but mostly out of time) / Molly and tenbrooks / Kentucky waltz / Blue light / Tallahassee / Highland dream / Last thing on my mind / Hello operator / Great American banjo tune / Nothing is left but the blues / Cabin on a mountain / Done gone
FF 70112 / May '97 / Flying Fish

☐ KEEP ON PUSHING
Rosa Lee McFall / Forgive and forget / Get up there and dance / Lovely lovely world / Anywhere the wind blows / Keep on pushing / Pretty boy Floyd / Picking at Snuffy's / Going back to Alabam' / Lucky dog / Marching through Georgia / Live and love / We've got a good fire going / Durang's hornpipe
FF 70561 / May '97 / Flying Fish

☐ TRAITOR IN OUR MIDST/DON'T GIVE UP YOUR DAY JOB
Lost indian / Keep on pushin' / I wish you knew / Hot burrito breakdown / I might take you back again / Forget me not / Tried so hard / Anna / If you're ever gonna love me / Aggravation / Sound of goodbye / Swing low, sweet chariot / Huckleberry hornpipe / Fallen eagle / I don't believe you met my baby / Deputy Dalton / Teach your children / My Oklahoma / Down the road / Winterwood / Honky cat / Snowball / Lonesome blues / Singin' all day and dinner on the ground
BGOCD 298 / Nov '95 / Beat Goes On

Country Gentlemen

☐ CLASSIC COUNTRY GENTS REUNION
Fare thee well / Stewball / I'll be there in the morning / Champagne breakdown / Here today, gone tomorrow / Gonna get there soon / Hey Lala / Casey's last ride / Wild side of life / Wait a little longer / Say won't you be mine
SHCD 3772 / Oct '89 / Sugar Hill

☐ COUNTRY GENTLEMEN SUGAR HILL COLLECTION, THE
SHCD 2207 / Aug '95 / Sugar Hill

☐ COUNTRY SONGS OLD AND NEW
SFCD 40004 / Dec '94 / Smithsonian Folkways

☐ EARLY REBEL RECORDINGS 1962-1971, THE (4CD Set)
Christmas time back / Heavenward bound / I am weary (let me rest) / Sad and lonesome day / Bluebirds are singing / White rose / Gentlemen is blue / Philadelphia lawyer / Spanish two step / Bringing Mary home / Convict and the rose / Banks of the Ohio / Down where the river bends / Battle hymn of the republic / This world's no place to live / Uncle Joe / Northbound / Let the light shine down / Girl from the north country / Cold wind a blowing / Jingle bells / Silent night / We three kings / Blue bell / It's all over now baby blue / Matterhorn / Dark as a dungeon / Big Bruce / When they ring those golden bells / Buffalo girls / Beautiful life / I'm working on the road / Border affair / Johnny Reb / Many a mile / Amelia Earhart's last flight / Traveller / Silver bell / Theme from Exodus / Love and wealth / He was a friend of mind / Daybreak in Dixie / Some old day / Raggy mountain shakedown / Banana boat song / Going to the races / Waiting for the boys to come home / Darling little Joe / El Dedo / I'll be there Mary dear / Blue ridge cabin home / Take me in a lifeboat / Sentence / Where I'm bound / To the rescue / Rodger Young / Green green grass of home / Along the way / Let's / Rambling boy / Gentlemen's concerto / Take me back to the valley / Fare thee well Cisco / Preaching praying singing / Mrs. Robinson / Two little boys / Doin' my time / Rank strangers to me / Heaven / Gone home / Rank strangers to me / I'm using my bible as a roadmap / Over the hills to the poorhouse / Little white church / Heaven / Bill Bailey / He will set your fields on fire / Are you washed in the blood / One wide river / On the sunny side of life / Born again / I'll break out again / Less of me / I am a pilgrim / Weapon of prayer / If I were free / Teach your children / Fox on the run / Johnny and Jack medley / I'd rather live by the side of the road / These men of God / Cowboy's and Indians / Sea of heartbreak / Orange blossom mandolin / Yesterday / Girl behind the bar / Son of hickory holler's tramp / Country roads / Redwood hill / Secret of the waterfall / Walkin' down the line / Breakin' it down / New freedom bell / Old pine tree / Legend of the rebel soldier / c.C.G. express / Little Bessie / Fields have turned brown / Get in line buddy
REB 4002 / Jun '98 / Rebel

Country Teasers

☐ BACK TO THE FUTURE
GUIDE 27CD / 27 Apr '98 / Guided Missile

☐ COUNTRY TEASERS
EFA 115942 / Apr '95 / Crypt

☐ SATAN IS REAL AGAIN
EFA 128772 / Jul '96 / Crypt

Counts

☐ IT'S WHAT'S IN THE GROOVE
Medley / Dedicated man / Tecalli / Flies over watermelon / Riding high / Jazzman / Since we said goodbye / Magic ride / At the fair / I'm the music / Funk / Funk pump / Too bad (you don't love me) / Chicken pox / Munchies / Short cut / Sacrifice / Love sign / Just you, just me / Counts say goodbye
CDSEWD 109 / Aug '96 / Southbound

☐ WHAT'S UP THE FRONT THAT - COUNTS
What's up front that counts / Rhythm changes / Thinking single / Why not start all over again / Pack of lies / Bills / Motor city / What's it all about
CDSEWM 063 / Nov '94 / Southbound

County, Jayne

☐ LET YOUR BACKBONE SLIP
Max's / Are you a boy or are you a boy / '28 Model T / Berlin / Lady Dye twist / Time machine (I wish I had) / Mr. Normal / Fun in Amerika / Where Queens collide (part 1) / No one woman can satisfy no one man all the time / Tomorrow is another day / Plain of nazca / I fell in love with a Russian soldier / Love lives in lies / Black black window / Midnight pal / Waiting for the marines / Bad in bed
RPM 145 / Jul '95 / RPM

☐ ROCK 'N' ROLL CLEOPATRA (From Sneakers To Stilettos) (County, Wayne & The Electric Chairs)
Eddie and Sheena / Rock 'n' roll Cleopatra / (If you don't want to fuck me) fuck off / Toilet love / Mean mutha fuckin' man / Night time / Trying to get on the radio / Evil minded momma / I had too much to dream last night / Crest / Waiting for the marines / Midnight pal / Berlin / Storm the gates of heaven / Cry of angels / Speed demon / Mr. Norman / Man enough to be a woman / Tomorrow is another day / Wonder woman / Wall city girl / Boy with the stolen face / C3 / Think straight
RPM 119 / Oct '93 / RPM

Couper, Tommy F.

☐ PIPERS MUSE, THE
Rachel and Rosslyns jig / Hector's jig / Cosla bay / Merry harriers / Urnaigh a'bhan thigreach / Elbow knock / Sheepwife / Caber feidh / Pipers muse / Flee the glen / Men in hodden grey / Cockerel in the creel / Think of a name for Friday / Jewel of Scotland / Hiush the cat / Little house under the hill / Cael e'sin don ti' sin / Uist bridal march / Thailer a bha mi sherridh is freaer a thuair mi / In and out the harbour / Air / Falls of dochart
CDLDL 1275 / 24 Jul '98 / Lochshore

Coupland, Gary

☐ A' THE BEST FAE SCOTLAND
GCD 1 / May '96 / Gary Coupland

Courage Of Lassie

☐ SING OR DIE
TMCD 055 / Oct '90 / Third Mind

☐ THIS SIDE OF HEAVEN
BBQCD 146 / Oct '94 / Beggars Banquet

Courbois, Pierre

☐ LIVE IN GERMANY (Courbois, Pierre Quintet)
Recuperation / Ralos / Chocolatine / Opaque / Aminona
AL 73071 / Dec '97 / A

Course Of Empire

☐ INITIATION
Hiss / White vision blowout / Gear / Breed / Apparition / Infested / Invertebrate / Sacrifice / Minions / Initiation / Chiluahaphile
72445110542 / Aug '94 / Zoo Entertainment

Court Music Ensemble Of Hue

☐ MUSIC FROM HUE (Music From Vietnam)
W 260073 / Dec '96 / Inedit

Courtney Melody

☐ COURTNEY MELODY CLASH WITH SANCHEZ (Courtney Melody & Sanchez)
RNCD 2072 / Jul '94 / Rhino

Courvoisier, Sylvie

☐ OCRE
Gugging / Anecdote 1 / La goulante de l'idiot / Andecdote 2 / Machines a sons / Ensorcelirradiant / Triton et demi / Ancedote 3 / Curio in Trivia / Anecdote 4 / Terre d'agala / Viable / Paradiso perduto / Tabular / Gnou gnou valse
ENJ 93232 / Jun '97 / Enja

Cousens

☐ CORNER OF THE SKY
OCRCD 6043 / Jun '96 / First Night

Cousin Joe

☐ BAD LUCK BLUES
Boxcar shorty / Life is a one way ticket / Take a lesson from your teacher / Bad luck blues / I'm living on borrowed time / That's enough / Goin' down slow / Chicken and the hawk / Levee blues / Railroad porter blues / I don't want no second hand love / Tore down
ECD 260462 / Mar '94 / Evidence

☐ COMPLETE VOL.1 1945-1947, THE
BMCD 6001 / Sep '95 / Blue Moon

☐ COMPLETE VOL.2 1946-1947, THE
BMCD 6002 / Sep '95 / Blue Moon

☐ COUSIN JOE VOL.3 1947-1955
BMCD 6013 / 1 Jun '98 / Blue Moon

Cousins, Dave

☐ BRIDGE, THE (Cousins, Dave & Brian Willoughby)
RGFCD 020 / Aug '94 / Road Goes On Forever

☐ OLD SCHOOL SONGS (Cousins, Dave & Brian Willoughby)
RGFCD 004 / '92 / Road Goes On Forever

Couturier, Francois

☐ PASSAGIO
LBLC 6543 / Jun '92 / Label Bleu

Couvez, Remy

☐ ITINERANCES
829392 / Apr '97 / BUDA

Couza, Jim

☐ APPALACHIAN BEACH PARTY (Couza, Jim & Durberville)
DRGNCD 922 / Jan '93 / Dragon

☐ JUBILEE
Mississippi jubilee (year of jubilo) / You've joined our hearts / My old man / Invention No. 13 / Gallo del cielo / Cranes over Hiroshima / Puncheon floor (Oklahoma rooster) / St. Paul's song / Poor wayfaring stranger / There were roses / If you don't love your neighbour / Jubilee
FSCD 6 / Aug '89 / Folksound

☐ MUSIC FOR THE HAMMERED DULCIMER
Jenny Lind polka / Johnny get your hair cut / Intrada and Minuet / Londonderry Air / Maid at the spinning / Nola / High cauled cap / As I roved out / Miss Hamilton / Christine's Waltz / Bells of St. Mary's / Devil's dream / Enchanted valley / La belle Katherine / Fisher's hornpipe / Swinging on a gate / Norwegian wood / Flower of England / Snowflake / Los ejes de mi carreta / Perfect cure me / Starry night for a ramble / Peel the carrot / Take five
CDSDL 335 / Mar '94 / Saydisc

☐ OUT OF THE SHADOWLAND
Canon in D / Song of the whale / Falls of Richmond / Hard love / Kitchen girl / I'll tickle Nancy / Christmas concerto / Forever / Green Willis / Out of the Shadowland / Concerto no. 1 / Jonah and the whale / Wish I could fall in love / William Tell overture / St. Francis prayer / Seek ye first
FSCD 14 / Jun '97 / Folksound

Covenant

☐ NEXUS POLARIS
Sulphur feast / Bizarre cosmic industries / Planetarium / Last of the dragons / Bringer of the sixth sun / Dragon heart / Planetary black elements / Chariots of thunder
NB 301CD / 23 Mar '98 / Nuclear Blast

☐ SPECTRES AT THE FEAST
COVCD 0002 / Nov '94 / Covenant

Coventry City FC

☐ SKY BLUES, THE (15 Coventry Classics) (Various Artists)
Go for it: *Coventry City FC 1987 FA Cup Squad* / Coventry city song: *Randall, Alan* / Count me in: *Taylor, Steve* / Sky blues song: *Taylor, Steve* / Sky blues song: *Willetts, Dave* / Jimmy Hill's sky blues: *Miekle, Jim* / Sky blue dream: *Coventry City FC* / Come on Cov: *Taylor, Steve & Heather* / Born not bred: *M45* / Highfield high: *Universal* / Dion Dion Dublin: *Judge Dread* / This is our year: *Leyland Blues*
CDGAFFER 25 / 10 Aug '98 / Cherry Red

Coverdale, David

☐ WHITESNAKE/NORTHWINDS
Lady / Time on my side / Blindman / Goldies place / Whitesnake / Peace lovin' man / Sunny days / Hole in the sky / Celebration / Keep on giving me love / Northwinds / Give me kindness / Time and again / Queen of hearts / Only my soul / Say you love me / Breakdown
VSOPCD 118 / Nov '88 / Connoisseur Collection

Coverdale-Page

☐ COVERDALE PAGE (Coverdale, David & Jimmy Page)
Shake my tree / Waiting on you / Take me for a little while / Pride and joy / Over now / Feeling hot / Easy does it / Take a look at yourself / Don't leave me this way / Absolution blues / Whisper a prayer for the dying
CDEMD 1041 / Jul '94 / EMI

Covington, Robert

☐ BLUES IN THE NIGHT
Trust in me / I just want to make love to you / Better watch your step / I Don't care / Playing on me / Blues in the night / I want to know / Mean mistreater / I want to thank ya
ECD 260742 / Oct '95 / Evidence

Cowan, Johnny

☐ SOUL'D OUT
634-5789 / Here I am / Dark end of the street / 99 and a half / I was made to love her / When a man loves a woman / Groove me / Two steps from the blues / Mustang Sally / I thank you / I found a love
SHCD 9101 / 9 Mar '98 / Sugar Hill

Coward, Sir Noel

☐ 20TH CENTURY BLUES (The Songs Of Sir Noel Coward) (Various Artists)
Parisian pierrott: *Texas* / I've been to a marvellous party: *Divine Comedy* / Room with a view: *McCartney, Paul* / Sail away: *Pet Shop Boys* / Someday I'll find you: *Ama, Shola & Craig Armstrong* / There are bad times just around the corner: *Williams, Robbie* / I'll see you again: *Ferry, Bryan* / Mad about the boy: *Faithfull, Marianne* / Mad dogs and Englishmen: *Space* / Poor little rich girl: *Suede & Raissa* / I'll follow my secret heart: *Sting* / London pride: *Albarn, Damon & Michael Nyman* / Mrs. Worthington: *Reeves, Vic* / 20th Century blues: *John, Elton*
4946312 / 13 Apr '98 / EMI

☐ CLASSIC RECORDINGS 1928-1938
CDCHD 168 / Jul '90 / Happy Days

☐ COMPACT COWARD, THE
I'll see you again / Dance little lady / Poor little rich girl / Room with a view / Mad dogs and Englishmen / Mary make believe / Mrs. Worthington / Parisian pierrot / Love scene (act 1 private lives) / Some day I'll find you / Let's say goodbye / Twentieth century blues / I'll follow my secret heart / Has anybody seen our ship / Men about town / Most of ev'ry day / I travel alone / Any little fish / Could you please oblige me with a Bren gun / London pride / I wonder what happened to him / There are bad times just around the corner / I like America / You were there / If love were all / Play orchestra play / Party's over
CDP 7922802 / Apr '98 / EMI

☐ I'LL SEE YOU AGAIN (His Greatest Recordings 1928-1941)
Could you please oblige me with a Bren Gun / Dearest love / Dream is over / I travel alone / I'll see you again / Imagine the duchess's feelings / Let's say goodbye / London pride / Lorelei / Lover of my dreams / Mad dogs and Englishmen / Mary Make-Believe / Most of ev'ry day / Mrs. Worthington / Medley / Private lives: *Coward, Sir Noel & Gertrude Lawrence* / Shadow play: *Coward, Sir Noel & Gertrude Lawrence* / Stately homes of England / We were dancing / Where are the songs we sung / World weary
CDAJA 5126 / Mar '94 / Living Era

☐ LIVE IN LAS VEGAS AND NEW YORK
CD 47253 / Nov '91 / Sony Classical

☐ LONDON PRIDE
Lorelei / Dream is over / Zigeuner / World weary / Let's say goodbye / We were dancing / Parisian Pierrot / Poor little rich girl / Room with a view / Dance little lady / Someday I'll find you / Any little fish / If you could only come with me / I'll see you again / London pride / Last time I saw Paris / Could you please oblige us with a bren gun / Imagine the Duchess's feelings / Private Lives / Shadowplay / Red peppers / Family album
CDHD 216 / Feb '97 / Happy Days

☐ MASTER
Room with a view / Dance little lady / Poor little rich girl / Something to do with spring / Where are the songs we sung / We were so young / Just let me look at you / Dearest love / Play orchestra play / Don't lets be beastly to the Germans / Mad dogs and Englishmen / Stately homes of England / London pride / Don't put your daughter on the stage Mrs. Worthington / I'm old fashioned / Lover of my dreams / Fare thee well / Half caste women / Gyspy melody / I'll see you again
300692 / Jul '96 / Hallmark

☐ MASTER'S VOICE, THE (His HMV Recordings 1928-1953)
Room with a view / Dance little lady / Mary make-believe / Try to learn to love / Lorelei / Dream is over / Zigeuner / World weary / Private lives / Half caste woman / Any little fish / Cavalcade prologue / Cavalcade - vocal selection / Lover of my dreams / Cavalcade vocal selection part 2 / Cavalcade epilogue / Noel Coward medley part 1 / Noel Coward medley part 2 / Let's say goodbye / Party's over now / Something to do with Spring / Mad dogs and Englishmen / Medley / I'll follow my secret heart / Melanie's aria part 1 / Melanie's aria part 2 / I travel alone / Most of ev'ry day / Love in bloom / Fare thee well / Mrs. Worthington / We were so young / Then play, orchestra, play / You were there / Has anybody seen our ship / Man about town / Family album / Parisian Pierrot / We were dancing / Dearest love / Where are the songs we sung / Stately homes of England / Gypsy melody / Dearest love (Operetta) / I'll see you again / Just let me look at you / Poor little rich girl / London pride / Last time I saw Paris / Could you please oblige us with a bren gun / There have been songs in England / Imagine the Duchess's feelings / It's only you / Don't let's be beastly to the Germans / Welcoming land / I'm old fashioned / You'd be so nice to come home to / Sigh no more ladies / I wonder what happened to him / Matelot / Nina / Never again / Wait a bit Joe / Bright was the day / This is a changing world / His excellency regrets / 1-2-3 / Uncle Harry / I never knew / I saw no shadow / Josephine / Don't make fun of the fair / Sail away / Why does love get in the way / I like America / Time and again / There are bad times just around the corner
COWARD 1 / Sep '92 / EMI

☐ ROOM WITH A VIEW, A
CDGFR 098 / Jun '92 / Tring

☐ SONGS OF NOEL COWARD, THE (Various Artists)
Mrs. Worthington / Parisian Pierrot / There's life in the old girl yet / Poor little rich girl / I'll see you again / If love were all / Zigeuner / Room with a view / Dance little lady / I'll follow my secret heart / Regency rakes / There's always something fishy about the french / Has anybody seen our ship / You were there / Someday I'll find you / Dearest love / Stately homes of England / London pride / Any little fish / Mad about the boy / Mad dogs and englishmen / Party's over now
PASTCD 7080 / Jul '96 / Flapper

☐ TOGETHER WITH MUSIC (Coward, Sir Noel & Mary Martin)
Together with music / 90 minutes is a long, long time / Get out those old records / They didn't believe me (foxtrot) / 's wonderful / Time on my hands / I didn't know what time it was / Anything goes / Dancing in the dark / Ballerina / I won't dance / Papa, won't you dance with me / Charleston / Way you look tonight / You're an old smoothie / Young and foolish / Always true to you in my fashion / Stumbling / Japanese sandman / Shall we dance / Continental / Uncle harry / Nina / Mad dogs and englishmen / I'll see you again / Dance little lady / Poor little rich girl / Room with a view / Someday I'll find you / I'll follow my secret heart / If love were all / Play orchestra play / World weary / What's going to happen to the tots / Deep in the heart of texas / I only have eyes for you / I get a kick out of you / Les filles de cadiz (delibes) / Ditesmol / A cock-eyed optimist / Some enchanted evening / Wash that man right out of my hair / Wonderful guy / London pride-I happen to like new york / My heart belongs to daddy
CDXP 1103 / '88 / DRG

Cowboy Junkies

☐ 200 MORE MILES (2CD Set)
Blue moon revisited (A song for Elvis) / 200 More miles / Me and the devil / State trooper / Sun comes up, it's Tuesday morning / Oregon hill / Where are you tonight / Casue cheap is how I feel / Floorboard blues / Murder, tonight, in the trailer park / Sweet Jane / If you were the woman and I was the man / Pale sun / Hunted / Lost my driving wheel / Forgive me / Misguided angel / I'm so lonesome I could cry / Walking after midnight
74321296432 / Feb '96 / RCA

☐ CAUTION HORSES, THE
Sun comes up, it's Tuesday morning / 'Cause cheap is how I feel / Thirty summers / Mariner's song / Powder finger / Where are you tonight / Witches / Rock and bird / Escape is so easy / You will be loved again
74321183572 / Feb '94 / RCA

☐ LAY IT DOWN
Something more besides you / Common disaster / Lay it down / Hold on to me / Come calling / Just want to see / Lonely sinking feeling / Angel mine / Bea's song / Musical key / Speaking confidentially / Come calling / Now I know
GED 24952 / Feb '96 / Geffen

☐ PALE SUN, CRESCENT MOON
Crescent moon / First recollection / Ring on the sill / Anniversary song / White sail / Seven years / Pale sun / Post / Cold tea blues / Hard to explain / Hunted / Floorboard blues
74321168082 / Feb '96 / RCA

☐ STUDIO
Shining moon / Misguided angel / Blue moon revisited / Sweet Jane / Sun comes up, it's Tuesday morning / 'Cause cheap is how I feel / Powderfinger / Southern rain / Horse in the country / This street, that man, this life / Anniversary song / Ring on the sill / Common disaster / Lost my driving wheel
07863674122 / 2 Feb '98 / RCA

☐ TRINITY SESSION, THE
Mining for gold / I don't get it / To love is to bury / Dreaming my dreams with you / Postcard blues / Misguided angel / I'm so lonesome I could cry / 200 more miles / Sweet Jane / Walkin' after midnight / Blue moon revisited (song for Elvis) / Working on a building
74321183562 / Feb '94 / RCA

Cowboy Killers

☐ DAI LAUGHING
DISC 9 / Jan '94 / Discipline

☐ THANK YOU FUCK YOU AND GOODNIGHT
REJ 1000025 / 3 Aug '98 / Rejected
CD 001 / 30 Mar '98 / TJ's

Cowboy Mouth

☐ LIFE AS A DOG
MA 8 / Jan '95 / Marina

☐ LOVE IS DEAD
MA 17 / Mar '96 / Marina

Cowboy Nation

☐ COWBOY NATION
RPM / Remember the Alamo / Cowboy way / Old paint / Cowboy nation / Way out west / Blizzard / Tender foot / Revolution / Cowboy's lament / Big train / Rifle, pony and me / Clock
FIENDCD 793 / May '97 / Demon

Cowdrey, Lewis

☐ IT'S LEWIS
ANT 0029CD / Jul '94 / Antones

Cowell, Henry

☐ PIANO MUSIC
SFCD 40801 / Jul '93 / Smithsonian Folkways

Cowell, Stanley

☐ BACK TO THE BEAUTIFUL
Theme for Ernie / Wall / It don't mean a thing if it ain't got that swing / But beautiful / Sylvia's place / Come Sunday / Carnegie six / St. Croix / Prayer for peach / Nightingale sang in Berkeley Square
CCD 4398 / Nov '89 / Concord Jazz

☐ HEAR ME ONE (Cowell, Stanley Quartet)
SCCD 31407 / Apr '97 / Steeplechase

☐ MUSA
CDGR 244 / 27 May '98 / Charly

☐ REGENERATION
CDGR 247 / 1 Jun '98 / Charly

☐ SUCH GREAT FRIENDS (Cowell, Stanley, Billy Harper, Reggie Workman & Billy Hart)
Sweet song / Destiny is yours / Layla joy / East harlem nostalgia
66051008 / May '91 / Strata East

☐ TRAVELLIN' MAN
BLCD 760178 / Mar '93 / Black Lion

☐ WE THREE
DIW 807 / Jul '94 / DIW

Cowie, Charlie

☐ UNSQUARE DANCE
Le reel de grandmere / Centennial jig / Joys of Quebec / Paris waltz / American rag / Maitland River / Ned Kendall / Snowshoer / Spin and glow / McDowall's breakdown / Mamou two step / Coryn Street / Rocky mountain / Kinloss clog / Cowal gathering / Duncan Johnstone / Silver spear / Salley Gardens / Jackie Coleman's / Knotted chord / Last cheater's waltz / Turnpike reek / Schottische / Lilting fisherman / Rose wood / Syracuse / Snug in the blanket / Spanish two step / Mouth of the tobique / Janet's piano lesson / Mrs. Forbes Leith / Little house on the hill / Paddy Carey's / Pet of the pipers / House in the garden / Rowe's division / Baker's breakdown
LCOM 5207 / '91 / Lismor

Cowlan, Paul F.

☐ PAPER DEVILS & SPIRITS OF FIRE
BRAM 1992362 / Nov '93 / Brambus

☐ SECOND CLASS HOTEL
BRAM 1989042 / Nov '93 / Brambus

Cown, Bobby

☐ BOBBY COWN
ALP 302CD / 22 Dec '97 / Atavistic

Cows

☐ OLD GOLD 1989-1991
ARRCD 68011 / Jan '96 / Amphetamine Reptile

☐ ORPHAN'S TRAGEDY
ARRCD 55/335 / Sep '94 / Amphetamine Reptile

☐ WHORN
ARR 70013CD / Mar '96 / Amphetamine Reptile

Cowslingers

☐ THAT'S TRUCKDRIVING
SFTRI 364 / Jul '98 / Sympathy For The Record Industry

Cox, Carl

☐ CARL COX FACT VOL.1 (2CD Set) (Various Artists)
Hot the heels of love: *DJ Hell* / Late night: *Mills, Jeff* / Secrets of meditation: *Trancesetters* / Cactus: *Union Jack* / Ego acid: *Pump Panel* / Hope: *Quench* / Orange theme: *Cygnus X* / Amphetamine: *Heckman, Thomas* / Psycho trip: *Gorl, Robert* / Elektra: *Source* / Phat man: *Wild, Morgen* / Like that: *DJ Hell* / Drum: *Aloof* / Singularity: *Brainchild Vol.2* / Kosmos: *Semisphere* / Raz: *Borealis, Aurora* / Pulsar cycle: *Galactic Spiral Sound* / Fuzz: *Beltram, Joey* / Sacred circles: *Lazonby, Peter* / First question: *Sister Cyrex* / Deep in you: *Stone Circle* / Phosphene: *Heckman, Thomas* / Tonight: *Stone Circle* / No more worry: *Lesamis* / Coda back again: *Coda* / Motorway: *Cox, Carl* / Meet my modern: *Bassxpansion*
REACTCD 056 / Feb '95 / React

☐ CARL COX NON-STOP (2CD Set) (Various Artists)
5560302 / 27 Jul '98 / London

☐ MIXMAG LIVE VOL.1 (Carl Cox/Dave Seaman) (Various Artists)
MMLCD 001 / Jul '96 / Mixmag Live

Cox, Derek

☐ 20 PIANO FAVOURITES (Cox, Derek & His Music)
As time goes by / One day I'll fly away / Canadian sunset / With one more look at you / Impossible dreams / Can't smile without you / Three times a lady / Eleanor Rigby / Michelle / With a little help from my friends / Memory / I know him so well / Serenata / Hello / Moonlight serenade / She's out of my life / Greensleeves / How deep is your love / I just called to say I love you / My way
CDSIV 1126 / Jul '95 / Horatio Nelson

☐ MAGIC OF ANDREW LLOYD WEBBER
Phantom of the opera / All I ask of you / Music of the night / Memory / King Herod's song / Any dream will do / Jesus Christ superstar / I don't know how to love him / Don't cry for me Argentina / Mr. Mistoffelees / Starlight express / Close every door / Unexpected song
CDSIV 1113 / Jul '95 / Horatio Nelson

☐ VIVA BRAZIL (Cox, Derek & his Bossa Nova Rhythm)
One Note Samba / Desafinado / Quiet nights and quiet stars / Once I Loved / So many stars / Wave / Someone to light up my life / Girl From Ipanema / How Insensitive / Dindi / Tristeza / Manha de carnaval / Surfboard / Abanda / Meditation / Sheila's Theme / Just a little bossa nova / Samba d'Orpheus / Adieu Tristeza / Brazil
CDSIV 1136 / Jul '95 / Horatio Nelson

Cox Family

☐ BEYOND THE CITY
ROUCD 0327 / May '95 / Rounder

☐ EVERYBODY'S REACHING OUT FOR SOMEONE
Standing by the bedside of a neighbour / Look me up by the ocean door / Everybody's reaching out for someone / Little white washed chimney / Cry baby cry / I've got that old feeling / But I do / Why not confess / Pardon me / My favorite memory / When God dips his pen of love in my heart / Backroads
ROUCD 0297 / May '93 / Rounder

Cox, Ida

☐ I CAN'T QUIT MY MAN
CDAFS 1015 / Sep '91 / Affinity

☐ IDA COX VOL.1 1923
DOCD 5322 / Mar '95 / Document

☐ IDA COX VOL.2 1924-1925
DOCD 5323 / Mar '95 / Document

☐ IDA COX VOL.3 1927-1938
DOCD 5324 / Mar '95 / Document

☐ IDA COX VOL.4 1927-1938
DOCD 5325 / Mar '95 / Document

☐ UNCROWNED QUEEN OF THE BLUES, THE
BBCD 7 / Nov '96 / Black Swan

Cox, Norrie

☐ MOVE THE BODY OVER (Cox, Norrie & His New Orleans Stompers)
You always hurt the one you love / Working man blues / One sweet letter from you / Yes yes in your eyes / City of a million dreams / San jacinto stomp / Franklin street blues / Royal telephone / Make me a pallet on the floor / Move the body over / Maryland my Maryland
DE 231 / Nov '97 / Delmark

Cox, Peter

☐ PETER COX
Ain't gonna cry again / If you walk away / Change / One more kiss / I'll be good to you / Tender heart / Believe / Wanting you / Enemy / They whisper to me / If you walk away / What a fool believes
4949692 / 22 Jun '98 / Chrysalis

Coxhill, Lol

☐ BOUNDLESS (Coxhill, Lol & Veryan Weston)
EM 4021 / Jun '98 / Emanem

☐ EAR OF BEHOLDER
Introduction / Hungerford / Deviation dance / Two little pigeons / Don Alfonso / Open Piccadilly / Feedback / How insensitive / Conversation / Mango walk / Piccadilly with hoofs / Rasa moods / Collective improvisation / I am the walrus / Rhythmic hooter / Lover man / Zoological fun / Little trip one shoot / Dat's why darkies were born / Series of superbly played mellotron codas
SEECD 414 / Oct '94 / See For Miles

☐ HOLYWELL CONCERT, THE (Coxhill, Lol & George Haslam/Paul Rutherford/ Howard Riley)
In transit / Half pisced / No how / Bliss / Gliss / Duet for trombone and piano / Oxford
SLAMCD 302 / Jan '90 / Slam

☐ SLOW MUSIC (Coxhill, Lol & Morgan-Fisher)
Que en paz descanse / Flotsam / Vase / Jetsam / Matt finish / Slow music / Pretty little girl
BP 160CD / Nov '96 / Blueprint

☐ TOVERBAL SWEET
Five to four / Clompen stomp / Spirit of Maasluis / Association / Or alternatively nine / One to three / PC one / Toverbal / Toverbal sweet / Jasper and out / Un-tempered klavier and heavy friends / Toverbal revisited
SEECD 480 / Jul '97 / See For Miles

Coyabalites

☐ UNHINGED
SH 45036 / Nov '97 / Shanachie

Coyle & Sharp

☐ ON THE LOOSE
213CD 005 / Jun '96 / 2.13.61

Coyle, Peter

☐ SEASON
TLGCD 008 / Jan '97 / Telegraph

Coyne, Kevin

☐ ADVENTURES OF CRAZY FRANK, THE
Born crazy / Drunk again / Moon madness / You're so wonderful / Crazy dream / Devil calling / Married / Deep the darkness / I stood up / Playing the fool / Heart of hearts / Perversion / Frankies dream No.1 / Frankies dream No.2 / Time for tears / Blast of glory / Never ending
CD 388701742 / Oct '95 / Rockport

☐ CASE HISTORY ...PLUS
God bless the bride / White horse / Uggy's song / Need somebody / Evil island home / Araby / My message to the people / Mad boy / Sand all yellow / I'm all aching / Leopard never changes it's spots
SEECD 410 / Sep '94 / See For Miles

☐ DYNAMITE DAZE
Dynamite daze / Brothers of mine / Lunatic / Are we dreaming / Take me back to Dear old Blighty / I really live round here (false friends) / I am / Amsterdam / I only want to see you smile / Juliet and Mark / Woman, woman, woman / Cry / Dance of Bourgeoise
CDV 2096 / Jun '91 / Virgin

☐ ELVIRA: SONGS FROM THE ARCHIVES 1979-83
Stand up for England / I'm a girl / Debutante / Leopard never changes it's spots / Golden days / Bad boys / Long arm of the law / Think of sunshine / Elvira / Better than you / Rambling Germany blues / Bimbo / Up North / Born in 1944 / Blood in the night
GH 70122 / Mar '95 / Golden Hind

☐ LEGLESS IN MANILA
Big money man / Gina's song / Money machine / Raindrop on the river / Nigel in Napoli / Zoo wars / Black cloud / Legless in Manila / Don't raise an argument / Cycling
GH 70062 / Nov '94 / Golden Hind

☐ MARJORY RAZORBLADE
Marjory Razorblade / Marlene / Talking to no one / Eastbourne ladies / Old soldier / I want my crown / Nasty, lonesome valley / House on the hill / Cheat me / Jack and Edna / Everybody says / Mummy / Heaven in my view / Karate king / Dog Latin / This is Spain / Chairman's ball / Good boy / Chicken wing
CDVM 2501 / Sep '90 / Virgin

☐ MATCHING HEAD AND FEET
Saviour / Lucy / Lonely lovers / Sunday morning sunrise / Rock 'n' roll hymn / Mrs. Hooley go home / It's not me / Turpentine / Tulip / One fine day
CDV 2033 / Jun '91 / Virgin

☐ RABBITS (Coyne, Kevin & Siren)
Stride / Mandy Lee / Marilyn / Why why why / Cheat me / Whole lotta shakin' goin' on / Flowering cherry / Trouble in mind / God bless the bride / Bottle up and go / Blues before sunrise / I need you / John the baptist / Lunatic laughs / Big pistol Mama / Hot potato / Start walking / Let's dance / Forked lightening / Wait until dark
DJC 001 / Oct '94 / DJC

☐ ROMANCE ROMANCE (Coyne, Kevin & The Paradise Band)
Ready for love / Happy, happy / Chances / It's all over / Seventeenth Floor / Theresa / No kindness, no pity / Heaven song / Lovers and friends / Wild eyes / Best friend / Impossible child / Neighbourhood girl
SPV 8492602 / Dec '94 / Voiceprint

☐ SIGN OF THE TIMES
Marjory razorblade / Marlene / Eastbourne ladies / House on the hill / Dog latin / Good boy / Karate king / Fat girl / Saviour / Brothers of mine / Dynamite daze / Having a party / I'm just a man / Only one / Children's crusade / Mona, where's my trousers / Sign of the times / Witch / Blame it on the night
CDVM 9029 / Aug '92 / Virgin

☐ STUMBLING ONTO PARADISE
I'm still here / Pack of lies / How is your luck / Sunshine home / Tear me up / No revolution / Victoria smiles / Charming / Winter into summer / Love for five minutes / Back home boogie
GH 70102 / Nov '94 / Golden Hind

☐ TOUGH AND SWEET
Little Miss Dynamite / Precious love / Burning head II / Really in love / Ponytail song / Elvis is dead / Totally naked II / Walls have ears / Baby blue / Talking money / Slow burner / All the loving / No lullabies / It's amazing II / Tell me Tony / Now's the time / Getting old / Some day / Love and money / Let's get romantic / Creeper
GH 70092 / Jun '94 / Golden Hind

☐ WILD TIGER LOVE (Coyne, Kevin & The Paradise Band)
Bungalow / Sensual / Cafe crazy / Looking in your eyes / Open up the gates / Go Sally go / American girls / Fish brain / Fooled again / Don't you look (that way) / Raindrops on the window / Passions pleasure
CD 3887001240 / Oct '94 / Golden Hind

Coyotes

☐ COYOTES, THE
RTMCD 85 / Nov '96 / Round Tower

Cozens, Chris

☐ SYNTHESIZER GREATEST HITS
Eve of the war / Chariots of fire / Oxygene / Axel F / Crockett's theme / Magic fly / Autobahn / Telstar / Toccata / Chung kuo / Tokyo rendezvous / Miami Vice / Pulstar / Love theme from Bladerunner / Equinoxe / Birdland / Sweet lullaby / Moments in love / Friends of Mr. Cairo
CDMFP 6134 / Sep '94 / Music For Pleasure

Crabbe, Frisco

☐ EMMERDALE WEDDING SET/SOUL SELECTION
Dancing in the street / Dock of the bay / Gotcha / Hard to handle / Hold on I'm coming / Knock on wood / My girl / Respect / Satisfaction / Soul man / Walkin' the dog / Can't buy me love
FC 1998CD / 6 May '98 / Frisco

Crabs

☐ WHAT WERE FLAMES NOW SMOULDER
K 74CD / 22 Aug '97 / Kranky

Crabs

☐ BRAINWASHED
KLP 56CD / Sep '96 / K

Crack

☐ IN SEARCH OF THE CRACK
My world / Take me away / You keep me running / Hard road / Don't just sit there / Don't you ever let me down / Glory boys / Everybody's dreaming / I'll be there / Giddy house / Nag nag nag / You kept me waiting / Going out / Cum on feel the noize / Don't stop me / Where are they now
AHOYCD 011 / 6 Jul '98 / Captain Oi

Crack

☐ SO 92
Happy birthday / For he's a jolly good fellow / For she's a jolly good lady / Auld lang syne / Congratulations / Happy anniversary / Christmas megamix / Irish national anthem / Number one (jingle)
SUNCD 5 / Sep '94 / Sound

Crack

☐ DEMOS & RARITIES
Don't you ever let me down / I can't take you out / Going out / Troops have landed / All or nothing / I caught you out / We've got a right to know / Take me away / Nag nag nag / That's the way / Wait till the day arrives / Battle song / My world / Hard road / Where are the glory boys / Don't just sit there / Everybody's dreaming / Saturday night's alright / One of the boys / Listen to me
AHOYCD 069 / 3 Nov '97 / Captain Oi

Crack Up

☐ FROM THE GROUND
NB 257CD / Jun '97 / Nuclear Blast

Cracker

☐ KEROSENE HAT
Low / Movie star / Get off this / Kerosene hat / Take me down to the infirmary / Nostalgia / Sweet potato / Sick of goodbyes / I want everything / Lonesome Johnny blues / Let's go for a ride / Loser / Hi-desert biker meth lab / Euro-trash girl / I ride my bike / Kerosene hat (Accoustic)
CDVU 67 / Jun '94 / Virgin

Crackerbash

☐ TIN TOY
EFA 11397CD / Aug '93 / Musical Tragedies

Cracknell, Sarah

☐ LIPSLIDE
Ready or not / Desert baby / Coastal town / Home / Anymore / How far / Goldie / Taxi / Taking off for France / If you leave me / Penthouse girl basement boy / Can't stop now
GUTCD 2 / May '97 / Gut

Craddock, Billy

☐ CRASH'S SMASHES (The Hits Of Billy 'Crash' Craddock)
RAZCD 2095 / Apr '96 / Razor & Tie

☐ WELL DON'T YOU KNOW
Sweet pie / School day dreams / Lulu Lee / Ah poor little baby / I miss you so much / Blabbermouth / Am I to be the one / Sweetie Pie / Well don't you know / Boom boom baby / Don't destroy me / (What makes you) Treat me like you do / I want that / Since she turned seventeen / All I want is you / Letter of love / One last kiss / Is it true or is it false / Report card of love / Heavenly love / Goodtime Billy
BCD 15610 / Jun '92 / Bear Family

Cradle

☐ BABA YAGA
TOPPCD 042 / Jun '96 / Ultimate

Cradle Of Filth

☐ CRUELTY AND THE BEAST
Thirteen autumns and a widow / Cruelty beneath the orchids / Beneath the howling stars / Venus in fear / Desire in violent overture / Twisted nails of faith / Bathory aria / Portrait of the dead countess / Lustmord and wargasm (the lick of carnivorous winds)
CDMFN 242 / 4 May '98 / Music For Nations

☐ DUSK & HER EMBRACE
Human inspired to nightmare / Heaven torn asunder / Funeral in Carpathia / Gothic romance / Malice through the looking glass / Dusk and her embrace / Graveyard moonlight / Beauty sleeps in sodom / Haunted shores / Hell awaits / Camilla's masque
CDMFN 208 / Nov '96 / Music For Nations

☐ PRINCIPLE OF EVIL MADE FLESH
Darkness our bride (jugular wedding) / Principle of evil made flesh / Forest whispers my name / Iscariot / Black goddess rises / One final graven kiss / A crescendo of passion bleeding / To eve the art of witchcraft / Of mist and midnight skies / In secret love we drown / Dream of wolves in the snow / Summer dying fast
NIHIL 001 / 20 Jul '98 / Cacophonous

☐ VEMPIRE
Ebony dressed for sunset / Forest whispers my name / Queen of winter throned / Nocturnal supremacy / She mourns a lengthening shadow / Rape and ruin of angels (hosannas in extremis)
NIHIL 006 / 20 Jul '98 / Cacophonous

Cradle Of Spoil

☐ SOLAR ECLIPSE
EFA 125192 / Apr '95 / Celtic Circle

Cragg, Steven

☐ DISCOVERY
CD 434 / 6 Jul '98 / New World

Craig, Carl

☐ DJ KICKS (Various Artists)
K7 042CD / Apr '96 / Studio K7

☐ LANDCRUISING
Mind of a machine / Wonderful life / Technology / They were / Landcruising / Einbahn / One day soon / Home entertainment / Science fiction
4509998652 / Dec '96 / Blanco Y Negro

☐ MORE SONGS ABOUT FOOD AND REVOLUTIONARY ART
Es30 / Televised green smoke / Goodbye world / Alien talk / Red lights / Dreamland / Butterfly / Act 2 / Dominas / At Les / Suspiria / As time goes by (sitting under a tree) / Attitude / Frustration / Food and art (in the spirit of revolution)
SSR 188CD / Mar '97 / Crammed Discs

Craig, Cathryn

☐ CATHRYN CRAIG
Runnin from love / Talk to you / Are you out there / Never / Colorado / Love coming down on me / My window faces the south / New Paint / Voyager / If you don't weaken
GOLDCD 002 / Aug '97 / Goldrush

☐ PORCH SONGS
GOLDCD 001 / Jul '95 / Goldrush

Craig, Sara

☐ SWEET EXHAUST
0072112ATT / Jul '95 / Edel

Craig's Brother

☐ HOMECOMING
TNR 1106CD / 9 Aug '98 / Tooth & Nail

Crain

☐ HEATER
Foot sanding / Save me your head / Valium and alcohol / Waste kings / Blistering / Knock your daylights out / Hey cops / Bricks / One who hangs / Broken heart of a neutron star
727512 / Apr '94 / Restless

Cramer, Floyd

☐ ESSENTIAL FLOYD CRAMER, THE
Last date / Fancy pants / I'm so lonesome I could cry / San Antonio rose / Flip flop and bop / Your last goodbye / Corrina corrina / Drown in my own tears / I need you now / On the rebound / Georgia on my mind / Lovesick blues / Chattanooga choo choo / Losers weepers / Java / Shrum / (These are) the young ears / All keyed up / Stood up / What'd I say
74321665912 / Feb '96 / RCA

☐ KING OF COUNTRY PIANO
PWKS 4222 / Nov '94 / Carlton

☐ MASTERS, THE
EABCD 106 / 30 Mar '98 / Eagle

Cramps

☐ BIG BEAT FROM BADSVILLE
Cramp stomp / God monster / It thing hard on / Like a bad girl should / Sheena's in a goth gang / Queen of pain / Monkey with your tail / Devil behind that bush / Super goo / Hypno sex ray / Burn she devil, burn / Wet nightmare / Badass bug / Haulass hyena
65162 / 29 Sep '97 / Epitaph

☐ DATE WITH ELVIS, A
How far can too far go / Hot pearl snatch / People ain't no good / What's inside a girl / Kizmiaz / Cornfed dames / Chicken / Womanneed / Aloha from hell / It's just that song
CDWIK 46 / Apr '86 / Big Beat

☐ FLAMEJOB
Mean machine / Ultra twist / Let's get fucked up / Nest of cuckoo birds / I'm customized / Sado county auto show / Naked girl falling down the stairs / How come you do me / Upside down and upside down / Trapped love / Swing the big eyed rabbit / Strange love / Blues blues blues / Sinners / Route 66
CRECD 170 / Oct '94 / Creation

☐ OFF THE BONE
Human fly / Way I walk / Domino / Surfin' bird / Lonesome town / Garbage man / Fever / Drug train / Love me / I can't hardly stand it / Goo goo muck / She said / Crusher / Save it / New kind of kick
4938372 / 13 Apr '98 / EMI

☐ ROCKINNREELININAUCKLAND NEWZEALANDXXX
Hot pearl snatch / People ain't no good / What's inside a girl / Cornfed Dames / Sunglasses after dark / Heartbreak Hotel / Chicken / Do the clam / Aloha from Hell / Can your pussy do the dog / Blue moon baby / Georgia Lee Brown / Lonesome town
CDWIKD 132 / Aug '94 / Big Beat

☐ SMELL OF FEMALE
Most exalted potentate of love / You got good taste / Call of the wig hat / Faster pussycat / I ain't nothin' but a gorehound / Psychotic reaction
CDWIKM 95 / Feb '91 / Big Beat

☐ SONGS THE CRAMPS TAUGHT US (Various Artists)
APECALL 007 / Mar '97 / Jungle Noise

☐ SONGS THE LORD TAUGHT US
TV set / Rock on the moon / Garbageman / I was a teenage werewolf / Sunglasses / Mad daddy / Mystery plane / Zombie dance / What's behind the mask / Strychnine / I'm cramped / Tear it up / Fever / I was a teenage werewolf / Mystery plane / Twist and shout / I'm cramped / Mad daddy
4938362 / 6 Jul '98 / EMI

☐ STAY SICK
Bop pills / God damn rock 'n' roll / Bikini girls with machine guns / All women are bad / Creature from the black leather lagoon / Shortnin' bread / Daisys up your butterfly / Everything goes / Journey to the center of a girl / Mama oo pow pow / Saddle up a buzz buzz / Mule skinner blues / Her love rubbed off
CDWIKD 126 / Jan '94 / Big Beat

Cran

☐ BLACK BLACK BLACK
CC 63CD / Jul '98 / Claddagh

☐ CROOKED STAIR
CBM 002CD / Oct '93 / Cross Border Media

Cranberries

☐ CRANBERRIES, THE (Fully Illustrated Book & Interview Dics)
SAM 7034 / Jun '97 / Sound & Media

☐ EVERYBODY ELSE IS DOING IT, SO WHY CAN'T WE
I still do / Dreams / Sunday / Pretty / Waltzing back / Not sorry / Linger / Wanted / Still can't... / I will always / How / Put me down
CID 8003 / Feb '94 / Island

☐ EVERYBODY ELSE IS DOING IT, SO WHY CAN'T WE/NO NEED TO ARGUE (2CD Set)
I still do / Dreams / Sunday / Pretty / Waltzing back / Not sorry / Linger / Wanted / Still can't... / I will always / How / Put me down / Ode to my family / I can't be with you / Twenty one / Zombie / Empty / Everything I said / Icicle melts / Disappointment / Ridiculous thoughts / Dreaming my dreams / Yeats' grave / Daffodil lament / No need to argue
ISDCD 1 / Nov '95 / Island

☐ NO NEED TO ARGUE
Ode to my family / I can't be with you / Twenty one / Zombie / Empty / Everything I said / Icicle melts / Disappointment / Ridiculous thoughts / Dreaming my dreams / Yeats grave / Daffodils lament / No need to argue
CID 8029 / Aug '94 / Island

☐ TO THE FAITHFUL DEPARTED
Hollywood / Salvation / When you're gone / Free to decide / Warchild / Forever yellow skies / Rebels / I just shot John Lennon / Electric blue / I'm still remembering / Will you remember / Joe / Bosnia
CID 8048 / Apr '96 / Island

Crane

☐ 345S
ELM 7CD / Jan '93 / Elemental

Crane River Jazz Band

☐ CRANE RIVER JAZZ BAND
SGC/MELCD 202 / Nov '96 / Cadillac

☐ GREAT BRITISH TRADITIONAL JAZZBANDS VOL.5
Balling the Jack / Maryland my Maryland / After dark / Moose march / Canal street blues / Down by the riverside / Winnin' boy blues / You tell me your dream / Tishomingo blues / When I leave the world behind / Saturday night function / Ain't gonna give nobody none of my jellyroll / I'm travelling / Washington and Lee swing / South
LACD 57 / Dec '95 / Lake

Crane, Tony

☐ FEEL LIKE DANCING
You make me feel like dancing / Mack the knife / Time in a bottle / Charade / Old fashioned way / Soul coaxin' / Women in love / Me and my shadow / Pretty world / Copacabana / Hot hot hot / Small world / Love changes everything / Route 66 / Choo choo ch'boogie
DLD 1020 / '92 / Dance & Listen

☐ GEE BUT IT'S GOOD
DLD 1036 / May '93 / Dance & Listen

Cranes

☐ POPULATION FOUR
Tangled up / Fourteen / Breeze / Can't get free / Stalk / Sweet unknown / Angel bell / On top of the world / Brazil / Let go / To be / Lemon tree
DEDCD 026S / Feb '97 / Dedicated

Cranioclast

☐ ICONCLASTER
EEE 09CD / Sep '93 / Musica Maxima Magnetica

Cranitch, Matt

☐ IRISH FIDDLE BOOK, THE
OSS 4CD / Jan '87 / Ossian

☐ SMALL ISLAND, A (Cranitch, Milne & Sullivan)
OSS 70CD / Dec '94 / Ossian

☐ TAKE A BOW
CDOSS 05 / Apr '93 / Ossian

Cranium

☐ SPEED METAL SATAN
NR 6669CD / 19 Jan '98 / Necropolis

☐ SPEED METAL SLAUGHTER
NR 033CD / 17 Aug '98 / Necropolis

Cranium HF

☐ OFF
RSNCD 52 / 29 Sep '97 / PRD

Crank

☐ PICKING UP THE PIECES
Lonely man / Why did you go / You as well / Punk a 'a' right
SEMAPHORE 35662 / Nov '96 / Onefoot

Cranna, Hannah

☐ HANNAH CRANNA
BD 9039 / Nov '97 / Big Deal

Craobh Rua

☐ MORE THAT'S SAID THE LESS THE BETTER
CDLDL 1215 / Jul '94 / Lochshore

☐ NO MATTER HOW COLD AND WET YOU ARE
CDLDL 1237 / Mar '96 / Lochshore

☐ SOH IT IS
Red crow / Dawn / Bianzano / Ye lovers all / Paddy Fahey's / Handy with the bottle / Wearing the britches / Cook in the kitchen / Na' tar ach san oiche / Tosa waltz / My charming Nancy Bell / Lads of Laois / London lasses / Miss McClouds / High road to Linton / Shore 'neath the tide / Ivy leaf / Fox on the town
CDLDL 1259 / Mar '97 / Lochshore

Crary, Dan

☐ BLUEGRASS GUITAR
SHCD 3806 / Jan '97 / Sugar Hill

☐ GUITAR
Cotton patch rag / Stanley Brothers medley / Sweet laree / Memories of Mozart / Green in the blue medley / Tom and Jerry / Bill Monroe medley
SHCD 3730 / Jan '97 / Sugar Hill

☐ HOLIDAY GUITAR
Santa baby / Silent night / O Holy night / What child is this / Little drummer boy / Coventry carol/Patapan / Christmas waltz/Fum fum fum / Silver bells / Last Noel / Carol of the bells / Masters in this hall / Christmas blues a-comin' / Jesu bambino/First Noel / God rest ye merry gentlemen/Joy to the world
SHCD 3871 / Mar '98 / Sugar Hill

☐ JAMMED IF I DO
SHCD 3824 / Oct '94 / Sugar Hill

☐ LADY'S FANCY
Huckleberry hornpipe / Lime rock / If the devil dreamed about playing flamenco / With a flatpick / Jenny's waltz / Sally Goodin / Julie's reel / Dill pickle rag / Pretty little indian / Grey eagle / Lady's fancy
ROUCD 0099 / Dec '94 / Rounder

☐ TAKE A STEP OVER
Bugle call rag / Take a step over / Great tunes/Dumb names medley / Raleigh and special / Come hither / Willow, the wandering gypsy / Hot canary / Traditional suite in "E" medley / Lord build me a cabin
SHCD 3770 / Oct '97 / Sugar Hill

☐ THUNDERATION
Banderilla / Depoe Bay / West o' the moon / Amsterdance / Songs of Makoraka-o / Thunderation / Lady's fantasy / Lime rock / Andante in steel / Denouement
SHCD 1135 / Oct '91 / Sugar Hill

Crash Museum

☐ CRASH MUSEUM
RD 3970003CD / 1 Dec '97 / Institute Of Art

Crash Test Dummies

☐ GHOST THAT HAUNTS ME, THE
Winter song / Comin' back song (the bereft man's song) / Superman's song / Country life / Here on earth (I'll have my cake) / Ghost that haunts me / Thick necked man / Androgynous / Voyage / At my funeral
74321283342 / Aug '95 / RCA

☐ GOD SHUFFLED HIS FEET
God shuffled his feet / Afternoons and coffespoons / Mmm mmm mmm mmm / In the days of the cinema / Swimming in you ocean / Here I stand before me / I think I've disappeared / How does a duck know / When I go out with artists / Psychic / Two knights and maidens / Untitled
74321165312 / 2 Feb '98 / RCA

☐ WORM'S LIFE, A
Overachievers / He liked to feel it / Worm's life / Our driver gestures / My enemies / There are many dangers / I'm outlived by that thing / All of this ugly / Old scab / My own sunrise / I'm a dog / Swatting flies
74321402012 / Sep '96 / RCA

Crash Worship

☐ ADRV
CHCD 3 / Jun '97 / Charnel House

☐ ASESINOS
RUSCD 8212 / Jul '95 / ROIR

Crass

☐ BEST BEFORE 1984
CRASS 5CD / Oct '90 / Crass

☐ CHRIST THE ALBUM
BOLLOX2U2 CD / Oct '90 / Crass

☐ CHRIST THE BOOTLEG
ALLIED 76CD / Nov '96 / Allied

☐ FEEDING OF THE 5,000
621984 CD / Oct '90 / Crass

☐ PENIS ENVY
321984 CD / Oct '90 / Crass

☐ STATIONS OF THE CRASS
Stations of the crass / Mother Earth / White punks on hope / You've got big hands / Darling / System / Bigman / Hurry up Gary / Gas man cometh / Democrats / Contaminational power / Time out / I ain't thick, it's just a trick / Fun going on / Crutch of society / Heard too much about / Chairman of the board / Tired / Walls / Upright citizen / System / Big man / Banned from the Roxy / Hurry up Gary / Middle class, working class / Fight war, not wars / Shaved women / Fun going on / Unknown songs / Do they owe us a living / Punk is dead
521984 CD / Oct '90 / Crass

☐ TEN NOTES ON A SUMMERS DAY
CATN 06CD / 24 Aug '98 / Crass

☐ YES SIR I WILL
121984/2 CD / Oct '90 / Crass

Craven, Beverley

☐ BEVERLEY CRAVEN
Promise me / Holding on / Woman to woman / Memories / Castle in the clouds / You're not the first / Joey / Two of a kind / I listen to the rain / Missing you
4670532 / 27 Jul '98 / Epic

☐ LOVE SCENES
Love scenes / Love is the light / Look no further / Mollie's song / In those days / Feels like the first time / Blind faith / Lost without you / Winner takes it all
4745172 / 27 Jul '98 / Epic

Cravens, Red

☐ 419 WEST MAIN (Cravens, Red & Bray Brothers)
WHOW introduction / This train / Glory in the meeting house / Bluegrass breakdown / Cora is gone / East Virginia blues / Jingle bell breakdown / Blue eyed darling / Little darling pal of mine / Pass me by / Cumberland gap / I never shall marry / Lost love / Sally Goodin / Gentle blues / Rawhide / Angel with the golden hair / Buckin' mule / Our darling's gone / Hazel Dell
ROUCD 0015 / May '97 / Rounder

Cravinkel

☐ CRAVINKEL
RR 7086 / Jul '98 / Repertoire

☐ GARDEN OF LONELINESS
RR 7087 / Jul '98 / Repertoire

Craw

☐ CRAW
CHK 002 / Feb '94 / Choke Inc.

☐ MAP, MONITOR, SURGE
CAM 004 / Jun '97 / Cambodia

Crawdaddys

☐ CRAWDADDY EXPRESS
I'm a lover not a fighter / You can't judge a book by the cover / Down the road apiece / Let's make it / Raining in my heart / I'm movin' on / Mystic eyes / Oh baby doll / Bald headed woman / Come see me / Got you in my soul / Times are getting tougher than tough / Down in the bottom / Crawdaddy Express / I wanna put a tiger in your tank
VOXXCD 2001 / Oct '94 / Voxx

☐ HERE TIS
VOXXCD 2046 / Oct '94 / Voxx

Crawford, Davell

☐ B3 AND ME, THE
CDBB 9603 / 19 Jan '98 / Bullseye Blues

Crawford, Hank

☐ SOUTH CENTRAL
Falling in love with love / I should care / South Central / I want to talk about you / In a mellow tone / Conjunction Mars / Fool that I am / Splanky / O holy night
MCD 9201 / Oct '93 / Milestone

Crawford, Johnny

☐ BEST OF JOHNNY CRAWFORD, THE
Cindy's birthday / Rumours / Your nose is gonna grow / Proud / Patti Ann / Daydreams / Cindy's gonna cry / Judy loves me / Janie please believe me / What happened to Janie / Lonesome town / Lucky star / Devil or angel / Sandy / Debbie / Your love is growing old / That's all I want from you / Cry on my shoulder / I don't need you / Mr. Blue / Girl next door (Once upon a time) / We belong together / No one really loves a clown / Sittin' and watchin'
CDCHD 429 / Oct '92 / Ace

Crawford, Kevin

☐ 'D' FLUTE ALBUM
KBSCD 77 / Oct '94 / Kerbstone

☐ RAISE THE RAFTERS
CCD 002 / Feb '96 / Celtic Prime

Crawford, Michael

☐ LOVE SONGS
TCD 2748 / Nov '94 / Telstar

☐ ON EAGLE'S WINGS
Spirit of the living God / Panis angelicus / Amazing grace / On eagle's wings / Joseph's lullaby / Walk with God / Not too far from here / Eternal love / Holy city / Ave Maria / Now the day is over
7567830762 / 23 Mar '98 / Atlantic

☐ PERFORMS ANDREW LLOYD WEBBER
Any dream will do / All I ask of you / Wishing you were somehow here again / And the money kept rolling in (and out) / Nothing like you've ever known / Tell me on a sunday / Gethsemane / Music of the night / Memory / Only you
TCD 2544 / Nov '91 / Telstar

Crawford, Randy

☐ ABSTRACT EMOTIONS
Can't stand the pain / Actual emotional love / World of fools / Betcha / Higher than anyone can count / Desire / Getting away with murder / Overnight / Almaz / Don't wanna be normal
9254232 / Jul '86 / WEA

☐ EVERY KIND OF MOOD
3984214022 / 16 Feb '98 / WEA

☐ EVERYTHING MUST CHANGE
Everything must change / I let you walk away / I'm easy / I had to see you one more time / I've never been to me / Don't let me down / Something so right / Soon as I touched him / Only your love song lasts / Gonna give lovin a try
7599273072 / Feb '92 / WEA

☐ NAKED AND TRUE
Cajun moon / Give me the night / Glow of love / Purple rain / Forget me nots / I'll be around / Joy inside my tears / Come into my life / What a difference a day makes / Holding back the years / All the king's horses
0630109612 / Jul '95 / WEA

☐ NOW WE MAY BEGIN
Now we may begin / Blue flame / When your life was low / My heart is not as young as it used to be / Last night at danceland / Tender falls the rain / One day I'll fly away / Same old story (same old song)
7599234212 / Feb '92 / WEA

☐ RAW SILK
I stand accused / Declaration of love / Someone to believe in / Endlessly / Love is like a newborn child / Where there was darkness / Nobody / I hope you'll be very unhappy without me / I got myself a happy song / Just to keep you satisfied / Blue mood
7599273862 / Feb '93 / WEA

☐ RICH AND POOR
Knockin' on heaven's door / Every kinda people / Wrap U up / This is love / Seperate lives / Believe that love can change the world / Rich and poor / Cigarette in the rain / Love is / I don't feel much like crying / All it takes is love
9260022 / Oct '89 / WEA

☐ SECRET COMBINATION
You might need somebody / Rainy night in Georgia / That's how heartaches are made / Two lives / You bring the Sun out / Rio De Janeiro blue / Secret combination / When I lose my way / Time for love / Trade winds
K2 56904 / Mar '87 / WEA

☐ THROUGH THE EYES OF LOVE
Who's crying now / It's raining / When love is new / If i were (in your shoes) / Rhythm of romance / Shine / Hold on, be strong / Lot that you can do / If you'd only believe / Like the sun out of nowhere / Just a touch / Diamante
7599267362 / Dec '96 / WEA

Crawford, Ray

☐ SMOOTH GROOVE
Compendium suite / Miss April / Impossible / I knew prez / Smooth groove
CCD 9028 / Feb '97 / Candid

Crawford, Stephanie

☐ TIME FOR LOVE, A (Crawford, Stephanie & Michel Graillier)
BBRC 9103 / Nov '92 / Big Blue

Crawler

☐ PASTIME DREAMER
RMCCD 0206 / Apr '97 / Red Steel

Crawley

☐ SUPERSONIC
SPV 08436202 / Oct '94 / SPV

Cray, Robert

☐ BAD INFLUENCE (Cray, Robert Band)
Phone booth / Grinder / Got to make a comeback / So many women, so little time / Where do I go from here / Waiting for a train / March on / Don't touch me / No big deal / Bad influence / Share what you've got, keep what you need / I got loaded
HCD 8001 / Apr '96 / Hightone

☐ FALSE ACCUSATIONS (Cray, Robert Band)
Porch light / Change of heart, change of mind / She's gone / Playin' in the dirt / I've slipped her mind / False accusations / Last time / Payin' for it now / Sonny
HCD 8005 / Apr '96 / Hightone

☐ I WAS WARNED (Cray, Robert Band)
Just a loser / I'm a good man / I was warned / Price I pay / Won the battle / On the road down / Whole lotta pride / Picture of a broken heart / He don't live here anymore / Our last time
5127212 / Jan '93 / Mercury

☐ MIDNIGHT STROLL (Cray, Robert Band & Memphis Horns)
8466522 / Sep '90 / Mercury

☐ NEW BLUES
Who's been talkin' / Nice as a fool can be / If you're thinkin' what I'm thinkin' / Welfare (turns its back on you) / I'm gonna forget about you / Sleeping on the ground / Too many cooks / I'd rather be a wino / Score / That's what I'll do
306642 / Apr '98 / Hallmark

☐ SCORE, THE (Charly Blues Masterworks Vol.16)
Too many cooks / Score / Welfare / That's what I'll do / I'd rather be a wino / Who's been talkin' / Sleeping in the ground / I'm gonna forget about you / Nice as a fool can be / If I'm thinkin' what I'm thinkin'
CDBM 16 / Apr '92 / Charly

☐ SHAME & SIN
5185172 / Oct '93 / Mercury

☐ SOME RAINY MORNING
5269282 / 15 Sep '97 / Mercury

☐ STRONG PERSUADER (Cray, Robert Band)
Smoking gun / I guessed I showed her / Right next door (because of me) / Nothin' but a woman / Still around / More than I can stand / Foul play / Ronettes / Fantasized / New blood
8305682 / Nov '86 / Mercury

☐ SWEET POTATO PIE (Cray, Robert Band)
5346982 / May '97 / Mercury

Crayton, Pee Wee

☐ BLUES AFTER HOURS
Win-o / Hurry hurry / Runnin' wild / I got news for you / Don't break my heart / Blues before dawn / Don't go / Telephone is ringing / Mistreated so bad / Poppa stoppa / Phone call from my baby / Tired of travellin' / California women / Blues for my baby / Rosa Lee / Guitar boogie / Dedicating the blues / Brand new woman / I love you so / Texas hop / Blues after hours / After hours boogie
CD 52045 / Oct '96 / Blues Encore

☐ MODERN LEGACY, THE
Texas hop / Central Avenue blues / Bounce Pee Wee / T for Texas (mistreated blues) / Rosa Lee / Blues after hours / I'm still in love with you / Pee Wee's boogie / Louella Brown / From blues to boogie / Please come back / Rock Island blues / Rockin' the blues / Change your way of lovin' / Pee Wee's wild / Black gal / Boogie woogie upstairs / When darkness falls / Bop hop / My everything / Blues for my baby / Tired of travellin' / Austin boogie
CDCHD 632 / Aug '96 / Ace

☐ THINGS I USED TO DO
Every night / But on the other hand / Peace of mind / Let the good times roll / Blues after hours / You were wrong / Things I used to do / Little bitty things / SK blues / Long tall Texan / My kind of woman
VMD 65662 / Oct '95 / Vanguard

Crazy

☐ CRAZIAH THAN EVER
JW 056CD / Feb '94 / Soca

☐ CRAZY FOR YOU
JW 067CD / Feb '95 / JW

Crazy Alice

☐ HEY JIMMY HAVE A GREAT SUMMER
CAT 013 / 13 Oct '97 / Catapult

Crazy Backward Alphabet

☐ CRAZY BACKWARD ALPHABET
Blood and the ink / Det Enda Raka / Get it you / Welfare elite / Ghosts / Lobster on the rocks / Sarayushka (La Grange) / Dropped D / Book of Joel / Bottoms up / We are in control / Maran II
SST 110CD / May '93 / SST

Crazy Cavan

☐ COOL AND CRAZY
107352 / Mar '94 / Musidisc

☐ HEY, TEENAGER
107332 / Mar '94 / Musidisc

☐ ROCKABILLY IN PARIS (Crazy Cavan & The Rhythm Rockers)
BBR 00040 / 6 Feb '98 / Big Beat

☐ ROLLIN' THROUGH THE NIGHT
107342 / Mar '94 / Musidisc

☐ ROUGH, TOUGH & READY
107072 / Mar '94 / Musidisc

☐ WILD, WEIRD AND CRAZY (Crazy Cavan & The Rhythm Rockers)
CRCD 01 / Nov '96 / Crazy Rhythm

Crazy Horse

☐ CRAZY HORSE
Gone dead train / Dance, dance, dance / Look at all the things / Beggar's day / I don't want to talk about it / Carolay / Dirty, dirty / Nobody / I'll get by / Crow Lady Jane
7599268082 / Apr '94 / Reprise

☐ CRAZY MOON
She's hot / Going down again / Lost and lonely feelin' / Dancin' lady / End of the line / New Orleans / Love don't come easy / Downhill / Too late / That day / Thunder and lightning
74321578212 / 27 Apr '98 / Camden

☐ LEFT FOR DEAD
SERV 009CD / Nov '89 / World Service

Crazy Rhythm Daddies

☐ CRAZY RHYTHM DADDIES
IR 001 / Sep '96 / Igloo

Crazyhead

☐ SOME KIND OF FEVER
Big sister / Above those things / Everything's alright / Magic eye / I can do anything / Movie theme / Talk about you / Rome / Train / Some kinda fever
REVXD 162 / Oct '90 / Black

Creach, Papa John

☐ I'M THE FIDDLE MAN
OW 30004 / Jul '94 / One Way

☐ ROCK FATHER
OW 30005 / Jul '94 / One Way

Cream

☐ ALTERNATIVE ALBUM, THE
ITM 960002 / Oct '92 / ITM

☐ CREAM BOX SET
CR 1 / Oct '92 / UFO

☐ CREAM LIVE VOL.2
Deserted cities of the heart / White room / Politician / Tales of brave Ulysses / Sunshine of your love / Steppin' out
8236612 / May '88 / Polydor

☐ DISRAELI GEARS
Strange brew / Sunshine of your love / World of pain / Dance the night away / Blue condition / Tales of brave Ulysses / We're going wrong / Outside woman blues / Take it back / Mother's lament
8236362 / Nov '90 / Polydor

☐ FRESH CREAM
I feel free / NSU / Sleepy time time / Dreaming / Sweet wine / Spoonful / Cat's squirrel / Four until late / Rollin' and tumblin' / I'm so glad / Toad / Coffee song / Wrapping paper
8275762 / Nov '90 / Polydor

☐ THOSE WERE THE DAYS (4CD Set)
5390022 / Sep '97 / Polydor

☐ VERY BEST OF CREAM, THE
White room / I feel free / Tales of brave Ulysses / I'm so glad / Toad / Sunshine of your love / Strange brew / NSU / Born under a bad sign / Badge / Crossroads
5237522 / Jan '95 / Polydor

Cream 8

☐ EMERALD TOUCH, THE
SPV 08423622 / May '95 / SPV

Creaming Jesus

☐ END OF AN ERROR
FREUDCD 52 / Oct '96 / Jungle

☐ TOO FAT TO RUN, TO STUPID TO HIDE
FREUDCD 36 / Dec '90 / Jungle

Creams

☐ ARE YOU REAL (Or Are You Just Some Sort Of Disgusting Fridge Magnet)
JAR 018 / 13 Oct '97 / Jar Music

☐ MALCOLM (2CD Set)
JAR 016 / 13 Oct '97 / Jar Music

Creation

☐ HOW DOES IT FEEL TO FEEL
How does it feel to feel / Life is just beginning / Through my eyes / Ostrich man / I am the walker / Tom Tom / Girls are naked / Painter man / Try and stop me / Biff bang pow / Making time / Cool jerk / For all that I am / Nightmares / Midway down / Can I join your band
EDCD 106 / Aug '90 / Edsel

☐ LAY THE GHOST
COCRD 001 / Oct '93 / Cohesion

☐ MARK FOUR/THE CREATION (Mark Four/Creation)
842058 / May '94 / EVA

☐ OUR MUSIC IS RED WITH PURPLE FLASHES
Making time / Try and stop me / Painter man / Biff bang pow / If I stay too long / Nightmares / Cool jerk / Like a rolling stone / I am the walker / Can I join your band / Hey Joe / Life is just beginning / Through my eyes / How does it feel to feel / Tom tom / Midway down / Girls are naked / Bony Moronie / Mercy mercy mercy / For all that I am / Uncle Bert / Ostrich man / Sweet Helen
DIAB 857 / 6 Apr '98 / Diablo

☐ POWER SURGE
CRECD 176 / Jun '96 / Creation

Creation Of Sunlight

☐ CREATION OF SUNLIGHT
MYSTIC 7 / Jun '97 / Mystic

Creation Rebel

☐ HISTORIC MOMENTS VOL.1 (Dub From Creation Rebel Vibrations)
ONUCD 72 / Jul '94 / On-U Sound

☐ HISTORIC MOMENTS VOL.2
ONUCD 74 / Mar '95 / On-U Sound

☐ LOWS AND HIGHS
Independent man / Rebel party / Reasoning / No peace / Love I can feel / Rubber skirt / Creation rebel / Creative involvements
CDBRED 33 / 22 Sep '97 / Cherry Red

☐ THREAT TO CREATION (Creation Rebel & New Age Steppers)
Chemical specialists / Threat to creation / Eugenic device / Last sane dream / Pain staker / Earthwire line / Ethos design / Final frontier
CDBRED 21 / 22 Sep '97 / Cherry Red

Creative Music Studio

☐ WOODSTOCK JAZZ FESTIVAL VOL.1
Waltz / Isfahan / Stella by starlight / Round midnight
ADC 8 / Jul '97 / Douglas Music
DM 10008 / 15 Jun '98 / Douglas Music

☐ WOODSTOCK JAZZ FESTIVAL VOL.2
Impressions / No greater love / All blues
ADC 9 / Jul '97 / Douglas Music

Creator, Carlos

☐ PURE GUITAR
Radio guitar / Snake dance / Wet blues / Mad kisses / Making satanic train / Grand Prix / Bound for Istanbul / European guitars / Elixir of life / ET calling / 711Q / Nightmare continutes
PCOM 1113 / Jul '91 / President

Creators

☐ HAVE A MASTERPLAN
BS 002CD / Feb '96 / Blindside

Creatures

☐ CREATURES
591052 / 21 Aug '97 / Musidisc

Credit To The Nation

☐ DADDY ALWAYS WANTED ME TO GROW A PAIR OF WINGS
TPLP 54CD / Feb '96 / One Little Indian

Credo

☐ FIELD OF VISION
Rules of engagement / Goodboy / Don't look back / Alicia / Power to the Nth degree / Phantom / Sweet scarlet whisper / Party / Kindness
CYCL 012 / Jun '97 / Cyclops

Creedence Clearwater Revival

☐ BAYOU COUNTRY
Born on the bayou / Bootleg / Graveyard train / Good golly Miss Molly / Penthouse pauper / Proud Mary / Keep on chooglin'
CDFE 502 / Aug '87 / Fantasy

☐ CHOOGLIN'
I heard it through the grapevine / Keep on chooglin' / Suzie Q / Pagan baby / Born on the bayou
CDFE 517 / Jun '93 / Fantasy

☐ CHRONICLE VOL.1 (20 Greatest Hits)
Suzie Q / I put a spell on you / Proud Mary / Bad moon rising / Lodi / Green river / Commotion / Down on the corner / Fortunate son / Travellin' band / Who'll stop the rain / Up around the bend / Run through the jungle / Lookin' out my back door / Long as I can see the light / I heard it through the grapevine / Have you ever seen the rain / Hey tonight / Sweet hitch hiker / Some day never comes
CDCCR 2 / Jun '87 / Fantasy

☐ CHRONICLE VOL.2
Walk on the water / Suzie Q (Part 2) / Born on the Bayou / Good golly Miss Molly / Tombstone shadow / Wrote a song for everyone / Night time is the right time / Cotton fields / It came out of the sky / Don't look now / Midnight special / Before you accuse me / My baby left me / Pagan baby / I wish I could hide away / It's just a thought / Molina / Born to move / Lookin' for a reason / Hello Mary Lou
CDCCR 3 / Jun '87 / Fantasy

☐ COLLECTION, THE (10CD Set)
I put a spell on you / Working man / Suzie Q / Ninety nine and a half (won't do) / Get down woman / Porterville / Gloomy / Walk on the water / Born on the bayou / Bootleg / Graveyard train / Good golly miss molly / Penthouse pauper / Proud Mary / Keep on chooglin' / Green river / Commotion / Tombstone shadow / Wrote a song for everyone / Bad moon rising / Lodi / Sinister purpose / Night time is the right time / Down on the corner / It came out of the sky / Cotton fields / Poorboy shuffle / Feelin' blue / Don't look now / Midnight special / Side of the road / Effigy / Ramble tamble / Before you accuse me / Ooby dooby / Lookin' out my back door / Run through the jungle / Up around the bend / My baby left me / Who'll stop the rain / I heard it through the grapevine / Long as I can see the light / Pagan baby / Sailor's lament / Chameleon / Have you ever seen the rain / I wish I could hide away / Born to move / Hey tonight / It's just a thought / Molina / Rude awakening / Lookin' for a reason / Hello Mary Lou / Cross tie walker / Take it like a friend / Need someone to hold / Tearin' up the country / Someday never comes / What are you gonna do / Sail away / Door to door / Sweet Hitch-Hiker / Born on the bayou (live) / Green river (live) / Suzie Q (Live) / It came out of the sky (live) / Travellin' Band / Fortunate son / Commotion (live) / Lodi (live) / Bad moon rising (live) / Proud Mary (live) / Up around the bend (live) / Hey tonight (live) / Keep on chooglin' (live)
FCDCCR 10 / Oct '92 / Fantasy

☐ CONCERT, THE
Born on the bayou / Green river / Tombstone shadow / Don't look now / Travellin' band / Who'll stop the rain / Bad moon rising / Proud Mary / Fortunate son / Commotion / Midnight special / Night time (is the right time) / Down on the corner / Keep on chooglin'
CDFE 511 / Jul '89 / Fantasy

☐ COSMO'S FACTORY
Ramble tamble / Before you accuse me / Lookin' out my back door / Run through the jungle / Up around the bend / My baby left me / Who'll stop the rain / I heard it through the grapevine / Long as I can see the light / Travellin' band / Ooby dooby
CDFE 505 / Aug '87 / Fantasy

☐ CREEDENCE CLEARWATER REVIVAL
I put a spell on you / Working man / Suzie Q / Ninety nine and a half (won't do) / Get down, woman / Porterville / Gloomy / Walk on the water
CDFE 501 / Jul '87 / Fantasy

☐ CREEDENCE COUNTRY
Lookin' for a reason / Don't look now / Lodi / My baby left me / Hello Mary Lou / Ramble tamble / Cotton fields / Before you accuse me / Wrote a song for everyone / Ooby dooby / Cross tie walker / Lookin' out my back door
CDFE 518 / Sep '92 / Fantasy

☐ CREEDENCE GOLD
Proud Mary / Down on the corner / Bad moon rising / I heard it through the grapevine / Midnight special / Have you ever seen the rain / Born on the Bayou / Suzie Q
CDFE 515 / Aug '91 / Fantasy

☐ GREEN RIVER
Bad moon rising / Cross tie walker / Sinister purpose / Night time is the right time / Green River / Commotion / Tombstone Shadow / Wrote a song for everyone / Lodi
CDFE 503 / '88 / Fantasy

☐ LIVE IN EUROPE
Born on the bayou / It came out of the sky / Fortunate son / Lodi / Proud Mary / Hey tonight / Green River / Suzie Q / Travellin' band / Commotion / Bad moon rising / Up around the bend / Keep on chooglin'
CDFE 514 / Feb '90 / Fantasy

☐ MARDI GRAS
Lookin' for a reason / Take it like a friend / Need someone to hold / Tearin' up the country / Some day never comes / What are you gonna do / Sail away / Hello Mary Lou / Door to door / Sweet hitch hiker
CDFE 513 / Aug '89 / Fantasy

☐ MORE CREEDENCE GOLD
Hey tonight / Run through the jungle / Fortunate son / Bootleg / Lookin' out my back door / Molina / Who'll stop the rain / Sweet hitch-hiker / Good golly Miss Molly / I put a spell on you / Don't look now / Lodi / Porterville / Up around the bend
CDFE 516 / Aug '91 / Fantasy

☐ PENDULUM
Pagan baby / I wish I could hide away / It's just a thought / Rude awakening number two / Sailor's lament / Chameleon / Born to move / Hey tonight / Molina / Have you ever seen the rain
CDFE 512 / Aug '89 / Fantasy

☐ PROUD MARY (The Best Of Creedence Clearwater Revival)
27200644B / 23 Mar '98 / Zounds

☐ RECOLLECTION (2CD Set) (Creedence Clearwater Revisited)
SPV 08529232 / 29 Jun '98 / SPV

☐ WILLY AND THE POORBOYS
Down on the corner / It came out of the sky / Cotton fields / Poor boy shuffle / Feelin' blue / Fortunate son / Don't look now / Midnight special / Side of the road / Effigy
CDFE 504 / Aug '87 / Fantasy

Creedle

☐ WHEN THE WIND BLOWS
HED 057 / Oct '96 / Headhunter

Creep

☐ NO PAIN
SPCD 90262 / May '93 / Sub Pop

Creepmine

☐ CHIAROSCURO
M 7015CD / Oct '95 / Mascot

Crematory

☐ AWAKE
NB 269CDD
NB 269CD / 11 Aug '97 / Nuclear Blast

☐ ILLUSIONS
MASSCD 080 / Oct '95 / Massacre

☐ JUST DREAMING
MASSCD 031 / Jun '94 / Massacre

☐ TRANSMIGRATION
MASSCD 016 / Nov '93 / Massacre

Crenshaw, Marshall

☐ MIRACLE OF SCIENCE
GRACD 231 / Jun '97 / Grapevine

Creole Unit

☐ LATITUDES 30
KAR 993 / Apr '97 / IMP

Crepillon, Pierre

☐ DREUZ KRIEZ BREIZ (Crepillon, Pierre & L. Bigot)
KMCD 56 / Jul '95 / Keltia Musique

Crescent City

☐ ULTIMATE SESSION, THE
72902103242 / Feb '96 / High Street

Crescent City Maulers

☐ SCREAMIN'
CCM 001 / Oct '96 / Pollytone

Cresent

☐ NOW
PUNK 011CD / Dec '95 / Planet

Cressida

☐ ASYLUM
REP 4105 / Aug '91 / Repertoire

Crests

☐ BEST OF THE CRESTS, THE (Crests & Johnny Maestro)
Sixteen candles / Step by step / Trouble in Paradise / Angels listened in / Pretty little angel / Model girl / Six nights a week / I thank the moon / Journey of love / It must be love / Mr. Happiness / What a surprise / Gee (but I'd give the world) / Flower of love / Isn't it amazing / Year ago tonight / Young love / I'll remember in the still of the night
CDCHD 297 / May '90 / Ace

☐ BEST OF THE REST, THE
Learning 'bout love / Molly Mae / IOU / I do / Keep away from Carol / Paper crown / Way you look tonight / Earth angel / Let me be the one / Beside you / Always you / Test of love / Six nights a week / Let true love begin / My special angel / Step by step / Say it isn't so / Isn't it amazing / Out in the cold again / Besame baby / Strangelove / Rose and a baby Ruth / If my heart could write a letter / We've got to tell them / Silhouettes / Angels listened in / You took the joy out of Spring / Dream maker / Warning voice
CDCHD 322 / Apr '91 / Ace

Cretins

☐ I FEEL BETTER ALREADY
MLT 5 / Oct '97 / Melted

Crew Cuts

☐ BEST OF THE CREW CUTS, THE (The Mercury Years)
Crazy 'bout ya baby / Sh-boom / I spoke too soon / Oop shoop / Do me good baby / Ko ko mo (I love you so) / Earth angel / Chop chop boom / This is my story / Two hearts, two kisses (make one love) / Don't be angry / Mostly Martha / Story untold / Angels in the sky / Gum drop / Seven days / Honey hair, sugar lips, eyes of blue / Out of the picture / Tell me why / Young love / Be my only love / I like it like that
5527622 / Feb '97 / Spectrum

Crickets

☐ 25 GREATEST HITS
He's old enough to know better / Don't ever change / Someday (when I'm gone from you) / Parisian girl / Little Hollywood girl / Peggy Sue / Bo Diddley / Willie and the hand jive / Summertime blues / My little girl / Don't try to change me / April avenue / Right or wrong / Thoughtless / Everybody's got a little problem / I'm feeling better / Lonely avenue / A fool never learns / La bamba / I think I've caught the blues / Teardrops fall like rain / Playboy / All over you / Girl of my best friend / Now hear this
4954812 / 6 Jul '98 / EMI Gold

☐ COLLECTION, THE/CALIFORNIA SUN - SHE LOVES YOU
La Bamba / All over you / Everybody's got a little problem / I think I've caught the blues / We gotta get together / Playboy / Lonely avenue / My little girl / Teardrops fall like rain / Right or wrong / You can't be in between / Don't try to change me / Lost and alone / I'm not a bad guy / I want to hold your hand / California sun / She loves you / Fool never learns / Slippin' and slidin' / I saw her standing there / Lonely avenue / Please please me / Money / From me to you / You can't be in between / Come on
BGOCD 251 / Mar '95 / Beat Goes On

☐ ORIGINAL, THE
Please please me / Slippin' and slidin' / My little girl / Don't try to change me / Right or wrong / La bamba / I think I've called the blues / I saw her standing there / April avenue / All over you / I'm not a bad guy / I want to hold your hand / Teardrops fall like rain / Playboy / California boy / Money / Everybody's got a little problem / She loves you / Lost and alone
TO 862522 / 2 Feb '98 / Disky

☐ SOMETHING OLD SOMETHING NEW
Willie and the hand jive / Don't ever change / Summertime blues / Searchin' / Little Hollywood girl / Pretty blue eyes / What I'd say / Parisienne girl / Blue blue day / Love is strange / He's old enough to know better / Blue Monday / La bamba / Lonely adventure / Teardrops fall like rain / Thoughtless / My little girl / Playboy
BGOCD 242 / Sep '94 / Beat Goes On

☐ TOO MUCH MONDAY MORNING
As good as gone / Do you want to be loved: Crickets & *Nanci Griffith* / Picture this / Goin' out lovin' / Betty Sue's still breaking Jimmy Lee's heart / Letter of love / Say it isn't so / No kidding / (Get a little) closer / I gotta pass / Playing by the rules / Best in me / I had a dream / Too much Monday morning
3036000332 / Mar '97 / Carlton

Crime & The City Solution

☐ ADVERSARY - LIVE
CDSTUMM 110 / Sep '93 / Mute

☐ BRIDE SHIP, THE
Shadow of no man / Stone / Keepsake / Free world / Greater head / Dangling man / Bride ship / New world
CDSTUMM 65 / Apr '89 / Mute

☐ PARADISE DISCOTHEQUE
I have the gun / Sly persuaders / Dolphins and the sharks / Sun before the darkness / Motherless child / Last dictator I / Last dictator ii / Last dictator iii / Last dictator iv
CDSTUMM 78 / Aug '90 / Mute

☐ ROOM OF LIGHTS
Right man wrong man / No money no honey / Hey sinkiller / Six bells chime / Adventure / Untouchable / Brother song / Her room of lights / Rose blue / Coal train / Five stone walls / Wailing wall / Trouble come this morning / Dangling man
CDSTUMM 36 / '88 / Mute

☐ SHINE
All must be love / Fray so slow / Angel / On every train (grain will bear grain) / Hunter / Steal to the sea / Home is far from here / On every train (grain will bear grain)(12") / All must be love (early version)
CDSTUMM 59 / Apr '88 / Mute

Criminals

☐ NEVER BEEN CAUGHT
LOOKOUT 170CD / May '97 / Lookout

Crimpshine

☐ DUCT TAPE SOUP
LK 57CD / 2 Mar '98 / Lookout

☐ SOUND OF A NEW GENERATION, THE
LK 194CD / 6 Jul '98 / Lookout

Crimson Glory

☐ ASTRONOMICA
RS 0072892CD / Jul '98 / Rising Sun

☐ CRIMSON GLORY
Valhalla / Dragon lady / Heart of steel / Azrael / Mayday / Queen of the masquerade / Angels of war / Lost reflection
RR 349655 / Dec '88 / Roadrunner

☐ TRANSCENDENCE
Lady of winter / Red sharks / Painted skies / Masque of the red death / In dark places / Where dragons rule / Lonely / Burning bridges / Eternal world / Transcendence
RR 9508 2 / Nov '88 / Roadrunner

Crimson Midwinter

☐ RANDOM CHAOS
BMCD 131 / 27 Apr '98 / Black Mark

Crimson Relic

☐ PURGATORY'S REIGN
RAD 005CD / Apr '96 / Radiation

Crisis

☐ NOUS SOMMES TOUS LES JUIFS ET DES ALLEMANDS
Holocaust / PC 1984 / No town hall / White youth / UK 78 / Brukwood Hospital / Alienation / Laughing afraid / Red brigades / On TV / Back in the USSR / Frustration kanada kommando / Militant / Kill kill kill
CR 16CD / Mar '97 / Crisis

Crisis

☐ 8 CONVULSIONS
TOODAMNHY 72 / Jan '95 / Too Damn Hype

☐ BROKEN GLASS
SPV 08510032CD / 8 Jun '98 / Angular

☐ DEATHSHED
398414108CD / Mar '96 / Metal Blade

☐ HOLLOWING, THE
398414141CD / 13 Oct '97 / Metal Blade

Crisis Children

☐ I'D LIKE TO PAINT AN AEROPLANE
NEATCD 63 / Oct '92 / Neat

☐ ONE MORE TIME FOR THE STUPID PEOPLE
NEAT 1058CD / May '96 / Neat

Crisis NTI

☐ ALIEN CONSPIRACY, THE
SPV 08461262 / Jun '96 / SPV

Crisis Of Faith

☐ LAND OF THE FREE
LF 059CD / Aug '93 / Lost & Found

Crisp, Rufus

☐ CHICKENS ARE A-CROWING (Crisp, Rufus Experience)
In this ring two ladies fair / Betty Lickens / Green beds / Needle case / Omie Wise / Train on the island / June apple / Sherman's march / Fly around my pretty Miss / Sandy river belles / Cold rain and snow / Old grey mare / Chickens are a-crowing / Angeline the baker / I'm going to join the army / Sadie at the backdoor
FECD 113 / Feb '97 / Fellside

Crispell, Marilyn

☐ CASCADES (Crispell, Marilyn & Barry Guy/Gerry Hemingway)
CD 853 / Jan '96 / Music & Arts

☐ CIRCLES
VICTOCD 012 / Nov '94 / Victo

☐ CRISPELL & HEMINGWAY (Crispell, Marilyn & Hemingway)
KFWCD 117 / Oct '92 / Knitting Factory

☐ GAIA (Crispell, Marilyn/Reggie Workman/Doug James)
CDLR 152 / Feb '89 / Leo

☐ HIGHLIGHTS FROM THE 1992 AMERICAN TOUR (Crispell, Marilyn Trio)
CD 758 / Apr '93 / Music & Arts

☐ HYPERION (Crispell, Marilyn & Peter Brotzmann/Hamid Drake)
CD 852 / Dec '95 / Music & Arts

☐ INFERENCE (Crispell, Marilyn & Tim Berne)
CD 851 / Dec '95 / Music & Arts

☐ LABYRINTHS
VICTOCD 06 / Nov '94 / Victo

☐ LIVE IN BERLIN
1200692 / Nov '93 / Black Saint

☐ LIVE IN ZURICH (Crispell, Marilyn Trio)
CDLR 122 / '90 / Leo

☐ NOTHING EVER WAS ANYWAY (2CD Set) (Crispell, Marilyn & Gary Peacock/ Paul Motian)
Nothing ever was anyway / Butterflies that I feel inside of me / Open to love / Cartoon / Albert's love theme / Dreams (if time weren't) / Touching / Both / You've left me / Miracles / Ending / Blood
5372222 / Sep '97 / ECM

☐ SANTUERIO
CDLR 191 / Feb '94 / Leo

Criss, Sonny

☐ CRISS CRAFT
412320492 / 17 Mar '98 / Thirty Two

☐ OUT OF NOWHERE
All the things you are / Dreamer / El tiante / My ideal / Out of nowhere / Brother can you spare a dime / First one
MCD 5089 / Sep '92 / Muse

☐ SATURDAY MORNING
60170400072 / 14 Apr '98 / PREV

☐ THIS IS CRISS
Black coffee / Days of wine and roses / When sunny gets blue / Greasy / Sunrise, sunset / Steve's blues / Skylark / Love for sale
OJCCD 430 / Nov '95 / Original Jazz Classics

Critchinson, John

☐ EXCUSE ME DO I KNOW YOU (Ronnie Scott Remembered) (Critchinson, John Quartet)
This heart of mine / Let me count the ways / Turned into you / You don't know what love is / Excuse me do I know you / Carib blue / Little tear / Nippon soul / Back in love again / Weaver of dreams / Seven steps to heaven / Ssh Ronnie's talking
JHCD 056 / 31 Jul '98 / Ronnie Scott's Jazz House

☐ FIRST MOVES (Critchinson, John & Art Themen Quartet)
JHCD 052 / Feb '97 / Ronnie Scott's Jazz House

Critics

☐ BRAINTREE
BV 160952 / Nov '96 / Black Vinyl

Crivits

☐ DRIVE
LF 068 / Jan '94 / Lost & Found

☐ EYE TO EYE
LF 300CD / 23 Mar '98 / Lost & Found

☐ MORE THE TRUTH HURTS THE MORE I LEARN ABOUT MYSELF
IGN 009CD / 17 Aug '98 / Ignition

☐ STARE
LF 148CD / May '95 / Lost & Found

Cro Magnon

☐ BULL
LOW 008 / Jun '97 / Lowlands

Cro-Mags

☐ ALPHA OMEGA
CM 9730CD / Jun '92 / Century Media

☐ HARD TIMES IN AN AGE OF QUARREL
CM 770722 / Jun '94 / Century Media

☐ NEAR DEATH EXPERIENCE
CM 770502 / Sep '93 / Century Media

Croce, A.J.

☐ FIT TO SERVE
RUF 1023 / Feb '98 / Ruf

Croce, Jim

☐ 50TH ANNIVERSARY
Spin, spin, spin / Vespers / Big wheel / Searchin' / He don't love you / Chain gang / Chain gang medley / Hey tomorrow / Long time ago / Cigarettes, whiskey and wild, wild women / (And) I remember her / Cottom mouth river / More than that tomorrow / Migrant worker / Child of midnight / Stone walls / King's song / Mississipi lady / Which way are you goin' / Rapid Roy (the stcok car boy) / You don't mess around with Jim / Tomorrow's gonna be a brighter day / New York's not my home / Hard times losin' man / Photographs and memories / Walkin' back to Georgia / Operator (That's not the way it feels) / Time in a bottle / Box no.10
ESDCD 188 / Dec '92 / Essential

☐ BAD BOY LEROY BROWN (The Definitive Collection/2CD Set)
You don't mess around with Jim / Photographs amd memories / New York's not my home / Operator (that's not the way it feels) / Time in a bottle / Rapid Roy (the stock car boy) / Hey tomorrow / One less set of footsteps / Roller derby queen / Alabama rain / Bad, bad Leroy Brown / These dreams / Speedball tucker / It doesn't have to be that way / I got a name / Lover's cross / Working at the car wash blues / I'll have to say I love you in a song / Salon and saloon / Chain gang medley / Spin, spin, spin / Tomorrow's gonna be a bright new day / Hard time losin' man /

Walkin' back to Georgia / Box no.10 / Long time ago / Dreamin' again / Careful man / Good time man like me ain't got no business (singing the blu / Next time, this time / Five short minutes / Ages / Thursday / Top hat bar and grill / Recently / Hard way / Every time / Ol' man river / Which way are you goin' / Mississippi lady
SMDCD 102 / May '97 / Snapper

☐ **BEST OF JIM CROCE, THE**
I got a name / Bad, bad, Leroy Brown / Operator (that's not the way it feels) / You don't mess around with Jim / One less set of footsteps / Time in a bottle / Workin' at the car wash blues / Lover's cross / New York's not my home / I'll have to say I love you in a song / Chain gang medley / Rapid Roy (the stock car boy) / Photographs and memories / These dreams / Box no.10 / Age / Dreamin' again / Speedball tucker / It doesn't have to be that way
MCCD 295 / May '97 / Music Club

☐ **BOMBS OVER PUERTO RICO (Croce, Jim & Ingrid)**
Age / Spin, spin, spin / I am who I am / What do people do / Another day, another town / Vespers / Big wheel / Just another day / Next man that I marry / What the hell / Man that is me
BCD 15894 / May '96 / Bear Family

☐ **COLLECTION, THE**
Time in a bottle / Operator (that's not the way it feels) / Salon Saloon / Alabama rain / Dreamin' again / It doesn't have to be that way / I'll have to say I love you in a song / Lover's cross / Thursday / These dreams / Long time ago / Photographs and memories
CCSCD 154 / Jan '86 / Castle

☐ **DOWN THE HIGHWAY**
I got a name / Mississippi lady / New York's not my home / Chain gang medley / Chain gang / He don't love you / Searchin' / You don't mess around with Jim / Ol' man river / Which way are you going / Bad, Bad Leroy Brown / Walkin' back to Georgia / Box no.10 / Speedball Tucker / Alabama rain
CLACD 118 / '88 / Castle

☐ **FINAL TOUR, THE**
Operator (that's not the way it feels) / Roller derby queen dialogue / Roller derby queen / Next time,this time / Trucker dialogue / Speedball trucker / New York's not my home / Hard time losin' man / Ball of Kerrymuir dialogue / Ball of Kerrymuir / You don't mess around with Jim / It doesn't have to be that way / Careful man dialogue / Careful man / Shopping for clothes / These dreams
CLACD 341 / Jun '94 / Castle

☐ **PHOTOGRAPHS AND MEMORIES (His Greatest Hits)**
Bad, Bad Leroy Brown / Operator (that's not the way it feels) / Photographs and memories / Rapid Roy (the stock car boy) / Time in a bottle / New York's not my home / Workin' at the car wash blues / I got a name / I'll have to say I love you in a song / You don't mess around with Jim / Lover's cross / One less set of footsteps / These dreams / Roller Derby Queen
CLACD 119 / Jun '88 / Castle

☐ **SIMPLY THE BEST**
WMCD 5703 / Oct '94 / Disky

☐ **TIME IN A BOTTLE**
Time in a bottle / Operator (that's not the way it feels) / Salon and saloon / Alabama rain / Dreamin' again / It doesn't have to be that way / I'll have to say I love you in a song / Lover's cross / Thursday / These dreams / Long time ago / Photographs and memories
CLACD 117 / Nov '86 / Castle

☐ **VERY BEST OF JIM CROCE, THE**
Time in a bottle / Bad bad Leroy Brown / Operator (That's not the way it feels) / I'll have to say I love you in a song / One less set of footsteps / You don't mess around with Jim / Photographs and memories / Next time this time / I got a name / Doesn't have to be that way / Alabama rain / Which way are you goin' / Lovers cross / Dreamin' again / New York's not my home / Working at the carwash blues / Mississippi lady
SELCD 505 / Mar '98 / Castle Select

Crocker, Barry

☐ **EMOTIONS**
HADCD 192 / Nov '95 / Javelin

Crocker, John

☐ **ALL OF ME**
Smiles / Don't blame me / My gal Sal / I love you / All of me / Between the devil and the deep blue sea / Tangerine / Poor butterfly / She's funny that way / Exactly like you / Stealin' apples
CDTTD 585 / May '94 / Timeless Traditional

☐ **EASY LIVING (Crocker, John Quartet)**
Avalon / I can't get started (with you) / Oh lady be good / Shine / Fine time / I hadn't anyone till you / Have you met Miss Jones / Easy living / Rose room / After you've gone
CDTTD 561 / Aug '91 / Timeless Traditional

Crockett, Valerie

☐ **UNBUTTON YOUR HEART (Crockett, Valerie & Walter)**
Unbutton your heart / On the road to Cleveland / Starlight / Apron of care / My heartache, my heartache / As I fall in love with you / Southbound trucker / Tell me now / Don't make her afraid / Nobody / I never thought about it / Computer song / I said goodbye
DARINGCD 3030 / Feb '97 / Daring

Crocketts

☐ **WE MAY BE SKINNY AND WIREY**
BDG 1002412 / 7 Sep '98 / Blue Dog

Croft, Paul

☐ **BROTHER JUKE BOX**
Chet Atkins voice mail liner notes / Blue heartache / Brother jukebox / Through the bottom of the glass / Raised by the railroad line / Take another swing at me / My own sweet time / Jealous / Teardrops will kiss the morning dew / Hank Williams you wrote my life / Ancient history / Ashley Judd / More love than I know what to do with / We know better / Midnight flyer / Walkin' home in the rain / Fallin' out with the blues
SCR 49 / May '98 / Strictly Country

Croisette

☐ **BEST OF CROISETTE, THE (Landslide)**
Keep it on ice / Under hypnosis / Jokers are wild / Shipwrecked in a storm / Landslide / Nothing but blackmail / Wasted nights / You're a time waster / My hands are tied / Do you know the way to San Jose / Ten years ago / Backfired
HTCD 60 / 20 Apr '98 / Hot Productions

Croker, Brendan

☐ **REDNECK STATE OF THE ART**
WFRCD 004 / Oct '95 / World Famous

Cromwell, Rodney

☐ **LET THE PICTURE PAINT ITSELF**
Let the picture paint itself / Give my heart a rest / Stuff that works / Big heart / Loving you makes me strong / Best years of our lives / I don't fall in love so easy / That ol'door / Rose of Memphis / Once in a while
MCD 11042 / Aug '94 / MCA

Cronos

☐ **DANCIN' IN THE FIRE**
NEAT 1048 / May '96 / Neat

☐ **ROCK 'N' ROLL DISEASE**
Message of war / Rock 'n' roll disease / Midnight eye / Lost and found / Love is infectious / Sexploitation / Super power / Aphrodisiac / Sweet savage sex / Bared to the bone / Dirty tricks dept.
NEATCD 1051 / Jan '96 / Neat

☐ **VENOM**
NM 003CD / Oct '97 / Neat Metal

Cronshaw, Andrew

☐ **ANDREW CRONSHAW CD, THE**
Voice of silence / Wexford carol / Andro and his cutty gun / Galician processional / Harry Bloodgood's famous jig/American Boot dance / Blacksmith / Fingal's cave / Yowe came to our door / Ships in distress/St Kilda rowing song/Go to sea no more / Pandeirada de entrimo/Gentle dark eyed Mary / Empty places / Dark haired youth/Taladh ar slanair / Freumh as craobh taigh challadair / Wasps in the woodpile / Turning the tide / Seana Mheallan / Giullan nam bo / Ho ho nighean donn/First of May/ Prince of Wale's jig / Saratoga hornpipe / Old highland air
TSCD 447 / Sep '89 / Topic

☐ **LANGUAGE OF SNAKES, THE**
SPDCD 1050 / Sep '93 / Special Delivery

Crooked Jack

☐ **AUDIENCE WITH CROOKED JACK & BILLY MCGUIRE, AN (A Night In A Scottish Pub) (Crooked Jack & Billy McGuire)**
Bonnie lass o'Tyvie / Barnyards of Dalgety / It's good to see you / Alan McPherson of Mosspark / Auld fiddler / Massacre of Glencoe / Continental Ceili / Sook blaw / Crooked Jack / Mary Mack / Heart song / John McMillan meets the Cajuns / When I'm 64 / Don't call me early in the morning / Red rose cafe / I'm my own Grandpa / Royal Scots Polka / Fairy dance / Piper O'Dundee / A the wae fae Dysart / Love is teasing / Pheasant plucker / Rolling home / Atholl Highlanders / Mrs. McLeod's reel
CDLOC 1098 / Nov '96 / Lochshore

☐ **TOMORROW MUST WAIT**
Rambling rover / Hermless / Magie cockabendie / Jigs and reels / Belfast mill / Working man / Auchtertool / Loch tay boat song / New teacher / March, strathspey and reel / Come by the hills / In search of you
LCOM 5224CD / Jan '94 / Lismor

Crooklyn Dub Consortium

☐ **CERTIFIED DOPE VOL.1**
WSCD 003 / Nov '95 / Word Sound Recordings

☐ **CERTIFIED DOPE VOL.2**
WSCD 012 / Feb '97 / Word Sound Recordings

Crooks

☐ **LIVE IN NOVOSIBIRSK**
PAN 151CD / Mar '95 / Pan

Crooks, Richard

☐ **ALL OF MY HEART**
All of my heart / My song goes round the world / Ah' fuyez / Douce image / Mother o' mine / Thora / E Lucevan le stelle / Ah / Moon of my delight / Neapolitan love song (t'amo) / Il mio tesoro / Until una furtive lagrima / Little love / Little kiss (Un peu d'amour) / Preislied / Songs my mother taught me / Nirvana / O song divine
CDHD 167 / Oct '89 / Happy Days

☐ **FOR YOU ALONE**
Serenade / Little love, a little kiss / Because / Castles in the air / Holy city / For you alone / Angels guard thee / En ferment les yeux (le reve) (manon) / Love everlasting / Waltz song / Vienna, city of my dreams (sieczyinski) / Neapolitan love song / Lost chord (sullivan) / How lovely are thy dwellings / O,lola (cavalleria rusticana) / Nazareth / Beautiful dreamer / Songs my mother taught me / Green hills of ireland / Just to linger in your arms / Goodbye
CDMOIR 431 / Oct '95 / Memoir

☐ **RICHARD CROOKS SERENADE, A**
Overhead the moon is beaming / Ah, sweet mystery of life / Song of songs / When you're away / Rio Rita / Only a rose / Because / I bring a love song / Vienna, city of my dreams / Only my song / Gipsy moon / Macushla / Smilin' through / If I should send a rose to you / Holy city / Songs my mother taught me / Beautiful dreamer / Oh Susannah / Ah may the red rose live always / Jeanie with the light brown hair / Serenade / Be thou faitful unto death
CDAJA 5240 / Dec '97 / Living Era

Cropdusters

☐ **IF THE SOBER GO TO HEAVEN**
Yesterday's cakes / Just poppin' out to fight a war (original version) / Coyote / Hard times / Banjo hill / You were the pilot / Gold against the soul / Oliver reed (goes to salt creek) / Jammit o'reilly / Just poppin' out to fight a war / Can't slow down on the old hoedown / Alligator come across / Proverb / Mason's apron-lannigan's ball / John henry / Southern life
DOJOCD 202 / Nov '94 / Dojo

Cropper, Steve

☐ **WITH A LITTLE HELP FROM MY FRIENDS**
Crop dustin' / Land of 1000 dances / Ninety nine and a half (won't do) / Boogaloo down Broadway / Funky Broadway / With a little help from my friends / Oh pretty woman / I'd rather drink muddy water / Way I feel tonight / In the midnight hour / Rattlesnake
CDSXE 008 / Aug '92 / Stax

Crosby, Bing

☐ **50TH ANNIVERSARY CONCERT AT THE LONDON PALLADIUM**
Where the blue of the night meets the gold of the day / Pleasure of your company / Mary Lou / Where the morning glories grow / At my time of life / On a slow boat to China / By myself / Tenderly / 50 ways to leave your lover / Send in the clowns / Gone fishin': *Crosby, Bing & Ted Rogers* / Now you has jazz / Man that got away/Hallelujah / Great day / Just one of those things / I surrender, dear / Swinging on a star / Wrap your troubles in dreams / True love / Don't fence me in / Pennies from heaven / Blue Hawaii / Sweet Leilani / Too-ra-loo-ra-loo-ra that's an Irish lullaby / Just one more chance / Them there eyes / Moonlight becomes you / You are my sunshine / I'll be seeing you / White cliffs of Dover / When the lights go on again all over the world / Accentuate the positive / Please / Baby face / South of the border / Galway boy / Dinah / San Fernando valley / I found a million dollar baby / San Antonio rose / I'm an old cowhand / In a little Spanish town / Wait till the sun shines, Nellie: *Crosby, Bing & Kathryn* / Easy to remember / Blue skies / It's been a long, long time / Mississippi mud / Ol' man river / That's what life is all about / Where the blue of the night meets the gold of the day
CDMFP 6389 / Jun '97 / Music For Pleasure

☐ **ALL THE CLOUDS WILL ROLL AWAY (Crosby, Bing & Judy Garland/Andrews Sisters)**
Wait till the sun shines nellie / Liza / Old buttermilk sky / Gotta get me somebody to love / Connecticut / Huggin' and chalkin' / I've got you under my skin / Tearbucket jim / And so to bed / Over the rainbow / Love somebody / Rambling rose / For me and my gal / Who / Embraceable you / Confess / Donovans / Katrina / I don't care / Ma, he's making eyes at me / Maybe it's because / Sam's song quadling / Get happy / I cross my fingers / Mona lisa / Goodnight irene / All my love (extended) / Tzena, tzena, tzena / Friendly star / High on the list / Pretty baby
JSPCD 702 / May '93 / JSP

☐ **ANYTHING GOES**
PDSCD 532 / Aug '96 / Pulse

☐ **BEST OF BING CROSBY & THE ANDREWS SISTERS, THE (Crosby, Bing & The Andrews Sisters)**
HMNCD 029 / 16 Mar '98 / Half Moon

☐ **BING CROSBY & FRIENDS**
Gone fishin' / Couple of song and dance men / Swinging on a star / Pennies from heaven / Zing a little zong / You are my sunshine / Moonlight bay / In the cool, cool, cool of the evening / Where the blue of the night meets the gold of the day / Anything you can do / White Christmas / Road to Bali / Spaniard that blighted my life / Whiffenpoof song / Life is so peculiar / MacNamara's band / Too ra loo ra loo ra / Moon came up with a great idea / Mr. Gallagher and Mr. Shean / Connecticut
MCCD 089 / Nov '92 / Music Club

☐ **BING CROSBY 1926-1932**
Pretty lips / Muddy water / I'm coming Virginia / Mississippi mud/I left my sugar standing in the rain / Changes / Mary / Ol' man river / Make believe / From Monday on / Lovable / Louisiana / You took advantage of me / T'ain't so honey, t'ain't so / Susianna / Spell of the blues / Let's do it / My kinda love / So the bluebirds and the blackbirds got together / If I had a talking picture of you / Happy feet / Three little words / One more time / Dinah / St. Louis blues
CBC 1004 / Jan '92 / Timeless Historical

☐ **BING CROSBY AND FRIENDS**
GO 3808 / 1 Dec '97 / Golden Options

☐ **BING CROSBY CHRISTMAS SPECIAL**
YHP 1 / 10 Nov '97 / YHP/NMC

☐ **BING CROSBY COLLECTION, THE**
(There'll be bluebirds over) The white cliffs of Dover / Yankee doodle dandy / I don't want to walk without you baby / You'd be so nice to come home to / As time goes by / I'll be seeing you / Bless 'em all / I'll get by (as long as I have you) / Basin Street blues / You belong to my heart / Swingin' on a star / Temptation / Too marvellous for words / June in January / I'm an old cowhand (from the Rio Grande) / Pennies from heaven / Mr. Gallagher and Mr. Shean / You must have been a beautiful baby / Sunday, Monday or always / Sierra Sue / Deep in the heart of Texas / Long ago (and far away)
PAR 2067 / Sep '96 / Parade

☐ **BING SINGS BERLIN, RODGERS AND HART**
Soft lights and sweet music / On a roof in Manhattan / How deep is the ocean / I'm playing with fire / Soon / Down by the river / It's easy to remember / Alexander's ragtime band / Now it can be told / When I lost you / God bless America / Bombardier song / Angels of mercy / I'll capture your heart / Lazy / Happy holiday / Let's start the New Year right / Abraham / Be careful it's my heart / Easter Parade / Song of freedom / I've got plenty to be thankful for / White Christmas
CDHD 232 / Feb '97 / Happy Days

☐ **BING SWINGS WITH JOHN SCOTT TROTTER ORCHESTRA (Crosby, Bing & John Scott Trotter Orchestra)**
Painting the clouds with sunshine / Shanghai / Oh lady be good / Everywhere you go / So tired / Easter parade / Bali Ha'i / Lazybones
DAWE 48 / Nov '93 / Magic

☐ **BING'S BUDDIES (1951 Crosby And Guests)**
Bright eyes / Painting the clouds with sunshine / Sweet violets / Wang wang blues / Domino / I only have eyes for you / Buttermilk sky
DAWE 41 / Sep '93 / Magic

☐ **BLUE SKIES**
Waiting for the evening mail / I wish you love / Chances are / Where or when / What is there to say / Sunday / They didn't believe me / This can't be love / I can't get started (with you) / I guess I'll have to change my plan / Try a little tenderness / What is this thing called love / Mandy / My ideal / Don't take your love from me / Tender trap / Love is just around the corner / Crazy rhythm / I've grown accustomed to her face / Come rain or come shine / She's funny that way / We're in the money / Little man you've had a busy day / At sundown
TRTCD 151 / 26 Jan '98 / TrueTrax

☐ **CHRISTMAS WITH BING CROSBY**
MCCDX 002 / Nov '93 / Music Club

☐ **COLLECTION, THE**
Just one more chance / Blues my naughty sweetie gives to me / Sweet and lovely / When the midnight train leaves for alabama / Glow-worm / Where the blue of the night meets the gold of the day / Blacksmith blues / A cock-eyed optimist / Come what may / Dancing in the dark / Dark moon / Down yonder / Feet up (pat him on the po-po) / Thousand violins / I apologise / I found a million dollar baby (in a five and ten cent store / I surrender dear / I'm thru with love / Maybe it's because / Now that I need you / Now that you're gone / Pittsburgh, pennsylvania / Please mr. sun / Rudolph the red-nosed reindeer / White christmas
COL 009 / Jan '95 / Collection

☐ **COMPLETE UNITED ARTISTS SESSIONS (3CD Set)**
That's what life is all about / We've only just begun / Best things in life are free / Great day / Children / More I see you / Igot rhythm / No time at all / Little love and understanding / Good old times / Cabaret / Send in the clowns / Change partners / Looking at you / Yours sincerely / How are things in glocca morra / Woman in your arm / Bon vivant / When a child is born / That's what life is all about / Pleasure of your company / Good companions/And points beyond / Introduction to the way we were / Way we were / Cuando cliente el sol / Sing / You've got a friend / My cup runneth over / SOng for you / Top billing / Roxie / Pick yourself up / Mr Keyboard man / How lucky can you get / Spring spring spring / I've a shooting box in Scotland / In the cool cool cool of the evening / Couple of song and dance men / Top billing / Session sound bites / Paris holiday / Nothing in common / Come share the wine / I love to dance like they used to dance / Beautiful memories / Hello dolly / My heart stood still / My resistance is low / With a song in my heart / Breezin' along with the breeze / Razzle dazzle / Have a nice day / Heat wave / Something to remeber you by / I'll never fall in love again / What I did for love / De ja vu / Some sunny day / Thou swell / At my time of life / Only way to go
CDBING 1 / 15 Sep '97 / EMI Gold

☐ **EP COLLECTION, THE**
Road to Morocco / That's a plenty / Moments to remember / Suddenly there's a valley / Oh loneliness of evening / Sailing down the Chesapeake Bay / Sing soft, sing sweet, sing gentle / Me and the moon / Got the moon in my pocket / Young at heart / Mademoiselle de Paris / Morgen / Domenica / It had to be you / Something in common / Look at your heart / Possibility's there / Longest walk / Sweetheart waltz / Moon was yellow / Pale moon / Chicago style / Oh baby mine I get so lonely / La mer / Under Paris skies / White Christmas / Road to Morocco: *Crosby, Bing & Bob Hope*
SEECD 360 / Aug '97 / See For Miles

☐ **EVERYTHING I HAVE IS YOURS**
Blacksmith blues / Come what may / I dreamt I dwelt in Marble Hall / Glow worm / Feet up / Pittsburgh, Pennsylvania / Please Mr. Sun / Cockeyed optimist / When the red roses grow / Girl in the bonnet of blue / Everything I have is yours / Thousand violins / Dark moon / Now that I need you / Maybe it's because / When the midnight choo choo leaves for Alabam' / If I had my way / Blues my naughty sweetie gives to me / Down yonder / Lady of Spain / Zip a dee doo dah / PS I love you / If this isn't love / Ole buttermilk sky / Great day / I git the sun in the morning / It's a good day / You go to my head / Old lamp lighter
GRF 016 / '93 / Tring

☐ **EVERYTHING I HAVE IS YOURS**
Blacksmith blues / Come what may / Glow worm / Feet up / Pitsburgh pennsylvania / Please Mr. Sun / Cockeyed optimist / Everything I have is yours / Thousand violins / Dark moon (come out from the clouds above) / Now that I need you / Maybe it's because / Blues my naughty sweetie gives to me / Down yonder / Lady of spain / Zip a dee doo dah / Ps I love you / If this isn't love / Ole buttermilk sky / Great day / I got the sun in the morning / It's a good day / You go to my head / Old lamplighter
QED 111 / Nov '96 / Tring

☐ **FUN WITH BING & LOUIS (Crosby, Bing & Louis Armstrong)**
Theme and Introduction: *Armstrong, Louis & Bing Crosby* / Lazy river: *Armstrong, Louis & Bing Crosby* / Lazybones: *Armstrong, Louis & Bing Crosby* / Baby won't you please come home: *Armstrong, Louis & Bing Crosby* / Blueberry hill: *Armstrong, Louis & Bing Crosby* / Lazy bones: *Armstrong, Louis & Bing Crosby* / Blueberry Hill: *Armstrong, Louis & Bing Crosby* / Rockin' chair: *Armstrong, Louis & Bing Crosby* / Rockin' chair parody: *Armstrong, Louis & Bing Crosby* / La vie en rose: *Armstrong, Louis & Bing Crosby* / My honey's loving arms: *Armstrong, Louis & Bing Crosby* / You're just in love: *Armstrong, Louis & Bing Crosby* / On the sunny side of the street: *Armstrong, Louis & Bing Crosby* / Gone fishin': *Armstrong, Louis & Bing Crosby* / Song is born: *Armstrong, Louis & Bing Crosby* / Gone fishin': *Armstrong, Louis & Bing Crosby* / I get ideas: *Armstrong, Louis & Bing Crosby* / Memphis blues: *Armstrong, Louis & Bing Crosby* / Kiss to build a dream on: *Armstrong, Louis & Bing Crosby*
JASCD 336 / 8 Nov '97 / Jasmine

☐ **GOING HOLLYWOOD (2CD Set)**
Stein song / Out of nowhere / Ya got love / You're getting to be a habit with me / I don't stand a ghost of a chance with you / Please / Here lies love / Down the old ox road / 1-2 Button your shoe / House that Jack built for Jill / Where the turf meets the surf / After all / Incurably romantic / It came upon a midnight clear / You tell me your dream / Second time around / Mr. Booze / Style / Don't be a do-badder
JASCD 108/9 / 6 Apr '98 / Jasmine

☐ **GREAT MOMENTS WITH BING CROSBY (2CD Set)**
Theme from Where the blue of the night meets the cold of / Don't fence me in / Moonlight becomes you / Accentuate the positive: *Crosby, Bing & The Charioteers* / Philco advertisement: *Crosby, Bing & The Charioteers* / Moonlight bay: *Crosby, Bing & The Charioteers* / Hut song: *Crosby, Bing & Connie Boswell* / Sleigh ride in July: *Crosby, Bing & Connie Boswell* / It makes no difference now / Amor / Maybe you'll be there: *Crosby, Bing & Peggy Lee* / Sentimental journey: *Crosby, Bing & The Charioteers* / Where the blue of the night meets the gold of the day: *Crosby, Bing & The Charioteers* / Way you look tonight: *Crosby, Bing & Trudy Erwin* / Please / Lazy bones: *Crosby, Bing & Louis Armstrong* / It's always you / Ghost riders in the sky / Remember me / Connecticut: *Crosby, Bing & Judy Garland* / Home on the range: *Crosby, Bing & Judy Garland* / If I had my way: *Crosby, Bing & The Charioteers* / You don't have to know the language: *Crosby, Bing & The Rhythmaires* / I'm always chasing rainbows: *Crosby, Bing & Eddy Duchin* / Night train to Memphis: *Crosby, Bing & The Charioteers* / People will say we're in love: *Crosby, Bing & Trudy Erwin* / More and more / White Christmas: *Crosby, Bing & The Charioteers/Music Maids/Trudy Erwin* / Pistol packin' mama: *Crosby, Bing & The Charioteers* / Oh what a beautiful mornin': *Crosby, Bing & Trudy Erwin* / Deep in the heart of Texas: *Crosby, Bing & The Music Maids* / Poinciana / Thank your lucky stars: *Crosby, Bing & The Music Maids* / All my love (bolero): *Crosby, Bing & The Music Maids* / Manhattan: *Crosby, Bing & Connie Boswell* / Now is the hour / I've got a crush on you: *Crosby, Bing & Peggy Lee* / Easter parade: *Crosby, Bing & Jeannie Durelle* / War bonds message: *Crosby, Bing & Jeannie Durelle* / I used to love you but it's all over now: *Crosby, Bing & Jeannie Durelle* / You've got me where you want me: *Crosby, Bing & Eugenie Baird* / Medley from Missisippi / Some enchanted evening / Between 18th and 19th on Chestnut Street: *Crosby, Bing & Connie Boswell* / Loch Lomond: *Crosby, Bing & The Music Maids* / Put it there pal: *Crosby, Bing & Bob Hope* / Whistle while you work / As time goes by / Maybe it's because: *Crosby, Bing & Judy Garland* / It's only a paper moon / Kraft advertisement / Marie Elena / I'll be home for Christmas: *Crosby, Bing & The Charioteers/Music Maid* / Mona Lisa: *Crosby, Bing & The Charioteers/Music Maid* / Goodnight Irene: *Crosby, Bing & Bob Hope/Judy Garland*
OTA 101978 / Jun '97 / On The Air

☐ **GREAT YEARS, THE**
Deep in the heart of Texas / White Christmas / Wait till the sun shines Nellie / Moonlight becomes you / Road to Morocco / You are my sunshine / Walking the floor over you / Yes indeed / Mr. Meadowlark / Where the blue of the night meets the gold of the day / Let's all meet at my house / Do you ever think of me / Between a kiss and a sigh / When day is done / Be honest with me / Sing me a song of the Islands / Tea for two / Tumbling tumbleweeds / Miss you / Along the Santa Fe trail / Start the day right / I want my Mama
PASTCD 7027 / Nov '93 / Flapper

☐ **HAVIN' MORE FUN (Crosby, Bing & Louis Armstrong)**
JUCD 2035 / Aug '97 / Jazz Unlimited

☐ **HERE LIES LOVE (A Selection of Love Songs)**
Very thought of you / Love thy neighbour / June in January / You've got me crying again / May I / With every breath I take / Temptation / Let me call you sweetheart / Sweet and lovely / Love in bloom / You're getting to be a habit with me / I love you truly / Someday, sweetheart / You're beautiful tonight my dear / Love is just around the corner / Just a wearyin' for you / It must be true / Here lies love
CDAJA 5043 / Sep '90 / Living Era

☐ **HEY, LOOK US OVER (Crosby, Bing & Rosemary Clooney)**
Introduction / Isn't it a lovely day / Anything you can do / They say it's wonderful / Ain't we got fun / Let's take a walk around the block / Summertime / Let's call the whole thing off / People will say we're in love / Lover / Hey look me over / Let's put out the lights / They can't take that away from me / Everytime I see you I'm in love again / Paris medley
JASCD 318 / Nov '93 / Jasmine

☐ **HOLLYWOOD GUYS AND DOLLS VOL.1**
PARCD 005 / Dec '94 / Parrot

☐ **HOLLYWOOD GUYS AND DOLLS VOL.2**
PARCD 006 / Dec '94 / Parrot

☐ **I'M AN OLD COWHAND**
Don't fence me in: *Crosby, Bing & Andrews Sisters/Vic Schoen Orchestra* / Home on the range: *Crosby, Bing & Lennie Hayton Orchestra* / I'm an old cowhand (from the Rio Grande): *Crosby, Bing & Jimmy Dorsey Orchestra* / Take me back to my boots and saddle: *Crosby, Bing & Victor Young Orchestra* / Silver on the sage: *Crosby, Bing & John Scott Trotter Orchestra* / When the bloom is on the sage: *Crosby, Bing & Foursome/John Scott Trotter Five* / Tumbling tumbleweeds: *Crosby, Bing & John Scott Trotter Orchestra* / After sundown: *Crosby, Bing & Lennie Hayton Orchestra* / El rancho grande: *Crosby, Bing & Foursome/John Scott Trotter Orchestra* / Singing hills: *Crosby, Bing & John Scott Trotter Orchestra* / Along the Sante Fe trail: *Crosby, Bing & John Scott Trotter Orchestra* / Clementine: *Crosby, Bing & Music Maids/Hal Hoppe/John Scott Trotter* / San Antonio rose: *Crosby, Bing & Bob Crosby Orchestra* / Deep in the heart of Texas: *Crosby, Bing & Woody Herman/Woodchoppers* / Who calls: *Crosby, Bing & John Scott Trotter Orchestra* / Pistol packin' Mama: *Crosby, Bing & Andrews Sisters/Vic Schoen Orchestra* / Ridin' down the canyon: *Crosby, Bing & Victor Young Orchestra* / San Fernando valley: *Crosby, Bing & John Scott Trotter Orchestra* / Empty saddles (In the old corral): *Crosby, Bing & Victor Young Orchestra* / Round up lullaby: *Crosby, Bing & Victor Young Orchestra* / Old oaken bucket: *Crosby, Bing & Music Maids/Hal Hoppe/John Scott Trotter* / We'll rest at the end of the trail: *Crosby, Bing & Victor Young Orchestra* / Twilight on the trail: *Crosby, Bing & Victor Young Orchestra* / Goodbye little darlin' goodbye: *Crosby, Bing & John Scott Trotter Eight* / Last round-up: *Crosby, Bing & Lennie Hayton Orchestra*
CDAJA 5160 / Apr '96 / Living Era

☐ **IMMORTAL BING CROSBY**
AVC 535 / May '94 / Avid

☐ **JAZZIN' BING CROSBY 1927-1940, THE (2CD Set)**
I'm coming Virginia / Side by side / Mississippi mud / I left my sugar standing in the rain (and she melted away) / Mary / There ain't no sweet man that's worth the salt of my tears / From Monday on / High water / Louisiana / T'ain't so honey, t'ain't so / Because my baby don't mean maybe now / Rhythm king / I'm crazy over you / Susianna / If I had you / Spell of the blues / Let's do it / My kinda love / So the bluebirds and the blackbirds got together / Oh Miss Hannah / Waiting at the end of the road / After you've gone / One more time / I'm sorry dear / Dinah / St. Louis blues / Shine / Shadows on the window / Cabin in the cotton e / How deep is the ocean / Sweet Sue, just you / My honey's lovin' arms / Somebody stole Gabriel's horn / Stay on the right side of the road / Blue prelude / I'm hummin', I'm whistlin', I'm singin' / Someday sweetheart / Moonburn / Pennies from heaven / Don't be that way / Mr. Gallagher and Mr. Shean / You must have been a beautiful baby / Yodelin' jive / Rhythm on the river / Yes indeed
CDAFS 10212 / Jun '93 / Affinity

☐ **KING BING**
You're getting to be a habit with me / Dinah / Temptation / With every breath I take / May I / Sweet Georgia Brown / June in January / Sunday Monday or always / I love you / New San Antonio rose / Mr.Gallagher and Mr.Shean / I'm an old cow hand (from the Rio Grande) / Deep in the heart of Texas / Sierra Sue / You must have been a beautiful baby / Swinging on a star / Trade winds / Moonlight becomes you / Too marvellous for words / Pennies from heaven
300222 / Feb '98 / Hallmark

☐ **KING OF THE CROONERS**
Dinah / Temptation / Please / I've got the world on a string / Pennies from heaven / How deep is the ocean / Blue Hawaii / Thanks / Did you ever see a dream walking / I'm an old cowhand / St. Louis blues / Where the blue of the night / Wrap your troubles in dreams / Some of these days / I don't stand a ghost of a chance with you / Someday sweetheart
HADCD 219 / Jun '97 / Spotlight On

☐ **L'ART VOCAL 1928-1945**
700202 / Jul '97 / L'Art Vocal

☐ **LIVE DUETS 1947-1949**
Then I'll be happy: *Crosby, Bing & Ethel Merman* / Your all time flop parade: *Crosby, Bing & Ethel Merman* / Chidabee chidabee chidabee: *Crosby, Bing & Jimmy Durante* / Clementine: *Crosby, Bing & Dinah Shore/Burl Ives* / You was: *Crosby, Bing & Kay Starr* / Little bird told me: *Crosby, Bing & Hattie McDaniel/Ernie Whiteman* / Just a gigolo: *Crosby, Bing & Bob Burns* / When it's night time in little Italy: *Crosby, Bing & Groucho Marx* / April showers / Ma blushin' Rosie: *Crosby & Jolson* / Swanee: *Crosby & Jolson* / One I love (belongs to somebody else): *Crosby, Bing & Al Jolson* / So in love: *Crosby, Bing & Peggy Lee* / Blue shadows: *Crosby, Bing & The Four Crosby Brothers* / If you stubb your toe on the moon: *Crosby, Bing & Jud Conlon's Rhythmaires* / Once and for all: *Crosby, Bing & Peggy Lee* / For your all time flop parade: *Crosby, Bing & Ethel Merman* / There's a flaw in my flue: *Crosby, Bing & Ethel Merman* / Your all time flop parade: *Crosby, Bing & Ethel Merman* / Lazybones: *Crosby, Bing & Louis Armstrong*
VN 1003 / Nov '96 / Viper's Nest

☐ **MEMORIES**
MCLD 19360 / 26 Sep '97 / MCA

☐ **OLD LAMPLIGHTER, THE**
CDSGP 0127 / Dec '94 / Prestige

☐ **ON THE ROAD (Crosby, Bing & Bob Hope/Dorothy Lamour)**
VJB 19492 / Jun '98 / Vintage Jazz Band

☐ **ON THE SENTIMENTAL SIDE (20 Classic Tracks Of The 30's)**
Black moonlight / How deep is the ocean / Stardust / Dancing in the dark / I'm through with love / Sweet is the word for you / Between a kiss and a sigh / Funny old hills / I found a million dollar baby / I have eyes / If you should ever need me / I'm building a sailboat of dreams / Joobalai / My heart is taking lessons / On the sentimental side / Our big love scene / Sing a song of sunbeams / That sly old gentleman / Thine alone / You're a sweet little headache
CDAJA 5072 / Aug '90 / Living Era

☐ **ON THE SENTIMENTAL SIDE, THE**
My heart is taking lessons / Funny old hills / Joobalai / East side of heaven / Hang your heart on a hickory limb / On the sentimental side / This is my night to dream / I have eyes / You're a sweet little headache / That sly old gentleman / Apple for the teacher / Man and his dream / Still the bluebird sings / April played the fiddle / I haven't time to be a millionaire / In my merry oldsmobile / Medley of Gus Edwards / Go fly a kite / Meet the sun halfway / Moon and the willow tree
MUCD 9030 / Apr '95 / Musketeer

☐ **ONLY FOREVER**
Only forever / Rhythm on the river / That's for me / When the moon comes over Madison Square / You're dangerous / Birds of a feather / Apple for the teacher / Still the bluebird sings / Go fly a kite / If I had my way / Too romantic / Sweet potato piper / April played the fiddle / I haven't time to be a millionaire / Meet the sun halfway / Man and his dream / I have eyes / You're a sweet little headache / It's always you / Birth of the blues / My melancholy baby / Waiter and the porter and the upstairs maid
RAJCD 802 / Dec '97 / Empress

☐ **PORTRAIT OF BING CROSBY, A**
GALE 403 / May '97 / Gallerie

☐ **SOME FINE OLD CHESTNUTS/NEW TRICKS**
Do you ever think of me / I never knew / I can't give you anything but love / In a little Spanish town / Ol' man river / Honeysuckle rose / Swanee / When I take my Sugar to tea / On the Alamo / I'm confessin' / Between the devil and the deep blue sea / Georgia on my mind / Chicago / You're driving me crazy / Avalon / Chinatown my Chinatown / If I could be with you / Softly as in a morning sunrise / Alabamy bound / More than you knew / Sleepy time gal / Dinah / After you've gone / Somebody loves me / More than you know / Rain / Church bells / Day by day / Prove it by the things you do
MCLD 19377 / 22 Jun '98 / MCA

☐ **SPOTLIGHT ON BING CROSBY & ROSEMARY CLOONEY (Crosby, Bing & Rosemary Clooney)**
White Christmas: *Crosby, Bing* / Have yourself a merry little Christmas: *Clooney, Rosemary* / Silent night: *Crosby, Bing* / It came upon a midnight clear: *Clooney, Rosemary* / Away in a manger: *Crosby, Bing* / Christmas song: *Clooney, Rosemary* / O'litte town of Bethlehem: *Crosby, Bing* / Little drummer boy: *Clooney, Rosemary* / Rudolph the red nosed reindeer: *Crosby, Bing* / Jingle bells: *Clooney, Rosemary* / O come all ye faithful (Adeste fidelis): *Crosby, Bing*
HADCD 110 / Feb '94 / Javelin

☐ **SWINGIN' ON A STAR (2CD Set)**
(There'll be bluebirds over) The white cliffs of Dover / Yankee doodle dandy / I don't want to talk without you baby / You'd be so nice to come home to / It's all over now / As time goes by / I'll be seeing you / Shoo shoo baby / Long ago (and far away) / Bless'em all / I'll get by (as long as I have you) / Is you is or is you ain't my baby / Saturday night / Wait for me Mary / It's always you / Basin Street Blues / You belong to my heart / Too ra loo ra loo ra (that's an Irish lullaby) / Swingin' on a star / Trade winds / New San Antonio Rose / Dinah / I love you / Sweet Georgia Brown / You're getting to be a habit with me / Temptation / Too marvellous for words / May I / June in January / With every breath I take / I'm an old cowhand (from the Rio Grande) / Pennies from heaven / Mr. Gallagher and Mr. Shean / You must have been a beautiful baby / Sunday, Monday or always / Sierra Sue / Deep in the heart of Texas / I'll be home for Christmas / White Christmas
MUCD 9515 / May '96 / Musketeer

☐ **SWINGING ON A STAR**
PASTCD 7065 / Jun '95 / Flapper

☐ **THAT'S JAZZ**
St. Louis blues / Please / Temptation / Did you ever see a dream walking / I don't stand a ghost of a chance with you / Down the old ox road / Black moonlight / Where the blue of the night meets the gold of the day / Last round-up / Someday sweetheart / How deep is the ocean / Our big love scene / Song of the Islands / Dinah / I'm an old cowhand (from the Rio Grande) / Wrap your troubles in dreams (and dream your troubles away) / Blue Hawaii / Sailor beware / Sweet Leilani / Pennies from heaven / Happy go lucky you and broken hearted me / Thanks
PASTCD 9739 / Mar '91 / Flapper

☐ **THOSE GREAT WORLD WAR II SONGS**
(there'll be bluebirds over) the white cliffs of dover / Army air corps song / Yankee doodle dandy / I don't want to walk without you baby / Song of freedom / You'd be so nice to come home to / What do you do in the infantry / Riding herd on a cloud tonight / Get on the road to victory / Sunday, monday or always / Victory polka / It's all over now / As time goes by / I'll be seeing you / Shoo shoo baby / (there'll be a) hot time in the town of berlin / Song of the bombadiers / Long ago and far away / Bless 'em all / I'll get by / Is you is or is you ain't my baby / Saturday night (is the loneliest night of the week) / Fifth marines-the amphibians battle march / Comin' in on a wing and a prayer / Comin' in on a wing and a prayer / Wait for me, mary / Brother bill / Stardust / It's always you / Basin street blues / Introduction / Swinging on a star / You belong to my heart / Too-ra-loo-ra-loo-ral (that's an irish lullaby) / Ida
DBG 53042 / Apr '95 / Double Gold

☐ **TOO MARVELLOUS FOR WORDS (25 Chart Toppers)**
CDGR 105 / Jan '96 / Charly

☐ **TOP O' THE MORNING**
MCD 11406 / 16 Feb '98 / MCA

☐ **TWO ON ONE: BING CROSBY & FRANK SINATRA (Crosby, Bing & Frank Sinatra)**
All or nothing at all / Night and day / I'll never smile again / Imagination / Let's get away from it all / Daybreak / There are such things / Everything happens to me / This love of mine / It's always you / Moonlight becomes you / Deep in the heart of texas / San antonio rose / Road to morocco / Only forever / Where the blue of the night meets the gold of the day / Temptation / Pennies from heaven / Sweet leilani / You are my sunshine
CDTT 6 / Apr '94 / Charly

☐ **VERY BEST OF BING CROSBY, THE (2CD Set)**
Swinging on a star / Alexander's ragtime band / Moonlight becomes you / Gone fishin' / Busy doing nothing / So would I / Friend of yours / Gigi / I've never been in love before / Among my souvenirs / Weaver of dreams / Where the blue of the night meets the gold of the day / I whistle a happy tune / Wrap your troubles in dreams / Dear hearts and gentle people / Very though of you / Sweet leilani / Give me the simple life / San Antonio rose / Spaniard that blighted my life / People will say we're in love / Folks that live on the hill / Sentimental music / Moonlight on a white picket fence / Blue skies / Anything you can do / Embraceable you / Fella with an umbrella / McNamara's band / Now is the hour / Getting to know you / Galway bay / Don't fence me in / Just one of those things / Sam's song / Like someone in love / Stardust / In the cool cool cool of evening / Too ra loo ra loo ra / Oh, what a beautiful morning / Pennies from heaven / Play a simple melody / Things we did last summer / Just for you / I can't begin to tell you / Marrying for love / Nightingale sang in Berkeley Square / Silent night, holy night / Deck the halls/away in a manger/I saw three ships / White Christmas
MCD 11561 / 16 Feb '98 / MCA

☐ **VISIT TO THE MOVIES, A**
Thoroughly modern millie / Talk to the animals / Ding dong the witch is dead / Where the rainbow ends / What's more american / Up, up and away / High hopes / My friend the doctor says / Puff the magic dragon / Chim chim cheree / Love is blue
15411 / Jan '93 / Laserlight

☐ **YOU AND THE NIGHT AND THE MUSIC**
I love you truly / Sweetheart waltz / Touch of your lips / Lovely lady / Two for tonight / Would you / For love alone / Way you look tonight / Too marvellous for words / Sweet is the word for you / All you want to do is dance / Dancing under the stars / Lets waltz for old times sake / This is my night to dream / Let me whisper I love you / Sweethearts / I'm falling in love with someone / Yours is my heart alone / You are the one / Don't break the spell / Anniversary waltz / Dearly beloved / Let me call you sweetheart / Strange music / Does your heart beat for me
AMSC 633 / 22 Jun '98 / Avid

Crosby, Bob

☐ **22 ORIGINAL BIG BAND RECORDINGS**
That's plenty: *Crosby, Bob & His Orchestra* / Lazy mood: *Crosby, Bob & His Orchestra* / March of the mustangs: *Crosby, Bob & His Orchestra* / March of the bob cats: *Crosby, Bob & His Orchestra* / Ghost of a chance: *Crosby, Bob & His Orchestra* / Washington and lee swing: *Crosby, Bob & His Orchestra* / San antonio shout: *Crosby, Bob & His Orchestra* / Jazz me blues: *Crosby, Bob & His Orchestra* / What's new: *Crosby, Bob & His Orchestra* / Big noise from winnetka: *Crosby, Bob & His Orchestra* / Stomp, mr. henry lee: *Crosby, Bob & His Orchestra* / High society: *Crosby, Bob & His Orchestra* / Dixieland shuffle: *Crosby, Bob & His Orchestra* / Sugar foot stomp: *Crosby, Bob & His Orchestra* / Mississippi mud: *Crosby, Bob & His Orchestra* / In a sentimental mood: *Crosby, Bob & His Orchestra* / Solitude: *Crosby, Bob & His Orchestra* / Alabamy bound: *Crosby, Bob & His Orchestra* / On the alamo: *Crosby, Bob & His Orchestra* / Our monday date: *Crosby, Bob & His Orchestra* / Rose of the rio grande: *Crosby, Bob & His Orchestra* / Grandpa: *Crosby, Bob & His Orchestra* / Spells: *Crosby, Bob & His Orchestra*
HCD 409 / Sep '92 / Hindsight

☐ **BIG APPLE 1936-1940, THE (Crosby, Bob & His Orchestra)**
RACD 7111 / May '96 / Aerospace

☐ **BIG NOISE STATUS, THE**
DHDL 126 / Dec '94 / Halcyon

☐ **BOB CROSBY & HIS DIXIELAND BOBCATS 1939-1942 (Crosby, Bob & His Bobcats)**
JH 1043 / Jun '95 / Jazz Hour

☐ BOB CROSBY & HIS ORCHESTRA (Crosby, Bob & His Orchestra)
It had to be you (vocal bob crosby) / Lover / Ostrich walk / My baby just cares for me (vocal bob crosby) / Over the waves / Love is just around the corner (vocal june christy) / Song of the islands / Exactly like you (vocal bob crosby) / Skaters waltz, the (les patineurs) (waldteufel) / Willow weep for me / Aunt haggar's blues / Let's fall in love (vocal polly bergen) / She's funny that way (vocal bob crosby) / Tales from hoffman / Wolverine blues / Fidgety feet
HCD 245 / Sep '94 / Hindsight

☐ BOB CROSBY ORCHESTRA VOL.11 (Crosby, Bob Orchestra)
HDL 131 / Mar '97 / Halcyon

☐ COMPLETE DISCOGRAPHY VOL.12 (So Far So Good)
DHDL 132 / Oct '97 / Halcyon

☐ DIXIELAND FAVOURITES
Big noise from Winnetka / Washington and Lee swing / I don't stand a ghost of a chance with you / Sugarfoot stomp / Stomp, Mr. Henry Lee / March of the Mustangs / High society / Mississippi mud / What's new / On the Alamo / San Antonio shout / March of the Bob Cats
HCD 332 / Mar '96 / Hindsight

☐ EYE OPENER
Savoy blues / Royal garden blues / Gin mill blues / Little Rock getaway / Who's sorry now / Coquette / Fidgety feet / South Rampart Street Parade / Dogtown blues / Panama / Wolverine blues / Yancey special / Big foot jump / I hear you talking / Call me a taxi / Big noise from Winnetka / I'm free (what's new) / Diga diga doo / Eye opener / Mournin' blues / Till we meet again / Jazz me blues / Vultee special / Tin roof blues
TPZ 1054 / Sep '96 / Topaz Jazz

☐ FROM ANOTHER WORLD VOL.13
DHDL 133 / Mar '98 / Halcyon

☐ GONE BUT NOT FORGOTTEN VOL.14 (Crosby, Bob & His Orchestra)
Don't call me boy / Gone but not forgotten / Do you know why / Isn't that just like love / Take me back again / I'll come back to you / You're bound to look like a monkey / Tea for two / Yes indeed / Christmas greetings (jingle bells) / San Antonio rose / It makes no difference now / Mark hop / Burnin' the candle at both ends / Dolores / Pale moon / Big noise in Winnetka / Something I dreamed / No doubt / Chick ee chick / Blue echoes / Until you fall in love / Much more lovely
DHDL 135 / Jul '98 / Halcyon

☐ HIGH SOCIETY VOL.10
DHDL 130 / Oct '96 / Magic

☐ HOW CAN YOU FORGET (Crosby, Bob & His Orchestra)
DHDL 125 / Nov '93 / Halcyon

☐ JAZZ ME BLUES (Crosby, Bob & The Bobcats)
South Rampart Street Parade / Washington and Lee swing / Gin mill blues / Yancey special / Love nest / I'm praying humble / All by myself / I hear you talking / Jazz me blues / Squeeze me / Till we meet again / Call me a taxi / Mournin' blues / Who's sorry now / Tin roof blues / Spain
305152 / Jul '97 / Hallmark

☐ MARCH OF THE BOBCATS (Crosby, Bob & The Bop Cats)
JHR 73534 / May '93 / Jazz Hour

☐ MARCH OF THE BOBCATS (Crosby, Bob & The Bobcats)
Dixieland shuffle / Muskrat ramble / Can't we be friends / Squeeze me / Coquette / Fidgety feet / Stumbling / You're driving me crazy / Who's sorry now / South Rampart Street Parade / Big Foot jump / March of the Bobcats / Slow mood / Big crash from China / Big noise from Winnetka / What's new
CWNCD 2037 / Jun '97 / Crown

☐ REMINISCING TIME
DHDL 131 / Apr '97 / Halcyon

☐ STOMP OFF, LET'S GO
Big noise from Winnetka / Call me a taxi / Diga diga doo / Dixieland shuffle / Dogtown blues / Gin mill blues / Gypsy love song: *Crosby, Bob & Connie Boswell* / Grand terrace rhythm / I'm free / March of the bob cats / Milk cow blues / Muskrat ramble / Ooh looka there, ain't she pretty / Panama / Savoy blues / Smoky Mary / South Rampart Street Parade / Spain / Stomp off, let's go / Stumbling / Swing Mister Charlie: *Crosby, Bob & Judy Garland* / Till we meet again / Wolverine blues / Yancey special
CDAJA 5097 / Nov '92 / Living Era

☐ STRANGE ENCHANTMENT (Vol. 8/ 1938-39) (Crosby, Bob & His Orchestra)
My inspiration / Your lovely, Madame / Deep in a dream / Summertime / Loopin' the loop / Skater's waltz / Stomp off and let's go / Smoky Mary / South Rampart Street Parade / Song of the wanderer / Cherry / Eye opener / Begin the beguine / Hindustan / Long time no see / Mournin' blues / Don't worry 'bout me / I never knew heaven could speak / If I were sure of you / Strange enchantment
DHDL 127 / May '95 / Halcyon

☐ STRANGE NEW RHYTHM IN MY HEART VOL.4 (Crosby, Bob Orchestra)
DHDL 122 / Nov '93 / Halcyon

☐ SUGARFOOT STOMP 1936-1942 (Crosby, Bob & His Orchestra)
RACD 7121 / May '96 / Aerospace

☐ THEM THERE EYES
DHDL 128 / Jul '96 / Halcyon

☐ YOU CAN CALL IT SWING (Crosby, Bob & His Orchestra)
DHDL 121 / Sep '93 / Halcyon

☐ YOU'RE DRIVING ME CRAZY (Crosby, Bob & His Orchestra)
DHDL 123 / Mar '93 / Halcyon

Crosby, David

☐ IF I COULD ONLY REMEMBER MY NAME
Music is love / Cowboy movie / Tamalpais high at about 3 / Laughing / What are their names / Traction in the rain / Song with no words / Tree with no leaves / Orleans / I'd swear there was somebody here
7567814152 / May '95 / Rhino

☐ KING BISCUIT PRESENTS...
Tracks in the dust / Guinnevere / Compass / In my dreams / Drive my car / Lady of the harbour / Oh yes I can / Monkey and the underdog / Deja vu / Night time for the Generals / Wooden ships / Almost cut my hair / Long time gone
KBFHCD 009 / 13 Jul '98 / King Biscuit

☐ THOUSAND ROADS
Hero / Too young to die / Old soldier / Through your hands / Yvette in english / Thousand roads / Columbus / Helpless heart / Coverage / Natalie
7567824842 / May '93 / Atlantic

☐ WIND ON THE WATER (Crosby, David & Graham Nash)
Carry me / Mamma Lion / Bittersweet / Take the money and run / Naked in the rain / Love work out / Low down payment / Cowboy of dreams / Homeward through the haze / Fieldworker / To the last whale / Wind on the water
REMCD 523 / 27 Apr '98 / Reactive

Crosby, Stills & Nash

☐ 4 WAY STREET (2CD Set) (Crosby, Stills, Nash & Young)
On the way home / Cowgirl in the sand / Southern man / Teach your children / Don't let it bring you down / Ohio / Triad / Forty nine bye byes / Carry on / Lee shore / Love the one you're with / Find the cost of freedom / Chicago / Pre-road downs / Right between the eyes / Long time gone / Suite: Judy blue eyes / King Midas in reverse / Black Queen / Loner/ Cinnamon girl/Down by the river
7567824082 / May '95 / Atlantic

☐ AFTER THE STORM
In my life / Camera / Find a dream / Panama / After the storm / Bad boyz / Street to lean on / These empty days / It won't go away / Till it shines / Unequal love / Only waiting for you
7567826542 / May '95 / Atlantic

☐ AMERICAN DREAM (Crosby, Stills, Nash & Young)
American dream / Got it made / Name of love / Don't say goodbye / This ole house / Nighttime for the generals / Shadowland / Drivin' thunder / Clear blue skies / That girl / Compass / Soldiers of peace / Feel your love / Night song
7818862 / Nov '88 / Atlantic

☐ CARRY ON
Woodstock / Marrakesh express / You don't have to cry / Teach your children / Love the one you're with / Almost cut my hair / Wooden ships / Dark star / Helpless / Chicago/We can change the world / Cathedral / Four plus twenty / Our house / AMass/ BWind on the water / Change partners / Just a song before I go / Ohio / Wasted on the way / Southern cross / Suite: Judy blue eyes / Carry on/questions / Horses through a rainstorm / Johnny's garden / Guinevere / Helplessly hoping / Lee shore / Taken at all / Shadow captain / As I come of age / Drive my car / Dear Mr. Fantasy / In my dreams / Yours and mine / Haven't we lost enough / After the dolphin / Find the cost of freedom
7567804872 / Dec '91 / Atlantic

☐ CROSBY, STILLS AND NASH
Suite: Judy blue eyes / Marrakesh express / Guinevere / You don't have to cry / Pre-road downs / Wooden ships / Lady of the island / Helplessly hoping / Long time gone / Forty nine bye byes
7567826512 / Aug '94 / Atlantic

☐ CSN
Shadow captain / See the changes / Carried away / Fair game / Anything at all / Cathedral / Dark star / Just a song before I go / Run from tears / Cold rain / In my dreams / I give you give blind
7567826502 / Jan '95 / Atlantic

☐ DAYLIGHT AGAIN
Turn your back on love / Wasted on the way / Southern cross / Into the darkness / Delta / Since I met you / Too much love to hide / Song for Susan / You are alive / Might as well have a good time / Daylight again
7567826722 / Oct '94 / Atlantic

☐ DEJA VU (Crosby, Stills, Nash & Young)
Carry on / Teach your children / Almost cut my hair / Helpless / Woodstock / Deja vu / Our house / Four plus twenty / Country girl / Everybody I love you
7567826492 / Aug '94 / Atlantic

☐ LIVE IT UP
Live it up / If anybody had a heart / Tomboy / Haven't we lost enough / Yours and mine / (Got to keep) open / Straight line / House of broken dreams / Arrows / After the dolphin
7567821072 / Jun '90 / Atlantic

☐ REPLAY
Carry on / Marrakesh express / Just a song before I go / First things first / Shadow captain / To the last whale / Love the one you're with / Pre-road downs / Change partners / I give you give blind / Cathedral
7567826792 / Dec '94 / Atlantic

☐ SO FAR (Crosby, Stills, Nash & Young)
Deja vu / Helplessly hoping / Wooden ships / Teach your children / Ohio / Find the cost of freedom / Woodstock / Our house / Helpless / Guenevere / Suite: Judy Blue eyes
7567826482 / Sep '94 / Atlantic

Crosland, Ben

☐ NORTHERN RUN, THE
Blues for Lex / Sunshower / Away too long / Don't you dare / Northern run / Break a leg / Pause for thought / Blue / Take the coltrane / Confluence
JCCD 101 / Sep '95 / Jazz Cat

Cross

☐ SHOVE IT
Shove it / Heaven for everyone / Love on a tightrope (like an animal) / Cowboys and indians / Stand up for love / Love lies bleeding / Rough justice / Second shelf mix / Contact
CDV 2477 / '88 / Virgin

Cross

☐ DREAM REALITY
Changing / Fire / Armoury show / Uncovered heart / Courage / Run for rescue / Fake / Dream reality / Fanfare song / Poison into medicine / Yearning
CYCL 054 / Aug '97 / Cyclops

☐ GAZE
CYCL 039 / Aug '96 / Cyclops

Cross, Christopher

☐ BEST OF CHRISTOPHER CROSS, THE
9548306562 / Nov '96 / WEA

☐ CHRISTOPHER CROSS
Say you'll be mine / I really don't know anymore / Spinning / Never be the same / Poor Shirley / Ride like the wind / Light is on / Sailing / Minstrel gigolo
256789 / Jul '89 / WEA

☐ RENDEZVOUS
Rendezvous / Deputy Dan / Night across the world / Angry young men / In the blink of an eye / Is there something / Isn't it love / Nothing will change / Driftin' away / Fisherman's tale
74321102912 / Jun '97 / Arista

☐ WINDOW
Been there, done that / Wild wild West / Wishing well / Thinkin' bout you / Jan's tune / Open up my window / Nature's way / Uncharted hearts / Before I go / Love is calling
74321246542 / Jun '97 / Arista

Cross, David

☐ EXILES
CDR 109 / '96 / Red Hot
CLP 0146 / Dec '97 / Cleopatra

☐ TESTING TO DESTRUCTION (Cross, David Band)
CDR 107 / Nov '94 / Red Hot

Cross, Keith

☐ BORED CIVILIANS (Cross, Keith & Peter Ross)
Last ocean rider / Bored civilians / Peace in the end / Story to a friend / Loving you takes so long / Pastels / Dead salute / Boo Radley / Fly home
SRMC 0036 / 5 Jan '98 / Siwan

Cross, Mike

☐ BEST OF THE FUNNY STUFF, THE (Creme De La Cross)
SHCD 1010 / Mar '94 / Sugar Hill

☐ BOUNTY HUNTER
SHCD 1003 / Jan '97 / Sugar Hill

☐ CAROLINA SKY
SHCD 1006 / Jan '97 / Sugar Hill

☐ HIGH POWERED, LOW FLYING
SHCD 1011 / Nov '94 / Sugar Hill

☐ IRREGULAR GUY
SHCD 1009 / Jan '97 / Sugar Hill

☐ LIVE AND KICKIN'
SHCD 1005 / Jan '97 / Sugar Hill

☐ PRODIGAL SON
SHCD 1008 / Jan '97 / Sugar Hill

Cross, Sandra

☐ 100% LOVERS ROCK
ARCD 096 / Jun '94 / Ariwa Sounds

☐ COMET IN THE SKY
Who's finally won / Comet in the sky / Blinded by love / White wash / I need a man / My only desire / Styler boy / Why oh why / Free South Africa / I want you so badly
ARICD 034 / Oct '88 / Ariwa Sounds

☐ COUNTRY LIFE
Country living / We miss you / I hope / You're lying / Break up to make up / Listen dj / Is there a message / It's you / I will go / Stepping into dubwise / Missing dub / Dubbing and hoping / Dub of lies / Can't let dub go / Dub up to rub up / Dub the dj / Dubwise message / I will dub
ARICD 026 / Feb '89 / Ariwa Sounds

☐ FOUNDATION OF LOVE
ARICD 047 / Jun '92 / Ariwa Sounds

Cross, Tim

☐ CLASSIC LANDSCAPE
NAGE 3CD / Jan '86 / Art Of Landscape

Crouch, Andrae

☐ MERCY
Say so / Give it all back to me / Lord is my light / Love somebody like me / Nobody else like you / Mercy / This is the Lord's doing / We love it here / He's the light / Mercy interlude / God still loves me
9362454322 / Jul '95 / Warner Bros.

Crow

☐ PLAY WITH LOVE
74321569442 / 27 Apr '98 / Roo Art

Crow, Dan

☐ OOPS
Oops / My mouth / I had ham / Ballad of reuben rooster / American gum / Potato goat / Miranda (was born in a barn) / In that bubble / Kiss a cow / Dogs / Apples and bananas / Skinny pig / Best bugs of all bugs / Chicken's speech / Yambo
ROUCD 8007 / '88 / Rounder

Crow, Rob

☐ LACTOSE ADEPT
EAR 017 / Oct '96 / Earth Music

Crow, Sheryl

☐ SHERYL CROW
Maybe angels / Change / Home / Sweet Rosalyn / If it makes you happy / Redemption day / Hard to make a stand / Everyday is a winding road / Love is a good thing / Oh Marie / Superstar / Book / Ordinary morning / Free man
5405902 / Sep '96 / A&M

☐ SHERYL CROW (Special Edition/2CD Set)
5407192 / 3 Nov '97 / A&M

☐ TUESDAY NIGHT MUSIC CLUB
Run baby run / Leaving Las Vegas / Strong enough / Can't cry anymore / Solidity / Na-na song / No-one said it'd be easy / What can I do for you / All I wanna do / We do what we can / Reach around jerk / Can't cry anymore (live) / What can I do for you (live) / Leaving Las Vegas (live) / No-one said it would be easy (live) / Volvo cowgirl
5401262 / Oct '93 / A&M
5403682 / May '95 / A&M

Crowbar

☐ BROKEN GLASS
Conquering / Like broken glass / (Can't) Turn away from dying / Wrath of time / Nothing / Burn your world / I am forever / Above, below and in between / You know (I'll live again) / Reborn thru me
CDVEST 77 / Oct '96 / Bulletproof

☐ CROWBAR
IRS 981200CD / 6 Oct '97 / Pavement

☐ CROWBAR/LIVE + 1
High rate extinction / All I had (I gave) / Will that never dies / No quarter / Self inflicted / Negative pollution / Existance is punishment / Holding nothing / I have failed / Self inflicted (Live) / Fixation / I have failed (Live) / All I had (Live) / Numb sensitive
CDVEST 5 / Apr '94 / Bulletproof

☐ OBEDIENCE THRU SUFFERING
CDVEST 42 / Feb '95 / Bulletproof

☐ ODD FELLOWS REST
Intro / Planets collide / And suffer as one / 1000 year internal war / To carry the load / December's spawn / It's all the gravity / Behind the black horizon / New man born / Scattered pieces lay / Odd fellows rest / On frozen ground
MAIM 111162 / 6 Jul '98 / Mayhem

☐ TIME HEALS NOTHING
CDVEST 51 / May '95 / Bulletproof

Crowd Of Isolated

☐ MEMORIES & SCARS
XM 025CD / Apr '92 / X-Mist

Crowded House

☐ CROWDED HOUSE
World where you live / Now we're getting somewhere / Don't dream it's over / Mean to me / Love you till the day I die / Something so strong / Hole in the river / I walk away / Tombstone / That's what I call love
CDEST 2016 / Feb '94 / Capitol

☐ CROWDED HOUSE/TEMPLE OF LOW MEN/WOODFACE (The Originals/3CD Set)
World where you live / Now we're getting somewhere / Don't dream it's over / Mean to me / Love you 'til the day I die / Something so strong / Hole in the river / I walk away / Tombstone / That's what I call love / I feel possessed / Kill eye / Into temptation / Mansion in the slums / When you come / Never be the same / Love this life / Sister madly / In the lowlands / Better

be home soon / Chocolate cake / It's only natural / Fall at your feet / Tall trees / Weather with you / Whispers and moans / Four seasons in one day / There goes God / Fame is / All I ask / As sure as I am / Italian plastic / She goes on / How will you go
CDOMB 001 / 27 Jul '98 / Capitol

☐ RECURRING DREAM (The Very Best Of Crowded House)
Weather with you / World where you live / Fall at your feet / Locked out / Don't dream it's over / Into temptation / Pineapple head / When you come / Private universe / Not the girl you think you are / Instinct / I feel possessed / Four seasons in one day / It's only natural / Distant sun / Something so strong / Mean to me / Better be home soon / Everything is good for you
CDEST 2283 / Jun '96 / Capitol

☐ RECURRING DREAM (The Very Best Of Crowded House/2CD Set)
Weather with you / World where you live / Fall at your feet / Locked out / Don't dream it's over / Into temptation / Pineapple head / When you come / Private universe / Not the girl you think you are / Instinct / I feel possessed / Four seasons in one day / It's only natural / Distant sun / Something so strong / Mean to me / Better be home soon / Everything is good for you / There goes God / Newcastle jam / Love U 'til the day I die / Hole in the river / Pineapple head / Private universe / How will you go / Left hand / Whispers and moans / Kill eye / Fingers of love / Don't dream it's over / When you come / Sister Madly / In my command
CDESTX 2283 / Nov '96 / Capitol

☐ TEMPLE OF LOW MEN
I feel possessed / Kill eye / Into temptation / Mansion in the slums / When you come / Never be the same / Love this life / Sister madly / In the lowlands / Better be home soon
CDEST 2064 / Jul '88 / Capitol

☐ TOGETHER ALONE
Kare kare / In my command / Nails in my feet / Black and white boy / Fingers of love / Pineapple head / Locked out / Private Universe / Walking on the spot / Distant sun / Catherine wheels / Skin feeling / Together alone
CDESTU 2215 / Sep '97 / Capitol

☐ WOODFACE
Chocolate cake / It's only natural / Fall at your feet / Tall trees / Weather with you / Whispers and moans / Four seasons in one day / There goes God / Fame is / All I ask / As sure as I am / Italian plastic / She goes on / How will you go
CDEST 2144 / Jun '91 / Capitol

☐ WOODFACE (2CD Set)
Chocolate cake / It's only natural / Fall at your feet / Weather with you / Whispers and moans / Four seasons in one day / There goes god / Fame is / All I ask / As sure as I am / Italian plastic / She goes on / How will you go / Weather with you / Four seasons in one day / It's only natural / Chocolate cake / How will you go / In love with it all
8230982 / 1 Dec '97 / Capitol

Crowe, Bobby

☐ SCOTTISH COUNTRY DANCING
EMPRCD 784 / 16 Mar '98 / Emporio

☐ SHORES OF LOCH ALVIE, THE (Crowe, Bobby & His Scottish Band)
GRCD 48 / '92 / Grasmere

Crowe, J.D.

☐ FLASHBACK (Crowe, J.D. & The New South)
ROUCD 0322 / Nov '94 / Rounder

☐ GOING BACK (Crowe & McLaughlin)
ROUCD 314 / Jan '94 / Rounder

☐ J.D. CROWE AND THE NEW SOUTH (Crowe, J.D. & The New South)
Old home place / Some old day / Rock salt and nails / Sally Goodin / Ten degrees / Nashville blues / You are what I am / Summer wages / I'm walkin' / Home sweet home revisited / Cryin' Holly
ROUCD 0044 / '88 / Rounder

☐ LIVE IN JAPAN (Crowe, J.D. & The New South)
She's gone gone gone / Don't give your heart to a rambler / Shuckin' the corn / Blue eyes crying in the rain / Railroad lady / Sugar coated love / Memphis mandolin / Rose coloured glasses / Red rocking chair / Martha White theme / Ballad of Jed Clampett / Foggy mountain breakdown / My window faces South / I'm walkin'
ROUCD 0159 / Oct '97 / Rounder

☐ STRAIGHT AHEAD
Say you lied / God's own singer / Stony mountain twist / Helplessly hoping / Sugar coated love / Runaround / You're no longer mine / Belleville, georgia / Miner's lady / Ride the train
ROUCD 0202 / Jun '87 / Rounder

Crowforce

☐ CROWFORCE
White king / Strange voyage / Judas kiss / Showtime / Eaten by dogs / Chinese whispers / Change / Possession / Candytown / Don't look down
CDDVN 1 / Jul '92 / Devotion

Crowley, Jimmy

☐ UNCORKED
CDTRAX 165 / Jul '98 / Greentrax

Crown Heights

☐ MORE PRICKS THAN KICKS
Greed kicks in / More pricks than kicks / Foxy looser / Learn to breathe / Unkind / Margaret / Dear Sir / Call king sour / Wired for sound / Moving from the small room to the big room / Out of Carolina
74321438312 / May '97 / American

Crown Heights Affair

☐ DREAM ON DANCELAND (2CD Set)
SMDCD 170 / 22 Sep '97 / Snapper

☐ ESSENTIAL DANCEFLOOR ARTISTS VOL.1
Dreaming a dream / Foxy lady / Dancin' / Far out / I'm gonna love you forever / Galaxy of love / You gave me love / Use your body and soul / Say a prayer for two
DGPCD 665 / Mar '94 / Deep Beats

☐ STRUCK GOLD (The Best Of Crown Heights Affair)
DEEPM 014 / Mar '97 / Deep Beats

Crown Of Autumn

☐ TREASURE'S OF ARCANE
ELN 001CD / 13 Apr '98 / Elnor

Crown Of Thorns

☐ 21 THORNS (2CD Set)
IRSCD 993026 / Nov '96 / Hengest

☐ BREAKTHROUGH
IRSCD 993025 / Nov '96 / Hengest

☐ BURNING, THE
BS 005CD / Jan '96 / Black Sun

☐ CROWN OF THORNS
NTHEN 008CD / Apr '96 / Now & Then

☐ ETERNAL DEATH
BS 010CD / Mar '97 / Burning Sun

☐ LOST CATHEDRAL
Lost cathedral / Live and die / Motorcycle Loretta / Lyin' / Free me / Greed of love / Cold bloodied bitch / End of the road / Although we're fools / Wasted prime / Hell of a night / If you need me
FRCD 003 / 18 May '98 / Frontier

☐ LOST CATHEDRAL
DM 300012 / 22 Jun '98 / Deshima

☐ RAW THORNS
NTHEN 013CD / Apr '96 / Now & Then

Crown Of Thornz

☐ TRAIN YARD BLUES
LF 151CD / May '95 / Lost & Found

Crown Royals

☐ ALL NIGHT BURNER
ES 1236CD / May '97 / Estrus

Crowsdell

☐ DREAMETTE
ABB 83CD / Apr '95 / Big Cat

☐ WITHIN THE CURVE OF AN ARM
Popsick / Five stars / Mooncalf / Lurking in sagas / You want me dead / Floridian lamb / WC Haley / Pharmeceutical fingers / Patches / Sunny sparkle / Cut and paste / Wake the lass / Foul
ABB 125CD / Jun '97 / Big Cat

Croydon SDA Gospel Choir

☐ VERY BEST OF GOSPEL, THE
Oh happy day / You're all I need to get by / New order / Jesus lover of my soul / People get ready / Come and go with me (to my Father's house) / Joy / Let my people go / Said he would / I'll take you there / I still haven't found what I'm looking for / Closer to the light / Stand by me / Time to heal / Family of man / Send out love
MCCD 310 / 8 Sep '97 / Music Club

Cru

☐ DA DIRTY 30
5376072 / 15 Sep '97 / Def Jam

Crucial Robbie

☐ CRUCIAL VIEW
ARICD 056 / Oct '90 / Ariwa Sounds

Crucial Vibes

☐ CONTROL YOURSELF
CDSGP 061 / Jun '93 / Prestige

Crucifix

☐ DEHUMANIZATION
18523 2 / Sep '94 / Southern

Crucifucks

☐ OUR WILL BE DONE
VIRUS 111 / '92 / Alternative Tentacles

Crudup, Arthur

☐ AFTER HOURS (Crudup, Arthur 'Big Boy')
That's all right / Crudup's after hours / My baby left me / Coal black mare / If you have ever been to Georgia / Help me bear this heavy load / Ethel Mae / Too much competition / Standing at my window / Greyhound bus / Who's been fooling you / If I get lucky / War is over / Shout sister shout / She ain't nothing but trouble / Cool disposition / I love you / She's got no hair / Keep your arms around me / So glad you're mine / My wife and woman / Chicago blues / I'm gonna dig myself a hole / Mean old Frisco blues / That's all right
74321523802 / 29 Sep '97 / Camden

☐ ARTHUR 'BIG BOY' CRUDUP MEETS THE MASTER BLUES BASSISTS (Crudup, Arthur 'Big Boy')
DD 621 / Mar '95 / Delmark

☐ ARTHUR 'BIG BOY' CRUDUP VOL.1 (Crudup, Arthur 'Big Boy')
DOCD 5201 / Oct '93 / Document

☐ ARTHUR 'BIG BOY' CRUDUP VOL.2 (Crudup, Arthur 'Big Boy')
DOCD 5202 / Oct '93 / Document

☐ ARTHUR 'BIG BOY' CRUDUP VOL.3 (Crudup, Arthur 'Big Boy')
DOCD 5203 / Oct '93 / Document

☐ ARTHUR 'BIG BOY' CRUDUP VOL.4 (Crudup, Arthur 'Big Boy')
DOCD 5204 / Oct '93 / Document

☐ FATHER OF ROCK 'N' ROLL, THE
I'm in the mood / Ethel Mae / My mama don't allow me / Look no yonder wall / Too much competition / My baby left me
CD 52025 / Feb '93 / Blues Encore

☐ LOOK ON YONDER'S WALL (Crudup, Arthur 'Big Boy')
Look on yonder's wall / Questionnaire blues / Keep your hands off that woman / That's all right / Rock me mama / Katie Mae / Dust my broom / Landlord blues / Coal black mare / Life is just a gamble / Walk out on the road / I'm all alone / You'll be old before your time / Ramblin' blues / When I lost my baby (I almost lost my mind)
DE 614 / Jul '97 / Delmark

☐ MEAN OL' FRISCO (Charly Blues Masterworks)
CDBM 50 / Jun '93 / Charly

Cruel Frederick

☐ BIRTH OF THE CRUEL
SST 127CD / May '93 / SST

☐ WE ARE THE MUSIC WE PLAY
SST 290CD / May '93 / SST

Cruel Sea

☐ THIS IS NOT THE WAY HOME
REDCD 25 / Aug '94 / Red Eye

☐ THREE LEGGED DOG
5275372 / 15 Sep '97 / Polydor

Cruickshank, Ian

☐ DJANGO MEETS DUKE (Cruickshank, Ian Gypsy Jazz)
Ultrafox / Billets doux / Tears / Djangologie / Nocturne / Lotus blossom / Caravan / Django meets the duke / Fleche d'or / Ina sentimental mood / Vous et moi
FJCD 109 / 17 Nov '97 / Fret

Cruise, Julee

☐ FLOATING INTO THE NIGHT
Floating / Falling / I remember / Mysteries of love / Into the night / I float alone / Nightingale / Swan / World spins
7599258592 / Feb '90 / WEA

☐ VOICE OF LOVE, THE
This is our night / Space for love / Movin' in on you / Friends for life / Up in flames / Kool kat walk / Until the end of the world / She would die for love / In my other world / Questions in a world of blues / Voice of love
9362453902 / Oct '93 / WEA

Crumb, R.

☐ CHASIN' RAINBOWS (Crumb, R & The Cheap Suit Serenaders)
Alabama jubilee / Chasin' rainbows / Fine artiste blues / Hula medley / I want a little girl / Persian rug / Mysterious mose / Crying my blues away / She lived down by the firehouse / Diane / Make my cot where the cot-cot-cotten grows / Moana march
SHCD 6002 / Mar '98 / Shanachie

Crumbs

☐ CRUMBS
LOOKOUT 161CD / Jan '97 / Lookout

Crumbsuckers

☐ LIFE OF DREAMS
Sit there / Trapped / Knterlude / Super tuesday / Shits creek / Return to the womb / Longest war / Shot down / Prelude / Life of dreams / Brainwashed / Faces of death / Hub run / Bullshit society / Live to work / Moment of silence / War hyde
CDJUST 4 / Aug '91 / Rough Justice

Crumit, Frank

☐ MOUNTAIN GREENERY
Bride's lament / Mountain greenery / Abdul Abulbul Amir / Thanks for the buggy ride / Kingdom coming and the year of Jubilo / Ukelele lady / Jack is every inch a sailor / Oh by jingo, oh by gee / Prune song / Girlfriend / Billy boy / King of Borneo / Get away old man get away / Down in the cane break / Crazy words crazy tune / Gay caballero / Insurance man
CDAJA 5001 / Oct '93 / Living Era

☐ SONG OF THE PRUNE
Song of the prune / Jack is every inch a sailor / I'm bettin' the roll on roamer / Donald the dub / Abdul Abulbul Amir / And then he took up golf / Around the corner / Sissy / Grandfather's clock / Would you like to take a walk / Old apple tree / I can't stand sittin' in a cell / Sunday in the park / Girl with the paint on her face / Return of Abdul Abulbul Amir / Gay Caballero / Get away old man get away / Crazy words crazy tune / Ukelele lady / Thanks for the buggy ride / Girl friend / Bride's lament / Mountain greenery / Billy boy
SWNCD 018 / Oct '97 / Sound Waves

Crumly, Pat

☐ BEHIND THE MASK (Crumly, Pat Quartet)
Behind the mask / Voyage / I'll remember April / You don't know what love is / Island / Carib-blue / This heart of mine / Tears inside / Little off beat / Polka dots and moonbeams / Contemplation / If I should lose you / Behind the mask (Second version)
SPJCD 549 / May '93 / Spotlite

☐ FLAMINGO
Nightwalk / Beautiful love / Bewitched, bothered and bewildered / Slow burn / Flamingo / Here's that rainy day / Eucalpyso / Days of wine and roses / Three little words / My old flame / Flamebirds / Two degrees East - three degrees West / It might as well be spring / Way you look tonight
SPJCD 550 / Jun '94 / Spotlite

Crummer, Annie

☐ SEVENTH WAVE
0630194872 / 3 Nov '97 / Coalition

Crunt

☐ CRUNT
TR 19CD / Feb '94 / Trance

Crusaders

☐ CRUSADERS AND BEYOND, THE
Street life / Inherit the wind / Stomp and buck dance / Burnin' up the carnival / (No matter how high I get) I'll still be looking up to you / Keep that same old feeling / Snowflakes / Brazos river / Breakdown / Soul shadows / Let's dance together / Time bomb / Voices in the rain
MCCD 163 / Jul '94 / Music Club

☐ CRUSADERS BEST, THE
Street life / Way back home / Feeling funky / Tough talk / Do you remember when / Message from the inner city / Eleanor Rigby / Carnival of the night / My Mama told me / I'm so glad I'm standing here today / Put it where you want it
PWKS 4231 / Nov '94 / Carlton

☐ GREATEST CRUSADE, THE
Street life: *Crusaders & Randy Crawford* / Hustler / Rodeo drive (High steppin') / Marcella's dream / Rainbow seeker: *Sample, Joe* / Burning up the carnival: *Sample, Joe & Josie James* / Snowflake / Spiral / Nite crawler / Rainbow visions / Hold on (I feel our love is changing): *Crusaders & B.B. King* / Chain reaction: *Crusaders & B.B. King* / Carnival of the night / Ballad for Joe (Louis) / Inherit the wind: *Felder, Wilton & Bobby Womack* / Some people just never learn / (No matter how high I get) I'll still be looking up to you: *Felder, Wilton & Bobby Womack/ Altrina Grayson* / Oasis: *Sample, Joe* / It happens every day / Fly with the wings of love: *Sample, Joe* / Soul caravan / Fairy tales / I'm so glad I'm standing here today: *Crusaders & Joe Cocker* / Put it where you want it / Elegant evening / Free as the wind / Search for soul / Survivor: *Sample, Joe & Phyllis Hyman*
CLBCD 5501 / Feb '95 / Calibre

☐ HAPPY AGAIN (Jazz Crusaders)
Lock it down / When your so far away / Midnite moods / Top of the world / Fool's rush in / Are you a part of me / Slyzappit / Rockslide / La luz el dia / Jamaica / Travellin' inside your love / Young rabbits / Uh huh oh yea
9950322 / Jul '95 / Sin-Drome

☐ HEALING THE WOUNDS
Pessimisticism / Mercy mercy mercy / Little things mean a lot / 'Cause we've ended as lovers / Shake dance / Maputo / Running man / Healing the wounds
GRD 9638 / May '91 / GRP

☐ HOLLYWOOD
5303062 / Apr '94 / Verve

☐ OLD SOCKS, NEW SHOES
5303072 / Apr '94 / Verve

☐ PASS THE PLATE
5303082 / Nov '94 / PolyGram Jazz

☐ PRICELESS JAZZ
Street life / Marcella's dream / Keep that same old feeling / Feeling funky / Soul shadows / Feel it / Carnival of the night / Serenity / Chain reaction
GRP 98922 / 23 Mar '98 / GRP

☐ SOUL SHADOWS
Night theme / Stomp and buck dance / Spiral / Street life / Feel it / 'Cause we've ended as lovers / Ballad for Joe (Louis) / Destiny / I felt the love / Soul shadows / Way it goes / Night ladies
VSOPCD 212 / Feb '95 / Connoisseur Collection

☐ STREET LIFE
MCLD 19004 / Apr '92 / MCA

☐ WAY BACK HOME (The Complete Authorised Collection) (4CD Set)
Young rabbits / Freedom sound / Brother Barnard / Tough talk / Scratch / Blues up tight / Eleanor Rigby / Inside the outside / Jazz / Thank you / Golden slumber / Way back home / Put it where you want it / So far away / Sweet revival / That's how I feel / Three children / Mosadi / Shade of blue / Don't let it get you down / Message from the inner city / Search for soul / Scratch / Hard times / Stomp and buck dance / Double bubble / Crossfire / Lilies of the Nile / When there's love around / Ballad for Joe (Louis) / Whispering pines / Chain reaction / Creole / Free as the wind / Sweet 'n' sour / I felt the love / Spiral / Night crawler / Keep that same old feeling / It happens every day / Snowflake / Fairy tales / Street life / Way back home
BTD 4700 / Sep '96 / Blue Thumb

Crusaders

☐ FAT DRUNK AND STUPID
ID 123360CD / 22 May '98 / Dionysus

Crusaders For Real Hip Hop

☐ DEJA VU/ IT'S '82
PCD 1428 / Jul '92 / Profile

Crush, Bobby

☐ DOUBLE DECKER PARTY
PLATCD 5920 / Jul '92 / Platinum

☐ HOLLYWOOD AND BROADWAY
Why God / Bohemian rhapsody / I dreamed a dream / Tears in heaven / Love moves in mysterious ways / (Everything I do) I do it for you / Beauty and the beast / Love can't happen / Places that belong to you / Any dream will do / Music of the night / Someone to watch over me
PLATCD 3919 / Apr '93 / Platinum

Crusher

☐ ACT 2-UNDERMINE
N 02312 / Nov '93 / Noise

Crust

☐ CRUSTY LOVE
TR 23CD / May '94 / Trance

Crustation

☐ BLOOM
Hey / Purple / Close my eyes / Face the waves / Reverie / Down down / Falling / Flame / Life as one / Ride on
CHIP 184 / 26 Jan '98 / Jive

Crux

☐ OI - THE COLLECTION
CIA / Keep on running / Streets at night / Brighton front / I'll die with my boots on / Liddle towers / Give us work / Riot / War / Skinhead / Vendetta / Computer future / Rabies / Government downfall / Dead hero / Fire another round / Suspicion / 1984 / Nobody cares / Fight for your life / Running down the world
AHOYCD 079 / 24 Nov '97 / Captain Oi

Cruz, Brandon

☐ COURTSHIP OF EDDIE
TAANG 141CD / 29 Jun '98 / Taang

Cruz, Celia

☐ AZUCAR
Sueno el cuero / Abre la Puerta Querida / La cumbanchera / Llego la zafra / Pegao / Me voy pa' el pueblo / Aguinaldo Antillano / Mi so den boso / Ven Bernabe / El Guajirito contento / Camadde / Traigo para ti / Asi quiero morir / Saludo a elegua / Tuya, y mas que tuya / Hasta fuerate con ti mambo / Baho kende / Munecas del cha-cha-cha / El Lleva y trae / Feliz Navidad
CDHOT 630 / Nov '97 / Charly

☐ CUBA GUARACHA Y SON (Cruz, Celia & Albita Rodriguez)
9944132182 / 3 Mar '98 / Orfeon

☐ CUBAN LEGEND
Pa la paloma / Burundanga / Con mucho cachet / Baila yemaya / Cao cao mani picao / Lo tuyo es mio / Chango ta veni / La guagua / Esperame en el cielo / Sun sun babae / La negrita sandunguera / Bambolalle / Vengan a la charanga / Cha cha guere / Me voy a pinar del rio / Quien sera / Mambo del amor / Agua pa mi / El barracon / Elegua quiere tambo
CDHOT 610 / Jan '97 / Charly

☐ EL MERENGUE
CD 62002 / Apr '94 / Saludos Amigos

☐ IRREPETIBLE
Que le den candela / Bembelequa / Limon Y menta / Marion ague / Drume negrita / Caballero y dama / Enamorada de ti / La guagua / Cuando cuba se acabe de liberar
66058054 / Feb '95 / RMM

☐ MADRE RUMBA
CD 62016 / Apr '94 / Saludos Amigos

☐ MADRE RUMBA (Cruz, Celia & La Sonora Matancera)
Madre rumba / Madre rumba / El merengue / Munecas del cha cha cha / Y mi negro esta cansao / Oya diosa fe / Contestacion de el marinero / Yerbero moderno / A todos mis amigos / Matiagua / Vailan vallende / Cha cha guere / La cumbanchera de belen / Chango ta viene / Palmeras tropicales / Tumba
CD 3557 / Jul '95 / Cameo

☐ MAMBO DEL AMOR
CD 62007 / Apr '94 / Saludos Amigos

☐ RITMOY Y CALOR DE CUBA CON
BMB 504CD / Nov '95 / Blue Moon

☐ SALSA SUPERSTAR (2CD Set)
Agua pa' mi / Reina rumba / La Mucura / Suavecito / Guede Zaina / Pa' La Paloma / Cao, Cao Mani Picao / Sun, sun babae / Me voy a pinar Del Rio / Quien sera / El Merengue / Ritmo / Tambo Y Flores / Mi bomba sono / Tamborilero / Baila Balla Vicente / Chango ta veni / Vengan a la Charanga / Rock and roll / Rumbanacao / Pila Pilandera / Mi Soncito / Juancito Trucupey / Mango mangue / Tumba La Cana Jibarito / Baila Yemaya / Melao de cana / Pepe Antonio / Los Ritmos Cambian / Matiagua / Mambo del amor / Hay comentario / Tatalibaba / El pai y la mai / Madre rumba / Vamos a Guarachar / Elegua quiere tambo / Saoco / Cha cha guere / Tu voz / Lalle lalle
CPCD 82532 / Nov '96 / Charly

Cryhavoc

☐ SWEETBRIERS
Bloodtie / Repent (whore) / Come with me / Wolfdance / Pagan uprise / I fade away / Armageddon y'know / Misanthropy
SPI 58CD / 25 May '98 / Spinefarm

Cryner, Bobbie

☐ GIRL OF YOUR DREAMS
Son of a preacher man / I didn't know my own strength / Girl of your dreams / Vision of loneliness / Lesson in leaving / You'd think he'd know me better / I just can't stand to be unhappy / Nobody leaves / Oh to be the one / Just say so
MCD 11324 / Jan '96 / MCA

Crypt Of Kereberos

☐ WORLD OF MYTHS
CDAR 013 / Feb '94 / Adipocre

Cryptic Slaughter

☐ SPEAK YOUR PEACE
Born too soon / Insanity by the numbers / Death styles of the poor and lonely / Divided minds / Killing time / Still born, again / Co-exist / One thing or another / Speak your piece
CDZORRO 6 / Jul '90 / Metal Blade

Cryptkickers

☐ CRYPTKICKERS
ACCD 002 / Dec '97 / Alley Cat

Cryptopsy

☐ BLASPHEMY MADE FLESH
D 00054CD / 10 Nov '97 / Displeased

Crystal Method

☐ VEGAS
Trip like I do / Busy child / Cherry twist / High roller / Comin' back / Keep hope alive / Vapor trail / She's my pusher / Jaded / Bad stone
VEGCDX 1CD / 23 Feb '98 / Sony Soho2

Crystal Palace FC

☐ GLAD ALL OVER (A Tribute To Crystal Palace FC & Supporters) (Various Artists)
Glad all over: *Crystal Palace FC FA Cup Final Squad 1990* / Claret and blue: *Crystal Palace FC 1972* / Power to the Palace: *Palace* / Why can't we all get together: *Crystal Palace FC 1972 & Wives* / Bye bye blackbird: *Venables, Terry & Friends* / Flying high: *Palace* / Gonna build a Palace: *Gary's Construction Company* / Our Crystal Palace: *Crystal Band* / Where eagles fly: *Crystal Palace FC FA Cup Final Squad 1990* / Follow the eagles: *Universal* / We all follow the Palace: *Eastern Eagles* / We are the eagles: *Eastern Eagles* / Eagles are flying high: *Garage Mechanics* / I'm in love with Harry Bassett: *Lady Helen Of Selhurst* / Where's Joyce: *Lower Tier* / We're back where we belong: *Eddie Eagle* / Yes we're back: *Back Five*
CDGAFFER 19 / Aug '97 / Cherry Red

Crystal Trip

☐ CRYSTAL TRIP
GULL 2CD / Sep '93 / Seagull

Crystallized Movements

☐ MIND DISASTER
TW 1001 / Nov '97 / Twisted Village

Csardas, Slovak

☐ DANCE TUNES FROM THE PENNSYLVANIA COAL MINES
HTCD 37 / Jun '97 / Heritage

Cua, Rick

☐ TIMES TEN
CD 58002 / Apr '96 / Salt

Cuarteto Caney

☐ CUARTETO CANEY 1936-1939
HQCD 75 / Jun '96 / Harlequin

Cuarteto Cedron

☐ PARA QUE VOS Y YO
088742 / 24 Feb '98 / Melodie

Cuarteto Coculense

☐ VERY FIRST MARIACHI RECORDINGS 1908-1909, THE
El periquito / El limoncito / Petrita / El carretero / La guacamaya / La indita / El ausente / Las abajenas / El chivo / Las olas de la laguna / El frijolito / El cuervo / Chaparrita de mi vida / El zihualteco / El becerrero / El tecolote / La malaguena / El tejon / Arenita de oro / Las campanitas / El arriero
ARHCD 7036 / Jul '98 / Arhoolie

Cuarteto Marcano

☐ CUARTETO MARCANO 1939-1945
HQCD 74 / Jun '96 / Harlequin

Cuarteto Patria

☐ UNA COQUETA, A
CO 106 / Jan '94 / Corason

Cuarto Espacio

☐ CUARTO ESPACIO
Tumbania / Sancho / Reencuentro / Pantera / Tranquilidad / Polka and son / Reencuentro / Hay Gritos / Momo
ASHECD 2004 / Sep '97 / Ashe

Cub

☐ MAULER
ANDA 214 / Feb '97 / Au-Go-Go

Cuba, Joe

☐ SALSA Y BEMBE (Cuba, Joe Sextet)
CDHOT 606 / Aug '96 / Charly

Cuban All Stars

☐ PASSPORTE
Presentation / Rumberos de ayer / Descarga pa' gozar / Donde va mulata / Anga / Blem blem blem / Tata se ha vuelto loco / La clave de los primros
ENJ 90192 / Apr '95 / Enja

Cubanate

☐ ANTIMATTER
Blackout / Bodyburn / Revolution time / Autonomy / Junky / Exert / Disorder / Sucker / Switch / Forceful / Bodyburn (remix) / Kill or cure
DYCD 12 / Sep '93 / Dynamica

☐ BARBAROSSA
Vortech 1 / Barbarossa / Joy / Why are you here / Exultation / Musclemen / Come alive / Vortech 2 / Lord of the flies
DY 172 / Jun '96 / Dynamica

☐ CYBERIA
DY 82E / Nov '95 / Dynamica

☐ INTERFERENCE
TVT 72472 / 13 Apr '98 / TVT/Wax Trax

☐ SUCK TASTE SPIT
DY 202 / Jul '96 / Dynamica

Cubanismo

☐ MALEMBE
Mulence / Salsa pilon / Montuno allegre / El prugunton / Now in Marinao / Cubanismo lleho / Danson Daulen / Mar y tierra / Malembe
HNCD 1411 / Apr '97 / Hannibal

Cuber, Ronnie

☐ LOVE FOR SALE (Cuber, Ronnie & The Netherlands Metropole Orchestra)
369142 / 1 Sep '98 / Koch

☐ SCENE IS CLEAN, THE
Scene is clean / Adoracion / Song for Pharoah / Arroz con pollo / Mazambo / Fajardo / Tee's bag / Flamingo
MCD 92182 / Jul '94 / Milestone

Cucchi, Flavio

☐ FLAVIO CUCCHI PLAYS BARRIOS & VILLA-LOBOS
EUCD 1096 / Jan '92 / ARC

☐ FROM YESTERDAY TO PENNY LANE
EUCD 1247 / Mar '94 / ARC

☐ GUITAR - CROSSING OVER
EUCD 1326 / Nov '95 / ARC

☐ PLAYS BROUWER
EUCD 1192 / Apr '92 / ARC

Cuccurullo, Warren

☐ MACHINE LANGUAGE
You are here / Machine language / Nightmare on dickens street / Crystal clear / Deja view / Delilah in action / Old photographs / 6th sense / Deep sleep
IMA 24001 / Jul '98 / Imago

☐ THANKS TO FRANK
Canarsie daiquiri / Orgasmatron / Ass man / Jam man jam / Hey zawinal / Galactic ballerina / Low speed chase / Indian time zones / Tardinha / Spider / Thanks to Frank
72787230022 / Jul '98 / Imago

Cuchulainn

☐ THREE MONTHS IN WINTER
PTICD 3006 / Aug '96 / Pure Traditional Irish

Cuckoo

☐ BREATHING LESSONS
GED 25162 / 13 Jul '98 / Geffen

Cuckooland

☐ POP SENSIBILITY
DAMGOOD 67CD / Jun '95 / Damaged Goods

Cud

☐ ASQUARIUS
Rich and strange / Easy / Sometimes rightly, sometimes wrongly / Spanish love song / Magic alex / Beyond hair / Pink flamingo / Possession / Through the roof / Soul food / Once again / No smoking
3953902 / Apr '95 / A&M

☐ SHOWBIZ
Somebody snatched my action / ESP / Waving and drowning / Sticks and stones / Mystery deepens / Slip away / One giant love / I reek of chic / Not neccessarily evil / You lead me / Tourniquet / Neurotica
5402112 / Apr '95 / A&M

Cudgels

☐ GOD'S CHILDREN
BULL 90CD / Jul '92 / Bring On Bull

Cuenca, Juanita

☐ NINA BONITA TE ILAMAN
ALCD 045 / Jul '97 / Alma Latina

Cues

☐ WHY
Yes sir / Why / Crackerjack / Burn that candle / Poppa loves momma / Charlie Brown / Crazy crazy party / You're on my mind / Ladder / Destination 2100 and 65 / Prince or pauper / Rock 'n' roll Mr. Oriole / Warm spot / Girl I love / Oh my darlin' / Killer diller / I pretend / Be my wife / Don't make believe / Only you / Fell for your loving, I / Hot rotten soda pop / So near and yet so far / Forty leven dozen ways / Schoochie schoochie / Yes sir / Ol' man river
BCD 15510 / May '91 / Bear Family

Cuesta, Ivan

☐ A TI, COLOMBIA (Cuesta, Ivan Y Sus Baltimore Vallent)
ARHCD 388 / Apr '95 / Arhoolie

Cueva, Julio

☐ DESTINTEGRANDO
TCD 083 / Apr '97 / Tumbao Cuban Classics

Cuevas, Sergio

☐ LA HARPE INDIENNE DU PARAGUAY
Camino de San Juan / Maquinita / Feliz Navidad / Harpa serenata / Pajaro campana / A mi dos amores / Nuevo baile / Poncho cuatro colores / Golpe llanero / Danza indiana / Barrio rincon / Magnolia / Balada de mi sueno / Pa i Zacaria
ARN 64040 / '88 / Arion

Cuffe, Tony

☐ WHEN FIRST I WENT TO CALEDONIA
When first I went to Caledonia / Miss Wharton Duff/ The mare / Iron horse / Caledonia / Dr. MacInnes' fancy / Buchan turnpike / Lass o' paties mill / Weary pund o' tow / Paddy Kelly's brew / Otterburn / Scalloway lasses / Humours of Tulla / Miss Forester
IRCD 011 / Feb '94 / Iona

Cugat, Xavier

☐ CONGAS, CHIHUAHUAS & RUMBAS 1940-1945
HQCD 83 / Sep '96 / Harlequin

☐ CUBAN LOVE SONG 1939-1940
Society conga / Mi espana / Cuban love song / Havana love song / Calientito / Tu volveras / Pa ran pan pan / At a time like this / Loca ilusion / Long live love / Siboney / I want my mama / Blen blen blen / Cat's serenade / Almendra / Adios / Green eyes / Adversidad / Agua agua / Serenta tropical / Los carnavales de oriente / Batucada / Ah Que bonita eres tu / Cuatro personas
HQCD 103 / Oct '97 / Harlequin

☐ CUBAN MAMBO
CD 62003 / Apr '94 / Saludos Amigos

☐ CUGAT'S NUGATS
Echale cinco al piano / Bambarito / Chupa-chupa / Brazil / Coconito / El cabonaro / Jesusita / Chiu-chui / Bim bam bum / Linda mujer / Tico tico / Toca-tu samba / Good good good / Stars in your eyes / My shawl / Tierra va tembla / La ola marina / Drume negrita / I'll never love again / Rhumba at the Waldorf / Miami beach rhumba / Come to the mardi gras / Papa knows / Cugat's nugats
HQCD 125 / Jul '98 / Harlequin

☐ DANCING PARTY VOL.5 (2CD Set)
1917552 / Jul '97 / EPM

☐ EL AMERICANO
El Americano / Yo quiero un mambo / Strangers in the dark / Que rico el mambo / Uuuh / Anything can happen - mambo / Mambo ay ay ay / Riviera mambo / Jamay / Maracaibo / Humpty dumpty / Mambo mania / Flute nightmares / Mambo gitano / Mambo OK / El Marijuano / Mondongo / Mambo at the Waldorf
CD 62078 / Jan '96 / Saludos Amigos

☐ HIT SOUND OF XAVIER CUGAT AND HIS ORCHESTRA, THE
Brazil / Perfidia / South America, take it away / Babalu / Quierme mucho / Breeze and I / Para vigo me voy / Green eyes / Stars in your eyes / Baia / You belong to my heart / I yi yi yi, I like you very much / No can do / Tico, Tico / Lady in red / Rumba-cardi / Night must fall / Coconut pudding vendor / La Paloma / Frenesi
CDHOT 631 / Nov '97 / Charly

☐ LE GRAN ORQUESTA DE XAVIER CUGAT
BM 513 / Feb '97 / Blue Moon

☐ ME GUSTA LA CONGA (Cugat, Xavier & His Orchestra)
Siboney / Babalu / Bim bam bum / Me gusta la conga / Tumbao / Bambarito / Yo ta'namora / Anna boroco tinde / Negra leonor / El mondonguero / Son los dandies / Rosita la bonita / Cachita / Negro a reza / Auto-conga / Calentito / Stars in your eyes / My shawl
CD 62009 / Jan '93 / Saludos Amigos

☐ PARA VIGO ME VAY (Cugat, Xavier & His Orchestra)
Para vigo me voy / Habanera / Bruca manigua / Nueva conga / Tunare / Mi conga / Guaira / Elube chango / Los hijos de buda / Rumba rumbero / Benabe / Cinco hijos / Blen, blen, blen / Adios africa / Enlloro / Tabu
CD 62044 / Nov '93 / Saludos Amigos

☐ ROMANTIC SOUND OF XAVIER CUGAT, THE (Cugat, Xavier & His Orchestra)
CDHOT 635 / 30 Mar '98 / Charly

☐ SOUTH AMERICA, TAKE IT AWAY (24 Latin Hits) (Cugat, Xavier & His Waldorf-Astoria Orchestra)
Lady in red / Jalouise / Estrellita / Ahi viene la conga / Cielito lindo / La paloma / Night must fall / Perfida / Yours / La cumparsita / Jungle drums / Breeze and I / Frenesi / Green eyes / I yi yi yi I like you very much / Brazil / Tico tico / Siboney / Baia / Hasta manana / You belong to my heart / No can do / South America, take it away
CDAJA 5223 / Mar '97 / Living Era

☐ TO ALL MY FRIENDS
New Cucaracha / Golden sunset / La Bamba / Que lindas in Mexicanas / Despedida / Cielito lindo / Banana boat song (Day O) / Cuban holiday / Adius marquita Linda / Barbados baila / Diamante negro / Braziliana
ISCD 146 / Jun '95 / Intersound

☐ XAVIER CUGAT (Cugat, Xavier & His Band)
HQCD 14 / '92 / Harlequin

☐ XAVIER CUGAT & DINAH SHORE 1939-1945 (Cugat, Xavier & Dinah Shore)
HQCD 29 / Oct '93 / Harlequin

☐ XAVIER CUGAT 1944 & 1945 (Cugat, Xavier & His Orchestra)
CCD 59 / Aug '94 / Circle

☐ XAVIER CUGAT ON THE RADIO 1935-1942
HQCD 95 / Apr '97 / Harlequin

Cujo

☐ ADVENTURES IN FOAM
NOZACD 03 / 10 Aug '98 / Ninebar

Cullen, Noreen

☐ BOW BRIDGES (Cullen, Noreen & Adrian Burns)
CMCD 063 / Nov '97 / Celtic Music

Cullum, Jim

☐ BATTLE OF THE BANDS (Cullum, Jim Jazz Band & Banv Gibson)
RWCD 4 / Jun '96 / Riverwalk

☐ BOOGIE WOOGIE (Cullum, Jim Jazz Band & David Holt/Dick Hyman)
RWCD 2 / Jun '96 / Riverwalk

☐ HOORAY FOR HOAGY (Cullum, Jim Jazz Band)
ACD 251 / '91 / Audiophile

☐ MUSIC OF JELLY ROLL MORTON (Cullum, Jim Jazz Band)
SOSCD 1254 / Jul '93 / Stomp Off

☐ SUPER SATCH (Cullum, Jim Big Band)
SOSCD 1148 / Jan '88 / Stomp Off

Cult

☐ CULT
BBL 164CD / 10 Nov '97 / Beggars Banquet

☐ DREAMTIME
Horse nation / Butterflies / Flower in the desert / Bad medicine waltz / Spiritwalker / 83rd dream / Go West / Gimmick / Dreamtime / Rider in the snow
BBL 57 CD / Oct '88 / Beggars Banquet

☐ ELECTRIC
Wild flower / Peace dog / Li'l devil / Aphrodisiac jacket / Electric ocean / Bad fun / King country man / Born to be wild / Love removal machine / Outlaw / Memphis hip shake
BBL 80CD / Apr '97 / Beggars Banquet

☐ GHOST DANCE (Death Cult)
BBL 2008CD / Sep '96 / Beggars Banquet

☐ INTERVIEW DISC
CBAK 4027 / Sep '90 / Baktabak

☐ LOVE
Nirvana / Big neon glitter / Love / Brother wolf, sister moon / Rain / Phoenix / Hollow man / Revolution / She sells sanctuary / Black angel
BBL 65CD / Apr '97 / Beggars Banquet

☐ PURE CULT (The Best Of The Cult)
She sells sanctuary / Fire woman / Lil' devil / Spiritwalker / Witch / Revolution / Wild hearted son / Love removal machine / Rain / Edie (ciao baby) / Heart of soul / Love / Wildflower / Go west / Ressurection joe / Sun king / Sweet soul sister / Earth mofo
BEGA 130CD / Jan '93 / Beggars Banquet

☐ SONIC TEMPLE
Fire woman / Sun king / Sweet soul sister / Soul asylum / Soldier blue / Edie (ciao baby) / American horse / Automatic blues / Wake up time for freedom / New York City
BBL 98CD / Apr '97 / Beggars Banquet

☐ SOUTHERN DEATH CULT (Southern Death Cult)
All glory / Fat man / Today / False faces / Crypt / Crow / Faith / Vivisection / Apache / Moya
BBL 2009CD / Sep '96 / Beggars Banquet

Cult Maniax

☐ LIVE AT ADAM AND EVE'S
RRCD 012 / 13 Apr '98 / Retch

Cultural Roots

☐ PRETTY WOMAN
LG 21073 / Mar '93 / Lagoon

Culture

☐ BALDHEAD BRIDGE
Them a payaka / How can I leave jah / Bald head bridge / Behold I come / Love shine bright / Jah love / Zion gate / So long babylon / Fool I (and I)
SHCD 44017 / Mar '94 / Shanachie

☐ CULTURE AT WORK
SHANCD 43047 / '89 / Shanachie

☐ CULTURE IN DUB - 15 DUB SHOTS
HBCD 173 / Aug '94 / Heartbeat

☐ CUMBOLO
They never love in this time / Innocent blood / Cumbolo / Poor Jah people / Natty never get weary / Natty dread naw run / Down in Jamaica / This train / Payday / Mind who you beg for help
SHANCD 44005 / '88 / Shanachie

☐ GOOD THINGS
Hand 'a' bowl / Good things / Love music / Psalm of Bob Marley / Cousin rude boy / Youthman move / Righteous loving / Chanting on
RASCD 3048 / Aug '96 / Ras

☐ LION ROCK
NETCD 1005 / Apr '95 / Network

☐ ONE STONE
RASCD 3188 / Apr '96 / Ras

☐ PEACE AND LOVE
Peace and love / Peace and love / Peace and love / Capture rasta / Capture rasta / Capture rasta / Old tattoo / Praise him / Old tattoo / This way / This way / Etc. / Step along / Step along / Five to one strip me / Five to one strip me / Praise him / Praise him / Mr. music / Mr. music / Soon come / Soon come / Pure war / Pure war
CPCD 8024 / Feb '94 / Charly

☐ PEACE AND LOVE
RN 7023 / Jun '97 / Rhino

☐ PRODUCTION SOMETHING
Too long in slavery / Garvey / Trod on / Weeping / Production something / Pyaka / Dog a go nyam dog / Black rose / Children of Israel
CDHB 151 / 27 Apr '98 / Heartbeat

☐ RAS PORTRAITS
One stone / Youth man move / Addis Ababa / Good things / Lazybones / Chanting on / Mark of the beast / I tried / Psalm of Bob Marley / Stoned again / Slice of Mount Zion / Righteous dub
RAS 3321 / Jun '97 / Ras

☐ STONED
Dubbing in the capital / Eye of the needle / Stoned again / We need answers / And the river ran red / Determined / Lazybones / Firm up yourself / Mark of the beast / Can't get we out / It's about time / One track mind
RAS 3177 / Feb '97 / Ras

☐ STRICTLY CULTURE
Behold / Two sevens clash / Holy mount zion / International herb / Natty never get weary / Calling rasta for I / Natty dread taking over / Zion gate / Jah love / See them a come / Stop the fussing and fighting / I'm not ashamed / Tell me where you get it / Iron sharpening iron / Get ready to ride the lion to zion / Work on natty / Jah pretty face / Cumbolo
MCCD 158 / May '94 / Music Club

☐ TOO LONG IN SLAVERY
Behold / Poor jah people / Stop the fussing and fighting / Cumbolo / Work on Natty / Tell me where you get it / Iron sharpening iron / International herb / Too long in slavery / Shepherd / Holy mount zion / Never get weary / Citizen as a peaceful dub
CDFL 9011 / Sep '90 / Frontline

☐ TROD ON
HBCD 137 / Jun '93 / Heartbeat

☐ TRUST ME
Trust me / Riverside / Outcast / Writing on the wall / No night / Walk with Jah / Chant down Babylon / Dirty tricks / Black starliner / Jah pretty face / Reasoning / Babylon a weep / Jah pretty face
RASCD 3240 / Sep '97 / Ras

☐ TWO SEVENS CLASH
Callin' rasta for I / I'm alone in the wilderness / Pirate days / Two sevens clash / I'm not ashamed / Get ready to ride the lion to Zion / Black starliner / Jah pretty face / See them a-come / Natty dread taking over
SHANCD 44001 / '88 / Shanachie

☐ WINGS OF A DOVE
Marcus / Why worry about them / Marriage in canaan / Wings of a dove / Freedom time / Rub-a-dub style / Pass on / Campyard / Too much pressure / England fireplace
SHCD 43097 / Jul '92 / Shanachie

Culture Beat

☐ CULTURE BEAT
Inside out / Intro / Walk the same line / Get it right / Troubles / Nothing can come ... take me away / Miracle / Crying in the rain / Do I have you / Under my skin / Worth the wait / In the mood
4874042 / Jun '96 / Epic

☐ REMIX ALBUM
Der erdbeermund / No deeper meaning / I like you / Tell me that you wait / Mr. Vain / Got to get it / Anything / World in your hands / Adelante / DMC Megamix
4776692 / 2 Feb '98 / Epic

☐ SERENITY
Serenity (prolog) / Mr. Vain / Got to get it / World in your hands / Adelante / Rocket to the moon / Anything / Key to your heart / Other side of me / Hurt / Mother Earth / Serenity (epilog) / ID Tania / ID Jay
4741012 / Sep '96 / Epic

Culture Ceilidh Band

☐ AFTER THE CEILIDH
Loch lomond / Dark island / Skye boat song / Mist covered mountains / Castlebay / Fir na fhata / Skye boat song / Will ye no come back again / Leezie lindsay / Let's have a ceilidh / Mhari's wedding / Leaving of liverpool / Macpherson's rant / Macauley's silver spoon / Mhari's wedding / Let's have a ceildh / Wild mountain thyme / Ye banks and braes / Auld lang syne
CDITV 543 / May '93 / Scotdisc

Culture Club

☐ 12" COLLECTION PLUS
11152 / Sep '97 / Caroline

☐ BEST OF CULTURE CLUB, THE
Do you really want to hurt me / White boy / Church of the poison mind / Changing everyday / War song / I'm afraid of me / It's a miracle / Dream / Time (Clock of the heart) / Dive / Victims / I'll tumble 4 ya / Miss me blind / Mistake no. 3 / Medal song / Karma chameleon
CDVIP 102 / Sep '94 / Virgin

☐ BEST OF CULTURE CLUB, THE (18 Original Hits/3CD Set)
Karma chameleon / Church of the poison mind / It's a miracle / White boy / Dream / Victims / Do you really want to hurt me / Time (clock of the heart) / Mistake no.3 / Changing everyday / Dive / Move away / War song / I'll tumble 4 ya / Medal song / I'm afraid of me / Miss me blind / God thank you woman
LAD 873182 / Nov '96 / Disky

☐ COLLECT 12" MIXES PLUS
Move away / Miss me blind/It's a miracle / God thank you woman / I'll tumble 4 ya / Love is cold / Do you really want to hurt me / Everything I own / Colour by numbers / From luzury to heartache / Time / Black money / Love is love / Man shake / War song
CDVIP 116 / Mar '94 / Virgin VIP

☐ COLOUR BY NUMBERS
Karma chameleon / It's a miracle / Black money / Changing everyday / That's the way / Church of the poison mind / Miss me blind / Mr. Man / Storm keeper / Victims
CDV 2285 / Feb '92 / Virgin

☐ KISSING TO BE CLEVER
White boy / You know I'm not crazy / I'll tumble 4 ya / Take control / Love twist / Boy boy (I'm the boy) / I'm afraid of me / White boys can't control it / Do you really want to hurt me
CDVIP 158 / Oct '96 / Virgin VIP

☐ THIS TIME
Do you really want to hurt me / Move away / I'll tumble 4 ya / Love is love / Victims / Karma chameleon / Church of the poison mind / Miss me blind / Time (Clock of the heart) / It's a miracle / Black money / War song / I'll tumble 4 ya (US 12" mix) / Miss me blind (US 12" mix)
CDVTV 1 / Apr '92 / Virgin

☐ WAKING UP WITH THE HOUSE ON FIRE
Dangerous man / War song / Unfortunate thing / Crime time / Mistake no.3 / Dive / Medal song / Don't talk about it / Mannequin / Hello goodbye
CDVIP 205 / 3 Aug '98 / Virgin VIP

Culture Musical Club

☐ TAARAB MUSIC OF ZANZIBAR VOL.4
Sibadili / Mwiko / Bingwa amekwenda kapa / Subalkheri mpenzi / Kupendana kwetu sisi / Sasa sinaye / Jipeleleze / Nimtakaye hataki / Mbuzi / Nieye / Umenita azizi
CDORBD 041 / May '89 / Globestyle

Culturemix

☐ CULTUREMIX (Culturemix & Bill Nelson)
Luna park / Radio head / Housewives on drugs / Dancematic / Four postcards home / Zebra / Exile / Tangram / Cave paintings
RES 113CD / Apr '97 / Resurgence

Cultus Sanguine

☐ CULTUS SANGUINE
WLR 006CD / Jul '95 / Wounded Love

☐ SHADOW'S BLOOD
CANDLE 021CD / 23 Feb '98 / Candlelight

Cunliffe, Bill

☐ PAUL SIMON SONG BOOK, A
You can call me Al / I do it for your love / Oh, Marion / One trick pony / Scarborough Fair / Jonah / Still crazy after all these years / Mrs. Robinson / America / Boxer / 59th Street Bridge song / Bridge over troubled water
77005 / Nov '93 / Discovery

☐ RARE CONNECTION, A
Stella by starlight / Chick it out / Jamaican lounge lizards / Cityscape / Rare connection / Big slide / Joyous dance / Minnesota / Miyako / Nobody else but me
77007 / Apr '94 / Discovery

Cunningham, David

☐ ARTIFICIAL HOMELAND (Cunningham, David & Angela Jaegar)
Silver thread / Artificial homeland / Beyond that star / Wood and glass / Fortuna / Turning left / Made of sand / Unlock the hills / Blue gold seven / Forsythia / Hot day / Time can make a difference / Radioloop / River west
PIANO 509 / 10 Aug '98 / Piano

☐ WATER
Stars / Next day / Once removed / Fourth sea / White, blue and grey / Shade creek / Short winter's day / Blue river / Beneath the vines / Yellow river / Low sun / Only shadows / Liquid hand / Dark ocean / Same day
MTM 31 / Sep '96 / Made To Measure

Cunningham, Deirdre

☐ CITY OF TRIBES
City of tribes / Dig for water / Mystical island / Secret pathway / Stormy heart / Fire on the line / Terror times / Darlin' Corey / September 1913 / Stoney fingers and star of Munster
CDLDL 1246 / Jan '97 / Lochshore

☐ CRY FROM THE HEART, A
CDLDL 1277 / 14 Aug '98 / Lochshore

Cunningham, John

☐ FAIR WARNING
Celtic society's quickstep/42nd Highlander's farewell / Archibald MacDonald of Keppoch / Planxty Drew/Planxty Wilkinson / Sad is my fate / Lord Drummond/Lady Margaret Stewart/Crarae / Logan water / Drovers lads/Mug of brown ale / Waulkin o' the fauld / Fair warning
GLCD 1047 / Oct '88 / Green Linnet

Cunningham, John

☐ SHANKLY GATES
LADIDA 020 / Jul '94 / La-Di-Da

Cunningham, Larry

☐ AT HIS BEST
Good old country music / They wouldn't do it now / Ballybunion by the sea / Night coach to Dallas / I love you because / 90 years on / My Kathleen / Is his love any better than mine / Forty shades of green / Pretty little girl from Omagh / Emerald Isle Express / Come back to Erin / Blue side of lonesome / Lough Gowna / Me ould tamborine / Lovely Leitrim / There's been a change in you / Seems like I'm always leaving / I used to be a railroad bum / Old Bog road / Annaghdown
3036000922 / Feb '97 / Carlton

☐ VERY BEST OF IRELAND, THE
CDC 038 / Dec '97 / Ceol

Cunningham, Matt

☐ DANCE MUSIC OF IRELAND VOL.10
ARCD 026 / May '98 / Ainm

☐ DANCE MUSIC OF IRELAND VOL.9
ARCD 019 / May '98 / Ainm

☐ GREEN HILLS OF ERIN, THE
ARCD 020 / May '98 / Ainm

☐ MEMORIES OF IRELAND
ARCD 021 / May '98 / Ainm

☐ SPIRIT OF IRELAND
ARCD 025 / May '98 / Ainm

☐ WEST OF THE OLD RIVER SHANNON
ARCD 022 / May '98 / Ainm

Cunningham, Phil

☐ AIRS AND GRACES
Andy m. stewart's reel-the harsh february / House in rose valley / Miss rowan davies / Flodigarry island-the wee man from skye / Joey's tune / Log splitter jig-you'll have a dram / Margaret mackinnon of digg / Farewell to ireland-hogties reel
GLCD 3032 / Nov '93 / Green Linnet

☐ PALOMINO WALTZ, THE
Bombardier beetle/Webbs wonderful / Ross Memorial Hospital / Palomino waltz/Donna's waltz / Four stroke reel/Martin O'Connor's flying clog / Leaving Glen Affric / Ceilidh funk / Wedding / Violet Tulloch's welcome to the Crask of Aigas / Laird of Drumblair / Ciara McCarthy's lullaby
GLCD 1102 / Nov '92 / Green Linnet

☐ REBOX
GLCD 200 / May '94 / Green Linnet

☐ RELATIVITY (Cunningham, Phil & Johnny/M. O Domhnaill/T. Ni Dhomhnail)
Hut on Staffin Island / Sandy MacLeod of Garafad / Soft horse reel / There was a lady / Gile Mear / Gracelands / When Barney flew over the hills / Leaving Brittany / Pernod waltz / An seanduine doite / John Cunningham's return to Edinburgh / Heather bells/Bell reel / Limerick lasses / Ur-Chill an Chreagain
GLCD 1059 / Feb '88 / Green Linnet

Cunningham, Woody

☐ NEVER SAY NEVER
Highways of my life / Animal / Forgive me / Body to body / Remove your halo / Tonite / You fooled me / Love is taking over / Hung up on your love / Never say never
EXCDP 15 / May '97 / Expansion

Cuppini, Gil

☐ WHATS NEW VOL.2 (Cuppini, Gil Quintet)
RTCL 811CD / Jul '96 / Right Tempo

Curbelo, Jose

☐ LIVE AT CHINA DOLL (New York 1946)
TCD 086 / Jan '98 / Tumbao Cuban Classics

Curd Duca

☐ MINIMALISTIC MOOD (Switched On Wagner)
EFA 006812 / Nov '96 / Mille Plateau

Cure

☐ 100 TEARS (A Tribute To The Cure) (Various Artists)
CLP 00012 / 15 Dec '97 / Cleopatra

☐ BOYS DON'T CRY
Boys don't cry / Plastic passion / 10.15 Saturday night / Accuracy / Object / Jumping someone else's train / Subway song / Killing an arab / Fire in Cairo / Another day / Grinding halt / World War / Three imaginary boys
8150112 / Jun '92 / Fiction

☐ CONCERT - THE CURE LIVE
Shake dog shake / Primary / Charlotte sometimes / Hanging gardens / Give me it / Walk / Hundred years / Forest / 10.15 Saturday night / Killing an arab / Heroin face / Boys don't cry / Subway song / At night / In your house / Drowning man / Other voices / Funeral party / All mine / Forever
8236822 / Jun '92 / Fiction

☐ CURE (Interview Disc)
3D 003 / Dec '96 / Network

☐ CURE: INTERVIEW PICTURE DISC
CBAK 4003 / Apr '88 / Baktabak

☐ DISINTEGRATION
Plainsong / Closedown / Last dance / Fascination Street / Same deep water as you / Homesick / Pictures of you / Love song / Lullaby / Prayers for rain / Disintegration / Untitled
8393532 / Jun '92 / Fiction

☐ FAITH
All cats are grey / Carnage visors / Doubt / Drowning man / Faith / Funeral party / Holy hour / Other voices / Primary
8276872 / Jun '92 / Fiction

☐ GALORE (The Singles 1987-1997)
Why can't I be you / Catch / Just like heaven / Hot hot hot / Lullaby / Fascination Street / Love song / Pictures of you / Never enough / Close to me / High / Friday I'm in love / Letter to Elise / 13th / Mint car / Strange attraction / Gone / Wrong number
FIXCD 30 / 3 Nov '97 / Fiction

☐ HEAD ON THE DOOR, THE
In between days / Kyoto song / Blood / Six different ways / Push / Baby screams / Close to me / Night like this / Screw / Sinking
8272312 / Jun '92 / Fiction

☐ INTERVIEW, THE
SPEEK 015 / 16 Mar '98 / Talking Music

☐ JAPANESE WHISPERS
Let's go to bed / Walk / Love cats / Dream / Just one kiss / Upstairs room / Lament / Speak my language
8174702 / Jun '92 / Fiction

☐ KISS ME, KISS ME, KISS ME
Kiss / Catch / Torture / If only tonight we could sleep / Why can't I be you / How beautiful you are... / Snakepit / Just like heaven / Hot hot hot / All I want / One more time / Like cockatoos / Icing sugar smooth / Perfect girl / Thousand hours / Shiver and shake / Fight
8321302 / Jun '92 / Fiction

☐ PORNOGRAPHY
Pornography / Hanging gardens / Hundred years / Siamese twins / Figurehead / Strange day / Cold / Short term effect
8276882 / Jun '92 / Fiction

☐ SEVENTEEN SECONDS
At night / Final sound / Forest / In your house / M / Play for today / Reflection / Secrets / Seventeen seconds / Three
8253542 / Jun '92 / Fiction

☐ THREE IMAGINARY BOYS
Accuracy / Another day / Fire in Cairo / Foxy lady / Grinding halt / It's not you / Meat hook / Object / So what / Subway / 10.15 Saturday night / Three imaginary boys
8276862 / Jun '92 / Fiction

☐ TOP, THE
Caterpillar / Piggy in the mirror / Empty world / Bananafishbones / Top / Shake dog shake / Bird mad girl / Wailing wall / Give me it / Dressing up
8211362 / Jun '92 / Fiction

☐ WILD MOOD SWINGS
Want / Club America / This is a lie / 13th / Strange attraction / Mint car / Jupiter crash / Round and round and round / Gone / Numb / Return / Trap / Treasure / Bare
FIXCD 28 / Apr '96 / Fiction

Curiosity Killed The Cat

☐ VERY BEST OF CURIOSITY KILLED THE CAT, THE
Down to Earth / Name and number / Free / Misfit / First place / Go go ahead / Keep on trying / Ball and chain / Cascade / Curiosity killed the cat / Treat you so well / Who are you / Bullet / Mile high / We just gotta do it (for us) / Something new, something blue / Shallow memory / Ordinary day
5525482 / Sep '96 / Spectrum

Curious Digit

☐ HESSIAN HILLS
JAG 06 / 16 Mar '98 / Jagjaguwar

Curless, Dick

☐ DRAG 'EM OFF THE INTERSTATE SOCK IT TO 'EM (The Hits Of Dick Curless)
RE 821682 / 1 Jun '98 / Razor & Tie

☐ TOMBSTONE EVERY MILE, A (7CD Set)
Coat of Maine / Ida dance / Jelly doughnuts / Fiddlers dance / Cottage in the pines / Cupid's arrow / Baby darling / Naponee / Rocky mountain queen / Streets of Laredo / Foggy foggy dew / China nights / Blues in my mind / Lovin' Dan sixty minute man / Blue yodel no.6 / Bright lights and blonde / Travellin' man / I'm ragged but I'm right / St. James infirmary / I am a pilgrim / Tuck me to sleep in my old kentucky home / I ain't got nobody / Rainbow in my heart / Something's wrong with you / Evil hearted man blues / I dreamed of a hillbilly heaven / Deck of cards / High noon / Strawberry roan / Red river valley / Cowboy Jack / On top of old smokey / Home on the range / Bury me not on the lone prairie / Chisholm trail / I ride an old paint / Whoopie ti yi yo / Green grow the lilacs / Last roundup / Crawdad song / Rock Island line / Don't fence me in / Big rock candy mountain / Rovin' gambler / Molly darlin' / Yellow rose of texas / Liza Jane / Careless love / Buffalo girl / San Antonio Rose / What a friend we have in Jesus / Whispering hope / My old kentucky home / Beautiful dreamer / I was seeing Nellie home / You tell me your dream, I'll tell you mine / Silver threads among the gold / I've been working on the railroad / Little brown jug / Rock of ages / Church in the wildwood / Bring them in / Onward Christian soldiers / Nearer my God to thee / In the garden / Jesus loves me / I love to tell the story / Old rugged cross / Tombstone every mile / Heart talk / King of the road / Uncle Tom / Six times a day / Down by the old river / Teardrops in my heart / Nine pound hammer / Sunny side of the mountain / Tater raisin / Down by the river / Tater raisin' man / Friend that makes it four / Mama's hand / Mom and Dad's waltz / Mama's hands / Daddy and home / I'm going home / Buckaroo / Little Terry / Please don't make me go / You, you only you / Terrible tangles web / Devil like me needs / No fool like an old fool / Old standby / Too late / I can't stop (lovin' you) / For ever and ever / Congratulations, you're absolutely / Highwayman / Baron / Memories / Old picture and a ring / Good job hunting and fishing / How do I say goodbye / I didn't know love was this way / House of memories / All of me belongs to you / My side of the night / Game of love and poker / Try and leave me / On the outside looking in / Hello honey / Hobo / Tears of Saint Ann / I went bad for a pretty girl / Tornado tillie / Life goes on / Big foot / Mumble boogy / You can't go back again / Shoes / When Dad was around / End of the road / Bury the bottle with me / Wrinkled, crinkled, wadded dollar bill / Just for the record / I'm worried about me / Heartline special / Secret of your heart / Bummin' on track E / Wild side of town / Nobody knows you (when you're down and out) / Things / Easy woman / Down at the corner at Kelly's / Tonight's the night my angels halo fell / Maybe I'll cry over you / It's nothing to me / Good old days / Over the edge / Blue is a beautiful color / Good year for the wine / Tears instead of cheers / All I need is you / Brand new bed of roses / Be here to love me / Kentucky boy / Fanning the flame / Sun / Somebody else / Jamaica farewell / Golden rocket / Just a closer walk with thee / I'm in love again / I walk the line / Marianne / Down by the riverside / Oh, lonesome me / Where is your heart tonight / I can get along without you now / What do I care / There's been a change in me / After all I ain't got much to lose / Monday night / Just a little lovin' / Tuck me to sleep / Montreal express / Station breaks / Tumbleweed kid
BCD 15882 / Feb '96 / Bear Family

☐ TRAVELLING THROUGH
ROUCD 3137 / Aug '95 / Rounder

☐ WELCOME TO MY WORLD
RRCD 007 / Aug '93 / Rocade

Curlew

☐ BEAUTIFUL WESTERN SADDLE, A
RUNE 50 / Nov '87 / Cuneiform

Current 93

☐ ALL THE PRETTY LITTLE HORSES
DURTRO 030CD / Oct '96 / Durtro

☐ AS THE WORLD DISAPPEARS
DURTRO 007CD / Oct '96 / Durtro

☐ CHRIST AND THE PALE QUEENS
MAL 666CD / Oct '96 / Maldoror

☐ CROOKED CROSSES FOR THE NODDING
UD 033CD / Sep '90 / United Dairies

☐ CROWLEYMASS
Crowleymass / As for the other side (Christmassacre) / Crowleymass / I arise
DURTRO 418CD / Jul '97 / Durtro

☐ CURRENT 93 & DOGS BLOOD ORDER (Current 93 & Dogs Blood Order)
Maldoror is dead / Maldoror ceases to exist
DURTRO 039CD / Oct '97 / Durtro

☐ DAWN
DURTRO 002CD / Oct '96 / Durtro

☐ DOG'S BLOOD RISING
DURTRO 027CD / Oct '96 / Durtro

☐ EARTH COVERS EARTH
DURTRO 012CD / Oct '96 / Durtro

☐ HITLER AS KHALKI
DURTRO 014CD / Oct '96 / Durtro

☐ HORSEY
Diana / Death of the corn / Tree / Broken birds fly / Horsey
DURTRO 032 / Apr '97 / Durtro

☐ IMPERIUM
DURTRO 008CD / Oct '96 / Durtro

☐ IN A FOREIGN TOWN, IN A FOREIGN LAND (Current 93 & Thomas Ligotti)
His shadow shall rise to a higher place / Bells shall sound forever / Soft voice whispers nothing / When you hear the singing you will know it is time
DURTRO 035CD / Jul '97 / Durtro

☐ ISLAND
DURTRO 006CD / Oct '96 / Durtro

☐ LIVE AT THE BAR MALDOROR
DURTRO 001CD / Jan '89 / Durtro

☐ LIVE IN FRANKFURT 1991 (Current 93 & Death In June/Sol Invictus)
WSBLCD 001 / Oct '96 / World Serpent

☐ LOONEY RUNES
DURTRO 004CD / Oct '96 / Durtro

☐ MEET THEIR WATERLOO (Current 93 & Aryan Aquarians)
Cry cry cry / My secret gardener / Bugs Bunny at Waterloo / Dangerous / Desperado / Aryan Aquarians' theme
DURTRO 038CD / Oct '97 / Durtro

☐ MENSTRUAL NIGHT
DURTRO 020CD / Oct '96 / Durtro

☐ MENSTRUAL YEARS (2CD Set)
DURTRO 016CD / Oct '96 / Durtro

☐ NATURE UNVEILED
DURTRO 009CD / Oct '96 / Durtro

☐ OF RUINE...
DURTRO 018CD / Oct '96 / Durtro

☐ SWASTIKAS FOR NODDY
Benediction / Blessing / North / One eye / Black sun bloody moon / Oh coal black Smith / Panzer rune / Black flowers please / Final church / Summer of love / Hey ho the Noddy (oh) / Beau soleil / Scarlet woman / Stair song / Angel / Since yesterday / Valediction / Malediction
DURTRO 017CD / Oct '96 / Durtro

☐ THUNDER PERFECT MIND
DURTRO 011CD / Oct '96 / Durtro

Current Value

☐ FREQUENCY HUNT
EFA 060782 / 15 Jun '98 / Position Chrome

Currie, Cherie

☐ MESSIN' WITH THE BOYS (Currie, Cherie & Marie)
RME 0189CD / 19 Jan '98 / Renaissance

Curry, Clifford

☐ CLIFFORD'S BLUES
APCD 122 / May '97 / Appaloosa

Curse

☐ TEENAGE MEAT
OPM 2110CD / May '97 / Other People's Music

Curse Of The Golden Vampire

☐ CURSE OF THE GOLDEN VAMPIRE, THE
Caucasian deathmask / Escape the earth / Substance X: *Curse Of The Golden Vampire & MC Beans* / Low-tech predator / Anti-matter / Kamikaze space programme / Temple of the yellow snake
DHRCD 014 / 22 Jun '98 / Digital Hardcore

Curson, Ted

☐ PLENTY OF HORN
Caravan / Nosruc / Things we did last summer / Dem's blues / Ahma (see ya) / Flatted fifth / Bali Ha'i / Antibes / Mr. Teddy
CDBOP 018 / Mar '94 / Boplicity

☐ TEARS FOR DOLPHY
BLCD 760190 / Jun '94 / Black Lion

☐ TED CURSON GROUP FEATURING ERIC DOLPHY
COD 016 / Jun '92 / Jazz View

Curtin, Dan

☐ ART AND SCIENCE
Airport martini / America / Ride / A 23 / Art and science / One evening at Mrs. Applebee's / Lunar groove / Mist / More
PF 051CD / Oct '96 / Peacefrog

☐ NEW WORLD
SBLCD 5026 / 16 Mar '98 / Sublime

☐ WEB OF LIFE
Matter of sound / Quantum / Biotic / Intersellar perception / Out of sight and mind / Path / Subconscious / Awareness / 3rd from the sun / Envision
PF 038CD / Sep '95 / Peacefrog

Curtin, Glen

☐ WILD COLONIAL BOY
MACCD 316 / Aug '96 / Autograph

Curtis, Amy

☐ PEACE FOR LOVE
FSR 5004CD / Mar '95 / Fresh Sound

Curtis, Charles

☐ LESSER WRITINGS (Curtis, Charles Trio)
CD 12632E / 24 Nov '97 / Strange Ways

Curtis, Mac

☐ BLUE JEAN HEART
Grandaddy's rockin' / Just so you call me / Half hearted love / If I had me a woman / Low road / That ain't nothing but right / Don't you love me / You ain't treatin' me right / I'll be gentle / Say so / Blue jean heart / Goosebumps / You are my very special baby / What you want / Little Miss Linda / Missy Ann
CDCHARLY 164 / Feb '91 / Charly

☐ BLUE JEAN HEART
KCD 6011 / 17 Nov '97 / King

☐ ROCKABILLY READY
Rockabilly ready / Love Doctor / Show me the money / Tell me what'll do / Old rock 'n' rollers like me / Miss Linda's still fine / One foot loose / Blues man / Let's go downtown / Keep on rockin' / Hey hey little lady / Mesmerized / Are you ready to rumble / Side wind / Little mama have mercy / Frantic
JRCD 31 / 27 Apr '98 / Jappin' & Rockin'

☐ ROCKABILLY UPRISING (The Best Of Mac Curtis)
HMG 6601 / Aug '97 / Hightone

Curtis, Ronald

☐ THANKS FOR THE MEMORY
There's a blue ridge round my heart / Old pianna rag / I can't give you anything but love / Liza / Flamingo / Sylvia / Ma curly headed baby / Oh lady be good / Sweet Sue, just you / Happy feet / Bye bye blues / Love is / O' my beloved father / Crackin' corn / Memories of you / Thanks for the memory / I've got a pocketful of dreams / Cabaret / I've got my love to keep me warm / Powder your face with sunshine / Dambuster's march / Butterflies in the rain / Happy wanderer / Dixie / De camptown races / Old black Joe / Swanee river / Turkey in the straw / Marching through Georgia / Out of the blue / Storm at sea / Anchors aweigh / What shall we do with a drunken sailor / Hornpipe / Life on the ocean wave / Skye boat song / Eternal father / Strong to save / Comedian's galop / Tiger rag / Lucky old sun / Cactus polka / Here's to the next time / When day is done
CDGRS 1287 / May '96 / Grosvenor

Curtis, Winston

☐ WINSTON'S GREATS
CRCD 71 / 11 Aug '97 / Charm

Curtis, Yvonne

☐ BEST OF YVONNE CURTIS
BROWNCD 002 / Mar '96 / Brown

Curve

☐ COME CLEAN
UMD 80475 / 18 May '98 / Universal

Curved Air

☐ AIR CONDITIONING
It happened today / Stretch / Screw / Blind man / Vivaldi / Hide and seek / Propositions / Rob one / Situation
7599264332 / Jan '96 / WEA

☐ LIVE
HTDCD 49 / Dec '95 / HTD

☐ LOVECHILD
Exsultate Jubilate / Lovechild / Seasons / Flasher / Joan / Dancer / Widow / Paris by night
CLACD 342 / Jun '94 / Castle

☐ MIDNIGHT WIRE
Woman on a one night stand / Day breaks my heart / Pipe of dreams / Orange Street blues / Dance of love / Midnight wire / It happened today
HTDCD 50 / Dec '95 / HTD

☐ SECOND ALBUM
Young mother / Backstreet luv / Jumbo / You know / Puppets / Everdance / Bright summer's day / Piece of mind
7599264342 / Jan '96 / WEA

Cusack, Michael

☐ PIPERS OF DISTINCTION
Macphail of bunessan / Muir of ord / Bobbie cuthbertson / Troy's wedding / P / M jimmy macgregor / Colin thomson / Braes of castle grant / Lament for donald dougal mackay / Loch lubnaig / Orange and blue / Rose among the heather / Dalnahasaig / Deel amang the tailors / Miss girdle / Fairy dance / Reel of tulloch / High road to linton (reels) / P / M doanald maclean of lewis / Rab's wedding / Loch maree / Ist argylls crossing the river poe / My own land / Lovely stornoway / Flying scotsman / St. ninians parish centre ceildh / John macdonald's exercise / Major manson of clachnatrushal / Arniston castle / Cecily ross / Inveraray castle / Caledonian society of london / Loch carron / Mrs. mcpherson of inveran / Donald maclean's farewell to oban / Kantara to el arish / Irish washerwoman / P / M george allan
CDMON 807 / Jul '90 / Monarch

Cusan Tan

☐ CUSAN TAN
FFLACH 113CD / Aug '97 / Fflach

☐ RIDGE, THE
SCD 2116 / Jan '96 / Sain

Custy, Mary

☐ MARY CUSTY BAND, THE (Custy, Mary Band)
MCB 003CD / Nov '96 / MCB

☐ WAYS OF THE WORLD, THE
CMCD 065 / Dec '97 / Celtic Music

☐ WITH A LOT OF HELP FROM...
CMCD 064 / Dec '97 / Celtic Music

Custy, Tola

☐ SETTING FREE (Custy, Tola & Cyril O'Donoghue)
CICD 098 / Aug '94 / Clo Iar-Chonnachta

Cut Chemist

☐ FUTURE PRIMITIVE SESSIONS (Cut Chemist/Shortkut)
FPRCD 001 / 4 Apr '98 / Future Primitive/Ubiquity

Cutler, Chris

☐ LIVE IN MOSCOW, PRAGUE AND WASHINGTON (Cutler, Chris & Fred Frith)
RERCCFFCD / Apr '90 / ReR/ Recommended

☐ LIVE IN TRONDHEIM, BERLIN AND LIMOGES (Cutler, Chris & Fred Frith)
RERCCFF 2 / Oct '96 / ReR/ Recommended

Cutler, Ivor

☐ FLAT MAN
CRECD 236 / 29 Jun '98 / Creation

☐ LIFE IN A SCOTCH SITTING ROOM
CREV 035CD / May '95 / Rev-Ola

☐ LUDO
CREV 49CD / Mar '97 / Creation

☐ WET HANDLE, A
Her tissues / American drink / One day / Out of decency / My disposition / No I won't / It's stupid / By the bus / Thatcher generation / My vest / Goosie / When it warts / Her Zimmer / Farmers wife / Bets / Just in time / Specific sundry / Just listen / Breaking point / Spring back / Hell / Man / Place / Hello explorer / Not asking / His slow hand / Local creatures / Heptagon / Where's my razor / One side / Singing to my foot / Ride off / Great albatross / Berd / Half and half / Get off the road / Fine example / Face of people / Stand well clear / Naughty Sydney / Perverse / Bargain / Space sandwich / Baked beetle / Taking hands / Entitles / It / Kitchen knife / Not from Hens / Carpet / Beyond / Way out / To take / Do you call that living / On holiday / Taste of gunny / Blunt yashmak / Kiddies / I give up / My window box / Pain in the neck / Not even / Tablets / Flat thin chests / Good girl / He himself / Uncrossing her legs / Crete/ Greece / Squeaky / Oddly comforting / Original sweet / Bridge / Butterfly / Snaps / Just / Hummed and hawed / Thursday / Cosy nest / Slice of seedcake / What a funny room / Heavy rock / Whole forest / Little Hetty
CRECD 217 / May '97 / Creation

Cutting Crew

☐ BEST OF CUTTING CREW, THE
(I just) died in your arms / Any colour / Fear of falling / Everything but my pride / Contact high / Tip of your tongue / One for the mockingbird / I've been in love before / Life in a dangerous time / Don't look back / Scattering / Christians / (I just) died in your arms (mix) / Reach for the sky / (Between a) rock and a hard place / If that's the way you want it
CDVIP 121 / Dec '93 / Virgin VIP

Cutting Edge

☐ TURNING THE TIDE
Turning the tide / Seagate salsa / Beechgrove / Jig of slurs / When she sleeps / Sniffer's delight / Ass in the graveyard / Silver spire / O'Keefe's no.7 / Ceilidh Dave / Miss Rowan Davies / Shandon bells / Gorgon's Ola / Rudy's reggae / Lilly
NGCD 1007 / Jan '95 / Ninegates Music

Cutty Ranks

☐ 60 MILLION WAYS TO DIE
P 253871 / Nov '96 / Priority

☐ FROM MI HEART
SHCD 45001 / Jun '93 / Shanachie

Cutty Wren

☐ PARSON'S HAT
CICD 101 / Dec '94 / Clo Iar-Chonnachta

Cuzner, Kate

☐ FLY BY WIRE
Tell me know / Snake in the grass / Metamorphosis / Savannah song / Jim'll mix it / Fly by wire / Contemplation / Rain dance / Twisting shadows / Ballad for Paul / Rodent rap
FMRCD 28 / Jun '97 / Future

Cwithe

☐ ILLEGAL (2CD Set)
BR 028CD / Mar '97 / Blue Room Released

Cyan Kills E Boli

☐ DO NOT OPEN
EFA 155862 / Nov '95 / Gymnastic

Cyber-Tec

☐ LET YOUR BODY DIE
SPV 07661112 / Jan '96 / SPV

Cybermen

☐ CYBERMEN, THE
ES 111CD / Nov '96 / Estrus

Cybertron

☐ INTERFACE (The Roots Of Techno)
Clear / Eden / Enter / Techno city / Cosmic cars / Alleys of your mind / Megiddo / R 9 / Cosmic raindance / El Salvador / Vision
CDSEWD 069 / Jan '94 / Southbound

Cyborg

☐ CHRONICLES
RRS 951CD / Sep '96 / Die Hard/ Progress

Cyclone

☐ BRUTAL DESTRUCTION
3038652 / 29 Jun '98 / Axe Killer

Cyco Mike

☐ LOST MY BRAIN... (ONCE AGAIN)
I love destruction / All I ever get / FUBAR / All kinda crazy / Gonna be alright / Save a peace for me / Nothing to lose / Ain't gonna get me / Lost my brain once again / It's always something / Cyco Mike wants you / Ain't mess'n around
4811362 / Oct '95 / Epic

Cygnet Committee

☐ ROMANTIC
DANCECOP 13CD / 16 Feb '98 / Dancecop

Cykle

☐ CYKLE
GF 106 / 6 Jul '98 / Gear Fab

Cylob

☐ CYLOBIAN SUNSET
CAT 033CD / Jul '96 / Rephlex

☐ PREVIOUSLY UNAVAILABLE ON COMPACT DISC
Flicklife / Quadrephlex / Kobal / Flad / German / 4J / Plouth / Lave trader / Sanq / Triachus / Sixed / Durftal
CAT 055CD / 13 Apr '98 / Rephlex

Cymande

☐ CYMANDE
Message / Brothers on the slide / Dove / Bra / Fug / For baby woh / Rickshaw / Equitorial forest / Listen / Getting it back / Anthracite / Willy's headache / Genevieve / 'Pon de jungle / Rastafarian folk song / One more / Zion I
NEX CD 202 / Jul '92 / Sequel

Cynical Smile

☐ STUPAS
ORGAN 035CD / 10 Nov '97 / Org

Cypher In The Snow

☐ BLOW AWAY THE GLITTER DIAMONDS
CAR 24 / Jul '97 / Candy Ass

Cypress Hill

☐ BLACK SUNDAY
I wanna get high / I ain't goin' out like that / Insane in the brain / When the ship goes down / Lick a shot / Cock the hammer / Interlude / Li'l Putos / Legalize it / Hits from the bong / What go around come around, kid / A to the K / Hand on the glock / Break 'em off some
4740752 / Jul '93 / Ruff House

☐ CYPRESS HILL
Pigs / How I could just kill a man / Hand on the pump / Hole in the head / Ultraviolet dreams / Light another / Phuncky feel one / Break it up / Real estate / Stoned is the way of the walk / Psycobetabuckdown / Something for the blunted / Latin lingo / Funky Cypress Hill shit / Tres eqyis / Born to get busy
4688932 / Feb '97 / Ruff House

☐ TEMPLE OF BOOM
Spark another owl / Throw your set in the air / Stoned raiders / Illusions / Killa hill niggas / Boom biddy bye bye / No rest for the wicked / Make a move / Killafornia / Funk freakers / Locotes / Red light visions / Strictly hip hop / Let it rain / Everybody must get stoned
4781272
4781279 / Oct '95 / Ruff House

☐ UNRELEASED AND REVAMPED
Boom biddy bye bye / Throw your hands in the air / Intellectual dons: Cypress Hill & Call O Da Wild / Hands on the pump / Whatta you know / Hits from the bong / Illusions / Latin lingo / When the ship goes down
4852302 / Aug '96 / Columbia

Cyrille, Andrew

☐ DOUBLE CLUTCH (Cyrille, Andrew & Richard Teitelbaum)
SHCD 146 / Oct '97 / Silkheart

☐ METAMUSICIANS' STOMP (Cyrille, Andrew & Maono)
1200252 / Nov '93 / Black Saint

☐ MY FRIEND LOUIS (Cyrille, Andrew Quintet)
DIW 858 / Jun '92 / DIW

☐ NAVIGATOR, THE
1210622 / May '94 / Soul Note

☐ NUBA
1200302 / May '94 / Black Saint

☐ X-MAN
RN 1210982 / Oct '94 / Soul Note

Cyrka, Jan

☐ BEYOND THE COMMON GROUND
Horse of another colour / Equaliser / Two wheels are better than four / In search of common ground / On the contrary / From your lips / Western eyes / Missing the motive / I remember / Sitting on eggs / Hoodlum
CDGRUB 22 / Mar '92 / Food For Thought

☐ PRICKLY PEAR
Back in the saddle / In a broken dream / Yours is mine / Hard rain falls / Gonna make it happen / This land / Road to glory / Je t'embrasse / Scratching the fixtures / One whole heart
CDGRUB 32 / Feb '97 / Food For Thought

☐ SPIRIT
CDGRUB 29 / Oct '93 / Food For Thought

Cyrus, Billy Ray

☐ COVER TO COVER (The Best Of Billy Ray Cyrus)
It's all the same to me / Cover to cover / Bluegrass state of mind / Trail of tears / One last thrill / Storm in the heartland / Words by heart / Somebody new / In the heart of a woman / She's not cryin' anymore / Could've been me / Achy breaky heart
5348372 / Aug '97 / Mercury

☐ IT WON'T BE THE LAST
514758242 / Jul '93 / Mercury

☐ SOME GAVE ALL
Could've been me / Achy breaky heart / She's not cryin' anymore / Wher'm I gonna live / These boots are made for walkin' / Someday, somewhere, somehow / Never thought I'd fall in love with you / Ain't no good goodbye / I'm so miserable / Some gave all
5106352 / Mar '92 / Mercury

☐ STORM IN THE HEARTLAND
5260812 / Mar '95 / Mercury

☐ TRAIL OF TEARS
5328292 / Aug '96 / Mercury

Cythara

☐ CYTHARA
GLCD 001 / Feb '96 / Realwood

☐ CYTHARA
Sherwood forest / Alfonso XIII el Sabio / Brittany / Star of county down / For Ireland I'd not tell her name / Maids of Mounre Shore / Xchanter / Carolans concerto / Scarborough fair / Watkins ale / Planxty Irwin/Planxty Howard glasser / Mwynder maldwyn / Hachas / Grenadier and the lady / Canon
CDLDL 1245 / Mar '97 / Lochshore

☐ PLUCKIN' HAMMERED
Karla with a K / P.J. Cunninghams's odd dance / Tuesday morning/Dusty windmills / Let no man steal your thyme / Buxton races/About she goes / Lady Marian / Ramble away / Sam McGrady's/Denis Murphy's/Holm Band/Jemima's jig / Reel a bouche / Julia Delaney/Bristol hornpipe / Women of Ireland/ Morrison's jig/Over the hills and far away
CDLDL 1253 / Sep '97 / Lochshore

Czech Army Central Band

☐ FESTIVE CONCERT IN RUDOLFINUM
Intrada / Scherzo / Concerto for piccolo in C major / Allegro / Largo / Allegro molto / Bolero / Symphonic march / West Side Story / Florentine march
CQ 00332431 / May '98 / Clarton

☐ **FESTIVE MUSIC OF PRAGUE**
Towards a new life / Slavonic dance no.1 / Aus dem studentenleben / Bajarderen galopp / St. Hubert / Thousand and one nights / Cradle for sinful maidens / Festive music of Prague / Festivo ben ritmico / Musica Bohemica / Music for festival / Salsa verde / Prelude / Victory march
CQ 00372431 / May '98 / Clarton

☐ **KAREL BELOHOUBEK**
Bartered bride overture / First movement allegro con brio / Thais / Moto perpetuo op.11 / Rustle of spring / Dresdener / Night prelude / Candide overture / Mattinata for soprano saxophone / Bolero / Concertino for clarinet / Polonaise / Little etude / Metamorphoses of the wind waltz / Intrada / Welcome march / Devil's gallop
CQ 00342431 / May '98 / Clarton

☐ **PRAGUE PANORAMA**
CQ 00092 / Mar '96 / Clarton

Czukay, Holger

☐ **CANAXIS**
SPOONCD 15 / Jan '95 / Grey Area

☐ **CLASH (2CD Set) (Czukay, Holger & Dr. Walker)**
TCCD 9827 / 15 Jun '98 / Tone Casualties
EFA 123392 / 6 Mar '98 / Sideburn

☐ **FULL CIRCLE (Czukay, Holger/Jah Wobble/Jaki Liebezeit)**
How much are they / Where's the money / Full circle R.P.S. (No. 7) / Mystery R.P.S. (No. 8) / Trench warfare / Twilight world
CDOVD 437 / May '92 / Virgin

☐ **MOVIES**
Cool in the pool / Oh Lord give us more money / Persian love / Hollywood symphony
SPOONCD 35 / 19 Jan '98 / Spoon

☐ **MOVING PICTURES**
Longing for daydreams / All night long / Radio in an hourglass / Dark moon / Floatspace / Rhythms of a secret life
CDSTUMM 125 / May '93 / Mute

☐ **ON THE WAY TO THE PEAK OF NORMAL**
Witches multiplication table / Two bass shuffle / Hiss 'n' listen
SPOONCD 36 / 19 Jan '98 / Spoon

☐ **ROME REMAINS ROME**
Hey ba ba re bop / Blessed Easter / Sudetenland / Hit hit flop flop / Perfect world / Music in the air / Der osten ist rot (the east is red) / Das massenmedium / Photo song / Ronrad / Michy / Esperanto socialiste / Traum mal wieder
CDV 2408 / '88 / Virgin

Ode to perfume / On the way to the peak of normal /

D

D-Maximillian
☐ MY STORY
BLKMCD 10 / Oct '94 / Blakamix

D:Ream
☐ BEST OF D:REAM, THE
Things can only get better / U R The best thing / Take me away / Shoot me with your love / Unforgiven / I like it / Party up the world / Power / Blame it on me / Heart of gold / Star / Hold me now
0630190692 / May '97 / Magnet

☐ D:REAM ON VOL.1
Take me away / U R the best thing / Unforgiven / I like it / Glorious / So long movin' on / Picture my world / Blame it on me / Things can only get better / Star
4509933712 / Dec '96 / Magnet

D+
☐ D PLUS
KCD 72 / Aug '97 / K

D-Influence
☐ GOOD 4 WE
Good lover / I'm the one / Funny (how things change) / Good 4 we / No illusions / Journey / Changes / For you I sing this song / Sweetest things
7567951882 / Aug '92 / East West

☐ LONDON
Hypnotize / Good life / Shake it / I've got my mind made up / Magic / Hold on / Good morning heart ache are you with me / Lonely / There can be / Running away / Falling / Loving you / High life
ECHCD 016 / 7 Sep '98 / Echo

☐ PRAYER 4 UNITY
Waiting / will I / Should I / You're all I need / Afrojam / Brasilia interview interlude / Prayer for unity / Break up / Midnight / Phuncky times / Simmer down / Always
7559617512 / Jul '95 / East West

D-Note
☐ BABEL
Judgement / Babel / Now's the time / Aria / Bronx bull / Rain / Pharoah / More I see / Message / Lychia / Scheme of things / D notion
DOR 12CD / Aug '97 / Dorado

☐ COMING DOWN (The Soundtrack)
Lost and found / Short goodbye / 'Avin' it / Deep water / Just a little chaser / Coming down / Kite hill
VCRD 19 / Mar '97 / Virgin

☐ CRIMINAL JUSTICE
DOR 32CD / Aug '97 / Dorado

☐ D-NOTE
Moody / Lost and found / Coming up / Waiting hopefully / Long goodbye / Say what you mean / Tri-cyclic / Black dog / Changeless
CDVCR 2 / 21 Jul '97 / Virgin

D-Train
☐ GO FOR IT BABY
Go for it baby / Fight / End of the road / Ridin' on the I and n / Sleep keeps me awake / Turnin' me on / Funky mama / What's wrong with you / Take my warning / Bad is bad / Sweet mama / Born in georgia / Bettie lou
TRCD 9916 / Nov '93 / Tramp

☐ MUSIC/SOMETHING'S ON YOUR MIND
I treasure your pleasure / Something's on your mind / You're the reason / Hustle and bustle of the city / Thank you / I'll do anything / So far away / Keep giving me love / Shadow of your smile / Are you ready for me / Music / Children of the world / Let me show you / Don't you wanna ride
DEEPM 012 / Mar '97 / Deep Beats

☐ YOU'RE THE ONE FOR ME
You're the one for me / Walk on by / Tryin' to get over / Lucky day / D-Train theme / Keep on / Love vibrations / You're the one for me / You're the one for me / Keep on / D-Train dub / You're the one for me
DEEPM 010 / Jan '97 / Deep Beats

Da Beat Goes
☐ NEW FRATERNITY OF HOUSE
DST 305102 / Nov '96 / House Nation

Da Brat
☐ ANUTHATANTRUM
Anuthatantrum / My beliefs / Sittin' on top of the world / Let's all get high / West Side interlude / Just a little bit more / Keepin' it live / Ghetto love / Lyrical molestation / Live it up / Make it happen
4841982 / Oct '96 / Columbia

Da Costa, Paulino
☐ SUNRISE
Taj Mahal / I'm going to Rio / African sunrise / Walkman / O mar e meu chao / You came into my life / My love / You've got a special kind of love / Carioca / Groove
CD 2312143 / Apr '94 / Pablo

Da Costa, Raie
☐ KEYBOARD WIZARDS OF THE GERSHWIN ERA VOL.7
GEMMCD 9207 / Jul '98 / Pearl

Da Costa, Tico
☐ BRAZIL ENCANTO
CDC 211 / Jun '93 / Music Of The World

Da Fustra
☐ FOAMING SEA, THE
Introduction / Boston two step / Billt Thom's reel / Inside oot fish eater / Brydon Morrison's reel / Veleta waltz / Boston two step / Gay Gordons / Scandinavian waltz / Cape Breton fiddler's welcome to Shetland / Mrs. Norman MacKeigan / Miss Susan MacLean / When you and I were young Maggie / Joe Foster's jig/Mrs. Stewart's jig of Bombay / Rosewood / Kiwi reels / Miss CM Barbour / James Forester Rankine / Quickstep / Brittania two step / Calum Donaldson / Brumley brae / Wing commander Donald McKenzies reel / Strip the willow / St. Bernard's waltz / Mrs McPherson of Clunie / Wee murdie / Alex little MC
HRMCD 002 / 1 Nov '97 / Highlander

Da Lench Mob
☐ GUERILLAS IN THE MIST
Capital punishment in America / Buck tha devil / Lost in tha system / You and your heroes / All on my nut sac / Guerillas in tha mist / Lenchmob also in tha group / Ain't got no class / Freedom got an AK / Ankle blues / Who ya gonna shoot wit that / Lord have mercy / Inside tha head of a black man
7567922062 / Nov '92 / Street Knowledge

☐ PLANET OF DA APES
Scared lil' nigga / Chocolate city / Cut throats / King of the jungle / Who is it / Planet of da apes / Goin' bananas / Mellow madness / Enviromenial terrorist / Set the shit straight / Trapped / Final call
CDPTY 110 / Dec '94 / Priority/Virgin

Da Silva, Jorginho
☐ EL BOSSA NOVA
12385 / Feb '95 / Strictly Dancing

Da Steppas Project
☐ MOON STEPPIN'
ONER 005CD / Nov '96 / One Drop

Da Vila, Martinho
☐ BATUCA NO CHAO
ML 51017 / 14 Apr '98 / Musica Latina

☐ MEU SAMBA FELIZ
Mangueirense feliz / Vai ou nao vai / Casa de bamba / en tenho / Ao povo em forma de arte / Canta canta minha gente / Mudiakime / Camafeu / Minha comadre / Isto e o amor / Meu pais
68911 / Jul '97 / Tropical

Da Willys
☐ SATUHDAY NITE PALSY
OUT 1052 / Sep '97 / Brake Out

Da Youngstas
☐ NO MERCY
Hip hop ride / No more hard times / Stayed away / Push me on / What u feel / People round town / In the city / Reality / Grim reaper / Illy filly funk / Backstabbers / Mad props / No mercy
7567923702 / Nov '94 / WEA

Daams, Menno
☐ MY CHOICE (Daams, Menno Sextet)
CHR 70031 / Sep '96 / Challenge

Dabagian, Gevorg
☐ MUSIC OF ARMENIA VOL.3, THE (The Duduk)
131172 / Sep '96 / Celestial Harmonies

Dabany, Patience
☐ CENTRAL AFRICAN REPUBLIC
Levekisha / Pitie / Sango ya mawa / Opoungou / Mbala / Magali alobi / Jalousie / Ayangal kelio / Ne t'inquietes pas / Patience II / Fly girl
CDEMC 3677 / May '94 / Hemisphere

Dabire, Gabin
☐ AFRIKI DJAMANA (Music From Burkina Faso)
ARNR 0494 / Oct '97 / Amiata

Daboa
☐ FROM THE GEKKO
TRECD 115 / Feb '97 / Triple Earth

Dada
☐ EL SUBLIMINOSO
Time is your friend / Sick in Santorini / Bob the drummer / I get high / Spirit of 2009 / Star you are / Trip with my Dad / You won't know me / Rise / No one / Fleecing of America / Hollow man / California dreamin'
EIRSCD 1080 / Jun '96 / IRS/EMI

Dada
☐ DADA
Big dipper / Last time / This is my song / Seed of peace / Organ interlude / Tonite / She walks away / Aspen Colorado / Eyes of the warren / Jasamin / Dada
LICD 901014 / Sep '97 / Line

Dadamah
☐ THIS IS NOT A DREAM
KRANK 002 / Mar '97 / Kranky

Daddy Cool
☐ EAGLE ROCK
PCD 10148 / Oct '97 / Castle

Daddy Rings
☐ STAND OUT
Stand out / Herb fi bun / Cat and the fiddle / Can I trust a stranger / Rumours / Stick to the man / Stand out / Secret life / Tell me what yuh dealing / Religion / Bonifide / Judgement day / Friend enemy / Don't you cry again / Mothers cry
GRELCD 237 / Jul '97 / Greensleeves

Dadi, Marcel
☐ COUNTRY GUITAR FLAVOURS
982532 / Nov '92 / EPM

Dad's Porno Mag
☐ DAD'S PORNO MAG
DPM 1977 / Sep '97 / Wax Tone

Daemion
☐ DARK OPERA OF THE ANCIENT WAR SPIRIT
CDAR 020 / May '94 / Adipocre

☐ SEVEN DEADLY SINS
RRS 947CD / Dec '96 / Progress

Daemon
☐ ENTRANCE TO HELL, THE
KSCD 9491 / Jun '97 / Kissing Spell

Daemonarch
☐ HERMETICUM
CM 77240CD / 17 Aug '98 / Century Media

Daere, Kim
☐ SHAMANISTIC CEREMONIES OF CHINDO
VICG 52142 / Mar '96 / JVC World Library

DAF
☐ DIE KLEINEN UN DIE BOSEN (Deutsch Amerikanische Freundschaft)
Osten wahrt am langsten / Essen dann schlafen / Coco pino / Kinderfunk / Nacht arbeit / Ich gebe dir ein stuck von mir / De pane / Gewalt / Gib's mir / Auf wiedersehen / Das ist liebe / Was ist eine welle / Anzufassen und anzufassen / Volkstanz / Die lustigen stiefel / Die kleinen und die bosen / Die fesche iola / El basilon / Y la gracia
CDSTUMM 1 / Apr '92 / Mute

Daft Punk
☐ HOMEWORK
Daftendirekt / WDPK 83.7 FM / Revolution 909 / Da funk / Phoenix / Fresh / Around the world / Rollin' and scratchin' / Teachers / High fidelity / Rock 'n' roll / Oh yeah / Burnin' / Indo silver club / Alive / Funk AD
CDV 2821 / Jan '97 / Virgin

Dafunkshun
☐ ALBUM, THE
CDSPV 08516522 / Jul '97 / SPV

Dag Nasty
☐ 1985 - 1986
SFLS 52 / Nov '92 / Selfless

☐ FIELD DAY
WB 3040CD / Sep '93 / We Bite

Dagar Brothers
☐ DHRUPAD (The Vocal Art Of Hindustan)
JVC 53902 / Sep '96 / JVC World Library

Dagar, Zia Mohiuddin
☐ RUNDRA VINA
NI 5402CD / Jul '94 / Nimbus

D'Agostino, Peppino
☐ CLOSE TO THE HEART
BEST 1039CD / Nov '93 / Acoustic Music

Dagradi, Tony
☐ DREAMS OF LOVE
Child's play / Prayer / Morning star / Call / Dreams of love / Parading / I cover the waterfront
ROUCD 2071 / '88 / Rounder

Dahinden, Roland
☐ NAIMA
MODE 62 / Mar '98 / Mode

Dahl, Carsten
☐ WILL YOU MAKE MY SOUP HOT AND SILVER (Dahl, Carsten Trio)
Autumn leaves / Giant steps / Will you make my soup hot and silver / On green dolphin street / Take five / All blues / Caravan / Freddie the freeloader / I thought about you / There is no greater love / Someday my prince will come / Ain't sorry blues
STCD 4203 / Dec '97 / Storyville

Dahl, Jeff
☐ HEART FULL OF SNOT
TX 51240CD / 13 Apr '98 / Triple XXX

☐ I WAS A TEENAGE GLAM FAG
UUCD 502 / 8 Jun '98 / Fan Club

Dahlander, Nils-Bertil
☐ FROM SWEDEN WITH LOVE
ECD 102 / Jun '95 / Everyday

Dahlgren, Chris
☐ SLOW COMMOTION
378132 / Oct '96 / Koch Jazz

Daho, Etienne
☐ EDEN
Les passagers / Les bords de Seine / New world / L'enfer enfin / Soudain / Me manquer / Un serpant sans importance / Les pluies chaudes de l'ete / Au commencement / Timide intimite / Des adieux tres heureux / Rendez-vous au jardin des plaisirs / Quand tu m'appelles Eden
CDVIRX 61 / 23 Mar '98 / Virgin

Daigrepont, Bruce
☐ PETIT CADEAU
ROUCD 6060 / May '94 / Rounder

☐ STIR UP THE ROUX
Laissez-faire / La valse de la riviere rouge / Disco et fais do-do / Les traces de mon bogue / Le two-step de marksville / Les filles cajines / Un autre soir ennuyant / Frisco zydeco / Stir up the roux
ROUCD 6016 / '88 / Rounder

Dailey, Juanita
☐ FREE
D21Z 24946 / 1 Jun '98 / Ichiban

Daily Flash
☐ I FLASH DAILY
FLASH 60 / 1 Jun '98 / Flash

Daily Planet
☐ CLARK'S SECRET
GRP 003CD / Dec '96 / Get Real

Dairo, I.K.

☐ ASHIKO
GL 4018CD / Aug '94 / Green Linnet

☐ DEFINITIVE DAIRO
Okin omo ni / Baba ngbo ti wa / Omo Owa o Ijesa / Ta lo ba mi ri / Labondo / Omo alaro / Chief Okeyemi Otubusin / Ore arakunrin temi / Congo kinshasa / President Mobutu
XENO 4045CD / Oct '96 / Xenophile

☐ JUJU MASTER
OMCD 009 / Nov '90 / Original Music

Daisy Chainsaw

☐ ELEVENTEEN
I feel insane / You be my friend / Dog with shaper teeth / Hope your dreams come true / Natural man / Love your money / Lovely ugly brutal world / Use me use you / Future free / Pink flower / Waiting for the wolves / Everthing is weird
TPLP 100CD / Sep '92 / One Little Indian

Dako, Del

☐ BALANCING ACT
SKCD 22021 / Jun '93 / Sackville

Dakota

☐ LAST STANDING MAN
ESM 023 / 2 Mar '98 / Escape

☐ MR. LUCKY
ESM 005 / 2 Mar '98 / Escape

Dakota Moon

☐ DAKOTA MOON
Another day goes by / A promise I make / Violet / Won't be alone tonight / If I can't love you / Sing you to sleep / She Knows / Call on me / Black moon day / Snow in July / Sweet lady Jane / Your smiling face / Til we meet again
7559621632 / 27 Jul '98 / Elektra

Dalakopa

☐ EVI ALLE IHOPA
HCD 7109 / Nov '95 / Helio

Dalal, Yair

☐ AL OL (Ud, Clarinet & Voices)
ALCD 202 / Sep '96 / Al Sur

Dalaras, George

☐ GREEK SPIRIT, THE
68966 / Apr '97 / Tropical

☐ GREEK VOICE, THE
68954 / Apr '97 / Tropical

☐ LIVE AND UNPLUGGED
68991 / 24 Apr '98 / Tropical

☐ PORTRAIT, A
Konstadis the only son / I was chosen / You were a God / Stranger / Don't read my life / Take gyspy your hammer and bellows / Death's / Mr. Kostaki join us / Sky darkens / Trip to cytheria / Manuella / You finished me / Tough one / August / You many faces / Year conviction / As long as the shutting door echoes / Songs are illness / To Thomas' place
HEMICD 29 / 6 Oct '97 / Hemisphere

Dalby, Graham

☐ GREAT LEGENDS OF JAZZ AND SWING, THE (Dalby, Graham & The Grahamophones)
Because my baby don't mean maybe now / Makin' whoopee / Cotton club stomp / Mooche / Sing, sing, sing / Blues in the night / I can't get started / Stompin' at the Savoy / Pennsylvania 6500 / Moonlight serenade / Fools rush in / Who (stole my heart away) / Deep purple / Eager beaver / Mack the knife
CDMFP 6397 / May '97 / Music For Pleasure

☐ LET'S DANCE FOXTROT (Dalby, Graham & The Grahamophones)
Top hat, white tie and tails / Anything goes / Zing went the strings of my heart / All of me / Jeepers creepers / Lullaby of broadway / Lady is a tramp / Isn't this a lovely day / American patrol / In the mood / Nice work if you can get it / I got rhythm / Baby face (foxtrot) / I've got a gal in kalamazoo / I'm the yankee doodle boy
LTD 102702 / Apr '95 / Let's Dance

☐ LET'S DANCE LATIN AMERICAN
Brazil / I've got you under my skin / Continental / Salamanca / Carnival / Cherry pink and apple blossom white / Suco suco / Tequila / Call me irresponsible / Theme from 'm.a.s.h.'
LTD 102705 / May '95 / Let's Dance

☐ LET'S DANCE THE BOSSA NOVA (Dalby, Graham & The Grahamophones)
Carol's theme / Te ame / Sweet inspiration / Bahia bosa nova / Cinnamon and clove / Latin snowfall / Way you look tonight / Pink polo / Desafinado / Soul bossa / Il silenzio
LTD 102713 / Apr '96 / Let's Dance

☐ LET'S DANCE THE CHA CHA CHA (Dalby, Graham & The Grahamophones)
Cha cha Mama Brown / Makin' whoopee / Ida, sweet as apple cider / Eternally / Last night on the back porch / Isle of Capri / If you knew Susie / Little serenade / C'est si bon / Christopher Columbus / L'Abeille et la Papillon / El canguro / In the mood / In a shady nook / My prayer / Chestnut tree / South of the border / How wonderful to know / Calcutta / Sucu Sucu / Any old iron cha cha / Isn't this a lovely day / Eye level / Dancin' easy / Rivers of Babylon / Sunny / Daddy Cool / Rasputin
LTD 102712 / Nov '96 / Let's Dance

☐ LET'S DANCE THE JIVE (Dalby, Graham & The Grahamophones)
Copper coloured girl / Is you is or is you ain't my baby / Little brown jug / Steppin' out with my baby / Jersey bounce / Don't sit under the apple tree / (I'll be glad when you're dead) you rascal you / Chicago / When I see an elephant fly / Hold tight hold tight / Bugle call rag / Eager beaver / Boogie woogie bugle boy / Can't buy me love / (We're gonna) Rock around the clock / See you later alligator / Hound dog / Under the moon of love / When / Dancing party
LTD 102711 / Apr '96 / Let's Dance

☐ LET'S DANCE THE PASO DOBLE (Dalby, Graham & The Grahamophones)
El pico / Islas canarias / Ven a bailir / Valencia / Viva el rumbo / Rafaelillo / Bizas andaluzas / Manolo vazquez / El nino de jerez / Gallito / Gitaneria andaluza / Jeronimo pimentel
LTD 102714 / Apr '96 / Let's Dance

☐ LET'S DANCE THE RUMBA (Dalby, Graham & The Grahamophones)
Savoy rumba medley / Angela Mia / Miami Beach rumba / Begin the beguine / You do something to me / Once in a while / Green eyes / Hill Street blues / I am a song / Laughter in the rain / That's when the music takes me / Lady in red / Romantica
LTD 102715 / Nov '96 / Let's Dance

☐ LET'S DANCE THE SLOW FOXTROT (Dalby, Graham & The Grahamophones)
Cheek to cheek / Blue moon / Am I blue / At last / I only have eyes for you / Mean to me / Heaven can wait / Pennies from heaven / These foolish things (remind me of you) / Two sleepy people / Stormy weather / Ill wind (you're blowing me no good) / They can't take that away from me / Night and day / Deep purple / A nightingale sang in berkeley square
LTD 102704 / Apr '95 / Let's Dance

☐ LET'S DANCE THE TANGO (Dalby, Graham & The Grahamophones)
Golden earrings / Isle of capri / La cumparsita / Music box tango / Tango de la nostalgia / Lapland tango / Play to me gypsy / Jealousy / Olvidado / On the sea / Night and day / In the still of the night / Poinciana
LTD 102703 / Apr '95 / Let's Dance

☐ LET'S DANCE THE WALTZ (Dalby, Graham & The Grahamophones)
True love / If you don't know me by now / Theme from "the-god father" / Great waltz / Cruising down the river / Alice blue gown / What'll I do / Theme from "the thornbirds"
LTD 102701 / Apr '95 / Let's Dance

☐ LET'S DANCE VOL.1 (Dalby, Graham & The Grahamophones)
Am I blue (slow foxtrot) / Isle of capri (tango) / True love (waltz) / Top hat, white tie and tails (foxtrot) / Brazil (samba) / I've got you under my skin (rumba) / La cumparsita (tango) / Cheek to cheek (slow foxtrot) / Anything goes (quickstep) / Great waltz (waltz) / Golden earrings (tango) / Continental (cha cha cha) / Salamanca (paso doble) / What'll I do (waltz) / American patrol (foxtrot) / In the still of the night (tango)
LTD 102706 / Jun '95 / Let's Dance

☐ LET'S DANCE VOL.2 (Dalby, Graham & The Grahamophones)
Zing went the strings of my heart (foxtrot) / Jeepers creepers (quickstep) / Music box (tango) / Carnival (samba) / Theme from mash (rumba) / Cherry pink and apple blossom white (cha cha) / Blue moon (slow foxtrot) / Tango de la nostalgia (tango) / If you don't know me by now (waltz) / Baby face (foxtrot) / Tequila (samba) / At last (slow foxtrot) / Poinciana (tango)
LTD 102707 / Jun '95 / Let's Dance

☐ LET'S DANCE VOL.3 (Dalby, Graham & The Grahamophones)
All of me (foxtrot) / Theme from 'the godfather' (waltz) / I only have eyes for you (slow foxtrot) / Lapland tango / In the mood (quickstep) / Call me irresponsible (cha cha) / Lullaby of broadway (foxtrot) / Play to me gypsy (tango) / Mean to me (slow foxtrot) / Cruising down the river (waltz) / Jealousy (tango) / Lady is a tramp (foxtrot) / I'm the yankee doodle boy (quickstep)
LTD 102708 / Jun '95 / Let's Dance

☐ LET'S DANCE VOL.4 (Dalby, Graham & The Grahamophones)
Isn't this a lovely day (foxtrot) / Olvidado (tango) / Heaven can wait (slow foxtrot) / I got rhythm (quickstep) / On the sea (tango) / I've got a gal in kalamazoo (foxtrot) / Suco suco (samba) / Deep purple (slow foxtrot) / Alice blue gown (waltz) / Night and day (tango) / Nice work if you can get it (foxtrot) / A nightingale sang in berkeley square (slow foxtrot) / Theme from 'the thornbirds' (waltz)
LTD 102709 / Jun '95 / Let's Dance

☐ LET'S DANCE VOL.5 (Dalby, Graham & The Grahamophones)
I get a kick out of you (quickstep) / Mais que nada (samba) / Ob-la-di ob-la-da (cha cha cha) / Ole guapa (tango) / Rock around the clock (jive) / Three quarter (waltz) / Spanish gipsy dance (paso doble) / O sole mio (rumba) / Black bottom (charleston) / In the mood (jive) / Noche de estrella (tango) / Vienne, mon amour (waltz) / New york, new york (slow foxtrot) / Coffee song (samba) / My prayer (rumba) / Over the rainbow (cha cha cha)
LTD 102710 / Jun '95 / Let's Dance

☐ MAD DOGS AND ENGLISHMEN (Dalby, Graham & The Grahamophones)
Everything's in rhythm with my heart / Continental / Mad dogs and englishmen / You're as pretty as a picture / Everything stops for tea / Vo do do de o dodo / I'm going to get lit up when the lights go up in london / A nightingale sang in berkeley square / Sarawaki / I'm singing a swing song now / Very thought of you / Leicester square rag / I'm in a dancing mood / I never see maggie alone / Deep secret / Love is the sweetest thing
PCOM 1097 / Feb '89 / President

☐ TRANSATLANTIQUE (Dalby, Graham & The Grahamophones)
Jeeves and Wooster / La mer / Anything goes / Easy come, easy go / Mackie Messer / My canary has circles under his eyes / Top hat, white tie and tails / Ces petites choses / 42nd Street / Once in a while / Crazy words crazy tune / I would sooner be a crooner / Ill wind / Hollywood's got nothing on you / Let's misbehave
PCOM 1128 / Aug '93 / President

Dalcan, Dominique

☐ ENTRE L'ETOILE & LE CARRE
Typical blues / Entre l'etoilr and le carre / Promesse celeste / Un jour sur deux / Une epee dans le dos / Comment faut-il faire / Up and down / Les annees bleues / Naked and so shy / Une direction contraire
CRAM 074 / Nov '93 / Crammed Discs

Dale, Colin

☐ OUTER LIMITS VOL.1 (Various Artists)
KICKCD 10 / Jun '94 / Kickin'

☐ OUTER LIMITS VOL.2 (Various Artists)
KICKCD 21 / May '95 / Kickin'

Dale, Dick

☐ CALLING UP SPIRITS
BBQCD 184 / May '96 / Beggars Banquet

☐ GREATEST HITS (Dale, Dick & His Del-Tones)
Victor / Surf beat / Sloop John B / King of the surf guitar / Wedge / Let's go trippin' / Peppermint man / Misirlou / Those memories of you / Scavenger / Surf buggy / Hot rod racer / Grudge run / Mr. Eliminator / Surfin' drums / Night rider / Del-tone rock / Mag wheels / Death of a gremmie
GNPD 2095 / '88 / GNP Crescendo

☐ TRIBAL THUNDER
HCD 8046 / Mar '95 / Hightone

☐ UNKNOWN TERRITORY
HCD 8055 / Mar '95 / Hightone

DaLeath, Vaughn

☐ EDISON LATERALS VOL.5, THE
DCP 304D / Jul '98 / Diamond Cut

Dalewood Auckland Pipe Band

☐ SOUTHERN GAEL
Lairg / Colonial conundrum / Competition set / Oldershaws / March past / Red coats / Hectors / Solo marches / Southern gael / From the fronce were reels / Nt / Eith / Mackay / Youngest ancient mariner
CDMON 828 / May '98 / Monarch

Daley & Lorien

☐ DREAMS OF THE YES MEN
EUCD 1193 / Apr '92 / ARC

Daley, Lloyd

☐ IT'S SHUFFLE 'N' SKA TIME
JMC 200221 / Jun '95 / Jamaican Gold

Daley, Martin

☐ ARCHITECTS OF TIME (Daley, Martin & Duncan Lorien)
Structure / Bermuda / Architects of time / Into the oasis / Eleven days / Thank you / Waiting for Karl / Spirit warrior
EUCD 1154 / Jun '91 / ARC

Dalida

☐ A MA MANIERE
PGCCD 987 / 15 Jun '98 / Orlando

Dalienst, Ntesa

☐ BEST OF NTESA DALIENST VOL.1, THE
CD 36563 / Jan '97 / Sonodisc

☐ BEST OF NTESA DALIENST VOL.2, THE
CD 36564 / Jan '97 / Sonodisc

Dali's Car

☐ WAKING HOUR
Dali's car / His box / Cornwall stone / Artemis / Create and melt / Moonlife / Judgement is the mirror
BBL 52CD / Jan '89 / Beggars Banquet

Dall, Cindy

☐ CINDY DALL
WIGCD 023 / Mar '96 / Domino

Dallas Jazz Orchestra

☐ THANK YOU, LEON
Back in town / Anand / Miami beach / Willow weep for me / Latin dream / Alison's tune / Basin Street blues / Reggae blues / Tickle toe / Yesterdays / Bikini beach / Thank you, Leon
SBCD 2041 / Oct '91 / Sea Breeze

Dalli, Toni

☐ BEST OF TONI DALLI, THE
C5CD 570 / Jul '91 / See For Miles

Dallwitz, Dave

☐ HOOKED ON RAGTIME VOL.1 (Dallwitz, Dave Euphonic Ragtime Ensemble)
BCD 321 / Jan '94 / GHB

☐ HOOKED ON RAGTIME VOL.2 (Dallwitz, Dave Euphonic Ragtime Ensemble)
BCD 322 / Jan '94 / GHB

Dalriada

☐ ALL IS FAIR
Haughs o' Cromdale / Scots wha hae / Green grow the rashes / Jock o'Hazeldean / Ye Jacobites by name / Will ye no' come back again / Johnny Cope / Loch Lomond / Macphersons' farewell / Ae fond kiss / Caledonia / Grey man
IR 015 CD / Nov '91 / Iona

Dalseth, Laila

☐ SOME OTHER TIME (Dalseth, Laila & Frode Thingnaes/Bjorn Johansen)
GMCD 66 / Apr '98 / Gemini

☐ TIME FOR LOVE, A
GEMCD 151 / Oct '90 / Gemini

Dalton, Joe

☐ I STILL DO
FCRCD 201 / Mar '96 / Flat Canyon

Dalton, Karen

☐ IT'S SO HARD TO TELL WHO'S GOING TO LOVE YOU THE BEST
379182 / Jul '97 / Koch International

Daltrey, Roger

☐ ANTHOLOGY
RR 4670 / Jul '98 / Repertoire

☐ DALTREY
One man band / Way of the world / You are yourself / Thinking / You and me / It's a hard life / Giving it all away / Story so far / When the music stops / Reasons / Reprise - One man band
5272592 / Apr '95 / Polydor
REP 4536 / 13 Jul '98 / Repertoire

☐ ONE OF THE BOYS
Parade / Single man's dilemma / Avenging Annie / Prisoner / Leon / One of the boys / Giddy / Written on the wind / Satin and lace / Doing it all again
REP 4643 / 15 Jan '98 / Repertoire

☐ RIDE A ROCK HORSE
Get your love / Hearts right / Oceans away / Proud the world over / Near to surrender / Feeling / Walking the dog / Milk train / I was
REP 4642 / 15 Jan '98 / Repertoire

Daltry, Peter

☐ DREAM ON
Dust / Going back to Bohemia / Fitzgerald / Tender is the night / Ravenswing / Richard and I / Nothing more than this / Felt like the moon / Unicorn / Eighteen summers / Dream on / Roundway Hill
BP 182CD / May '97 / Blueprint

Daly, Jackie

☐ BUTTONS AND BOWS (Daly, Jackie/ Seamus & Manus McGuire)
Blue Angel / Esther's reel/Trip to Kinvara / Old resting chair / Crowley's reels / Norwegian waltz/ Liza Lynn / Dionne reel / Waltz from Orsa / Barn dances / My love is an Arbutus / Waltz clog / La Bastringue / Bog carrot
GLCD 1051 / Jun '93 / Green Linnet

☐ JACKIE DALY
OSS 30CD / Mar '94 / Ossian

☐ JACKIE DALY & SEAMUS CREAGH (Daly, Jackie & Seamus Creagh)
CEFCD 057 / Jan '94 / Gael Linn

☐ MANY'S A WILD NIGHT
CEFCD 176 / Dec '95 / Gael Linn

☐ MUSIC FROM SLIABH LUACHRA (Vol.6)
Tom Sullivan's / Johnny Leary's / Jim Keefe's / Keefe's / Clog / Tir na nog / Callaghan's hornpipe / Rising sun / Pope's toe / Glin cottage polkas / Paddy scully's / Gallant tipperay / Walsh's / Ballyvourine polka / Johnny Mickey's / Trip to the Jacks / Where is the cat / Banks of Sullane / Biddy Martin's / Ger the rigger / Glenside cottage / Tdim gan airgead / Willie Reilly / Murphy's / Going to the well for water
GLCD 3065 / Jun '92 / Green Linnet

Daly, Vic

☐ SO AM I
ADITZ 1 / Dec '95 / Album Zutique

Dama & D'Gary

☐ LONG WAY HOME
SH 64052CD / Oct '94 / Shanachie

Damad

☐ RISE AND FALL
PRANK 011CD / Feb '97 / Prank

Damage

☐ FOREVER
Love II love / Love guaranteed / Girlfriend / Let it be me / Wonderful tonight / By my baby / Love lady / Anything / Forever / Do me that way / Storyteller / In your eyes
BLRCD 31X / Apr '97 / Big Life

D'Ambrosio, Meredith

☐ IT'S YOUR DANCE
Giant steps / Once upon a tempo / Listen little girl / Devil may care / August moon / Nobody else but me / Humpty dumpty heart / It's your dance / Underdog / It isn't so good it couldn't be better / Off again on again / No one remembers but me / Miss Harper goes bizarre / Strange meadowlark
SSC 1011 D / Feb '86 / Sunnyside

☐ LOVE IS NOT A GAME
Daybreak / In April / Autumn serenade / Young and foolish / I love you / You, I love / Quiet now / Get used to it baby / That old sweet song / Heaven sent / All or nothing at all / This lament / Indian summer / Peace / Oh look at me now / But now look at me / Love is not a game
SSC 1051D / Jun '91 / Sunnyside

☐ MEREDITH....ANOTHER TIME
All of us in it together / Aren't you glad you're you / It's so peaceful in the country / Rain rain (don't go away) / Dear Bix / Lazy afternoon / Where's the child I used to hold / Love is a simple thing / You are there / While we're young / Small day tomorrow / Child is born / Piano player / Someday my Prince will come / Such a lonely girl am I / Wheelers and dealers / I was doing all right / Skylark
SSC 1017D / Nov '90 / Sunnyside

☐ SHADOWLAND
500602 / Nov '92 / Sunnyside

☐ SILENT PASSION
SSC 1075 / Apr '97 / Sunnyside

Dambuilders

☐ GOD DAMBUILDERS BLESS AMERICA
CTX 066CD / Feb '97 / Cortex

Dameron, Tadd

☐ MAGIC TOUCH, THE (Dameron, Tadd Orchestra)
On a misty night / Fontainebleau / Just plain talkin' / If you could see me now / Our delight / Dial b for beauty / Look, stop and listen / Bevan's birthday / You're a joy / Swift as the wind
OJCCD 143 / Jan '97 / Original Jazz Classics

☐ MATING CALL
OJCCD 212 / Oct '92 / Original Jazz Classics

Damia

☐ 1928-35
123 / Nov '92 / Chansophone

☐ LA TRAGEDIENNE DE LA CHANSON
Les goelands / La mauvaise priere / Johnny palmer / La guinguette a ferme ses volets / L'etranger / La chaine / La grand frise / Berceuse tendre / Quand c'est lui / Dis-moi tout bas / Du soleil dans ses yeux / Je sens en moi / Tu ne sais pas amier / Moi, je m'ennuie / Sombre dimanche / La garde de nuit a l'yser / Tout fout l'camp / L'angelus de la mer
UCD 19075 / Jun '95 / Forlane

☐ LA TRAGEDIENNE DE LA CHANSON
701622 / Nov '96 / Chansophone

Damianio, Peter

☐ MERRY XMAS AND A HAPPY NEW YEAR (Damianio, Peter & His Orchestra)
White Christmas / Jingle bells / Do they know it's Christmas / Stille nacht / Notte d'amore / Last Christmas / Oh happy day / Once upon a long ago / This is the night / Bonne Noel / Happy Xmas (war is over) / Tanti auguri
CDSGP 0116 / Feb '96 / Prestige

Damn Yankees

☐ DAMN YANKEES
Coming of age / Bad reputation / Runaway / High enough / Damn yankees / Come again / Mysified / Rock city / Tell me how you want it / Pile driver
7599261592 / Mar '94 / WEA

Damnation

☐ BURIED ALIVE
BJR 96001 / Mar '97 / Black Jack

☐ DAMNATION
LRR 021 / Oct '96 / Last Resort

☐ NO MORE DREAMS OF HAPPY ENDINGS
JT 1020CD / Sep '95 / Jade Tree

Damned

☐ BALLROOM BLITZ - LIVE
Fall / I just can't be happy / Plan 9 channel 7 / Smash it up / Drinking about my baby / Looking at you / I feel alright / Love song / Ballroom blitz / New rose / In a rut / Dr. jekyll and mr. hyde / Melody lee / Neat, neat, neat - new rose (medley) / Shakin' all over
RRCD 159 / Jul '93 / Receiver

☐ BBC RADIO 1 SESSIONS, THE
CDNT 011 / Jun '96 / Strange Fruit

☐ BEST OF THE DAMNED
New rose / Neat neat neat / I just can't be happy today / Jet boy jet girl / Hit and miss / There ain't no sanity clause / Smash it up (parts 1 and 2) / Plan 9 channel 7 / Ra bid (over you) / Wait for the blackout / History of the world (part 1)
CDDAM 1 / Oct '87 / Big Beat

☐ BLACK ALBUM, THE
Wait for the blackout / Lively arts / Silly kids games / Drinking about my baby / Hit and miss / Dr. Jekyll and Mr. Hyde / Thirteenth floor vendetta / Curtain call / Twisted nerve / Sick of this and that / History of the world (part 1) / Therapy
CDWIK 906 / '87 / Big Beat

☐ BORN TO KILL (2CD Set)
Thanks for the night / Billy bad breaks / Disco man / I think I'm wonderful / Lovely money / Some girls are ugly / Ignite / Generals / Dozen girls / Bad time for Bonzo / Gun fury / Fun factory / Neat neat neat / Fan club / Wait for the blackout / I fall / Noise noise noise / Last time / I just can't be happy today / Smash it up / I feel alright / Love song / In a rut / Dr. Jeckyll and Mr. Hyde / Plan 9 channel 7 / Teenage dream / Problem child / Born to kill / Ballroom blitz / Stretcher case baby / Melody Lee / Suicide / New rose / Looking at you / Ignite / Disco man
SMDCD 143 / May '97 / Snapper

☐ CHAOS YEARS, THE
CLP 9960 / Mar '97 / Cleopatra

☐ COLLECTION, THE
Ignite / Generals / Dozen girls / Bad time for Bonzo / Gun fury / Thanks for the night / History of the world (part 1) / Lively arts / There ain't no sanity clause / White rabbit / Melody Lee / Lovely money / Disco man / I think I'm wonderful / Help / I just can't be happy today / Love song / Neat neat neat / New rose / Noise noise noise / Smash it up / Wait for the blackout
CCSCD 278 / Dec '90 / Castle

☐ DAMNED BUT NOT FORGOTTEN
Dozen girls / Lovely money / I think I'm wonderful / Disguise / Take that / Torture me / Disco man / Thanks for the night / Take me away / Some girls are ugly / Nice cup of tea / Billy bad breaks
ESMCD 472 / Feb '97 / Essential

☐ DAMNED, DAMNED, DAMNED
Neat neat neat / Fan club / I fall / Born to kill / Stab your back / Feel the pain / New rose / Fish / See her tonite / One of the two / So messed up / I feel alright
FIENDCD 91 / Apr '87 / Demon
310332 / 24 Nov '97 / Frontier

☐ ETERNALLY DAMNED (The Very Best Of The Damned)
Neat neat neat / New rose / Problem child / Don't cry wolf / Stretcher case baby / Sick of being sick / Love song / Smash it up / I just can't be happy today / History of the world (Part 1) / White rabbit / Disco man / Nasty / There ain't no sanity clause / Shadow of love / Grimly fiendish / Eloise / Is it a dream / Alone again or / Gigolo
MUSCD 017 / May '94 / MCI Music

☐ FIENDISH SHADOWS
CLP 9804 / Oct '96 / Cleopatra

☐ I'M ALRIGHT JACK AND THE BEANSTALK
MOCDR 1 / Apr '97 / The Record Label

☐ LIVE AT SHEPPERTON
Love song / Second time around / I just can't be happy today / Melody Lee / Help / Neat neat neat / Looking at you / Smash it up (parts 1 and 2) / New rose / Plan 9 channel 7
CDWIKM 27 / Jun '88 / Big Beat

☐ MACHINE GUN ETIQUETTE
Love song / Machine gun etiquette / I can't be happy today / Melody Lee / Anti-pope / These hands / Plan 9 channel 7 / Noise noise noise / Looking at you / Liar / Smash it up (Part 1) / Smash it up (Part 2) / Ballroom blitz / Suicide / Rabid (over you) / White rabbit
CDWIK 905 / '86 / Big Beat

☐ MCA SINGLES A'S AND B'S, THE
Grimly fiendish (spic 'n' span mix) / Edward the bear (single version) / Shadow of love / Nightshift / Would you / Is it a dream / Curtain call (single version) / Eloise / Beat girl / Temptation (tango) / Anything / Year of the jackal / Gigolo (12" remix version) / Portrait (extended version) / Alone again or (mixed again) / In dulce decorum
VSOPCD 174 / Jul '92 / Connoisseur Collection

☐ MUSIC FOR PLEASURE
Problem child / Don't cry wolf / One way love / Politics / Stretcher case baby / Idiot box / You take my money / Alone / Your eyes / Creep (you can't fool me) / You know
FIENDCD 108 / Apr '88 / Demon

☐ NOISE (The Best Of The Damned Live)
New rose / In a rut / Dr. Jeckyl and Mr. Hyde / Ballroom blitz / Love song / Born to kill / Generals / Melody lee / Drinking about my baby / Looking at you / Problem child / I feel alright / Stretcher case baby / Plan 9- channel 7 / Shakin' all over
EMPRCD 592 / Oct '95 / Emporio

☐ SESSIONS OF THE DAMNED, THE
Stab you back / Neat neat neat / New Rose / So messed up / I fall / Sick of this and that / Stretcher case baby / Fan club / Feel the pain / Melody Lee / I'm a burglar / Love song / Looking at you / I just can't be happy today / Smash it up / I'm bored / Curtain call / Therapy / Is it a dream / Nasty / We love you / Thanks for the night
SFRSCD 070 / 20 Jul '98 / Strange Fruit

☐ SKIP OFF TO SCHOOL TO SEE THE DAMNED
New rose / Help / Neat neat neat / Stab your back / Singalongascabies / Stretcher case baby / Sick of being sick / Problem child / You take my money / Don't cry wolf / One way love
VEXCD 12 / Sep '92 / Demon

☐ STRAWBERRIES
Ignite / Generals / Stranger on the town / Dozen girls / Dog / Gun fury / Pleasure and pain / Life goes on / Bad time for Bonzo / Under the floor again / Don't bother me
DOJOCD 46 / Dec '92 / Dojo
CLEO 10292 / Dec '93 / Cleopatra
ESMCD 473 / Mar '97 / Essential

☐ TALES FROM THE DAMNED
CLEO 71392 / Oct '94 / Cleopatra

☐ TOTALLY DAMNED
Fun factory / Generals / Stranger / On the town / Gun fury / Born to kill / I fall / Fish / Help / New rose / I just can't be happy today / Wait for the blackout / Noise noise noise / Looking at you / Disguise / Take that / Torture me / Take me away / Some girls are ugly / Billy bad breaks
DOJOCD 65 / Feb '94 / Dojo

Damon

☐ SONG OF A GYPSY
DAMON 1 / 27 Apr '98 / Damon

Damon & Naomi

☐ PLAYBACK SINGERS
Turn of the century / Eye of the storm / In the sun / Navigator / I'm yours / Kinetoscope / Awake in a muddle / We're not there / Translucent carriages
RCD 10438 / 6 Apr '98 / Rykodisc

☐ WONDEROUS WORLD OF...
SP 322B / Nov '95 / Sub Pop

Damone, Vic

☐ BEST OF VIC DAMONE, THE (The Mercury Years)
I have but one heart / You do / Again / You're breaking my heart / Four winds and the seven seas / My bolero / Why was I born / Vagabond shoes / Tzena tzena tzena / Just say I love her / Cincinatti dancing pig / My heart cries for you / Music by the angels / Night is young and you're so beautiful / My truly truly fair / Longing for you / Calla calla / Here in my heart / Rosanne / Sugar / April in Portugal / Eternally / Ebb tide / Breeze and I / In my own quiet way
5527572 / Feb '97 / Spectrum

☐ BEST OF VIC DAMONE, THE
Goin' out of my head / Time after time / More I see you / Shadow of your smile / It makes no difference / Why can't I walk away / Stardust / Watch what happens / Meditation / On the South side of Chicago / Make me rainbows / Quiet tear / Stay with me / I never go there anymore / Stay / What is a woman / Two for the road / I got it bad and that ain't good / When you've laughed all your laughter / You don't have to say you love me
74321451912 / Feb '97 / Camden

☐ CLOSER THAN A KISS/THIS GAME OF LOVE
Closer than a kiss / Out of nowhere / I kiss your hand / Madame / We kiss in a shadow / Cuddle up a little closer / Toujours / You and the night and the music / Prelude to a kiss / How deep is the ocean / Day by day / As time goes by / Close as pages in a book / Game of love / Alone together / My romance / Ain't misbehavin' / But beautiful / End of a love affair / Things we did last summer / Am I blue / I'll be around / It's a lonesome old town / Me and my shadow / I like the likes of you / Fellow needs a girl
4871902 / Mar '97 / Columbia

☐ FEELINGS
Feelings / Lazy afternoon / Ghost riders in the sky / Softly / Windmills of your mind / People / Top of the world / Farewell to paradise / Over the rainbow
MU 3004 / Oct '92 / Musketeer

☐ LINGER AWHILE WITH/MY BABY LOVES TO SWING
Linger awhile / Close your eyes / Stella by starlight / Change partners / After the lights go down / Let's face the music and dance / Soft lights and sweet music / Deep night / One love / There I've said it agin / When lights are low / In still of the night / I'm nobody baby / All right okay you win / My melancholy baby / Let's sit this one out / My baby just cares for me / Is you is or is you ain't / Baby baby all the time / Baby won't you please come home / Make this a slow goodbye
CTMCD 123 / 15 Sep '97 / EMI

☐ ON THE STREET WHERE YOU LIVE
MU 5074 / Oct '92 / Musketeer

☐ ON THE STREET WHERE YOU LIVE
When lights are low / Close your eyes / Tender is the night / No strings / Once upon a time / Little girl / Alright, OK you win / What kind of fool am I / Ooh looka there, ain't she pretty / Affair to remember / Call me irresponsible / Wives and lovers / Again / I'm gonna miss you / Cathy / Vieni vieni / Dearly beloved / Maria / Lost in the stars / On the street where you live
CDSL 8277 / Nov '95 / Music For Pleasure

☐ THAT TOWERING FEELING/YOUNG AND LIVELY
You stepped out of a dream / Wait till you see her / Song is you / Spring is here / Let's fall in love / Smoke gets in your eyes / Time on your hands / I'm glad there is you / Touch of your lips / All the things you are / Cheek to cheek / Last night when we were young / We could make such beautiful music / It had to be you / In the blue of evening / I got it bad and that ain't good / Serenade in blue / Very thought of you / Spring will be a little late this year / Imagination / Solitude / What is there to say / Evert time we say goodbye
4810142 / Aug '95 / Columbia

☐ VIC DAMONE COLLECTOR'S EDITION
DVAD 6022 / Apr '95 / Deja Vu

Dan Air Scottish Pipe Band

☐ BEST OF SCOTTISH PIPES AND DRUMS, THE
EUCD 1150 / '91 / ARC

Dan Ar Bras

☐ SEPTEMBER BLEU
KMCD 38 / May '94 / Keltia Musique

☐ THEME FOR THE GREEN LANDS
KMCD 48 / May '94 / Keltia Musique

Dan 'n' Dad

☐ DAYLIGHT
Years go by / Skiing wild / Don't look over your shoulder / Surfer's paradise / Guiding light / Strike while the iron's hot / Mon ami / It all takes time / Tender zone / Daylight
ZYZCD 2 / May '96 / Pink Whistle

Dan, Teddy

☐ UNITED STATES OF AFRICA
RMCD 013 / Nov '94 / Roots Man

Dana

☐ BEST OF DANA, THE
All kinds of everything / Who put the lights out / Please tell him that I said hello / There's nothin' you can do to change my mind / It's gonna be a cold cold christmas / I'm not in love / Never gonna fall in love again / There's a kind of hush: *Fairytale* / All my loving: *Fairytale* / I get a little sentimental over you: *Fairytale* / Rose garden: *Fairytale* / Totas tuus: *Fairytale* / If: *Fairytale* / Over the rainbow / Girl is back (in town) / Something's cookin' in the kitchen / I can't get over getting over you / Cry like a baby / Everynight
4914522 / 3 Aug '98 / Epic

☐ DANA THE COLLECTION
Fairytale / Never gonna fall in love again / Right back where we started / Girl is back / Something's cooking in the kitchen / Can't find a way / Far away / Rainy days and mondays / If you leave me now / All kinds of everything / Magic / I feel love / Who put the lights out / Cold cold Christmas / Please tell him I said hello / Baby come back / Dream lover / Bridge over troubled water
3036400112 / Mar '96 / Carlton

☐ HEAVENLY PORTRAIT
I saw my Lord this morning / Portrait of Jesus / He careth for you / Let there be love / Hosanna / Oh so wonderful / Praise the Lord / Sing for me / Little baby / Mary's song / Run that race / Hallelujah / Diamond in the rough / Oh Lord / Christ is my light / Ag croist an siol / Home where I belong / Soft rain / Totus tuus / Simple song of love
TIMED 025 / Nov '97 / Timeless Classics

Dana, Vic

☐ RED ROSES FOR A BLUE LADY
BRM 4301 / 19 Jan '98 / Late Nite

Dance 2 Trance

☐ REVIVAL
Surrealistic pillow / Purple onions / Neil's aurora / Land of Oz / Enuf Eko / Christopher / Mrs. Canabis / Morning star / Fly, fly dragonfly / Warrior
74321260282 / Feb '95 / Logic

Dance Hall Crashers

☐ HONEY I'M HOMELY
MCD 11676 / 27 Jul '98 / MCA

☐ OLD RECORD
DON 002 / Dec '96 / Fatwreck Chords

Dance, Heather

☐ HIGHLAND WELCOME
CDLOC 1083 / Oct '94 / Lochshore

Danceable Weird Shit

☐ HERE'S THE RECORD
WD 6662CD / Sep '90 / World Domination

Dancefloor Virus

☐ BALLROOM, THE
Message in a bottle / De do do do de da da da / Bed's too big without you / When the world is running down / Walking on the moon / Synchronicity / Every breath you take / Spirits in a material world / Don't stand so close to me
4804872 / Nov '95 / Epic

Dancetime Orchestra

☐ OLD TIME CHAMPIONSHIP DANCES
SAV 183CD / May '93 / Savoy

Dancing Feet

☐ IN THAT LAND ACROSS THE SEA
DFO 2CD / Apr '94 / Diffusion Breizh

Dancing French Liberals

☐ POWERLINE
SKIP 342 / May '95 / Broken

Dancing Strings

☐ ENCORE
LCOM 5225 / Oct '93 / Lismor

Dando Shaft

☐ REAPING THE HARVEST
Coming home to me / Railway / Magnetic beggar / Pass it on / Kalyope driver / Prayer / Sometimes / Waves upon the ether / Dewet / Riverboat / Harp lady I bombed / Black prince of paradise / When I'm weary / Till the morning comes / Whispering Ned / Road song / Is it me / It was good / Rain / Cold wind / In the country / End of the game
SEECD 291 / Jan '90 / See For Miles

☐ SHADOWS ACROSS THE MOON
HT 001CD / 11 May '98 / Happy Trails

D'Andrea, Franco

☐ ENROSADIRA (D'Andrea, Franco & Luis Agudo)
1232432 / Nov '91 / Red

Dandridge, Putney

☐ CLASSICS 1935-1936
CLASSICS 846 / Nov '95 / Classics

☐ CLASSICS 1936 (Dandridge, Putney & His Orchestra)
CLASSICS 869 / Mar '96 / Classics

☐ PUTNEY DANDRIDGE 1935-1936
CBC 1023 / Sep '95 / Timeless Jazz

Dandruff Deluxe

☐ DEAL WITH THE DEVIL, THE
EFA 043762 / Jan '97 / Crippled Dick Hot Wax

Dandy Jack

☐ DANDY JACK AND THE COSMIC TROUSERS
RI 033CD / Jan '96 / Rather Interesting

Dandy Warhols

☐ COME DOWN
Be in / Boys better / Minnasoter / Orange / I love you / Not if you were the last junkie on Earth / Every day should be a holiday / Good morning / Whipping tree / Green / Cool as Kim Deal / Hard on for Jesus / Pete International Airport
8365052 / 4 May '98 / Parlophone

Dandys

☐ SYMPHONIC SCREAMS
Intro / Merry go round / Drag Queen / You make me want to scream / English country garden / Dirty weekend / All that you do / I wanna be like you / Walter ego / Long live the King / Butterfly song / Johnny foxtrot
5580912 / 15 Jun '98 / Artificial

Dane, Barbara

☐ ANTHOLOGY OF AMERICAN FOLK SONGS
TCD 1062 / 12 Jan '98 / Tradition

☐ SOMETIMES I BELIEVE SHE LOVES ME (Dane, Barbara & Lightnin' Hopkins)
I'm going back baby / I know you got another man / Sometimes I believe she loves me / Baby shake that thing / It's a lonesome old town / Don't push me / Let me be your rag doll / Mother Earth / Mama told Papa / Careless love / Love with a feeling / Betty and Dupree / Don't you push me down / Bury me in my overalls / Deportees / Hold on / Jesus won't you come by here
ARHCD 451 / Nov '96 / Arhoolie

Danemo, Peter

☐ BARABAN
DRAGON 206 / Sep '89 / Dragon

D'Angelo

☐ BROWN SUGAR
Brown sugar / Alright / Jonz in my bonz / Me and those dreaming eyes of mine / Shit, damn Motherfucker / Smooth / Cruisin' / When we get by / Lady / Higher
CTCD 46 / Jun '95 / Cooltempo

Danger Danger

☐ DANGER DANGER
ZK 44342 / 13 Apr '98 / Imagine

☐ FOUR THE HARD WAY
Still kickin' / Sick little twisted mind / Jaded / Captain bring me down / Girl ain't built to sleep alone / Goin' goin' gone / Afraid of love / Heartbreak suicide / I don't need you
199634 / 22 Sep '97 / Made To Measure

☐ SCREW IT
Ginger snaps (intro) / Monkey business / Slipped her the big one / C'est loupe (prelude) / Beat the bullet / I still think about you / Get you s**t together / Crazy nites / Puppet show / Everybody wants some / Don't blame it on love / Comin' home / Horny SOB / Find your way back home / Yeah, you want it / DFNS
ZK 46977 / 13 Apr '98 / Imagine

Dangerous Toys

☐ PISSED
CDVEST 30 / Sep '94 / Bulletproof

Daniele, Pino

☐ YES I KNOW MY WAY (The Best Of Pino Daniele)
3984228182 / 14 Apr '98 / CGD

Daniels, Bebe

☐ FEMALE VOCALISTS (3CD Set) (Daniels, Bebe & Dorothy Carless/Anne Shelton)
While the mucic plays on / Daddy / Better not roll those blue blue eyes / Minnie from Trinidad / Russian rose / St. Louis blues / Yes my darling daughter / Until you fall in love / Little steeple pointing to a star / Let there be love / Amapola / Tomorrow's sunrise / Fools rush in / Always in my heart / How about you / How green was my valley / I don't want to walk without you / My devotion / Taxi driver's serenade / South wind / Only you / My yiddishe Momme / Daddy / It can't be wrong / My sister and I / Room 504 / That lovely weekend / You too can have a lovely romance / Love stay in my heart / We three / Where's my love / I want to be in Dixie / This is no laughing matter / When the sun comes out / Our love affair / I can't love you anymore / I'll always love you / I'd know you anywhere / I guess I'll have to dream the rest / I'm sending my blessing / Ragtime cowboy Joe / Never a day goes by / Walkin' by the river / Deep purple / Stop it's wonderful / As round and round we go / Start the day right / Your company's requested / It's a small world / Give me a little whistle / I'm singing to a million / There I go / Rio Rita / Little Swiss whistling song / Imagination / Nursie nursie / Somewhere in France with you / Mother's prayer at twilight / Our love / Three little fishes / With the wind and rain in your hair / Little Sir Echo / Masquerade is over / Ling ring on your doorstep / Little boy who never told a lie
EMPRESS 1002 / Jul '96 / Empress

☐ STOP IT'S WONDERFUL
Deep purple / Stop it's wonderful / As round and round we go / Start the day right / Your company's requested / It's a small world / Give a little whistle / I'm singing to a million / There I go / Rio Rita / Little swiss whistling song / Imagination / Nursie Nursie / Somewhere in France with you / Mother's prayer at twilight / Our love / Three little fishes / With the wind and rain in your hair / Little Sir Echo / Little boy who never told a lie / Ling'ring on your doorstep / (I'm afraid) the masquerade is over
RAJCD 850 / Nov '97 / Empress

Daniels, Eddie

☐ BEAUTIFUL LOVE (Intimate Jazz Portraits)
SH 5029 / Mar '97 / Shanachie

☐ BLUE BOSSA
Blue bossa / Wistful moment / Emily / Samia / Etude no.14 in F minor Op.25 no.2 / Variations on an Autumn theme / As long as I live / Shine / Two for the road / Entr'acte / Afterthought / Samia / Flower for all seasons / Blue bossa
CHCD 71002 / May '97 / Candid

☐ BRIEF ENCOUNTER
Brief encounter / Child is born / Path / Sway / There is no greater love / Ligia
MCD 5154 / Sep '92 / Muse

☐ FIVE SEASONS, THE
SHCD 5017 / Nov '96 / Shanachie

☐ MEMO'S FROM PARADISE
Spectralight / Dreaming / Heartline / Love of my life / Homecoming / Memo's from Paradise / Seventh heaven / Capriccio twilight / Impressions from ancient dreams / Flight of the dove / Eight-pointed star
GRPD 9651 / May '88 / GRP

Daniels, Joe

☐ SWING IS THE THING (Daniels, Joe & His Hotshots)
Avalon / Basin Street blues / It don't mean a thing if it ain't got that swing / Power house / Who / Crashing through / Somebody stole my gal / No name jive / Swing is the thing / Steepin' out to swing / Darktown strutters ball / Red light / Whirlwind / Downbeat / Oh lady be good / Red robin rag / When you're smiling / Swing fan / Honeysuckle rose / Time on my hands / Drum boogie / Jammin' sessions / Beat me Daddy, eight to the bar / Fats' in the fire
RAJCD 853 / Jan '97 / Empress

Daniels, Luke

☐ LUKE DANIELS & FRANK KILKELLY (Daniels, Luke & Frank Kilkenny)
ACS 019CD / Aug '94 / Acoustics

☐ TARANTELLA
Patsy Denning set / Musette a Teresa / Golden eagle / Tommy Peoples' jigs / King of Prussia / Wednesday's tune / Baby, Isle of Ewe/The snoring barber / Bandolim / Badinerie / Wounded Hussar / Reels for Nadine / Tarantella sonata
ACS 023CD / May '97 / Acoustics

Daniels, Maxine

☐ MEMORY OF TONIGHT, A
Memory of tonight / Miss you / My one and only love / Moving into Spring / Everybody loves my baby / Ill wind / Cottage for sale / Blues for Holly Ann / That's the way it is / I'm nobody's baby / Come rain or come shine / Waltzing round the moon / Smoke gets in your eyes / I've got a crush on you / Who knows how much I love you / They can't take that away from me / Everything happens to me / I fall in love with you every day / You keep coming back like a song
CLGCD 032 / Sep '96 / Calligraph

☐ POCKETFUL OF DREAMS, A
I've got a pocketful of dreams / With you in mind / Deep purple / Seems like old times / Change partners / Sunshine of love / Something 'bout you baby I like / When you wish upon a star / Leaning on a lamp-post / Into each life some rain must fall / Broken doll / For all we know / Over the rainbow / Talk to the animals
CLGCD 016 / Oct '93 / Calligraph

Danielsson, Lars

☐ CONTINUATION
Hit man / Continuation / Long ago and far away / Flykt / Falin' down / Hymn / It never entered my mind / Namtih / Fatima / Solar / Postludium
CDLR 45085 / Aug '94 / L&R

☐ LIVE AT VISIONES NEW YORK 1996 (Danielsson, Lars & Dave Liebman/Jon Christensen/Bobo Stenson)
DRCD 309 / Aug '97 / Dragon

☐ NEW HANDS
DRAGON 125 / Jan '89 / Dragon

☐ POEMS
DRAGON 209 / May '87 / Dragon

Danielsson, Tamara

☐ SO IT GOES
PER 45312 / Aug '97 / Ichiban

Danish Radio Big Band

☐ CRACKDOWN (1st UK Tour (1987))
Mr. CT / Vismanden / Ballad for Benny / Crackdown / From one to another / Say it / Malus scorpio ritus / Cherry juice / Big dipper
HEPCD 2041 / Apr '90 / Hep

☐ SUITE FOR JAZZ BAND
Nervous Charlie / November / Daydream / Suite for jazz band / This is all I ask / On Green Dolphin Street / Groove merchant / Well you needn't
HEPCD 2051 / May '92 / Hep

Danko, Harold

☐ AFTER THE RAIN
SCCD 31356 / Sep '95 / Steeplechase

☐ TIDAL BREEZE
SCCD 31411 / Jul '97 / Steeplechase

Danko, Rick

☐ DANKO/FJELD/ANDERSEN (Danko, Rick & Jonas Fjeld/Eric Andersen)
Driftin' away / Blue hotel / One more shot / Mary I'm comin' back home / Blue river / Judgement day / When morning comes to America / Wrong side of town / Sick and tired / Angels in the snow / Blaze of glory / Last thing on my mind
RCD 10270 / Oct '93 / Rykodisc

☐ RICK DANKO
What a town / Brainwash / New Mexico / Tired of waiting / Sip the wine / Java blues / Sweet romance / Small town talk / Shake it / Once upon a time
ED CD 317 / Apr '90 / Edsel

☐ RIDIN' ON THE BLINDS (Danko, Rick & Jonas Fjeld/Eric Andersen)
GR 4080CD / Apr '95 / Grappa

Dankworth, Jacqui

☐ FIVE HOUSMAN SETTINGS (Dankworth, Jacqui & New Perspectives)
On Green Dolphin Street / Bachiana brasileiras No.5 / Sinner's rue / Terence this is stupid stuff / On the idle hill of summer / White in the moon the long road lies / When summer's end is nighing / Creole love call / Reflections in D / Maids of Cadiz / Down hill all the way
SPJCD 559 / Jul '96 / Spotlite

Dankworth, John

☐ MOON VALLEY
Moon valley / Stompin' at the savoy / Down the line / Son of sparky / Close to you / Days of wine and roses / Casa 50 / Spooks / Autumn in New York
ABCD 7 / Jul '98 / ABCD

☐ NEBUCHADNEZZAR (Dankworth Generation Big Band)
Maggot / It ain't necessarily so / Early June / Song for my lad / Day I met Kenny G / Every time we say goodbye / Black narcissus / Ida Lupino / Down to earth / Up for an oscar / Emily / Song for my lady
JHCD 029 / Mar '94 / Ronnie Scott's Jazz House

☐ RHYTHM CHANGES (Dankworth Generation Big Band)
I got rheumatics / Just once more / Around the track / Jelly mould blues / Going back, going on / Thoughts / Pigs head copanitza / All things
JHCD 043 / Nov '95 / Ronnie Scott's Jazz House

Danleers

☐ ONE SUMMERNIGHT
One summer night / My flaming heart / Perlude to love / Wheelin' and dealin' / Picture of you / Really love you, I / You're everything / Whole mess of trouble / Just look around / Can't sleep, I / Your love / (I live) half a block from an angel / If you don't care / Little lover / I'll always believe in you / Light of love / I'll be forever yours / I'm looking around / Foolish / Angels sent you / Were you there / If / Where is love / Think it over baby / Love you better leave me alone
BCD 15503 / May '91 / Bear Family

Danny & Dusty

☐ LOST WEEKEND, THE
SID 006 / Mar '96 / Prima

Danny & The Juniors

☐ BACK TO THE HOP (Original Swan Recordings 1960-1962)
Back to the hop / Twistin' england / Pony express / Let's stomp again / Doin' the continental walk / Twistin' usa / Tallahassee lassie / Thousand miles away / Your hair's too long / Funny / Some kind of nut / Daydreamer / Down I go / Oh holy night / Candy cane sugary plum / Cha cha go go / Cathedral bells / Twistin' italy / Back to the hop / Doin' the continental walk / Do the mashed potato / Just because / Twist-mother's club twist (medley) / When the saints go twistin' in / Twistin' all night long / Together you and I (joe terry and mystery) / Twistin' germany
RCCD 3005 / Sep '92 / Rollercoaster

Danny Wilson

☐ BEBOP MOPTOP
Imaginary girl / Second summer of love / I can't wait / If you really love me (let me go) / If everything you said was true / Loneliness / I was wrong / Charlie boy / Never gonna be the same / Desert hearts / NYC Shanty / Goodbye Shanty Town / Ballad of me and Shirley MacLaine
CDV 2594 / Aug '91 / Virgin

☐ BEST OF DANNY WILSON, THE
Davy / Mary's prayer / Girl I used to know / I won't forget / Second summer of love / Get happy / Never gonna be the same / I'll be waiting / Living to learn / Nothing ever goes to plan / Broken china
CDVIP 139 / Sep '95 / Virgin VIP

☐ MEET DANNY WILSON
Davy / Mary's prayer / Lorraine parade / Aberdeen / Nothing ever goes to plan / Broken china / Steamtrains to the milkyway / Spencer Tracey / You remain an angel / Ruby's golden wedding / Girl I used to know / Five friendly aliens / I won't be here when you get home
CDV 2419 / '87 / Virgin

☐ SWEET DANNY WILSON (2CD Set)
Never gonna be the same / Ballad of me and Shirley MacLaine / If you really love me (let me go) / Mary's prayer / Girl I used to know / Pleasure to pleasure / Davy / Ruby's golden wedding / I can't wait / I won't be here when you get home / Second summer of love / From a boy to a man / Three in a bed romp / Get

happy / Kathleen / Growing emotional / I'll be waiting / Living to learn / I won't forget / Kooks / Broken china / Aberdeen / Steamtrains (to the milky way) / Knowing me, knowing you / Don't know who I am / I was wrong / Loneliness
CDVIP 206 / 3 Aug '98 / Virgin VIP

☐ SWEET DANNY WILSON
Never gonna be the same / Ballad of me and Shirley MacLaine / If you really love me (Let me go) / Mary's prayer / Girl I used to know / Pleasuer to pleasure / Davy / Ruby's golden wedding / I can't wait / I won't be here when you get home / Second Summer of love / From a boy to a man
CDV 2669 / Aug '92 / Virgin

Danse Macabre
☐ TOTENTANZ
M 7029CD / 11 May '98 / Mascot

Dantalian's Chariot
☐ CHARIOT RISING
WHCD 005 / Mar '97 / Wooden Hill

Dante Fox
☐ UNDER SUSPICION
NTHEN 030CD / 16 Feb '98 / Now & Then

Danu
☐ DANU
TM 002CD / Aug '97 / TM

Danzas Panama
☐ INSTRUMENTAL FOLK MUSIC OF PANAMA
VICG 53382 / Mar '96 / JVC World Library

Danzig
☐ BLACK ACID DEVIL
1620842 / Oct '96 / Polydor

☐ DANZIG
Twist of Cain / Not of this world / She rides / Soul on fire / Am I demon / Mother / Possession / End of time / Hunter / Evil thing
74321248412 / Apr '95 / American

☐ DANZIG VOL.4
Brand new God / Little whip / Cantspeak / Going down to die / Until you call on the dark / Dominion / Bringer of death / Sadistikal / Son of the morning star / I don't mind the pain / Stalker song / Let it be captured
74321236812 / Oct '94 / American

☐ HOW THE GODS KILL
Godless / Anything / Bodies / How the gods kill / Dirty black summer / Left hand black / Heart of the devil / Sistinas / Do you wear the mark / When the dying calls
74321248432 / Apr '95 / American

☐ LUCIFUGE
Long way back from hell / Killer wolf / I'm the one / Devil's plaything / Blood and tears / Pain in the world / Snakes of Christ / Tired of being alone / Her black wings / 777 / Girl
74321248422 / Apr '95 / American

Daphne's Flight
☐ DAPHNE'S FLIGHT
FLE 1005CD / Apr '96 / Fledg'ling

Dapogny, Jim
☐ JAMES DAPOGNY & HIS CHICAGOANS
SOSCD 1263 / Oct '93 / Stomp Off

Darby, Blind Teddy
☐ BLIND TEDDY DARBY 1929-1937
BDCD 6042 / May '93 / Blues Document

D'Arby, Terence Trent
☐ INTRODUCING THE HARDLINE ACCORDING TO TERENCE TRENT D'ARBY
If you all get to Heaven / If you let me stay / Wishing well / I'll never turn my back on you (fathers words) / Dance little sister / Seven more days / Let's go forward / Rain / Sign your name / As yet untitled / Who's loving you
4509112 / 27 Jul '98 / Columbia

☐ TERENCE TRENT D'ARBY'S SYMPHONY OR DAMN (Exploring The Tension Inside The Sweetness)
Welcome to the Monasteryo / She kissed me / Do you love me like you say / Baby let me share my love / Delicate / Neon messiah / Penelope please / Wet your lips / Turn the page / Castilian blues / TITS/ FandJ / Are you happy / Succumb to me / I still love you / Seasons / Let her down easy
4735612 / 27 Jul '98 / Columbia

☐ TERENCE TRENT D'ARBY'S VIBRATOR
Vibrator / Supermodel sandwich / Holding onto you / Read my lips (I dig your scene) / Undeniably / We don't have that much time / Together / Epilog / CYFLAY / If you go before me / Surrender / TTD's recurring dream / Supermodel sandwich with cheese / Resurrection / It's been said
4785052 / 2 Feb '98 / Columbia

Darby, Tom
☐ COMPLETE RECORDINGS (Darby, Tom & Jimmie Tarlton)
Down in Florida on a hog / Birmingham town / Birmingham jail / Columbus Stockade blues / Gamblin' Jim / Lonesome in the pines / After the ball / I can't tell you why / I love you / Irish police / Hobo tramp / Alto waltz / Mexican rag / Birmingham jail # 2 / Rainbow division / Country girl valley / Lonesome railroad / If you ever learn to love me / If I had listened to my Mother / Travelling yodel blues / Heavy hearted blues / New York hobo / All bound down in Texas / Touring yodel blues / Slow wicked blues / Black Jack moonshine / Ain't gonna marry no more / Down in the old cherry orchid / When the bluebirds nest again / Beggar Joe / When you're far away from home / Birmingham rag / Sweet Sarah blues / Little Bessie / I left her heart at the river / Jack and May / Captain won't you let me go home / Going back to my Texas home / Whistling songbird / Freight train ramble / Lonesome Frisco line / Down among the sugar cane / Black sheep / Little ola / Once I had a sweetheart / Maple on the hill / My father died a drunkyard / Franke Dean / Pork chops / On the banks of a lonely river / Faithless husband / Hard time blues / Rising sun blues / My little blue heaven / Carleless love / By the old oaken bucket / Louise / Lowe Bonnie / After the sinking of the Titanic / New Birmingham jail / Roy Dixon / Moonshine blues / She's waiting for me / That lonesome Frisco line / Thirteen years in Kilbie prison / Once I had a fortune / Dixie mail / Weaver's blues / Sweetheart of my dreams / Ooze up to me / Let's be friends again / By the oaken bucket
BCD 15764 / Jun '95 / Bear Family

Darc, Daniel
☐ PARCE QUE (Darc, Daniel & Bill Pritchard)
BIAS 100CD / '90 / Play It Again Sam

Dardanelle
☐ COLORS OF MY LIFE, THE
STCD 544 / '91 / Stash

☐ DARDANELLE & DAG WALTON'S BIG BAND (Dardanelle & Dag Walton)
ACD 227 / Oct '92 / Audiophile

☐ DOWN HOME
ACD 214 / Oct '92 / Audiophile

☐ ECHOES SINGING LADIES
ACD 145 / Mar '95 / Audiophile

☐ NEW YORK NEW YORK
STCD 547 / '92 / Stash

☐ SWINGIN' IN LONDON
ACD 278 / Jan '94 / Audiophile

Dare
☐ CALM BEFORE THE STORM
Walk on the water / Some day / Calm before the storm / Rescue me / Silence in your head / Rising sun / Ashes / Crown of thorns / Deliverance / Still in love with you
199649 / 1 Jun '98 / Made To Measure

Darensbourg, Joe
☐ LIVE 1957 (Darensbourg, Joe & His Dixie Flyers)
AMCD 103 / Dec '97 / American Music

☐ N'ORLEANS STATESMEN
BCD 313 / Aug '94 / GHB

D'Arienzo, Juan
☐ JUAN D'ARIENZO 1937-1944
HQCD 71 / Jul '96 / Harlequin

☐ LA PUNALADA
BMT 011 / Jan '98 / Blue Moon

☐ TIPICA 1935-1939
EBCD 84 / Jan '97 / El Bandoneon

Darin, Bobby
☐ AS LONG AS I'M SINGIN'
JASSCD 4 / Oct '91 / Jass

☐ BEST OF BOBBY DARIN VOL.1, THE
7567917942 / Dec '96 / Atlantic

☐ DREAM LOVER
La mer / Clementine / That's the way love is / I got a woman/What'd I say/When the saints go marching in / Mack the knife / By myself/When your lover has gone / Splish splash / Queen of the hop / Quarter to nine / You're nobody till somebody loves you / Girl who stood beside me / Dream lover / This could be the start of something big/Just in time / I wish I were in love again / Don't rain on my parade / Toot toot tootsie goodbye/Don't worry 'bout me / Plain Jane / Early in the morning / Swing low, sweet chariot/ Lonesome road/When the saints / If I were a carpenter / That's all
CD 6040 / Sep '96 / Music

☐ DREAM LOVER (The Concert Collection)
Mack the knife / Dream lover / Splish splash / If I were a carpenter / Queen of the hop / Early in the morning / Plain Jane / Girl who stood beside me / Funny what love can do / Quarter to nine / Once upon a time / I wish I were in love again
PLACD 111 / Feb '97 / Platinum

☐ GREATEST HITS
Mack the knife / Dream lover / Splish splash / If I were a carpenter / Queen of the hop / Early in the morning / Plain Jane / Girl who stood beside me / Funny what love can do / Quarter to nine / Once upon a time / I wish I were in love again
HADCD 152 / May '94 / Javelin

☐ I GOT RHYTHM
Eighteen yellow roses / If a man answers / True true love / I wonder who's kissing her now / Hello Dolly / All by myself / Roses of Picardy / You'll never know / You made me love you (I didn't want to do it) / Nightingale sang in Berkeley Square / Days of wine and roses / Goodbye Charlie / Softly as I leave you / Call me irresponsible / I got rhythm / All of you / Fly me to the moon / In a world without you / I'm sitting on top of the world / Party's over
CDMFP 6247 / Aug '96 / Music For Pleasure

☐ LIVE
Mack the knife / Dream lover / Splish splash / Funny what love can do / Quarter to nine / I wish I were in love again / Early in the morning / Queen of the hop / Plain jane / If I were a carpenter / Girl who stood beside me / Once upon a time
305772 / Jul '97 / Hallmark

☐ SPOTLIGHT ON BOBBY DARIN
Alabamy bound / Blue skies / You'll never know / Standing on the corner / I'm beginning to see the light / Good life / Oh look at me now / Just in time / You made me love you / All of you / There's a rainbow 'round my shoulder / Fly me to the moon / I got rhythm / All by myself / I wanna be around / Nightingale sang in Berkley Square / Call me irresponsible / My buddy / Always / I'm sitting on top of the world
CDP 8285122 / Apr '95 / Capitol

☐ TOUCH OF CLASS, A
18 Yellow roses / If a man answers / True true love / I wonder who's kissing her now / Hello Dolly / All by myself / Roses of Picardy / You'll never know / You made me love you / Nightingale sang in Berkley Square / Days of wine and roses / Goodbye Charlie / Softly as I leave you / Call me irresponsible / I got rhythm / All of you / Fly me to the moon / In a world without you / I'm sitting on top of the world / Party's over
TC 877052 / 2 Feb '98 / Disky

☐ YOU'RE THE REASON I'M LIVING/I WANNA BE AROUND
Sally was a good girl / Be honest with me / Oh lonesome whistle / You're the reason I'm living / It keeps right on hurtin' / You're the reason I'm livin' / Please help me I'm falling under your spell again / Here I am / Who can I count on / Now you're gone / RElease me / Venice blue / I wanna be around / Somewhere / Good life / Dear life / Dear heart / Softly as I leave you / You just don't know / There ain't no girl worth the salt of my tears / Who can I turn to / Taste of honey / World without you
CTMCD 122 / 15 Sep '97 / EMI

Dario G
☐ SUNMACHINE
Sunchyme / Carnaval de Paris / Sunmachine / Voices / Be my friend / Peaches / Malaway / Revolution / Voices / End of the beginning
3984233782 / 8 Jun '98 / WEA

Darius
☐ DARIUS
FLASH 009 / Jun '97 / Flashback

Dark
☐ ENDLESS DREAMS OF SADNESS
GUN 117CD / Mar '97 / Gun

☐ ZYEZN GAMBALLE & MENTALWORLD
MABCD 008 / Sep '94 / MAB

Dark
☐ ANONYMOUS DAYS
DRCD 2371 / 24 Nov '97 / Dark

☐ DARK
KSCD 9204 / Jun '97 / Kissing Spell

Dark Angel
☐ DARKNESS DESCENDS
Darkness descends / Burning of Sodom / Hunger of the undead / Merciless death / Death is certain (life is not) / Black prophesies / Perish in flames
CDFLAG 6 / '89 / Under One Flag

Dark Carnival
☐ LAST GREAT RIDE
SFTRI 431CD / Jan '97 / Sympathy For The Record Industry

Dark Comedy
☐ SEVEN DAYS
Electic / Bar / March / Ina room / Solace / Darkness / War of the worlds / Without a sound / Paranoid / Bar
ELY 007CD / May '97 / Elypsia

Dark Funeral
☐ SECRETS OF THE BLACK ARTS
NFR 011CD / Feb '96 / No Fashion

☐ VOBISCUM SATANAS
NFR 027CD / 13 Apr '98 / No Fashion

Dark Illumination
☐ REALIZE THE ERROR
ZOTH 190CD / Oct '97 / Zoth Ommog

Dark Lantern
☐ DARK LANTERN
SP 002CD / Nov '95 / Silent Pocket

Dark Magus
☐ NIGHT WATCHMEN
In the blood / Fire underwater / Solid / Nothing has been said / Arma Gideon / Ocean spray / Funck '48 / Plastic paradise
ALPHACD 3 / 3 Nov '97 / Alphaphone

Dark Side Cowboys
☐ APOCRYPHAL, THE
MACDL 948 / Nov '96 / Resurrection

Dark Throne
☐ GOATLORD
FOG 013CD / Nov '96 / Moonfog

☐ PANZERFAUST
FOG 005CD / May '95 / Moonfog

☐ TOTAL DEATH
FOG 011CD / Mar '96 / Moonfog

Dark Tranquility
☐ ENTER SUICIDAL ANGELS
OPCD 049 / Nov '96 / Osmose

☐ GALLERY, THE
OPCD 033L / Apr '96 / Osmose
OPCD 033 / Jan '96 / Osmose

☐ MINDS VOL.1
OPCDL 052
OPCD 052 / Apr '97 / Osmose

☐ OF CHAOS AND ETERNAL LIGHT
SPI 023CD / May '95 / Spinefarm

☐ SKYDANCER
SPI 016CD / Apr '96 / Spinefarm

☐ SKYDANCER/OF CHAOS AND ETERNAL LIGHT
SPI 034CD / Oct '96 / Spinefarm

Dark Woods My Betrothed
☐ AUTUMN ROARS THUNDER
SOL 006CD / 28 Jul '97 / Solistium

Darkman
☐ WORLDWIDE
Who's the darkman / Brand new day (I'm no puppet) / Yabba dabba do / What's not yours / Wicked / She used to call me / Worldwide ting / What is hardcore / Lighter / Come with the funk / Flip da script / Hot and cold
5294162 / Oct '95 / Wild Card

Darko, George
☐ HIGH LIFE IN THE AIR
BLDCD 522 / Sep '96 / Boulevard

Darkroom
☐ DAYLIGHT
HAL 8002CD / 31 Aug '98 / Halloween Society

Darkseed
☐ MIDNIGHT SOLEMNLY DANCE
SR 008CD / 28 Jul '97 / Serenades

☐ ROMANTIC TALES
IR 010CD / Apr '95 / Invasion

Darkside
☐ MELANCHOLIA OF A DYING WORLD
SPV 8453552 / Aug '96 / SPV

Darling, David
☐ CELLO
Darkwood / No place nowhere / Fables / Darkwood II / Lament / Two or three things / Indiana Indian / Totem / Psalm / Choral / Bell / In November / Darkwood III
5119822 / Sep '92 / ECM

CYCLES
Cycle song / Cycle 1: Namaste / Fly / Ode / Cycle 2: Trio / Cycle 3: Quintet and coda / Jessica's sunwheel
8431722 / Nov '91 / ECM

DARKWOOD
Dawn / In motion / Journey / Light / Earth / New morning / Returning / Picture / Medivial dance / Searching / Up side down / Beginning / Passage
5237502 / Feb '95 / ECM

Darling, Erik
☐ BLUEGRASS MUSIC
Cripple creek / Pateroller song / One dime blues / Sourwood mountain / Goin' down road feelin' bad / Amazing grace / Girl I left behind me / Marching jaybird / John brown's dream / Sally goodin / Railroad bill / Soldier's joy / Molly brooks / Pretty polly / Johnson boys / John henry / Drunken hiccups / Shady grove / Bully of the town / Skip to my lou / Hard and it's hard / Bowling green / I'll fly away / Darby ram / Willie moore / Little birdie / Banks of the ohio / Wagoner's lad / Poor ellen smith / What will we do with the baby-o
12181 / May '94 / Laserlight

☐ BORDER TOWN AT MIDNIGHT
FE 1417 / Dec '94 / Folk Era

D'Arnell, Andrea
☐ VILLERS-AUX-VENTS
422498 / May '94 / New Rose

Darren, James
☐ BEST OF JAMES DARREN, THE
Angel face / I ain't sharin' Sharon / Because they're young / Goodbye cruel world / Her royal majesty / Conscience / Gotta have love / Mary's little lamb / Life of the party / Hail to the conquering hero / Pin a medal on Joey / They should have given you the oscar / Put on a happy face / Just think of tonight / Punch and Judy
NEMCD 694 / Aug '94 / Sequel

Darrid, Brad
☐ BRAD DARRID
ESM 016 / 2 Mar '98 / Escape

Darrow, Chris
☐ FRETLESS
TX 2012CD / Jan '94 / Taxim

Darshan
☐ AWAKENING
AFRCD 10 / 9 Mar '98 / Flying Rhino

Dart
☐ 36 CENTS AN HOUR
CHE 39CD / Mar '96 / Che

Darwyn
☐ CATALOGUE OF MYSTERIES, A
Better by far / Coming up for air / People / Dear Mrs. Bryan / Through the looking glass / Lifeline / Can I help it / My pretty one / Sheep fever / Give me space / Origin of the species / Far way star
7115857 / 6 Apr '98 / Scorpio

Daryll-Ann
☐ COME AROUND
Come around / Doll / Shamrock / Good thing / Mirror mind / Ocean girl
HUTDM 44 / May '94 / Hut

☐ SEABORNE WEST
Stay / Low light / Doctor and I / Sheila / Allright / Holida why / You're so alien / Birthmark / Boy you were / Liquid / HP confirm / Soft and fat
CDHUT 26 / Apr '95 / Hut

Das Baul
☐ REAL SUGAR (Das Baul, Paban & Sam Mills)
Dil ki doya / Nacho kali / Porojonome / Ore poinkha / Boshondharar buke / Mon fakira / Choncholo mon / Mon moti / Gopun premer kotha
CDRW 65 / May '97 / Realworld

Das Bose Ding
☐ CLEANHAPPYDIRTY
BEST 1090CD / Apr '96 / Acoustic Music

Das Damen
☐ DAS DAMEN
SST 040CD / May '93 / SST

☐ TRISKAIDEKAPHOBE
SST 190CD / May '93 / SST

Das EFX
☐ DEAD SERIOUS
Mic checka / Jussummen / They want efx / Looseys / Dum dums / East coast / If only / Brooklyn to T-neck / Klap ya handz / Straight out the sewer
7567918272 / May '92 / Atlantic

GENERATION EFX
Intro / Raw breed / Shine / Somebody told me / Set it off / Rap scholar / Generation EFX / Rite now / Whut goes around / Make noise / New stuff / Take it back / Change
7559620632 / 30 Mar '98 / East West

☐ HOLD IT DOWN
Intro (once again) / Real hip-hop / Microphone master / Buck-buck / 40 a blunt / Bad news / Hardcore rap act / Comin' thru / Represent the real / Ready to rock rough rhymes / Dedicated / Hold it down / Alright / Real hip hop / Can't have nuttin' / Here it is / Here we go / No diggedy / Knockin' niggaz off
7559618292 / Sep '95 / Atlantic

☐ STRAIGHT UP SEWASIDE
Intro / Undaground rappa / Gimme dat microphone / Check it out / Interlude / Freak it / Rappaz / Interview / Baknaffek / Kaught in da ak / Wontu / Krazy wit da books / It'z lik dat / Host wit da most
7567922652 / Dec '93 / Atlantic

Das Ich
☐ DIE PROPHETEN
EFA 11201 / Apr '93 / Danse Macabre

☐ SATANISCHE VERSE
EFA 112322 / Jul '94 / Danse Macabre

☐ STAUB
EFA 112362 / Nov '94 / Danse Macabre

☐ STIGMA
EFACD 112332 / Jun '94 / Danse Macabre

Das Klown
☐ LAUGHIN' STACK
EFA 122152 / Oct '94 / Poshboy

Das, Partho
☐ MUSIC OF THE SITAR
VICG 52222 / Mar '96 / JVC World Library

Das Pferd
☐ KISSES (Das Pferd & Randy Becker)
ITM 1430 / Jan '91 / ITM

Das, Puma Chandra
☐ SONGS OF THE BAULS
VICG 52672 / Mar '96 / JVC World Library

Dash, Julian
☐ JULIAN DASH 1950-1953
BMCD 1050 / Apr '97 / Blue Moon

Dash Rip Rock
☐ GET YOU SOME OF ME
SECT2 10021 / Jan '96 / Sector 2

Datacook
☐ ONDAS
RI 040CD / Dec '96 / Rather Interesting

Datblygu
☐ LIBERTINO
ANKST 037CD / Jun '93 / Ankst

☐ WYAU/PYST
ANKST 60CD / Sep '95 / Ankst

Daugherty, Michael
☐ AMERICAN ICONS (Daugherty, Michael & Paul Crossley/Markus Stenz/David Zinman)
Dead Elvis / Snap / What's that spell / Jackie's song / Le tombeau de Liberace / Motown metal / Flamingo
4581452 / 22 Jun '98 / Argo

☐ METROPOLIS SYMPHONY/BIZARRO (Daugherty, Michael & Baltimore Symphony Orchestra)
4521032 / Oct '96 / Argo

Daughters Of Zion
☐ AISHA
NGCD 538 / May '93 / Twinkle

Daun, Tom
☐ ALL IN A GARDEN GREEN (Harp Music)
TUT 167 / Oct '94 / Wundertute

Dauner, Wolfgang
☐ GET UP AND DAUNER
5335482 / Feb '97 / MPS Jazz

Dave & Deke Combo
☐ MOONSHINE MELODIES
NOHITCD 009 / Jan '94 / No Hit

Dave Dee, Dozy, Beaky, Mick & Tich
☐ ALL THE HITS PLUS MORE
Save me / Legend of Xanadu / Wreck of Antoinette / Okay / Bend it / It's hard to love you / Zabadak / Last night in Soho / Here's a heart / Touch me touch me / Hideaway / Hold tight
CDSGP 0323 / 1 Dec '97 / Prestige

☐ BEST OF DAVE DEE, DOZY, BEAKY, MICK & TICH
Legend of Xanadu / Bend it / Save me / Hold tight / Touch me, touch me / Wreck of the Antoinette / Snake in the grass / No time / My woman's man / Zabadak / Okay / You make it move / Mr. President / Don Juan / Sun goes down / Is it love / Last night in Soho / Legend of Xanadu
5518232 / Nov '95 / Spectrum

☐ GREATEST HITS
Legend of Xanadu / Hideaway / Bend it / Zabadak / It's so hard to love you / Okay / Hold tight / Wreck of the Antoinette / Save me / Here's a heart / Touch me touch me / Last night in Soho
QED 122 / Nov '96 / Tring

☐ GREATEST HITS
Save me / Legend of Xanadu / Wreck of the Antoinette / Okay / Bend it / It's hard to love you / Touch me touch me / Hideaway / Hold tight
300362 / Jul '96 / Hallmark

☐ HITS
Hold tight / Hideaway / Bend it / Save me / Here's a heart / Legend of xanadu / Touch me, touch me / Okay / Zabadak / It's hard to love you / Last night in soho / Wreck of the antointete
12274 / Apr '94 / Laserlight

☐ HOLD TIGHT
Hold tight / Hideaway / Bend it / Save me / Touch me touch me / Okay / Zabadak / Legend of Xanadu / Last night in Soho / Wreck of the Antoinette / Here's a heart / It's so hard to love you / Matthew and son / Do wah diddy diddy
PLATCD 205 / Feb '97 / Platinum

☐ TOGETHER
BX 4362 / Nov '97 / BR Music

☐ ZABADAK
Legend of Xanadu / Bend it / Save me / Mr. President / My woman's man / All I want to do / Master Llewellyn / I'm on the up / If I were a carpenter / Zabadak / Okay / Don Juan / She's so good / Hands off / Help me / Hard to love you / Nose for trouble / We've got a good thing goin'
5509392 / Jan '95 / Spectrum

☐ ZABADAK (The Best Of Dave, Dee, Dozy, Beaky, Mick & Tich)
MACCD 263 / Feb '97 / Autograph

Davenport, Bob
☐ RED HAIRED LAD, THE (Davenport, Bob & The Rakes)
Blarney stone / I am a rambling man / Durham city / Greenwich Park/Red haired lad / Come all ye tramps and hawkers / Begging I will go / Hallelujah I'm a bum / Star of County Down / Bonny at Morn/My bonny lad / Close of an Irish day/Wild hills of Wannies / Bells of Rhymney/Johnny Miner / Moving day / Kerry polka/I have a bonnet trimmed with blue / I'll make my way to Liverpool / Caw market a roving / Doran's Ass/The Liverpool no. 2 / Wild wild whiskey / Wealthy squire / An Coleen Deas/Down the Glen / Green banks of Yarrow / Three around three/Flowers of Edinburgh / Young man came to my Daddy's door / Stone outside Dan Murphy's door / Goodbye Mick / I wish they'd do it now
FECD 122 / 1 Nov '97 / Fellside

Davenport, Cow Cow
☐ ACCOMPANIST, THE
BDCD 6040 / May '93 / Blues Document

☐ UNISSUED PRIVATE ACETATE RECORDINGS
DOCD 5586 / Dec '97 / Document

Davenport, Jeremy
☐ JEREMY DAVENPORT
Was it something I did / Night we met in Paris / They don't take that away from me / I see your face before me / Why oh why / Joy zones in the Temple of Doom / I'm old fashioned / Watch out / I'm confessin' that I love you / Love a with an O / Just in case / I'm in the mood for love
CD 83376 / Jul '96 / Telarc

Davenport, N'Dea
☐ N'DEA DAVENPORT
VVR 1002022 / 22 Jun '98 / V2

Davern, Kenny
☐ BREEZIN' ALONG
ARCD 19170 / May '97 / Arbors Jazz

☐ I'LL SEE YOU IN MY DREAMS
MM 5020 / Oct '94 / Music Masters

LAST REUNION, THE (Davern, Kenny Trio)
I never knew / There'll be some changes made / Buddy Bolden's blues / I would do anything for you / New Orleans / Exactly like you / Love for sale / Art's interlude / Love me or leave me / After you've gone / Sometimes I'm happy / Save it pretty mama / All of me
URCD 135 / Apr '98 / Upbeat

☐ LIVE AND SWINGING (Davern, Kenny & John Petters Swing Band)
That's a plenty / Man I love / Poor butterfly / Royal Garden blues / Blue Monk / Love me or leave me
CMJCD 001 / Jul '98 / CMJ

☐ NEVER IN A MILLION YEARS (Davern, Kenny & Dick Wellstood)
CHR 70019 / Jun '95 / Challenge

☐ ONE HOUR TONIGHT (Davern, Kenny & Dick Wellstood)
Elsa's dream / Pretty baby / Love is the thing / If I could be with you one hour tonight
MM 5003 / Oct '94 / Music Masters

☐ SUMMIT REUNION 1992
CRD 324 / Feb '95 / Chiaroscuro

☐ THIS OLD GANG OF OURS (Davern, Kenny & Humphrey Lyttelton)
Mood Hollywood / Porter's love song to a chamber maid / My mama socks me / Jackass blues / Undecided / Of all the wrongs you've done to me / Buddy Bolden's blues / Legacy: Lyttelton, Humphrey
URCD 138 / Jul '98 / Upbeat

Dave's True Story
☐ SEX WITHOUT BODIES
JD 164 / 23 Feb '98 / Chesky

Davey, Alan
☐ BEDOUIN
Rock palace / Medi dhar / Passion is an animal / Al hadan / Space rock cafe / One moon circles / Queen of the night / Eyes in the dark / Sand devil
EBSCD 133 / 8 Dec '97 / Emergency Broadcast System

☐ CAPTURED ROTATION
Call / Never come down / Higher than before / Ancient light / Space bass / Hawkstrel / Nebula / Thunderbird / Nova dive / Spacial wave / Quirk / Pre-Med
EBSSCD 122 / 24 Nov '97 / Emergency Broadcast System

Davey, Shaun
☐ GRANUALI
Dubhbarra / Ripples in the rockpools / Defence of Hens Castle / Free and easy / Rescue of Hugh de Lacy / Dismissal / Hen's march / Death of Richard-an-Irainn / Sir Richard Bingham / Spanish Armada / New age
TARACD 3017 / Dec '96 / Tara

☐ PILGRIM, THE
TARA 3032CD / Oct '94 / Tara

☐ RELIEF OF DERRY SYMPHONY
TARACD 3024 / Jul '92 / Tara

David & Jonathan
☐ VERY BEST OF DAVID & JONATHAN
Michelle / Softly whispering your name / You ought to meet my baby / This golden ring / Bye bye brown eyes / I know / Speak her name / Ten storeys high / I've got that girl on my mind / You've got your troubles / Lovers of the world unite / Laughing fit to cry / Be gone / Scarlet ribbons / Gilly gilly ossenfeffer katzenellenbogen by the sea / How bitter the taste of love / Every now and then / One born every minute / See me cry / She's leaving home
C5CD507 / Jul '90 / See For Miles

David
☐ ANOTHER DAY ANOTHER LIFETIME
852123 / 1 Jun '98 / EVA

David Devant & His Spirit Wife
☐ WORK LOVELIFE MISCELLANEOUS
KINDCD 1 / Jun '97 / Rhythm King

David J
☐ DAVID J ON GLASS
CLEO 2102 / 14 Apr '98 / Cleopatra

☐ ETIQUETTE OF VIOLENCE
Gospel according to fear / I hear only silence now / No one's spending roses / Fugitive / Betrayel / Joe Orton's wedding / Promised land / With the indians permanent / Say Uncle / Disease / Roulette / St. Jackie
SITL 8CD / '88 / Situation 2

David, Jean
☐ CHIR HACHIRIM - THE SONG OF SONGS
926282 / Jul '95 / BUDA

David, Kal

☐ DOUBLE TUFF
SC 880042 / May '95 / Lipstick

Davidson, Fiona

☐ FONNSHEEN
FONOCD 13 / Mar '96 / Watercolour

☐ LANGUAGE OF BIRDS, THE
WCMCD 017 / Jul '98 / Watercolour

Davidson, Matthew

☐ SPACE SHUFFLE & OTHER FUTURISTIC RAGS
SOSCD 1252 / May '93 / Stomp Off

Davies, 'Blind' John

☐ INCOMPARABLE
Everyday I have the blues / Blues for Jimmy / How long blues / Jim town blues / Crazy boogie / I wish I could shimmy like my sister Kate / Boogie woogie on St. Louis blues / 12th Street rag / Martin's boogie / Let's move to the outskirts of town / Cow cow blues / Goin' to Kansas city / Pine Top's boogie woogie / After hours / Rocking chair boogie / Lonesome blues
OLCD 7003 / Nov '97 / Oldie Blues

Davies, Debbie

☐ I GOT THAT FEELING
BPCD 5039 / Feb '97 / Blind Pig

☐ LOOSE TONIGHT
BPCD 5015 / Dec '94 / Blind Pig

☐ ROUND EVERY CORNER
Sittin' and cryin' / Homework / Who'll stop the rain / Time work your magic / Scratches / Blue and lonesome / Such a fine man / Round every corner / Little sister / Room with a view / A.C. strut / Backseat driver
SHANCD 9010 / Jun '98 / Shanachie

Davies, Gail

☐ GREATEST HITS
Waiting here for you / Tell me why / Jagged edge of a broken heart / Someone is looking for someone like you / I'll be there / It's a lovely lovely world / Blue heartache / Grandma's song / Bucket to the South / I'm hungry I'm tired / You turn me on I'm a radio / Boys like you / You're a hard dog / Not a day goes by / Singing the blues / Kentucky / Unwed Fathers / What can I say / Round the clock lovin' / Mama I'm sick
GAIL 0096 / Jul '97 / Gail Davies

Davies, Hugh

☐ INTERPLAY
FMRCD 39 / Sep '97 / Future

Davies, Ray

☐ STORYTELLER
Storyteller / Introduction / Victoria / My name / 20th century man / London song / My big sister / That old black magic / Tired of waiting / Set me free / Dad and the green lamp / Set me free / Front room / See my friends / Autumn almanac / Hunchback / X-Ray / Art school / Art school / Babe / Back in the front room / Writing the song / When big Bill speaks / Man who knew a man / It's alright / It's alright / Julie Finkle / Ballad of Julie Finkle / Third single / You really got me / London song
4941682 / 23 Mar '98 / EMI

Davies, Ray

☐ BEST OF BUTTON DOWN BRASS & RAY DAVIES, THE (Button Down Brass & Ray Davies)
5545162 / Jul '98 / Spectrum

☐ SWAY (20 Latin Ballroom Classics) (Davies, Ray Button Down Band & Orchestra)
Sway (quie sera) / Zorba the Greek/Zorba's dance / Never on Sunday / La cumparsita / Punta prima / Over the rainbow / Adios mariquita Linda / Our man in Brazil / La bamba / Shadow of your smile / Choo choo samba / Little brown jug / Sweet and gentle / Good the bad and the ugly / La golondrina / Tengo un amor / Fame / Kiss kiss jive / Holiday in Davos / Historia un amor
308822 / 11 May '98 / Hallmark

☐ TEQUILA (Davies, Ray & Button Down Brass)
Tequila / This guy's in love with you / Do you know the way to San Jose / Somethin' stupid / Chitty chitty bang bang / Can't take my eyes off you / More I see you / Up up and away / Let the heartaches begin / Green grow the rushes-o / Love is blue / Bonnie and Clyde / Look of love / Delilah / By the time I get to Phoenix / MacArthur park / What a wonderful world / It's not unusual / They say it's wonderful / Young girl / Fool on the hill / Last waltz
5329392 / Aug '96 / Mercury

Davies, Richard

☐ TELEGRAPH
BRRC 1001152 / 23 Mar '98 / Blue Rose

Davies, Steve Gwyn

☐ AN UBHAL AS AIRDE
VITAL 02CD / Nov '95 / Vital Spark

Davilita

☐ DAVILITA 1932-1939
Lamento borincano / Boton de rosa / Mis amores / Muchos besos / Desmayo / Campanitas de cristal / Perfume de gardenias / Maria belen chacon / Vuelve otra noche / Luisa Linda / Mi sol (o sole mio) / Oh Mari / Tiempos viejos / Tu no sabes mentir / Alma borincana / Borinquenita / Jabla la conga / Pobre gaviota / El buen borincano / A mi que / El perro que ladra / Dolorosa / Madreselva / Buen borincano
HQCD 102 / Sep '98 / Harlequin

Davina

☐ BEST OF BOTH WORLDS, THE
Come over to my place / Comin' for you / So good / When it rains / Love's coming down / I can't help it / Give me love / Mercy / Getz nowhere / Only one reason / Way I feel about you / After the rain / My cryin' blues / Is it the way
74321522992 / 30 Mar '98 / Loud

Davis, Alvin

☐ LET THE VIBES DECIDE
Call me baby / Rising / Money or love / Organ grinder / Mia / Need you / Guidance / Let the vibes decide / Greeting / Message from the heart / End of the day
RIPEXD 213 / Feb '95 / Ripe

Davis, Anthony

☐ HIDDEN VOICES (Davis, Anthony & James Newton Quartet)
IN 1041CD / Jan '97 / India Navigation

☐ LADY OF THE MIRRORS
IN 1047CD / Jan '97 / India Navigation

☐ MIDDLE PASSAGE
Behind the rock / Middle passage / Particle W / Proposition for life
GRCD 8401 / Feb '85 / Gramavision

☐ TRIO 2 (Davis, Anthony & James Newton/Abdul Wadud)
Who's life / Thursday's child / Eclipse / Kiano / Invisible island / First movement / Second movement / Third movement / Simultaneity / Flat out
794 412 / Mar '90 / Gramavision

Davis, Art

☐ LIFE
SN 1143CD / Sep '95 / Soul Note

Davis, Betty

☐ CRASHIN' FROM PASSION
RAZCD 2099 / May '96 / Razor & Tie

☐ HANGIN' OUT IN HOLLYWOOD
CPCD 8148 / Mar '96 / Charly

Davis, Blind John

☐ BLIND JOHN DAVIS 1938
I had a dream / I know the baby loves me / Hey hey Mama / Woman I love / I heard an echo / Trick's done turned on you / Don't lie to me / Harlem blues / When the blues came out to sing / Pretty blues for listening / When I've been drinking / Bartender's bounce / Penny pinching blues
ECD 260562 / Sep '94 / Evidence

☐ FIRST RECORDING SESSIONS
SOB 35202 / Dec '92 / Story Of The Blues

Davis, Carlene

☐ REGGAE SONGBIRD
Brown eyes blue / Come to me softly / You are the one I need / When I call your name / I remember / Strange things / Money can't buy life / Don't stay away
RRTGCD 7703 / '88 / Rohit

☐ SONGS OF FREEDOM
Better give love a try / She is not for sale / Don't walk away / No charge / Brother bob / Tell me a lie / Reggae rebel / Everything I own / First word in memory / No bias / Jailer man's ballad / Welcome home mr mandela / Taking control / Redemption song (live)
LG 21076 / Mar '93 / Lagoon

Davis, Charles

☐ REFLECTIONS (Davis, Charles & Barry Harris)
1232472 / Nov '92 / Red

Davis, Daniel

☐ I KNOW A PLACE
I know a place / I'm not listening anymore / It's been a pleasure (not knowing you) / Better half of my heart / What I wouldn't give / Ruth Ann / My heart's not in it / Beer and money / From where I stand / Here's lookin' at you
5311722 / Aug '96 / A&M

Davis, Eb

☐ GOOD TIME BLUES (Davis, Eb Bluesband)
BEST 1016CD / Nov '93 / Acoustic Music

Davis, Eddie 'Lockjaw'

☐ EDDIE 'LOCKJAW' DAVIS & MICHAEL STARCH TRIO/KARL RATZER (Davis, Eddie 'Lockjaw' & Michael Starch Trio/ Karl Ratzer)
WOLF 120588 / Jul '96 / Wolf

☐ EDDIE 'LOCKJAW' DAVIS/ MICHEL ATTENOUX & HIS ORCHESTRA (Davis, Eddie 'Lockjaw' / Michel Attenoux & his Orchestra)
STCD 5009 / May '93 / Storyville

☐ HEAVY HITTER, THE
When your lover has gone / Just one of those things / Old folks / Out of nowhere / Secret love / Comin' home baby / You stepped out of a dream / Jim dog
60412320572 / 7 Apr '98 / Thirty Two

☐ JAWS
I let a song go out of my heart / I'll never be the same (mm solo) / You stepped out of a dream / Old devil moon / Too close for comfort / Body and soul / But not for me / Tangerine
OJCCD 218 / Nov '95 / Original Jazz Classics

☐ LIGHT AND LOVELY
BB 883 / Apr '97 / Black & Blue

☐ LOCKJAW COOKBOOK VOL.1
Avalon / Have horn will blow / Chef / But beautiful / In the kitchen / Three deuces
OJCCD 652 / Feb '92 / Original Jazz Classics

☐ LOCKJAW COOKBOOK VOL.2
Willow weep for me / Rev / Stardust / Skillet / I surrender dear / Broilers
OJCCD 653 / Feb '92 / Original Jazz Classics

☐ SWINGIN' TIL GIRLS
SCCD 31058 / Jul '88 / Steeplechase

☐ TRANE WHISTLE
Trane whistle / Whole Nelson / You are too beautiful / Stolen moment / Walk away / Jaws
OJCCD 429 / Apr '97 / Original Jazz Classics

☐ WITH MILT (Davis, Eddie 'Lockjaw' & Sonny Stitt)
CDC 9028 / Mar '91 / LRC

Davis, Frank

☐ GOLDEN MELODIES (2CD Set) (Davis, Frank Orchestra)
Smoke gets in your eyes / Into each life some rain must fall / When I fall in love / Put your head on my shoulder / Cry / Dancin' / Blue velvet / (You are) my special angel / Serenade in blue / Misty / What a difference a day made / Great pretender / Stranger in paradise / Laura / Let it be me / Crazy / Little things mean a lot / Waht a wonderful world / On the sunny side of the street / Only you / Unforgettable / Travellin' / Crying in the chapel / Red roses for a blue lady / Sentimental journey / Nightingale / Somewhere over the rainbow / Sweetlips / Cheek to cheek / You'll never walk alone
SD 886372 / 2 Feb '98 / Disky

Davis, Guy

☐ CALL DOWN THE THUNDER
RHRCD 89 / Nov '96 / Red House

☐ STOMP DOWN RIDER
RHRCD 80 / Dec '95 / Red House

☐ YOU DON'T KNOW MY MIND
RHRCD 113 / May '98 / Red House

Davis, Janet-Lee

☐ MISSING YOU
FADCD 30 / Apr '95 / Fashion

Davis, Jesse

☐ FIRST INSIGHT
First insight / Nola / Little R and R / BYOG / Midnight blue / J's idea / Funny thing / Jetlagged / Donkey stomp
CCD 47962 / 5 May '98 / Concord Jazz

☐ FROM WITHIN
Journey to Epiphany / Tai's tune / Portrait of Desiree / You've changed / Introspection / You never know / If I should lose you / From within / Six and four
CCD 4727 / Oct '96 / Concord Jazz

☐ HIGH STANDARDS
Rush hour / I hear a rhapsody / Isms / Peace / Jubilation / Hues / Big push / On a misty night / Strike up the band / Just a little blues
CCD 4624 / Nov '94 / Concord Jazz

☐ YOUNG AT ART
East of the sun and west of the moon / Brother Roj / I love Paris / Ask me now / Georgiana / Waltz for Andre / Little flowers / One for cannon / Tipsy / Fine and dandy
CCD 4565 / Aug '93 / Concord Jazz

Davis, Jesse Ed

☐ JESSE ED DAVIS
7567803032 / Jan '96 / Atlantic

Davis, Jimmie

☐ NOBODY'S DARLIN' BUT MINE (5CD Set)
Barroom message / Baby's lullaby / Out of town blues / Home town blues / Settling down for life / My dixie sweetheart / You're the picture of your mother / Doggone that train / My Louisiana girl / Cowboy's home sweet home / She's a hum-dum dinger / Before you say farewell / Where the old red river flows / Penitentiary blues / Arabella blues / In Arkansas / Lonely hobo / I'll be happy today / Woman's blues / Bear cat mama from Horner's Corner / My Arkansas sweetheart / Ramona / You'd rather forget thabn forgive / Think of me thinking of you / Way out on the mountain / Hobo's warning / Wild and reckless hobo / Davis limited / She left a runnin' like a sewing machine / Down at the old country church / She's a hum-dum dinger / Market house blues / Get on board Aunt Susan / Midnight blues / There's evil in ye children gather round / Pea pickin' papa / I'll get mine by and by / Barnyard stomp / I wonder (if she is blue) / 1982 blues (Davis' last day blues) / High behind blues / Saturday night stroll / Sewing machine blues / Red nightgown blues / Davis' salty dog / You can't tell about the women nowadays / Shotgun wedding / Hold 'er newt / Yo yo mama / Tom cat and pussy blues / Organ-grinder blues / Rockin' blues / Wampas kitty mama / Bury me in old Kentucky / Jealous lover / Gambler's return / Home in Caroline / It's all coming home to you / I wonder if she's blue / When it's round-up time in heaven / Would you / You've been tom cattin' around / Alimony blues / Keyhole in the door / Beautiful Texas / Triflin' mama blues / I want her tailor-made / Alimony blues / That's why I'm nobody's darling / Do you ever think of me / Prairie of love / There ain't gonna be no afterwhile / Sweet Loraine / Easy rider blues / Just forgive and forget / Pal of long ago / Nobody's darlin' but mine / If I ever cry you'll never know / Sweetheart of West Texas / When it's round up time in heaven / Ten tiny toes / I wonder where you are / In the west where life is free / You'll be comin' back some day / Hard hearted mama / Jimmie's travelin' blues / I wonder who's kissing her now / Pi-rootin' around / High geared daddy / Honky tonk blues / Good time papa blues / I wish I had never seen sunshine / Shirt tail blues / Nobody's darling but mine / High geared Mama / One two three four / Bed bug blues / Have you ever been in heaven / Greatest mistake in my life / It's been years (since I've seen my mother) / I ain't gonna let ol' Satan turn me 'round / Beautiful Mary / (Sweetheart) please be true to me / My brown eyed Texas rose / It will be sweet when we meet / By the grave of nobody's darling (my darling's promise) / Moonlight and skies / My blue bonnet girl / Shackles and chains / Jellyroll blues / Ridin' down the Arizona trail / Call me back pal o'mine / Graveyard blues / Just a girl that men forget / Are you tired of me darling / Mama's getting hot and papa's getting cold / Red river blues / When it's peach pickin' time in Georgia / Come on over to my house (ain't nobody home but me) / Answer to nobody's darling but mine / In my cabin tonight / When a boy from the mountains (weds a girl from the valley) / Don't say goodbye if you love me
BCD 15943 / May '98 / Bear Family

☐ YOU ARE MY SUNSHINE (5CD Set)
All alone in this world / Goodbye old booze / You're as welcome as the flowers in May / I saw your face inm the moon / I love evrything you do / Hard hearted moma / There's a goldmine in the sky / Nobody's lonesome for me / Meet me tonight in dreamland / There's a ranch in the rockies / Headin' home / Farewell to the range / I'm drifting back to dreamland / Memories / I'm waiting for ships that never come in / It makes no differnce now / Curse of an aching heart / You tell me your dream I'll tell you mine / Don't break my heart boy / I've tried so hard to forget you / What good will it do / Same old moon is shining / I'm wondering now / Dream of love / If tomorrow never comes / When you know you're not forgotten by the girl you can't for / Some must win some lose / Down at the end of memory lane / In my heart you'll always be mine / Last letter / Born to be blue / Never break a promise / What else can I do / Why should I care / It's hard but it's true / Last trip of the old ship / Why do you treat me like the dirt under your feet / Walls of white / I'm still a fool over you / My blue heaven / Two more years (and I'll be free) / Leanin' on the old top rail / You are my sunshine / Your promise was broken / I'd love to call you sweetheart / Old timer / Baby your mother (like she babied you) / Roll along Kentucky moon / There's a chill on the hill tonight / Write a letter to your mother / My mother's bible / Why should I be to blame / I feel the same as you / You're my darling / On the sunnyside of the Rockies / Love I have for you / Sweethearts or strangers / Same other moon / I'm sorry now / Prisoner's song / My Mary / There's an old fashioned house on the hillside / Too late / I'm knocking at your door again / What more can I say / I told you so / I hung my head and cried / I'll be true to the one I love / Just because (of you little girl) / You're breaking my heart / I loved you once / Pay me no mind / Won't you forgive me / I'm thinking tonight / Of my blue eyes / You told me a lie / End of the world / You'll be sorry / Sweetheart of the valley / I'm the one / Tears on my pillow / I wosh I had a sweetheart (like that old sweetheart of mine) / I dreamed of an old love affair / I've got my heart on my sleeve / Don't you cry over me / Live and let live / All because you said goodbye / What's the matter with you darlin' / Sinner's prayer / Where is my boy tonight / Columbus stockade blues / Plant some flowers by my grave / Walkin;' my blues away / What happened / I never say goodbye / It is too late now / There's a new moon over my shoulder / Grievin' my heart out for you / I'm happy I can ride the open range / Time alone will tell / Love please don't let me down / No good for nothin' / I'm hurt too much to cry / I'm sorry if that's the way you feel / When it's harvest time (sweet Angeline) / When you were a boy on my knee / I'm only in the way / Just thinking of you / Beginning of the end / Bang bang / In the pines / I'm gonna write myself a letter / Tired of cryin' over you / There's a new love in my heart tonight / Atlanta Georgia / Wave to me my lady / Woman's blues / Down at the old country church / When a boy from the mountains (weds a girl from the valley) / Don't say goodbye if you love me / My blue bonnet girl / Ridin' down the Arizona trail / Mama's getting hot and papa's getting cold / Nobody's lonesome for me / Same old moon is shining / Born to be blue / My blue heaven / Old timer / There's a chill on the hill tonight / Why should I be to blame / I'm knocking at your door / What more can I say / I hung my head and cried / I'll be true to the one I love / Live and let live
BCD 16216 / May '98 / Bear Family

Davis, John

☐ BLUE MOUNTAINS
SHR 90CD / Jan '97 / Shrimper

☐ I'LL BURN
SHR 85CD / Nov '96 / Shrimper

☐ LEAVE HOME
COMM 37CD / Dec '96 / Communion

☐ ROOM FOR SPACE (Davis, John & Dennis Callaci)
SHR 74CD / Dec '96 / Shrimper

Davis, Larry

☐ BLUES KNIGHTS (Davis, Larry/Byther Smith)
Giving up on love: *Davis, Larry* / I tried: *Davis, Larry* / Teardrops: *Davis, Larry* / That's alright Mama: *Davis, Larry* / I don't have a mother: *Smith, Byther* / I'm a honey bee: *Smith, Byther* / What is this: *Smith, Byther* / Don't make me talk to much: *Smith, Byther* / Addressing the nation with the blues: *Smith, Byther* / I'm broke: *Smith, Byther*
ECD 260422 / Mar '94 / Evidence

☐ I AIN'T BEGGIN' NOBODY
ECD 26016 / Feb '93 / Evidence

☐ SOONER OR LATER
How could you do it to me / I'm working on it / Penitentiary blues / You'll need another favour / Help the poor / Letter from my darling / Goin' out west (part 1 and 2) / 102 St. blues / How long / Bluebird / Littlerock
CDBB 9511 / Sep '92 / Bullseye Blues

Davis, 'Little' Sammy

☐ I AIN'T LYIN'
I ain't lyin' / Daniel / Sammy's shuffle / Shorty / That's my girl / Someday / Devil's trail / When I leave / Bad luck blues / Somebody's fool / Hey little girl / California blues / I-man stomp / Play me for a fool
DE 682 / Mar '97 / Delmark

Davis, Linda

☐ SOME THINGS ARE MEANT TO BE
Some things are meant to be / Love story in the making / Walk away / Always will / Neither one of us / She dosen't ask / Cast iron heart / There isn't one / What do I know / If I could live your life
07822188042 / Jan '96 / Arista

Davis, Link

☐ 1948-1963
KKCD 06 / Jul '93 / Krazy Kat

Davis, Meg

☐ CLADDAGH WALK, THE
For Ireland I'd not tell her name / Castle of Dromore / Burning West Indies / She moved through the fair / Broom o'the Cowdenknowes / Claddagh walk / Lake of Ponchartrain / If I were a blackbird / P stands for Paddy / Eileen Aroon / My Lagan love / Loch Tay boat song / Queen of May / Last Leviathan
LCDM 9030 / Nov '90 / Lismor

Davis, Miles

☐ '58 SESSIONS
On Green Dolphin Street / Fran dance / Stella by starlight / Love for sale / Straight no chaser / My funny valentine / Oleo
4679182 / Apr '92 / Columbia

☐ AGHARTA
Prelude / Maiysha / Interlude / Theme from Jack Johnson
4678972 / Sep '93 / Columbia

☐ AMANDLA
Catembe / Big time / Jo Jo / Jilli / Cobra / Hannibal / Amandla / Mr. Pastorius
K 9258732 / May '89 / WEA

☐ AND MODERN JAZZ GIANTS
Man I love (take 2) / Swing spring / 'round midnight / Bemsha swing / Man I love (take 1)
OJCCD 347 / Feb '92 / Original Jazz Classics

☐ ASCENSEUR POUR L'ECHAFAUD (Lift To The Scaffold/Original 1957 Soundtrack)
Nuit sur Les Champs-Elysee / Assassinat / Motel / Final / Le petit bal / Sequence voiture / Generique / L'assassinat de Carala / Sur l'autoroute / Julien dans l'ascenseur / Florence dans l'ascenseur / Florence sur Les Champs-Elysee / Diner au motel / Evasion de Julien / Visite du vigile / Au bar du petit bac / Chez le photographe du motel
8363052 / Mar '94 / Fontana

☐ AT CARNEGIE HALL (2CD Set)
So what / Spring is here / No blues / Oleo / Someday my prince will come / Meaning of the blues / Lament / New rhumba / Concierto de Aranjuez (part 1) / Concierto de Aranjuez (part 2) / Teo / Walkin' / I thought about you
4723572 / Apr '96 / Sony Jazz

☐ AT FILLMORE (2CD Set)
Wednesday miles / Thursday miles / Friday miles / Saturday miles
4769092 / Oct '94 / Columbia

☐ AT LAST (Davis, Miles & The Lighthouse All Stars)
Infinity promenade / 'Round midnight / Night in Tunisia / Drum conversation / At last
OJCCD 480 / Feb '92 / Original Jazz Classics

☐ AT THE ROYAL ROOST 1948 & BIRDLAND 1950-53
52nd street / Half Nelson / You go to my head / Chasin' the Bird / Hot house / Wee / Tempus fugit / Evance (out of the blue) / Move / Tenderly / Night in Tunisia / Dig
LEJAZZCD 45 / Jun '95 / Le Jazz

☐ AUDIO ARCHIVE
Out of nowhere / Night in Tunisia / Yardbird suite / Scrapple the apple / Ornithology / Don't blame me / Moose the mooche / Bird of paradise / Embraceable you / My old flame / Bird's nest / Tweet bop / Slam blam blues / Cool head blues / Riff raff
CDAA 027 / Jun '92 / Tring

☐ AURA
Intro / White / Yellow / Orange / Red / Green / Blue / Electric red / Indigo / Violet
4633512 / Oct '89 / Columbia

☐ BALLADS
Baby, won't you please come home / I fall in love too easily / Bye bye blackbird / Basin Street blues / Once upon a summertime / Song no.2 / Wait till you see her / Corcovado
4610992 / Apr '89 / Columbia

☐ BALLADS AND BLUES
I waited for you / Yesterdays / One for Daddy-O / Moon dreams / How deep is the ocean / Weirdo / Enigma / It never entered my mind / Autumn leaves
CDP 8366332 / Apr '96 / Blue Note

☐ BEST OF MILES DAVIS, THE
Move / Godchild / Budo / Dear old Stockholm / Donna / Yesterdays / Tempus fugit / Enigma / CTA / Well you needn't / It never entered my mind / Weirdo / Something else / Autumn leaves
BNZ 286 / Feb '92 / Blue Note

☐ BIRDLAND DAYS
FSCD 124 / Jan '91 / Fresh Sound

☐ BIRDLAND SESSIONS
LEJAZZCD 23 / Feb '94 / Le Jazz

☐ BIRTH OF THE COOL
Move / Jeru / Moon dreams / Venus De Milo / Budo / Deception / Darn that dream / Godchild / Boplicity / Rocker / Israel / Rouge
CDP 7928622 / Sep '92 / Capitol

☐ BIRTH OF THE COOL/MILES DAVIS VOL.1/MILES DAVIS VOL.2 (The Originals/3CD Set)
Move / Jeru / Moon dreams / Venus de Milo / Budo / Deception / Godchild / Boplicity / Rocker / Israel / Rouge / Tempus fugit / Kelo / Enigma / Ray's idea / How deep is the ocean / CTA / Dear old Stockholm / Chance it / Yesterdays / Donna / CTA / Would'n you / Take off / Weirdo / Would'n you / I waited for you / Ray's idea / Donna / Well you needn't / Leap / Lazy Susan / Tempus fugit / It never entered my mind
CDOMB 007 / Mar '97 / Blue Note

☐ BITCHES BREW
Pharaoh's dance / Bitches brew / Spanish key / John McLaughlin / Miles runs the voodoo down / Sanctuary
4606022 / Oct '91 / Columbia

☐ BLACK BEAUTY (Live At Filmore West)
Directions / Miles runs the voodoo down / Willie Nelson / I fall in love too easily / Sanctuary / It's about that time / Bitches brew / Masqualero / Spanish key
65138 / Aug '97 / Sony Jazz

☐ BLUE HAZE
I'll remember april / Four / Old devil moon / Smooch / Blue haze / When lights are low / Tune up / Miles ahead
CDSGP 042 / Mar '93 / Prestige

☐ BLUE MOODS
Nature boy / Alone together / There's no you / Easy living
OJCCD 432 / Oct '93 / Original Jazz Classics

☐ BLUING (Miles Davis Plays The Blues)
Bluing / Blue 'n' boogie / Bag's groove / Green haze / Dr. Jackle / No line / Vierd blues / Trane's blues / Blues by five
PRCD 11004 / Jun '97 / Prestige

☐ BOPPING THE BLUES
Don't sing me the blues / I've always got the blues / Don't explain to me baby / Baby, won't you make up your mind
BLCD 760102 / Jun '88 / Black Lion

☐ BYE BYE BLACKBIRD
CDSGP 0264 / Jan '97 / Prestige

☐ CBS YEARS 1955-85 (4CD Set)
Generique / All blues / Eighty one / Blues for Pablo / Summertime / Straight no chaser / Footprints / Florence sur les Champs Elysees / I thought about you / Someday my Prince will come / Bye bye blackbird / My funny valentine / Love for sale / Budo / Miles / Files de Kilimanjaro / Fran dance / Seven steps to heaven / Flamenco sketches / So what / Water babies / Saeta / Masqualero / Pinocchio / Summer night / Fall / It's about that time / Sivad / What it is / Ms. Morrisine / Shout / Honky Tonk / Star on Cicely / Thinkin' one thing and doin' another / Miles runs the voodoo down
4632462 / Jan '95 / Columbia

☐ CHRONICLE: THE COMPLETE PRESTIGE RECORDINGS (8CD Set)
Ahmad's blues / Airegin / Bag's groove / Bemsha swing / Bitty ditty / Blue haze / Blue 'n' boogie / Blue room / Blues by five / But not for me / Changes / Compulsion / Conception / Denial / Diane / Dig / Dr. Jackle / Down / Doxy / Ezz-thetic / Floppy / For adults only / Four / Gal in Calico / Green haze / Half nelson / Hibeck / How am I to know / I could write a book / I know / I didn't / I see your face before me / I'll remember April / If I were a bell / In your own sweet way / It could happen to you / It never entered my mind / It's only a paper moon / Just squeeze me / Love me or leave me / Man I love / Miles ahead / Minor march / Morpheus / My funny valentine / My old flame / Night in Tunisia / No line / Odjenar / Old devil moon / Oleo / Out of the blue / 'Round midnight / Salt peanuts / Serpent's tooth / Smooch / Solar / Something I dreamed last night / S'posin' / Stablemates / Surrey with the fringe on top / Swing spring / Tasty pudding / Theme / There is no greater love / Trane's blues / Tune up / Vierd blues / Walkin' / Well you needn't / When I fall in love / When lights are low / Whispering / Will you still be mine / Willie the wailer / Wouldn't you / Yesterdays / You don't know what love is / You're my everything
8 PCD 012 / Apr '92 / Prestige

☐ CIRCLE IN THE ROUND
Circle in the round / Two bass hit / Love for sale / Blues No. 2 / Teo's bag / Side car / Splash sanctuary / Guinevere
4679892 / Sep '93 / Columbia

☐ COLLECTORS ITEM
Compulsion / Serpent's tooth / 'Round midnight / In your own sweet way / Vierd blues / No line / My old flame / Nature boy / There's no you / Easy living / Alone together
OJCCD 71 / Feb '92 / Original Jazz Classics

☐ COMPLETE BIRTH OF THE COOL, THE
Move / Jeru / Moon dreams / Venus De Milo / Budo / Deception / Godchild / Boplicity / Rocker / Israel / Rouge / Darn that dream / Move / Why do I love you / Godchild / S'il vous plait / Moon dreams / Budo / Darn that dream / Move / Moon dreams / Budo
4945502 / 1 Jun '98 / Capitol Jazz

☐ COMPLETE COLUMBIA STUDIO RECORDINGS (6CD Set) (Davis, Miles & Gil Evans)
CXK 67397 / Sep '96 / Sony Jazz

☐ COMPLETE CONCERT 1964, THE (My Funny Valentine & Four More)
Introduction by Mort Fega / My funny valentine / All of you / Go go (Theme and re-introduction) / Stella by starlight / All blues / I thought about you / So what / Walkin' / Joshua / Go go (Theme and announcement) / Four / Seven steps to heaven / There is no greater love / Do go
4712462 / May '93 / Columbia

☐ COMPLETE PRESTIGE RECORDINGS, THE (Chronicle 1951-1965/8CD Set)
Morpheus / Down / Blue room / Whispering / I know / Odjenar / Ezz-thetic / Hibeck / Yesterdays / Conception / Out of the blue / Denial / Bluing / Dig / My old flame / It's only a paper moon / Compulsion / Serpent's tooth / 'Round midnight / Tasty pudding / Willie the wailer / Floppy / For adults only / When lights are low / Tune up / Miles ahead / Smooch / Four / Old devil moon / Blue haze / Solar / You don't know what love is / Love me or leave me / I'll remember April / Blue 'n' boogie / Walkin' / Airegin / Oleo / But not for me / Doxy / Bag's groove / Bemsha / Swing swing Spring / Man I love / I didn't / Will you still be mine / Green haze / I see your face before me / Night in Tunisia / Gal in Calico / Dr. Jackle / Bitty ditty / Minor march / Changes / No line / Vierd blues / Stablemates / How am I to know / Just squeeze me / There is no greater love / Theme / In your own sweet way / S'posin' / In your own sweet way / Diane / Trane's blues / Something I dreamed last night / It could happen to you / Woody 'n' you / Ahmad's blues / Surrey with the fringe on top / It never entered my mind / When I fall in love / Salt peanuts / Four / Theme / If I were a bell / Well, you needn't / Round midnight / Half Nelson / You're my everything / I could write a book / Oleo / Airegin / Tune up / When lights are low / Blues by five / My funny valentine
PCD 0122 / Nov '96 / Prestige

☐ CONCIERTO DE ARANJUEZ
CD 14543 / Jan '94 / Jazz Portraits

☐ COOKIN' WITH THE MILES DAVIS QUINTET
Airegin / Tune up / Blues by five / My funny valentine / When lights are low
OJC20 128 / Sep '98 / Original Jazz Classics

☐ COOKIN', WALKIN', WORKIN', STEAMIN' (4CD Set)
It never entered my mind / Four / In your own sweet way / Theme / Trane's blues / Ahmad's blues / Half Nelson / Theme / Surrey with the fringe on top / Salt peanuts / Something I dreamed last night / Diane / Well you needn't / When I fall in love / My funny valentine / Blues by five / Airegin / Tune up/When lights are low / Walkin' / Blue 'n' boogie / Solar / You don't know what love is / Love me or leave me
4PRCD 8805 / Nov '96 / Prestige

☐ COOL JAZZ CLASSICS
I'll remember April / Compulsion / Serpent's tooth / Max is making wax / That old black magic / Whispering / Bird of paradise / Conception / Miles ahead / Morpheus / Ray's idea / When lights are low / 'Round midnight / Ornithology / Yardbird suite / Embraceable you / Don't blame me
BN 008 / Nov '96 / Blue Nite

☐ COTE BLUES
JMY 10102 / Aug '93 / JMY

☐ DARK MAGUS
Moja / Moja / Wili / Wili / Tatu / Tatu / Nne / Nne
65137 / Aug '97 / Sony Jazz

☐ DAVISIANA (Davis, Miles Quintet)
MCD 0332 / Jan '92 / Moon

☐ DIG (Davis, Miles & Sonny Rollins)
Dig / It's only a paper moon / Denial / Bluing / Out of the blue / My old flame / Conception
OJCCD 5 / Feb '92 / Original Jazz Classics

☐ DOO BOP
Mystery / Doo bop song / Chocolate chip / High speed chase / Blow / Sonya / Fantasy / Duke booty / Mystery (reprise)
7599269382 / Mar '94 / WEA

☐ ESP
ESP / Eighty one / Little one / RJ / Agitation / Iris / Mood
4678992 / Oct '91 / Columbia

☐ ESSENTIAL MILES DAVIS, THE
'Round midnight / My funny valentine / Concierto de Aranjuez / Summertime / All blues / Milestones / Walkin'
4671442 / Aug '92 / Columbia

☐ FESTIVAL INTERNATIONAL DE JAZZ PARIS 1949 (Davis, Miles & Tadd Dameron Quintet)
Rifftide / Good bait / Don't blame me / Lady bird / Wah hoo / Allen's alley / Embraceable you / Ornithology / All the things you are
4852572 / Sep '96 / Sony Jazz

☐ FILLES DE KILIMANJARO
Frelon brun (brown hornet) / Tout de suit / Petits machins (little stuff) / Filles de Kilimanjaro (girls of Kilimanjaro) / Mademoiselle Mabry
4670882 / Oct '91 / Columbia

☐ FIRST MILES
Mile stone / Little Willie leaps / Half nelson / Sippin' at bells / That's the stuff you gotta watch / Pointless Mama blues / Deep sea blues / Bring it on home
SV 0159 / Oct '97 / Savoy Jazz

☐ FRIDAY NIGHT AT THE BLACK HAWK, SAN FRANCISCO VOL.1
4633342 / Jan '95 / Columbia

☐ GET UP WITH IT
He loved him madly / Maiysha / Honky tonk / Rated X / Calypso frelimo / Red China blues / Mtume / Billy Preston
LICD 9211552 / Nov '96 / Line
4852562 / Sep '96 / Sony Jazz

☐ GREAT JAZZ PERFORMANCES (2CD Set)
Whispering / I'll remember April / Compulsion / Serpent's tooth / Blue haze / Smooch / Down / Night in Tunisia / Embraceable you / Moose the mooch / Ornithology / Yardbird suite / 'Round midnight / Autumn leaves / That old devil moon / Four / Miles ahead / Blue room / Morpheus / When lights are low / Bird of paradise / Don't blame me / My old flame / Out of nowhere / Scrapple the apple / So what / All of you
TNC 96211 / Aug '96 / Natural Collection

☐ GREATEST HITS
Seven steps to heaven / All blues / Someday my prince / Walkin' / My funny valentine / ESP / 'Round midnight / So what
CK 65418 / 26 Jan '98 / Sony Jazz

☐ HIGHLIGHTS FROM THE PLUGGED NICKEL
Milestones / Yesterdays / So what / Stella by starlight / Walkin' / 'Round midnight
4814342 / Nov '95 / Sony Jazz

☐ IN A SILENT WAY
Ssh peaceful / In a silent way / It's about that time
4509822 / Oct '93 / Columbia

☐ IN CONCERT
Miles davis in concert (side one) / Miles davis in concert (side two) / Miles davis in concert (side three) / Miles davis in concert (side four)
4769102 / Oct '94 / Columbia

☐ JAZZ AT THE PLAZA VOL.1
4715102 / Jan '95 / Columbia

☐ JAZZ PORTRAITS
Now's the time / Night in Tunisia / Donna Lee / Cheryl / Milestones / Half nelson / Marmaduke / Jeru / Boplicity / Rocker / Ezz-thetic / Yesterdays / Compulsion / Tempus fugit / Tune up / It never entered my mind / Old devil moon / I'll remember April
CD 14503 / May '94 / Jazz Portraits

☐ KIND OF BLUE
So what / Freddie Freeloader / Blue in green / Al blues / Flamenco sketches / Flamenco sketches
CK 64935 / Apr '97 / Sony Jazz

☐ KIND OF BLUE/PORGY AND BESS/ SKETCHES OF SPAIN (3CD Set)
So what / Freddie freeloader / Blue in green / Al blues / Framenco sketches / Flamenco sketches / Buzzard song / Bess you is my woman / Gone gone gone / Summertime / Bess oh where's my bed / Prayer / O doctor Jesus / Fisherman / Strawberry and devil country / My man's gone now / It ain't necessarily so / Here comes de honey man / I loves you porgy / There's a boat that's leaving / I loves you porgy / Gone / Concierto de aranjuez / Amor brujo / Pan piper / Saeta / Solea
4893452 / 1 Dec '97 / Sony Jazz

☐ LIVE (2CD Set)
Intruders / New blues / One phone call / Street scenes / Perfect way / Senate / Me and you / Tutu / Movie stars / Splatch / Time after time / Wayne's tune / Full Nelson
24327 / Mar '96 / Laserlight

☐ **LIVE AROUND THE WORLD**
In a silent way / Time after time / Tutu / Full nelson / Amandla / Intruder / Mr pastorius / Wrinkle / Human nature / New blues / Hannibal
9362460322 / Jul '96 / Warner Bros.

☐ **LIVE AT CARNEGIE HALL (2CD Set)**
So what / Spring is here / Teo / Walkin' / Meaning of the blues / Lament / New rhumba / Someday my Prince will come / Oleo / No blues / I thought about you / En Aranjuez con tu amor
C2K 65027 / 6 Apr '98 / Sony Jazz

☐ **LIVE AT MONTREUX (Davis, Miles & Quincy Jones)**
Introduction by Claude Nobs and Quincy Jones / Boplicity / Introduction to Miles ahead medley / Springsville / Maids of cadiz / Duke / My ship / Miles ahead / Blues for pablo / Introduction to Porgy and Bess medley / Orgone / Gone gone gone / Summertime / Here come de honey man / Pan piper / Solea
9362452212 / Sep '93 / Warner Bros.

☐ **LIVE AT NEWPORT 1958 & 1963 (2CD Set) (Davis, Miles/Thelonious Monk)**
Introduction: *Davis, Miles* / Ah-leu-cha: *Davis, Miles* / Straight no chaser: *Davis, Miles* / Fran dance: *Davis, Miles* / Two bass hit: *Davis, Miles* / Bye bye blackbird: *Davis, Miles* / Theme: *Davis, Miles* / Introduction: *Monk, Thelonious* / Criss cross: *Monk, Thelonious* / Light blue: *Monk, Thelonious* / Nutty: *Monk, Thelonious* / Blue monk: *Monk, Thelonious* / Epistrophy: *Monk, Thelonious*
C2K 53585 / Oct '94 / Columbia

☐ **LIVE AT THE PLUGGED NICKEL 1965 (8CD Set)**
If I were a bell / Stella by starlight / Walkin' / I fall in love too easily / Theme / My funny valentine / Four / When I fall in love / Agitation / 'Round midnight / Milestones / All of you / Oleo / No blues / I thought about you / On green dolphin street / So what / Autumn leaves / All blues / Yesterdays
CXK 66955 / Jul '95 / Sony Jazz

☐ **LIVE EVIL**
Sivad / Little church / Gemini/Double image / What I say / New um talvez / Selim / Funky tonk / Inamorata
4852552 / Sep '96 / Sony Jazz
65135 / Aug '97 / Sony Jazz

☐ **LIVE IN 1958-59 (Davis, Miles All Stars)**
EBCD 21012 / Dec '90 / Flyright

☐ **LIVE IN STOCKHOLM 1960 COMPLETE (Davis, Miles & John Coltrane/Sonny Stitt)**
DRCD 228 / Sep '89 / Dragon

☐ **MAN WITH THE HORN (Davis, Miles & John Coltrane)**
Fat time / Backseat Betty / Shout Aida / Man with the horn / Ursula
4687012 / Sep '93 / Columbia

☐ **MELLOW MILES**
Miles / Summertime / So what / Time after time / Miles ahead / Freddie freeloader / Bye bye blackbird / Pfrancing / 'Round midnight / It ain't necessarily so / Human nature
4694402 / Dec '91 / Columbia

☐ **MEMORIAL ALBUM, THE**
UAE 34082 / 27 Apr '98 / Memorial Album

☐ **MILES AHEAD**
Springsville / Maids of Cadiz / Duke / My ship / Miles ahead / Blues for Pablo / New rhumba / Meaning of the blues / Lament / I don't wanna be kissed
CK 65121 / 6 Oct '97 / Sony Jazz

☐ **MILES AHEAD**
Vierd blues / Diane / In your own sweet way / 'round midnight / Well you needn't / Springsville / Maids of cadiz / Duke / My ship / Miles ahead / Miles milestones
CD 14540 / Jan '94 / Jazz Portraits

☐ **MILES AHEAD 1956-58**
Vierd blues / Diane / In your own sweet way / 'round midnight / Well you needn't / Springsville / Maids of cadiz / Duke / My ship / Miles ahead / Miles milestones
CD 56038 / Jul '95 / Jazz Roots

☐ **MILES AND COLTRANE (Davis, Miles & John Coltrane)**
Ah-leu-cha / Straight / No chaser / Fran dance (put your little foot right out) / Two bass hit / Bye bye blackbird / Little melonae / Budo
4608242 / Oct '93 / Columbia

☐ **MILES AND HORNS**
Tasty pudding / Floppy / Willie the wailer / For adults only / Morpheus / Down / Blue room / Blue room (alternate take) / Whispering
OJCCD 53 / Feb '92 / Original Jazz Classics

☐ **MILES DAVIS**
That old devil moon / Four / Ladybird / Woody 'n' you / Squirrel / Blue room / Confirmation / Down / Out of the blue / Move / Smooch / Moose the Mooch / My old flame / Out of nowhere / Scrapple the apple / Night in Tunisia
BN 009 / Feb '97 / Blue Nite

☐ **MILES DAVIS**
I'll remember April / Tempus Fugit / It never entered my mind / Walkin' / Compulsion / Old devil moon / Tune up / Jeru / Ezzthetic / Rocker / Boplicity / Now's the time / Milestones
399548 / Jun '97 / Koch Presents

☐ **MILES DAVIS & MILT JACKSON (Davis, Miles & Milt Jackson)**
Dr. jackie / Bitty ditty / Minor march / Changes
OJCCD 12 / Feb '92 / Original Jazz Classics

☐ **MILES DAVIS & THE JAZZ GIANTS**
Dig / Serpent's tooth (take 1) / Four, walkin' / Doxy / Bags' groove / Gal in calico / Minor march / Vierd blues
FCD 60015 / Oct '93 / Fantasy

☐ **MILES DAVIS AND THELONIOUS MONK (Davis, Miles & Thelonious Monk)**
BMCD 3043 / 23 Feb '98 / Blue Moon

☐ **MILES DAVIS AT FILLMORE**
Wednesday miles / Thursday miles / Friday miles / Saturday miles
65139 / Aug '97 / Sony Jazz

☐ **MILES DAVIS COLLECTION**
Blue haze / Whispering / Night in tunisia / Bird of paradise / Embraceable you / Four / That old devil moon / Blue room / Compulsion / Don't blame me / Down / Miles ahead / Morpheus / My old flame / Ornithology / Out of nowhere / Smooch / When lights are low / Yardbird suite / Moose the mooch / Scrapple the apple
COL 035 / Jun '95 / Collection

☐ **MILES DAVIS IN CONCERT**
710455 / Apr '95 / RTE/Europe 1

☐ **MILES DAVIS IN CONCERT (Live At The Philarmonic Hall)**
Foot fooler in concert / Rated x / Honky tonk / Thene from Jack Johnson / Black satin / Slickaphonics in concert / Ife / Right off/The Theme
65140 / Aug '97 / Sony Jazz

☐ **MILES DAVIS SAMPLER**
There is no greater love / If I were a bell / Man I love / Love me or leave me / Salt peanuts
OJCX 015 / Jan '98 / Original Jazz Classics

☐ **MILES IN ANTIBES**
4629602 / Jan '95 / Columbia

☐ **MILES IN BERLIN**
CD 62976 / Jan '95 / Columbia

☐ **MILES IN MONTREUX 1989 (2CD Set)**
JD 1287/88 / 12 Jan '98 / Jazz Door

☐ **MILES IN THE SKY**
Stuff / Paraphernalia / Black comedy / Country son
4772092 / Sep '93 / Columbia

☐ **MILES SMILES**
Orbits / Circle / Footprints / Dolores / Freedom jazz dance / Gingerbread boy
4710042 / Apr '92 / Columbia

☐ **MILESTONES**
Dr. jekyll / Sid's ahead / Two bass hit / Miles / Billy boy / Straight / No chaser
4608272 / Oct '93 / Columbia

☐ **MILESTONES 1945-54**
Now's the time / Night in tunisia / Donna lee / Cheryl / Milestones / Half nelson / Marmaduke / Jeru / Boplicity / Rocker / Ezz-thetic / Yesterdays / Compulsion / Tempus fugit / Tune up / It never entered my mind / Old devil moon / I'll remember april
CD 56009 / Aug '94 / Jazz Roots

☐ **MISCELLANEOUS DAVIS**
Hackensack / 'Round midnight / Now's the time / Four / Walkin' / Oh lady be good / All of you / Four
JUCD 2050 / Nov '94 / Jazz Unlimited

☐ **MOSTLY MILES (Newport Jazz Festival July 3rd/6th 1958)**
NCD 8813 / '93 / Phontastic

☐ **MUSINGS OF MILES, THE**
I didn't / Will you still be mine / Green haze / I see your face before me / Night in Tunisia / Gal in Calico
OJCCD 4 / Feb '92 / Original Jazz Classics

☐ **NEFERTITI**
Nefertiti / Fall / Hand jive / Madness / Riot / Pinocchio
4670892 / Oct '91 / Columbia

☐ **NEW MILES DAVIS QUINTET**
Just squeeze me / There is no greater love / How am I to know / S'posin' / Theme / Stablemates
OJCCD 6 / Feb '92 / Original Jazz Classics

☐ **ON THE CORNER**
On the corner / New York girl / Thinkin' one thing and doin' another / Vote for Miles / Black satin / One and one / Helen Butte / Mr. Freedom X
4743712 / Feb '94 / Columbia

☐ **OUT OF THE BLUE**
Out of the blue / Half nelson / Ray's idea / Move / Lady bird / Max is making wax / Squirrel / That old black magic / Down / Confirmation / Woody 'n' you / Conception / Move
307732 / Aug '97 / Hallmark

☐ **PANGAEA (2CD Set)**
Zimbabwe / Gondwana
4670872 / Sep '93 / Columbia

☐ **PANTHALASSA (Davis, Miles & Bill Laswell)**
In a silent way / Shhh / Peaceful / It's about that time / Black Satan / What if / Agharta / Rated X / Billy Preston / He loved him madly
CK 67909 / 9 Feb '98 / Sony Jazz

☐ **PARAPHERNALIA**
JMY 10132 / Aug '92 / JMY

☐ **PORGY AND BESS (Davis, Miles & Gil Evans Orchestra)**
Buzzard song / Bess you is my woman now / Gone gone gone / Summertime / Bess, oh where's my Bess / Prayer / O Doctor Jesus / Fisherman / Strawberry and devil crab / My man's gone now / It ain't necessarily so / Here come de honey man / I loves you Porgy / There's a boat that's leavin' soon for New York / I loves you Porgy / Gone
CK 65141 / Apr '97 / Sony Jazz

☐ **QUIET NIGHTS**
Song no.2 / Once upon a summertime / Aos pes da cruz / Song no.1 / Wait 'til you see her / Corcovado / Summer night / Time of the barracudas
CK 65293 / 6 Oct '97 / Sony Jazz

☐ **REAL BIRTH OF THE COOL, THE**
BS 18005 / Jul '96 / Bandstand

☐ **RELAXIN' WITH MILES (Davis, Miles Quintet)**
If I were a bell / You're my everything / If I could write a book / Oleo / It could happen to you / Woody 'n' you
OJC20 1902 / Sep '98 / Original Jazz Classics

☐ **ROUND ABOUT MIDNIGHT**
'Round midnight / Ah leu cha / All of you / Bye bye blackbird / Tadd's delight' / Dear old Stockholm
4606052 / Oct '91 / Columbia

☐ **SATURDAY NIGHT AT THE BLACK HAWK, SAN FRANCISCO VOL.2**
4651912 / '88 / Columbia

☐ **SEVEN STEPS TO HEAVEN**
Basin Street blues / Seven steps to heaven / I fall in love too easily / So near, so far / Baby, won't you please come home / Joshua
4669702 / Apr '92 / Columbia

☐ **SKETCHES OF SPAIN**
Concierto de Aranjuez / Amor brujo / Pan piper / Saeta / Solea
CK 65142 / 6 Oct '97 / Sony Jazz

☐ **SOME DAY MY PRINCE WILL COME**
Someday my Prince will come / Old folks / Drad-dog / Teo / I thought about you / Pfancing
4663122 / Jan '95 / Columbia

☐ **SORCERER**
Prince of Darkness / Vonetta / Limbo / Masqualero / Pee Wee / Sorcerer
4743692 / Sep '93 / Columbia

☐ **STAR PEOPLE**
Come get it / It gets better / Speak / Star people / U'un I / Star on Cicely
CD 25395 / Sep '93 / Columbia

☐ **STEAMIN' WITH THE MILES DAVIS QUINTET**
Surrey with the fringe on top / Salt peanuts / Something I dreamed last night / Diane / Well you needn't / When I fall in love
OJCCD 391 / Feb '92 / Original Jazz Classics
OJC20 3912 / Sep '98 / Original Jazz Classics

☐ **STOCKHOLM 1960**
TAXCD 3716 / Aug '95 / Tax

☐ **THIS IS JAZZ**
'Round midnight / Stella by starlight / Springsville / Summertime / So what / Someday my prince will come / Seven steps to heaven / Walkin' / ESP
CK 64616 / May '96 / Sony Jazz

☐ **THIS IS JAZZ**
Circle / My ship / Old folks / Mood / Dear old Stockholm / I loves you Porgy / Basin street blues / Time after time / Flamenco sketches
CK 65038 / May '97 / Sony Jazz

☐ **THIS IS JAZZ (Electric Miles Davis)**
Water on the pond / Frelon brun / Directions II / Honky tonk / Spanish key/The theme / Little church / Aida / U 'n' I / Human nature
CK 65449 / 4 May '98 / Sony Jazz

☐ **TIME AFTER TIME (1989 Live/2CD Set)**
JD 1256/57 / 12 Jan '98 / Jazz Door

☐ **TRIBUTE TO JACK JOHNSON**
Right off / Yesternow
4710032 / Sep '93 / Columbia

☐ **TUTU**
Tutu / Tomaas / Portia / Splatch / Backyard ritual / Perfect way / Don't lose your mind / Full nelson
9254902 / Oct '86 / WEA

☐ **VERY BEST OF MILES DAVIS, THE**
Time after time / Summertime / Bye bye blackbird / It ain't necessariy so / Once upon a summertime / Concierto de Aranjuez / 'Round midnight / I don't wanna be kissed (by anyone but you) / So what / Jean Pierre / Human nature / Shout / Miles
SONYTV 17CD / Sep '96 / Sony TV

☐ **WALKIN' (Davis, Miles All Stars)**
Walkin' / Blue 'n' boogie / Solar / You don't know what love is / Love me or leave me
OJCCD 213 / Feb '92 / Original Jazz Classics
911900472 / 31 Mar '98 / JVC

☐ **WALKIN'**
Walkin' / But not for me / Bags' groove / Man I love / Budo / S'posin' / There is no greater love / Just squeeze me
CD 14537 / Jan '94 / Jazz Portraits

☐ **WE WANT MILES**
Jean Pierre / Backseat Betty / Fast track / My man's gone now / Kix
4699022 / Sep '93 / Columbia

☐ **WHAT I SAY VOL.1**
JMY 10152 / Apr '94 / JMY

☐ **WHAT I SAY VOL.2**
JMY 10162 / Apr '94 / JMY

☐ **WORKIN' (Davis, Miles Quintet)**
It never entered my mind / Four / In your own sweet way / Theme (take no.1) / Trane's blues / Ahmad's blues / Half nelson / Theme (take no.2)
OJCCD 296 / Feb '92 / Original Jazz Classics

☐ **YOU'RE UNDER ARREST**
One phone call / Street scenes / Human nature / Ms. Morrisine / Katia (prelude) / Time after time / You're under arrest / Then there were none / Something's on your mind
4687032 / Sep '93 / Columbia

☐ **YOUNG MILES 1945-1946**
M7J 131 / 14 Apr '98 / Karonte

Davis, Morgan

☐ **MORGAN DAVIS**
SP 1148CD / Oct '93 / Stony Plain

Davis, Nathan

☐ **HAPPY GIRL/THE HIP WALK**
Flute in the blues / Spring can really hang you up the most / Happy girl / Evolution / Theme from Zoltan / Along came Byrd / Mr. E / Hip walk / While children sleep / Train of thought / Yesterdays / That Kaycee thing / Carmell's Black Forest waltz / B's blues
5390822 / 26 May '98 / MPS Jazz

Davis, Rev. Gary

☐ **COMPLETE EARLY RECORDINGS, THE**
I belong to the band-hallelujah / Great change in me / Angel's message to me / I saw the light / Lord, stand by me / I am the light / O lord, search my heart / Have more faith in jesus / You got to go down / I am the true vine / Twelve gates to the city / You can go home / I'm throwin' up my hand / Cross and evil woman blues / I can't bear my burden by myself / Meet me at the station
YAZCD 2011 / Oct '94 / Yazoo

☐ **FROM BLUES TO GOSPEL**
Talk on the corner / Sally where'd you get your whiskey from / Crow Jane / Eagle rocking blues / Cocaine blues / Lost John / Samson and Delilah / I heard the angels singing / Children of Zion / Lord I wish I could see / Down by the river / You better get right / I'll do my last singing
BCD 123 / May '98 / Biograph

☐ **GOSPEL BLUES & STREET SONGS (Davis, Rev. Gary & Pink Anderson)**
John Henry / Everyday in the week / Ship / Titanic / Greasy greens / Wreck of ol' 97 / I've got mine / He's in the jailhouse now / Blow Gabriel / Twelve gates to the city / Samson and Delilah / Oh Lord / Search my heart / Get right church / You got to go down / Keep your lamp trimmed and burning / There was a time that I was blind
OBCCD 524 / Nov '92 / Original Blues Classics

☐ **HARLEM STREET SINGER**
Samson and Delilah / Let us get together right down here / I belong to the band / Pure religion / Great change since I been born / Death don't have no mercy / Twelve gates to the city / Goin' to sit down on the banks of the river / Tryin' to get home / Lo I be with you always / I am the light of this world / Lord I feel just like goin' on
OBCCD 547 / Nov '92 / Original Blues Classics

☐ **I AM A TRUE VINE (1962-1963)**
I am a true vine / Lord stand by me / Won't you hush / Mean ol' world / Moon is goin' down / Sportin' life blues / Get right church / Blow Gabriel / Slippin' til my gal comes in partner / Wall hollow blues / Blues in E / Piece without words / Whoopin' blues / I want to be saved
HTCD 07 / '91 / Heritage

☐ **LIVE AND KICKIN'**
Make believe stunt / Maple leaf rag / Coon chase / Samson and Delilah / Twelve gates to the city / Mind how you're living / You got to move / How much we can bear / I will do my last singing
JAM 91332 / 23 Feb '98 / Just A Memory

☐ **O GLORY**
EDCD 482 / Jun '96 / Edsel

☐ PURE RELIGION AND BAD COMPANY
Pure religion / Mountain jack / Right now / Buck dance / Candy man / Devil's dream / Moon going down / Cocaine blues / Runnin' to the judgement / Hesitation blues / Bad company / I didn't want to join the band / Evening sun goes down / Seven sisters / My heart is fixed / Time is drawing near / Crucifixion
SFWCD 40035 / Oct '94 / Smithsonian Folkways

☐ REVEREND BLIND GARY DAVIS
I'm going to sit down on the banks of the river / Twelve gates to the city / I heard the angels singing / Twelve sticks / Make believe stunt / Waltz time candyman / C rag / Walking dog blues
HTCD 02 / Oct '89 / Heritage

☐ REVEREND GARY DAVIS
Walkin' dog blues / Cincinnati flow rag / She's funny that way / Whoopin' blues / Twelve sticks / Children of Zion / Buck rag / Hesitation blues / C-rag / Baby let me lay it on you / Cocaine blues / Buck dance / Candyman / Wall hollow blues / Little boy little boy who made your britches / Whistlin' blues
SH 97024 / Mar '98 / Shanachie

☐ SAY NO TO THE DEVIL
Say no to the devil / Time is drawing near / Hold to God's unchanging hand / Bad company brought me here / I decided to go down / Lord I looked down the road / Little Bitty baby / No one can do me like Jesus / Boy in the wilderness / Trying to get to heaven in due time
OBCCD 519 / Nov '92 / Original Blues Classics

☐ SIGN OF THE SUN
Sun is going down / When the train comes along / If I had my way / Twelve gates / God's gonna separate / Get right Church / Saints / God don't work like a natural man / There's destruction in this land
HTCD 03 / Oct '90 / Heritage

Davis, Richard

☐ NOW'S THE TIME
MCD 6005 / Sep '92 / Muse

Davis, Sara

☐ TUNDRA
CAKECD 14 / Jun '94 / Soundcakes

Davis Sisters

☐ MEMORIES
I forgot more than you'll ever know / Sorrow and pain / Rock-a-bye boogie (master) / You're gone / Sorrow and pain (fast version) / You're gone (swinging version) / Heartbreak ahead / Jealous love / Kaw-Liga / Rag mop / Your cheatin' heart / Crying steel guitar waltz / Just when I needed you / It wasn't God who made honky tonk angels / Tomorrow's just another day to cry / Tomorrow I'll cry / Jambalaya / Takin' time out for tears / Rock-a-bye boogie (alt.) / Gotta git a goin' / You weren't ashamed to kiss me last night / Foggy mountain top / Just like me / Don't take him for granted / I've closed the door / Medley / She loves him and he loves me / Single girl / Show me / Christmas boogie / Fiddle diddle boogie / Everlovin' / Come back to me / Tomorrow I'll cry over you / When I stop lovin' you / I'll get him back / It's the girl who gets the blame / Toodle-ooh (to you) / Baby be mine / Blues for company / Lonely and blue / Let's go steady / Lying brown eyes / Everywhere he went / Take my hand, precious Lord / Dig a little deeper in God's love
BCD 15722 / Jul '93 / Bear Family

Davis, Skeeter

☐ END OF THE WORLD, THE
End of the world / Silver threads and golden needles / Mine is a lonely life / Once upon a time / Why I'm walkin' / Don't let me cross over / My colouring book / Where nobody knows me / Keep your hands off my baby / Something precious / Longing to hold you again / He called me baby
TC 017 / Mar '94 / That's Country

☐ ESSENTIAL SKEETER DAVIS, THE
I forgot more than you'll ever know / Set him free / Am I that easy to forget / One you slip around with / (I can't help you) I'm falling too / No, never / My last date (with you) / Optimistic / End of the world / Gonna get along without ya now / Where I ought to be / I can't stay mad at you / I'm saving my love / Silver threads and golden needles / Mine is a lonely life / Let me get close to you / Fuel to the flame / What does it take (to keep a man like you satisfied) / I'm a lover (not a fighter) / Bus fare to Kennedy
74321665362 / Feb '96 / RCA

☐ SHE SINGS THEY PLAY (Davis, Skeeter & NRBQ)
Things to you / Everybody wants a cowboy / I can't stop loving you now / Heart to heart / Ain't nice to talk like that / Everybody's clown / Someday my Prince will come / How many tears / You don't know what you got till you lose it / Roses on my shoulder / Temporarily out of order / May you never be alone
ROUCD 3092 / '88 / Rounder

Davis, Spencer

☐ 24 HOURS (Live In Germany) (Davis, Spencer Band)
24 hours / Lady cop / Sensitive kind / Moon is a harsh mistress / On the green line / Pockey way / I'll take your love / Don't want you no more / Strong love / Route 66 / Easy rider / Knock on your door / Spiral times
INAK 859CD / Nov '97 / In Akustik

☐ 8 GIGS A WEEK (2CD Set) (Davis, Spencer Group)
Dimples / I can't stand it / Jump back / Here right now / Searchin' / Midnight train / It's gonna work out fine / My babe / Kansas City / Every little bit hurts / Sittin' and thinkin' / I'm blue / She put the hurt on me / I'll drown in my own tears / I'm getting better / Goodbye Stevie / Strong love / Georgia on my mind / It hurts me so / Oh pretty woman / Look away / This hammer / Please do something / Let me down easy / Somebody help me / Watch your step / Nobody knows you (When you're down and out) / Midnight special / When I come home / High time baby / Hey darling / I washed my hands in muddy water / You must believe me / Trampoline / Since I met you baby / Mean woman blues / Dust my broom / When a man loves a woman / Neighbour neighbour / On the green light / Stevie's blues / Take this hurt off me / Stevie's groove / I can't get enough of it / Waltz for Lumumba / Together till the end of time / Gimme some lovin' / Back into my life again / I'm a man / Blues in F
CRNCD 5 / Mar '96 / Island

☐ CATCH YOU ON THE REBOP (Live '73) (Davis, Spencer Group)
Let's have a party / Catch you on the rebop / I'm a man / Man jam / Gimme some lovin' / Living in a back street / Today, gluggo, tomorrow the world / Lega eagle shuffle / Fastest thing on / One night / Trouble in mind / Tumble down tenament row / Hanging around / Mr. Operator
RPM 150 / Jun '95 / RPM

☐ FUNKY (Davis, Spencer Group)
OW 34529 / Jun '97 / One Way

☐ FUNKY (Davis, Spencer Group)
I met a woman / Letter from Edith / Raintree River / What a way to die / Funky / Magical day / I guess I'm wasting my time / Poor misguided woman / And the Gods came down / New Jersey turnpike / With their new face on / Time seller / Feel your way / Taking out time / Mr. Second Class / After tea / Groove extra / Moonshine / Girls song / Dust my blues
SJPCD 021 / Jun '98 / Angel Air

☐ GIMME SOME LOVIN'
Gimme some lovin' / Crossfire / Such a good woman / Somebody help me / It must be love / Mistakes / Keep on running / I'm a man / No other baby / Love is on a roll / Blood runs hot / Don't want you no more / Private number: *Davis, Spencer & Dusty Springfield*
304312 / Jun '97 / Hallmark

☐ GLUGGO (Davis, Spencer Group)
Catch on the bebop / Don't let it bring you down / Living in a backstreet / Today gluggo tomorrow the world / Feeling rude / Mr. Operator / Edge / Screw / Tumble down tenement row / Alone / Legal eagle shuffle / Trouble in mind / Touching cloth
REP 4683 / Oct '97 / Repertoire

☐ LIVE TOGETHER (Davis, Spencer & Pete York/Colin Hodgkinson)
Keep on running / Midnight special / Walking blue / Mistakes / Sliding delta / I'm a man / Crossfire / Blood runs hot / Trouble in mind / Somebody help me / Don't leave me / Tulsa time / Gimmie some lovin' / Muddy waters
INAK 8410CD / Nov '97 / In Akustik

☐ LIVING IN A BACK STREET (Davis, Spencer Group)
REP 4682 / 24 Nov '97 / Repertoire

☐ SPOTLIGHT ON SPENCER DAVIS
Love is on a roll / Keep on running / It must be love / Somebody help me / Don't want you no more / Crossfire / I'm a man / Private number / Such a good woman / Gimme some lovin' / No other baby / Blood runs hot / Mistakes
HADCD 123 / Feb '94 / Javelin

☐ TAKING OUT TIME 1967-69 (Davis, Spencer Group)
RPMCD 127 / May '94 / RPM

☐ WITH THEIR NEW FACE ON (Davis, Spencer Group)
With his new face on / Mr. Second Class / Alec in transitland / Sanity inspector / Feel your way / Morning sun / Moonshine / Don't want you no more / Time seller / Stop me when I'm falling / After tea / Aqaurious der wassermann / Let the sunshine / Feel your way / I'm lost / Pools winner / Morning sun
REP 4684 / 24 Nov '97 / Repertoire

Davis, Steve

☐ DIG DEEP (Davis, Steve Sextet)
One for all / Dig deep / Little boy's bossa / Blues noble / Detour ahead / I should care / Summertime / Payne's window / Trippin'
CRISS 1136CD / Sep '97 / Criss Cross

☐ JAUNT, THE (Davis, Steve Quintet)
CRISS 1113CD / Jun '95 / Criss Cross

Davis, Thornetta

☐ SUNDAY MORNING MUSIC
SPCD 324 / Oct '96 / Sub Pop

Davis, Tyrone

☐ BEST OF THE FUTURE YEARS, THE
ICH 1153CD / Feb '94 / Ichiban

☐ I'LL ALWAYS LOVE YOU
I'll always love you / Prove my love / Talk to you / Let me love you / Do U still love me / Can I change my mind / Woman needs to be loved / Mom's apple pie
ICH 1103CD / Oct '93 / Ichiban

☐ SOMETHING'S MIGHTY WRONG
Something's mighty wrong / Running in and out of my life / Big cat / Ain't gonna get it / Wishin' well / I'm learning / Don't make me choose / I've gotta get over you
ICH 1135CD / Apr '94 / Ichiban

☐ YOU STAY ON MY MIND
You stay on my mind / Let me be your pacifier / I found myself when I lost you / All because of your love / You can win if you want / I won't let go / Something good about a woman / You're my heart / You're my soul
ICH 1170CD / May '94 / Ichiban

Davis, 'Wild' Bill

☐ LIVE AT THE CAVEAU DE LA HUCHETTE (Davis, 'Wild' Bill & Dany Doriz)
Struttin' with some barbecue / Lullaby of birdland / Indiana / Body and soul / Wild Bill Davis blues at the Huchette / Gone with the wind / Lil' darlin / Jumpin' with symphony kid
17156 / Sep '97 / Laserlight

☐ SING SYSTEM D LIVE 1978 (Davis, 'Wild' Bill & Dany Doriz/Michel Denis)
In a mellotone / Take the 'A' train / In the evening / Jitteburg waltz / Cute / Stolen sweets / After you've gone / Misty / Indiana / Rockville / Things ain't what they used to be / Limoges hot club blues
17150 / Apr '98 / Laserlight

Davison, 'Wild' Bill

☐ 'S WONDERFUL (Davison, 'Wild' Bill & His New Yorkers)
JCD 181 / '92 / Jazzology

☐ 'WILD' BILL
STCD 5524 / May '97 / Storyville

☐ 'WILD' BILL AT BULL RUN
JCD 30 / Nov '96 / Jazzology

☐ 'WILD' BILL DAVISON
SKCD 3002 / Dec '97 / Sackville

☐ 'WILD' BILL DAVISON & HIS FAMOUS JAZZ BAND (Davison, 'Wild' Bill & His Famous Jazz Band)
JCD 103 / '92 / Jazzology

☐ 'WILD' BILL DAVISON & PAPA BUE'S VIKING JAZZ BAND (Davison, 'Wild' Bill & Papa Bue Viking Jazz Band)
STCD 5523 / May '97 / Storyville

☐ 'WILD' BILL DAVISON WITH FRESSOR'S BIG CITY JAZZ BAND (Davison, 'Wild' Bill & Fessor's Big City Jazz Band)
Sweet Georgia Brown / Blue and brokenhearted / I can't believe that you're in love with me / Do you know what it means to Miss New Orleans / Open ears / General Booze / Blue again / Louisiana / Keepin' out of mischief now / I would do anything for you / Just a closer walk / Duet / Sweet Lorraine / My friend Bill
STCD 5525 / Dec '97 / Storyville

☐ AFTER HOURS
JCD 22 / '92 / Jazzology

☐ BUT BEAUTIFUL
If I had you / Sunday / I can't get started / Georgia / But beautiful / B flat blues / Someday you'll be sorry / Am I blue / You took advantage of me / I don't stand a ghost of a chance with you / I'm confessin' / Rainy day / Everything happens to me / Memories of you / Blue turning grey over you / Exactly like you
STCD 8233 / Oct '97 / Storyville

☐ COMMODORE MASTER TAKES
That's a plenty / Panama / River boat shuffle / Muskrat ramble / Clarinet marmalade / Original Dixieland one step / At the Jazz band ball / Baby, won't you please come... / I don't stand a ghost of a chance with you / Jazz me blues / Little girl / Squeeze me / Monday day / I'm confessin' that I love you / Big butter and egg man / I wish I could shimmy like my... / Sensation rag / Who's sorry now / On the Alomo / Someday sweetheart / High society / Wrap your troubles in dreams / I'm coming Virginia / Wabash blues
CMD 14052 / Feb '97 / Commodore Jazz

☐ JAZZ ON A SATURDAY AFTERNOON VOL.1
JCD 37 / '92 / Jazzology

☐ JAZZ ON A SATURDAY AFTERNOON VOL.2
JCD 38 / '92 / Jazzology

☐ JUST A GIG
JCD 191 / '91 / Jazzology

☐ LADY OF THE EVENING
JCD 143 / '92 / Jazzology

☐ MEMORIES
JCD 201 / Dec '97 / Jazzology

☐ RUNNING WILD
Blue room / I surrender dear / Monday date / Am I blue / You took advantage of me / If I had you / I never knew / (Back home again in) Indiana / When it's sleepy time down South / I want to be happy / Sunny side of the street / Running wild
JSPCD 1044 / Oct '90 / JSP

☐ SHOWCASE
JCD 83 / '92 / Jazzology

☐ SOLO FLIGHT
JCD 114 / '92 / Jazzology

☐ STARS OF JAZZ (Davison, 'Wild' Bill/ Freddy Randall Band)
JCD 62 / Oct '91 / Jazzology

☐ STARS OF JAZZ VOL.2 (Davison, 'Wild' Bill/Freddy Randall Band)
JCD 63 / Oct '91 / Jazzology

☐ SWEET AND LOVELY (Davison, 'Wild' Bill & Strings)
STCD 4060 / Feb '90 / Storyville

☐ THIS IS JAZZ (Volume 1)
JCD 42 / '92 / Jazzology

☐ TOGETHER AGAIN (Davison, 'Wild' Bill & Ralph Sutton)
Limehouse blues / Am I blue / Grandpa's spells / Three little words / Reunion blues / Back in your own backyard / I've got the world on a string / Rockin' chair
STCD 8216 / Dec '95 / Storyville

Daweh Congo

☐ MILITANCY
RN 0050 / Jul '97 / Runnetherlands

Dawkins, Ernest

☐ CHICAGO NOW VOL.2 (Dawkins, Ernest New Horizons Ensemble)
SHCD 141 / Oct '97 / Silkheart

Dawkins, Jimmy

☐ ALL FOR BUSINESS
All for business / Cotton country / Moon man / Down so long / Welfare blues / Having such a hard time / Sweet home Chicago / Born in poverty / Jammin' with Otis / Hippies playground / Moon man
DD 634 / Mar '97 / Delmark

☐ B PHUR REAL
DOG 9110CD / Aug '95 / Wild Dog

☐ BLISTERSTRING (Dawkins, Jimmy Band)
Feel so bad / Blue Monday / Chitlins con carne / She got the blues too / If you're ready / Blues with a feeling / Ode to Billie Joe / Welfare line / Shufflin' the blues / People will talk / Sea of luv
DE 641 / Nov '96 / Delmark

☐ BLUES AND PAIN
DOG 9108CD / Jun '94 / Wild Dog

☐ BLUES FROM ICELAND (Dawkins, Jimmy/Chicago Beau/Blue Ice Bragason)
Welfare line / That's alright / You don't love me / Feel so bad / Too much alcohol / Sometimes I have a heartache / Nightlife / One room country shack / Help me / Tin pan alley
ECD 26064 / Mar '95 / Evidence

☐ COME BACK BABY
STCD 8035 / Sep '97 / Storyville

☐ FAST FINGERS
It serves me right to suffer / I wonder why / I'm good for nothing / triple trebles / I finally learned a lesson / You got to keep on trying / Night rock / Little angel child / I don't know what love is / Breaking down / Sad and blues / Back home blues
DD 623 / Jul '98 / Delmark

☐ FEEL THE BLUES
(If you got to) Love somebody / Highway man / So good to be me / Last days / Feel the blues / Christmas time blues / Have a little mercy / We got to go / So good to me
JSPCD 282 / Jan '97 / JSP

☐ HOT WIRE 81
You just a baby child / Ruff times / Welfare line / Kold actions / Roc-kin-sole / Peeper's music / My way
ECD 260432 / Mar '94 / Evidence

☐ TRIBUTE TO ORANGE (Dawkins, Jimmy & Gatemouth Brown/Otis Rush)
All for business / You've got to keep on trying / Ain't never had nothing / Born in poverty / Marcelle Morgantini's Cassoulet / Your love / Tribute to orange / Mississippi bound / Life is a mean mistreater / Mean Atlantic ocean / Serves you right to suffer / Marcelle, Jacques et Luc / Ode to Billy Joe
ECD 260312 / Feb '93 / Evidence

Dawn

☐ CANDIDA
RE 21192 / 3 Aug '98 / Charlotte

☐ TIE A YELLOW RIBBON
Candida / Knock three times / Look at... / I play and sing / Summer sand / Country / What are you doing sunday / Runawayhappy together / Vaya con dios / You're a lady / Tie a yellow ribbon round the old oak tree / Say, has anybody seen my sweet gypsy rose / Who's in the strawberry patch with sally / Steppin' out (gonna boogie tonight) / You say the sweetest things / Look in my eyes pretty woman / Up on the roof / Love in your eyes / He don't love you (like I love you) / Cupid
BR 1452 / Jun '94 / BR Music

☐ TIE A YELLOW RIBBON (The Very Best Of Dawn/Tony Orlando)
Tie a yellow ribbon / Knock three times / Up on the roof / Rainy day man / Candida / Jolie / Let's run away girl / Carolina in my mind / What are you doing Sunday / Personality / Did you ever think she'd run away from you / You're a lady / Vaya con dios / Steppin' out gonna boogie tonight / Home / All in the game / Who's in the strawberry patch with Sally / Country / She can't hold a candle to you / Sweet gypsy rose
74321454762 / Feb '97 / Camden

Dawn

☐ NIER SOLEN GAR NIFER FUR EVUGHER
NR 006CD / Apr '95 / Necropolis

☐ SLAUGHTERSUN (CROWN OF THE TRIARCHY)
NR 021CD / 18 May '98 / Necropolis

Dawn

☐ 5 DAYS WISER
Feel like living / Five days wiser / Sister mystery / Mesmerize / Make it right / Good luck
R 4062 / Aug '97 / Rough Trade

☐ GETTING BY ON THE GOOD TIMES
Beautiful / Where do your dreams go / Lousiana / Testify 5 / Above my mind / Blue skies
VRT 001CD / 11 May '98 / One Little Indian

Dawn, Dolly

☐ MEMORIES OF YOU
ACD 201 / Feb '91 / Audiophile

☐ SMOOTH AS SILK (Dawn, Dolly & The Manhattan Nighthawks)
ACD 51 / Dec '97 / Audiophile

Dawn Of Dreams

☐ FRAGMENTS
CANDLE 022CD / 25 May '98 / Candlelight

Dawn Of The Replicants

☐ 1 HEAD 2 ARMS 2 LEGS
Cocaine on the catwalk / Candlefire / Ten sea birds / Lisa Box / Return of the board game / Windy Miller / Radars / So sleepy / Let them eat coal / Sgt Growley / Hogwash farm / Sleepy spiders / Float on a raft / Mary Louise / Fatal firework
0630196002 / 16 Feb '98 / East West

Dawson

☐ CHEESE MARKET
GRUFF 11CD / Nov '95 / Gruff Wit

Dawson, Julian

☐ LIVE ON THE RADIO
WM 1003 / Jun '93 / Watermelon

☐ LOST ALBUM, THE
HYCD 296161 / Mar '96 / Hypertension

☐ MOVE OVER DARLING
If I neede rain / Move over darling / Every tear's a weapon / Waiting for the moon / It came from Memphis / All the King's horses / Ghost of his own name / Locked out of paradise / Never take a fall / It's not time now / Pilgrims / Action man / There's more to love
FLED 3012 / Jun '97 / Fledg'ling

☐ TRAVEL ON
Uneasy rider / Never alone / Just can't say no / Sigh heart don't break / New Columbus / You're listening now / Hosanna / Queen of the bayou / My own damn bed / Brando's perfect girl / Gabriel's hill
HYCD 296160 / Feb '97 / Hypertension

Dawson, Nick

☐ NICK DAWSON & JOHN PETTERS/ KEITH DONALD (Dawson, Nick & John Petters/Keith Donald)
RRCD 1014 / Jul '98 / Rose

Dawson, Peter

☐ PETER DAWSON
Floral dance / Drake goes west / Glorious Devon / Up from Somerset / When the Sergeant Major's on parade / Vulcan's song / Non piu'andrai / Largo al factotum / Toreador's song (Bizet 'Carmen') / Bachelor gay / Smuggler's song / Yeomen of England / Old father Thames / Phil the fluter's ball / Waltzing Matilda / Ol' man river / Waiata poi / Drum major / I am a roamer
GEMMCD 9336 / '90 / Pearl

☐ PETER DAWSON
I travel the road / Old Father Thames / Smuggler's song / Boots / Soldier's dream / When the Sergeant Major's on parade / Danny Deever / Old comrades - the boys of the old brigade / Yeoman of England / Drake goes West / Glorious Devon / Fishermen of England / Friend o' mine / Floral dance / Drake's drum / Phil the flutter's ball / Cobbler's song / Bachelor gay / Whalin' up the Lochlan / Admiral's broom / By the side of the road / Gentleman Jim / Joggin' along the highway
CDMFP 6351 / Jun '97 / Music For Pleasure

☐ SCOTTISH AND IRISH SONGS
Auld sangs o'home / Auld hoose / O sing to me an Irish song / Mountains of Mourne / Star o' Rabbie Burns / Jug of punch / Border ballad / Off to Philadelphia / There far far awa' / Away in Athlone / Paddy's wedding / Father O'Flynn / Molly of Donegal / Pride of Tipperary / Turn ye tae me / She is far from the land / With my shillelagh under me arm / Fiddler of Dooney / Kerry dance / Phil the fluter's ball
MIDCD 008 / Jul '95 / Moidart

☐ SINGS THE YEOMAN OF ENGLAND
Floral dance / Glorious devon / Old father thames / On the road to mandalay / Boots / Drake's drum / Phil the flutter's ball / When the sergeant major's on parade / Fishermen of england / Cobbler's song / Smuggler's song / I heard a forest praying / A bachelor gay / Drum major / Admiral's broom / Whalin' up the lochlan / Waltzing matilda / Yeomen of england / By the side of the road / Gentleman jim / Joggin' along the highway / I travel the road
PASTCD 7007 / Jun '93 / Flapper

☐ SOMEWHERE A VOICE IS CALLING
El Abanico / Banjo song / Boots / Cobbler's song / Down among the dead men / Drum major / Fishermen of England / Fleet's not in port very long / Floral dance / Friend o' mine / Give me the rolling sea / Glorious Devon / If those lips could only speak / In a monastery garden / Jerusalem / Love and wine / Man who brings the sunshine / Mountains o' Mourne / Snowbird / Somewhere a voice is calling / Tomorrow is another day / Waiata poi / Waltzing Matilda / We saw the sea / Winding road
CDAJA 5114 / Sep '93 / Living Era

☐ SONGS OF THE SEA
Drake's drum / Outward bound / Old superb / Devon, O Devon / Homeward bound / Sons of the sea / Shipmates o'mine / Admiral Broom / At Santa Barbara / Cargoes / Rocked in the cradle of the deep / Tune the bosun played / Jolly Roger / Anchored / Rolling down to Rio / Little Admiral
GEMMCD 9381 / '90 / Pearl

Dawson, Ronnie

☐ JUST ROCKIN' AND ROLLIN'
Just rockin' and rollin' / You got a long way to go / Veronica / Fish out of water / Home cookin' / Club wig wam / You're humbuggin' me / Mexigo / It wouldn't do no good / She's a bad un / High on love / Sucker for a cheap guitar / Hoodlum / Tired of travellin' / No dice / Party town
NOHIT 019CD / May '97 / No Hit

☐ MONKEY BEAT
NOHITCD 008 / Jan '94 / No Hit

☐ ROCKIN' BONES
Rockin' bones / Congratulations to me / Do do do / Who's been here / Action packed / Tied down / I make the love / Riders in the sky / Jump and run / Tired of waitin' / I'm on your wagon / Who put the cat out / Reelin' and rockin' / Straight skirts / Searchin' for my baby / Everybody clap your hands
NOHITCD 001 / Jan '94 / No Hit

Dax, Danielle

☐ COMATOSE NON-REACTION (2CD Set)
BOT131 06CD / Oct '96 / Biter Of Thorpe

☐ INKY BLOATERS
BOT131 04CD / Oct '96 / Biter Of Thorpe

☐ POP EYES
Here come the harvest buns / Bed caves / Tower of lies / Numb companions / Everyone squeaks quietly
BOT131 01CD / Oct '96 / Biter Of Thorpe

Day Behaviour

☐ ADORED
Carouse / Cinematic / Shortness of breath / Hello / Il sogno / Clown / Beginning of something else / Movie / Momentary laughter / Remarkable rocket / Gullible / Treno notturno
NONS 352 / Mar '97 / Nons

Day Blindness

☐ DAY BLINDNESS
FLASH 42 / 1 Jun '98 / Flash

Day, Bobby

☐ ROCKIN' ROBIN
Rockin' Robin / Bluebird, the buzzard and the oriole / Over and over / Come seven / Honeysuckle baby / My blue Heaven / I don't want to / When the swallows come back to Capistrano / Beep beep beep / Ain't gonna cry no more / Little bitty pretty one / Life can be beautiful / That's all I want / Mr. and Mrs. rock 'n' roll / Sweet little thing / Three young rebs from Georgia
CDCH 200 / May '91 / Ace

Day, Darren

☐ ALBUM, THE
DAYCD 01 / 6 Apr '98 / Tailormade

Day, Doris

☐ 'S WONDERFUL
HCD 226 / Mar '95 / Hindsight

☐ 'S WONDERFUL
'S wonderful / My blue Heaven / You oughta be in pictures / Hundred years from today / September in the rain / I'm a big girl now / Don't worry 'bout me / Just you, just me / I gotta sing away these blues / Sentimental journey / I can't give you anything but love / Light your lamp / Singin' in the rain / Blues skies / I got it bad and that ain't good / Be anything but mine / Crying my heart out for you / Let's be buddies / While the music plays on / Dig it
SUMCD 4008 / Nov '96 / Summit

☐ 16 MOST REQUESTED SONGS
Sentimental journey / My dreams are getting bigger all the time / It's magic / Love somebody / Again / Bewitched, bothered and bewildered / Would I love you (love you, love you) / Why did I tell you I was going to Shanghai / Starbust / Guy is a guy / When I fall in love / Secret love / If I give my heart to you / I'll never stop loving you / Whatever will be will be (Que sera sera) / Everybody loves a lover
4721952 / May '95 / Columbia

☐ BEST OF DORIS DAY, THE
Move over darling / Love me or leave me / Sentimental journey / Whatever will be will be (Que sera sera) / Secret love / Everybody loves a lover / Softly as I leave you / It had to be you / Singin' in the rain / Make somebody happy / Very thought of you / Fly me to the moon / Bewitched, bothered and bewildered / April in Paris / When I fall in love / I'll never stop loving you
4837222 / 27 Jul '98 / Columbia

☐ BEST OF DORIS DAY, THE
Sentimental journey / September in the rain / 'S wonderful / You brought a new kind of love to me / Stardust / Blue skies / I've gotta sing away these blues / I can't give you anything but love / My blue heaven / I could write a book / Hundred years from today / I'm a big girl now / S'posin' / You oughta be in pictures / I'm in the mood for love / Be anything, but be mine / I got it bad and that ain't good / Light your lamp / Singin' in the rain / Just you, just me / Don't worry 'bout me / Crying my heart out for you
CD 6056 / Jan '97 / Music

☐ BLUE SKIES
PLSCD 213 / Apr '97 / Pulse

☐ BLUE SKIES
Stardust / I could write a book / Don't worry 'bout me / You oughta be in pictures / Sentimental journey / Singin' in the rain / I got it bad and that ain't good / Blue skies / Light your lamp / You bought a new kind of love to me / I'm in the mood for love / I'm a big girl now / I can't give you anything but love / My blue heaven / Just you, just me / Hundred years from today / 'S wonderful / I gotta sing away the blues / S'posin' / September song
306472 / Jun '97 / Hallmark

☐ COLLECTION, THE
Sentimental journey / Embraceable you / I can't give you anything but love / Blue skies / I'm in the mood for love / My blue heaven / Stardust / Singin' in the rain / 's wonderful / Hundred years from today / Be anything (but be mine) / September in the rain / Crying my heart out for you / Light your lamp / Dig it / Don't worry 'bout me / I gotta sing away these blues / I'm a big girl now / I've got a feelin' you're foolin' / Let's be buddies / S'posing / While the music plays on / You brought a new kind of love to me / You oughta be in pictures / I got it bad and that ain't good
COL 071 / Mar '95 / Collection

☐ COMPLETE DORIS DAY & LES BROWN, THE (Day, Doris & Les Brown)
61774200292 / 21 Apr '98 / Collectables

☐ CUTTIN' CAPERS/BRIGHT AND SHINY (2CD Set)
Cuttin' capers / Steppin' out with my baby / Makin' whoopee / Lady's in love with you / Why don't we do this more often / Let's take a walk around the block / I'm sitting on top of the world / Get out and get under the moon / Fit as a fiddle / Me too / I feel like a feather in the breeze / Let's fly away / Bright and shiny / I want to be happy / Keep smilin' keep laughin' be happy / Singin' in the rain / Gotta feelin' / Happy talk / Make someone happy / Riding high / On the sunny side of the street / Clap yo' hands / Stay with the happy people
4775932 / Oct '94 / Columbia

☐ DAY BY DAY/DAY BY NIGHT (2CD Set)
Song is you / Hello my lover, goodbye / Goodbye / But not for me / I remember you / I hadn't anyone till you / But beautiful / Autumn leaves / Don't take your love from me / There will never be another you / Gone with the wind / Gypsy in my soul / Day by day / I see your face before me / Close your eyes / Night we called it a day / Dream a little dream of me / Under a blanket of blue / You do something to me / Stars fell on Alabama / Moon song / Wrap your troubles in dreams (and dream your troubles away) / Soft as the starlight / Moonglow / Lamp is low
4757492 / Feb '94 / Columbia

☐ DAY BY DAY/LATIN FOR LOVERS/ SHOWTIME (3CD Set)
Song is you / Hello my lover, goodbye / But not for me / I remember you / I hadn't anyone till you / But beautiful / Autumn leaves / Don't take your love from me / There will never be another you / Gone with the wind / Gypsy in my soul / Day by day, night by night / I see your face before me / Close your eyes / Night we called it a day / Dream a little dream of me / Under a blanket of blue / You do something to me / Stars fell on Alabama / Moon song / Wrap your troubles in dreams (and dream your troubles away) / Soft as the starlight / Moonglow / Lamp is low / Quiet nights of quiet stars / Fly me to the moon / Meditation / Dansero / Summer has gone / How insensitive / Slightly out of tune / Our day will come / Be true to me / Latin for lovers / Perhaps, perhaps, perhaps / Be mine tonight / Love him more / Can't help falling in love / Since I fell for you / Losing you / (Now and then there's) A fool such as I / As long as he needs me / Night life / Funny / Softly as I leave you / Lollipops and roses / Love him / Moonlight lover / Whisper away / Showtime / I got the sun in the morning / Ohio / I love Paris / When I'm not near the boy I love / People will say we're in love / I've grown accustomed to his face / Surrey with the fringe on top / They say it's wonderful / Wonderful guy / On the street where you live / Sound of music / Showtime / Tea for two / Lullaby of broadway / Cuddle up a little closer / I may be wrong / Makin' whoopee / Be my little baby bumble bee / Secret love / Till we meet again / Ain't we got fun / Just one of those things / It had to be you / Love me or leave me
4853132 / 3 Nov '97 / Columbia

☐ DAYDREAMING (The Very Best Of Doris Day)
Move over darling / Secret love / Whatever will be will be (Que sera sera) / Lullaby of broadway / Love me or leave me / It's magic / Everybody loves a lover / Dream a little dream of me / Pillow talk / Cheek to cheek / Fly me to the moon / Close your eyes / Quiet night of quiet stars / Night and day / Let's face the music and dance / Pennies from heaven / Over the rainbow / I'll never stop loving you / If I give my heart to you / Bewitched / Very precious love / Black hills of Dakota / Teacher's pet / Makin' whoopee / Ready, willing and able / Sentimental journey
4873612 / Apr '97 / Columbia

☐ DORIS DAY COLLECTOR'S EDITION
DVGH 7032 / Apr '95 / Deja Vu

☐ DORIS DAY SINGS SONGS FROM CALAMITY JANE/PAJAMA GAME
Deadwood stage / I can do without you / Black of hills of dakota / Just blew in from the windy city / A woman's touch / Higher than a hawk (deeper than a well) / 'tis harry I'm plannin' to marry / Secret love / Pajama game (opening) and racing with the clock / I'm not at all in love / I'll never be jealous again / Once-a-year day / Small talk / There once was a man / Hernanado's hideaway / Finale
4676102 / Jul '93 / Columbia

☐ HOORAY FOR HOLLYWOOD VOL.1 & 2
Hooray for Hollywood / Cheek to cheek / It's easy to remember / Way you look tonight / I'll remember April / Blues in the night / Over the rainbow / Love is here to stay / In the still of the night / Night and day / Easy to love / I had the craziest dream / I've got my love to keep me warm / Soon / That old black magic / You'll never know / Foggy day / It's magic / It might as well be spring / Nice work if you can get it / Three coins in the fountain / Let's face the music and dance / Pennies from heaven / Oh, but I do
4871892 / Mar '97 / Columbia

☐ I HAVE DREAMED/LISTEN TODAY
I have dreamed / I believe in dreams / I'll buy that dream / My ship / All I do is dream of you / When I grow too old to dream / We'll love again / Periwinkle blues / Someday I'll find you / You stepped out of a dream / Oh what a beautiful dream / Time to say goodnight / Listen today / Pillow talk / Heart full of love / Anyway the wind blows / Oh what a lover you'll be / No / Love me in the daytime / I enjoy being a girl / Tunnel of love / He's so married / Roly Poly / Possess me / Inspiration
4840312 / Jun '96 / Columbia

☐ IT'S MAGIC
It takes time / Pete / My young and foolish heart / Tell me, dream face (What am I to you) / I'm still sitting under the apple tree / Just an old love of mine / That's the way he does it / Why she we both be lonely / Papa, won't you dance with me / Say something nice about me baby / It's magic / Just imagine / Pretty baby / Confess / Love somebody / Tacos, Enchilados and Beans / No moon at all / Put 'em in a box / Imagination / It's the sentimental thing to do / I've only myself to blame / Thoughtless / It's a quiet town (In Crossbone county) / Someone like you / My dream is yours / I'm in love / It's you or no one / My darling, My darling / That certain party / His fraternity pin / If you will marry me / You was / I'll string along with you / Powder your face with sunshine / Don't gamble with romance / I'm beginning to miss you / That old feeling / When your lover has gone / You go to my head / How it lies, how it lies, how it lies / If I could be with you one hour tonight / Everywhere you go / Again (Where are you) Now that I need you / Blame my absent minded heart / Let's take an old fashioned walk / You're my thrill / Bewitched, bothered and bewildered / At the cafe rendezvous / It's a great feeling / It's better to conceal than reveal / You can have him / Sometimes, I'm happy / Land of love (come my love and live with me) / I didn't know what time it was / I'm confessin' that I love you / Last mile home / Canadian capers (Cuttin' capers) / Here comes Santa Claus / Ol' St Nicholas / It's on the tip of my tongue / River Seine (La Seine) / (It happened at the) festival of roses / Three rivers, The (The Allegheny, Susquehanna and the Old Mo / (There's a) Bluebird on your windowsill / Crocodile tears / Game of broken hearts / Quicksilver / I'll never slip around again / I don't wanna be kissed by anyone but you / With you anywhere you are / Save a little sunbeam (For a rainy, rainy day) / Mama what'll I do / I said my pyjamas / Enjoy yourself / I may be wrong, but I think you're wonderful / Very thought of you / Too marvellous for words / With a song in my heart / Spesh'lly you / Marriage ties / Before I loved you / I went a wooing / I didn't slip, I wasn't pushed, I fell / Hoop dee doo / I can't get over a boy like you (Loving a girl like me) / I've forgotten you / I'll be around / Darn that dream / Here in my arms / Tea for two / I only have eyes for you / Do do do / Crazy rhythm / I know that you know / Oh me, oh my / I want to be happy / He's such a gentleman / Load of hay / I love the way you say goodnight / Orange coloured sky / Comb and paper polka / Pumpernickel / You are my sunshine / Everlasting arms / David's Psalm / Christmas story / I've never been in love before / Bushel and a peck / You love me / Best thing for you / If I were a bell / Silver bells / It's a lovely day today / From this moment on / I am loved / Nobody's chasing me / Ten thousand four hundred thirty-two sheep / You're getting to be a habit with me / Somebody loves me / Please don't talk about me when I'm gone / Just one of those things / Lullaby of Broadway / I love the way you say good night / (In) a shanty in old Shanty Town / Fine and dandy / Would I love you (Love you, love you) / Say something nice about me baby / It's magic / Pretty baby, / Thoughtless / It's you or no one / My darling, my darling / His fraternity pin / Let's take an old fashioned walk / You're my thrill / Do do do
BCD 15609 / Mar '93 / Bear Family

☐ LATIN FOR LOVERS/LOVE HIM
Quiet nights of quiet stars / Fly me to the moon / Meditation / Dansero / Summer has gone / How insensitive / Slightly out of tune / Our day will come / Be true to me / Latin for lovers / Perhaps, perhaps, perhaps / Be mine tonight / Can't help falling in love / Since I fell for you / Losing you / Fool such as I / As long as he needs me / Whisper away / Moonlight lover / Love him / Lollipops and roses / Softly as I leave you / Funny / Night life
4810182 / Aug '95 / Columbia

☐ LES BROWN & HIS ORCHESTRA WITH DORIS DAY
HCD 103 / Nov '94 / Hindsight

☐ MOVE OVER DARLING 1960-1968 (8CD Set)
What does a woman do / Please don't eat the daisies / Falling / Blue train / Daffa down dilly / Here we go again / On the street where you live / When I'm not near the boy I love / Love Paris / Surrey with the fringe on top / Ohio / I've grown accustomed to his face / They say it's wonderful / Wonderful guy / Show time / People will say we're in love / I've got the sun in the morning / Happy talk / Ridin' high / Stay with the happy people / Clap yo' hands / Singin' in the rain / I want to be happy / Make someone happy / On the sunny side of the street / Lucky shine / Bright and shiny / Gotta feelin' / Keep smilin' keep laughin' be happy / Oh what a beautiful dream / I'll buy that dream / Time to say goodnight / All I do is dream of you / My ship / We'll love gain / I believe in dreams / Periwinkle blue / Let no walls divide / Look all around

/ In the secret place / As a child / Someday I'll find you / You stepped out of a dream / I have dreamed / Let no walls divide / When I grow too old to dream / Who knows what might have been / Should I surrender / Lover come back / Close your eyes / Fools rush in / Remind me / Yes / Control yourself / Day dreaming / You're good for me / Nobody's heart / Wait till you see him / Give me time / Who are we to stay / Day dreaming / Close your eyes / My one and only love / In love in vain / Falling in love again / Nearer my God to thee / I need thee every hour / Abide with me / Lord's prayer / Walk with Him / In the garden / Prodigal son / If I can help somebody / Scarlet ribbons / Bless this house / You'll never walk alone/Be still and know/Let the little gir / Let the little girl limbo / Move over darling / Twinkle lullaby / More / Lollipops and roses / Can't help falling in love / Softly as I leave you / As long as he needs me / Losing you / Since I fell for you / Love him / Night life / Fool such as I / Funny / Moonlight lover / Send me no flowers / Rainbow's end / Oowee baby / Have yourself a merry little Christmas / Toyland / Christmas song / Winter wonderland / Silver bells / White Christmas / Be a child at Christmas time / Snowfall / Let it snow, let it snow, let it snow / Christmas waltz / I'll be home for Christmas / Christmas present / Getting to know you / Sleepy baby / With a smile and a song / Whatever will be will be (Que sera sera) / Zip-a-dee-doo-dah / Give a little whistle / Inch worm / Swinging on a star / Lilac tree / Children's marching song / Do re mi / High hopes / Send me no flowers / I remember you / Sentimental journey / It could happen to you / At last / I'll never smile again / Serenade in blue / It's been a long, long time / More I see you / I'm beginning to see the light / I had the craziest dream / Come to baby do / Slightly out of tune / Quiet night for quiet stars / Meditations / Summer has gone / Fly me to the moon / Perhaps, perhaps, perhaps / Our day will come / Be true to me / Dansero / Por favor / How insensitive / Be mine tonight / Catch the bouquet / Another go around / Whisper away / Do not disturb / Au revoir is goodbye with a smile / There they are / Every now and then (you come around) / Glass bottom boat / Sorry / Caprice / For all we know / Snuggled on your shoulder / Are you lonesome tonight / Wonderful one / Street of dreams / Oh how I miss you tonight / Life is just a bowl of cherries / All alone / Faded summer love / Sleepy lagoon / If I had my life to live over / Blue train / Daffa down dilly / Let the little girl limbo / Catch the bouquet / Another go around / Do not disturb / Glass bottom boat / Circus is on parade: *Day, Doris & Martha Raye/Jimmy Durante* / Over and over again / Why can't I: *Day, Doris & Martha Raye* / This can't be love / Most beautiful girl in the world: *Day, Doris & Stephen Boyd* / My romance / Most beautiful girl in the world: *Day, Doris & Jimmy Durante* / Little girl blue / Sawdust, spangles and dreams: *Day, Doris & Stephen Boyd/Martha Raye/Jimmy Durante* / Overture / Colonel Buffalo Bill: *Day, Doris & Leonard Stokes* / I'm a bad, bad man: *Day, Doris & Robert Goulet* / Doin' what comes naturally / Girl that I marry: *Day, Doris & Robert Goulet* / You can't get a man with a gun / They say it's wonderful: *Day, Doris & Robert Goulet* / My defences are down: *Day, Doris & Robert Goulet* / Moonshine lullaby / I'm an Indian too / I got lost in his arms / Who do you love I hope: *Day, Doris & Kelly Brown/Renee Winters* / I got the sun in the morning / Anything you can do: *Day, Doris & Robert Goulet* / There's no business like show business: *Day, Doris & Ensemble*
BCD 15800 / Apr '97 / Bear Family

☐ **PERSONAL CHRISTMAS COLLECTION**
Christmas song / Silver bells / Here comes Santa Claus / Ol' Saint Nicholas / Christmas story / Have yourself a merry little Christmas / Be a child at Christmas time / Toyland / Christmas present / Christmas waltz / Winter wonderland / Snowfall / White Christmas / Let it snow, let it snow, let it snow
4777712 / 3 Nov '97 / Columbia

☐ **QUE SERA SERA (5CD Set)**
Whatever will be will be (Que sera sera) / Somebody somewhere / We'll love again / Julie / Love in a home / Gone with the wind / Song is you / Don't take your love from me / Gypsy in my soul / Autumn leaves / I remember you / Hello, my lover, goodbye / Day by day / But beautiful / There will never be another you / But not for me / I hadn't anyone till you / Today, will be yesterday tomorrow / Party's over / Nothing in the world / Whad'ja put in that kiss / Man who invented love / Twelve O'clock / Tonight / Rickety rackety rendevous / Through the eyes of love / I'm not at all in love / Once a year day / Small talk / There once was a man / Seven and a half cents / Under a blanket of blue / I see your face before me / Moon song / Dream a little dream of me / You do something to me / Wrap your troubles in dreams / Close your eyes / Wrap your toubles in dreams / Let's face the music and dance / I've got my love to keep me warm / Nice work if you can get it / Cheek to cheek / Moonglow / Lamp is low / Soft as the starlight / Night we called it a day / Stars fell in Alabama / It's easy to remember / It might as well be spring / I'll remember April / Three coins in the fountain / In the still of the night / Soon / Foggy day / Our love is here to stay / Run away, skidaddle skidoo / Teacher's pet / Walk a chalk line / You'll never know / I had the craziest dream / Over the rainbow / Oh, but I do / Easy to love / That old black magic / Pennies from heaven / Way you look tonight / Night and day / Hooray for Hollywood / Very precious love / Blues in the night / Everybody loves a lover / Tunnel of love / Instant love / Posses me / Kissin' my honey / That Jane from Maine / Steppin' out with my baby / Lady's in love with you / I enjoy being a girl / Let's fly away / Why don't we do this more often / Fit as a fiddle (and ready for love) / Let's take a walk around the block / Makin' whoopee / You're driving my crazy / Get out and under the moon / I feel like a feather in the breeze / I'm sitting on top of the world / Cuttin' capers / Me too (ho-ho-ha-ha) / Love me in the daytime / Anyway the wind blows / Be prepared / Perfect understanding / It happend to Jane / He's so married / Deck the halls with boughs of holly / Inspiration / Posess me / What does a woman do / Pillow talk / Roly poly / Heart full of love / Sound of music / Oh what a lover you'll be / No / Fellow needs a girl / What every girl should know / Mood indigo / What's the use of wonderin' / My kinda lover / When you're smiling / You can't have everything / Hundred years from today / Everlasting arms / Something wonderful / Not only should you love him
BCD 15797 / Feb '96 / Bear Family

☐ **SECRET LOVE**
It's so laughable / Something wonderful / We kiss in a shadow / Very good advice / Tell me (why nights are lonely) / Till we meet again / Moonlight baby / My life's desire / I'm forever blowing bubbles / Every little moment / Love ya / Cuddle up a little closer / Why did I tell you I was going to Shanghai / Lonesome and sorry / Ask me (because I'm so in love) / Kiss me goodbye love / Got him off my hands / Baby doll / Oops / If that doesn't do it / Domino / Makin' whoopee / It had to be you / My buddy / One I love / Moonlight bay / I'll see you in my dreams / I wish I had a girl / Ain't we got fun / Nobody's sweetheart / How lovely cooks the meat / Sugarbush / Guy is a guy / Little kiss goodnight / Gently Johnny / Who who who / Take me in your arms / Make it soon / My love and devotion / It's magic / When I fall in love / Cherries / April in Paris / No two people / You can't lose me / I know a place / That's what makes Paris Paree / I'm gonna ring the bell tonight / Second star to the right / Your Mother and mine / Mr. Tip toe / Ma says, Pa says / Full time job / Beautiful music to love you by / You have my sympathy / Let's walk that way / Candy lips / Be my little baby / King Chanticleer / If you were the only girl in the world / Your eyes have told me so / Just one girl / By the light of the silvery moon / When the red, red robin comes bob, bob, bobbin' along / Purple cow / Kiss me again stranger / Black hills of Dakota / 'Tis Harry I'm planning to marry / Just blew in from the windy city / This too shall pass away / Woman's touch / Choo choo train / Secret love / I can do without you / Deadwood stage / Love you Dearly / Lost in loveliness / I speak to the stars / What every girl should know / Blue bells of broadway / Kay Muleta / Anyone can fall in love / Jimmy unknown someone / Else's roses / If I give my heart to you / There's a rising moon for every falling star / You, my love / Hold me in your arms / Till my love comes to me / Ready, willing and able / Two hearts, two kisses (make one love) / Foolishly yours / I'll never stop loving you / Love's little island / Ooh bang jiggly jang let it ring / I've gotta sing away these blues / Live it up / I'm a big girl now / When I'm happy / Love's little island / It all depends on you / You made me love you / Stay on the right side / Mean to me / Everybody loves my baby / Sam the old accordion man / Shaking the blues away / Ten cents a dance / Never look back / At sundown / Love me or leave me / Overture / You made me love you (I didn't want to do it)
BCD 15746 / Mar '95 / Bear Family

☐ **SENTIMENTAL JOURNEY**
HCD 200 / Nov '94 / Hindsight

☐ **SENTIMENTAL JOURNEY**
My blue heaven / September in the rain / 'S wonderful / You brought a new kind of love to me / Stardust / Blue skies / I've gotta sing away these blues / I can't give you anything but love / Sentimental journey / I could write a book / Singin' in the rain / I'm a big girl now / S'posin' / You ought to be in pictures / I'm in the mood for love / Be anything, but be mine / I got it bad and that ain't good / Light your lamp / Hundred years from today / Just you, just me / Don't worry 'bout me / Crying my heart out for you
TRTCD 164 / 28 Jan '98 / TrueTrax

☐ **SENTIMENTAL JOURNEY**
Singin' in the rain / I've got it bad, and that ain't good / Blue skies / Crying my heart out for you / I'm in the mood for love / S'posin' / My blue heaven / Stardust / I gotta sing away these blues / I'm a big girl now / September in the rain / You brought a new kind of love to me / Hundred years from today / Be anything, but be mine / Light up your lamp / Don't worry 'bout me / Sentimental journey
MUCD 9015 / Apr '95 / Musketeer

☐ **SENTIMENTAL JOURNEY (2CD Set)**
'Til the end of time / He'll have to cross the atlantic / I'd rather be with you / Aren't you glad you're you / Last time I saw you / Come to baby / You won't be satisfied / Red kiss on a blue letter / We'll be together again / Day by day / In the moon mist / There's good blues tonight / All through the day / Devil devil devil / I got the sun in the morning / Whole world is singing my song / Sooner or later / My number one dream came true / You should have told me / It could happen to you / Christmas song / Let's be buddies / Three at a table for two / Dig it / While the music plays / Between friends / Broom street / Barbara Allen / Amapola / Easy as pie / Booglie wooglie piggy / Celery stalks at midnight / Beau night in hotchkiss corners / Alexander the swoose / Keep cool fool / Made up my mind / Sentimental journey / My derams are getting better all the time / He's home for a little while / T'ain't me / I'll always be with you
CDGR 1632 / Sep '97 / Charly

☐ **SENTIMENTAL JOURNEY**
GO 3807 / 1 Dec '97 / Golden Options

☐ **SHOW TIME/DAY IN HOLLYWOOD (2CD Set)**
Showtime (part one) / I got the sun in the morning / Ohio / I love Paris / When I'm not near the boy I love / People will say we're in love / I've grown accustomed to his face / Surrey with the fringe on top / They say it's wonderful / Wonderful guy / On the street where you live / Showtime (part two) / Tea for two / Lullaby of Broadway / Cuddle up a little closer / I may be wrong, but I think you're wonderful / Makin' whoopee / Be my little baby bumble bee / Secret love / Till we meet again / Ain't we got fun / Just one of those things / It had to be you / Love me or leave me
4757502 / Feb '94 / Columbia

Day, Jimmy

☐ **STEEL & STRINGS (Golden Steel Guitar Hits)**
Panhandle rag / Roadside rag / Texas playboy rag / Remington ride / Coconut grove / Boot hill drag / Bud's bounce / B Bowman's hop / Georgia steel guitar / Steelin' the blues / Indian love call / Please help me, I'm falling / I love you because / Am I that easy to forget / Fallen star / She thinks I still care / Making believe / I love you so much it hurts / Wild side of life / Release me / Funny how time slips away / I can't stop loving you / I fall to pieces
BCD 15583 / Apr '92 / Bear Family

Day One

☐ **HALLOWED GROUND**
BV 131182 / Nov '96 / Black Vinyl

Dayglo Abortions

☐ **CORPORATE WHORES**
AR 62112 / Mar '97 / A&R International

☐ **LITTLE MAN IN THE CANOE**
AR 1105CD / Mar '97 / A&R International

Dayinthelife

☐ **DAYINTHELIFE**
TVT 71102 / 22 Sep '97 / Building/TVT

Dayjah

☐ **URBAN JUNGLE (Dayjah & The Disciples)**
TEMCD 3 / Aug '97 / Third Eye

Dayne, Taylor

☐ **GREATEST HITS**
Say a prayer / Tell it to my heart / I'll always love you / Can't get enough of your love / With every beat of my heart / Love will lead you back / Don't rush me / Prove your love / I'll be your shelter / Heart of stone / Send me a lover / I'll wait
7822187742 / 2 Feb '98 / Arista

Days

☐ **MELLOW**
Park and ride / Dazed / Now I know / Hello boys / Sheila / Crushed / Why I hate the sixties / Heavy wait / My crap life / Alone / Saturday girl / Shy / Spearhead
3215558 / 10 Nov '97 / No Organisation

Days Of The New

☐ **DAYS OF THE NEW**
OPD 30004 / 9 Mar '98 / Outpost

Dayspring

☐ **DREAMSTATE**
NA 023CD / Jul '96 / New Age

Daytona

☐ **MY OBSESSION WITH ELIZABETH MONTGOMERY**
BDG 1001172 / 1 Jun '98 / Blue Dog

Dazzie Dee

☐ **REBIRTH (Dazzie Dee & Coolio/Ice Cube)**
50545 / Jun '97 / Raging Bull

Dazzling Killmen

☐ **FACE OF COLLAPSE**
GR 12CD / Apr '94 / Skingraft

☐ **RECUERDA**
GR 36CD / Jul '96 / Skingraft

DBF

☐ **NOT BOUND BY THE RULES**
You deceive yourself / Election's just a farce / Suicide Billy / Make it a lie / Too wide apart / Narrow-minded / Not bound to rules / Nothing to prove / Rape your mind / Too much wasn't said / Am I too weak / Religion / Blank minds / No personality
853881 / Jul '89 / SPV

DB's

☐ **PARIS AVENUE**
MON 6122 / Jan '95 / Monkey Hill

☐ **RIDE THE WILD TOM TOM**
We should be in bed / Everytime anytime / Let's live for today / Little hands / You got it wrong / Tell me two times / Nothing is wrong / Purple hose / Ash / I read New York Rocker / Walking the ceiling (it's good to be alive) / Baby talk / Dynamite (original demo) / Soul kiss (part one) / Bad reputation / Modern boys and girls / What about that cat / What's the matter with me / Fight / She's green, I'm blue / If and when / Soul kiss (part two) / Death of rock / Purple hose (slight return) / Hardcore Judy / Spy in the house of love
RSACD 805 / Dec '94 / Sequel

DC 3

☐ **VIDA**
SST 156CD / Jul '89 / SST

DC Talk

☐ **FREE AT LAST**
Luv is a verb / That kinda girl / Jesus is just alright / Say the words / Socially acceptable / Free at last / Time is... / Hard way / Lean on me / I don't want it / Word 2 the Father
FFD 3002 / Jul '95 / Alliance Music

D'Cruze

☐ **CONTROL**
SUBBASECD 2 / Oct '95 / Suburban Base

DDC

☐ **PLATE FULLA FUNK**
GT 0230 / May '96 / Grapetree

De Alicante, Montoya

☐ **FLAMENCO FIRE (De Alicante, Montoya & Flamenco Ensemble)**
Sevillanas / Noche granadina / Bulerias de la samaritana / Fandangos / Torremolinos / Zapateado de las campanas / Los ojos mios / Levante / Danza egipcia / Temas de huelva
TCD 1073 / 15 Jun '98 / Rykodisc

De Almaden, Escudero & Ramos

☐ **FLAMENCO DE TRIANA**
TCD 1041 / Mar '97 / Tradition

De Alvear, Maria

☐ **EN AMOR DURO**
ARTCD 6112 / Jan '93 / Hat Art

De Angelis, Alfredo

☐ **ATENTI DE ANGELIS**
BMT 016 / Jan '98 / Blue Moon

☐ **BAJO BELGRANO**
BMT 012 / Jan '98 / Blue Moon

De Babalon, Christoph

☐ **IF YOU'RE INTO IT I'M OUT OF IT**
Opium / Nostep / Expressure / What you call a life / Water / Brilliance / Dead / Damaged / Release / High life / My confession
DHRCD 008 / 15 Sep '97 / Digital Hardcore

De Barro, Joao

☐ **NASCE UM COMPOSITOR**
RVCD 119 / 12 May '98 / Revivendo

De Boignard, Faubourg

☐ **LA RAVINE**
495012 / Mar '96 / Acousteak

De Bora, Naomi

☐ **PRIVATE EYES**
BRAM 1991282 / Nov '93 / Brambus

De Buddelschipper

☐ **SHANTIES AND SEEMANNSLIEDER**
EUCD 1178 / '91 / ARC

De Burgh, Chris

☐ **AT THE END OF A PERFECT DAY**
Broken wings / Round and round / I will / Summer rain / Discovery / Brazil / In a country churchyard / Rainy night in Paris / If you really love her let her go / Perfect day
CDMID 112 / Oct '92 / A&M

☐ **BEAUTIFUL DREAMS**
Missing you / Carry me (Like a fire in your heart) / Discovery / Snows of New York / In love forever / Shine on / Lady in red / In dreams / I'm not crying over you / Always on my mind / Say goodbye to it all / One more mile to go
5404322 / Oct '95 / A&M

☐ **BEST MOVES**
Every drop of rain / In a country churchyard / Patricia the stripper / Satin green shutters / Spanish train / Waiting for the hurricane / Broken wings / Lonely sky / Spaceman came travelling / Crusader / Traveller
3950832 / Apr '95 / A&M

☐ **CRUSADER**
Carry on / I had the love in my eyes / Something else again / Girl with April in her eyes / Just in time / Devil's eyes / It's such a long way home / Old fashioned people / Quiet moments / Crusader / You and me
CDMID 113 / Oct '92 / A&M

☐ **EASTERN WIND**
Traveller / Record company bash / Tonight / Wall of silence / Flying home / Shadows and light / Some things never change / Tourist attraction / Eastern wind
CDMID 167 / Aug '91 / A&M

☐ **FAR BEYOND THESE CASTLE WALLS**
Hold on / Key / Windy night / Sin City / New moon / Watching the world / Lonesome cowboy / Satin green shutters / Turning around / Goodnight
CDMID 110 / Oct '92 / A&M

☐ **FLYING COLOURS**
Sailing away / Carry me (like a fire in your heart) / Tender hands / Night on the river / Leather on my shoes / Suddenly love / Missing you / I'm not scared anymore / Don't look back / Just a word away / Risen Lord / Last time I cried / Simple truth (a child is born)
3952242 / Apr '95 / A&M

☐ **GETAWAY, THE**
Don't pay the ferryman / Living on the island / Crying and laughing / I'm counting on you / Getaway / Ship to shore / Borderline / Where peaceful waters flow / Revolution / Light a fire / Liberty
3949292 / Apr '95 / A&M

☐ HIGH ON EMOTION - LIVE FROM DUBLIN
Last night / Sailing away / Revolution / I'm not scared anymore / Spanish train / Borderline / Risen Lord / Last time I cried / Lady in red / Spaceman came travelling / Patricia the stripper / Missing you / Say goodbye to it all / Don't pay the ferryman / High on emotion
3970862 / Apr '95 / A&M

☐ HITS OF CHRIS DE BURGH, THE (David, Ron Orchestra)
Don't pay the ferryman / Getaway / Spaceman came travelling / Sailing away / Diamond in the dark / High on emotion / Lady in red / Borderline / Missing you / Tender hands / Ship to shore
QED 217 / Nov '96 / Tring

☐ INTO THE LIGHT
One word straight to the heart / For Rosanna / Leader / Vision / What about me / Last night / Fire on the water / Ballroom of romance / Lady in red / Say goodbye to it all / Spirit of man / Fatal hesitation
3951212 / Apr '95 / A&M

☐ LOVE SONGS, THE
Here is your paradise / Missing you / So beautiful / In love forever / Borderline / Lady in red / Much more than this / It's me (and I'm ready to go) / Seperate tables / Fatal hestitaion / Forevernmore / Head and the heart / Lonely sky / Suddenly love / If you really love her let her go / In a country churchyard
5407942 / 29 Sep '97 / A&M

☐ MAN ON THE LINE
Ecstasy of flight (I love the night) / Sight and touch / Taking it to the top / Head and the heart / Sound of a gun / High on emotion / Much more than this / Man on the line / Moonlight and vodka / Transmission ends
CDMID 188 / Jul '93 / A&M

☐ POWER OF TEN
Where will we be going / By my side / Heart of darkness / In your eyes / Separate tables / Talk to me / Brother John / Connemara coast / Shine on / Celebration / She means everything to me / Making the perfect man
3971882 / Apr '95 / A&M

☐ SPANISH TRAIN AND OTHER STORIES
Spanish train / Lonely sky / This song for you / Patricia the stripper / Spaceman came travelling / I'm going home / Painter / Old friend / Tower / Just another poor boy
CDMID 111 / Oct '92 / A&M

☐ SPARK TO A FLAME
This waiting heart / Don't pay the ferryman / Much more than this / Sailing away / Lady in red / Borderline / Say goodbye to it all / Ship to shore / Missing you / Diamond in the dark / Tender hands / Spaceman came travelling / Where peaceful waters flow / High on emotion / Spanish train / Fatal hesitation
CDBCD 100 / Oct '89 / A&M

☐ THIS WAY UP
This silent world / This is love / This weight on me / Here is your paradise / Oh my brave hearts / Blonde hair, blue jeans / Son and the father / Up here in heaven / You are the reason / Love's got a hold on me / Snows of New York
5402332 / May '94 / A&M

De Cadiz, Beni

☐ GREAT FIGURES OF FLAMENCO VOL.17
LDX 274992 / Jun '94 / La Chant Du Monde

De Cana, Flor

☐ MUEVETE (MOVE IT)
FF 70463 / Jul '89 / Flying Fish

De Carlo, Julio

☐ TODO CORAZON 1924-1928
EBCD 83 / Jan '97 / El Bandoneon

De Chiaro, Giovanni

☐ SCOTT JOPLIN ON GUITAR VOL.2
Sugar cane / Peacherine rag / Cascades / Country club ragtime two step / Leola two step / Wall street rag / Kismet rag / Antoinette / Roseleaf rag / Augustan club waltz / Lily queen / March majestic / Favourite / Euphonic sounds
CRC 2379 / Aug '98 / Centaur

De Courson, Hughes

☐ CHARLEMAGNE
669412 / Mar '96 / Melodie

De Dakar, Etoile

☐ VOL.2 (Phiapathioloy)
Thiapathioly / Dokhama say ne ne / Diandioli / Dounyan / Defal gnou guess / Dagotte
STCD 3006 / Mar '94 / Stern's

De Danann

☐ ANTHEM
Wren's nest / Let it be / Johnstone hornpipe / Connie from Constantinople / Johnny I hardly knew you / Ril and Spideal / Anthem for Ireland / Jimmy Byrnes and Dinkies / Diglake fields / Duo in G / Paddy's lamentation
DARCD 013 / 8 Sep '97 / Dara

☐ BALLROOM
GLCD 3040 / Feb '95 / Green Linnet

☐ DE DANANN
Cuckoo's nest medley / Come back again to me Mavourneen / Conlon's jig/Padraig O'Keefe's head of cabbage/Boys of Malin / My Irish Molly-O / Hey Jude / Maggie / Coleraine jig/Derrane's/John Stenson's / Kitty's wedding/The rambler / Teetotlar/ St. Anne's / Then you'll remember me / Morrison's/ The tailor's thimble/Wellington's / I'm leaving Tipperary
KCD 430 / Jan '97 / Celtic Collections

☐ HALF SET IN HARLEM
CMCD 057 / Dec '97 / Celtic Music

☐ HIBERNIAN RHAPSODY
PED 9601 / Dec '96 / Bee's Knees

☐ JACKET OF BATTERIES, A
CMCD 066 / Oct '94 / Celtic Music

☐ MIST COVERED MOUNTAINS, THE
Mac's fancy/Mist covered mountain / Cameronian reel/Doon reel / Seamaisin / Mulvihill's reel/Dawn / Banks of the Nile / Johnny Leary's polka/O'Keefe's polka/Johnny do I miss you / Mr. O'Connor / Henry Joy / Cottage in the grove/Sean Ryan's reel / Maire Mhor / Langstrom's pony/Tap room/Lord Ramsey's reel
CEFCD 087 / Jan '94 / Gael Linn

☐ SONG FOR IRELAND
SHCD 1130 / Oct '97 / Sugar Hill

☐ STAR SPANGLED MOLLY, THE
TFCB 5006CD / Oct '94 / Third Floor

De Diego, Victor

☐ AMAIA
FSNT 012 / 5 Jan '98 / Fresh Sound New Talent

De Fabriek

☐ PWZ
EFA 015622 / Sep '95 / Apocalyptic Vision

De Forest, Carmaig

☐ DEATHGROOVELOVEPARTY
KFWCD 145 / Feb '95 / Knitting Factory

De France, Jean Michel

☐ FEELINGS (Music Of The Pan Flute)
Woman in love / Man and a woman / La mer / My heart in my hands / About the clouds / Love serenade / Dolannes melodie / Guernica / We are the world / Feelings / Autumn leaves / Adagio / Song for Anna / Liebestraum / L for love / Ave Maria / Summer love affair / El condor pasa
PWK 130 / May '90 / Carlton

De Franco, Buddy

☐ BLUES BAG (De Franco, Buddy & Louis Hayes)
VJ 010 / 23 Feb '98 / Vee Jay

☐ BORN TO SWING
Don't be that way / Skyliner / I wanna be loved / I remember clifford / Yesterday / Tenderly / Mr. lucky / Melancholy stockholm / Buy it and fry it
HCD 701 / Nov '94 / Hindsight

☐ BUENOS AIRES CONCERTS, THE
Billie's bounce / Triste / Ja da / Yesterdays / Mood indigo / Scrapple from the apple / Street of dreams / Song is you
HEPCD 2014 / Nov '95 / Hep

☐ FIVE NOTES OF BLUES
500302 / Nov '93 / Musidisc

☐ FREE FALL
Free fall / Please send me someone to love / Free sail / Yesterdays / Threat of freedom / Free fall / Free sail
CHCD 71008 / Mar '97 / Candid

☐ HARK (De Franco, Buddy & Oscar Peterson Quartet)
All too soon / Summer me, Winter me / Llovisna (Light rain) / By myself / Joy spring / This is all I ask / Hark / Why am I
OJCCD 867 / Nov '95 / Original Jazz Classics

☐ MR. LUCKY (2CD Set)
In a mellow tone / Lamp is low / Mood indigo / Scrapple from the apple / Mar descancado / You do something to me / Mr. Lucky / In a sentimental mood / Billie's bounce / Meditation
JLR 103610 / Apr '97 / Live At EJ's

De Fresnes, Roberto

☐ ATLANTIS
Atlantis / Discovery / Poseidia / Dolphin / Kimmeriou / Aleinous / Visions from the past / Gateway to the gods / Requiem / Dolphin reprise
AD 22CD / 11 May '98 / AD

De Goal, Charles

☐ DOUBLE FACE
ROSE 96CD / Dec '86 / New Rose

De Gonzaga, Luizinho

☐ GONZAGUINHA
Baiao / Guardo / Humanos / Respeita januario / Asa branca / Gonzaga / Uma vez por semana / Borboleta prateda / Avassaladora / Olha pro ceu / A vida do viajante
68951 / Apr '97 / Tropical

De Graaf, Dick

☐ NEW YORK STRAIGHT AHEAD (De Graaf, Dick & Tony Lakatos Trio)
CHR 70033 / Sep '96 / Challenge

☐ SAILING
CHR 70024 / Sep '95 / Challenge

De Grassi, Alex

☐ BEYOND THE NIGHT SKY
Rain is pouring / Beyond the night sky / Bells of London / Boo maramba / Mama Papa / When my soul embraces you / Sleepytime / A La Nanita Nan / As you drift away / Swedish lullaby / Waters of time / Brahms lullaby
R 272537 / Nov '96 / Earthbeat

De Haidouks, Taraf

☐ DUMBALA DUMBA
Introduction / Dumbala dumba / Sabarelu / Rustem / Foii de prun si foli de praz / Cuculetu / Catar o birtu mai opre / Pe deasupra casei mele / Mesteru manole / Cintece de jale / Pe drumul minastiresc / APadure verde padure / Tambal solo / Tot taraful / Hora ca la ursari / Terno chelipe / Catar o birto mai opre / Mestreu maole / Padure verde padure
CRAW 21 / 18 May '98 / Cramworld

De Johnette, Jack

☐ ALBUM ALBUM (Special Edition)
Festival / New Orleans strut / Zoot suite / Ahmad the terrible / Monk's mood / Third world anthem
8234672 / Jan '89 / ECM

☐ DANCING WITH NATURE SPIRITS
Dancing with nature spirits / Anatolia / Healing song for Mother earth / Amanations / Time warps
ECM 55310242 / Jun '96 / ECM

☐ DEJOHNETTE COMPLEX, THE
Equipoise / Major general / Miles' mode / Requiem / Mirror image / Papp-Daddy and me / Brown, warm and wintry / Requiem
OJCCD 617 / Jun '96 / Original Jazz Classics

☐ NEW DIRECTIONS
Bayou fever / Where or wayne / Dream stalker / One handed woman / Silver hollow
8293742 / Jan '89 / ECM

☐ NEW DIRECTIONS IN EUROPE
Salsa for Eddie / Bayou fever / Where or Wayne / Multo spillagio
8291582 / '88 / ECM

☐ ONENESS
Welcome blessing / Free above the sea / Priestess of the mist / Jack in / From the heart / CMA
5373432 / 27 Oct '97 / ECM

☐ PARALLEL REALITIES (2CD Set)
Jack in / Exotic isles / Dancing / Nine over reggae / John McKee / Indigo dreamscapes / Parallel realities
JD 1251/52 / 13 Jul '98 / Jazz Door

☐ PIANO ALBUM, THE
Minority / Lydia / Countdown to love / Spiral / Time after time / Milton / Ahmad the terrible / Quiet now
LCD 15042 / Aug '88 / Landmark

☐ PICTURES
Picture 1 / Picture 2 / Picture 3 / Picture 4 / Picture 5 / Picture 6
5192842 / Jun '93 / ECM

☐ SPECIAL EDITION (De Johnette, Jack Special Edition)
One for Eric / Zoot suite / Central Park West / India / Journey to the twin planet
8276942 / Jan '89 / ECM

☐ TIN CAN ALLEY (De Johnette, Jack Special Edition)
Tin can alley / Pastel rhapsody / Riff raff / Gri gri man / I know
51775422 / Nov '93 / ECM

☐ WORKS
Bayou fever / Gri gri man / To be continued / One for Eric / Unshielded desire / Blue
8254272 / Jun '89 / ECM

De Jong, Michael

☐ GROWN MAN MOAN
Vienna breakdown / Between you and me / Mean old world / Grown man moan / St Peters got the blues / Drowning and drowning / Jailhouse letter / I won't cry / Mind if I pass / Wondering when she's coming home / Slow slow loving / Goo37 / 37 goodbyes
MRCD 190 / 9 Mar '98 / Munich

De Jong, Tracie

☐ LONGEST DAY, THE
CDMANU 1440 / Dec '93 / Manu

De Jonge, Henk

☐ JUMPING SHARK
BVHAASTCD 9103 / Nov '90 / Bvhaast

De Jorge, Juan

☐ SONGS FROM THE SOUL (De Jorge, Juan Group)
Cascabeles de oro / Camino sin horizonte / Margarita por tu amor / Querer o amar / Bajan los comechingones / Hermano / Indio soy de Tucuman / Por que te ame / Galopando voy / Buscando la paz / Sabes mi amor / El humahuaqueno / Quisiera volver a verte / La donosa
PS 65186 / Jun '97 / PlayaSound

De La Isla, Camaron

☐ GRAND FIGURES OF FLAMENCO VOL.15
LDX 274957 / May '94 / La Chant Du Monde

De La Matrona, Pepe

☐ GREAT SINGERS OF FLAMENCO VOL.2
LDC 274 829 / '88 / La Chant Du Monde

De La Rosa, Tony

☐ ATOTONILCO
La palomilla (polka) / Lost tiliches (huapango) / El sube y baja (polka) / Adios amor (bolero) / Sylvia (polka) / El guaracha (huapango) / La grulla (polka) / Paloma sin nido (ranchera) / El celo me tortura (bolero) / Sufriendoypenando (ranchera) / Los frijoles bailan (polka) / Copas de placer (ranchera) / El circo (polka) / Amores que van y vienen (ranchera) / Atotonilco (polka) / Todo lo conciento (ranchera) / Anita (polka) / Dos lindas palomitas (ranchera) / Mis brazos te esperan (ranchera) / Paloma negra (ranchera) / Ana rosa (polka) / Tantas mentiras (ranchera) / Una cualquiera (ranchera) / Perdi el albur (ranchera)
ARHCD 362 / Apr '95 / Arhoolie

☐ ES MI DERECHO
ROUCD 6066 / Jun '95 / Rounder

De Lange, Andre

☐ WORTH THE WAIT
EXCDP 16 / 1 Sep '97 / Expansion

De Lay, Paul

☐ NICE AND STRONG (De Lay, Paul Band)
Over and done / Fourteen dollars in the bank / Too old to scold / Love on a roll / She doesn't work that way / I'm gonna miss talkin' to you / Nice and strong / What do you want in a man / I know you got another man / Come on with it / Punchy
ECD 26091 / 3 Feb '98 / Evidence

☐ OCEAN OF TEARS
Bottom line / Don't shame me / Ocean of tears / Maybe our luck will change / Hopefully / If she is / Slip, stumble, fall / What went wrong / Stop your groanin' / I win
ECD 260792 / Oct '96 / Evidence

☐ TAKE IT FROM THE TURNAROUND
Merry way / Ain't that right / Other one / Great round world / Chalk and roll / Silly smile / Why can't you love me / Every woman I get / Oat bran / Worn out shoe / Second hand smoke / I can't quit you no / No use worryin' / What's the big idea / I missed you bad / Don't feel nothin' / Lou's blues / Just this one / Prisoner's song
ECD 260762 / Apr '96 / Evidence

De Lucia, Paco

☐ ANTOLOGIA
Almoraima / Cancion de amor / Gloria al Nino Ricardo / Solo quiero caminar / Punta umbria / Rio ancho / Danza ritual del fuego / Compadres / Fuente y caudal / Casilda / Cepa Andaluza / Rumba improvisada
5284212 / Apr '96 / Mercury

☐ LIVE IN AMERICA (De Lucia, Paco Sextet)
Mi nino curro / La barrosa / Alcazar de Sevilla / Peroche / Tio sabas / Soniquete / Zyryab / Buana buana King Kong
5188092 / Mar '93 / Philips

☐ LUZIA
Rio de la Miel / La villa Vieja / Calle municion / Me regale / Luzia / Manteca colora / El chorruelo / Cameron
5581652 / 1 Jun '98 / Mercury

☐ ZYRYAB
8467072 / Jan '93 / Phonogram

De Marcos, Juan

☐ A TODA CUBA LE GUSTA (De Marcos, Juan Afro Cuban All Stars)
Amor verdadero / Alto songo / Habana del este / A toda cuba le gusta / Fiesta de la rumba / Los sitio' asere / Pio mentiroso / Maria Caracoles / Clasiqueando con Ruben / Elube chango
WCD 047 / Mar '97 / World Circuit

De Mbanga, Labiro

☐ NDINGA MAN CONTRE-ATTAQUE : NA WOU GO PAY (Protest Songs From Cameroon)
LBLC 2506 / Jan '93 / Indigo

De Melo, Armenio

☐ SPIRIT OF FADO, A (De Melo, Armenio & Jose Maria Nobrega)
PS 65705 / Feb '93 / PlayaSound

De Might Trini

☐ STILL THE BEST
JWCD 148 / Mar '98 / JW

De Moor, Vincent

☐ ORION CITY
ZYX 204522 / 29 Jun '98 / ZYX

De Moron, Bernabe

☐ FLAMENCO ESPANOLA
TCD 1020 / May '96 / Tradition

De Norte A Sur

☐ FOLKSONGS FROM VENEZUELA
EUCD 1149 / '91 / ARC

☐ INSPIRATION MEXICANA - SONGS & DANCES FROM MEXICO (De Norte A Sur & Friends)
EUCD 1196 / Sep '93 / ARC

De Palma, Victor

☐ BEGUINE/BOSSA NOVA/RUMBA (De Palma, Victor Orquesta)
9163 / Oct '96 / Divusca

☐ CHA CHA CHA/CALYPSO/MAMBO (De Palma, Victor Orquesta)
9161 / Oct '96 / Divusca

☐ COME DANCING (De Palma, Victor & His Orchestra)
CDSGP 060 / Oct '93 / Prestige

☐ SAMBA (De Palma, Victor Orquesta)
9166 / Oct '96 / Divusca

☐ SLOW/SWING/FOXTROT (De Palma, Victor Orquesta)
9162 / Oct '96 / Divusca

De Paris, Wilbur

☐ DOCTOR JAZZ VOL.7 (De Paris, Wilbur & His Rampart Street Ramblers)
STCD 6047 / Jul '96 / Storyville

De Paul, Lynsey

☐ BEST OF LYNSEY DE PAUL, THE
Sugar me / Rock bottom / Won't somebody dance with me / All night / Getting a drag / If I don't get you the next one will / Brandy / Storm in a teacup / Rockadile / Just visiting / Sleeping blue nights / Way it goes / Blind leading the blind / Water / So good to you / Fur immer
12842 / Nov '96 / Laserlight

☐ LYNSEY DE PAUL
Sugar me / Getting a drag / Words don't mean a thing / We got love / Storm in a teacup / (Dancing) on a Saturday night / Just a little time / Instant love / Now and then / Won't somebody dance with me / Sugar me / Getting a drag
QED 128 / Nov '96 / Tring

De Paula, Borba

☐ AS MELHORES
ATR 21211 / 12 May '98 / Atracao

De Phazz

☐ DETUNIZED GRAVITY
MOLECD 0072 / 2 Feb '98 / Mole

De Ridder, Willem

☐ SNUFF (De Ridder, Willem & Hafler Trio)
SPL 2 / Oct '95 / Touch

De Sa, Sandra

☐ ENTRE NOS
ML 51018 / 14 Apr '98 / Musica Latina

De Shelter, Jacque

☐ SHOUT IT LOUD
Can't stop talking / I walk by faith / All things are possible / Everything that has breath / Love you so much / Step by step (oh God you are my god) / Where you lead me / Shout it loud / Who shall seperate us / We have come / Let the rain of your presence / Even now / Only you
12952 / May '98 / Hosanna

De Souza, Dennis

☐ CARIBBEAN PARADISE
CSS 009 / 17 Nov '97 / Coral

De Souza, Raul

☐ 20 PREFERIDAS
55022 / 12 May '98 / RGE

De Trebert, Irene

☐ MADEMOISELLE SWING 1938-1946 (2CD Set)
FA 056 / Jan '97 / Fremeaux

De Utrera, Pitine

☐ GUITARRA FLAMENCA
ARN 64237 / Jun '93 / Arion

De Ville, Willy

☐ BEST OF WILLY DE VILLE, THE
3018902 / Jan '97 / Wotre Music

☐ BIG EASY FANTASY
122151 / Jan '96 / Wotre Music

☐ MIRACLE
Due to gun control / Could you would you / Heart and soul / Assassin of love / Spanish Jack / Storybook love / Southern politician / Angel eyes / Miracle
RVCD 41 / Nov '94 / Raven

☐ VICTORY MIXTURE
Hello my lover / It do me good / Key to my heart / Beating like a tom tom / Every dog has its day / Big blue diamonds / Teasin' you / Ruler of my heart / Who shot the la la / Junkers blues
652304 / Mar '95 / New Rose

De Vit, Tony

☐ TONY DE VIT LIVE IN TOKYO (Various Artists)
GU 005CD / 6 Oct '97 / Boxed

De Wilde, Laurent

☐ BACK BURNER, THE
Yesterdays / Basame mucho / Late bloomer / What is this thing called love / Lost / Gallop's gallop / You've changed / Ba-Lue Bolivar Ba-Lues-Are
4807842 / Apr '96 / Sony Jazz

☐ SPOON-A-RHYTHM
Edward K / Relaxin' at Camarillo / Fathers / 'Round midnight / Spoon-a-rhythm / Invitation / Tune for T / Totem / Live and Dyrek / So long Barney
4872532 / May '97 / Sony Jazz

De Zes, Winden

☐ SAX SEXTET - MAN MET MUTS
BVHAASTCD 9004 / Dec '87 / Bvhaast

Deacon Blue

☐ OUR TOWN (Greatest Hits Of Deacon Blue)
Dignity / Wages day / Real gone kid / Your swaying arms / Fergus sings the blues / I was right and you were wrong / Chocolate girl / I'll never fall in love again / When will you (make my telephone ring) / Twist and shout / Your town / Queen of the new year / Only tender love / Cover from the sky / Love and regret / Beautiful stranger / Will we be lovers / Loaded / Bound to love / Still in the mood
4766422 / Apr '94 / Columbia

☐ RAINTOWN
Born in a storm / Raintown / Ragman / He looks like Spencer Tracy now / Loaded / When will you (make my telephone ring) / Chocolate girl / Dignity / Very thing / Love's great fears / Town to be blamed / Riches / Kings of the Western world / Shifting sands / Suffering / Ribbons and bows / Angeliou / Just like boys
4505492 / 27 Jul '98 / Columbia

☐ RICHES AND MORE
Which side are you on / Kings of the western world / Angeliou / Just like boys / Riches / Church / Shifting sand / Suffering / Ribbons and bows / Dignity / I'll never fall in love again / Look of love / Are you there / Message to Michael
4871472 / Feb '97 / Columbia

☐ WHEN THE WORLD KNOWS YOUR NAME
Queen of the New Year / Real gone kid / Circus lights / Sad loved girl / Hundred things / Silhouette / Wages day / Love and regret / This changing light / Fergus sings the blues / Orphans / World is lit by lightning
4633212 / 27 Jul '98 / Columbia

Dead And Gone

☐ GOD LOVES EVERYONE BUT YOU
VIRUS 191CD / Jan '97 / Alternative Tentacles

Dead Beat

☐ FILE UNDER FUCK
LF 134MCD / May '95 / Lost & Found

Dead Boys

☐ ALL THIS AND MORE (2CD Set)
BCD 4066 / 10 Aug '98 / Bomp

☐ NIGHT OF THE LIVING DEAD BOYS
Detention home / Caught with the meat in your mouth / Kill this and more / 3rd generation nation / Tell me / Catholic boy / Won't look back / Ain't it fun / What love is / Ain't nothin' to do / I need lunch / Sonic reducer / Route 66 / Hang on sloopy / It's all over now / Ain't it fun / Sonic reducer
BCD 4017 / Mar '94 / Bomp

☐ TWISTIN' ON THE DEVIL'S FORK
BA 1121CD / 10 Nov '97 / Bacchus Archives

☐ YOUNGER, LOUDER AND SNOTTIER
BCD 4064 / Jun '97 / Bomp

Dead C

☐ HARSH 70'S REALITY
SB 1112 / 13 Apr '98 / Siltbreeze

☐ REPENT
SB 66 / Feb '97 / Siltbreeze

☐ TRAPDOOR FUCKING EXIT
Heaven / Hell is now love / Mighty / Power / Bury / Bury (refutation, omnium, haeresium) / Sky / Bone / Krossed / Calling slowly / Helen said this / Acoustico
SB 021 / Feb '97 / Siltbreeze

☐ TUSK
SB 64 / 27 Oct '97 / Siltbreeze

☐ WHITE HOUSE, THE
Voodoo spell / New snow / Your hand / (PROCHAM) / Bitcher / Outside
SB 402 / Aug '95 / Matador

Dead Can Dance

☐ AION
Arrival and the reunion / Mephisto / Fortune presents gifts not according / End of words / Wilderness / Garden of Zephirus / Saltarello / Song of Sibyl / As the bell rings the Maypole sign / Black sun / Promised womb / Radharc
CAD 0007CD / Apr '90 / 4AD

☐ DEAD CAN DANCE
Fatal impact / Trial / Frontier / Fortune / Ocean / East of Eden / Threshold / Passage in time / Wild in the woods / Musica eternal
CAD 404 CD / Feb '87 / 4AD

☐ INTO THE LABRYNTH
Yulunga (spirit dance) / Ubiquitous mr lovegrove / Wind that shakes the barley / Carnival is over / Ariadne / Saldek / Towards the within / Bird / Tell me about the forest (you once called home) / Spider's stratagem / Spirit / Emmeleia / How fortunate the man with none
CAD 3013CD / Jun '93 / 4AD

☐ PASSAGE IN TIME, A
Saltarello / Song of sophia / Ullyses / Cantara / Garden of zephirus / Engima of the absolute / Wilderness / Ost of seraphim / Anywhere out of the world / Writing on my fathers hand / Severance / Song of the sybil (traditional verson. catalan. 16th ce / Fortune presents gifts not according to the book / In the kingdom of the blind the one-eyed are kings / Bird / Spirit
CAD 1010CD / Oct '91 / 4AD

☐ SERPENTS EGG, THE
Host of Seraphim / Orbis de ignis / Severance / Writing on my father's hand / In the kingdom of the blind / Chant of the paladin / Song of Sophia / Echolalia / Mother tongue / Ulysses
CAD 808CD / Oct '88 / 4AD

☐ SPIRITCHASER
Nierika / Song of the stars / Indus / Song of the disposessed / Dedicace outo / Snake and the moon / Song of the nile / Devorzhum
CAD 6008CD / Jun '96 / 4AD

☐ SPLEEN AND IDEAL
This tide / De profundis / Ascension / Circumradiant dawn / Cardinal sin / Mesmerism / Enigma of the absolute / Advent / Abatar / Indoctrination / Out of the depth of sorrow / Design for living
CAD 512CD / Jan '86 / 4AD

☐ TOWARD THE WITHIN
Rakim / Persian love song / Desert song / Yulunga (spirit dance) / Piece for solo flute / Wind that shakes the barley / I am stretched on your grave / I can see now / American dreaming / Cantara / Oman / Song of the sibyl / Tristan / Sanvean / Don't fade away
DAD 4015CD / Oct '94 / 4AD

☐ TRIBUTE TO DEAD CAN DANCE, A (Various Artists)
CLP 0131 / 2 Feb '98 / Cleopatra

☐ WITHIN THE REALM OF A DYING SUN
Anywhere out of the world / Windfall / In the wake of adversity / Xavier / Dawn of the iconoclast / Cantara / Summoning up the muse / Persphone (the gathering of flowers)
CAD 705CD / Jul '87 / 4AD

Dead Famous People

☐ ALL HAIL THE DAFFODIL
LADIDA 016CD / Jul '94 / La-Di-Da

Dead Flowers

☐ ALTERED STATE CIRCUS
Elephant's eye was eerie / Altered state circus / Warm within - chemical binolculas / Slough factor 9 / Full fist / Free the weed / Vodaphone in Oz
DELECCD 022 / Oct '94 / Delerium

☐ SMELL THE FRAGRANCE
Absolution / Drowning / Jesus toy / Piece of sky / So far gone / Can't understand / Swimming around / Manic depression / Third eye shades / Crack down / Our tabs
CDRUNE 002 / Oct '93 / Mystic Stones

Dead Fly Boy

☐ DEAD FLY BOY
SECT2 1001 / Jul '95 / Sector 2

Dead Fucking Last

☐ GRATEFUL
Alien/We are the dead / 300lb mushroom / Leave me alone / Grateful song / You and me / Live 4 today / Short breath / Retribution / All in your head / Four twenty / You can't make me / Help wanted / Ought to be a law / 14 acre mosh / Camel toe / Powerless / Alcohol/Autumn's fall
64932 / Apr '97 / Epitaph

☐ PROUD TO BE
864532 / Aug '95 / Epitaph

Dead Kennedys

☐ BEDTIME FOR DEMOCRACY
Take this job and shove it / Hop with the jet set / Dear abby / Rambozo the clown / Fleshdunce / Great wall / Shrink / Triumph of the swill / Macho insecurity / I spy / Cesspools in eden / One-way ticket to pluto / Do the slag / A commercial / Gone with my wind / Anarchy for sale / Chickenshit conformist / Where do ya draw the line / Potshot heard round the world / D.m.s.o. / Lie detector
VIRUS 50CD / 22 Jun '98 / Alternative Tentacles

☐ FRANKENCHRIST
Soup is good food / Hellnation / This could be anywhere (this could be everywhere) / A growing boy needs his lunch / Chicken farm / Macho-rama / Goons of hazzard / Mtv-get off the air / At my job / Stars and stripes of corruption
VIRUS 45CD / 22 Jun '98 / Alternative Tentacles

☐ FRESH FRUIT FOR ROTTING VEGETABLES
Kill the poor / Forward to death / When ya get drafted / Let's lynch the landlord / Drug me / Your emotions / Chemical warfare / California uber alles / I kill children / Stealing people's mail / Funland at the beach / Ill in the head / Holiday in Cambodia / Viva Las Vegas
VIRUS 1CD / '88 / Alternative Tentacles
CDBRED 10 / Mar '95 / Cherry Red

☐ GIVE ME CONVENIENCE OR GIVE ME DEATH
VIRUS 57CD / Sep '87 / Alternative Tentacles

☐ PLASTIC SURGERY DISASTERS
Government flu / Terminal preppie / Trust your mechanic / Well paid scientist / Buzzbomb / Forest fire / Halloween / Winnebago warrior / Riot / Bleed for me / I am the owl / Dead end / Moon over marin / In God we trust
VIRUS 27CD / Mar '92 / Alternative Tentacles

☐ PLASTIC SURGERY DISASTERS/IN GOD WE TRUST INC.
Government flu / Terminal preppie / Trust your mechanic / Well paid scientist / Buzzbomb / Forest fire / Halloween / Winnebago warrior / Riot / Bleed for me / I am the owl / Dead end / Moon over Marin / Religious vomit / Moral majority / Hyperactive child / Kepone factory / Dog bite / We've got a bigger problem now / Nazi punks fuck off / Rawhide
VIRUS 627CD / 22 Jun '98 / Alternative Tentacles

☐ VIRUS 100 (Dead Kennedy's Cover Versions Album) (Various Artists)
Ill in the head: *Victim's Family* / Saturday night holocaust: *Neurosis* / Police truck: *Didjits* / Winnebago warrior: *Nixon, Mojo* / Too drunk to fuck: *Johns, Evan* / California uber alles: *Disposable Heroes Of Hiphoprisy* / Forward to death: *No Means No* / Halloween: *Alice Donut*
VIRUS 100CD / Mar '92 / Alternative Tentacles

Dead Man Ray

☐ BERCHEM
HH 98008 / 11 May '98 / Heaven Hotel

Dead Man's Curve

☐ WORLD CATASTROPHE GENERATOR
GORGD 002 / Mar '98 / Gorgeous

Dead Man's Shadow

☐ 4P'S, THE
GET 22CD / 11 Nov '97 / Get Back

Dead Milkmen

☐ BIG LIZARD ON MY BACK
720542 / 16 Mar '98 / Restless

Dead Moon

☐ HARD WIRED (Live)(2CD Set)
MM 067CD
MM 067DCD / 11 Aug '97 / Music Maniac

☐ HARD WIRED IN LJUBLJANA (CD/CD-Rom Set)
MMCD 067
MMCD 06768 / Jul '97 / Music Maniac

Dead Mould
☐ POLYMOG
Hit / Almost natural / Drape / Screwball / Second half / Through the lungs / What it takes / Tall / Big muff / Diggin' a hole
SPV 08545872 / Jan '97 / SPV

Dead Or Alive
☐ MAD, BAD AND DANGEROUS TO KNOW
Brand new lover / I'll save you all my kisses / Son of a gun / Then there was you / Come inside / Something in my house / Hooked on love / I want you / Special star
4655742 / Mar '97 / Epic

☐ YOUTHQUAKE
You spin me round / I wanna be a toy / DJ hit that button / In too deep / Big daddy of the rhythm / Cake and eat it / Lover come back to me / My heart goes bang / It's been a long time / Lover come back to me (extended mix)
4778532 / Oct '94 / Epic

Dead Orchestra
☐ SOUNDS LIKE TIME TASTES
MASSCD 064 / Aug '95 / Massacre

Dead Reckoners
☐ NIGHT OF RECKONING, A
Intro / I desire fire / Cryin' for nothing / You tell me / Rocky road / Workin' on it / Always will / Waiting for the assassin / Pearl earrings / Too much love / When we're gone, long gone / Outro
DR 00072 / Dec '97 / Dead Reckoning

Dead Ringer Band
☐ HOME FIRES
Home fires / More about love / Always be me / Australian son / Honky tonk from hell / I'd go home if I had one / Why / Family man / Burning flame / Just wanted to see you so bad / Sin city / Guitar talk / Gypsy bound
FIENDCD 798 / Aug '97 / Demon

☐ RED DESERT SKY
LARRCD 302 / Nov '94 / Larrikin

Dead Voices On Air
☐ FIRE IN THE BRONX ZOO, A (Dead Voices On Air & Not Breathing)
INV 096CD / 26 Aug '97 / Invisible

☐ PISS FROND
INV 120CD / 3 Aug '98 / Invisible

Dead World
☐ MACHINE, THE
NB 0892 / Jan '94 / Nuclear Blast

Dead Youth
☐ INTENSE BRUTALITY
GCI 9800 / Jun '92 / Plastic Head

Deadbolt
☐ TIJUANA HIT SQUAD
HED 059 / Oct '96 / Headhunter

☐ ZULU DEATH MASK
CDHED 074 / 8 Jun '98 / Headhunter

Deadcats
☐ BUCKET O' LOVE
FLY 1001 / Jun '96 / Flying Saucer

Deadfall
☐ CUT LOOSE HOWLING
41287CD / 23 Mar '98 / V&V

Deadguy
☐ FIXATION ON A CO WORKER
VR 030 / Jan '96 / Victory Europe

Deadline
☐ DOWN BY LAW
Makossa rock / Gammatron / Doo root / Afro beat / Boat peoples / Baliphone dub
CPCD 8192 / Jun '96 / Charly

Deadly Nighshades
☐ DEADLY NIGHTSHADES, THE
Totally female / Monster / Love blackmailer / James / That song / Vampire / Train / Who's that living next door / Nocturnal / Stray cats / Red turns to brown / Twilight
HOT 1051 / Feb '96 / Hot

Deadspot
☐ ADIOS DUDE
Addiction / Right through you / Inside / Deadspot / Friday night in hell / This means war / Power tool / Another day / My death / Jesus is my best friend
HMRXD 149 / May '90 / Heavy Metal

Deadstock
☐ DEADSTOCK
Monophonic man / Suite 303 / Oedipus sucks / Nobody / Fold unfold fold / Six sided something
TRUCD 12 / Nov '96 / Internal

Deaf Heights Cajun Aces
☐ LES FLAMMES D'ENFER
Les flames d'enfer / Madame Edourarde / New pinegrove blues / Grand Mamou / Moi et mon cousin / La danse de la limonade / Bosco strip / Bayou pom pom / Colinda / La robe barree / Allons a Lafayette / 'Tit galop pour Mamou / Hackberry zydeco
COMD 2025 / Jul '98 / Temple

Deaf Shepherd
☐ SPARK O' NATURES FIRE, A
Gie's a drink / Waltzes / Minister's set / Logan braes / New Pa / Finbarr / Ah surely / Peggy Gordon / Double pipe set / Lost for words at sea / Foreign set
CDTRAX 104 / Mar '96 / Greentrax

☐ SYNERGY
Jean Carignan / Strathspeys / Winter o' life / First light / Pawkie Paiterson / Father John / Weepers I shall wear / Reverend's revenge / Huntin' the buntin' / Clanranald / Coarncraik / Keys money fags
CDTRAX 143 / 1 Dec '97 / Greentrax

Deal, Bill
☐ BEST OF BILL DEAL AND THE RHONDELS (Deal, Bill & The Rhondells)
I've been hurt / What kind of fool do you think I am / May I / Are you ready for this / Can I change my mind / Words / Touch me / I've gotta be me / Soulful strut / It's too late / Everybody's got something to hide / Nothing succeeds like success / Swinging tight / I'm gonna make you love me / I've got my needs / Harlem shuffle / River deep, mountain high / Hooked on a feeling / Hey bulldog / Tuck's theme / So what if it rains / I live in the night
NEMCD 644 / Apr '94 / Sequel

Deal, Kelley
☐ BOOM BOOM BOOM (Deal, Kelley 6000)
Brillo hunt / Shag / My boyfriend died / Baby I'm king / When he calls me kitten / Box / Stripper / Where did the home team go / Total war / Scary / Future boy / Drum solo / Skylark / Confidence girl / Get the writing off my back
BIAS 361CD / 10 Nov '97 / Play It Again Sam

Deals Gone Bad
☐ LARGE AND IN CHARGE
JUMP 015 / 16 Mar '98 / Jump Up

Dean Brothers
☐ CHANCE TO DANCE VOL.1, A
MTNCD 003 / Jan '97 / Milltown
DVCD 004 / Sep '97 / Deansville

☐ CHANCE TO DANCE VOL.2, A
DVCD 005 / Sep '97 / Deansville

☐ FAMILY ALBUM, THE (2CD Set)
DVCD 008 / Nov '97 / Deansville

☐ LET'S DANCE
DVCD 009 / Mar '98 / Deansville

☐ ON THE RIGHT TRACKS
DVCD 003 / Sep '97 / Deansville

☐ SAME TRAIN DIFFERENT TRACK
DVCD 002 / Jun '97 / Deansville

☐ WILD WEST HERO
DVCD 007 / Nov '97 / Deansville

Dean Close School Chapel Choir
☐ MICHAELMAS TO WHITSUNTIDE
Sing lullaby / And there were shepherds / Break forth / Lo now we count them blessed / Miserere mei / Three kings / When to the temple Mary went / Spirit of the Lord / Little road to Bethlehem / Crucifixus / I waited for the Lord / Ascendit Deus / Tibi Christe / Beata nobis gaudia / Haec dies / Caelos ascendit hodie / Wash me throughly / Alleluia, a new work / Strife is o'er
CDPS 405 / '91 / Alpha

Dean, Elton
☐ ALL THE TRADITION (Dean, Elton & Howard Riley Quartet)
Darn that dream / Longest day / Crescent / Convivial convocation / I remember Clifford
SLAMCD 201 / Apr '91 / Slam

☐ ELTON DEAN & HIS UNLIMITED SAXOPHONE COMPANY
OGCD 002 / Oct '92 / Ogun

☐ IF DUBOIS ONLY KNEW (Dean, Elton & Paul Dunmall)
See the melody / Janet and Corina / Wide asleep / If dubois only knew / That's your plot / Deep awake / Lomu / Tale of two horns
BP 194CD / 6 Oct '97 / Blueprint

☐ NEWSENSE
SLAMCD 229 / Jun '98 / Slam

☐ RUMOURS OF AN INCIDENT (Dean, Elton Quartet & Roswell Rudd)
SLAMCD 223 / May '97 / Slam

☐ TWO'S AND THREE'S
He who dares / PR Department / Uprising / Reconciliation / KT / Riolity / Duke
BP 167CD / Jul '97 / Blueprint

☐ VORTEX TAPES, THE
Second thoughts / First impressions / Going fourth / Third time lucky / Taking the fifth
SLAMCD 203 / Oct '96 / Slam

Dean, Graham
☐ GRAHAM DEAN QUARTET, THE
GFD 001 / Jun '94 / Scorpio

Dean, Hazell
☐ GREATEST HITS
Searchin' / Whatever I do (wherever I go) / Evergreen / Jealous love / Back in my arms once again / They say it's gonna rain / Turn it into love / You're too good to be true / Who's leaving who / Maybe (we should call it a day) / No fool (for love) / Ain't nothing like the real thing: *Dean, Hazell & Daryl Pandy* / Searchin'/ Whatever I do/Stand up / Who's leaving who (Bobs tambourine mix)
CDGOLD 1023 / May '96 / EMI Gold

Dean, Jimmy
☐ BIG BAD JOHN
Big bad John / I won't go huntin' with you Jake / Smoke, smoke, smoke / Dear Ivan / To a sleeping beauty / Cajun Queen / PT 109 / Walk on boy / Little bitty big John / Steel man / Little black book / Please pass the biscuits / Gonna raise a ruckus tonight / Day that changed the world / Gotta travel on / Sixteen tons / Oklahoma Bill / Night train to Memphis / Make the waterwheel roll / Lonesome road / Grasshopper MacClean / Old Pappy's new banjo / You're nobody 'til somebody loves you / Cajun Joe / Nobody / Kentucky means paradise
BCD 15723 / Jul '93 / Bear Family

☐ INSPIRATIONAL SMASHES
CRB 77930 / 2 Feb '98 / Curb

Dean/Riley
☐ DECREASING CIRCLES
BP 221CD / Oct '96 / Blueprint

Deanta
☐ DEANTA
Flight of the termite / Green fields of canada / King of the blues / Cold grey fairyland / Willie taylor / Harp airs / Thousands are sailing / Gravelley groove / Dark iniseoghain
GLCD 1126 / May '93 / Green Linnet

☐ READY FOR THE STORM
GL 1147CD / Oct '94 / Green Linnet

☐ WHISPER OF A SECRET
Two days to go / Willie and Mary / Usual suspects / Paddy and the bandit / Lone shanakyle / Waltz of the white lilies / At the crossroads / Blacksmith / Cogair ruin / Druid's mountain / Where are you / Scarta Glen road
GLCD 1173 / Jun '97 / Green Linnet

Dear Janes
☐ NO SKIN
TRACD 107 / Apr '96 / Transatlantic

☐ SOMETIMES I
Girl of your dreams / Niagara tears / Brides of the cross / Dear Jane / Air traffic / Sometimes I / Outside my window / My guilty hand / Some small corner / Jesus put me down / I'm heading home / PMP
TRACD 104 / Feb '95 / Transatlantic

Dearie, Blossom
☐ BLOSSOM DEARIE - VOCAL CLASSICS
'Deed I do / Lover man / Everything I've got / Comment allez vous / More than you know / Thou swell / It might as well be Spring / Tout doucement / You for me / Now at last / I hear music / Wait till you see her / I won't dance / Fine Spring morning / They say it's Spring / Johnny one note / Blossom's blues
8379342 / Feb '93 / Verve

☐ BLOSSOM TIME AT RONNIE SCOTT'S
On Broadway / When the world was young / When in Rome / Shadow of your smile / Everything I've got belongs to you / Once upon a Summertime / I'm hip / Mad about the boy / Shape of things / Satin doll
5586832 / 3 Aug '98 / Redial

☐ CHRISTMAS SPICE, IT'S SO NICE
CHECD 00103 / '91 / Master Mix

☐ ET TU BRUCE
Bruce / Hey John / Someone's been sending me flowers / You have lived in autumn / Alice in Wonderland / Satin doll / Riviera / Inside a silent tear
CDCHE 5 / Aug '89 / Master Mix

☐ GIVE HIM THE OOH LA LA
Just one of those things / Like someone in love / Between the devil and the deep blue sea / They say it's spring / Try your wings / Bang goes the drum (and you're in love) / Riviera / Middle of love / Plus je t'embrasse / Give him the ooh la la / Let me love you / I walk a little faster / Give him the ooh la la
5170672 / 3 Aug '98 / Verve

☐ JAZZ MASTERS
5299062 / 5 May '98 / Verve

☐ NEEDLEPOINT MAGIC
Ballad of the shape of things / Lush life / When the world was young / I'm hip / Baby, it's cold outside / I like you, you're nice / Sweet surprise / I'm shadowing you / Sweet Georgie fame / Peel me a grape / Two sleepy people
CDCHE 3 / Oct '91 / Master Mix

☐ ONCE UPON A SUMMERTIME
Tea for two / Surrey with the fringe on top / Moonlight saving time / It amazes me / If I were a bell / We're together / Teach me tonight / Once upon a summertime / Down with love / Manhattan / Doop doo de doop / Our love is here to stay
5172232 / Feb '93 / Verve

☐ SONGS OF CHELSEA
My attorney Bernie / Everything I've got / C'est Le Printemps / When in Rome / Let the flower grow / My new celebrity is you / What time is it now / You fascinate me so / There ought to be moonlight saving time / Chelsea Aire
CDCHE 2 / Jan '90 / Master Mix

☐ TWEEDLE DUM AND TWEEDLE DEE (Dearie, Blossom & Mike Renzi)
CHECD 00101 / '91 / Master Mix

☐ WINCHESTER IN APPLE BLOSSOM TIME
Spring can really hang you up the most / Sunday afternoon / Wonderful guy / To touch the hand of love / Wheelers and dealers / Jazz musician / Surrey with the fringe on top / Love is an elusive celebration / Lucky to be me / You're for loving / Summer is gone / Sammy / It amazes me / If I were a bell
CHECD 8 / '89 / Master Mix

Dearly Beheaded
☐ CHAMBER OF 1
Thankless task / Generations / Dead issue / Moment of clarity / Escape / Chamber of 1 / Giving up the lies / Faceless / Tribal convictions / Haunting your horizons
CDMFN 232 / 6 Oct '97 / Music For Nations

☐ TEMPTATION
CDMFN 203
CDMFNX 203 / Jun '96 / Music For Nations

Deason, Sean
☐ RAZORBACK
K7R 008CD / Oct '96 / Studio K7

Death
☐ SYMBOLIC
RR 89572 / Sep '96 / Roadrunner

Death Angel
☐ FROLIC THROUGH THE PARK
Third floor / Road mutants / Why you do this / Bored / Confused / Guilty of innocence / Open up / Shores of sin / Cold gin / Mind rape
7725492 / Jul '94 / Restless

☐ ULTRA-VIOLENCE
Thrashers / Evil priest / Voracious souls / Kill as one / Ultra violence / Mistress of pain / Final death / IPFS
7725482 / Jul '94 / Restless

Death Cube K
☐ DISEMBODIED
ION 2004 / 15 Sep '97 / Ion

Death In June
☐ 93 DEAD SUNWHEELS
BADVCCD 93 / Oct '96 / New European

☐ BLACK WHOLE OF LOVE BOX SET
BADVC 39 / Oct '96 / New European

☐ BURIAL
UBADVCCD 4 / Oct '96 / New European

☐ BUT WHAT ENDS WHEN THE SYMBOLS SHATTER
Death is the martyr of beauty / He's disabled / Mourner's bench / Because of him / Daedalus rising / Little black angel / Golden wedding of sorrow / Giddy edge of light / Ku ku ku / This is not paradise / Hollows of devotion / But what ends when the symbols shatter
BADVCCD 36 / Oct '97 / New European

☐ CATHEDRAL OF TEARS, THE
BADVCCD 34 / Oct '96 / New European

☐ CORN YEARS, THE
Heiligel / Torture by roses / Love murder / Zimmerit / We are the lust / To drown a rose / Break the black ice / Behind the rose / Punishment initiation / Rocking horse night / Break the black ice / Runes and men / Rule again / Hail the white grain / Blood of winter / Fog of the world / Europa / Gates of heaven / Come before Christ and murder love
BADVCCD 7 / Oct '97 / New European

☐ DEATH IN JUNE PRESENT OCCIDENTAL MARTYR
NERO 8CD / Oct '96 / Twilight Command

☐ DEATH IN JUNE PRESENTS KAPO
NERO 13CD / Jan '97 / Twilight Command

☐ GUILTY HAVE NO PAST, THE
BADVCCD 3 / Jan '90 / New European

☐ NADA
BADVCCD 13 / Jan '90 / New European

☐ OSTENBRAUN
SD 01 / Oct '96 / New European

☐ PARADISE RISING
BADVCCD 63 / Oct '96 / New European

☐ ROSE CLOUDS OF HOLOCAUST
Lord winter / God's golden sperm / Omen filled season / Symbols of the sun / Jerusalem / Black / Luther's army / 13 years of carrion / Accidental protege / Rose clouds of holocaust / Lifebooks
BADVCCD 38 / Oct '97 / New European

☐ SCORPION WIND - HEAVEN SENT
NERO 39CD / Oct '96 / Twilight Command

☐ SOMETHING IS COMING (Death In June Live)
Death is the martyr of beauty / Hullo angel / Giddy giddy carousel / Hollows of devotion / Rocking horse night / He's disabled / Fall apart / Heaven Street / Break the black ice / Leper lord / Golden wedding of sorrow / Torture by roses / Little black angel / But what ends when the symbols shatter / Fields of rape / Ku ku ku / Giddy giddy carousel / Runes and men / Golden wedding of sorrow / Death is the martyr of beauty
BADVCCD 96 / Oct '97 / New European

☐ WALL OF SACRIFICES, THE
BADVCCD 88 / Jan '90 / New European

Death In Vegas

☐ DEAD ELVIS
HARD 22LPCD / Jun '97 / Concrete

Death SS

☐ HEAVY DEMONS
BABEDISCCD 002 / Jul '92 / Plastic Head

Deathcore

☐ SPONTANEOUS
842976 / Sep '90 / Nuclear Blast

☐ SPONTANEOUS UNDERGROUND
NB 034CD / Oct '92 / Nuclear Blast

Deathfolk

☐ DEATHFOLK
NAR 047CD / May '93 / New Alliance

Deathline International

☐ ARASHI SYNDROME
COPCD 029 / May '97 / Cop International

Deaville, Gillman

☐ WAYS TO FLY
FF 70636 / Nov '94 / Flying Fish

DeBarge, El

☐ HEART, MIND & SOUL
Where you are / Can't get enough / Where is my love / You got the love I want / It's got to be real / Slide / I'll be there / Special lady / Starlight, moonlight, candlight / You are my dream / Heart, mind and soul
9362453752 / Jun '94 / Warner Bros.

Debriano, Santi

☐ OBEAH
FRLCD 008 / Oct '92 / Freelance

☐ PANAMANIACS (Debriano, Santi Group)
FRLCD 019 / Nov '93 / Freelance

☐ SOLDIERS OF FORTUNE
Awake at last / Plants / Soldiers of fortune / Air / Our quiet place / Morming melody / Dream research / Eventual return
FRLCD 012 / Oct '92 / Freelance

Debustrol

☐ NEUROPATOLOG
MONITOR 2 / Jan '92 / Monitor

Decameron

☐ THIRD LIGHT/TOMORROW'S PANTOMIME
Rock and roll away / All the best wishes / Strawman / Saturday / Wide as the years / Journey's end / Road to the sea / Trapeze / Ungodly / Morning glory / Deal / Fallen over / Ask me tomorrow / Tomorrow's pantomime / Shadows on the stairs / So this is God's country / Peace with honour
ESMCD 568 / Jul '97 / Essential

Decameron

☐ MY SHADOW
NFR 013CD / Jun '96 / No Fashion

Decan, Chen

☐ CHINESE FOLK MUSIC (Decan, Chen Chinese Ensemble)
EUCD 1167 / '91 / ARC

Deceased

☐ BLUEPRINTS
RR 6920CD / Dec '96 / Nuclear Blast

☐ FEARLESS UNDEAD MACHINES
Silent creature / Contamination / Fearless undead machines / From the ground they came / Night of the deceased / Graphic repulsion / Mysterious research / Beyound science / Unhuman drama / Psychic / Destiny
RR 69572 / Aug '97 / Relapse

December Band

☐ DECEMBER BAND VOL.2
BCD 198 / Dec '97 / GHB

☐ MOOSE LODGE HALL VOL.1 1965
BCD 197 / Mar '97 / GHB

December Moon

☐ SOURCE OF ORIGIN
Exhaltation of power / You can't bless the damned / Nocturnal transcendency / Winter sunset / Black millenium / Apparition of Mother Earth / Twinned with destiny / Empty gesture
SP 1032CD / 24 Nov '97 / Spinefarm

Decimator

☐ CARNAGE CITY STATE MOSH PATROL
Raider / Mutoids / F H Blood Island / CCSMP / Devil's bridge / Rogue decimator / Dustbowl / Stealer of souls
NEAT 1047D / '89 / Neat

☐ DIRTY, HOT & HUNGRY
I'll strangle you / First evening / Ophelie / Lines / To a reason / Hapolot kenym / Hunger / Sahara blue (brussels) / Amdyaz / Victim of stars / Harar et les gallas / Lettre au directeur des messageries maritimes
NEATCD 1052 / Nov '92 / Neat

Decollation

☐ CURSED LANDS
POSH 0004 / Oct '93 / Listenable

Decomposed

☐ FUNERAL OBSESSION
CYBERCD 2 / May '92 / Cybersound

☐ HOPE FINALLY DIED
CANDLE 003CD / Jan '94 / Candlelight

Decoryah

☐ BREATHING THE BLUE
398414130CD / Jun '97 / Metal Blade

☐ FALL DARK WATERS
398414111CD / Jun '96 / Metal Blade

Decree

☐ WAKE OF DEVASTATION
08543432 / Mar '97 / Westcom

Decry

☐ COMPLETE DECRY (2CD Set)
CLP 9908 / Feb '97 / Cleopatra

Dedale

☐ ALIVE FACE A
DPCD 97015 / Dec '97 / Mustradem

☐ CHRONIQUES URBAINES
DP 93009CD / Apr '94 / Mustradem

☐ LE MAITRE DHU
DP 91007CD / Apr '94 / Mustradem

☐ NO PAST
DP 9501CD / Aug '95 / Mustradem

☐ OBSESSION
DP 92008CD / Apr '94 / Mustradem

Dede, Amayke

☐ OKYENA SESEE
KO 3 / Jan '97 / Kotoko

Dedeyan, Garo

☐ GIFT OF THE GODS
WAV 1004 / Apr '97 / Wave

Dedication Orchestra

☐ IXESHA
OGCD 102/103 / Dec '94 / Ogun

☐ SPIRITS REJOICE
OGCD 101 / Feb '98 / Ogun

Dee, Brian

☐ CLIMB EVERY MOUNTAIN
I have dreamed / I should care / Your song / Pete Kelly's blues / Nuages / Koo / Instep / Day by day / You are the sunshine of my life / Uncle's friend / Triple play / I surrender Dear / How insensitive / Dream / To the shores of Tripoli / Unforgettable / Homebase / Climb every mountain
SPJCD 552 / May '95 / Spotlite

☐ SECOND SIGHT (Dee, Brian Trio)
Bruised blues / Certain smile / Dream dancing / Elba mel delba / Second sight / Seven steps to heaven / In your own sweet way / Hermitage / Promised land / More bruised blues
SPJCD 543 / May '93 / Spotlite

Dee, David

☐ GOIN' FISHIN'
Heatin' me up / Rainy night in Georgia / If I knew then / Special way of making love / Part time love / Goin' fishin' / Workin' this dream overtime / Lead me on / Thought my lovin' was over
ICH 1114CD / Oct '93 / Ichiban

Dee Jay & The Runaways

☐ PETER RABBIT
AA 067 / Sep '97 / Arf Arf

Dee, Kiki

☐ ALMOST NAKED
TB 01 / Oct '95 / Tickety Boo

☐ AMOUREUSE
Amoureuse / I got the music in me / Loving and free / (You don't know) How glad I am / Chicago / First thing in the morning / One jump ahead of the storm / Dark side of your soul / Stay with me baby / Why don't I run away from you / Runnin' out of fools / You hold me too tight / Can't take my eyes off you / On a magic carpet ride / Step by step / You need help / One step / Talk to me
5521162 / Mar '96 / Spectrum

Dee, Sonny

☐ CHICAGO - THAT'S JAZZ VOL.2 (Dee, Sonny Allstars)
Who's sorry now / My cutie's due at two to two / You're in kentucky sure as you're born / Trouble in mind / Mandy, make up your mind / Is it true what they say about Dixie / When / Mama's gone goodbye / Goodbye / Do you know what it means to miss New Orleans / Moonglow / Who cares / It's been so long / Lady's in love with you / Blue and broken hearted / Miss Annabelle Lee / Since my best gal turned me down
LACD 26 / Mar '93 / Lake

Deebank, Maurice

☐ INNER THOUGHT ZONE
Watery song / Four corners of the earth / Study No.1 / Golden hills / Silver fountain of Paradise Square / So Serene / Dance Of Deliverance / Pavanne / Tale from Scriabins lonely trail / Maestoso Con Anima
CDMRED 61 / Nov '92 / Cherry Red

Deedrah

☐ SELF OSCILLATION
Self oscillation / Blissfull blonde / Essential / Japonicus delphinus / Wizard demo / Christiana high life / Funkybootik / Alien dick / Warheads / Lion blue
SUB 48352 / 22 Sep '97 / Distance

Deee-Lite

☐ DEW DROPS IN THE GARDEN
Bring me your love / Party happening people / Say ahhh / Picnic in the summertime / River of freedom / When you told me you loved me / Call me / Sampladelic / DMT (Dance music trance) / Apple juice kissing / What is this music / Music selector is the soul reflector / Stay in bed forget the rest / Somebody / Bittersweet loving / Mind melt
7559615262 / Jul '94 / Elektra

☐ REMIX ALBUM, THE
7559618722 / Feb '97 / Elektra

☐ WORLD CLIQUE
Good beat / Power of love / Try me on...I'm very you / Smile on / What is love / World clique / ESP / Groove is in the heart / Who was that / Deep ending w/gloop / Deee-lite theme / Build the bridge
7559609572 / Sep '90 / Elektra

Deejays

☐ DIMPLES 1965-1966
CDHM 46254 / Oct '97 / HM

Deele

☐ BEST OF THE DEELE, THE
Two occasions / Shoot 'em up movies / Body talk / I surrender / Just my luck / Sexy love / You're all I've ever known / Suspicious / Material thangz / I'll send you roses / Sweet November / Let no one separate us / Can-U-dance / Dry your eyes / Crazy 'bout cha / Eyes of stranger
DEEPM 001 / Nov '96 / Deep Beats

Deems, Barrett

☐ DEEMUS
Deed I do / New Orleans / Shine / After you've gone / Seven come eleven / Six appeal / I love Paris / Get happy
DD 492 / Jul '97 / Delmark

☐ HOW D'YOU LIKE IT SO FAR
DE 472 / Dec '95 / Delmark

Deene, Carol

☐ JOHNNY GET ANGRY
Sad movies / Don't forget / Norman / On the outside looking in / Johnny get angry / Somebody's smiling / Some people / Kissin' / James (hold the ladder steady) / It happened last night / Let me do it my way / Growin' up / Want to stay here / Oh oh oh Willie / Who's been sleeping in my bed / Love is wonderful / Hard to say goodnight / Very first kiss / I can't forget someone like you / Most people do / He just don't know / Up in the penthouse / Dancing in your eyes / Please don't be unfaithful again / Time / Love not have I
GEMCD 005 / Jan '97 / Diamond

Deep Blue Something

☐ HOME
Gammer Gerten's needle / Breakfast at Tiffany's / Halo / Josey / Water prayer / Done / Song to make love to / Kadinski Prince / Home / Red light / I can wait / Wouldn't change a thing
IND 90002 / 8 Sep '97 / Interscope

Deep Dish

☐ CREAM SEPARATES VOL.1 (Mixed By Deep Dish) (Various Artists)
Never tell you: *Rhythm & Sound/Tikiman* / Rise: *Rivera, Sandy & Kings Of Tomorrow Presents* / Flirt: *Horn* / Glide by shooting: *Two Lone Swordsmen* / Fade II black: *Kot* / Love revolution: *Mysterious People* / Fly life: *Basement Jaxx* / Untitled: *Listenin' Parlour* / Gosp: *LWS* / Summer madness: *Daemyon, Jerald* / Twenty minutes of disco glory: *DJ Garth & ETI* / Tick tock: *Chia Pet* / Don't ever stop: *Dubbing Double* / Theme from the Blue Cucaracha: *Innocent* / Samba magic: *Summer Daze* / In your soul: *Latino Circus*
74321462002 / Mar '97 / De-Construction

☐ DJ'S TAKE CONTROL VOL.1 (Mixed By Deep Dish - 2CD Set) (Various Artists)
ORCD 028 / May '96 / One

☐ JUNK SCIENCE
Intro / Morning Wood / Future of the future (stay gold) / Summer's over / Mohammad is Jesus / Stranded / Junk science / Sushi / My only sin / Monsoon / Persepolis / Chocolate city (love songs) / Mohammad is Jesus (in dub) / Wear the hat
74321580342 / 15 Jun '98 / De-Construction

Deep Forest

☐ BOHEME
Anathasia / Marta's song / Gathering / Lament / Bulgarian melody / Deep folk song / Freedom cry / Twosome / Cafe europa / Katharina / Boheme
4786232 / May '95 / Columbia

☐ COMPARSA
Noonday sun / Green and blue / Madazalu / 1716 / Deep weather / Comparsa / Earthquake / Tres Maria / Radio Belize / Ekue ekue / La lune se bat avec etoiles / Forest power / Media luna
4887252 / 19 Jan '98 / Columbia

☐ DEEP FOREST
Deep forest / Sweet lullaby / Hunting / Night bird / First twilight / Savannah dance / Desert walk / White whisper / Second twilight / Sweet lullaby (mix) / Forest hymn
4741782 / Feb '94 / Columbia

Deep Freeze Mice

☐ I LOVE YOU LITTLE BOBO WITH YOUR DELICATE GOLDEN LIONS (2CD Set)
JAR 011 / Jul '97 / Jar Music

Deep Freeze Productions

☐ IF THEY MOVE KILL 'EM
Who the hell / Inda soupe / 5th dimension / Burnt sienna / Let sleeping dogs lie / Instant mayhem / Inda soupe / Beat the hell
SSRCD 002 / Apr '97 / Sureshot

Deep Purple

☐ 24 CARAT PURPLE
Woman from Tokyo / Fireball / Strange kind of woman / Never before / Black night / Speed king / Smoke on the water / Child in time
CDFA 3132 / Oct '87 / Fame

☐ ABANDON
Any fule know that / Almost human / Don't make me happy / Seventh heaven / Watching the sky / Fingers to the bone / Jack Ruby / She was / Whatsername / '69 / Evil Louie / Bludsucker
4953062 / 25 May '98 / EMI

☐ ANTHOLOGY (2CD Set)
Hush / Mandrake root / Shield / Wring that neck / Bird has flown / Bloodsucker / Speed king / Black night / Child in time / Fireball / Strange kind of woman / Highway star / Smoke on the water / Pictures of home / Woman from Tokyo / Smooth dancer / Sail away / Lay down stay down / Burn / Stormbringer / Hold on / Gypsy / Mistreated / Gettin' tighter / Love child / You keep on moving / No one came
CDEM 1374 / Mar '91 / EMI

☐ BATTLE RAGES ON, THE
Battle rages on / Lick it up / Anya / Talk about love / Time to kill / Ramshackle man / Twist in the tale / Nasty piece of work / Solitaire / One man's meat
74321154202 / Aug '95 / RCA

☐ BLACK NIGHT (A Tribute To Deep Purple) (Various Artists)
DER 092 / 24 Nov '97 / De Rock

☐ BOOK OF TALIESYN, THE
Listen, learn, read on / Wring that neck / Kentucky woman / Exposition / We can work it out / Shield / Anthem / River deep, mountain high
CZ 171 / Feb '96 / Premier/EMI

☐ BOOK OF TALIESYN, THE/SHADES OF DEEP PURPLE/DEEP PURPLE (The Originals Vol.1/3CD Set)
Listen, learn, read on / Wring that neck / Kentucky woman / Exposition / We can work it out / Shield / Anthem / River deep, mountain high / And the address / Hush / One more rainy day / Prelude / Happiness / I'm so glad / Mandrake / Root / Help / Love help me / Hey Joe / Chasing shadows / Blind / Lalena / Fault line / Painter / Why didn't Rosemary / Bird has flown / April
CDOMB 002 / 27 Jul '98 / EMI

☐ BURN
Burn / Might just take your life / Lay down stay down / Sail away / You fool no one / What's goin' on here / Mistreated / A-Zoo
CZ 203 / Jul '89 / EMI

☐ CALIFORNIA JAMMING
Burn / Might just take your life / Mistreated / Smoke on the water / Your fool no-one/The mule / Space truckin'
PRMUCD 2 / May '96 / Premier/EMI

☐ CHILD IN TIME
Nobody's home / Mean streak / Wasted sunsets / Hungry daze / Unwritten law / Mad dog / Spanish archer / Mitzi dupree / Woman from Tokyo (live) / Child in time (live) / Strange kind of woman (live) / Highway star (live)
5513392 / Aug '95 / Spectrum

☐ COLLECTION, THE
Mandrake root / Wring that neck / Living wreck / Black night / Smoke on the water / Demon's eye / Lady double dealer / Comin' home / Never before
CDGOLD 1080 / Feb '97 / EMI Gold

☐ COLLECTION, THE
Mandrake root / Wring that neck / Living wreck / Black night / Smoke on the water / Demon's eye / Lady double dealer / Comin' home / Never before
DC 878642 / Mar '97 / Disky

☐ COME HELL OR HIGH WATER
Highway star / Black night / Twist in the tale / Perfect strangers / Anyone's daughter / Child in time / Anya / Speed king / Smoke on the water
74321234162 / Feb '97 / RCA

☐ COME TASTE THE BAND
Comin' home / Lady Luck / Gettin' tighter / Dealer / I need love / Drifter / Love child / This time around / Owed to 'G' / You keep on moving
CDFA 3318 / Jul '95 / Fame

☐ CONCERTO FOR GROUP AND ORCHESTRA
Wring that neck / Child in time / Moderato - allegro: First movement / Andante: Second movement / Vivace - presto: Third movement
CZ 342 / Jul '90 / EMI

☐ DEEP PURPLE
Chasing shadows / Blind / Lalena / Fault line / Painter / Why didn't Rosemary / Bird has flown / April part 1
CDFA 3317 / Apr '95 / Fame

☐ DEEP PURPLE FAMILY ALBUM, THE (Various Artists)
If you've gotta pick a baby: *Collins, Glenda & The Outlaws* / You'll never stop me loving you: *MI5* / I take what I want: *Artwoods* / I can see through you: *Episode Six* / Hush: *Deep Purple* / Snowbound: *Mouson, Alphonse* / Black night: *Deep Purple* / Into the fire: *Deep Purple* / Burn: *Deep Purple* / Love is all: *Glover, Roger & Guests* / You keep on moving: *Deep Purple* / Kill the king: *Rainbow* / Arabella: *Paice, Ashton, Lord* / Northwinds: *Whitesnake* / LA cutoff: *Hughes, Glenn* / Stallion: *Simper, Nick* / Nervous: *Gillan* / Clouds and rain: *Gillan & Glover* / Perfect strangers: *Deep Purple*
VSOPCD 187 / May '93 / Connoisseur Collection

☐ DEEPEST PURPLE
Black night / Speed king / Fireball / Strange kind of woman / Child in time / Woman from Tokyo / Highway star / Space truckin' / Burn / Demon's eye / Stormbringer / Smoke on the water
CDFA 3239 / Jul '90 / Fame

☐ FINAL CONCERTS, THE (Deep Purple Mark 3) (2CD Set)
DPVSOPCD 230 / Jul '96 / Connoisseur Collection

☐ FIREBALL
Fireball / No, no, no / Demon's eye / Mule / Fools / No one came / Anyone's daughter
CZ 30 / Jan '88 / EMI

☐ FIREBALL (25th Anniversary Edition)
Fireball / No no no / Demon's eye / Anyone's daughter / Mule / Fools / No one came / Strange kind of woman / I'm alone / Freedom / Slow train / Demon's eye / Midnight in Moscow / Robin Hood / William Tell / Fireball (take 1) / Piano insert / No one came
CDDEEPP 2 / Sep '96 / EMI

☐ GEMINI SUITE LIVE, THE
Guitar/Voice / Organ/Bass / Drums/Finale
RPM 114 / Jul '93 / RPM

☐ GEMINI SUITE LIVE, THE
CLEO 2342 / 12 May '98 / Cleopatra

☐ GREEN BULLFROG SESSIONS, THE (Green Bullfrog)
My baby left me / Makin' time / Lawdy Miss Clawdy / Bullfrog / I want you / I'm a free man / Walk a mile in my shoes / Lovin' you is good for me baby / Who do you love / Ain't nobody home / Louisiana man
NSPCD 503 / Nov '91 / Connoisseur Collection

☐ HOUSE OF BLUE LIGHT
Bad attitude / Unwritten law / Call of the wild / Mad dog / Black and white / Hard lovin' woman / Spanish archer / Strangeways / Mitzi dupree / Dead or alive
8313182 / Jan '87 / Polydor

☐ IN ROCK (25th Anniversary Edition)
Speed king / Blood sucker / Child in time / Flight of the rat / Into the fire / Living wreck / Hard lovin' man / Black night / Studio chat 1 / Speed king / Studio chat 2 / Cry free / Studio chat 3 / Jam stew / Studio chat 4 / Flight of the rat / Studio chat 5 / Woffle and speed king / Studio chat 6 / Black night
CDDEEPP 1 / Jun '95 / Harvest

☐ IN THE ABSENCE OF PINK (Knebworth 1985) (2CD Set)
Highway star / Nobody's home / Strange kind of woman / Gypsy's kiss / Perfect strangers / Lazy / Knocking at your back door / Space truckin' / Difficult to cure / Speed king / Black night / Smoke on the water
DPVSOPCD 163 / Jun '91 / Connoisseur Collection

☐ INTERVIEW PICTURE DISC
CBAK 4054 / Apr '92 / Baktabak

☐ KNOCKING AT YOUR BACK DOOR
Knocking at your back door / Bad attitude / Son of Aleric / Nobody's home / Black night / Perfect strangers / Unwritten law / Call of the wild / Hush / Smoke on the water / Space trucking
5114382 / Mar '92 / Polydor

☐ LIVE AT THE OLYMPIA (2CD Set)
Fireball / Maybe I'm a leo / Ted the mechanic / Pictures of home / Black night / Cascades / I'm not your lover / Sometimes I feel like screaming / Woman from Tokyo / No one came / Purpendicular walls / Rosa's cantina / Smoke on the water / When blind man cries / Speed king / Perfect strangers / Hey cisco / Highway star
CDEM 1615 / Jun '97 / EMI

☐ LIVE IN JAPAN (3CD Set)
Highway star / Child in time / Mule / Strange kind of woman / Lazy / Space truckin' / Black night / Speed king
CDEM 1510 / Nov '93 / EMI

☐ MACHINE HEAD
Highway star / Maybe I'm a leo / Pictures of home / Never before / Smoke on the water / Lazy / Space truckin'
CDFA 3158 / May '89 / Fame

☐ MACHINE HEAD
Highway star / Maybe I'm a Leo / Pictures of home / Never before / Smoke on the water / Lazy / Space truckin' / When a blind man cries / Highway star / Maybe I'm a Leo / Pictures of home / Never before / Smoke on the water / Lazy / Space truckin' / When a blind man cries / Maybe I'm a Leo / Lazy
CDDEEPP 3 / 8 Sep '97 / EMI

☐ MADE IN EUROPE (Live)
Burn / Mistreated / Lady double dealer / You fool no one / Stormbringer
CZ 344 / Jul '90 / EMI

☐ MADE IN JAPAN
Highway star / Child in time / Smoke on the water / Mule / Strange kind of woman / Lazy / Space truckin'
CDFA 3268 / Oct '92 / Fame

☐ MADE IN JAPAN
Highway star / Child in time / Smoke on the water / Mule / Strange kind of woman / Lazy / Space truckin' / Black night / Speed king / Lucille
8578642 / 19 Jan '98 / EMI

☐ NOBODY'S PERFECT - LIVE
Highway star / Strange kind of woman / Perfect strangers / Hard lovin' woman / Bad attitude / Knocking at your back door / Child in time / Lazy / Black night / Woman from Tokyo / Smoke on the water / Space truckin'
8358972 / Jun '88 / Polydor

☐ ON THE WINGS OF A RUSSIAN FOXBAT (Live In California 1976/2CD Set)
Burn / Lady Luck / Getting tighter / Love child / Smoke on the water / Lazy / Grind / This time around / Stormbringer / Highway star / Going down
DPVSOPCD 217 / May '95 / Connoisseur Collection

☐ PERFECT STRANGERS
Knocking at your back door / Under the gun / Nobody's home / Mean streak / Perfect strangers / Gypsy's kiss / Wasted sunsets / Hungry daze / Not responsible
8237772 / Mar '91 / Polydor

☐ PROGRESSION
Perfect strangers / Under the gun / Knocking at your back door / Gypsy's kiss / Not responsible / Black night / Smoke on the water / Hush / Bad attitude / Dead or alive / Hard lovin' woman / Call of the wild
5500272 / May '93 / Spectrum

☐ PURPENDICULAR
Vavoom Ted the mechanic / Loosen my strings / Soon forgotten / Sometimes I feel like screaming / Cascades - I'm not your lover / Aviator / Rosa's cantina / Castle full of rascals / Touch away / Hey Cisco / Somebody stole my guitar / Purpendicular waltz
74321338022 / Jan '96 / RCA

☐ PURPLE RAINBOWS
Black night / Speed king / Child in time / Strange kind of woman / Fireball / Smoke on the water / Highway star / Woman from Tokyo / Perfect strangers / Hush / Since you been gone: *Rainbow* / I surrender: *Rainbow* / Fool for your loving: *Whitesnake* / Here I go again: *Whitesnake* / Night games: *Bonnet, Graham* / Rock 'n' roll children: *Dio*
8455342 / Apr '94 / PolyGram TV

☐ PURPLEXED
Highway star / Battle rages on / King of dreams / Speed king / Aviator / Love conquers all / Anya / Loosen my strings / Solitaire / Child in time / Smoke on the water
74321597372 / 27 Jul '98 / Camden

☐ SCANDINAVIAN NIGHTS (2CD Set)
Wring that neck / Speed king / Into the fire / Paint it black / Mandrake root / Child in time / Black night
DPVSOPCD 125 / Oct '88 / Connoisseur Collection

☐ SHADES OF DEEP PURPLE
And the address / Hush / One more rainy day / Prelude: happiness / I'm so glad / Mandrake root / Help / Love help me / Hey Joe
CDFA 3314 / Apr '97 / Fame

☐ SINGLES A'S AND B'S
Hush / One more rainy day / Emmaretta / Wring that neck / Hallelujah / April, part 1 / Black night / Speed king / Strange kind of woman / I'm alone / Demon's eye / Fireball / Kentucky woman / Bird has flown / Never before / When a blind man cries / Smoke on the water / Black night (live) / Might just take your life / Coronarias redig / You keep on moving / Lovechild
CDP 7810092 / Apr '97 / EMI

☐ SLAVES AND MASTERS
King of dreams / Cut runs deep / Fire in the basement / Truth hurts / Breakfast in bed / Love conquers all / Fortune teller / Too much is not enough / Wicked ways
74321187192 / Apr '94 / RCA

☐ SMOKE ON THE WATER (Various Artists)
RR 89672 / Nov '94 / Roadrunner

☐ STORMBRINGER
Stormbringer / Love don't mean a thing / Holy man / Hold on / Lady double dealer / You can't do it right / High ball shooter / Gypsy / Soldier of fortune
CZ 142 / Oct '88 / EMI

☐ STORMBRINGER/WHO DO WE THINK WE ARE/COME TASTE THE BAND (The Originals Vol.2/3CD Set)
Stormbringer / Love don't mean a thing / Holy man / Hold on / Lady Double Dealer / You can't do it right / High ball shooter / Gypsy / Soldier of fortune / Woman from Tokyo / Mary Long / Super trouper / Smooth dancer / Rat bat blue / Place in line / Our lady / Comin' home / Lady Luck / Gettin' tighter / Dealer / I need love / Drifter / Love child / This time around / Owed to 'G' / You keep on moving
CDOMB 017 / Mar '97 / EMI

☐ WHO DO WE THINK WE ARE
Woman from Tokyo / Mary Long / Super trouper / Smooth dancer / Rat bat blue / Place in line / Our lady
CDFA 3311 / Dec '94 / Fame

☐ WHO DO WE THINK WE ARE/ STORMBRINGER/COME TASTE THE BAND (The Originals Vol.2/3CD Set)
Woman from Tokyo / Mary Long / Super trouper / Smooth dancer / Rat bat blue / Place in line / Our lady / Stormbringer / Love don't mean a thing / Holy man / Hold on / Lady double dealer / You can't do it right / High ball shooter / Gypsy / Soldier of fortune / Comin' home / Lady luck / Gettin' tighter / Dealer / I need love / Drifter / Love child / This time around / Owed to G (instrumental) / Keep on moving
DOMB 017 / 27 Jul '98 / EMI

Deep Space Network

☐ DSN & HIA (Deep Space Network & Higher Intelligence Agency)
EFA 006242 / Feb '97 / Source

Deep Throat

☐ VERSION 3.0
CDDVN 20 / Jun '93 / Devotion

Deep Wound

☐ DEEP WOUND
LF 284CD / 6 Oct '97 / Lost & Found

Deepika

☐ I ALT SLAGS LYS
FXCD 118 / Jul '93 / Kirkelig Kultuverksted

Deerheart

☐ QUEEN, WORKER, DRONE
GR 044CD / Oct '96 / Goldenrod

Deerhoof

☐ MAN THE KING THE GIRL, THE
KRS 4444 / Nov '97 / Kill Rock Stars

Dees, Sam

☐ SECOND TO NONE
We always come back strong / Tag / Your love is like a boomerang / Number one, second to none / Home wreckers / Your fool or your man / World don't owe you nothing / I like to party / I'm gonna give you just enough rope (To hang yourself) / Cry to me / Who are you gonna love (Your woman or your wife) / Good guys don't always win / Vanishing love / Nothing comes to a sleeper but a dream / I wish that I could be him / False alarm / You've been doing wrong for so long / Win or lose / Run to me / Help me my Lord / Touch me with your love / Just my alibi / Worn out broken heart
CDKEND 125 / Jun '95 / Kent

Def Leppard

☐ ADRENALIZE
Let's get rocked / Heaven is / Make love like a man / Tonight / White lightning / Stand up (kick love into motion) / Personal property / Have you ever / I wanna touch you / Tear it down
5109782 / Mar '92 / Bludgeon Riffola

☐ CONVERSATIONALIZE
CBAK 4029 / Feb '94 / Baktabak

☐ HIGH 'N' DRY
High 'n' dry (Saturday night) / You got me runnin' / Let it go / Another hit and run / Lady strange / On through the night / Mirror mirror (look into my eyes) / No, no, no / Bringin' on the heartbreak / Switch 625
8188362 / Jan '89 / Bludgeon Riffola

☐ HYSTERIA
Women / Rocket / Animal / Love bites / Pour some sugar on me / Armageddon it / Gods of war / Don't shoot shotgun / Run riot / Hysteria / Excitable / Love and affection
8306752 / '87 / Bludgeon Riffola

☐ INTERVIEW DISC
SAM 7020 / Nov '96 / Sound & Media

☐ ON THROUGH THE NIGHT
Answer to the master / Hello America / It could be you / It don't matter / Overture / Rock brigade / Rocks off / Satellite / Sorrow is a woman / When the walls came tumblin' down
8225332 / Jan '89 / Bludgeon Riffola

☐ PYROMANIA
Rock rock (til you drop) / Photograph / Stagefright / Too late for love / Die hard the hunter / Foolin' / Rock of ages / Comin' under fire / Action not words / Billy's got a gun
8103082 / '88 / Bludgeon Riffola

☐ RETRO ACTIVE
Desert song / Fractured love / Two steps behind (acoustic) / Only after dark / Action / She's too tough / Miss you in a heartbeat / Only after dark / Ride into the sun / From the inside / Ring of fire / I wanna be your hero / Miss you in a heartbeat / Two steps behind
5183052 / Oct '93 / Bludgeon Riffola

☐ SLANG
Truth / Turn to dust / Slang / All I want is everything / Breathe a sigh / Deliver me / Gift of flesh / Blood runs cold / Where does love go when it dies / Pearl of Euphoria
5324862 / May '96 / Bludgeon Riffola

☐ SLANG (Ltd. Edition)
Truth / Turn to dust / Slang / All I want is everything / Work it out / Breathe a sigh / Deliver me / Gift of flesh / Blood runs cold / Where does love go when it dies / Pearl of Euphoria / Armageddon it / Two steps behind / From the inside / Animal / When love and hate collide / Pour some sugar on me
5324932 / May '96 / Bludgeon Riffola

☐ TELLTALES (Interview Disc)
TELL 11 / Jun '97 / Network

☐ VAULT
Pour some sugar on me / Photograph / Love bites / Let's get rocked / Two steps behind / Animal / Heaven is / Rocket / When love and hate collide / Action / Make love like a man / Armageddon it / Have you ever needed someone so bad / Rock of ages / Hysteria / Bringin' on the heartbreak
5286562
5286572 / Oct '95 / Bludgeon Riffola

Def Squad

☐ EL NINO
Shower / Check n' me out / Countdown / Full cooperation / Ride wit' us / Lay 'em down / Rhymin' wit' biz / Game / World announcement / Can u dig it / You do I do / Ya'll niggas ain't ready / Say word / No guest list / Babies father committee / Def squad delite
5583432 / 6 Jul '98 / Def Jam

Deface

☐ GOVERNMENT DENIES KNOWLEDGE
LF 301CD / 25 May '98 / Lost & Found

Defecation

☐ PURITY DILUTION
NB 018CD / Nov '92 / Nuclear Blast

Definition Of Sound

☐ EXPERIENCE
Boom boom / Pass the vibes / Lucy / Will you love me / Experience / Here comes the sun / Feels like heaven / Child / Take me on / Mama's not coming home / Wishes in the wind
5287402 / Sep '97 / Fontana

☐ LOVE AND LIFE
When a lion awakens / Now is tomorrow / Passion and pain / Wear you love like heaven / Reality / Rise like the sun / What's going on / Dream girl / Change / Blues / Moira Jane's cafe / Won / City lights / Time is running out
CIRCD 14 / Jun '91 / Circa

Defleshed

☐ MA BELLE SCALPELLE
IR 009CD / Apr '95 / Invasion

☐ UNDER THE BLADE
IR 032CD / 13 Oct '97 / Invasion

DeFrancesco, Joey

☐ ALL IN THE FAMILY (DeFrancesco, Joey & Papa John)
Bag's groove / Sunny / Slammin' at the slims / Those were the days / My buddy / Tuxedo junction / Blues for sweet Sue / When the saints go marchin' in
HCD 7021 / 16 Mar '98 / Highnote

☐ STREET OF DREAMS, THE
BIGMO 20252E / Nov '95 / Big Mo

DeFranco, Buddy

☐ PLAYS GERSHWIN (Defranco, Buddy & Oscar Peterson)
I want to stay here / I was doing alright / 'S wonderful / Bess you is my woman now / Strike up the band / They can't take that away from me / Man I love / I got rhythm / Someone to watch over me / It ain't necessarily so / I wants to stay here / Someone to watch over me
5570992 / 3 Aug '98 / Verve

Deftones

☐ AROUND THE FUR
My own summer (shove it) / Lhabia / Mascara / Around the fur / Be quiet and drive / Lotion / Dai the flu / Headup / MX
9362468102 / 27 Oct '97 / Maverick

Defunkt

☐ AVOID THE FUNK (Defunkt Anthology)
Make them dance / Strangling me with your love (revisited) / Defunkt (live) / Big bird (au private) / For the love of money / Razor's edge / Avoid the funk / In the good times
HNCD 1320 / May '89 / Hannibal

☐ CRISIS
EMY 1352 / Sep '97 / Enemy

☐ CUM FUNKY
EMY 1442 / Nov '94 / Enemy
EMY 1402 / Sep '97 / Enemy

☐ DEFUNKT SPECIAL EDITION (Live Tribute To Muddy Waters & Jimi Hendrix)
EMY 1482 / Sep '97 / Enemy

☐ LIVE AND REUNIFIED
EMY 1452 / Sep '97 / Enemy

☐ LIVE AT THE KNITTING FACTORY
KFWCD 104 / Nov '94 / Knitting Factory

☐ LIVE AT THE KNITTING FACTORY, NYC
EMY 122 / Sep '91 / Enemy

Degen, Bob

☐ CATABILITY
Courage / My old flame / Sophie / Worth a week's anguish / Catability / MC / Ode to Sammy Davis Jr. / Colleen / Fading day / Round trip / Parting
ENJ 93322 / 29 Jun '98 / Enja

Deiana, Gesuino

☐ PINTADERAS (Made In Sardinia)
Tutu tutu / Ateras ninnas / Arvekes et tenores / Abu et Mont' Arbu / Sole de Oriente / Istorias de intro et fora / Andhendhe a benalonga / Arbeskidas / Sonos a de notte / Pintaderas / Zocculas de prata / Terra de 'entos / Carignos de luna / Biddh' 'e babois / Uas / Cuccos et arteros sonos / Froredillu / Turulu 'e monachus / In sa rena et in su mar-ea
WSCD 007 / May '97 / Womad Select

Deicide

☐ AMON : FEASTING THE BEAST
Lunatic of God's creation / Sacrificial suicide / Crucifixation / Carnage in the temple of the damned / Dead by dawn / Blasphererelon / Feasting the beast / Day of darkness / Oblivious to nothing
RR 91112 / Feb '93 / Roadrunner

☐ DEICIDE (Remastered)
Lunatic of God's creation / Sacrificial suicide / Oblivious to evil / Dead by dawn / Blasphererelon / Deicide / Carnage in the temple of the damned / Mephistopheles / Day of darkness / Crucifixation
RR 87442 / 8 Jun '98 / Roadrunner

☐ LEGION
Satan spawn, the caco-daemon / Dead but dreaming / Repent to die / Trifixion / Behead the prophet (no lord shall live) / Holy deception / In hell I burn / Revocate the agitator
RC 91922 / Mar '96 / Roadrunner

☐ ONCE UPON THE CROSS
RR 89492 / May '95 / Roadrunner

☐ SERPENTS OF THE LIGHT
RR 88112 / 20 Oct '97 / Roadrunner

Deighton Family

☐ ROLLING HOME
I love you because / I can see clearly now / Save the last dance for me / Road to Newcastle / Green rolling hills of West Virginia / Reuben's train / Under the Boardwalk / I forgot to remember to forget / When I get home / Leather britches / Rollin' home / Has he got a friend / Gilbert Clancy's reel
GLCD 1116 / '92 / Green Linnet

Deine Lakaien

☐ ACOUSTIC
EFA 155882 / Sep '95 / Gymnastic

☐ DARK STAR TOUR '92
EFA 15567 / Apr '93 / Gymnastic

☐ WINTER FISH TESTOSTERONE
EFA 155952 / Mar '96 / Gymnastic

Deinonychus

☐ SILENCE OF DECEMBER, THE
Black sun / I, ruler of paradise in black / Silencer of December / Final affliction of Xafan / Shining blaze over darkland / Under the autumn tree / Here lies my kingdom / My travels through the midnight sky / Red is my blood, cold is my heart / Bizarre landscape
NIHIL 5CD / Jun '97 / Cacophonous

☐ WEEPING OF A THOUSAND YEARS
NIHIL 13CD / Jul '96 / Cacophonous

Deiseal

☐ LONG LONG NOTE, THE
Shores of loch Ghamhna / Si beag si mor / Raindrops/The first of May / My love I miss her so / Long (long) note / Soporific/The rights of man / Mna na hEireann / Stranger at the gate/Boston blues / Lord inchiquin / Lakeside
SCD 193 / Jan '94 / Starc

☐ SUNSHINE DANCE
Sporting Nell/The 8th of October / Flowing tide/ Biddy Walsh's hornpipe / Cup of tea/The pinch of snuff/The newly-mowed meadow / Marbhna Luimni / Mairseail Ui Neill / Sunshine dance / Chanson gamme / Johnny Henry's/The abbey/Jimmy's return / Stepping stones / Out with the boys/The rocky road to Dublin / Wind of Rose Green / Wise maid
SCD 596 / Oct '97 / Starc

Deity Guns

☐ TRANS LINES APPOINTMENT
Tv blackscreen / Bob / Distance / Billy dracks / Crusing coast shadows / Tinnitus / Radio kill / Desert / Map
ABBCD 047 / May '93 / Big Cat

Dekker, Desmond

☐ ACTION (Dekker, Desmond & The Aces)
Mother pepper / Don't blame me / Unity / 007 / You're got your troubles / Personal posession / It pays / Your generation / Mother long tongue / Sabotage / Unforgettable / Mother young gal / Keep a cool head / Jump a ting a ling / Gimme gimme / Fu manchu
HSCD 1001 / Oct '96 / Hot Shot
444012 / Mar '97 / Beverly

☐ BLACK & DEKKER
Israelites / Lickin' stick / It mek / Please don't bend / Many rivers to cross / Hippo / 007 / Workout / Problems / Rude boy train / Pickney girl / Why fight
STIFFCD 11 / Jan '94 / Disky

☐ COMPASS POINT
I'll get by / Moving on / We can and shall / Hurt so bad / Isabella / Come back to me / Cindy / I do believe / My destiny / Big headed / That's my woman / Allamanna
REP 4223 / Aug '91 / Repertoire

☐ CRUCIAL CUTS (The Best Of Desmond Dekker)
Israelites / King of ska / You've got your troubles / Pretty africa / 007 (shanty town) / Writing on the wall / Reggae recipe / Keep a cool head / It mek / I believe / Too much too soon / It's a shame / You can get it if you really want / Rudy got soul / Archie wah wah / Problems / Pickney gal / More you live
MCCD 115 / Jun '93 / Music Club

☐ DESMOND DEKKER ARCHIVE
007 / Please don't bend / Go tell my people / Shing a ling / Mother nature / Yakety yak / When I'm cold / First time for a long time / It pays / Israelites / It mek / Life, hope and faith / Where did it go / What will you gain / Look what they're doing to me / You can get it if you really want / Trample / Little darling / Warlock / Baby come back
RMCD 208 / Nov '97 / Rialto

☐ FIRST TIME FOR A LONG TIME
Hanging tree / Fu man chu / Generosity / Pickney gal / Hippopotamus / Licking stick / Perserverance / Where did it go (the song we used to sing) / Get up little Suzie / It gotta be so / First time for a long time / What will you gain / Little darling / My reward / Please don't bend / Stop the wedding / Go and tell my people / Look what you're doing to me / Life, hope and faith / Trample / Reggae recipe / Mother nature / Father Noah / Life of opportunity / When I'm cold / Yakety yak
CDTRL 379 / May '97 / Trojan

☐ GREATEST HITS
You can get it if you really want it / Archie wah wah / Mother nature / Where did it go / More you live / What will you gain / Look what they're doing to me / Israelites / Reggae recipe / Licking stick / Pickney gal / It mek / Life of opportunity / I believe / My reward / 007
QED 123 / Nov '96 / Tring

☐ INTENSIFIED (Dekker, Desmond & The Aces)
0444022 / Mar '97 / Rhino

☐ ISRAELITES
Israelites / Beware / Everybody join hands / It mek / Sing a little song / Busted lad / My world is blue / Mother nature / Money and friends / No place like home
CDTRO 9104 / Aug '92 / Trojan

☐ ISRAELITES
Israelites / It miek / You can get it if you really want / Money and friends / No place like home / Busted lad / My world is blue / Mother nature / Beware / Everybody join hands / Pick up the phone / Sugar dumpling / Travel on / Get up little suzie / Sing a little song / Pickney gal
12361 / May '94 / Laserlight

☐ ISRAELITES, THE
MACCD 233 / Aug '96 / Autograph

☐ KING OF KINGS (Dekker, Desmond & The Specials)
CDTRL 324 / Mar '94 / Trojan

☐ KING OF SKA
CDTRL 292 / Mar '94 / Trojan

☐ MOVING ON
CDTRL 369 / Aug '96 / Trojan

☐ MUSIC LIKE DIRT
King of Ska / It's a shame / Rudie got soul / Rude boy train / Mother's young gal / Sweet music / You've got your troubles / Keep a cool head / Mother long tongue / Personal possession / Bongo gal / Don't blame me / Hey Grandma / Music like dirt / Nincompoop / It mek / Problems / Coconut water
CDTRL 301 / Mar '94 / Trojan

☐ OFFICIAL LIVE AND RARE (Dekker, Desmond & The Aces)
CDTRD 404 / Nov '89 / Trojan

☐ ORIGINAL REGGAE HITSOUND, THE (Dekker, Desmond & The Aces)
007 / Get up, Edina / Beautiful and dangerous / Shing a ling / Pretty Africa / Wise man / Sabotage / Unity / It pays / Israelites / It mek / Warlock / Archie wah wah / Pickney girl / Reggae recipe / You can get it if you really want / Hippopotamus song / Lickin' stick / More you live
CDTRL 226 / Mar '94 / Trojan

☐ VOICE OF SKA (Dekker, Desmond & The Aces)
007 / Wise man / Pickney gal / It mek / Unity / Music like dirt / Mother long tongue / Warlock / Licking stick / Sweet music / Personal possession / Hippopotamus / Beautiful and dangerous / Get up Edina / Sabotage / Rude boy train
EMPRCD 594 / Oct '95 / Emporio

☐ WRITING ON THE WALL, THE
Honour your mother and father / Madgie / Dracula / Parents / Labours of learning / Jeserine (and cherry pies) / It was only a dream / This woman / Mount Zion / Young generation / I've got the blues / Mother pepper / Writing on the wall / Tips of my fingers / Too much too soon / My precious love / Gimme gimme / For once in my life / I believe / Peace of mind / Cindy / You got soul / Coomyah / That's the way life goes / Polka dot
CDTRL 397 / Jun '98 / Trojan

Del Amitri

☐ CHANGE EVERYTHING
Be my downfall / Just like a man / When you were young / Surface of the moon / I won't take the blame / First rule of love / Ones that you love lead you nowhere / Always the last to know / To last a lifetime / As soon as the tide comes in / Behind the fool / Sometimes I just have to say your name
3953852 / Jun '92 / A&M

☐ DEL AMITRI
Heard through a wall / Hammering heart / Former owner / Sticks and stones girl / Deceive yourself (in ignorant heaven) / I was here / Crows in a wheatfield / Keepers / Ceasefire / Breaking bread
CCD 1499 / Dec '90 / Chrysalis

☐ SINGLES 1989-1998 (2CD Set)
Cry to be found / Roll to me / Kiss this thing goodbye / Not where it's at / Nothing ever happens / Always the last to know / Here and now / Just like a man / Spit in the rain / When we were young / Driving with the breaks on / Stone cold sober / Tell her this / Move away Jimmy Blue / Be my downfall / Some other sucker's parade / Don't come home to soon / Scared to live / Return of Maggie Brown / In the frame / Sleep instead of teardrops / Long journey home / Paper thin / Last love song / Verb to do / In the meantime / Long way down / Whiskey remorse / Before the evening steals the afternoon / So many souls to change
5409402
5409942 / 6 Jul '98 / A&M

☐ SOME OTHER SUCKER'S PARADE
Not where it's at / Some other sucker's parade / Won't make it better / What I think she sees / Medicine / High times / Mother nature's writing / No family man / Cruel light of day / Funny way to win / Through all that nothing / Life is full / Lucky guy / Make it always be too late
5407052 / Jun '97 / A&M

☐ TWISTED
Food for songs / Start with me / Here and now / One thing left to do / Tell her this / Being somebody else / Roll to me / Crashing down / It might as well be you / Never enough / It's never too late to be alone / Driving with the brakes on
5403112 / 15 Sep '97 / A&M

☐ WAKING HOURS
Kiss this thing goodbye / Opposite view / Move away Jimmy Blue / Stone cold sober / You're gone / When I want you / This side of the morning / Empty / Hatful of rain / Nothing ever happens
3970102 / Apr '95 / A&M

Del Ferro, Mike

☐ LIVE (Del Ferro, Mike & Frank Vaganee Group)
To John / Feels like summer / I don't know why / Sal's delight / Waltz three / Jump'n joy / Seven dwarfs / Due duel / Mooch / Little thing / Lanotas circle
AL 73057 / Nov '96 / A

Del Gastor, Paco

☐ FLAMENCO DE LA FRONTERA
NI 5352 / Oct '94 / Nimbus

Del Monte, Dino

☐ ENTRE LOS TIEMPOS
21096CD / Nov '96 / Sonifolk

Del Rey, Teisco

☐ MANY MOODS OF TEISCO DEL REY
UPSTART 007 / Jul '94 / Upstart

☐ PLAY MUSIC FOR LOVERS
UPSTART 030 / Feb '96 / Upstart

Del Tha Funky Homosapien

☐ I WISH MY BROTHER GEORGE WAS HERE
What is a booty / Mistadobalina / Wacky world of rapid transit / Pissin' on your steps / Dark skin girls / Money for sex / Ahonetwo, ahonetwo / Prelude / Dr. Bombay / Sunny meadowz / Sleepin' on my couch / Hoodz come in dozens / Same old thing / Ya lil crumbsnatchers
7559611332 / Dec '91 / Elektra

Del-Vikings

☐ BEST OF THE DEL-VIKINGS, THE (The Mercury Years)
Cool shake / Jitterbug Mary / Come along with me / Somewhere over the rainbow / Voodoo man / Can't wait / Sunday / Kind of love / I'm sitting on top of the world / Oh baby (I need your kisses) / Big beat / I'm spinning / When I come home / Nobody's kisses but yours / Meeting of the eyes / Friendly eyes / Oh tonight / That's why (I love you so) / You are invited / Bells / Heaven on Earth / Flat tyre
5527532 / Feb '97 / Spectrum

☐ COME GO WITH ME
Come go with me / Don't be a fool / In the still of the night / Yours / I'm spinning / Over the rainbow / White cliffs of Dover
FLYCD 34 / Apr '91 / Flyright

☐ DEL-VIKINGS VOL.2
FLYCD 53 / Nov '92 / Flyright

Delafose, Geno

☐ FRENCH ROCKIN' BOOGIE
ROUCD 2131 / Aug '94 / Rounder

☐ LA CHANSON PERDUE
Ja va's jamais la voir encore / Bernadette / Tite monde / Bon soir Moreau / Chere ici chere la bas / La chanson perdue / Un autre soir ennuyante / Mon vrai amour / Bayou pon pon / I want it all / Double D two step / Valse de Opelousas / Quo faire/Jolie Bassette / Tits yeux noir / Save the last dance for me
ROUCD 2151 / Jun '98 / Rounder

Delafose, John

☐ BLUES STAY AWAY FROM ME (Delafose, John & The Eunice Playboys)
ROUCD 2121 / Jan '94 / Rounder

☐ JOE PETE GOT TWO WOMEN
Joe pete got two women / One hour too late / Lonesome road / Prudhomme stomp / Co-fe (why) / You took my heartache (english) / Bye bye mo neg / Rag around your head (english) / I just want to be your lovin' man (english) / Petite et la grosse / Joe pete lost his two women / Crying in the streets (english) / Mardi gras song / Mother's day blues (english) / Arthritis two-step / Grand mamou / Uncel bud zydeco (english) / Sweet girl in texas (english) / Oh, negresse / Las valse de freole / Hippity hop / Johnny can't dance
ARHCD 335 / Apr '95 / Arhoolie

☐ LIVE AT RICHARD'S ZYDECO DANCE HALL VOL.2 (Delafose, John & The Eunice Playboys)
ROUCD 2070 / '88 / Rounder

Delagado, Luis

☐ AL ANDALUS
21042CD / Jun '94 / Sonifolk

Delakian, Michel

☐ BIARRITZ
BBRC 9107 / Dec '91 / Big Blue

Delaney & Bonnie

☐ ON TOUR WITH ERIC CLAPTON (Delaney & Bonnie/Friends)
Things get better / Poor Elijah / Only you know and I know / I don't want to discuss it / That's what my man is for / Where there's a will / Comin' home / Little Richard medley: *Clapton, Eric*
7567903972 / Feb '92 / Atlantic

Delano, Peter

☐ BITE OF THE APPLE
Spontaneous / Heartfelt / Distant stage / Reflected spirit / Sweetest sounds / Sunrise remembered / Improvisation #2 blues / On the spot / Demonic disorder / Castellaras
5218692 / Jul '94 / Verve

☐ PETER DELANO
Elephants in the sky / Experiencing change / Gesticulations / Entranced / Miles' mode / Piano improvisation / I remember Clifford / Say Uncle / Central Park waltz / Anicca / Autumn leaves / Reminiscence
5196022 / Mar '94 / Verve

Delavier, Katrien

☐ IRISH HARP, THE
PS 65095 / Sep '92 / PlayaSound

Delerium

☐ FACES FORMS AND ILLUSIONS
DCD 9008 / May '89 / Dossier

☐ KARMA (2CD Set)
067003011327
067003011421 / Apr '97 / Delerium

☐ MORPHEUS
DCD 9010 / '89 / Dossier

☐ SEMANTIC SPACES
W 230092 / Apr '95 / Nettwerk

☐ SPHERE
EFA 084532 / Feb '94 / Dossier

☐ SPHERES VOL.2
EFA 08460 2 / Sep '94 / Dossier

☐ SYROPHENIKAN
DCD 9015 / '89 / Dossier

Delevantes

☐ LONG ABOUT THAT TIME
ROUCD 9041 / May '95 / Rounder
CRCDM 6 / Sep '96 / CRS

☐ POSTCARDS FROM ALONG THE WAY
Suitcase of leather / My daddy's cadillac / This engine runs on faith / I know I promised / Reminds me of you / I'm your man / If I was / Blame it on the horizon line / Ring about now / John Wayne lives in Hoboken
CDEST 2302 / 15 Sep '97 / Capitol

Delfin, Eusebio

☐ EN EL TRONCO DE UN ARBOL
TCD 088 / 24 Apr '98 / Tumbao

Delfonics

☐ LA-LA MEANS I LOVE YOU
La-La means I love you / I'm sorry / Break your promise / Ready or not here I come (can't hide from love) / Somebody loves you / Funny feeling / Loving him / You got yours and I'll get mine / Didn't I blow your mind this time / Trying to make a fool of me / When you get right down to it / Over and over / Delfonics theme / Hey love / Walk right up to the sun / Tell me this is a dream / Think it over / I don't want to make you wait / I told you so / Lying to myself
07822189792 / 2 Feb '98 / Arista

Delgado, Andre

☐ ESSENTIAL PANPIPES
SPLCD 003 / Apr '96 / Sloane

Delgado, Isaac

☐ CON GANAS
74321342772 / Jun '96 / Milan

☐ EL CHEVERE DE LA SALAS/EL CABELLERO DEL SON (Delgado, Isaac & Adalberto Alvarez)
74321331192 / May '96 / Milan

☐ RARITIES
RMD 82276 / 24 Mar '98 / RMM

Delgado, Junior

☐ DANCE A DUB
Dance a dub / Hooligan stew / Mr. Dub / Crack a dub / Kidnapped on a subway / Ups / Downs / Enter / Torture / Herb eye
ABB 133CD / Jun '97 / Big Cat

☐ FREEDOM HAS IT'S PRICE
IMCD 0016 / Apr '97 / Incredible Music

☐ MR. FIXIT
Tichen (original) / Shelter / Lady / Rock me baby / Tell me how you feel / Look at the trees / Gimme your love / What's the matter with the people / Mr. fixit / Bad girls / Song of love / Runaway love / Hipo / Rebel soul in captive / Jah say / Warrior / Tichen (original 12" mix)
RNCD 2055 / May '94 / Rhino

☐ SISTERS AND BROTHERS
Row fisherman row / Caution / Warning / Effort / Hold me tighter / She's gonna marry me / Easy girl / Live like a hermit / My miss world / Sisters and brothers
CDBM 027 / 31 Jul '98 / Blue Moon

☐ TREASURE FOUND VOL.1
IMCD 001 / Mar '95 / Incredible Music

☐ TREASURE FOUND VOL.2 (More Treasure Found)
IMCD 0014 / Apr '97 / Incredible Music

Delgados

☐ BBC SESSIONS, THE
Primary alternative / I've only just started to breathe / Lazarwalker / Indian fables / Under canvas under wraps / Sucrose / Teen elf / Thirteen gliding principles / Friendly conventions / Tempered not tamed / Falling and landing
SFRSCD 037 / 15 Sep '97 / Strange Fruit

☐ DOMESTIQUES
CHEM 10CD / Nov '96 / Chemikal Underground

☐ PELOTON
Everything goes around the water / Arcane model / Actress / Clarinet / Pull the wires from the wall / Repeat failure / And so the talking stopped / Don't stop / Blackpool / Russian orthodox / Weaker argument defeats the stronger
CHEM 024CD / 8 Jun '98 / Chemikal Underground

Delicatessen

☐ HUSTLE INTO BED
STFCD 2 / 1 Sep '98 / Starfish

☐ SKIN TOUCHING WATER
I'm just alive / CF Kane / Zebra/Monkey/Liar / Red, blue and green / Watercress / Classic adventure / Appeased / Chomsky / You cut my throat, I'll cut yours / Sick of flying saucers / Smiling you're stupid / Inviting both sisters out to dinner / Advice / Love's liquid / Froth / If she was anybody else
STFCD 001X / May '95 / Starfish
STFCD 1 / 1 Sep '98 / Starfish

☐ THERE'S NO CONFUSING SOME PEOPLE
Another meal turns up / Lightbulbs and moths / Various pets / Psycho / He killed himself in 1980 / Boy dough / Cruel country / Priest in half / Sweet
VIP 002CD / 23 Feb '98 / Viper

Delico, Stephane

☐ AQUARELLES
ED 13024CD / Jul '95 / L'Empreinte Digitale

Delinquent Habits

☐ DELINQUENT HABITS
Tres delinquentes / Lower Eastside / Juvy / What it be like / I'm addicted / Realm / SALT (shit ain't like that) / Good times / Break 'em off / What's real iz real / If you want some / Another fix / Underground connection / When the stakes are high
07863669292 / Nov '96 / Loud

☐ HERE COME THE HORNS
This is LA / It's the delinquentes / I Adam 12 / Think you're bad / Here come the horns / Western ways / Shed a tear / Wallah / Orphan of the industry / Life is a struggle / Super DJ / Life I live / Get up get on it / No identity
74321537102 / 16 Mar '98 / Loud

Delirium

☐ PRIMER DIALOGO
SR 2012 / Dec '97 / Smogless

Delius, Toby

☐ HERON, THE (Delius, Toby Quartet)
ICP 033 / Apr '98 / ICP

Dellamorte

☐ UGLIER AND MORE DISGUSTING
KRONH 09CD / 27 Oct '97 / Kronh

Dello, Pete

☐ INTO YOUR EARS...PLUS (Dello, Pete & Friends)
It's what you've got / There's nothing that I can do for you / I'm a gambler / Harry the earwig / Do I still figure in your life / Uptight Basil / Taking the heart out of love / Here me only / On a time said Sylvie / Good song / It's the way / Go away / Arise Sir Henry / Madam Chairman (of the committee)
SEECD 257 / Sep '89 / See For Miles

Dells

☐ CLASSIC BALLADS
MCD 09395 / 23 Feb '98 / Chess/MCA

☐ I TOUCHED A DREAM/WHATEVER TURNS YOU ON
So you are love / All about the paper / Passionate breezes / I touched a dream / Just a little love / Look at us now / Your song / Happy song / It took a woman like you to make a man out of me / Whatever turns you on / How can we find the love we lost when we don't know how it g / Ain't it ashame / Heaven's just a step away / Is it it / Stay in my corner
CDSEWD 118 / 23 Feb '98 / Southbound

☐ ON THEIR CORNER
Oh what a night / Wear it on our face / Love is so simple / I can sing a rainbow/Love is blue / O-O, I love you / There is / Nadine / Love we had / Run for cover / Stay in my corner / Give your baby a standing ovation / Always together / Open up my heart / I miss you / Since I found you / My pretending days are over / Learning to love you was easy / I wish it was me you loved
MCD 09333 / Apr '97 / Chess/MCA

Delmar, Elaine

☐ 'S WONDERFUL
Some of my best friends / Touch of your lips / In a sentimental mood / 'S Wonderful / Stardust / I did it all for you / Little girl blue / Carioca / They can't take that away from me / We could be flying / They say it's wonderful / Ol' man river / There's a small hotel / Joy / My foolish heart / Like a lover / Love for sale
JHCD 027 / Sep '91 / Ronnie Scott's Jazz House

☐ NOBODY ELSE BUT ME
Nobody else but me / Where or when / Hymn for Jobim / I will say goodbye / Down with love / Once upon a summertime / Little girl blue / Isn't it a pity / Let's fall in love / Weaver of dreams / Lush life / You stepped out of a dream / All the things you are / My foolish heart / It had to be you
SPJCD 563 / 5 Jan '98 / Spotlite

Delmonas

☐ DELMONAS/DELMONAS 5
Dr. Goldfoot / Heard about him / Why don't you smile now / Black elk speaks / Hound dog / Delmona / I feel like giving in / Keep your big mouth shut / When I want you / Black Ludella / Your love / Don't fall in love (every single time) / Jealousy / Jealousy (French version) / That boy of mine / Can't sit down / Kiss me honey / I've got everything I need / Uncle Willy / Farmer John / You did him wrong / Dangerous charms / Long drop / I feel alright
ASKCD 032 / Oct '93 / Vinyl Japan

Delmore Brothers

☐ FREIGHT TRAIN BOOGIE
Blues stay away from me / Freight train boogie / Trouble ain't nothin' but the blues / Boogie woogie baby / Rounder's blues / Mobile boogie / Used car blues / Pan American blues / Pan American boogie / Field hand man / Brown's ferry blues / Peach tree street boogie / Blues you never lose / Steamboat boogie / Muddy water / Sand mountain blues / Hillbilly boogie / You can't do wrong and get by / Kentucky Mountain / Weary day / Take it to the Captain
CDCHD 455 / Aug '93 / Ace

Delpech, Michel

☐ 1960'S FRENCH EP COLLECTION, THE
174652 / Nov '97 / Magic

Delphines

☐ DELPHINES
DEL 100CD / Jun '97 / Abstract

Delphium

☐ HOW CAN YOU HIDE FROM WHAT NEVER GOES AWAY
OUT 003CD / Jul '97 / Outsider

Delray, Leon

☐ I'M STILL WAITIN'
All the lonely girls / Please don't ask me why / Macho man / I'm not in love / My love for you / Day by day / Good mornin' / I wanna be free / Unfree / I'm still waiting (for your call) / I wonder will we ever learn / I wanna be free (reprise)
101S 8770572 / Nov '93 / 101 South

Delta 72

☐ R & B OF MEMBERSHIP, THE
TG 172CD / Jul '96 / Touch & Go

☐ SOUL OF A NEW MACHINE, THE
TG 182CD / 8 Jun '98 / Touch & Go

Delta 9

☐ ALPHA DECAY
VC 109CD / Mar '97 / Vinyl Communication

☐ DISCO INFERNO
Welcome to hell / Drox / In the void / Watch yer back / Son of a bitch / Headstrong / Oblivion / Atomizer / Yellow fever / Abomination / Only way out / Trained to hate and destroy / Real hardcore / 246 / Sine / Headstrong / Infidel / Mortified
MOSH 165CD / Jan '97 / Earache

☐ NO BLUFF
503632 / Apr '95 / Declic

☐ UNEQUALIBRIUM
VC 138 / 27 Apr '98 / Vinyl Communication

Delta Accordion Band

☐ 50 PARTY FAVOURITES
It's a sin to tell a lie / Ain't she sweet / I want to be happy / Baby face / My blue heaven / Your cheatin' heart / From a Jack to a King / Walk on by / I love you because / Take these chains from my heart / You are my sunshine / Blackpool belle / She'll be coming round the mountain / Down by the riverside / When the saints go marching in / Whiskey in the jar / Muirsheen Durkin / Holy ground / Mountain dew / I'll tell me Ma / She's a lassie from Lancashire / I belong to Glasgow / On top of Old Smokey / In my Liverpool home / Wild colonial boy / Yellow rose of Texas / Little brown jug / Happy wanderer / Marie's wedding / Scotland the brave / Kiss me goodnight Sergeant Major / We're gonna hang out the washing on the Siegfried Line / Run rabbit run / Oh Johnny, oh Johnny oh / Hey little hen / Daisy bell / Home on the range / Cockles and mussels / Goodnight Irene / My Bonnie lies over the ocean / Rothesay / Campbeltown Loch / Campbells are coming / Coming through the rye / Road to the Isles / Lily of Laguna / By the light of the silvery moon / Barefoot days / Maybe it's because I'm a Londoner / Roll me over
CD 6058 / Feb '97 / Music

Delta Four

☐ MEMORIES OF NEW ORLEANS 1991-1992
PKCD 014 / Jul '96 / PEK

Delta Line Dance Band

☐ BOOT SCOOTIN' BOOGIE
Boot scootin' boogie / Mercury blues / My baby loves me / Achy breaky heart / Love's gotta hold on you / Hillbilly rock, hillbilly roll / Black coffee / One step forward / Dream baby / He thinks he'll keep her / Cherokee boogie / Guitars and cadillacs / Ancient history / Elvira / Bug / When will I be loved / Passionate kisses / Honky tonk blues / Wild one / One more last chance
CD 6083 / Aug '97 / Music

Delta Of Venus

☐ NEUTRAL A
SR 1006 / Jan '96 / Scout

Delta Plan

☐ INDELIBLE
NZCD 055 / Jun '96 / Nova Zembla

Delta Rhythm Boys

☐ DRY BONES
MCCD 028 / Nov '96 / Magnum America

Delta T

☐ LOST ARKS
HOLCD 29 / 6 Oct '97 / Holistic

Deltas

☐ BOOGIE DISEASE
NERDCD 002 / Jun '95 / Nervous

☐ LIVE
Raging sea / You can't judge a book by the cover / As you like it / Tuffer than tuff / Boogie disease / Gimme the drugs / Cigarette / Cool off baby / Teenage ball / Long black train / Honky tonk women / Nine below zero / I got you / How come you do me / Kokomo
JE 256 / Mar '93 / Visionary/Jettisoundz

☐ TUFFER THAN TUFF LIVE
LOMACD 34 / Nov '94 / Loma

Deltones

☐ NANA CHOC CHOC IN PARIS
PHZCD 31 / Jan '89 / Unicorn

Deluigi, Silvana

☐ TANGOS
SM 16132 / Jan '96 / Wergo

☐ TANGUERA - WOMAN IN TANGO
SM 15032 / Nov '92 / Wergo

Delyle, Lucienne

☐ LUCIENNE DELYLE 1939-1946 (2CD Set)
FA 151 / 24 Apr '98 / Fremeaux

Demasse, Seleshe

☐ SONGS FROM ETHIOPIA
SM 15162 / Nov '93 / Wergo

DeMent, Iris

☐ MY LIFE
Sweet is the melody / You've done nothing wrong / Calling for you / Childhood memories / No time to cry / Troublesome waters / Mom and Dad's waltz / Easy's getting harder every day / Shores of Jordan / My life
9362454932 / Mar '94 / Warner Bros.

☐ WAY I SHOULD, THE
When my mornin' comes around / Trouble / Walkin' home / Quality time / I'll take my sorrow straight / This kind of happy / Way I should / Keep me god / Letter to mom / Wasteland of the free / There's a wall in washington
9362461882 / Oct '96 / Warner Bros.

Demented Are Go

☐ BEST OF DEMENTED ARE GO, THE
Pervy in the park / Busty hymen / Holy hack jack / Pickled and preserved / Transvestite blues / PVC chair / Nuke mutants / Satan's rejects / Cripple in the woods / Call of the wired / Surf ride to oblivion / Shadow crypt / Human slug / Sick spasmoid / Country woman / One shrp knife / Brain damaged chile / Flight 103
DOJOCD 125 / May '93 / Dojo

☐ DAY THE EARTH SPAT BLOOD
RAUCD 035 / 22 Jun '98 / Raucous

☐ IN SICKNESS AND IN HEALTH/KICKED OUT OF HELL
Be bop a lula / Pervy in the park / (I was born on a) Busted hymen / Holy hack Jack / Frenzied beat / Pickled and preserved / Crazy horses / Transvestite blues / Rubber buccaneer / Vibrate / Rubber love / Nuke mutants / PVC chair / Don't go into the woods / Satan's rejects / Human slug / Cripple in the woods / Decomposition / Cast iron arm / Call of the wired / Rubber plimsoles / Shadow crypt / Surf ride to oblivion / Old black Joe / Sick spasmoid / Vietnam / Jet tune boogie
LOMACD 15 / Feb '94 / Loma

☐ SATANS REJECTS (The Best Of Demented Are Go)
Pervy in the park / Busted hymen / Holy hack jack / Pickled and preserved / Transvestite blues / PVC chair / Nuke mutants / Satans rejects / Cripple in the woods / Call of the wired / Surf ride to oblivion / Shadow crypt / Human slug / Sick spasmoid / Country women / One sharp knife / Brain damaged chile / Flight 103
CDMPSYCHO 19 / 3 Nov '97 / Anagram

☐ TANGENITAL MADNESS
DAGCD 1 / Apr '95 / Fury

☐ WHO PUT GRANDMA UNDER THE STAIRS
RRCD 218 / May '96 / Receiver

Demolition Doll Rods

☐ TASTY
ITR 048CD / Jun '97 / In The Red

Demolition Hammer

☐ EPIDEMIC OF VIOLENCE
CM 97282 / Sep '94 / Century Media

☐ TIMEBOMB
CM 770712 / Aug '94 / Century Media

Demon

☐ ANTHOLOGY
Night of the demon / Into the nightmare / Father of time / Don't break the circle / Spell / Sign of the madman / Plague / Nowhere to run / Blackheath / Touching the ice / From the outside / Hear of our time / Crossfire / Life on the wire / Breakout / Hollywood / England's glory
CLAYCD 108 / Apr '93 / Clay

☐ BLOW OUT
SONICCD 11 / May '92 / Sonic

☐ BRITISH STANDARD APPROVED
SONICCD 4 / Sep '90 / Sonic

☐ ONE HELLUVA NIGHT (Live In West Germany)
DEMONCD 1 / Aug '90 / Sonic

☐ PLAGUE, THE
Plague / Nowhere to run / Fever in the city / Blackheath / Writings on the wall / Only sane man / Step to far
HTDCD 36 / Jul '95 / HTD

☐ TAKING THE WORLD BY STORM
Commercial dynamite / Taking the world by storm / Life brigade / Remembrance day / What do you think about hell / Blue skies in Red Square / Time has come
HTDCD 32 / Mar '95 / HTD

Demone, Gitane

☐ AM I WRONG
TX 60011CD / 22 Jun '98 / Triple XXX

☐ DEMONIX (Demone, Gitane & Marc Ickx)
CLP 9816 / Oct '96 / Cleopatra

☐ LOVE FOR SALE
CD 004 / Jan '94 / Dark Vinyl

Demoniac

☐ EMPIRE OF AGONY
NR 018CD / 13 Apr '98 / Necropolis

☐ PREPARE FOR WAR
EOR 003CD / Apr '95 / Osmose

☐ STORMBLADE
EOR 005CD / May '97 / Evil Omen

Dempsey, Kevin

☐ ALWAYS WITH YOU
SPINCD 136 / Dec '97 / Spindrift

☐ CRY OF LOVE
WPSCD 006 / Apr '98 / WPS

Dempsey, Little Jimmy

☐ GUITAR MUSIC
CNCD 5937 / Jun '92 / Disky

Dempsey, Peter

☐ LOVE'S GARDEN OF ROSES
It's only a tiny garden / Zinetta / Go lovely Rose / E'en as a lovely flower / Ah, may the red rose live alway / In the garden of your heart / Vucchella / English rose / Child's song / Roses of Picardy / Raindrop kissed a rose / Yearning / Thank God for a garden / Now sleeps the crimson petal / To a wild rose / Old flagged path / Mighty like a rose / Love sends a little gift of roses / Thora / Do you know my garden / Rose of Tralee / There's a bower of roses by Bendemmer's stream / Garden in the rain / Rose still blooms in Picardy / Love's garden of roses
MDMCD 005 / May '96 / Moidart

Dempsey, Tom

☐ BLUES IN THE SLOPE
79116498052 / 21 Apr '98 / IGM

Den Fule

☐ LUGUMLEIK
Tuss ola / Nordafjells / Pal karls vals / Raddascottis / Lugumleik / Dickapolskan / Langdans / Vallat / Tre strommingar / Slangpolska / Kopmanpolska / Modus mats / Pslam / Nordic wolf
XOUCD 104 / May '97 / Xource

☐ SKALV
Skalv / Snail / Skagget / Fly med mig / Gammel husin / Den bla slatten / Ormsla / Det ar jag / Munnharpevals / Offerklippans sang / Koptespakte / Jagaren och algen / Rammeslatten / Paki / Storebackepolskan / Vinge
XOUCD 109 / May '97 / Xource

Denayer, Oscar

☐ ACCORDION FAVOURITES
HRCD 8056 / Sep '94 / Disky

Dene, Terry

☐ REAL TERRY DENE, THE
Pick a bale of cotton / Come on train / That's all right / Good rockin' tonight / Lock and chain / Blue suede shoes / Mystery train / Baby she's gone / Market place / My baby left me / Pretty little Pearly / Shakin' all over / Lawdy Miss Clawdy / Move it / I'm left, you're right, she's gone / Learning to rock 'n' roll / C'min and be loved / White sport coat / Blue moon of Kentucky / All shook up / Heartbreak hotel / Love me tender / Poor boy / Like a baby / Shake, rattle and roll / Whole lotta shakin' goin' on / Rip it up / Off 'n' on
CDROLL 3015 / Dec '97 / Rollercoaster

Denham, Jay

☐ ESCAPE TO BLACK PLANET
EFA 294642 / 30 Mar '98 / Disko B

Denio, Amy

☐ BIRTHING CHAIR BLUES
KFWCD 111 / Nov '94 / Knitting Factory

Denison/Kimball Trio

☐ NEUTRONS
QS 48CD / Aug '97 / Quarter Stick

☐ SOUL MACHINE
GR 22CD / May '95 / Skingraft

☐ WALLS IN THE CITY
GR 16CD / Oct '94 / Skingraft

Denissenkov, Vladimir

☐ BAJAN
FY 8002CD / Aug '97 / Robi Droli

Deniz Tek

☐ BAD ROAD
CITCD 917 / Jul '97 / Citadel

☐ EQUINOX
CITCD 537 / 16 Mar '98 / Citadel

☐ TAKE IT TO THE VERTICAL
5170162 / 26 Jan '98 / Red Eye

Denman, John

☐ ENGLAND - NEW ENGLAND (Denman, John & Paula Fan)
BML 002 / Jan '96 / British Music

☐ SPLENDID BRITISH CLARINET WORKS (Denman, John & Paula Fan)
BML 009 / Jan '96 / British Music

Denman, Todd

☐ LIKE MAGIC (Denman, Todd & Bill Dennehy)
ANR 001CD / Dec '97 / Aniar

☐ REEDS AND ROSIN (Denman, Todd & Dale Russ)
ANR 003CD / Dec '97 / Aniar

Dennehy, Tim

☐ FAREWELL TO MILTOWN MALBAY
SRCD 002 / Dec '97 / Sceilig

☐ WINTER'S TEAR, A (Traditional & Original Songs Of Love, Loss & Longing)
CICD 087 / Dec '93 / Clo Iar-Chonnachta

Dennis, Cathy

☐ AM I THE KIND OF GIRL
West End pad / Fickle / When dreams turn to dust / Stupid fool / Am I the kinda girl / Homing the rocket / That is why you love me / Waterloo sunset / Don't take my heaven / Date / Crazy ones
5331512 / Mar '97 / Polydor

Dennis, Denny

☐ I SING YOU A THOUSAND LOVE SONGS
May I have the next romance with you / I stumbled over love / Time on my hands / Hurry home / Rosita / Sweet is the word for you / I have eyes / If I should fall in love again / Will you remember / Goodnight my love / Sweet someone / Pretty little quaker girl / Thru the courtesy of love / Deep purple / I let a song go out of my heart / Blue Hawaii / South of the border (Down Mexico way) / Always and always / Dearest love / Where are the songs we sung
PAR 2026 / Jul '94 / Parade

☐ TRIBUTE, A
Angels never leave heaven / Bird on the wing / Blue skies are just around the corner / Did you ever see a dream walking / Glory of love / Goodbye to summer / Hear my song Violetta / I fall in love with you every day / I was lucky / I wished on the moon / I'll string along with you / If you please / In the middle of a kiss / In the mission by the sea / Just one more chance / Let's call the whole thing off / Let's face the music and dance / Louise / Mexicali Rose / South of the border (Down Mexico way) / Stardust / Two sleepy people: *Dennis, Denny & Vera Lynn* / Way you look tonight / Whispers in the dark / Would you
CDAJA 5127 / '94 / Living Era

Dennison, Jeff

☐ THEY'RE COMING BACK TO THE WATER (Songs Of The Waterways) (Dennison, Jeff & Benny Graham)
They're coming back to the water / Manchester Canal or the SS Irwell / When Leeds becomes a seaport town / All hail this grand day / Wandering navvy boy / Rochdale nine / Still waters / Broken boats / Narrow lock gate / Moving up the cuts / Tommy note / Rosemary / Push boys push / Girl on the cut/Keep your hands off / Bristol through to Reading / I know that I'll be back again / Down at the pub on the cut
FSCD 47 / Nov '97 / Folksound

Denny & Dunipace Pipe Band

☐ PLAY SCOTLANDS BEST
Scotland the brave / Rowan tree / Bonnie Galloway / Old rustic bridge / Black Watch polka / Mull of Kintyre / Green hills / When the battle is over / Lynn Shannon's wedding / Dunipace / Danish knife grinder's spring song / Crossing the Minch / AA Cameron's strathspey / Miller of Drone / Donald's wedding / McFarlane's reel / John Wilson / Muckin' o' Geordie's byre / Glendaurel highlanders / Bonnie Dundee / Amazing grace / Day thou gavest Lord is ended / Flower of Scotland / MacKay's farewell to the 71st / Rose among the heather / Fiddlers' joy / De'il among the tailors / Pigeon on the gate / Kate Dalrymple / Going home / Mist covered mountains of home / Morag of Dunvegan / Skye boat song / Dark island / Highland wedding / Susan Macleod / Kate Robertson / Barren rocks of Aden / Highland laddie / Mhairi's wedding / Black bear / Flowers of the forest / Drum salute
CD ITV 385 / May '87 / Scotdisc

Denny, Martin

☐ COCONUT CREAM OF MARTIN DENNY, THE
3036400152 / Jun '98 / Hallmark

☐ EXOTIC SOUNDS OF MARTIN DENNY, THE
CREV 039CD / Jul '95 / Rev-Ola

☐ EXOTICA VOL.1 & 2
SCP 97122 / Nov '97 / Scamp

☐ HYPNOTIQUE/EXOTICA 3
SCP 9713 / Mar '97 / Scamp

☐ QUIET VILLAGE/ENCHANTED SEA
SCP 9715 / 18 Aug '97 / Scamp

Denny, Sandy

☐ ATTIC TRACKS 1972-1984 (Denny, Sandy & Trevor Lucas)
SPDCD 1052 / Jun '95 / Special Delivery
RVCD 46 / Dec '97 / Raven

☐ BEST OF SANDY DENNY, THE
Listen listen / Lady / One way donkey ride / It'll take a long time / Farewell, farewell / Tam Lin / Pond in the stream / Late November / Solo / Sea / Banks of the Nile / Next time around / For shame of doing wrong / Stranger to himself / I'm a dreamer / Who knows where the time goes
IMCD 217 / Mar '96 / Island

☐ GOLD DUST (Live At The Royalty)
IMCD 252 / 18 May '98 / Island

☐ LISTEN LISTEN (An Introduction To Sandy Denny)
Late November / Blackwaterside / Next time around / Wretched Wilbur / Northstar grassman and the ravens / It'll take a long time / Listen listen / Lady / Music weaver / Solo / Like an old fashioned waltz / Dark the night / No end / One way donkey ride / I'm a dreamer / All our days / No more sad refrains / Here in silence
IMCD 253 / 4 May '98 / Island

☐ NORTH STAR GRASSMAN AND THE RAVENS
Late November / Blackwater side / Sea Captain / Down in the flood / John the gun / Next time around / Optimist / Let's jump the broomstick / Wretched Wilbur / North star grassman and the ravens / Crazy lady blues
IMCD 133 / Jun '91 / Island

☐ RENDEZVOUS
I wish I was a fool for you / Gold dust / Candle in the wind / Take me away / One way donkey ride / I'm a dreamer / All our days / Silver threads and golden needles / No more sad refrains
HNCD 4423 / Jan '87 / Hannibal

☐ SANDY
It'll take a long time / Sweet rosemary / For nobody to hear / Tomorrow is a long time / Quiet joys of brotherhood / Listen, listen / Lady / Bushes and briars / It suits me well / Music weaver
IMCD 132 / Jun '91 / Island

☐ SANDY AND THE STRAWBS (Denny, Sandy & The Strawbs)
Nothing else will do / Who knows where the time goes / How everyone but Sam was a hypocrite / Sail away to the sea / And you need me / Poor Jimmy Wilson / All I need is you / Tell me what you see in me / I've been my own worst friend / Two weeks last summer / Always on my mind / Stay a while with me / On my way
HNCD 1361 / Jul '91 / Hannibal

☐ WHO KNOWS WHERE THE TIME GOES (3CD Set)
Lady / Nothing more / Memphis Tennessee / Solo / John the gun / Knockin' on Heaven's door / Who knows where the time goes / Music weaver / Take away the load / Sweet Rosemary / Now and then / By the time it gets dark / What is true / Sail away to the sea / Farewell, farewell / Quiet joys of brotherhood / Tamlin / You never wanted me / Autopsy / One more chance / Stranger to himself / Pond and the stream / Banks of the Nile / Two weeks last summer / Late November / Gypsy Davey / Winter winds / Sea / When will I be loved / Listen listen / Next time around / Tomorrow is a long time / One way donkey ride / Burton Town / Blackwater side / It'll take a long time / Walking the floor over you / Friends / For shame of doing wrong / I'm a dreamer / Full moon
HNCD 5301 / Jun '96 / Hannibal

Denson, Karl

☐ D STANDS FOR DIESEL
GB 002CD / Jul '96 / Greyboy

Dent De Lion

☐ LES BEAUX YEAUX BLEUS
MINCD 795 / Mar '96 / Minuit

Dentists

☐ BEHIND THE DOOR I KEEP THE UNIVERSE
This is not my flag / Space man / Sorry is not enough / In orbit / Faces on stone / Smile like oil on water / Tremendous Many / Gas / Brittle sin and flowers / Apple beast / Water for a man on fire / Waiter
7567922882 / Mar '94 / WEA

☐ DRESSED
Strawberries are growing in my garden (and it's wintertime / Strawberries are growing in my garden (and it's wintertime (/ I had an excellent dream / A strange way to go about things / Chainsaw the horse / Peppermint dreams / Just like oliver reed / Turquoise castle / I can see your house from up here / Pailino / Dawn overdone / Writhing on the shagpile / Flowers around me / I'm not the devil / Tony bastable v john noakes / You make me say it somehow / Mary won't come out to play / Kinder still / Little engineers set / Tangerine / Arrow points to the spot / One of our psychedelic beakers is missing
ME 2001 / Aug '92 / Metwo

☐ POWDERED LOBSTER FIASCO
Pocket of silver / Charms and the girls / Outside your inside / Box of Sun / Beautiful day / I can see your house from up here / We thought we'd gone to Heaven / Leave me alive / All coming down / Snapdragon
SHED 002CD / Jun '93 / Ball Product

Denver, John

☐ ANNIE'S SONG
Windsong / Annie's song / Potter's wheel / Two different directions / Chained to the wheel / Country girl in Paris / All this joy / Thanks to you / Gift you are / I want you to live
12924 / Dec '97 / Laserlight

☐ BEST OF JOHN DENVER LIVE, THE
Rocky mountain high / Country road / Back home again / I guess he'd rather be in Colorado / Matthew / Sunshine on my shoulders / Darcy Farrow / Wild montana skies / Medley / Bet on the blues / I think I'd rather be a cowboy / Fly away / I'm sorry / Annie's song / Poems / Prayers and promises / Calypso
4873902 / Jul '97 / Epic

☐ CALYPSO
Calypso / Flower that shattered the stone / American child / Postcard from Paris / In a far away land / Little further north / Sing Australia / Alaska and me / Stonehaven sunset / Potter's wheel / Flower that shattered the stone
12927 / Dec '97 / Laserlight

☐ COLLECTION, THE
280729 / Nov '96 / Universe

☐ COLLECTION, THE (5CD Set)
15978 / 29 Sep '97 / Laserlight

☐ COUNTRY ROADS COLLECTION, THE (4CD Set)
Leaving on a jet plane / Circus / Rhymes and seasons / Catch another butterfly / Daydream / Follow me / Aspenglow / Molly / Sticky summer weather / Isabel / Sunshine on my shoulders / My sweet lady / Take me home country roads / I guess he'd rather be in Colorado / Poems prayers and promises / Starwood in Aspen / City of New Orleans / All of my memories / Casey's last ride / Eagle and the hawk / Friends with you / Calypso / Come and let me look in your eyes / Like a sad song / Polka dots and moonbeams / In the grand way / How can I leave again / Ripplin' waters / It amazes me / Singing skies and dancing waters / Dearest Esmerelda / Thirsty boots / I want to live / Southwind / Garden song / What's on your mind / You're so beautiful / In my heart / Mountain song / Song for the life / Autograph / Rocky Mountain high / For baby (for Bobbie) / Goodbye again / We don't live here no more / I'd rather be a cowboy / Farewell Andromeda / Rocky Mountain suite / Annie's song / Back home again / Grandma's feather bed / Sweet surrender / Eclipse / Thank god I'm a country boy / This old guitar / Spirit / Song of Wyoming / I'm sorry / Looking for a space / Fly away / Some days are diamonds / Country love / Dreams / Heart to heart / Shanghai breezes / Seasons of the heart / Perhaps love / Falling out of love / It's about time / Wild Montana skies / Dreamland express / If ever / I'm in the mood to be desired / Don't close your eyes tonight / Love is the master / I can't escape / Love again / Flying for me
07863674372 / 30 Mar '98 / RCA

☐ DIFFERENT DIRECTIONS
Potters wheel / Ponies / Chained to the wheel / Two different directions / Hold on to me / Chosen ones / Amazon (let this be a voice) / Tenderly calling
MCCD 237 / Mar '96 / Music Club

☐ EARTH SONGS
Windsong / Rocky mountain suite / Rocky mountain high / Sunshine on my shoulders / Eagle and the hawk / Eclipse / Flower that shattered the stone / Raven's child / Children of the universe / To the wild country / American child / Calypso / Islands / Earth day every day (celebrate)
MCCD 035 / Sep '91 / Music Club

☐ FLOWER THAT SHATTERED THE STONE, THE
Thanks to you / Postcard from Paris / High, wide and handsome / Eagles and horses / Little further north / Raven's child / Ancient rhymes / Gift you are / I watch you sleeping / Stonehaven sunset / Flower that shattered the stone
MCCD 154 / Feb '94 / Music Club

☐ GREATEST COUNTRY HITS, THE
Take me home country roads / Sunshine on my shoulders / Annie's somg / Back home again / Sweet surrender / Thank God I'm a country boy / I'm sorry / Fly away / Looking for space / Like a sad song / Baby you look good to me tonight / How can I leave you again / What's on your mind / Autograph / Some days are diamonds (some days are stone) / Cowboy and the lady / Wild Montana skies / Dreamland express
07863676042 / 11 May '98 / RCA

☐ HIGHER GROUND
Higher ground / Home grown tomatoes / Whispering jesse / Never a doubt / Deal with the ladies / Sing australia / Country girl in paris / For you / All this joy / Falling leaves (the refugees) / Bread and roses / Alaska and me
MCCD 197 / Mar '95 / Music Club

☐ REFLECTIONS (Songs Of Love And Life)
You're so beautiful / Dearest Esmerelda / Annie's song / My sweet lady / Polka dots and moonbeams / For baby (for Bobbie) / Come and let me look in your eyes / Daydream / Let it be / What's on your mind / I'm sorry / Rhymes and reasons / Molly / Sunshine on my shoulders / I can leave you again / Fire and rain / Isabel / Goodbye again / Autograph / Calypso
07863669872 / 11 May '98 / RCA

☐ ROCKY MOUNTAIN COLLECTION, THE (2CD Set)
Leaving on a jet plane / Rhymes and reasons / Follow me / Aspenglow sunshine on my shoulders / My sweet lady / Take me home country roads / Poems, prayers and promises / Eagle and the hawk / Starwood in Aspen / Friends with you / Goodbye again / Rocky mountain high / I'd rather be a cowboy / Farewell Andromeda / Back home again / Annie's song / Thank God I'm a country boy / Sweet surrender / This old guitar / Fly away / Looking for space / Windsong / Calypso / I'm sorry / Like a sad song / Come and let me look in your eyes / How can I leave you again / Thirsty boots / It amazes me / I want to live / Autograph / Some days are diamonds / Seasons of the heart / Shanghai breezes / Perhaps love: *Denver, John & Placido Domingo* / Wild Montana skies: *Denver, John & Emmylou Harris* / Love again / Flying for me
0786366837202 / 24 Nov '97 / RCA

☐ ROCKY MOUNTAIN HIGH
Rocky mountain high / Mother nature's son / Paradise / For baby (for Bobbie) / D'Arcy farrow / Prisoners / Goodbye again / Season suite
12925 / Dec '97 / Laserlight

☐ SUNSHINE ON MY SHOULDERS
Sunshine on my shoulders / Deal with the ladies / Amazon / Eclipse / Earth day every day / Ancient rhymes / Tenderly calling / Falling leaves / Islands / Children of the universe
12926 / Dec '97 / Laserlight

☐ TAKE ME HOME
Take me home, country roads / Back home again / Thank God I'm a country boy / I'm sorry / Grandma's feather bed / Eagle and the hawk / Children of the universe / Potter's wheel / Tenderly calling / Windsong / Rocky mountain suite (Cold nights in Canada) / Bread and roses / Alaska and me / Home grown tomatoes / Never a doubt / Country girl in Paris
CTS 55434 / Apr '96 / Country Stars

☐ TAKE ME HOME COUNTRY ROADS
Take me home country roads / Homegrown tomatoes / Eagles and horses / Ponies / High wide and handsome / Hold on to me / Whispering Jesse / Never a doubt / Eagle and the hawk / I watch you sleeping / For you
12923 / Dec '97 / Laserlight

☐ TWO DIFFERENT DIRECTIONS (2CD Set)
DBP 102008 / Oct '95 / Double Platinum

☐ UNPLUGGED COLLECTION, THE
Annie's song / Perhaps love / Dreamland express / Rocky mountain high / Seasons of the heart / Whispering Jesse / Take me home / For you / Windsong / Leaving on a jetplane / I'm sorry / Back home again / Sunshine on my shoulders / Thank God I'm a country boy / Christmas for Cowboys / Love again
8231372 / 3 Nov '97 / EMI

☐ WILDLIFE CONSERVATION SOCIETY CONCERT
Rocky mountain high / Rhymes and reasons / Country roads / Back home again / I guess he'd rather be in Colorado / Matthew / Sunshine on my shoulders / You say the battle is over / Eagles and horses / Darcy Farrow / Whispering Jesse / Me and my uncle / Wild mountain skies / Leaving on a jet plane/Goodbye again / Bet on the blues / Harder they fall / Shanghai breezes / Fly away / Song for all lovers / Dreamland express / For you / Is it love / Falling out of love / Annie's song / Poems prayers and promises / Calypso / Amazon / This old guitar
4806942 / Aug '95 / Columbia

Denver, Karl

☐ JUST LOVING YOU
From a Jack to a King / Garden party / I can't stop loving you / San Fernando / King of the road / Just loving you / Song for Maria / Walk on by / Won't give up / Runaway / Voices of the Highlands / Little bitty tear / Travelling light / Answer to everything / Story of my life
PZA 004CD / Oct '93 / Plaza

Denzil

☐ PUB
Fat loose and fancies me / Running this family / Rake around the grave / Useless / Sunday service Hengistbury Head / Too scared to be true / Bastard son of Elvis / Funny moon / Shame / Who made you so cynical about me / Autistic / If only Alan won the pools / Seven years in these boots / Your sister song / Cutie / Goodnight darling
74321189662 / Jan '95 / RCA

Deodato, Eumir

☐ OS CATEDRATICOS 73
100001CD / Apr '97 / Rare Brazil

☐ PRELUDE
Also sprach Zarathustra / Spirit of summer / Carly and Carole / Baubles, bangles and beads / Prelude to the afternoon of a faun / September 13 / Area code 808 / Pina Colada / Love Island / Whistle bump / San Juan sunset / Take the 'A' train / Tahiti hut (Ta Pa E) / Chariot of the Gods
ZK 65129 / 8 Sep '97 / Sony Jazz

☐ PRELUDE/DEODATO VOL.2
4505582 / Jan '94 / CBS

Departure

☐ DEPARTURE
ESM 028 / 2 Mar '98 / Escape

Depeche Mode

☐ 101
Pimpf / Behind the wheel / Strangelove / Sacred / Something to do / Blasphemous rumours / Stripped / Somebody / Things you said / Black celebration / Shake the disease / Nothing / Pleasure little treasure / People are people / Question of time / Never let me down again / Question of lust / Master and servant / Just can't get enough / Everything counts
CDSTUMM 101 / Jan '89 / Mute

☐ BLACK CELEBRATION
Black celebration / Fly on the windscreen (Final) / Question of lust / Sometimes / It doesn't matter / Question of time / Stripped / Here is the house / World full of nothing / Dressed in black / New dress / But not tonight / Breathing in fumes / Black day
CDSTUMM 26 / Jan '86 / Mute

☐ BROKEN FRAME, A
Leave in silence / My secret garden / Monument / Nothing to fear / See you / Satellite / Meaning of love / A photograph of you / Shouldn't have done that / Sun and the rainfall
CDSTUMM 9 / ' / Mute

☐ CONSTRUCTION TIME AGAIN
Love in itself / More than a party / Everything counts / Pipeline / Two minute warning / Shame / Landscape is changing / Told you so / And then
CDSTUMM 13 / Jan '86 / Mute

☐ INTERVIEW SESSIONS
CHAT 14 / 1 Dec '97 / Chatback

☐ INTERVIEW, THE
SPEEK 013 / 16 Mar '98 / Talking Music

☐ MUSIC FOR THE MASSES
Things you said / Strangelove / Sacred / Little 15 / Behind the wheel / I want you now / To have and to hold / Nothing / Pimpf / Agent Orange / Never let me down again / To have and to hold (Spanish taster) / Pleasure little treasure
CDSTUMM 47 / Sep '87 / Mute

☐ SINGLES '81-'85
People are people / Master and servant / It's called a heart / Just can't get enough / See you / Shake the disease / Everything counts / New life / Blasphemous rumours / Leave in silence / Get the balance right / Love in itself / Dreaming of me
CDMUTEL 1 / '85 / Mute

☐ SOME GREAT REWARD
If you want to / Master and servant / Lie to me / Something to do / Blasphemous rumours / Somebody / People are people / It don't matter / Stories of old / Pipeline / Everything counts / Two minute warning
CDSTUMM 19 / '84 / Mute

☐ SONGS OF FAITH AND DEVOTION
I feel you / Walking in my shoes / Condemnation / Mercy in you / In your room / Get right with me / Rush / One caress / Higher love / Judas
CDSTUMM 106 / Apr '93 / Mute

☐ SONGS OF FAITH AND DEVOTION - LIVE
I feel you / Walking in my shoes / Condemnation / Mercy in you / Judas / In your room / Get right with me / Rush / One caress / Higher love
LCDSTUMM 106 / Dec '93 / Mute

☐ SPEAK AND SPELL
New life / Just can't get enough / I sometimes wish I was dead / Puppets / Boys say go / No disco / What's your name / Photographic / Tora tora tora / Big muff / Any second now
CDSTUMM 5 / Jun '88 / Mute

☐ SPEAKING ONLY (Interview Disc)
3D 011 / Dec '96 / Network

☐ ULTRA
Barrel of a gun / Love thieves / Home / It's no good / Uselink / Useless / Sister of night / Jazz thieves / Freestate / Bottom line / Insight
CDSTUMM 148 / Apr '97 / Mute

☐ VIOLATOR
World in my eyes / Sweetest perfection / Personal Jesus / Halo / Waiting for the night / Enjoy the silence / Policy of truth / Blue dress / Clean
CDSTUMM 64 / Mar '90 / Mute

Depravity

☐ SILENCE OF THE CENTURIES
CDAR 017 / May '94 / Adipocre

Depth Charge

☐ NINE DEADLY VENOMS
STEAM 100CD / Nov '94 / Vinyl Solution

Der Dritte Raum

☐ DER DRITTE RAUM
HHCD 008 / Nov '94 / Harthouse

Derailers

☐ JACKPOT
WTM 1051 / 2 Feb '98 / Watermelon

Derby County FC

☐ RAMS SONG, THE (14 Derby Anthems) (Various Artists)
Going back to Derby: *Austin, Rockin' Johnny* / Forward Derby County: *Derby County FC* / Rams song: *Wynton, Carl Sound 1975* / Supporter's lament: *Wynton, Carl Sound 1975* / We will follow you: *Syndrome* / Sure beats going to work on a Sunday: *Syndrome* / Roy McFarland: *Austin, Rockin' Johnny* / It's only a game: *Clough, Brian & Friends* / I wish I could play like Charlie George: *Strikers* / Vintage football: *Derby County FC* / Dambuster's march: *Central Band of The Royal Air Force* / Jim Smith's mission: *Universal* / Paulo Wanchope: *Derby County FC*
CDGAFFER 24 / 3 Aug '98 / Cherry Red

Derek & The Dominoes

☐ DEREK AND THE DOMINOES IN CONCERT (2CD Set)
Why does love got to be so sad / Got to get better in a little while / Let it rain / Presence of the Lord / Tell the truth / Bottle of red wine / Roll it over / Blues power / Have you ever loved a woman
8314162 / Jan '94 / Polydor

☐ LAYLA REMASTERED - 20TH ANNIVERSARY EDITION (2CD Set)
I looked away / Bell bottom blues / Keep on growing / Nobody knows you when you're down and out / I'm yours / Anyday / Keep to the highway / Tell the truth / Why does love got to be so sad / Have you ever loved a woman / Little wing / It's too late / Layla / Thorn in the garden / Jam I / Jam ii / Jam iii / Jam iv / Jam v / Have you ever loved a woman (alternate master 1) / Have you ever loved a woman (alternate master 2) / Tell the truth (jam i) / Tell the truth (jam ii) / Mean old world (rehearsal) / Mean old world (band version master take) / Mean old world (duet version master take) / (when things go wrong) it hurts me too (jam) / Tender love (incomplete master) / It's too late (alternate master)
8470832 / Oct '90 / Polydor

☐ LIVE AT THE FILLMORE
Got to get better in a little while / Why does love got to be so sad / Key to the highway / Blues power / Have you ever loved a woman / Bottle of red wine / Tell the truth / Nobody knows you when you're down and out / Roll it over / OPresence of the Lord / Little wing / Let it rain / Crossroads
5216822 / Apr '96 / Polydor

Deris, Andi

☐ COME IN FROM THE RAIN
House of pleasure / Come in from the rain / Think higher / Good bye Jenny / King of 7 eyes / Foreign rainbow / Somewhere, someday, someway / They wait / Now that I know this ain't love / Could I leave forever / 1000 Years away
SRECD 701 / May '97 / Reef

Derise, Joe

☐ HOUSE OF FLOWERS
ACD 153 / Apr '93 / Audiophile

☐ SINGS & PLAYS THE JIMMY VAN HEUSEN ANTHOLOGY
ACD 234 / Oct '92 / Audiophile

Derome, Jean

☐ CONFITURES DE GAGAKU
VICTOCD 05 / Oct '94 / Victo

Derrane, Joe

☐ GIVE US ANOTHER
GLCD 1149 / Jun '95 / Green Linnet

☐ IRISH ACCORDION MASTERS
COPCD 5009 / Feb '96 / Copley

☐ IRISH ACCORDION, THE
COP 5008CD / Mar '94 / Cop

☐ RETURN TO INIS MOR (Derrane, Joe & Carl Hession)
GLCD 1163 / Jun '96 / Green Linnet

☐ TIE THAT BINDS, THE
Visitors / Old copperplate / O'Connors favorite / Frieze breeches / Ann from Monaghan / Gan ainm / Caprice / Short road / Cavan's own / Buttermilk Mary / Dever the dancer / McDonagh's
SHANCD 78009 / 9 Mar '98 / Shanachie

Derrero

☐ DERRERO
BNR 102CD / Jun '97 / Big Noise

☐ SMALL POCKET MACHINE
BNR 103CD / 27 Oct '97 / Lookout

Derriere Le Miroir

☐ ALIBI
EFA 119022 / Jan '94 / Apollyon

☐ PREGNANT
EFA 119312 / Mar '94 / Derriere

Derringer, Rick

☐ ARCHIVE ALIVE
ACHV 80012 / Sep '97 / Archive

☐ BACK TO THE BLUES
Trouble in paradise / Blue suede blues / Mean town blues / Sorry for your heartache / Sink or swim / Diamond / Cry baby / Unsolved mystery / Blue velvet
RR 90482 / Sep '96 / Roadrunner

☐ BLUES DELUXE
2039 / 22 Jun '98 / Blues Bureau

☐ ELECTRA BLUES
RR 89682 / Sep '94 / Roadrunner

☐ GUITARS AND WOMEN
Something warm / Guitars and women / Everything / Man in the middle / It must be love / Desires of the heart / Timeless / Hopeless romantic / Need a little girl / Don't ever say goodbye
RE 821702 / 30 Jun '98 / Razor & Tie

☐ KING BISCUIT PRESENTS...
Guitars and women / On my way up / Party at the hotel / Rock and roll hoochie koo / Let me in / Beyond the universe / Jump jump jump / Just another night / All the young dudes / Right place wrong time
KBFHCD 021 / 24 Aug '98 / King Biscuit

☐ RICK DERRINGER AND FRIENDS
88036 / 20 Apr '98 / KNB

☐ WOMEN AND GUITARS
RE 82170 / 3 Aug '98 / Razor & Tie

Dervish

☐ AT THE END OF THE DAY
Touching cloth / Ar eirinn ni neosfainn ee hi / Jim Coleman's set / An spailpin fanach / Packie Duignan's / Lone shanakyle / Drag her round the road / Peata beag / Trip to Sligo / Sheila Nee Iyer / Kilavill set / I courted a wee girl / Josefin's waltz / Thirty seconds / Eileen McMahon
WHRL 003 / Sep '96 / Whirling Discs

☐ BOYS OF SLIGO, THE
Donegal set / Dolphin / Clapton jigs / Thos Byrnes / Man of Arran / Jackson's / Cliffs of Glencolumbkille / Silgo set / Martin Wynne's / Lad O'Beirne's / McDermotts / Raphoe reel / Chestnut tree / Boys of silgo / Montaghan twig / World's end set / Eddie Kelly's jigs / Return from Camden Town / Key of the Convent / Tommie people's reel / Dancing bear / Oreaga / Walsh's fancy / Congress / Spoil the dance
SUNCD 1 / Sep '94 / Sound

☐ HARMONY HILL
WHRL 001CD / Aug '93 / Whirling Discs

☐ LIVE IN PALMA (2CD Set)
WHRL 004 / Sep '97 / Whirling Discs

☐ PLAYING WITH FIRE
WHRL 002 / Apr '95 / Whirling Discs

Des, Henri

☐ DES NO.5
MCD 237 684 / '88 / Accord

Des Plantes, Ted

☐ CHRISTMAS NIGHT IN HARLEM STRIDE STYLE
SACD 125 / Jan '97 / Solo Art

☐ TED DES PLANTES
JCD 225 / Oct '93 / Jazzology

Desai, Ashit

☐ MANGAL DHWANI
Mangalam / Anand / Prakash / Sundaram / Paawan / Shobeet / Aashiwaad
NRCD 4001 / Feb '98 / Navras

Desanto, Sugar Pie

☐ DOWN IN THE BASEMENT (The Chess Years)
In the basement / I want to know / Mama didn't raise no fools / There's gonna be trouble / I don't feel sorry / Maybe you'll be there / Do I make myself clear / Use what you got / Can't let you go / Soulful dress / I don't wanna fuss / Going back to where I belong / It won't be long / She's got everything / Wish you were mine / Slip-in mules
MCD 09275 / Apr '97 / Chess/MCA

Desaster

☐ STORMBRINGER
MRCD 005 / 1 Sep '97 / Merciless

☐ TOUCH OF MEDIEVAL DARKNESS, A
MRCD 003 / 1 Sep '97 / Merciless

Descendents

☐ ALL
All / Coolidge / No, all / Van / Cameage / Impressions / Iceman / Jealous of the world / Clean sheets / Pep talk / All-o-gistics / Schizophrenia / Uranus
SST 112CD / May '93 / SST

☐ BONUS FAT
SST 144CD / May '93 / SST

☐ ENJOY
Enjoy / Floater / 50/50 / Sausage / Barnacle / Loaf / Carbuncle / Choda / Half pipe / Cable service / Lockout
SST 242CD / Sep '90 / SST

☐ EVERYTHING SUCKS
64812 / Sep '96 / Epitaph

☐ HALLRAKER
Global probing / My world / Hurtin crue / Hey hey / Kabuki girl / All / Pep talk / Jealous of the world / Christmas vacation / I like food / Iceman / Good good things / Cheer / Rock star / No fb / Cameage
SST 205CD / May '93 / SST

☐ I DON'T WANT TO GROW UP
Descendents / I don't want to grow up / Pervert / Rock star / No fb / Can't go back / Gcf / My world / Theme / Silly girl / In love this way / Christmas vacation / Good good things / Ace
SST 143CD / Feb '88 / SST

☐ LIVEAGE
All / I'm not a loser / Silly girl / I wanna be a bear / Coolidge / Weinerschnitel / I don't want to grow up / Kids / Wendy / Get the time / Descendents / All-o-gistics / Myage / My dad sucks / Van / Surburban home / Hope / Clean sheets
SST 163CD / Jan '88 / SST

☐ MILO GOES TO COLLEGE
SST 142CD / May '93 / SST

☐ SOMERY
SST 259CD / May '93 / SST

☐ TWO THINGS AT ONCE
My age / I wanna be a bear / I'm not a loser / Parents / Tonyage / M-16 / I'm not a punk / Catalina / Suburban home / Statue of liberty / Kabuki girl / Marriage / Hope / Bikeage / Jean is dead / My dad sucks / Mr. bass / I like food / Hey hey / Weinerschnitzel / Global probing / Ride the wild / It's a hectic world
SST 145CD / May '93 / SST

Desde El Sur De Europa

☐ ESTAMPAS
21101CD / Aug '97 / Sonifolk

Desecration

☐ MURDER IN MIND
Intro / Murder in mind / Impaled / Cerebal annoxia / Stillborn climax / Beyond recognition / Bathroom autopsy / Victimised / IS / Obscene publication / Crave for rot
COP 06 / 11 May '98 / Copro

Desford Colliery Band

☐ ANDREW LLOYD WEBBER IN BRASS (Desford Colliery Caterpillar Band)
340472 / Dec '94 / Koch

☐ GREGSON (Desford Colliery Caterpillar Band)
Dances and arias / Concerto for french horn and brass band / Connotations / Of men and mountains
DOYCD 017 / Nov '92 / Doyen

☐ MAKING TRACKS (Desford Colliery Caterpillar Band)
Westward go / London overture / Little red bird / Russky percussky / River city serenade / Impromptu for tuba / Mountain song / Folks who live on the hill / Poinciana / Pantomime / Trumpet blues and cantabile / Make believe / Oceans
QPRL 045D / Jun '90 / Polyphonic

Desfougeres

☐ WAROK
L'OZ 09CD / Dec '97 / L'Oz

Designer

☐ GOIN' DE DISTANCE
JW 057CD / Feb '94 / Soca

Desmond, Johnny

☐ ONCE UPON A TIME/BLUE SMOKE
All the things you are / My heart stood still / Night and day / Where or when / Symphony / Together / I'll be seeing you / I'll walk alone / I'll remember April / Sweet Lorraine / Amor / Time on my hands / I'm through with love / No-one ever tells you / Party's over / I gotta right to sing the blues / It's a lonesome old town / Blue smoke / Last night when we were young / Why shouldn't I / Imagination / That old feeling / You go to my head / I'm glad there is you / Bluesmoke
4810162 / Aug '95 / Columbia

Desmond, Paul

☐ BEST OF PAUL DESMOND, THE
Song to a seagull / Take ten / Romance de amor / Was a sunny day / Summer song/Summertime / Squeeze me / I'm old fashioned / Nuages / You'd be so nice to come home to / Autumn leaves / Skylark / Vocalise
ZK 45484 / Feb '96 / Sony Jazz

☐ COMPLETE RCA VICTOR RECORDINGS, THE (5CD Set)
My funny valentine / Desmond blue / Then I'll be tired of you / I've got you under my skin / Late lament / I should care / Like someone in love / Ill wind / Body and soul / Advise and consent / Autumn leaves / Imagination / Take ten / El prince / Alone together / Embarcadero / Black orpheus / Nancy / Samba de orphue / One I love belongs to someone else / Out of nowhere / El prince / Glad to be unhappy / Poor butterfly / Stranger in town / Taste of honey / Any other time / Hi Lili / Hi Lo / Angel eyes / By the river Sainte Marie / All across the city / All through the night / Bossa antigua / Night has a thousand eyes / O gato samba cantina / Curacao doloroso / Ship without a sail / Alianca / Girl from east 9th street / Night has a thousand eyes / Samba cepeda / O Gato
09026686872 / 9 Feb '98 / RCA Victor

☐ DESMOND BLUE
My funny Valentine / Desmond blue / Then I'll be tired of you / I've got you under my skin / Late lament / I should care / Like someone in love / Ill wind / Body and soul / Advise and consent / Autumn leaves / Imagination
09026687082 / Feb '97 / RCA Victor

☐ FEELING BLUE
When Joanna loved me / Alone together / Here's that rainy day / Body and soul / Samba d'Orpheu / Polka dots and moonbeams / Bewitched / That old feeling / I've got you under my skin / I've grown accustomed to her face / One I love (belongs to someone else) / Easy living / Embarcadero / All the things you are
74321400552 / Sep '96 / Camden

☐ JAZZ GREATS
Take ten / I've grown accustomed to her face / Black Orpheus theme / Hi lili hi lo / Desmond blue / Embarcadero / Polka dot and moonbeams / All the things you are / El prince / Alone together / Taste of honey / O gato
74321556872 / Feb '98 / RCA Victor

☐ LIKE SOMEONE IN LOVE
Just squeeze me / Tangerine / Meditation / Nuages / Like someone in love / Things ain't what they used to be
CD 83319 / Nov '92 / Telarc

☐ PAUL DESMOND & THE MJQ (Desmond, Paul & The MJQ)
Greensleeves / You go to my head / Blue dove (la paloma azul) / Jesus christ superstar / Here's that rainy day / East of the sun / Bag's new groove
4749842 / May '94 / Sony Jazz

☐ PURE DESMOND
Squeeze me / I'm old fashioned / Nuages / Why shouldn't I / Everything I love / Warm valley / Till the clouds roll by / Mean to me / Song from MASH / Wave
ZK 40806 / Feb '96 / Sony Jazz
ZK 64767 / Jan '96 / Mastersound

☐ SKYLARK
Take ten / Romance de amor / Was a sunny day / Music for a while / Skylark / Indian summer / Music for a while / Skylark / Indian summer
ZK 65133 / 8 Sep '97 / Sony Jazz

☐ TAKE TEN
Take ten / El prince / Alone together / Embarcadero / Black orpheus / Nancy / Samba d'Orpheus / One I love
07863661462 / Apr '93 / Bluebird

☐ TRIBUTE TO PAUL DESMOND, A (Various Artists)
JD 156 / May '97 / Chesky

☐ TWO OF A MIND (Desmond, Paul & Gerry Mulligan)
All the things you are / Stardust / Two of a mind / Blight of the fumble bee / Way you look tonight / Out of nowhere
09026685132 / Oct '96 / RCA Victor

Desmond, Trudy

☐ MAKE ME RAINBOWS
378032 / May '96 / Koch Jazz

☐ MY ONE AND ONLY
I got rhythm / Fascinatin' rhythm / Somebody loves me / Things are lookin' up / My one and only / Promenade / They all laughed / For you for me for evermore / Nice work if you can get it / Piano prelude II / They can't take that away from me / Shall we dance / Love is here to stay
JTR 84682 / 27 Jul '98 / Justin Time

☐ TAILOR MADE
Day by day / Goody goody / I see your face before me / Lucky to be me / I'm shadowing you / By myself / Anyone can whistle / I thought about you / Make someone happy / Guess I'll hang my tears out to dry / People will say we're in love / I'll never be the same
TJA 10015 / Oct '92 / Jazz Alliance

Desotos

☐ CRUISIN' WITH THE DESOTOS
WCD 9026 / Sep '91 / Wilson Audiophile

Desperadoes Steel Orchestra

☐ JAMMER, THE
Jammer / No pan / Ah goin an party tonight / Moliendo cafe / Africa / Rebecca / Symphony in G / Musical volcano
DE 4023 / Jan '94 / Delos

Des'ree

☐ I AIN'T MOVIN'
Herald the day / Crazy maze / You gotta be / Little child / Strong enough / Trip on love / I ain't movin' / Living in the city / In my dreams / Love is here / I ain't movin' (Percussion reprise)
4758432 / May '94 / Sony Soho2

☐ MIND ADVENTURES
Average man / Feel so high / Sun of '79 / Why should I love you / Stand on my own ground / Competitive world / Mind adventures / Laughter / Save me / Momma, please don't cry
4712632 / Mar '96 / Sony Soho2

☐ SUPERNATURAL
What's your sign / God only knows / Life / Best days / Proud to be a dread / I'm kissing you / Indigo daisies / Time / Down by the river / Darwin Star / Fire
4897192 / 29 Jun '98 / Sony Soho2

Destination

☐ AEOA
FX 168 / Aug '96 / Kirkelig Kultuverksted

Destinations

☐ HERE WE ARE
LI 1001 / Oct '96 / Little Italy

Destiny

☐ NOTHING LEFT TO FEAR
Nothing left to fear / Mediaeval rendezvous / Evil trinity / Sirens in the dark / Sheer death / F.o.s. / Beyond all sense / No reservation / Raven / Rest in peace / Du gamla du fria
CDATV 18 / May '91 / Active

☐ UNDISCOVERED COUNTRY
GNW 01CD / 25 May '98 / GNW

Destiny's Child

☐ DESTINY'S CHILD
Second nature / No no no / With me / Tell me / Bridges / No no no / With me / Show me the way / Killing time / Illusion / Birthday / Sail on / My time has come / Know that
4885352 / 2 Mar '98 / Columbia

Destroy

☐ NECROPOLIS
POLLUTE 19 / Aug '97 / Sound Pollution

Destroy All Monsters

☐ BORED
You're gonna die / November 22nd 1963 / Meet the creeper / Nobody knows / What do I get / Goin' to lose / Bored
CDMRED 94 / Apr '97 / Cherry Red

☐ SILVER WEDDING
SFTRI 444 / Oct '96 / Sympathy For The Record Industry

Destroyer 666

☐ UNCHAIN THE WOLVES
MIM 7325CD / Jun '97 / Modern Invasion

☐ VIOLENCE IS THE PRINCE OF THIS WORLD
MIM 7320CD / Jan '96 / Modern Invasion

Destruction

☐ BEST OF DESTRUCTION, THE (2CD Set)
SPV 08476482 / Mar '97 / SPV

☐ DESTRUCTION
UAM 0447 / Oct '95 / UAM

☐ ETERNAL DEVASTATION
5035032 / 30 Mar '98 / Axe Killer

☐ INFERNAL OVERKILL/SENTENCE OF DEATH
857529 / '89 / Steamhammer

☐ LIVE WITHOUT SENSE
CDNUK 126 / Feb '89 / Noise

☐ MAD BUTCHER/ETERNAL DEVASTATION
851860 / '89 / SPV

Desultory

☐ SWALLOW THE SNAKE
398414109CD / Sep '96 / Metal Blade

Det Hedenske Folk

☐ DET HEDENSKE FOLK/ABYSSIC HATE (United By Heathen Blood) (Det Hedenske Folk/Abyssic Hate)
BLCR 7002CD / Jun '97 / Bloodless Creations

Det-Ri-Mental

☐ XENOPHOBIA
Bhangra attack / Informer / Total revolution / Richmans world (suffering pt 2) / Children of a rat race (aye man) / Sista India / Bank robber / Babylon / Living on the edge / Unkown identity (Inn-a-England)
DEBTCD 003 / Oct '95 / Debt

Detective

☐ DETECTIVE
Recognition / Got enough love / Grim reaper / Nightingale / Detective man / Ain't none of your business / Deep down / Wild hot summer / One more heartache
7567914152 / Jan '96 / Atlantic

☐ IT TAKES ONE TO KNOW ONE
Help me up / Competition / Are you talkin' to me / Dynamite / Something beautiful / Warm love / Betcha won't dance / Fever / Tear jerker
7567804032 / Jan '96 / Atlantic

Deteriorate

☐ SENECTUOS ENTRANCE, THE
RRS 952CD / Sep '96 / Die Hard/ Progress

Detest

☐ DORVAL
NB 104 / Mar '94 / Nuclear Blast

Dethmuffen, Miles

☐ CLUTTER
QTZ 012 / Apr '94 / Quartz

Detroit

☐ GET OUT THE VOTE (Detroit & Mitch Ryder)
NER 3010CD / May '97 / Total Energy

Detroit Cobras

☐ MINK RAT OR RABBIT
SFTRI 525CD / 23 Mar '98 / Sympathy For The Record Industry

Detroit Emeralds

☐ DO ME RIGHT/YOU WANT IT YOU GOT IT
Do me right / Wear this ring / Long live the king / What you gonna do about me / You can't take this love for you, from me / Just now and then / Lee / If I lose your love / And I love her / I can't see myself (Doing without you) / Holding on / Admit your love is gone / You want it, you got it / There's love for me somewhere / I'll never sail the sea again / Take my love / Feel the need / I've got to move / Baby let me take you (in my arms) / I bet you get the one you love / Till you decide to come home / Radio promo medley:
CDSEWD 067 / Apr '93 / Westbound

☐ GREATEST HITS
Do me right / Holding on / I think of you / Feel the need in me / I bet you get the one / Baby let me take you / You're gettin' a little too smart / You wan t it you got it / Long live the king / Guess who's been talking / I'm qualified / Yes I know I'm in love / Lee / Something you got / Set it out / My dreams have got the best of me / Feel the need / I can't seem to forget / There's a love for me somewhere / I can't see myself (doing without you) / Heaven couldn't be like this / I'll never sail the sea again / Lonely corner / Only the young
CDSEWD 119 / 23 Feb '98 / Westbound

☐ I'M IN LOVE WITH YOU
Shake your head / You're getting a little too smart / What'cha gonna wear tomorrow / My dreams have got the best of me / So long / I think of you / Heaven couldn't be like this/Without you baby
CDSEW 006 / Jun '89 / Westbound

☐ I'M IN LOVE WITH YOU/FEEL THE NEED IN ME
Shake your head / So long / You're getting too smart / I think of you / What'cha gonna wear tomorrow / Heaven couldn't be like this/without you baby / My dreams have got the best of you / Set it out / Take it or leave it / Feel the need in me / Wednesday / Love for you / Look what has happened to our love / Sexy ways / Love has come to me
CDSEWD 068 / Nov '93 / Westbound

Detroit Spinners

☐ DANCIN' AND LOVIN'
Disco ride / Body language / Let's boogie, let's dance / Working my way back to you / Forgive me girl / With my eyes / 1122 Boogie Woogie Avenue
8122711152 / Jan '96 / Atlantic

☐ FROM HERE TO ETERNITY/LOVE TRIPPIN' (Spinners)
CCLCD 62022 / 3 Aug '98 / Collectables

☐ HAPPINESS IS BEING WITH THE SPINNERS/SPINNERS NO.8 (Spinners)
CCLCD 62012 / 3 Aug '98 / Collectables

☐ LOVE TRIPPIN'
Love trippin' / Heavy on the sunshine / Cupid / I've loved you for a long time / I just want to be with you / Street wise / Working my way back to you / I just want to fall in love / Now that you're mine again / Split decision / I'm takin' you back / Pipe dream / Body language
7567803782 / Jan '96 / Atlantic

☐ SPINNERS LIVE (Spinners)
CCLCD 62002 / 3 Aug '98 / Collectables

☐ YESTERDAY TODAY AND TOMORROW/LABOUR OF LOVE (Spinners)
CCLCD 62032 / 3 Aug '98 / Collectables

Detroiters

☐ OLD TIME RELIGION (Detroiters & Golden Echoes)
He walks with me / Mother on the train take 2 / Mother on the train take 3 / Angels watching over me / I trust in Jesus / Ride on king Jesus / Mother, don't cry about your child / Let Jesus lead you / Mother, I need your prayer / Old time religion / Sometimes / Body and soul / Shady green pastures / Where shall I be / Down on my knees / My life is in his hands / When the saints go marching in (take 2) / When the saints go marching in / When I lay my burden down / I'm so happy in the service of the lord / Waiting and watching / Yield not to temptation take 1 / Yield not to temptation take 2 / Yield not to temptation take 3
CDCHD 467 / Mar '93 / Ace

Deuce

☐ ON THE LOOSE
Call it love / Talk to me / What you wanna be / Rumours / Let's call it a day / I need you / Boyfriend girlfriend / I'll be there for you / I was wrong / Kiss it
8286642 / Aug '95 / London

dEUS

☐ IN A BAR UNDER THE SEA
I don't mind whatever happens / Fell off the floor man / Opening night / Theme from turnpike / Little arithmetics / Gimme the heat / Serpentine / Shocking lack thereof / Supermarketsong / Memory of a festival / Guilty pleasures / Nine threads / Disappointed in the sun / Roses / Wake me up before I sleep
CID 8052 / Oct '96 / Island

☐ MY SISTER IS MY CLOCK
Middlewave / Almost white / Health insurance / Little ghost / How to row a cat / Only a colour to her / Sick sugar / Sweetness / Horror party jokes / Void / Sans titre pour sira / Glovesong / Lorre in the forest
IMCD 8031 / Jan '95 / Island

☐ WORST CASE SCENARIO
Intro / Suds and soda / WCS (1st draft) / Jigsaw you / Morticiachair / Via / Right as rain / Mute / Let's get lost / Hotellounge (be the death of me) / Shake your hip / Great American nude / Secret hell / Divebomb djingle
CID 8028 / 8 Feb '98 / Island

Deutsch, Alex

☐ PINK INC. (Deutsch, Alex, George Garzone & Jamaladeen Tacuma)
DIW 852 / Nov '91 / DIW

Deutscher, Drafi

☐ DIE DECCA JAHRE 1963-68
Teeny / Shu-bi-do the slop / Grun, grun ist Tennessee / Kleine Peggy Lou / Shake hands / Come on let's go / Cinderella baby / Es ist besser, wenn du gebst / Keep smiling / Es war einmal / Hast du alles vergessen / Heute male ich dein Bild, Cindy Lou / Mr. Tambourine man / Keiner weiss, wie es morgen sein wird / Nimm mich so wie ich bin / Ich geh' durch's Feuer fur dich / Marmor, Stein und Eisen bricht / Das sind die einsamen jahre / Honey bee / Hello little girl / Ich hab' den mond in meiner tasche / An deiner seite / Old old Germany / Mit schirm, Frack und Melone / Mit schirm, charme und melone / Die goldene zeit: *Deutscher, Drafi & Manuela* / Take it easy: *Deutscher, Drafi & Manuela* / Was sind sie ohne Regen: *Deutscher, Drafi & Manuela* / Sweet dreams for you my love / Darlin' / Der hauptmann von Kopenick / Zwei fremde augen / Rock 'n' roll lady / Alice im Wunderland / Marble breaks, iron bends / Wanna take you home / Summertime / Bachelor boy / Trouble / Amanda / Wake up / Crying in the morning / Bleib, oh bleib / Junge leute brauchen liebe / Shake your hands / Good golly Miss Molly / Memphis Tennessee / Roll over Beethoven / What'd I say / What's the matter baby / Mit siebzehn fangt das Leben erst an / Komm zu mir / Zip a dee doo dah / Lion sleeps tonight / Hippy hippy shake / Shakin' all over / Ready Teddy / Marnor, stein und eisen bricht / Wunder / I don't need that kind of lovin' / Language of love / Tranen der liebe / Ich will frei sein / Welche farbe had die welt / He's got the whole world in his hands / Noah's arche / Waterloo / Denn da waren wir beide noch kinder / Liebe, gluck und treue / Bring grusse zu Mary
BCD 15416 / Dec '87 / Bear Family

☐ HITS, PSEUDONYMC AND RARITATEN
REP 4113 / Aug '91 / Repertoire

Deutschmark Bob

☐ BAD WITH WIMMIN (Deutschmark Bob & The Deficits)
CD 12878 / Apr '97 / Crypt

☐ BUSH HOG'N MAN
EFA 12894CD / Jul '97 / Crypt

Deux Filles

☐ SILENCE AND WISDOM
Letter / L'intrigue / Drinking at a stream / Oakwood green / Children of clay / Sur la plage / Her masters voice / Draw in room / She slides / Fleurs doll / Mortuary / City sleeps / Birds / Silence and wisdom / Festival
BAH 1 / Feb '93 / Humbug

Devan

☐ RAGGAFUNKIN'
WCCD 001 / Sep '96 / Wild Cherry

DeVaughan, William

☐ BE THANKFUL FOR WHAT YOU GOT/ FIGURES CAN'T CALCULATE
Give the little man a great big hand / Something's being done / Blood is thicker than water / Kiss and make up / You gave me a brand new start / Be thankful for what you got / Sing a love song / You can do it / We are his children / Be thankful for what you've got / Hold on to love / Boogie Dan / Figures can't calculate (the love I have for you) / Love comes so easy with you / You send me / I've never found a girl
NEMCD 700 / Nov '94 / Sequel

Devi, Girija

☐ GIRIJA DEVI IN CONCERT
C 560056 / Oct '95 / Ocora

Deviant Electronics

☐ BRAINWASHING IS CHILD'S PLAY
HEXCD 2 / Mar '97 / Helix

Deviants

☐ DEVIANTS VOL.3
CTCD 061 / Jul '97 / Captain Trip

☐ DISPOSABLE
CTCD 042 / Jul '97 / Captain Trip

☐ DISPOSABLE
PILOT 032 / 27 Apr '98 / Burning Airlines

☐ HUMAN GARBAGE (Live At Dingwalls 1984)
CTCD 092 / 27 Apr '98 / Captain Trip

☐ PTOOFF
Opening / Opening / Child of the sky / Charlie / Nothing man / Garbage / Bun / Deviation street
DOCD 1988 / Nov '92 / Drop Out

Deviate

☐ CRISIS OF CONFIDENCE
MASSCD 042 / Oct '94 / Massacre

☐ THORN OF THE LIVING
IS 889890CD / Jun '97 / I Scream Music

☐ WRECK STYLE
IS 889860CD / 15 Dec '97 / I Scream Music

Deviated Instinct

☐ RE-OPENING OLD WOUNDS
DAR 011CD / Nov '94 / Desperate Attempt

Device

☐ 22B3
Hanging on a heart attack / Who says / Pieces on the ground / Tough and tender / When love is good / Didn't I read you right / Fall apart, golden heart / I've got no room for your love / Who's on the line / Sandstone, cobwebs and dust
RME 0107CD / 19 Jan '98 / Renaissance

Devil Dogs

☐ 30 SIZZLING SLABS
EFA 11561 CD / Jun '93 / Crypt

☐ CHAOS BLAST
MTR 218CD / Sep '95 / Empty

☐ CHOAD BLAST
EFA 123572 / Mar '94 / Empty

☐ NO REQUESTS TONIGHT
SFTRI 310CD / Oct '97 / Sympathy For The Record Industry

☐ SATURDAY NIGHT FEVER
EFA 115362 / Jan '97 / Crypt

Devilyn

☐ ANGER
POSH 009CD / 15 Jun '98 / Listenable

Devine, Ian

☐ CARDIFFIANS (Devine, Ian & Alison Statton)
TWI 9062 / Oct '96 / Les Disques Du Crepuscule

Devine, Sydney

☐ 50 COUNTRY WINNERS
Country roads / Early morning rain / Gentle on my mind / Hello Mary Lou / Oh lonesome me / Sea of heartbreak / Lonesome number one / Blue blue day / Four walls / He'll have to go / You're free to go / Sweet dreams / Send me the pillow that you dream on / Satin sheets / Wild side of life / This song is just for you / Blackboard of my heart / Married by the bible, divorced by the law / Crying time / Together again / I can't stop loving you / Take these chains from my heart / Dear God / Where could I go but to the Lord / House of gold / You'll never walk alone / Blanket on the ground / Old flames / Blowin' in the wind / Sing me / Tiny bubbles / Early shells / Stand beside me / Gypsy woman / You're my best friend / Till the rivers all run dry / Please help me, I'm falling / Fraulein / I fall to pieces / It keeps right on a-hurtin' / Eighteen yellow roses / Ramblin' rose / Red roses for a blue lady / Irene / Lucille / Amanda / Lovesick blues / Singin' the blues / Knee deep in the blues / Long gone lonesome blues
PLATCD 18 / Oct '87 / Platinum

☐ BIG COUNTRY LINE DANCE PARTY VOL.1, THE
CDTIV 620 / Dec '96 / Scotdisc

☐ BIG COUNTRY LINE DANCE PARTY VOL.2, THE (20 Non Stop Line Dances)
Outback / Cherokee boogie / Hucklebuck / Macarena / Fly like a bird / No way Jose / Jazzy Joe / Cowboy strut / Red neck girl / Cowboy cha cha / Rock 'n' roll waltz / Elvira / Electric reel / Fallsview rock / Lightning cha cha / Slosh / I like it / Just for grins / Macarena / Cotton eye Joe / Break down of dances
CDITV 625 / 3 Nov '97 / Scotdisc

☐ CRYING TIME
Crying time / Broken engagement / My son calls another man daddy / Long black limousine / Two little orphans / Eighteen yellow roses / Old Shep / Letter edged in black / Nobody's child / I ain't crying, mister / Gentle mother / Come home rolling stone
EMPRCD 505 / Apr '94 / Emporio

☐ GREEN GRASS OF HOME, THE
Scotland forever / Mexicali rose / Way up in clachan / It's now or never / Nobody's child / Jealous heart / Green green grass of home / Loch lomond / I'm afraid to go back home / My mother's eyes / Have I told you lately that I love you / Sweet caroline / When your old wedding ring was new / Down in the glen / American trilogy
CDITV 530 / Dec '90 / Scotdisc

☐ NORFOLK COUNTRY
Bill's riff / China doll / Your cheatin' heart / Married by the bible / Crazy / Lightning express / Faded love / Just out of reach / Corrina corrina / Old rugged cross / Look at us / Don't fence me in / Sioux city sue / You are my sunshine / Miracle song / Nobody's darlin / Hear my song / Laura / This song's just for you / Wild side of life / Blackboard of my heart / Last farewell / Happy whistler
CDITV 598 / Nov '94 / Scotdisc

☐ VERY BEST OF SYDNEY DEVINE, THE
I can't stop loving you / Blackboard of my heart / Lovesick blues / Two little orphans / Bye bye love / Take these chains from my heart / Ain't that a shame / Blueberry hill / Corrine corrina / I ain't cryin' mister / Room full of roses / Crying time / Help me make it through the night / May the bird of paradise fly up your nose / Donna / Send me the pillow that you dream on / You're sixteen / It keeps right on hurtin' / She wears my ring / Rose Marie / Maggie
MCVD 30011 / Nov '96 / Emerald Gem

Deviser

☐ TRANSMISSION TO CHAOS
TM 1206CD / 3 Aug '98 / Mascot

Devlins

☐ WAITING
UND 53102 / 15 Jun '98 / Universal

Devo

☐ DEVO LIVE
Gates of steel / Be stiff / Planet Earth / Freedom of choice / Whip it / Girl U want
CDV 2106 / May '93 / Virgin

☐ DUTY NOW FOR THE FUTURE
Devo corporate anthem / Clockout / Timing x / Wiggly world / Block head / Strange pursuits / SIB (swelling itching brain) / Triumph of the will / Day my baby gave me a surprise / Pink pussycat / Secret agent man / Smart patrol / Redeye express / Mr. DNA
CDV 2125 / May '93 / Virgin

☐ DUTY NOW FOR THE FUTURE/OH NO IT'S DEVO/ARE WE NOT MEN (3CD Set)
TPAK 38 / Oct '94 / Virgin

☐ FREEDOM OF CHOICE
Girl u want / It's not right / Snowball / Ton o' lov / Freedom of choice / Gates of steel / Cold war / Don't you know / That's pep / Mr. B's ballroom / Planet Earth
CDV 2241 / May '93 / Virgin

☐ HARD CORE DEVO
422105 / May '94 / New Rose

☐ HARDCORE VOL.2
Booji / Boy's funeral / Can u take it / Bamboo bimbo / A plan for u / Rope song / Goo goo itch / Be stiff / All of us / Baby talkin' bitches / I need a chick / You got me bugged / Chango / Fraulein / Dogs of democracy / "37" / Bottled up / Working in the coal mine / I been refused / Fountain of filth / Clockout / Let's go
RCD 20208 / Sep '91 / Rykodisc

☐ HOT POTATOES: THE BEST OF DEVO
Jocko Homo / Mogoloid / Satisfaction / Whip it / Girl u want / Freedom of choice / Peek-a-boo / Through being cool / That's good / Working in a coalmine / Devo corporate anthem / Be stiff / Gates of steel / Come back Jonee / Secret agent man / Day my baby gave me a surprise / Beautiful world / Big mess / Whip it (remix)
CDVM 9016 / Aug '93 / Virgin

☐ LIVE MONGALOID YEARS
Satisfaction (i can't get no) / Too much paranoias / Praying hands / Uncontrollable urge / Mongoloid / Smart patrol-mr. dna / Gut feeling slap your mammy / Sloppy / Come back jonee / Clockout / Soo bawls / Space junk / Blockhead / Subhuman woman / Bamboo bimbo / Beulah / Jocko homo-i need a chick
RCD 20209 / Oct '92 / Rykodisc

☐ NEW TRADITIONALISTS
Through being cool / Jerkin' back 'n' forth / Pity you / Soft things / Race of doom / Going under / Love without anger / Super thing / Beautiful world / Enough said
CDV 2125 / May '93 / Virgin

☐ NOW IT CAN BE TOLD
727552 / Feb '95 / Restless

☐ OH NO IT'S DEVO
Time out for fun / Peek-a-boo / Out of sync / Explosions / That's good / Patterns / Big mess / Speed racer / What I must / I desire / Deep sleep
CDV 2241 / May '93 / Virgin

☐ Q. ARE WE NOT MEN (A. We Are Devo)
Uncontrollable urge / Satisfaction / Praying hands / Space junk / Monogoloid / Jocko homo / Too much paranoias / Gut feeling / Slap your mammy / Sloppy (I saw my baby gettin') / Shrivel up / Come back Jonee
CDV 2106 / May '93 / Virgin

☐ SMOOTH NOODLE MAPS
Stuck in a loop / Post post-modern man / When we do it / Spin the wheel / Morning dew / Chance is gonna cum / Big picture / Pink jazz trancers / Jimmy / Devo has feelings too / Dawghaus
727572 / Feb '95 / Restless

☐ TOTAL DEVO
Baby doll / Disco dancer / Some things never change / Plain truth / Happy guy / Shadow / I'd cry if you died / Agitated / Man turned inside out / Blow up
727562 / Feb '95 / Restless

☐ WE ARE NOT DEVO (A Tribute To Devo) (Various Artists)
CR 001CD / 30 Sep '97 / Centipede

Devolver

☐ GRAND STORM MATINEE
MILE 5 / 20 Oct '97 / Trans Siberian

Devon

☐ SKIN DEEP
D 003 / 30 Mar '98 / Devon

Dew Scented

☐ IMMORTELLE
SPV 08518262 / Mar '96 / SPV

☐ INNOSCENT
Shattered insanity / Bereaved / Burn with me / Star spangled / Sicker things / Everred / Grapes of wrath / Aentity / Underneath / Fatal if swallowed
SON 3252 / 27 Jul '98 / Nuclear Blast

Dewar, Colin

☐ COLLINS POCKET REFERENCE VOL.1 (Ceilidh Dances) (Dewar, Colin Scottish Country Dance Band)
Bluebell polka / Boston two step / Britannia two step / Canadian barn dance / Circle waltz / Elephant walk / Eva three step / Friendly waltz / Gay Gordons / Hesitation waltz / Highland Scottische / Kelvingrove two step / Lambeth walk / Lomond waltz / Military two step / Mississippi dip / Palais glide / Pride of Erin waltz / St. Bernard's waltz / Sheena's saunter / Social swing / Stern polka / Suzuki circle / Swedish masquerade / La va / Veleta / Virginia reel / Dunnet head / Auld lang syne
RSCDSCD 008 / Jul '98 / Royal Scottish Country Dance Society

☐ COLLINS POCKET REFERENCE VOL.2 (Scottish Country Dances) (Dewar, Colin Scottish Country Dance Band)
Dashing white sergeant / Eightsome reel / Foursome reel / Hamilton House / Inverness country dance / Duke and Duchess of Edinburgh / Machine without horses / Reel of the 51st Division / Duke of Perth / Scottish reform / Waltz country dance / Mairi's wedding / Postie's jig / Petronella / Dunedin Festival dance/Highland welcome / Strip the willow
RSCDSCD 009 / Jul '98 / Royal Scottish Country Dance Society

☐ SPECIAL REQUESTS VOL.3 (Dewar, Colin Quartet)
Tomtain brae / West's hornpipe / Cashmere shawl / Jennifer's jig / Polharrow burn / Hermitage Castle / Blooms of Bon Accord / New Scotland strathspey / MacDonald of Sleet / Fisherman's reel / Luckenbooth brooch / Mairi's wedding
SRCD 003 / Jul '98 / Colin Dewar

Dewar, James

☐ STUMBLEDOWN ROMANCER
Out of time / Goodbye love / Stumbledown romancer / Bright lights / Hosanna / Love's melody / Sands of time / Heartbeat / Lay down the night / Dance with me / Nature child
4931532 / 11 May '98 / EMI

D'Ewondo, Zogo

☐ KING OF BIKOUTSI
795972 / 5 Jan '98 / Melodie

Dexter, Levi

☐ POMP
Other side of midnight / Just go wild / Hot 'n' cold / Lolita / Joint jumpin' / Dub-scratch-boogie / Crazy blues / Everytime / Stealin' corn / Motorhead baby / All night rockin'
JRCD 3 / Sep '97 / Jappin' & Rockin'

Dexy's Midnight Runners

☐ BBC RADIO 1 SESSIONS 1980-1982, THE
Tell me when my light turns green / Let's make this precious / Dubious / Until I believe in my soul / Liars A to E / Jackie Wilson said / All in all / Old
SFRSCD 044 / 8 Dec '97 / Strange Fruit

☐ DON'T STAND ME DOWN
CRECD 154 / Jun '97 / Creation

☐ IT WAS LIKE THIS
Breakin' down the walls of heartache / Tell me when my light turns green / Teams that meet in Caffs / Dance stance / Geno / I'm just looking / Thankfully not living in Yorkshire it doesn't apply / Seven days too long / I couldn't help it if I tried / Respect / Horse / Keep it / Love part 1 / There there my dear / Keep it part 2 (Inferiority part 1) / One way love / Plan B / Soul finger
PRMUCD 1 / May '96 / Premier/EMI

☐ SEARCHING FOR THE YOUNG SOUL REBELS
Burn it down / Tell me when my light turns green / Teams that meet in the caffs / I'm just looking / Geno / Seven days too long / I couldn't help it if I tried / Thankfully not living in Yorkshire it doesn't apply / Keep it / Love part one / There there my dear
CZ 31 / Jan '88 / EMI

☐ TOO RYE AYE (Remastered)
Celtic soul brothers / Let's make this precious / All in all (this one last wild waltz) / Jackie Wilson said (I'm in heaven when you smile) / Old / Plan B / I'll show you / Liars A to E / Until I believe in my soul / Come on Eileen
5148392 / Mar '96 / Mercury

☐ TOO RYE AYE/DON'T STAND ME DOWN (2CD Set)
Celtic soul brothers / Let's make this precious / All in all (this one last wild waltz) / Jackie Wilson said (I'm in heaven when you smile) / Old / Plan B / I'll show you / Liars A to E / Until I believe in my soul / Come on Eileen / Occasional flicker / This is what she's like / Knowledge of beauty / One of those things / Reminisce part 2 / Listen to this / Waltz
5286082 / Aug '95 / Mercury

☐ VERY BEST OF DEXY'S MIDNIGHT RUNNERS, THE
Come on Eileen / Jackie Wilson said (I'm in heaven when you smile) / Let's get this straight / Because of you / Show me / Celtic soul brothers / Liars A to E / One way love / Old / Geno / There there my dear / Breakin' down the walls of heartache / Dance stance / Plan B / Keep it / I'm just looking / Soon / This is what she's like / Soul finger
8464602 / May '91 / Mercury

Deyess

☐ LITTLE GODDESS
STCD 1040 / Oct '92 / Stern's

DFA

☐ OM23
Empire / Oo su kushi / Heckmondwike / Jewels and calories / Dark matter / OM23 / Sonic soul surfer / Departure / Mondo cahoona / Heaven's inferno
CDKTB 97 / May '97 / Dreamtime

DFL

☐ MY CRAZY LIFE
GR 002CD / Apr '97 / Grand Royal

D'Gary

☐ MALAGASY GUITAR
SHCD 65009 / May '93 / Shanachie

☐ MBO LOZA
Gofo libre / Atahora fabiby / Mibaby diavolana / Mare rano / Lehibeny / Te-beheloky / Ragnandria / Kinanga / Mbo loza / Asmine / Manoro
LBLC 2535 / Apr '97 / Indigo

DGM

☐ CHANGE DIRECTION
Brain storming / In my heart / Last memory / Lonely nights / Anthem / Do what you want / Change direction / Flyin' fantasy
ERO 2003 / 23 Feb '98 / Cyclops

Dhar, Sheila

☐ VOYAGE INTERIEUR
C 560017/18 / Jan '93 / Ocora

Dhomont, Francis

☐ ACOUSMATRIX 8/9
BVHAASTCD 9107/8 / Oct '93 / Bvhaast

☐ FORET PROFONDE
IMED 9634 / Jun '97 / Diffunzioni Musicali

☐ FRANKENSTEIN SYMPHONY NO.1
Allegro / Andante / Scherzo / Finale
ASP 0978CD / 22 Jun '98 / Asphodel

☐ SOUS LE REGARD D'UN SOLEIL NOIR
IMED 9633 / Jun '97 / Diffunzioni Musicali

DI

☐ STATE OF SHOCK
Hated / Clownhouse / What is life / Runaround / Colors and blood / It's not right / Paranoid's demise / Dream / Better than expected / Martyr man / Lexicon devil
CDVEST 14 / May '94 / Bulletproof

Di Bart, Tony

☐ FALLING FOR YOU
Falling for you / Real thing / Secrecy / Turn your love around / Do it / Father / Why did ya / What am I gonna do / We got the love / Stay a little while
CLECD 555 / Oct '96 / Cleveland City

Di Battista, Stefano

☐ VOLARE (Di Battista, Stefano & Flavio Boltro)
Prima di partire / Blues for Michel / Widows walk / Funky porcini / Stars fell on Alabama / Matbon / My foolish heart / Patacchione / Volare / Rap (hip criminal time pop) / Caligola / One finger snap
LBLC 6613 / 29 Jun '98 / Label Bleu

Di Franco, Ani

☐ ANI DI FRANCO
Both hands / Talk to me now / Slant / Work your way out / Dog coffee / Lost woman song / Pale purple / Rush hour / Fire door / Story / Every angle / Out of habit / Letting the telephone ring / Egos like hairdos
RBR 001CD / Jul '95 / Righteous Babe
COOKCD 112 / Jan '97 / Cooking Vinyl

☐ DILATE
Untouchable face / Outta me, onto you / Superhero / Dilate / Amazing grace / Napoleon / Shameless / Done wrong / Going down / Adam and eve / Joyful girl
COOKCD 103 / Jul '96 / Cooking Vinyl
RBR 8 / May '96 / Righteous Babe

☐ IMPERFECTLY
RBR 003CD / Jul '95 / Righteous Babe

☐ LIKE I SAID - SONGS 1990-91
RBR 005CD / Jul '95 / Righteous Babe

☐ LITTLE PLASTIC CASTLE
Little plastic castle / Fuel / Gravel / As is / Two little girls / Deep dish / Loom / Pixie / Swan dive / Glass house / Independence day / Pulse
COOKCD 140 / 9 Feb '98 / Cooking Vinyl

☐ LIVING IN CLIP (2CD Set)
Whatever / Wherever / Gravel / Willing to fight / Shy / Joyful girl / Hide and seek / Napoleon / I'm no heroine / Amazing Grace / Anticipate / Tiptoe / Sorry I am / Diner/Slant / 32 Flavours / Out of range / Untouchable face / Shameless / Distracted / Adam and Eve / Fire door / Both hands / Out of habit / Every state line / Not so soft / Travel tips / Wrong with me / In or out / We're all gonna blow / Letter to a John / Overleaf
COOKCD 122 / Jun '97 / Cooking Vinyl

☐ MORE JOY LESS SHAME
Joyful girl / Shameless / Both hands
COOKCD 119 / Dec '96 / Cooking Vinyl

☐ NOT A PRETTY GIRL
Worthy / Tiptoe / Cradle and all / Shy / Sorry I am / Light of some kind / Not a pretty girl / Million you never made / Hour follows hour / 32 flavors / Asking too much / This bouquet / Crime for crime
RBR 007CD / Nov '95 / Righteous Babe
COOKCD 113 / Jan '97 / Cooking Vinyl

☐ NOT SO SOFT
Anticipate / Rockabye / She says / Make me stay / On every corner / Small world / Not so soft / Roll with it / Itch / Gratitude / Whole night / Next big thing / Brief bus stop / Looking for the holes
COOKCD 133 / 29 Sep '97 / Cooking Vinyl

☐ OUT OF RANGE
HAVENCD 3 / Jan '95 / Haven

☐ PUDDLE DIVE
Names and dates and times / Anyday / 4th of July / Willing to fight / Ego's like hairdos / Back around / Blood in the boardroom / Born a lion / My IQ / Used to u / Pick yer nose / God's country
COOKCD 132 / 29 Sep '97 / Cooking Vinyl

☐ WOMEN IN (E)MOTION FESTIVAL
T&M 105 / Nov '94 / Tradition & Moderne

Di Fulvio, Hedgar

☐ CHACARA DEL PORQUE
BMF 007 / Jan '98 / Blue Moon

☐ MIS CHANGUITOS ASI SON
BMF 002 / Jan '98 / Blue Moon

☐ Y SO DE AQUEL PAGO POBRE
BMF 003 / Jan '98 / Blue Moon

☐ ZAMBITA PARA MI AUSENCIA
BMF 001 / Jan '98 / Blue Moon

Di Gojim

☐ NOCH A SJOH
SYNCD 161 / Jun '94 / Syncoop

Di Meola, Al

☐ CASINO
Egyptian danza / Chasin' the voodoo / Dark eye tango / Senor mouse / Fantasia suite for two guitars / Viva la danzarina / Guitars of the exotic isle / Rhapsody Italia / Bravoto fantasia / Casino
4682152 / Jan '95 / Sony Jazz

☐ ELECTRIC RENDEZVOUS
God bird / Change / Electric rendezvous / Passion, grace and fire / Cruisin' / Black cat shuffle / Ritmo de la noche / Somalia / Jewel inside a dream
4682162 / Nov '93 / Columbia

☐ ELEGANT GYPSY
Flight over Rio / Midnight tango / Mediterranean sundance / Race with devil on Spanish highway / Lady of Rome / Sister of Brazil / Elegant gypsy suite
4682132 / Jan '95 / Sony Jazz

☐ LAND OF THE MIDNIGHT SUN
Wizard / Sarabande from violin sonata in B minor / Pictures of the sea (love theme) / Land of the midnight sun / Golden dawn suite (morning fire) / Calmer of the tempests / From ocean to the clouds / Short tales of the Black Forest
4682142 / Jan '95 / Sony Jazz

☐ ORANGE & BLUE
5237242 / Oct '94 / PolyGram Jazz

☐ SCENARIO
CK 38944 / Aug '97 / Sony Jazz

☐ SPLENDIDO HOTEL
4670902 / Jan '95 / Sony Jazz

☐ THIS IS JAZZ
Race with the devil on Spanish highway / Ritmo de la noche / Short tales of the black forest / Nena / Fantasia suite for two guitars / Viva la danzarina / Guitars of the exotic isle / Rhapsody italia / Bravoto fantasia / African night / Cruisin / Spanish eyes / Passion / Grace and fire / Silent story in her eyes / Sarabande
CK 65047 / May '97 / Sony Jazz

☐ TOUR DE FORCE
4682172 / Jan '95 / Sony Jazz

Di Novi, Gene

☐ LIVE AT THE MONTREAL BISTRO TORONTO (Di Novi, Gene Trio)
Introduction / TNT / Happy harvest / Things we did last summer/Indian summer / Terry's little tune / Nieves / Tune for Mac / AB's blues / It happened in Monterey / You better go now / Coffee time / Tiny's blues
CCD 79726 / Jan '97 / Candid

☐ RENAISSANCE OF A JAZZ MASTER
Cockeyed optimist / Springsville / Till the clouds roll by / Right as the rain / Bill / It never entered my mind / Budding memories / Elegy / My old flame / Have a heart / Speak low
CCD 79708 / Feb '97 / Candid

Di Sarli, Carlos

☐ A LA GRAN MUNECA
BMT 003 / Feb '97 / Blue Moon

☐ PORTENO Y BAILARIN
BMT 014 / Jan '98 / Blue Moon

Diabate, Abdoulaye

☐ DJIRIYO
STCD 1066 / Mar '96 / Stern's

Diabate, Djanke

☐ SABOU SABOU
SMCD 1169 / Jan '97 / Sonima

Diabate, Mama

☐ N'NA NIWALE
PAMOA 205 / Mar '95 / PAM

Diabate, Sekou Bembeya

☐ DIAMOND FINGERS
2002849 / Jan '97 / Dakar Sound

Diabate, Sekouba

☐ LE DESTIN
OA 202 / Feb '94 / PAM

Diabate, Sona

☐ KANKELE TI
PAM 401 / Feb '94 / PAM

Diabate, Toumani

☐ DJELIKA
Djelika / Mankoman djan / Cheik oumar bah / Marielle / Kandjoura / Aminata santoro / Tony vander / Sankoun djabi
HNCD 1380 / Sep '95 / Hannibal

☐ KAIRA
Alla l'aa ke / Jarabl / Kaira / Konkoba / Tubaka
HNCD 1338 / May '89 / Hannibal

Diablos Rising

☐ 666
CD 023 / Oct '94 / Osmose

☐ BLOOD, VAMPIRISM AND SADISM
KRONH 02CD / Feb '96 / Osmose

Diabolical Masquerade

☐ PHANTOM LODGE, THE
CDAR 039 / May '97 / Adipocre

☐ RAVENDUSK IN MY HEART
CDAR 036 / Dec '96 / Adipocre

Diaboliks

☐ DANGER
ID 123341CD / Nov '96 / Dionysus

Diabolique

☐ WEDDING THE GROTESQUE
BS 011CD / Mar '97 / Burning Sun

Diagne, Boubacar

☐ TABALA WOLOF (Sufi Drumming From Senegal)
VPU 1002CD / May '97 / Village Pulse

Diamond Accordion Band

☐ COUNTRY CRAZY (45 Great Country Hits)
Blanket on the ground / Top of the world / Take me home country roads / Hey good lookin' / Old faithfull / Don't fence me in / Spanish eyes / Yellow bird / South of the border / Tie a yellow button / Are you lonesome tonight / Adios amigo / Yellow rose of texas / You're cheatin heart / San antonio rose / Cryin' time / Only you / Crazy / Sweet dreams / I fall to pieces / She's got you / Oh lonesome me / Sea of heartbreak / Hello Mary Lou / Things / One day at a time / King of the road / From a jack to a king / Walk on by / Lil 'ole wine drinker me / Blueberry hill / Who's sorry now / You're my best freind / Paper roses / Roses of picardy / Red roses for a blue lady / Ramblin' rose / Wolverton mountain / Jambalaya / Pretty brwon eyes / Welcome to my world / Distant drums / Ten guitars / Beautiful sunday / Is this the way to Amarillo / Stand by your man / You're cheatin' heart / Send me the pillow you dream on
MCVD 30007 / Nov '96 / Emerald Gem

☐ PLAY COUNTRY GREATS
Help me make it through the night / Rhinestone cowboy / You're my best friend / One day at a time / Once around the dance floor / Where the blue and lonely go / My son calls another man daddy / I walk the line / I love you because / Crystal chandeliers / Tie a yellow ribbon round the old oak tree / Down river road / Blanket on the ground
EMPRCD 510 / Apr '94 / Emporio

☐ SINGALONG PARTY
Robert E Lee / California here I come / Baby face / I'm looking over a four leaf clover / Carolina in the morning / Pretty baby / My mammy / Toot toot tootsie / Chinatown my chinatown / Ma he's making eyes at me / April showers / Rock bye baby / Don't dilly dally / Goodbye Dolly Gray / Run rabbit run / Wish me luck / Swanee / You made me love / Maybe it's because I'm a Londoner / Underneath the arches / Whatever will be will be (Que sera sera) / Liverpool Lou / How much is that doggie / After the ball is over / Happy wanderer / Roll out the barrel / It's a long way to Tipperary / Pack up your troubles / By the light of the silvery moon / If you were the only girl in the world / Lily of laguna / Mocking bird hill / Oh dear what can the matter be / Two lovely black eyes / Two little girls in blue
EMPRCD 591 / Oct '95 / Emporio

☐ WALTZES
Annie's song / Tulips from Amsterdam / By the side of Zuder Zee / Miller's daughter / Carnival of Venice / Tippi-tippi-tin / Softly softly, good luck, good health, god bless you / Old rockin' chair / There goes my everything / My Florence / We will make love / Delilah / Lady of Spain / Cruisin' down the river / Windmill song / Under the bridges of Paris / Gordon for me / Northern lights of Aberdeen / These are my mountains / Home on the range / Carolina moon / When I grow too old to dream / I wonder whose kissing her now / Far away places / Ramona / Where the blue of the night / Whiffenspoof song / It's sin to tell a lie / Four in the morning / Morning has broken / Oh what a beautiful morning / Three o'clock in the morning / Anniversary waltz / Now is the hour / Beautiful dreamer / Moon river / Plaisir d'amour / Edelweiss / Somewhere my love / Loveliest night of the year / Reine de musette / You take the high road / I belong to glasgow / Flower of Scotland / Auld lang syne / Twelfth of never / Are you lonesome tonight / Eternally / Daisy bell / Irene goodnight / My bonnie lies over the ocean / On top of old smokey / Anna Marie / When the girl in your arms / You're the only good thing that's happened to me / I'll be with you in apple blossom time / Always / Let me call you sweetheart
MCVD 30009 / Nov '96 / Emerald Gem

Diamond Head

☐ AM I EVIL
Am I evil / Heat of the night / Don't you ever leave me / Borrowed time / To Heaven from Hell / Dead reckoning / Lightning to the nations / Sucking my love
WKFMXD 92 / Sep '94 / FM

☐ BEHOLD THE BEGINNING
It's electric / Prince / Sweet and innocent / Sucking my love / Streets of gold / Play it loud / Shoot out the lights / Waited too long / Helpless
HMRXD 165 / May '91 / Heavy Metal

☐ DEATH & PROGRESS
Starcrossed (lovers of the night) / Truckin' / Calling your name (the light) / I can't help myself / Paradise / Dust run / Wild on the streets / Damnation street / Home
ESMCD 387 / Jul '96 / Essential

☐ DIAMOND HEAD
HMRXD 92 / May '87 / Heavy Metal

☐ DIAMOND HEAD - IN THE BEGINNING
WKFMCD 165 / Feb '91 / FM

Diamond Rio

☐ FOUR IV
Holdin' / Walkin' away / That's what I get for loving you / She misses him on Sunday the most / She sure did like to run / It's all in your head / Who am I / Love takes you there / Is that askin' too much / Just another heart / Big
07822188122 / Apr '96 / Arista

☐ GREATEST HITS
How your love makes you feel / Meet me in the middle / Mirror mirror / Mama don't you forget to pray for me / Norma Jean Riley / In a week or two / Love a little stronger / Night is fallin' in my heart / Bubba Hyde / Walkin' away / It's all in your head / Holdin' / She misses him on Sunday the most / Imagine that
07822188442 / Jul '97 / Arista

☐ LITTLE STRONGER, A
07822187452 / Aug '94 / Arista

Diamond Wookie

☐ FOXBURY RULES, THE
Avenue du bois / Hand me downs / Back to the flat / Oscar / Unglamorous madness / To Monte Carlo Mr Noyes / Dance of the dibnah
IBCD 7 / Apr '97 / Internal Bass

Diamond, Jim

☐ JIM DIAMOND
I won't let you down / I should have known better / Hi ho silver / Not man enough / Our love / I still love you / We dance the night away / It's true what they say / If you're gonna break my heart / Devil in my eyes / Child's heart / Goodnight tonight
8438472 / May '93 / PolyGram TV

Diamond, Neil

☐ 12 GREATEST HITS VOL.2
Beautiful noise / Hello again / Forever in blue jeans / September morn / Desiree / You don't bring me flowers / America / Be / Longfellow serenade / If you know what I mean / Yesterday's songs / Love on the rocks
CD 85844 / May '87 / CBS

☐ 20 GOLDEN GREATS: NEIL DIAMOND
Sweet caroline (good times never seemed so good) / Holly holy / And the singer sings his song / Shilo / Play me / Mr. bojangles / Song sung blue / Cherry cherry / Solitary man / Kentucky woman / Crackling rosie / Soolaimon / Canta libre / Stones / He ain't heavy, he's my brother / Brother love's travelling salvation show / Cold water morning / Walk on water / And the grass won't pay no mind / I am...i said / Girl, you'll be a woman soon
MCD 11452 / May '96 / MCA

☐ BEAUTIFUL NOISE
Beautiful noise / Stargazer / Lady oh / Don't think / Feel / Surviving the life / If you know what I mean / Street life / Home is a wonderful heart / Jungletime / Signs / Dry your eyes
4504522 / Mar '91 / CBS

☐ BEAUTIFUL NOISE/JONATHON LIVINGSTONE SEAGULL/JAZZ SINGER (3CD Set)
Beautiful noise / Stargazer / Lady oh / Don't think feel / Surviving the life / If you know what I mean / Street life / Home is a wonderful heart / Jungletime / Signs / Dry your eyes / Jonathan Livingstone Seagull / Flight of the gull / Dear father / Skybird (part 1) / Lonely looking sky / Be (part 1) / Odyssey / Anthem / Skybird (part 2) / Be (part 3) / America / Adorn O lume / You baby / Love on the rocks / Amazed and confused / Robert E. Lee / Summer love / Hello again / Acapulco / Hey Louise / Songs of life / Jerusalem / Kol nidre / My name is Yussel / America (reprise)
4886762 / 3 Nov '97 / Columbia

☐ CHRISTMAS ALBUM, THE
O come o come Emmanuel/We three kings of Orient are / Silent night / Little drummer boy / Santa Claus is coming to town / Christmas song / Morning has broken / Happy Christmas (war is over) / White Christmas / God rest ye merry gentlemen / Jingle bell rock / Hark the herald angels sing / Silver bells / You make it feel like Christmas / Holy night
4724102 / 3 Nov '97 / Columbia

☐ CHRISTMAS ALBUM, THE VOL.2
Joy to the world / Mary's boy child / Deck the halls/ We wish you a merry Christmas / Winter wonderland / Have yourself a merry little Christmas / I'll be home for Christmas / Rudolph the red nosed reindeer / Sleigh ride / Candlelight carol / Away in a manger / O come all ye faithful (Adeste Fidelis) / O little town of Bethlehem / Angels we have heard on high / First Noel / Hallelujah chorus
4775982 / Nov '94 / Columbia

☐ CLASSICS (The Early Years)
Kentucky woman / Cherry, Cherry / Solitary man / You got to me / I got the feelin' (oh no no) / Thank the Lord for the night time / I'm a believer / Girl, you'll be a woman soon / Shilo / Do it / Red red wine / Boat that I row
4777842 / 11 May '98 / Columbia

☐ DIAMOND SYMPHONIES, THE (London Philharmonic Orchestra)
Overture / Holly Holy / Cracklin' Rosie / Brother love's travelling / Salvation show / Play me / Forever in blue jeans / Sweet Caroline / September morn / I am...I said / Beautiful noise / You don't bring me flowers / Song sung blue / Shilo / Kentucky woman / Song sung blue reprise
QED 053 / Nov '96 / Tring

☐ DIAMOND SYMPHONIES, THE (The Music Of Neil Diamond) (London Philharmonic Orchestra)
Overture / Holly holy / Medley / Play me / Forever in blue jeans / Sweet Caroline / September morn / I am...I said / Beautiful noise / You don't bring me flowers / Medley
ECD 3300 / Feb '97 / K-Tel

☐ GREATEST HITS (1966-1992)
Solitary man / Cherry, Cherry / I got the feelin' (oh no no) / Thank the Lord for the night time / Girl, you'll be a woman soon / Kentucky woman / Shilo / You got to me / Brooklyn roads / Red red wine / I'm a believer / Sweet caroline / Soolaimon / Cracklin' rosie / Song sung blue / Play me / Holly holy / Morning side / Crunchy granola suite / Brother love's travelling salvation show / I am...I said / Longfellow serenade / Beautiful noise / If you know what I mean / Desiree / September morn / You don't bring me flowers / Forever in blue jeans / Hello again / America / Love on the rocks / Yesterday's songs / Heartlight / Headed for the future / Heartbreak hotel: *Diamond, Neil & Kim Carnes* / All I really need is you
4715022 / Jun '92 / Columbia

☐ HEADED FOR THE FUTURE
Headed for the future / Man you need / I'll see you on the radio (Laura) / Stand up for love / It should have been me / Lost in Hollywood / Story of my life / Angel / Me beside you / Love don't live here anymore
4894532 / 2 Feb '98 / Columbia

☐ HOT AUGUST NIGHTS VOL.2
Song of the whales / Headed for the future / September morn / Thank the Lord for the night time / Cherry, Cherry / Sweet Caroline / Hello again / Love on the rocks / America / Forever in blue jeans / You don't bring me flowers / I dreamed a dream / Back in LA / Song sung blue / Cracklin' Rosie / I am...I said / Holly holy / Soolaimon / Brother Love's travelling salvation show / Heartlight
4604082 / Nov '87 / CBS

☐ IN MY LIFETIME (3CD Set)
In my lifetime / Hear them bells / Blue destiny / Million miles away / Good kind of lonely / What will I do / At night / Clown town / Flame / Straw in the wind / Solitary man / Cherry, Cherry / I got the feelin' (oh no no) / I'm a believer / Kentucky woman / Boat that I row / Girl, you'll be a woman soon / You got to me / Thank the Lord for the night time / Red red wine / Shilo / Brooklyn roads / And the grass won't pay no mind / Sweet Caroline / Holly holy / Brother love's travelling salvation show / Cracklin' Rosie / Done too soon / Morningside / Soolaimon / He ain't heavy, he's my brother / Crunchy Granola suite / Play me / I am...I said / Song sung blue / Jonathan Livingston Seagull suite / Prologue / Lonely looking sky / Skybird / Dear father / Be / I've been this way before / Longfellow serenade / Beautiful noise / If you know what I mean / Dry your eyes / Desire / September morn / Forever in blue jeans / You don't bring me flowers: *Diamond, Neil & Barbra Streisand* / America / Love on the rocks / Scotch on the rocks / Hello again / Yesterday's songs / I'm alive / Heaven can wait / Heartlight / Just need to love you more / You make it feel like Christmas / Falling / Dancing to the party next door / Story of my life / I'm sayin' I'm sorry / If there were no dreams / Headed for the future / Hooked on the memory of you / Angel above my head / Everybody
C3K 65013 / Oct '96 / Columbia

☐ INSTRUMENTAL MEMORIES (Various Artists)
I am I said / Tennesse moon / Beautiful noise / Cherry cherry / Red red wine / I'm a believer / Love on the rocks / He ain't heavy he's my brother / Cracklin' rosie / Song sung blue / You don't bring me flowers / America / Hello again / September morn / Forever in blue jeans
307282 / Aug '97 / Hallmark

☐ JAZZ SINGER, THE (Original Soundtrack)
America / Adam Olom / You baby / Love on the rocks / Amazed and confused / On the Robert E. Lee / Summerlove / Hello again / Acapulco / Hey Louise / Songs of life / Jerusalem / Kol nidre / My name is Yussel / America
4839272 / 27 Jul '98 / Columbia

☐ LIVE IN AMERICA (2CD Set)
America / Hello again / Kentucky woman / You got me / Cherry, Cherry / I'm a believer / Sweet Caroline / Love on the rocks / Hooked on the memory of you / Lady oh / Beautiful noise / Play me / Up on the roof / You've lost that lovin' feelin' / River deep, mountain high / I who have nothing / Missa / Soolaimon / Holly holy / Grass won't pay no mind / You don't bring me flowers / September morn / Hava nagila / Solitary man / Red red wine / Song sung blue / Forever in blue jeans / Heartlight / Cracklin' Rosie / I am...I said / Crunchy granola suite / Brother Love's travelling salvation show
4772112 / Jun '97 / Columbia

☐ LOVE SONGS
Theme / If you go away / Last thing on my mind / Coldwater morning / Juliet / Both sides now / Play me / Hurtin' you don't come easy / Husbands and wives / Until it's time for you to go / And the grass won't pay no mind / Modern day version of love / Suzanne
MCBD 19525 / Apr '97 / MCA

☐ LOVESCAPE
If there were no dreams / Mountains of love / Someone who believes in you / When you miss your love / Fortunes of the night / One hand, one heart / Hooked on the memory of you / Wish everything was alright / Way / Sweet LA days / All I really need is you / Lonely lady no.17 / I feel you / Common ground
4688902 / Oct '91 / Columbia

☐ MOODS
Song sung blue / Porcupine pie / High rolling man / Canta Libre / Captain sunshine / Play me / Gitchy goomy / Walk on water / Theme / Prelude in E Major / Morningside
MCLD 19043 / Apr '92 / MCA

☐ SALUTE TO NEIL DIAMOND, A (Various Artists)
I am I said / Love on the rocks / Song sung blue / Cracklin' rose / Sweet Caroline / Mr. Bojangles / Longfellow serenade / America / September morn' / Heartlight / Red red wine / You don't bring me flowers
309192 / 13 Jul '98 / Hallmark

☐ SEPTEMBER MORN
September morn / Mama don't know / That kind / Jazz time / Good Lord loves you / Dancing in the street / Shelter of your arms / I'm a believer / Sun ain't gonna shine anymore / Stagger Lee
4844552 / Feb '97 / Columbia

☐ SERENADE
I've been this way before / Rosemary's wine / Lady Magdelene / Last Picasso / Longfellow serenade / Yes I will / Reggae strut / Gift of song
4650122 / Dec '95 / Columbia

☐ STONES
I am...I said / Last thing on my mind / Husbands and wives / Chelsea morning / Crunchy Granola Suite / Stones / If you go away / Suzanne / I think it's going to rain today
MCLD 19118 / Apr '92 / MCA

☐ TAP ROOT MANUSCRIPT
Cracklin' Rosie / Free life / Coldwater morning / Done too soon / He ain't heavy, he's my brother / African trilogy / I am the lion / Madrigal / Soolaimon / Missa / African suite / Child's song
MCLD 19119 / Aug '92 / MCA

☐ TENNESSEE MOON (The Nashville Collection)
Tennessee moon / One good love / Shame / Matter of love / Marry me / Deep inside of you / Gold don't rust / Like you do / Can anybody hear me / Win the world / No limit / Reminisce for a while / Kentucky woman / If I lost my way / Everybody / Talking optimist blues (good day today) / Blue highway
4813782 / Feb '96 / Columbia

☐ ULTIMATE COLLECTION, THE
Sweet Caroline / Song sung blue / Cracklin Rosie / Love on the rocks / Beautiful noise / Forever in blue jeans / Hello again / Red, red wine / Everybody's talkin' / Girl, you'll be a woman soon / I'm a believer / Heartlight / Up on the roof / Desiree / If you know what I mean / Longfellow serenade / Play me / You got to me / I (who have nothing) / I am...I said / Solitary man / He ain't heavy, he's my brother / Cherry, Cherry / Walk on water / Soolaimon / Sun ain't gonna shine anymore / Stones / You've lost that loving feelin': *Diamond, Neil & Dolly Parton* / Morning has broken / Chelsea morning / Mr. Bojangles / Yesterdays songs / Thank the lord for the night time / Brother Love's travelling salvation show / September morn / Kentucky woman / I got the feelin' (oh no, no) / America / Holly Holy / You don't bring me flowers: *Diamond, Neil & Barbra Streisand*
MOODCD 45 / Aug '96 / Sony Music

☐ UP ON THE ROOF (Songs From The Brill Building)
You've lost that lovin' feelin' / Up on the roof / Love potion no.9 / Will you still love me tomorrow / Don't be cruel / Do wah diddy diddy / I who have nothing / Do you know the way to San Jose / River deep, mountain high / Groovy kind of love / Spanish Harlem / Sweets for my sweet / Happy birthday sweet sixteen / Ten lonely guys / Save the last dance for me
4743562 / Oct '93 / Columbia

☐ VERY BEST OF NEIL DIAMOND, THE
Sweet Caroline / Girl, you'll be a woman soon / Walk on water / Soolaimon / Morningside / Cracklin' Rosie / Play me / Holly holy / Stones / Song sung blue / Brooklyn roads / I am...I said
PWKS 510 / Feb '96 / Carlton

Diamonds

☐ BEST OF THE DIAMONDS, THE (The Mercury Years)
Why do fools fall in love / Church bells may ring / Cool baby cool / Ka ding dong / My judge and my jury / Every minute of the day / Little darlin' / Zip zip / Don't say goodbye / Words of love / Dance with me / Daddy cool / Silhouettes / Stroll / Walking along / High sign / She say (oom dooby doom) / Batman, Wolfman, Frankenstein or Dracula / Oh Carol / Believe me / Chimes in my heart / One summer night
5527592 / Feb '97 / Spectrum

Di'Anno, Paul

☐ CHILDREN OF MADNESS (Di'Anno, Paul Battlezone)
ZCRCD 3 / 23 Mar '98 / Zoom Club

☐ FIGHTING BACK (Di'Anno, Paul Battlezone)
Fighting back / Welcome to the battlezone / War child / In the darkness / Land God gave to Caine / Running blind / Too much to heart / Voice on the radio / Welfare warriors / Feel the rock
ZCRCD 2 / 23 Mar '98 / Zoom Club

☐ HARD AS IRON (Di'Anno, Paul & Dennis Stratton)
CDTB 176 / Jun '96 / Thunderbolt

☐ HEARTUSER
Heartuser / Tales of the unexpected / Antigue
WKFMPD 1 / Aug '84 / FM

☐ SOUTH AMERICAN ASSAULT
SPV 08438952 / Aug '94 / SPV

Dianogah

☐ AS SEEN FROM ABOVE
OHIOGOLD 002CD / 6 Oct '97 / Ohio Gold

Diaouled Ar Menez

☐ CHAUFFE LA BREIZH
CD 875 / Aug '97 / Arfolk

Diary Of Dreams

☐ END OF FLOWERS
EFA 036012 / Mar '96 / Accession

Dias, Jose Barrense

☐ ESCULTOR DE IMAGEM
KAR 973 / Sep '93 / Kardum

Dias, Sergio

☐ MIND OVER MATTER
EXPALCD 8 / Aug '91 / Expression

☐ SONG OF THE LEOPARD, THE
150242 / Aug '97 / Black Sun

Diatribe

☐ DIATRIBE
REC 007 / Nov '96 / Re-Constriction

Diaz, Alirio

☐ ART OF SPANISH GUITAR, THE
14129 / Jun '94 / Laserlight

Diaz, Daniel

☐ YEARS ALONE, THE
XENO 4031CD / Mar '96 / Xenophile

Diaz, Diomedes

☐ CANTANDO (Diaz, Diomedes & Nicholas Colacho Mendoza)
Esperanza / Cantando / Te necesito / Myriam / Cardon guarjiro / El medallon / Por amor a dios / Paisana mia / Siempre contigo / Las cosas del amor
CDORB 055 / Mar '90 / Globestyle

Diaz, Hugo

☐ 20 BEST OF CLASSICAL "TANGO ARGENTINO" (Diaz, Hugo Trio)
EUCD 1094 / '91 / ARC

☐ TANGO ARGENTINO (Diaz, Hugo Trio)
EUCD 1327 / Nov '95 / ARC

Diaz, Joaquin

☐ AFFINITES
CD 001CD / Nov '95 / Caskabel

Diaz, Servando

☐ POSTALES DE MI TIERRA 1940-1942 (Diaz, Servando Trio)
TCD 081 / Jul '96 / Tumbao Cuban Classics

Dibango, Manu

☐ AFRIJAZZY
Masa lemba / Bushman promenade / Gombo sauce / Soir au village / Makossa / Kango / Doula serenade / Abelley sphere
EMY 1372 / Sep '97 / Enemy

☐ BAO BAO
Makossa rock / Afro beat / Boat people / Big blow / Bao Bao / Chapo-So jam
MPG 74035 / Jan '97 / Movieplay Gold

☐ ELECTRIC AFRICA
Pata piya / Electric africa / Echos beti / L'arbre a palabres
CPCD 8152 / Nov '95 / Celluloid
TRS 40212 / Jul '98 / Terrascape

☐ LAMASTABASTANI
859062 / Apr '96 / Melodie

☐ LES INOUBLIABLES DE...
592137 / Feb '97 / Flarenasch

☐ NEGROPOLITAINES
859052 / Nov '92 / Melodie

☐ PAPA GROOVE
382025 / Jul '96 / Wotre Music

☐ POLYSONIK
Senga Abele lion roar / Yeke Tenge lion line / Soma Loba / Polysonik / Mincalor lion feeling / Kwala Kwala / Negriers / Jazzeries / Polysonik / Mincalor
EXVP 7CD / Feb '97 / Expression

☐ SAX AND SPIRITUALS - LAMBASTINI
859072 / 21 Aug '97 / Melodie

☐ SOUL MAKOSSA
Soul makossa / Rencontre / Taoumba / Moni / New bell 'hard pulsation' / O Boso / Kata kata / Soukouss / Pepe soup / Essimo / Nights in Zeralda
139 215 / Aug '90 / Musidisc

☐ WAKAFRIKA
Soul Makossa / Biko / Wakafrika / Emma / Homeless / Lady / Hi-life / Wimoweh / Am oh / Jingo / Pata pata / Diarabi / Ca va chouia
BLM 001CD / Jun '94 / Blue Music

Dibenn

☐ DIBENN
ANCD 1 / Mar '98 / An Naer

Diblo

☐ MONDO RY
410082 / '91 / Melodie

Dicabor

☐ DICABOR
EFA 004102 / Feb '95 / Space Teddy

☐ LIVE AT THE INTERFERENCE FESTIVAL (Dicabor & Dr. Motte)
EFA 004122 / Feb '96 / Space Teddy

Dice Of The Dixie Crew

☐ FIRST THROW
Sweet Georgia Brown / At a Georgia camp meeting / Struttin' with some barbecues / Black and blue / Wolverine blues / After you've gone / Dr. Jazz / I can't give you / China boy
INAK 811CD / Nov '97 / In Akustik

☐ SECOND SIGHT
Sheik of Araby / Jazz me blues / Sweet Lorraine / Please don't talk about me / As long as I live / Indiana / Girl / Royal garden blues
INAK 822CD / Nov '97 / In Akustik

Dick Nixons

☐ PAINT THE WHITE HOUSE BLACK
422106 / Jun '94 / New Rose

Dick, Robert

☐ JAZZ STANDARDS ON MARS (Dick, Robert & The Soldier String Quartet)
India / Gazzeloni / Water babies / Machine gun / Somehthing sweet something tender / Sometimes perpetually / Three wishes
ENJ 93272 / 23 Mar '98 / Enja

☐ THIRD STONE FROM THE SUN
804352 / Sep '93 / New World

Dickens, 'Little' Jimmy

☐ COUNTRY BOY (4CD Set)
Take an old cold 'tater (and wait) / Pennies for papa / Crazy worried mind / Golden haired darlin' / Country boy / I'm fading fast with the time / I'll be back a-Sunday / My heart's bouquet / I'm in love up to my ears / Rose from the bride's bouquet / Beautiful morning glory / Lovin' lies / Rose from the bride's bouquet / Lovin' lies / A-sleepin' at the foot of the bed / Sign by the highway / Be careful of stones that you throw / I'm in love up to my ears / Then I had to turn around and get married / If it ain't one thing it's another / FOOLISH me me / Hillbilly fever / Walk chicken walk ('cause you're too fat to fly) / Just when I needed you / When that love bug bites you / Waitin' for the tide to change / Cold feet / Out of business / Bessie the heifer / Lola Lee / I'm little but I'm loud / Bible on the table (and the flag upon the wall) / What about you / Galvanised washing tub / He turned up his nose / It may be silly (but ain't it fun) / I wish you didn't love me so much / Bring your broken heart to me / I sure would like to set a spell with you / On the sea of broken dreams / Poor little darlin' / They don't know nothin' at all / I've just got to see you once more / They locked God outside the iron curtain / Brother do you take time to pray / Hot diggity dog / Waitress waitress / On the sea of broken dreams / No tears in heaven / He spoke not a word / That little old country church / Take up thy cross / Just a closer walk with thee / Old country preacher / Take my hand precious Lord / I shall not be moved / Wedding bell waltz / You don't have love at all / I'm gettin' nowhere fast / Love must be catching / Thick and thin / Teardrops (fell like raindrops) / Sidemeat and cabbage / Forever is too long to be alone / Would you mind / I'll dance at your wedding (if you marry me) / I'm making love to a stranger / Barefooted little cowboy / No place like home on christmas / Rockin' with Red / You all come / Out behind the barn / Lovesong of the Bayou / You better not do that / Closing time / Slow suicide / Take me as I am (or let me go) / Where's Willie / Blackeyed Joe's / Ribbon and a rose / Stinky passed the hat around / Salty boogie / Conscience (set me free) / We could / Hey worm (you wanna wiggle) / Where did the sunshine go / I'm braver now / Are you insured beyond the grave / When they get too rough (they're just right) / I feel for you (but I can't quite reach you) / Big Sandy / It scares me half to death / You gotta have a heartbreak / Red wing / Country boy bounce / Buddy's boogie / Raisin' the Dickens / I never thought it would happen to me / Say it now / I'm coming over tonight / Cornbread and buttermilk / I don't love you anymore / Happy heartaches / Last time / Let's quit before we start
BCD 15848 / Nov '97 / Bear Family

☐ I'M LITTLE BUT I'M LOUD (The Little Jimmy Dickens Collection)
RE 21072 / Jul '96 / Razor & Tie

☐ OUT BEHIND THE BARN (4CD Set)
Making the rounds / I never had the blues / Happy heartaches / Let's quit before the start / Wabash cannonball / I can't help it / Jambalaya / Tramp is on the street / Family reunion / Goodbye / Whatever you were / Recipe for the blues / (I got) a hole in my pocket / Darling my darling / Me and my big loud mouth / Country ways and city ideas / Hannah / When your house is not a home / Honeymoon is over / Hey ma (hide the daughter) / We lived it up (now we've got to live it down) / Hot tears / I'm just blue enough (to do 'most anything) / We could / Alone with God / Careless darlin' / Fireball mail / I cried again / Tomorrow never comes / John Henry / Have I told you lately that I love you / Tomorrow's just another day to cry / Petal from a faded rose / Singing waterfall / Pins and needles (in my heart) / My heart's bouquet / Talking to the wall / Eight more miles / Farewell party / Twenty cigarettes / It's me that hurts the most / Honky tonk troubles / Whole world seems different / String eraser and blotter / Before I met you / Best years of your life / Slowly / Out behind the barn / I'm making love to a stranger / Night train to Memphis / Violet and the rose / Out behind the barn / Running into memories of you / Sorrow's tearing down the house / Police police / Another bridge to burn / I ain't comin' home tonight / I'll sit this one out / Is goodbye that easy to say / I leaned over backwards for you / Too many irons in the fire / Watching the fire go down / He stands real tall / Stepping stone / She's not forgotten yet / Things have gone to pieces / Life turned her that way / Handle with care / I can't get over me / He knocked me right out of the box / Collection of failures / Back of my hand / Twice the fool / May the bird of paradise fly up your nose / Call him me / My eyes are jealous / Halfway loved / Little Jack Daniel / Make me an offer / Rose from the bride's bouquet / When the ship hit the sand / Where the buffalo trod / Jenny needs a g-string (for her old guitar) / Truck load of starvin' kangaroos / Possum holler / Butter beans / Where there's a will / Who licked the red off your candy / You don't have time for me / Doggone it / I just had a bar of soap / You've destroyed me / Big John / Don't forget your hat / Your little red riding hood / Country music lover
BCD 16218 / Feb '98 / Bear Family

Dickens, Hazel

☐ FEW OLD MEMORIES, A
Few old memories / Beyond the river bend / Busted / Old and in the way / It's hard to tell the singer from the song / Don't bother to cry / Hills of home / Pretty bird / Only the lonely / Coal tattoo / Little lenaldo / Old calloused hands / Scars from an old love / You'll get no more of me / Mama's hand / Working girl blues / West virginia my home / Play us a waltz
ROUCD 11529 / '88 / Rounder

☐ HAZEL & ALICE (Dickens, Hazel & Alice Gerrard)
Mining camp blues / Hello stranger / Green rolling hills of West Virginia / Few more years shall roll / Two soldiers / Sweetest gift, a mother's smile / Tomorrow I'll be gone / My better years / Custom made woman blues / Don't put her down, you helped put her there / You gave me a song / Pretty bird / Gallop to Kansas
ROUCD 0027 / May '95 / Rounder

☐ PIONEERING WOMEN OF BLUEGRASS (Dickens, Hazel & Alice Gerrard)
SFWCD 40065 / Jun '96 / Smithsonian Folkways

Dickenson, Vic

☐ BREAKS, BLUES AND BOOGIES
My favourite blues / Downtown cafe boogie / Uptown cafe blues / Breaks / I can't believe that you're in love with me / Blues mizz / Victory stride / Joy-mentin' / After you've gone / Just you, just me / Ygon mili jam session / I'm through with love / My blue Heaven / DB blues / Lester blows again / Jammin' with Lester / GUMPEY / Sugar / Blues in the South / Blues for yesterday / I want a little girl
TPZ 1065 / Jul '97 / Topaz Jazz

☐ DING DONG (Dickenson, Vic Quintet)
Rosetta / Blue and brokenhearted / Isle of golden dreams / Dear old Southland / Ding dong / Penthouse serenade / Black bottom / Five o' clock whistle / Isle of golden dreams / Blue and brokenhearted / Five o' clock whistle
STCD 8229 / Feb '98 / Storyville

☐ ESSENTIAL VIC DICKENSON, THE
Russian lullaby / Keeping out of mischief now / Sir Charles at home / Jeepers creepers / I cover the waterfront / Runnin' wild / Nice work if you can get it / Old fashioned love / Everybody loves my baby / Suspension blues
VCD 99/100 / 27 Apr '98 / Vanguard

Dickerson, Walt

☐ LIFE RAYS
1210282 / May '98 / Soul Note

☐ SHADES OF LOVE
SCCD 31424 / Nov '97 / Steeplechase

Dickey, Walt

☐ TRANSONIC (Dickey, Walt Trio)
AUM 005 / 6 Jul '98 / Aum Fidelity

Dickie, Neville

☐ CHARLESTON MAD AND OTHER SONGS OF THE 1920'S
SOSCD 1324 / May '97 / Stomp Off

☐ HARLEM STRUT
SOSCD 1302 / Jul '96 / Stomp Off

☐ NEVILLE DICKIE & HIS RHYTHM KINGS (Dickie, Neville Rhythm Kings)
SCD 31 / Dec '97 / Southland

☐ OH PLAY THAT THING
SOSCD 1309 / Jul '96 / Stomp Off

☐ WE GOT RHYTHM (Dickie, Neville & Mike Goetz)
DOWNTOWN 9214 / Dec '97 / Downtown

Dickies

☐ DOGS FROM THE HARE THAT BIT US
TX 51232CD / 22 Jun '98 / Triple XXX

☐ IDJIT SAVANT
CDHOLE 002 / May '95 / Golf

☐ STUKAS OVER DISNEYLAND
OVER 76CD / 6 Jul '98 / Overground

☐ WE AREN'T THE WORLD
RE 140CD / Nov '94 / ROIR

Dickinson, Bruce

☐ ACCIDENT OF BIRTH
RAWCD 124 / May '97 / Raw Power

☐ ALIVE IN STUDIO A (2CD Set)
Surrender to the city / She's the one that I adore / Wasted / D f dogs / Shipyard song / Past is another country
RAWDD 102 / Apr '96 / Raw Power

☐ SKUNKWORKS
RAWCD 106 / Apr '96 / Raw Power

Dickinson, Jim

☐ THOUSAND FOOTPRINTS IN THE SAND, A (Dickinson, Jim & Chuck Prophet)
3018392 / Apr '97 / Last Call

Dickinson, Rev. Emmett

☐ REV. EMMETT DICKINSON VOL.1 1929-1930
DOCD 5441 / May '96 / Document

Dicks

☐ DICKS 1980-1986
VIRUS 200CD / Apr '97 / Alternative Tentacles

Dickson, Barbara

☐ AFTER DARK
Right moment / Same sky / Only a dream in Rio / Lush life / I don't believe in you / Caravan / Fortress around your heart / I think it's going to rain today / It's money that I love / Pride (in the name of love) / No milk today / I know him so well
CLACD 302 / Aug '92 / Castle

☐ BEST OF BARBARA DICKSON, THE
Caravan song / January February / In the night / Crying game / Run like the wind / Tonight / With a little help from my friends / Answer me / Can't get by without you / Will you love me tomorrow / Stop in the name of love / As time goes by / Stardust / It's really you / I don't believe in miracles / Now I don't know / Tell me it's not true / I believe in you
4837962 / 27 Jul '98 / Columbia

☐ DARK END OF THE STREET
Young man cut down in his prime / Ballad of springhill / Fine horseman / First time ever I saw your face / Brother, can you spare a dime / Love needs a heart / Who knows where the time goes / All the pretty little horses / Dark end of the street / Sandman's coming / Just one smile / Love hurts
TRACD 117 / Apr '96 / Transatlantic

☐ DON'T THINK TWICE IT'S ALL RIGHT
Don't think twice, it's alright / With God on our side / When the ship comes in / Maggie's farm / Tears of rage / Oxford town / You ain't goin' nowhere / When I paint my masterpiece / Times they are a changin' / Ring them bells / Hard rain's gonna fall / Blowin' in the wind
MOODCD 25 / Mar '96 / Columbia

☐ GOLD
I know him so well / Missing you / Another good day for goodbye / Touch touch / Anyone who had a heart / Day in the life / You send me / What is love
CLACD 297 / '92 / Castle

☐ NOW AND THEN
Follow you follow me / Fine partly cloudy / I think it's going to rain today / Friend in need / It might be you / Fortress around your heart / If you go away / Same sky / September song / If you're right / How long / Peter / West coast of Clare / Tenderly / I don't believe in you / Angie baby / Who are you anyway / Caravans / No milk today / Day in the life / Thousands are sailing / Dream of you / It's raining again today / Every now and then
VSOPCD 166 / Jul '91 / Connoisseur Collection

☐ PARCEL OF ROGUES, A
Van Diemen's land / My lagan love / My Johnny was a shoemaker / Fine flowers in the valley / I once loved a lad / Jock O'Hazeldean / Sule skerry / Farewell to whisky / Lovely Joan / Donald Og / Geordie / Oh dear me / Parcel o' rogues
CTVCD 126 / Feb '94 / Castle

☐ RIGHT MOMENT, THE
Right moment / Tenderly / She moved through the fair / Time after time / Follow you, follow me / It's raining again today / Wouldn't it be good / Boulder to Birmingham / Who are you anyway / Vanishing days of love / Angie baby / Making history / Fine partly cloudy / If you go away
CLACD 310 / Sep '92 / Castle

☐ WORLD OF BARBARA DICKSON, THE
Answer me / Here comes the sun / Lover's serenade / Morning comes quickly / Deep into my soul / High tide / Who was it stole your heart away / Give me space / Drift away / People get ready / From now on / When you touch me this way / I could fall / There's a party in my heart / Stolen love / It makes me feel good / Lean on me / Long and winding road
5520122 / May '96 / Spectrum

Dictators

☐ DICTATORS FOREVER VOL.1 (A Tribute To The Dictators) (Various Artists)
RTI 205 / 24 Nov '97 / Roto

☐ DICTATORS FOREVER VOL.2 (A Tribute To The Dictators) (Various Artists)
RTI 206 / Dec '97 / Roto

☐ FUCK 'EM IF THEY CAN'T TAKE A JOKE
DANCD 052 / Nov '94 / Danceteria

Diddley, Bo

☐ AIN'T IT GOOD TO BE FREE
Ain't it good to be free / Bo Diddley put the rock in rock 'n' roll / Gotta be a change / I don't want your welfare / Mona, where's your sister / Stabilize yourself / I don't know where I've been / I ain't gonna force it on you / Evil woman / Let the fox talk
422107 / May '94 / New Rose

☐ BO DIDDLEY - THE CHESS YEARS (12CD Box Set)
I'm a man / Little girl / Bo Diddley / You don't love me (You don't care) / Diddley daddy / She's fine, she's mine / Pretty thing / Heart o-matic love / Bring it to Jerome / Spanish guitar / Dancing girl / Diddy wah diddy / I'm looking for a woman / I'm bad / Who do you love / Cops and robbers / Down home special / Hey Bo Diddley / Mona (I need you baby) / Say boss man / Before you accuse me / Say man / Hush your mouth / Bo's guitar / Clock strikes twelve / Dearest Darling / Willie and Lillie / Bo meets the monster / Crackin' up / Don't let it go / I'm sorry / Oh yeah / Blues blues / Great Grandfather / Mamma mia / Bucket / What do you know about love / Lazy woman / Come on baby / Nursery rhyme (Puttentang) / Mumblin' guitar / I love you so / Story of Bo Diddley / She's alright / Limber / Say man back again / Run Diddley Daddy / Roadrunner / Spend my life with you / Love you baby / Diddlin' / Cadillac / Limbo / Look at my baby / You know I love you / Let me in / Signifying blues / Live my life / Scuttle bug / Love me / Deed and deed I do / Walkin' and talkin' / Travellin' west / Crawdad / Ride on Josephine / No more lovin' / Do what I say / Doing the crawdaddy / Whoa / Mule (shine) / Cheyenne / Sixteen tons / Working man / Gunslinger / Somwhere / Sick and tired / Huckleberry bush / All together / Mess around / Shank / Twister / Bo Diddley is a lover / Love is a secret / Bo diddley is loose / Congo / Aztec / Call me / Bo's vacation / Hong Kong / Mississippi / Quick draw / You're looking good / Back home / Not guilty / Moon baby / Untitled instrumental / My babe / Detour / Stay sharp / Pills (love's labours lost) / Bo's bounce / I want my baby / Two flies / Background / Please Mr. Engineer / Doin' the jaguar / I know, I'm alright / For the love of Mike / Mr. Khrushchev / You all green / Bo's twist / I can tell / You can't judge a book by the cover / Sad sack / Rock 'n' roll / Mama don't allow no twistin' / Give me a break / Babes in the woods / Who may your lover be / Here 'tis / Bo's a lumberjack / (Extra read all about) Ben / Help out / Gimme gimme / Same old thing / Diana / Met you on a Saturday / Put the shoes on willie / Pretty girl / Ol' man river / Surfer's love call / Cookie headed Diddley / Greatest lover in the world / Surf sink or swim / Low tide / Africa speaks / Memphis / Old smokey / Bo Diddley's dog / I'm alright / Mr. Custer / Bo's waltz / What's buggin' you / Monkey Diddle / Hey good lookin' / Mama keep your big mouth shut / Jo-Ann / When the saints go marching in / Mush mouth Millie / London stomp / Rooster stew / Mummy walk / La la la / Yeah yeah yeah / Rain man / I wonder why (people don't like me) / Brother bear / Bo Diddley's hoot'nanny / Let's walk awhile / You ain't bad / Somebody beat me / Greasy spoon / Let me pass / Tonight is ours / Soul food / Let the kids dance / Hey red riding hood / He's so mad / Stop my monkey / Root hoot / Stinkey / Cornbread / Fireball / 500% more man / We're gonna get married / Easy / Do the frog / Yakky doodle / Ooh baby / Back to school / Juke / Long distance call / I just want to make love to you / Sad hours / Wrecking my love life / Boo-ga-loo before you go / Little red rooster / Sweet little angel / Goin' down slow / Spoonful / I'm high again / Another sugar Daddy / Bo Diddley 1969 / Soul train / Elephant man / I've got a feeling / If the bible's right / Power house / Funky sly / Shut up woman / Back soul / You Bo Diddley / I don't like you / Hot buttered blues / Bo's beat / Chuck's beat / I love you more than you'll ever know / Shape I'm in / Pollution / Bad moon rising / Down on the corner / I said shutup woman / Bad side of the moon / Lodi / Go for broke / Look at granma / Woman / Hey Jerome / Take it all off / I've had it hard / Bad trip / Good thing / Infatuation / Bo Diddley-itis / I hear you knocking / Make a hit record / Do the robot / Get out of my life / Don't want no lyin' woman / Bo-jam / Husband in law / Sneakers on a rooster / Going down / I've been workin' / Hit or miss / He's got all the whisky / Bite you / Evelee / Stop the pusher / You've got a lot of nerve / I'm sweet on you baby / You got to love me baby / Rollercoaster / I got to go / Billy's blues / Billy's blues / She's alright (unedited) / Signifying blues (extended version) / Pretty baby / You can shimmy / I'm hungry / Oh yes / Watusi bounce / Soup maker / Hey, go go
CDREDBOX 8 / Feb '94 / Charly

☐ BO DIDDLEY IS A LOVER
Not guilty / Hong Kong, Mississippi / You're looking good / Bo's vacation / Congo / Bo Diddley is a lover / Aztec / Back home / Bo Diddley is loose / Love is a secret / Quick draw / Two flies / Help out / Diana / Mamma mia / What do you know about love / My babe
SEECD 391 / Dec '93 / See For Miles

☐ BO'S BLUES
Down home special / You don't love me (you don't care) / Blues blues / 500% more man / Live my life / She's fine, she's mine / Heart-o-matic love / Bring it to Jerome / Pretty thing / You can't judge a book by the cover / Clock strikes twelve / Cops and robbers / Run diddley daddy / Before you accuse me / Diddy wah diddy / Bo's blues / Little girl / I'm a man / I'm bad / Who do you love / I'm looking for a woman / Two flies
CDCHD 396 / Aug '93 / Ace

☐ EP COLLECTION, THE
Little girl / Put the shoes on Willie / Run Diddley daddy / Bo Diddley / I'm a man / Bring it on Jerome / Pretty thing / Greatest lover in the world / She's fine, she's mine / Hey good lookin' / Deed and deed I do / I'm sorry / Dearest darling / Bo meets the monster / Rooster stew / Bo's a lumberjack / Let me in / Hong Kong, Mississippi / Hey Bo Diddley / Before you accuse me / Story of Bo Diddley / You're looking good / I'm looking for a woman / Hush your mouth
SEECD 321 / Jul '91 / See For Miles

☐ HEY BO DIDDLEY
Bo Diddley / Hey Bo Diddley / I'm a man / Bring it to Jerome / Diddley daddy / Before you accuse me / Pretty thing / Who do you love / Dearest darling / You can't judge a book by the cover / Say, mam / I'm looking for a woman / Roadrunner / Mona / Cops and robbers / Story of Bo Diddley / Say bossman / Hush your mouth / Nursery rhyme / I'm sorry / Live my life
CDRB 1 / Apr '94 / Charly

☐ HEY BO DIDDLEY/BO DIDDLEY
Hey Bo Diddley / I'm a man / Detour / Before you accuse me / Bo Diddley / Hush your mouth / My babe / Roadrunner / Shank / I know / Here 'tis / I'm looking for a woman / I can tell / Mr. Khrushchev / Diddlin' / Give me a break / Who may your lover be / Bo's bounce / You can't judge a book by the cover / Babes in the woods / Sad sack / Mama don't allow no twistin' / You all green / Bo's twist
BGOCD 287 / Jul '95 / Beat Goes On

☐ HIS BEST
MCD 09373 / Aug '97 / Chess/MCA

☐ IN CONCERT WITH MAINSQUEEZE
AIM 1023CD / Oct '93 / Aim

☐ LET ME PASS...PLUS
Let me pass / Stop my monkey / Greasy spoon / Tonight is ours / Root toot / Slinkey / Hey red riding hood / Let the kids dance / He's so mad / Soul food / Cornbread / Somebody beat me / 500% more man / Mama keep your big mouth shut / We're gonna get married / Easy
SEECD 392 / Jan '94 / See For Miles

☐ LIVING LEGEND
ROSE 188CD / Sep '89 / New Rose

☐ MIGHTY BO DIDDLEY, THE
TX 51161CD / Sep '95 / Triple X

☐ RARE AND WELL DONE
She's alright / Heart-o-matic love / I'm a man / Little girl / She's fine, she's mine / Bo meets the monster / I'm bad / Blues blues / Rock 'n' roll / No more lovin' / Cookie headed Diddley / Moon baby / Please Mr. Engineer / We're gonna get married / I'm high again
MCD 09331 / Apr '97 / Chess/MCA

Die Art

☐ BUT
RTD 19519042 / Nov '94 / Our Choice

Die Cheerleader

☐ FILTH BY ASSOCIATION
ABT 097CD / Oct '93 / Abstract

Die Drei Travellers

☐ EINE TUTE LUFT AUS BERLIN
Manana/Fridericus-Rex-marsch/Helenen-marsch / Berlin ist auch 'ne schone stadt genau wie Bonn / Wenn ich minister war / Eine tute luft aus Berlin / Es geht wieder los / Neubau swing / Der neue hut / 3D song (Ich mochte dich gern plastisch sehn) / Bella Ida / Wann darf ich sie besuchen / Tina Marie / Ein kleiner Eskimo traumt von melonen / 08/15 cocktail / Fraulein/Ich kusse ihre hand, Madame/Schoner / Gigolo/Heut liegt was in der luft / Rechts um / Das schonste am tag ist der morgen / Mich hat's erwischt / Hatschi-boogie / Sieben kleine spatzen / Musikanten tango / Ja, ja die sachsen / Janz weit weg von Berlin / Ich hab' so'n appetit uff'ne bulette / Rosalinde / Sind sie ringer, sind sie boxer / August / Komm herab von deinem esel, schone Gina / Ach kunigunde / Katja polka
BCD 16014 / Apr '97 / Bear Family

☐ ICH TRAUME NUR VON BERLIN
Hol' dir 'ne braut aus Berlin / Ich traume nur von Berlin / Tina Marie / Parodie / Benny's bierbar / Ich will keine sauren gurken / Das alte boot am Havelstrand / Barbier mambo / Klapperstorch song / Noch ein tor / Blau weisse hertha / Bleib nicht gleich schiessen / Fahren sie langsam / Heimweh nach dem kurfurstendamm / Die duften madchen von Berlin / 0-3-1-1 Berlin Berlin: *Oldorp, Fred* / Orchestra Italiana: *Oldorp, Fred* / Wer mal am kurfurstendamm seinen kaffee trank: *Oldorp, Fred* / Lucky aus Texas: *Oldorp, Fred* / Die polizei die regelt den verkehr: *Oldorp, Fred* / Ein fensterplatz im himmel: *Oldorp, Fred* / Kleiner bar von Berlin: *Oldorp, Fred* / Ich hab' nach einen koffer in Berlin: *Oldorp, Fred* / Afrika: *Oldorp, Fred* / Au revoir: *Oldorp, Fred* / Nim kein bier mit nach Munchen: *Oldorp, Fred* / Im endeffekt da hast du ja nach mich: *Oldorp, Fred* / Der Berliner liebt musike: *Oldorp, Fred* / Ich bin een Berliner junge: *Oldorp, Fred* / Zu vaters zeiten: *Oldorp, Fred*
BCD 16026 / May '97 / Bear Family

Die Goldenen Zitronen

☐ DEAD SCHOOL HAMBURG
Weil wir einverstanden sind / Nur ein bisschen noch / On y va / Der Wiederholer / Yes I am / Ketten bilden / 98 local invention / ICE Bertholt Brecht / Loser und normalos / Orange / Bird / L'avance du millenaire / Moderne classic
COOKCD 154 / 10 Aug '98 / Cooking Vinyl

Die Hard

☐ LOOKING OUT FOR...
CR 007CD / Jul '96 / Conversion

Die Haut

☐ HEAD ON
INDIGO 29222 / Oct '96 / Strange Ways

☐ SWEAT (Die Haut Live)
INDIGO 29402 / Oct '96 / Strange Ways

Die Kreuzen

☐ CENTURY DAYS
TGLP 30CD / Aug '88 / Touch & Go

Die Krupps

☐ FOUNDATION
CTCD 057 / Jul '97 / Captain Trip

☐ METALLE MASCHINEN MUSIK
KRUPPS 1CD / Aug '91 / Grey Area

☐ METAMORPHOSIS 1981-1992
CLP 9812 / Oct '96 / Cleopatra

☐ ODYSSEY OF THE MIND
Last flood / Scent / Metalmorphasis / Isolation / Final option / Alive / Odyssey / LCD / Eggshell / Jekyll or Hyde
CDXMFN 187
CDMFN 187 / Jul '95 / Music For Nations

☐ PARADISE NOW
Moving beyond / Gods of void / Paradise now / Black beauty / Reconstruction / Behind taste of taboo / Rise up / Fire / Full circle / Vortex / 30 Seconds / Society treaty
CDMFN 218 / May '97 / Music For Nations

Die Laughing

☐ GLAMOUR AND SUICIDE
FEATSHIH 13CD / Apr '96 / Grave News

☐ HEAVEN IN DECLINE
FETISH 15CD / Jun '96 / Grave News

Die Lustigen Junggesellen

☐ EDELWEISS
CNCD 5996 / Jul '94 / Disky

Die Monster Die

☐ CHROME MOLLY
JBM 1 CD / Mar '93 / Johnson Brothers Music

Die Moulinettes

☐ 20 BLUMEN
MA 34 / 14 Apr '98 / Marina

Die Sonne Satan

☐ SIGILLO
SMCD 1 / Sep '96 / Cacophonous

Die Toten Hosen

☐ LOVE, PEACE AND MONEY
Return of Alex / Year 2000 / All for the sake of love / Love song / Sexual / Diary of a lover / Put your money where your mouth is (Buy me) / Love is here / More and more / My land / Wunsch dir was / Wasted years / Perfect criminal / Love machine / Chaos bros
CDVIR 27 / Dec '94 / Virgin

Die Verbannten Kinder Evas

☐ COME HEAVY SLEEP
MOS 11CD / 6 Jul '98 / Trinity

Dieform

☐ ARCHIVES AND DOCUMENTS
NORMAL 95CD / '89 / Normal

☐ ARCHIVES AND DOCUMENTS
Face against ground / Bondage / New York / Serenade / Serial clones / Deadline 2 / North valley / Necron x / Third generation / Shaved girls / Was / Nostalgia / Tomorrow / Crash in the sky / Eternal language / Reflex 3 / Criminal passion / Sing song / Dance msuic / Maldoror / Es lebe der tod 3 / Murder / projection / Tote kinder aus deutschland / Ataxia / Uns kill / Psychotrope / Dog handler / Purple rain / Newel/light / Crypt / Song of parlysis / Oltre / Fleshwounds / Post mortem / Sad memory
TUECD 9202 / Mar '95 / Tuesday

☐ DIE PUPPE
NORMAL 81CD / '89 / Normal

☐ PHOTOGRAMMES
NORMAL 106CD / '89 / Normal

☐ POUPEE MECHANIQUE
NORMAL 83CD / '89 / Normal

☐ SOME EXPERIENCES WITH SHOCK
NORMAL 82CD / '89 / Normal

Diego, Don

☐ FEEL ME
D 2248992 / Aug '97 / Ichiban

Dieheim, Susan

☐ DESERT EQUATIONS (Dieheim, Susan & Richard Horowitz)
Ishtar / Got away / I'm a man / Tear / Azax attra / Jum jum / Armour / Desert equations
MTM 8CD / Nov '97 / Made To Measure

Diesel Boy

☐ VENUS ENVY
DON 014CD / 16 Feb '98 / Honest Don's

Diesel Park West

☐ LEFT HAND BAND (The Very Best Of Diesel Park West)
All the myths on Sunday / Here I stand / Jackie's still sad / When the hoodoo comes / Fall to love / Boy on top of the news / Bell of hope / I want no mystery / Fine Lily fine / Girl with the name / Like Princes do / King fluid / Let's talk American / Heathen a go go / Above these things / While the world cries decency
CDCHRM 105 / Feb '97 / Chrysalis

Dietrich, Marlene

☐ COLLECTION, THE
Lili marlene / Boys in the backroom / Johnny / Falling in love again / You do something to me / Lola / Nimm dich in acht vor blonden frauen / Peter (nelson) / Leben ohne liebe kannst du nicht / Give me the man / Quand l'amour meurt / Allein in einer grossen stadt / Assez / Moi, je m'ennuie / Mein blondes baby / Wo ist der mann
COL 054 / Mar '95 / Collection

☐ DIVAS GOLD COLLECTION, THE (2CD Set) (Dietrich, Marlene/Rita Hayworth)
R2CD 4059 / 9 Mar '98 / Deja Vu

☐ ESSENTIAL MARLENE DIETRICH, THE
Ich bin von kopf bis fuss auf liebe eingestellt / Quand l'amour meurt / Give me the man / Leben ohne liebe kannst du nicht / Mein blondes baby / Allein in einer grossen stadt / Peter / Lola / Wer wird den weinen / Johnny wenn du geburtstag hast / Lili Marlene / Dejeuner du matin / Ou vont les fleurs / Wenn die soldaten / In den kasernen / Und wenn er wiederkommt / Wenn der sommer wieder einzieht / Blowin' in the wind / Der welt war jung / Where have all the flowers gone / Ich werde dich lieben / Der trommelmann / Auf der mundharmonika
CDEMS 1399 / May '91 / EMI

☐ FALLING IN LOVE AGAIN
Falling in love again / You do something to me / Ich bin die fesche Lola / You go to my head / Blonde woman / Peter / Boys in the back room / Hot voodoo / Wo ist der man / I've been in love before / Johnny / Give me the man / Moi, je Mennuie / You've got that look / Assez / I gotta get a man
HADCD 217 / Jun '97 / Spotlight On

☐ FOR THE BOYS IN THE BACKROOM
Lili Marlene / Black market / Johnny / Boys in the backroom / You've got that look / This world of ours / You do something to me
BSTCD 9109 / May '92 / Best Compact Discs

☐ HIGHLIGHTS AND EVERGREENS (Marlene Dietrich On Radio 1930-1947)
Lili Marlene / Johnny / Quand l'amour / Meurt / Black market / Falling in love again / Illusions / Ich bin die fesche / Lola / Peter / You go to my head / Give me the man
RY 89 / Aug '97 / Radio Years

☐ LILI MARLENE
AC 75104 / 27 Apr '98 / Arkadia

☐ MARLENE
Kinder, heute'abend / Leben ohne liebe kannst du nicht / Falling in love again / Ich bin die fesche Lola / Quand l'amour meurt / Johnny / Mein blondes baby / Wenn die beste freundin / Wenn ich mir'was wunschen durfte / Allein in einer grossen stadt / Ich bin von kopf bis fuss auf liebe eingestellt / Es liegt in der luft/potpourri / Nimm dich in acht vor blonden frauen / Give me the man
CDAJA 5039 / Oct '88 / Living Era

☐ MARLENE DIETRICH
Lili marlene / La vie en rose / Lola / Boys in the backroom / I may never go home anymore / Another spring another love / Go away from my window / Honeysuckle rose / Such trying times / Near you / Allien / Johnny I can give you anything but love / Laziest gal in town / Frag nicht warum ich gehe / I wish you love / I will come back again / Illusions / Falling in love again / Shir hatan / You go to my head
LCD 6006/7 / Jan '93 / Fresh Sound

☐ MARLENE DIETRICH
16058 / May '94 / Laserlight

☐ MARLENE DIETRICH
Lili Marlene / La vie en rose / Lola / Boys in the backroom / I may never go home anymore / Another Spring, another love / Go away from my window / Honeysuckle rose / Such trying times / Near you / Allein / Johnny / I can't give you anything but love / Laziest gal in town / Frag nicht warum ich gehe / I wish you love / I'll come back again (maybe I'll come back) / Illusions / Falling in love again / Shir hatan / You go to my head
399536 / May '97 / Koch Presents

☐ MARLENE DIETRICH COLLECTOR'S EDITION
DVGH 7012 / Apr '95 / Deja Vu

☐ MARLENE DIETRICH IN LONDON
I can't give you anything but love / Laziest girl in town / Shir Hatan / La vie en rose / Jonny / Go away from my window / Allein in einer grossen stadt / Lili Marlene / Das lied ist aus / Lola / I wish you love
CDSBL 13110 / Nov '92 / DRG

☐ SEI LIEB ZU MIR
Lili marlene / Sei lieb zu mir / Das hobellied / Fraulein annie wohnt schon lange nicht hier (annie doesn't / Du liegst mir im herzen (you have taken my heart) / Schlittenfahrt (the surrey with the fringe on top) / Sag'mir'adieu' (time on my hands) / Dass ich dich wiederseh' (taking a chance on love) / Muss I denn / Mein mann ist verhindert (miss otis regrets) / Du hast die seele mein (you have taken my soul) / Ich hab'die ganze nacht geweint (i couldn't sleep a wink / Look me over closely / You're the cream in my coffee / My blue heaven / Boys in the backroom / Das lied ist aus / Je tire ma reverence / Alright, okay, you win / Makin' whoopee / I've grown accustomed to her face / One for my baby (and one more for the road) / Maybe I'll come back / Luar do serto
RMB 75056 / Aug '93 / Remember

Diez Brothers

☐ CLOSE UP
ISCD 114 / Oct '91 / Intersound

Diez, Stefan

☐ BAY SONGS (Diez, Stefan Group)
ISCD 158 / Sep '96 / Intersound

☐ IPANEMA (Diez, Stefan & Joerg Reiter band)
ISCD 173 / May '98 / Intersound

Dif Juz

☐ EXTRACTIONS
Crosswinds / Starting point / Love insane / Twin and earth
GAD 505CD / 6 Jul '98 / 4AD

Difference Engine

☐ BREADMAKER
Five listens / Simon's day / Never pull / Tsunami / Flat / Bugpowder / Epiphany
LADIDA 034 / Jul '94 / La-Di-Da

☐ CALIDAD
BDZ 34 / Oct '97 / Bedazzled

Different Trains

☐ ON THE RIGHT TRACK
Birth / This is life / Bits of dust / Dust in the wind / Market place / In my house / Sweet children / Class / To be continued / Workmen / Work / Rain / Tired tide / Swim against the tide / Cruel trick
GEPCD 1008 / Apr '94 / Giant Electric Pea

Dig D'Diz & Mondriaan Quartet

☐ ONTAARDE MOEDERS
BVHAASTCD 9702 / Aug '97 / Bvhaast

Diga Rhythm Band

☐ DIGA
Sweet sixteen / Magnificent sevens / Happiness is drumming / Razooli / Tal mala
RCD 10101 / Sep '91 / Rykodisc

Digable Planets

☐ BLOWOUT COMB
May 4th movement / Black ego / Dog it / Jettin' / Borough check / Highing fly / Dial 7 (Axiomos of creamy spices) / Art of easing / KB's Alley (mood dudes groove) / Graffiti / Blowing down / Ninth Wonder (Blackitolism) / For corners
CDCHR 6087 / Oct '94 / Cooltempo

☐ REACHIN' (A NEW REFUTATION OF TIME AND SPACE)
It's good to be here / Pacifics / Where I'm from / What cool breezes do / Time and space / Rebirth of slick / Last of the spiddyocks / Jimi diggin' cats / La femme fetal / Escapism / Appointment at the fat clinic / Nickel bags / Swoon units / Examination of what
CDCHR 6064 / Jan '94 / Cooltempo

Digance, Richard

☐ BEST OF THE TRANSATLANTIC YEARS, THE
England's green and pleasant land / My friend upon the road / Migration memoirs / Natural gas / As the crow flies / Mr. Jailer / How the west was lost / Drag queen blues / Working class millionaire / Dear River Thames / Edward Sayer's brass band / Show me the door / I hear the press gang / Midnight windmill / Money machine / Will we ever see them again / Red lights of Antwerp / Rosemary McLaren of The Strand / Final bow
ESMCD 497 / Apr '97 / Essential

☐ LIVE AT THE QEH/COMMERCIAL ROAD
Dear Diana / Summertime day in Stratford / Down petticoat lane / Drinking with Rosie / Journey of the salmon / Up on the seventh floor / Drag queen blues (nearly) / Right back where I started / Taken my lifetime away / I want to be there when you make it / Suicide Sam / Jungle cup final / East end ding dong / Think of me / Jumping Jack frog / Nightingale sang in Berkeley Square / Beauty Queen / Goodbye my friend, goodbye / Heavyweight Albert / Back Street international / Jimmy Greaves
BGOCD 304 / Nov '95 / Beat Goes On

Digger

☐ PROMISE OF AN UNCERTAIN FUTURE
HR 630CD / 18 May '98 / Hopeless

Diggers

☐ MOUNT EVEREST
CRECD 193 / Mar '97 / Creation

Diggle, Steve

☐ HERE'S ONE I MADE EARLIER
AXSO 2CD / Aug '96 / AX-S

Digi Dub

☐ 5 YEARS OF DIGI DUB
DDCD 002 / Mar '97 / Digi Dub

Digital Information Ensemble

☐ DIGITAL INFORMATION ENSEMBLE
MSS 0222 / 20 Apr '98 / Mutant Sound System

Digital Orgasm

☐ COME DANCIN'
Another world / Startouchers / Time to believe / Switch the mood / Magick / Running out of time (remix) / Moog eruption / Keep on flying / This generation / Reality / Running out of time / Moog eruption (remix)
4509905022 / Aug '92 / Dead Dead Good

Digital Poodle

☐ DIVISION
Division / Forward march / Totalitarian / Head of Lenin / Left/right / Binary / Elektronic espionage / Reform / Crack / Red star / Rifle
LUDDITECD 222 / Mar '94 / Death Of Vinyl

Digital Sun

☐ SPIRAL OF POWER
PR 0016CD / Jun '97 / Polytox

Digital Underground

☐ FUTURE RHYTHM
0097782RAP / Jul '97 / Edel

☐ SONS OF THE P
DFLO shuffle / Heartbeat props / No nose job / Sons of the P / Flowin' on the D-line / Kiss you back / Tales of the funky / Higher heights of spirituality / Family of the underground / D-flowstrumental / Good thing we're rappin'
BLRCD 12 / Oct '91 / Big Life

Digitalis

☐ 3RD STATE
MPCD 16 / 15 Jun '98 / Matsuri

Digits

☐ LITTLE MISCARRIAGE
TG 103CD / Oct '92 / Touch & Go

Digweed, John

☐ JOURNEYS BY DJ VOL.4
JDJCD 4 / Feb '94 / JDJ

☐ LIVE IN SYDNEY (Various Artists)
GU 006CD / 13 Apr '98 / Global Underground

☐ MIXMAG LIVE VOL.8 (Gordon Kaye/ John Digweed) (Various Artists)
MMLCD 008 / Jul '96 / Mixmag Live

Dikongue, Henri

☐ C'EST LA VIE
926882 / Nov '97 / BUDA

Dillard & Clark

☐ FANTASTIC EXPEDITION OF DILLARD & CLARK (Dillard, Doug & Gene Clark)
Out on the side / She darked the sun / Don't come rollin' / Train leaves here this morning / Radio song / Git it on brother (git in line brother) / In the plan / Something's wrong / Why not your baby / Lyin' down the middle / Don't be cruel
EDCD 192 / Jun '90 / Edsel

☐ FANTASTIC EXPEDITION OF DILLARD & CLARK/THROUGH THE MORNING
Out on the side / She darked the sun / Don't come rollin' / Train leaves here this morning / Why not your baby / Lyin' down the middle / With care from someone / Radio song / Git it on brother (git in line brother) / In the plan / Something's wrong / Don't be cruel / No longer a sweetheart of mine / Through the morning through the night / Rocky top / So sad / Corner street bar / I bowed my head and cried holy / Kansas city southern / Four walls / Polly / Roll in my sweet baby's arms / Don't let me down
5409752 / Jul '98 / A&M

☐ THROUGH THE MORNING, THROUGH THE NIGHT (Dillard, Doug & Gene Clark)
No longer a sweetheart of mine / Through the morning, through the night / Rocky top / So sad / Corner street bar / I bowed my head and cried holy / Kansas City Southern / Four walls / Polly / Rollin' in my sweet baby's arms / Don't let me down
EDCD 195 / Feb '91 / Edsel

Dillard, Rodney

☐ LET THE ROUGH SIDE DRAG
FF 537CD / Jul '92 / Flying Fish

Dillard, Varetta

☐ GOT YOU ON MY MIND
Square dance rock / If (you want to be my baby) / Got you on my mind / Mama don't want (what papa don't want) / One more time / I'm gonna tell my Daddy on you / Skinny Jimmy / Darling listen to the words of this song / Leave a happy fool alone / CC rider / That's why I cry / I got a lot of love / Undecided / Pray for me mother / I miss you Jimmy / Star of fortune / Rules of love / Falling / Old fashioned / Honey / What'll I do / Just multiply / Give me the right / Time was / I can't help myself / That old feeling / Cherry blossom / Pennies from Heaven / Night is never long enough
BCD 15431 / Jul '89 / Bear Family

☐ LOVIN' BIRD, THE
(Twee twee twee) the lovin' bird / Teaser / Good to me / Mercy Mr. Percy / Whole lot of lip / What can I say / I don't know what it is but I like it / Hey sweet love / You don't know what you're missing / Little bitty tear / Positive love / You ain't foolin' nobody / You better come home / You know I'm too good for you / Wondering where you are / Scorched / Good gravy baby / One more time / Star of fortune / Rules of love / Old fashioned
BCD 15432 / Jul '89 / Bear Family

Dillard-Hartford-Dillard

☐ GLITTER GRASS/PERMANENT WAVE
Don't come rollin' / Cross the borderline / Two hits and the joint turned brown / Don't lead me on / Bear Creek hop / No end love / Biggest whatever / Lost in a world / High dad in the morning / California is nicer than you / Artificial limitations / Get no better / Break it to me gently / That'll be the day / Blue morning / Same thing / Yakety yak / Something's wrong / Boogie on reggae woman / Country boy rock and roll / No beer in heaven
FF 036CD / Feb '93 / Flying Fish

Dillards

☐ HOMECOMING AND FAMILY REUNION
Old bald eagle / Hop high ladies / Cripple Creek / Whole world round / Ground hog / High dad in the morning / Douglas and I used to sit around and play / Old Joe Clark / Tennessee breakdown / Ebo Walker / Old man at the mill / Listen to the sound / Daddy was a mover / Banjo signal / Interview fragment
FF 70215 / Sep '96 / Flying Fish

☐ MOUNTAIN ROCK
Caney Creek / Don't you cry / Reason to believe / Big bayou / Walkin' in Jerusalem / I've just seen a face / High sierra / Never see my home again / Somebody touched me / Fields have turned brown / Orange blossom special
15295 / Aug '91 / Laserlight

☐ TAKE ME ALONG FOR THE RIDE
Someone's throwing stones / In my life / Like a hurricane / Take me along for the ride / Against the grain / Hearts overflowing / Bed of clover / Banks of the rouge bayou / Move on (life of the common man) / Food on the table / Wide wide Dixie highway / Great connection
VCD 79464 / Jan '97 / Vanguard

☐ TRIBUTE TO THE AMERICAN DUCK/ ROOTS & BRANCHES
BGOCD 306 / Mar '96 / Beat Goes On

Dilleshaw, John

☐ COMPLETE RECORDED WORKS 1929-1930
DOCD 8002 / Jan '97 / Document

Dillinger

☐ 3 PIECE SUIT
CP 445042 / 7 Jul '98 / Rhino

Dillinger

☐ CB 200
CB 200 / No chuck it / Cokane in my brain / General / Power bank / Plantation heights / Race day / Natty kick like lightning / Buckingham Palace / Crankface
RRCD 30 / Sep '91 / Reggae Refreshers

☐ COCAINE
Cocaine in my brain / Jah love / Funkey punk / Mickey Mouse crab louse / I thurst / Loving pauper / Flat foot hustlin' / Crabs in my pants / Marijuana in my brain / Cocaine (remix)
CPCD 8020 / Feb '94 / Charly

☐ FUNKY PUNK
Cocaine / Rockers / Super cock / Sex me baby / Get on the good side / LSD / Funky punk / Rock to the music / Soul food / Rebel with a cause
LG 21061 / Nov '92 / Lagoon

☐ I NEED A WOMAN
RB 3004 / May '94 / Reggae Best

☐ MARIJUANA IN MY BRAIN
Marijuana in my brain / Addis Ababbaithiopia / Bouncing ball / Step it in Ethiopia / Stop stealing in the name of Jah / Come praise Jah Jah / Hard being Thomas / Rasta vibration / African roots reggae
CDBS 559 / Jul '97 / Burning Sounds

☐ SAY NO TO DRUGS
No sound contest / Money it a lick / Gun hawk / Say no to drugs / Freedom fighter / Short and stout / You I love / Wey you wann me do / Rub it down / Child abuse / Jealously / Ball of fire
LG 21003 / Jun '93 / Lagoon

☐ THREE PIECE SUIT
Answer my question / Natty dread a the ruler / Fernando sancho / Leggo violence / Lier linda / Everybody girl / Three piece suit and thing / Tickle me girl / Fool and his money / Babylon leggo vah children / African world wide / Into the african dub / Thruth and right / Right dub wise / Don't take another man's life / Man size dub / Jah show them the way / 12 tribe dub / Trial and crosses / Into bradforth dub / See and blind / Striker see da dub ya
LG 21081 / Aug '93 / Lagoon

☐ TOP RANKING
RNCD 2129 / Nov '95 / Rhino

Dillinger Four

☐ MIDWESTERN SONGS OF THE AMERICAS
HR 633CD / 29 Jun '98 / Hopeless

Dillingham, Todd

☐ ART INTO DUST
Little visions / Girl of the scene / You don't mind / Art into dust / Celebration bonfire / It really matters / Never want to see / Fading (just for you) / Fine time no time / African device / Fly / Crabs advancing / Luminous glow / Green pears / Am I alone / Interstellar overdrive
VP 121CD / Jan '93 / Voiceprint

☐ SGT. KIPPER
WO 25CD / Jul '95 / Woronzow

☐ VAST EMPTY SPACES
Vast empty spaces / Shiny girl / Myriad girl-paintings / Rely on me / Dollis broof / Millero / Wonderland / Mullardo / Tranquil water / Nine you dont' want to / Up the ass of a swan / Animal bizarre / Where is the brave
BP 153CD / 6 Oct '97 / Blueprint

☐ VOICEPRINT RADIO SESSION
VPR 002CD / Oct '94 / Voiceprint

Dillon, Cheralee

☐ CITRON
GRCD 380 / Dec '95 / Glitterhouse

☐ POOL
GRCD 310 / Feb '94 / Glitterhouse

Dillon Fence

☐ ROSEMARY
Daylight / Hey mockingbird / Summer / Sad inheritance / Danger / I'll wait / Playful / Something for you / Guilty / How did you get so high / I will break
MR 00332 / Nov '92 / Mammoth

Dillon, Leonard

☐ ONE STEP FORWARD
Name of the game (is survival) / (Cool it) amigo / On the road again / One step forward (and two steps back) / Love you, little lover / In day, mi dey / Feed the fire (fan the flame) / Woman of babylon / Done I' done / You are my first love / You got the dough / Train to skaville / Dread prophesy / No bad woman / Whip / I'm ready
PRCDSP 400 / Jun '92 / Prestige

Dillon, Phyllis

☐ LOVE WAS ALL I HAD
RNCD 2088 / Dec '94 / Rhino

☐ ONE LIFE TO LIVE
TICD 15004 / Mar '95 / Studio One

Dillon, Sandy

☐ DANCING ON THE FREEWAY
GY 004 / Mar '94 / NMC

Dils

☐ I HATE THE RICH
DAMGOOD 008 / Jul '92 / Damaged Goods

Dim Dim

☐ NECTARINE (CD/Book Set)
BRCD 057 / Apr '97 / Brinkman

Dim Sum Clip Job

☐ HARMOLODIC JEOPARDY
AVAN 051 / Oct '96 / Avant

Dime Bag

☐ DIME BAG
HB 10 / Mar '93 / Heatblast

Dime Store Prophets

☐ FANTASTIC DISTRACTION
246654 / May '97 / Sara Bellum

Dimension 5

☐ TRANSDIMENSIONAL
INTALCD 001 / Jun '97 / Intastella

Dimension Zero

☐ PENETRATIONS FROM THE LOST WORLD
WAR 97929CD / 18 May '98 / War

Dimisich, Victor

☐ MY NAME IS K (Dimisich, Victor Band)
MEDICATION 002CD / 24 Nov '97 / Medication

Dimitri

☐ HI TEC SOUL (Dimitri From The Roxy)
8530152 CD / 16 Jul '97 / Kubin

Dimitri From Paris

☐ MONSIEUR DIMITRI'S DE-LUXE HOUSE OF FUNK (Various Artists)
Free ton style: *Dimitri From Paris* / Free lovin': *Morning Kids* / You love my music: *Switchblade Sisters* / Number one: *Sir Mang, Raymond* / May the funk be with you: *Second Crusade* / Captain dobbey: *Teddy G* / Visions of paradise: *Sinclair, Bob* / High priestess: *Karma* / Vibe PM: *Mondo Grosso* / Ola-Le: *Takada* / Spy's spice: *UFO* / N'ssi n'ssi: *Khaled, Cheb* / Sometimes: *Brand New Heavies* / Isobel: *Bjork*
MMLCD 024 / 26 Aug '97 / Mixmag Live

☐ SACRE BLEU
Prologue / Sacre francais / Monsieur Dimitri joue du stylophone / Nothing to lose / Un termede / Reveries / Attente musicale / Dirty Larry / Free ton style / Un terlude / Une very stylish fille / Un woman's paradis / La rythme et le cadence / Le moogy reggae / Encore un terlude / Un world myterious / Par un chemin different / Nothing to lose (lounge instrumentale) / Epilogue
YP 011ACD / Nov '96 / Yellow
0630178322 / Apr '97 / East West

Dimizio, Pat

☐ SONGS AND SOUNDS
Where am I going / Nobody but me / 124mph / Running jumping standing still / Everyday world / No love lost / World apart / Today it's you / Liza / Somewhere down the line / You should know / I'd rather have the blues
VEL 79706 / 13 Jul '98 / Velvel

Dimmu Borgir

☐ DEVIL'S PATH
SHAGRATH 006CD / Oct '96 / Hot

☐ ENTHRONE DARKNESS TRIUMPHANT
NB 247CD / Jun '97 / Nuclear Blast

☐ FOR ALL TID
NB 279CD / 25 Aug '97 / Nuclear Blast

☐ GODLESS SAVAGE GARDEN
Moonchild domain / Hunnerkongene / Chaos without prophecy / Raabjorn speiler draugheimens skodde / Metal heart / Stormblast / Master of disharmony / In death's embrace / Mourning place
NB 3002 / 3 Aug '98 / Nuclear Blast

☐ STORMBLAST
Alt lys er svunnet hen / Broderskapets ring / Nar sjelen hentes til helvete / Sorgens kammer / Da den kristne satte livet til / Stormblast / Dodsferd / Antikrist / Vinder fra en ensom grav / Guds fortapelse - apenbaring av dommedag
NIHIL 012 / 20 Jul '98 / Cacophonous

D'Imperio, Danny

☐ OUTLAW, THE
SKCD 3060 / Dec '97 / Sackville

Dimple Minds

☐ DRUNK ON ARRIVAL
38226 / 29 Sep '97 / Semaphore

☐ LIVE IN ALZHEIM
SPV 08476932 / May '95 / SPV

Dimuzio, Tom

☐ HEADLOCK
RERTD 1 / Jun '98 / ReR/ Recommended

Dinger, Thomas

☐ FUR MICH
CTCD 078 / 2 Feb '98 / Captain Trip

Dingoes

☐ DINGOES, THE
D 19463 / Oct '97 / Festival

Dinner Is Ruined

☐ ELEVATOR MUSIC FOR NON-CLAUSTROPHOBIC PEOPLE
SUNCD 035 / 20 Oct '97 / Sonic Unyon

Dinorock

☐ DINOSAUR ROCK
ROUCD 8081 / 19 Jan '98 / Rounder

☐ GREAT DINOSAUR MYSTERY, THE
ROUCD 8083 / 19 Jan '98 / Rounder

Dinosaur Jr.

☐ BUG
BFFP 31 CD / Oct '88 / Blast First

☐ FOSSILS
SST 275CD / Oct '96 / SST

☐ GREEN MIND
Wagon / Puke and cry / Flying cloud / How'd you pin that one on me / Water / Muck / Thumb / Green mind / Blowing it/I live for that look
9031734482 / Feb '91 / Blanco Y Negro

☐ HAND IT OVER
I don't think / Never bought it / Nothin's goin' on / I'm insane / Can't we move this alone / Sure not over you / Loaded / Mick / I know yer insane / Gettin' rough / Gotta know
0630183122 / Mar '97 / Blanco Y Negro

☐ WHERE HAVE YOU BEEN
Out there / Start choppin' / What else is new / On the way / Not the same / Get me / Drawerings / Hide / Goin' home / I ain't sayin'
4509916272 / Feb '93 / Blanco Y Negro

☐ WITHOUT A SOUND
Feel the pain / I don't think so / Yeah right / Outta hand / Grab it / Even you / Mind glow / Get out of this / On the brink / Seemed like the thing to do / Over your shoulder
4509969332 / Aug '94 / Warner Bros.

☐ YOU'RE LIVING ALL OVER ME
SST 1330CD / May '93 / SST

Dio

☐ ANGRY MACHINES
08518292 / Nov '96 / SPV

☐ ANTHOLOGY
Holy diver / Rainbow in the dark / Stand up and shout / Straight through the heart / Last in line / One night in the city / We rock / Egypt (the chains are on) / Shoot shoot / Time to burn / All the fools sailed away / I could have been a dreamer / Sunset superman / Shine on the night
VSOPCD 245 / 17 Nov '97 / Connoisseur Collection

☐ DIAMONDS (The Best Of Dio)
Holy diver / Rainbow in the dark / Don't talk to strangers / We rock / Last in line / Evil eyes / Rock 'n' roll children / Sacred heart / Hungry for heaven / Hide in the rainbow / Dream evil / Wild one / Lock up the wolves
5122062 / Jun '92 / Vertigo

☐ ELF ALBUMS, THE (Carolina County Ball/Trying To Burn The Sun) (Elf)
Carolina county ball / LA 59 / Ain't it all amusing / Happy / Annie New Orleans / Rocking chair rock 'n' roll blues / Rainbow / Do the same thing / Blanche / Black swampy water / Prentice wood / When she smiles / Good time music / Liberty road / Shotgun boogie / Wonderworld / Street walker
VSOPCD 167 / Sep '91 / Connoisseur Collection

☐ HOLY DIVER
Stand up and shout / Holy diver / Gypsy / Caught in the middle / Don't talk to strangers / Straight through the heart / Invisible / Rainbow in the dark / Shame on the night
8110212 / Mar '88 / Vertigo

☐ INFERNO (Live In Line/2CD Set)
Intro / Jesus and Mary / Straight through the heart / Don't talk to strangers / Holy diver / Drum solo / Heaven and Hell / Double Monday / Stand up and shout / Hunter of the heart / Mistreated / Guitar solo / Last in line / Rainbow in the dark / Mob rules / Man on a silver mountain / Long live rock 'n' roll / We rock
908611115CD / 16 Mar '98 / Mayhem

Dion

☐ BEST OF DION & THE BELMONTS (Dion & The Belmonts)
Teenager in love / I wonder why / Where or when / Every little thing I do / Lover's prayer / No one knows / That's my desire / Don't pity me / In the still of the night / Will you love me still / Run around Sue / Lonely teenager / Sandy / Lovers who wander / Runaway girl / Queen of the hop / Lonely world / King without a Queen / Kissin' game / Tonight, tonight / Wanderer
CDMFP 6218 / Apr '96 / Music For Pleasure

☐ BEST OF THE GOSPEL YEARS, THE
Centre of my life / Still in the spirit / I put away my idols / Truth will set you free / New Jersey wife / New breed of man / Sweet surrender / Healing / Train for glory / I believe (sweet Lord Jesus) / Hymn to him / Come to the cross / He's the one / Simple ironies / Daddy / Golden sun, silver moon / You need a love / Day of the Lord
CDCHD 644 / Apr '97 / Ace

☐ DREAM ON FIRE
VR 3327 / Oct '92 / Vision

☐ LAURIE, SABINA & UNITED ARTISTS SIDES VOL.1, THE (Belmonts)
Come on little angel / Tell me why / Smoke from your cigarette / That background sound / How about me / My love is real / Searching for a new love / I don't know how to cry / I need someone / Hombre / Don't get around much anymore / Why / You're like a mystery / Today my love has gone away / I got a feeling / I don't know why / We belong together / Such a long way / Come take a walk with me / Ann-Marie / Diddle-dee-dum / I confess / Summertime time / Walk on boy / Now it's all over / Not responsible / Time to dream / Dancin' girl / Have you heard / (I've got) More important things to do / Tell my why
CDCHD 58C / Aug '95 / Ace

☐ LOVERS WHO WANDER/SO WHY DIDN'T YOU DO THAT... (Dion & The Belmonts/Dion)
Lovers who wander: *Dion* / Come go with me: *Dion* / King without a queen: *Dion* / So long friend (by the way I love you): *Dion* / Twist: *Dion* / Mi muchacha (little girl): *Dion* / Stagger Lee: *Dion* / Shout: *Dion* / Tonight tonight: *Dion* / (I was) born to cry: *Dion* / Queen of the hop: *Dion* / Candy man: *Dion* / Sandy: *Dion* / Lost for sure: *Dion* / Wanderer: *Dion & The Belmonts* / Moon river: *Dion & The Belmonts* / Ain't that better baby: *Dion & The Belmonts* / In a room in a house: *Dion & The Belmonts* / Crying: *Dion & The Belmonts* / It was never meant to be: *Dion & The Belmonts* / Baby what you want me to do: *Dion & The Belmonts* / My private joy: *Dion & The Belmonts* / Every little thing I do: *Dion & The Belmonts* / We went away: *Dion & The Belmonts* / Come take a walk with me: *Dion & The Belmonts* / Tag along: *Dion & The Belmonts* / Will you love me still: *Dion & The Belmonts* / Teenager in love: *Dion & The Belmonts* / That's how I need you: *Dion & The Belmonts*
CDCHD 943 / 23 Mar '98 / Ace

☐ PRESENTING DION & THE BELMONTS (Dion & The Belmonts)
I wonder why / Teen angel / Where or when / You better not do that / Just you / I got the blues / Don't pity me / Teenager in love / Wonderful girl / Funny feeling / I've cried before / That's my desire / No one knows / I can't go on
CDCHM 107 / Jul '89 / Ace

☐ RETURN OF THE WANDERER/FIRE IN THE NIGHT
Looking for the heart of Saturday night / You've awakened something in me / Pattern of my lifeline / Street heart theme / Spanish Harlem incident / Fire in the night / Hollywood / Street mama / You are my star / Midtown American main street gang / Guitar queen / (I used to be a) Brooklyn dodger / Power of love within / Do you believe in magic / We don't talk anymore / Midnight lover / All quiet on 34th Street / Poor boy
CDCHD 936 / Jun '90 / Ace

☐ ROAD I'M ON, THE (A Retrospective/2CD Set)
Can't we be sweethearts / Ruby baby / Will love ever come my way / This little girl of mine / Sunday kind of love / Gonna make it alone / This little girl / Fever / Donna the prima donna / Drip drop / Baby please don't go / 900 miles / Work song / Chicago blues / Road I'm on (Gloria) / Ruby baby / Donna the prima donna / Too much monkey business / I'm the hoochie koochie man / Katie May / You can't judge a book by its cover / Johnny B Goode / Spoonful / Kickin' child / Drop down baby / It's all over now, baby blue / Knowing I won't go back there / My love / Tomorrow won't bring the rain / Time in my heart for you / All I want to do is live my life / I can't help but wonder where I'm bound / Two ton feather / Born to cry / You move me
4868232 / Feb '97 / Legacy

☐ RUNAROUND SUE
Runaround Sue / Somebody nobody wants / Dream lover / Life is but a dream / Wanderer / Runaway girl / I'm gonna make it somehow / Majestic / Could somebody take my place tonight / Little star / Lonely world / In the still of the night / Kansas City / Take good care of my baby
CDCHM 148 / Aug '89 / Ace

☐ RUNAROUND SUE (The Best Of The Rest)
Runaround Sue / Lonely teenager / Kissin' game / Havin' fun / Little Miss Blue / Wanderer / Tonight tonight / My one and only / PS I love you / One for my baby (and one more for the road) / Close your eyes / North east end of the room / Little Diane / In a room / Ain't that better baby / Baby, what you want me to do / Moon river / Crying / After the dance / Somebody nobody wants / Heaven help me / I'm gonna make it somehow / Could someone take my place tonight
CDCH 915 / 30 Mar '98 / Ace

☐ WISH UPON A STAR/ALONE WITH DION (Dion & The Belmonts/Dion)
When you wish upon a star: *Dion & The Belmonts* / Lover's prayer: *Dion & The Belmonts* / My day: *Dion & The Belmonts* / Every little thing I do: *Dion & The Belmonts* / It's only a paper moon: *Dion & The Belmonts* / I'm through with love: *Dion & The Belmonts* / September song: *Dion & The Belmonts* / Lonely teenager: *Dion* / PS I love you: *Dion* / Little Miss Blue: *Dion* / Heaven help me: *Dion* / Fools rush in: *Dion* / North East end of the corner: *Dion* / Then I'll be tired of you: *Dion* / In the still of the night: *Dion & The Belmonts* / My private joy: *Dion & The Belmonts* / Swinging on a star: *Dion & The Belmonts* / All the things you are: *Dion & The Belmonts* / Fly me to the moon: *Dion & The Belmonts* / When the red, red robin comes bob, bob, bobbin' along: *Dion & The Belmonts* / Faith: *Dion & The Belmonts* / After the dance: *Dion* / Save the last dance for me: *Dion* / Havin' fun: *Dion* / Close your eyes: *Dion* / My one and only love: *Dion* / One for my baby (and one more for the road): *Dion* / Kissin' game: *Dion*
CDCH 945 / 23 Mar '98 / Ace

Dion, Celine

☐ CELINE DION
Introduction / Love can move mountains / Show your emotion / If you asked me to / If you could see me now / Halfway to heaven / Beauty and the beast / With this tear / Did you give enough love / If I were you / I love you, goodbye / Little bit of love / Water from the moon / Nothing broken but my heart / Where does my heart beat now
4715089 / Nov '92 / Epic

☐ CELINE DION/UNISON
Love can move mountains / Show some emotions / If you asked me to / If you could see me now / Halfway to heaven / Did you give enough love / If I were you / Beauty and the beast / I love you, goodbye / Little bit of love / Water from the moon / With this tear / Nothing broken but my heart / (If there was) Any other way / If love is out of the question / Where does my heart beat now / Last to know / I'm loving every moment with you / Love by another name / Unison / I feel too much / If we could start over / Have a heart
DIONCD 2 / May '95 / Epic

☐ COLLECTION 1982-1988, THE (2CD Set)
Ne partez pas sans moi / D'amour ou d'amitie / Visa pour les beaux jours / Les oiseaux du bonheur / Tellement j'ai d'amour pour toi / La religieuse / C'est pour toi / Avec toi / Mon reve de toujours / Du soleil au couer / A quatre pas d'ici / Un amour pour moi / Billy / Comment t'aimer / Mon ami m'a quittee / La dodo la do / Hymne a l'amitie / Je ne veux pas / C'est pour vivre / En amour / Ne me plaignez pas / Les chemins de ma maison / Hello Mister Sam / Trois heures vingt / Trop jeune a dix sept ans / Paul et Virginie / La voix du bon dieu / Benjamin
BS 81012 / May '97 / BR Music

☐ COLOUR OF MY LOVE, THE
Power of love / Misled / Think twice / Only one road / Everybody's talkin' my baby down / Next plane out / Real emotion / When I fall in love / Love doesn't ask why / Refuse to dance / I remember LA / No living without loving you / Lovin' proof / Just walk away / Colour of my love
4747432 / Feb '94 / Epic

☐ D'EUX
Pour que tu maimes encore / Le ballet / Regarde moi / Je seia pas / La moire d'abraham destin / Les derniers seront les premiers / Mrai ou tu iras / J'attendais / Priere paienne / Vole
4802862 / Sep '95 / Epic

☐ DION CHANTE PLAMONDON
Des mots qui sonnent / Le monde est stone / Le fils de superman / Je danse dans ma tete / Le blues du businessman / Un garcon pas comme les autres (ziggy) / Quelqu'un pue j'aime quelqu'un qui m'aime / Les uns contres les autres / Oxygene / L'amour existe encore
4772152 / 8 Sep '97 / Epic

☐ FALLING INTO YOU
It's all coming back to me now / Because you loved me / Falling into you / Make you happy / Seduces me / All by myself / Declaration of love / (You make me feel like) A natural woman / Dreaming of you / I love you / If that's what it takes / I don't know / River deep, mountain high / Your light / Call the man / Fly
4837922 / Mar '96 / Epic

☐ FOR YOU
D'amour ou d'amitie / Visa pour les beaux jours / Ne partez pas sans moi / Les oiseaux du bonheur / Tellement j'ai d'amour pour toi / La religieuse / C'est pour toi / Avec toi / Mon reve de toujours / Du soleil au coeur / A quatre pas d'ici / Un amour pour moi / Billy / Comment t'aimer
DSHLCD 7021 / Jan '96 / D-Sharp

☐ LES PREMIERES ANNEES
D'amour ou d'amitic / Visa pour les beaux jours / En amour / Les oiseaux du bonheur / Tellement j'ai d'amour pour toi / La religieuse / C'est pour toi / Ne partez pas sans moi / Mon ami m'a quitce / Avec toi / Mon reve de toujours / Du soleil au coeur / A quatre pas d'ici / Un amour pour moi / Billy / Comment t'aimer / Je ne veux pas / C'est pour vivre
4881042 / Jun '97 / Epic

☐ LET'S TALK ABOUT LOVE
Reason / Immortality / Treat her like a lady / Why oh why / Love is on the way / Tell him: *Dion, Celine & Barbara Streisand* / Amar haciendo el amor / When I need you / Miles to go (before I sleep) / Us / Just a little bit of love / My heart will go on / Where is the love / Be the man (on this night) / I hate you then I love you: *Dion, Celine & Luciano Pavarotti* / Let's talk about love
4891592 / 17 Nov '97 / Epic

☐ LIVE A PARIS
J'attendais / Destin / Power of love / Regarde, moi / River deep mountain high / Ziggy les derniers seront les premiers / J'irai ou tu iras / Je sais pas / Le ballet priere paienne / Pour que tu m'aimes encore / Quand on n'a que l'amour / Vole / To love you more
4866062 / Oct '96 / Epic

☐ NE PARTEZ PAS SANS MOI
Ne partez pas sans moi / D'amour ou d'amitie / Visa pour les beaux jours / Les oiseaux du bonheur / Teliment j'al d'amour pour tol / La religeuse / C'est pour toi / Avec toi / Mon reve de tourjours / Du soileil au coeur / A quatre pas d'ici / U amour pour moi / Billy / Comment t'aimer
CD 2005 / Jun '96 / BR Music

☐ UNISON
(If there was) any other way / If love is out of the question / Where does my heart beat now / Last to know / I'm loving every moment with you / Love by another name / Unison / I feel too much / If we could start over / Have a heart
4672032 / Sep '94 / Epic

Dion, Claudette

☐ CHANTE EDITH PIAF
3020232 / 24 Apr '98 / Arcade

Diop, Mapathe

☐ SABAR WOLOF (Dance Drumming Of Senegal)
VPU 1003CD / May '97 / Village Pulse

Diop, Wasis

☐ NO SANT
African dream / Di na wo / Hoaal du Baah / TGV / Ma na / Dames electriques / NOP / No sant / Issa thiaw / La danse des Maures / Den ma ba / SB-LE voyager
5265652 / Jan '96 / Mercury Black Vinyl

☐ TOXU
Soweto / My son / Everything (is never quite enough) / Que faut-il faire / Toxu / Once in a lifetime / Accident / Rat 'n belle / After dreaming / Julia / Mori / Samba le berger / Colobane (hymne a l'amour)
5581982 / 29 Jun '98 / Mercury Black Vinyl

Diorio, Joe

☐ DOUBLE TAKE
RMCD 4502 / Sep '93 / Ram

☐ MORE THAN FRIENDS
RMCD 4514 / Apr '94 / Ram

☐ WE WILL MEET AGAIN
RMCD 4501 / Sep '93 / Ram

Dioubate, Oumou

☐ LANCEY
STCD 1046 / Oct '93 / Stern's

Dioulasso, Bob

☐ BALAFONS, PERCUSSIONS, ETC
824812 / Nov '90 / BUDA

Dip Tse Chok Ling Monks

☐ SACRED CEREMONIES VOL.1 (Tantric Hymns & Music Of Tibetan Buddhism)
170742 / Jan '95 / Celestial Harmonies

☐ SACRED CEREMONIES VOL.2 (Tantric Hymns & Music Of Tibetan Buddhism)
170792 / Jan '95 / Celestial Harmonies

☐ SACRED CEREMONIES VOL.3 (Ritual Music Of Tibetan Buddhism)
131323 / Oct '96 / Celestial Harmonies

Diplomats

☐ DON'T FAKE THE JAZZ
Just another day / Elegant evening / Don't fake the jazz / Old Jack swang / Iva's groove / Last chance / It's you / Jean Pierre / 6 AM
RIPEXD 197 / Nov '95 / Ripe

Dir Han Tan

☐ CHANTS TRADITIONAL DU PAYS VANNETAIS
ARN 64364 / Feb '97 / Arion

Dire Straits

☐ ALCHEMY - LIVE (2CD Set)
Once upon a time in the west / Expresso love / Private investigations / Sultans of swing / Two young lovers / Telegraph Road / Solid rock / Going home / Romeo and Juliet
8182432 / Jun '96 / Vertigo

☐ BROTHERS IN ARMS
So far away / Money for nothing / Walk of life / Your latest trick / Why worry / Ride across the river / Man's too strong / One world / Brothers in arms
8244992 / Jun '96 / Vertigo

☐ COMMUNIQUE
Angel of mercy / Follow me home / Lady writer / News / Once upon a time in the West / Communique / Portobello belle / Single headed sailor / Where do you think you're going / So far away / Money for nothing / Walk of life / Your latest trick / Why worry / Ride across the river / Man's too strong / One world / Brothers in arms
8000522 / Jun '96 / Vertigo

☐ DIRE STRAITS
Down to the waterline / Water of love / Setting me up / Six blade knife / Southbound again / Sultans of swing / In the gallery
8000512 / Jun '96 / Vertigo

☐ LIVE AT THE BBC
Down to the waterline / Six blade knife / Water of love / Wild West End / Sultans of swing / Lions / What's the matter baby / Tunnel of love
WINCD 072
WINCD 072X / Jun '95 / Windsong

☐ LOVE OVER GOLD
Telegraph Road / Private investigations / Industrial disease / It never rains / Love over gold
8000882 / Jun '96 / Vertigo

☐ MAKING MOVIES
Tunnel of love / Romeo and Juliet / Skateaway / Expresso love / Les boys / Hand in hand / Solid rock / Down to the waterline / Water of love / Setting me up / Six blade knife / Southbound again / Sultans of swing / In the gallery / Wild West End / Lions
8000502 / Jun '96 / Vertigo

☐ MONEY FOR NOTHING
Sultans of swing / Down to the waterline / Portobello belle / Twisting by the pool / Romeo and Juliet / Where do you think you're going / Walk of life / Private investigations / Money for nothing / Tunnel of love / Brothers in arms / Telegraph Road
8364192 / Jun '96 / Vertigo

☐ ON EVERY STREET
Calling Elvis / On every street / When it comes to you / Fade to black / Bug / You and your friend / Heavy fuel / Iron hand / Ticket to heaven / My parties / Planet of New Orleans / How long
5101602 / Jun '96 / Vertigo

☐ ON THE NIGHT
Calling Elvis / Walk of life / Heavy fuel / Romeo and Juliet / Private investigations / Your latest trick / On every street / You and your friend / Money for nothing / Brothers in arms
5147662 / Jun '96 / Vertigo

Direct Hits

☐ MAGIC ATTIC
TANGCD 9 / Oct '94 / Tangerine

Directions In Groove

☐ DIG DEEPER
Two way dreamtime / Medium rare / Favourite / DNA / Pythonicity / Shelflife / Hip replacement / Suffer the children / Gil / Big theme / Den / Terrified from dizzy heights / Re-invent yourself / Inner blue funk
5186092 / Dec '93 / Verve

☐ DIRECTIONS IN GROOVE
Re-invent yourself / Sweet thing / Taylor's cube / Heaven on Earth / Freezerville
5184362 / Dec '93 / Mercury

☐ SPEAKEASY
5285392 / May '96 / Verve

Dirk K

☐ BEACH BALL
65013000022 / 5 May '98 / Fuzz

Dirt

☐ BLACK AND WHITE (2CD Set)
SKULD 027CD / May '97 / Skuld

Dirtball

☐ HILLBILLY SOUL
HYMN 1 / 24 Nov '97 / Fundamental

Dirtbombs

☐ DIRTBOMBS HORNDOG FEST, THE
ITR 55CD / 14 Sep '98 / In The Red

Dirtcoldfight

☐ HYMNAL
CSR 017CD / Oct '95 / Cavity Search

Dirtsman

☐ ACID
Nah put it down / Trailer load come / Roughest / Nah sell it / Me a nuh bad boy / Bubble and wine / Sample / It a worry them / Check seh me done / Acid / Rough this year / Original d.j.
VYDCD 011 / Jul '96 / Vine Yard

Dirty Beatniks

☐ ONE ONE SEVEN IN THE SHADE
WALLCD 011 / Nov '96 / Wall Of Sound

Dirty Deeds

☐ DANGER OF INFECTION...
Nothing to lose / Cry out / Dividing line / Too scared to run / Promised land / In the name of the law / Call of the wild / I am the one / I'm no angel / Facing the enemy / Ruled by the gun
BTDCD 1 / 18 May '98 / Beast

Dirty Dogs

☐ FREE LUNCH
DDCD 4401 / Apr '97 / Dog's Dinner

Dirty Dozen Brass Band

☐ LIVE (Mardi Gras In Montreux)
Who took the happiness out / Mardi gras in new orleans / It ain't what you think / Do it fluid do it again / Flinstones meets the president (meets the dirty dozen) / Night train / Blue monk-stormy monday / Lickity split / Blackbird special (part 2) (encore)
ROUCD 2052 / '88 / Rounder

☐ THIS IS JAZZ
Charlie dozen / It's all over now / Georgia swing / Voodoo / Don't you feel my leg / Lost souls (of Southern Louisiana) / Cortege / Do I have to go / Mourning march / Memoirs / Inquest / Shout / Moose the mooche / Monkey / Gemini rising / Open up (Whatcha gonna do for the rest of your life) / Remember when / New Orleans blues / When I'm walking (Let me walk) / Old rugged cross
CK 65046 / May '97 / Sony Jazz

Dirty Old Man River

☐ DIRTY OLD MAN RIVER
RDL 102 / May '97 / Radial

Dirty Three

☐ DIRTY 3
ABB 93CD / Aug '95 / Big Cat

☐ HORSE STORIES
ABB 115CD / Sep '96 / Big Cat

☐ OCEAN SONGS
Sirena / Restless waves / Distant shore / Authentic celestial music / Backwards voyager / Last horse on the sand / Sea above sky below / Black tide / Deep waters / Ends of the Earth
BELLACD 003 / 30 Mar '98 / Bella Union

☐ SAD AND DANGEROUS
ABB 107CD / Apr '96 / Big Cat

Dirtys

☐ YOU SHOULD BE SINNIN'
EFACD 12897 / 10 Nov '97 / Crypt

Dis Bonjour A La Dame

☐ DIS BONJOUR A LA DAME
Chris'tal / Sheherazade groove / This funk / Soul body / Sister / Moi je dort / Hall blues / J m f groove / Just like before / Mama had to tell me / Sa ka passe / Ta mere en short bleu / Mon ange / Super foolish baby / La nuit toute les chattes sont grises / Children of war / You want to know / Hey mama
0630104362 / Jul '95 / East West

Disappear Fear

☐ DEEP SOUL DIVER
CDPH 1173 / May '95 / Philo

☐ DISAPPEAR FEAR
CDPH 1171 / Aug '95 / Philo

☐ LIVE AT THE BOTTOM LINE
CDPH 1172 / Jun '95 / Philo

☐ SEED IN THE USA
CDPH 1180 / Jun '96 / Philo

Disaster Area

☐ SLAM SECTION
N 03022 / 23 Mar '98 / Noise

Disbelief

☐ DISBELIEF
CRS 046CD / Jun '97 / Nuclear Blast

☐ INFECTED
Infected / Mindstrip / First / Fetish 97 / Again / Down / Pounding / Without a kiss / Now
NB 3302 / 27 Jul '98 / Nuclear Blast

Disc

☐ DISC (2CD Set)
VC 134CD / 20 Apr '98 / Vinyl Communication

Discepolo, Enrique S.

☐ HOMENAJE A LOS POETAS DEL TANGO
EBCD 76 / Jul '96 / El Bandoneon

Discharge

☐ DISCHARGED (A Tribute To Discharge) (Various Artists)
PREACH 001CD / Jun '92 / Rhythm Vicar

☐ HEAR NOTHING SEE NOTHING SAY NOTHING
Hear nothing, see nothing, say nothing / Nightmare continues / Final bloodbath / Protest and survive / I won't subscribe / Drunk with power / Meanwhile / Hell on earth / Cries of help / Possibilities of lifes destruction / Q - and children? A - and children / Blood runs red / Free speech for the dumb / End
CLAYCD 3 / Mar '95 / Clay
RRCD 255 / 25 May '98 / Receiver

☐ LIVE AT THE CITY GARDEN NEW JERSEY
Warning / Nightmare continues / Never again / Blood runs red / Protest and survive / State violence/State control / More I see / Angel burning (encore) / Hear nothing, see nothing, say nothing / Where there is a will / Anger burning / Born to die in the gutter / In defence of our future / Price of silence / Decontrol / Blood runs red, The (encore)
CLAYCD 103 / Apr '93 / Clay

☐ MASSACRE DIVINE
City of fear / FED / Lost tribe rising / Challenge terror / White knuckle ride / New age / Terror police / Kiss tomorrow goodbye / Sexpolosion / Dying time / E 230
CLAYCD 110 / Apr '93 / Clay

☐ NEVER AGAIN
Warning / Never again / Hear nothing, see nothing, say nothing / Nightmare continues / Where there is a will / Drunk with power / Final bloodbath / Anger burning / Two monstrous nuclear stockpiles / Price of silence / Protest and survive / Born to die in the gutter / Doomsday / More I see / State violence/State control / In defence of our future / Decontrol
CLAYCD 12 / Apr '93 / Clay
RRCD 256 / 13 Jul '98 / Receiver

☐ NIGHTMARE CONTINUES, THE
Never again / Hear nothing, see nothing, say nothing / Nightmare continues / Realities of war / State violence/State control / Hell on earth / Cries of help / Possibilities of lifes destruction / Final bloodbath / Protest and survive / Doomsday / Drunk with power / Why / Blood runs red / Two monstrous nuclear stockpiles / Decontrol
CLAYCD 107 / Apr '93 / Clay

☐ PROTEST & SURVIVE
Never again / Hear nothing, See nothing, Say nothing / Nightmare continues / Realities of war / Ain't no feeble bastard / War's no fairytale / Anger burning / Hell on earth / Cries of help / Possibilities of lifes destruction / Visions of war / Stockpiles / More I see / Look at tomorrow / Society's victim / Protest and survive / Death dealers / Tomorrow belongs to us / Final bloodbath / Is this to be / Price of silence / Fight back / Doomsday / Why / Drunk with power / Religion instigates / Warning / Massacre of innocence / State violence / Decontrol
CLAYDCD 113 / Oct '94 / Clay

☐ PROTEST AND SURVIVE (2CD Set)
Realities of war / Fight back / War's no fairytale / Decontrol / It's no TV sketch / Warning / Anger burning / Hear nothing, see nothing, say nothing / Nightmare continues / Protest and survive / I won't subscribe / Blood runs red / Never again / Too monstrous nuclear stockpiles / Why / Ain't no feeble bastard / Visions of war / Does this system work / Look at tomorrow / Massacre of innocents / State violence, state control / Price of silence / Born to die in the gutter / More I see / Ignorance / Where there is a will / Anger burning / In defence of our future / Hell on earth / Cries of help / Final bloodbath / Drunk with power / City of fear / Kiss tomorrow goodbye / Terror police / Exiled in hell / Psycho active / Shootin' up the world
SMDCD 131 / May '97 / Snapper

☐ SEEING, FEELING, BLEEDING
NB 085 / Dec '93 / Nuclear Blast

☐ SHOOTIN' UP THE WORLD
CLAYCD 118 / Oct '93 / Clay

☐ SINGLES COLLECTION, THE
Realities of war / They declare it / But after the gig / Society's victim / Fight back / War's no fairytale / Always restrictions / You take part in creating this system / Religion instigates / Decontrol / It's no tv sketch / Tomorrow belogs to us / Never again / Death dealers / Two monstrous nuclear stockpiles / State violence-state control / Doomsday / Warning / Where there is a will / In defence of our future / Anger burning / Price of silence / Born to die in the gutter / More I see you / Protest and survive / Ignorance / No compromise
CLAYCD 120 / Jul '95 / Clay

☐ WHY
Vision of war / Look at tomorrow / Maimed and slaughtered / Ain't no feeble bastard / Massacre of innocence / Doomsday / Does this system work / Why / Mania for conquest / Is this to be / State violence / State control
PLATE 2CD / Apr '93 / Clay
RRCD 259 / 17 Aug '98 / Receiver

Disciples

☐ FOR THOSE WHO UNDERSTAND
BSL101CD / Nov '95 / Boomshakalacka

☐ INFINITE DESTINY OF DUB
DBHD 004CD / Oct '96 / Dubhead

☐ REBIRTH (Disciples & Rootsman)
TEMCD 007 / Aug '97 / Third Eye

Disciplin A Kitschne

☐ I THINK I SEE MYSELF ON CCTV
BABACDL 1 / Sep '96 / The Record Label

Discipline

☐ BULLDOG STYLE
LF 289CD / 27 Oct '97 / Lost & Found

Disco Inferno

☐ IN DEBT
Entertainment / Arc in round / Broken / Emigre / Interference / Leisure time / Set sail / Hope to God / Freethought / Bleed clean / Next in line / Incentives / Waking up / Glancing away / Fallen down the wire / No edge no end
CHE 4CD / Sep '95 / Che

☐ TECHNICOLOUR
R 4102 / Jul '96 / Rough Trade

Discocks

☐ LONG LIVE OI
KOCD 061 / 29 Sep '97 / Knock Out

Discolor

☐ DISCOLOR
SGCD 16 / 15 Dec '97 / September Gurls

Discordia

☐ LIVING DEAD
HL 07CD / 23 Feb '98 / Nightbreed

Discount

☐ ATAXIA'S ALLRIGHT TONIGHT
LM 16 / Jun '97 / Liquid Meat

☐ HALF FICTION
KAT 023CD / 24 Aug '98 / Kat

Disembowelment

☐ TRANSCENDENCE INTO THE PERIPHERAL
NB 0962 / Jan '94 / Nuclear Blast

Disfear

☐ EVERYDAY SLAUGHTER
With each dawn I die / Anthem of agony / Crimescene worldwide / Race for power / Spectre of genocide / Everyday slaughter / Subsistance / Totalitarian control / Frustration / Aftermath / 101 Overkill / Captured by life / ...in fear
KRONH 08CD / 27 Oct '97 / Kronh

Disgrace

☐ SUPERHUMAN DOME
SPV 08412652 / Mar '96 / SPV

Disgust

☐ WORLD OF NO BEAUTY, A
NB 232CD / Mar '97 / Nuclear Blast

Disgusting

☐ DISGUSTING
HNF 030CD / 22 Jun '98 / Head Not Found

☐ SHAPESHIFTERBIRTHBLUES
HNF 011CD / Nov '95 / Head Not Found

Disharmonic Orchestra

☐ EXPOSITIONSPROPHYLAXE
8429812 / Dec '90 / Nuclear Blast

☐ PLEASURE DOME
SPV 08476772 / Jun '94 / SPV

Dishrags

☐ LOVE IS SHIT
OPM 2112CD / Feb '97 / Other People's Music

Dishwalla

☐ PET YOUR FRIENDS
Pretty babies / Haze / Counting blue cars / Explode / Charlie Brown's parents / Give / Miss Emma Peel / Moisture / Feeder / All she can / Only for so long / Date with Sarah / It's gonna to take some time
5403432 / Oct '96 / A&M

Disinformation

☐ R&D VOL.1
ASH 29CD / Apr '96 / Ash International

☐ R&D VOL.2
ASH 92 / 30 Mar '98 / Ash International

Disjam

☐ MONEY
YO 40242 / May '97 / Yo Mama

Disjecta

☐ CLEAN PIT AND LID
WARPCD 41 / Apr '96 / Warp

Disley, Diz

☐ DIZ DISLEY & HIS STRING QUARTET AT THE WHITE BEAR
JCD 212 / Mar '95 / Jazzology

Dismember

☐ CASKET GARDEN
NB 1302 / Mar '95 / Nuclear Blast

☐ INDECENT AND OBSCENE
NB 077CD / Jul '93 / Nuclear Blast

☐ LIKE AN EVER FLOWING STREAM
Override of the overture / Soon to be dead / Bleed for me / And so is life / Dismembered / Skin her alive / Sickening art / In death's sleep / Deathevocation / Defective decay
NB 163CD / Jun '96 / Nuclear Blast

☐ MASSIVE KILLING CAPACITY
NB 123CD / Sep '95 / Nuclear Blast

☐ MISANTHROPIC
NB 254CD / Jun '97 / Nuclear Blast

☐ PIECES
Pieces / I wish you hell / Carnal tomb / Soon to be dead
NB 060CD / Apr '92 / Nuclear Blast

Disorder

☐ COMPLETE DISORDER
Today's war / Violent crime / Complete disorder / Insane youth / You've got to be someone / More than fights / Daily life / Rampton song / Provocated war / Bullshit everyone / Three blind mice / Buy I gurt pint / Stagnation / Life / Out of order / Condemned / Media / Suicide children / Preachers / Remembrance day
CDPUNK 46 / Oct '96 / Anagram

☐ LIVE IN OSLO/VIOLENT WORLD
Complete disorder / Daily life / More than fights / Remembrance day / Maternal obsession / Bent edge / Provocated wars / God nose / Education / Driller killer / Prisoner of conscience / Stagnation / Life / Rampton / After 16 / Fuck your nationality / Out of order / Rhino song / Intro 21 / Ate seconds 22 / Another fight another gig / Gods are born in the USA / I don't like war / Joleen 26 / Fur else / Health hazard / Todays world / Violent world / Dope not Pope / Distortion til U vomit / Take what you need
CDPUNK 39 / Oct '94 / Anagram

☐ MASTERS OF THE GLUENIVERSE (Disorder/Mushroom Attack)
DAR 010CD / Nov '94 / Desperate Attempt

☐ REST HOME FOR SENILE OLD PUNKS
CDPUNK 88 / Feb '97 / Anagram

☐ SLICED PUNX ON MEATHOOKS
Fight the right / Fast food / Free society / Therefore we shout / Giro song / Boring / Insane war / Cry of death / Tied down / Pass the gluebag (to the right hand side) / To be continued / Intro / Army of aggressors / Warfear / Drop the bomb / Profanators and lies / Brutal attack / Anti-social reject / Jack hammer / Fight the right / Fuck your nationality
CDMGRAM 118 / 2 Feb '98 / Anagram

☐ UNDER THE SCALPEL BLADE
Driller killer / Education / Security guard / Go-song / Lambeth / Victim of the NHS / Bent edge / Rhino song / God nose / Overproduction / Other side of the fence / Fuck your nationality / Men make frontiers / Prisoner of conscience / After / Double standards / Be bad be glad / Marriage story / Love and flowers / Togetherness and unity
CDPUNK 19 / Apr '96 / Anagram

Disposable Heroes Of Hiphoprisy

☐ HYPOCRISY IS THE GREATEST LUXURY
Satanic reverses / Famous and dandy (like Amos 'n' Andy) / Television (the drug of a nation) / Language of violence / Winter of the long hot summer / Hypocrisy is the greatest luxury / Everyday life has become a health risk / INS Greencard A-19 191 500 / Socio-genetic experiment / Music and politics / Financial leprosy / California uber alles / Water pistol man
IMCD 250 / Mar '97 / Island

Disrupt

☐ UNREST
RR 69062 / Dec '94 / Nuclear Blast

Dissect

☐ SWALLOW SWOUMING MASS
CYBERCD 5 / Sep '93 / Cyber

Dissecting Table

☐ HUMAN BREEDING
Least mean square algorithm for personality alteration / Man in the black box / Behind the ethereal thorns / Human breeding market
RR 69542 / May '97 / Relapse

☐ ULTIMATE PSYCHOLOGICAL
DVLR 003CD / Aug '94 / Dark Vinyl

☐ ZIGOKU
DV 016CD / Sep '93 / Dark Vinyl

Dissection

☐ PAST IS ALIVE, THE
NR 017DP / 24 Nov '97 / Necropolis
NR 017CD / 9 Mar '98 / Necropolis

☐ SOMBERLAIN
NFR 006 / Jan '95 / No Fashion

☐ STORM OF THE LIGHTS BANE
NB 129CD / Jan '96 / Nuclear Blast

☐ WHERE DEAD ANGELS LIE
NB 167CD / May '96 / Nuclear Blast

Dissidenten

☐ INSTINCTIVE TRAVELLER
Taste of melon / Instinctive traveller / Broken moon / Dreamcatcher / Blue world / Seek to sigh / Lobster song / Shine on me / Live and experience / Never say no / World is like a mirror
EXIL 55352 / Jul '97 / Exil

☐ MIXED UP JUNGLE
EXIL 55312 / Jun '97 / Exil

Dissober

☐ SOBER LIFE
DISTCD 6 / Jun '94 / Distortion

Dissolve

☐ DISMANTLE
ELM 013CD / 2 Mar '98 / Elevator

☐ THAT THAT IS...IS (NOT)
KRANK 005CD / Mar '97 / Kranky

☐ THIRD ALBUM FROM THE SUN
KRANK 018CD / 22 Aug '97 / Kranky

Distance

☐ DISTANCE, THE
ESM 022 / 2 Mar '98 / Escape

Distorted Pony

☐ INSTANT WINNER
TR 22CD / Apr '94 / Trance

Distortion

☐ BROTHERS UNDER THE SKIN
RRCD 009 / 13 Apr '98 / Retch

Distortion Felix

☐ RECORD
AKR 07 / 22 Jun '98 / Akashic

District Singers

☐ TWELFTH PARTY SINGALONG
Green grassy slopes / South down militia / Enniskillen dragoons / Ducks of Magheralin / Sash / Aughalee heroes / My Aunt Jane / Lily O / Ould Lammas fair / B for Barney / I'll tell me ma / Auld orange flute / My bonnie lies over the ocean / Northern lights of old Aberdeen / End of the road / Orange and blue / Black velvet band / Old mud cabin on the hill / Sprigs of Kilkrea / Wild rover / Love is teasin' / Muirsheen durkin / Home boys home / No surrender / Derry's walls / When you and I were young Maggie / Mountains of Mourne / Battle of Garvagh / Star of County Down / Courtin' in the kitchen / Protestant boys / Scottish soldier / Roamin' in the gloamin' / Old rustic bridge / London lights / Twenty one years
CDUCD 11 / Apr '97 / Ulster Music

Disturbed Company

☐ CABIN FEVER
IND 049CD / Jun '96 / Incentive

Ditch Croaker

☐ CHIMPFACTOR
SYM 0072 / May '97 / Symbiotic

Ditch Witch

☐ EVERYWHERE, NOWHERE
GROW 122 / Apr '94 / Grass

Diverse Interpreten

☐ CLASSIC REFERENCE
BLR 84 008 / May '91 / L&R

☐ REFERENCE
BLR 84 001 / May '91 / L&R

☐ REFERENCE VOL.2
BLR 84 020 / May '91 / L&R

☐ REHEARSAL
BLR 84 010 / May '91 / L&R

Diversion

☐ JAM TOMORROW
TOAD 3CD / May '94 / Newt

Divine

☐ BEST OF DIVINE, THE
Shoot your shot / Shout it out / Native love / Love reaction / Divine madness / Kick your butt / Alphabet rap / Shoot it out / Shake it up / T-shirts and tight blue jeans / Love reaction / Native love
21024 / Sep '97 / Laserlight

☐ BEST OF DIVINE, THE (Native Love)
Shoot your shot / Jungle jezebel / Native love / Love reaction / Shoot it out / T-shirts and tight blue jeans / Psychedelic rock / Shake it up / Kick your butt / Alphabet rap / You think you're a man / Walk like a man / I'm so beautiful / Hey you
HTCD 16 / 20 Apr '98 / Hot Productions

☐ BORN TO BE CHEAP
Gang bang / Alphabet rap / Native love / Shake it up / Shoot your shot / Love reaction
CDMGRAM 84 / Aug '94 / Anagram

☐ CREAM OF DIVINE
PWKS 4228 / Nov '94 / Carlton

☐ ORIGINALS
AVEXCD 30 / Apr '96 / Avex

☐ ORIGINALS/REMIXES (2CD Set)
AVEXCD 33X / Apr '96 / Avex

☐ REMIXES
AVEXCD 29 / Apr '96 / Avex

☐ YOU THINK YOU'RE A MAN
Divine's theme / You think you're a man / Give it up / I'm so beautiful / Show me around / Walk like a man / Twistin' the night away / Good time / Hard magic / Little baby / Hey you / Divine reprise
QED 226 / Nov '96 / Tring

Divine Comedy

☐ CASANOVA
Something for the weekend / Becoming more like Alfie / Middle class heroes / In and out of Paris and London / Charge / Songs of love / Frog Princess / Woman of the world / Dogs and the horses / Theme from Casanova / Through a long and sleepless night
SETCD 025 / Apr '96 / Setanta

☐ FANFARE FOR THE COMIC MUSE
SETCDM 002 / Aug '90 / Setanta

☐ FIN DE SIECLE
Generation Sex / Thrillseeker / Commuter Love / Sweden / Eric the gardener / National express / Life on Earth / Certainty of chance / Here comes the flood / Sunrise
SETCD 057
SETCDL 057 / 31 Aug '98 / Setanta

☐ LIBERATION
Festive Road / Death of a supernaturalist / Bernice bobs her hair / I was born yesterday / Your Daddy's car / Europop / Timewatching / Popsinger's fear of the pollen count / Queen of the South / Victoria falls / Three sisters / Europe by train / Lucy
SETCD 011 / Aug '97 / Setanta

☐ PROMENADE
Going downhill fast / Booklovers / Seafood song / Geronimo / When the lights go out all over Europe / Summerhouse / Neptune's daughter / Drinking song / Ten seconds to midnight / Tonight we fly
SETCD 013 / Aug '97 / Setanta

☐ SHORT ALBUM ABOUT LOVE, A
In pursuit of happiness / Everybody knows (except you) / Someone / Timewatching / If / If I were you (I'd be through me) / I'll all you need
SETCD 036 / Feb '97 / Setanta

Divine Horsemen

☐ DEVIL'S RIVER
ROSE 102CD / Dec '86 / New Rose

Divine Soma Experience

☐ WELCOME TO THE LAND OF DRAGONS
Ravi Shankar's bizarre sitar / Soma / Music is magic / Impossible possibilities / Chillout and chill'um / Icaro (Magical curing song)
DIVINE 001CD / 7 Oct '97 / Taste/Divine

Divine Works

☐ DIVINE WORKS
Divine works I / Ancient person of my heart / O' Ecclesia / Interlude I / Divine works II / Father of eternal life / Gloria deo patri / Graces naked danced / Tranquility / Interlude II / Da nobis indicio / Divine
VTCD 119 / 4 Aug '97 / Virgin

Divinyls

☐ MAKE YOU HAPPY 1981-1993
Boys in time / Girlfriends / Only lonely / Science fiction / Siren / I'll make you happy / 9.50 / Pleasure and pain / Good die young / Sleeping beauty / Hey little boy / Back to the wall / Tempremental / I touch myself / Love school / I'm on your side / Wild thing / Ain't gonna eat out my heart / Love is the drug / Love in motion
RVCD 67 / Nov '97 / Raven

Divisia

☐ WIFEBEATER
T 62CD / Jun '97 / Theologian

Dixie Cups

☐ BEST OF DIXIE CUPS, THE
Chapel of love / Girls can tell / I'm gonna get you yet / All grown up / Ain't that nice / Gee baby gee / Iko iko / Another boy like mine / Poeple say / Thank you mama, thank you papa / Gee the moon is shining bright / Little bell / Wrong direction / True true love / You should have seen the way he looked at me
12659 / May '97 / Laserlight

☐ HIT SINGLE COLLECTABLES
DISK 4511 / Apr '94 / Disky

Dixie Dregs

☐ KING BISCUIT PRESENTS...
880312 / Sep '97 / King Biscuit

Dixie Hummingbirds

☐ DIXIE HUMMINGBIRDS 1939-1947
DOCD 5491 / Nov '96 / Document

Dixie Jubilee Singers

☐ DIXIE JUBILEE SINGERS 1924-1928
DOCD 5438 / May '96 / Document

Dixie Stompers

☐ AIN'T GONNA TELL NOBODY
DD 224 / Aug '94 / Delmark

Dixieland All Stars

☐ DIXIELAND ALL STARS AND BUCK CLAYTON (Dixieland All Stars & Buck Clayton)
Someone to watch over me / Strike up the band / Sweet SUe / Billboard match / Ballin' the jack / Muskat ramble / Somebody loves me / Bugle call rag / Synthetic blues / When the saints go marching in / Embraceable you / Fascinating rhythm / St james infirmary / Deed I do / Dinah / Sunday
JUCD 2037 / 9 Mar '98 / Jazz Unlimited

Dixon, Bill

☐ VADE MECUM VOL.1
SN 1212082 / Oct '94 / Soul Note

☐ VADE MECUM VOL.2
1212112 / Jul '97 / Soul Note

Dixon, Don

☐ ROMANTIC DEPRESSIVE
SHCD 5501 / Apr '95 / Sugar Hill

Dixon, Dorsey

☐ BABES IN THE MILL
HMG 2502 / Feb '98 / Hightone

Dixon, Errol

☐ MISTER BOOGIE WOOGIE
DM 10015 / Jul '96 / DMA Jazz

Dixon, Floyd

☐ MARSHALL TEXAS IS MY HOME
Hard living alone / Please don't go / Old memories / Hole in the wall / Time brings about a change / Me quieras / Call operator 210 / Ooh eee ooh eee / Chicken growing / Carlos / Nose trouble / Reap what you sow / Judgement day / Instrumental shuffle / Hey bartender / Never can tell when a woman changes her mind / Oh baby / What is life without a home / Rita / I'll always love you / Oooh little girl
CDCHD 361 / Nov '93 / Ace

☐ MR. MAGNIFICANT HITS AGAIN
IMP 706 / Sep '95 / IMP

☐ WAKE UP AND LIVE
ALCD 4841 / May '96 / Alligator

Dixon, Prince

☐ BEST OF PRINCE DIXON, THE
HMG 5503 / Aug '97 / Hightone

Dixon, Reginald

☐ AT THE BLACKPOOL TOWER WURLITZER
Blackpool song mixture medleys 7 and 8: *Dixon, Reginald & Cavan O'Connor* / Canadian capers / Dixon hits medleys 3 and 7 / Dixonland medley 2 / Dixontime medleys 1, 2, 3, 9 and 10 / Dixon request medley / Fifty years of song medley / Goodnight: *Dixon, Reginald & Cavan O'Connor* / In a Persian market / It's time to sing Sweet Adeline again: *Dixon, Reginald & Cavan O'Connor* / Parade of the tin soldiers / Sanctuary of the heart / Spoonful / Tauber memories medley / Waltz memories medley / Was love a dream
CDAJA 5134 / Jul '94 / Living Era

☐ BESIDE THE SEASIDE
I do like to be beside the seaside / Begin the beguine/ Night and day / Smoke gets in your eyes/Who/Ol' man river / Little Sir Echo/Summer/Sweetheart/ South of the border / Deep purple/The Masquerade is over/Boomps-a-daisy / Bolero / Sunrise serenade / At the Cafe Continental/Empty saddles / Pretty girl is like a melody / Across the great divide/Delyse/ Boo-hoo / In a monastery garden / In a Persian market / Blue Danube/Vienna blood/Fledermaus/ The kiss / Lagoon/Wine, women and song/Tales from the Vienna woods / Voices of Spring/Blue Danube / Bill Bailey/Get your hair cut/Champagne Charlie / Ta-ra-ra-boom-de-ay/Good old summertime/Dolly Grey / Tiddy fol Lol, where the sunset turns/Little Alabama Coon / I don't want to play in your yard/He's only a working man / Guards parade / Piano concerto no.1 in B flat minor/ Chanson sans paroles / Valse (Eugen Onegin) / Riff song (Desert song)/Serenade/Lover come back to me / Will you remember (May time)/Desert song waltz/Drinking song / Soldiers of the King/Ta-ra-ra-boom-de-ay/Lily of Laguna / Man who broke the bank at Monte Carlo/After the ball / I love a lassie/ Let's all go down the Strand/Ramona / You made me love you/Swanee/Love I the sweetest thing / Rustle of Spring / I do like to be beside the seaside (reprise)
SWNCD 009 / 15 Sep '97 / Sound Waves

☐ MISTER BLACKPOOL
Riff song/Serenade/Love come back to me / Will you remember/Desert song waltz/Drinking song / Impatience/Ave Maria/Dream waltz / Medley / Medley / Andante cantabile/Valse des fleurs/ Barcarolle/1812 overture / In the mood/Highland swing/Darktown strutters ball / Stardust/Solitude/ After you've gone / Automne / Medley / Medley / Orpheus in the underworld / Skaters waltz / Fledermaus selection part.1 / Fledermaus selection part.2 / Medley / Medley / Fingal's cave/Bees wedding/Violin concerto/Wedding march / Merry widow waltz/You're in love/You are my hearts delight / Dutiful wife/Gipsy love waltz/Cavalier/ Gipsy song/Boys / Medley / Medley
RAJCD 893 / 9 Mar '98 / Empress

☐ REGINALD DIXON AT THE BLACKPOOL TOWER
Medley / St. Louis blues/Limehouse blues/Jealousy / My blue heaven/Star dust/Goodnight sweetheart / Bolero / I hate myself/Isle of Capri/My song for you / I won't dance/Lovely to look at/Smoke gets in your eyes / Rustle of spring / With my eyes open I'm dreaming/If/I never had a chance / Harlemania/Ain't misbehavin'/My sweetie went away / Ma, he's making eyes at me/Alexander's ragtime band / Medley / I'll walk beside you / Dream lover/Nobody's using it now/March of the Grenadiers/Lo / Skater's waltz / Why do I love you/You are my love/Ol' man river / Somebody stole my gal / Love makes the world go round/Change partners / Sweet music/Ev'ryday/ Fare thee well Annabelle / Sunrise serenade / When Mother Nature sings her lullaby / Bugle call rag / Medley
PASTCD 7039 / May '94 / Flapper

☐ TOWER BALLROOM FAVOURITES
Tiger rag / Autumn leaves / Moonlight serenade / These foolish things / Dardanella / Elizabethan serenade / La paloma / Russian rag / Peanut vendor / Wedding of the painted doll / Temptation rag / Czardas / Sabre dance / Sweet and lovely / Canadian capers / Continental / Jealousy / 12th Street rag / Deep purple / Cherokee / Toy trumpet / Stardust
CC 255 / May '90 / Music For Pleasure

☐ WONDERFUL WORLD OF REGINALD DIXON, THE
EMPRCD 787 / 16 Mar '98 / Emporio

Dixon, Willie

☐ CHESS BOX, THE (2CD Set) (Various Artists)
My babe: *Little Walter* / Violent love: *Big Three* / Third degree: *Boyd, Eddie* / Seventh son: *Mabon, Willie* / Crazy for my baby: *Dixon, Willie* / Pain in my heart: *Dixon, Willie* / Hoochie coochie man: *Waters, Muddy* / Evil: *Howlin' Wolf* / Mellow down easy: *Little Walter* / When the lights go out: *Witherspoon, Jimmy* / Young fashioned ways: *Waters, Muddy* / Pretty thing: *Diddley, Bo* / I'm ready: *Waters, Muddy* / Do me right: *Fulson, Lowell* / I just want to make love to you: *Waters, Muddy* / Tollin' blues: *Fulson, Lowell* / 29 ways: *Dixon, Willie* / Walkin' the blues: *Dixon, Willie* / Spoonful: *Howlin' Wolf* / You know my love: *Rush, Otis* / You can't judge a book by its cover: *Diddley, Bo* / I ain't superstitious: *Howlin' Wolf* / You need love: *Waters, Muddy* / Little red rooster: *Howlin' Wolf* / Back door man: *Howlin' Wolf* / Dead presidents: *Little Walter* / Hidden charms: *Howlin' Wolf* / You shook me: *Waters, Muddy* / Bring it on home: *Williamson, Sonny Boy* / 300 pounds of joy: *Howlin' Wolf* / Weak brain, narrow mind: *Dixon, Willie* / Wang dang doodle: *Taylor, Koko* / Same thing: *Waters, Muddy* / Built for comfort: *Howlin' Wolf* / I can't quit you baby: *Little Milton* / Insane asylum: *Taylor, Koko*
MCD 16500 / Apr '97 / Chess/MCA

☐ CRYIN' THE BLUES (Live At Liberty Hall) (Dixon, Willie & Johnny Winter)
Sittin' and cryin' the blues / Spoonful / I just want to make love to you / Chicago here I come / Tore down / You know it ain't right / Mean mistreater/Baby what you want me to do / Roach stew / Killing floor
CDTB 166 / Mar '95 / Thunderbolt

☐ HIDDEN CHARMS
Blues you can't lose / I don't trust myself / Jungle swing / Don't mess with the messer / Study war no more / I love the life I live, I live the life I love / I cry for you / Good advice / I do the job
ORECD 515 / Mar '94 / Silvertone

☐ I'M THE BLUES
Pain in my heart / My babe / Walking the blues / (Back home again in) Indiana / Hoochie coochie man / Little red rooster / Spoonful
CD 52026 / Mar '93 / Blues Encore

☐ POET OF THE BLUES
Back door man / I can't quit you babe / Seventh son / Spoonful / I ain't superstitious / You shook me / I'm your hoochie coochie man / Little red rooster / Same thing / Big three stomp / Tell that woman / I ain't gonna be your monkey man no more / It's all over now / You don't love me no more / If the sea were whiskey / O C bounce / Money tree blues / No one to love me / Cool kind woman / Juice head bartender / Signifying monkey
4898952 / 20 Jul '98 / Sony Blues

☐ WILLIE DIXON
WCD 120271 / Dec '97 / Wolf

☐ WILLIE'S BLUES (Dixon, Willie & Memphis Slim)
Nervous / Good understanding / That's my baby / Slim's thing / That's all I want baby / Don't you tell nobody / Youth to you / Sittin' and cryin' the blues / Bluit for comfort / I got a razor / Go easy / Move me
CDCHD 349 / Jun '92 / Ace
OBCCD 501 / Nov '92 / Original Blues Classics

DIY

☐ STRICTLY FOR GROOVERS (Various Artists)
Orange is orange: *Firenze* / Elevator: *Victor Dynagroove Ensemble* / Up there out there: *Essa* / Be still: *Overview* / Thelma: *Sandmen* / Cassiopeia: *Nail* / Eve's theme: *Serve Chilled*
WARPCD 18 / Dec '93 / Warp

Diyici, Senem

☐ TAKALAR (Diyici, Senem Sextet)
CDLLL 17 / Aug '93 / La Lichere

Dizrhythmia

☐ DIZRHYTHMIA
RES 117CD / Nov '96 / Resurgence

DJ 6666

☐ DEATH BREATHING (DJ 6666 & The Illegals)
Dead nation / Silver pills / Steel cum / Welcome to the shit / Generation / Acid's not enough / Global holocaust / Zion battles/The dope / 6666 girls / Slow drive / Death breathin'
DHRCD 012 / 23 Mar '98 / DHR

DJ 7

☐ TECHNODROME (DJ 7 & The Sound Generators)
Back in the UK / I wanna be a hippie / Inside out / Forever young / There is a star / Endless summer / Tears don't lie / Stars / I kiss your lips / Come take my hand / Move your ass / Spaceman / Hardcore vibes / Knockin' / Texas cowboys / Power rangers
12840 / May '96 / Laserlight

DJ Acucrack

☐ MUTANTS OF SOUND
60086331212 / 14 Apr '98 / SLPP

DJ Andy Smith

☐ DOCUMENT, THE
GB beats: *Barrow, Geoff* / How ya want it: *Jungle Brothers* / Come clean: *Jeru The Damaja* / Cissy Strutt: *Meters* / Funk no.49: *James Gang* / Can't seem to find him: *White, Barry* / Stop ya skemes: *Jeep Beat Collective* / T plays it cool: *Gaye, Marvin* / Looking out of my window: *Jones, Tom* / Deaf Mick's throwdown: *Clockwork Voodoo Freaks* / Adventures of Grandmaster Flash on the wheels of steel: *Grandmaster Flash & Melle Mel* / Sittin' on the dock of the bay: *Lee, Peggy* / Movement: *SL Troopers* / I'm a man: *Davis, Spencer Group* / Can't seem to find him (reprise): *White, Barry*
5556692 / 18 May '98 / Polydor

DJ Cam

☐ BEAT ASSASINATED, THE
I love hip hop / Broadcasting live / Success / Renegade / Inside a mind / Raise up / Hardcore freestyle / Baron Samedi / L'Invasion / Danger interlude / Brooklyn 1-2 / Interlude
4895102 / 11 May '98 / Columbia

☐ DJ CAM (2CD Set)
SDW 010CD / Feb '97 / Shadow

☐ DJ KICKS (Various Artists)
Dieu reconnaitra le siens: *DJ Cam* / Zero G: *Minus 8* / Dark jazz: *Daphreephunkateerz* / Prelude to cycle 6: Part 2 / Tell the world: *Sci Fi Select* / Ride a way: *Mighty Bop* / Gettin' down again: *Tek 9* / Things in time: *Rodney P* / Freestyle 1: *Awesome Two & Channel Five* / Unassisted: *Rasco* / Freestyle 2: *Awesome Two & Jem* / Visitor: *Grand* / Juggling: *Ragga Twins* / Milan: *Hools, Tommy* / Bronx theme: *DJ Cam*
K 7060CD / 1 Sep '97 / Studio K7

☐ MAD BLUNTED JAZZ (2CD Set)
SDW 0102 / Nov '96 / Shadow

☐ SUBSTANCES
Intro:friends and enemies / Essence part one / Meera / Essence part two / Sound system children / Alexandra's interlude / Innervisions / Essence part three / Hip hop pioneer / Essence part four / Lost kingdom / Essence part five / Angel dust / Essence part six / Twilight zone / Outro
4854052 / Mar '97 / Columbia

☐ UNDERGROUND LIVE ACT
IRCD 1 / Jul '96 / Inflammable

☐ UNDERGROUND VIBES
Intro / Gansta shit / Mad blunted jazz / Suckers never play that / Sang lien / Underground vibes / Romanic love / Return of the Jedi / Other aspect / Dieu reconnaitra les siens / Free your tunrtable and your scratch will follow / Dieu reconnaitra les siens minux 8
CAMCD 004 / Jul '96 / Street Jazz
4877142 / Aug '97 / Epic

DJ Choc

☐ MODERNISTIC ACID TRANCE VOL.1 (Various Artists)
VCFCD 001 / 27 Apr '98 / VCF

DJ Cyclone

☐ BEST OF MY BOX, THE (Various Artists)
MDMA 9704CD / May '97 / Acid Fever

DJ Dara

☐ RINSIMUS MAXIMUS
Kah / Jade / Sleepers / RNA / Discipline / Nation / Scorpio rising / Night stepper / Stasis
SM 80392 / 29 Sep '97 / Smile Communications

DJ Darren Jay

☐ TOTAL SCIENCE VOL.3 (2CD Set)
MECDD 001 / 27 Oct '97 / Mecca

DJ Dimitri

☐ JOURNEYS BY DJ VOL.3
JDJ 13CD / Mar '95 / JDJ

DJ Dougal

☐ ABSOLUTELY HECTIC (Mixed By DJ Dougal) (Various Artists)
Sunshine: *Ramos & Supreme/Sunset Regime* / Are you ready: *DJ Sy & Unknown* / Choirs of heaven: *Druid & Vinyl Groover* / Crowd control: *Slipmatt* / Soothe my soul: *Eliminators* / Gotta believe: *Ramos & Supreme/Sunset Regime* / Phantasm: *Vinyl Groover* / Pumpin' it up: *Eye On Life* / Moments in time: *DJ Sy & Unknown* / Journey: *Ramos & Supreme* / True love: *Mystic & Fire* / Kounter attack: *Druid & Vinyl Groover*
MMCCD 002 / 20 Oct '97 / Massive

☐ DJ DOUGAL TAKES CONTROL
KICKCD 39 / Jun '96 / Kickin'

DJ Duke

☐ JOURNEYS BY DJ VOL.2 (Various Artists)
JDJ 12CD / Jan '95 / JDJ

DJ Faust

☐ MAN OR MYTH
BOMB 20072 / 30 Mar '98 / Bomb

DJ Flavours

☐ THROW YOUR HANDS UP
Throw your hands up
ROWTCD 96008 / Apr '97 / Ruff On Wax

DJ Food

☐ RECIPE FOR DISASTER, A
Dark river / Inosan / Scratch yer head / Brass neck / Fungle junk / Half step / Dusk / Bass city roller / Spiral / Scratch yer butt / Akaire / Little samba / Scientific youth / SE 1 / Hipslop
ZENCD 020 / Oct '95 / Ninja Tune

☐ REFRIED FOOD VOL.1
Strange taste / Spiral dub / Freedom / Sexy bits / Scratch yer head / Mella / Half step / Turtle soup / Spiral / Dark lady / Dark river / Dark blood / Consciousness
ZENCD 021 / Feb '96 / Ninja Tune

DJ Greyboy

☐ GREYBREAKS VOL.1
GBR 006CD / 23 Mar '98 / Greyboy

DJ Hell

☐ X-MIX VOL.5 (Wildstyle) (Various Artists)
K7 039CD / Nov '95 / Studio K7

DJ Hixxy

☐ **BONKERS VOL.1 (Mixed By DJ Hixxy/ MC Sharkey/Dougal) (Various Artists)**
Toytown: *DJ Hixxy & MC Sharkey* / Steam train: *Hopscotch* / Love of my life: *DJ Dougal* / A-ha ha ha: *DJ Hixxy* / Together forever: *DJ Hixxy & Banana Man* / Let the music: *Eruption* / Party Time: *DJ Dougal & Eruption* / Funfair: *Force & Styles* / Airhead: *DJ Brisk* / Now is the time: *Brown, Scott* / Calypso summer: *Vinyl Groover & DJ Quatro* / Hold me now: *Highlander* / Like a dream: *Bass D & King Matthew* / Bust a new jam: *Seduction & Eruption* / Step to the side: *DJ Seduction* / On top: *Sense Of Summer* / Thumper: *DJ Hixxy* / Wantin' to get high: *DJ Hixxy & Ikon* / Frantik: *Druid & Sharkey* / Rocket to the moon: *Druid & Sharkey* / Tweedledum: *Druid & Bananaman* / Rainbow islands: *Seb* / Is there anybody there: *DJ Ham* / Techno round the world: *Sense Of Summer* / On and on: *DJ Brisk* / Wonder land: *Force & Styles* / All systems go: *Force & Styles* / Teknostorm: *Vampire* / Outside world: *Bunter, Billy & D'Zyne/ Supreme* / Revolution: *Sharkey* / Truth: *Smith, Marc & Sharkey* / Bonkers anthem: *Druid & Sharkey* / Pumpin: *Druid & Sharkey* / Feel the heat: *DJ Sy & Sharkey* / Burns this joint: *Terrible twins*
REACTCD 083 / Jul '96 / React

☐ **BONKERS VOL.2 (Mixed By DJ Hixxy/ MC Sharkey/Dougal - 2CD Set) (Various Artists)**
Rave station: *Ramos & Supreme/UFO* / Tekniq: *Ramos & Supreme/UFO* / Future dimensions: *Druid & DJ Energy* / Body slam: *Bang The Future* / Twister: *GSI* / Whores in the house: *DJ Darryl* / Rock 'n' roll: *DJ Quatro* / E-motion: *Druid & Trixxy* / Inside beat: *Rapido* / Boom 'n' pow: *Smith, Marc* / Droppin' bombs: *DJ Fury* / Genesis: *Trixxy & Sharkey* / UR Everything: *Helix* / Living dream: *Evolve* / Ultraworld 5: *DJ Eclipse* / See the stars trixxy: *DJ Eclipse* / Revolution part 1: *Sharkey* / Therapy: *Trixxy & Sharkey* / My way: *Anti Social* / On top: *Sense Of Summer* / Now you've got: *Anti Social* / Forever young: *Anti Social* / Whistle: *Anti Social* / People's party: *DJ Hixxy & Sunset Regime* / Critical heights: *Unkown Project* / Paradise and dreams: *Force & Styles* / Scream: *Anti Social* / 24-7: *Anti Social* / Big up the bass: *Blitz, Blaze & Revolution* / Sugar and spice: *Evolve* / Your mind: *DJ Demo* / Antisocial: *Anti Social* / Dream surprise: *Dougal & Micky Skeedale* / Is this love: *DJ Fade & Melody* / Wham bam: *Vinyl Groover*
REACTCD 101 / Apr '97 / React

☐ **BONKERS VOL.3 (Mixed By DJ Hixxy/ MC Sharkey/Dougal - 3CD Set) (Various Artists)**
Fly away: *Clock* / Return to toytown: *Hixxy & Sharkey* / Happy days: *Anti Social* / Lullaby: *DJ Hixxy* / Together forever: *Hixxy & Bananaman* / Legends: *Anti Social* / Make your own kind of music: *Daydream* / Need your love: *Anti Social* / PA 3 sides: *Anti Social* / One spliff: *DJ Hixxy* / Starry night: *DJ Hixxy* / Feel this way: *Spitfire* / Power of love 97: *Q-Tex* / Cloudy daze: *Bang* / Take me to wonderland: *4 Tune Fairytales* / Inner sanctum: *UFO* / Trip to the other side: *RSR Recordings* / Ravechief: *RSR Recordings* / Sound assassin: *Sharkey* / Procrastinator: *Smith, Mark* / Acid break: *Slam & Helix* / Influence: *DJ Slam* / Back to the top: *Brisk & Trixxy* / Temperal riff: *Druid & UFO* / Overdose: *Energy & Loopy* / Here to invade: *Trixxy/Terranova: Sharkey & UFO* / FBI: *DJ Quattro* / East: *DJ Quattro* / Can u feel it: *Go Mental* / Ruff Muff: *2 Damn Tuff* / Follow the sun: *Triple J* / Have it all: *Triple J* / Stop me: *Innovate* / Talking 'bout love: *Innovate* / Out there...: *Innovate* / Set you free: *Force & Styles* / Steamtrain: *Hopscotch & Dougal* / Follow me: *Stompy* / Tranquility: *Dougal* / Jump a little higher: *Breeze* / Gotta go: *Dougal & Micky Skeedale* / Recreate creation: *Dougal & Micky Skeedale* / Going all the way: *Elagic & DNA* / Tears in your eyes: *Dougal & DNA* / Dreams: *DJ Fade & Bananaman* / Muzik: *DJ Demo* / Big spill: *Ham & Demo/Justin Time*
REACTCD 115 / 20 Oct '97 / React
REACTCTCDL 115 / 9 Feb '98 / React

☐ **BONKERS VOL.4 (Mixed By DJ Hixxy/ MC Sharkey/Dougal - 3CD Set) (Various Artists)**
It's a hard life: *Sharkey* / Death by stereo: *Sharkey & Marc Smith* / Product of society: *Sharkey* / Back to the top: *Brisk & Trixxy* / De-sensitize: *DJ Fury* / Mindless pleasure: *Tekno Dred & Helix* / Bell: *DJ Slam* / Acid rain: *Johnny Go Fruity Mental* / Future dimension 2: *DJ Energy* / King of rock: *DJ Energy* / Encounters: *Dark Myth* / 2 turntables: *Smith, Marc* / Gotta hold on: *Smith, Marc* / Light cycle: *DJ Eclipse* / Hustler: *Equinox* / Express yourself: *S-Cape* / Dub star: *Datcha & DNA* / Zurich: *Dougal & Skeedale* / Life is like a dance: *Dougal* / Don't you realise: *Dougal & Skeedale* / Words of wisdom: *Dougal & Skeedale* / Underground: *Dyanoiss* / Innovate: *Innovate* / Shooting star: *Bang* / Sail away: *Bang* / Open your eyes: *Brisk & Trixxy* / Let's fly: *Breeze* / Leaving the world behind: *Seduction* / Sweet thing: *Project* / My dreams: *Subase & Aura* / Feelin' fine: *Unique* / Universe: *Innovate* / Equazion part 9: *Q-Tex* / U and me: *2 Without Heads* / Don't go away: *Visa* / Imigination: *Slashing Funkids* / Lights: *Los Bonitos* / 3rd chapter: *Sequel Bass* / Fire: *Saints* / Power of love: *Q-Tex* / Distant skies: *Unique* / Guiding light: *Subase & Aura* / One: *OMG* / Different outlook: *OMG* / 14th dream: *OMG* / Better days: *Devil Licious*
REACTCD 122 / 18 May '98 / React

DJ Honda

☐ **HII**
Intro: *DJ Honda & Roc Raider* / Trouble in the water: *DJ Honda & De La Soul* / Five seconds: *DJ Honda & Black Attack* / Hai: *DJ Honda & Keith Murray/50 Grand* / Every now and then: *DJ Honda & Syndicate* / Mista sinista interlude / Team players: *DJ Honda & Doe-V/KRS-One* / For every day that goes by: *DJ Honda & The Rawcoticks* / WCRC interlude: *DJ Honda & Stretch Armstrong/Lord Seer* / Who the trifest: *DJ Honda & The Beatnuts* / Talk about it: *DJ Honda & Al Tariq* / Blaze it up: *DJ Honda & Black Attack* / Go crazy: *DJ Honda & S-On* / Around the clock: *DJ Honda & Problemz* / When your hot you hot: *DJ Honda & No ID/Dug Infinite* / Travellin' man: *DJ Honda & Mos Def*
4897592 / 20 Apr '98 / Epic

DJ Hurricane

☐ **HURRA, THE**
Now you do / Elbow room / Four fly guys / Can we all get along / Stick em up / Pat your foot / Get blind / Comin' off / What's really going on / Where's my niggas at / Hurra / Pass me the gun / Feel the blast
WIJ 043CD / Feb '95 / Wiiija

DJ Jazzy Jeff

☐ **CODE RED (DJ Jazzy Jeff & The Fresh Prince)**
Somethin' like dis / I'm looking for the one to be with me / Boom, shake the room / Can't wait to be with you / Twinkle twinkle (I'm not a star) / Code red / Shadow dreams / Just kickin' it / Ain't no place like home / I wanna rock / Scream / Boom shake the room
CHIP 140 / Mar '97 / Jive

☐ **GREATEST HITS (DJ Jazzy Jeff & The Fresh Prince)**
Boom shake the room / Summertime / Men In Black / Girls ain't nothing but trouble / Twinkle twinkle (I'm not a star) / Things that you do / I think I can beat Mike Tyson / Just cruisin' / Ring my bell / I wanna rock / Parents just don't understand / I'm looking for the one (to be with me) / Nightmare on my street / Can't wait to be with you / Brand new funk / Fresh Prince of Bel Air / Lovely day
0518482 / 4 May '98 / Jive

☐ **HOME BASE (DJ Jazzy Jeff & The Fresh Prince)**
I'm all that / Summertime / Things that U do / This boy is smooth / Ring my bell / Dog is a dog / Caught in the middle / Trapprd on the dancefloor / Who stole the DJ / You saw my blinker / Dumb dancin' / Summertime
CHIP 116 / Mar '97 / Jive

DJ K. Alexi Shelby

☐ **DJ K. ALEXI SHELBY BRINGS YOU ABSOLUTE...**
NPTCD 007 / 20 Oct '97 / Nepenta

☐ **FLAWLESS VICTORY**
ACVCD 015 / Mar '96 / ACV

DJ Keoki

☐ **JOURNEYS BY DJ INTERNATIONAL (Keoki)**
JDJIL 50202 / Aug '94 / JDJ

☐ **WE ARE ONE**
SUB 4D / Oct '95 / Subversive

DJ Kool

☐ **LET ME CLEAR MY THROAT**
I'm not from Philly / Let me clear my throat / I got dat feelin' / Put the hump (in your back) / Music ain't loud enuff / Twenty minute workout / Let me clear my throat / I'm done
74321421152 / Feb '97 / Loud

DJ Krush

☐ **DJ KRUSH**
SDW 0042 / May '97 / Shadow

☐ **HOLONIC (The Self Megamix)**
Forward: *DJ Krush & Lee Q/Stash* / Anticipation / Yeah / What's behind the darkness / Freestyle 1 / To be continued / Fucked up pendulum / Freestyle 2 / AM3:00TYO / Duality: *DJ Krush & DJ Shadow* / Light (can you see it) / Dig this vibe / Le temps: *DJ Krush & DJ Cam* / Only the strong survive / Real: *DJ Krush & Tragedy* / Shin-sekai: *DJ Krush & Rhino* / Kemuri / Bypath-Would you take it
MW 088CD / 19 Jan '98 / Mo Wax

☐ **KI OKU (DJ Krush & Toshinori Kondo)**
AMB 8949CD
AMB 8949CDX / 26 Jan '98 / Apollo

☐ **MEISO**
Only the strong survive / Anticipation / What's behind the darkness / Meiso / By path 1 / Blank / Ground / By path 2 / Most wanted man / By path 3 / 3rd eye / Oce 9504 / Duality / By path - would you take it
MW 039CD / Sep '95 / Mo Wax

☐ **MILIGHT**
Intro / Shin sekkai / Jikan no hashi I / Real / Listen / Supanova / Jikan no hashi II / Le temps / Hitotsu no mirai / Shinjiro / Light (can you see it) / Mind games / Skin against skin / Jugoya / Jikan no hashi III / To-u-kyo
MW 077CD / Aug '97 / Mo Wax

☐ **STRICTLY TURNTABILIZED**
Intro / Lunation / Fucked up pendulum / Kemuri / Loop / Silent ungah / Interlude / Dig this vibe / Yeah / To the infinity / Nightmare of ungah (sandro in effect)
MW 025CD / Apr '96 / Mo Wax

DJ Linus

☐ **FANTASMAGORIQUE**
COMPOSE 1232 / 15 Sep '97 / Compose

DJ Loops

☐ **BEATS TO SAMPLE**
Evil / Bone / Slip / Light up / Stuffed / Moved / Pumped / Middle / Fatso / Tooty / Tooty 11 / So bad / Mash up / Holey / Buzz / Baz / Batty / Slam
BRCD 608 / Feb '94 / 4th & Broadway

DJ Phantasy

☐ **ELEMENTS OF FREEDOM**
LIBTCD 003 / 8 Dec '97 / 4 Liberty

DJ Q

☐ **FACE THE MUSIC**
We are one / Delirious / Flying home / Make your mind up / Glasgow's jazz / Paranoid impulses / Up space dance / Fila / Tracking / She'll be gone / Going forward in reverse
FILT 24CD / 27 Oct '97 / Filter

DJ Quicksilver

☐ **QUICKSILVER**
Arabescu / I have a dream / Free / Synphonica / Bellissima / Bingo bongo / Techno macht spass / FFM / Deep in motion / African rain / Adagio / Planet love
4934942 / 23 Feb '98 / Positiva

DJ Quik

☐ **QUIK IS THE NAME**
FILERCD 402 / Apr '91 / Profile

☐ **SAFE & SOUND**
FILECD 462 / Feb '95 / Profile

DJ Rap

☐ **JOURNEY INTO DRUM 'N' BASS**
JDJDB 1CD / Mar '95 / JDJ

DJ Rectangle

☐ **DEADLY NEEDLES/TABLES HAVE TURNED, THE (2CD Set)**
CDRD 3 / 5 May '98 / Sound Chamber

☐ **LIGHTNING FIST**
RCD 007SR / 13 Jul '98 / Sound Chamber

DJ Red Alert

☐ **SLAMMIN' VINYL (DJ Red Alert & Mike Slammer)**
GUMH 011 / Nov '94 / Gumh

DJ Rodriguez

☐ **WORLD WIDE FUNK**
489601CD / 20 Apr '98 / Irma

DJ Seeq

☐ **INSTRUMENTAL BREAKBEAT**
3020262 / Jul '97 / Jimmy Jay

DJ Shadow

☐ **CAMEL BOBSLED RACE**
Napalm brain / Midnight in a perfect world / Organ donor / Hardcore / Bonus beat / In flux / Number song
MW 084CD / 8 Dec '97 / Mo Wax

☐ **ENDTRODUCING...**
Best foot forward / Building steam with a grain of salt / Number song / Changeling / Transmission / What does your soul look like / Untitled / Stem/Long stem / Transmission / Mutual slump / Organ donor / Why hip hop sucks in '96 / Midnight in a perfect world / Napalm brain/Scatter brain / What does your soul look like / Transmission
MW 059CD / Sep '96 / Mo Wax

DJ Skribble

☐ **TRAFFIC JAMS**
Skribble's intro / Step into the World: *KRS 1* / Theme: *Lee, Tracey* / Love is all we need: *Blige, Mary J.* / Must be the music: *Big Punisher & Cuban Link* / Franklyns: *Crooklyn Clan & DJ Riz/Sizza Hands* / I need your love: *Big Bub* / What Cru is number one: *Cru* / I'll do anything: *K7* / Battle / Get up: *Lost Boyz* / Streets are like a jungle: *Wyclef Jean* / Ladies: *Crooklyn Clan & DJ Riz/Sizza Hands* / Get me home: *Brown, Foxy* / Loungin': *LL Cool J* / You can't stop the Pras: *Prakazrel* / Beat of the year: *DJ Skribble & DJ Slynke* / Shimmy: *Ol' Dirty Bastard* / Everybody come on / Treat me right: *Mack, Craig* / Love dancing: *Pleasant Russell* / Ain't no nigga: *Jay-Z* / Big mama thing: *Lil' Kim* / In my bed: *Dru Hill* / Keep it tight: *Hill, Lauryn* / Morning tribute: *DJ Skribble & Dr. Dre*
5560192 / 22 Jun '98 / FFRR

DJ Sneak

☐ **BLUE FUNK FILES**
Computer games / Grinder / Sneak attack / Grace of tracks / Sounds in my head / For the love of house / Jugglin' thoughts / Who's knockin' / Psychic bounty killaz / Futuristic cipher / Junglist steelos
ULTRA 2002 / Jun '97 / Ultra

☐ **KINKY TRAX COLLECTION, THE (DJ Sneak/Princess Juliana/2CD Set) (Various Artists)**
Moist womanly needs: *Weebles & Princess Julia* / Do it your way: *Mood II Swing* / Deeper go deeper: *Juice Company* / Love love love: *Those Guys* / Version 10: *Swag* / I'm the baddest bitch: *Bell, Norma Jean* / I'm ready: *Donald O* / Get hi: *Roger S* / So in love: *Wild Pursuit* / Stand up: *Jones, Nick* / Night: *Roach Motel* / Yeah yeah: *Dixon, Daniel* / Find your way: *Crosby, B.J.* / If Madonna calls: *Vasquez, Junior* / Get lost: *Alan X* / Stickin' to my groove: *Chunky Kutz* / Transaxual: *Armando* / Mack Daddy shoot: *Kenlou* / Something I feel: *Alias* / Love potion: *Baby Pop* / Let's go disco: *Southern Comfort & Nolan Epps* / Only 4 U: *Cajmere* / Latin Seoul: *DJ Sneak* / Pain in my brain: *Outsider* / Free: *Morel, Nasty* / Play it again: *DJ Sneak* / Disco breaks: *DJ Sneak* / Ooh: *Mood II Swing* / Psychic bounty killaz: *DJ Sneak & Armand Van Helden* / It's a damn shame: *Long, Wyndell* / Salsa break: *G-Dubs & Ben Starr* / Check this out: *Fisher, Cevin* / What I want: *Groove Source* / Fly away: *Edwards, Todd* / Day and night: *Baby Pop*
REACTCD 091 / Oct '96 / React

DJ Soulslinger

☐ **DON'T BELIEVE**
JS 120CD / Jun '97 / Jungle Sky

☐ **MISSING TIME (The Abducted Remixes)**
JS 127 / 17 Nov '97 / Jungle Sky

DJ Spike

☐ **GLOBAL 2000**
BLCCD 9 / Feb '95 / Blanc

☐ **TASTELESS CUTS**
Baby bye / Gaps in space / Mr. President / Spike part one / MPB 105 / German / Designer drugs / Stick out
BL 001 CD / Apr '92 / Blanc

DJ Spooky

☐ **NECROPOLIS (The Dialogic Project)**
KFWCD 185 / Oct '96 / Knitting Factory

☐ **SONGS OF A DEAD DREAMER**
ASP 0961CD / 29 Jun '98 / Asphodel

☐ **SYNTHETIC FURY**
ASP 110CD / 23 Mar '98 / Asphodel

DJ SS

☐ **ROLLERS CONVENTION**
FORM 4CD / Nov '94 / Formation

☐ **WORLD DANCE (Mixed By DJ SS & Kenny Ken/2CD Set) (Various Artists)**
97 Style: *Ellis Dee & MC Fats* / Step on VIP: *Majistrate* / Quantize: *Kenny Ken* / Killamanjaro: *Ed Rush* / Threshold: *Dillinja* / Domination: *G-Squad* / Protocal 4: *Riley, Bill* / Recharge: *Andy C* / Reminiscence: *DJ Mace* / One: *Swift* / Gold: *DJ Mace* / Quest: *Andy C* / Tune your bass: *Macko* / It's jazzy: *Roni Size* / Ding dong bass: *L-Double* / Bad ass: *Aphrodite* / Enter the dragon: *DJ Red* / Doom moods: *Aphrodite* / Earls dream: *Helen T* / On the streets: *A-Sides* / Soul in motion: *Krust* / Mutation: *Andy C* / Systems: *Nemesis* / Stakes is high: *DT* / Cold stil pressure: *Acetate* / Mind control: *Boymerang* / Subzero: *3 Way* / Memphis bliss: *Rogue Unit* / Special treat: *DJ Die* / Unexplored terrain: *Dillinja* / Going gets tough: *Lemon D* / 2 Degrees: *TNT* / Circuit breaker: *Technical Itch* / Breakdown: *Perfect Combination* / Captain Nemo: *Barcode* / A Side: *9.0* / Dark soldier: *Keith, Ray*
HLPCD 5 / 22 Sep '97 / Higher Limits
MSS 0035 / 20 Jul '98 / Fuel

DJ Stealth

☐ **TEMPTATION**
BULLCD 3 / 8 Jun '98 / Bullion

DJ Stix

☐ **DIFFERENT WORLDS**
KSRCD 3 / 24 Nov '97 / Kingsize

DJ Sy

☐ **SOUND OF HAPPYCORE '98 VOL.3, THE (Mixed By DJ Sy/2CD Set) (Various Artists)**
Discoland: *Tiny Tot* / Heaven's gate: *Brown, Scott* / Voices of tomorrow: *Vinyl Groover* / Insomniak: *Rapido* / Hyperspace: *Digital Manouvers* / Tranquility: *Dougal & DNA* / Have it all: *Triple J* / Shooting star: *Bang* / Here I am: *DJ Demo* / Devotion: *DJ Sy & DJ Demo* / Million miles: *DJ Demo & Mickey Skeedale* / Till we meet again: *DJ Slam*
CDRAID 540 / 4 May '98 / Rumour

DJ Toolz

☐ **BREAKBEATS 'N' GROOVES VOL.1**
Takin 1 back / Slots / Funky donkey / To the beat y'all / Eight ins for Rita / Drummer / Thirteenth break / Flute of the groove / Col' favor / Smoove B / Bus stop / Gimmi gimmi / Twenty dollars / Biz beat / Congo soul / Texas B boy
TOOLCD 001 / Jul '93 / Ninja Tune

DJ Triple

☐ **JUNGLE BREAKS & BEATS (DJ Triple & Bassman)**
MOLCD 38 / Mar '95 / Music Of Life

DJ Twist

☐ **HELL RAZOR**
CDTH 001 / 6 Jul '98 / Sound Chamber

DJ Vadim

☐ **USSR RECONSTRUCTION**
Scematics / Theme from the conquest of the irrational / Breaks / Conquest of the irrational / Pimp theme / Beyond thought / USSR reconstruction / Variations in USSR / Abstractions / USSR repetoire / Who the hell am I / More melodies in vertical theory
ZENCD 31 / 26 Jan '98 / Ninja Tune

☐ USSR REPERTOIRE
Intro / Relax with Pep / Headz ain't ready / Next shit / Lounge vibes / Live in Paris / Lord forgive me / Relax with Pep / Suckas wearing tainted sunglasses / Aural prostitution / Knowledge be born / This goes out / Buggin' out / Melodies in Hinge Creek / Times are hard / Schematics / Call me / Bloke 1 / Who the hell am I / Relax with Pep / Abstractions / Mental gymnastics / Foundation / USSR Repetoire / Help me / Melodies in vertical theory / Reality (who is the realist) / Nuisance caller / Level test / Variations in chair creek and cradle / Lounge shiznits / Live from Paris / Morning prayer / Knowledge vs wisdom / Heads still ain't ready
ZENCD 025 / Oct '96 / Ninja Tune

DJ Wally
☐ DJ WALLY'S GENETIC FLAW
Japaneez wine / Possi purple / Fractured beaker / Feelin' groovy / Mr. Beaver saves the day / Space people / Ricco's love / At war / Last chance to comprehend / Mustard plaster / Ridiculous sound / Bitchley's kow korn
HE 117CD / Feb '97 / Home Entertainment

☐ DOG LEG LEFT (DJ Wally & Swingsett)
UR 025CD / 16 Dec '97 / Ubiquity

Djalti
☐ CHARMING RAI
829272 / Sep '96 / BUDA

Djavan
☐ FLOR DE LIS
1919362 / 24 Apr '98 / EPM

Djiboudjep
☐ PARFUM D'EPICES ET GOUT DE SEL
869CD / May '97 / Escalibur

Djip
☐ SOUMBAYO
3020302 / Jun '97 / Arcade

Djur Djura
☐ VOICES OF SILENCE (Adventures In Afropea 2)
9362452112 / May '94 / Luaka Bop

Djwahl Khul
☐ SCHLACHTUNGSKIND
EFA 121632 / Aug '95 / Apollyon

DKV Trio
☐ BARAKA
OD 12012 / Feb '98 / Okka Disk

DLP
☐ ON THE DL
EFA 610232 / 26 Aug '97 / Bassment

DM Bob & The Deficits
☐ BAD WITH WIMMEN
EFA 128782 / Jul '96 / Crypt

DM3
☐ DIG IT THE MOST
BCD 4067 / Sep '97 / Bomp

☐ GARAGE SALE
CITCD 533 / Jul '97 / Citadel

☐ ROAD TO ROME
CITCD 532 / 6 Apr '98 / Citadel

DMX
☐ IT'S DARK AND HELL IS HOT
5582272 / 1 Jun '98 / Def Jam

DMX Krew
☐ FFRESSSHH
Introduction / You can't hide your love / Bonkers goes back to school / Radio DMX / Body rock / Sound of the DMX / We are gonna make you move / I'm all alone / Space pirate / Europa / Ready to roll / Black music / Acknowledgement
CAT 053CD / Jul '97 / Rephlex

☐ NU ROMANTIX
Come to me / Can you feel the power / Mouse / You are not there / End of the night / You can do it / Place called love / I'm all alone
CAT 061CD / 1 Jun '98 / Rephlex

☐ SOUND OF THE STREET
CAT 029CD / Sep '96 / Rephlex

DMZ
☐ WHEN I GET OFF
Busy man / Can't stand the pain / You're gonna miss me / When I get off / Do not enter / Guilty child / Shirt loop / Lift up your hood / Barracuda / Comin' after me / Bloody englishmen / First time / Oedipus show / Rosalyn / Might he i.d. / From home / Are you gonna be there / Pretty girl
VOXXCD 2004 / Jul '93 / Voxx

DNA
☐ DNA
AVAN 006 / Sep '93 / Avant

DNA Production
☐ VIRTUAL JUNGLE
20742 / 12 Jan '98 / Phonokol

DNS
☐ BOMBS AND CLOUDS
MA352 / Dec '93 / Machinery

Do Bandolim, Jacob
☐ MANDOLIN MASTER OF BRAZIL
ACD 3 / Jul '97 / Acoustic Disc

Do Carmo, Lucilia
☐ PORTUGAL - A SPIRIT OF FADO VOL.4
PS 65704 / Oct '92 / PlayaSound

Do'A
☐ ANCIENT BEAUTY (Do'A World Music Ensemble)
CDPH 9004 / Dec '86 / Philo

☐ COMPANIONS OF THE CRIMSON COLOURED ARK (Do'A World Music Ensemble)
CDPH 9009 / Dec '86 / Philo

☐ EARLY YEARS, THE (Do'A World Music Ensemble)
Zenith / Crystal streams / Song of the dove / Oneness / Village earth / Ornament of hope / Valley of search / Kalimba / Light upon light / Meditation / Majesty / Celebration for world peace
ROUCD 11539 / '88 / Rounder

DOA
☐ BLACK SPOT, THE
352992 / Dec '96 / Frantic

☐ FESTIVAL OF ATHEISTS, A
CDHOLE 014 / 4 May '98 / Golf

☐ LOGGERHEADS
VIRUS 130CD / Sep '93 / Alternative Tentacles

☐ LOST TAPES, THE
CDHOLE 015 / 30 Mar '98 / Golf

☐ MURDER
723762 / Feb '95 / Restless

☐ NEW YORK CITY SPEEDCORE
Total annihilation / Ya mutha / Brooklyn mob / NYC speedcore / Wanna be a gangsta / Zu leiten / Uncle Bill's message / Pound down on your brain / Kill / Uncle Bill's message / Minute madness / Extreme gangsta / Our father / Ya mutha III / Noize core / I'll give you hard / Ya mutha II / You're dead / This is DOA
MOSH 164CD / Jan '97 / Earache

☐ TALK - ACTION = 0
725062 / Feb '95 / Restless

☐ THIRTEEN FLAVOURS OF DOOM
Already dead / Death machine / Bombs away / Living dead / I played the fool / Too fin' heavy / Hole in the sky / Hey sister / Use your raincoat / Legalized theft / Rosemary's baby / Beatin' rock 'n' roll to death / Time of illusion / Phantom zone
VIRUS 117CD / Oct '92 / Alternative Tentacles

Dob
☐ LA LU LA ROO
BUNG 0102 / Jan '97 / City Slang

Dobie
☐ SOUND OF ONE HAND CLAPPING
PUSSYCD 009 / 27 Apr '98 / Pussy Foot

Dobkins, Carl Jr.
☐ MY HEART IS AN OPEN BOOK
My heart is an open book / If you don't want my lovin' / Love is everything / My pledge to you / Lucky devil / Fool such as I / Promise me / Take time out / Chance to belong / In my heart / Ask me no questions / Sawdust Dolly / Pretty little girl in the yellow dress / Open up your arms / I'm sorry / Three little piggies / Class ring / Exclusively yours / For your love / True love / Raining in my heart / Sue / That's what I call true love / One little girl / Genie / Different kind of love / Lovelight / That's all I need to know
BCD 15546 / Feb '91 / Bear Family

Dobrogosz, Steve
☐ FINAL TOUCH, THE
DRAGONCD 195 / May '86 / Dragon

☐ JADE
DRCD 203 / Jul '87 / Dragon

☐ TRIO
1232 / Dec '87 / Caprice

Dobson, Dobby
☐ AT LAST
ANGCD 22 / Jul '94 / Angella

☐ GREATEST HITS
SONCD 0072 / Nov '94 / Sonic Sounds

☐ IF I ONLY HAD TIME
ANGCD 018 / Jun '97 / Angella

☐ NOTHING BUT LOVE VOL.3
PILCD 303 / Feb '96 / Pioneer

☐ SWEET DREAMS
PKCD 32993 / 23 Mar '98 / K&K

☐ SWEET DREAMS AGAIN VOL.2
PILCD 301 / Feb '96 / Pioneer

Dobson, Richard
☐ HEARTS & RIVERS (Dobson, Richard & State Of The Heart)
BRAM 1990142 / Nov '93 / Brambus

☐ ONE BAR TOWN
199568CD / Jul '95 / Brambus

☐ RICHARD DOBSON SINGS TOWNES VAN ZANDT
BRAMBUS 1994502 / Jul '94 / Brambus

DOC
☐ HELTER SKELTER
Return of da livin' dead / From Ruthless to Death Row / Secret plan / Komurshell / For my dawgs / 45 Automatic / Sonz o'light / Bitches / Da hereafter / Erotix shit / Welcome to the new world / Killa instinct / Brand new formula / Crazy bitches
74321288282 / Jan '96 / RCA

Doc Holliday
☐ SON OF THE MORNING SUN
CDIRS 972190 / Aug '93 / Intercord

Doc Houlind
☐ TRIBUTE TO GEORGE LEWIS, A (Doc Houlind Copenhagen Ragtime Band)
MECCACD 1037 / Nov '94 / Music Mecca

Doc Martin
☐ UNITED DJ'S OF AMERICA VOL.4/LOS ANGELES (Various Artists)
UNDJACD 4 / Jul '96 / Stress

Doc Scott
☐ MIXMAG LIVE VOL.22 (Various Artists)
Trichonic cycle: Jonny L / Last day: *DJ Krust* / Eye of a needle: *Art Of Noise* / Re-transitions: *Deep Blue & Blame* / Life: *Decoder* / Threshold: *Dillinja* / Metropolis: *Adam F* / Shadow boxing: *Nasty Habits* / Brief encounter: *DJ Krust* / Trippin' on broken beats: *Omni Trio* / Circuit breaker: *Decoder* / Red lights: *Hokusai* / Symbiosis: *Jonny L*
MMLCD 022 / Nov '96 / Mixmag Live

Doc Tahri
☐ EINSTEIN WAS A BULLFIGHTER
EFA 12363 / Jul '97 / Musical Tragedies

Doc Wor Mirran
☐ GARAGE PRETENSIONS
EFA 113642 / Jan '94 / Musical Tragedies

Dockery, Doc
☐ LOUISVILLE GUITAR SLUGGER, THE
Daddy played those Jimmie Rodgers blues / Waiting for a train / Diamonds and gold / Smoke and drink / Oh Kentucky girl / Eyes of a faraway dancer / I'll fix your flat tyre Merle / I wanna go where the angels fly / Beacon street / Everybody's talkin' / I like it that way
PRPCD 3 / Dec '97 / Proper

Doctor Bison
☐ BLOATED VEGAS YEARS, THE
Clean the air / Sweet embrace / Place for us / Sense / Kentucky red hair / Make me yours / Come around / Ocean of dreams / Cut down / Baptism of vodka / Right about you
PLAYCD 20 / Apr '97 / Workers Playtime

Dodds, Baby
☐ BILL RUSSELL'S HISTORIC RECORDINGS
AMCD 17 / Feb '95 / American Music

Dodds, Johnny
☐ BLUE CLARINET STOMP (1926-1928)
Weary blues / New Orleans Stomp / Wild man blues / Melancholy / Come on and stomp, stomp, stomp / After you've gone / Joe Turner blues / When Erastus plays his old kazoo / Blue clarinet stomp / Blue piano stomp / Bucktown stomp / Weary city / Bull fiddle blues / Blue washboard stomp / Sweet Lorraine / Pencil papa / My little Isabel-A / Heah' me talkin' / Goober dance / Too tight-A
DGF 3 / Oct '94 / Frog

☐ CLASSICS 1926
CLASSICS 589 / Aug '91 / Classics

☐ CLASSICS 1927
CLASSICS 603 / Sep '91 / Classics

☐ CLASSICS 1927-1928
CLASSICS 617 / Sep '92 / Classics

☐ CLASSICS 1928-1940
CLASSICS 635 / Nov '92 / Classics

☐ INTRODUCTION TO JOHNNY DODDS 1923-1940, AN
4014 / Apr '95 / Best Of Jazz

☐ JOHNNY DODDS & JELLY ROLL MORTON (Dodds, Johnny & Jelly Roll Morton)
DGF 9 / Nov '96 / Frog

☐ JOHNNY DODDS 1926-1940 (3CD Set)
What a man / Who's gonna do your lovin' / Nobody else will do / Bohhunkus blues / Buddy Burton's jazz / Little bits / Struggling / Perdido street blues / Gatemouth / Too tight / Papa did / Mixed salad / I can't say / Flat foot floogie / Mad dog / Messin' around / Adam's apple / East coast trot / Chicago buzz / Idle hour special / 47th street stomp / Someday sweetheart / Stock yards strut / Salty dog / Ape man / Yours folks / House rent rag / Memphis shake / Carpet alley breakdown / Hen party blues / Stomp time blues / It must be the blues / Oh daddy / Loveless love / 19th street blues / San / Oh Lizzie (A lovers lament) / New St. Louis blues / Clarinet wobble / Easy come, easy go blues / Blues stampede / I'm goin' huntin' / If you want to be my sugar papa / Weary blues / New Orleans stomp / Wild man blues / Melancholy / Wolverine blues / Mr. Jelly Lord / There'll come a day / Weary way blues / Cootie stomp / Poutin' papa / Hot stuff / Have mercy
CDAFS 10233 / Jan '93 / Affinity

☐ JOHNNY DODDS 1926-40
CD 14559 / Jul '94 / Jazz Portraits

☐ JOHNNY DODDS STORY 1923-1929
158412 / Feb '96 / Jazz Archives

☐ KING OF THE NEW ORLEANS CLARINET (1926-1938)
Perdido street blues / Gatemouth / Too tight / I can't say / Flat foot / Mad dog / Clarinet wobble / New st. louis blues / Hot stuff / Come on and stomp, stomp, stomp / Joe turner's blues / When erastus plays his old kazoo / Blue piano stomp / Bucktown stomp / Weary city / Blue fiddle blues / Blue washboard stomp / Goober dance / Piggly wiggly / Wild man blues / Melancholy / 29th and dearborn / Blues galore
BLE 592352 / Dec '92 / Black & Blue

☐ MYTH OF NEW ORLEANS, THE (1926-1940)
Wild man blues / Melancholy / Heah me talkin' / Bull fiddle boogie / Blue clarinet stomp / Bucktown stomp / Get 'em again blues / Lady love / Weary way blues / After you've gone (take 2) / Carpet alley breakdown / Gravier street stomp / Weary city / Perdido street blues / Oriental man / Gate mouth / My baby / New orleans stomp / Ballin' the jack / Grandma's ball / Indigo stomp / Pencil papa / Flat foot / Too tight
CD 53077 / Mar '92 / Giants Of Jazz

☐ OH DADDY
Riverside blues / Jackass blues / Frog tongue stomp / East coast stomp / Chicago buzz / In the alley blues / Someday sweetheart / Oh Daddy / Loveless love / 19th Street blues / New Orleans stomp / Wild man blues / Potato head blues / Melancholy blues / Beale Street blues / Wolverine blues / Mr. Jelly Lord / There'll come a day / Come on and stomp stomp stomp / After you've gone / Joe Turner's blues / When Erastus plays his old kazoo / Oriental man / Piggly wiggly
TPZ 1060 / Jan '97 / Topaz Jazz

☐ WILD MAN BLUES (24 Clarinet Classics 1923-1940)
Canal Street blues: *Oliver, Joe 'King' & His Creole Jazz Band* / Yes I'm in the barrel: *Armstrong, Louis Hot Five/Hot Seven* / Weary blues: *Armstrong, Louis Hot Five/Hot Seven* / Gatemouth: *New Orleans Wanderers/Bootblacks* / Too tight: *New Orleans Wanderers/Bootblacks* / Mixed salad: *New Orleans Wanderers/Bootblacks* / Flat foot: *New Orleans Wanderers/Bootblacks* / Wild man blues: *Dodds, Johnny Black Bottom Stompers* / When Erastus plays his old Kazoo: *Dodds, Johnny Black Bottom Stompers* / Clarinet wobble: *Dodds, Johnny Trio* / Wolverine blues: *Morton, Jelly Roll Trio* / Mr. Jellylord: *Morton, Jelly Roll Trio* / Hot stuff: *Blythe, Jimmy Owls* / Ballin' a jack: *Chicago Foot Warmers* / Grandma's ball: *Chicago Foot Warmers* / Southbound rag: *Blake, Arthur 'Blind'* / Get 'em again blues: *Chicago Foot Warmers* / Lady love: *Chicago Foot Warmers* / Bull fiddle blues: *Dodds, Johnny Washboard Band* / Indigo stomp: *Dodds, Johnny Trio* / Heah' me talkin': *Dodds, Johnny Orchestra/Chicago Boys* / Melancholy: *Dodds, Johnny Orchestra/Chicago Boys* / Gravier Street blues: *Dodds, Johnny Orchestra/Chicago Boys*
CDAJA 5252 / Dec '97 / Living Era

Dodge, Arthur

☐ ARTHUR DODGE & THE HORSEFEATHERS (Dodge, Arthur & The Horsefeathers)
BIR 045 / Feb '97 / Barber's Itch

☐ CADILLACS PONYTAILS AND DIRTY DREAMS (Dodge, Arthur & The Horsefeathers)
BIR 52CD / 29 Jun '98 / Barber's Itch

Dodgeball

☐ HOORAY FOR EVERYTHING
GR 58 / Jun '97 / Goldenrod

Dodgy

☐ DODGY ALBUM, THE
Water under the bridge / I need another / Lovebirds / Satisfied / Grand old english oak tree / Stand by yourself / As my time goes by / Never again / Cold tea / We're not going to take this anymore
5400822 / Jun '93 / A&M

☐ FREE PEACE SWEET
Intro / In a room / Trust in me / You've gotta look up / If you're thinking of me / Good enough / Ain't no longer asking / Found you / One of those rivers / Prey for drinking / Jack the lad / Long life / UKRIP / Homegrown
5405732 / Jun '96 / A&M

☐ HOMEGROWN
Staying out for the summer / Melodies haunt you / So let me go far / Crossroads / One day / We are together / Whole lot easier / Making the most of / Waiting for the day / What have I done wrong / Grassman
5402822 / Oct '94 / A&M

Dodheimsgard

☐ MONUMENTAL POSSESSION
MR 010CD / 22 Sep '97 / Malicious

Doernberg, Ferdy

☐ JUST A PIANO AND A HANDFUL OF DREAMS
08412112 / Jan '96 / SPV

Dog Age

☐ AS IT WERE
VOW 067CD / 3 Aug '98 / Voices Of Wonder

Dog Boy Jones

☐ OUT FOR KICKS
Train / I'm going walking / Spin your partner / Hey na na / Dear Jane / Out for kicks / Blue dress / Cross the river / Almost gone / Louisiana bayou / Billy and Rebecca / Boys in the rodeo / White lies / Let it rain
LCD 80009 / May '97 / Lizard

Dog Eat Dog

☐ ALL BORO KINGS
If these are good times / Think / No fronts / Pull my finger / Who's the king / Strip song / Queen / In the dog house / Funnel king / What comes around
RR 90208 / Feb '96 / Roadrunner

☐ PLAY GAMES
Bulletproof / Isms / Hi lo / Rocky / Step right in / Rise above / Games / Getting live / Buggin' / Numb / Sore loser / Games / Getting live / Rocky
RR 88762
RR 88765 / Aug '97 / Roadrunner

☐ WARRANT
It's like that / Dog eat dog / World keeps spinnin' / In the dog house / Psychorama / In the dog house (remix)
RR 90712 / Jun '93 / Roadrunner

Dog Faced Hermans

☐ BUMP AND SWING
K 153CD / Jun '94 / Konkurrel

☐ HUM OF LIFE
K147D / Mar '93 / Konkurrel

☐ THOSE DEEP BUDS
K 155C / Oct '94 / Konkurrel

Dog God

☐ GOD IS LOVE
NWM 007CD / 26 Sep '97 / Ninth World

Dog Town Balladeers

☐ ANTIQUE WINE AND ROSES
RE 10034 / Mar '97 / Relative

Dogfeet

☐ DOGFEET
CA 36002 / Jun '97 / Kissing Spell

Doggett, Bill

☐ 14 HITS (Doggett, Bill Combo)
KCD 5009 / Apr '97 / King

☐ DOGGETT BEAT FOR DANCING FEET, THE
Soft / And the angels sing / Ding dong / Honey / Easy / Hammerhead / Ram-bunk-shush / Chloe / Hot ginger / King Bee / What a difference a day makes / Shinding
KCD 557 / Mar '90 / King

☐ LEAPS AND BOUNDS
Bo-do rock / Honky tonk / Rainbow riot / Blue largo / Big boy / You ain't no good / Big dog / Hippy dippy / Backwards / Shindig / After hours / Peacock alley / In the wee hours / Leaps and bounds / Your kind of woman / Yocky dock / Wild oats
CDCHARLY 281 / Sep '91 / Charly

Dogheimsgard

☐ KRONET TIL KONGE
MR 006CD / Oct '95 / Malicious

Dogs D'Amour

☐ DOG'S HITS AND THE BOOTLEG ALBUM
WOLCD 1020 / Aug '91 / China

☐ ERROL FLYNN
Drunk like me / Hurricane / Errol Flynn / Princess valium / Trail of tears / Prettiest girl in the world / Goddess from the gutter / Satellite kid / Planetary pied piper / Dog's hair / Ballad of Jack / Girl behind the glass
8397002 / Sep '89 / China

☐ GRAVEYARD OF EMPTY BOTTLES, A
I think it's love again (for lucie) / So once was (for the angels) / Comfort of the devil (for my soul) / Saviour (for ever) / Errol flynn (for what the silver screen did to them) / Bullet proof poet (for charles bukowski) / When the dream has gone (how come it never rains part 2) / Angel (so you shall be)
WOLCD 1005 / Mar '91 / China

☐ MORE UNCHARTERED HEIGHTS OF DISGRACE
What's happening here / What you do / Pretty, pretty once / World's different now (an ode to drug hill) / Mr. addiction / Johnny silvers / Cach / More unchartered heights of disgrace / Scared of dying / Mr. barfly / Put it in her arm
WOLCD 1032 / Apr '93 / China

☐ STRAIGHT
Cardboard town / Cardboard town / Lie in this land / You can't burn the devil / No gypsy blood / Empty world / Back on the juice / Evil / Victims of success / Flyin' solo / Heroine / Chiva / Lady nicotine
WOLCD 1007 / Mar '91 / China

Dogs Deluxe

☐ DOGS DELUXE
Moon fever / Wreckin' ball / Fast track / Blue / From above the clouds / Sex and bass / Missing in action / Snow queen / Dreamtime / Colorado / Slopes / Coffee / Last dance
SKINCD 003 / 3 Aug '98 / Second Skin

Dogstar

☐ ILLUMINATE FABRICATI
LALACD 3 / Apr '94 / La La Land

Doherty, John

☐ BUNDLE AND GO
Hudie Gallagher's march / Black mare of Fanad / March of the meena toiten bull / Kiss the maid behind the bier/The bargain is over / 21 Highland / Paps o' Glencoe / Hare in the corn / Knights of St. Patrick / Dispute at the crossroads / Roaring Mary / Miss Patterson's slippers / Cat that kittled in Jamie's wig / Welcome home royal Charlie / Darby Gallagher / Teelin highland / Heathery breeze / Monaghan switch / Black haired lass / Paddy's rambles through the park
OSS 17CD / Jan '94 / Ossian

☐ FLOATING BOW, THE (Traditional Folk Music From Donegal)
Spirits of wine/Madame Bonaparte / Further in the deeper / An chuilfhionn/The flogging reel / Drops of brandy / Miss Patterson's slipper / Day I listed/ Fantastic reel / Willie McLennan's / Lancer's jig/ Gusty's frolics / Tom Tailor's / Scots Mary / Sligo maid's lament/Hand me down the tackle / Enniskillen Dragoons/Nora Crionna/Piobaire an cheideadh / Cameronian / Dulaman na binne bui / Within a mile of Dublin/Old Simon's hornpipe / Glenconwell's hornpipe / Mint in the corn / Highlanders/The wind that shakes the barley / Sean sa cheo / King George IV / Lancer's jig/The silver slipper / Mountain road / Braes of Maas / Bonnie Kate / Maidin fhomhair/Miss McLeod
CCF 31CD / Nov '96 / Claddagh

☐ TAISCE (The Celebrated Recordings)
CEFCD 072 / Jul '97 / Gael Linn

Doherty, Tom

☐ TAKE THE BULL BY THE HORNS
Three sisters reels / Donegal reel/The maid I daren't tell / Cathy Jones/The keel row / Road to the Isles/ Auld Rigadoo / Maggie pickie / I've a polkie trimmed with blue/The gallope / Liverpool/Derry / Connaught man's rambles / Sally gardens/Cooley's / Humours of whiskey / Take the bull by the horns / Primrose lass / Corn rigs / Bridge O'Leary's / Paddy McGinty's goat/Green grow the rushes-o / Sweet cup of tea/ Drowsy Maggie / Miss Drummond of Perth/ Mollymusk / Silver spear/Mountain road/Maid behind the bar / Queen of the fair/Off she goes
GLCD 1131 / Jul '93 / Green Linnet

Doiron, Julie

☐ LONELIEST IN THE MORNING
SPCD 398 / 1 Sep '97 / Sub Pop

Dokken

☐ BACK IN THE STREETS
REP 4005 / Aug '91 / Repertoire

☐ ONE NIGHT LIVE
Into the fire / Unchain the night / Maze / Nothing left to say / From the beginning / Tooth and nail / Just got lucky / I will remember / Alone again / In my dreams / Nowhere man / It's not love
06076862062 / Apr '97 / CMC

Dokken, Don

☐ UP FROM THE ASHES
GED 24301 / Jun '97 / Geffen

Dol-Lop

☐ CRYPTIC AUDIO
Shadow / Bluehouse / Doum / Hybrid / Phase / Qoke / Stem
VWM 16 / Jun '97 / Swim

Dolan, Joe

☐ 32 GREATEST HITS (2CD Set)
CDP 001 / Dec '97 / Ceol

☐ BEST OF JOE DOLAN, THE
PDSCD 509 / Sep '97 / Pulse

☐ COLLECTION, THE
ARCD 004 / May '98 / Ainm

☐ GREATEST HITS COLLECTION VOL.1
CDJOE 001 / Jun '98 / Outlet

☐ GREATEST HITS COLLECTION VOL.2
Make me an island / Most wanted man in USA / Mysterious lady / What have you done to me / This is my life / Tropical girl / Maybe some day my love / Bonjour madamoiselle / You belong to me baby / Boogie mama / Sentimental and blue / One step ahead / Home is where the heart is / Dreaming (ghost on the moon) / Sister Mary / 12th of never / Runaway / Heart breaker
CDJOE 002 / Jun '98 / Outlet

☐ GREATEST HITS VOL.1
You're such a good looking woman / Sixteen brothers / Hush hush Maria / Home is where the heart is / Lady in blue / If I could put my life on paper / Disco crazy / Only you / Gypsy lady / Little boy big man / Rock 'n' roll fever / Anushka balalaika / Fly me Atlantic / Hang tough / Crazy woman / Suspicious minds / All outta love / Sad lady
CDC 001 / Feb '97 / Ceol

☐ GREATEST HITS VOL.2
CDC 002 / Feb '97 / Ceol

☐ LOVE SONG COLLECTION
DHCD 721 / Jan '95 / Outlet

☐ LOVE SONGS
Always on my mind / Only you / Tonight I celebrate my love / If I said you had a beautiful body / Without you / Runaway / All in the game / Sad lady / All outta love / Twelfth of never / Help me make it through the night / Heartbreaker / You needed me / Suspicious minds / When I need you / It's a heartache
CDIRISH 025 / Jun '98 / Outlet

☐ MAKE ME AN ISLAND (The Best Of Joe Dolan)
PLSCD 201 / Apr '97 / Pulse

☐ MAKE ME AN ISLAND
Make me an island / You're such a good looking woman / I need you / Hush hush Maria / Lady in blue / Frozen rivers / You belong to me baby / Lady sentimental / Most wanted man in the USA / Sixteen brothers / This is my life / Dreaming (ghosts on the moon) / More and more / Crazy woman / Disco crazy / Home is where the heart is
ECD 3398 / 23 Feb '98 / K-Tel

☐ MEMORIES
Love me tonight / My way / Lover come back to me / Here am I / Games people play / Proud Mary / Sometimes a man just has to cry / Daytime nightime / My love / She / Be my fire / Little boy, big man / Love grows (where my Rosemary goes) / My first love / Can't help falling in love / Something's burning / Las Vegas / She's so beautiful / I only dream of you / Bridge over troubled water
PLSCD 256 / 27 Oct '97 / Pulse

☐ MORE & MORE
It's you, it's you, it's you (remix '85) / Secret love / Spirit of love / When your lover leaves you / Queen of the broken hearts / It's only make believe / More and more / Love me, love me, aloha / Limerick you're a lady / Let me in / Ave maria / Come back home
RZSCD 416 / Apr '93 / Ritz

☐ MUSIC OF JOE DOLAN, THE
Sixteen brothers / You're such a good looking woman / You belong to me baby / Hypnotise / Frozen rivers / Sister Mary / More and more / Lady in blue / Maybe someday my love / Disco crazy / Most wanted man in the USA / Hush hush Maria
12644 / Apr '96 / Laserlight

Dolan, Michael

☐ TRIBUTE TO MICHAEL DOLAN, A (Various Artists)
GLCD 3097 / Jan '95 / Green Linnet

Dolan, Packie

☐ FORGOTTEN FIDDLE PLAYER OF THE 1920'S, THE
VVCD 1 / Jul '94 / Viva Voce

☐ PACKIE DOLAN
VIVAVOCE 006CD / Nov '94 / Viva Voce

Dolby, Thomas

☐ ASTRONAUTS AND HERETICS
I love you, goodbye / Cruel / Silk pyjamas / I live in a suitcase / Eastern block (the sequel) / Close but no cigar / That's why people fall in love / Neon sister / Beauty of a dream
CDV 2701 / Jul '92 / Virgin

☐ FLAT EARTH, THE
Flat earth / Screen kiss / Mulu the rain forest / I scare myself / Hyperactive / White City / Dissidents
CDP 746 028 2 / Jul '84 / Parlophone

☐ GATE TO THE MIND, THE
74321233862 / Mar '95 / RCA

☐ GOLDEN AGE OF WIRELESS, THE
She blinded me with science / Radio silence / Airwaves / Flying north / Weightless / Europa and the pirate twins / Windpower / Commercial break-up / One of our submarines is missing / Cloudburst at Shingle Street
CDFA 3319 / Apr '95 / Fame

☐ RETROSPECTACLE - THE BEST OF THOMAS DOLBY
Europa and the pirate twins / Urges / Leipzig / Windpower / Airwaves / She blinded me with science / One of our submarines is missing / Screen kiss / Hyperactive / I scare myself / Flat earth / Pulp culture / Budapest by Blimp / Cruel / Close but no cigar / I love you, goodbye
CDEMC 3659 / Sep '96 / EMI

Doldinger, Klaus

☐ DOLDINGER'S BEST
Blues for George / Two getting together / Minor kick / Quartenwaizer / Guachi guaro / Viva Brasilia / Fiesta / Raga up and down / Saragossa / Waltz of the jive cats / Comin' home baby / I feel free / Stormy Monday blues / Compared to what
92242 / Feb '96 / Act

Doldrums

☐ ACUPUNCTURE
KRANK 016 / Feb '97 / Kranky

☐ FENG SHUI
VHF 32 / 27 Apr '98 / VHF

Dole, Gerard

☐ CO CO COLINDA (15 Original Songs)
PS 65086 / Apr '92 / PlayaSound

Doleful Lions

☐ MOTEL SWIM
PARCD 032 / 26 May '98 / Parasol

Dollar

☐ BEST OF DOLLAR, THE
Mirror, mirror (mon amour) / I wanna hold your hand / Love's gotta hold on me / Shooting star / Who were you with in the moonlight / We walked in love / Takin' a chance on you / Hand held in black and white / Oh l'amour / Videotheque / Kiss / Outta my head, outta my heart / It's nature's way (no problem) / I don't want our love thing to die / She said she said / Give me some kind of magic
ECD 3370 / Jun '97 / K-Tel

☐ DOLLAR
Shooting star / We walked in love / Ring ring / Who were you with in the moonlight / Kiss / Love's gotta hold on me / Takin' a chance on you / Outta my head outta my head / I wanna hold your hand / It's nature's way / Oh l'amour / No dull moments / She said, she said / Addicted to love / I don't want our love thing to die / Give me some kind of magic / Give me some kind of kind
306142 / Jan '97 / Hallmark

Dollface

☐ GIANT
KCCD 3 / Jul '95 / Kill City

Dollis, Bo

☐ 1313 HOODOO STREET (Dollis, Bo & The Wild Magnolias)
I been hoodood / Run Joe / Angola bound / Might mighty chief / Hey hey / Louisiana / Walk on gilded spiders / Voodoo / Quitters never win / I know you Mardi Gras / Injuns here they come / Indian red
AIMA 3CD / Nov '96 / Aim

Dolphino, Jim

☐ IRON LEGS (The Fun Runners' Ballad)
Iron legs / Wind / Very special place / Goldfish song / Walking on air / I've got a great big hole in my shoe / Seasons of my love / Little boy / Looking for nuts / As I sit and watch the rain / Kiss me, my amore / Wise old man
MYSCD 001 / Jul '97 / Myson

Dolphy, Eric

☐ AT THE FIVE SPOT VOL.1
Fire waltz / Bee vamp / Prophet / Bee vamp (alternate)
OJCCD 133 / Feb '92 / Original Jazz Classics

☐ CANDID DOLPHY
Reincarnation of a love bird / Stormy weather / African lady / Quiet please / Moods in free time / Hazy hues / It ain't nobody's business if I do / Body and soul
CCD 79033 / Feb '97 / Candid

☐ CARIBE
Caribe / Blues in 6-8 / First bass line / Mambo Ricci / Spring is here / Sunday go meetin'
OJCCD 819 / Jun '96 / Original Jazz Classics

☐ COMPLETE PRESTIGE RECORDINGS, THE (9CD Set)
GW / On Green Dolphin Street / Les / 245 / Glad to be unhappy / Miss Toni / April fool / GW / 245 / Screamin' the blues / March on, march on / Drive / Meetin' / Three seconds / Alto-itis / Lautir / Curtsy / Geo's tune / They all laughed / Head shakin' / Dianna / Out there / Serene / Baron / Eclipse / 17 West / Sketch of melba / Feather / Caribe / Blues in 6/8 / First bass line / Mambo ricci / Spring is here / Sunday go meetin' / Trane whistle / Whole Nelson / You are too beautiful / Stolen moment / Walk away / Jaws / Mrs. Parker of K.C. / Ode to Charlie Parker / Far cry / Miss Ann / Left alone / Tenderly / It's magic / Serene / Images / Six and four / Mama Lou / Ralph's new blues / Straight ahead / III-44 / Rally / Bass duet / Softly as in a morning sunrise / Where / Yes indeed / Saucer eyes / Status seeking / Duquility / Thirteen / We diddit / Warm canto / Warp and woof / Fire waltz / Like someone in love / God bless the child / Aggression / Like someone in love / Fire waltz / Bee vamp / Prophet / Booker's waltz / Status seeking / Number eight / Bee vamp / Don't blame me / When lights are low / Don't blame me / Les / Way you look tonight / Woody 'n' you / Laura / Glad to be unhappy / God bless the child / In the blues / Hi-fly / Oleo
9PRCD 44182 / Nov '96 / Prestige

☐ CONVERSATIONS
CDGR 187 / Oct '97 / Charly

☐ ERIC DOLPHY 1961
CD 14553 / Jul '94 / Jazz Portraits

☐ ERIC DOLPHY IN EUROPE VOL.2
OJCCD 414 / Mar '93 / Original Jazz Classics

☐ ERIC DOLPHY SAMPLER
Ode to Charlie Parker / GW / Mrs. Parker of KC (Bird's mother) / Oleo / Feathers
OJCX 008 / Jan '98 / Original Jazz Classics

☐ ESSENTIAL, THE
GW / Les / Meetin' / Feathers / Eclipse / Ode to Charlie Parker / Bird's mother / Ralph's new blues / Status seeking
FCD 60022 / Apr '94 / Fantasy

☐ FAR CRY (Dolphy, Eric & Booker Little)
OJCCD 4002 / Mar '93 / Original Jazz Classics

☐ HOT, COOL AND LATIN
BMCD 3057 / Jul '97 / Blue Moon

☐ IN EUROPE VOL.1
Hi fly / Glad to be unhappy / God bless the child / Oleo
OJCCD 413 / Apr '93 / Original Jazz Classics

☐ IN EUROPE VOL.3
Woody 'n' you / When lights are low / In the blues
OJCCD 416 / Apr '93 / Original Jazz Classics

☐ IRON MAN
Iron man / Mandrake / Come Sunday / Burning spear / Ode to the CP
CDGR 147 / May '97 / Charly

☐ LAST DATE
Epistrophy / South Street exit / Madrig speaks, the panther walks / Hypochristmutrreefuzz / You don't know what love is
5101242 / Sep '92 / EmArCy

☐ MEMORIAL ALBUM (Dolphy, Eric & Booker Little)
Number eight (posta lotsa) / Booker's waltz
OJCCD 353 / May '93 / Original Jazz Classics

☐ MUSIC MATADOR
Jitterbug waltz / Music matador / Alone together / Love me
LEJAZZCD 14 / Jun '93 / Le Jazz
FSRCD304 / 5 Jan '98 / Fresh Sound

☐ OTHER ASPECTS
Jim Crow / Inner flight / Dolphy'n / Improvisations and tukras
7480412 / 1 Jun '98 / Blue Note

☐ OUT THERE
Out there / Serene / Baron / Eclipse / 17 west / Sketch of melba / Feathers
OJCCD 23 / May '93 / Original Jazz Classics

☐ OUT TO LUNCH
Hat and beard / Something sweet, something tender / Gazzellioni / Out to lunch / Straight up and down
CDP 7465242 / Mar '95 / Blue Note

☐ OUTWARD BOUND
GW / Green Dolphin Street / Les / 245 / Glad to be unhappy / Miss tonl
OJCCD 222 / Feb '91 / Original Jazz Classics

☐ STOCKHOLM SESSIONS
ENJA 30552 / 17 Nov '97 / Enja

Dom Um Romao

☐ SAUDADES
WLACS 16CD / Nov '95 / Waterlily Acoustics

Domaci Kapela

☐ JEDNE NOCI SNIL
R 0010 / Jun '97 / Rachot

Domancich, Sophia

☐ L'ANNEE DES TREIZE LUNES
A 15 / Oct '95 / Seventh

Dome

☐ DOME VOL.1 & 2
DOME 12CD / Aug '92 / Grey Area

☐ DOME VOL.3 & 4
DOME 34CD / Aug '92 / Grey Area

Dominator

☐ FORBIDDEN PLEASURES
SHWL 304CD / Oct '96 / World Serpent

Domine

☐ CHAMPION ETERNAL
CHAOS 001CD / 13 Apr '98 / Dragonheart

Domingo, Enrico

☐ STRICTLY DANCING: MAMBO (Domingo, Enrico & His Big Band)
15335 / May '94 / Laserlight

Domingo, Placido

☐ FROM MY LATIN SOUL VOL.1
CDC 7548782 / Jul '96 / Premier/EMI

☐ FROM MY LATIN SOUL VOL.2
Sabra dios / Un minuto de amor / Sabor a mi / La paloma / Capullito de aleli / Cuando calienta el sol / Guantanamera / Que daria / Alma latino / Volver, volver / El rey / Perdon / Obsession / Maria Elena / Corazon, corazon / Fina / Estampa / Bahia / Copacabana / Princesita / Ay, ay, ay
724355636928 / May '97 / EMI

☐ GOLDEN VOICE, THE
MU 5041 / Oct '92 / Musketeer

☐ POR AMOR
Mujer / Solamente una vez / Guitarra Guajira / Palmera / Noche de ronda / Noche criolla / Te quiero / Maria bonita / Granada / Rosa / Mi rival / Veracruz / Se me hizo facil / Piensa en mi / Arrancame la vida / Palabras de mujer / Farolito/Arroyito
3984237942 / 31 Aug '98 / WEA

☐ PURE DOMINGO
Somewhere over the rainbow / Recondita armonia / Softly, so softly / Amor, vida de mi vida / Somewhere my love / Donna non vida mai / Girls where made to love and kiss / Love story / Vienna, city of my dreams / Be my love / Un 'aura amorosa / You are my heart's delight / Spanish eyes / Mi aidea / E lucevan le stelle / Do not ask me / Flor roja / Celeste aida
CDC 5556162 / Jul '96 / Premier/EMI

Dominguez, Chano

☐ CHANO
NUBA 7756 / 1 Jun '98 / Nuba

☐ EN DIRECTO (2CD Set)
NUBA 77601 / 1 Jun '98 / Nuba

☐ HECHO A MANO
NUBA 7759 / 1 Jun '98 / Nuba

Dominguez, Lorenzo

☐ ALMA GITANO
65011310172 / 14 Jul '98 / SVLL

Dominic Sonic

☐ COLD TEARS
CRAMCD 065 / Nov '89 / Southern

Dominion

☐ BLACKOUT
Unseen / Distortion / Ill effect / Covet / Threshold / Prism / Blackout / Down / Release / Today's tomorrow / Fuelling nothing
CDVILE 71 / 24 Nov '97 / Peaceville

☐ INTERFACE
CDVILE 63 / Aug '96 / Peaceville

Dominique, Lisa

☐ ROCK 'N' ROLL LADY
Rock 'n' roll lady / All fall down / Gamble / Somebody special / Holding on to your love / Time bomb / Jealous heart / Slow down / One foot back in your door / Trouble
WKFMXD 117 / May '89 / FM

Dominique, Natty

☐ NATTY DOMINIQUE 1953
AMCD 18 / Aug '94 / American Music

Domino

☐ DOMINO
Diggady Domino / Ghetto jam / AFD / Do you qualify / Jam / Money is everything / Sweet potato pie / Raincoat / Long beach thang / That's real
4757592 / Feb '94 / Columbia

Domino, Anna

☐ ANNA DOMINO
TWICD 600 / Oct '96 / Les Disques Du Crepuscule

☐ COLOURING THE EDGE AND OUTLINE
TWI 8652 / Oct '96 / Les Disques Du Crepuscule

☐ MYSTERIES OF AMERICA
TWI 8882 / Oct '96 / Les Disques Du Crepuscule

☐ THIS TIME
TWI 7772 / Oct '96 / Les Disques Du Crepuscule

Domino, Fats

☐ 20 GREAT LOVE SONGS
Blueberry Hill / Three nights a week / I want to walk you home / Goodnight sweetheart / Trouble in mind / When my dreamboat comes home / Shame on you / Red sails in the sunset / Valley of tears / I've got a right to cry / Just a lonely man / Can't go on without you / Song for Rosemary / Blue Monday / Land of make believe / Tell me the truth baby / I don't want to set the world on fire / Love me / I'm a fool to care / Girl I love
LS 886342 / 2 Feb '98 / Disky

☐ 50 GREATEST HITS
Fat man / Every night about this time / Rockin' chair / Goin' home / How long / Goin' to the river / Please don't leave me / Rose mary / Something's wrong / You done me wrong / Don't you know / Ain't it a shame / All by myself / Poor me / I can't go on / Bo weevil / Don't blame it on me / I'm in love again / My blue heaven / When my dreamboat comes home / So long / Blueberry hill / Honey chile / Blue monday / What's the reason I'm not pleasin' you / I'm walkin' / Rooster song / Valley of tears / It's you I love / What will I tell my heart / When I see you / Wait and see / Big beat / Yes my darling / Sick and tired / Little mary / Whole lotta loving / Telling lies / I'm ready / I want to walk you home / I'm gonna be a wheel someday / Be my guest / I've been around / Walking to new orleans / Don't come knockin' / Three nights a week / My girl josephine / What a price / Ain't that just like a woman / Let the four winds blow
DBP 102006 / Feb '95 / Double Platinum

☐ AUDIO ARCHIVE
CDAA 048 / Jun '92 / Tring

☐ BEST OF FATS DOMINO, THE
Blueberry Hill / Ain't that a shame / Please don't leave me / Blue Monday / Fat man / I'm in love again / I'm walkin' / I'm ready / I'm gonna be a wheel someday / I want to walk you home / Whole lotta lovin' / Be my guest / My girl Josephine / Walking to New Orleans / Let the four winds blow / Jambalaya
CDP 7902942 / Jul '88 / EMI

☐ BEST OF FATS DOMINO, THE
When the saints go marching in / Blueberry Hill / So long / Whole lotta loving / Walking to New Orleans / Heartbreak Hill / Jambalaya / Blue Monday / Ballin' the jack / Kansas City / My blue Heaven / I'm walking
399232 / May '97 / Koch Presents

☐ BEST OF FATS DOMINO, THE
MATCD 325 / Feb '95 / Castle

☐ BEST OF FATS DOMINO, THE
MACCD 148 / Aug '96 / Autograph

☐ BLUEBERRY HILL
Blueberry hill / I'm ready / Ain't that a shame / So long / CC rider / Hello josephine / Blue monday / Jambalaya / Oh what a price / I'm in the mood for love / Let the four winds blow / I want to walk you home / I'm gonna be a wheel someday / Whole lotta loving / Domino twist / Fat man / Please don't leave me
PWK 021 / '88 / Carlton

☐ BLUEBERRY HILL
KWEST 5400 / Oct '94 / Kenwest

☐ DOMINO EFFECT, THE (2CD Set)
CPCD 83392 / 27 May '98 / Charly

☐ EP COLLECTION VOL.2, THE
You said you love me / Rose Mary / Baby please / Where did you stay / Love me / Don't you hear me calling you / Don't you know / I can't go on / When my dream boat comes home / What's the reason (I'm not pleasing you) / Honey chile / What will I tell my heart / My happiness / Rooster song / It's you I love / Valley of tears / Wait and see / Big beat / When I see you / I still love you / I want you to know / Country boy / Be my guest / Won't you come on back / What a party / My real name
SEECD 455 / Oct '96 / See For Miles

☐ EP COLLECTION, THE
Ain't that a shame / All by myself / My blue heaven / Bo weevil / Coquette / Tired of crying / It must be love / Sick and tired / Telling lies / Please don't leave me / Margie / Blueberry Hill / I want to walk you home / I'm ready / I'm in the mood for love / So long / Walking to New Orleans / Country boy / Let the four winds blow / I'm in love again / Poor me / Don't blame it on me / Blue Monday / Fat man
SEECD 416 / Nov '94 / See For Miles

☐ FAT MAN SINGS, THE
Ain't that a shame / All by myself / Blueberry Hill / Margie / I hear you knocking / Don't blame it on me / You always hurt the one you love / Walking to New Orleans / Honey Chile / My happiness / Sick and tired / Country boy / Your cheatin' heart / You win again / One night / It keeps rainin' / Trouble blues / Nothing new (Same old thing) / My blue heaven / Fat man
CDMFP 5938 / Apr '92 / Music For Pleasure

☐ FAT MAN, THE (3CD Set)
When I'm walking (let me walk) / I got a right / There goes my heart again / Just a lonely man / Red sails in the sunset / Bye baby bye bye / Forever forever / I'm livin' right / Can't go on without you / Land of a 1000 dances / Song for Rosemary / Tell me the truth baby / I don't want to set the world on fire / You know I miss you / Fats on fire / Land of make believe / Old man trouble / Love me / Mary, oh Mary / Gotta get a job / Fat man / Valley of tears / Fats' shuffle / I'm a fool to care / When my dreamboat comes home / Wigs / Trouble on mind / Man that's all / Kansas City / Reelin' and rockin' / Slowboat to China / Monkey business / Heartbreak hill / (I met) the girl I'm gonna marry / Why don't you do right / Ballin' the Jack / Lazy lady / Goodnight sweetheart / Let me call you sweetheart / That certain someone / Nobody needs you like me / Who cares / Something you got baby / If you don't know what love is / Packin' up / (All of my life) for you / Sally was a good old girl / Whole lot of trouble / If I get rich / My old time used to be / Any old time / Shame on you / Sleeping on the job / Girl I love / After hours/I almost lost my mind / Just can't get New Orleans (off my mind) / Move with the groove / Something about you baby / If I get rich / I'm walkin' / Blueberry hill, 1990
SA 872622 / Sep '96 / Disky

☐ FATS DOMINO
LECD 047 / May '94 / Dynamite

☐ FATS DOMINO IN CONCERT
CDSGP 0162 / Aug '95 / Prestige

☐ GOLD COLLECTION, THE (2CD Set)
R2CD 4053 / 13 Apr '98 / Deja Vu

☐ GREATEST HITS
MU 5015 / Oct '92 / Musketeer

☐ HITS ALIVE (2CD Set)
CPCD 82912 / Jul '97 / Charly

☐ IMPERIAL SINGLES VOL.1 1950-1952, THE
Fat man / Detroit city blues / Boogie woogie baby / Little bee / Hide away blues / She's my baby / Brand new baby / Hey La Bas boogie / Every night about this time / Korea blues / Tired of crying / What's the matter baby / Don't lie to me / Sometimes I wonder / No no baby / Right from wrong / Careless love / Rockin' chair / You know I miss you / I'll be gone / Goin' home / Reelin' and rockin' / Trust in me / Poor poor me / Dreaming / How long / Cheatin' / Nobody loves me / Fat man's hop / Hey fat man
CDCHD 597 / Jun '96 / Ace

☐ IMPERIAL SINGLES VOL.2 1953-1956, THE
Going to the river / Mardi Gras in New Orleans / Please don't leave me / Girl I love / You said you love me / Rose Mary / Don't leave me this way / Something's wrong / Little school girl / You done me wrong / Baby please / Where did you stay / You can pack your suitcase / I lived my life / Don't you hear me calling you / Love me / I know / Thinking of you / Don't you know / Helping hand / Ain't that a shame / La la / All by myself / Troubles of my own / Poor me / I can't go on (Rosalie) / Bo weevil / Don't blame it on me / Swanee river hop / If you need me
CDCHD 649 / Apr '97 / Ace

☐ IMPERIAL SINGLES VOL.3 1956-1958, THE
I'm in love again / My blue heaven / When my dreamboat comes home / So long / Blueberry Hill / Honey chile / Blue Monday / What's the reason I'm not pleasing you / I'm walkin' / I'm in the mood for love / Valley of tears / It's you I love / When I see you / What will I tell my heart / Wait and see / I still love you / Big beat / I want you to know / Yes my darling / Don't you know I love you / Sick and tired / No no / Little Mary / Prisoner's song / Young school girl / It must be love / Whole lotta loving / Coquette / Telling lies / When the saints go marching in
CDCHD 689 / 29 Jun '98 / Ace

☐ IN CONCERT
Blueberry Hill / I'm ready / Ain't that a shame / I'm walking / Domino twist / My toot toot / My girl Josephine / Jambalay (on the bayou) / Fat man / So long/CC Rider / Walking to New Orleans / Whole lotta loving / I want to walk you home / Blue Monday / Going to the river / Let the four winds blow / I'm in love again / I'm gonna be a wheel someday
100392 / May '97 / A-Play Collection

☐ JAMBALAYA
Jambalaya / Ain't that a shame (live) / Let the four winds blow / Blue Monday / I'm walkin' / When the Saints go marching in / Blueberry Hill / Walking to New Orleans / My blue heaven / I left my heart in San Francisco / You win again / I done got over it / Mardi Gras in New Orleans
5501792 / Mar '94 / Spectrum

☐ KINGS OF BEAT
REP 4160 / Aug '91 / Repertoire

☐ MAGIC OF FATS DOMINO IN CONCERT
Blueberry hill / I'm ready / Ain't that a shame / My girl Josephine (hello Josephine) / Blue Monday / Jambalaya / What a price / I'm in the mood for love / Let the four winds blow / I want to walk you home / I'm gonna be a wheel someday / Whole lotta loving / Dance with Mr. Domino / Fat man / Please don't leave me / I'm in love again / Be my guest / Red sails in the sunset / Goin' home
QED 060 / Nov '96 / Tring

☐ SPOTLIGHT ON FATS DOMINO
Ain't that a shame / Blueberry hill / Lawdy Miss Clawdy / Fat man / When the saints go marching in / Blue Monday / Domino twist / I'm in the mood for love / I'm in love again / Jambalaya / Lady Madonna / There goes my heart again / Honest papa's love their mama's / Oh what a price / Whole lotta lovin' / Be my guest
HADCD 133 / Feb '94 / Javelin

☐ THAT'S FATS
Sally was a good old girl / Reelin' and rockin' / Fat man / Blueberry Hill / If you don't know what love is / When my dreamboat comes home / Why don't you do right / On a slow boat to China / Trouble in my mind / Monkey business / Heartbreak Hill / I'm gonna be a wheel today / Be my guest / Ballin' the jack / Wigs / Man that's all
12661 / Sep '96 / Laserlight

☐ VERY BEST OF FATS DOMINO, THE
I'm walkin' / Blueberry Hill / I'm ready / Going to the river / My girlfriend Josephine / I want to walk you home / Let the four winds blow / Ain't that a shame / Jambalaya / I'm gonna be a wheel some day / Blue Monday / I'm in love again / Walking to New Orleans / Whole lotta loving / My toot toot / When the saints go marching in
PLATCD 128 / Feb '97 / Platinum

☐ WALKING TO NEW ORLEANS
Detroit City blues / Fat man / Hide away blues / She's my baby / Brand new baby / Little Bee / Boogie woogie baby / Hey la bas boogie / Korea blues / Every night about this time / Careless love / Hey fat man / Tired of crying / Tired of crying / What's the matter baby / I've got eyes for you / Stay away / Don't you lie to me / My baby's gone / Rockin' chair / Sometimes I wonder / Right from wrong / You know I'll miss you / I'll be gone / No, no baby / Reelin' and rockin' / Goin' home / Fat man's hop / How long / How long / Long lonesome journey / Long lonesome journey / Poor, poor me / Poor, poor me / Trust in me / Cheatin' / Mardi Gras in New Orleans / I guess I'll be on my way / Nobody loves me / Dreaming / Going to the river / I love her / Second line jump / Goodbye / Swanee river hop / Rosemary / Please don't leave me / Domino stomp / You said you love me / Rosemary / Fats Domino blues / Ain't it good / Girl I love / Don't leave me this way / Something's wrong / Fats' frenzy / Goin' back home / You left me / You left me / 44 / Barrell house / Little school girl / If you need me / You done me wrong / Thinking of you / Baby please / Where did you stay / You can pack your stay / I lived my life / Little Mama / I know / Love me / Don't you hear me calling you / Don't you know / Helping hand / Help me / All by myself / Ain't it a shame / Oh ba-a-aby / La la / Blue Monday / Troubles of my own / What's wrong / Poor me / I can't go on / I'm in love / Bo Weevil / Don't blame it on me / Howdy podner / So long / I can't go on this way / My blue heaven / Don't know what's wrong / Ida Jane / When my dreamboat comes home / What's the reason / Twist set me free / Blueberry Hill / Honey chile / I'm walkin' / What will I tell my heart / I'm in the mood for love / Would you / My happiness / Don't deceive me / Rooster song / Telling lies / As time goes by / Town talk / Twistin' the spots / It's you I love / Valley of tears / Valley of tears / Wait and see / True confession / Sailor boy / It must be love / Big beat / Little Mary / Stack and Billy / When I see you / Oh whee / I still love you / My love for her / I want you to know / Yes my darling / Don't you know I love you / Sick and tired / No, no / Prisoner's song / One of these days / (I'll be glad when you're dead) you rascal you / Young school girl / I'm gonna be a wheel someday / How can I be happy / Lazy woman / Isle of Capri / Coquette / Once in a while / Sheikh of Araby / Whole lotta lovin' / I miss you so / Margie / I'll always be in love with you / HAnds across the table / If you need me / So glad / At the Darktown strutter's ball / Margie / Sheikh of Araby / My heart is bleeding / I hear you knocking / Li'l Liza Jane / Every night / When the saints go marching in / Country boy / I'm ready / I'm ready / I want to walk you home / When I was young / When I was young / Easter Parade / I've been around / Be my guest / Tell me that you love me / Before I grow too old / Walking to New Orleans / Walking to New Orleans / Don't come knockin' / Don't come knockin' / La la / Put your arms around me honey / Three nights a week / Shu Rah / Rising Sun / My girl Josephine / You always hurt the one you love / Magic Isles / Natural born lover / Am I blue / It's tha talk of the town / It keeps rainin' / What a price / Ain't that just like a woman / Fell in love on Monday / Fell in love on Monday / Trouble in mind / Hold hands / Bad luck and trouble / I've been calling / I just cry / Ain't gonna do it / Won't you come on back / I can't give you anything but love / I'm alone because I love you / Good hearted man / (In) a shanty in old Shanty Town / Along the Navajo trail / One night / Let the four winds blow / Trouble blues / You win again / Your cheatin' heart / Let the four winds blow / What a party / Rockin' bicycle / Did you ever see a dream walking / Birds and the bees / Wishing ring / Jambalaya / Do you know what it means to miss New Orleans / South of the border (Down Mexico way) / Teenage love / Stop the clock / Goin' home / My real name / Hum diddy doo / Those eyes / I want to go home / Dance with Mr. Domino / Nothing new (same old thing)
BCD 15541 / Oct '93 / Bear Family

☐ WHEN I'M WALKING
Lazy lady / When I'm walking / Kansas city / There goes my heart again / I got a right to cry / Red sails in the sunset / Just a lonely man / Land of 1000 dances / Forever forever / Song for rosemary / Bye baby, bye baby / I'm livin' right / Tell me the truth baby / Can't go on without you / Let me call you sweetheart / Girl I'm gonna marry
12362 / May '94 / Laserlight

Dominoes

☐ 14 HITS (Dominoes & Jackie Wilson)
KCD 5007 / Apr '97 / King

☐ 18 HITS (Dominoes & Clyde McPhatter)
KCD 5006 / Apr '97 / King

☐ DOMINOES MEET THE RAVENS (Dominoes & Ravens)
Take me back to heaven: *Dominoes* / Green eyes: *Ravens* / On Chapel Hill: *Ravens* / Stop you're sending me: *Dominoes* / Happy go lucky baby: *Ravens* / Bells of San Raquel: *Ravens* / We'll raise a ruckus tonight: *Ravens* / Gimme gimme gimme: *Dominoes* / Rockin' at the record hop: *Ravens* / She's fine, she's mine: *Ravens* / Take me back to heaven (Faster version): *Dominoes* / Boots and saddles: *Ravens* / Ashamed: *Ravens* / Come to me baby: *Dominoes* / Same sweet wonderful one: *Ravens* / Sweethearts on parade: *Dominoes* / I'll always be in love with you: *Ravens* / Unbeliever: *Ravens* / Take me back to heaven (Unreleased version): *Dominoes* / Bye bye baby blues: *Ravens*
NEMCD 716 / Mar '95 / Sequel

Dominus

☐ FIRST 9
POD 030 / Nov '96 / Progress

☐ VIEW TO THE DIM
RRS 942CD / Sep '95 / Lost & Found

☐ VOL BEAT
PCD 040 / 10 Nov '97 / Diehard

Domnerus, Arne

☐ ANTIPHONE BLUES
PCD 7744 / Dec '95 / Proprius

☐ ARNE DOMNERUS
NCD 8831 / Aug '94 / Phontastic

☐ ARNE DOMNERUS SEXTET (Domnerus, Arne Sextet)
PHONTCD 9303 / Feb '95 / Phontastic

☐ DOMPAN AT THE SAVOY
Rombacksbotten / Morning glory / Nearness of you / Solitude / Honeysuckle rose / Take the train
NCD 8806 / '93 / Phontastic

☐ DOWNTOWN MEETING (Domnerus, Arne & Bengt Hallberg)
Gone with the wind / Embraceable you / On the sunny side of the street / I cover the waterfront / Song from Utanmyra
PHONT CD 7518 / Apr '88 / Phontastic

☐ IN CONCERT LIVE 1996 (Domnerus, Arne Septet)
CAP 21526CD / Aug '97 / Caprice

☐ JAZZ AT THE PAWNSHOP VOL.1
PCD 7778 / Dec '95 / Proprius

☐ JAZZ AT THE PAWNSHOP VOL.2
PCD 9044 / Dec '95 / Proprius

☐ JAZZ AT THE PAWNSHOP VOL.3
PCD 9058 / Dec '95 / Proprius

☐ SKETCHES OF STANDARDS
PCD 9036 / Dec '95 / Proprius

Don & Dewey

☐ JUNGLE HOP
Jungle hop / Little love / Hey Thelma / Baby gotta party / Miss Sue / Good morning / Leavin' it all up to you / Jelly bean / Sweet talk / Farmer John / Just a little lovin' / Letter / When the sun has begun to shine / Bim bam / Day by day / Koko Joe / Justine / Little Sally Walker / Kill me / Big boy Pete / Pink champagne / Jump awhile / Mammer-jammer / Get your hat
CDCHD 358 / Nov '91 / Ace

Don

☐ YEAR IN THE GUTTER STARING AT THE STARS, A
5560292 / 17 Aug '98 / Island

Don Caballero

☐ DON CABALLERO VOL.2
TG 143CD / Sep '95 / Touch & Go

Don Carlos

☐ 7 DAYS A WEEK
Movin' (to the top) / Africa / Fight the revolution / Civilised / Guide us (jah jah oh jah jah) / 7 Days a week / Sunshine / Baby you know / Holiday / Time / Come let's party / Hotty totty (fast food) / You've changed
RASCD 3233 / 5 May '98 / Ras

☐ DAY TO DAY LIVING
Hog and goat / I like it / Dice cups / Roots man party / Hey Mr. Babylon / Street life / English woman / I'm not crazy / At the bus stop
GRELCD 45 / Sep '89 / Greensleeves

☐ DEEPLY CONCERNED
Deeply concerned / Cool Johnny cool / Ruff we ruff / Jah people unite / Black station white station / Satan control them / Money lover / Night rider / Crazy girl
RASCD 3029 / Apr '89 / Ras

☐ EASE UP (Don Carlos & Gold)
RASCD 3150 / Jun '94 / Ras

☐ HARVEST TIME
Fuss fuss / I Love Jah / Harvest time / In pieces / White squall / Magic man / Young girl / Music crave / Hail the roots
CDBM 066 / Jul '93 / Blue Moon

☐ PLANTATION
Plantation / Promise to be true / Teardrops / Declaration of rights / Ain't too proud to beg / Pretty baby / Nice time (late night blues) / Get up / Unity is strength / Leggo me shirt gate man
CPCD 8188 / Sep '96 / Charly
TWCD 1062 / 13 Jul '98 / Tamoki Wambesi

☐ PROPHECY
Gimme gimme your love / Crucial situation / Version / Working everyday / Live in harmony / Prophecy / Jah hear my plea
CDBM 054 / Nov '88 / Blue Moon

☐ RAS PORTRAITS
Jah Jah hear my plea / Just a passing glance / Deeply concerned / Harvest time / Johnny big mouth / Springheel skanking / Prophecy / Cool Johnny cool / Laser beam / Ease up the pressure / Jah people unite / Christine / You are my sunshine
RAS 3307 / Jun '97 / Ras

☐ RAVING TONIGHT (Don Carlos & Gold)
RASCD 3005 / Nov '92 / Ras

☐ THEM NEVER KNOW NATTY DREAD HAVE HIM CREDENTIAL (Don Carlos & Gold)
78249700084 / Jun '96 / Channel One

☐ TIME IS THE MASTER
RASCD 3217 / Nov '92 / Ras

Donahue, Jerry

☐ BRIEF ENCOUNTERS (Donahue, Jerry & Doug Morter)
Brief encounters / False hands / Shifting sands / Say what you say / Deep in the darkest night / Girl on a Harley / I don't want / Two dancers / Five minutes more / Taking the easy way out
ARIS 883510CD / Sep '93 / Hypertension
STRCD 003 / Oct '97 / Stormy Turtle

☐ NECK OF THE WOOD
RGFCD 011 / Mar '91 / Road Goes On Forever

Donahue, Sam

☐ CONVOY 1945 VOL.1
Convoy / Deep night / I've found a new baby / Moten swing / Homeward bound / Lonesome nights / Saxophone Sam / Without a song / Bugle call rag / You was right, baby / Just you, just me / Out of this world / Take me in your arms / C jam blues / Gypsy love song / On the sunny side of the street / My silent love / Please get us out
HEPCD 2 / Jun '94 / Hep

☐ LST PARTY - 1945 VOL.2
World is waiting for the sunrise / Dinah / I can't give you anything but love / Play fiddle play / Cocktails for two / Mean to me / Minor de luxe / C jam blues / C jam blues (Breakdown) / Liza / My heart stood still / LST Party / St. Louis blues / Moten swing / Convoy take / Paradise / Dear Al / My melancholy baby / Bugle call rag
HEPCD 5 / Oct '94 / Hep

Donahue, Tim

☐ VOICES IN THE WIND
44030 / Jun '97 / Eclipse

Donaldson, Eric

☐ KEEP ON RIDING
3021452 / Jun '97 / Arcade
RN 7017 / 23 Mar '98 / Rhino

☐ KENT VILLAGE PLUS
RNCD 2119 / Sep '95 / Rhino

☐ LOVE OF COMMON PEOPLE
Cherry oh baby / Miserable woman / Got to get you off my mind / Please let me love you / Go away / Lion sleeps tonight / Love of the common people / Never on sunday / Can't happen this way / Build my world / Sylvia's mother / Breaking my heart / I'm indebted to you / Blue boots / What a festival
JMC 200116 / Jun '95 / Jamaican Gold

☐ OH WHAT A FEELING
RN 7037 / 30 Mar '98 / Rhino

☐ VERY BEST OF ERIC DONALDSON
RNCD 2054 / May '94 / Rhino

Donaldson, John

☐ MEETING IN BROOKLYN
BDV 9405 / Mar '95 / Babel
378082 / May '96 / Koch Jazz

☐ SING THE LINE (Donaldson, John & Andrew Cleyndert/Dave Mattacks)
Sing the line / Ladies in Mercedes / Wedding / Unrelated incident / Sad to say / Fruit / Chanterelle / Only child / Wild mountain thyme / Compensation
RD 00123 / Jan '97 / Red Dot
378422 / Jun '97 / Koch Jazz

Donaldson, Lou

☐ BEST OF LOU DONALDSON VOL.1, THE
CDARC 509 / Apr '94 / Charly

☐ BIRDSEED
Cherry / Walkin' again / Pennies from heaven / Red top / Blue bossa / Black door blues / Dorothy / Bird seed
MCD 91982 / Apr '94 / Milestone

☐ BLUE BREAKBEATS
Turtle walk / Brother Soul / Minor bash / Pot belly / One cylinder / Caracas
4947092 / 13 Jul '98 / Blue Note

☐ CARACUS
Hot dog / Just a dream / Ornithology / I don't know why (I just do) / Night train / I be blue / Caracus / Li'l darlin'
MCD 92172 / Jul '94 / Milestone

☐ FORGOTTEN MAN (Donaldson, Lou Quartet)
CDSJP 153 / Jan '88 / Timeless Jazz

☐ GOOD GRACIOUS
Bad John / Holy ghost / Cherry / Caracas / Good gracious / Don't worry 'bout me
CDP 8543252 / Feb '97 / Blue Note

☐ GRAVY TRAIN
Gravy train / South of the border / Polka dots and moonbeams / Avalon / Candy / Twist time / Glory of love / Gravy train / Glory of love
CDP 8533572 / Nov '96 / Blue Note

☐ LIVE: FRIED BUZZARD
Fried buzzard / Summertime / Peck time / Thang / Best things in life are free / We
GRP 18292 / 27 Jul '98 / Chess Mates

☐ MR. SHING-A-LING
Ode to Billy Joe / Humpback / Shadow of your smile / Peepin' / Kid
CDP 7842712 / Jan '97 / Blue Note

☐ RIGHTEOUS REED - BEST OF LOU DONALDSON
Alligator boogaloo / Reverend Moses / Peepin' / Midnight creeper / Say it loud, I'm black and I'm proud / Snake bone / Turtle walk / Everything I do gohn be funky / Hamp's hump / (Don't worry) If there's a hell below, we're all gonna go / Sassy soul strut / Gravy train / Crosstown shuffle / Who's making love / Caterpillar
CDP 8307212 / Sep '94 / Blue Note

☐ SUNNY SIDE UP
Blues for JP / Man I love / Politely / It's you or no one / Truth / Goose grease / Softly as in a morning sunrise
CDP 8320952 / Aug '95 / Blue Note

Donaldson, Walter

☐ YES SIR, THAT'S MY BABY (The Songs Of Walter Donaldson) (Various Artists)
How ya gonna keep 'em down on the farm: *Cantor, Eddie & Victor Young Orchestra* / My mammy: *Jolson, Al* / Carolina in the morning: *Whiteman, Paul & His Orchestra* / That certain party: *Lewis, Ted & His Band* / I wonder where my baby is tonight: *Hylton, Jack & His Orchestra* / Yes sir, that's my baby: *Cantor, Eddie* / When you're in love: *Schipa, Tito & Rosario Bourdon Orchestra* / Where'd you get those eyes: *Lewis, Ted & His Band* / My blue heaven: *Austin, Gene & Nat Shilkret Orchestra* / Sam the old accordion man: *Etting, Ruth* / At sundown: *Spanier, Muggsy Ragtime Band* / Just like a melody out of the sky: *Edwards, Cliff* / Because my baby don't mean maybe now: *Whiteman, Paul & His Orchestra* / Love me or leave me: *Etting, Ruth* / Makin' whoopee: *Cantor, Eddie & Orchestra* / Hello beautiful: *Chevalier, Mauice & Leonard Joy Orchestra* / My baby just cares for me: *Payne, Jack & His Band* / Little white lies: *Hanshaw, Annette* / You're driving me crazy: *Armstrong, Louis Orchestra* / That's what I like about you: *Teagarden, Jack & His Orchestra* / Evening in Caroline: *Boswell Sisters & Dorsey Brothers Orchestra* / Sleepy head: *Mills Brothers* / I've had my moments: *Quintet De Hot Club Du France* / It's been so long: *Fox, Roy & His Orchestra* / Did I remember: *Holiday, Billie & Her Orchestra* / Mr. Meadowlark: *Crosby, Bing & Johnny Mercer/Victor Young Orchestra*
CDAJA 5206 / Nov '96 / Living Era

Donato, Edgardo

☐ A MEDIA LUZ
EBCD 95 / 24 Apr '98 / El Bandoneon

Donatto, L.C.

☐ TEXAS ZYDECO
It's too late / Jolie blonde / Lucille / How can I love you baby / Houston walz / Baby please don't go / Oh mama / Zydeco express / Texas two step / Stop down little girl / Don't tell me about your worries / Virgie mae / Take me back / Tequila / Twist (zydeco twist) / Lucille
CD 52038 / Oct '95 / Blues Encore

Done Lying Down

☐ JOHN AUSTIN RUTLEDGE
ABT 0992 / Oct '94 / Abstract

Doneda, Michel

☐ OGOOUE OGOWAY (Live At Banlieu Blues Festival 1994)
TE 003 / Jul '95 / BUDA

Donegan, Dorothy

☐ COPENHAGEN 1980 (Donegan, Dorothy Trio)
STCD 8262 / Dec '97 / Storyville

☐ DOROTHY DONEGAN
ACD 281 / Aug '95 / Audiophile

☐ EXPLOSIVE, THE
ACD 209 / May '95 / Audiophile

☐ LIVE AT THE 1991 FLOATING JAZZ FESTIVAL
CRD 318 / Mar '96 / Chiaroscuro

☐ LIVE AT THE 1992 FLOATING JAZZ FESTIVAL
CRD 323 / Mar '96 / Chiaroscuro

☐ LIVE AT THE WIDDER BAR
Lover / Tea for two / Autumn in New York / Makin' whoopee / Take the 'A' train / Prelude to a kiss / Like someone in love
CDSJP 247 / Aug '90 / Timeless Jazz

☐ MAKIN' WHOOPEE
Here's that rainy day / Lullaby in rhythm / Am I blue / These foolish things / All of me / Makin' whoopee / I can't get started (with you) / Poor butterfly
BLE 591462 / Dec '90 / Black & Blue

Donegan, Lonnie

☐ BEST OF LONNIE DONEGAN
Rock island line / Pick a bale of cotton / Gamblin' man / Grand coulee dam / When the sun goes down / It takes a worried man / Stewball / Battle of new orleans / My dixie darling / I've got rocks in my bed / Dead or alive / I'm a ramblin' man / Sal's got a sugar lip / There's a big wheel / Bring a little water, sylvie / Lost john / Cumberland gap / Midnight special / Golden vanity / How long, how long blues / Wreck of the old '97 / Lonesome traveller / Don't you rock me daddy-o / Nobody's child / Joshua...battle of jericho / Tom dooley
KAZCD 21 / Jul '92 / Kaz

☐ BEST OF LONNIE DONEGAN, THE
Rock island line / Jack o'diamonds / Tom dooley / Puttin' on the style / I'm alabammy bound / Wabash cannonball / Wreck of the old '97 / Battle of new orleans / Bring a little water, sylvie / Nobody loves like an irishman / Michael row the boat ashore / Gamblin' man / Nobody's child / San miguel / Talking guitar blues / Jimmy brown the news boy / Does your chewing gum lose its flavour / My old man's a dustman / Cumberland gap / Don't you rock me daddy-o / Grand coulee dam / Have a drink on me
GOLD 213 / May '94 / Disky

☐ COLLECTION, THE
Rock Island line / Lost John / Nobody's child / Bring a little water Sylvie / Frankie and Johnny / Cumberland gap / Mule skinner blues / Puttin' on the style / My Dixie darling / Ham 'n' eggs / Grand coulee dam / Times are getting hard boys / Long summer day / Does your chewing gum lose its flavour on the bedpost... / Whoa Buck / Battle of New Orleans / Fancy talking tinker / Miss Otis regrets / Talking guitar blues / My old man's a dustman / Have a drink on me / Keep on the sunny side / Pick a bale of cotton / This train
CCSCD 223 / Feb '93 / Castle

☐ EP COLLECTION VOL.2, THE
Midnight special / Worried man blues / Railroad Bill / Ballad of Jesse James / Mule skinner blues / On a monday / Bewildered / It is no secret / Corine Corina / Nobody understands me / No hiding place / Lorelei / Party's over / New burying ground / When the sun goes down / Stagger Lee / Ol' Riley / Old Hannah / Glory / Kevin Barry / My laggan love / Junko partner / Sorry, but I'm gonna have to pass / Pick a bale of cotton / Losing by a hair
SEECD 382 / Oct '93 / See For Miles

☐ EP COLLECTION, THE
Lost John / Stewball / Railroad Bill / Ballad of Jesse James / Little water, Sylvie / Dead or alive / Don't you rock me daddy-o / Cumberland Gap / Puttin' on the style / Gamblin' man / My dixie darling / Jack O'Diamonds / Grand coulee dam / Sally, don't you grieve / Betty, Betty, Betty / Tom Dooley / Does your chewing gum lose its flavour on the bedpost... / Fort Worth jail / Battle of New Orleans / Sal's got a sugar lip / My old man's a dustman / I wanna go home / Have a drink on me / Michael, row the boat ashore / Lumbered
SEECD 346 / Oct '96 / See For Miles

☐ FAVOURITE FLAVOURS
Cumberland gap / Battle of New Orleans / Pick a bale of cotton / Michael, row the boat ashore / Bring a little water Sylvie / Sorry, but I'm gonna have to pass / Comancheros / Frankie and Johnny / Lorelei / Nobody's child / Have a drink on me / Joshua Fit De Battle Of Jericho / Tom Dooley / Aunt Rhody (The old grey goose) / Mule skinner blues / Nobody knows the trouble I've seen / Miss Otis regrets / 500 miles away from home / Corine Corina / Does your chewing gum lose its flavour on the bedpost....
5507612 / Mar '95 / Spectrum

☐ KING OF SKIFFLE
MACCD 165 / Aug '96 / Autograph

☐ MORE THAN 'PYE IN THE SKY
Rock Island line / John Henry / Nobody's child / Wabash cannonball / Hard time blues / You don't know my mind / Midnight special / Precious Lord lead me on / Passing stranger / On a christmas day / Take my hand, precious Lord / When the sun goes down / New burying ground / Worried man blues / Harmonica blues / Ballad of Jesse James / Ol' Riley / Railroad Bill / Lost John / Stewball / Stagger Lee / Bring a little water Sylvie / Dead or alive / Frankie and Johnny / How long blues / I'm a ramblin' man / I'm Alabamy bound / Wreck of ol' 97 / Nodody's child / I shall not be moved / Don't you rock me Daddy-o / Cumberland Gap / Love is strange / Light fingers / Gamblin' man / Puttin' on the style / My Dixie darling / I'm just a rolling stone / Jack O'Diamonds / Grand coulee dam / Hard travellin' / Ham 'n' eggs / Nobody loves like an Irishman / Sally don't you grieve / Ain't you glad you got religion / Lonesome traveller / Light from the lighthouse / I've got rocks in my bed / I've got rocks in my bed (alt.) / Long summer day / Sunshine of his love / Times are getting hard boys / Ain't no more cane on the Brazos / Lazy John / Betty, Betty, Betty / Whoa Buck / Shorty George / Baby don't you know that's love / Lonnie with Alan Freeman / Lonnie's skiffle party / Lonnie's skiffle party (part 2) / Darling Corey / Bewildered / It is no secret / My Lagan love / Rock of my soul / Aunt Rhody (the old grey goose) / Tom Dooley / Does your chewing gum lose its flavour on the bedpost... / Kevin Barry / My only son was killed in Dublin / Chesapeake Bay / Ace in the hole / Fortworth Jail / Battle of New Orleans / Sal's got a sugar lip / Just a closer walk with thee / Ice cream / Fancy talking tinker / Gloryland / Gold rush is over / House of the rising sun / Miss Otis regrets / Take this hammer / San Miguel / Jimmie Brown the newsboy / John Hardy / John Hardy (alt.) / Mr. Froggie / You pass me by / Talking guitar blues (American version) / Talking guitar blues (British version) / Golden vanity / My old man's a dustman / I wanna go home / I wanna go home (alt.) / Corine Corina / In all my wildest dreams / Beyond the sunset / Nobody understands me / Junco partner / Lorelei / Wreck of the John B / Sorry, but I'm gonna have to pass / Lively / Black cat (crossed my path today) / Banana split for my baby / Leave my woman alone / Bury me beneath the willow / When I was young / Virgin Mary / Just a wearyin' for you / Ramblin' round / Have a drink on me / Seven daffodils / Keep on the sunny side / Tiger rag / Michael, row the boat ashore / Lumbered / Michael, row the boat ashore (stereo) / Red berets / Comancheros / Party's over / Over the rainbow / I'll never fall in love again / It was a very good year / I'll never smile again / I'll never fall in love again (alt.) / His eye is on the sparrow / Nobody knows the trouble I've seen / Steal away / Good news, chariot's a-comin' / Born in Bethlehem / Joshua fit de battle of Jericho / No hiding place / Noah found grace in the eyes of the Lord / Sing hallelujah / This train / We shall walk through the valley / Pick a bale of cotton / Market song / Tit bits / Losing by a hair / Trumpet sounds / Rise up / I've got a girl so fine / It's a long road to travel / Lemon tree / 500 miles away from home / Cajun Joe (the bully of the bayou) / Fisherman's luck / Louisiana man / Interstate 40 / Bad news / There's a big wheel / Diamonds of dew / Nothing to gain / Lovey told me goodbye / Beans in my ears / Get out of my life / Blistered / Bound for Zion / Where in this world are we going / Doctor's daughter / Reverend Mr. Black / Farewell (fare thee well) / Wedding bells / Won't you tell me / My sweet Marie / After taxes / I'm gonna be a bachelor / She was a T-bone talking woman / World Cup Willie / Ding ding / Leaving blues / Auntie Maggie's remedy / Over in the new buryin' ground / Leavin' blues / Bury my body / Diggin' my potatoes / When I move to the sky / On a Monday / In the evening / Old Hannah (go down old Hannah) / Mule skinner blues / Precious memories / Brother Moses smote the water / Ella speed / Glory (false start) / Black girl / Glory
BCD 15700 / Oct '93 / Bear Family

☐ ORIGINALS
Wabash cannonball / How long, how long blues / Nobody's child / I shall not be moved / I'm alabammy bound / I'm a ramblin' man / Wreck of the old '97 / Frankie and johnny / Lonesome traveller / Sunshine of his love / Ain't no more cane on the brazos / Ain't you glad you've got religion / Times are getting hard boys / Lazy john / Light from the lighthouse / I've got rocks in my bed / Long summer day
SEECD 331 / Sep '91 / See For Miles

☐ PUTTING ON THE STYLE
Cumberland gap / Railroad bill / Jack o'diamonds / Take this hammer / Tom dooley / Bring a little water, sylvie / Gamblin' man / Ballad of jesse james / This train / Hard travelling / My dixie darling / Frankie and johnny / Lonesome traveller / Grand coulee dam / Ramblin' round / Old hannah / Lost john / Ham 'n' eggs / Wabash cannonball / Darling corey / Sally don't you grieve / Lazy john / Rock o' my soul / Pick a bale of cotton / Glory / Puttin' on the style / Dead or alive / Noah found grace in the eyes of the lord / Battle of new orleans / World cup willie / I'm gonna be a bachelor / My old man's a dustman / Market song / Mr. froggy / Lively / After taxes / Auntie maggie's remedy / Nobody lives like an irishman / Don't you rock me daddy-o / Beans in my ears / Tit-bits / She was t-bone talking woman / Talking guitar blues (uk version) / Does your chewing gum lose its flavour / Lumberee / Fancy talking tinker / Stewball / Have a drink on me / Talking guitar blues (us version) / Ding ding / Party's over / Love is strange / Sorry but I'm gonna have to pass / Interstate forty / Times are getting hard boys / Over the rainbow / Comancheros / We shall walk through the valley / In all my wildest dreams / Miss otis regrets (she's unable to lunch today) / I wanna go home (the wreck of the john b) / I'll never fall in love again / Seven daffodils (seven golden daffodils) / In the evening when the sun goes down / San miguel / Nobody understands me / It is no secret / 500 miles away from home / Nobody's child / I'll never smile again / Beyond the sunset / I'm a ramblin' man / Virgin mary / Bewildered / You pass me by / Farewell (fare thee well)
NXTCD 233 / Nov '92 / Sequel

☐ ROCK MY SOUL
Rock Island line / Bring a little water Sylvie / Have a drink on me / Does your chewing gum loose its flavour / My old man's a dustman / Don't you rock me daddy o / Pick a bale of cotton / Battle of New Orleans / Cumberland gap / Midnight special / Stewball / Wreck of the old '97 / Rock my soul / Joshua fit the battle of Jericho / Michael row the boat ashore
21040 / Jul '97 / Laserlight

Donelly, Tanya

☐ LOVESONGS FOR UNDERDOGS
Pretty deep / Bright light / Landspeed song / Mysteries of the unexplained / Lantern / Acrobat / Breath around you / Bum / Clipped / Goat girl / Manna / Swoon
CAD 7008CD / 8 Sep '97 / 4AD

Donkey

☐ I AIN'T YER HOUSE NIGGER
GUIDE 4CD / 15 Sep '97 / Guided Missile

☐ STROKE MY WINGS GENTLY
GUIDE 26CD / 8 Dec '97 / Guided Missile

Donn, Larry

☐ THAT'S WHAT I CALL A BALL
CLCD 4429 / Aug '96 / Collector/White Label

Donna

☐ MY HAPPINESS
SPCD 12 / Nov '95 / Spindle

Donna Maria

☐ REGGAE LOVE MUSIC VOL.4
PILCD 204 / Nov '94 / Pioneer

Donna The Buffalo

☐ ROCKIN' IN THE WEARY LAND
Times of tide / Funky side / Sailing / Each and every direction / All the time / Mr. King / Seminole wind / Conscious evolution / It will be right / Life is strange / Faith to believe / Let love move me
SHCD 3877 / Jun '98 / Sugar Hill

Donnas

☐ AMERICAN TEENAGE ROCK 'N' ROLL MACHINE
LK 191CD / 9 Feb '98 / Lookout

Donnelly, Des

☐ REMEMBER
DDCD 001 / Dec '94 / Des Donnelly

☐ WELCOME
MMRCD 1005 / Mar '96 / Magnetic

Donnelly, Martin

☐ STONE AND LIGHT
RTMCD 72 / Feb '96 / Round Tower

Donockley, Troy

☐ UNSEEN STREAM, THE
Wild black coast / sights / Air / Yearl / Carousel / Tunnels / Finlandia / Death of rainbows
1901162 / 10 Aug '98 / EMI

Donohoe, Martin

☐ FREE SPIRIT (Donohoe, Martin & Phil Cunningham)
CICD 089 / Mar '96 / Clo Iar-Chonnachta

Donohue, Pat

☐ YE OLDE WOODEN GUITAR CHRISTMAS (Donohue, Pat & Phil Heywood/Dan 'Fancy Dog' Neale)
Silent night / Here comes Santa Claus / Sleigh ride / Friendly beasts / Hark the herald angels sing / O' christmas tree / It came upon a midnight clear / Jingle bells / White christmas / Little drummer boy / Jesus loves me / Blue christmas / Away in a manger / We three kings / O' holy night
ATM 1136 / Nov '97 / Atomic Theory

Donovan

☐ CATCH THE WIND
PLSCD 130 / Jul '96 / Pulse

☐ COSMIC WHEELS
Cosmic wheels / Earth sign man / Sleep / Maria Magenta / Wild witch lady / Music makers / Intergalactic laxative / I like you / Only the blues / Appearance
4773782 / Aug '94 / Epic

☐ DEFINITIVE COLLECTION, THE
Sunshine superman / Season of the witch / Mellow yellow / Epistle to Dippy / There is a mountain / Jennifer Juniper / Hurdy gurdy man / Lalena / Atlantis / To Susan on the West Coast waiting / Barabajagal / Riki tiki tavi / Celia of the seals / Sailing homeward / Earth sign man / Maria Magenta / Salvation stomp / Colours / Catch the wind / Universal soldier
4805522 / 13 Jul '98 / Epic

☐ DONOVAN
Local boy chops wood / Astral angel / Light / Dare to be different / Brave new world / Lady of the stars / International man / Sing my song / Maya's dance / Kalifornia kiddies
BGOCD 375 / 15 Jun '98 / Beat Goes On

☐ DONOVAN IN CONCERT
Isle of Islay / Young girl blues / There is a mountain / Poor cow / Celeste / Fat angel / Guinevere / Widow with a shawl / Preachin' love / Lullaby of Spring / Writer in the sun / Pebble and the man / Rules and regulations / Mellow yellow
BGOCD 90 / Dec '90 / Beat Goes On

☐ DONOVAN LIVE IN CONCERT
Jennifer Juniper / Catch the wind / Hurdy gurdy man / Sunshine superman / Sadness / Universal soldier / Cosmic wheels / Atlantis / Wear your love like heaven / To Susan on the west coast waiting / Colours / Young girl blues / Young but growing / Stealing / Sailing homeward / Love will find a way / Lalena
QED 063 / Nov '96 / Tring

☐ EP COLLECTION, THE
Hey gyp (dig the slowness) / Josie / Catch the wind / To sing for you / Remember the alamo / Oh deed I do / Ballad of a crystal man / Universal soldier / Do you hear me now / Colours / Turquoise / There is a mountain / Rambling boy / Sunny goodge street / Hurdy gurdy man / War drags on / Jersey thursday / Why do you treat me like you do / Jennifer juniper / Mellow yellow
SEECD 300 / '90 / See For Miles

☐ ESSENCE TO ESSENCE
Operating manual for spaceship Earth / Lazy days / Life goes on / There is an ocean / Dignity of man / Yellow star / Divine days of deathless delight / Boy for every girl / St.Valentine angel / Life is a merry go round / Sailing homeward
4894432 / 26 Jan '98 / Epic

☐ FAIRYTALE
Colours / I'll try for the sun / Sunny Goodge Street / Oh deed I do / Circus of sour / Summer day reflection song / Candy man / Jersey Thursday / Belated of a crystal man / Little tin soldier / Ballad of Geraldine
CLACD 226 / Feb '91 / Castle

☐ FAIRYTALES AND COLOURS
Catch the wind / Universal soldier / Colours / Turquoise / Sunny Goodge Street / Oh deed I do / Little tin soldier / Candy man / Donna Donna / Summer day reflection song / To try for the sun / Ballad of Geraldine / Hey Gyp (Dig the slowness) / Josie / Jersey Thursday / Why do you treat me like you do / Ballad of crystal man / Goldwatch blues / Tangerine puppet / Circus of sour
SELCD 506 / Mar '98 / Castle Select

☐ GIFT FROM A FLOWER TO A GARDEN, A
Song of the naturalist's wife / Enchanted gypsy / Isle of Islay / Mandolin man and his secret / Lay of the last tinker / Tinker and the crab / Widow with shawl portrait / Lullaby of spring / Magpie / Starfish on the toast / Epistle to Derroll / Voyage into the golden screen / Wear your love like heaven / Mad John's escape / Skip-a-long Sam / Sun / There was a time / Oh gosh / Little boy in corduroy / Under the greenwood tree / Land of doesn't have to be / Someone's singing
BGOCD 194 / Apr '97 / Beat Goes On

☐ GREATEST HITS
Jennifer Juniper / Catch the wind / Hurdy gurdy man / Sunshine superman / Sadness / Universal soldier / Cosmic wheels / Atlantis / Wear your love like heaven / To Susan on the west coast waiting / Colours / Young girl blues / Young but growing / Stealing / Sailing homeward / Love will find a way / Lalena
RM 1513 / Aug '97 / BR Music

☐ HMS DONOVAN
BGOCD 372 / 12 Jan '98 / Beat Goes On

☐ INTROSPECTIVE
CINT 5007 / Feb '92 / Baktabak

☐ LOVE IS HOT TRUTH IS MOLTEN 1965-1973
RVCD 66 / Apr '98 / Raven

☐ MELLOW (2CD Set)
SMDCD 158 / Jul '97 / Snapper

☐ ORIGINALS
Sunshine superman / Legend of a girl child Linda / Three King Fishers / Ferris wheel / Bert's blues / Season of the witch / Trip / Guinevere / Fat angel / Celeste / Mellow yellow / Writer in the sun / Sand and foam / Observation / Bleak City woman / House of Jansch / Young girl blues / Museum / Hampstead incident / Sunny South Kensington / Hurdy gurdy man / Peregrine / Entertaining of a shy girl / As I recall it / Get thy bearings / Hi it's been a long time / West Indian lady / Jennifer Juniper / River song / Tangier / Sunny day / Sun is a very magic fellow / Teas / Barabajagal / Superlungs my supergirl / Where is she / Happiness runs / I love my shirt / Love song / To Susan on the West Coast waiting / Atlantis / Trudi / Pamela Jo
DONOVAN 1 / Oct '94 / EMI

☐ SUNSHINE SUPERMAN
Sunshine superman / Legend of a girl child linda / Observation / Guinevere / Celeste / Writer in the sun / Season of the witch / Hampstead incident / Sand and foam / Young girl blues / Three kingfishers / Bert's blues
BGOCD 68 / Feb '91 / Beat Goes On
HADCD 197 / Nov '95 / Javelin

☐ SUNSHINE SUPERMAN
Catch the wind / Colours / Sunshine superman / Turquoise / Oh deed I do / Belated forgiveness plea / Remember the alamo / War drags on / Ramblin' boy / To try for the sun / Ballad of the crystal man / Hey gyp / Lady of the stars / Season of the witch / Living for the love light / Every reason / Boy for every girl / Till I see you again
RMB 75059 / Sep '93 / Remember

☐ SUNSHINE SUPERMAN
Sunshine superman / Legend of a girl child Linda / Three king fishers / Ferris wheel / Bert's blues / Season of the witch / Trip / Guiney ere / Fat angel / Celeste
CDGOLD 1066 / Oct '96 / EMI Gold

☐ SUNSHINE SUPERMAN
Lady of stars / I love you baby / Bye bye girl / Every reason / Season of the witch / For every boy there is a girl / Local boy chops wood / Sunshine superman / Living for the lovelight in your eyes / Till I see you again
100082 / May '97 / A-Play Collection

☐ SUNSHINE TROUBADOR
Season of the witch / For every boy there is a girl / Every reason / Till I see you again / Bye bye girl / Lady of the stars / Living for the love light in your eyes / I love you baby / Local boy chops wood / Sunshine superman
305012 / Jul '97 / Hallmark

☐ SUTRAS
Please don't bend / Give it all up / Sleep / Everlasting sea / High your love / Clear-browed one / Way / Deep peace / Nirvana / Eldorado / Be mine / Lady of the lamp / Evernow / Universe am I
74321397432 / Oct '96 / RCA

☐ UNIVERSAL SOLDIER
Colours / Catch the wind / Ballad of a crystal man / Josie / Do you hear me now / Candy man / Belated forgiveness plea / Tangerine puppet / Ballad of Geraldine / Universal soldier / Turquoise / I'll try for the sun / Summer day reflection song / Why do you treat me like you do / Hey gyp (Dig the slowness) / To sing for you / You're gonna need somebody on your bond / Little tin soldier
5507212 / Jan '95 / Spectrum

☐ VERY BEST OF DONOVAN, THE
ARTFULCD 5 / Mar '97 / Artful

Donovan, Jason

☐ GREATEST HITS
Nothing can divide us / Especially for you / Too many broken hearts / Sealed with a kiss / Everyday / When you come back to me / Hang on to your love / Another night / Rhythm of the rain / I'm doing fine / R.s.v.p. / Happy together / Fool such as I
HFCD 20 / Sep '91 / PWL

Donovan's Brain

☐ 50,000,000 YEARS BEFORE
GH 1069CD / 27 Apr '98 / Get Hip

Doo Rag

☐ CHUNCKED AND MUDDLED
BLT 10048 / Dec '96 / Bloat

Doobie Brothers

☐ CAPTAIN AND ME, THE
Natural thing / Long train runnin' / China grove / Dark eyed Cajun woman / Clear as the driven snow / Without you / South City midnight lady / Evil woman / Busted down around O'Connelly Corners / Ukiah / Captain and me
K 246217 / Feb '95 / Warner Bros.

☐ DOOBIE BROTHERS
Nobody / Slippery St. Paul / Greenwood Creek / It won't be right / Travellin' man / Feeling down farther / Master / Growin' a little each day / Beehive state / Closer every day / Chicago
7599262152 / May '95 / Warner Bros.

☐ LISTEN TO THE MUSIC (The Very Best Of The Doobie Brothers)
Long train runnin' / China grove / Listen to the music / Takin' it to the streets / Black water / Jesus is just alright / Rockin' down the highway / Take me in your arms / Without you / South city midnight lady / It keeps you runnin' / Little darlin' / You belong to me / Minute by minute / Here to love you / Real love / What a fool believes / Long train runnin' (mix)
9548328032 / May '94 / Warner Bros.

☐ LIVIN' ON THE FAULT LINE
Nothin' but a heartache / Little darlin' / Livin' on the fault line / Larry the logger two-step / Need a lady / You're made that way / Chinatown / There's a light / You belong to me / Echoes of love
K 9273152 / Jun '89 / Warner Bros.

☐ MINUTE BY MINUTE
Here to love you / What a fool believes / Minute by minute / Dependin' on you / Don't stop to watch the wheels / Open your eyes / Sweet feelin' / Streamer lane breakdown / You never change / How do fools survive
256486 / '88 / Warner Bros.

☐ ROCKIN' DOWN THE HIGHWAY - THE WILDLIFE CONCERT
China grove / What a fool believes / Dangerous / Jesus is just alright / Rockin' down the highway / Dependin' on you / Eyes of silver / Another park another Sunday / Slack key sequel rag (instrumental) / South city midnight lady / Clear as the driven snow / Black water / Wild ride / Slow burn / Doctor / Take me in your arms (rock me) / Long train runnin' / Without you / Excited / Dark eyed Cajun woman / Neal's fandango / Listen to the music / Minute by minute / Takin' it to the streets
4844522 / Aug '96 / Columbia

☐ TOULOUSE STREET
Listen to the music / Rockin' down the highway / Mamaloi / Toulouse Street / Cotton mouth / Don't start me talkin' / Jesus is just alright / White sun / Disciple / Snakeman
7599272632 / May '93 / Warner Bros.

☐ WHAT WERE ONCE VICES ARE NOW HABITS
Another park another Sunday / Black water / Daughters of the sea / Down in the track / Eyes of silver / Flying cloud / Pursuit on 53rd street / Road angel / Song to see you through / Spirit / Tell me what you want (and I'll give you what you need) / You just can't stop it
759927802 / Jul '93 / Warner Bros.

Doof

☐ LET'S TURN ON
TIPCD 10 / Nov '96 / Tip

Doom

☐ DOOMED FROM THE START
DISCCD 5 / Sep '96 / Discipline

☐ FUCK PEACEVILLE
EXIST 024CD / Apr '97 / Profane Existence

☐ GREATEST INVENTION, THE
DISCCD 10 / Aug '93 / Discipline

☐ PEEL SESSIONS, THE
Symptom of the universe/Multinationals / Exploitation / Circles / No religion / Relief / Sold out/ War crimes / Means to an end/A dream to come true / Natural abuse/Days go by / Life lock/Bury the debt / Life in freedom/Money drug/Fear of the future
DISCCD 16 / 20 Apr '98 / Discipline

☐ RUSH HOUR OF THE GODS
FE 021CD / Mar '97 / Flat Earth

Doonan Family

☐ FENWICK'S WINDOW
FSCD 12 / Jan '91 / Folksound

Doonican, Val

☐ 50 YEARS OF LOVE SONGS
Way we were / Where is love / Secret love / Groovy kind of love / On the wings of love / Somewhere / Unforgettable / You needed me / Can't help falling in love / All my loving / Unchained melody / We've only just begun / Sometimes when we touch / Hello young lovers / Our love is here to stay / Alomost like being in love / Mind if I make love to you / April love / When I fall in love / Save the best for last
3036000152 / May '96 / Carlton

☐ CHRISTMAS ALBUM
It's the most wonderful time of the year / Christmas song / When a child is born / Silent night / Let it snow, let it snow, let it snow / Do you hear what I hear / O little town of bethlehem / Have yourself a merry little christmas / Santa claus is coming to town / Mary's boy child / O holy night / I sing noel / Light the candles 'round the world' / White christmas
PWKS 4218 / Oct '95 / Carlton

☐ VERY BEST OF VAL DOONICAN, THE
Special years / Elusive butterfly / If the whole world stopped loving / Morning / For the good times / First time ever I saw your face / Heaven is my woman's love / Now / Paddy McGinty's goat / Walk tall / If I knew then what I know now / What would I be / O'Rafferty's motor car / Marvellous toy / Song sung blue / King of the road / Two streets / I'm just a country boy / Delaney's donkey
MCCD 008 / Feb '91 / Music Club

Doors

☐ AMERICAN PRAYER, AN (Music By The Doors) (Morrison, Jim/Doors)
Awake / To come of age / Poet's dreams / World on fire / American prayer
7559618122 / May '95 / Elektra

☐ BEST OF THE DOORS, THE (2CD Set)
Break on through / Light my fire / Crystal ship / People are strange / Strange days / Love me two times / Five to one / Waiting for the sun / Spanish caravan / When the music's over / Hello I love you / Roadhouse blues / LA Woman / Riders on the storm / Touch me / Love her madly / Unknown soldier / End
9603452 / Nov '85 / Elektra

☐ CEREMONY CONTINUES, THE
CBAK 4052 / Mar '92 / Baktabak

☐ DIONYSUS (A Collection Of Words Spoken By Jim Morrison) (Morrison, Jim)
OZITCD 0035 / 6 Jul '98 / Ozit

☐ DOORS BOX SET, THE (4CD Set)
Five to one / Queen of the highway / Hyacinth house / Who scared you / Black train song / Whiskey mystics and men / I will never be untrue / My eyes have seen you / End of the night / Moonlight drive / Moonlight drive / Rock is dead / Albinoni / Roadhouse blues / Ship of fools / Peace frog/Blue Sunday / Celebration of the lizard / Gloria / Crawling king snake / Money / Poontang blues/Build me a woman/Sunday trucker / End / Hello to the cities / Break on through / Rock me / Money / Someday soon / Go insane / Mental floss / Summer's almost gone / Adolph Hitler / Hello I love you / Crystal ship / I can't see your face in my mind / Soft parade / Tightrope ride / Orange county suite / I can't see your face in my mind / LA Woman / Land ho / Light my fire / Love me two times / When the music's over / Peace frog / Riders on the storm / Shaman's blues / Take it as it comes / Yes the river knows / Unknown soldier / Wild child / Wishful sinful / You're lost little girl
7559621232 / 27 Oct '97 / Elektra

☐ DOORS IN CONCERT, THE
House announcer / Who do you love / Medley / Alabama song / Backdoor man / Love hides / Five to one / Build me a woman / When the music's over / Universal mind / Petition the Lord with prayers / Dead cats / Dead rats / Break on through / Celebration of the lizard / Soul kitchen / Roadhouse blues / Gloria / Light my fire / You make me real / Texas radio and the big beat / End / Unkown soldier / Close to you / Moonlight drive / Little red rooster / Love me two times
7559610822 / May '91 / Elektra

☐ DOORS LIVE, THE
Soul kitchen / Alabama song / Five to one / Love hides / Build me a woman / Who do you love / Break on through no.2 / Dead cats dead rats / Petition the lord with prayers / House announcer / Hill dwellers / Wake up / Universal mind / Close to you / Palace of exile / Names of the kingdom / Little game / Lions in the street / Not to touch the earth / When the music's over / Backdoor man
7559619722 / Nov '96 / Elektra

☐ DOORS, THE
Break on through / Soul kitchen / Crystal ship / Twentieth Century Fox / Alabama song / Light my fire / Back door man / I looked at you / End of the night / Take it as it comes / End
9740072 / Feb '89 / Elektra

☐ GREATEST HITS
Light my fire / Break on through / Roadhouse blues / People are strange / End / Touch me / Hello I love you / LA woman / Love her madly / Ghost song / Riders on the storm / Love me two times
7559618602 / Nov '95 / Elektra

☐ INTERVIEW, THE
SPEEK 011 / 16 Mar '98 / Talking Music

☐ LA WOMAN
Changeling / Love her madly / Cars hiss by my window / LA woman / L'America / Hyacinth house / Crawlin' kingsnake / Wasp / Riders on the storm
9750112 / Feb '89 / Elektra

☐ MORRISON HOTEL
Roadhouse blues / Waiting for the sun / You make me real / Peace frog / Blue Sunday / Ship of fools / Land ho / Spy / Queen of the highway / Indian summer / Maggie McGill
9750072 / Feb '89 / Elektra

☐ MYTH AND REALITY (Spoken Word History/2CD Set) (Manzarek, Ray)
MSE 1018 / 23 Mar '98 / Monster

☐ OPENING THE DOORS OF PERCEPTION - INTERVIEWS
RVCD 33 / May '94 / Raven

☐ SOFT PARADE
Tell all the people / Touch me / Shaman's blues / Do it / Easy rider / Wild child / Running blue / Wishful sin / Soft parade
9750052 / Feb '89 / Elektra

☐ STONED BUT ARTICULATE (Pronouncements Of Jim Morrison 1968) (Morrison, Jim)
OZITCD 0020 / Mar '97 / Ozit

☐ STRANGE DAYS
Strange days / You're lost little girl / Love me two times / Unhappy girl / Horse latitudes / Moonlight drive / People are strange / My eyes have seen you / I can't see your face in my mind / When the music's over
9740142 / '89 / Elektra

☐ ULTIMATE COLLECTED SPOKEN WORDS 1967-1970 (Interview Disc/ 2CD Set) (Morrison, Jim)
OZITCD 0025 / May '97 / Ozit

☐ WAITING FOR THE SUN
Hello I love you / Love street / Not to touch / Earth / Summer's almost gone / Winter time love / Unknown soldier / Spanish caravan / My wild love / We could be so good together / Yes the river knows / Five to one
9740242 / '89 / Elektra

DOP

☐ MUSICIANS OF THE MIND
DOP Chant / Oh yeah / Take me / Groovy beat (part 1) / Dance spirit / Future le funk / Let's party / Get out on this dancefloor / Dancefloor / Oh no / Don't stop the music / Ric / Groovy beat
GRCD 003 / Jul '94 / Guerilla

☐ MUSICIANS OF THE MIND VOL.2
Come to me / Together / String vest / Lion / Party rockin' / Satisfy / Here I go / Ooh la la / Electronic funk / Lust / Catwalk
GRCD 010 / Jul '94 / Guerilla

Dope Fiends

☐ HELTER SKELTER
SEVE 007CD / Jun '96 / 7

Doppler 20-20

☐ KLANGFARBENMELODIE
ADOR 2311 / 23 Mar '98 / Law & Auder

Doran, Christy

☐ WHAT A BAND
ARTCD 6105 / May '92 / Hat Art

Dorau, Andreas

☐ ARGER MIT DER UNSTERBLICHKEIT
EFA 037532 / Apr '95 / Atatak

☐ ERNTE
EFA 037642 / Apr '95 / Atatak

Dordan

☐ IRISH TRADITIONAL & BAROQUE
CEFCD 150 / Jan '94 / Gael Linn

☐ JIGS TO THE MOON
CEFCD 168 / Oct '94 / Gael Linn

☐ NIGHT BEFORE A CELTIC CHRISTMAS, THE
Enniscorthy Christmas carol / Leanbh Ghil Mhilis / Christmas eve reel / Mistletoe waltz / Draiocht na Hoiche / Winter solstice / Oiche nollag / March of the Dreolin / Oiche chiuin / Failte an Fhanai / Don oiche ud I'mBeithil / Polly in the holly / Gartan mother's lullaby / Ding dong merrily on high / Shades of auld lang syne
ND 61063 / 17 Nov '97 / Narada

Dore, Charlie

☐ THINGS CHANGE
BICD 1 / Aug '95 / Black Ink

Dorge, Christian

☐ LYCIA
DW 100 / Feb '95 / Isol

Dorge, Pierre

☐ BALLAD ROUND THE LEFT CORNER
SCCD 31132 / Jul '88 / Steeplechase

Dorham, Kenny

☐ ARRIVAL
FSRCD 7002 / 23 Feb '98 / Fresh Sound

☐ ARRIVAL OF KENNY DORHAM, THE
FSRCD 200 / Dec '92 / Fresh Sound

☐ ART OF THE BALLAD, THE
Darn that dream / Ruby my dear / Old folks / It might as well be spring / Falling in love with love / I'll be seeing you / My ideal / My old flame / What's new / I should care / Passion flower / So in love
PRCD 110132 / Sep '98 / Prestige

☐ HORN SALUTE
JHR 73590 / May '98 / Jazz Hour

☐ JAZZ CONTRASTS
OJCCD 28 / Oct '92 / Original Jazz Classics

☐ KENNY DORHAM AND THE JAZZ PROPHETS VOL.1
Prophet / Blues elegante / DX / Don't explain / Tahitian suite
GRP 18202 / 27 Jul '98 / Chess Mates

☐ OSMOSIS
Osmosis / Soul support / Grand street / Like someone in love / Oscar for Oscar / BMT express / Just friends / Soul support / Grand street / Like someone in love / Osmosis
BLCD 760146 / May '91 / Black Lion

☐ QUIET KENNY
Lotus blossom / Old folks / My ideal / My ideal / Blue Friday / Blue spring shuffle / Alone together / Lotus blossom / Blue spring shuffle / I had the craziest dream / I had the craziest dream / Alone together / Old folks / Blue friday / Mack the knife / Mack the Knife
OJCCD 250 / Sep '93 / Original Jazz Classics
911900492 / 7 Apr '98 / JVC

☐ ROUND ABOUT MIDNIGHT AT THE CAFE BOHEMIA VOL.2
Royal roost / My heart stood still / Prophet / KD's Blues / Riffin' / Who cares / Monaco / NY
BNZ 26 / May '87 / Blue Note

☐ WEST 42ND STREET
BLCD 760119 / Oct '92 / Black Lion

Doris

☐ DID YOU GIVE THE WORLD SOME LOVE TODAY BABY
MRBCD 010 / 2 Mar '98 / Mr. Bongo

Doriz, Dany

☐ THIS ONE'S FOR BASIE
BB 8602 / Apr '96 / Black & Blue

Dorough, Bob

☐ DEVIL MAY CARE (Bethlehem Jazz Classics)
Old devil moon / It could happen to you / I had the craziest dream / You're the dangerous type / Ow / Polka dots and moonbeams / Yardbird suite / Baltimore Oriole / Midnight sun / Johnny one note / I don't mind / Devil may care / Yardbird suite
CDGR 138 / Apr '97 / Charly

☐ JUST ABOUT EVERYTHING
Don't think twice, it's alright / Baltimore Oriole / I've got just about everything / Message / Crawdad song / Better than anything / But for now / 'Tis autumn / Baby, you should know it / Lazy afternoon
ECD 220942 / Jul '94 / Evidence

☐ MEMORIAL CHARLIE PARKER (Dorough, Bob & Bill Takas)
214 W242 / Aug '91 / Philology

Dorset, Ray

☐ COLD BLUE EXCURSION
Got to be free / Cold blue excursion / With me / Have pity on me / Time is now / Livin' ain't easy / Help your friends / I need it / Because I want you / Nightime / Maybe that's the way / Always on my mind
BGOCD 282 / Oct '96 / Beat Goes On

Dorsey Brothers

☐ BEST OF THE BIG BANDS, THE
Somebody stole Gabriel's horn / Mood Hollywood / Sing (it's good for ya) / By heck / My dog loves your dog / Old man Harlem / She reminds me of you / Shim sham shimmy / She's funny that way / Blue room / But I can't make a man / Judy / Nasty man / Annie's cousin Fanny / I'm getting sentimental over you
4716492 / Jun '92 / Columbia

☐ DORSEY BROTHERS 1955
JUCD 2026 / Jul '96 / Jazz Unlimited

☐ DORSEY BROTHERS VOL.1 NEW YORK 1928
BDW 8004 / May '97 / Jazz Oracle

☐ DORSEY BROTHERS VOL.2 NEW YORK 1929-1930
BDW 8005 / May '97 / Jazz Oracle

☐ DORSEY BROTHERS VOL.3 NEW YORK 1930-1933
BDW 8006 / May '98 / Jazz Oracle

☐ HARLEM LULLABY
Somebody stole Gabriel's horn / Stay on the right side of the road / Here is my heart / Stormy weather / Love is the thing / Don't blame me / Shadows on the Swanee / I like a guy what takes his time / Easy rider / You've got me crying again / I gotta right to sing the blues / Is that religion / Harlem lullaby / There's a cabin in the Pines / Lazybones / Shoutin' in the Amen Corner / Snowball / Give me Liberty or give me love / Doin' the uptown lowdown
HEPCD 1006 / Dec '91 / Hep

☐ LIVE IN THE MEADOWBROOK, 28 OCTOBER 1955 (Dorsey Brothers Orchestra)
JH 1003 / Feb '91 / Jazz Hour

☐ MOOD HOLLYWOOD
I'm getting sentimental over you / It don't mean a thing / Shim sham shimmy / Blue room / It's the talk of the town / Dinah / Mood Hollywood / By heck / Dr. Heck / Dr. Heckle and Mr. Jibe / Mean to me
HEPCD 1005 / Apr '96 / Hep

Dorsey, Don

☐ BACH BUSTERS
Italian concerto, bwv971 / Two and three part inventions / Diverse kanons, bwv1087 / Toccata and fugue in d minor / Jesu, joy of man's desiring
CD 80123 / '87 / Telarc

☐ BUSTED
CD 80473 / 6 Oct '97 / Telarc

Dorsey, Jimmy

☐ 1939-40 (Dorsey, Jimmy Orchestra)
CCD 30 / May '93 / Circle

☐ 1940 (Dorsey, Jimmy Orchestra)
CCD 46 / May '93 / Circle

☐ 22 ORIGINAL BIG BAND RECORDINGS (Dorsey, Jimmy & His Orchestra)
Contrasts / Julia / Blueberry hill / Shine on harvest moon / Imagination (bob eberly) / Out of nowhere / In a little spanish town / Just for a thrill (helen o'connell) / Blue lou / Fools rush in (bob eberly) / Carolina in the morning / Tangerine (claire hogan and kenny martin) / I got rhythm / I'm stepping out with a memory tonight (helen o'connell) / Grand central getaway / Nearness of you (bob eberly) / Perfidia / Green eyes / Everywhere you go / You, you darling (helen o'connell) / On the alamo / After all (bob eberly)
HCD 415 / Sep '92 / Hindsight

☐ DON'T BE THAT WAY 1935-1940 (Dorsey, Jimmy Orchestra)
RACD 7120 / May '96 / Aerospace

☐ GREAT JIMMY DORSEY, THE
Contrasts / Imagination / Just for a thrill / Perfidia / Fools rush in / I'm steppin' out with a memory tonight / Blueberry hill / You, you darling / Green eyes / In a little Spanish town / Tangerine / Nearness of you
HCD 333 / Apr '96 / Hindsight

☐ I REMEMBER YOU
Tangerine / Keep a knockin' / Dixieland dectour / Begone / Cherokee / I remember you / Green eyes / Always in my heart / Tropical magic / Time was / You make me love you / Holiday for strings / My ideal / They're either too young or too old / Besame mucho / Amapola / Maria elena / Yours / Brazil / At the crossroads
RAJCD 852 / Nov '97 / Empress

☐ JIMMY DORSEY
15759 / Aug '92 / Laserlight

☐ JIMMY DORSEY 1939-1940
Contrasts / Shine on harvest moon / Imagination / Blue Lou / Just for a thrill / Fools rush in / Carolina in the morning / At least you could say hello / Moonlight on the river / I'm stepping out with a memory tonight / Julia / Nearness of you / Shoot the meatballs to me Dominick boy / You, you darlin' / Blueberry hill / Flight of the jitterbug
HCD 101 / Jul '96 / Hindsight

☐ JIMMY DORSEY AT THE 400 RESTAURANT 1946 (Dorsey, Jimmy Orchestra)
All the things you ain't / Grand Central getaway / Sunset Strip / Together / Opus no.1 / I've got a crush on you / Outer drive / Come to baby do / Town hall tonight / Lover / It's the talk of the town / Super chief / Lover man / King Porter stomp / Here I go again / I can't believe that you're in love with me / Man with the horn / This can't be love / Contrasts
HEPCD 41 / Dec '91 / Hep

☐ PENNIES FROM HEAVEN
It's the natural thing to do / Slap that bass / Love bug will bite you / Dorsey Dervish / Pick yourself up / Moon got in my eyes / In a sentimental mood / Rap tap on wood / I love to sing / All you want to do is dance / They can't take that away from me / Serenade to nobody in particular / Let's call a heart a heart / Swingin' the jinx away / Stompin' at the Savoy / After you / Listen to the mockingbird / Pennies from Heaven
CDAJA 5052 / May '88 / Living Era

☐ PERFIDIA (Dorsey, Jimmy Orchestra)
In a little spanish town / You taught me to love again (vocal by tommy mercer) / Pet me pappa (vocal by lynn roberts) / Perfidia / (love is) the tender trap (vocal by tommy mercer) / Bula beige / Love for sal / End of a love affair (vocal by lynn roberts) / How little we know (vocal by tommy mercer) / Manhattan / Moten swing / Hip hop / Oh what a beautiful mornin' / Open up that door
15768 / Jul '92 / Laserlight

☐ SHINE ON HARVEST MOON
I've got rhythm / Grand Central getaway / Sowing wild oats / Just you, just me / Sophisticated swing / Together hit the note / (I would do) anything for you / Three little words / Shine on harvest moon / Imagination / I'm stepping out with a memory tonight / Carolina in the morning / Nearness of you / Moonlight on the river / Someday sweetheart / Fools rush in / Begin the beguine / Sunset strip
GRF 067 / '93 / Tring

☐ THEN AND NOW (Dorsey, Jimmy Orchestra)
7567818012 / Jul '93 / Atlantic

Dorsey, Lee

☐ FREEDOM FOR THE FUNK
Yes we can (part 1) / Work work work / Can you hear me / Occapella / Games people play / When the bill gets paid / Ride your pony / Wonder woman / Love lots of lovin / Little baby / Take care of our love / Neighbours daughter / Confusion / O me-o, my-o / Sneakin' sally thru the alley / Freedom for the stallion / If she won't (find someone who will) / Get out of my life / Woman / Working in the coal mine / Yes we can (part 2)
CPCD 8068 / Nov '94 / Charly

☐ MASTERS, THE
EABCD 049 / 24 Nov '97 / Eagle

☐ WHEELIN' AND DEALIN' (The Definitive Lee Dorsey Collection)
Ya ya / Do-re-mi / Ride your pony / Work work work / Can you hear me / Get out of my life woman / Confusion / Working in the coal mine / Holy cow / Operation heartache / Gotta find a job / Love lots of lovin' / My old car / Go go girl / I can't get away / Loppie Mo '68 / Love was born / Everything I do gohn be funky / Give it up / Candy yam
07822189802 / 2 Feb '98 / RCA

☐ WORKING IN A COALMINE
REP 4169 / Aug '91 / Repertoire

☐ WORKING IN A COALMINE
Ya ya / Ride your pony / Get out of my life woman / Working in the coal mine / Holy cow / My old car / Go-go girl / Everything I do gohn be funky / Can you hear me / Love lots of lovin' / Sneakin' sally thru the alley / Yes we can / Greatest love / Mellow good time / Mexico / Confusion / Don't you ever leave me / Neighbours daughter / Kitty cat song / Shortnin' bread / So long / People I wish you could see me / Work work work / Here comes the hurt again / Hello mama / Feelin' / Little dab a doya
RMB 75055 / Nov '93 / Remember

☐ WORKING IN A COALMINE
Ya ya / Ride your poney / Can you hear me / Get out of my life woman / Working in the coal mine / Holy cow / My old car / Go-go girl / Love lots of lovin' / Everything I do gohn be funky / Sneakin' sally thru the alley / Yes we can
QSCD 6007 / Jan '95 / Charly

Dorsey, Tommy

☐ 1944- ALL TIME HIT PARADE
On the sunny side of the Street / April in Paris / What is this thing called love / I may be wrong, but I think you're wonderful / East of the sun and west of the moon / Embraceable you / Cheek to cheek / I'll be seeing you / Dancing in the dark / I can't give you anything but love / I'll walk alone / South of the border (Down Mexico way) / Summertime / If you are but a dream / Amor / Lover come back to me / Top hat, white tie and tails / Lamp is low / Boogie woogie / I'll never smile again / Song of India / As time goes by / Hawaiian war chant
HEPCD 39 / Apr '90 / Hep

☐ AT THE FAT MAN'S
Blue skies / Dawn on the desert / At the Fat Man's / Bingo, bango, boffo / Marie / Chloe / Well git it / At sundown / Opus one / Candy / Continental / Call you sweetheart / Feels so good / Pussy Willow / Broadcasts from 1945-1948
HEPCD 43 / Jun '93 / Hep

☐ BEST OF TOMMY DORSEY
Maria / Stardust / Little white lies / I'll never smile again / Yes indeed / Boogie woogie / Opus one / Song of India / Who / Royal Garden blues / Once in a while / I'm getting sentimental over you
DCD 5330 / Dec '93 / Disky

☐ BIG BAND BASH (Dorsey, Tommy Orchestra)
Opus one / On the sunny side of the street / I'm getting sentimental over you / Boogie woogie / Blue skies / Royal garden blues / Chicago / Stardust / Sheel of Araby / Song of India / Swing low, sweet chariot / There are such things / Well git it / Marie / What is this thing called love / Imagination / Weary blues / Yes indeed / Liebestraum / East of the sun and west of the moon / Hawaiian war chant / Whispering / Mendelssohn's spring song
CD 53082 / Mar '90 / Giants Of Jazz

☐ BROADCASTS 1928-1941 (Dorsey, Tommy Orchestra)
JH 1052 / Feb '98 / Jazz Hour

☐ BROADCASTS 1938-1939 (Dorsey, Tommy Orchestra)
JH 1053 / Feb '98 / Jazz Hour

☐ CARNEGIE HALL V-DISC SESSION APRIL 1944, THE (Dorsey, Tommy Orchestra)
Minor goes muggin' / I dream of you / Milkman keep those bottles quiet / I never knew / Song of India / Tess's torch song / Irresistible you / Losers weepers / Wagon wheels / Paramount on parade / TD chant / Then I'll be happy / Small fry / Pennies from heaven / Somebody loves me / Indian summer / I'm in the mood to be loved / Sweet and lovely / Chicago / Lady in red / For all we know / I'm nobody's baby / Three little words
HEPCD 40 / Dec '90 / Hep

☐ CLASSICS 1928-1935
CLASSICS 833 / Sep '95 / Classics

☐ CLASSICS 1935-1936
CLASSICS 854 / Feb '96 / Classics

☐ CLASSICS 1936
CLASSICS 878 / Apr '96 / Classics

☐ CLASSICS 1936-1937
CLASSICS 916 / Jan '97 / Classics

☐ CLASSICS 1937 VOL.1
CLASSICS 955 / Nov '97 / Classics

☐ CLASSICS 1937 VOL.2
CLASSICS 995 / 1 Jun '98 / Classics

☐ COMPLETE RECORDINGS 1940-42, THE (4CD Set) (Dorsey, Tommy & Frank Sinatra)
852137 / May '94 / New Rose

☐ DANCE WITH DORSEY
Opus One / Lamp Is Low / You grow sweeter as the years go by / How Am I To Know / All I remember is you / Well alright / Big Dipper / Tin Roof Blues / Sweet Sue, Just You / Copenhagen / Panama / Chinatown, my Chinatown / When the midnight choo choo leaves for Alabam' / Big Apple / Hawaiian War Chant / Song Of India / Chicago / Marie
PAR 2068 / Jul '94 / Parade

☐ GO THEIR SEPARATE WAYS (Dorsey, Tommy & Jimmy)
Sinner kissed an angel / Blue skies / What'cha know Joe / East of the sun and west of the moon / Too romantic / How about you / Lady is a tramp / Fools rush in / Hawaiian war chant / Be careful it's my heart / Night in Sudan / Six lessons from Madame La Zonga / Bogg it / Arthur Murray taught me dancing in a hurry / Not mine / If you build a better mousetrap / Whispering grass / Dolimite / Aurora / I can't resist you / So do I / Contrasts
RAJCD 817 / Mar '97 / Empress

☐ GREAT TOMMY DORSEY, THE
Music maestro please / Stardust / Who / Marie / Song of India / Hawaiian war chant / East of the sun and west of the moon / Night in Sudan / That's a plenty / Night and day / Smoke gets in your eyes / Tea for two / Beale Street blues / Lonesome road / Turn off the moon / After you've gone / Lady is a tramp / Call of the canyon / After I say I'm sorry / Polka dots and moonbeams / Too romantic
PASTCD 9740 / Mar '91 / Flapper

☐ INTRODUCTION TO TOMMY DORSEY 1928-1942, AN
4029 / Feb '96 / Best Of Jazz

☐ JAZZ GREATS
Opus one / Song of India / Once ina while / Marie / Little white lies / Stardust: *Dorsey, Tommy & Frank Sinatra* / I'm getting sentimental over you / Indian summer: *Dorsey, Tommy & Jack Leonard* / You / Music goes 'round and 'round / All the things you are: *Dorsey, Tommy & Jack Leonard* / Our love: *Dorsey, Tommy & Jack Leonard* / In the blue of evening: *Dorsey, Tommy & Frank Sinatra* / Song is you: *Dorsey, Tommy & Frank Sinatra* / I'm in the mood for love: *Dorsey, Tommy & Charlie Shavers* / Summertime: *Dorsey, Tommy & Charlie Shavers* / Birmingham bounce: *Dorsey, Tommy & Charlie Shavers*
74321499872 / Feb '98 / RCA Victor

☐ MAN AND HIS TROMBONE, A
BMCD 3055 / Nov '97 / Blue Moon

☐ MASTERPIECES VOL.15 1935-44
158342 / Mar '95 / Masterpieces

☐ MOONLIGHT IN VERMONT
Marie / You're my everything / Song of India / Love for sale / Taking a chance on love / This love of mine / Opus one / Swanee river / I'm getting sentimental over you / Boogie woogie / Melancholy serenade / Autumn in New York / I should care / Oo do do / It started all over again / I dream of you / Moonlight in Vermont / There are such things / High and mighty / Who / In a little Spanish town / Little girl / Granada
GRF 068 / '93 / Tring

☐ OPUS ONE (Dorsey, Tommy Orchestra & Frank Sinatra)
Opus one / On the sunny side of the street / I'm getting sentimental over you / Boogie woogie / Blue skies / Royal garden blues / Stardust / Chicago / Well git it / Marie (ranchera) / Imagination / Yes indeed / Weary blues / Liebestraum / Hawaiian war chant / Whispering / Mendelssohn's spring song / Song of india
CD 14526 / Jan '94 / Jazz Portraits

☐ PORTRAIT OF TOMMY DORSEY, A
GALE 404 / May '97 / Gallerie

☐ SONG OF INDIA (Dorsey, Tommy Orchestra)
They didn't believe me / Cheek to cheek / Opus one / Tico-tico / Blue skies / I'll never smile again / Begin the beguine / There's no you / Midriff / Cuttin' out / Pussy willow / Hollywood hat / Then I'll be happy / Lovely weather for ducks / And the angels sing / Somebody loves me / Boogie woogie / Song of India / On the sunny side of the street / Non drastic / Swanee river
DBCD 08 / Jul '87 / Dance Band Days

☐ STOP, LOOK AND LISTEN
After you've gone / Beale Street blues / Boogie woogie / Chinatown, my Chinatown / Davenport blues / Easy does it / He's a gypsy from Poughkeepsie / Liebestraum / Lonesome road / Mandy, make up your mind / Maple leaf rag / Marie / Night and day / Royal Garden blues / Sheikh of araby / Song of India / Stomp it off / Stop, look and listen / Swanee river / Symphony in riffs / Tin roof blues / Twilight in Turkey / Weary blues
CDAJA 5105 / May '93 / Living Era

☐ SWEET & HOT (Meadowbrook Broadcast 24/2/40)
TAX 37052 / Aug '94 / Tax

☐ TOMMY DORSEY
Royal garden blues / Music goes round and round / Boogie woogie / After you've gone / Little white lies / Hollywood hat / Capitol idea / All of me / Lullabye in boogie / Pussy willow / I got rhythm / Let me love you tonight / Sweet georgia brown / Dry bones / Chloe / Puddle wamp / Boogie woogie blues / On the sunny side of the street
22709 / Nov '95 / Music

☐ TOMMY DORSEY & HIS ORCHESTRA 1935-47 (Dorsey, Tommy Orchestra)
TAXS 42 / Aug '94 / Tax

☐ TOMMY DORSEY & HIS ORCHESTRA 1940-43
JH 1035 / Oct '93 / Jazz Hour

☐ TOMMY DORSEY 1942 (Dorsey, Tommy Orchestra)
JH 1013 / Feb '92 / Jazz Hour

☐ TOMMY DORSEY AND HIS CLAMBAKE SEVEN 1936-1938 (Dorsey, Tommy & His Clambake Seven)
At the codfish ball / Milkman's matinee / Twilight in Turkey / He's a gypsy from Poughkeepsie / Alibi baby / Is this gonna be my lucky summer / Who'll be the one this summer / Posin' / All you want to do is dance / Having wonderful time (wish you were here) / After you / Stardust on the moon / Big apple / Lady is a tramp / Tears in my heart / Josephine / If the man in the moon / Nice work if you can get it / You're a sweetheart / When the midnight choo choo leaves for Alabam' / Everybody's doing it
RTR 79012 / Jul '97 / Retrieval

☐ TOMMY DORSEY AND HIS GREATEST BAND
Boogie woogie / Amor / But she's my buddy's chick / Swing high / Like a leaf in the wind / Marie / Opus No.1 / Wagon wheels / Clarinet cascades / Land of dreams / Song of India / Swanee river / Losers weepers / There is no breeze to cool the flames / Minor goes muggin' / We'll git it / On the sunny side of the street / Rest stop / I'm in love with someone / That's my home / I'm getting sentimental over you
JASMCD 2537 / Nov '94 / Jasmine

☐ TOMMY DORSEY ORCHESTRA/DAVID ROSE STRING ORCHESTRA (Dorsey, Tommy Orchestra & Dave Rose)
Dance of the spanish onion / My dog has fleas / Our waltz / Da easta time / Holiday for strings / Vienna swings again / Humoresque / Buy my violets / Leibestraum / Song of india / Barcarole / Dark eyes / Blue danube waltz (strauss) / Spring song
15777 / Jul '93 / Laserlight

☐ TOMMY DORSEY VOL.1
15755 / Aug '92 / Laserlight

☐ TOMMY DORSEY WITH FRANK SINATRA (Dorsey, Tommy & Frank Sinatra)
Marie: *Dorsey, Tommy* / Too romantic: *Dorsey, Tommy* / Polka dots and moonbeams: *Dorsey, Tommy* / This is the beginning of the end: *Dorsey, Tommy* / Hear my song: *Dorsey, Tommy* / I haven't time to be a millionaire: *Dorsey, Tommy* / Head on my pillow: *Dorsey, Tommy* / I'll never smile again: *Dorsey, Tommy* / One I love: *Dorsey, Tommy* / Call of the canyon: *Dorsey, Tommy* / Shadows on the sand: *Dorsey, Tommy* / Do you know why: *Dorsey, Tommy* / Yearning: *Dorsey, Tommy* / Not so long ago: *Dorsey, Tommy* / Stardust: *Dorsey, Tommy* / How am I to know: *Dorsey, Tommy* / Oh look at me now: *Dorsey, Tommy* / You lucky people you: *Dorsey, Tommy* / Without a song: *Dorsey, Tommy* / Everything happens to me: *Dorsey, Tommy* / Let's get away from it all: *Dorsey, Tommy* / Love me as I am: *Dorsey, Tommy* / Love of mine: *Dorsey, Tommy* / Blue skies: *Dorsey, Tommy* / How do you do without me: *Dorsey, Tommy* / Violets for your furs: *Dorsey, Tommy* / How about you: *Dorsey, Tommy* / My melancholy baby: *Dorsey, Tommy* / Dig down deep: *Dorsey, Tommy* / It started all over again: *Dorsey, Tommy* / I'll take Tallulah: *Dorsey, Tommy* / Song is you: *Dorsey, Tommy*
7432115182 / Jun '94 / Jazz Tribune

☐ TOMMY DORSEY WITH FRANK SINATRA (Dorsey, Tommy & Frank Sinatra)
Opus one / On the sunny side of the street / I'm getting sentimental over you / Boogie woogie / Blue skies / Royal garden blues / Stardust / Chicago / Well git it / Marie (ranchera) / Yes indeed / Weary blues / Liebestraum / Hawaiian war chant / Whispering / Mendelssohn's spring song / Song of india / Imagination
CD 56004 / Aug '94 / Jazz Roots

☐ WELL, GIT IT (Dorsey, Tommy Orchestra)
JASSCD 14 / Oct '91 / Jass

Dos

☐ UNO CON DOS
NAR 061CD / May '93 / New Alliance

Dos Of Soul

☐ COME AROUND
5318422 / Sep '96 / Mercury

Dos Santos, Jovino

☐ CABO VERDE NHA TERRA
PS 65174 / Nov '96 / PlayaSound

☐ MORNAS & COLADERAS FROM CAPE VERDE
PS 65127 / May '94 / PlayaSound

Dotsero

☐ JUBILEE
NOVA 9136 / Jan '93 / Nova

☐ OFF THE BEATEN PATH
NOVA 9023 / Jan '93 / Nova

Double Exposure

☐ BEST OF DOUBLE EXPOSURE, THE
CDGR 149 / Jul '97 / Charly

☐ TEN PERCENT
Ten percent / Gonna give my love away / Everyman / Baby I need your loving / Just can't say hello / My love is free / Pick me
CPCD 8062 / Nov '94 / Charly

Double Muffled Dolphin

☐ LIONS ARE GROWING
APR 011CD / Aug '96 / April

☐ MY LEFT SIDE IS OUT OF SYNC
APR 004CD / 6 Oct '97 / April

Double Nelson

☐ LE GRAND CORNET
RM 002 / Feb '97 / Room Tone

Double Trio

☐ GREEN DOLPHY SUITE (Arcado String Trio/Trio De Clarinettes)
Green Dolphy Street / Cold water music / Clic / Bosnia / Muhu / Suite domestique
ENJ 90112 / Jul '95 / Enja

Double U

☐ ABSURD FJORD
COMM 041CD / Dec '96 / Communion

☐ GLANDS OF EXTERNAL SECRETION (2CD Set)
VHF 31 / 17 Nov '97 / VHF

Double Vision

☐ DOUBLE VISION
Conscience / Somebody / Trouble / Torn to pieces / Time / Ain't never giving up / Should I stay / Shades / Dawning / Kickstart / Summer never ending
JAZIDCD 104 / Aug '94 / Acid Jazz

Double Vision

☐ UNSAFE BUILDING
HV 295012 / Dec '96 / Happy Vibes

Doubt

☐ PROFIT
CD 7913003 / Jun '93 / Progress Red

Doucet, David

☐ QUAND J'AI PARTI
T'en as eu / Balfa waltz / Zydeco sont pas sales / J'ai passe / Bee la manche / Ton papa / French blues (Je m'endors) / J'etais au bal / Les bons temps rouler / Pacquent d'epingles / Coulee rodair / J'ai fait la tour / La valse des cajuns
ROUCD 6040 / '91 / Rounder

Doucet, Michael

☐ BEAU SOLO
Grand tasso / Valse acadienne / One-step d'amedee / La valse d'amedee / Contredanse de freeman / Bee's blues / Valse a pop mcgee / Blues acadiens / Isabeau se promene (ballad) / Grand mamou / Perrodin two-step / Chez varise connor / La betaille / Gigue d'acadie / Wade's waltz (caillette est cr evee) / Sept ans sur mer (ballad) / Creole french blues / La malheureuse / Valse d'avant-hier / Two-step d'ambrose / La valse d'auguste / Two-step de maman
ARHCD 321 / Apr '95 / Arhoolie

☐ GREAT CAJUN (Doucet, Michael & Cajun Brew)
Wooly bully / Bayou pom pom / Un autre soir ennuyant / Hey good lookin' / Last wednesday night / Louie louie / Woman or a man / Pauline / Zydeco boogaloo / Like a real cajun / J'ai passe devant ta porte / Do you want to dance
ROUCD 6017 / Apr '93 / Rounder

☐ MAD REEL, THE (Doucet, Michael & Beausoleil)
ARHCD 397 / Apr '95 / Arhoolie

☐ MICHAEL DOUCET & CAJUN BREW (Doucet, Michael & Cajun Brew)
Wooly bully / Bayou pom pom / Un autre soir ennuyant / Hey good lookin' / Last Wednesday night / Louie louie / Woman or a man / Pauline / Zydeco boogaloo / Like a real cajun / J'ai passe devant ta porte / Do you want to dance
ROUCD 6017 / May '93 / Rounder

Doughboys

☐ HAPPY ACCIDENTS
Countdown / Sorry wrong number / Deep end / Intravenus DeMilo / Happy home / Sunflower honey / Far away / Happy sad day / Wait and see / Every bit of nothing / Dream day / Apprenticeship of Lenny Kravitz / Tupperware party
LC 9336 2 / Nov '90 / Restless

Doughnuts

☐ AGE OF CIRCLE
VR 025CD / Nov '95 / Victory

Doughten, John

☐ TIME FOR LOVE, A
SSC 1073D / Feb '97 / Sunnyside

Douglas, Blair

☐ BENEATH THE BERET
SKYECD 02 / Jan '92 / Macmeanmna

☐ SUMMER IN SKYE, A
SKYECD 09 / Oct '96 / Macmeanmna

Douglas, Carl

☐ BEST OF CARL DOUGLAS, THE (Kung Fu Fighting)
Kung fu fighting / When you got love / I want to give you my everything / Run back / I don't care what people say / Love peace and happiness / Too hot to handle / Witchfinder general / Girl you're so fine / Changing times / Mistakes of mine / Green tangerines and wild evergreens / Dance the kung fu / I'll be your light / What's good for the goose / Never had this dream before
HTCD 51 / 20 Apr '98 / Hot Productions

☐ KUNG FU FIGHTING
Kung fu fighting / Witchfinder general / When you got love / Changing times / I want to give you everything / Dance the kung fu / Never had this dream before / I don't care what people say / Blue eyed soul / Blue eyed soul / Shanhaid / Honest woman / Loving you / Kung fu fighting
21023 / Jul '97 / Laserlight

Douglas, Carol

☐ BEST OF CAROL DOUGLAS, THE (Doctor's Orders)
Dancing queen / Midnight love affair / Baby don't let this good love die / Hurricane is coming tonight / Doctor's orders / Night fever / Light my fire / Burnin' / In the morning / Lie to me / Fell in love for the first time / I want to stay with you / Who what where when and why / I got the answer / My simple heart / You're not so hot
HTCD 24 / 20 Apr '98 / Hot Productions

Douglas, Craig

☐ ONLY SIXTEEN
Our favourite melodies / Time / Hundred pounds of clay / Change of heart / Rainbows / Riddle of love / When my little girl is smiling / Pretty blue eyes / There is no greater love / Girl next door / Wish it were me / Sandy / Hello spring / Another you / Teenager in love / Only sixteen / Oh what a day / Dream lover / Ring-a-ding doo
SEECD 34 / Feb '90 / See For Miles

Douglas, Dave

☐ CHARMS OF THE NIGHT SKY
9100152 / Aug '98 / Winter & Winter

☐ CONSTELLATIONS (Douglas, Dave Tiny Bell Trio)
ARTCD 6175 / Oct '95 / Hat Art

☐ MOVING PORTRAIT
DIW 934 / Jul '98 / DIW

☐ PARALLEL WORLDS
1212262 / Jan '94 / Soul Note

☐ SANCTUARY
AVAN 066 / Oct '97 / Avant

Douglas, Jerry

☐ EVERYTHING'S GONNA WORK OUT FINE
ROU 11535 / '89 / Rounder

☐ RESTLESS ON THE FARM
Things in life / Turkish taffee / Passing the bar / Don't take your guns to town / Tribute to Peador O'Donnell / Takarasaka / Follow on / Like it is / Ride / TV doctor / For those who've gone clear
SHCD 3875 / Jun '98 / Sugar Hill

☐ SKIP, HOP AND WOBBLE (Douglas, Jerry & Russ Barenberg/Edgar Meyer)
SHCD 3817 / Sep '96 / Sugar Hill

☐ SLIDE RULE
Ride the wild turkey / Pearlie Mae / When papa played the dobro / We hide and seek / Shoulder to shoulder / Uncle Sam / It's a beautiful life / I don't believe you've met my baby / Rain on Oliviatown / Hey Joe / New day medley / Shenandoah breakdown
SHCD 3797 / Jul '92 / Sugar Hill

☐ UNDER THE WIRE
TOB / Dhaka rock / Time gone by / Monroe's hornpipe / Before the blues / Trip to Kilkerrin / Grant's corner / Redhill / Two friends / New day
SHCD 3831 / Apr '95 / Sugar Hill

☐ YONDER (Douglas, Jerry & Peter Rowan)
Wayside tavern / Cannonball blues / Lullaby of the leaves / Tuck away my lonesome blues / Texas Rangers / Can't get there from here / Tribulations / When you and I were young Maggie / Girl in the blue velvet band / Chicka-li-lee-lo / You taught me how to lose / Where angels weep
SHCD 3847 / 27 Apr '98 / Sugar Hill

Douglas, John

☐ SCOTTISH LOVE SONGS
Until my heart stands still / My love is like a red red rose / Culzean Bay / Flow gently sweet Afton / Ye banks and braes o' bonnie Doon / Skye boat song / Loch Lomond / Roamin' in the gloamin' / Jean / Down in the glen / Bonnie lass o'Fyvie / Almost like being in love / Heather on the hill / Crooked bawbee
LCCD 004 / '89 / Lapwing

Douglas, Johnny

☐ IT'S MAGIC (Douglas, Johnny Strings)
All the things you are / Only love / Music of the night / It's magic / At this time of year / Sleepy shores / Warsaw concerto / Dulcima / Secret love / Dream of Olwen / Birthday waltz / Time / Quiet nights and quiet stars / Moonlight serenade / Windows of Paris / I can tell by the look in your eye
DLCD 115 / Apr '95 / Dulcima

☐ MORE ROMANCE WITH THE CLASSICS (Douglas, Johnny Strings)
Swan / Eighteenth variation from a Rhapsody on a theme of Paganini / Serenade / Piano concerto no.2 / Adagio / Romance no. 2 / Dreaming / Intermezzo from Cavalleria Rusticana / Swan lake / Spring song / Requiem for a love affair / Moonlight sonata / Symphony No. 5 / Romeo and Juliet / Sonata in D
DLCD 105 / Sep '88 / Dulcima

☐ ON SCREEN (Douglas, Johnny Strings)
Days of wine and roses / Gigi / Call me irresponsible / Summer knows / Laura / Dungeons and dragons / Like someone in love / Affair to remember / Smile / Young at heart / Railway children / As time goes by / Dulcima / Somewhere in time / Way we were
DLCD 110 / May '91 / Dulcima

☐ ON STAGE (Douglas, Johnny Strings)
I could write a book / Bali Ha'i / Tap your troubles away / Hey there / All I ask of you / Ascot Gavotte / If I loved you / Sweetest sounds / I won't send roses / Stranger in paradise / Where or when / Heather on the hill / I have dreamed / Try to remember / Love changes everything
DLCD 109 / Oct '90 / Dulcima

☐ ROMANCING WITH THE CLASSICS
Melody in f / Fantaisie impromptu / Andante / Consolation no.3 / Lullaby / Clair de lune / Romance / Nocturne no. 2 (chopin) / Piano concerto / Etude no.3 in e major op 10 'tristesse' (chopin) / L'inverno / Return to mijas / Chant sans paroles / Ballade op.23 / Romance (spanish folk song) / Barcarolle (the seasons - june)
DLCD 103 / May '94 / Dulcima

Douglas, K.C.

☐ BIG ROAD BLUES
Big road blues / Buck dance / Tore your playhouse down / Whisky headed woman / Catfish blues / Howlin' blues / Kansas City blues / Bottle up and go / KC blues / Key to the highway
OBCCD 569 / Oct '95 / Original Blues Classics

☐ KC'S BLUES
Broken heart / Hen house blues / Wake up, workin' woman / Rootin' ground hog / Meanest woman / Born in the country / Love me all night long / Tell me / No more cryin' / K.c.'s doctor blues / You got a good thing now / Watch dog blues
OBCCD 533 / Nov '92 / Original Blues Classics

Douglass, Greg

☐ MAELSTROM
TX 2007CD / Jan '94 / Taxim

Doumbia, Mamadou

☐ YAFA (Doumbia, Mamadou & Mandinka)
JCD 90132 / May '97 / JVC

Dour, Yann

☐ JOB DAOULAS
CAR 013CD / Apr '95 / Diffusion Breizh

Dove

☐ WRECKING BALL
LF 041CD / Nov '92 / Lost & Found

Dove Shack

☐ THIS IS THE SHACK
5279332 / Oct '95 / RAL

Dover, Connie

☐ IF EVER I RETURN
TPMD 301 / May '98 / Taylor Park

☐ SOMEBODY
TPMD 101 / May '98 / Taylor Park

☐ WISHING WELL
TPMD 201 / May '98 / Taylor Park

Dowd, Johnny

☐ WRONG SIDE OF MEMPHIS, THE
Murder / Papa oh papa / Ft Worth Texas / One way / Just like a dog / Average guy / Ballad of Frank and Jesse James / Idle conservation / Wages of sin / John Deere yeller / Thanksgiving day / Heavenly feast / First there was / I don't exist / Welcome Jesus
MRCD 193 / Jun '98 / Munich

Dowling Dowling & Sproule

☐ THOUSAND FAREWELLS, A
CM 001CD / Dec '97 / Cottage Music

Dowling, Leslie Rae

☐ UNBOUNDED WATERS
4509971082 / Aug '94 / Warner Bros.

Dowling, Mike

☐ BEATS WORKIN'
Police dog blues / Train that carried my girl from town / Beats workin' / DW Washburn / Ace in the hole / Jan's song / Louis Collins / Lonely at the bottom / Jitterbug waltz / Bottleneck march / Nothin' could be better / Jump children
SCR 46 / Feb '97 / Strictly Country

☐ SWAMP DOG BLUES
SCR 39 / Sep '95 / Strictly Country

Down But Not Out

☐ CEMETERY CONFINEMENT
IS 889950CD / 13 Oct '97 / I Scream Music

Down By Law

☐ BLUE
E 864192 / Nov '92 / Epitaph

☐ LAST OF THE SHARPSHOOTERS
USA today / No equalizer / Call to arms / Gun of '96 / Get out / Burning heart / Question marks and periods / Urban napalm / DJG / Concrete times / No one gets away / Last goodbye / Factory day / Cool crowd / Self destruction
65012 / Aug '97 / Epitaph

Down Home Jazzband

☐ PADDLE WHEELIN' ALONG
SOSCD 1300 / Jul '96 / Stomp Off

☐ RAGS TURK MURPHY STYLE
SOSCD 1316 / Feb '98 / Stomp Off

Down Low

☐ IT AIN'T OVER
KTR 100052 / Nov '97 / K-Town

Down To Reality

☐ PERVERT INHUMANITY
LF 270CD / May '97 / Lost & Found

Down To The Bone

☐ FROM MANHATTAN TO STATEN
Staten island groove / Brooklyn heights / Savour the flavour / Meesli brown / Yo mama's so phat / Touch of voodoo / 17 mile drive / Carliot's way / 3 days in Manhattan / On the corner of Darcy street
IBCD 3 / Nov '96 / Internal Bass

Down Town Jazzband

☐ DOWN TOWN HIGHLIGHTS (2CD Set)
Tears / Bird of Bleekerstreet / Knock out stomp / On the street where you live / Jada / Song of the islands / Saint Louis blues / Muskrat ramble / Third little girl / Cheerin' rag / You must have been a beautiful baby / Eurovision blues / Down town blues / 1919 Rag / I'm coming Virginia / I've got what it takes / Royal garden blues / Mame / Thinking blues / Mabel's dream / As long as I live / Change / Buddy's habbits / Kenia blues / Pearls / Wouldn't it be lovely / Jazz me blues / New Orleans function / Little bird / Lonesome road / Psychotechnical change / High society / Basin Street blues / Wolga song / St James infirmary / Baboon rag / Jamie's blues / Potato head blues / Do you know what it means to Miss New Orleans / New Orleans stomp / John's boogie / King Porter stomp
CDTTD 606 / Apr '96 / Timeless Jazz

Downchild

☐ GONE FISHING
SP 1139CD / Oct '93 / Stony Plain

Downes, Bob

☐ SONGS FOR MOTHER EARTH
SACD 90773 / Aug '97 / Sacral

Downes, David

☐ PAVILION
WCL 11006 / May '94 / White Cloud

☐ RUSTED WHEEL OF THINGS, THE
WCL 110112 / May '95 / White Cloud

Downes, Geoffrey

☐ EVOLUTION
BP 215CD / Jun '96 / Blueprint

☐ LIGHT PROGRAM, THE
Ethnic dance / East West / Urbanology / Symphonie electronique / Oceania electronique
BP 216CD / Mar '96 / Blueprint

☐ VOX HUMANA
Tears / Video killed the radio star / Roads of destiny / Plastic age / Ave Maria / Network / All of the time / Concerto / Satellite blues / England / Moon under the water / White car / Adagio
BP 214CD / Oct '95 / Blueprint

Downes, Paul

☐ OVERDUE
HTDCD 55 / Mar '96 / HTD

Downey, Morton

☐ IRISH NIGHTINGALE, THE
CDAJA 5173 / May '96 / Living Era

Downing, 'Big' Al

☐ BACK TO MY ROOTS
RCCD 3026 / Oct '97 / Rollercoaster

Downing, Will

☐ DREAM FULFILLED, A
She / I'll wait / Giving my all to you / I try / For all we know / Something's going on / Don't make me wait / I go crazy / No love intended / World is a ghetto
IMCD 212 / Mar '96 / 4th & Broadway

☐ LOVE'S THE PLACE TO BE
There's no living without you / Sailing on a dream / One moment / Nothing has ever felt like this / Love's the place to be / Lover's paradise / Everything to me / Do you still love me / Hey girl / Break up to make up / That's all
IMCD 218 / Mar '96 / 4th & Broadway

☐ MOODS
BRCD 612 / Nov '95 / 4th & Broadway

☐ WILL DOWNING
In my dreams / Do you / Free / Love supreme / Security / Set me free / Sending out an SOS / Dancing in the moonlight / Do you remember love
IMCD 190 / Mar '94 / Island

Downliners Sect

☐ BIRTH OF SUAVE, THE
HOG2 / Sep '94 / Hangman's Daughter

☐ SAVAGE RETURN
Bad girls looking for fun / Piccadilly run / Ain't I got you / Hard case / Midnight call / Pan American boogie / Eel pie memories / Down the road apiece / Talking 'bout you / Studio 51 / Bad penny / Who do you love / Cadillac / Bye bye Johnny / Just like I treat you / Before you accuse me
CDKVL 9033 / May '94 / Kingdom

☐ SHOWBIZ
Frustration / Wild time / Red hot mama / Mismanagement / Richmond rhythm and blues / Downloading / Showbiz / Break up / Out of school / Playing my guitar / Blue coup de ville / Loose ends / Blue night / Love is blind / Let's ride
IGOCD 2084 / Jun '98 / Indigo

☐ SINGLES A'S AND B'S
Cadillac / Roll over Beethoven / Beautiful Delilah / Shame shame shame / Green onions / Nursery rhymes / Baby what's wrong / Be a sect maniac / Little Egypt / Sect appeal / Find out what's happening / Insecticide / Wreck of ol' 97 / Leader of the sect / I want my baby back / Midnight hour / Now she's dead / I got mine / Waiting in heaven somewhere / Bad storm coming / Lonely and blue / All night worker / He was a square / Glendora / I'll find out / Cost of living / Everything I've got to give / I can't get away from you / Roses
SEECD 398 / May '97 / See For Miles

Download

☐ EYES OF STANLEY PAIN
8522502 / May '96 / Westcom

☐ III
38543812 / 9 Feb '98 / Offbeat

☐ SIDEWINDER
07322472 / May '96 / Westcom

Downset

☐ DO WE SPEAK A DEAD LANGUAGE
Intro / Empower / Eyes shut tight / Keep on breathing / Hurl a stone / Fire / Touch / Against the spirits / Sickness / Pocket full of fatcaps / Sangre de mis manos / Horrifying / Permanent days unmoving / Ashes in hand / Sickness (Reprise)
5324162 / Jun '96 / Talkin' Loud

☐ DOWNSET
Anger / Ritual / Take 'em out / Prostitutionalized / Downset / My American prayer / Holding hands / About to blast / Breed the killer / Dying of thirst
5188802 / 15 Sep '97 / Mercury

Dowsett, Janet

☐ KALEIDOSCOPE
I could have danced all night / Groovy kind of love / Tea for two / Water fountain / Splanky / Pavanne / Elizabethan serenade / Disney medley / Dizzy fingers / Aranjuez mon amour / Walking in the sunshine / Adagio for organ and strings in G minor / Hello Dolly/Mame / West Side story medley / Prelude in classic style / Forgotten dreams
CDGRS 1259 / Feb '95 / Grosvenor

Doy, Carl

☐ PIANO BY CANDLELIGHT VOL.1
NELCD 101 / Aug '93 / Timbuktu

☐ PIANO BY CANDLELIGHT VOL.2
NELCD 102 / Aug '93 / Timbuktu

☐ PIANO BY CANDLELIGHT VOL.3
NELCD 103 / Aug '93 / Timbuktu

Doyle, Matthew

☐ LYREBIRD
150232 / Aug '96 / Celestial Harmonies

Doyle, Roger

☐ BABEL VOL.1
SIDO 001CD / Oct '96 / Silver Door

☐ BABEL VOL.2
Entry level 1 / Mr. Brady's room / Temple music (Earth to Earth) / Yunnus / Entry level 2 / Dressing room / Concert music - pagoda charm / Mansard / Squat
SIDO 002CD / Jul '97 / Silver Door

Dp-Sol

☐ LIVE IN OSLO
TSF 9006 / Apr '95 / Play It Again Sam

Dr. & The Medics

☐ INSTANT HEAVEN
MAMA 005 / May '96 / Madman

Dr. Alban

☐ SECOND EDITION
74321135652 / Apr '93 / Arista

Dr. Alimantado

☐ BEST DRESSED CHICKEN IN TOWN
Gimme mi gun / Plead I cause / Poison flour / Ride on / Just the other day / Best dressed chicken in town / Unitone skank / I killed the barber / Ital galore / I am the greatest says Muhammed Ali / Johnny was a baker / Tribute to the dark / Can't conquer natty dreadlock / I shall fear no evil
KMCD 1 / May '97 / Keyman

☐ BORN FOR A PURPOSE
Chant to Jah / Return of Muhammed Ali / Sons of thunder / Dreadlocks dread / Call on Jah / Born for a purpose / Careless Ethiopians repent / Oil crisis / Sitting in the park / Marriage licence
GRELCD 22 / Jul '87 / Greensleeves

☐ IN THE MIX
In the mix / In the kingdom of dub / My mother's eyes in my eyes / Dub eyes / Memories buy the dub / Whirl delight / Raiders of the dub art / Dubin it easy / Dub at high noon / For a few dub more
KMCD 003 / Oct '88 / Keyman

☐ KING'S BREAD
Just because a bit of bread / Marcus garvey school / Babylon let I go / Jah loving feeling / Jah love forever / Mama mama / Conscious man / Zion steppers / Find the one / Oh this world / Love mama mama dub chapter 2 / Jah love forever dub chapter 2 / Babylon let I go dub chapter 2
ISDACD 5000 / Apr '94 / Keyman

☐ LOVE IS
Stop yer fighting / Stop yer fighting / Go deh natty / Jah jah great / Step upon u prophecy / Love is / Mek a little move / Satta in the park / She wreng ep
KMCD 1001 / Nov '83 / Keyman

☐ PRIVILEGED FEW
Privileged few / She used to live next door (sha ba da ba day) / Come into my life / New kinda dick / Na go mek (dem buss I shhut) / Gift of god (cheer up) / Where is jah love / Jah pon mi mind
KMCD 009 / Nov '94 / Keyman

☐ REGGAE REVUE VOL.1
Riding high on a windy day / No more heartache / Duke of earl / Playfool / Zion gates / Tonight / Fatty fatty / Happy go lucky girl / Same song / Country boy
KMCD 002 / Oct '88 / Keyman

☐ WONDERFUL TIME
KMCD 006 / 27 Jul '98 / Keyman

Dr. Brown

☐ DREAMSCAPE
GRCD 013 / 23 Mar '98 / Garageland

Dr. Didg

☐ OUT OF THE WOODS
Street music / Devon / Easy / King tut / Ever increasing circles / Brolga / Suntan / Rave on / Say what you like / Under the influence
HNCD 1384 / Apr '95 / Hannibal

☐ SEROTONALITY
Son of Tut / Later / Serotonality / Retro rockets / Bob's clouds / Bouncy / Made ya mine / My little pony / Brand new shoes / Whirligig
HNCD 1406 / 16 Feb '98 / Hannibal

Dr. Dixie

☐ BEST OF DOCTOR DIXIE JAZZ BAND (Dr. Dixie Jazz Band)
CDTTD 521 / Jan '88 / Timeless Traditional

Dr. Dre

☐ AFTERMATH (Various Artists)
Aftermath (intro) / East coast, west coast killas: *Group Therapy* / Sh'tin' on the world: *Mel Man* / Blunt time: *RBX* / Been there done that: *Dr. Dre* / Choices: *Summerson, Kim* / As the world keeps turning: *Miscellaneous* / STR-8 gone: *King T* / Please: *Wilcher, Maurice* / Do 4 love: *Lockhart, Jheryl* / Sexy dance: *RC* / No second chance: *Whoz Who* / Lyrical assault weapon: *Sharief* / Nationowl: *Nowl* / Fame: *RC*
IND 90044 / Dec '96 / Interscope

☐ CHRONIC, THE
Chronic / Fuck wit Dre day (and everybody's celebratin') / Let me ride / Day the niggaz took over / Nuthin' but a G thang / Deeez nuuuts / Li'l ghetto boy / Nigga witta gun / Rat-tat-tat-tat / Twenty dollar sack pyramid / Lyrical gangbang / High powered / Doctor's office / Stranded on death row / Roach (the chronic outro)
IND 57128 / Feb '97 / Interscope

Dr. Feelgood

☐ 25 YEARS OF DR. FEELGOOD (2CD Set)
She does it right / I don't mind / All through the city / Keep it out of sight / Roxette / I can tell / Sneakin' suspicion / Back in the night / Going back home / Riot in cell block No.9 / She's a wind up / That's it, I quit / Nighttime / Milk and alcohol / Put him out of your mind / Shotgun blues / No mo do yakamo / Jumping from love to love / Violent love / Rat race / Crazy 'bout girls / Dangerous / Mad man blues / Dimples / Hunting shooting fishing / See you later alligator / King for a day / Baby Jane / Sugar turns to alcohol / Down by the jetty blues / Double crossed / Wolfman callin' / One step forward / Roadrunner / Down at the doctors / Heart of the city / World keeps turning / Instinct to survive / Going out west / You got me
GRAND 20 / May '97 / Grand

☐ AS IT HAPPENS
Take a tip / Every kind of vice / Down at the doctors / Baby Jane / Sugar shaker / Things get better / She's a windup / Ninety nine and a half (won't do) / Buddy Buddy friends / Milk and alcohol / Matchbox / As long as the price is right / Night time / Riot in cell block 9 / Blues had a baby and they named it rock 'n' roll
GRANDCD 15 / Sep '95 / Grand

☐ BE SEEING YOU
Ninety nine and a half (won't do) / She's a wind up / I thought I had it made / I don't wanna know / That's it I quit / As long as the price is right / Hi rise / My buddy buddy friends / Blues had a baby and they named it rock 'n' roll / Looking back / Sixty minutes
GRANDCD 14 / Sep '95 / Grand

☐ BRILLEAUX
I love you so you're mine / You've got my number / Big enough / Don't wait up / Get rhythm / Where is the next one / Play dirty / Grow too old / Rough ride / I'm a real man / Come over here / Take what you can get
GRANDCD 04 / Sep '95 / Grand

☐ CASE OF THE SHAKES, A
Jumping from love to love / Going some place else / Best in the world / Punch drunk / King for a day / Violent love / No mo do yakamo / Love hound / Coming to you / Who's winning / Drives me wild / Case of the shakes
GRANDCD 10 / Sep '95 / Grand

☐ CENTENARY COLLECTION, THE (The Best Of Dr. Feelgood)
She does it right / Route 66 / Roxette / Sneakin' suspicion / She's a wind up / Baby Jane / Down at the doctors / Night time / Milk and alcohol / Looking back / I'm a man / As long as the price is right / Hong Kong money / Jumping from love to love / Violent love / Blues had a baby and they called it rock'n'roll / Tequila / Going back home
CTMCD 335 / 8 Sep '97 / EMI

☐ CLASSIC
Hunting shooting fishing / Break these chains / Heartbeat / (I wanna) make love to you / Hurricane / Quit while you're behind / Nothing like it / Spy Vs. spy / Highway 61 / Crack me up
GRANDCD 11 / Sep '95 / Grand

☐ DOCTOR'S ORDERS
Close but no cigar / So long / You don't love me / My way / Neighbour, neighbour / Talk of the devil / Hit, git and split / I can't be satisfied / Saturday night fish fry / Drivin' wheel / It ain't right / I don't worry about a thing / She's in the middle / Dangerous
GRANDCD 06 / Sep '95 / Grand

☐ DOWN AT THE DOCTORS
If my baby quit me / Styrofoam / Tanqueray / Roadrunner / Wolfman callin' / Double crossed / One step forward / Mojo workin' / Milk and alcohol / Down at the doctors / Freddie's footsteps / Heart of the city
GRANDCD 18 / Sep '95 / Grand

☐ DOWN BY THE JETTY
She does it right / Boom boom / More I give / One weekend / I don't mind / Twenty yards behind / Keep it out of sight / All through the city / Cheque book / Oyeh / Bony Moronie / Tequila
GRANDCD 05 / Sep '95 / Grand

☐ FAST WOMEN AND SLOW HORSES
She's the one / Sweet sweet lovin' (gone sour on me) / Trying to live my life without you / Rat race / Baby jump / Crazy about girls / Sugar bowl / Educated fool / Bum's rush / Baby why do you treat me this way / Beautiful Delilah / Monkey
GRANDCD 03 / Sep '95 / Grand

☐ FEELGOOD FACTOR, THE
Feelgood factor / Tanqueray / Tell me no lies / Styrofoam / I'm in the mood for you / Double crossed / Lying about the blues / She moves me / Wolfman callin' / One step forward / One to ten / Fool for you
GRANDCD 17 / Sep '95 / Grand

☐ LET IT ROLL
Java blues / Feels good / Put him out of your mind / Bend your ear / Hong Kong money / Keeka smeeka / Shotgun / Pretty face / Ridin' on the L and N / Drop everything and run
GRANDCD 07 / Sep '95 / Grand

☐ LIVE IN LONDON
King for a day / As long as the price is right / Baby Jane / See you later alligator / You upset me / She does it right / Back in the night
GRANDCD 08 / Sep '95 / Grand

☐ LOOKING BACK (5CD Set)
Roxette / All through the city / Cheque book / 20 yards behind / She does it right / Bonie moronie/ Tequila / Going back home / You shouldn't call the doctor (if you can't afford the pills / I can tell / Back in the night / I'm a man / I don't mind / I'm a hog for you baby / Checkin' up on my baby / Stupidity / Johnny B Goode / Lights out / You'll be mine / Walking on the edge / Hey Mama keep your big mouth shut / Nothin' shakin' (but the leaves on the trees) / Sneakin' suspicion / She's a windup / Looking back / 99 and a half won't do / Baby Jane / As long as the price is right / Down at the doctors / Take a tip / Every kind of vice / Milk and alcohol / Sugar shaker / Night time / Riot in cell block 9 / My buddy buddy friends / Great balls of fire / Pretty face / Put him out of your mind / Java blue / Hong Kong money / No mo do Yakamo / Jumping from love to love / Violent love / Shotgun blues / Waiting for Saturday night / Trying to live my life without love / She's the one / Crazy about girls / Monkey / Rat race / You don't love me / She's in the middle / Dangerous / I can't be satisfied / Close but no cigar / My way / Rock me baby / Tore down / Dust my broom / I love you so you're mine / Don't wait up / Come over here / Get rhythm / I'm a real man / See you later alligator / Quit while you're behind / Hunting shooting fishing / (I wanna) Make love to you / Mad man blues / King for a day / Primo blues / Standing at the crossroads again / Two times nine / Down by the jetty blues / No time / Wolfman calling / Feelgood factor / If my baby quits me / Roadrunner / One step forward / Mojo workin' / Heart of the city / Route 66 / Keep it out of sight / Homeward / You upset me baby / Down at the (other) doctor's / Love hound / Don't take but a few minutes / Eileen / Touch of class / She's got her eyes on you / Solitary blues / Looking at you
ACDFEEL 195 / Oct '95 / Liberty

☐ MAD MAN BLUES
Dust my broom / Something you got / Dimples / Living on the highway / Tore down / Madman blues / I've got news for you / My babe / Can't find the lady / Rock me baby
GRANDCD 02 / Sep '95 / Grand

☐ MALPRACTICE
I can tell / Going back home / Back in the night / Another man / Rollin' and tumblin' / Don't let your daddy know / Watch your step / Don't you just know it / Riot in cell block 9 / Because you're mine / You shouldn't call the doctor
GRANDCD 09 / Sep '95 / Grand

☐ ON THE JOB
Drives me wild / Java blues / Jumping from love to love / Pretty face / Nomo do yakamo / Love hound / Best in the world / Who's winning / Ridin' on the L 'n' N / Case of the shakes / Shotgun blues / Goodnight Vienna
GRANDCD 16 / Sep '95 / Grand

☐ ON THE ROAD AGAIN
Wine, women and whisky / Sweet Louise / World keeps turning / On the road again / Instinct to survive / Mellow down easy / Going out West / Cheap at half the price / Second opinion / What am I to believe / Repo man / You got me
GRAND 19 / Aug '96 / Grand

☐ PRIMO
Heart of the city / My sugar turns to alcohol / Going down / No time / World in a jug / If my baby quit me / Primo blues / Standing at the crossroads again / Been down so long / Don't worry baby / Down by the jetty blues / Two times nine
GRANDCD 12 / Sep '95 / Grand

☐ PRIVATE PRACTICE
Down at the doctors / Every kind of vice / Things get better / Milk and alcohol / Night time / Let's have a party / Take a tip / It wasn't me / Greaseball / Sugar shaker
GRANDCD 01 / Sep '95 / Grand

☐ SINGLES - THE UA YEARS
Roxette / She does it right / Back in the night / Going back home / Riot in cell block 9 / Sneakin' suspicion / She's a wind up / Baby Jane / Down at the doctors / Milk and alcohol / As long as the price is right / Put him out of your mind / Hong Kong money / No mo do yakamo / Jumping from love to love / Violent love / Waiting for Saturday night / Monkey / Trying to live my life without you / Crazy about girls / My way / Madman blues / See you later alligator / Hunting shooting fishing / Don't wait up / Milk and alcohol (New recipe)
CDEM 1332 / May '89 / Liberty

☐ SNEAKIN' SUSPICION
Sneakin' suspicion / Paradise / Nothin' shakin' (but the leaves on the trees) / Time and the devil / Lights out / Lucky seven / All my love / You'll be mine / Walking on the edge / Hey mama keep your mouth shut
GRANDCD 13 / Sep '95 / Grand

☐ STUPIDITY
Talking about you / Twenty yards behind / Stupidity / All through the city / I'm a man / Walking the dog / She does it right / Going back home / I don't mind / Back in the night / I'm a hog for you baby / Checkin' up on my baby / Roxette / Riot in cell block no.9 / Johnny B. Goode
GRANDCD 21 / Jun '98 / Grand

Dr. Fink

☐ HOOKED ON THE BEATLES (The Ultimate Fab Four Tribute Album) (Dr. Fink & The Mystery Band)
Please please me / All my loving / Eight days a week / Hard day's night / Can't buy me love / Help / Ticket to ride / Day tripper / Paperback writer / Got to get you into my life / Lady Madonna / Drive my car / Nowhere man / Taxman / Eleanor Rigby / Sgt. Pepper's Lonely Hearts Club Band / Lucy in the sky with diamonds / Magical mystery tour / I am the walrus / Strawberry fields forever / Ob la di ob la da / Get back / Back in the USSR / Polythene Pam / She came in through the bathroom window / If I fell / Michelle / Yesterday / Blackbird / Hey Jude / End
ECD 3227 / Jun '97 / K-Tel

☐ I'M IN THE MOOD FOR THE BEATLES (Dr. Fink & The Mystery Band)
LPCD 1024 / Apr '94 / Disky

Dr. Hector

☐ BAD CONNECTION (Dr. Hector & The Groove Injectors)
Fever / Mr. Right Now / High cost of living / Safe in your arms again / Midnight run / Eyes of a child / Bad connection / No mercy at all / Doing all the wrong things right / City lights / Fool like me / Psychotherapy
KS 025 / May '98 / King Snake

Dr. Hook

☐ 20 GREAT LOVE SONGS
Better love next time / Sharing the night together / Sexy eyes / When you're in love with a beautiful woman / If not you / Little bit more / Oh Jesse / Years from now / Sweetest of all / In over my head / I don't feel much like smilin' / I don't want to be alone tonight / Only sixteen / All the time in the world / Everybody's makin' it big but me / Storms never last / More like the movies / What about you / Couple more years / Making love and music
LS 866622 / 2 Feb '98 / Disky

☐ DR. HOOK (Dr. Hook & The Medicine Show)
Sylvia's mother / Marie Lavauz / Sing me a rainbow / Hey Lady Godiva / Four years older than me / Kiss it away / Making it natural / I call that true love / When she cries / Judy / Mama I'll sing one song for you
4805222 / May '95 / Columbia

☐ MAKING LOVE AND MUSIC - THE 1976-79 RECORDINGS
When you're in love with a beautiful woman / Little bit more / If not you / Up on the mountain / Bad eye Bill / Who dat / Let the loose end drag / I'm a lamb / Making love and music / Radio / Everybody loves me / Oh Jesse / Jungle in the zoo / More like the movies / I don't feel much like smilin' / Mountain Mary / Leviate / Dooley Jones / Sexy energy / Love monster
CDMFP 5979 / Apr '93 / Music For Pleasure

☐ PLEASURE AND PAIN (The History Of Dr. Hook/3CD Set)
Sylvia's mother / Cover of the 'Rolling Stone' / Ballad of Lucy Jordon / Levitate / Only sixteen / I got stoned and missed it / Millionaire / Everybody's makin' it big but me / Cooky and Lila / Everybody loves me / More like the movies / Little bit more / If not you / Radio / Jungle to the zoo / What about you / I need the high / Couple more years / Making love and music / Lay too low too long / Sleeping late / Walk right in / Let the loose end drag / I'm a lamb / Sharing the night together / Sweetest of all / Storms never last / I don't want to be alone tonight / Knowing she's there / Clyde / When you're in love with a beautiful woman / I gave her comfort / You make my pants want to get up and dance / Better love next time / In over my head / Sexy eyes / Oh Jessie / Years from now / I don't feel much like smilin' / What do you want / Love monster / Mountain Mary / Girls can get it / Baby makes her blue jeans talk / Feels good / I couldn't believe / Rings of grass / Stuck on the wrong side of love / That plane / Lonely man / I never got to know her / You can't take it with you / I've been him / Bread upon the water / Here comes the blues again / Stagolee / Shadow knows / No.1 rock radio station / Pleasure and pain / There's a light / Walkin' my cat named dog / Carry me Carrie / Oo poo pa doo
HOOKBOX 1 / Oct '96 / Capitol

☐ SHARING THE NIGHT TOGETHER
Better love next time / Sharing the night together / Sexy eyes / When you're in love with a beautiful woman / If not you / Little bit more / Oh Jesse / Years from now / Sweetest of all / In over my head / I don't feel much like smilin' / I don't wanna be alone tonight / Only sixteen / All the time in the world / Everybody is making it big but me / Storms never last / More like the movies / What about you / Couple more years / Makin' love and music
CDGOLD 1051 / Jul '96 / EMI Gold

☐ VERY BEST OF DR. HOOK & RAY SAWYER, THE (Dr. Hook & Ray Sawyer)
Sylvia's mother / When your in love with a beautiful woman / Baby makes her blue jeans talk / Everyone is making it big but me / Only sixteen / Sexy eyes / Walk right in / Little bit more / Cover of the rolling stones / Sharing the night together / Queen of the silver dollar / Soup stone
10302 / Oct '97 / Go On Deluxe

Dr. Israel

☐ 7 TALES OF ISRAEL
WSCD 009 / Aug '96 / Word Sound Recordings

☐ NEXT STEP (Dr. Israel & Brooklyn Jungle Soundsystem)
BKA 0003 / 1 Dec '97 / Baraka Foundation

Dr. John

☐ AFTERGLOW
I know what I've got / Gee baby ain't I good to you / I'm just a lucky so and so / Blue skies / So long / New York City blues / Tell me you'll wait for me / There must be a better world somewhere / I still think about you / I'm confessin' that I love you
GRB 70002 / Jun '95 / GRP

☐ ANUTHA ZONE
Zonata / Ki ya gris gris / Voices in my head / Hello God / John Gris / Party hellfire / I don't wanna know about evil / Anutha zone / I like ki yoka / Olive tree / Soulful warrior / Stroke / Sweet home New Orleans
4954902 / 8 Jun '98 / Parlophone

☐ BABYLON
Babylon / Glowin' / Black widow spider / Barefoot lady / Twilight zone / Patriotic flag waver / Lonesome guitar strangler
7567804382 / Feb '92 / Atco

☐ BRIGHTEST SMILE IN TOWN, THE
Saddled the cow / Boxcar boogie / Brightest smile in town / Waiting for a train / Monkey puzzle / Average kind of guy / Pretty Libby / Marie Le Veau / Come rain or come shine / Suite home New Orleans
FIENDCD 9 / Oct '90 / Demon

☐ CRAWFISH SAUCE
Crawfish soiree (bring your own) / Tipitina / In the night / Woman is the root of all evil / Time had come / Shoo raa / Zu zu man / Baldhead / Mean cheatin' woman / Make your own bed well / Little closer to my home / Della
AIMA 4CD / May '97 / Aim

☐ CUT ME WHILE I'M HOT
Time has come / Loser for you baby / Ear is on strike / Little closer to my home / I pulled the cover off you two lovers / Go ahead on / Just like a mirror / Bring your love / Make your own / She's just a square / Woman is the root of all evil / Mean cheatin' woman / Cat and mouse game / Shoo ra / Zu zu man / In the night / Tipitina / Bald head / Helpin' hand
CDTB 158 / Mar '95 / Thunderbolt

☐ DESITIVELY BONNAROO
Quitters never win / Stealin' / What comes around (goes around) / Me, you, loneliness / Mos' scocious / (Everybody wanna get rich) Rite away / Let's make a better world / R U 4 Real / Sing along song / Can't git enough / Go tell the people / Destitively bonnaroo
7567804412 / Dec '93 / Atco

☐ DOCTOR JOHN PLAYS MAC REBENNACK
Dorothy / Mac's boogie / Memories of Professor Longhair / Nearness of you / Delicado / Honey dripper / Big Mac / New island midnight / Saints / Pinetop / Silent night / Dance a la negres / Wade in the water
FIENDCD 1 / '88 / Demon

☐ DR. JOHN
GRP 7002 / Jun '95 / GRP

☐ DR. JOHN
AOP 64 / 6 Apr '98 / Dressed To Kill

☐ GOIN' BACK TO NEW ORLEANS
Litanie des saints / Careless love / My indian red / Milneburg joys / I thought I heard Buddy Bolden say / Basin Street blues / Didn't he ramble / Do you call that a buddy / How come my dog don't bark / Goodnight Irene / Fess up / Since I fell for you / (I'll be glad when you're dead) you rascal you / Cabbagehead / Goin' home tomorrow / Blue Monday / Scald dog medley / I can't go on / Goin' back to New Orleans
7599269402 / Mar '94 / Atco

☐ GRIS GRIS
Gris gris gumbo ya ya / Danse Kalinda ba doom / Mama roux / Danse fambeaux / Croker courtbullion / Jump sturdy / Walk on gilded splinters
7567804372 / Jan '95 / Atlantic

☐ GUMBO
Iko Iko / Blow wind blow / Big chief / Somebody changed the lock / Mess around / Let the good times roll / Junko partner / Stagger Lee / Tipitina / Those lonely lonely nights / Huey Smith medley / Little Liza Jane
7567803982 / Mar '93 / Atco

☐ HOLLYWOOD BE THY NAME
New Island soiree / Reggae doctor / Way you do the things you do / Swanee river boogie / Yesterday / Babylon / Back by the river / Medley / Hollywood be thy name / I wanna rock
BGOCD 62 / 17 Aug '98 / Beat Goes On

☐ IN A SENTIMENTAL MOOD
Makin' whoopee / Candy / Accentuate the positive / My buddy / In a sentimental mood / Black night / Don't let the sun catch you crying / Love for sale / More than you know
K 9258892 / Apr '89 / Atco

☐ IN THE RIGHT PLACE
Right place wrong time / Same old same old / Just the same / Qualified / Travelling mood / Peace brother peace / Life / Such a night / Shoo fly marches on / I been hoodood / Cold cold cold
7567803602 / Mar '93 / Atco

☐ LOSER FOR YOU BABY
Time had come / Loser for you baby / Ear is on strike / Little close to my home / I pulled the cover off you two lovers / New Orleans / Go ahead on / Just like a mirror / Bring your love / Bald head / Make your own
MM 006 / 1 Jun '98 / MagMid

☐ MASTERS, THE
In the night / Tipitina / Grass is greener / Did she mention my name / Shoo ra / Zu zu man / One night late / She's just a square / Mean cheatin' woman / Helpin' hand / Time had come / Loser for you baby / Ear is on strike / Little closer to home / I pulled the cover off you two lovers / New Orleans / Go ahead on / Just like a mirror / Bring your love / Make your own / Bald head
EABCD 077 / 30 Mar '98 / Eagle

☐ MOS'SCOCIOUS (Dr. John Anthology)
Bad neighborhood / Morgus the magnificent / Storm warning / Sahara / Down the road / Gris gris gumbo ya ya / Mama Roux / Jump sturdy / I walk on guilded splinters / Black widow spider / Lop garoo / Wash Mama wash / Mardi gras day / Familiar reality / Opening / Zu zu mamou / Mess around / Somebody changed the lock / Iko iko / Junko partner / Tipitina / Huey Smith medley / Right place wrong time / Travelling mood / Life / Such a night / I been hoodood / Cold cold cold / Quitters never win / What comes around (goes around) / Mos' scocious / Let's make a better world / Back by the river / I wanna rock / Memories of Professor Longhair / Honey dripper / Pretty libby / Makin' whoopee / Accentuate the positive / More than you know
8122714502 / Feb '94 / Atco

☐ REMEDIES
Loop garoo / What goes around / Wash Mama wash / Chippy, chippy / Mardi gras day / Angola anthem
7567804392 / Feb '91 / Atco

☐ SUCH A NIGHT (Live In London)
SPINCD 107 / Dec '97 / Spindrift

☐ SUN, MOON AND HERBS, THE
Black John the conqueror / Where ya at mule / Craney crow / Familiar reality / Opening / Pots on fiyo (file gumbo) / Who I got to fall on / Zu zu mamou / Familiar reality (reprise)
7567804402 / Jan '89 / Atco

☐ TELEVISION
Television / Lissen / Limbo / Witchy red / Only the shadow knows / Shut D Fonk up / Spaceship relationship / Hold it / Money / U lie too much / Same day service
GRM 40252 / 25 May '98 / GRP

☐ TRIPPIN' LIVE
EAGCD 003 / 25 Aug '97 / Eagle

☐ VERY BEST OF DR. JOHN, THE
Wash mama wash / Litanie des saints / Makin' whoopee / Accentuate the positive / Honey dripper / I walk on guilded splinters / Jump sturdy / Tipitina / Iko iko / Loop garoo / Junko partner / Goin' back to new orleans / Right place wrong time / Such a night / What comes around (goes around) / Mos' scocious / Qualified / Mama roux
9548335532 / May '95 / Atco

☐ VOODOO BLUES
Zu zu man / One late night / Mean cheatin' woman / Woman is the root of all evil / She's just a square / In the night / Tiptina / Shoo-ra / Bald headed / Trader John / Helpin' hand / Cat and mouse game
305982 / Apr '98 / Hallmark

☐ ZU ZU MAN
In the night / Tipitina / Grass is greener / Did she mention my name / Shoo ra / Zu zu man / One night late / She's just a square / Mean cheatin' woman / Helpin' hand
CDTB 069 / May '89 / Thunderbolt

Dr. K's Blues Band

☐ ROCK THE JOINT
I can't lose / Walkin' / Key to the highway / Crippled Clarence / Pet cream man / Feel so bad / Messin' with kid / Don't quit the man you love, for me / Rolty's banjo shuffle / Strobe lemming's lament / Lond distance call
SEECD 361 / Oct '92 / See For Miles

Dr. Nerve

☐ ARMED OBSERVATION/OUT OF BOMB FRESH
RUNE 38X / Apr '86 / Cuneiform

☐ EVERY SCREAMING EAR
RUNE 88 / Jun '97 / Cuneiform

Dr. Numa

☐ DR. NUMA
RA 012CD / Oct '96 / Radikal Ambience

Dr. Octagon

☐ DR. OCTAGON
Into / 3000 / I got to tell you / Earth people / No awareness / Technical difficulties / General hospital / Blue flowers / Visit to the gynaecologist / Bear witness / Dr. Octagon / Girl let me touch you / I'm destructive / Wild and crazy / Elective surgery / On production / Biology 101 / Waiting list
MW 046CD / Apr '96 / Mo Wax

☐ INSTRUMENTALYST
Blue flowers / Girl let me touch you / 3000 / Mosebumps / Tricknology 101 / I'm destructive / No awareness / Waiting list / On production / Technical difficulties / Catapillar / Wild 'n' crazy / Earth people / Dr. Octagon
MW 064CD / Nov '96 / Mo Wax

Dr. Robert

☐ OTHER FOLK
ROOTCD 1 / May '97 / Art Bus

Dr. Rockitt

☐ MUSIC OF SOUND
CLR 424CD / Oct '96 / Clear

Dr. Space Toad Experience

☐ DR. SPACE TOAD EXPERIENCE WITH CAP
BP 222CD / Sep '96 / Blueprint

Dr. Strangely Strange

☐ ALTERNATIVE MEDICINE
Lilty's / Darksome burn / Heat came down / James gang / Hale Bopp/Jig for Jack / Hames and traces / Wishing / Whatever happened to the blues / Too much of a good thing / Hard as nails / Planxty Roland / Epilog / Strange world / Pulp kayak
CDWIKD 177 / 3 Nov '97 / Big Beat

Drag

☐ CLASSIC CURVE
FSRC 004CD / 26 May '98 / Football Stars Record Club

Dragonfly

☐ DRAGONFLY
842970 / Sep '97 / EVA

☐ TIMESTREAM
SM 01 / 20 Apr '98 / Sweetmother

Dragonmilk

☐ WOLFMAN MACABRE
AACD 027 / 20 Apr '98 / Audio Archive

Dragons

☐ CHEERS TO ME
168222 / 25 May '98 / Nitro

Dragonsfire

☐ ROYAL ARRAY, A
Sumer is y-cumen in / Earl of Salisbury's Pavan and Galliard / Boar's head carol / Courtly capers: English dance tunes / Greensleeves / Come again - Sweet love doth now invite / Agincourt song / Woods so wilde / Now is the month of Maying / Blame not my lute / Ampleforth / Green grow'th the holly
URCD 102 / Jul '90 / Upbeat

Drags

☐ DRAGSPLOITATION
ES 110CD / Nov '95 / Estrus

☐ STOP ROCK 'N' ROLL
ES 1239CD / Aug '97 / Estrus

Drain

☐ HORROR WRESTLING
Stench / Smile / Mirrors eyes / Serve the shame / Unforgiving hours / Mind over body / Crucified / Don't mind / Crack the liars smile / Unreal
0630137742 / Apr '96 / East West

☐ OFFSPEED AND IN THERE
TR 49CD / Apr '96 / Trance

Drain Bramaged

☐ HAPPY DRUNX
KNR 117 / Jun '97 / Know

Draiocht

☐ DRUID & THE DREAMER, THE
CBM 006CD / Oct '93 / Cross Border Media

Drake, Nick

☐ BRYTER LAYTER
Introduction / Hazey Jane / At the chime of the city clock / One of these things first / Hazey Jane / Bryter layter / Fly / Poor boy / Northern sky / Sunday
IMCD 71 / '89 / Island

☐ FIVE LEAVES LEFT
Time has told me / River man / Three hours / Day is done / Way to blue / Cello song / Thoughts of Mary Jane / Man in a shed / Fruit tree / Saturday Sun
IMCD 8 / '89 / Island

☐ FRUIT TREE (4CD Set)
HNCD 5402 / Jun '96 / Hannibal

☐ PINK MOON
Pink moon / Place to be / Road / Which will / Horn / Things behind the sun / Know / Parasite / Ride / Harvest breed / From the morning
IMCD 94 / Feb '90 / Island

☐ TIME OF NO REPLY
Joey / Clothes of sand / May fair / I was made to love magic / Strange meetings II / Been smoking too long
HNCD 1318 / May '89 / Hannibal

☐ WAY TO BLUE (An Introduction To Nick Drake)
Cello song / Hazey Jane / Way to blue / Things behind the sun / River man / Poor boy / Time of no reply / From the morning / One of these things first / Northern sky / Which will / Time has told me / Pink moon / Black eyed dog / Fruit tree
IMCD 196 / May '94 / Island

Drake, Tony

☐ TEXTURE
Birth of love / These lips of gold / This is how much I love you / Cherish / Strangest dream / One / Haunting / In the hearts of angels / Night descends / Moisture/After the moment / These moments fade / Love's release / Texture
ELECTM 30CD / Nov '96 / New Electronica

Drama

☐ DRAMA
CDP 1046DD / Nov '97 / Pseudonym

Dramarama

☐ 10 FROM 5
Work for food / What are we gonna do / Last cigarette / Haven't got a clue / Shadowless heart / Some crazy dame / Would you like / Memo to Turner / It's still warm / Work for food (acoustic version)
3705615842 / Sep '93 / Chameleon

☐ BOX OFFICE BOMB
Steve and Edie / New dream / Whenever I'm with her / Spare change / 400 blows / Pumpin (my heart) / It's still warm / Out in the rain / Baby rhino's eye / Worse than being by myself / Modesty personified
ROSE 138CD / Jan '88 / New Rose

☐ CINEMA VERITE
ROSE 74CD / Nov '85 / New Rose

Dramatics

☐ BEST OF THE DRAMATICS, THE
Get up and get down / Thank you for your love / Whatcha see is whatcha get / In the rain / (Gimme some) good soul music / Fall in love, lady love / Devil is dope / You could become the very heart of me / Fell for you / Hey you get off my mountain / Beware the man with the candy in his hand / And I panicked / I dedicate my life to you / I made myself lonely / Highway to heaven / Toast to the fool
CDSXD 115 / Jul '97 / Stax

☐ WHATCHA SEE IS WHATCHA GET/ DRAMATIC EXPERIENCE, A
Get up and get down / Thank you for your love / Hot pants in the summertime / What'cha see is what'cha get / In the rain / Good soul music / Fall in love, lady love / Mary don't cha wanna / Devil is dope / You could become the very heart of me / Now you got me loving you / Fell for you / Jim, what's wrong with him / Hey you get off my mountain / Beautiful people / Beware of the man
CDSXD 963 / Jan '91 / Stax

Drambuie Kirkliston Pipe Band

☐ LINK WITH THE '45
King has landed in Moidart / Glenfinnan highland gathering / March of the Cameron men / Johnny Cope / Southward bound / Wae's me for Prince Charlie / Forty five revolution / Link with the '45 / Young pretender / White rose of Culloden / Skye boat song / Fugitive / Tribute to the lost souls / Will ye no' come back again
CDTRAX 084 / Apr '95 / Greentrax

Drame, Adama

☐ 30 YEARS OF DJEMBE
PS 65177 / Dec '96 / PlayaSound

☐ MANDINGO DRUMS
PS 65085 / Apr '92 / PlayaSound

☐ MANDINGO DRUMS VOL.2 (Drame, Adama & Foliba)
PS 65122 / Feb '94 / PlayaSound

Dranes, Arizona

☐ ARIZONA DRANES 1926-1929
DOCD 5186 / Oct '93 / Document

Dransfield

☐ FIDDLER'S DREAM
Up to now / Blacksmith / Alchemist and the pedlar / It's dark in here / Handsome meadow boy / Fool's song / Ballad of Dickie Lubber / Blacksmith / What will we tell them / Violin
ESMCD 462 / Jan '97 / Transatlantic

Dransfield, Robin

☐ UP TO NOW (A History Of Robin & Barry Dransfield/2CD Set) (Dransfield, Robin & Barry)
Rout of the blues / Trees they do grow high / Morpeth rant/Nancy / Lord of all I behold / Bold Nelson's praise/Princess Royal/Saddle the pony / Werewolf / Girl of dances / Cuckoo's nest / Up to now / Blacksmith / Alchemist and the pedlar / It's dark in here / Handsome meadow boy / Fool's song / Ballad of Dickie Lubber / What will we tell them / Violin / You can't change me now / Talcahuano girls / Conscript's farewell / Bogie's bonnie belle / Sligo fancy/Coleman's two halves / Seeds of love / Peggy Gordon / Banks of the sweet Dundee / Holmfirth anthem / Two ravens / Good ale for my money / Doctor Slime / Too much to do / Catch the morning dew / Fiddler's progress / O'Carolan's concerto / Tidewave / Spencer the rover / Be your own man / Daddy fox / Week before Easter / Irish session
FRDCD 18 / Jun '97 / Free Reed

Drax

☐ TALES FROM THE MENTAL PLANE
TROPE 013 / May '95 / Trope

Drayton, Luce

☐ SUICIDAL ANGEL
Dreamer / I said hey / Drown in you / Holding on alone / What about sky / Bitter blisters / La la la / All in vain / To be loved / Tears of our youth / Kiss the blues goodbye
0097984WHE / Jul '97 / What So Ever

Drazy Hoops

☐ STRAIGHT TO BLACK
SHMCD 5089 / 10 Aug '98 / Shimmy Disc

Dread & Fred

☐ IRON WORKS VOL.3
SHAKA 937CD / Mar '94 / Jah Shaka

Dread Knight

☐ ELECTRONIC BAND
TASTE 60CD / Aug '95 / Taste

Dread, Mikey

☐ MIKEY DREAD
MCCD 343 / 20 Apr '98 / Music Club

Dread Zeppelin

☐ FUN SESSIONS (Tortelvis Sings The Classics)
Baba O'Riley / Sunshine of your life / Born on the bayou / Light my fire / Smoke on the water / Freebird / Feel like making love / BBWAGS / Siute Judy blue eyes / Golden slumbers carry that weight the end
72787230042 / Jul '98 / Imago

Dread Zone

☐ 360 DEGREES
CRECD 162 / Oct '93 / Creation

☐ PERFORMANCE DEADZONE...LIVE
TTPCD 002 / Oct '94 / Totem

Dreadful Shadows

☐ BEYOND THE MAZE
CD 08561912 / 23 Feb '98 / SPV

☐ ESTRANGEMENT
SPV 08423612 / Jul '94 / SPV

Dreadful Snakes

☐ SNAKES ALIVE
ROUCD 177 / Jun '95 / Rounder

Dreadline

☐ BRAVEDANCES
CDSGP 0212 / Sep '96 / Prestige

Dreadzone

☐ BIOLOGICAL RADIO
Biological radio / Moving on / Third wave / Lost tribe / Earth angel / Messengers / Heat the pot / Alli Baba / Dream within a dream
CDV 2808 / 28 Jul '97 / Virgin

☐ SECOND LIGHT
Life, love and unity / Little Britain / Canterbury tale / Captain Dread / Cave of angels / Zion youth / One way / Shining path / Out of heaven
CDV 2778 / May '95 / Virgin

Dream

☐ DREAM, THE
Take your time / Tender touch / Makes no sense / All over again / Tipsy on the brink of love / You / Here is the love / Desires / Suzanne / Wonderful world / Last monday / Thirteen years / Here is the love
REVXD 143 / Apr '90 / Black

Dream Academy

☐ DREAM ACADEMY
Life in a northern town / Edge of forever / Johnny new light / In places on the run / This world / Bound to be / Moving on / Love parade / Party / One dream
7599252652 / Jan '96 / Blanco Y Negro

Dream City Film Club

☐ DREAM CITY FILM CLUB
Night of nights / Shit tinted shades / Pissboy / Because you wanted it / Filth dealer / Mama / Porno Paradiso / Situation desperate / Perfect piece of trash / Vague / If I die I die / 'Til the end of the world
BBQCD 191 / Jun '97 / Beggars Banquet

Dream Disciples

☐ CURE FOR PAIN, A
CR 00303CD / Oct '96 / Resurrection

☐ IN AMBER
In amber / Rememeber Bethany / Walk the wire / Mark 13 / Burn the sky / Dream is dead / Love letters / Sweet dreams / Where the weeping lie
DDICK 007CD / 10 Nov '97 / Dick Bros.

☐ SUB ATOMIC
CR 00666CD / 29 Sep '97 / Resurrection

☐ VEIL OF TEARS
Pray / Crimson white / Eternal / Resting place / Lights / Aradia
0020CR001 / Sep '96 / Carrion

Dream Sequence

☐ ENDLESS REFLECTION (Dream Sequence & Blake Baxter)
EFA 017802 / Jun '95 / Tresor

Dream State

☐ CLOCKWORK MANNEQUIN
Mannequin man / Alive in the rain / Innocence / Highway / Spirit in you / Rampage / My friend / Operator
ZUCD 1 / Mar '97 / Zukris

Dream Syndicate

☐ 3 & 1/2
NORM 156CD / Nov '93 / Normal

☐ DAY BEFORE WINE AND ROSES, THE
NORMAL 176CD / Dec '94 / Normal

☐ LOST TAPES 1985-88, THE
NORMAL 156CD / Mar '94 / Normal

☐ OUT OF THE GREY
Out of the grey / Forest for the trees / 50 in a 25 zone / Boston / Blood money / Slide away / Dying embers / Now I ride alone / Drinking problem / Dancing blind / You can't forget / Let it rain / Cinnamon girl / Ballad of Dwight Frye / Shake your hips / I won't forget / Lonely bull
NORMAL 184CD / Jul '97 / Normal

Dream Team

☐ DRUM 'N' BASS WORLD SERIES, THE
12 am / Suka DJ / Time / Check the tekniq / Switch / Dedicated / Rollin' raw / Survival of the fit / Mad / Insane / Click
JOK 25CD / Feb '97 / Joker

☐ TRILOGY
Sta warz: *Drum 'n' Bass Dream Team* / Switch: *Drum 'n' Bass Dream Team* / Kung fu: *Drum 'n' Bass Dream Team* / Lucky: *Drum 'n' Bass Dream Team* / Deal with the matter: *Drum 'n' Bass Dream Team* / Different: *Drum 'n' Bass Dream Team* / Coast 2 coast: *Drum 'n' Bass Dream Team* / Throat: *Drum 'n' Bass Dream Team* / Ladies and gentlemen: *Drum 'n' Bass Dream Team* / Da shit: *Drum 'n' Bass Dream Team*
JKSUBCD 6 / 27 Oct '97 / Suburban Base

Dream Theater

☐ AWAKE
Lie / 6:00 / Erotomania / Silent man / Lifting shadows off a dream / Scarred / Innocence faded / Mirror / Voices / Caught in a web / Space-dye vest
7567901262 / Oct '94 / Atlantic

☐ CHANGE OF SEASON, A
Song remains the same / Achilles last stand / Rover / Crimson sunrise / Carpe diem / Innocence / Cruise control / Lovin touchin squeezin / Carry on wayward son / In the flesh / Turn it on again / Perfect strangers / Love lies bleeding / Funeral for a friend / Crimson sunset / Inevitable summer / Another world / Darkest winters / Bohemian rhapsody
7559618422 / Sep '95 / Atlantic

☐ FALLING INTO INFINITY
New millennium / You not me / Peruvian skies / Hollow years / Burning my soul / Hells kitchen / Lines in the sand / Take away my pain / Just let me breathe / Anna Lee / Trial of tears
7559620602 / 20 Oct '97 / Elektra

☐ IMAGES AND WORDS
Pull me under / Another day / Take the time / Surrounded / Metropolis / Miracle and the sleeper / Under a glass moon / Wait for sleep / Learning to live
7567921482 / Feb '92 / Atlantic

☐ LIVE AT THE MARQUEE
Metropolis / Miracle and the sleeper / Fortune in lies / Bombay vindaloo / Surrounded / Pull me under / Killing hand / Another hand
7567922862 / Feb '92 / Atlantic

Dream Warriors

☐ AND NOW THE LEGACY BEGINS
Mr. Bibbinut spills his guts / My definition of a boombastic jazz style / Follow me not / Ludi / U never know a good thing till u lose it / And the legacy begins / Tune from the missing channel / Wash your face in my sink / Voyage through the multiverse / U could get arrested / Journey on / Face in the basin / Do not feed the alligators / Twelve sided dance / Maximum 60 lost in a dream
IMCD 204 / Apr '95 / Island

☐ MASTER PLAN, THE
Fear none / Era of Stay real / Here today gone tomorrow / Sound clash / Master plan / Float on / What do you want ladies / From the beginning / Test of purity / Luvz history lesson / Dem no ready / Who's the crook / First ya live / Times are changing / Sound clash
CTCD 56 / Jan '97 / Cooltempo

Dreamcatcher

☐ DREAMCATCHER
CIDM 1118 / May '97 / Mango

Dreamgrinder

☐ AGENTS OF THE MIND
CDBLEED 15 / Nov '95 / Bleeding Hearts

Dreamhouse

☐ DREAMHOUSE
78864740032 / 14 Jul '98 / TRAA

Dreamies

☐ AURALGRAPHIC ENTERTAINMENT
GCR 015 / 9 Feb '98 / Growing Concern

Dreamlovers

☐ BEST OF THE DREAMLOVERS, THE
When we get married / Just because / Welcome home / Let them love and be loved / Zoom, zoom, zoom / While we were dancing / If I should lose you / Pretty little girl / I'm thru with you / Together / Amazons and coyotes / Oh baby mine / These will be the good old days / You gave me somebody to love / Doin' things together with you / Bad times make the good times / Bless your soul / Calling jo-ann / Let's twist again / Mother / Happiness / I need you
NEMCD 673 / May '94 / Sequel

Dreams & Emotion

☐ MOODS OF LOVE
I will always love you / When a man loves a woman / Love is all around / You've lost the lovin' feelin' / Wonderful tonight / How deep is your love / Without you / Think twice / When I fall in love / Unchained melody / Power of love / All out of love / I'm not in love / First time ever I saw your face / Lady in red / Woman / Three times a lady / I don't want to talk about it / Feelings / Because I love you
RECD 501 / Dec '97 / REL

Dreams Of Ireland

☐ 22 SONGS OF HOME
PLATCD 3930 / May '94 / Platinum

Dreams Of Sanity

☐ KOMODIA
HOS 7061CD / 27 Apr '98 / Hall Of Sermon

Dreamscape

☐ TRANCE LIKE STATE
RS 0072932CD / Jul '98 / Rising Sun

Dredge

☐ YEARS OF VIOLATION
SCCD 05 / 29 Nov '97 / Scenario

Dreem Teem

☐ DREEM TEEM IN SESSION (Various Artists)
74321549032 / 13 Dec '97 / De-Construction

Dremmwel

☐ HEOL LOAR
862CD / Nov '96 / Escalibur

Dresher, Paul

☐ OPPOSITES ATTRACT
804112 / Aug '92 / New World

Dresser, Mark

☐ BANQUET
TZA 7027 / 27 Oct '97 / Tzadik

☐ CABINET OF DR. CALIGARI
KFWCD 155 / Feb '95 / Knitting Factory

☐ FORCE GREEN
1212732 / Jan '96 / Soul Note

☐ INVOCATION
KFWCD 173 / Oct '96 / Knitting Factory

Drever, Ivan

☐ BACK TO BACK
ATCD 036 / Dec '97 / Attic

☐ EVERY BREAKING HEART
ATCD 030 / Dec '97 / Attic

☐ FOUR WALLS
Ballad of Jimmy Fry / Catching the dream / Timmer the Tartar / Colonel Sir Neil Macrae of Howden end / How far / Called to fire / Christy Jane Drever / We sometimes hurt too / Kinnairdie's awa wi' the geese / John Boocock's reel / Brave souls / Braes O'Gleniffer
IRCD 037 / Jul '96 / Iona

☐ ORKNEY YEARS, THE (1986-1992 Vol.1)
ATCD 051 / May '98 / Attic

Drew, Kenny

☐ AND FAR AWAY (Drew, Kenny Quartet)
And far away / Rianne / Serenity / I love you, goodbye / Twice a week / Autumn leaves (french version) / Blues run
SNCD 1081 / Jan '86 / Soul Note

☐ FALLING LEAVES, THE (Drew, Kenny Trio)
Falling leaves / Stella by starlight / All blues / Django / In your own sweet way / Blues
MCD 042 / 23 Feb '98 / Limetree

☐ KENNY DREW & NIELS-HENNING ORSTED PEDERSON (Drew, Kenny & Niels-Henning Orsted Pederson)
STCD 8274 / May '96 / Storyville

☐ KENNY DREW TRIO (Drew, Kenny Trio)
OJCCD 65 / Nov '95 / Original Jazz Classics

☐ MORNING
SCCD 31048 / Jul '88 / Steeplechase

☐ YOUR SOFT EYES (Drew, Kenny Trio)
SNCD 1031 / Jan '86 / Soul Note

Drew, Kenny Jr.

☐ CRYSTAL RIVER (Drew, Kenny Jr. Sextet)
Confrontation / Undercurrent / White gardenia / Largo / First love letter / Manhattan sunset / Crystal river / Sweet and lovely / Straight jacket
TCB 98202 / 26 May '98 / TCB

☐ FOLLOW THE SPIRIT
Serial blues / Wrap your troubles in dreams / Soldier in the rain / Star crossed lovers / All the things you are / Your soft eyes / Flame within / Four in one / Invierno portena
SJL 1004 / 18 May '98 / Sirocco

☐ LIVE AT MAYBECK RECITAL HALL VOL.39
Stella by starlight / Peace / After you / Ugly beauty / Well you needn't / Coral sea / Images / Straight no chaser / Waitin' for my dearie / Autumn leaves
CCD 4653 / Jul '95 / Concord Jazz

☐ LOOK INSIDE, A
5142112 / Feb '94 / Antilles/New Directions

☐ PASSIONATA
AJ 70561 / 27 Apr '98 / Arkadia

Drew, Ray

☐ TOO MUCH LOVIN'
MCR 10012 / 7 Apr '98 / Midnight Creeper

Drew, Ronnie

☐ COLLECTION, THE
CHCD 1053 / Feb '95 / Chyme

☐ IRISH ROVER, THE
CDRONNIE 001 / Mar '97 / Outlet

☐ RONNIE DREW WITH THE DUBLINERS (Drew, Ronnie & The Dubliners)
Master McGrath / Finnegans wake / Champion at keeping them rollin' / Johnston's motor car / Kimmage / Ojos negros / Donegal Danny / Mero / When Margaret was eleven / Lowlands of Holland / Sam Hall / McAlpines fusiliers / Oul triangle / Waltzing Matilda / Irish rover / Whack fol de diddle / Rebel pearse / Free the people / Seven drunken nights / Biddy mulligan / Weile weile weile / Greenland whale fishery / Louse house in Kilkenny / Now I'm easy / Hi for the beggarman / Se faith mo bhurta / Johnny McGory / Bonny boy / Building up and tearing down England / Danny Farrell / James Larkin / Monto / All for me grog / Smith of Bristol / Comical genius / Cuanla
PTICD 2003 / Dec '97 / Outlet

Dreyblatt, Arnold

☐ NODAL EXCITATION
DEX 15CD / 23 Mar '98 / Dexter's Cigar

☐ SOUND OF ONE STRING
RUTHENIUM 44 / 30 Mar '98 / Table Of The Elements

DRI

☐ 4 OF A KIND
398417012CD / May '96 / Metal Blade

☐ CROSSOVER
ROTCD 2092 / Nov '95 / Rotten

☐ DEALING WITH IT
Snap / Marriage / Counter attack / Nursing home blues / Give my taxes back / Equal people / Bail out / Evil minds / I'd rather be sleeping / Yes ma'am / God is broke / I don't need society / Explorer / On my way home / Argument the war / Slit my wrists
ROTCD 2091 / Nov '95 / Rotten

☐ DEFINITION
ROTCD 2093 / Nov '95 / Rotten

☐ DIRTY ROTTEN
ROTCD 001 / Nov '95 / Rotten

☐ FULL SPEED AHEAD
ROTCD 2099 / Nov '95 / Rotten

☐ THRASH ZONE
Thrashard / Beneath the wheel / Enemy within / Strategy / Labeled uncurable / You say I'm scum / Gun control / Kill the words / Drown you out / Trade / Standing in line / Give a hoot / Worker bee / Abduction
398147002CD / Oct '95 / Metal Blade

Drift Pioneer

☐ METAL ELF BOY
TEQM 95004 / Jun '97 / TEQ

Drifters

☐ 70'S CLASSICS
Kissin' in the back row of the movies / You're more than a number in my little black book / Hello happiness / Like sister and brother / There goes my first love / Sweet Caroline / Harlem child / Like a movie I've seen before / Songs we used to sing / Love games / Down on the beach tonight / Every night's a Saturday night with you / Can I take you home little girl / Anothe lonely weekend / Summer in the city / Midnight cowboy
MCCD 100 / Mar '93 / Music Club

☐ BEST OF THE DRIFTERS, THE
74321265062 / Aug '95 / RCA

☐ BOOGIE WOOGIE ROLL (Greatest Hits 1953-58)
White christmas / Drip drop / Adorable / Don't dog me / Let the boogie woogie roll / Honey bee / Hot ziggety / Some day you'll want me to want you / If I didn't love you like I do / Bells of st mary's / Lucille / What'cha gonna do / Warm your heart / I gotta get myself a woman / Sadie my lady / Honky tonky / I should have done right / Drifting away from you / Steamboat / Your promise to be mine / No sweet lovin' / Suddenly there's a valley / Souvenirs / Hypnotized / I know / Yodee yakee / Soldier of fortune / It was a tear / Way I feel / Three thirty three / Everyone's laughing / Try try baby / There you go / Honey love / Bip bam / Such a night / Gone / Fools fall in love / Ruby baby / Money honey
7567819272 / Mar '95 / Atlantic

☐ CLYDE MCPHATTER & THE DRIFTERS (McPhatter, Clyde & The Drifters)
Honey love / Money honey / Someday (you'll want me to want you) / Such a night / Bells of St. Mary's / Warm your heart / Whatcha gonna do / White Christmas / Lucille / Way I feel / Gone / Let the boogie woogie roll / Don't dog me / Bip bam / If I didn't love you like I do / There you go / Try try baby / Everyone's laughing / Hot ziggety / Three thirty three
RSACD 803 / Sep '96 / Sequel

☐ CLYDE MCPHATTER & THE DRIFTERS/ROCKIN' & DRIFTIN'
CCLCD 62262 / 3 Aug '98 / Collectables

☐ DRIFTERS COLLECTION, THE
Stand by me / Save the last dance for me / Another saturday night / Under the boardwalk / On broadway / (sittin' on) the dock of the bay / Saturday night at the movies / Dance with me / Sweets for my sweet / Some kind of wonderful / Bring it on home to me / Cupid / I can help / Ruby baby / Third rate romance / Please stay / True love / Up on the roof / When my little girl is smiling / There goes my baby / Little drummer boy / I saw mommy kissing santa claus / Oh holy night / Christmas song (chestnuts roasting on an open fire) / Auld lang syne
COL 011 / Jun '95 / Collection

☐ DRIFTERS COLLECTION, THE
Under the boardwalk / I count the tears / Up on the roof / Please stay / On Broadway / When my little girl is smiling / (If you cry) True love true love / There goes my baby / This magic moment / Some kind of wonderful / Dance with me / Save the last dance for me / Sweets for my sweet / Saturday night at the movies / Stand by me: *King, Ben E.* / Spanish Harlem: *King, Ben E.*
PLATCD 175 / Mar '96 / Platinum

☐ DRIFTERS, THE
LECD 039 / May '94 / Dynamite

☐ DRIFTERS, THE
On Broadway / Save the last dance for me / Dance with me / There goes my baby / Up on the roof / Under the boardwalk / This magic moment / Please stay / Sweets for my sweet / Some kind of wonderful / Third rate romance / Night moves / Another Saturday night / I can help / Cupid / Any day now / Wonderful world / Bring it on home to me / Stand by me / Short people
QED 039 / Nov '96 / Tring

☐ GOOD LIFE WITH THE DRIFTERS, THE
What kind of fool am I / I wish you love / More / Tonight / On the street where you live / Who can I turn to / Quando quando quando / Desafinado / As long as she needs me / Good life / Temptation / Christmas song / I remember Christmas / In the park / Looking through the eyes of love
RSACD 835 / Sep '96 / Sequel

☐ GREATEST
Hello happiness / Kissin' in the back row of the movies / Always something there to remind me / Every night / Sweet Caroline / If it feels good do it / Save the last dance for me / There goes my first love / Like sister and brother / I can't live without you / Harlem child / You've got your troubles / Love games / Down on the beach tonight
CDMFP 5734 / Oct '91 / Music For Pleasure

☐ GREATEST HITS
CDSGP 0153 / Apr '95 / Prestige

☐ GREATEST HITS AND MORE 1959-1965
There goes my baby / Oh my love / Baltimore / Hey senorita / Dance with me / (If you cry) True love, true love / This magic moment / Lonely winds / Nobody but me / Save the last dance for me / I count the tears / Sometimes I wonder / Please stay / Room full of tears / Sweets for my sweet / Some kind of wonderful / Loneliness of happiness / Mexican divorce / Somebody new dancing with you / Jackpot / She never talked to me that way / When my little girl is smiling / Stranger on the shore / What to do / Up on the roof / Another night with the boys / I feel good all over / Let the music play / On Broadway / I'll take you home / If you don't come back / Didn't it / One way love / He's just a playboy / Under the Boardwalk / I don't want to go on without you / I've got sand in my shoes / Saturday night at the movies / At the club / Come on over to my place
7567819312 / Jul '93 / Atlantic

☐ I'LL TAKE YOU WHERE THE MUSIC'S PLAYING
I'll take you where the music's playing / Nylon stockings / We gotta sing / Up in the streets of Harlem / Memories are made of this / You can't love them all / My islands in the sun / Aretha / Baby what I mean / Ain't it the truth / Up jumped the devil / Still burning in my heart / I need you now / Country to the city / Your best friend / Steal away / Black silk / You've got to pay your dues / Rose by any other name / Be my lady / It takes a good woman
RSACD 836 / Nov '96 / Sequel

☐ ON BROADWAY
On broadway / Save the last dance for me / Dance with me / There goes my baby / Up on the roof / Under the boardwalk / (sittin' on) the dock of the bay / Another saturday night / Stand by me / Cupid / Wonderful world / You send me / Unchained melody summertime / Bring it on home to me / Tie a yellow ribbon round the old oak tree
15074 / Aug '92 / Laserlight

☐ ON BROADWAY (The Best Of The Drifters)
Dance with me / There goes my baby / True love / This magic moment / Save the last dance for me / Some kind of wonderful / Sweets for my sweet / Please stay / I count the tears / Up on the roof / On Broadway / I'll take you home / Under the boardwalk / Saturday night at the movies / Kissing in the back row / You're more than a number in my little red book / Ol' man river / I feel so good / I'm gonna move across the river / Fools fall in love
AIM 2014CD / 20 Oct '97 / Aim

☐ PLEASE COME HOME FOR CHRISTMAS
Santa Claus got the blues / White Christmas / Silent night / I saw Mummy kissing Santa Claus / We wish you a merry Christmas / Please come home for Christmas / Santa Claus is coming to town / Little drummer boy / Christmas song / Winter wonderland / Little St.Nick / Christmas just ain't christmas / O holy night / Auld lang syne
120032 / Oct '97 / Jingle

☐ ROCKIN' AND DRIFTIN'
Moonlight bay / Ruby baby / Drip drop / I got to get myself a woman / Fools fall in love / Hypnotized / Yodee Yakee / I know / Soldier of fortune / Drifting away from you / Your promise to be mine / It was a tear / Adorable / Steamboat / Honey bee / I should have done right / No sweet lovin' / Honky tonk / Sadie my lady / Souvenirs / Suddenly there's a valley / On bended knee: *Pinkney Flyers* / My only desires: *Pinkney Flyers*
RSACD 815 / Nov '96 / Sequel

☐ SAVE THE LAST DANCE FOR ME
AVC 511 / Dec '92 / Avid

☐ SAVE THE LAST DANCE FOR ME
MACCD 156 / Aug '96 / Autograph

☐ SAVE THE LAST DANCE FOR ME
Dance with me / Baltimore / Hey Senorita / Lonely winds / Oh my love / There goes my baby / This magic moment / (If you cry) true love, true love / Sometimes I wonder / I count the tears / I feel good all over / Save the last dance for me / Nobody but me / Roomfull of tears / Sweets for my sweet / When my little girl is smiling / Night shift / Lonely winds
RSACD 817 / Sep '96 / Sequel

☐ SPOTLIGHT ON DRIFTERS
Under the boardwalk / I count the tears / Up on the roof / Please stay / On Broadway / When my little girl is smiling / (If you cry) true love, true love / There goes my baby / This magic moment / Some kind of wonderful / Dance with me / Save the last dance for me / Sweets for my sweet / Saturday night at the movies
HADCD 122 / Feb '94 / Javelin

☐ UNDER THE BOARDWALK
Under the boardwalk / Please stay / Twist / Some kinda wonderful / My girl / Sand in my shoes / This magic moment / I count the tears / Money honey / True, true love / Honey love / When my little girl is smiling / On broadway / Dance with me / Lonely winds / There goes my baby / Sweets for my sweet / Save the last dance for me
MUCD 9016 / Apr '95 / Musketeer

☐ UNDER THE BOARDWALK
If you don't come back / I'll take you home / Didn't I / One way love / Under the boardwalk / He's just a playboy / I don't want to go without you / I've got sand in my shoes / Saturday night at the movies / Under the boardwalk / There goes my baby / Spanish lace / At the club / Answer the phone / Saturday night at the movies / Under the boardwalk / Follow me / Chains of love / Far from the maddening crowd / Come on over to my place / Outside place
RSACD 834 / Nov '96 / Sequel

☐ UP ON THE ROOF
Please stay / Some kind of wonderful / Loneliness or happiness / Mexican divorce / Somebody new dancing with you / Jackpot / She never talked to me that way / Stranger on the shore / What to do / Another night with the boys / Up on the roof / Let the music play / On Broadway / I don't want nobody: *Lewis, Rudy* / Baby I dig love: *Lewis, Rudy* / Only in America / Rat race / In the land of make believe / Beautiful music / Vaya con dios
RSACD 833 / Sep '96 / Sequel

☐ UP ON THE ROOF/UNDER THE BOARDWALK
CCLCD 62112 / 3 Aug '98 / Collectables

☐ VERY BEST OF THE DRIFTERS
Up on the roof / Some kind of wonderful / I count the tears / I'll take you home / Sweets for my sweet / When my little girl is smiling / Please stay / Saturday night at the movies / Under the boardwalk / On broadway / There goes my baby / Dance with me / This magic moment / Save the last dance for me / (if you cry) true love true love / I've got sand in my shoes
8122712112 / Jun '93 / Atlantic

☐ VERY BEST OF THE DRIFTERS, THE
Save the last dance for me / There goes my first love / Kissin' in the back row of the movies / Down on the beach tonight / Like sister and brother / Can I take you home little girl / You're more than a number in my little red book / Every night's a Saturday night with you / Sweet Caroline / Love games / Harlem child / Summer in the city / Songs we used to sing / Something tells me (something's gonna happen tonight) / If only I could start again / Another lonely weekend / Midnight cowboy / Always something there to remind me / Don't cry on the weekend / Hello happiness
74321446742 / Feb '97 / Camden

Driftwood, Jimmie

☐ AMERICANA
Unfortunate man / Fair Rosamund's bower / Soldier's joy / Country boy / I'm too young to marry / Pretty Mary / Sailor man / Zelma Lee / Rattlesnake song / Old Joe Clark / Tennesee stud / Razor back steak / First covered wagon / Maid of Argenta / Bunker Hill / Song of the cowboys / Peter Francisco / Four little girls in Boston / Slack your rope, hangman / Run Johnny run / Arkansas traveller / Damn Yankee lad / Chalamette / Battle of New Orleans / Land where the bluegrass grows / Widders of Bowling green / Get along boys / Sweet Betsy from pike / Shoot the buffalo / Song of the pioneer / I'm leavin' on the wagon train / Jordan am a hard road to travel / Marshall of Silver City / Wilderness road / Pony express / Mooshatonio / Shanty in the holler / Big river man / Big John Davy / On top of Pikes peak / Fi di diddle um-a-dazey / Song of creation / Battle of San Juan hill / Banjer pickin' man / Tucumcari / St. Brendan's Isle / He had a long chain on / Big Hoss / Sal's got a sugar lip / Ox driving song / General Custer / What was your name in the States / Billy the kid / Jesse James / Billy Yank and Johnny Reb / Won't you come along and go / Rock of Chickamauga / How do you like the army / Git along little yearlings / Oh Florie / I'm a poor rebel soldier / My black bird has gone / Goodbye Reb, you'all come / On top of Shiloh's hill / When I swim the Golden River / Giant of the Thunderhead / Shanghai'd / Santy Anny O-Roe / Bullies Row / Land of the Amazon / What could I do / Driftwood at sea / In a cotton shirt and a pair of dungarees / Davy Jones (Song of a dead soldier) / Sailor, sailor marry me / Diver boy / Ship that never returned / Sailing away on the ocean / John Paul Jones / Bear flew over the ocean
BCD 15465 / Apr '92 / Bear Family

Drill

☐ SKIN DOWN
ABT 092 CD / May '91 / Abstract

Driller Killer

☐ BRUTALIZED
DISTCD 8 / Jun '94 / Distortion

☐ FUCK THE WORLD
KRONH 006CD / Apr '97 / Osmose

☐ LIFE
DISTEP 20 / Nov '95 / Distortion

Drink Small
☐ BLUES DOCTOR, THE
Tittie man / Little red rooster / So bad / Something in the milk ain't clean / Rub my belly / Baby leave your panties home / Stormy Monday blues / I'm gonna move to the outskirts of town / John Henry Ford
ICH 1062CD / Oct '93 / Ichiban

☐ ROUND TWO
DUI / Steal away / Thank you, pretty baby / Don't let nobody know / Widow woman / I'm tired now / Honky tonk / They can't make me hate you / Bishopville women / Can I come over tonight
ICH 9009CD / Jun '94 / Ichiban

Drippin' Honey
☐ DRIP DRIP
MMBCD 4 / 9 Mar '98 / Me & My Blues

Driscoll, Julie
☐ 1969
OW 30013 / Sep '94 / One Way

☐ ROCK GENERATION (Driscoll, Julie/ Sonny Boy Williamson)
14559 / 23 Mar '98 / Spalax

Driscoll, Phil
☐ LIVE WITH FRIENDS
I can feel your love / Make us one / Place in my heart / Shout / Unbearable spirit / You are so beautiful / You're all I need to get by
7019956602 / Nov '97 / Word

Drisket
☐ CELTIC HARP
Plangstigh Ewen / Dainty davie / Dime ramo verdi / Iona / Sun and shadow / Vincenta / Enezen du / Plantxy / George brabazon / Vieux chateau sous la lune / Boulavogue / King william's march / Dafydd y garreg wen / Pardon sant fiakr / Piljadur ha displijadur
ANT 016 / Nov '96 / Tring

Drive She Said
☐ ROAD TO PARADISE, THE (The Very Best Of Drive She Said)
Look at what you got / Fallin' again / Suddenly closer / If this is love / Don't you know / It's gonna take a miracle / Think of love / Maybe it's love / Wherever you go / Love has no pride / Drivin' wheel / Just for the moment / Inside you / Hard to hold / Won't keep beggin' / Water from a stone / Road to paradise / All I'm livin' for
FRCD 002 / 18 May '98 / Frontier

Driver, Betty
☐ GIRL FROM THE STREET, THE
I'll take romance / I fall in love with you every day / Moon remembered / I'm getting sentimental over you / What goes on here in my heart / With you / So little time / Red maple leaves / Sweetest song in the world / Twitterpated / World will sing again / Sailor with the navy blue eyes / It's spring again/Potato Pete / Swing bugler / We mustn't miss the last bus home / What more can I say/Booglie wooglie piggy/Rose O'Day / Red silken stockings / Dreamer's holiday / Leprechaun lullaby / Bullfrog (samba)
CDMFP 6209 / Feb '96 / Music For Pleasure

D'Rivera, Paquito
☐ 40 YEARS OF CUBAN JAM
158262 / Sep '97 / Messidor

☐ CARIBBEAN JAZZ PROJECT, THE
One for Tom / Abracadabra / Carousel / Como un bolero / Paco and Dave / Valsetriste / Latin quarter / Todo Aquelayer / Three amigos / Afro / Cafe' Espana
INAK 9038CD / Nov '97 / In Akustik

☐ LA HABANA
MES 158202 / Nov '92 / Messidor

☐ LIVE AT THE MANCHESTER CRAFTSMEN'S GUILD (D'Rivera, Paquito & The United Nation Orchestra)
Tocache / King of Cancun / Puerto Padre / Recife's blues / Memories / Andulucia medley / Guasi moodi / Groove for Diz / Despojo / Night in Tunisia
BJAC 1003 / 24 Nov '97 / Blue Jackel

☐ NIGHT IN ENGLEWOOD, A (D'Rivera, Paquito United Nations Orchestra)
158292 / Sep '97 / Messidor

☐ RETURN TO IPANEMA
70544665162 / 5 May '98 / Town Crier

☐ REUNION (D'Rivera, Paquito & Arturo Sandoval)
Mambo influenciado / Reunion / Tanga / Claudia / Friday morning / Part I, II, III / Body and soul / Caprichosos de la habana
158052 / Sep '97 / Messidor

☐ WHO'S SMOKING (D'Rivera, Paquito & James Moody)
Who's smoking / Giant steps / Irremediablemente solo (incurably alone) / Linda's moody / Desert storm / Nuestro bolero / I mean you / You got it, diz / Out of nowhere
CCD 79523 / Feb '97 / Candid

Drivin' n' Cryin'
☐ DRIVIN' N' CRYIN'
D 2249212 / Oct '97 / Ichiban

Droge, Pete
☐ FIND A DOOR (Droge, Pete & The Sinners)
Mr. Jade / Wolfgang / Don't have to be that way / Dear Dianne / Brakeman / You should be running / That ain't right / Find a door / Out with you / Sooner or later / Lord is busy
743213745022 / Sep '96 / American

☐ NECKTIE SECOND
If you don't love me (I'll kill myself) / Northern bound train / Strayin street / Faith in you / Two steppin' monkey / Sunspot stopwatch / Hardest thing to do / So I am over you / Dog on a chain / Hampton Inn Room 306
743212242302 / Apr '95 / American

☐ SPACEY AND SHAKIN'
Spacey and shakin' / Please the ghost / Eyes on the ceiling / Motokid / Song four / Mile of fence / I want to go away / Blink of a kiss / Evan's radio / Walking by my side / Blindly
4898492 / 1 Jun '98 / Epic

Drolma, Choying
☐ CHO (Drolma, Choying & Steve Tibbetts)
Ngakso / Kyema mimin / Kyamdro semkye / Ngani troma pt1 / Ngani troma pt2 / Cho chendren / Kangyi tengi / Ney ogmin choying podrang / Shengshik pema jungney / Om nama phem / Leymon tendrel 2 / Nubchok dechen / SSenge wangchuk / Dechen monlam / Tal
HNCD 1404 / Jan '97 / Hannibal

Drome
☐ FINAL CORPORATE COLONIZATION OF THE UNCONSCIOUS
Age of the affordable retina / Hinterland, Kassler Kessel / Down at heels / Hoax what did you get / Steel lung, bye one / Nuzzling / Wonderland / Squirrel / Marathon/Texas / Party in the woods 4
ZENCD 011 / Feb '94 / Ninja Tune

Drone
☐ DRONE
FFR 024 / Dec '96 / Freek

☐ FAT CONTROLLER, THE
QDKCD 007 / Mar '94 / Normal

Drone Summit
☐ DRONE SUMMIT
DR 005CD / Jul '97 / Drug Racer

Drones
☐ FURTHER TEMPTATIONS
Persecution complex / Bone idol / Movement / Be my baby / Corgi crap / Sad so sad / Change / Lookalikes / Underdog / No more time / City drones / Just want to be myself / Lift off the bans / Lookalikes / Corgi crap / Hard on me / You'll lose / Just want to be myself / Bone idol / I can't see / Fooled today
CDPUNK 20 / Oct '93 / Anagram

☐ TAPES FROM THE ATTIC
OVER 60CD / Apr '97 / Overground

Drones
☐ GIANT BONSAI
DRO 1996CD / Aug '96 / Drones

Droney, Chris
☐ FERTILE ROCK, THE
CICD 110 / Jul '95 / Clo Iar-Chonnachta

Drop
☐ WITHIN BEYOND
CHAPMCD 061 / Nov '91 / Chapter 22

Drop 19's
☐ DELAWARE
HUTCD 004 / Aug '92 / Hut

☐ NATIONAL COMA
Limp / All swimmers are brothers / Skull / Cuban / Rot winter / Martini love / 7/8 / Franco inferno / My hotel deb / Moses brown / Superfeed / Dead / Royal
CDHUT 14 / Sep '93 / Hut

Drop The Box
☐ HONEYTRAP
Run dry / Dancing / Silver fox / Honeytrap / Badger things / Red bee / Molasses / Sexuality / Wings / Here with me
CDLDL 1268 / May '98 / Lochshore

Dropkick Murphys
☐ BOYS ON THE DOCKS
CYCD 105 / 16 Mar '98 / Cyclone

☐ DO OR DIE
04072 / 9 Mar '98 / Epitaph

Droste, Silvia
☐ AUDIOPHILE VOICINGS
BLR 84 004 / May '91 / L&R

Drovers
☐ TIGHTROPE TOWN
TX 2010CD / Jan '94 / Taxim

Drovers Old Time Medicine Show
☐ SUNDAY IN PETERS CREEK
HYMN 6 / Aug '97 / Fundamental

Dru Hill
☐ DRU HILL
Anthem / Nothing to prove / Tell me / Do U believe / Whatever U want / Satisfied / April showers / All alone / Never make a promise / So special / In my bed / Love's train / Share my world / 5 steps
5243062 / 1 Dec '97 / 4th & Broadway

Drug Free America
☐ NARCOTICA
CBKTB 21 / Jul '95 / Dreamtime

☐ TRIP
Detroit walkabout / One Alien/Nation / Out on the blue horizon / Orient pearl and cherry blue / Drop zone (reprise,live) / Cygni X-1
CYBERCD 001 / Oct '92 / Cybersound

☐ TRIP - THE DREAMTIME REMIXES
Cyberspace / Detroit walkabout / One alien nation under a groove / Out on the blue / Horizon / Orient pearl and cherry blue / Can you feel / Drop zone / Cygni X-1 / Drop zone (free Yibet)
CDKTB 14 / Apr '95 / Dreamtime

Drugstore
☐ WHITE MAGIC FOR LOVERS
Mondo cane / Say hello / El President / I know I could / I don't want to be here / Song for Pessoa / Space girl / Never come down / White magic for lovers / Tips for travelling
RR 87112 / 4 May '98 / Roadrunner

Druid
☐ TOWARD THE SUN/FLUID DRUID
Voices / Remembering / Theme / Toward the sun / Red carpet for an evening / Dawn of evening / Shangri-La / Razor truth / Painters clouds / FM 145 / Crusade / Nothing but morning / Barnaby / Kestrel / Left to find / Fisherman's friend
BGOCD 285 / Aug '95 / Beat Goes On

Druids Of Stonehenge
☐ CREATION
1610985 / 22 Jun '98 / Synton

Druidspear
☐ ...SLOW
ANEWCD 1 / Jun '97 / Anew

Drukpa Tibetan Monks
☐ TIBETAN BUDDHIST RITES FROM BHUTAN MONASTRIES BOX SET
LYRCD 9001 / May '94 / Lyrichord

☐ TIBETAN BUDDHIST RITES FROM BHUTAN MONASTRIES VOL.1
LYRCD 7255 / Feb '94 / Lyrichord

☐ TIBETAN BUDDHIST RITES FROM BHUTAN MONASTRIES VOL.2 (Drukpa & Nyingmapa Tibetan Monks)
LYRCD 7256 / Feb '94 / Lyrichord

☐ TIBETAN BUDDHIST RITES FROM BHUTAN MONASTRIES VOL.3
LYRCD 7257 / May '94 / Lyrichord

☐ TIBETAN BUDDHIST RITES FROM BHUTAN MONASTRIES VOL.4
LYRCD 7258 / May '94 / Lyrichord

Drum Club
☐ DRUMS ARE DANGEROUS
BFLCD 10 / 1 Sep '98 / Butterfly

☐ EVERYTHING IS NOW
BFLCD 3 / 1 Sep '98 / Butterfly

☐ LIVE IN ICELAND
Oscillate and infiltrate / Bug / Follow the sun / Reefer / Crystal express / De-lushed / Plateau of wolves / U make me feel so good
SBR 003 / Aug '95 / Sabres Of Paradise

Drum Island
☐ DRUM ISLAND
Drum island
AMB 7946CDX / 17 Nov '97 / R&S

Drumhead
☐ DANGEROUS DUB VOL.2 (Drumhead & Ninja Shark)
COPCD 4 / Mar '96 / Copasetic

Drummers Of Burundi
☐ DRUMMERS OF BURUNDI
RWMCD 1 / Mar '92 / Realworld

Drummond, Bill
☐ MAN, THE
True to the trail / Ballad for a sex god / Julian cope is dead / I want that girl / Going back / Queen of the south / I believe in rock 'n' roll / Married man / I'm the king of joy / Son of a preacher man / Such a parcel of rogues in a nation
CRECD 14 / May '94 / Creation

Drummond, Billy
☐ GIFT, THE (Drummond, Billy Quartet)
CRISS 1083CD / May '94 / Criss Cross

☐ NATIVE COLOURS (Drummond, Billy Quintet)
CRISS 1057CD / May '92 / Criss Cross

Drummond, Don
☐ BEST OF DON DRUMMOND, THE
SOCD 9008 / Mar '95 / Studio One

☐ GREATEST HITS
Corner stone / Musical communion / Mesopotamia / Cool smoke / Burning torch / Alipang / Don memorial / Stampede / Thorough fare
TICD 004 / May '89 / Treasure Isle

☐ MEMORIAL
Silver dollar / Let george do it / Woman a come / Knock out punch / Dr. decker / Occupation / Garden of love / Feeling fine / Street corner / Latin goes ska / Green island / Cool smoke / Burning torch / Stampede / Musical communion
LG 21023 / Jul '93 / Lagoon

Drummond, Ray
☐ CAMERA IN A BAG (Drummond, Ray Quintet)
CRISS 1040CD / Nov '90 / Criss Cross

☐ CONTINUUM
Blues from the sketchpad / Some serious steppin' / Intimacy of the blues / Sakura / Blues in the closet / Equipoise / Gloria's step / Sail away / Sophisticated lady
AJ 0111 / Aug '94 / Arabesque

☐ EXCURSION
Susanita / Penta-major / Prelude / Quads / Invitation / Well you needn't / Andei / Blues African / Excursion
AJ 0106 / Jun '93 / Arabesque

☐ VIGNETTES
Susanita-like / Ballade poetique / Dance to the lady / Dedication (to John Hicks) / 1-95 / Poor butterly / Eleanor Rigby / Ballade poetique
AJ 0122 / Jun '96 / Arabesque

Drumpact
☐ NEW MUSIC
EPC 886 / Oct '92 / European Music Production

Drunk
☐ DERBY SPIRITUAL, A
JAG 02 / May '97 / Jagjaguwar

☐ TO CORNER WOUNDS
JAG 07CD / May '98 / Jagjaguwar

Drunk In Punk
☐ TAPPED
FO 25CD / Apr '97 / Fearless

Drunken Boat
☐ DRUNKEN BOAT
Tragic hands / New pop / Accidents / Home skull crusher / Pony / Jubilee / Lisa's dream / Shit suit / Uniform gold / Stacko / Spin around / What's going on
EFACD 6185 / Oct '92 / House In Motion

Drunken State
☐ KILT BY DEATH
Time to stop / Blind faith / Forgotten ones / Lament / Call to arms / Resurrection / E.r.i.c. / Line up / Deal with the cliche / Prophets on the wind
HMRXD 151 / May '90 / Heavy Metal

Drunks With Guns
☐ DRUNKS WITH GUNS
BET 15 / 24 Nov '97 / Behemoth

Drupi
☐ GOLDEN YEARS
74321455802 / Nov '97 / Ricordi

243

Drusky, Roy

☐ 18 ORIGINAL COUNTRY CLASSICS
El Paso / Crystal chandeliers / Honey come back / Ring of fire / End of the world / (I'd be a) legend in my time / Take good care of her / Battle ofNew Orleans / Abilene / Early morning rain / Together again / Talk back trembling lips / Lonely street / Waitin' for a train / Cryin' time / Sunday morning coming down / Almost persuaded / When two worlds collide
5525562 / Sep '96 / Spectrum

Dry Branch Fire Squad

☐ FERTILE GROUND
Devil, take the farmer / Darling Nellie across the sea / Where we'll never die / Turkey in the straw / There's nothing between us / Love has bought me to dispair / Honest farmer / Great Titanic / Golden morning / Do you ever dream of me / Old time way / Bonaparte's crossing the Rhine
ROUCD 0258 / '89 / Rounder

☐ JUST FOR THE RECORD
ROUCD 306 / Jan '94 / Rounder

☐ LIVE AT LAST
Late last night / True historia / Aragon Mill / Economical talk / John Henry / Pitiful thing / Cowboy song / Housework is my life / Red rocking chair / Cultural exchange / Someone play Dixie for me / Hambone/Balo's song / Testosterone poisoning / Midnight on the stormy deep / Banjo jokes / Bluegrass breakdown / World's greatest folk singer / Hard times / Goin' up the mountain / Walk the streets of glory
ROUCD 0339 / Oct '96 / Rounder

☐ TRIED AND TRUE
Down south in new orleans / Brand new tennessee waltz / Someone play dixie for me / Going up on the mountain / Auction at the home place / Legend of the johnson boys / Aragon mill / Goin' across the mountain / Faded coat of blue / Wild mountain honey / Little girl and the dreadful snake / Oh what a storm / She's more to be pitied / Cripple creek / Golden ring / There's dust on the bible / Cowboy jim / Walking back to richmond / Golgotha
ROUCD 11519 / '88 / Rounder

Dry Throat Fellows

☐ DO SOMETHING
SOSCD 1226 / '92 / Stomp Off

DSB

☐ DON'T SAY THAT YOU'LL BELIEVE IT 2
IS 88993CD / 13 Oct '97 / I Scream Music

Dschinn

☐ DSCHINN
SB 037 / Jun '97 / Second Battle

Duarte, Chris

☐ TAILSPIN HEAD WHACK
Cleopatra / Crimino / Thrill is gone / Driving south / Catch the next line / Tailspin head whack / People say / Crazy / 32 Blues / Walls
ORECD 548 / 13 Oct '97 / Silvertone

Dub Chandra

☐ EUPHONISM'S
UWCD 002 / 29 Jun '98 / Ultrawave

☐ OUTLANDS
UWCD 001 / 16 Feb '98 / Ultrawave

Dub Doctor

☐ ZULU DUB
ROTCD 011 / Sep '96 / Reggae On Top

Dub Funk Association

☐ CONFRONTATION IN DUB
TNTYCD 004 / 22 Jun '98 / Tanty

☐ SPIRITS UNDER PRESSURE
TNTYCD 003 / Oct '96 / Tanty

Dub Ghecko

☐ LOVE TO THE POWER OF EACH
DBHD 003CD / Oct '96 / Dubhead

Dub Judah

☐ BETTER TO BE GOOD
DJCD 004 / Aug '94 / Dub Jockey

Dub Lion 2000

☐ EARTHQUAKE
EQCD 001 / 9 Feb '98 / Higher Science

Dub Mix Specialists

☐ DUB MIX SPECIALISTS VOL.1
DMSCD 101 / Sep '96 / DMS

Dub Monsters

☐ IN THE FAST LANE
KICKCD 70 / 30 Mar '98 / Kickin'

Dub Narcotic

☐ BOOT PARTY
KLP 40CD / Jun '96 / K

☐ INDUSTRIAL BREAKDOWN
SOUL 8CD / Jul '95 / Soul Static Sound

☐ OUT OF YOUR MIND
KLP 83CD / 24 Aug '98 / K

☐ RIDING SHOTGUN
KCD 50 / Nov '95 / K

☐ SHIP TO SHORE
KLP 60CD / Oct '96 / K

Dub Specialists

☐ 17 DUB SHOTS
CDHB 142 / Aug '95 / Heartbeat

☐ DUB TO DUB VOL.1 (Break To Break)
Dust bowl / Go west / Dusted out / Mother road / Needles / Rose of sharon / Milk 'n' honey / End of the line / Storm clouds / Cotton camp / Broken banks / Sheet rain / Whispers / Little rivers and little rose / Hopeless anger / Whispers in the rain
CP 001CD / May '95 / Crispy

☐ DUB TO DUB VOL.2 (Beat To Beat)
Slow yourself down / Mystic queen / Six ate / Separation / Never let go / Curiosity / Arubaluba
CP 002CD / Jun '96 / Crispy

☐ DUB TO DUB, BREAK TO BREAK
CP 001CD / Apr '97 / Crispy

Dub Syndicate

☐ CLASSIC SELECTION VOL.1
ONUCD 5 / Jul '89 / On-U Sound

☐ CLASSIC SELECTION VOL.3
ONUCD 69 / Jul '94 / On-U Sound

☐ ECHOMANIA
ONUCD 24 / Sep '93 / On-U Sound

☐ FEAR OF A GREEN PLANET
SH 45038 / 6 Apr '98 / Shanachie
EFA 398022 / May '98 / Lion & Roots

☐ ITAL BREAKFAST
ONUCD 84 / Mar '96 / On-U Sound

☐ LIVE
ONUCD 19 / Mar '93 / On-U Sound

☐ MELLOW & COLLY
EFA 398012 / 27 Jul '98 / Lion & Roots

☐ ONE WAY SYSTEM
DANCD 115 / Nov '94 / Danceteria

☐ POUNDING SYSTEM, THE
ONUCD 18 / 9 Feb '98 / On-U Sound

☐ RESEARCH AND DEVELOPMENT
ONUCD 85 / Oct '96 / On-U Sound

☐ STONED IMMACULATE
ONUCD 15 / '93 / On-U Sound

☐ STRIKE THE BALANCE
ONUCD 0047 / 8 Jun '98 / On-U Sound

☐ TUNES FROM THE MISSING CHANNEL
Ravi Shankar / Show is coming / Must be dreaming / Overboard / Forever more / Geoffrey Boycott / Wellie / Jolly / Out and about
ONUCD 18638 / Aug '97 / On-U Sound

Dub Tractor

☐ EVENING WITH DUB TRACTOR, AN
Scary hi hat loop / 104 dub / Ten eighty on its own / Klappesangen / Overheated livingroom / Elvis monk / Snappy bloom / B.a.t. / Spinet in yer face / Evening lost / A c tractor
CDADA 1001 / Feb '97 / Additive

Dub War

☐ DUB WARNING
WOWCD 37 / '94 / Words Of Warning

☐ PAIN
Why / Mental / Nar say a ting / Mad zone / Strike it / Respected / Pain / Nations / Gorrit / Spiritual warfare / Fool's gold / Over now / Anadin
MOSH 121CD / 1 Sep '97 / Earache

☐ WORDS OF DUB WARNING
WOWCD 47 / Dec '95 / Words Of Warning

☐ WRONG SIDE OF BEAUTIFUL
Control / Armchair thriller / Greedee / Baseball bat / One chill / Enemy maker / Million dollar love / Silencer / Cry dignity / Can't stop / Prisoner / Love is / Mission / Universal jam / One chill / Million dollar love / Armchair thriller / Nar say a ting / Prisoner / Million dollar love
MOSH 159CD / Sep '96 / Earache
MOSH 159CDL / 3 Nov '97 / Earache

Dubadelic

☐ 2001: A BASS ODYSSEY
WSCD 007 / Apr '96 / Word Sound Recordings

☐ BASS INVADERS
EFA 012272 / 29 Jun '98 / Word Sound & Power

Dubas, Marie

☐ INTEGRAL 1927-1945 (2CD Set)
FA 053 / Oct '96 / Fremeaux

Dubber, Goff

☐ CLARINET MARMALADE (Dubber, Goff & The Neville Dickie Trio)
Clarinet marmalade / Lonesome (si tu vois ma mere) / South side strut / Memphis blues / Black bottom stomp / Indian summer / Shreveport stomp / Saturday night out / Memories of you / Louisiana and me / I hear ya talkin' / Lou-easy-an-i-a / Gone but not forgotten (my inspiration) / Your folks / Wrap up your troubles in dreams / At the jazz band ball
LACD 78 / May '97 / Lake

Dube, Lucky

☐ HOUSE OF EXILE
SHCD 43094 / Apr '92 / Shanachie

Dublin City Ramblers

☐ BEST OF THE DUBLIN CITY RAMBLERS
Ferryman / Rare ould times / Paddy lie back / O'Carolan's draught / Green hills of Kerry / Mary's song / John O'Dreams / Punch and Judy man / Town of Ballybay / Nancy Spain / Belfast mill / Slievenamon / My green valleys / Crack was ninety in the Isle of Man
DOCDX 9005 / Jul '96 / Dolphin

☐ CRACK WAS 90, THE
CDIRLSH 022 / Jul '97 / Outlet

☐ CRAIC AND THE PORTER BLACK, THE (The Best Of Irish Pub Songs)
DOCDK 107 / Nov '95 / Dolphin

☐ FLIGHT OF THE EARLS
DOCD 9015 / Nov '93 / Delmark

☐ FROM IRELAND - WHISKEY IN THE JAR (Dublin City Ramblers/Spailpin)
Sweet Betsy from Pike: *Dublin City Ramblers* / Foggy dew: *Dublin City Ramblers* / Rising of the moon: *Spailpin* / Scarce o' tatties: *Spailpin* / Gentleman soldier: *Dublin City Ramblers* / Nightingale: *Spailpin* / Loch Lomond: *Dublin City Ramblers* / White, orange and green: *Spailpin* / Greensleeves: *Dublin City Ramblers* / Fiddler's green: *Spailpin* / Feilims' little boat Phelims: *Spailpin* / Night visiting sun: *Dublin City Ramblers* / Beggar man: *Spailpin* / Gartan mother's lullaby: *Dublin City Ramblers* / Ramblin' Irishman: *Spailpin* / Lord Randall: *Dublin City Ramblers* / Port Lairge: *Spailpin* / Turtle dove: *Dublin City Ramblers* / Arthur McBride: *Spailpin*
15160 / '91 / Laserlight

☐ HOME AND AWAY (20 Collected Irish Ballads)
DOCD 101 / Aug '96 / Dolphin

Dublin Concert Orchestra

☐ SHAMROCK FAVOURITES (Dublin Concert Orchestra/Alan Loraine Orchestra)
Wearing of the green / Believe me if all those endearing young charms / Harp that once thro' Tara's halls / Kerry dance / Ould orange flute / Minstrel boy / Londonderry air / Galway piper / Down went McGinty / Rose of Tralee / Cockles and mussels / Kitty of Coleraine / Daughters of Erin / Dear little Shamrock / Tis the last rose of Summer / Irish washerwoman / Teetotaler's reel / I know where I'm going / Bendemeer's stream / Rakes of mallow / Fairy dance / Patrician theme / Happy Colleen / Spring theme / Farmer's frolic / Postman's knock / Killarney / Low back'd car / Erin is my home / Aileen aroon / Rory O'Moore / Fisher's hornpipe / Kathleen Mavoureen / I'm sitting by the stile / Mary / Sprig of shillelagh / Rakes of Kildare / Shamus O'Brien / Pretty girl milking her cow / St. Patrick was a gentleman / St. Patrick's day / Come back to Erin / Barndoor / Miss McLeod's / Silent oh Moyle / Off to Philadelphia / I'll take you home again Kathleen / Nursery song / Balladeer / Pastorale / Fairy builder / Industrial theme / Merry theme
SUMCD 4075 / Nov '96 / Summit

Dubliners

☐ 15 YEARS ON
Wild rover / Ploughboy lads / Three sea captains / Bunclody / Seven drunken nights / Belfast hornpipe / Black Velvet Band / Carrickfergus / Last night's fun / Congress reel / Bank of the sweet primroses / Weila weila weila / Four green fields / Town I loved so well / Salamanca / Spancil Hill / McAlpine's fusiliers / Boulavogue / Old triangle / Spanish lady / O'Carolans devotion / Thirty foot trailer / Down by the glenside / Fiddlers green / Molly Malone
CHCD 1025 / Jan '95 / Chyme

☐ 20 ORIGINAL GREATEST HITS VOL.1
Farewell to carlingford / Finnegan's wake / Whiskey in the jar / Free the people / Rebel / Lord of the dance / Molly maguires / Champion at keepin' them rolling / Town I loved so well / Donegal danny / Sam hall / Springhill disaster / Night visiting song / Fiddler's green / Farewell to ireland / Dirty old town / Three sea captains / Gentleman soldier / Seven drunken nights / Louse house at kilkenny
CHCD 1028 / Dec '88 / Chyme

☐ 20 ORIGINAL GREATEST HITS VOL.2
Monto / Black Velvet Band / Johnston's motorcar / Drops of brandy/Lady Carberry / Button pusher / Old triangle / Downfall of Paris / Johnny McGory / Spanish lady / Killieburne brae / Molly Malone / God save Ireland / Spancil Hill / Peat bog soldiers / Joe Hill / Molly Maguires / Hand me down me bible / Musical priest/Blackthorn stick / Schoolday's over / Wild Rover
CHCD 1014 / Jul '93 / Chyme

☐ 20 ORIGINAL GREATEST HITS VOL.3
Kimmage / Biddy Mulligan / Waltzing Matilda / Lord Inchquinn / All for me grog / Lifeboat Mona / Lark in the morning / Mero / Down by the Glenside / McAlpine's fusiliers / Dublin in the rare oul times / Weile weile waile / Acrobat/Village bells / Scorn not his simplicity / Smith of Bristol / Parcel of rogues / Barney's banjo selection / Parting glass
CHCD 1015 / Jun '96 / Chyme

☐ 25TH ANNIVERSARY (2CD Set)
Rose of Allendale / Salonika / Reels / Now I'm easy: *Dubliners & Stockton's Wing* / Sally Wheatley / Oro se do bheatha bhaile / Irish rover: *Dubliners & Pogues* / Molly Malone / Protect and survive / Planxty Irwin / Three score and ten / Don't get married / Luke - a tribute / Ballad of St. Anne's reel / Cil chais / Cunla: *Dubliners & Stockton's Wing* / Clavalitos / Jigs / Leaving Nancy / O'Connell's steam engine / Rambling rover / Last of the great whales / Mountain dew: *Dubliners & Pogues* / Red roses for me: *Dubliners & Finbar Furey* / Marino waltz / Cod liver oil / I loved the ground she walked on / Love is pleasing / Sick note
ESDCD 422 / Aug '96 / Essential

☐ 30 YEARS A-GREYING
Rose / Eileen oge / Three jigs / Death of the bear / Galway shawl / Auld triangle / Will the circle be unbroken / Sands of Sudan / Manchester rambler / Drag that fiddle / Call and the answer / Boots of Spanish leather / Two hornpipes / I'll tell me Ma / Sweet Thames flow softly / Whiskey in the jar / Deportees / Nora / Three reels / Liverpool Lou / What will we tell the children / Man you don't meet every day
ESDCD 423 / Aug '96 / Essential

☐ 40 TRADITIONAL IRISH TUNES
CHCD 1052 / Dec '94 / Chyme

☐ AGELESS CLASSICS (2CD Set)
SMDCD 160 / 9 Feb '98 / Snapper

☐ AT HOME WITH THE DUBLINERS
EUCD 1093 / '89 / ARC

☐ AT THEIR BEST
PLSCD 161 / Feb '97 / Pulse

☐ BEST OF THE DUBLINERS, THE
Off to Dublin in the green / Sunshine hornpipe/The mountain road / Will you come to the bower / Peggy Lettermore / Donegal reel/Longford collector / Roddy McCorley / I'll tell my Ma / Mason's apron / Foggy dew / Old orange flute / Roisin dubh / Holy ground
HILLCD 4 / Sep '96 / Wooded Hill

☐ BEST OF THE DUBLINERS, THE
TRTCD 205 / Feb '96 / TrueTrax

☐ BEST OF THE DUBLINERS, THE
Seven drunken nights / Weile weile weila / Whiskey in the jar / Lord of the dance / Free the people / Blavk velvet band / Wild rover / Skibereen / Springhill disaster / Monto / Danny Farrell / Lifeboat Mona / Joe Hill / Mero / Dirty old town / Gentleman soldier / Champion at keeping them rolling / Louse house in Kelkenny / And the band played Waltzing Matilda / Lark in the morning / Down by the glenside
EURCD 400 / 24 Aug '98 / Eureka

☐ COLLECTION VOL.2, THE
Roddy McCorley / Twwang man / Sligo maid/Colonel Rodney / Woman from Wexford / Roisin Dubh / Air fa la la la lo / Peggy Lettermore / Easy and slow / Kerry recruit / Donegal reel / Longford collector / Tramps and hawkers / Home boys home / Sunshine hornpipe / Mountain road / Will you come to the bower / I'll tell me ma / Mason's apron / Holy ground / Boulavogue / Master McGrath / Walking in the dew / Nightingale / Sea shanty
CCSCD 270 / Sep '90 / Castle

☐ COLLECTION, THE
Wild rover / Chief O'Neill's favourite / Glendalough Saint / Off to Dublin in the green / Love is pleasing / Nelson's farewell / Monto / Dublin fusiliers / Rocky road to Dublin / Leaving of Liverpool / Old orange flute / Jar of porter / Prefad san ol / High reel / Patriot game / Swallow tail reel / McAlpine's fusiliers / Hot asphalt / Within a mile of Dublin / Finnegan's wake / Banks of the roses / My love in America / Foggy dew / Sea around us
CCSCD 164 / Sep '87 / Castle

☐ COMPLETE DUBLINERS (2CD Set)
SMDCD 150 / Jul '97 / Snapper

☐ DEFINITIVE TRANSATLANTIC COLLECTION, THE
Wild rover / Ragman's ball / Holy ground / Tramps and hawkers / Rocky road to Dublin / Banks of the roses / Swallow tail reel / Sligo maid/Colonel Rodney / Woman from Wexford / Patriot game / Roisin dubh / Fa la la lo / My love is in America / Kerry recruit / Leaving of Liverpool / Finnegan's wake / Sea around us / McAlpine's fusiliers / Hot asphalt / Glendalough saint / Within a mile of Dublin / Will you come to the bower / Boulavogue / Walking in the dew
ESMCD 518 / Jul '97 / Essential

☐ DUBLIN
Finnegan's wake / Raglan Road / Zoo / Logical Gardens / Sez she
CLACD 337 / Aug '93 / Castle

☐ **DUBLINERS COLLECTION VOL.1, THE (2CD Set)**
Biddy Mulligan / Springhill disaster / Doherty's reel / Down the broom/The honeymoon reel / Foggy dew / Weila weila weila / Kimmage / Donegal Danny / Queen of the fair/Tongs by the fire / Louse house in Kilkenny / Home boys home / High Germany / Whiskey in the jar / Champion at keeping them rolling / Scholar/Teetotaler / Joe Hill / Free the people / Sun is burning / Monto / Johnston's motorcar / Musical priest/Blackthorn stick / Battle of the Somme / Smith of Bristol / Button pusher / Molly Maguires / Kid on the mountain / Parcel o' rogues / School day's over / Jail of Claun Meala / Skibereen / Ojos negros / Killieburne brae / Saxon shilling / Lowlands of Holland / Holy ground
CHCD 1011 / Jul '93 / Chyme

☐ **DUBLINERS COLLECTION VOL.2, THE (2CD Set)**
Black velvet band / Hey Johnny McGory / Night visiting song / Drops of brandy/Lady Carberry / Farewell to Carlingford / Bunch of red roses / Lord of the dande / Rebel/Padraig Pearse / Ploughboy lads / Irish rover / Avondale / Downfall of Paris / Spancil Hill / Fiddler's green / Gentleman soldier / Dicey Reilly / God save Ireland / Song for Ireland / Master Magrath / Building up and tearing England down / Three sea Captains / Sam Hall / Town I love so well / Lark in the morning / I knew Danny Farrell / All for me grog / Humpty dumpty / Gartan Mother's lullaby / Home boys home / Maid behind the bar/Toss the feathers / On Raglan Road / Cuanla / Dublin in the rare ol' times / Molly Malone / Farewell to Ireland
CHCD 1094 / Aug '96 / Chyme

☐ **DUBLINERS LIVE**
Fairmoyle lassies/Sporting Paddy / Black velvet band / Whiskey in the jar / All for me grog / Belfast hornpipe/Tim Maloney / Four poster bed/Colonel Rodney / Finnegan's wake / McAlpine's fusiliers / Waterford boys/Humours of Scariff/Flannel jacket / Galway races / Btuilding up and tearing England down / Sick note-Murphy and the bricks / Seven drunken nights / Scholar/Teetotaller/High reel / Home boys home / Dirty old town / Blue mountain rag / Wild rover / Wealia waile / Holy ground
CHCD 1006 / Jun '96 / Chyme

☐ **DUBLINERS, THE**
Wild rover / Ragman's ball / Preab san ol / High reel / Holy ground / Tramps and hawkers / Home boys home / Rocky road to Dublin / Banks of the roses / I'll tell my ma / Swallow's tail reel / Jar of porter / Love is pleasing / Nightingale
HILLCD 12 / Feb '97 / Wooded Hill

☐ **ESSENTIAL COLLECTION, THE**
CDMFP 6345 / May '97 / Music For Pleasure

☐ **FURTHER ALONG**
Step out mary / Back in durham / Sailing in-alive's reel / Coming of the road / If you ever go to dublin town / Ar eireann ni neosainn ce hl / Dirty old town / Ta an coilech ag fogairt an lae / St. patrick's cathedral / Crack was ninety in the isle of man / Song for ireland / Job of journeywork / Cavan girl / Further along / Jigs / Miss zanussi-st. martin's day / Working man
TRACD 243 / Jun '96 / Transatlantic

☐ **GREATEST HITS**
Wild rover / Lark in the morning / Lifeboat Mona / Weila weila waile / Down by the glenside / Lord of the dance / Danny Farrell / Seven drunken nights / Mero / Champion at keepin' them rolling / Free the people / Dirty old town / Skibbereen / Louse house at Kilkenny / Gentleman soldier / Monto / Band played waltzing Matilda / Springheel disaster / Joe Hill / Whiskey in the jar
CDIRISH 007 / Mar '97 / Outlet

☐ **INSTRUMENTAL**
CH 1052CD / Sep '94 / Outlet

☐ **IRISH PUB SONGS**
CDPUB 027 / Oct '95 / Outlet

☐ **IRISH REBEL BALLADS**
Johnston's motorcar / Ould triangle / Four green fields / God save Ireland / Charles Stewart Parnell / Town I loved so well / Free the people / Down by the glenside / Boulavogue / Take it down from the mast / Rebel / Wrap the green flag 'round me / West's awake / Nation once again
CHCD 1055 / Oct '95 / Chyme

☐ **LIVE AT THE ROYAL ALBERT HALL**
Black velvet band / McAlpine's fusiliers / Peggy Gordon / Wella walla / Monto / Cork hornpipe / Leaving of Liverpool / Whisky on a Sunday / I wish I were back in Liverpool / Flop eared mule (Donkey Reel) / Navvy boots / Whiskey in the jar / Maids, when you're young never wed an old man / Seven drunken nights
CDMFP 6127 / May '97 / Music For Pleasure

☐ **LIVE IN CARRE, AMSTERDAM**
Sweets of May / Dicey Reilley / Song for Ireland / Building up and tearing England down / Dunphy's hornpipe / Leitrim fancy / Down the broom / Dirty old town / Old triangle / Whiskey in the jar / Humours of Scariff / Flannel jacket / Galway races / Prodigal son / Sick note / Wild rover / Seven drunken nights
5509292 / Jul '95 / Spectrum

☐ **MILESTONES**
TRACD 110 / Apr '96 / Transatlantic

☐ **ORIGINAL DUBLINERS**
Seven drunken nights / Galway races / Old alarm clock / Colonel Fraser and O'Rourke's reel / Rising of the moon / McCafferty / I'm a rover / Weila waila / Travelling people / Limerick rake / Zoological gardens / Fairmoye lasses and sporting Paddy / Black velvet band / Poor Paddy on the railway / Seven deadly sins / Net hauling song / Nancy Whiskey / Many young men of twenty / Paddy's gone to France/Skylark / Molly Bawn / Dundee weaver / Irish navvy / Tibby Dunbar / Inniskillen Dragoons / I wish I were back in Liverpool / Go to sea no more / Instrumental medley / Darby O'Leary / Cork hornpipe / Peggy Gordon / Maid of the sweet brown knowe / Quare bungle rye / Flop eared mule (Donkey reel) / Poor old Dicey Riley / Whiskey on a Sunday / Gentleman soldier / Navvy boots / Maids, when you're young never wed an old man / Rattlin' roarin' Willie / Mrs. McGrath / Carolan concerto / Partin' glass / Muirsheen durkin / Nation once again / Whiskey in the jar / Old triangle / Pub with no beer / Kelly, the boy from Killane / Croppy boy / Sullivan's John / Come and join the British Army / Shoals of herring / Mormon braes / Drink it up men / Maloney wants a drink
CDEM 1480 / Mar '93 / EMI

☐ **PARCEL OF ROGUES, A**
Spanish lady / Foggy dew / Kid on the mountain / Avondale / Acrobats / Village bells / Blantyre explosion / False hearted lover / Thirty foot trailer / Boulavogue / Doherty's reel / Down the broom / Honeymoon reel / Killieburne brae
EUCD 1061 / '89 / ARC

☐ **REVOLUTION**
Alabama 58 / Alabama 58 / Scorn not his simplicity / School days over / Se' fath mo bhuartha / Ojos negros / For what died the sons of roison / Joe hill / Bonny boy / Biddy mulligan / Button pusher / Battle of the somme-freedom come all ye / Peat bog soldiers
CHCD 1002 / Jan '95 / Chyme

☐ **SEVEN DRUNKEN NIGHTS**
Seven Drunken nights / Finnegan's wake / Monto / Auld triangle / Dirty old town / Sam Hall / Holy ground / Black velvet ground / Whiskey in the jar / McAlpine's fusileers / All for me grog / Wild rover / Weila wallia / Home boys home
CHCD 1032 / '88 / Chyme

☐ **SEVEN DRUNKEN NIGHTS**
Seven drunken nights / Poor Paddy on the railway / Whiskey on a Sunday / I'm a rover / Galway races / Darby O'Leary / Limerick rake / Dundee weaver / I wish I were back in Liverpool / Kelly the boy from Killan / Rising of the moon / Maid of the sweet brown knowe
WB 885812 / 2 Feb '98 / Disky

☐ **SONGS FROM IRELAND**
Wild rover / Leaving of liverpool / I'll tell my ma / Will you come to the bower / Easy and slow / Home boys home / Rocky road to dublin / Old orange flute / Nelson's farewell / Mason's apron / Off to dublin in the green / Peggy lettermore / Glendalough saint / Roisin dubh / Twang man / Boulavogue
SOW 90108 / Oct '95 / Sounds Of The World

☐ **SONGS OF DUBLIN**
CHCD 1054 / Oct '95 / Chyme

☐ **ULTIMATE IRISH FOLK ALBUM, THE**
Monto / Town I loved so well / Raglan Road / Wild rover / Spring Hill disaster / Seven drunken nights / Whiskey in the jar / Dirty old town / Auld triangle / Dublin in the rare old times / Finnegan's wake / Song for Ireland
KCD 445 / Jan '97 / Celtic Collections

☐ **WHISKEY IN THE JAR (3CD Set)**
Whiskey in the jar / Galway races / Old alarm clock / Rising of the moon / Poor paddy on the railway / Nancy Whiskey / Darby O'leary / Maid of the sweet brown knowe / Quare bungle rye / Poor old Dicey Riley / Mursheen Durkin / McCafferty / Travelling people / Molly bawn / Seven drunken nights / Weila waila / Limerick rake / Net hauling song / Whiskey on a Sunday / Mrs McGrath / Partin' grass / (The Bonny) shoals of herring / Mormon braes / Dundee weaver / I wish I were back in Liverpool / Go to sea no more / All for me grog / Gentleman soldier / I'm a rover / Fairmoye lasses and sporting paddy / Black velvet band / Seven deadly sins / Many young men of twenty / Maloney wants a drink / Croppy boy / Come and join the British army / Maids when you're young never wed an old man / Tibby Dunbar / Inniskillen dragoons / Peggy Gordon / Kelly, the boy from Killan / Nation once again
SA 872862 / Sep '96 / Disky

☐ **WILD ROVER, THE**
295943 / Oct '94 / Ariola

☐ **WILD ROVER, THE**
PDSCD 535 / Aug '96 / Pulse

Dubmerge

☐ **WAKE UP**
BUD 1 / May '96 / Bud Urge

Dubois, Kerwin

☐ **WE BUILD DIS CITY**
FBCD 010 / 9 Feb '98 / First Beat

Duboniks

☐ **2 BLIND MICE**
Don't get pushy / Nite 'n' day / Fi don givit / Stuck in the middle with you / Panic / Bad dogs / Drunk on something / Duboniks / Pushy dub
KOBICD 006 / 29 Sep '97 / Delancey Street

Dubplate Vibe Crew

☐ **VOICE OF DUB**
SOLDCD 003 / May '97 / Solardub

Dubrovniks

☐ **AUDIO SONIC LOVE AFFAIR**
NORMAL 127 / May '94 / Normal

☐ **DUBROVNIK BLUES**
NORMAL 117 / May '94 / Normal

☐ **MEDICINE WHEEL**
NORMAL 167CD / Dec '94 / Normal

Dubstar

☐ **DISGRACEFUL**
Stars / Anywhere / Just a girl she said / Elevator song / Day I see you again / Week in week out / Not so manic now / Popdorian / Not once, not ever / St. Swithin's day / Disgraceful
FOODCD 13 / Oct '95 / Food

☐ **DISGRACEFUL: REPACKAGED & REMIXED (2CD Set)**
Stars / Anywhere / Just a girl she said / Elevator song / Day I see you again / Week in week out / Not so manic now / Popdorian / Not once, not ever / St. Swithin's day / Disgraceful / Stars (Mother Dub mix) / Elevator song (Biff and Memphis mix) / Anywhere (Crunch chill) / Not once, not ever / Not so manic now (Way out West mix) / Stars (Way out West mix) / Not so manic now (Mother's whole dub) / Disgraceful (Steve Hillier mix)
FOODCOR 13 / Jul '96 / Food

☐ **GOODBYE**
I will be your girlfriend / Inside / No more talk / Polestar / Say the worst thing first / Cathedral park / It's over / View from here / My start in wallsend / It's clear / Ghost / Can't tell me / Wearchest / When you say goodbye / Let's go
FOODCD 23 / 22 Sep '97 / Food

Dubtribe

☐ **SELENE SONGS**
ORG 013CD / 23 Feb '98 / Organico

☐ **SOUND SYSTEM**
ORG 007CD / 23 Feb '98 / Organico

☐ **VERSIONS**
ORG 025CD / 23 Feb '98 / Organico

Duchaine, Kent

☐ **JUST ME AND MY GUITAR**
CAD 01CD / Jun '94 / Cadillac

☐ **LOOKIN' BACK**
CAD 1313CD / Jun '94 / Cadillac

☐ **TAKE A LITTLE RIDE WITH ME**
CAD 1414CD / Apr '95 / Cadillac

Duchesne, Andre

☐ **L' OU 'L**
VICTOCD 010 / Nov '94 / Victo

Duchin, Eddie

☐ **EDDIE DUCHIN ORCHESTRA 1933-1937, THE (Duchin, Eddie Orchestra)**
TT 413 / May '98 / Take Two

☐ **EDDIE DUCHIN STORY, THE (Original Mono Recordings 1933-1938) (Duchin, Eddie Orchestra)**
I cover the waterfront / Let's fall in love / Ill wind / She reminds me of you / Riptide / Easy come, easy go / I only have eyes for you / Learning / One night of love / Lovely to look at / I won't dance / Isn't this a lovely day / Moon over Miami / I'm an old cowhand / Follow your heart / Love will tell / It's de-lovely / Moonlight and shadows / Someone to care for me / Too marvellous for words / Merry-go-round broke down / Star is born / 10 o'clock town / Get out of town
CDAJA 5205 / Oct '96 / Living Era

☐ **SOPHISTICATED STYLING 1933-1937 (Duchin, Eddie Orchestra)**
TT 417 / May '98 / Take Two

Ducks Deluxe

☐ **ALL TOO MUCH**
622402 / Mar '96 / Skydog

☐ **TAXI TO THE TERMINAL ZONE**
Coast to coast / Nervous breakdown / Daddy put the bomp / I got you / Please please please / Fireball / Don't mind rockin' tonite / Heart's on my sleeve / Falling on my sleeve / Falling for the woman / West Texas trucking board / It's all over now / Cherry pie / It don't matter tonite / I'm crying / Love's melody / Teenage head / Rio Grande / My my music / Rainy night in Kilburn / Paris 9
MAUCD 610 / Oct '91 / Mau Mau

Ducksoup

☐ **PLANET SKA**
JABSCO 007CD / 16 Mar '98 / Burning Heart

Ducret, Marc

☐ **DETAIL**
9100032 / Oct '97 / Winter & Winter

☐ **IN THE GRASS (Ducret, Marc & Bobby Previn)**
Fifty is a hundred a hundred is a thousand... / 7 families / Handy / Very handy / Tight lipstick / Du du du / Walking in the dust / Very handy indeed / And the rest are what they are / Qui parle
ENJ 93432 / 26 May '98 / Enja

☐ **UN CERTAIN MALAISE**
What did I forget / Old brown shoe / Mefiance / Un certain malaise / Le bruit court / La mazurka
SCREWU 70005 / 5 May '98 / ScrewGun

Dudley, Anne

☐ **ANCIENT AND MODERN**
Canticles of the sun and the moon / Veni sanct spiritus / Communion / Veni veni emmanuel / Tallis canon / Holly and the ivy / Coventry carol / Prelude / Vater unser im himmelreich
ECHCD 003 / 20 Apr '98 / Echo

☐ **SONGS FROM THE VICTORIOUS CITY (Dudley, Anne & Jaz Coleman)**
Awakening / Endless festival / Minarets and memories / Force and fire / Habebe / Ziggarats and Cinnamon / Hannah / Conqueror / Survivor's tale / In a timeless place
WOLCD 1009 / Apr '91 / China

Dudley-Smith, Timothy

☐ **TELL OUT, MY SOUL (Dudley-Smith, Timothy & All Souls Church Orchestra/ Choir)**
When the Lord in glory comes / As water to the thirsty / Born by the Holy Spirit's breath / Christ is risen as He said / Christ is the one who calls / Fill your hearts with joy and gladness / Holy child / How still you lie / I lift my eyes / Lighten our darkness / Lord, for the years / Name of all Majesty / Safe in the shadow of the Lord / We come as guests invited
KMCD 936 / Aug '96 / Kingsway

Due Nueva America

☐ **FIESTA LATINA - LATIN AMERICAN SONGS**
Maria Paleta / Pampa Lirima / Brasileirinho / Patricia / El condor pasa / Delicado / LA llorona / Candombe mulato / Seleccion san juanitos / Del caribe a los Andes / Senora tentacion / Camino real / La partida / Flor de cacao / Aptao
EUCD 1203 / Sep '93 / ARC

Duellists

☐ **ENGLISH HURDY GURDY MUSIC**
Starters, Alfriston / Miserden, indigo / Duellists / Doyenne / Capriole, drystone / Kate at the gate / Magog, monkey puzzle / Bluesaussis, biscuit shuffle / Baba yaga's cat / Poolside
PATCCD 20397D / May '97 / Panic ATC

Duet Emmo

☐ **OR SO IT SEEMS**
Hill of men / Or so it seems / Friano / First person / A.n.c. / Long sledge / Gatemmo / Last's card / Heart of hearts
CDSTUMM 11 / Aug '92 / Mute

Duetones

☐ **JUST IN TIME**
CH 807101 / Jul '98 / Cherokee

Duff, Mary

☐ **COLLECTION, THE**
RZRCD 550 / Oct '95 / Ritz

☐ **JUST LOVING YOU**
She broke her promise / End of the world / Moonlighter / What do they know / More than I can say / Power of love / Secret love / When you're not a dream / If anything should happen to you / What the eyes don't see / Tonight we might fall in love again / Cliffs of Dooneen / Strangers / Just loving you
RZCD 0075 / Jun '95 / Ritz

☐ **LOVE SOMEONE LIKE ME**
Love someone like me / She's got you / Are you teasing me / Crazy / Forever and ever Amen / It's not over (if I'm not over you) / Daddy's hands / Pick me up on your way down / Dear God / Chicken every Sunday / There won't be any patches in heaven / Do me with love
RZCD 503 / '91 / Ritz

☐ **SHADES OF BLUE**
Road to Eden / Wounded heart / Face in the crowd / Just like yesterday / I just knew / Michael / Suffering in silence / I don't blame you / I'd just as soon go / No one's living here / Love lines / Isle of hope / Dark island
RZCD 0082 / Apr '97 / Ritz

☐ **SILVER AND GOLD**
Your one and only / Picture of me (without you) / Walk the way the wind blows / Deep water / Silver and gold / Mama was a working man / Sunshine and rain / Homeland / One you slip around with / Where would that leave me / I'll be your San Antone rose / Fields of Athenry / Beautiful meath / Down by the Sally gardens
RZCD 0066 / May '92 / Ritz

☐ **WINNING WAYS**
Goin' gone / Yellow roses / Eighteen wheels and a dozen roses / Can I sleep in your arms / Once a day / Does Fort Worth ever cross your mind / One bird on a wing / Just out of reach / Heartaches by the number / I'm not that lonely yet / Come on in / Maggie
RZCD 506 / '91 / Ritz

Duffy, Stephen

☐ **I LOVE MY FRIENDS (Duffy)**
Tune in / Eucharist / 17 / Lovers beware / You are / Deal / She belongs to all / Autopsy / What if I fell in love / Just good / Twenty three / Postcard / One day one of these fucks will change your lives
COOKCD 144 / 27 Apr '98 / Cooking Vinyl

☐ MUSIC IN COLOURS
It sparkles / Transitoire I / Natalie / Transitoire II / She wants to share her magic / Transitoire III / Music in colours / Galaxy / Transitoire IV / Totem / Transitoire V / Holte end hotel / Transitoire VI / Charlotte's conversation / Transitoire VII / Fall from the sky
7894202 / 1 Jun '98 / EMI

☐ UPS AND DOWNS, THE (Duffy, Stephen 'Tin Tin')
Kiss me / She makes me quiver / Masterpiece / But is it art / Wednesday Jones / Icing on the cake / Darkest blues / Be there / Believe in me / World at large alone
DIXCD 5 / Apr '85 / 10

Dufourcet, Marie

☐ DUETS FOR ORGAN AND PIANO (Dufourcet, Marie Bernadette & Francoise Dechico Cartier)
PRCD 347 / Sep '92 / Priory

Dug

☐ BEWARE OF FAFNER
NIX 05CD / Aug '97 / Nix

Dug Dug's

☐ DUG DUG'S
PECD 472 / Jun '97 / Cirula Elect

Duggan Family

☐ DUGGAN'S TRAD, THE
CICD 090 / Dec '93 / Clo Iar-Chonnachta

Duggan, John

☐ MISSION, THE
Memories of the mission / Night the telly blinked / Country boy / Michael mor agus city Sue / Radioholic / Cigarettes / Barmaid I met in Kinsale
SUNCD 9 / '93 / Sound

Duh

☐ BLOWHARD
TUPCD 032 / Feb '92 / Tupelo

☐ UNHOLY HAND JOB, THE
K 163C / Nov '95 / Konkurrel

Duhan, Johnny

☐ FAMILY ALBUM
Room / Ordinary town / Trying to get the balanace right / Young mothers / Couple of kids / Corner stone / Well knit family / We had our trouble then / Storm is passed / Voyage
RTMCD 16 / Jul '90 / Round Tower

Duignan, Eoin

☐ COUMINEOL
CEFCD 163 / Jan '94 / Gael Linn

Duisit, Lorraine

☐ FEATHER RIVER (Duisit, Lorraine & Tom Espinola)
CDPH 9012 / '88 / Philo

Duke, George

☐ BRAZILIAN LOVE AFFAIR
Brazilian love affair / Summer breezin' / Cravo E Canela / Alone / 6 a.m. / Brazilian sugar / Sugar loaf mountain / Love reborn / Up from the sea it arose and ate Rio in one / I need you now / Ao que vai Nascer
4712832 / Jan '95 / Sony Jazz

☐ DON'T LET GO
EK 35366 / Aug '97 / Sony Jazz

☐ DREAM ON
EK 37532 / Aug '97 / Sony Jazz

☐ GUARDIAN OF THE LIGHT
Overture / Light / Shane / Born to love you / Silly fightin' / You / War fugue interlude / Reach out / Give me your love / Stand / Soon / Celebrate / Fly away
4738982 / Jul '95 / Sony Jazz

☐ RENDEZVOUS
Got to get back to love / Stay awhile / Powersecret rendezvous / Thinking of you / Take it on / She can't wait forever / Better ways / Your life / Ipanema lady
EK 39262 / Jul '95 / Sony Jazz

☐ THIS IS JAZZ
Diamonds / Love reborn / Cravo e canela / Positive energy / Sugar loaf mountain / Pathways / Brazilian sugar / Hot fire / Summer breezin' / Omi (freshwater)
EK 65054 / 4 May '98 / Sony Jazz

Dukes Of Dixieland

☐ DIXIE ON PARADE (2CD Set)
Sweet Georgia Brown / Basin street blues / South Rampart Street Parade / Washington and Lee swing / My blue heaven / Sheik of Araby / Waiting for the Robert E Lee / Toot toot tootsie / Tailgate ramble / High society / Clarinet marmalade / When my sugar walks down the street / (There'll be a) Hot time on the old town tonight / Darktown strutters ball / Mama don't allow it / Limehouse blues / Missisippi mud / Milenberg joys / Down by the old mill stream / Ol'man river / St. Louis blues / Tiger rag / Original Dixieland one-step / Wolverine blues / Slide, frog, slide / Dill pickles rag / After you've gone / Riverside blues / Lazy river / Dear old southland / Down by the riverside / Ain't she sweet / Twelfth street rag / Johnson rag / Bugle call rag / Swanee river / St. James infirmary / Copenhagen / San / When it's sleepy time down south / Beale Street blues
DBG 53051 / Aug '96 / Double Gold

Dukes Of Stratosphear

☐ CHIPS FROM THE CHOCOLATE FIREBALL
Twenty five o'clock / Bike ride to the moon / My love explodes / What in the world... / Your gold dress / Mole from the ministry / Vanishing girl / Have you seen Jackie / Little lighthouse / You're a good man Albert Brown (curse you red barrel) / Collideascope / You're my drug / Shiny cage / Brainiac's daughter / Affiliated / Pale and precious
COMCD 11 / Aug '87 / Virgin

Dulac, Jacqueline

☐ FLAGRANT DELICE
984402 / 24 Apr '98 / EPM

Dulcimer

☐ DULCIMER
Sonnet to the fall / Pilgrim from the city / Morman's casket / Ghost of the wandering minstrel boy / Gloucester City / Starlight / Caravan / Lisa's song / Time in my life / Fruit of the musical tree / While it lasted / Suzanne
SEECD 266 / Sep '89 / See For Miles

☐ ROOM FOR THOUGHT
HBG 122/6 / Apr '94 / Background

Dulfer, Candy

☐ BIG GIRL
Wake me when it's over / ILU / Tommygun / Jazz it's me / Miles / Funkyness / Capone / Get funky / Chains / September / Upstairs / I'll still be looking up to you / Big girl
74321315132 / 1 Sep '97 / RCA

☐ SAX-A-GO-GO
2 funky / Sax-a-go-go / Mister marvin / Man in the desert / Bob's jazz / Jamming / I can't make you love me / Pick up the pieces / Compared to what / Sunday afternoon
74321111812 / Mar '93 / RCA

☐ SAXUALITY
Pee wee / Saxuality / So what / Jazzid / Heavenly city / Donja / There goes the neighborhood / Mr. Lee / Get the funk / House is not a home
260696 / Aug '95 / RCA

Dulfer, Hans

☐ EXPRESS DELAYED (Dulfer, Hans & Herbert Noord)
Home is not a house / Troubleshooter / Take it away babe / Carrow / Meeting the six / Troubleshooter 2
MCD 0041 / Apr '96 / Limetree

Dull Knife

☐ ELECTRIC INDIAN
SB 026 / Jun '97 / Second Battle

Dulzaineros Del Vilorio

☐ SIERTERIA
20084 / Aug '96 / Sonifolk

Dumb

☐ THIRSTY
UP 040 / Jan '97 / Up

Dumisani Ras

☐ MISTER MUSIC
505322 / Oct '96 / Declic

Dumitrescu, Iancu

☐ A PRIORI
A priori / 5 implosions / Mythos de sacrae / Lamentationem / Icarus
EDMN 1006 / Oct '95 / Editions Modern

☐ AU DELA DE MOVEMUR
Au dela de mouvemur / Monades / Ekagrata / Signum gemini / Zodiaque
EDMN 1003 / Oct '95 / Editions Modern

☐ GALAXY
Galaxy / Movemur / Reliefs / Memorial / Basoreliefs
EDMN 1005 / Oct '95 / Editions Modern

☐ IANCU DUMITRESCU & ANA-MARIA AVRAM (Dumitrescu, Iancu & Ana-Maria Avram)
EDMN 1008 / Jun '97 / Editions Modern

☐ MEDIUM III
Medium III / Cogito / Trompe l'oeil / Aulodie moiritica / Apogeum / Perspectives
EDMN 1001 / Oct '95 / Editions Modern

☐ MNEMOSYNE/IMPULSE
EDMN 1007 / Jun '98 / Editions Modern

☐ MUISIQUE DE PAROLES
Muisique de paroles / Astalos
EDMN 1004 / Oct '95 / Editions Modern

☐ SACREES
Sacrees / Harryphones (alpha and epsilon) / Grande ourse
EDMN 1002 / Oct '95 / Editions Modern

Dummer, John

☐ CABAL...PLUS (Dummer, John Blues Band)
I need love / Just a feeling / No chance with you / Young fashioned ways / Sitting and thinking / Low down Santa Fe / When you got a good friend / Welfare blues / Hound dog / Blue guitar / After hours / Daddy please don't cry / Doblee dooblee jubilee / Monkey speaks his mind / Travelling man / 40 days / Nine by nine / Going in the out / Medicine weasel / Endgame
SEECD 456 / Oct '96 / See For Miles

☐ NINE BY NINE
World's in a tangle / Soulful dress / Let me love you baby / Screaming and crying / Big feeling blues / New skin game / No chance now / Reconsider baby / Down home girl / I can't be satisfied / Nine by nine / I love you honey / Riding in the moonlight / Walkin' blues / Lovin' man / Statesboro' blues / Monkey speaks his mind / Young blood / Be careful what you do / Shame shame shame / Walking the dog
IGOCD 2021 / May '95 / Indigo

Dump

☐ I CAN HEAR MUSIC
BRCD 0729 / 22 May '98 / Brinkman

☐ PLEA FOR TENDERNESS, A
BRCD 070 / 22 May '98 / Brinkman

☐ SUPERPOWERLESS
BRCD 013 / 19 Jan '98 / Brinkman

Dumpster Juice

☐ GET THAT OUT OF YOUR MOUTH
Clown midget / DDS / Hud / Bowl / Stockton / Pound / Chisel you weasel / Farmer gatherer / Living dead / Gerald / Mommy's sobbin' / Kwan tu
892712 / May '94 / Spanish Fly

Dunaj

☐ LA LA LA
R 0009 / Jun '97 / Rachot

Dunbar, Aynsley

☐ AYNSLEY DUNBAR RETALIATION, THE (Dunbar, Aynsley Retaliation)
MCAD 22101 / May '94 / One Way

☐ BLUE WHALE
Willing to fight / Willie the pimp / It's your turn / Days / Going home
14814 / May '96 / Spalax

☐ DOCTOR DUNBAR'S PRESCRIPTION (Dunbar, Aynsley Retaliation)
MCAD 22102 / May '94 / One Way

☐ TO MUM FROM AYNSLEY AND THE BOYS (Dunbar, Aynsley Retaliation)
MCAD 22069 / May '94 / One Way

Dunbar, Valerie

☐ BEST OF VALERIE DUNBAR, THE
Always Argyll / Mull of Kintyre / How great thou art / Medley / Loch Lomond / Old rugged cross / Scotland again / Bonnie Gallowa' / Annie Laurie / Medley / Lochingar / Scotland forever / Dumbartons drums / Lovely Argyll / Mingulay boat song / Flower of Scotland / Medley / Medley
CDLOC 1099 / Nov '96 / Lochshore

☐ SCARLET RIBBONS
Mingulay boat song / Bonnie mary of argyll / Till we meet again / Dumbarton's drums / Scarlet ribbons (for her hair) / Lovely argyll / Beneath the lights of home / Annie laurie / Wind beneath my wings / Eriskay love lilt / Waters of kylesku / Falkland hero / Lovely oban bay / Isle of innesfree / Haste ye back
CDKLP 69 / Sep '90 / Klub

Duncan, Gordon

☐ CIRCULAR BREATH, THE
Macdonald's / High drive / Jolly tinker / Clan meets tribe / Contradiction / Herring in salt / Circular breath / Shepherd's crook / Blow my chanter / MacFadden's / MacDougall's / Gathering
CDTRAX 122 / Mar '97 / Greentrax

☐ JUST FOR SEAMUS
Hornpipe and jig / 4 strathspeys and 3 reels / 2 x 2\4 marches / 3 jigs / Selection / Slow air / Jigs / 3 x strathspeys and 3 x reels / Slow air and 4 reels / 3 jigs / Jig and 3 reels / Piobaireachd / Just for seamus set
CDTRAX 075 / Aug '94 / Greentrax

Duncan, Hugo

☐ IRISH COLLECTION, THE
CDIRISH 005 / Oct '95 / Outlet

Duncan, Jock

☐ YE SHINE WHAR YE STAN
Gruel / Rhynie / Lothian hairst/Hairsters' reel / Cruel mother / Hash O' Benagoak / Bogie's bonnie belle / Glenlogie / Bonnie Udny / Bonnie lass O' Fyvie / Sleepytoon / Mormond braes / Hairst O' Rettie / Macfarlan O' the Sprotts / Plouboy lads / Drumdelgie / Battle of Harlaw/Desperate battle / Banks of Inverurie / Barnyards O' Delgaty
SPRCD 1039 / Feb '97 / Springthyme

Duncan, John

☐ SEND
TO 20 / Oct '95 / Touch

Duncan, Johnny

☐ LAST TRAIN TO SAN FERNANDO (4CD Set) (Duncan, Johnny Bluegrass Boys)
Last train to San Fernando / Rockabilly baby / Footprints in the snow / Blue blue heartache / Jig along home / If you love me baby / Goodnight Irene / Freight train blues / Press on / Johnny's blue yodel / Out of business / Get along home Cindy / Old Blue / Calamity Mose / Just a little lovin' / Which way did he go / More and more / Just a closer walk with thee / Travellin' blues / St. James Infirmary / Mind your own business / Kaw-Liga / Ella speed / Doin' my time / Where could I go / Can't you line 'em / Gypsy Davy / Blue yodel / Old dusty road / Itching for my baby / I heard the bluebirds sing / Railroad, steamboat, rivers and canals / More and more / Geisha girl / All the monkeys ain't in the zoo / This train / Rosalie / Hey good lookin' / Wedding bells / Moanin' the blues / Cold cold heart / Jambalaya / Your cheatin' heart / Long gone lonesome blues / Half as much / May you never be alone / Salute to Hank Williams / My son calls another man Daddy / My lucky love / Any time / Kansas City / That's alright darlin' / Yellow yellow moon / Rockabilly medley / Waltz medley / Railroad medley / Gospel medley / Sleepy eyed John / Tobacco Road / Legend of Gunga Din / Hannah / Waitin' for the sandman / Long time gone / Will you be mine / She's my baby / You shouldn't have cried / Baby we're really in love / Bluebird Island / Ballad of Jed Clampett / Dang me / Which way did he go / My little baby / I thank my lucky stars / Beyond the sunset / Just a little walk with Jesus / Amazing grace / Where could I go to but to the Lord / Just a closer walk with thee / Walking in Jerusalem just like John / Precious Lord hold my hand / No hiding place down there / I've just told Mama goodbye / In the garden / Press on / When God dips his pen of love in my heart / Last train to San Fernando / Little things / I fought the law / Out of business / I wonder where you are tonight / Someone stole my steel guitar / Joe and Mabel's 12th Street Bar and Grill / Margie's at Lincoln's Park Inn / Footprints in the snow / Kaw-Liga / I ain't buyin' / Mustang prang / Life can be beautiful / Hello heartache / If it feels good, do it / Wild side of life / Just for what I am / Salty dog blues / Just a little lovin' / Footprints in the snow / Blue blue heartaches / Someone to give my love to / Hank Williams medley / Smoke smoke smoke (that cigarette) / Tom Dooley / Last train to San Fernando / Mustang prang
BCD 15947 / Dec '96 / Bear Family

Duncan, Sammy

☐ SAMMY DUNCAN & HIS HOT SOUTH JAZZ BAND
JCD 264 / Jun '96 / Jazzology

Duncan, Stuart

☐ STUART DUNCAN
Bushy fork of John Creek/Mason's apron / G Forces / Thai clips / Passing / Miles to go / Lee highway blues / Lonely moon / Whistling Rufus / Summer of my dreams / My dixie home / Two o'clock in the morning
ROUCD 0263 / '92 / Rounder

Duncan, Tommy

☐ BENEATH A NEON STAR IN A HONKY TONK
Gossip song / California waltz / Got a letter from my kid today / Jesus is mine / Take your burden to the Lord / Nancy Jane / Relax and take it easy / Move a little closer / I was just walking out the door / I've turned a gadabout / I hit the jackpot / I don't want to hurt you / Excuse me, I gotta go / Tomato can / Who drank my beer / Where oh where has my little... / It may take a long long time / Grits and gravy blues / Beneath a neon star in a honky tonk / Stars over San Antone / I reckon in a Texan / I guess you were right / Tennessee church bells / Hound dog / That certain feeling / San Antonio rose / Daddyo loves Mammyo / Crazy mixed up kid
BCD 15957 / Dec '96 / Bear Family

☐ TEXAS MOON
I'm thru wastin' time on you / Take me back to Tulsa / Worried over you / Time changes everything / September / Gamblin' polka dot blues / You put me on my feet / Just a plain old country boy / In the jailhouse now / Chattanooga shoe shine boy / I don't believe you're mine / Never no mo' blues / Texas moon / Just a little bit jealous / We got good business / Please come back home / High country / All star boogie / There's not a cow in Texas / See who's sorry now / Sick, sober and sorry / Mississippi river blues / Wrong road home blues / Sweet Mama hurry home or... / My sweet wildflower / I'm swing you
BCD 15907 / Dec '96 / Bear Family

Dundee Strathspey & Reel Society

☐ FIDDLE ME JIG
Moray reel/Willie Tate / O'er the hills to Ardentinny/ Flo'er o'the heather / Farewell to the creeks/Mo caillreag fhein (68 pipe marches) / Perth accordion and fiddle club/The skymen of Arnhem / A land for all seasons / Australian ladies/Atholl and Breadalbane gathering / Ronald Cooper/Jim Anderson's delight / Lassie wi' the yellow coatie / Dumbarton Castle/Blin' Jamie-David / Lee light o'the moon
LCOM 9047 / Aug '91 / Lismor

Dunham Jazz & Jubilee Singers

☐ DUNHAM JAZZ & JUBILEE SINGERS 1927-1931
DOCD 5498 / Nov '96 / Document

Dunham, Sonny

☐ SONNY DUNHAM
CCD 085 / Oct '93 / Circle

Dunkelziffer

☐ DUNKELZIFFER III
FUNFUNDVIERZ 23 / Jun '97 / Funfundvierz

☐ IN THE NIGHT
FUNFUNDVIERZ 2 / Jun '97 / Funfundvierz

☐ LIVE
CTCD 058 / Jun '97 / Captain Trip

Dunkley, Errol

☐ EARLY YEARS, THE
RNCD 2104 / May '95 / Rhino

☐ ERROL AGAIN
SCHCD 01 / Jul '97 / Schema

☐ OK FRED
O.k. fred / Ok fred dub / Love brother love / Give (if you can give) / Oh lord (hear my humble prayer) / Repatriation / Peek-a-boo / Sit and cry over you / Letter to mummy and daddy / If the world were mine / Don't go nowhere / Patricia I love you
RNCD 2017 / Jul '93 / Rhino

☐ PLEASE STOP YOUR LYING
RGCD 0041 / Apr '97 / Rocky One

☐ PROFILE
665432 / Jul '97 / Melodie

Dunlavy

☐ I RUINED AMERICA
SGCD 8 / Sep '97 / September Gurls

Dunmall, Paul

☐ DESIRE AND LIBERATION (Dunmall, Paul Octet)
SLAMCD 225 / Aug '97 / Slam

☐ FOLKS (Dunmall, Paul & Paul Rogers)
Dingle at Leigh / Malvern Hills / S-round / Pete's reel / Himalayan balsam / Lament 4 / Nan / Grandad / Francis Thompson / St. Edburga / Alfrick's swan / Hornpipe / Cruck barn / Lucky Oscar / Lament 1 and 2 / Hairy fox / Grassnake / Nu / Nibly point / Bank Farm / Two dogs at Pigeon House
SLAMCD 212 / Oct '96 / Slam

☐ GHOSTLY THOUGHTS (Dunmall, Paul & John Adams/Mark Sanders)
HATOLOGY 503 / Dec '97 / Hatology

☐ QUARTET, SEXTET AND BABU TRIO (2CD Set)
Dubunni / Moths and spiders / In the haddock / Devil's chair / Lert / Trickly hausen / Shun fat / Separate balls
SLAMCD 207 / Oct '96 / Slam

☐ SOLILOQUY - 1986
MR 15 / '90 / Matchless

Dunn, Holly

☐ LIFE, LOVE AND ALL THE STAGES
5141611402 / Mar '96 / River North

Dunn, Johnny

☐ JOHNNY DUNN VOL.1 (1921-1922)
JPCD 1522 / Jul '96 / Jazz Perspectives

☐ JOHNNY DUNN VOL.2 (1922-1928)
JPCD 1523 / Jul '96 / Jazz Perspectives

Dunn, Larry

☐ LOVER'S SILHOUETTE (Dunn, Larry Orchestra)
Lover's silhouette / 2000 SKY-5 / Don't it make you wanna cry / Italian lady (A song for Mama) / Heaven sent (Michael's song) / Where's the love / Between 7 and earth / Pure faith (guitar interlude) / Maybe in my dreams / Jahap / Enchanted
101S 870712 / Nov '93 / 101 South

Dunn, Roy

☐ KNOW'D THEM ALL
She cooked cornbread for her husband / Further on down the line / Everything I get a hold to / CC rider / You're worrying me / Lost lover blues / Stranger's blues / Move to Kansas city / Red cross store / Don't tear my clothes / I changed the lock / Pearl Harbour blues / Mr. Charlie / Bachelor's blues / Roy's matchbox blues
TRIX 3312 / Nov '93 / Trix

Dunn, Willie

☐ AKWESASNE NOTES
TRIK 032 / Oct '94 / Trikont

☐ PACIFIC
TRIK 075 / Oct '94 / Trikont

Dunn-Packer Band

☐ LOVE AGAINST THE WALL
Love against the wall / Broken dreams / Dear john / 21 days / Close to you / Mama talk to your daughter / Heart's desire / House with a cardboard gate / Look what you've done / I get so worried / Bring it on home / I don't care / Can't help it / Certain girl / Pallet on the floor / Pedal to the metal
TRCD 9905 / Nov '93 / Tramp

Dunne, Mary

☐ COOLATEE
Song of De Dannan / Do you love an apple / Athru / Changes / Spancil Hill / Danny / Coolatee / Baidin fheilimi / Tell me / Star of County Down / Mary from Dungloe / Cliffs of Dooneen/Margaret's waltz
JVC 90172 / Nov '97 / JVC

Dunne, Mickey

☐ LIMERICK LASSIES
SD 001CD / Apr '94 / SD Recordings

Dunne, Pecker

☐ TRAVELLIN' PEOPLE (Dunne, Pecker & Margaret Barry)
Dirty old town / Come back Paddy Reilly / Last of the travellin' people / She moved through the fair / Ballybunion by the sea / Down by the broom / Portlaoise jail / Cottage with the horseshoe / Wexford / Her mantle so green / Whiskey in the jar / Leprachaun / Tinker's lullaby / If you ever go o'er to Ireland / Down by the Liffeyside / Half door / Ould Morris van / Blarney stone / McAlpines fusiliers / Lovely Derry on the banks of the Foyle / Roisin dubh
MCVD 30012 / Nov '96 / Emerald Gem

Dunnery, Francis

☐ LET'S GO DO WHAT HAPPENS
RE 82834 / 27 Apr '98 / Razor & Tie

☐ ONE NIGHT IN SAUCHIEHALL STREET
COTINDCD 2 / May '95 / Cottage Industry

☐ TALL BLOND HELICOPTER
48 hours / Too much saturn / In my dreams / Johnny Podell song / Because I can / Immaculate / Father and Son
7567828252 / Apr '96 / Atlantic

Dunphy, Sean

☐ IRELAND TO REMEMBER
DOCDX 9014 / Jul '96 / Dolphin

Dunvant Male Choir

☐ WELSH CELEBRATION
Fanfare / Capital city / Cwm rhondda / Soldiers' chorus / Where shall I be / Goin' home / Ar hyd y nos / Sospan fach patrol / Rhythm of life / Memory / 76 trombones / David of the white rock / Investiture music / Morte criste (when I survey the wondrous cross) / Tydi a roddaist / Moab / Rose / An evening's pastorale / Battle hymn of the republic / Day thou gavest / Rising of the lark / Men of harlech
BNA 5057 / Sep '91 / Bandleader

Duo Bertrand

☐ DUO BERTRAND
AVPL 12CD / Apr '94 / Diffusion Breizh

Duo Dre

☐ TRE
Ouverture - strange new world / Vogel tut noot / Waltz in the woods / Veteran's day / Plan / Sushi moto / Unseren lieben frauen
8379502 / Oct '94 / Amadeo

Duo Peylet-Cunilot

☐ MUSIQUE DES KLEZMORIM
925672 / Jun '93 / BUDA

☐ MUSIQUE KLEZMER
925682 / Jun '93 / BUDA

Duochrome

☐ ALL DAY I DREAM ABOUT SEX
COG 004 / 13 Apr '98 / Vital Cog

Dupa, Sangwa

☐ BUDDHIST TANTRAS OF GYUTO
7559791982 / Jan '95 / Nonesuch

Dupree, 'Champion' Jack

☐ 1945-53
KKCD 08 / Nov '92 / Krazy Kat

☐ BIGTOWN PLAYBOYS BURNLEY FESTIVAL
JSPCD 231 / Oct '89 / JSP

☐ BLUES FOR EVERYBODY
Heartbreaking women / Watchin' my stuff / Ain't no meat on de bone / Blues got me rockin' / Tongue tied blues / Please tell me baby / Harelip blues / Two below zero / Let the doorbell ring / Blues for everybody / That's my pa / She cooks me cabbage / Failing health blues / Stumbling block / Mail order woman / Silent partner / House rent party / Rub a little boogie / Walking the blues / Daybreak rock
CD 52029 / Mar '93 / Blues Encore

☐ BLUES FROM THE GUTTER
Strollin' / TB Blues / Can't kick the habit / Evil woman / Nasty boogie / Junkers blues / Bad blood / Goin' down slow / Frankie and Johnny / Stack-o-lee
7567824342 / Jul '93 / Atlantic

☐ BLUES OF CHAMPION JACK DUPREE VOL.1, THE
STCD 8019 / Jul '96 / Storyville

☐ BLUES OF CHAMPION JACK DUPREE VOL.2, THE
STCD 8020 / Jul '96 / Storyville

☐ CHAMPION JACK DUPREE
DOCD 5444 / May '96 / Document

☐ CHAMPION JACK DUPREE 1945-1946 (The Joe Davis Sessions)
Rum cola blues / She makes good jelly / Johnson street boogie / I'm a doctor for women / Wet neck mama / Love strike blues / Gin Mill Sal / Fisherman's blues / FDR blues
FLYCD 22 / Sep '90 / Flyright

☐ CHAMPION JACK DUPREE 1977-1983
157712 / Feb '93 / Blues Collection

☐ GAMBLIN' MAN 1940-1947
159192 / 1 Jun '98 / Blues Collection

☐ GET BACK JACK, DO IT AGAIN
Wine wine wine / Bring me flowers when I'm living / Junkers blues / I keep on drifting / In the evening / Freedom blues / One scotch one bourbon one beer / She's gone / Lawdy lawdy / I used to love you / Rock the boogie woogie / Sweet little baby
KATCD 103 / 29 Sep '97 / Catfish

☐ HOME (Charly Blues Masterworks Vol.40)
My baby's coming home / (I'll be glad when you're dead) you rascal you / No tomorrow / Heart of the blues is sound / Japanese special / Hard feeling / Blues from 1921 / Don't mistreat your woman
CDBM 40 / Jan '93 / Charly

☐ JACK DUPREE, JIMMY RUSHING & MUDDY WATERS (Dupree, Jack & Jimmy Rushing/Muddy Waters)
Get some more you fool / Way I feel / In the moonlight / She's mine, she's yours / Somebody's been spoiling these woman / Harelip blues / Everybody blues / Walking the blues / Silent partner / Overhead blues / Sugar sweet / All aboard / I'm ready / Forty days and forty nights
17062 / Jul '96 / Laserlight

☐ LIVE WITH THE BIG TOWN PLAYBOYS (Dupree, 'Champion' Jack & The Big Town Playboys)
JSPCD 807 / 27 Jul '98 / JSP

☐ NEW ORLEANS BARRELHOUSE 1960
PYCD 53 / Oct '93 / Magpie

☐ ONE LAST TIME
BB 9522CD / Aug '93 / Bullseye Blues

☐ TRUCKIN' ON DOWN
How long blues / Blues before sunrise / Rocky mountain blues / Deep sea diver / Automobile blues / Midnight hour blues / You gotto do asitell you / Truckin' on down / It's too late / Doctor Dupree blues / Come back baby / Alberta / My baby's gone / Calcutta blues / Please don't dog your woman / Tee na nee na / Rock me mama / Big fat mama
STCD 8029 / Jun '98 / Storyville

Dupree, Cornell

☐ CAN'T GET THROUGH
Can't get through / Southern comfort / Double clutch / Sweet thing / Slippin' in / Let the sun shine on me again / Duck soup / Could it be
CDMT 020 / Mar '93 / Meteor

☐ CHILD'S PLAY
Bumpin' / Short stuff / Putt's pub / For blues sake / Child's play / Smooth sailin' / Ramona / Just what you need / Mr. Bojangles
CDMT 024 / Jan '94 / Meteor

Dupree, Simon

☐ KITES (Dupree, Simon & The Big Sound)
Kites / Like the sun like the fire / Sleep / For whom the bell tolls / Broken hearted pirates / Sixty minutes of your love / Lot of love / Love / Get off my Bach / There's a little picture playhouse / Daytime, nightime / I see the light / What is soul / Amen / Who cares / She gave me the sun / Thinking about my life / It is finished / I've seen it all before / You need a man / Reservations
SEECD 368 / May '97 / See For Miles

Duprees

☐ BEST OF THE DUPREES, THE
You belong to me / Why don't you believe me / Check yourself / Save your heart for me / Carousel / Two different worlds / Hope / Goodnight my love / Sky's the limit / People / My own true love / Have you heard / Delicious / Groovin' is easy / My love, my love / Ring of love / One in a million / Beautiful / My special angel / Delicious (Disco version)
NEMCD 674 / Apr '94 / Sequel

☐ THEIR COMPLETE COED MASTERS
You belong to me / Unbelievable / I gotta tell her now / Ginny / I wish I could believe you / Please let her know / Have you heard / September in the rain / These foolish things / So little time / Exodus / Where are you / I'm yours / Try to remember / My own true love / So many have told me / It isn't fair / Sand and the sea / My dearest one / As time goes by / Sunset to sunrise / Take me as I am / Why don't you believe me / Gone with the wind / Wishing ring / Things I love / It's no sin / Yours / Love eyes / I'd rather be in your arms / Let's make love again
CDCHD 617 / Feb '96 / Ace

Dura Delinquent

☐ DURA DELINQUENT
K 173 / May '97 / Konkurrent

Duran Duran

☐ BIG THING
Big thing / I don't want your love / All she wants is / Too late Marlene / Drug (It's just a state of mind) / Do you believe in shame / Palomino / Interlude one / Land / Flute interlude / Edge of America / Lake shore driving / Drug (It's just a state of mind)
DC 881642 / Aug '97 / Disky
CDPRG 1007 / Jun '97 / Parlophone

☐ DURAN DURAN
Girls on film / Planet Earth / Anyone out there / To the shore / Careless memories / Night boat / Sound of thunder / Friends of mine / Tel Aviv
CDPRG 1003 / Aug '95 / Parlophone

☐ DURAN DURAN TRIBUTE ALBUM, THE (Various Artists)
32059 / Oct '97 / Mojo

☐ LIBERTY
Violence of summer / Liberty / Hothead / Serious / All along the water / My Antarctica / First impressions / Read my lips / Can you deal with it / Venice drowning / Downtown
CDPRG 1009 / Aug '93 / Parlophone

☐ NOTORIOUS
Notorious / American science / Skin trade / Hold me / Vertigo (do the demolition) / So misled / Meet el presidente / Winter marches on / Proposition / Matter of feeling
CDPRG 1006 / Aug '93 / Parlophone

☐ RIO
Rio / My own way / Lonely in your nightmare / Hungry like the wolf / Hold back the rain / New religion / Last chance on the stairway / Save a prayer / Chauffeur
CDPRG 1004 / Aug '93 / Parlophone

☐ SEVEN AND THE RAGGED TIGER
Reflex / New moon on Monday / I'm looking for cracks in the pavement / I take the dice / Of crime and passion / Union of the snake / Shadows on your side / Tiger tiger / Seventh stranger
CDPRG 1005 / Aug '93 / Parlophone

☐ THANK YOU
White lines (don't don't do it) / I want to take you higher / Perfect day / Watching the detectives / Lay lady lay / 911 is a joke / Success / Crystal ship / Ball of confusion / Thank you / Drive-by / I want to take you higher again
CDDDB 36 / Mar '95 / Parlophone

☐ WEDDING ALBUM, THE
Too much information / Ordinary world / Love voodoo / Drowning man / Shotgun / Stop dead / Breath after breath / UMF / None of the above / Time for temptation / Shelter / To whom it may concern / Sin of the city
CDDDB 34 / Feb '93 / Parlophone

Duran, Hilario

☐ KILLER TUMBAO
Homage to Chano Pozo / Alfredo's mood / Longina / Song for Yemaya / Brasiliangada / Three for one / Los Tres Golpes / Killer Tumbao / Timba Mabo
JUST 1012 / Aug '97 / Justin Time

Durant, Jon

☐ SILENT EXTINCTION BEYOND THE ZERO
Crossing zero / RC 11.21 / Easter / Clutching razors / Tears trickle down / Breath of the wind / Danger boy / Three things no-one knew / Hope
ALCD 1012 / 24 Nov '97 / Alchemy

☐ THREE IF BY AIR
Pale and crystal / Was there something out there / Shadows beginning to fade / Escalator / Sombrero fallout / Final frontiers / Alien communication technique
ALCD 1005 / Aug '97 / Alchemy

Durante, Jimmy

☐ AS TIME GOES BY (The Best Of Jimmy Durante)
As time goes by / If I had you / Smile / Hi lili hi lo / Make someone happy / Young at heart / Hello, young lovers / Try a little tenderness / Glory of love / I'll be seeing you / September song / I'll see you in my dreams
9362454562 / Nov '96 / WEA

☐ GREAT SCHNOZZLE, THE
Inka dinka do / Can Broadway do without me / Hot Patatta / Umbriago / Durante the patron of the arts / Start off each day with a song / Who will be with you when I'm far away / So I ups to him and he ups to me / Joe goes up I come down / Jimmy the well dressed man / There are two sides are every girl / G'wan home your mudder's callin / I'm feeling mighty low /

DURANTE, JIMMY | MAIN SECTION | R.E.D. CD CATALOGUE

I'll do the strutaway in my cutaway / I'm the guy who found the lost chord / Little bit of this little bit of that / Chidabee-ch-ch / Day I read a book / Fugitive from Esquire / Song's gotta come from the heart / Real piano player / It's my nose's birthday / Inka dinka do
CDAJA 5271 / Aug '98 / Living Era

☐ I SAY IT WITH MUSIC
VN 169 / Aug '95 / Viper's Nest

Durao, Eduardo

☐ TIMBILA
Ngono utane vuna kudima / Walamba kudja mundino / Haguma nguma tekenha / Eduardo Durao mauaia / Magueleguele / Nhantumbuane / Unichenguile
CDORBD 065 / Jan '91 / Globestyle

Durbin, Deanna

☐ BEST OF DEANNA DURBIN
It's raining sunbeams / My own / Spring in my heart / One fine day / Love is all / Perhaps / Last rose of summer / Can't help singing / Blue Danube dream / Californ-i-ay / Because / Turntable song / Spring will be a little late this year / Home sweet home / Waltzing in the clouds / Ave Maria
MCLD 19183 / May '93 / MCA

☐ CAN'T HELP SINGING
JASCD 101 / Nov '95 / Jasmine

☐ FAN CLUB, THE
Amapola / Because / When April sings / Waltzing in the clouds / My own / Brindisi / Beneath the lights of home / Spring in my heart / It's raining sunbeams / Musetta's waltz song / Love is all / Perhaps / One fine day / Home sweet home / Last rose of summer / Il bacio / Ave Maria / Loch Lomond / Alleluia
PASTCD 9781 / May '92 / Flapper

☐ GOLDEN VOICE OF DEANNA DURBIN, THE
Can't help singing / More and more / Spring in my heart / Californ-i-ay / Always / One fine day / Les filles de Cadiz / Ave Maria / Love is all / Home sweet home / Beneath the lights of home / Any moment now / My own / Last rose of summer / Spring will be a little late this year / Someone to care for me / It's foolish but it's fun / Waltzing in the clouds / Annie Laurie / Love's old sweet song
308182 / 13 Oct '97 / Hallmark

☐ KISS ME AGAIN
Can't help singing / Spring will be a little late this year / Les filles de Cadiz / Someone to care for me / Love at last / My hero / Poor butterfly / Californ-i-ay / More and more / Any moment now / Always / Cielito Lindo / Estrellita / Kiss me again / Something in the wind / It's only love / When the roses bloom again / Love's old sweet song / Adeste fidelis / Silent night / Annie Laurie / Turntable song / God bless America
PASTCD 7828 / 29 Jun '98 / Flapper

☐ SENSATIONAL SONGBIRD
Turntable song / More and more / Spring will be a little late this year / Un bel di vedremo / Always / Beneath the lights of home / Any moment now / Californ-i-ay / Can't help singing / Love is all / Ave Maria / Old folks at home / Someone to care for me / Il bacio / Allelujah / It's foolish but it's fun / When the roses bloom again / Love's old sweet song / Amapola / Les filles de Cadiz / Ave Maria / Say a prayer for the boys over there
PLCD 567 / 5 May '98 / President

☐ ULTIMATE COLLECTION, THE (24 Greatest Hits)
It's foolish but it's fun / Waltzing in the clouds / Beneath the lights of home / Spring in my heart / Estrellita / Il bacio / Because / Cielito lindo / When April sings / Spring will be a little late this year / Always / It's raining sunbeams / My hero / When the roses bloom again / Brindisi / Ave Maria / Amapola / Love's old sweet song / Poor butterfly / Les filles de Cadiz / Musetta's waltz song / Last rose of summer / Perhaps / Can't help singing
PLATCD 143 / Mar '96 / Platinum

☐ WITH A SONG IN MY HEART
Waltzing in the clouds / My own / Brindisi / It's raining sunbeams / Beneath the lights of home / Love is all / Les filles de cadiz / Perhaps / One fine day / Spring in my heart / Amapola / Estrellita / When April sings / Musetta's waltz song / Because / Blue Danube dream / Poor butterfly / Last rose of summer / It's foolish but it's fun / Home sweet home
PLCD 534 / Mar '93 / President

Durham Constabulary Brass Band

☐ GENTLE TOUCH, THE
In celebration / Where no man has gone before / Here's that rainy day / I could be so good for you / Fascination / Shepherd's hey (grainger) / Love changes everything / Jaguar / La virgen de la macarena / Born free / Sullivan at sea / World traveller / St. clement / Songs of the quay
BNA 5079 / Mar '93 / Bandleader

Durham, Judith

☐ MONA LISA
Catch the wind / Love song / Someone out there / Heart on my sleeve / Turn turn turn / Adios amor / Saltwater / Northern lights / Put a little love in your heart / Morning has broken / Mona Lisas and Mad Hatters / You've got a friend / End of the world
CDJDTV 1 / Feb '97 / EMI TV

Durham, Mike

☐ BOUNCING AROUND (West Jesmond Rhythm Kings)
BCD 352 / Nov '96 / GHB

☐ CHICAGO BUZZ (West Jesmond Rhythm Kings)
Mama's gonna slow you down / Big boy / Anywhere Sweetie goes / Sweet Emmalina / 2.19 blues / Down among the sugar cane / Chicago buzz / Breeze / Brownskin Mama / Candy lips / One I love just can't be bothered with me / Oh sister, ain't that hot / That's my stuff / Shout 'em Aunt Tillie / Magnolia's wedding day / Angry / Sweet substitute / Wa wa wa
LACD 74 / Mar '97 / Lake

☐ SHAKE 'EM LOOSE
Worn out blues / Cushion foot stomp / Anytime / Tree top tall papa / Frog-i-more rag / Take your pick / Dead man blues / Shootin' the pistol / Sadie green (the vamp of new orleans) / Oh baby / Gatemouth / Someday sweetheart / Shake 'em loose / Cole smoak / Lovely came back / Papa dip / Travelling blues / My little bimbo down on the bamboo isle
LACD 45 / Feb '95 / Lake

Duro, Christian

☐ SONNEUR FISEL
BUR 872CD / Dec '97 / Escalibur

Durrant, Phil

☐ SOWARI
ACTA 10 / Sep '97 / Acta

Durrant, Richard

☐ RICHARD DURRANT'S DUELLIN' BANJOS
Duellin' banjos / Old Joe Clarke / Bill Cheetham / Dance of the Welsh vicar / Stoney creek / Jerusalem ridge / Frosty morning / Foggy mountain breakdown / Billy in the low ground / Wild wood flower / Mason's apron / Salamanca / Byrne's hornpipe / Nine points of roguery / Star of Munster / Loch Neagh / Czardas / Down in the swamp / Speed the plough / Swing low, sweet chariot
QED 172 / Nov '96 / Tring

Durutti Column

☐ BREAD AND CIRCUSES
Pauline / Tomorrow / Dance 11 / Hilary / Street fight / Royal infirmary / Black horses / Dance 1 / Blind elevator girl / Osaka
TWI 9882 / Nov '93 / Les Disques Du Crepuscule

☐ FIDELITY
TWI 9762 / Apr '96 / Les Disques Du Crepuscule

☐ GUITAR AND OTHER MACHINES, THE
Arpeggiator / What is it to me (woman) / Red shoes / Jongleur grey / When the world / USP / Bordeaux sequence / Pol in B / English landscape tradition / Miss Haymes / Don't you think you're funny / LFO mod / Dream topping / 28 oldham street / Otis / ELT / Finding the sea / Bordeaux
8288282 / Dec '96 / Factory Too

☐ LC
Sketch for dawn / Portrait for Fraser / Jacqueline / Messidor / Sketch for dawn / Never known / Act committed / Detail for Paul / Missing boy / Sweet cheat gone / For Mimi / Belgian friends / Self portrait / One christmas for your thoughts / Danny / Enigma
8288272 / Dec '96 / Factory Too

☐ LIPS THAT WOULD KISS
FBN 2CD / Nov '96 / Les Disques Du Crepuscule

☐ LIVE AT THE BOTTOM LINE
RE 512CD / Nov '94 / ROIR

☐ RETURN OF THE DURUTTI COLUMN
Sketch for summer / Requiem for a father / Katherine / Conduct / Beginning / Jazz / Sketch for winter / Collete / In d
8288292 / Dec '96 / Factory Too

☐ SEX & DEATH
Anthony / Rest of my life / For Colette / Next time / Beautiful lies / My irascible friend / Believe in me / Fermina / Where should I be / Fado / Madre mio / Blue period
FACD 201 / Nov '94 / Factory Too

☐ VINI REILLY
Love no more / Poling / Opera I / People's pleasure park / Red square / Finding the sea / Otis / William B / They work every day / Opera II / Homage to the Catalonea / Requiem again / My country / Paradise passage road / Les preger's tune / Bhuddist prayer / Misere / Real drums - real drummer / Pathway / Rob Grey's elegy / Shirt no.7
8188262 / Dec '96 / Factory Too

Dury, Ian

☐ BEST OF IAN DURY, THE
DC 869752 / Aug '96 / Disky

☐ BUS DRIVER'S PRAYER & OTHER STORIES, THE
That's enough of that / Bill Haley's last words / Poor Joey / Quick quick slow / Fly in the ointment / O'Donegal / Poo poo in the prawn / Have a word / London talking / D'orine the cow / Your horoscope / No such thing as love / Two old dogs without a name / Bus driver's prayer
FIENDCD 702 / Nov '92 / Demon

☐ DO IT YOURSELF
In betweenies / Quiet / Don't ask me / Sink my boats / Waiting for your taxi / This is what we find / Uneasy sunny day hotsy totsy / Mischief / Dance of the screamers / Lullaby for Francies
AHLCD 58 / 24 Aug '98 / Hit

☐ IAN DURY AND THE BLOCKHEADS
Intro / Wake up and make love with me / Clevor Trever / If I was with a woman / Billericay dickie / Quiet / My old man / Spasticus autisticus / Plaistow Patricia / There ain't half been some clever bastards / Sweet Gene Vincent / What a waste / Hit me with your rhythm stick / Blockheads
FIENDCD 777 / Aug '91 / Demon

☐ LAUGHTER (Dury, Ian & The Blockheads)
Superman's big sister / Pardon / Delusions of grandeur / Yes and no / Dance of the crackpots / Over the points / Take your elbow out of the soup... / Uncoolohol / Hey hey take me away / Manic depression / Oh Mr. Peanut / Fucking Ada
AHLCD 59 / 24 Aug '98 / Hit

☐ MR. LOVE PANTS
DUR 1 / 29 Jun '98 / Ronnie Harris

☐ NEW BOOTS AND PANTIES (Dury, Ian & The Blockheads)
Sweet Gene Vincent / Wake up and make love with me / I'm partial to your Abracadabra / My old man / Billericay Dickie / Clevor Trever / If I was with a woman / Plaistow Patricia / Blockheads / Blackmail man
AHLCD 57 / 24 Aug '98 / Hit

Dusk

☐ DUSK
CYBERCD 15 / Feb '95 / Cyber

Duskin, 'Big' Joe

☐ CINCINNATI STOMP
Mean old frisco blues / Roll 'em pete / Stormin' in texas / Cincinnati stomp / Little red rooster / Tribute / Down the road apiece / Well, well baby / Honky tonk train / Beat me daddy, eight to the bar / Tender hearted women / Sloop down baby
ARHCD 422 / Sep '95 / Arhoolie

☐ DON'T MESS WITH THE BOOGIE MAN
Don't mess with the boogie man / Down on my bended knees / Big Joe's boogie prayer / Oodle adle / Mean and evil / Dirty rat swing / Cuban sugar mill / Call my job / Keep it to yourself / Low down dog / CC rider / So long / Boogie woogie on St. Louis blues / Ida B / Yancey special
IGOCD 2062 / May '97 / Indigo

☐ DOWN THE ROAD APIECE
WOLF 120713 / Jul '96 / Wolf

Dust

☐ DUST
REP 4002 / Aug '91 / Repertoire

☐ HARD ATTACK
REP 4030 / Aug '91 / Repertoire

Dust In My Head

☐ WIND IN MY HEART
PARCD 019 / Oct '96 / Parasol

Dust Junkys

☐ DONE AND DUSTED
Nothin' personal / What time is it / Fever / Middle man / Non stop operation / Movin' on / Daddy / Here I am / Remember / Living in the pocket of a drug Queen / Get the funk up / Wasting hard time
5570432
5571282 / 9 Mar '98 / Polydor

Dustball

☐ QUALITY BUT HERS
Owe it all / Let me lie / Rude me out / Ten feet small / Such an eyesore / Useless / Flusher / My life thrill / Mind / Sent apart / Talkback back / Intravolvo
SHIFTY 9802 / 4 May '98 / Shifty Disco

Duster

☐ STRATOSPHERE
UP 050CD / 30 Mar '98 / Up

Dutch Jazz Orchestra

☐ PORTRAIT OF A SILK THREAD
Blue star / Bagatelle / Love has passed me by again / La sacre supreme / Portrait of a silk thread / Tonk / Wounded love / Cashmere cutie / Lana Turner / Pentonsilic / Lament for an orchid
KOKO 1310 / Aug '96 / Kokopelli

Dutch Swing College Band

☐ 40 YEARS AT ITS BEST 1945-85
CDTTD 516 / Sep '86 / Timeless Traditional

☐ DUTCH SAMBA
Corro / Velas blancas / Girl from Ipanema / Samba de Orfeu / Menina flor meditacao / Manana / Corcovado / Poinciana / Samba de Quena / Eso es el amor / La adelita
CDTTD 552 / Jun '89 / Timeless Traditional

☐ DUTCH SWING COLLEGE BAND & TEDDY WILSON (Dutch Swing College Band & Teddy Wilson)
Limehouse blues / Riverboat shuffle / Undecided / Rhythm king / Sweet Georgia Brown / China boy / Runnin' wild / How come you do me like you do / You must have been a beautiful baby / Paradise island / Happy days are here again
CDTTD 525 / Oct '96 / Timeless Traditional

☐ JOINT IS JUMPIN', THE
Milenberg joys / Grandpa's spells / Squeeze me / Bugle call rag / Peg o' my heart / King Porter stomp / Ballin' the Jack / Clarinet marmalade / Drop me off in Harlem / Freeze and melt / Snowy morning blues / Limehouse blues / Keepin' out of mischief now / Joint is jumpin'
CDTTD 594 / Jul '95 / Timeless Jazz

☐ LIVE IN 1960 (Best Of Dixieland)
Way down in yonder in New Orleans / South Rampart Street Parade / Apex blues / Ory's creole underground / Mood indigo / King of the zulus / Opus 5 / Tin roof blues / Freeze and melt / Please don't talk about me when I'm gone / Out of the gallion / Carry me back to old Virginny / Jazz me blues / Waery blues / Way down yonder in New Orleans
8387652 / May '90 / Philips

☐ LIVE IN CONCERT 1974
Way down yonder in New Orleans / Charleston hound / Apex blues / Shiny stockings / Muskrat ramble / Jump the rabbit / At the jazz band ball / I'm coming Virginia / Bag O'Blues / My inspiration / Runnin' wild / De bas van drakestein / Chimes blues / That's a plenty / Face to face / I surrender dear / Original Dixieland one step
AL 73080 / Mar '97 / Challenge

☐ OLD FASHIONED WAY, THE
JHR 73566 / Nov '93 / Jazz Hour

☐ STOMPIN' THE HITS
Bad bad leroy brown / Can't buy me love / Georgia / Hello mary lou (goodbye heart) / Chanson d'amour / Waterloo / I will wait for you / Rosetta / Blueberry hill / Girls, girls, girls / Winchester cathedral / More I see you / What a diff'rence a day made / You are the sunshine of my life / When you smile / Champs elysees
15137 / May '94 / Laserlight

☐ SWINGING STUDIO SESSIONS
At the Jazz Band Ball / Savoy blues / Fidgety feet / CC rider / Royal Garden blues / Some of these days / Tiger rag / Just a closer walk with thee / March of the Indians / Mood indigo / I wish I could shimmy like my sister Kate / I've been working on the railroad / East St. Louis toodle-oo / Cornet chop suey / When it's sleepy time down South / Dippermouth blues / Davenport blues / Shake it and break it
8242562 / May '85 / Philips

Duterte, Jean-Francois

☐ TRADITIONAL FRENCH SONGS
926662 / Feb '97 / BUDA

Dutronc

☐ DUTRONC
DAMGOOD 70CD / Jan '96 / Damaged Goods

Dutronc, Jacques

☐ GREATEST HITS
670009 / Nov '97 / Vogue

Duval, Maria

☐ NE DUFTE PARTY (Duval, Maria & Franco)
BCD 16237 / Jul '98 / Bear Family

Duvall, Huelyn

☐ THREE MONTHS TO KILL
CLCD 4415 / Oct '96 / Collector/White Label

Dvergmal

☐ VISOR OG KVAEDE FRA BLABERGLANDET
GR 4121CD / Aug '97 / Grappa

Dwarves

☐ DWARVES ARE YOUNG AND GOOD LOOKING
Unrepentent we must have / Blood I will deny / Demonica / Everybodies girl / Throw that world away / Hits / Ballad of Vadge Moore / One time only pimp / Crucifixion is now / You gotta burn
65122 / 3 Nov '97 / Epitaph

☐ HORROR STORIES
VOXXCD 2037 / Aug '88 / Voxx

☐ SUGAR FIX
Anybody out there / Evil primeval / Reputation / Lies / Saturday night / New Orleans / Action man / Smack city / Cain novacaine / Underworld / Wish that I was dead
SPCD 76/243 / Jul '93 / Sub Pop

☐ TOOLIN' FOR LUCIFER'S CRANK
RECESS 32CD / Feb '97 / Recess

Dweeb

☐ TURN YOU ON
Intro / Oh yeah baby / 100 mph / Beautiful thing (she's so radical) / Scooby doo / Everything's fine / Buzzsong / Intermission / IOU everything / Me and you / Last girl in the world / No hit wonder / I need you / Elastic love / Retard / Goodbye / Theme from Dweeb / Born with style / Reprise
3984206062 / 3 Aug '98 / Blanco Y Negro

Dwyer, Finbarr

☐ PURE TRADITIONAL IRISH ACCORDIAN
PTICD 1004 / Apr '94 / Pure Traditional Irish

Dyani, Johnny

☐ BORN UNDER THE HEAT (Dyani, Johnny Mbizo)
DRCD 288 / Feb '98 / Ogun

Dyer, Johnny

☐ JUKIN
BP 5028CD / Feb '96 / Blind Pig

☐ LISTEN UP
BT 1101CD / Apr '94 / Black Top

☐ SHAKE IT
BT 1114CD / Apr '95 / Black Top

Dyer-Bennet, Richard

☐ DYER-BENNET
SFWCD 40078 / Dec '97 / Smithsonian Folkways

Dyewitness

☐ BATTLE FOR YOUR MIND
MMCD 1003 / Feb '97 / Mo's Music Machine

Dying Fetus

☐ PURIFICATION THROUGH VIOLENCE
RRS 960CD / Mar '97 / Progress

Dyke & The Blazers

☐ SO SHARP
Funky Broadway (part 1) / Funky Broadway (part 2) / Uhh (part 1) / Runaway people / We got more soul / It's your thing / Shot gun Slim / So sharp / Let a woman be a woman - let a man be a man / You are my sunshine / Funky walk (part 2) / Wrong house / Don't bug me / City dump / My sisters and my brothers / Funky walk (part 1) / Uhh part 2 / Broadway combination / Stuff / Funky bull part 1 / Funky bull part 2 / Wobble / Uhh (edit) / I'm so all alone
CDKEND 004 / Aug '91 / Kent

Dykes, Omar

☐ MUDDY SPRINGS ROAD
Muddy springs road / Black bottom / Midnight ramblin' man / Hoo doo ball / Life is just a circle / Life without you / Exactly what I thought she'd do / Everywhere I go / Get hip / Hurry hurry / Dangerous man
PRD 70602 / Mar '94 / Provogue

Dykstra, Jorrit

☐ EUROPEAN ECHOES (Dykstra, Jorrit & Benoit Delbecq)
BVHAASTCD 9704 / Aug '97 / Bvhaast

Dylan, Bob

☐ 30TH ANNIVERSARY CONCERT CELEBRATION (2CD Set) (Various Artists)
Like a rolling stone: *Mellencamp, John Cougar* / Leopardskin pillbox hat: *Mellencamp, John Cougar* / Introduction: *Kristofferson, Kris* / Blowin' in the wind: *Wonder, Stevie* / Masters of war: *Vedder, Eddie/Mike McCready* / Foot of pride: *Reed, Lou* / Times they are a changin': *Chapman, Tracy* / It ain't me babe: *Carter, June/Johnny Cash* / What was it you wanted: *Nelson, Willie* / I'll be your baby tonight: *Kristofferson, Kris* / Seven days: *Winter, Johnny* / Highway 61: *Winter, Johnny* / Just like a woman: *Havens, Richie* / Just like Tom Thumb's blues: *Young, Neil* / All along the watchtower: *Young, Neil* / When the ship comes in: *Clancy Brothers & Tommy Makem* / I shall be released: *Hynde, Chrissie* / Don't think twice, it's alright: *Clapton, Eric* / Emotionally yours: *O'Jays* / When I paint my masterpiece: *Band* / You ain't goin' nowhere: *Cash, Rosanne & Mary Chapin-Carpenter/Shawn Colvin* / Absolutely sweet Marie: *Harrison, George* / Licence to kill: *Petty, Tom & The Heartbreakers* / Rainy day women 12 and 35: *Petty, Tom & The Heartbreakers* / Mr. Tambourine man: *McGuinn, Roger* / It's alright Ma (I'm only bleeding): *Dylan, Bob* / My back pages: *Dylan, Bob* / Girl from the North Country: *Dylan, Bob* / Knockin' on Heaven's door: *Dylan, Bob*
4740002 / Jun '97 / Columbia

☐ AND THE TIMES THEY WERE A CHANGIN' (18 Classic Covers Of Bob Dylan's Songs) (Various Artists)
Mr. Tambourine Man: *Byrds* / Mighty Quinn: *Manfred Mann* / All along the watchtower: *Hendrix, Jimi* / It's all over now baby blue: *Them* / Only a hobo: *Stewart, Rod* / Knockin' on heaven's door: *Clapton, Eric* / Hard rain's a-gonna fall: *Ferry, Bryan* / Highway 61 revisited: *Winter, Johnny* / Absolutely sweet Marie: *Jason & The Scorchers* / It takes a lot to laugh it takes a train to cry: *Stills/Kooper/Bloomfield* / Tears of rage: *Band* / Percy's song: *Fairport Convention* / Buckets of rain: *Midler, Bette* / It ain't me babe: *Cash, Johnny* / Love is a four letter word: *Baez, Joan* / With God on our side: *Neville Brothers* / Chimes of freedom: *N'Dour, Youssou* / It's alright ma I'm only bleeding: *McGuinn, Roger*
5554312 / Feb '98 / Debutante

☐ ANOTHER SIDE OF BOB DYLAN
All I really want to do / Black crow blues / Spanish Harlem incident / Chimes of freedom / I shall be free / To Ramona / Motorpsycho nightmare / My back pages / I don't believe you (she acts like we never have met) / Ballads in plain D / It ain't me babe
CD 32034 / Nov '89 / CBS

☐ ANOTHER SIDE OF.../TIMES THEY ARE A CHANGIN'/FREEWHEELIN' (3CD Set)
All I really want to do / Crow blues / Spanish Harlem incident / Chimes of freedom / I shall be free no.1 / To Ramona / Motorpsycho nightmare / My back pages / I don't believe you / Ballad in plain D / It ain't me babe / Times are a changin' / Ballad of hollis brown / With god on our side / One's too many mornings / North country blues / Only a pawn in their game / Boots of Spanish leather / When the ship comes in / Lonesome death of hattie carroll / Restless farewell / Blowin' in the wind / Girl from the north country / Masters of war / Down the highway / Bob Dylan's blues / Hard rain's gonna fall / Don't think twice it's alright / Bob Dylan's dream / Oxford town / Talking world war III blues / Corrina corrina / Honey just allow me one more chance / I shall be free
4886732 / 3 Nov '97 / Columbia

☐ BASEMENT TAPES (Dylan, Bob & The Band)
Odds and ends / Orange juice blues (blues for breakfast) / Million dollar bash / Yaroo Street scandal / Goin' to Acapulco / Kate's been gone / You ain't goin' nowhere / Don't ya tell Henry / Nothing was delivered / Open the door, Homer / Long distance operator / This wheel's on fire / Lo and behold / Bessie Smith / Clothes line saga / Apple suckling tree / Mrs. Henry / Tears of rage / Too much of nothing / Yea, heavy and a bottle of bread / Ain't no more cane / Crash on the levee (down in the flood) / Ruben Remus / Tiny Montgomery
4661372 / Nov '89 / CBS

☐ BEFORE THE FLOOD (2CD Set) (Dylan, Bob & The Band)
Most likely you'll go your way and I'll go mine / Lay lady lay / Rainy day women 12 and 35 / Knockin' on Heaven's door / It ain't me babe / Ballad of a thin man / Up on Cripple Creek / I shall be released / Endless highway / Night they drove old Dixie down / Stagefright / Don't think twice, it's alright / Just like a woman / It's alright Ma (I'm only bleeding) / Shape I'm in / When you awake / Weight / All along the watchtower / Highway 61 revisited / Like a rolling stone / Blowin' in the wind
CD 22137 / Jun '96 / CBS

☐ BEST OF BOB DYLAN, THE (2CD Set)
Blowin' in the wind / Times they are a-changin' / Don't think twice, it's alright / Mr. Tambourine man / Like a rolling stone / Just like a woman / All along the watchtower / Lay lady lay / If not for you / Knockin' on Heaven's door / Forever young / Tangled up in blue / Shelter from the storm / I shall be released / Oh sister / Gotta serve somebody / Jokerman / Everything is broken / Times they are a changin' / Don't think twice it's all right
SONYTV 28CD / Jun '97 / Sony TV

☐ BIOGRAPH (3CD Set)
Lay lady lay / If not for you / Times they are a changin' / Blowin' in the wind / Masters of war / Percy's song / Like a rolling stone / Subterranean homesick blues / Mr. Tambourine man / It ain't me babe / Million dollar bash / It's all over now baby blue / Positively 4th Street / Heart of mine / I believe in you / Time passes slowly / Forever young / Baby let me follow you down / I'll be your baby tonight / I'll keep it with mine / Lonesome death of Hattie Carroll / Mixed-up confusion / Tombstone blues / Groom's still waiting at the altar / Most likely you'll go your way and I'll go mine / Jet pilot / Lay down your weary tune / I don't believe you (she acts like we never have met) / Visions of Johanna / Every grain of sand / Quinn the Eskimo / Dear landlord / You angel you / To Ramona / You're a big girl now / Abandoned love / Tangled up in blue / Can you please crawl out of your window / Isis / Caribbean wind / Up to me / Baby I'm in the mood for you / I wanna be your lover / I want you / On a night like this / Just like a woman / Romance in Durango / Senor (tales of Yankee power) / Gotta serve somebody / I shall be released / Knockin' on Heaven's door / All along the watchtower / Solid rock
4880992 / 25 Aug '97 / Columbia

☐ BLONDE ON BLONDE
Rainy day women 12 and 35 / Pledging my time / Visions of Johanna / One of us must know / I want you / Stuck inside a mobile with the Memphis blues again / Leopardskin pillbox hat / Just like a woman / Most likely you'll go your way and I'll go mine / Temporarily like Achilles / Absolutely sweet Marie / Fourth time around / Obviously five believers / Sad eyed lady of the Lowlands
CK 64411 / Feb '95 / Columbia
4804172 / Jul '95 / Columbia

☐ BLOOD ON THE TRACKS
Tangled up in blue / Simple twist of fate / You're a big girl now / Idiot wind / You're gonna make me lonesome when you go / Meet me in the morning / Lily Rosemary and the jack of hearts / If you see her / Say hello / Shelter from the storm / Buckets of rain
4678422 / Sep '93 / Columbia

☐ BOB DYLAN
She's no good / Talkin' New York blues / In my time of dying / Man of constant sorrow / Fixing to die blues / Pretty Peggy-O / Highway 51 blues / Gospel plow / Baby let me follow you down / House of the rising sun / Freight train blues / Song to Woody / See that my grave is kept clean
CD 32001 / Nov '89 / CBS

☐ BOB DYLAN AT BUDOKAN (2CD Set)
Mr. Tambourine man / Shelter from the storm / Love minus zero / No limit / Ballad of a thin man / Don't think twice, it's alright / Maggie's farm / One more cup of coffee / Like a rolling stone / I shall be released / Is your love in vain / Going going gone / Blowin' in the wind / Just like a woman / Oh, sister / Simple twist of fate / All along the watchtower / I want you woman / All I really want to do / Knockin' on Heaven's door / It's alright Ma (I'm only bleeding) / Forever young / Times they are a changin'
4678502 / Nov '96 / Sony Music

☐ BOOTLEG SERIES VOL.1-3, THE (Rare & Unreleased 1961-1991/3CD Set)
Hard times in New York Town / He was a friend of mine / Man on the street / No more auction block / House carpenter / Talkin' Bear Mountain picnic massacre blues / Let me die in my footsteps / Rambling gambling Willie / Talkin' Hava negeilah blues / Quit your low down ways / Worried blues / Kingsport Town / Walkin' down the line / Walls of red wing / Paths of victory / Talkin' John Birch paranoid blues / Who killed Davey Moore / Only a hobo / Moonshiner / When the ship comes in / Time they are a changin' / Last thoughts on Woody Guthrie / Seven curses / Eternal circle / Suze (The cough song) / Mama you been on my mind / Farewell, Angelina / Subterranean homesick blues / If you gotta go, go now / Sitting on a barbed wire fence / Like a rolling stone / It takes a lot to laugh, it takes a train to cry / I'll keep it with mine / She's your lover now / I shall be released / Santa Fe / If not for you / Wallflower / Nobody 'cept you / Tangled up in blue / Call letter blues / Idiot wind / If you see her / Golden loom / Catfish / Seven days / Ye shall be changed / Every grain of sand / You changed my life / Need a woman / Angelina / Someone's got a hold of my heart / Tell me / Lord protect my child / Foot of pride / Blind Willie McTell / When the night comes falling from the sky / Series of dreams
4881002 / 25 Aug '97 / Columbia

☐ BRINGING IT ALL BACK HOME
Subterranean homesick blues / She belongs to me / Maggie's farm / Love minus zero / Outlaw blues / On the road again / Bob Dylan's 15th dream / Mr. Tambourine man / Gates of Eden / It's alright Ma (I'm only bleeding) / It's all over now baby blue
CD 32344 / Jun '89 / CBS

☐ DESIRE
Hurricane / Isis / Mozambique / One more cup of coffee / Oh sister / Joey / Romance in Durango / Black Diamond Bay / Sara
CD 32570 / 27 Jul '98 / Columbia

☐ DESIRE/BLOOD ON THE TRACKS/ STREET LEGAL (3CD Set)
Hurricane / Isis / Mozambique / One more cup of coffee / Oh sister / Joey / Romance in durango / Black diamond bay / Sara / Tangled up in blue / Simple twist of fate / You're a big girl now / Idiot wind / You're gonna make me lonesome when you go / Meet me in the morning / Lily / Rosemary and the jack of hearts / If you see her say hello / Shelter from the storm / Buckets of rain / Changing of the guard / New pony / Not time to think / Baby stop crying / Is your love in vain / Senot tales of yankee power / True love tends to forget / We'd better talk this over / Where are you tonight
4853142 / 3 Nov '97 / Columbia

☐ DYLAN (A Fool Such As I)
Lily of the west / Can't help falling in love / Sarah Jane / Ballad of Ira Hayes / Mr. Bojangles / Mary Ann / Big yellow taxi / Fool such as I / Spanish is the loving tongue
CD 32286 / Feb '91 / Columbia

☐ DYLAN AND THE DEAD (Dylan, Bob & Grateful Dead)
Slow train / I want you / Gotta serve somebody / Queen Jane approximately / Joey / All along the watchtower / Knockin' on Heaven's door
4633812 / Apr '94 / CBS

☐ EMPIRE BURLESQUE
Tight connection to my heart (has anybody seen my love?) / Seeing the real you at last / I'll remember you / Clean cut kid / Emotionally yours / Dark eyes / Something's burning baby / Never gonna be the same again / Trust yourself / When the night comes / Falling from the sky
4678402 / Feb '91 / Columbia

☐ FREEWHEELIN' BOB DYLAN, THE
Blowin' in the wind / Girl from the North Country / Masters of war / Down the highway / Bob Dylan's blues / Hard rain's a-gonna fall / Don't think twice, it's alright / Bob Dylan's dream / Oxford Town / Talking World War III blues / Corine Corina / Honey just allow me one more chance / I shall be free
CD 32390 / 27 Jul '98 / Columbia

☐ GOOD AS I'VE BEEN TO YOU
Frankie and Albert / Jim Jones / Blackjack Davy / Canadee-I-O / Sittin' on top of the world / Little Maggie / Hard times / Step it up / Tomorrow night / Arthur McBride / You're gonna quit me / Diamond Joe / Froggie went a-courtin'
4727102 / Feb '97 / Columbia

☐ GREATEST HITS
Blowin' in the wind / It ain't me babe / Times they are a changin' / Mr. Tambourine man / She belongs to me / It's all over now baby blue / Subterranean homesick blues / One of us must know / Like a rolling stone / Just like a woman / Rainy day women 12 and 35 / I want you
4609079 / Apr '97 / Columbia

☐ GREATEST HITS
TF 34 / 9 Mar '98 / CTA

☐ GREATEST HITS VOL.2
I want you / One of us must know (sooner or later) / It takes a lot to laugh, it takes a train to cry / Just like Tom Thumb's blues / Masters of war / Chimes of freedom / Just like a woman / Obviously 5 believers / Rainy day woman no.s 12 and 35 / Gates of eden / Leopardskin pillbox hat / Absolutely sweet Marie
4712432 / Jul '93 / Columbia

☐ GREATEST HITS VOL.3
Tangled up in blue / Changing the guards / Groom's still waiting at the alter / Hurricane / Forever young / Jokerman / Dignity / Silvio / Ring them bells / Gotta serve somebody / Series of dreams / Brownsville girl / Under the red sky / Knockin' on heaven's door
4778052 / Nov '94 / Columbia

☐ HARD RAIN'S A-GONNA FALL, A
Maggie's farm / One too many mornings / Stuck inside a mobile with the Memphis blues again / Oh sister / Lay lady lay / Shelter from the storm / You're a big girl now / I threw it all away / Idiot wind
CD 32308 / Nov '89 / CBS

☐ HIGHWAY '61 REVISITED
Like a rolling stone / Tombstone blues / It takes a lot to laugh, to train to cry / From a Buick 6 / Ballad of a thin man / Queen Jane approximately / Highway 61 revisited / Just like Tom Thumb's blues / Desolation Row
4609532 / Nov '89 / CBS

☐ INFIDELS
Jokerman / Sweetheart like you / Neighbourhood bully / Licence to kill / Man of peace / Union sundown / I and I / Don't fall apart on me tonight
4607272 / Nov '89 / CBS

☐ JOHN WESLEY HARDING
John Wesley Harding / As I went out one morning / I dreamed I saw St. Augustine / Drifter's escape / All along the watchtower / I am a lonesome hobo / Ballad of Frankie Lee and Judas Priest / Dear landlord / I pity the poor immigrant / Wicked messenger / Down along cove / I'll be your baby tonight
4633592 / Nov '89 / CBS

☐ KNOCKED OUT LOADED
You wanna ramble / They killed him / Drifting too far from the shore / Precious memories / Maybe someday / Brownsville girl / Got my mind made up / Under your spell
4670402 / Feb '91 / Columbia

☐ MORE GREATEST HITS (2CD Set)
Watching the river flow / Don't think twice, it's alright / Lay lady lay / Stuck inside a mobile with the Memphis blues again / I'll be your baby tonight / All I really want to do / My back pages / Maggie's farm / Tonight I'll be staying here with you / Positively 4th Street / All along the watchtower / Mighty Quinn / Just like Tom Thumb's blues / Hard rain's gonna fall / If not for you / New morning / Tomorrow is a long time / When I paint my masterpiece / I shall be released / You ain't goin' nowhere / Down in the flood
4678512 / Jun '96 / Columbia

☐ NASHVILLE SKYLINE
Girl from the North Country / Nashville skyline rag / To be alone with you / I threw it all away / Peggy Day / Lay lady lay / One more night / Tell me that it isn't true / Country pie / Tonight I'll be staying here with you
CD 63601 / Jan '86 / CBS

☐ NEW MORNING
If not for you / Day of the locusts / Time passes slowly / Went to see the gypsy / Winterlude / If dogs run free / New morning / Sign in the window / One more weekend / Man in me / Three angels / Father of night
CD 32267 / Feb '94 / Columbia

☐ OH MERCY
Political world / Where teardrops fall / Ring them bells / Man in the long black coat / Most of the time / What good am I / Disease of conceit / What was it you wanted / Shooting star
4658002 / Sep '89 / CBS

☐ PLANET WAVES
On a night like this / Going going gone / Tough mama / Hazel / Something there is about you / Forever young / Dirge / You angel you / Never say goodbye / Wedding song
CD 32154 / Nov '89 / CBS

☐ SAVED
Satisfied mind / Saved / Covenant woman / What can I do for you / Solid rock / Pressing on / In the garden / Saving grace / Are you ready
CD 32742 / Feb '91 / Columbia

☐ SELF PORTRAIT
All the tired horses / Alberta no.1 / I've forgotten more than you'll ever know / Days of 49 / Early morning rain / In search of little Sadie / Let it be me / Woogie boogie / Belle Isle / Living the blues / Like a rolling stone / Copper kettle / Gotta travel on / Blue moon / Boxer / Mighty Quinn / Take me as I am / It hurts me too / Minstrel boy / She belongs to me / Wigwam / Alberta no.2
4601122 / Feb '91 / Columbia

☐ SHOT OF LOVE
Shot of love / Heart of mine / Property of Jesus / Lenny Bruce / Watered-down love / Dead man dead man / In the Summertime / Trouble / Every grain of sand
4746892 / Feb '97 / Columbia

☐ SLOW TRAIN COMING
Gotta serve somebody / Precious angel when you gonna wake me up / I believe in you / Slow train / Gonna change my way of thinking / Do right to me baby / When he returns / Man gave names to all the animals / Changing of the guard / New pony / No time to think / Baby stop crying / Is your love in vain / Senor / True love tends to forget / We better talk this over / Where are you tonight / Journey through dark heat
CD 32524 / Apr '89 / CBS

☐ STREET LEGAL
Changing of the guard / New pony / No time to think / Baby stop crying / Is your love in vain / Senor (tales of Yankee power) / True love tends to forget / We better talk this over / Where are you tonight / Journey through dark heat
CD 32389 / Apr '95 / Columbia

☐ SUBTERRANEAN/HIGHWAY 61/ NASHVILLE SKYLINE (3CD Set)
4673912 / Dec '90 / CBS

☐ TIME OUT OF MIND
Love sick / Dirt road blues / Standing in the doorway / Million miles / Tryin' to get to heaven / 'Til I fell in love with you / Not dark yet / Cold irons bound / Make you feel my love / Can't wait / Highlands
4869362 / 29 Sep '97 / Columbia

☐ TIMES THEY ARE A-CHANGIN', THE
Times they are a changin' / Ballad of Hollis Brown / With God on our side / One too many mornings / North Country blues / Only a pawn in their game / Boots of Spanish leather / When the ship comes in / Lonesome death of Hattie Carroll / Restless farewell
CD 32021 / Nov '89 / CBS

☐ UNDER THE RED SKY
Wiggle wiggle wiggle / Under the red sky / Unbelievable / Born in time / TV talkin' song / 10,000 men / Two times two / God knows / Handy Dandy / Cat's in the well
4671882 / Sep '90 / CBS

☐ UNPLUGGED
Tombstone blues / Shooting star / All along the watchtower / Times they are a-changin' / John Brown / Desolation row / Rainy day women 12 and 35 / Dignity / Love minus zero / No limit / Knockin' on heaven's door / Like a rolling stone / With God on our side
4783742 / 2 Feb '98 / Columbia

☐ WORLD GONE WRONG
World gone wrong / Love Henry / Ragged and dirty / Blood in my eyes / Broke down engine / Delia / Stagger Lee / Two soldiers / Jackaroe / Lone pilgrim
4748572 / 27 Jul '98 / Columbia

Dylan Group

☐ IT'S ALL ABOUT (RIMSHOTS AND FAULTY WIRING)
EFA 805082 / 23 Mar '98 / Bubblecore

☐ RE-INTERPRETED
EFA 805182 / 5 May '98 / Bubblecore

Dynamic Blues Band

☐ ONE MORE KISS AND ONE MORE BEER
STINGCD 039 / Jul '97 / Blue Sting

Dynamics

☐ WHAT A SHAME
What a shame / She's for real (Bless you) / Let me be your friend / You'll never find a man like me / Woe is me / Voyage through the mind / You're the only one funkey key / Count your chips / Shucks I love you / We're gonna be together / Show the world (we can do it) / Sweet games of love / Let's start all over / Baby, baby I love you / I've been blessed / I'm thinking / Beautiful music (makes you dance) / Get myself high
NEMCD 720 / Feb '95 / Sequel

Dynamix II

☐ ELECTRO MEGAMIX
Introduction / Don't touch that dial / Feel the bass / Technology / 1 million mHz / Ignition / Techno bass / Dj's go berzerk / Bass generator / Atomic age / Just give the DJ a break / Energy / II evolve / Dreamscape / Hypnotic 808 / Just give the DJ a break / Technology / Atomic age / Feel the bass / Techno bass / 1 million mHz / Bass generator / Ignition / II evolve / DJ's go berzerk / Don't touch that dial / Energy
CAT 065CD / 4 May '98 / Rephlex

Dynasty

☐ BEST OF DYNASTY, THE
I don't want to be a freak (but I can't help myself) / I've just begun to love you / Do me right / Adventures in the land of music / Love in the fast lane / Check it out / Something to remember / Groove control / Here I am / Strokin' / Does that ring a bell / Only one
NEMCD 679 / Oct '94 / Sequel

Dyoxen

☐ FIRST AMONG EQUALS
CDATV 17 / Jul '92 / Active

DYS

☐ FIRE AND ICE
TG 2981CD / Jul '91 / Taang

Dysart & Dundonald Pipe Band

☐ IN CONCERT, BALLYMENA 1983
COMD 2053 / Jan '94 / Temple

☐ PIPE BANDS OF DISTINCTION
Fallen stag / Fulmar's flight / Pm g. allan / Swagger / Doug boyd's favourite / Paddy's green isle / Doug boyd's favourite 2 / 1. a.d. macleod / Cuckoo / J.f. mackenzie / Balmoral castle / Marry me now / Miss stewart / Dans le jardin / Man's a man / Corn rigg / Aye love nae a lassie but yin / Rantin' rovin' robin / Star o' rabbie burns / Seann thomais / Cpl. macritchie / Lady bowhill / Children's song / Chasm / Rose of allandale / All thro' the night / Auld hoose / Lea rig / Jimmy young / Cameronian rant / Loch carron / Tulloch castle / Poisoned dwarf / Faut or cartsonia / Murdoch macallister / Merlins meeting /

Kelly's walk / Major wilson / Within a mile of edinburgh toon / Laggan love / Shepherd's building / Laggan love 2 / Kiwi clipper / Craig cluny salute / Mother's fancy / How great thou art / Fairy dance / Circassion circle / Clumsy lover
CDMON 803 / Dec '89 / Monarch

Dysney Moon

☐ RUNAWAY
WHALE 101CD / Aug '93 / Christine

Dyson, Ronnie

☐ SOUL SESSION
Let the love begin / Constantly / Tender loving care / Waiting for you / I gave you all of me / Are we so far apart / My fantasy / It's all over your face / Don't need you now / You better be fierce
303072 / Jun '97 / Hallmark

Dystrophy

☐ SPIEGEL MEINER KALTE
SR 0003CD / Nov '95 / Serenades

Dzintars

☐ SONGS OF AMBER
Blow wind blow / Breaking flax / Sun moves quickly / Sleep my child / Song of the wind / Autumn landscape / Tomtit's message / Where have you been, brother / Orphan girl in white / Di raike / Christmas masquerade / Oi hanuke / So silent is the Ukranian night / Forest shook from dancing
RCD 10130 / Sep '91 / Rykodisc

E

E-40

□ HALL OF GAME
CHIP 174 / Mar '97 / Jive

E-De-Cologne

□ SYNTHETIC OVERDOSE
EFA 008782 / Sep '96 / Shockwave

E-Types

□ LIVE AT THE RAINBOW BALLROOM 1966
BR 103 / 9 Mar '98 / Beatrocket

E-Z Rollers

□ DIMENSIONS OF SOUND
ASHADOW 5CD / Jul '96 / Moving Shadow

□ WEEKEND WORLD
ASHADOW 12CD / 5 May '98 / Moving Shadow

EA

□ ORIPANDO
78942851522 / 17 Mar '98 / Tinder

Each Dawn I Die

□ NOTES FROM A ...
DVLR 009CD / Nov '95 / Dark Vinyl

Eade, Dominique

□ WHEN THE WIND WAS COOL
Moonray / Ridin' high / Something cool / All about Ronnie / Poor little rich girl / When the wind was cool / I'll take romance / Wind / Intrigue / Lullaby of Birdland / Bad and the beautiful / Tea for two / Goodbye
09026688582 / 8 Nov '97 / RCA Victor

Eagle Brass Band

□ LAST OF THE LINE, THE
BCD 170 / Jul '96 / GHB

Eagles

□ BEST OF THE EAGLES, THE (Vienna Classic Rock Orchestra)
323834 / May '97 / Koch International

□ COMMON THREAD (The Songs Of The Eagles) (Various Artists)
Take it easy: *Tritt, Travis* / Peaceful easy feeling: *Little Texas* / Desperado: *Black, Clint* / Heartache tonight: *Anderson, John* / Tequila sunrise: *Jackson, Alan* / Take it to the limit: *Bogguss, Suzy* / I can't tell you why: *Gill, Vince* / Lyin' eyes: *Diamond Rio* / New kid in town: *Yearwood, Trisha* / Saturday night: *Dean, Billy* / Already gone: *Tucker, Tanya* / Best of my love: *Brooks & Dunn* / Sad cafe: *Morgan, Lorrie*
74321166772 / 19 Jan '98 / Giant

□ DESPERADO
Doolin Dalton / Twenty one / Out of control / Tequila sunrise / Desperado / Certain kind of fool / Outlaw man / Saturday night / Bitter Creek
K 253008 / '89 / Asylum

□ EAGLES
Take it easy / Witchy woman / Chug all night / Most of us are sad / Nightingale / Train leaves here this morning / Take the devil / Earlybird / Peaceful easy feeling / Trying / Doolin Dalton / Twenty one / Out of control / Tequila sunrise / Desperado / Certain kind of fool / Outlaw man / Saturday night / Bitter creek
2530092 / Feb '87 / Asylum

□ EAGLES LIVE
Hotel California / Heartache tonight / I can't tell you why / Long run / New kid in town / Life's been good / Seven Bridges Road / Wasted time / Take it to the limit / Doolin Dalton / Desperado / Saturday night / All night long / Life in the fast lane / Take it easy
7559605912 / Feb '92 / Asylum

□ HELL FREEZES OVER
Get over it / Love will keep us alive / Girl from yesterday / Learn to be still / Tequila sunrise / Hotel California / Wasted time / Pretty maids all in a row / I can't tell you why / New York minute / Last resort / Take it easy / In the city / Life in the fast lane / Desperado
GED 24725 / Nov '94 / Geffen

□ HOTEL CALIFORNIA
Hotel California / New kid in town / Life in the fast lane / Wasted time / Wasted time (reprise) / Pretty maids all in a row / Try and love again / Last resort / Victim of love
253051 / May '87 / Asylum

□ LONG RUN, THE
Long run / I can't tell you why / In the city / Disco strangler / King of Hollywood / Heartache tonight / Those shoes / Teenage jail / Greeks don't want no freaks / Sad cafe
252181 / '86 / Asylum

□ ON THE BORDER
Already gone / You never cry like a lover / Midnight flyer / My man (mon homme) / On the border / James Dean / 01 55 / Is it true / Good day in hell / Best of my love
243005 / Jun '83 / Asylum

□ ONE OF THESE NIGHTS
One of these nights / Too many hands / Hollywood waltz / Journey of the sorcerer / Lyin' eyes / Take it to the limit / Visions / After the thrill is gone / I wish you peace
K253014 / '89 / Asylum

□ TELLTALES (Interview Disc)
TELL 13 / Jun '97 / Network

□ VERY BEST OF THE EAGLES, THE
Take it easy / Witchy woman / Peaceful easy feeling / Doolin dalton / Desperado / Tequila sunrise / Best of my love / James Dean / I can't tell you why / Lyin' eyes / Take it to the limit / One of these nights / Hotel California / New kid in town / Life in the fast lane / Hertache tonight / Long run
9548323752 / Jul '94 / Asylum

Eagles

□ SMASH HITS...PLUS
March of the Eagles / Dance on / Lonely bull / Desperados / Scarlett O'Hara / Stranger on the shore / Al di la / Exodus / Johnny's tune / Bristol express / Pipeline / Some people / Old Ned (theme from Steptoe and son) / Maigret / Happy Joe / Special agent / Hava nagila / Sukiyaki / Desafinado / Theme from Station Six Sahara / Wishin' and hopin' / Come on baby (to the Floral Dance) / Moonstruck / Andorra / Theme to Oliver Twist / Telstar
SEECD 277 / '89 / See For Miles

Eaglesmith, Fred

□ DRIVE-IN MOVIE
VER 42182 / Apr '96 / Vertical

Eaglin, Snooks

□ BABY YOU CAN GET YOUR GUN
You give me nothing but the blues / Oh sweetness / Lavinia / Baby you can get your gun / Drop the bomb / That certain door / Mary Joe / Nobody knows / Pretty girls everywhere
FIENDCD 96 / Mar '92 / Demon

□ COUNTRY BOY DOWN IN NEW ORLEANS
ARHCD 348 / Apr '95 / Arhoolie

□ LIVE IN JAPAN
Quaker city / I went to the Mardi Gras / Soul train / Don't take it so hard / Josephine / Down yonder (we go ballin) / Lillie Mae / Nine pound steel / It's your thing / Yours truly / (Boogie on) Reggae woman / Black night / Traveling mood / Reprise
CDBT 1137 / Mar '97 / Black Top

□ NEW ORLEANS STREET SINGER
Alberta / That's alright / Malaguena / When they ring the golden bells / Remember me / Fly right back baby / I don't know / Mean ol' world / I must see Jesus / She's one black rat / Don't you lie to me / Well I had my fun / Brown skin woman / Mama don't you tear my clothes / Who's been foolin' you / When shadows fall / One more drink / I got a woman / Come back baby / Trouble in mind / I got my questionaire / Drifter
STCD 8023 / Dec '94 / Storyville

□ OUT OF NOWHERE
Oh lawdy, my baby / Lipstick traces / Young girl / Out of nowhere / You're so fine / Mailman blues / Well-a, well-a, baby-la / Kiss of fire / It's your thing / Playgirl / West side baby / Cheetah
JJCD 13 / Apr '90 / Black Top

□ SOUL'S EDGE
Josephine / Show me the way back home / Ling ting tong / Aw'some funk / I'm not ashamed / Nine pound steel / Answer now / Skinny minnie / Thrill on the hill / You and me / I went to the mardi gras / Talk to me / Mama and papa / God will take care
BT 1112CD / Apr '95 / Black Top

□ TEASIN' YOU
BT 1072CD / '92 / Black Top

□ THAT'S ALL RIGHT (Eaglin, Blind Snooks)
OBCCD 568 / Jul '95 / Original Blues Classics

Ealey, Robert

□ I LIKE MUSIC WHEN I PARTY
Shake your butt / See about me / Don't I love you / Is your bathroom clean / Too many ways / Cristena / Elloise / Shoo-be-doo / Graveyard blues / When the lights go out (let's push it) / Picture on the wall / Wild wild west
CDBT 1138 / May '97 / Black Top

□ IF YOU NEED ME (Texas Blues Legend)
IMP 705 / Jul '95 / Iris Music

Ealey, Theodis

□ IF YOU LEAVE ME, I'M GOING WHI CHA
ICH 1164CD / Jan '94 / Ichiban

□ RAW
70630249342 / 21 Apr '98 / Ichiban

□ STUCK BETWEEN RHYTHM AND BLUES
Bluesman lover / Do you love me / You're on my mind / Was it me / Dreamin' / (tell me) why I can't trust you / I don't wanna talk about it / Goody sack / Lonely sunday / Stuck between rhythm and blues
ICH 1185CD / Dec '95 / Ichiban

Earl 16

□ NOT FOR SALE
NXXCD 01 / Dec '93 / Next Step

□ ROOTSMAN
RNCD 2038 / Jan '94 / Rhino

□ STEPPIN' OUT
Cyber town / Natural roots / Herbman corner / Promised land / Purify / Zion City / Zion dub / Steppin' out / Inner city blues / Going to Africa / Is it because I'm black / Going to Africa (Rockers Hi-Fi mix)
3984205501 / 6 Oct '97 / WEA

Earl Brutus

□ TONIGHT YOU ARE THE SPECIAL ONE
SAS and the glam that goes with it / Universal plan / God let me be kind (bitterfeld) / Midland red / Come taste my mind / Second class war / Your majesty we are here / Don't die Jim / 99p (take me away) / East / Edelweiss (blown away) / Male wife
FRUCD 1003 / 1 Jun '98 / Fruition

□ YOUR MAJESTY, WE ARE HERE
Navyhead / I'm new / Male milk / On me not in me / Don't leave me behind mate / Thelmex / Black speedway / Motorola / Shrunken head / Curtsy / Blind date / Life's too long / Karl Brutus / Single seater Xmas
BLUFF 036CD / Sep '96 / Deceptive

Earl Grey

□ PURVEYORS OF THE NEW GROOVE
0090952COX / 15 Sep '97 / Edel

Earl, Jimmy

□ JIMMY EARL
EFA 120672 / May '95 / Hotwire

Earl, Johnny

□ AMERICAN DREAM, THE
Lucille / U.s. of a. / Your cheatin' heart / In a modern world / Jeanie, jeanie, jeanie / Give me your love / American dream / You're the one / Look away / Sittin' in the balcony / Memory lingers on / Our love was always meant to be / Game of love / Fool for your love
F 3020 P / Nov '91 / Fury

□ BURNING THE FLOOR
PCM 001 / Apr '97 / Pollytone

□ GIVE ME THE RIGHT (Earl, Johnny & The Jordonaires)
Give me the right / Hallo mary lou-it's late / Don't / Until then / Love me / Run boy run / Too much / Finders keepers losers weepers / Love come back / I want you, I need you, I love you / Crying / I can count on you / Just can't help believing
WCPCD 1007 / Sep '92 / West Coast

□ PRESLEY STYLE OF..., THE
ROCKCD 9115 / Oct '91 / Rockhouse

□ SINGER MAN, THE
Singer man / Next time that I see you / Power in me / Knocked for six / She won't / Wherever love can be found / Born a country boy / No no no no / London town / Daddy's leaving home / Always forever / Love's on fire / When hearts break / Radio man
CDRPM 008 / Feb '97 / JEM

□ WITH ELVIS IN MIND
Long live the King / Don't / Queen of the night / Santa's party / Suspicion / I tried / Too much / Born to rock / Faithful and true / Fame and fortune / It's been too long / Blind date / Only one love / Christmas bells ring / Next time that I see you / Reckless heart / Power in me / Skiff-a-billy line dance / I have a dream
CDRPM 0024 / Oct '97 / RP Media

Earl, Ronnie

□ BLUES & FORGIVENESS (Earl, Ronnie & The Broadcasters)
CCD 11042 / Jun '94 / Crosscut

□ COLOUR OF LOVE (Earl, Ronnie & The Broadcasters)
5375622 / Jul '97 / Verve

□ DEEP BLUES (Earl, Ronnie & The Broadcasters)
CD 1033 / '88 / Black Top

□ GRATEFUL HEART - BLUES & BALLADS (Earl, Ronnie & The Broadcasters)
CDBB 9565 / Mar '96 / Bullseye Blues

□ I LIKE IT WHEN IT RAINS
Ridin' with ronnie / Linda / Midnite clothes / Mutcika / I like it when it rains / Walkin' and cryin' / Down on guadalupe / Anne lee / Sittin' on top of the world / Blues for jimmie and jessie
ANTCD 0002 / Jan '93 / Antones

□ LANGUAGE OF THE SOUL (Earl, Ronnie & The Broadcasters)
Eddie's gospel groove / Beautiful child / Indigo burell / Blues for Martin Luther King / Harvard square stomp / Barcelona morning / I am with you / Green light / Through floods and storms / Blue guitar / Bill's blues
BBCD 9554 / Nov '94 / Bullseye Blues

□ PEACE OF MIND (Earl, Ronnie & The Broadcasters)
I want to shout about it / I wish you could see me now / Peace of mind / T-Bone boogie / Wayne's blues / Bonehead too / More than I deserve / Can't keep from cryin' / I cried my eyes out / No use crying / Stickin' / Wayward angel
FIENDCD 169 / yun '90 / Demon

□ PLAYS BIG BLUES
CDBTEL 7002 / Mar '97 / Black Top

□ SOUL SEARCHIN' (With Jerry Portnoy) (Earl, Ronnie & The Broadcasters)
CD 1042 / '88 / Black Top

Earland, Charles

□ BLACK TALK
Black talk / Mighty burner / Here comes charlie / Aquarius / More today than yesterday
OJCCD 335 / Nov '95 / Original Jazz Classics

□ BLACK TALK/BLACK DROPS
Black talk / Mighty burner / Here comes Charlie / Aquarius / More today than yesterday / Sing a simple song / Don't say goodbye / Lazybird / Letha / Raindrops keep falling on my head / Buck green
CDBGPD 093 / Apr '95 / Beat Goes Public

□ BLOWING THE BLUES AWAY
Blowing the blues away / Sweet love / For the love of you / This is the day (the Lord has made) / Dolphin dance / Put it where you want it / Strollin' / Quicksilver
HCD 7010 / Jan '98 / Highnote

□ JAZZ ORGAN SUMMIT
CBD 27102 / 22 Jun '98 / Cannonball

□ LEAVING THIS PLANET
Leaving this planet / Red clay / Warp factor 8 / Brown eyes / Asteroid / Mason's galaxy / No me esqueca (Don't forget me) / Tyner / Van jay / Never ending melody
PRCD 660022 / Jan '94 / Prestige

□ LIVING BLACK (Live At The Lighthouse)
Key club cookout / Westbound 9 / Killer Joe / Milestones / Smiling / We've only just begun / Black gun / Spinky / Freedom jazz dance / Moontrane
CDBGPD 118 / 27 Jul '98 / Beat Goes Public

□ WHIP APPEAL
MCD 5409 / Nov '91 / Muse

Earle, Steve

□ COPPERHEAD ROAD
Copperhead Road / Snake oil / Back to the wall / Devil's right hand / Johnny come lately / Even when I'm blue / You belong to me / Waiting on you / Once you love / Nothing but a child
MCLD 19213 / Sep '93 / MCA

□ EARLY TRACKS
7903 / 2 Feb '98 / Koch

□ EL CORAZON
Christmas in Washington / Taneytown / If you fall / I still carry you around / Telephone road / Someone out there / You know the rest / NYC / Poison lovers / Other side of town / Here I am / Fort Worth blues
9362467892 / 6 Oct '97 / Warner Bros.

□ ESSENTIAL STEVE EARLE, THE
Guitar town / Hillbilly highway / Devil's right hand / Goodbye's all we got left to say / Six days on the road / Someday / Good ol' boy (gettin' tough) / Copperhead road / Rain came down / I ain't ever satisfied / Nowhere road / Week of living dangerously / Continental trailways blues
MCLD 19325 / Sep '96 / MCA

□ EXIT O
Nowhere road / Sweet little '66 / No. 29 / Angry young man / San Antonio girl / Rain came down / I ain't ever satisfied / Week of living dangerously / I love you too much / It's all up to you
MCLD 19070 / Oct '92 / MCA

☐ I FEEL ALRIGHT
I feel alright / Hard-core troubadour / More than I can do / Hurtin' me, hurtin' you / Now, she's gone / Poor boy / Valentine's day / Unrepentant / CCKMP / Billy and Bonnie / South Nashville blues / You're still standin' there
TRACD 227 / Apr '96 / Transatlantic

☐ SHUT UP AND DIE LIKE AN AVIATOR (Live)
Good ol' boy (gettin' tough) / Devil's right hand / I ain't ever satisfied / Someday / West Nashville boogie / Snake oil / Blue yodel no.9 / Other kind / Billy Austin / Copperhead road / Fearless heart / Guitar town / I love you too much / She's about a mover / Rain came down / Dead flowers
MCLD 19326 / Sep '96 / MCA

☐ TRAIN A COMIN'
TRACD 111 / Apr '96 / Transatlantic

Earls

☐ REMEMBER THEN (The Best Of The Earls)
Remember then / Life is but a dream / Eyes / Out in the cold again / Looking for my baby / Remember me baby / Never / Lookin' my way / All through our teens / Don't forget / Cry cry cry / Without you / Amor / Let's waddle / I believe / Oh what a time / Cross my heart / Kissing / Ol' man river / Never (alt take) / Ask anybody / Our day will come / I keep a tellin' you
CDCHD 366 / May '92 / Ace

Earls, Jack

☐ HEY SLIM, LET'S BOP (His Complete Sun Recordings)
CPCD 8197 / Jun '96 / Charly

Earls Of Suave

☐ BASEMENT BAR AT THE HEARTBREAK HOTEL, THE
Ain't that lovin' you baby / Cheat / Fool such as I / Ring of fire / Sea of love / She's my witch / Mondo moodo / Stranger in my own hometown / Nothing takes the place of you / Somebody buy me a drink / Really gone this time / You can call (But I won't answer) / Cheap wine / Yabba dabba doo (So are you) / One more beer / Little ole wine drinker me / Nobody knows
ASKCD 042 / Jul '94 / Vinyl Japan

Earth

☐ CAPSULAR EXTRACTION
8P123B / Feb '94 / Sub Pop

☐ EARTH VOL.2
SPCD 65/222 / Feb '93 / Sub Pop

☐ PENTASTAR: IN THE STYLE OF DEMONS
SPCD 361 / Jul '96 / Sub Pop

Earth Crisis

☐ DESTROY THE MACHINES
VE 022CD / Aug '95 / Victory

☐ FIRESTORM
VR 122 / Apr '94 / Victory

☐ GOMORRAH'S SEASON ENDS
VR 044CD / Dec '96 / Victory

☐ LIVE
VR 066CD / 2 Mar '98 / Victory

☐ LIVE CALIFORNIA TAKEOVER (Earth Crisis/Snapcase/Strife)
VR 042CD / Sep '96 / Victory

Earth Nation

☐ THOUGHTS IN PAST FUTURE
Lord giveth / Falling tears / Revelation / In your mind / World in blue / Chilled dreams / Claim for passion / Alienated / Isolation / In retrospect / Lord taketh
4509955572 / May '94 / Eye Q

Earth Water Air Fire

☐ AVALON
Hydroscope / Red fish / Miditation / Nautical dream / Cumana / Thunderdome / Earthbound / Gemini / Moontribe / Stereogen / Nautical mix / Gothama
SSR 128 / Nov '93 / SSR

Earth, Wind & Fire

☐ BEST OF EARTH, WIND AND FIRE VOL.1, THE
Got to get you into my life / Fantasy / Saturday night / Love music / Getaway / That's the way of the world / September / Shining star / Reasons / Sing a song
CD 32536 / Jun '89 / Columbia

☐ BEST OF EARTH, WIND AND FIRE VOL.2, THE
Turn on (the beat box) / Let's groove / After the love has gone / Fantasy / Devotion / Serpentine fire / Love's holiday / Boogie wonderland / Saturday nite / Mighty mighty
4632002 / May '91 / Columbia

☐ BOOGIE WONDERLAND (The Best Of Earth, Wind & Fire)
Boogie wonderland / Let's groove / September / Fantasy / Got to get you into my life / Saturday nite / In the stone / Mighty mighty / I've had enough / Love's holiday / Star / Reasons / Getaway / System of survival / Spread your love / Let me talk / After the love has gone / Let your feelings show
TCD 2879 / Aug '96 / Telstar

☐ DEFINITIVE COLLECTION, THE
Shining star / That's the way of the world / Sing a song / Getaway / Fantasy / Got to get you into my life / September / Boogie wonderland: *Earth, Wind & Fire/The Emotions* / After the love has gone / Star / Can't let go / Love goes on / Let's groove / Fall in love with me / Magnetic / Systems of survival / Thinking of you
4805542 / 13 Jul '98 / Columbia

☐ EARTH, WIND & FIRE
Help somebody / Moment of truth / Love is life / Fan the fire / C'mon children / World today / Bad tune
7599268612 / Jan '96 / Warner Bros.

☐ ETERNAL DANCE, THE (3CD Set)
Fan the fire / Love is life / I think about lovin' you / Interlude / Time is on your side / Where have all the flowers gone / Power / Keep your head to the sky / Mighty mighty / Feelin' blue / Hey girl / Open our eyes / Shining star / That's the way of the world / Kalimba story/Sing a message to you (live) / Head to the sky / Devotion / Sun goddess (live) / Mighty mighty (Live) / Can't hide love / Sing a song / Sunshine / Getaway / Saturday nite spirit / Ponta de areia / Fantasy / Saturday night spirit / Ponta de Ariea 'Brazilian rhyme' / Serpentine fire / I'll write a song for you / Be ever wonderful / Beijo / Got to get you into my life / September / Boogie wonderland / After the love has gone / In the stone / Dirty / Let me talk / And love goes on / Pride demo / Let's groove / Wanna be with you / Little girl / Night dreamin' / Fall in love with me / Magnetic / System of survival / Thinking of you / Gotta find out
4726142 / Jan '93 / Columbia

☐ FACES
Let me talk / Turn it into something good / Pride / You / Sparkle / Back on the road / Song in my heart / You went away / Love goes on / Sailaway / Take it to the sky / Win or lose / Share your love / In time / Faces
4746792 / Feb '97 / Columbia

☐ IN THE NAME OF LOVE
EAGCD 002 / Jul '97 / Eagle

☐ LET'S GROOVE (The Best Of Earth, Wind & Fire)
Let's groove / Boogie wonderland / Saturday nite / In the stone / I've had enough / Can't let go / Fall in love with me / Star / September / Jupiter / Got to get you into my life / Fantasy / Evil / That's the way of the world / You can't hide love / Reasons / After the love has gone
4865112 / Apr '97 / Columbia

☐ LIVE AND UNPLUGGED
AVEXCD 20 / Nov '95 / Avex

☐ LOVE SONGS, THE
After the love has gone / I'm in love / You / Reasons / Sailaway / Fantasy / Could it be right / All about love / Be ever wonderful / We're living in our own time / Daydreamin' / I'll write a song for you / Wait / That's the way of the world / You can't hide love / Miracles
4677682 / Oct '95 / Columbia

☐ MILLENNIUM, YESTERDAY, TODAY
Even if you wonder / Sunday morning / Blood brothers / Kalimba interlude / Spend the night / Divine / Two hearts / Honor the magic / Love is the greatest story / L word / Just another lonely night / Super hero / Wouldn't change a thing about you / Love across the wire / Chicago (Chi-town) blues / Kalimba blues
9362452742 / Sep '93 / WEA

☐ POWER LIGHT/ELECTRIC UNIVERSE/SPIRIT (3CD Set)
4688042 / Jul '94 / Columbia

☐ SMOOTH ELEMENTS (The Songs Of Earth, Wind & Fire) (Various Artists)
Evil: *Coryell, Larry* / After the love has gone: *Benoit, David & Russ Freeman* / Sun goddess: *Lewis, Ramsey & Earth, Wind & Fire* / Devotion: *Johnson, Mark* / Fantasy: *Grant, Tom & Peter White* / Shining star: *Johnson, Mark* / Reasons: *Turrentine, Stanley* / Tuck and patti: *Getaway* / Can't hide love: *Evans, Carl Jr.* / That's the way of the world: *Pensyl, Kim* / September: *Tesh, John*
SH 5036 / Mar '98 / Shanachie

☐ SWEET SWEETBACK'S BAADASSS SONG (Original Soundtrack)
Sweetback losing his cherry / Sweetback getting it so hard... / Come on feet / Sweetback's theme / Hoppin' John/Voices/Mojo woman/Voices / Sanra Z/Voices / Reggin hanging on in there as best they can/Voices / Won't bleed me / Man tries running his usual game...
CDSXE 103 / Mar '97 / Stax

☐ THAT'S THE WAY OF THE WORLD
Shining star / That's the way of the world / Happy feelin' / All about love / Yearnin' learnin' / Reasons / Africano / See the light
4844672 / Feb '97 / Columbia

Earthlan

☐ BEAUTIFUL COLLISON OF NATIONS, THE
SH 66001 / Nov '97 / Shanachie

Earthlings

☐ EARTHLINGS
ZD 21CD / 17 Aug '98 / Crippled Dick Hot Wax

Earthmen

☐ FALL AND RISE OF MY FAVORITE SIXTIES GIRL
Figure 8 / Brittle / Fall and rise of my favorite sixties girl / Things that worry grown-ups / Tell the women we're going / Language of you and me
958882 / Jul '94 / Seed

☐ TEEN SENSATIONS
Cool chick / Stacey's cupboard / Blonde / Momentum / Encouragement kiss / Roll / Too far down / In the south / Flyby / Elephant
142412 / Nov '93 / Seed

Earthquake

☐ DUB LION 2000
EQCD 001 / 2 Mar '98 / Earthquake

Earthrise

☐ DEEPER THAN SPACE
SR 9344 / Mar '94 / Silent

Earthtone 9

☐ LO-DEF(INTION) DISCORD
COP 07 / 17 Aug '98 / Copro

Earwig

☐ UNDER MY SKIN I AM LAUGHING
LADIDA 024CD / Jul '94 / La-Di-Da

Easley, Bill

☐ WIND INVENTIONS
SSC 1022CD / Sep '96 / Sunnyside

East 17

☐ AROUND THE WORLD - THE JOURNEY SO FAR (The Hit Singles)
Stay another day / Around the world / Let it rain / Deep / Thunder / It's alright / Do U still / Steam / Hey child / Hold my body tight / House of love / If you ever: *East 17 & Gabrielle* / Someone to love / Slow it down / Gold / West End girls
8288502 / Nov '96 / London

☐ AROUND THE WORLD - THE JOURNEY SO FAR (The Hit Singles/Limited Edition 2CD Set)
House of love / Deep / It's alright / Stay another day / Steam / Let it rain / Slow it down / If you ever: *East 17 & Gabrielle* / West End girl / Around the world / Thunder / Gold / Do u still / Someone to love / Hey child / Hold my body tight / Stay another day / Let it rain / Hold my body tight / House of love / Deep / Gold / Do u still / Steam / Deep / Let it rain / Slow it down
8288522 / Nov '96 / London

☐ STEAM
Steam / Let it all go / Hold my body tight / Stay another day / Around the world / Let it rain / Be there / MF Power / Generation XTC
8285422 / Oct '94 / London

☐ UP ALL NIGHT
Innocent erotic / Thunder / I remember / Do U still / Gotta keep on / Ghetto / It's all over / Someone to love / Right here with you / Free your mind / Don't you feel so good / Best days / Looking for
8286992 / Oct '95 / London

East Down Septet

☐ CHANNEL SURFING
East 9th street / Which Ralph are you / Knock knock / Mist flower / Abeyance / Once upon a time in the west / Downside / Tell me when / Joke's on me / Take it home
HEPCD 2069 / Mar '97 / Hep

☐ OUT OF GRIDLOCK
Claudia's car / Three views of a secret / Mothers of the veil / Suite from Taxi Driver / It smells good / Knew rhythm / Black Monday / Gray whale / Cowboy song / Dedication
HEPCD 2063 / Jun '95 / Hep

East London Chorus

☐ ESSENTIALLY CHRISTMAS
372022 / Nov '97 / Koch International

East Meets West

☐ DUBOLOGY PRESENTS MEGADUB
DOR 100CD / Sep '95 / Dubology

☐ MEGADUB
DOR 001CD / Apr '97 / Dubology

☐ TIME IS THE MASTER
Time is the master / Time dub / Distant dub / Plea for peace / Over the rainbow / Rainbow dub / Valve dub / Gates of Zion / London calling / London's dubbing / Prophet lives / Give love / Ghost killer / Jah say / Feel good / Feel good dub
DBHD 005CD / 29 Sep '97 / Dubhead

East Of Eden

☐ JIG A JIG
REP 7073 / 15 Dec '97 / Repertoire

☐ KALIPSE
HTDCD 80 / 1 Dec '97 / HTD

☐ MERCATOR PROJECTED
PMS 7040 / 22 Jun '98 / Repertoire

☐ SNAFU
SRMC 0071 / 5 Jan '98 / Siwan

East Of Java

☐ IMP AND THE ANGEL, THE
PLASCD 018 / Jan '90 / Plastic Head

East River Pipe

☐ MEL
SHINKANSEN 7CD / Dec '96 / Shinkansen

☐ POOR FRICKY
Bring on the loser / Ah dictaphone / Crawl away / Metal detector / Put down / Superstar in France / Keep all your windows tight tonight / Make it real / Hey, where's your girl / Walking the dog / Million trillion
SARAH 621CD / Nov '94 / Sarah

East Texas Serenaders

☐ COMPLETE RECORDED WORKS 1927-1937, THE
DOCD 8031 / 15 Jun '98 / Document

East West Ensemble

☐ ZURNA
ITM 001478 / Nov '92 / ITM

East Yorkshire Brass Band

☐ FACE THE MUSIC
EYBCD 1 / May '96 / Lone Wolf Audio

Eastbound Expressway

☐ BEST OF EASTBOUND EXPRESSWAY, THE (You're A Beat)
Danger zone / Cloudburst / Better look before you leap / Turn back the tide / Never let go / Primitive desire / Frantic love / You're a beat / Knock me senseless / Rainstorm / Whiplash / Theme from K-9 and company
HTCD 59 / 20 Apr '98 / Hot Productions

Eastern Standard Time

☐ SECOND HAND
Tick tock / Oh no / Tenor madness / Bemsha swing / Mad dog / Housewive's choice / Richard Bruce / Be bop / On the trail / Barbados / Urban lullaby
BVR 1001 / May '98 / Beatville

Eastley, Max

☐ NEW AND REDISCOVERED MUSICAL INSTRUMENTS (Eastley, Max & David Toop)
Hydrophone / Metallophone / Elastic aerophone / Centriphone / Do the bathosphere / Divination of the bowhead whale / Chairs story
CDOVD 478 / Jun '97 / EG

Easton, Sheena

☐ 20 GREAT LOVE SONGS
You could have been with me / Follow my rainbow / Moody / Paradox / Forever friends / When he shines / Summer's over / Wind beneath my wings / Fire and rain / I wouldn't beg for water / Calm before the storm / To anyone / If you go away / Savoir faire / Next time / Almost over you / I don't need your word / Magic of love / Ice out in the rain / So we say goodbye
LS 887012 / 2 Feb '98 / Disky

☐ GOLD COLLECTION, THE
Morning train (9 to 5) / Moody (my love) / Modern girl / Paradox / For your eyes only / One man woman / Summer's over / Take my time / Calm before the storm / Just another broken heart / Savoir faire / Are you man enough / Back in the city / Letters from the road / I don't need your word / So we say goodbye
CDGOLD 1008 / Mar '96 / EMI Gold

Easton, Ted

☐ KIDNEY STEW (Easton, Ted & His Band)
DD 631 / Nov '93 / Delmark

Easy Access Orchestra

☐ RIVIERA ROYALE
Cable car / Los banditos / Boy with beautiful hair / Wichita lineman / Swinging London / Wet Wednesday / Easy breezin' / Bermuda playboy / Cocktails and cheese / Riviera femline
EASYCD 1 / 13 Jul '98 / Beechwood

Easy Club

☐ ESSENTIAL
Easy club reel - Janine's reel / Dirty old town / Diamond / Euphemia / Free journey north / Black is the colour of my true love's hair / Little cascade / Quiet man / Fause, fause hae ye been / Skirlie beat / Auld toon shuffle / Road to Gerenish / Innocent railway / Auchengeich / North sea chinaman / Desert march / This for that / Murdo Mackensie of Torridon / Collier's 8 hour day / Arnish light / Eyemouth disaster / Easy club reel
ECLCD 9103 / Jan '96 / Eclectic

Easy Riders

☐ MARIANNE (2CD Set)
What'cha gonna do / So true blues / Marianne / US Adam / Rollin' home / Everybody loves Saturday night / Lonesome rider / Goodbye Chiquita / Champagne wine / South coast / Hot crawfish / Red sundown / Yermo's nightmare and Yermo red / Sky is high / Send for the captain / Don't hurry worry me / True love and tender care / Tina / Sweet sugar cane / I won't tell / Strollin' blues / Fare thee well / Weary travellin' blues / Blues ain't nothin' / Times / Man about town / Shorty Joe / Green fields / Blue mountain / Windjammer / Kari waits for me / Delia / (I heard that) Lonesome whistle / Wanderin' blues / Eddystone light / Drill ye tarriers drill / East Virginia / I ride an old paint / Mayfield mountain / Ravin' gambler / Gambler's blues / John Henry / Six wheel driver / I'm gonna leave you now / Saturday's child / Love is a golden ring / Ride away / Vaquero / Take off your old coat / Il fait si beau / Glory glory / My pretty quadron / Forever new / Poor boy / Lights of town / Cry of the wild goose / Young in love / Ballad of the Alamo / Green leaves of summer / Remember the Alamo / Laredo / Green grow the lilacs / Long lean Deliah / Leina / Plain old plainsmen / Girl I left behind / Here's to the ladies / Tennessee babe / Mi amor, mi corazon / Haven't we met before / Silver and gold / Go tell her for me / Brother Simon and sister Mary / Ten men from Tennessee / Deerfoot Dan / Sam Hall/ Nellie / Maggie Gonzales / Along comes me / 900 Miles / Bachelor's boy / Jeb Jone's daughter / See all the people / Bill goat hill / Ta pedia tou pirea (never on a sunday) / Marianne P / Pajarillo barranquero / Toro / Wabash cannon ball / Run come see Jerusalem / Adieu Cherie / Dead eye Sam / Devil cat / Speak a word of love (I wish, I wish) / Lady from Laramie / Little King / Oh Brandy leave me alone / Boll weevil / Black eyed Susie / Story of creation / Cotton eyed Joe / Billy boy / Roving gambler / Jennie Jenkins / Black is the colour / I know where I'm going / Ev'ryone's crazy ceptin me / Running away / Secret / Nellie Lou / Last freight / Solitary singer / Mr. Buzzard / Tick tock song / Across the wild Missouri / Girl in the wood / Fast freight / Hoofbeat serenade / Stay a while / Rollin' stone / World belongs to me / Three jolly rogues of Lynne / Charmin' bells / Nine hundred miles / Greensleeves / John Hardy / Fond affection / Box of rosewood / Man you don't meet every day / Tom Jack / Wait by the willow / Golden minute / Mackerel feet / Sparrow grass and brown bread / Gypsy Davey / Tall timber / Come home Zelda / Ride away Vaquero / Quit kicking my dog around / Man of the sky / Christopher Columbus
BCD 15780 / Aug '95 / Bear Family

Easybeats

☐ FRIDAY ON MY MIND
422126 / May '94 / New Rose

☐ GOOD FRIDAY
REP 4162 / Aug '91 / Repertoire

☐ LIVE - STUDIO AND STAGE
RVCD 40 / Oct '95 / Raven

☐ VERY BEST OF THE EASYBEATS
Friday on my mind / Hello how are you / Land of make believe / She's so fine / Bring a little lovin' / St. louis / Good time / Falling off the edge of the world / Music goes 'round my head / Come in, you'll get pneumonia / It's so easy / Hard road / Evie (part 1) / Evie (part 2) / Evie (part 3)
BRCD 118 / Jan '95 / BR Music

Eat Static

☐ ABDUCTION
BARKCD 001 / Jul '94 / Ultimate

☐ B-WORLD
BARKCD 034 / 31 Aug '98 / Planet Dog

☐ IMPLANT
BARKCD 005 / May '94 / Ultimate

☐ SCIENCE OF THE GODS
Science of the gods / Interceptor / Kryll / Spawn / Dissection / Pseudopod / Body stealers / Contact / Hangar
BARKCD 029 / 13 Oct '97 / Planet Dog

Eater

☐ ALL OF EATER
CMD 024 / 9 Mar '98 / Creativeman Disc

☐ COMPLETE EATER, THE
You / Public toys / Room for one / Lock it up / Sweet Jane / I don't need it / Ann / Get raped / Space dreaming / Queen Bitch / My business / Waiting for the man / Fifteen / No more / No brains / Peace and love (H-Bomb) / Outside view / Thinking of the USA / Michael's monetary system / She's wearing green / Notebook / Jeepster / Debutante's ball / Holland / What she wants she needs / Reach for the sky / Point of view / Typewriter babes
CDPUNK 10 / Apr '93 / Anagram

Eatman, Heather

☐ MASCARA FALLS
Goodbye Betty-Jean / Barbs / Miss Liberty / City of your heart / Amelia waltz / Halfway hotel / Lucky you / Sheila / Big bass drum / Used car / Greyhound
OBR 014 / May '97 / Oh Boy

Eaton, John

☐ INDIANA ON OUR MINDS
CRD 304 / Mar '96 / Chiaroscuro

☐ MADE IN AMERICA
CRD 333 / Jan '97 / Chiaroscuro

Eaton, Nigel

☐ MUSIC OF THE HURDY-GURDY, THE
Il Pastor Fido (Vivaldi) / Les Amusements d'une heure (Baton) / Crocodile bourree / Lady Diamond/ New Jig / Satins blanc / Malashevska / Laride / Queen Adelaide
CDSDL 374 / Mar '94 / Saydisc

Eazy E

☐ EAZY-DUZ IT
(prelude) still talkin' / Nobody move / 2 hard mutha's / Boyz-n-the hood / Eazy-duz-it / We want eazy / Eazy-er said than dunn / Radio / No more 's / I'mma break it down / Eazy-chapter 8 verse 10
IMCD 124 / Apr '91 / 4th & Broadway

☐ ETERNAL E
Boyz-n-the-hood / 8 ball: NWA / Eazy duz it / Eazy-er said than dunn / No more questions: NWA / We want Eazy / Nobody move / Radio / Only if you want it / Neighborhood sniper / I'd rather fuck you: NWA / Automobile: NWA / Niggaz my height don't fight / Eazy Street
CDPTY 122 / Jan '96 / Priority/Virgin

☐ STR8 OFF THA STREETZ OF MUTHAPHUKKIN COMPTON
First power / Old school shit / Sorry Louis / Just tah let U know / Sippin' on a 40 / Nutz on ya chin / Tha muthaphukkin real / Lickin', suckin', phukkin' / Hit the hooker / My baby's mama / Creep n' oh crawl / Wut would you do / Gangsta beat for the street / Eternal E
4835762 / Jan '96 / Ruthless

Ebbage, Len

☐ SAY IT WITH MUSIC (Ebbage, Len Band)
CDTS 054 / Dec '95 / Maestro

Eberhardt, Cliff

☐ 12 SONGS OF GOOD AND EVIL
RHRCD 105 / Oct '97 / Red House

☐ MONA LISA CAFE
SHCD 8017 / Oct '95 / Shanachie

☐ NOW YOU ARE MY HOME
SHAN 8008CD / Dec '93 / Shanachie

Ebérle, Ray

☐ GLENN MILLER'S MEN 1943-1947 (Eberle, Ray & His Orchestra)
JH 1011 / '91 / Jazz Hour

Ebi

☐ TEN
EFA 004132 / Feb '96 / Space Teddy

☐ ZEN
EFA 117572 / May '94 / Space Teddy

Ebogo, Ange

☐ EXPLOSION
DTC 027 / Jan '91 / Stern's

Ebony Band

☐ MUSIC FROM THE SPANISH CIVIL WAR
BVHAASTCD 9203 / Jan '86 / Bvhaast

Ebony Steel Drum Band

☐ CARIBBEAN CARNIVAL
Imagine / Island in the sun / I shot the sheriff / Carnival time / Crying / Bounce / Wind beneath my wings / One note samba / Skettle in the city / Hey Jude / Wait / Killing me softly with his song / Movin' / Ain't nobody / Yellow bird
EURCD 003 / 24 Aug '98 / Eureka

Ebony Tears

☐ TORTURA INSOMIE
BS 012CD / 19 Jan '98 / Black Sun

Ebrel, Annie

☐ TRE HO TI HA MA HINI
GWP 012 / May '96 / Gwerz

EC8OR

☐ EC8TOR
Cocain duck / You will never find / Think about / Pick the best one / Victim / Overload / Discriminate / We are pissed / Lichterloh / Plastic creatures / Intro / Speed erection / Short circuit / Iche suche nichts / Cheap drops
DHRCD 003 / Nov '95 / Digital Hardcore

☐ SPEX IS A FAT BITCH
Spex is a fat bitch / I don't wanna be a part of this / One track minded fuckhead / Notorious 30's / Need / All of us can be rich
DHRMCD 009 / Nov '96 / Digital Hardcore

☐ WORLD BEATERS
Mean / Whack / Until everything explodes / Wouldn't you agree / Unable to balance / Shit you dig / Dirt / Gash in your subversive idyll / Our present is our piss / Stick to the sight / Alert (live Tokyo) / 199EC8OR
DHRCD 009 / 25 May '98 / Digital Hardcore

Eccles, Clancy

☐ FATTY FATTY 1967-1970 (Eccles, Clancy & Friends)
CDTRL 262 / 19 Jan '98 / Trojan

Echo & The Bunnymen

☐ BALLYHOO (The Best Of Echo & The Bunnymen)
Rescue / Do it clean / Villiers terrace / All that jazz / Over the wall / Promise / Disease / Back of love / Cutter / Never stop / Killing moon / Silver / Seven seas / Bring on the dancing horses / People are strange / Game / Lips like sugar / Bedbugs and ballyhoo
0630191032 / Jun '97 / WEA

☐ CROCODILES
Going up / Stars are stars / Pride / Monkeys / Crocodiles / Rescue / Villiers Terrace / Pictures on the wall / All that jazz / Happy death man / Do it clean
2423162 / '89 / Korova

☐ EVERGREEN (2CD Set)
Don't let it get you down / In my time / I want to be there (when you come) / Evergreen / I'll fly tonight / Nothing lasts forever / Baseball Bill / Altamont / Just a touch away / Empire state halo / Too young to kneel / Forgiven / Villiers terrace / Read it in books / All that jazz / Over the wall / All my colours / Back of love / Seven seas / Ocean rain / Nocturnal me / Rescue me
8289802 / 17 Nov '97 / London

☐ EVERGREEN
Don't let it get you down / In my time / I want to be there (when you come) / Evergreen / I'll fly tonight / Nothing lasts forever / Baseball Bill / Altamont / Just a touch away / Empire state halo / Too young to kneel / Forgiven
8289052 / Jul '97 / London

☐ HEAVEN UP HERE
Show of strength / With a hip / Over the wall / It was a pleasure / Promise / Heaven up here / Disease / All my colours / No dark things / Turquoise days / All I want
2423172 / Jul '88 / Korova

☐ OCEAN RAIN
Silver / Nocturnal me / Crystal days / Yo yo man / My kingdom / Thorn of crowns / Killing moon / Seven seas
2403882 / Apr '84 / Korova

☐ PORCUPINE
Cutter / Back of love / My white devil / Clay / Porcupine / Heads will roll / Ripeness / Higher hell / Gods will be gods / In bluer skies
2400272 / Jul '88 / Korova

Echo Art

☐ COREOGRAFIE
NT 6712 / Jan '94 / Robi Droli

Echo City

☐ SONIC SPORT 1983-88
Shirtful of ice / Tour tuns / Singaraja bemo ride / Night strike / On tarr catch / In the field / In aluminium / Red red red / Spiv / Song for the black economy / Engineer and more
GR 001CD / Mar '95 / Voiceprint

Echo Park

☐ RETURN TO HEAR
HE 2 / Nov '96 / Helium

Echo System

☐ HEADLAND
Bosphoressence / Jahan (The vast world) / Ish / Modulator / Chant 96 (The dome of light) / Mystic ships / Hydrophonics / Shimmer / Drum fish
DVNT 009CD / Jun '96 / Deviant

Echobelly

☐ LUSTRA
Bulldog baby / I'm not a saint / Here comes the big rush / Iris art / World is flat / Everyone knows better / Wired on / O / Bleed / Paradise / Angel B / Lustra
4889679
4889672 / 10 Nov '97 / Epic

Echolyn

☐ AS THE WORLD
All ways the same / As the world / Uncle / How long have I waited / Best regards / Cheese stands alone / Prose / Short essay / My dear wormwood / Entry 11/19/93 / One for the show / Wiblet / Audio verite / Settled land / Habit worth forming / Never the same
CYCL 025 / May '95 / Cyclops

☐ WHEN THE SWEET TURNS
CYCL 036 / Jun '96 / Cyclops

Eckert, Rinde

☐ FINDING MY WAY HOME
DIW 859 / Jun '92 / DIW

☐ STORY IN STORY OUT
Sign says West / Indian summer / Bad feelin' / Hit the desert / Day by day / Out on the mesa / Whatever the reason / Amnesia / Slow train breakdown / Last ride / Carlo dreams / Locked in amazement / Thin walls / Street don't sleep / Beyond these walls / Mechanical bird / Fearful dark streets / In the morning light / Winding the world
INT 35072 / 27 Apr '98 / Intuition

Eckhoff, Ditlef

☐ IMPRESSIONS OF ANTIBES
GMCD 92 / Feb '98 / Gemini

Ecklund, Peter

☐ IN ELKHART
JCD 246 / Aug '95 / Jazzology

Eckstine, Billy

☐ AT BASIN STREET EAST (Eckstine, Billy & Quincy Jones)
Alright, OK you win / Caravan / Don't get around much anymore / I'm just a lucky so and so / Sophisticated lady / In the still of the night / Ma, she's making eyes at me / Everything I have is yours / Fool that I am / I'm falling for you / Work song
8325922 / Feb '94 / EmArCy

☐ BEST OF THE MGM YEARS, THE (2CD Set)
8194422 / May '94 / Verve

☐ BILLY ECKSTINE
I got a date with the rhythm man / I stay in the mood for you / Good jelly blues / If that's the way you feel / I want to talk about you / Blowing the blues away / Opus X / I'll wait and pray / Real thing happend to me / Cottage for sale / I apologize / I hear a rhapsody / I'm beginning to see the light / That old black magic / Misty
17070 / Aug '96 / Laserlight

☐ BILLY'S BEST
5264402 / Feb '95 / PolyGram Jazz

☐ BOPPIN' WITH B
I want to talk about you / Together / If that's the way you feel / Opus X / I only have eyes for you / You're my everything / Jitney man / Blue / Second balcony jump / Tell me pretty baby / Love is the thing / Without a song / Don't take your love from me / Oo bop sh'bam / Cool breeze / Oo bop sh'bam / In the still of the night / Jelly jelly / My silent love / Time on my hands / All the things you are / In a sentimental mood
IGOCD 2069 / Sep '97 / Indigo

☐ CLASSICS 1944-1945
CLASSICS 914 / Jan '97 / Classics

☐ IMAGINATION
It was so beautiful / I gotta right to sing the blues / Love is just around the corner / I don't stand a ghost of a chance with you / Faded summer love / What a little moonlight can do / Imagination / Lullaby of the leaves / I cover the waterfront / I wished on the moon / That's all
8481622 / Mar '94 / EmArCy

☐ JAZZ MASTERS
I left my hat in Haiti / My foolish heart / Imagination / Kiss of fire / Now it can be told / I apologize once / I lost my sugar in Salt Lake City / So far / Jealousy / Everything I have is yours / Strange sensation / Because you're mine / Sitting by the window / Have a good time / Passing strangers
5166932 / 5 May '98 / Verve

☐ MAGNIFICENT MR. B
PASTCD 7086 / Feb '96 / Flapper

☐ MISTER B AND THE BAND
Lonesome lover blues / Cottage for sale / I love the rhythm in a riff / Last night / Prisoner of love / I ain't like that / I'm in the mood for love / You call it madness / All I sing is blues / Long long journey / I only have eyes for you / You're my everything / Jitney man / Blue / Second balcony jump / Tell me pretty baby / Love is the thing / Without a song / Cool breeze / Don't take your love from me / Oop bop sh'bam / In the still of the night / Jelly jelly / My silent love / Time on my hands / All the things you are
SV 0264 / Oct '97 / Savoy Jazz

☐ MR. B
Blowing the blues away / If that's the way you feel / I want to talk about you / Real thing happened to me / I'll wait and pray / I got a date with rhythm / Good Jelly blues / Opus X / I stay in the mood for you / I'm the caring kind
EMBCD 3338 / 29 Jun '98 / Ember

☐ MR. B & THE BE BOP BAND
Blowing the blues away / I stay in the mood for you / Good jelly blues / I got a date with rhythm / If that's the way you feel / Opus x / Real thing happened to me / I want to talk about you / Without a song / Mean to me / Mr. Chips / Don't blame me / Air mail special / Love me or leave me / Lonesome lover blues / A cottage for sale / I love the rhythm in a riff / Last night / Prisoner of love / I'm in the mood for love / You call it madness but I call it love / All I sing is blues / Long long journey / It ain't like that no more
PLCD 545 / Aug '96 / President

Eclectic Chameleon

☐ CHRISTMAS FROM TOMORROW
God rest ye merry gentleman / Jingle bells / O come o come Emmanuel / Pat-a-pan / Coventry carol / We three kings / O come all ye faithful (adeste fidelis) / Away in a manger / Angels we have heard on high / First Noel / It came upon a midnight clear / While shepherds watched
BR 104 / 7 Nov '97 / Brioso

☐ JOYOUS CHRISTMAS, A
Deck the halls / Jolly old St. Nick / Silent night / Carol of the bells / Still still / O little town of Bethlehem / Holly and the ivy / Silent night / Watchman tell us of the night / Three carols went a fuguing / Twelve days of Christmas
BR 108 / 7 Nov '97 / Brioso

Eclipse First

☐ ECLIPSE FIRST
IRCD 012 / Oct '90 / Iona

☐ NAMES AND PLACES (Eclipse First & Scotrail Vale Of Atholl Pipe Band)
Landing at roscoff / West wind / Isle de groix / La grande nuit du port de peche / Games / Road to copshie / Oban inn / Victoria bar / Craigdarroch arms
IRCD 133 / Sep '91 / Iona

Ecllerzie

☐ MUSIQUES A DANSER
CDUP 68 / May '93 / Diffusion Breizh

Economist

☐ NEW BUILT GHETTO
MASSCD 030 / Jun '94 / Massacre

Ectogram

☐ I CAN'T BELIEVE IT'S NOT REGGAE
ANKST 069CD / Oct '96 / Ankst

Ecume

☐ ECUME
CDLLL 127 / Aug '93 / La Lichere

Eddie & The Hot Rods

☐ CURSE OF THE HOT RODS/TIES THAT BIND
LOMACD 44 / Jan '95 / Loma

☐ DOING ANYTHING THEY WANNA DO...
Get out of Denver / Horseplay / All I need is money / Writing on the wall / Wooly bully / Been so long / Get across to you / Double checkin' woman / GLORIA / At night / I got mine / I see the light / Teenage depression / Do anything you wanna do / Quit this town / Telephone girl / Moon tears / You better run
CDMGRAM 108 / Oct '96 / Anagram

☐ END OF THE BEGINNING, THE (The Best Of Eddie & The Hot Rods)
Anything you wanna do / Quit this town / Telephone girl / Teenage depression / Kids are alright / Get out of Denver / Till the night is gone let's rock / Schoolgirl love / Hard drivin' man / On the run / Power and the glory / Ignore them still life / Life on the line / Circles / Take it or leave it / Echoes / We sing the cross / Beginning of the end / Gloria / Satisfaction
IMCD 156 / Jul '94 / Island

☐ GASOLINE DAYS
CMCD 008 / Apr '96 / Creative Man

☐ GET YOUR BALLS OFF
622412 / Mar '96 / Skydog

☐ LIVE AND RARE
RRCD 177 / Aug '93 / Receiver

☐ TEENAGE DEPRESSION
Get across to you / Why can't it be / Show me / All I need is money / Double checkin' woman / Kid's are alright / Teenage depression / Horseplay / Been so long / Shake / On the run
EDCD 563 / 4 May '98 / Edsel

☐ TIES THAT BIND
Get across to you / GLORIA / Wolly bully / Double checkin' woman / Get out of Denver / Ties that bind / Wide eyed kids / Hit or miss / I got mine / Red light blue light / At night / Hey tonight / Teenage deepression (Live) / Quit this town (Live) / Do anything you wanna do
DOJOCD 173 / Feb '94 / Dojo

Eddie Fingers

☐ TILL DEATH DO US DISCO (Eddie Fingers Music)
Till death do us disco / Silicon mysteries / Long hard funky dreams / Midnight safari / Graveyard shuffle / Transilvania transcendental / Hot summer dreams / Apres minuit
MASSCD 022 / Nov '94 / Infinite Mass

Eddy, Duane

☐ BECAUSE THEY'RE YOUNG
Because they're young / Rebel rouser / Peter gunn theme / Yep / Forty miles of bad road / Some kinda earthquake / Cannon ball / Pepe / Shazam / Ring of fire / Ramrod / Theme from dixie / My blue heaven / Top of old smokey / Kommotion / Scarlet ribbons (for her hair) / Lonely one / Bonnie came back / Moovin' 'n' groovin' / Play me like you play your guitar / Peter gunn theme
BR 1492 / May '94 / BR Music

☐ BEST OF DUANE EDDY, THE
(Dance with) The guitar man / Peter Gunn theme / Because they're young / Some kinda earthquake / Theme from Dixie / Shazam / Kommotion / Trambone / Bonnie came back / Detour / Rebel rouser / Play me like you play your guitar / Lonely one / Movin' and groovin' / Cannonball / Yep / Ramrod / Ring of fire / Ragbone / Forty miles of bad road
ECD 3314 / Mar '97 / K-Tel

☐ BEST OF DUANE EDDY, THE
Because they're young / Peter gunn theme / Shazam / Kommotion / Theme from dixie / Bonnie came back / Trambone / Rebel rouser / Cannonball / Some kinda earthquake / Yep / Forty miles of bad road / Detour / Ring of fire / Lonely one / Ragbone / Movin' 'n' groovin' / (Dance with) The guitar man / Ramrod / Play me like you play your guitar
SUMCD 4146 / Sep '97 / Summit

☐ BEST OF DUANE EDDY, THE/LONELY GUITAR
OW 34541 / 15 Jun '98 / One Way

☐ BOSS GUITAR
Deep in the heart of Texas / Ballad of paladin / Dance with the guitar man / Boss guitar / Lonely boy lonely guitar / Your baby's gone surfin' / Limbo rock / Scrape / Loco locomotion / Creamy mashed potatoe / High noon / Rebel rouser / Twistin' n' twangin' / Blowin' up a storm / Soul twist / Rumble tequila / Moonshot / Iguana / Roughneck / Wild westerners / Jerky jalopy / Saint 'n' sinners / Marauder / Feud / Desert rat
74321511982 / 1 Sep '97 / Camden

☐ DANCE WITH THE GUITAR MAN/ TWISTIN' AND TWANGIN'
OW 34542 / 15 Jun '98 / One Way

☐ ESPECIALLY FOR YOU/GIRLS, GIRLS, GIRLS
Peter Gunn / Only child / Lover / Fuzz / Yep / Along the Navajo trail / Just because / Quiniela / Trouble in mind / Tuxedo junction (stereo) / Hard times / Along came Linda / Tuxedo junction (mono) / I want to be wanted / That's all you got / I'm sorry / Sioux City Sue / Tammy / Big Liza / Mary Ann / Annette / Tuesday / Sweet Cindy / Patricia / Mona Lisa / Connie / Carol
BCD 15799 / Apr '94 / Bear Family

☐ GHOSTRIDER
CURCD 032 / Nov '96 / Hit

☐ HIS TWANGY GUITAR AND THE REBELS
Kicking asphalt / Rockestra theme / Theme for something really important / Spies / Blue city / Trembler / Los Companeros / Lost innocence / Rockabilly holiday / Last look back
SEECD 417 / Oct '96 / See For Miles

☐ MASTERS, THE
EABCD 024 / 24 Nov '97 / Eagle

☐ PETER GUNN
Rebel rouser / Movin' 'n' groovin' / Cannonball / Lonely one / Peter Gunn / Yep / Ramrod / Trambone / Forty miles of bad road / Some kinda earthquake / Bonnie came back / Detour / Shazam / Because they're young / Kommotion / Theme from Dixie
308592 / 20 Apr '98 / Hallmark

☐ RCA YEARS, THE
74321127012 / Jun '96 / RCA

☐ SHAZAM
Guitar man / Peter Gunn / Because they're young / Some kinda earthquake / Dixie / Shazam / Kommotion / Trambone / Bonnie come back / Detour / Rebel rouser / Play me like you play your guitar / Lonely one, (The) / Movin' and groovin' / Cannonball / Yep / Ramrod / Ring of fire / Ragbone / Forty miles of bad road
CD 6010 / Apr '96 / Music

☐ THAT CLASSIC TWANG
Rebel rouser / Moovin 'n' groovin / Ramrod / Cannonball / Mason Dixon lion / Lonely one / 3.30 blues / Yep / Peter Gunn / Forty miles of bad road / Quiet three / Some kinda earthquake / Bonnie come back / First love, first tears / Shazam / Because they're young / Kommotion / Pete / Theme from Dixie / Ring of fire / Drivin' home / Gidget goes Hawaiian / Avenger / Shazam
BCD 15702 / Apr '94 / Bear Family

☐ TWANG'S THE THANG/SONGS OF OUR HERITAGE
My blue heaven / Tiger love and turnip greens / Last minute of innocence / Route 1 / You are my sunshine / St. Louis blues / Night train to Memphis / Battle / Trambone / Blueberry hill / Rebel walk / Easy / Cripple creek / Riddle song / John Henry / Streets of Laredo / Prisoner's song / In the pines / Ole Joe Clark / Wayfaring stranger / On top of old smokey / Mule train / Scarlet ribbons
BCD 15807 / Apr '94 / Bear Family

☐ TWANGIN' (The Golden Hits)
OW 34543 / 15 Jun '98 / One Way

☐ TWANGIN' FROM PHOENIX TO LA (The Jamie Years/7CD Set)
I want some lovin' baby / Soda fountain girl / Ramrod (ford, version) / Caravan (ford version) / Up and down / Moovin 'n' groovin / Pretty jane / Want me / Rebel rouser / Stalkin' / Have love will travel / Look at me / Doo waddie / Dear 53310761 / Walker / Lonely one / Cannonball / Mason Dixon lion / Lonesome road / I almost lost my mind / Loving you / Anytime / Three 30 blues / Yep / Yep (take 7) / Dixie, part 1 / Dixie, part 2 / Yep (master) / Raid / Quiet three (basic track) / Peter Gunn / Lover / Along the Navajo trail / First love, first tears / Quiet three (master) / Forty miles of bad road / Some kinda earthquake / Some kind of earthquake (UK version) / Route 1 / Tiger love and turnip greens / Trambone / My blue heaven / Secret seven / You are my sunshine / Last minute of innocence / Rebel walk (without overdub) / Blueberry hill / Battle (without overdub) / St. Louis blues / Nightrain to Memphis / Bonnie came back / Lost island (master) / Kommotion / Rebel walk (master) / Battle (master) / Easy / Lost island (lost flute version) / Cripple creek / Riddle song / John Henry / Streets of Laredo / Prisoner's song / In the pines / Old Joe Clark / Old Joe Clark (take 27 master) / Wayfaring stranger / Top of old smokey / Mule train / Scarlet ribbons / Shazam / Kommotion / Kommotion / Because they're young / Theme for moon children (take 1) / Because they're young (take 27 master) / Theme for moon children (take 4, master) / Back porch, part 1 / Back porch, part 2 / Words mean nothing / Girl on death row / Pepe / Lost friend / Runaway pony / Drivin' home / I want to be wanted / That's all you gotta do / I'm sorry / Mary Ann / Sioux City Sue / Sweet Cindy / Tuesday / Jo Ann / Big Liza / Mona Lisa / Patricia / Connie / Carol / Dixie / Gidget goes Hawaiian / Ring of fire / Bobbie / Avenger / Londonderry air / Just because / Caravan part 1 / Caravan part 2 / Stalkin / Along came Linda / Back porch / Battle / Trouble in mind
BCD 15778 / Nov '94 / Bear Family

☐ TWANGY GUITAR/WATER SKI
OW 34545 / 15 Jun '98 / One Way

Eddy, Nelson

☐ 16 CLASSIC PERFORMANCES
CWNCD 2025 / Jul '96 / Javelin

☐ 16 MOST REQUESTED SONGS (Eddy, Nelson & Jeanette MacDonald)
Ah sweet mystery of life / I'm falling in love with someone / Tramp, tramp, tramp along the highway / Italian street song / When I grow too old to dream / Mounties / Rose Marie / Indian love call / Farewell to dreams / Will you remember / Lover come back to me / One kiss / Softly as in a morning sunrise / Stouthearted men / At the balalaika / Toreador's song
CWNCD 2042 / Jun '97 / Crown

☐ AH, SWEET MYSTERY OF LIFE (Eddy, Nelson & Jeanette MacDonald)
Indian love call / Who are we to say (obey your heart) / Isn't it romantic / Hills of home / Auf wiedersehen / Ah sweet mystery of life / Rose Marie / Lover come back to me / Mounties / 'Neath the southern moon / Beyond the blue horizon / When I grow too old to dream / Italian street song / Song of love / Sylvia / Senorita / Farewell to dreams / I'm falling in love with someone / Goodnight / Trees / One kiss / Will you remember
PASTCD 7026 / Nov '93 / Flapper

☐ IN THE STILL OF THE NIGHT
That great come and get it day / In the still of the night / You and the night and the music / Rosalie / It ain't necessarily so / Bess you is my woman now / Stout hearted men / June is bustin' out all over / Shortnin' bread / It's a grand day for singing / Beyond the blue horizon / Shadrack
12597 / May '97 / Laserlight

☐ LOVE'S OLD SWEET SONG
When I grow too old to dream / Rose Marie / 'Neath the southern moon / Deep river / Perfect day / Rosary / Thy beaming eyes / Sylvia / Dusty road / Auf wiedersehen / Smilin' through / Ah sweet mystery of life / Love's old sweet song / At dawning / Oh promise me / Hills of home / Mounties / Trees / Dream / Through the years
CDHD 150 / '89 / Happy Days

☐ SMILIN' THROUGH
Great day / Without a song / Song of the Volga boatmen / At the balalaika / Magic of your love / Dear little cafe / Call of life/If you could come with me / Tokay / I'll see you again / I'm falling in love with someone / Sympathy / My hero / Chocolate soldier / At dawning / Trees / Smilin' through / Perfect day / Waterboy / Shortnin' bread / None but the lonely heart / Pilgrim's song / Chanson du toreador / Vision fugitive
CDMOIR 436 / Oct '96 / Memoir

Eddy, Samuel

☐ STRANGERS ON THE RUN
SPV 08589422 / Jan '96 / SPV

Edegran Orchestra

☐ SHIM SHAM SHIMMY (Edegran Orchestra & New Orleans Jazz Ladies)
BCD 323 / Mar '95 / GHB

Edegran, Lars

☐ LARS EDEGRAN PRESENTS COOKIE GABRIEL (Edegran, Lars & Cookie Gabriel)
BCD 380 / Dec '97 / GHB

Edelman, Judith

☐ ONLY SUN
742532 / 3 Aug '98 / Compass

☐ PERFECT WORLD
FIENDCD 787 / Sep '96 / Demon

Eden 224

☐ HOLOCAUSTIC SODA
TOPYCD 075 / May '94 / Temple

Eden's Bridge

☐ CELTIC PSALMS
Fear no evil / Praise the holy Lord above / Lord is my light / I lift up my eyes / El shaddai / He will never be shaken / Blessed is the man / In the Lord my heart takes refuge / How long o Lord / Shout for joy / In the morning / Psalm 23 / Your love is better than life
SSD 0180 / Jun '98 / Word

☐ CELTIC WORSHIP
Awesome God / Into the light / Stones and sea / For thou o Lord (I exalt thee) / Shadow of your hand / Lamb of God / Prodigal / He is exalted / Tell me now / Spirit of the living God / Be thou my vision
SSD 0181 / Jun '98 / Word

Eden's Children

☐ EDEN'S CHILDREN/SURE LOOKS REAL
3797 / Jun '97 / Head

Edge Of Sanity

☐ CRYPTIC
BMCD 125 / Oct '97 / Black Mark

☐ NOTHING BY DEATH REMAINS
BMCD 10 / '92 / Black Mark

☐ PURGATORY AFTERFLOW
BMCD 061 / Oct '94 / Black Mark

☐ SPECTRAL SORROWS, THE
BMCD 37 / Nov '93 / Black Mark

☐ UNORTHODOX
Unorthodox / Enigma / Incipience to the butchery / In the veins/Darker than black / Human aberration / Everlasting / After afterlife / Beyond the unknown / Nocturnal / Curfew for the damned / Cold sun / Day of maturity / Requiscon by page / Dead but dreaming / When all is said
BMCD 018 / Jun '92 / Black Mark

Edgewise

☐ EDGEWISE
Angel face / In my hands / Crime pays / In the past / Orange / Virgo / Lost in space / Cardinal / Piss and vinegar
GG 009CD / Mar '97 / Gain Ground

Edguy

☐ VAIN GLORY OPERA
AFM 024CD / 8 Jun '98 / AFM

Edison, Harry

☐ COPENHAGEN STUDIO SESSION 1976 (Edison, Harry 'Sweets' & Eddie 'Lockjaw' Davis)
STCD 8225 / May '97 / Storyville

☐ EDISONS LIGHTS (Edison, Harry 'Sweets')
OJCCD 804 / Jun '95 / Original Jazz Classics

☐ SWING SUMMIT (Live At Birdland 1990) (Edison, Harry 'Sweets' & Buddy Tate)
Centrepiece / S'wonderful / Out of nowhere / Bags groove / Just friends / Blue creek / Idaho
CCD 79050 / Feb '97 / Candid

☐ WHISPERING (2CD Set) (Edison, Harry 'Sweets' & Eddie 'Lockjaw' Davis)
What is this thing called love / My funny valentine / I'll remember April / But beautiful / Just squeeze me / Shiny stockings / Whispering / Ain't misbehavin' / Out of nowhere / Corcovado / Meet the flintstones / Satin doll
JLR 103612 / Apr '97 / Live At EJ's

Edison, Harry 'Sweets'

☐ JUST YOU JUST ME (Edison, Harry 'Sweets' & Earl 'Fatha' Hines)
BB 885 / Nov '97 / Black & Blue

☐ LIVE AT THE IRIDIUM (Edison, Harry 'Sweets' & The Golden Horns)
Helena's theme / Mean greens / 'Sweets' bossa / Doggin' around / Emily / Midgets / I wish I knew / Centerpiece
CD 83425 / Feb '98 / Telarc Jazz

Edith Strategy

☐ EDITH STRATEGY
ABB 19 CD / Jul '90 / Big Cat

Edmunds, Dave

☐ BEST OF DAVE EDMUNDS, THE
Deborah / Girls talk / I knew the bride / A1 on the jukebox / Race is on / I hear you knocking / Almost saturday night / Sabre dance / Queen of hearts / Crawling from the wreckage / Here comes the weekend / Trouble boys / Ju ju man / Singin' the blues / Born to be with you
7567903382 / Mar '97 / Warner Bros.

☐ CHRONICLES
Sabre dance: *Love Sculpture* / You can't catch me: *Love Sculpture* / I hear you knocking / Down down down / Baby I love you / Born to be with you / Warmed over kisses (leftover love) / From small things, big things come / Slippin' away / Something about you / Get out of Denver / I knew the bride / Trouble boys / Girls talk / Queen of hearts / Crawling from the wreckage / Singin' the blues / Almost Saturday night / Race is on / Baby ride easy
VSOPCD 209 / Nov '94 / Connoisseur Collection

☐ COLLECTION, THE
I hear you knockin' / You can't catch me / Stumble / Sabre dance / In the land of the few / Blues helping / Down down down / Farandole / Wang dang doodle / (I am) a lover not a fighter / Egg or the hen / 3 o'clock blues / So unkind / Promised land / Dance dance dance / Outlaw blues / Sweet little rock 'n' roller / Don't answer the door
DC 878622 / Mar '97 / Disky

☐ I HEAR YOU KNOCKING
You can't catch me / Stumble / Sabre dance / In the land of the few / Blues helping / Down, down, down / I hear you knocking / Farandole / Wang-dang-doodle / (I am) a lover not a fighter / Egg or the hen / 3 o'clock blues / So unkind / Promised land / Dance, dance, dance / Outlaw blues / Sweet little rock 'n' roller / Don't answer the door
CDGOLD 1083 / Feb '97 / EMI Gold

☐ ROCKIN' (The Best Of Dave Edmunds)
From small things / Slipping away / Don't you doublecross me / Shape I'm in / Information / Bail you out / Feel so right / Don't call me tonight / Louisiana man / Warmed over kisses / Deep in the heart / Steel claw / SOS / Can't get enough / Something about you / Girls talk / Here comes the weekend / Queen of hearts / Wanderer / Crawlin' from the wreckage / I hear you knocking / I knew the bride (when she used to rock 'n' roll)
74321451922 / Feb '97 / Camden

☐ SUBTLE AS A FLYING MALLET
Baby I love you / Leave my woman alone / Maybe da doo ron ron / Let it be me / No money down / Shot of rhythm 'n' blues / Billy The Kid / Born to be with you / She's my baby / I ain't never / Let it rock
OW 34504 / 15 Jun '98 / One Way

Ed's Redeeming Qualities

☐ AT FISH AND GAME CLUB
SRRCD 021 / 17 Mar '98 / Slow River

☐ BIG GRAPEFRUIT CLEAN UP JOB
SRRCD 032 / 17 Mar '98 / Slow River

Edsel

☐ EDSEL EP
DIS 1145CD
1145 / Mar '97 / Radiopaque

Edsels

☐ EVERLASTING BEST CO
GROW 122 / Apr '94 / Grass

Edu Lobo

☐ MISSA BREVE
MOFB 3748CD / Apr '97 / Rare Brazil

Edward II

☐ TWO STEPS TO HEAVEN (Edward II & The Red Hot Polkas/Mad Professor)
Bjorn again polka / Swing easy / Untitled polka / Steamboats / Lover's two step / Pomp and pride / Queen's jig / Cliffhanger / Staffordshire hornpipe / Jenny Lind / Stack of wheat / Brimfield hornpipe / Swedish polka / Two step to heaven
COOKCD 019 / Jul '96 / Cooking Vinyl

☐ ZEST
OCKCD 0042 / Oct '96 / Ock

Edward, John

☐ BLUE RIDGE (Edward, John & The Seldom Scene)
Don't that road look rough and rocky / How long have I been waiting for you / Blue ridge / Seven daffodils / Sunshine / Only a hobo / God gave you to me / Little hands / I don't believe I'll stay here anymore / Don't crawfish me baby
SHCD 3747 / Mar '89 / Sugar Hill

Edwards, Clarence

☐ I LOOKED DOWN THAT RAILROAD
7422508 / Jun '98 / Last Call

☐ SWAMPIN'
422398 / Feb '97 / Last Call

Edwards, Cliff

☐ SINGING IN THE RAIN
ACD 17 / Jun '95 / Audiophile

☐ VINTAGE RECORDINGS OF UKELELE IKE 1922-1944, THE
TT 419 / May '98 / Take Two

Edwards, David

☐ CRAWLING KING SNAKE (Edwards, David 'Honeyboy')
TCD 6002 / Aug '97 / Hightone

☐ DELTA BLUESMAN (Edwards, David 'Honeyboy')
Roamin' and ramblin' blues / You got to roll / Water Coast blues / Stagolee / Just a spoonful / Spread my raincoat down / Hellatakin' blues / Wind howlin' blues / Worried life blues / Tear it down rag / Army blues / Big Katie Allen / Black cat / Number 12 at the station / Rocks in my pillow / Decoration Day / Who may your regular be / Eye full of tears / Bad whiskey and cocaine
IGOCD 2003 / Jun '95 / Indigo

☐ I'VE BEEN AROUND (Edwards, David 'Honeyboy')
Pony blues / Sad and lonesome / Ham bone blues / Ride with me tonight / I'm a country man / Banty rooster / Take me in your arms / You're gonna miss me / I feel so good today / Things have changed / Big fat Mama / Eyes full of tears / Woman I'm loving / Big road blues
TRIX 3319 / Mar '95 / Trix

☐ WHITE WINDOWS (Edwards, David 'Honeyboy')
West Helena blues / Don't say I don't love you / Build myself a cave / Don't you lie to me / 61 Highway / Drop down Mama / It's been so long since I laughed and talked with you / Shake 'em on down / Take a walk with me / War is over / Roll and tumble / Goin' down slow / Lay my burden down
ECD 260392 / Sep '93 / Evidence

☐ WORLD DON'T OWE ME (Edwards, David 'Honeyboy')
EARWIGCD 4940 / Dec '97 / Earwig

Edwards, Don

☐ MY HERO GENE AUTRY (A Tribute To Gene Autry)
Back in the saddle again / Way out West in Texas / That silver haired Daddy of mine / Ridin' down the canyon / Dear old Western skies / My hero Gene Autry / It's my lazy day / Twilight on the trail / Cowboy blues / Mexicali rose / Have I told you lately that I love you / There's a rainbow on the Rio Colorado / South of the Border / Let the rest of the world go by / Back in the saddle again (outro)
SHANCD 6032 / Jun '98 / Shanachie

☐ SADDLE SONGS (2CD Set)
Ballad of Jack Thorp / Old Chisholm trail / Whoopi ti yi yo / Pecos river queen / Cowboy Jack / Chopo / Zebra dun / Patonio / Sam bass / Streets of Laredo / Night herding song / Little Joe the wrangler / Little Joe the wrangler's sister Nell / Railroad corral / Pecos stream / What's become of the punchers / Minstrel of the range / Long road West / Miss Aledo / Ridin' / 'Longside the Santa Fe trail / Wanderin' cowboy / Strawberry roan / Glory trail / I'd like to be in Texas / Doney gal / Stompede/Masters call / After the roundup / Rounded up in glory / Philosophical cowboy / Old cow man
SHCD 6025 / Mar '98 / Shanachie

☐ WEST OF YESTERDAY
Habit / Bad half hour / Gypsy Davey / Rose of old pawnee / Run along little dogies / Jim I wore a tie / I wanted to die in the desert / Freedom song / At the end of a long lonely day / Blue bonnet lane / West of yesterday / Texas plains
9461872 / Nov '96 / Warner Western

Edwards, Jackie

☐ 20 SUPER HITS
SONCD 0026 / Apr '92 / Sonic Sounds

☐ DO IT SWEET
CSDSGP 074 / Apr '95 / Prestige

☐ IN PARADISE
CDTR 344 / Jun '94 / Trojan

☐ MEMORIAL
RNCD 2026 / Jan '94 / Rhino

☐ SINGING HITS FROM STUDIO ONE AND MORE
Sad news / Love I can feel / Mean girl / I'm still waiting / OK Fred (my name is Fred) / Mr. Fix It (do it sweet) / Sugar plum / Welcome you back home / Dearest you're nearest to my heart / Vow (I'll be your very own king of the ghetto) / You're mine / I'm a peaceful man / Money in your pocket / Ali Baba / Never never / Further you look / Before the next teardrop / Last farewell / Pretty star
RN 7014 / Apr '97 / Rhino
3020762 / Jul '97 / Arcade

Edwards, John

☐ CAREFUL MAN
Cold hearted woman / How can I make it without you / Vanishing love / Tin man / Look on your face / It's those little things that count / It's got to be the real thing this time / Ain't that good enough / Time / We always come back strong / I had a love / Everybody don't get a second chance / Way we were / Stop this merry go round / Spread the news / Careful man / Claim jumpin / I'll be your puppet / You we're made for love / You're messing up a good thing / It's a groove / Exercise my love / Danny Boy
CDKEND 127 / Jan '96 / Kent

Edwards, Rupie

☐ DUB BASKET
RNCD 2014 / Jun '93 / Rhino

☐ HIT PICKS
BFMCD 116 / 11 May '98 / Bushranger

☐ IRIE FEELINGS
Wanderer / Dub master / Rasta Dreadlocks / Free the wind / Wandering dub / Feeling horn / Dub master special / Spangy / Rasta Dreadlocks dub / What can I do / Feeling time / Ten dread commandment
CDTRL 281 / May '90 / Trojan

☐ LET THERE BE VERSION
CDTRL 280 / May '90 / Trojan

☐ RUPIE'S GEMS (Various Artists)
RNCD 2009 / Jun '93 / Rhino

☐ SWEET GOSPEL VOL.4
RECD 06 / Oct '94 / Rupie Edwards

Edwards, Scott

☐ DISTANT HORIZONS
CD 0001 / Jul '94 / Out Of Orbit

Edwards, Stoney

☐ POOR FOLKS STICK TOGETHER (The Best Of Stoney Edwards)
RE 821692 / 1 Jun '98 / Razor & Tie

Edwards, Teddy

☐ MIDNIGHT CREEPER
Midnight creeper / Walking in the rain / Sensitive / Lady be good / Don't blame me / Sunday / Tenderly / Almost like being in love
HCD 7011 / Jan '98 / Highnote

☐ SUNSET EYES
Tempo de blues / Vintage '57 / I hear a rhapsody / Up in Teddy's new flat / Sunset eyes / Teddy's tune / Takin' off / New symphony Sid / My kinda blues / Takin' off
4948482 / 20 Jul '98 / Pacific Jazz

Edwards, Teddy

☐ BIG BOY TEDDY EDWARDS 1930-1936 (Edwards, 'Big Boy' Teddy)
DOCD 5440 / May '96 / Document

Edwards, Terry

☐ DORA SUAREZ (Edwards, Terry & James Johnston)
Dora / Empire Gate / Voice / Mourning / College Hill / Season of storms
HUNKACDL 006 / Nov '93 / Clawfist

☐ I DIDN'T GET WHERE I AM TODAY (Edwards, Terry & The Scapegoats)
King of the cheap thing / Boots off / I like my low-life low / Asthma / Lurch / Ditch / Good-time-strange-thing / Out of the clear / Evening falls / Tallis's canon / Dog food / I didn't get where I am today
WIJCD 1061 / Jun '97 / Wiiija

☐ LARGE DOOR (Edwards, Terry & The Scapegoats)
DAMGOOD 148 / 27 Apr '98 / Damaged Goods

☐ MY WIFE DOESN'T UNDERSTAND ME
STIM 7CD / Sep '95 / Stim

☐ NO FISH IS TOO WEIRD FOR HER AQUARIUM
STIM 005 / Jul '94 / Stim

☐ PLAYS, SALUTES AND EXECUTES
STIM 4 / Oct '93 / Stim

Edwards, Todd

☐ TALES FROM THE UNDERGROUND (Various Artists)
Thankyou: *Sunshine Brothers* / Take my hand: *Moreso & Damon Trueitt* / Push the love: *Edwards, Todd* / Don't turn your back on love: *Collins, Jay Super 20* / Gimmie me all: *Fifth Gear* / Vybe: *Ultymate* / Deep dub instrumental re-visit edit: *RIP* / *ESQ* (The esquire): *MC Ward* / Too-nite: *Filthy Rich* / Key dub: *Tuff & Jam* / 2HD: *MC Ward* / Can't live without you: *Edwards, Todd* / Sweet Jesus: *Edwards, Todd* / Keep holdin': *Tuff & Jam Klubb Conektion*
DI 0932 / 10 Aug '98 / Distance

Edwards, Willie

☐ EVERLASTIN' TEARS
Everlastin' tears / Dollar in / Been a long time / Read between the lines / Helpless, hopeless feeling / True what they say / Heart of deception / Can't create desire / Won't be back / Bottom's falling out / Company store / 90's blues
JSPCD 281 / Jan '97 / JSP

Eek-A-Mouse

☐ MOUSE-A-MANIA
RASCD 30616 / '88 / Ras

☐ RAS PORTRAITS
Freak / Penni walli / I like them all / Oh me oh my / Do me / Gun shot a cry / Assasinator / Macho man / What me ago do / De di doo / Night before Christmas
RAS 3308 / Jun '97 / Ras

☐ SKIDIP
Sensee party / Looking sexy / Modelling queen / You na love reggae music / Always on my mind / Do you remember / Skidip / Na make mi girl go away / Fat and slim / Where is my baby
GRELCD 41 / Sep '89 / Greensleeves

☐ VERY BEST OF EEK-A-MOUSE, THE
Anarexol / Star daily news or cleaner / Noah's ark / Terrorists in the city / Peeni walli / Wild like a tiger / Wa-do-dem / Assassinator / Christmas a come
GRELCD 105 / Aug '87 / Greensleeves

☐ WA DO DEM
Ganja smuggling / Long time ago / Operation eradication / There's a girl in my life / Slowly but surely / Wa-do-dem / Lonesome journey / I will never leave my love / Noahs ark / Too young to understand
GRELCD 31 / May '87 / Greensleeves

Eel Grinders

☐ AQUAMARINE
EEL 001CD / Aug '96 / Sargasso Sounds

Eels

☐ BEAUTIFUL FREAK
Novocaine for the soul / Susan's house / Rags to rags / Beautiful freak / Not ready yet / My beloved monster / Flower / Guest list / Mental / Spunky / Your lucky day in hell / Manchild
DRD 50001 / Feb '97 / Dreamworks

Eerk & Jerk

☐ DEAD BROKE
PCD 1409 / Nov '91 / Profile

Effective Force

☐ BACK AND TO THE LEFT (2CD Set)
In the beginning / Reality labyrinth / Make me forget / Back and to the left / Big surprise / Left hand, right hand / Fish / Ultimate flower / Trouble and desire / So / My time is yours (Past, present and future) / Diamond bullet will to power / Illuminate the planet world in order / Time zero / Complete mental breakdown / My time is yours the end amen / Illumination / Everglade (Effective force remix) / Punishing the atoms / Super illuminated
DVNT 011CD / Jun '96 / Deviant

Effigies

☐ REMAINS NONVIEWABLE
TG 135CD / Oct '95 / Touch & Go

Eg

☐ TURN ME ON, I'M A ROCKET MAN
Nothing comes easy / Stay home / I wish you could be happy too / Angel / Do it for myself / My lovely valentine / Sister blue / Holding it in / Made my baby cry / Mr cool / What can I do
0630132962 / Feb '96 / WEA

Eg & Alice

☐ 24 YEARS OF HUNGER
Rockets / In a cold way / Mystery man / I have seen myself / So high, so low / New year's eve / Indian / Doesn't mean that much to me / Crosstown / IOU / I wish
9031753882 / Aug '91 / WEA

Egan, Mark

☐ MOSAIC
EFA 034512 / Nov '95 / Wavetone

Egan, Seamus

☐ TRADITIONAL MUSIC FROM IRELAND
SHCD 34015 / Dec '95 / Shanachie

☐ WHEN JUNIPER SLEEPS
Winding hills / Weep not for the memories / Masons apron/My love is in America / Lark / Mick O'Connor's / Along the way / When juniper sleeps / Faubert's lilt / Farewell to Glasgow / To an old rose / When last we met / Czar of Munster / Lullaby
SHCD 79097 / Mar '98 / Shanachie

Egdom, Emiel Van

☐ HYBRID GROOVE
You're in my heart / Modal mood / Elegance d'etiquette / Gentle giant Aussi / Hybrid groove / Sad nostalgia / These things do happen / Star of the sea / Dig this / NY dream / Emmelage / How's my heart
AL 73081 / Jul '97 / Nefertiti

Ege Bam Yasi

☐ HOW TO BOIL AN EGG
UGTCD 001 / Oct '95 / UGT

☐ MOTHER GOOSE
SUB 40D / 27 Oct '97 / Subversive

Egebjer, Boo

☐ BOO EGEBJER AND STEVE DOBROGOSZ/MARGARETA ANDERSSON (Egebjer, Boo & Steve Dobrogosz/Margareta Andersson)
LW 9601 / Jan '97 / Supreme

Egg

☐ ALBUMEN
Fat boy goes to the cinema / Time to enjoy / Get some money to get her / Bend / Jam together / Big duck / Sunglasses / Roche (don't you ever stop) / Shopping / Shoplifting / 284 windows and a door
ZEN 011CD
ZEN 011CDM / Jul '96 / Indochina

☐ TRAVELATOR
Number cruncher / Hey Billy / Willow / Getting away with it / Anyway / Port Meadow / Encore les oeufs / Ben Hur / Bunmela / Ambassador
ZEN 019CD / 13 Jul '98 / Indochina

Eggman

☐ FIRST FRUITS
CRECD 201 / May '96 / Creation

Eggs

☐ BRUISER
TEENBEAT 76CD / Sep '94 / Teenbeat

☐ HOW DO YOU LIKE YOUR LOBSTER
TB 156CD / Jul '95 / Teenbeat

Egmose, Willy

☐ PA GYNGENDE GRUND (Egmose, Willy Trio & Asger Rosenberg)
MECCACD 2023 / May '97 / Music Mecca

Egmose, Willy Trio

☐ BARE DET SWINGER
MECCACD 1046 / Nov '94 / Music Mecca

Ego On The Rocks

☐ ACID IN WONDERLAND
SB 048 / 9 Mar '98 / Second Battle

Egypt

☐ PRESERVING THE DEAD
Baby, please don't go / Coal train union / Egypt / Khartoom / Legend of the lighthouse / Ecccentric man / Pearl of the orient / Lady luck
HTDCD 21 / Sep '96 / HTD

Ehrlich, Marty

☐ CAN YOU HEAR A MOTION
Black hat / Welcome / Pictures in a glass house / North star / Ode to Charlie Parker / Reading the river / One for Robin / Comme il faut
ENJ 80522 / May '94 / Enja

☐ EMERGENCY PEACE (Ehrlich, Marty Dark Woods Ensemble)
Emergency peace / Dusk / Painter / Tucked sleave of a one-armed boy / Unison / Double dance / Circle the heart / Charlie in the Parker / Tribute
804092 / Jun '91 / New World

☐ JUST BEFORE THE DAWN (Ehrlich, Marty Dark Woods Ensemble)
804742 / Aug '95 / New World

☐ LIVE WOOD (2CD Set) (Ehrlich, Marty Dark Woods Ensemble)
CD 986 / Aug '97 / Music & Arts

☐ NEW YORK CHILD
New York child / Generosity / Georgia blue / Tell me this / Elvin's exit / Prelude / Time and the wild words / Untitled / Turn again
ENJ 90252 / Aug '96 / Enja

☐ PLIANT PLIANT
ENJA 506548 / Jul '88 / Enja

Ehrling, Thore

☐ JAZZ HIGHLIGHTS
DRCD 236 / Sep '87 / Dragon

☐ SWEDISH SWING (1945 & 1947)
ANC 9503 / Jun '95 / Ancha

Eide, Khalifa Ould

☐ MOORISH MUSIC FROM MAURITANIA (Eide, Khalifa Ould & Dimi Mint Abba)
Waidalal waidalal / Yar allahoo / Hassaniya song for dancing / Hassaniya love poem / Tortoise's song / Independence / Art's plume / Oh lord bring apartheid crashing down / Mauritania my beloved country / My young people do the youth of nations invite / Autoot
WCD 019 / Oct '90 / World Circuit

Eightball

☐ WHERE GRAVITY ENDS
IS 88991CD / 13 Oct '97 / I Scream Music

Eighth Wonder

☐ FEARLESS
Cross my heart / When the phone stops ringing / Baby baby / Will you remember / Wild love / I'm not scared / Use me / Anything at all / My baby's heartbeat / Dress / Stay with me
4884082 / Jun '97 / Epic

Eikas, Sigmund

☐ JOLSTRING
HCD 7101 / Apr '95 / Musikk Distribujson

Eiliff

☐ EILIFF
SPMWWRCD 0067 / Jul '97 / SPM

☐ GIRLRLS
SPMWWRCD 0068 / Jul '97 / SPM

Eimerman, Herb

☐ FROM YOUR WINDOW
DLS 123782 / Nov '96 / Black Vinyl

☐ STORY IN YOUR EYES
DLS 102750 / Nov '96 / Black Vinyl

Einheit, F.M.

☐ RADIO INFERNO
INV 097CD / Oct '97 / Invisible

☐ SENSATION DEATH
INV 086CD / Nov '97 / Invisible

Einherjer

☐ AURORA BOREALIS
NR 6662 / Sep '96 / Necropolis

☐ FAR FAR NORTH
CM 77197CD / 10 Nov '97 / Century Media

☐ ODIN OWNS YE ALL
CM 77206CD / 8 Jun '98 / Century Media

Einhorn, Andreas

☐ OCEAN BLUE (Einhorn, Andreas & Wilhelm Magnus)
ISCD 157 / Sep '96 / Intersound

Einniu

☐ EINNIU
CICD 086 / Dec '93 / Clo Iar-Chonnachta

Einstein

☐ THEORY OF EMCEES SQUARED, THE
Rhymes unlimited / Are we ready to party / Can I get a witness / Ladies / Friday night and saturday morning (1990 remix) / Gotstago / My rhymes are smokin' / Only the funkiest / Food for thought / On the ill tip / Every nigger's a star / Talk like a yardie
STEIN 1 CD / Jun '90 / Music Of Life

Einsturzende Neubauten

☐ 2X4
RUSCD 8235 / 24 Nov '97 / ROIR

☐ ENDE NEU
BETON 504CD
BETON 504CDX / Aug '96 / Grey Area

☐ ENDE NEU REMIXED
Ende neu / Installation no.1 / Nnnnaaammm / Stella maris / Garden / Nnnaaammm / Ende neu / Was ist ist / Nnnaaammm / Die explosion im festspielhaus
BETON 602CD / 22 Sep '97 / Grey Area

☐ FAUSTMUSIK
EG 0501 / Feb '96 / Mute

☐ KOLLAPS
INDIGO 25172 / Oct '96 / Zick Zack
14537 / 30 Mar '98 / Spalax

☐ MALADICTION
Blume (french version) / Blume (english version) / Blume (japanese version) / Ubique media version / 3 thoughts / (ein gansz kleines loch in einem) diapositiv / Ring my bell
BETON 206CD / Mar '93 / Mute

☐ STRATEGIES AGAINST ARCHITECTURE
CDSTUMM 14 / Apr '88 / Mute

☐ TABULA RASA
Die interimsliebenden / Zebulon / Blume / 12305 (te nacht) / Sie / Wuste / Headcleaner
BETON 106CD / Jan '93 / Mute

Eisel, Helmut & Jem

☐ PASSIONS FOR KLEZMER
CHCD 87057 / 3 Mar '98 / Music & Words

Either/Orchestra

☐ ACROSS THE OMNIVERSE (10 Years In The Life Of A Band/2CD Set)
AC 3272 / May '97 / Accurate

☐ DIAL E
Doxy / Nicole is always in Tokyo / 17 December / Lady's blues
AC 2222 / May '97 / Accurate

Eitzel, Mark

☐ 60 WATT SILVER LINING
There is no easy way down / Sacred heart / Always turn away / Saved / Cleopatra Jones / When my plane finally goes down / Mission rock / Wild sea / Aspirin / Some bartenders have the gift of pardon / Southend on sea / Everything is beautiful
CDV 2798 / Mar '96 / Virgin

☐ CAUGHT IN A TRAP AND I CAN'T BACK OUT... (Cause I Love You Too Much Baby)
Are you the trash / Xmas lights spin / Auctioneers song / White rosary / If I had a gun / Goodbye / Queen of no one / Cold light of day / Go away / Atico 18 / Sun smog seahorse
OLE 1792 / 2 Feb '98 / Matador

☐ CAUGHT IN A TRAP AND I CAN'T BACK OUT... (Cause I Love You Too Much Baby/Japanese Issue)
APCY 8427 / 27 Apr '98 / Apollon

☐ SONGS OF LOVE
Firefly / Channel No. 5 / Western sky / Blue and grey shirt / Gary's song / Outside this bar / Blue under the club / Last harbour / Kathleen / Crabwalk / Jenny / Take courage / Nothing can bring me down
DIAB 838 / 3 Nov '97 / Diablo

☐ WEST
If you have to ask / Free of harm / Helium / Stunned and frozen / Then it really happens / In your life / Lower Eastside tourist / Three inches of wall / Move myself ahead / Old photographs / Fresh screwdriver / Live or die
9362466022 / Jun '97 / Warner Bros.

Ejected

☐ TOUCH OF CLASS, A
Young tribes of England / Fast 'n' loud / Gang warfare / Class of '82 / England ain't dead / Carnival / Football song / Man of war / Fifteen / Have you got 10p / Mr. Muggins / East End kids / I'm gonna get a gun / Dressed to kill / Karnal dub / Sky's in love / Have you got 10p / Class of '82 / One of the boys / Fast 'n' loud / I don't care / What am I gonna do End kids / What am I gonna do
AHOYCD 024 / 20 Jul '98 / Captain Oi

Ekdahl, Lisa

☐ WHEN DID YOU LEAVE HEAVEN (Ekdahl, Lisa & Peter Nordahl Trio)
When did you leave heaven / But not for me / Cry me a river / Love for sale / Life / You're gonna see a lot of me / It's oh so quiet / It was just one of those things / Boy next door / I'm a fool to want you / My heart belongs to daddy / Blame it on my youth / It's oh so quiet
74321562662 / May '98 / RCA Victor

Ekholm, Anders

☐ ABASH JAZZ (Ekholm, Anders & Tommy Skotte/Nils Danell)
DRCD 295 / Feb '98 / Dragon

Ekstrom, Lars

☐ SO FAR SO GOOD
FLCCD 155 / Oct '97 / Four Leaf Clover

El Amin, Muhamed

☐ VOICE OF SUDAN
SM 15232 / Feb '97 / Wergo

El Bad

☐ BAD MOTHERFUCKERS
SST 33OCD / Jun '96 / SST

☐ TRICK OR TREAT
Eternity / I turned into a misfit / Trick or treat / Last time / Death race 2000 / Shrink / Alien invasion / No one / SNG no.53 / Liquid Jesus / Transistor / Don't go down into the basement / Heaven can wait / Bitter end
SST 348CD / 29 Sep '97 / SST

El Caminos

☐ REVERB EXPLOSION
71260 / Sep '97 / Del-Fi

El Chino

☐ VIEJA LETANIA
B 6836 / Dec '96 / Auvidis/Ethnic

El Din, Hamza

☐ AVAILABLE SOUND
Er'rasoul / Saqiat darius / Ashranda / Nabra / Shortunga / El aranya / Shams esh'shamusa
LR 9621 / Nov '96 / Lotus

☐ ECLIPSE
RCD 10103 / Nov '91 / Rykodisc

☐ LILY OF THE NILE
WLAAS 11CD / Nov '95 / Waterlily Acoustics

☐ MUWASHSHAH
VICG 5416 / Jul '96 / JVC World Library

☐ SONGS OF THE NILE
VICG 50072 / Mar '96 / JVC World Library

☐ WATER WHEEL
7559720412 / 26 Jan '98 / Nonesuch

El Dorados

☐ ROCK 'N' ROLL'S FOR ME
Bim bam boom / At my front door / Rock 'n' roll's for me / She don't run around / Trouble trouble / Boom diddie boom / Chop ling soon / Little Miss love / I'll be forever loving you / Oh what a girl / Baby I need you / Annie's answer / Tears on my pillow / Fallen tear / Language of love / My loving body / Love of my own / Baby I'm lonely I tried / Now that you've gone / Home chance / Lights are low / I began to realise / Rose for my darling / It's no wonder why / Always my love / There in the night / Why must I / Three reasons why I love you
CDGR 197 / Nov '97 / Charly

El Flaco

☐ THUB
SECT2 10016 / Aug '95 / Sector 2

El Ghiwan, Nass

☐ CHANSONS DE NASS EL GHIWAN
824672 / Nov '90 / BUDA

☐ CHANTS GNAWA DU MAROC
824682 / Nov '90 / BUDA

El Kabli, Abdel Karim

☐ LIMAZA
RPM 0032 / 9 Mar '98 / Rags Productions

El Lebrijano

☐ CASABLANCA
Coge la onda / Calle de San Francisco / Del placer que irrita / A canela y menta / Ay por dios / Rezo / El sueno vencio al Leon / A calzon quitao / Salada claridad
4931572 / 2 Mar '98 / Hemisphere

El Lobo, Paco

☐ FLAMENCO SONGS
926852 / 24 Feb '98 / BUDA

El Malo

☐ STARSHIP IN WORSHIP
99 2126 / Jul '96 / Ninetynine

☐ WORST UNIVERSAL JET SET, THE
99 2142 / Jul '96 / Ninetynine

El Masry, Hussein

☐ ARABIAN EMOTIONS
Ra'etak (i protected you) / Wa hallaftak (i asked you) / Ela awwel ma habena (our first love) / Wah'hashtani (I'm longing for you) / Ya wabour el-saa (oh, you twelve-o'clock train) / Tismah te olly (please tell me) / Allah, alik, allah / Meddy l'dek (give me your hand)
12455 / Jul '95 / Laserlight

☐ NOMADE
KAR 994 / Jun '97 / Kardum

☐ ZAGAL
AUB 006781 / Aug '93 / Auvidis/Ethnic

El Medioni, Maurice

☐ CAFE ORAN (El Medioni, Maurice Et Son Pianoriental)
CDPIR 1045 / Jan '97 / Piranha

El Mondao

☐ FLAMENCO NUEVO
EUCD 1116 / '91 / ARC

☐ FLAMENCO TOTAL
EUCD 1089 / '89 / ARC

El Mubarak, Abdel Aziz

☐ ABDEL AZIZ EL MUBARAK
Tahrimni minnak / Ahla eyyoun / Ah'laa jarah / Tarig ash-shoag / Bitgoohil la
CDORB 023 / Jan '89 / Globestyle

El Nino De Almaden

☐ GREAT SINGERS OF FLAMENCO VOL.1
LDC 274 830 / '88 / La Chant Du Monde

El Nino De Marchena

☐ ART OF FLAMENCO VOL.15, THE (The Bloom Of Decadence)
MAN 4898 / May '97 / Mandala

☐ ARTE FLAMENCO VOL.15
Soleares / Fandango de Galeana / Canto de la roda de Sevilla / Punto del Platanal / Fandangos de Marchena / Columbiana / Punto Cubano / Tarantas de Linares / Petenera / Guajira / Buleras por Solea / Fandangos / Aire de la sierra de Cordoba / Columbiana
HMCD 78 / May '97 / Harmonia Mundi

El Nino De Ronda

☐ REAL FLAMENCO
La vuelta / Sagrario Montes / Carino del legionario / Consuelo la granadina / Los hierros / Rodenos
TCD 1072 / 15 Jun '98 / Rykodisc

El Periquin

☐ SONAKAY
Engano / Sonakay / A mi madre / Luz marina / El duende de triana / El guadalquivir / Recuerdo de Madrid
AL 73095 / Dec '97 / A

El Ritual

☐ EL RITUAL
CDDCD 3020 / 9 Feb '98 / Denver

El Rumbero

☐ EL RUMBERO
Chica ven / Rumba del amor / Cada vez que the encuentro solo / Pasa / Quireme / Sei bellissima / Delilia / Angelina / Historia de amor / Sin saber
CDGRUB 23 / Sep '92 / Food For Thought

El Sexteto Tabala

☐ EL SEXTETO TABALA
C 560126 / Apr '98 / Ocora

El Shari, Hamid

☐ AINY
3106892 / 23 Mar '98 / Odeon

El Sonido De La Ciudad

☐ GRAND TANGO, THE
MVCD 1079 / Jul '95 / CBC

El Tachuela, Rafa

☐ GIPSY FLAMENCO GUITARRAS
EUCD 1330 / Nov '95 / ARC

Elahi, Ostad

☐ DIALOGUE WITH THE BELOVED
CMT 2741100 / Jan '98 / Le Chant Du
Monde

☐ PATHS OF DIVINE LOVE, THE
CMT 2741083 / Jan '98 / Le Chant Du
Monde

Elanara

☐ MOSAIC D'ESPANA (Spanish And
Sephardic Songs)
CDE 84334 / Jul '97 / Meridian

Elastic

☐ BEND YOUR EARS
TO3CD 002 / 22 Jun '98 / 21-3
Productions

Elastic Band

☐ EXPANSIONS ON LIFE
CDP 1001DD / Jun '97 / Pseudonym

Elastic Purejoy

☐ ELASTIC PUREJOY
If Samuel Beckett had met Lenny Bruce / Soul and
fire / Unchain my sister / Element of doubt / Stiff /
Suburban yoke / You are my perfect PFM / Claxton
vs the Fourth Estate / Monkey bone-walker / Witness
WDOM 010CD / Jun '94 / World
Domination

Elastica

☐ ELASTICA
Line up / Annie / Connection / Car song / Smile / Hold
me now / SOFT / Indian / Blue / All-nighter / Waking
up / Two to one / Vaseline / Never here / Stutter /
Cleopatra
BLUFF 014CD / Mar '95 / Deceptive

Elbert, Donnie

☐ R & B MAVERICK (2CD Set)
Get ready / Time hangs on my mind / Along came
pride / Baby please come home / Without you / Can't
get over losing you / If I can't have you / Will you ever
be mine / Little piece of leather / One thousand, nine
hundred and seventy years / Where did our love go /
What can I do / Get myself together / Sweet baby /
That's if you love me / This feeling of losing you / Love
is strange / You're gonna cry when I'm over / (In
between the heartaches) another tear will take its
place / Come see me / Free / Love of your own / You
don't have to be a star (to be in my show) / What a
difference a day made / Back in my arms again / Will
you still love me tomorrow / What do you do /
Reachin' for a dream / Cry cry cry / Mr. Peanut in the
White House / You should be dancing
NEDCD 288 / Jul '97 / Sequel

☐ ROOTS OF DONNIE ELBERT, THE
Run little girl / Whose it gonna be / Never again /
Memphis / Do what cha wanna / Your red wagon /
Doen home blues / Alittle piece of leather / Lilly Lu
EMBCD 3421 / 27 Mar '98 / Ember

Elcka

☐ LIKE STALLIONS
CID 8057 / Aug '97 / Island

ELD

☐ CARVED
DISC 026 / Oct '96 / Discordia

Elders, Betty

☐ CRAYONS
FF 642CD / Nov '95 / Flying Fish

Eldon, Jim

☐ JIM AND LYNETTE ELDON (Eldon, Jim
& Lynette)
Died for love / Still I love him / Champagne Charlie /
Tommy Bell / Folkestone murder / Red bush / Lord
Bateman / Rakes of Mallow / No my love not I / Robin
Hood and the three squires / Oh what a windy night /
Pip's among Cod / Green castle hornpipe/The
steamboat hornpipe / Laidly worm / Candlelight
fisherman / Derby lamb / As I was going to Alston /
Nobleman lived in a mansion / Napoleon crossing
the Alps / Freddy Archer / Bold Dickie and bold

Archie / Father had a knife / Bold Princess Royal /
Dogger bank/The cliff hornpipe / Bonny labouring
boy / What shall I draw the water in / Two
schottisches / Mrs. Cuddledee / Step dance tune /
Robin to Bobbin / Acre of land / Hopping down in
Kent
SDCD 008 / Oct '97 / Stick

Eldopa

☐ 1332
EBM 006CD / Jun '97 / East Bay Menace

Eldridge, Roy

☐ 1935-1941
After you've gone / Where the lazy river goes by /
Heckler's hop / Florida stomp / Wabash stomp /
Fallin' in love again / That thing / Warmin' up / Let me
off uptown / Blues in c sharp minor / Wham (be-boop-
boom-bam) / Big chief de sota (grand terrace swing)
/ Blue lou / I'm nobody's baby / Stealin' apples / Mary
had a little lamb / When I grow to old to dream /
Lookie, lookie, lookie here comes cookie
CD 56066 / Jul '95 / Jazz Roots

☐ BIG SOUND OF LITTLE JAZZ
TPZ 1021 / May '95 / Topaz Jazz

☐ CLASSICS 1935-1940
CLASSICS 725 / Dec '93 / Classics

☐ CLASSICS 1943-1944
CLASSICS 920 / Apr '97 / Classics

☐ CLASSICS 1945-1947
CLASSICS 983 / 24 Feb '98 / Classics

☐ FIESTA IN JAZZ
Sittin' in / Sittin' in no.2 / Stardust / Body and soul /
46 West 52 / 46 West 52 no.2 / Gasser / Jump
through the wind / Minor jive / Don't be that way / I
want to be happy / Fiesta in brass / Fiesta in brass /
St. Louis blues / I can't get started / After you've
gone / Fish market / Twilight time
LEJAZZCD 46 / Oct '95 / Le Jazz

☐ FRENCHIE ROY
VGCD 655009 / Jan '93 / Vogue

☐ HECKLERS HOP
I hope Gabriel likes my music / Mutiny in the parlour /
I'm gonna clap my hands / Swing is here / Wabash
stomp / Florida stomp / Heckler's hop / Where the
lazy river goes by / That thing / After you've gone /
Sittin' in / Stardust / Body and soul / Forty six, west
fifty two / It's my own soul / You're a lucky guy /
Pluckin' the bass / I'm gettin' sentimental over you /
High society / Muskrat ramble / Who told you I cared
/ Does your heart beat for me
HEPCD 1030 / Mar '91 / Hep

☐ HIS LITTLE JAZZ VOL.1
It don't mean a thing (if it ain't got that swing) / Man I
love / Man I love / Wrap your troubles in dreams /
Wrap your troubles in dreams / Ain't no flies on me /
Undecided / Undecided / Undecided / Undecided /
King David / Wild driver / If I had you / Nuts / Easter
parade / Easter parade / Goliath bounce / Someone
to watch over me
74321511412 / Mar '98 / Vogue

☐ INTRODUCTION TO ROY ELDRIDGE
1935-1946, AN
4051 / 5 Jan '98 / Best Of Jazz

☐ LITTLE JAZZ
158362 / Jul '95 / Jazz Archives

☐ LIVE IN 1959 (Eldridge, Roy & Coleman
Hawkins)
STCD 531 / Feb '91 / Stash

☐ MONTREUX 1977 (With Oscar
Peterson, Niels Pederson & Bobby
Durham)
Between the Devil and the deep blue sea / Go for / I
surrender Dear / Joie De Roy / Perdido / Bye bye
blackbird
OJCCD 373 / Apr '93 / Original Jazz
Classics

☐ NIFTY CAT, THE
Jolly Hollis / Cotton / 5400 North / Ball of fire /
Wineola / Nifty cat
803492 / Jan '96 / New World

☐ ROY & DIZ (Eldridge, Roy & Dizzy
Gillespie)
Sometimes I'm happy / Algo bueno / Trumpet blues /
I'm through with love / Can't we be friends / Don't
you think I don't know why / If I had you / Blue moon /
I've found a new baby / Pretty-eyed baby / I can't get
started / Limehouse blues
5216472 / Jul '94 / Verve

☐ ROY ELDRIDGE (1935-41)
CD 14571 / May '95 / Jazz Portraits

☐ ROY ELDRIDGE AND VIC DICKENSON
(Eldridge, Roy & Vic Dickenson)
STCD 8239 / Jan '97 / Storyville

Eleanor Rigby

☐ BEST OF ELEANOR RIGBY VOL.1, THE
(The Singles Collection)
FLEGCD 3 / Mar '95 / Future Legend

☐ BEST OF ELEANOR RIGBY VOL.2, THE
I'm not like everybody else / She's got everything /
Play with fire / Getting thru the day / Mod girls / Gotta
move / For the video / Till the end of the day /
Censorship / My Christmas card to you / More than
the truth / Don't take me what I say / All or nothing
FLEGCD 7 / Jul '96 / Future Legend

Elecktronauten

☐ COLLECTIVE INDUCED FICTION
Collective induced fiction / Heart / Barbarella sisters
/ Invisible music / Nanoscale / Wheel of life /
Throwdown / Mondfinsternis / I go with you /
Outsider / Chase / Robbery / Assault on the 13th
precinct / Push / Segelflieger
INCCD 3320 / 3 Aug '98 / Incoming

Electrafixion

☐ BURNED
Zephyr / Mirrorball / Lowdown / Feel my pulse /
Timebomb / Sister pain / Bed of nails / Hit by
something / Who's been sleeping in my head / Too
far gone / Never
0630112482 / Sep '95 / WEA

Electric Band

☐ VOLTAGE
92624 / May '94 / Oberoi

Electric Bluebirds

☐ BACK ON THE TRAIN
Back on the train / Trouble with me / Alligator man /
Tell it like it is / I don't need you / City limits / La Vie
Malheureuse (Cajun Belle) / Stranger's just a friend /
When the money's all gone / Dixieland rock / Dark
hollow / Un Majada sin licencia / Rockin'n'rollin' with
Granmaw / Sad memory / Delia live / Colinda (Queen
Ida's tune) / Careless love / Bluebird two-step / You
don't miss your water / Alison's Lafayette / Madame
Etienne / Square dancin' Mama / Los amores del
Flaco / Waltz across Texas
GEMCD 001 / Oct '96 / Diamond

Electric Blues Duo

☐ OUT ON THE HIGHWAY
You gonna suffer / Steady rollin' man / White lady /
My jug and I / Texas / Make mine a double / Going
down slow / B and Q / Last fair deal / San Francisco
Bay blues / No money down / Sweet home Chicago /
Bitch / Louise / Roberta
INAK 11002CD / Nov '97 / In Akustik

Electric Boys

☐ FREEWHEELIN'
5217222 / Mar '94 / Polydor

Electric Family

☐ MARIOPAINT
55IRDCOM 3CD / Oct '95 / Irdial

Electric Frankenstein

☐ ACTION HIGH
LOUDEST 24 / Jun '97 / One Louder

☐ ELECTRIC FRANKENSTEIN
CONQUERS THE WORLD
198192 / Jun '97 / Nesak

☐ FRACTURED
41286 / Nov '97 / V&V

☐ SICK SONGS
198292 / Jun '97 / Kado

☐ TIME IS NOW
NITR 005 / Jan '97 / Demolition Derby

Electric Groove Temple

☐ SEQUENCE ME
TCNCD 4 / Sep '96 / Trichone

Electric Hellfire Club

☐ CALLING DR. LUV
CLP 9797 / Oct '96 / Cleopatra

☐ UNHOLY
CLEO 1932 / 14 Apr '98 / Cleopatra

Electric Kings

☐ NOT FOR SALE
MWCD 2017 / Dec '95 / Music & Words

Electric Mojo

☐ NEW FORMAT JAZZ SESSIONS VOL.1
553679 CD / 16 Jul '97 / Mojo

Electric Orange

☐ CYBERDELIC
Cyberdelic/Unaffected fruit / Vaporized dance /
Funny in the bathroom / Kirschen / Sweet absurd / B-
movie / Steal no egg / Mothers cake / Tartisma
zemini / She-wah / More end/Cyberdelic
DELECCD 041 / Apr '97 / Delerium

☐ ORANGE COMMUTATION
Electripity chapter 99 / Journey through weird
scenes featuring cows in space / Return of Eugene,
be careful / Back in a strange world / Reflections of
2072 and everywhere
DELECCDS 036 / Mar '96 / Delerium

Electric Playboys

☐ GOOD TIMES
IMPCD 046 / Sep '97 / Impossible

Electric Preachers

☐ GASHEAD
Face down / Hold me down / I got the ride / Sorry for /
Mixer / Gashead / Puffhead / Maggot / Gasoline
highs / Swear
HTT 0902 / 23 Feb '98 / Holier Than Thou

Electric Prunes

☐ I HAD TOO MUCH TO DREAM LAST
NIGHT/UNDERGROUND
3397 / 24 Nov '97 / Head

☐ RELEASE OF AN OATH
HEAD 4097 / 15 Jun '98 / Head

☐ SINGLES, THE
EPCD 77013 / 10 Nov '97 / Gone Beat

☐ STOCKHOLM 1967
CDHB 67 / May '97 / Heartbeat

Electric Skychurch

☐ KNOWONENESS
MM 800322 / Apr '96 / Moonshine

Electric Universe

☐ STARDIVER
Alien encounter (part 2) / From the heart / Radio
SPACE / Rising sun / Online information / Luna
overdrive / Technologic / Astral voyage / Sunset
skyline / Stardiver / Alien encounter (part 1)
SUB 48412 / Jun '97 / Distance

Electric Wizard

☐ ELECTRIC WIZARD/ORANGE GOBLIN
(Electric Wizard/Orange Goblin)
MR 071 / 8 Dec '97 / Man's Ruin

☐ SUPERCOVEN
TRIP 001CD / 3 Aug '98 / Bad Acid

Electro Assassin

☐ BIOCULTURE
HY 39100692 / Nov '93 / Hyperium

☐ DIVINE INVASION
SPV 08461252 / Jun '96 / SPV

Electroids

☐ ELEKTRO WORLD
WARPCD 35 / Aug '95 / Warp

Electronic

☐ ELECTRONIC
Idiot country / Reality / Tighten up / Patience of a
saint / Gangster / Getting away with it / Soviet / Get
the message / Try all you want / Some distant
memory / Feel every beat
CDPRG 1012 / Feb '94 / EMI

☐ RAISE THE PRESSURE
Forbidden city / For you / Dark angel / One day / Until
the end / Second nature / If you've got love / Out of
my league / Interlude / Freefall / Visit me / How long /
Time can tell
CDPCS 7382 / Jul '96 / Parlophone

Electronic Eye

☐ IDEA OF JUSTICE, THE
RBADCD 14 / Oct '95 / Beyond

Electroscope

☐ HUMAN ELECTROSCOPE, THE
WJ 27CD / Sep '97 / Wurlitzer Jukebox

Elegeion

☐ ODYSSEY INTO DARKNESS
CANDLE 020MCD / 23 Feb '98 /
Candlelight

Elegy

☐ LABYRINTH OF DREAMS
TT 00052 / Apr '97 / T&T

☐ LOST
TT 00172 / Apr '97 / T&T

☐ MANIFESTATION OF FEAR
TT 00362 / 24 Aug '98 / T&T

☐ PRIMAL INSTINCT
Take my love / Labyrinth of dreams / Always with you
/ Spirits / Erase me
TT 00253 / Sep '96 / T&T

☐ STATE OF MIND
Equinox / Visual vortex / Trust / Beyond / Shadow
dancer / Aladdin's cave / State of mind / Destiny
calling / Resurrection / Losers game / Suppression
TT 00302 / Jun '97 / T&T

☐ SUPREMACY
TT 00092 / Apr '97 / T&T

Elektraws

☐ SHOCK ROCK
NERCD 083 / Jan '96 / Nervous

Elektric Music

☐ ESPERANTO
TV / Showbusiness / Kissing the machine / Lifestyle / Crosstalk / Information / Esperanto / Overdrive
4509929992 / Jun '93 / East West

Elektrosushi

☐ ELEKTROSUSHI
NO 32662 / 24 Aug '98 / Noise-O-Lution

Elem, Big Mojo

☐ MOJO BOOGIE (Live At The Golden Slipper 1977)
STCD 8041 / Aug '97 / Storyville

Element

☐ HOLD MY BREATH
LF 238CD / Sep '96 / Lost & Found

Elementales

☐ AL BANO MARIA
21060CD / Apr '95 / Sonifolk

☐ ELEMENTALES
J 1030CD / Jun '94 / Sonifolk

Elements

☐ FAR EAST VOL.2
EFA 034522 / Nov '95 / Wavetone

Elend

☐ LECONS DE TENEBRES
HOLY 008CD / Nov '94 / Holy

☐ LES TENEBRES DU DEHORS
HOLY 017CD / Apr '96 / Holy

☐ UMBERSUN
Du trefonds des tenebres / Melpmene / Moon of amber / Apocalypse / Umbra / Umbersun / In the embrasure of heaven / Wake of the angel / Au trefonds des tenebres
CDMFN 239 / 26 May '98 / Music For Nations

☐ WEEPING NIGHTS
HOLY 026CD / Jun '97 / Elend

Elephant

☐ ELEPHANT
HB0162 / Feb '94 / Heatblast

Elephant Talk

☐ IN A BIG SEA
INFRACD 0001 / Apr '97 / Knock On Wood

Elevate

☐ ARCHITECT, THE
FLOWCD 002 / Mar '96 / Flower Shop

☐ BRONZEE
FLOWCD 001 / Oct '94 / Flower Shop

Elevator

☐ CURD DUCA
EFA 006972 / 16 Mar '98 / Mille Plateau

Elevator To Hell

☐ EERIECONSILIATION
SPCD 399 / 29 Sep '97 / Sub Pop

Elevators

☐ LINOLEUM
No business / Separator / Cockroach / 3am / Banana bells / Tijuana extension / Somewhere in Mukkula / Night in Hesberia / Link-a-ping / Khe sanh / Just say oh / Jehovah / Burn the kitchen
ODOR 20 / 17 Nov '97 / Spinefarm

Eleven Pictures

☐ INTIALS
M 7022CD / Feb '97 / Mascot

Eleven Years From Yesterday

☐ ELEVEN YEARS FROM YESTERDAY
BEADCD 1 / May '90 / Bead

Eleventh Dream Day

☐ EIGHTH
For a King / Writes a letter home / Two smart cookies / Insomnia / View from the rim / April / Motion sickness / Last call
EFA 049892 / Feb '97 / City Slang

☐ PRAIRIE SCHOOL FREAKOUT
422128 / May '94 / New Rose

☐ URSA MAJOR
EFA 049432 / Jan '95 / City Slang

Elf Power

☐ WHEN THE RED KING COMES
AR 007 / 1 Dec '97 / Arena Rock

Elgart, Charlie

☐ BALANCE
On the breeze of a shadow / My sentiments exactly / Balance / Bryanna / Sight unseen / Goodbye my friend / Sundance
PD 83068 / Dec '89 / Novus

☐ SIGNS OF LIFE
Float / Sojourn / This thing we share / Signs of life / I cry for you / When I'm with Stu / Summer dusk
PD 83045 / Mar '89 / RCA

Elgart, Larry

☐ SENSATIONAL SWING (Six Medleys Of Timeless Swing Favourites) (Elgart, Larry & His Manhattan Swing Orchestra)
Switched on swing / Switched on big bands / Switched on a star / Switched on Astaire / Switched on the blues / Switched on Broadway
ECD 3042 / Jan '95 / K-Tel

Elharrachi, Dahmane

☐ DAHMANE ELHARRACHI
AAA 142 / Dec '96 / Club Du Disque Arabe

Eli, Billy

☐ SOMETHING'S GOING ON (Eli, Billy & Lost In America)
MRCD 1295 / Jun '96 / Club De Musique

Eliane Do Forro

☐ ELIANE DO FORRO
61132 / 19 May '98 / RGE

Elias, Elaine

☐ ELAINE ELIAS SINGS JOBIM
Garota de Ipanema / Samba de uma nota / So danco samba / Ela e carioca / Anos dourados / Desafinado / Falando de amor / Samba de aviao / A felicidade / Por toda a minha vida / How insensitive / Esquecendo voce / Pois e / Amor em paz / Modinha / Caminhos cruzados / Continental
4950502 / 11 May '98 / Blue Note

☐ SOLOS AND DUETS
Autumn leaves / Masquerade is over / Interlude / Way you look tonight: *Elias, Elaine & Herbie Hancock* / All the things you are / Joy spring / Have you met Miss Jones / Just enough: *Elias, Elaine & Herbie Hancock* / Messages: *Elias, Elaine & Herbie Hancock* / Asa branca
CDP 8320732 / Oct '95 / Blue Note

☐ THREE AMERICANS, THE
Up dawn / Time is now / Caipora / Chorango / Chega de saudade / Crystal and lace / Brigas nunca mais / Introduction to Guarani / O Guarani / Jungle journey / Missing you / Jumping fox
CDP 8533282 / Jun '97 / Blue Note

Elias Hulk

☐ UNCHAINED
Anthology of dreams / Nightmare / Been around too long / Yesterday's trip / We can fly / Free / Delhi blues / Ain't got you
SEECD 286 / Jan '90 / See For Miles

Elijah's Mantle

☐ ANGELS OF PEVERSITY
DNDC 001CD / Oct '96 / De Nova Da Capo

☐ BETRAYALS AND ECSTASIES
DNDC 006CD / Oct '96 / De Nova Da Capo

☐ POETS AND VISIONARIES
Preface / Hymn to beauty / Windows / Spleen / Vampire / Ophelia / Night in hell / Adieu
DNDC 009 / Jan '97 / De Nova Da Capo

☐ REMEDIES IN HERESIES
DNDC 002CD / Oct '96 / De Nova Da Capo

☐ SORROWS OF SOPHIA
DNDC 003CD / Oct '96 / De Nova Da Capo

Elite

☐ FULL TEN INCHES
WWRCD 022 / 6 Apr '98 / Walzwerk

Elite Syncopators

☐ RAGTIME SPECIAL
SOSCD 1286 / Mar '95 / Stomp Off

Elixir

☐ PHOBEUS INCIDENT
Orpheus / Magic orange / Isis / Theme from galaxian / 35 prophetic signs / Phobus incident / Deep speed diving / Pegasus 51 / Dark spheres of / Yesterday / 1060 / Alien rainbow / Deimos / March of osiris
WORD 006 / 29 Sep '97 / Language

Elizalde, Fred

☐ BEST OF FRED ELIZALDE 1928-1929, THE (Elizalde, Fred & Anglo-American Band)
Under the moon / Dixie / Tiger rag / Sugar / Shy Anna / Arkansas blues / Sugar step / How long has this been going on / Here am I broken hearted / Smile / Dance little lady / Darktown strutters ball / Somebody stole my gal / My pet / Blue baby / Wherever you are / Crazy rhythm / If I had you / Misery farm / Singapore sorrows / Nobody's sweetheart / After the sun kissed the world goodbye
RTR 79011 / Dec '97 / Retrieval

Elkanger Bjorsvik Musikklag

☐ KING'S MESSENGER
Songs for BL / King messenger / Frogs of aristophanes / River dance / Arctic funk / Intrada / Concertine for trombone / Alle fugler / American dream
DOYCD 047 / Oct '95 / Doyen

Elkin, A.P.

☐ ARNHEM LAND
LARRCD 288 / Jun '94 / Larrikin

Elkins-Payne Jubilee Singers

☐ ELKINS-PAYNE JUBILEE SINGERS (1923-1929)
DOCD 5356 / Jun '95 / Document

Ellefson, Art

☐ AS IF TO SAY
SKCD 22030 / Jun '93 / Sackville

Ellen James Society

☐ RELUCTANTLY WE
DR 01CD / Sep '90 / Daemon

Ellen Jamesians

☐ IN SEARCH OF
BIRD 089 / Jun '97 / Birdnest

Elles

☐ AALLE KREKAJENTE
ELLES 9401CD / Dec '94 / Musikk Distribujson

Elliman, Yvonne

☐ FOOD OF LOVE
Casserole me over / More than one, less than five / I want to make you laugh / Muesli dreams / I can't explain / Sunshine / Hawaii / I don't know how to love him blues / Moon struck one / Happy ending / Love's bringing me down
CSAPCD 124 / Nov '96 / Connoisseur Collection

Elling, Kurt

☐ MESSENGER
Nature boy / April in Paris / Suite / Beauty of all things / Dance / Prayer for Mr. Davis / Endless / It's just a thing / Ginger bread boy / Prelude to a kiss / Time of the season
CDP 8527272 / Apr '97 / Parlophone

Ellington, Duke

☐ 1952 SEATTLE CONCERT, THE
Skin deep / How could you do a thing like that to me / Sophisticated lady / Perfido / Caravan / Harlem suite / Hawk talks / Don't get around much anymore / In a sentimental mood / Mood indigo / I'm beginning to see the light / Prelude to a kiss / It don't mean a thing if it ain't got that swing / Solitude / Let a song go out of my heart / Jam with Sam
07863665312 / Apr '95 / Bluebird

☐ 20 JAZZ CLASSICS
Thing's ain't what they used to be / Satin doll / Flamingo / Liza / In a sentimental mood / My old flame / If I give my heart to you / Caravan / Stardust / Harlem air shaft / Band call / Bakiff / In the mood / One-o'clock jump / Flying home / Warm valley / C jam blues / Black and tan fantasy / Reflections in D / Rockin' in rhythm
CDMFP 6161 / May '95 / Music For Pleasure

☐ 22 ORIGINAL BIG BAND RECORDINGS
Take the A train / Crosstown / Passion flower / Perdido / Pretty woman / 9.20 special / One o'clock jump / Moon mist / How high the moon / Just squeeze me / Happy go lucky local / Come rain or come shine / Just you, just me / Double ruff / Mooche / Swamp fire / Blue lou / On the alamo / Frisky / Tea for two / Who struck john / Park at 106th
HCD 410 / Sep '92 / Hindsight

☐ 70TH BIRTHDAY CONCERT (2CD Set)
Rockin' in rhythm / BP / Take the 'A' train / Tootie for Cootie / 4.30 blues / El Gato / Black butterfly / Things ain't what they used to be / Laying on mellow / Satin doll / Azure / In triplicate / Perdido / Fifi / Prelude to a kiss / I'm just a lucky so and so / I let a song go out of my heart / Prelude to a kiss / I'm just a lucky so and so / Do nothin' 'til you hear from me / Just squeeze me / Don't get around much anymore / Mood indigo / Sophisticated lady / Caravan / Black swan / Final Ellington speech
CDP 8327462 / Sep '95 / Blue Note

☐ AFRO EURASIAN ECLIPSE, THE
OJCCD 645 / Mar '93 / Original Jazz Classics

☐ ANATOMY OF A MURDER
4691372 / Jan '95 / Sony Jazz

☐ AT NEWPORT (Ellington, Duke & Buck Clayton)
Take the 'A' train: *Ellington, Duke Orchestra* / Sophisticated lady: *Ellington, Duke Orchestra* / I got it bad and that ain't good: *Ellington, Duke Orchestra* / Skin deep: *Ellington, Duke Orchestra* / You can depend on me: *Clayton, Buck All Stars* / Newport jump: *Clayton, Buck All Stars* / In a mellow tone: *Clayton, Buck All Stars*
4773202 / Nov '94 / Columbia

☐ AT THE COTTON CLUB
8464604592 / 24 Mar '98 / Special Music

☐ AT THE GREEK 1966 (Ellington, Duke & Ella Fitzgerald)
DSTS 1013 / '94 / Status

☐ AUDIO ARCHIVE
Mooche / Honeysuckle rose / Take the 'A' train / Mood indigo / Sophisticated lady / Crosstown / Caravan / Tea for two / Frustration / Perdido / One O'clock jump / Colatura / 920 special / Love you madly / Moon mist / Rose of the Rio Grande / Just squeeze me / Jam with Sam / Black and tan fantasy / Primin' at the prom
CDAA 014 / Jun '92 / Tring

☐ AZURE ELLINGTON (Blue Note Plays The Duke) (Various Artists)
Rockin' in rhythm: *Ellington, Duke* / It don't mean a thing: *Simone, Nina* / Caravan: *Burrell, Kenny* / Take the a train: *Ervin, Booker* / Satin doll: *Holmes, Richard 'Groove' & Jimmy Witherspoon* / Mood indigo: *Cole, Nat 'King'* / Don't get around much anymore: *Kenton, Stan* / Cottontail: *Newton, James* / Just squeeze me: *Rawls, Lou* / Duke's place: *Armstrong, Louis & Duke Ellington* / Lush life: *Williams, Joe* / In a sentimental mood: *Eubanks, Kevin* / In a mellow tone: *McGriff, Jimmy* / Sophisticated lady: *Jordan, Clifford* / Chelsea bridge: *Newborn, Phineas Jr.* / Passion flower: *Strayhorn, Billy*
4940350 / 22 Jun '98 / Blue Note

☐ BATTLE OF THE BANDS (Ellington, Duke & Count Basie)
Bill's mill / C jam blues / Backstage at Stuff's / Just squeeze me (but don't tease me) / Bye bye baby / In a mellotone / Swingin' the blues / Memphis blue / St. Louis' boogie / Suddenly it jumped / South / Royal garden blues / One o' clock boogie / Concerto for cootie / House rent boogie / Main stem / Seventh Avenue express / Take the A train
09026631302 / 10 Aug '98 / RCA Victor

☐ BEST OF THE FORTIES VOL.1 (1940-1942)
BMCD 3019 / Sep '95 / Blue Moon

☐ BLACK, BROWN AND BEIGE
ND 86641 / Oct '95 / Bluebird

☐ BLANTON-WEBSTER YEARS, THE
You, you darlin' / Jack the bear / Koko / Morning glory / So far, so good / Conga brava / Do nothin' 'til you hear from me / Me and you / Cotton tail / Never no lament / Dusk / Bojangles / Portrait of Bert Williams / Blue goose / Harlem air shaft / At a Dixie roadside diner / All too soon / Rumpus in Richmond / My greatest mistake / Sepia panorama / There shall be no night / In a mellow tone / Five o'clock whistle / Warm valley / Flaming sword / Jumpin' punkins / Across the track blues / John Hardy's wife / Blue Serge / After all / Chloe / Bakiff / Are you sticking / I never felt this way before / Just a sittin' and a rockin' / Giddybug gallop / Sidewalks of New York / Chocolate shake / Flamingo / I got it bad and that ain't good / Clementine / Brown skin gal / Girl in my dreams tries to look like you / Jump for joy / Moon over Cuba / Take the 'A' train / Five o'clock drag / Rocks in my bed / Blip blip / Chelsea Bridge / Raincheck / What good would it do / I don't know what kind of blues I got / Perdido / C jam blues / Moon mist / What am I here for / I don't mind / Someone / My little brown book / Main stem / Johnny come lately / Hayfoot strawfoot / Sentimental lady / Slip of the lip (can sink a ship) / Sherman shuffle
74321131812 / Mar '93 / Bluebird

☐ BLUE FEELING
Black and tan fantasy / Creole love call / Harlem twist / Black Beauty / Swampy river / Cotton club stomp / Shout 'em Aunt Tillie / Ring dem bells / Echoes of the jungle / Blue Harlem / Drop me off at Harlem / Bundle of blues / Harlem speaks / Hyde Park / Blue feeling / Merry go round / Clarinet lament / I'm slapping Seventh Avenue with the sole of my shoe / Riding on a blue note / I let a song go out of my heart / Blue light / Koko / Conga Brava / Jack the Bear
PPCD 78103 / Feb '95 / Past Perfect

☐ BLUES IN ORBIT
Blues in orbit / Track 360 / Villes ville is the place, man / Brown penny / Three J's blues / Smada / Pie eye's blues / C jam blues / Sweet and pungent / In a mellow tone / Sentimental lady / Blues in blueprint / Swingers get the blues too / Singer's jump
4608232 / Jan '95 / Sony Jazz

☐ CHEEK TO CHEEK 1935
PHONTCD 7657 / Apr '94 / Phontastic

☐ CLASSIC DUKE ELLINGTON, THE (2CD Set)
Rockin' in rhythm / I let a song go out of my heart / Concerto for Cootie / Tonight I shall sleep / I got it bad and that ain't good / Misty mornin' / Jump for joy / East St. Louis toodle-oo / Ring dem bells / Mood to be wooed / Perdido / Black and tan fantasy / Solitude / Main stem / Chelsea Bridge / Three little words / Jack the bear / Azure / Cotton club stomp / Mood indigo / Drop me off in Harlem / Mooche / Moonglow / Take the 'A' train / Creole love call / Sophisticated lady / Harlem air shaft / All too soon / In a sentimental mood / Sepia panorama / Echoes of Harlem / Gal from Joe's / Bojangles / Prelude to a kiss / Black beauty / Things ain't what they used to be / I'm beginning to see the light / Ko Ko / It don't mean a thing (if it ain't got that swing) / Caravan / Black, brown and beige suite
CPCD 82592 / Jan '97 / Charly

☐ CLASSICS 1924-1927
CLASSICS 539 / Dec '90 / Classics

☐ CLASSICS 1927-1928
CLASSICS 542 / Dec '90 / Classics

☐ CLASSICS 1928
CLASSICS 550 / Dec '90 / Classics

☐ CLASSICS 1928-1929
CLASSICS 559 / Oct '91 / Classics

☐ CLASSICS 1929
CLASSICS 569 / Oct '91 / Classics

☐ CLASSICS 1929-1930
CLASSICS 577 / Oct '91 / Classics

☐ CLASSICS 1930 VOL.1
CLASSICS 586 / Aug '91 / Classics

☐ CLASSICS 1930 VOL.2
CLASSICS 596 / Sep '91 / Classics

☐ CLASSICS 1930-1931 (Ellington, Duke Orchestra)
CLASSICS 605 / Oct '92 / Classics

☐ CLASSICS 1931-1932 (Ellington, Duke Orchestra)
CLASSICS 616 / Sep '92 / Classics

☐ CLASSICS 1932-1933 (Ellington, Duke Orchestra)
CLASSICS 626 / Sep '92 / Classics

☐ CLASSICS 1933
CLASSICS 637 / Nov '92 / Classics

☐ CLASSICS 1933-1935
CLASSICS 646 / Nov '92 / Classics

☐ CLASSICS 1935-1936
CLASSICS 659 / Nov '92 / Classics

☐ CLASSICS 1936-1937
CLASSICS 666 / Nov '92 / Classics

☐ CLASSICS 1937 VOL.1
CLASSICS 675 / Mar '93 / Classics

☐ CLASSICS 1937 VOL.2 (Ellington, Duke Orchestra)
CLASSICS 687 / Mar '93 / Classics

☐ CLASSICS 1938 VOL.1 (Ellington, Duke Orchestra)
CLASSICS 700 / Jul '93 / Classics

☐ CLASSICS 1938 VOL.2
CLASSICS 717 / Jul '93 / Classics

☐ CLASSICS 1938 VOL.3
CLASSICS 726 / Dec '93 / Classics

☐ CLASSICS 1938-1939
CLASSICS 747 / Aug '94 / Classics

☐ CLASSICS 1939 VOL.1
CLASSICS 765 / Aug '94 / Classics

☐ CLASSICS 1939 VOL.2
CLASSICS 780 / Nov '94 / Classics

☐ CLASSICS 1939-1940
CLASSICS 790 / Jan '95 / Classics

☐ CLASSICS 1940 VOL.1
CLASSICS 805 / Mar '95 / Classics

☐ CLASSICS 1940 VOL.2
CLASSICS 820 / Jul '95 / Classics

☐ CLASSICS 1940-1941
CLASSICS 837 / Sep '95 / Classics

☐ CLASSICS 1941
CLASSICS 851 / Feb '96 / Classics

☐ CLASSICS 1942-1944
CLASSICS 867 / Mar '96 / Classics

☐ CLASSICS 1944-1945
CLASSICS 881 / Jul '96 / Classics

☐ CLASSICS 1945 VOL.1
CLASSICS 915 / Jan '97 / Classics

☐ CLASSICS 1945 VOL.2
CLASSICS 951 / Nov '97 / Classics

☐ CLASSICS 1945-1946
CLASSICS 985 / 24 Apr '98 / Classics

☐ COLLECTION, THE
HBCD 501 / Sep '92 / Hindsight

☐ COMPLETE DUKE ELLINGTON VOL.1
KAZCD 501 / May '96 / Kaz

☐ COMPLETE DUKE ELLINGTON VOL.10
KAZCD 510 / May '96 / Kaz

☐ COMPLETE DUKE ELLINGTON VOL.2
KAZCD 502 / May '96 / Kaz

☐ COMPLETE DUKE ELLINGTON VOL.3
KAZCD 503 / May '96 / Kaz

☐ COMPLETE DUKE ELLINGTON VOL.4
KAZCD 504 / May '96 / Kaz

☐ COMPLETE DUKE ELLINGTON VOL.5
KAZCD 505 / May '96 / Kaz

☐ COMPLETE DUKE ELLINGTON VOL.6
KAZCD 506 / May '96 / Kaz

☐ COMPLETE DUKE ELLINGTON VOL.7
KAZCD 507 / May '96 / Kaz

☐ COMPLETE DUKE ELLINGTON VOL.8
KAZCD 508 / May '96 / Kaz

☐ COMPLETE DUKE ELLINGTON VOL.9
KAZCD 509 / May '96 / Kaz

☐ COMPLETE PRIVATE COLLECTION, THE (10CD Set)
March 19th blues / Feet bone / In a sentimental mood / Discontented / Jump for joy / Just scratchin' the surface / Prelude to a kiss / Miss Lucy / Uncontrived / Satin doll / Do not disturb / Love you madly / Short street cluster / Moon mist / Long time blues / Things ain't what they used to be / Something sexual / Riff / Bluer / Wailing 'bout / I cover the waterfront / Blues a la Willie Cook / Slow blues ensemble / Circle of forths / Perdido / Three trumps / Deep blues / Things ain't what they used to be / Paris blues / I got it bad and that ain't good / Circle blues / Sky fell down / Perdido / Passion flower / Cotton tail / ESP / Blue too-the shepherd / Tune up / Take it slow / Telstar / To know you is to love you / Like late / Major / Minor / G for groove / Lonely ones / Monk's dream / Frere monk / Cordon bleu / New concerto for cootie / September 12th blues / Bad woman / Jeep's blues / Stoona / Serenade to Sweden / Harmony in Harlem / Action in Alexandria / Tajm / Isfahan / Killian's lick / Blousons noir / Elysee / Butter and oleo / Got nobody now / MG / Blue rose / July 18th blues / Countdown / When I'm feeling kinda blue / El viti / Draggin' blues / Cotton tail / Now ain't it / Last go round / Moon mist / Skillipoop / Banquet scene (Timon of Athens) / Love scene / Rod la roque / Rhythm section blues / Lele / Ocht o' clock rock / Lady / Rondolet / I can't get started / Waiting for you / Knuf / Gigl / Meditation / Sophisticated lady / Just squeeze me / Mood indigo / I let a song (go out of my heart)/Don't get around much anym / Reva / Ortseam / Cool and groovy / Elos / C-jam blues / Degas suite-Introduction / River / Black / Comes Sunday / Light / West Indian dance / Emancipation celebration / Blues / Cy runs rock waltz / Beige / Sugar Hill penthouse / Harlem / Ad lib on Nippon / Main stem / Dancing in the dark / Stompy Jones / Time on my hands / Stompin' at the Savoy / Sophisticated lady / Take the 'A' train / All heart / Just a-settin' and a-rockin' / Take the 'A' train / Where or when / Mooche / One o' clock jump / Autumn leaves / Oh lady be good / Such sweet thunder / Blues to be there / Juniflip / Star-crossed lovers / Together / Californio mello / Suburban beauty / C jam blues / Blues in orbit / Mood indigo / Honeysuckle rose / Willow weep for me / Caravan / Wailing interval
PBXCD 010 / 30 Mar '98 / Pulse

☐ CONCERT OF SACRED MUSIC
DSTS 1015 / Jul '97 / Status

☐ CONNECTICUT JAZZ FESTIVAL
IAJRCCD 1005 / Jun '94 / IAJRC

☐ COOL ROCK (Ellington, Duke Orchestra)
Cool rock / P.s. 170 / Don't you know I care / Hi, june / Hi, jane / Anatomy of a murder / Alone together / Chinoiserie / Vancouver lights / Hello dolly-mame / Twitch / Things ain't what they used to be
15782 / Aug '92 / Laserlight

☐ CORNELL UNIVERSITY CONCERT (2CD Set)
MM 65114 / Oct '96 / Music Masters

☐ COTTON CLUB STOMP (Ellington, Duke Orchestra)
Some of these days / Nagasaki / Sweet georgia brown / Tiger rag / Rockin' chair / Miss otis regrets / My gal sal / Limehouse blues / There goes my headache / Sweet lucy brown / Don't be afraid to tell your (mother) / Moanin' for you / What's the reason I'm not pleasin' you / Old fashioned love / Lulu's back in town / Since we fell out of love / Ida, sweet as apple cider / Sweeter than suger
CD 14544 / Jan '94 / Jazz Portraits

☐ COTTON CLUB STOMP 1927-1931 (Ellington, Duke Orchestra)
Rockin' in rhythm / Cotton club stomp / Ring dem bells / Creole love call / Mooche / Black and tan fantasy / Black beauty / East st. louis toodle-oo / Blues I love to sing / Washington wobble / Hot and bothered / Misty mornin' / Jubilee stomp / Mood indigo / Doin' the voom voom / Old man blues / Take it easy / Echoes of the jungle
CD 56051 / Mar '95 / Jazz Roots

☐ COTTON TAIL (Ellington, Duke Orchestra)
Cotton tail / All too soon / Toby: *Moten, Bennie Kansas City Orchestra* / Lafayette: *Moten, Bennie Kansas City Orchestra* / Voice of old man river: *Bryant, Willie & His Orchestra* / Early session hop: *Hampton, Lionel & His Orchestra* / Conga brava / Bojangles / My greatest mistake / Chloe / Mobile ray: *Stewart, Rex & His Orchestra* / Linger awhile: *Stewart, Rex & His Orchestra* / Blue serge / Just a sittin' and a rockin' / Some Saturday: *Stewart, Rex & His Orchestra* / Five o'clock drag / Chelsea bridge / Rain check / Perdido / What am I here for / Main stem / Cadillac slim: *Carter, Benny & Chocolate Dandies*
07863667902 / 11 Sep '97 / RCA Victor

☐ COUNT MEETS THE DUKE, THE (Ellington, Duke Orchestra & Count Basie Orchestra)
Battle royal / To you / Take the 'a' train / Until I met you / Wild man / Segue in 'c' / B d b / Jumpin' at the woodside
4505092 / Jan '95 / Sony Jazz

☐ CRYSTAL BALLROOM, FARGO VOL.1 1940
TAX 37202 / Aug '94 / Tax

☐ CRYSTAL BALLROOM, FARGO VOL.2 1940
TAX 37212 / Aug '94 / Tax

☐ DRUM IS A WOMAN, A
4713202 / Jan '95 / Sony Jazz

☐ DUKE ELLINGTON (2CD Set)
R2CD 4019 / 13 Apr '98 / Deja Vu

☐ DUKE ELLINGTON
22710 / Feb '96 / Music

☐ DUKE ELLINGTON & HIS GREAT VOCALISTS
It don't mean a thing if it ain't got that swing / St. Louis blues / I can't give you anything but love / Diga diga doo / I must have that man / Solitude / Woman'll get you / Don't get around much anymore / Take love easy / On a turquoise cloud / Love you madley / Take the 'A' train / Sophisticated lady / Autumn leaves / Love (my everything)
CK 66372 / Jul '95 / Columbia

☐ DUKE ELLINGTON & HIS ORCHESTRA 1963
CD 14564 / May '95 / Jazz Portraits

☐ DUKE ELLINGTON 1927-1934
Creole love call / Black beauty / Got everything but you / Duke steps out / Jungle nights in Harlem / Blue feeling
HRM 6001 / Jan '89 / Hermes

☐ DUKE ELLINGTON 1927-1941 (Ellington, Duke Orchestra)
East St. Louis toodle-oo / Blues I love to sing / Black and tan fantasy / Washington wobble / Creole love call / Black beauty / Mooche / Misty mornin' / Hot and bothered / Jubilee stomp / Take it easy / Cotton club stomp / Tiger rag / Ring dem bells / Old man blues / Mood indigo / Dicty glide / Doing the voom voom / Hop head / Wall Street wail / Saratoga swing / Echoes of the jungle / Rockin' in rhythm / Take the 'A' train / Don't get around much anymore / Cotton tail / I got it bad and that ain't good / Conga brava / Do nothin' 'til you hear from me / Portrait of Bert Williams / Warm valley / Solitude / Country gal / Prelude to a kiss / I let a song go out of my heart / Diminuedno in blue / Crescendo in Ibue / Echoes of Harlem / Caravan / Clarinet lament / Merry go round / In a sentimental mood / Live and love tonight / Sophisticated lady / Harlem speaks / Slippery horn / In a mellow tone / Koko / Jack the bear / Harlem air shaft / Just a sittin' and a rockin' / Sepia panorama / Jumpin' punkins / Mr. J.B. blues / Body and soul / Bojangles / Sidewalks of New York / Pitter panther patter / Across the track blues / Plucked again / Blues / Chloe / C Blues / Weely / Junior hop / Dusk / Blue Serge / Morning glory
CDB 1201 / '92 / Giants Of Jazz

☐ DUKE ELLINGTON 1931-1932 (Ellington, Duke Orchestra)
Take the 'a' train / Don't get around much anymore (never no lament) / Cotton tail (shuckin' and stiffin') / I got it bad and that ain't good / Conga brava / Concerto for cootie (do nothing till you hear from me) / A portrait of bert williams / Warm valley / Solitude / Country gal / Prelude to a kiss / I let a song go out of my heart / Diminuendo in blue / Crescendo in blue / Echoes of harlem (cootie's concerto) / Caravan / Clarinet lament (barney's concerto) / Merry go round / In a sentimental mood / Live and love tonight / Sophisticated lady / Harlem speaks / Slippery horn
CD 53046 / Mar '90 / Giants Of Jazz

☐ DUKE ELLINGTON 1941
UCD 19003 / Jul '88 / Forlane

☐ DUKE ELLINGTON AND HIS ORCHESTRA 1927-1931 (Ellington, Duke Orchestra)
East st. louis toodle-oo / Blues I love to sing / Black and tan fantasy / Washington wobble / Creole love call / Black beauty / Mooche / Misty mornin' / Hot and bothered / Jubilee stomp / Take it easy / Cotton club stomp / Tiger rag / Ring dem bells / Old man blues / Mood indigo / Dicty glide / Doin' the voom voom / Hop head / Wall street wail / Saratoga swing / Echoes of the jungle / Rockin' in rhythm
CD 53030 / Aug '88 / Giants Of Jazz

☐ DUKE ELLINGTON AND JOHN COLTRANE (Ellington, Duke & John Coltrane)
In a sentimental mood / Take the Coltrane / Big Nick / Stevie / My little brown book / Angelica / Feeling of jazz
IMP 11662 / Oct '95 / Impulse Jazz

☐ DUKE ELLINGTON AND THE SMALL GROUPS 1936-1950
Dancers in love / Clothed woman / C jam blues / Charlie the chulo / Johnny come lately / Caravan / Chasin' chippies / Rent party blues / Tonk / Tip toe topic / Great times / Frankie and johnny / Subtle slough / Without a song / Blues for blanton / Dooji wooji / Oscalypso / Jeep's blues / Things ain't what they used to be / Good queen bess / Squaty roo / Menelik the lion of judah / A lull at dawn / Goin' out the back way / Who knows
CD 53070 / May '92 / Giants Of Jazz

☐ DUKE ELLINGTON COLLECTORS' EDITION
DVX 08042 / Apr '95 / Deja Vu

☐ DUKE ELLINGTON GOLD (2CD Set)
D2CD 4019 / Jun '95 / Deja Vu

☐ DUKE ELLINGTON IN CONCERT
RTE 15032 / Apr '95 / RTE/Europe 1

☐ DUKE ELLINGTON PRESENTS... (Big Band Bounce & Boogie) (Ellington, Duke Orchestra)
Summertime / Laura / I can't get started (with you) / My funny Valentine / Everything but you / Frustration / Cotton tail / Daydream / Deep purple / Indian summer / Blues
CDGR 123 / Mar '97 / Charly

☐ DUKE ELLINGTON SAMPLER
Latin American sunshine / C-jam blues / Caravan / Paris blues / Afrique / Take the 'A' train
OJCX 012 / Jan '98 / Original Jazz Classics

☐ DUKE ELLINGTON TRIBUTE
8747192 / 18 Dec '97 / DA Music

☐ DUKE ELLINGTON VOL.1
Take the "a" train / Black and tan fantasy / Perdido / Rain check / Day dream / Grievin / Gal from joe's / Day in day out
15710 / Apr '94 / Laserlight

☐ DUKE ELLINGTON VOL.1
UAE 30042 / Jan '98 / Members Edition

☐ DUKE ELLINGTON VOL.10 (Rockin' In Rhythm 1930-1931)
152312 / May '95 / Hot 'n' Sweet

☐ DUKE ELLINGTON VOL.12 (Echoes Of The Jungle 1931-1932)
152332 / Mar '96 / Hot 'n' Sweet

☐ DUKE ELLINGTON VOL.2 (Creole Rhapsody)
152322 / Feb '95 / Hot 'n' Sweet

☐ DUKE ELLINGTON VOL.2
15753 / Apr '94 / Laserlight

☐ DUKE ELLINGTON VOL.2
UAE 30062 / Jan '98 / Members Edition

☐ DUKE ELLINGTON VOL.7 (Wall Street Wail 1929)
152232 / Dec '93 / Hot 'n' Sweet

☐ DUKE ELLINGTON VOL.8 (Jungle Blues 1929-1930)
152242 / Dec '93 / Hot 'n' Sweet

☐ DUKE ELLINGTON VOL.9 (Mood Indigo 1930)
152252 / May '94 / Hot 'n' Sweet

☐ DUKE PLAYS ELLINGTON
TPZ 1020 / May '95 / Topaz Jazz

☐ DUKE'S BIG FOUR (Ellington, Duke Quartet)
Cotton tail / Blues / Hawk talks / Prelude to a kiss / Love you madly / Just squeeze me / Everything but you
CD 2310703 / Nov '95 / Pablo

☐ ECHOES OF HARLEM
MACCD 276 / Aug '96 / Autograph

☐ ELLINGTON '56
East St. Louis toodle-oo / Creole love call / Stompy Jones / Jeep is jumpin' / Jack the bear / In a mellow tone / Koko / Midriff / Stomp, look and listen / Unbooted character / Lonesome lullaby / Upper Manhattan medical group / Cotton tail / Daydream / Deep purple / Indian summer / Laura / Blues
LEJAZZCD 27 / Aug '94 / Le Jazz

☐ ELLINGTON AT BASIN STREET EAST (Ellington, Duke Orchestra)
CD 908 / Jun '98 / Music & Arts

☐ ELLINGTON AT NEWPORT (Ellington, Duke Orchestra)
Festival junction (newport jazz festival suite) / Blues to be there / Newport up / Jeep's blues / Diminuendo and crescendo in blue
4509862 / Jan '95 / Sony Jazz

☐ **ELLINGTON INDIGOS**
Solitude / Where or when / Mood indigo / Night and day / Prelude to a kiss / All the things you are / Willow weep / For me / Tenderly / Dancing in the dark / Autumn leaves / Sky fell down
4723642 / Jun '96 / Sony Jazz

☐ **ELLINGTON MEETS HAWKINS (Ellington, Duke & Coleman Hawkins)**
Limbo jazz / Mood indigo / Ray Charles' place / Wanderlust / You dirty dog / Self portrait (of the bean) / Jeep is jumpin' / Ricitic / Solitude
IMP 11622 / Oct '95 / Impulse Jazz

☐ **ELLINGTON SUITES, THE**
Queen's suite / Goutelas suite / Uwis suite
OJCCD 446 / Feb '92 / Original Jazz Classics

☐ **ESSENTIAL DUKE ELLINGTON, THE (4CD Set)**
CDDIG 13 / Apr '95 / Charly

☐ **ESSENTIAL RECORDINGS, THE**
LEJAZZCD 2 / Mar '93 / Le Jazz

☐ **ETERNAL DUKE ELLINGTON**
PHONTCD 7666 / Apr '94 / Phontastic

☐ **FAR EAST SUITE - SPECIAL MIX, THE**
Tourist point of view / Bluebird of Delhi / Ifashan / Depk / Mount Harissa / Blue pepper (Far East of the blues) / Agra / Amad / Ad lib on Nippon / Tourist point of view (Alt. Take) / Bluebird of Delhi (Alt. Take) / Isfahan / Amad (Alt. Take)
07863665512 / Jun '95 / Bluebird

☐ **FEELING OF JAZZ, THE**
BLCD 760123 / Feb '89 / Black Lion

☐ **FOUR SYMPHONIC WORKS**
Harlem / Three black kings / New world a comin' / Black, brown and beige
MM 65096 / Oct '96 / Music Masters

☐ **GENEROSITY OF MOOD, A**
Mood Indigo / It don't mean a thing if it ain't got that swing / East St. Louis toodle-oo / Black and tan fantasy / Rockin' in rhythm / Mooche / Solitude / Caravan / Wall Street wail / When your smiling / Cotton Club Stomp / Running wild / Wang wang blues / Twelfth street rag / Creole rhapsody / Is that religion / Hot and bothered / Old man blues / Ring dem bells
PAR 2036 / Oct '94 / Parade

☐ **GREAT CHICAGO CONCERTS, THE (The Travelog Edition/Unreleased Masters/2CD Set)**
Ring dem bells / Jumpin' punkins / Beale Street blues / Memphis blues / Golden feather / Air conditioned jungle / Very unbooted character / Sultry sunset / Magnolias just dripping with molasses / Hearsay / There was nobody looking / Happy go lucky local / Things ain't what they used to be / Hiawatha / Ride Red ride / Blues riff / Improvisation / Honeysuckle rose / Blue skies / Star spangled banner / In a mellotone / Solid old man / Come Sunday/Work song / Rugged Romeo / Circe / Dancers in love / Coloratura / Frankie and Johnny / Caravan / Take the 'A' train / Mellow ditty / Fugue / Jam a ditty / Magenta haze / Pitter panther patter / Suburbanite
8444012 / Jun '94 / Limelight
MM 65110 / Oct '96 / Music Masters

☐ **GREAT DUKE ELLINGTON**
Take the 'A' train / Just you, just me / Come rain or come shine / Blue Lou / Tea for two / How high the moon / One o'clock jump / Crosstown / Pretty woman / 9.20 Special / On the Alamo / Perdido
HCD 335 / Mar '96 / Hindsight

☐ **GREAT ELLINGTON UNITS, THE**
Daydream / Good Queen Bess / That's the blues, old man / Junior hop / Without a song / My Sunday gal / Mobile bay / Linger awhile / Charlie the chulo / Lament for Javanette / Lull at dawn / Ready Eddy / Some Saturday / Subtle slough / Menelik, the lion of Judah / Poor bubber / Squatty roo / Passion flower / Things ain't what they used to be / Going out the back way / Brown suede / C jam blues
ND 86751 / Nov '88 / Bluebird

☐ **GREAT JAZZ VOCALISTS SING ELLINGTON AND STRAYHORN (Various Artists)**
I got it bad (and that ain't good): *Reeves, Dianne* / I ain't got nothin' but the blues: *Rawls, Lou* / Prelude to a kiss: *Wilson, Nancy* / Do nothin' 'til you hear from me: *Lincoln, Abbey* / Lush life: *Wilson, Nancy* / Something to live for: *Horne, Lena* / Just a sittin' and a rockin': *Nance, Ray* / Warm valley: *Lincoln, Abbey* / It don't mean a thing (if it ain't got that swing): *Ross, Annie & Gerry Mulligan* / I didn't know about you: *Christy, June* / Jump for joy: *Vaughan, Sarah* / Sophisticated lady: *Vaughan, Sarah* / Medley:prelude to a kiss/I'm beginning to see the light: *Vaughan, Sarah* / Drop me off in Harlem: *Armstrong, Louis* / I'm just a lucky so and so: *Armstrong, Louis* / Day dream: *Christy, June* / It's kind of lonesome out tonight: *Cole, Nat 'King' Trio* / Come Sunday: *Williams, Joe*
CDP 8552212 / Mar '97 / Blue Note

☐ **GREAT LONDON CONCERTS, THE (The Travelog Edition/Unreleased Masters)**
Take the 'A' train / Intro / Perdido / Caravan / Isfahan / Opener / Harlem / Take the 'A' train / Mood indigo / C jam blues / Don't get around much anymore / Diminuendo and crescendo in blue / Single petal of a rose / Kinda Dukish / Rockin' in rhythm
5184462 / Jun '94 / Limelight
MM 65106 / Oct '96 / Music Masters

☐ **GREAT PARIS CONCERT, THE**
Kinda dukish / Rockin' in rhythm / On the sunny side of the street / Star crossed lovers / All of me / Asphalt jungle / Do nothin' 'til you hear from me / Tutti for cootie / Suite Thursday / Perdido / Eighth veil / Rose of the Rio Grande / Cop out / Bula / Jam with Sam / Happy go lucky local / Tone parallel to Harlem / Don't get around much anymore / Black and tan fantasy / Creole love call / Mooch / Things ain't what they used to be / Pyramid / Blues / Echoes of Harlem / Satin doll
7567813032 / Feb '92 / Atlantic

☐ **GREAT TIMES (Ellington, Duke & Billy Strayhorn)**
Cotton tail / C jam blues / Flamingo / Bang-up blues / Tonk / Johnny come lately / In a blue summer garden / Great times / Perdido / Take the 'A' train / Oscarlypso / Blues for blanton
OJCCD 108 / Sep '93 / Original Jazz Classics

☐ **GREATEST HITS**
Take the 'A' train / Sophisticated lady / Perdido / Prelude to a kiss / C jam blues / Mood indigo / Mooche / Satin doll / Solitude / What am I here for / I got it bad and that ain't good / Skin deep
4629592 / Oct '93 / Sony Jazz

☐ **GREATEST HITS**
Satin doll / Don't get around much anymore / Do nothing 'til you hear from me / Take the 'A' train / Solitude / C jam blues / Mood indigo / I'm beginning to see the light / Prelude to a kiss / Perdido
CK 65419 / 26 Jan '98 / Sony Jazz

☐ **GREATEST JAZZ BAND IN THE WORLD...EVER, THE (2CD Set)**
Take the 'A' train / Sophisticated lady / Harlem speaks / I let a song go out of my heart / Merry go round / Echoes of Harlem / Country gal / Caravan / Don't get around much anymore / Cotton tail / In a sentimental mood / Crescendo in blue / I got it bad and that ain't good / Concerto for Cootie (do nothing till you hear from me) / Prelude to a kiss / Hyde park / Diminuendo in blue / Solitude / Drop me in Harlem / Mooche / Showboat shuffle / Harmony in Harlem / Creole rhapsody pts. 1 and 2 / Slippery horn / Steppin' into swing society / Warm valley / It don't mean a thing (if it ain't got that swing) / In a jam / East St. Louis toodle-oo / Clarinet lament (Barney's concerto) / Gal from Joe's / Black and tan fantasy / Doin the voom voom / Stompy Jones / Ring dem bells / Merry go round 2
330222 / Jul '96 / Hallmark

☐ **HAPPY BIRTHDAY DUKE VOL.2 (Ellington, Duke Orchestra)**
Summertime / Warm valley / Sultry serenade / Hy-ah-sue / Sophisticated lady / I let a song go out of my heart-don't get around much anym / Just squeeze me (but don't tease me) / Caravan / Perdido / Without a song
15784 / Jul '92 / Laserlight

☐ **HAPPY BIRTHDAY DUKE VOL.3 (Ellington, Duke Orchestra)**
Things ain't what they used to be / Hawk talks / C jam blues / Tenderly / All the things you are / Solitude / She moved / Happy birthday to you / Mood indigo / Trumpet no end / Take the 'a' train
15785 / Jul '92 / Laserlight

☐ **HAPPY BIRTHDAY DUKE VOL.4 (Ellington, Duke Orchestra)**
Coffee and kisses / Johnny come lately / (maybe I should) change my ways / Primping at the prom / Band call / Satin doll / Blue jean beguine / Tulip or turnip (tell me, tell me, dream face) / Honeysuckle rose / Theme for trambeam / Blue moon
15786 / Aug '92 / Laserlight

☐ **HAPPY BIRTHDAY DUKE VOL.5 (Ellington, Duke Orchestra)**
V.i.p.'s boogie / Jam with sam / Bunny hop mambo / Isle of capri / Take the "a" train (vocal by ray nance) / Take the "a" train (instrumental) / Famingo / I got it bad and that ain't good-I'm just a lucky so-and-/ Ballin' the blues / Satin doll
15787 / Aug '92 / Laserlight

☐ **HAPPY-GO-LUCKY LOCAL (Ellington, Duke Orchestra)**
MVSCD 52 / Jul '88 / Musicraft

☐ **HARLEM (Ellington, Duke Orchestra)**
Blow by blow / Caravan / Satin doll / Harlem: *Ellington, Duke Orchestra & Johnny Hodges* / Things ain't what they used to be / All of me / Prowling cat / Opera / Happy reunion / Tutti for cootie
CD 2308245 / Oct '92 / Pablo

☐ **HIS ORCHESTRA AND HIS SMALL GROUPS**
C Jam blues / Perdido / Sultry sunset / Blue skies (trumpet no end) / It don't mean a thing if it ain't got that swing / Magenta haze / Things ain't what they used to be (times's-a-wastin') / I'm beginning to see the light / Moonmist / Chelsea bridge / Jump for joy / Main stem / What am I here for / Johnny come lately / Do nothin' 'til you hear from me / Snibor / On a turquoise cloud / Park at 106th / In a sentimental mood / Black and tan fantasy / Caravan / Creole love call / Great times / Brown Betty / Dancers in love / Clothed man / Charlie the chulo / Chasin' chippies / Rent party blues / Tonk / Tip toe topic / Frankie and Johnny / Subtle slough / Without a song / Blues for blanton / Dooji wooji / Oscarlypso / Jeep's blues / Things ain't what they used to be / Good Queen Bess / Squaty roo / Menelik, the Lion of Judah / Lull at dawn / Goin' out the back way / Who knows / In a mellow tone / East St. Louis toodle-oo / Koko / Sophisticated lady / Cotton tail / Mooche / Bensonality / Prelude to a kiss / Satin doll / Mood indigo / Just a sittin' and a rockin' / I got it bad and that ain't good / Harlem air shaft / Blues in orbit / Hawk talks / El gato / Trambean / Smada / Take the 'A' train
CDB 1211 / '92 / Giants Of Jazz

☐ **HOLLYWOOD HANGOVER**
MCCD 019 / Nov '96 / Magnum America

☐ **IN CONCERT AT THE PLEYEL PARIS**
DAWE 39 / Oct '92 / Magic

☐ **IN CONCERT AT THE PLEYEL PARIS VOL.2 1958**
El Gato / Take the 'A' train / MB blue / VIP boogie / Jam with Sam / Stompy Jones / Hi fi fo fun / Medley / Hawkes talks
DAWE 40 / May '90 / Magic

☐ **IN THE UNCOMMON MARKET**
Bula / Silk lace / Asphalt jungle / Star crossed lovers / Getting sentimental over you / ESP (extra sensory perception) / Paris blues / Shepherd / Kinda Dukish
CD 2308247 / Apr '94 / Pablo

☐ **INCOMPARABLE, THE (Ellington, Duke Orchestra)**
Rockin' in rhythm / Such sweet thunder / Newport up / St. Louis blues / Walkin' and singin' the blues / Anatomy of a murder / El gato / Hank cinq (hank sank) / Jam with Sam / Things ain't what they used to be / Don't get around much anymore / Do nothin' 'til you hear from me / I've got it bad, and that ain't good / I'm beginning to see the light / Caravan / I let a song go out of my heart
DBCD 11 / Dec '88 / Dance Band Days

☐ **INDISPENSABLE DUKE ELLINGTON VOL.5 & 6, THE**
Koko / Bojangles / Pitter panther patter / Body and soul / Sophisticated lady / Jack the bear / Koko / Morning glory / Conga brava / Do nothin' 'til you hear from me / Bojangles / Cotton tail / Never no lament / Dusk / Portrait of Bert Williams / Blue goose / Harlem air shaft / At a Dixie roadside diner / All too soon / Rumpus in Richmond / Sepia panorama / In a mellow tone / Five o'clock whistle / Warm valley / Across the track blues / Chloe / Sidewalks of New York / Pitter panther patter / Body and soul / Sophisticated lady / Mr. J.B. Blues
ND 89750 / May '94 / Jazz Tribune

☐ **INDISPENSABLE DUKE ELLINGTON VOL.7 & 8, THE**
Take the 'A' train / Jumpin' punkins / John Hardy's wife / Blue serge / After all / Are you sticking / Just a sittin' and a rockin' / Giddybug gallop / Chocolate shake / I got it bad and that ain't good / Clementine / Brown skin gal / Jump for you / Five o'clock drag / Rocks in my bed / Bli-blip / Raincheck / I don't know what kind of blues I got / Chelsea bridge / Perdido / C jam blues / Moon mist / What am I here for / I don't mind / Someone / My little brown book / Main stem / Johnny come lately / Hayfoot strawfoot / Sentimental lady / Slip of the lip (can sink a ship) / Sherman shuffle
74321155242 / Jun '94 / Jazz Tribune

☐ **INDISPENSABLE DUKE ELLINGTON VOL.9 & 10, THE (The Small Groups)**
Daydream / Good Queen Bess / That's the blues, old man / Junior hop / Without a song / My Sunday gal / Mobile Bay / Linger awhile / Charlie the Chulo / Lament for Javanette / Lull at dawn / Ready Eddy / Dear old Southland / Solitude / Some Saturday / Subtle slough / Menelik, the Lion of Judah / Poor bubber / Squattyroo / Passion flower / Things ain't what they used to be / Going out the back way / Brown suede / Noir blue / C jam blues / June / Frankie and Johnny / Jumpin' room only / Tonk / Drawing room blues
74321115232 / Mar '94 / RCA

☐ **INDISPENSABLE DUKE ELLINGTON, THE**
74321155252 / Apr '94 / RCA

☐ **INTIMACY OF THE BLUES, THE (Ellington, Duke Small Bands)**
Intimacy of the blues / Out south / Tell me 'bout my baby / Kentucky Avenue / Near North / Soul country / Noon morning / Rockochet / Tippy-toeing through the jungle garden / Just a sittin' and a rockin' / All too soon
OJCCD 624 / Jun '96 / Original Jazz Classics

☐ **INTRODUCTION TO DUKE ELLINGTON 1927-1941, AN**
4024 / Sep '95 / Best Of Jazz

☐ **JACK THE BEAR**
AMSC 573 / Jun '96 / Avid

☐ **JAZZ AT THE PHILHARMONIC (Berlin 1965/Paris 1967) (Ellington, Duke Orchestra)**
Midriff / Ad lib on Nippon / Chelsea Bridge / Happy go lucky local / Blood count / Harmony in Harlem / Things ain't what they used to be / Drag / Rockin' in rhythm / Second portrait of the lion
PACD 5304 / Oct '97 / Pablo

☐ **JAZZ COCKTAIL (Ellington, Duke Orchestra)**
Stevedore stomp / Creole love call / It don't mean a thing if it ain't got that swing / Hot and bothered / Rose room / Old man blues / Jungle nights in Harlem / Tiger Bay / Sweet jazz o'mine / Mood indigo / Sing you sinners / Limehouse blues / Double check stomp / Swing low, sweet chariot / Jazz cocktail / Creole rhapsody
CDAJA 5024 / Oct '88 / Living Era

☐ **JAZZ COLLECTION (2CD Set)**
Take the 'A' train / Black and tan fantasy / Perdido / Rain check / Satin doll / Diminuendo in blue / Happy golucky local (part 1) / Happy go lucky local (part 2) / Flippant fury / Glory / Cool rock / Chinoiserie / Vancover lights / Things ain't what they used to be / Lullaby of birdland / Liza (All the clouds'll roll away) / Creole love call / Hy-ah Sue / Sophisticated lady / Caravan / C jam blues / Coffee and kisses / Johnny come lately / Honeysuckle rose / Theme for trambeam / VIP's boogie / Jam with Sam
24369 / Nov '97 / Laserlight

☐ **JAZZ GREATS**
Take the 'A' train / Mood indigo: *Davis, Kay* / I'm beginning to see the light / Sophisticated lady / I got it bad and that ain't good / Perdida / Solitude / I can't give you anything but love / Prelude to a kiss / Drawing room blues / Caravan / In a sentimental mood / It don't mean a thing if it ain't got that swing: *Sherrill, Joya & Kay Davis/Marie Ellington* / Lover man: *Cox, Marion* / Lotus blossom
74321499882 / 6 Oct '97 / RCA Victor

☐ **JAZZ MASTERS**
Take the 'A' train / La plus belle / Africaine / Flirtibird / Diminuendo in blue/Blow by blow / Loveless love / Going up / St. Louis blues / Stompy Jones / Caravan / Total jazz / Perdido / Jam with Sam / Rockin' in rhythm
5163382 / 5 May '98 / Verve

☐ **JAZZ MASTERS (Ellington, Duke Orchestra)**
Satin doll / Flamingo / Liza / In the mood / Things ain't what they used to be / Caravan / My old flame / Black and tan fantasy / Star dust / Flying home / Band call / Rockin' in rhythm / If I give my heart to you / In a sentimental mood / Harlem air shaft / Warm valley / One o'clock jump / Bakiff / Reflections in d / C jam blue
CDMFP 6298 / Mar '97 / Music For Pleasure

☐ **JAZZ PARTY**
4600592 / Jan '95 / Sony Jazz

☐ **JAZZ PORTRAITS (Ellington, Duke Orchestra)**
Take the 'A' train / Don't get around much anymore / Cotton tail / I got it bad and that ain't good / Conga brava / Do nothin' 'til you hear from me / Portrait of Bert Williams / Solitude / I let a song go out of my heart / Prelude to a kiss / Caravan / Merry go round / In a sentimental mood / In a mellow tone / Sophisticated lady / Koko / Harlem air shaft / Just a sittin' and a rockin'
CD 14505 / May '94 / Jazz Portraits

☐ **JUMP FOR JOY (The Genius Of Duke Ellington)**
CECD 8 / Jul '96 / Collector's Edition

☐ **JUMP FOR JOY**
JC 98001 / 26 May '98 / Jazz Classix

☐ **KEEP IT MOVIN'**
Dick's boogie / Skirts / Between some place goin' no place / Sittin' on a tree top / Venetian sunset / J for Johnny / Accentuate the positive / Stringin' the blues / Mexican bandit / Rooftop / Like dig / Wilt the stilt / Savoy non-stop / Dedicated to the Duke / Coffee mornin' / Keep it movin'
CDMT 015 / Oct '96 / Meteor

☐ **KEEP IT MOVIN'**
Sittin' on a treetop / Stringin' the blues / Creole love call / Mexican bandit / Between someplace and goin' no place / Ac-cent-tchu-ate the positive / Daydream / Skirts / Venetian sunset / Coffee mornin' / Midriff / Dick's boogie / Like dig / Dedicated to Duke / Jeep is jumpin' / Wilt the stilt / Keep it movin' / J for Johnny / Savoy non-stop / Roof top rhapsody
SUMCD 4198 / 11 May '98 / Summit

☐ **LATIN AMERICAN SUITE (Ellington, Duke Orchestra)**
OJCCD 469 / Mar '93 / Original Jazz Classics

☐ **LIVE AT MONTEREY 1960 (The Unheard Recordings Part 1) (Ellington, Duke Orchestra)**
Deep river/Take the 'A' train / Perdido / Overture: Nutcracker suite / Half the fun / Jeep's blues / Newport up / Sophisticated lady / Suite Thursday / Dance of the floreadores / Jam with Sam / Jones
DSTS 1008 / May '95 / Status

☐ **LIVE AT MONTEREY 1960 (The Unheard Recordings Part 2) (Ellington, Duke Orchestra & Cannonball Adderley Quintet)**
Big P / Blue Daniel / Chant / Old country / Dis here / Sunny side of the street / Goin' to Chicago / Sent for you yesterday / You can't run around / Red carpet
DSTS 1009 / May '95 / Status

☐ **LIVE AT NEWPORT 1958 (2CD Set) (Ellington, Duke Orchestra)**
Introduction / Take the 'A' train / Princess blue / Duke's place / Just scratchin' the surface / Happy reunion / Junie flip / Mr. Gentle and Mr. Cool / Jazz festival jazz / Feet bone / Hi fi fo fum / I got it bad and that ain't good / Bill Bailey, Won't you please come home / Won't you please come home / Prima bara dubla / El gato / Multicoloured blue / Introduction to Mahalia Jackson / Come Sunday / Keep your hands on the plow / Take the 'A' train / Jones
C2K 53584 / Oct '94 / Columbia

☐ **LIVE AT THE BLUE NOTE**
Take the 'A' train / Newport up / Haupe (Polly's theme) / Flirtibird / Pie Eye's blues / Almost cried / Dual fuel (dual filter) / Sophisticated lady / Mr. Gentle and Mr. Cool / El Gato / C Jam blues / Tenderly / Honeysuckle rose / Drawing room blues / Tonk / In a mellow tone / All of me / Things ain't what they used to be / Jeep's blues / Mood indigo / Perdido / Satin doll / A disarming visit / Medley
CDS 8286372 / Feb '94 / Roulette

☐ **LIVE AT THE RAINBOW GRILL (Ellington, Duke Octet)**
MCD 0492 / Nov '93 / Moon

☐ **LIVE AT THE SALLE PLEYEL**
JMY 10112 / Aug '91 / JMY

□ LIVE AT THE WHITNEY
Black and tan fantasy / Prelude to a kiss / Do nothin' 'til you hear from me / Caravan / Meditation / Mural from two perspectives / Sophisticated lady / Solitude / Soda fountain rag / New world a-coming / Amour, amour / Soul soothing beach / Lotus blossom / Flamingo / Le sucrier velors / Night shepherd / C jam blues / Mood indigo / I'm beginning to see the light / Dancers in love / Kixx / Satin doll
IMP 11732 / Oct '95 / Impulse Jazz

□ LIVE IN PARIS 1959
Black and tan fantasy / Creole love call / Mooche / Newport up / Sonet in search of amour / Kinda duckish/Rockin in rhythm / El gato / All of me / Won't you come home, Bill Bailey / Walkin' and singin' the blues / VIP boogie / Jam with Sam / Skin deep / Ellington medley
CDAFF 777 / Sep '91 / Affinity

□ MASTERPIECES BY ELLINGTON
4694072 / Jan '95 / Sony Jazz

□ MASTERS OF JAZZ (2CD Set)
R2CD 8005 / 13 Apr '98 / Deja Vu

□ MASTERS OF JAZZ VOL.6 (Ellington, Duke Orchestra)
STCD 4106 / Feb '89 / Storyville

□ MASTERS, THE (2CD Set)
EDMCD 010 / 24 Nov '97 / Eagle

□ MELLOW
Do nothin' 'til you hear from me / Mood indigo / Chelsea bridge / Morning glory / Sophisticated lady / Blue serge / Black and tan fantasy / Perdido / 'A' train / In a mellotone / Moon mist / I got it bad and that ain't good / Solitude / Creole love call / Prelude to a kiss / Dusk / Midriff / Across the track blues / Sentimental lady / Esquire Swank / In a sentimental mood / Dusk
74321487312 / May '97 / Camden

□ MEMORIAL ALBUM, THE
UAE 34102 / 27 Apr '98 / Memorial Album

□ MONEY JUNGLE
Money jungle / Fleurette Africaine (the African flower) / Very special / Warm valley / REM blues / Little Max / Wig wise / Switchblade / Caravan / Backward country boy blues / Solitude
CDP 7463982 / Mar '95 / Blue Note

□ MOOD INDIGO
CDSGP 087 / Sep '94 / Prestige

□ MOOD INDIGO (The Best Of Duke Ellington)
TRTCD 194 / Jun '95 / TrueTrax

□ MOOD INDIGO
HADCD 193 / Nov '95 / Javelin

□ MR. ELLINGTON
BN 011 / Apr '98 / Blue Nite

□ NEW ORLEANS SUITE
Blues for New Orleans / Bourbon Street jingling jollies / Portrait of Louis Armstrong / Thanks for the beautiful land on the delta / Portrait of Wellman Braud / Second line / Portrait of Sidney Bechet / Aristocracy of Jean Lafitte / Portrait of Mahalia Jackson
7567813762 / Mar '93 / Atlantic

□ NEW YORK CONCERTS, THE (Ellington, Duke Orchestra)
Take the "a" train / Satin doll / Caravan / Skillipoop / Into each life some rain must fall / Carolina shout / Tonk / Things ain't what they used to be / Melancholia-reflections in d / Little african flower / Bird of paradise / Single petal of a rose
MM 65122 / Oct '96 / Music Masters

□ NEWPORT 1958
4684362 / Jan '95 / Sony Jazz

□ PASSION FLOWER
MCD 0742 / Aug '95 / Moon

□ PIANIST, THE
Don Juan / Slow blues / Looking glass / Shepherd / Tap dancer's blues / Sam Woodyard's blues / Duck amok / Never stop remembering Bill / Fat mess
OJCCD 717 / Aug '96 / Original Jazz Classics

□ PIANO IN THE BACKGROUND (Ellington, Duke Orchestra)
4684042 / Jan '95 / Sony Jazz

□ PIANO IN THE FOREGROUND (Ellington, Duke Orchestra)
4749302 / Jan '95 / Sony Jazz

□ PLAY THE BLUES BACK TO BACK (Remastered) (Ellington, Duke & Johnny Hodges)
5214042 / Oct '97 / Verve Master Edition

□ PLAYING THE BLUES 1927-1939
BLE 592322 / Nov '92 / Black & Blue

□ POPULAR DUKE ELLINGTON, THE
Take the 'A' train / I got it bad and that ain't good / Perdido / Mood indigo / Black and tan fantasy / Twitch / Solitude / Do nothin' 'til you hear from me / Mooche / Sophisticated lady / Creole love call
09026687052 / Mar '97 / RCA Victor

□ PORTRAIT OF DUKE ELLINGTON, A
GALE 405 / May '97 / Gallerie

□ PRELUDE TO A KISS (Ellington, Duke & Dee Dee Bridgewater/Hollywood Bowl Orch.)
Mood indigo / Daydream / Come Sunday / Bli blip / Solitude / Fleurette Africaine / Midnight indigo / I'm beginning to see the light / Prelude to a kiss / Caravan / Night creature
4467172 / Nov '96 / Philips

□ QUINTESSENCE, THE (1926-1941/2CD Set)
FA 204 / Oct '96 / Fremeaux

□ RECOLLECTIONS OF THE BIG BAND ERA
Minnie the moocher / For dancers only / It's a lonesome old town / Cherokee / Midnight sun will never set / Let's get together / I'm getting sentimental over you / Chant of the weed / Ciribiribin / Contrasts / Christopher Columbus / Auld lang syne / Tuxedo junction / Smoke rings / Artistry in rhythm / Waltz you saved for me / Woodchopper's ball / Sentimental journey / When it's sleepy time down South / One o'clock jump / Goodbye / Sleep, sleep, sleep / Rhapsody in blue
7567900432 / Feb '94 / Atlantic

□ REMEMBERING DUKE ELLINGTON (RTE Concert Orchestra)
8990053 / Oct '95 / Naxos

□ RING DEM BELLS
Mooche / Ring dem bells / Frustration / Colortura / Rose of the Rio Grande / Love you madly / Harlem speaks / Caravan / Primpin' at the prom / Jam with Sam / One O'Clock jump / Take the 'A' train / Crosstown / Perdido / Pretty woman / 920 special / Moon mist / Just squeeze me / Prelude to a kiss (medley) / Tootie for cootie
GRF 039 / Jun '92 / Tring

□ ROCKIN' IN RHYTHM VOL.1 (Ellington, Duke Orchestra)
Shoe shine boy / Trumpet in spades / Solitude / Happy as the day is long / Cootie's concerto / In a jam / Uptown beat / Yearning for love / Love is like a cigarette / Exposition swing / Showboat shuffle / Barney's concerto / It was a sad night in Harlem / East St. Louis toodle-oo / Mooche / It don't mean a thing if it ain't got that swing / Rockin' in rhythm / Black and tan fantasy
CDAJA 5057 / Nov '88 / Living Era

□ ROCKIN' IN RONNIE'S (Echoes Of Ellington)
JHCD 050 / Mar '97 / Ronnie Scott's Jazz House

□ SARATOGA SWING (Ellington, Duke Cotton Club Orchestra)
Take the 'A' train / Perdido / Five o'clock whistle / Sidewalks of New York / At a Dixie roadside diner / Sophisticated lady / Harlem air shaft / Me and you / Concerto for Cootie / My greatest mistake / Johnny come lately / Sepia panorama / Cotton tail / Don't get around much anymore / Blue goose / C jam blues / Pitter panther patter / Raincheck / Hayfoot strawfoot / Moon mist / Morning glory / Saratoga swing
RAJCD 842 / Jan '97 / Empress

□ SECOND SACRED CONCERT
Praise god / Supreme being / Heaven / Something about believing / Almighty god / Shepherd (who watches over the night flock) / It's freedom / Meditation / Biggest and busiest intersection / T.g.t.t. / Praise god and dance
PCD 24045 / Nov '95 / Prestige

□ SIDE BY SIDE (Ellington, Duke & Johnny Hodges)
Stompy Jones / Squeeze me / Big shoe / Going up / Just a memory / Let's fall in love / Ruin / Bend one / You need go rock
8215782 / Sep '93 / Verve

□ SONNY LESTER COLLECTION
CDC 9066 / Nov '93 / LRC

□ SOPHISTICATED LADY
Take the 'A' train / I got it bad and that ain't good / Chelsea Bridge / Perdido / C Jam blues / Caravan / Mood indigo / It don't mean a thing if it ain't got that swing / Sophisticated lady / Things ain't what they used to be (time's a wasting) / Just squeeze me / Concerto for Cootie / Never no lament / Just a-settin' and a-rockin' / Prelude to a kiss / In a sentimental mood / I let a song go out of my heart / Solitude / St. Louis blues
09026685162 / Oct '96 / RCA Victor

□ SOPHISTICATED LADY
9026685162 / Jul '96 / RCA

□ SUCH SWEET THUNDER
4691402 / Jan '95 / Sony Jazz

□ TAKE THE 'A' TRAIN
Taffy twist / Flirtibird / Smada / What am I here for / Take the 'A' train / I'm gonna go fishin' / Boo-dah / Black and tan fantasy / Feeling of jazz / Jump for joy / I let a song out of my heart / Don't get around much anymore
EMPRCD 565 / May '95 / Emporio

□ TAKE THE 'A' TRAIN
MU 5035 / Oct '92 / Musketeer

□ TAKE THE 'A' TRAIN
Mooche / Ring dem bells / Frustration / Colorotura / Rose of the Rio Grande / Love you madly / Caravan / Primpin' at the prom / Jam with Sam / One o'clock jump / Take the 'A' train / Crosstown / Perdido / Pretty woman / 9.20 special / Moon mist / Just squeeze me / Medley / Do nothin' 'til you hear from me / Tootie for cootie
QED 070 / Nov '96 / Tring

□ TAKE THE 'A' TRAIN
BN 012 / Apr '98 / Blue Nite

□ TAKE THE 'A' TRAIN 1933-1941 (Ellington, Duke Orchestra)
Take the 'a' train / Don't get around much anymore / Cotton tail / I got it bad and that ain't good / Conga brava / Concerto for cootie (do nothing till you hear from me) / A portrait of bert williams / Solitude / I let a song go out of my heart / Prelude to a kiss / Caravan / Merry go round / In a sentimental mood / In a mellotone / Sophisticated lady / Ko ko / Harlem air shaft / Just a sittin' and a rockin'
CD 56012 / Aug '94 / Jazz Roots

□ THIS IS JAZZ (Duke Ellington Plays Standards)
Take the 'A' train / Tenderly / St. Louis blues / Stormy weather / I can't get started / On the sunny side of the street / Autumn leaves / I can't believe that you're in love with me / Mood indigo / Willow weep for me / Sophisticated lady / Body and soul / Satin doll
CK 65056 / 4 May '98 / Sony Jazz

□ TIMON OF ATHENS
Black and tan fantasy (overture) / Timon's theme / First banquet / Toasts / Bonding of friendship (dinner music) / Skillipoop-the moochie (dance) / Creole love call - timon's theme (compulsive giving) / Market crash / Banquet theme (false friends) / Revolutionary march / Creditors draggin' blues / Senate-second banquet / Creole love call (soured for the second banquet) / Entr'acte / Gold / Ring dem bells (alcibiades' camp) / Revolutionary march / Poet and painter / Timon's theme / Revolutionary march-timon's theme (finale and curtain call
VSD 5466 / Mar '94 / Varese Sarabande

□ TRIBUTE TO DUKE ELLINGTON (Live At The Montreux Jazz Festival) (Various Artists)
BLCD 760208 / Nov '95 / Black Lion

□ TRIBUTE TO DUKE ELLINGTON VOL.1, A (Various Artists)
Take the 'A' train / Satin doll / I'm beginning to see the light / It don't mean a thing / In my solitude / Don't get around much anymore / Satin doll / Jeep is jumpin' / Blue light / Sophisticated lady
8747012 / Jul '96 / DA Music

□ TRIBUTE TO DUKE ELLINGTON, A (Hendricks, Barbara & Monty Alexander Trio)
CDC 5553462 / Nov '96 / EMI Classics

□ TRIPLE GOLD (3CD Set)
Mood indigo / It don't mean a thing / I let a song go out of my heart / Transblucency / Jack the bear / Morning glory / Jump for joy / Louisiana / Sweet mama / Warm valley / Ring dem bells / Chelsea bridge / Misty morning / Slap happy / Creole rhapsody / Sergeant was shy / Showboat shuffle / Raincheck / Awful sad / Solitude / Take the 'A' train / Concerto for cootie / Double check stomp / Cottontail / Slippery horn / Never no lament / Azure / Saddest tale / Sweet chariot / Daybreak express / Harlem flat blues / Lightnin' / Stepping into swing society / Bojangles / Doin' the voom voom / Yearning for love / Rent party blues / Battle of swing / Lost in meditation / Moonglow / Caravan / St. Louis blues / Main stem / John Hardy's wife / Bundle of blues / Sophisticated lady / Ducky wucky / Subtle lament / Portrait of Bert Williams / Harmony in Harlem / Serenade to Sweeden / Blue serge / Blues with a feeling / Trumpet in spades / It was a sad night in Harlem / Hot and bothered / Jungle jamboree / Drop me off in Harlem / Moon mist / In a mellotone
TG 333 / 8 Sep '97 / Start

□ TWO GREAT CONCERTS IN EUROPE
Take the 'A' train / Caravan / Do nothin' 'til you hear from me / Fancy dance / Hawk talks / Swamp drum / Main stem / Tattooed bride / Threesome / Take the 'A' train (version) / Satin doll/Sophisticated lady / Meow, shorted encore / I got it bad and that ain't good / Harmong in Harlem / Things ain't what they used to be / Perdido / New concerto for Cootie / Carolina shout
302284 / Dec '89 / Accord

□ TWO ON ONE (Ellington, Duke & Count Basie)
It don't mean a thing (if it ain't got that swing) / Prelude to a kiss / Mooche / In a sentimental mood / Concerto for cootie (do nothing till you hear from me) / Solitude / Take the 'a' train / Black and tan fantasy / Sophisticated lady / Drop me off in harlem / One o'clock jump / Pannasie stomp / Blue and sentimental / Honeysuckle rose / Roseland shuffle / Swinging at the daisy chain / You can depend on me / Cherokee (parts 1 and 2) / Jive at five / Jumpin' at the woodside
CDTT 7 / Apr '94 / Charly

□ UNKNOWN SESSION
Everything but you / Black beauty / All too soon / Something to live for / Mood indigo / Creole blues / Don't you know I care (or don't you care to) / Flower is a lovesome thing / Mighty like the blues / Tonight I shall sleep / Dual highway / Blues
4720842 / Nov '93 / Columbia

□ YALE CONCERT (Ellington, Duke Orchestra)
Little purple flower (parts 1 and / Put-tin / A chromatic love affair / Boola boola / Warm valley-drag (a johnny hodges medley) / Salome / Swamp goo / Up jump / Take the 'a' train
OJCCD 664 / Feb '92 / Original Jazz Classics

□ YOUNG DUKE 1927-1940, THE (Ellington, Duke Orchestra)
Jazz cocktail / Drop me off in Harlem / Slippery horn / Blue ramble / Merry go round / In the shade of the old apple tree / Raisin' the rent / Blue tune / Kissin' my baby goodnight / Bundle of blues / Stompy Jones / Baby, when you ain't there / Blue feeling / Rockin' chair / East St. Louis Toodle-oo / Rockin' in rhythm / Awful sad / Jazz convulsions / Dusk / Blue goose / Girl in my dreams tries to look like you / Flamingo
PASTCD 9771 / Jan '92 / Flapper

Elliot Green

□ UNITED STATES
Come on / X / Red Rum / Lonely rider / Crying screaming / Rectify / Runaway / Seed about to happen / Push I needed / It's alright we love you / Reflections dawn to dusk
AMUSE 36CD / 30 Mar '98 / Playtime

Elliot, Richard

□ JUMPIN' OFF
All night / If you want my love / Here and now / Tell me about it / Slow burn / In the groove / One last kiss / Nobody knows
8382512 / 19 Jan '98 / Metro Blue

Elliot, Tim

□ TIM ELLIOT & THE TROUBLEMAKERS (Elliot, Tim & Troublemakers)
Cat squirrel / Ridin' the freights / Hobo blues / Good morning blues / Judgement day / Come on in my kitchen / Calling out to jesus / Down on the farm / Chain gang bound / I'm gonna tell god all my sorrows / Evil / Rollin' and tumblin' / Thunder and lightnin' / Sally mae / Morning train / Cow cow blues / Me and the devil
TRCD 9918 / Nov '93 / Tramp

Elliott

□ US SONGS
REV 068CD / 20 Jul '98 / Revelation

Elliott, G.H.

□ GOLDEN AGE OF MUSIC HALL, THE
I'se a-waiting for yer Josie / If the man on the moon were a coon / There's a little cupid in the moon / Lou, Sue, Mary, Dinah / Chocolate Major / Hello Susie Green / On the Mississippi / She has such dreamy eyes / My southern maid / Waiting / Way down yonder / My picture girl / You'd never know that old home town of mine / When the sun goes down in dixie / Give her a great big kiss for me / My Michaelmas daisy / If you're going back to dixie / Mississippi honeymoon / In Carolina / Tickle the keys of your silvery saxophone / Maybe it's the moon / My gal's given me the go-bye / That's just like heaven to me / Sue, Sue, Sue / I used to sigh for the silvery moon
PASTCD 7033 / Jan '94 / Flapper

Elliott, Jack

□ ESSENTIAL RAMBLIN' JACK ELLIOT, THE (Elliott, Ramblin' Jack)
Roving gambler / Will the circle be unbroken / Diamant Joe / Guabi Guabi / Sowing on the mountain / Roll on Buddy / 1913 massacre / House of the rising sun / Shade of the old apple tree / Black snake / Portland Town / More pretty girls / San Francisco bay blues / Buffalo skinners / Sadie Brown / Don't think twice it's alright / Blind Lemon Jefferson / Ramblin' round your city / Talkin' Columbia / Tennessee stud / Night herding song / Love sick blues / I belong to Glasgow
VCD 89 / Jun '98 / Vanguard

□ FRIENDS OF MINE (Elliott, Ramblin' Jack)
Rex's blues / Me and Billy The Kid / Louise / Walls of red wing / Hard travellin' / He was a friend of mine / Ridin' down the canyon / Last letter / Dark as a dungeon / Friend of the devil / Reason to believe / Bleeker street blues
HCD 8089 / 16 Mar '98 / Hightone

□ HARD TRAVELLIN' (Songs by Woody Guthrie & Others)
Hard travellin' / Grand coulee dam / New York Town / Tom Joad / Howdido / Dust bowl blues / This land is your land / Pretty Boy Floyd / Philadelphia lawyer / Talking Columbia blues / Dust storm disaster / Riding in my car / 1913 massacre / So long (it's been good to know yuh) / Sadie Brown / East Virginia blues / I belong to glasgow / Cuckoo / Rollin' in my sweet baby's arms / South coast / San Francisco Bay blues / Last letter / Candy man / Tramp on the street / Railroad Bill
CDWIK 952 / Aug '90 / Big Beat

□ KEROUAC'S LAST DREAM (Elliott, Ramblin' Jack)
TUT 72163 / Jan '94 / Wundertute
APRCD 1021 / Nov '97 / Appleseed

□ ME AND BOBBY MCGEE
ROUCD 0368 / Nov '95 / Rounder

□ RAMBLIN' JACK
TSCD 477 / Feb '96 / Topic

□ SOUTH COAST (Elliott, Ramblin' Jack)
RHRCD 59 / Jul '95 / Red House

Elliott, Missy

□ SUPA DUPA FLY
Busta's intro / Hit 'em wit da he / Sock it 2 me / Rain (Supa dupa fly) / Beep me 911 / They don't wanna fuck wit me / Pass da blunt / Bite our style / Friendly skies / Best friends / Don't be comin' (in my face) / Izzy izzy ahh / Why you hurt me / I'm talkin' (the biz) / Gettaway / Busta's outro / Missy's finale
7559620622 / Jul '97 / East West

Elliott, Paul & Glen

☐ APRIL PAVES THE WAY
April paves the way / Ballybay / Red Rose cafe / Peat bog soldiers / Monto / Tarry Flynn / Murshin Durkin / Tipperary / Between us both / Banks of the roses / Shoals of herring / Patrick was a gentleman / Happy go lucky / Blarney roses / Song about nothing / Wild colonial boy / Galway races / Tell me ma / Walk on talk on / Stop giving out / Roots
FSCD 44 / Jun '97 / Folksound

Ellis, Alton

☐ BEST OF ALTON ELLIS
SOCD 8019 / Mar '95 / Studio One

☐ CRY TOUGH
CDHB 106 / May '93 / Heartbeat

☐ DUKE REID COLLECTION
RNCD 2083 / Dec '94 / Rhino

☐ MORE ALTON ELLIS
JGMCD 003072 / 22 Dec '97 / Joe Gibbs

☐ SOUL GROOVER
Dance crasher / Girl I've got a date / Rocksteady / Duke of Earl / All my tears (come rolling) / Ain't that loving you / Why birds follow spring / Oowee baby(Baby I love you) / How can I / Willow tree / My time is the right time / Message / Trying to reach my goal / If I had the right / Give me your love / Breaking up / Personality / Diana / Remember that Sunday / What does it take to win your love / You've made me so very happy / I'll be waiting / Soul groover / Lord deliver us / You are mine / All that we need is love
CDTRL 385 / Jul '97 / Trojan

☐ SUNDAY COMING
CDHB 3511 / Feb '95 / Heartbeat

☐ VALLEY OF DECISION
CDSGP 071 / Sep '94 / Prestige

Ellis, Brad

☐ CHICAGO AND ALL THAT JAZZ (Ellis, Brad Group)
VSD 5798 / Mar '97 / Varese Sarabande

Ellis, Don

☐ DON ELLIS
I'll remember April / Sweet and lovely / Out of nowhere / All things you are / You stepped out of a dream / My funny valentine / I love you / Just one of those things / Johnny come lately / Angel eyes / Lover / Form / Sallie / How time passes / Simplex one
CD 53262 / Jan '96 / Giants Of Jazz

☐ HOW TIME PASSES
How time passes / Sally / Simplex one / Waste / Improvisational suite
CCD 9004 / Feb '97 / Candid

☐ OUT OF NOWHERE
Sweet and lovely / My funny valentine / I love you / I'll remember April / Just one of those things / You stepped out of a dream / All the things you are / Out of nowhere / Just one of those things / I love you
CCD 9032 / Feb '97 / Candid

Ellis, Herb

☐ DOGGIN' AROUND (Ellis, Herb & Red Mitchell)
CCD 4372 / Apr '89 / Concord Jazz

☐ EVENING WITH HERB ELLIS, AN
JFCD 019 / Apr '98 / Jazz Focus

☐ JAZZ MASTERS, THE (Ellis, Herb/Ray Brown/Serge Ermoll)
AIM 1039CD / Jun '95 / Aim

☐ SOFT WINDS 1946-1996 (Ellis, Herb & Lou Carter/Johnny Frigo)
CRD 342 / May '97 / Chiaroscuro

☐ TEXAS SWINGS
JR 10022 / Apr '94 / Justice

☐ TOGETHER (Ellis, Herb & Stuff Smith)
378052 / Jan '96 / Koch

☐ TWO FOR THE ROAD (Ellis, Herb & Joe Pass)
Love for sale / Am I blue / Seven come eleven / Guitar blues / Oh lady be good / Cherokee (concept 1) / Cherokee (concept 2) / Gee baby ain't I good to you / Try a little tenderness / I found a new baby / Angel eyes
OJCCD 726 / Jun '94 / Original Jazz Classics

☐ WINDFLOWER (Ellis, Herb & Remo Palmier)
CCD 4056 / Jul '96 / Concord Jazz

Ellis, Hortense

☐ HITS FROM STUDIO ONE AND MORE
RN 7035 / 23 Feb '98 / Rhino

Ellis, John

☐ ACRYLIC
OPT 0041CD / Apr '97 / Optic Nerve

☐ DANCIN' WI' CLAYMORES (Ellis, John & His Highland Country Band)
Twa bonnie reels / Pipe jig and march / GS Manclennan selection / Folk waltz / Grand march / Eva three step / Slow air and march / Strip the willow / Mackay's music medley / Pipe march / Locl Leven castle (Reel set) / March, strathspey and reel / Gaelic waltzes / Polka / Highland fair (jig set) / Highland hornpipes / Gay gordons / Braes of breadalbane / Queens bridge (reel set)
LCOM 5210 / Mar '92 / Lismor

☐ FIRE IN THE KILT (Ellis, John & His Highland Country Band)
Grand march / Pipe march / Strip the willow / Waltz, strathspey and pipe reel / Fiddle hornpipes / Fife hunt / Gaelic waltzes / Two pipe marches / Pipe hornpipe / Highland lass / Orcadian polkas / Old fashioned waltz / Two step-Canadian jigs / Hornpipe and pipe reel / Scottish waltz / March, strathspey and reel / Gay Gordons
LCOM 5158 / Feb '97 / Lismor

☐ REEL KICK, A (Ellis, John & His Highland Country Band)
Gates of Edinburgh / Quaker jig / Gaelic waltz / Polka / Eight men of Moidart / March, strathspey and reel / Highland Schottische / Pipe tunes / Hornpipes / Pipe marches
LCOM 5120 / Oct '96 / Lismor

Ellis, Lisle

☐ ELEVATIONS
VICTOCD 027 / Oct '94 / Victo

Ellis, Osian

☐ CLYMAU CYTGERDD/DIVERSIONS
Caneuon plant / Tri darn byrfyfyr / Clymau cytgerdd i ddwy delyn / Consierto i'r delyn / Canu penillion / Gavotte / Caniadau llanelwy / Sonata yn f leiaf / Caneuon atgof
SCD 4038 / Jun '89 / Sain

Ellis, Paul

☐ CARNIVAL OF VOICES, A
CDPH 1191 / Aug '96 / Philo

☐ STORIES
CDPH 1181 / Oct '95 / Philo

Ellis, Steve

☐ LOVE THAT'S EVERYTHING
HADCD 210 / Jul '96 / Javelin

Ellis, Tinsley

☐ COOL ON IT (Ellis, Tinsley & Heartfixers)
Drivin' woman / Cool on it / Hong Kong Mississippi / Second thoughts / Sailor's grave on the prairie / Greenwood chainsaw boogie / Tulane / Time to quit / Sugaree / Wild weekend
ALCD 3905 / May '93 / Alligator

☐ FANNING THE FLAMES
Leavin' here / Pawnbroker / Loneliness is here to stay / Put me where you want me / Born in Georgia / Fender blender / Deaf, dumb, crippled and blind / So many tears / Must be the devil / Dangling by a thread / Mr. night time
ALCD 4778 / May '93 / Alligator

☐ FIRE IT UP
Diggin' my own grave / Just dropped in / Standing on the edge of love / Soulful / Are you sorry / I walk alone / Change your mind / Break my rule / One sunny day / If that's how he loves you / Look what you done / Everyday
ALCD 4852 / May '97 / Alligator

☐ GEORGIA BLUE
Can't you lie / You picked a good time / Crime of passion / Double eyed whammy / Look ka py py / Free manwells / Texas stomp / I've made nights by myself / Hot potato / She wants to sell my monkey / As the years go passing by / Lucky lot
ALCD 4765 / Apr '93 / Alligator

☐ STORM WARNING
To the devil for a dime / Cut you loose / Quitter never wins / Panhead / Next miss wrong / Early in the morning / When I howl / Side tracked / Wanted man / Sun is shining / Bush doctor / Mercy mercy mercy
ALCD 4823 / Oct '94 / Alligator

☐ TROUBLE TIME
Highway man / Hey hey baby / Sign of the blues / What have I done wrong / Big chicken / Axe / Come morning / Restless heart / Bad dream No.108 / Hulk / Now I'm gone / Red dress
ALCD 4805 / May '93 / Alligator

Ellis, Tony

☐ DIXIE BANNER
Dixie banner / Stephen / One rose / Sally ann / Barefoot boys / Little brown dog waltz / Big bad red / Father's pride / Rocky road to kansas / Old friends / Cactus reel / Courtner's country ham / Doc mongle's blues / My sweet highland girl / Peninsula / Beaver creek
FF 444CD / Apr '94 / Flying Fish

☐ FAREWELL MY HOME (Ellis, Tony & Bill)
Rain on the water / Merrywang / T-model Ford / Hartford's waltz / Farewell my home / Montana march / Wild fox / Cherry blossom waltz / Red dog / Kate bride of Matt / Snow camp / Wind chimes and nursery rhymes / Going to the country fair / Straw dolls / Wade's dixieliner special railroad blues no.9 / My Mama loves me / Uncle Shorty / Johnny come-a-running / Trail of tears / Dawson George / One horned goat / Hangman's song / Come thy fount of every blessing
FF 70620 / Jul '97 / Flying Fish

Ellwood, William

☐ NATURAL SELECTIONS
Half moon / First love / Laughing earth / Summer words / Elysain fields / Simpatico / Barefoot dance / Blue period / Night calling / Spirit river / Cotton wood / Gymnopedie No.1
ND 61049 / Aug '95 / Narada

Elman, Ziggy

☐ CLASSICS 1938-1939
CLASSICS 900 / Nov '96 / Classics

☐ ZIGGY ELMAN AND FRIENDS - 1947 (Elman, Ziggy & His Orchestra)
CCD 70 / '92 / Circle

Elmerhassel

☐ BILLYOUS
Dehydration / Nearing home / Business as usual / Calm and collected / Bare back / Pert host / Safeish / Simian / Almost at one / Exposure / Common flowers
DPROMCD 18 / Mar '94 / Dirter Promotions

ELO

☐ AFTERGLOW (3CD Set)
10538 Overture / Mr. Radio / Kuiama / In old England town (Boogie no.2) / Mama / Roll over beethoven / Bluebird is dead / Ma-ma-ma belle / Showdown / Can't get it out of my head / Boy blue / One summer dream / Evil woman / Tightrope / Strange magic / Do ya / Nightrider / Waterfall / Roackarial / Telephone line / So fine / Livin' thing / Mr. Blue Sky / Sweet is the night / Turn to stone / Sweet talkin' woman / Steppin' out / Midnight blue / Don't bring me down / Twilight / Julie don't live here / Shine a little love / When time stood still / Rain is falling / Bouncer / Hello my old friend / Hold on tight / Four little diamonds / Mandalay / Buildings have eyes / So serious / Matter of fact / No way out / Getting to the point / Destination unkown / Rock 'n' roll is king
CD 46090 / Jul '94 / Legacy

☐ ALL TIME GREATEST
Standing in the rain / Evil woman / Showdown / Can't get it out of my head / Livin' things / Mr. Blue Sky / Telephone line / Strange magic / Sweet talking woman / Confusion / Do ya / Rockaria / Roll over Beethoven / Hold on tight / Turn to stone / Rock and roll is king / Don't bring me down
RM 1546 / Jun '97 / BR Music

☐ BALANCE OF POWER
Heaven only knows / So serious / Getting to the point / Secret lives / Is it alright / Sorrow about to fall / Without someone / Calling America / Endless lies / Send it
4685762 / Jun '91 / Epic

☐ BEST OF ELO II LIVE, THE (ELO II)
Standing in the rain / Evil woman / Can't get it out of my head / Do ya / Rockaria / Mr Blue Sky / Telephone line / Strange magic / Sweet talkin' woman / Roll over Beethoven / Livin' thing / Last train to London / Rock and roll is King / Turn to stone / Hold on tight / Showdown
3036000722 / Apr '97 / Carlton

☐ DEFINITIVE COLLECTION, THE
Showdown / Eldorado overture / Can't get it out of my head / Evil woman / Strange magic / Livin' thing / So fine / Rockaria / Sweet talking woman / Turn to stone / Mr. Blue sky / Don't bring me down / Shine a little love / Diary of Horace Wimp / All over the world / Twilight / Rock 'n' roll is king / Hold on tight / Secret messages / Definitive collection
4724212 / 13 Jul '98 / Epic

☐ DISCOVERY
Shine a little love / Confusion / Need her love / Diary of Horace Wimp / Last train to London / Midnight blue / On the run / Wishing / Don't bring me down
4500832 / Jun '91 / Epic

☐ DISCOVERY/OUT OF THE BLUE/TIME (3CD Set)
Shine a little love / Confusion / Need her love / Diary of Horace Wimp / Last train to London / Midnight blue / On the run / Wishing / Don't bring me down / Turn to stone / It's over / Sweet talkin' woman / Across the border / Night in the city / Starlight / Believe me now / Steppin' out / Whale / Standin' in the rain / Big wheels / Summer and lightning / Mr. Blue Sky / Sweet is the night / Birmingham blues / Wild West hero / Jungle / Prlogue / Twilight / Yours truly 2095 / Ticket to the moon / Way life's meant to be / Another heart breaks / Rain is falling / From the end of the world / Lights go down / Hear is the news / 21st century man / Hold on tight / Epilogue
4853402 / 3 Nov '97 / Epic

☐ ELDORADO
Eldorado overture / Can't get it out of my head / Boy blue / Laredo tornado / Poorboy (The Greenwood) / Mr. Kingdom / Nobody's child / Illusions in G Major / Eldorado / Eldorado (finale)
4768312 / May '94 / Epic

☐ ELDORADO/NEW WORLD RECORD/ OUT OF THE BLUE (3CD Set)
4722672 / Oct '92 / Epic

☐ GOLD COLLECTION, THE
10538 Overture / Mr. Radio / All over the world / Look at me now / Manhattan rumble / In old England town (boogie no.2) / Ma ma belle / Roll over Beethoven / Battle of Marston Moor / Queen of the hours / Showdown / First movement (Jumping biz) / Whisper in the night / Momma
CDGOLD 1002 / Mar '96 / EMI Gold

☐ GREATEST HITS VOL.1
Telephone line / Evil woman / Livin' thing / Can't get it out of my head / Showdown / Turn to stone / Rockaria / Sweet talkin' woman / Ma-ma-ma belle / Strange magic / Mr. Blue sky
4503572 / 3 Aug '98 / Epic

☐ GREATEST HITS VOL.2
Rock 'n' roll is King / Hold on tight / All over the world / Wild West hero / Diary of Horace Wimp / Shine a little love / Confusion / Ticket to the moon / Don't bring me down / I'm alive / Last to train / Don't walk away / Here is the news / Calling America / Twilight / Secret messages
4719562 / Jul '93 / Epic

☐ LIVE AT WEMBLEY
Intro: *Curtis, Tony* / Standing in the rain / Night in the city / Turn to stone / Tight rope / Telephone line / Rock aria / Wild west hero / Show down / Sweet talking woman / Mr. Blue Sky / Ma-ma-ma belle / Living thing / Roll over Beethoven
EAMCD 039 / 28 Mar '98 / Eagle

☐ LIVE AT WINTERLAND
Fire / Poker / Nightrider / Showdown / Strange magic / 10538 overture / Evil woman / Ma-ma-ma belle / Roll over Beethoven
EAMCD 038 / 30 Mar '98 / Eagle

☐ NIGHT THE LIGHTS WENT ON (IN LONG BEACH), THE
Daybreaker / Showdown / Day tripper / 10538 Overture / Mik's solo / Orange blossom special / In the hall of the mountain king / Great balls of fire / Roll over Beethoven
4911032 / 11 May '98 / Columbia

☐ ONE NIGHT (Live In Australia/2CD Set) (ELO II)
Standing in the rain / Evil woman / Don't wanna / Showdown / Can't get you out of my head / Whiskey girl / Livin' thing / One more tomorrow / Mr. Blue Sky / Telephone line / Ain't necessarily so / Fox / Strange magic / Sweet talking woman / Confusion / Rockaria / Roll over Beethoven / All fall down / Witness / 1000 eyes / Hold on tight / Turn to stone / Rock 'n' roll is king / Last train to London / Don't bring me down
SPV 08944072 / Sep '96 / SPV

☐ ONE NIGHT IN AUSTRALIA LIVE VOL.1
Standing in the rain / Evil woman / Don't wanna / Showdown / Can't get you out of my head / Whiskey girl / Livin' girl / One more tomorrow / Mr. blue sky / Telephone line / Ain't necessarily so / Fox
30132 / Oct '97 / Go On Deluxe

☐ ONE NIGHT IN AUSTRALIA LIVE VOL.2
Strange magic / Sweet talking woman / Confusion / Do ya / Rockaria / Roll over Beethoven / All fall down / Witness / 1,000 Eyes / Hold on tight / Turn to stone / Rock and roll is king / Last train to London / Don't bring me down
30142 / Oct '97 / Go On Deluxe

☐ OUT OF THE BLUE
Turn to stone / It's over / Sweet talkin' woman / Across the border / Night in the city / Starlight / Jungle / Believe me now / Steppin' out / Standing in the rain / Summer and lightning / Mr. Blue sky / Sweet is the night / Whale / Wild West hero
4508852 / 27 Jul '98 / Epic

☐ POWER OF A MILLION LIGHTS (ELO II)
96125 ULT / Aug '94 / Ultra Pop

☐ SECRET MESSAGES
Secret messages / Loser gone wild / Take me on and on / Bluebird / Four little diamonds / Stranger / Danger ahead / Letter from Spain / Train of gold / Rock 'n' roll is king
4624872 / Jun '91 / Epic

☐ TIME
Prologue / Twilight / Yours truly 2095 / Ticket to the moon / Way life's meant to be / Another heart breaks / Rain is falling / From the end of the world / Lights go down / Here is the news / 21st century man / Hold on tight / Epilogue
4602122 / Jun '91 / Epic

☐ TIME/SECRET MESSAGE/DISCOVERY (3CD Set)
Prologue / Twilight / Yours truly / Ticket to the moon / 2095 / Way life's meant to be / Another heart breaks / Rain is falling / From the end of the world / Lights go down / Here is the news / 21st Century man / Hold on tight / Epilogue / Secret messages / Loser gone wild / Bluebird / Take me on and on / Four little diamonds / Stranger / Danger ahead / Letter from Spain / Train of gold / Rock 'n' roll is king / Shine a little love / Confusion / Need her love / Diary of Horace Wimp / Last train to London / Midnight blue / On the run / Wishing / Don't bring me down
4775262 / Oct '94 / Epic

☐ VERY BEST OF ELO, THE (2CD Set)
Turn to stone / Evil woman / Livin' thing / Twilight / Telephone line / Four little diamonds / Xanadu / Last train to London / Strange magic / Ma ma ma belle / Confusion / Rock 'n' roll is king / Way life's meant to be / Can't get it out of my head / Secret messages / Calling America / Don't walk away / Don't bring me down / Mr. Blue sky / Sweet talkin' woman / I'm alive / Shine a little love / Ticket to the moon / Illusions in G minor / So serious / Nightrider / All over the world / Here is the news / Diary of Horace Wimp / Across the border / Showdown / Wild west hero / Do ya / 10538 overture / Getting to the point / Rockaria / Roll over Beethoven
4890392 / 27 Oct '97 / Epic

Elonkorjuu

☐ HARVEST TIME
FJD 030 / 15 Dec '97 / FJD Sound

Eloy

☐ CHRONICLES VOL.1
SPV 08448182 / Feb '97 / SPV

☐ CHRONICLES VOL.2
SPV 08448192 / Feb '97 / SPV

☐ DESTINATION
SPV 08448082 / Dec '96 / SPV

☐ METROMANIA
HMIXD 21 / Sep '84 / Heavy Metal

☐ RA
REVXD 120 / Aug '89 / Revolver
SPV 0854802 / Dec '96 / SPV

☐ TIDES RETURN FOREVER
SPV 08448202 / Dec '96 / SPV

Els Cosins Del Sac

☐ AL FINAL DELL BALL T'ESPERO
20057CD / Dec '94 / Sonifolk

Els Trobadors

☐ ET ADES SERA L'ALBA
F 1016CD / Jun '94 / Sonifolk

Elsafty, Roisin

☐ ART OF SEAN-NOS, THE (Elsafty, Roisin & T. Ni Cheannabain)
927112 / 1 Jun '98 / BUDA

Elsdon, Alan

☐ JAZZ JOURNEYMEN
Lord Randal / Saturday afternoon blues / Diga diga doo / There's yes yes in your eyes / Panama rag / Four or five times / Two deuces / Come back sweet Papa / Lovely Rita, meter maid / Satisfaction
BLCD 760519 / Apr '96 / Black Lion

☐ KEEPERS OF THE FLAME
PARCD 504 / Dec '94 / Parrot

Elsdon, Tracy

☐ RELATIVELY SPEAKING
Half the moon / Relatively speaking / Only a woman's heart / Somewhere under the sun / Heaven / You were my lover / Lonely street / One careful owner / Just when I needed you most / Water is wide / Dream a little dream of me / Loving arms / Golden years / I'll walk beside you
RCD 534 / Oct '93 / Ritz

Elstak, Paul

☐ MAY THE FORZE BE WITH YOU
ROTC 09 / 29 Apr '98 / Rotterdam

Elusion

☐ THINK ABOUT IT
Reality / Good and plenty / Giving it up / How can u / I need a real man / Bring that lovin' on / Got to have it / Medicine / Pretty baby / Chillin' / Better think about it
74321593952 / 1 Jun '98 / RCA

Elvis Hitler

☐ HELLBILLY
LS 94362 / Dec '89 / Restless

Elwood, Michael

☐ ROLLING VALENTINE (Elwood, Michael & Beth Galiger)
DJD 3219 / Sep '95 / Dejadisc

Ely, Brother Claude

☐ SATAN GET BACK
I'm crying holy unto the lord / There's a leak in this old building / Send down the rain / There ain't no grave gonna hold my body down / Talk about Jesus / I'm just a stranger here / Thank you Jesus / I want to rest / You've got to move / Farther on / Jesus is the rock / Little David play your harp / There's a higher power / Holy holy holy (That's all right) / Dip your finger in the water (And cool my thumb) / Do you want to shout / Those prayers and words still guide me / My crucified one / Old fireside / Fare you well / I want to go to heaven / You took the wrong road again / Stop that train
CDCHD 456 / Sep '93 / Ace

Ely, Joe

☐ DIG ALL NIGHT
Settle for love / For your love / My eyes got lucky / Maybe she'll find me / Drivin' man / Dig all night / Grandfather blues / Jazz street / Rich man, poor boy / Behind the bamboo shade
FIENDCD 130 / Oct '88 / Demon

☐ LETTER TO LAREDO
TRACD 222 / Apr '96 / Transatlantic

☐ LIVE AT THE CAMBRIDGE FOLK FESTIVAL
I had my hopes up high / She never spoke Spanish to me / Me and Billy the kid / Rich man/poor man / Boxcars / My eyes got lucky
CAFECD 003 / 27 Jul '98 / Strange Fruit

☐ LORD OF THE HIGHWAY
Lord of the highway / (Don't put a) lock on my heart / Me and Billy The Kid / Letter to LA / No rope, Daisy-o / Thinks she's French / Everybody got hammered / Are you listening Lucky / Row of dominoes / Silver city
FIENDCD 101 / Sep '87 / Demon

☐ LOVE AND DANGER
Sleepless in love / Pins and needles / Love is the beating of hearts / Slow you down / Road goes on forever / Settle for love / Highways and heartaches / Whenever kindness fails / She collected / Every night about this time
MCD 10584 / 8 Sep '97 / MCA

☐ NO BAD TALK OR LOUD TALK
Honky tonk masquerade / If you were a bluebird / Dallas / Fingernails / Boxcars / Tonight I think I'm gonna go downtown / I had my hopes up high / Fools fall in love / Treat me like a Saturday night / Maria / Down on the drag / Hard livin' / Musta notta gotta lotta / Suckin' a big bottle of gin / Johnny's blues / She never spoke Spanish to me / Because of the wind / West Texas waltz
EDCD 418 / Mar '95 / Edsel

☐ TIME FOR TRAVELLIN'
Mardi gras waltz / Tennessee's not the state I'm in / Gambler's pride / All my love / Jericho(now all your walls must come tumbling down) / I'll be your fool / Cornbread moon / Standin' at the big hotel / Crazy lemon / Crawdad train / In another world / She leaves you where you are / Time for travellin' / Wishin for you / Hold on / I keep gettin paid the same / Road hawg / Dam of my heart / Bet me
EDCD 486 / Aug '96 / Edsel

☐ TWISTING IN THE WIND
UMD 80488 / 6 Apr '98 / Universal

Elysian Fields

☐ BLEED YOUR CEDAR
RAD 11505 / 3 Nov '97 / Radioactive

Elysium

☐ DANCE FOR THE CELESTIAL BEINGS
NZCD 039 / Sep '95 / Nova Zembla

El'Zabar, Kahil

☐ RENAISSANCE OF THE RESISTANCE (El'Zabar, Kahil Ritual Trio)
Sweet meat / Ornette / Renaissance of the resistance / Trane in mind / Golden sea / Fatsmo / Save your love for me
DE 466 / Mar '97 / Delmark

EM & I

☐ HEAVENLY
99 1600 / Jul '96 / Ninetynine

Emanuel, Carol

☐ TOPS OF TREES
378022 / Sep '96 / Koch Jazz

Embale, Carlos

☐ RUMBERO MAYOR
CD 0020 / Mar '96 / Egrem

Embalmer

☐ THERE WAS BLOOD EVERYWHERE
There was blood everywhere / Necro-philing cabinet / Bloodsucking freaks / May the wounds bleed forever / Rotten body fluids / Bone box / Morbid confessions / Cellar
RR 69702 / Aug '97 / Relapse

Emblow, Jack

☐ ENJOY YOURSELF (Emblow, Jack & The French Collection)
Good morning/The sun has got his hat on / Kerry dances/The Irish washerwoman / Trail of the lonesome pine / Up a lazy river/Lazy bones / Enjoy yourself / Frenesi / Nola / April love/A certain smile / Chanson d'amour / Milord/The poor people of Paris / Louise / Way down yonder in New Orleans / Singing piano / J'attendrai/La vie en rose / Tango musette / Zip a dee doo dah-heigh ho / White cliffs of Dover/I'll be seeing you / Here you come again/Spread a little happiness / Canadian capers / 'Allo 'allo / Waiter and the porter and the upstairs maid / Sleepy time gal / Makin' whoopee / Ain't we got fun/Happy talk
CDTS 001 / Aug '93 / Maestro

☐ PICK YOURSELF UP (Emblow, Jack & The French Collection)
Pick yourself up / Hot time in the old town tonight / Boiled beef and carrots / Don't dilly dally on the way / Any old iron / I don't want to walk without you / Little on the lonely side / Dance of the hours / Guantanamera / Yes, we have no bananas / Whilst strolling in the park / Lily of laguna / Narcissus / La cucuracha / I yi yi yi yi (I like you very much) / Black orpheus samba / No strings / I'm putting all my eggs in one basket / I'm a dreamer (aren't we all) / I double dare you / Moonstruck / Bill Bailey, won't you please come home / Question and answer / Dubarry waltz / Endearing young charms / Rose of tralee / Mother McChree / Slow rhumbas / La golondrina / Indian summer / Pokarekareana / Estrellita / Too marvellous for words / Chihuahua / Opus one
GRCD 46 / '91 / Grasmere

Embodyment

☐ EMBRACE THE ETERNAL
TNR 1113CD / 20 Jul '98 / Tooth & Nail

Embrace

☐ GOOD WILL OUT, THE
Now you're nobody / You've got to say yes / Retread / That's all changed forever / I want the world / Fireworks / My weakness is none of your business / Last gas / Higher sights / All you good good people / Intro / Good will out / One big family / Come back to what you know
CDHUT 46 / 8 Jun '98 / Hut

Embracing

☐ DREAMS LEFT BEHIND
IR 031CD / 13 Oct '97 / Invasion

Embryo

☐ ROCK SESSION
REP 7077 / 16 Mar '98 / Repertoire

Embryo's Reise

☐ AFGHANISTAN, PAKISTAN AND INDIA
30202 / May '97 / Schneeball

Emerald Accordian Band

☐ IRELAND'S DANCING DAYS
Catch me if you can / Golden jubilee / Come back Paddy Reilly / Believe me if all those endearing young charms / Come back to Erin / Westmeath bachelor / Old woman from Wexford / Rose of Killarney / Sweet slievenamon / Galway shawl / Hucklebuck / Athole highlanders / Champion / Irish washerwoman / Rose of tralee / Banks of my own lovely lee / I'll tell me ma / Marie's wedding / Forty shades of green / Mursheen durkin / Wild colonial boy / Leaving of Liverpool / Red rose cafe / Kathleen / Village where I went to school / If your Irish (come into the parlour) / Bold O'Donaghue / St Bernard waltz / Green glens of Antrim / Boys from the county Armagh / Simple Simon says / Bluebell polka / How can you buy Kilarney / My wild Irish rose / Bunch of Thyme / I'll take you home again Kathleen / Old rustic bridge
MCVD 30002 / Nov '96 / Emerald Gem

Emerald Girls

☐ IRISH FIDDLES AND PIPES
PLSCD 285 / 1 Jun '98 / Pulse

Emergency

☐ GET OUT OF COUNTRY
RR 7048 / 1 Jun '98 / Repertoire

Emerson & Waldron

☐ BEST OF EMERSON & WALDRON, THE
Early morning rain / I'm bound to ride / There's no room in my heart for the blues / Fox on the run / Spanish grass / Lonesome night / Deep river / If I were a carpenter / Shiloh / Little maggie / Our darling's gone / Wheels / Proud Mary / I know you're married / You didn't say goodbye / Who will sing for me
REBCD 1123 / 9 Mar '98 / Rebel

Emerson, Billy

☐ MOVE BABY, MOVE (Emerson, Billy 'The Kid')
No teasing around / If lovin's believin' / Hey little girl / I'm not going home / Woodchuck / When my baby quit me / Move baby, move / When it rains it pours / Little fine healthy thing / Something for nothing / Cherry pie / Satisfied / When my baby quit me / No greater love / Red hot / Shim sham shimmy / Every woman I know (crazy 'bout automobiles) / Tomorrow never comes / Don't start me to lying / If you won't stay home / Don't be careless / Do the chicken / Somebody show me the pleasure is all mine / Do yourself a favour / You never miss the water
CPCD 8276 / Jan '97 / Charly

Emerson, Darren

☐ CREAM SEPARATES VOL.2 (Mixed By Darren Emerson) (Various Artists)
Seawall: *Envoy* / Modus vivendi: *Modus Vivendi* / Paper moon: *51 Days* / Indulge: *Howard, Neal* / In a vision: *Virgo Four* / Unicorn: *Blue Maxx* / Warrior: *Oniero* / Airport martini: *Curtin, Dan* / Party: *Willpower* / Sugar: *Nimbus Quartet* / Sueno latino: *Sueno Latino* / Song for Olivia: *Cliff Hanger* / Art Lukm: *Holy Ghost Inc.* / Confusion the waitress: *Underworld*
74321462012 / Mar '97 / De-Construction

☐ MIXMAG LIVE VOL.13 (Techno - Darren Emerson/Dave Angel) (Various Artists)
MMLCD 013 / Jul '96 / Mixmag Live

Emerson, Keith

☐ CHANGING STATES
AMPCD 026 / Apr '95 / AMP

☐ CHRISTMAS ALBUM, THE
O little town of Bethlehem / We three kings / Snowman's land / Aria / Captain starship christmas / I saw three ships / Petites litanies de jesus / It came upon the midnight clear / Silent night
AMPCD 018 / Feb '95 / AMP

Emerson, Lake & Palmer

☐ BEST OF EMERSON, LAKE AND PALMER, THE
ESSCD 296 / Nov '95 / Essential

☐ BLACK MOON
Black moon / Paper blood / Affairs of the heart / Romeo and Juliet / Farewell to arms / Changing states / Burning bridges / Close to home / Betterdays / Footprints in the snow
ESMCD 506 / May '97 / Essential

☐ BRAIN SALAD SURGERY
Jerusalem / Toccata / Still you turn me on / Benny the bouncer / Karn evil 9 / First impression (part 1) / First impression / Second impression / Third impression
ESMCD 344 / Mar '96 / Essential

☐ EMERSON, LAKE AND PALMER
Barbarian / Take a pebble / Knife edge / Three fates / Clotho / Lachesis / Auropos / Tank / Lucky man
ESMCD 340 / Mar '96 / Essential

☐ KING BISCUIT PRESENTS...
Peter Gunn theme / Tiger in a spotlight / C'est la vie / Piano improvisation / Maple leaf rag / Drum solo / Enemy god / Watching over you / Pirates / Fanfare for the common man / Hoe down / Still you turn me on / Lucky man / Piano improvisation
KBFHCD 003 / 27 Apr '98 / King Biscuit

☐ LIVE AT THE ROYAL ALBERT HALL
Karn evil 9 / Tarkus (medley) / Knife edge / Paper blood / Romeo and Juliet / Creole dance / Still, you turn me on / Lucky man / Black moon / Pirates / Finale (medley)
ESMCD 504 / May '97 / Essential

☐ LOVE BEACH
All I want is you / Love beach / Taste of my love / Gambler / For you / Canario / Memoirs of an officer and a gentleman / Prologue / Education of a gentleman / Love at first sight / Letters from the front / Honourable company
ESMCD 363 / Aug '96 / Essential

☐ PICTURES AT AN EXHIBITION
Promenade / Gnome / Sage / Old castle / Blues variation / Hut of Baba Yaga / Curse of Baba Yaga / Great gate of Kiev / End (nutrocker)
ESMCD 342 / Mar '96 / Essential

☐ RETURN OF THE MANTICORE (4CD Set)
Touch and go / Hang on to a dream / 21st Century schizoid man / Fire / Pictures at an exhibition / I believe in Father Christmas / Introductory Fanfare/ Peter Gunn / Tiger in a spotlight / Toccata / Trilogy / Tank / Lucky man / Tarkus / From the beginning / Take a pebble / Knife edge / Paper blood / Hoedown / Rondo / Barbarian / Still ... you turn me on / Endless enigma / C'est la vie / Enemy God dances with the black spirits / Bo Diddley / Bitches crystal / Time and a place / Living sin / Karn evil 9 / Honky tonk train blues / Jerusalem / Fanfare for the common man / Black moon / Watching over you / Toccata con fuoco / For you / Prelude and fugue / Memoirs of an officer and a gentleman / Pirates / Affairs of the heart
ESFCD 421 / Nov '96 / Essential

☐ TARKUS
Tarkus / Eruption / Stones of years / Iconoclast / Mass / Manticore / Battlefield / Aquatarkus / Jeremy Bender / Bitches crystal / Only way / Infinite space (conclusion) / Time and a place / Are you ready Eddy
ESMCD 341 / Mar '96 / Essential

☐ TRILOGY
Endless enigma (part 1) / Fugue / Endless enigma (part 2) / From the beginning / Sheriff / Hoedown / Trilogy / Living sin / Abaddon's bolero
ESMCD 343 / Mar '96 / Essential

☐ WELCOME BACK MY FRIENDS TO THE SHOW THAT NEVER ENDS
Hoedown / Jerusalem / Toccata / Tarkus / Take a pebble / Piano improvisations / Jeremy Bender/The Sheriff / Karn evil 9
ESDCD 359 / Aug '96 / Essential

☐ WORKS LIVE
Introductory Fanfare / Peter Gunn / Tiger in a spotlight / C'est la vie / Watching over you / Maple leaf rag / Enemy God dances with the black spirits / Fanfare for the common man / Knife edge / Show me the way to go home / Abaddon's bolero / Pictures at an exhibition / Closer to believing / Piano concerto no. 1 / Tank
ESDCD 362 / Aug '96 / Essential

☐ WORKS VOL.1
Piano concerto no. 1 / Lend your love to me tonight / C'est la vie / Hallowed be thy name / Nobody loves you like I do / Closer to believing / Enemy God dances with the black spirits / LA nights / New Orleans / Two part invention in D minor / Food for your soul / Tank / Fanfare for the common man / Pirates
ESDCD 360 / Aug '96 / Essential

☐ WORKS VOL.2
Tiger in the spotlight / When the apple blossoms bloom in the windmills of your mind / I'll be your valentine / Bullfrogs / Brain salad surgery / Barrelhouse shake down / Watching over you / So far to fall / Maple leaf rag / I believe in Father Christmas / Close but not touching
ESMCD 361 / Aug '96 / Essential

Emery, B.J.

☐ HORNS (Emery, B.J. & Maurice John Vaughan)
I want to take you higher / I'm ready for you / Big bad circle / Talk to me baby / Talk to me baby (reprise) / You ought to be dancing / Drowning in the sea of love / Nothin' but a woman / I want to hear some blues / Fridgidare woman / I gamble I gamble / Problems
APCD 129 / 31 Jul '98 / Appaloosa

Emery, James

☐ STANDING ON A WHALE FISHING FOR MINNOWS
New water / In a secret place / Cobalt blue / Strings of thread / Texas koto blues / Crepusule with Nellie / Standing on a whale fishing for minnows / Arc into distant night / Black diamonds and pink whisper / Epicenter / Poetry in stillness
ENJ 93122 / Jul '97 / Enja

☐ TURBULENCE (Emery, James & Iliad Quartet)
KFWCD 106 / Nov '94 / Knitting Factory

Emery, Jon

☐ IF YOU DON'T BUY THIS I'LL FIND SOMEBODY WHO WILL
She was bad / I let the freight train carry me on / I'm the fool (who told you to go) / If you don't leave me / I bought her roses / Midnight, music city USA / Rockin' Rhonda ain't rockin' no more / Fool in El Paso / I'm comin' home / Old that train / Christy-Ann / Fiddlin' John Carson / God don't never change / Chicken pickin' (break song) / Man who never lies
BCD 15897 / Aug '95 / Bear Family

EMF

☐ SCHUBERT DIP
Children / Long Summer days / When you're mine / Travelling not running / I believe / Unbelievable / Girl of an age / Admit it / Lies / Long time / Live at the Bilson
CDPCS 7353 / Feb '94 / Parlophone

Emler, Andy

☐ HEAD GAMES (Emler, Andy Mega Octet)
LBLC 6553 / Jan '93 / Label Bleu

Emmanuel, Ivor

☐ BEST OF IVOR EMMANUEL, THE
Men of Harlech / My little Welsh home / Sospan fach / Idle days in summertime / Dove / Sweet Gwen of Aberdovey / All through the night / David of the white rock / Forth to the battle / Ash grove / Land of my fathers / My life belongs to you / I can give you the starlight / We'll gather lilacs / My dearest dear / Shine through my dreams / Keep the home fires burning / Glamorous night / Fly home little heart / Fold your wings / If this were love / Someday my heart will awake / Rose of England
PLSCD 242 / 27 Oct '97 / Pulse

Emmett, Rik

☐ SPIRAL NOTEBOOK
IRS 993515CD / Jan '96 / Intercord

Emotional Outburst

☐ IF THE FIRMAMENT TREMBLES
EFA 112892 / 13 Oct '97 / Glasnost

Emotions

☐ EMOTIONS LIVE IN 1996
50548 / Feb '97 / Raging Bull

Emperor

☐ ANTHEMS TO THE WELKIN AT DUSK
CANDLE 023CD / May '97 / Candlelight

☐ IN THE NIGHTSIDE ECLIPSE
CANDLE 008CD / Jan '95 / Candlelight

Emperor Sly

☐ HEAVY ROTATION
ZD 6CD / Nov '95 / Zip Dog

☐ SPARKING UP
ZD 16CD / 3 Nov '97 / Zip Dog

Emperor's New Clothes

☐ WISDOM & LIES
Luke's idea / Mystery daydream / Missing the sea / What's gone has disappeared / Stone's throwing / Making photographs underwater / Wishing hues of green / Don't you / Nowhere / Colours make waves
JAZIDCD 122 / Apr '95 / Acid Jazz

Empire Brass

☐ EMPIRE BRASS ON BROADWAY
Phantom of the opera / Hello Dolly / Man of La Mancha / Macavity / Don't cry for me Argentina / Mambo / Easy Street / Till there was you / Seventy six trombones / Fugue for tinhorns / At the end of the day / Lonely goatherd / Night and day / Bali Ha'i / Put on a happy face / Big spender
80303 / Jun '92 / Telarc

☐ PASSAGE
CD 80355 / Jan '95 / Telarc

Empirion

☐ ADVANCED TECHNOLOGY
XLCD 117 / Oct '96 / XL

Empress Of Fur

☐ HOW DOES THAT MAD BAD HAWAIIAN VOODOO GRAB YOU
RAUCD 011 / Jan '95 / Raucous

Empty Set

☐ THIN, SLIM AND NONE
FLIP 96100 / Oct '96 / Flippaut

Empty Tremor

☐ APOCOLOKYNTOSYS
RS 72902CD / Jul '98 / Rising Sun

Empyria

☐ BEHIND CLOSED DOORS
TT 00232 / Apr '96 / T&T

Emsland Hillbillies

☐ ENDLICH/BAUER BARNES MUHLE
Ich weiss etwas, was keiner weiss / Liebe Mama / Country freak / Ich liebe meinen diesel / Der geburtstag / Jungs, ab morgen / Popstar / Endlich / Hey hey / Emslander / Das alte lied / Original aschendorfer countryband / Wieder auf dem sofa / Der letzte joint zum aschied / Ich ging ins casino / Radarwagen / Erika's sonnenburg der liebe / Schroder goes country / Bauer barnes muhle / Cowboy roadie / Der fremde / Iglu himmel / Die gute alte sonne / Rechts vom kanal / Der krzeste countrysong der welt / Fernfahrer harmann
BCD 16183 / May '97 / Bear Family

Emtidi

☐ SAAT
CD 9019 / 16 Feb '98 / Galaxis

En Slave

☐ HALF PAST HUMAN
WSCD 005 / Oct '96 / World Serpent

En Vogue

☐ BORN TO SING
Party / Strange / Lies / Hip hop bugle boy / Hold on / Part of me / You don't have to worry / Time goes on / Just can't stay away / Don't go / Luv lines / Waitin' on you
7567820842 / Jun '90 / Atlantic

☐ EV3
Whatever / Don't let go (love) / Right direction / Damn I want to be your lover / Too gone, too long / You're all I need / Let it flow / Sitting by heaven's door / Love makes you do thangs / What a difference a day makes / Eyes of a child / Does anybody hear me
7559620972 / Jun '97 / Atlantic

☐ FUNKY DIVAS
This is your life / My lovin' / Hip hop lover / Free your mind / Desire / Give him something he can feel / It ain't over till the fat lady sings / Give it up, turn it loose / Yesterday / Hooked on your love / Love don't love you / What is love / Runaway love / Whatta man: *Salt n' Pepa & En Vogue*
7567923102 / Dec '96 / Atlantic

Enaid & Einalem

☐ CELTIC NIGHTS
2689 / Aug '96 / NorthSound

Enbor

☐ ENBOR
LV 007 / 15 Jun '98 / Lost Vinyl

☐ KATEBEGIAK
LV 008 / 15 Jun '98 / Lost Vinyl

Enchantment

☐ DANCE THE MARBLE NAKED
CM 770662 / May '94 / Century Media

End

☐ GUSTO
Powerblind / Powerblind / City of lost souls / Weapon / Smack of shame / Waste or gain / Cut me loose / Nowhere no good / Redman / Cavaliers / Weirdo / Stuck in the middle
GUSTCD 1 / Aug '91 / Expression

☐ IN REGION OF SUMMER STARS 1984-1987
SRMC 4021 / 5 Jan '98 / Siwan

☐ INTROSPECTION
SRMC 0065 / 5 Jan '98 / Siwan

End Of Green

☐ INFINITY
NB 140CD / Jan '96 / Nuclear Blast

Endemic Void

☐ EQUATIONS
Hydrosphere / Tidal / Lionstone / Serious intent / Knight moves / Infectious / Evolution / Turn da tide / Inner daze / Confused / Intermission
WORDD 004 / Nov '96 / Language

Enders, Johannes

☐ BRIGHT NIGHTS
Thanksgiving / Bright nights / Brooklyn blue / Egon / 400 years ago tomorrow / Butterfly / So near so far
ENJ 93522 / 24 Aug '98 / Enja

Endpoint

☐ AFTERTASTE
DOG 024CD / Nov '94 / Doghouse

☐ LAST RECORD
DOG 030CD / Aug '95 / Doghouse

Endraum

☐ IN FLIMMANDER NACHT
EFA 112292 / Mar '94 / Danse Macabre

Endresen, Sidsel

☐ DUPLEX RIDE (Endresen, Sidsel & Bugge Wesseltoft)
Singles / Fifty ways to leave your love / And later the rain / You call me / River / Duplex ride / Six minutes or so / Trying times / Pennywhistle poem / Okay / Epilogue
ACT 90002 / 26 May '98 / Act

☐ EXILE
Here the moon / Quest / Stages, I, II, III / Hunger / Theme I / Waiting train / Dreaming / Dust
5217212 / Apr '94 / ECM

Endsley, Melvin

☐ I LIKE YOUR KIND OF LOVE
I like your kind of love / Is it true / I got a feeling / Keep a lovin' me baby / Let's fall out of love / Just want to be wanted / I ain't gettin' nowhere with you / Hungry eyes / Loving on my mind / Lonely all over again / There's bound to be / Gettin' used to the blues / Bringin' the blues to my door / I'd just be fool enough
BCD 15595 / May '93 / Bear Family

Endura

☐ DREAMS OF DARK WAVES
NACD 202 / Oct '95 / Nature & Art

☐ GREAT GOD PAN
Oriflamme / Alpha- wolf / Dark face of Eve / From sickening skies / Sucking the sour vine / Sperm of metals / Truth is a sharp knife / Saturns tree / Black dog crossed my path / Hymn to Pan / Battle song of Endura
SAG 5 / Jul '97 / Elfinblut

Enekk

☐ FYRA NAETUR FYRI JOL
SHD 27 / 2 Apr '98 / Tutl

Energy Orchard

☐ ENERGY ORCHARD
Belfast / Somebody's brother / Lion / One two brown eyes / King of love / Sailortown / Walk in love / This house must fall / Sweet irish rose / Hard street / Good day to die / Belfast-instrumental
MNMCD 2 / Oct '95 / M&M

☐ PAIN KILLER
Surrender to the city / She's the one I adore / Wasted / D F Dogs / Shipyard song / Past is another country / Remember my name / Sight for sore eyes / Pain killer / I hate to say goodbye
TRACD 100 / Apr '96 / Transatlantic

☐ SHINOLA
Coming through / Madame George / Atlantic City / Stay away / Don't fail me now / In my room / Seven sisters / Star of County Down / London Fields / Big town / I'm no angel
TRACD 103 / Feb '95 / Transatlantic

Enertopia

☐ MAGIC FOR ETERNITY
KRBCD 003 / 1 Sep '97 / Krembo

Engel, Detlef

☐ EIN ENGEL, OHNE FLUGEL
Ein Engel, ohne flugel / Komm' zu mir darling / So klar wie die sterne / Mr. Blue / Traumen / Sugar baby / Ich such ein herz / Junges gluck / Oh I love you / War' nur nicht der and're gekommen / Isabella / Alle twens geh'n heut' tanzen / Zeig' mir bei nacht die sterne / Vier kleine schuhe / Mein herz schlagt nur fur Susie / Sweety sleepy melodie / Schenk mir doch ein bild von dir / Du du bist ja so sch'n / Wenn du nicht bei mir bist / Ist das liebe oder nicht / Was kann das sein / Ich bin nicht so, wie alle andern / Bitte gib mir einen kuss / Lass mich heute nicht allein / Oh no / Rote rosen / Das ist leicht gesagt / Goodnight / Let's go / Geh'n wir
BCD 16106 / Dec '96 / Bear Family

Engelstaub

☐ IGNIS FATUUS: IRRLICHTER
EFA 121542 / Jul '94 / Apollyon

Engin, Esin

☐ BELLY DANCE MUSIC
EUCD 1309 / Jul '95 / ARC

Engine 54

☐ 54-95
EFA 127682 / Sep '95 / Heatwave

Engine 88

☐ CLEAN YOUR ROOM
Bottle / Funny car / Mangos / Pelican / Spinach / Des Moines / Lonely pimp / GTO / Drowning / Crackers / Baby doll / Firefly / Twenty
CAROL 17842 / May '96 / Caroline

☐ SNOWMAN
Ballerina / Seconal / Stairway / Manclub / Istanbul / Snowman / Curious / Trouble / Cold-blooded / Mustard / Butchery / Killer willow / Precious
CAR 7588 / Mar '97 / Caroline

Engine Kid

☐ ANGEL'S WINGS
REV 038CD / May '95 / Revelation

Engkilde, August

☐ BAND OF INNER URGE
STCD 4210 / May '97 / Storyville

England

☐ GARDEN SHED
RWE 004CD / 5 Jan '98 / Forward

☐ LAST OF THE JUBBLIES
MARBEL 001CD / 2 Feb '98 / Vinyl Tap

England FC

☐ ENGLAND'S GLORY 1966 (From 1966 To Euro '96) (Various Artists)
Back home: *England World Cup Squad 1970* / Red shirt explained: *Hurst, Geoff & Martin Peters* / Up there England: *Portwood, Cliff & World Cup Squad 1966* / Was it over the line: *Hurst, Geoff & Martin Peters* / You'll never walk alone: *Portwood, Cliff & World Cup Squad 1966* / Who pinched the ball: *Hurst, Geoff & Martin Peters* / World cup willie: *Donegan, Lonnie* / Sugar sugar: *Lee, Francis & Bobby Moore* / Here we are: *Lee, Francis & Bobby Moore* / Viva England: *Lees, Ian 'Sludge'* / Ballad of bulldog Bobby: *Dave & The Bulldogs* / England: *Keegan, Kevin* / This time we'll get it right: *England World Cup Squad 1982* / England we'll fly the flag: *England World Cup Squad 1982* / Land of hope and glory: *England World Cup Squad 1982* / We are the champions: *Hoddle, Glen* / Oh sweet England: *Nationwide England Supporters* / Red white and blue: *Marsden, Gerry & The Supporters Club* / Viva Bobby Moore: *Business* / Fog on the Tyne: *Gazza & Lindisfarne* / Can we kick it (no we can't): *Wall Of Orange* / Euromania: *Eleven V Eleven* / World in motion: *Cortez, Hector & His Formation* / Home of football: *Billy Bluebeat* / England (we shall not be moved): *Billy Bluebeat* / England's glory: *England's Glory*
CDGAFFER 6 / 5 May '98 / Cherry Red

England, Buddy

☐ FATE'S A FIDDLER, LIFE'S A DANCE
LARRCD 304 / Nov '94 / Larrikin

England, Ty

☐ TWO WAYS TO FALL
It starts with L / Two ways to fall / I'll take today / Never say never / Last dance / Backslider's prayer / Irresistible you / Kick back / All of the above / Sure
07863669302 / Oct '96 / RCA Nashville

☐ TY ENGLAND
Redneck son / Smoke in her eyes / Should've asked her faster / Her only bad habit is me / New faces in the fields / Swing like that / You'll find somebody new / Blues ain't news to me / It's lonesome everywhere / Is that you
74321285932 / Aug '95 / RCA

England's Glory

☐ LEGENDARY LOST ALBUM
Devotion / Wide waterway / City of fun / First time I saw you / Broken arrows / Bright lights / It's been a long time / Guest / Peter and the pets / Showdown / Predictably blonde / Weekend / Trouble in the world
CDMGRAM 73 / Sep '96 / Anagram

Englesstaub

☐ ALLEUS MALEFICARUM
AP 00310593 / Dec '93 / Apollyon

English Brass Ensemble

☐ LYRIC BRASS
CDDCA 660 / Apr '89 / ASV

English Chorale

☐ CHORAL CHRISTMAS, A
O come all ye faithful (adeste fidelis) / While shepherds watched / We three Kings / God rest ye merry gentlemen / In dulce jubilo / Silent night / Good King Wenceslas / O little town of Bethlehem / In the bleak midwinter / First Noel / Once in royal David's city / Away in a manger / Hark the herald angels sing
CDVIP 168 / Nov '96 / Virgin VIP

English Dogs

☐ ALL THE WORLD'S A RAGE
SPV 08453632 / Jun '96 / SPV

☐ ALL THE WORLD'S A RAGE
IRC 053 / Jun '97 / Impact

☐ BOW TO NONE
IRC 021 / Mar '97 / Impact

☐ TO THE ENDS OF THE EARTH/ FORWARD INTO BATTLE
STEPCD 041 / 24 Nov '97 / Step 1

☐ WHERE LEGEND BEGAN
Trauma / Eye of shamahn / Enter the domain / Premonition / Calm before the storm / Flashback / A tomb of traveller's past / Middle earth / Epilogue
PRAGE 003CD / Jun '97 / Powerage

English Philharmonic Orchestra

☐ PHILHARMONIC ROCK
Jesus Christ Superstar selection / When I fall in love / Whiter shade of pale / Greatest love of all / Reach out I'll be there / Beatles selection / Lady in red / Bohemian rhapsody / Dream theme
QED 089 / Nov '96 / Tring

English, Barbara Jean

☐ JUST LIKE A LADY
I'm sorry / I'm living a lie / Little baby / Danger signs / Baby I'm a want you / So many ways to die / Just like a lady / All this / Don't make me over / Where do I begin / You're gonna need somebody to love / Comin' or goin' / Love's arrangement / Guess who / Fair weather lover / Breakin' up a happy home / He knows my key / I wanna be ready
NEMCD 932 / 29 Sep '97 / Sequel

Enid

☐ AERIE FAERIE NONSENSE
Prelude / Mayday galliard / Ondine / Childe Roland / Fand: first movement / Fand: second movement
MNTLCD 6 / May '94 / Newt

☐ ANARCHY ON 45 (2CD Set)
MNTLCD 13 / Jul '96 / Mantella

☐ AT THE HAMMERSMITH
MNTLCD 10 / May '94 / Newt

☐ FINAL NOISE
Childe Roland / Hall of mirrors / Song for Europe / Something wicked this way comes / Sheets of blue / Chaldean crossing / La rage / Earth born / Jerusalem
MNTLCD 3 / May '94 / Newt

☐ IN THE REGION OF THE SUMMER STARS
Fool / Falling tower / Death the reaper / Lovers / Devil / Sun / Last judgement / In the region of the Summer stars
MNTLCD 7 / May '94 / Newt

☐ SALOME
O Salome / Streets of blue / Change / Jack / Flames of power
MNTLCD 9 / May '94 / Newt

☐ SEED AND THE SOWER, THE
Children crossing / Bar of shadow / La rage / Longhome / Earth born
MNTLCD 2 / Apr '94 / Newt

☐ SIX PIECES
Sanctus / Once she was / Ring master / Punch and Judy man / Hall of mirrors / Dreamer / Joined by the heart
MNTLCD 4 / May '94 / Newt

☐ SOMETHING WICKED THIS WAY COMES
Raindown / Jessica / And then there was none / Evensong / Bright star / Song for Europe / Something wicked this way comes
MNTLCD 1 / May '94 / Newt

☐ SUNDIALER
MNTLCD 12 / Oct '95 / Mantella

☐ TOUCH ME
Humoresque / Cortege / Elegy (touch me) / Gallevant / Albion fair / Joined by the heart
MNTLCD 5 / May '94 / Newt

☐ TRIPPING THE LIGHT FANTASTIC
Ultraviolet cat / Little shiners / Gateway / Tripping the light fantastic / Freelance human / Dark hydraulic / Biscuit game
MNTLCD 11 / Nov '94 / Newt

Enigma

☐ CROSS OF CHANGES
Second chapter / Eyes of truth / Return to innocence / I love you... I'll kill you / Silent warrior / Dream of the dolphin / Age of loneliness (Carly's song) / Out from the deep / Cross of changes / Return to innocence (mix) / Age of loneliness (mix) / Eyes of truth (mix)
CDVIR 20 / Jan '94 / Virgin

☐ LE ROI EST MORT, VIVE LE ROI
Le Roi est mort, vive le Roi / Morphing thru time / Third of its kind / Beyond the invisible / Why / Shadows in silence / Child in us / TNT for the brain / Almost full moon / Roundabout / Prism of life / Odyssey of the mind
CDVIR 60 / Nov '96 / Virgin

☐ MCMXC AD
Voice of Enigma / Principles of lust / Sadness / Find love / Sadness (reprise) / Callas went away / Mea culpa / Voice and the snake / Knocking on forbidden doors / Back to the rivers of belief / Way to eternity / Hallelujah / Rivers of belief
CDVIR 1 / Dec '90 / Virgin

Enigma

☐ DISCO MEGAMIX
SUMCD 4137 / Jan '98 / Summit

Enloe, Lyman

☐ FIDDLE TUNES I RECALL
CUY 2707CD / Apr '96 / County

Ennen, Thea

☐ ALL ABOARD (Ennen, Thea & The Algorythms)
Surfboard / Patience / Warm North / Your own prison / Mama Mama / Common sense / Ain't that something / Promised land / Lonely love / Cradle / Cream corn / Standing
ATM 1122 / Oct '96 / Atomic Theory

Ennis, Seamus

☐ BEST OF IRISH PIPING
Pure drop/The flax in bloom / Fairy boy / Grove's hornpipe/Dwyer's hornpipe / O'Sullivan the great / When sick, is it tea you want/The humours of Drinagh / By the river of gems/The rocky road to Dublin / Ask my father/Pat Ward's jig / Valencia harbour (slow air) / Standing abbey/The stack of barley (hornpipes) / Leitrim thrush/Miss Johnson (reels) / Return from Fingal (march) / Chase me Charlie/The dingle regatta / White Connor's daughter, Nora / Slieve Russell/ Sixpenny money / Stay for another while/I have no money/The cushogue / Brown thorn (slow air) / Music at the gate/The pigeon on the gate (reels) / Blooming meadows/Kitty's rambles / Ned of the hill / Smash the windows/The dark girl in blue / Derry hornpipe/The cuckoo's nest (hornpipes) / Trip we took over the mountain / Merry sisters/Music in the forge/Castle Kelly (reels) / Johnny Cope / Rainy day/ A fair wind / Fox chase / Braes of Busby/Colonel Frazer / Kid on the mountain (slip jig)
TARACD 1002/9 / Aug '95 / Tara

☐ BONNY BUNCH OF ROSES
TCD 1023 / Aug '96 / Tradition

☐ PURE DROP/FOX CHASE
TARA 1002/9CD / Jul '95 / Tara

☐ RETURN FROM FINGAL, THE
RTECD 199 / Dec '97 / RTE/Europe 1

☐ WANDERING MINSTREL, THE
Wandering minstrel/Jackson's morning brush / Boys of Bluehill/Dunphy's hornpipe / Glennephin cuckoo/Littlefair Cannavans / Frieze breeches / Flags of Dublin/Wind that shakes the barley / Little stack of barley/Cronin's hornpipe / New Demesne / Blackbird / Gillan's apples / Walls of Liscarroll/Stone in the field / Molly O'Malone / Kiss the maid behind the barrel / Happy to meet and sorry to part
OSS 12CD / Mar '94 / Ossian

Ennis, Skinnay

☐ 1956/57 LIVE IN STEREO
When summer is gone / Cheek to cheek / Got a date with an angel / Love for sale / You've got me crying again / I've got you under my skin / Breathless / Rhythm is our business / Whispers in the night / Scatterbrain / Josephine / I went out of my way / There ought to be a moonlight savings time / Foggy day / Untitled instrumental / Boy, a girl, and a lamplight / Girlfriend
JH 1027 / Feb '93 / Jazz Hour

Eno, Brian

☐ ANOTHER GREEN WORLD
Sky saw / Over Fire Island / St. Elmo's fire / In dark trees / Big ship / I'll come running / Another green world / Sombre reptiles / Little fishes / Golden hours / Becalmed / Zawinul / Lava / Everything merges with the night / Spirits drifting
EGCD 21 / May '87 / EG

☐ APOLLO (Atmospheres & Soundtracks)
Under stars / Secret place / Matta / Signals / Ending (ascent) / Under stars II / Drift / Silver morning / Deep blue day / Weightless / Always returning / Stars
EGCD 53 / Jan '87 / EG

☐ BEFORE & AFTER SCIENCE/WARM JETS/ANOTHER GREEN WORLD (Compact Collection 3CD Set)
No one receiving / Backwater / Kurt's rejoinder / Energy fools the magician / King's lead hat / Here he comes / Julie with... / By this river / Through hollow lands / Spider and I / Needles in the camel's eye / Paw paw negro blowtorch / Baby's on fire / Cindy tells me / Driving me backwards / On some faraway beach / Blank Frank / Dead fink's don't talk / Some of them are old / Here come the warm jets / Sky saw / Over Fire Island / St. Elmo's fire / In dark trees / Big ship / I'll come running / Another green world / Sombre reptiles / Little fishes / Golden hours / Becalmed / Zawinul / Lava / Everything merges with the night / Spirits drifting
TPAK 36 / Oct '94 / Virgin

☐ BEFORE AND AFTER SCIENCE
No one receiving / Backwater / Kurt's rejoinder / Energy fools the magician / King's lead hat / Here he comes / Julie with... / By this river / Through hollow lands / Spider and I
EGCD 32 / Jan '87 / EG

☐ BRIAN ENO VOL.2 (3CD Set)
Needle in the camel's eye / Baby's on fire / Cindy tells me / On some faraway beach / Blank Frank / Dead finks don't talk / Some of them are old / Here come the warm jets / Seven deadly finns / Burning airlines... / Back in Judy's jungle / Great pretender / Third uncle / Put a straw... / True wheel / Taking tiger mountain / Lion sleeps tonight / Sky saw / Over fire island / St. Elmo's fire / In dark trees / Big ship / I'll come running / Sombre reptiles / Golden hours / Becalmed / Zawinul/Lava / Everything merges / Spirits drifting / No one receiving / Backwater / Kurt's rejoinder / King's lead hat / Here he comes / Julie with... / By this river / Through hollow lands / Spider and I / RAF / America is waiting / Regiment / Jezebel spirit / Very very hungry / Spinning away / One word / Empty frame / River / Soul of Carmen Miranda / Belldog / I fall up / Stiff / Are they thinking of me / Some words / Under / Over
ENOBX 2 / Oct '93 / Virgin

☐ DISCREET MUSIC
Discreet music 1 and 2 / Fullness of wind (part 1) / French catalogues (part 2) / Brutal adour (part 3)
EEGCD 23 / '87 / EG

☐ DROP, THE
Slip, dip / But if / Belgiam drop / Cornered / Block drop / Out/out / Swanky / Coasters / Blissed / MC Organ / Boomcubist / Hazard / Rayonism / Dutch blur / Back clack / Dear world / Iced world
ASCD 032 / Jun '97 / All Saints

☐ HEADCANDY
6896400052 / Jan '95 / EG

☐ HERE COME THE WARM JETS
Needles in the camel's eye / Paw paw negro blowtorch / Baby's on fire / Cindy tells me / Driving me backwards / On some faraway beach / Blank Frank / Dead finks don't talk / Some of them are old / Here come the warm jets
EGCD 11 / Jul '93 / EG

☐ MORE BLANK THAN FRANK (Desert Island Selection)
Here he comes / Everything merges with the night / On some faraway beach / I'll come running (to tie your shoe) / Taking tiger mountain / Backwater / St. Elmo's fire / No one receiving / Great pretender / King's lead hat / Julie with ... / Back in Judy's jungle
EGCD 65 / Jun '87 / EG

☐ MUSIC FOR AIRPORTS (Ambient 1)
1/1 / 2/1 / 1/2 / 2/2
EEGCD 17 / Jan '87 / EG

☐ MUSIC FOR FILMS
M 386 / Aragon / From the same hill / Inland sea / Two rapid formations / Slow water / Sparrow fall 1 / Sparrow fall 2 / Sparrow fall 3 / Quartz / Events in dense fog / There is nobody / Patrolling wire borders / Task force / Strange light / Final sunset / Measured room / Alternative 3
EEGCD 5 / '87 / EG

☐ MUSIC FOR FILMS VOL.3 (Various Artists)
Tension block: *Lanois, Daniel & Brian Eno* / Err: *Eno, Brian & Michael Brook* / 4 minute warning: *Eno, Brian & Michael Brook* / For her atoms: *Mahlin, Misha & Lydia Kavina* / Balthus bemused by colour: *Budd, Harold* / Theme from Creation: *Eno, Brian* / Saint Tom: *Eno, Brian* / White mustang: *Lanois, Daniel & Brian Eno* / Sirens: *Lanois, Daniel & Brian Eno* / Asian river: *Eno, Brian* / Zaragoza: *Laraaji* / Quixote: *Eno, Roger* / Fleeting smile: *Eno, Roger* / Theme for Opera: *Eno, Brian & Roger Eno* / Kalimba: *Laraaji*
ASCD 004 / Mar '96 / All Saints

☐ MY LIFE IN THE BUSH OF GHOSTS (Eno, Brian & David Byrne)
America is waiting / Mea culpa / Help me somebody / Regiment / Jezebel spirit / Moonlight in glory / Come with us / Carrier / Secret life / Mountain of needles / Very very hungry
EGCD 48 / Jul '93 / EG

☐ NEROLI
Neroli
ASCD 015 / Jun '93 / All Saints

☐ NERVE NET
Fractal zoom / Wire shock / What actually happened / Pierre and mist / My squelchy life / Decentre / Juju space jazz / Roil the choke / Ali click / Distributed being
9362450332 / Aug '92 / WEA

☐ ON LAND (Ambient 4)
Lizard point / Lost day / Tal coat / Shadow / Lantern marsh / Unfamiliar wind (Leeks hills) / Clearing / Dunwich Beach, Autumn 1960
EEGCD 20 / Apr '82 / EG

☐ PLATEAUX OF MIRRORS (Ambient 2) (Eno, Brian & Harold Budd)
First light / Steal away / Plateaux of mirror / Above Chiangmai / Arc of doves / Not yet remembered / Chill air / Among fields of crystal / Wind in lonely fences / Failing light
EEGCD 18 / Jan '87 / EG

☐ SPINNER (Eno, Brian & Jah Wobble)
Where we lived / Like Organza / Steam / Garden recalled / Marine radio / Unusual balance / Space diary / Spinner / Transmitter and trumpet / Left where it fell
ASCD 023 / Oct '95 / All Saints

☐ TAKING TIGER MOUNTAIN BY STRATEGY
Burning airlines give you so much more / Back in Judy's jungle / Fair lady of Limbourg / Mother whale eyeless / Great pretender / Third uncle / Put a straw under baby / True wheel / China my china / Taking tiger mountain
EGCD 17 / Jul '93 / EG

☐ THURSDAY AFTERNOON
Thursday afternoon
EGCD 64 / Jul '93 / EG

☐ TRIBUTE TO BRIAN ENO, A (Various Artists)
CLP 0016 / Jul '97 / Cleopatra

☐ WRONG WAY UP (Eno, Brian & John Cale)
Lay my love / One word / In the backroom / Empty frame / Cordoba / Spinning away / Footsteps / Been there done that / Crime in the desert / River
ASCD 12 / Jun '92 / All Saints

Eno, Roger

☐ BETWEEN TIDES
Out at dawn / Field of gold / Prelude for St. John / Ringinglow / Frost / One gull / Silent hours / Between tides / Winter music / While the city sleeps / Sunburst / Autumn / Almost dark
ASCD 01 / Feb '96 / All Saints

☐ FAMILIAR, THE (Eno, Roger & Kate St. John)
Our man in Havana / Wonderful year / We stay still / Rain outside an open door / Song of songs / Mister bosco / Familiar / Blue sea / Lament / Heartland / I've been searching / Days of delay / In a lonely world
ASCD 013 / Apr '97 / All Saints

☐ ISLANDS
SINE 001 / Sep '95 / Sine

☐ LOST IN TRANSLATION
Occham's close shave / Ne cede melia / Last resort / Ventis secundis / Slow and slender / Mariachi funeral (pennies on a dead man's eyes) / Newton's statue / Quando solus / Whispering gallery / Hunch / Domus in nebulae / Emberdays / Rain stopped play / Nostalgia isn't what it used to be / My little darling / Docet umbra / Lost in translation / Evening paragraphs / Green grass
ASCD 018 / Feb '95 / All Saints

☐ MUSIC OF NEGLECTED ENGLISH COMPOSERS
Heavenly sarum / In a old mellow air / Zimzally bim / Tango for the new woman / Ragtime / Old winter / Telestrion / Holiday of a lifetime / Strewwlpeter / Travellen / Bright September / Hour of darkness 1 / Hour of darkness 2 / Hour of darkness 3 / Hour of darkness 4 / Petersfield / How the years turn / Ely diamond / Love affair (version 873) / Love affair (final version) / Anonymous postcard / Still day
RES 126CD / Apr '97 / Resurgence

☐ SWIMMING
Paddington frisk / Whole wide world / Slow river / In water / Amukidi / Swimming / Over the hils / Boatman / Little things left behind / Hewendaway / Aryis / Where the road leads to nowhere / How you shone / Parting glass / Subcircus: *Subcircus*
ASCD 028 / Sep '96 / All Saints

☐ VOICES
Place in the wilderness / Day after / At the water's edge / Grey promenade / Paler sky / Through the blue / Evening tango / Recalling winter / Voices / Old dance / Reflections on IKB
EEGCD 42 / Jul '93 / EG

Enriquez, Bobby

☐ WILDMAN RETURNS, THE
Pink Panther / Our love is here to stay / Groovin' high / Walkin' shoes / Starlight souvenirs / Easy living / I'm confessin' that I love you / As long as I live / Blue Hawaii / Misty
ECD 22059 / Oct '93 / Evidence

Ensemble Bash

☐ LAUNCH
Shiftwork / Apple blossom / Gene pool / Kumpo / Shining through / Shaken not stirred / Suite d'Lorenzo / Dash me something
SK 69246 / Feb '97 / Sony Classical

Ensemble Berehinya

☐ VOROTARCHILC: THE GATEKEEPER
PAN 7002 / Feb '94 / Pan

Ensemble Crai

☐ ROMANIAN PAN PIPES
PS 65176 / Dec '96 / PlayaSound

Ensemble Dede Gorgud

☐ HEYVA GULU: DANCES & ASHUG MELODIES FROM NAKHICHEVAN (Anthology Of Azerbaijanian Music No.3)
PAN 2021CD / Mar '94 / Pan

Ensemble Del Doppio Bordonne

☐ JESUS CHRIST WAS BORN
NT 6722 / Jan '94 / Robi Droli

Ensemble Folk-Art

☐ BULGARIA - WOMEN'S CHORUS
PS 65102 / Mar '93 / PlayaSound

Ensemble Kolkheti

☐ BATONEBO
PAN 7004CD / Apr '96 / Pan

☐ OH BLACK EYED GIRL
PANCD 2006 / May '93 / Pan

Ensemble Kutaisi

☐ MAKRULI: POLYPHONIC SONGS FROM GEORGIA
PAN 7001 / Feb '94 / Pan

Ensemble Morkos

☐ CEDRE
ED 13067 / Jan '97 / L'Empreinte Digitale

Ensemble Musica Criolla

☐ MUSIQUE TRADITIONALE DU CHILI
824742 / Nov '90 / BUDA

Ensemble Nihon No Oto

☐ TRADITIONAL CHAMBER MUSIC OF JAPAN
AUB 6784 / Feb '94 / Auvidis/Ethnic

Ensemble Nipponia

☐ KABUKI AND OTHER TRADITIONAL MUSIC
7559720842 / Jan '95 / Nonesuch

☐ TRADITIONAL VOCAL AND INSTRUMENTAL MUSIC
7559720722 / Jan '95 / Nonesuch

Ensemble Of The Bulgarian Republic

☐ HARVEST, A SHEPHERD, A BRIDE, A (Village Music Of Bulgaria/Original 1955 Recording)
7559720112 / Jan '95 / Nonesuch

Ensemble Recherche

☐ MORTON FELDMAN/SAMUEL BECKETT - WORDS & MUSIC (Ensemble Recherche & Omar Ebrahim/Stephen Lind)
MO 782084 / Oct '96 / Montaigne

Ensemble Tirana

☐ CHANTS POLYPH D'ALBANIE
3001807 / 24 Feb '98 / IMP

Ensemble Tzigane Chiokerly

☐ SERENADE
PV 785092 / Jul '93 / Disques Pierre Verany

Ensign

☐ DIRECTION OF THINGS TO COME
IND 012CD / 10 Nov '97 / Revelation

Enslaved

☐ ELD
OPCD 053 / Mar '97 / Osmose

☐ ENSLAVED
ANTIMOSH 008CD / Apr '94 / Deathlike Silence

☐ ENSLAVED/EMPEROR (Enslaved/Emperor)
CANDLE 12CD / Jan '94 / Candlelight

☐ FROST
OP 025 / Nov '94 / Osmose

ENT

☐ DAMAGE 381
Utopia burns / Punishment solitude / Icon off guilt / Jesus on my side / Cold world / Damage / Shallow existence / Chaos perverse / Crawl / Downside
MOSH 173CD / Jul '97 / Earache

Enteli

☐ ENTELI
PSCD 77 / Oct '94 / Phono Suecia

☐ LIVE
AMCD 738 / May '97 / Amigo

Enthrall

☐ PROPHECIES OF THE DYING
HR 009CD / 28 Jul '97 / Hot

Enthroned

☐ PROPHECIES OF PAGAN
EORCD 004 / May '96 / Osmose

☐ REGIS SATHANAS
BLACK 009MCD / 6 Apr '98 / Blackend

☐ TOWARDS THE SKULLTHRONE OF SATAN
BLACK 008CD / 13 Oct '97 / Blackend

Entombed

☐ CLANDESTINE
Living dead / Sinners bleed / Evilyn / Blessed be / Stranger aeons / Chaos breed / Crawl / Severe burns / Through the underworld
MOSH 037CD / 1 Sep '97 / Earache

☐ ENTOMBED
Out of hand / God of thunder / Black breath / Stranger aeons / Dusk / Shreds of flesh / Crawl / Forsaken / Bitter loss / Night of the vampire / State of emergency / Vandal X / Hey bitch
MOSH 125CD / Mar '97 / Earache

☐ LEFT HAND PATH
Left hand path / Drowned / Revel in flesh / When life has ceased / Supposed to rot / But life goes on / Bitter loss / Morbid devourment / Deceased / Truth beyond / Carnal leftovers
MOSH 021CD / 1 Sep '97 / Earache

☐ RIDE, SHOOT STRAIGHT AND SPEAK THE TRUTH
To ride, shoot straight and speak the truth / Lights out / Wound / They / DCLXVI / Parasight / Somewhat vulgar / Put me out / Just as sad / Damn deal done / Wreckage / Like this with the devil / Boats / Mr. Uffe's horrorshow
CDMFN 216
CDMFNX 216 / Mar '97 / Music For Nations

☐ WOLVERINE BLUES
Eyemaster / Rotten soil / Wolverine blues / Demon / Contempt / Full of hell / Blood song / Hollowman / Heavens die / Out of hand
MOSH 082CD / 1 Sep '97 / Earache

☐ WRECKAGE
Wreckage / Tear it loose / Satan / Lost / Ballad of Hollis Brown
CDMFNM 233 / 6 Oct '97 / Music For Nations

Entwined

☐ DANCING UNDER GLASS
Sound of her wings / Shrad nightward beauty / Under a killing moon / Forgotten / Moment's sadness / Sacrifice of Spring / Red winter / Heaven rise / XIII
MOSH 194CD / 30 Mar '98 / Earache

Entwistle, John

☐ KING BISCUIT PRESENTS...
Heaven and hell / Whiskey man / My size / Boris the spider / Not fade away / Cell number seven / Who cares / Give me that rock and roll / My wife / Interview
KBFHCD 006 / 26 May '98 / King Biscuit

☐ ROCK, THE
REP 4696 / 6 Jul '98 / Repertoire

☐ SMASH YOUR HEAD AGAINST THE WALL
SC 6116 / 22 Sep '97 / Sundazed

☐ WHISTLE RHYMES
SC 6117 / 22 Sep '97 / Sundazed

Enuff Z Nuff

☐ LIVE
Kiss the clown / Indian angel / She wants more / Baby loves you / In the groove / Piano vie / Social disease / Runaway / Way home / Fly high Michelle / New thing / Revolution
PCCY 011932 / 16 Feb '98 / Pony Canyon
MAIM 111252 / 6 Jul '98 / Mayhem

☐ SEVEN
Wheels / Still have tonight / Down hill / Its no good / 5 miles away / LA burning / New kind of motion / Clown on the town / U and I / Oh my way back home / We don't have to be / So sad to see you / Jealous guy / For you girl / I won't let you go
CDMFN 212 / Feb '97 / Music For Nations

☐ TWEAKED
Stoned / Life is strange / If I can't have / Love song / Bullet from a gun / Without your love / Jesus closed his eyes / Mr. Jones / We're all right / Style / My dear dream / My heroin / It's 2 late
CDMFN 190 / Sep '95 / Music For Nations

Enya

☐ BOX OF DREAMS, A (3CD Set)
Orinoco flow / Caribbean blue / Book of days / Anywhere is / Only if / Celts / Cursum perficio / I want tomorrow / China roses / Storms in Africa / Pax deorum / Longships / Ebudae / On my way home / Boadicea / Watermark / Portrait / Miss Clare remembers / Shepherd moons / March of the Celts / Lothlorien / Fire and ice / After ventus / Oriel window / River / Tea-house moon / Willows on the water / Morning glory / No holly for Miss Quinn / Marble halls / Evening falls / Paint the sky with stars / Angeles / Deireadh an tuath / Eclipse / Exile / On your shore / Evacuee / Marble halls / Hope has a place / Sun in the stream / Na laetha geal m'oige / Smaointe
3984213332 / 8 Dec '97 / WEA

☐ CELTS, THE
Celts / Aldebaran / I want tomorrow / March of the celts / Deireadh an tuath / Sun in the stream / To go beyond / Fairytale / Epona / Triad: St. Patrick cu chulainn sister / Portrait / Boadicea / Bard dance / Dan y dwr / To go beyond
4509911672 / Nov '92 / WEA

☐ MEMORY OF TREES, THE
Memory of trees / Anywhere is / Pax deorum / Athair ar neamh / From where I am / China roses / Hope has a place / Tea-house moon / Once you had gold / La sonadora / On my way home
0630128792 / Nov '96 / WEA

☐ PAINT THE SKY WITH STARS (The Best Of Enya)
Orinoco flow / Caribbean blue / Book of days / Anywhere is / Only if / Celts / China roses / Shepherd moons / Ebudae / Storms in Africa / Watermark / Paint the sky with stars / Marble halls / On my way home / Memory of trees / Boadicea
3984208952 / 3 Nov '97 / WEA

☐ SHEPHERD MOONS
Shepherd moons / Caribbean blue / How can I keep from singing / Ebudae / Angeles / No holly for Miss Quinn / Book of days / Evacuee / Lothlorien / Marble halls / After ventus / Smaointe
9031755722 / Nov '91 / WEA

☐ WATERMARK
Watermark / Cursum perfico / On your shore / Storms in Africa / Exile / Miss Clare remembers / Orinoco flow / Evening falls / River / Longships / Na laetha geal m'oige / Storms in Africa (part II)
2292438752 / Aug '93 / WEA

Eon

☐ VOID DWELLER
STEAM 45 CD / Oct '92 / Vinyl Solution

Epic Soundtracks

☐ DEBRIS
RTS 20 / Jan '96 / Return To Sender

☐ SLEEPING STAR
NORMAL 186CD / Aug '95 / Normal

Epicycle

☐ ORANGE
ISAM 1005 / 23 Mar '98 / Idiot Savant Music

Epidemics

☐ EPIDEMICS, THE
Never take no for an answer / What would I do without you / Situations / You don't love me anymore / Love is alright / You can be anything / No cure / Don't I know you / Give an inch / Full moon
8275222 / May '87 / ECM

Epilepsy

☐ BAPHOMET - TAROT OF THE UNDERWORLD (CD Box With Tarot Cards & Book)
KK 144CD / Jan '96 / KK

☐ ROZIS
PA 009CD / Aug '95 / Paragoric

Epilogue

☐ HIDE
Swords and knives / Hide / Wheel of love / Living a lie / In the city / Travelling man / No sign of life / Into the clock / Matthew / Flame
CYCL 010 / Aug '97 / Cyclops

Epinette, Georges

☐ EPINETTE & BARON (Epinette, Georges & Jean Baron)
KMCD 57 / Feb '96 / Keltia Musique

Episode Six

☐ COMPLETE PYE SESSIONS
My babe / Put yourself in my place, baby / That's all I want / I hear trumpets blow / True love is funny that way / Here, there and everywhere / Mighty morris ten / I will warm your heart / Incense / Love hate revenge / Baby, baby, baby / Morning dew / Sunshine girl / I won't hurt you / U.f.o. / I can see through you / When I fall in love / Way you look tonight / My little red book / Little one / Wide smiles / Luck sunday / Mr. universe / Mozart vs the rest / Jack d'or
NEXCD 156 / Jul '91 / Sequel

☐ LIVE AT THE RADIO 1 CLUB SESSIONS 1969
RPM 178 / 29 Sep '97 / RPM

Epitaph

☐ EPITAPH
Moving to the country / Visions / Hopelessly / Little Maggie / Early morning / London girl / Visions / I'm trying / Changing world
RR 7084 / 20 Apr '98 / Repertoire

☐ STOP LOOK AND LISTEN
Crossroads / Nightingale / Uptight / Fly / Stop look and listen / Autumn / Are you ready / We love you / Alice / Paradise for sale
RR 7083 / 20 Apr '98 / Repertoire

EPMD

☐ BACK IN BUSINESS
5363892 / 29 Sep '97 / Def Jam

☐ BUSINESS AS USUAL
I'm mad / Hardcore / Rampage / Manslaughter / Jane 3 / For my people / Mr. Bozack / Gold digger / Give the people / Rap is outta control / Brothers on my jock / Underground / Hit squad heist / Funky piano
5235102 / Jan '96 / Def Jam

☐ BUSINESS NEVER PERSONAL
Boon dox / Nobody's safe chump / Can't hear nothing but the music / Chill / Headbanger / Scratch bring it back / Crossover cummin' at cha / Play the next man / It's going down / Who killed Jane
4719632 / Sep '92 / Def Jam/CBS

Epperley

☐ SOPHOMORE SLUMP
TX 51234CD / 8 Jun '98 / Triple XXX

Epstein Brothers

☐ KINGS OF FREYLEKH
SM 16112 / Dec '95 / Wergo

Equals

☐ ALL THE HITS PLUS MORE
Baby come back / Softly softly / Viva bobby joe / Black skinned blue eyed boys / Laurel and hardy / Rub a dub dub / Michael and the slipper tree / I get so excited / Bad boy / No place to go / Back streets / Domino
CDPT 001 / Jun '92 / Prestige

☐ GREATEST HITS
Viva bobby joe / Baby come back / Backstreet / Laurel and hardy / Rub a dub dub / Michael and the slipper / No place to go / Black skinned blue / Bad boy / Gimme some lovin' / Black is black domino / I get so excited / Softly softly
AHLCD 38 / May '96 / Hit

☐ GREATEST HITS
Viva Bobby Joe / Baby come back / Backstreet / Laurel and Hardy / Rub a dub dub / Michael and the slipper tree / No place to go / Black skinned blue eyed boys / Bad boy / Gimme some lovin' / Black is black / Domino / I get so excited / Softly, softly
399349 / Jun '97 / Koch Presents

☐ SUPREME/SENSATIONAL
REP 4673 / Sep '97 / Repertoire

☐ ULTIMATE HIT COLLECTION, THE
REP 4214 / Aug '91 / Repertoire

☐ VERY BEST OF THE EQUALS, THE
Baby come back / Hold me closer / Viva Bobby Joe / Laurel and Hardy / Another sad and lonely night / Rub-a-dub-dub / Softly, softly / Soul brother Clifford / I get so excited / Teardrops / You'd better tell her / I can see, but you don't know / Black skinned blue eyed boys / I won't there / I'm a poor man / Michael and his slipper tree / Cinderella / Christine / Friday night / Honey gum / No love can be sweeter / Ain't got nothing to give you / Leaving you is hard to do / Put some rock 'n' roll in your soul / Diversion
SEECD 374 / Jun '96 / See For Miles

☐ VIVA EQUALS
MCCD 289 / Mar '97 / Music Club

Equation

☐ HAZY DAZE
Safe and sound / My world / Sister / What did you do today / Kissing crime / Communion / Ataxia / Sad the girl / Clueless / Choose your moves / Myself
3984208242 / 2 Feb '98 / Blanco Y Negro

☐ RETURN TO ME
He loves me / Return to me / Song of the well / Wake up / No goodbyes / Can't cry hard enough / Let him cry / Cross the river / Sad the girl / Golden bird / Strange love / Cloths of heaven
0630153422 / Jun '98 / Blanco Y Negro

Equidad Bares

☐ MES ESPAGNES
Y 225049CD / Apr '95 / Silex

Equinox

☐ LABYRINTH
PRO 017 / Feb '97 / Progress

Equipe 84

☐ RACCOLTA DI SUCCESSI V2
182562 / Aug '93 / Ricordi

Era

☐ AMENO
5349812 / Aug '97 / Mercury

Erasure

☐ CHORUS
Chorus / Waiting for the day / Joan / Breath of life / Am I right / How I love to hate you / Turns the love to anger / Siren song / Perfect stranger / Home
CDSTUMM 95 / Oct '91 / Mute

☐ CIRCUS, THE
It doesn't have to be / Hideaway / Don't dance / If I could / Sexuality / Victim of love / Leave me to bleed / Sometimes / Circus / Spiralling
CDSTUMM 35 / '87 / Mute

☐ COWBOY
Rain / Worlds on fire / Reach out / In my arms / Don't say your love is killing me / Precious / Treasure / Boy / How can I say / Save me darling / Love affair
CDSTUMM 155 / Mar '97 / Mute

☐ ERASURE
Guess I'm into feeling / Rescue me / Sono luminus / Fingers and thumbs (Cold summer's day) / Rock me gently / Grace / Stay with me / Love the way you do so / Angel / I love you / Long goodbye
CDSTUMM 138 / Oct '95 / Mute

☐ I SAY, I SAY, I SAY
CDSTUMM 115 / May '94 / Mute

☐ INNOCENTS, THE
Little respect / Ship of fools / Phantom bride / Chains of love / Hallowed ground / 65,000 / Heart of stone / Yahoo / Imagination / Witch in the ditch / Weight of the world
CDSTUMM 55 / Apr '88 / Mute

☐ POP - THE FIRST 20 HITS
Who needs love like that / Heavenly action / Oh l'amour / Sometimes / It doesn't have to be / Victim of love / Circus / Ship of fools / Chains of love / Little respect / Stop / Drama / You surround me / Blue savanna / Star / Chorus / Love to hate you / Am I right / Breath of life / Take a chance on me / Who needs love like that (remix)
CDMUTEL 2 / Nov '92 / Mute

☐ RAIN
Rain / In my arms / First contact / Sometimes / Rain / Rain / Love to hate you / Sometimes / In my arms / First contact
CDLPMUTE 208 / 17 Nov '97 / Mute

☐ TWO RING CIRCUS
CDSTUMM 35 R / '87 / Mute

☐ WILD
Piano song (instrumental) / Blue Savannah / Drama / How many times / Star / La Gloria / You surround me / Brother and sister / 2000 miles / Crown of thorns / Piano song
CDSTUMM 75 / Oct '89 / Mute

☐ WONDERLAND
Who needs love like that / Reunion / Cry so easy / Push me, shove me / Heavenly action / Say what / Love is a loser / Senseless / My heart... so blue / Oh l'amour / Pistol
CDSTUMM 25 / '86 / Mute

Erazerhead

☐ SHELLSHOCKED - BEST OF ERAZERHEAD
AHOY 28 / Dec '94 / Captain Oi

Erblast

☐ 2
12985 CD / 3 Nov '97 / Kodex

Erdegran, Lars

☐ CRESCENT CITY CHRISTMAS
BCD 425 / Jan '97 / GHB

Erdmann, Dietrich

☐ WORKS FOR STRING ORCHESTRA
CTH 2145 / Jul '92 / Thorofon

Erguner Brothers

☐ PRELUDE TO CEREMONIES OF THE WHIRLING DERVISHES
VICG 50052 / Mar '96 / JVC World Library

Erguner, Kudsi

☐ DERVISHES OF TURKEY - SUFI MUSIC
PS 65120 / Feb '94 / PlayaSound

☐ PESHREV & SEMAI OF TANBURI DJEMI BEY
Seddiaraban peshrev / Taksim on tanbur / Seddiaraban saz semaisi / Muhayyer peshrev / Muhayyer saz semaisi / Taksim on oud and kanun / Ferahfeza peshrev / Taksim on the ney / Ferahfeza saz semaisi / Neva peshrev / Huseyni / Nikriz sirto
CMPCD 3013 / Oct '94 / CMP

☐ SUFI MUSIC OF TURKEY
CMPCD 3005 / 30 Mar '98 / CMP

Eric B & Rakim

☐ PAID IN FULL
I ain't no joke / Eric B is on the cut / My melody / I know you got soul / Move the crowd / As the rhyme goes on / Chinese arithmetic / Eric B for president / Extended beat / Paid in full
IMCD 9 / '89 / 4th & Broadway

Erick

☐ ESTRANGED
Progress / Terry / Anarchy / 4004 BC 9 a.m. / Beast / Martini 2000 / Egyptians in space / Half hearted Jon / 2 Ways 2 love U / Moral village / Death boll tell
CLOD 14 / Aug '93 / Fragment

Erickson, Eddie

☐ ON EASY STREET
ARCD 19111 / Nov '94 / Arbors Jazz

Erickson, Lenita

☐ LENITA ERICKSON
DCD 9628 / Nov '96 / Dream Circle

Erickson, Roky

☐ ALL THAT MAY DO MY RHYME
TR 33CD / Feb '95 / Trance

☐ CLICK YOUR FINGERS APPLAUDING THE PLAY
422130 / May '94 / New Rose

☐ GREMLINS HAVE PICTURES
Night of the vampire / Interpreter / Song to Abe Lincoln / John Lawman / Anthem / Warning / Sweet honey pie / I am / Cold night for alligators / Heroin / I have always been here before / Before in the beginning
FIENDCD 66 / Oct '90 / Demon

☐ I THINK OF DEMONS (Erickson, Roky & The Aliens)
Two headed dog / I think of demons / I walked with a zombie / Don't shake me Lucifer / Night of the vampire / Bloody hammer / White faces / Cold night for alligators / Creature with the atom brain / Mine mine mind / Stand for the fire / Wind and more
EDCD 528 / Jun '97 / Edsel

☐ LIVE DALLAS 1979 (Erickson, Roky & The Nervebreakers)
422404 / May '94 / New Rose

☐ LOVE TO SEE YOU BLEED
Bloody hammer / Every time I look at you / Miss elude / Haunt / Laughing things / You don't love me yet / Creature with the atom brain / I think of demons / Two headed dog / Red temple prayer / Bumblebee zombie / Click your fingers applauding / Play / Mine mine mind / Things that go bump in the night / Here today, gone tomorrow / Realise your my sweet brown angel eyes / I love to see you bleed / Please don't kill my baby
SFMDCD 2 / Feb '93 / Swordfish

Eric's Trip

☐ ALBUM
SPCD 136336 / Oct '94 / Sub Pop

☐ LOVE TARA
SPCD 115293 / Nov '93 / Sub Pop

☐ PETER
SPCD 102/274 / Jun '93 / Sub Pop

☐ PURPLE BLUE
SPCD 333 / Jan '96 / Sub Pop

Ericson, Rolf

☐ STOCKHOLM SWEETNIN'
DRCD 256 / Oct '94 / Dragon

Ericsson, Lena

☐ DOODLIN'
Days of wine and roses / Doodlin' / Too long at the fair / Love for sale / My second home / Cheek to cheek / Hey John / But not for me / (I'm afraid) the masquerade is over
NCD 8808 / Dec '94 / Phontastic

Erin's Isle Singers

☐ IRISH SONGS YOU KNOW BY HEART
If you're Irish/McNamara's band/Hannigan's hooley / Isle of Innisfree / Molly Malone / Peggy O'Neill/ Sweet Rosie O'Grady/My wild Rose / Grace / I'll take you home again Kathleen/Green glens of Antrim / Moonlight mayo/Wild colonial boy/Lovely Leitrim / Galway Bay/Fields of Athenry / When Irish eyes are smiling / Mountains of Mourne / Banks of my own lovely Lee / Come back Paddy Reilly to Ballyjamesduff / Rare oul times / Dear old Donegal/ It's a long way to Tipperary / Hello Patsy Fagan / Rose of Tralee / Danny boy
21115 / Aug '97 / Laserlight

Erkose Ensemble

☐ TURKISH TZIGANE MUSIC
Bahriye ciftetellisi / Taksim on the kanun / Taksim on the ud / Taksim on the clarinet / Harmandali zeybek / Taksim on the kaman
CMPCD 3010 / Jul '92 / CMP

Eroglu, Musa

☐ INSTRUMENTAL MUSIC FROM ANATOLIA (Eroglu, Musa & Arif Sag)
926202 / Jul '95 / BUDA

Erosion

☐ DOWN
WB 1138CD / Feb '96 / We Bite

☐ EROSION VOL.3
WB 095CD / Nov '92 / We Bite

☐ MORTAL AGONY
WB 036CD / Dec '88 / We Bite

Erotic Dissidents

☐ NAKED ANGEL
Introduction / Jack to the air / Sure beats are working / Right rhythm, right time / Off your ass / Mind fuck / TWAT / Body language / I wanna be loved by you / Move your ass / Shake your hips
SD 4005 CD / Jul '89 / SPV

Erotic Suicide

☐ ABUSEMENT PARK
341972 / Oct '95 / No Bull

Erraji, Hassan

☐ IA DOUNIA (Erraji, Hassan & Arabesque/Sabra)
TUGCD 002 / Nov '90 / Riverboat

☐ MUSIC FOR ARABIAN DULCIMER AND LUTE
SDL 415CD / Mar '96 / Saydisc

Errobi

☐ BIZI BIZIAN
KD 11100 / 15 Jun '98 / Elkar

Error Type

☐ 11
SOM 006CD / 15 Jun '98 / Some

Erskine, Lisa

☐ SEE YOU ON THE OTHER SIDE
SBDCD 5 / 3 Aug '98 / Southbound

Erskine, Peter

☐ AS IT IS
Glebe ascending / Lady in the lake / Episode / Woodcocks / Esperanca / Touch her soft lips and part / Au contraire / For Ruth / Romeo and Juliet
4290852 / May '96 / ECM

☐ BEHIND CLOSED DOORS
65013000052 / 5 May '98 / Fuzz

☐ FROM KENTON TO NOW (Erskine, Peter & Richard Torres)
65013000032 / 5 May '98 / Fuzz

☐ LAVA JAZZ (Erskine, Peter Lounge Art Ensemble)
65013000042 / 5 May '98 / Fuzz

☐ PETER ERSKINE
Leroy Street / ESP / All's well that ends / Coyote blues / In statu nascendi / Change of mind / My ship
OJCCD 610 / Feb '92 / Original Jazz Classics

☐ SWEET SOUL
Touch her soft lips and part / Press enter / Sweet soul / To be or not to be / Ambivalence / Angels and devils / Speak low / Scholastic / Distant blossom / But is it art / In your own sweet way
PD 90616 / May '92 / Novus

☐ TIME BEING (Erskine, Peter & John Taylor/Palle Danielsson)
5217192 / Sep '94 / ECM

Erstrand, Lars

☐ DREAM DANCING
OP 9101CD / Sep '91 / Opus 3

☐ LARS ERSTRAND
CD 19405 / May '96 / Opus 3

☐ LARS ERSTRAND AND FOUR BROTHERS (Erstrand, Lars & Four Brothers)
OP 8402CD / Sep '91 / Opus 3

☐ TRIBUTE TO LIONEL HAMPTON (Erstrand, Lars & Wobbling Woodwinds)
NCD 8835 / Feb '95 / Phontastic

☐ WE'LL MEET AGAIN (Erstrand, Lars & Ove Lind)
NCD 8854 / Jan '98 / Phontastic

Ervin, Booker

☐ BLUES BOOK
Blues book / Eeerie dearie / One for Mort / No booze blooze / True blue
OJCCD 780 / Jan '94 / Original Jazz Classics

☐ COOKIN'
Dee da do / Mr. Wiggles / You don't know what love is / Down in the dumps / Well well / Autumn leaves
SV 0150 / Oct '97 / Savoy Jazz

☐ DOWN IN THE DUMPS
Down in the dumps / Well well / Mr. Wiggles / When you're smiling / Dee da do / You don't know what love is / Autumn leaves / Trolley song
SV 0245 / Oct '97 / Savoy Jazz

☐ SONG BOOK, THE
Lamp is low / Come Sunday / All the things you are / Just friends / Yesterdays / Our love is here to stay
OJCCD 779 / Apr '94 / Original Jazz Classics

☐ SPACE BOOK, THE
Number two / I can't get started / Mojo / There is no greater love
OJCCD 896 / Oct '96 / Original Jazz Classics

☐ THAT'S IT
Mojo / Uranus / Poinciana / Speak low / Booker's blues / Boo
CCD 79014 / Feb '97 / Candid

Eschete, Ron

☐ CLOSER LOOK, A
Like someone in love / One for Pop / When it's sleepy time down South/Stars fell on Alabama / Do you know what it means to miss New Orleans / You stepped out of a dream / I'll be seeing you / Mona Lisa / Amazing Grace / Stardust / Coquette / My foolish heart / Manha De Carnaval / My blue heaven
CCD 4607 / Jul '94 / Concord Jazz

☐ COME RAIN OR COME SHINE
Azul serape / Some other time / Come rain or come shine / Theme for Jeff / Naima / Girl next door / Moanin' / Nuages / Loads of love / Goodbye
CCD 4665 / Sep '95 / Concord Jazz

☐ SOFT WINDS
I'll close my eyes / Sleepwalk / 1-5 blues / Where or when / Because of you / Sweet and lovely / But beautiful / Soft winds / Rumpled silk skin / My romance
CCD 4737 / Dec '96 / Concord Jazz

Escorts

☐ FROM THE BLUE ANGEL
Dizzy Miss Lizzy / All I want is you / One to cry / Tell me baby / I don't want to go without you / Don't forget to write / C'mon home baby / You'll get no lovin' that way / Let it be me / Mad mad world / From head to toe / Night time
EDCD 422 / May '95 / Edsel

Escorts

☐ PRISONERS OF SOUL
I'll be sweeter tomorrow / By the time I get to Phoenix / Little green apples / All we need (is another chance) / Look over your shoulder / I'm so glad I found you / Ooh baby baby / Disrespect can wreck / Let's make love (at home sometimes) / Corruption (man's self destruction) / We've come too far to end it now / Brother / I only have eyes for you / Shoo nough / La la means I love you / Within without / I can't stand to see you cry
NEMCD 931 / Jul '97 / Sequel

Escoude, Christian

☐ HOLIDAYS (Escoude, Christian Gipsy Trio)
Bird alone / J'aime Paris au mois de Mai / Holiday for strings / Nem um talvez / Que nadie sepa mi sufrir / La foule / Cavatina / Day I met Bill Evans / After you've gone / Lyle's song
5143042 / Feb '94 / EmArCy

Escovedo, Alejandro

☐ 13 YEARS
WMCD 1017 / Sep '96 / Watermelon

☐ END, THE/LOSING YOUR TOUCH
WMCD 0017 / Sep '96 / Watermelon

☐ GRAVITY
Paradise / Broken bottle / By eleven / Bury me / Five hearts breaking / Oxford / Last to know / She doesn't live here anymore / Pyramid of tears / Gravity/Falling down again
422409 / May '94 / New Rose
WMCD 1007 / Nov '96 / Watermelon

☐ MORE MILES THAN MONEY (Live 1994-1996)
Timber / Bowling green / High on cruel / Karoline / Lonely old ladies / Honky tonk hiccups / Virginia / Duchess / Thanks a lot / Led me away / Misfire
BS 027 / 9 Mar '98 / Bloodshot

☐ WITH THESE HANDS
Put you down / Slip / Crooked frame / 2 am / Nickel and a spoon / Little bottles / Sometimes / Guilty was his name / Tired skin / With these hands / Tugboat (fro Sterling Morrison)
RCD 10343 / Mar '96 / Rykodisc

Escovedo, Pete

☐ E STREET
Another star / Sambacu / Fantasy / Boomerang / Smile please / Like a volcano / You're my little girl / La familia / Waterfall / Lord remember me
CCD 47482 / Apr '97 / Concord Vista

☐ FLYING SOUTH
Flying South / All this love / Cabo frio / Tiemblas / Flying easy / Still life / Esta noche / Como rien / Leyte / Canto para changó / El alma de carnival
CCD 4684 / Feb '96 / Concord Jazz

☐ YESTERDAY'S MEMORIES - TOMORROW'S DREAMS
Charango sunrise / Moving pictures / Azteca Mozambique / Ah ah / Cueros / Modern dance / Zina's Zamba / Yesterday's memories, tomorrow's dreams / Revolt
CCD 45002 / Jul '87 / Concord Jazz

Eskalte Gaeste

☐ KUNSTSCHEISSE
EFA 11891 / Apr '93 / EFA

Eskelin, Ellery

☐ FIGURE OF SPEECH
1212322 / Apr '93 / Soul Note

☐ ONE GREAT DAY
HATOLOGY 502 / Nov '97 / Hatology

☐ SUN DIED, THE
1212822 / Oct '96 / Soul Note

Eskenazi, Roza

☐ REBETIKO
ML 0088 / 11 May '98 / Musurgia Graeca

☐ REMBETISSA
Rast Gazel / Ousak Mare / Mes'tou Zambikou ton teke / Ferte Birres / Derti ke Pono Apoktisa / Yiati Foumaro Kokaini / Hariklaki / Yinome Andhras / Konialis / Dhodheka Cronon Koritsi / Barberaki / Yiannoula / Me Zournadhes Ke Daoulia / Yiannousena / Ouzo, hasis / O Xenitevmenos / Mes' to Vathi Skotadhi / Tou Psara o Tios / To Gri Gri / Ta Dhika Sou Ta Sfalmata
ROUCD 1080 / Sep '96 / Rounder

☐ REMBETISSA 1933-1936
HTCD 35 / Jun '97 / Heritage

Eskens, Margot

☐ EIN HERZ, DAS KANN MAN NICHT KAUFEN
BCD 15952 / Jun '96 / Bear Family

☐ OB IN BOMBAY, OB IN RIO
Ob in Bombay, ob in Rio / Coeur blesse, armes herz / Mein schonster traum / Gluck und tranen / Si petite / Melodie von laramie / Oh Smoky, oh Smoky / Sole, sole / Schau' mich an / Eine reise in die vergangerheit / Ich tausche mit keinem auf der welt / Ein bisschen seligkeit / Moonlight song / Mama / Vergiss mein nicht / Serenade der liebe / Lieberlei ist leider keine liebe / Wenn die sonne hinter den dachern versinkt / Eine weisse hochzeitskutsche: *Eskens, Margot & Kurt Stelly* / Mutti, du darfst doch nicht weinen / Es kam der fruhling / Einsamer sonntag / Bald schon da sehen wir uns wieder / Sail to Bombay, sail to Rio / Mama / Si tu m'aimes tant que ca / Melancolie / Quaranta notti / Ma melodie
BCD 16138 / Apr '97 / Bear Family

Eskimos & Egypt

☐ PERFECT DISEASE
TPLP 37CD / Sep '93 / One Little Indian

Eskovitz, Bruce

☐ ONE FOR NEWK
Moving out / No moe / Airegin / Poor butterfly / Valse hot / Paradox / Strode rode / Pent-up house / Count your blessings / Tenor madness
378012 / May '96 / Koch Jazz

ESP Summer

☐ ESP SUMMER
PER 005 / May '97 / Perdition Plastics

Espacio, Cuarto

☐ REENCUENTRO
Tumbania / Sancho / Reencuentro / Pantera / Tranquilidad / Polka and son / Reencuentro (reprise) / Hay gritos / Momo
INT 30602 / Nov '93 / Intuition

Esperanto

☐ ESPERANTO
You're the one / Are you the best / Only a miracle / Turning point / All good things / Love affair / Don't let love pass away / Something that you said / Glad that you were mine
SJRCD 023 / Mar '95 / Soul Jazz

Espinasse, Philippe

☐ CAMINS (Espinasse, Philippe & J.M.)
173192 / Jan '97 / Musidisc

Espiritu

☐ ANOTHER LIFE
Baby I wanna live / Man don't cry / Sleeper / Another life / My reality / You don't get me / Beat of my heart / Deep end / Nocturno carrusel / So scared / U send me
HVNLP 18CD
HVNLP 18CDX / Aug '97 / Heavenly

Esplendor Geometrico

☐ CONTOL REMOTO 1.0
EFA 015642 / Feb '96 / Apocalyptic Vision

☐ ESPLENDOR GEOMETRICO 1980-1988
AV 020CD / Nov '96 / Apocalyptic Vision

Esplin, Joss

☐ SCOTLAND 'TIL I RETURN (Esplin, Joss & Sandra Wright)
JJCD 1020 / Jan '93 / Beechwood

Esposito, Favio

☐ NEAPOLITAN SONGS
926702 / Apr '97 / BUDA

Esposito, Gene

☐ RHYTHM SECTION
PS 004CD / Sep '95 / P&S

Esquerita

☐ ROCKIN' THE JOINT
CD 2713 / 22 Jun '98 / Collectables

☐ SOCK IT TO ME BABY
Introduction by Little Richard / Sock it to me baby / Nobody want you when you're down and out / Mississippidod damn / Wig wearin' baby / I can't stand it anymore / Get along, honey, honey / I guess I'll go through life alone / Never again / Till then / At the Dewdrop Inn / (I don't want nobody gonna) steal my love from me / What's wrong with you
BCD 15504 / Nov '93 / Bear Family

Esquire

☐ COMING HOME
WCPCD 1011 / Sep '96 / West Coast
RME 0185CD / 19 Jan '98 / Renaissance

☐ ESQUIRE
To the rescue / Sunshine / Knock twice for heaven / Up down turnaround / Blossom time / Hourglass / Moving together / Silent future / Special greeting / What you've been saying
RME 0177CD / Oct '97 / Renaissance

Esquires

☐ GET ON UP...AND GET AWAY WITH THE ESQUIRES (Classic Chicago Soul 1966-1969)
Get on up / You got the power / Everybody's laughing / You say / I know I can / Groovin' / No doubt about it / I don't know / My sweet baby / Part angel / State Fair / Feeling's gone / Woman / When I'm ready / How was I to know / Listen to me / Why can't I stop / Things won't be the same / (That) ain't no reason / Reach out / Ain't gonna give it up (baba daba dop) / How could it be / And get away
WESA 803 / 15 Jun '98 / Westside

Esquires

☐ FLASHIN' RED 1963-1965
00042 / Nov '97 / Bacchus Archives

Esquivel, Juan Garcia

☐ CABARET MANANA
Mini skirt / Johnson rag / Night and day / El cable / Harlem nocturne / Mucha muchacha / Time on my hands / Malaguena / Guanacoa / Sentimental journey / Estrellita / Limehouse blues / Todavia / April in Portugal / Take the 'A' train / Question mark / It had to be you / Yeyo / Lullaby of Birdland / Flower girl from Bordeaux
07863666572 / Aug '96 / RCA

☐ LOUNGECORE
Mucha muchacha / Jesusita de chihuahua / Mini skirt / Night and day / Yeyo / Vereda tropical / Puerto prinicpe / Besame mucho / La raspa / Nature boy / Cachita / La palome / Carioca / Speak low / Johnson rag / El cable / Poinciana / Sentimental journey / Limehouse blues / Question mark / Ballerina / Lullaby of Birdland / Flower girl from Bordeaux / Harlem nocturne
74321578152 / 27 Apr '98 / Camden

Essence

☐ DANCING IN THE RAIN (Best Of Essence)
Out of grace / Like Christ / Only for you / Cat / Everything / Drifting / Mirage / In your heart / Time / Forever in death / Waves of death / Burned in heaven / Endless lakes / Ice / U 4 life / Angelic / How to make me hate / Mirage '94 / Afterworld / Thirty second song
CDMGRAM 82 / Aug '94 / Anagram

☐ ECSTASY/NOTHING LASTS FOREVER
Burned in Heaven / Only for you / Like Christ / Angelic / Ice / Afterworld / So gorgeously / Despair / One more wasted night / Separation / How you make me hate / September / Out of grace / Everything / Never let go / Air / Thirtysecond song / All is empty
CDMGRAM 103 / Mar '96 / Anagram

☐ MONUMENT OF TRUST, A
Mirage / Drifting / In teats / Nothing / Waves of death / Happiness / Lollipop / Years of doubt / Fire / Death cell / Monument of trust
CDMGRAM 96 / Sep '95 / Anagram

☐ PURITY
Last preach / Reflected dream / Cat / Blind / Never mine / Endless lakes / Forever in death / Salvation / Waving girl / Purity / Confusion / From my mouth / Swaying wind
CDMGRAM 95 / Sep '95 / Anagram

Essence All-Stars

☐ AFRO CUBANO CHANT
HIBD 8009 / Feb '96 / Hip Bop

☐ BONGO BOP
HIBD 8017 / 6 May '97 / Hip Bop

☐ ORGANIC GROOVES
Broadway / Luny tune / True blue / Old wine, new bottles / Smokin'
HIBD 8010 / Sep '96 / Hip Bop

Essex

☐ BEST OF THE ESSEX, THE
Easier said than done / Whenever I need my baby / Where is he / Every night / I love her / Come on to my party / Walkin' miracle / She's got everything / More than it would help / Marriage license / In my dreams / You talk too much / There's no fool like a young fool / Where there's a will / Make him feel like a man / Don't fight it baby / When somethin's hard to get / Just for the boy / I'm making it over / Everybody's got you (for their own) / Be my baby / Be sure / When the music stops / Real true lover
NEMCD 714 / Nov '94 / Sequel

Essex, David

☐ BACK TO BACK
Africa / Father and son / Fall at your feet / Here comes the rain / True love ways / Love train / Singin' the blues / Never meant to hurt you / You really got me / Really nice / Won't back down / Oh Father
5542152 / Mar '98 / Spectrum

☐ BEST OF DAVID ESSEX, THE
Hold me close / Gonna make you a star / If I could / Lamplight / Coming home / Cool out tonight / Bring in the sun / For Emily, whenever I might find her / Rolling stone / City lights / Stardust / Good ol' rock and roll / Turn me loose / America / On and on
4810362 / Dec '95 / Columbia

☐ COLLECTION, THE
Oh what a circus / Heart on my sleeve / No substitutes / Imperial wizard / Silver dream machine / Hot love / Ships that pass in the night / Me and my girl (Night-clubbing) / High flying, adored / Winter's tale / Smile / Won't change me now / Goodbye first love / Tahiti / Fishing for the moon / You're in my heart / Falling angels riding
5517952 / Nov '95 / Spectrum

☐ COVER SHOT
Everlasting love / Time after time / Waterloo sunset / First cut is the deepest / Here comes the night / Paint it black / Out of time / Horse with no name / Letter / I can't let Maggie go / New York mining disaster 1941 / Summer in the city
5145632 / Mar '93 / PolyGram TV

☐ GREATEST HITS
Rock on / Gonna make you a star / Hold me close / Winter's tale / Oh what a circus / Silver dream machine / My and my girl (nightclubbing) / Tahiti / Lamplight / Stardust / Cool out tonight / If I could / Myfanwy / Rollin' stone / You're in my heart / Sun ain't gonna shine anymore / Africa - you shine / Rock on (new version)
5103082 / Oct '91 / Mercury

☐ MISSING YOU
5295822 / Nov '95 / PolyGram TV

☐ NIGHT AT THE MOVIES, A
Girl, you'll be a woman soon / Can you feel the love tonight / Crying game / Wind beneath my wings / Stardust / Together in electric dreams / Oh what a circus / Seperate lives / St. Elmo's fire / Kiss from a rose / Somewhere out there / Silver dream machine / Sea of love / If I had words (anthem)
55376082 / May '97 / PolyGram TV

☐ VERY BEST OF DAVID ESSEX, THE (2CD Set)
Rock on / Lamplight / America / Gonna make you star / Rolling stone / Hold me close / If I could / Oh what a circus / Silver dream machine / Me and my girl (night clubbing) / Winters tale / Tahiti / True love ways / Missing you magic / Myfanwy / Forever and a day / Sun ain't gonna shine anymore / Coming home / Cool out tonight / River / Stardust / City lights / Father and son / Everlasting love / Really nice / First cut is the deepest / Look at the shining sun / New York mining disaster 1941 / Here comes the rain / Fall at your feet / Imperial wizard / Girl you'll be a woman soon / Crying game / Africa you shine / Wind beneath my wings / Will you still love me tomorrow / Singin' the blues / Light my fire / Heart beats like a drum / Shoulder to cry on
5584842 / 1 Jun '98 / PolyGram TV

Essig, David

☐ REBEL FLAG
APCD 072 / '92 / Appaloosa

☐ REDBIRD COUNTY AND HIGH GROUND
Falling / Candyman / Flo's cafe / Norman's glory / Lonesome vigil / Circus song / Waiting game / Wake up smiling / New eighth of January / Redbird country / Poor Ellen Smith / Cripple creep / Rebel flag / Rising star / Watch dog / Woman in the snow / Kick the stone / Paint me a picture / She burned up in the footlights / Albert's cove / Antigonish breakdown / High ground / Sault creek
APCD 133 / 31 Jul '98 / Appaloosa

☐ TREMBLE AND WEEP
APCD 126 / Jun '96 / Appaloosa

Essix, Eric

☐ FIRST IMPRESSIONS
NOVA 8920 / Sep '92 / Nova

☐ SECOND THOUGHTS
NOVA 9138 / Sep '92 / Nova

Estefan, Gloria

☐ ABRIENDOS
Abriendo puertas / Tres deseos / Mas alla / Dulce amor / Farolita / Nuevo dia / La parranda / Milagro de amor / Lejos de ti / Felicidade
4809922 / Oct '95 / Epic

☐ ANYTHING FOR YOU (Estefan, Gloria & Miami Sound Machine)
Betcha say that / Let it loose / Can't stay away from you / Give it up / Surrender / Rhythm is gonna get you / Love toy / I want you so bad / 1-2-3 / Anything for you / Rhythm is gonna get you (12" mix) / Betcha say that (remix)
4631252 / Oct '88 / Epic

☐ ANYTHING FOR YOU/CUTS BOTH WAYS
Betcha say that / Let it loose / Can't stay away from you / Give it up / Surrender / Rhythm is gonna get you / Love toy / I want you so bad / 1-2-3 / Anything for you / Rhythm is gonna get you (12" mix) / Betcha say that (Mix) / Ay ay ay / Here we are / Say / Think about you now / Nothin' new / Oye mi canto (Hear my voice) / Don't wanna lose you / Get on your feet / Your love is bad for me / Cuts both ways
4784852 / Mar '95 / Epic

☐ ANYTHING FOR YOU/CUTS BOTH WAYS/INTO THE LIGHT (3CD Set)
Betcha say that / Let it loose / Can't stay away from you / Give it up / Surrender / Rhythm is gonna get you / Love toy / I want you so bad / 1-2-3 / Anything for you / Ay, ay / Here we are / Say / Think about you now / Nothin' new / Oye mi canto / Don't wanna lose you / Get on your feet / Your love is bad for me / Cuts both ways / Coming out of the dark / Seal our fate / What goes around / Nayib's song (I am here for you) / Remember me with love / Heart with your name on it / Sex in the 90's / Don't wanna lose you (Portugese version) / Close my eyes / Language of love / Light of love / Can't forget you / Live for loving you / Mama yo can't go / Desda la oscuridad / Words get in the way
4853152 / 3 Nov '97 / Epic

☐ CHRISTMAS THROUGH YOUR EYES
Overture / Silver bells / Christmas song / Have yourself a merry little Christmas / Let it snow, let it snow, let it snow / This Christmas / I'll be home for Christmas / White Christmas / Silent night / Christmas through your eyes / Arbolito de navidad / Christmas auld lang syne
4746602 / 3 Nov '97 / Epic

☐ CUTS BOTH WAYS
Ay ay ay / Here we are / Say / Think about you / Nothin' oye mi canto / Don't wanna lose you / Get on your feet / Your love is bad for me / Cuts both ways
4651452 / Sep '94 / Epic

☐ DESTINY
Destiny / I'm giving you up / Steal your heart / Heart never learns / You'll be mine (party time) / Path of the right love / Show me the way back to your heart / Along came you (a song for Emily) / Higher / Reach
4839322 / Jun '96 / Epic

☐ EXITOS DE GLORIA ESTEFAN
Renacer / Conga / No sera facil / Dr. Beat / Regresa a mi / No ti olvidare / Dingue li bangue / No me vuelvoa ennamorar / Si voy a perderte / Oye mi canto (hear my voice)
4675202 / 8 Sep '97 / Epic

☐ EYES OF INNOCENCE (Miami Sound Machine)
Dr. Beat / Prisoner of love / OK / Love me / Orange express / I need a man / Eyes of innocence / When someone comes into your life / I need your love / Do you want to dance
4746872 / Feb '97 / Epic

☐ GLORIA
Heaven's what I feel / Don't stop / Oye / Real women / Feelin' / Don't release me / Don't let this moment end / Touched by an angel / Lucky girl / I wanna be happy / Cubre libre / Feelin' / Don't release me / Heaven's what I feel / Cuba libre / Oye
4898502 / 1 Jun '98 / Epic

☐ GREATEST HITS
Dr. Beat / Can't stay away from you / Bad boy / 1-2-3 / Anything for you / Here we are / Rhythm is gonna get you / Get on your feet / Don't wanna lose you / Coming out of the dark / Christmas through your eyes / I see your smile / Go away / Always tomorrow
4723322 / Nov '92 / Epic

☐ HOLD ME, THRILL ME, KISS ME
Hold me, thrill me, kiss me / How can I be sure / Everlasting love / Traces / Don't let the sun catch you crying / You've made me so very happy / Turn the beat around / Breaking up is hard to do / Love on a two way street / Cherchez la femme / It's too late / Goodnight my love / Don't let the sun go down on me
4774162 / Oct '94 / Epic

☐ INTO THE LIGHT
Coming out of the dark / Seal our fate / What goes around / Nayib's song (I am here for you) / Remember me with love / Heart with your name on it / Sex in the '90s / Close my eyes / Language of love / Light of love / Can't forget you / Live for loving you / Mama you can't go / Desde la oscuridad
4677822 / Apr '95 / Epic

☐ MI TIERRA
Con los anos que me quedan / Mi Tierra / Ayer / Mi buen Amor / Tus Ojos / No hay mal Que por bien no Venga / Si senor / Volveras / Montuno / Hablemos el Mismo Idioma / Hablas de mi / Tradicion
4737992 / Jun '93 / Epic

Estes, Gene

☐ IN A SENTIMENTAL MOOD
STJC 101 / Sep '97 / Arbors Jazz

☐ ON THE EDGE (Estes, Gene Quartet)
PCD 7095 / Jul '96 / Progressive

Estes,'Sleepy'John

☐ BLUES, THE (2CD Set)
Broken-hearted ragged and dirty too / Girl I love she got long curly hair / Divin' duck blues / Milk cow blues / Poor John blues / Stack o' dollars / My black gal blues / Down south blues / Stop that thing / Someday baby blues / Who's telling you Buddy Brown / Married woman blues / Drop down mama / Government money / Vernita blues / Floating bridge / Need more blues / Jack and Jill blues / Poor man's friend / Hobo jungle blues / Airplane blues / Everybody ought to make a change / Liqour store blues / Easin' back to Tennessee / Fire department blues / Clean it up at home / New someday baby / Brownsville blues / Special agent / Maliman blues / Time is drawing near / Jailhouse blues / Tell me about it / Drop down / Lawyer clark blues / Working man blues
FA 258 / 21 Aug '97 / Fremeaux

☐ BROKE AND HUNGRY
DD 608 / Dec '95 / Delmark

☐ BROWNSVILLE BLUES
DD 613 / Jan '93 / Delmark

☐ ELECTRIC SLEEP
DD 619 / Dec '88 / Delmark

☐ GOIN' TO BROWNSVILLE
TCD 6008 / 30 Mar '98 / Testament

☐ I AIN'T GONNA BE WORRIED NO MORE
CD 2004 / Sep '92 / Yazoo

☐ LEGEND OF SLEEPY JOHN ESTES, THE
DD 603 / May '87 / Delmark

☐ SLEEPY JOHN ESTES 1929-1937
DOCD 5015 / Aug '91 / Document

☐ SLEEPY JOHN ESTES 1935-1938
Down south blues / Stop that thing / Someday baby blues / Who's telling you buddy brown blues / Married woman blues / Drop down mama / Government money / Vernita blues / Need more blues / Jack and jill blues / Poor man's blues / Hobo jungle blues / Air plane blues / Everybody oughta make a change / Liquor store blues / Easin' back to tennessee / Fire department blues (martha hardin) / Clean up at home / New someday baby / Brownsville blues / Special agent (railroad police blues)
BLE 592542 / Dec '92 / Black & Blue

☐ SLEEPY JOHN ESTES 1937-1941
DOCD 5016 / Aug '91 / Document

☐ SOMEDAY BABY (The Essential Recordings Of 'Sleepy' John Estes)
This girl I love / She's got long curly hair / Broken hearted / Ragged and dirty too / Divin' duck blues / Milk cow blues / Poor John blues / Stack o'dollars / Stop that thing / Someday baby blues / Married woman blues / Drop down Mama / I ain't gonna be worried no more / Floating bridge / Jack and Jill blues / Everybody oughta make a change / Liquor store blues / New someday baby / Brownsville blues / Special agent / Time is drawing near / Tell me how about it / You shouldn't do that / Lawyer clerk blues
IGOCD 2041 / Nov '96 / Indigo

Estevan, Pedro

☐ NOCTURNOS Y ALLEVOSIAS
21050CD / Jun '94 / Sonifolk

Estragon, Vladimir

☐ THREE QUARKS FOR MISTER MARK
888803 / Nov '89 / Tiptoe

Estrand, Lars

☐ BEAUTIFUL FRIENDSHIP, A
SITCD 9204 / Feb '94 / Sittel

☐ SECOND SET: BEAUTIFUL FRIENDSHIP
Oh lady be good / Someone to watch over me / 'S wonderful / Our love is here to stay / Man I love / Tiger rag / Dream dancing / Between the devil and the deep blue sea / Things ain't what they used to be
SITCD 9205 / Aug '94 / Sittel

Estrellas Caiman

☐ DESCARGA IN NEW YORK
CCD 9035 / Jan '97 / Fresh Sound

Estudiantina Invasora

☐ ESTUDIANTINA TRADITION, THE
NI 5448 / Nov '96 / Nimbus

Etant Donnes

☐ ROYAUME
Royaume / Matin / Quatre / Bleu
SPL 2 / Mar '91 / Spiral

Etchingham Steam Band

☐ ETCHINGHAM STEAM BAND, THE
FLED 3002 / Apr '95 / Fledg'ling

Eternal

☐ ALWAYS AND FOREVER
Stay / Crazy / Save our love / Oh baby, I / I'll be there / Sweet funky thing / Never gonna give you up / Just a step from heaven / Let's stay together / This love's for real / So good / If you need me tonight / Don't say goodbye / Amazing grace
CDEMD 1053 / Nov '93 / EMI

☐ BEFORE THE RAIN
Don't you love me / I wanna be the only one / How many tears / Grace under pressure / Someday / Think about me / Promises / I'm still crying / All my love / What do you mean / Why am I waiting / It's never too late
CDEMD 1103 / Mar '97 / EMI

☐ GREATEST HITS
Angel of mine / Stay / Save our love / Just a step from heaven / So good / Oh baby I / Crazy / Power of a woman / I am blessed / Good thing / Someday / Secrets / Don't you love me / I wanna be the only one / Who are you / Finally / Might as well be me
8217982 / 20 Oct '97 / EMI

☐ POWER OF A WOMAN
Power of a woman / I am blessed / Good thing / Telling you now / Hurry up / Redemption song / It will never end / Who are you / Secrets / Your smile / Don't make me wait / Up to you / Faith in love
CDEMD 1090 / Sep '97 / EMI

Eternal Afflict

☐ JAHWEH KDRESH
EFA 112642 / Mar '94 / Danse Macabre

☐ LUMINOGRAPHIC AGONY
EFA 11252 / Apr '93 / Glasnost

☐ NOW MIND REVOLUTION
EFA 11258 / Apr '93 / Glasnost

☐ WAR
EFA 155762 / Dec '94 / Gymnastic

Eternal Dirge

☐ KHAOS MAGICK
SPV 08412662 / Aug '96 / SPV

Eternal Solstice

☐ DEMONIC FERTILIZER
PP 35021CD / 27 Oct '97 / Displeased

☐ HORRIBLE WITHIN
PP 35020CD / 10 Nov '97 / Displeased

☐ WISH IS FATHER TO THE THOUGHT, THE
PP 35019CD / 10 Nov '97 / Displeased

Eterne

☐ STILL DREAMING
CANDLE 009CD / Sep '95 / Candlelight

Ethel The Frog

☐ ETHEL THE FROG
Eleanor Rigby / Apple of your eye / Staying on my mind / You need wheels / Bleeding heart / Fight back / Don't do it / Why don't you ask / Whatever happened to love / Fire bird
CDMETAL 11 / Jun '97 / Anagram

Ether

☐ STRANGE
She could fly / Watching you / I love her anyway / He say yeah / Wasting time / When she woke / Best friend / If you really want to know / World that she sees / Roadworks / Without you / Strange
4941822 / 6 Jul '98 / Parlophone

Ethereal Winds

☐ FIND THE WAY
CYBERCD 14 / May '95 / Cyber

Etheridge, John

☐ ASH
In / Ash / Venerable bede / Ugetsu / Baiere / Your own sweet way / Chips / Infant eyes / Nardis / You don't know what love is / There is no greater love / Little wing / 81 / Out
VP 175CD / Sep '94 / Voiceprint

Etheridge, Melissa

☐ BRAVE AND CRAZY
No souvenirs / Brave and crazy life / You used to love to dance / Angels / You can sleep while I drive / Testify / Let me go / My back door / Skin deep / Royal station 4/16
IMCD 241 / Mar '97 / Island

☐ MELISSA ETHERIDGE
Similar features / Chrome plated heart / Like the way I do / Precious pain / Don't need / Late September dogs / Occasionally / Watching you / Bring me some water / I want you
CID 9879 / May '88 / Island

☐ NEVER ENOUGH
2001 / It's for you / Letting go / Keep it precious / Boy feels strange / Meet me in the back / Must be crazy for me / Place your hand / Dance without sleeping / Ain't it heavy
IMCD 214 / Mar '96 / Island

☐ YES I AM
I'm the only one / If I wanted to / Come to my window / Silent legacy / I will never be the same / All American girl / Yes I am / Resist / Talking to my angel
CID 8010 / Apr '94 / Island

☐ YOUR LITTLE SECRET
Your little secret / I really like you / Nowhere to go / Unusual kiss / I want to come over / All the way to heaven / I could have been you / Shriner's park / Change / War is over
CID 8042 / Nov '95 / Island

Ethik

☐ INDIVIDUAL TRAFFIC (Ethik II)
EAT 003CD / Oct '95 / Eat Raw

☐ MUSIC FOR STOCK EXCHANGE
DIGI 1001CD / Oct '95 / Digitrax

Ethiopians

☐ CLAP YOUR HANDS
Feel the spirit / So you look on it / Everyday talking / Don't let him go / One / Sharing you / Joy joy / High high / Your promise / Opportunity / Things a get from bad to worse / I'll never get burn / Woman capture man / I want you my baby
LG 21086 / Sep '93 / Lagoon

☐ LET'S SKA AND ROCK STEADY
Engine '54 / My love / You got the dough / Train to skaville (original) / Give me your love / Train to glory / Long time now / Woman's world / Unchanged love / Come on now / Love and respect / Train to skaville (version)
JMC 200103 / Nov '92 / Jamaican Gold

☐ ORIGINAL REGGAE HIT SOUNDS
Free man / Train to Skaville / Engine 54 / Come on now / Train to glory / Whip / Everything crash / Things a get bad to worse / Well red / One / Hong Kong flu / Gun man / What a fire / Woman capture man / Feel the spirit / Drop him / Good ambition / No baptism / Selah / Pirate / Word is love
CDTRL 228 / Mar '94 / Trojan

☐ OWNER FE DE YARD
HBCD 127 / Apr '94 / Heartbeat

☐ SIR JJ & FRIENDS
Well red / Mango tree / Drop him / Version drop / My testimony / Everything crash / Bigger boss / Mek you go on so / Removers / Rock ma dine / Wire version / My girl / I'm a believer / I'm a believer version / Selah / Selah version / Selah
LG 21088 / Sep '93 / Lagoon

☐ SLAVE CALL
Ethiopian national anthem / Ethiopian national anthem / Guilty conscience / Hurry on / Mus follow babylon / Train to skaville / Culture / Obeah book / Let it be / I love jah
HBCD 56 / Nov '92 / Heartbeat

☐ TRAIN TO SKAVILLE
CDGR 229 / 30 Mar '98 / Charly

☐ WOMAN CAPTURE MAN
RB 3006 / Jul '94 / Reggae Best

☐ WORLD GOES SKA, THE
I need you / Do it sweet / Stay loose mama / World goes ska / Give me your love / You get the dough / Sh-boom / Long time now / I'm not losing now / Everyday talking / Wreck it up / Hang on (don't let it go) / I'll never get burnt / So you look on it / He's not a rebel / Mothers tender care / Sad news / Rim bam bam / I need someone / Solid as a rock
CDTRL 312 / Mar '94 / Trojan

Ethnic Heritage Ensemble

☐ 21ST CENTURY UNION MARCH
SHCD 142 / Oct '97 / Silkheart

☐ CONTINUUM, THE
DE 496 / Jan '98 / Delmark

Ethyl Meatplow

☐ HAPPY DAYS, SWEETHEART
Suck / Devil's johnson / Car / Queenie / Close to you / Tommy / Mustard requiem / Abazab / Ripened peach / Feed / Rise / For my sleepy lover / Sad bear / Coney island
3704613542 / Oct '90 / WEA

Etitude Du Temps

☐ PREMIER PARTIE
PNMCD 02 / 22 Sep '97 / Pik 'n' Mix

Etnica

☐ ALIEN PROTEIN
BR 014CD / Apr '96 / Blue Room Released

Etoile 2000

☐ DAKAR SOUND VOL.1
2002868 / Jan '97 / Dakar Sound

Etoile De Dakar

☐ XALIS
ADC 303 / Feb '94 / PAM

Etting, Ruth

☐ CENTENARY
Nothing else to do / I'm nobody's baby / After you've gone / Keep sweeping the cobwebs off the moon / Love me or leave me / My blackbirds are bluebirds / Place to call home / Ain't misbehavin' / Crying for the Carolines / More than you know / Button up your overcoat / I'll get by / Mean to me / I'll be blue / Ten cents a dance / Just a little closer / If I could be with you / All of me / Guilty / Hey young fella / Were your ears burning baby / It's been so long / Take my heart / There's a lull in my life
CDGSE 785074 / Nov '97 / Claremont

☐ GLORIFIER OF AMERICAN SONG 1931-1937, THE
TT 422 / May '98 / Take Two

☐ GOODNIGHT MY LOVE 1930-1937
TT 403 / May '98 / Take Two

☐ LOVE ME OR LEAVE ME
PASTCD 7061 / Jan '96 / Flapper

☐ TEN CENTS A DANCE
Ten cents a dance / Button up your overcoat / Funny, dear, what love can do / But I do, you know I do / Mean to me / I'm yours / If I could be with you one hour tonight / Don't tell him what happened to me / Body and soul / Sam, the old accordion man / Dancing with tears in my eyes / Hello baby / What wouldn't I do for that man / Could I, certainly could / Kiss waltz / Shakin' the blues away / You're the cream in my coffee / Lonesome and sorry / Laughing at life / Love me or leave me
CDAJA 5008 / '88 / Living Era

Etzel, Roy

☐ SERENADE
INT 860196 / '88 / Interchord

Eubanks, Kevin

☐ FACE TO FACE
Face to face / That's what friends are for / Essence / Silent waltz / Moments aren't moments / Wave / Relaxin' at Camarillo / Ebony surprise / Trick bag
GRP 95392 / Jan '93 / GRP

Eubanks, Robin

☐ WAKE UP CALL
United / Ceora / Soliloquy / Oriental folk song / Wake up call / You are too beautiful / Scrapple from the apple / Rush hour
SJL 1001 / Sep '97 / Sirocco

Eugenius

☐ MARY QUEEN OF SCOTS
Pebble-shoe / On the breeze / Blue above the rooftops / Moon's a balloon / Mary queen of scots / Easter bunny / Let's hibernate / Friendly high / River clyde song / Tongue rock / Fake digit / Love, bread and beers
RUST 008CD / Jan '94 / Creation

Eulogy

☐ ESSENCE
SPV 077140782 / Sep '94 / SPV

Euphone

☐ EUPHONE
SUPERCD 006 / 29 Sep '97 / Tiny Superhero

Euphonic

☐ EUPHONIC
Aerosol / Bombscared / Space in my soul / Revolution/Solution / Cattleprod / Onehelluvanorgan / Stakeout / 7 Orbits / Way of the exploding fist / Jah science / RHYTHM / Chewin' marbles / Slinky
DIFCD 1 / 9 Mar '98 / Different Drummer

Euphoria

☐ GIFT FROM EUPHORIA, A
Lisa / Stone river hill song / Did you get the letter / Through a window / Young Miss Pflugg / Lady Bedford / Suicide on the hillside, Sunday morning, after tea / Sweet Fanny Adams / I'll be home to you / Sunhine woman / Hollyville train / Docker's son / Something for the milkman / Too young to know
SEECD 465 / Apr '98 / See For Miles

Euro Boys

☐ JET AGE
SFTRI 519CD / 10 Nov '97 / Sympathy For The Record Industry

Euro Grass

☐ MADE IN EUROPE
Headin' West / When I get to the border / Lookin' out my back door / Once upon a heartbeat / Que Rico Chacoli De Sopuerta / Ocean front property / Woodstock / You've got a crazy heart / Old Indian dream / Pure homemeade love / Cajun girl / Don't think twice, it's alright / TPPC
SCRA 6 / Feb '97 / Strictly Country

Eurogroove

☐ IN THE GROOVE
AVEXCD 28
AVEXCDX 28X
AVEXCD 29R / Apr '96 / Avex

Europa Philharmonic

☐ MEMORIAL TRIBUTE TO DIANA PRINCESS OF WALES, A
CDMO 004 / 27 Mar '98 / Magnum Opus

Europa String Choir

☐ STARVING MOON, THE
Monkey never lies / Sermon on the Mount / Waltz / Mama Tequila / Delicate little me / Carol / Saving grace / Camomilla / La pasta / Prelude / Dancing bride / Little Sinfonie / Health food frenzy / Starving moon
DGM 9509 / Nov '95 / Discipline

Europe

☐ DEFINITIVE COLLECTION, THE
Final countdown / Rock the night / Carrie / Cherokee / Time has come / Heart of stone / Love chaser / On broken wings / Superstitious / Open your heart / Let the good times rock / Sign of the times / Tomorrow / Prisoners in paradise / I'll cry for you / Halfway to heaven / Break free / Sweet love child
4865762 / 20 Jul '98 / Epic

☐ EUROPE
In the future to come / Female / Seven doors hotel / King will return / Boyazant / Children of the time / Words of wisdom / Paradise beach / Memories
4777862 / Feb '97 / Columbia

☐ EUROPE 1982-1992
In the future to come / Seven doors hotel / Stormwind / Open your heart / Scream of anger / Dreamer / Final countdown / On broken wings / Rock the night / Carrie / Cherokee / Superstitious / Ready or not / Prisoners in paradise (Single edit) / I'll cry for you / Sweet love child / Yesterday's news
4735892 / Mar '96 / Epic

☐ FINAL COUNTDOWN, THE
Love chaser / On the loose / Heart of stone / Time has come / Final countdown / Cherokee / Ninja / Danger on the track / Rock the night / Carrie
4663282 / 27 Jul '98 / Epic

European Music Orchestra

☐ GUEST
SN 1212992 / Oct '94 / Soul Note

Eurythmics

☐ BE YOURSELF TONIGHT
It's alright (baby's coming back) / Would I lie to you / There must be an angel (playing with my heart) / I love you like a ball and chain / Sisters are doin' it for themselves: Eurythmics & Aretha Franklin / Conditioned soul / Adrian / Here comes that sinking feeling / Better to have lost in love than never to have loved at all
ND 74602 / May '90 / RCA

☐ EURYTHMICS LIVE 1983-1989 (2CD Set)
Never gonna cry again / Love is a stranger / Sweet dreams (are made of this) / This city never sleeps / Somebody told me / Who's that girl / Right by your side / Here comes the rain again / Sexcrime (1984) / I love you like a ball and chain / Would I lie to you / There must be an angel (playing with my heart) / Thorn in my side / Let's go / Missionary man / Last time / Miracle of love / I need a man / We too are one / (My my) Baby's gonna cry / Don't ask me why / Angel / I need you / You have placed a chill in my heart / Here comes the rain again (acoustic) / Would I lie to you (acoustic) / It's alright (Baby's coming back) / Right by your side (acoustic) / When tomorrow comes
74321177042 / Aug '95 / RCA

☐ IN THE GARDEN
English summer / Belinda / Take me to your heart / She's invisible now / Your time will come / Caveman head / Never gonna cry again / All the young people (of today) / Sing, sing / Revenge
ND 75036 / Aug '91 / RCA

☐ REVENGE
Let's go / Take your pain away / Little of you / Thorn in my side / In this town / I remember you / Missionary man / Last time / When tomorrow comes / Miracle of love
74321125292 / Sep '93 / RCA

☐ SAVAGE
Beethoven (I love to listen to) / I've got a lover back in Japan / Do you want to break up / You have placed a chill in my heart / Shame / Savage / I need a man / Put the blame on me / Heaven / Wide eyed girl / I need you / Brand new day
74321134402 / May '93 / RCA

☐ SWEET DREAMS (ARE MADE OF THIS)
Love is a stranger / I've got an angel / Wrap it up / Could give you a mirror / Walk / Sweet dreams (are made of this) / Jennifer / Somebody told me / This city never sleeps / This is the house
ND 71471 / Aug '95 / RCA

☐ TOUCH
Here comes the rain again / Regrets / Right by your side / Cool blue / Who's that girl / First cut / Aqua / No fear, no hate, no pain (no broken hearts) / Paint a rumour
ND 90369 / Sep '89 / RCA

☐ TOUCH DANCE
Cool blue / Paint a rumour / Regrets / First cut / Cool blue (instrumental) / Paint a rumour (instrumental)
ND 75151 / Jan '92 / RCA

☐ WE TOO ARE ONE
We too are one / King and Queen of America / (My my) Baby's gonna cry / Don't ask me why / Angel / Revival / You hurt me (I hate you) / Sylvia / How long / When the day goes down
74321208982 / Jun '94 / RCA

EVA

☐ EXTRA VEHICULAR ACTIVITY
KICKCD 26 / Jul '95 / Kickin'

Eva-lution

☐ SOUL GLIDE
SUNFCD 001 / Jul '95 / Sunflower

Evangelos, Boudounis

☐ LET IT BEATLES
ML 0185 / 11 May '98 / Musurgia Graeca

Evans, Adriana

☐ ADRIANA EVANS
Love is all around / Seeing is believing / Heaven / Reality / Hey brother / Trippin' / I'll be there / Love me / Looking for your love / Swimming / Say you won't / In the sun
7863675092 / Jul '97 / Loud
07863669582 / Mar '97 / Loud

Evans, Bill

☐ ALONE
Here's that rainy day / Time for love / Midnight mood / One a clear day / Never let me go / All the things you are/Midnight mood / Time for love
8338012 / Feb '94 / Verve

☐ AT SHELLY'S MANNE-HOLE (Evans, Bill Trio)
Isn't it romantic / Boy next door / Wonder why / Swedish pastry / Our love is here to stay / Blues in F / 'Round midnight / Stella by starlight
OJCCD 263 / Feb '92 / Original Jazz Classics

☐ AT THE MONTREUX JAZZ FESTIVAL 1968
One for Helen / Sleepin' bee / Mother of earl / Nardis / I loves you Porgy / Touch of your lips / Embraceable you / Someday my Prince will come / Walkin' up / Quiet now
8278442 / Mar '94 / Verve

☐ AT THE MONTREUX JAZZ FESTIVAL 1968 (Remastered)
One for Helen / Sleeping bee / Mother of Earl / Nardis / Quiet now / I loves you Porgy / Touch of your lips / Embraceable you / Someday my prince will come / Walkin' on up
5397582 / 16 Mar '98 / Verve Master Edition

☐ AT THE VILLAGE VANGUARD (Evans, Bill Trio)
My foolish heart / My romance (take 1) / Solar / Gloria's step (take 2) / My man's gone now / All of you / I loves you Porgy / Milestones / Waltz for Debby / Jade visions
FCD 60017 / Apr '94 / Fantasy

☐ BEST OF BILL EVANS LIVE 1964-1968, THE
5338252 / Mar '97 / Verve

☐ BILL EVANS ALBUM, THE
Funkallero / Two lonely people / Sugar plum / Waltz for Debby / TTTT / Re: person I knew / Comrade Conrad
4809892 / Dec '95 / Sony Jazz

☐ BILL EVANS ALBUM, THE
Funkallero / Two lonely people / Sugar plum / Waltz for Debby / TTT / Re: person I knew / Comrade Conrad / Waltz for Debby / Re: person I knew / Funkallero
CK 64963 / Sep '96 / Sony Jazz

☐ BILL EVANS AT TOWN HALL VOL.1 (Live At The New York Town Hall 21/2/66)
I should care / Spring is here / Who can I turn to / Make someone happy / Solo - In memory of his Father / Beautiful love / My foolish heart / One for Helen
8312712 / Jan '94 / Verve

☐ BILL EVANS SAMPLER
Waltz for Debby / What is there to say / Peace piece / Milestones / My foolish heart / Epilogue
OJCX 011 / Jan '98 / Original Jazz Classics

☐ BILL EVANS TRIO 1964 (Remastered) (Evans, Bill Trio)
5390582 / Oct '97 / Verve Master Edition

☐ BILL EVANS TRIO WITH SYMPHONY ORCHESTRA (Arranged/Conducted By Claus Ogerman) (Evans, Bill Trio)
Granados / Valse / Prelude / Time remembered / Pavanne / Elegie / My bells / Blue interlude
8219832 / Mar '94 / Verve

☐ BLUE IN GREEN
Elsa / Detour ahead / Skidoo / Alfie / Peri's scope / Blue in green / Emily / Who can I turn to / Some other time / Nardis / Waltz for Debby
LEJAZZCD 42 / Jun '95 / Le Jazz

☐ BRILLIANT BILL EVANS, THE
Laurie / Letter to Evans / Mornin' glory / Mash / Up with the lark / Gary's theme / Bill's hit tune / Knit for Mary F
CDSJP 329 / Apr '96 / Timeless Jazz

☐ BRILLIANT BILL EVANS, THE/ CONSECRATION VOL.1 & 2 (3CD Set)
Laurie / Letter to Evan / Mornin' glory / Theme from MASH / Up with the lark / Gary's theme / Bill's hit tune / Knit for Mary F / You and the night and the music / Emily / Two lonely people / I do it for your love / Re: person I knew / Polka dots and moonbeams / Knit for Mary F / Someday my Prince will come / Tiffany / My foolish heart / Days of wine and roses / Your story / Turn out the stars / Like someone in love / My romance
CDSJP 009 / Oct '96 / Timeless

☐ BUT BEAUTIFUL (Evans, Bill Trio & Stan Getz)
Grandfather's waltz / Stan's blues / But beautiful / Emily / Lover man / Funkallero / Peacocks / You and the night and the music / See saw / Two lonely people
MCD 9249 / Aug '96 / Milestone

☐ BUT BEAUTIFUL (Live At Middelheim Jazz Festival Antwerp 1974) (Evans, Bill Trio & Stan Getz)
JD 1208 / Oct '96 / Jazz Door

☐ COMPLETE BILL EVANS RECORDINGS, THE (18CD Set)
53769532 / Oct '97 / Verve

☐ COMPLETE FANTASY RECORDINGS 1973-1979, THE (9CD Set)
Mornin' glory / Up with the lark / Yesterday / I heard the rain / My romance / When Autumn comes / TTTT / Hullo Bolinas / Gloria's step / On Green Dolphin Street / Up with the lark / Quiet now / Gloria's step / When in Rome / It amazes me / Since we met / Midnight mood / See saw / Elsa / Sareen Jurer / Time remembered / Turn out the stars / But beautiful / Re: person I knew / Sugar plum / Alfie / TTT / Dolphin Dance/Very early / 34 skidoo / Emily / Are you all the things / Invitation / Blue Serge / Show-type tune / Nature of things / Are you all the things / Face without a name / Falling grace / Hi lili hi lo / Gone with the wind / Saudade do Brasil / My foolish heart / Touch of your lips / Some other time / When in Rome / We'll be together again / Young and foolish / Waltz for Debby / But beautiful / Days of wine and roses / Elsa / Milano / Venutian rhythm dance / Django / But beautiful / Minha / Driftin' / I love you / Summer knows / In a sentimental mood / Touch of your lips / In your own sweet way / Make someone happy / All of you / What kind of fool am I / People / Since we met / But not for me/Isn't it romantic/The opener / Sweet Dulcinea / Martina / Second time around / Child is born / Bass face / Nobody else but me / Sugar plum / Time remembered / 34 skidoo / TTTT / Turn out the stars / Someday my prince will come / Minha / All of you / Waltz for Debby / Eiderdown / Every time we say goodbye / Pensativa / Speak low / When I fall in love / Night and day / I will say goodbye / Dolphin dance / Seascape / Peau douce / Nobody else but me / I will never say goodbye / Opener / Quiet light / House is not a home / Orson's theme / Marian McPartland's piano jazz interview / Kaleidoscope / Waltz for Debby / All of you / In your own sweet way / Touch of your lips / Reflections in D / I love you / Days of wine and roses / This is all I ask / While we're young
FCD 10122 / Nov '96 / Fantasy

☐ COMPLETE RIVERSIDE RECORDINGS, THE (12CD Set)
I love you / Five / Conception / Easy living / Displacement / Speak low / Our delight / No cover, no minimum / No cover, no minimum / I got it bad and that ain't good / Waltz for Debby / My romance / Minority / Young and foolish / Night and day / Oleo / Tenderly / What is there to say / Peace piece / Lucky to be me / Some other time / Epilogue / You and the night and the music / When I fall in love / Woody 'n' you / Woody 'n' you / My heart stood still / On Green Dolphin Street / Peri's scope / Witchcraft / Spring is here / What is this thing called love / Come rain or come shine / Blue in green / Blue in green / Autumn leaves / Autumn leaves / Someday my prince will come / When I fall in love / Elsa / Sweet and lovely / Beautiful love / Beautiful love / I wish I knew / Boy next door / Haunted heart / Nardis / Nardis / How deep is the ocean / Israel / Who cares / Who cares / Goodbye / Nancy / Toy / Elsa / Waltz for Debby / Venice / Know what I mean / Know what I mean / Alice in Wonderland / My foolish heart / All of you / My romance / Some other time / Solar / Gloria's step / My man's gone now / All of you / Detour ahead / Waltz for Debby / Alice in wonderland / I loves you Porgy / My romance / Milestones / Detour ahead / Gloria's step / Waltz for Debby / All of you / Jade visions / Jade visions / Few final bars / Danny boy / Like someone in love / In your own sweet way / Easy to love / How my heart sings / Summertime / If you could see me now / Waking up / Very early / Show-type tune / Re: person I used to know / 34 skidoo / Polka dots and moonbeams / I should care / I fall in love too easily / Everything I love / In love in vain / Stairway to the stars / In your own sweet way / It might as well be Spring / Wrap your troubles in dreams / When you wish upon a star / You go to my head / You and the night and the music / Interplay / I'll never smile again / I'll never smile again / Loose bloose / Loose bloose / Fudgesickle built for four / Time remembered / Funkallero / My bells / Then came you / Fun ride / What kind of fool am I / My favourite things/Easy to love/Baubles, bangles and beads / When I fall in love / Spartacus/Nardis / Everything happens to me / April in Paris / All the things you are / Santa Claus is coming to town / I loves you Porgy / What kind of fool am I / Love is here to stay / Ornithology / Autumn in New York/How about you / How about you / All the things you are / Lover man / Love is here to stay / Stella by starlight / 'Round midnight / Boy next door / Isn't it romantic / What is this thing called love / How about you / Blues in F/five / Everything happens to me / In a sentimental mood / My heart stood still / Time remembered / Wonder why / Swedish pastry
12RCD 0182 / Nov '96 / Riverside

☐ CONSECRATION VOL.1 (Evans, Bill Trio)
You and the night and the music / Emily / Two lonely people / I do it for your love / Re: person I knew / Polka dots and moonbeams / Knit for Mary F / Someday my Prince will come
CDSJP 331 / Apr '96 / Timeless Jazz

☐ CONSECRATION VOL.2 (Evans, Bill Trio)
Tiffany / My foolish heart / Days of wine and roses / Your story / Turn out the stars / Like someone in love / My romance
CDSJP 332 / Apr '96 / Timeless Jazz

☐ CONVERSATIONS WITH BILL EVANS (Thibaudet, Jean-Yves)
Song for Helen / Waltz for Debby / Turn out the stars / Noelle's theme / Reflections in D / Here's that rainy day / Hullo Bolinas / Spartacus / Since we met / Peace piece / Your story / Lucky to be me
4555122 / May '97 / Decca

☐ CONVERSATIONS WITH MYSELF (Remastered)
5214092 / Oct '97 / Verve Master Edition

☐ EMPATHY/A SIMPLE MATTER OF CONVICTION
Washington twist / Danny boy / Let's go back to the waltz / With a song in my heart / Goodbye / I believe in you / Simple matter of conviction / Stella by starlight / Orbit / Laura / My melancholy baby / I'm getting sentimental over you / Star eyes / Only child / These things called changes
8377572 / Jan '90 / Verve

☐ EVERYBODY DIGS BILL EVANS
Minority / Young and foolish / Lucky to be me / Night and day / Epilogue / Tenderly / Peace piece / What is there to say / Oleo
OJCCD 68 / Feb '92 / Original Jazz Classics

☐ EXPLORATIONS
Israel / Haunted heart / Beautiful love / Elsa / Nardis / How deep is the ocean / I wish I knew / Sweet and lovely
OJCCD 37 / Feb '92 / Original Jazz Classics

☐ HOW MY HEART SINGS (Evans, Bill Trio)
How my heart sings / I should care / In your own sweet way (take 1) / In your own sweet way (take 2) / Walking up / Summertime / 34 skidoo / Ev'rything I love / Show-type tune
OJCCD 369 / Feb '92 / Original Jazz Classics

☐ INTERMODULATION (Evans, Bill & Jim Hall)
I've got you under my skin / My man's gone now / Turn out the stars / Angel face / Jazz samba / All across the city
8337712 / Jan '93 / Verve

☐ INTERPLAY (Evans, Bill & Freddie Hubbard)
You and the night and the music / When you wish upon a star / I'll never smile again / Interplay / You go to my head / Wrap you troubles in dreams
OJCCD 308 / Feb '92 / Original Jazz Classics

☐ JAZZ MASTERS
Israel / Here's that rainy day / Just you, just me / Sleepin' bee / Let's go back to the waltz / Funkallero / NYC's no lark / Mother of earl / Bemsha swing / Angel face / Alfie / On Green Dolphin Street / Quiet now
5198212 / 5 May '98 / Verve

☐ JAZZHOUSE
How deep is the ocean / How my heart sings / Goodbye / Autumn leaves / California here I come / Sleepin' bee / Polka dots and moonbeams / Stella by starlight / Five
MCD 91512 / Apr '94 / Milestone

☐ LIVE IN TOKYO
Mornin' glory / Up with the lark / On Green Dolphin Street / Gloria's step / Hullo bolinas / TTTT / When autumn comes / My romance / Yesterday I heard the rain
4812652 / Dec '95 / Sony Jazz

☐ LOOSE BLUES
Loose bloose / Time remembered / Funkallero / My bells / There came you / Fudgesickle built for four / Fun ride
MCD 92002 / Aug '94 / Milestone

☐ MONTREUX VOL.2
Very early / Alfie / 34 Skidoo / How my heart sings / Israel / I hear a rhapsody / Peri's scope
4812642 / Dec '95 / Sony Jazz

☐ MONTREUX VOL.3 (Evans, Bill & Eddie Gomez)
Elsa / Milano / Venutian rhythm dance / Django / Minha (all mine) / Driftin' / I love you / Summer knows
OJCCD 644 / Feb '92 / Original Jazz Classics

☐ MOODS UNLIMITED (Evans, Bill & Hank Jones/Red Mitchell)
Yesterdays / There is no greater love / All the things you are / In a sentimental mood / Night and day
ECD 220722 / Nov '93 / Evidence

☐ MOONBEAMS (Evans, Bill Trio)
Re person I knew / Polka dots and moonbeams / I fall in love too easily / Stairway to the stars / If you could see me now / It might as well be spring / In love in vain / Very early
OJCCD 434 / Feb '92 / Original Jazz Classics

☐ NEW JAZZ CONCEPTIONS
I love you / Five / I got it bad and that ain't good / Conception / Easy living / Displacement / Speak low / Waltz for Debby / Our delight / My romance / No cover, no minimum
OJCCD 25 / Feb '92 / Original Jazz Classics

☐ PERSON I KNEW
Re: Person I knew / Sugar plum / Alfie / TTT / Excerpt from Dolphin dance / Very early / 34 skidoo / Emily / Are you all the things
OJCCD 749 / Apr '93 / Original Jazz Classics

☐ PORTRAIT IN JAZZ
Come rain or come shine / Autumn leaves / Witchcraft / When I fall in love / Peri's scope / What is this thing called love / Spring is here / Someday my Prince will come / Blue in green
OJCCD 88 / Feb '92 / Original Jazz Classics

☐ QUIET NOW
Very airy / Sleepin' bee / Quiet now / Turn out the stars / Autumn leaves / Nardis
LEJAZZCD 32 / Sep '94 / Le Jazz

☐ SECRET SESSIONS, THE (8CD Set)
Very early / 'Round midnight / One for helen / Blue in green / Turn out the stars / Waltz for Debby / Time remembered / Autumn leaves / I should care / Elsa / Who can I turn to (when nobody needs me) / My foolish heart / In your own sweet way / Five / Gloria's step / Nardis / Someday my Prince will come / Who can I turn to (when nobody needs me) / Come rain or come shine / If you could see me now / Spring is here / Re: person I knew / Sleepin' bee / Emily / Alfie / Walkin' up / You're gonna hear from me / Some other time / I'll remember april / Alice in wonderland / I love you / Very early / Round midnight / Stella by starlight / My man's gone now / Turn out the stars / In a sentimental mood / When I fall in love / Nardis / Come rain or come shine / Gloria's step / Round midnight / Blue in green / Waltz for Debby / Detour ahead / On green dolphin street / My foolish heart / If you could see me now / Elsa / How deep is the ocean / Polka dots and moonbeams / I'm getting sentimental over you / I should care / Star eyes / Peri's scope / Haunted heart / Airegin / Little lulu / Five (theme) / Turn out the stars / Nardis / California, here I come / Very early / Easy living / Wonder why / Time remembered / You and the night and the music / Beautiful love / Waltz for Debby / I fall in love too easily / My man's gone now / Who can I turn to (when nobody needs me) / Polka dots and moonbeams / Emily / Ev'rything I love / Someday my prince will come / Shadow of your smile / Sleepin' bee / Blue in green / For heaven's sake / Love is here to stay / In a sentimental mood / How my heart sings / On green dolphin street / My foolish heart / Stella by starlight / Midnight mood / What are you doing the rest of your life / I should care / Autumn leaves / Re: person I knew / Alfie / Very early / Polka dots and moonbeams / Mornin' glory / Yesterday I heard the rain / Emily / Time remembered / Who I can I turn to (when nobody needs me) / Dolphin dance / Sugar plum / Turn out the stars / Quiet now / Waltz for Debby
MCD 44212 / Jan '97 / Milestone

☐ SERENITY
LEJAZZCD 5 / Mar '93 / Le Jazz

☐ SINCE WE MET
Since we met / Midnight mood / See saw / Sareen jurer / Time remembered / Turn out the stars / But beautiful
OJCCD 622 / Aug '94 / Original Jazz Classics

☐ SMALL HOTEL, A (Evans, Bill Trio)
FDM 365612 / Jul '93 / Dreyfus

☐ SOLO SESSIONS VOL.1
What kind of fool am I / My favourite things-easy to love-baubles bangles and beads(/ When I fall in love / Spartacus love theme-nardis (medley) / Everything happens to me / April in paris
MCD 9170 / Oct '93 / Milestone

☐ SUNDAY AT THE VILLAGE VANGUARD
Gloria's step / My man's gone now / Solar / Alice in wonderland / All of you / Jade visions
911900512 / 19 May '98 / JVC
OJC20 1402 / Sep '98 / Original Jazz Classics

☐ SUNDAY NIGHT AT THE VILLAGE VANGUARD
Gloria's step / My man's gone now / Solar / Alice in wonderland / All of you / Jade visions
OJCCD 140 / Feb '92 / Original Jazz Classics

☐ TOKYO CONCERT, THE
Mornin' glory / Up with the lark / Yesterday I heard the rain / My romance / When autumn comes / T.t.t.t. (twelve tone tune two) / Hullo bolinas / Gloria's step / On green dolphin street
OJCCD 345 / Feb '92 / Original Jazz Classics

☐ TURN OUT THE STARS (The Music Of Bill Evans) (Repertory Quartet)
MECCACD 1098 / May '97 / Music Mecca

☐ WALTZ FOR DEBBY (Evans, Bill Trio)
My foolish heart / Waltz for debby / Detour ahead / My romance / Some other time / Milestones
OJC20 2102 / Sep '98 / Original Jazz Classics

☐ YOU'RE GONNA HEAR FROM ME
You're gonna hear from me / Waltz for Debby / Time remembered / Emily / Someday my Prince will come / 'Round midnight / Nardis / Who can I turn to / Our love is here to stay
MCD 91642 / Aug '94 / Milestone

Evans, Bill

☐ ESCAPE
Swing hop / Escape / Reality / Sunday after / Rattletrap / Flash in dreamland / Coravilas / Easilee / Undercover / La di da / Armsakimbo / Aftermath
ESC 036502 / Apr '96 / Escapade

☐ PETITE BLONDE
Prize hat / Branca's hal / Millenium / Oh so hip / Daddy's long leg / Watcher / Stansfield
LIP 890122 / Jun '96 / Lipstick

☐ STARFISH AND THE MOON
Something in the rose / Starfish and the moon / Little slow poke / I'll miss you / Whiskey talk / Last goodbye / Red dog / It's only history / Big blue hat / Shady lady
ESC 036542 / Sep '97 / Escapade

Evans, Bill

☐ NATIVE AND FINE
ROUCD 0295 / Nov '95 / Rounder

Evans, Ceri

☐ HIDDEN TREASURE (Evans, Ceri Sextet)
BLJCD 001 / 1 Sep '98 / Big Life Jazz

Evans, Dave

☐ GOIN' ROUND THIS WORLD
REB 1602CD / Dec '96 / Rebel

Evans, Delyth

☐ DELTA
Taith ar y fferi / Pibddawns y sipsi newydd / Pibddawns y gof / Branle / Mwynder maldwyn / Merch megan / Pandeirada de nebra / Y maerdy/ Pibddawns merthyr / Eleanor Plunkett / Beto o Lansanffraid / Elsie Marley / Er gwell er gwaeth / A l'rntree de l'este / Carolan's receipt for drinking / Jackson's bottle of brandy / Baltiorum / Cariad pur / Gymnopedie III / Carolan's farewell to music / Ysbryd Kilvrough
SAIN 4062CD / Aug '94 / Sain

Evans, Doc

☐ STOMP AND BLUES (Evans, Doc Jazzband)
JCD 195 / Oct '93 / Jazzology

Evans, Faith

☐ FAITH
Faith (interlude) / No other love / Fallin' in love / Ain't nobody / You are my joy / Love don't live here anymore / Come over / Soon as I get home / All this love / Thank you Lord / You used to love me / Give it to me / You don't understand / Reasons
78612730032 / Aug '95 / Arista

Evans, Gil

☐ BLUES IN ORBIT
ENJA 30692 / 17 Nov '97 / Enja

☐ BUD AND BIRD (Evans, Gil & The Monday Night Orchestra)
Bud and bird: *Evans, Gil* / Half man, half cookie: *Evans, Gil* / Gates-illumination: *Evans, Gil* / Nicaragua blues: *Evans, Gil* / Cosmos: *Evans, Gil* / Groove from the louvre: *Evans, Gil*
K32Y 6171 / Sep '88 / Electric Bird

☐ GIL EVANS & TEN
Remember / Ella Speed / Big stuff / Nobody's heart / Just one of those things / If you could see me now / Jambangle
OJCCD 346 / Sep '93 / Original Jazz Classics

☐ HONEY MAN
RD 5022CD / Apr '95 / Robi Droli

☐ INDIVIDUALISM OF GIL EVANS, THE
8338042 / Oct '93 / Verve

☐ JAZZ MASTERS
Time of the barracudas / Greensleeves / Last night when we were young / Moon and sand / Las Vegas tango / Spoonful / Concorde / I will wait for you / Barbara song
5218602 / 5 May '98 / Verve

☐ LIVE AT THE PUBLIC THEATRE NEW YORK 1980 VOL.1
Anita's dance / Jelly roll / Alyrio / Variation on the misery / Orgone / Up from the skies
ECD 220892 / Jun '94 / Evidence

☐ LIVE AT THE PUBLIC THEATRE NEW YORK 1980 VOL.2
Copenhagen sight / Zee zee / Sirhan's blues / Stone free / Orange was the colour of her dress, then silk blue
ECD 220902 / Jun '94 / Evidence

☐ LUNAR ECLYPSE (Evans, Gil & His Orchestra)
1298067112 / Jun '93 / Robi Droli

☐ OUT OF THE COOL
La Nevada / Where flamingos fly / Bilbao song / Stratusphunk / Sunken treasure / Sister Sadie
IMP 11862 / Mar '96 / Impulse Jazz

☐ PLAYS THE MUSIC OF JIMI HENDRIX (Evans, Gil Orchestra)
Angel / Crosstown traffic / Castles made of sand / Up from the skies (take 1) / 1983 / Voodoo chile / Gypsy eyes / Little wing / Up from the skies (take 2) / Little Miss Lover
ND 88409 / Nov '88 / Bluebird

☐ PRICELESS JAZZ
Where flamingos fly / Push de button / Cheek to cheek / La Nevada / Travlin' light / Coconut sweet / Bilbao song / Aren't you glad you're you / Savanna / Sunken treasure / Napolean
GRP 98952 / 23 Mar '98 / GRP

☐ SVENGALI
Thoroughbred / Blues in orbit / Eleven / Cry of hunger / Summertime / Zee zee
92072 / Apr '94 / Act

☐ WHERE FLAMINGOS FLY
Zee zee / Nana / Love your love / Jelly rolls / Where flamingos fly / El matador
3908312 / Jul '94 / A&M

Evans, Guy

☐ LONG HELLO VOL.4, THE
Holsworthy market place / Trick or treat / Der traum von julius / Rock of riley / Caretaker's wife / Wonderful brothers / Martha's express wishes / Hamburg station / Solo kabine / Finger points / Haben sie waffen oder funk dabei / Slow slither loop / My feet are freezing but my knees are warm
VP 112CD / Mar '93 / Voiceprint

☐ UNION CHAPEL CONCERT, THE (2CD Set) (Evans, Guy & Peter Hammill)
Fireworks / Forest of pronouns / Anatol's proposal / After the show / Roger and out / Accidents / Soundbeam melody / Women of Ireland / Ship of fools / Hamburg station / Seven wonders / Barber's adagio / Red shift / Lemmings / Traintime
FIE 9115 / Mar '97 / Fie

Evans, Jenny

☐ SHINY STOCKINGS
Shiny stockings / Good old days / Softly as in a morning sunrise / That's what zoot said / You go to my head / In a mellow tone / Caravan / Willow weep for me / Alright, ok you win / Honeysuckle rose / Song of autumn / April in Paris / All of me
ENJ 93172 / May '97 / Enja

Evans, Paul

☐ FABULOUS TEENS AND BEYOND, THE
Midnite special / Hushabye little guitar / I'm in love again / Hambone rock / Over the mountain, across the sea / Tutti frutti / Butterfly / Slippin' and slidin' / Honey love / I'm walkin' / Since I met you baby / 60 Minute man / Fool / Seven little girls sitting in the back seat / Worshipping an idol / Happy go lucky me / Fish in the ocean / Brigade of broken hearts / Blind boy / Twins / After the hurricane / Just because I love you / Show folk / Why / Roses are red / Disneyland Daddy / Willie's sung with everyone (but me) / Hello, this is Joanne
CDCHD 551 / Nov '95 / Ace

Evans, Rev. Clay

☐ I'VE GOT A TESTIMONY
What a fellowship / Lead me on / God's grace is sufficient for me / God rose in a windstorm / Blessed quietness / I've got a testimony / Praise God / It's me again / Worship the lord / Lost sheep / Everything will be alright
FA 426 / Nov '97 / Fremeaux

Evans, Sara

☐ THREE CHORDS AND THE TRUTH
True lies / Shame about that / Three chords and the truth / If you ever want my lovin' / Imagine that / Even now / I don't wanna see the light / I've got a tiger by the tail / Unopened / Walk out backwards / Week the river raged
74321482512 / Jun '97 / RCA

Evans, Terry

☐ BLUES FOR THOUGHT
Too many cooks / Hey Mama, keep your big mouth shut / Shakespeare didn't quote that / Natcha bone lover / That's the way love turned out for me / So fine / Get your lies straight / Live, love and friends / Honey boy / I want to be close to you, God
VPCD 16 / Jan '93 / Pointblank

Evans, Tony

☐ FALLING INTO YOU
Falling into you / La piu bella del mondo / Dance away / I wanna dance with somebody / I love to love / I'm so excited / Love ain't here anymore / Dream a little dream / Amore scusami / Another time another place / Young hearts run free / I am what I am / Memory / Boom bang a bang
CDE 1034 / May '96 / Tema

☐ I WON'T SEND ROSES (Evans, Tony & His Orchestra)
I won't send roses (foxtrot) / J'attendrai (foxtrot) / It's the smile in your eyes (foxtrot) / 's wonderful (quickstep) / It could happen to you (quickstep) / Dancing with the night (quickstep) / Kiss in your eyes (waltz) / Our waltz (waltz) / Eternally (waltz) / La coumparsita (tango) / Take two to tango (tango) / Adios muchachos (tango)
CDE 1025 / May '93 / Tema

☐ WHERE DID YOU LEARN TO DANCE (Evans, Tony Orchestra & Singers)
Where did you learn to dance / What a little moonlight can do / Night lights / That Sunday, that summer / Dance only with me / Waltzing in the clouds / Sunset tango / Starlight tango / Words get in the way / When you tell me that you love me / Young girl / Don't cry for me Argentina / Love is in the air / Choo choo ch'boogie / Tell him / Spaniard that blighted my life
CDE 1035 / Mar '97 / Tema

☐ WRAP YOUR ARMS AROUND ME (Evans, Tony & His Orchestra)
Wrap your arms around me / Portrait of my love / Let's do it / Too young / April in Portugal / You can't hurry love / Malaguana / Sweet Heaven / Let there be love / This can't be love / I love Paris / Daddy's little girl / Plaisir d'amour / Tropicana tango / Under the bridges of Paris
CDE 1033 / Mar '96 / Tema

EVE

☐ IN THE BEGINNING
THE 4177CD / Apr '94 / Ichiban

Even

☐ LESS IS MORE
RUB 052CD / Jan '97 / Rubber

Evenson, Dean

☐ OCEAN DREAMS
SP 7140CD / Aug '96 / Soundings Of The Planet

☐ WIND DANCER (Evenson, Dean & Tom Barabas)
SP 7149CD / Jul '96 / Soundings Of The Planet

Everclear

☐ SO MUCH FOR THE AFTERGLOW
So much for the afterglow / Everything to everyone / Ataraxia / Normal like you / I will buy you a new life / Father of mine / One hit wonder / El distorto de melodica / Amphetamine / White men in black suits / Sunflower / Why don't I believe in God / Like a California king
8365032 / 2 Mar '98 / Capitol

☐ SPARKLE AND FADE
Electra made me blind / Heroin girl / You made me feel like a whore / Santa Monica / Summerland / Strawberry / Heartspark dollarsign / Twistinside / Her brand new skin / Nehalem / Queen of the air / Pale green stars / Chemical smile / My sexual life
CDEST 2257 / Mar '96 / Capitol

☐ SPARKLE AND FADE
Electra made me blind / Heroin girl / You make me feel like a whore / Santa Monica / Summerland / Strawberry / Heartspark dollarsign / Twistinside / Her brand new skin / Nehalem / Queen of the air / Pale green stars / Chemical smile / My sexual life / Heroin girl / Summerland / Annabella / Sparkle / Heartspark dollarsign / American girl
CDESTX 2257 / Oct '96 / Capitol

☐ WHITE TRASH HELL
Heroin girl / Pacific wonderland / Blondes / Detroit / 1975 / For Pete's sake / Fire maple song
FIREMCD 45 / Mar '97 / Fire

Everdawn

☐ POEMS BURN THE PAST
IR 029CD / 22 Sep '97 / Invasion

Everett, Betty

☐ GREATEST HITS
It's in his kiss (shoop shoop song) / You're no good / I can't hear you / Getting mighty crowded / Chained to your love / Hands off / It hurts to be in love / Hound dog / Until you were gone
CDSGP 0235 / 2 Feb '98 / Prestige

☐ LOVE RHYMES/HAPPY ENDINGS
Sweet Dan / I gotta tell somebody / I wanna be there / Be anything, but be mine / Wondering / Who will your next fool be / I'm your friend / Just a matter of time / I'm afraid of losing you / La la la / Try it you'll like it / Here's the gift / God only knows / Things I say to his shoulder / Bedroom eyes / Keep it up / Just a little piece of you / Don't let it end ('til you let it begin) / As far as we can go / Happy endings
CDSEWD 085 / Jul '93 / Southbound

Everett, Neil

☐ LATE NIGHTS AND EARLY MORNINGS
MGBCD 4002 / 11 May '98 / Mobius

Everett, Sangoma

☐ COURAGE TO LISTEN TO YOUR HEART
Mombasa / Crossroads / Murivel / Auburn prive / Liberated / African plains
TCB 97202 / Jun '97 / TCB

Evereve

☐ STORMBIRDS
Embittered / Fields of ashes / Escape / On lucid wings / Martyrium / Failure / Downfall / Dedications / Stormbirds / As I breathe the dawn / Spleen / Universe / Part of you / Valse bizarre
NB 3142 / 6 Apr '98 / Nuclear Blast

Everfresh

☐ EVERFRESH
Book of lies / Heart / Make up / It needs to be said / Memories / Sanka / Another day / Mileage / Easy / Best friend / Exhausted
LJCD 007 / 25 May '98 / Lockjaw

Evergreen

☐ EVERGREEN
HBLP 0996CD / Mar '97 / Hi-Ball

Evergreen Classic Jazz Band

☐ EVERGREEN CLASSIC JAZZ BAND
SOS 1202 / Oct '92 / Stomp Off

Evergreens

☐ 20 MOST REQUESTED IRISH SONGS
EHCD 1 / Nov '97 / Emerald Hour

☐ IRISH ROVER, THE (20 Classics From The Emerald Isle)
Star of County Down / Do you want your old lobby washed down / Irish rover / Old folks at home / Maggie / Cumberland Road / Marie's wedding / New York girls / Gentle mother / She moved through the fair / Come back Paddy Reilly / MacNamara's band / Seven drunken nights / Your mother's eyes / Red is the rose / Cliffs of Dooneen / Water is deep / Three drunken maidens / Holy ground / Parting glass
EMPRCD 659 / Jun '96 / Emporio

☐ SONGS OF IRELAND
Wild rover / I'll tell me ma / Leaving of Liverpool / Black velvet band / Galway bay / Old bog road / Spanish lady / Mountains of mourne / I'll take you home again Kathleen / Danny boy / Rovin' I will go / Molly malone / Peggy Gordon / Spinning wheel / Muirsheen durkin / Bunch of thyme / Rose of tralee / Whistling gyspy rover / Whiskey in the jar / Carrickfergus
EMPRCD 578 / Jul '95 / Emporio

Evergrey

☐ DARK DISCOVERY
GNW 02CD / 25 May '98 / GNW

☐ LIKE CUTTING THE SLEEPING
HNF 044CD / 29 Jun '98 / Head Not Found

Everly Brothers

☐ ALL I HAVE TO DO IS DREAM (Original Hits & Rarities)
All I have to do is dream / Claudette / Bye bye love / Devoted to you / Hey doll baby / Roving gambler / Rip it up / When will I be loved / Bird dog / Oh true love / Wake up little Susie / Maybe tomorrow / Poor Jenny / Let it be me / Be bop a lula / Put my little shoes away / Long time gone / Love of my life / Leave my woman alone / All I have to do is dream
3036000832 / Jun '97 / Carlton

☐ BEST OF THE EVERLY BROTHERS
DCD 5324 / Dec '93 / Disky

☐ BEST OF THE EVERLY BROTHERS, THE
Bye bye love / All I have to do is dream / Claudette / When will I be loved / I wonder if I care as much / ('til) I kissed you / Rip it up / Maybe tomorrow / Bird dog / Devoted to you / Leave my woman alone / I'm here to get my baby out of jail / Problems / Be bop a lula / Brand new heartache / This little girl of mine / Love of my life / Since you broke my heart / Oh so many years / Should we tell him
MCCD 209 / Jul '95 / Music Club

☐ BROTHERS IN RHYTHM (2CD Set)
SMDCD 179 / 9 Feb '98 / Snapper

☐ CLASSIC EVERLY BROTHERS (1955-60)
Keep a lovin' me / Suns keeps shining / If here love isn't true / That's the life I have to live / I wonder if I care as much / Bye bye love / Should we tell him / Wake up little Susie / Hey doll baby / Maybe tomorrow / Brand new heartache / Keep a knockin' / Leave my woman alone / Rip it up / This little girl of mine / Be bop a lula / All I have to do is dream / Claudette / Devoted to you / Bird dog / Problems / Love of my life / Take a message to Mary / Poor Jenny (one o'clock version) / Poor Jenny (ten o'clock version) / Oh true love / Till I kissed you / Oh what a feeling / Let it be me / Since you broke my heart / Like strangers / When will I be loved / Roving gambler / Who's gonna shoe your pretty little feet / Rockin' alone in an old rocking chair / Put my little shoes away / Down in the willow garden / Long time gone / Lightning express / That silver haired daddy of mine / Barbara Allen / Oh so many years / I'm here to get my baby out of jail / Kentucky
BCD 15618 / Feb '92 / Bear Family

☐ EB84
RE 2040 / Aug '96 / Razor & Tie

☐ EP COLLECTION, THE
I'm here to get my baby out of jail / Rockin' alone in an old rockin' chair / Long time gone / (Til) I kissed you / Oh, what a feeling / Let it be me / Since you broke my heart / Bye bye love / I wonder if I care as much / Maybe tomorrow / Wake up little Susie / That silver haired daddy of mine / Devoted to you / Rip it up / Leave my woman alone / Should we tell him / Hey, doll baby / Claudette / Birddog / All I have to do is dream / Brand new heartache / This little girl of mine / Keep a knockin' / Be bop a lula / Problems / Poor Jenny
SEECD 482 / Aug '97 / See For Miles

☐ EVERLY BROTHERS AND THE FABULOUS STYLE OF...
This little girl of mine / Maybe tomorrow / Bye bye love / Brand new heartache / Keep a knockin' / Be bop a lula / Poor Jenny / Rip it up / I wonder if I care as much / Wake up little Susie / Leave my woman alone / Should we tell him / Hey doll baby / Claudette / Like strangers / Since you broke my heart / Let it be me / Oh what a feeling / Take a message to Mary / Devoted to you / When will I be loved / Bird dog / Till I kissed you / Problems / Love of my life / Poor Jenny (2nd version) / All I have to do is dream
CDCH 932 / Apr '90 / Ace

☐ EVERLY BROTHERS ON WARNER BROTHERS, THE (2CD Set)
Cathy's clown / So sad (to watch good love go bad) / Walk right back / Love hurts / Sleepless nights / Nashville blues / Lucille / What kind of girl are you / Made to love / Radio and tv / Stick with me baby / Always it's you / Temptation / Ebony eyes / Crying in the rain / Don't blame me / True love / That's old fashioned (that's the way love should be) / Nancy's minuet / I'm not angry / How can I meet her / Burma shave / Muskrat / Just one time / Lonely street / Sweet dreams / Price of love / Man with money / Love is strange / Give me a sweetheart / You're the one I love / You're my girl / Kiss your man goodbye / Gone, gone, gone / Don't let the whole world know / Don't forget to cry / Nothing matters but you / It's all over / Empty boxes / Bowling green / Love of the common people / (I'd be) a legend in my time / I'm movin' on / T for Texas / I wonder if I care as much / Lord of the manor / Sing me back home / Shady grove / Cuckoo bird / I'm on my way home again
9362451642 / Jul '96 / Warner Bros.

☐ EVERLY BROTHERS, THE
When will I be loved / Problems / Bye bye love / Wake up little Susie / Barbara Allen / This little girl of mine / Bird dog / I'm here to get my baby out of jail / Claudette / Roving gambler / Leave my woman alone / Long time gone / Oh so many years / All I have to do is dream / Poor Jenny / Be bop a lula / Like strangers / Take a message to Mary
399540 / May '97 / Koch Presents

☐ EVERLY COUNTRY
VSOPCD 237 / Jun '97 / Connoisseur Collection

☐ FABULOUS EVERLY BROTHERS, THE
Bye bye love / Wake up little Susie / All I have to do is dream / Bird dog / Problems / Till I kissed you / Let it be me / When will I be loved / Take a message to Mary / Claudette / Poor Jenny / Devoted to you
CDFAB 006 / Sep '91 / Ace

☐ GOLDEN YEARS OF THE EVERLY BROTHERS, THE
Walk right back / Crying in the rain / Wake up little Susie / Love hurts / Claudette / Till I kissed you / Love is strange / Ebony eyes / Temptation / Let it be me / Don't blame me / Cathy's clown / All I have to do is dream / Lucille / So sad (to watch good love go bad) / Bird dog / When will I be loved / No one can make my sunshine smile / Ferris wheel / Price of love / Muskrat / Problems / How can I meet her / Bye bye love
9548319922 / May '93 / Warner Bros.

☐ GREATEST HITS LIVE
Wake up little Susie / Bird dog / ('Till) I kissed you / Let it be me / Cathy's clown / Lucille / Crying in the rain / Love is strange / Price of love / Walk right back / Claudette / All I have to do is dream / So sad / Temptation / For the love of Barbara Allen / Bye bye love
RM 1528 / Jun '97 / BR Music

☐ GREATEST LOVE SONGS VOL.1 (Live At The Royal Albert Hall)
Price of love / Walk right back / Claudette / Crying in the rain / Love is strange / (Take a) message to Mary / Maybe tomorrow / I wonder if I care as much / When will I be loved / Bird dog / Devoted to you / Ebony eyes / Love hurts / For the love of Barbara Allen / Lightning express / Put my little shoes away / Long time gone / Down in the willow garden / Step it up and go
PLATCD 168 / Mar '96 / Platinum

☐ GREATEST LOVE SONGS VOL.2 (Live At The Royal Albert Hall)
Cathy's clown / Gone gone gone / You send me / So sad (to watch a good love go bad) / Blues stay away from me / Bye bye love / All I have to do is dream / (Till) I kissed you / Temptation / Be bop a lula / Lucille / Let it be me / Good golly Miss Molly
PLATCD 169 / Mar '96 / Platinum

☐ GREATEST RECORDINGS
Wake up little Susie / Problems / Take a message to Mary / I wonder if I care as much / Poor Jenny / Love of my life / Bird dog / Like strangers / Hey doll baby / Leave my woman alone / Till I kissed you / Claudette / Should we tell him / All I have to do is dream / Rip it up / When will I be loved / Bye bye love / Let it be me
CDCH 903 / '88 / Ace

☐ HIT SINGLE COLLECTABLES
DISK 4502 / Apr '94 / Disky

☐ MASTERS, THE
EABCD 032 / 24 Nov '97 / Eagle

☐ ORIGINAL BRITISH HIT SINGLES, THE
Bye bye love / I wonder if I care as much / Wake up little Susie / Maybe tomorrow / Should we tell him / This little girl of mine / All I have to do is dream / Claudette / Bird dog / Devoted to you / Problems / Love of my life / Poor Jenny / Take a message to Mary / Till I kissed you / Oh what a feeling / Let it be me / Since you broke my heart / When will I be loved / Be bop a lula / Like strangers / Leave my woman alone
CDCHM 544 / Nov '94 / Ace

☐ ORIGINAL, THE
Wake up little Susie / Bird dog / Keep a knockin' / Rip it up / Claudette / Bye bye love / Problems / Devoted to you / Take a message to Mary / Till I kissed you / Let it be me / Be bop a lula / Like strangers / Poor Jenny / Love of my life / This little girl of mine / When will I be loved / All I have to do is dream
TO 865522 / 2 Feb '98 / Disky

☐ RARE SOLO CLASSICS
Let it be me / So sad (to watch a good love go bad) / Sweet southern love / Brother jukebox / Dare to dream again / Since you broke my heart / Lonely days / Yesterday just passed my way / Nighht rider / Deep water / Love at last sight / Never like this / Lettin' go / Turn the memories loose again / In your eyes / Oh, I'd like to go away / What a feeling / Love angel
PWKS 4259 / Mar '96 / Carlton

☐ RE-UNION
Price of love / Walk right back / Claudette / Crying in the rain / Love is strange / (Take a) message to Mary / When will I be loved / Bird dog / Devoted to you / Ebony eyes / Love hurts / Gone gone gone / Cathy's clown / You send me / So sad (to watch good love go bad) / Bye bye love / All I have to do is dream / Wake up little Susie / Till I kissed you / Temptation / Be bop a lula / Lucille / Let it be me / Good golly Miss Molly
MOCD 3002 / Feb '95 / More Music

☐ REUNION CONCERT (2CD Set)
Price of love / Walk right back / Claudette / Crying in the rain / Love is strange / (Take a) message to Mary / Maybe tomorrow / I wonder if I care as much / When will I be loved / Bird dog / Devoted to you / Ebony eyes / Love hurts / For the love of Barbara Allen / Lightning express / Put my little shoes away / Long time gone / Down in the willow garden / Step it up and go / Cathy's clown / Gone gone gone / You send me / So sad (to watch good love go bad) / Blues (stay away from me) / Bye bye love / All I have to do is dream / Wake up little Susie / Till I kissed you / Temptation / Be bop a lula / Lucille / Let it be me / Good golly Miss Molly
PLATCD 5901 / Oct '93 / Platinum
24316 / Mar '96 / Delta Doubles

☐ REUNION CONCERT, THE
Price of love / Walk right back / Claudette / Crying in the rain / Love is strange / Take a message to Mary / When will I be loved / Bird dog / Devoted to you / Ebony eyes / Love hurts / Cathy's clown / Gone, gone, gone / You send me / Bye bye love / All I have to do is dream / Wake up little Susie / (Til) I kissed you / Temptation / Be bop a Lula / Lucille / Let it be me / Good golly miss moll
EMPRCD 587 / Oct '95 / Emporio

☐ REUNION CONCERT, THE (2CD Set)
CPCD 82992 / May '97 / Charly

☐ SIMPLY THE BEST
WMCD 5704 / Oct '94 / Disky

☐ SONGS OUR DADDY TAUGHT US
Roving gambler / Down in the willow garden / Long time gone / Lightning express / That silver haired daddy of mine / Who's gonna shoe your pretty little feet / Barbara Allen / Oh so many years / I'm here to get my baby out of jail / Rockin' alone in an old rocking chair / Kentucky / Put my little shoes away
CDCHM 75 / Nov '90 / Ace

☐ STORIES WE COULD TELL
All I really want to do / Breakdown / Green river / Mandolin wind / Up in Mabel's room / Del Rio Dan / Ridin' high / Christmas Eve can kill you / Three armed poker playin' river rat / I'm tired of singing my song in Las Vegas / Brand new Tennessee waltz / Lay it down / Husbands and wives / Woman don't you try to tie me down / Sweet memories / Ladies love outlaws / Not fade away / Somebody nobody knows / Good hearted woman / Stories we could tell
74321432552 / Jan '97 / Camden

Everly, Phil

☐ PHIL EVERLY
She means nothing to me: *Richard, Cliff & Phil Everly* / I'll mend your broken heart: *Richard, Cliff & Phil Everly* / God bless older ladies / Sweet pretender / Never gonna dream again / Better than now / Woman and a man / Louise / When I'm dead and gone / Sweet Suzanne / Oh baby oh (you're the star)
BGOCD 199 / Feb '95 / Beat Goes On

Everon

☐ VENUS
M 7030CD / 27 Oct '97 / Mascot

Everton Blender

☐ LIFT UP YOUR HEAD
CDHB 169 / Jan '95 / Heartbeat

☐ WORLD CORRUPTION
Coming harder / World corruption / Just wanna be / Man / Live up / Bob Marley / Piece a di Blender / Blow your nose / Blend dem / Material girl / Baa baa white sheep / When you wrong / If you want to dance: *Everton Blender & Prezident Brown* / Blow your nose: *Everton Blender & Prezident Brown*
GRELCD 231 / Oct '96 / Greensleeves

Everton FC

☐ FOREVER EVERTON (Everton FC/ Supporters)
CDGAFFER 5 / Apr '96 / Cherry Red

Every New Dead Ghost

☐ ENDLESS NIGHTMARE
NIGHTCD 001 / Jul '92 / Plastic Head

☐ NEW WORLD, A
PLASCD 024 / Nov '90 / Plastic Head

☐ RIVER OF SOULS
APOREK 1110893 / Feb '95 / Apollyon

Everyman Band

☐ WITHOUT WARNING
Patterns which connect / Talking with himself / Multibluetonic blues / Celebration / Trick of the wool / Huh what he say / Al ur
8254052 / '88 / ECM

Everything But The Girl

☐ AMPLIFIED HEART
Rollercoaster / Troubled mind / I don't understand anything / Walking to you / Get me / Missing / Two star / We walk the same line / 25th December / Disenchanted
4509964822 / Jun '94 / Blanco Y Negro

☐ BABY THE STARS SHINE BRIGHT
Come on home / Don't leave me behind / Country mile / Cross my heart / Don't let the teardrops rust your shining heart / Careless / Sugar Finney / Come hell or high water / Fighting talk / Little Hitler
2409662 / Aug '86 / Blanco Y Negro

☐ BEST OF EVERYTHING BUT THE GIRL
Missing / Driving / Old friends / One place / I don't want to talk about it / Love is strange / Only living boy in New York / Apron strings / When all's well / Another bridge / Each and every one / Rollercoaster / Better things / Protection
0630166372 / Oct '96 / Blanco Y Negro

☐ EDEN
Each and every one / Bittersweet / Tender blue / Another bridge / Spice of life / Dust bowl / Crabwalk / Even so / Frost and fire / Fascination / I must confess / Soft touch
2403952 / '84 / Blanco Y Negro

☐ IDLEWILD
Love is here where I live / These early days / Oxford Street / Night I heard Caruso sing / Goodbye Sunday / Shadow on a harvest moon / Blue moon rose / Tears all over town / Lonesome for a place I know / Apron strings / I don't want to talk about it
K 2438402 / Nov '94 / Blanco Y Negro

☐ LANGUAGE OF LIFE, THE
Driving / Get back together / Meet me in the morning / Me and Bobby D / Language of life / Take me / Imagine America / Letting love go / My baby don't love me / Road
2462602 / Jan '90 / Blanco Y Negro

☐ LOVE NOT MONEY
When all's well / Ugly little dreams / Shoot me down / Are you trying to be funny / Sean / Ballad of the times / Anytown / This love (not for sale) / Trouble and strife / Angel / Heaven help me / Kid
2406572 / May '85 / Blanco Y Negro

☐ WALKING WOUNDED
Before today / Wrong / Single / Heart remains a child / Walking wounded / Flipside / Big deal / Mirrorball / Good cop bad cop
CDV 2803 / Jun '96 / Virgin

Evidence

☐ SEE YOU LATER
TRIOCD 301 / Jul '98 / Triple Earth

Evil Dead

☐ ANNIHILATION OF CIVILISATION
847603 / '90 / Steamhammer

☐ RISE ABOVE
557590 / '88 / Steamhammer

Evil Mothers

☐ CROSSDRESSER
Teen strap party / Articles of faith / Hardware / Warm wire / Lust horse / You had enough / God's will / For kicks / Bad blood flows / P.g.f.c.
CDDVN 26 / Dec '93 / Devotion

☐ SPIDER SEX AND CAR WRECKS
Free poison / Something wicked this way please / Spider sex and car wrecks / I like fur / You had enough / Backbiter / Give up the ghost / Loud and clear / Geek / Corpse / Last suffer / Ready set die
VIRUS 193 / Mar '97 / Alternative Tentacles

Evil Superstars

☐ BOOGIE CHILDREN-R-US
BABY / If you cry (I'll go to hell) / I've been wrong before / Can't seem to fuck things up / Gimme animal rights / Just a princess / Oh girl / It's a sad sad planet / Holy Spirit come home / First comes farewell / Song off the record / My little dead one / Laserblack / Love happened
PDOX 018CD / 1 Jun '98 / Paradox

☐ LOVE IS OKAY
No more people / Power of Haha / Go home for lunch / Parasol / Your dump or mine / Rocking all over / Pantomiming with her parents / Oh funlump / We need your head / 1,000,000 demons can't be wrong / Satan is in my ass / Death by summer / Miss your disease
PDOXCD 002 / Feb '96 / Paradox

Evil's Toy

☐ BEST OF EVIL'S TOY, THE
HYP 0860469CD / 13 Apr '98 / Hypnobeat

☐ HUMAN REFUSE
HY 85921053 / Jun '94 / Hyperium

Evol
☐ DREAMQUEST
CDAR 037 / Dec '96 / Fatwreck Chords

☐ SAGA, THE
CDAR 026 / May '95 / Adipocre

Evolution
☐ THEORY OF EVOLUTION
WARPCD 29 / Apr '95 / Warp

Evora, Cesaria
☐ CABO VERDE
Tchintchirote / Sabine larga'm / Partida / Sange de berona / Apocalipse / Mar e morada de sodade / Bo e di meu cretcheu / Coragem irmon / Quem bo e / Regresso / Zebra / Mae velha / Pe di boi / Ess pais
74321453932 / Feb '97 / RCA

☐ CESARIA EVORA
Petit pays / Xandinha / Tudo tem se limite / Consedjo / D'nhirim reforma / Rotcha 'scribida / Oriundina / Tudo dia e dia / Nha cancera ka tem medida / Areia de salamansa / Flor na paul / Doce Guerra
74321254192 / Nov '96 / RCA

☐ DIVA AUX PIEDS NUS
824532 / Jun '93 / BUDA

☐ LIVE A L'OLYMPIA
795912 / Oct '96 / Melodie

☐ MUSIC FROM CAPE VERDE
824842 / Nov '90 / BUDA

Ewell, Don
☐ DON EWELL MEETS PAMELA & LLEW HIRD
BCD 342 / Jun '95 / GHB

☐ IN JAPAN 1975 (Ewell, Don & Yoshio Toyama)
JCD 179 / Oct '91 / Jazzology

☐ IN NEW ORLEANS (Ewell, Don & Herb Hall Quartet)
JCD 256 / Jul '94 / Jazzology

☐ LIVE AT THE 100 CLUB
SACD 89 / Jul '93 / Solo Art

Ewigkeit
☐ BATTLE FURIES
ELD 001 / 2 Mar '98 / Eldethorn

Ex
☐ BLUEPRINTS FOR A BLACKOUT
EX 19D / May '93 / Konkurrel

☐ INSTANT
EX 063064D / Nov '95 / Konkurrel

☐ JOGGERS AND SNOGGERS
EX 40/41 / Apr '92 / Ex

☐ TUMULT
EX 14D / May '93 / Konkurrel

☐ WEATHERMEN SHRUB
EX 57CD / Feb '94 / Ex

Ex-Cathedra
☐ TARTAN MATERIAL
DAMGOOD 106CD / Sep '96 / Damaged Goods

Ex-Press
☐ DEFINITIVE ARTICLE, THE
YP 007ACD / Jul '96 / Yellow

Exact Life
☐ GERONIMO
SOH 023CD / Jan '96 / Suburbs Of Hell

Excelsior Brass Band
☐ EXCELSIOR NEW ORLEANS JAZZ BAND
BARX 051CD / Nov '95 / Bartrax

Excession
☐ JONG AND HUGA
ABCD 019 / 23 Feb '98 / Resurrection

Excessive Force
☐ CONQUER YOUR WORLD
Conquer your house il / Conquer your world / Blow your house down / To death il / Ride the bomb / We like war / Worship me / Finger on the trigger
CDDVN 12 / Jul '92 / Devotion

Excidium
☐ INNOCENT RIVER
CDAR 034 / Jan '96 / Adipocre

Exciter
☐ DARK COMMAND
OPCD 059 / 24 Nov '97 / Osmose

☐ KILL AFTER KILL
Rain of terror / No life no future / Cold blooded murder / Smashin' 'em down / Shadow of the cross / Dog eat dog / Anger, hate and destruction / Second coming / Born to kill
N 01922 / Apr '92 / Noise

Exciters
☐ BEST OF THE EXCITERS, THE (Reaching For The Best)
HTCD 65 / 20 Apr '98 / Hot Productions

☐ SOMETHING TO SHOUT ABOUT (Complete Roulette Sessions)
Something to shout about / I want you to be my boy / Stars are shining bright / Run mascara / I knew you would / Talkin' 'bout my baby / Tonight, tonight / I know, I know / Baby did you change your mind / Love, life, peace / There they go / Are you satisfied / That's how love starts / My father / Just not ready
NEMCD 730 / May '95 / Sequel

Excrement
☐ SCORCHED
IR 012CD / Apr '95 / Invasion

Excrement Of War
☐ CATHODE RAY COMA
FINNREC 07CD / Jun '94 / Finn

Excretion
☐ VOICE OF HARMONY
WAR 007CD / Apr '96 / Wrong Again

Excruciating Terror
☐ DIVIDED WE FALL
PESS 27CD / 13 Jul '98 / Pessimiser

Excuse Seventeen
☐ EXCUSE SEVENTEEN
CHSW 9 / 16 Feb '98 / Chainsaw

Exile
☐ LATEST AND GREATEST
CDI 9149 / Nov '96 / Intersound

Exit
☐ EXIT
To hyena / Infinite gain / Horsa
IRE 1022 / Jul '96 / I

☐ SET
Am nil / Idiot house
IRE 2092 / Aug '97 / I

Exit 13
☐ ETHOS MUSICK
RR 69132 / Dec '94 / Roadrunner

☐ JUST A FEW MORE
RR 6966CD / Nov '95 / Relapse

☐ SMOKING SONGS
RR 69342 / Feb '97 / Relapse

Exit EEE
☐ EPIDEMIC
NRR 0185 / Nov '93 / No Respect

Exocet
☐ CONFUSION
MASSCD 068 / Sep '95 / Massacre

Exodus
☐ ANOTHER LESSON IN VIOLENCE
CM 77173CD / Jun '97 / Century Media

Exodus Quartet
☐ WAY OUT THERE
EX 3372 / Nov '96 / Instinct

Exp
☐ EXP
DV 027CD / 10 Nov '97 / Dark Vinyl

Experiment Fear
☐ ASSUMING
MASSCD 054 / Jun '95 / Massacre

Experimental Audio Research
☐ BEYOND THE PALE
ABB 96CD / Jun '96 / Big Cat

☐ DATA RAPE
ORBIT 013CD / 27 Jul '98 / Space Age

☐ KONER EXPERIMENT, THE
EFA 006862 / Mar '97 / Mille Plateau

☐ MILLENIUM MUSIC
ALP 72CD / 19 Jan '98 / Atavistic

☐ PHENOMENA 256
ORBIT 005CD / 27 Apr '98 / Space Age

Experimental Flux
☐ MODULATION RENOVATIO
EFA 001 / Oct '94 / Clubscene

Experimental Pop Band
☐ DISCGROTESQUE
SF 017 / Jun '97 / Swarf Finger

☐ WOOF
SF 009CD / Jan '97 / Swarf Finger

Explainer
☐ KAISO POTPOURRI
EXPLAINER 97 / 13 Oct '97 / Kismet

Exploder
☐ THIS SOUND STARTS RIGHT NOW
REP 028CD / 26 May '98 / Reptilian

Exploding Thumbs
☐ FLYING WITHOUT WINGS
Too many buns / Good time to be born / Hairy mouth / Speak highly / Redcliff / Thumb dub / Goose map / On me bonce / Desert song / Chewy / Falcon jam / Things are tame / Full swing live at the park
HOLCD 31 / 30 Mar '98 / Holistic

Exploding White Mice
☐ EXPLODING WHITE MICE
NORMAL 119CD / Aug '90 / Normal

Exploited
☐ BEAT THE BASTARDS
If you are sad / They lie / Sea of blood / I syrs / Fight back / Police TV / Law for the rich / Don't blame me / Beat the bastards / System fucked up / Massacre of innocents / Affected by them / Serial killer
CDJUSTX 22
CDJUST 22 / Mar '96 / Rough Justice

☐ DEATH BEFORE DISHONOUR
Anti uk / Power struggle / Scaling the derry wall / Barry prossitt / Don't really care / No forgiveness / Death before dishonour / Adding to their fears / Police informer / Drive me insane / Pulling us down / Sexual favours / Drug squad man / Privacy invasion / Jesus is dead / Politicians / War now / United chaos and anarchy / Sexual favours (dub version)
CDJUST 6 / Sep '90 / Rough Justice

☐ HORROR EPICS
Horror epics / Don't forget the chaos / Law and order / I hate you / No more idols / Maggie / Dangerous vision / Down below / Treat you like shit / Forty odd years ago / My life
DOJOCD 184 / Feb '94 / Dojo
SMMCD 532 / 2 Mar '98 / Snapper

☐ LET'S START A WAR (SAID MAGGIE ONE DAY)
Let's start a war (said Maggie one day) / Insanity / Safe below / Eyes of the vulture / Should we, can't we / Rival leaders / God save the Queen / Psycho / Kidology / False hopes / Another day to go nowhere / Wankers
SMMCD 531 / 2 Mar '98 / Snapper

☐ LET'S START A WAR/HORROR EPICS
Let's start a war (said Maggie one day) / Insanity / Safe below / Eye's of the vulture / Should we, can't we / Rival leaders / God saved the queen / Psycho / Kidology / False hope / Another day to go nowhere / Horror epics / Wankers / Don't forget the chaos / Law and order / I hate you / No more idols / Maggie / Dangerous vision / Down below / Treat you like shit / Forty odd years ago / My life
LOMACD 3 / Feb '94 / Loma

☐ LIVE AND LOUD
Law and order / Let's start a war (said Maggie one day) / Horror epics / Cop cars / Blown to bits / Hitler's in the charts again / Belsen was a gas / Alternative / I hate you / UK 82 / Rival leaders / Maggie / Troops of tomorrow / Sex and violence / Daily news / Crashed out / SPG / Exploited barmy army / Dead cities / I believe in anarchy
CDPUNK 18 / Apr '96 / Anagram

☐ LIVE AT THE WHITEHOUSE
Let's start a war / Jimmy Boyle / Don't forget the chaos / I believe in anarchy / God save the Queen / Alternative / Horror epics / Wankers / Dead cities / Rival leaders / I hate you / Dogs of war / Army life / Sex and violence / Daily news / Punks not dead
PINCD 104 / 13 Jul '98 / PinHead

☐ LIVE IN JAPAN
Let's start a war (said Maggie one day) / Scaling the Derry Walls / Dogs of war / Massacre / UK 82 / About to die / Alternative / Rival leaders / Maggie / I still believe in anarchy / Death before dishonour / Dead cities / Troops of tomorrow / Army life / USA / Punk's not dead / Exploited barmy army / Sex and violence
DOJOCD 109 / Feb '94 / Dojo

☐ LIVE ON STAGE 1981/LIVE AT THE WHITEHOUSE 1985
Cop cars / Crashed out / Dole Q / Dogs of war / Army life / Out of control / Ripper / Mod song / Exploited barmy army / Royalty / SPG / Sex and violence / Punk's not dead / Maggie one day) / Jimmy Boyle / Don't forget the chaos / God saved the Queen / Alternative / Horror epics / Wankers / Dead cities / Rival leaders / I hate you / Daily news
LOMACD 2 / Feb '94 / Loma

☐ MASSACRE, THE
Massacre / Sick bastard / Porno slut / Now I'm dead / Boys in blue / Dog soldier / Don't pay the poll tax / F religion / About to die / Blown out of the sky / Police shit / Stop the slaughter
CDJUST 15 / Sep '90 / Rough Justice

☐ PUNKS NOT DEAD
Punk's not dead / Mucky pup / Cop cars / Free flight / Army life / Blown to bits / Sex and violence / SPG / Royalty / Dole Q / Exploited barmy army / Ripper / Out of control / Son of a copper / I believe in anarchy
SMMCD 530 / 27 Apr '98 / Snapper

☐ SINGLES, THE
CLEO 5000CD / Jan '94 / Cleopatra

☐ TOTALLY EXPLOITED/LIVE IN JAPAN (2CD Set)
SMDCD 136 / 22 Sep '97 / Snapper

☐ TROOPS OF TOMORROW
Jimmy Boyle / Daily news / Disorder / Alternative / Rapist / Troops of tomorrow / UK 82 / Sid Vicious was innocent / War / They won't stop / So tragic / Germs / USA
SMMCD 529 / 5 May '98 / Snapper

Explorers
☐ LIVE AT CAMDEN PALACE
Ship of fools / Lorelei / Crack the whip / Robert Loius Stevenson / Breath of life / It's over / Voodoo isle / You go up in smoke / Soul fantasy / Prussian blue / Two worlds apart / Venus de Milo
EXVP 3CD / 20 Oct '97 / Expression

Explorers Club
☐ AGE OF IMPACT
MAX 9021CD / 20 Jul '98 / Mascot

Exponents
☐ BETTER NEVER THAN LATE
Once in a lifetime / Change your mind / Shouldn't be alloeed / Close / Come and go / Only you are / You started me thinking / Happy today / Help me / Smith's getting through / Infinity / Everything at all
4877082 / 8 Sep '97 / Columbia

Expresion
☐ Q'EROS
TUMICD 031 / '93 / Tumi

☐ WASICHAKUY
TUMICD 067 / 24 Apr '98 / Tumi

Expulsion
☐ MAN AGAINST
GOD 027CD / Jun '97 / Godhead

☐ OVERFLOW
GOD 011CD / May '95 / Godhead

Exquisite Corpse
☐ INNER LIGHT
KK 107CD / Oct '93 / KK

☐ SEIZE
Etoiles / Sitting in a tree (time flies) / B k s / Sacrifice / Strange attractor / Elevator
KK 083CD / Aug '92 / KK

Extra Prolific
☐ LIKE IT SHOULD BE
Intro / Brown sugar / In front of the kids / Is this right / Sweet potato pie / Cash (cash money) / One motion / Never changing / First sermon / No what / It's alright / In 20 minutes / Go back to school / Fat outro
CHIP 150 / Sep '94 / Jive

Extrema
☐ POSITIVE PRESSURE
FLY 190CD / Nov '95 / Flying

Extremadura
☐ PULSES
WWCD 018 / Apr '96 / Universal Egg

Extreme
☐ BEST OF EXTREME, THE
Play with me / Song for love / Kid ego / Get the funk out / Tragic comic / Hip today / Stop the world / More than words / Cupid's dead / Leave me alone / Hole hearted / Am I ever gonna change
5408362 / 2 Mar '98 / A&M

☐ III SIDES TO EVERY STORY
5400062 / Sep '92 / A&M

☐ PORNOGRAFFITI
Decadance dance / Li'l Jack horny / When I'm president / Get the funk out / More than words / Money (In God we trust) / It's a monster / Pornograffiti / When I first kissed you / Suzi / He-man woman hater / Song for love / Hole hearted
CDMID 191 / May '94 / A&M

☐ WAITING FOR THE PUNCHLINE
There is no God / Cynical / Tell me something I don't know / Hip today / Naked / Midnight express / Leave me alone / No respect / Evilangelist / Shadow boxing / Unconditionally / Fair-weather faith / Waiting for the punchline
5403052 / Jan '95 / A&M

Extreme Noise Terror

☐ PEEL SESSIONS, THE (10.11.87/ 16.2.90)
False profit / Use your mind / Human error / Only in it for the music / Subliminal music / Punk, fact and fiction / Deceived / Another nail in the coffin / Carry on screaming / Conned thru life / Work for never / Third world genocide / I am a bloody fool / In it for life / Shock treatment
SFPSCD 208 / Aug '90 / Strange Fruit

☐ RETROBUTION (Ten Years Of Terror)
Raping the earth / Bullshit propaganda / Love brain / Work for never / We the helpless / Invisible war / Subliminal music / Human error / Murder / Think about it / Pray to be saved / Conned thru life / Deceived / Third World genocide
MOSH 083CD / 1 Sep '97 / Earache

Exxplorer

☐ RECIPE FOR POWER, A
MASSCD 041 / Oct '94 / Massacre

Eye Hate God

☐ DOPESICK
CM 77114CD / Apr '96 / Century Media

☐ TAKE AS NEEDED FOR PAIN
CM 770522 / Sep '93 / Century Media

Eyeless In Gaza

☐ ALL UNDER THE LEAVES
ASCALESR 021 / Oct '96 / Ambivalent Scale

☐ BACK FROM THE RAINS
Between these dreams / Twilight / Back from the rains / Lie still, sleep long / Catch me / Evening music / She moved through the fair / Sweet life longer / New love here / Welcome now / Your rich sky / Flight of swallows / My last lost melody / New risen / Bright play of eyes / Scent on evening air / Drumming the beating heart
CDBRED 69 / Jul '89 / Cherry Red

☐ BITTER APPLES
ASCALE 020CD / Oct '96 / Ambivalent Scale

☐ CAUGHT IN FLUX
Sixth sense / Point You / Voice from the tracks / Scale Amiss / Decoration / Continual / Soul on thin ice / Rose petal knot / Skeletal framework / See red / Half light / Every which way / Eyes of the beautiful losers / Still air / Out from the day-to-day / True colour / Keynote inertia
CDMRED 145 / 15 Sep '97 / Cherry Red

☐ DRUMMING THE BEATING HEART/ PALE HANDS I LOVED SO WELL
Transcience blues / Ill wind blows / One by one / Picture the day / Dreaming at rain / Two / Veil like calm / Throw a shadow / Pencil sketch / At arms length / Lights of April / Before you go / Tall and white nettles / Warm breath soft and slow / Blue distance / Sheer cliffs / Falling leaf/Fading flower; Goodbye to summer / Lies of love / To Ellen / Pale Saints / Letters to she / Light sliding / Big clipper ship
CDMRED 127 / Mar '96 / Cherry Red

☐ MYSTERY SEAS
ASCALE 018CD / Oct '96 / Ambivalent Scale

☐ RUST RED SEPTEMBER
Changing stations / Pearl and pale / New risen / September hills / Taking steps / Only whispers / Leaves are dancing / No perfect stranger / Corner of dusk / Bright play of eyes / Stealing Autumn
CDMRED 111 / Jun '96 / Cherry Red

☐ TRANSIENCE IN BLUE
IR 006CD / Jan '90 / Integrity

☐ VOICE - THE BEST OF EYELESS IN GAZA (Recollections 1980-1986)
Kodak ghosts run amok / No noise / Seven years / From A to B / Speech rapid fire / Invisibility / Others / Rose petal knot / Out from the day today / Transcience blues / Picture the day / Two / Veil like calm / One by one / Pencil sketch / Through eastfields / Changing stations / Corner of dusk / Drumming the beating heart / New risen / Sun bursts in / Welcome now / Back from the rains / Lilt of music / Evening music / Between these dreams
CDBRED 104 / Jun '96 / Cherry Red

Eyelids

☐ IF IT KILLS
IND 013CD / 18 May '98 / Revelation

Eyeliners

☐ CONFIDENTIAL
SFTRI 484CD / May '97 / Sympathy For The Record Industry

Eyephone

☐ EVERGREENS
39130092 / Mar '97 / Hypnotism

Eyes Of Blue

☐ CROSSROADS OF TIME
BR 102 / 15 Dec '97 / Black Rose

☐ IN FIELDS OF ARDATH
BR 114 / 15 Dec '97 / Black Rose

Eyes Of The Nightmare Jungle

☐ FATE
SPC 08425152 / Jan '94 / SPV

☐ INNOCENCE
SPV 08461722 / May '95 / SPV

Eyewitness

☐ EYEWITNESS
NTHEN 017CD / Apr '95 / Now & Then

Eyges, David

☐ LIGHTNIN' STRIKES (Eyges, David & Byard Lancaster)
BLE 592212 / Feb '93 / Black & Blue

eYT

☐ CUBIC SPACE
MEYCD 12 / Nov '95 / Magick Eye

Eyuphuro

☐ MAMA MOSAMBIKI
Samukeha (the nostalgic man) / Mwanuni (the bird) / Akakswela / We awaka (you are mine) / Kihiyeny / Nifungo (the key of the house) / Oh mama (oh mother) / Nuno maalani (single mother of a single mother
CDRW 10 / '90 / Realworld

Ezio

☐ BLACK BOOTS ON LATIN FEET
Saxon street / Thirty and confused / Just to talk to you again / Cancel today / Go / Steal away / Further we stretch / Tuesday night / 1000 years / Agony / Wild side / Brave man / Angel song
74321240152 / Jun '97 / Arista

☐ DIESEL VANILLA
Deeper / Moon / Accordion girl / Cinderella / One more walk round the dancefloor / Maybe sometimes / Alex / Call you tomorrow / Back on your own again
MCD 60038 / Jun '97 / MCA

F

Fab 5

☐ BEST OF FAB 5, THE
PKCD 32593 / Jul '93 / K&K

☐ GOOD BUDDY
VPCD 2043 / Sep '96 / VP

Fabares, Shelly

☐ BEST OF SHELLY FABARES, THE
Johnny Angel / What did they do before rock n' roll / Johnny loves me / I'm growing up / Welcome home / Big star / Things we did last summer / I left a note to say goodbye / Telephone (Won't you ring) / Billy boy / Ronnie, call me when you get a chance / How lovely to be a woman / Bye bye birdie / Football seasons over / He don't love me
NEMCD 695 / Aug '94 / Sequel

Fabian

☐ HOLD THAT TIGER
REP 4157 / Aug '91 / Repertoire

☐ THIS IS FABIAN
Tiger / Turn me loose / Got the feeling / Mighty cold (to a warm warm heart) / Tomorrow / I'm a man / Hypnotised / Come on and get me / Tongue tied / Gonna get you / Steady date / King of love / Stop thief / Hound dog man / Lilly Lou / Long before / Wild party / Shivers / This friendly world / I'm gonna sit right down and write myself a letter / String along / Girl like you / About this thing called love / Kissin' and twistin' / Love that I'm giving to you / Grapevine
CDCHD 321 / Jul '91 / Ace

Fabian, Lara

☐ PURE
Tout / J'ai zappe / La difference / Humana / Urgent desir / Les amoureux de l'an deux mille / Ici / Alleluia / Je t'aime / Je t'appartiens / Perdere l'amore
5376362 / 9 Feb '98 / Polydor

Fabich, Rainer

☐ BACK ON EARTH
ISCD 161 / Sep '96 / Intersound

Fabre, Candido

☐ POQUITO POCO
TMGCD 2 / 21 Aug '97 / Tumi

☐ SON DE CUBA
TUMICD 057 / May '96 / Tumi

Fabulous Flee Rekkers

☐ JOE MEEK'S FABULOUS FLEE REKKERS
Lone rider / Stage to Cimarron / Sunburst / Fireball / Shiftless Sam / Blue tango / Isle of Capri / Brer Robert / Miller like wow / Twistin' the chestnuts / Black buffalo / Fandango / Sunday date / Bitter rice / Hangover / PF and (Phil the fluter's ball)
C5CD 564 / May '97 / See For Miles

Fabulous Poodles

☐ HIS MASTERS VOICE
Mirror star / Mirror star / Bionic man / B movies / Toytown people / Pinball pinup / You wouldn't listen / Stomping on the cat / Mr. mike / Cherchez la femme / Talkin' trash / Rumbaba boogie / When the summer's thru / Rosie pink / Man with money / Bike blood / Chicago boxcar (boston back) / Annarexia / Suicide bridge / Pink city twist / Vampire rock
NEMCD 697 / Jun '95 / Sequel

Fabulous Sister Brothers

☐ LIVE IN KEMP TOWN
Intro / Here I am / Let your love / I lift up my voice / I will comfort you / Capitol Hill / Lead me on / Glory day / That the world / Up jump shout
FSB 01 / Sep '95 / FSB

Fabulous Thunderbirds

☐ BEST OF THE FABULOUS THUNDERBIRDS, THE
Wait on time / Scratch my back / Rock with me / Let me in / Runnin' shoes / I'm a good man (if you give me a chance) / Dirty work / I believe I'm in love / One's too many / Tell me why / Can't tear it up enuff / Diddy wah diddy / Give me all your lovin' / My babe / 'Neighbour' tend to your business / Monkey / Crawl / Roll, roll, roll / How do you spell love / You ain't nothing but fine / Sugar coated love / She's tuff
CDCHRM 100 / Feb '97 / Chrysalis

☐ BUTT ROCKIN'/T-BIRD RHYTHM
I believe I'm in love / One's too many / Give me all your lovin' / Roll roll roll / Cherry pink and apple blossom white / I hear you knocking / Tip on in / I'm sorry / Mathilda / Tell me why / In orbit / Can't tear it up enuff / How do you spell love / You're humbuggin' me / My babe / Neighbour tend to your business / Monkey / Diddy wah diddy / Lover's crime / Poor boy / Tell me (pretty baby) / Gotta have some/Just got some
BGOCD 193 / Jun '93 / Beat Goes On

☐ COLLECTION, THE
Crawl / She's tuff / Baby scratch my back / Tip on in / That's enough of that stuff / Full time lover / Sugar-coated love / Wait on time / Los fabulosos thunderbirds / I'm a good man (if you give me a chance) / You ain't nothin' but fine / Walkin' to my baby / Marked deck / Learn to treat me right / I believe I'm in love / How do yo spell love / Mathilda / One's too many / Dirty work / Can't tear it up enuff / Cherry pink and apple blossom white / Monkey / Give me all your lovin' / Diddy wah diddy / My babe / Roll roll roll
DC 886092 / 2 Feb '98 / Disky

☐ FABULOUS THUNDERBIRDS, THE/ WHAT'S THE WORD
Wait on time / Scratch my back / Rich woman / Full time lover / Pocket rockets / She's tuff / Marked deck / Walkin' to my baby / Rock with me / C-boy's blues / Let me in / Running shoes / You ain't nothing but fine / Low-down woman / Extra Jimmies / Sugar coated love / Last call for alcohol / Crawl / Jumpin' bad / Learn to treat me right / I'm a good man if you treat me right / Dirty work / That's enough of that stuff / Los Fabulosos Thunderbirds
BGOCD 192 / Jun '93 / Beat Goes On

☐ HIGH WATER
Too much of everything / Do right by me / Tortured / High water / Hurt on me / Hand to mouth / Promises you can't keep / Can't have you / Too hot to handle / Save it for someone who cares / It's about time / That's all I need
1005821572 / 29 Sep '97 / High Street

☐ HOT STUFF (The Greatest Hits)
Tuff enuff / Twist of the knife / Why get up / Got love if you want it / Rock this place / Stand back / You can't judge a book by its cover / Powerful stuff / Wrap it up / Two time my lovin / Look at that, look at that
4722262 / Feb '97 / Epic

☐ PORTFOLIO
Crawl / She's tuff / Scratch my back / Tip on in / That's enough of that stuff / Full time lover / Sugar coated love / Wait on time / Los Fabulosos Thunderbirds / I'm a good man if you treat me right / You ain't nothing but fine / Walkin' to my baby / Marked deck / Learn to treat me right / I believe I'm in love / How do you spell love / Mathilda / One's too many / Dirty work / Can't tear it up enuff / Cherry pink and apple blossom white / Monkey / Give me all your lovin' / Diddy wah diddy / My babe / Roll roll roll
MPCD 1599 / 15 Sep '97 / Chrysalis

☐ ROLL OF THE DICE
Roll of the dice / Too many irons / How do I get you back / Here comes the night / Taking it too easy / I don't want to be / Mean love / I can't win / Memory from hell / Looking forward / Do as I say / Zip a dee do dah
01005821032 / Sep '95 / Private Music

Face Down

☐ MINDFIELD
RR 89022 / Apr '96 / Roadrunner

☐ TWISTED RULE OF THE WICKED, THE
NB 194CD / 13 Oct '97 / Nuclear Blast

Face To Face

☐ DON'T TURN AWAY
FAT 515CD / Mar '94 / Fatwreck Chords

☐ LIVE
VG 331CD / 3 Mar '98 / Vagrant

Face Value

☐ CHOICES
WB 2130CD / Sep '95 / We Bite

☐ FACE VALUE
CR 012CD / Jul '96 / Conversion

Faceless

☐ ACHIEVMENT
NBX 010 / May '95 / Noisebox

☐ FACELESS
Dusty empire / Sequin ocean / Summer of dub / Interlude / Beamer / Angel / Dark the day / APB (Night drive) / Summer of version
PLAN ONE / 8 Sep '97 / Planet Noisebox

Faceplate

☐ CASUAL OBSERVATION
RR 85201CD / Jun '96 / Rokaroola

Faces

☐ ALL SHAPES AND SIZES FAMILY ALBUM (Various Artists)
Black coffee: *Humble Pie* / Heartbreaker: *Free* / Won't get fooled again: *Who* / In a broken dream: *Python Lee Jackson* / Reason to believe: *Stewart, Rod* / Poacher: *Lane, Ronnie & Slim Chance* / Waiting for a girl like you: *Foreigner* / Can feel the fire: *Wood, Ronnie* / Cindy incidentally: *Faces* / Afterglow of your love: *Small Faces* / Whatcha gonna do about it: *Marriott, Steve* / Ready or not: *Jones, Kenny* / Looking for a love: *Small Faces* / La di da: *McLagan, Ian* / Sorry she's mine: *Winston, Jimmy*
VSOPCD 231 / Sep '96 / Connoisseur Collection

☐ FIRST STEP
Wicked messenger / Devotion / Shake shudder shiver / Stone / Around the plynth / Flying / Pinapple and the monkey / Nobody knows / Looking out the window / Three button hand me down
7599263762 / Sep '93 / Warner Bros.

☐ LONG PLAYER
Bad 'n' ruin / Tell everyone / Sweet Lady Mary / Richmond / Maybe I'm amazed / Had me a real good time / On the beach / I feel so good / Jerusalem
7599261912 / Sep '93 / Warner Bros.

☐ NOD'S AS GOOD AS A WINK TO A BLIND HORSE, A
Miss Judy's farm / You're so rude / Love lived here / Last orders please / Stay with me / Debris / Memphis / Too bad / That's all you need
7599259292 / Sep '93 / Warner Bros.

☐ OOH LA LA
Silicone grown / Cindy incidentally / Flags and banners / My fault / Borstal boys / Fly in the ointment / If I'm on the late side / Glad and sorry / Just another honky / Ooh la la
7599263682 / Sep '93 / Warner Bros.

Facil

☐ FACIL
IAE 004 / May '95 / Instinct Ambient Europe

Faction

☐ HEAVEN
TMCD 056 / Oct '90 / Third Mind

Faction Zero

☐ LIBERATION
IJT 002 / Feb '97 / Idjit

Faddis, Jon

☐ JON AND BILLY (Faddis, Jon & Billy Harper)
Jon and Billy / Water bridge-mizu hashi san / Ballad for Jon Haddis / Two d's from Shinjyuku, dig and dug / Seventeen bar blues / This all-koredake
ECD 22052 / Jul '93 / Evidence

☐ REMEMBRANCES
JD 166 / 24 Feb '98 / Chesky

Fadela, Cheb

☐ MANICH MANA (Fadela, Cheb & Cheb Sahraoui)
DECLI 50630 / 3 Mar '98 / Munich

☐ WALLI (Fadela, Cheb & Cheb Sahraoui)
Bab Wahran / Walli / Dellali (my lover) / Dance the Rai / Dawh (they took him away) / Hasni / Wayala / Mani / Dougih / Waadi (just my luck) / N'sel fik
ROUCD 5076 / Feb '97 / Rounder

Fading Colours

☐ I'M SCARED OF...
SPV 08558972 / 30 Mar '98 / SPV

Fading Out

☐ FADING OUT
PR 12CD / Dec '96 / Palace

Faeber, Will

☐ NO SMALL COMFORT
No small comfort / Elena / I ain't living like that / Tire tracks / She reads me like a book / Bottle of whiskey and a woman for the night / Frontier breakdown / Picture this / Waiting for the Texas sun / Coyote / Runaway hearts / Another roadside attraction / Fast train / One thing right
TOP 101CD / 6 Oct '97 / Topless

Fagen, Donald

☐ KAMAKIRIAD
Trans island skyway / Countermoon / Springtime / Snowbound / Tomorrow's girls / Florida room / On the dunes / Teahouse on the tracks
9362452302 / Dec '96 / Warner Bros.

☐ NIGHTFLY, THE
New frontier / IGY / Green Flower Street / Ruby baby / Maxine / Walk between raindrops / Goodbye look / Night fly
9236962 / Oct '82 / Warner Bros.

☐ ORIGINS OF STEELY DAN, THE (Fagen, Donald & Walter Becker)
CDSGP 029 / Mar '94 / Prestige

Fagin, Joe

☐ BEST OF JOE FAGIN
Am I asking too much / Crazy in love / That's livin' alright / (Cry) for no one / Younger days / Forever now / Only love can show the way / Epitaph (for a drunk) / Why don't we spend the night / Put out the light / Get it right / Love hangs by a thread / As time goes by / So much for saying goodbye / Breaking away / She's leaving home / Annie
CDWM 107 / Jan '96 / ACL

Fahey, John

☐ AMERICA
Jesus is a dying bedmaker / Amazing grace / Song no.3 / Special rider blues / Dvorak / Jesus is a dying bedmaker / Finale / America / Dalhart Texas / Knoxville blues / Mark 1:15 / Voice of the turtle / Waltz that carried us away and then a mosquito came...
CDTAK 8903 / 27 Apr '98 / Takoma

☐ CHRISTMAS GUITAR VOL.1
Joy to the world / What child is this / Hark the herald angels sing-o come, all ye faithful / Auld lang syne / Bells of saint mary's / Good christian men, rejoice / We three kings / Away in a manger / God rest ye merry gentlemen / Jolly old saint nicholas / Santa claus is coming to town / Skater's waltz / Christmas song / Christmas time's a coming-rudolph the red-nosed reindeer (/ Holly and the ivy-the cherry tree carol (medley) / Apple blossom time / White christmas / First nowell / Good king wenceslas / Of the father's love begotten / Away in a manger / In the bleak midwinter / It came upon the midnight clear / Jesus, won't you come by here-go tell it on the mountain (/ Lo, how a rose e'er blooming / Silent night, holy night
CDVR 002 / Dec '94 / Varrick

☐ COMPLETE BLIND JOE DEATH
On doing all evil deed blues / St. Louis blues / Poor boy long way from home / Uncloudy day / John Henry / In Christ there is no East or West / Desperate man blues / Sun gonna shine in my back door / Sligo river blues / On doing all evil deed blues / St. Louis blues / Poor boy long way from home / Uncloudy day / John Henry / In Christ there is no East or west / Desperate man blues / Sun gonna shine in my backdoor / Sligo river blues / I'm gonna do all I can for my Lord / Transcendental waterfall / West coast blues
CDTAK 1002 / Apr '96 / Takoma

☐ ESSENTIAL JOHN FAHEY, THE
VCD 55 / Nov '96 / Vanguard

☐ FARE FORWARD VOYAGERS
SHANCD 99005 / '92 / Shanachie

☐ LET GO
Let go / Black Mommy / Dvorak / World is waiting for the sunrise / Deep river/Old man river / Lights out / Pretty afternoon / Sunset on Prince George's country / Layla / Old country rock
CDVR 008 / Feb '97 / Varrick

☐ OLD FASHIONED LOVE
In a Persian market / Jaya shiva shankaram / Marilyn / Assassination of Stefan Grossman / Old fashioned love / Boodle am shake / Keep your lamp trimmed and burning / I saw the light shining 'round and 'round
SHCD 99001 / Jun '91 / Shanachie

☐ OLD GIRLFRIENDS AND OTHER HORRIBLE MEMORIES
CDVR 031 / Feb '92 / Varrick

☐ POPULAR SONGS OF CHRISTMAS AND NEW YEAR
VR 012CD / Feb '95 / Varrick

☐ RAILROAD
SHAN 99003CD / '92 / Shanachie

☐ RAIN FORESTS, OCEANS AND OTHER THEMES
CDVR 019 / Dec '86 / Rounder

☐ REQUIA
Requiem for John Hurt / Requiem for Russell Blaine Cooper / When the catfish is in bloom / Requiem for Molly / Fight on Christians fight on
VMD 79259 / 27 Apr '98 / Vanguard

☐ TRANSFIGURATION OF BLIND JOE DEATH, THE
Beautiful Linda Getchell / Orinda-moraga / I am the resurrection / On the sunny side of the ocean / Tell her to come back home / My station will be changed after a while / 101 is a hard road to travel / How green was my valley / Bicycle built for two / Death of the Clayton Peacock / Brenda's blues / Old southern medley / Come back baby / Poor boy / St. Patrick's hymn
CDTAK 7015 / May '97 / Takoma

☐ VOICE OF THE TURTLE, THE
Bottleneck blues / Bill Cheatham / Lewisdale blues / Bean vine blues / Bean vine blues / Raga called Pat part 3 / Raga called Pat part 4 / Train / Je ne me suis reveillais matin pas en May / Story of Dorothy Gooch part 1 / Nine pound hammer / Lonesome valley
CDTAK 1019 / Jul '96 / Takoma

☐ WOMBLIFE
RUBIDIUM 37 / 18 Aug '97 / Table Of The Elements

Faine Jade

☐ INTROSPECTION: A FAINE JADE RECITAL
Tune up / Dr. Paul overture / People games play / Cold winter sun symphony in D major / I lived tomorrow yesterday / Ballad of the bad guys (1956 AD) / Piano interlude / Introspection / In a brand new groove / On the inside there's a middle / Don't hassle me / Grand finale / Stand together in the end / Dr. Paul / People games play / Don't hassle me (instrumental)
CDWIKD 141 / Mar '95 / Big Beat

Faint Sound Of Shovelled Earth

☐ FAINT SOUND OF SHOVELLED EARTH
Precursor / Detour / Boxer's son / Colour of his shoes / Jack / Shroud / Promise / Fires of this town / Endnotes / Gods and punks
SIMBA 012 / 3 Aug '98 / Simba

Fair Warning

☐ GO
GUN 148CD / 17 Nov '97 / Gun

Fairburn, Werly

☐ EVERYBODY'S ROCKIN'
I'm a fool about your love / Everybody's rockin' / All the time / My heart's on fire / Speak to me baby / Telephone baby / No blues tomorrow / I'm jealous / I guess I'm crazy / That sweet love of mine / Nothin' but lovin' / Love spelled backwards is evol / Broken hearted me / Stay close to me / It's heaven / Old mem'ries come back / Good deal Lucille / Baby he's a wolf / Won't it be nice / Little bit of nothing / Prison cell of love / Spiteful heart / It's a cold weary world / I feel like cryin' / Camping with Marie / Let's live it over / Doggone that moon / Black widow spider woman / You are my sunshine
BCD 15578 / Nov '93 / Bear Family

Fairclough Group

☐ SHEPHERD WHEEL
Jacob's ladder / Shepherd wheel / Yaller belly / Saint Monda / Rattening / Stoneburst / Racing / When there's nothing left to burn
ASCCD 1 / Jun '95 / ASC

Fairclough, Peter

☐ PERMISSION
Relic / Misnomer / Sandscribe / Wildlife / Kenya at dawn / Permission / Manifesto / Naive / In / Truth / Ice and lemon / Higger tor part I / Carl Wark / Higger tor part II
ASCCD 18 / 29 Sep '97 / ASC

☐ WILDSILK (Fairclough, Peter & Keith Tippett)
Emerald lake / Under thunder / Wild silk / Skretch for Gary / Casting the net / Recurring dream / In the glade of the woodstone bird / Through the gate / Fountain / Humble
ASCCD 8 / May '96 / ASC

Fairer Sax

☐ DIVERSIONS WITH THE FAIRER SAX
Arrival of the Queen of Sheba / Sixteenth century dances / Fugue in D minor (Bach) / Aria / Moment musicale (Schubert) / Something doing
CDSDL 365 / Oct '87 / Saydisc

Fairey Engineering Works Band

☐ BRASS BAND GALA (25 Favourite Classics - 2CD Set)
Die Fledermaus / Nimrod / Grand march / Rondo / Gypsy baron / Prelude / Radetzky march / Morning / Festive overture / Trumpet tune and air / Rondo a la turque / Royal water music / Slavonic dance no.8 / Academic festival overture / Saltarello / Flight of the bumblebee / L'italiana in Algeri / Chorus of the Hebrew slaves / Polonaise / Moorside suite / Russlan and Ludmilla / Intermezzo / Hungarian march / Carnival of Venice / Orpheus in the underworld
4529072 / 16 Mar '98 / Decca

☐ SPECTRUM (The Music Of Gilbert Vinter Vol.1)
Spectrum / Vizcaya / Mattheson's air / Resilience (salute to youth) / Romance (salute to youth) / Relaxation (salute to youth) / Centenary march / Caprice (entertainments) / Elegy (entertainments) / March (entertainments) / Lisbon carnival / Challenging brass / James cook, circumnavigator
QPRL 058D / Aug '93 / Polyphonic

☐ TOP BRASS
King cotton / Perpetuum mobile / Send in the clowns / Lohengrin - intro to act 3 / Girl I left behind me / If / Round the clock / Queen of Sheba / Can can / Don't cry for me Argentina / Polly wolly doodling / Hustle / Peace / Fanfare and soliloquy
SUMCD 4131 / Jun '97 / Summit

☐ TRIUMPHANT RHAPSODY
Triumphant rhapsody (fantasy for brass band) / Triumphant rhapsody (fantasy for brass band) / Simon called peter (rhapsody for brass band) / Taproom ballade / John o'gaunt (overture) / Dover coach / Variations on a ninth / Cavatina / Maestro-grave-brioso (symphony of marches)
QPRL 068D / Sep '94 / Polyphonic

Fairfield Four

☐ STANDING ON THE ROCK
Don't leave me by myself / Hope to shout in glory / I can tell you the time / My prayer / Come on to this altar / I love the name Jesus / Does Jesus care / Leave it there / Love like a river / Who is that knocking / His eye is on the sparrow / How I got over / This evening our father / Hear me when I pray / When the battle is over / Standing on the rock / Somebody touched me / On my journey now / Old time religion / Talking about Jesus / No room at the inn / When we bow / Let's go / Don't drive your children away / Packin' every burden / Poor pilgrim
CDCHD 449 / Aug '93 / Ace

Fairground Attraction

☐ AY FOND KISS
Jock O'Hazeldean / Walkin' after midnight / Trying times / Winter rose / Allelujah (live) / Watching the party / Game of love / You send me / Mystery train / Do you want to know a secret / Cajun band / Ae fond kiss
74321193712 / Apr '94 / RCA

☐ FIRST OF A MILLION KISSES
Smile in a whisper / Perfect / Moon on the rain / Find my love / Fairground attraction / Wind knows my name / Clare / Comedy waltz / Moon is mine / Station Street / Whispers / Allelujah / Falling backwards / Mythology
74321134392 / May '93 / RCA

☐ PERFECT - THE BEST OF FAIRGROUND ATTRACTION
74321292772 / Jul '95 / RCA

☐ VERY BEST OF FAIRGROUND ATTRACTION, THE
Perfect / Find my love / Fairground attraction / Smile in a whisper / Clare / Walkin' after midnight / Do you want to know a secret / Allelujah / Moon is mine / Watching the party / Winter rose / Wind knows my name / Jock O'Hazeldean / Comedy waltz / You send me / Aye fond kiss
74321446752 / Feb '97 / Camden

Fairhurst, Richard

☐ HUNGRY ANTS
BDV 9504 / Jan '96 / Babel

Fairies Fortune

☐ SNOWFISH
EFA 155852 / Aug '95 / Gymnastic

Fairport Convention

☐ ANGEL DELIGHT
Lord Marlborough / Sir William Gower / Bridge over the river Ash / Wizard of the wordly game / Journeyman's grace / Angel delight / Banks of the sweet primroses / Instrumental medley / Bonnie black hare / Sickness and diseases
IMCD 166 / Mar '93 / Island

☐ BONNY BUNCH OF ROSES
Adieu adieu / Bonnie bunch of roses / Eynsham poacher / General Taylor / James O'Donnell's jig / Last waltz / Poor ditching boy / Royal selleccion number 13 / Run Johnny run
WRCD 011 / Oct '88 / Woodworm

☐ CLOSE TO THE WIND
Red and gold / All your beauty / Summer before the war / Cup of tea/Loaf of bread/Miss Monohan's / London river / Gold / Wounded whale / Set me up / Open the door Richard / Rhythm of the time / Mock Morris / Beggar's song / Dark eyed Molly / Claudy banks / Sock in it / Close to the wind
CRESTCD 035 / Apr '98 / Mooncrest

☐ CROPREDY BOX (3CD Set)
Intro / Wings / Jack O'Diamonds / Time will show the wiser / Mr. Lacey / Suzanne / Genesis Hall / Million dollar bash / Come all ye / Reynardine / Matty Groves / Danny Boy / Intro / Walk awhile / Now be thankful / Poor Will and the Jolly Hangman / Angel delight / Rain / Cut across shorty / Sloth / Rosie / Solo / John Barleycorn / Wat Tyler / Red and gold / Jewel in the crown / Woodworm swing / John Gaudie / Fiddlestix / Dirty linen / Si tu dois partir / Meet on the ledge / Seventeen come Sunday / April fool tape
WR3CD 026 / 18 May '98 / Woodworm

☐ ENCORE ENCORE (Farewell Farewell Remastered)
Matty groves / Orange blossom special / John Lee / Bridge over the river Ash / Sir Patrick Spens / Mr. Lacey / Walk awhile / Bonny black hare / Journeyman's grace / Meet on the ledge / Rubber band / Hen's march/Four poster bed / Flatback caper / Dirty linen
FP 001CD / 15 Sep '97 / Folkprint

☐ EXPLETIVE DELIGHTED
Rutland reel-sack the juggler / Cat on the mixer-three left feet / Bankruptured / Portmeirion / James o'donall's jigs / Expletive delighted / Sigh beg sigh mor / Innstuch / Hanks for the memory
TRUCKCD 16 / Nov '95 / Terrapin Truckin'

☐ FAIRPORT CONVENTION
Time will show the wiser / I don't know where I stand / Decameron / Jack O'Diamonds / Portfolio / Chelsea morning / Sun shade / Lobster / It's alright ma, it's only witchcraft / One sure thing / MI breakdown
8352302 / Oct '90 / Polydor

☐ FAIRPORT CONVENTION 9
Hexhamshire lass / Polly on the shore / Brilliancy medley and Cherokee shuffle / To Althea from prison / Tokyo / Bring 'em down / Big William / Pleasure and pain / Possibly parsons green
IMCD 154 / Aug '92 / Island

☐ FIVE SEASONS, THE
Claudy banks / All your beauty / Gold / Rhythm of the time / Card song/Shuffle the pack / Mock Morris / Sock in it / Ginnie / Wounded whale
HTCD 48 / 9 Mar '98 / HTD

☐ FULL HOUSE
Walk awhile / Dirty linen / Sloth / Sir Patrick Spens / Flatback caper / Doctor of physick / Flowers of the forest
HNCD 4417 / Nov '91 / Hannibal

☐ GLADY'S LEAP/EXPLETIVE DELIGHTED (2CD Set)
How many times / Bird from the mountain / Honour and praise / Hiring fair / Instrumental medley '85 / My feet are set for dancing / Wat Tyler / Head in a sack / Sack the juggler / Three left feet / Bankruptured / Portmeirion / Jam's O'Donnell's jigs / Expletive delighted / Sigh beg sigh mor / Innstruck / Gas almost works / Hanks for the memory
FP 002CD / 9 Feb '98 / Folkprint

☐ GLADYS LEAP
How many times / Bird from the mountain / Honour and praise / Hiring fair / Instrumental medley '85 / My feet are set for dancing / Wat tyler / Head in a sack
SIVCD 0003 / May '96 / Red Steel

☐ HEYDAY (BBC Radio Sessions)
Close the door lightly when you go / I don't know where I stand / Some sweet day / Reno nevada / Suzanne / If it feels good you know it can't be wrong / I still miss someone / Bird on a wire / Gone, gone, gone / Tried so hard / Shattering live experience / Percy's song
HNCD 1329 / Oct '87 / Hannibal

☐ HISTORY OF FAIRPORT CONVENTION, THE
Meet on the ledge / Fotheringay / Mr. Lacey / Book song / Sailor's life / Si tu dois partir / Who knows where the time goes / Matty Groves / Crazy man Michael / Now be thankful (Medley) / Walk awhile / Sloth / Bonnie black hare / Angel delight / Bridge over the river Ash / John Lee / Breakfast in Mayfair / Hanging song / Hen's march / Four poster bed
IMCD 128 / Jun '91 / Island

☐ HOUSE FULL (Live In Los Angeles)
Sir Patrick Spens / Banks of the sweet primroses / Toss the feathers / Sloth / Staines morris / Matty groves / Mason's apron / Battle of the Somme
HNCD 1319 / Jul '90 / Hannibal

☐ IN REAL TIME
Reynard the fox / Widow of Westmorland's daughter / Hiring fair / Crazy man Michael / Close to the wind / Big three medley / Meet on the ledge
IMCD 10 / '90 / Island

☐ JEWEL IN THE CROWN
WRMCD 023 / Jan '95 / Woodworm

☐ JOHN BABBACOMBE LEE
John's reflections / This was the happiest period of his life / Tragedy now strikes hard / John was hardly more than a bewildered observer / When it comes he can cannot sleep
IMCD 153 / Aug '92 / Island

☐ LIEGE AND LIEF
Come all ye / Reynardine / Matty groves / Farewell farewell / Deserter / Lark in the morning (medley) / Tamlin / Crazy man Michael / Rakish paddy / Foxhunters jigs / Toss the feathers
IMCD 60 / '89 / Island

☐ LIVE
Matty Groves / Rosie / Fiddlestix / John the gun / Something you got / Sloth / Dirty linen / Down in the flood / Sir B MacKenzie
IMCD 95 / Feb '90 / Island

☐ OLD, NEW, BORROWED AND BLUE
WRCD 024 / May '96 / Woodworm

☐ RED AND GOLD
Set me up / Red and gold / Battle / London river / Noise club / Beggars song / Dark eyed Molly / Open the door Richard
HTDCD 47 / 9 Mar '98 / HTD

☐ RISING FOR THE MOON
Rising for the moon / Restless / White dress / Let it go / Stranger to himself / What is true / Iron lion / Dawn / After halloween / Night-time girl / One more chance
IMCD 155 / Aug '92 / Island

☐ ROSIE
Rosie / Matthew, Mark, Luke and John / Knights of the road / Peggy's pub / Plainsman / Hungarian rhapsody / My girl / Me with you / Hen's march / Furs and feathers
IMCD 152 / Aug '92 / Island

☐ UNHALFBRICKING
Genesis hall / Si tu dois partir / Autopsy / Cajun woman / Who knows where the time goes / Percy's song / Million dollar bash / Sailor's life
IMCD 61 / Nov '89 / Island

☐ WHAT WE DID ON OUR HOLIDAYS
Fotheringay / Mr. Lacey / Book song / Lord is in this place / No man's land / I'll keep it with mine / Eastern rain / Nottamun town / Tale in hard time / She moved through the fair / Meet me on the ledge / End of a holiday
IMCD 97 / Feb '90 / Island

☐ WHO KNOWS WHERE THE TIME GOES
John Gaudie / Sailing boat / Tom Paine / Bowman's retreat / Spanish main / Golden glove / Slipolgy / Wishful waltz / Life's a long song / Dangerous / Heard it throught the grapevine / Who knows where the time goes
WRCD 025 / Aug '97 / Woodworm

☐ WOODWORM YEARS, THE
Level pegging / Hiring fair / Wat Tyler / Portmeirion / Honour and praise / Deserter / From a distance / Rosemary's sister / Red and gold / Summer before the war / Tripping up the stairs / Claudy banks / Three jigs for Jamie / Ginnie
FP 003CD / 9 Feb '98 / Folkprint

Fairuz

☐ LEGENDARY FAIRUZ, THE
Beirut Hal Zarafat / Ya mina el habayeb / Amman / Al Kuwait / Hamaltu Beirut / Misr Adat / Bagdad wal chouarra
724382357223 / 19 Jan '98 / Hemisphere

Fairweather, Al

☐ MADE TO MEASURE (Fairweather, Al & Friends)
By the fireside / Music goes round and round / Sue's blues / Exactly like you / Goody goody / Easy to love / Sometimes I'm happy / Tin roof blues / I can't give you anything but love / Red for go / September in the rain / If I had you / Coe-pilot / Grapevine / Doin' the racoon
LACD 75 / Mar '97 / Lake

Fairweather, Digby

☐ DIGBY FAIRWEATHER (Various Artists)
LOTCD 4310 / 8 Dec '97 / Loose Tie

☐ PORTRAIT OF DIGBY FAIRWEATHER
BLCD 760505 / Apr '91 / Black Lion

☐ SONGS FOR SANDY
Prologue/Sandy and Al / Singing away the cold in Edinburgh / Hi-life in Hampstead / Sandy's blues / Requiem for a weeping willow/Singing away the cold Edinburgh / It's always fairweather / Pal Sandy / Rosetta / Blue turning grey / Everybody loves Saturday night / Straighten up and fly right / When my sugar walks down the street / Easy living / After supper / Hanid / One for Sandy
HEPCD 2016 / 13 Jul '98 / Hep

☐ WITH NAT IN MIND (Fairweather, Digby & His New Georgians)
JCD 247 / Aug '95 / Jazzology

Faitelson, Dalia

☐ COMMON GROUND (Faitelson, Dalia Group)
Dahab / Eye of the morning / East west / My treasure / Trail of a trail / Captain / Mustafa / Common ground / Cheek to cheek / Alone with you
STCD 4196 / Nov '94 / Storyville

Faith & The Muse

☐ ANNWYN, BENEATH THE WAVES
EFACD 6486 / Jul '96 / Tess

Faith, Adam

☐ ADAM
Wonderful time / Diamond ring / Summertime / Greenfinger / Piper of love / Girl like you / Turn me loose / So many ways / Singin' in the rain / Fare thee well my pretty maid / I'm a man / Hit the road to dreamland / Wonderful time / Diamond ring / Summertime / Greenfinger / Piper of love / Girl like you / Turn me loose / So many ways / Singin' in the rain / Fare thee well my pretty maid / I'm a man / Hit the road to dreamland
DORIG 106 / Aug '97 / EMI

☐ ADAM FAITH SINGLES COLLECTION (His Greatest Hits)
Got a heartsick feeling / What do you want / Poor me / Someone else's baby / When Johnny comes marching home / Made you / How about that / Lonely pup / Who am I / Easy going me / Don't you know it / Time has come / Lonesome / As you like it / Don't that beat all / What now / First time / We are in love / Message to Martha / Someone's taken Maria away / Cheryl's goin' home
CZ 260 / Jan '90 / EMI

☐ BEST OF ADAM FAITH
What do you want / Poor me / Someone else's baby / Johnny comes marching home / Made you / How about that / Lonely pup (in a christmas shop) / This is it / Who am I / Easy going me / Don't you know it / Time has come / Lonesome / As you like it / Don't that beat all / What now / Walkin' tall / First time: *Faith, Adam & The Roulettes* / We are in love: *Faith, Adam & The Roulettes* / If he tells you: *Faith, Adam & The Roulettes* / I love being in love with you: *Faith, Adam & The Roulettes* / Message to Martha / Stop feeling sorry for yourself / Someone's taken Maria away: *Faith, Adam & The Roulettes* / Cheryl's goin' home
CDMFP 6048 / Jan '89 / Music For Pleasure

☐ BEST OF THE EMI YEARS, THE
What do you want / (Got a) Heartsick feeling / From now until forever / Ah poor little baby / Poor me / Summertime / Wonderful time / Someone else's baby / When Johnny comes marching home / Made you / Hit the road to dreamland / I'm a man / How about that / With open arms / Singin' in the rain / Fare thee well my pretty maid / Lonely pup (in a Christmas shop) / This is it / Who am I / Sho' know a lot about love / As long as you keep loving me / I'm gonna love you too / Easy going me / Wonderin' / Watch your step / Don't you know it / Time has come / Help each other romance / Lonesome / Ballad of a broken heart / (I'm) Knockin' on wood / As you like it / Learning to forget / You 'n' me / Face to face / You can do it if you try / Don't that beat all / Mix me a person / Baby take a bow / What now / What have I got / Walkin' tall / Forget me not / First time / So long baby / Made for me / We are in love / If he tells you / Come closer / Talk to me / It's alright / I love being in love with you / Message to Martha / I've gotta see my baby / Stop feeling sorry for yourself / I'll stop at nothing / Hand

me down things / Talk about love / Someone's taken Maria away / I don't need that kind of lovin' / If you ever need me / Cheryl's goin' home / What more can anyone do / Cowman milk your cow / To hell with love / Close the door / You make my life worthwhile
CDEM 1513 / Feb '94 / EMI

☐ VERY BEST OF ADAM FAITH, THE
What do you want / Poor me / Someone's elses baby / Johnny comes marching home / How about that / Lonely pup / This is it / Who am I / Easy going me / Don't you know it / Time has come / Lonesome / As you like it / Don't that beat all / Baby take a bow / What now / Walkin' tall / First time / We are in love / If he tells you / I love being in love with you / Message to Martha / Stop feeling sorry for yourself / Someone's taken Maria away / Cheryl's goin' home
CDMFP 6380 / 13 Oct '97 / Music For Pleasure

Faith, George

☐ REGGAE GOT SOUL
CDGR 204 / Dec '97 / Charly

☐ SOULFUL
CDSGP 073 / Jul '95 / Prestige

Faith Healers

☐ IMAGINARY FRIEND
PURECD 027 / Oct '93 / Too Pure

Faith No More

☐ ALBUM OF THE YEAR (2CD Set)
Collision / Strip search / Last cup of sorrow / Naked in front of the computer / Helpless / Mouth to mouth / Ashes to ashes / She loves me not / Got that feeling / Paths of glory / Home sick home / Pristina / Last cup of sorrow / Last cup of sorrow / Ashes to ashes / Ashes to ashes / She loves me not / Ashes to ashes
8288022 / Jun '97 / Slash
8289012 / 19 Jan '98 / Slash

☐ ANGEL DUST
Land of sunshine / Caffeine / Mid life crisis / Rv / Smaller / Everything's ruined / Malpractise / Kindergarten / Be aggressive / Small victory / Crack hitler / Jizz lobber / Midnight cowboy / Easy
8284012 / Jan '93 / Slash

☐ INTERVIEW SESSIONS
CHAT 15 / 11 May '98 / Chatback

☐ INTRODUCE YOURSELF
Faster disco / Anne's song / Introduce yourself / Chinese arithmetic / Death march / We care a lot / R 'N' R / Crab song / Blood / Spirit
8280512 / Apr '87 / Slash

☐ KING FOR A DAY, FOOL FOR A LIFETIME
Get out / Ricochet / Evidence / Gentle art of making enemies / Star AD / Cuckoo for caca / Caralho voador / Ugly in the morning / Digging the grave / Take this bottle / King for a day / What a day / Last to know / Just a man
8285602 / 15 Sep '97 / Slash

☐ LIVE AT THE BRIXTON ACADEMY
Epic / From out of nowhere / We care a lot / Falling to pieces / Real thing / Warriors / Zombie eaters / Edge of the world / Grade / Cowboy song
8282382 / Feb '91 / Slash

☐ REAL THING, THE
From out of nowhere / Epic / Falling to pieces / Surprise you're dead / Zombie eaters / Real thing / Underwater love / Morning after / Woodpecker from Mars / War pigs / Edge of the world
8281542 / Jun '89 / Slash

☐ WE CARE A LOT
We care a lot / Jungle / Mark Bowen / Jim / Why do you bother / Greed / Pills for breakfast / As the worm turns / Arabian disco / New beginnings
8288052 / Sep '96 / Slash

Faith Over Reason

☐ EYES WIDE SMILE
ABBCD 027 / Sep '91 / Big Cat

Faith, Percy

☐ SUMMER PLACE, A (Faith, Percy Orchestra)
304842 / Jun '98 / Hallmark

☐ VIVA THE MUSIC OF MEXICO/THE MUSIC OF BRAZIL
Granada / La golondrina / La cucaracha / Chiapanecas / Estrellita / El rancho grande / La paloma / Noche de ronda / Mexican hat dance / Guadalajara / Zandunga / Jesusita en chihuahua / Cuanto la gusta / Solamente una vez / Brazil / Delicado / Tu sabes / Ba-tu-ca-da / Amorada / Bandit / Baia / Tico-tico / Little dreamer / Maxixe / Atrevido / Minute samba
4871922 / Mar '97 / Columbia

Faithful Dawn

☐ TEMPERANCE
NIGHTCD 014 / May '97 / Nightbreed

Faithfull, Marianne

☐ 20TH CENTURY BLUES
Alabama song / Want to buy some illusions / Pirate Jenny / Salomon song / Boulevard of broken dreams / Complainte de la Seine / Ballad of the soldier's wife / Intro / Mon ami, my friend / Falling in love again / Mack the knife / 20th Century blues / Don't forget me / Surabaya Johnny / Outro
74321386562 / Sep '96 / RCA Victor

☐ BLAZING AWAY
Les prisons du roy / Guilt / Sister Morphine / Why'd ya do it / Ballad of Lucy Jordan / Blazing away / Broken English / Strange weather / Working class hero / As tears go by / When I find my life / Times Square / She moved through the fair
IMCD 207 / Apr '95 / Island

☐ BROKEN ENGLISH
Working class hero / What's the hurry / Ballad of Lucy Jordan / Why d'ya do it / Broken English / Witch's song / Guilt / Brain drain
IMCD 11 / '89 / Island

☐ CHILD'S ADVENTURE, A
Times square / Blue millionaire / Falling from grace / Morning come / Ashes in my hand / Running for our lives / Ireland / She's got a problem
IMCD 206 / Apr '95 / Island

☐ DANGEROUS ACQUAINTANCES
Sweetheart / Intrigue / Easy in the city / Strange one / Tenderness / For beauty's sake / So sad / Eye communication / Truth, bitter truth
IMCD 205 / May '95 / Island

☐ FAITHFULL - A COLLECTION OF HER BEST SONGS
Broken english / Ballad of Lucy Jordan / Working class hero / Guilt / Why'd ya do it / Ghost dance / Trouble in mind / Times Square / Strange weather / She / As tears go by
CID 8023 / Aug '94 / Island

☐ FAITHLESS
Dreamin' my dreams / Vanilla O'Lay / Wait for me down by the river / I'll be your baby tonight / Lady Madelaine / All I wanna do in life / Way you want me to be / Wrong road again / That was the day (Nashville) / This time / I'm not Lisa / Honky tonk angels
CLACD 148 / Apr '89 / Castle

☐ RICH KID BLUES
Rich kid blues / Long black veil / Sad Lisa / It's all over now baby blue / Southern butterfly / Chords of fame / Visions of Johanna / It takes a lot to laugh it takes a train to cry / Beware of darkness / Corinne Corinna / Mud slide Slim / Crazy lady blues
DIAB 861 / 6 Jul '98 / Diablo

☐ SECRET LIFE, A
Prologue / Sleep / Love in the afternoon / Flaming September / She / Bored by dreams / Losing / Wedding / Stars line up / Epilogue
IMCD 225 / Sep '96 / Island

☐ STRANGE WEATHER
Stranger intro / Boulevard of broken dreams / I ain't goin' down to the well no more / Yesterdays / Sing of judgement / Strange weather / Love life and money / I'll keep it with mine / Hello stranger / Penthouse serenade / As tears go by / Stranger on earth
IMCD 12 / '89 / Island

☐ VERY BEST OF MARIANNE FAITHFULL, THE
As tears go by / Come and stay with me / Scarborough Fair / Monday, Monday / Yesterday / Last thing on my mind / What have they done to the rain / This little bird / In my time of sorrow / Is this what I get for loving you / Tomorrow's calling / Reason to believe / Sister Morphine / Go away from my world / Summer nights
8204822 / Sep '87 / Deram

Faithless

☐ REVERENCE
CHEKXCD 500 / Nov '97 / Cheeky
CHEKCD 500 / 10 Nov '97 / Cheeky

Fajt, Pavel

☐ PAVEL FAJT & PLUTO (Fajt, Pavel & Pluto)
MAMO 402 / Jun '97 / Indies

Fake ID

☐ DREAMING EZEKIEL
Above and beyond the call of love / Heartbreak moon / Nothing next to you / Tied to the mast / Half a heart / Even the strong / Tears don't put out the fire / Heartbreak like promises / Go easy / I'm a fighter
199624 / Aug '97 / Made To Measure

Falay, Maffy

☐ HANK'S TUNE (Falay, Maffy Sextet)
LICD 3157 / Jan '97 / Liphone

Falco, Tav

☐ BEHIND THE MAGNOLIA CURTAIN/ BLOW YOUR TOP (Falco, Tav Panther Burns)
422135 / May '94 / New Rose

☐ DISAPPEARING ANGELS (Falco, Tav Panther Burns)
SFTRI 460CD / Oct '96 / Sympathy For The Record Industry

☐ LIFE SENTENCE (Falco, Tav Panther Burns)
422136 / May '94 / New Rose

☐ LOVE'S LAST WARNING (The Best Of Tav Falco's Panther Burns) (Falco, Tav Panther Burns)
422088 / Nov '96 / Last Call

☐ MIDNIGHT IN MEMPHIS (Falco, Tav Panther Burns)
422141 / May '94 / New Rose

☐ RED DEVIL
ROSE 140CD / Feb '88 / New Rose

☐ SHADOW ANGELS AND DISAPPEARING DANCERS
MRCD 111 / Mar '97 / Munster

☐ SHADOW DANCER
IRS 993513CD / Feb '96 / Intercord
4222462 / Nov '96 / Last Call

☐ SUGAR DITCH REVISITED
422137 / May '94 / New Rose

☐ WORLD WE KNEW, THE (Falco, Tav Panther Burns)
422140 / May '94 / New Rose

Falcon, Bobby

☐ SOMETHING WONDERFUL
EMCD 1003 / May '96 / Don One

Falcon, Joseph

☐ CAJUN MUSIC PIONEER
Joe's breakdown / 99 year waltz / Corrine, Corrina / Jole blonde / Lacasine special / Le traces de mon buggy / Osson two-step / Le valse de St. Landry / Hip et taiaut / Creole stomp / Myer's waltz / Allons a lafayette / La valse a nonc gustave / Allons danser Colinda / Les flambes D'Enfer
ARHCD 459 / Sep '97 / Arhoolie

Falconer, Elizabeth

☐ ISSHIN EMERGING (Koto Music)
CD 973 / Jul '97 / Music & Arts

Falkenbach

☐ MAGNI BLANDINN OK MEGINTIRI
NPR 037CD / 15 Jun '98 / Napalm

Fall

☐ 15 WAYS TO LEAVE YOUR MAN (Live)
Chilinist / Don't call me darling / 15 ways to leave your man / DIY meat / Pearl city / Feeling numb / LA / Big new prinz / Mr. Pharmacist / Everything hurtz / Mixer / Das vaulture ans ein nutter-wain / M5 6-7pm / Return / Reckoning / Hey student
RRCD 239 / 25 Aug '97 / Receiver

☐ CHEETHAM HILL
RRCD 247 / 1 Dec '97 / Receiver

☐ CODE: SELFISH
Birmingham School Of Business / Free range / Return / Time enough at last / Everything hurtz / Immortality / Two face / Just waiting / So-called dangerous / Gentlemen's agreement / Married two kids / Crew filth
5121622 / Mar '96 / Cog Sinister

☐ EXTRICATE
Sing Harpy / I'm Frank / Bill is dead / Black monk theme / Popcorn double feature / Telephone thing / Hilary / Chicago now / Littlest rebel / And therein... / Black monk theme / Arms control poseur / British people in hot weather / Extricate
8422042 / Mar '96 / Cog Sinister

☐ FALL ARCHIVES, THE
I feel voxish / Guest informant / Arid Al's dream / Bad news girl / Fiend with a violin / Edinburgh man / Get a hotel / Blood outta stone / Carry bag man / Gut out the quantifier / Man whose head exploded / Pumpkin head escapes / Oswald defence lawyer / DKTR Faustus / Just waiting
RMCD 214 / Nov '97 / Rialto

☐ FALL IN A HOLE
Impression of J Temperance / Man whose head expanded / Room to live / Hip priest / Lie dream of a casino soul / Prole art theatre / Hard life in country / Classical / Mere pseud maged / Marquis Cha - Cha / Backdrop / Fantastic life / English scheme / Joker hysterical face / No Xmas for John Quays / Solicitor in studio
COGVP 102CD / Apr '97 / Cog Sinister

☐ FALL IN A HOLE (2CD Set)
RSG 4016 / 17 Nov '97 / Resurgence

☐ FALL, THE (2CD Set)
SMDCD 132 / Jul '97 / Snapper

☐ FIEND WITH A VIOLIN
I feel voxish / Man whose head expanded / Ed's babe / What you need / LA / Petty thief lout / Fiend with a violin / Spoilt Victorian child / Bombast / Married, two kids / Haven't found it yet / Gentleman's agreement
RRCD 211 / Apr '96 / Receiver

☐ GROTESQUE
Pay your rates / English scheme / New face in hell / C'N'Cs mithering / Container drivers / Impression of J Temperance / In the park / WMC blob 59 / Gramme Friday / NWRA
ESMCD 640 / 27 Jun '98 / Essential

☐ HEX ENDUCTION HOUR
Classical / Hip priest / Mere pseud mac editor's father / Who makes the Nazis / And this day / Jawbone and the air rifle / Fortress/Deer park / Winter / Just step s'ways / Iceland/Island
LICD 900126 / 16 Mar '98 / Line

☐ LEGENDARY CHAOS TAPES, THE
Middle class rap / English scene / New face in hell / That man / Old lover / Male slags / Prole art threat / Container drivers / Jawbone and the air rifle / In the park / Leave the capital / Spectre versus rector / Pay your rates / Impression of J Temperance
SAR 1005 / Nov '96 / Scout
COGVP 101CD / Jul '97 / Cog Sinister

☐ LEVITATE
ARTFULCD 9
ARTFULCDX 9 / 16 Feb '98 / Artful

☐ LIGHT USER SYNDROME, THE
DIY meat / Das vulture ans ein nuttter-wain / He pep / Hostile / Stay away (old white train) / Spinetrak / Interlude/chilinism / Powder keg / Oleano / Cheetham hill / Coliseum / Last chance to turn around / Ballad of J.Drummer / Oxymoron / Secession man
JETCD 1012 / Feb '98 / Jet

☐ LIVE AT THE WITCH TRIALS
Frightened / Like to blow / Rebellious jukebox / No Xmas for John Quays / Mother sister / Industrial estate / Underground medicine / Two steps back / Live at the witch trials / Futures and pasts / Music scene
COGVP 103CD / Jun '97 / Cog Sinister

☐ LIVE IN THE CITY
ARTFULCD 3 / 29 Jun '98 / Artful

☐ LIVE ON AIR IN MELBOURNE 1982
I feel voxish / Hard life in the country / I'm into CB / Lie dream of casino soul / Solicitor in the studio / Tempo house / Classical / Marquis cha cha / Room to live / Hexen strife / Knot deer park
COGVP 108CD / 27 Apr '98 / Cog Sinister

☐ LIVE VARIOUS YEARS
Deadbeat descendant / Big new prinz / Grudgeful / Free range / Shiftwork / Strychnine / Das vulturs / Spine track / Behind the counter / Interfrancs / Hip priest / Interfranc
COGVP 111CD / 24 Aug '98 / Cog Sinister

☐ NORTHERN ATTITUDE
Telephone thing / Das vulture ans ein nutter wain / Oxymoron / M5 6-7PM / Powder keg / Victoria / Edinburgh man / Oswald defence lawyer / I feel voxish / L.A. / Guest informant / E.S.P. disco / Mr. Pharmacist / Italiano / Fiend with a violin / Bremen nacht / Man whose head expanded / Bombast
MCCD 350 / 15 Jun '98 / MCI Music

☐ OSWALD DEFENCE LAWYER
Just waiting / Oswald defence lawyer / Victoria / Frenz / Two by four / Bad news girl / Get a hotel / Guest information / Big new prinz / Bremen nacht / Crazy bag man / Bombast
RRCD 213 / Apr '96 / Receiver

☐ OTHER SIDE OF THE FALL, THE (Sinister Waltz/Fiend With A Violin/ Oswald Defence/3CD Set)
Talk a lot of wind / Couldn't get ahead / Blood outta stone / Arid Al's dream / Knight / Devil and death / Chicago now / Birthday / Pumpkin head escapes / Wings / Dr. Faustus / Telephone thing / Black monk theme / Get out of the quantifier / Edinburgh man / I feel voxish / Man whose head expanded / Ed's babe / What you need / LA / Petty thief lout / Fiend with a violin / Spoilt Victorian child / Bombast / Married, two kids / Haven't found it yet / Gentleman's agreement / Just waiting / Oswald defence lawyer / Victoria / Frenz / Two by four / Bad news / Bad news girl / Get a hotel / Guest informant / Big new prinz / Bremen nacht / Crazy big man / Bombast
RRXCD 506 / Oct '96 / Receiver

☐ OXYMORON
Oxymoron / Powder keg / White lines / Pearl city / Birmingham school of business school / Hostile / Glam racket / Italiano / He pep / Rainmaster / Bill is dead / ESP Disco / Interlude/Chilinism / Life just bounces
RRCD 246 / 3 Nov '97 / Receiver

☐ PEEL SESSIONS, THE
Rebellious jukebox / Mess of my / New face in hell / Winter / Smile / Middlemass / Two by four / Cruisers creek / What you need / Athlete cured / Dead beat descendant / Black monk theme / Idiot joy showland / Free range / Strychnine / Past gone mad / M5
SFRSCD 048 / 2 Mar '98 / Strange Fruit

☐ PERVERTED BY LANGUAGE
Eat y'self fitter / Neighbourhood of infinity / Garden / Hotel Bloedel / Smile / I feel voxish / Tempo house / Hexen definitive/Strife knot
ESMCD 639 / 27 Jun '98 / Essential

☐ ROOM TO LIVE
COGVP 105CD / 20 Apr '98 / Cog Sinister

☐ SHIFT WORK
So what about it / Idiot joy showland / Edinburgh man / Pitsville direkt / Book of lies / High tension line / War against intelligence / Shiftwork / You haven't found it yet / Mixer / White lightning / Lot of wind / Rose / Sinister waltz
8485942 / Mar '96 / Cog Sinister

☐ SINISTER WALTZ
Talk a lot of wind / Couldn't get ahead / Blood outta stone / Arid Al's dream / Knight / Devil and the death / Chicago now / Birthday / Pumpkin head escapes / Wings / Dr. Faustus / Telephone thing / Black monk theme / Get out of the quantifier / Edinburgh man
RRCD 209 / Apr '96 / Receiver

☐ SLATES/PART OF AMERICA THEREIN 1981
Middle mass / Older lover / Prole art threat / Fit and working / Slates slags etc / Leave the capitol / NWRA / Hip priest / Totally wired / Lie dream of a casino soul / Cash 'n' carry / Older lover / Deep park / Winter
LOMACD 10 / Feb '94 / Loma

☐ SMILE...IT'S THE BEST OF THE FALL
CCSCD 823 / 30 Mar '98 / Castle

☐ THIS NATION'S SAVING GRACE
Mansion / Bombast / Barmy / What you need / Spoilt Victorian child / LA / Gut of the quantifier / My new house / Paintwork / I am Damo Suzuki / To Nkroachment : Yarbles
BBL 67CD / Feb '90 / Beggars Banquet

☐ TOTALES TURN
Fiery Jack / Rowche rumble / Muzorewi's daughter / In my area / Choc stock / Spector vs Rector 2 / Cary Grant's wedding / That man / New puritan / No xmas for John Quays
DOJOCD 83 / Nov '92 / Dojo

Fall From Grace

☐ FALL FROM GRACE
Snake eyed saviour / Seven shades of grey / It ain't like that / Gone / Violent truth / Sin (takes over) / Feel / Never / Before it grows / Hero zero / Open arms and broken hands
CDMFN 217 / 29 Sep '97 / Music For Nations

Falla Trio

☐ WEST SIDE STORY/PULCINELLA/ JAZZ SONATA
Prologue / Something's coming / Mambo / Cha cha / Maria, my own / Cool / One hand, one heart / Gee, officer krupke / America / Finale / Introduzione / Serenata / Tarantella / Gavotta / Vivo / Menuetto / Finale / 4th movement
CCD 42013 / Feb '89 / Concord Jazz

Fallen Angels

☐ HAPPY EVER AFTER
Happy ever after / Millworker / Aililiu na gamhna / Love is a rose / Throwing doves / Sunrise sunset / Virtual strangers / Greatest gift / Tha mullad / She moved through the fair / Madam I'm a darlin' / Starfish and coffee / Fragile / That lonesome road / I saw my Jesus
TARACD 4005 / Apr '97 / Tara

Falling Joys

☐ PSYCHOHUM
Black bandages / Incinerator / God in a dustbin / Challenger / Dynamite / Lullaby / Parachute / Natural scene / Fortune teller / Psychohum / Winter's tale / Ending or beginning
VOLTCD 059 / Jun '92 / Volition

☐ WISH LIST
VOLTCD 029 / Jan '92 / Volition

Falling Wallendas

☐ FALLING WALLENDAS
VAGUE 1001 / Apr '97 / Vague

False Virgins

☐ INFERNAL DOLL
OUT 1072 / Sep '97 / Brake Out

☐ SKIN JOB
OUT 1042 / Sep '97 / Brake Out

Falstaff

☐ FALSTAFF VOL.2
HMS 2342 / Mar '97 / Homestead

Faltskog, Agnetha

☐ BEST OF AGNETHA FALTSKOG 1968-1979, THE
I was so in love / My life goes on without you / Everything has changed / Sweedish summer (chic a chic a dee) / Gipsy friend / If tears were gold / Song and a fairy tale / So many good times to come / Dream's a dream / I don't know how to love him / Happiness in your eyes / Union silver / SOS / Doctor / Thanks for a wonderful day / When you take me in your arms
4652982 / 2 Feb '98 / Columbia

☐ EYES OF A WOMAN
One way love / Eyes of a woman / Just one heart / I won't let you go / Angels cry / Click track / We should be together / I won't be leaving you / Save me / I keep turning off lights / We move as one
8256002 / Jan '93 / Polydor

☐ THAT'S ME
Heat is on / Last time / Let it shine / Winner takes it all / I wasn't the one (who said goodbye) / Way you are / It's so nice to be rich / I won't let you go / Never again / Eyes of a woman / Slipping through my fingers / One way love / Can't shake loose / Wrap your arms around me / Queen of hearts / That's me / Turn the world around / You're there / Fly like the eagle
5399282 / 25 May '98 / Polydor

☐ WRAP YOUR ARMS AROUND ME
Heat is on / Can't shake loose / Shame / Stay / Once burned, twice shy / Mr. Persuasion / Wrap your arms around me / To love / I wish tonight could last forever / Man / Take good care of your children / Stand by my side
8132422 / Jan '93 / Polydor

Falu, Eduardo

☐ RESOLANA
NI 5281 / Sep '94 / Nimbus

Falu Spelmanslag

☐ I STOTEN
AW 18CD / Aug '97 / Tongang

Fambrough, Charles

☐ CITY TRIBES
Canto de Guebra / Hunt / Add a lesson / Dolores / Alligators / Irish lullaby / Laura Marie / Past time / City tribes
ECD 221492 / Apr '96 / Evidence

☐ KEEPER OF THE SPIRIT
Angels at play / Pop pop's song / Life above the means / Little this, a little that / Keeper of the spirit / Tears of romance / Save that time / Descent / Kaln / Secret hiding place
AQCD 1033 / Aug '95 / Audioquest

Fame, Georgie

☐ 20 BEAT CLASSICS
Yeh yeh / Getaway / Do re mi / My girl / Sweet things / Point of no return / Get on the right track baby / Baby / Ride your pony / Moody's mood for love / Funny how time slips away / Sunny sitting in the park / Green onions / In the meantime / Papa's got a brand new bag / Blue Monday / Pride and joy / Pink champagne / Let the sunshine in / I love the life I live, I live the life I love
8478102 / Jan '92 / Polydor

☐ BEST OF GEORGIE FAME 1967-1971, THE (2CD Set)
Ballad of Bonnie and Clyde / This guy's in love with you / Seventh son / Try my world / And I love her / Peaceful / Mellow yellow / Because I love you / By the time I get to Phoenix / Rosetta: *Fame, Georgie & Alan Price* / When I'm sixty four / Everything happens to me / Knock on wood / St. James Infirmary / Ask me nice / Hideaway / Exactly like you / Yellow man: *Fame, Georgie & Alan Price* / Blossom / Bird in a world of people
4851272 / Aug '96 / Columbia

☐ COOL CAT BLUES
Cool cat blues / Every knock is a boost / You came a long way from St. Louis / Big brother / It should have been me / Yeah yeah / Moondance / Cats' eyes / I love the life I live, I live the life I love / Survival / Little pony / Rockin' chair
GOJ 60022 / 8 Jun '98 / Go Jazz

☐ FIRST THIRTY YEARS, THE
Do the dog / Yeh yeh / Getaway / Ballad of Bonnie and Clyde / Rosetta / Daylight / Samba (toda menina baiana) / In crowd / C'est la vie / Fully booked / That ol' rock and roll / Sitting in the park / Do re mi / Like we used to be / Sunny / Seventh son / Ali shuffle / Hurricane / Moody's mood for love / Dawn yawn / Mellow yellow / Woe is me / Funny how time slips away / Old music master
VSOPCD 144 / Dec '89 / Connoisseur Collection

☐ GEORGIE FAME & THE DANISH RADIO BIG BAND 1992-93 (Fame, Georgie & Danish Radio Big Band)
MECCACD 1040 / Oct '93 / Music Mecca

☐ IN HOAGLAND (Fame, Georgie & Annie Ross)
Old music master / Hong Kong blues / Georgia on my mind / My resistance is low / One morning in May / I get along without you very well / Rockin' chair / Drip drop / Stardust / Upa lazy river / Small fry / Two sleepy people / Hoagy help / Hoagland
DRGCD 5197 / 23 Mar '98 / DRG

☐ NAME DROPPIN'
Jimmy McGroove / Cool cat blues / Tell me how do you feel / Zulu / Was / Vinyl / Mercy mercy mercy/ Vanlose stairway / Groove's groove/Red top/ Centrepiece/Don't Getz scared
GOJ 60212 / 29 Jun '98 / Go Jazz

☐ NO WORRIES (Fame, Georgie & The Australian Blue Flames)
Oh lady be good / Ole buttermilk sky / Eros hotel / Little Samba / It ain't right / On a misty night / Cats' eyes / Parchman farm / Zulu / Saturday night fish fry / Try na get along with the blues / Yeh yeh / Get away
FLCD 5099 / May '88 / Four Leaf Clover

☐ SELECTION OF STANDARDS... (Fame, Georgie & Hoagy Carmichael/Annie Ross)
CDSL 5197 / '88 / DRG

Familia Valera Miranda

☐ SON, THE
NI 5421 / Feb '95 / Nimbus

Family

☐ ANYWAY
Good news bad news / Willow tree / Holding the compass / Strange band / Normans / Part of the load / Lives and ladies / Anyway
ESMCD 615 / 30 Mar '98 / Essential

☐ BANDSTAND
Burlesque / Bolero babe / Coronation / Dark eyes / Broken nose / My friend the sun / Glove / Ready to go / Top of the hill / Rockin' R's
ESMCD 565 / Aug '97 / Essential

☐ COLLECTION, THE
Burlesque / My friend the sun / Children / Sweet desiree / It's only a movie / Holding the compass / In my own time / Ready to go / No mule's fool / Larf and sing / Cat and the rat / A song for me
CCSCD 374 / Mar '93 / Castle

☐ ENTERTAINMENT
Weaver's answer / Observations from a hill / Hung-up down / Summer '67 / How-hi-the-li / Second generation woman / From the past archives / Dim / Processions / Face in the crowd / Emotions
SEECD 200 / Oct '96 / See For Miles

☐ FEARLESS
Between blue and me / Sat'dy barfly / Larf and sing / Spanish tide / Save some for thee / Take your partners / Children / Crinkley grin / Blind / Burning bridges / In my own time / Seasons
ESMCD 567 / Aug '97 / Essential

☐ IT'S ONLY A MOVIE
It's only a movie / Leroy / Buffet tea for two / Boom bang / Boots 'n' roots / Banger / Sweet desiree / Suspicion / Check out / Stop this car / Drink to you
ESMCD 566 / Aug '97 / Essential

☐ MUSIC IN A DOLL'S HOUSE
Chase / Mellowing grey / Never like this / Me, my friend / Hey Mr. Policeman / See through windows / Variation on a theme of hey Mr. policeman / Winter / Old songs new songs / Variation on the theme of the breeze / Variation on a theme of me my friend / Peace of mind / Voyage / Breeze / Three times time
SEECD 100 / Apr '94 / See For Miles

☐ PEEL SESSIONS, THE
DEI 83332 / Mar '93 / Dutch East India

☐ SONG FOR ME, A
Drowned in wine / Some poor soul / Love is a sleeper / Stop for the traffic (through the heart of me) / Wheels / Song for sinking lovers / Hey let it rock / Cat and the rat / 93's OK J / Song for me
ESMCD 616 / 30 Mar '98 / Essential

Family Cat

☐ TELL 'EM WE'RE SURFING
BCRLCD 1 / Mar '90 / Big Cat

Family Dogg

☐ WAY OF LIFE, A
BX 4532 / Oct '95 / BR Music

Family Of God

☐ FAMILY OF GOD (2CD Set)
OCH 004LCD / 27 Apr '98 / Ochre

Family Stand

☐ CONNECTED
Keepin' you satisfied / Butter / When Heaven calls / Connected / It should've been me / What must I do now / You don't have to worry / Fienin' / You're mine / Don't ask why / More and more / What must I do now
7559620732 / 27 Apr '98 / Perfecto/East West

Famous Castle Jazz Band

☐ FAMOUS CASTLE JAZZ BAND
Sweet georgia brown / Royal garden blues / I've been floating down the old green river / At a georgia camp meeting / Careless love / Tiger rag / Dippermouth blues / Smokey mokes / Kansas city stomp / Torch / Ory's creole trombone / Farewell blues
GTCD 10030 / Oct '93 / Good Time Jazz

Famous Five

☐ LOST IN FISHPONDS
UNCCD 3 / Jun '95 / Uncle

Fan Modine

☐ SLOW ROAD TO TINY EMPIRE
Cardomon chai / Tinseltown / Mesopotamian pop soda / Tiny empire / Do it for love / Rodeo driving / Rhubarb pie / Oh to be a perfect servant / Oi ya lyubyu / Maigold / Trash in romance
SRRCD 031 / 23 Feb '98 / Slow River

Fanatik

☐ SEISMIC ACTIVITY
Mission one / Big world / Hallucinate / Ramadan / Catacombs of conscience / Kontortion / Post millennium / Sun torture / Disk jock no.2 / Parallel / Soundscape / Produce man / Remedy / Home improvement / Subwoofer contents / Deep sleep / Chameleon, the aftershock / Home-made remedy / Q vibe / Comatose / Aftershock / Unrankable talent
AGV 010CD / Feb '97 / All Good Vinyl

Fancy

☐ SOMETHING TO REMEMBER/WILD THING
Wild thing / Love for sale / Move on / I don't need your love / One night / Touch me / US Surprise / Between the devil and me / I'm a woman / Feel good / Fancy / She's riding the rock machine / I was made to love him / You've been in love too long / Something to remember / Everybody's cryin' mercy / Tour song / Stop / Music maker / Bluebird
SRH 802 / Feb '97 / Rock Heritage

Fane, Alan

☐ KALAMAN N'GONE/DOZON N'GONI (Fane, Alan Fote Mocoba)
2002850 / Jan '97 / Dakar Sound

Fania Allstars

☐ BEST OF THE FANIA ALLSTARS, THE
EDE 1063 / 14 Apr '98 / Karonte

☐ BRAVO
PTPM 1014 / 14 Apr '98 / Actual

Fankhauser, Merrell

☐ FAPARDOKLY
SC 6059 / Jun '97 / Sundazed

☐ THINGS
Things / Girl / What does she see in you / Lost in the city / Your painted lives / Drivin' sideways / In a minute not too soon / Visit with Ashiya / Big gray sky / Rich man's fable / Ice cube island / Madame Silky / I'm flying home
SC 6094 / Jun '97 / Sundazed

Fantastic Four

☐ ALVIN STONE (BIRTH AND DEATH OF A GANGSTER)/NIGHT PEOPLE
Alvin Stone (birth and death of a gangster) / Have a little mercy / County line / Let this moment last forever / Words / My love won't stop at nothing / Medley: Night people/Lies divided by jive / If I lose my job / Hideaway / By the river under the tree / Don't risk your happiness on foolishness / They took the show on the road
CDSEWD 057 / Jan '93 / Westbound

☐ GOT TO HAVE YOUR LOVE/BRING YOUR OWN FUNK
She'll be right for me / Mixed up moods and attitudes / There's fire down below / Ain't I been good to you / Cash money / I got to have your love / Disco pool blues / Give me all the love you got / Super lover / I just want to love ya baby / Shout (Let it all hang out) / Cold and windy night / Sexy lady / Realize (When you're in love) / BYOF (Bring your own funk)
CDSEWD 92 / Jun '94 / Westbound

Fantastic Plastic Machine

☐ FANTASTIC PLASTIC MACHINE, THE
Bon voyage / L'adventure fantastique / Steppin' out / Bachelor pad / Fantastic plastic world / Dear Mr. Salesman / Allen Ginsberg / First class '77 / Philter / Pleas estop / Pura saudade / L'adventure fantastic
BUNG 0302 / 13 Apr '98 / Bungalow

Fantasy

☐ BEST OF FANTASY, THE (You're Too Late)
HTCD 89 / 20 Apr '98 / Hot Productions

Fantasy

☐ BEYOND THE BEYOND
AACD 001 / 27 Apr '98 / Audio Archive

Fantasy Band

☐ KISS
SH 5028 / Mar '97 / Shanachie

Fantasyy Factoryy

☐ TALES TO TELL
LC 3163 / Jun '97 / Ohrwaschl

Far

☐ WATER AND SOLUTIONS
Bury white / Really here / Water and solutions / Mother Mary / I like it / System / Nestle / In 2 again / Wear it so well / Man overboard / Another way out / Waiting for Sunday
4892332 / 9 Mar '98 / Epic

Far Tulla

☐ BEST OF IRISH BALLADS
Sullivan's john / Fields of athenry / Spancil hill / Flight of earls / Only our rivers run free / Rose of mooncoin / Sick note / Cliffs of dooneen / Green fields 'round ferbane / Wild rover / Galway bay / Mary from dunloe / Luke a tribute / Paddy's green shamrock shore / Dirty old town / Old dungarvan oak
CHCD 017 / May '96 / Chart

Farafina

☐ FASO DENOU
Mama Sara / Kara mogo mousso / Dounouia / Nanore / Faso denou / Hereyo mibi / Ourodara sidiki / Lanaya / Bi mousso
CDRW 35 / May '93 / Realworld

☐ NEMAKO
Nemako / Africa Denou / Kora / Bana / Badeya / Fana / La paix / Djigui / Miribali / Kedo / Ai bamba / Touma / Fien
INT 32412 / 29 Jun '98 / Intuition

Farah Dance Orchestra

☐ TURKISH DELIGHT
CNCD 5957 / Jul '93 / Disky

Farantouri, Maria

☐ 17 SONGS
68950 / Apr '97 / Tropical

Farber, Mitch

☐ STARCLIMBER
Starclimber / Lonely promises / Chooser / Sky dance / Monuments / Time line
MCD 5400 / Sep '92 / Muse

Fardon, Don

☐ INDIAN RESERVATION (The Best Of Don Fardon)
Indian reservation / Gimme gimme good lovin' / Letter / Treat her right / I'm alive / Follow your drum / Delta queen / Running bear / Belfast boy / Take a heart / Lola / It's been nice loving you / Hudson Bay / On the beach / Tobacco Road / California maiden / Coming on strong / Mr. Station Master / Miami sunset / Riverboat / I need somebody / For your love / Girl / Sunshine woman
C5CD 540 / Jun '96 / See For Miles

☐ LINE DANCE PARTY
Folsom Prison blues / Letter / It doesn't get countrier than this / Della and the dealer / Achy breaky heart / Bad moon rising / Have you ever seen the rain / Hello Mary Lou, goodbye heart / Games people play / Let's work together / Will you love me tomorrow / All fired up
GRCD 84 / 22 Sep '97 / Grasmere

☐ NEXT CHAPTER, THE
Indian reservation / Good woman's love / Cocktail bar blues / Brown eyed and blue / Fear of losing you / Champion of the rodeo / Gone country / Who's that man / Caught in the crossfire / Belfast boy / Jodie's song / Take a heart / Do you remember / Indian reservation
CDSGP 0353 / May '97 / Prestige

Farflung

☐ SO MANY MINDS, SO LITTLE TIME
CLP 0009 / Jul '97 / Purple Pyramid

Farholt, Ann

☐ SECRET LOVE (Farholt, Ann & Henrik Bay Duo)
MECCACD 1085 / May '97 / Music Mecca

Farian, Frank

☐ HIT COLLECTION (Hits Of Frank Farian) (Various Artists)
74321199402 / Jun '94 / Arista

Farina, Geoff

☐ USONIAN DREAM
185502 / 14 Apr '98 / Southern

Farina, Mark

☐ FRISKO DISKO (Various Artists)
Flame: *Crustation* / Dreams of you: *Peter Funk* / I know: *Tim Deluxe* / Non sensical existence: *Primary Colours* / Feel your body talkin': *DJ Sneak* / Scrumpin': *Rainbow Garden* / Inhibitions: *Belizbeha* / Glasgow's jazz: *DJ Q* / C'mon clap your hands: *Magi* / Home: *Mateo & Matos* / Let's go disco: *Southern Comfort* / It's love: *Naked Music NYC* / Late night jam: *Sixteen Souls*
UNDJACD 009 / 23 Mar '98 / United DJ's Of America

Farina, Mimi

☐ SOLO
CDPH 1102 / Dec '86 / Philo

Farina, Mimi & Richard

☐ BEST OF MIMI & RICHARD FARINA, THE
Reflections in a crystal wind / Bold marauder / Swallow song / Sell-out agitation waltz / Hard loving loser / Pack up your sorrows / Michael, Andrew and James / One way ticket / Mainline prosperity blues / House un-American / Blues activity dream / Raven girl / Miles / Children of darkness / Hamish / Another country / Tuileries / Falcon / Reno Nevada / Celebration for a grey day
VCD 21 / 27 Jul '98 / Vanguard

☐ MEMORIES
Quiet joys of brotherhood / Joy 'round my brain / Lemonade lady / Downtown / Almond joy / Blood red roses / Morgan the pirate / Dopico / House of un-American blues activity dream / Shallow song / All the world has gone by / Pack up your sorrows
VMD 79263 / Oct '95 / Vanguard

☐ REFLECTIONS IN A CRYSTAL WIND
Reflections in a crystal wind / Bold marauder / Dopico / Swallow song / Chrysanthemum / Sell out agitation waltz / Hard loving loser / Mainline prosperity blues / Allen's interlude / House of un-American blues activity dream / Raven girl / Miles / Children of darkness
VMD 79204 / Oct '95 / Vanguard

Farina, Rafael

☐ LOS GRANDES EXITOS
DCD 62111 / 14 Apr '98 / DCD

Farjami, Hossein

☐ PLAYS SANTOOR (Folk Music From Iran)
EUCD 1100 / '91 / ARC

Farkas, Andras

☐ FAMOUS HUNGARIAN GIPSY TUNES (Farkas, Andras & Budapest Ensemble)
EUCD 1133 / '91 / ARC

☐ POPULAR GIPSY MELODIES (Farkas, Andras & Budapest Ensemble)
EUCD 1197 / Sep '93 / ARC

Farley & Heller

☐ JOURNEYS BY DJ VOL.12 (2CD Set) (Various Artists)
JDJCD 12 / Oct '96 / JDJ

Farley Jackmaster Funk

☐ REAL HOUSE ALBUM, THE
LIBTCD 001 / May '96 / 4 Liberty

Farlow, Billy C.

☐ GULF COAST BLUES
APCD 102 / Nov '95 / Appaloosa

☐ I AIN'T NEVER HAD TOO MUCH FUN
APCD 074 / '92 / Appaloosa

Farlow, Tal

☐ CHROMATIC PALETTE
All alone / Nuages / I hear a rhapsody / If I were a bell / St Thomas / Blue art too / Stella by starlight / One for my baby (And one more for the road)
CCD 4154 / Mar '94 / Concord Jazz

☐ COOKIN' ON ALL BURNERS
You'd be so nice to come home to / If I should lose you / I've got the world on a string / Love letters / Lullaby of the leaves / I thought about you / I wished on the moon / Why shouldn't I / Just friends
CCD 4204 / Jul '96 / Concord Jazz

☐ JAZZ MASTERS
5273652 / 5 May '98 / Verve

☐ LEGENDARY TAL FARLOW, THE
You stepped out of a dream / When your lover has gone / I got it bad and that ain't good / When lights are low / Who cares / I can't get started (with you) / Prelude to a kiss / Everything happens to me
CJ 266 390 / '88 / Concord Jazz

☐ RETURN OF TAL FARLOW, THE/1969
Straight no chaser / Darn that dream / Summertime / Sometime ago / I'll remember april / My romance / Crazy she calls me
OJCCD 356 / Nov '95 / Original Jazz Classics

☐ SIGN OF THE TIMES
Fascinating rhythm / You don't know what love is / Put a happy face / Stompin' at the Savoy / Georgia on my mind / You are too beautiful / In your own sweet way / Bayside blues
CCD 4026 / May '92 / Concord Jazz

☐ THIS IS TAL FARLOW
5377462 / 22 Sep '97 / Verve Elite

Farlowe, Chris

☐ AS TIME GOES BY
Bewitched / Glow / Sunday kind of love / As time goes by / Drinking again / These foolish things / At last / Blues as blues can get / You don't know me / Trust in me / I thought of you / Don't let me be lonely
CDEC 4 / Feb '97 / Out Of Time

☐ EXTREMELY (Farlowe, Chris & Spencer Davis/Pete York/Colin Hodgkinson)
Intro / Let the good times roll / Key to the highway / Feets too big / Tamp 'em up solid / Ain't nothing shakin' but the bacon / Intro / I think it's gonna rain today / Thrill is gone / Watch the river flow / Stormy Monday
INAK 8905CD / Nov '97 / In Akustik

☐ FROM HERE TO MAMA ROSA
Travelling into make believe / Fifty years / Where do we go from here / Questions / Head in the clouds / Are you sleeping / Black sheep / Winter of my life / Mama Rosa / Put out the light
CDEC 6 / Nov '96 / Out Of Time

☐ HIT SINGLE COLLECTABLES
DISK 4509 / Apr '94 / Disky

☐ I'M THE GREATEST
Paint it black / Think / Satisfaction / Handbags and gladrags / Baby make it soon / Looking for you / My colouring book / Don't just look at me / Moanin' / It was easier to hurt her / What becomes of the broken hearted / In the midnight hour / North west south east / Out of time / Yesterdays papers / Ride on baby / My way of giving / Headlines / Don't play that song (You lied) / I just don't know what to do with myself / You're so good for me / Life is but nothing / Dawn / Reach out, I'll be there / Mr. Pitiful
SEECD 396 / Oct '96 / See For Miles

☐ LONESOME ROAD
Who's been sleeping in my bed / Lonesome road / Jealous kind / My foundation / Tough on me, tough on you / I don't wanna sing the blues no more / Guitar don't lie / Watching the river flow / Have a little faith in me / Miss you fever / Out of time
IGOXCD 500 / Dec '95 / Indigo

☐ OLYMPIC ROCK AND BLUES CIRCUS (Farlowe, Chris, Brian Auger & Pete York)
BLR 84 013 / May '91 / L&R

☐ OUT OF TIME
Try me / Rock 'n' roll soldier / Some mother's son / Hold on / Blues anthem / Waiting in the wings / Function to function / Working in a parking lot / Make it fly / On the beach / Out of time
JHD 054 / Jan '93 / Tring

☐ R & B YEARS, THE
I remember / Push push / Girl trouble / Itty bitty pieces / Just a dream / What you gonna do / Hey hey hey hey / Hound dog / Buzz with the fuzz / You're the one / They call it stormy monday (parts 1 and 2) / Voodoo / Think / Lipstick traces / Don't play that song / Rockin' pneumonia and the boogie woogie flu / Baby make it soon / Cuttin' in / North south east west / My way of giving
CDRB 5 / Apr '94 / Charly

☐ VOICE, THE
I want to do everything for you / Easy as that / Language of the heart / Private number / Feel so good / Loving arms / Handbags and gladrags / All or nothing / She knows / Borderline blues
CIT 4CD / Apr '98 / Citadel

Farm

☐ BEST OF THE FARM, THE (2CD Set)
Stepping stone / Groovy train / All together now / Don't let me down / Mind / Love see no colour / Hearts and minds / Family of man / Good morning sinners / News International / Rising sun / Creepers / Messiah / All American world / Groovy train / Groovy train / All together now / All together now / Don't let me down / Mind / Love see no colour / Love see no colour / Love see no colour
ESSCD 595 / 2 Mar '98 / Essential

☐ HULLABALOO
Messiah / Shake some action / Comfort / Man who cried / Hateful / Golden vision / To the ages / All American world / Distant voices
9362455882 / Aug '94 / Warner Bros.

☐ SPARTACUS
Hearts and minds / How long / Sweet inspiration / Groovy train / Higher and higher / Don't let me down / Family of man / Tell the story / Very emotional / All together now / Higher and higher / Very emotional / Groovy train / All together now
ESMCD 580 / Jul '97 / Essential

Farm Dogs

☐ IMMIGRANT SONS
Foreign windows / Distance to the mountain / Daria / Lightning on the hill / This face / Whiskey in the bathtub / Bird of prey / Leaving Buffalo / Working in the fields / America on trial / Nothin' gonna kill the kid / Aimless driving / Deep driving secret / Stars and seeds
4344310142 / 23 Mar '98 / Sire

Farmer, Art

☐ ART FARMER & LEE KONITZ/JOE CARTER
STCD 571 / Mar '94 / Stash

☐ ART FARMER SEPTET (Farmer, Art Septet)
OJCCD 54 / Sep '93 / Original Jazz Classics

☐ EARLY ART
Soft shoe / Confab in tempo / I'll take romance / Wisteria / Autumn nocturne / I've never been in love before / Gone with the wind / Alone together / Pre amp
OJCCD 880 / Jun '96 / Original Jazz Classics

☐ FOOLISH
Larry's delight / Al-leu-cha / D's dilemma / In a sentimental mood / Foolish memories / Farmer's market
CDLR 45008 / Dec '88 / L&R

☐ IN CONCERT
Half Nelson / Darn that dream / Barbados / I'll remember April
ENJ 40882 / Jul '95 / Enja

☐ LISTEN TO ART FARMER AND THE ORCHESTRA
5377472 / 22 Sep '97 / Verve Elite

☐ LIVE AT THE HALF NOTE
What's new / I want to be happy / Swing spring / Stompin' at the savoy / I'm getting sentimental over you
7567906662 / Apr '95 / Atlantic

☐ MANHATTAN (Farmer, Art Quintet)
SNCD 1026 / '86 / Soul Note

☐ MEANING OF ART, THE
On the plane / Just the way you look tonight / Lift your spirit high / One day forever / Free verse / Home / Johnny one note
AJ 0118 / Dec '95 / Arabesque

☐ MEETS MULLIGAN & HALL
MCD 0512 / Apr '94 / Moon

☐ MIRAGE (Farmer, Art Quintet)
Barbados / Passos / My kind of love / Mirage / Cherokee sketches / Smiling billy
SNCD 1046 / '86 / Soul Note

☐ PHD
PhD / Affaire d'amour / Mr. Day's dream / Summary / Blue wail / Like someone in love / Rise to the occasion / Ballade art
CCD 140552 / Apr '94 / Contemporary

☐ SOMETHING TO LIVE FOR (The Music Of Billy Strayhorn)
Isfahan / Bloodcount / Johnny come lately / Something to live for / Upper Manhattan medical group / Raincheck / Daydream
CCD 140292 / Apr '94 / Contemporary

☐ TWO TRUMPETS (Farmer, Art & Donald Byrd)
OJCCD 18 / Nov '95 / Original Jazz Classics

☐ WARM VALLEY
Moose the mooche / And now there's you / Three little words / Eclypso / Sad to say / Upper Manhattan medical group / Warm valley
CCD 4212 / Mar '92 / Concord Jazz

☐ WORK OF ART, A (Farmer, Art Quartet)
She's funny that way / Love walked in / Change partners / Red cross / You know I care
CCD 4179 / Jul '96 / Concord Jazz

☐ YOU MAKE ME SMILE (Farmer, Art Quintet)
SNCD 1076 / '86 / Soul Note

Farmer Boys

☐ FLASH CRASH AND THUNDER
Flash crash and thunder / Cool down Mame / Yearnin' / Burning heart / Somehow, someway, someday / Flip flop / Charming Betsy / Lend a helpin' hand / It pays to advertise / Someone to love me / My baby done left me / Oh how it hurts / No one / You lied / You're a hungdinger / I'm just too lazy / Onions, onions
BCD 15579 / Mar '92 / Bear Family

Farmer Not So John

☐ FARMER NOT SO JOHN
742392 / May '98 / Compass

Farmer's Daughter

☐ FARMER'S DAUGHTER
HERCD 282 / Mar '98 / Heritage

Farmer's Manual

☐ EXPLORERS WE
SQUISH 4 / 18 May '98 / Or

☐ FSCK
TRAY 2CD / Aug '97 / Ashtray

Farmer's Market

☐ MUSIKK FRA HYBRIDENE
FX 182CD / Aug '97 / Kirkelig Kultuverksted

☐ SPEED/BALKAN/BOOGIE
FX 148CD / Apr '95 / Musikk Distribujson

Farmers

☐ ROCK ANGEL
FF 548CD / '92 / Flying Fish

Farnham, Allen

☐ ALLEN FARNHAM MEETS THE RIAS BIG BAND (Farnham, Allen & The RIAS Big Band)
RIAS-ticity / Work song / Lost in Zurich / There will never be another you / Triste / Gai-Kichi / My foolish heart / Samba de Sorvete / Cousin Mary
CCD 47892 / 16 Feb '98 / Concord Jazz

☐ COMMON THREAD, THE
Common thread / Hamma-ron / Nocturne / Glide / Falling grace / Interlude / How deep is the ocean / In a sentimental mood / No more blues / Very early
CCD 4634 / Mar '95 / Concord Jazz

☐ PLAY CATION
M'kashi b'nashi / Play cation / Long ago and far away / My man's gone now / Foot prince / Alone together / Stablemates / Daymeam / Cheek to Chico
CCD 4521 / Sep '92 / Concord Jazz

Farnham, John

☐ AGE OF REASON
Age of reason / Blow by blow / Listen to the wind / Two strong hearts / Burn down the night / Beyond the call / We're no angels / Don't tell me it can't be done / Fire / Some do, some don't / When the war is over / It's a long way to the top (if you wanna rock 'n' roll)
74321138982 / Sep '95 / RCA

☐ ANTHOLOGY VOL.1 (The Greatest Hits 1986-1997)
You're the voice / Pressure down / Touch of paradise / Reasons / Two strong hearts / Age of reason / That's freedom / Chain reaction / Burn for you / Seemed like a good idea (at the time) / Talk of the town / Angels / Have a little faith (in us) / Simple life / Heart's of fire / When something is wrong with my baby: *Farnham, John & Jimmy Barnes* / Everything you cry: *Farnham, John & Human Nature*
74321518692 / Jul '98 / RCA

☐ WHISPERING JACK
Pressure down / You're the voice / One step away / Reasons / Going going gone / No one comes close / Love to shine / Trouble / Touch of paradise / Let me out
74321187202 / Apr '94 / RCA

Farnon, Dennis

☐ MOTHER MAGOO SUITE (Metropole Orchestra)
Half the King's men / Very contrary Mary / Hip pocket full of rye / Little Miss muffed it / Not-so-simple Simon / Sheepish Bo-Peep / Little boy blew / Portrait of Mr. Magoo / Wormwood Scrubs march
EW 9631 / Sep '97 / Eigen Wijs

Farnon, Robert

☐ AT THE MOVIES (Farnon, Robert & His Orchestra)
Moment I saw you / Early one morning / Best things in life are free / Wouldn't it be loverly / How beautiful is night / You're the cream in my coffee / Pictures in the fire / I guess I'll have to change my plan / Great day / When I fall in love / Melody fair / Just imagine / Lady Barbara / Trolley song / Way we were / Sunny side up
CDSIV 6111 / Jul '95 / Horatio Nelson

☐ JOURNEY INTO MELODY (Farnon, Robert & His Orchestra)
Journey into melody / My heart stood still / To each his own / Darktown Strutters' Ball / Goodbye goodbye Cherie / Carioca / This is always / You keep coming back like a song / Nearness of you / Oh Susannah / Begin the beguine / All through the day / What is the thing called love / Love walked in / Stars will remember / Getting nowhere / Along the Navajo trail / My fickle eye / So would I / Hora staccato / South American way / Journey into melody
PLCD 564 / Oct '97 / President

Farr, Deitra

☐ SEARCH IS OVER, THE
Anywhere but here / Bad company / You've got to choose / Waiting for you / I refuse to lose / How much longer / Taking the long way home / Waiting for the blues / Search is over / Must have been an angel / Stealin' your love / This I know to be free
JSPCD 284 / Jul '97 / JSP

Farr, Gary

☐ ROCK GENERATION (Farr, Gary/Soft Machine)
14556 / 23 Mar '98 / Spalax

Farrar, John

☐ JOHN FARRAR
Reckless / Tell someone who cares / Can't hold back / Gettin' loose / Cheatin' his heart out again / Recovery / It'll be me babe / Falling / From the heart
SEECD 484 / Jul '97 / See For Miles

Farrell, Eileen

☐ EILEEN FARRELL SINGS ALEC WILDER
Lady sings the blues / Where do you go / Moon and sand / Worm has turned / Blackberry winter / I'll be around
RR 36CD / '90 / Reference Recordings

☐ EILEEN FARRELL SINGS HAROLD ARLEN
Let's fall in love / Out of this world / I wonder what became of me / I've got the world on a string / Like a straw in the wind / Down with love / Happiness is a thing called Joe / Woman's prerogative / Come rain or come shine / Little drops of rain / Over the rainbow / When the sun comes out / As long as I live / My shining hour / Last night when we were young
RR 30CD / '90 / Reference Recordings

☐ EILEEN FARRELL SINGS RODGERS AND HART
I could write a book / I wish I were in love again / Wait 'til you see him / I didn't know what time it was / Love me tonight / Nobody's heart / It never entered my mind / Mountain greenery / Sing for your supper / Can't you do a friend a favour / Lover / My heart stood still / Little girl blue / You're nearer
RR 32CD / '90 / Reference Recordings

☐ EILEEN FARRELL SINGS TORCH SONGS
Stormy weather / 'Round midnight / End of a love affair / Black coffee / When your lover has gone / Don't explain / This time the dream is on me / I get along without you very well / Something cool ... and more
RR 34CD / '90 / Reference Recordings

☐ LOVE IS LETTING GO
Just in time / Why did I choose you / Love is letting go / I've never been in love before / Country boy / Where were you this afternoon / Everyday / I dream of you / Quiet thing / Time after time / My love turned me down today / I'll be tired of you / For Eileen
DRGCD 91436 / Oct '95 / DRG

☐ WITH THE LOONIS MCGLOHON QUARTET
ACD 237 / Apr '93 / Audiophile

Farrell, Pat

☐ PAT FARRELL 1966-1968
AA 072 / 27 Apr '98 / Arf Arf

Farren, Mick

☐ FRAGMENTS OF BROKEN PROBES (Farren, Mick & The Deviants)
CTCD 046 / Jun '97 / Captain Trip

☐ GRINGO MADNESS (Farren, Mick & Tijuana Bible)
Leader hotel / Mark of zorro / Lone sungularity / Solitaire devil / Spider kissed / Jezebel / Long walk with the devil/Jumping Jack flash / Movement of the whores on revolution plaza / Hippie death cult / Last night the alhambra burned down / Eternity is a very long time / Memphis psychosis / Riot in cell block 9
CDWIK 117 / Feb '93 / Big Beat

Farrenden, Bernie

☐ ON THE ALAMO (Farrenden, Bernie Jazz Quintet)
RSCD 668 / Feb '98 / Raymer

Farrenden, Shaun

☐ YIDAKI
ALUNA 001 / May '96 / Aluna

☐ YODAKI (DIDJERIDU)
ALUNA 1995 / Apr '97 / Knock On Wood

Farreyrol, Jacqueline

☐ REUNION ISLAND TRADITIONS
PS 65091 / Jul '92 / PlayaSound

Farris, Dionne

☐ WILD SEED WILD FLOWER
I know / Reality / Stop to think / Passion / Food for thought / Now or later / Don't ever touch me (again) / Eleventh hour / Water blackbird / Old ladies / Human / Find your way / Audition
4777552 / 2 Feb '98 / Columbia

Farside

☐ RIGGED
REV 033CD / Aug '94 / Revelation

Fascinating Aida

☐ IT WIT DON'T GIVE A SHIT GIRLS
SCENECD 23 / 29 Sep '97 / First Night

☐ LOAD OF OLD SEQUINS, A
Boring / Radiating love / Yuppies / Shattered illusions / Songs of the homesick / Lieder / Another man / Whites blues / My dream man / All bonjour monsieur / Jealousy / Sew on a sequin / Taboo
OCRCD 6018 / Mar '96 / First Night

Fascinations

☐ OUT TO GET'CHA
Girls are out to get you / You'll be sorry / I'm so lucky (He loves me) / Such a fool / I'm in love / OK for you / I can't stay away from you / Say it isn't so (Take four) / Say it isn't so (Take eight) / Just another reason / Hold on / Trust in you / Crazy / I've been trying / If / Still trying / Don't start none / Little bird / Lucky / Foolish one / So sorry / Out to get'cha
NEMCD 881 / Mar '97 / Sequel

Fasoli, Claudio

☐ CITIES (Fasoli, Claudio & Dalla Porta/ Elgart/Goodrick)
RMCD 4503 / Nov '93 / Ram

Fassaert, Tammy

☐ JUST PASSIN' THROUGH
SCR 36 / Nov '95 / Strictly Country

Fast Freddie's Fingertips

☐ NEW TOWN SOUL
323184 / Aug '94 / Koch

Fastbacks

☐ ANSWER THE PHONE DUMMY
SPCD 259 / Nov '94 / Sub Pop

☐ QUESTION IS NO
SP 146B / Mar '94 / Sub Pop

☐ WIN LOSE OR BOTH
PLCD 6 / 23 Feb '98 / Pop Llama

☐ ZUCKER
SP 231 CD / Jan '93 / Sub Pop

Fastball

☐ ALL THE PAIN MONEY CAN BUY
1621302 / 27 Jul '98 / Polydor

Fat & Frantic

☐ QUIRK
Too late / Last night my wife hoovered my head / Rise up / Who's your friend Eddy / I don't want to say goodbye / Africa / It's you / If I could be your milkman / Aggressive sunbathing / Senator's daughter / I'm sorry / I wish / Darling Doris / River
5018524 01102 / Aug '90 / I'll Call You

Fat

☐ AUTOMAT HIGHLIFE
RERFATCD / Apr '91 / ReR/ Recommended

Fat Larry's Band

☐ CLOSE ENCOUNTERS OF A FUNKY KIND
Close encounters of a funky kind / Stand up / Good time / Can't keep my hands to myself / Last chance to dance / Everything is disco / Hey Pancho, it's disco / Zoom / Play with me / Boogie town / I love you so / Dirty words / Lookin' for love / You gotta help yourself
CDSEWD 095 / Jan '95 / Southbound

☐ OFF THE WALL
Sparkle / Peaceful journey / Castle of joy / Passing time / Easy / Don't you worry about tomorrow / Time / I love you so / In the pocket
CDSXE 069 / Nov '92 / Stax

Fat Mattress

☐ FAT MATTRESS VOL.1
All nightdrinker / I don't mind / Bright new way / Petrol pump assistant / Mr. Moonshine / Magic forest / She came in the morning / Everything's blue / Walking through a garden / How can I live / Little girl in white / Marguerita / Which way to go / Future days / Cold wall of stone
NEXCD 196 / May '92 / Sequel

Fat Tony

☐ LAST NIGHT A DJ (Various Artists)
21CCCD 003 / Mar '96 / 21st Century Opera

Fat Tulips

☐ STARFISH
So unbelievable / World away from me / Ribs / Sweetest child / Chainsaw / I promise you / My secret place / Double decker bus / Clumsy / If God exists / Big toe / Nothing less than you deserve / Letting go / Death of me / Never
ASKCD 034 / Jul '94 / Vinyl Japan

Fatal

☐ IN THE LINE OF FIRE
Intro / MOB / Everyday / Friday / I know the rules / Outlaws / Time's wastin / Whta's your life worth / Ghetto star / Take your time / World is changing
4898112 / 23 Mar '98 / Relativity

Fatal Embrace

☐ SHADOWLANDS
CANDLE018CD / 6 Oct '97 / Candlelight

Fatal Opera

☐ FATAL OPERA
MASSCD 051 / Apr '95 / Massacre

Fatala

☐ GONGOMA TIMES
Timini / Yekeke / Maane / Gongoma times / Seoraba / Boke (N'yaraloum-ma) / Limbadji toko / Sohko / Soisisa
RWMCD 4 / Jan '93 / Realworld

Fatback Band

☐ 14 KARAT
Let's do it again / Angel / Backstrokin' / Concrete jungle / Without your love / Gotta get my hands on some (money) / Your love is strange / Lady groove / Chillin' out
CDSEWM 060 / Jun '93 / Southbound

☐ 21 KARAT FATBACK
I found lovin' / Girl is fine / Night fever / (Are you ready) Do the bus stop / Double Dutch / King Tim III (Personality jock) / Wicky wacky / I like girls / Gotta get my hands on some (money) / Let's do it again / Master Booty / Backstrokin' / Keep on steppin' / Freak the freak the funk (rock) / Take it any way you want it / Spanish hustle / Rockin' to the beat / On the floor / Booty / Yum yum (gimme some) / Is this the future / Party time
CDSEWD 101 / Mar '95 / Southbound

☐ BRITE LITES/ BIG CITY
Freak the freak the funk (rock) / Let me do it to you / Big city / Do the boogie woogie / Hesitation / Wild dreams
CDSEWM 045 / Jan '92 / Southbound

☐ FEEL MY SOUL
Feeling mellow (Instrumental) / Meet me over my house / Three dimensional world / Sketches of life / You've got a friend / Feeling mellow / Makin' love / Why is it so hard to do (Things I wanna do) / Feel my soul
DEEPM 018 / Mar '97 / Deep Beats

☐ FIRED UP 'N' KICKIN'
I'm fired up / Boogie freak / Get out on the dance floor / At last / I like girls / Snake / Can't you see
CDSEW 041 / Jul '91 / Southbound

☐ GIGOLO
Rockin' to the beat / Rub down / I'm so in love / Higher / Do it / Gigolo / Oh girl / Na na hey hey kiss her goodbye
CDSEWM 081 / Nov '93 / Southbound

☐ HOT BOX
Hot box / Come and get the love / Love spell / Gotta get my hands on some (money) / Backstrokin' / Street band
CDSEWM 056 / Sep '92 / Southbound

☐ IS THIS THE FUTURE
Is this the future / Double love affair / Spread love / Funky aerobics (Body movement) / Up against the wall / Finger lickin' good / Sunshine lady / Girl is fine
CDSEWM 058 / Apr '94 / Southbound

☐ KEEP ON STEPPIN'
Mr. Bass man / Stuff / New York style / Love / Can't stop the flame / Wicky wacky / Feeling / Keep on stepping / Breaking up with someone you love is hard to do
CDSEW 001 / Jun '89 / Southbound

☐ LET'S DO IT AGAIN
Street dance / Free form / Take a ride (On the soul train) / Wichita lineman / Baby I'm want you / Let's do it again / Goin' to see my baby / Give me one more chance / Green green grass of home
DEEPM 020 / Mar '97 / Deep Beats

☐ MAN WITH THE BAND
Man with the band / Master Booty / Funk backin' / Mile high / I gotta thing for you / Midnight freak / Zodiac man
CDSEW 036 / Jan '91 / Southbound

☐ NIGHT FEVER
Night fever / Little funky dance / If that's the way you want it / Joint (you and me) / Disco crazy / Booty / No more room on the dancefloor / December '63 (oh what a night)
CDSEW 008 / Aug '89 / Southbound

☐ NYCNYUSA
Double Dutch / Soul finger (gonna put on you) / Spank the baby / Duke walk / NYCNYUSA / Love street / Changed man / Cosmic woman
CDSEW 030 / Jul '90 / Southbound

☐ ON THE FLOOR
On the floor / UFO (Unidentified funk object) / Burn baby burn / She's my shining star / Hip so slick / Do it to me now
CDSEWM 091 / Mar '94 / Southbound

☐ PEOPLE MUSIC
Nija walk (Street walk) / Gotta have you (Day by day) / Fatbackin' / Baby doll / Clap your hands / Soul march / Soul man / To be with you / Kiba
DEEPM 019 / Mar '97 / Deep Beats

☐ RAISING HELL
(Are you ready) do the bus stop / All day / Put your love (in my tender care) / Groovy kind of day / Spanish hustle / I can't help myself / Party time
CDSEW 028 / Apr '90 / Southbound

☐ TASTY JAM
Take it any way you want it / Wanna dance / Keep your fingers out of the jam / Kool whip / High steppin' lady / Get ready for the night
CDSEWM 088 / Feb '94 / Southbound

☐ WITH LOVE
He's a freak undercover / Rastajam / I love your body language / I found lovin' / I wanna be your lover / Please stay / Wide glide
CDSEW 024 / Feb '90 / Southbound

☐ XII
You're my candy sweet / Disco bass / Gimme that sweet, sweet lovin' / King Tim III (personality jock) / Disco queen / Love in perfect harmony
CDSEWM 049 / Apr '92 / Southbound

☐ YUM YUM
Yum yum (gimme some) / Trompin' / Let the drums speak / Put the funk on you / Feed me your love / Boogie with Fatback / Got to learn how to dance / If you could turn into me / (Hey) I feel real good
CDSEW 016 / Nov '89 / Southbound

Fatboy Slim

☐ BETTER LIVING THROUGH CHEMISTRY
BRASSIC 2CD / 3 Nov '97 / Skint

☐ ON THE FLOOR AT THE BIG BEAT BOUTIQUE (Mixed By Fatboy Slim) (Various Artists)
BRASSIC 9CD / 13 Jul '98 / Skint

Fates Warning

☐ CHASING TIME
398414085CD / Apr '97 / Metal Blade

☐ INSIDE OUT
MASSCD 037 / Jun '94 / Massacre

☐ NIGHT ON BROCKEN
398414053CD / May '96 / Metal Blade

☐ NO EXIT
No exit / Anarchy divine / Silent cries / In a word / Shades of heavenly death / Ivory gate of dreams
398414047CD / Apr '96 / Metal Blade

☐ PLEASANT SHADE OF GREY
MASSCD 125 / Jun '97 / Massacre

☐ SPECTRE WITHIN
398414054CD / May '96 / Metal Blade

Fathead

☐ BLUES WEATHER
EF 3357 / Jun '98 / Electro-Fi

Father MC

☐ THIS IS FOR THE PLAYERS
Interlude (interview) / Treat me right / This is for the players / Sexual playground / You can do me / Interlude (studio talk) / High rollers / Sexual healing / I am what you want / Funkin with father / Interlude (farewell) / Life
CDMISH 3 / Nov '95 / Mission

Fatman

☐ FATMAN VS. SHAKA (First, Second & Third Generation Of Dub) (Fatman & Jah Shaka)
FM 001CD / May '95 / Fatman

☐ SAME SONG DUB (Fatman Riddim Section)
LG 21103 / Apr '95 / Lagoon

Fatool, Nick

☐ NICK FATOOL AND HIS JAZZ BAND/ QUARTET
JCD 158 / Sep '97 / Jazzology

Fatskins

☐ THINKIN' LIKE A FATSKIN
STEPCD 108 / 23 Mar '98 / Step 1

Fatso Jetson

☐ POWER OF THREE
Builders and collectors / Ugly man ugly name / Mummified / Orgy porgy / El taurino / Phil the hole / Phantom of the opry / Handgun / Sandy the clockfarmer / Bored stiff / Itchy brother / Drones pills
SST 341CD / 20 Oct '97 / SST

Fattburger

☐ ALL NATURAL INGREDIENTS
SH 5026CD / Oct '96 / Shanachie

☐ LIVIN' LARGE
Anything's possible / Love is like a river / Creepin' / Livin large' / Nine lives / Just can't get enough / Intuition / Rockin' the walk / In your eyes / Sheezateez
SHCD 5012 / 9 Mar '98 / Shanachie

☐ SUGAR
Show me the honey / Spice / Groovin' / Sugar / Emerald hills / Soothing / It's about time / Valencia / Hole in one / Mad cow
SHANCD 5044 / Jun '98 / Shanachie

Fatty George

☐ FATTY'S SALON 1958
RST 91425 / Oct '92 / RST

Faubert, Michel

☐ CAREME ET MARDI-GRAS
MPCD 1095 / Apr '96 / Mille Pattes

☐ MAUDITE MEMOIRE
MPCD 995 / Apr '96 / Mille Pattes

Faubert, Shane

☐ SQUIRRELBOY BLUE
MMCD 056 / Sep '97 / Music Maniac

Faucett, Dawnett

☐ TAKING MY TIME
Slow dancing / Don't stop to count the memories / Mama never told me / Bus won't be stopping / Heart heart / Cheap perfume / Good for you / Taking my time / As far as love can throw me / Dusty road / Two empty arms / Unwanted
SORCD 0054 / Oct '94 / D-Sharp

Faulk, Dan

☐ FOCUSING IN (Faulk, Dan Quintet)
CRISS 1076CD / Nov '93 / Criss Cross

Faulkner, John

☐ KIND PROVIDENCE
Sweet Thames flow softly / Walecatchers/Drunken landlady / Planxty gan ainm / Wild rover / Johnny Coughlin / McCaffery / Banks of Newfoundland / Forger's farewell / Road to Cashel/Jackie Daly's reel / Newry town
GLCD 1064 / Feb '93 / Green Linnet

☐ NOMADS/FANAITHE
MacCrimmon will never come back / MacCrimmon's lament / Sucah a Parcel of Rogues in a Nation / Farewell to Scotland/In the mist / Young Munroe / La reel du Pendu / Cape Sky waltz/Joe Tom's reels / I am a little orphan/Two step too / I loved a lass / Jolly bold robber / Flowers of Finae / Child owlet/ Erskine's folly / Nomads of the road/Pristina
CIC 071CD / Jan '92 / Clo Iar-Chonnachta

Fauna Flash

☐ AQUARIUS
COMP 042CD / 8 Dec '97 / Compost

Fausko, Ola & Knut

☐ HULDREHATTEN
H 4001CD / Sep '97 / Fausko

Faust

☐ FAUST
KLANG 01 / Nov '96 / Klangbad

☐ FAUST CONCERTS VOL.1
2655847 / Dec '97 / Table Of The Elements

☐ FAUST CONCERTS VOL.2
589332 / Dec '97 / Table Of The Elements

☐ FAUST IV
Krautrock / Sad skinhead / Jennifer / Jus' a second / Picnic on a frozen river, Deuxieme tableux / Giggy smile / Lauft... Heist das es lauft oder es kommt bald... Lauft / It's a bit of a pain
CD 0501 / Oct '92 / Virgin

☐ LIVE IN EDINBURGH - AUGUST 1997
EFA 035602 / 8 Dec '97 / Think Progressive
FAUSTLIVECD 1 / Nov '97 / Klangbad

☐ OUTSIDE THE DREAM SYNDICATE (Faust & Tony Conrad)
LITHIUM 3 / Jan '94 / Southern

☐ RIEN
CHROMIUM 24 / Jun '97 / TOE

☐ UNTITLED
KLANG 001 / Feb '97 / Klangbad

☐ WAKES NOSFERATU
C 8173 / 20 Apr '98 / Klangbad

Faust, Alban

☐ BORDUNMUSIK FRAN DALSLAND
TONART 41CD / Nov '96 / Tonart

Faux, George

☐ TIME FOR A LAUGH AND A SONG
Birthday reel / Farewell to the building / Cultural dessert / Kellswater / Parker's fancy / Farewell to London / Artesian water / Leggett's reel - the old grey cat / Do me amma / Gallant brigantine / Dominic's march / Time for a laugh and a song
HARCD 006 / Oct '93 / Harbour Town

Favata, Enzo

☐ AJO (Favata, Enzo & Dino Saluzzi)
FY 7001CD / Aug '97 / Robi Droli

Faver, Colin

☐ TECHMIX VOL.1 (On The Decks With Colin Faver) (Various Artists)
KICKCD 40 / Aug '96 / Kickin'

Favre, Pierre

☐ SOUFFLES (Favre, Pierre Singin' Drums)
INTAKTCD 049 / Jan '98 / Intakt

☐ WINDOW STEPS
Snow / Cold nose / Lea / Girimella / En passant / Aguilar / Passage
5293482 / Feb '96 / ECM

Favreau, Eric

☐ VIOLIN & ACCORDION (Favreau, Eric & Joaquin Diaz)
B 6837 / Nov '96 / Auvidis/Ethnic

Fawkes, Wally

☐ FIDGETY FEET
SOSCD 1248 / Jul '93 / Stomp Off

Fay, Colin

☐ DANCING ON THE CEILING
Snowbird / Walking the floor / Swanee / Please baby please / Ain't we got fun / Melody in F / Oh my Papa / Andantiono / Dancing on the ceiling / Silver threads among the gold / Rose room / Coppelia / Love theme from The Thorn Birds / Nocturne in Eb / If those lips could only speak / I'll be your sweetheart / Let the rest of the world go by / Pretty baby / Make mine love / Strollin' / Underneath the arches / Louise / Broken doll / Honeysuckle and the bee / Nola / Glory of love / Waiting at the church / Oh Mr Porter / Daddy wouldn't buy me a bow-wow / On the banks of wabash / Lily of Laguna / Man who broke the bank at Monte Carlo / Let's all go down the strand / Wot'cher (Knocked 'em in the Old Kent Road) / Fall in and follow me / Light of foot / Life on the ocean wave / Stephanie Gavotte / Kind regards / Tell me pretty maiden / Ascot gavotte / Ay ay ay / La concordia / Pablo the dreamer / Creole tango
GRCD 52 / Aug '92 / Grasmere

Fay, Rick

☐ AMONG THE REEDS
ARCD 19177 / 1 Jun '98 / Arbors Jazz

☐ GLENDENA FOREVER (Fay, Rick & Jackie Coon)
ARCD 19104 / Nov '94 / Arbors Jazz

☐ HELLO HORN
ARCD 19102 / Nov '94 / Arbors Jazz

☐ LIVE AT LONE PINE
ARCD 19101 / Nov '94 / Arbors Jazz

☐ LIVE AT THE STATE THEATRE
ARCD 29102 / Nov '94 / Arbors Jazz

☐ MEMORIES OF YOU
ARCD 19103 / Nov '94 / Arbors Jazz

☐ OH BABY
ARCD 19105 / Nov '94 / Arbors Jazz

☐ ROLLING ON
I double dare you / Blues (my naughtie sweetie gives to me) / Somebody loves me / Tishomingo blues / Manoir de mes reves / Come back Papa
ARCD 19108 / Nov '94 / Arbors Jazz

☐ SAX-O-POEM
ARCD 19113 / Nov '94 / Arbors Jazz

☐ THIS IS WHERE I CAME IN
ARCD 19106 / Nov '94 / Arbors Jazz

Faye, Alice

☐ GOT MY MIND ON MUSIC (2CD Set)
Oh I didn't know / According to the moonlight / You belong to me / Music is magic / Whose baby are you / I'm shooting high / I love to ride the horse on a merry-go-round / But definitely / When I'm with you / You've got to eat your spinach / Sing sing baby / You turned the tables on me / One never knows does one / Goodnight my love / He ain't got rhythm / This year's kisses / Slumming on Park Avenue / You can't have everything / Danger love at work / Afraid to dream / Please pardon us we're in love / My fine feathered friend / Got my mind on music / Think twice / This is where I came in / Alexander's ragtime / International rag / When the midnight choo choo leaves for Alabam' / Everybody's doing it / Now it can be told / Remember/Alone / Are you in the mood for mischief / I'm sorry I made you cry / Vamp / I'm just wild about Harry / I never knew heaven could speak / Rose of Washington Square / My man / I'll see you in my dreams / I'm always chasing rainbows / Blue lovebird / Hawaii-A / You say the sweetest things baby / Moonlight bay / America I love you / Sheik of Araby / Get out and get under / They met in Rio / Boa noite / It's all in a lifetime / I take to you / Where you are / Long ago last night / Romance and rhumba / Tropical magic / Ragtime cowboy Joe / Sweet cider time / Grizzly bear / Why do they always pick on me / By the light of the silvery moon / You'll never know / Hello Frisco hello / No love no nothing / Polka dot polka / Journey to a star
JASCD 105/6 / 8 Nov '97 / Jasmine

☐ ON SCREEN & RADIO 1932-1943
VJB 1947 / May '96 / Vintage Jazz Band

Faye, Glenda

☐ FLATPICKIN' FAVORITES
FF 70432 / Oct '89 / Flying Fish

Fays, Raphael

☐ VOYAGES
BEST 1015CD / Nov '93 / Acoustic Music

Faze Action

☐ PLANS AND DESIGNS
Plans and designs / Original disco motion / In and out / In the trees / Astral projection / Turn the point / Vortex
NUX 115CD / May '97 / Nuphonic

Fear

☐ HAVE ANOTHER BEER WITH FEAR
SECT2 10020 / Jan '96 / Sector 2
HR 0052 / 8 Jun '98 / Fear

Fear Disorder

☐ IN A RAGE
REVXD 217 / Feb '98 / Revolver

Fear Factory

☐ DEMANUFACTURE
Demanufacture / Self bias resistor / Zero signal / Replica / New breed / Dog day sunrise / Body hammer / Flashpoint / H-K (Hunter killer) / Pisschrist / Therapy for pain
RR 89562 / Jun '95 / Roadrunner

☐ FEAR IS THE MINDKILLER
Martyr / Self immolation / Scapegoat / Scumgrief / Self immolation / Self immotation (lp version)
RR 90822 / Apr '93 / Roadrunner

☐ OBSOLETE
Shock / Edgecrusher / Smasher devourer / Securiton / Descent / Hi-tech hate / Freedom or fire / Obsolete / Resurrection / Timelessness
RR 87522 / 27 Jul '98 / Roadrunner

☐ REMANUFACTURE
RR 88342 / Jun '97 / Roadrunner

☐ SOUL OF A NEW MACHINE
Martyr / Leechmaster / Scapegoat / Crisis / Crash test / Flesh hold / Lifeblind / Scumgrief / Natividad / Big god-raped souls / Arise above oppression / Self immolation / Suffer age / W.o.e. / Desecrate / Escape confusion / Manipulation
RR 91602 / Jun '96 / Roadrunner

Fearing, Stephen

☐ ASSASSIN'S APPRENTICE, THE
CSCCD 1001 / Aug '95 / CRS

☐ BLUE LINE
TNMD 0076 / Nov '97 / True North

☐ INDUSTRIAL LULLABY
RHRCD 120 / 3 Aug '98 / Red House

☐ OUT TO SEA
CROCD 222 / Dec '97 / Black Crow

Fearon, Phil

☐ BEST OF PHIL FEARON & GALAXY, THE (Fearon, Phil & Galaxy)
Dancing tight / Head over heels / What do I do / Nothing is too good for you / I can prove it / Everybody's laughing / Burning my bridges / Wait until tonight (my love) / All I give to you / You don't need a reason / This kind of love / Ain't nothing but a house party / If you're gonna fall in love / Fantasy real
MCCD 150 / Feb '94 / Music Club

☐ DANCING TIGHT (Fearon, Phil & Galaxy)
Dancing tight / Wait until tonight (my love) / Head over heels / Ain't nothing but a house party / Fantasy real / This kind of love / You don't need a reason / I can prove it / Everybody's laughing / What do I do / I can prove it (edit)
MOCD 3006 / Feb '95 / More Music

☐ GREATEST HITS (Fearon, Phil & Galaxy)
Dancing tight / Wait until tonight / What do I do / This kind of love / If you're gonna fall in love / Nothing is too good for you / Fantasy real / Everybody's laughing / I can prove it / Ain't nothing but a house party / You don't need a reason / All I give to you / Anything you want / Head over heels / This kind of love (Morales mix) / Fantasy real (12" mix)
CDGOLD 1032 / May '96 / EMI Gold

Feast

☐ HONEYSUCKLE SIPS
Crazy / Not gonna cry / For your heart / Anastasia / All over / Let you down / Still walking / Trust me / Staring out of stars / Obsession / Say we'll meet again / Above the water
HOT 1062CD / Mar '97 / Hot

Feather, Leonard

☐ CLASSICS 1937-1945
CLASSICS 901 / Nov '96 / Classics

Feathers, Charlie

☐ CHARLIE FEATHERS
Man in love / When you come around / Pardon me mister / Fraulein / Defrost your heart / Mean woman blues / I don't care if tomorrow never comes / Cootzie coo / We can't seem to remember to forget / Long time ago / Seasons of my heart / Uh huh honey / Oklahoma hills
7559611472 / Jul '91 / Nonesuch

☐ GET WITH IT (Essential Recordings 1954-1969/2CD Set)
RVNCD 209 / 10 Aug '98 / Revenant

☐ GONE GONE GONE
Peepin' eyes / I've been deceived / Defrost your heart / Wedding gown of white / We're getting closer to being apart / Bottle to the baby / One hand loose / Can't hardly stand it / Everybody's lovin' my baby / Too much alike / When you come around / When you decide / Nobody's woman / Man in love / I forgot to remember to forget / Uh huh honey / Mound of clay / Tongue tied Jill / Gone gone gone / Two to choose / Send me the pillow that you dream on / Folsom Prison blues
CDCHARLY 278 / Sep '91 / Charly

☐ GOOD ROCKIN' TONITE
Good rockin' tonight / Corina corina / Call dog / She's gone (long gone lonesome blues) / Break song / Baby let's play house / Mound of clay / Blues stay away from me / Matchbox / Two to choose / Rain / Rockin' with red / Kansas city / Honky tonk man / Shake, rattle and roll / Rock and roll ruby / It's all over now / Tongue tied jill / Roll over beethoven / Blueberry hill / I got a woman / Wild side of life / Hello josephine / Send me the pillow that you dream on / Blue moon of kentucky
EDCD 355 / Sep '92 / Edsel

☐ HONKY TONK MAN
422407 / Feb '97 / Last Call

☐ ROCK-A-BILLY 1954-1973 (The Definitive Collection Of Rare & Unissued Recordings)
Bottle to the baby / So ashamed / Honky tonk kind / Frankie and Johnny / Defrost your heart / Runnin' around / I've been deceived / Corine Corina / Wedding gown of white / Defrost your heart / Bottle to the baby / I can't hardly wait / One hand loose / Everybody's lovin' my baby / Dinky John / South of Chicago / I'm walking the dog / Today and tomorrow / Wild wild party / Where's she at tonight / Don't you know / Wild side of life / Long time ago / Tongue tied Jill / Folsom Prison blues / Gone gone gone
CDZ 2011 / Apr '94 / Zu Zazz

February

☐ EVEN THE NIGHT
FEBCD 1 / Oct '96 / February

☐ TOMORROW IS TODAY
SAK 1019 / 13 Oct '97 / Carrot Top

Fedchock, John

☐ ON THE EDGE (Fedchock, John New York Big Band)
RSRCD 153 / Apr '98 / Reservoir

Feddy, Jason

☐ FISH ON THE MOON
REDHEDCD 1 / Nov '94 / Redhead

☐ I THOUGHT THE MOON WAS MEANT FOR ME
Even the rain / No faith / All that you do to me / Ragtime to riches / Road / Anyway / I depend on you / Let it be summer / Kicking up the pavement / She's not to blame / Angels / I want holding
TACD 2 / 1 Sep '97 / Blueprint

Federal Music Society

☐ COME AND TRIP IT (Hyman, Dick & Gerard Schwarz Orchestras)
Prima donna waltz / Jenny Lind polka / Minuet and gavotte / Country fiddle music / Natilie polka-mazurka / Flying cloud / Victoria gallop / Flirt polka / La sonnambula / Eliza Jane McCue / Blaze-away / Hiawatha / Sweet man
802932 / Aug '94 / New World

Federation

☐ EARTH LOOP
ZEN 008CD / Feb '96 / Indochina

☐ HEADSPINZ
Intro / Headspinz / See through / It could happen / Lo fi lullaby / Sea of green / Twisted / Dr umlaut plays uptempo / Antidote / Ordinary day / Could be mine / My cyphiere
COTCD 014 / 27 Oct '97 / Cup Of Tea

Federici, Danny

☐ FLEMINGTON
Flemington / Mingle mangle / My little cow / Mr. Continental / Carousel breeze / Egg beater / Doorman's life / Sea bright / Round and round / In the next five minutes / Pennsylvania Avenue
MM 65173 / 9 Mar '98 / Music Masters

Feds

☐ CHICAGO BUREAU
DSR 060CD / May '97 / Dr. Strange

Feed Your Head

☐ AMBIENT COMPILATION
BARKCD 002 / Jul '94 / Planet Dog

Feedback Bleep

☐ ENGRAM
EFA 119712 / Apr '95 / Electro Smog

Feeder

☐ POLYTHENE
Polythene girl / My perfect day / Cement / Crash / Radiation / Suffocate / Descend / Stereo world / Tangerine / Waterfall / Forgive / Twentieth century trip
ECHCD 015 / May '97 / Echo

Feedtime

☐ BILLY
ARR 72015CD / Jun '96 / Amphetamine Reptile

Feelings

☐ DEARLING DARLING
DRL 035 / Jun '97 / Darla

Feels So Good

☐ VOLUME 3
UJA 034CD / 16 Jul '97 / Ujammin

Feenjon/Avram

☐ SALUTE TO ISRAEL
MCD 71746 / Jun '93 / Monitor

Feeny, Michael

☐ MY OLD IRISH ROSE
CNCD 5951 / Jul '93 / Disky

Feidman, Giora

☐ MAGIC OF THE KLEZMER, THE (Feidman, Giora & The Feidman Ensemble)
Song of rejoicing / Mr. Mzirion / Mothers in law / Happiness is a nigon / Cigarettes / With much sentiment / Frilling / Market place in jaffa / Hopkefe / Nigon / Dudele / Music for ghetto / Humoresque / Gershwin suite / Freilach
DE 4005 / Jan '94 / Delos

☐ SILENCE AND BEYOND (Feidman Plays Ora Bat Chaim)
Skipping (Improv no.19) / Im waltz spirit / Grain of sand / Not for our sake / Beyond the now / In the self / In silence and joy / Love and joy / Elokim Eli Ata / Prayer / Psalm of thanks / Golem / At dawn / In freilach spirit
364992 / Jun '97 / Koch Schwann

Felder, Don

☐ AIRBORNE
Bad girls / Winners / Haywire / Who tonight / Never surrender / Asphalt jungle / Night owl / Still alive
7599602952 / Jul '96 / Warner Bros.

Felder, Wilton

☐ FOREVER ALWAYS
Lillies of the nile / For lovers only / My way / My one and only love / Rainbow visions / Forever / Goin' crazy / Asian flower / African queen / Mr. Felder
CPCD 8141 / Nov '95 / Charly

☐ NOCTURNAL MOODS
Feel so much better / Night moves / Southern pearl / If I knew then what I know now / Sugar loaf / Love steps / Out of sight not out of mind / Since I fell for you / Music of the night
CPCD 8124 / Oct '95 / Charly

Feldman, Morton

☐ FOR CHRISTIAN WOLFF
ARTCD 36120 / Apr '93 / Hat Art

☐ FOR PHILIP GUSTON
ARTCD 46104 / Jul '92 / Hat Art

☐ FOR SAMUEL BECKETT
ARTCD 6107 / Jan '93 / Hat Art

☐ NEITHER
HATN 102 / Dec '97 / Hat Now

☐ PIANO AND STRING QUARTETS (Feldman, Morton & Aki Takahashi/ Kronos Quartet)
7559793202 / Jan '95 / Nonesuch

☐ TRIO
ARTCD 6195 / Jul '97 / Hat Art

Feldman, Victor

☐ ARTFUL DODGER, THE
Limehouse blues / Haunted ballroom / Walk on the heath / Isn't she lovely / Smoke gets in your eyes / Agitation / Artful Dodger / St. Thomas
CCD 4038 / Jun '89 / Concord Jazz

☐ FIESTA AND MORE
Fiesta / Elusive spirit / With your love / Forever / Summer games / Amigos / Viva Zapata / Heart to heart / Brazilia / Candy dance / Villa nueva / So much time
JVC 90232 / Aug '97 / JVC

☐ HIS OWN SWEET WAY
Fine romance / Alley blues / Thought about you / Autumn leaves / Swinging on a star / Azul serape / Llevestraum / Too blue / In your own sweet way / Fly me to the moon / Basin Street blues
JHAS 605 / Jun '96 / Ronnie Scott's Jazz House

☐ TO CHOPIN WITH LOVE (Feldman, Victor Trio)
Mr. C meets Mr. T. / Star drift / Dream dance / Pola nova / Polka surprise / Night flight / Waltz for Scotty
HCD 610 / Jul '97 / Hindsight

Feleus, Pali

☐ ZIGEUNERORKEST ZIGEUNERKAPELLE (Feleus, Pali & Gipsy Band)
SYNCOOP 5755CD / Feb '95 / Syncoop

Felice, Dee

☐ DEE FELICE (Felice, Dee & The Sleep Cat Band)
JCD 168 / Feb '91 / Jazzology

Felice, John

☐ NOTHING PRETTY (Felice, John & The Lowdowns)
Don't be telling me / Ain't we having fun / I'll never sing that song again / Not the one / Perfect love / Nowadaze kids / Nothing pretty / Dreams / Don't make me wait / Can't play it safe
ROSE 141CD / Mar '88 / New Rose

Feliciano, Jose

☐ AND I LOVE HER
And I love her / Light my fire / For my love / You're no good / Always something there to remind me / Yesterday / Don't let the sun catch you crying / I want to learn a love song / Find somebody and the sun will shine / Rain / Twilight time
743213394626 / Jan '96 / Camden

☐ AND THE SUN WILL SHINE
Light my fire / Hi heel sneakers / Hitchcock railway / Susie-Q / Hey baby / Marley purt drive / And the sun will shine / Adios amour (Goodbye my love) / Rain / Girl (you'll never get away from me) / Point of view / Destiny / She's a woman / I got a woman / Go on your way / Sleep late my lady friend / Don't let the sun catch you crying / First of May / Life is that way / Chico and the man / Take me to the pilot / Wild world / Not that kind of guy / Felice navidad
RVCD 70 / Feb '98 / Raven

☐ BEST OF JOSE FELICIANO
Light my fire / California dreamin' / And the sun will shine / Windmills of your mind / Miss Otis regrets / Rain / First of May / Guantanamera / Che sara / Destiny / Suzie Q / Hi-heel sneakers / Cico and the man / Hitchcock railway / Malaguena / No dogs allowed
ND 89561 / Feb '90 / RCA

☐ BEST OF JOSE FELICIANO, THE
TRTCD 203 / Jul '96 / TrueTrax

☐ CHE SERA SERA
WMCD 6544 / May '94 / Disky

☐ COLLECTION, THE
Che sera sera / Light my fire / Hi-heel sneakers / La bamba / California dreamin' / Jealous guy / Samba Pati / This could be the last time / Daniel / Right here waiting / Chico (and the man) / Time after time / In my life / Angela / Volvere / Stay with me / Affirmation / Pegao / Rain / You send me
COL 074 / Apr '96 / Collection

☐ GOLD COLLECTION, THE (2CD Set)
R2CD 4054 / 13 Apr '98 / Deja Vu

☐ HITS COLLECTION, THE
Time after time / In my life / Light my fire / California dreamin' / You send me / Que sera / Daniel / Right here waiting / Jealous guy / Last time / La bamba / Chico and the man / Stay with me / Hi-heel sneakers / Angela / Affirmation / Rain / Pegao / Mule skinner blues / Y volere
100262 / May '97 / A-Play Collection

☐ JOSE FELICIANO
Bamboleo / La bamba / Che sera sera / Angela / Malaguena / Y volvere / Samba pa ti / Pegao / Daniel / Right here waiting / Affirmation / Chico and the man / La entrada de Bilbao
CD 62110 / Oct '96 / Saludos Amigos

☐ JOSE FELICIANO
GFS 090 / Nov '97 / Going For A Song

☐ LIGHT MY FIRE
PLSCD 101 / Apr '96 / Pulse

☐ LIGHT MY FIRE
Light my fire / Stay with me / Chico and the man / And I love her / You're no good / Don't let the sun catch you crying / Daytime dreams / Pegao / Always something there to remind me / California dreamin' / And the sun will shine / Here, then and everywhere / Essence of your love / Sunny / By the time I get to Phoenix / Yesterday / Nature boy / Rain / In my life / And the feeling's good
74321449252 / Feb '97 / Camden

☐ LIGHT MY FIRE
Daniel / Right here waiting / You send me / Hi-heel sneakers / Rain / Angela / Mule skinner blues / Affirmation / Chico the man / Samba pati / Che sera sera / La bamba / Light my fire / In my life / Last time / California dreamin' / Time after time / Jealous guy
PLATCD 110 / Feb '97 / Platinum

☐ LIGHT MY FIRE
Light my fire / California dreamin' / Daniel / Jealous guy / Volvere / Pegao / Rain / In my life / You send me / Right here waiting / Stay with me / Affirmation / Mystery train / Last time / Hi-heel sneakers / Mule skinner blues / La bamba / Chico and the man / Bamboleo
WB 870972 / Mar '97 / Disky

☐ LIGHT MY FIRE
Light my fire / Che sera sera / California dreamin' / Rain / La bamba / High heel sneakers / Jealous guy / In my life / Last time / Time after time / Daniel / Affirmation / Mystery train / Samba pati / Chico and the man / Bombelo
RM 1504 / Aug '97 / BR Music

☐ MEMPHIS MENU
Magnolia / River song / One more mile / Never leave you / Tale of Maria / It doesn't matter / Good times / Lay lady lay / Where is my woman / Movin'
EDCD 570 / 4 Aug '98 / Edsel

☐ TRIBUTE TO THE BEATLES, A
290810 / Dec '92 / RCA

Feline

☐ FELINE
Just as you are / Sun in my eyes / Drama queen / Shocks and surprises / Not what it seems / Bad habit / Fantasy world / Play with fire / Can't help myself / Mother / Property / Release
4947862 / 3 Aug '98 / Chrysalis

☐ SAVE YOUR FACE
Just as you are / Sun in my eyes / Shocks and surprises / Not what it seems / Fantasy world / Play with fire / Can't help myself / Mother / Property / Release
CDCHR 6126 / 3 Nov '97 / Chrysalis

Felix Da Housecat

☐ THEE ALBUM - 'METROPOLIS PRESENT DAY'
Some kinda special / Marine mood / Metropolis present day / Little bloo / Trippin' on a trip / Ano.Th.A. Level / Submarine / B4 wuz then / Cycle spin / Footsteps of rage / Thee dawn / Radikal thanx
FEAR 011CD / May '95 / Radikal Fear

Felix, Julie

☐ EL CONDOR PASA
Amazing grace / Mr. Tambourine man / Early morning rain / San Francsico / Vincent / Where have all the flowers gone / Going to the zoo / Scarborough fair / Blowing in the wind / Let it be / Dona Dona / Soldier from the 60's / If I could / Where you are / Last thing on my mind / Man gave names to all the animals / I miss you / Bring on Lucie (free da people) / So much trouble / Changing / We better talk this over / Steal away again / My preservation kit / Big bang / Yoko (we believe)
SCD 26 / Feb '97 / Start

Fell, Simon H.

☐ COMPILATION VOL.1
CDBF 01 / Oct '93 / Bruce's Fingers

☐ COMPILATION VOL.2
CDBF 04 / Oct '93 / Bruce's Fingers

Fell, Terry

☐ TRUCK DRIVIN' MAN
Truck driving man / Caveman / Don't drop it / Play the music / I'm hot to trot / Mississippi River shuffle / Get aboard my wagon / You don't give a hang about me / He's in love with you / I believe my heart / What am I worth / Over and over / I nearly go crazy / That's the way the big ball bounces / Don't do it Joe / Consolation prize / Let's stay together till after Christmas / (We wanna see) Santa do the mambo / Wham bam hot ziggity zam / If I didn't have you / That's what I like / Fa-so-la / I can hear you cluckin' / What's good for the goose
BCD 15762 / Nov '93 / Bear Family

Fellow Travellers

☐ FEW GOOD DUBS, A
OKCD 33023 / Dec '94 / Okra

☐ JUST A VISITOR
OKCD 33016 / Sep '93 / Okra

☐ LOVE SHINES BRIGHTER
RTS 4 / Nov '94 / Return To Sender

☐ NO EASY WAY
OKRACD 010 / Mar '94 / Okra

☐ THINGS AND TIME
OKCD 33020 / Sep '93 / Okra

Fells

☐ FELLS
ES 1237CD / Nov '97 / Estrus

Felony, Jayo

☐ TAKE A RIDE
5282912 / Sep '95 / Island

☐ WATCHA GONNA DO
5587622 / 24 Aug '98 / Mercury

Felsons

☐ ONE STEP AHEAD OF THE POSSE
TMC 9607 / May '96 / Music Corporation

Felsons

☐ GLAD
Boomerang boy / Heart is home / Missing you / Postcards / Born to lose you / Is there a dreamer here / Joseph Black / You're everything / Wake me up / Is it yesterday yet / What about me / Belfast blues / On fire / Meet me after the show
G2CD 7001 / 6 Jul '98 / G2

Felt

☐ ABSOLUTE CLASSIC MASTERPIECES
Primitive painters / Day the rain came down / My darkest light will shine / Textile ranch / Sunlight bathed the golden glow / Crystal ball / Dismantled King is off the throne / Fortune / Dance of deliverance / Stagnant pool / Red indians / World is a soft as lace / Penelope tree / Trails of colour dissolve / Evergreen dazed / Templeroy / Something sends me to sleep / Index
CDBRED 97 / Oct '96 / Cherry Red

☐ ABSOLUTE CLASSIC MASTERPIECES VOL.2
Ballad of the band / I didn't mean to hurt you / Magellan / I will die with my head in flames / Sandman's on the rise again / Final resting of the ark / Autumn / There's no such thing as victory / Space blues / Be still / Song for william s. harvey / Indian scriptures / Jewel sky / Voyage to illumination / Grey streets / A wave crashed on rocks / Hours of darkness have changed my mind / She lives by the castle / Stained glass windows in the sky / Dark red birds / Bitter end / Don't die on my doorstep / Darkest ending / Train above the city / On weegee's sidewalk / Run chico run
CRECD 150 / Sep '93 / Creation

☐ BUBBLEGUM PERFUME
I will die with my head in flames / I didn't mean to hurt you / Autumn / There's no such thing as victory / Final resting place of the ark / Don't die on my doorstep / Book of swords / Gather up your wings and fly / Bitter end / Voyage to illumination / Stained glass windows / Space blues / Be still / Magellan / Sandman's on the rise again / Wave crashed on my doorstep / Declaration / Darkest ending / Rain of crystal spires / Ballad of the band
CRECD 69 / Apr '90 / Creation

☐ CRUMBLING THE ANTISEPTIC BEAUTY/SPLENDOUR OF FEAR, THE
Evergreen dazed / Fortune / Birdman / Cathedral / I worship the sun / Templeroy / Red Indians / World is as soft as lace / Optimist and the poet / Mexican bandits / Stagnant pool / Preacher in New England
CDBRED 72 / May '96 / Cherry Red

☐ FOREVER BREATHES THE LONELY WORD
Forever breathes the lonely word / Rain of crystal spires / Down but not yet out / September lady / Grey streets / All the people I like are those that are dead / Gather up your wings and fly / A wave crashed on rocks / Hours of darkness have changed my mind / Let the snakes crinkle their heads to death / Song for william s. harvey / Ancient city where I lived / Seventeenth century / Palace / Indian scriptures / Nazca plain / Jewel sky / Viking dress / Voyage to illumination / Sapphire mansions
CRECD 011 / Oct '90 / Creation

☐ GOLDMINE TRASH
Something sends me to sleep / Trails of colours dissolve / Dismantled King is off the throne / Penelope tree / Sunlight bathed the golden glow / Crystal ball / Day the rain came down / Fortune / Vasco da Gama / Primitive painters
CDMRED 79 / Sep '87 / Cherry Red

☐ IGNITE THE SEVEN CANNONS
My darkest night will shine / Day the rain came down / Scarlet servants / I don't know which way to turn / Primitive painters / Textile ranch / Black ship in the harbour / Elegance of an only dream / Serpent shade / Caspian see / Southern state tapestry / Roman litter / Sempiternal darkness / Spanish house / Imprint / Sunlight bathed the golden glow / Vasco da Gama / Crucifix heaven / Dismantled King is off the throne / Crystal ball / Whirlpool vision of shame
CDBRED 65 / May '96 / Cherry Red

☐ KISS YOU KIDNAPPED CHARABANC/ DEAD MEN TELL NO TALES
CRECD 862 / May '88 / Creation

☐ LET THE SNAKES CRINKLE THEIR HEADS TO DEATH
Song for william s. harvey / Ancient city where I lived / Seventeenth century / Palace / Indian scriptures / Nazca plain / Jewel sky / Viking dress / Voyage to illumination / Sapphire mansions
CRECD 009 / May '94 / Creation

☐ ME AND A MONKEY ON THE MOON
Can't make love / Mobile shack / Free / Budgie jacket / Cartoon sky / New day dawning / August path / Never let you go / Hey sister / Get out of my mirror
ACME 24CD / Oct '96 / El

☐ PICTORIAL JACKSON REVIEW
CRELP 030CD / Mar '88 / Creation

☐ POEM OF THE RIVER
Declaration / Silver plane / She lives by the castle / Stained glass windows in the sky / Riding on the equator / Dark red birds
CRECD 017 / May '94 / Creation

☐ STRANGE IDOLS PATTERN & OTHER SHORT STORIES
Roman litter / Sempiternal darkness / Spanish house / Imprint / Sunlight bathed the golden glow / Vasco da Gama / Crucifix heaven / Dismantled King is off the throne / Crystal ball / Whirlpool vision of shame
CD BRED 65 / Feb '93 / Cherry Red

☐ TRAIN ABOVE THE CITY
Train above the city / On weegee's sidewalk / Run chico run / Press softly on the brakes holly / Spectral morning / Teargardens / Book of swords / Seahorses on broadway / Sending lady load / Darkest ending / Apple boutique / Ivory past / Until the fools get wise / Bitter end / How spook got her man / Christopher st / Under a pale light / Don't die on my doorstep
CRECD 035 / Oct '88 / Creation

Felten, Eric

☐ GRATITUDE
1212962 / Sep '95 / Soul Note

☐ T-BOP (Felten, Eric & Jimmy Knepper)
1211962 / Sep '93 / Soul Note

Felts, Narvel

☐ DRIFT AWAY (The Best Of Narvel Felts 1973-1979)
Drift away / Before you have to go / All in the name of love / Rockin' little angel / When your good love was mine / Fraulein / Until the end of time / She loves me like a rock / I want to stay / Wrap my arms around the world / Reconsider me / Foggy misty morning / Funny how time slips away / Blue suede shoes / Somebody hold me / Away / Lonely teardrops / Lonely kind of love / My prayer / Garden of Eden / Feeling's right / Moments to remember / To love somebody / Stirrin' up feelin's / One run for the roses / Never again / Everlasting love / End
BCD 15690 / May '96 / Bear Family

☐ MEMPHIS DAYS
Night creature / Your true love / Blue darlin' / What you're doing to me / Sad and blue / She's in your heart to stay / Return / Welcome home / Love is gone / Tear down the wall / Four seasons of life / Come what may / Lola did a dance / Lovelight man / Mr. Pawnshop broker / Tongue tied Jill / All that heaven sent / I had a girl / Slippin' and slidin' / Larry and Joellen / You were mine / Get on the right track baby / Sweet sweet loving / Mountain of love / Private detective / One man at a table
BCD 15515 / Oct '90 / Bear Family

☐ MORE RADIO ROCKABILLIES (Felts, Narvel & Jerry Mercer)
Lawdy Miss Clawdy / Five foot two, eyes of blue / Bonaparte's retreat / Gone gone gone / Boogie / Closing theme / Boogie woogie country girl / Blue suede shoes / Lawdy Miss Clawdy / Mystery train / In the mood / My baby left me / Seven nights to rock / Go go go / Merle's boogie woogie / All Mama's children / Tommy Dorsey boogie / Hound dog / Closing theme / Jack and Jill boogie / Heartbreak Hotel / Boogie / Kansas city blues / Gone gone gone / Maybelline / Corrine Corrina / Seven nights to rock / There'll be no teardrops tonight / Woman love / Dixie fried / Georgia steel guitar / Closing theme
RSRCD 012 / Dec '97 / Rockstar

Fem 2 Fem

☐ ANIMUS
AHLCD 33 / Aug '95 / Hit

Female

☐ INTO THE EXOTIC
DNCD 004 / 13 Oct '97 / Downwards

Feminine Complex

☐ LIVIN' LOVE
TB 196 / Jun '97 / Teenbeat

☐ TO BE IN LOVE
TB 236 / Oct '97 / Teenbeat

Fender, Freddy

☐ CANCIONES DE MI BARRIO
ARHCD 366 / Apr '95 / Arhoolie

☐ COLLECTION, THE
Man can cry / Before the next teardrop falls / Wasted days and wasted nights / She's about a mover / Donna / What'd I say / Silver wings / Ooh poo pah doo / You'll lose a good thing / Wild side of life / Baby I want to love you / But I do / Almost persuaded / Crazy baby / Going out with the tide / I'm leaving it up to you / Just because / Lovin' cajun style / Mathilda / Mean woman blues / Running back / Sweet summer day / Girl who waits on tables / Rains came / Enter my heart
COL 013 / Oct '95 / Collection

☐ CRAZY BABY
Crazy baby / Wasted days and wasted nights / What'd I say / Something on your mind / Loving cajun / Style / Mean woman / La Bamba / Get out of my life woman / Only one / Coming home soon / Before the next teardrop falls / Since I met you baby / Wild side of life / Rains came / Mathilda / You'll lose a good thing / Just because / Black shirt / You made a fool / Coming round the mountain
CDSB 012 / 24 Aug '98 / Starburst

☐ GREATEST HITS
Your cheatin' heart / These arms of mine / She's about a mover / Baby I want to love you / High school dance / Talk to me / Let the good times roll / In the still of the night / Man can cry / Wasted days and wasted nights / Crazy baby / Enter my heart / La Bamba / I'm leaving it all up to you / Wild side of life / Sweet summer day / Mathilda / Silver wings / Since I met you baby / Before the next teardrop falls
HADCD 167 / May '94 / Javelin

☐ IN HIS PRIME
Before the next teardrop falls / Wasted days and wasted nights / You'll lose a good thing / Vaya con dios / Living it down / Rains came / If you don't love me / Think about me / Walking piece of heaven / Wild side of life / Since I met you baby / I'm a fool to care / She's about a mover / It's raining / Talk to me / Tell it like it is / Just out of reach of my two open arms / I can't help it (if I'm still in love with you) / What a difference a day made / Pass me by (if you're only passing through)
EDCD 516 / Aug '97 / Edsel

☐ WASTED DAYS & WASTED NIGHTS
Wasted days and wasted nights / Rains came / You'll lose a good thing / Almost persuaded / I'm leaving it all up to you / Man can cry / Wild side of life / She's about a mover / Crazy baby / Girl who waits on tables / Before the next teardrop falls / Lovin' cajun style / But I do / Sweet summer day / Silver wings / Running back / Enter my heart / Going out with the tide / Baby I want to love you / Just because
GRF 072 / Feb '93 / Tring

Fenech, Paul

☐ DADDY'S HAMMER
Guitar slinger / Daddy's hammer / Hear me howl / Running back to you / Scrape your sanity / Snakin' with the bad guys / Locked in a room with Betty / Cold cold baby / (We're) not like you / One fine day / (Alone) In the killing room / 1000 Guns for Pablo
CDGRAM 87 / Mar '95 / Anagram

☐ DISEASE
HRCD 003 / 16 Mar '98 / Knock Out

Feng Shui

☐ SACRED SPACE
AHLCD 55 / 3 Aug '98 / Hit

Fenton, George

☐ TRAILS OF LIFE
CDSGP 030 / Oct '92 / Prestige

Fenwick, Ray

☐ GROUPS AND SESSIONS 1962-1976 (Various Artists)
It's for you: *Rupert & The Red Devils* / Everytime I do: *Rupert & The Red Devils* / Crawdaddy Simone: *Syndicats* / Please call me: *Tee Set* / So I came back to you: *Tee Set* / Long ago: *After Tea* / After tea: *After Tea* / After Tea: *Davis, Spencer Group* / Mr. 2nd class: *Davis, Spencer Group* / Bad boy: *Musicians Union Band* / Let the circle stay unbroken: *Fenwick, Ray* / USA: *Fenwick, Ray* / Have mercy: *Hardin, Eddie & Pete York* / Ghost town: *Guitar Orchestra* / Get out of my life: *Diddley, Bo* / Blue bird: *Fenwick, Ray* / She's riding the rock machine: *Fancy* / Catch you on the rebop: *Davis, Spencer Group* / Livin' in a black street: *Davis, Spencer Group* / Magpie: *Murgatroyd Band* / Trying to get to you: *Gillan, Ian* / Clear air turbulence: *Gillan, Ian*
RPM 176 / Jun '97 / RPM

☐ KEEP AMERICA BEAUTIFUL, GET A HAIRCUT
Stateside / Anniversary / I wanna stay here / City ride / Dream / Back USA / New Jersey turnpike
SJPCD 013 / Aug '97 / Angel Air

Feon, Daniel

☐ EVIT DANSAL (Feon, Daniel & Jil Lehart)
432CD / Jul '95 / Diffusion Breizh

Ferber, Mordy

☐ MR. X
EFA 015052 / Jul '95 / Ozone

Ferbos, Lionel

☐ AT THE JAZZ BAND BALL
At the jazz band ball / Over the rainbow / Shake it and break it / Walking my baby back home / Cherry pink and apple blossom white / My blue heaven / Sobbin' blues / Bogalusa strut / Pretty baby / Sweethearts on parade / Once in awhile / Put on your old grey bonnet / Let me call you sweetheart / Girl of my dreams / Beautiful dreamer / You're all I want for Christmas / Pretty doll/Ugly child / Shine / I'm sorry I made you cry
504CDS 18 / Jun '98 / 504

☐ LIONEL FERBOS & LARS EDEGRAN'S NEW ORLEANS BAND (Ferbos, Lionel & Lars Edegran)
BCD 340 / Jun '96 / GHB

Fergani, Cheikh Salim

☐ TROUBADOUR FROM CONSTANTINE, A
926762 / 24 Apr '98 / BUDA

Ferguson, Maynard

☐ AMERICAN MUSIC HALL 1972, THE
DSTS 1004 / '94 / Status

☐ BODY AND SOUL
Expresso / Body and soul / MOT / Mira Mira / Last dive / Beautiful hearts / Central Park
TJA 10027 / Feb '96 / Jazz Alliance

☐ JAZZ MASTERS
5299052 / 5 May '98 / Verve

☐ LIVE AT PEACOCK LANE (Ferguson, Maynard & His Orchestra)
JH 1030 / Jul '93 / Jazz Hour

☐ LIVE AT THE GREAT AMERICAN MUSIC HALL
DSTS 1007 / May '95 / Status

☐ MAYNARD FERGUSON ORCHESTRA 1967
JAS 9504 / Dec '95 / Just A Memory

☐ MAYNARD FERGUSON SEXTET 1967
JAS 9503 / Dec '95 / Just A Memory

☐ NEW SOUNDS OF...1964
FSCD 2010 / Nov '94 / Fresh Sound

☐ ONE MORE TRIP TO BIRDLAND (Ferguson, Maynard & Big Bop Nouveau)
You got it / Manteca / Vibe / Cajun cookin' / Milestones / She was too good to me / Birdland / Blues from around here / It don't mean a thing (if it ain't got that swing)
CCD 4729 / Oct '96 / Concord Jazz

☐ STORM
Admiral's horn / Jar star / Take the 'A' train / Latino lovewalk / Sesame Street / As time goes by / Go with the flo / Hit in the head
74321374872 / Feb '97 / Bluebird

☐ THESE CATS CAN SWING (Ferguson, Maynard & Bip Bop)
Sugar / Caravan / I don't wanna be a hoochie coochie man no mo' / Sweet bab suite (Bai Rav) / I'll be around / He can't swing / It's the gospel truth
CCD 4669 / Oct '95 / Concord Jazz

☐ THIS IS JAZZ
Birdland / Everybody loves the blues / McArthur Park / Fox hunt / Cheshire cat walk / 'Round midnight / Gospel John / Gonna fly now
CK 64970 / Oct '96 / Sony Jazz

Fermenting Innards

☐ MYST
INV 016CD / Nov '95 / Invasion

Fernandel

☐ ANTHOLOGIE
EN 522 / Feb '96 / Fremeaux

☐ ETOILES DE LA CHANSON
878152 / Jun '93 / Music Memoria

☐ L'IRRESISTIBLE
Felicie aussi / Ignace / Quelle famille / L'amour incompris / Barnabe / Je suis une petite nature / Ernestito / Pourquoi tu me vexes, victor / Un dur, un vrai, un tatoue / C'est toujours comme ca / Lequel des deux / Redis le moi / Si j'osais / C'est la fete a tante aurore / C'est une voleuse d'ames / Ne me dis plus tu / Maintenant je sais ce que c'est / Quand ca me prend / C'est comme ca a calcutta / Idylle a bois le roi
UCD 19028 / Jun '95 / Forlane

Fernandez, Fernando

☐ EL CROONER DE MEXICO
ALCD 026 / Apr '97 / Alma Latina

☐ GRANDES EXITOS VOL.1
ALCD 028 / Apr '97 / Alma Latina

☐ GRANDES EXITOS VOL.2
ALCD 031 / Apr '97 / Alma Latina

Fernandez, Roberto

☐ NEW YORK SESSIONS (Fernandez, Roberto 'Fats')
CDCH 564 / Feb '91 / Milan

Fernandez, Vicente

☐ MANO A MANO (Fernandez, Vicente & Pedro Infante)
9944132042 / 3 Mar '98 / Orfeon

Fernando, Alfredo

☐ MILONGAS FROM URUGUAY
EUCD 1098 / '91 / ARC

☐ TRIBUTE TO CARLOS GARDEL
EUCD 1134 / '91 / ARC

Fernhill

☐ CA NOS
Ffarwel i Aberystwyth / Cowboi / Brigg fair / Gwenith gwyn / Ridees pastwn mawr / March glas / Le gabier de Terre-Neuve / Lloer dirion / Banks of the Nile / Pilons l'herbe
BEJOCD 14 / Nov '96 / Beautiful Jo

☐ LLATAI
BEJOCD 23 / Jun '98 / Beautiful Jo

Ferrante & Teicher

☐ COLLECTION, THE
VSD 5919 / 21 Apr '98 / Varese Sarabande

Ferrara, Luigi

☐ LIFE ALWAYS, THE
LFX 001 / 1 Jun '98 / LFX

Ferrari, Luc

☐ ACOUSMATRIX VOL.3
BVHAASTCD 9009 / Oct '93 / Bvhaast

☐ CELLULE 75
TZA 7033 / 27 Apr '98 / Tzadik

Ferrat, Jean

☐ 1960'S FRENCH EP COLLECTION, THE
174632 / Nov '97 / Magic

Ferre, Boulou

☐ NEW YORK NY
SCCD 31404 / Apr '97 / Steeplechase

☐ TRINITY
SCCD 31171 / Jul '88 / Steeplechase

Ferre, Leo

☐ PREMIERE CHANSON
LDX 274967 / Sep '93 / La Chant Du Monde

Ferreira, Johnny

☐ CRAZY 'BOUT A SAXOPHONE (Ferreira, Johnny & The Swing Machine)
JF 1015115 / 19 Mar '98 / Johnny Ferreira

Ferrel, Frank

□ BOSTON FIDDLE
ROUCD 7018 / Aug '96 / Rounder

Ferrell, Rachelle

□ FIRST INSTRUMENT
You send me / You don't know what love is / Bye bye blackbird / Prayer dance / Inchworm / With every breath I take / What is this thing called love / My funny valentine / Don't waste your time / Extensions / Autumn leaves
CDP 8728202 / Jun '95 / Blue Note

Ferrero, Medard

□ INOUBLIABLES DE L'ACCORDEON
882392 / Aug '93 / Music Memoria

Ferrick, Melissa

□ MASSIVE BLUR
Honest eyes / Happy song / Hello dad / What have I got to lose / Love song / Ten friends / For once in my life / Blue sky night / Massive blur / Take me all / Wonder why / Meaning of love / In a world like this / Breaking vows
7567825022 / Dec '93 / Elektra

Ferrio, Gianni

□ LA MORTE ACCAREZZA
ET 902CD / 23 Mar '98 / Easy Tempo

Ferris, Gene

□ PLANET HOUSE
FIM 128CD / 2 Feb '98 / Force Inc.

Ferris, Glenn

□ FLESH AND STONE
ENJACD 80882 / Jan '95 / Enja

Ferro, Nina

□ OUT OF THE BLUE
NINAFERRO / Dec '97 / Australian Jazz

Ferron

□ PHANTOM CENTER
9425762 / Jan '96 / Earthbeat

Ferry, Bryan

□ ANOTHER TIME, ANOTHER PLACE
In crowd / Smoke gets in your eyes / Walk a mile in my shoes / Funny how time slips away / You are my sunshine / What a wonderful world / It ain't me babe / Finger poppin' / Help me make it through the night / Another time another place
EGCD 14 / Sep '91 / EG

□ BETE NOIRE
Limbo / Kiss and tell / New town / Day for night / Zamba / Right stuff / Seven deadly sins / Name of the game / Bete noire
CDV 2474 / Nov '87 / Virgin

□ BOYS AND GIRLS
Sensation / Slave to love / Don't stop the dance / Wasteland / Windswept / Chosen one / Valentine / Stone woman / Boys and girls
EGCD 62 / Sep '91 / EG

□ BRIDE STRIPPED BARE, THE
Sign of the times / Can't let go / Hold on I'm comin' / Same old blues / When she walks in the room / Take me to the river / What goes on / Carrickfergus / That's how strong my love is / This island Earth
CDVIP 220 / 3 Aug '98 / Virgin VIP

□ IN YOUR MIND
This is tomorrow / All night operator / One kiss / Love me madly again / Tokyo Joe / Party doll / Rock of ages / In your mind
CDVIP 219 / 3 Aug '98 / Virgin VIP

□ LET'S STICK TOGETHER
Let's stick together / Casanova / Sea breezes / Shame shame shame / 2HB / Price of love / Chance meeting / It's only love / You go to my head / Re-make/Re-model / Heart on my sleeve
EGCD 24 / Jan '84 / EG

□ MAMOUNA
Don't want to know / NYC / Your painted smile / Mamouna / Only face / Thirty nine steps / Which way to turn / Wild cat days / Gemini moon / Chain reaction
CDV 2751 / Sep '94 / Virgin

□ MORE THAN THIS (The Best Of Bryan Ferry & Roxy Music)
Virginia Plain: *Roxy Music* / Hard rain's gonna fall / Street life: *Roxy Music* / These foolish things / Love is the drug: *Roxy Music* / Dance away: *Roxy Music* / Let's stick together / Angel eyes: *Roxy Music* / Slave to love / Oh yeah: *Roxy Music* / Don't stop the dance / Same old scene: *Roxy Music* / Is your love strong enough / Jealous guy: *Roxy Music* / Kiss and tell / More than this: *Roxy Music* / I put a spell on you / Avalon: *Roxy Music* / Your painted smile / Smoke gets in your eyes
CDV 2791 / Oct '95 / Virgin

□ TAXI
I put a spell on you / Will you still love me tomorrow / Answer me / Just one look / Rescue me / All tomorrow's parties / Girl of my best friend / Amazing grace / Taxi / Because you're mine
CDV 2700 / Mar '93 / Virgin

□ THESE FOOLISH THINGS
Hard rain's gonna fall / River of salt / Don't ever change / Piece of my heart / Baby I don't care / It's my party / Don't worry baby / Sympathy for the devil / Tracks of my tears / You won't see me / I love how you love me / Loving you is sweeter than ever / These foolish things
EGCD 9 / Jul '93 / EG

Fertile Crescent

□ FERTILE CRESCENT
KFWCD 118 / Nov '92 / Knitting Factory

Fertilizer

□ PAINTING OF ANNOYANCE
IR 008CD / Apr '95 / Invasion

Fervant, Thierry

□ LEGENDS OF AVALON
QMCD 7042 / Sep '90 / Quartz

□ UNIVERSE
QMCD 7012 / Sep '90 / Quartz

Fesov, Oleg

□ LALAIKI PAMIR
39840592 / 21 Aug '97 / Blue Flame

Fest, Manfredo

□ AMAZONAS
Secret love / Florianopolis / Amazonas / Caminhos crizados (Crossed paths) / O Pato (The Duck) / Madison Square / Over the rainbow / Guarana / Tristeza de nos dois (Sad for both of us) / Lullaby of birdland / Ela E Carioca (She's a child of Rio) / Estate (Summer)
CCD 47662 / Apr '97 / Concord Picante

□ COMECAR DE NOVO
Fetuccini Manfredo / Voce e eu / You must believe in spring / Where's montgomery / Bonita / Seresta / Lush life / Morning / How insensitive / Brazilian divertimento # 2 / Comecar de novo / Vera cruz
CCD 4660 / Aug '95 / Concord Jazz

□ FASCINATING RHYTHM
Fascinating rhythm / Berimbau / Samba do aviao / Marcia / Summertime / Samba do soho / Spring can really hang you up the most / Triste / Route 66 / Tenderly / Eyes of love / Arigo
CCD 4711 / Jul '96 / Concord Picante

Fester

□ WINTER OF SIN
NFR 002 / Oct '94 / No Fashion

Festival

□ RESURRECTION
EFA 294672 / 22 Jun '98 / Disko B

Fetish 69

□ ANTI-BODY
NB 087 / Dec '93 / Nuclear Blast

□ BRUTE FORCE
Void / Marooned / Stares to nowhere / Stomach turner / Tough center/harter ken / Hellville (pop 7,000)
SPASM 005CD / Jul '93 / Intellectual Convulsion

Fever Tree

□ FEVER TREE/ANOTHER TIME ANOTHER PLACE
Imitation situation (tocatta and fugue) / Where do you go / San Francisco girls (return of the natives) / Ninety nine and one half / Man who paints the pictures / Filigree and shadow / Sun also rises / Day tripper/We can work it out / Nowadays Clancy can't even sing / Unlock my door / Come with me / Man who paints the pictures (part 2) / What time did you say it was in salt lake city / Don't come crying to me girl / Fever / Grand candy young sweet / Jokes are for sad people / I've just seen evergreen / Peace of mind / Death is the dancer
SEECD 364 / Jun '97 / See For Miles

□ LIVE AT LAKE CHARLES 1978
SP 98004 / 13 Jul '98 / Shroom

Few Good Men

□ TAKE A DIP
Tonite / Walk you thru / Let's take a dip / All of my love / Please baby don't cry / Have I never / Thang for you young girl / Don't cry (behind my back) / Sexy day / Good man / 1-900-G-Man (How I say I love you)
73008260212 / Nov '95 / Arista

Fez Combo

□ FOLLOW THE SPIRIT
RTCD 403 / Jul '96 / Right Tempo

Fez Petting Zoo

□ ALL SYSTEMS GONE
BB 002 / Sep '97 / Blue Baby

FFA Coffi Pawb

□ HEI VIDAL
AMKSTCD 036 / Mar '93 / Ankst

Fflaps

□ AMHERSAIN
PROBE 21C / Jul '89 / Probe Plus

FFW

□ KILLER (Freaky Fukin Weirdoz)
EFA 15525CD / Feb '92 / Sub Up

Fiahlo, Fransico

□ BEST OF FADO PORTUGUESE
EUCD 1165 / '91 / ARC

□ MEU ALENTEJO
EUCD 1113 / '91 / ARC

□ O FADOAL LATINO
EUCD 1075 / '89 / ARC

Fiction Factory

□ THROW THE WARPED WHEEL OUT
Feels like heaven / Heart and mind / Hanging gardens / All or nothing / Hit the mark / Ghost of love / Tales of tears / First step / Warped wheel
4805232 / May '95 / Columbia

Fiddle, Johnny

□ CAJUN GIRL
RPCDS 001 / Dec '94 / Rivet Productions

Fiddle Puppets

□ LIFT UP YOUR WINGS
HEE 009CD / Jun '94 / Yodel-Ay-Hee

Fiddler, John

□ RETURN OF THE BUFFALO
RMCCD 0197 / May '96 / Red Steel

Fiddler's Green

□ KING SHEPHERD
EFA 127502 / May '95 / Deaf Shepherd

Fiddlers Five

□ FIDDLE MUSIC FROM SCOTLAND
Farewell to ravenscraigthe steel reel / Centennial waltzwilliam ritchie esqhugh mcke / Neil gow's farewell to whiskythe poppy leaf
COMD 2044 / Feb '94 / Temple

Fidler, Jim

□ GYPSY
IRCD 059 / Feb '98 / Iona

Fiedler, Arthur

□ POPS CHRISTMAS PARTY (Boston Pops Orchestra/Arthur Fiedler)
09026616852 / Nov '95 / RCA Victor

Field Day

□ BIG WHEELS
CARTCD 1 / Dec '96 / Car Tunes

Field Mice

□ FOR KEEPS
SARAH 607CD / Mar '95 / Sarah

Field Of Blue

□ FIELD OF BLUE
HUBCD 001 / Nov '96 / Hubba Dots

Fields, Brandon

□ OTHER PLACES
NOVA 9025 / Sep '92 / Nova

□ OTHER SIDE OF THE STORY, THE
NOVA 8602 / Jan '93 / Nova

□ TRAVELER
NOVA 8811 / Sep '92 / Nova

Fields, Dorothy

□ EVENING WITH DOROTHY FIELDS, AN
DRGCD 5167 / 27 Jul '98 / DRG

Fields, Ernie

□ IN THE MOOD (Fields, Ernie Orchestra)
In the mood / Annie's rock / Strollin' after school / Chattanooga choo choo / Workin' out / Honky tonk / Tuxedo junction / Volare cha cha / My prayer / Knocked out / Dipsy doodle / Raunchy / Tea for two cha cha / It's all in the game / Boot / Christopher Columbus / Things ain't what they used to be / Begin the beguine / Teen flip / Honeydripper / Charleston / Castle rock / String of pearls / Ernie's tune / Hucklebuck
CDCHD 540 / Mar '96 / Ace

Fields, Gracie

□ BEST OF GRACIE FIELDS, THE
Sally / Clatter of the clogs / Singing in the bathtub / Laugh at life / I took my harp to a party / She fought like a tiger for 'er 'onour / Will you love me when I'm mutton / Little pudden basin / Let's all go posh / Eee by gum / Nowt about owt / Smile when you say goodbye / Biggest aspidistra in the world / She's one of those old fashioned ladies / Ring down the curtain / Pass shoot goal / Sing as we go / Dicky bird hop / You've got to be smart to be in the army / Fall in and follow the band / Wish me luck as you wave me goodbye
CD 6057 / Feb '97 / Music

□ CLASSIC YEARS, THE
Sing as we go / Because I love you / Little love, a little kiss / Little pudden basin / Sally / Just a dancing sweetheart / Underneath the arches / Mary Rose / It isn't fair / I took my harp to a party / Just a catchy little tune / Did I remember / Biggest aspidistra in the world / Swing your way to happiness / Wish me luck / I love the moon / Over the rainbow / Christopher Robin is saying his prayers / Rochdale hounds / Perfect day / Fonzo (my hot Spanish knight) / September song / When I grow too old to dream / Turn 'Erbert's face to the wall / Charmaine / My Bonnie lies over the ocean / Walter, Walter / Don't be angry with me Sergeant / Put your shoes on Lucy / Now is the hour
RPCD 320 / 26 Jan '98 / Robert Parker Jazz

□ GRACIE FIELDS
Sally / Smoke gets in your eyes / Nature boy / Indian summer / Ciao ciao bambino / Young at heart / You didn't want me when you had me / Autumn leaves / Take me to your heart again / Moon river / Happy talk / September song / Jealousy / Ugly duckling / Carefree heart / My favourite things / People / Kerry dance / House is haunted / You're breaking my heart / Little donkey / Lord's prayer / Blow the wind southerly / Sing as we go
CDMFP 6360 / Jun '97 / Music For Pleasure

□ GRACIE FIELDS COLLECTORS EDITION
DVX 08052 / Apr '95 / Deja Vu

□ OUR GRACIE (23 Favourites 1928-1947)
Sing as we go / My blue heaven / I'm a dreamer aren't we all / Singin' in the bathtub / Just a dancing sweetheart / Just one more chance / I took my harp to a party / Looking on the bright side / Isle of Capri / Ave Maria / In my little bottom drawer / Love in bloom / Roll along prarie moon / Would you / What can you give a nudist on his birthday / Little old lady / Holy city / Donkey's serenade / Biggest aspidistra in the world / Pedro the fisherman / Christopher Robin is saying his prayers / Wish me luck as you wave me goodbye / Now is the hour
CDAJA 5259 / Feb '98 / Living Era

□ OUR GRACIE'S GREATEST SELECTION
Sally / Pedro the fisherman / We've got to keep up with the Joneses / Bleeding heart / Biggest aspidistra in the world / Danny boy / He's dead but he won't lie down / I took my harp to a party / In my little bottom drawer / Stop and shop at the co-op shop / Wish me luck (as you wave me goodbye) / Little old lady / I never cried so much in all my life / Sing as we go / Isle of Capri / Walter Walter lead me to the alter / Turn 'Erbert's face to the wall / Smile when you say goodbye
EMPRCD 754 / 8 Sep '97 / Emporio

□ SALLY
Sally / Sing as we go / Red sails in the sunset / One of the little orphans of the storm / There's a lovely lake in London / Isle of Capri / We've got to keep up with the Joneses / In my little bottom drawer / Roll along prairie moon / It looks like rain in Cherry Blossom Lane / Greatest mistake of my life / I never cried so much in all my life / Smile when you say goodbye / I haven't been the same girl since / You haven't altered a bit / Did your mother come from Ireland / Turn 'Erbert's face to the wall mother / When I grow too old to dream
CDGFR 099 / Jun '92 / Tring

□ SING AS WE GO
Sally / Oh sailor behave / Just one more chance / It isn't fair / Bargain hunter / Mary Rose / My lucky day / There's a lovely lake in London / Walter, Walter, lead me to the altar / Chapel in the moonlight / Sing as we go / It's a sin to tell a lie / I'll never say Never Again again / Pity the poor goldfish / In my little bottom drawer / Laugh at life / I took my harp to a party / Mocking bird went cuckoo / Fred Fanna / Stop and shop at the Co-op shop / We've got to keep up with the Joneses / Have you forgotten so soon / Roll along prairie moon / Goody goody / Daisy daisy / Light in the window
RAJCD 833 / 2 Feb '98 / Empress

□ THAT OLD FEELING
Sweetest song in the world / Turn 'Erbert's face to the wall mother / Home / Remember me / Round the bend of the road / Will you remember / When I grow too old to dream / That old feeling / Fred Fannakapan / My first love song / Walter, Walter, lead me to the altar / Goodnight my love / Red sails in the sunset / Ah sweet mystery of life / Smilin' through / Giannina mia / There's a lovely lake in London / We've got to keep up with the Joneses / I never cried so much in all my life / First time I saw you / Fall in and follow the band / Saily
CDAJA 5062 / Jun '89 / Living Era

☐ THAT OLD FEELING
Turn 'erbert's face to the wall / Remember me / Fred fannakapan / Walter, walter lead me to the altar / There's a lovely lake in london / We've got to keep up with the joneses / I never cried so much in all my life / Home / Round the bend of the road / That old feeling / Red sails in the sunset / Goodnight my love / Sally / Biggest aspidistra in the world / In my little bottom drawer / Wish me luck (as you wave me goodbye) / Sing as we go / If I should fall in love again / Will you love me when I'm mutton / I took my harp to a party / Three green bonnets / Little old lady
PASTCD 7050 / Sep '94 / Flapper

Fields Of The Nephilim

☐ BURNING THE FIELDS
MOO 1CD / Dec '93 / Jungle

☐ DAWNRAZOR
Intro / Slow kill / Volcane / Vet for the insane / Dust / Reanimator / Dawnrazor / Sequel / Power / Preacher man / Secrets / Tower
SITL 18CD / '88 / Situation 2

☐ ELIZIUM
(Dead but dreaming) for her light / At the gates of silent memory (paradise regained) / Submission / Summer land / Wail of summer.. and will your heart be also
BEGA 115CD / Oct '90 / Beggars Banquet

☐ REVELATIONS
BEGA 137CD / Jul '93 / Beggars Banquet

☐ ZOON (Nefilim)
BBL 172CD / 10 Nov '97 / Beggars Banquet

Fields, Scott

☐ DISASTER AT SEA (Fields, Scott Ensemble)
CD 961 / Feb '97 / Music & Arts

☐ SONOTROPISM (Fields, Scott Ensemble)
CD 1007 / Sep '97 / Music & Arts

Fields, Shep

☐ THANKS FOR THE MEMORY (Fields, Shep & His Rippling Rhythm Orchestra)
September in the rain / Melody for two / Twinkle twinkle little star / That's life I guess / In the still of the night / Who knows / Whistle while you work / Till the clock strikes three / Moon at sea / My walking stick / Little heaven of the seven seas / Thanks for the memory / There's a new moon over the old mill / Teacher's pet / 'S wonderful / I must see Annie tonight / Good evenin' good lookin' / You're lovely madame / What have you got that gets me / I go for that / Kinda lonesome / With a smile and a song
RAJCD 889 / 6 Oct '97 / Empress

Fieldstones

☐ MEMPHIS BLUES TODAY
HMG 6505 / Nov '97 / Hightone

Fiend

☐ CALEDONIAN GOTHIC
NOIR 001CD / 13 Oct '97 / God Bless

Fier, Anton

☐ DREAMSPEED
AVAN 009 / Nov '93 / Avant

Fiestas

☐ OH SO FINE
So fine / Dollar bill / That was me / Mr. Dillon, Mr. Dillon / Come on and love me / Mexico / Last night I dreamed / Lawman / Our anniversary / Railroad song / Try it one more time / Mama put the law down / Fine as wine / You can be my girlfriend / Anna / I'm your slave
CDCHD 382 / Feb '93 / Ace

Fife

☐ GYPSY SPIRIT
Raggle taggle gypsy / Star of the County Down / Ye Jacobites by name / Western lilt / Atholl Highlanders / Real old mountain dew / Drunken sailor / Roll in my sweet baby's arms / Leaving of Liverpool / Whiskey in the jar / Irish washerwoman / Tenpenny bit
SMD 612 / Dec '97 / Smiddy Made

Fifteen

☐ BUZZ
GROW 152 / Nov '94 / Grass

Figarova, Amina

☐ ANOTHER ME
Nomads / Another me / Could you / Grey circle / Southern dreams / Say no / Touch / Invisible / If you get it / Talkin' bass / Calling you
BMCD 294 / 9 Mar '98 / Munich

Figgy Duff

☐ AFTER THE TEMPEST
CMCD 023 / Dec '97 / Celtic Music

☐ RETROSPECTIVE
AMBER 50325CD / Mar '98 / Amber

Fighting Cause

☐ PINT OF SPITE
LRR 022 / Oct '96 / Last Resort

Figlin, Arkadi

☐ PARTS OF A WHOLE (A Jazz Portrait)
MK 437061 / Jul '92 / Mezhdunarodnaya Kniga

Figueres, Miguel

☐ FLAMENCO
Guantanamera / La tani / Maruja limon / Carmen Carmela / Campanilleros / Javeras / Taka taka ta / Pasadoble campero / Maria Isabel / Zorongo / Martinetes / Y no te olvido / Esperanza / Triana morena / A mi me pesa / Bata de lunares / Camino verde / Fandangos de Isabel / Tangos de grana
QED 221 / Nov '96 / Tring

Fila Brazillia

☐ BLACK MARKET GARDENING
PORK 037 / Nov '96 / Pork

☐ LUCK BE A WEIRDO TONIGHT
PORK 045 / May '97 / Pork

☐ MESS
PORK 030 / Apr '96 / Pork

☐ POWER CLOWN
PORK 055 / 1 Sep '98 / Pork

Filarfolket

☐ SMUGGLE
CDAM 71 / Jul '95 / Temple

☐ VINTERVALS
Tartan / Cowboyhalling / Polska / Polska to Ola Laingen / Rida ranka / Se makaroni / Svalan/Bosse buses marsch / Vintervalsen / Slangen / Hallingpolska / Lyckovalsen / Honsafotter and gulerotter / Gustav vasa / Potatisvalsen / Dammsugare efter bodil i / Ravmarschen / Daggvisa / Rockan / Tuffpolska
RESCD 504 / Jul '97 / Resource

File

☐ 2 LEFT FEET
FF 507CD / '92 / Flying Fish

☐ LA VIE MARRON
GLCD 2124 / Aug '96 / Green Linnet

Filipinos

☐ PEEL BACK THE SKIN
TWIST 003CD / Jun '92 / Wild

Fille Qui Mousse

☐ TRIXIE STAPLETON 291
14919 / 2 Feb '98 / Spalax

Filska

☐ HARVEST HOME
ATCD 044 / May '96 / Attic

Filter

☐ SHORT BUS
Hey man nice shot / White like that / Gerbil / So cool / Consider this / Under / Take another / Stuck in here / It's over / Spent / Dose
9362458642 / Apr '95 / Warner Bros.

Filthy Lucre

☐ POP SMEAR
NM 025CD / Oct '97 / Neat Metal

Fimbulwinter

☐ SERVANTS OF SORCERY
HR 001CD / Feb '96 / Hot

Fin De Siecle

☐ END OF THE CENTURY
TIRCD 003 / Apr '96 / Totem

Final Conflict

☐ ASHES TO ASHES
FLY 008CD / Jun '97 / Tackle Box

☐ REBIRTH
FLY 005CD / Feb '97 / Tackle Box

Final Cut

☐ ATONEMENT
60086331242 / 27 Apr '98 / SLPP

Final Exit

☐ TEG
DFR 6 / Oct '96 / Desperate Flight

☐ UMEA
DFR 15 / Jun '97 / Desperate Flight

Finchley Boys

☐ EVERLASTING TRIBUTES
852127 / 1 Jun '98 / EVA

Finchley Children's Choir

☐ LITTLE DONKEY
75605515142 / 10 Nov '97 / RCA Victor

Fine Arts Brass Ensemble

☐ LIGHTER SIDE OF FINE ARTS BRASS ENSEMBLE, THE
CDSDL 381 / Aug '90 / Saydisc

Fine Tooth Combine

☐ BIG BIG SOUR
FTC 003CD / Jun '96 / FTC

Fine Young Cannibals

☐ FINEST
She drives me crazy / Flame / Johnny come home / Good thing / Suspicious minds / Blue / Ever fallen in love / Don't look back / Tell me what / I'm not the man I used to be / Couldn't care more / Funny how love is / Take what I can get / Since you've been gone / She drives me crazy
8288542 / Nov '96 / FFRR

☐ FINEST (2CD Limited Edition Set)
She drives me crazy / Flame / Johnny come home / Good thing / Suspicious minds / Blue / Ever fallen in love / Don't look back / Tell me what / I'm not the man I used to be / Couldn't care more / Funny how love is / Take what I can get / Since you've been gone / She drives me crazy / Motherless child / Wade in the water / Love for sale / Prick up your ears / Pull the sucker off / You never know
8288552 / Nov '96 / FFRR

☐ RAW AND THE COOKED, THE
She drives me crazy / Good thing / I'm not the man I used to be / I'm not satisfied / Tell me what / Don't look back / It's OK (It's alright) / Don't let it get you down / As hard as it is / Ever fallen in love
8280692 / Jan '89 / London

Finger

☐ SWOLLEN
Third eye / Distortek / Done ravin' / Grout / Funghi / Bloop / Sore / Breakdown no.1 / On the double / Bloop (remix)
MILCD 001 / 29 Jun '98 / Milk

Finger, Peter

☐ BETWEEN THE LINES
BEST 1079CD / Nov '95 / Acoustic Music

☐ INNERLEBEN
BEST 1019CD / Nov '93 / Acoustic Music

☐ NIEMANDSLAND
BEST 1001CD / Nov '93 / Acoustic Music

☐ SOLO
BEST 1032CD / Nov '93 / Acoustic Music

Finitribe

☐ GROSSING 10K
Eyeball / Instant access / A earth creature / Whale of a tail / Ask a silly question / Monster in the house / Asstrax / 3aaas / Put your trunk in it / Built in monster / Animal farm / Ouch ya go
TPLP 24 CD / Dec '89 / One Little Indian

☐ NOISE LUST AND FUN
TPCD 21 / Nov '89 / One Little Indian

☐ SLEAZY LISTENING
Sleazy rider / Mind my make up / Frantic / Chiller / Waltzer / Flying peppers / Electrician / Bells / Shining / Oxbow incident / Theme
INFECT 43CD / 2 Mar '98 / Infectious

☐ UNEXPECTED GROOVY TREAT, AN
Forevergreen / 101 (sonic shuffle edit) / Come and get it / Mellowman / Yer crazy / Forevergreen / Bagomatix 2 (there can only be one) / Ace love duece / Hypnopaedia / Glisten / An unexpected groovy treat / Forevergreen (forevermost excellent) / Ace love duece / Forevergreen (foreverdreaming)
TPLP 34CD / Aug '92 / One Little Indian

Fink, Cathy

☐ CATHY FINK & MARCY MARXER (Fink, Cathy & Marcy Marxer)
Last night I dreamed / Love's last chance / Frieght train blues / My prairie home / I've endured / Early / I'm not alone anymore / Names / Walking in the glory / Are you tired of me / Tune medley / Crawdad song
SHCD 3775 / Jul '89 / Sugar Hill

☐ CHANGING CHANNELS
Turn it off change the channel leave the room / 50 things that I can do instead of watch TV / Ballet dancing truck driver / Count to 10 and try again / That's what I like about you / Use a word / Talk to me / Dad threw the TV out the window / Buy me this and buy me that / TV way / Power in me / Sharing
ROUCD 8048 / Apr '98 / Rounder

☐ COLLECTION FOR KIDS, A (Fink, Cathy & Marcy Marxer)
ROUCD 8029 / Apr '94 / Rounder

☐ DOGGONE MY TIME
Where the west begins / I'm so lonesome I could cry / Cuckoo / Sara McCutcheon / Cat's got the measles / Coal mining woman / Monkey medley / Midnight prayerlight / No tell motel / When it's darkness on the delta / Cotton patch rag / Coming home / Little Billy Wilson / Shenandoah Falls / My old Kentucky home
SHCD 3783 / Jul '90 / Sugar Hill

☐ GRANDMA SLID DOWN THE MOUNTAIN
New river train / Brush your teeth / Yodeling lesson / Grandma slid down the mountain / Jazzy three bears / It's a shame / I'd like to be a cowgirl / Cuckoo rock / Oh susanna / Peanut butter and jelly / Little rabbit, where's your mammy / A flea and a fly in a flue / What does your mama do / Yodel polka / Cat and the fiddle-briarpicker brown
ROUCD 8010 / Oct '88 / Rounder

☐ NOBODY ELSE LIKE ME (Fink, Cathy & Marcy Marxer)
Hello hello hello / Kye kye kule / Nobody else like me / Special kids / Little like you and a little like me / I see with my hands / Twins / Kid like me / May there always be sunshine / Walkin' on my wheels / Harry's glasses / Everything possible
ROUCD 8079 / Jun '98 / Rounder

☐ PARENTS' HOME COMPANION, A (Fink, Cathy & Marcy Marxer)
ROUCD 8031 / Feb '95 / Rounder

☐ WHEN THE RAIN COMES DOWN
When the rain comes down / Magic penny / Susie and the alligator / Alphabet boogie / Rock, old joe (old joe clark) / Uncle noah's ark / Martin luther king / Cookies / Betty botter / Skip to my lou / Banjo song / Shakin' hands / Whoever shall have some good peanuts / Seven days to rock / Soon as we all cook sweet potatoes / Happy trails
ROUCD 8013 / '88 / Rounder

Finkel, Sigi

☐ DERVISH DANCES (Finkel, Sigi & Tim Richards)
ORFCD 155 / Sep '97 / Orf

☐ HEARTBEAT (Finkel, Sigi & American Heart)
332752 PC08 / May '98 / Koch

Finley, Karen

☐ CERTAIN LEVEL OF DENIAL, A (2CD Set)
Hello mother / He's going home / Woman's best friend / Session / Aunt enid / Roadkill / It's my body / Testomony of the reality that life is unfair and unjust / Lost hope / An act of conscience / In memory of / Aunt enid 2 / Epilogue
RCD 40317 / Feb '95 / Rykodisc

Finn

☐ FINN
Only talking sense / Eyes of the world / Mood swinging man / Last day of June / Suffer never / Angel's heap / Niwhai / Where is my soul / Bullets in my hairdo / Paradise (wherever you are) / Kiss the road of Raratonga
CDFINN 1 / Sep '97 / Parlophone

Finn, Alec

☐ BLUE SHAMROCK
Micky finn's air / Water is wide / Mountains of pomeroy / West's awake / Slan le maighe / Dark island / Eamon an chnuic / Down by the sally gardens / Sean o duibhir an ghleanna / Lakes of coolfinn
7567827352 / Apr '95 / Warner Bros.

Finn, Neil

☐ TRY WHISTLING THIS
Last one standing / Souvenir / King Tide / Try whistling this / She will have her way / Sinner / Twisty bass / Loose tongue / Truth / Astro / Dream date / Faster than light / Addicted
4951392 / 15 Jun '98 / Parlophone

Finn, Steve

☐ BEFORE THE FLOOD (Finn, Steve & Andrew Dinan/John Joe Kelly)
It's not what you've been born with / Jenny picking cockles/Mouseskin shoe/The bunny's hat / Before the flood / Strong storm rising / Out on the road/The first pint/Cathal McConnell's / All come to reap the goldrush / Song of the strings / Countdown/The big reel from Ballynacaslly / Marian's favourite / Struggle / Arkle Mountain/Padraig's favourite / Sailing into Warpoles Marsh
JAS 9801 / Jun '98 / Smallworld

Finnegan, Brian

☐ WHEN THE PARTY'S OVER
ARADCD 101 / Mar '94 / Acoustic Radio

Finnegans

☐ FINNEGANS, THE
CDMANU 1439 / Dec '93 / Manu

Finneus Gauge

☐ MORE ONCE MORE
More wants more / King of the chord change / Press the flesh / Desire / Doogins (the evil spawn) / Customer service / Mess of finesse / Sidewalk sale / Calling card / Salvation / Abandon / Finding the strength
CYCL 055 / Aug '97 / Cyclops

Finnigan, Jim

☐ IRISH HARVEST DAY
DHCD 722 / Jan '95 / Outlet

Fiorentino, Francisco

☐ CANTA
EBCD 97 / 1 Jun '98 / El Bandoneon

Firat, Ozan

☐ TURKEY: MUSIC OF THE TROUBADORS
AUB 006771 / Jun '93 / Auvidis/Ethnic

Fire & Ice

☐ GUIDED BY THE SUN
BADVCCD 144 / Oct '96 / New European

☐ HOLLOW WAYS
Lord of secrets / Militia templi / Seeker / Old grey widowmaker / Huldra's maze / Rising of the moon / Holy vehm / Ershebeth / Fetter / Svartalfar
FREMDCD 211 / Jul '97 / Fremdheit

☐ RUNA
FREMDCD 24 / Oct '96 / Fremdheit

☐ SEASONS OF ICE
Call up the four winds / Noxialicht / Old grey bolverker / Bolverker / Michael / Care charmer sleep / Hamarr and the raven / Suppose my name / Seekers prayer / Wind that shakes the barley / Annabel Lee / Reyn again / Corpus Christie / Annar runa / Goddess of the north / Hollow ways / Purity / Paladin
FREMDCD 10 / Jan '98 / Fremdheit

Fire

☐ MAGIC SHOEMAKER
Children of immagination / Tell you a story / Magic shoes / Reason for everything / Only a dream / Flies like a bird / Like to help you if I can / I can see the sky / Shoemaker / Happy man am I
SEECD 294 / '90 / See For Miles

Fire Crow, Joseph

☐ NORTHERN CHEYENNE FLUTE
14995 / Jan '97 / Spalax

Fire Dept.

☐ ELPEE FOR ANOTHER TIME
YEPCD 3 / May '96 / Yep

Fire Escape

☐ PSYCHOTIC REACTION/RAW AND ALIVE (Fire Escape & The Seeds)
Psychotic reaction: *Fire Escape* / Talk talk: *Fire Escape* / Love special delivery: *Fire Escape* / Trip: *Fire Escape* / 96 tears: *Fire Escape* / Blood beat: *Fire Escape* / Trip maker: *Fire Escape* / Journey's end: *Fire Escape* / Pictures and designs: *Fire Escape* / Fortune teller: *Fire Escape* / No escape: *Seeds* / Satisfy you: *Seeds* / Night time girl: *Seeds* / Up in her room: *Seeds* / Gypsy plays his drums: *Seeds* / Can't seem to make you mine: *Seeds* / Mumble and bumble: *Seeds* / Forest outside your door: *Seeds* / 900 million people daily (all making love): *Seeds* / Pushin' too hard: *Seeds*
DOCD 1990 / Oct '91 / Drop Out

Fire Facts

☐ REMAND CENTRE
SHCD 6016 / Jul '95 / Sky High

Fire Merchants

☐ LANDLORDS OF ATLANTIS
EFA 130012 / May '94 / Ozone

Fire This Time

☐ STILL DANCING ON JOHN WAYNE'S HEAD
I love the future / Sisters and brothers / No white borders / Ohtokin / At least American Indian people know exactly how they've bee / Oka / Reluctant warrior
FILT 029CD / 27 Apr '98 / Filter

Fireballs

☐ BEST OF THE FIREBALLS, THE (The Original Norman Petty Masters)
Torquay / Bulldog / Carioca / Yacky doo / Foot patter / Dumbo / Vaquero / Long long ponytail / Gunshot / Nearly sunrise / Rik-a-tik / Quite a party / Really big time / Peg leg / Fireball / Panic button / Cry baby / Tuff-a-nuff / Find me a golden street / Blacksmith blues / Daytona drag / Kissin' / Chief whoopin' koff / El ringo / Torquay
CDCHD 418 / Sep '92 / Ace

☐ BEST OF THE FIREBALLS, THE
Do you think / Wishing / True love ways / Call in the sheriff / Don't stop / Good good lovin' / Won't be long / Sugar shack / Ain't gonna tell anybody / Daisy petal pickin' / When my tears have dried / Look at me / I'll send for you / What kind of love / Cry baby / Bull moose / Lonesome tears / Indian giver / Red Cadillac and a black moustache / Almost eighteen / Pretend / I wonder why / Maybe baby / Everyday / Little baby / It's so easy / Bottle of wine / Come on react / Goin' away / Can't you see I'm trying
CDCHD 468 / Oct '94 / Ace

☐ BLUE FIRE / RARITIES
Blue fire / Blues in the night / Bluesday / Wang wang blues / Birth of the blues / Blacksmith blues / Blue tinted blues / Wabash blues / Big daddy blues / Basin Street blues / Bye bye blues / St. Louis blues / Almost paradise / Sweet talk / Sneakers / I doubt it / Yacky doo / Clink clink classic / Spotnick / Power packed / Vaquero (Latino) / Vaquero / Wicked / Rik-a-tik / Teekee / Gunshot / Dooop / Tuff-a-nuff / Joshi / Don't lie to me / Torquay
CDCHD 472 / Oct '93 / Ace

☐ BOTTLE OF WINE/COME ON REACT (The Original Norman Petty Masters)
Three minutes time / Ain't that rain / Where can tomorrow be found / Bottle of wine / Mason street / Barbara White / Groovy motions / Goin' away / I don't have the right / Girl as perfect as you / Baby listen to me / Chicken little / Hurry hurry / Cod'ine / Come on react / Light in the window / It's easy for me / Woman help me / Mr. Reeves / Good lovin's so hard to find / Get out of my life woman / Lonely too long / Litty bitty bucket / Louie go home
CDCHD 677 / 23 Feb '98 / Ace

☐ FIREBALLS/VAQUERO
Torquay / Guess what / Panic button / Let there be love / Nearly sunrise / Long long ponytail / Bulldog / I wonder why / Foot patter / Blind date / Kissin' / Cry baby / Vaquero / La raspa / In a little Spanish town / Cielito lindo / La golondrina / Tequila / Spur / Spanish legend / Jesusita en chihuahua / La borachita / Gay ranchero / El rancho grande
CDCHD 447 / Mar '93 / Ace

☐ TORQUAY/CAMPUSOLOGY
Torquay / Alone / Joey's song / Last date / Chief whoopin' koff / El ringo / Wheels / Honey / Rawhide / Tuff-a-nuff / Dumbo / Quite a party / Ahhh soul / Campusology / Daytona drag / Evermore / Peg leg / Sheezburger / In the mood / Mr. Mean / Mrs. Mean / Gently, gently / Mr. Reed / Find me a golden street
CDCHD 452 / Apr '93 / Ace

Firebirds

☐ LET'S GO
PEPCD 123 / 26 May '98 / Pollytone

☐ TAKING BY STORM
FBCD 101 / Jan '95 / Pollytone

☐ THIS IS IT
PEPCD 105 / Mar '95 / Pollytone

☐ TOO HOT TO HANDLE
PEPCD 103 / Jan '95 / Pollytone

Firefall

☐ FIREFALL
It doesn't matter / Love isn't all / Livin' ain't livin' / No way out / Dolphin's lullaby / Cinderella / Sad ol' love song / You are the woman / Mexico / Do what you want
8122703792 / Mar '93 / WEA

Firehose

☐ IF'N
Sometimes / Honey please / For the singer of REM / Anger / Hear me / Backroads / From one comes one / Making the freeway safe for the freeway / Operation solitaire / Windmilling / Me and you remembering / In memory of Elizabeth Cotton / Soon / Thunderchild
SST 115CD / May '93 / SST

☐ RAGIN' FULL ON
Locked in / Brave captain / Under the influence of meat puppets / Chemical wire / Another theory shot to shit on your ... / It matters / On your knees / Candle and the flame / Choose any memory / Perfect pairs / This / Caroms / Relatin' dudes to jazz / Things could turn around
SST 079CD / May '93 / SST

Firehouse Five

☐ AT DISNEYLAND
Anvil stomp / Muskrat ramble / You've got to see mamma ev'ry night or you can't see mam / Lassus trombone / Coney island washboard / Ja-da / Baby won't you please come home / Tiger rag
GTCD 10049 / Oct '93 / Good Time Jazz

☐ DIXIELAND FAVOURITES (Firehouse Five Plus Two)
Fidgety feet / Storyville blues / Muskrat ramble / Canal street blues / That's a plenty / Doctor jazz / Working man blues / Jazz me blues / Royal garden blues / Sister kate / A hot time in the old town tonight / Come back sweet papa / Firehouse stomp / Yellow dog blues / Bill bailey won't you please come home / When the saints go marching in
FCD 60008 / May '95 / Fantasy

☐ GOES SOUTH
Alabama jubilee / Swanee river / Basin street blues / Birmingham papa (your memphis mama's comin' to town) / Tuck me to sleep in my old kentucky home / Milneberg joys / I'm gonna charleston back to charleston / At a georgia camp meeting / Tishomingo blues / Original dixieland one-step
GTCD 12018 / Oct '93 / Good Time Jazz

Firewater

☐ GET OFF THE CROSS
TWA 04CD / Apr '97 / Jetset

☐ PONZI SCHEME
TWA 11 / 30 Mar '98 / Jetset

Fireworks

☐ LIT UP
LB 0020 / Jun '97 / Last Beat

☐ OFF THE AIR
ANDA 195 / Feb '97 / Au-Go-Go

☐ SET THE WORLD ON FIRE
EFA 115732 / Apr '94 / Crypt

Firk, Backwards Sam

☐ TRUE BLUES & GOSPEL
STCD 0002 / Aug '94 / Stella

Firkins, Michael Lee

☐ CACTUS CRUZ
RR 88482 / Oct '96 / Roadrunner

☐ CHAPTER 11
RR 88952 / Sep '96 / Roadrunner

Firm

☐ FIRM, THE
Firm fiasco / Phone tap / Executive decision / Firm family / Firm all stars / Fuck somebody else / Hardcore / Untouchable / Five minutes to flush / Desperados / Firm biz / I'm leaving / Throw your guns
4890712 / 27 Oct '97 / Columbia

Firpo, Roberto

☐ MILONGA ORILLERA
EBCD 75 / Jul '96 / El Bandoneon

First Choice

☐ BEST OF FIRST CHOICE, THE
Armed and extremely dangerous / Smarty pants / One step away / Newsy neighbours / This little woman / This is the house (where love is) / Love and happiness / Runnin' out of fools / Wake up to me / Player / Guilty / Love freeze / Boy named Junior / All I need is time / Guess what Mary Jones did / Hustler Bill / You took the words right out of my mouth / You've been doing wrong for so long / Don't fake it / Why can't I touch you (if you let me make love to you) / This is the house
CDSEWD 096 / Aug '94 / Southbound

☐ BEST OF FIRST CHOICE, THE
CDGR 141 / Jul '97 / Charly

☐ DELUSIONS
Dr. love / Indian giver / Love having you around / Gamble on love / Chances go around / I love you more than before / Let no man put asunder / Do me again / Jimmy "d"
CPCD 8060 / Nov '94 / Charly

☐ HOLD YOUR HORSES
Let me down easy / Good morning midnight / Great expectations / Hold your horses / Love thang / Double cross
CPCD 8096 / Apr '95 / Charly

First Class

☐ FIRST CLASS/SST
Beach baby / Won't someone help me / What became of me / Surfer Queen / First day of your life / Long time gone / Dreams are ten a penny / Bobby Dazzler / Disco kid / I was always a joker / I was a star / Ain't no love / Child's play / Old time love / Baby blue / Life is whatever you want it to be / Carry on singing my song / Smiles on a summer night / Seven Ten to nowhere / Autumn love / And she cried / Wake up America / Song was wrong
SEECD 443 / Jun '96 / See For Miles

First Class

☐ BATTLE OF THE BANDS VOL.2 (First Class/Continental Four)
What is life / What about me / Me and my gemini / Don't you know what you're doing / I wasn't there / Beginning of my end / Let's make love / Coming back to you / Day by day / What you gave from love / Dream world / Way I love you / Take a little time / How can I pretend / Heaven must have sent you / Love you gave to me / I don't have you
NEMCD 991 / 19 Aug '97 / Sequel

First Class Bluesband

☐ FIRST CLASS BLUES
BEST 1031CD / Nov '93 / Acoustic Music

First Down

☐ WORLD SERVICE
EFA 610092 / Apr '95 / Blitzvinyl

First House

☐ ERINDIRA
Day away / Innocent erendira / Journeyers to the east / Bracondale / Grammenos / Stranger than paradise / Bridge call / Doubt / Further away
8275212 / Apr '86 / ECM

Fisc

☐ HANDLE WITH CARE
Come run riot / Won't let go / Love fight / Hold your head up / Let me leave / Live it up / Lover under attack / Handle with care / Got to beat the clock / Speed limit 55
CDMFN 91 / Mar '89 / Music For Nations

Fischbacher Group

☐ MYSTERIOUS PRINCESS (Fischbacher Group & Adam Nussbaum)
BEST 1025 / Nov '93 / Acoustic Music

Fischer, Clare

☐ JUST ME - SOLO PIANO EXCURSIONS
Autumn leaves / Pra braden / 'Round midnight / I'm gettin' sentimental over you / I'd do anything for you / Liebesleid / After you've gone / Guajira / Ill wind / Pensativa / Topsy
CCD 4679 / Feb '96 / Concord Jazz

☐ LATIN SIDE, THE
369072 / 3 Aug '98 / Koch Jazz

☐ LEMBRANCAS (REMEMBRANCES)
CP (Charlie Palmieri) / Fina / Coco B / Curumim / Endlessly / On Green Dolphin Street / Xapun / Gilda / Pan pipe dance / And miles to go / Strut
CCD 4404 / Mar '90 / Concord Jazz

Fischer-Z

☐ KAMIKAZE SHIRT
Peaches and cream / Killing time / Marlon / And this we call crime / Kamikaze shirt / Polythene / Human beings / Stripper in the mirror / Stars / Blue anenome / Radio k.i.l.l.
WELFD 6 / Apr '94 / Welfare

☐ STREAM
WELFD 8 / Mar '95 / Recognition

☐ WORKER, THE
Pretty paracetemol / Acrobats / Worker / Spiders / Remember Russia / French let her / Lies / Wax dolls / Headlines / Nice to know / Billy and the motorway police / Lemmings / Limbo / Marliese
DC 882812 / 2 Feb '98 / Disky

Fish

☐ FORTUNES OF WAR
Somebody special / State of mind / Fortunes of war / Warm wet circles / Jumpsuit city / Company / Kayleigh / Internal exile / Just good friends / Sugar mice / Dear friend / Lady let it lie / Lucky / Work tapes, The
DDICK 30CD / 27 Jul '98 / Dick Bros.

☐ OUTPATIENTS 1993 (Various Artists)
Time and a word: *Fish* / Mark 13: *Dream Disciples* / One love: *One Eternal* / Don't ask me: *Joyriders* / Seeker: *Fish* / Swing your bag: *Guaranteed Pure* / Traveller's tales: *Avalon* / Out of my life: *Fish* / Best friend: *Joyriders* / Dream is dead: *Dream Disciples*
DDICK 1CD / Sep '96 / Dick Bros.

☐ PIGPENS BIRTHDAY
DDICK 16CD / Sep '96 / Dick Bros.

☐ SUITS
1470 / Lady let it lie / Emperor's song / Fortunes of war / Somebody special / No dummy / Pipeline / Jumpsuit city / Bandwagon / Raw meat
DDICK 4CD / Sep '96 / Dick Bros.

☐ SUNSETS ON EMPIRE
DDICK 25CD / May '97 / Dick Bros.

☐ SUSHI (2CD Set)
Fearless / Big wedge / Boston tea party / Credo / Family business / View from a hill / He knows you know / She chameleon / Kayleigh / White Russian / Company / Just good friends / Jeepster / Hold your head up / Lucky / Internal exile / Cliche / Last straw / Poets moon / Five years
DDICK 2CD / Sep '96 / Dick Bros.

☐ TALES FROM THE BIG BUS (2CD Set)
Perceptions of Johnny Punter / What colour is God / Family business / Mr. 1470 / Jungle ride / Assassing / Credo / Tongues / Fugazi / White feather / Cliche / Brother 52 / Lucky / Internal exile / Company
DDICK 29CD / 1 Jun '98 / Dick Bros.

☐ VIGIL IN A WILDERNESS OF MIRRORS
Vigil / Big wedge / State of mind / Company / Gentlemen's excuse me / Voyeur / Family business / View from the hill / Cliche
CDEMD 1015 / Feb '90 / EMI

☐ VIGIL IN A WILDERNESS OF MIRRORS (Remastered)
Vigil / Big wedge / State of mind / Company / Gentleman's excuse me / Voyeur / Family business / View from a hill / Cliche / Jack and Jill / Internal exile / Gentleman's excuse me / Whiplash
DDICK 28CD / 16 Mar '98 / Dick Bros.

☐ YANG
Lucky / Big wedge / Lady let it lie / Lavender / Credo / Gentlemen's excuse me / Kayleigh / State of mind / Somebody special / Sugar mice / Punch and Judy / Fortunes of war / Internal exile
DDICK 12CD / Sep '96 / Dick Bros.

☐ YIN
Incommunicado / Family business / Just good friends / Pipeline / Institution waltz / Tongues / Time and a word / Company / Incubus / Solo / Favourite stranger / Boston tea party / Raw meat
DDICK 11CD / Sep '96 / Dick Bros.

Fish Heads & Rice

☐ SOMETHING SMELLS FISHY
APCD 121 / Nov '96 / Appaloosa

Fish Karma

☐ SUNNYSLOPE
422433 / May '94 / New Rose

Fish Out Of Water

☐ LUCKY SCARS
Just like in the movies (Part 1) / Once in a lifetime / Take it easy / Cry from the city / Belfast boy / Her old man / Parisienne prelude / Persistence of memory / MS Madness / He like a drink / Take it easy (Instrumental) / Cry from the city (Dub) / Lucky scars / Just like the movies (Part 2)
SRCD 004 / Nov '96 / Stream

Fish, R.A.

☐ RHYTHMIC ESSENCE (The Art Of The Dumbek)
LYRCD 7411 / Jan '92 / Lyrichord

Fish, Robert

☐ DANCES WITH FISH (Fish, Robert Band)
CDTT 1002 / Dec '97 / Tartan Tapes

Fishbelly Black

☐ FISHBELLY BLACK
BBCD 72107 / Jul '96 / Backbeat

☐ MOVIN'
BBCD 721172 / Jul '96 / Backbeat

Fisher, Andy

☐ MAN IN THE WOODS, A
Oh what a kiss / Mr. Cannibal / Computer no.9 / Man in the woods / Crazy bull fandango / Der babyspeck ist weg / Carnaby Street / No wine in Texas / Telephone / Heinzelmannchen's hitparade / Sleep well / Bunte papageien und ein grunes krokodil / Olympia ole / Ich will das nicht / Who really wants it / Kartoffelbeat / Walter, Walter / Mrs. Thunderbird / Monsieur controleur / Max nix / Fraulein, fraulein / Very nice day / Mademoiselle bon bon / German beer drinking song / Forgotten cafe in Berlin / Gilly, Gilly Oxenpfeffer / If they ever made me a king / General Bum Bum / Comrade Komzak / Equal goes it lose
BCD 16163 / Apr '97 / Bear Family

Fisher, Archie

☐ ARCHIE FISHER
CMCD 007 / Dec '97 / Celtic Music

☐ MAN WITH THE RHYME
FLEG 61CD / Mar '98 / Folk Legacy

☐ SUNSET'S I'VE GALLOPED INTO... (Fisher, Archie & Garnet Rogers)
Ashfields and Brine / Yonder banks / Shipyard apprentice / Cuillins of Home / Southside blues / Silver coin / Prescence / Gunsmoke and whiskey / Bill Hosie / I wandered by a brookside / Merry England / Great North road / Eastfield / Black horse / All that you ask
CDTRAX 020 / Apr '92 / Greentrax

☐ WILL YE GANG, LOVE
O charlie, o charlie / Lindsay / Broom o' the cowdenknowes / Mally lee / Will ye gang love / Flower of france and england, o / Laird o' windy wa's / Men o' worth / Looly, looly / Dreg song / Adam cameron / Blackbirds and thrushes / Gallant ninety two / Rovin' ploughboy
GLCD 3076 / May '93 / Green Linnet

Fisher, Cilla

☐ CILLA AND ARTIE (Fisher, Cilla & Artie Trezise)
Norland wind / Beggarman / What can a young lassie / Fisher lassies / Generations of change / Fair maid of London Town / Wicked wife / Gypsy laddie / Blue bleezin' blind drunk / John Grumlie / Jeannie C
CDTRAX 9050 / 5 May '98 / Greentrax

Fisher, Eddie

☐ EDDIE FISHER
DVAD 6062 / May '95 / Deja Vu

Fisher, King

☐ KING FISHER & HIS ALL-STARS
JCD 13 / Jul '96 / Jazzology

Fisher, Laurie

☐ SWEETHEART TREE, THE
Over the river to Charlie / Gentle maiden / Ashe grove / Bare necessities / Merry widow / Artists life / Emperor waltz / Jalousie / Margaret's waltz / Farewell to Devon / Melancholy waltz
STRINGCD 2 / May '98 / Laurie Fisher

Fisher, Matthew

☐ SALTY DOG RETURNS, A
Dance band on the Titanic / Salty dog returns / Nutrocker / Whiter shadow of pale / Pilgrimage / Rathunter / Strange conversation continues / G String / Sex and violence / Green onions / Linda's theme / Downliners Sect manifesto / Peter Grump
CDKVL 9032 / May '94 / Kingdom

☐ STRANGE DAYS
BGOCD 308 / Mar '96 / Beat Goes On

Fisher, Morgan

☐ CLAWS
We three Kings / O come all ye faithful (adeste fidelis) / Deck the halls / Coventry carol / Holly and the ivy / Bernard / Listen / Dead duck / Good King Wenceslas / Happy Christmas / Coventry carol / Holly and the ivy / We three kings / O come all ye faithful (adeste fidelis)
BP 273CD / 17 Nov '97 / Blueprint

☐ HYBRID KIDS VOL.1 (A Collection Of Classic Mutants) (Various Artists)
MacArthur Park: *Burtons* / God save the lean: *Punky & Porky* / Pretty bacon: *Punky & Porky* / Wuthering Heights: *Jah Wurzel* / Catch a falling star: *Rififi* / Fever: *Galaxy, Malcolm* / Save your kisses for me: *Kapital Punishment* / D'ya think I'm sexy: *British Standard Unit* / Enlightenment: *Combo Satori* / Get back: *US Nurds* / Something better change: *Incestors* / You've lost that lovin' feelin': *Atom, R.W.* / Take me I'm yours: *Cage* / All the young dudes: *Pipettes* / Emergency: *666*
BP 262CD / 3 Nov '97 / Blueprint

Fisher, Natalie

☐ NATALIE FISHER
Grasp (l'etreinte) / To granny (a granny) / End of a dream (fin d'un reve) / Boat (le bateau) / Amber (ambre) / Night in moureau (une nuit a moureau) / Green cedar (le cedre vert) / Child (un enfant) / Lamasquere / Wonders (les splendeurs)
4509966412 / Aug '94 / Warner Bros.

Fisher, Ray

☐ TRADITIONAL SONGS OF SCOTLAND (Fisher, Ray & Colin Ross/Martin Carthy/John Kirkpatrick)
Night visiting song / Wark o' the weavers / Lady Keith's lament / Gallowa' hills / Coulter's candy / Willie's fatal visit / Twa recruiting sergeants / Floo'ers o' the forest / MacGinty's meal and ale / Baron o'Brackley / Gypsy laddie / Lang biding here / Jute mill song / Hie, Jeannie hie / Johnny my man / My laddie's bedside / What can a young Lassie / Nicky Tams
CDSDL 391 / Mar '94 / Saydisc

Fisher-Turner, Simon

☐ EDWARD THE II (Original Soundtrack) (Fisher-Turner 5)
IONIC 8CD / Nov '91 / The Fine Line

☐ GARDEN, THE (Original Soundtrack)
IONIC 5CD / Jan '91 / The Fine Line

☐ LIVE BLUE ROMA (The Archaeology Of Sound)
CDMUTE 149 / Jun '95 / Mute

☐ LIVE IN JAPAN
BAH 7 / May '93 / Humbug

☐ NADJA
IONIC 16CD / Apr '96 / Mute

☐ REVOX
Scott / I just woke up man, is it too early / Miaw / Blackouts / Sappora sky / Pop song 93 / Fall / Boxer / Luch at Great Rissington / Recover / Where are we going / Iona / Stuck inside lady / Mr. Davidson's tube / Moist
BAH 16 / Feb '94 / Humbug

☐ SEX APPEAL
Prettiest star / Wild thing / 17 / Love around / Sit down, I think I love you / Shoe shine boy / I wanna love my life away / Sex appeal / Surf city-fun fun-so you wanna be a rock 'n' roll sta / Simon talk / A picture of dorian gray / Vallerl / Rubens room / Smash hit wonder / Trial of dr. fancy / Lee remick / Flirt / Personality parade / Straits of malacca / Poptones / I've been a bad boy
MONDE 7 CD / Oct '92 / Cherry Red

☐ SIMON TURNER
Almost bliss / Warm melt / Dark melt / Muzak / Bliss
CRECD 64 / May '94 / Creation

Fisherstreet

☐ OUT IN THE NIGHT
LUNCD 057 / Feb '86 / Mulligan

Fishtank No.9

☐ ITSELF
COPCD 030 / Jun '97 / Cop International

Fisk, Steve

☐ 448 DEATHLESS DAYS
Invocation / No 2nd chance / Ragged old flag / Weekend review / Diamond club / Oh little seeds / Johnny smoke (swamp thing) / Emerging nation / Trasheap / Further demo of an assist / Break on thru / Tongues / Soul of spain / Tragedy at sea / This vacuum / Chakiri bushl / She walks / Barretta / To abide in the flesh / Priorities
SST 159CD / May '93 / SST

Fisk University Jubilee Singers

☐ FISK UNIVERSITY JUBILEE SINGERS VOL.1 1909-1911
DOCD 5533 / Apr '97 / Document

☐ FISK UNIVERSITY JUBILEE SINGERS VOL.2 1915-1920
DOCD 5534 / Apr '97 / Document

☐ FISK UNIVERSITY JUBILEE SINGERS VOL.3 1924-1940
DOCD 5535 / Apr '97 / Document

Fits

☐ TOO MANY RULES
GET 18CD / Oct '97 / Get Back

Fitz Of Depression

☐ SWING
KLCD 41 / May '96 / K

Fitzgerald, Ella

☐ ALL THAT JAZZ
Dream a little dream of me / My last affair / Baby don't you quit now / Oh look at me now / Jersey bounce / When your lover has gone / That ole devil called love / All that jazz / Just when we're falling in love / Good morning heartache / Little jazz / Nearness of you
CD 2310938 / Nov '95 / Pablo

☐ AT THE MONTREUX JAZZ FESTIVAL 1975
Caravan / Satin doll / Teach me tonight / Wave / It's all right with me / Let's do it / How high the moon / Girl from Ipanema / Ain't nobody's business if I do
OJCCD 789 / May '94 / Original Jazz Classics

☐ AT THE OPERA HOUSE (Live In Chicago & Los Angeles 1957)
It's all right with me / Don't cha go 'way mad / Bewitched, bothered and bewildered / Stompin' at the Savoy / These foolish things / Ill wind / Goody goody / Moonlight in Vermont / Oh lady be good
8312692 / Jan '94 / Verve

☐ AUDIO ARCHIVE
Don't be that way / Fine romance / Flying home / That old black magic / Cryin' mood / If you should ever leave / Everyone's wrong but me / Cheek to cheek / Basin Street blues / Tisket-a-tasket / Starlit hour / Chewing gum / We can't go on this way / Sing song swing / Stairway to the stars / Can't we be friends / Lover come back to me / Moonlight in Vermont / Is there someone else / Who you hunchin
CDAA 001 / Jun '92 / Tring

☐ BASIN STREET BLUES
Basin Street blues / Starlit hour / We can't go on this way / Stairway to the stars / Lover come back to me / Is there somebody else / Tisket-a-tasket / Sing song swing / That old black magic / Sugar blues / It's a blue world / Flying home / Who ya hunchin' / Chewing gum / Goin' and gettin' it / I wanna be a rug cutter / Don't be that way / Can't we be friends / Cheek to cheek / Fine romance / Moonlight in Vermont / Foggy day
GRF 064 / Jun '92 / Tring

☐ BASIN STREET BLUES
Basin street blues / Starlit hour / We can't go on this way / Stairway to the stars / Lover come back to me / Tisket-a-tasket / Sing song swing / That old black magic / Sugar blues / It's a blue world / Flying home / Chewin' gum / Don't be that way / Can't we be friends / Cheek to cheek / Fine romance / Moonlight in Vermont / Foggy day
QED 050 / Nov '96 / Tring

☐ BEST IS YET TO COME (Fitzgerald, Ella & Nelson Riddle)
I wonder where our love has gone / Don't be that way / God bless the child / You're driving me crazy / Goodbye / Any old time / Autumn in New York / Best is yet to come / Deep purple / Somewhere in the night
CD 2312138 / Apr '87 / Pablo

☐ BEST IS YET TO COME, THE (2CD Set)
I ain't got nothin' but the blues / One note samba / (I don't stand a) Ghost of a chance with you / I get a kick out of you / Something to live for / Cotton tail / Take love easy / Don't be that way / Sweet Georgia Brown / They can't take that away from me / You've got a friend / Satin doll / How high the moon / How long has this been going on / When your lover has gone / That old feeling / I've got you under my skin / Tennessee waltz / Dream dancing / Mack the knife / Fine and mellow / I'm in the mood for love / Speak low / Jersey bounce / All that jazz / Please don't talk about me when I'm gone / After you've gone / Ain't misbehavin' / Honeysuckle rose / I wonder where our love has gone / Summertime / Foggy day / How long has this been going on / Dreamer (vivo sonhando) / Best is yet to come
PACD 0032 / Jan '97 / Pablo

☐ BEST OF ELLA FITZGERALD & LOUIS ARMSTRONG, THE (Fitzgerald, Ella & Louis Armstrong)
5379092 / 10 Nov '97 / Verve

☐ BEST OF ELLA FITZGERALD, THE
Tisket-a-tasket / Stairway to the stars / Into each life some rain must fall / It's only a paper moon / Flying home / (I love you) for sentimental reasons / Oh lady be good / How high the moon / Basin Street blues / My one and only love / I've got the world on a string / Walkin' by the river / Lover come back to me / Mixed emotions / Smooth sailin' / If you can't sing it, you'll have to swing it (Mr. Paganini) / I wished on the moon / That old black magic / It's too soon to know / Tender trap
MCBD 19521 / Apr '95 / MCA

☐ BEST OF ELLA FITZGERALD, THE
Dreamer / Fine and mellow / Street of dreams / This love that I've found / How long has this been going on / You're blase / Honeysuckle rose / I'm walkin' / I'm getting sentimental over you / Don't be that way
CD 24054212 / Apr '94 / Pablo

☐ BEST OF THE SONGBOOKS - BALLADS, THE
Oh lady be good / I'm old fashioned / Laura / Daydream / Easy to love / It was written in the stars / How long has this been going on / Let's begin / Now it can be told / There is a small hotel / Do nothin' 'til you hear from me / Ill wind / You're laughing at me / Ship without a sail / Travellin' light / This time the dream's on me
5218672 / Aug '94 / Verve

☐ BEST OF THE SONGBOOKS, THE
Something's gotta give / Our love is here to stay / Bewitched, bothered and bewildered / I've got my love to keep me warm / Lady is a tramp / I got it bad and that ain't good / Miss Otis regrets / 'S wonderful / Between the devil and the deep blue sea / Love for sale / They can't take that away from me / Midnight sun / Hooray for love / Why was I born / Cotton tail / Every time we say goodbye
5198042 / Dec '93 / Verve

☐ BIG BOY BLUE
Big boy blue / Dedicated to you / You showed me the way / Cryin' mood / Love is the thing so they say / All over nothing at all / If you ever should leave / Everyone's wrong but me / Deep in the heart of the south / Just a simple melody / I got a guy / Holiday in Harlem / Rock it for me / I want to be happy / Dipsy doodle / If dreams come true / Hallelujah / Bei mir bist du schon / It's my turn now / 'S wonderful / I was doing all right / Tisket-a-tasket
GRF 091 / '93 / Tring

☐ BLUELLA (Ella Fitzgerald Sings The Blues)
Smooth sailing / Duke's place / St. Louis blues / C jam blues / Fine and mellow / Happy blues / Billie's bounce / I'm walkin' / Fine and mellow / St. Louis blues / Basella
23109602 / Feb '97 / Pablo

☐ CELEBRATED
Organ grinder's swing / If dreams come true / Crying my heart out for you / I'll chase the blues away / It ain' what you do / Sugar blues / Sing song swing / My heart belongs to daddy / Baby won't you please come home / Undecided / Under the spell of the blues / A-tisket a-tasket / My man / Chew chew chew / Shine / My last affair
CDMT 029 / Nov '96 / Meteor

☐ CHEEK TO CHEEK (Fitzgerald, Ella & Louis Armstrong)
Fine romance / I can't give you anything but love: *Fitzgerald, Ella* / Foggy day / Cheek to cheek / Can't we be friends / Don't be that way / I'm puttin' all my eggs in one basket / I've got my love to keep me warm / Let's call the whole thing off / Love is here to stay / Moonlight in Vermont / Stars fell on Alabama / Tenderly / Nearness of you / They can't take that away from me / St. James Infirmary: *Armstrong, Louis* / How high the moon: *Fitzgerald, Ella* / What a wonderful world: *Armstrong, Louis*
BN 010 / Nov '96 / Blue Nite

☐ CLAP HANDS, HERE COMES CHARLIE
Night in Tunisia / You're my thrill / My reverie / Stella by starlight / 'Round midnight / Jersey bounce / Signing off / Cry me a river / This year's kisses / Good morning heartache / I was born to be blue / Clap hands, here comes Charlie / Spring can really hang you up the most / Music goes 'round and around / One I love belongs to somebody else / I got a guy / This could be the start of something big
8356462 / Mar '90 / Verve

☐ CLASSIC ELLA FITZGERALD, THE (2CD Set)
Sing, song, swing / 'S wonderful / Organ grinder's swing / Tisket-a-tasket / Sing me a swing song (and let me dance) / All over nothing at all / If you can't sing it, you'll have to swing it (Mr. Paganini) / My melancholy baby / Undecided / Darktown strutters ball / Stairway to the stars / I'll chase the blues away / Big boy blue / Goodnight, my love / Imagination / I was doing all right / Moon Ray / Dedicated to you / Baby, won't you please come home / My man (mon homme) / I'm beginning to see the light / Can't help lovin' dat man / Into each life some rain must fall / Benny's coming home on Saturday / This love of mine / He's my guy / Cow cow boogie / It's only a paper moon / Somebody nobody loves / Time alone will tell / Mama, come home / Kiss goodnight / Stone cold dead in de market / Make love to me / Jim / And her tears flowed like wine / Once too often / Cry you out of my heart / Petootie pie / Flying home
CPCD 82502 / Nov '96 / Charly

☐ CLASSICS 1935-1937
CLASSICS 500 / Apr '90 / Classics

☐ CLASSICS 1937-1938
Big boy blue / Dedicated to you / You showed me the way / Cryin' mood / Love is the thing so they say / All over nothing at all / If you ever should leave / Everyone's wrong but me / Deep in the heart of the south / Just a simple melody / I've got a guy / Holiday in Harlem / Rock it for me / I want to be happy / Dipsy doodle / If dreams came true / Hallelujah / Bei mir bist du schon / It's my turn now / 'S Wonderful / I was doing all right / Tisket-a-tasket
CLASSICS 506 / Apr '90 / Classics

☐ CLASSICS 1938-1939
CLASSICS 518 / Apr '90 / Classics

☐ CLASSICS 1939
CLASSICS 525 / Apr '90 / Classics

☐ CLASSICS 1939-1940
CLASSICS 566 / Oct '91 / Classics

☐ CLASSICS 1940-1941
CLASSICS 644 / Nov '92 / Classics

☐ CLASSICS 1941-1944
CLASSICS 840 / Nov '95 / Classics

☐ CLASSICS 1945-1947
CLASSICS 998 / 1 Jun '98 / Classics

☐ CLASSY PAIR, A (Fitzgerald, Ella & Count Basie)
I'm getting sentimental over you / Organ grinder swing / Just a sittin' and a rockin' / My kind of trouble is you / Ain't misbehavin' / Some other Spring / Teach me tonight / Don't worry 'bout me / Honeysuckle rose / Sweet Lorraine / Please don't talk about me when I'm gone
CD 2312132 / May '94 / Complete

☐ COLE PORTER SONGBOOK, THE (Remastered/2CD Set)
5372572 / Oct '97 / Verve Master Edition

☐ COLE PORTER SONGBOOKS (Parts 1 & 2/2CD Set)
All through the night / Anything goes / Miss Otis regrets / Too darn hot / In the still of the night / I get a kick out of you / Do I love you / Always true to you in my fashion / Let's do it / Just one of those things / Every time we say goodbye / All of you / Begin the beguine / Get out of town / I am in love / From this moment on / I love Paris / You do something to me / Riding high / Easy to love / It's all right with me / Why can't you behave / What is this thing called love / You're the top / Love for sale / It's de-lovely / Night and day / Ace in the hole / So in love / I've got you under my skin / I concentrate on you / Don't fence me in
8219892/9902 / Mar '93 / Verve

☐ COLLECTION, THE
I can't give you anything but love / How high the moon / Mack the knife / Fine romance / Goody goody / It's only a paper moon / We can't go on this way / That old black magic / Stars fell on alabama / Tisket a tasket / Can't we be friends / I've got my love to keep me warm / Sing song swing / Baby it's cold outside / You'll have to swing it (mr. paganini) / I can't get started / Smooth sailing / You'll never know / Taking a chance on love / Flying home / Oh lady be good / Sugar blues / Cow cow boogie / Oh johnny, oh johnny, oh / Lover come back to me
COL 014 / Apr '95 / Collection

☐ COMPLETE ELLA FITZGERALD & LOUIS ARMSTRONG ON VERVE, THE (3CD Set) (Fitzgerald, Ella & Louis Armstrong)
5372842 / May '97 / Verve

☐ COMPLETE RECORDINGS 1933-40, THE (3CD Set)
I'll chase the blues away / Love and kisses / Rhythm and romance / Crying my heart out for you / Under the spell of the blues / When I get low I get high / Sing me a swing song / Little bit later on / Love you're just a laugh / Devoting my time to you / If you can't sing it, you'll have to swing it (Mr. Paganini) / Swinging on the reservation / I've got the spring fever blues / Vote for Mr. Rhythm / My melancholy baby / All my life / Goodnight my love / Oh yes take another guess / Did you mean it / My last affair / Organ grinder swing / Shine / Darktown strutters ball / Big boy blues / Dedicated to you / Wake up and live / You showed me the way / Cryin' mood / Love is the thing so they say / Just a simple melody / I got a guy / Holiday in Harlem / Rock it for me / I want to be happy / Dipsy doodle / If dreams come true / Hallelujah / Tisket-a-tasket / Heart of mine / I'm just a jitterbug / All over nothing at all / If you ever should leave / Everyone's wrong but me / Deep in the heart of the south / Bei mir bist du schon / It's my turn now / 'S Wonderful / I was doing all right / This time it's real / What do you know about love / You can't be mine (and someone else's too) / We can't go on this way / Saving myself for you / If you only knew / Strictly from Dixie / Woe is me / Pack up your sins and go to the devil / MacPherson is rehearsin' / Everybody step / Ella / Wacky dust / Gotta pebble in my shoe / I can't stop loving you / I let a tear fall in the river / FDR Jones / I love each move you make / It's foxy / I found my yellow basket / Undecided / T'ain't what you do (it's the way that you do it) / One side of me / My heart belongs to Daddy
CDAFS 10203 / Oct '93 / Affinity

☐ COMPLETE SONGBOOKS, THE
5198322 / Dec '93 / Verve

☐ CONCERT YEARS 1953-1983, THE (4CD Set)
On the sunny side of the street / Body and soul / Why don't you do right / Oh lady / Oh lady be good / I got it bad and that ain't good / How high the moon / My funny valentine / Smooth sailing / Frim fram sauce / Perdido / Imagine my frustration / Duke's place / Satin doll / Something to live for / So danco samba / Don't be that way / You've changed / Let's do it / On the sunny side of the street / Cotton tail / Night and day / Cole Porter medley / Ballad medley / Bossa medley / They can't take that away from me / St. Louis blues / St. Louis blues / Love / Begin the beguine / Indian summer / You've got a friend / Spring can really hang you up the most / Shiny stockings / I can't stop loving you / C jam blues / Sweet Georgia Brown / They can't take that away from me / Man I love / It don't mean a thing if it ain't got that swing / Lemon drop / Very thought of you / Happy blues / Caravan / Teach me tonight / Wave / It's all right with me / How high the moon / Ain't nobody's business if I do / Too close for comfort / I ain't got nothin' but the blues / Day by day / Ordinary fool / Billie's bounce / Please don't talk about me when I'm gone / Make me rainbows / After you've gone / 'Round midnight / You've changed / Basella / Manteca / Willow weep for me / All of me / Blue moon / Night and day / Flying home
4PACD 4414 / Nov '96 / Pablo

☐ DAYDREAM: THE BEST OF THE DUKE ELLINGTON SONGBOOK
Take the 'a' train / Day dream / Everything but you / Azure / Solitude / E and d blues (e for ella, d for duke) / Bli-blip / It don't mean a thing (if it ain't got that swing) / I ain't got nothin' but the blues / I got it bad and that ain't good / Just squeeze me (but don't tease me) / Cotton tail / Squatty roo / Rocks in my bed / Rockin' in rhythm / Mood indigo / All too soon
5272232 / Jun '95 / Verve

☐ DEDICATED TO YOU
My heart belongs to Daddy / My last affair / Dedicated to you / If dreams come true / Goodnight my love / T'ain't what you do (it's the way that you do it) / Love and kisses / Rhythm and romance / What do you know about love / I want to be happy / Tisket-a-tasket / My melancholy baby / I've got the Spring fever blues / If you ever should leave / Devoting my time to you / I can't stop loving you
SUMCD 4012 / Nov '96 / Summit

☐ DIGITAL III AT MONTREUX (Fitzgerald, Ella & Count Basie/Joe Pass)
I can't get started (with you) / Good mileage / I don't stand a ghost of a chance with you / Flying home / I cover the waterfront / Li'l darlin' / In your own sweet way / Oleo
CD 2308223 / May '94 / Pablo

☐ DREAM DANCING (Fitzgerald, Ella & Cole Porter)
Dream dancing / I've got you under my skin / I concentrate on you / My heart belongs to Daddy / Love for sale / So near and yet so far / Down in the depths / After you / Just one of those things / I get a kick out of you / All of you / Anything goes / At long last love / C'est magnifique / Without love
CD 2310 814 / May '94 / Pablo

☐ DUKE ELLINGTON SONGBOOK, THE (3CD Set)
Rockin' in rhythm / Drop me off in Harlem / Daydream / Caravan / Take the 'A' train / I ain't got nothin' but the blues / Clementine / I didn't know about you / I'm beginning to see the light / Lost in meditation / Perdido / Cotton tail / Do nothin' 'til you hear from me / Just a sittin' and a rockin' / Solitude / Rocks in my bed / Satin doll / Sophisticated lady / Just squeeze me (but don't tease me) / It don't mean a thing if it ain't got that swing / Azure / I let a song go out of my heart / In a sentimental mood / Don't get around much anymore / Prelude to a kiss / Mood indigo / In a mellow tone / Love you madly / Lush life / Squatty roo / I'm just a lucky so and so / All too soon / Everything but you / I got it bad and that ain't good / Bli-blip / Chelsea Bridge / Portrait of Ella Fitzgerald / E and D blues
8370352 / Apr '89 / Verve

☐ EASY LIVIN' (Fitzgerald, Ella & Joe Pass)
CD 2310921 / Oct '92 / Pablo

☐ ELLA & LOUIS (3CD Set) (Fitzgerald, Ella & Louis Armstrong)
Fine romance / Foggy day / Cheek to cheek / St. James Infirmary / Can't we be friends / Don't be that way / I'm puttin' all my eggs in one basket / I've got my love to keep me warm / How high the moon / Let's call the whole thing off / Love is here to stop / Moonlight in Vermont / Stars fell on Alabama / Tenderly / Nearness of you / They can't take that away from me / I can't give you anything but love: *Fitzgerald, Ella* / What a wonderful world: *Armstrong, Louis* / Jeepers creepers: *Armstrong, Louis* / Kiss to build a dream on: *Armstrong, Louis* / When the saints go marching in: *Armstrong, Louis* / Mack the knife: *Armstrong, Louis* / C'est si bon: *Armstrong, Louis* / St. Louis blues: *Armstrong, Louis* / Black and blue: *Armstrong, Louis* / Dippermouth blues: *Armstrong, Louis* / Bye and bye: *Armstrong, Louis* / Rockin' chair: *Armstrong, Louis* / C jam blues: *Armstrong, Louis* / Stardust: *Armstrong, Louis* / Royal Garden blues: *Armstrong, Louis* / Indiana: *Armstrong, Louis* / I used to love you: *Armstrong, Louis* / Where did you sleep last night: *Armstrong, Louis* / If I could be with you: *Armstrong, Louis* / Way down yonder in New Orleans: *Armstrong, Louis* / Goody goody: *Fitzgerald, Ella* / It's only a paper moon: *Fitzgerald, Ella* / We can't go on this way: *Fitzgerald, Ella* / That old black magic: *Fitzgerald, Ella* / Tisket a-tasket: *Fitzgerald, Ella* / Sing song swing: *Fitzgerald, Ella* / Baby it's cold outside: *Fitzgerald, Ella & Sarah Vaughan* / You'll have to swing it: *Fitzgerald, Ella* / You'll never know: *Fitzgerald, Ella* / Taking a chance on love: *Fitzgerald, Ella* / Flying home: *Fitzgerald, Ella* / Oh lady be good: *Fitzgerald, Ella* / Cow cow boogie: *Fitzgerald, Ella* / Oh Johnny: *Fitzgerald, Ella* / Lover come back to me: *Fitzgerald, Ella* / Body and soul: *Fitzgerald, Ella* / I can't get it started: *Fitzgerald, Ella* / Smooth sailing: *Fitzgerald, Ella*
KBOX 359 / Nov '96 / Collection

☐ ELLA A NICE
Night and day / Get out of town / Easy to love / You do something to me / Body and soul / Man I love / Porgy / Bossa scene / Girl from Ipanema / Fly me to the moon / O nosso amor / Cielito lindo / Magdalena / Aqua de beber / Summertime / They can't take that away from me / Mood indigo / Do nothin' 'til you hear from me / It don't mean a thing if it ain't got that swing / Something / St. Louis blues / Close to you / Put a little love in your heart
OJCCD 442 / Feb '92 / Original Jazz Classics

☐ ELLA ABRACA JOBIM
CD 2630201 / Oct '92 / Pablo

☐ ELLA AND BASIE (Remastered) (Fitzgerald, Ella & Count Basie)
5390592 / Oct '97 / Verve Master Edition

☐ ELLA AND DUKE AT THE COTE D'AZUR (2CD Set) (Fitzgerald, Ella & Duke Ellington)
5390302 / 10 Nov '97 / Verve

☐ ELLA AND FRIENDS
Frim fram sauce / Dream a little dream of me / Can anyone explain / Would you like to take a walk / Who walks in when I walk out / Into each life some rain must fall / I'm making believe / I'm beginning to see the light / I still feel the same about you / Petootie pie / Baby, it's cold outside / Don't cry, cry baby / Ain't nobody's business but my own / I'll never be free / It's only a paper moon / Cry you out of my heart / For sentimental reason / It's a pity to say goodnight / Fairy tales / I gotta have my baby back
GRP 16632 / Jul '96 / American Decca

☐ ELLA AND LOUIS (Fitzgerald, Ella & Louis Armstrong)
Can't we be friends / Isn't this a lovely day (to be caught in the rain) / Moonlight in Vermont / They can't take that away from me / Under a blanket of blue / Foggy day / Tenderly / Stars fell on Alabama / Nearness of you / April in Paris / Cheek to cheek
8253732 / Sep '85 / Verve

☐ ELLA AND LOUIS AGAIN (Fitzgerald, Ella & Louis Armstrong)
Don't be that way / They all laughed / Autumn in New York / Stompin' at the Savoy / I won't dance / Gee baby ain't I good to you / Let's call the whole thing off / I've got my love to keep me warm / I'm putting all my eggs in one basket / Fine romance / Our love is here to stay / Learnin' the blues
8253742 / Feb '93 / Verve

☐ ELLA AND OSCAR (Fitzgerald, Ella & Oscar Peterson)
Mean to me / How long has this been going on / When your lover has gone / More than you know / There's a lull in my life / Midnight sun / I hear music / Street of dreams / April in Paris / Hear music
CD 2310759 / '94 / Pablo

☐ ELLA AT DUKE'S PLACE (Fitzgerald, Ella & Duke Ellington Orchestra)
5297002 / Jun '96 / Verve

☐ ELLA FITZGERALD
CD 109 / Oct '94 / Timeless Treasures

☐ ELLA FITZGERALD
Lover come back to me / Basin street blues / Starlit hour / Don't be that way / Tenderly / Tisket a tasket / Sing song swing / Let's call the whole thing off / That old black magic / Sugar blues / It's a blue world / Chewin' gum / Flying home / Who ya hunchin' / Goin' and gettin it / I'm putting all my eggs in one basket
22708 / Nov '95 / Music

☐ ELLA FITZGERALD (2CD Set)
R2CD 4018 / 13 Apr '98 / Deja Vu

☐ ELLA FITZGERALD (4CD Set)
You showed me the way / Love is the thing so they say / If you should ever leave / Everyone's wrong but me / All or nothing at all / Big boy blue / Deep in the heart of the south / Just a simple melody / I gotta guy / Holiday in Harlem / Rock it for me / I want to be happy / Dipsy doodle / If dreams come true / Hallelujah / Dedicated to you / Cryin' mood / Bei mir bist du schoen / It's my turn now / 'S wonderful / I was doin' all right / Tisket a tasket / Basin street blues / Starlit hour / We can't go on this way / Stairway to the stars / Lover come back to me / Sing song swing / That old black magic / Little white lies / Sugar blues / Smooth sailing / Chewin' gum / Don't worry 'bout me / Don't be that way / Can't we be friends / Cheek to cheek / Fine romance / Moonlight in Vermont / Foggy day / My wubba dolly / Baby won't you please come home / Imagination / Taking a chance on love / One I love belongs to someone else / I got it bad and that ain't good / My heart belongs to daddy / What can I say after I say I'm sorry / Cabin in the sky / Three little words / Ella / FDR Jones / I must have that man / My melancholy baby / Goodnight my love / My last affair / Wake up and live / Darktown strutters ball
QUAD 009 / Nov '96 / Tring

☐ ELLA FITZGERALD
Lover come back to me / Basin street blues / Starlit hour / We can't go on this way / Stairway to the stars / Is there somebody else / Tisket a tasket / Sing song swing / That old black magic / Sugar blues / It's a blue world / Flying home / Who ya hunchin' / Chewin' gum / Goin' and gettin' it / I wanna be a rug cutter
15705 / Apr '94 / Laserlight

☐ ELLA FITZGERALD
UAE 30072 / Jan '98 / Members Edition

☐ ELLA FITZGERALD & JOE PASS AGAIN (Fitzgerald, Ella & Joe Pass)
I ain't got nothin' but the blues / 'Tis autumn / My old flame / That old feeling / Rain / I didn't know about you / You took advantage of me / I've got the world on a string / All too soon / One I love (belongs to somebody else) / Solitude / Nature boy / Tennessee waltz / One note samba
CD 2310772 / Oct '93 / Pablo

☐ ELLA FITZGERALD AND LOUIS ARMSTRONG SING GERSHWIN (Fitzgerald, Ella & Louis Armstrong)
5396792 / 9 Feb '98 / Verve

☐ ELLA FITZGERALD COLLECTION
Little white lies / Imagination / Taking a chance on love / Three little words / When my sugar walks down the street / Can't help lovin' dat man / Darktown strutters ball / Just a simple melody / I want to be happy / Bei mir bist du schon / Tisket-a-tasket / FDR Jones / I found my yellow basket / This love of mine / Make love to me / Cow cow boogie / Once too often / Into each life rain must fall / I'm making believe / I'm confessin' that I love you / I'm beginning to see the light / It's only a paper moon
PAR 2066 / Aug '96 / Parade

☐ ELLA FITZGERALD COLLECTOR'S EDITION
DVAD 6032 / Apr '95 / Deja Vu

☐ ELLA FITZGERALD GOLD (2CD Set)
D2CD 4018 / Jun '95 / Deja Vu

☐ ELLA FITZGERALD SINGS CHRISTMAS
O holy night / It came upon a midnight clear / Hark the Herald Angels sing / Away in a manger / Joy to the world / First Noel / Silent night / O come all ye faithful (adeste fidelis) / Sleep my little Jesus / Angels we have heard on high / O little town of Bethlehem / We three kings / God rest ye merry gentlemen
CDMFP 6241 / Oct '96 / Music For Pleasure

☐ ELLA FITZGERALD SONGBOOK, THE
Deedle-de-dum / Shake down the stars / Gulf coast blues / Five o'clock whistle / So long / Louisville, K-Y / Taking a chance on love / I'm the loneliest gal in town / Three little words / Hello ma, I done it again / One I love (belongs to somebody else) / Keep cool, fool / My man / I can't believe that you're in love with me / I must have that man / When my sugar walks down the street / I got it bad and that ain't good / Melinda the mousie / Can't help lovin' dat man / Into each life some rain must fall / Paper moon / Flying home / Stone cold dead in de market / Petootie pie / That's rich / One side of me / My heart belongs to daddy / Sugar pie / It's slumbertime along the swanee / Chew chew chew (your bubble gum) / Don't worry 'bout me / If that's what you're thinking, you're wrong / If you ever change your mind / Little white lies / Coochi coochi coo / That was my heart / Betcha nickel / Stairway to the stars / I want the waiter / That's all, brother / Out of nowhere / My last goodbye / Billy (I always dream of Billy) / I'm not complainin' / You're gonna lose your gal / After I say I'm sorry / My wubba dolly / Sugar blues / Starlit hour / I got a guy / Holiday in Harlem / Rock it for me / I want to be happy / Dipsy doodle / Hallelujah / I was doing all right / Tisket-a-tasket / I'm just a jitterbug / This time it's real / You can't be mine (and somebody else's too) / We can't go on this way / Pack up your sins and go to the devil / Everybody step / Ella / Wacky dust / Gotta pebble in my shoe / Strictly from dixie / Woe is me / FDR Jones / I love each move you make / It's foxy / I found my yellow basket / Undecided / T'ain't what you do (it's the way that you do it) / I'll chase the blues away / Love and kisses / Rhythm and romance / My melancholy baby / Crying my heart out for you / When I get low I get high / Sing me a swing song (and let me dance) / Little bit later on / Love, you're just a laugh / Devoting my time to you / Vote for Mr rhythm / Goodnight my love / Didja mean it / Organ grinder's swing / Shine / Darktown strutters ball / Take another guess / Big boy blue / Dedicated to you / Cryin' mood / Love is the thing, so they say / If you ever should leave / Everyone's wrong but me / Somewhere deep in the heart of the south / Just a simple melody
MBSCD 451 / Dec '96 / Castle

☐ ELLA FITZGERALD WITH THE CHICK WEBB BAND
Harlem Congo / I gotta guy / I'll chase the blues away / If you can't sing it, you'll have to swing it (Mr. Paganini) / Squeeze me / Vote for Mr. Rhythm / If dreams come true / Down home rag (sweatman) / Crying my heart out for you / Sing me a swing song / Liza / Tisket-a-tasket / Little bit later on / Strictly jive / Rock it for me / Everybody step / Sweet Sue, just you / Pack up your sins and go to the devil / When I get low I get high / Midnite in Harlem / Love you're just a laugh / Take another guess
PASTCD 9762 / Aug '91 / Flapper

☐ ELLA FITZGERALD WITH THE TOMMY FLANAGAN TRIO (Fitzgerald, Ella & Tommy Flanagan Trio)
I won't dance / That old black magic / Medley / Cabaret / I love you madly / Man and a woman / Alright, OK you win / People / I concentrate on you / Mr. Paganini / I'm beginning to see the light / My heart belongs to Daddy / Just one of those things / I can't give you anything but love baby
17109 / Mar '97 / Laserlight

☐ ELLA IN LONDON
Sweet Georgia Brown / They can't take that away from me / Every time we say goodbye / It don't mean a thing if it ain't got that swing / You've got a friend / Lemon drop / Very thought of you / Happy blues / Man I love
CD 2310711 / Apr '94 / Pablo

☐ ELLA IN ROME 1958 (The Birthday Concert)
St. Louis blues / These foolish things / Just squeeze me / Angel eyes / That old black magic / Just one of those things / I loves you Porgy / It's alright with me / I can't give you anything but love / When you're smiling / Foggy day / Midnight sun / Lady is a tramp / Sophisticated lady / Caravan / Stompin' at the Savoy
8354542 / Mar '93 / Verve

☐ ELLA RETURNS TO BERLIN (1961 Live)
Give me the simple love / Take the 'A' train / I'd like to get to know you on a slow boat to China / Why was I born / Can't help lovin' dat man / You're driving me crazy / Rock it for me / Witchcraft / Anything goes / Cheek to cheek / Misty / Caravan / If you can't sing it, you'll have to swing it (Mr. Paganini) / Mack the knife / Fanfare for Ella / 'Round midnight / Joe Williams' blues / Fanfare for Ella / This can't be love
8377582 / Apr '91 / Verve

☐ ELLA SINGS CHICK SWINGS (Fitzgerald, Ella & Chick Webb)
Oh Johnny / Blue Lou / Diga diga do / I want the waiter with the water / Limehouse blues / T'ain't what you (it's the way that you do it) / Traffic jam / I'm confessin' / Breakin' down / Swing out
EMBCD 3431 / 1 Jun '98 / Ember

☐ ELLA SWINGS BRIGHTLY WITH NELSON (Fitzgerald, Ella & Nelson Riddle Orchestra)
When your lover has gone / Don't be that way / Love me or leave me / I hear music / What am I here for / I'm gonna go fishin' / I won't dance / I only have eyes for you / Gentleman is a dope / Mean to me / Alone together / Pick yourself up / Call me darling / Somebody loves me / Cheerful little earful
5193472 / Mar '93 / Verve

☐ ELLA SWINGS EASY
All or nothing at all / If dreams come true / 'S wonderful / I was doing alright / A-tisket a-tasket / Undecided / T'ain't what you do (it's the way that you do it) / My heart belongs to Daddy / Little white lies / Stairway to the stars / Baby what else can I do /

Sugar blues / Baby won't you please come home / Imagination / Five o'clock whistle / Taking a chance on love / Cabin in the sky / I'm the lonesomest gal in town / Three little words / One I love belongs to somebody else / When my sugar walks down the street / I got it bad and that ain't good / Can't help lovin' dat man / You don't know what love is / He's my guy
CDMOIR 508 / Jan '95 / Memoir

☐ **ELLA SWINGS GENTLY WITH NELSON (Fitzgerald, Ella & Nelson Riddle Orchestra)**
Sweet and slow / Georgia on my mind / I can't get started / Street of dreams / Imagination / Very thought of you / It's a blue world / Darn that dream / She's funny that way / I wished on the moon / It's a pity to say goodnight / My one and only love / Body and soul / Call me darling / All of me
5193482 / Mar '93 / Verve

☐ **ELLA SWINGS LIGHTLY**
Little white lies / You hit the spot / What's your story Morning Glory / Just you, just me / As long as I live / Teardrops from my eyes / Gotta be this or that / Moonlight on the Ganges / My kinda love / Blues in the night / If I were a bell / You're an old smoothie / Little Jazz / You brought a new kind of love to me / Knock me a kiss / 720 in the books / Oh what a night for love / Little jazz / Dreams are made for children / Oh what a night for love
5175352 / Feb '93 / Verve

☐ **ELLA WITH (1936-1937/2CD Set)**
All over nothing at all / If you ever should leave / It's my turn now / Everyone's wrong but me / Bei mir bist du schon / Little bit later on / I want to be happy / Hallelujah / Crying my heart out for you / If you can't sing it, you'll have to swing it (Mr. Paganini) / Holiday in Harlem / Cryin' mood / Devoting my time to you / Rock it for me / At the Darktown strutter's ball / Sing me a swing song / Vote for Mr. Rhythm / Just a simple melody / Swinging on the reservation / Under the spell of the blues / I got the spring fever blues / Rhythm and romance / If dreams come true / Take another guess / Dipsy doodle / I've got a guy / When I get low I get high / Did you mean it / Dedicated to you / Big boy blues / Goodnight my love / Shine
CDAJD 055 / Jul '96 / Living Era

☐ **FABULOUS ELLA FITZGERALD, THE (2CD Set)**
T'ain't what you do (it's the way that you do it) / My heart belongs to Daddy / Don't worry 'bout me / Little white lies / I want the waiter / Imagination / Five o'clock whistle / Taking a chance on love / Three little words / My man (mon homme) / When my sugar walks down the street / I got it bad and that ain't good / Can't help lovin' dat man / Sing me a swing song (and let me dance) / Organ grinder's swing / Darktown strutters ball / If you ever should leave / Just a simple melody / Rock it for me / I want to be happy / If dreams come true / Bei mir bist du schoen / 'S wonderful / Tisket-a-tasket / McPherson is rehearsin' (to swing) / FDR Jones / I found my yellow basket / This love of mine / Somebody nobody loves / You don't know what love is / Make love to me / My heart and I decided / He's my guy / Cow cow boogie / Once too often / Into each life some rain must fall / I'm making believe / I'm confessin' that I love you / I'm beginning to see the light / It's only a paper moon
MUCD 9505 / May '96 / Musketeer

☐ **FINE AND MELLOW**
Fine and mellow / I'm just a lucky so and so / I don't stand a ghost of a chance with you / Rockin' in rhythm / I'm in the mood for love / 'Round midnight / I can't give you anything but love / Man I love / Polka dots and moonbeams
CD 2310829 / May '94 / Pablo

☐ **FIRST LADY OF JAZZ**
Tisket-a-tasket / Darktown strutters ball / I want to be happy / Everybody step / If you can't sing it, you'll have to swing it (Mr. Paganini) / Crying my heart out for you / Little bit later on / If dreams come true / Rock it for me / All over nothing at all / Sing me a swing song / When I get low I get high / I'll chase the blues away / Holiday in Harlem / I gotta guy / Everyone's wrong but me
HADCD 154 / May '94 / Javelin

☐ **FIRST LADY OF SONG (3CD Set)**
Perdido / Lullaby of Birdland / Too young for the blues / Too darn hot / Miss Otis regrets / April in Paris / Undecided / Can't we be friends / Bewitched, bothered and bewildered / Just a sittin' and a rockin' / I'm just a lucky so and so / Airmail special / Tisket-a-tasket / Baby don't you go away mad / Angel eyes / I won't dance / Summertime / Oh lady be good / More than you know / Lush life / Blue skies / These foolish things / Travellin' light / You're an old smoothie / Makin' whoopee / How long has this been going on / Detour ahead / Mack the knife / How high the moon / Black coffee / Let it snow, let it snow, let it snow / Get happy / Heart and soul / If you can't sing it, you'll have to swing it (Mr. Paganini) / Night in Tunisia / I can't get started / Don't be that way / After you've gone / Hernando's hideaway / Fine romance / 'Deed I do / Hear me talkin' to ya / Can't buy me love / Day in, day out / Something to live for / You've changed / Jazz samba / It don't mean a thing if it ain't got that swing
5178982 / Jan '93 / Verve

☐ **FLYING HOME**
Flying home / How high the moon / Basin street blues / Moonlight in vermont / Tenderly / Smooth sailing / Air mail special / Angel eyes / Lullaby of birdland / Foggy day / April in paris / Oh lady be good
CDSGP 084 / Oct '93 / Prestige

☐ **FOR THE LOVE OF ELLA FITZGERALD (2CD Set)**
Tisket-a-tasket / Oh lady be good / Stompin' at the Savoy / How high the moon / Mr. Paganini / Sweet Georgia Brown / Mack the knife / Caravan / Night in Tunisia / Rockin' in rhythm / Honeysuckle rose / I got rhythm / Fine romance / On the sunny side of the street / Party blues / Cotton tail / Misty / Sophisticated lady / Midnight sun / Solitude / How long blues / I loves you Porgy / Summertime / Mood indigo / Laura / Stormy weather / Autumn in New York / These foolish things / I can't get started / CC rider / I love Paris / Blues in the night
8417662 / Jan '90 / Verve

☐ **FOREVER ELLA**
5293872 / Mar '96 / Verve

☐ **FOREVER GOLD**
ST 5008 / Apr '95 / Star Collection

☐ **GEORGE & IRA GERSHWIN SONGBOOK, THE (3CD Set)**
Sam and Delilah / But not for me / My one and only / Let's call the whole thing off / I've got beginner's luck / Oh lady be good / Nice work if you can get it / Things are looking up / Just another rhumba / How long has this been going on / 'S wonderful / Man I love / That certain feeling / By Strauss / Who cares / Someone to watch over me / Real American folk song / They all laughed / Looking for a boy / My cousin from Milwaukee / Somebody from somewhere / Foggy day / Clap yo' hands / For you, for me, for evermore / Stiff upper lip / Strike up the band / Soon / I've got a crush on you / Bidin' my time / Aren't you kind of glad we did / Of thee I sing / Half of it dearie blues / I was doing all right / He loves and she loves / Love is sweeping the country / Treat me rough / Our love is here to stay / Slap that bass / Isn't it a pity / Shall we dance / Love walked in / You've got what gets me / They can't take that away from me / Embraceable you / I can't be bothered now / Boy what love has done to me / Fascinating rhythm / Oh so nice / Lorelei / Let's kiss and make up / I got rhythm / Boy wanted / Funny face
8250242 / Feb '93 / Verve

☐ **GEORGE & IRA GERSHWIN SONGBOOK, THE (Remastered/4CD Set)**
5397592 / 26 May '98 / Verve Master Edition

☐ **GOLDEN YEARS 1936-1945, THE (2CD Set)**
FA 973 / Feb '97 / Fremeaux

☐ **HAROLD ARLEN SONGBOOK VOL.1 (Fitzgerald, Ella & Billy May Orchestra)**
Blues in the night / Let's fall in love / Stormy weather / Sing my heart / Between the devil and the deep blue sea / My shining hour / Hooray for love / This time's the dream's on me / That old black magic / I've got the world on a string / Let's take a walk around the block / Ill wind / Accentuate the positive
8175272 / Oct '88 / Verve

☐ **HAROLD ARLEN SONGBOOK VOL.2 (Fitzgerald, Ella & Billy May Orchestra)**
When the sun comes out / Come rain or come shine / As long as I live / Happiness is a thing called Joe / It's only a paper moon / Man that got away / One for my baby (and one more for the road) / It was written in the stars / Get happy / I gotta right to sing the blues / Out of this world / Ding dong the witch is dead / Over the rainbow
8175282 / Jan '97 / Verve

☐ **HOW HIGH THE MOON**
Basin street blues / Starlit hour / We can't go on this way / Stairway to the stars / Lover come back to me / Sing song swing / That old black magic / Little white lies / Sugar blues / Flying home / Don't worry 'bout me / Chewin' gum / Don't be that way / Can't we be friends / Cheek to cheek / Fine romance / Moonlight in Vermont / Foggy day in London
101662 / May '97 / A-Play Collection

☐ **I WANT TO BE HAPPY**
GO 3801 / 1 Dec '97 / Golden Options

☐ **IMMORTAL VOICE 1918-1996, THE**
BN 013 / Apr '98 / Blue Nite

☐ **INCOMPARABLE ELLA, THE**
Lady is a tramp / Manhattan / Very thought of you / From this moment on / I've got you under my skin / Foggy day / With a song in my heart / Cheek to cheek / I've got a crush on you / Night and day / Every time we say goodbye / It's only a paper moon / I get a kick out of you / I got rhythm / My funny valentine / That old black magic
8356102 / Apr '94 / PolyGram TV

☐ **INTIMATE ELLA, THE**
Black coffee / Angel eyes / I cried for you / I can't give you anything but love baby / Then you've never been blue / I hadn't anyone till you / My melancholy baby / Misty / September song / One for my baby (and one more for the road) / Who's sorry now / I'm getting sentimental over you / Reach for tomorrow
8398382 / Mar '90 / Verve

☐ **IRVING BERLIN SONGBOOK VOL.1**
Let's face the music and dance / You're laughing at me / Let yourself go / You can have him / Russian lullaby / Puttin' on the Ritz / Get thee behind me, Satan / Alexander's ragtime band / Top hat, white tie and tails / How about me / Cheek to cheek / I used to be colour blind / Lazy / How deep is your love / All by myself / Remember
8295342 / Mar '93 / Verve

☐ **IRVING BERLIN SONGBOOK VOL.2**
Reaching for the moon / Slumming on Park Avenue / Song is ended (but the melody lingers on) / I'm putting all my eggs in one basket / Now it can be told / Always / It's a lovely day today / Change partners / No strings / I've got my love to keep me warm / How's chances / Heatwave / You keep coming back like a song / Blue skies / Suppertime
8295352 / Mar '93 / Verve

☐ **IT AIN'T WHAT YOU DO**
CWNCD 2023 / Jul '96 / Javelin

☐ **JAZZ COLLECTOR EDITION (5CD Set) (Fitzgerald, Ella & Louis Armstrong)**
15910 / Jan '92 / Laserlight

☐ **JAZZ MASTERS**
I hear music / I ain't got nothin' but the blues / Everything I've got / I loves you Porgy / Mack the knife / I'm putting all my eggs in one basket / Man that got away / Just you, just me / I've got the world on a string / Tisket-a-tasket / These foolish things / Heatwave / I never had a chance / How high the moon / In the evening / Signing off
5198222 / 5 May '98 / Verve

☐ **JAZZ MASTERS (Fitzgerald, Ella & Louis Armstrong)**
I've got my love to keep me warm / Isn't this a lovely day (to be caught in the rain) / Learnin' the blues / I got plenty o' nuttin' / Moonlight in Vermont / Under a blanket of blue / I'm puttin' all my eggs in one basket / Our love is here to stay / April in Paris / Tenderly / Bess you is my woman now / They all laughed
5218512 / 5 May '98 / Verve

☐ **JAZZ MASTERS (The Jazz Sides)**
5276552 / 5 May '98 / Verve

☐ **JAZZ PORTRAITS**
If you can't sing it, you'll have to swing it (Mr. Paganini) / Love you're just a laugh / Swinging on the reservation / I got the spring fever blues / Rock it for me / Holiday in Harlem / Cryin' mood / Just a simple melody / Love is the thing so they say / You showed me the way / My melancholy baby / All my life / If dreams come true / Take another guess / Pack up your sins and go to the devil / I love each move you make / Sugar pie / I got a guy
CD 14524 / May '94 / Jazz Portraits

☐ **JEROME KERN SONGBOOK, THE**
Let's begin / Fine romance / All the things you are / I'll be hard to handle / You couldn't be cuter / She didn't say yes / I'm old fashioned / Remind me / Way you look tonight / Yesterdays / Can't help lovin' dat man / Why was I born
8256692 / Oct '92 / Verve

☐ **JOHNNY MERCER SONGBOOK, THE**
Too marvellous for words / Early Autumn / Day in, day out / Laura / This time the dream is on me / Skylark / Single-o / Something's gotta give / Travellin' light / Midnight sun / Dream / I remember you / When a woman loves a man
8232472 / Feb '92 / Verve

☐ **JOHNNY MERCER SONGBOOK, THE (Remastered)**
5390572 / Oct '97 / Verve Master Edition

☐ **LADY TIME**
I'm walkin' / All or nothing at all / I never had a chance / I cried for you / What will I tell my heart / Since I fell for you / And the angels sing / I'm confessin' that I love you / Mack the knife / That's my desire / I'm in the mood for love
OJCCD 864 / Nov '95 / Original Jazz Classics

☐ **LEGENDARY ELLA FITZGERALD, THE**
My heart belongs to Daddy / 'S wonderful / Shine / T'ain't what you do (it's the way that you do it) / If you can't sing it, you'll have to swing it (Mr. Paganini) / Tisket-a-tasket / My melancholy baby / Goodnight my love / Dedicated to you / My last affair / Darktown Strutters ball / Rock it for me / All over nothing at all / If you ever should leave / It's my turn now / Saving myself for you / This time it's real / Love is the thing so they say
REMCD 517 / Feb '98 / Reactive

☐ **LET'S GET TOGETHER**
Let's get together (intro) / Rock it for me / My heart belongs to daddy / Love and kisses / Rhythm and romance / Crying my heart out for you / Under the spell of the blues / When I get low I get high / Big boy blue / Vote for mr. rhythm / T'aint what you do (it's the way that cha do it)
17003 / Jul '94 / Laserlight

☐ **LIKE SOMEONE IN LOVE**
There's a lull in my life / More than you know / What will I tell my heart / I never had a chance / Close your eyes / We'll be together again / Then I'll be tired of you / Like someone in love / Midnight sun / I thought about you / You're blase / Night wind / What's new / Hurry home / How long has this been going on / I'll never be the same / Lost in a fog / Everything happens to me / So rare
5115242 / Sep '93 / Verve

☐ **LOVE & KISSES**
Oh johnny, oh johnny, oh / It's a blue world / Chew, chew, chew (your bubble gum) / Sugar blues / Love that boy / Too soon / You'll have to swing it (mr. paganini) / Bop boogie / Heatwave / Hallelujah / Love and kisses
17009 / Aug '93 / Laserlight

☐ **LULLABIES/HOT AND SWEET**
Lullaby of birdman / Rough ridden / Angel eyes / Smooth sailing / Oh lady be good / Later / Ella hums the blues / How high the moon / Basin street blues / Air mail special / Flying home / Thanks for the memory / It might as well be spring / You'll never know / I can't get started / Moaning low / Taking a chance on love / That old black magic called love again / Old devil moon / Lover come back to me / Between the devil and the deep blue sea / You have to swing it
MCLD 19365 / 23 Mar '98 / MCA

☐ **MACK THE KNIFE (The Complete Ella In Berlin - Live 1960)**
That old black magic / Our love is here to stay / Gone with the wind / Misty / Lady is a tramp / Man I love / Love for sale / Just one of those things / Summertime / Too darn hot / Lorelei / Mack the knife / How high the moon
5195642 / Oct '93 / Verve

☐ **MASTERS, THE**
EABCD 047 / 24 Nov '97 / Eagle

☐ **MASTERS, THE (2CD Set)**
EDMCD 005 / 24 Nov '97 / Eagle

☐ **MEMORIAL ALBUM, THE**
UAE 34072 / 27 Apr '98 / Memorial Album

☐ **MY HAPPINESS (Fitzgerald, Ella & Bing Crosby)**
Stay with the happy people / I hadn't anyone till you / A dreamer's holiday / My happiness / Basin street blues / Can anyone explain / Five foot two, eyes of blue / Silver bells / Trying, my favourite song-between the devil and the deep bl / I can dream can't I / Rudolph the red-nosed reindeer / Someone to watch over me / White christmas / Marshmallow world / Moanin' low / That's a plenty / Taking a chance on love / Way back home / Istanbul / Looking for a boy / Chicago style / Everything I have is yours / Undecided / Memphis blues
PARCD 002 / Jan '96 / Parrot

☐ **MY HEART BELONGS TO DADDY**
MU 5040 / Oct '92 / Musketeer

☐ **NEWPORT JAZZ FESTIVAL LIVE AT CARNEGIE HALL, JULY 5, 1973 (2CD Set)**
I've gotta be me / Good morning heartache / Miss Otis regrets / Medley: Don't worry about me/These foolish things / Any old blues / Tisket-a-tasket / Indian summer / Smooth sailin' / You turned the tables on me / Nice work if you can get it / I've got a crush on you / Medley: I can't get started / Young man with the horn / 'Round midnight / Stardust / C Jam blues / Medley: Taking a chance on love / I'm in the mood for love / Lemon drop / Some of these days / People
C 2K66809 / Aug '95 / Sony Jazz

☐ **NICE WORK IF YOU CAN GET IT (Fitzgerald, Ella & Andre Previn)**
Let's call the whole thing off / How long has this been going on / Who cares / I've got a crush on you / Someone to watch over me / Embraceable you / They can't take that away from me / Foggy day / But not for me / Nice work if you can get it
CD 2312140 / '94 / Pablo

☐ **ONE AND ONLY ELLA FITZGERALD, THE**
Tisket-a-tasket / My man (mon homme) / I want to be happy / Got a pebble in my shoe / This love of mine / Once too often / Billy / Rock it for me / Hellelujah / Gulf coast blues / Undecided / I'm confessin' that I love you / I got it bad and that ain't good / Strictly from Dixie / MacPherson is rehearsin' / Wake up and live / Bei mir bist du shon / Darktown strutters ball / Ella / Taking a chance on love
ECD 3302 / Feb '97 / K-Tel

☐ **ONE SIDE OF ME**
When my sugar walks down the street / My man / Someone to watch over me / If dreams come true / I let a tear fall in the river / Dipsy doodle / Don't worry 'bout me / I was doing all right / 'S wonderful / All over nothing at all / Starlit hour / Looking for a boy / Time alone will tell / Rhythm and romance / Sugar blues
AMSC 565 / Aug '96 / Avid

☐ **PABLO YEARS, THE (20CD Set)**
PACD 0202 / Nov '96 / Pablo

☐ **PERFECT MATCH, A (Fitzgerald, Ella & Count Basie)**
Please don't talk about me when I'm gone / Sweet Georgia Brown / Some other Spring / Make me rainbows / After you've gone / 'Round midnight / Fine and mellow / You've changed / Honeysuckle rose / St. Louis blues / Basella
CD 2312110 / Apr '94 / Pablo

☐ **PLATINUM COLLECTION, THE (2CD Set)**
Don't worry about me / Imagination / Taking a chance on me / When my sugar walks down the street / Can't help lovin' dat man / Sing me a swing song / Darktown strutters ball / If you ever should leave / I want to be happy / Bei mir bist du schon / It's wonderful / A-tisket a-tasket / McPherson is rehearsin' / FDR Jones / This love of mine / Somebody know body loves / You don't know what love is / Make love to me / My heart and I decided / He's my guy / Cow cow boogie / Once too often / Into each life some rain must fall / I'm making believe / I'm confessin' that I love you / It's only a paper moon / You'll have to swing it / Dedicated to you / Little white lies / Big boy blues / If you ever should leave me / All or nothing at all / I got a guy / I found my yellow basket / Wacky dust / I didn't mean a word I said / I'm just a lucky so and so / Frim fram sauce / You won't be satisfied (till you break my heart) / My heart belongs to daddy
PC 605 / 10 Nov '97 / Platinum Collection

☐ **PORTRAIT**
This love of mine / It's only a paper moon / Into each life some rain must fall / I got a guy (sunshine) / Swing me a swing song (and let me dance) / Shine / Somebody nobody knows / Make love to me / That's the way it is / When I get low I get high / Farktown strutters ball / Cryin' mood / Time alone will tell / Her tears flowed like wine / Once too often / If you should ever leave / Little bit later on / Just a simple melody
SUMCD 4164 / 26 Jan '98 / Summit

☐ **PORTRAIT OF ELLA FITZGERALD, A**
GALE 406 / May '97 / Gallerie

☐ **RHYTHM AND ROMANCE**
Rhythm and romance / Take another guess, oh yes / Dedicated to you / Tisket-a-tasket / Ella / Baby won't you please come home / I'm the lonesomest gal in town / I got it bad and that ain't good / My heart and I decided / Cow cow boogie / Time alone will tell / I'm confessin' / I'm beginning to see the light / That's the way it is / It's only a paper moon / Benny's coming home on Saturday / Flying home / Stone cold dead in the market / Petootie pie / You won't be satisfied / Frim fram sauce / I'm just a lucky so-and-so / I didn't mean a word I said / (I love you) for sentimental reasons / It's a pity to say goodnight
CDAJA 5212 / Feb '97 / Living Era

☐ RODGERS & HART SONGBOOK, THE (Remastered/2CD Set)
5372582 / Oct '97 / Verve Master Edition

☐ SING ME A SWING SONG (Fitzgerald, Ella & Chick Webb Orchestra)
Sing me a swing song (and let me dance) / Little bit later on / Devoting my time / You'll have to swing it (mr. paganini) / Vote for mister rhythm / Swinging on the reservation / I got the spring fever blues / Shine / Darktown strutters' ball / Cryin' mood / All over nothing at all / If you ever should leave / Everyone's wrong but me / Rock it for me / Holiday in harlem / Just a simple melody / I got a guy / I want to be happy / Hallelujah / If dreams come true
JHR 73512 / '91 / Jazz Hour

☐ SING SONG SWING
17008 / Jul '93 / Laserlight

☐ SONGBOOKS, THE (The Silver Collection)
Oh lady be good / Nice work if you can get it / Fascinating rhythm / All the things you are / Yesterdays / Can't help lovin' dat man / Come rain or come shine / It's only a paper moon / Over the rainbow / Laura / Skylark / This time the dream is on me / Puttin' on the Ritz / Alexander's ragtime band / Cheek to cheek / My funny Valentine / Lady is a tramp / Have you met Miss Jones / Manhattan
8234452 / Nov '84 / Verve

☐ SPEAK LOVE
Speak love / Come love / There's no you / I may be wrong, but I think you're wonderful / At last / Thrill is gone / Gone with the wind / Blue and sentimental / Girl talk / Georgia on my mind
CD 2310888 / Apr '94 / Pablo

☐ STAIRWAY TO THE STARS
MACCD 163 / Aug '96 / Autograph

☐ STOCKHOLM 1957
TAX 37032 / Aug '94 / Tax

☐ STOCKHOLM CONCERT 1966 (Fitzgerald, Ella & Duke Ellington)
Imagine my frustration / Duke's place / Satin doll / Something to live for / Wives and lovers / So danco samba / Let's do it / Lover man / Cotton tail
CD 2308242 / May '94 / Pablo

☐ SUNSHINE OF YOUR LOVE
Hey Jude / Sunshine of your love / This girl's in love with you / Watch what happens / Alright, OK you win / Give me the simple life / Useless landscape / Old devil moon / Don't cha go 'way mad / House is not a home / Trouble is a man / I love you madly
5331022 / Nov '96 / MPS Jazz

☐ SWING IT
'S wonderful / Do you mean it / One I love (belongs to somebody else) / Shake down the stars / Goodnight my love / Out of nowhere / Jim / Baby won't you please come home / (What can I say) after I say I'm sorry / Melancholy baby / When my baby walks down the street / Imagination / My last affair / All my life / Oh yes, take another guess / You don't know what love is / Sing, song, swing / I was doin' alright / If you can't sing it, you'll have to swing it (Mr. Paganini) / He's my guy
306512 / Jun '97 / Hallmark

☐ SWINGS
You got me singin' the blues / Angel eyes / Lullaby of birdland / Tenderly / Do nothin' 'til you hear from me / April in Paris / I can't give you anything but love / Love for sale / Papa loves mambo / Lover come back to me / Just one of those things / Airmail special / I'm beginning to see the light / Sophisticated lady / Old mother hubbard / How high the moon
BSTCD 9111 / Apr '94 / Best Compact Discs

☐ SWINGSATION (Fitzgerald, Ella & Chick Webb)
Sing me a swing song (and let me dance) / Blue minor / When I get low I get high / Little bit later on / Don't be that way / Vote for Mr. Rhythm / Organ grinder's swing / Blue Lou / Oh yes take another guess / I want to be happy / Clap hands here comes Charlie / A-tisket A-tasket / I'm just a jitterbug / Harlem congo / Wacky dust / Undecided / Tain't what you do (it's the way that cha do it) / Liza (all the clouds'll roll away)
GRP 99212 / 24 Aug '98 / GRP

☐ TAKE LOVE EASY (Fitzgerald, Ella & Joe Pass)
Take love easy / Once I loved / Don't be that way / You're blase / Lush life / Foggy day / Gee baby ain't I good to you / You go to my head / I want to talk about you
CD 2310702 / Jan '92 / Pablo

☐ THESE ARE THE BLUES
Jailhouse blues / In the evening / CC rider / You don't know my mind / Trouble in mind / How long how long blues / Cherry red / Down hearted blues / St. Louis blues / Hear me talkin' to ya
8295362 / Nov '93 / Verve

☐ TISKET A-TASKET
GO 3802 / 1 Dec '97 / Golden Options

☐ TISKET-A-TASKET
You showed me the way / Love is the thing, so they say / If you ever should leave / Everyone's wrong but me / All or nothing at all / Big boy blue / Deep in the heart of the South / Just a simple melody / I gotta guy / Holiday in Harlem / Rock it for me / I want to be happy / Dipsy doodle / If dreams come true / Hallelujah / Dedicated to you / Cryin' mood / Bei mir bist du schone / It's my turn now / 'S wonderful / I was doing all right / Tisket-a-tasket
QED 090 / Nov '96 / Tring

☐ ULTIMATE DIVAS
5390542 / 10 Nov '97 / Verve

☐ UNFORGETTABLE SOUND OF ELLA FITZGERALD, THE (40 Swing Classics From The First Lady Of Jazz/2CD Set)
If you can't sing it, you'll have to swing it (Mr. Paganini) / Somebody nobody loves / Make love to me / Benny's coming home on Saturday / If it weren't for you / 'S wonderful / When my sugar walks down the street / Jim / Rock it for me / Baby, what else can I do / Imagination / Cow cow boogie: *Fitzgerald, Ella & The Ink Spots* / You won't be satisfied (until you break my heart): *Fitzgerald, Ella & Louis Armstrong* / It's only a paper moon / Goodnight, my love: *Fitzgerald, Ella & Benny Goodman Orchestra* / All my life / Dedicated to you: *Fitzgerald, Ella & The Mills Brothers* / And her tears flowed like wine / Mama, come home / Petootie pie: *Fitzgerald, Ella & Louis Jordan* / Undecided / This love of mine / Sugar blues / Out of nowhere / Sing song swing / Moonray / Shake down the stars / I was doing all right / Baby, won't you please come home / You don't know what love is / He's my guy / Tisket-a-tasket / Oh yes, take another guess / I'm beginning to see the light: *Fitzgerald, Ella & The Ink Spots* / My melancholy baby / It's a pity to say goodnight / I'm just a lucky so and so / Into each life some rain must fall / Stone cold dead in the market: *Fitzgerald, Ella & Louis Jordan* / Frim fram sauce: *Fitzgerald, Ella & Louis Armstrong*
330352 / Mar '97 / Hallmark

☐ VERY BEST OF ELLA FITZGERALD, THE
PLSCD 120 / Apr '96 / Pulse

☐ WITH TOMMY FLANAGAN
Too close for comfort / I ain't got nothin' but the blues / My man / Come rain or come shine / Day by day / Ordinary fool / One note samba / I let a song go out of my heart / Billie's bounce / You are the sunshine of my life
OJCCD 376 / Feb '92 / Original Jazz Classics

☐ YOUNG ELLA (4CD Set)
CDDIG 10 / Aug '96 / Charly

Fitzi Niceness

☐ IMPRESSIONS OF LOVE
0133CD / Jun '97 / Fitzinicen

Fiuczynski, David

☐ LUNAR CRUSH
Vog / Pacifica / Gloria ascending / Pineapple / Quest / Freelance Brown / Slow blues for Fuzy's Mama / Lillies that fester / 122 St. Marks / Fima's sunrise
R 279498 / Jun '94 / Gramavision

Five

☐ FIVE
Slam dunk da funk / When the lights go out / Everybody get up / Got the feelin' / It's the things you do / Human / Until the time is through / Satisfied / Partyline 555-on-the-line / That's what you told me / It's all over / Don't you want it / Shake / Cold sweat / Straight up funk / My song / Switch
74321589762 / 22 Jun '98 / RCA

Five Americans

☐ I SEE THE LIGHT
I see the light / Losing game / Goodbye / I know they lie / Twist and shout / She's a-my-own / Train / It's a crying shame / I'm so glad / Don't blame me / Outcast / What'd I say / Train (unissued version) / Good times (unissued version)
CDSC 6018 / Apr '94 / Sundazed

Five Blind Boys Of Alabama

☐ DEEP RIVER (Five Blind Boys Of Alabama & Clarence Fountain)
Deep river (part one) / Don't play with God / Reminiscing / God said it / Look where he brought me from / Down on bended knees / I believe in you / I'm getting better all the time / Brother Moses / Every time I feel the spirit / Just a closer walk with thee / I've got the love of Jesus / Deep river (part two)
7559614412 / Nov '92 / Nonesuch

☐ FIVE BLIND BOYS OF ALABAMA 1948-1951
FLYCD 946 / Jul '96 / Flyright

☐ HOLDIN' ON
161311 / Sep '97 / Am

☐ I BROUGHT HIM WITH ME
Rain / He's got what I want / Do Lord / Better all the time / Listen to the lambs / If I had a hammer / No dope / Hush / King Jesus / Walking Jerusalem / Lord will make a way / Praying time / Amazing grace / Looking back
70010870032 / Nov '95 / Private Music

☐ OH LORD STAND BY ME/ MARCHING UP TO ZION
Oh Lord / Stand by me / You got to move / Lord have mercy / Living for Jesus / Take my hand, precious Lord / I'll fly away / This may be the last time / Alone and motherless / Since I met Jesus / Our father's praying ground / Broken hearts of mine / Here am I / Marching up to Zion / Servant's prayer amen / Count me in / When I lost my mother / There is a fountain / I've been born again / He'll be there / Think about me / Does Jesus care / Fix it Jesus / Goodbye mother / I've got a home
CDCHD 341 / Nov '93 / Ace

☐ SERMON, THE
Sermon / All the way / I'll fly away / Without the help of Jesus / I'm on the battlefield / Heavenly light / Sit down servant / Standing by the bedside / When I need him most / Precious Lord / This may be the last time / Our father's praying ground / Marching up to Zion / God's promise / You got to move / Old time religion / Does Jesus care / Swingin' on the golden gate / I cried / Hallelujah / Golden bells / Heaven on my mind / I'm going through / Fix it Jesus / I've been born again / When death comes / In the garden
CDCHD 479 / Jul '93 / Ace

☐ SWING LOW SWEET CHARIOT
JEWEL 3127 / Apr '96 / Jewel

Five Blind Boys Of Mississippi

☐ JESUS IS A ROCK
Let's have a church / I'm willing to run / Leave you in the hands of the Lord / Where there's a will / You don't know / I'm a soldier / Jesus loves me / I'm a-rolling / My robe will fit me / All over me / Somebody's mother / No need to cry / I never heard a man / Oh why / Don't forget the bridge / Waiting at the river / Jesus is a rock in a weary land / I've been weeping for a mighty long time / One talk with Jesus / I haven't been home in a mighty long time
CPCD 8086 / Apr '95 / Charly

☐ MEET THE BLIND BOYS
JEWEL 3126 / Apr '96 / Jewel

Five Day Train

☐ ROUGH MARMALADE
HBG 123/1 / Apr '93 / Background

Five Eight

☐ ANGRIEST MAN, THE
SKYCD 3101 / Sep '94 / Sky

☐ WEIRDO
SKYCD 3102 / May '94 / Sky

Five Hand Reel

☐ COLLECTION, THE
Bratach bana / Pinch of snuff / Man's not a man / Haughs o' Cromdale / Fond kiss / P is for Paddy / Cruel brother / Carrickfergus / My love is like a red red rose / Bonny Earl O' Mornay / Trooper and the maid / Beef can close / Knight and the shepherd's daughter / When a man's in love / Maid of Listowell / Medley
74321451932 / Feb '97 / Camden

Five Horse Johnson

☐ DOUBLE DOWN
SMALL 006 / Nov '97 / Small Stone

Five HT

☐ NEUROTRANSMITTER
HYPOXIA 003CD / Jun '96 / Hypoxia

Five Keys

☐ DREAM ON
I burned your letter / How can I forget you / Gonna be too late / I took your love for a toy / Dancing senorita / Dream on / Your teeth and your tongue / I've always been a dreamer / You broke the only heart / When Paw was courtin' Maw / Rosetta / Ziggus / I can't escape from you / Will you / Wrapped in a dream / Do something for me / Valley of love / No say's my heart / That's what you're doing to me / Now I know I love you / Stop your crying / Girl you better stop it / I'll never stop loving you / Bimbo
CDCHARLY 26 / Mar '91 / Charly

Five Red Caps

☐ FIVE RED CAPS 1943-1945
Boogie woogie on a Saturday night / It's got a hole in it / Mary had a little jam / Don't fool with me / Mama put your britches on / Just for you / Somebody's lyin' / I learned a lesson I'll never forget / Sugar lips / Lennox Avenue jump / Monkey and the baboon
FLYCD 60 / May '96 / Flyright

Five Star

☐ FIVE STAR
Slightest touch / System addict / Can't wait another minute / Another weekend / With every heartbeat / Stay out of my life / Rain or shine / Find the time / RSVP / Love take over / If I say yes / Let me be the one / Strong as steel / There's a brand new world / Rock my world / All fall down
74321183252 / Feb '94 / Ariola Express

☐ GREATEST HITS
Can't wait another minute / Whenever you're ready / Rain or shine / Find the time / System addict / Stay out of my life / Let me be the one / Rock my world / With every heartbeat / Slightest touch / All fall down / If I say yes / Somewhere somebody / RSVP / Strong as steel / Love take over / Another weekend / Something about my baby
74321578222 / 27 Apr '98 / Camden

Five-A-Slide

☐ STRIKE UP THE BAND
BLCD 760509 / Oct '93 / Black Lion

Fivepenny Piece

☐ VERY BEST OF FIVEPENNY PIECE, THE
Watercolour morning / Ee by gum / Pete was a lonely mongrel dog who lived in central Wigan / Down our street / King Cotton / Mi Grandfather's day / Stories from the wishing well / Gradely prayer / Gotta get away / Tell you owt / Mountain climber / Spanish holiday / I don't know if I wanna go home / Tuppence change / Fred Fannakapan / Stalybridge station / Homemade brew / Winter sun / Molly Kershaw / Stalybridge market / Watering can / Where there's muck there's brass / Sail away tin soldier / Big Jim
4943542 / 13 Apr '98 / EMI Gold

Fix

☐ COLD DAYS
LF 078 / Mar '94 / Lost & Found

Fixtures

☐ DEVIL'S PLAYGROUND
VIRUS 187CD / Dec '96 / Alternative Tentacles

Fixx

☐ ELEMENTAL
86244 / 6 Apr '98 / CMC

FJF

☐ BLOW HORN
OD 12019 / Feb '98 / Okka Disk

Flack, Roberta

☐ BEST OF ROBERTA FLACK - SOFTLY WITH THESE SONGS
First time ever I saw your face / Will you still love me tomorrow / Where is the love / Killing me softly / Feel like makin' love / Closer I get to you / More than everything / Only heaven can wait (for love) / Back together again / Making love / Tonight I celebrate my love / Oasis / And so it goes / You know what it's like / Set the night to music / My foolish heart / Uh-uh ooh-ooh look out (here it comes)
7567824982 / Feb '94 / Atlantic

☐ BORN TO LOVE (Flack, Roberta & Peabo Bryson)
Tonight I celebrate my love / Blame it on me / Heaven above me / Born to love / Maybe / I just came here to dance / Comin' alive / You're lookin' like love to me / Can we find love again
MUSCD 508 / Nov '94 / MCI Original Masters

☐ CHAPTER TWO
Reverend Lee / Do what you gotta do / Just like a woman / Let it be me / Gone away / Until it's time for you to go / Impossible dream / Business goes on as usual
7567813732 / Jan '96 / Atlantic

☐ FEEL LIKE MAKIN' LOVE
Feeling that glow / I wanted it too / I can see the sun in late December / Some gospel according to Mathew / Feel like makin' love / Mr. Magic / Early every midnight / Old heart break top ten / She's not blind
7567803332 / Feb '91 / Atlantic

☐ LIVE AND MORE (Flack, Roberta & Peabo Bryson)
Killing me softly with his song / Feel like makin' love / Only heaven can wait (for love) / Back together again / Feel the fire / Love is a waiting game / More than everything / Love in every season / When will I learn / I believe in you / Reachin' for the sky / If only for one night / Don't make me wait too long / God don't like ugly / You are my heaven / Make the world stand still
7567814112 / Dec '96 / Atlantic

☐ QUIET FIRE
Go up Moses / Bridge over troubled water / Sunday and Sister Jones / See you then / Will you still love me tomorrow / To love somebody / Let them talk / Sweet bitter love
7567813782 / Feb '91 / Atlantic

☐ ROBERTA
Angel eyes / Cottage for sale / Sweet georgia brown / It might be you / Thrill is gone / You'll never know ('til you let go) / Prelude to a kiss / I don't care who knows (baby I'm yours) / Looking for another pure love / In a sentimental mood / Let's stay together / My romance / Isn't it romantic / Tenderly
7567825972 / Nov '94 / Atlantic

Flag Of Convenience

☐ BEST OF STEVE DIGGLE & FLAG OF CONVENIENCE (The Secret Public Years 1981-1989) (Diggle, Steve & Flag Of Convenience)
Fifty Years comparative wealth / Shut out the light / Here comes the fire brigade / Life on the telephone / Picking up on audio sound / Other mans sin / Men from the city / Who is innocent / Drift away / Change / Longest life / Arrow has come / Keep on pushing (live) / Pictures in my mind / Last train to safety / Exiles / Can't stop the world / Shot down with a gun / Tragedy in Market Street / Tomorrows sunset / Life with the lions
CDMGRAM 74 / Feb '94 / Anagram

Flag Of Democracy

☐ EVERYTHING SUCKS
BC 1708CD / Nov '96 / Blitzcore

Flake

☐ REFLECTIONS
D 19012 / Oct '97 / Festival

Flamborough Head

☐ UNSPOKEN WHISPER
Schoolyard fantasy / Wolves at war / Childscream / Unspoken whisper / Legend of the old man's tree / Xymphonia / Heroes
CYCL 063 / 18 May '98 / Cyclops

Flame, Frankie

☐ INFERNO
PCR 4302 / Sep '97 / Pub City Royal

Flamin' Groovies

☐ FLAMINGO
Gonna rock tonite / Comin' after me / Headin' for the Texas border / Sweet roll on down / Keep a knockin' / Second cousin / Childhood's end / Jailbait / She's falling apart / Roadhouse / Walking the dog / Something else / Hello / Josephine / Louie Louie / Rockin' pneumonia and the boogie woogie flu / Going out theme II
REP 4020 / Aug '91 / Repertoire

☐ GREASE (The Complete Skydog Singles 1973-1981)
FREUDCD 072 / 8 Jun '98 / Jungle

☐ GROOVE IN
890011 / May '94 / New Rose

☐ GROOVIES GREATEST, THE
7599259482 / Jan '96 / Sire

☐ IN PERSON
CED 255 / Jul '97 / Norton

☐ LIVE 1968/1970
842070 / May '94 / EVA

☐ LIVE AT THE FESTIVAL OF THE SUN BARCELONA
AIM 1051CD / Apr '95 / Aim

☐ OLDIES BUT GROOVIES (The Best Of The Flamin' Groovies)
Shake some action / Married woman / Slow death / Tallahassee lassie / Teenage head / Way over my head / Searching / She's got a hold on me / You tore me down / Money / I'm only what you want me to be / I can't hide
AIM 2001CD / May '97 / Aim

☐ ONE NIGHT STAND
Kicks / Bittersweet / I can't hide / Money / Call me lightning / Shake some action / Slow death / Teenage head / Slow down / Tallahasse lassie
AIM 1008CD / Oct '93 / Aim

☐ SHAKE SOME ACTION
Shake some action / Sometimes / Yes it's true / St. Louis blues / You tore me down / Please please girl / Let the boy rock 'n' roll / Don't you lie to me / She said yeah / I'll cry alone / Misery / I say her / Teenage confidential / I can't hide
AIM 1017CD / Oct '93 / Aim

☐ SNEAKERS/ROCKFIELD SESSIONS
COLLECT 12 / Oct '93 / Aim

☐ STEP UP
AIM 1030CD / Oct '93 / Aim

☐ SUPERSNEAKER
SC 6077 / Nov '96 / Sundazed

☐ TEENAGE HEAD LP
Teenage head / Evil hearted Ada / Dr. Boogie / Whiskey woman / High flyin' baby / City lights / Have you seen my baby / Yesterday's numbers / Rumble / Shakin' all over / That'll be the day / Around and around / Going out theme
REP 4042 / Aug '91 / Repertoire

☐ YESTERDAY'S NUMBERS
Teenage head / Doctor Boogie / Yesterday's numbers / Headin' for the Texas border / High flyin' baby / Comin' after you / City lights / Have you seen my baby / 32-20 / Whiskey woman / Gonna rock tonite / She's falling apart / Evil hearted Ada / Jailbait / Sweet roll me on down / Second cousin / Childhood's end / Keep a knockin' / Walking the dog / Around and around / Rockin' pneumonia and the boogie woogie flu / Going out theme
74321558432 / 26 Jan '98 / Camden

Flaming Lips

☐ CLOUDS TASTE METALLIC
Abandoned hospital ship / Placebo headwound / Brainville / When you smile / Guy who got a headache and accidentally saves / Bad days (aurally excited version) / Evil will prevail / Christmas at the zoo / Lightning strikes the postman / They punchured my yolk / Kim's watermelon gun / This here giraffe / Psychiatric explorations of the fetus with needles
9362459112 / Sep '95 / Warner Bros.

☐ HERE IT IS
7721732 / 1 May '98 / Restless

☐ IN A PRIEST DRIVEN AMBULANCE
Shine on sweet Jesus-Jesus song no.5 / Unconsciously screamin' / Rainin' babies / Take metamars / Five stop mother superior rain / Stand in line / God walks among us now-Jesus song no.7 / Mountain side / What a wonderful world / Lucifer rising / Let me be it
7723592 / 1 May '98 / Restless

☐ TELEPATHIC SURGERY
Drug machine / Michael time to wake up / Miracle on 42nd Street / UFO story / Shaved gorilla / Begs and achin' / Right now / Hare Krishna stomp wagon / Chrome plated suicide / Redneck school of technology / Spontaneous combustion of John / Last drop of morning dew
7723502 / 1 May '98 / Restless

☐ TRANSMISSIONS FROM THE SATELLITE HEART
Turn it on / Pilot can at the queer of God / Oh my pregnant head (Labia in the sunlight) / She don't use jelly / Chewin' the apple of your eye / Superhumans / Be my head / Moth in the incubator / #@#@@#@ (Plastic Jesus) / When yer twenty two / Slow nerve action
9362453342 / Jun '93 / Warner Bros.

Flaming Stars

☐ BRING ME THE REST OF ALFREDO GARCIA
ASKCD 067 / Mar '97 / Vinyl Japan

☐ SELL YOUR SOUL TO THE FLAMING STARS
Sweet smell of success / Blood money / London after midnight / Street that never closes / I remembered to forget to remember / New hope for the dead / Find yourself another drunk / Don't need the sunshine / What you want / Just too bad / Don't mean a thing if you haven't got the king / Better than that / Day the earth caught fire
ASKCD 076 / 27 Oct '97 / Vinyl Japan

☐ SONGS FROM THE BAR ROOM FLOOR
Face on the bar room floor / Forget my name / You can't lie / Who's out there / Burnt out wreck of a man / Bring me the rest of Afredo Garcia / Kiss tomorrow goodbye / Ballad of the walking wounded / Downhill without brakes / Theme from Dog Instruction / Back of my mind / Down to you / Oncoming train / Tubs twist / Like trash / 3 A.M. On the bar room floor
ASKCD 062 / Jun '96 / Vinyl Japan

Flamingos

☐ COMPLETE CHESS MASTERS, THE
MCD 09378 / Jul '97 / Chess/MCA

☐ FLAMINGO SERENADE/FLAMINGO FAVOURITES
Love walked in / Music maestro please / Begin the beguine / Breeze and I / Time was / Goodnight sweetheart / I only have eyes for you / I'm in the mood for love / As time goes by / Where or when / Yours / But not for me / Besame mucho / Dream girl / Crazy crazy crazy / That's why I love you / Heavenly angel / Mio amore / Maria Elena / Sweet and lovely / Tell me how long / My foolish heart / You belong to my heart / Bridge of tears
WESM 532 / Feb '98 / Westside

☐ I ONLY HAVE EYES FOR YOU
Lovers never say goodbye / That love is you / Jump children / I shed a tear at your wedding / Time was / Goodnight sweetheart / Love walked in / I only have eyes for you / At the prom / I was such a fool / Nobody loves me like you / Besame mucho / At night / Mio amore / Kokomo / That's why I love you / I'll be home / Your other love / A kiss from your lips / My memories of you
NEMCD 609 / Apr '91 / Sequel

☐ REQUESTFULLY YOURS/THE SOUND OF THE FLAMINGOS
In the still of the night / Beside you / Never in this world / When I fall in love / You me and the sea / Everybody's got a home / Nobody loves me like you / Tenderly / I was such a fool (to fall in love with you) / Everytime I think of you / At night / You'll never walk alone / Too soon to know / Flame of love / Sinner / I'm coming home / (When you're young and) only seventeen / Ol' man river / You're mine / My lovely one / I know better / Moonlight in Vermont / Without his love / Danny boy
WESM 537 / Feb '98 / Westside

Flanagan & Allen

☐ ARCHES AND UMBRELLAS
Music, maestro please / Umbrella song / Oi / Milking time in Switzerland / Nice people / New MP / Run rabbit run / (We're gonna hang out the) washing on the Siegfried Line / Sending out an SOS for you / Down and out blues / Sport of kings / Home town / If a grey-haired lady says How's yer father / Free / Digging holes / FDR Jones / Dreaming / How do you do Mr. Right / Crazy Gang at sea / Underneath the arches / Flanagan and Allen memories
PASTCD 9720 / '90 / Flapper

☐ LET'S BE BUDDIES
Are you having any fun / Round the back of the arches / Let's be buddies / Smiths and the Jones / Don't ever walk in the shadows / Why don't you fall in love with me / Down forget-me-not lane / Corn silk / We'll smile again / What more can I say / Yesterday's dreams / Down every street / I don't want to walk without you / If a grey-haired lady says How's yer father / Umbrella man / Can't we meet again / Underneath the arches / Rose o'day / I'm nobody's baby / In a little rocky valley / On the outside looking in / Miss you / Washing on siegfried line / Million years
RAJCD 832 / 6 Oct '97 / Empress

☐ UNDERNEATH THE ARCHES
Run rabbit run / Miss you / Smiths and the Jones / In a little rocky valley / Two very ordinary people / Down every street / Flying through the rain / FDR Jones / On the outside looking in / Roll on tomorrow / There's a boy coming home on leave / Shine on harvest moon / We'll smile again / Underneath the arches
CDDL 1209 / Jun '91 / Music For Pleasure

☐ WE'LL SMILE AGAIN
Underneath the arches / Dreaming / Wanderer / Can't we meet again / Million tears / Home town / Music, maestro, please / Umbrella man / Nice people / Run, rabbit, run / We're gonna hang out the washing on the Siegfried / FDR Jones / If a grey haired lady says "How's your Father" / On the outside looking in / Yesterday's dream / Down forget me not lane / Rose O'Day (The filla-ga-dusha-song) / What more can I say / I don't want to walk without you / Miss you / We'll smile again / Round the back of the arches / Flying through the rain / Shine on, harvest moon / Two very ordinary people
CDAJA 5194 / May '96 / Living Era

Flanagan Brothers

☐ TUNES WE LIKE TO PLAY
VV 007 / Aug '96 / Viva Voce

Flanagan, Kevin

☐ ZANZIBAR (Flanagan, Kevin & Chris Ingham Quartet)
Don't loook at me like that / Po-town / Walk between raindrops / Born to be blue / Pent-up house / Waiting for dusko / It's your dance / Gloryhound / Sleepin' bee / Zanzibar
GBCD 2 / 29 Sep '97 / Gray Brothers

Flanagan, Ralph

☐ DANCE AGAIN
DAWE 75 / Jul '96 / Magic

☐ HOT TODDY
AERO 1032 / Jul '96 / Aerospace

☐ LET'S DANCE WITH RALPH FLANAGAN (Flanagan, Ralph Orchestra)
DAWE 74 / Jan '96 / Magic

Flanagan, Tommy

☐ 3 FOR ALL (Flanagan, Tommy & Red Mitchell/Phil Woods)
ENJACD 308167 / Jan '95 / Enja

☐ CATS, THE (Flanagan, Tommy & John Coltrane/Kenny Burrell)
Minor mishap / How long has this been going on / Eclypso / Solacium / Tommy's time
OJCCD 79 / Jun '86 / Original Jazz Classics

☐ JAZZ POET
Raincheck / Lament / Willow weep for me / Caravan / That tired routine called love / Glad to be happy / St. Louis blues / Mean streets
CDSJP 301 / Nov '89 / Timeless Jazz

☐ LADY BE GOOD...FOR ELLA
Oh lady be good / Love you madly / Isn't it a pity / How high the moon / Smooth sailing / Alone too long / Angel eyes / Cherokee / Rouge ridin' / Pete Kelly's blues / Oh lady be good
5216172 / Jun '94 / Groovin' High

☐ LET'S
Let's / Mean what you say / To you / Bird song / Scratch / Thadrack / Child is born / Three in one / Quietude / Zec / Elusive
ENJ 80402 / Nov '93 / Enja

☐ MAGNIFICENT TOMMY FLANAGAN, THE
PCD 7059 / Oct '91 / Progressive

☐ MASTER TRIO
PRCDSP 204 / May '94 / Prestige

☐ MONTREUX 1977 (Flanagan, Tommy Trio)
Barbados / Woody 'n' you / Blue bossa / Heat wave
OJCCD 372 / Nov '95 / Original Jazz Classics

☐ THELONICA
ENJA 40522 / 17 Nov '97 / Enja

☐ YOU'RE ME (Flanagan, Tommy & Red Mitchell)
You're me / Darn that dream / What am I here for / When I have you / All the things you are / Milestones / Whisper not / There'll never be another you
PHONTCD 7528 / Apr '94 / Phontastic

Flanders & Swann

☐ AT THE DROP OF A HAT
Transport of delight / Song of reproduction / Gnu song / Design for living / Je suis les tenebreux / Songs for our time / Song of the weather / Reluctant cannibal / Greensleeves / Misalliance / Kokoraki / Madeira m'dear / Too many cookers / Vanessa / Tried by the centre court / Youth of the heart / Hippopotamus song / Happy song / Satellite moon / Philogical waltz
CZ 515 / Sep '92 / EMI

☐ AT THE DROP OF ANOTHER HAT
Gas man cometh / Sounding brass / Los Olivados / In the desert / Ill wind / First and second law / All gall / Horoscope / Friendly duet / Bedstead men / By air / Slow train / Song of patriotic prejudice / Built up area / In the bath / Sea fever / Hippo encore
CZ 517 / Sep '92 / EMI

☐ COMPLETE FLANDERS AND SWANN
Transport of delight / Song of reproduction / Gnu song / Design for living / Je suis les tenebreux / Songs for our time / Song of the weather / Reluctant cannibal / Greensleeves / Misalliance / Kokoraki / Madeira m'dear / Too many cookers / Vanessa / Tried by the centre court / Youth of the heart / Hippopotamus song / Gas man cometh / Sounding brass / Los olivados / In the desert / Ill wind / First and second law / All gall / Horoscope / Friendly duet / Bedstead men / By air / Slow train / Song of patriotic prejudice / Built up area / In the bath / Sea fever / Hippo encore / Warthog / Sea horse / Chameleon / Whale / Sloth / Rhinoceros / Twosome - Kang and Jag / Dead ducks / Elephant / Armadillo / Spider / Threesome / Wild boar / Ostrich / Wompom / Twice shy / Commonwealth fair / Paris / Eine kleine nachtmusik cha cha cha / Hundred song / Food for thought / Bed / Twenty tons of TNT / War of 14-18
CDFSB 1 / Aug '91 / EMI

☐ TRANSPORT OF DELIGHT, A (The Best Of Flanders & Swann)
Act 1: Introduction / Transport of delight / Song of reproduction / Gnu song / Songs for our time, Philological waltz, Satelite moon, Happy / Song of the weather / Greensleeves / Misalliance / Madeira m'dear / Hippopotamus song / Act 2: introduction / All gall / Horoscope / Gas man cometh / Sounding brass / Ill wind / First and second law / By air / Song of patriotic prejudice / Hippo encore / Encore / Wompon
CDGO 2061 / Aug '94 / EMI

Flare

☐ RE-GRIP
Turbinates / Cycling around / Curved flow / Clinch / Parts and wholes / Sweet katharsis / Curved sunburst / Transition / One blink / Grip
SBLCD 5012 / Feb '97 / Sublime

Flash & The Pan

☐ FLASH & THE PAN/LIGHTS IN THE NIGHT
RMED 0124CD / 8 Jun '98 / Renaissance

Flash

☐ FLASH
OW S2117796 / Sep '94 / One Way

☐ FLASH IN THE CAN
Lifetime / Monday morning eyes / Black and white / Stop that banging / There no more
OW S2156841 / Sep '94 / One Way

☐ OUT OF OUR HANDS
OW S2117414 / Sep '94 / One Way

Flat Duo Jets

☐ FLAT DUO JETS
DOG 004CD / Sep '94 / Wild Dog

☐ GO GO HARLEM BABY
SKYCD 5031 / Sep '94 / Sky

☐ IN STEREO
SKYCD 5023 / Sep '94 / Sky

☐ WHITER TREES
SKYCD 5033 / Sep '94 / Sky

☐ WILD BLUE YONDER
CED 259 / 16 Mar '98 / Norton

Flat Earth Society

☐ WALEECO/LOST SPACE KIDS
AA 042 / 16 Mar '98 / Arf Arf

Flatlanders

☐ MORE A LEGEND THAN A BAND
Dallas / Tonight I'm gonna go downtown / You've never seen me cry / She had everything / Rose from the mountain / One day at a time / Jolie blon / Down in my hometown / Bhagavan decreed / Heart you left behind / Keeper of the mountain / Stars in my life / One more road
SSCD 34 / '90 / Rounder

Flatley, Michael

☐ MICHAEL FLATLEY
BUA 9501CD / Apr '95 / BUA

Flatt & Scruggs

☐ AT CARNEGIE HALL
379292 / May '98 / Koch

☐ DON'T GET ABOVE YOUR RAISIN' (Flatt, Lester & Earl Scruggs)
SSCD 08 / Feb '94 / Rounder

☐ FLATT AND SCRUGGS 1948-1959 (4CD Set) (Flatt, Lester & Earl Scruggs)
God loves his children / I'm going to make Heaven my home / We'll meet again sweetheart / My cabin in Caroline / Baby blue eyes / Bouquet in Heaven / Down the road / Why don't you tell me so / I'll never shed another tear / No mother or dad / Is it too late now / Foggy mountain breakdown / Cora is gone / Preaching, praying, singing / Pain in my heart / Rollin' in my sweet baby's arms / Back to the cross / Farewell blues / Old salty dog blues / Take me in a lifeboat / Will the roses bloom / I'll just pretend / Come back darling / I'm head over heels in love / I'm waiting to hear you call me darling / Old home town / I'll stay around / We can't be darlings anymore / Jimmie Brown the newsboy / Somehow tonight / Don't get above your raising / I'm working on a road / He took your place / I've lost you / 'Tis sweet to be remembered / I'm gonna settle down / Earl's breakdown / I'm lonesome and blue / Over the hills to the poorhouse / My darling's last goodbye / Get in line brother / Brother I'm getting ready to go / Why did you wander / Flint Hill special / Thinking about you / If I should wander back tonight / Dim lights,

thick smoke / Dear old Dixie / Reunion in Heaven / Pray for the boys / I'll go stepping too / I'd rather be alone / Foggy mountain chimes / Someone took my place with you / Mother prays loud in her sleep / That old book of mine / Your love is like a flower / Be ready for tomorrow may never come / Till the end of the world rolls around / You're not a drop in the bucket / Don't that road look rough and rocky / Foggy mountain special / You can feel it on your soul / Old fashioned preacher / Before I met you / I'm gonna sleep with one eye open / Randy Lynn rag / On my mind / Blue Ridge cabin home / Some old day / It won't be long / No mother in this world / Gone home / Bubbling in my soul / Joy bells / What's good for you / No doubt about it / Who will sing for me / Give mother my crown / Six white horses / Shuckin' the corn / I'll take the blame / Don't let your deal go down / Hundred years from now / Give me the flowers while I'm living / Is there room for me / Let those brown eyes smile at me / I won't be hanging around / I don't care anymore / Big black train / Mama's and daddy's little girl / Crying alone / Million years in glory / Heaven / Building on sand / Jesus saviour pilot me / Crying my heart out over you / Ground speed / Who knows right from wrong / Iron curtain / Cabin on the hill / Someone you have forgotten / Foggy mountain rock / You put me on my feet

BCD 15472 / Jan '94 / Bear Family

☐ **FLATT AND SCRUGGS 1959-1963 (5CD Set) (Flatt, Lester & Earl Scruggs)**

Angel band / When the angels carry me home / I'll never be lonesome again / Get on the road to glory / Take me in your lifeboat / Bubbling in my soul / Heaven / Joy bells / Give me flowers while I'm living / You can feel it in your soul / Give mother my crown / Great historical bum / I've lost you forever / Polka on a banjo / All I want is you / Shuckin' the corn / Home sweet home / Fireball mail / Cripple creek / Reuben (Instrumental) / John Henry / Cumberland gap / Lonesome road blues / Sally Goodin (instrumental) / Little darlin', pal of mine (Instrumental) / Sally Ann / Bugle call rag / I ain't gonna work tomorrow / If I should wander back tonight / Cold, cold loving / Welcome to the club / False hearted lover / Picking in the wildwood / Homestead on the farm / Foggy mountain top / You are my flower / Forsaken love / Storms are on the ocean / Gathering flowers from the hillside / Worried man blues / On the rock where Moses stood / Keep on the sunny side / Jimmie brown the newsboy / Just ain't / Where will I shelter my sheep / I saw mother with God last night / Go home / Old Joe Clark / Sally Goodin / Black mountain rag / Billy in the lowground / Twinkle little star / Old fiddler / Soldier's joy / Georgia shuffle / Golden slippers / Tennessee Wagner / Handsome Molly / Coal loadin' Johnny / Hear that whistle blow (a hundred miles) / Too old for a broken heart / Legend of the Johnson boys / All the good times are past and gone / George Alley's FFV / This land is your land / Philadelphia lawyer / Sun's gonna shine in my back door some day / Hear the wind blow / I'll be no man's wife / McKinley's gone / Nine pound hammer / Ellen Smith / Life of trouble / Hard travellin' / Wreck of ol' 97 / Ninety nine years is almost for life / Over the hills to the poorhouse / New York town / Dixie home / Pastures of plenty / Bound to ride / When I left East Virginia / Drowned in the deep blue sea / My native home / Coal miner's blues / Salty dog blues / Durham's reel / Down the road / Rainbow / Big ball in Brooklyn / Flint Hill special / Dig a hole in the meadow / I hung my head and cried / Hot corn, cold corn / Little darlin', pal of mine / Mama don't allow it / Footprints in the snow / Martha White theme / I wonder where you are tonight / Old Macdonald / He will set your fields on fire / Let the church roll on / Picking the wildwood flower / Fiddle and banjo / Old leather britches / Ballad of Jed Clampett / Yonder stands little Maggie / Reuben / Mama blues / I know what it mean to be lonesome / Foggy mountain rock / Take this hammer / Rollin' in my sweet baby's arms / Gotta travel on / Mountain dew / Pearl, Pearl, Pearl / What about you / Rambling gambler / I'm troubled / My Sarah Jane / Train that carried my girl from town / Little birdy / Po' rebel soldier

BCD 15559 / Jun '92 / Bear Family

☐ **FLATT AND SCRUGGS 1964-1969 (6CD Set) (Flatt, Lester & Earl Scruggs)**

Petticoat junction / Have you seen my dear companion / Good things (outweigh the bad) / Working it out / Amber tresses (tied in blue) / Jimmie Brown / Newsboy / When Papa played the dobro / Fireball / Father's table grace / I'm walking with him / My wandering boy / Sally don't you grieve / Faded red ribbon / Bummin' an old freight train / Georgia Buck / Hello stranger / Please don't wake me / You're gonna miss me when I'm gone / I still miss someone / Wabash cannonball / Rose conelly / You've been fooling my baby / Will you be lonesome too / Big shoes to fill / Branded wherever I go / Starlight on the rails / Loafer's glory / I'll be on the good road some day / Confessing / Gonna have myself a ball / Rock, salt and nails / Soldier's return / Memphis / Jackson / Colours / For lovin' me / Houston / Detroit city / Foggy mountain breakdown / Kansas City / Nashville blues / Take me back to Tulsa / Last public hanging in West Virginia / Boys form Tennessee / Ten miles from Natchez / Seattle town / Green acres / I had a dream / When the saints go marching in / God gave Noah the rainbow sign / Call me on home / Stone that builders refused / Wait for the sunshine / No Mother in this world / Thank God I'm on my way / Troublesome waters / Last thing on my mind / Mama, you been on my mind / It was only the wind / Why can't I find myself with you / Southbound / I'm gonna ride the steamboat / Roust-a-bout / Nashville cats / Train number 1262 / Bringin in the Georgia mail / Going across the sea / Atlantic coastal line / East bound train / Orange blossom special / Last train to Clarksville / California up tight band / Don't think twice it's alright / Four strong winds / Blowin' in the wind / It ain't me babe / Down in the flood / Buddy don't you roll so slow / Where have all the flowers gone / This land is your land / Mr. Tambourine man / Ode to Billie Joe / Like a rolling stone / I'd like to say a word for Texas / I'll be your baby tonight / Folsom Prison blues / Gentle on my mind / Times they are a-changin' / If I were a carpenter / Universal soldier / Long road to Houston / Catch the wind / Rainy day women / Frieda Florentine / Nashville skyline rag / I walk the line / Ruby, don't take your love to town / Boy named Sue / Maggie's farm / Wanted man / One more night / One too many mornings / Girl from the north country / Honey, just allow me one more chance / Tonight will be fine / Story of Bonnie and Clyde / Another ride with Clyde / Picture of Bonnie / Barrow gang will get you little man / Bang you're alive / See Bonnie die, see Cly die / Get away / Chase / Highway's end / Pick along / John Hardy was a desperate little man / Jazzing / Evelina / Tommy's song / Lonesome Ruben / Spanish two step / Careless love / Liberty / Bill Cheatham / Nothin' to it / Lost all my money / Maggie blues / Steamboat whistle blues / Paul and Silas / Cannonball blues / You are my flower / Old leather britches / Across the blue ridge mountains / Old folks / Going back to Harlan / Poor rebel soldier / No hiding place down here / Going up cripple creek / Foggy mountain special / Bile them cabbage down / Old Joe Clark / Sally goodine / Black mountain rag / Billy in the lowground / Twinkle little star / Old fiddler / Soldier's joy / Cheyenne / Down yonder / Georgia shuffle / Golden slippers / Tennessee Wagner / Chicken reel / Theme from Beverly Hillibilies / Beverly Hills / Vittles / Long talk with that boy / Jethro's a powerful man / Elly's spring song / Back home USA / Critters / What a great doctor Granny is / Lady lessons / Birds and the bees / Love or money / Close

BCD 15879 / Nov '95 / Bear Family

☐ **FOGGY MOUNTAIN JAMBOREE**

CUY 118CD / Aug '96 / County

☐ **GOLDEN ERA, THE (Flatt, Lester & Earl Scruggs)**

Flint Hill special / Your love is like a flower / I'm waiting to hear you call me darling / I'm head over heels in love / I'm working on a road / Till the end of the world rolls around / Jimmie Brown the newsboy / Earl's breakdown / Someone took my place with you / I'm gonna sleep with one eye open / Dim lights, thick smoke / Don't that road look rough and rocky / Randy lynn rag / Old home town / Brother I'm getting ready to go

SSCD 05 / '92 / Rounder

☐ **MERCURY SESSIONS VOL.1 (Flatt, Lester & Earl Scruggs)**

SSCD 18 / Dec '87 / Rounder

☐ **MERCURY SESSIONS VOL.2 (Flatt, Lester & Earl Scruggs)**

My little girl in Tennessee / Will the roses bloom / I'll never shed another tear / Bouquet in heaven / Cabin in Caroline / I'll never love another / God loves his children / Pain in my heart / Baby blue eyes / Doing my time / Preaching, praying, singing / Why don't they tell me so / Foggy mountain breakdown / I'm going to make heaven my home

SSCD 19 / Dec '87 / Rounder

Flatt, Lester

☐ **LESTER RAYMOND FLATT**

Come back darling / Wreck of ol' 97 / Some old day / Listen to my mockingbird / When it's time for the whippoorwill to sing / Down the road / I won't care / It was only the wind / My cabin in Caroline / Sleep with one eye open / Foggy mountain chimes / That old book of mine

FF 700015 / 6 Oct '97 / Flying Fish

Flatts, Vincent

☐ **FLATT OUT**

MYSCD 101 / May '96 / Mystic

Flatville Aces

☐ **CRAWFISHTROMBONES**

FLATCD 123 / Apr '94 / Flat

Flavin, Mick

☐ **COUNTRY ALL THE WAY**

California okie / She's got a way (of makin' me forget) / Writing on the wall / I'll be there (if you ever want me) / Cotton Jenny / Family tree / In my father's house / Flowers in the snow / I met a friend of yours today / What we love to do / Lovin' understanding man / I sleep just like a baby / Old man on the porch / You beat all I've ever seen / I won't be in Atlanta anynore

RZRCD 564 / Jul '97 / Ritz

☐ **COUNTRY SOUNDS**

In the echoes of my mind / You're the reason / Walk softly on the bridges / Love bug / I wish it was that easy going home / County of Fermanagh / Can you feel it / Yours to hurt tomorrow / Life's too short to be unhappy / Grand tour / Dreams of Donegal / If you remember me / Maria's heading out to California / Take my back home to Mayo

RZRCD 545 / Nov '94 / Ritz

☐ **LIGHTS OF HOME, THE**

Someday you'll love me / I see an angel every day / On the wings of love / It started all over again / For a minute there / One of these days (I want to be in your nights) / I never loved you more / Little things in life / Lights of home / Connemara rose / Keeper of my heart / You done me wrong / Old home in Mayo / Table in the corner / Little mountain church mouse / Longford on my mind

RZRCD 533 / Aug '93 / Ritz

☐ **SWEET MEMORY**

If you're gonna do me wrong (do it right) / Gonna have love / What she don't know won't hurt her / Way down deep / I took a memory to lunch / Old school yard / She's my rose / Haven't you heard / Wine flowed freely / Lady Jane / Hills of Tyrone / All I can be (is a sweet memory)

RZRCD 517 / Jun '92 / Ritz

☐ **TRAVELLIN' LIGHT**

Jennifer Johnson and me / Blue blue day / Hard times lovin' can bring / Where have all the lovers gone / Home to Donegal / Old side of town / Roads and other reasons / Travellin' light / There is no other way / Rarest flowers

RZCD 507 / '91 / Ritz

☐ **VERY BEST OF MICK FLAVIN, THE**

RZCD 086 / 13 Jul '98 / Ritz

Flavournaughts

☐ **MY INBRED PEDIGREE CHUMS**

Enchantress (stone cold heartbreaker) / Shivers / Asa quebrada / Flower of the valley / Keeping the rabble in line / Mexican rave / If you know me / Double decker / Jamie's magic ending / Bustin' outta no way street / Last drag / New dawn / Magic ending (Reprise)

NOZACD 005 / May '97 / Ninebar

Fleck, Bela

☐ **DAYBREAK**

Texas barbeque / Spain / Twilight / Reading in the dark / Growling old man and the grumbling old woman / How can you face me now / Bill cheatham / Christina's jig-plain brown jig / Silver bell / Fiddler's dream / Daybreak / Dawg's due / Flexibility / Old hickory waltz / Crossfire / Applebutter / Natural bridge suite / Punch drunk

ROUCD 11518 / '88 / Rounder

☐ **DEVIATION (Fleck, Bela & The New Grass Revival)**

ROUCD 0196 / Jul '95 / Rounder

☐ **DOUBLE TIME**

Spunk / Black forest / Double play / Lowdown / Bullfrog shuffle / Another morning / Light speed / Sweet rolls / Ladies and gentleman / Right as rain / Far away / Ready to go / Fast lane

ROUCD 0181 / May '97 / Rounder

☐ **DRIVE**

Whitewater / Slipstream / Up and around the bend / Natchez trace / See rock city / Legend / Lights of home / Down in the swamp / Sanctuary / Open road

ROUCD 0255 / Aug '88 / Rounder

☐ **INROADS**

Tonino / Somerset / Cecata / Four wheel drive / Ireland / Perplexed / Old country / Hudson's bay / Close to home

ROUCD 0219 / May '93 / Rounder

☐ **PLACES**

ROUCD 11522 / '88 / Rounder

☐ **TABULA RASA (Fleck, Bela & V.M. Batt/ Jie-Bing Chen)**

WLACS 44CD / Aug '96 / Waterlily Acoustics

☐ **THREE FLEW OVER THE CUCKOOS'S NEST**

Vix 9 / At last we meet again / Spunky and Clorissa / Bumbershoot / Blues for Gordon / Monkey see / Message / Interlude (return of the ancient ones) / Drift / Celtic melody / Peace, be still / Longing / For now

9362453282 / Jun '94 / Warner Bros.

Flecknor, Gregory

☐ **MONKEY BOOTS (Flecknor, Gregory Quartet)**

CLR 419CD / Oct '95 / Clear

Fleetwood Mac

☐ **25 YEARS - SELECTIONS FROM THE CHAIN (2CD Set)**

Paper doll / Love shines / Love in store / Goodbye angel / Heart of stone / Silver springs / Oh Diane / Big love / Rhiannon / Crystal / Chain / Over my head / Dreams / Go your own way / Sara / Hold me / Gypsy / Make me a mask / Don't stop / Everywhere / Tusk / Not that funny / Beautiful child / Teen beat / Need your love so bad / Did you ever love me / Oh well, part 1 / I believe my time ain't long / Bermuda triangle / Why / Station man / Albatross / Black magic woman / Stop messin' around / Trinity / Heroes are hard to find / Green manalishi

9362451882 / Feb '93 / WEA

☐ **25 YEARS - THE CHAIN (4CD Set)**

Paper doll / Love shines / Stand back / Crystal / Isn't it midnight / Big love / Everywhere / Affairs of the heart / Heart of stone / Sara / That's all for everyone / Over my head / Little lies / Eyes of the world / Oh Diane / In the back of my mind / Make me a mask / Save me / Goodbye angel / Silver springs / What makes you think you're the one / Think about me / Gypsy / You make loving fun / Second hand news / Love in store / Chain / Teen beat / Dreams / Only over you / I'm so afraid / Love is dangerous / Gold dust woman / Not that funny / Warm ways / Say you love me / Don't stop / Rhiannon / Walk a thin line / Storms / Go your own way / Sisters of the moon / Monday morning / Landslide / Hypnotised / Lay it all down / Angel / Beautiful child / Brown eyes / Save me a place / Tusk / Never go back again / Songbird / I believe my time ain't long / Need your love so bad / Rattlesnake shake / Oh well, part 1 / Stop messin' around / Green manalishi / Albatross / Man of the world / Love that burns / Black magic woman / Watch out / String-a-long / Station man / Did you ever love me / Sentimental lady / Come a little bit closer / Heroes are hard to find / Trinity / Why

9362451292 / Feb '93 / WEA

☐ **ALBATROSS (Fleetwood Mac & Christine Perfect)**

Albatross / Rambling pony / I believe my time ain't long / Dr. Brown / Stop messin' around / Love that burns / Jigsaw puzzle blues / Need your love tonight / I'd rather go blind / Crazy about you baby / And that's saying a lot / I'm on my way / No road is the right road / Let me go (leave me alone) / I'm too far gone (to turn around) / When you say

CD 31569 / Feb '91 / Columbia

☐ **BEHIND THE MASK**

Skies the limit / Love is dangerous / In the back of my mind / Do you know / Save me / Affairs of the heart / When the sun goes down / Behind the mask / Stand on the rock / Hard feelings / Freedom / When it comes to love / Second time

7599261112 / Feb '95 / WEA

☐ **BEST OF FLEETWOOD MAC, THE**

Albatross / Black magic woman / Doctor Brown / Long grey mare / Love that burns / Merry go round / My baby's good to me / No place to go / Ramblin' pony / World keep on turning / Watch out

4837242 / Feb '96 / Columbia

☐ **BLUES COLLECTION, THE**

Green manalishi (live) (shortened version) / Sandy mary (live) / Jumping at shadows (live) / Oh well (live) / Black magic woman (live) / World in harmony (live) / Like it this way (live) / Rattlesnake shake (live) / Got to move (live) / Madison blues (live) / Teenage darling (live) / Red hot mamma (live)

CCSCD 216 / Apr '89 / Castle

☐ **BLUES YEARS, THE**

PLSCD 198 / Apr '97 / Pulse

☐ **BOSTON LIVE**

Oh well / Like it this way / World in harmony / Only you / Black magic woman / Jumping at shadows / Can't hold on

CLACD 152 / Oct '89 / Castle

☐ **CLASSIC MAC (Plays Fleetwood Mac Classics) (London Rock Orchestra)**

Oh well (Part one) / Black magic woman / Future games / Green manalishi / Dragon fly / Need your love so bad / Tusk / Albatross / Jigsaw puzzle blues / Sentimental lady / Man of the world / Oh well (Part two) / Hypnotised / Don't stop

DCD 5368 / Apr '94 / Disky

☐ **DANCE, THE**

Chain / Dreams / Everywhere / Rhiannon / I'm so afraid / Temporary one / Bleed to love her / Big love / Landslide / Say you love me / My little demon / Silver springs / You make loving fun / Sweet girl / Go your own way / Tusk / Don't stop

9362467022 / Aug '97 / Warner Bros.

☐ **FLEETWOOD MAC**

Monday morning / Warm always / Blue letter / Rhiannon / Over my head / Crystal / Say you love me / Landslide / I'm so afraid / World turning / Sugar daddy

254043 / Dec '85 / Reprise

☐ **FLEETWOOD MAC**

My heart beats like a hammer / Merry go round / Long grey mare / Hellhound on my trail / Shake your moneymaker / Looking for somebody / No place to go / My baby's good to me / I loved another woman / Cold black night / World keeps on turning / Got to move

4773582 / Aug '94 / Columbia

☐ **FLEETWOOD MAC FAMILY ALBUM, THE (Various Artists)**

Respectable: *Cheynes* / If you wanna be happy: *Peter B's Looners* / Double trouble: *Mayall, John & The Bluesbreakers* / I'd rather go blind: *Chicken Shack* / Shape I'm in: *Spencer, Jeremy* / When you say: *Perfect, Christine* / Ram Jam city: *Kirwan, Danny* / Put a record on: *Tramp* / Sentimental lady: *Welch, Bob* / Stop draggin' my heart around: *Nicks, Stevie & Tom Petty & The Heartbreakers* / Rattlesnake shake: *Fleetwood, Mick* / Now I know: *McVie, John* / Don't say no: *Burnette, Billy* / We just disagree: *Mason, Dave* / Fleetwood Mac: *Fleetwood Mac*

VSOPCD 222 / Feb '96 / Connoisseur Collection

☐ **FLEETWOOD MAC LIVE**

SSLCD 207 / Jun '95 / Savanna

☐ **FLEETWOOD MAC/PIOUS BIRD OF GOOD OMEN/MR. WONDERFUL (3CD Set)**

My heart beats like a hammer / Merry go round / Long grey mare / Hellbound on my trail / Shake your moneymaker / Looking for somebody / No place to go / My baby's good to me / I loved another woman / Cold black night / World keeps on turning / Got to move / Need your love so bad / Coming home / Rambling pony / Big boat: *Fleetwood Mac & Eddie Boyd* / I believe my time ain't long / Sun is shining / Albatross / Black magic woman / Just the blues: *Fleetwood Mac & Eddie Boyd* / Jigsaw puzzle blues / Looking for somebody / Stop messin' around / Stop messin' round / I've lost my baby / Rollin' man / Dust my broom / Love that burns / Doctor Brown / Need your love tonight / If you be my baby / Evenin' boogie / Lazy poker blues / Comin' home / Tryin' so hard to forget

4853162 / Nov '97 / Columbia

☐ **GREATEST HITS**

Green Manalishi / Oh well / Shake your moneymaker / Need your love so bad / Rattlesnake shake / Dragonfly / Black magic woman / Albatross / Man of the world / Stop messin' around / Love that burns

4607042 / 27 Jul '98 / Columbia

☐ **GREATEST HITS**

As long as you follow / No questions asked / Rhiannon / Don't stop / Go your own way / Hold me / Everywhere / Gypsy / Say you love me / Dreams / Little lies / Sara / Tusk / Oh Diane / Big love / You make loving fun / Seven wonders

9258382 / Nov '88 / WEA

☐ **LEGACY (A Tribute To Fleetwood Mac's Rumours) (Various Artists)**

Second hand news: *Tonic* / Dreams: *Corrs* / Never going back again: *Matchbox 20* / Don't stop: *John, Elton* / Go your own way: *Cranberries* / Songbird: *Sheik, Duncan* / Chain: *Colvin, Shawn* / You make loving fun: *Jewel* / I want to know: *Goo Goo Dolls* / Oh daddy: *Tallulah* / Gold dust woman: *Sister Hazel*

7567830542 / 25 May '98 / Atlantic

☐ **LIVE AT THE BBC (2CD Set)**

EDFCD 297 / Sep '95 / Essential

☐ **LONDON LIVE '68**

Got to move / I held my baby last night / My baby's sweet / My baby's a good un / Don't know which way to go / Buzz me / Dream / World keeps turning / How blue can you get / Bleeding heart

CDTB 11038 / Mar '95 / Thunderbolt

☐ MADISON BLUES LIVE
MACCD 187 / Aug '96 / Autograph

☐ MASTERS, THE
Got to move / I held my baby last night / My baby's sweet / My baby's a good 'un / Don't know which way to go / Buzz me / Worried dream / World keeps on turning / How blue can you get / Bleeding heart
EABCD 091 / 30 Mar '98 / Eagle

☐ MIRAGE
Love in store / Can't go back / That's alright / Book of love / Gypsy / Only over you / Empire State / Straight back / Hold me / Oh Diane / Eyes of the world / Wish you were here
K 256952 / '89 / WEA

☐ MISTER WONDERFUL
Stop messin' round / Coming home / Rollin' man / Dust my broom / Love that burns / Dr. Brown / Need your love tonight / If you be my baby / Evenin' boogie / Lazy poker blues / I've lost my baby / Trying so hard to forget
4746122 / Mar '96 / Columbia

☐ ORCHESTRAL FLEETWOOD MAC (London Rock Orchestra)
Oh well (part one) / Black magic woman / Future games / Greem manalishi / Dragonfly / Need your love so bad / Tusk / Albatross / Jigsaw puzzle blues / Sentimental lady / Man of the world / Oh well (part two) / Hypnotised / Don't stop
EMPRCD 546 / Nov '94 / Emporio

☐ PATRON SAINTS OF POP, THE (A Tribute To Fleetwood Mac) (Various Artists)
UNCV 009 / Nov '97 / Undercover

☐ PIOUS BIRD OF GOOD OMEN, THE
Need your love so bad / Coming home / Rambling pony / Big boat / I believe my time ain't long / Sun is shining / Albatross / Black magic woman / Just the blues / Jigsaw puzzle blues / Looking for somebody / Stop messin' around
4805242 / May '95 / Columbia

☐ RUMOURS
Second hand news / Dreams / Never going back again / Don't stop / Go your own way / Songbird / Chain / You make loving fun / I don't want to know / Oh daddy / Gold dust woman
256344 / Dec '83 / Reprise

☐ TANGO IN THE NIGHT
Big love / Seven wonders / Everywhere / Caroline / Tango in the night / Mystified / Little lies / Family man / Welcome to the room...Sara / Isn't it midnight / When I see you again / You and I (part 2)
9254712 / Apr '87 / WEA

☐ THEN PLAY ON
Coming your way / Closing my eyes / Fighting for Madge / When you say / Showbiz blues / Underway / One sunny day / Although the sun is shining / Rattlesnake shake / Without you / Searching for Madge / My dream / Like crying / Before the beginning
9274482 / '88 / WEA

☐ TIME
Talkin' to my heart / Blow by blow / Winds of change / Hollywood (some other kind of town) / I do / Dream the dream / I wonder why / I got it in for you / Nights in estoril / These strange times / All over again / Sooner or later / Nothing without you
9362459202 / Oct '95 / WEA

☐ TUSK
Over and over / Ledge / Think about me / Save me a place / Sara / What makes you think you're the one / Storms / That's all for everyone / Not that funny / Sisters of the moon / Angel / That's enough for me / Brown eyes / Never make me cry / I know I'm not wrong / Honey hi / Beautiful child / Walk a thin line / Tusk / Never forget
K2 66088 / Mar '87 / WEA

Fleming & John

☐ DELUSIONS OF GRANDEUR
REX 460122 / Nov '95 / Rex

Fleming, Don

☐ JOJO ASS RUNNNE
NOIR 006CD / 13 Apr '98 / God Bless

Flesh & Blood

☐ BLUES FOR DAZE
NTHEN 037CD / May '97 / Now & Then

Flesh Eaters

☐ SEX DIARY OF MR. VAMPIRE
SST 292CD / May '93 / SST

Flesh 'n' Bone

☐ THUGS
5335392 / Dec '96 / Mo Thugs/Def Jam

Fleshcrawl

☐ BLOOD RED MASSACRE
BMCD 122 / 3 Nov '97 / Black Mark

☐ DESCEND INTO THE ABSURD
Between the shadows they crawl / Phrenetic Tendencies / Perpetual dawn / Purulent bowel erosion / Lost in a grave / Never to die again / Festering flesh / Infected subconscious / Evoke the excess
BMCD 027 / Oct '92 / Black Mark

☐ IMPURITY
BMCD 48 / Mar '94 / Black Mark

Fleshold

☐ PATHETIC
MASSCD 049 / May '95 / Massacre

Fleshrevels

☐ STONED AND OUT
FINNREC 009CD / Jun '96 / Finn

Fleshtones

☐ BLAST OFF
RE 107CD / Jul '97 / ROIR

☐ FLESHTONES
BYOB / Critical list / Shadowline / American beat / Cara - Lin / Watch Junior go / Atom spies / Way I feel / Comin' in dead stick / Judy / Soul struttin' / Rockin' this joint / Rocket USA
ESMCD 573 / Jul '97 / Essential

☐ LABORATORY OF SOUND
Let's go / High on drugs / Sands of our lives / Nostradamus Jr / Sweetest thing / Hold you / Accelerated emotion / Train of thought / One step less / Motor needs gas / Psychedelic swamp / Fading away / We'll never forget
118542 / Oct '95 / Musidisc UK

☐ MORE THAN SKIN DEEP
65292 / 26 Jan '98 / Epitaph

Fleshy Ranks

☐ BUSTIN' OUT
HBCD 163 / Oct '94 / Heartbeat

Fleta, Elia

☐ GRANDES EXITOS (Fleta, Elia & Paloma)
ALCD 050 / 1 Jun '98 / Alma Latina

Fletcher, Liz

☐ MELLOW MANIA
Come in out of the rain / My foolish heart / Occasional man / Sunshine / Wild child / Scotch mist / Serenade in blue / Stormy weather / You stepped out of a dream / Lullaby / Since you asked me / Green / Softly as in a morning sunrise / If you ever loved (the meaning of the blues)
BBJ 1001 / Sep '97 / Black Box Music

Fleur Des Lys

☐ FACING MORNING
FJD 031 / 15 Dec '97 / FJD Sound

Fleurety

☐ MIN TID SKAL KOMME
AMAZON 005CD / 3 Nov '97 / Misanthropy

Fleurine

☐ MEANT TO BE
Lazay and satisfied / My souldance with you / Favourite love affair / Velejar / Meant to be / My hearts escapade / I've got just about everything / When I think of one / Escolher / It's all in the mind / Call me now / One dream gone / High in the sky
BM 1001 / Feb '97 / Blue Music

Flex

☐ STEPPIN' OUT
OMCD 11 / Jul '96 / One Movement

Flibbertigibbet

☐ WHISTLING JIGS TO THE MOON
KSCD 9510 / Jun '97 / Kissing Spell

Flies Inside The Sun

☐ AN AUDIENCE OF OTHERS (INCLUDING HERSELF)
KRANK 008CD / Mar '97 / Kranky

☐ FLIES INSIDE THE SUN
MET 002 / Dec '96 / Metonymic

Flight Recorder

☐ PINKERTON'S COLOURS/FLYING MACHINE (2CD Set)
Smile a little smile for me / Send my baby home again / Marie take a chance / Waiting on the shores of nowhere / Maybe we've been loving too long / There she goes / That same old feeling / Baby make it soon / Broken hearted me, evil hearted you / Thing called love / My baby's coming home / Memories of Melinda / Devil has posession of your mind / Hey little girl / Pages of your life / Yes I understand / Hanging on the edge of sadness / Flying machine / Mirror mirror / Don't stop loving me baby / Magic rocking horse / Mum and Dad / On a street car / Duke's jetty / There's nobody I'd sooner love / Kentucky woman / Behind the mirror / Look at me, look at me / People say / One man band / Lies in your eyes / Me without you / Can't break the habit / Shadows on a foggy day / If you were true / Shine a little light / St. Louis child / 4 o'clock in New York / Hard, hard year / Strawberry fool / Angel (she was born out of love)
NEDCD 290 / Jul '97 / Sequel

Flinner, Matt

☐ VIEW FROM HERE, THE
742472 / 30 Mar '98 / Compass

Flint, Tim

☐ SHOW TUNES - AND THEN SOME
Overture / All I need is the girl / We kiss in a shadow / I have dreamed fugue for tin horns / Anything goes / On the street where you live / This can't be love / I've never been in love before / They say that falling in love is wonderful / Once in love with Amy / Give my regards to Broadway / Bandology / La Calinda / Love walked in/Forgotten dreams / Autumn concerto / April in Paris / Thunder and lightning polka / Tritach tratsch polka / 9.20 Special
CDGRS 1264 / Sep '93 / Grosvenor

☐ TOO MARVELLOUS FOR WORDS
Moment of truth / Where are you / Too marvellous for words / Sweet Lorraine / Shiny stockings / Somewhere along the way / Bahn frei / Rock revolution / Disney selection / When you wish upon a star / Heigh ho / Whistle while you work / Party gras / Jolly holiday / With a smile and a song / So this is love / Unbirthday song / It's a small world / Pomp and circumstance No.1
KGRS 1242 / '91 / Grosvenor

Flip Flap

☐ MORNING TRACKS VOL.1
Dawn / 4th insight: *Suger Plant & Flip Flap* / Spiritual healing: *Muses Rapt* / White light into you: *Suger Plant* / Express way to your mind: *Fractal Express* / ISP (Indian Summer Project): *Okino, Shuntaro* / Party continues: *Fractal Express* / Phenix: *Okino, Shuntaro* / Niji - morning track
KSC 2187 / Jul '97 / Ki-Oon

Flippen, Benton

☐ OLD TIMES, NEW TIMES
ROUCD 0326 / Oct '94 / Rounder

Flipper

☐ BLOW'N CHUNKS
RE 126CD / Nov '94 / ROIR

☐ LIVE AT CBGB'S 1983
OVER 63CD / Jul '97 / Overground

☐ SEX BOMB BABY
Sex bomb / Love canal / Ha ha ha / Sacrifice / Falling / Ever get away / Earthworm / Games' got a price / Old lady who swallowed a fly / Brainwash / Lowrider / End the game
74321298982 / Oct '95 / Infinite Zero

Flipside

☐ FLIPSIDE
Magic beans / Muses / Elder days / High times / Numero 6 / Stretch nude / Big dea
860132 / Jul '98 / Naxos Jazz

Flirts

☐ BEST OF THE FLIRTS, THE (Calling All Boys)
Passion / Calling all boys / (Don't put another dime in the) jukebox / Boy crazy / On the beach / We just wanna dance / Jungle rock / Helpless / Danger / Dancing madly backwards / You and me / New toy / All you ever think about is sex / After midnight / Miss you
HTCD 14 / 20 Apr '98 / Hot Productions

Flitcroft, Iain

☐ GRANADALAND WURLITZER
Wurlitzer march / Reilly, ace of spies / Rose medley / Cavaquinho / Waltz medley / Tango Havana / Musetta's waltz song / White Horse Inn / Granada television medley / Masterpiece / Quickstep / City of Chester / Vija / Ballet Egyptien / Paris medley / Samba incognito / Medley / Buffoon / Granada connection
OS 213 / Aug '95 / Bandleader

Floaters

☐ FLOAT ON (The Best Of The Floaters)
HMNCD 030 / 16 Mar '98 / Half Moon

Floating Jazz Festival Trio

☐ FLOATING JAZZ FESTIVAL TRIO, THE
CRD 340 / May '97 / Chiaroscuro

☐ MUSIC OF DUKE ELLINGTON, THE (Live At The 1996 Floating Jazz Festival)
In a sentimental mood / Single petal of a rose / Sunset and the mocking bird / In a mellotone / Creole love call / Do nothin' 'til you hear from me / Jeep's blues
CRD 352 / 8 Nov '97 / Chiaroscuro

Flock Of Seagulls

☐ 20 CLASSICS OF THE 80'S
Tokyo / Who's that girl she's got it / DNA / How could you ever leave me / ELectrics / Remember David / Messages / Don't ask me / Traveller / Rosenmontag / 2.30 / Better and better / Euorpean I wish I was / Say so much / Telecommunication / End / Space age love song / It's not me talking / Over my head / Love on your knees
EMPRCD 562 / Mar '95 / Emporio

☐ BEST OF A FLOCK OF SEAGULLS, THE
I ran / Space age love song / Telecommunication / More you live, the more you love / Nightmares / Wishing (if I had a photograph of you) / It's not me talking / Transfer affection / Who's that girl / DNA I ran
CHIP 41 / Jun '91 / Jive

☐ BEST OF A FLOCK OF SEAGULLS, THE
Wishing (if I had a photograph of you) / Nightmares / Space age love song / Never again / I ran / Heartbeat like a drum / Transfer affection / D.n.a. / More you live, the more you love / Windows / Who's that girl (she's got it) / Committed / Living in heaven / (it's not me) talking / Telecommunications / Modern love is automatic
MCCD 114 / Jun '93 / Music Club

☐ BEST OF A FLOCK OF SEAGULLS, THE
I ran / Space age love song / Telecommunication / More you live, the more you love / Nightmares / Wishing (if I had a photograph of you) / (It's not me) talking / Transfer affection / Who's that girl (she's got it) / DNA / Wishing (if I had a photograph of you) / More you live, the more you love
QED 082 / Nov '96 / Tring

Floh De Cologne

☐ PROFIT GEIER LIVE
14891 / 16 Feb '98 / Spalax

Flood

☐ RISE OF THE FLOOD
FLASH 64 / 1 Jun '98 / Flash

Flood, Goran

☐ VERNISSAGE
FLCCD 154 / Oct '97 / Four Leaf Clover

Floodgate

☐ PENALTY
RR 88902 / Oct '96 / Roadrunner

Flook

☐ LIVE
Branohm/Trip to Herve's / Knocknamoe jig/Custy's/ Trip to Brittany / Jizique / Brian's reel/Peter's epic journey / In another life / Blackberry blossom/The independence / History man / Dub reel
SMALLCD 9405 / Feb '97 / Smallworld

Floorpunch

☐ TWIN KILLING
EVR 038CD / 27 Oct '97 / Equal Vision

Floppy Sounds

☐ DOWNTIME
Actual footage / Durexx / Daisy / Since I split / Superhype / Ultrasong / Oblivion / Excursions / Deliverance / Sprawl / Weird
SLIPCD 040 / Feb '96 / Slip 'n' Slide

Florence

☐ OCCURRENCES
Dream the dream / Departure / Transit / Arrival / Jump shock / Undiscovered / Instantaneous drive / Second hand culture / Collapse of commerce / Coincidental harmony
ELEC 32CD / Apr '97 / New Electronica

Florence, Bob

☐ BOB FLORENCE & HIS BIG BAND (Florence, Bob Big Band)
Party harty / Trinity fair / BBC / Jewels / Willowcrest / Invitation / Forgetful / Samba de rollins / Collage
HEPCD 2064 / Jun '95 / Hep

☐ SOARING (Florence, Bob Limited Edition)
SB 2082 / Jan '97 / Sea Breeze

☐ STATE OF THE ART (Florence, Bob Limited Edition)
Just friends / Moonlight serenade / Silky / Crunch / Stella by starlight / All the things you are / Mr. Paddington / BBC / Auld lang syne
CDPC 797 / Oct '90 / Prestige

☐ TRIO
FSRCD 303 / 5 Jan '98 / Fresh Sound

Flores, Caledonio E.

☐ HOMENAJE A LOS POETAS DEL TANGO
EBCD 73 / Jul '96 / El Bandoneon

Flores, Lola

☐ OLE
SCCD 995 / Mar '96 / Seeco

Flores, Pedro

☐ 1938-1942
HQCD 49 / May '95 / Harlequin

☐ PEDRO FLORES 1933-1942
Azucenas / Blanca estrella / Arturito / Ciego de amor / El triunfo / Vencido / Cuando vuelvas / Los cisnes / Tu seras mia / El ultimo adios / Olga / Yo no se nada / Venganza / Borracho no vale / El cafetero / Mentirosa / Desilusion / Ciego de amor / Que extrana es la vida / Entre mar y cielo / Celos de amor
HQCD 116 / May '98 / Harlequin

☐ PEDRO FLORES 1935-1938
HQCD 72 / Jun '96 / Harlequin

Flores, Rosie

☐ AFTER THE FARM
HACD 8033 / Jul '94 / Hightone

☐ HONKY TONK REPRISE, A
ROUCD 3136 / Jun '96 / Rounder

☐ LITTLE BIT OF HEARTACHE, A (Flores, Rosie & Ray Campi)
This song is just for you / Seperate ways / Where honky tonk angels spread there wings / Train kept a rollin' / All I have to do is dream / I'm gonna wear the pants / Bandera highway / There ain't a cow in Texas / Little bit of heartache / Eighteen wheels / If teardrops were pennies / Joe and old merle / My baby's doin' alright / Living on love / Crazy / Let's say goodbye
WMCD 1059 / May '97 / Watermelon

☐ ONCE MORE WITH FEELING
HCD 8047 / Jun '94 / Hightone

☐ ROCKABILLY FILLY
HITCD 8067 / Oct '95 / Hightone

Florida

☐ BRASS ROOTS
FLP 003CD / Nov '95 / Florida

Flory, Chris

☐ CITY LIFE
Alexandria, VA / Besame mucho / S'posin' / Tin tin por tin tin / Good morning heartache / JA Blues / My shining hour / So danco samba / Drafting / Come back to me / New York / Penthouse serenade / Cafe solo
CCD 4589 / Feb '94 / Concord Jazz

☐ FOR ALL WE KNOW
Soft winds / T'ain't me / Avalon / Tenderly / Close your eyes / Lee's blues / It had to be you / For all we know / Airmail special / Ninth Avenue shuffle / Lullaby of the leaves
CCD 4403 / Jan '90 / Concord Jazz

Flotsam & Jetsam

☐ DOOMSDAY FOR THE DECEIVER
Hammerhead / Iron tears / Desecrator / Fade to black / Doomsday for the deceiver / Metal shock / She took the axe / U.s.i.w. / Der fuhrer / Flotzilla
398414077 CD / Mar '96 / Metal Blade

☐ HIGH
398414126CD / Jun '97 / Metal Blade

Flotsam & Jetsam

☐ FLOTSAM AND JETSAM
Introduction / King Canute / Mrs. Peer Gynt / PC Lamb / Maude-Marie / Optimist and pessimist / Polonaise in the Mall / Melodrama of the mice / Only a few of us left / Businessman's love song / Simon the bootlegger / Song of the air / Move into my house / Little Betty Bouncer / Weather reports / We never know what to expect / Schubert's toy shop / Village blacksmith / Alsation and the pekinese / Modern diver / Little Joan / What was the matter with Rachmaninov / British pantomime / Ghost of old king's jester / High-brow sailor / When I grow old, dad / Postscript
PASTCD 9723 / '90 / Flapper

☐ FLOTSAM AND JETSAM VOL.2
Sing a song of england / Sing a song of england / Little chap / Big ben calling / Speed / Song of love / New words for old / Down amongst the dead men / Two different men / Pipe and cigarette / Bats in the belfry / Merry peasant / Harmonious blacksmith / Down with dora / Our war book / Londoner and the hun / Old bill and young bill / Spooning of the knife and fork / Love and kisses / A musical confession / My grandfather's clock / Piano impressions / A british spelling song
PASTCD 9749 / Jul '91 / Flapper

Flour

☐ FOURTH AND FINAL
TG 125CD / Apr '94 / Touch & Go

Flouride, Klaus

☐ BECAUSE I SAY SO
VIRUS 67CD / Jul '89 / Alternative Tentacles

☐ LIGHT IS FLICKERING, THE
VIRUS 95CD / '92 / Alternative Tentacles

Flow

☐ FLOW
809971 / 16 Feb '98 / Synton

Flowchart

☐ CUMULUS MOOD TWANG
SAKI 0171CD / 22 Sep '97 / Carrot Top

☐ IN THE SPIRIT OF KENNY G
BBPTC 60CD / Jun '97 / Black Bean & Placenta Tape Club

☐ MULTI PERSONALITY TABLETOP VACATION
SAKI 008 / 24 Nov '97 / Carrot Top

Flower

☐ HOLOGRAM SKY
SR 330491CD / Jul '91 / Semaphore

Flower Kings

☐ SCANNING THE GREENHOUSE
In the eyes of the world / World of adventures / Pipes of peace / Flower king / There is more to this world / Stardust we are / Retropolis / Compassion
OM 2008CD / 10 Aug '98 / Outer Music

Flowerpot Men

☐ LET'S GO TO SAN FRANCISCO
Let's go to San Francisco / Walk in the sky / Am I losing you / You can never be wrong / Man without a woman / In a moment of madness / Young birds fly / Journey's end / Mythological Sunday / Blow away / Piccolo man / Silicon City
C5CD 526 / Mar '97 / See For Miles

☐ VERY BEST OF THE FLOWERPOT MEN, THE
Let's go to San Francisco / Walk in the sky / Am I losing you / Man without a woman / You can never be wrong / Piccolo man / Mythological Sunday / Sweet baby Jane / Journey's end / Let's go to San Francisco / Silicon city / Busy doin' nothing / White dove / Cooks of cake kindness / Gotta be free / Heaven knows when / Brave new world / Children of tomorrow / Let's go to San Francisco
SUMCD 4111 / Mar '97 / Summit

Flowers Of Romance

☐ BRILLIANT MISTAKES
3132 / 25 Aug '97 / Hyperium

Flowers, Mike

☐ GROOVY PLACE, A (Flowers, Mike Pops Orchestra)
Groovy place / Wonderwall / In crowd / Light my fire / Please release me / Venus as a boy / Crusty girl / Velvet Underground medley / Freebase / 1999
8287432 / 15 Sep '97 / London

Flowerz

☐ GARAGE RECORDINGS 1967-1968
AA 071 / 27 Apr '98 / Arf Arf

Floyd, Eddie

☐ ALL THE HITS PLUS MORE
On a Saturday night / Gotta make a comeback / Never found a girl / I got a reason to smile / Raise your hand / California girl / Knock on wood / Bring it on home to me / Mr. Blue / Things get better
CDSGP 0393 / 13 Jul '98 / Prestige

☐ CALIFORNIA GIRL/DOWN TO EARTH
California girl / Didn't I blow your mind this time / Why is the wine sweeter (on the other side) / Rainy night in Georgia / Love is you / People, get it together / Laurie / Hey there lonely girl / I feel good / Too much is too little for me / You got that kind of love / People get ready / Linda Sue Dixon / My mind was messed around at the time / When the sun goes down / Salvation / I only have eyes for you / Tears of joy / Changing love
CDSXD 087 / Jul '95 / Stax

☐ I'VE NEVER FOUND A GIRL
Bring it on home to me / Never gonna give you up / Girl I love you / Hobo / I need you woman / I've never found a girl / I'll take her / Slip away / I'm just the kind of fool / Water / Sweet things you do
CDSXE 059 / Jul '92 / Stax

☐ KNOCK ON WOOD
Knock on wood / Something you got / But it's alright / I stand accused / If you gotta make a fool of somebody / I don't want to cry / Raise your hand / Got to make a comeback / 634 5789 / I've just been feeling bad / Hi-heel sneakers / Warm and tender love
7567802832 / Oct '94 / Atlantic

☐ KNOCK ON WOOD (The Best Of Eddie Floyd)
Knock on wood / Raise your hand / Big bird / On a Saturday night / Things get better / Love is a doggone good thing / I've never found a girl / Consider me / Bring it on home to me / I've got to have your love / Blood is thicker than water / Baby, lay your head down / Too weak to fight / Oh how it rained / Why is the wine sweeter (on the other side) / Soul Street / Don't tell your mama / Girl, I love you / People, get it together / Something to write home about / Check me out / Stealing love
CDSX 010 / Mar '88 / Stax

☐ KNOCK ON WOOD (The Best Of Eddie Floyd)
California girl / Knock on wood / Bring it on home to me / Mr. Blue / When I'm with you / On a Saturday night / Got to make a comeback / I've never found a girl / I've got a reason to smile / Raise your hand
AIM 2009CD / May '97 / Aim

☐ RARE STAMPS/I'VE NEVER FOUND A GIRL
Bring it on home to me / Never give you up / Girl I love you / Hobo / I need you woman / I've never found a girl / I'll take her / Slip away / I'm just the kind of fool / Water / Sweet things you do / Knock on wood / Raise your hand / Love's a doggone good thing / On a Saturday night / Thing's get better / Big bird / Got to make a comeback / I've just been feeling bad / This house / I've got to have your love / Consider me / Never let you go / Ain't that good / Laurie
CDSXD 096 / Jul '93 / Stax

Floyd, Frank

☐ GREAT MEDICAL MENAGERIST, THE (Floyd, 'Harmonica' Frank)
Mosquito bar britches / Blue yodel No.6 / Swanproot / Tour De Floyd / Great medical menagerist / Sweet temptation / Howlin' tomcat / Shampoo / Blue yodel No.7 / Steppin' to Covington / Movement like Elgin / Knothole blues
EDCD 384 / Apr '97 / Edsel

Floyd, Gary

☐ BROKEN ANGELS
GRCD 367 / Jun '97 / Glitterhouse

☐ WORLD OF TROUBLE
GRCD 316 / 17 Nov '97 / Glitterhouse

Floyd, Ruth Naomi

☐ PARADIGMS FOR DESOLATE TIMES
BLJCDX 2 / 1 Sep '98 / Big Life Jazz

Floyd, Tina

☐ TINA FLOYD
1385329132 / 17 Mar '98 / Caiman

Flu Thirteen

☐ SPIN CYCLE
ITU 001613 / Feb '97 / Interplanetary

Flue

☐ SOMETIMES
TORSO 12031 / May '87 / Torso

Fluf

☐ ROAD RAGE
J'n it on the net / Leo and George / Living it up / Not that kind / Hang out / Fuck up / Feel good / Ocean song / Wake up / Just like you / Garden weasel / $79 / Something's wrong / You and I agree
DON 017CD / 17 Aug '98 / Honest Don's

☐ WAIKIKI
HED 070CD / Jun '97 / Headhunter

Fluffy

☐ BLACK EYE
Nothing / Hypersonic / Black eye / Scream / I wanna be your lush / Crossdresser / Psychofudge / Too famous / Technicolour yawn / Cosmetic dog / Crawl / Husband / Dirty old bird / Cheap
CDV 2817 / Oct '96 / Virgin

Flugschadel

☐ FLUGSCHADEL
EFA 800232 / Mar '94 / Platten Meister

☐ OTHNIEL
EFA 800312 / Apr '95 / Platten Meister

Fluke

☐ OTO
Bullet / Tosh / Cut / Freak / Wobbler / Squirt / OK / Setback
CIRCD 31 / Jul '95 / Circa

☐ RISOTTO
Absurb / Atom bomb / Kitten moon / Mosh / Bermuda / Setback / Amp / Referendum / Squirt / Goodnight lover
CIRCD 33 / 29 Sep '97 / Circa

☐ SIX WHEELS ON MY WAGON
Groovy feeling / Love letters / Glidub / Electric guitar / Top of the world / Slid / Slow motion / Spacey (catch 22 dub) / Astrosapiens / Oh yeah / Eko / Life support / Philly / Glorious / Cool hand flute / Joni / Easy peasy / Phin / Jig / Taxi / Coolest
CIRCD 27 / Oct '93 / Circa

Flush

☐ LOCUST FUDGE
GRCD 280 / 17 Nov '97 / Glitterhouse

Flute Force 4

☐ FLUTISTRY
1201642 / Nov '97 / Black Saint

Flux

☐ PROTOPLASMIC
Patterns of traffic / Hollow spaces / Unknown codes / Light fuse / Protoplasmic / Stretched out / Airtrap / Immanence
RR 69582 / Jul '97 / Relapse

☐ USCHI'S HOUSE
MA 010 / Jun '97 / M

Flux Of Pink Indians

☐ FUCKING CUNTS TREAT US LIKE PRICKS
TPCD 3 / Jun '88 / One Little Indian

☐ NOT SO BRAVE
OVER 67CD / Jul '97 / Overground

☐ UNCARVED BLOCK
TPCD 1 / Jun '88 / One Little Indian

Fly Ashtray

☐ CLUMPS TAKES A RIDE
Second song / Soft pack / L'age-nt-sno-pee / Dolphin brain / Sink / Man who stayed in ed all day / Ssssss / Do what you can / Best boy / Hypoblast / Ignells 2 / Crows / It doesn't matter / Hoafie hoafie / Ostrich atmosphere / Bad head park / Anyway / Head park rev / Non-ignells
WORD 0042 / Aug '92 / See Eye

Fly Right Trio

☐ WILD ABOUT
TBCD 2008 / Mar '93 / Tombstone

Fly-Rite Boys

☐ BIG SANDY PRESENTS HIS FLY-RITE BOYS
HCD 8090 / 1 Jun '98 / Hightone

Flying Burrito Brothers

☐ BACK TO THE SWEETHEART OF THE RODEO (Burrito Brothers)
Back to the sweethearts of the rodeo / Burning embers / Red shoes / Shoot for the moon / Moonlight rider / Carry me / Baby, won't you let me be the one / Gold guitar / True, true love / I'm impressed / Let's do something crazy / You're a fool to love / Mean streets / Like a shadow / I don't believe you met my baby / My heart skips a beat / Do you know Mary Lou / One man woman / Roadmaster / I've got a new heartache / You should know me by now / My shoes keep walkin' back to you / This could be the night / You're running wild / Should we tell him / Burn the midnight oil / Last call / Take a message to merry
AP 054552 / Jun '95 / Appaloosa
CDSD 502 / Feb '96 / Sundown

☐ BURRITO DELUXE
Lazy days / Image of me / High fashion queen / If you gotta go, go now / Man in the fog / Farther along / Older guys / Cody, Cody / God's own singer / Down in the churchyard
EDCD 194 / 27 Oct '97 / Edsel

☐ DIM LIGHTS, THICK SMOKE AND LOUD MUSIC
Train song / Close all the honky tonks / Sing me back home / Tonight the bottle let me down / Your angel steps out of heaven / Crazy arms / Together again / Honky tonk women / Green green grass of home / Bony Moronie / To love somebody / Break my mind / Dim lights, thick smoke
EDCD 197 / Mar '87 / Edsel

☐ DOUBLE BARREL (Burrito Brothers)
She's single again / New shade of blue / Price of love / Ain't love just like the rain / One more time / Sailor / No easy way out / Tonight / Hearts in my eyes / Ain't worth the powder / Late in the night / I'm confessing / Let your heart do the talking
CDSD 079 / Nov '95 / Sundown

☐ ENCORE (Live 1990) (Burrito Brothers)
Dim lights, thick smoke / You ain't goin' nowhere / Hickory wind / White line fever / Sweet little Colette / Big bayou / Sweet Suzanna / Wild horses / Silverwings / Help wanted / Cannonball rag / When it all comes down to love / Wheels
CDSD 069 / Nov '90 / Sundown

☐ EYE OF A HURRICANE
Wheel of love / Like a thief in the night / Bayou blues / Angry words / Rosetta knows / Heart highway / I sent your saddle home / Jukebox Saturday night / Arizona moon / Wild wild West / Eye of a hurricane / Sunset boulevard / Smile
CDSD 075 / Nov '93 / Sundown
OW 30330 / Jul '94 / One Way

☐ FROM ANOTHER TIME
Diggi diggi li / Wheels / Dim lights, thick smoke / Faded love / Devil in disguise / Building fires / Bon soir blues / White line fever / Sin City / She thinks I still care / Why baby why / Close all the honky tonks
CDSD 072 / Apr '91 / Sundown

☐ GILDED PALACE OF SIN, THE
Christine's tune / Sin City / Do right woman, do right man / Dark end of the street / My uncle / Wheels / Juanita / Hot burrito / Do you know how it feels to be lonesome / Hippie boy
EDCD 191 / '88 / Edsel

☐ GUILDED PALACE OF SIN/BURRITO DELUXE
Christine's tune / Sin city / Do right woman / Dark end of the street / My uncle / Wheels / Juanita / Hot Burrito / Hot burrito / Do you know how it feels / Hippie boy / Lazy days / Image of me / High fashion queen / If you gotta go / Man in the fog / Farther along / Older guys / Cody, cody / God's own singer / Down in the churchyard / Wild horses
5407042 / Mar '97 / A&M

☐ HOLLYWOOD NIGHTS 79-82
She belongs to everyone but me / Somewhere tonight / Baby, how'd we ever get this way / Too much honky tonkin' / My abandoned heart / She's a friend of mine / Louisiana / Why must the ending always be so sad / That's when you know it's over / She's a hell of a deal / Another shade of grey / Damned if I'll be lonely tonight / If something should come between us / Run to the night / Coast to coast / Closer to you / True love never runs dry / Tell me it ain't so
CDSD 067 / May '90 / Sundown

☐ LIVE FROM TOKYO
Big bayou / White line fever / Dim lights, thick smoke / There'll be no teardrops tonight / Rollin' in my sweet baby's arms / Hot burrito / Colorado / Rocky top / Six days on the road / Truck drivin' man
CDSD 025 / '86 / Sundown

☐ LIVE IN EUROPE
SUMCD 4157 / Jan '98 / Summit

☐ MASTERS, THE
She belongs to everyone but me / Somewhere tonight / Baby how'd we ever get this way / Too much honky tonkin' / Midnight magic woman / My abandoned heart / She's a friend of a friend / Louisiana / Cheating kind of love / Why must the ending always be so sad / That's when you know its over / You / I swear I don't miss her anymore / She's a hell of a deal / Another shade of grey / Damned if I'll be lonely tonight / If something should come between us / When you're giving yourself to a stranger / Run to the night / Coast to coast / Closer to you / True love never runs dry / Tell me it ain't so
EABCD 079 / 30 Mar '98 / Eagle

☐ OUT OF THE BLUE (2CD Set)
Sing me back home / Hot burrito no.2 / Break my mind / Dark end of the street / Cody, Cody / Wheels / Hot burrito no.1 / Sin city / Do right woman / God's own singer / Older guys / Train song / Lazy days / Christine's tune / Close up the honky tonks / Do you know how it feels / High fashion queen / Man in the fog / To love somebody / My uncle / Hippie boy / Juanita / Image of me / Farther along / If you gotta go / Bony Moronie / Six days on the road / Wild horses / Down in the churchyard / Wake up little Susie / Pick me up on your way down / Just because / Lodi / Money honey / I shall be released / White line fever / Ain't that a lot of love / Don't fight it / Losing game / Tried so hard / All alone / 100 years from now
5404082 / Apr '96 / A&M

☐ TOO MUCH HONKY TONKIN'
She belongs to everyone but me / She's a friend of a friend / If sometehing should come between us / Closer to you / Somewhere tonight / Baby how'd we ever get this way / Too much honky tonkin' / Midnight magic woman / My abandoned heart / Louisiana / Cheating king of love / Why must the ending always be so sad / That's when you know it's over / You / I swear I son't miss her anymore / She's a hell of a deal / Damned if I'll be lonely tonight / When you're gicing yourself to a stranger / Run to the night / Coast to coast / True love never runs dry / Another shade of gray / Tell me it ain't so
CTS 55439 / May '96 / Country Stars

☐ WHEELS (A Tribute To Clarence White & Gram Parsons) (Burrito Brothers & Co.)
Six white horses / Emmy / Bugler / Promised land / Freeborn man / Games people play / Detroit city / 500 miles away from home / Four strong winds / Shame on me / Streets of Baltimore / Millers cave / Christine's tune / Wheels
APCD 049 / '88 / Appaloosa

Flying Dutchman Jazzband

☐ IN FULL SWING
KLM march / Just a closer walk with thee / Makin' whoopy / Don't get around much anymore / She's funny that way / That's plenty / Tennessee waltz rock / Out of the gallion / Ory's creole trombone / St. James infirmary / Goody goody / Apex blues / Alexander's ragtime band / After you've gone / When it's sleepytime down south / Honeysuckle rose / World is waiting for the sunrise / Farewell blues
AL 73121 / Jun '98 / A

Flying Luttenbachers

☐ DESTROY ALL MUSIC
GR 51CD / 29 Jun '98 / Skingraft

☐ REVENGE
GR 37CD / Sep '96 / Skingraft

Flying Neutrinos

☐ I'D RATHER BE IN NEW ORLEANS
FIXCD 29 / Jan '97 / Fiction

Flying Nun

☐ PILOT
Submarine / Frank / Shades / Carousel of freaks / Life on the ground
OLE 1512 / Sep '95 / Matador

Flying Pickets

☐ LOST BOYS
Remember this / I heard it through the grapevine / Disco down / So close / Tears of a clown / When you're young and in love / You've lost that lovin' feelin' / Psycho killer / Wide boy / Factory / Monica engineer / Only you / Masters of war / Who's that girl
MTD 021 / Dec '93 / Moving Target

☐ ONLY YOU - THE BEST OF THE FLYING PICKETS
Only you / I heard it through the grapevine / Tears of a clown / You've lost that lovin' feelin' / Sealed with a kiss / Only the lonely / Space oddity / Who's that girl / When you're young and in love / Groovin' / Coral island / Buffalo soldier / I got you babe / Summer in the city / Get off my cloud / Higher and higher
CDVIP 115 / Mar '94 / Virgin VIP

Flying Saucer Attack

☐ CHORUS
Feedback song / Light in the evening / Popul vuh ill / Always / Feedback song demo / Second hour / Beach red lullaby / There, but not there / February 8th / There dub
WIGCD 022 / Nov '95 / Domino

☐ DISTANCE
WIGCD 012 / Oct '94 / Domino

☐ FLYING SAUCER ATTACK
VHF 11 / Dec '96 / VHF

☐ FURTHER
WIGCD 020 / Apr '95 / Domino

☐ NEW LANDS
Past / Present / Up in her eyes / Respect / Night falls / Whole day song / Sea / Forever
WIGCD 038 / 13 Oct '97 / Domino

Flyscreen

☐ COUNCIL POP
WOWCD 42 / May '95 / Words Of Warning

☐ GIRLS CAN'T MAKE GUN NOISES
MCD 60018 / 2 Mar '98 / MCA

Flyte Reaction

☐ CREATE A SMILE
SPLENCD 3 / Jun '95 / Backs

Flyy, Kenny

☐ MY GOD
SB 32266CD / 3 Nov '97 / NMG/ Southboy

FM

☐ APHRODISIAC
Breathe fire / Blood and gasoline / All or nothing / Closer to heaven / Ain't too proud / Take the money / Aphordisia / Inside out / Run no more / Play dirty / Rivers run dry / Hard day in hell
CDMFN 141 / Oct '92 / Music For Nations

☐ DEAD MAN'S SHOES
RAWCD 107 / Apr '96 / Raw Power

☐ NO ELECTRICITY REQUIRED
Seagull / Need your love so bad / Rocky mountain way / Blood and gasoline / Superstition / Heard it through the grapevine / Some kind of wonderful / Midnight hour-dancing in the street (medley) / Closer to heaven / Only the strong survive / Little bit of love / Rockin' me / Tush / Long way to go / Burning my heart down ('93 version) / Flesh and blood / Don't stop ('93 version) / All or nothing
CDMFN 155 / Oct '93 / Music For Nations

☐ ONLY THE STRONG (The Best Of FM 1984-1994)
That girl / Other side of midnight / American girls / Face to face / Frozen heart / Tough it out / Don't stop / Bad luck / Burning my heart down / Let love be the leader / I heard it through the grapevine / Only the strong survive / Dangerous ground / Breathe fire / Blood and gasoline / All or nothing / Closer to heaven
VSOPCD 203 / Aug '94 / Connoisseur Collection

☐ TAKIN' IT TO THE STREETS
I'm ready / I heard it through the grapevine / Only the strong survive / Just can't leave her alone / She's no angel / Dangerous ground / Bad blood / Crack alley / If it feels good, do it / Girl's gone bad / Thrill of it all
CDMFN 119 / Oct '91 / Music For Nations

Fochabers Fiddlers

☐ ORANGE BLOSSOM SPECIAL
CDGR 163 / Apr '98 / Ross

Focus

☐ FOCUS VOL.3
Round goes the gossip / Love remembered / Sylvia / Carnival fugue / Focus III / Answers Questions Answers Questions / Anonymus II / Elspeth of Nottingham / House of the king
PRMCD 10 / Jun '96 / Premier/EMI

☐ HOCUS POCUS: THE BEST OF FOCUS
Hocus pocus / Anonymus / House of the king / Focus / Janis / Focus II / Tommy / Sylvia / Focus III / Harem scarum / Mother focus / Focus IV / Bennie Helder / Glider / Red sky at night / Hocus pocus (US single version)
CDP 8281622 / May '94 / EMI

☐ LIVE AT THE RAINBOW
7489692 / 1 Jun '98 / EMI

☐ MOVING WAVES
Hocus pocus / Le clochard (bread) / Janis / Moving waves / Focus II / Eruption
PRMCD 9 / Jun '96 / Premier/EMI

Foden Motor Works Band

☐ WORLD OF THE BRASS BAND, THE (Foden Motor Works Band & Fairey Aviation/Morris Motors Band)
Coronation march / Shepherd's hey / Lilac time / Ruy blas overture / Perpetuum mobile / Marche Slave / Czech polka / Orpheus in the underworld / Trumpet voluntary / Elizabethan serenade / Merrie England / Swedish rhapsody / Finlandia / Chit chat polka / William Tell overture
4529392 / Aug '97 / Decca

Foden OTS Band

☐ BRASS BAND CHRISTMAS
PLSCD 260 / 29 Sep '97 / Pulse

☐ ELGAR IN BRASS (Foden OTS Band & Desford Colliery Dowty Band)
Pomp and circumstance marches / Serenade Op.20 / Enigma variations
QMPR 605D / Oct '97 / Polyphonic

Fodor, Eugene

☐ WITCHES BREW
CCD 1017 / Jul '98 / Clarity

Foehn

☐ INSIDE OUT EYES
SF 018CD / 24 Nov '97 / Swarf Finger

Foetus

☐ ACHE
THI 570352 / 30 Mar '98 / Thirsty Ear

☐ BOIL
ABB 119CD / Aug '96 / Big Cat

☐ DEAF
THI 570342 / 30 Mar '98 / Thirsty Ear

☐ GASH
ABB 88CD / May '95 / Big Cat

☐ MALE (Foetus Corruptus)
ABB 31/2CD / Feb '92 / Big Cat

☐ NAIL (Scraping Foetus Off The Wheel)
WOMBFIP 004CD / Apr '86 / Some Bizarre

☐ NULL AND VOID
CLP 99312 / Jun '97 / Cleopatra
ABB 149CD / 20 Oct '97 / Big Cat

☐ YORK
ABB 148XCD / 20 Oct '97 / Big Cat

Fogelberg, Dan

☐ INNOCENT AGE, THE (2CD Set)
Nexus / Innocent age / Sand and the foam / In the passage / Lost in the sun / Run for the roses / Leader of the band/Washington Post / March / Same auld lang syne / Stolen moments / Lion's share / Only the heart may know / Reach / Aireshire lament / Times like these / Hard to sat / Empty cages / Ghosts
4874822 / Jun '97 / Epic

Fogerty, John

☐ BLUE MOON SWAMP
Southern streamline / Hot rod heart / Blueboy / Hundred and ten in the shade / Rattlesnake highway / Bring it down to Jelly Roll / Walking in a hurricane / Swamp river days / Rambunctions boy / Joy of my life / Blue moon nights / Bad bad boy
9362454262 / Jun '97 / Warner Bros.

☐ BLUE RIDGE RANGERS (Blue Ridge Rangers)
Blue Ridge Mountain blues / Somewhere listening (for my name) / You're the reason / Jambalaya / She thinks I still care / California blues / Workin' on a building / Please help me, I'm falling / Have thine own way / I ain't never / Hearts of stone / Today I started loving you again
CDFE 506 / Oct '87 / Fantasy

☐ CENTERFIELD
Old man down the road / Rock 'n' roll girls / Big train / I saw it on TV / Mr. Greed / Searchlight / Centerfield / I can't help myself / Zanz kant danz
9252032 / Feb '85 / WEA

☐ JOHN FOGERTY
Rockin' all over the world / (I'll be glad when you're dead) you rascal you / Wall / Travellin' high / Lonely teardrops / Almost Saturday night / Where the river flows / Sea cruise / Dream song / Flying away / Comin' down the road / Ricochet
CDFE 507 / Sep '87 / Fantasy

☐ PREMONITION (John Fogerty Live)
Born on the Bayou / Green river / Susie-Q / I put a spell on you / Who'll stop the rain / Premonition / Almost Saturday night / Rockin' all over the world / Joy of my life / Down on the corner / Centerfield / Swamp river days / Hot rod heart / Old man down the road / Bad moon rising / Fortunate son / Proud Mary / Travelin' band
9362469082 / 8 Jun '98 / Reprise

Foghat

☐ BEST OF FOGHAT
I just want to make love to you / Maybellene / Ride ride ride / Take it or leave it / Home in my hand / Drivin' wheel / Fool for the city / Slow ride / Stone blue / Honey hush / Night shift / Wild cherry / Third time lucky (first time I was a fool) / Easy money / Chateau lafitte '59 boogie / Eight days on the road
8122700882 / Jul '93 / WEA

☐ NIGHTSHIFT
Drivin' wheel / Don't run me down / Burning the midnight oil / Nightshift / Hot shot love / Take me to the river / I'll be standing by
8122708882 / Mar '93 / WEA

☐ ROAD CASE
8255156282 / 27 Apr '98 / Plum

Fohlin, Ingvar

☐ MAGDEBURGERSPELMAN
AW 11CD / Aug '96 / Tongang

Foil

☐ SPREAD IT ALL AROUND
AC Rocket / High wire / Acid kewpie / Control freak / Penicillin / Place to hide / Soup / Don't come around / Are you enemy / Coup d'etat / Reviver gene / Carstairs
13THCD 5 / 19 Jan '98 / Thirteenth Hour

Fol, Raymond

☐ PARIS SWINGS THE 60'S (Fol, Raymond & Pierre Michelot)
Le printemps: *Fol, Raymond Big Band* / L'ete: *Fol, Raymond Big Band* / L'automne: *Fol, Raymond Big Band* / L'hiver: *Fol, Raymond Big Band* / Cherokee: *Michelot, Pierre & His Orchestra* / Gavotte: *Michelot, Pierre & His Orchestra* / Akkilino: *Michelot, Pierre & His Orchestra* / Elephant green: *Michelot, Pierre & His Orchestra* / Sous les ponts de Paris: *Michelot, Pierre & His Orchestra* / Chet: *Michelot, Pierre & His Orchestra* / Bye bye blackbird: *Michelot, Pierre & His Orchestra* / Sweet feeling: *Michelot, Pierre & His Orchestra* / Klook's shadow: *Michelot, Pierre & His Orchestra*
8326572 / Mar '88 / ECM

Folan, Declan

☐ SKIN AND BOW (Folan, Declan & J. Davey)
SUN 23CD / Nov '96 / Sun

Folds, Ben

☐ BEN FOLDS FIVE (Folds, Ben Five)
Jackson Cannery / Philosophy / Julianne / Where's summer B / Alice Childress / Underground / Sports and wine / Uncle Walter / Best imitation of myself / Video / Last polka / Boxing
CAROL 002CD / Apr '96 / Caroline

☐ NAKED BABY PHOTOS (Folds, Ben Five)
Eddie Walker / Jackson Cannery / Emaline / Alice Childress / Dick Holdress / Tom and Mary / For those of y'al who wear Fanny Packs / Bad idea / Underground / Ultimate scarifice / Satan is my master / Julianne / Song for the dumped / Philosophy / Twin falls / Boxing
CAR 7554 / 12 Jan '98 / Caroline

☐ WHATEVER AND EVER AMEN (Folds, Ben Five)
One angry dwarf and 200 solemn / Faces / Fair / Brick / Song for the dumped / Selfless / Cold and composed / Kate / Smoke / Cigarette / Steven's last night in town / Battle of who could care less / Missing the war
4866982 / Mar '97 / Epic

Folds, Chuck

☐ HITTING HIS STRIDE
ARCD 19117 / Nov '94 / Arbors Jazz

Foley, Sue

☐ TEN DAYS IN NOVEMBER
Highwayside / Baltimore skyline / Long way to go / Waiting game / Give my love to you / She don't belong to you / Through the night / Winds of change / Forest / Promised land / 11 new roads
SHANCD 8031 / Jun '98 / Shanachie

☐ WITHOUT A WARNING
ANTCD 0025 / May '94 / Antones

☐ YOUNG GIRL BLUES
Queen Bee / (Me and my) Chauffeur blues / Cuban getaway / Mean old lonesome train / Gone blind / Walkin' home / But I forgive you / Off the hook / Hooked on love / Little mixed up / Time to travel
ANTCD 0019 / Jun '92 / Alligator

Folk & Rackere

☐ FOLK & RACKERE 1976-1985
Vanner och frander / En sjomansbrud skall blakladd ga / Harpans kraft / Nas ingars polska / Inga litimor / Major brack / Maria / Naktergalen / Aggavisan / Haugebonden / Ruben ranzo / De tva systrarna / Silibrand / Flickan gar pa golvet / Det blaser nordost
RES 515CD / Jul '97 / Resource

Folk Aerobics

☐ FOLK YOUR WAY TO FITNESS
HTDCD 75 / Jul '97 / HTD

Folk Friends

☐ 1
TUT 72160 / Jan '94 / Wundertute

☐ 2
CDTUT 72150 / '89 / Wundertute

Folk Implosion

☐ DARE TO BE SURPRISED
COMM 45CD / Jun '97 / Communion

☐ TAKE A LOOK
COMM 032CD / Dec '96 / Communion

Folke Rabe

☐ WAS (WHAT)
DEX 12CD / Jun '97 / Dexter's Cigar

Folkloyuma

☐ MUSIC FROM THE ORIENTE DE CUBA: THE RUMBA
NI 5425 / Apr '95 / Nimbus

Foly, Liane

☐ REVE ORANGE
Au fur et a mesure / Nuit halogene / Goodbye lover / Reve orange / Blue notes / Va savoir / Be my boy / Sun / S'en balancer
CDVIR 7 / Jun '91 / Virgin

☐ SWEET MYSTERY
A trace of you (doucement) / Sweet mystery / When you smile / Les parfums d'autrefois / Voler la nuit / Tell me why / Tear of desire / No sweat / Who knows why / Anywhere anyplace anytime / Au fur et a mesure / Les petites notes
CDVIR 19 / Apr '94 / Virgin

Fon, Bryn

☐ DAWNSIO AR Y DIBYN
Coedwig ar dan / Fy nghalon I / Un funud fach / Boddi wrth y lan / Gwaed ar aur / Dawnsio ar y bibyn / Y bai / Chwarae'r gem / Llythyrau tyddyn-y-gaseg / Tan ar fynydd cennin / Strydoedd aberstalwm / Yn yr ardd
CRAICD 061 / Jun '98 / Crai

☐ DYDDIAU DI-GYMAR
Cwm yr aur / Gwybod yn iawn / Ceidwad y goleudy / Rebal wieend / Diwedd y gan / Yr un hen gwestynau / Lar i'r niwl / Angen y gan / Diane o'r ddinas / Cofio dy wyneh / Can i ems
CRAICD 044 / Jun '98 / Crai

Fonsea

☐ ET SE ANGES NOIRS
CNCD 5981 / Apr '94 / Disky

Fonseca

☐ MELODIES FROM PORTUGAL
EUCD 1087 / '89 / ARC

Fontaine, Seb

☐ ELEMENTS (Mixed By Seb Fontaine & Tony De Vit - 2CD Set) (Various Artists)
Rapper's delight: *Sugarhill Gang* / Spin me wild: *Freak & Mac Zimms* / Uprising: *Ecomo, Silvio* / That lemon dub: *CBQ* / Storm club / Untidy dubs: *To The Beat* / Expressions: *Black, Steve* / Black is back: *All Nighters* / What ya got for me: *Signum* / Joansey independents / Freaks come out: *Fisher, Cevin Big Freak* / Ripped in two minutes: *A vs. B* / Keep on dancin': *Perpetual Motion* / Can you feel it: *CIS & Todd Terry* / Get up stand up: *Phunky Phantom* / Union Jack: *Two Full Moons & A Trout* / Grease 2000 / Gamesmaster: *Lost Tribe* / Hold it now: *Johan & Beastie Boys* / To the world: *Organ* / Rights of passage: *Sophie's Men* / NRG 52: 3 In 1 / In my mind: *In My Mind* / In the socket: *Bones, Frankie* / Scott Mac Project: Boo / Just let go: *Petra & Co* / Meet her at the love parade: *Da Hool* / Let me show you: *Camisra*
3984238682 / 6 Jul '98 / Warner ESP

Fontana, Wayne

☐ WORLD OF WAYNE FONTANA & THE MINDBENDERS, THE (Fontana, Wayne & The Mindbenders)
Game of love / Groovy kind of love / Pamela Pamela / Um um um um um um / Just a little bit too late / Ashes to ashes / It was easier to hurt her / Hello Josephine / Uncle Joe, the ice cream man / Words of Bartholomew / Like I did / Letter / Come on home / First taste of love / Goodbye bluebird / She needs love / (Can't live with you) can't live without you / Storybook children / Stop, look and listen / Something keeps calling me back
5514362 / May '96 / Spectrum

Fontenot, Canray

☐ LOUISIANA HOT SAUCE CREOLE STYLE
Les barres de la prison (the prison bars) / Canray's one step / Joe pitre a deux femmes (joe pitre got two women) / Allons danser / Bernadette / Bonsoir, moreau (good evening moreau) / Lorita's blues / La valse de mom et pop / Two-step de grand mallet / Les plats sont tous mis sur la table (the table's already / Hey hey blues / Midland two step / La coulee rodair / Le slow drag a nonc adam / La robe barree / Old carpenter's waltz / Bee de la manche / La jog a plombeau / Jig cajin / Malinda / Fi-do (dixieland) / Shoo, black / Canray's breakdown / La table ronde (the round table) / Les blues a canray (canray's blues) / Bernadette
ARHCD 381 / Apr '95 / Arhoolie

Foo Fighters

☐ COLOUR AND THE SHAPE, THE
Doll / Monkey wrench / Hey Johnny Park / My poor brain / Wind up / Up in arms / My hero / See you / Enough space / February stars / Everlong / Walking after you / New way home
CDEST 2295 / May '97 / Roswell

☐ FOO FIGHTERS
This is a call / I'll stick around / Big me / Alone and easy target / Good grief / Floaty / Weenie beenie / Oh George / For all the cows / X-static / Watershed / Exhausted
CDEST 2266 / Jul '95 / Roswell

☐ INTERVIEW SESSIONS
CHAT 5 / 23 Feb '98 / Chatback

Fool

☐ FOOL...PLUS
Fly / Voice on the wind / Rainbow man / Cry for me / No one will ever know / Reincarnation / Hello little sister / Keep on pushin / Inside your mind / Lay it down / We are one / Shining light
SEECD 496 / 10 Aug '98 / See For Miles

Fool Proof

☐ NO FRICTION
Beale and baxter / Lower east side jazzbo panorama / August wilson's urban blue blues / Popeye's blues / Leg blues / Red car / Girl's gonna drive me mad / West broadway and 125th / Love and happiness / Shelter man / Sidewalking / Title 9 blues
188804 2 / Feb '89 / Gramavision

Foot

☐ FOOT
NOIR 009CD / 27 Jul '98 / God Bless

For Against

☐ SHELF LIFE
WDM 10072 / 2 Mar '98 / World Domination

For Carnation

☐ PROMISED WORKS
RUNT 30 / Jun '97 / Runt

For Love Not Lisa

☐ MERGE
Softhand / Slip slide melting / Lucifer for now / Daring to pick up / Simple line of decline / Travis Hoffman / Just a phase / Traces / Mother's faith / Swallow / More than a girl / Merge
7567922832 / Oct '93 / WEA

For Real

☐ FREE
Intro / Like I do / Good morning sunshine / Hold me / So in love / Remember / Will you love me / Saddest song I ever heard / Nothing without you / How can I get close to you / Love will be waiting at home / Free
75444370132 / Jul '97 / Rowdy

☐ IT'S A NATURAL THANG
Easy to love / Where did your love go / You don't wanna miss / Just a matter of time / Li'l bit / Don't wanna love you now / You don't know nothin' / With this ring (say yes) / D'yer mak'er / Harder I try / I like / Thinking of you / Prayer
5401562 / Feb '95 / A&M

Forbert, Steve

☐ AMERICAN IN ME, THE
GED 24459 / Jun '97 / Geffen

☐ HERE'S YOUR PIZZA
Stop breakin' down blues / What kinda guy/Rockin' Robin / One after 909 / Years ago / Everybody does it in Hawaii / You're darn right / Runaway train of love / All because of you / Song for Katrina / Honky tonker / Samson and Delilah / You cannot win (if you do not play) / Polk salad Annie / His was the sound/La Bamba / Sweet pea
9246922 / Nov '97 / Paladin
FIENDCD 936 / 29 Sep '97 / Demon

☐ JACKRABBIT SLIM
Romeo's tune / Sweet love that you give (sure goes a long, long way) / I'm in love with you / Say goodbye to little Jo / Wait / Make it all so real / Baby / Complications / Sadly sorta like a soap opera
4851072 / Nov '96 / Epic

☐ MISSION OF THE CROSS
74321259902 / Apr '95 / RCA

☐ ROCKING HORSE HEAD
If I want you now / My time ain't long / Shaky ground / Dear Lord / Moon man (I'm waiting on you) / Don't stop / Some will rake the coals / I know what I know / Good planets are hard to find / Big new world / Open house / Dream, dream
74321407482 / Nov '96 / RCA

☐ STREETS OF THIS TOWN
Running on love / Don't tell me, I know / I blinked once / Mexico / As we live and breathe / On the streets of this town / Hope, faith and love / Perfect stranger / Wait a little longer / Search your heart
GED 24194 / Jun '97 / Geffen

Forbes, Roy

☐ LOVE TURNS TO ICE
FF 70499 / Jul '89 / Flying Fish

Forbidden

☐ POINT OF NO RETURN, THE (The Best Of The Forbidden)
Chalice of blood / Out of body (out of mind) / Feel no pain / Step by step / Off the edge / One foot in hell / Through the eyes of glass / Tossed away / March into fire / Victim of changes
CDMFLAG 73 / Nov '92 / Under One Flag

Force & Styles

☐ HARDCORE EXPLOSION '97 (Remixed By Force & Styles/Hixxy & Dougal/2CD Set) (Various Artists)
Heart of gold: *Force & Styles* / Surrender: *Eruption* / People's party: *DJ Hixxy & Sunset Regime* / Come on: *Walford Project* / Apollo 13: *Force & Styles* / Euro bounce: *Force & Styles* / Love of my life: *Dr. Who* / Stay with me: *Eruption* / I'm gonna get ya: *Eruption & Dougal* / Sunshine: *Slipmatt & Eruption* / Pacific sun: *Force & Styles* / Muzik: *Happy Rollers* / Rock dis place: *Chewy* / Wonderland: *Force & Styles* / Techno wonderland: *Ravers Choice* / Shinning down: *Force & Styles* / Set you free: *Zoom* / Fun fair: *Force & Styles* / Pretty green eyes: *Force & Styles* / Simply electric: *Force & Styles* / Let the music: *Eruption* / Party time: *Eruption & Dougal* / Poison fruit: *Walford Project* / Fantasy: *Eruption* / Party people: *Slipmatt & Eruption* / SMD 5: *SMD* / Something like dis: *Slippery Project* / Kick your leg in the air: *Elogic & DNA* / Forever together: *DJ Hixxy & Banana Man* / Frantic: *Druid & Sharkey*
SUMCD 116 / Feb '97 / Supreme Underground

☐ SIMPLY ELECTRIC (2CD Set)
SPIN 35684 / 8 Jun '98 / Death Becomes Me

☐ SIMPLY ELECTRIC (Remixes/2CD Set)
SPIN 3810 / 1 Sep '98 / Death Becomes Me

Force Dimension

☐ DEUS EX MACHINA
KK 049CD / Aug '90 / KK

☐ FORCE DIMENSION
KK 020CD / '90 / KK

Force Mass Motion

☐ MOTIONS BEYOND
CUTCD 003 / Oct '96 / Rabbit City

Force Of Music

☐ KINGS AND QUEENS OF DUB
TWCD 1017 / Oct '94 / Tamoki Wambesi

Force One Network

☐ SOUL NETWORK PROGRAMME VOL.2
Force One theme / Vibe / Somethin' about you / Sista sista / Force One theme / Static: *Force One Network & 2Pac* / Everybody wants to be black / Miss you / Always / Don't go / Never in a million years / Over and over / Love interlude / Spirit
AIM 4002CD / Oct '97 / Aim

Forcefield

☐ INSTRUMENTALS
Tokyo / Talisman / Perfect world / I lose again / Secret waters / Look don't touch / Three card shuffle / Rendezvous / Osaka
PCOM 1121 / Jun '92 / President

☐ LET THE WILD RUN FREE (Forcefield IV)
Let the wild run free / Can't get enough of your love / Money talks / I will not go quietly / Ball of confusion / Wind cries mary / Living by numbers / In a perfect world
PCOM 1110 / Nov '90 / President

☐ TALISMAN, THE (Forcefield II)
Talisman / Year of the dragon / Tired of waiting for you / Heartache / Good is good / Carrie / Without your love / I lose again / Mercenary / Black night / I lose again (instrumental)
PCOM 1095 / Aug '88 / President

☐ TO OZ AND BACK (Forcefield III)
Hit and run / Always / Stay away / Desire / Tokyo / Who'll be the next in line / Wings on my feet / Firepower / Hold on / Rendezvous
PCOM 1100 / Oct '89 / President

Forcione, Antonio

☐ ACOUSTIC REVENGE
NAIMCD 017 / Dec '97 / Naim Audio

☐ DEDICATO
NAIMCD 013 / Mar '97 / Naim Audio

Ford, Charles

☐ AS REAL AS IT GETS (Ford, Charles Band)
CCD 11048 / Feb '97 / Crosscut

☐ CHARLES FORD BAND, THE (Ford, Charles Band)
Blue and lonesome / Gibson creek shuffle / My time after a while / Rest my mind on jesus / Reconsider baby / Black night / Wild woman / I know what you're puttin' down / Live the life I love / Tell him I was flyin' / Promise
ARHCD 353 / Apr '95 / Arhoolie

☐ REUNION - LIVE
CCD 11043 / Nov '94 / Crosscut

Ford, Douglas

☐ PIPES AND DRUMS OF SCOTLAND (Ford, Douglas & The Gordon Highlanders)
Amazing grace / My home in the hills / Conund rum / Miss Kirkwood / Scotland the brave / Reveille / Rustic bridge by the mill / Miss McLeod O'Raasey / Cock of the north / Skye boat song / Bonnie Dundee
SOW 90149 / Jan '96 / Sounds Of The World

Ford, Emile

☐ EMILE FORD AND THE CHECKMATES (Ford, Emile & The Checkmates)
REP 4097 / Aug '91 / Repertoire

☐ GREATEST HITS
Keep on doin' what you're doin / I ran all the way home / Counting teardrops / Doin' the twist / Endlessly / Half of my heart / I'll be satisfied / Mona lisa / On a slow boat to china / Red sails in the sunset / Still / Them there eyes / To know her is to love her / What am I gonna do / What do you want to make those eyes at me for / You'll never know what you're missing
SSLCD 201 / Jun '95 / Savanna

☐ VERY BEST OF EMILE FORD & THE CHECKMATES (Ford, Emile & The Checkmates)
What do you want to make those eyes at me for / After you've gone / Hold me, thrill me, kiss me / Keep on doin' what you're doin' / Them there eyes / Questions / Still / You'll never know what you're missing / Trouble / Lawdy Miss Clawdy / Joker / Yellow bird / Buona sera / I don't / Danny boy / That lucky old sun / Counting teardrops / Heavenly / What am I gonna do / On a slow boat to China / Don't tell me your troubles / Red sails in the sunset / Send for me / Kiss to build a dream on / Scarlet ribbons / Vaya con dios / Move along
SEECD 309 / Jan '91 / See For Miles

☐ VERY BEST OF EMILE FORD, THE
What do you want to make those eyes at me for / Don't tell me your troubles / Endlessly / Mona lisa / On a slow boat to china / You'll never know what you're missing / Red sails in the sunset / Them there eyes / That lucky old sun / Counting teardrops / Blue moon / What am I gonna do / Vaya con dios / Fever / Half of my heart / Always / On the sunny side of the street / Danny boy / I wonder who's kissing her now / Hold me, thrill me, kiss me
SOW 703 / May '94 / Sound Waves

Ford, Frankie

☐ OOO-WEE BABY (The Very Best Of Frankie Ford)
Cheatin' woman / Last one to cry / You can't stop her / Sea cruise / Roberta / Rockin' teenage wedding / Baby it's love / Alimony / Can't tell my heart what to do / I want to be your man / Time after time / Chinatown / What's going on / Morgus the magnificent / Lonely boy / Ocean full of tears / Hour of need / Blow wind blow / It must be jelly / Your game is over / St. Louis blues / Watch dog / Pretending you're mine / Sea cruise
WESM 519 / 16 Mar '98 / Westside

Ford, Jim

☐ HARLAN COUNTY
Harlan County / I'm gonna make her love me / Changing colors / Dr. Handy's dandy candy / Love on my brain / Long road ahead / Under construction / Working my way to LA / Spoonful / To make my life beautiful
EDCD 519 / Jun '97 / Edsel

Ford, Lita

☐ INTERVIEW COMPACT DISC: LITA FORD
CBAK 4020 / Nov '89 / Baktabak

☐ KISS ME DEADLY
Kiss me deadly / Hungry / Shot of poison / What do ya know about love / Only women bleed / Stiletto / Lisa / Bad boy / Larger than life / Playin' with fire / Back to the cave / Bad love / Black widow / Fatal passion / Cherry red / Broken dreams / Can't catch me
74321512002 / 1 Sep '97 / Camden

Ford, Oscar

☐ COMPLETE RECORDED WORKS 1926-1930, THE (Ford, Oscar & Walter Morris)
DOCD 8024 / 20 Apr '98 / Document

Ford Pier

☐ MECONIUM
WRONG 15 / Nov '95 / Wrong

Ford, Ricky

☐ AMERICAN - AFRICAN BLUES
American - African blues / Environ / Of / Complex harmony / Descent / Mostly arco / Encore / American - African blues
CCD 79528 / Feb '97 / Candid

☐ EBONY RHAPSODY
Intro / Ebony rhapsody / Mon amour / Independence blues / Mirror man / In a sentimental mood / Setting sun blues / Broadway / Red, crack and blue
CCD 79053 / Feb '97 / Candid

☐ HOT BRASS
Ford variations / Banging, bashing, bowing and blowing / Night in Valencia / 11/15/91 / Cop out / Hot brass / Mood blues / Speak now / Carbon / It don't mean a thing if it ain't got that swing
CCD 79518 / Feb '97 / Candid

☐ LOXODONTA AFRICANA (The Jazz Sound)
Loxodonta Africana / UCIL / Blues Peru / Dexter / My romance / One up one down / Aerolinos
802042 / Oct '97 / New World

☐ MANHATTAN BLUES
In walked Bud / Misty / Ode to crispus attacks / Bop nouveau / My little strayhorn / Manhattan blues / Half nelson / Portrait of Mingus / Land preserved
CCD 79036 / Feb '97 / Candid

☐ SAXOTIC STOMP
MCD 5349 / Sep '92 / Muse

Ford, Robben

☐ AUTHORIZED BOOTLEG, THE (Ford, Robben & The Blue Line)
When I leave here / Chevrolet / Top of the hill / Start it up / Don't let the sun catch you crying / Help the poor / Lovin' cup / Tired of talkin'
BTR 70132 / 23 Mar '98 / Blue Thumb

☐ BLUES COLLECTION 1971-1991, THE
CCD 11054 / Jun '97 / Crosscut
BRR 127CD / May '97 / Blue Rock-It

☐ FORD BLUES BAND, THE (Ford Blues Band)
Shuffle for walter / Parchman farm / Self preservation / Mojo boogie / Down in mississippi / Blues are back / One way out / Take out some insurance / Too late / Alabama march / Crying for my baby / I gotta know / Can't you see / Cadillac walk
CCD 11024 / '92 / Crosscut

☐ FORDS AND FRIENDS (Ford Blues Band)
Tell me Mamma / Another fine day / Happy anniversary baby / I'm in love / Sign / Baby please / Sahara moon / Hey sister / Old Bill / Little baby / That happy look in your eye / Luther's lament
BRCD 126 / Dec '96 / Blue Rock-It
CCD 11052 / Jun '97 / Crosscut

☐ HANDFUL OF BLUES (Ford, Robben & The Blue Line)
Rugged road / Chevrolet / When I leave here / Strong will to live / I just want to make love to you / Think twice / Good thing / Tired of talking / Running out on me / Top of the hill / Don't let me be misunderstood / Miller's son
BTR 70042 / Aug '95 / Blue Thumb

☐ HOTSHOTS (Ford Blues Band)
CCD 11041 / Nov '95 / Crosscut

☐ INSIDE STORY, THE
Tee time for eric / North carolina / Magic sam / For the one I love / There's no one else / Need somebody / Inside story / Far away
7559610212 / Jan '96 / Elektra

☐ LIVE AT THE BREMINALE '92 (Ford Blues Band)
Take out some insurance / Oh why / Dance with me / Long as I have you / Self preservation / I ain't got you / Walking by myself
CCD 11038 / Jul '93 / Crosscut

☐ LIVE IN SAN FRANCISCO
JD 1283 / Nov '97 / Jazz Door

☐ MYSTIC MILE
He don't play nothin' but the blues / Busted up / Politician / Worried life blues / Misdirected blues / Trying to do the right thing / Say what's on your mind / Plunge / I don't play / Mystic mile
GRS 00082 / 25 May '98 / GRP

☐ ROBBEN FORD & THE BLUE LINE
Brother / You cut me to the bone / Real man / My love will never die / Prisoner of love / Tell me I'm your man / Start it up / Life song
GRS 11022 / 25 May '98 / GRP

☐ TIGER WALK
In the beginning / Ghosts / Freedom / Red lady / Oasis / Just like it is / I can't stand the rain / Champ / Tiger walk / Comin' up / Don't let the sun catch you crying / Chevrolet
BTR 70122 / May '97 / Blue Thumb

Ford, Tennessee Ernie

☐ COUNTRY CLASSICS
I've been to Georgia on the fast train / King of the road / Detroit City / I don't hurt anymore / Take me home country roads / I can't stop loving you / No one will ever know / Give me your word / River of no return / Sixteen tons / Sweet dreams / By the time I get to Phoenix / Release me / Funny how time slips away / Make the world slip away / I forgot more than you'll ever know / Rainy night in Georgia / There goes my everything / Okie from Muskogee / Cold cold heart
4949212 / 1 Jun '98 / EMI Gold

☐ SHOWTIME
Night train to Memphis / Catfish boogie / You gotta see Mama tonight / Cool water / Just because / My little red wagon / Do the hucklebuck / Up the lazy river
DATOM 7 / Apr '94 / Touch Of Magic

☐ SIXTEEN TONS
Milk 'em in the morning blues / Country junction / Smoky mountain boogie / Anticipation blues / Mule train / Cry of the wild goose / My hobby / Feed 'em in the morning blues / Shot gun boogie / Tailormade woman / You're my sugar: *Ford, Tennessee Ernie & Kay Starr* / Rock City boogie / Kissin' bug boogie / Hey good lookin': *Ford, Tennessee Ernie & Helen O'Connell* / Ham bone: *Ford, Tennessee Ernie & Bucky Tibbs* / Everybody's got a girl but me / Snow shoe Thompson / Blackberry boogie / Hey Mr. Cotton Picker / Kiss me big / Catfish boogie / Ballad of Davy Crockett / Sixteen tons / Roving gambler / Black eyed Susan Brown
BCD 15487 / Feb '90 / Bear Family

☐ ULTIMATE COLLECTION, THE
RE 2134 / Jul '97 / Razor & Tie

Ford-Payne, Sherree

☐ SHERREE FORD-PAYNE
ALMOCD 009 / May '96 / Almo Sounds

Forde, Aiden

☐ DUBLIN YOU'RE BREAKING MY HEART
WWCD 003 / Dec '97 / West Winds

Fordham, Julia

☐ FALLING FORWARD
I can't help myself / Caged bird / Falling forward / River / Blue sky / Different time, different place / Threadbare / Love and forgiveness / Honeymoon / Hope, prayer and time / Safe
CIRCD 28 / May '94 / Circa

☐ JULIA FORDHAM
Happy ever after / Comfort of strangers / Few too many / Invisible war / My lover's keeper / Cocooned / Where does the time go / Woman of the 80's / Other woman / Behind closed doors / Unconditional love
CIRCD 4 / Apr '92 / Circa

☐ PORCELAIN
Lock and key / Porcelain / Girlfriend / For you only for you / Genius / Did I happen to mention / Towerblock / Island / Your lovely face / Prince of peace
CIRCD 10 / Sep '89 / Circa

☐ SWEPT
CIRCD 18 / Oct '91 / Circa

Forebitter Shantymen

☐ MYSTIC SEAPORT
SCM 038CD / Mar '98 / Chasse Maree

Foreheads In A Fishtank

☐ STRIPPER
TOAD 5CD / Jun '94 / Newt

Foreigner

☐ AGENT PROVOCATEUR
Tooth and nail / That was yesterday / I want to know what love is / Growing up the hard way / Reaction to action / Stranger in my own house / Love in vain / Down on love / Two different worlds / She's too tough
7819992 / Jan '85 / Atlantic

☐ CLASSIC HITS LIVE
Double vision / Cold as ice / Damage is done / Women / Dirty white boy / Fool for you anyway / Head games / Not fade away / Waiting for a girl like you / Jukebox hero / Urgent / Love maker / I want to know what love is / Feels like the first time
7567825252 / Dec '93 / Atlantic

☐ DOUBLE VISION
Hot blooded / Blue morning, blue day / You're all I am / Back where you belong / Love has taken it's toll / Double vision / Tramontane / I have waited so long / Lonely children / Spellbinder
K250 476 / Aug '83 / Atlantic

☐ FOREIGNER
Feels like the first time / Cold as ice / Starrider / Headknocker / Damage is done / Long long way from home / Woman oh woman / At war with the world / Fool for the anyway / I need you
250356 / Apr '83 / Atlantic

☐ RECORDS
Cold as ice / Double vision / Head games / Waiting for a girl like you / Feels like the first time / Urgent / Dirty white boy / Jukebox hero / Long long way from home / Hot blooded
7567828002 / Nov '95 / Atlantic

☐ VERY BEST OF FOREIGNER...AND BEYOND
Soul doctor / Prisoner of love / With heaven on our side / Jukebox hero / Hot blooded / Cold as ice / Head games / Waiting for a girl like you / Urgent / Double vision / I want to know what love is / Say you will / That was yesterday / I don't want to live without you / Rev on the red line / Dirty white boy / Feels like the first time
7567899992 / Dec '92 / Atlantic

Forest

☐ FOREST/FULL CIRCLE
Bad penny / Glade somewhere / Lovemaker's ways / While you're gone / Sylvie / Fantasy you / Fading light / Do you want some smoke / Don't want to go / Nothing else will matter / Mirror of life / Rain is on my balcony / Hawk the hawker / Bluebell dance / Midnight hanging of a runaway serf / To Julie / Gypsy girl and rambleaway / Do not walk in the rain / Much ado about nothing / Graveyard / Famine song / Autumn child
BGOCD 236 / Sep '94 / Beat Goes On

Forest, Andy J.

☐ BLUE ORLEANS
APCD 128 / Nov '96 / Appaloosa

☐ HOG WILD
APCD 036 / '92 / Appaloosa

☐ HOGSHEAD CHEESE (Forest, Andy J. & Kenny Holladay)
APCD 118 / Oct '95 / Appaloosa

☐ LIVE (Forest, Andy J. Band)
APCD 066 / '92 / Appaloosa

Forest Called Mulu

☐ SEARCH FOR THE UNEXPLORED, A
SPV 08564032 / 6 Apr '98 / SPV

Forest For The Trees

☐ FOREST FOR THE TREES
DRD 50002 / 10 Oct '97 / Dreamworks

Forest, Helen

☐ ON THE SUNNY SIDE OF THE STREET
ACD 047 / Oct '93 / Audiophile

Forest Mighty Black

☐ MELLOW DRAMATIC
CMPOST 492 / 24 Aug '98 / Compost

☐ MELLOWDRAMATIC
COMP 038CD / 8 Dec '97 / Compost

Forest Of Souls

☐ CONTES ET LEGENDES D'EFEANDAY
CDAR 041 / 15 Dec '97 / Adipocre

Forever Amber

☐ LOVE CYCLE
HBG 122/7 / Apr '94 / Background

Forgodsake

☐ BLASTHEAD
Armchair enthusiast / Wake up now / If this is what it takes / Bad sex / Half past anything / Blasthead / Strange / Negative / In front of me / Crash / This one / Not today / Sky high / Dumbtown
CDBLEED 3 / Apr '93 / Bleeding Hearts

Forgotten Rebels

☐ EXECUTIVE OUTCOMES
BA 1120CD / 23 Feb '98 / Bacchus Archives

☐ PRIDE AND DISGRACE, THE
OPM 2105CD / Oct '96 / Other People's Music

☐ TOMORROW BELONGS TO US
OPM 2115CD / Nov '97 / Other People's Music

Forlorn

☐ CRYSTAL PALACE
HNF 041CD / 3 Aug '98 / Head Not Found

Forman, Bruce

☐ PARDON ME (Forman, Bruce Quartet)
CCD 4368 / Feb '89 / Concord Jazz

☐ THERE ARE TIMES (Forman, Bruce Quartet)
There are times / Milan k / All the things you are / Nearness of you / Con alma / Strike up the band / Prelude to a kiss / Little rootie tootie
CCD 4332 / Dec '87 / Concord Jazz

Forman, Mitchel

☐ CHILDHOOD DREAMS
1210502 / Jan '93 / Soul Note

Formanek, Michael

☐ NATURE OF THE BEAST
Emerger / Dry season / Grand bizarre / Don't go there / Excruciation / El Nino / Lickin' center / Thick skin / Dangerous crustaceans
ENJ 93082 / Apr '97 / Enja

Format

☐ MEDIA CIRCUS
CDC 001 / Sep '96 / Christel Deesk

Formby, George

☐ AT THE FLICKS
I could make a living at that / Baby / It's in the air / They can't fool me / Goodnight, little fellow, goodnight / Pardon me / I'm making headway now / I could not let the stable down / I wish I was back on the farm / Count your blessings and smile / Oh don't the wind blow cold / Emperor of Lancashire / You're everything to me / You can't go wrong in these / I played on my Spanish guitar / I'd do it with a smile / Barmaid at the Rose and Crown / Get crackin' / Home Guard blues / Bell bottom George / Serves you right / Got to get your photo in the press / Hillbilly Willie / Unconditional surrender
PLCD 554 / Nov '96 / President

☐ BELL-BOTTOM GEORGE (George Formby Vol. 2)
Bell bottom George / When the lads of the village get crackin' / When the waterworks caught fire / It serves you right / Got to get your photo in the press / If I had a girl like you / Thirty thirsty sailors / I'd do it with a smile / Home guard blues / Swim little fish / At the baby show / Hold your hats on / Mr. Wu's an air raid warden now / Bar maid at the Rose and Crown / I wish I was back on the farm / Delivering the morning milk / Grandad's flannelette nightshirt / Guarding the homes of the Home Guard / Our Sergeant Major / Baby / She's never been seen since then / Swimmin' with the wimmin'
PASTCD 7043 / May '94 / Flapper

☐ BEST OF GEORGE FORMBY, THE
MU 3006 / Oct '92 / Musketeer

☐ BEST OF GEORGE FORMBY, THE
Auntie Maggie's remedy / Why don't women like me / With my little ukelele in my hand / When I'm cleaning windows (The window cleaner) / Chinese laudry blues / Leaning on a lampost / With my little stick of Blackpool rock / Swimmin' with the wimmin' / Mother what'll I do now / In my little snapshot album / Mr. Wu's a window cleaner now / Wedding of Mr Wu / Lancashire toreador / Our Sergeant Major / Madame Moscovitch / Sitting on the ice on the ice rink / I told my baby with the ukelele / It's turned out nice again / Sitting on the sands allnight / When I'm cleaning windows (The window cleaner) / Hid tiddley hi ti island / Bless em' all
CD 6019 / Apr '96 / Music

☐ EMPEROR OF LANCASHIRE
It could be / We've been a long time gone / Mad march hare / You don't need a license for that / Our Fanny's gone all yankee / Swim little fish / It's in the air / Keep fit / Said the little / If I had a girl like you / Up in the air and down in the dumps / She's got two of everything / Leaning on a lampost / Auntie Maggie's remedy / Window cleaner / Emperor of Lancashire / Bell bottom George / Mr. Wu's a window cleaner now / Chinese laundry blues / Why don't women like me
EMPRCD 777 / Nov '97 / Music Club

☐ FORMBY AT WAR - LIVE
Auntie Maggie's remedy / Frank on his tank / Guarding the homes of the home guard / Chinese laundry blues / Cleaning windows / Little stick of Blackpool rock / Imagine me in the maginot line / When the lads of the village get crackin' / Thirty thirsty sailors / Out in the Middle East / Mr. Wu's an air raid warden now / It's in the air / Little ukulele / Down the old coal hole / Bless 'em all
CDGRS 1224 / '91 / Grosvenor

☐ HIS GREATEST FAVOURITES
I'm the ukelele man / Leaning on a lamp-post / Auntie Maggie's remedy / With my little stick of Blackpool rock / When I'm cleaning windows (The window cleaner) / Mr. Wu's a window cleaner now / Chinese laundry blues / Do de o do / Blue eyed blonde next door / Like the big pots do / When I'm cleaning windows (The window cleaner) / I don't like / Easy going chap / Biceps, muscle and brawn / Lancashire hot pot swingers / You can't go wrong in these / Who are you a-shoving off / I'm the husband of the wife of Mr.Wu / Hitting the high spots / Kiss your mansy pansy / I can tell it by my horoscope / I'm the emperor of Lancashire
PASTCD 7001 / Feb '93 / Flapper

☐ I'M THE UKELELE MAN
When I'm cleaning windows (the window cleaner) / Auntie Maggie's remedy / Leaning on a lamp-post / In my little snapshot album / With my little stick of Blackpool rock / Mr. Wu's a window cleaner now / Our Sergeant Major / I'm the ukelele man / Bless 'em all / I don't like / Joo-jah tree / Chinese laundry blues / Baby / Why don't women like me / Running round the fountains in Trafalgar Square / My ukelele / De do o'do / Believe it or not / It's all hot and cold / Wedding of Mr. Woo / In a little Wigan garden / Alexander's ragtime band
RAJCD 801 / Dec '97 / Empress

☐ IT'S TURNED OUT NICE AGAIN
Keep your seats please / On the beat / It ain't nobody's biz'ness what I do / Goody goody / I like bananas / Sitting on the sands all night / On the Wigan Boat Express / Talking to the moon about you / Some of these days / Hard hearted Hannah / Sweet Georgia Brown / Sweet Sue, just you / Dinah / Tiger rag / Hitting the high spots / Home guard blues / Goodnight little fellow, goodnight / When I'm cleaning windows (The window cleaner) / Lad from Lancashire / Oh you have no idaea / Riding in the TT races / They can't fool me / Under the blasted oak / I always get to bed by half-past nine / Down the old coal hole / I wonder who's under her balcony now / Delivering the morning milk / Leaning on a lamp-post / It's turned out nice again
PPCD 78105 / Feb '95 / Past Perfect

☐ IT'S TURNED OUT NICE AGAIN
Sitiing on the ice rink / Do de oh doh / Chinese laundry blues / Madame Moskovitch / My ukelele / Fanlight Fanny / Keep fit / Biceps, muscle and brawn / Gallant Dick Turpin parts 1 and 2 / When we feather our nest / Our Sergeant Major / Isle of Man / Hitting the high spots now / Said the little brown hen / Trailing around in a trailor / Men of Harlech / John Peel / Heart of oak / On Ilkley Moor / Loch Lomond /

Come landlord fill the flowing bowl / Auld lang syne / My old Kentucky home / Camptown races / She'll be coming round the mountain / Old folks at home (Swanee river) / Oh Suzanna / Over there / Anchors aweigh / If I had a girl like you / Ring your little bell / Under the blasted oak / Oh you have no idea / Blackpool Prom / Daring young man / I'd like a dream like that / Up in the air and down in the dumps / She's got two of everything / Old cane bottom chair / It's a grand and healthy life / With my little stick of Blackpool rock / I'm the husband of the wife of Mr. Wo / When I'm cleaning windows (The window cleaner)
RAJCD 878 / May '96 / Empress

☐ RAF TAKES TO THE AIR/MAX WITH THE FORCES (Formby, George/Max Miller)
RAF takes the air: *Formby, George* / Jingle jangle jingle: *Formby, George* / Don't go in the lion's cage tonight: *Formby, George* / Oh how I hate to get up in the morning: *Formby, George* / You walk by: *Formby, George* / Thirsty thirsty sailors: *Formby, George* / Out in the Middle East: *Formby, George* / Mr. Wu's an air raid warden now: *Formby, George* / It's in the air: *Formby, George* / New kind of old fashioned girl: *Miller, Max* / Cheeky chappie picks from the white book and the blue book: *Miller, Max* / Is there no end to his cleverness: *Miller, Max* / He now recites what Ju-Ju wants: *Miller, Max* / Stringing along with you: *Miller, Max* / Sitting in the old armchair: *Miller, Max* / Max gives Jean some chocolates: *Miller, Max* / Hiking song: *Miller, Max* / All good things come to an end: *Miller, Max*
PLCD 565 / Oct '97 / President

☐ ULTIMATE COLLECTION, THE (2CD Set)
Leaning on a lampost / Hi-tiddly-hi-ti island / Happy go lucky me / Banjo boy / It's no use looking at me / Little stick of Blackpool rock / Our Fanny's gone all yankee / Bell bottom George / On the beat / I wish I was back on the farm / I blew a little blast on my whistle / Andy the handy man / Ghost / Lancashire toreador / Oh dear mother / Mr. Wu's a window cleaner now / Delivering the morning milk / Oh don't the wind blow cold on the left hand side of Egypt / Chinese laundry blues / When I'm cleaning windows / Pleasure cruise / Levi's monkey mine / You're everything to me / Isle of Man / Riding in the TT races / I'm making headway now / I could not let the stable down / I wonder who's under her balcony now / Fanlight Fanny / Hindoo man / Springtime here again / Sitting in the ice in the ice rink / Grand and healthy life / Noughts and crosses / Share and share alike / Grandad's flannelette nightshirt / Baby we've been a long time gone / It's turned out nice again
PDSCD 547 / 13 Oct '97 / Pulse

☐ V FOR VICTORY
Introduction 'v' sign song / Little stick of blackpool rock / Imagine me on the maginot line / Auntie maggie's remedy / Frank on his tank / Guarding the homes of the home guard / Chinese laundry blues / Cleaning windows / Thirsty thirsty sailors / Out in the middle east / Mr. woo is now an air raid warden / It's in the air / George's story 'v' sign song
RKD 23 / Mar '95 / Redrock

☐ VERY BEST OF GEORGE FORMBY, THE (20 Great Songs)
Leaning on a lamp-post / With my little stick of Blackpool rock / Chinese laundry blues / When I'm cleaning windows (The window cleaner) / Swimmin' with the wimmin' / With my little ukelele in my hand / Why don't women like me / You can't keep a growing lad down / Mother, what'll I do now / There's nothing proud about me / In my little snapshot album / Old kitchen kettle / Isle of Man / Lancashire toreador / Our sargeant major / Believe it or not / Madame moscovitch / As the hours and the days and the months and the years roll / Sitting on the ice in the ice rink / I told my baby with the ukelele
PLATCD 28 / Aug '90 / Platinum

☐ VERY BEST OF GEORGE FORMBY, THE
Leaning on a lamp post / Riding in the TT races / Auntie Maggie's remedy / When I'm cleaning windows / With my little stick of Blackpool rock / Window cleaner / I'm the ukelele man / Lancashire toreador / Sitting on the top of Blackpool tower / I don't like / Bless 'em all / Mother what'll I do now / Frigid air Fanny / It's turned out nice again / Grandad's flanelette nightshirt / Hi-Tiddley-Hi-Ti island / Mr. Wu's a window cleaner now / Window cleaner no.2 / Oh don't the wind blow cold / Emperor of Lancashire / In my little snapshot album / Home Guard blues
SWNCD 017 / Oct '97 / Sound Waves

☐ WHEN I'M CLEANING WINDOWS
When I'm cleaning windows (The window cleaner) / Oh don't the wind blow cold / It's turned out nice again / With my little stick of Blackpool rock / Hi tiddly hi ti island / It's in the air / Count your blessings and smile / Easy going chap / Grandad's flannelette nightshirt / Hillbilly Willie / Hitting the high spots / I don't like / I'm a froggie / Keep your seats please / Lancashire hot pot swingers / Leaning on a lamp-post / Like the big pots do / Mr. Wu's a window cleaner now / My plus fours / Our sergeant major / Rhythm in the alphabet / Somebody's wedding day / They can't fool me / You can't stop me from dreaming
CDAJA 5079 / Apr '91 / Living Era

☐ WHEN I'M CLEANING WINDOWS
Sitting on the ice in the ice rink / Do de o do / Chinese laundry blues / You can't stop me from dreaming / Pleasure cruise / Keep fit / Riding in the TT races / Hindoo man / It ain't nobody's biz'ness what I do / Goody goody / I like bananas / Lancashire Toreador / Farmer's boy / You can't keep a growing lad down / You're a li-a-ty / With my little stick of Blackppol rock / Trailing around in a trailer / Why don't women like me / Dare devil Dick / Somebody's wedding day / Sitting on the sands all night / Madame Moscovitch / With my little ukelele in my hand / Fanlight Fanny / When I'm cleaning windows (The window cleaner) / Leaning on a lamp-post
PLCD 538 / Jul '95 / President

☐ WINDOW CLEANER
GO 3804 / 1 Dec '97 / Golden Options

Formell, Juan

☐ AY DIOS AMPARAME (Formell, Juan Y Los Van Van)
74321401352 / Sep '96 / Milan

☐ GRACIAS FORMELL (Various Artists)
RMD 82249 / 24 Mar '98 / RMM

☐ SANDUNGUERA (Formell, Juan Y Los Van Van)
Que palo es ese / Por encima del nivel (sandunguera) / Artesano del espacio / La habana no aguanta mas / Habla claro camara / Sera que se acabo / Quien bien te quiere te hara llorar / El baile del buey cansao / Cuentame
MES 159892 / Jun '93 / Messidor

Formula 3

☐ SONGANDO E RISOGNANDO
SRMC 1004 / 5 Jan '98 / Siwan

Formula 7

☐ EXPRESSIONS
HLCD 5 / 29 Jun '98 / Hardleaders

Forrest, Helen

☐ CREAM OF HELEN FORREST
PASTCD 7062 / May '95 / Flapper

☐ DOUBLE DATE WITH HELEN FORREST AND CHRIS CONNOR (Forrest, Helen & Chris Connor)
STCD 14 / Oct '91 / Stash

☐ EMBRACEABLE YOU (Previously Unreleased 1949-1950)
Embraceable you / I'll get by / I've got a crush on you / I can't get started / What's the use of wond'rin' / Little white lies / My heart belongs to daddy / How deep is the ocean / I'll always be in love with you / Someone to watch over me / Between the devil and the deep blue sea / Ain't misbehavin' / They say it's wonderful / What can I say after I say I'm sorry / Bewitched, bothered and bewildered / Come rain or come shine / I can't give you anything but love / Baby won't you please come home
HCD 257 / Jul '95 / Hindsight

☐ I WANNA BE LOVED
That's my desire / My idea / Paradise / Too marvellous for words (vocal george melachrino) / I hadn't anyone till you / I'm confessin' (that I love you) / I'm in the mood for love / I can't believe that you're in love with me / You go to my head / I wanna be loved / Bill / Mad about the boy / I only have eyes for you / One I love belongs to somebody else / I don't stand a ghost of a chance (with you) / Deep purple / East of the sun (and west of the moon) / My man
HCD 250 / Mar '94 / Hindsight

☐ NOW AND FOREVER (1983 Studio Sessions)
I've heard that song before / I don't want to walk without you / Happiness is a thing called Joe / But not for me / I cried for you / I had the craziest dream / You made me love you / I didn't want to do it / You'll never know more than you know
VN 1006 / Nov '96 / Viper's Nest

☐ VOICE OF THE BIG BANDS, THE
Deep in a dream: *Forrest, Helen & Artie Shaw Orchestra* / Deep purple: *Forrest, Helen & Artie Shaw Orchestra* / Comes love: *Forrest, Helen & Artie Shaw Orchestra* / Day in, day out: *Forrest, Helen & Artie Shaw Orchestra* / All the things you are: *Forrest, Helen & Artie Shaw Orchestra* / Moonray: *Forrest, Helen & Artie Shaw Orchestra* / How high the moon: *Forrest, Helen & Benny Goodman Orchestra* / Shake down the stars: *Forrest, Helen & Benny Goodman Orchestra* / It never entered my mind: *Forrest, Helen & Benny Goodman Orchestra* / I'm nobody's baby: *Forrest, Helen & Benny Goodman Orchestra* / Taking a chance on love: *Forrest, Helen & Benny Goodman Orchestra* / Yes my darling daughter: *Forrest, Helen & Benny Goodman Orchestra* / Bewitched: *Forrest, Helen & Benny Goodman Orchestra* / I found a million dollar baby: *Forrest, Helen & Benny Goodman Orchestra* / When the sun comes out: *Forrest, Helen & Benny Goodman Orchestra* / Devil sat down and cried: *Forrest, Helen & Harry James Orchestra* / I don't want to walk without you: *Forrest, Helen & Harry James Orchestra* / Skylark: *Forrest, Helen & Harry James Orchestra* / He's my guy: *Forrest, Helen & Harry James Orchestra* / I had the craziest dream: *Forrest, Helen & Harry James Orchestra* / I've heard that song before: *Forrest, Helen & Harry James Orchestra* / Close to you: *Forrest, Helen & Harry James Orchestra* / Long ago and far away: *Forrest, Helen & Dick Haymes* / It had to be you: *Forrest, Helen & Dick Haymes*
JASMCD 2545 / May '97 / Jasmine

Forrest, Jimmy

☐ ALL THE GIN IS GONE
All the gin is gone / Laura / You go to my head / Myra / Caravan / What's new / Sunkenfoal
DD 404 / Jul '97 / Delmark

☐ BLACK FORREST
DD 427 / Oct '86 / Delmark

☐ FORREST FIRE
Forrest fire / Remember / Dexter's deck / Jim's jam / Bag's groove / When your love has gone / Help
OJCCD 199 / Jan '94 / Original Jazz Classics

☐ HONKERS AND BAR WALKERS VOL.1 (Forrest, Jimmy & Tab Smith)
DD 438 / Mar '97 / Delmark

☐ NIGHT TRAIN
DD 435 / Apr '86 / Delmark

☐ SIT DOWN AND RELAX WITH JIMMY FORREST
Tuxedo junction / Moonglow / Rocks in my bed / Organ grinder's swing / Tin tin deo / Moon was yellow and the night was cold / That's all
OJCCD 895 / Oct '96 / Original Jazz Classics

Forrester, Joel

☐ STOP THE MUSIC
378432 / Oct '97 / Koch Jazz

Forrester, Sharon

☐ THIS TIME
VPCD 1434 / Oct '95 / VP

Forsberg, Ebba

☐ BEEN THERE
Lost count / Most of all / Carried / Photographs / I'll do fine / You surprise me / Take me some time / Hold me / Once upon a time / Fine is the line / Didn't treat me right
9362467402 / 1 Jun '98 / WEA

Forsen, Arne

☐ UR HJARTANS DJUP (Forsen, Arne & Pia Olby)
DRCD 198 / Apr '87 / Dragon

Forster, John

☐ ENTERING MARION
PH 1164CD / Jan '94 / Philo

☐ HELIUM
CDPH 1214 / Aug '97 / Philo

Forster, Robert

☐ CALLING FROM A COUNTRY PHONE
BBL 127CD / Sep '95 / Beggars Banquet

☐ I HAD A NEW YORK GIRLFRIEND
BBQCD 161 / Aug '94 / Beggars Banquet

☐ WARM NIGHTS
BEGL 185CD / Jul '96 / Beggars Banquet

Forsythe, Guy

☐ HIGH TEMPERATURE (Forsythe, Guy Band)
LDCD 80001 / Aug '94 / Lizard

Fortaleza

☐ SOY DE SANGRE KOLLA
FF 529CD / '92 / Flying Fish

Forte

☐ DESTRUCTIVE
MASSCD 123 / 1 Sep '97 / Massacre

☐ DIVISION
MASSCD 035 / Jun '94 / Massacre

Forte, John

☐ POLYSCI
Hot / They got me: *Forte, John & Fat Joe* / Ninety-nine (flash the message) / God is love/God is war / We got this: *Forte, John & DMX* / Right one / Madina passage / All you gotta do / All fucked up / Born to win / Poly sci / Flash the message / Hot (outro)
4891172 / 13 Jul '98 / Refugee Camp/ Columbia

Fortran 5

☐ BAD HEAD PARK
CDSTUMM 104 / Jun '93 / Mute

☐ BLUES, THE
Groove / Look to the future / Two curious friends / Blues (part 1) / Xx 21 / Heart on the line / Bike (syd sing sid) / Love baby / Blues (part 2) / Inanga / Crazy earth (l'edit de syd) / Midnight trip / Blues (part 3)
CDSTUMM 79 / Sep '91 / Mute

Fortunairs Barber Shop Quartet

☐ SWEET ADELINE
Sweet Adeline / Alabama jubilee/Down yonder / Heart of my heart / Auctioneer / Danny boy / Ride the chariot / In the evening by the moonlight / If the good Lord's willing and the creek don't rise / You made me love you/It had to be you / Sunny side up / No more sorrows / Wedding ball rag / Roses of Picardy / Start off each day with a song / Wonderful day like today / When day is done / California here I come / April showers / Gonna build a mountain / When somebody thinks you're wonderful / I'm looking over a four leaf clover / I'll take you home again Kathleen / How could Little Red Riding Hood
GRCD 77 / Oct '96 / Grasmere

Fortune, Jesse

☐ FORTUNE TELLIN' MAN
Dark is the night / Fortune tellin' man / Get mad at my money / Sandu / Too many cooks / Lovingest woman in town / Specter's walk / Gambler's blues / Be careful with a fool / Ain't about money / Losing hand
DD 658 / Mar '97 / Delmark

Fortune, Johnny

☐ LIFE GOES ON
Z 501 / Apr '97 / Zorch

Fortune, Sonny

☐ MONK'S MOOD
Little rootie tootie / Mysterioso / Nutty / I mean you / Monk's wood / Ruby my dear / In walked bud / Off minor
KCD 5048 / Nov '93 / Konnex

☐ SOUND OF SOUNDS (2CD Set) (Fortune, Sonny Quartet)
Diabolo / Big bop shuffle / Turning it over / Come in come out of the rain / Sunshower / Paravillion / Invitation / Sound of sounds / Caravan
JLR 103613 / Apr '98 / Live At EJ's

Fortunes

☐ FORTUNES
GRF 186 / Jan '93 / Tring

☐ SPOTLIGHT ON FORTUNES
You've got your troubles / Here comes that rainy day feeling again / Caroline / Seasons in the sun / Don't throw your love away / When your heart speaks to you / Anna Maria / Storm in a teacup / Mumba Sarah / Half way to paradise / It's a beautiful dream / Funny how love can be
HADCD 113 / Feb '94 / Javelin

☐ STORM IN A TEACUP/HERE COMES THAT RAINY DAY FEELING AGAIN
Storm in a teacup / Man is a man / Red Clay county line / Whether you like it or not / Today I killed a man / Freedom come, freedom go / Someone is standing outside / Four and twenty hours / Excuse me friend / There's a man / Here comes that rainy day feeling again / Night started to cry / I gotta dream / Just a line to let you know / All my calender is you / Hear the band / Oh babe / Eye for the main chance / Thoughts / Noises (in my head)
BGOCD 310 / Jun '96 / Beat Goes On

☐ WORLD OF THE FORTUNES, THE
Caroline / You've got your troubles / Looking through the eyes of love / Here it comes again / All cried out / Maria / Won't you give him (one more chance) / Truly yours / Coloured lights / I'll have my tears to remind me / This golden ring / Our love has gone / Am I losing my touch / This empty place / Laughing fit to cry / Look homeward angel / You can have her / You gave me somebody to love / Silent street / Time to be going
5520232 / May '96 / Spectrum

Foskett, Jeffrey

☐ OTHER TAKES, THE
NC 961011 / Jul '97 / New Surf

☐ THRU MY WINDOW
NC 961007 / Jul '97 / New Surf

Foster & Allen

☐ 100 GOLDEN GREATS
TCD 2791 / Oct '95 / Telstar

☐ 100 GOLDEN LOVE SONGS (2CD Set)
STAC 2846 / Oct '96 / Telstar

☐ AFTER ALL THESE YEARS
Old Dungarvan oak / When I dream / Bluebell polka / Do you think you could love again / Leaving of Liverpool / Rose of Allendale / I still love you / Cottage by the sea / Old Ardboe / Scots polka / Rose of Mooncoin / Six foot seven woman / When my blue moon turns gold again / After all these years
RZSCD 420 / Jun '92 / Ritz

☐ BEST FRIENDS
Way old friends do / Try to remember / You're my best friend / Have you ever been lonely / Nobody's child / My grandfather's clock / I swear / Unicorn / Between the two of them / I still miss someone / Cuckoo waltz / Mother's way / Little shirt me mother made for me / Carnival is over / Matchstalk men and matchstick cats and dogs / Reminisce for a while / You stand all alone / Sergeant Murphy / Would you lay with me (in a field of stone) / Heaven round Galway bay / Old house / Valetta waltz / Another town / Shine your light / If the whole world stopped loving
TTVCD 2935 / 3 Nov '97 / Telstar TV

☐ BUNCH OF THYME
Bunch of thyme / Fiddler / Come back Paddy Reilly / Drink up the cider / Green willow / Living here London / Blacksmith / Alice Benbolt / Benbulben of Sligo / Wise maid / Cooley's reel / Foster's fancy / Nancy Miles / Courtin' in the kitchen
RZSCD 408 / Apr '93 / Ritz

☐ CHRISTMAS ALBUM
TCD 2459 / Nov '90 / Telstar

☐ FOSTER & ALLEN SELECTION, THE
Blind / Green willow / Jacqueline waltz / Cocky farmer / Polkas / Fagins wake / Sligo maid / Nancy Myles / Old flames / Oslo waltz / Salonika / Boys of Bluehill / Bally James Duff / Green groves of Erin / Gentle Annie / Sweets of May
RZSCD 409 / Apr '93 / Ritz

☐ I WILL LOVE YOU ALL OF MY LIFE
I will love you all my life / Whiskey on a Sunday / Birdie song / Mull of Kintyre / Swedish rhapsody / Forever and ever / I'll take you home again Kathleen / Cock o' the North / If those lips could only speak / Mountains of Mourne / Happy hour / When I grow too old to dream
RZSCD 419 / Jun '92 / Ritz

☐ MAGGIE
Maggie / Old rustic bridge by the mill / Harvest moon / Isle of Innisfree / Mist upon the morning / Hornpipes / Sweethearts in the spring / Blue eyes cryin' in the rain / Molly my lovely Molly / Seasons of my heart / Reels / Nell Flaherty's drake / Farewell to Derry / Johnny Brown
RZSCD 418 / Jun '92 / Ritz

☐ SHADES OF GREEN
TCD 2899 / Apr '97 / Telstar

☐ VERY BEST OF FOSTER & ALLEN, THE
Bunch of thyme / Old flames / Maggie / I will love you all my life / Blacksmith / Oslo waltz / Place in the choir / Just for old times sake / Job of journeywork / Spinning wheel / We will make love / Maid behind the bar / My love is in America / Molly darling / Before I met you / Gentle mother
RZRCD 523 / Apr '93 / Ritz

☐ VERY BEST OF THE LOVE SONGS VOL.2
After all these years / Blues eyes crying in the rain / Red river valley / Rose of allendale / Moutains of mourne / I still love you / Rose of mooncoin / When my blue moon turns to gold again / When I dream / Morning glory / Old rustic bridge / I'll take you home again kathleen / Do you think you could love me again / Alice ben bolt / Molly my lovely molly / Gentle annie
RZRCD 524 / Apr '93 / Ritz

Foster, David

☐ CHRISTMAS ALBUM, THE
Carol of the bells / Blue Christmas / First Noel / It's the most wonderful time of the year / Grown up Christmas list / O holy night / Go tell it on the mountain / Mary had a baby, yes Lord / I'll be home for Christmas / Mary's boy child / Christmas song / Away in a manger / White Christmas
6544922952 / Feb '93 / Atlantic

Foster, Eboni

☐ JUST WHAT YOU WANT
MCAD 11750 / 29 Jun '98 / MCA

Foster, Frank

☐ FRANKLY SPEAKING (Foster, Frank & Frank Weiss)
When did you leave Heaven / Up and coming / One morning in May / Two Franks / This is all I ask / Blues backstage / An' all such stuff as'dat / Summer knows
CCD 4276 / Sep '86 / Concord Jazz

☐ SWING
Joy spring / Chiquito loco / Simone / Shiny stockings / Theme for Ernie / Giant steps
CHR 70051 / Jun '98 / Challenge

Foster, Gary

☐ MAKE YOUR OWN FUN
Alone together / Peacocks / Warne-ing / Nica's dream / What a life / I concentrate on you / Some other Spring / Teef / I'll close my eyes / Easy living / Sweet lips
CCD 4459 / May '91 / Concord Jazz

Foster, Mo

☐ BEL ASSIS (Foster, Mo & Gary Moore)
Light in your eyes / Walk in the country / Gaia / Crete re-visited / So far away / Analytical engine / Pump II / Jaco / Bel assis / And then there were ten / Nomad
INAK 11003CD / Jul '97 / In Akustik

☐ SOUTHERN REUNION (Foster, Mo & Gary Moore)
Gil / Blue / Achill island / Waves / Tricotism / National anthem / Southern reunion / Grand unified boogie / Fractal landscape / Shin kan sen
INAK 11006CD / Jul '97 / In Akustik

Foster, Radney

☐ DEL RIO, TX 1959
Just call me lonesome / Don't say goodbye / Easier said than done / Fine line / Went for a ride / Nobody wins / Louisiana blue / Closing time / Hammer and nails / Old silver
07822187132 / Jun '94 / Arista

☐ LABOR OF LOVE
Willing to talk / Labor of love / My whole wide world / Never say die / Jesse's soul / Everybody gets the blues / If it were me / Broke down / Precious pearl / Last chance for love / Fine line / Nobody wins / Making it up as I go along / Walkin' talkin' woman
74321229842 / Apr '95 / Arista

Fotheringay

☐ FOTHERINGAY (Fotheringay & Sandy Denny)
Nothing more / Sea / Ballad of Ned Kelly / Winter winds / Peace in the end / Way I feel / Pond and the stream / Too much of nothing / Banks of the Nile
HNCD 4426 / May '89 / Hannibal

Foulplay

☐ SUSPECTED
ASHADOW 2CD / Oct '95 / Moving Shadow

Foundations

☐ ALL THE HITS PLUS MORE
Every one's a winner / Born to live and born to die / If there were no music / Baby now that I've found you / Same sad feeling / Bring back / In the bad, bad old days / Tender touch / Any old time / It's a burning love / Everyday / Back on my feet again / Let's make this love last forever / Build me up buttercup
CDSGP 0244 / Apr '97 / Prestige

☐ BRITISH 60'S, THE (Foundations/ Equals)
Baby come back: *Equals* / Viva Bobby Joe: *Equals* / Black skin blue eyed boys: *Equals* / Michael and the slipper tree: *Equals* / Laurel and Hardy: *Equals* / Rub a dub dub: *Equals* / I get so excited: *Equals* / Softly softly: *Equals* / Get back: *Equals* / Hey baby: *Equals* / Baby now that I found you: *Foundations* / Build me up buttercup: *Foundations* / Dock of the bay: *Foundations* / Any old time you're sad and lonely: *Foundations* / Back on my feet again: *Foundations* / Born to live and born to die: *Foundations* / In the bad old days: *Foundations* / Keep loving you: *Foundations* / Knock on wood: *Foundations* / Together flowers: *Foundations*
PLATCD 202 / Feb '97 / Platinum

☐ BUILD ME UP BUTTERCUP
SELCD 527 / 27 Jun '98 / Castle Select

☐ DIGGIN' THE FOUNDATIONS
REP 4183 / Aug '91 / Repertoire

☐ FROM THE FOUNDATIONS
REP 4182 / Aug '91 / Repertoire

☐ STRONG FOUNDATIONS
Baby now that I've found you / In the bad bad old days (before you loved me) / Build me up buttercup / I can take or leave your loving / Baby I couldn't see / Take agirl like you / Show me / Walk through the trees / Any old time you're lonely and sad / Call me / Born to live born to die / Let the heartaches begin / That same old feeling / I'm gonna be a rich man / Back on my feet again / Writing's on the wall / Love is alright (the horse) / Harlem shuffle / Look of love / Stop her on sight (SOS)
MCCD 327 / Nov '97 / Music Club

☐ THAT SAME OLD FEELING
Baby now that I've found you / Back on my feet again / Tomorrow / Harlem shuffle / Mr. Personality man / I can take or leave your lovin' / Let the heartaches begin / Am I groovin' you / We are happy people / That same old feeling / Any old time / Build me up buttercup / Born to live, born to die / Waiting on the shores of nowhere / Come on back to me / In the bad, bad old days
21041 / Jul '97 / Laserlight

Foundland

☐ EVERYBODY'S NEIGHBOUR
XOUCD 112 / Mar '96 / Xource

Foundry Bar Band

☐ ROLLING HOME
Conundrum / Rollin' home / Murdo's wedding / Weaver / Braes of Castlegrant / Come by the hills / Dashing white sergeant / Muckin' O' Geordie's byre / Row her in ma plaide / Barren rocks of Aden / Aince upon a time / Skye gathering / Angus MacLeod / All for me grog / Scotland the brave
SPRCD 1026 / Dec '88 / Springthyme

Fountain, Pete

☐ DIXIELAND KING
TCD 1068 / 23 Mar '98 / Tradition

☐ DO YOU KNOW WHAT IT MEANS TO MISS NEW ORLEANS
BCD 300 / Aug '94 / GHB

☐ NEW ORLEANS ALL-STARS
TCD 1047 / May '97 / Tradition

☐ PETE FOUNTAIN
Waiting for the Robert E Lee / South Rampart Street Parade / Angry / Bonaparte's retreat / Original dixieland one-step / Land of dreams / Mahogany Hall Stomp / Royal Garden blues / Sailing down the Cheseapeake Bay / Up a lazy river / Milenburg joys / Margie / High society / I'm going home / Farewell blues
504CD 16 / Mar '98 / 504

☐ PETE FOUNTAIN AT PIPER'S OPERA HOUSE
JCD 217 / Aug '94 / Jazzology

Fountainhead

☐ DRAIN
DOG 021 / Nov '94 / Doghouse

Fountains Of Wayne

☐ FOUNTAINS OF WAYNE
Radiation vibe / Sink to the bottom / Joe Rey / She's got a problem / Survival car / Barbara H / Sick day / I've got a flair / Leave the biker / You curse at girls / Please don't rock me tonight / Everything's ruined
7567927252 / May '97 / Atlantic

FOUR

☐ ORDER
Going to extremes / Sweetest surrender / New York Jamaica London Ethiopia / SMILE / Non-stop traffic / Wait until tonight / Lay of the land / Hold me like china / Little more love / Four reasons unknown
CDKUFF 1 / Sep '96 / Kuff

Four 80 East

☐ ALBUM, THE
BOOMCD 001 / 16 Jul '97 / Boom Tang

Four Aces

☐ FOUR ACES
CD 113 / Oct '94 / Timeless Treasures

☐ LOVE IS A MANY SPLENDOURED THING
Love is a many splendored thing / Mr. sandman / In the chapel in the moonlight / Stranger in paradise / Feelings / Believe in love / Heart and soul / I write the songs / Time alone will tell / You are my way of life / Three coins in the fountain / Heart of my heart / Tell me why / Sin / A garden in the rain / Written on the wind / And I love you so / Now I need you / God's greatest gift / Tonight must last forever
RMB 75060 / Aug '92 / Remember

Four Bitchin' Babes

☐ BUY ME, BRING ME, TAKE ME
Oh great spirit / Bald headed men / Save me a seat (homeward bound) / From a distance / Sealed with a kiss / Butter / Graceful man / Try love / Take me out to eat / As close to flying / (fun to be) perfect / Choice / Good night, new york
PHCD 1150 / May '93 / Philo

☐ OUT OF THE MOUTH OF BABES
SH 8028 / Nov '97 / Shanachie

Four Blazes

☐ MARY JO
DE 704 / Feb '98 / Delmark

Four Brothers

☐ MAKOROKOTO
Makorokoto / Rugare / Wapenga nayo bonus / Ndakatadzeiko / Sara Tasangana / Pamusoroi / Nhaka yemusiiranwa / Uchandifunga / Guhwa uri mwana waani / Ndakatambura / Vimbayi / Rumbidzai / Rudo imoto / Pasi pano pane zviedzo / Maishoko ababa namai / Siya zviriko
BAKECD 004 / May '90 / Cooking Vinyl

Four Champions

☐ IRISH TRADITIONAL ACCORDION
Hill 60 / Spring well / Jackie Coleman's / Reel of Rio / McGuires / Maud Millar's / Molly's / Return from Camden Town / Tom Moyland's frolic / Paddy Ryan's dream / Farewell to Cailroe / Miller's maid / Skylark / Josie McDermott / Bunch of green rushes / Richard Dwyer's / Paddy Kelly's / Concert flute / Upstairs in a tent / Mason's apron / Pigeon on the gate / Drunken tinker / Fahy's / Finbar Dwyer's No.2 / Meadow / Ballinasloe fair / Bunch of Keys / Lady Montgomery / Farrell Garret / Dillan Brown's / Sonny McDonagh's
PHCD 1027 / Mar '97 / Outlet

Four Courts

☐ TRADITIONAL IRISH MUSIC AND SONG FROM COUNTY CLARE
TRADCD 001 / Feb '91 / GTD

Four Drop Bop

☐ FOUR DROP BOP
SLAMCD 224 / Aug '97 / Slam

Four Freshmen

☐ DAY BY DAY
Day by day / Day by day / Polka dots and moonbeams / Teach me tonight / It's only a paper moon / This october / Their hearts were full of spring / Candy / Once in love with amy / Show me the way to get out of this world / Fools rush in / Somebody loves me / Taps miller / (get your kicks on) route 66 / In this whole wide world
HCD 604 / Feb '95 / Hindsight

☐ EASY STREET (Live On The Ray Anthony TV Show 1958)
Day by day / You're so far above me / Love is just around the corner / You stepped out of a dream / Charmaine / Get a date with an angel / Easy Street / After you've gone / Somebody loves me / He who loves and runs away / Crazy bones / Day isn't long enough / How do you like your eggs in the morning / Someone like you / We'll be together again / This can't be love / Graduation day / Frosty the snowman / Love turns Winter to Spring / There'll never be another you / It's a blue world
RACD 1023 / Jun '97 / Aerospace

☐ FIVE SAXES/FIVE GUITARS
Liza / You've got me crying again / This can't be love / Very thought of you / East of the sun / I may be wrong / There's no one but you / Sometimes I'm happy / For all we know / Lullaby in rhythm / This love of mine / I get along without you very well / Rain / More I see you / October / Don't worry 'bout me / It's a pity to say goodbye / Oh lonely winter / It all depends on you / Nancy / I never knew / Invitation / I understand / Come rain or come shine
4950022 / 8 Jun '98 / EMI

☐ FIVE TROMBONES FIVE TRUMPETS
61774200172 / 21 Apr '98 / Collectables

☐ IT'S A BLUE WORLD
VN 170 / Mar '96 / Viper's Nest

☐ LIVE AT BUTLER UNIVERSITY (Four Freshmen & Stan Kenton Orchestra)
There will never be another you / After you / Byrd Avenue / Surfer girl / Girl talk / When the feeling hit you / Walk on by / What are you doing the rest of your life / Brand new key / Teach me tonight / Beautiful friendship / Summer has gone / Hymn to her / Come back to me / It's not unusual / Coming round the mountain / Walk softly / Artistry in rhythm
GNPD 1059 / Aug '95 / GNP Crescendo

☐ VOICES IN STANDARDS
Come fly with me / Young at heart / I've got you under my skin / Nearness of you / You'd be so nice to come home to / All the way / Embraceable you / I'm a fool to want you / All or nothing at all / In the wee small hours / Witchcraft / Time after time / How insensitive / Nancy / Nice 'n' easy / Put your dreams away
HCD 801 / Jul '96 / Hindsight

Four Horsemen

☐ GETTIN' PRETTY GOOD AT BARELY GETTIN' BY
4701440252 / Apr '96 / SPV

Four Letter Word

☐ NASTY PIECE OF WORK
BYO 049CD / 16 Feb '98 / BYO

Four Lovers

☐ JOYRIDE
What is a thing called love / Joyride / Such a night / Girl in my dreams / Diddilly diddilly baby / Shake a hand / Please don't leave me / You're the apple of my eye / Stranger / White Christmas / It's too soon to know / San Antonio rose / Night train / Cimarron / Lawdy Miss Clawdy / This is my story / (I love you) for sentimental reasons / I want a girl - just like the girl that married dear old Dad / Memories of you / Jambalaya / Be lovey lovey / Love sweet love / Happy am I / Never never / Honey love / (I love you) for sentimental reasons / White Christmas / Girl in my dreams / Diddilly diddilly baby / Such a night / Honey love
BCD 15424 / Apr '89 / Bear Family

Four Men & A Dog

☐ BARKING MAD
Hidden love/Sheila Coyles / Wee Johnny set / Wrap it up / Foxhunters / Waltzing for dreamers / Reel / Polkas / Swing set / Short fat Fanny / Jigs / Cruel father / High on a mountain / McFadden's reels
CBMMCCD 001 / Sep '91 / Special Delivery

☐ DR. A'S SECRET REMEDIES
Papa Genes Tree / Bertha / Last month of Summer / Mother of mercy / Punch in the dark / Take it on back / Samba / Hollow time / Last nite / Woodstock set / Heading West / Hector the hero
TRACD 106 / Apr '96 / Transatlantic

☐ LONG ROADS
She's on my mind / She's on my mind / Nancy / Meet me / Sally gardens / Joefy spokes / Long roads / Poor fool polka / Over the river she goes / Restless / Hold on I'm comin'
TRACD 223 / Jun '96 / Transatlantic

☐ SHIFTING GRAVEL
SPDCD 1047 / May '93 / Special Delivery

Four Pennies

☐ TWO SIDES OF FOUR PENNIES/MIXED BAG
Da doo ron ron / Sweeter than you / Claudette / If you love me / Do you want me to / Love's journey / You went away / Will you love me tomorrow / Now we are through / Pony time / Come to me / Why do you cry / Cryin' inside / Look down / I'm on my own / She didn't say yes / It is no secret / Iko Iko / Without love / Try to find another man / Maracabama / Stewball / All my sorrows / Someday soon / Wild goose / Let it be me
BGOCD 346 / Mar '97 / Beat Goes On

☐ WORLD OF THE FOUR PENNIES, THE
Juliet / Black girl / Keep the freeway open / I found out the hard way / Tell me girl / Till another day / If you love me / Miss bad Daddy / You went away / Running scared / Love's journey / No sad songs for me / Square peg / Sweeter than you / Way out love / Trouble is my middle name / Now we are through / San Francisco Bay / Do you want me to / Until it's time for you to go
5511012 / May '96 / Spectrum

Four Preps

☐ THREE GOLDEN GROUPS IN ONE
Hello again / Big man / Summer place / Church bells may ring / Can't take my eyes off you / Got a girl / Graduation day / Hurt so bad / I'll sing for you / MacArthur Park / I heard it through the grapevine / You've lost that lovin' feelin' / Hard habit to break / Why do fools fall in love / When I fall in love / Stroll / Little darlin' / Put your head on my shoulder / Ride like the wind / Stand by me / Love love love / Down by the station / Going out of my head / Lazy summer night / Silhouettes / Twenty six miles (Santa Catalina) / Shangri-La / Over the rainbow / I'll still be loving you / Somewhere
C5MCD 588 / Aug '92 / See For Miles

Four Sides

☐ SQUARE ONE
SQUARE 1 / Mar '97 / Square 1

Four Star Trio

☐ SQUARE TRIANGLE, THE
CR 02CD / Dec '97 / Craft

Four Tops

☐ FOUR TOPS
MCCD 340 / 20 Apr '98 / Music Club

☐ FOUR TOPS SINGLES COLLECTION
Reach out, I'll be there / Standing in the shadows of love / Bernadette / Walk away Renee / If I were a carpenter / Simple game / Seven rooms of gloom / Loving you is sweeter than ever / You keep running away / Yesterday's dreams / I'm in a different world / What is a man / Loco in Acapulco / Indestructible / When she was my girl / It's all in the game / Still water (love) / I can't help myself / Do what you gotta do / Keeper of the castle / Don't walk away
5157102 / Sep '92 / Motown

☐ MOTOWN EARLY CLASSICS
Reach out I'll be there / Love feels like fire / I can't help myself / I'm grateful / It's the same old song / Just as long as you need me / Baby I need your loving / Call on me / Where did you go / Your love is amazing / Tea house in Chinatown / Ask the lonely / Sad souvenirs / Don't turn away / Love has gone / Is there anything that I can do / Darling, I hum our song / Helpless
5521192 / Jul '96 / Spectrum

☐ MOTOWN'S GREATEST HITS
Reach out I'll be there (original version) / I can't help myself (sugar pie honey bunch) / It's the same old song / 7 rooms of gloom / Standing in the shadows of love / Walk away renee / Yesterday's dreams / Bernadette / I'm in a different world / Do what you gotta do / It's all in the game / River deep, mountain high / Still water (love) / You keep running away / If I were a carpenter / Just seven numbers (can straighten out my life) / Loving you is sweeter that ever / What is a man / Simple game / Reach out, I'll be there
5300162 / Jan '92 / Motown

☐ REACH OUT I'LL BE THERE
I can't help myself / Loving you is sweeter than ever / Reach out I'll be there / Bernadette / Walk away Renee / Yesterday's dreams / Do what you gotta do / It's all in the game / Still water / Simple game / MacArthur park / Cherish / River deep mountain high / Helpless / Ask the lonely / Climb every mountain / I got a feeling / Just seven numbers / In these changing times / For once in my life
5307912 / Apr '97 / Spectrum

☐ ULTIMATE COLLECTION
5308252 / 10 Aug '98 / Motown

☐ VERY BEST OF THE FOUR TOPS LIVE, THE
Intro / MacArthur Park / Shake me wake me (when it's over) / Baby I need your lovin' / In the still of the night / Ain't no woman like the one I got / When she was my girl / Ask the lonely / I've got you under my skin / Medley
WB 885522 / 2 Feb '98 / Disky

Fourmost

☐ FIRST AND FOURMOST
Till you say you'll be mine / Yakety yak / Girls, girls, girls / My block / So fine / Some kind of wonderful / Girl can't help it / Today I'm in love / In crowd / Baby sittin' boogie / Heebie jeebies / Sure to fall (in love with you) / Bound to lose my heart / Something's got a hold on me / Till you say you'll be mine / Yakety yak / Girls, girls, girls / My block / So fine / Some kind of wonderful / Girl can't help it / Today I'm in love / In crowd / Baby sittin' boogie / Heebie jeebies / Sure to fall (in love with you) / Bound to lose my heart / Something's got a hold on me
DORIG 116 / Aug '97 / EMI

Fourplay

☐ 4
Still the one / Little foxes / Sexual healing / Charmed I'm sure / Someone to love / Rio rush / Place of my heart / Slow slide / Vest pocket / Swamp jazz
9362469212 / 8 Jun '98 / Warner Bros.

☐ BEST OF FOURPLAY, THE
Max-o-man / 101 Eastbound / Higher ground: *Fourplay & Take 6* / Fourplay and pleasure / Chant / After the dance: *Fourplay & El Debarge* / Bali run / Play lady play / Between the sheets: *Fourplay & Chaka Khan* / Amorose / Any time of day / Why can't it wait till morning: *Fourplay & Phil Collins*
9362466612 / Jul '97 / Warner Bros.

☐ BETWEEN THE SHEETS
Chant / Monterrey / Between the sheets / Li'l darlin' / Flying east / One in the AM / Gulliver / Amoroso / Summer child / Anthem / Song for Somalia
9362452402 / Aug '93 / WEA

☐ FOURPLAY
Bali run / 101 eastbound / Foreplay / Moonjogger / Max-o-man / After the dance / Quadrille / Midnight stroll / October morning / Wish you were here / Rainforest
7599266562 / Mar '94 / WEA

Fourth Wall

☐ FOURTH WALL
CD 9801 / 16 Mar '98 / RBN

Fourth Way

☐ FOURTH WAY, THE
COD 022 / Aug '92 / Jazz View

Fourth World

☐ FOURTH WORLD
Fourth world / Sao felipe / Lua flora / Time one / Step seven / Rainha de noite / Sea horse / Africa
JHCD 026 / Jan '94 / Ronnie Scott's Jazz House

Fowler, Lemuel

☐ LEM FOWLER (1923-27) (Fowler, Lem & Helen Baxter/H. McDonald)
JPCD 1520 / May '95 / Jazz Perspectives

Fowley, Kim

☐ ANIMAL GOD OF THE STREET
622482 / Apr '97 / Skydog

☐ DAY THE EARTH STOOD STILL, THE
14260 / Jan '97 / Spalax

☐ HIDDEN AGENDA AT THE 13TH NOTE (Fowley, Kim & The BMX Bandits)
Jaded / Ugly dream / Crabmeat / Ballad of a suicidal teenager / Medicine girl / Secret and sometimes cunning exploits of a Glaswegian mortua / Volcano / Sleep / Alice Cooper's roadie's lovechild / Dancing with death on the lilac / Super highway / Tokyo summertime love affair number 69 / Susan was bleeding / Do you want to dance / It's my party / Peaches / Vampire scarecrow / Kimotronix / Sight surfing
RRCD 231 / Mar '97 / Receiver

☐ KINGS OF SATURDAY NIGHT (Fowley, Kim & Ben Vaughn)
SECT2 1002 / Jul '95 / Sector 2

☐ MICHIGAN BABYLON
DE 2 / 22 May '98 / Detroit Electric

☐ MONDO HOLLYWOOD
CREV 036CD / Nov '95 / Rev-Ola

☐ OUTLAW SUPERMAN
BA 1113CD / 5 Jan '98 / Bacchus Archives

☐ OUTRAGEOUS/GOOD CLEAN FUN
CREV 033CD / Feb '95 / Rev-Ola

Fowlkes, Eddie

☐ BLACK TECHNOSOUL (Fowlkes, Eddie 'Flashin')
EFA 017952 / Jun '96 / Tresor

☐ IN DA MIX (Fowlkes, Eddie 'Flashin')
OL 1 / Apr '97 / On The Lid

☐ TECHNOSOUL (Fowlkes, Eddie 'Flashin' & 3MB)
My soul / Computee / Move me / Tribal joy / Hoodlum child / Golden apple / Image-a-nation
TRESOR 8CD / Apr '93 / Tresor

Fox

☐ VERY BEST OF FOX, THE
AHLCD 51 / 6 Oct '97 / Hit

Fox

☐ FOR FOX SAKE
FLASH 34 / 1 Jun '98 / Flash

Fox, Bill

☐ TRANSIT BYZANTIUM
SPART 63CD / 19 May '98 / Spin Art

Fox, Bob

☐ HOW ARE YOU OFF FOR COALS (Songs Of The Mining Communities Of North East England) (Fox, Bob & Benny Graham/Celebrated Working Men)
Celebrated working man/Oakey's strike evictions / Funny names at Tanfield / South Medomsley strike / I wish pay Friday wad come / Old miner / Trimdon Grange explosion / Geordie Black / Have a game for the crack / Little chance / Wor Nanny's a maizor / Going to the mine / Big hewer / When it's ours / Blackleg mining man / Farewell Johnny miner / Miner's lifeguard
FECD 111 / Feb '97 / Fellside

Fox, Donal

☐ GONE CITY
805152 / Nov '97 / New World

☐ UGLY BEAUTY (Fox, Donal & David Murray)
Ugly beauty / Vamping with TT / 'Round midnight / Hope scope / Song for Murray / Icarus / Becca's ballad / Picasso / Golden ladders / Hope scope (Live)
ECD 221312 / Dec '95 / Evidence

Fox, Mandy

☐ FIRST TIME EVER (Fox, Mandy & HARA)
Invocation / Missing / Here it comes / You / Flight of the eagle / First time ever / Zoodat / She moved through the fair / Let me go soldier / Bliss / Prayer / Soukhous by night / Call
SLAMCD 220 / Oct '96 / Slam

Fox, Paul

☐ TRIBULATION DUB VOL.1
WSPCD 002 / Nov '93 / WSP

Fox, R.J.

☐ RETROSPECTIVE DREAMS (2CD Set)
BBCD 211 / 23 Mar '98 / Black Bamboo

Fox, Robert

☐ GATHERING OF SPIRITS, A
FXCD 4 / Aug '96 / FX

Fox, Roy

☐ RISE 'N' SHINE
Rise 'n' shine / You leave me breathless / It's been so long / Touch of your lips / Saddle your blues to a wild mustang / Please believe me / It's the natural thing to do / Roses in December / Things are looking up / Waterlillies in the monlight / Quicker than you can say Jack Robinson / No regrets / Fine romance / In my cabin of dreams / How'd ya like to love me / These foolosh things / So rare / Miracles sometimes happen / You took the words right out of my heart / Harbour lights / Thanks for the memory / Whispering
CDEA 6003 / Feb '98 / Vocalion

☐ ROY FOX
Whispering / Roll on, mississippi, roll on / Cherie, c'est vous / Them there eyes / Tell me, are you from georgia / Bathing in the sunshine / My temptation / When the waltz was through / Writing a letter to you / Maybe it's love / That's what I like about you / Jungle drums / Lady play your mandoline / Drowsy blues / Can't we be friends / You're the one I care for / That lindy hop / Oh monah / I'd rather be a beggar with you / Ya got love / You rascal you / Between the devil and the deep blue sea
PASTCD 9745 / Aug '91 / Flapper

Fox, Samantha

☐ GREATEST HITS
CHIP 122 / Sep '92 / Jive

☐ GREATEST HITS
Touch me (I want your body) / Do ya do ya (wanna please me) / Nothing's gonna stop me now / I only wanna be with you / I surrender (to the spirit of the night) / I wanna have some fun / Hold on tight / Just one night / Naughty girls (need love too) / I promise you (get ready) / (I can't get no) satisfaction / Love house / Another woman / Spirit of America / Hot lovin' / Giving me a hard time / Even in the darkest hours
100032 / May '97 / A-Play Collection

☐ GREATEST HITS OF SAMANTHA FOX, THE
Touch me touch me (I want your body) / Do ya do ya (wanna please me) / Nothing's gonna stop me now / I only wanna be with you / I surrender (to the spirit of the night) / I wanna have some fun / Hold on tight / Just one night / Naughty girls (need love too) / I promise you (get ready) / Satisfaction / Love house / Another woman (too many people) / Spirit of America / Hot lovin' / Giving me a hard time / Even in the darkest hours
QED 046 / Nov '96 / Tring

☐ HITS ALBUM, THE
Touch me (I want your body) / Nothing's gonna stop me now / I only wanna be with you / Do ya do ya (wanna please me) / Love house / Satisfaction / I wanna have some fun / Hot for you / More more more / Love to love you baby / Naughty girls (need love too) / Hurt me hurt me / But the pants stay on / Hot lovin' / Even in the darkest hours / Just one night / Another woman (too many people) / Pleasure zone / Spirit of America / I surrender (to the spirit of the night)
EMPRCD 557 / Mar '95 / Emporio

☐ INTERVIEW COMPACT DISC: SAM FOX
CBAK 4023 / Nov '89 / Baktabak

Foxley, Ray

☐ PROFESSOR FOXLEY'S SPORTING HOUSE MUSIC
BLR 84 021 / May '91 / L&R

☐ RAY FOXLEY & BLACK EAGLE JAZZBAND (Foxley, Ray & Black Eagle Jazzband)
SOSCD 1257 / Oct '93 / Stomp Off

Foxx, Inez & Charlie

☐ COUNT THE DAYS
CDRB 26 / Aug '95 / Charly

Foxx, John

☐ ASSEMBLY
New kind of man / Underpass / Burning car / This city / Twilight's last gleaming / Ghosts on water / This jungle / Endlessly / Someone / Sitting at the edge of the world / In mysterious ways / Morning glory / Europe after the rain / Systems of romance / Walk away / When I was a man and you were a woman / Pater noster / Garden
CDVM 9002 / Jun '92 / Virgin

☐ CATHEDRAL OCEANS
Cathedral oceans / City as memory / Through Summer rooms / Geometry and coincidence / If only... / Shifting perspective / Floating islands / Infinite in all directions / Avenham collanade / Sunset rising / Invisible architecture
META 001 / Mar '97 / Metamatic

☐ GARDEN, THE
Europe after the rain / Systems of romance / When I was a man and you were a woman / Dancing like a gun / Pater Noster / Night suit / You were there / Fusion / Walk away / Garden / Fission
CDV 2194 / Jul '93 / Virgin

☐ METAMATIC
Plaza / He's a liquid / Underpass / Metal beat / No-one driving / New kind of man / Blurred girl / 030 / Tidal wave / Touch and girl
CDV 2146 / Jul '93 / Virgin

☐ SHIFTING CITY (Foxx, John & Louis Gordon)
Crash / Noise / Here we go / Shadow man / Through my sleeping / Forgotten years / Everyone / Shifting city / Concrete / Bulletproof / Invisible / Ocean we can breathe
META 002 / Mar '97 / Metamatic

Foxy

☐ BEST OF FOXY, THE
Get off your aaahh and dance / Let's love / People fall in love (while dancing) / Get off / Tena's song / Party boys / Rrrrock / Hot number / Head hunter / Chicapbon-chicapbon / Lady / Let's make love: *Ish* / Faster than a speeding bullet: *Ish* / Deep down I'm funky: *Ish*
HTCD 31 / 20 Apr '98 / Hot Productions

☐ GET OFF/HOT NUMBERS
CCLCD 62332 / 3 Aug '98 / Collectables

Foyer Des Arts

☐ DIE UNFAEHIGKETT ZU FRUEHSTUECKEN
EFA 4522 CD / Jun '89 / Funfundvierz

Fracasso, Michael

☐ LOVE AND TRUST
DJD 3205 / May '94 / Dejadisc

☐ WHEN I LIVED IN THE WILD
BOHB 003 / Feb '95 / Bohemia Beat

☐ WORLD IN A DROP OF WATER
Hospital / Chain link fence / Jar of pennies / Started on the wrong foot / Changed your mind / Gold / Your gift to me / Our finest hour / World / Marie / Sleep becomes you
BBEA 0008 / 9 Mar '98 / Bohemia Beat

Fraction

☐ MOON BLOOD
ANT 2411 / May '97 / Anthology

Fracture

☐ KILLERNET
SPV 0822462 / Oct '96 / SPV

Fracus, Dimitru

☐ IMPROVISATIONS ON FAMOUS ROMANIAN THEMES (Fracus, Dimitru & Marcel Cellier)
Marie Polale ciurate / Cinrec de unstrainare / Quand dieu crea les montagnes / Les moutons, les bergers / Dooina prieteniei / Doina Cind eram copil d-un an / Bruil lui cepzan / Doina Cresta frunza / Entre ciel et terre / Appels des sommets et danse du berger / Doina lui constantin gherghina / Poarga din pomezau / Doina au sommet de la collines / Suite: Un soir en transylvanie / Doina: Les plaines du banat / Duex danses dominicales / Oh montagnes aux sapins majesteux / Ardalean de la zarvesti / Cind s a pierduit ciobanul oile
PV 750003 / Jul '94 / Disques Pierre Verany

Fradon, Amy

☐ TAKE ME HOME (Fradon, Amy & Leslie Ritter)
SHCD 8013 / Dec '94 / Shanachie

Fraley, J.P.

☐ MAYSVILLE (Fraley, J.P. & Annadeene)
ROUCD 0351 / Nov '95 / Rounder

Frames

☐ FITZCARRALDO (Frames DC)
Say it to me now / Denounced / Red chord / Angel at my table / Revelate / Roger / Monument / Giving it all away / Fitzcarraldo / In this boat together
ZTT 110CD / 17 Aug '98 / ZTT

Frampton Hill

☐ WELCOME TO FRAMPTON HILL
0630179842 / May '97 / East West

Frampton, Peter

☐ FRAMPTON COMES ALIVE
(Baby) Something's happening / Doobie wah / Show me the way / It's a plain shame / All I want to be (is by your side) / Wind of change / Baby, I love your way / I wanna go to the sun / Penny for your thoughts / (I'll give you) money / Shine on / Jumpin' Jack Flash / Lines on my face / Do you feel like we do
5407162 / Mar '97 / A&M

☐ FRAMPTON COMES ALIVE VOL.2
Day in the sun / Lying / For now / Most of all / You / Waiting for your love / I'm in you / Talk to me / Hang on to a dream / Can't take that away / More ways than one / Almost said goodbye / Off the hook / Show me the way / Baby I love your way / Lines on my face / Do you feel like we do
EIRSCD 1074 / Oct '95 / IRS/EMI

☐ LOVE TAKER
HADCD 199 / Nov '95 / Javelin

☐ MOON'S TRAIN
Life I lead / Say what I mean / Telephone talker / Bakerman / I get excited / Home and dry / Marriage is for old folks / Nervous / I'm not the marrying kind / You got me / My town / What's that you got / Wait for me / My love for you / Gotta go catch me a woman / It's in my mind / Moaning
INAK 11004 / Nov '97 / In Akustik

☐ PACIFIC FREIGHT
CDSGP 0243 / Feb '96 / Prestige

☐ SHINE ON
CDMID 174 / Oct '92 / A&M

☐ SHOWS THE WAY
Friday on my mind / Roadrunner / Signed, sealed, delivered (I'm yours) / Baby, I love your way / I can't stand it no more / You don't know like I know / Wind of change / Show me the way / We've just begun / (I'll give you) money / Breaking all the rules / All night long / Jumpin' Jack Flash
5501032 / Mar '94 / Spectrum

Fran, Carol

☐ SEE THERE (Fran, Carol & Clarence Holliman)
BT 1100CD / Apr '94 / Black Top

☐ SOUL SENSATION (Fran, Carol & Clarence Holliman)
BT 1071CD / Feb '92 / Black Top

France, Laila

☐ ORGONON
Trashy like TV / Trance cocktail airlines / Wonderhood / Japanese especially / Pink song / David Hamilton / Synthesizer wizard / First love blood / Orgonon / Bilitis / Sensations of orgasm
RTD 3460018243 / 17 Nov '97 / Bungalow

France, Marie

☐ MARIE FRANCE
3014632 / Feb '97 / Last Call

Francini-Pontier

☐ A MIS AMORES
BMT 006 / Jan '98 / Blue Moon

Francis, Connie

☐ 24 GREATEST HITS
Where the boys are / If I didn't care / Hurt / Vacation / Are you lonesome tonight / Together among my souvenirs / Everybody's somebody's fool / Old time rock 'n' roll / My heart has a mind of its own / Crying time / My happiness / Lipstick on your collar / Who's sorry now / Stupid cupid / Misty blue / Torn between two lovers / Breakin' in a brand new broken heart / Many tears ago / Don't break the heart that loves you / Cry / Frankie / Second hand love / Something stupid
PLATCD 3910 / Nov '90 / Platinum

☐ 24 GREATEST HITS
Who's sorry now / Stupid cupid / My happiness / If I didn't care / Lipstick on your collar / Frankie / Among my souvenirs / Everybody's somebody's fool / My heart has a mind of its own / Many tears ago / Where the boys are / Breakin' in a brand new broken heart / Together / Don't break the heart that loves you / Second hand love / Vacation / I'm gonna be warm this winter / Cry / Are you lonesome tonight / Hurt / Cryin' time / Old time rock and roll / Misty blue / Torn between two lovers
RMB 75069 / Jan '94 / Remember

☐ COLLECTION, THE
Stupid Cupid / Lipstick on your collar / Don't break the heart that loves you / Jealous heart / Where the boys are / Breakin' in a brand new broken heart / Plenty good lovin' / Singin' the blues / Valentino / You always hurt the one you love / My heart has a mind of its own / Heartaches by the number / Bye bye love / Your cheatin' heart / I can't stop loving you / Walk on by / Among my souvenirs / My happiness
5518222 / Nov '95 / Spectrum

☐ KISSIN', TWISTIN', GOIN' WHERE THE BOYS ARE (The Early Sixties/5CD Set)
Teddy / It would be worth it / No one / No one / My dream / Cashin' in / Valentino / Yes indeed / Amen / Accentuate the positive / Lonesome Road / I think of you / Millionaire / Jealous of you / Robot man / Everybody's somebody's fool / I think of you / Robot man / My heart has a mind of it's own / My heart has a mind of it's own / My heart has a mind of it's own / I've got reason to worry / My heart has a mind of it's own / My heart has a mind of it's own / Love is where you find it / Swanee / My love, my love / Angel eyes / I got lost in his arms / Gone with the wind / How long has this been going on / It might as well be Spring / Ol' man Mose / Dat's love / Taboo / You're nobody 'til somebody loves you / Where the boys are / On the outside lookin' in / Many tears ago / Happy New Year baby / Breakin' in a brand new broken heart / No one / Without your love / Auf wiederseh'n / Baby Roo / One tear too many / Let the rest of the world go by / Someone else's boy / It's time to say goodnight / Too many rules / You love / Your love / Together / Together / O Suzanna / On top of Old Smokey / Every night (when the sun goes in) / Boll weevil / Clementine / She'll be comin' round the mountain / Come on Jerry / Careless love / True love, true love / Aura Lee / Red River valley / Beautiful brown eyes / High noon / Love is a many splendored thing / Three coins in the fountain / Around the world / Tammy / April love / Anna / Where is your heart / Love me tender / Young at heart / Never on Sunday / Moonglow / Pretty little baby / (He's my) Dreamboat / He's just a scientist / Hollywood / Sing along / You tell me your dream / In the good old summertime / I love you truly / Home on the range / And the band played on / My wild Irish rose / Auld lang syne / Tavern in the town / Down in the valley / When the boy in your arms / I'm falling in love with yiou / Baby's first Christmas / Don't break the heart that loves you / White cliffs of Dover / White cliffs of Dover / Mr. Twister / Mr. Twister / Ain't that better baby / Don't cry on my shoulder / Love bird / Does ol' Broadway ever sleep / Gonna git that man / Johnny darlin' / Teach me how to twist / Kiss 'n' twist / Cha cha twist / Lovey dovey twist / Telephone lover / Drop it Joe / Hey ring a ding / Mommy your daughter's fallin' in love / I won't be home to you / My real happiness / Little bit of heaven / Mother Machree / How can you buy Killarney / Danny Boy / How are things in Glocca Morra / My wild Irish rose / When Irish eyes are smiling / Too-ra-loo-ra-loo-ral / It's a great day for the Irish / Great day for the Irish / Dear old Donegal / MacNamara's band / Did your mother come from Ireland / I'm so alone / It happened last night / No one ever sends me roses / I was such a fool / Second hand love / Second hand love / You'll never know / Lullaby of Broadway / Zip-a-dee-doo-dah / Moon river / Whatever will be will be (Que sera sera) / (Somewhere) Over the rainbow / Secret love / When you wish upon a star / Buttons and bows / High hopes / Last time I saw Paris / All the way / Way you look tonight / It's time to say goodnight
BCD 15826 / Jun '96 / Bear Family

☐ SING GREAT COUNTRY FAVORITES (Francis, Connie & Hank Williams Jr.)
Bye bye love / Send me the pillow that you dream on / Wolverton mountain / No letter today / Please help me, I'm falling / Singin' the blues / Walk on by / If you've got the money, I've got the time / Mule skinner blues / Making believe / Blue blue day / No letter today (alt) / Wabash cannonball / Mule skinner blues (Alt.take)
BCD 15737 / Aug '93 / Bear Family

☐ SINGLES COLLECTION, THE
Lipstick on your collar / Everybody's somebody's fool / I'm sorry I made you cry / I'm gonna be warm this winter / Together / V-A-C-A-T-I-O-N / I'll get by / Frankie / Many tears ago / Mama/Robot man / Fallin' / Among my souvenirs / In the valley of love / Who's sorry now / Stupid cupid/Carolina moon / Breakin' in a brand new broken heart / Plenty good lovin' / Baby's first Christmas / You always hurt the one you love / Don't break the heart that loves you / My happiness / Valentino / Where the boys are/Baby Roo / My heart has a mind of its own / Senza fine / Jealous heart / My child
5191312 / Apr '93 / PolyGram TV

☐ SOUVENIRS (2CD Set)
5333822 / Nov '96 / Polydor

☐ SWINGING CONNIE, THE (Francis, Connie & Joe Mazzu Orchestra)
ACD 286 / Nov '96 / Audiophile

☐ WHITE SOX, PINK LIPSTICK AND STUPID CUPID (5CD Set)
Didn't I love you enough / Freddy / (Oh please) Make him jealous / Goody goodbye / Are you satisfied / My treasure / My first real love / Believe in me / Forgetting / Send for my baby / I never had a sweetheart / Little blue wren / Everyone needs someone / My sailor boy / No other one / I leaned on a man / Faded orchid / Eighteen / My sisters clothes / Majesty of love / You my darling you / Who's sorry now / You were only fooling (while I was falling in love) / I'm beginning to see the light / Rudolph the red nosed reindeer / Wheel of fortune / How can I make you believe in me / You belong to me / Daddy's little girl / I'm sorry I made you cry / I cried for you / You always hurt the one you love / I'll get by / Lock up your heart / Heartaches / I'm nobody's baby / My melancholy baby / I miss you so / It's the talk of the town / If I had you / How deep is the ocean / Carolina moon / Stupid Cupid / Happy days and lonely nights / Fallin' / You're my everything / My happiness / Don't speak of love / Love eyes / Never before / In the valley of love / Time after time / Blame it on my youth / How did he look / That's all / Toward the end of the day / I really don't want to know / No-one to cry to / If I didn't care / If you love me tonight / Come rain or come shine / All by myself / Hold me, thrill me, kiss me / Song is ended (but the melody lingers on) / There will never be another you / Melancholy serenade / Rock-a-bye your baby with a Dixie melody / Hallelujah, I love him so / My thanks to you / Bells of St. Mary's / Good luck, good health, God bless you / Garden in the rain / Try a little tenderness / Goodnight sweetheart / Cruising down the river / I'll close my eyes / Very thought of you / These foolish things / Tree in the meadow / Gypsy / Now is the hour / You're gonna miss me / Frankie / Lipstick on your collar / Oh, Frankie / I almost lost my mind / I'm walkin' / Just a dream / Heartbreak hotel / I hear you knocking / Tweedle dee / Ain't that a shame / It's only make believe / Sincerely / Don't be cruel / Bye bye love / Earth angel / Hearts of stone / Silhouettes / Plenty good lovin' / Singin' the blues / My special angel / Tennessee waltz / Let me go, lover / Young love / Half as much / Anytime / Your cheatin' heart / Cold cold heart / Peace in the valley / Too young / Temptation / You made me love you / Prisoner of love / Young at heart / It's not for me to say / Thinking of you / That's my desire / Because of you / Where the blue of the night meets the gold of the day / April love / Cry / God bless America / Among my souvenirs / Snapdragon / No one / Tiger and the mouse / Forgetting (take 10) / Lock up your heart (slow version) / My melancholy baby (take 2) / No one (take 2) / Tiger and the mouse, The (take 4)
BCD 15616 / Jul '93 / Bear Family

☐ WITH LOVE TO BUDDY
Heart beat / Maybe baby / That'll be the day / It doesn't matter anymore / Love made a fool out of you / Not fade away / Bo Diddley / It's so easy / Love is strange / Oh boy / Well alright / Everyday / Peggy Sue / Raining in my heart / Think it over / You've got love / Early in the morning / Rave on
3036000412 / May '96 / Carlton

☐ WORLD OF CONNIE FRANCIS, THE
Look of love / What kind of fool am I / Hold me, thrill me, kiss me / White cliffs of Dover / True love / Strangers in the night / Moon river / Young at heart / Tammy / Three coins in the fountain / Love me tender / Love is a many splendoured thing / Stardust / Last waltz / My foolish heart / Am I blue / My heart cries for you / I wish I had a wooden heart / Wayward wind / Trains, boats and planes
5513092 / May '96 / Spectrum

Francis, Dean

☐ THIS GROOVE'S FOR YOU
This groove's for you / Just funkin' around / Without guns / I got the hots / It's okay / Got a funky disposition / Dancefloor jazz / In the rain / Know when to leave it alone
ME 000332 / Sep '95 / Soulciety

Francis, Deloris

☐ HERE TO STAY
Here to stay
VDACD 001 / 30 Mar '98 / Voida

Francis, Karen

☐ LITTLE SUNFLOWER (Francis, Karen Sextet)
SCCD 31431 / 24 Feb '98 / Steeplechase

Francis, Panama

☐ GETTIN' IN THE GROOVE (Francis, Panama & The Savoy Sultans)
Song of the Islands / Stitches / Rhythm Dr Man / Freezy / Chequered had / Second balcony jump / Nuages / Little John special
BLE 233320 / Dec '90 / Black & Blue

Francis, Terry

☐ TERRY FRANCIS PRESENTS ARCHITECTURE (Various Artists)
Dreamers: *Damon Dreamers* / Voice: *Electrospy* / Web of deceit: *Primary Colours* / Marathon: *Aubrey* / Fight against oppression: *Aubrey* / Halftoo: *DJ Profile* / 5 O'Clock: *FFN* / You say: *Digital Boogie* / Only house music: *Yusef & Loveys* / Keep on: *Jackson, Gideon* / Straight ahead then take the next wrong: *Two Right Wrongans* / Free your mind: *Skymaster* / Shakedown: *Blaze* / Lovelee dae: *Ame Strong* / Tous est blue: *Ame Strong* / Better day: *Presence* / Marathon: *Aubrey* / Fight against oppression: *Pure Science* / You say: *Digital Boogie* / Tout est bleu: *Ame Strong* / Two point five: *Francis, Terry* / Furry: *Francis, Terry* / Three point five: *Francis, Terry* / Snake charmed: *Francis, Terry*
PAGANCD 1005 / 16 Feb '98 / Pagan

Francis, W.J.

☐ RAGGA LOVE
MRCD 002 / Dec '92 / Metronome

Francis, Winston

☐ MR FIX-IT/CALIFORNIA DREAMING
Same old song / Fools fall in love / Games people play / Too experienced / Eretta / Send me some loving / Love me today not tomorrow / Don't change / Venus / Mr Fix-It / Chain gang / I'll make you my own / What does it take to win / Never had a dream come true / California dreaming / Yester me yester you / Groovy situation / Turn back the hands of time / I've lost everything I ever had / Angie girl / There's always something there / By the time I get to Phoenix / Baby please
SOCD 011 / 20 Apr '98 / Studio One

☐ SWEET ROCK STEADY
LKJCD 017 / Jun '97 / LKJ

Franck, Albert

☐ UN PARISIEN A PARIS
ROSE 236CD / Feb '91 / New Rose

Franck, Thomas

☐ THOMAS FRANCK IN NEW YORK (Franck, Thomas Quartet)
CRISS 1052CD / Nov '91 / Criss Cross

Franco, Gian

☐ SEA, THE (Franco, Gian Reverberi)
Rendezvous / Eclipse / Sunset / Sand ripples / Nice words / Moonlight / Sweet touches / After love / Again and again / Golden sky / Sea dawn / Sea
CDPM 6001 / Mar '90 / Prestige

Franco, Jess

☐ MANACOA EXPERIENCE, THE (A Dazzling Lesson In Cinematic B-Film Jazz)
EFA 043942 / 9 Mar '98 / Crippled Dick Hot Wax

Francois, Claude

☐ LES CONCERTS INEDITS DE MUSICORAMA (2CD Set)
3036112 / 24 Apr '98 / Arcade

Frank & Walters

☐ GRAND PARADE, THE
Colours / Indian ocean / Little dolls / Russian ship / I suppose / Saturday night / How can I exist / Mrs. Xavier / Have you ever / Tony Cochran / Landslide / Lately
SETCD 054 / Jun '97 / Setanta

Frank Bango

☐ FUGITIVE GIRLS
NL 045 / 29 Jun '98 / Not Lame

Frank Chickens

☐ CLUB MONKEY
RES 137CD / 3 Aug '98 / Resurgence

☐ GET CHICKENIZED
We say you say / Sacred marriage / Street angels Tokyo / Two little ladies / Solid life / Japanese girl / Island inside island / Young summer / Chicken ondo / Yellow toast / Dark / One million hamburgers / Monster
RES 136CD / 3 Aug '98 / Resurgence

☐ YUKASITA UNDERFLOOR
CMCD 009 / Jun '96 / Creative Man

Frank, Ed

☐ NEW NEW ORLEANS MUSIC VOL.1 (Frank, Ed Quintet)
ROUCD 2065 / '88 / Rounder

Frank, Emilio

☐ LECUONA
74321430522 / 8 Nov '97 / Milan

Frank, Erik

☐ NOVELTY ACCORDION 1936-1968
DRCD 310 / May '97 / Dragon

Frank, Jackson C.

☐ BLUES RUN THE GAME
CRESTCD 021 / Jun '96 / Mooncrest

Frank, Keith

☐ YOU'D BE SURPRISED
MDSCD 1063 / Mar '98 / Maison De Soul

Franke, Bob

☐ HEART OF THE FLOWER, THE
DARINGCD 3016 / Oct '95 / Daring

☐ LONG ROADS SHORT VISITS
Roads are long in Canada / Inland sea / There's a last time for everything / In the place of trust / For real / I won't feel lucky ('til I get lucky with you) / Slow down / Je t'adore / William the streak / Straw against the chill / Saturn blues
DARINGCD 3031 / Sep '97 / Daring

Franke, Christopher

☐ ENCHANTING NATURE
ET 7401 / 16 Feb '98 / Earthtones

☐ KLEMANIA
Scattered thoughts of a canyon flight / Inside a morphing space / Silent waves
SI 85042 / Sep '95 / Sonic Images

Frankel, Judy

☐ SEPHARDIC SONGS OF LOVE & HOPE
Los bilbilicos / Tres hermanicas / Alta, alta va la luna / Puncha la rosa / La vida do por el rakl / Bendigamos / A la una / El dio alto / Morena / O mis hermanos / Fiestaremos / Avram avinu
GVMCD 157 / May '93 / Global Village

Frankfurt Jazz Ensemble

☐ ATMOSPHERIC CONDITIONS PERMITTING (2CD Set)
5173542 / Dec '95 / ECM

Frankie

☐ MY HEART BELONGS TO YOU
Heart-interlude / If I had you / One last time / I have love / Wait-interlude / Dear love / Think of you / All I do / Life without you-interlude / I can tell / Forever with me / Have I told you (I love you) / My heart
4882072 CD / 1 Sep '97 / Epic

Frankie Goes To Hollywood

☐ BANG (Greatest Hits)
Relax / Two tribes / War / Ferry 'cross the Mersey / Warriors of the wasteland / For heaven's sake / World is my oyster / Welcome to the pleasure dome / Watching the wildlife / Born to run / Rage hard / Power of love / Bang
ZTT 108CD / 20 Jul '98 / ZTT

Franklin, Aretha

☐ AMAZING GRACE
Mary don't you weep / Precious Lord, take my hand / You've got a friend / Old landmark / Give yourself to Jesus / How I got over / What a friend we have in Jesus / Amazing grace / Precious memories / Climbing higher mountains / God will take care of you / Wholly Holy / You'll never walk alone / Never grow old
7567813242 / Jun '93 / Atlantic

☐ ARETHA ARRIVES
Satisfaction / You are my sunshine / Never let me go / 96 tears / Prove it / Night life / That's life / Ronettes / Ain't nobody / Going down slow / Baby I love you
8122712742 / Jan '93 / Atlantic

☐ ARETHA GOSPEL
There is a fountain filled with blood / Precious Lord (take my hand) / Precious Lord (take my hand) / You grow closer / Never grow old / Day is past and gone / He will wash you white as snow / While the blood runs warm / Yield not to temptation
MCD 91521 / Apr '97 / Chess/MCA

☐ ARETHA IN PARIS
Satisfaction / Don't let me lose this dream / Soul serenade / Night life / Baby I love you / Groovin' / Natural woman / Come back baby / Dr. Feelgood / Respect / Since you've been gone / I never loved a man (the way I love you) / Chain of fools
8122718522 / Dec '94 / Atlantic

☐ ARETHA NOW
Think / I say a little prayer / See saw / Night time is the right time / You send me / You're a sweet sweet man / I take what I want / Hello sunshine / Change / I can't see myself leaving you
8122712732 / Feb '93 / Atlantic

☐ DELTA MEETS DETROIT, THE (Aretha's Blues)
Today I sing the blues / Ramblin' / Pitiful / I never loved a man (the way I love you) / Night life / I wonder / Takin' another man's place / Night time is the right time / River's invitation / Good to me as I am to you / It ain't fair / Going down slow / Drown in my own / You are my sunshine / Dr. Feelgood / Thrill is gone
8122729422 / 4 May '98 / Rhino

☐ GREATEST HITS 1980-1994
74321162022 / Feb '96 / Arista

☐ HEY NOW HEY (The Other Side Of The Sky)
Angel / Hey now hey (the other side of the sky) / Somewhere / Master of eyes (the deepness of your eyes) / Just right tonight / Moody's mood for love (moody's mood) / That's the way I feel about cha / Mister spain / Sister from texas / So swell when you're well
8122718532 / Dec '94 / Atlantic

☐ I NEVER LOVED A MAN THE WAY I LOVE YOU
Respect / Drown in my own tears / I never loved a man (the way I love you) / Soul serenade / Don't let me lose this dream / Baby baby baby / Dr. Feelgood / Good times / Do right woman, do right man / Save me / Change is gonna come
7567814392 / Mar '93 / Atlantic

☐ JAZZ TO SOUL (2CD Set)
Today I sing the blues / (Blue) by myself / Maybe I'm a fool / All night long / Blue holiday / Nobody like you / Sweet lover / Just for a thrill / If ever I would leave you / Once in a while / This bitter Earth / God bless the child / Skylark / Muddy water / Drinking again / What a difference a day makes / Unforgettable / Love for sale / Misty / Impossible / This could be the start of something / Won't be long / Operation heartbreak / Soulville / Runnin' out of fools / Trouble in mind / Walk on by / Every little bit hurts / Mockingbird / You'll lose a good thing / Cry like a baby / Take it like you give it / Land of dreams / Can't you just see me / (No no) I'm losing you / Bit of soul / Why was I born / Until you were gone / Lee cross
4772342 / Jun '96 / Columbia

☐ LADY SOUL
Chain of fools / Money won't change you / People get ready / Niki Hoeky / Natural woman / Since you've been gone / Good to me as I am to you / Come back baby / Groovin' / Ain't no way
7567818182 / Mar '93 / Atlantic

☐ LET ME IN YOUR LIFE
Let me in your life / Every natural thing / Ain't nothing like the real thing / I'm in love / Until you come back to me / (I'm afraid) the masquerade is over / With pen in hand / Oh baby / Eight days on the road / If you don't think / Song for you
8122718542 / Dec '94 / Atlantic

☐ LIVE AT FILLMORE WEST
Respect / Love the one you're with / Bridge over troubled water / Eleanor Rigby / Make it with you / Don't play that song (You lied) / Dr. Feelgood / Spirit in the dark / Reach out and touch
8122715262 / Feb '94 / Atlantic

☐ LOVE SONGS
Baby I love you / I say a little prayer / You send me / You make me feel like a natural woman / Day dreaming / You and me / Call me / Oh me oh my (I'm a fool for you baby) / I'm in love / Look into your heart / Crazy he calls me / Something he can feel / This girl's in love with you / Brand new me / If you don't think / Ain't nothing like the real thing
8122725762 / Mar '97 / Rhino

☐ QUEEN OF SOUL
I never loved a man (the way I love you) / Do right woman, do right man / Dr. Feelgood / Baby I love you / (You make me feel like) A natural woman / Chain of fools / Since you've been gone / Ain't no way / Save me / House that Jack built / Think / I say a little prayer / See saw / Daydreaming / Call me / Don't play that song (You lied) / Border song (Holy Moses) / You're all I need to get by / I'm in love / Spanish Harlem / Rock steady / Angel / Until you come back to me
7567806062 / Oct '94 / Atlantic

☐ QUEEN OF SOUL - THE ATLANTIC RECORDINGS (4CD Set)
Eleanor rigby / Thrill is gone / I never loved a man (the way I love you) / Tracks of my tears / Dark end of the street / Dr feelgood / (you make me feel like) a natural woman / Since you've been gone (sweet sweet baby) / Think / Ain't no way / You're all I need to get by / Spirit in the dark / Spirit in the dark / Don't play that song / Bridge over troubled water / See saw / I say a little prayer / House that jack built / Ain't nothing like the real thing / Every natural thing / Until you come back to me (that's what I'm gonna d / Rock steady / Today I sing the blues / You are my sunshine / Call me / Let it be / Drown in my own tears / Somewhere / I wonder / Oh me oh my / Angel / With everything I feel in me / Without love / I'm in love / I can't see myself leaving you / My song / You're a sweet sweet man / Change / Going down slow / (son of a) preacher man / Honest I do / Come back baby / Mr d j (5 for the d j) / Master of eyes (the deepness of your eyes) / How I got over / Brand new me / Border song (holy moses) / Young gifted and black / You and me / Try matty's / Pullin' / One way ticket / Weight / Sit down and cry / It ain't fair / Pitiful / Good to me as I am to you / Why I sing the blues / River's invitation / All the king's horses / Share your love with me / So swell when you're well / I take what I want / Rock with me / Break it to me gently / Look into your heart / Sparkle / Day dreaming / When the battle is over / Something he can feel / People get ready / Ain't nobody (gonna turn me around) / Night life / Prove it / Never let me go / Save me / Good times / Baby baby baby / Soul serenade / Night time is the right time / You send me / Chain of fools / Baby I love you / Do right woman do right man / Respect / Spanish harlem
8122710632 / Nov '92 / Atlantic

☐ ROSE IS STILL A ROSE, A
Rose is still a rose / Never leave you again / In case you forgot / Here we go again / Every lil' bit hurts / In the morning / I'll dip / How many times / Watch my back / Love pang / Woman
07822189872 / 11 May '98 / Arista

☐ SOUL '69
Ramblin' / Today I sing the blues / River's invitation / Pitiful / Crazy he calls me / Bring it on home to me / Tracks of my tears / If you gotta make a fool of somebody / Gentle on my mind / So long / I'll never be free / Elusive butterfly
8122715232 / Feb '94 / Atlantic

☐ SOUL SISTER (The Best Of Aretha Franklin)
Unforgettable / My guy / Sweet lover / Today I sing the blues / Maybe I'm a fool / All night long / Nobody like you / If ever I would leave you / Soulville / Shoop shoop song (it's in his kiss) / Lee cross / Operation heartbreak / Misty / Trouble in mind / God bless the child / Runnin' out of fools / Muddy water / What a difference a day makes / Walk on by / Try a little tenderness / Every little bit hurts / Mokingbird / People
4914542 / 3 Aug '98 / Columbia

☐ SPIRIT IN THE DARK
Don't play that song (You lied) / Thrill is gone / Pullin' / You and me / Honest I do / Spirit in the dark / When the battle is over / One way ticket / Try Matty's / That's all I want from you / Oh no, not my baby / Why I sing the blues
8122715252 / Feb '94 / Atlantic

☐ THIS GIRL'S IN LOVE WITH YOU
Son of a preacher man / Share your love with me / Dark end of the street / Let it be / Eleanor Rigby / This girl's in love with you / It ain't fair / Weight / Call me / Sit down and cry
8122715242 / Feb '93 / Atlantic

☐ THIS IS JAZZ
Evil gal blues / Today I sing the blues / Skylark / Nobody knows the way I feel this morning / Unforgettable / Love for sale / Only the lonely / I'd rather drink muddy water / God bless the child / All night long / It ain't necessarily so / What a difference a day made / Over the rainbow / Maybe I'm a fool / Drinking again / Trouble in mind / This bitter Earth
CK 65050 / 4 May '98 / Sony Jazz

☐ UNFORGETTABLE (A Tribute To Dinah Washington)
Unforgettable / Cold cold heart / What a difference a day makes / Drinking again / Nobody knows the way I feel this morning / Evil gal blues / Don't say you're sorry again / This bitter Earth / If I should lose you / Soulville / Lee cross
4805082 / May '95 / Columbia

☐ WHO'S ZOOMIN' WHO
Freeway of love / Another night / Sweet bitter love / Who's zoomin' who / Sisters are doin' it for themselves: *Eurythmics & Aretha Franklin* / Until you say you love me / Push / Ain't nobody ever loved you / Integrity
259053 / Aug '88 / Arista

☐ YOUNG, GIFTED AND BLACK
Oh me oh my / Daydreaming / Rock steady / Young, gifted and black / All the king's horses / Brand new me / April fools / I've been loving you too long / First snow in Kokomo / Long and winding road / Didn't I / Border song
8122715272 / Feb '94 / Atlantic

Franklin, Kirk

☐ KIRK FRANKLIN AND FAMILY (Franklin, Kirk & The Family)
Why we sing / He's able / Silver and gold / Call on the lord / Real love / He can handle it / Letter from my friend / Family worship / Speak to me / Till we meet again
GCD 2119 / Jun '95 / Alliance Music

☐ WHATYA LOOKIN' 4 (Franklin, Kirk & The Family)
Saviour more than life / Whatcha lookin' 4 / Melodies from heaven / Conquerors / Don't take your joy away / When I think about Jesus / Mama's song / Jeus paid it all / I love you Jesus / Washed away / Where the spirit is / Let me touch you / Anything
GCD 2127 / Oct '96 / Alliance Music

Franko, Mladen

☐ FUN AND ROMANCE (Franko, Mladen & Norman Candler)
ISCD 123 / '91 / Intersound

Franks, Michael

☐ ART OF TEA
Nightmoves / Egg plant / Monkey see, Monkey do / St. Elmo's fire / Don't know why I'm so happy I'm sad / Jive / Popsicle toes / Mr. Blue / Sometimes I just forget to smile
7599272242 / Aug '81 / WEA

☐ DRAGONFLY SUMMER
Coming to life / Soul mate / Dragonfly summer / Monk's new tune / Learning what love means / I love Lucy / Practice makes perfect / String of pearls / Keeping my eye on you / Dream / You were meant for me / How I remember you
9362452272 / May '93 / Warner Bros.

☐ OBJECTS OF DESIRE
Jealousy / Ladies night / No deposit love / Laughing gas / Wonderland / Tahitian moon / Flirtation / Love duet / No one but you
7599236482 / May '94 / Warner Bros.

Franks, Nick

☐ DARK ANDROMEDA
Dark andromeda / Girl by the lough / Land of the rising moon / Gone to Texas / Love will find a way / Sugar loaf / Stone mountain breakdown / Long time ago
WMMSCD 1003 / Apr '97 / Warner Sisters

Franks, Rebecca

☐ ALL OF A SUDDEN (Franks, Rebecca Coupe)
JR 009022 / Sep '92 / Justice

☐ SUIT OF ARMOUR (Franks, Rebecca Coupe)
JR 009012 / Nov '92 / Justice

Franky D

☐ CULTURE FLYIE
MRCC 1003 / 17 Nov '97 / Marston

Frantic

☐ CONCEPTION
FLASH 31 / Jul '97 / Flash

Frantic Flintstones

☐ CUTTIN' A FINE LINE
RUMCD 009 / Sep '91 / Rumble

☐ ENJOY YOURSELF
Enjoy yourself / Cradle baby / Black Caddi / I gotta baby / You don't love me anymore / Tip of my tongue / Ain't got a / Draw your breaks / She done me wrong / Mummy's boy / Sunset of my tears / Up your nose / Crazy Clems dream / Chop one up Chuck
CDGRAM 86 / Sep '94 / Anagram

☐ JAMBOREE
Detroit dirt box / Love for a nutter / Your time is up / Mean mean woman / Diablo / Saty with me / Sweet Georgia Brown / Lunatics (are raving) / Busted / Mindkill / (To the Devil) a son / Oh 898 / Candy man / He's waiting / Sad 'n' lonely / Suspended / Chop chop splash splash / Honeychild / Hey Chuck / Detroit blood box
CDMPSYCHO 15 / Aug '97 / Anagram

☐ MY WOMAN IS...
TBCD 2006 / Mar '93 / Tombstone

☐ NIGHTMARE ON NERVOUS
Hellfire / Monte Carlo or bust / 44 / Please cool baby / Oh baby oh baby / Alley cat king / Gone gone well gone / Red chevy / Ring ring ringin' / What the hell / Sugar daddy / Frantic Flintstones
NERCD 034 / Oct '97 / Nervous

Franzen & Trace Dog

☐ UP ALL NITE PAPER CHASE
60515120202 / 21 Apr '98 / MNME

Fraser, Alasdair

☐ DAWN DANCE
CUL 106CD / Jul '95 / Culburnie

☐ DRIVEN BOW, THE (Fraser, Alasdair & Jody Stretcher)
CUL 102CD / Jul '95 / Culburnie

☐ HEAT THE HOOSE
CDTT 1004 / 24 Jul '98 / Tartan Tapes

☐ PORTRAIT OF A SCOTTISH FIDDLER
CUL 009CD / Jul '96 / Culburnie

☐ ROAD NORTH (Fraser, Alasdair & Paul Machlis)
24384553920 / 24 Mar '98 / Narada

☐ SKYEDANCE (Fraser, Alasdair & Paul Machlis)
CUL 101CD / Oct '95 / Culburnie

☐ WAY OUT TO HOPE STREET (Fraser, Alasdair & Eric Rigker/Nick Limden)
Way out to Hope Street / Walking the plank / Donostia / Year's turning / Midnight on Raasay / Braemar cappuccino / Dizzy / Stoney run / Lupine / Dark jewel / Tathaich nam fonn / Skyedance reels / Skerray / Reel de Flores / Bannockburn
CUL 111CD / 27 Sep '97 / Culburnie

Fraser, Dean

☐ BIG UP
Dick Tracy / None a jah jah children no cry / Big up/ Armageddon time / Shine eye gal / Place called Africa / Queen of the minstrels / Natty never get weary / Bank of the river / Have mercy / African elation / It's me again Jah
IJCD 4003 / May '97 / Island Jamaica Jazz

☐ CLASSICS
RNCD 2080 / Dec '94 / Rhino

☐ DEAN PLAYS BOB VOL.1
RASCD 3127 / Jun '96 / Ras

☐ DEAN PLAYS BOB VOL.2
RASCD 3186 / Feb '96 / Ras

☐ JESUS LOVES ME
SONCD 0091 / Jul '97 / Sonic Sounds

☐ RAS PORTRAITS
Roots rock raggae / Johnny was / One drop / Africa unite / Zimbabwe / Ram dancehall / Bad card / Crazy baldheads / Rastaman chant / Chant down babylon / Unforgettable / Just because
RAS 3325 / Jul '97 / Ras

☐ RAW SAX
GRELCD 129 / Sep '89 / Greensleeves

☐ SINGS AND BLOWS
Falling in love / Jamaican lady / Girlfriend / Magnet and steel / Voyage to Atlantis
GRELCD 113 / Jun '88 / Greensleeves

☐ TAKING CHANCES
RASCD 3106 / Jun '93 / Ras

Fraser, Donald

☐ WORLD ANTHEMS (Fraser, Donald & English Chamber Orchestra)
Olympic theme / Marcha real / Advance Australia fair / Jeszche Polska / Patra amada, Brasil / King Christian / Ee mungu nguvu ye tu / O Canada / God save the Queen / Ch'i lai / La brabanconne / Maamme laulu / Isten aldd meg a Magyard / Ja vi elsker dette landet / Einigkeit und recht und freiheit / Kde domov kuj / Star spangled banner / Segnorees apo tin kopsi / Wilhelmus Van Nassouwe / Peaceful reign / Hatikvah / Walla zaman algunud / La Marseillaise / Sean eternos los laurales / Du canta, du fria / Mexicanos al grito de guerra / Ethiopia / Land der berge / Lietuva / Inno di mameli
09026613442 / Jul '92 / RCA

Fraser, Fi & Jo

☐ FRASER SISTERS, THE
Garden of love / Lowlands of Holland / Rose of Raby/ FIM / Stitch in time / Bonny light horseman / Man of passion / Hold back the tide / Friday the 12th/Havero polka/Friday the 13th / Hug you like a mountain / Tiennet/Tourdion / Coldness of winter / Bird in cage / All the way with you / Jumper song / Bramble and the rose / Swedelska
NMCD 12 / Jul '98 / No Master's Cooperative

Fraser Highlanders

☐ LIVE IN CONCERT IN IRELAND
Lord Lovat's lament / Beverley's wedding / Ishabel T MacDonald / Catrina Baker / Gordon MacRae's favourite / Cliffs of Dooneen / Brig Gen Ronald Cheape of Tiroran / Laggan love song / Lament for the children / Up to the line / John MacColl's farewell to the Scottish / Farewell to Erin / Journey to Skye / Mason's apron / Fair maid of Barra
LCDM 8003 / '89 / Lismor

☐ MEGANTIC OUTLAW CONCERT, THE
4/4 marches / Medley / Solo piping: *Black Hairy Tongue* / Drum fanfare / Waulking songs / Hornpipes / Megantic outlaw / Piping duet: *Branch, Billy & The Sons Of Blues* / Airs / Jigs
LCOM 8014 / Sep '92 / Lismor

Fraser, Hugh

☐ IN THE MEANTIME (Fraser, Hugh Quintet)
JFCD 020 / Sep '97 / Jazz Focus

Fraser, Iain

☐ NORTHLINS
Old fincastle / Northlins / Pride of the north / Blue bonnets / Devil in the kitchen / Golden mile / Walnut grove / Valparaiso / Loup / Tummelside / Drummossie moor / North wall / Farewell to whiskey / Am balachan siubhlach / Merry making / Last light
IRCD 027 / Aug '94 / Iona

Fraser, Simon

☐ ALIVE IN AMERICA (Fraser, Simon University Pipe Band)
Trad II / 6/8 Marches / Hornpipes and jigs / Set / Scotstoun medley / Do mo chara maith / Slow air and reels / Compound II / Medley / Calleach an dudain / Drops / Hornpipes / Drums
LDDC 8017 / Jul '96 / Lismor

☐ DO MO CHARA MAITH (Fraser, Simon University Pipe Band)
Lochanside / McPhedran's Strathspey / AA Cameron's Strathspey / Lexy McAskill / Blackberry bush / Our ain fireside / MacLeod medley / Compound / 420 Byng Street / Buskin' / Flowers of Edinburgh / Drops / Highland Set / Maestro and the minions / Sorcerer Set / Three Fours / Boys / Do mo chara maith / Three stripes / Caileach an Dudain
LCOM 5236 / Jul '94 / Lismor

Fraternity Of Man
☐ FRATERNITY OF MAN
EDCD 437 / Oct '95 / Edsel

☐ GET IT ON
EDCD 438 / Oct '95 / Edsel

Fraunhofer Saitenmusik
☐ VOLSMUSIK
TRIK 0107 / Oct '94 / Trikont

Frazier Chorus
☐ SUE
Dream kitchen / Forty winks / Sloppy heart / Sugar high / Typical / Little chef / Storm / Ha ha happiness / Living room / Forgetful / Shi-head
CDV 2578 / Dec '88 / Virgin

☐ WIDE AWAKE
PINKCD 1 / Jul '95 / Pinkerton

Freak Of Nature
☐ FREAK OF NATURE
Turn the other way / What am I / Rescue me / '92 / People / World doesn't mind / Possessed / Where can I go if I leave / Love was here
CDMFN 146 / Mar '93 / Music For Nations

☐ GATHERING OF FREAKS
CDMFN 169 / Sep '94 / Music For Nations

Freak Scene
☐ PSYCHEDELIC PSOUL
HEAD 2896 / 20 Apr '98 / Head

Freakpower
☐ DRIVE-THRU BOOTY
Moonbeam woman / Turn on tune in cop out / Get in touch / Freak power / Running away / Change my mind / What it is / Waiting for the story to end / Rush / Big time / Whip
BRCD 606 / 2 Feb '98 / 4th & Broadway

☐ MORE OF EVERYTHING FOR EVERYBODY
BRCD 619 / Jun '96 / 4th & Broadway

Freaks Of Desire
☐ INTOXICATED
Beast inside / So it goes / I'm on fire / Everything must die / Messiah / Exit / Intoxicated / Heaven with a gun / Strange things / (this is my) religion
0630139852 / Mar '96 / Anxious

Freakwater
☐ DANCING UNDER WATER
THRILL 040CD / May '97 / Thrill Jockey

☐ FEELS LIKE THE THIRD TIME
THRILL 010CD / 16 Feb '98 / Thrill Jockey

☐ OLD PAINT
EFA 049652 / Oct '95 / City Slang
THRILL 022CD / 20 Apr '98 / Thrill Jockey

☐ SPRINGTIME
THRILL 047CD / 16 Feb '98 / Thrill Jockey

Freaky Chakra
☐ FREAKY CHAKRA & SINGLE CELL ORCHESTRA (Freaky Chakra & Single Cell Orchestra)
Intro / Lurking / Piledriver / Trepidations in love / I want to fall / Wishfullness / Trying to find you / Anthem of the forgotten / Way
ASW 6166 / Sep '96 / Astralwerks

Fred, John
☐ AGNES ENGLISH (Fred, John & His Playboy Band)
REP 4153 / Aug '91 / Repertoire

☐ AGNES ENGLISH/PERMANENTLY STATED (Fred, John & The Playboys)
528872 / Jul '97 / Magic

Fred Locks
☐ BLACK STAR LINER
STCD 001 / Nov '94 / Starlight
VPCD 2037 / Sep '95 / VP

☐ CULTURALLY
TYCD 008 / Jan '96 / Tan Yah
SDCD 918 / May '96 / Starlight

☐ LOVE & ONLY LOVE
TMCD 2 / Nov '94 / Tribesman

☐ NEVER GIVE UP
EXTCD 10 / 9 Feb '98 / Exterminator

Fred, Maguy
☐ SUCCES ET RARETES 1930-1933
701642 / Nov '96 / Chansophone

Freddie & The Dreamers
☐ EP COLLECTION, THE
Do the freddie / Zip a dee doo dah / Windmill in old amsterdam / I'm telling you now / Feel so blue / Money (that's what I want) / Kansas city / I'm a hog for you baby / I just don't understand / I love you baby / Don't make me cry / You were made for me / Sally ann / Just for you / Silly girl / Little bitty pretty one / Over you / She belongs to you / Love like you / Come back when you're ready / Short shorts / If you gotta make a fool of somebody
SEECD 299 / '90 / See For Miles

☐ VERY BEST OF FREDDIE & THE DREAMERS, THE
If you gotta make a fool of somebody / I understand / It doesn't matter anymore / Jailer bring me water / I think of you / If you've got a minute, baby / Feel so blue / Do the Freddie / Thou shalt not steal / See you later alligator / I'm telling you now / I don't love you anymore / Viper / You were made for me / Over you / Money (that's what I want) / Tell me when / Playboy / Don't make me cry / Little you
CDSL 8261 / Jul '95 / Music For Pleasure

☐ VERY BEST OF FREDDIE & THE DREAMERS, THE
I'm telling you now / I understand / It doesn't matter anymore / If you gotta make a fool of somebody / You were made for me / See you later alligator / Do the freddie / I think of you / Feel so blue / Over you / I love you baby / Viper / If you've got a minute baby / Just for you / Money (that's what I want) / Little you / Thou shalt not steal / Jailer bring me water / I don't love you anymore / Playboy / Windmill in old Amsterdam / Tell me when / Come back when you're ready / Sally ann / Don't make me cry / I just don't understand / Silly girl / Love like you
CDMFP 6382 / 13 Oct '97 / Music For Pleasure

Freddie Fresh
☐ ACCIDENTALLY CLASSIC
Flow / Gimme / Baroque / Dilema / Hey / Chupacabbra / Fat beat / Bum bum / Cherrish electronique / Open spaces / Ah / Represent / Flava / Portion / Menagerie
HHCD 23 / Mar '97 / Harthouse

Freddy K
☐ RAGE OF AGE
ACVCD 8 / Jun '95 / ACV

Frederic
☐ PHASES AND FACES 1967-1969
AA 061 / Jul '97 / Arf Arf

Frederick The Great
☐ BROADWAY USA
HIICD 804 / Oct '94 / Hard Hat

Frederiksen/Phillips
☐ FREDERIKSEN/PHILLIPS
ERCD 1021 / Jul '95 / Now & Then

Free
☐ ALL RIGHT NOW
Wishing well / All right now / Little bit of love / Come together in the morning / Stealer / Sail on / Mr. Big / My brother Jake the hunter / Be my friend / Travellin' in style / Fire and water / Travelling man / Don't say you love me
CIDTV 2 / Feb '91 / Island

☐ FIRE AND WATER
Oh I wept / Remember / Heavy load / Fire and water / Mr. Big / Don't say you love me / All right now
IMCD 80 / Apr '90 / Island

☐ FREE
I'll be creepin' / Songs of yesterday / Lying in the sunshine / Trouble on double time / Mouthful of grass / Woman / Free me / Broad daylight / Mourning sad mourning
IMCD 64 / '89 / Island

☐ FREE AT LAST
Catch a train / Soldier boy / Magic ship / Sail on / Travelling man / Little bit of love / Guardian of the Universe / Child / Goodbye
IMCD 82 / Feb '90 / Island

☐ FREE LIVE
All right now / I'm a mover / Be my friend / Fire and water / Ride on pony / Mr. Big / Hunter / Get where I belong
IMCD 73 / '89 / Island

☐ FREE STORY, THE
I'm a mover / I'll be creepin' / Mourning sad morning / All right now / Heavy load / Fire and water / Be my friend / Stealer / Soon I will be gone / Mr. Big / Hunter / Get where I belong / Travelling man / Just for the box / Lady / My brother Jake / Little bit of love / Sail on / Come together in the morning
IMCD 226 / Sep '96 / Island

☐ HEARTBREAKER
Wishing well / Come together in the morning / Travellin' in style / Heartbreaker / Muddy water / Common mortal man / Easy on my soul / Seven angels
IMCD 81 / Feb '90 / Island

☐ HIGHWAY
Highway song / Stealer / On my way / Be my friend / Sunny day / Ride on pony / Love you so / Bodies / Soon I will be gone
IMCD 63 / '89 / Island

☐ MOLTEN GOLD (The Anthology)
I'm a mover / Hunter / Walk in my shadow / I'll be creepin' / Songs of yesterday / Woman / Broad daylight / Mouthful of grass / All right now / Oh I wept / Heavy load / Don't say you love me / Stealer / Highway song / Be my friend / Soon I will be gone / My brother Jake / Fire and water / Ride on pony / Mr. Big / Time away / Molten gold / Catch a train / Travelling man / Little bit of love / Sail on / Wishing well / Come together in the morning / Travellin' in style / Heartbreaker
CRNCD 2 / May '94 / Island

☐ TONS OF SOBS
Over the green hills (part 1) / Worry / Walk in my shadow / Wild Indian woman / Going down slow / I'm a mover / Hunter / Moonshine sweet tooth / Over the green hills (Part 2)
IMCD 62 / '89 / Island

Free Flow
☐ FREE FLOW
RR 103CD / Jul '96 / Roots

Free Hot Lunch
☐ EAT THIS
FF 540CD / '92 / Flying Fish

Free Jazz Quartet
☐ PREMONITIONS - 1989
MR 18 / '90 / Matchless

Free Kitten
☐ NICE ASS
Harvest spoon / Rock of ages / Proper band / What's fair / Kissing well / Call back / Blindfold test / Greener pastures / Revlon liberation orchestra / Boasta / Scratch tha DJ / Secret sex fiend / Royal flush / Feelin' / Alan Licked has ruined music for an entire generation
WIJ 041CD / Jan '95 / Wiiija

☐ SENTIMENTAL EDUCATION
Teenie weenie boppie / Top 40 / Never gonna sleep / Strawberry milk / Played yrself / Dr Spooky's spatialized chinatown express / Bouwerie boys / Records sleep / Picabo who / Sentimental education / One forty five / Eat cake / Gaa / Daddy long legs / Noise doll
WIJCD 1076 / 27 Oct '97 / Wiiija

☐ UNBOXED
Skinny butt / Platinumb / Smack / Falling backwards / Oneness / Dick / Yoshimi Vs. Mascis / Oh bondage up yours / 1-2-3 / Party with me punker / John stark blues / Guilty pleasure / Sex boy / Cleopatra / Loose lips / Oh baby
WIJ 036CD / Jun '94 / Wiiija

Free, Mark
☐ LONG WAY FROM LOVE (2CD Set)
FRCD 009 / 6 Jul '98 / Frontier

Free The Spirit
☐ PAN PIPE MOODS
I will always love you / (Everything I do) I do it for you / Holding back the years / Love theme from Bladerunner / Sacrifice/Nikita / From a distance / Wonderful tonight / Without you / Circle of life / Love is all around / Can you feel the love tonight / Mission / Careless whisper / Cockeye's song / Wonderful life / It must have been love / Evergreen / World in union
5271972 / Jan '95 / PolyGram TV

Freeborne
☐ PEAK IMPRESSIONS
AFT 14 / Nov '97 / Afterglow

Freed Unit
☐ FIELD REPORTS FROM OUT THERE
SRCD 002 / May '97 / Sorted

☐ THINGS ARE LOOKING UP
RAPTCD 19 / 11 May '98 / Enraptured

Freedom
☐ THROUGH THE YEARS
REP 4226 / Aug '91 / Repertoire

Freeez
☐ FREEEZ FRAME (The Best Of Freeez)
Southern freeez / Caribbean winter / Flying high / One to one / Alone / Sunset / Anti-freeez / Easy on the onions / Mariposa / I.o.u. / Can't keep my love / Love's gonna get you / Pop goes my love / Freezin'
MCCD 131 / Sep '93 / Music Club

Freeform
☐ HETERARCHY
WISE 01 / Jun '97 / Worm Interface

Freelon, Nnenna
☐ MAIDEN VOYAGE
Come into my life / Four women / Maiden voyage / Buy and sell / Future news blues / Until it's time for you to go / Woman be wise / Sepia wing / Pick yourself up / I won't dance / Inside a silent tear / Sing me down
CCD 47942 / 6 Apr '98 / Concord Jazz

☐ SHAKING FREE
Out of this world / Black is the colour of my true love's hair / I live to love you / Shaking free / Stories we hold / Birk's works / My shining hour / Visions / I thought about you / What am I here for / Nature boy / Blue daughter
CCD 4714 / Aug '96 / Concord Jazz

Freeman
☐ ROUGH ROADS
NAR 116CD / Dec '94 / New Alliance

Freeman, Bud
☐ BUD FREEMAN 1928/1937
CD 53272 / May '98 / Giants Of Jazz

☐ CHICAGO/AUSTIN HIGH SCHOOL JAZZ IN HI-FI (Freeman, Bud Summa Cum Laude)
China boy / Sugar / Liza / Nobody's sweetheart / Chicago / At sundown / Prince of wails / Jack hits the road / Forty seventh and state / There'll be some changes made / At the jazz band ball
74321130312 / Sep '93 / RCA

☐ CLASSICS 1928-1938
CLASSICS 781 / Nov '94 / Classics

☐ CLASSICS 1939-1940
CLASSICS 811 / May '95 / Classics

☐ CLASSICS 1945-1946
CLASSICS 942 / Jun '97 / Classics

☐ CLASSICS 1946
CLASSICS 975 / 24 Feb '98 / Classics

☐ SOMETHING TO REMEMBER YOU BY
BLCD 760153 / Jul '91 / Black Lion

Freeman, Chico
☐ CHICO
IN 1031CD / Jan '97 / India Navigation

☐ DESTINY'S DANCE
OJCCD 799 / Nov '95 / Original Jazz Classics

☐ EMISSARY, THE
CCD 1015 / Jul '98 / Clarity

☐ FOCUS (Freeman, Chico Quintet)
Bemsha swing / Blackfoot / Ah, George, we hardly knew ya / To hear a tear drop in the rain / Playpen / Peacemaker / Rhythm-a-ning
CCD 140732 / Jan '97 / Contemporary

☐ FREEMAN AND FREEMAN (Freeman, Chico & Von Freeman)
IN 1070CD / Jan '97 / India Navigation

☐ LUMINOUS (Freeman, Chico & Arthur Blythe)
Footprints / Luminous / Naima's love song / Avotja / You are too beautiful
JHCD 010 / Jan '94 / Ronnie Scott's Jazz House

☐ NO TIME LEFT (Freeman, Chico Quartet)
BSR 0036CD / '86 / Black Saint

☐ OUTSIDE WITHIN, THE
IN 1042CD / Jan '97 / India Navigation

☐ SPIRIT SENSITIVE
IN 1045CD / Jan '97 / India Navigation

☐ STILL SENSITIVE
IN 1071CD / Jan '97 / India Navigation

☐ UNSPOKEN WORD, THE (Freeman, Chico Quintet)
Unspoken word / Gano club / Playpen / Infant eyes / Peace maker / Misty / Rhythm-a-ning
JHCD 030 / Aug '94 / Ronnie Scott's Jazz House

☐ UP AND DOWN (Freeman, Chico & Mal Waldron)
1201362 / Sep '92 / Black Saint

Freeman, Ernie

☐ RAUNCHY (The Imperial Recordings) (Freeman, Ernie Combo)
Raunchy / Puddin' / Dumplin's / Lost dreams / Walking the beat / River boat / Swing it / Turtle / Leaps and bounds / Shape up / Theme from igor / Indian love call / After sunset / Jamboree / Junior jive / School room rock / Blues after hours / Live it up / Marshmallows popcorn and sodapop / Night / Sounds / Swamp meeting / Twist / Touch of the blues / Jivin' around / Jivin' around
CDCHD 659 / Aug '97 / Ace

Freeman, George

☐ BIRTH SIGN
Mama, papa, brother / Cough it up / My scenery / Must be, must be / Birth sign / Hoss / My ship
DD 424 / Mar '97 / Delmark

Freeman, Ken

☐ TRIPODS
GERCD 1 / Nov '95 / GR Forrester

Freeman, Louise

☐ LISTEN TO MY HEART
When push comes to shove / Save your love / Nothin's gonna win me (but love) / Love is gone / Back in stride / I don't want to talk about it / Fever / Unchained melody
ICH 1111CD / Oct '93 / Ichiban

Freeman, Russ

☐ BRAVE NEW WORLD (Freeman, Russ & The Rippingtons)
Brave new world / Urban wanderer / Key to the Forbidden City / Hideaway / Caravan of love / Faith / First time I saw her / Cicada / While my guitar gently weeps / Ain't no stoppin' us now / Virtual reality
GRP 98352 / Mar '96 / GRP

Freestyle Files

☐ FUTURISTIC ELECTRONICS (2CD Set)
K7 048CD / Sep '96 / Studio K7

Freestylers

☐ WE ROCK HARD
Freestyle noize / Dancehall vibes / Drop the boom / Don't stop / Here we go / Lower level / B-boy stance / We rock hard / Breaker beats / Scratch 22 / Ruffneck / Hold up your hands / Warning
FNTCD 004 / 3 Aug '98 / Freskanova

Freewheelers

☐ WAITIN' FOR GEORGE
Best be on your way / What's the matter Ruth / Mother nature lady / Ghost of Tchoupitulas Street / My little friend / (Chico's sellin') Maps to the stars / Crime pays / Walkin' funny / About Marie / Kiss her for the punk / Elevator man / Blame / Let the music bring a smile
74321279682 / Mar '96 / American

Freewill

☐ ALMOST AGAIN
LF 181CD / Dec '96 / Lost & Found

Freeze

☐ CRAWLING BLIND
LF 075 / Mar '94 / Lost & Found

☐ FREAKSHOW
LF 198CD / Jan '96 / Lost & Found

☐ FREEZE/KILLRAYS (Freeze/Killrays)
LF 143MCD / Jul '95 / Lost & Found

☐ TOKEN BONES
DSR 062CD / Jun '97 / Dr. Strange

Frehel

☐ CHANSOPHONE 1933-1939
701252 / Jun '93 / Chansophone

Frehley, Ace

☐ 12 PICKS
Into the night / Words are not enough / Insane / Hide your heart / Trouble walkin' / Rock soldiers / Rip it out / Breakout / Cold gin / Shock me / Rocket ride / Deuce
SPV 08518712 / May '97 / Steamhammer

☐ ACE FREHLEY
Rip it out / Speedin' back to my baby / Snow blind / Ozone / What's on your mind / New York groove / I'm in need of love / Wiped out / Fractured mirror
5323852 / 22 Sep '97 / Casablanca

☐ FREHLEY'S COMET (Frehley's Comet)
Rock soldiers / Breakout / Into the night / Something moved / We got your rock / Love me right / Calling to you / Dolls / Stranger in a strange land / Fractured too
7567817492 / Jan '96 / Atlantic

☐ LIVE PLUS ONE (Frehley's Comet)
Rip it out / Breakout / Something moved / Rocket ride / Words are not enough
7567818262 / Jan '96 / Atlantic

☐ LOADED DECK
ME 1997 / 19 Jan '98 / Megaforce
SPV 08518872 / Mar '98 / SPV

☐ RETURN OF THE COMET, THE (A Tribute To Ace Frehley) (Various Artists)
SR 01 / 6 Jul '98 / Shock Canada

☐ SECOND SIGHTING (Frehley's Comet)
Insane / Time ain't runnin' out / Dancin' with danger / It's over now / Loser in a fight / Juvenile delinquent / Fallen angel / Separate / New kind of lover / Acorn is spinning
7567818622 / Jan '96 / Atlantic

☐ TROUBLE WALKING (Frehley's Comet)
Shot full of rock / Do ya / Five card stud / Hide your heart / Lost in limbo / Trouble walkin' / 2 young 2 die / Back to school / Remember me / Fractured III
7567820422 / Jan '96 / Atlantic

Freiberg, David

☐ BARON VON TOLLBOOTH AND THE CHROME NUN (Freiberg, David & Grace Slick/Paul Kantner)
Ballad of the chrome nun / Fat / Flowers of the night / Walkin' / Your mind has left your body / Across the board / Harp tree lament / White boy / Fishman / Sketches of China
7863674182 / 11 May '98 / RCA

Freight Hoppers

☐ WHERE'D YOU COME FROM, WHERE'D YOU GO
Sandy river / Cotton eyed Joe / Mississippi Joe / Little Sadie / Texas gals / Johnson boys / Logan County blues / Gray cat on a Tennessee Farm / Four cent cotton / Cornbread, molasses and sassafras / Dark hollow blues / Elzick's farewell / Pretty little girl / How many biscuits can you eat this morning / Kentucky whiskey / Bright morning stars
ROUCD 0403 / Nov '96 / Rounder

Frejlechs

☐ YIDDISH KLEZMER MUSIC
EUCD 1185 / Apr '92 / ARC

Frej's Jazz

☐ NORDLYD
MECCACD 1039 / Nov '94 / Music Mecca

French Alligators

☐ SOUS LA GALLERIE
FA 003CD / Jan '95 / French Alligator

French Charleston Orchestra

☐ STRICTLY DANCING: CHARLESTON
Charleston / I'm looking over a four leaf clover / Back to charleston / Chicago / Whispering / Avalon / Some of these days / Japanese sandman / Tiger rag / Old charleston / Tres moutarde / Mandy make up your mind / Alexander's ragtime band / Sugar papa / 12th street rag / Yes we have no bananas today / Ain't she sweet
15339 / May '94 / Laserlight

French, Frank

☐ BUCKTOWN (French, Frank & Scott Kirby)
SOSCD 1306 / Jul '96 / Stomp Off

French, John

☐ INVISIBLE MEANS (French, Frith, Kaiser & Thompson)
Peppermint rock / To the rain / Lizard's tail / March of the cosmetic surgeons / Suzanne / Quick sign / Invisible means / Book of lost dreams
FIENDCD 199 / Oct '90 / Demon

☐ LIVE, LOVE, LARF, LOAF (French, Frith, Kaiser & Thompson)
Wings a la mode / Killerman gold posse / Where's the money / Hai sai oji-san / Drowned dog black night / Surfin' USA / Blind step away / Second time / Tir-nan darag / Disposable thoughts / Bird in god's garden/ Lost and found
FIENDCD 102 / '88 / Demon

French, Robert

☐ ROBERT FRENCH, HEAVY D & FRIENDS (French, Robert & Heavy D)
RASCD 3148 / Aug '95 / Ras

Frenchy

☐ CHE'S LOUNGE
ID 123350CD / 23 Mar '98 / Dionysus

Frente

☐ MARVIN THE ALBUM
TVD 93367 / May '94 / Mushroom

☐ SHAPE
D 93429 / Oct '96 / Mushroom

Frenzy

☐ (IT'S A) MAD, MAD WORLD
(It's a) mad mad world / So far away / Part of me / CC rider / Pressure / Hot rod satellite / Rock hard / Brand new gun / Crunch / I can't tell you / Ready or not / Show me the way / This is the fire / Can't stop thinkin' about you / Reward / Scandalous / Forever young / Wild night / Ready or not (mix)
RAGECD 111 / Mar '93 / Rage

☐ BEST OF FRENZY
Hall OF Mirrors / Robot Riot / Misdemeanour / Clockwork Toy / I See Red / Schitzophrenic / Emotions / Hot Rod Satellite / Gotta Go / Cry Or Die / Long Gone / Sweet Money / Wound up / Aftermath / Ain't nobody's business if I do / Don't Give Up / House On Fire / Hunt / Howard Hughes / Can't Stop Thinking About You
RAGECD 107 / Nov '90 / Rage

☐ CLOCKWORK TOY
Clockwork toy / Misdemeanour / Love is the drug / Howard hughes / Aftermath / Whose life / Gotta go / House on fire / I see red / Nightmares / Mexican radio / In my prison / Nobody's business / Don't give up / Hunt
NERCD 065 / '91 / Nervous

☐ HALL OF MIRRORS
One last chance / Schizophrenic emotions / Choice / Hall of mirrors / Frenzy / Asylum moves / Skeleton rock / Sweet money / Ghost train / Long gone / Surfin' bird / Was it me / Wound up / Frustration
NERDCD 016 / Jul '90 / Nervous

☐ THIS IS THE FIRE
Ready Or Not / Robot Riot / This Is The Fire / Come back my love / Wild night / Can't Stop Thinking About You / Another Day / I Want Your Lovin' / Scandalous / Forever Young / Reward
RAGECD 101 / Aug '92 / Rage

Frequenzia Mod

☐ SONG AUS LATCHINAMERIKA
REP 4193 / Aug '91 / Repertoire

Fresh Claim

☐ BROKEN
Broken man / Pillar sways / Morning ashtray blues / Wayfaring stranger / Driving through the rain / Defiled / Slow burning candle / Broken jam
PCDN 146 / Nov '95 / Plankton

☐ ROCK COMMUNION, THE
What a friend we have in Jesus / Peruvian Gloria / Father hear the prayer we offer / Sanctus (Holy, holy, holy) / Blessed is he / Christ has died / Agnus dei (Lamb of God) / Purple robe / Broken by / Jesus light of the world / Eternal love / Father on high / Swing low, sweet chariot / Oh sacred head / Crown him with many crown
PCN 142 / Aug '94 / Plankton

Fresh, Doug E

☐ PLAY
Where's da party at / It's on / Take 'em uptown / I-ight / Original old school / Freaks / Freak it out / It's really goin' on here / Who's got all the money / Get da money / Hands in the air / Doug E got it going on / Keep it going / Breath of fresh air
GEECD 17 / Oct '95 / Gee Street

Fresh Maggots

☐ FRESH MAGGOTS
SRMC 1039 / 5 Jan '98 / Siwan

Freshies

☐ VERY VERY BEST OF THE FRESHIES, THE
CDMRED 129 / Apr '96 / Cherry Red

Fresi, Sandro

☐ ISKELIU
APG 002CD / Dec '97 / Robi Droli

Fresu, Paolo

☐ CONDAGHES (Fresu, Paolo & Erik Marchand)
Me 'bokehe an douar / Fenoz d'an gwele me na n'enn han / Ar Serjant Major / Firibich / Berseuz / Ar sorserez / Ar riblou dall / Ar riblou dall / Ton braz manuel kryann / Ton kozh / Steredenn / Maenkuzh
Y 225067 / Mar '98 / Silex

☐ WANDERLUST (Fresu, Paolo Quartet)
Trunca peltunta / Favole / Wanderlust / Geremeas variazione quattro / Children of 10,000 years / Appuntamento sol treno / Soul eyes / Seven up / Hush / In quelle sere d'autunno / Simplicity / Touch her soft lips and parts
74321464352 / Aug '97 / RCA Victor

Fretblanket

☐ JUNK FUEL
5219972 / Aug '94 / Polydor

Fretless AZM

☐ ASTRAL CINEMA
Framed in funk / Rhythm in bass / Thought for food / Air conditioning / Swamp thing swing / Steppin' on the cracks / Rake island / Big wheel butterflies / Streets of old / Out house
HOLCD 27 / May '97 / Holistic

☐ DISTANT EARTH
Manipulation / Jam sandwich / Brass lines and basses / Descend / Electronic arms / Distant earth
HOLCD 26 / Jun '97 / Holistic

☐ FROM MARZ WITH LOVE
HOLCD 24 / Aug '96 / Holistic

☐ OCEANS OF LIGHT
HOLCD 32 / 20 Apr '98 / Holistic

Frey, Glenn

☐ SOLO CONNECTION
This way to happiness / Who's been sleeping in my bed / Common ground / Call on me / One you love / Sexy girl / Smuggler's blues / Heat is on / You belong to the city / True love / Soul searchin' / Part of me, part of you / I've got mine / River of dreams / Rising high / Brave new world
MCD 11227 / 8 Sep '97 / MCA

☐ SOUL SEARCHING/STRANGE WEATHER (2CD Set)
Livin' right / True love / I did it for your love / Working man / Two hearts / Some kind of blue / Can't put out this fire / Let's pretend we're still in love / Soul searching / It's your life / Silent spring / Long hot summer / Agua tranquillo / Love in the 21st century / He took advantage / River of dreams / Before the ship goes down / I've got mine / Rising sun / Brave new world / Delicious / Walk in the dark / Big life / Part of me, part of you
MCD 33727 / Jul '96 / MCA

☐ STRANGE WEATHER
Silent spring / Long hot summer / Strange weather / Agua tranquillo / Love in the 21st century / He took advantage / River of dreams / Before the ship goes down / I've got mine / Rising sun / Brave new world / Delicious / Walk in the dark / Big life / Part of me, part of you
MCD 10599 / 8 Sep '97 / MCA

Freya, Jo

☐ LUSH (Freya, Jo & Kathryn Locke)
NMCD 5 / Feb '96 / No Master's Voice

☐ TRADITIONAL SONGS OF ENGLAND
All things are quite silent / As I set off to Turkey / As Sylvie was walking / General Wolfe / Though I live not where I love / Sailor's life / Rounding the Horn / Lord Franklin / Unquiet grave / Broomfield wager / There was a lady all skin and bone / Geordie / Maids, when you're young never wed an old man / Bold William Taylor / Lovely Joan / Blacksmith courted me / Carnal and the crane / Green Cockade / Fourpence a day / Streams of lovely Nancy / Sweet England
CDSDL 402 / Mar '94 / Saydisc

Freyja

☐ FREYJA
Entradilla / Freylech / Csardas / Le moulin des deux roues / Snieder danz/reelin' over the rooftops / Krummshots / Rossignolet / Lost papers / Setalos kopogos tusszentos csardas / Vecinos
OSMOCD 006 / Jul '96 / Osmosys

☐ GLOBALULLABIES
9425712 / Jan '96 / Music For Little People

Friction

☐ REPLICANT WALK
EMY 1092 / Sep '97 / Enemy

Frida

☐ SHINE
Shine / One little lie / Face / Twist in the dark / Slowly / Heart of the country / Come to me / Chemistry tonight / Don't do it / Comfort me
8235802 / Jan '93 / Polydor

☐ SOMETHING'S GOING ON
Tell me it's over / I see red / I got something / Strangers / To turn the stone / I know there's something going on / Threnody / Baby don't you cry no more / Way you do / You know what I mean / Here we'll stay
8001022 / Jan '93 / Polydor

Friday, Gavin

☐ EACH MAN KILLS THE THING HE LOVES
Each man kills the thing he loves / He got what he wanted / Tell tale heart / Man of misfortune / Apologia / Rags to riches / Dazzle and delight / Next thing to murder / Next / Love is just a word / You take away the sun / Another blow on the bruise / Death is not the end
IMCD 175 / Jul '93 / Island

☐ SHAG TOBACCO
IMCD 227 / Sep '96 / Island

Fridge

☐ CEEFAX
EDM / Helicopter / Tricity / More eh4-800 / Jazz loop / Robots in disguise / EDM 2 / Oracle / EDM 3 / Zed ex ay-ti-wan
OPR 6CD / 6 Jul '98 / Output

☐ SEMAPHORE
Cassette / Furniture boy / Slow / Motorbuss / Teletexed / Chroma / Low fat diet / Swerve and spin / Curdle / Lign / Stamper / There is no try / Michael Knight
OPR 12CD / 23 Feb '98 / Output

Friedlander, Erik

☐ CHIMERA
AVAN 057 / Jan '96 / Avant

Friedman, Al

☐ EDISON LATERALS VOL.1, THE
DCP 201D / Jul '98 / Diamond Cut

Friedman, Dean

☐ DEAN FRIEDMAN/WELL WELL SAID THE ROCKING CHAIR
Company / Ariel / Solitaire / Woman of mine / Song for my mother / Letter / I may be young / Humor me / Funny papers / Love is not enough / Rocking chair / I've had enough / Lucky stars / Shopping bag ladies / Don't you ever dare / Deli song (corned beef on wry) / Lydia / S and M / Let down your hair
CDWIKD 98 / Apr '91 / Chiswick

☐ RUMPLED ROMEO
First date / McDonald's girl / Are you ready yet / Hey Larry / Love is real / Buy my baby a car / Special effects / I depend on you, Jesus / Marginal middle class / I will never leave you
CDWIK 106 / May '92 / Chiswick

☐ SONGS FOR GROWN UPS (2CD Set)
EDGCD 022 / 5 May '98 / Eagle

☐ VERY BEST OF DEAN FRIEDMAN
Lucky stars / Company / Solitaire / Letter / Humor me / Love is not enough / Woman of mine / Lydia / Ariel / Rocking chair / I've had enough / Shopping bag ladies / Deli song (corned beef on wry) / S and M / Funny papers / I may be young
MCCD 036 / Sep '91 / Music Club

Friedman, Don

☐ DAYS OF WINE AND ROSES (Friedman, Don Trio)
1212722 / Feb '97 / Soul Note

☐ FRIEDMAN/PEPPER/KNEPPER (Friedman, Don/Pepper Adams/Jimmy Knepper)
PCD 7036 / Jun '93 / Progressive

☐ I HEAR A RHAPSODY
ST 577 / Jul '94 / Stash

☐ LIVE AT MAYBECK RECITAL HALL VOL.33
In your own sweet way / Alone together / Prelude to a kiss / Invitation / Memory for Scotty / I concentrate on you / How deep is the ocean / Sea's breeze
CCD 4608 / Aug '94 / Concord Jazz

☐ MY ROMANCE
SCCD 31403 / Apr '97 / Steeplechase

☐ OPUS D'AMOUR (Friedman, Don & Don Thompson)
SKCD 3058 / Jul '96 / Sackville

Friedman, Kinky

☐ SOLD AMERICAN
We reserve the right to refuse service to you / Highway Cafe / Sold American / Flyin' down the freeway / Ride 'em Jewboy / Get your buisquits in the oven and your buns in the bed / High on Jesus / Ballad of Charles Whitman / Top ten commandments / Western union wire / Silver Eagle Express
VMD 79333 / Jun '98 / Vanguard

Friedman, Maria

☐ MARIA FRIEDMAN
I happen to like New York / Man with the child in his eyes / Golden days / If you go away / I'm gorgeous / My romance / In the sky / Paris in the rain / Toby's song / Man that got away / Guess who I saw today / Play the song again / Finishing the hat / Now and then / Broadway baby
3036000012 / Oct '95 / Carlton

Friedman, Marty

☐ DRAGON'S KISS
Saturation point / Dragon mistress / Evil thrill / Namida (tears) / Anvils / Jewel / Forbidden city / Thunder march
RR 9529 2 / '89 / Roadrunner

☐ INTRODUCTION
Arrival / Bittersweet / Be / Escapism / Luna / Mama / Loneliness / Siberia
RR 8950 2 / Dec '94 / Roadrunner

☐ SCENES
Tibet / Angel / Valley of entirety / Night / Realm of the senses / West / Trance / Triumph
RR 91042 / Sep '96 / Roadrunner

☐ TRUE OBSESSIONS
398414219CD / Oct '96 / Metal Blade

Friedmann

☐ INDIAN SUMMER
BIBERCD 66301 / '88 / In Akustik

☐ LEGENDS OF LIGHT
Fairies of sternsea / Mount belenos / Joy of Beltane / Seven silver stars / Spring has come to wiesental / Sunday in Alsace / Memories of Lugnasad / Black cherries, white wine / Lament of the white goddess / Sun at midnight
ND 63033 / Oct '95 / Narada

☐ VOYAGER IN EXPANSE
INAK 860 CD / '88 / In Akustik

Friedmann, Bernd

☐ LEISURE ZONES
ASH 25 / Jan '96 / Ash International

Friend

☐ HOT ROD
DOTCD 03 / 12 Jan '98 / Dot

Friend, Constance

☐ HOME (Friend 'N' Fellow)
One more day / Home / I wonder / Livin' in a world / Bluebird / How will I know / All of it / Liar / I gave it all / I know / This love / Love child / Other side / Cajun moon
RUF 1011 / Feb '98 / Ruf

Friends

☐ TALKIN' BOUT US
GRCD 031 / 6 Apr '98 / Garageland

Friends From Rio

☐ FRIENDS FROM RIO
Batacuda com mongo / Casa forte / Para Lennon E McCartney / Fransisco cat / Maracatudo / Os grilos (The crickets) / Bebe / Batunk / Aquila coisas todas
F 007CD / Jul '96 / Far Out

☐ MISTURADA VOL.1 (Friends From Rio Remixes) (Various Artists)
Francisco cat: *Pressure Drop* / Casa forte: *Natural Element* / Os grilos: *Takemura, Nobukazu* / Batacuda com mingo: *Mighty Black Forest* / Batunk: *DJ First Klas* / Maracatudo: *Wax Doctor* / Bebe: *Hightower Set* / Aquilas coisas todas: *APE* / Para Lennon and McCartney: *Da Lata* / Bebe: *Takemura, Nobukazu*
FARO 010CD / Oct '96 / Far Out

Friends Of Dean Martinez

☐ RETROGRADE
SPCD 375 / 1 Sep '97 / Sub Pop

☐ SHADOW OF YOUR SMILE, THE
SPCD 306 / Sep '95 / Sub Pop

Frier, Tich

☐ MAN O' INDEPENDENT MIND
CMCD 078 / Nov '97 / Celtic Music

Friesen, David

☐ 1,2,3 (Friesen, David Trio)
My funny valentine / Come rain or come shine / Getting sentimental over you / How deep is the ocean / Only trust your heart / Sarabande / Dark sky / Going forth
BCD 00172 / May '96 / Burnside

☐ LONG TRIP HOME
ITM 970073 / Sep '92 / ITM

☐ RETURNING (Friesen, David & Glen Moore)
BCD 00132 / Jul '96 / Burnside

☐ THREE TO GET READY
ITMP 970084 / Oct '95 / ITM

☐ TWO FOR THE SHOW
ITM 960079 / Oct '95 / ITM

☐ UPON THE SWING
SHAM 1020CD / Nov '95 / Shamrock

Frifot

☐ JARVEN
CAP 21551CD / Nov '96 / Caprice

Frijid Pink

☐ DEFROSTED
REP 4172 / Aug '91 / Repertoire

☐ FRIJID PINK
REP 4156 / Aug '91 / Repertoire

Fringe

☐ IT'S TIME FOR THE FRINGE
1212052 / Sep '93 / Soul Note

Fripp, Robert

☐ 1995 SOUNDSCAPES VOL.1
DGM 9505 / Mar '96 / Discipline

☐ BLESSING OF TEARS, A (1995 Soundscape)
Cathederal of tears / First light / Midnight blue / Reflection 1 / Second light / Blessing of tears / Returning 1 / Returning 2
DGM 9506 / Aug '95 / Discipline

☐ BRIDGE BETWEEN
Kan-non power / Yamanashi blues / Hope / Chromatic fantasy / Contrapunctus / Bicycling to Afghanistan / Blue / Blockhead / Passacaglia / Therenody for souls in torment
DGM 9303 / Sep '94 / Discipline

☐ ESSENTIAL FRIPP & ENO, THE (Fripp, Robert & Brian Eno)
Heavenly music corporation / Swastika girls / Wind on water / Evening star / Healthy colours
CDVE 920 / Apr '94 / Venture

☐ EVENING STAR (Fripp, Robert & Brian Eno)
Wind on water / Evening star / Evensong / Wind on wind / Index of metals
EEGCD 3 / '87 / EG

☐ EXPOSURE
Breathless / Chicago / Disengage / Exposure / First inaugural address to the IACE Sherbourne House / Here comes the flood / I may not have had enough of me but I've had enough of you / Mary / North star / NY3 / Urban landscape / Water music 1 / You burn me up I'm a cigarette / Preface / Postscript / Haaden two / Water music 2
EGCD 41 / Jan '87 / EG

☐ GATES OF PARADISE
DGM 9608 / 27 Apr '98 / Discipline

☐ GOD SAVE THE KING
God save the King / Under heavy manners / Heptaparaparshinokh / Inductive resonance / Cognitive dissonance / Dislocated / HG Wells / Eye needles / Trap
EEGCD 9 / Jun '85 / EG

☐ INTERGALACTIC BOOGIE EXPRESS LIVE
Connecticut yankee in the court of King Arthur / Rhythm of the universes / Lark's thrak / Circulation I / Intergalactic boogie express / G Force / Eye of the needle / Corrente / Driving force / Groove penetration / Flying home / Circulation II / Fireplace / Fragments of skylab / Asturias / Prelude circulation / Cheeseballs / Prelude in C minor / Wabash cannonball
DGM 9502 / Sep '95 / Discipline

☐ LET THE POWER FALL (An Album Of Frippertronics)
1984 / 1985 / 1986 / 1987 / 1988 / 1989
EEGCD 10 / '87 / EG

☐ NO PUSSY FOOTING (Fripp, Robert & Brian Eno)
Heavenly music corporation / Swastika girls
EEGCD 2 / Jan '87 / EG

☐ ROBERT FRIPP AND THE LEAGUE OF CRAFTY GUITARISTS - LIVE
Guitar craft theme 1: Invocation / Tight muscle party at love beach / Chords that bind / Guitar craft theme 3: Eye of the needle / All or nothing / Crafty march / Guitar craft theme 2: Aspiration / All or nothing / Circulation / Fearful symmetry / New world
EEGCD 43 / Nov '86 / EG

☐ SHOW OF HANDS (Fripp, Robert & The League Of Crafty Guitarists)
Listen: *Fripp, Robert* / Eye of the needle: *Fripp, Robert* / Askesis: *Fripp, Robert* / Bicycling to afghanistan: *Fripp, Robert* / Here comes my sweetie: *Fripp, Robert* / An easy way: *Fripp, Robert* / Scaling the whales: *Fripp, Robert* / Moving force: *Fripp, Robert* / A connecticut yankee in the court of king arthur: *Fripp, Robert* / This yes: *Fripp, Robert* / Are you abel (ready and able to rock 'n' roll): *Fripp, Robert* / Spasm for juanita: *Fripp, Robert* / Hard times: *Fripp, Robert* / Burning siesta: *Fripp, Robert* / Empty magazine: *Fripp, Robert* / Circulation: *Fripp, Robert* / Chiara: *Fripp, Robert* / Asturias: *Fripp, Robert* / Ease god's sorrow: *Fripp, Robert*
EEG 21022 / Jul '93 / EG

☐ THAT WHICH PASSES
On acceptance / On the approach of doubt / Leap / Worm in paradise / New worlds / On triumph / On awe / This too shall pass / Fear of light / Time to die
DGM 9507 / Sep '96 / Discipline

Frisco Syncopators

☐ SAN FRANCISCO BOUND
SOSCD 1211 / Oct '92 / Stomp Off

Frisell, Bill

☐ BEFORE WE WERE BORN
Before we were born / Pip squeak / Hard plains drifter / Steady girl / Some song and dance / Goodbye / Lone ranger
7559608432 / Jan '94 / Nonesuch

☐ GONE JUST LIKE A TRAIN
Blues for Los Angeles / Godson song / Pleased to meet you / Nature's symphony / Ballroom / Sherlock Jr. / Wife and kid / Lonesome / Verona / Girl asks boy (part 1) / Lookout for hope / Egg radio / Girl asks boy (part 2) / Gone, just like a train / Raccoon cat
7559794792 / 26 Jan '98 / Nonesuch

☐ HAVE A LITTLE FAITH
Billy the kid / Saint-gaudens in boston common / Colonel shaw and his colored regiment / Just like a woman / I can't be satisfied / Live to tell / No moe / Washington post, the (sousa) / When I fall in love / Little jenny dow / Have a little faith in me / Billy boy
7559793012 / Jan '94 / Nonesuch

☐ IN LINE
Start / Throughout / Two arms / Shorts / Smile on you / Beach / In line / Three / Godson song
8370192 / Jul '91 / ECM

☐ IS THAT YOU
7559609562 / Jan '94 / Nonesuch

☐ LOOKOUT FOR HOPE (Frisell, Bill Band)
Lookout for hope / Little brother Bobby / Hangdog / Remedios / Beauty / Lonesome / Melody for Jack / Hackensack / Little bigger / Animal race / Alien prints (for D Sharpe)
8334952 / Feb '88 / ECM

☐ QUARTET
7559794012 / May '96 / Nonesuch

☐ RAMBLER
Tone / Music I heard / Rambler / When we go / Resistor / Strange meeting / Wizard of odds
8252342 / May '85 / ECM

☐ SAFETY BY NUMBERS - AMERICAN BLOOD (Frisell, Bill & Victor Godsey)
VBR 20642 / Oct '94 / Vera Bra

☐ THIS LAND
7559793162 / Jun '94 / Nonesuch

☐ WORKS
Monica Jane / Beach / When we go throughout / Black is the colour of my true love's hair / Wizard of odds / Conception vessel / Etude
8372732 / Jun '89 / ECM

Frishberg, Dave

☐ BY HIMSELF
ARCD 19185 / 1 Jun '98 / Arbors Jazz

☐ DOUBLE PLAY (Frishberg, Dave & Jim Goodwin)
ARCD 19118 / Nov '94 / Arbors Jazz

☐ GETTING SOME FUN OUT OF LIFE
CCD 4037 / Jul '96 / Concord Jazz

☐ LET'S EAT HOME
Brenda Starr / Let's eat home / Mr. George / Matty / Mooche / I was ready / Strange music / Ship without a sail / Lookin' good / Underdog
CCD 4402 / Jan '90 / Concord Jazz

Frith, Fred

☐ DROPERA
RECDEC 32 / Oct '95 / Rec Rec

☐ EYE TO EAR
TZA 7503 / Feb '97 / Tzadik

☐ IMPROVISATIONS (Frith, Fred & J.P. Drouet)
TE 012 / Jul '97 / EPM

☐ NOUS AUTRES (Frith, Fred & Rene Luiser)
VICTOCD 01 / Nov '94 / Victo

☐ PACIFICA 1993-1995
TZA 7034 / 1 Jun '98 / Tzadik

☐ PREVIOUS EVENING, THE
RERFF 1 / Jan '98 / ReR/Recommended

☐ STEP ACROSS THE BORDER
RECDEC 30 / May '93 / Rec Rec

☐ TECHNOLOGY OF TEARS
RECDEC 20 / Apr '88 / Rec Rec

☐ TOP OF HIS HEAD, THE
Title theme / Driving to the train / Wheels within / Hold on hold / Lucy leaves a note / Gus escapes / Gravity's a rule / Channel change / Orbit / Fall to call / Underwater dream / This old earth / Donuts / Long drive / Lucy / Premonition / Questions and answers / Performance / Title theme (conclusion) / Way you look tonight
MTM 21 / Apr '96 / Made To Measure

☐ WITH ENEMIES LIKE THESE, WHO NEEDS FRIENDS (Frith & Kaiser)
Trace / Three languages / Love in hell / Twisted memories give way to the angry pheasant / One of nature's mistakes / Roy rogers / It sings / Drowsy maggie / Kirghiz light / Golden eighties / Objects everyday / Changing of names / It moves... / One-eyed theater / Dog puppet born out of a sock / Hard time killin' floor blues
SST 147CD / May '93 / SST

Fritts, Donnie

☐ EVERYBODY'S GOT A SONG
OBR 017CD / 24 Nov '97 / Oh Boy

Frizzell, Lefty

☐ LIFE'S LIKE POETRY (12CD Set)
I love you a thousand ways / If you've got the money, I've got the time / Shine, shave shower / Cold feet / Don't think it ain't been fun dear / When payday comes around / My baby's just like money / Look what thoughts will do / You want everything but me / I want to be with you always / Give me more more more (of your kisses) / How long will it take (to stop loving you) / Always late (with your kisses) / Mom and dad's waltz / You can go on your way now / Treasure untold / Blue yodel / Travellin' blues / My old pal / Lullaby yodel / Brakeman's blues / My rough and rowdy ways / I love you (Though you're no good) / It's just you (I could love always) / (Darling now) you're here so everything's alright / I've got reasons to hate you / Don't stay away / If you can spare the time (I won't miss the money) / King without a Queen / Forever (and always) / I know you're lonesome (while waiting for me) / Lost love blues / That's me without you / Send her here to be mine / I won't be good for nothin' / If I lose you (I'll lose my world) / I'm an old old man (Tryin' to love while I can) / You're just mine (Only in my dreams) / I'll try / Bring your sweet self back / Time changes things / All of me (loves all of

you) / California blues / Never no' mo' blues / We crucified our Jesus / When it comes to measuring love / Sleep, baby, sleep / (I'm) Lonely and blue / Before you go, make sure you know / Two friends of mine in love / Hopeless love / Then I'll come back to you / Tragic letter (The letter that you left) / You can always count on me / I've been away way too long / Run 'em off / Darkest moment (Is just before the light of da / You're too late / My little her and him / I love you mostly / You're there, I'm ere / Let it be so / Mama / Making believe / Moonlight, Darling and you / I'll sit alone and cry / Forest fire (Is in your heart) / Sweet lies / Your tomorrows will never come / It gets late so early / I'm lost between right and wrong / Promises (promises, promises) / My love and baby's gone / Today is that tomorrow (I dreamed of yesterday) / First to have a second chance / These hands / You can't divorce my heart / Treat her right / Heart's highway / I'm a boy left alone / Just can't live that fast (anymore) / Waltz of the angels / Lullaby waltz / Glad I found you / Now that you are gone / From an angel to a devil / Lover by appointment / Sick, sober and sorry / No one to talk to (but the blues) / Is it only that you're lonely / Mailman bring me no more blues / You've still got it / Tell me dear / To stop loving you (means cry) / Torch within my heart / Time out for the blues / (Darling) let's turn back the years / You win again / Why should I be lonely / Signed, sealed, delivered (I'm yours) / Nobody knows but me / If you're ever lonely darling / Silence / Release me / Our love's no bluff / You're humbuggin' me / She's gone / Cigarettes and coffee blues / I need your love / My bucket's got a hole in it / Sin will be the chaser for the wine / Knock again, true love / Long black veil / One has been to another / Farther than my eyes can see / My blues will pass / Ballad of the blue and grey / That's all I can remember / So what, let it rain / What you gonna do, Leroy / I feel sorry for me / Heaven's plan / Looking for you / Stranger / Few steps away / Forbidden lovers / Just passing through / That reminds me of me / Don't let her see me cry / Through the eyes of a fool / James river / Preview of coming attractions / Lonely heart / What good did you get (out of breaking my heart) / When it rains the blues / I'm not the man I'm supposed to be / Saginaw Michigan / There's no food in this house / Rider / Nester / I was coming home to you / Hello to him (goodbye to me) / I can tell / Make that one for the road a cup of coffee / Gator hollow / It costs too much to die / She's gone, gone, gone / Confused / How far down can I go / It's bad (when it's that way) / I don't trust you anymore / Little unfair / Woman let me sing you a song / Preparations to be blue / Love looks good on you / It's hard to please you / You don't want me to get well / Writing on the wall / I just couldn't see the forest (for the trees) / I'm not guilty / It couldn't happen to a nicer guy / Everything keeps coming back (but you) / Heart (don't love her anymore) / You don't have to be present to win / My feet are getting cold / Is there anything I can do / Old gang's gone / Song from a lonely heart / You gotta me puttin' me on / There in the mirror / Get this stranger out of me / Money tree / Hobo's pride / When the rooster leaves the yard / Anything you can spare / Only way to fly / Only way to fly (Laughing version) / Prayer on your lips is like freedon in your hands / Little ole wine drinker me / Word or two to Mary / Almost persuaded / Have you ever been untrue / When the grass grows green again / Marriage bit / I'll remember you / Wasted way of live / Blind street singer / Honky tonk hill / My baby is a tramp / She brought love sweet love / Watermelon time in Georgia / I must be getting over you / Out of you / It's raining all over the world / There's something lonley in this house / Three cheers for the good guys / Article from life / Honky tonk hill (without overdub) / Honky tonk stardust cowboy / What am I gonna do / Give me more, more, more (of your kisses) / You babe / This just ain't a good day for leavin' / Down by the railroad track / Let me give her the flowers / If I had half the sense (A fool was born with) / Somebody's words / Lucky arms / True love needs to be in touch / My house is your honky tonk / I buy the wine / If she just helps me to get over you / Falling / Railroad lady / I can't get over you to save my life / I never go around mirrors / That's the way love goes / She found the key / I wonder who's building the bridge / My wishing room / I'm gonna hang out my mind today / Sittin' and thinkin' / I'm not that good at goodbye / Yesterday just passed my way again / Life's like poetry / Darling I'm missing you / I'll never cry over you / My confession / I hope you're not lonely when I'm gone / My baby and my wife / It's all over now / Worried mind / Maiden's prayer / I'm wasting my life away / You nearly lose your mind / Just can't live that fast (anymore) / Just can't live that fast (anymore) / Honey baby, you were wrong / Please me mine, dear blue eyes / I'm yours if you want me / I'll be a bachelor till I die / Yesterday's mail / Shine, shave and shower / I want to be with you / Always / Ida red / Always late / Theme and If you've got the money / Make the one for the road a cup of coffee / Darling let's turn back the years / Things / At the woodchoppers' ball / Stay all night / Somebody's pushing / Mona Lisa / Sunday down in Tennessee / I'll make it up to you / Too much love / My abandoned heart / Wait till I'm asleep / Not this time / Why didn't you tell me our love was wrong / Forever and always / Please don't stay away so long / Please don't stay away so long / You have never known to be wrong / Reason why my heart's in misery / Just little things like that / I love you so / Fool's advice / When me and my baby go steppin' out / When me and my baby go steppin' out / Brakeman's blues

BCD 15550 / Feb '92 / Bear Family

Froboess, Conny

☐ DIE SINGLES 1958-1959

Diana / Teenager Susan / I love you baby / Schicke schicke schuh / Auch du hast dein schicksal in der hand / Glockergiesser rock / Blue jean boy / Sunshine / Hey boys, how do you do / Jolly joker / Teenager melodie: *Froboess, Conny & Will Brandes* / Ich mocht mit dir traumen: *Froboess, Conny & Will Brandes* / Holiday in Honolulu: *Froboess, Conny & Will Brandes* / Ob 15 ob 16 ob 17 jahre alt / Mr. Music / Wenn das mein grosser bruder wusste / Kleine Lucienne / Such das gluck des lebens / Little girl / Ein madchen mit sechzehn / Lieber disc jockey / Billy, Jack and Joe / Een meisje ven zestien / Liefde als zonneschijn

BCD 15410 / Dec '87 / Bear Family

☐ DIE SINGLES 1960-1962

Yes my darling: *Froboess, Conny & Rex Gildo* / Lippenstift am jacket / Midi midinette / Wer wird der erste sein / Lago maggiore / Junge mach musik / Sag mir was du denkst: *Froboess, Conny & Peter Kraus* / Das geht di leute gar nichts an: *Froboess, Conny & Rex Gildo* / Papa liebt mama / Nicht so schuchtern, junger mann / Ich bin fur die liebe nicht zu jung / Mein vater war ein cowboy / Firulin: *Froboess, Conny & Rex Gildo* / Oky doky: *Froboess, Conny & Rex Gildo* / Mariandl / Nur ein kleines medaillon / Einen kuss und noch einen kuss / Tanz noch einmal mit mir / Zwei kleine Italiener / Hallo, hallo, hallo / Das tu' ich alles nur fur dich (Italian) / Un bacio al' Italiano (Italian) / Hallo, hallo, hallo (Italian) / Twe kleine Italianen (Dutch) / Hallo, hallo, hallo (Dutch)

BCD 15411 / Dec '87 / Bear Family

☐ DIE SINGLES 1962-1964

BCD 15452 / Feb '90 / Bear Family

☐ DIE SINGLES 1964-1967

Diese nacht hat viele lichter / Ist es wahr / Meine hochzeitsreise mach'ich auf den mond / Schone manner sind nicht sehr gefahrlich / Gestern um dreiviertel zehn / Es muss nicht dies sein / Ich geh' durch den regen / Tausend und noch ein paar traume / Der sommer geht / Und das leben geht weiter / Schreib' es in den sand / So ist das leben / Ich komme nie mehr los von dir / Oh Gloria / Georgy girl / Frage und antwort / Adios, adios / Arme kleine sterne / Mein herz schlagt daba daba dab / Liverpool waltz / Die sommerballade von der armen Louise / Folg dem sonnenschein / Um die welt geht die reise / L'amourette / Dis moi si tu veux / Les yeux de Paris / On peux bien dire / Jolly Joker / Hey boys / How do you do

BCD 15491 / Aug '91 / Bear Family

Frodus

☐ CONGLOMERATE INTERNATIONAL

TNR 1102CD / 30 Mar '98 / Tooth & Nail

Froese, Edgar

☐ AGES

Metropolis / Era of the slaves / Tropic of Capricorn / Nights of automatic women / Icarus / Children's deeper study / Ode to Granny / Pizarro and Atahuallpa / Golgatha and the circle closes

CDOVD 480 / Jun '97 / Virgin

☐ AQUA

Upland / Panorphelia / NGC / Aqua

CDV 2016 / Jun '87 / Virgin

☐ AQUA/BLACKOUTS/TIMEWIND (Froese, Edgar & Ashra Tempel/Klaus Schulze)

TPAK 12 / Oct '90 / Virgin

☐ BEYOND THE STORM

Heatwave city / Dome of yellow turtles / One fine day in Siberia / Magic lantern / Walkabout / Genesta in the afternoon glow / Moonlight on a crawler lane / Scarlet score for Mescalero / Upland / Santa Elena Marisal / Macula transfer / Drunken Mozart in the desert / Descent like a hawk / Carneol / Light cone / Detroit snackbar dreamer / Epsilon in Malaysian pale / Tierra del fuego / Bobcats in the sun / Metropolis / Year of the falcon / Juniper mascara / Shores of Guam / Pinnacles / Stuntman / Days of camouflage / Tropic of Capricorn / Vault of the heaven

AMBT 5 / Jun '95 / Virgin

☐ PINNACLES

Specific gravity of smile / Light cone / Walkabout / Pinnacles

CDV 2277 / May '88 / Virgin

☐ STUNTMAN

Stuntman / It would be like Samoa / Detroit snackbar dreamer / Drunken Mozart in the desert / Dali-esque sleep fuse / Scarlet score for Mescalero

CDV 2139 / '87 / Virgin

Froggatt, Raymond

☐ COLLECTION, THE

RBMCD 0017 / May '97 / Red Balloon

☐ MOONSHINE

CRESTCD 025 / 19 Jan '98 / Mooncrest

☐ SOMEDAY

RBMCD 0016 / Oct '95 / Red Balloon

Frogs

☐ MY DAUGHTER THE BROAD

OLE 1552 / Jun '96 / Matador

Frohmader, Peter

☐ GATES

EFA 127612 / Sep '95 / Atonal

Frolic Froth

☐ EPONYMOUS

SR 2013 / Dec '97 / Smogless

From The Fire

☐ 30 DAYS & DIRTY NIGHTS

Hold on / Same song / Tears cried in the rain / Over your head / Take my heart / Lovestruck / Spark and flame / Go all the way / Where are you now

CDATV 22 / Jul '92 / Active

Froman, Jane

☐ CAPITOL RECORDINGS, THE

61774200262 / 21 Apr '98 / Collectables

☐ MY HEART SPEAKS

My melancholy baby / I only have eyes for you / You let me down / Lost in a fog / But where are you / Summertime/It ain't necessarily so / Please believe me / If you love me / Maybe/Do do do/Clap yo' hands/Someone to watch over me / Man I love / Did I remember / Speak your haert / La bomba boy / What love has done to me / Tonight we love / You are romance/Swing low sweet harriot / At your service madam / I get a kick out of you / Begin the beguine / You go to my head / Who cares/So am I/I got rhythm/ Somebody loves me

JASCD 107 / Feb '98 / Jasmine

Fromenteau, Michele

☐ L'ART DE LA VIELLE A ROUE VOL.1

ARN 60355 / Feb '97 / Arion

Frongia, Enrico

☐ ARGIA (Frongia, Enrico & Alberto Balia)

NT 6713 / Jan '94 / Robi Droli

Front 242

☐ LIVE CODE 5413356424225

Der verfluchte engel / Motion / Masterhit / Flag / Tragedy for you / Im rhythmus bleiben / Skin / Headhunter / Welcome to paradise / Crapage / Soul manager / Punish your machine / Religion

BIAS 242CD / Oct '94 / Play It Again Sam

☐ LIVE TARGET

Rhythm of time / Soul manager / Don't crash / Im rhythmus bleiben / DSM 123 and Moldavia / No shuffle / Gripped by fear / Never stop / Headhunter / Tragedy for you / Welcome to paradise / Punish your machine / Intro/Circling overland

GUZZ 1888 / Dec '92 / Guzzi

☐ NO COMMENT (1984-1985)

Commando mix / S fr nomenklatura pt 1/2 / Deceit / Lovely day / No shuffle / Special forces / See the future (live) / In November / Body to body

MK 002CD / Jun '92 / Mask

☐ REBOOK 98

ZOT 242CD / 20 Jul '98 / Zoth Ommog

Front Page Review

☐ MYSTIC SOLDIERS

Prophecies/Morning blue / Prism fawn / One eyed minor / Feels like love / Silver children / Valley of eyes / Without you / For the best offer

CDWIKD 166 / Feb '97 / Big Beat

Front Range

☐ BACK TO RED RIVER

SHCD 3811 / Jan '94 / Sugar Hill

☐ NEW FRONTIER, THE

Waiting for the real thing / Chains of darkness / Down in Caroline / Without you / Why don't you leave me baby / Lonesome night / When I still needed you / So far away / Burning the breakfast / Shady river / Building on the rock / Happy after all

SHCD 3801 / Jul '92 / Sugar Hill

☐ ONE BEAUTIFUL DAY

SHCD 3830 / Mar '95 / Sugar Hill

☐ RAMBLIN' ON MY MIND

Under the influence of love / Ramblin' on my mind / Way back in the hills / Fergus County jail / He's everywhere / Lantern / Jenny dear / You're only lonely / Willoughby Gap / Home in San Antone / With body and soul / Kissing the blues goodbye

SHCD 3861 / Mar '98 / Sugar Hill

Frontier

☐ 4

EJ 17CD / 16 Mar '98 / Emperor Jones

☐ FRONTIER

Frontier

103 FR / Nov '96 / Humboldt Pie

☐ HEATER

TOW 004 / May '97 / Tug O' War

Frontline Assembly

☐ CAUSTIC GRIP

Resist / Victim / Overkill / Forge / Provision / Force fed / Iceolate / Threshold / Mental distortion / Chair

TM 91162 / Sep '96 / Roadrunner

☐ COLUMBIAN NECKTIE

MET 073 / 5 Jan '98 / Metropolis

☐ CORRODED DISORDER

08422332CD / Jan '96 / Westcom

☐ FLAVOUR OF THE WEAK

08543792 / 9 Feb '98 / Offbeat

☐ GASHED SENSES AND CROSSFIRE

No limit / Hypocrisy / Prayer / Big money / Sedation / Anti-social / Shut down / Digital tension dementia / Fools game

TM 91152 / Sep '96 / Roadrunner

☐ HARD WIRED

08522292CD / May '96 / Westcom

☐ INITIAL COMMAND

ZOT 189CD / 29 Sep '97 / Zoth Ommog

☐ LIVE WIRED (2CD Set)

08843262 / Sep '96 / Westcom

☐ MILLENNIUM

RR 90192 / Sep '96 / Roadrunner

☐ RECLAIMATION

Covered

RR 87902 / 27 Oct '97 / Roadrunner

☐ STATE OF MIND

DCD 9005 / Aug '88 / Dossier

☐ TACTICAL NEURAL IMPLANT

Final impact / Blade / Mindphaser / Remorse / Bio-mechanic / Outcast / Gun / Lifeline

TM 91882 / Sep '96 / Third Mind

☐ TOTAL TERROR VOL.1

EFA 08451CD / Nov '93 / Dossier

☐ TOTAL TERROR VOL.2

EFA 08452CD / Nov '93 / Dossier

Froom, Mitchell

☐ DOPAMINE

Tastes good: *Froom, Mitchell & David Hidalgo* / Bunny: *Froom, Mitchell & M. Doughty* / Kitsum: *Froom, Mitchell & Lisa Germano* / Dopamine: *Froom, Mitchell & Suzanne Vega* / Watery eyes: *Froom, Mitchell & Mark Eitzel* / Monkey mind: *Froom, Mitchell & Sheryl Crow* / Noodletown: *Froom, Mitchell & Steve Donnelly* / Wave: *Froom, Mitchell & Miho Atori* / I'd better not: *Froom, mitchell & Louie Perez* / Permanent midnight: *Froom, Mitchell & Jerry Stahl* / Overcast: *Froom, Mitchell & Ron Sexsmith* / Fruta prohibida: *Froom, Mitchell & Mark Feldman*

7567831022 / 6 Jul '98 / East West

Frost

☐ FROST MUSIC

VMD 6520 / Oct '96 / Vanguard

☐ ROCK 'N' ROLL MUSIC

VMD 6541 / Oct '96 / Vanguard

Frost, Edith

☐ CALLING OVER TIME

DC 89CD / Jun '97 / Drag City

Frost, Frank

☐ DEEP BLUES

Nothin' I wouldn't do for you / Sweet woman / Born to be wise / Pocket full of shells / My baby / Ride with your daddy tonight / Repo man blues / Pocket full of money / Janie on my mind / Somebody tell me / Deep blues

ECD 26094 / 23 Jun '98 / Evidence

☐ JELLY ROLL KING (Charly Blues Masterworks Vol.36)

Everything's alright / Lucky to be living / Jelly roll king / Bay you're so kind / Gonna make you mine / Now twist / Big boss man / Jack's jump / So tired of living by myself / Now what you gonna do / Pocket full of shells / Just come on home / Crawlback / My back scratcher / Things you do / Ride with your daddy tonight / Pocket full of money / Didn't mean no harm

CDBM 36 / Jan '93 / Charly

☐ KEEP YOURSELF TOGETHER (Frost, Frank & Sam Carr)

Keep yourself together / Frank's boogie woogie / Tired of living by myself / You're so kind / Going to Chicago / Just a feeling / Cotton needs pickin' / Come on home / All my life / Everything's gonna be alright / My soul lover

ECD 260772 / Apr '96 / Evidence

Frostbite

☐ CAROUSEL

NM 022CD / Oct '97 / Neat Metal

☐ SECOND COMING

Loose my mind / Frostbite / Bartender / Depressed / Sand / Only the light / Goldfish

TPLP 666CD / Aug '93 / One Little Indian

☐ SECRET ADMIRER

USCD 011 / Nov '96 / Underground Symphony

Frosted

☐ COLD

RR 88022 / 6 Oct '97 / Roadrunner

Frozen Brass

☐ ASIA

PANCD 2020 / May '93 / Pan

Frozen Doberman

☐ BONZAI

FD 019CD / Jul '95 / Modern Invasion

Frugivore

☐ BIONAUT, THE

DIGI 1002CD / Oct '95 / Digitrax

Fruitcake

☐ ONE MORE SLICE

Joke / Spirit of this day / Hell's kitchen / Between reality and dream / Have a slice / Somewhat late for supper / Final signals / Just another weird vector

CYCL 057 / 10 Nov '97 / Cyclops

☐ ROOM FOR SURPRISE

CYCL 032 / May '96 / Cyclops

Fruko Y Sus Tesos

☐ TODOS BAILAN SALSA (The Best Of Fruko)
El preso / El ausente / Lupita / La pachanga del futbol / El patillero / Barranquillero arrebatao / Manyoma / Mambo no.5 / Cerezo rosa / Tanai / Los charcos / Chachacha con pachanga / Swing pachanga / Salsa brava / Oye como va / Mambo del politenico / Mambo del marcardo la merced / Todos bailan salsa
TUGCD 1014 / 18 May '98 / World Music Network

Fruminous Bandersnatch

☐ YOUNG MAN'S SONG
You gotta believe / Chain reaction / Rosemary's baby / What is a Bandersnatch / Woodrose syrup / Now that you've gone / 45 Cents / Pulpit huff / Paper / Cheshire / Black box / Can-a-bliss
CDWIKD 169 / Jun '96 / Big Beat

Frumpy

☐ ALL WILL BE CHANGED
REP 4146 / Aug '91 / Repertoire

☐ BY THE WAY
REP 4231 / Aug '91 / Repertoire

Frusciante, John

☐ NIANDRA LADES AND USUALLY JUST A T-SHIRT
74321236792 / Nov '95 / American

☐ SMILE FROM THE STREETS YOU HOLD
BMR 016 / Oct '97 / Birdman

Frustrated

☐ ANTHOLOGY OF EXPERIMENTAL MUSIC
DIS 011CD / Jun '94 / Disturbance

Fruupp

☐ FUTURE LEGENDS/SEVEN SECRETS
Future legends / Decision / As day breaks with dawn / Garveyard epistle / Lord of the incubus / Olde tyme future / Song for a thought / Wise as wisdom / White eyes / Garden lady / Three spires / Elizabeth / Seventh secret
C5HCD 645 / Aug '96 / See For Miles

☐ PRINCE OF HEAVEN'S EYES/MODERN MASQUERADES
It's all up now / Prince of Darkness / Jaunting car / Annie Austere / Knowing you / Crystal Brook / Seaward sunset / Perfect wish / Misty morning way / Masquerading with Dawn / Mystery might / Why / Janet Planet / Sheba's song
C5HCD 646 / Jul '96 / See For Miles

☐ SEVEN SECRETS
SRMC 1045 / Oct '97 / Siwan

Fry, Albert

☐ THIAR I DTIR CHONAILL
CIC 081CD / Nov '93 / Clo Iar-Chonnachta

Frye, Howard

☐ GYPSY MANDOLIN
MCD 71463 / Jun '93 / Monitor

FSK

☐ INTERNATIONAL
EFA 155482 / Mar '96 / Sub Up

☐ PEEL SESSIONS, THE (3.8.86/21.5.87)
I wish I could sprechen sie Deutch / Die musik finik findet immer nach haus / Dr. Arnold Fanck / Am tafelberg von kepstadt / Komm gib mir deine hand / Girl / Birthday / Don't pass me by
SFPMCD 204 / '89 / Strange Fruit

Fu Manchu

☐ ACTION IS GO
3549801732 / Nov '97 / Mammoth

☐ ACTION IS GO
5570702 / 16 Mar '98 / Polydor

☐ EARLY RECORDINGS
ELS 014 / May '97 / Elastic

☐ IN SEARCH OF...
Lazy magician / Missing link / Asphalt risin' / Neptune's convoy / Redline / Cyclone launch / Strat-o-streak / Solid hex / Falcon has landed / Sea hag / Bargain / Supershooter
MR 1342 / Mar '96 / Mammoth

☐ NO ONE RIDES FOR FREE
BL 10CD / 27 Jul '98 / Bongload

Fu-Schnickens

☐ NERVOUS BREAKDOWN
Breakdown / Sum dum monkey / Visions (20/20) / Watch ya back door / Aaahh ooohhh / Sneakin' up on ya / Got it covered / Who stole the pebble / Hi Lo / What's up doc (Can we rock): *Fu-Schnickens & Shaquille O'Neal* / Breakdown (remix)
CHIP 153 / Oct '94 / Jive

Fuchs, Wolfgang

☐ BITS AND PIECES
OWN 90004 / May '97 / Full Moon

Fuck

☐ BABY LOVES A FUNNY BUNNY
Boy meets girl / Swinger / Love me 2 / Flight of the mongeese / Tired / 22 no / Nice burg lettuce / Talent or / Ballet high / Part of me / Rococo / Like you / Loosened mind / Crush a butterfly / Whimper and cry
NORMAL 204CD / Feb '97 / Normal
WLR 2229 / Jun '97 / Walt Rhesus Lamplighter

☐ PARDON MY FRENCH
L'il Hilda / Fuck Motel / Le serpent / Bestest friend / Compromise / One lb of In / La Jolla / For Lori / Raggy rag / Tether / Dirty brunette / To my gurl / Thoroughfare / Sometimes / Am I losin' / Scribble dribble
OLE 2612 / Jun '97 / Matador

☐ PRETTY...SLOW
WALT 008 / May '97 / Walt Rhesus Lamplighter

Fugain, Michel

☐ 1960'S FRENCH EP COLLECTION, THE (2CD Set)
174712 / Nov '97 / Magic

☐ DIAMOND COLLECTION, THE
3009412 / Feb '97 / Arcade

☐ SES MEILLEURS MOMENTS (2CD Set)
3018532 / Feb '97 / Flarenasch

Fugazi

☐ 13 SONGS
Waiting room / Bulldog front / Bad mouth / Burning / Give me the cure / Suggestion / Glue man / Margin walker / And the same / Burning too / Provisional / Lockdown / Promises
DIS 36CD / 6 Apr '98 / Dischord

☐ END HITS
DIS 100CD / 30 Mar '98 / Dischord

☐ FUGAZI
Waiting room / Bulldog front / Bad mouth / Burning / Give me the cure / Suggestion / Glue man
DIS 30CD / Dec '88 / Dischord

☐ IN ON THE KILLTAKER
Facet squad / Public witness programme / Returning the screw / Smallpox champion / Rend it / Twenty three beats off / Sweet and low / Cassavetes / Great cop / Walken's syndrome / Instrument / Last chance for a slow dance
DIS 70CD / 6 Apr '98 / Dischord

☐ MARGIN WALKER
Margin walker / And the same / Burning too / Provisional / Lockdown / Promises
DIS 35CD / Jul '89 / Dischord

☐ RED MEDICINE
Do you like me / Bed for the scraping / Latest disgrace / Birthday pony / Forensic scene / Combination lock / Fell, destroyed / By you / Version / Target / Back to base / Downed city / Long distance runner
DIS 90CD / 6 Apr '98 / Dischord

☐ REPEATER
Turnover / Repeater / Brendan No.1 / Merchandise / Blueprint / Sieve-fisted find / Greed / Two beats off / Styrofoam / Reprovisional / Shut the door
DIS 44CD / 6 Apr '98 / Dischord

☐ STEADY DIET OF NOTHING
Exit only / Reclamation / Nice new outfit / Stacks / Latin roots / Steady diet of nothing / Long division / Runaway return / Polish / Dear justice letter / KYEO
DISCHORD 60CD / 6 Apr '98 / Dischord

Fugees

☐ BLUNTED ON REALITY
Introduction / Nappy heads / Blunted interlude / Recharge / Free-style interlude / Vocab / Special new bulletin interlude / Boof baf / Temple / How hard is it / Harlem chit chat interlude / Some seek stardom / Giggles / Da kid from Haiti interlude / Refugees on the mic / Living like there ain't no tomorrow / Shouts out from the block
4747132 / Jul '96 / Ruff House

☐ SCORE, THE (Refugee Camp)
Red intro / How many mics / Ready or not / Zealots / Beast / Fu-gee-la / Family business / Killing me softly / Score / Mask / Cowboys / No woman no cry / Manifesto/Outro
4835492 / Feb '96 / Ruff House

☐ SCORE, THE (The Bootleg Versions)
Ready or not / Nappy heads / Don't cry, dry your eyes / Vocab / Killing me softly / No woman no cry
4868242 / Nov '96 / Ruff House

Fugs

☐ FIRST ALBUM
Slum Goddess / Ah sunflower weary of time / Supergirl / Swinburne stomp / I couldn't get high / How sweet I roamed / Carpe diem / My baby done left me / Boobs a lot / Nothing / We're the fugs / Defeated / Ten commandments / CIA man / In the middle of their first recording session The Fugs sign / I saw the best minds of my generation rock / Spontaneous salute at Andy Warhol / War kills babies / Fugs national anthem / Fugs spaghetti death / Rhapsody of Tuli
CDWIKD 119 / Jun '93 / Fugs/Big Beat

☐ FUGS LIVE FROM THE 60'S
Doin' alright / Swedish nada / Homage to Catherine and William Blake / I couldn't / Johnny pissoff and the red angel / JOB / My baby done left me / Garden is open / Exorcism of the grave of Senator Joseph McCarthy / Yodeling yippie / Ten commandments / Swinburne stomp
CDWIKD 125 / May '94 / Fugs/Big Beat

☐ NO MORE SLAVERY
No more slavery / Cold war / Dreams of sexual gratification / South Africa / Dover beach / Smoking gun / Working for the yankee dollar / Just like a jail / Here come the levellers / What would Tom Paine do / Technology is going to set us free / Hymn to America / Days of auld lang hippie / Ballad of the League Of Militant Agnostics / You can't go into the same river twice
CDWIKD 145 / Sep '96 / Big Beat

☐ REAL WOODSTOCK FESTIVAL, THE (Byrdcliffe Barn, Woodstock NY - 14th August 1994/2CD Set) (Fugs & Allen Ginsberg/Friends)
Nova slum goddess / Poe job / Cia man / Crystal liason / Golden age / Rock 'n' roll hall of fame / Frenzy / Sonnet 29: Fortune and men's eyes / Postmodern nothing / Ramses the II is dead, my love / When the mode of the music changes / Ten commandments, together with the ten amendments / Woodstock nation / Augries of innocence / They're closing up the loopholes of life / Einstein never wore socks / Shadows of paradise / I want to know / Song for Janis Joplin / Cave 64 / Down by the Salley Gardens / Coming down / Wide wide river / How sweet I roamed from field to field / Morning morning / Nurse's song (and all the hills echoed)
CDWIK2 160 / Sep '95 / Fugs/Big Beat

☐ REFUSE TO BE BURNT-OUT (Live In The 1980s)
Five feet / If you want to be President / Nova slum goddess / Nicaragua / Fingers of the sun / Wide wide river / How sweet I roamed / Refuse to be burnt-out / Country punk / CIA man / Ban the bomb / Keeping the issues alive / Dreams of sexual perfection / Summer of love
CDWIKD 139 / Mar '95 / Fugs/Big Beat

☐ SECOND ALBUM
Frenzy / I want to know / Skin flowers / Group grope / Coming down / Dirty old man / Kill for peace / Morning morning / Doin' alright / Virgin forest / Mutant stomp / Carpe diem / Wide wide river / Nameless voices crying for kindness
CDWIKD 121 / Sep '93 / Fugs/Big Beat

☐ STAR PEACE
ROSE 115CD / Jun '87 / New Rose

Fuji Dub

☐ LAGOS-BROOKLYN-BRIXTON
TRECD 116 / Jun '97 / Triple Earth

Fujieda, Mamourn

☐ PATTERNS OF PLANTS
TZ 7025 / 15 Sep '97 / Tzadik

Fukushima, Kazuo

☐ WORKS FOR FLUTE AND PIANO
ARTCD 6114 / Oct '92 / Hat Art

Fulham FC

☐ VIVA EL FULHAM (Fulham FC/ Supporters)
Fulham stomp / Viva el Fulham: *Rees, Tony & The Cottagers* / Julie Brown loves Captain Cook: *Barrett, Les* / Love me: *Barrett, Les & Paul* / Maybe it's because I'm a Londoner: *Mullery, Alan & Friends* / Sugar sugar: *Moore, Bobby & Friends* / You lucky people / These boots are made for walking: *Fulham Flurries* / Interview with Johnny Haynes / Victory / You and me and Fulham: *Bay, Tony* / Interview with George Cohen / Interview with Jimmy Hill / Going up: *Stevenage Road Boys*
CDGAFFER 17 / Apr '97 / Cherry Red

Fulks, Robbie

☐ COUNTRY LOVE SONGS
BS 011 / 19 Jan '98 / Bloodshot

☐ SOUTH MOUTH
BS 023 / 19 Jan '98 / Bloodshot

Full House

☐ SPACIOUSLY DECEPTIVE
101REC 3CD / Feb '96 / 101

Full Monte

☐ SPARK IN THE PARK
Bubbling marsh / Spark in the dark / Mogadonic tonic / Lift life / Grand Hotel ascenseur / Spiritual cleavage / Wind dance
SLAMCD 209 / Oct '96 / Slam

Full Moon

☐ EUPHORIA
DMCD 1031 / Feb '92 / Demi-Monde

Full Moon Scientists

☐ DO WE LOOK LIKE COMEDIANS
Fly low / Wild whips of Westminster / Stroller / Doc hope / Till kingdom come / We demand a shrubbery / Shake me out of my tree / Nuke speak train / You've got me howling / Lunar base to big ben 6am / I'll tell you when to panic
BOS 2002CD / 6 Oct '97 / Botchit & Scarper

Fuller, Blind Boy

☐ 1935-1940
Baby you gotta change your mind / Baby I don't have to worry / Looking for my woman / Precious lord / Jesus is a holy man / Bye bye baby / You got to have your dollar / Shake that shimmy / Truckin' my blues away
TMCD 01 / Apr '90 / Travellin' Man

☐ BLIND BOY FULLER VOL.1 1935-1936
DOCD 5091 / '92 / Document

☐ BLIND BOY FULLER VOL.2 1937
DOCD 5092 / '92 / Document

☐ BLIND BOY FULLER VOL.3 1937
DOCD 5093 / '92 / Document

☐ BLIND BOY FULLER VOL.4 1937-1938
DOCD 5094 / '92 / Document

☐ BLIND BOY FULLER VOL.5 1938-1940
DOCD 5095 / '92 / Document

☐ BLIND BOY FULLER VOL.6 1940
DOCD 5096 / '92 / Document

☐ HARMONICA & GUITAR 1937-1945 (Fuller, Blind Boy & Sonny Terry)
158562 / Oct '96 / Blues Collection

☐ TRUCKIN' MY BLUES AWAY
Truckin' my blues away / Untrue blues / Homesick and lonesome blues / You never can tell / Mamie / Jivin' woman blues / Weeping willow / Funny feeling blues / I crave my pigmeat / Corrine what makes you treat me so / Meat shakin' woman / Walking my troubles away / Painful hearted man / Sweet honey hole
YAZCD 1060 / Apr '91 / Yazoo

☐ UNTRUE BLUES
KATCD 109 / 1 Sep '98 / Catfish

Fuller, Bobby

☐ BEST OF THE BOBBY FULLER FOUR (Fuller, Bobby Four)
I fought the law / Love's made a fool of you / Another sad and lonely night / She's my girl / New shade of blue / My true love / Pamela / Let her dance / Never to be forgotten / Thunder reef / Baby my heart / Fool of love / Only when I dream / Don't ever let me know / King of the wheels / Think it over / Magic touch / Keep a knockin'
CDCHM 388 / Mar '92 / Ace

☐ EL PASO ROCK VOL.1
CED 252 / 15 Dec '97 / Norton

☐ EL PASO ROCK VOL.2
CED 260 / 15 Dec '97 / Norton

☐ I FOUGHT THE LAW (Fuller, Bobby Four)
842614 / May '94 / EVA

☐ I FOUGHT THE LAW/THE KRLA KING OF THE WHEELS (Fuller, Bobby Four)
Thunder reef / Wolfman / She's my girl / King of the wheels / Lonely dragster / Phantom dragster / KRLA top eliminator / Let her dance / Julie / New shade of blue / Only when I dream / You kiss me / Little Annie Lou / I fought the law / Another sad and lonely night / Saturday night / Take my word / Fool of love / Never to be forgotten / Love's made a fool of you / Don't ever let me know / My true love / Magic touch / I'm a lucky guy
CDCHD 956 / Nov '90 / Ace

☐ LIVE AT PJ'S PLUS (Fuller, Bobby Four)
Anytime at all / Wooly bully / Gloria / Oh boy / Think it over / Thunder reef / Hi-heel sneakers / Slow down / I fought the law / New shade of blue / Let her dance / CC rider / My babe / Keep a knockin' / Long tall Sally / Baby my heart / Pamela / My true love / Our favourite Martian / Never to be forgotten
CDCHD 314 / Jul '91 / Ace

☐ NEVER TO BE FORGOTTEN (3CD Set) (Fuller, Bobby Four)
DLF 3903 / 20 Apr '98 / Del-Fi

☐ SHAKEDOWN (The Texas Tapes Revisited/2CD Set)
DFBX 2902 / Nov '96 / Del-Fi

Fuller, Curtis

☐ BLUES-ETTE VOL.1
Five spot after dark / Undecided / Bluesette / Minor vamp / Love your spell is everywhere / Twelve inch
SV 0127 / Oct '97 / Savoy Jazz

☐ BLUES-ETTE VOL.2 (Fuller, Curtis Quintet)
Love your spell is everywhere / Sis / Bluesette / Is it all a game / Captain Kidd / Five spot after dark / How am I to know / Along came Betty / Autumn in New York / Manhattan serenade
CY 75624 / Oct '97 / Savoy Jazz

☐ BOSS OF THE SOUL STREAM TROMBONE, THE
FSRCD 209 / Oct '96 / Fresh Sound

☐ CURTIS FULLER JAZZTETTE, THE
It's all right with me / Wheatleigh Hall / I'll walk alone / Arabia / Judy's dilemma
SV 0134 / Oct '97 / Savoy Jazz

☐ IMAGES OF CURTIS FULLER
Accident / Darryl's mirror / Be back / Ta-reckla / Judyful / New date
SV 0129 / Oct '97 / Savoy Jazz

☐ IMAGINATION
Kachin / Bang bang / Imagination / Blues de funk / Lido Road
SV 0128 / Oct '97 / Savoy Jazz

☐ NEW TROMBONE
Vonce / Transportation blues / Namely you / What is this thing called love / Blue Lawson / Alicia
OJCCD 77 / Aug '96 / Original Jazz Classics

Fuller, Jesse

☐ FRISCO BOUND
ARHCD 360 / Apr '95 / Arhoolie

☐ FULLER'S FAVOURITES
Red river blues / How long blues / You can't keep a good man down / Key to the highway / Tickling the strings / Midnight special / Stranger blues / Fables aren't nothing but doggone lies / Brown skin gal I got my eyes on you / Cincinnati blues / Hump in your back / Trouble if I don't use my head
OBCCD 528 / Nov '92 / Original Blues Classics

☐ JAZZ, FOLK SONGS, SPIRITUALS & BLUES
Take this hammer / Linin' track / I'm going to meet my lovign mother / Tiger rag / Memphis boogie / Raise a ruckus / By and by / Fingerbuster / Stagolee / 99 years / Hesitation blues
OBCCD 564 / Jan '94 / Original Blues Classics

☐ LONE CAT, THE
Leavin' Memphis, Frisco bound / Take it slow and easy / Monkey and the engineer / New Corrine / Guitar blues / Running wild / Hey hey / In that great land / Way you treat me / Down home waltz / Beat it on down the line / Buck and wing
OBCCD 526 / Nov '92 / Original Blues Classics

☐ RAILROAD WORKSONG
Move on down the line / Stealing / Ninety nine years and one dark day / Animal fair / Sleeping in the midnight cold / Stagolee / Bill Bailey, Won't you please come home / San Francisco Bay blues / Crazy waltz / Railroad worksong / Meet my loving mother / I love my baby / Tune (Creole love call) / Running wild / Stranger blues / Hanging around a skin game / Monkey and the engineer / Buck dancer's jump
LACD 24 / Jan '93 / Lake

☐ SAN FRANCISCO BAY BLUES
San Francisco Bay blues / Jesse's new midnight special / Morning blues / Little black train / Midnight cold / Whoa mule / John Henry / I got a mind to ramble / Crazy about a woman / Where could I go but to the Lord / Stealin' back to my old time used to be / Brown skin gal
OBCCD 537 / Nov '92 / Original Blues Classics

Fuller, Robert

☐ AM FUSS DER BLAUEN BERGE
Riding / Fighting (Am fuss der blauen berge) / Uberall auf der Welt / Schone madchen sind wie blumen / My only friend / Margerita (einmal ist die Reise aus) / Hang my hat out in the prairie / My blue mountains / Adios Mexicana / Baby come home / Beide heissen Jenny / Horse and no saddle / Ein einsamer cowboy
BCD 15963 / May '96 / Bear Family

Fully

☐ NEW BEGINNING, A (Fully/Lady Luck)
IJT 004 / Jun '97 / Idjit

Fulson, Lowell

☐ COMPLETE CHESS MASTERS, THE (2CD Set)
MCD 09394 / 23 Feb '98 / Chess/MCA

☐ HOLD ON
Working man / Shake, rattle and roll / Me and my woman / Ain't that sweet / Quicker the better / It's no need / Real name is danger zone / I'm just a fool about you / Cryin' won't help / Hold on / Love is the bottom line
BBCD 9525 / Jan '93 / Bullseye Blues

☐ I'VE GOT THE BLUES
Teach me / I've got the blues / Every second a fool is born / Searchin' out / Crying won't help you / Last one to know / Sleeper / Man on the run / Don't destroy me / Cheatin' woman / Do you feel it / Lonesome Christmas (parts 1 and 2)
JEWEL 5009CD / Mar '98 / Jewel

☐ IT'S A GOOD DAY
Thanks a lot / It's a good day / Ten more shows / Your love for me is gone / I'm tough / Keep that smile / Slow down baby / Blues and my guitar / One more blues / Push on
ROUCD 2088 / '88 / Rounder

☐ MY FIRST RECORDINGS
Western Union blues / Lazy woman blues / River blues (part 1) / River blues (part 2) / I walked all night / Between midnight and day / Blues is killing me / Did you ever feel lucky / I'm wild about you / Three o'clock blues / Crying blues (street walking woman) / You're gonna miss me / Miss Katy Lee blues / Rambling blues / Fulson blues / San Francisco blues / I want to see my baby / Trouble blues / Don't be so evil / Black widow spider blues / I'm prison bound / My baby left me / Blues with a feeling / Why can't you cry for me / There is a time for everything / Lowell jumps one
ARHCD 443 / Sep '97 / Arhoolie

☐ OL' BLUES SINGER, THE
Do you love me / Step at a time / Name of the game / Walk on / Old blues singer / Monday morning blues / Cloudy day / Just a kiss / Kansas city bound / Something's wrong
IGOCD 2022 / May '95 / Indigo

☐ ONE MORE BLUES
Hot mama (atta ride atta ride) / I can't stand it / Ten more shows to play / Thanks a lot for the offer / Guitar shuffle / One room country shack (a thousand miles from nowhere) / Worried about the blues / Your love for me is gone / Think about it / One more blues / Jump children
BLE 597242 / Dec '90 / Black & Blue

☐ SAN FRANCISCO BLUES
BLC 760176 / Dec '92 / Black Lion

☐ THEM UPDATE BLUES
What's the matter baby / Think about it / Don't lie / My secret love / Sun going down / Get on down (them update blues) / Lonely man / Forty four / Too soon to tell / Not a dime / L and L special
CDBB 9558 / Aug '95 / Bullseye Blues

☐ TRAMP/ SOUL
Tramp / I'm sinking / Get your game up tight / Back door key / Two way wishing / Lonely day / Black nights / Year of 29 / No hard feelings / Hustlers game / Goin' home / Pico / Talkin' woman / Shattered dreams / Sittin' here thinkin' / Little angel / Change your ways / Blues around midnight / Everytime it rains / Just one more time / Ask at any door in town / Too many drivers / My aching back
CDCHD 339 / Nov '93 / Ace

Fun Boy Three

☐ BEST OF FUN BOY THREE, THE
DC 864262 / Mar '96 / Disky

☐ FUN BOY THREE
Sanctuary / Way on down / Lunatics (have taken over the asylum) / Life in general (Lewe in Algemeen) / Faith hope and charity / Funrama 2 / Best of luck mate / T'ain't what you do (it's the way that you do it) / Telephone always rings / I don't believe it / Alone
CDGOLD 1013 / Mar '96 / EMI Gold

☐ REALLY SAYING SOMETHING (The Best Of The Fun Boy Three)
Lunatics (have taken over the asylum) / 'Tain't what you do it's the way that you do it: *Fun Boy Three & Bananarama* / Really saying something: *Fun Boy Three & Bananarama* / Summertime / Summer of '82 / Funrama theme: *Fun Boy Three & Bananarama* / Lunacy legacy / Tunnel of love / Our lips are sealed / Faith, hope and charity / More I see (the less I believe) / Telephone always rings / Alibi / Farmyard connection / Going home / We're having all the fun / Pressure of life (takes weight off the body) / Things we do / Well fancy that
CDCHRM 102 / Feb '97 / Chrysalis

☐ SINGLES, THE (Fun Boy Three/ Colourfield)
VSOPCD 196 / Apr '94 / Connoisseur Collection

☐ WAITING
Murder, she said / More I see (the less I believe) / Going home / We're having all the fun / Farmyard connection / Tunnel of love / Our lips are sealed / Pressure of life / Things we do / Well fancy that
CDGOLD 1048 / Jul '96 / EMI Gold

Fun Factory

☐ ALL THEIR BEST
0042172REG / Jul '97 / Edel

☐ NON STOP
0041062REG / Jul '97 / Edel

Fun Fun

☐ BEST OF FUN FUN, THE
HTCD 107 / 20 Apr '98 / Hot Productions

Fun Horns

☐ LIVE IN SOUTH AMERICA
KR 30060 / Feb '96 / Babel

Fun Lovin' Criminals

☐ 100% COLOMBIAN
Up on the hill / Love unlimited / View belongs to everyone / Korean bodega / Back on the block / 10th street / Sugar / Southside / We are all very worried about you / All for self / All my time is gone / Big night out / Mini bar blues / Fisty nuts
4970562 / 24 Aug '98 / Chrysalis

☐ COME FIND YOURSELF
Fun lovin' criminal / Passive/Aggressive / Grave and the constant / Scooby snacks / Smoke 'em / Bombin' the L / I can't get with that / King of New York / We have all the time in the world / Bear hug / Come find yourself / Crime and punishment / Mathadonia / I can't get with that (smoove) / Coney Island girl
CDCHR 6113 / Jun '97 / Chrysalis

Fun Republic

☐ HAPPY PEOPLE AND MORE REALITY TV
EFA 046212 / Oct '95 / Pork Pie

Fun With Atoms

☐ NORTHERN DISTORTION
BV 162962 / Nov '96 / Black Vinyl

Fun-Da-Mental

☐ EROTIC TERRORISM
Oh Lord / Demonised soul / Godevil / Ja sha'taan / Blood in transit / Repent / Deathening silence / Furious / See I A / Distorted C / One ness / Sliced lead / Tongue gone cold
NATCD 1080 / 23 Mar '98 / Nation

☐ SEIZE THE TIME
Dog tribe / Seize the time / Mera mazab / President propaganda / No more fear / Dollars or sense / Mother india / Mr. bubbleman / English breakfast / Bullet solution / Fartherland / New world order / White gold burger / Back to basix
NATCD 33 / May '94 / Nation

☐ WITH INTENT TO PERVERT THE COURSE OF JUSTICE
NATCD 56 / Jul '95 / Nation

Funbug

☐ SPUNKIER
CDHOLE 006 / Oct '95 / Golf

Funderburgh, Anson

☐ ANSON FUNDEBURGH AND THE ROCKETS (Featuring Sam Myers) (Funderburgh, Anson & The Rockets)
CD 1038 / '88 / Black Top

☐ BLACK TOP BLUES-A-RAMA VOL.1 (Live At Tipitina's) (Funderburgh, Anson & The Rockets)
CD 1044 / '88 / Black Top

☐ HARPOON MAN
APCD 117 / Oct '95 / Appaloosa

☐ LIVE AT THE GRAND
BT 1111CD / Apr '95 / Black Top

☐ LIVE AT THE GRAND EMPORIUM (Funderburgh, Anson & The Rockets)
BT 1111CD / Feb '95 / Black Top

☐ THAT'S WHAT THEY WANT (Funderburgh, Anson & Sam Myers)
Lookin' the world over / Oh-oh / Last time around / Monkey around / That's what they want / Dew is falling / Mudslide / I don't play / I don't want you cutting off your hair / Don't quit the one you love for me / I've been dogged by women / Meanest woman / I'm shakin'
CDBT 1140 / May '97 / Black Top

Funeral Dress

☐ BEST OF FUNERAL DRESS, THE
STEPCD 113 / 23 Mar '98 / Step 1

☐ SONGS 'BOUT SEX, BEER AND PUNK ROCK
WB 1174CD / 18 Aug '97 / We Bite

Funeral Oration

☐ BELIEVER
HR 616CD / Jan '97 / Hopeless

☐ FUNERAL ORATION
HR 606CD / Nov '95 / Hopeless

☐ SURVIVAL
HR634CD / 20 Jul '98 / Hopeless

Fung, Trevor

☐ ESSENTIAL SKOOL HOUSE
DCID 005 / 20 Apr '98 / Dance Club International

Funhouse

☐ GENERATION GENERATOR
Preacher (down in the hole) / Y.r.s. / One funhouse / Self denial / One more time for love / Rocks and roses / Generation generator / Christine in chains
HMAXD 160 / Oct '90 / Heavy Metal

☐ NEVER AGAIN
NACDL 949 / Oct '96 / Resurrection

Funk D'Void

☐ TECHNOIR
Light / Martian love dance / Herbie on rhodes / Fewshun / Bad coffee / Dope lullaby / Angelic upstart / Lucky strike / Soundtrack / Snakebite / V-Ger / Thank you
SOMACD 8 / Jun '97 / Soma

Funk Inc.

☐ ACID INC - THE BEST OF FUNK INC
Chicken lickin' / Sister Jane / Jung bongo / Where are we going / Smokin' at Tiffany's / Kool's back again / Give me your love / Let's make love and stop the war / Better half / Bowlegs
CDBGP 1011 / Oct '91 / Beat Goes Public

☐ FUNK INC./CHICKEN' LICKIN'
Kool is back / Bowlegs / Sister Janie / Thrill is gone / Whipper / Chicken lickin' / Running away / They trying to get me / Better half / Let's make peace and stop the war / Jung bongo
CDBGPD 040 / Sep '92 / Beat Goes Public

☐ HANGIN' OUT/SUPERFUNK
Smokin' at Tiffany's / Give me your love / We can be friends / Dirty red / I can see clearly now / I'll be around / Message from the Meters / Goodbye so long / Hill where the lord hides / Honey, I love you / Just don't mean a thing / I'm gonna love you just a little bit more baby
CDBGPD 058 / Feb '93 / Beat Goes Public

☐ PRICED TO SELL
It's not the spotlight / Priced to sell / God only knows / Where are we going / Gimme some lovin' / Somewhere in my mind / Girl of my dreams
CDBGPM 075 / Jun '93 / Beat Goes Public

☐ URBAN RENEWAL
Ants in yo pants / Urban renewal / Spasms / Sneaky / Thang / Days and nights in St. Ignace / Still called the blues / Get some more / 6th Street stroll / Memphis underground
CDBGPD 104 / Apr '96 / Beat Goes Public

Funkadelic

☐ AMERICA EATS ITS YOUNG
You hit the nail on the head / If you don't like the effects, don't produce the cause / Everybody is going to make it this time / Joyful process / We hurt too / Loose booty / Philmore / I call my baby pussycat / America eats its young / Biological speculation / That was my girl / Balance / Miss Lucifer's love / Wake up
CDSEWD 029 / Jul '90 / Westbound

☐ BEST OF FUNKADELIC 1976-1981, THE
One nation under a groove / Cholly (funk getting ready to roll) / Who says a funk band can't play rock / Coming round the mountain / Smoky / Cosmic slop / Electric spanking of war babies / Funk gets stronger / Uncle Jam / Icka prick / (Not just) knee deep
CDGR 104 / Aug '96 / Charly

☐ ELECTRIC SPANKING OF WAR BABIES
Electric spanking of war babies / Electro-cuties / Funk gets stronger / Brettino's bounce / She loves you / Shockwaves / Oh, I / Icka prick
CDGR 102 / Jun '93 / Charly

☐ FINEST
I'll bet you / I got a thing, you got a thing, everybody got a thing / Funky dollar bill / I wanna know if it's good to you / Hit it and quit it / You and your folks, me and my folks / Joyful process / Loose booty / You can't miss what you can't measure / Cosmic slop / Red hot Mama / Standing on the verge of getting it on / Let's take it to the stage / Get off your ass and jam / Undisco kidd / Maggot brain / Maggot brain / Maggot brain
CDSEWD 115 / Jul '97 / Westbound

☐ FUNKADELIC LIVE
Funkentelechy / Cosmic slop / Maggot brain / Bop gun / Funk gettin' ready to roll / It ain't legal / Flashlight / Mothership connection / Give up the funk / Let's take it to the stage / Do that stuff / Undisco kidd / Children of production / Atomic dog / Maceo, not Charlie / Red hot Mama / Into you / Standing on the verge of getting it on / One nation under a groove / Coming round the mountain / Won't you dance / Quickie / Aquaboogie / I wanna know if it's good to you / Up for the down stroke / Hit it and quit it / Gamin' on ya / Put your hands together / Dog you out / P-funk / You do me / Nickel bag o'solos / Dope dog / I call my baby pussycat / Lampin / Microphone fiend underground angel / Yank my doodle sum'else / I got a thing, you got a thing, everybody got a thing / All your goodies are gone / Lifted
NEFCD 273 / Oct '94 / Sequel

☐ FUNKADELIC LIVE (Live At Meadowbrook, Rochester, Michigan 12/9/71)
Alice in my fantasies / Maggot brain / I call my baby pussycat / I call my baby pussycat / Good old music / I got a thing, you got a thing, everybody got a thing / All your goodies are gone (The loser's seat) / I'll bet you / You and your folks, me and my folks / Free your mind and your ass will follow
CDSEWD 108 / Apr '96 / Westbound

☐ FUNKADELIC PICTURE DISC BOX SET
WBOXPD 1 / Aug '90 / Westbound

☐ FUNKADELIC PICTURE DISC BOX SET VOL.2
WBOXPD 5 / Feb '94 / Westbound

☐ HARDCORE FUNK JAM
Uncle jam (full length album version) / Oh, I / Groovallegiance / You scared the lovin' outta me / Funk gets stronger (killer millimetre longer version) - she I / Freak of the week / Into you / Electro-cuties / If you got funk / You got style / One nation under a groove
CPCD 8064 / Nov '94 / Charly

☐ MUSIC FOR YOUR MOTHER (Funkadelic 45's - 2CD Set)
Music for my mother / Music for my mother (instrumental) / Can't shake it loose / As good as I can feel / I'll bet you / Qualify and satisfy / Open our eyes / I got a thing, you got a thing, everybody got a thing / Fish, chips and sweat / I wanna know if it's good to you / You and your folks, me and my folks / Funky dollar bill / Can you get to that / Back in our minds / I miss my baby / Baby I owe you something good / Hit it and quit it / Whole lot of BS / Loose booty / Joyful process / Cosmic slop / If you don't like the effects, don't produce the cause / Standing on the verge of getting it on / Jimmy's got a little bit of bitch in him / Red hot Mama / Vital juices / Better by the pound / Stuffs and things / Let's take it to the stage / How do yeaw view you
CDSEW 2055 / Oct '92 / Westbound

☐ ONE NATION UNDER A GROOVE
One nation under a groove / Groovallegiance / Who says a funk band can't play rock / Promentalshitbackwashipsychosisenema squad / Into you / Cholly (funk getting ready to roll) / Lunchmeataphobia / PE squad / Doodoo chasers / Maggot brain
CDGR 100 / Jul '93 / Charly

☐ ULTIMATE FUNKADELIC
One nation under a groove / Who says a funk band can't play rock / Comin' round the mountain / Smokey / Promentalshitbackwashpsychosis enema squad / If you got funk you got style / Icka prick / Cholly (funk getting ready to roll) / (Not just) knee deep / Freak of the week / You scared the lovin' outa me
MCCD 307 / 8 Sep '97 / Music Club

☐ UNCLE JAM WANTS YOU
Freak of the week / (Not just) knee deep / Uncle Jam / Field manoeuvers / Holly wants to go to California / Foot soldiers
CDGR 103 / Jun '93 / Charly

☐ VERY BEST OF FUNKADELIC, THE (2CD Set)
CPCD 83062 / 16 Mar '98 / Charly

Funkdoobiest

☐ BROTHERS DOOBIE
This it it (interlude) / Rock on / What the deal / Lost in thought / Dedicated / Ka sera sera / Pussy ain't shit / XXX Funk / It ain't going down / You're dummin' / Tomahawk bang / Super hoes / Who ra ra
4783812 / Jul '95 / Epic

Funker Vogt

☐ TAKE CARE
ZOT 192CD / 29 Sep '97 / Zoth Ommog

Funki Porcini

☐ HED PHONE SEX
Word of vice / B Monkey / Dubble / King ashababapal part 1 / Deep / King Ashabanapal part 2 / Michael's little friend / White slave / Poseathon / Wicked, cruel, nasty and bad / Pork alumen / Softest thing in the world (motorway accident) / Tiny kangeroo dolphin / Long road / Mushroom head / Pork kiss head
ZENCD 017 / May '95 / Ninja Tune

☐ LOVE, PUSSYCATS & CAR WRECKS
Purrfect / Groover / Last song / Snip and lick / Car wreck / Afterlife / 12 points off your licence / Venus / Hyde Park / Theme music for nothing / I'm such a small thing / Going down
ZENCD 023 / Jun '96 / Ninja Tune

Funkmaster Flex

☐ 60 MINS OF FUNK VOL.1
7863674722 / Feb '97 / RCA

☐ MIX TAPE VOL.1 - 60 MINUTES OF FUNK
07863668052 / Nov '95 / RCA

Funkturm

☐ URBAN MANTRAS
ADOR 409 / 16 Feb '98 / Law & Auder

Funky Aztecs

☐ DAY OF THE DEAD
50502 / Apr '97 / Raging Bull

Funky Company

☐ EVERYTIME
FARCD 414 / 20 Apr '98 / Family Affair

☐ TENDENCY OF LOVE
FARCD 402 / Jul '96 / Family Affair

Funky DL

☐ CLASSIC WAS THE DAY
32 bar summary / I've lost my microphone / Underground hip hop / 20-20-8-8 / On ya own / Pink panther / Confidental information / Worldwide / Soul sihouette / Classic moves / Queen of diamonds / Off key / Make decisions / Circles (going round) / Eye remember / If I had a day to live / It's about time
UTMCD 01 / 26 Aug '97 / Utmost

Funky Green Dogs

☐ GET FIRED UP
Way / Firedup / Noticiasuno / Somekindoflove / Untiltheday / Noticiasdos / Sogood / Why / Pigsty / Noticiastres / Icametostomp / Ride / Nightofthefunkygreendogsfromouterspace
TWCD 90001 / Apr '97 / Twisted UK

Funky Monkey

☐ COME TOGETHER PEOPLE OF FUNK
FINK 4CD / 15 Sep '97 / Funky Inc.

Funky New Orleans Jazz Band

☐ FUNKY NEW ORLEANS JAZZ BAND
MMRCCD 5 / Feb '94 / Merry Makers

Funny Farm

☐ AMPUTATE
PRO 026 / May '97 / Progress

☐ BITING THE HAND
33842 / Feb '97 / Progress

Funny Hill

☐ COWBOY BOOTS
BRAM 1989062 / Nov '93 / Brambus

☐ LIVE IN NASHVILLE
BRAM 1990152 / Nov '93 / Brambus

Furbowl

☐ AUTUMN YEARS
BMCD 47 / Mar '94 / Black Mark

Furey, Finbar

☐ BEST OF FINBAR & EDDIE FUREY, THE (Furey, Finbar & Eddie)
Rakish Paddy / Curragh of Kildare / Lonesome boatman / Bogy's bonny belle / Blackbird / Her Father didn't like me anyway / Drops of brandy / Planxty Davy / Eamonn an chnuic / Farewell to Tarwathy / Eddie's fancy / My Lagan love / Fox chase / Prickly bush / Coppers and brass / Reynardine / Bonny bunch of roses / Sliabh na mban / This town is not your own / Dawning of the day
MCCD 293 / Jun '97 / Music Club

☐ DAWNING OF THE DAY
BGOCD 291 / Oct '95 / Beat Goes On

☐ FINBAR & EDDIE FUREY/THE LONESOME BOATMAN (Furey, Finbar & Eddie)
Spanish cloak / Come by the hills / Sliabh na mban / Dainty Davy / Tattered Jack Welch / Flowers in the valley / Pigeon on the gate / Graham's flat / Leezy Lindsay / Piper in the meadow straying / Curragh of Kildaire / Eamonn an Chnuic / This town is your own / Rocking the baby / Bill Hart's favourite / Dance around the spinning wheel / Let me go to the mountains / McShane / Colonel Fraser / Lonesome boatman / Carron Lough bay / Prickly bush / Bogy's bonny belle / Fox chase
ESMCD 524 / Apr '97 / Essential

☐ TRADITIONAL IRISH PIPE MUSIC
Rakish Paddy / Hag with the money / Castle terrace / Madam Bonaparte / Young girl milking the cow / Fin's favourite / Peter Byrnes fancy / O'Rouke's reel / Roy's hands / Planxty Davy / Bonny bunch of roses / Eddie's fancy / Silver spear / Spanish cloak / Sliabh na mban (mountain of the women) / Piper in the meadow straying (set dance) / Rocking the baby (jig)
HILLCD 13 / Feb '97 / Wooded Hill

☐ WIND AND THE RAIN, THE
Aran girl / Ocean / Anac cuan / Gypsy goboy / You enter my soul / My song of emigration / Roy's tribute / Journey's of love / Wind and the rain / Amandan / Travelling lady / Takes two / Garrickfergus / Mrs. A
ECD 3371 / Jun '97 / K-Tel

Fureys

☐ BEST OF THE FUREYS
Spanish cloak / Dainty Davie / Castle Terrace / Roy's hands / Dance around the spinning wheel / Let me go to the mountains / McShane / Colonel Fraser / Carron Lough Bay / Prickly bush / Fox chase / Bill Hart's favourite / Silver spear / Tattered Jack Welch / Pigeon on the gate / Fin's favourite / Peter Byrne's fancy / Bonny bunch of roses / Eddie's fancy / O'Rourke's reel
TRTCD 137 / Dec '94 / TrueTrax

☐ BEST OF THE FUREYS AND DAVEY ARTHUR (Fureys & Davey Arthur)
When you were sweet sixteen / Maggie / Morning has broken / Twelfth of never / Annie's song / I'll take you home again Kathleen / Love is pleasin' / Beautiful dreamer / Bonnie Mary of Argyle / Just a song at twilight / Bless this house / I'll be your sweetheart / Last rose of summer / If I had my life to live over / Wait till the clouds roll by / Scarlet ribbons / Perfect day / When I grow too old to dream / Come by the hills / Anniversary waltz
MCCD 010 / Feb '91 / Music Club

☐ CLADDAGH ROAD
Sound of thunder / Donegal / Mary Skeffington / Liffey walls / Roy's tribute / Living on the edge of your town / America cried / 6000 lonely miles / I remember Mary / Amadan / Cross me heart / Mo Chuileann
CDDPR 132 / Jan '95 / Premier/MFP

☐ COLLECTION, THE (Fureys & Davey Arthur)
Paddy in Paris / Reason I left Mullingar / Mountains of Mourne / Irish eyes / Who do you think you are / Lovers / Ted Furey's selection / Evening falls / Night Ferry / Portland town / Ned of the hill / October song / Leaving Nancy / Garrett Barry's jig / Sitting alone / Big ships / From where I stand / Morning cloud/New copperplate / Dreaming my dreams / Lament / I'll be there / First leaves of Autumn
CCSCD 231 / Oct '89 / Castle

☐ FINEST (Fureys & Davey Arthur)
When you were sweet sixteen / Dublin / When I leave behind Neidin / Green fields of France / Lonesome boatman / I will love you ev'ry time / Stealaway / Red rose cafe / Maggie
CLACD 319 / '92 / Castle

☐ FOUR GREEN FIELDS (Furey, Finbar & Eddie)
TUT 72166 / Jan '94 / Wundertute

☐ FUREYS & DAVEY ARTHUR,THE (Fureys & Davey Arthur)
When you were sweet sixteen / Alchoholidays / Steals away / Poem to the lonesome boatman / Lonesome boatman / Silver threads among the gold / Green fields of France / Siege of a nation / I will love you every time / Gallipoli / Old man / She came to me
EMPRCD 518 / Jul '94 / Emporio

☐ FUREYS, THE (The Ultimate Irish Love Songs Experience)
When you were sweet sixteen / Leezy Lindsay / Grand affair / Steal away / I will love you / My love is like a red red rose / Lonesome boatman / I'll take you home again Kathleen / Red Rose Cafe / Maggie / Yesterday's people / Old man / Old Joe / Siege of a nation / Anniversary waltz / Green fields of France
KCD 425 / Jan '97 / Celtic Collections

☐ MAY WE ALL MEET AGAIN
CDC 008 / Feb '97 / Ceol

☐ SPANISH CLOAK, THE
PLSCD 106 / Apr '96 / Pulse

☐ TOMORROW WE PART (Fureys & Bob Stewart)
CMBCD 001 / Apr '98 / CMB

☐ WHEN YOU WERE SWEET SIXTEEN (Fureys & Davey Arthur)
Green fields of France / When you were sweet sixteen / My love is like a red red rose / Anniversary song / I will love you ev'ry time / Yesterdays people / Lonesome boatman / Old man / Oh Babushka / Belfast mill / Siege of a nation / Yesterdays men
CLACD 171 / Feb '90 / Castle

☐ WINDS OF CHANGE
Oro oro / It's good to see you / Sweet and gentle love / Old george / Didn't it rain / North by north / Mary and me / Campfire in the dark / Travelling lady / If I don't bring you flowers / Cry of the celts / Man of our times / Noraleen / Song for the fox / Goodbye booze
RZLCD0069 / Oct '92 / Ritz

Furholt, Ragnhild

☐ SEGNER SYNG
H 7128CD / Aug '97 / Heilo

Furic, Stephane

☐ STEPHANE FURIC
1212152 / May '91 / Soul Note

Furioso

☐ FURIOSO
Labyrinth / Get out / Don't you wanna rock / Furioso / Evil lady (satin's call) / Pacific highway / Magic tokyo girl / Ten screaming guitars / Just keep holding on / Poussiere d'etoiles / Turn off your radio / Sex on the telephone line / Dark waltz
CDGRUB 24 / Sep '92 / Food For Thought

Furious IV

☐ WHAT'S BECOME OF THE BABY
HB8 002 / 11 Aug '97 / Hairball 8

Furnaceface

☐ UNSAFE AT ANYSPEED
FURCD 1 / Dec '96 / Cargo

Furniture

☐ FURNITURE SCRAPBOOK, THE
Brilliant mind / Make believe I'm him / Forever / Song for a doberman / Dancing the hard bargain / Love your shoes / Robert nightman's story / Slow motion kisses / I miss you / How I've come to hate the moon / Bullet / Turnupspeed / One step behind you / She gets out the scrapbook
SURCD 013 / Sep '91 / Survival

Furtado, Tony

☐ FULL CIRCLE
ROUCD 0323 / Oct '94 / Rounder

☐ ROLL MY BLUES AWAY
Waterslide / Ghost of Blind Willie Johnson / Stark raven / Can you hear the rain / Willow tree / Knave's bane / Song for Early / Boat's up the river / Bolinas / Mudville / Sundin / Crow Canyon
ROUCD 0343 / Feb '97 / Rounder

☐ WITHIN REACH
Ralph Trischka / St. John's fire / I will / Waiting for Guiteau/President Garfield's Hornpipe / Queen Anne's lace / Sao Miguel / Julia Dealaney/The Drunken landlady / Drake's bay / Magpie on the gallows / Duskus
ROUCD 0290 / '92 / Rounder

Further

☐ 5 FURTHER JOURNEYS
FUR 100CD / Sep '94 / Abstract

☐ SUPER GRIP TAPE
SHED 003CD / Aug '93 / Ball Product

Furudate, Tetsuo

☐ AUTREMENT QU'ETRE
DSA 54040 / Dec '95 / Les Disques Du Soleil

Fury 66

☐ FOR LACK OF A BETTER WORD
SESCD 1 / 26 May '98 / Sessions

Fury, Billy

☐ ALL THE BEST
I will / Like I've never been gone / Last night was made for love / I'm lost without you / When will you say I love you / Run to my lovin' arms / It's only make believe / Maybe tomorrow / In thoughts of you / Give me your word / That's love / Once upon a dream / Colette / Wonderous place / Thousand stars / I'll never find another you / Fools errand (Do you really love me) / Jealousy / Someone else's girl / Halfway to paradise
ECD 3041 / Jan '95 / K-Tel

☐ AM I BLUE
Wondrous place / That's enough / Tell me how you feel / Am I blue / What am I living for / Baby, what you want me to do / This diamond ring / Away from you / Give me your word / I'll never quite get over you / Didn't see the real thing come along / Letter full of tears / Last night was made for love / I'm hurting all over / Somebody else's girl / I will / Don't jump / Don't walk away / (Here I am) Broken hearted / I'm lost without you
8289022 / Jul '93 / London

☐ BILLY FURY HIT PARADE, THE
Maybe tomorrow / Colette / That's love / Thousand stars / Halfway to paradise / Jealousy / I'd never find another you / Last night was made for love / Once upon a dream / Because of love / Like I've never been gone / When will you say I love you / In summer / Somebody else's girl / Do you really love me too / I will / It's only make believe / Lost without you / In thoughts of you / Run to my lovin' arms
8205032 / Jan '87 / London

☐ HALFWAY TO PARADISE (The Greatest Hits)
Colette / That's love / Thousand stars / Fools errand (do you really love me) / I'd never find another you / I will / Like I've never been gone / I'm lost without you / Jealousy / Halfway to paradise / Last night was made for love / When will you say I love you / It's only make believe / In thoughts of you / Once upon a dream / Maybe tomorrow
PLATCD 49 / Feb '97 / Platinum

☐ HALFWAY TO PARADISE (The Very Best Of Billy Fury)
Halfway to Paradise / In thoughts of you / Colette / Give me your word / Jealousy / Once upon a dream / Fool's errand / I'll never find another you / Wondrous place / Like I've never been gone / Last night was made for love / Maybe tomorrow / That's love / Somebody else's girl / Thousand stars / It's only make believe / When will you say I love you / Run to my loving arms
309172 / 13 Jul '98 / Hallmark

☐ ONE AND ONLY, THE
Be mine tonight / No trespassers / Love or money / Love sweet love / Let me go lover / Devil or angel / Don't tell me lies / Deborah / This little girl of mine / I'm telling you / Someday
5298612 / Mar '96 / Polydor

☐ ONE AND ONLY, THE
PLSCD 279 / 1 Jun '98 / Pulse

☐ PARADISE
Halfway to paradise / It's only make believe / Last night was made for love / I will / Wonderous place / Don't worry / We were meant for each other / Our day will come / I'll never fall in love again / Forget him / Love or money / Begin the beguine / Be mine tonight / Don't leave me this way
5500112 / May '93 / Spectrum

☐ ROUGH DIAMONDS AND PURE GEMS
Sticks 'n' stones / Things are changing / Loving you / I'll go along with it / Suzanne in the mirror / Phone box / Any morning now / Lady / Certain things / All the way to the USA / Well alright / Baby get yourself together / Driving nicely / Your words / Maybe baby / Sheila / Lazy life / I'm gonna love you too / In my room / I love you / Lyanna / Going back to Germany / Come outside and play / Easy living / Day by day / Dreaming of St. Louis
CDMF 072 / Apr '91 / Magnum Force

☐ VERY BEST OF BILLY FURY
SOW 709 / Jul '93 / Sound Waves

☐ VERY BEST OF BILLY FURY, THE
I will / Like I've never been gone / Last night was made for love / I'm lost without you / When will you say I love you / Run to my loving arms / It's only make believe / Maybe tomorrow / In thoughts of you / Give me your word / That's love / Once upon a dream / Colette / Wonderous place / Thousand stars / I'd never find another you / Fools errand / Jealousy / Somebody else's girl / Halfway to paradise
SUMCD 4144 / Sep '97 / Summit

☐ WE WANT BILLY/BILLY
Sweet little sixteen / Wedding bells / I'm movin' on / I'd never find another you / Like I've never been gone / How many nights, how many days / She cried / Our day will come / One kiss / Baby come on / Sticks and stones / Just because / Once upon a dream / When will you say I love you / Willow weep for me / Let me know / Million miles from nowhere / All my hopes /

Hard times / That's alright / Unchain my heart / Halfway to paradise / Last night was made for love / We were meant for each other / Bumble bee / Chapel on the hill / I'll show you / One step from heaven / (Here I am) Broken hearted
BGOCD 258 / Feb '95 / Beat Goes On

Fury In The Slaughterhouse

☐ NOWHERE...FAST
SPV 08529072 / 1 Jun '98 / SPV

Fury Of Five

☐ AT WAR WITH THE WORLD
CM 77159CD / 2 Feb '98 / Century Media

☐ NO REASON TO SMILE
GAIN 007CD / Dec '96 / Gain Ground

Fury Things

☐ BIG SATURDAY ILLUSION, THE
TR 43CD / Apr '96 / Trance

☐ FREQUENT LUNACY
TR 64CD / 13 Oct '97 / Trance Syndicate

FU's

☐ ORIGIN OF, THE
LF 020CD / Apr '92 / Lost & Found

☐ REVENGE
LF 037CD / Jun '92 / Lost & Found

Fuse

☐ DIMENSION INTRUSION
WARPCD 12 / May '93 / Warp

Fushitsusha

☐ FUSHITSUSHA VOL.1 (2CD Set)
PSFD 34 / 16 Mar '98 / PSF

☐ GOLD BLOOD
CHCD 30 / Jun '98 / Charnel House

Fusion

☐ BEST OF BRITISH, THE (2CD Set)
FUSCD 002 / Nov '96 / Future Vinyl

Fusion Orchestra

☐ SKELETON IN ARMOUR
SRMC 6003 / 5 Jan '98 / Siwan

Fusioon

☐ FUSIOON VOL.1
32516 / Dec '97 / Divusca

☐ FUSIOON VOL.2
32517 / 16 Mar '98 / Divusca

Futique

☐ PAGING MR. SO AND SO
SDW 0312 / 17 Nov '97 / Shadow

Futterman, Joel

☐ NICKELSDORF KONFRONTATION
(Futterman, Joel & Kidd Jordan Quintet)
SHCD 143 / Oct '97 / Silkheart

Future

☐ 1998
RRCD 1998 / May '90 / Receiver

Future 3

☐ STAY WITH...
APR 020CD / 20 Apr '98 / April

☐ WE ARE THE FUTURE
APR 010CD / Aug '96 / April

Future Bible Heroes

☐ MEMORIES OF LOVE
Lonely days / She devil of the deep / Hopeless / Death opened a boutique / You pretend to be the moon / Blonde adonis / But you're so beautiful / A you you never knew / Real summer / Memories of love / You steal the scene
SETCD 056 / 20 Apr '98 / Setanta

Future Breeze

☐ CLUB MIX VOL.1
FRIE 0062 / 6 Jul '98 / Friends

Future Funk

☐ EARLY YEARS
PLACUKCD 0052 / 30 Mar '98 / Plastic City UK

☐ FUTURE FUNK
DAN 487243 / Jun '97 / Dance Pool

Future Loop Foundation

☐ TIME AND BASS
BARKCD 020 / Jul '96 / Planet Dog

Future Sound Of London

☐ ACCELERATOR
Expander / Stolen documents / While others cry / Calcium / It's not my problem / Papua New Guinea / One in eight / Pulse state / Central industrail
CLP 97072 / Nov '97 / Cleopatra

☐ DEAD CITIES
Herd killing / Dead cities / Her face forms in summertime / We have explosive / Everyone in the world is doing something without me / My kingdom / Max / Antique toy / Quagmire / In a state of permanent abyss / Glass / Yage / Vit drowning / Through your gills I breathe / First death in the family
CDV 2814

☐ ISDN
Just a fuckin' idiot / Far out son of lung and the ramblings of a madman / Appendage / Slider / Smokin' Japanese babe / You're creeping me out / Eyes pop - skin explodes - everybody dead / It's my mind that works / Dirty shadows / Tired / Egypt / Are they fighting us / Kai / Amoeba / Study of six guitars / Snake hips
CDV 2755 / Dec '94 / Virgin
CDVX 2755 / Jun '95 / Virgin
ASW 6144 / 20 Apr '98 / Astralwerks

☐ LIFEFORMS
Cascade / III flower / Flak / Bird wings / Dead skin cells / Lifeforms / Eggshell / Among myselves / Domain / Spineless jelly / Interstat / Vertical pig / Cerebral / Life Form Ends / Vit / Omnipresence / Room 208 / Elaborate burn / Little brother
CDV 2722 / May '94 / Virgin

Futuresound

☐ BEST OF FUTURESOUND, THE
CAT 025CD / Jan '96 / Rephlex

Fuxa

☐ 3 FIELD ROTATION
IRE 1012 / Sep '96 / I

☐ ACCRETION
MEO 24 / 18 May '98 / Mind Expansion

☐ VERY WELL ORGANISED
IRE 1062 / Mar '97 / Che

Fuzzbird

☐ WELCOME TO SANTA'S SEX SHOP
MKCD 06 / Apr '97 / Mook

Fuzztones

☐ FLASHBACKS
1-2-5 / Nine month later / Heathen set / I never knew / 81 / Strychnine / In heat / All the kings horses / Rise / Down on the street / Look for the question mark / She's my witch / Blue's theme / Blood from a stone / Hurt on hold / Romilar D / I'm the wolfman / She's wicked / Cinderella
SC 11045 / 17 Nov '97 / Sundazed

☐ LYSERGIC EMANATIONS
1-2-5 / Gotta get some / Ward 81 / Radar eyes / Cinderella / Highway 69 / Just once / Living sickness / She's wicked
MMCD 036 / 10 Nov '97 / Music Maniac

Fuzzy Mountain String Band

☐ FUZZY MOUNTAIN STRING BAND
ROUCD 11571 / Jul '95 / Rounder

FX Randomiz

☐ GOFLEX
A9 / 15 Oct '97 / A Musik

Fyffe, Will

☐ WILL FYFFE (Legendary Scottish Singer Performs His Best Songs)
It isn't the hen that cackles the most / Sketch of a man from Aberdeen / Wedding of Mary Maclean / I'm the landlord at the inn at Aberfoyle / He's been on the bottle since a baby / She was the belle of the ball / Railway guard / Train that's taking you home / Twelve and a tanner a bottle / Will Fyffe's war-time sketch: Clyde built / I belong to Glasgow / I'm 94 today
LCOM 5234 / May '94 / Lismor

Fygi, Laura

☐ BEWITCHED
Dream a little dream / It's crazy / Good morning heartache / Let there be love / I only have eyes for you / Bewitched / End of a love affair / Love you for sentimental reasons / Just one of those things / Girl talk / I wish you love / Willow weep for me
5147242 / Sep '94 / Verve

☐ INTRODUCING/BEWITCHED (2CD Set)
5329792 / Jan '97 / Verve

☐ LADY WANTS, THE
5189242 / Nov '94 / PolyGram Jazz

☐ WATCH WHAT HAPPENS WHEN
(Laura Fygi Meets Michel Legrand)
5345982 / May '97 / Mercury

G

G&K Ceili Band

☐ SONGS JIGS AND REELS
PLSCD 168 / Apr '97 / Pulse

G-Anx

☐ FLASHBACKS
POLLUTE 13 / 22 May '98 / Sound Pollution

G-Flame & Mr. G

☐ WHO KNOWS G
Songs of the underground / Do it right / Oooohh / Fenness / No sell out / Make me high / Who knows / Deep lovin' / Polly / Lizard / Take a chance / Thoughts / Just another B-line / D bunk
74321583002 / 15 Jun '98 / Metalbox

G-Force

☐ ELECTRONIC LESSON VOL.2
KKT 003CD / 27 Mar '98 / KK

G-Love & Special Sauce

☐ COAST TO COAST MOTEL
Sweet sugar Mama / Leaving the city / Nancy / Kiss and tell / Chains no.3 / Sometimes / Everybody / Soda pop / Bye bye baby / Tomorrow night / Small fish / Coming home
4809792 / Jan '96 / Okeh/Epic

☐ G-LOVE & SPECIAL SAUCE
Things I used to do / Blues music / Garbage man / Eyes have miles / Baby's got sauce / Rhyme for the summertime / Cold beverage / Fatman / This ain't living / Walk to slide / Shooting hoops / Some peoples like that / Town to town / I love you
4766322 / Jul '94 / Okeh/Epic

☐ YEAH IT'S THAT EASY
Stepping stones / 1-76 / Lay down the law / Slipped away / You shall see / Take you there / Willow tree / Yeah it's that easy / Recipe / 200 Years / Making amends / Pull the wool / When we meet again
4869072 / 3 Nov '97 / Okeh/Epic

G-Squad

☐ G-SQUAD
YUMECD 001 / Oct '96 / MC Projects

Gaar, Burton

☐ ONE HUNDRED POUNDS OF TROUBLE
One hundred pounds of trouble / Real good woman / No / I won't cry / It's still raining / Bim bam thank you Mam / Step out lady / Tear it up / Short red dress / Face down on the bottom / Because of you / I be gone / Where the girl is
CCD 11053 / Jun '97 / Crosscut

Gaard Quintet

☐ GAARD QUINTET
MECCACD 1036 / Nov '94 / Music Mecca

Gaberlunzie

☐ FOR AULD LANG SYNE
CDLDL 1224 / Oct '95 / Lochshore

☐ HIGHLAND LINES
Rob rhuadh / First orra loon / Maccrimmon / Kelty clippie / Girl behind the bar / Liverpool hornpipe / Bonnie earl o' moray / Arthur mcbride / Ullapool ullapool / Raglan road / Tae the beggin' / Voice of my island
CDLOC 1056 / Jul '90 / Lochshore

☐ TWA CORBIES
Twa corbies / Loch Tay boat song / Flower in the snow / Born beyond the border / Slow goin' easy / MacPherson's rant / Wallace / Old Balgedie road / Margaret's waltz medley / Jute mill song / Lonely in the bothy
CDLDL 1260 / May '97 / Lochshore

Gabin, Jean

☐ JEAN GABIN ANTHOLOGY
EN 525 / Sep '96 / Encyclopaedia

☐ LA COMPILATION
Maintenant je sais / Quande on s'promene au bord de l'eau / Qu'est -ce que tu dis d'ca / Avec ma petite gueule / Leo, lea, elie / C'est chouette d'etre un monsieur / Quand on a ca / Ingenuement, naivement / Je ne dis pas non / Viens fifine / C'est moi le marl / La mome caoutchouc / Chanson de mariniers / C'est un petit rien / On m'suit
UCD 19033 / Jun '95 / Forlane

Gable, Tony

☐ SEVEN HILLS
INAK 3031 / Oct '96 / In Akustik

☐ TONY GABLE & 206
Slip / Tailwind / Island lady / Bus song / Camano island / Pockets / Lake Union / Homeport / Futon fun
101S 71462 / Nov '93 / 101 South

Gabrels, Reeves

☐ SECRET SQUALL OF NOW, THE
UPSTART 020 / Sep '95 / Upstart

Gabriel, John

☐ FROM JOHN WITH LOVE
I remember you / Quando quando quando (tell me when) / Long before I knew you / Love walked in / It was a very good year / Because of you / I hadn't anyone till you / Good morning heartache / Day by day / Now that I have everything / Room without windows / East river drive / Long ago and far away / It could happen to you / Painted mem'ries / I see your face before me / Doomed, damned and delighted / Time after time
HCD 1601 / 24 Aug '98 / DRG

Gabriel, Peter

☐ PETER GABRIEL VOL.1
Moribund the burgermeister / Solsbury Hill / Modern love / Excuse me / Humdrum / Slowburn / Waiting for the big one / Down the dolce vita / Here comes the flood
PGCD 1 / May '87 / Charisma

☐ PETER GABRIEL VOL.1-3 (Compact Collection/3CD Set)
On the air / DIY / Mother of violence / Wonderful day in a one way world / White shadow / Indigo / Animal magic / Exposure / Flotsam and jetsam / Perspective / Home sweet home (instrumental) / Intruder / No self control / I don't remember / Family snapshot / And through the wire / Games without frontiers / Not one of us / Lead a normal life / Biko / Moribund the burgermeister / Solsbury hill / Modern love / Excuse me / Humdrum / Slow burn / Waiting for the big one / Down the dolce vita / Here comes the flood
TPAK 9 / Oct '90 / Charisma

☐ PETER GABRIEL VOL.2
On the air / DIY / Mother of violence / Wonderful day in a one way world / White shadow / Indigo / Animal magic / Exposure / Flotsam and jetsam / Perspective / Home sweet home
PGCD 2 / May '87 / Charisma

☐ PETER GABRIEL VOL.3
Intruder / No self control / I don't remember / Family snapshot / And through the wire / Games without frontiers / Not one of us / Lead a normal life / Biko
PGCD 3 / May '87 / Charisma

☐ PETER GABRIEL VOL.3/DEUSTCHES ALBUM
Eindringling / Keine selbstkontrolle / Frag mich nicht immer / Schnappshub (ein familienfoto) / Und durch den draht / Spiel ohne grenzen / Du bist nicht wie wir / Ein normales leben / Biko
XCDSD 4019 / '88 / Charisma

☐ PETER GABRIEL VOL.4
Rhythm of the heat / San Jacinto / I have the touch / Family and the fishing net / Shock the monkey / Lay your hands on me / Wallflower / Kiss of life
PGCD 4 / '86 / Charisma

☐ PETER GABRIEL VOL.4 (German)
Der rythmus der hitze / Das fischernetz / Kontakt / San Jacinto / Schock den affen / Handauflegen / Nicht die erde hat dich verschluckt / Mundzumundeatmung
XPGCD 4 / Apr '88 / Charisma

☐ PLAYS LIVE (2CD Set)
San Jacinto / Solsbury Hill / No self control / Shock the monkey / I don't remember / Humdrum / On the air / Biko / Rhythm of the heat / I have the touch / Not one of us / Family snapshot / DIY / Family and the fishing net / I go swimming
CDPGD 100 / '88 / Charisma

☐ SECRET WORLD LIVE (2CD Set)
Come talk to me / Steam / Across the river / Slow marimbas / Shaking the tree / Red rain / Blood of Eden / Kiss that frog / Washing of the water / Solsbury Hill / Digging in the dirt / Sledgehammer / Secret world / Don't give up / In your eyes
PGDCD 8 / Aug '94 / Charisma

☐ SHAKING THE TREE
Solsbury Hill / I don't remember / Sledgehammer / Family snapshot / Mercy Street / Shaking the tree / Don't give up: *Gabriel, Peter & Kate Bush* / Here comes the flood / Games without frontiers / Shock the monkey / Big time / Biko / San Jacinto / Zaar / Red rain / I have the touch
PGTVD 6 / Nov '90 / Charisma

☐ SO
Red rain / Sledgehammer / Don't give up / That voice again / In your eyes / Mercy street / Big time / We do what we're told (Milgram's 37) / This is the picture (excellent birds)
PGCD 5 / '86 / Charisma

☐ US
Come talk to me / Love to be loved / Blood of Eden / Steam / Only us / Washing of the water / Digging in the dirt / Fourteen black paintings / Kiss that frog / Secret world
PGCD 7 / Sep '92 / Charisma

Gabriela

☐ DETRAS DEL SOL
Verano en la pampa / Sueno transparente / Noches de Tilcara / Tren de la medianoche/Rambler / Luz del mundo / Estos son mis dias / Estrella austral / Cuando me vaya / Hermana Maria / Duerme
INT 35062 / Aug '97 / Intuition

Gabrielle

☐ FIND YOUR WAY
Going nowhere / Who could love you / Find your way / I wanna know / Dreams / I wish / We don't talk / Second chance / Say what you gotta say / Because of you / Inside your head
8284412 / Oct '93 / Go Beat

☐ GABRIELLE
Forget about the world / People may come / I live in hope / Baby I've changed / Give me a little more time / If you really cared / There she goes / Our love is over / If I could / Alone / Have you ever wondered / So glad / Miracle / If you ever: *Gabrielle & East 17* / Walk on by / Forget about the world
8288582 / Nov '96 / Go Beat

Gad, Pablo

☐ BEST OF PABLO GAD, THE
ROTCD 001 / 20 Apr '98 / Reggae On Top

☐ EPISTLES OF DUB VOL.1 (Gad, Pablo & Conscious Sounds)
ROTCD 002 / Nov '94 / Reggae On Top

☐ LIFE WITHOUT DEATH
ROTCD 005 / Jul '95 / Reggae On Top

Gadd, Eric

☐ DO YOU BELIEVE IN GADD
4509967772 / Oct '94 / East West

Gade, Jacob

☐ TANGO JALOUSIE
MECCACD 1005 / Nov '94 / Music Mecca

Gadgets

☐ BLUE ALBUM, THE
PLASCD 016 / May '89 / Plastic Head

☐ GADGETREE
PLASCD 013 / May '89 / Plastic Head

☐ INFANTREE/FRUITS OF AKELDAMA
PLASCD 012 / Jul '89 / Plastic Head

☐ LOVE, CURIOSITY, FRECKLES AND DOUBT
PLASCD 014 / Jul '89 / Plastic Head

Gadzouk

☐ GADZOUK
REVCC 013 / Jul '96 / Revco

Gaelforce Orchestra

☐ ABIDE WITH ME
Lord's my shepherd / By cool siloam's shady rill / There is a green hill faraway / When I survey the wondrous cross / O worship the king (all glorious above) / Lead kindly light / Praise my soul the king of heaven / Day thou gavest Lord is ended / O for a closer walk with God / O God of Bethel by whose hand / I to the hills will lift mine eyes / All people that on earth do dwell / Behold the mountain to the lord / Holy holy holy, Lord God almighty / Child in a manger
LCOM 5230 / Oct '93 / Lismor

☐ CELTIC AIRS
LCOM 5265 / Feb '98 / Lismor

☐ FROM HIGHLANDS TO LOWLANDS
Maciain of Glencoe / Dream Angus / Ca' the yowes / Crimond / Green grow the rushes-o / Mingulay boat song / Aye waukin' o / Queen's Maries / Mo mathair (my mother) / Bluebells of Scotland / Jock O'Hazeldean / Cradle song / Proud lion rampant / Old Scots songs
LCDM 9025 / '90 / Lismor

☐ FROM THE GREEN ISLAND TO THE LAND OF THE EAGLE
Green Island / Pat Murphy's meadow / Meeting of the waters / After all these years / Rose of Tralee / My cavan girl / Danny boy / Song for Ireland / Boolavogue / Flight of Earls / Little grey home in the West / Banks of my own lovely Lee / Green glens of Antrim / Shores of Amerikay
LCDM 9029 / '90 / Lismor

☐ SCOTLAND AGAIN
Skye boat song / Loch Lomond / Westering home / Red red rose / Glencoe / Flowers of the forest / Mull of Kintyre / Bonnie lass O'Ballochmyle / Scotland again / Star o' Rabbie Burns / Annie Laurie / Man's a man for a' that / Auld lang syne
LCOM 5169 / May '96 / Lismor

☐ SCOTLAND FOREVER
Scotland forever / Loch tay boat song / Calling me home / Scotland for me / Ae fond kiss / Culloden / John Anderson, my Jo / Highland cathedral / Mull of the cool bens / Bonnie Galloway / Scotland my home / Flower o' the Quern / Land for all seasons / Scotland yet
LCOM 5179 / May '96 / Lismor

☐ SKYE HIGH
Of a' the airts / Abide with me / Northern lights of old Aberdeen / Afton water / Skye high / Bonnie wee thing / Durisdeer / Annie McKelvie / Cuillin / Fair maid of Barra / Broom o' the cowdenknowes / Isle of Mull / Clearcall a'chuain / Amazing grace
LCOM 5215 / Oct '91 / Lismor

☐ STOIRM (Gaelforce)
GH 002CD / Oct '94 / Goatshed

Gaffney, Chris

☐ LOSER'S PARADISE
HCD 8062 / Aug '95 / Hightone

Gage, Pete

☐ OUT OF HOURS
GRCD 6077 / 24 Oct '97 / Goofin'

Gaia

☐ 777 (Gaia 1991-1997)
POLLUTE 38 / Oct '97 / Sound Pollution

Gaida Orchestra

☐ BAGPIPE MUSIC FROM THE RHODOPE MOUNTAINS
VICG 52242 / Mar '96 / JVC World Library

Gaillard, Slim

☐ ANYTIME, ANYPLACE, ANYWHERE
How high the moon / Anytime anyplace anywhere / I can't get started (with you) / Slim's jam No.2 / Everything's OK in the UK / Music goes 'round and around / Satin doll / Honeysuckle rose
HEPCD 2020 / Mar '96 / Hep

☐ AT BIRDLAND 1951
Flat foot floogie, no 1 / Cement mixer / Laughin' in rhythm / Imagination / Oh lady be good / Sabroso / Flat foot flogie, No.2 / Fine and dandy / Srenade in sulfur 8 / Sound off / Serenade in vout / Ya ha ha
HEPCD 21 / Jan '96 / Hep

☐ CEMENT MIXER PUTTI PUTTI
Cement mixer / Vout Orenee / Please wait for me / Slim Gaillard's boogie / Harlem hunch / Tutti frutti / Travellin' blues / Laguna / Boogin' at Berg's / Dunkin' bagel / Novachord boogie / Tee say Malee / Atomic cocktail / Yep roc heresay / Penicilin boogie / Jumpin' at the record shop / Minuet in vout / Dreisix cents / Early mornin' boogie / That ain't right baby / Riff city / Mean Mama blues / Chicken rhythm / Santa Monica jump / Mean pretty Mama / School kids' hop
PLCD 558 / Mar '97 / President

☐ CLASSICS 1937-1938
CLASSICS 705 / Jul '93 / Classics

☐ CLASSICS 1939-1940
CLASSICS 724 / Dec '93 / Classics

☐ CLASSICS 1940-1942
CLASSICS 753 / May '94 / Classics

☐ CLASSICS 1945 VOL.1
CLASSICS 864 / Mar '96 / Classics

☐ CLASSICS 1945 VOL.2
CLASSICS 911 / Jan '97 / Classics

☐ CLASSICS 1946
CLASSICS 962 / Nov '97 / Classics

☐ GROOVE JUICE SPECIAL, THE (Gaillard, Slim & Slam Stewart)
Flat foot floogie / Chinatown, my Chinatown / Oh lady be good / Ti-pi-tin / Vol vistu gaily star / Dopey Joe / Sweet Safronia / Chicken rhythm / Matzoh balls / Chittlin switch blues / Swingin' in the key of C / Boot-ta-la-za / Bongo / Lookin' for a place to park / Tip on the numbers / B19 / African jive / Palm springs jump / Ra-da-da-da / Groove juice special
4851002 / Nov '96 / Sony Jazz

☐ LAUGHING IN RHYTHM (The Best Of The Verve Years 1946-1954)
Opera in vout / Arabian boogie / Boip boip / Bartender's just like my Mother / Serenade to a poodle / Soony roony / Laughing in rhythm / Genius / Babalu / Oh lady be good / Yo yo yo / Federation blues / Chicken rhythm / Yip roc heresy / Make it do / You goofed / Gomen nasai / Potato chips / Mishugana mambo / Tip light
5216512 / Aug '94 / Verve

☐ LEGENDARY MCVOUTIE
Voutoreene / Operatic aria / Hey stop that dancing up there / Chicken rhythm / Yep roc heresi / Gaillard special / Matzoh balls / Advocado seed soup symphony / Sonny boy / Cement mixer / Fried chicken o routie / African jive / Ya ha ha / Advocado seed soup symphony (part 2)
HEPCD 6 / Jul '90 / Hep

☐ SHUCKIN' & JIVIN'
Vout orenee / Please wait for me / Sighing boogie / Voot boogie / Nightmare boogie / Slim Gaillard's boogie / Harlem hunch / Tutti frutti / Travellin' blues / Sightseeing boogie / Central avenue boogie / Boogie / Slim's cement boogie / Still wailin' / Shuckin' and jivin' / House rent party / She's just right for me / Be bop Santa Claus / Watch them resolutions
CDCHARLY 279 / Nov '92 / Charly

☐ SIBONEY
Siboney / Cocinero / Voodoo / Midnight congas / Havana / La comparsa / Lecumi / 10,000 congas / Nanjigo / Carnival / Memories of Maria
IGOCD 2066 / Jun '97 / Indigo

☐ SLIM & SLAM (Gaillard, Slim & Slam Stewart)
Flat foot floogie / Chinatown, my Chinatown / That's what you call romance / Ti-pi-tin / 8,9 and 10 / Dancing on the beach / Oh lady be good / Ferdinand the bull / Tutti frutti / Look-a there / Humpty Dumpty / Jump session / Laughin' in rhythm / Vol vist du gaily star / Dopey Joe / Sweet Safronia / It's gettin' kinda chilly / Buck dance rhythm / Dark eyes / Bei mir bist du schoen / I got rhythm / Lady's in love with you / Caprice pagannini
CD 53270 / Jun '96 / Giants Of Jazz

☐ SLIM & SLAM - COMPLETE RECORDINGS 1938-1942 (3CD Set) (Gaillard, Slim & Slam Stewart)
Flat foot floogie / Chinatown, my Chinatown / That's what you call romance / Ti-pi-tin / Eight, nine and ten / Dancing on the beach / Oh Lady be good / Ferdinand the bull / Tutti frutti / Look-a-there / Humpty dumpty / Dark eyes / Bei mir bist due schoen / Jump session / Laughin' in rhythm / Vol vistu gaily star / Dopey Joe / Sweet Safronia / It's gettin' kinda chilly / Buck dance rhythm / I got rhythm / Lady's in love with you / Caprice paganini / That's a bringer / A-well-a-take-um-a-Joe / Chicken rhythm / Swingin' in C / Boot-ta-la-za / It's you, only you / Beatin' the board / Look out / Matzoh balls / Early in the morning / Chitlin' switch blues / Huh uh-huh / Windy city hop / Baby be mine / Sploghm / Fitzwater Street / Don't let us say goodbye / Rhythm mad / Bongo / Broadway jump / Put your arms around me / Baby / Lookin' for a place to park / Hit that mess / Hey chef / Ah now / Tip on the numbers / Slim slam boogie / Bassology / Bingie-bingie-scootie / B-19 / Champagne lullaby / African jive / Palm springs jump / Groove juice special-1 / Ra-da-da-da
CDAFS 10343 / Jun '93 / Affinity

☐ SLIM & SLAM 1938 (Gaillard, Slim & Slam Stewart)
TAXS 12 / Aug '94 / Tax

☐ SLIM & SLAM 1938-1939 (Gaillard, Slim & Slam Stewart)
TAXS 22 / Aug '94 / Tax

☐ SLIM & SLAM 1940-1942 (Gaillard, Slim & Slam Stewart)
TAXS 72 / Aug '94 / Tax

☐ SLIM'S JAM
8, 9 and 10: *Gaillard, Slim & Slam Stewart* / Ferdinand's the bull: *Gaillard, Slim & Slam Stewart* / Tutti frutti: *Gaillard, Slim & Slam Stewart* / Jump session: *Gaillard, Slim & Slam Stewart* / Laughin' in rhythm: *Gaillard, Slim & Slam Stewart* / Sweet safronia: *Gaillard, Slim & Slam Stewart* / Vout orenee: *Gaillard, Slim Orchestra* / Sighing boogie: *Gaillard, Slim Trio* / Harlem hunch: *Gaillard, Slim Orchestra* / Travelling blues: *Gaillard, Slim Orchestra* / Scotchin' with the soda: *Gaillard, Slim Trio* / Cement mixer: *Gaillard, Slim Trio* / Cuban rhumbarini: *Gaillard, Slim Trio* / Dizzy boogie: *Gaillard, Slim Orchestra* / Flat foot floogie: *Gaillard, Slim Orchestra* / Poppity pop: *Gaillard, Slim Orchestra* / Slim's jam: *Gaillard, Slim Orchestra* / Jumpin' at the record shop: *Gaillard, Slim Quartet* / Drel six cents: *Gaillard, Slim Quartet* / Laguna: *Gaillard, Slim Quartet* / Dunkin' bagel: *Gaillard, Slim Quartet* / Buck dance rhythm: *Gaillard, Slim Quartet* / Chicken rhythm: *Gaillard, Slim Orchestra*
TPZ 1068 / May '97 / Topaz Jazz

Gailmor, Jon

☐ GENERATIONS
Solo / One room / Don't tell me to smile / Generations / Somebody gonna change my name to dada / Jacob and eva / Flail away / Lost in song / Killyloo caper / Randy's tail / Bone of contention
GLCD 1082 / Jul '88 / Green Linnet

Gaines, Earl

☐ I BELIEVE IN YOUR LOVE
APCD 119 / Oct '95 / Appaloosa

Gaines, Grady

☐ HORN OF PLENTY (Gaines, Grady & The Texas Upsetters)
Baby workout / I'm packin' up / Upsetter / Stamp house blues / Have fun, baby / Walking with robert / Alligator rock / G.g. shuffle / Looking for one real good friend / Baby don't do it / My baby changed me / When something's wrong with my baby / Jumbo
BT 1084CD / Jan '93 / Black Top

Gaines, Jeffrey

☐ GALORE
First chapters last page / Right my wrongs / Simple prayer / Step by step / Belle du jour / Everything / Praise or blame / Toast and tea / Goodbye / To love her inside / Anything new / Alone / Leave her to me
RCD 10400 / 22 Jun '98 / Rykodisc

Gaines, Rosie

☐ CLOSER THAN CLOSE
5305782 / Aug '97 / Polydor

Gaines, Roy

☐ BLUESMAN FOR LIFE
Bluesman for life / It's midnight baby / Roy jumps the gator / You went back on your word / Lulu Mae / Sweet pig porker / Jump in my cadillac / Cat came back / BWR / You're gonna wish I had stayed / Fly away to glory
JSPCD 2110 / Jul '98 / JSP

Gaines, Steve

☐ ONE IN THE SUN
Give it to get it / It's alright / Black jack David / On the road / One in the sun / Talkin' about love / Nothin' is now / Take my time / Summertime's here
WKFMXD 136 / Nov '89 / FM

Gainsbourg, Serge

☐ COULEUR CAFE
Cha cha cha du loup / Mambo miam miam / L'anthracite / Laissez-moi tranquille / Leau a la bouche / Les amours perdues / Erotico tico / Ces petits riens / Baudelaire / Couleur cafe / Pauver Lola / Les cigarillos / New York / Tatou Jeremie / Ce grand merchant vous / Labas c'est naturel / Joanna / Marabout / L'ami caouette
5289492 / Oct '96 / Philips

☐ DU JAZZ DANS LE RAVIN
Angoisse / Du jazz dans le ravin / Requiem pour un twisteur / Chez les ye ye / Black march / Black trombone / Ce mortel ennui / Generique / Coco and co / Intoxicated man / Elaeudania teitia / Le talkie-walkie / Some small chance / Quand tu t'y mets / La fille au rasoir / Quand mon / Me fair les yeux deux / Fugue / Machins choses / Negative blues / Wake me at five
5226292 / Oct '96 / Philips

☐ GREAT JEWISH MUSIC (Various Artists)
TZA 7116 / 6 Oct '97 / Tzadik

Gaither, Bill

☐ BILL GAITHER VOL.1 1935-1941
DOCD 5251 / May '94 / Document

☐ BILL GAITHER VOL.2 1935-1941
DOCD 5252 / May '94 / Document

☐ BILL GAITHER VOL.3 1935-1941
DOCD 5253 / May '94 / Document

☐ BILL GAITHER VOL.4 1935-1941
DOCD 5254 / May '94 / Document

☐ BILL GAITHER VOL.5 1940-1941
DOCD 5255 / Dec '94 / Document

Gala

☐ COME INTO MY LIFE
BLRCD 33 / 24 Nov '97 / Big Life

Galactic Cowboys

☐ FEEL THE RAGE
398414117CD / Oct '96 / Metal Blade

☐ HORSE THAT BUD BOUGHT, THE
3984144127CD / Jun '97 / Metal Blade

☐ MACHINE FISH
3984114105CD / Jan '96 / Metal Blade

Galactic Disco

☐ FINAL COUNTDOWN
NASA 12CD / 26 May '98 / Galactic Disco

Galahad

☐ CLASSIC ROCK LIVE
GHCRS 1 / Jul '96 / Avalon

☐ FOLLOWING GHOSTS
Myopia / Imago / Short reflection on two past lives (part 1) / Karmam for one / Perfection personified / Bug eye / Short reflection on two past lives (part two) / Ocean blue / Rejuvenation / Easier said than done / Shine / Like a bolt out of the blue / Pain she feels inside / Shine on
GHCD 6 / 22 Jun '98 / Velvel

☐ OTHER CRIMES AND MISDEMEANOURS VOL.2
Dreaming from the inside / Opiate / Reach in to the flames / Dreams of tomorrow / GSX / Truth of you / Aqua nimue / Painted lady / Pretty in the sun / There must be a way / Rollercoaster / Suffering in silence
GHCD 5 / Jul '97 / Avalon

☐ SLEEPERS
Sleepers / Julie Anne / Live and learn / Dentist song / Picture of bliss / Before, after and beyond / Exorcising demons / Middleground / Amaranth
GHCD 4 / Aug '95 / Avalon

☐ VOICEPRINT RADIO SESSION
VPR 018CD / Oct '94 / Voiceprint

Galahad Acoustic Quintet

☐ NOT ALL THERE
Sir Galahad / Mother mercy / Club 18-30 / Dreaming from the inside / Melt / White lily / Through the looking glass / Looking up at the apple trees / Shrine / Legless in Gaza / Iceberg / Where there's all or nothing
GAQ 001CD / Jan '95 / Avalon

Galal, Aziz

☐ HOWAEL HOB LA' ABA
3106792 / 23 Mar '98 / Odeon

Galante, Inessa

☐ JEWISH FOLK SONGS
RRCD 1340 / Nov '97 / Campion

Galas, Diamanda

☐ LITANIES OF SATAN (Original Soundtrack)
CDIS 001 / Apr '89 / The Fine Line

☐ MASQUE OF THE RED DEATH
GALAS 001 / Dec '88 / Mute

☐ SAINT OF THE PIT/DIVINE PUNISHMENT
La treizieme revient / E-eaoyme / L'heautontimoroumenos / Artemis / Cris d'aveugle
CDSTUMM 33 / Apr '88 / Mute

☐ SCHREI X LIVE/SCHREI 27
CDSTUMM 146 / Sep '96 / Mute

☐ SINGER, THE
My love will never die / Reap what you sow / Were you there when they crucified my lord / Gloomy sunday / Balm in gilead-swing low, sweet chariot / Insane asylum / I put a spell on you / Let my people go / See that my grave is kept clean / Judgement day
CDSTUMM 103 / Apr '92 / Mute

☐ SPORTING LIFE (Galas, Diamanda & John Paul Jones)
CDSTUMM 127 / Sep '94 / Mute

☐ VENA CAVA
CDSTUMM 119 / Sep '93 / Mute

☐ YOU MUST BE CERTAIN OF THE DEVIL
Swing low, sweet chariot / Let's not chat about despair / You must be certain of the devil / Malediction / Double barrel prayer / Birds of death / Let my people go / Lord's my shepherd
CDSTUMM 46 / Jun '88 / Mute

Galaxie 500

☐ COPENHAGEN
Decomposing trees / Fourth of July / Summertime / Sorry / When will you come home / Spook / Listen, the snow is falling / Here she comes now / Don't let our youth go to waste
RCD 10363 / Apr '97 / Rykodisc

☐ GALAXIE 500 BOX SET (4CD Set)
Flowers / Pictures / 3.23 / Parking lot / Don't let our youth go to waste / Temperature's rising / Oblivious / It's getting late / Instrumental / Tugboat / 3.53 / King of Spain / Blue thunder / Tell me / Snowstorm / Strange / When will you come home / Decomposing trees / Another day / Leave the planet / 2.40 / Plastic bird / Isn't it a pity / Victory garden / Ceremony / Cold night / Fourth of July / Hearing voices / Spook / Summertime / Way up high / Listen, the snow is falling / Sorry / Melt away / King of Spain (part 2) / Here she comes now / Cheese and onions / Them / Final day / Blue thunder / Maracas song / Crazy / Jerome / Song in 3 / Oblivious (alternate) / I can't believe it's me / Walking song / Other side / On the floor / Rain/Don't let our youth go to waste
RCD 10355 / Sep '96 / Rykodisc

☐ ON FIRE
RCD 10357 / Apr '97 / Rykodisc

☐ THIS IS OUR MUSIC
Fourth of July / Hearing voices / Spook / Summertime / Way up high / Listen, the snow is falling / Sorry / Melt away / King of Spain, part two
RCD 10358 / Apr '97 / Rykodisc

☐ TODAY
Flowers / Pictures / Parking lot / Don't let our youth go to waist / Temperature's rising / Oblivious / It's getting late / Instrumental / Tugboat / King of Spain / Crazy
RCD 10356 / Apr '97 / Rykodisc

Galaxy

☐ DAYS WITHOUT THE SUN
AK 008 / Jul '98 / Akarma
FLASH 47 / 1 Jun '98 / Flash

Galaxy

☐ ANGEL
BR 051CD / 13 Jul '98 / Blue Room Released

Galaxy P

☐ OLD FRIENDS
CRCD 23 / Sep '93 / Charm

Galaxy Trio

☐ IN THE HAREM
ES 107CD / Jun '95 / Estrus

Galbraith, Alastair

☐ MIRRORWORK
EJ 22CD / 8 Jun '98 / Emperor Jones

☐ MORSE AND GAUDY LIGHT
EJ 08CD / Sep '96 / Emperor Jones

Gales, Larry

☐ MESSAGE FROM MONK, A (Gales, Larry Sextet)
Straight no chaser / 'Round midnight / Off minor / Ruby my dear / Let's call this / Message from the high priest
CCD 79503 / Feb '97 / Candid

Gall, Gunter

☐ TIVOLI
BEST 1007CD / Nov '93 / Acoustic Music

Gallagher & Lyle

☐ BEST OF GALLAGHER & LYLE, THE
Heart on my sleeve / I wanna stay with you / Showdown / You're the one / Song and dance man / I believe in you / Wilie / Mhairu / Love on the airwaves / Runaway / Breakaway / Heartbreaker / All grown up / I'm amazed / Country morning / Never give up on love / Hurts to learn / We / Sittin' down music / Every little teardrop
5518302 / Nov '95 / Spectrum

☐ LIVE IN CONCERT
SFRSCD 059 / 27 Apr '98 / Strange Fruit

Gallagher, Bridie

☐ GIRL FROM DONEGAL, THE
Girl from Donegal / At the close of an Irish day / Boys from the coArmagh / Cottage by the Lee / My lovely Irish rose / When will you marry me Johnny / Tumble down shack in Athlone / Road by the river / Killarney and you / My mother's last goodbye / Noreen Brown / Lovely Derry on the banks of the Foyle / Irish jaunting car / Faithful sailor boy / Hills of Donegal / I'll forgive but I'll never forget / Two little orphans / Heart of Donegal / Rose of Kilkenny / Cutting the corn in Cresslough
MCVD 30010 / Nov '96 / Emerald Gem

Gallagher, Eve

☐ WOMAN CAN HAVE IT ALL
Heaven has to wait / You can have it all / Love come down / Good enough / Change your mind / Master of disguise / Love don't slip away / Crimes of the heart / Last night / Amazing grace
CLECD 444 / Mar '97 / Cleveland City

Gallagher, Rory

☐ LIVE IN EUROPE
Messin' with the kid / Laundromat / I could've had religion / Pistol slapper blues / Going to my home town / In your town / Bullfrog blues
CLACD 406 / '95 / Castle

☐ STAGE STRUCK
Shin kicker / Wayward child / Brute force and ignorance / Moonchild / Follow me / Bought and sold / Last of the independents / Shadow play
CLACD 407 / '95 / Castle

Gallant, Joe

☐ BLUES FOR ALLAH PROJECT, THE (Gallant, Joe & Illuminati)
KFWCD 188 / Oct '96 / Knitting Factory

Gallardo, Joe

☐ LATINO BLUE
Mongo / Lady guajira / Sambita / Amanecer / Slidin' home / El brujo / Once there was you / Lady guajira
INAK 853CD / Nov '97 / In Akustik

Gallen, Ray

☐ CELTIC BEAT (Bodhran Masterclass)
Man of the house/The Galway rambler / New mown meadow / Hawk on the Strand/The jig of slurs / Home ruler/Kitty's wedding / Dublin reel/The reconciliation / Rocky road to Dublin / Donncha Lynch/Una Brady's polka / Monaghan twist / Johnny's gone to France / Tom Busby's jig/The Atholl Highlanders / Maids of Mount Cisco/Christmas Eve / Coleman's jig/Hammy's / Virginia reel/The 3 R's / Eddie Duffy's barndance / Ruairi Wallace's/The star above the Carter / Miss Galvin's/Cooley's hornpipe / Hungrey eye/The rolling wave / Pinch of snuff/The gravel walks / Mist on the meadow/The Killavil jig / Maid on the green / Craig's pipes/The bush in bloom
CHCD 1010 / Jun '98 / Outlet

Gallery

☐ WIND THAT SHAKES THE BARLEY
KSCD 9503 / Jun '97 / Kissing Spell

Gallery

☐ DREAMSCAPES
HOS 7051CD / 27 Apr '98 / Hall Of Sermon

Galli, Sandro

☐ SPECTRUM
ACVCD 9 / Oct '95 / ACV

Galli-Curci, Amelita

☐ LO HERE AND THE GENTLE LARK (25 Songs And Arias)
Una voce poca fa / Ah talor del tuo pensiero / Love's old sweet song / My old Kentucky home / Comin' thro' the rye / Russian nightingale song / Estrellita / Clavelitos / La paloma / Al pensar en el dueno de mis amores / Parla / La serenata / No te vayas, te lo pido / Dreamin' time / Sometime / Say a little prayer for me / Kiss me again / Kiss in the dark / Pretty mocking bird / Lo here the gentle lark / Deh, torna, mio bene / Sevillana / Dov'e l'indiana bruna / Nella calma
AJA 5201 / Jun '96 / ASV

Galliano

☐ 4OUR
Who ate the fly / Ease your mind / Slack hands / Roofing tiles / Slighty frayed / Best lives of our days / Thunderhead / Freefall/Anyone else / Some came / Funny how / Western front / Who's in charge / Battles are brewing
5328112 / Sep '96 / Talkin' Loud

☐ IN PURSUIT OF THE 13TH NOTE
Leg in the sea of history / Welcome to the story / Coming on strong / Sweet you like your favourite gears / Cemetary of drums (Theme from Buhaina) / Five sons of the Mother / Storm clouds gather / Nothing has changed / Fifty seventh minute of the twenty third hour / Power and glory / Stoned again / Reviewing the situation / Little ghetto boy / Me, my Mike, my lyrics / Love bomb / Welcome to the story (summer breeze)
8484932 / Apr '91 / Talkin' Loud

☐ JOYFUL NOISE UNTO THE CREATOR, A
Grounation part 1 / Jus' reach / Skunk funk / Earth boots / Phantom / Jazz / New world order / So much confusion / Totally together / Golden flower / Prince of peace / Grounation part 2
8480802 / Jun '92 / Talkin' Loud

☐ LIVE AT THE LIQUID ROOM
Intro/Slack hands / Jus' reach / Freefall / Twyford Down / Roofing tiles / Prince of peace / Storm clouds / Jazz / Thunderhead / Long time gone/Outro
5360272 / Jul '97 / Talkin' Loud

☐ PLOT THICKENS, THE
Was this the time / Blood lines / Rise and fall / Travels the road / Twyford down / Little one / Down in the gulley / Long time gone / Believe / Do you hear them / Better all the time / What colour our flag / Cold wind
5224502 / May '94 / Talkin' Loud

☐ THICKER PLOT, A (Remixes)
Long time gone (mix) / Bloodlines / Believe / Skunk funk / Travels the road / Long time gone / Twyford down / Rise and fall / Better all the time
5264262 / Oct '94 / Talkin' Loud

Galliano, Frederick

☐ ESPACES BAROQUES
Plis infinis / Pils infinis / Pils infinis / Pils infinis / Nomades monades / Multiples un
F 077CD / 6 Apr '98 / F-Communications

Galliano, Richard

☐ BLOW UP (Galliano, Richard & Michel Portal)
Mozambique / Libertango / Taraf / Little tango / Oblivion / Chorinho pra ele / Ten years ago / Viaggio / Leo estante num instante / Blow up
FDM 365892 / 6 Oct '97 / Dreyfus

☐ NEW MUSETTE (Galliano, Richard Quartet)
LBLC 6547 / Jan '92 / Label Bleu

☐ NEW YORK TANGO
Vuelvo al sur / Soleil / New York tango / Ten years ago / Fou rire / Sertao / A l'encre rouge / Blue day / Perle / To Django / Three views of a secret
FDM 365812 / Oct '96 / Dreyfus

☐ PANAMANHATTAN
Summer in Central Park / Spleen / Doom / Allee des brouillards / Small ballad / Portrait of Jenny / Ballade pour Marion / Little waltz / Des voiliers
FDM 365142 / Aug '96 / Dreyfus

☐ VIAGGIO
Waltz for Nicky / Java indigo / Viaggio / Billie / Tango pour claude / Christopher's bossa / Coloriage / Romance / Little muse / La liberte est une fleur
FDM 365622 / Mar '94 / Dreyfus

Galliard

☐ STRANGE PLEASURE/NEW DAWN
002 / 16 Feb '98 / Two Of Us

Galliard Brass Ensemble

☐ CAROLS FOR BRASS
Joy to the world / Rejoice and be merry / It came upon a midnight clear / O come, all ye faithful / Once in Royal David's City / Deck the halls with boughs of holly / Wexford carol / Ding dong merrily on high / Hosanna to the Son of David / Rejoice in the Lord always / Queum vidistis pastores / Boston and Judea / Puer natus in Bethlehem / Hodie Christus natus est / In dulci jubilo
CD QS 6035 / Oct '89 / Quicksilva

Galliards

☐ STRANGE NEWS
HOP 941CD / Apr '95 / Grasshopper

Gallinger, Karen

☐ LIVE AT THE JAZZ BAKERY
SBCD 3016 / Jun '96 / Sea Breeze

Gallivan, Joe

☐ ORIGIN OF MAN, THE (Gallivan, Joe & Brian Cuomo/Elton Dean)
NB 102 / May '97 / No Budget

Gallon Drunk

☐ IN THE LONG STILL NIGHT
EFA 049822 / Sep '96 / City Slang

Galloway, Jim

☐ JIM AND JAY'S CHRISTMAS (Galloway, Jim & Jay McShann)
SKCD 23054 / Sep '97 / Sackville

☐ KANSAS CITY NIGHTS
SKCD 3057 / Jul '96 / Sackville

Gallucio, Lo

☐ BEING VISITED
KFWCD 186 / Jun '97 / Knitting Factory

Galos

☐ DECLARACIONES
4001440292 / 24 Mar '98 / ARES

Galper, Hal

☐ PORTRAIT: HAL GALPER TRIO (Galper, Hal Trio)
After you've gone / Giant steps / In your own sweet way / I'll be seeing you / What is this thing called love / I didn't care / I should care
CCD 4383 / Jun '89 / Concord Jazz

☐ REBOP
All the things you aren't / Laura / It's magic / Jackie-ing / I don't stand a ghost of a chance with you / Take the Coltrane
ENJ 90292 / Oct '95 / Enja

Galvin, Mick

☐ AT HOME IN IRELAND
FRCD 031 / Oct '94 / Foam

Galway, James

☐ CELTIC MINSTREL, THE
Over the sea to Skye / I dreamt I dwelt in marble halls / Cath chiem an fhia / Shoheen Sholyoh / I'll take you home again Kathleen / Dark Island / Minstrel boy / She moved through the fair / Slievenamon / When you and I were young, Maggie / Carrickfergus / Last rose of summer / Down by the Salley Gardens / Fields of Athenry / Danny boy
74321383502 / Jul '96 / RCA Victor

☐ ENCHANTED FOREST, THE (Melodies Of Japan)
Enchanted forest / Lyrical shortpiece / Nakasendo (The old road) / Zui zui zukkorobashi (Children's play song) / Star children / Song of the deep forest (Improvisation) / Tokuyama lullaby / Hietsuki bushi (Love song) / Usuhiki uta (Song of the mill) / Love song / Echoes / Song of clay / Harukoma (Spring horse-dance) / Sakura / Romantic world
RD 87893 / Sep '90 / RCA

☐ GALWAY AT THE MOVIES
0926613262 / Sep '93 / RCA Victor

☐ GREATEST HITS VOL.1
Annie's song / Thorn birds / Memory / Danny boy / Perhaps / Kanon in D / Pink panther / Sabre dance / Clair de Lune
RD 87778 / Jul '88 / RCA

☐ I WILL ALWAYS LOVE YOU
Wind of change / I will always love you / Here, there and everywhere / Tears in heaven / Whole new world / Dreamlover / Belle-ile-en-mer / Holding back the years / When a man loves a woman / Last song / Golden slumbers / Little Jeannie / Always on my mind / If you leave me now / Caruso / Can't help falling in love / I just called to say I love you / Tu
74321262212 / Feb '95 / RCA Victor

☐ IN THE PINK (Galway, James & Henry Mancini)
Pink panther / Thorn birds / Breakfast at Tiffany's / Penny whistle jig / Crazy world / Pie in the face polka / Baby elephant walk / Two for the road / Speedy Gonzalez / Molly McGuires / Cameo for flute / Days of wine and roses / Roses / Charade / Moon River
RD 85315 / Jan '85 / RCA

☐ LARK IN THE CLEAR AIR
09026619552 / Apr '94 / RCA Victor

☐ LEGENDS (Galway, James & Phil Coulter)
Riverdance / Harry's game / Believe me if all those endearing young charms / Mna na h-Eireann / Battle of Kinsale / Thornbirds / Lannigan's ball/The Kerry dances / Ddanny boy / Music for a found harmonium / Lament for the wild geese / My Lagan love / Ashokan farewell / An Cailin Fionn / Hoedown
09026687762 / May '97 / RCA Victor

☐ PORTRAIT, A
090266862726 / 8 Sep '97 / RCA Victor

☐ WIND BENEATH MY WINGS, THE
El condor pasa (if I could) / Unchained melody / From a distance / La vie en rose / Come to my garden / Memory / Smoke gets in your eyes / Windmills of your mind / Perhaps love / Basque / Ceremony / Send in the clowns / Angel of music / Wind beneath my wings
RD 60862 / Oct '91 / RCA

Gambale, Frank

☐ GREAT EXPLORERS, THE
Frankly speaking / Final frontier / Jaguar / Great explorers / Duet tuet / She knows me well / Thunder current / Dawn over the Nullarbor / Cruising altitude / Naughty business
JVC 20202 / Jun '93 / JVC

☐ NOTE WORKER
Lunar rotation / Mr. Hollywood Line / Calafia / Jet rag / Stay with me / Schmooze / High five / Awakening / My silent heart
JMID 2001 / Nov '97 / JVC

☐ THUNDER FROM DOWN UNDER
Humid being / Faster than an arrow / Samba di somewhere / Kuranda / Obsessed for life / Leave ozone alone / Land of wonder / Obrigado fukuoka / Robo roo / Forgotten but not gone / Mambo jambo / One not two
JVC 20242 / Apr '94 / JVC

Gambetta, Beppe

☐ DIALOGS
BRAM 1991222 / Nov '93 / Brambus

☐ GOOD NEWS FROM HOME
GLCD 2117 / Mar '95 / Green Linnet

Gambit Jazzmen

☐ GAMBIT JAZZMEN AND FRIENDS
RSC 658 / Mar '97 / Raymer

☐ KING OF THE MARDI GRAS
Dreaming the hours away / Bedelia / Glory of love / King of the mardi gras / Just a closer walk with thee / Smiles / Sweet substitute / Dippermouth blues / Shim-me-sha-wabble / Si tu vois ma mere / Original dixieland one-step
LACD 54 / Oct '95 / Lake

Gameface

☐ REMINDER
DSR 071CD / 8 Dec '97 / Dr. Strange

☐ THREE TO GET READY
DSR 038CD / Jun '97 / Dr. Strange

Gamelan Batel

☐ RAMAYANA, THE
CMPCD 3003 / 3 Aug '98 / CMP

Gamelan Jegog Werdi Sentana

☐ BAMBOO GAMELAN OF BALI
CMPCD 3011 / 3 Aug '98 / CMP

Gamez, Celia

☐ EL AGUILA DE FUENGO
20100CD / Aug '97 / Sonifolk

☐ LA GRAN ESTRELLA DE MADRID VOL.1
20082 / Aug '96 / Sonifolk

☐ LA GRAN ESTRELLA DE MADRID VOL.2
20083 / Aug '96 / Sonifolk

Gamez, Jose Luis

☐ COLORES
FSNT 028 / 5 Jan '98 / Fresh Sound New Talent

Gamil, Soliman

☐ ANKH
Dance of ka / Lamentation / Pharoah funeral process / Isis looks for osiris / Supplication / Echos of memphis / Dance of gaiety / Shadows in the desert / Alexandrian dance / Cairo at dawn / Dance of the campaign / Village and town / Ghost dance / Dervish dance / Clown dance
TO 14CD / Apr '90 / Touch

☐ EGYPTIAN MUSIC
Black minute waltz / Goodnight irene / Pixie / On the sunny side of the street / Make a better world / Junco partner / Put out the light / Pop's dilemma / I'll be seeing you
TO 7 / Oct '95 / Touch

☐ L'ART DU QUANUN EGYPTIEN
ARN 60273 / Feb '97 / Arion

Gamma Ray

☐ ALIVE 1995
Land of the free / Man on a mission / Rebellion in dreamland / Space eater / Fairytale / Tribute to the past / Heal me / Saviour / Abyss of the void / Ride the sky / Future world / Heavy metal mania
N 02652 / Jun '96 / Noise

☐ FUTURE MADHOUSE
N 02033 / Jun '93 / Noise

☐ INSANITY AND GENIUS
Tribute to the past / No return / Last before the storm / Cave principle / Future madhouse / Gamma ray (edited version) / Insanity and genius / Eighteen years / Your torn is over / Heal me / Brothers
N 02032 / Jun '93 / Noise

☐ LAND OF THE FREE
N 02272 / May '95 / Noise

☐ SIGN NO MORE
N 01782 / Oct '91 / Noise

☐ SOMEWHERE OUT IN SPACE
Beyond the black hole / 2 Men martians and machines / No stranger / Somewhere out in space / Guardians of mankind / Landing / Valley of the kings / Pray / Winged horse / Cosmic chaos / Lost in the future / Watcher in the sky / Rising star / Shine on
N 02832 / 8 Sep '97 / Noise

Ganc, David

☐ BALADAS BRASILIERAS
829282 / Jul '96 / BUDA

Gandalf

☐ COLOURS OF THE EARTH
SKV 080CD / Jul '95 / Sattva Art

☐ GANDALF
Golden earrings / Hang on to a dream / Never too far / Scarlet ribbons / You upset the grace of living / Can you travel alone / Nature boy / Tiffany rings / Me about you / I watch the moon
SEECD 326 / Jun '97 / See For Miles

Gandy, Bruce

☐ COMPOSERS SERIES VOL.2
LCOM 5242 / Aug '95 / Lismor

Ganelin Trio

☐ ANCORA DA CAPO
CDLR 108 / Aug '97 / Leo

☐ ENCORES
CDLR 106 / Oct '94 / Leo

☐ OPUSES
CDLR 171 / '90 / Leo

☐ POCO A POCO
CDLR 101 / Feb '89 / Leo

☐ TRIO ALLIANCE
LEOLABCD 042 / Feb '98 / Leo Lab

Gang Green

☐ ANOTHER CASE OF BREWTALITY
TAANG 135CD / 3 Oct '97 / Taang

☐ ANOTHER WASTED NIGHT
Another wasted night / Skate to hell / Last chance / Alcohol / Have fun / Nineteenth hole / Skate hate / Let's drink some beer / Protect and serve / Another bomb / Voices carry / Sold out Alabama
TAANG 13CD / 11 Aug '97 / Taang

Gang Of Four

☐ ENTERTAINMENT
Ether / Naturals not in it / Damaged goods / Return the gift / Guns before butter / I found that essence rare / Glass / Contract / At home he's a tourist / 5-45 / Love like anthrax / Not great men / Outside the trains don't run on time / He'd send in the army / It's her factory
CZ 541 / Jan '95 / EMI

☐ SHRINKWRAPPED
WENCD 003 / Oct '95 / When

☐ SOLID GOLD
Paralysed / What we all want / If I could keep it for myself / Outside the trains don't run on time / Why theory / Cheeseburger / Republic / In the ditch / Hole in the wallet / He'd send in the army / To hell with poverty / Capital (it fails us now) / History's bunk / Cheeseburgher / What we all want (live)
CZ 561 / Feb '96 / Premier/EMI

Gang Starr

☐ DAILY OPERATION
Daily operation (intro) / Place where we dwell / Flip the script / Ex girl to next girl / Soliloquy of chaos / I'm the man / 92 interlude / Take it personal / 2 deep / 24-7-365 / No shame in my game / Conspiracy / Illest brother / Hardcore composer / BYS / Much too much (Mack A Mil) / Take two and pass / Stay tuned
CCD 1910 / May '92 / Cooltempo

☐ HARD TO EARN
Intro (the first steps) / Alongwaytogo / Code of the streets / Brainstorm / Tonz 'o' gunz / Planet / Aiiight chill... / Speak ya clout / Dwyck / Words from the Nutcracker / Mass appeal / Blowin' up the spot / Suckas need bodyguards / Now you're mine / Mostly the voice / FALA / Comin' for the datazz
CTCD 38 / Feb '94 / Cooltempo

☐ MOMENT OF TRUTH
Bl and friendship / Rep growz bigga / Above the clubs / You know what she wantz / In memory of / JFK 2 / LAX / She knows what she wantz / Militia / Robbin' hood theory / Royalty / Itz a set up / My advice 2 you / Mall / What I'm here for / Betrayal / Next time / Pause mixin'
8455852 / 30 Mar '98 / Cooltempo

☐ STEP IN THE ARENA
Name tag (Premier and The Guru) / Step in the arena / Form of intellect / Execution of a chump (No more Mr. Nice Guy) / Who's gonna take the weight / Beyond comprehension / Check the technique / Lovesick / Here today, gone tomorrow / Game plan / Take a rest / What you want this time / Street ministry / Just to get a rep / Say your prayers / As I read my S-A / Precisely the right rhymes / Meaning of the name
CCD 1798 / Jan '91 / Cooltempo

Ganger

☐ FORE
Hollywood loaf / Missile that back-fired / Drummers arms and bionic thumbs / Smorgasbord / Fore / Jellyneck / Anomovieshot / Prisoner of my eyeball
WIGCD 30 / Apr '97 / Domino

☐ HAMMOCK STYLE
Cats dogs and babies jaws / Upye / Capo (south of Caspian) / First thing in the morning / What happened to the king happened to me / Blau / Lid of the stars
WIGCD 047 / 27 Jul '98 / Domino

Gangsta Tribe

☐ GOTTA COME UP
CON 45022 / May '96 / Ichiban

Ganguly, Rita

☐ THUMRI AND DADRA (Vocal Art Of Hindustan)
VICG 53472 / Mar '96 / JVC World Library

Gangwar

☐ STREET FIGHTING
622582 / Apr '97 / Skydog

Ganksta C

☐ STEPCHILD
FILECD 455 / Jan '95 / Profile

Gant, Cecil

☐ CECIL GANT
Cecil boogie / Hit that jive Jack / Hogan's alley / I gotta girl / Boogie blues / Sloppy Joe / Playing myself the blues / Time will tell / Cecil's mop top / Train time blues
KKCD 03 / Apr '90 / Krazy Kat

☐ CECIL GANT 1944-1945
Killer driller boogie / I wonder / Cecil boogie / Blues in LA / When I wanted you / Little baby you're running wild / Rhumba boogie woogie / I gotta gal / Cecil's mop top / Wake up Cecil wake up / New Cecil boogie / Soft and mellow / Hit that jive jack / Special delivery / That's the stuff you've got to watch / I'll remember / Midnight on central avenue / Boogie blues / Jump jack jump / It's all over darling / What's on your worried mind
FLYCD 61 / 3 Sep '97 / Flyright

Gantry, Elmer

☐ VERY BEST OF ELMER GANTRY/ VELVET OPERA, THE (Gantry, Elmer & Velvet Opera)
Mother writes / Long nights of summer / Mary Jane / Air / Looking for a happy life / Reactions of a young man / Flames (single version) / Dreamy / Talk of the devil / And I remember / To be with you / Painter / Volcano / Raga / Eleanor Rigby / Money by / Raise the light / Warm day in July / Black Jack Davy / Anna Dance square / Statesboro blues / There's a hole in my pocket
SEECD 437 / May '97 / See For Miles

Ganxsta Rid

☐ OCCUPATION HAZARDOUS
If I die, let me roll / Chilling on the west side / One life, last breath / Happy feelings / Karson makes u bounce / Gs from the otha side / Born May 1st / Occupation hazardous / Rid is coming / Operation green light / Tell em who sent yo ass / Once upon a mossburg
CDVEST 65 / Nov '95 / Bulletproof

Ganzie, Terry

☐ TEAM UP
VYDCD 012 / Jul '96 / Vine Yard

Gap Band

☐ AIN'T NOTHIN' BUT A PARTY
50532 / Feb '97 / Raging Bull

☐ BEST OF THE GAP BAND, THE
Early in the morning / Shake / Outstanding / Why you wann hurt me / Yearning / Open your mind / You dropped a bomb on me / You can always count on me / I don't believe you want to get up and dance / Steppin' out / Humping around / Boys are back in town / Party train
5224572 / Jun '94 / Mercury

☐ LIVE AND WELL
Intro / Gap Band party / Wide / Oops upside your head / Outstanding / Humpin' / No hiding place / Burn rubber / Gotta get up / Early in the morning / Party train / Drop the bomb / Yearning for your love / Yearning - reprise / Mega mix
ESMCD 442 / Oct '96 / Essential

☐ OOPS UPSIDE YOUR HEAD
Oops upside your head / Outstanding / Burn rubber on me (why you wanna hurt me) / Party lights / Jammin' in America / You dropped a bomb on me / Boys are back in Town / Baby baba boogie / Steppin' (out) / Humpin' (edit version) / When I look in your eyes / Yearning for your love / Sweet Caroline / You can count on me / Open your mind (wide) / I don't believe you want to get up and dance (oops)
5511722 / Aug '95 / Spectrum

Garbage

☐ GARBAGE
Super vixen / Queer / Only happy when it rains / As Heaven is wide / Not my idea / Stroke of luck / Vow / Stupid girl / Dog new tricks / My lover's box / Fix me now / Milk
D 31450 / Oct '95 / Mushroom

☐ VERSION 2.0
MUSH 29CD / 11 May '98 / Mushroom

Garbarek, Jan

☐ AFTENLAND
Aftenland / Aftenland / Linje / Bue / Enigma / Kilden / Spill / Iskirken / Tegn
8393042 / Nov '89 / ECM

☐ ALL THOSE BORN WITH WINGS
Last clown / Yellow fever / Soulful Bill / La divetta / Cool train / Loop
8313942 / Feb '87 / ECM

☐ DANSERE
Dansere / Svevende / Bris / Skrik and hyl / Lokk / 'til vennene
8291932 / Oct '86 / ECM

☐ DIS
Vandrere / Krusning / Viddene / Skygger / YR / Dis
8274082 / Feb '86 / ECM

☐ ESOTERIC CIRCLE (Garbarek, Jan & Terje Rypdal)
Traneflight / Rabalder / Esoteric circle / VIPs / SAS 644 / Nefertiti / Gee / Karin's mode / Breeze ending
FCD 41031 / Aug '96 / Freedom

☐ EVENTYR
Soria maria / Lillekort / Eventyr / Weaving a garland / Once upon a time / Companion / Snipp snapp snute / East of the sun (and west of the moon)
8293842 / Aug '88 / ECM

☐ GRAY VOICE, THE
White noise of forgetfulness / Crossing place / One day in march I go down to the sea and listen / To be where I am / It's ok to phone the island that is a mirage / It's ok to listen to the gray voice / I'm the knife-thrower's partner
8254062 / Aug '88 / ECM

☐ I TOOK UP THE RUNES
Gula gula / Molde canticle (parts 1-5) / His eyes were suns / I took up the runes / Buena hora, buenos vientos
8438502 / Nov '90 / ECM

☐ LEGENDS OF THE SEVEN DREAMS
He comes from the North / Aichuri, the song man / Tongue of secrets / Brother wind / It's name is secret road / Send word / Voy cantando / Mirror store
8373442 / Oct '88 / ECM

☐ OFFICIUM (Garbarek, Jan & The Hilliard Ensemble)
4453692 / Sep '94 / ECM

☐ PHOTO WITH BLUE SKY (Garbarek, Jan Group)
Blue sky / White cloud / Windows / Red roof / Wives / Picture
843 168 2 / Oct '90 / ECM

☐ PLACES
Reflections / Entering / Going places / Passing
8291952 / Oct '86 / ECM

☐ ROSENSFOLE (Garbarek, Jan & Maria Buen-Garnas)
Innferd / Innferd / Margjit og targjei risvollo / Maalfri mi fruve / Venelite / Stolt Oll / Signe lita / Lillebroer og storebroer / Grisilla / Utferd
8392932 / Jun '89 / ECM

☐ STAR
Star / Jumper / Lamenting / Anthem / Roses for you / Clouds in the mountain / Snowman / Music of my people
8496492 / Oct '91 / ECM

☐ TRIPTYKON
Rim / Selji / JEV / Sang / Triptykon / Etu hei / Bruremarsi
8473212 / Jun '92 / ECM

☐ TWELVE MOONS
Twelve moons / Psalm / Brother wind march / There were swallows / Tall tear trees / Arietta / Gautes-Margjit / Darvanan / Huhai / Witch-tai-to
5195002 / May '93 / ECM

☐ USTAD SHAUKAT HUSSAIN-MADAR (Garbarek, Jan & Anouar Brahem)
Sull lull / Madar / Sebika / Bahia / Ramy / Jaw / Joron / Qaws / Epilogue
5190752 / Feb '94 / ECM

☐ VISIBLE WORLD
Red wind / Creek / Survivor / Healing smoke / Visible world (Chiaro) / Desolate mountains I / Desolatae mountains II / Visible world (Scuro) / Giulietta / Desolate mountains III / Pygmy lullaby / Quest / Arrow / Scythe / Evening land
5290862 / Apr '96 / ECM

☐ WAYFARER
Gesture / Wayfarer / Gentle / Pendulum / Spor / Singsong
8119682 / Aug '86 / ECM

☐ WITCHI-TAI-TO
AIR / Kukka / Hasta siempre / Witchi-tai-to / Desireless
8333302 / Mar '88 / ECM

☐ WORKS
Folk songs / Skirk and hyl / Passing / Selje / Viddene / Snipp, snapp, snute / Beast of Kommodo / Svevende
8232662 / Jun '89 / ECM

Garber, Jan

☐ GREAT JAN GARBER, THE
My dear / S'wonderful / More than you know / Maria Elena / Star dust / It's a wonderful world / Lovely to look at / Oh lady be good / It's only a paper moon / Birth of the blues / I'll see you in my dreams / Things we did last summer
HCD 331 / Apr '96 / Hindsight

Garbo, Chuck

☐ BARBER'S BLUES, THE
ROUCD 2140 / Feb '96 / Rounder

☐ DRAWERS TROUBLE
Meet me with your black drawers on / Drawers trouble / Average kind of guy / Changing scenes / Hurt coming on / Meet me at the station / New york city blues / Can't straighten your mind / After tears / Rock me in your arms / Take off that dress
ROUCD 2123 / Aug '93 / Rounder

Garbutt, Vin

☐ BANDALIZED
HROCD 9 / Apr '96 / Home Roots

☐ BYPASS SYNDROME, THE
HROCD 8 / Apr '96 / Home Roots

☐ PLUGGED
HROCD 11 / Apr '96 / Home Roots

☐ WHEN THE TIDE TURNS
CMCD 050 / Dec '97 / Celtic Music

Garcia, Carlos

☐ TANGO VOL.2 (Garcia, Carlos & The Tango Allstars)
VICG 53432 / Mar '96 / JVC World Library

Garcia, Chris

☐ CHUTNEY BUCCHANAL
JMC 1120 / May '96 / JMC

Garcia, Jerry

☐ ALMOST ACOUSTIC (Garcia, Jerry Acoustic Band)
Swing low, sweet chariot / Blue yodel no. 9 (Standing on the corner) / I'm troubled / Oh babe, it ain't no lie / Casey Jones / Ripple / Deep elem blues / I'm here to get my baby out of jail / Girl at the crossroads bar / Diamond Joe / Spike diver blues / I've been all around this world / Oh the wind and the rain / Gone home
GDCD 4005 / Feb '89 / Grateful Dead

☐ COMPLIMENTS OF GARCIA
Let it rock / That's what love will make us do / Turn on the bright lights / What goes around / Mississippi moon / Hunter gets captured by the game / Russian lullaby / He ain't give you none / Let's spend the night together / Midnight town
GDCD 4011 / Mar '89 / Grateful Dead

☐ HOOTEROLL (Garcia, Jerry & Howard Wales)
Morning in marin / Da bird song / South side strut / Up from the desert / Dc-502 / One a.m. approach / Uncle martin's / Evening in marin
RCD 10052 / Oct '87 / Rykodisc

☐ HOW SWEET IT IS... (Garcia, Jerry Band)
How sweet it is / Tough Mama / That's what love will make you do / Someday baby / Cats under the stairs / Tears of rage / Think / Gomorrah / Tore up over you / Like a road
GDCD 4051 / Jun '97 / Grateful Dead

☐ JERRY GARCIA AND DAVID GRISMAN (Garcia, Jerry & David Grisman)
ACD 2 / Jun '97 / Acoustic Disc

☐ REFLECTIONS
Might as well / Mission in the rain / They love each other / I'll take a melody / It must have been the roses / Tore up (over you) / Catfish John / Comes a-time
GDCD 4008 / May '89 / Grateful Dead

☐ SHADY GROVE (Garcia, Jerry & David Grisman)
ACD 21 / Apr '97 / Acoustic Disc

☐ TALK WITH JERRY GARCIA
74833700602 / 14 Apr '98 / Blackheart

☐ WHEEL, THE
Deal / Sugaree / Late for supper / Eep hour / Odd little place / Bird song / Loser / Spidergawd / To lay me down / Wheel
GDCD 4003 / Feb '89 / Grateful Dead

Garcia-Fons, Renaud

☐ ALBOREA
Al Cameron / Alborea / Natgo / Secret zambra / Eosine / Gus's smile / Amadu / Sacre coeur / Tropea / Fort apache / Rue de buci
ENJ 90572 / Feb '96 / Enja

☐ LEGENDS
Funambule / Aube / Sesame / Inanga / Moreno / Like someone in love / Procession / Fille des sables / La guitare a King Kong / Legendes / Elle / Mi saeta
ENJ 93142 / Feb '97 / Enja

☐ ORIENTAL BASS
Oriental bass / San Juan / Goodjinns / Oryssa / Ghazali / Jullundur / Hommage a Ostad / Bajo Andaluz / Jam Buleria / Djani
ENJ 93342 / 23 Feb '98 / Enja

Garcons

☐ DIVORCE
French boy / Critics / 25th Street / French boy reprise / French boy / Critics / 25th Street / French boy reprise / Encore l'amour
THECD 107 / Jun '97 / Other

Gardel, Carlos

☐ BEST OF CARLOS GARDEL, THE
Mi buenos aires querido / Melodia de arrabal tango / Leguisamo solo tango / Tomo y obligo tango / Silencio tango / Golondrinas tango cancion / Por una cabeza tango / Sus ojos se cerraron tango / Volver tango / Rubias de Nueva York / El Dia que me quieras / Cuesta ababjo / Madreselva / Amargura / Estudiante / Soy una fiera / Buenos Aires / Arrabal amargo / Volvio una noche / Lejana tierra mia
724382350521 / 19 Jan '98 / Hemisphere

☐ CANTA A BUENOS AIRES Y SU GENTE (2CD Set)
BM 99910 / Nov '97 / Blue Moon

☐ CARLOS GARDEL
Tomo y obligo / Almagro / Viejo rincon / Silencio / Rencor / Secreto / Volvio una noche / La cancion de Buenos Aires / Juventud / Volver / Senda florida / Bandoneon arrabalero / Lo han visto con otra / Cuesta abajo / Muneca brava / Tango Argentino / Palomita blanca / Dandy / La garconniere / Milonga sentimental / Viejo smocking / Tortazos / Sueno de juventud / El dia que me quieras / Silbando / Mi Buenos Aries querido / Paseo de Julio / Farolito de papel / Por una cabeza / Caprichosa / Parlez moi d'amour / Mi noche triste / Medianoche / Pompas / Vieja recova / Tu vieja ventana / Lejana tierra mia / La cumparsita
FA 054 / Oct '96 / Fremeaux

☐ EL REY DEL TANGO (2CD Set)
R2CD 7003 / 13 Apr '98 / Deja Vu

☐ LA CUMPARSITA
La cumparasita / Mano a mano / Tomo y obligo / Milonga sentimental / Chorra / Compadron / Lo han visto con otra / Bandoneon arrabalero / Mi noche triste / Barrio reo / Rencor / Viejo smoking / Dandy / Muneca / Senda Florida / Carnaval / Malevaje / Melodia de arrabal
CD 62128 / Jul '97 / Saludos Amigos

☐ LAS 60 MEJORES CANCIONES (2CD Set)
BMCD 99909 / Jan '98 / Blue Moon

☐ MANO A MANO
BM 506CD / Jul '96 / Blue Moon

☐ ORATORIO CARLOS GARDEL (Various Artists)
873086 / Feb '97 / Milan Sur

☐ PASSION OF THE TANGO, THE
74321447942 / Feb '97 / Milan Sur

☐ POR UNA CABEZA
BM 507CD / Jul '96 / Blue Moon

☐ TANGO ARGENTINO
Mano a mano / Lo han visto con orta / La cumparsita / Me da penda confesarlo / La cancion de beunos aires / Yra yra / Misa de once / A la luz del candil / Caminot / Alma, en pena / Desden / Adios muchachos / Melodia de arrabal / Guitarra mia / Tomo y obligo / Tango Argentino
CD 12527 / Jun '96 / Music Of The World

Garden, Bill

☐ BILL GARDEN'S HIGHLAND FIDDLE ORCHESTRA (Garden, Bill & His Highland Fiddle Orchestra)
French Canadian special / Stings to the bow (reels and jigs) / De'il among the tailors / Blackthorn stick / Roaring jelly / Brumley brae / Slow air, strathspey and reel / Hornpipes / Reel of Tulloch / Robert Burns waltz / March, strathspey and reel / Scots and Irish (reels and jigs) / Polka / Country hoedown / Intercity waltz / Schottische reel / Sir Harry Lauder selection
CD ITV 423 / Dec '86 / Scotdisc

☐ IOLAIRE (Garden, Bill Fiddle Orchestra)
CDITV 514 / Jul '90 / Scotdisc

☐ REFLECTIONS OF SCOTLAND
CDITV 637 / Apr '98 / Scotdisc

☐ TRAVEL THE LAKES (Garden, Bill Fiddle Orchestra)
Out on the lake / Early one morning / Barbara allan / John peel / Water is wide / I gave my love a cherry / Greensleeves / Evening sunset / Raggle taggle gypsy / Home sweet home / English country garden / Mountain pass / Day has ended / At the waters edge
CDITV 577 / Sep '94 / Scotdisc

Gardiner, Bobby

☐ MASTER'S CHOICE, THE
Fermoy lassies, Doon reel, concertina reel / Paul Halfpenny, Mulvihills / Reel of Rio, the ash plant / Shoe the donkey, Sonnys / Cathaoir an phiobaire, Chorus jig / Blind Mary / Tailor's thimble, Lilies in the field, Take your choice / McDermotts, Humours of Lissadell / Colleys delight / Banbridge town, Mr. McGuire, Pride of the Bronx / Jack Gorman's favourite showjumper drinking whiskey / Road to Ballymac/Silver birch / Johnson's / Kilty town, The lobster / Gentian waltz / Sporting nell/Earl's chair
OSS 86CD / Aug '93 / Ossian

☐ MEMORIES OF CLARE
COPCD 5010 / Feb '96 / Copley

Gardiner, Boris

☐ IT'S NICE TO BE WITH YOU
LPKK 2000 / 20 Apr '98 / K&K

☐ IT'S WHAT'S HAPPENING
RNCD 2125 / Nov '95 / Rhino

☐ REGGAE HAPPENING
Dynamic pressure / Commanding wife / News flash / Barbwire / Reggae me dis, reggae me dat / Mr. sandman / Spooky / Merry jig / Something tender / Lock jaw
JMC 200110 / Sep '93 / Jamaican Gold

☐ THIS IS BORIS GARDINER
I want to wake up with you / Wrong end of the rainbow / Jean / Cara mia / Next to you / All in my dreams / Take care of my heart / You're everything to me / This old house / Let's keep it that way / Friends and lovers / Woman behind the man / Falling in love again / Make it tonight / Guilty / Last night / She's everything a man could want
RNCD 2006 / May '93 / Rhino

Gardiner, Paula

☐ TALES OF INCLINATION
SCDC 2103 / Nov '95 / Sain

Gardiner, Ronnie

☐ MY SWEDISH HEART
SITCD 9225 / Aug '95 / Sittel

Gardner, Dave

☐ EMPTY DREAMS
PLAN 006CD / Jul '95 / Planet

Gardner, Freddy

☐ FREDDY GARDNER AND HIS SWING ORCHESTRA 1937-1939 (Gardner, Freddy & His Swing Orchestra)
Japanese sandman / Baby won't you please come home / Indiana / Sweet Georgia Brown / I ain't got nobody / Blue strings / Swing as it comes / Keep goin' / You can't stop me from dreaming / That old feeling / I want to be happy / Limehouse blues / I double dare you / Have you got any castles baby / Snake charmer / Dipsy doodle / Music maestro please / It's d'lovely / Jeeper's creeper's / Tom Tom the piper's son / They say / Someday sweetheart / 10am blues
HQCD 118 / May '98 / Harlequin

Gardner, Jeff

☐ SECOND HOME
500722 / 21 Aug '97 / Musidisc

☐ SKY DANCE
500332 / 21 Aug '97 / Musidisc

☐ SPIRIT CALL
087142 / Mar '96 / Ulysse

Gardner, Joanna

☐ JOANNA GARDNER
I never thought / We can make it / Special feelings / Friday night / Watching you / I could never love another like you / Pick up the pieces / Spooky
EXCDM 1 / Sep '96 / Expansion

Gardony, Laszlo

☐ BREAKOUT
74321378872 / May '96 / RCA

Garfunkel, Art

☐ ACROSS AMERICA (The Very Best Of Art Garfunkel)
Heart in New York / Crying in the rain / Scarborough Fair / Poem on the underground wall / I only have eyes for you / Homeward bound / All I know / Bright eyes / El Condor Pasa / Bridge over troubled water / Mrs. Robinson / 59th Street Bridge song (Feelin' groovy) / I will / April come she will / Sound of silence / Grateful / Goodnight, my love
VTCD 113 / Dec '96 / Virgin

☐ ART GARFUNKEL ALBUM, THE
Bright eyes / Breakaway / Heart in New York / I shall sing / Ninety nine miles from LA / All I know / I only have eyes for you / Watermark / Sometimes when I'm dreaming / Travellin' boy / Same old tears on a new background / What a wonderful world / I believe / Scissors cut
4663332 / Oct '90 / Columbia

☐ BEST OF ART GARFUNKEL, THE
Bright eyes / Break away / I believe (when I fall in love it will be forever) / Disney girls / Miss you nights / She moved through the fair / Scissors cut / Since I don't have you / Watermark / What a wonderful world / When a man loves a woman / Looking for the right one / I only have eyes for you / Crying in the rain: *Garfunkel, Art & JT* / Another lullaby / 99 miles from LA / Heart in New York / Saturday suit / Why worry / Crying in my sleep
4914502 / 3 Aug '98 / Columbia

☐ BREAKAWAY
I believe / Rag doll / Breakaway / Disney girls / My little town / Waters of March / I only have eyes for you / Looking for the right one / Ninety nine miles from LA / Same old tears on a new background
4688732 / Feb '97 / Columbia

☐ FATE FOR BREAKFAST
In a little while / Since I don't have you / I know / Sail on a rainbow / Miss you nights / Bright eyes / Finally found a reason / Beyond the tears / Oh how happy / When someone doesn't want you / Take me away
4879462 / Jul '97 / Columbia

Garibian, Ludwig

☐ ARMENIA (Garibian, Ludwig Trio & Folk Lab)
MWCD 9303 / Jul '93 / Music & Words

Garing, Greg

☐ ALONE
My love is real / Safe within your arms / Say what you mean / Alone / Dream too real to hold / Walk away from me / How the road unwinds / Where the bluegrass grows / Don't cry baby / All ym stars are in your eyes / Fallen angel
74321441132 / 27 Oct '97 / RCA

Garioch Fiddlers

☐ AT HAME
CDR 038 / Mar '96 / Donside

Garland, Hank

☐ HANK GARLAND AND HIS SUGAR FOOTERS
Sugarfoot rag / Third man theme / Flying eagle polka / Sugarfoot boogie / Hillbilly express / Seventh and union / Lowdown Billy / Sentimental journey / Doll dance / Chic, No. 1 / Chic, No. 2 / E string rag / Guitar shuffle / I'm movin' on / This cold war with you / I'll never slip around again / Some other world / I'm crying
BCD 15551 / Apr '92 / Bear Family

Garland, Judy

☐ ALWAYS CHASING RAINBOWS (The Young Judy Garland)
All God's chillun got rhythm / Buds won't bud / Cry baby cry / Embraceable you / End of the rainbow / Everybody sing / FDR Jones / I'm always chasing rainbows / I'm just wild about Harry / I'm nobody's baby / In between / It never rains but it pours / Oceans apart / Our love affair / Over the rainbow / Sleep my baby sleep / Stompin' at the Savoy / Sweet sixteen / Swing Mister Charlie / Ten pins in the sky / You can't have everything / Zing went the strings of my heart
CDAJA 5093 / Jul '92 / Living Era

☐ BEST OF JUDY GARLAND, THE
On the Atchison, Topeka and The Santa Fe / I'm always chasing rainbows / But not for me / Meet me in St. Louis / For me and my gal / In between / Dear Mr. Gable / FDR Jones / Embraceable you / Trolley song / I got rhythm / Boy next door / Zing went the strings of my heart / When you wore a tulip / I'm nobody's baby / Over the rainbow
DCD 5332 / Dec '93 / Disky

☐ BEST OF JUDY GARLAND, THE
That's entertainment / More / Come rain or come shine / It's yourself / Lucky day / I could go on singin' (till the cows come home) / Day in, day out / Foggy day / Almost like being in love/This can't be love / Fly me to the moon / Battle Hymn of the Republic / Zing went the strings of my heart / You'll never walk alone / Old devil moon / Maggie May / You made me love you/For me and my girl/The trolley song / Man that got away / Rock-a-bye your baby with a Dixie melody / As long as he needs me / Over the rainbow
CDSL 8258 / Sep '95 / Music For Pleasure

☐ CHASING RAINBOWS
I never knew / Oceans apart / Love / But not for me / Embraceable you / Over the rainbow / Blues in the night / How about you / Poor little rich girl / No lover no nothing / For me and my gal / Trolley song / This heart of mine / You made me love you
RMB 75007 / Nov '93 / Remember

☐ COLLECTOR'S GEMS FROM THE MGM FILMS (2CD Set)
Waltz with a swing / Americana, opera vs jazz / Everbody sing / Yours and mine / Your broadway and my broadway / Got a pair of new shoes / Sun showers / Down on melody farm / Why, because / Ever since the world began / Shall I sing a melody / In between / It never rains, but what it pours / Bei mir bist du schoen / Meet the beat of my heart / Zing went the strings of my heart / On the bumpy road to love / Ten pins in the sky / I'm nobody's baby / All I do is dream of you / Alone / It's a great day for the Irish / Danny boy / Pretty girl milking her cow / Singin' in the rain / Easy to love / We must have music / I'm always chasing rainbows / Minnie from Trinidad / Every little moment has a meaning of its own / Tom, Tom, the piper's son / When I look at you / Paging Mr. Greenback / Where there's music / Joint is really jumping at Carnegie hall / D'ya love me / Mack the black / Love of my life / Voodoo / You can't get a man with a gun / There's no business like show business / They say it's wonderful / Girl that I marry / I've got the sun in the morning / Let's go west, again / Anything you can do / There's no business like show business
CDODEON 22 / Jan '97 / EMI

☐ EARLY YEARS, THE
AVC 536 / May '94 / Avid

☐ IT WAS A GOOD TIME (Garland, Judy & Liza Minnelli)
777772 / 3 Aug '98 / Curb

☐ JUDY GARLAND
DVGH 7062 / May '95 / Deja Vu

☐ JUDY GARLAND ON RADIO (2CD Set)
Balboa / Feelin' like a million / They can't take that away from me / Thanks for the memory / Could you pass in love / Sweet sixteen / FDR Jones / Comes love / All the things you are / Don't get around much anymore / But not for me / I lost my sugar in Salt Lake City / Taking a chance on love / Over the rainbow / I may be wrong / Program introduction / Trolley song / Have yourself a merry little Christmas / Judy's spoken tribute to Jerome Kern / I won't dance / Can't help lovin' dat man / Why do I love you / Look for the silver lining
JZCL 5006 / Nov '96 / Jazz Classics

☐ JUDY GARLAND SHOW, THE (5CD Set)
15942 / Oct '95 / Laserlight

☐ JUDY GARLAND SHOWS, THE
Introdustion / Just in time / When you're smiling (the whole world smiles with you) / You do something to me / Too marvellous for words: *Sinatra, Frank* / You do something to me: *Garland, Judy & Dean Martin* / You must have been a beautiful baby: *Martin, Dean* / You do something to me (reprise): *Garland, Judy & Frank Sinatra/Dean Martin* / One I love belongs to someone else: *Sinatra, Frank & Dean Martin* / I can't give you anything but love / You're nobody 'til somebody loves you: *Garland, Judy & Frank Sinatra/Dean Martin* / You made me love you / Rock-a-bye your baby with a Dixie melody / Swanee / I never will forget / San Francisco / Fly me to the moon / Old soft shoe: *Garland, Judy & Donald O'Connor* / Chicago (that toddling town) / Closing theme
OTA 101911 / Feb '97 / On The Air

☐ LEGENDARY AMSTERDAM CONCERT 1960, THE (2CD Set)
When you're smiling (The whole world smiles with you) / Almost like in love / This can't be love / Do it again / You go to my head / Alone together / Who cares (As long as you care for me) / Puttin' in the ritz / How long has this been going on / Just you, just me / Man that got away / San Francisco / That's entertainment / I can't give you anything but love / Come rain or come shine / You're nearer / If love were all / Foggy day (In London town) / Zing went the strings of my heart / Stormy weather / You made me love you (I didn't want to do it) / For me and my gal / Trolley song / Rock-a-bye your baby with a Dixie melody / Swanee / It's a great day for the Irish / After you've gone / San Francisco (Reprise) / Sail away / Something's coming / Just in time / Get me to the church on time / Joey, Joey, Joey / Never will I marry / Hey, look me over / Party's over / Some people
DBG 53044 / Jul '96 / Double Gold

☐ MAIL CALL (Garland, Judy & Bing Crosby)
Mail call / Trolley song / It's love, love, love / Can do, will do / Amor / Groaner, canary and nose / Mail call / Dixieland band / I love you, goodbye / All the things you are / You're the top / Something to remember you by
15413 / Jan '93 / Laserlight

☐ MISS SHOWBUSINESS
Zing went the strings of my heart / Stompin' at the savoy / All God's chillun got rhythm / Everybody sing / You made me love you / Over the rainbow / Sweet sixteen / Embraceable you / (Can this be) The end of the rainbow / I'm nobody's baby / Pretty girl milking her cow / It's a great day for the Irish / Sunny side of the street / For me and my gal / That old black magic / When you wore a tulip
HADCD 156 / May '94 / Javelin

☐ ONE AND ONLY, THE
This is the time of evening / While we were young / Carolina in the morning / Danny boy / Pretty girl milking her cow / Last night when we were young / April showers / Dirty hands, dirty face / Memories of you / Be myself / Me and my shadow / Little girl blue / I get the blues when it rains / Zing went the strings of my heart / I hadn't anyone till you / More than you know / That's entertainment / Down with love / Old devil moon / I've confessed to the breeze (I love you) / Hello bluebird / I could go on singing / Trolley song / Over the rainbow / Man that got away / When you're smiling / Day in, day out / I can't give you anything but love / When the sun comes out / Who cares (as long as you care for me) / Puttin' on the Ritz / How long has this been going on / Just you, just me / Hey look me over / Joey Joey Joey / Party's over / I wish you love / As long as he needs me / More / Battle hymn of the Republic / Maybe I'll come back (I will come back) / We could make such beautiful music / Bob White / Don't rain on my parade / Smile / Just in time / Make someone happy / Once in a lifetime / Lucky day / Judy at the palace / Shine on harvest moon / Some of these days / My man (mon homme) / I don't care / Stormy weather / You go to my head / Come rain or come shine / San Francisco / Swanee / Rock-a-bye your baby with a dixie melody / Happiness is a thing called Joe / It's a great day for the Irish / You'll never walk alone / I happen to like New York / You made me love you / For me and my gal / Why was I born / Do it again / Chicago / After you've gone
CDGFR 017 / Jun '92 / Tring

☐ PLATINUM COLLECTION, THE (2CD Set)
Over the rainbow / Embraceable you / Swanee / Buds won't bud / I'm nobody baby/End of the rainbow / Wearing of the green / Sweet sixteen / Zing went the strings of my heart / Fascinaing rhythm / How about you / FDR Jones / Blues in the night / Last call for love / On the sunny side of the street / Poor little rich girl / That old black magic / I never knew / No love no nothin' / Journey to a star / This heart of mine / Love / For me and my girl / When you wore a tulip(and I wore a big red rose) / I'm wild about Harry / Could you use me: *Garland, Judy & Mickey Rooney* / But not for me: *Garland, Judy & Mickey Rooney* / Bidin' my time: *Garland, Judy & Mickey Rooney* / I got rhythm: *Garland, Judy & Mickey Rooney* / Meet me in St Louis: *Garland, Judy & Mickey Rooney* / Boy next door: *Garland, Judy & Mickey Rooney* / Skip to my Lou: *Garland, Judy & Mickey Rooney* / Boys and girls like you and me: *Garland, Judy & Mickey Rooney* / Trolley song / Have yourself a merry Christmas / Poor you / Yah ta ta yah ta ta / In the valley where the evening goes down / You'll never walk alone / On the Actison Topeka and the Santa Fe
PC 602 / 10 Nov '97 / Platinum Collection

☐ PORTRAIT OF JUDY GARLAND, A
GALE 407 / May '97 / Gallerie

☐ SOMEWHERE OVER THE RAINBOW
GO 3806 / 1 Dec '97 / Golden Options

☐ SONGS FROM THE MOVIES
Somewhere over the rainbow / Come rain or come shine / Give my regards to Broadway / Carolina in the morning / Rock-a-bye baby
BSTCD 9110 / May '92 / Best Compact Discs

☐ TOUCH OF CLASS, A
That's entertainment / Over the rainbow / Old devil moon / Who cares (as long as you care for me) / Just you just me / Down with love / Alone together / If I love again / How long has this been going on / Among my souvenirs / April showers / More than you know / Happiness is a thing called Joe / After you've gone / I get the blues when it rains / You'll never walk alone
TC 885302 / 2 Feb '98 / Disky

☐ VERY BEST OF JUDY GARLAND, THE
HMNCD 015 / 3 Nov '97 / Half Moon

☐ WHEN YOU'RE SMILING (Garland, Judy & Bing Crosby)
PARCD 003 / Jan '96 / Parrot

☐ YOU MADE ME LOVE YOU
Fascinating rhythm / (Can this be) the end of the rainbow / Buds won't bud / In between / Swing Mr. Charlie / How about you / Our love affair / Friendship / I'm just wild about Harry / Nobody's baby / I'm always chasing rainbows / Swanee / Dear Mr. Gable, you made me love you / All God's chillun got rhythm / FDR Jones / Cry baby cry / Sweet sixteen / Embraceable you / Zing went the strings of my heart / Over the rainbow
304592 / Jul '97 / Hallmark

☐ YOUNG JUDY GARLAND
Swanee / Friendship / Embraceable you / Pretty girl milking her cow / It's a great day for the Irish / Zing went the strings of my heart / Oceans apart / FDR Jones / I'm just wild about Harry / How about you / In between / Figaro / Sweet sixteen / Jitterbug / Over the rainbow / Dear Mr. Gable / You can't have everything / It never rains but it pours / Ten pins in the sky / Buds won't bud / Our love affair / I'm always chasing rainbows / Everybody sing / All God's chillun got rhythm / I'm nobody's baby
PASTCD 7014 / Jun '93 / Flapper

☐ ZING WENT THE STRINGS OF MY HEART
Trolley song / Boy next door / For me and my gal / Jitterbug / Pins in the sky / I'm just wild about Harry / I'm always chasing rainbows / Figaro / Zing went the strings of my heart / You've got me where you want me / It never rains but what it pours / Oceans apart / Buds won't bud / I'm nobody's baby / When you wore a tulip / Over the rainbow / Friendship / Embraceable you / Our love affair / Can this be the end of the rainbow / Meet me in St. Louis, Louis / Yah-ta-ta, yah-ta-ta
RAJCD 873 / Apr '96 / Empress

Garland, Peter

☐ NANA & VICTORIO
AVAN 012 / Nov '92 / Avant

Garland, Red

☐ ALL MORNIN' LONG (Garland, Red Trio)
All mornin' long / They can't take that away from me / Our delight
OJCCD 293 / Feb '92 / Original Jazz Classics

☐ CAN'T SEE FOR LOOKIN'
I can't see for lookin' / Soon / Blackout / Castle rock
OJCCD 918 / May '97 / Original Jazz Classics

☐ GROOVY (Garland, Red Trio)
OJCCD 61 / Nov '95 / Original Jazz Classics

☐ MANTECA (Garland, Red Trio)
Manteca / S'wonderful / Lady be good / Exactly like you / Mort's report / Portrait of Jenny
OJCCD 428 / May '97 / Original Jazz Classics

☐ PC BLUES, THE
Ahmad's blues / Lost April / Why was I born / Tweedle dee dee / PC blues
OJCCD 898 / Sep '96 / Original Jazz Classics

☐ RED GARLAND TRIO & EDDIE 'LOCKJAW' DAVIS (Garland, Red Trio & Eddie 'Lockjaw' Davis)
We'll be together again / Stella by starlight / I heard you cried last night / Softly baby / When your lover has gone / Wonder why / Blue room / Red blues
OJCCD 360 / Nov '95 / Original Jazz Classics

☐ RED IN BLUESVILLE
He's a real gone guy / CC rider / M squad theme / Your red wagon / Trouble in mind / St. louis blues
OJCCD 295 / Sep '93 / Original Jazz Classics

☐ ROJO (Red Garland Trio & Ray Barretto)
Rojo / We kiss in a shadow / Darling je vous aime beaucoup / Ralph J Gleason blues / You better go now / Mr. Wonderful
OJCCD 772 / Jun '94 / Original Jazz Classics

☐ SOUL BURNIN'
On Green Dolphin Street / If you could see me now / Rocks in my bed / Soul burnin' / Blues in the night / Little bit of Basie
OJCCD 921 / Jun '97 / Original Jazz Classics

☐ SOUL JUNCTION (Garland, Red Quintet & John Coltrane)
Soul junction / Woody 'n' you / Birk's works / I got it bad and that ain't good / Hallelujah
OJCCD 481 / Jun '95 / Original Jazz Classics

Garland, Tim

☐ ENTER THE FIRE
Simple Simon / Only child / Great spirit / Suite / I loves you Porgy / Rejoicing / Inconclusion
AKD 074 / 15 Sep '97 / Linn

☐ PLAYING TO THE MOON (Garland, Tim Quartet)
JHCD 047 / Oct '96 / Ronnie Scott's Jazz House

☐ POINTS ON THE CURVE - NORTH SHIP SUITE
FMRCD 01 / Oct '87 / Future

Garlaza, Faustino

☐ MARIMBA DE GUATEMALA
Me lo dijo adela / Quien sera / Corazon de melon / Aquarla do Brasil (Brazil) / Tico tico / Adios / Besame mucho / Cachito / Quando calienta el sol / Solamente una vez / Noches de ronda / Perfida / Frenesi / Cielito lindo / Guadalajara / Vereda tropical / Maria Elena / Grandada / Autumn leaves (Las hojas muertas)
CD 12531 / Jun '96 / Music Of The World

Garling, Tom

☐ MAYNARD FERGUSON PRESENTS
Shrimp tales / Trinology / Bill Evans / I'm getting sentimental over you / Forging behind / Rainer's dream / How my heart sings / Ilene's dance / Here's that rainy day
CCD 47522 / May '97 / Concord Jazz

Garmarna

☐ GARMARNA
MASS 54CD / Jul '95 / Mass Productions

☐ GUDS SPELEMAN
Herr mannelig / Vanner och Frander / Hailing fran Makedonien / Min man / Hilla lilla / Drew drusnaar/ Idar som igar / Njaalkeme / Herr holger / Guds speleman
MASSCD 69 / Mar '96 / Mass Productions
XOUCD 113 / May '97 / Xource

☐ LE MYSTERE DES CHANTS VIKINGS
7992107 / Jul '97 / Arcade

☐ VITTRAD
MASS 61CD / Jul '94 / Mass Productions

Garner, Erroll

☐ BODY AND SOUL
Way you look tonight / Body and soul / (Back home again in) Indiana / Honeysuckle rose / I'm in the mood for love / I can't get started (with you) / Play piano play / Undecided / You're blase / Sophisticated lady / Ain't she sweet / I didn't know / Fine and dandy / Robbin's nest / Please don't talk about me when I'm gone / It's the talk of the town / You're driving me crazy / Ja da / Summertime / I never knew
4679162 / '91 / Sony Jazz

☐ CLASSICS 1940-1945
CLASSICS 873 / Apr '96 / Classics

☐ CLASSICS 1944 VOL.1
CLASSICS 802 / Mar '95 / Classics

☐ CLASSICS 1944 VOL.2
CLASSICS 818 / May '95 / Classics

☐ CLASSICS 1944 VOL.3
CLASSICS 850 / Feb '96 / Classics

☐ CLASSICS 1945-1946
CLASSICS 924 / Apr '97 / Classics

☐ CLOSEUP IN SWING/A NEW KIND OF LOVE
Something to me / My silent love / All of me / St. Louis blues / Some of these days / I'm i the mood for love / El Papa Grande / Best things in life are free / Back in your own backyard / You've brought a new kind of love to me / Louise / Fashion interlude / Steve's song / Paris mist / Mimi / Theme from a new kind of love / In the park in Paree / Paris mist (waltz swing) / Tease
CD 83383 / 8 Sep '97 / Telarc Archive

☐ CONCERT BY THE SEA
I'll remember April / Teach me tonight / Mambo Carmel / It's all right with me / Red top / April in Paris / They can't take that away from me / Where or when / Erroll's theme
4510422 / Oct '93 / CBS

☐ CONTRASTS (Garner, Erroll Trio)
You are my sunshine / I've got the world on a string / 7-11 jump / Part time blues / Rosalie / In a mellow tone / Don't worry 'bout me / All of a sudden / There's a small hotel / Misty / I wanna be a rugcutter / Sweet and lovely / Exactly like you
5580772 / 26 May '98 / Verve Master Edition

☐ DREAMSTREET/ONE WORLD CONCERT
Just one of those things / I'm gettin' sentimental over you / Blue Lou / Come rain or come shine / Lady is a tramp / Sweet Lorraine / Dreamstreet / Mambo Gotham / Oklahoma medley / Way you look tonight / Happiness is a thing called Joe / Sweet and lovely / Mack the knife / Lover come back / Misty / Dancing tambourine / Thanks for the memory
CD 83350 / Feb '96 / Telarc

☐ ENCORES IN HI FI
Moonglow / Sophisticated Lady / Robbin's nest / Creme De Menthe / Humoresque / How high the moon / Fancy / Groovy day / Man I love
4677072 / Jan '95 / Sony Jazz

☐ ERROLL GARNER COLLECTION VOL.3
Cecilia / Idaho / Margie / Stars fell on Alabama / Way down yonder in New Orleans / Louise / Peg o' my heart / Heart / Kittin on the keys / Ramona / My gal Sal / I've got the world on a string / Dinah / Too marvellous for words / California here I come
8424192 / Mar '93 / EmArCy

☐ JAZZ MASTERS
I wanna be a rug cutter / Misty / Smooth one / Love in bloom / (All of a sudden) My heart sings / Don't be that way / Jump / St. James infirmary / Don't worry 'bout me / Is you is or is you ain't my baby / Part time blues / Yesterdays / Oh lady be good / Fandango / I've got the world on a string
5181972 / 5 May '98 / Verve

☐ JAZZ PORTRAITS
Misty / Play piano play / Pastel / Trio / Turquoise / Frankie and Johnny Fantasy / Impressions / This can't be love / Moonglow / I can't give you anything but love / Blue and sentimental / Way you look tonight / She's funny that way / I can't believe that you're in love with me / Cool blues / Bird's nest / Frantonality / Man I love
CD 14508 / May '94 / Jazz Portraits

☐ LIVE IN LA
DM 15006 / Jul '96 / DMA Jazz

☐ LONG AGO AND FAR AWAY
When Johnny comes marching home / It could happen to you / I don't know why / It could happen to you / My heart stood still / When you're smiling / Long ago and far away / Poor butterfly / Spring is here / Petite waltz / Petite waltz bounce / Lover / How high the moon / People will say we're in love / Laura / I cover the waterfront / Penthouse serenade
4606142 / Jan '95 / Sony Jazz

☐ MAGICIAN & GERSHWIN & KERN
Close to you / It gets better every time / Someone to watch over me / Nightwind / One good turn / Watch what happens / Yesterdays / I only have eyes for you / Muncho gusto / Strike up the band / Love walked in / I got rhythm / Foggy day / Nice work if you can get it / Lovely to look at / Can't help lovin' dat man / Only make believe / Ol' man river / Dearly beloved / Why do I love you / Fine romance
CD 83337 / Apr '95 / Telarc

☐ MISTY
Misty / Very thought of you / It might as well be spring / Dreamy / I didn't know what time it was / Moment's delight / On the street where you live / Other voices / This is always / Solitaire / St. Louis blues / Summertime / 'S wonderful / Easy to love / Way you look tonight / I'm in the mood for love
CD 56019 / Aug '94 / Jazz Roots

☐ MOONGLOW
CDSGP 098 / May '94 / Prestige
TCD 1010 / Feb '96 / Tradition

☐ MOONGLOW
BN 014 / Apr '98 / Blue Nite

☐ NOW PLAYING - A NIGHT AT THE MOVIES/UP IN ERROLL'S ROOM
You made me love you / As time goes by / Sonny boy / Charmaine / I found a million dollar baby / I'll get by / Three o'clock in the morning / Stella by starlight / Jeannine I dream of lilac time / Just a gigolo / How deep is the ocean / It's only a paper moon / Newsreel tag / Watermelon man / It's the talk of the town / Groovin' high / Girl from Ipanema / Coffee song / Cheek to cheek / Up in Erroll's room / Lot of living to do / I got rhythm
CD 83378 / Sep '96 / Telarc Archive

☐ ORIGINAL MISTY, THE
Misty / I've got the world on a string / 7-11 jump / Don't worry 'bout me / You are my sunshine / Part time blues / All of a sudden / In a mellow tone / There's a small hotel / I wanna be a rug cutter / Exactly like you / Oh lady be good
8349102 / Feb '94 / Mercury

☐ OVERTURE TO DAWN
LEJAZZCD 49 / Nov '95 / Le Jazz

☐ PARIS IMPRESSIONS
4756242 / Jan '95 / Sony Jazz

☐ PENTHOUSE SERENADE
(Back home again in) Indiana / Love walked in / Body and soul / Penthouse serenade / Stompin' at the Savoy / Stardust / More than you know / Over the rainbow
SV 0162 / Oct '97 / Savoy Jazz

☐ PIANO MAGIC
Play piano play / Pastel / Frankie and Johnnie fantasy / Star dust / Indiana / Gas light / Trio / Don't worry 'bout me / On the sunny side of the street / Frantonality / Opus one / Yesterdays / Everything happens to me / Cool blues / Gliss in the dark / Perdido / Boogie woogie boogie / I'm in the mood for love / This is always / Laura
308552 / 20 Apr '98 / Hallmark

☐ PLAY PIANO PLAY
78067422222 / 7 Apr '98 / Drive Archive

☐ SEPARATE KEYBOARDS (Garner, Erroll & Billy Taylor)
Cottage for sale / Rosalie / Everything happens to me / Stairway to the stars / September song / All the things you are / Mad Monk / Solace / Night and day / Alexander's ragtime band / Misty blues / Bug
SV 0223 / Oct '97 / Savoy Jazz

☐ SERENADE TO LAURA
Laura / This can't be love / Man I love / Moonglow / I want a little girl / It's easy to remember / Goodbye / She's funny that way / Until the real thing comes along / Confessin' / Stormy weather / I surrender dear / I'm in the mood for love / All of me
SV 0221 / Oct '97 / Savoy Jazz

☐ SOLILOQUY - AT THE PIANO
Caravan / There is no greater love / Avalon / Lullaby of Birdland / Memories of you / Will you still be mine / You'd be so nice to come home to / You's be so nice to come home to / No more time / I surrender dear / If I had you / Don't take your love from me
4656312 / Jan '95 / Sony Jazz

☐ SOLITAIRE
I'll never smile again / Then you've never been blue / It's the talk of the town / Solitaire / Cottage for sale / That old feeling / Over the rainbow / Yesterdays / Who / When a gypsy makes his violin cry / Salud segovia
5182792 / May '94 / Mercury

☐ THAT'S MY KICK/GEMINI
That's my kick / Shadow of your smile / Like it is / It ain't necessarily so / Autumn leaves / Blue moon / More / Gaslight / Nervous waltz / Passing through / Afinidad / How high the moon / It could happen to you / Gemini / When a gypsy makes his violin cry / Tea for two / Something / Eldorado / These foolish things
CD 83332 / Sep '94 / Telarc

☐ THIS IS JAZZ
Lover / It's the talk of the town / When you're smiling / Laura / Dancing in the dark / How high the moon / Easy to love / Moonglow / Lullabye of Birdland / Poor butterfly / If I had you / My heart stood still / Love for sale / Dreamy / St. Louis blues
CK 64968 / Oct '96 / Sony Jazz

☐ TRIO AND SOLO 1945-1947
159102 / 24 Feb '98 / Jazz Archives

☐ YESTERDAYS
Play fiddle play / Dark eyes / Laff slam laff / Jumpin' at the Deuces / September song / Everything happens to me / I only have eyes for you / Cottage for sale / On the sunny side of the street / All the things you are / Rosalie / Stairway to the stars / Yesterdays
SV 0244 / Oct '97 / Savoy Jazz

Garner, Larry

☐ DOUBLE DUES
Scared of you / No free rides / Buster / Shut it down / Dreaming again / Taxman / Broke bluesman / Tale spreaders / California sister / Past 23
JSPCD 273 / Jan '97 / JSP

☐ STANDING ROOM ONLY
RUF 1024 / Jun '98 / Ruf

Garner, Lynn

☐ KEEP THE CIRCLE TURNING
DLD 1063 / Dec '95 / Dance & Listen

Garner, Sue

☐ TO RUN MORE SMOOTHLY
Nightfall / Dear darling / Rose coloured glue / Box and you / Glazed / Silver wings / Intuition / Life / Sense enough / Item's song / Something else / Goodbye / Continuous play
087082 / 2 Mar '98 / City Slang

Garnet Silk

☐ GARNET SILK & THE DJ'S RULE THING
RNCD 2035 / Oct '93 / Rhino

☐ GARNET SILK GOLD
CRCD 20 / Aug '93 / Charm

☐ IT'S GROWING
NWSCD 1 / Mar '93 / New Sound
VYDCD 4 / Sep '95 / Vine Yard

☐ LIVE IN CONCERT
CDC 03 / 12 Jan '98 / Power Play

☐ LIVE REBIRTH
SILKCD 1 / 12 Jan '98 / Christian Souljahs

☐ LORD WATCH OVER OUR SHOULDERS
Lord watch over our shoulders / Cry of my people / So divine / Fill us up with your mercy / Zion in a vision / Let them talk / You gonna need love / Home town / Spread the love / Babylon be still / Retreat wicked man / Lord watch over our shoulders
GRELCD 219 / Aug '95 / Greensleeves

☐ LOVE IS THE ANSWER
SCCD 3 / Nov '94 / Steely & Cleevie

☐ NOTHING CAN DIVIDE US
CRCD 38 / Apr '95 / Charm

☐ REGGAE MAX
JSRNCD 4 / Jun '96 / Jet Star

Garnett, Carlos

☐ FUEGO EN MI ALMA (FIRE IN MY SOUL)
Fuego en mi alma / Catch me if you can / Eternal justice / Fuego en mi alma / Little sunflower / Urd14me / Love thy neighbor / Mystic moon / Shalome
HCD 7001 / Apr '97 / Highnote

Garnier, Laurent

☐ 30
Deep sea diving / Sweet mellow d / Crispy bacon / Formax / Hoe / Mid summer night / Kall it / La minute du repondeur le plus casse-couilles / Theme from Larry's dub / Feel the fire / Flashback / I funk up / Asterix question mark asterix / Le voyage de Simone / Last winter in Alaska
F 063CD
F 063CDLTD / Mar '97 / F-Communications

☐ LABORATOIRE MIX (2CD Set) (Various Artists)
Jungle: *Jungle Wonz* / Moon Walk: *Funky People* / Help me: *Green Velvet* / People everyday (we just wanna be free): *Holmes, Braxton* / Basemental: *AJ Sound* / Ruhrschnellweg: *Broccoli Brothers* / Sides of iron: *Chaser* / Tomorrow is the first day: *6K* / You gotta believe: *FRD* / Takks: *Landstrumm, Neal* / House-O-matic: *DJ Deeon* / Ambulance: *Armani, Robert* / Speaker: *Speaker* / Gas mask: *Brown, Steven* / Bleu: *Scan X* / Flash: *Kosmic Messenger* / XTC: *K-Hand* / Bytes accapellas: *Aux 88* / Amazon: *World 2 World* / Force: *Garnier, Laurent* / Die Kosmischen Kuriere: *3MB & Juan Atkins* / Let it go: *Tyree* / Wipe: *Teste* / All the way in: *Big Foot Part 2* / Conflexx: *Ratio* / Mind control music: *Club MCM* / Reverting: *Purpose Maker* / Te qua: *Timeblind* / Man-Me: *DJ Shufflemaster* / Essit musique: *Essit Musique* / Nervous acid: *Konders, Bobby* / Acid Eiffel: *Choice* / Beyond the dance: *Rhythim Is Rhythim* / Icct Hedral: *Aphex Twin*
REACTCD 087 / Oct '96 / React

☐ MIXMAG LIVE VOL.19 (Various Artists)
MMLCD 019 / Jul '96 / Mixmag Live

☐ SHOT IN THE DARK
Shapes under water / Astral dreams / Bouncing metal / Rising spirit / Harmonic grooves / Force / Geometric world / 022 / Rex attitude / Raw cut / Track for Mike / Silver string
F 014CD / Oct '94 / F-Communications

Garrett, Amos

☐ AMOSBEHAVIN'
SP 1189CD / Oct '93 / Stony Plain

☐ BURIED ALIVE IN THE BLUES
Home in my shoes / Move on down the line / Don't tell me / Smack dab in the middle / Ha ha in the daytime / Stanley Street / Hair of the dog / Too many rivers / Buried alive in the blues / What a fool I was / Lost love / All my money / Bert's boogie / Got to get you off my mind
VDCD 110 / Jun '96 / Voodoo

☐ I MAKE MY HOME IN MY SHOES
SP 1132CD / Oct '93 / Stony Plain

☐ OFF THE FLOOR LIVE
VDCD 113 / Jun '96 / Voodoo

☐ RETURN OF THE FORMERLY BROTHERS, THE (Garrett, Amos & Doug Sahm/Gene Taylor)
Smack dab in the middle / Big mamou / Teardrops on your letter / Drunk / Don't tell me / Coming back home / Sure is a good thing / Amarillo highway / Banks of the old Ponchartrain / Just like a woman / Gene's boogie / Queen of the Okanagan
RCD 10127 / Aug '92 / Rykodisc

☐ THIRD MAN IN
SP 1179CD / Oct '93 / Stony Plain

Garrett, Vernon

☐ CAUGHT IN THE CROSSFIRE
Lonely, lonely nights / Bottom line / Drifting apart / Love me right / If you can't help me baby / Somebody done messed up / Don't make me pay for his mistakes / Walkin' the back streets and crying / Caught in the crossfire
ICH 1128CD / Oct '93 / Ichiban

☐ HALF PAST THE BLUES
D 2249082 / Oct '97 / Ichiban

☐ TOO HIP TO BE HAPPY
Are you the one / You just call me / You don't know nothin' about love / Too hip to be happy / Doors of my heart / Special kind of lady / She's a burgular / I'll be doggone / Gonna have to use my head / Li'l black woman
ICH 1169CD / May '94 / Ichiban

Garrick, David

☐ ALL THE HITS PLUS MORE
CDSGP 0261 / May '96 / Prestige

☐ BOY CALLED DAVID, A
REP 4091 / Aug '91 / Repertoire

Garrick, Michael

☐ FOR LOVE OF DUKE AND RONNIE
Webster's mood / Samba changes / Swallows on the water / StormFor love of Duke / Two trumpets / Kyrie / Salvation march / Water patterns / Blue dusk girl / Trick of the light or grandma's spells / Shadowplay / And Ronnie; The open question
JAZA 4 / Jul '97 / Jazz Academy

☐ LADY IN WAITING, A (Garrick, Michael Trio)
JAZA 1 / Oct '94 / Jazz Academy

☐ METEORS CLOSE AT HAND (2CD Set)
JAZA 2 / Dec '95 / Jazz Academy

Garrido, David

☐ EL SONIDO DEL TIEMPO
20051CD / Dec '94 / Sonifolk

Garrido, Lolita

☐ CON SABOR TROPICAL
CCD 805 / 24 Apr '98 / Caney

☐ LA VOL DEL BOLERO EN ESPANA VOL.1
ALCD 041 / Jul '97 / Alma Latina

☐ LA VOL DEL BOLERO EN ESPANA VOL.2
ALCD 043 / Jul '97 / Alma Latina

Garside, Robin

☐ RAGMAN'S TRUMPET, THE
GET 2CD / Aug '94 / Get

Garson, Michael

☐ GERSHWIN FANTASIA, A
RR 84CD / May '96 / Reference Recordings

☐ OXFORD SESSIONS VOL.1
RR 37CD / May '96 / Reference Recordings

☐ OXFORD SESSIONS VOL.2
RR 53CD / May '96 / Reference Recordings

☐ REFLECTIONS (Garson, Michael & Jim Walker)
Portrait of a friend / Love / First song / Waltz of the Arts / Ethereal / Yearnings / Syrinx / Pied Piper / Park / Magic spell / Homecoming / You're one of a kind / Reflections / Reason / Admiration
RR 18CD / May '96 / Reference Recordings

☐ SERENDIPITY
Serendipity / Lady / Autumn leaves / I should care / Spirit of play / Trio blues / My romance / Promise / Tam's jam / Searching / My one and only love
RR 20CD / May '96 / Reference Recordings

Gary D

☐ D-TRANCE VOL.3 (3CD Set) (Various Artists)
PIAS 55600526 / Oct '96 / DJ's Present

☐ D-TRANCE VOL.4 (3CD Set) (Various Artists)
PIAS 556200925 / Dec '96 / DJ's Present

☐ D-TRANCE VOL.5 (3CD Set) (Various Artists)
PIAS 556201325 / Apr '97 / DJ's Present

Gary, John

☐ SINGS COLE PORTER
ACD 274 / Apr '95 / Audiophile

Garzon, Armando

☐ BOLEROS (Garzon, Armando & Quinteto Oriente)
Dos gardenias / Pensamiento / Sublime ilusion / Reclamo mistico / Quiereme mucho / Si llego a besarte / Mienteme mas / Y tu que has hecho / Contigo en la distancia / La puerta / Juramento / Chan chan / Se te olvida / Si me pudieras querer
CORA 131 / Oct '96 / Corason

Garzone, George

☐ FOUR'S & TWO'S
Four's and two's / Have you met Miss Jones / In memory of Lauren Nichols / One time / To my papa / Snow place like home / Mingus that I knew / Tutti Italiani / Hey open up / In a sentimental mood
NYC 60242 / Sep '96 / NYC

Gas

☐ GAS
EFA 006822 / 9 Feb '98 / Mille Plateau

☐ ZAUBERBERG
EFA 006952 / 9 Feb '98 / Mille Plateau

Gas 0095

☐ EMIT 0095
EMIT 0095 / Feb '95 / Time Recordings

Gas Huffer

☐ BEER DRINKING
EFA 11396D / Apr '93 / Musical Tragedies

☐ INHUMAN ORDEAL OF SPECIAL AGENT GAS HUFFER, THE
864592 / Feb '96 / Epitaph

☐ INTERGRITY TECHNOLOGY AND SERVICE
MT 181CD / Sep '95 / Burning Heart

☐ JUST BEAUTIFUL MUSIC
Rotten egg / Beware of the viking / Over that side / Is that for me / Clay pigeon / Old man winter / Hacked / Last act / Princess / Don't panic / Jungles of guam / Surgeona / Mr. Inbetween / Cut the check / Bridge to the 21st century / You may already have won
65112 / 18 May '98 / Epitaph

☐ MTI
E 11373 CD / Jan '93 / Musical Tragedies

☐ ONE INCH MASTERS
E 864392 / Aug '94 / Epitaph

Gas Mark 5

☐ GUIZERS
REGULO 3 / Oct '94 / Regulo

☐ JUMP
REGULO 2 / Oct '94 / Regulo

Gascoyne, Geoff

☐ VOICES OF SPRING
Breakfast with Jr / Pao de acucar / John Brown's body / Pass the pepper / Voices of Spring / Black Nile / On the street where you live / Spring break / To itch his own / Tyrone / If it's magic
JITCD 9605 / Sep '96 / Jazzizit

☐ WINTER WONDERLAND (Gascoyne, Geoff & Pete Churchill)
Winter wonderland / Christmas song / Let it snow let it snow / Little Jesus sweetly sleep / O come o come Emmanuel / O little town of Bethlehem / Have yourself a merry little Christmas / ANgels from the realm of glory / It came upon a midnight clear / In the bleak midwinter clear / Jingle bells / Silent night / Huron carol / White Christmas
JITCD 9710 / 17 Nov '97 / Jazzizit

Gaseneta

☐ SOONER OR LATER
PSFD 17 / Sep '97 / PSF

Gash

☐ GASH
WDM 10056 / 23 Mar '98 / World Domination

Gaskin

☐ END OF THE WORLD/NO WAY OUT
CDMETAL 6 / Feb '97 / British Steel

Gaskins, Ray

☐ REACH
Reach / Down home / Lovin' factor / Never say die / Knee deep / Lullabye / Blues "R" gonna' get you / Song for my son / No one has wanted more / I want to talk about God
MTCD 1006 / Apr '96 / MT

☐ SHADY LANE
Just imagine me / Who's right, who's wrong / Outstanding / Yo funky Mama / Chilli funk / We had to say goodbye / Shady lane / Mo' chicken / Again and again / Spain (I can recall) / PY / Mo chicken
LIPHOT 89532 / May '97 / Lipstick Hot

☐ SOUL CRUSADE
Come back to me / London strut / Soul crusade / Fall / About the music / Ain't easy / I know it's you / Kissing you / All about love / Easy sax
MTCD 1002 / May '96 / MT

Gaslini, Giorgio

☐ AYLER'S WINGS
1212702 / Apr '91 / Soul Note

☐ GASLINI PLAYS MONK
1210202 / May '92 / Soul Note

☐ LAMPI (LIGHTNINGS)
1212902 / May '94 / Soul Note

☐ SCHUMANN REFLECTIONS
Von fremden landern und menschen / Kuriose geschichte / Hasche-mann / Schmann reflections / Bittendes kind / Gluckes genius / Wichtige begebenheit / Traumerei / Am kamin / Ritter vom steckenpferd / Fast zu ernst / Furchtenmachen / Kind im einschlummern / De ditcher spricht
1211202 / May '92 / Soul Note

Gasoline

☐ GASOLINE
ES 1243CD / 16 Mar '98 / Estrus

Gasp

☐ DROME TRILER OF PUZZLE ZOO PEOPLE
SAH 46CD / 27 Jul '98 / Slap A Ham

Gasparyan, Djivan

☐ I WILL NOT BE SAD IN THIS WORLD
Cool wind is blowing / Brother hunter / Look here, my dear / I will not be sad in this world / Little flower garden / Your strong mind / Ploughman / Dle Yaman
ASCD 06 / Mar '96 / All Saints

☐ MOON SHINES AT NIGHT
Lovely spring / Sayat nova / 7th December 1988 / Don't make me cry / You have to come back to me / Tonight / They took my love away / Moon shines at night / Apricot tree / Mother of mine
ASCD 016 / 26 Jan '98 / All Saints

Gaster, Marvin

☐ UNCLE HENRY'S FAVORITES
ROUCD 382 / May '96 / Rounder

Gastr Del Sol

☐ CAMOFLEUR
Seasons reverse / Blues (No sense of wonder) / Black horse / Each dream is an example / Mouth Canyon / Putt of dew / Bauchredner
WIGCD 044 / 23 Feb '98 / Domino

☐ CROOKT, CRACKT OR FLY
DC 43CD / Dec '96 / Drag City

☐ SERPENTINE SIMILAR
DEX 13CD / Jun '97 / Dexter's Cigar

☐ UPGRADE AND AFTERLIFE
DC 90CD / Dec '96 / Drag City

Gate

☐ MONOLAKE
KRYPTON 36 / Mar '97 / Table Of The Elements

Gatecrashers

☐ TWENTY GOOD REASONS
PT 603001 / Jun '96 / Part

Gates, Bruce

☐ JOYOUS REUNION (Gates, Bruce Jazz Consortium Big Band)
SB 2086 / Sep '97 / Sea Breeze

Gates, David

☐ FIRST ALBUM
Sail around the world / Soap (I use the) / Ann / Sight and sound / Loriee / Help is on the way / Suite clouds rain / Sunday rider / Do you believe he's comin'
7559609102 / Jan '96 / Elektra

☐ GOODBYE GIRL
Goodbye girl / Took the last train / Overnight sensation / California lady / Ann / Drifter / He don't know how to love you / Clouds suite / Loriee / Part time love / Sunday rider / Never let her go
7559611722 / Jan '96 / Elektra

Gates Of Ishtar

☐ BLOODRED PATH
SP 1031CD / Jun '96 / Spinefarm

☐ DAWN OF FLAMES, THE
IR 027CD / May '97 / Cyclone Empire

Gates, Rev. J.M.

☐ REV. J.M. GATES VOL.2 1926
DOCD 5432 / Jul '96 / Document

☐ REV. J.M. GATES VOL.3 1926
DOCD 5433 / Jul '96 / Document

☐ REV. J.M. GATES VOL.4 1926
DOCD 5442 / May '96 / Document

☐ REV. J.M. GATES VOL.5 1927
DOCD 5449 / May '96 / Document

☐ REV. J.M. GATES VOL.6 1928-1929
DOCD 5457 / Jun '96 / Document

☐ REV. J.M. GATES VOL.7 1929-1930
DOCD 5469 / Jul '96 / Document

☐ REV. J.M. GATES VOL.8 1930-1934
DOCD 5483 / Nov '96 / Document

☐ REV. J.M. GATES VOL.9 1934-1941
DOCD 5484 / Nov '96 / Document

Gateway Jazz Band

☐ IN THE MOMENT
5293462 / Sep '96 / ECM

Gateway Trio

☐ HOMECOMING
Homecoming / Waltz new / Modern times / Calypso falto / Short cut / How's never / In your arms / 7th D / Oneness
5276372 / Oct '95 / ECM

Gathering

☐ ADRENALINE
CM 77135CD / May '96 / Century Media

☐ ALMOST A DANCE
FDN 2008CD / Dec '93 / Foundation 2000

☐ ALWAYS
FDN 2004CD / Jul '92 / Foundation 2000

☐ KEVIN'S TELESCOPE
CM 77192CD / 20 Oct '97 / Century Media

☐ MANDYLION
CM 77098CD / Sep '95 / Century Media

☐ NIGHT TIME BIRDS
CM 77168CD / Jun '97 / Century Media

Gato Negro

☐ BLACK CAT DUB
RE 203CD / Nov '94 / ROIR

☐ VITAL FORCE DUB
RUSCD 8210 / May '97 / ROIR

Gatto, Roberto

☐ ASK (Gatto, Roberto & John Scofield)
Ask / There will never be another you / 100 flowers waltz / Tango's time / Blue Christmas / Oh what
INAK 8802CD / Jul '97 / In Akustik

☐ NOTES (Gatto, Roberto & Michael Brecker)
Streggae / Town Street / Green ice blue eyes / Can you make it / Long step / First blues / Pedals / La coda del Gatto
INAK 8805CD / Jul '97 / In Akustik

Gatton, Danny

☐ AMERICAN MUSIC
NCD 34222 / 19 Jan '98 / NRG

☐ IN CONCERT
BIG MO 2028 / 20 Jul '98 / Big Mo

☐ REDNECK JAZZ
NCD 2916 / 19 Jan '98 / NRG

☐ REDNECK JAZZ EXPLOSION (Live In Washington 1978)
NCD 3760 / 19 Jan '98 / NRG

☐ RELENTLESS (Gatton, Danny & Joey DeFrancesco)
BIGMO 2023 / Aug '94 / Big Mo

☐ UNFINISHED BUSINESS
NCD 2479 / 19 Jan '98 / NRG

Gaudreau, Jimmy

☐ LIVE IN HOLLAND (Gaudreau, Jimmy Bluegrass Unit)
SCR 21 / Jul '95 / Strictly Country

Gaughan, Dick

☐ CALL IT FREEDOM
CMCD 041 / Dec '97 / Celtic Music

☐ COPPERS AND BRASS (Scots & Irish Dance Music On Guitar)
Coppers and brass / Gander in the pratie hole / O'Keefe's / Foxhunter's / Flowing tide / Fairies hornpipe / Oak tree / Music in the glen / Planxty Johnson / Gurty's frolics / Spey in spate / Hurricane / Alan MacPherson of Mosspark / Jig of slurs / Thrush in the storm / Flogging reel pipes / Ask my father / Lads of Laois / Connaught heifers / Bird in the bush / Boy in the gap / MacMahon's reel / Strike the gay harp / Shores of Lough Gowna / Jack broke da prison door / Donald blue / Wha'll dance wi' wattie
GLCD 3064 / Oct '93 / Green Linnet

☐ DIFFERENT KIND OF LOVE SONG, A
CMCD 017 / Dec '97 / Celtic Music
APRCD 1018 / Nov '97 / Appleseed

☐ GAUGHAN
Bonnie Jeannie O'Bethelnie / Bonnie lass among the heather / Crooked Jack / Recruited colliers / Pound a week rise / My Donald / Willie o' Winsbury / Such a parcel of rogues in a nation / Gillie Mor
TSCD 384 / Nov '90 / Topic

☐ LIVE IN EDINBURGH
CMCD 030 / Dec '97 / Celtic Music

☐ NO MORE FOREVER
LERCD 2072 / Dec '97 / Leader

☐ PARALLEL LINES (Gaughan, Dick & Andy Irvine)
CDTUT 724007 / Oct '89 / Wundertute

☐ SAIL ON
Land of the North Wind / Son of man / Ruby Tuesday / Waist deep in the big muddy / No cause for alarm / 51st (Highland) Division's farewell to Sicily / No gods and precious few heroes / Geronimo's cadillac / 1952 Vincent black lightning / Sail on / Freedom come all ye
CDTRAX 109 / Jun '96 / Greentrax

☐ SONGS OF EWAN MACCOLL, THE (Gaughan, Dick & Dave Burland/Tony Capstick)
Ballad of accounting / Moving on song / Jamie Foyers / Freeborn man / Manchester rambler / Schooldays end / Thirty foot trailer / Big hewer / First time ever I saw your face
CROCD 215 / Jul '97 / Black Crow

☐ TRUE AND BOLD
STUCCD 002 / Dec '97 / STUC

☐ WOODY LIVES
Hard travellin' / Vigilante man / Deportees / Do re mi / Tom Joad / This land is your land / Pretty boy Floyd / Philadelphia lawyer / Pastures of plenty / Will you miss me
CROCD 217 / Jun '88 / Black Crow

Gaunt

☐ I CAN SEE YOUR MOM FROM HERE
EFACD 115872 / Nov '94 / Crypt

☐ YEAH, ME TOO
ARRCD 66009 / Dec '95 / Amphetamine Reptile

Gauss

☐ ESTRUCTURAS PRIMARIAS
ED 017CD / 6 Apr '98 / Elefant

Gauthe, Jacques

☐ CASSOULET STOMP (Gauthe, Jacques & His Creole Rice Jazzband)
SOSCD 1170 / Feb '89 / Stomp Off

☐ CLARINET SERENADERS (Gauthe, Jacques & Alain Marquet Clarinet Serenaders)
SOSCD 1216 / Oct '92 / Stomp Off

☐ JACQUES GAUTHE & CLAUDE LUTER/ BOB WILBER/CREOLE RICE BAND (Gauthe, Jacques & Claude Luter/Bob Wilber/Creole Rice Band)
BCD 397 / May '98 / GHB

☐ JACQUES GAUTHE & CREOLE RICE YERBA BUENA JAZZBAND
SOSCD 1256 / Apr '94 / Stomp Off

☐ JACQUES GAUTHE & HIS CREOLE RICE JAZZ BAND OF NEW ORLEANS
BCD 331 / Jun '96 / GHB

Gauty, Lys

☐ LYS GAUTY 1932-1933
122 / Nov '92 / Chansophone

Gauze

☐ COLLECTION, THE
JPC 02 / Nov '96 / Japan Punk Collection

Gavin, Frankie

☐ BEST OF FRANKIE GAVIN, THE
RTE 187CD / Dec '95 / RTE/Europe 1

☐ FRANKIE GAVIN & ALEC FINN (Gavin, Frankie & Alec Finn)
SHANCD 34009 / Jan '95 / Shanachie

☐ FRANKIE GOES TO TOWN
John mckenna's reels / Paddy canney's toast / Humours of galway / Walls of liscarroll / Alice's reel / Oak tree / Green fields of america / St. patrick's day / Reels from the 1920's / Mama's pet / Doberman's wallet / Ladies' choice / Maid behind the barrel / Dowry reels / Pigeon on the gate / All about weaving
GLCD 3051 / Oct '93 / Green Linnet

☐ IRELAND
C 570400 / Mar '97 / Ocora

☐ IRISH CHRISTMAS
BK 003CD / Jan '94 / Bee's Knees

☐ IRLANDE (Gavin, Frankie & Arty McGlynn)
C 560021CD / Apr '94 / Oscora

☐ SHAMROCKS AND HOLLY (An Irish Christmas Celebration)
First Noel / Children's first chimes / Silent night / Turkey reel / Adeste fideles / Holly and the ivy / Tommy Cohen's Christmas eve / Angels we have heard on high / Ragtime rudolph / Ding dong merrily / Away in a manger / Holly reel / Hark the Herald angels sing / Jingle bell jazz
SHANCD 78004 / 9 Mar '98 / Shanachie

☐ TRIBUTE TO JOE COOLEY (Gavin, Frankie & Paul Brock)
CEFCD 115 / Jan '94 / Gael Linn

☐ UP AND AWAY
CEFCD 103 / Jan '94 / Gael Linn

Gavioli Fair Organ

☐ TWELFTH STREET RAG
GRCD 63 / May '94 / Grasmere

Gay Gordon

☐ ULTIMATE PARTY ALBUM (Gay Gordon & The Mince Pies)
Happy Birthday to you / 21 today / Celebration / Congratulations / Happy birthday / Birthday medley / Wedding / Wedding march / Wedding march / Conga / Knees up Mother Brown / Hokey cokey / Charleston / Glenn Miller megamix / Essential wally party medley / Anniversary waltz / Last waltz / Agadoo / Can can / Birdie song / Simple Simon says / Big Ben strikes 12 / Auld lang syne / National anthem
XMAS 007 / Nov '96 / Tring

Gay, Noel

☐ SONGS OF NOEL GAY, THE
PASTCD 7035 / Jan '95 / Flapper

Gayden, Mac

☐ NIRVANA BLUES
WH 3305CD / Apr '96 / Winter Harvest

Gaye, Marvin

☐ BEST OF MARVIN GAYE, THE
5302922 / Mar '94 / Motown

☐ DIANA & MARVIN (Gaye, Marvin & Diana Ross)
You are everything / Love twins / Don't knock my love / You're a special part of me / Pledging my love / Just say just say / Stop, look, listen (to your heart) / I'm falling in love with you / My mistake (was to love you) / Include me in your life
5300482 / Jan '93 / Motown

☐ DISTANT LOVER
Third World girl / I heard it through the grapevine / Come get to this / Let's get it on / God is my friend / What's going on / Inner city blues / Joy / Ain't nothing like the real thing / Heaven must have sent you / If this world were mine / Rockin' after midnight / Distant lover / Sexual healing
MU 3003 / Oct '92 / Musketeer

☐ DISTANT LOVER
HADCD 165 / May '94 / Javelin

☐ HERE, MY DEAR
Here my dear / I met a little girl / When did you stop loving me, when did I stop loving you / Anger / Funky space reincarnation / You can leave but it's goin' to cost you / Falling in love again / Is that enough / Everybody needs love / Time to get it together / Sparrow / Anna's song
5302532 / Mar '96 / Motown

☐ I HEARD IT THROUGH THE GRAPEVINE
Stubborn kind of fellow / Pride and joy / Can I get a witness / How sweet it is / Little darling I need you / Chained / I heard it through the grapevine / What's going on / Let's get it on / I want you / World is rated X / Ego tripping out / Trouble man / Unforgettable / What's the matter with you baby / It takes two / If this world were mine / Yesterday / Got to give it up / You are everything
5307932 / Apr '97 / Spectrum

☐ I WANT YOU
I want you / Come live with me angel / Angel / After the dance / Feel all my love inside / I wanna be where you are / All the way round / Since I had you / Soon I'll be loving you again / I want you (intro jam) / After the dance (plus instrumental)
5300212 / Jul '94 / Motown

☐ IN CONCERT
I heard it through the grapevine / Come get to this / Let's get it on / God is love / What's going on / Inner city blues (make me wanna holler) / Joy / Medley / Rockin' after midnight / Distant lover / Sexual healing
CDSGPO 152 / Dec '96 / Prestige

☐ IN CONCERT
I heard it through the grapevine / Sexual healing / Let's get it on / Medley / Come get to this / Distant lover / God is love / Inner city blues / Intermission/ Percussion interlude / What's going on / Joy
100302 / May '97 / A-Play Collection

☐ INNER CITY BLUES (A Tribute To Marvin Gaye) (Various Artists)
Save the children: *Bono* / Let's get it on: *Boyz II Men* / Trouble man: *Cherry, Neneh* / You're the man: *Digable Planets* / Inner city blues: *Gaye, Nona* / I want you: *Madonna & Massive Attack* / God is love/ Mercy mercy me: *Sounds Of Blackness* / What's going on: *Speech* / Just to keep you satisfied: *Stansfield, Lisa* / Stubborn kind of fellow: *Wonder, Stevie*
5304522 / Sep '95 / Motown

☐ LEGENDARY MARVIN GAYE, THE (2CD Set)
Intro / Third world girl / I heard it through the grapevine / Come get to this / Let's get it on / God is my friend / What's goin' on / Inner city blues / Rockin' after midnight / Medley/Ain't nothing like the real thing/Heaven must have se / Joy / Distant lover / Interlude / Sexual healing / Pride and joy / Stubborn kind of fellow / Highlight
ALPCD 102 / Sep '97 / Alpha Entertainments

☐ LET'S GET IT ON
Let's get it on / Please don't stay (once you go away) / If I should die tonight / Keep gettin' it on / Distant lover / You sure love to ball / Just to keep you satisfied / Come get to this
5300552 / Jul '92 / Motown

☐ MASTER 1961 - 1984, THE (4CD Box Set)
5304922 / May '95 / Motown

☐ MIDNIGHT LOVE
Joy / My love is waiting / Midnight lady / Sexual healing / Rockin' after midnight / Till tomorrow / Turn on some music / Third world girl
CD 85977 / Jul '94 / Columbia

☐ MIDNIGHT LOVER, THE (Live In Concert)
I heard it through the grapevine / Come get to this / Let's get it on / God is love / What's going on / Inner city blues / Joy / Ain't nothing like the real thing / Heaven must have sent you / If this world were mine / Rockin' after midnight / Distant lover / Sexual healing
SUMCD 4043 / Nov '96 / Summit

☐ MOTOWN EARLY CLASSICS
How sweet it is (to be loved by you) / No good without you / I'll take care of you / You've been a long time coming / Lucky lucky me / Little darling (I need you) / Stubborn kind of fellow / Never let you go (sha-lu-bop) / I'm yours, you're mine / Wherever I lay my hat (that's my home) / One of these days / Got to get my hands on some lovin' / She's got to be real / Can I get a witness / Now that you've won me / You're a wonderful one / Stepping closer to your heart / Need somebody
5521182 / Jul '96 / Spectrum

☐ ROMANTICALLY YOURS
More / Why did I choose you / Maria / Shadow of your smile / Fly me to the moon / I won't cry anymore / Just like / Walking in the rain / I live for you / Stranger in my life / Happy go lucky
4631582 / Dec '95 / Columbia

☐ SEXUAL HEALING (Live In Indianapolis)
Third world girl / Heard it through the grapevine / Come get to this / Let's get it on / God is my friend / What's going on / Inner city blues (makes me wanna holler) / Joy / Ain't nothing like the real thing / Heaven must have sent your precious love / If this world were mine / Rockin' after midnight / Distant lover / Sexual healing
CD 6047 / Oct '96 / Music

☐ TROUBLE MAN
Trouble man main theme / T plays it cool / Poor Abbey Walsh / Break in (police shoot big) / Cleo's apartment / Trouble man / Trouble man / T stands for trouble / Trouble man main theme / Life is a gamble / Deep in it / Don't mess with Mr. T / There goes mister 'T'
5300972 / Jan '92 / Motown

☐ VULNERABLE
5307862 / Aug '97 / Motown

☐ WHAT'S GOING ON
What's going on / What's happening brother / Flyin' high / Save the children / God is love / Mercy mercy me / Right on / Wholly holy / Inner city blues
5300222 / Jul '94 / Motown

Gaylads

☐ AFTER STUDIO ONE
MRCD 001 / Apr '97 / Metronome

☐ FIRE AND RAIN
HSCD 1004 / Oct '96 / Hot Shot

☐ OVER THE RAINBOW'S END
CDTRL 351 / Apr '95 / Trojan

☐ SOUL BEAT
SOCD 001 / Mar '95 / Studio One

Gayle, Charles

☐ BERLIN MOVEMENT FROM FUTURE YEARS (Gayle, Charles Trio)
FMPCD 90 / Jan '98 / Full Moon

☐ CONSECRATION
1201382 / Nov '93 / Black Saint

☐ DELIVERED (Gayle, Charles Quartet)
Yes God is real / Lord's prayer / Sought me / AMAZING GRACE / Go down Moses / Motherless child / Come out / Receive / These things / Delivered
213CD 024 / Jun '97 / 2.13.61

☐ KINGDOM COME (Gayle, Charles Trio)
KFWCD 157 / Feb '95 / Knitting Factory

☐ MORE LIVE AT THE KNITTING FACTORY (Gayle, Charles Quartet)
KFWCD 137 / Feb '95 / Knitting Factory

☐ RAINING FIRE
SHCD 137 / Oct '94 / Silkheart

☐ REPENT
KFWCD 122 / Nov '94 / Knitting Factory

☐ SOLO IN JAPAN
PSFD 94 / Feb '98 / PSF

☐ TESTAMENTS
KFWCD 174 / Oct '96 / Knitting Factory

☐ TRANSLATION VOL.1
SHCD 134 / Oct '94 / Silkheart

Gayle, Crystal

☐ 20 GREAT LOVE SONGS
Don't it make my brown eyes blue / I wanna come back to you / Going down slow / Make a dream come true / Heart mender / Talking in your sleep / Too good to throw away / Cry me a river / I still miss someone / Dreaming my dreams with you / Someday soon / Hello I love you / Right in the palm of your hand / Beyond you / Woman's heart (is a handy place to be) / I'll get over you / Coming closer / I'll do it all over again / When I dream / Paintin' this old town blue
LS 866612 / 2 Feb '98 / Disky

☐ BEST ALWAYS
Ready for the times to get better / Crazy / For the good times / Silver threads and golden needles / When I dream / Talkin' in your sleep / Oh Lonesome me / I fall to pieces / Beyond you / Don't it make my brown eyes blue / Break my mind
RZRCD 530 / Jun '93 / Ritz

☐ BEST OF CRYSTAL GAYLE, THE
Cry / Turning away / Baby what about you / Straight to the heart / Till I gain control again / Only love can save me now / Long and lasting love / Our love is on the faultline / I don't wanna lose your love / Sound of goodbye
7599256222 / May '94 / Warner Bros.

☐ BEST OF CRYSTAL GAYLE, THE
PLSCD 122 / Jun '96 / Pulse

☐ BEST OF CRYSTAL GAYLE, THE
TRTCD 168 / Jul '96 / TrueTrax

☐ BLUE (All Her Greatest Hits)
Don't it make my brown eyes blue / Take it easy / I don't wanna lose your love / God bless the child / Baby what about you / Lover man / Cry / Love found me / Talking in your sleep / Other side of me / Blue side / Dancing the night away / When I dream / Turning away from love / Crying in the rain / He is beautiful to me / Take me home
308642 / 20 Apr '98 / Hallmark

☐ COUNTRY CLASSICS
Somebody loves you / Don't it make my brown eyes blue / Ready for times to get better / You never miss a real good thing / You / Trouble with me is you / River road / Wrong road again / Talking in your sleep / Why have you left the one you left me for / Green door / Wayward wind / High time / Sweet baby on my mind / Never ending story of love
CDMFP 6324 / Apr '97 / Music For Pleasure

☐ EMI COUNTRY MASTERS (2CD Set)
Somebody loves you / High time / I'll get over you / Woman's heart (Is a handy place to be) / Restless / You / Wrong road again / Beyond you / Hands / Counterfeit love / This is my year for Mexico / Dreaming my dreams with you / One more time (Karneval) / Oh my soul / Come home Daddy / You never miss a real good thing ('Til he says goodbye) / I'll do it all over again / It's all right with me / Going down slow / Make a dream come true / Funny / We must believe in magic / Cry me a river / Wayward wind / Why have you left the one you left me for / Don't it make my brown eyes blue / Ready for the

times to get better / Someday soon / I still miss someone / Talking in your sleep / Green door / Paintin' this old town blue / All I wanna do in life / When I dream / Time will prove I'm right / Your kisses will / Your old cold shoulder / Too deep for tears / We should be together / River road / I wanna come back to you / Heart mender / Everybody's reaching out for someone / Just an old love / Never ending song of love / Once in a very blue moon / Trouble with me is you / Love to, can't do / 99% Of the time / Faithless love
CDEM 1499 / May '93 / EMI

☐ HOLLYWOOD TENNESSEE/TRUE LOVE
Keepin' power / Woman in me / Ain't no sunshine / You never gave up on me / Hollywood / Lovin' in these troubled times / Love crazy love / Lean on me / Crying in the rain / Tennessee / Our love is on the faultline / Deeper in the fire / 'Til I gain control again / Baby what about you / You bring out the lover in me / Take me to the dance / True love / Everything I own / Let your feelings show / Easier said than done / He is beautiful to me
ESMCD 549 / Jun '97 / Essential

☐ LOVE SONGS
Hello I love you / Cry me a river / Dreaming my dreams with you / Someday soon / I'll do it all over again / I wanna come back to you / Somebody loves you / It's all right with me / Coming closer / Don't it make my brown eyes blue / When I dream / I'll get over you / Heart mender / Funny / I still miss someone / Talking in your sleep / Right in the palm of your hand / Beyond you / Going down is slow / Woman's heart (is a handy place to be)
CDMFP 5629 / Aug '96 / Music For Pleasure

☐ MISS THE MISSISSIPPI/THESE DAYS
Half the way / Other side of me / Room for one more / Don't go my love / Dancing the night away / It's like we never said goodbye / Blue side / Little bit of the rain / Danger zone / Miss the Mississippi and you / Too many lovers / If you ever change your mind / Ain't no love in the heart of the city / Same old story (same old song) / Help yourselves to each other / Take it easy / I just can't leave your love alone / You've almost got me believin' / Lover man / What a little moonlight can do
ESMCD 520 / Jun '97 / Essential

☐ SINGLES ALBUM
Somebody loves you / Wrong road again / I'll get over you / High time / Ready for the times to get better / You never miss a real good thing ('Til he says goodbye) / River road / Don't it make my brown eyes blue / When I dream / Talking in your sleep / Why have you left the one you left me for / All I wanna do in life / We should be together / Too deep for tears
CZ 204 / Jul '89 / Liberty

☐ SOMEDAY
Anchor deep / Diamonds from dust / My old friend / He'll be there / I saw / Medley / Medley
RZCD 0083 / Apr '97 / Ritz

☐ SONGBIRD/NOBODY WANTS TO BE ALONE
Sound of goodbye / I don't wanna lose your love / Me against the night / Cage the songbird / Turning away / Come back (when you can stay forever) / Victim or a fool / You made a fool of me / On our way to love / Take me home / Long and lasting love / Tonight, tonight / Nobody wants to be alone / Love does that to fools / Coming to the dance / You were there for me / Touch and go / Someone like you / New way to say I love you / God bless the child
ESMCD 553 / Jul '97 / Essential

☐ STRAIGHT TO THE HEART/NOBODY'S ANGEL
Straight to the heart / Cry / Take this heart / Little bit closer / Do I have to say goodbye / Deep down / Crazy in the heart / Only love can save me now / Nobody should have to love this way / Lonely girl / Nobody's angel / Prove me wrong / Old habits die hard / Tennessee nights / When love is new / Hopeless romantic / Love may find you / Love found me / Heat / After the beast
ESMCD 554 / Jul '97 / Essential

Gayle, Michelle

☐ MICHELLE GAYLE
Get off my back / Happy just to be with you / Walk with pride / Looking up / Girlfriend / Freedom / Personality / It doesn't matter / Your love / Sweetness / One day / Say what's on your mind / Rise up / Baby don't go / All night long
74321234122 / 1 Sep '97 / RCA

Gaynor, Gloria

☐ ALL THE BEST
Heat is on / Everybody wants to rule the world / What a wonderful world / Every breath you take / Suddenly / Every time you go away / Don't you dare call it love / I will survive / Never can say goodbye / Reach out (I'll be there) / I am what I am / I want to know what love is / Broken wings / Careless whisper / He's out of my life / Top shelf / Eye of the tiger / Power of love / Feel so real
305922 / Jan '97 / Hallmark

☐ CARELESS WHISPER
Eye of the tiger / Every breath you take / Broken wings / What a wonderful world / I want to know what love is / Feel so real / He's out of my life / Every time you go away / Everybody wants to rule the world / Careless whisper / Heat is on / Suddenly / Power of love / I will survive / Never can say goodbye / Reach out (I'll be there) / I am what I am / Don't you dare call it love / Top shelf
MU 5075CD / Apr '97 / Start

☐ COLLECTION, THE
I will survive / Reach out, I'll be there / How high the moon / Let me know (I have a right) / All I need is your sweet lovin' / Don't stop us / Substitute / Goin' out of my head / Anybody wanna party / (If you want it) Do it yourself / Can't fight the feeling / One number 1 / I've got you under my skin / Tonight / Honey bee / This love affair / We can start all over again / Walk on by / I am what I am
5518392 / Mar '96 / Spectrum

☐ GLORIA GAYNOR - THE HITS
OVCCD 003 / Mar '94 / Satellite Music

☐ GLORIA GAYNOR ALBUM, THE
MACCD 374 / 30 Mar '98 / Autograph

☐ GREATEST HITS
13885992 / Jun '97 / Galaxy

☐ HITS OF GLORIA GAYNOR, THE
Stop in the name of love / I will survive / Runaround love / For you, my love / Mack side / Love me real / Tease me / America / Even a fool would let go
12665 / Apr '96 / Laserlight

☐ I AM WHAT I AM
MU 5045 / Oct '92 / Musketeer

☐ I WILL SURVIVE (The Best Of Gloria Gaynor)
I will survive / Honey bee / Never can say goodbye / Reach out, I'll be there / Let me know (I have a right) / How high the moon / Casanova Brown / (If you want it) Do it yourself / I am what I am / All I need is your sweet lovin / Walk on by / We can start all over again / Let's mend what's been broken / I will survive (Classic 12" mix)
5196652 / Mar '96 / Polydor

☐ I WILL SURVIVE
I will survive / Reach out, I'll be there / (If you want it) do it yourself / I am what I am / Reason for the season / Can't take my eyes off you / How high the moon / Never can say goodbye / Feelings / Mama San
QED 026 / Nov '96 / Tring

☐ I WILL SURVIVE
I will survive / Mack-side / Runaround love / Even a fool would let go / Stop in the name of love / America / For you, my love / Love me real / Tease me / I will survive
100042 / May '97 / A-Play Collection

☐ POWER OF LOVE, THE
Everytime you go away / Don't you dare call it love / Everybody wants to rule the world / What a wonderful world / Broken wings / Top shelf / Hits medley (I will survive, never can say goodbye, reach ou / Power of love / Eye of the tiger / Heat is on / Feel so real / Suddenly / He's out of my life / Every breath you take / I want to know what love is
ECD 3098 / Jan '95 / K-Tel

Gaze

☐ MITSUMERU
Shady / Jelly bean / Bob again 3 / 400 AD / Anyway 6 / Portrait / Preppy villain / Peeking shows his ignorance / Listen / Eric Idol / Seedless / Turquoise / X reel / You glow
KLP 80 / 2 Feb '98 / K

GBH

☐ CHURCH OF THE TRULY WARPED
Pure greed / Not enough / Leather coffin / Candy man / Lords of discipline / Where the wild things are / Church of the truly warped / Back / I need energy / Evil Evar / All for the cause
PRAGE 008CD / Oct '96 / Powerage

☐ CITY BABIES REVENGE
Diplomatic immunity / Drugs party in 526 / In 526 / See the man run / Vietnamese blues / Womb with a view / Forbidden zone / Valley of death / City baby's revenge / Pins and needles / Christianised cannibals / Faster faster / High octane fuel / I feel alright / Skanga (Herby weed)
CLAYCD 8 / May '90 / Clay
RRCD 258 / 17 Aug '98 / Receiver

☐ CITY BABY ATTACKED BY RATS
Boston babies / Sick boy / Slit your own throat / Willie Whitelaw's willie / Big women / Heavy discipline / Bellend bop / Self destruct / No survivors / Passenger on the menu
CLAYCD 4 / May '90 / Clay
RRCD 257 / 13 Jul '98 / Receiver

☐ CLAY RECORDINGS, THE (2CD Set)
Necrophilia / Generals / No survivors / Sick boy / Time bomb / City baby attacked by rats / Give me fire / Diplomatic immunity / City baby's revenge / Self destruct / Maniac / Boston babies / I feel alright / Slut / Faster faster / Race against time / Dead on arrival / Big women / Freak / Hell hole / Alcohol / Drugs party in 526 / Vietnamese blues / Valley of death / Skanga (Herby weed) / War dogs / Gunned down / Heavy discipline / Do what you do / Children of dust
CLAYDCD 112 / Jul '93 / Clay

☐ CLAY YEARS 1981-1984, THE
Necrophilia / Generals / No survivors / Sick boy / Time bomb / I am the hunted / City baby attacked by rats / Give me fire / Catch 23 / Diplomatic immunity / Womb with a view / City baby's revenge / Christianised cannibals / Four men
CLAYCD 21 / Apr '93 / Clay

☐ DIPLOMATIC IMMUNITY
No survivors / Self destruct / Give me fire / Catch 23 / City baby attacked by rats / Time bomb / Maniac / I am the hunted / Sick boys / Boston babies / I feel alright / Slut / Diplomatic immunity / Pins and needles / Faster, faster / City baby's revenge / Necrophilia / Generals / Womb with a view / Christianised cannibals / Four men
CLAYCD 106 / Apr '93 / Clay

☐ FRIDGE TOO FAR, A
Go home / Twenty floors below / Checking out / Needle inna haystack / See you bleed / Pass the axe / Crossfire / Captain Chaos / Fist of regret / Nocturnal journal
CDJUST 13 / Oct '89 / Rough Justice

☐ FROM HERE TO REALITY
New decade / Trust me, I'm a doctor / B.m.t. / Mass production / Old school of self-destruction / You don't do enough / From here to reality / Dirty too long / Destroy / Just in time for the epilogue / Don't leave your honey down the pits / Moonshine song
PRAGE 007CD / Oct '96 / Powerage

☐ LEATHER BRISTLES STUDS ACNE
Race against time / Knife edge / Lycanthropy / Necrophilia / Sick boy / State executioner / Dead on arrival / Generals / Freak / War dogs / City baby attacked by rats / City baby's revenge
PLATECD 3 / Apr '93 / Clay

☐ LEATHER, BRISTLES/NO SURVIVORS/ SICK BOYS
Race against time / Knife edge / Lycanthropy / Necrophilia / Sale executioner / Dead on arrival / Generals / No surviviors / Self destruct / Big women / Sick boy / Slit your own throat / Am I dead yet freak
CLAYCD 5 / May '90 / Clay

☐ LIVE IN LOS ANGELES
CDPUNK 82 / Sep '96 / Anagram

☐ MIDNIGHT MADNESS AND BEYOND
Limpwristed / Future fugitives / Too much / Iroquis / Guns and guitars / Horror story / Midnight madness / Chance for living / Seed of madness / Sam is your leader / How come / Blood
CDJUST 2 / Aug '87 / Rough Justice

☐ NO NEED TO PANIC
Transylvanian perfume / Hearing screams (for the last time) / To understand / Makin' whips / I shot the marshall / Electricity through space / Hit the deck / Rumblin' underground / Desperate times / Gunning for the president / Avenues and alleyways / Unanswered prayers
CDJUST 7 / '89 / Rough Justice

☐ NO SURVIVORS
Sick boy / Maniac / Time bomb / Necrophilia / I am the hunted / Generals / Catch 23 / Give me fire / City baby attacked by rats / No survivors / Alcohol / Bell end stop
CLAYCD 102 / Apr '93 / Clay

☐ PUNK JUNKIES
WB 1151CD / Sep '96 / We Bite

☐ SINGLES COLLECTION, THE
No survivors / Self destruction / Big woman / Sick boy / Slit your own throat / Am I dead yet / Give me fire / Mantrap / Catch 23 / Hell hole / Race against time / Knife edge / Lycanthropy / Necrophilia / State executioner / Dead on arrival / Generals / Freak / Do what you do / Four men / Children of dust
CLAYCD 119 / Jul '95 / Clay

Gealtra

☐ GEALTRA
GEAL 001CD / Mar '98 / Geal

Gean, Ralph

☐ STAR UNBORN, A
Homicidal me / Hey Doctor Casey / Japanese rain song / Planet of the rain / Granny's grave / You're drivin' me crazy / Asshole song / Bobbit song / Star trekkin' rock 'n' roll cowboy / Hard to be a killer / Godess of love / Experimental love / Guitar pickin' teabag / Wearin' that loved on look
HH 3307CD / Jul '97 / Hierarchy

Gear

☐ BED AND BREAKFAST
HAIR 7 / Feb '96 / Hair

Geballe, Tony

☐ NATIVE OF THE RAIN
DGM 9703 / 29 Sep '97 / Discipline

Geckoes

☐ ART GECKO
OCK 003CD / Jul '95 / Ock

Gee, Jonathan

☐ CLOSER TO (Gee, Jonathan Trio)
Lifecycle / Prayer to love / Bye bye blackbird / In a sentimental mood / Serious red / Why / Everybody's song but my own / Closer to
ASCCD 14 / Mar '97 / ASC

☐ YOUR SHINING HEART (Gee, Jonathan Trio)
Fevo dreaming / Lions of jaffa / Welcome / Love thoughts / Your shining heart / Cawoman / Limbe / William's treat / Blues for plews / Happy Birthday Winston
ASCCD 21 / 9 Feb '98 / ASC

Gee, Peter

☐ VISION OF ANGELS, A
PEND 8CD / Apr '97 / Pendragon/Toff

Geers, Didier

☐ IT AIN'T THE MEAT, IT'S THE MOTION (Geers, Didier Group)
MECCACD 1072 / May '97 / Music Mecca

Geesin, Ron

☐ RAISE OF EYEBROWS, A/AS HE STANDS
Raise of eyebrows / Freedom for four voices and me / Psychedelia / Positives / It's all very new, you know / Female / Certainly random / Eye that nearly saw / Two fifteen string guitars for nice poeple / From an electric train / World of too much sound / Another female / We're all going to Liverpool / Ha ha but reasonable / Can't stop that thing / Looming view / Rise up Sebastian / Concrete line up / Upon composition / Mr. Peugeot's trot / To Roger Waters wherever you are / Cymbal and much electronics / Up above my heart / Twist and knit for two guitars / Wrap a keyboard round a plant / Middle of whose night / Waiting for life / On-through-out-up / Duet for two and street market / Roll 'em, bowl 'em - in three movements
SEECD 433 / Nov '97 / See For Miles

Geet

☐ NO PROBLEM
CDSR 012 / May '90 / Star

Geezer

☐ BLACK SCIENCE
EAGCD 001 / Jul '97 / Eagle
TVT 60202 / Jun '97 / TVT

Geezer Lake

☐ KING FROST PARADE
THK 040 / Feb '97 / Thick

Gege & The Mother Tongue

☐ MOTHER TONGUE
GOJ 60182 / 8 Jun '98 / Go Jazz

Gehenna

☐ ADIMIRION BLACK
FOG 016CD / 6 Jul '98 / Moonfog

☐ FIRST SPELL
HNF 003CD / Jun '96 / Head Not Found

☐ MALICE
NIHIL 16CD / Sep '96 / Cacophonous

☐ SEEN THROUGH THE VEILS OF DARKNESS (The Second Spell)
Lord of flies / Shairak Kinnummh / Vinterriket / Witch is born / Through the veils of darkness / Mystical play of shadows / Eves of the sun / Myth / Dark poems author
NIHIL 9CD / Jun '97 / Cacophonous

Gehhenah

☐ DECIBEL REBEL
OPCD 065 / 2 Mar '98 / Osmose

☐ KING OF THE SIDEWALK
OPCD 046 / Nov '96 / Osmose

Gehrman, Shura

☐ ENGLISH SONGS
Songs of travel / Shropshire lad / Selected songs
NI 5033 / '88 / Nimbus

☐ FOLKSONGS OF THE BRITISH ISLES
NI 5082 / '88 / Nimbus

Geils, J. Band

☐ BEST OF THE J. GEILS BAND, THE
Southside shuffle / Give it to me / Where did our love go / Ain't nothing but a house party / Detroit breakdown / Whammer jammer / I do / Must of got lost / Looking for a love
7567815572 / Feb '84 / WEA

☐ CENTREFOLD
Sanctuary / One last kiss / Take it back / Come back / Love stinks / Til the walls come tumbling down / Just can't wait / Centrefold / Flamethrower / Freeze-frame / Piss on the wall / Angel in blue / I do / Land of 1,000 dances / Concealed weapons / You're getting even while I'm getting odd
VSOPCD 234 / Mar '97 / Connoisseur Collection

☐ FREEZE FRAME
Freeze frame / Rage in the cage / Centrefold / Do you remember when / Insane, insane again / Flamethrower / River blindness / Angel in blue / Piss on the wall
BGOCD 196 / Jul '93 / Beat Goes On

☐ LADIES INVITED
Chimes / Did you no wrong / Diddyboppin' / I can't go on / Lady makes demands / Lay your good thing down / My baby don't love me / No doubt about it / Take a chance (on romance) / That's why I'm thinking of you
7567814312 / Feb '95 / Atlantic

☐ LOVE STINKS
Just can't wait / Come back / Takin' you down / Night time / No anchovies, please / Love stinks / Tryin' not to think about it / Desire / Till the walls come tumblin' down
BGOCD 254 / Dec '94 / Beat Goes On

☐ SANCTUARY
I could hurt you / One last kiss / Take it back / Sanctuary / Teresa / Wild man / I can't believe you / I don't hang around much anymore / Jus' can't stop me
BGOCD 262 / May '95 / Beat Goes On

☐ SANCTUARY
RE 821732 / 1 Sep '98 / Razor & Tie

☐ SHOWTIME
Jus' can't stop me / Just can't wait / Till the walls come tumblin' down / Sanctuary / I'm falling / Love rap / Love stinks / Stoop down 39 / I do / Centrefold / Land of 1000 dances
BGOCD 264 / Nov '95 / Beat Goes On

Geissler, Ladi

☐ MINOR SWING
Kissin' on the beach / ADAC / Samba pa ti / Persian market / Dos Pajasos / Wave / Minor swing / Sunrise serenade / Siboney / Ballade fur Birgit / Andalusia / Johnny Guitar / Lovesong for Effi / One more for my lady
BCD 16227 / Nov '97 / Bear Family

☐ MR. GUITAR
Mason Dixon line / Cannonball / Lonely guitar / Navajo / 40 miles of bad road / Colorado rock / Wheels / Gesterreiter / Red River rock / Dreaming guitar / Tomahawk / Stormy night guitar / Zwei gitarren / Johnny Guitar / Swing guitar / Ladi's guitar boogie / Gitarren spielt auf / Amazonas paddleboot / La guitara Brasiliana / Guitar lullaby / Zwei gitarren am Meer / Mr. Guitar / Tango Helena / Little Geisha / Indigo / Yellow bird / Immer nur Lacheln / Auf einem persischen Markt / Little darlin' / Banana boat song
BCD 16197 / Nov '97 / Bear Family

Geist, Morgan

☐ DRIVING MEMOIRS, THE
Doorbell / Flat out / Resolved / Linking tunnel / This too shall pass / Highway hipnosis / Food and fuel / Detoured / Self-init / You didn't see me
CLR 437CD / 24 Nov '97 / Clear

☐ INTO A SEPERATE SPACE
Embark / Airpour / Current / Minijupe / Postcard / Cusp / Intronic / Frebics / Inyour electronic arms / Overcast / Outronic
PHONOCD 3 / 2 Feb '98 / Phonography

Gelato, Ray

☐ FULL FLAVOUR, THE (Gelato, Ray's Giants Of Jive)
AKD 034 / Mar '95 / Linn

☐ GANGSTERS OF SWING
ND 20742 / 10 Nov '97 / Durium

☐ GELATO ALL'ITALIANA
NDCD 209 / May '97 / Durium

☐ GELKATO ESPRESSO
NDCD 203 / May '97 / Durium

Geldof, Bob

☐ LOUD MOUTH (The Best Of Bob Geldof/Boomtown Rats)
I don't like Mondays: *Boomtown Rats* / This is the world calling / Rat trap: *Boomtown Rats* / Great song of indifference / Love or something / Banana republic: *Boomtown Rats* / Crazy / Elephant's graveyard: *Boomtown Rats* / Someone's looking at you: *Boomtown Rats* / She's so modern: *Boomtown Rats* / House on fire: *Boomtown Rats* / Beat of the night / Diamond smiles: *Boomtown Rats* / Like clockwork: *Boomtown Rats* / Room 19 (Sha la la la lee) / Mary of the 4th form: *Boomtown Rats* / Looking after no. 1: *Boomtown Rats*
5222832 / Apr '94 / Vertigo

Geller, Herb

☐ HERB GELLER PLAYS AL COHN
Mr. George / Danielle / Mr. Music / Halley's comet / Pensive / Flugelbird / High on you / You 'n me / Woody's lament / El cajon / Underdog / Tasty pudding / T'ain't no use / Infinity
HEPCD 2066 / Mar '96 / Hep

☐ JAZZ SONG BOOK, A
60062 / Nov '89 / Tiptoe

☐ PLAYING JAZZ
FSR 5011CD / Nov '97 / Fresh Sound

☐ THAT GELLER FELLER
FSRCD 091 / Jul '92 / Fresh Sound

Gema Y Pavel

☐ COSA DE BROMA
La caminadora / Jurame / Aixa / Ay del amor / Longina / Mayeya / Noche de ronda / El zun zun / Te amo / Girl / 'Hacia donde / Oshe
INT 31812 / Sep '96 / Intuition

☐ TRAMPAS DEL TIEMPO
Domingo AM / El bobo / Lo feo / Habana, devorando claridad / Trampas del tiempo / Parar de fumar / Ay, Maria / La capital / Marginal DS / Huella del azar / Helado sobre ruedas / La carretera, fuera de tiempo / Bajo la luna / Al bord de la locura / Guajira a la Algeria / Parar de fumar
INT 31792 / Dec '96 / Intuition

Gemini

☐ IN AND OUT OF FOG AND LIGHTS
New style of / Deep shade / Freefall / I / Pelargonium / 2007 / Z funk / Fizz
PF 070CD / 22 Sep '97 / Peacefrog

☐ IN NEUTRAL
SUB 48442 / 1 Dec '97 / Distance

Gemini Gemini

☐ FLAVOURS OF THELONIUS MONK, THE
ITMP 970082 / Oct '95 / ITM

☐ GEMINI GEMINI
ITMP 970063 / Oct '95 / ITM

Genaro, Tano

☐ PIONNIER DU TANGO ARGENTIN
883142 / Aug '93 / Music Memoria

Genaside II

☐ NEW LIFE 4 THE HUNTED (2CD Set)
New life 4 the hunted / Distant noises: *Genaside II & Rose Windross* / Waistline firecracker: *Genaside II & Killerman Archer* / Come to the fools: *Genaside II & Sharon Williams* / Just as rough: *Genaside II & Eek-A-Mouse* / Narra mine: *Genaside II & Sharon Williams* / Choose ya weapon: *Genaside II & Killerman Archer/Otherized FAM* / Blacker shade: *Genaside II & Rose Windross* / Why you watching me: *Genaside II & Rose Windross* / Basic killer instinct: *Genaside II & Killerman Archer/Otherized FAM/Cappadonna* / Under the bridge: *Genaside II & Rose Windross* / Blue precious metal / New life II the hunted: *Genaside II & Rose Windross* / Waistline firecracker: *Genaside II & Killerman Archer* / Distant noises: *Genaside II & Rose Windross* / Blue precious metal / Why you watching me: *Genaside II & Rose Windross*
TRUCD 14
TRUDC 14 / Sep '96 / Internal

Gencturk, Vedad

☐ ART OF THE TURKISH UD, THE
ARN 60265 / Sep '96 / Arion

Gene

☐ DRAWN TO THE DEEP END
GENEC 3
GENED 3 / Feb '97 / Costermonger

☐ OLYMPIAN
Haunted by you / Your love, it lies / Truth, rest your head / Car that sped / Left-handed / London, can you wait / To the city / Still can't find the phone / Sleep well tonight / Olympian / We'll find our own way
5274462 / Feb '97 / Costermonger

☐ TO SEE THE LIGHTS
Be my light, be my guide / Sick, sober and sorry / Her fifteen years / Haunted by you / I can't decide if she really loves me / Car that sped / For the dead (version) / Sleep well tonight / How much for love / London, can you wait / I can't help myself / Child's body / Don't let me down / I say a little prayer / Do you want to hear it from me / This is not my crime / Olympian / For the dead
5298072 / Feb '97 / Costermonger

Gene Loves Jezebel

☐ HOUSE OF DOLLS, THE
Gorgeous / Motion of love / Set me free / Suspicion / Every door / Twenty killer hurts / Treasure / Message / Drowning crazy / Up there
BEGA 87CD / Oct '87 / Beggars Banquet

☐ IMMIGRANTS
Always a flame / Shame / Stephen / Immigrant / Thin things / Cow / Worth waiting for / Rhino plasty / Deep south Wales / Cole Porter / One someone / Gorgeous
SITU 14CD / Jan '88 / Situation 2

☐ IN THE AFTERGLOW (2CD Set)
PINKGCD 1 / Oct '95 / Pink Gun

☐ PROMISE
Screaming for Emmalie / Bread from heaven / Wraps and arms / Upstairs / Psychological problems / Scheming / Influenza / Punch drunk
SITL 7CD / '88 / Situation 2

General Degree

☐ GENERAL DEGREE
VPCD 1491 / May '97 / VP

General Echo

☐ 12" OF PLEASURE
Lorna she love young boy banana / It's my desire to set your crutches on fire / Me know everything about she pum pum / Old man love young gal vegie / This are the cockie tribulation / Bathroom sex / This a loves corner / Love me waist don't bother me face / Love bump / She have a pair of headlamp breast
GRELCD 15 / Mar '97 / Greensleeves

General Lafayette

☐ JESTER
Oh my beloved Father / Power of music / Love in the eyes of a child / Blow the trumpet at the new moon / Trumpet on fire / Going back to Scotland / Jester / Gentle to the soul / Lizzie's song (Is on the radio) / Sentimental value / Jupiter / Burn's theme / Silent anguish / Country barn dance
PZA 003CD / Mar '93 / Plaza

☐ KING OF THE BROKEN HEARTS
King of the broken hearts / True love will never die / Like a story you read in a book / Country blues / Strictly continental / Arrivederci magdalena / Song for ray / Only love can break your heart / Man and the fool / Trapped in the webs of love / Impossible to do / Sad samba / Lonely is the night / Trumpet concerto for the girl who doesn't believe
PZA 007CD / Nov '89 / Plaza

☐ LOVE IS A RHAPSODY
Angel in blue / For the girl who couldn't find love / Melody for you / Florence serenade / Love is a rhapsody / Life is for loving / Lonely trumpet / Love you love me Aloha
PZA 001CD / Jul '88 / Plaza

☐ PIERROT
PZA 009CD / Apr '91 / Plaza

General Levy

☐ RUMBLE IN THE JUNGLE VOL.1 (General Levy & Top Cat)
Birk's works / Birk's works / Japanese folk song / Misterioso / Lulu's back in town / Ruby my dear / Wrap your troubles in dreams / Blues for strayhorn / For you again / Creator has a master plan / Child within / Mood indigo
JFCD 001 / Jan '95 / Fashion

☐ WICKEDER GENERAL, THE
FADCD 024 / Dec '92 / Fashion

General Pecos

☐ BACK WITH A VENGEANCE
Controversy / Run come / Ghetto life / Gummy glue don / Hardcore lover / Love me so bad / Right stuff / Mad house / See dem deh / Under bondage
WRCD 010 / Nov '97 / World

☐ TALK BOUT GUN
GRELCD 185 / Jun '93 / Greensleeves

General Public

☐ RUB IT BETTER
Tough / Rainy days / Hold it deep / Big bed / Punk / Friends again / It's weird / Never not alone / Handgun / Blowhard / Warm love / Rub it better
4783582 / Oct '95 / Epic

General TK

☐ I SPY
GRELCD 183 / Mar '93 / Greensleeves

General Trees

☐ RAGGA RAGGA RAGAMUFFIN
Break my lyric store / Ragga ragga ragamuffin / Lover's affair / Pick up my chick / Mash mouth bus / Granit / Youth stop the gaze / I like the thing / Girl love I / Dangerous
RRTGCD 7702 / Aug '88 / Rohit

Generation

☐ BRUTAL REALITY
CDZORRO 82 / Nov '94 / Metal Blade

Generation X

☐ GENERATION X
Hundred punks / Listen / Ready steady go / Kleenex / Promises, promises / Day by day / Invisible man / Kiss me deadly / Too personal / Valley of the dolls / Running with the boss sound / Night of the cadillacs / Friday's angels / King rocker / Wild youth / Dancing with myself / Triumph / Revenge / Youth youth youth / From the heart
CDGOLD 1039 / Jul '96 / EMI Gold

☐ SWEET REVENGE
MUTINY 14 / 18 May '98 / Mutiny

Generators

☐ WELCOME TO THE END
TX 51249CD / 1 Jun '98 / Triple XXX

Genesis

☐ ABACAB
No reply at all / Me and Sarah Jane / Keep it dark / Dodo / Lurker / Man on the corner / Who dunnit / Like it or not / Another record / Abacab
CBRCDX 102 / Oct '94 / Charisma

☐ AND THEN THERE WERE THREE
Scenes from a night's dream / Snowbound / Ballad of big / Burning rope / Deep in the motherlode / Down and out / Follow you follow me / Lady lies / Many too many / Say it's alright Joe / Undertow
CDSCDX 4010 / Oct '94 / Charisma

☐ ARCHIVE 1967-1975 (4CD Set)
Stagnation / Broadway melody of 1974 / Firth of fifth (live) / Watcher of the skies / One day (demo) / Where the sour turns to sweet / Counting out time / Hey / She is beautiful (demo) / Patricia (demo) / Magic of time / More fool me (live) / Hidden in the world of dawn (demo) / Sea bee (demo) / Mystery of the Flannen Isle lighthouse (demo) / Riding the scree / In the rapids / Shepherd / Lilywhite Lilith / Cuckoo cocoon / Going out to get you / Dusk / Image blown out / Hair on the arms and legs / Lamb lies down on Broadway / Let us now make love / It / Anyway / Fly on the windshield / Dancing on the moonlit knight / Twilight alehouse / I know what I know what I like (live) / Suppers ready (live) / Light dies down on Broadway / Build me a mountain / Chamber of 32 doors / Hairless heart / Here comes the supernatural anaesthetist / Lamia / Pacidy / Waiting room / Silent sorrow in empty boats / In the beginning / Happy the man / In the cage / Ravine / Colony of slippermen / Try a little sadness (demo) / Back in NYC / Grand parade of lifeless packaging / In the wilderness
CDBOX 6 / 22 Jun '98 / Charisma

☐ CALLING ALL STATIONS
Calling all stations / Congo / Shipwrecked / Alien afternoon / Not about us / If that's what you need / Dividing line / Uncertain weather / Small talk / There must be some other way / One man's fool
GENCD 6 / 1 Sep '97 / Virgin

☐ DUKE
Behind the lines / Duchess / Guide vocal / Man of our times / Misunderstanding / Heathaze / Turn it on again / Alone tonight / Cul-de-sac / Please don't ask / Duke's end / Duke's travels
CBRCDX 101 / Oct '94 / Charisma

☐ FOX LIES DOWN, THE (Tribute To Genesis) (Various Artists)
CLP 0287 / 6 Jul '98 / Cleopatra

☐ FOXTROT
Watcher of the skies / Time table / Get 'em out by Friday / Can-utility and the coastliners / Horizon / Supper's ready
CASCDX 1058 / Aug '94 / Charisma

☐ GENESIS
Mama / Illegal alien / That's all / Taking it all too hard / Just a job to do / Home by the sea / Second home by the sea / It's gonna get better / Silver rainbow
GENCD 1 / Dec '83 / Charisma

☐ GENESIS LIVE
Watcher of the skies / Get 'em out by friday / Knife / Return of the giant hogweed / Musical box
CLACDX 1 / Aug '94 / Charisma

☐ INTERVIEW COMPACT DISC
CBAK 4028 / Sep '90 / Baktabak

☐ INTERVIEW, THE
SPEEK 010 / 16 Mar '98 / Talking Music

☐ INVISIBLE TOUCH
Invisible touch / Tonight tonight tonight / Land of confusion / In too deep / Anything she does / Domino / Throwing it all away / Brazilian
GENCD 2 / Dec '86 / Charisma

☐ LAMB LIES DOWN ON BROADWAY, THE
Lamb lies down on Broadway / Riding the scree / In the rapids / It / Fly on a windshield / Broadway melody of 1974 / Cuckoo cocoon / In the cage / Grand parade of lifeless packaging / Back in NYC / Hairless heart / Counting out time / Carpet crawlers / Chamber of 32 doors / Lilywhite lilith / Waiting room / Anyway / Here comes the supernatural anaesthetist / Lamia / Silent sorrow in empty boats / Colony of slippermen (The arrival) / Colony of slippermen (A visit to the doctor) / Colony of slippermen (The-Raven) / Ravine / Light dies down on Broadway
CGSCDX 1 / Aug '94 / Charisma

☐ NURSERY CRYME
Musical box / For absent friends / Return of the giant hogweed / Seven stones / Harold the barrel / Harlequin / Fountain of Salmacis
CASCDX 1052 / Aug '94 / Charisma

☐ RIVER OF CONSTANT CHANGE, A (A Tribute To Genesis/2CD Set) (Various Artists)
MMP 270 / 27 Apr '98 / Mellow

☐ SECONDS OUT
Squonk / Carpet crawlers / Robbery, assault and battery / Afterglow / Firth of fifth / I know what I like (in your wardrobe) / Lamb lies down on Broadway / Musical box (closing section) / Supper's ready / Cinema show / Dance on a volcano / Los Endos
GECDX 2001 / Sep '94 / Virgin

☐ SELLING ENGLAND BY THE POUND
Dancing with the moonlit knight / I know what I like (in your wardrobe) / Firth of fifth / More fool me / Battle of Epping Forest / After the ordeal / Cinema show / Aisle of plenty
CASCDX 1074 / Aug '94 / Charisma

☐ SELLING ENGLAND BY THE POUND/ THE LAMB LIES DOWN ON BROADWAY (3CD Set)
TPAK 17 / Nov '91 / Virgin

☐ SUPPER'S READY (A Tribute To Genesis) (Various Artists)
RR 89122 / Nov '95 / Roadrunner

☐ THREE SIDES LIVE
Behind the lines / Duchess / Me and Sarah Jane / Follow you follow me / One for the vine / Fountain of Salmacis / Watcher of the skies / Turn it on again / Dodo / Abacab / Misunderstanding / In the cage / Afterglow / Paperlate / You might recall / Me and Virgil / Evidence of autumn / Open door
GECDX 2002 / Oct '94 / Virgin

☐ TRESPASS
Looking for someone / White mountain / Visions of angels / Stagnation / Dusk / Knife
CASCDX 1020 / Aug '94 / Charisma

☐ TRESPASS/NURSERY CRYME/ FOXTROT (3CD Set)
Looking for someone / White mountain / Visions of angels / Stagnation / Dusk / Knife / Watcher of the skies / Time table / Get 'em out by friday / Can-utility and the coastliners / Horizons / Supper's ready / Musical box / For absent friends / Return of the giant hogweed / Seven stones / Harold the barrel / Harlequin / Fountain of salmacis
TPAK 1 / Oct '90 / Virgin

☐ TRICK OF THE TAIL, A
Dance on a volcano / Entangled / Squonk / Madman moon / Robbery, assault and battery / Ripples / Trick of the tail / Los Endos
CDSCDX 4001 / Oct '94 / Charisma

☐ WAY WE WALK, THE (The Shorts)
Land of confusion / No son of mine / Jesus he knows me / Throwing it all away / I can't dance / Mama / Hold on my heart / That's all / In too deep / Tonight tonight tonight / Invisible touch
GENCD 4 / Nov '92 / Virgin

☐ WAY WE WALK, THE (The Longs)
Drum duet / Dance on a volcano / Lamb lies down on broadway / Musical box / Firth of fifth / I know what I like (in your wardrobe) / Driving the last spike / Domino / Fading lights / Home by the sea / Second home by the sea
GENCD 5 / Jan '93 / Virgin

☐ WE CAN'T DANCE
No son of mine / Jesus he knows me / Driving the last spike / I can't dance / Never a time / Dreaming while you sleep / Tell me why / Living forever / Hold on my heart / Way of the world / Since I lost you / Fading lights
GENCD 3 / Nov '91 / Virgin

☐ WE KNOW WHAT WE LIKE (The Music Of Genesis) (London Symphony Orchestra/David Palmer)
Turn it on again (guide vocal) / Mad man moon / Entangled / Follow you follow me / I know what I like / Horizons / Can-utility and the coastliners / Undertow-supper's ready
07863562422 / Jul '95 / RCA Victor

☐ WIND AND WUTHERING
Eleventh Earl of Mar / One for the vine / Your own special way / Wot gorilla / All in a mouse's night / Blood on the rooftops / Unquiet slumbers for the sleepers / In that quiet earth / Afterglow
CDSCDX 4005 / Oct '94 / Charisma

Genetic

☐ WE ARE GENETIC
Floor (sonic shakedown) / Gala / Uptown downtown / Transmission / Change / Drop the bomb / Fat boy / 42nd Street hustle / Lexus / Analogico
BFLCD 30 / 11 May '98 / Butterfly

Genetic Control

☐ FIRST IMPRESSIONS
LF 069 / Jan '94 / Lost & Found

Genetic Drugs

☐ KARMA CLUB
39850102 / 24 Feb '98 / Blue Flame

☐ KARMA PHARMA
398501112 / 24 Feb '98 / Blue Flame

Genetik System

☐ INITIATIK
DI 432 / Feb '97 / Distance

Geneva

☐ FURTHER
NUDE 7CD / Jun '97 / Nude

Genf

☐ IMPORT/EXPORT
COMP 035CD / Jun '97 / Compost

Genie

☐ ONE WORLD EXPERIENCE
Rhythm talking / One world / Who killed Jesus / Rhythm talking / Attitude / Attitude / Some people / Black rock / Attitude / Utopia / Wild friends / One world / Mary's freedom train / Comet hopper / Some people / City life / Lonely world / Acid tribe
JUMPCD 1 / Jun '97 / Strobe

Genitorturers

☐ 120 DAYS OF GENITORTURE
CDFLAG 81 / Oct '93 / Under One Flag

☐ SIN CITY
SPV 08518912 / 6 Apr '98 / SPV
CLEO 239 / 7 Apr '98 / Cleopatra

Genius/GZA

☐ LIQUID SWORDS
Liquid swords / Duel of the iron mic / Living in the world today / Gold / Cold world / Labels / 4th Chamber / Shadowboxin' / Hell's wind staff / Killah hills 10304 / Investigate reports / Swordsman / I gotcha back / Basic instructions / Before leaving earth: *Genius At Work*
GED 24813 / Nov '95 / Geffen

Gente, Misma

☐ CALICHE
RMD 81290 / 24 Mar '98 / RMM

Gentiane

☐ MUSIQUE D'AUVERGNE
MW 4013CD / Aug '97 / Music & Words

Gentle Giant

☐ ACQUIRING THE TASTE
Pentagruel's nativity / Edge of twilight / House the street the room / Acquiring the taste / Wreck / Moon is down / Black cat / Plain truth
8429172 / Feb '97 / Vertigo

☐ CIVILIAN
A 28591 / Nov '97 / One Way

☐ EDGE OF TWILIGHT (2CD Set)
Advent of panurge / Funny ways / Peel the paint / Acquiring the taste / Cogs in cogs / House, the street, the moon / Boys in the band / Schooldays / Raconteur troubadour / Wreck / Nothing at all / Why not / Playing the game / Mister class and quality / Three friends / Proclaimation / Cry for everyone / Isn't it quiet and cold / Plain truth / Knots / Alucard / Aspirations / Pantagruel's nativity / River / Face / Moon is down / Edge of twilight / No God's a man / So sincere / Think of me with kindness / Valedictory
5341012 / Oct '96 / Vertigo

☐ GENTLE GIANT
Alucard / Funny ways / Giant / Isn't it quiet and cold / Nothing at all / Queen / Why not
8426242 / Feb '97 / Vertigo

☐ KING BISCUIT PRESENTS...
Proclamation / Funny ways / Runaway / Experience / So sincere / Knots / Advent of panurge
KBFHCD 004 / 27 Apr '98 / King Biscuit

☐ LAST TIME - LIVE 1980, THE
TRUCKCD 1010 / Apr '94 / Terrapin Truckin'

☐ LIVE - PLAYING THE FOOL
Just the song / Proclamation / On reflection / Excerpts from Octopus / Funny ways / Runaway / Experience / So sincere / Freehand / Breakdown in Brussels / Peel the paint / I lost my head
TRUCKCD 1009 / Dec '94 / Terrapin Truckin'

☐ LIVE IN CONCERT
Two weeks in Spain / Free hand / On reflection / Just the same / Playing the game / Memories of old days / Betcha thought we couldn't do it / I'm turning around / For nobody / Mark time
WINCD 066 / Oct '94 / Windsong

☐ OCTOPUS
Advent of panurge / Raconter troubadour / Cry for everyone / Knots / Boys in the band / Dog's life / Think of me with kindness / River
8426942 / Feb '97 / Vertigo

☐ OUT OF THE FIRE (2CD Set)
HUX 008 / 1 Sep '98 / Hux

Gentle People

☐ SOUNDTRACKS FOR LIVING
CAT 045CD / Jan '97 / Rephlex

Gentle Readers

☐ YOU IN BLACK AND WHITE
FLT 112CD / 29 Jun '98 / Flat Earth

Gentlemen Of Jazz

☐ 10 YEARS ANNIVERSARY
MECCACD 1067 / May '97 / Music Mecca

☐ BLUE AND GENTLE
MECCACD 2053 / Jan '98 / Music Mecca

☐ THIRD TIME ROUND
MECCACD 130591 / Nov '94 / Music Mecca

☐ WE'LL MEET AGAIN
MECCACD 1026 / Nov '94 / Music Mecca

Gentry, Bobbie

☐ BEST OF BOBBIE GENTRY, THE
Ode to Billie Joe / All I have to do is dream / I'll never fall in love again / Raindrops keep falling on my head / Mississippi delta / Little green apples / Natural to be gone / Son of a preacher man / Season come, seasons go / Gentle on my mind / Touch 'em with love / Where's the playground Johnny / My elusive dreams / Grey hound goin' somewhere / You've made me so very happy / Mornin' glory / I wouldn't be surprised / Ace insurance man / Glory hallelujah, how they'll sing / Let it be me
CDMFP 6115 / Mar '94 / Music For Pleasure

☐ TOUCH 'EM WITH LOVE
CREV 038CD / Nov '95 / Rev-Ola

Génty, Alain

☐ LA COULEUR DU MILIEU
GWP 006CD / Jul '94 / Gwerz

☐ LE GRAND ENCRIER
KMCD 92 / 1 Jun '98 / Keltia Musique

Geordie

☐ DON'T BE FOOLED BY THE NAME
REP 4124 / Aug '91 / Repertoire

☐ HOPE YOU LIKE IT
REP 4033 / Aug '91 / Repertoire

☐ VERY BEST OF BRIAN JOHNSON AND GEORDIE, THE
All because of you / Black cat woman / House of the Rising Sun / Electric lady / Natural born loser / Geordie stomp / I cried today / We're all right now / Francis was a rocker / Going to the city / Rock 'n' roll fever / You do this to me
100632 / May '97 / A-Play Collection

George Banton

☐ BEST OF GEORGE BANTON, THE
LDRCD 022 / Apr '97 / Londisc

☐ JESUS IS EVERYTHING 2 ME
CRCD 57 / Jan '97 / Charm

☐ YOU'RE ALL I NEED
CRCD 58 / Jul '97 / Charm

George, Iwer

☐ AH READING
JW 142CD / 14 Apr '98 / JW

George, Lowell

☐ ROCK 'N' ROLL DOCTOR (A Tribute To Lowell George) (Various Artists)
607686242 / 24 Mar '98 / CMC

☐ THANKS I'LL EAT IT HERE
What do you want the girl to do / Honest man / Two trains / Can't stand the rain / Cheek to cheek / Easy money / Twenty million things / Find a river / Himmler's ring
7599267552 / Jul '93 / WEA

George, Siwsann

☐ CANEUON TRADDODIADOL CYMRU (Traditional Songs Of Wales)
Adar man y mynydd / Y gwcw fach / Can Merthyr / Miner's life / Blodau'r flwyddyn / Hen ferchetan / Hiraeth / Can y Cardi / Cainc yr aradwr / Titrwm tatrwm / Yr hen wr mwyn / Yr eneth gadd ei gwrthod / Bachgen bach o dincer / Mae'r ddaear yn glasu / Ar fore Dydd Nadolig / Clywch clywch / Llangollen market / Can y bugail / Lisa lan / Marwnad yr ehedydd / Llongau Caernarfon / Yr insiwrans agent / Rhybudd i'r carwr
CDSDL 406 / Sep '94 / Saydisc

George, Sophia

☐ LATEST SLANG
Latest slang / Runnings well dread / Final decision / Magadawg / Girlie girlie / Rockers in the rain / Physique / It burm mi belly / You never knew / Love again / Love's on the way / Ain't no meaning / Lazy body / Tenement yard / I just love you / Dance with you
RNCD 2004 / May '93 / Rhino

Georgia Melodians

☐ GEORGIA MELODIANS 1924-1926
Why did you do it / Red hot Mamma / Charley, my boy / San / Everybody loves my baby / Doo wac a doo (A 'wow-wow') / I'm satisfied (Beside that sweetie o'mine) / I'm bound for Tennessee / My Mammy's blues / Give us the charleston / Yes, Sir, that's my baby / She's drivin' me wild / Red hot Henry Brown / Spanish shawl / Charleston ball / I've found a new baby / Hangin' around / Rhythm of the day / Ev'ry body's charleston crazy / I can't get the one I want
CBC 1031 / Aug '96 / Timeless Jazz

Georgia Satellites

☐ KEEP THE FAITH
SPRAYCD 301 / Jul '87 / Making Waves

☐ LET IT ROCK (The Best Of Georgia Satellites)
Don't pass me by / Keep your hands to yourself / Battleship chains / Myth of love / Can't stand the pain / Nights of mystery / Let it rock / Open all night / Sheila / Mon cheri / Down and down / Saddle up / Hippy hippy shake / I dunno / All over but the crying / Six years gone / Hard luck boy / Almost Saturday night/Rockin' all over the world / Dan takes five / Another chance
7559613362 / Feb '93 / Elektra

☐ VERY BEST OF THE GEORGIA SATELLITES, THE
Hippy hippy shake / Deep in the heart of dixie / Battleship chains / Let it rock / Games people play / Can't stand the pain / Don't pass me by / Running out / Six years gone / Anna lee
10322 / Oct '97 / Go On Deluxe

Georgians

☐ GEORGIANS 1922-1923, THE
I wish I could shimmy like my sister Kate / Chicago (that toddling town) / Way down yonder in New Orleans / Nothing but / Loose feet / Aggravatin' Papa / You tell her, I stutter / You've got to see Mama every night / Farewell blues / Snakes hips / Old King Tut / Barney Google / Henpecked blues / Long lost Mama / Land of cotton blues / Mamma loves Papa / Mamma goes where Papa goes / Somebody's wrong / I'm sitting pretty in a pretty little city / Learn to do the strut / Home town blues / You maybe fast but Your Mamma's gonna slow you down / Shake your feet / Old fashioned love
RTR 79003 / Nov '96 / Retrieval

Georgius

☐ SURREALISTIC FUNNY MAN (2CD Set)
FA 075 / Jan '98 / Fremeaux

Geraci, Little Anthony

☐ TAKE IT FROM ME (Geraci, Little Anthony & Sugar Ray Norcia)
CDTC 1149 / Nov '94 / Tonecool

Geraldine Fibbers

☐ BUTCH
California fluffy / Toybox / I killed the cuckoo / Trashman infurs / Swim back to me / Seven or in 10 / Claudine / Folks like me / Pet angel / Butch / Arrow to my drunken eye / You doo right / Dwarf song / Heliotrope
CDVUS 133 / 6 Oct '97 / Virgin

☐ GERALDINE FIBBERS, THE
Marmalade / Get thee gone / Grand tour / Outside of town / They suck / Fancy / Blue cross
DGHUTM 22 / Jan '95 / Hut

☐ LOST SOMEWHERE BETWEEN THE EARTH AND MY HOME
Lily Belle / Small song / Marmalade / Dragon lady / Song about walls / House is falling / Outside of town / French song / Dusted / Richard / Blast of baby / Get thee gone
CDHUT 28 / Jul '95 / Hut

Geraldo

☐ DANCE BAND YEARS, THE (2CD Set) (Geraldo & His Orchestra)
You'll never know / Don't get around much anymore / Why don't you fall in love with me / Pavanne / Walkin' by the river / Don't say that nobody loves you / All of my life / Moonlight mood / In the blue of the evening / MacNamara's band / Shoo shoo baby / Take the 'A' train / Is my baby blue tonight / I'm sending my blessing / Poinciana / Come to baby do / Concerto for drums / I heard you cried last night / Tenement symphony / I'm going to build a future world / San Fernando valley / This is always / Patience and fortitude / Come with me, my honey / Rhapsody for reeds / How sweet you are / I've got a gal in Kalamazoo / Never a day goes by / Gettin' nowhere / I'm confessin' / Saturday night / Barrel organ rhapsody / Can't you read between the lines / Robin Hood / Laura / Two moods / I'm beginning to see the light / June comes around every year / Little yellow bird / I begged her / In Charlie's footsteps / Summertime / Symphony / Don't fence me in / Let him go, let him tarry / There must be a way / Just a prayer away / My heart sings / Chewing a piece of straw / And then you kissed me
PDSCD 555 / 13 Oct '97 / Pulse

☐ DANCING IN THE BLITZ
Good morning / I'm nobody's baby / Whose little what is it are you / I've got my eyes on you / Where or when / When night is through / Don't worry bout me / Sierra Sue / Singing hills / I can't love you anymore / Let's top the clock / Ferryboat serenade / Sweetheart it's you / Don't you ever cry / Love stay in my heart / World is waiting for the sunrise / Blue orchids / We'll go smiling along / Nightingale sang in berkely square / Goodnight again
PAR 2009 / Apr '95 / Parade

☐ GERALDO
All of me / C'est si bon / Carnival time / That's you / Russian lullaby no.4 / Can't you read between the lines / Box 155 / Old master painter / Orange coloured sky / I still love you / Medley / I do, I do, I do / We all have a song in our hearts / Taps Miller / Patience and fortitude / Music, music, music / Jungle fantasy / Undecided / I never loved anyone / In Charlie's footsteps / Slow coach / Two moods / I only have eyes for you / Sometimes / Medley
CDMFP 6359 / Jun '97 / Music For Pleasure

☐ JOURNEY TO A STAR, A (Geraldo & His Orchestra)
Sweet Sue, just you / Goodnight again / World is waiting for the sunrise / I can't love you anymore / Singing hills / Don't you ever cry / Breathless / Elmer's tune / Hey Mabel / Jim / Jingle jangle jingle / My devotion / Canzonetta / Russian rose / Waiter and the porter and the upstairs maid / Humpty dumpty heart / Frenes / Ain't it a shame about mame / Blue in the night / What is this thing called love / Journey to a star / Don't ask me why
RAJCD 811 / May '97 / Empress

☐ TIP-TOP TUNES
In a little Spanish town: *Geraldo Strings* / Nearness of you: *Geraldo & His Concert Orchestra* / Top hat, white tie and tails: *Geraldo & His Dance Orchestra* / Autumn concerto: *Geraldo & His Concert Orchestra* / Hallelujah: *Geraldo & His Dance Orchestra* / Signature tune: *Geraldo & His Concert Orchestra* / My heart stood still: *Geraldo & His Concert Orchestra* / There's a small hotel: *Geraldo & His Concert Orchestra* / Heather on the hill: *Geraldo & His Concert Orchestra* / Rockin' through Dixie: *Geraldo & His Dance Orchestra* / Nature boy: *Geraldo Strings* / What is this thing called love: *Geraldo & His Concert Orchestra* / I'm on a see-saw: *Geraldo & His Concert Orchestra* / So many times I have cried over you: *Geraldo Strings* / When Johnny comes marching home: *Geraldo & His Dance Orchestra* / Begin the beguine: *Geraldo & His Concert Orchestra* / Isle of Innisfree: *Geraldo Strings* / Arkansas traveller: *Geraldo & His Dance Orchestra*
CDHD 135 / '89 / Happy Days

☐ TOP HAT, WHITE TIE AND TAILS (Geraldo & His Orchestra)
Top hat, white tie and tails / Lullaby of Broadway / My foolish heart / Somebody loves me / Night and day / Great day / Hallelujah / I get a kick out of you / Stardust / Strike up the band / Embraceable you / Continental / Pavanne / Time after time / Folks who live on the hill / Trombonology / Ding dong, the witch is dead / Trolley song / Without a song
302942 / Jun '97 / Hallmark

☐ VERY BEST OF GERALDO & HIS ORCHESTRA, THE (Geraldo & His Orchestra)
Waiter, the porter and the upstairs maid / Blues in the night / Humpty dumpty heart / Frenesi / Mocking bird / Ain't it a shame about Mame / To your heart's content / Smoke gets in your eyes / Besame mucho / What is this thing called love / Journey to a star / Flamingo / Rose of Washington Square / Don't ask me why / Lonesome road / Song of the Volga boatmen / As time goes by / Dolores / Starlight serenade / Somebody loves me / Song of the rose / Night and day / Be careful it's my heart / Do I worry
PLCD 566 / Oct '97 / President

Gerbils

☐ ARE YOU SLEEPY
AHA 006 / 30 Mar '98 / Hidden Agenda

Gerd

☐ THIS TOUCH IS GREATER THAN MOODS
First crisium appearance / Nautiloidea / Qare scent spangled arcanum / Vulcan Princess / Carxan 71 / Carxan 72 / Century city / Trendor vualda / Austaris solalia / Osiris' starshaft
EVOGD 03CD / May '97 / Universal Language

Geremia, Paul

☐ GAMBLIN' WOMAN BLUES
RHRCD 54 / Dec '96 / Red House

☐ LIVE FROM UNCLE SAM'S BACKYARD
RHRCD 101 / Aug '97 / Red House

☐ REALLY DON'T MIND/MY KIND OF PLACE
FF 395CD / May '93 / Flying Fish

☐ SELF PORTRAIT IN BLUES
SHAM 1024CD / Apr '95 / Shamrock
RHRCD 77 / Dec '96 / Red House

Germ

☐ GONE
GPRCD 6 / Aug '94 / GPR

Germano, Lisa

☐ EXCERPTS FROM A LOVE CIRCUS
Baby on a plane / Beautiful schizophrenic / Bruises / I love a snot / Forget it, it's a mystery / Victoria's secret / Small heads / We suck / Lovesick / Singing to the birds / Messages from Sophia / Big big world
CAD 6012CD / Sep '96 / 4AD

☐ GEEK THE GIRL
My secret reason / Trouble / Geek the girl / Just geek / Cry wolf / ...a psychopath / Sexy little girl princess / Phantom love / Cancer of everything / Guy like you / ...of love and colours / Stars
GAD 4017CD / 6 Jul '98 / 4AD

☐ HAPPINESS
Bad attitude / Destroy the flower / Puppet / Everyone's victim / Energy / Cowboy / Happiness / Earth / Around the world / Sycophant / Miamo-tutti / Dresses song / Darkest night of all
GAD 4005CD / 6 Jul '98 / 4AD

☐ LOVE CIRCUS
GAD 6012CD / 6 Jul '98 / 4AD

Germer, Richard

☐ GEH'N WIR MAL ZU HAGENBECK
BCD 16249 / May '98 / Bear Family

Germs

☐ GERMICIDE: LIVE AT THE WHISKEY
RE 108CD / Nov '94 / ROIR

☐ MEDIA BLITZ
CLEO 3736CD / Jan '94 / Cleopatra

Geronimo

☐ PEACE TO THE CHIEF
TRP 002CD / Sep '95 / Trechoma

Gerrard, Alice

☐ PIECES OF MY HEART
COP 134CD / May '97 / Copper Creek

Gerrard, Lisa

☐ DUALITY (Gerrard, Lisa & Peter Bourke)
Shadow magnet / Tempest / Forest veil / Comforter / Unfolding / Pilgrimage of lost children / Human game / Circualtion of shadows / Sacrifice / Nadir
CAD 8004CD / 14 Apr '98 / 4AD

☐ MIRROR POOL, THE
Violina: The last embrace / La bas: Song of the drowned / Persian love song : The silver gun / Sanvean: I am your shadow / Rite / Ajhon / Glorafin / Majhnavea's music box / Largo / Werd / Laurelei / Celon / Ventelas / Swans / Nilleshna / Gloradin
GAD 5009CD / 6 Jul '98 / 4AD

Gerry & The Pacemakers

☐ AT ABBEY ROAD 1963-1966
How do you do it / Away from you / I like it / You'll never walk alone / Chills / Shot of rhythm and blues / Hello little girls / Summertime / Slow down / I'm the one / You've got what I like / Dont' let the sun catch you crying / Show me that you care / It's gonna be alright / It's just because / Ferry cross the mersey / I'll wait for you / Why oh why / I'll be there / Reelin' and rockin' / WHole lotta shakin' goin' on / Rip it up / You win again / It'll be me / Walk hand in hand / La la la / Girl on a swing / Big bright green pleasure machine
CDABBEY 102 / 6 Oct '97 / EMI

☐ BEST OF GERRY & THE PACEMAKERS, THE
PLSCD 129 / Apr '96 / Pulse

☐ BEST OF GERRY & THE PACEMAKERS, THE
How do you do it / I'm the one / Ferry across the mersey / Just the way you are / It's still rock 'n' roll to me / Roll over Beethoven / Unchained melody / Imagine / Running man / Don't let the sun catch you crying / Save the last dance for me / Rock 'n' roll rush / It's only make believe / Rock me gently / Do you wanna dance / You'll never walk alone
CD 6087 / 29 Sep '97 / Music

☐ EMI YEARS, THE
How do you do it / Maybellene / I like it / Chills / Pretend / Jambalaya / You're the reason / Hello little girl / You'll never walk alone / Shot of rhythm and blues / Slow down / It's alright / I'm the one / Don't let the sun catch you crying / You've got what I like / It's just because / You, you, you / It's gonna be alright / Ferry 'cross the Mersey / I'll wait for you / Hallelujah, I love her so / Reelin' and rockin' / Why oh why / Baby you're so good to me / Walk hand in hand / Dreams / Give all your love to me / I'll be there / La la la / Fool to myself / Girl on a swing
CDEMS 1443 / May '92 / EMI

☐ EP COLLECTION, THE
How do you do it / Away from you / I like it / Chills / You'll never walk alone / Shot of rhythm and blues / You've got what I like / I'm the one / Don't let the sun catch you crying / Where have you been all my life / Maybellene / You're the reason / It's gonna be alright / I'll wait for you / Ferry 'cross the Mersey / You win again / Reelin' and rockin' / Whole lotta shakin' goin' on / Skinny Lizzie / My babe / What'd I say
SEECD 95 / Mar '95 / See For Miles

☐ FERRY CROSS THE MERSEY (Remastered)
It's gonna be all right / Why oh why / Fall in love / Think about love / I love you too: *Fourmost* / All quiet on the Mersey front: *Martin, George Orchestra* / This thing called love / Baby you're so good to me / I'll wait for you / She's the only girl for me / Is it love: *Black, Cilla* / Ferry cross the Mersey / It's gonna be alright / I love you too: *Fourmost* / All quiet on the Mersey front: *Martin, George Orchestra* / This thing called love / Baby you're so good to me / I'll wait for you / She's the only girl for me / Is it love: *Black, Cilla* / Ferry cross the Mersey / Why oh why / Fall in love / Think about love
DORIG 114 / Jul '97 / EMI

☐ GERRY & THE PACEMAKERS
GRF 191 / Jan '93 / Tring

☐ HOW DO YOU DO IT
How do you do it / Roll over Beethoven / You'll never walk alone / It's still rock and roll to me / Imagine / Don't let the sun catch you crying / Ferry 'cross the Mersey / Run for home / I want you just the way you are / I'm the one / Unchained melody
308922 / 15 Sep '97 / Hallmark

☐ HOW DO YOU LIKE IT
Shot of rhythm and blues / Where have you been / Pretend / You'll never walk alone / You're the reason / You can't fool me / Summertime / Jambalaya / Here's hoping / Maybellene / Right string baby, but the wrong yo-yo / Chills / Don't you ever / Slow down
DORIG 120 / 3 Nov '97 / EMI

☐ NON STOP PARTY ALBUM, THE
Party medley / 60's medley / Light's down low medley / 70's medley / Roll 'n' roll medley / You'll never walk alone
EMPRCD 658 / Jun '96 / Emporio

☐ VERY BEST OF GERRY & THE PACEMAKERS, THE
How do you do it / I like it / It's gonna be alright / I'll be there / Girl on a swing / Come back to me / When, oh when / Don't let the sun catch you crying / You'll never walk alone / I'm the one / Walk hand in hand / La la la / It's alright / Give all your love to me / Hallelujah, I love her so / Ferry 'cross the Mersey
CDMFP 6379 / 13 Oct '97 / Music For Pleasure

Gershwin, Frances

☐ FOR GEORGE & IRA 1928-1938
ACD 116 / Mar '97 / Audiophile

Gershwin, George

☐ 'S MARVELLOUS (Gershwin, George & Ira)
5216582 / Feb '94 / Verve

☐ 'S WONDERFUL
5139282 / Apr '92 / Verve

☐ 20 INTRUMENTAL GREATS
But not for me / Embraceable you / Fascinating rhythm / Foggy day / I got rhythm / It ain't necessarily so / Let's call the whole thing off / Liza / Man I love / Nice work if you can get it / Shall we dance / Someone to watch over me / 'S wonderful / They can't take that away from me / Who cares / Long ago and far away / Summertime / There's a boat that's leavin' soon for New York / Oh I can't sit down / Somebody loves me
GRF 108 / '93 / Tring

☐ BY GEORGE (2CD Set) (Various Artists)
3036701297 / Jun '98 / Hallmark

☐ CENTURY OF GLORY, A (2CD Set) (Various Artists)
FA 152 / 24 Apr '98 / Fremeaux

☐ COMPLETE ORCHESTRAL COLLECTION, THE (The Gershwin Centennial Edition) (Various Artists)
CD 80445 / 6 Jul '98 / Telarc

☐ CRAZY FOR GERSHWIN (Various Artists)
VN 165 / Mar '96 / Viper's Nest

☐ CRAZY FOR GERSHWIN (Lythgoe, Clive)
Fascinating rhythm / Man I love / I'll build a stairway to paradise / Somebody loves me / Strike up the band / Clap yo' hands / Oh lady be good / Liza / Do it again / 'S wonderful / Who cares / My one and only / Do do do / That certain feeling / Sweet and low down / I got rhythm
EMPRCD 558 / May '95 / Emporio

☐ CRAZY FOR GERSHWIN (Various Artists)
CDMOIR 502 / Apr '95 / Memoir

☐ FOREVER GEORGE GERSHWIN (Various Artists)
S'Wonderful: *London, Julie* / Bidin' my time: *Cole, Nat 'King'* / American in Paris: *Brown, Les* / Do it again: *Garland, Judy* / I got rhythm: *Darin, Bobby* / Fascinating rhythm: *Damone, Vic* / Gershwin - king of rhythm: *Adler, Larry* / How long has this been going on: *Christy, June* / Embraceable you: *Cole, Nat 'King' Trio* / I'll build you a stairway to paradise: *Minnelli, Liza* / It ain't necessarily so: *MacKintosh, Ken* / Nice work if you can get it: *Southern, Jeri* / Love walked in: *Haymes, Dick* / Rhapsody in blue: *Adler, Larry* / Slip that bass: *Roy, Harry & His Band* / Someone to watch over me: *Wilson, Nancy* / Strike up the band: *Getz, Stan* / Summertime: *Rawls, Lou* / Our love is here to stay: *Shore, Dinah* / Man I love: *Lee, Peggy*
CDMFP 6261 / Nov '96 / Music For Pleasure

☐ GENIUS OF GEORGE GERSHWIN, THE (Starlight Orchestra)
But not for me / Embraceable you / Fascinating rhythm / Foggy day / I got rhythm / It ain't necessarily so / Lets call the whole thing off / Liza / Man I love / Nice work if you can get it / Shall we dance / Someone to watch over me / 'S wonderful / They can't take that away from me / Who cares / Long ago and far away / Summertime / There's a boat that leaving soon for new york / Oh I can't sit down / Somebody loves me
QED 109 / Nov '96 / Tring

☐ GEORGE GERSHWIN PLAYS GEORGE GERSHWIN
Rhapsody in blue / Hang on to me / Fascinating rhythm / Half of it dearie blues / I'd rather charleston / Sweet and low down / That certain feeling / Looking for a boy / Then do we dance / Do do do / Someone to watch over me / Clap yo' hands / Maybe / My one and only / Three preludes / Andante / 'S wonderful/Funny face / Rhapsody in blue / American in Paris / It ain't necessarily so / Buzzard song / Summertime / Bess you is my woman now / My man's gone now / Concerto in F (Third movement) / I got rhythm/Of thee I sing
GEMMCDS 9483 / Mar '91 / Pearl

☐ GEORGE GERSHWIN PLAYS GERSHWIN
Rhapsody in blue / American in Paris / It ain't necessarily so / Buzzard song / Summertime/ Crapgame/A woman is a sometime thing / Bess you is my woman now / I got plenty o' nuthin' / Where is my Bess / Summertime / My man's gone now / Concerto in F / I got rhythm/Of thee I sing
CD 48035 / Oct '96 / Magic Talent

☐ GEORGE GERSHWIN SONGBOOK, THE (18 Gershwin Songs With Gershwin's Own Piano Improvisations) (Hill, Julie & Craig Bohmler)
Man I love / Swanee / Nobody like you / I'll build a stairway to paradise / Do it again / Fascinating rhythm / Oh lady be good / Somebody loves me / Sweet and low down / Clap yo' hands / Do do do / My one and only / 'S wonderful / Strike up the band / I got rhythm / Who cares / That certain feeling / Liza
CRC 2322 / 15 Jun '98 / Centaur

☐ GERSHWIN (2CD Set) (Various Artists)
Rhaposdy in blue: *Gershwin, George* / When do we dance: *Gershwin, George* / But not for me: *Garland, Judy* / Someone to watch over me: *Gershwin, George* / Man I love: *Shaw, Artie* / Maybe: *Gershwin, George* / Long ago and far away: *Gershwin, George* / Nice work if you can get it: *Gershwin, George* / Summertime: *Holiday, Billie* / How long has this been going on: *Lee, Peggy* / Fascinating rhythm: *Lee, Buddy & The Gilt-Edged Four* / They all laughed: *Astaire, Fred* / Somebody loves me: *Carter, Benny* / Swanee: *Jolson, Al* / So am I: *Gershwin, George* / Love walked in: *Armstrong, Louis* / Rhapsody in blue: *Gershwin, George* / Embraceable you: *Garland, Judy* / Tee oodle um bum bo: *Gershwin, George* / Foggy day: *Grathan, Cyril* / Kickin' the clouds away: *Gershwin, George* / Liza: *Webb, Chick & His Orchestra* / S'wonderful: *Gershwin, George* / Shall we dance: *Astaire, Fred* / Sweet and low down: *Gershwin, George* / Drifting along with the tide: *Gershwin, George* / I've got a crush on you: *Wiley, Lee* / Looking for a boy: *Gershwin, George* / My one and only: *Gershwin, George* / They can't take that away from me: *McRae, Carmen* / I got rhythm: *Waller, Fats & His Orchestra*
PC 611 / 10 Nov '97 / Platinum Collection

☐ GERSHWIN PLAYS GERSHWIN: THE PIANO ROLLS VOL.1
Sweet and low down / Novelette in fourths / That certain feeling / So am I / Rhapsody in blue / Swanee / When you want 'em you can't get 'em / Kickin' the clouds away / Idol dreams / On my mind the whole night long / Scandal walk / American in paris
7559792872 / Jul '94 / Nonesuch

☐ GERSHWIN PLAYS GERSHWIN: THE PIANO ROLLS VOL.2
7559793702 / Nov '95 / Nonesuch

☐ GERSHWIN SONGBOOK, A (Marshall, Wayne)
Fascinating rhythm / I love you Porgy / Can't take that away / Summertime / Oh lady be good / Let's call the whole thing off / Embraceable you / Someone to watch over me / Love walked in / By Strauss / Our love is here to stay / Porgy trio / Clara Clara / I got rhythm
VC 5452982 / 6 Oct '97 / Virgin Classics

☐ GERSHWIN STORY (Amsterdam Saxophone Quartet)
I 9611502 / Dec '96 / Masters Music

☐ GERSHWIN TRIBUTE (Various Artists)
Strike up the band / Embraceable you / Fascinating rhythm / Rhapsody in blue / But not for me / Bidin' my time / Foggy day / They can't take that away from me / Oh lady be good / How long has this been going on / Man I love / Prelude no.2 / Somebody loves me / S'wonderful
HCD 266 / Jan '98 / Hindsight

☐ ONE AND ONLY GEORGE GERSHWIN, THE (Various Artists)
When do we dance: *Gershwin, George* / I got plenty o' nuttin': *Crosby, Bing* / Embraceable you: *Garland, Judy* / Half of it dearie blues: *Astaire, Fred* / 'S Wonderful: *Goodman, Benny* / Man I love: *Welch, Elisabeth & Benny Carter* / Swanee: *Jolson, Al* / I'll build a stairway to paradise: *Whiteman, Paul* / I was doing all right: *Fitzgerald, Ella* / I got rhythm: *Waller, Fats & his Rhythm Orchestra* / Someone to watch over me: *Lawrence, Gertrude* / Liza: *Wilson, Teddy* / Love walked in: *Armstrong, Louis* / Nice work if you can get it: *Andrews Sisters* / They can't take that away from me: *Holiday, Billie* / Oh Lady be good: *Lee, Buddy* / But not for me: *Forrest, Helen* / Let's call the whole thing off: *Astaire, Fred* / Summertime: *Crosby, Bing* / Somebody loves me: *Teagarden, Jack* / Andante: *Gershwin, George*
PAR 2033 / Sep '94 / Parade

☐ ORIGINAL HITS OF GEORGE GERSHWIN, THE (Various Artists)
DHDL 112 / Oct '92 / Halcyon

☐ RHAPSODY IN BLUE
Rhapsody in blue / American in Paris / Swanee / Walking the dog / Let's call the whole thing off / Somebody loves me / Our love is here to stay / 'S Wonderful / Embraceable you / Oh Lady be good
BCD 106 / Jul '91 / Biograph

☐ RHAPSODY IN BLUE (Black, Stanley & London Festival Orchestra)
Rhapsody in blue / American in Paris / Porgy and Bess
4489532 / Aug '97 / Decca

☐ RHAPSODY IN BLUE (Tilson Thomas, Michael)
SMK 60028 / 15 Sep '97 / Sony Classical

☐ RHAPSODY IN BLUE (Fiedler, Arthur & Boston Pops Orchestra/Earl Wild)
Rhapsody in blue / Concerto in F / American in Paris / I got rhythm
09026687922 / Mar '98 / RCA Victor

☐ RHAPSODY IN BLUE (The Music Of George Gershwin) (Brooks, Paul)
I got rhythm / 'S wonderful / Someone to watch over me / But not for me / Nice work if you can get it / Somebody loves me / They can't take that away from me / Foggy day in London Town / Do what you do / Rhapsody in blue / Embraceable you / I've got a crush on you / It ain't necessarily so / Man I love / Our love is here to stay / Bidin' my time / Swanee / Summertime
ECD 3395 / 23 Feb '98 / K-Tel

☐ SELF PORTRAIT
Rhapsody in blue / That certain feeling / Left all again blues / Grieving for you / I'm a lonesome little raindrop / Just snap your fingers at care / Make believe / Land where the good songs go / Some Sunday morning / American in Paris / Rhapsody in blue
SUMCD 4051 / Nov '96 / Summit

☐ STARS SALUTE GEORGE GERSHWIN, THE (Various Artists)
They all laughed: *Astaire, Fred* / But not for me: *Garland, Judy* / I was doing alright: *Fitzgerald, Ella* / Somebody loves me: *Carter, Benny Orchestra* / Swanee: *Jolson, Al* / They can't take that away from me: *McRae, Carmen* / Summertime: *Holiday, Billie* / Swonderful: *Day, Doris* / Someone to watch over me: *Wiley, Lee* / Man I love: *Forrest, Helen* / I got rhythm: *Waller, Fats Orchestra* / Liza: *Webb, Chick Orchestra* / Fascinating rhythm: *Lee, Buddy* / Love walked in: *Armstrong, Louis* / Shall we dance: *Astaire, Fred* / Nice work if you can get it: *Dorsey, Tommy* / Oh lady be good: *Shaw, Artie* / Foggy day: *Grantham, Cyril & Geraldo Orchestra* / Embraceable you: *Garland, Judy* / How long has this been going on: *Lee, Peggy*
300352 / Jul '96 / Hallmark

☐ SUMMERTIME (Various Artists)
MACCD 257 / Aug '96 / Autograph

☐ THEIR GREAT MELODIES (Gershwin, George/Cole Porter)
An American in Paris / Man I love / Our love is here to stay / Someone to watch over me / Foggy day / Strike up the band / They can't take that away from me / From me / Medley (Gershwin, a portrait) / Another openin' another show / I love you Samantha / Begin the beguine / I've got you under my skin / Let's do it / Love for sale / So in love / Anything goes
300582 / Jun '98 / Hallmark

☐ TRIBUTE TO GERSHWIN, A (Various Artists)
'S wonderful / Summertime / Fascinating rhythm / Oh lady be good / Man I love / Summertime / Man I love / I can't get started / But not for me / 'S wonderful/Summertime/But not for me/I got rhythm / Man I love
8747072 / Jul '96 / DA Music

☐ TWO SIDES OF GEORGE GERSHWIN, THE
Rhapsody in blue / Three piano preludes / Andante / American in Paris / Sweet and low down / That certain feeling / Looking for a boy / When do we dance / Do do do / Someone to watch over me / Clap yo' hands / Maybe / My one and only / 'S wonderful / Funny face
DHDL 101 / Oct '91 / Halcyon

☐ ULTIMATE GERSHWIN, THE (4CD Set) (Various Artists)
PBXCD 407 / 20 Apr '98 / Pulse

☐ WORLD OF GERSHWIN, THE (2CD Set) (Various Artists)
ZYX 111182 / 2 Feb '98 / ZYX

Gershwin, Ira

☐ 'S WONDERFUL (Various Artists)
Our love is here to stay: *Clooney, Rosemary* / Soon: *Sloane, Carol* / Liza: *Torme, Mel* / Fascinating rhythm: *McCorkle, Susannah* / Long ago and far away: *Clooney, Rosemary* / Love walked in: *Anderson, Ernestine* / I can't get started: *Sheldon, Jack* / 'S Wonderful: *Allyson, Karrin* / Things are looking up: *Stallings, Mary* / Embraceable you: *Maria, Tania* / He loves and she loves: *Sloane, Carol* / Isn't it a pity: *Torme, Mel & Cleo Laine* / But not for me: *Stallings, Mary* / Foggy day: *Clooney, Rosemary*
CCD 4741 / Nov '96 / Concord Jazz

Gertz, Bruce

☐ BLUEPRINT (Gertz, Bruce Quartet)
Proton / Neves / It should / Otto's motto / While you were out / Cryptic current / Other you / Backspace / Red yellow green / Blueprint / Proton II
FRLCD 017 / Nov '92 / Freelance
ECD 22196 / Aug '97 / Evidence

Gessle, Per

☐ WORLD ACCORDING TO GESSLE
(You make me feel so) stupid / Do you wanna be my baby / Saturday / Elvis in Germany / I want you to know / Reporter / B any 1 U wanna B / Wish you the best / Kix / T-t-take it / It'll be alright / There is my baby / Lay down your arms
CDEMD 1105 / May '97 / EMI

Get Up Kids

☐ FOUR MINUTE MILE
DOG 047 / 20 Oct '97 / Doghouse

Getaway Cruiser

☐ INSTRUMENTALS
ME 012CD / Mar '97 / Mind Expansion

☐ PHONES CALLING
SKL 201 / Mar '97 / Skillet

Geto Boys

☐ RESURRECTION, THE
Ghetto prisoner / Still / World is a ghetto / Open minded / Killer for scratch / Hold it down / Blind leading the blind / First light of day / Time taker / Geto boys and girls / Geto fantasy / I just wanna die / Niggas and flies / Visit with Larry Hoover / Point of no return
CDVUS 103 / Apr '96 / Virgin

Gettel, Michael

☐ ART OF NATURE, THE
Light of the land / When all is quiet (she dreams if horses) / Watershed / Shelter / Fire from the sky / Solace / Where eagles soar / Midsummer / Crosswind
ND 63032 / Jul '95 / Narada

☐ KEY, THE
Waiting / Turning of a key / Breaking the silence / When hearts collide / Search / Glimmer of hope / Broken / Light of a candle / Letting go / Awakening / Through the doorway
ND 63027 / Jun '94 / Narada

☐ SAN JUAN SUITE VOL.1
72438455962 / 21 Apr '98 / Narada

☐ SKYWATCHING
Anasazi Roads / Skywatching / Windows and walls / Prelude / Sacred side (in ruins) / Wellspring / Prelude: Kiva / Sipapu / Tekohananae (to the morning) / Prelude: Stilness / Scent of rain / Where the road meets the sky
ND 63025 / May '93 / Narada

Getz, Stan

☐ 'ROUND MIDNIGHT
All god's chillun got rhythm / 'round midnight / Broadway / A ghost of a chance / Topsy / East of the sun (and west of the moon) / Dear old stockholm / Lady bird / I remember clifford / Stuffy
JD 1266 / Nov '94 / Koch

☐ 'ROUND MIDNIGHT
Stuffy / I remember clifford / Laverne walk / Pennies from heaven / Broadway / A ghost of a chance / All god's chillun got rhythm / East of the sun (and west of the moon) / Topsy / 'round midnight / Dear old stockholm / Lady bird
JHR 73542 / May '93 / Jazz Hour

☐ 'ROUND MIDNIGHT IN PARIS
BS 18001 / Jul '96 / Bandstand

☐ ACADEMY OF JAZZ (Getz, Stan & Bob Brookmeyer)
COD 024 / Mar '92 / Jazz View

☐ ANNIVERSARY (Live At The Montmartre Club, Copenhagen)
El Cahon / I can't get started (with you) / Stella by starlight / Stan's blues / I thought about you / What is this thing called love / Blood count
8387692 / Jul '90 / EmArCy

☐ AT LARGE VOL.1
JUCD 2001 / Jan '89 / Jazz Unlimited

☐ AT LARGE VOL.2
JUCD 2002 / Dec '91 / Jazz Unlimited

☐ AT THE OPERA HOUSE (Live In Chicago & Los Angeles 1957) (Getz, Stan & J.J. Johnson)
Billie's bounce / My funny valentine / Crazy rhythm / Blues in the closet / Yesterdays / It never entered my mind
8312722 / Jan '93 / Verve

☐ AUDIO ARCHIVE
Autumn leaves / Billie's bounce / Heart place / Kali-au / Chappaqua
CDAA 028 / Jun '92 / Tring

☐ AUTUMN LEAVES
WWCD 2046 / Apr '90 / West Wind

☐ AUTUMN LEAVES
Autumn leaves / Chappaqua / Don't worry about me / Heart place / Kali au / Billie's bounce
BN 015 / Apr '98 / Blue Nite

☐ BEST OF TWO WORLDS, THE
4715112 / Jan '95 / Sony Jazz

☐ BIG BAND BOSSA NOVA
Manha de carnaval / Balanco no samba / Melancolico / Entre amigos / Chega de saudade / Noite triste / Samba de uma nota so / Bim bom
8257712 / Jan '93 / Verve

☐ BIRDLAND SESSIONS 1952 (Getz, Stan Quintet)
FSRCD 149 / Dec '90 / Fresh Sound

☐ BLUE SKIES
Spring is here / Antigny / Easy living / There we go / Blue skies / How long has this been going on
CCD 4676 / Dec '95 / Concord Jazz

☐ BROTHERS, THE
Five brothers / Five brothers / Battle of the saxes / Four and one moore / Four and one moore (alternate take) / Battleground / Battleground (alternate take) / Red door / Zootcase / Tangerine / Morning fun
OJCCD 8 / Apr '87 / Original Jazz Classics

☐ CAPTAIN MARVEL
4684122 / Jan '95 / Sony Jazz

☐ CHANGE OF SCENES (Getz, Stan & Kenny Clarke/Francy Boland Big Band)
Extravagances / Symptones / Quiproquos / Escarmouches / Touchstone / Provocations
5570952 / 20 Apr '98 / Verve

☐ COMPLETE ROOST RECORDINGS, THE (3CD Set)
On the Alamo / Gone with the wind / Yesterdays / Sweetie pie / You go to my head / Hershey bar / Tootsie roll / Strike up the band / Imagination / For stompers only / Navy blue / Out of nowhere / 'S wonderful / Penny / Split kick / It might as well be spring / Best thing for you / Signal / Budo / Thou swell / Song for you / Mosquito knees / Hershey bar / Rubberneck / Signal / Everything happens to me / Jumpin' with the symphany sid / Yesterdays / Budo / Wildwood / Melody express / Yvette / Potter's luck / Song is you / Wildwood / Lullaby of birdland / Autumn leaves / Autumn leaves / Fools rush in fools rush out / These foolish things / Where or when / Tabu / Moonlight in Vermont / Jaguar / Sometimes I'm happy / Stars fell on Alabama / Nice work if you can get it / Tenderly / Little pony / Easy living / Nails
8596222 / 10 Nov '97 / Roulette

☐ COMPLETE STOCKHOLM CONCERTS, THE (3CD Set) (Getz, Stan & Chet Baker)
Stablemates / We'll be together again / On the up and up / How long has this been going on / O grande amor / Just friends / My funny Valentine / Sipping at Bell's / Stella by starlight / Airegin / Baggage room blues / We'll be together again / I'll remember April / Just friends / My funny Valentine / Sippin' at Bell's / Blood count / Milestones / Airegin / Dear old Stockholm / Line for Lyons
5375552 / 29 Jun '98 / Verve

☐ DOLPHIN,THE (Getz, Stan Quartet)
Time for love / Joy Spring / Dolphin / Close enough for love
CCD 4158 / Jul '87 / Concord Jazz

☐ EARLY STAN (With Jimmy Raney & Terry Gibbs)
Motion / Lee / Michelle / T and S / Signal / 'Round midnight / Terry's tune (original, alternate and alternate two) / Cuddles (Speedway)
OJCCD 654 / Apr '93 / Original Jazz Classics

☐ ESSENTIAL STAN GETZ, THE
Ligia / Lester left town / Blue Serge / Hopscotch / Anna / Captain Marvel / What am I here for / Lush life / Double rainbow / Peacocks / La Fiesta
4715182 / Jul '93 / Columbia

☐ ESSENTIAL STAN GETZ, THE (3CD Set)
Song is you / O grande amor / For Jane / Dane's chant / Major General / Folk tune for bass / Tonight I shall sleep/Desafinado / All the things you are / Summer night / One note samba / All God's children got rhythm / Broadway / Ladybird / Dear old Stockholm / East of the sun (and West of the moon) / They all fall in love / Theme for Manuel / Our kind of Sabi / Two little pearls / Yesterdays / Song without words / Old folks / Don't get around much anymore / Cherokee / My funny Valentine / Stan's tune / Blues in Suburbia
55598 / Oct '97 / Laserlight

☐ FOCUS (Remastered)
5214192 / Oct '97 / Verve Master Edition

☐ GETZ MEETS MULLIGAN IN HI-FI (Getz, Stan & Gerry Mulligan)
Let's fall in love / Anything goes / Too close for comfort / That old feeling / This can't be love / Ballad / Scrapple from the apple / I didn't know what time it was
8493922 / Mar '91 / Verve

☐ GETZ/GILBERTO VOL.1 (Remastered) (Getz, Stan & Joao Gilberto/Antonio Carlos Jobim)
5214142 / Oct '97 / Verve Master Edition

☐ GETZ/GILBERTO VOL.2 (Live At Carnegie Hall) (Getz, Stan & Joao Gilberto)
Grandfather's waltz / Tonight I shall sleep with a smile on my face / Stan's blues / Here's that rainy day / Samba da minha terra / Rosa morena / Um braco no bronfa / Bim bom / Meditation / O pato / It might as well be Spring / Only trust your heart / Corcovado / Girl from Ipanema / Eu e voce
5198002 / Dec '93 / Verve

☐ GIRL FROM IPANEMA, THE (The Bossa Nova Years/4CD Set)
Desafinado / Samba dees days / O pato / Samba triste / Samba de uma nota so / E luxo so / Baia / Manha de carnival / Balanco no samba / Melancolico / Entre amigos / Chega de saudade / Noite triste / Samba de uma nota so / Bim bom / Sambalero / So danco samba / How insensitive / O morro nao tem vez / Samba de duas notas / Menina flor / Mania de Maria / Saudade vem correndo / Um abraco no Getz / Ebony samba / Ebony samba / Tribute to Stan / Girl from Ipanema / Doralice / Para machuchar mew coracao / Desafinado / Corcovado / So danco samba / O grande amor / Dreamer / Corcovado / It might as well be Spring / Eu e voce / Only trust your heart / Telephone song / Samba de uma nota so / Corcovado / Menina moca / Once again / Winter moon / Do what you do / Samba da Sahra / Maracatu - too / Eu e voce / Corcovado / Girl from Ipanema
8236112 / Jan '90 / Verve

☐ GITANES - JAZZ 'ROUND MIDNIGHT (Getz, Stan & Joao Gilberto/Astrud Gilberto)
Girl from Ipanema: *Getz, Stan & Astrud Gilberto* / Once upon a Summertime: *Gilberto, Astrud* / Once again: *Getz, Stan & Laurindo Almeida* / Thanks for the memory: *Getz, Stan* / I haven't got anything better to do: *Gilberto, Astrud* / How insensitive: *Getz, Stan & Luiz Bonfa* / Corcovado: *Gilberto, Astrud & Joao Gilberto* / Manha de carnaval: *Gilberto, Astrud* / Desafinado: *Getz, Stan & Charlie Byrd* / Avarandado: *Gilberto, Joao* / Look to the rainbow: *Gilberto, Astrud* / Sambalero: *Getz, Stan & Luiz Bonfa* / It might as well be Spring: *Getz, Stan & Astrud Gilberto* / Shadow of your smile: *Gilberto, Astrud* / Bronx blues: *Getz, Stan & Oscar Peterson*
8414452 / Oct '92 / Verve

☐ HIGHLIGHTS VOL.1 (The Best Of The Verve Years/2CD Set)
Stella by starlight / Exactly like you / It don't mean a thing if it ain't got that swing / Handful of stars / Wee / Ballad / You're blase / My funny valentine / 'Round midnight / Desafinado / Manha de carnaval / Girl from Ipanema / Corcovado / Melinda / Cool mix / With the wind and the rain / Night in Tunisia / Over the rainbow / Sniles / Blues for Herky / Gold rush / Goodbye / I'm late I'm late / I didn't know what it was / Sweet rain / I remember Clifford / Communication 72
8474302 / May '91 / Verve

☐ HIGHLIGHTS VOL.2 (The Best Of The Verve Years/2CD Set)
Thanks for the memory / Rustic hop / Round up time / Cherokee / East of the sun and West of the moon / Serenade in blue / Dark eyes / Where or when / Billie's bounce / Blues for junior / Honeysuckle rose / All the things you are / Folks who live on the hill / Airegin / Who could care / Chega de saudade / Corcovado / Maria Moca / My heart stood still / When the world was young / Litha / I remember Clifford
5173302 / Jan '93 / Verve

☐ IN CONCERT (Getz, Stan & Joe Farrell/ Paul Horn/Michael Garson)
Heartplace / Kali-au / Chappaqua / Nature boy / 500 miles high / Lady Day / Autumn leaves / Billie's bounce
CDGATE 7022 / '89 / Kingdom Jazz

☐ IN CONCERT
DM 15009 / Jul '96 / DMA Jazz

☐ JAZZ MASTERS
Desafinado / Shine / Body and soul / Gladys / It never entered my mind / Jordu / Windows / Dynsty / Her / Girl from Ipanema
5198232 / 5 May '98 / Verve

☐ JAZZ MASTERS (Getz, Stan & Dizzy Gillespie)
Dark eyes / Be bop / It's the talk of the town / Mooche / Way you look tonight / It don't mean a thing if it ain't got that swing
5218522 / 5 May '98 / Verve

☐ JAZZ MASTERS (Bossa Nova 1962-1967)
5299042 / 5 May '98 / Verve

☐ JAZZ MASTERS
Love and the weather / Spring is here / Pot luck / Willow weep for me / Crazy rhythm / Nearness of you
4934682 / 16 Feb '98 / EMI Jazz

☐ JAZZ PORTRAITS (Getz, Stan & Joao Gilberto/Astrud Gilberto)
Corcovado / It might as well be spring / Eu e voce / Girl from Ipanema / O pato (the duck) / Um abraco no bonfa / Meditation / Here's that rainy day / Samba de minha terra / One note samba / Telephone song / Only trust your heart / Stan's blues / Bim bom / Rosa morena / Singing song
CD 14514 / May '94 / Jazz Portraits

☐ JAZZ SAMBA (Remastered) (Getz, Stan & Charlie Byrd)
5214132 / Oct '97 / Verve Master Edition

☐ JAZZ SAMBA ENCORE (Getz, Stan & Luiz Bonfa)
Sambalero / So danco samba / O morro noa tem vez / How insensitive / Samba de duas notas / Mania de Maria suadade vem correndo / Um abraco no Getz / Ebony samba / Menina flor
8236132 / Mar '93 / Verve

☐ LIVE AT MONTMARTRE VOL.1
SCCD 31073 / '90 / Steeplechase

☐ LIVE AT MONTMARTRE VOL.2
SCCD 31074 / '90 / Steeplechase

☐ LIVE AT THE HAIG 1953 (Getz, Stan & Chet Baker)
FSRCD 8001 / 24 Feb '98 / Fresh Sound

☐ LIVE IN EUROPE (2CD Set)
Stuffy / I remember clifford / Laverne walk / Pennies from heaven / Broadway / A ghost of a chance / All god's chillun got rhythm / East of the sun (and west of the moon) / Topsy / 'round midnight / Dear old stockholm / Lady bird / Autumn leaves / Lady day / Heart place / Time after time / Kali au / Nature boy / Chappaqua / Billie's bounce
JWD 102304 / Nov '94 / JWD

☐ LIVE IN PARIS
Un grand amor / Blood count / Airegin / Blue skies / On the up and up / I wanted to say / Tempus fugit
FDM 365772 / Apr '96 / Dreyfus

☐ LYRICAL STAN GETZ, THE
Willow weep for me / La fiesta / Captain Marvel / Ligia / Misty / Lover man
4608192 / Jan '95 / Sony Jazz

☐ NATURE BOY VOL.2
Autumn leaves / Lady day / Heart place / Time after time / Kali au / Nature boy / Chappagua / Billie's bounce
JHR 73554 / Jan '93 / Jazz Hour

☐ NOBODY ELSE BUT ME
5216602 / Nov '94 / Verve

☐ OPUS DE BOP
Opus de bop / Running water / Don't worry 'bout me / And the angels swing / Fool's fancy / Be bop in pastel / Ray's idea / Bombay / Eb pob / Goin' to Minton's / Fat girl / Ice freezes red
SV 0118 / Oct '97 / Savoy Jazz

☐ PEOPLE TIME (2CD Set) (Getz, Stan & Kenny Barron)
East of the sun and west of the moon / Night and day / I'm okay / Like someone in love / Stablemates / I remember Clifford / Gone with the wind / First song / There is no greater love / Surrey with the fringe on top / People time / Softly as in a morning sunrise / Hush-a-bye / Soul eyes
5101342 / Mar '92 / Verve

☐ PURE GETZ (Getz, Stan Quartet)
On the up and up / Blood count / Very early / Sippin' at bells / I wish I knew / Come rain or come shine / Tempus fugit
CCD 4188 / Dec '86 / Concord Jazz

☐ QUARTETS
There's a small hotel / I've got you under my skin / What's new / Too marvellous for words / You stepped out of a dream / My old flame / My old flame (alternate take) / Long island sound / Indian summer / Marcia / Crazy chords / Lady in red / Lady in red / Wrap your troubles in dreams
OJCCD 121 / Feb '93 / Original Jazz Classics

☐ RARE DAWN SESSIONS
BCD 132 / Oct '94 / Biograph

☐ SERENITY (Live At The Cafe Montmartre Copenhagen 1987)
On green dolphin street / Voyage / Falling in love / I remember you / I love you
8387702 / May '91 / EmArCy

☐ SILVER COLLECTION, THE (Getz, Stan & Oscar Peterson)
I want to be happy / Pennies from heaven / Bewitched, bothered and bewildered / I don't know why I just do / How long has this been going on / I can't get started / Polka dots and moonbeams / I'm glad there is you / Tour's end / I was doing all right / Bronx blues / Three little words / Detour ahead / Sunday / Blues for Henry
8278262 / Oct '86 / Verve

☐ SONG IS YOU, THE
Song is you / O grande amor / For Jane / Dane's chant / Major General / Folk tune for bass / Tonight I shall sleep/Desafinado / All the things you are / Summer night / One night samba
17078 / Jan '97 / Laserlight

☐ SOUL EYES
Voyage / Soul eyes / Feijada / Blood count / (Real) Stan's blues / Slow boat to China / Warm valley / Hush-a-bye
CCD 47832 / 6 Oct '97 / Concord Jazz

☐ SPRING IS HERE
How about you / You're blase / Easy living / Sweet Lorraine / Old devil moon / I'm old fashioned / Spring is here
CCD 4500 / Mar '92 / Concord Jazz

☐ STAN & CHET (Getz, Stan & Chet Baker)
8374362 / Mar '96 / Verve

☐ STAN GETZ AT THE SHRINE (Live In Los Angeles 1954)
Flamingo / Lover man / Pernod / Tasty pudding / I'll remember April / Polka dots and moonbeams / Open country / It don't mean a thing if it ain't got that swing / We'll be together again / Feather merchant
5137532 / Jan '93 / Verve

☐ STAN GETZ GOLD COLLECTION, THE (2CD Set)
R2CD 4062 / 9 Mar '98 / Deja Vu

☐ STAN GETZ PLAYS
Stella by starlight / Time on my hands / 'Tis Autumn / Way you look tonight / Lover come back to me / Body and soul / Stars fell on Alabama / You turned the tables on me / Thanks for the memory / Hymn of the Orient / These foolish things / How deep is the ocean / Nobody else but me / Down by the sycamore tree / I hadn't anyone till you / With the wind and the rain in your hair
8335352 / Sep '93 / Verve

☐ STAN GETZ WITH LAURINDO ALMEIDA (Getz, Stan & Laurindo Almeida)
Menina moca / Once again / Winter moon / Do what you do / Samba da Sahra / Maracatu - too / Corcovado
8231492 / Jan '93 / Verve

☐ SWEET RAIN
Litha / O grande amor / Sweet rain / Con Alma / Windows / There will never be another you
8150542 / Jan '93 / Verve

☐ THIS IS JAZZ
La fiesta / Who cares / Ligia / Misty / Aguas de marco / Lester left / Town / Blue serge / Captain Marvel / Peacocks / Count Basie / This is jazz / One o'clock jump / Lester leaps in / 9:20 special / Oh lady be good / Goin' to Chicago blues / Red bank boogie / Dickie's dream / Miss thing / Tickle toe / How long blues / Broadway / Rock-a-bye Basie / Blow top / Let me see / Taxi war-dance / Moten swing jumpin' at the Woodside
CK 64969 / Oct '96 / Sony Jazz

☐ WEST COAST SESSIONS, THE (3CD Set)
5319352 / Dec '96 / Verve

☐ WEST COAST SESSIONS, THE (Highlights)
5370842 / May '97 / Verve

☐ WITH CAL TJADER SEXTET (Getz, Stan Sextet)
Ginza samba / I've grown accustomed to her face / For all we know / Crow's ghost / Liz anne / Big bear / My buddy
OJCCD 275 / Feb '92 / Original Jazz Classics

☐ WITH EUROPEAN FRIENDS
All God's chillun got rhythm / Broadway / Ladybird / Dear old Stockholm / East of the sun and west of the moon / They all fall in love / Theme for Manuel / Our kind of sabi
17079 / May '97 / Laserlight

☐ YOURS AND MINE
You'd be so nice to come home to / Joanne Julia / Yours and mine / Con alma / People time / What is this thing called love / Yesterdays
CCD 4740 / Dec '96 / Concord Jazz

GGFH

☐ HALLOWEEN
Little Missy / Blood is thicker / Chainsaw / She comes to you / Curiosity killed the cat / Thorns / Night stalker / As I touch you / Plaster Christ '88 / Ireland / Fetal infection / Dread / Missy '84 / Go away / Missy's revenge
KTB 012 / Oct '94 / Dreamtime

Ghanaian Inspiration

☐ RIVER PRA
MECCACD 1092 / May '97 / Music Mecca

Ghazal

☐ LOST SONGS OF THE SILK ROAD
SH 64096 / Oct '97 / Shanachie

Ghent, Aubrey

☐ CAN'T NOBODY DO ME LIKE JESUS (Ghent, Aubrey & Friends)
Just a closer walk with thee / CCan't nobody do me like Jesus / Amazing grace / I am thine oh lord / When the saints go marching in / Sweet sweet spirit / What he's done for me / Walk with me / There is a fountain filled with blood / How great thou art
ARHCD 463 / Jul '98 / Arhoolie

Ghetto Mafia

☐ DRAW THE LINE
FTR 4184CD / May '94 / Ichiban

Ghezzi, Wess

☐ GOLDEN YEARS (Ghezzi, Wess & Dori)
74321455912 / Nov '97 / Ricordi

Ghiglioni, Tiziana

☐ CANTA LUIGI TENCO
W 602 / Apr '94 / Philology

☐ I'LL BE AROUND (Ghiglioni, Tiziana, Enrico Rava & Mal Waldron)
1212562 / Jun '91 / Soul Note

☐ MY ESSENTIAL DUKE
CD214W 1222 / May '98 / Philology

☐ SOUNDS OF LOVE
Beautiful singing / My old flame / All of me / Ruby my dear / Naima / Sound of love / I remember you / My funny valentine / Straight no chaser
1210562 / Nov '90 / Soul Note

Ghillies

☐ NINETIES COLLECTION VOL.2
Hornpipes / Reels / Slow air / Marches / Slow air / Strathspey and reels / Jigs and reels / Hornpipes / Marches / Slow air / Jigs / Slow air / Strathspey and reels / Slow air and reels
CDTRAX 5006 / Feb '97 / Greentrax

Ghorwane

☐ MAJURUGENTA
Muthimba / Majurugenta / Matarlatanta / Xai-xai / Mavabwyi / Sathuma / Buluku / Terehuma / Akuhanha
CDRW 29 / Jul '93 / Realworld

Ghost

☐ ICH MACHINE
INDIGO 29152 / Dec '96 / Strange Ways

☐ LAMA RABI RABI
DCD 113 / Jan '97 / Drag City

☐ SECOND TIME AROUND
INDIGO 11752 / Dec '96 / Strange Ways

☐ TEMPLE STONE
INDIGO 11782 / Dec '96 / Strange Ways

Ghost

☐ OTHER SIDE, THE
NTHEN 020CD / Mar '96 / Now & Then

Ghostface Killah

☐ IRON MAIDEN
Iron maiden / Wildflower / Faster blade / 260 / Assassination day / Poisonous darts / Winter warz / Box in hand / Fish / Camay / Daytona 500 / Motherless child / Black Jesus / After the smoke is clear / All that I got is you / Soul controller / Marvel
4853892 / Oct '96 / Razor Sharp/Epic

Ghostings

☐ LIPS LIKE RED
SPV 08561772 / Aug '95 / SPV

Ghostland

☐ GHOSTLAND
Blue / Cowboys and Indians / Float / Gamgo / Guide me God / Seven arrows / Free / Ghostland / Your time will come
3984200502 / 15 Jun '98 / East West

Ghosts

☐ FULL FRONTAL DUBLOTOMY
CDZM 2 / Apr '96 / Zanders

Ghoststorm

☐ FROZEN IN FIRE
BMCD 65 / May '95 / Black Mark

Ghriallais, Nora

☐ NATIVE CONNEMARA IRISH SINGING
NGCD 001 / May '94 / Claddagh

Ghymes

☐ UZENET
GHYCD 001 / Mar '98 / Monique

Giammarco, Maurizio

☐ HORNITHOLOGY (Giammarco, Maurizio Quartet)
Old home / Sky walker / End of a bop affair / No Spanish night / Arboreal code / Unexpected flight / Voce vai ver
CDSGP 040 / Feb '93 / Prestige

☐ INSIDE (Giammarco, Maurizio Quartet)
1212542 / Jan '94 / Soul Note

Gianelli, Fred

☐ TELEPATHIC ROMANCE
EFA 501112 / Aug '96 / Sahko

☐ TELEPATHIC WISDOM VOL.1
Acid diji 3 / Salacious / Fox hunt / Precognition / Eloquence / Clairvoyance / Fingered / Kooky scientist / Painkiller / EOD / Excelsior / Sleeps with the foxes / Acid diji 2
SUPER 2025CD / Feb '95 / Superstition

☐ TELEPATHIC WISDOM VOL.2
SUPER 2062 / Sep '96 / Superstition

Giant

☐ LAST OF THE RUNAWAYS
I'm a believer / Innocent days / I can't get close enough / I'll see you in my dreams / No way out / Shake me up / It takes two / Stranger to me / Hold back the night / Love welcome home / Big pitch
CDA 5272 / Apr '90 / A&M

Giant Sand

☐ BACKYARD BARBECUE BROADCAST
OUT 1262 / Aug '96 / Brake Out
379142 / Jan '96 / Koch International

☐ BEST OF GIANT SAND VOL.1, THE (Giant Songs)
Down on town / Valley of rain / Thin line man / Body of water / Moon over Memphis / Uneven light of day / Big rock / One man's woman, no man's land / Mountain of love / Curse of a thousand flames / Barrio / Graveyard / Heartland / Underground train / Bigger than that / Wearing the robes of bible black / Fingernail moon, barracuda and me
GSCD 1 / Jul '89 / Demon

☐ BEST OF GIANT SAND VOL.2, THE
Can't find love / Get to leave / Town with a little or no pity / Dreamville New Mexico / October anywhere / Almost the politicians wife / Badlands / Christmas Day (maybe it'll help) / Sucker in a cage / Who am I / Death dying and channel 5 / Sandman / Sisters and brothers / Sage advice / Love like a train / Trickle down system
GSCD 2 / Jul '95 / Demon

☐ BUILD YOUR OWN NIGHT, IT'S EASY (Official Bootleg Series Vol.1)
No name guitars / Sled / Elevator music / Spit / Corridor of love / Mason card / Hank's rap city / Less the lie / Scorcher / Bed of nails / Crumb / TW's forgotten chorus / Smokey Joe's deep blue pancakes
GSFANCD 1 / Feb '97 / Epiphany

☐ CENTRE OF THE UNIVERSE
OUT 1092 / Nov '92 / Brake Out

☐ GOODS & SERVICES
OUT 1222 / Aug '96 / Brake Out

☐ LOVE SONGS
Wearing the robes of bible black / One man's woman / No man's land / Mad dog a man / Fingernail moon, barracuda and me / Mountain of love / Almost the politician's wife / Doors / Love like a train / Is that all there is
FIENDCD 129 / Sep '90 / Demon

☐ PURGE & SLOUCH
OUT 1152 / Nov '94 / Brake Out

☐ RAMP
Romance of falling / Warm storm / Wonder / Welcome to my world / Anti-shadow / Jazzer snipe / Shadow to you / Z.z. quicker foot / Neon filler / Seldom matters / Resolver / Nowhere / Always horses coming / Patsy's blues
R 2762 / Oct '91 / Rough Trade

☐ STORM
Town where no town belongs / Back to black and grey / Bigger than that / Right makes right / Three sixes / Replacement / Storm / Was is a big word / Town with little or no pity / Weight
FIENDCD 115 / Sep '90 / Demon

☐ STROMAUSFALL
RTS 7 / Nov '94 / Return To Sender

☐ SWERVE
Trickle down system / Dream stay / Former versions of ourselves / Angels at night / Can't find love / Swerver / Sisters and brothers / Swerving / Every grain of sand / Some kind of / Swervette / Final swerve
FIENDCD 204 / Oct '90 / Demon

☐ VALLEY OF RAIN/BALLAD OF A THIN LINE MAN
Down on town (love's no answer) / Black venetian blind / Curse of a thousand flames / Artists / Man of want / Valley of rain / Tumble and tear / October anywhere / Death, dying and channel 5 / Torture of love / Thin line man / All along the watchtower / Graveyard / Body of water / You can't put your arms around a memory / Hard man to get to know / Who am I / Desperate man
DIAB 831 / Jun '97 / Diablo

Giants Causeway

☐ IS THERE ANYWAY
MASSCD 070 / Aug '95 / Massacre

Giants Chair

☐ PURITY AND CONTROL
CR 022CD / Nov '96 / Caulfield

Gibb, Andy

☐ GREATEST HITS
I just want to be your everything / Thicker than water / Shadow dancing / Everlasting love / Don't throw it all away / Time is time / Me / Will you still love me tomorrow / After dark / Desire
5115852 / Jul '94 / Polydor

Gibb, Robin

☐ HOW OLD ARE YOU
Juliet / How old are you / In and out of love / Kathy's gone / Don't stop the night / Another lonely night in New York / Danger / He can't love you / Hearts on fire / I believe in miracles
8108962 / Apr '94 / Polydor

Gibbons, Carroll

☐ CALLS THE TUNES
FDR Jones / My heart belongs to Daddy / Apple for the teacher / Wish me luck / Moon love / They can't black out the moon / In an 18th Century drawing room / It's a lovely day tomorrow / Scatterbrain / It's a hap hap happy day / Faithful forever / Let the people sing / Midnight in Mayfair / Oh Johnny / When you wish upon a star / Walkin' thru' Mockin' Bird Lane / Over the rainbow / Little rain must fall / My Capri serenade / Nightingale sang in Berkeley Square / I've got my eyes on you / Shake down the stars / Indian summer / Woodpecker song / Fools rush in / Let's put out the lights / When that man is dead and gone / Give me something to remembr you by / Goodnight / Good luck and carry on / Weep no more / One look at you / We three / South American way / I hear a rhapsody / Dolores / Boa noite / You and your kiss / I yi yi yi yi / You are too beautiful / When the blackbird says bye bye / Imagination / All the things you are / Blueberry hill / Sleepy lagoon / Never took a lesson in my life / You're as pretty as a picture / My own / Be a good scout / I wanna go back to Bali / Daydreaming / Latin quarter / You never looked so beautiful / I've got a pocketful of dreams / Change partners / Blue skies are round the corner / Two sleepy people / Penny Serenade
RAJCD 863 / Apr '96 / Empress

☐ CARROLL GIBBONS
Grandma said / Ten little miles from town / They say / Say it's my heart / I have eyes / Remember me / Nice work if you can get it / Five o'clock whistle / You walk by / Breathless / Old black magic / You leave me breathless / Accentuate the positive / If I had a wishing ring / Mary Lou / We talk about you ev'ry night / Five minutes more / It's a beautiful day / As long as I live / To bed early / Prisoner of love / Saturday night / Pablo the dreamer / So ends my search for a dream / Let's take the long way home
CDMFP 6354 / Jun '97 / Music For Pleasure

☐ CARROLL GIBBONS WITH THE SAVOY HOTEL ORPHEANS
On the air / Sweet as a song / With thee I swing / Let me give my happiness to you / Three wishes / I need you / Certain age / Moonbeam dance / When anybody plays or sings / Every woman thinks / Cabin in the cotton / Living in dreams / Oo - that kiss / Gay imposters / Isn't it romantic / Remember (Carroll Gibbons medley) / Any broken hearts to mend / Tomorrow is another day / Bubbling over / Goodbye to summer / Shall we dance
PASTCD 9734 / Mar '91 / Flapper

☐ OH THAT KISS
Breaking in a pair of shoes / Sugar rose / You've got everything / You / Birth of the blues / Moonlight and roses / Smoke gets in your eyes / Got to admit / You never looked so beautiful / She's my lovely / Je vous aime beaucoup / For me for you / Touch of your lips / This year's kiss / I've got you to keep me warm / Cheek to cheek / Isn't it a lovely day / I've got you under my skin / Close my eyes / I'm getting sentimental over you / Body and soul / Can't we talk it over / Oh that kiss / On the air / I guess I'll have to change my plan
CDEA 6004 / Feb '98 / Vocalion

☐ ON THE AIR
Black coffee / Body and soul / By the fireside / Carroll calls the tunes / Everything I have is yours / Fascinating rhythm / Flamingo / For me, for you: *Gibbons, Carroll & Hildegarde* / Garden in the rain: *Gibbons, Carroll & George Metaxa* / Happy go lucky / Heaven can wait / I need some cooling off/My heart stood still / I'm just beginning to care / Life is just a bowl of cherries / Linda: *Gibbons, Carroll & Al Bowlly* / Lovely to look at / Moonbeam dance / On the air / Smoke gets in your eyes / Summer rain / Sweet and lovely: *Gibbons, Carroll & Al Bowlly* / Under a blanket of blue / When day is done / Whispers in the dark / With thee I swing
CDAJA 5142 / Oct '94 / Living Era

☐ TIME WAS
On the air / Always in my heart / Old Uncle Bud / Yankee doodle boy / Madelaine / Turn your money in your pocket / Tropical magic / Elmer's tune / Tomorrow's sunrise / Moonlight cocktail / Miss you / Concerto for two / Sinner kissed an angel / Darling / I walked into a dream without knocking / As time goes by / I don't want anybody at all / Tell me the truth / Put your arms around me honey / Amodola / I should have known years ago / Time
RAJCD 823 / Nov '97 / Empress

Gibbons, Leroy

☐ FOUR SEASON LOVER
FMCD 004 / Jan '97 / Fatman

Gibbons, Steve

☐ ANY ROAD UP/ROLLIN' ON (Gibbons, Steve Band)
Take me home / Johnny Cool / Rollin' / Spark of love / Standing on the bridge / Natural thing / Speed kills / Strange world / Sweetheart / Back street cat / Dick Malone / Wild flowers / Light up your face / Now you know me / Mr. Jones / Till the well runs dry / Tulane / Cross me over the road / Till the fire burns out / Low down man / Right side of heaven / Rollin' on / Please don't say goodbye / Tupelo Mississippi flash / Rounden / Gave his life to rock 'n' roll / Make the good times last / Dick leaps in
SGDCD 035 / Sep '97 / Road Goes On Forever

☐ BIRMINGHAM TO MEMPHIS
AKD 019 / Apr '93 / Linn

☐ CAUGHT LIVE IN THE ACT (Gibbons, Steve Band)
REP 4048 / Aug '91 / Repertoire

☐ DOWN IN THE BUNKER
No spitting on the bus / Any road up / Down in the bunker / Big j.c. / Mary ain't going home / Down in the city / Let's do it again / Eddy vortex / Chelita / When you get outside / Grace / Tulane / Gold coast / Body talk / Let me go / Satisfying moves / I am here / Great escape
REP 4047 / Aug '91 / Repertoire

☐ ON THE LOOSE (Gibbons, Steve Band)
Down the road apiece / Chuck in my car / Absolutely gone / Love part one / Trucker / On the loose / To be alone with you / Love 'n' peace / Like a rolling stone
CDMF 041 / May '92 / Magnum Force

☐ STEVE GIBBONS- LIVE
848829 / Sep '90 / SPV

Gibbs, Joe

☐ EXPLOSIVE ROCKSTEADY (Joe Gibbs Amalgamated 1967-1973) (Various Artists)
CDHB 72 / May '92 / Heartbeat

☐ GET ON UP (Rocksteady 1967-1968) (Various Artists)
You're gonna need me: *Dunkley, Errol* / Feel so fine: *McCook, Tommy* / Musically: *Blake, Keith* / My friends: *Dynamics* / I'm going home: *Dunkley, Errol* / Woo oh oh: *Blake, Keith* / Big take over: *Overtakers* / Dee's special: *Taitt, Lynn & The Jetts* / Tit for tat: *Hinds, Neville* / Give it to me: *Pioneers* / Soul glide: *Hinds, Neville* / Fat girl in the red: *Mellotones* / Dip and fall back: *Pioneers* / World needs love: *Shirley, Roy* / Having a party: *Walks, Dennis* / Day by day: *Groovers* / Get on up: *Creations* / This is soul: *Pioneers & Lyn Tait/The Jetts* / Over and over: *Robinson, Jackie* / I spy: *Taitt, Lynn & The Jetts* / Let the little girl dance: *Robinson, Jackie* / Cinderella: *Morris, Eric* / Tickle me for days: *Pioneers* / Sleepy lady: *Taitt, Lynn & The Jetts* / Mortgage: *Malcolm, Hugh* / Let me through (please Mr. Gateman): *Versatiles*
CDTRL 390 / Feb '98 / Trojan

☐ JOE GIBBS RARE GROOVES (Various Artists)
RGCD 014 / Nov '94 / Rocky One

☐ JOE GIBBS' MOOD (Various Artists)
Scorcher: *Dunkley, Errol* / Thank you baby: *Perry, Lee 'Scratch'* / That's the way you like it: *Overtakers* / People grudgeful: *Pioneers* / Time has come: *Versatiles* / Sweet dreams: *Pioneers* / Never see some see: *Royals* / Jumping Jack: *Cannonball Bryan Trio* / Hurry come up: *Intruders* / Mama look deh: *Reggae Boyz* / Decimal currency: *Blenders* / Them a laugh and kiki: *Soulmates* / Hippys are here: *Hippy Boys* / Wreck a buddy: *Soul Sisters* / Me no born yah: *Reggae Boyz* / It is I: *Count Matchuki* / One love: *Cobbs* / Reflections of Don D: *Moore, Johnny* / Alli Button: *Pioneers* / Man beware: *Slickers* / Joe Gibbs mood: *Collins, Ansell* / Long long time: *Versatiles* / Nevada Joe: *Johnny Lover* / Danzella: *Thomas, Nicky* / Movements: *Count Matchuki* / Seeing is believing: *Gibbs, Caly*
CDTRL 394 / 20 Apr '98 / Trojan

☐ MIGHTY TWO, THE (Gibbs, Joe & Errol Thompson)
HBCD 73 / Nov '92 / Heartbeat

☐ REGGAE TRAIN, THE (1968 - 1971) (Gibbs, Joe & Friends)
CDTRL 261 / Sep '94 / Trojan

☐ STATE OF EMERGENCY
RGCD 037 / Apr '96 / Rocky One

☐ UPTOWN TOP RANKING (Joe Gibbs Reggae Productions 1970-1978) (Various Artists)
Love of the common people: *Thomas, Nicky* / Ten feet tall: *Lizzy* / Don't be prejudice: *Max Romeo* / I've got a feeling: *Heptones* / Headcup: *Johnny Lover* / Maga dog: *Tosh, Peter* / Mandingo dog: *Bunny Flip* / Fat dog: *Gibbs, Joe* / You wrong fe trouble Joshua: *Ford, Eddie* / Pretty girl: *Wilson, Delroy* / Forman versus Frazier: *Big Youth* / Hello my little Queen (my girl Josephine): *Parker, Ken* / African Queen: *Pablo, Augustus* / Win them: *Graham, Leo* / News carrier: *I-Roy & Leo Graham* / Band you belly: *Ethiopians* / Burn Babylon: *Walker, Sylford* / Ghetto living: *Mighty Diamonds* / Heavy manners: *Prince Far-I* / Three piece suit and thing: *Trinity* / Uptown top ranking: *Althia & Donna* / Heart and soul: *Byles, Junior* / Money in my pocket: *Brown, Dennis*
CDTRL 392 / Apr '98 / Trojan

Gibbs, Kevin

☐ PIANO FOR ALL SEASONS, A
CCD 1004 / Jul '98 / Clarity

Gibbs, Louise

☐ INVITATION
Invitation / I wish you were here / Island / Thrill is gone / Gramercy Park / When we were one / Dulcinea / Man I remember / You have to try / You and the night and music / Words, nevertheless / Four
33JAZZ 040 / 29 Jun '98 / 33 Jazz

Gibbs, Michael

☐ CENTURY/CLOSE MY EYES (Original Soundtracks)
IONIC 10CD / Jan '94 / The Fine Line

☐ HARDBOILED (Original Soundtrack)
Hard-boiled overture / Tea house bust / Red car boogie / Library hit / Sad kong / Wong-kong / Wong loses it / Gun arsenal / Boatyard battle / Yuen and kong / Motorcade / Ko knocked out / Corridor creeping / Cut throat / Body count / Shirley and the babies / Hospital inferno
IONIC 11CD / Jul '93 / The Fine Line

☐ IRON AND SILK (Original Soundtrack)
Arrival/First impressions / Teacher Hei/The dining room / Iron fist / Mark and ming / Walking teacher Hei part-way home/Tai Chi / Mark's first lesson / Bamboo garden/Nearly morning/Tai Chi / Working out with bricks / Gorge / Confusion / Improving cultural relations / Mark's anger / Through the paces / On the steps/Pan's house / Farewell party/Blue Danube / Duel / End credits
IONIC 7CD / Nov '91 / The Fine Line

Gibbs, Mike

☐ BIG MUSIC (Gibbs, Mike Orchestra)
Wall to wall / Pride aside / Kosasa / Almost ev'ry day / Watershed / Mopsus / Adult / Pride outside
92312 / May '96 / Act

☐ BY THE WAY (Gibbs, Mike Orchestra)
Beauteous being / Blueprint / To Lady Mac: In sympathy / Something similar / World without / Rain before it falls / Jeunesse / Roses are red / Turn of the century / Out of the question / Just a head/Fanfare
AHUM 016 / Nov '93 / Ah-Um

☐ EUROPEANA - JAZZPHONY NO.1 (Gibbs, Mike & Joachim Kuhn)
Castle in heaven / Black is the colour of my true love's hair / Shepherd of Breton / Ingrian rune song / Groom's sister / Norwegian psalm / Three angels / Heaven has created / She moved through the fair / Crebe de chet / Midnight sun / Londonderry air / Otra jazzpana
92202 / Mar '95 / Act

☐ ONLY CHROME WATER FALL ORCHESTRA (Gibbs, Mike Orchestra)
To Lady Mac: In retrospect / Nairam / Blackgang / Antique / Undergrowth / Tunnel of love / Unfinished sympathy
BGOCD 273 / May '95 / Beat Goes On

Gibbs, Terry

☐ DREAM BAND VOL.1
Begin the beguine / Don't be that way / Cotton tail / Stardust / Opus one / After you've gone / You've gone to my head / Let's dance / Subtle sermon / Kissing bug / Jumpin' at the woodside
CCD 7647 / Jun '95 / Contemporary

☐ DREAM BAND VOL.2 (The Sundown Sessions)
Song is you / Moonglow / Fat man / It could happen to you / Back bay shuffle / Dancing in the dark / Bue lou / Softly as in a morning sunrise / No heat / My reverie / Claw
CCD 7652 / Jun '95 / Contemporary

☐ DREAM BAND VOL.3 (Flying Home)
CCD 7654 / Jun '95 / Contemporary

☐ DREAM BAND VOL.4 (The Main Stem)
Day in, day out / Summit blues / Limerick waltz / You don't know what love is / Sweet georgia brown / Nose cone / Too close for comfort / Main stem / Jada / T and s
CCD 7656 / Jun '95 / Contemporary

☐ DREAM BAND VOL.5 (The Big Cat)
Tico tico / Big bad bob / Big cat / Soft eyes / Billie's bounce / Pretty blue eyes / I'll take romance / Do you wanna jump, children / Nature boy / Jump the blues away / Sleep
CCD 7657 / Nov '95 / Contemporary

☐ KINGS OF SWING (Gibbs, Terry & Buddy De Franco/Herb Ellis)
Seven come eleven / Soft winds / Man I love / Undecided / Body and soul / Just one of those things / Stompin' at the savoy / These foolish things / Airmail special
CCD 14067 / Jan '94 / Contemporary

☐ MEMORIES OF YOU (Gibbs, Terry & Buddy De Franco/Herb Ellis)
Flying home / Rose room / I surrender dear / Dizzy spells / Don't be that way / Poor butterfly / Avalon / Memories of you / After you've gone
CCD 14066 / Apr '94 / Contemporary

☐ PLAY THAT SONG (Gibbs, Terry Quartet)
CRD 337 / Jun '96 / Chiaroscuro

Gibert, Allain

☐ CHARIOT D'OR
Y 225051CD / Aug '96 / Silex

Gibney, David

☐ SHAMAN JOURNEY
DD 101CD / May '96 / Subspace

Gibson, Anthony T.

☐ COMPLETE ANTHONY T. GIBSON, THE
Aint no way / Say it isn't so / Special kinda woman / My heart is in your hands / Sitting in the park / I want a lover / If you need someone / Girl on the sidelines / Is it for real / Take the money and run / At this moment / Searching for romance
ATCD 016 / Apr '93 / ATR

Gibson Brothers

☐ BEST OF GIBSON BROTHERS, THE (Cuba)
Cuba / Que sera mi vida (if you should go) / Better do it salsa / Ooh what a life / Non-stop dance / Come to America / Mariana / Latin America / Heaven / Baby it's the singer / My heart's beating wild / Rio Brasilia / West Indies / Dancin' the mambo
HTCD 57 / 20 Apr '98 / Hot Productions

☐ HITS
KWEST 5408 / Feb '93 / Kenwest

Gibson Brothers

☐ MEMPHIS
SFTRI 176 / Jun '98 / Sympathy For The Record Industry

Gibson, Banv

☐ JAZZ BABY (Gibson, Banv & NOR Hot Jazz)
SOSCD 1073 / Aug '90 / Stomp Off

Gibson, Bob

☐ PERFECT HIGH
78067417942 / 27 Apr '98 / Drive Archive

☐ REVISITED (Gibson, Bob & Hamilton Camp)
FE 1413 / Dec '94 / Folk Era

Gibson, Clifford

☐ BEAT YOU DOING IT
Bad luck dice / Levee camp moan / Hard headed blues / Blues without a dime / Jive me blues / Society blues / Ice and snow blues / Drayman blues / Old time rider / Tired of being mistreated (part 1) / Brooklyn blues / Beat you doing it / Sunshine moan / Stop your rambling
YAZCD 1027 / Mar '92 / Yazoo

Gibson, Debbie

☐ BODY MIND SOUL
Love or money / Do you have it in your heart / Free me / Shock your mama / Losin' myself / How can this be / When I say no / Little birdy / Kisses 4 one / Tear down these walls / Goodbye
7567824512 / Apr '93 / Atlantic

☐ OUT OF THE BLUE
Out of the blue / Staying together / Only in my dreams / Foolish beat / Red hot / Wake up to love / Shake your love / Fallen angel / Play the field / Between the lines
K 781 780 2 / Sep '87 / Atlantic

Gibson, Don

☐ BEST OF DON GIBSON, THE
Sea of heartbreak / Oh lonesome me / Lonesome no. 1 / (yes) I'm hurting / Who cares for me / So how come (no one loves me) / It's a long, long way to georgia / Blue blue day / I can mend your broken heart / Funny, familiar, forgotten feelings / I can't stop loving you / Don't tell me your troubles / Sweet dreams / Watch where you're going / Just one time / Head over heels in love with you / Far far away / I'm movin' on
74321218482 / Jun '94 / Arista

☐ COUNTRY CLASSICS
Oh lonesome me / Blue blue day / Give myself a party / I can't stop loving me / Who cares / Just one time / Sweet dreams / Sea of heartbreak / Lonesome number one / I need thee every hour / Bring back your love to me / One day at a time / Touch the morning / Woman (sensuous woman) / Country green / I can mend your broken heart
CD 6075 / Apr '97 / Music

☐ LEGEND IN MY TIME, A
Sittin' here cryin' / Blue blue day / Oh lonesome me / I can't stop loving you / Look who's blue / If you don't know it / Bad bad day / Sweet sweet girl / Give myself a party / Who cares / Didn't work out did it / Lonesome old house / Don't tell me your troubles / I couldn't care less / Just one time / Legend in my time / Far far away / Sweet dreams / Sea of heartbreak / I sat back and let it happen / Lonesome number one / I can mend your broken heart / If you knew me / If you don't know the sorrow / Think of me / I'm crying inside
BCD 15401 / Nov '87 / Bear Family

☐ MASTERS, THE
EABCD 034 / 24 Nov '97 / Eagle

☐ SEA OF HEARTBREAK (The Very Best Of Don Gibson)
Oh lonesome me / Bring back your love to me / Just one time / Touch in the morning / Sea of heartbreak / One day at a time / Who cares / I need thee every hour / Blu blue day / I can mend your broken heart / Woman (sensuous woman) / I can't stop loving you / Country green / Give myself a party / Lonesome number one / SSweet dreams
308762 / 11 May '98 / Hallmark

☐ SINGER SONGWRITER 1949-1960 (4CD Set)
I lost my love / Why am I so lonely / Automatic mamma / Cloudy skies / I love no one but you / Carolina breakdown / Roses are red / Wiggle wag / Dark future / Just let me love you / Blue million tears / Red lips, white lies and blue hours / Sample kisses / No shoulder to cry on / Let me stay in your arms / We're stepping out tonight / Waitin' down the road / Walkin' in the moonlight / I just love the way you tell a lie / You cast me out (forevermore) / Symptoms of love / Selfish with your kisses / Ice cold heart / Many times I've waited / Road of life alone / Run boy / Sweet dreams / I must forget you / Taller than trees / Satisfied / Wait for the light to shine / Cannan's land / Faith unlocks the door / Evening prayer / Lord I'm coming home / Climbing up the mountain / Where no one stands alone / Known only to him / My God is real / That lonesome valley / Who cares (for me) / When will this ever end / Sweet sweet girl / Stranger to me / Won't cha come back to me / Stranger to me / As much / Who cares (for me) / I wish it had been a dream / Ages and ages ago / Even tho' / Didn't work out did it / It's my way / Almost / Do you think / Foggy river / Midnight / Lonesome old house / Ah-ha / It happens every time / I ain't gonna waste my time / I ain't a-studyin' you baby / I'm gonna fool everybody / I believed in you / What a fool I was for you / You're the only one for me / I love you still / Everything turns out for the best / I can't leave / Sittin' here cryin' / Too soon to know / Pretty rainbow / Blue blue day / Tell it like it is / Oh lonesome me / I can't stop loving you / It has to be / Give myself a party / Look who's blue / Bad bad day / Take me as I am / Heartbreak Avenue / We could / If you don't know it / Blues in my heart / Give myself a party / Don't tell me your troubles / I couldn't care less / Don't tell me your troubles / Heartbreak Avenue / Big hearted me / Maybe tomorrow / Everybody but me / I'm movin' on / Just one time / I may never get to heaven / Lonely Street / On the banks of the old Ponchartrain / Why don't you love me / If I can stay away / Never love again / Streets of Laredo / My love for you / My hands are tied / It only hurts for a little while / Legend in my time / Far far away / Foolish me / My tears don't show / World is waiting for the sunrise / What about me / Next voice you hear / Hurtin' inside / Time hurts (as well as it heals) / What's the reason I'm not pleasin' you / Sweet dreams / Same street
BCD 15475 / Jan '92 / Bear Family

☐ SINGER SONGWRITER 1961-1966 (4CD Set)
Sweet dreams / I think it's best (To forget me) / That's how it goes / Sea of heartbreak / No one will ever know / Born to lose / Beautiful dreamer / Camptown races / Fireball mail / Last letter / White silver sands / Driftwood on the river / Lonesome road / Above and beyond / I sat back and let it happen / Lose the score / Same old trouble / So how come (no one loves me) / Lonesome number one / Let's fall out of love (Tonight) / I let her get lonely / I can mend your broken heart / For a little while / It makes no difference now / Settin' the woods on fire / Baby we're really in love / I love you so much it hurts / It's a sin / I'm sorry for you my friend / This cold war with you / Where is your heart tonight / Blue dream / How's the world treating you / May you never be alone / We live in two different worlds / Old ship of zion / Then I met the master / I'd rather have Jesus / Be ready / Can't see myself / For old time's sake / It was worth it all / Head over heels in love with you / I can't stop loving you / Legend in my time / Give myself a party / Oh lonesome me / Don't tell me your troubles / Love has come my way / Blue blue day / Just one time / Oh such a stranger / After the heartache / Anything new gets old (Except my love for you) / God walks these hills / Do you know my Jesus / Hide me rock of ages / Where else would I want to be / If I can help somebody / He's everywhere / You don't knock / When they ring the golden bells / There she goes (Let her go) / If you knew me / If you don't know the sorrow / Mixed up love / There she goes / Think of me / 'Cause I believe in you / Then i'll be free / Love that can't be / Waltz of regret / When your house is not a home / Watch where you're going / You're going away / Again / Too much hurt / Born loser / Wound time can't erase / Around the town / I'm crying inside / Dark as a dungeon / Right away / Lovin' lies / All the world is lonely now / Worried mind / There's a big wheel / Take these chains from my heart / Singin' the blues / With your love on my mind / Address unknown / My adobe hacienda / Lonely street / Cryin' heart blues / I can't tell my heart that / (Yes) I'm hurting / My whole world is hurt / You can't laugh (At a fool) / My tomorrows (They don't come easy) / Don't you ever get tired of hurting me / Once a day / My friends are gonna be strangers / Vaya con dios / Just call me lonesome / With love on my mind / Stranger to me / Maria Elena / Blues in my mind / Making believe / Somebody loves you darlin' / I'd just be fool enough / Lost highway / Let's fall out of love / I thought I heard you calling my name / Don't touch me / How do you tell someone / Just out of reach / When I stop dreaming / Cute little girls
BCD 15664 / Nov '93 / Bear Family

☐ VERY BEST OF DON GIBSON, THE
Oh lonesome me / Blue blue day / Give myself a party / I can't stop loving you / Who cares / Just one time / Sweet dreams / Sea of heartbreak / Lonesome number one / I can mend your broken heart / Country green / Woman (sensuous woman) / Touch the morning / One day at a time / Bring back your love to me / I need thee every hour
PLATCD 217 / Feb '97 / Platinum

Gibson, Harry

☐ WHO PUT THE BENZEDRINE IN MRS. MURPHY'S OVALTINE (Gibson, Harry 'The Hipster')
Hey man, you just made my day / Get hip to Shirley MacLaine / I flipped my wig in San Francisco / Back in the days of Dixieland and Bop / Boogity woogity blues / Thanks for the use of the hall / Get hip to Shirley MacLaine / They call him Harry The Hipster / Me and Max / Who put the benzedrine in Mrs Murphy's ovaltine / Lowdown slowdown inflationary blues / Maple Leaf rag and a little bit of The Entertainer / Ragtime raggedy Ann
DE 687 / Nov '96 / Delmark

Gibson, Lacy

☐ CRYING FOR MY BABY
You'd better be sure / Easy woman / Crying for my baby / Chicago women / Blackjack / CB blues / Pleading for love / Take my love (I want to give it all to you) / My love is real / Dirty old man / Shake it baby
DE 689 / Jun '97 / Delmark

Gibson, Lee

☐ NEARNESS OF YOU, THE
Time after time / Never let me go / They can't take that away from me / Good morning heartache / Here's that rainy day / Nice 'n' easy / Lady is a tramp / Foggy day / Please don't talk about me when I've gone / Nearness of you / Teach me tonight / I only have eyes for you
ZECD 3 / Mar '96 / Zephyr

Gibson, Steve

☐ BOOGIE WOOGIE ON A SATURDAY NIGHT (Gibson, Steve & The Red Caps)
Sidewalk shuffle / Bobbin' / Would I mind / Always / Freehearted / How I cry / Three dollars and ninety nine cents / D'ya eat yet, Joe / Boogie woogie on a Saturday night / I went to your wedding / My tzatskele (my little darling) / Feeling kinda happy / Nuff of that stuff / Win or lose / Two little kisses / I may hate myself in the morning / Wait / Big game hunter / Shame / Do I, do I, do I / Why don't you love me / Truthfully / When you come to me / Fussing and fighting (unissued) / Thing / Am I to blame / I'm to blame / Sleepy little cowboy
BCD 15490 / Jul '90 / Bear Family

Gidea Park

☐ ENDLESS SUMMER DAYS
Surf is up / Surfer's paradise / Have you seen that girl / Lai lo la limbo / Party beach / American girls / And your dreams come true / I got rhythm / Bring back those surfin' days / Lazin' on the beach / Back in '65 / Don't look back / Summertime city / Endless summer days / Stay healthy
304432 / Jun '98 / Hallmark

Gieco, Leon

☐ DESENCHUFADO
68977 / Apr '97 / Tropical

☐ MENSAJES DE ALMA
68964 / Apr '97 / Tropical

Gift

☐ MULTUM IN PARVA
Little deranged puppet / Sinking ship / OK this is the pops / Don't need a reason / Restless spirit / Little deranged puppet / Never too young / Social cleansing / Date with failure / Bayond the tears / Kelly K / Jezebel / Little deranged puppet
TK 93CD068 / Oct '94 / T/K

Gigantic

☐ ANSWER
HB 12CD / Mar '93 / Heatblast

Gigantor

☐ ATOMIC
LF 186CD / Nov '95 / Lost & Found

☐ GIGANTOR/BASEBALL ANNIE (Gigantor/Baseball Annie)
LF 240CD / Sep '96 / Lost & Found

☐ MAGIC BOZO SPIN
LF 074CD / May '94 / Lost & Found

☐ SINGLES AND MORE, THE
LF 129CD / Jan '95 / Lost & Found

Giger, Paul

☐ SCHATTENWELT
4377762 / Jun '93 / ECM

Gigli, Beniamino

☐ GREAT VOICES OF THE CENTURY
CDMOIR 417 / Apr '95 / Memoir

Gigolo Aunts

☐ WHERE I FIND MY HEAVEN (The Best Of The Gigolo Aunts)
REMCD 528 / 1 Jun '98 / Reactive

Gil, Gilberto

☐ AQUELE ABRACO
ML 51012 / 14 Apr '98 / Musica Latina

☐ GILBERTO EM CONCERTO
WWCD 2200 / Apr '92 / West Wind Latina

☐ LIVE IN TOKYO
CDGR 202 / Dec '97 / Charly

☐ LIVE IN TOKYO
ML 51019 / 14 Apr '98 / Musica Latina

☐ QUANTA
Quanta / Ciencia e arte / Estrela / Danca de Shiva / Vendedor de caranguejo / Chiquinho azevedo / Pilula de alho / Opachoro / Graca divina / Pela internet / Guerra santa / Atimo de po / Fogo liquido / Pop wu wei / O lugar do nosso amor / De ouro e marfim / Sala do som / Un abraco no Joao / O mar e o lago / La lune de goree
0630189192 / Jun '97 / Warner Bros.

☐ QUANTA GENTE VEIO VER
Introducao / Palco / Is this love / Stir it up / Refavela / Vendedor de caranguejo / Quanta / Estrela / Pela internet / Cerebro electronico / Opachoro / Copacabana / Novidade / O Ghandi / De ouro e marfim
3984232182 / 13 Jul '98 / Warner Bros.

☐ SOUNDS OF BRAZIL
SOW 90121 / Jun '94 / Sounds Of The World

☐ SOY LOCO POR TI AMERICA
Aquele abraco / Vida / Mamma / Soy loco por ti america / Jubiaba / Mar de copacabana / Mardi 10 mars
CDGR 168 / Sep '97 / Charly

Gila

☐ GILA
SBCD 021 / 26 Jan '98 / Second Battle

Gilbert & Lewis

☐ 8 TIME
GAD 016CD / 6 Jul '98 / 4AD

Gilbert, Bruce

☐ AB OVO
CDSTUMM 117 / Jan '96 / Mute

☐ IN ESSE
Soli / Bassi / Muzi
CDSTUUM 171 / 13 Oct '97 / Mute

☐ SONGS FOR FRUIT
Music for fruit (edited) / Push / You might be called
CDSTUMM 77 / Sep '91 / Mute

☐ THIS WAY TO THE SHIVERING MAN
Work for 'do you me? I did' / Hommage / Shivering man / Here visit / Epitaph for Henran Brenlar / Angelfood
STUMM 18 CD / Aug '84 / Mute

Gilbert, Paul

☐ KING OF CLUBS
Champagne / Vinyl / Girls who can read your mind / I'm just in love / Jig / Girlfriend's birthday / Bumblebee / Streetlights / My Naomi / Double trouble / Million dollar smile / Jam
111192 / 8 Jun '98 / Mayhem

Gilbert, Vance

☐ EDGEWISE
PH 1156CD / Mar '94 / Philo

☐ FUGITIVES
CDPH 1186 / Aug '95 / Philo

☐ SHAKING OFF GRAVITY
Hey lah dee dah song / Taking it all to Tennessee / Twice struck / Watching a good thing burn / Just can't go like that / House of pain / Fly / Charlene / Do what you do / Icarus by night / Oh little town / Could you believe / Noting for you
CDPH 1213 / Feb '98 / Philo

Gilberto, Astrud

☐ BEACH SAMBA
Stay / Misty roses / Face I love / Banda / Oba oba / Canoeiro / I had the craziest dream / Bossa na prai / My foolish heart / Dia das rosas / You didn't have to be so nice / Nao bate o corocoa / Goodbye sadness / Call me / Here's that rainy day / Tu meu delirio / It's a lovely day today
5198012 / Apr '93 / Verve

☐ GIRL FROM IPANEMA, THE
Girl from Ipanema / Black magic / Love for sale / Meu piao / Far away: *Gilberto, Astrud & Chet Baker* / Mamae eu quero/Chica chica boom chic / All I've got / Puppy song / Wanting you / We'll make today last night again
307672 / Jul '97 / Hallmark

☐ GIRL FROM IPANEMA, THE
BN 016 / Apr '98 / Blue Nite

☐ JAZZ MASTERS
Dreamer / Girl from Ipanema / Once upon a summertime / Felicidade / Certain sadness / Agua de beber / Frevo / Corcovado / Dindi / Look to the rainbow / Day by day / Shadow of your smile / Aruanda / Gentle rain / Tristeza / Berimbau
5198242 / 5 May '98 / Verve

☐ LOOK TO THE RAINBOW
Berimbau / Once upon a summertime / Felicidade / I will wait for you / Frevo / Maria Moita / Look at the rainbow / Bim bom / Lugar bonito / El preciso aprender a ser so / She's a carioca / Certain smile / Certain sadness / Nega do cabelo duro / So nice / Voce ja foi a Bahia / Portuguese washerwoman
8215562 / Sep '93 / Verve

☐ MUSIC FOR THE MILLIONS
Once I loved / Auga de beber / Meditation / And roses and roses / How insensitive / O morro / Dindi / Photograph / Dreamer / So tinha de ser com voce / All that's left is to say goodbye
8234512 / Feb '92 / Verve

☐ TALKIN' VERVE
Beginnings / On my mind / Maria Quiet / Wailing of the willow / Call me / Crickets sing for Anamaria / Bim bom / Don't leave me baby / Bossa na praia (beach samba) / Windy / Holiday / Stay / Berimbau / She's a caricoa / So nice (summer samba) / Nao bate o corocao
5396752 / 9 Feb '98 / Verve

☐ THIS IS...ASTRUD GILBERTO
Girl from Ipanema / How insensitive / Beach samba / Fly me to the moon / Without him / Face I love / It's a lovely day today / Parade (A banda) / Bim bom / Shadow of your smile / I haven't got anything better to do / Look at the rainbow / Agua de beber / Aruanda
8250642 / Sep '92 / Verve

Gilberto, Joao

☐ DESAFINADO
Corcovado / Voce e eu / Desafinado / Meditacao / Samba de una nota so (one note samba) / Chega de saudade / Rosa morena / O pato / Saudade da bahia / Manha de carnaval / O amor em paz / O barquinho / Insensatez / Coisa mais linda / Samba de minha terra / Doralice / Este seu olhar / E luxo so / Outra vez / Discussao
CD 62024 / Jan '93 / Saludos Amigos

Gilchrist, Hector

☐ LEA RIG, THE (Gilchrist, Hector & Liz Thomson)
WGS 274CD / May '96 / Wild Goose

Giles, Ian

☐ AMBER TRIANGLE
WGS 287CD / Mar '98 / Wild Goose

Gilgamesh

☐ GILGAMESH
One end more / Phil's little dance / Worlds of Zin / Lady and friend / Notwithstanding / Arriving twice / Island of Rhodes / Paper boat / As if your eyes were open / For absent friends / We are all / Someone else's food / Jamo and other boating disasters / 5 just C
CACD 2007 / Jun '97 / Charisma

Gill, John

☐ CAROLINA SHOUT
RQCD 1403 / Mar '94 / Request

☐ DOWN HOME FIVE
SDSCD 1264 / Jun '94 / Stomp Off

☐ JOHN GILL & HIS NOVELTY ORCHESTRA OF NEW ORLEANS
SOSCD 1270 / Apr '94 / Stomp Off

☐ MIDNIGHT CAKEWALK
SOSCD 1304 / Jul '96 / Stomp Off

☐ RAGTIME DYNASTY, THE
Original rags / Charleston rag / Sensation rag / Pork and beans / Evergreen rag / Pearls / Wildcat blues / Jingles / Keep your temple / Hobson Street blues / Root beer rag / Heliotrope bouquet / Grace and beauty / Silver swan rag / Reindeer rag / Chicago breakdown / Echo of spring / Crave / Piccadilly / Eubie's classical rag
RQCD 1405 / Nov '96 / Request

Gill, Johnny

☐ LET'S GET THE MOOD RIGHT
5307492 / 15 Sep '97 / Motown

Gill, Ron

☐ SONGS OF BILLY STRAYHORN, THE
76548148792 / 14 Jul '98 / WGBH

Gill, Vince

☐ ESSENTIAL VINCE GILL, THE
Victim of life's circumstances / Oh Carolina / I've been hearing things about you / Turn me loose / Radio / Livin' the way I do / Midnight train / True love / Ain't it always that way / Oklahoma borderline / With you / Way back home / Losing your love / Everybody's sweetheart / Don't say that you love me / Something's missing / Colder than winter / Cinderella / Let's do something / I never knew lonely
74321665352 / Feb '96 / RCA

☐ HIGH LONESOME SOUND, THE
One dance with you / High lonesome sound / Pretty little Adriana / Little more love / Down to New Orleans / Tell me lover / Given more time / You and you alone / Worlds apart / Jenny dreamed of trains
MCD 11422 / Jun '96 / MCA

☐ I STILL BELIEVE IN YOU
Don't let our love start slippin' away / No future in the past / Nothin' like a woman / Tryin' to get over you / Say hello / One more last chance / Under these conditions / Pretty words / Love never broke anyone's heart / I still believe in you
MCLD 19352 / Apr '97 / MCA

☐ KEY, THE
UMD 80523 / 10 Aug '98 / Universal

☐ MASTERS, THE
EABCD 028 / 24 Nov '97 / Eagle

☐ POCKET FULL OF GOLD
I quit / Look at us / Take your memory with you / Pocket full of gold / Strings that tie you down / Liza Jane / If I didn't have you in my world / Little left over / What's a man to do / Sparkle
MCLD 19321 / Sep '96 / MCA

☐ SOUVENIRS
MCD 11394 / Dec '95 / MCA

☐ WHEN I CALL YOUR NAME
Never alone / Sight for sore eyes / Oh girl (you know where to find me) / Oklahoma swing / When I call your name / Ridin' the rodeo / Never knew lonely / We won't dance / We could have been / Rita ballou
MCAD 42321 / Mar '94 / MCA

☐ WHEN LOVE FINDS YOU
Whenever you come around / You better think twice / Real lady's man / What the cowgirls do / When love finds you / If there's anything I can do / South side of Dixie / Maybe tonight / Which bridge to cross (which bridge to burn) / If I had my way / Go rest high on that mountain / Ain't nothing like the real thing / I can't tell you why
MCD 11078 / May '94 / MCA

Gillan, Ian

☐ ACCIDENTALLY ON PURPOSE (Gillan & Glover)
Clouds and rain / Evil eye / She took my breath away / Dislocated / Via Miami / I can't dance to that / Can't believe you wanna leave / Lonely Avenue / Telephone box / I thought no / Cayman Island / Purple people eater / Chet
EAMCD 049 / 8 Jun '98 / Eagle

☐ BBC SESSIONS VOL.1 1979, THE (Dead Of Night) (Gillan)
Sleeping on the job / Mr. Universe / Dead of night / Roller / Vengeance / Smoke on the water / Secret of the dance / Sleeping on the job / Mr. Universe / Vengeance
RPM 185 / 12 Jan '98 / RPM

☐ BBC SESSIONS VOL.2 1980, THE (Unchain Your Brain) (Gillan)
Unchain your brain / Are you sure / Mr Universe / No easy way / Trouble / If you believe me / On the rocks / Nervous / Running white face city boy / Vengeance / Lucille / If you believe me
RPM 186 / 12 Jan '98 / RPM

☐ CHERKAZOO AND OTHER STORIES
Intro / Cherkazoo / Monster in paradise / Bull of birantis / Intro / Hogwash / Driving me wild (take one) / Donkey ride dream / Trying to get to you / Ain't that lovin' you baby / Driving me wild (fast take) / Music in my head / You make me feel so good / She called me softly / Driving me wild (take three) / You led my heart astray / Little share of plenty / Night and day
RPM 104 / Jul '93 / RPM
EAMCD 052 / 8 Jun '98 / Eagle

☐ CHILD IN TIME (Gillan)
Lay me down / You make me feel so good / Shame / My baby loves me / Down the road / Child in time / Let it slide
CDVM 2606 / Apr '90 / Virgin

☐ CLEAR AIR TURBULENCE (Gillan)
Clean air turbulence / Five moons / Money lender / Over the hill / Goodhand Liza / Angel Manchenio
EAMCD 047 / 8 Jun '98 / Eagle

☐ DOUBLE TROUBLE (Gillan)
I'll rip your spine out / Restless / Men of war / Sunbeam / Nightmare / Hadely bop bop / Life goes on / Born to kill / No laughing in Heaven / No easy way / Trouble / Mutually assured destruction / If you believe me / New Orleans
CDVM 3506 / Nov '89 / Virgin

☐ FUTURE SHOCK (Gillan)
Future shock / Night ride out of Phoenix / Ballad of the Lucitania Express / No laughing in Heaven / Sacre bleu / New Orleans / Bite the bullet / If I sing softly / Don't want the truth / For your dreams / One for the road / Bad news / Take a hold of yourself / MAD / Maelstrom / Trouble / Your sister's on my list / Handles on her hips / Higher and higher / I might as well go home (mystic)
CDVIP 131 / Apr '95 / Virgin VIP

☐ GILLAN TAPES VOL.1 (Gillan, Ian Band)
Maelstrom / Bad news / Fiji / Take a hold of yourself / Come tomorrow / No easy way (writing session) / No easy way / Are you confident / Are you sure / Don't want the truth / It isn't going to die / Restless / Restless / Higher and higher / Smokin' and smowakin' / Night lights / MAD / Because you lied
SJPCD 004 / Apr '98 / Angel Air

□ GLORY ROAD (Gillan)
Unchain your brain / Are you sure / Time and again / No easy way / Sleeping on the job / On the rocks / If you believe me / Running white face city boy / Nervous / Your mother was right / Red watch / Abbey of Thelema / Trying to get to you / Come tomorrow / Dragon's tongue / Post-fade brain damage
CDVM 2171 / Nov '89 / Virgin

□ JAPANESE ALBUM (Gillan)
Street theatre / Secret of the dance / I'm your man / Dead of night / Fighting man / Message in a bottle / Not weird enough / Bringing joanna back / Abbey of thelema / Back in the game / Vengeance / Move with the times / Sleeping on the job / Roller
RPM 113 / Jul '93 / RPM
CLEO 3142 / 3 Aug '98 / Cleopatra

□ LIVE AT THE RAINBOW (Gillan, Ian Band)
Clear air turbulence / Money lender / Child in time / Smoke on the water / Woman from Tokyo / Twin exhausted
SJPCD 017 / 22 Apr '98 / Angel Air

□ MAGIC (Gillan)
What's the matter / Bluesy blue sea / Caught in a trap / Long gone / Driving me wild / Demon driver / Living a lie / You're so right / Living for the city / Demon driver (reprise) / Breaking chains / Fiji / Purple sky / South Africa / John / Helter skelter / Smokestack lightnin'
CDVM 2238 / Nov '89 / Virgin

□ MR. UNIVERSE (Gillan)
Mr. Universe / Second sight / Secret of the dance / She tears me down / Roller / Vengeance / Puget sound / Dead of night / Message in a bottle / Fighting man / On the rocks / Bite the bullet / Mr. Universe (version) / Smoke on the water / Lucille
CDVM 2589 / Mar '83 / Virgin

□ NAKED THUNDER
Gut reaction / No good luck / Sweet Lolita / Moonshine / Love gun / Talking to you / Nothing but the best / Nothing to lose / Long and lonely ride / No more can on the Brazos
EAMCD 050 / 8 Jun '98 / Eagle

□ ROCK PROFILE
Can I get a witness: *Gillan, Ian & The Javelins* / Little one: *Episode Six* / Driving me wild: *Gillan* / Strange kind of woman: *Deep Purple* / Temple: *Various Artists* / You make me feel so good: *Gillan, Ian Band* / Secret of the dance: *Gillan* / Roller: *Gillan* / Nervous: *Gillan* / Trouble: *Gillan* / MAD: *Gillan* / If I sing softly: *Gillan* / Bluesy blue sea: *Gillan* / Clouds and rain: *Gillan & Glover* / South Africa / No more cane on the Brazos / Dancing nylon shirt
VSOPCD 214 / Jul '95 / Connoisseur Collection

□ ROCKFIELD MIXES, THE (Gillan, Ian Band)
Over the hill / Clear air turbulence / Fire moons / Money lender / Angelo manchenio / This is the way / Goodhand Liza
SPJCD 007 / Mar '97 / Angel Air

□ SCARABUS (Gillan)
Scarabus / Twin exhausted / Poor boy hero / Mercury high / Pre-release / Slags to bitches / Apathy / Mad Elaine / Country lights / Fool's mate / My baby loves me
EAMCD 048 / 8 Jun '98 / Eagle

□ SOLE AGENCY & REPRESENTATION (Gillan, Ian & The Javelins)
Too much monkey business / It'll be me / You really got a hold on me / It's only make believe / Can I get a witness / Poison Ivy / Rave on / Blue Monday / You better move on / Something else / Money / Love potion no.9 / Let's dance / Roll over Beethoven
RPM 132 / Aug '94 / RPM

□ TOOL BOX
Hang me out to dry / Tool box / Dirty dog / Candy horizon / Don't hold me back / Pictures of hell / Dancing nylon shirt / Bed of nails / Gassed up / Everything I need
GILVP 102CD / 20 Apr '98 / Resurgence
EAMCD 051 / 8 Jun '98 / Eagle

□ TROUBLE (The Best Of Gillan) (Gillan)
Trouble / New Orleans / Fighting man / Living for the city / Helter skelter / Mr. Universe / Telephone box / Dislocated / Sleeping on the job / MAD (Mutually Assured Destruction) / No laughing in heaven / Nightmare / Restless / Purple sky / Born to kill / Smoke on the water
CDVIP 108 / Nov '93 / Virgin VIP

□ VERY BEST OF GILLAN, THE (Gillan)
Sleeping on the job / Secret of the dance / Time and again / Vengeance / Roller / MAD / Dead of night / Nightmare / Don't want the truth / If you believe me / Trouble / New Orleans / Living for the city / Restless / No laughing in heaven / Smoke on the water
MCCD 032 / Sep '91 / Music Club

Gille, Hans

□ PA VARAT VIS (Gille, Hans & Kurt Sodergren)
AW 23CD / Aug '97 / Tongang

Gillespie, Dana

□ BLUES IT UP
Lotta what you got / My man stands out / Fat Sam from Birmingham / Sweet meat / Ugly papa / Sweets / King size papa / One hour mama / 300 pounds of joy / Don't you make me high / Big ten inch record / Below the belt / Long lean baby / Tongue in cheek / Meat balls / Wasn't that good / Joe's joint / Organ grinder / Come on (if you're coming) / Nosey Joe / It ain't the meat / Sixty minute man / Snatch and grab it
CDCHD 950 / Aug '90 / Ace

□ HAVE I GOT NEWS FOR YOU
WCD 120942 / Oct '96 / Wolf

□ HOT STUFF
Lovin' machine / Pencil thin Papa / Easy does it / Meat on their bones / Raise a little hell / Empty bed blues / Play with your poodle / Big fat Mamas are back in style again / Too many drivers / Sailor's delight / Built for comfort / Fat meat is good meat / Hot stuff / Tall skinny Papa / Big car / Spoonful / Diggin' my potatoes / Mainline baby / Pint size Papa / Horizontal boogie
CDCHD 605 / Nov '95 / Ace

Gillespie, Dizzy

□ 'S WONDERFUL
VGCD 670508 / Jan '93 / Vogue

□ 20TH/30TH ANNIVERSARY
5335502 / Dec '96 / MPS Jazz

□ AFRO CUBAN JAZZ MOODS (Gillespie, Dizzy & Machito)
Oro, incienso y mirra / Calidoscopico / Pensativo / Exuberante
OJCCD 447 / Oct '92 / Original Jazz Classics

□ AT MONTREUX '75 (Gillespie, Dizzy Big Seven)
Lover come back to me / I'll remember april / What's new / Cherokee
OJCCD 739 / May '93 / Original Jazz Classics

□ AUDIO ARCHIVE
Long long summer / All these things you are / Ray's idea / Dizzy atmosphere / Oop bop sh'bam / Emanon / Lorraine / Things to love / Rumbop concerto/Study in soulphony / Groovin' high / Desafinado / Hot house / Good dues blues / Blue 'n' boogie / Oop-bop-a-da / Our delight / Three hearts in a tangle
CDAA 022 / Oct '91 / Tring

□ BAHIANA
Carnival / Samba / Barcelona / In the land of the living dead / Behind the moonbeam / Truth / Pele / Olinga
2625708 / Jun '96 / Pablo

□ BE BOP
Kush / Be bop / Swing low, sweet chariot / Brother K / Minor walk / Emanon / Two bass hit / Things to come / Oop-pop-a-dah
17126 / May '97 / Laserlight

□ BE BOP ENTERS SWEDEN 1947-1949 (Gillespie, Dizzy & Chubby Jackson/ James Moody)
DRCD 318 / Apr '98 / Dragon

□ BEBOP & BEYOND PLAYS DIZZY GILLESPIE (Gillespie, Dizzy & Benny Carter)
Wheatleigh Hall / Manteca / I waited for you / That's Earl, brother / Con Alma / Diddy wah diddy / Father time / Rhythm man
R 279170 / Feb '92 / Blue Moon

□ BEST OF DIZZY GILLESPIE, THE
Unicorn / Free ride / Pensavito / Exuberante / Behind the moonbeam / Shim-sham-shimmy
CD 2405411 / Apr '94 / Pablo

□ BIRD SONGS (The Final Recordings)
Ornithology / Con Alma / Confirmation / Night in Tunisia / Diamond jubilee blues / Theme
CD 83421 / 10 Nov '97 / Telarc Jazz

□ CHAMP, THE
Champ / Birk's works / Caravan / Time on my hands / On the sunny side of the street / Tin tin deo / Stardust / They can't take that away from me / Bluest blues / Swing low, sweet cadillac / Ooh-shoo-be-doo-bee
SV 0170 / Oct '97 / Savoy Jazz

□ CLASSICS 1945
CLASSICS 888 / Jul '96 / Classics

□ CLASSICS 1945-1946
CLASSICS 935 / Jun '97 / Classics

□ CLASSICS 1946-1947
CLASSICS 986 / 24 Apr '98 / Classics

□ COMPLETE DIAL SESSIONS 1946-1948 (Gillespie, Dizzy & Sonny Berman/ Fats Navarro)
Diggin' Diz / Confirmation / Diggin' for Diz / Dynamo / When I grow too old to dream / 'Round midnight / Curbstone souffle / Nocturne / Woodchopper's holiday / Somebody loves me / Blue Serge / Guilty / Yardbird suite / Stranger in town / As time goes by / Move
SPJCD 132 / Oct '96 / Spotlite

□ COMPLETE RCA VICTOR RECORDINGS 1947-1949, THE
Manteca / Anthropology / King Porter stomp / Yours and mine / Blue rhythm fantasy / Hot mallets / 52nd Street / Night in Tunisia / Ol' man rebop / Ow / Oop-bop-a-da / Stay on it / Algo bueno / Cool breeze / Cubana be, cubana bop / Ool-ya-koo / Minor walk / Good bait / Guarachi guaro / Duff capers / Lover come back to me / I'm beboppin' too / Swedish suite / St. Louis blues / I should care / That old black magic / You go to my head / Jump di-le ba / Dizzier and dizzier / Hey Pete / Let's eat more meat / Jumpin' and symphony Sid / If love is trouble / In the land of oo-bla-dee / Overtime / Victory ball
0786366528 / Apr '95 / Bluebird

□ COOL WORLD, THE/DIZZY GOES HOLLYWOOD (Original Soundtrack)
5312302 / Jul '96 / Verve

□ DEEGEE DAYS (Savoy Sessions)
Tin tin deo / Birk's works / We love to boogie / Oh lady be good / Champ / I'm in a mess / School days / Swing low, sweet cadillac / Bopsie's blues / I couldn't beat the rap / Caravan / Nobody knows / Bluest blues / On the sunny side of the street / Stardust / Time on my hands / Blue skies / Umbrella man / Confessin' / Ooh-shoo-be-doo-bee / They can't take that away from me
VGCD 650101 / Jan '93 / Vogue

□ DIGITAL AT MONTREUX
Christopher Columbus / I'm sitting on top of the world / Manteca / Get the booty / Kisses
CD 2308226 / Oct '92 / Pablo

□ DIZ 'N' BIRD AT CARNEGIE HALL (Gillespie, Dizzy & Charlie Parker)
Night in Tunisia / Dizzy atmosphere / Groovin' high / Confirmation / Koko / Cool breeze / Relazin' at Camarillo / One bass hit / Nearness / Salt peanuts / Cubano-be, cubano-bop / Hot house / Toccata for trumpet / Oop-pop-a-da / Things to come
CDP 8570612 / Jun '97 / Blue Note

□ DIZ AND GETZ (Gillespie, Dizzy & Stan Getz)
It don't mean a thing if it ain't got that swing / I let a song go out of my heart / Exactly like you / It's the talk of the town / Impromptu / One alone / Girl of my dreams / Siboney
8335592 / Aug '90 / Verve

□ DIZ MEETS STITT (Gillespie, Dizzy & Sonny Stitt)
MCD 0362 / Aug '92 / Moon

□ DIZZIER AND DIZZIER
52nd Street theme / Night in Tunisia / Anthropology / Two bass hit / Cool breeze / Cubana be / Minor walk / Good bait / Lover come back to me / I'm be boppin' too / St. Louis blues / That old black magic / You go to my head / Dizzier and dizzier / Hey Pete, let's eat more meat / Jumpin' with Symphony Sid / In the land of oo-bla-dee
09026685172 / Oct '96 / RCA Victor

□ DIZZY (Gillespie, Dizzy Big Seven)
CD 20038 / May '86 / Pablo

□ DIZZY ATMOSPHERE
BN 017 / Apr '98 / Blue Nite

□ DIZZY FOR PRESIDENT
Dizzy atmosphere / Morning of the carnival / Cup bearers / I'm in the mood for love / Desfinado / Gee baby ain't I good to you / No more blues / Vote Dizzy (Salt peanuts)
ADC 1 / May '97 / Douglas Music

□ DIZZY GILLESPIE
CD 14554 / Jul '94 / Jazz Portraits

□ DIZZY GILLESPIE
Blue 'n boogie / Groovin' high / All the things you are / Dizzy atmosphere / Hot house / Oop bop sh'bam / That's earl brother / Our delight / Good dues blues / Ray's idea / Things to come / Emanon / Relaxin' at Camarillo / Guarachi guarro / Soulphony in three hearts / Ooh-poo-pah-doo / Ool-ya-koo / I'm be-boppin' too
17071 / Aug '96 / Laserlight

□ DIZZY GILLESPIE 1940-1946
158812 / Feb '97 / Jazz Archives

□ DIZZY GILLESPIE 1946-1949 (2CD Set)
Manteca / Good bait / Ool-ya-koo / 52nd Street / Night in Tunisia / Ol' man rebop / Anthropology / Owl / Oop-bop-a-da / Cool breeze / Cubana be, Cubana bop / Minor walk / Guarachi guaro / Duff capers / Lover come back to me / I'm beboppin' too / Overtime / Victory ball / Swedish suite / St. Louis blues / Katy mo' meat / Jumpin' with Symphony Sid / In the land of oo-bla-dee
ND 89763 / May '94 / Jazz Tribune

□ DIZZY GILLESPIE MEETS PHIL WOODS QUARTET
CDSJP 250 / Jan '88 / Timeless Jazz

□ DIZZY GILLESPIE STORY, THE
Swing low, sweet chariot / Alone together / These are the things I love / Lullaby of the leaves / Boppin' the blues / Smoky hollow jump / On the Alamo / I found a million dollar baby / What is there to say / Interlude in C / Moody speaks / For hecklers only
SV 0177 / Oct '97 / Savoy Jazz

□ DIZZY'S 80TH BIRTHDAY CELEBRATION (Gillespie, Dizzy All Stars)
SH 5040 / Oct '97 / Shanachie

□ FREE RIDE
Unicorn / Incantation / Wrong number / Free ride / Ozone madness / Love poem for Donna / Last stroke of midnight
OJCCD 784 / Jun '94 / Original Jazz Classics

□ GIANT, THE
139 217 / '86 / Accord

□ GILLESPIANA/CARNEGIE HALL CONCERT 1961
Prelude / Blues / Panamericana / Africana / Manteca / This is the way / Ool-ya-koo / Kush / Tunisian fantasy
5198092 / Dec '93 / Verve

□ GOLD COLLECTION, THE (2CD Set)
R2CD 4043 / 13 Apr '98 / Deja Vu

□ GROOVIN' HIGH
Blue 'n' boogie / Groovin' high / Dizzy atmosphere / All the things you are / Salt peanuts / Hot house / Oop bop sh'bam / That's Earl brother / Our delight / One bass hit / Things to come / Ray's idea / Emanon
SV 0152 / Oct '97 / Savoy Jazz

□ GROOVING HIGH
I can't get started / Good bait / Be-bop / Groovin' high / Blue 'n' boogie / Groovin' high / All the things you are / Dizzy atmosphere / Salt peanuts / Shaw 'nuff / Hot house / Diggin' Diz / Confirmation / Diggin' for Diz / Dynamo / When I grow too old to dream / 'Round about midnight / 52nd Street theme / Night in Tunisia / Ol' man Rebop / Anthropology / One bass hit / Oop bop sh'bam / That's Earl brother
IGOCD 2068 / Sep '97 / Indigo

□ IN CONCERT (Gillespie, Dizzy Quintet)
RTE 710465 / May '95 / RTE/Europe 1

□ IN CONCERT
RTE 10082 / 7 Apr '98 / RTE/Europe 1

□ IT DON'T MEAN A THING
It don't mean a thing if it ain't got that swing / I let a song go out of my heart / It's the talk of the town / Impromptu / Siboney / Exactly like you / Girl of my dreams
CDSGP 062 / May '93 / Prestige

□ JAM AT MONTREUX '77
Girl of my dreams / Get happy / Once in a while-but beautiful-here's that rainy day (medle / Champ
OJCCD 381 / Feb '92 / Original Jazz Classics

□ JAMBO CARIBE
Fiesta mojo / Barbados Carnival / Jambo / Trinidad hello / Poor Joe / And then she stopped / Don't try to keep up with the Joneses / Trinidad goodbye
5574922 / 3 Aug '98 / Verve

□ JAZZ GREATS (Gillespie, Dizzy Orchestra)
Night in Tunisia / 52nd street theme / Good bait / Anthropology / Stay on it / Two bass hit / Manteca / Minor walk / Lover come back to me / Ool-ya-koo / I'm be boppin' too / You go to my head: *Gillespie, Dizzy Orchestra & Johnny Hartman* / St. Louis blues / Jumpin' with symphony Sid / Jump did-le ba / In the land of oo-bla-dee / Victory ball
74321499862 / Feb '98 / RCA Victor

□ JAZZ MASTERS
Manteca / November afternoon / Night in Tunisia / Tour de force / Trumpet blues / Con alma / I can't get started (with you) / 'Round midnight / Africana / Birk's works / Desafinado / Leap frog / Swing low, sweet Cadillac
5163192 / 5 May '98 / Verve

□ JAZZ MATURITY...WHERE IT'S COMING FROM (Gillespie, Dizzy & Roy Eldridge)
Quasi-boogaloo / Quasi-boogaloo / I cried for you (now it's your turn to cry over me) / Drebizks / When it's sleepy time down south / Indiana
OJCCD 807 / Oct '95 / Original Jazz Classics

□ JIVIN' IN BEBOP
MCD 0452 / Nov '93 / Moon

□ LIVE AT CHESTER (Gillespie, Dizzy Big Band)
JH 1029 / Jul '93 / Jazz Hour

□ LIVE AT THE 1986 FLOATING JAZZ FESTIVAL (Gillespie, Dizzy & Buddy Rich/Clark Terry)
CRD 300 / Mar '96 / Chiaroscuro

□ MANTECA
CD 14575 / Nov '95 / Complete

□ MASTERS OF JAZZ (2CD Set)
R2CD 8006 / 13 Apr '98 / Deja Vu

□ MOST IMPORTANT RECORDINGS
CDOFF 830562 / Mar '90 / Ogun

□ MUSICIAN, COMPOSER, RACONTEUR (2CD Set)
Introduction / Manteca / Dizzy rapping with the audience / Con Alma / SKJ / Night in Tunisia / Brother King / Body and soul / Tanga / Olinga
CD 26201162 / Jan '98 / Pablo

□ NIGHT IN TUNISIA
Night in Tunisia / Emanon / Chga de Saudade / Con Alma / This is the way / Kush
17108 / Mar '97 / Laserlight

□ ON THE SUNNY SIDE OF THE STREET
MCD 077 / Dec '95 / Moon

□ OO BOP
TCD 1027 / Aug '96 / Tradition

□ PERCEPTIONS
5377482 / 22 Sep '97 / Verve Elite

□ PLEYEL CONCERT 1948/PLEYEL CONCERT 1949 (Original Vogue Masters) (Gillespie, Dizzy & Max Roach Quintet)
Ooh-poo-pah-doo / Round about midnight / Algo bueno / I can't get started / Two bass hit / Good bait / Afro-Cuban drum suite / Ool-ya-koo / Things to come / Prince Albert / Baby sis / Tomorrow / Maximum
74321409412 / May '97 / Vogue

□ PLEYEL CONCERT 1953 (Original Vogue Masters) (Gillespie, Dizzy Quintet)
Intro / Champ / Good bait / Swing low, sweet Cadillac / Oh lady be good / Mon homme / Bluest blues / Birk's works / Ooh-shoo-be-doo-bee / They can't take that away from me / Play fiddle play / I can't get started (with you) / Embraceable you / Tin tin deo / On the sunny side of the street / School days
74321429212 / Apr '97 / Vogue

☐ PROFESSOR BOP
Blue 'n' boogie / Groovin' high / Dizzy atmosphere / All the things you are / Hot house / Oop bop sh'bam / Our delight / Things to come / Ray's idea / Emanon / Good dues blues
LEJAZZCD 25 / Feb '94 / Le Jazz

☐ QUINTESSENCE, THE (2CD Set)
FA 224 / 1 Jun '98 / Fremeaux

☐ QUINTET, THE
Perdido / Salt peanuts / All the things you are / Wee / Hot house / Night in tunisia
OJCCD 44 / Feb '92 / Original Jazz Classics

☐ SCHOOL DAYS
Oh lady be good / Pop's confessin' / Nobody knows the trouble I've seen / Bopsie's blues / I couldn't beat the rap / School days / I'm in a mess / Umbrella man / Love me pretty baby / We love to boogie
CY 18062 / Jun '98 / Savoy Jazz

☐ SOMETHING OLD SOMETHING NEW (Gillespie, Dizzy Quintet)
Be bop / Good bait / I can't get started / Round midnight / Dizzy atmosphere / November afternoon / This lovely feeling / Day after / Cup beareres / Early mornin' blues
5580792 / 26 May '98 / Verve Master Edition

☐ SONNY SIDE UP (Remastered) (Gillespie, Dizzy & Sonny Rollins/Sonny Stitt)
5214262 / Oct '97 / Verve Master Edition

☐ SOUL TIME
MACCD 274 / Aug '96 / Autograph

☐ SUMMERTIME (Gillespie, Dizzy & Mongo Santamaria)
Virtue / Afro blue / Summertime / Mambo Mongo
OJCCD 6266 / Feb '92 / Original Jazz Classics

☐ SWING LOW SWEET CADILLAC
Swing low, sweet cadillac / Mas que nada / Something in your smile / Kush / Bye
IMP 11782 / Feb '96 / Impulse Jazz

☐ SYMPHONY SESSIONS, THE
Manteca / Con alma / Lorraine / Brother K / Tin tin deo / Fiesta mojo / Night in Tunisia
SION 18110 / Jul '97 / Sion

☐ TALKIN' VERVE
5338462 / Mar '97 / Verve

☐ THINGS TO COME
Things to come / Ray's idea / Montego / Milan is love / N'Bani / Something in your smile / Yesterdays
17107 / Jan '97 / Laserlight

☐ TO BIRD WITH LOVE
Billie's bounce / Be bop / Ornithology / Anthropology / Oo pa pa da / Diamond jubilee blues / Theme
CD 83316 / Nov '92 / Telarc

☐ TO DIZ, WITH LOVE (Diamond Jubilee Recordings)
Billie's bounce / Confirmation / Mood indigo / Straight no chaser / Night in Tunisia
83307 / May '92 / Telarc

Gillespie, Hugh

☐ CLASSIC
Dowd's favorite (reel) / Mckenna's farewell (the liverpool-hennessey's) (hornpipes / Master crowley's reels (reels) / Irish mazurka / Jenny's welcome to charlie / Master crowley's favorites (jigs) / Finnea lassies-gurren's castle (highland flings) / Girl that broke my heart-dick cosgrove's reel (reels) / Farewell to leitrim-tom steele (reels) / Jackson's favorite-kips (jigs) / Paddy finley's fancy-joe o'connell's dream (reels) / Versevanna (waltz) / Donegal traveler-miss montgomery (reels) / Mountain stream-parker's fancy (hornpipes) / Contentment is wealth-finley's jig (jigs) / Dowd's no.9-jackson's (reels)
GLCD 3066 / Jun '92 / Green Linnet

Gillet & Greitez

☐ TERRACOTA
BEST 1056 / Oct '94 / Acoustic Music

Gillette, Steve

☐ LIVE IN CONCERT (Gillette, Steve & Cindy Mangsen)
BRAMBUS 199231 / Oct '94 / Brambus

Gilley, Mickey

☐ MICKEY GILLEY
Still care about you / Keepin' on / That's how it's going to be / I miss you so / Just out of reach / Grapevine / Fraulein / No greater love / Boy who didn't pass / Ain't goin' home / Black Mountain rag / Turn around / Rocky top / CC Rider
PRACD 4004 / Jun '97 / Prairie

☐ THAT HEART BELONGS TO ME
I'm to blame / Night after night / Suzie Q / I'll make it all up to you / Breathless / Is it wrong / Lonely wine / Forgive / My babe / Turn around and look at me / She's still got a hold on you / Running out of reasons / World of our own / That heart belongs to me / I'm gonna put my love in the want ads / Without you / It's just a matter of making up my mind / New way to live / There's no one like you / You can count me missing / Still care about you / Grapevine / That's how it's gotta be / Boy who didn't pass / Fraulein / I miss you so / Just out of reach / Keepin' on / Watching the way
GRF 074 / Feb '93 / Tring

Gillian, Ian

☐ DREAMCATCHER
CRMCD 001 / 3 Nov '97 / Caramaba

Gilliard

☐ GILLIARD
76192 / 19 May '98 / RGE

Gillies, Alasdair

☐ AMONG MY SOUVENIRS
Take me home / I dream of Jeannie with the light brown hair / Among my souvenirs / I will love you all my life / Tak a dram / Scarlet ribbons / Scotland my home / Banners of Scotland / Bonnie Mary of Argyle / Say you'll stay until tomorrow / Beautiful dreamer / More than yesterday / Maggie / Messin' about on the river
CD ITV 416 / Dec '86 / Scotdisc

☐ WORLD'S GREATEST PIPERS VOL.12, THE
2/4 Marches / Strathspey and Reel / Gaelic airs and hornpipes / 6/8 Marches / March, Strathspey and Reel / Gaelic Air and Jigs / Strathspeys and Reels / 2/4 Marches / Jigs / Gaelic Airs, Strathspeys and Reels
LCOM 5231 / Jul '94 / Lismor

Gillies, Anne Lorne

☐ HILLS OF LORNE
CDLOC 1008 / May '97 / Lochshore

☐ OH MY LAND
Sad am I far from my home / Lullaby for Donald gorm of Sleat / Great song of Macleod / Alasdair son of Great Colla / I'm asleep don't wake me / Silver whistle / My fair young love / Farewell to the lovely tartan / Oh my land / When I was young / Say goodbye for me/Young Alasdair son of the son of Nicol / Mavis comes in spring / Isle of joy / Surge of the sea / Freedom
RCD 052 / May '97 / Iona

☐ SONGS OF THE GAELS, THE
Am buachaille ban / Ho ro chall eile / Na h-uain air an tulaich / Cumha iain ghairbh ratharsair / Allt an t-siucair / Griogal cridhe / Coille'n fhasaich / Gur moch rinn mi dusgagh / Mo dhomhnallan fhin / Nach gorach mi'gad chaoinead / Orain luaidh / Iain glinn cuaich / A fhleasgaich a'chuil dualaich / A'chuairt shamhraidh
CDLOC 1014 / May '97 / Lochshore

Gillis, Brad

☐ GILROCK RANCH
Gilrock ranch / Lions, tigers and bears / Honest to god / Slow blow / Monster breath / Shades of pomposity / Gospel / Opus winfrus / Afterthought / If looks could kill
CDGRUB 27 / Jan '93 / Food For Thought

Gillman, Jane

☐ ONE LOOK BACK
Howlin' at the moon / Song on the radio / Song of Baltimore / Ready for the time to come / Open up / Three quarters / Falling in place / One look back / What tomorrow finds / Tell the rooster / Listen to the thunder / Elsa's tune
GLCD 2101 / Oct '93 / Green Linnet

☐ PICK IT UP
GLCD 1068 / Feb '92 / Green Linnet

Gillum, Bill 'Jazz'

☐ BLUEBIRD RECORDINGS 1934-1938, THE
Early in the morning / Harmonica stomp / Sarah Jane / I want you by my side / Jockey blues / Don't scandalize my name / My old Lizzie / Alberta blues / My old suitcase / Birmingham blues / Just like Jessie James / Reefer head woman / Gillum's windy blues / New 'Sail on little girl' / Sweet sweet woman / Boar hog blues / Worried and bothered / I'm that man down in the mine / Uncertain blues / Good old 61 highway / You're laughing now / I'm gonna get it
07863667172 / Feb '97 / Bluebird

☐ BLUES, THE (2CD Set)
FA 260 / 24 Feb '98 / Fremeaux

☐ HARMONICA AND WASHBOARD BLUES 1937-1940 (Gillum, Bill 'Jazz' & Washboard Sam)
My old lizzie / My old lizzie / Good old 51 highway / You're laughing now / I'm gonna get it / Let her go / She won't treat me kind / I'll get along somehow / Got to reap what you sow / Keyhole blues / She belongs to me / Key to the highway / Back door / We gonna move / Lowland blues / Mountain blues / Yellow black and brown / I'm gonna keep my hair parted / Warehouse blues / This time is my time / Booker t. blues / How can I play fair / She fooled me / Yes I got your woman
BLE 592522 / Dec '92 / Black & Blue

☐ JAZZ GILLUM VOL.1 1936-1938
DOCD 5197 / Oct '93 / Document

☐ JAZZ GILLUM VOL.2 1938-1941
DOCD 5198 / Oct '93 / Document

☐ JAZZ GILLUM VOL.3 1941-1946
DOCD 5199 / Oct '93 / Document

☐ JAZZ GILLUM VOL.4 1946-1949
DOCD 5200 / Oct '93 / Document

☐ KEY TO THE HIGHWAY 1935-1942
158402 / Sep '95 / Blues Collection

Gilmer, Jimmy

☐ LUCKY 'LEVEN/FOLKBEAT
Boom boom / Lucille / Shame shame shame / If you ever / Candy wrappers / My daddy walked in darkness / Hi heel sneakers / Your turn to cry / Fool / Note upon my door / Dixie fried / Codine / 500 miles / Let me follow you down / Bessie Barnes / Can't help but wonder where I'm bound / Blackland farmer / She belongs to me / Come on in / Rambler's blues / Blowin' in the wind / That's my song / Come on back
CDCHD 665 / 29 Sep '97 / Ace

☐ SUGAR SHACK/BUDDY'S BUDDY (Gilmer, Jimmy & The Fireballs)
Sugar shack / Let's talk / Linda Lu / Lonesome tears / Let the good times roll / Red Cadillac and a black moustache / Won't be long / Little baby / I wonder why / Suzie Q / Pretend / Almost eighteen / Look at me: Gilmer, Jimmy / Wishing: Gilmer, Jimmy / I'm gonna love you too: Gilmer, Jimmy / Think it over: Gilmer, Jimmy / Lonesome tears: Gilmer, Jimmy / Maybe baby: Gilmer, Jimmy / Listen to me: Gilmer, Jimmy / Everyday: Gilmer, Jimmy / Words of love: Gilmer, Jimmy / It's so easy: Gilmer, Jimmy / Little baby: Gilmer, Jimmy / Oh boy: Gilmer, Jimmy
CDCHD 646 / Apr '97 / Ace

Gilmore, Jimmie Dale

☐ AFTER AWHILE
Tonight I think I'm gonna go downtown / My mind's got a mind of its own / Treat me like a Saturday night / Chase the wind / Go to sleep alone / After a while / Number 16 / Don't be a stranger to your heart / Blue moon waltz / These blues / Midnight train / Story of you
7559611482 / Sep '91 / Nonesuch

☐ BRAVER NEW WORLD
Braver newer world / Come fly away / Borderland / Long long time / There she goes / Sally / Outside the lines / Because of the wind / Black snake moan / Where is love now / Headed for a fall
7559618362 / Jul '96 / Elektra

☐ SPINNING AROUND THE SUN
Where are you going / Santa fe thief / So I'll run / I'm so lonesome I could cry / Mobile line (France blues) / Nothing of the kind / Just a wave, reunion: Gilmore, Jimmie Dale & Lucinda Williams / I'm gonna love you / Another colorado / Thinking about you
7559615022 / Sep '93 / Elektra

Gilmour, David

☐ ABOUT FACE
Until we sleep / Murder / Love on the air / Blue light / Out of the blue / You know I'm right / Cruise / Let's get metaphysical / Near the end / All lovers are deranged
CDP 7460312 / Aug '84 / Harvest

Gilstrap, Jim

☐ SWING YOUR DADDY
Swing your daddy / House of strangers / Love talk / Never stop your loving me / Hello it's me / I'm on fire / Ain't that peculiar / One more heartache / Put out the fire / Special occasion / Swing your daddy / Move me
WB 885552 / 2 Feb '98 / Disky

Giltrap, Gordon

☐ GORDON GILTRAP/PORTRAIT
Gospel song / Fast approaching / Don't you feel good / Birth of spring / Won't you stay awhile Suzanne / Wilderness / Adolescent years / Saturday girl / Don't you hear your mother's voice / Ives horizon / Blyth Hill / Willow pattern / Portrait / Thoughts in the rain / Never ending solitude / Tuxedo / All characters fictitious / Lucifer's cage / Careful as you go / Free for all / William Taplin / Hands of fate / Confusion / Young love
TDEM 15 / Apr '94 / Trandem
ESMCD 526 / 24 Nov '97 / Essential

☐ MATTER OF TIME, A (Giltrap, Gordon & Martin Taylor)
CDSGP 007 / Aug '91 / Prestige

☐ MUSIC FOR THE SMALL SCREEN
MRCD 1 / May '95 / Munchkin

☐ ONE TO ONE
NP 002CD / Sep '89 / Nico Polo

☐ SOLO ALBUM
Jig / Roots / Shady tales / Ecchoing green / London / Empty / Magpie rag / Heartsong / Melancholy lullaby / Prelude to pastoral / Christmas carol / Fast approaching / Catwalk blues / Tailor bird / Prelude to morbid gorge / Lucifer's cage / From the four winds / Lord's seat / Country bluff
CDSGP 021 / Jul '96 / Prestige

☐ TROUBADOUR
ECD 3390 / 16 Mar '98 / K-Tel

Gimmicks

☐ HIGH HEELS
ES 118CD / 13 Jul '98 / Estrus

Gin Blossoms

☐ CONGRATULATIONS, I'M SORRY
Day job / Highwire / Follow you down / Not only numb / As long as it matters / Perfectly still / My car / Virginia / Whitewash / I can't figure you out / Memphis time / Competition smile / Til I hear it from you
5404702 / 15 Sep '97 / A&M

☐ NEW MISERABLE EXPERIENCE
Lost horizons / Hey jealousy / Mrs. Rita / Until I fall away / Hold me down / Cajun song / Hands are tied / Found out about you / Allison road / Twenty nine / Pieces of the night / Cheatin'
5404032 / 15 Sep '97 / A&M

Gin On The Rocks

☐ COOLEST GROOVE
847025 / Dec '90 / Steamhammer

Gina G

☐ FRESH
Just a little bit / Fresh / Ti amo / Every time I fall / Follow the light / Gimme some love / Rhythm of my life / Missin' you like crazy / I belong to you / Higher than love / It doesn't mean goodbye
0630178402 / Mar '97 / Eternal

Ginger

☐ FAR OUT
W 230096 / May '97 / Nettwerk

☐ GINGER
W 26320 / Jul '97 / Nettwerk

Gingrich, Brian

☐ WHITE RIM OF HEAVEN, THE
Knotted cord / Slowing in motion / White rim stories / Batterie of last resort / Fading days / Heavenly reception / Reversal of plans
ALCD 1008 / Aug '97 / Alchemy

Ginn, Greg

☐ DICK
Never change, baby / I want to believe / You wanted it / I won't give in / Creeps / Strong violent type / Don't tell me / You dirty rat / Disgusting reference / Walking away / Ignorant order / Slow fuse / You're going to get it
CRZ 032CD / Sep '93 / Cruz

☐ GETTING EVEN
I've changed / Kill burn fluff / You drive me crazy / Pig mf / Hard thing / Pay day / Nightmares / Torn / Pf flyer / I can't wait / Short fuse / Not that simple / Yes officer / Crawling inside
CRZ 029CD / May '93 / Cruz

☐ LET IT BURN BECAUSE
CRZ 036CD / Jul '94 / Cruz

☐ PAYDAY
CRZ 028CD / May '93 / Cruz

Ginsberg, Allen

☐ LION FOR REAL, THE
Scribble / Christmas gift / Lion for real / Shrouded stranger / Cleveland, the flats / Stanzas written at night in radio city / Hum bom / Guru / C'mon Jack / Gregory Corso's story / End / Sunset / Krai majales / Ode to failure
5349082 / Jun '97 / Mercury

Ginuwine

☐ BACHELOR, THE
Intro / Pony / Tell me do U wanna / Holler / Hello / Lonely daze / Ginuwine 4 Ur mind / Only when Ur lonely / I'll so anything/I'm sorry / World is so cold / When doves cry / G thang / 550 what
4853912 / Oct '96 / Epic

☐ BACHELOR, THE (2CD Set)
Intro / Pony / Interlude / Tell me / Holler / Hello / Lonely daze / Ginuwine 4 ur mind / Only when you're lonely / I'll do anything/I'm sorry / World is so cold / When doves cry / G thang / 550 what / Tell me do you wanna / When doves cry / I'll do anyhting/I'm sorry / Holler / Only when ur lonely
4895892 / 16 Mar '98 / Epic

Giordand, Vince

☐ QUALITY SHOUT
SOSCD 1260 / Apr '94 / Stomp Off

Giorgio, Gaber

☐ PER FORTUNA CHE C'E
3006172 / 17 Aug '98 / Carosello

Gipsy Fire

☐ GIPSY FIRE
INT 845149 / Feb '91 / Interchord

Gipsy Kings

☐ COMPAS
Solo por ti / Una rumba por aqui / MIRA La Itlana mora / Recuerdo apasionda / La fiesta comenza / Sueno de noche / Que si que no funicula funicula / Canto a brazil / Obsesion de amor / Mi nino / Di me lo / Lo mal y lo bien / Amor / Amnor gitano / Salsa de noche
4879932 / 18 Aug '97 / Columbia

☐ ESTRELLAS
La rumba / A ti a ti / Siempre acaba tu vida / Forever / Mujer / Campesino / Cata luna igual se entonces / Pararito / Tierra gitana / A tu vera / Mi carazon / Estrellas
4813452 / Nov '95 / Columbia

☐ GIPSY KINGS
Tu quieres volver / Moorea / Bem bem Maria / Un amor / Inspiration / Mi minera / Djobi djoba / Faena / Quiero saber / Amor amor / Duende / Bamboleo
4691232 / Jul '93 / Columbia

☐ GIPSY KINGS/MOSAIQUE/ESTE MUNDO (3CD Set)
Bamboleo / Tu quieres volver / Moorea / Bem, bem, Maria / Un amor / Inspiration / A mi manera (comme d'habitude) / Djobi djoba / Faena / Quiero saber / Amor, amor / Duende / Caminando por la calle / Viento del arena / Mosaique / Carmino / Passion / Soy / Volare (nel blu di pinto di blu) / Trista pena / Liberte / Serana / Bossamba / Vamos a bailar / Baila me / Sin Ella / Habla me / Lagrimas / Oy / Mi vada / El manuro / No volvere / Furia / Oh mai / Ternuras / Este mundo
4853172 / 3 Nov '97 / Columbia

☐ GREATEST HITS
Djobi djoba / Baila me / Bamboleo / Pida me la / Bem bem Maria / Voalre (Nel blu di pinto di blue) / Moorea / A mi manera (Comme d'habitude) / Un amor / Galaxia / Escucha me / Tu quieres volver / Soy / La quiero / Allegria / Vamos a bailar / La Dona / Djobi dojoba
4772422 / Jul '96 / Columbia

☐ LIVE
Intro / Allegria / La dona / El mauro / Bem bem Maria / Trista pena / Odeon / Sin ella / Quiero saber / Habla me / Galaxia / Fandango / Tu quieres volver / Oh mai / Djobi djoba / Bamboleo
4726482 / Feb '97 / Columbia

☐ LUNA DE FUEGO
Amor d'un dia / Luna de fuego / Calaverada / Galaxia / Ruptura / Gypsy rock / Viento del arean / Princessa / Olvidado / Ciento
4667632 / Feb '91 / Columbia

☐ MOSAIQUE
Caminando por la calle / Viento del arena / Mosaique / Camino / Passion / Soy / Volare / Trista pena / Liberte / Serana / Bossamba / Vamos a Bailar
4662132 / Jul '93 / Columbia

Girault, Martine

☐ REVIVAL
Intro interlude / Bring back our love / Good love / Been thinking 'bout you / Love to love you baby / These are the best days / Don't dog me / Revival / We've got tomorrow / Special / I wish / Soulfully yours / Outro interlude / Revival
74321432172 / Feb '97 / RCA

Girl

☐ SHEER GREED
Hollywood tease / Things you say / Lovely Lorraine / Strawberries / Little Miss Ann / Doctor doctor / Do you love me / Take me dancing / What's up / Passing clouds / My number / Heartbreak America
JETCD 1009 / Feb '98 / Jet

☐ WASTED YOUTH
Thru the twilight / Old dogs / Ice in the blood / Wasted youth / Standard romance / Nice 'n' nasty / McKitty's back / Nineteen / Overnight angels / Sweet kids
JETCD 1010 / Feb '98 / Jet

Girl

☐ FIRED UP
EBCD 29 / Jan '95 / Eightball

Girl Eats Boy

☐ COMIN' IN LOADED
DUKE 047CD / 17 Aug '98 / Hydrogen Dukebox

Girl Trouble

☐ NEW AMERICAN SHAME
EFA 11390CD / Jun '93 / Musical Tragedies

Girlandia

☐ CELTIC HEIR
BRAM 1993462 / Mar '94 / Brambus

Girlfriend

☐ MAKE IT COME TRUE
74321152172 / May '93 / Arista

Girls Against Boys

☐ 8 ROUNDS (Girls Against Boys/Guided By Voices)
RR 13CD / Mar '97 / Radiopaque

☐ CRUISE YOURSELF
TG 134CD / Oct '94 / Touch & Go

☐ FREAK-ON-ICA
GED 25156 / 18 May '98 / Geffen

☐ HOUSE OF GVSB
TG 149CD / 8 Jun '98 / Touch & Go

☐ NINETIES VS. EIGHTIES
AS 3CD / '93 / Touch & Go

☐ TROPIC OF SCORPIO
AS 4CD / '94 / Touch & Go

☐ VENUS LUXURE NO.1 BABY
TG 117CD / '94 / Touch & Go

Girls At Our Best

☐ PLEASURE
Getting nowhere fast / Warm girls / Politics / It's fashion / Go for gold / Pleasure / Too big for your boots / I'm beautiful now / Waterbed babies / Fun city teenagers / 600,000 / Heaven / China blue / Fast boyfriends / She flipped / Goodbye to that jazz / This train
ASKCD 047 / Oct '94 / Vinyl Japan

Girlschool

☐ BEST OF GIRLSCHOOL, THE
Take it all away / It could be better / Emergency / Nothing to lose / Race with the devil / Demolition boys / C'mon let's go / Yeah right / Hit and run / Tonight (Live) / Kick it down / Please don't touch: Headgirl / Bomber / Wildlife / Don't call it love / Screaming blue murder / 1-2-3-4 Rock 'n' roll / Burning in the heat / Twentieth century boy / Play dirty / I'm the leader of the gang (I am) / Play with fire / Fox on the run / Head over heels
DOJOCD 103 / Feb '94 / Dojo

☐ DEMOLITION/HIT AND RUN
Demoltion boys / Not for sale / Race with the devil / Take it all away / Nothing to lose / Breakdown / Midnight ride / Emergency / Baby doll / Deadline / C'mon let's go / Hunter / Victim / Kick it down / Following the crowd / Tush / Hit and run / Watch your step / Back to start / Yeah right / Future flash
LOMACD 1 / Feb '94 / Loma

☐ EMERGENCY (2CD Set)
SMDCD 126 / 22 Sep '97 / Snapper

☐ KING BISCUIT PRESENTS...
Screaming blue murder / Play dirty / You got me / Hit and run / Nothing to lose / Future flash / Running for cover / Burning in the heat / Demolition boys / Tush / I like it like that / C'mon let's go / Emergency / 20th century boy / Race with the devil
KBFHCD 007 / 26 May '98 / King Biscuit

☐ LIVE
CMGCD 013 / Nov '95 / Communique

☐ RACE WITH THE DEVIL
RRCD 254 / 25 May '98 / Receiver

Girly

☐ YOU'RE NEVER TOO YOUNG TO JUMP AND JIVE VOL.1 (Girly & The Blue Caps)
Go ahead and rock / Two hearts two kisses / Bloodshot eyes / 100 beer bottle boogie / Please tell me / True love / Bee see boogie / Bump bounce boogie / I'm gonna sit right down / We want cerveza / It's over baby / Except my baby does / Hamp's special / Daddy-o / Cat tune / Come rock with me / Twin guitars / Thirteen men / Oh babe / Bumble boogie
CDZR 96006 / Oct '97 / Zipp

☐ YOU'RE NEVER TOO YOUNG TO JUMP AND JIVE VOL.2 (Girly & The Blue Caps)
Sea cruise / Drum boogie / Honkin' at midnight / Shout hooray / Singin' in the rain / Just a closer walk with thee / Heart attack boogie / Hey good lookin' / Sing and swing / Late nite special / Sausage and bread boogie / Dig that crazy Santa Claus / Silent night / Blue Christmas / Ring-a-chime
CDZR 97011 / May '98 / Zipp

Gisbert, Greg

☐ HARCOLOGY (Gisbert, Greg Quintet)
CRISS 1084CD / May '94 / Criss Cross

Gismonti, Egberto

☐ ACADEMIA DE DANCAS
Palacio de pinturas / Jardim de prazeres / Celebracao de nupcias / A porta encantada / Scheherazade (the young prince and the young princess) (rim / Bodas de prata / Quatro cantos / Vila rica 1720 / Continuidade dos parques / Conforme a altura do sol / Conforme a altura da lua / Polichinelo / Trem noturno / Baiao do acordar
5112022 / Feb '92 / Carmo

☐ ALMA
Baiao Malandro / Palhaco / Loro / Maracuta / Karate / Agua and Vinho / Frevo / Cigana / Ruth / Sanfona / Fala de Peixao / Realejo / 7 Aneis
5291232 / Oct '96 / Carmo

☐ AMAZONIA
Dois Curumins na floresta / O senhor dos caminhos / Trenzinho amazonico / Forro na beira da mata / Os deuses da selva 1 / O baile dos caraibas / O coracao das trevas / Danca das amazonas / Todos os fogos O fogo / Ciranda no ceu / Os deuses da selva II / Sertao/Forrobodo / Ao redor da fogueira / Turma do mercado / Fuga and destruicao / Floresta (Amazonia) / Forro Amazonico / Ruth / No coracao dos homens
5177162 / Jun '93 / Carmo

☐ ARVORE
Luzes da ribalta / Memoria e fado / Academic de danca / Tango / Encontro no bar / Adagio / Variacoes sombre um tema de leo brouwer / Salvador
8490762 / May '91 / Carmo

☐ CIRCENSE
Karate / Cego aderaldo / Magico / Palhaco / Ta boa, santa / Equilibrista / Ciranda / Mais que a paixao
8490772 / May '91 / Carmo

☐ DANCA DOS ESCARVOS
2 violoes / Lundu / Trenzinho do caipira / Alegrinho / Danca dos escravos / Salvador / Memoria e fado
8377532 / Nov '89 / ECM

☐ DUAS VOZES (Gismonti, Egberto & Nana Vasconcelos)
Rio De Janeiro / Tomarapeba / Dancando / Fogueira / Bianca / Don Quixote / O dia / A noite
8236402 / Apr '86 / ECM

☐ INFANCIA
Ensaio de escola de samba (danca dos escravos) / 7 aneis (7 rings) / Infancia / A fala da paixao / Recife and o amor que o sol e outras estrelas / Danca no. 1 / Danca no. 2
8478892 / Sep '91 / ECM

☐ KUARUP
Senhores da Terra / Ossuario / Valsa de Francisca / Anta / Urucum / A Forca da Floresta / A Danca da Floresta / Aguas / Sonia / A Morte da Floresta / Valsa de Francisca / O Som da Floresta / Jogos da Floresta 1 / Jogos da Floresta 2 / Mutacao
8431992 / May '91 / Carmo

☐ MEETING POINT
Strawa zzabumba / Strawa maxixe / Musica para cordas / Frevo / A pedriha cai / Eterna / Musica de sobrevivencia
5336812 / May '97 / ECM

☐ NO CAIPIRA
Saudacoes / No caipira and zambumba / Noca and Garrafas / Pira and Bambuzal / Palacio de pinturas / Maracatu, sapo, queimada and Grilo / Frevo / Esquenta muie and banda de pffanos / Frevo rasgado / Sertao Brasiliero / Selva Amazonica / Uana Lua and Kalimbas / Cancao da espera / Danca das sombras
5177152 / Jun '93 / Carmo

☐ SANFONA
Maracatu / 10 anos / Frevo / Loro (parrot) / De repente / Vale do eco / Cavaquinho / 12 de fevereiro / Carta de amor
8293912 / Aug '88 / ECM

☐ SOL DO MEIO DIA
Palacio de pinturas / Raga / Kalimba / Coracao / Cafe / Sapain / Dance solitaria No.2 / Baiao Malandro
8291172 / Jun '86 / ECM

☐ SOLO
Selva Amazonica / Pau Rolou / And zero / Frevo / Salvador / Ciranda Nordestina
8271352 / Dec '85 / ECM

☐ TREM CAIPIRA
Trenzinho do Caipira / Dansa / Bachianas brasileiras No.5 / Desejo / Cantiga / Cancao de Carreiro / Preludio / Pobre cega
8417752 / Feb '92 / Carmo

☐ WORKS
Loro / Gismonti / Mauro senise / Zeca assumpcao / Nene raga / Vasconcelos / Colin Walcott / Ciranda nordestina / Magico / Garbarek / Charlie Haden / Maracutu / Nene salvador
8232692 / Jun '89 / ECM

☐ ZIG ZAG (Gismonti, Egberto Trio)
Mestico and Caboclo / Orixas / Carta de Amor / Um anjo / Forrobodo
5293492 / Feb '96 / ECM

Gitbox

☐ TOUCH WOOD
Engagement / Wedlock / Sipho / Les bouche du monde / Elfwalk / Springscape / Journey / Oceanscape / Be longing / Morman X and the Major's cheque / Icescape / Neither a candle for the angel nor a poker for the devil / Autumnscape / In vocation / Rajasthani heart / Panda miracle / Touch wood
DGM 9511 / Nov '95 / Discipline

Giuffre, Jimmy

☐ FLIGHT, BREMEN 1961
ARTCD 6071 / Oct '92 / Hat Art

☐ FREE FALL
Propulsion / Threewe / Ornothoids / Dichotomy / Man alone / Spasmodic / Yggdrasill / Divided man / Primordial call / Five ways
44807082 / Dec '95 / Sony Jazz

☐ JIMMY GIUFFRE THREE 1961, THE (2CD Set) (Giuffre, Jimmy Trio)
Jesus Maria / Emphasis / In the mornings out there / Scootin' about / Cry want / Brief hesitation / Venture / Afternoon / Trudgin' / Ictus / Carla / Sonic / Whirrr / That's true, that's true / Goodbye / Flight / Gamut / Me too / Temporarily / Herb and Ictus
8496442 / Mar '92 / ECM

☐ JIMMY GIUFFRE THREE, THE (Giuffre, Jimmy Three)
Song is you / Crazy she calls me / My all / Crawdad suite / That's the way it is / Forty-second street / Green country (new england mood) / Train and the river / Voodoo / Two kinds of blues / Gotta dance
7567909812 / Apr '95 / Atlantic

☐ JIMMY GIUFFRE VOL.1 1947-1952
BMCD 1046 / 21 Aug '97 / Blue Moon

☐ JIMMY GIUFFRE VOL.2 1953
BMCD 1047 / 21 Aug '97 / Blue Moon

☐ LIQUID DANCERS
1211582 / Apr '91 / Soul Note

☐ TRAIN AND THE RIVER, THE
Train and the river / Elephant / Tibetan sun / Listening / River chant / Tide is in / Tree people / Om / Celebration
CHCD 71011 / Mar '97 / Candid

☐ WILLISAU 1988 (Giuffre, Jimmy & Andre Jaume)
HATOLOGY 508 / Dec '97 / Hatology

Give Me Memphis

☐ HAIL
SIZE8CD 1 / 18 May '98 / Size 8

Gizavo, Regis

☐ MIKEA
Mpembe / Siniko / Tsikaholy / Malaso / Zeombanao / Misoholo / Mafy / Mikea / Mahavatse / Taligne
LBLC 2529 / Jun '96 / Indigo

Gjallarhorn

☐ RANAROP (The Call Of The Sea Witch)
0630196272 / 11 May '98 / Finlandia

Glackin, Kevin

☐ NORTHERN LIGHTS (Na Saighneain) (Glackin, Kevin & Seamus)
CEFCD 140 / Jan '94 / Gael Linn

Glackin, Paddy

☐ IN FULL SPATE
CEFCD 153 / Jan '94 / Gael Linn

☐ SEIDEAN SI
CEFCD 171 / Aug '95 / Gael Linn

☐ WHIRLWIND, THE (Glackin, Paddy & Robbie Hannon)
SHCD 79093 / Oct '95 / Shanachie

Gladiators

☐ CASH, THE
087962 / Jan '97 / Melodie

☐ DREADLOCKS THE TIME IS NOW
Mix up / Bellyfull / Looks is deceiving / Chatty chatty mouth / Soul rebel / Eli Eli / Hearsay / Rude boy ska / Dreadlocks the time is now / Jah works / Pocket money / Get ready / Stick a bush / Write to me / Naturality / Struggle / Day we go / Sweet so till / Hello Carol
CDFL 9001 / Jul '90 / Frontline

☐ STORM, THE
Lovin' you / Cuss cuss / Community / Fools rush in / Reggae music / Storm / Hello my love / Love got the power / Rewind / Sun comes out
111222 / Jul '95 / Musidisc UK

☐ TRUE RASTAMAN, A
No rice and peas / Let's face it / Think twice (A wise saying) / Sea breeze / Hearts on fire / South Africa / True Rastaman / Giddie head / Every moment / One way ticket
109632 / Feb '94 / Musidisc

Glam Rock Allstars

☐ NON STOP GLAM ROCK (35 All Time Glam Smash Hits Megamix)
Yeah glisten / Rock 'n' roll / Do you wanna touch me (oh yeah) / Can the can / Devil gate drive / 48 crash / My coo ca choo / Jealous mind / Blockbuster / Hot love / Metal guru / Get it on / Sugar baby love / Dynamite / Angel face / Goodbye my love / Cum on feel the noize / Mama weer all crazee now / Gudbuy 't Jane / Son of my father / Jean Genie / Waterloo / Mamma mia / SOS / Glass of champagne / (Dancing) on a Saturday night / Do you wanna dance / Tiger feet / John I'm only dancing / Ballroom blitz / Hell raiser / Fox on the run / I can do it / Tell him / Hello hello I'm back again / I'm the leader of the gang (I am)
305452 / Oct '96 / Hallmark

Glamorous Hooligan

☐ NAKED CITY SOUNTRAX
3984242012 / 17 Aug '98 / Arthrob

☐ WASTED YOUTH CLUB CLASSICS
Hooli cool downbeat / Billy Liar does De Niro / Stoned Island Estate / Lazy bomb / New age pension / Pure fiction / Tokyo heartwash / Next steppas / Naked beatbox / Charlie don't cybersurf
MOBCD 007 / Apr '96 / Mass Of Black

Glandien, Lutz

☐ SCENES FROM NO MARRIAGE
RERLG 1 / Oct '96 / ReR/ Recommended

Glands Of External Secretion

☐ NOSEJOB
STAR 4CD / Dec '96 / Starlight

☐ WHO'S WHO IN HOSPITALISATION (Glands Of External Secretion/Prick Decay)
STAR 6CD / 22 Sep '97 / Starlight

Glaser, Tompall

☐ OUTLAW, THE
It never crossed my mind / Bad times / What are we doing with our lives / How I love them old songs / On second thought / Drinkin' them beers / My mother was a lady / Duncan and Brady / Easy on my mind / Wonder of it all / You can have her / Release me / Tennessee blues / Come back Shane / It'll be her / It ain't fair / Sweethearts or strangers / Late nite show / I just want to hear the music / Storms never last
BCD 15605 / Jun '92 / Bear Family

☐ ROGUE, THE
Rogue / Tears on my pillow / Forever and ever / Shackles and chains / My pretty quadron / Lean on me / I'll hold you in my heart / True love / Open arms / I love you so much it hurts / Chattanooga shoe shine boy / You can't borrow back any time / Like an old country song / Sad country songs / What a town / Don't think you're too good for country music / Unwanted outlaw / Man you think you see / When I dream / Burn Georgia burn / Billy Tyler / Carry me on
BCD 15596 / Apr '92 / Bear Family

Glasgow Celtic FC

☐ GLASGOW CELTIC FC SUPPORTERS SONGS (2CD Set) (Various Artists)
Why I follow Celtic / I'll follow Celtic / 25th of May / Johnny Thompson we remember / Gemmell the great / Our famous Celtic team / Celtic is the name / O'Donnell Abu / We sing our Celtic songs / Men of the west / Flags are out for Celtic / Wrap the green flag / Choice / Celtic 4, Rangers 0 / Celtic and proud of it / Bold Celtic men / Old fenian gun / Celtic crazy / Johnny Thompson was his name / God save Ireland / Big Jock manager of Celtic / Wearing of the green / Three cheers for Tommy Gemmell / Celtic are the boys / Celtic story / When the Celts go marching in / Here to cheer the famous Glasgow Celtic / Celtic vocal waltz / Legend of Jimmy McCrory / After the game melody / Charlie Tully - Celtic's famous boy / Parkhead men / Wee Jimmy / Sir Robert Kelly / Big Jock Stein / Famous Glasgow Celtic / Nation once again / Sean South / Joe McDonnell / Glory Glory Glasgow Celtic / Bye bye rangers / Coatbridge shamrock / Celtic 7, Rangers 1 / I'm coming home Glasgow Celtic / On the one road / McAlpine's fusiliers / Boys of the old brigade / Fields of Athenry / Soldier's song
TSCD 1888 / Apr '97 / Outlet

☐ GLASGOW CELTIC SUPPORTERS SONGS VOL.1 (Various Artists)
Why I follow Celtic / I'll follow Celtic / 25th May / Johnny Thompson we remember / Gemmel the great / Our famous Celtic team / Celtic is the name / O'Donnell Abu / We sing our celtic songs / Men of the west / Flags are out for Celtic / Wrap the green flag / Choice / Celtic 4 Rangers 0 / Celtic and proud of it / Bold Celtic men / Old fenian gun / Celtic crazy / Johnny Thompson was his name / God save Ireland / Big Jock manager of Celtic / Wearing the green / Three cheers for Tommy Gemmel / Celtic are the bhoys
CDCFC 1240 / Jun '98 / Outlet

☐ GLASGOW CELTIC SUPPORTERS SONGS VOL.2 (Various Artists)
Celtic story / When the Celts go marching in / Here to cheer the famous Glasgow Celtic / Celtic vocal waltz / Parkhead men / Famous Glasgow Celtic / Nation once again / Sean south / Joe McDonnell / Glory glory Glasgow Celtic / Bye bye rangers / Coatbridge shamrock / Celtic 7 Rangers 1 / I'm coming home Glasgow Celtic / On the one road/Nation once again/ McAlpine's fusiliers / Boys of the old brigade / Fields of Athenry / Soldier's song
CDCFC 1241 / Jun '98 / Outlet

☐ HAIL HAIL CELTIC (Various Artists)
CDGAFFER 12 / Nov '96 / Cherry Red

Glasgow Gaelic Musical Association

☐ CENTENARY SELECTION, A
Fuadach nan gaidheal / Fuadach nan gaidheal / Ailean donn / Ho-ro mo nighean donn bhoidheach (choir) / Tillidh mi (quartet) / Aillte (choir) / Deoch slainte nam muileach / Gruagach og an fhuilt (alasdair gillies) / Chi m'in geamradh / Gu ma slan do na fearaibh (choir) / Brochan lom-bodachan a mhirein (puirt-a-beul) / An ubhal as airde / Nuair bha mi og (kirsteen grant) / Smeorach chlann domhnuill / Mi le m'uilinn air mo ghluin (quartet) / Illean bithibh sunndach (choir) / French
LCOM 5220 / Jun '93 / Lismor

☐ GAELIC GALORE
Tuireadh nan treun / 'S olc a dh' fhag an uiridh mi / O hi ri ri, tha e tighinn / Maighdeanan na h-airidh / Tir an airm / Seoladh dhachaidh / An ataireachd ard / Allt an t-siucair / An ubhal as airde / Nuair bha mi og / Strathspeys and reels / O righ nan dul / 'S cian bho dh'fhag mi Ieodhas / An t-Iarla diurach / Cathair a chulchinn / Cearcall a' chuain / Oran an lennaibh og / Och nan och, tha mi fo mhulad / Caberfeidh
LCOM 9037 / Oct '90 / Lismor

Glasgow Islay Gaelic Choir

☐ TRIBUTE TO RUNRIG
CDLOC 1094 / Jun '96 / Lochshore

Glasgow Orpheus Choir

☐ 20 CLASSIC RECORDINGS
All in the April evening / Belmont peat / Fire smoothing prayer / Bonnie Dundee Orlington / Eriskay love lilt / Lilt / Ca' the Yowes / Crimond / Hark, hark the echo falling / Bluebird / Ellan Vannin / Jesu joy of man's desiring / Cloud capp'd towers / Faery song / Campbells are coming / Far away / Iona boat song / Cradle song / Sea sorrow / All through the night
MOICD 007 / Nov '92 / Moidart

☐ O LIGHT OF LIFE
O light of life / Kendron / O can ye sew cushions / Far away/old woman / Herdmaiden's song / In silent night / I live not where I love / Ae fond kiss / White waves on the water / Dashing white sergeant / Scots wha hae / Laird of cockpen / Haste thee nymph / Come kindly death / Dumbarton's drum / Deep river / All creatures now are merry minded / Mice and men / Go lovely rose / Gretna green / Isle of Mull / To take the air (a bonny lass was walking) / Strathcathro / Shower
MOICD 012 / Dec '96 / Moidart

Glasgow Phoenix Choir

☐ FEEL GOOD
CDLOC 1080 / Jul '94 / Lochshore

☐ HIGHLAND CATHEDRAL
CDITV 634 / 10 Nov '97 / Scotdisc

☐ WITH VOICES RISING
Scots wha hae / In the Wheatfield / When the saints go marching in / Annie Laurie / Time for man go home / Brother James' air / Shenandoah / John Anderson, my Jo / Tumbalalaika / Little cherry tree / Corn rigs / Dream angus / Death o' death oh me lawd / Loch Lomond / Campbells are coming / All my trials / Lament of Mary Queen Of Scots / Battle of the republic
LCDM 9024 / Aug '90 / Lismor

Glasgow Police Pipe Band

☐ PIPES ARE CALLING, THE
EMPRCD 703 / Mar '97 / Emporio

Glasgow Rangers FC

☐ FAMOUS GLASGOW RANGERS (Various Artists)
CDGAFFER 11 / Nov '96 / Cherry Red

☐ GLASGOW RANGERS FC SUPPORTERS SONGS (2CD Set) (Various Artists)
Paisley (Town of) / Rangers ABC / Johnston king of the ball / Rangers in shirts of blue / Rangers our greatest pride / I'll follow rangers / Best team in the land / Stars of Ibbrox / March on to victory / Gers go marching on / Follow follow / Men of Ibrox / Rangers true and blue / Bonnie Rangers / Scottish nonsense song / Call them Glasgow rangers / Maggie McDonald / We are the people / Aye ready / Wonders of the world / Red, white and blue / King Kai / March on Glasgow rangers / Blue flag / No surrender / Green grassy slopes of the Boyne / Sash / Le reve passe - the Rangers story / We shall not be moved / Rangers over here / Every other Saturday / Old mud cabin / Glory glory / Scarf / Lambeg drums / Cry is Glasgow Rangers / My dear old Belfast town / Land of no surrender / Legend of Willie Woodburn / It's Rangers for me / Sandy Sandy / I'm off to join the orange walk / Ranger story / Flower of Scotland / Men of Harlech / God save the Queen
TSCD 300 / Apr '97 / Outlet

☐ GLASGOW RANGERS SUPPORTERS SONGS VOL.1 (Various Artists)
Paisley (town of) / Rangers ABC / Johnston king of the ball / Rangers in shirts of blue / Rangers our greatest pride / I'll follow Rangers / Best team in the land / Stars of Ibrox / March on to victory / Gers' go marching on / Follow follow / Men of Ibrox / Rangers true and blue / Bonnie Rangers / Scottish nonsense song / Call them Glasgow rangers / Maggie Macdonald / We are the people / Aye ready / Wonders of the world / Red white and blue / King kai / March on Glasgow Rangers / Blue flag
CDCFC 1242 / Jun '98 / Outlet

☐ GLASGOW RANGERS SUPPORTERS SONGS VOL.2 (Various Artists)
No surrender / Green grassy slopes of the Boyne / Sash / Le reve passe / We shall not be moved / Rangers over here / Every other Sunday / Thornlie bank medley / Scarf / Glory glory / Lambeg drums / Cry is Glasgow Rangers / My dear old Belfast Town / Land of no surrender / Ranger's waltz / I'm off to join the orange walk / Ranger story / Lambeg drums / Flower of Scotland / Men of Harlech / God save the Queen
CDCFC 1243 / Jun '98 / Outlet

Glasgow, Alex

☐ NOW AND THEN/THE SONGS OF ALEX GLASGOW VOL.3 (2CD Set)
MWMCDSP 21 / Nov '97 / Mawson & Wareham

Glasgow, Deborahe

☐ DEBORAHE GLASGOW
Give me that touch / Best friend / Perfect situation / This love / Hooked on this feeling / Don't test me (the don't test it mix) / Fantasy becomes reality / I know your cheating / Champion lover / Unconditionally / Champion lover
GRELCD 135 / Dec '89 / Greensleeves

☐ GIMME YOUR LOVE
Mind is willing / Gimme your love / Too late / Lonely hearts / Overflow / Ready for this / Easy rider / First / Mind is willing / St. Elizabeth Junction
WRCD 011 / Nov '97 / World

Glass Family

☐ BEST OF GLASS FAMILY, THE
HTCD 95 / 20 Apr '98 / Hot Productions

Glass, Philip

☐ 1000 AIRPLANES ON THE ROOF
1000 airplanes on the roof / City walk / Girlfriend / My building disappeared / Screens of memory / What time is grey / Labyrinth / Return to the hive / Three truths / Encounter / Grey cloud over New York / Where have you been as the doctor / Normal man running
CDVE 39 / Feb '89 / Venture

☐ AKHNATEN (2CD Set)
M2K 42457 / Feb '88 / Sony Classical

☐ EINSTEIN ON THE BEACH
7559793232 / Jan '95 / Nonesuch

☐ GLASSMASTERS (3CD Set)
Window of appearances / III/The dam / Vow / Open the kingdom / Attack and fall / Confrontation and rescue / Funeral of Amenhotep III / Floe / Dance No.5 / Spaceship / Photographer act III / Building/Train / Knee play 3 / Facades / Akhnaten Act III4 epilogue / Freezing / Akhnanten's hymn to the aten / Satyagraha Act III3 evening song / Knee play 5 / Mad rush
SM3K 62960 / Apr '97 / Sony Classical

☐ HEROES SYMPHONY, THE (The Music Of David Bowie/Brian Eno)
4543082 / Mar '97 / Point Music

☐ HYDROGEN JUKEBOX (Glass, Philip & Allen Ginsberg)
7559792862 / Jan '95 / Nonesuch

☐ ITAIPU
SK 46352 / Nov '93 / Sony Classical

☐ LA BELLE ET LA BETE (2CD Set) (Glass, Philip Ensemble)
7559793472 / Jan '98 / Nonesuch

☐ LOW SYMPHONY, THE (The Music Of David Bowie/Brian Eno)
4381502 / Mar '93 / Philips

☐ MUSIC IN 12 PARTS (3CD Set) (Glass, Philip Ensemble)
Music in 12 parts (parts 1 - 12)
7559793242 / Oct '96 / Nonesuch

☐ NORTH STAR
Etoile polaire (North star) / Victor's lament / River run / Mon pere, mon pere / Are years what? (for Marianne Moore) / Lady Day / Ange des orages / Ave / Ik-ook / Montage
CDV 2085 / Jun '88 / Virgin

☐ PASSAGES (Glass, Philip & Ravi Shankar)
Offering / Channels and winds / Meetings along the edge / Sadhanipa / Ragas in minor scale / Prashanti
260947 / Sep '90 / Private Music

☐ SATYAGRAHA (3CD Set)
M3K 39672 / Jan '94 / Sony Classical

☐ SOLO PIANO
SMK 45576 / Jan '96 / Sony Classical

☐ SYMPHONY NO.2 (Vienna Radio Symphony Orchestra/Rascher Quartet/Stuttgart CO)
Symphony No.2 / Interlude from Orphee / Concerto for saxophone quartet
7559794962 / 18 May '98 / Nonesuch

Glasse, Paul

☐ ROAD TO HOME, THE
DOSCD 7004 / May '94 / Dos

Glaz

☐ AR GEST
504362 / Mar '96 / Declic

☐ GLAZ
CD 848 / Aug '93 / Escalibur

Glazier, Richard

☐ SCOTT JOPLIN COLLECTED PIANO WORKS VOL.1
CRC 2403 / Aug '98 / Centaur

Gleason, Jackie

☐ HOW SWEET IT IS (The Jackie Gleason Velvet Brass Collection)
RE 21112 / Jul '96 / Razor & Tie

Gledhill, Simon

☐ SHALL WE DANCE
Shall we dance / Fleurette / El relicario / These foolish things / Garland of Judy / Canyon caballero / No matter what happens / Veradero / Dancing in the dark / Autumn crocus / June night on marlow reach / Swing time / My silent love / Themes from: Skyscraper fantasy / Haunted ballroom
OS 205 / Jul '94 / OS Digital

Glee Club

☐ MINE
Need / Blame / No reason / Bad child's dolly / Already there / Free to believe / Drives you away / Remember the years / All the promises / Take you there / Icy blue
SETCD 012 / Jan '94 / Setanta

Gleeson, Barry

☐ PATH ACROSS THE OCEAN
Path across the ocean / Mulligar recruit / Roy Roger um / Sleeveless charms / What will we do when we have no money / This is Macaronic / Irish jubilee / Sweet daffodil Mulligan / Sheila Nee Iyer (sile ni ghaidhre) / False false fly / Calf meal in Roscrea / Slip jigs and reels / Shrieken artaner / Cuppid's visitation to Mick Dwyer
CD 001 / Sep '94 / Wavelength
TERRCD 001 / Nov '96 / Terra Nova

Gleeson, Patrick

☐ FOUR SEASONS
Spring / Summer / Autumn / Winter
VCD 47212 / '87 / Varese Sarabande

Glen Or Glenda

☐ REASONS IN THE SUN
SHMCD 5136 / Apr '98 / Shimmy Disc

Glencastle Sound

☐ CELTIC JIGS AND REELS (Glencastle Sound & Waxie's Dargle/Gravel Walk)
Medley: *Glencastle Sound* / Duke of Perth/Caddam woods: *Glencastle Sound* / Father O'Flyn/Irish washerwoman/Blackberry blossom: *Waxie's Dargle* / Medley: *Glencastle Sound* / Maid behind the bar/ Gravel walk: *Gravel Walk* / Hamish's tune/Barnyards o' Delgaty: *Glencastle Sound* / Cumberland reel/ Rosin the bow: *Glencastle Sound* / Paddy Ryan's dream/Docherty's reel/McGinnely's reel: *Waxie's Dargle* / Swallow's tail: *Waxie's Dargle* / Parting glass/Brown gate/Yellow bonnet: *Waxie's Dargle* / La russe/Rakes of mallow: *Glencastle Sound* / Medley: *Glencastle Sound* / Paddy Fathy's reel/ Dinny's fancy: *Waxie's Dargle* / Mist on the bog/ Brunden laws/Seige of Ennis: *Glencastle Sound* / Merrily kissed the Quaker/Between worlds: *Waxie's Dargle* / Dashing white Sergeant/Rose tree/Donald Dunn: *Glencastle Sound* / Geese in the bog/Wind that shakes the barley: *Waxie's Dargle*
300542 / Feb '98 / Hallmark

Glenfiddle

☐ NEVERTHELESS
EFA 800392 / Dec '95 / Twah

Glenn, Glen

☐ GLEN GLENN STORY/EVERYBODY'S MOVIN' AGAIN
If I had me a woman / One cup of coffee / Hold me baby / Baby let's play house / Laurie Ann / Be bop a lula / Kitty Kat / Everybody's movin' / Shake, rattle and roll / Treat me nice / Blue jeans and a boy's shirt / I got a woman / Kathleen / Would ja' / I'm glad my baby's gone away / Down the line / Come on / Flip flop and fly / Jack and Jill boogie / I sure do love you baby / Bony Moronie / Mean woman blues / Rock 'n' roll Ruby / Sick and tired / Rockin' around the mountain / Why don't you love me / Ugly and slouchy / You win again / Everybody's movin' again
CDCHD 403 / Jun '92 / Ace

Glenn Underground

☐ ATMOSFEAR
Isralee night falls / Entercourse of the new age / Rising son / May datroit / Colouration / Dance slam / Sound struck / Midnight groove
PF 043CD / Apr '96 / Peacefrog

☐ FUTURE PARABLES
DFDCD 14 / 24 Nov '97 / Defender

☐ JERUSALEM EP'S, THE
Black slaves = Israel / Sun, moon and 12 stars / Keep the hidden treasures / Servants jazz house / H-Dance / Negro city / To the King Ol / There is a time
PF 066CD / May '97 / Peacefrog

☐ PARABLES
DFDCD 003 / Jul '96 / Defender

Glennie, Evelyn

☐ GREATEST HITS (2CD Set)
Entrances / Halasana / Sorbet no.1 / Rhythm song / My spine / Slaughter on 10th Avenue / Sorbet no.5 / Little prayer / Eldorado / Sorbet no.7 / Black key study / Divertimento / Taps in tempo / Born to be wild / Michi for marimba / Sorbet no.4 / Light in darkness / Anvil chorus / Rhapsody / Swan / Sorbet no.3
74321476292 / May '97 / RCA Victor

Glenside Ceili Band

☐ CELTIC PRIDE (Glenside Ceili Band & The Pat O'Brien Band)
Riverdance / Reels / Jigs / Jackie Coleman's reel/ The snake / Limerick is beautiful / Reels / Hurrican's victory/The providence / Golden jubilee / Morrison's jig/The bride's favourite / Glenside / Cod liver oil / Reels
PLSCD 258 / 27 Oct '97 / Pulse

Glide

☐ SPACE AGE FREAK OUT
OCH 001L / Jul '97 / Ochre

Glinn, Lillian

☐ LAST SESSION 1929 (Glinn, Lillian & Mae Glover)
SOB 035372 / Oct '92 / Story Of The Blues

☐ LILLIAN GLINN 1927-1933
DOCD 5184 / Oct '93 / Document

Glitter Band

☐ 20 GLITTERING GREATS
Angel face / People like you and people like me / Just for you / Sea cruise / Rock on / Game's up / Love in the sun / Twistin' the night away / Shout it out / I can hear music / Let's get together again / Sealed with a kiss / Dream baby / Don't make promises you can't keep / Tell him / Tears I cried / Pictures of you / Can't stop / Goodbye my love / Makes you blind
MCCD 357 / 20 Jul '98 / Music Club

☐ VERY BEST OF THE GLITTER BAND, THE
Angel face / Painted lady / Makes you blind / My first mistake / Let's get together again / Tell him / Love street / Sweet baby blue / Tears I cried / Rock on / People like you and people like me / Almost American / Let me love you / Gotta get a message back to you / Just for you / Write me a letter / Tuna biscuit / Love in the sun / Where have you been / Goodbye my love
3036400062 / May '96 / Essential Gold

Glitter, Gary

☐ 25 YEARS OF HITS (2CD Set)
Rock and roll (part 1) / Do you wanna touch me (oh yeah) / I'm the leader of the gang (I am) / I didn't know I loved you (till I saw you rock 'n' roll) / I love you love me love / Let's get together again: *Glitter Band* / Doing alright with the boys / Always yours / Sidewalk sinner / Angel face: *Glitter Band* / Oh yes you're beautiful / Love like you and me / Remember me this way / You belong to me / When I'm on / Rock hard men (need the power) / Hello hello I'm back again / Rock and roll (part 2) / Papa oom mow mow / Dance me up / Rock on / It takes all night / Goodbye my love: *Glitter Band* / Oh what a fool / What your Mama don't see / Little boogie woogie / I dare you to lay one on me / Just for you: *Glitter Band* / Be my baby / And then she kissed me / All that glitters / Another rock 'n' roll Christmas
GGCD 001 / 24 Nov '97 / Snapper

☐ GARY GLITTER
GRF 200 / Jan '93 / Tring

☐ GLITTER
Rock 'n' roll / Baby please don't go / Wanderer / I didn't know I loved you (till I saw you rock 'n' roll) / Ain't that a shame / School day (ring ring goes the bell) / Rock on / Donna / Famous instigator / Clapping song / Shaky sue / Rock 'n' roll part 2 / I am the leader of the gang (I am) / It's not a lot / Just fancy that / Thank you baby for myself
DOJOCD 100 / Jul '96 / Dojo

☐ LEADER VOL.2, THE
Ready to rock / Tonight / Why do you do it / Wild women / (The only way to) survive / Let's go party / Are you hard enough / Shake it up / It's enough / Am I losing you
CCSCD 443 / Oct '96 / Castle

☐ LEADER, THE
Rock and roll (part 1) / Rock and roll (part 2) / I didn't know I loved you (till I saw you rock and roll) / Ain't that a shame / Hello hello I'm back again / Oh yes you're beautiful / Doing alright with the boys / Hold on to what you got / Lonely boy / To know you is to love you / Didn't I do it right / Side walk sinner / Hard on me / I.o.u. / Happy birthday / Come on, come in, get on / Money honey / Do you wanna touch me / Leader of the gang / I love you love me love / Remember me this way / Always yours / Love like you and me / Papa com mow mow / Donna / Rock on / Wanderer / Baby please don't go / Famous instigator / Clapping song / Shakey sue / School days / Intro / Rock 'n' roll / Do you wanna touch me / Hello hello I'm back again / Leader of the gang / I belong to you / I love you love me love / Let's get together again / Always yours
TFP 026 / Nov '92 / Tring

☐ MANY HAPPY RETURNS - THE HITS
Rock 'n' roll (part 1) / Rock 'n' roll (part 2) / I didn't know I loved you (till I saw you rock 'n' roll) / Ready to rock / Rock on / Doing alright with the boys / I'm the leader of the gang (I am) / Wanderer / Do you wanna touch me (Oh yeah) / Hello hello I'm back again / I love you love me love / You belong to me / It takes all night long / Oh yes, you're beautiful / Love like you and me / Little boogie woogie (in the back of my mind) / Dance me up / Through the years / Always yours / Remember me this way / And the leader rocks on / Another rock 'n' roll Christmas
CDFA 3303 / Jan '94 / Fame

☐ TOUCH ME
Do you wanna touch me / Come on come in get on / Happy birthday / Hard on me / To know you is to love you / Money honey / Hello hello I'm backa again / Sidewalk sinner / Didn't I do it right / Lonely boy / Hold on to what you got / IOU / Oh yes you're beautiful / I would if I could but I can't / I'm right you're wrong I win / I'll carry your picture everywhere
DOJOCD 200 / Jul '96 / Dojo

Glitterbox

☐ TIED AND TANGLED
Houdini / Scared of all the world / Woody Allen / Superman / I can wait / You can't live on Mars / Jesus song / Summersong / Step inside / Sit back and watch her fly / Tonight to hell
SCANCD 30 / 18 May '98 / Radarscope

GLO

☐ EVEN AS WE
Deiea / I'm in your gravity / Travellers stargate / Crystal world / Doom ghosts / And / Pagli herbus / Spirit lover / Walk the streets / Goddesses love oranges / Let's GLO / Back to the sea
GLISSCD 002 / Jul '97 / GAS

Glo Worm

☐ GLIMMER
KLP 54CD / May '96 / K

Global

☐ GIG NA GIG
GLISSCD 003 / Jul '97 / GAS

Global Communication

☐ REMOTION
DEDCD 021 / Nov '95 / Dedicated

Global Goon

☐ CRADLE OF HISTORY
Sloe intro / Funky drunk / Jazz intro / Long whiney / Dum dar dee / Quirky till / Duck soup / DX / Afterlife / Grand piano / Prince / Snare rush / Rockford / Vocal loop / Aha / Basesy hip hop / Ready to roll / Hardcore symphony / Open hihat / Gallery / False epic
CAT 058CD / 6 Apr '98 / Rephlex

☐ GLOBAL GOON
CAT 0038CD / Dec '96 / Rephlex

Global Noise Attack

☐ RESTRAINED FURY
Desperate culture / Heal / Don'Don't fear the pain / Born again mutation / Drip feed / Sand and tears / Shrine / Shape-shifter / Trance talk / Desensitise / Secretion
ORGAN 040CD / 2 Mar '98 / Org

☐ SEIZURE
TCD 001 / Dec '96 / Tumult Productions

Glommin Geek

☐ DIG A HOLE IN THE SKY
WD 014CD / Aug '92 / Wide

Glommy Grim

☐ BLOOD MONSTERS AND DARKNESS
HOLY 034CD / 11 May '98 / Holy

Gloria

☐ 20 SONGS
PHCD 535 / Jan '95 / Outlet

Glory

☐ CRISIS VS. CRISIS
DCD 9622 / Mar '97 / Dream Circle

Glory Box

☐ BEGIN
CCD 512651 / Feb '97 / Celebration

Glory Stompers

☐ NINESIXNINESEVEN
KOCD 075 / 20 Jul '98 / Knock Out

Gloucester Cathedral Choir

☐ CHRISTMAS CAROLS
As with gladness men of old / We three Kings / Personent hodie / Infant King / Quem pastores Laudavere / In dulci jubilo / Sussex carol / Adam lay y bounden / Whence is that goodly fragrance / Of the Father's heart begotten / In the bleak mid-winter / Cherry tree carol / Tomorrow shall be my dancing day / Virgin most pure / O come, O come, Emmanuel / Joys seven / Twelve days of Christmas / See amid the winter's snow / Past three o'clock / Jingle bells / King Jesus hath a garden / Shepherd's pipe carol / Christmas is coming / Sans day carol / Torches / Great and mighty wonder / Angels from the realms of glory / Jeus Christ the apple tree
XMAS 002 / Nov '96 / Tring

☐ MUSIC FOR CHRISTMAS
There is no rose / O little one sweet / See amid the winter's snow / I sing of a maiden / Three mummers / Sing lullaby / Carol of praise / New Year carol / Hymn of the Nativity / Carol for today / Tomorrow shall be my dancing day / Lamb / O little town of Bethlehem / Silent night / Blessed be that maid Mary / Whence is that goodly fragrance / Ding dong merrily on high / It came upon a midnight clear / Once in Royal David's City
CDCA 917 / Nov '91 / Alpha

Glove

☐ BLUE SUNSHINE
Like an animal / Looking glass girl / Sex-eye-make-up / Blues in drag / Mr. Alphabet says / Punish me with kisses / This green city / Orgy / Perfect murder / Relax
8150192 / Aug '90 / Polydor

Glover, May

☐ MAY GLOVER 1927-1931
DOCD 5185 / Oct '93 / Document

Glover, Roger

☐ BUTTERFLY BALL, THE/WIZARD'S CONVENTION (Various Artists)
Dawn / Get ready / Saffron Dormouse and Lizzy Bee / Harlequin hare / Old blind mole / Magician moth / No solution / Behind the smile / Fly away / Aranea / Sitting in a dream / Waiting / Sir Maximus Mouse / Dreams of Sir Bedivere / Together again / Watch out for the bat / Little chalk blue / Feast / Love is all / Homeward / Craig song / When the sun stops shining / Loose ends / Money to burn / Who's counting on me / Make it soon / Until tomorrow / Light of my life / She's a woman / Swanks and swells
VSOPCD 139 / Oct '89 / Connoisseur Collection

Glu Gun

☐ JUST GLU IT
EFA 113892 / May '94 / Poshboy

Glue

☐ MACHINE KEEP ME WARM
FAN 1012 / Jun '94 / Fantastick

Glue Gun

☐ SCENE IS NOT FOR SALE, THE
FO 10CD / Apr '97 / Fearless

Glueball

☐ MAD DOGS AND SCHOOL GIRLS
PREACH 006CD / 25 May '98 / Rhythm Vicar

Gluecifer

☐ NINETEEN INCHES OF ROCK
GLUE 001CD / 29 Jun '98 / Voices Of Wonder

☐ RIDIN' THE TIGER
JAZZ 005CD / Jun '97 / White Jazz

Glutz, Sadie

☐ BOY FROM OUTER SPACE, THE
SILVER 12CD / 23 Mar '98 / Silver Planet

Glykeria

☐ 15 GREEK CLASSICS
4939022 / 1 Mar '98 / Atoll

Gnaoua, Jilala

☐ MOROCCAN TRANCE MUSIC VOL.1
SUBCD 01336 / Jul '97 / Sub Rosa

Go Getters

☐ ROCK AND ROLL IS EVERYWHERE
GRCD 6086 / Jul '98 / Goofin'

Go To Blazes

☐ ANY TIME
GRCD 374 / 22 Sep '97 / Glitterhouse

Go West

☐ ACES AND KINGS (The Best Of Go West)
We close our eyes / King of wishful thinking / Tracks of my tears / Call me / Faithful / Don't look down (the sequel) / One way street / What you won't do for love / From Baltimore to Paris / Goodbye girl / I want to hear it from you / Tell me / King is dead
CDCHR 6050 / Oct '93 / Chrysalis

☐ BANGS AND CRASHES
We close our eyes / Man in my mirror / Goodbye girl / SOS / Eye to eye / Ball of confusion / Call me / Haunted / Missing person / Don't look down / One way street / Innocence
CCD 1536 / 15 Sep '97 / Chrysalis

☐ GO WEST
We close our eyes / Don't look down / Call me / Eye to eye / Haunted / SOS / Goodbye girl / Innocence / Missing persons
CDGOLD 1014 / Mar '96 / EMI Gold

Go-Betweens

☐ 16 LOVERS LANE
Love goes on / Quiet heart / Love is a sign / You can't say no forever / Dive for your memory / Devil's eye / Streets of your town / Clouds / Was there anything I could do / I'm alright
BBL 2006CD / Mar '96 / Beggars Banquet

☐ BEFORE HOLLYWOOD
Bad debt follows you / Two steps step out / Before Hollywood / Dusty in here / Ask / Cattle and cane / By chance / As long as that / On my block / That way
BBL 2002CD / Mar '96 / Beggars Banquet

☐ LIBERTY BELLE AND THE BLACK DIAMOND EXPRESS
Spring rain / Ghost and the black hat / Wrong road / To reach me / Twin layers of lightning / In the core of a flame / Head full of steam / Bow down / Palm down / Apology accepted
BBL 2004CD / Mar '96 / Beggars Banquet

☐ SEND ME A LULLABY
Your turn my turn / One thing can hold us / People know / Girls have moved / Careless / All about strength / Ride / Hold your horses / Midnight to neon / Eight pictures / Arrow in a bow / It could be anyone
BBL 2001CD / Mar '96 / Beggars Banquet

☐ SPRING HILL FAIR
Bachelor kisses / Five words / Old way out / You've never lived / Part company / Slow slow music / Draining the pool for you / River of money / Unkind and unwise / Man o'sand to girl o'sea
BBL 2003CD / Mar '96 / Beggars Banquet

☐ TALLULAH
Right here / You tell me / Someone else's wife / I just get caught out / Cut it out / House that Jack Kerouac built / Bye bye pride / Spirit of a vampyre / Clarke sisters / Hope then strife
BBL 2005CD / Mar '96 / Beggars Banquet

Go-Getters

☐ REAL GONE
PT 601001 / Jun '96 / Part

Go-Nuts

☐ WORLD'S GREATEST SUPER HERO
PPC 022 / Sep '97 / Planet Pimp

Goat

☐ SACRED PILGRIM
RRS 950CD / Sep '96 / Die Hard/ Progress

Goat Of Mendes

☐ TO WALK UPON THE WICCAN WAY
PT 019CD / 22 Sep '97 / Perverted Taste

Goats Don't Shave

☐ OUT IN THE OPEN
Coming home / Help / Children of the highway / Rose street / Arranmore / This world / She's leaving / Song for Fionula / War / Let it go / Lock it in
COOKCD 075 / Sep '94 / Cooking Vinyl

☐ RUSTY RAZOR
Let the world keep on turning / Las Vegas (In the hills of Donegal) / Eyes / John Cherokee / Evictions / Biddy from Sligo/Connaught man's rambles / Ranger / Mary Mary / Closing time / What she means to me / Crooked Jack / When you're dead
COOKCD 074 / Jul '97 / Cooking Vinyl

Gob

☐ TOO LATE NO FRIENDS
FO33CD / 20 Jul '98 / Fearless

Goblins

☐ GOBLIN PRIDE
ALP 304
TRUCK 04CD / Jun '97 / Truckstop

Gobsmakt

☐ YOU WOT
STEPCD 114 / 4 May '98 / Step 1

God & Texas

☐ CRIMINAL ELEMENT
Incoming / Bury magnets / D 2 / Cold bringer / Chromalox / Breach / Drive time / In the blast furnace / Flat black wide / Cruel andunusual
729002 / Nov '93 / Restless

☐ DOUBLE SHOT
Confidential scrape / Codename: Soul albino / In the flesh again / Lower / Meet me at the inversion layer / Zappatos del diablo / Red room / Back on the downside / Profiteerings / Goodbye blacksheep / Chevalier / Outro
729022 / Sep '94 / Restless

God

☐ APPEAL TO HUMAN GREED
ABB 79XCD / Jun '95 / Big Cat

☐ POSSESSION
Pretty / Fucked / Return to hell / Soul fire / Hate meditation / Lord I'm on my way / Love / Black Jesus
CDOVD 485 / Jun '97 / Virgin

God Bullies

☐ KILL THE KING
VIRUSUK 152CD / 10 Nov '97 / Alternative Tentacles

God Dethroned
☐ GRAND GRIMOIRE
398414148CD / 13 Oct '97 / Metal Blade

God Forsaken
☐ DREAMS OF DESOLATION
CDAR 08 / Feb '94 / Adipocre
☐ TIDE HAS TURNED
CDAR 025 / May '95 / Adipocre

God Is My Co-Pilot
☐ BEST OF GOD IS MY CO-PILOT, THE
ALP 82CD / Nov '96 / Atavistic
☐ CHILDREN CAN BE SO CRUEL
MIGUEL 1 / May '97 / Miguel
☐ PEEL SESSIONS, THE
SFRSCD 004 / Jan '97 / Strange Fruit
☐ PUSS 02
DSA 54041 / Dec '95 / Les Disques Du Soleil
☐ TIGHT LIKE FIST
KFWCD 148 / Feb '95 / Knitting Factory

God Lives Underwater
☐ EMPTY
Still / All wrong / Empty / Don't know how to be / No more love / 23 / We were wrong / Weaken / Tortoise / Scared / Lonely again / Nothing / Try / Waste of time / Drag me down
74321295182 / Oct '95 / American

God Machine
☐ ONE LAST LAUGH IN A PLACE OF DYING
Tremelo song / Mama / Alone / In bad dreams / Painless / Love song / Life song / Devil song / Hunter / Evol / Train song / Flower song / Boy by the roadside / Sunday song
FIXCD 27 / Oct '94 / Fiction

Godard, Michel
☐ ABORIGENE
HOP 200002 / May '94 / Label Hopi
☐ LE CHANT DU SERPENT
CDLLL 37 / Oct '93 / La Lichere
☐ LOOSE WIRES
Chanson pour Lise / Stara pesma / Monster / It's still quite dark but there are some signs of light / Bakija / Les enfants qui s'aiment / Emilio / Spiritual / Locusts have returned and they are bigger than ever / Down home where the blowfish roam / Immaculate conception
ENJ 90712 / May '97 / Enja

Godard, Vic
☐ IN TROUBLE AGAIN
Up on icing sugar mountain / TROUBLE / 20th century blues / Tidal wave / Devil's in league with you / Caribb-blu / I'm gonna write a musical / Chainsmoking / (Stayin outta) view / Stop that girl / Nice on the ice / Holiday hymn / Ice on a volcano / Miss Sadie / Wave
TUG 001CD / 11 May '98 / Tugboat

Godchildren Of Soul
☐ GODCHILDREN OF SOUL, THE
TOTCD 4 / Sep '95 / Total

Godfathers
☐ AFTERLIFE
IRS 845255CD / Feb '96 / Intercord
☐ BIRTH, SCHOOL, WORK, DEATH (The Best Of The Godfathers)
Birth, school, work, death / She gives me love / Unreal world / Just because you're not paranoid / Cause I said so / Angela / Walking talking Johnny Cash blues / Miss that girl / This is war / If only I had time / Love is dead / Another you / Gone to Texas / Don't let me down / Lonely man / When am I coming down / Cold turkey / Birth, school, work, death (remix)
4784232 / Jul '96 / Epic
☐ GOLDEN DELICIOUS/THE GODFATHERS
IRS 988574CD / May '96 / Intercord
☐ ORANGE
986974 / Oct '93 / Intercord

Godflesh
☐ GODFLESH
Avalanche master song / Veins godhead / Spinebender weak flesh / Ice nerveshatter wounds / Streetcleaner 2
MOSH 020CD / 1 Sep '97 / Earache
☐ LOVE AND HATE IN DUB
Circle of shit / Wake / Almost heaven / Gift from heaven (breakbeat) / Frail (now broken) / Sterile prophet / Kingdom come / Time, death wastefulness in dub / Sterile prophet(in dub) / Domain / Gift from heaven
MOSH 178CD / Jul '97 / Earache

☐ PURE
Spite / Mothra / I wasn't born to follow / Predominance / Pure / Monotremata / Baby blue eyes / Don't bring me flowers / Love, hate (slugbaiting) / Pure ii
MOSH 032CD / 1 Sep '97 / Earache
☐ SELFLESS
Xnoybis / Bigot / Black bored angel / Anything is mine / Empyreal / Crush my soul / Body dome light / Toll / Heartless / Mantra / Go spread your wings
MOSH 085CD / 1 Sep '97 / Earache
☐ SONGS OF LOVE AND HATE
Wake / Sterile prophet / Circle of shit / Hunter / Gift from heaven / Amoral / Angel domain / Kingdom come / Time death and wastefulness / Frail / Almost heaven
MOSH 157CD / 1 Sep '97 / Earache
☐ STREETCLEANER
Like rats / Christbait rising / Pulp / Dream long dead / Head dirt / Devastator-mighty trust krusher / Life is eeay / Streetcleaner / Locust furnace / Tiny tears / Wound / Dead head / Suction
MOSH 015CD / 1 Sep '97 / Earache

Godheads
☐ ORDINARY SWOON
CDZOT 181 / Jul '97 / Zoth Ommog

Godheadsilo
☐ SKYWARD IN TRIUMPH
SPCD 347 / Apr '96 / Sub Pop

Godkiller
☐ END OF THE WORLD, THE
WLR 014CD / 6 Jul '98 / Wounded Love

Godplow
☐ RED GIANT JUDAS
GROW 0472 / May '95 / Grass

Godrays
☐ SONGS FOR TV STARS
Comforting Joe / Songs for TV stars / Vampires suck / Darling / Careless / Both your names (Janus' creepy girlfriend) / Still just a night thing / 30 second song / Crummy / Boyscout thriller / Crack you up / Bother (the blushes) / Crazy / Carkeys, ponytail and gum
YARDCD 017 / Oct '96 / Vernon Yard

God's Hotel
☐ GOD'S HOTEL
SKIRT 52 / 25 May '98 / Best Dressed

God's Reflex
☐ BRIEF LESSON IN AFFECTION
JFR 039 / 26 Jan '98 / Johann's Face

Godsend
☐ AS THE SHADOWS FALL
HOLY 003CD / May '94 / Holy
☐ WAYFARER'S TEARS, A
HOLY 031CD / 23 Feb '98 / Holy

Godspeed
☐ RIDE
Ride / Not enough / Hate / Abstract life / Stubborn ass / Downtown / Born and raised / Houston St. / Mind blaster / Christ / My brother
7567825732 / Mar '94 / WEA

Godspeed You Black Emperor
☐ F# A#
KRANKY 027 / 15 Jun '98 / Kranky

Godstar
☐ SLEEPER
TAANG 79CD / Dec '93 / Taang

Godzilla
☐ VOLUME
TOPYCD 073 / May '94 / Temple

Godzuki
☐ FREE WADE
GS 003 / Mar '97 / Time Stereo/Go Sonic

Goebbels, Heiner
☐ DISASTROUS LANDING
5279302 / Dec '95 / ECM
☐ HORSTUCKE
Liberation of prometheus / Despoiled shore / Maelstromsouthpole / Volokolamsk highway i-v
5133682 / Jun '94 / ECM
☐ LIVE A VICTORIAVILLE (Goebbels, Heiner & Alfred Harth)
VICTOCD 04 / Nov '94 / Victo

☐ MAN IN THE ELEVATOR, THE (Goebbels, Heiner & Heiner Muller)
8371102 / Nov '88 / ECM

Goforth, Gene
☐ EMMINENCE BREAKDOWN
Dialog / Charleston no.1 / Dialog / Dink's Dusty Miller / Dialog / Quail is a pretty bird / Black river / Wolves a howlin' / Roy Wooliver's money musk / Jawbone / Hamilton ironworks / Uncle Dink / Say old man / Fiddler's hornpipe / Emminence breakdown / Prettiest little girl in the county / Devil's hornpipe / Sally Goodin / Knockin' at your door / White river / Gettin' out the way of the Federalds / Little brown jug / Grandmammy look at Uncle Sam / Dialog / Rocky road to Denver / Comin' down from Denver / Hop skip squirrel
ROUCD 0388 / Feb '97 / Rounder

Gogan, Barbara
☐ MADE ON EARTH (Gogan, Barbara & Hector Zazou)
True love / Lost girl / Dangerous / Cradle your soul / Home again / Cruel guy / My love and I / Dance with me / Your radio's on / Breathe in breathe out / Life is an adventure
CRAM 091 / 15 Jun '98 / Crammed Discs

Gogh Van Go
☐ GOGH VAN GO
Bed where we hide / Say you will / Vinyl / Long shory short / Tunnel of trees / Call it romance / 97 / Have a whirl / Instant karma / Raise the ground / Say you will
ATLASCD 005 / Apr '94 / Equator

Gogogo Airheart
☐ GOGOGO AIRHEART
VC 122CD / Oct '97 / Vinyl Communication

Goikoetxea, Joxan
☐ GOAZEN LAGUN
AZ 000 / 1 Jun '98 / Karonte

Goins, Herbie
☐ SOULTIME (Goins, Herbie & The Nightimers)
Outside of heaven / Look at Granny run run / I don't mind / Pucker up buttercup / Coming home to you / No. 1 in your heart / Satisfaction / Good good lovin' / Cruisin' / Knock on wood / 36-22-36 / Turn on your love light / Coming home to you (Live)
SEECD 362 / Oct '92 / See For Miles

Gol
☐ SENSATIONS OF TONE
WOLCD 1065 / Mar '96 / China

Gola, Andy
☐ LIVE IN HAVANA
TUMICD 060 / Sep '96 / Tumi

Gold, Andrew
☐ GREETINGS FROM PLANET LOVE
JBI 80146 / 23 Mar '98 / J-Bird
☐ HALLOWEEN HOWLS
R 272532 / Nov '96 / Music For Little People

Gold, Angie
☐ BEST OF ANGIE GOLD, THE
HTCD 73 / 20 Apr '98 / Hot Productions

Gold Blade
☐ HOME TURF
Strictly hardcore / Soul power / Genius is pain / Soul on fire / Hail the people / Canal street / Breakdown / Saddest song / Black Elvis / Not even Jesus / Feel my disease / Down town / Jacknife / Meet thy saviour / Fastest man alive / True believers
TOPPCDX 058
TOPPCD 058 / Apr '97 / Ultimate

Gold, Brian & Tony
☐ BULLSEYE
VPCD 1435 / Oct '95 / VP

Gold, Graham
☐ CLUB CUTS '97 VOL.1 (Mixed By Graham Gold - 2CD Set) (Various Artists)
Fly life: Basement Jaxx / In the head: Gat Decor / Scared: Slacker / Encore une fois: Sash / I love you...stop: Red 5 / Sound of Eden: Casino / Get into the music: DJ's Rule & Karen Brown / Killin' time: Cousins, Tina / Underwater love: Smoke City / You got the love: Source & Candi Station / Ready or not: Course / Get up (everybody): Stingily, Byron / Fired up: Funky Green Dogs / Spin spin sugar: Antonio / Pimps / Show me love: Robin S / Where can I find love: Linin' Joy / Give me a reason: Portman / Up to no good: Pom Kings / Tha wildstyle: DJ Supreme / Just playin': JX Plavy / I have peace: Strike / So in love with you: Bass / Gotta love for you: Serial Diva / Driving south: Future Homosapiens / Funk phenomena: Van Helden, Armand / If Madonna calls: Vasquez, Junior / Morning light: Team Deep / Offshore: Chicane / Footprint: Disco Citizens / Comin' up: Chemical Heaven / Come with me: Qattara / Galaxia: Moonman / Going out of my head: Fatboy Slim / Remember me: Blueboy
TCD 2898 / May '97 / Telstar
☐ CLUB CUTS '97 VOL.2 (2CD Set) (Various Artists)
TTVCD 2916 / Jul '97 / Telstar TV
☐ CLUB CUTS '97 VOL.3 (Mixed By Graham Gold - 2CD Set) (Various Artists)
Stay: Sash / Discohopping: Klubb Heads / Plastic dreams: Jaydee / It's like that: Run DMC & Jason Nevins / Professional widow: Amos, Tori / Gipsy boy gipsy girl: Sharada House Gang / Favourite shirts: E-Motion / Playmate puzzle: Deconstruction / America: Full Intention / Dirty cash: Adventures Of Stevie V / Joy: Staxx / Nightmare: Brainbug / No stoppin': Big Band Experience / Belissima: DJ Quicksilver / Cloudburst: Niagra / Your face: Slacker / Epidemic: Exit EEE / On the run: De Bos / Open your motel: Chicane / Flaming June: BT / Joanna: Mrs. Wood / Why don't you dance with me: Future Breeze / Ooh la la la: Eivissa / Hyperfunky: Funktastica / Discobug: Freakyman / Lovemm: Klubb Heads / Happiness: Karmasutra / Player: First Choice / It's just a groove: Mighty Dub Katz / Oh boy: Fab Baker Boys / Just gets better: TJR & Xavier / London thing: Garcia, Scott / Anytime: Nu Birth
TTVCD 2933 / 29 Sep '97 / Telstar TV

Gold Tooth Display
☐ MONSTERPIECE
69012 / May '97 / Immigrant

Goldberg, Barry
☐ REUNION
OW 24833 / Jul '94 / One Way
☐ TWO JEWS BLUES
OW 27672 / Jul '94 / One Way

Goldberg, Ben
☐ BEN GOLDBERG & TREVOR DUNN/JOHN SCOTT/KENNY WOLLESEN PROJECT
KFWCD 160 / Feb '95 / Knitting Factory
☐ EIGHT PHRASES FOR JEFFERSON RUBIN
VICTOCD 057 / Jul '98 / Victo
☐ HERE BY NOW (Goldberg, Ben Trio)
CD 1004 / Feb '98 / Music & Arts
☐ TWELVE MINOR (Goldberg, Ben Sextet)
AVANT 35 / Aug '98 / Avant

Goldberg, Stu
☐ FANCY GLANCE
INAK 8614 CD / Dec '87 / In Akustik

Golden Bough
☐ BEST OF GOLDEN BOUGH, THE
EUCD 1145 / '91 / ARC
☐ BEYOND THE SHADOWS
EUCD 1092 / '89 / ARC
☐ BOATMAN'S DAUGHTER
EUCD 1037 / '89 / ARC
☐ FAR FROM HOME
EUCD 1065 / '89 / ARC
☐ FLIGHT OF FANTASY
EUCD 1045 / '89 / ARC
☐ GOLDEN BOUGH
EUCD 1123 / '91 / ARC
☐ WINDING ROAD
EUCD 1051 / '89 / ARC
☐ WINTER'S DANCE
EUCD 1046 / '89 / ARC

Golden Claw Music
☐ ALL BLUE REVIEW
INFECT 7CD / Jul '94 / Infectious

Golden Dawn
☐ POWER PLANT
Evolution / This way please / Starvation / I'll be around / Seeing is believing / My time / Nice surprise / Everyday / Tell me why / Reaching out to you
842969 / 1 Jun '98 / EVA

Golden Eagle Jazz Band
☐ MOROCCO BLUES
SOSCD 1192 / Aug '90 / Stomp Off

Golden Eagles

☐ LIGHTNING AND THUNDER (Golden Eagles & Monk Boudreaux)
Two-way-pak-e-way / Shallow water oh mama / Shotgun joe / Sew-sew-sew / Indian red / Hold 'em joe / Shoo fly / Little liza jane
ROUCD 2073 / '88 / Rounder

Golden Gate Quartet

☐ FROM SPIRITUALS TO SWING VOL.2
7805732 / Aug '93 / Jazztime

☐ GOLDEN GATE QUARTET 1937-1941
Massa' in the cold cold ground / Siants go marching in / Golden gate gospel train / Gabriel blows his horn / Lead me on and on / Sweet Adeline / Preacher and the bear / Noah / Take your burdens to God / Travellin' shoes / Packing up / Getting ready to go / Born ten thousand years ago / Jonah in the whale / I looked down the road and wondered / Everytime I feel the spirit / My walking sticks / Daniel saw the stones / Whoa babe
FA 057 / Apr '97 / Fremeaux

☐ GOLDEN GATE QUARTET VOL.1 1937-1938
DOCD 5472 / Sep '96 / Document

☐ GOLDEN GATE QUARTET VOL.2 1938-1939
DOCD 5473 / Sep '96 / Document

☐ GOLDEN GATE QUARTET VOL.3 1939
DOCD 5474 / Sep '96 / Document

☐ GOLDEN GATE QUARTET VOL.4 1939-1943
DOCD 5475 / Sep '96 / Document

☐ GOSPEL TRAIN (Golden Gate Jubilee Quartet)
Golden gate gospel train-1 / Golden gate gospel train-1 / Behold the bridegroom cometh-1 / Go where I send thee / Won't there be one happy time / Job / Stand in the test in judgement / Motherless child / Travelin' shoes / Remember me / Pure religion / Sampson / I was brave / When they ring the golden bells / My lord is waiting / Rock my soul / Saints go marching in / I heard zion moan / Noah / Lord, am I born to die / What are they doing in heaven today / Troubles of the world / Everything moves by the grace of god / This world is in a bad condition / Precious lord
JSPCD 602 / Jul '93 / JSP

☐ GOSPELS AND SPIRITUALS (2CD Set)
R2CD 7007 / 20 Apr '98 / Deja Vu

☐ GREATEST HITS 1946-1950
BMCD 3016 / Sep '95 / Blue Moon

☐ NEGRO SPIRITUALS VOL.1 (My Walking Stick)
My walking stick / Ol'man Mose / Stormy weather / Dipsy doodle / Motherless child / To the rock / Hide me in thy bosom / Golden gate gospel train / Bedside of a neighbor / Job / Travelin' shoes / Lead me on and on / Sampson / Take your burdens to God / Bye and bye little children / God almighty said / Let that liar alone / I heard Zion moan
CD 12537 / Jun '96 / Music Of The World

☐ NEGRO SPIRITUALS VOL.2 (When The Saints Go Marching Home)
When the saints go marching home / Massas in the cold cold ground / Packing up getting ready to go / If I had my way / I looked down the road and I wondered / Way down in Eygpt land / I'm a pilgrim / Every time that I feel the spirit / John the revelator / You'd better mind / Sweet Adeline / Bonnet / Timber / Our Father / Rock my soul / Cheer the weary traveller
CD 12541 / Jun '96 / Music Of The World

☐ RADIO TRANSCRIPTIONS 1941-1944
DOCD 5502 / Nov '96 / Document

☐ THEIR EARLY YEARS 1937-1939
BMCD 3015 / Sep '95 / Blue Moon

☐ WHEN THE SAINTS GO MARCHING
GO 3814 / 1 Dec '97 / Golden Options

Golden Palominos

☐ BEST OF THE GOLDEN PALOMINOS 1983-1989, THE
Clustering train / Angel of death / Buenos Aires / ID / Wild river / Strong simple silences / Animal speaks / Under the cap / Omaha / Faithless heart / (Something else is) working harder / Boy (go) / Clean plate / Darklands
MCCD 316 / 6 Oct '97 / Music Club

☐ BEST OF THE GOLDEN PALOMINOS, THE
Boy (go) / Omaha / Animal speaks / (Kind of) True / Only one party / Wild river / Shattered image / Darklands / Over / I've been the one / (Something else is) Working harder / Faithless heart / Brides of Jesus / Clean plate / Under the cap
CDNEW 112 / Oct '97 / Charly

☐ BLAST OF SILENCE
CPCD 8225 / Mar '97 / Charly
MPG 74051 / 3 Mar '98 / Movieplay Gold

☐ DEAD HORSE, A
A letter back / A letter back / Lucky / Angel of death / Darklands / Over the rainbow / Shattered image
CPCD 8185 / Jun '96 / Charly

☐ GOLDEN PALOMINOS, THE
Clean plate / Hot seat / Under the cap / Monday night / Cookout / ID / Two sided fist
CPCD 8198 / Dec '96 / Charly

☐ GOLDEN PALOMINOS, THE
Clean plate / Hot seat / Under the cap / Monday night / Cookout / ID / Two sided fist
MPG 74049 / Jan '98 / Movieplay Gold

☐ VISIONS OF EXCESS
CPCD 8151 / Nov '95 / Celluloid

☐ VISIONS OF EXCESS
Boy (go) / Clustering train / Omaha / Animal speaks / Silver bullet / (Kind of) true / Buenos Aires / Only one party
MPG 74050 / Jan '98 / Movieplay Gold

Golden Smog

☐ DOWN BY THE OLD MAINSTREAM
V / Ill-fated / Pecan pie / Yesterday I cried / Glad and sorry / Won't be coming home / He's a dick / Walk where he walked / Nowhere bound / Friend / She don't have to see you / Red headed stepchild / Williamton angel / Radio King
RCD 10325 / Mar '97 / Rykodisc

Golden Star

☐ DHOOTAKADA BAI DHOOTAKADA
CDSR 019 / Aug '90 / Star

Goldenrod

☐ GOLDENROD
FLASH 50 / 1 Jun '98 / Flash

Goldfinger

☐ GOLDFINGER
Mind's eye / Stay / Here in your bedroom / Only a day / King for a day / Anxiety / Answers / Anything / Mable / City with twp faces / My girlfriends shower sucks / Miles away / Nothing to prove / Pictures
UND 53007 / Nov '96 / Universal

Goldie

☐ SATURNZ RETURN (2CD Set)
Mother / Dream within / Truth / Temper temper / Digital / I'll be there for you / Believe / Dragonfly / Chico death of a rockstar / Letter of fate / Fury the origin / Crystal clear / Demonz
8289902 / 2 Feb '98 / FFRR

☐ TIMELESS
Timeless / Saint Angel / State of mind / This is a bad / Sea of tears / Jah the seventh seal / Sense of rage / Still life / Angel / Adrift / Kemistry / You and me
8286462 / Sep '95 / FFRR
8286142 / 2 Feb '98 / FFRR

Goldie, Don

☐ DON GOLDIE & HIS DANGEROUS JAZZ BAND
JCD 135 / Jul '96 / Jazzology

Golding, Peter

☐ STRETCHING THE BLUES
Good rockin' tonight / Stretching the blues / Thanks to the blues / Fashion designer blues / Burglar jump / Treasure of the blues / Stumble / Crucify me / Living in a memory / Chatanoogie shoe shine boy / Pete's bop / Blues in the night/train / Good rockin' tonight
IGOCD 2063 / May '97 / Indigo

Goldings, Larry

☐ CAMINHOS CRUZADOS
So danco samba / Caminhos cruzados / Ho-ba-la-la / O amor en paz / Where or when / Manine / Avarandado / Serenata / Menina-moca / Words / Una mas
01241631842 / Jun '95 / Novus

Goldsboro, Bobby

☐ HONEY (22 Greatest Hits)
See the funny little clown / Whenever he holds you / Me japanese boy, I love you / Summer (the first time) / Brand new kind of love / Watching scotty grow / Can you feel it / I'm a drifter / Glad she's a woman / Straight life / Autumn of my life / Honey / Blue autumn / It hurts me / It's too late / Broomstick cowboy / It breaks my heart / If you've got a heart / If you wait for love / Voodoo woman / Little things / I don't know you anymore
RMB 75084 / Jan '96 / Remember

Goldsby, John

☐ TALE OF THE FINGERS (Goldsby, John Quartet)
Op / Terrace / Three short stories for contrabass and piano / Tale of the fingers / Twilight time / Tricotism / Time and again / Beautiful / Seven minds / Pitter, panther, patter
CCD 4632 / Feb '95 / Concord Jazz

Goldschmidt, Per

☐ FRAME, THE
Blues for Trane / Snowgirl / Frame / Loneliness / Bermuda triangle
CDSJP 290 / Aug '90 / Timeless Jazz

☐ FRANKLY (A Tribute To Frank Sinatra)
You and the night and the music / It happend in Monterey / Theme for Eve / Forever Frank / Frankly speaking / Man alone / Too marvellous for words / Fly me to the moon / Come fly with me / You make me feel so young / Second to none
MCD 92242 / Mar '97 / Milestone

Goldson, Harry

☐ HARRY GOLDSON PLAYS THE BIG BAND SESSIONS
617817121325 / Feb '98 / Weatherbird

Golia, Vinny

☐ DANTE NO LONGER REPENTS
CD 992 / Sep '97 / Music & Arts

☐ HAUNTING THE SPIRITS INSIDE THEM (Golia, Vinny & Joelle Leandre/Ken Filiano)
CD 893 / Jan '96 / Music & Arts

☐ REGARDS FROM NORMAN DESMOND
FSNT 008CD / Mar '95 / Fresh Sound New Talent

Golson, Benny

☐ BENNY GOLSON IN PARIS
Stablemates / Blues on my hand / You're not the kind / Afternoon in paris / Calgary / Thursday's theme / Blues march / I remember clifford / Moanin' / Not serious / Stablemates
CDSW 8418 / Jan '89 / DRG

☐ BENNY GOLSON QUARTET
Up jump spring / Voyage / Beautiful love / Gypsy jingle-jangle / Stable mates
17076 / Mar '97 / Laserlight

☐ FREE
Sock cha / Mad about the boy / Just by myself / Shades of Stein / My romance / Just in time / You're my thrill / My heart belongs to Daddy / Best thing for you is me / Impromptune / Little Karine / Swing it / I fall in love too easily
GRP 18162 / 8 Jun '98 / Chess Jazz

☐ GONE WITH GOLSON
Staccato swing / Autumn leaves / Soul me / Blues after dark / Jam for bobbie / Bit of heaven
OJCCD 1850 / Jul '94 / Original Jazz Classics

☐ GROOVIN' WITH GOLSON
My blues house / Drum boogie / I didn't know what time it was / Stroller / Yesterdays
OJCCD 226 / Sep '93 / Original Jazz Classics

☐ PHILADELPHIANS
You're not the kind / Blues on my mind / Stablemates / Thursday's theme / Afternoon in Paris / Calgary / Blues march / I remember Clifford / Moanin' / Stablemates
4941042 / 22 Jun '98 / Pacific Jazz

☐ TENOR LEGACY
AJ 70742 / 27 Apr '98 / Arkadia

☐ THIS IS FOR YOU JOHN
Jam the avenue / Greensleeves / Origin / Change of heart / Times past (this is for you, John) / Page 12 / Vilia
CDSJP 235 / Jan '88 / Timeless Jazz

☐ THREE LITTLE WORDS
JHAS 609 / Apr '97 / Ronnie Scott's Jazz House

☐ TIME SPEAKS
I'll remember April / Time speaks / No dancin' / Jordu / Blues for Duane / Theme for Maxine
CDSJP 187 / Jan '87 / Timeless Jazz

☐ UP JUMPED BENNY
AJ 70741 / 27 Apr '98 / Arkadia

☐ WALKIN'
FSRCD 302 / 5 Jan '98 / Fresh Sound

Golub, Jeff

☐ UNSPOKEN WORDS
1390082 / May '89 / Gaia

Goma

☐ 14 ABRIL
LV 019 / 16 Mar '98 / Lost Vinyl

Gomes, Carmen

☐ CALLIN' FROM KC (Gomes, Carmen Inc.)
Dig dis / Freewheel blues / Big city / MMM, come on in my kitchen / And what if I don't / Matter of truth / It's about time / Sidekick / Topaz / I've grown accustomed to his face / Callin' from KC / What a little moonlight can do / Case of blues
BY 951018 / Oct '96 / Byton World Series

Gomez

☐ BRING IT ON
Get Miles / Tijuana lady / Bubble gum years / Rie's wagon / Here comes the breeze / Free to run / 78 stone wobble / Make no sound / Whippin' Piccadily / Love is better than a warm trombone / Comeback / Get myself arrested
CDHUT 49
CDHUTX 49 / 13 Apr '98 / Hut

Gomez, Alberto

☐ LA SERENATA DE AYER
EBCD 91 / Jan '98 / El Bandoneon

Gomez, Alice

☐ WHILE THE EAGLE SLEEPS
TTCD 130 / Mar '96 / Talking Taco

Gomez, Claudia

☐ SALAMANDRA
CCD 1002 / Jul '98 / Clarity

☐ TIERRADENTRO
XEPCD 4039 / Mar '96 / Xenophile

Gomez, Eddie

☐ NEXT FUTURE
Next future / Intro and body / Dreaming of you / North Moore St. / Lost tango (for Astor Piazzolla) / Tenderly / Cheeks (dedicated to Dizzy Gillespie) / Love letter (to my father) / Basic trane-ing / Walter (pigeon)
SCD 90052 / Mar '97 / Stretch

Gomez, Jill

☐ CABARET CLASSICS (Gomez, Jill & John Constable)
DKPCD 9055 / Aug '88 / Unicorn-Kanchana

Gomorrah

☐ REFLECTIONS OF AN INANIMATE MATTER
BMCD 067 / Aug '95 / Black Mark

☐ TRAUMA
14509 / Feb '97 / Spalax

Gonads

☐ PUNK ROCK WILL NEVER DIE
MOGCD 007 / 2 Mar '98 / Mog

Gonashvili, Hamlet

☐ HAMLET GONASHVILI
8557772 / Jul '97 / Origins

Gone

☐ ALL THE DIRT THAT'S FIT TO PRINT
SST 306CD / Sep '94 / SST

☐ COUNTRY DUMB
SST 344CD / 3 Aug '98 / SST

☐ CRIMINAL MIND
SST 300CD / Jan '94 / SST

☐ GONE II, BUT NEVER TOO GONE
Jungle law / New vengeance / Unglued / Turned over stone / Drop the hat / Adams / Time of entry / Left holding bag / Gtv / Daisy strut / Cut off / Put it there / Utility hole / Yesterday is teacher / How soon they forget / Cobra xviii
SST 086CD / May '93 / SST

☐ LET'S GET REAL, REAL GONE FOR A CHANGE
Insidious detraction / Get gone / Peter gone / Rosanne / Climbing rat's wall / Watch the tractor / Last days of being stepped on / Ch 69 / Lawndale rock city / Hypercharge-the wait (the fifth force suite)
SST 061CD / May '93 / SST

Gonella, Nat

☐ CRAZY VALVES (Gonella, Nat & His Georgians)
How'm I doin / Capri caprice / Skeleton in the cupboard / I can't dance / Crazy valves / Bessie couldn't help it / Take another guess / Nagasaki / Just a crazy song / Sheikh of Araby / Tiger rag / Copper coloured gal / Ol' man mose / Trumpetuous / I'm gonna clap my hands / Makin' a fool of myself / Bill Tell / Georgia on my mind
CDAJA 5055 / Sep '88 / Living Era

☐ CREAM OF NAT GONELLA, THE
Swing and sway / E flat blues / Ti-pi-tin / Flat foot floogie / Basin street blues / Bessie couldn't help it / Dipsy doodle / Bogey bogey / Delta serenade / Me myself and I / Nagasakl / Blue drag / T'aint what you do (it's the way that cha do it) / Now they call it swing / Tiger rag / Someone stole gabriel's horn / Rhythm is my romeo / Ol' man river / No, mamma, no / On the sunny side of the street / Never took a lesson in my life / Man who comes around
PASTCD 9750 / Aug '91 / Flapper

☐ DANCE BAND YEARS, THE (2CD Set) (Gonella, Nat & His New Georgians)
I got rhythm / I'm forever blowing bubbles / Seven days leave / Juanita / We three / Put the blame on Mame / One meat ball / Murder / Can't get Indiana off my mind / Tuxedo junction / I'm nobody's baby / It's a pair of wings for me / Time on my hands / Oh Mo'nah / Never took a lesson in my life / Sentimental interlude / Booglie wooglie piggy / You came along / Oh Susanna / Aurora / I saw, I conga'd / Big noise from Winnetka / Bad humour man / For no reason at all / All in favour say aye / I want my Mama / Beat me Daddy eight to a bar / In the mood / Mean to me / Down in Mexico / Sheik of Araby / Song of songs / Stardust / At the Woodchopper's ball / Thanks for the boogie ride / I understand / Hut-Sut song / I've

got sixpence / He stole my heart away / Playhouse party / That's my home / Hot mallets / Let him go, let him tarry / Gnat jump / Vox poppin' / If I could be with you one hour tonight / Jingle jangle jingle / Shoe fly pie and apple pan dowdy / Georgia on my mind
PDSCD 552 / 13 Oct '97 / Pulse

☐ **JAZZ SIDE, THE**
I ain't got nobody / Stormy weather / Nobody's sweetheart / (I'll be glad when you're dead) you rascal you / How'm I doin' / Continental / Troublesome trumpet / Black coffee / I heard / That's my home / E flat blues / Wabash blues / Harlem hokum blues / Mama don't allow it / Get hot / Way down yonder in New orleans / Crazy valves / Cocktail swing / Bill tell / Jeepers creepers / Georgia on my mind / For no reason at all / Seven days leave / Hot malletts
RAJCD 882 / Aug '96 / Empress

☐ **NAT GONELLA**
Nagasaki / Mayor of Alabam / When you're smiling / Medley / Bessie couldn't help it / You rascal you / Just a crazy song / I'd like to see Somoa of Samoa / Junk man's blues / Down t'Uncle Bill's / Crazy values / On the sunny side of the street / Twilight in Turkey / His old cornet / Tiger rag / Get hot / Some of these days / T'ain't what you do (it's the way that you do it) / Ain't misbehavin' / Ciribiribin / Flat foot floogie / Makin' a fool of myself / Swing and sway / Bill Tell / Medley
CDMFP 6350 / Jun '97 / Music For Pleasure

☐ **NATURALLY GONELLA (Gonella, Nat & His Georgians)**
Georgia on my mind / Tuxedo junction / Big noise from Winnetka / I understand / At the woodchoppers ball / South with the boarder / Hep hep the jumpin' jive / If you were the only girl in the world / Beat me daddy eight to the bar / In the mood / Ay ay ay / No mama no / I haven't time to be a millionaire / Vox poppin' / Oh buddy I'm in love / It's a pair of wings for me / Eep ipe wanna piece of pie / Sunrise serenade / Yes my darling daughter / Plucking on the golden harp / That's my home
RAJCD 804 / Sep '97 / Empress

☐ **PENNIES FROM HEAVEN (Gonella, Nat & His Georgians)**
Fascinating rhythm / Ol' man Mose / Mama don't allow it / Makin' a fool of myself / I'm gonna clap my hands / Tiger rag / Solitude / It happened down in Dixieland / There goes my attraction / Pennies from heaven / Bill Tell / Bessie couldn't help it / Let us be sweethearts over again / Gonna go / When you're smiling / Get hot Gonella / I can't get started / I can't dance (I've got ants in my pants) / Nagasaki / Afterglow / Capri caprice (Isle of Capri) / Sheik of Araby
SWNCD 014 / Oct '97 / Sound Waves

Gonen, Raya

☐ **VOCAL JEWELS FROM ISRAEL**
CRC 2324 / Aug '98 / Centaur

Gong

☐ **25TH BIRTHDAY PARTY (Gong Live October 8/9th 1994 At The Forum/2CD Set)**
Thom intro / Floating into a birthday gig / You can't kill me / Radio gnome 25 / I am you pussy / Pot head pixies / Never glid before / Eat that phonebook / Gnomic address / Flute salad / Oily way
VPGAS 101CD / Mar '97 / GAS

☐ **ABOUT TIME (El Alien's New Wave Dispensation) (New York Gong)**
Preface / Much too old / Black September / Materialism / Strong woman / I'm a Freud / O my photograph / Jungle windo / Hours gone
CDCRH 118 / Feb '97 / Charly

☐ **ANGEL'S EGG (Radio Gnome Invisible Vol.2)**
Other side of the sky / Sold to the highest Buddha / Castle in the clouds / Prostitute poem / Givin' my luv to you / Selene / Flute salad / Oily way / Outer temple / Inner temple / Love is how you make it / I never glid before / Eat that phonebook code
14833 / Oct '96 / Spalax
CDCRH 119 / Feb '97 / Charly

☐ **BEST OF GONG, THE**
Wet cheese delirum / Tropical fish / Seline / Flying teapot / Pot head Pixies / Outer temple / Eat the phone book coda / Magick mother invocation / Master builder / Mister long shanks / O Mother I am your fantasy / Squeezing sponges over policemen's heads / Octave doctors and the crystal machine / Zero the hero and the witches spell / Castle in the clouds / Inner temple / Sprinkling of clouds / Much too old
REMCD 508 / Feb '98 / Reactive

☐ **BEST OF GONG, THE**
3015912 / Nov '96 / Mantra

☐ **BEST OF GONG, THE**
1119611 / Dec '96 / Tumult Productions

☐ **BEST OF MOTHER GONG, THE (Mother Gong)**
Augment and lady / Lament / Time is a hurrying dog / Weather / Technamaid / Disco at the end of the world / Machine song / Superboots / Quantum impro / Wild child / Zen / Today is beautiful / Water / Magenta / It's you and me / Love poem / Children's song / Trees / She's the mother of... / Faces of women / Wapu / Spirit of the bush
BP 271CD / 17 Nov '97 / Blueprint

☐ **BREAKTHROUGH (Moerlen, Pierre & Gong)**
EUCD 1053 / '89 / ARC

☐ **CAMEMBERT ELECTIQUE (Not What You Think...Unreleased Studio Tracks)**
Cafe Montelieu demos / Garcon ou fille / Dynamite/ Goldilocks / Rock 'n' roll angel/Nightmare of Mr. Respectable / Hyp hypnotise you / Haunted chateau rehersals / Big city energy / Gongwash indelible
AGASCD 001 / Mar '97 / GAS

☐ **CAMEMBERT ELECTRIQUE**
Radio gnome predection / You can't kill me / I've bin stone before / Mr. Long Shanks: O Mother I am your fantasy / Dynamite: I am your animal / Wet cheese delirium / Squeezing sponges over policemen's heads / Fohat digs holes in space / And you tried so hard / Tropical fish/Selene / Gnome the second
14826 / Oct '96 / Spalax
CDCRH 111 / Feb '97 / Charly

☐ **CONTINENTAL CIRCUS**
642089 / May '96 / Mantra

☐ **EXPRESSO VOL.2**
Heavy tune / Golden dilemma / Sleepy / Soli / Boring / Three blind mice
CDV 2099 / Jun '90 / Virgin

☐ **EYE (Mother Gong)**
Fanfare / She's the mother of / Sunday / Beds / Time is a hurrying dog / Ancient / Zen / Quantum / Spirit canoe / What if we were gods and goddesses / Auction / Little boy / Magic stories / Excuses / Sax canoe / Fairy laughter / Virtual reality
VP 176CD / Sep '94 / Voiceprint

☐ **FAMILY JEWELS (2CD Set)**
Seven year itch: *Pyle, Pip* / Second wind: *Moerlen, Pierre & Gong* / Cyberwhale: *Smyth, Gilli* / So what: *Allen, Daevid* / Little house I used to live in: *Moerlen, Pierre & Orchestre Regional De Jazz D'Alsace* / Radio gnome transmission: *Allen, Daevid* / Guitar solo: *Steffe Sharpstrings & Gong* / Farewell flagship: *Allen, Daevid* / Say no more: *Moerlen, Pierre & Gong* / Master builder / You can't kill me / You are I and I / Hadouk: *Malherbe, Didier* / Lets GLO: *Lewry, Steffe & Gilli Smythe* / Blame the rich: *Allen, Daevid* / Back to the sea: *Lewry, Steffe & Gilli Smythe* / Zeff dance: *Malherbe, Didier* / Stroking the tail of the bird: *Smyth, Gille & Daevid Allen* / Mountains of venus: *Howlett, Mike* / Deia: *Lewry, Steffe & Gilli Smythe* / Blues d'horizon: *Malherbe, Didier* / Voice of Om: *Allen, Daevid*
AGASCD 008 / 11 May '98 / GAS

☐ **FLOATING ANARCHY 1977 (Planet Gong)**
Psychological overture / Floating anarchy / Stone innoc Frankenstein / New age transformation try / No more sages / Opium for the people / Allez Ali Baba black sheep have you any bullshit / Mama maya mantram
CDCRH 115 / Feb '97 / Charly
14829 / 23 Mar '98 / Spalax

☐ **FLYING TEAPOT (Radio Gnome Invisible Vol.1)**
Radio gnome invisible / Pot head pixies / Octave doctors and the crystal machine / Zero the hero and the witches spell / Witches song I am your pussy
CDCRH 114 / Feb '97 / Charly
14828 / 23 Mar '98 / Spalax

☐ **FULL CIRCLE LIVE 1988 (Moerlen, Pierre & Gong)**
Second wind / Deep end / Exotic / Leave it open / Drum alone / Soli / Breakthrough / Xtasea
OM 1006CD / 20 Jul '98 / Outer Music

☐ **GAZEUSE**
Expresso / Night illusion / Percolations (part 1) / Percolations (part 2) / Shadows of / Mireille / Esnuria
CDV 2074 / Jun '90 / Virgin

☐ **GLASTONBURY 1989 (Gong Maison)**
AGASCD 004 / Sep '96 / GAS

☐ **GONG EST MORT**
669152 / 23 Feb '98 / Melodie

☐ **GONG MAISON (Gong Maison)**
DMCD 1022 / 22 Sep '97 / Demi-Monde

☐ **HISTORY AND THE MYSTERY OF THE PLANET GONG, THE**
Concert intro / Captain Shaw and Mr. Gilbert / Love makes sweet music / DLT interview / Riot 1968 / Dreaming it / I feel so lazy / And I tried so hard / Radio gnome pre-mix / Pot head pixies / Majick brother / Line up / Clarence in Wonderland / Breakthrough interview / Where have all the hours gone / Gong poem / Dey a Goddess / Opium for the people / Red alert / 13/8 / Gliss-u-well / Future / Dream / Chernobyl rain / Let me be one
CDTB 116 / 26 Jun '98 / Thunderbolt

☐ **HOW TO NUKE THE EIFFEL TOWER**
Away away / Nuclear mega waste / Chernobyl rain
VPGAS 102CD / Oct '96 / GAS

☐ **LIVE 1990**
Planetary introduction / You can't kill me / I've been stoned before / Radio gnome / Post-head pixies / Voix lactee / Outer vision / Gorbachev cocktail / Flying teacup / I am you / Inner vision
NINETY 1 / Mar '93 / Code 90

☐ **LIVE AT SHEFFIELD 1974**
MANTRA 042 / 1 Jun '98 / Mantra

☐ **LIVE AU BATACLAN 1973**
890025 / May '96 / Mantra

☐ **LIVE ETC**
You can't kill me / Zero the hero and the witches spell / Flying teapot / Dynamite: I am your animal / 6/8 / Est-ce que je suis / Ooby-scooby doomsday or the D-day DJ's got / Radio gnome invisible / Oily way / Outer temple / Inner temple / Where have all the flowers gone / Isle of everywhere / Get it inner / Master Builder / Flying teapot (reprise)
CDVM 3501 / '90 / Virgin

☐ **LIVE IN PARIS**
MANTRA 025 / 1 Jun '98 / Mantra

☐ **MAGICK BROTHER**
Mystic sister: Magick brother / Magick brother / Glad to say to say / Rational anthem / Chainstore chant: pretty Miss Titty / Pretty miss titty / Fable of a Fredfish / Hope you feel OK / Ego / Gong song / Princess dreaming / Five and twenty schoolgirls / 'Cos you got green hair
14812 / 23 Mar '98 / Spalax

☐ **MYSTERY AND HISTORY OF GONG, THE (Gong Rarities 1971-1972)**
14518 / Jun '97 / Spalax

☐ **PARAGONG LIVE 1973 (Paragong)**
Camembert psilocybin flashback / Pourquoi dormons nous
AGASCD 002 / Oct '96 / GAS

☐ **RADIO GNOME TRILOGY (3CD Set)**
Radio Gnome invisible / Pot head pixies / Octave doctors and the crystal machine / Zero the hero and the witches spell / Witches song I am your pussy / Other side of the sky / Sold to the highest Buddha / Castle in the clouds / Prostitute poem / Givin' my luv to you / Selene / Flute salad / Oily way / Outer temple / Inner temple / Love is how you make it / I never glid before / Eat that phonebook code / APHP's advice / Thoughts for nought / Magick Mother invocation / Master builder / Sprinkling of clouds / Perfect mystery / Isle of everywhere / You never blow your trip forever
14707 / 23 Mar '98 / Spalax

☐ **SHAMAL**
Wingful of eyes / Chandra / Bambooji / Cat in Clark's shoes / Mandrake / Shamal
CDV 2046 / Jun '90 / Virgin

☐ **SHE MADE THE WORLD MAGENTA**
Magenta / Water / She made the world / Weather / Malicious sausage / Sea horse / Spirit calling / Tattered jacket / Warn / When the show is over / I am a witch / Spirit of the bush / Blessed be
VP 134CD / May '93 / Voiceprint

☐ **SUFFER (Gongzilla)**
Gongzilla / Bad habits / Sing / Gongzilla's dilemma / Mr. Sinister Minister / Almost you / Mezzanine / Hip hopnosis / Allan Qui / Senna / Camel
LOLO 0032 / Dec '96 / Blueprint

☐ **VERY BEST OF GONG, THE**
Dynamite I am your animal / Radio Gnome / Invisible / Zero the hero and the witches spell / Flute salad / Oily way / Outer temple, inner temple / I never glid before / Isle of Everywhere / You'll never blow yer trip forever / Eat that phonebook coda / Stone innocent Frankenstein
SUMCD 4117 / May '97 / Summit

☐ **VOICEPRINT RADIO SESSION (Mother Gong)**
VPR 007CD / Oct '94 / Voiceprint

☐ **WILD CHILD (Mother Gong)**
DMCD 1026 / Jul '94 / Demi-Monde
CD 14521 / Sep '97 / Spalax

☐ **WINGFUL OF EYES, A**
Heavy tune / Cat in Clark's shoes / Night illusion / Golden dilemma / Wingful of eyes / Three blind mice / Expresso / Soli / Shadows of / Mandrake / Bambouji
CDOVD 462 / Jan '96 / Virgin

☐ **YOU (Radio Gnome Invisible Vol.3)**
APHP's advice / Thoughts for nought / Magick mother invocation / Master builder / Sprinkling of clouds / Perfect mystery / Isle of everywhere / You never blow your trip forever
CDV 2019 / Jun '90 / Virgin
14834 / Oct '96 / Spalax
CDCRH 120 / Feb '97 / Charly

☐ **YOU (Remixes/2CD Set)**
GLISSCD 001 / Jul '97 / GAS

Gonk

☐ **WILL/WILL NOT ATTEND**
SF 029CD / 22 Jun '98 / Swarf Finger

Gonnella, Ron

☐ **RON GONNELLA'S INTERNATIONAL FRIENDSHIP FIDDLE**
BBC echoes / Cape Breton ceudh / Hector MacAndrews favourites / Congratulations all round / Sounds of Strathearn / Touch of Gaelic / Bonnie Dundee / Boston tea party / Jimmy Shand special / Strathspey king and friends / Scottish dance music corner / Canadian connection / Fiddlers two / My friend Adam Rennie / New York, New York / Music of William Marshall
CDITV 453 / Aug '88 / Scotdisc

Gonsalves, Paul

☐ **GETTIN' TOGETHER**
Yesterdays / J and b blues / I surrender dear / Hard groove / Low gravy / I cover the waterfront / Gettin' together / Walkin'
OJCCD 203 / Feb '92 / Original Jazz Classics

☐ **JAZZ TILL MIDNIGHT (Gonsalves, Paul & Eddie 'Lockjaw' Davis)**
STCD 4123 / Feb '90 / Storyville

☐ **JUST A-SITTIN' AND A-ROCKIN' (Gonsalves, Paul & Ray Nance)**
BP blues / Lotus blossom / Don't blame me / Just a sittin' and a rockin' / Hi ya, Sue / Angel eyes / I'm in the market for you / Tea for two
BLCD 760148 / May '91 / Black Lion

☐ **PAUL GONSALVES MEETS EARL HINES (Gonsalves, Paul & Earl Hines)**
BLCD 760177 / Mar '93 / Black Lion

Gonzaga, Luiz

☐ **SABIDO**
KAR 076 / Jan '98 / IMP

Gonzales, Tino

☐ **SMILES FOR MILES**
HP 30022 / 15 Jun '98 / Horseplay

Gonzalez

☐ **GONZALEZ/OUR ONLY WEAPON IS OUR MUSIC**
Pack it up / Clapham South / No way / Adelanto nightride / Underground railroad / Gonzalez / Together forever / Saoco / Funky Frith street / Got my eye on you / De me la cosa carmaba / Love you've given me / Ain't it funny / Rissoled / Nothing ever comes that easy / Ahwai five-O / DNS / Love me love me not / Our only weapon is our music / I haven't stopped dancing yet
C5HCD 668 / 22 Jun '98 / See For Miles

☐ **HAVEN'T STOPPED**
Closer to you / Neptune / Just my imagination / Cuidado / Got to get it / Virgin flight / Hey amiente / I believe in you / Leave old dreams / Tribute to Puente / Rissoled / Nothing ever comes that easy / Haven't stopped dancing yet
PRIMACD 5 / 6 Jul '98 / Prima Vera

Gonzalez, Celina

☐ **DESDE LA HABANA TE TRAIGO (Gonzalez, Celina & Revtilio)**
TUMI 074 / 15 Jun '98 / Tumi

☐ **FIESTA GUAJIRA**
Yo soy el punto Cubana / Muero de olivdo / Santa Barbara / Oye mi le lo ley / Guajiro Guarachero / Paisajes naturales / El refran se te Olivido / Aguacero aguacerito / Mi tierra es asi
WC 34CD / Oct '93 / World Circuit

☐ **QUE VIVA CHANGO**
Santa Barbara / Oye mi le lo lei / El refran se te olivido / Aurora / Mi terra es asi / El reto / Yo soy el punto Cubana / Camina y ven / Aguacero aguacerito / Guateque campesino / Paisajes / El hijo del sibony
PSCCD 1002 / Feb '95 / Pure Sounds From Cuba

☐ **RICH HARVEST**
Yo soy el punto Cubano / Rezo a oya / Mi son es un misterio / Tambores Africanos / Asi quiero vivir / Alla voy / San Lazaro / Que se yo / La verdad de mi verdad / Sin penas ni glorias / A la patrona de Cuba / Herencia paterna / Los soneros de mi Cuba / Rezo a oya / La casa de yagua / Popurri Cubano
TUMICD 066 / Sep '96 / Tumi

☐ **SANTA BARBARA**
CD 0042 / Mar '96 / Egrem

Gonzalez, Dennis

☐ **DEBENGE DEBENGE**
SHCD 112 / May '89 / Silkheart

☐ **NAMESAKE (Gonzalez, Dennis New Dallas Quartet)**
SHCD 106 / May '88 / Silkheart

☐ **WELCOME TO US**
378232 / Nov '96 / Koch Jazz

Gonzalez, Jerry

☐ **CROSSROADS (Gonzalez, Jerry & The Fort Apache Band)**
Malandro / Rumba Columbia I / Vonce / Thelingus / Guaguanco I / Ezekiel / Saw the wheel / Rumba Columbia II / Viva cepeda / Lament / Guaguanco II / Fort apache / Elegua
MCD 92252 / Mar '97 / Milestone

☐ **EARTH DANCE (Gonzalez, Jerry & The Fort Apache Band)**
SSC 1050D / May '91 / Sunnyside

☐ **FIRE DANCE (Gonzalez, Jerry & The Fort Apache Band)**
Isabel / Liberator / Elegua / Today's nights / Verdad amarga / Let's call this / Ugly beauty
MCD 92582 / Nov '96 / Milestone

☐ **PENSATIVO (Gonzalez, Jerry & The Fort Apache Band)**
MCD 92422 / Feb '96 / Milestone

☐ **RIVER IS DEEP, THE (Gonzalez, Jerry & The Fort Apache Band)**
ENJA 40402 / 17 Nov '97 / Enja

Gonzalez, Junior

☐ **TE SIGO AMANDO**
486710152 / 17 Mar '98 / Asefra

Gonzalez, Luis Felipe

☐ **20 GRANDES EXITOS**
6754213022 / 24 Mar '98 / Vedisco

Gonzalez, Pee

☐ WHUZ THE P
SR 129CD / 24 Nov '97 / Sub Rosa
PIAS 591000128 / 27 Oct '97 / Play It Again Sam

Gonzalez, Ruben

☐ INTRODUCING
La enganadora / Cumbanchero / Tres lindas Cubanas / Melodia del rio / Mandinga / Siboney / Almendra / Tumbao / Como siento yo
WCD 049 / May '97 / World Circuit

Goo Goo Dolls

☐ BOY NAMED GOO, A
Long way down / Naked / Name / Somethin' bad / So long / Disconnected / Slave girl / Eyes wide open / Ain't that unusual / Impersonality / Flat top / Burnin' up / Only one
9362457502 / Apr '95 / Warner Bros.

☐ HOLD ME UP
Laughing / Just the way you are / So outta line / There you are / You know what I mean / Out of the red / Never take the place of your man / Hey / On your side / 22 seconds / Kevin's song / Know my name / Million miles away / Two days in february
398417018CD / May '96 / Metal Blade

☐ JED
Out of sight / No way out / Down on the corner / Road to Salinas / Misfortune / Gimme shelter / Up yours / Sex maggot / Had enough / Em elbmuh / Artie / James Dean
398414035CD / Jun '97 / Metal Blade

Goober Patrol

☐ DUTCH OVEN
GOOD 001CD / 3 Aug '98 / Them's Good

☐ EXTENDED VACATION
GOOD 005CD / 3 Aug '98 / Them's Good

☐ TRUCK OFF
Timothy / Do it right / She knows / What's the point / I think it's time / Stop me / Hand in hand / Shadows and reflections / Playing with fire / 20 minute song / You can't repeat / Small gain / Wasn't it you
GOOD 004CD / 3 Aug '98 / Them's Good

☐ VACATION
GOOD 002CD / 3 Aug '98 / Them's Good

Gooch, Jon

☐ VELVET PIANO, THE
Music of the night/Memory / Chopin E' nocturne / Tea for two / Wind beneath my wings / Misty / West on sunset / Eddy Duchin medley / My one and only love / Up a lazy river / Daytona drift / All the things you are / Moonsway / As time goes by / Without you/All by myself / Stardust / (Everything I do) I do it for you / Vocal medley / Meditation - thais
AZJG 14CD / Jul '97 / Tinkling Ivories

Good Fellas

☐ GOOD FELLAS
Rap city / Witches / Head and out / Candy / Almost always / Secret love / Bossami / Cherokee / Taxi driver
ECD 22050 / Jul '93 / Evidence

☐ GOOD FELLAS VOL.2
Look out / Dr. Jamie / It's you or no one / In the dream / Anti-calypso / I'll miss you / Welcome / Pop gun / Quick way / Breezi-lee
ECD 220772 / Mar '94 / Evidence

Good Morning Blues

☐ NEVER MAKE A MOVE TO SOON
SITCD 9201 / Aug '94 / Sittel

Good Ol' Persons

☐ GOOD 'N' LIVE
SHCD 2208 / Jan '96 / Sugar Hill

☐ PART OF A STORY
Broken hearted lover / Easy substitute / My my my / I don't hurt anymore / It's gonna rain / You're a flower / Crossing the Cumberlands / It seems there's nothing I can do / This young boy / Part of a story
FR 104 / May '97 / Flat Rock

Good Pants

☐ ALL TALK, NO PANTS
Duelling banjos / Shady grove / I like likker / Grandma's feather bed / It takes no time / Rueben's train / Don't take your guns to town / Bitter creek / Oozlin' Daddy / Windy mountain / Hey Joe / One last match / Naughty little poem / Blues stay away from me / Girl I left behind me / Happy wanderer / Arkansas traveller
CRAW 001 / May '97 / Crawdaddy

Good Rats

☐ GOOD RATS
REP 4034 / Aug '91 / Repertoire

Good Riddance

☐ BALLADS FROM THE REVOLUTION
FAT 565CD / 16 Feb '98 / Fatwreck Chords

☐ COMPREHENSIVE GUIDE TO MODERN REBELLION, A
FAT 539CD / Jun '96 / Fatwreck Chords

☐ FOR GOD AND COUNTRY
FAT 23CD / Mar '95 / Fatwreck Chords

Good Sons

☐ SINGING THE GLORY DOWN
Help me to find / Leaving time / When the night comes / Gospel Hall / Riding the range / You are everything / God's other son / Tower of strength / Watch my dreamboat sail / Day to day / My own prayers / When I turn out the light
GRCD 379 / Nov '96 / Glitterhouse

☐ WINES LINES AND VALENTINES
GRCD 427 / 22 Sep '97 / Glitterhouse

Goodacre Bros.

☐ BAG UP YER TROUBLES
WHCD 02 / Dec '97 / White House

Goodall, Medwyn

☐ CLAN (A Celtic Journey)
CD 440 / 6 Jul '98 / New World

☐ EAGLE SPIRIT
CD 269 / 6 Jul '98 / New World

☐ MEDICINE WOMAN
CD 229 / 6 Jul '98 / New World

☐ MOON GODDESS
CD 409 / 6 Jul '98 / New World

☐ PAGAN DAWN
CD 424 / 6 Jul '98 / New World

☐ WAY OF THE DOLPHIN
CD 220 / 6 Jul '98 / New World

☐ WAY OF THE OCEAN
CD 446 / 7 Jul '98 / New World

Goodbye Harry

☐ FOOD STAMP BBQ
CRZ 037CD / Jan '95 / Cruz

☐ I CAN SMOKE
CRZ 038CD / Sep '96 / Cruz

Goodbye Mr. Mackenzie

☐ FIVE
Hard / Hard / Grip / Jim's killer / Niagara / Touch the bullseye / Day of storms / Yelloueze / Bugdive / Normal boy / Hands of the receiver / Titanic
BLOKCD 002 / Mar '96 / Blokshok

☐ GLORY HOLE, THE
Ugly child / Smile trash it / She's got eggs / Troubling you / Space / Neurotic / Overboard / Concrete / Prince of Wales / Crew cut / House on fire / Neuromental
BLOKCD 003 / 13 Jul '98 / Blokshok

☐ JEZEBEL
BLOKCD 004 / Jul '95 / Blokshok

☐ LIVE ON THE DAY OF STORMS
Goodwill city / Blacker than black / Face to face / Diamonds / Pleasure search / Sick baby / Goodbye Mr. Mackenzie / Dust
BLOKCD 001 / Apr '96 / Blokshok

Goodchilde

☐ STRAIGHT OUT THE FRIDGE
LZ 127 / Mar '96 / Backs

Goode, B.

☐ SHOCK OF THE NEW
Tribute to Clifford and Sonny / Old folks / You don't know what love is / Hermit / Winter's song / Stew's blues / Clock radio / New blues
DD 440 / Mar '97 / Delmark

Goodfellaz

☐ GOODFELLAZ
Sugar honey ice tea / Why you wanna flip on me / If you walk away / Hey / Show and prove / Backslidin' / Nothing at all / Anytime will do / For better or worse / No matter / Pour your love down / If you walk away
5333962 / May '97 / Polydor

Goodhouse, Sissy

☐ THIRD CIRCLE, THE
14936 / Jan '97 / Spalax

☐ TIWAHE
14569 / Nov '97 / Spalax

Goodies

☐ YUM YUM
Goodies theme / Funky gibbon / Inbetweenies / Please let us play / Custard pie / Black pudding Bertha / Cricklewood / Good old country music / Nappy love / Baby Samba / Wild thing / Rock with a policeman / Crickelwood shakedown / Panic / I'm a teapot / Working the line / Sick man blues / Last chance dance / Father Christmas do not touch me / Make a daft noise for Christmas
MCCD 294 / May '97 / Music Club

Gooding, Cuba

☐ MEANT TO BE IN LOVE
TRI 4162CD / Feb '94 / Ichiban

Goodman, Benny

☐ 16 MOST REQUESTED SONGS
Let's dance / Don't be that way / Avalon / Flying home / Memories of you / Somebody stole my gal / Clarinet a la King / Jersey bounce / Why don't you do right / After you've gone / Stompin' at the Savoy / Sing sing sing / Symphony / Liza / How am I to know / Goodbye
4743962 / Feb '94 / Columbia

☐ AIR CHECKS 1937-1938
Let's dance / Moten swing / Vibraphone blues / Peckin' / Nagasaki / St. Louis blues / Sugarfoot stomp / I'm a ding dong daddy from Dumas / Bumble Bee stomp / Naughty waltz / Vieni vieni / Roll 'em / Have you met Miss Jones / Shine / When Buddha smiles / Laughing at life / You turned the tables / My gal Sal / Mama that moon is here again / Time on my hands / In the shadow of the old apple tree / Benny sent me / Moonlight on the highway / Killer diller / Someday sweetheart / Goodbye / Riding high / Nice work if you can get it / Sheikh of Araby / Sunny disposish / Whispers in the dark / Life goes to a party / Moonglow / I hadn't anyone till you / Down south camp meeting / Sweet leilani / Sometimes I'm happy / King Porter stomp / Limehouse blues / Minnie The Moocher's wedding day / Running wild / At the Darktown strutter's ball / Bugle call rag / Clarinet marmalade / Stardust / Everybody loves my baby / Josephine / Caravan
4729902 / Oct '93 / Columbia

☐ AUDIO ARCHIVE
Stompin' at the Savoy / Jumpin' at the woodside / Jersey bounce / Let's dance / Christopher Columbus / Down South camp meeting / South of the border (down Mexico way) / I'm gonna sit right down and write myself a letter / Sing sing sing / Somebody stole my gal / You turned the tables on me / You bought a new kind of love to me / When Buddha smiles / When I grow too old to dream / What can I say after I say I'm sorry / King Porter stomp / You're a sweetheart / Bugle call rag / Fascinating rhythm / Big John special
CDAA 012 / Oct '91 / Tring

☐ AVALON - THE SMALL BANDS (Goodman, Benny Quartet)
Avalon / Handful of keys / Man I love / Smiles / Liza / Where or when: *Goodman, Benny Trio* / Vieni vieni / I'm a ding dong daddy from Dumas / Sweet Lorraine: *Goodman, Benny Trio* / Blues in your flat / Sugar / Dizzy spells / Opus 1/2 / I must have that man: *Goodman, Benny Trio* / Sweet Georgia Brown / 'S wonderful / Pick-a-rib (part 1): *Goodman, Benny Quintet* / Pick-a-rib (part 2): *Goodman, Benny Quintet* / I cried for you: *Goodman, Benny Quintet* / I know that you know / Opus 3/4
ND 82273 / Oct '90 / Bluebird

☐ BANGKOK 1956
Let's dance / Don't be that way / King Porter stomp / Trigger fantasy / Roll'em / One o'clock jump / Down South camp meeting / Yarm yen/In the evening / Sugar foot stomp / Big John special / Flying home / World is waiting for the sunrise / Oh lady be good / Sai fon/Falling rain / Stompin' at the Savoy / Thai Royal anthem
TCB 43042 / Jun '97 / TCB

☐ BASEL 1959
Let's dance / Airmail special / Rachel's dream / Memories of you / Slipped disc / Get happy / Tenbone / Go, Margot, go / Marchin' and swingin' / Breakfast feud / Body and soul / I want to be happy
TCB 43032 / Dec '96 / TCB

☐ BENNY & THE SINGERS (Goodman, Benny Orchestra)
CDMOIR 516 / Aug '96 / Memoir

☐ BENNY GOODMAN
295715 / Apr '93 / Ariola

☐ BENNY GOODMAN
CWNCD 2006 / Jun '95 / Javelin

☐ BENNY GOODMAN
22703 / Feb '96 / Music

☐ BENNY GOODMAN (Goodman, Benny & Arturo Toscanini/Bela Bartok)
Clarinet Quintet in A major KV 581: *Goodman, Benny & Budapest String Quartet* / Contrasts: *Goodman, Benny & Joseph Szigeti/Bela Bartok* / Rhapsody in blue: *Goodman, Benny & Arturo Toscanini/Earl Wild*
CD 48047 / Oct '96 / Magic Talent

☐ BENNY GOODMAN (Goodman, Benny Orchestra)
Let's dance / Memories of you / Stompin' at the savoy / One o'clock jump / King porter stomp / Henderson stomp / Sing, sing, sing (with a swing) / Limehouse blues / After you've gone / Down south camp meeting / Bugle call rag / Avalon
15703 / Apr '94 / Laserlight

☐ BENNY GOODMAN & HIS GREAT VOCALISTS
Riffin' the scotch / Blue moon / Gal in Calico / Blue skies / Symphony / It's only a paper moon / Gotta this or that / Close a pages in a book / Every time we say goodbye / Serenade in blue / Somebody else is taking my place / I got it bad and that ain't good / Taking a chance on love / Peace, brother / There'll be some changes made / Loch Lomond
CK 66198 / Jul '95 / Columbia

☐ BENNY GOODMAN 1934
CCD 111 / Oct '91 / Circle

☐ BENNY GOODMAN 1935-1938
Dinah / Sweet sue, just you / Moonglow / After you've gone / Body and soul / Who / Exactly like you / Tiger rag / Stompin' at the savoy / Whispering / China boy / Oh lady be good / Nobody's sweetheart / Tea for two / Runnin' wild / Avalon / Sugar / Blues in my flat
CD 56060 / Mar '95 / Jazz Roots

☐ BENNY GOODMAN AND HIS ORCHESTRA 1935-1939 (Goodman, Benny Orchestra)
Don't be that way / King porter stomp / Roll 'em / Down south camp meeting / Goodbye / Christopher columbus / One o'clock jump / Bugle call rag / Goody goody / Sing, sing, sing / I want to be happy / Smoke house rhythm / Stompin' at the savoy / Topsy / Sugar foot stomp / Kingdom of swing / Bach goes to town / St. louis blues / Sent for you yesterday and here you come today / He ain't got rhythm / Sing me a swing song (and let me dance)
CD 53042 / Jan '89 / Giants Of Jazz

☐ BENNY GOODMAN AND HIS ORCHESTRA 1935-1939 (Goodman, Benny Orchestra)
Don't be that way / King Porter stomp / Roll 'em / Down south camp meeting / Goodbye / Christopher Columbus / One o'clock jump / Bugle call rag / Sing sing sing / I want to be happy / Smoke house rhythm / Stompin' at the Savoy / Topsy / Sugarfoot stomp / Kingdom of swing / Bach goes to town / Sent for you yesterday / Sing me a swing song
CD 56005 / Aug '94 / Jazz Roots

☐ BENNY GOODMAN IN STOCKHOLM (1959) (Goodman, Benny & Flip Phillips)
PHONTCD 8801 / '88 / Phontastic

☐ BENNY GOODMAN ORCHESTRA & SEXTET (Goodman, Benny Orchestra)
CD 14562 / May '95 / Jazz Portraits

☐ BENNY GOODMAN ORCHESTRA/ TRIO/QUARTET (6CD Set)
NCD 8841-8846 / Jan '97 / Phontastic

☐ BENNY GOODMAN PLAYS EDDIE SAUTER
Love never went to college / Darn that dream / Faithful forever / Fable of the rose / Shake down the stars / Coconut grove / Hour of parting / Who cares / Nostalgia / Man I love / Benny rides again / These things you left me / Superman / More than you know / Time on my hands / Intermezzo / Something new / When the sun comes out / Birth of the blues / Clarinet a la king / Let's give love a chance / Tangerine / Moonlight on the Ganges
HEPCD 1053 / Jan '97 / Hep

☐ BENNY GOODMAN PLAYS FLETCHER HENDERSON
Japanese sandman / Get rhythm in your feet / Blue skies / Sometimes I'm happy / King Porter stomp / Devil and the deep blue sea / Sandman / Basin Street blues / If I could be with you one hour tonight / When Buddha smiles / Christopher Columbus / Down south camp meeting / St. Louis blues / Alexander's ragtime band / I want to be happy / Chloe (song of the swamp) / Rosetta / Can't we be friends / Sugarfoot stomp / Wrappin' it up / Bumble bee stomp / Rose of Washington square
HEPCD 1038 / Nov '93 / Hep

☐ BENNY GOODMAN PLAYS MEL POWELL
HEPCD 1055 / 5 Jan '98 / Hep

☐ BENNY GOODMAN SEXTET & CHARLIE CHRISTIAN 1939-1941
4656792 / Jan '95 / Sony Jazz

☐ BENNY GOODMAN STORY, THE
Down South camp meetin' / And the angels sing / Goodbye / Sing sing sing / Shine / One o'clock jump / Bugle call rag / King Porter stomp / Let's dance / Don't be that way / It's been so long / Sometimes I'm happy / Goody goody / Avalon / Moonglow / Alicia's blues / Memories of you / China boy / Seven come eleven
CDP 8335692 / Nov '95 / Capitol Jazz

☐ BENNY GOODMAN STORY, THE
MCD 04005 / 16 Feb '98 / MCA

☐ BENNY GOODMAN SWINGS AGAIN
4756252 / Jan '95 / Sony Jazz

☐ BENNY GOODMAN TRIO AND QUARTET SESSIONS VOL.1 (Goodman, Benny Trio & Quartet)
After you've gone / Body and soul / Who / Someday, sweetheart / China boy / More than you know / All my life / Oh lady be good / Nobody's sweetheart / Too good to be true / Moonglow / Dinah / Exactly like you / Vibraphone blues / Sweet Sue, just you / My melancholy baby / Tiger rag / Stompin' at the Savoy / Whispering / Ida / Tea for two / Running wild
ND 85631 / Apr '88 / Bluebird

☐ BENNY GOODMAN TRIO/QUARTET 1935-1938 (Goodman, Benny Trio & Quartet)
159132 / 24 Apr '98 / Jazz Archives

☐ **BENNY GOODMAN VOL.3 & 4**
Smiles / Liza / Where or when / Silhouetted in the moonlight / Vieni vieni / I'm a ding dong daddy from Dumas / Bei mir bist du schon / Sweet Lorraine / Blues in your flat / Sugar / Dizzy spells / Opus onen half / I must have that man / Sweet Georgia Brown / 'S wonderful / Pick-a-rib / I cried for you / I know that you know and you know that I know
ND 89754 / Jun '94 / Jazz Tribune

☐ **BENNY RIDES AGAIN (2CD Set)**
CPCD 82632 / Jan '97 / Charly

☐ **BENNY'S BOP**
Mary's idea / Bye bye blues bop / There's a small hotel / Blue views / I can't give you anything but love / You took advantage of me / Where oh where has my little dog gone / Pepper (Patsy's idea) / String of pearls / I'll see you in my dreams / Undercurrent blues
HEPCD 36 / Oct '93 / Hep

☐ **BERLIN 1980**
Oh lady be good / Here's that rainy day / Hary Pepl's blues / Avalon / Poor butterfly / Airmail special / You must meet my wife / Don't be that way/Stompin' at the Savoy / If I had you / World is waiting for the sunrise / Stompin' at the Savoy / Bei mir bist du schon / Sing sing sing / Good-bye
TCB 43022 / Nov '96 / TCB

☐ **BEST OF BENNY GOODMAN, THE**
Don't be that way / Sing sing sing / And the angels sing / Loch Lomond / King Porter stomp / Stompin' at the Savoy / One o'clock jump / After you've gone / Goodnight my love / Goodbye
DCD 5331 / Dec '93 / Disky

☐ **BIG BAND 1939-1946**
158962 / 21 Aug '97 / Jazz Archives

☐ **BREAKFAST BALL (Goodman, Benny Orchestra)**
Georgia jubilee / Junk man / Ol' pappy / Emaline / I ain't lazy, I'm just dreamin' / As long as I live / Moonglow / Breakfast ball / Take my word / It happens to the best of friends / Nitwit serenade / Bugle call rag / Learning / Stars fell on alabama / Solitude / I'm getting sentimental over you / I'm a hundred percent for you / Cokey / Like a bolt from the blue / Music hall rag
TQ 201 / Jun '93 / Happy Days

☐ **CAMEL CARAVAN BROADCASTS 1939 VOL.1**
Jeepers creepers / Hold tight / I cried for you / Undecided / Angels sing / Basin Street blues / Roll 'em
NCD 8817 / '93 / Phontastic

☐ **CAMEL CARAVAN BROADCASTS 1939 VOL.2**
NCD 8818 / '93 / Phontastic

☐ **CAMEL CARAVAN BROADCASTS 1939 VOL.3 (Goodman, Benny Orchestra)**
NCD 8819 / '93 / Phontastic

☐ **CAMEL CARAVAN SHOWS VOL.1, THE (14/10/39-28/10/39) (Goodman, Benny Orchestra/Sextet)**
EBCD 2138 / Oct '97 / Jazzband

☐ **CAMEL CARAVAN SHOWS VOL.2, THE (4/11/39-18/11/39) (Goodman, Benny Orchestra/Sextet)**
EBCD 2139 / Oct '97 / Jazzband

☐ **CARNEGIE HALL CONCERTS VOL.1 1938**
Don't be that way / One o'clock jump / Shine / Honeysuckle rose / Body and soul / Avalon
CD 53101 / May '92 / Giants Of Jazz

☐ **CARNEGIE HALL CONCERTS VOL.2 1938-1939**
Loch Lomond / Stompin' at the Savoy / Dizzy spells / Don't be that way / Stardust
CD 53102 / May '92 / Giants Of Jazz

☐ **CLASSIC YEARS, THE**
CDSGP 0175 / Feb '96 / Prestige

☐ **CLASSICS 1928-1931 (Goodman, Benny Orchestra)**
CLASSICS 693 / May '93 / Classics

☐ **CLASSICS 1931-1933**
CLASSICS 719 / Jul '93 / Classics

☐ **CLASSICS 1934-1935**
CLASSICS 744 / Feb '94 / Classics

☐ **CLASSICS 1935**
CLASSICS 769 / Aug '94 / Classics

☐ **CLASSICS 1935-1936**
CLASSICS 789 / Nov '94 / Classics

☐ **CLASSICS 1936 VOL.1**
CLASSICS 817 / May '95 / Classics

☐ **CLASSICS 1936 VOL.2**
CLASSICS 836 / Sep '95 / Classics

☐ **CLASSICS 1936-1937**
CLASSICS 858 / Feb '96 / Classics

☐ **CLASSICS 1937**
CLASSICS 879 / Apr '96 / Classics

☐ **CLASSICS 1937-1938**
CLASSICS 899 / Oct '96 / Classics

☐ **CLASSICS 1938 VOL.1**
CLASSICS 925 / Apr '97 / Classics

☐ **CLASSICS 1938 VOL.2**
CLASSICS 961 / Nov '97 / Classics

☐ **CLASSICS 1938-1939**
CLASSICS 990 / 24 Apr '98 / Classics

☐ **COMPLETE CAMEL CARAVAN SHOWS 1938 (Goodman, Benny Orchestra)**
JH 1038 / Feb '95 / Jazz Hour

☐ **COMPLETE CAMEL CARAVAN SHOWS 20 & 28/9/1938**
JH 1025 / Feb '93 / Jazz Hour

☐ **COMPLETE RCA VICTOR SMALL GROUP RECORDINGS, THE (3CD Set)**
After you've gone / Body and soul / Who / Someday sweetheart / China boy / More than you know / All my life / Oh lady be good / Nobody's sweetheart / Too good to be true / Moonglow / Dinah / Exactly like you / Vibraphone blues / Sweet Sue / My melancholy baby / Tiger rag / Stompin' at the Savoy / Whispering / Ida sweet as apple cider / Tea for two / Runnin' wild / Avalon / Handful of keys / Man I love / Smiles / Liza (all the clouds roll away) / Where or when / Sihouetted in the moonlight / Vieni, vieni / I'm a ding dong Daddy (from Dumas) / Bei mir bist du schon (part 1) / Bei mir bist du schon (part 2) / Sweet Lorraine / Blues in your flat / Blues in my flat / Sugar / Dizzy spells / Opus 1/2 / I must have been that man / Sweet Georgia Brown / 'S wonderful / Pick a rib (part 1) / Pick a rib (part 2) / Pick a rib (part 1) / Pick a rib (part 2) / I cried for you / I know that you know / Opus 3/4
09026687642 / 12 Jan '98 / RCA Victor

☐ **CREAM SERIES, THE**
Stompin' at the Savoy / Sing sing sing / My melancholy baby / Louise / 'S Wonderful / Avalon / Who / Make believe / When a lady meets a gentleman down South / Chloe / Bach goes to town / Handful of keys / Take another guess / Dear old Southland / Sandman / Goodnight my love / Nobody's sweetheart / He ain't got rhythm / Japanese sandman / Vibraphone blues / Did you mean it
PASTCD 9743 / Sep '91 / Flapper

☐ **DIFFERENT VERSION VOL.1 (1939-1942)**
NCD 8821 / Apr '94 / Phontastic

☐ **DIFFERENT VERSION VOL.2**
NCD 8822 / Jun '94 / Phontastic

☐ **DIFFERENT VERSION VOL.3**
NCD 8823 / Jun '94 / Phontastic

☐ **DIFFERENT VERSION VOL.4 (1942-1945)**
NCD 8824 / Apr '94 / Phontastic

☐ **DIFFERENT VERSION VOL.5**
NCD 8825 / Jun '94 / Phontastic

☐ **DON'T BE THAT WAY (Goodman, Benny Orchestra)**
Don't be that way / King porter stomp / Roll 'em / Down south camp meeting / Goodbye / Christopher columbus / One o'clock jump / Bugle call rag / Sing, sing, sing / I want to be happy / Smoke house rhythm / Stompin' at the savoy / Topsy / Sugar foot stomp / Kingdom of swing / Bach goes to town / Sent for you yesterday and here you come today / Sing me a swing song (and let me dance)
CD 14527 / Jan '94 / Jazz Portraits

☐ **EARLY YEARS**
Old man Harlem / Keep on doin' what you're doin' / Nobody's sweetheart now / Ain't cha glad / Dr. Heckle and Mr. Jibe / Georgia jubilee / Texas tea party / Honeysuckle rose / Sweet Sue, just you / Hundred years from today / Riffin' the scotch / Your mother's son-in-law / Love me or leave me / I can't give you anything but love / Baby / I gotta right to sing the blues
BCD 109 / Jul '91 / Biograph

☐ **ESSENTIAL BENNY GOODMAN, THE**
Let's dance / Flying home / Good enough to keep / Sm-o-o-oth one / Scarecrow / Clarinet a la King / Jersey bounce / Mission to Moscow / Body and soul / After you've gone / Liza / King Porter stomp / Down South camp meeting / South of the border (Down Mexico way) / Wrappin' it up
4671512 / Jul '93 / Columbia

☐ **GOLD COLLECTION, THE (2CD Set)**
R2CD 4045 / 13 Apr '98 / Deja Vu

☐ **GREATEST HITS**
Let's dance / Six flats unfurnished / Clarinet ala king / Don't be that way / Jersey bounce / Sing sing sing / Flying home / Slipped disc / Air mail special / Benny rides again / Goodbye
CK 65421 / 26 Jan '98 / Sony Jazz

☐ **HAPPY SESSION**
Happy session blues / You'd be so nice to come home to / King and me / Indian summer / What a diff'rence a day made / Batunga train / Having a ball / Clarinet a la king / Macedonia lullaby / Diga diga doo
4765232 / May '94 / Sony Jazz

☐ **HARRY JAMES YEARS VOL.1**
I want to be happy / Chloe / Rosetta / Peckin' / Can't we be friends / Sing sing sing / Roll 'em / When it's sleepy time down South / Changes / Sugarfoot stomp / I can't give you anything but love / Minnie the moocher's wedding day / Camel hop - Take 1/2 / Life goes to a party / Don't be that way
07863661552 / Apr '93 / Bluebird

☐ **HOW HIGH THE MOON**
Don't be that way / Moonglow / This year's kisses / There'll be some changes made / How high the moon / Take a chance on love / I let a song go out of my heart / Goodnight my love / Glory of love / Stardust / Clarinet a la king / Angels sing / Body and soul / I know that you know / These foolish things / Love me or leave me / It's been so long / Stompin' at the Savoy / Darn that dream / You turned the tables on me
307932 / 15 Sep '97 / Hallmark

☐ **I'M NOT COMPLAININ' (Goodman, Benny & His Band)**
Clarinet a la King / My old flame / Cornsilk / Birds of a feather / I'm not complainin' / Time on my hands / I can't give you anything but love / Gilly / Yes my darling daughter / I'm always chasing rainbows / Let the door knob hitcha / Good evenin' good lookin' / Something new / I found a million dollar baby / When the sun comes out / Smoke gets in your eyes / I hear a rhapsody / It's always you / Tuesday at ten / Elmer's tune / Down down down / Cherry
RAJCD 813 / May '97 / Empress

☐ **IN STOCKHOLM 1958**
NCD 8801 / Apr '94 / Phontastic

☐ **INDISPENSABLE BENNY GOODMAN VOL.1 & 2 1935-1936, THE (Goodman, Benny Orchestra)**
Blue skies / Dear old Southland / Sometimes I'm happy / King Porter stomp / Between the Devil and the deep blue sea / Mad house / If I could be with you one hour tonight / When Buddha smiles / Stompin' at the Savoy / Breakin' in a pair of shoes / I hope Gabriel likes my music / Mutiny in the parlour / I'm gonna clap my hands / Swing is here / Get happy / Christopher Columbus / I know that you know / Stardust / You forgot to remember / House hop / (I would do) anything for you / I've found a new baby / Swingtime in the Rockies / Pick yourself up / Down south camp meeting / St. Louis blues / Love me or leave me / Bugle call rag / Organ grinder swing / Riffin' at the Ritz / Somebody loves me
74321155212 / Mar '94 / RCA

☐ **INTRODUCTION TO BENNY GOODMAN 1928-1941, AN**
4007 / May '94 / Best Of Jazz

☐ **JAZZ GREATS**
Stompin' at the Savoy / Body and soul / Get happy / King Porter stomp / Goodbye / Always / Moonglow / Goodnight my love / You turned the tables on me / After you've gone / Bugle call rag / Tea for two / Love me or leave me / In a sentimental mood / Sing sing sing (with a swing)
74321499622 / 6 Oct '97 / RCA Victor

☐ **JAZZ HOLIDAY, A (The Early Benny Goodman 1926-1931)**
Jazz holiday: *Goodman, Benny Boys* / Indeed I do: *Pollack, Ben Californians* / Waitin' for Katie: *Pollack, Ben & His Orchestra* / Buy buy for baby: *Pollack, Ben Park Central Orchestra* / Bashful baby: *Pollack, Ben Park Central Orchestra* / Yellow dog blues: *Pollack, Ben Bad Boys* / Dinah: *Nichols, Red & His Five Pennies* / Carolina in the morning: *Nichols, Red & His Five Pennies* / Who: *Nichols, Red & His Five Pennies* / How come you do me like you do: *Nichols, Red & His Five Pennies* / Royal Garden blues: *Lewis, Ted & His Band* / I'm crazy 'bout my baby: *Lewis, Ted & His Band* / Crazy 'bout my gal: *Mills, Irving Orchestra* / Railroad man: *Mills, Irving Orchestra* / Sweetest melody: *Pettis, Jack Orchestra* / Mysterious Mose: *Bloom, Rube & His Bayou Boys* / That's a plenty / Clarinetitis / Jungle blues: *Goodman, Benny Boys* / Room 1411: *Goodman, Benny Boys* / Blue: *Goodman, Benny Boys* / After a while: *Goodman, Benny Boys* / Basin Street blues: *Charleston Chasers* / Farewell blues: *Venuti, Joe All Star Orchestra*
CDAJA 5263 / Feb '98 / Living Era

☐ **JAZZ MASTERS**
8444102 / 5 May '98 / Verve

☐ **JAZZ MASTERS**
Let's dance / There'll be some changes made / Stompin' at the savoy / Don't be that way / Big john's special / One o'clock jump / And the angels sing / Avalon / It's been so long
CDMFP 6304 / Mar '97 / Music For Pleasure

☐ **JAZZ PORTRAIT**
CD 14573 / Nov '95 / Complete

☐ **JAZZ PORTRAITS (Goodman, Benny Trio & Quartet)**
Dinah / Sweet Sue, just you / Moonglow / After you've gone / Body and soul / Who / Exactly like you / Tiger rag / Stompin' at the Savoy / Whispering / China boy / Oh lady be good / Nobody's sweetheart / Tea for two / Running wild / Avalon / Sugar / Blues in my flat
CD 14520 / May '94 / Jazz Portraits

☐ **KING OF SWING (36 Joyful Jazz Masterpieces/2CD Set) (Goodman, Benny Orchestra)**
Bugle call rag / I've found a new baby / I know that you know / Blue skies / Dear old southland / When Buddha smiles / Somebody loves me / Swingtime in the rockies / Get happy / Christopher Columbus / Sometimes I'm happy / Goody goody / King porter stomp / Stardust / Airmail special / Bewitched / Earl / Superman / Henderson stomp / How long has this been going on / Peace brother / Clarinet a la king / Zaggin' with zig / Cherry / Solo flight / All the cats join in / Tangerine / How deep is the ocean / It never entered my mind / When the sun comes out / My old flame / Pound ridge / Honeysuckle rose / Beyond the moon
330362 / Mar '97 / Hallmark

☐ **KING OF SWING 1935-1955, THE (3CD Set)**
Don't be that way / King Porter stomp / Roll 'em / Down South camp meeting / Goodbye / Christopher Columbus / One o'clock jump / If I could be with you one hour tonight / Bugle call rag / Goody goody / Sing sing sing / I want to be happy / Smoke house rhythm / Stompin' at the Savoy / Topsy / Sugarfoot stomp / Kingdom of swing / Bach goes to town / St. Louis blues / Sent for you yesterday / He ain't got rhythm / Sing me a swing song / After you've gone / Body and soul / Who / China boy / Oh Lady be good / Nobody's sweetheart / Moonglow / Dinah / Exactly like you / Sweet Sue, just you / Just you / Tiger rag / Whispering / Tea for two / Running wild / Avalon / Sugar / Blues in my flat / Pick a rib / Shivers / Rose room / Boy meet god / On the Alamo / Let's dance / Jumpin' at the woodside / Get happy / Blue Lou / Seven come eleven / Memories of you / Somebody stole my gal / Rock Rimmon / And the angels sing / Airmail special / Jersey bounce / Lullaby of the leaves / What can I say after I say I'm sorry / East of the sun and west of the moon / Temptation rag / You brought a new kind of love to me / Four or five times / Big John special / I got rhythm / Loved walked in / Stealin' apples / Undercurrent blues / Clarinet a la King
CDB 1206 / '92 / Giants Of Jazz

☐ **KING OF SWING, THE**
300154 / Dec '89 / Accord

☐ **KING OF SWING, THE**
Don't be that way / Stompin' at the Savoy / One o'clock jump / Bach goes to town / Bugle call rag / St. Louis blues / Kingdom of swing
BSTCD 9106 / May '92 / Best Compact Discs

☐ **KING PORTER STOMP**
King Porter stomp / Clarinade / And the angels sing / All the cats join in / Mad boogie / One o'clock jump / Clarinet a la King / 'S Wonderful / Jealousy / Rattle and roll / I want to be loved / Remember / Somebody stole my gal / Don't be that way / Tattle tale / Blue skies / Mahzel / Moon-faced and starry eyed / Old buttermilk / Oh baby / Theme (goodbye)
DBCD 02 / Jun '86 / Dance Band Days

☐ **KINGS OF SWING (Goodman, Benny/ Harry James)**
78067422032 / 7 Apr '98 / Drive Archive

☐ **LET'S DANCE**
Let's dance / Stompin' at the savoy / Somebody stole my gal / You brought a new kind of love to me / Sent for you yesterday and here you come today / Close your eyes (demo) / You're blase / World is waiting for the sunrise / I want to be happy / Mission to moscow / King porter stomp / That's a plenty
15780 / Jan '93 / Laserlight

☐ **LIVE 1937**
Whispers in the dark / Avalon / Roses in December / I'm a ding dong daddy / Body and soul / Sweet Sue-just you / Where or when / Nagasaki / Handful of keys / Oh, lady be good / Everybody loves my baby / More than you know / Vieni, vieni / Who / Limehouse blues / Where or when / Dinah / Can't help lovin' that man / Avalon
VN 1009 / Nov '96 / Viper's Nest

☐ **LIVE AT CARNEGIE HALL (2CD Set)**
Don't be that way / One o'clock jump / Sensation rag / I'm coming Virginia / When my baby smiles at me / Shine / Blue reverie / Life goes to a party / Honeysuckle rose / Body and soul / Avalon / Man I love / I got rhythm / Blue skies / Loch Lomond / Blue room / Swingtime in the Rockies / Bei mir bist du schon / China boy / Stompin' at the Savoy / Dizzy spells / Sing sing sing / Big John's special
4509832 / Oct '93 / Sony Jazz

☐ **LIVE AT THE CARNEGIE HALL 6 OCTOBER 1939 (Goodman, Benny & Glenn Miller)**
EBCD 21032 / Dec '90 / Flyright

☐ **LIVE AT THE INTERNATIONAL WORLD EXHIBITION (Brussels 1958: Unissued Recordings) (Goodman, Benny Orchestra)**
Let's dance / When you're smiling / Sent for you yesterday / Pennies from Heaven / Goin' to Chicago / Soon / Who cares / 'Deed I do / I hadn't anyone till you / I've got you under my skin / There's no fool like an old fool / Sometimes I'm happy / Oh boy I'm lucky / Song is ended (but the melody lingers on) / I'm coming Virginia / Fine romance / Harvard blues / If I had you / Goodbye theme
DAWE 36 / Sep '93 / Magic

☐ **LIVE DOWN UNDER 1973 (Goodman, Benny Sextet)**
TMCD 21302 / Jul '97 / Jazzband

☐ **MANHATTAN ROOM VOL.1 1937 (Satan Takes A Ride)**
VN 171 / Aug '95 / Viper's Nest

☐ **MANHATTAN ROOM VOL.1-6 1937 (6CD Set)**
VN 177 / Mar '96 / Viper's Nest

☐ **MANHATTAN ROOM VOL.2 1937 (One O'Clock Jump)**
VN 172 / Aug '95 / Viper's Nest

☐ **MANHATTAN ROOM VOL.3 1937 (Jam Session)**
VN 173 / Aug '95 / Viper's Nest

☐ **MANHATTAN ROOM VOL.4 1937**
VN 174 / Mar '96 / Viper's Nest

☐ **MANHATTAN ROOM VOL.5 1937**
VN 175 / Mar '96 / Viper's Nest

☐ **MANHATTAN ROOM VOL.6 1937**
VN 176 / Mar '96 / Viper's Nest

☐ **MASTERPIECES 1935-1942**
158172 / Mar '94 / Masterpieces

☐ **MASTERPIECES OF BENNY GOODMAN, THE**
393322 / Jul '96 / Music Memoria

☐ ON RADIO WITH ARTURO TOSCANINI/ BUDAPEST STRING QUARTET (Goodman, Benny & Arturo Toscanini)
Clarinet quintet in A major KV 581 / Rhapsody in blue / American in Paris
RY 60 / Jun '96 / Radio Years

☐ PERMANENT GOODMAN VOL.1 1926-1938
PHONTCD 7659 / Feb '89 / Phontastic

☐ PERMANENT GOODMAN VOL.2 1939-1945
PHONTCD 7660 / Apr '94 / Phontastic

☐ PLATINUM COLLECTION, THE (2CD Set)
Let's dance / Don't be that way / When the Buddah smiles / Down south camp meeting / You turned the tables on me / King Porter stomp / Sometimes I'm happy / Blue skies / Sugar foot stomp / I know that you know / Why don't you do right / Perfidia / Smoke gets in your eyes / Stardust / Clarinet a la King / After you've gone / Someday sweetheart / Big John's special / What's new / Air mail special / Clarinade / And the angels sing / All the cats join in / Mad boogie / One o'clock jump / I want to be loved / Remember / Somebody stole my gal / Sing sing sing / Get happy / Lady be good / Jersey bounce / Stompin' at the Savoy / Jumpin' at the woodside / Bugie call rag / Lucky / Rattle and roll / Oh baby / Body and soul / Darktown strutter's ball
PC 625 / 29 Jun '98 / Start

☐ PLAY BENNY GOODMAN VOL.2 (International Allstars)
NHCD 045 / May '98 / Nagel Heyer

☐ PLAYS JIMMY MUNDY
Mad house / You can't pull the wool over my eyes / House hop / Sing me a swing song / In a sentimental mood / Swingtime in the rockies / These foolish things / There's a small hotel / Bugle call rag / Jam session / Did you mean it / When you and I were young / Swing low, sweet chariot / He ain't got rhythm / Sing sing sing / I'm like a fish out of water / Sweet stranger / Margie / Farewell blues / Roll' em / Camel hop
HEPCD 1039 / Feb '94 / Hep

☐ PORTRAIT OF BENNY GOODMAN, A
GALE 408 / May '97 / Gallerie

☐ RADIO TRANSCRIPTS VOL.1 1935 (Goodman, Benny & His Rhythm Makers)
Makin' whoopee / Poor butterfly / Between the Devil and the deep blue sea / Farewell blues / I would do almost anything for you / Bugle call rag
TAX 37082 / Aug '94 / Tax

☐ RADIO TRANSCRIPTS VOL.2 1935 (Goodman, Benny & His Rhythm Makers)
Royal Garden blues / Down South camp meeting / Lovely to look at / Stardust / Sugarfoot stomp / Wrappin' it up
TAX 37192 / Aug '94 / Tax

☐ RARE RECORDINGS FROM YALE UNIVERSITY MUSIC LIBRARY VOL.1-5 (Swing Swing Swing/6CD Set)
Sweet Georgia Brown / Macedonia lullaby / Soft lights and sweet music / Broadway / Marching in rhythm / Marching and swinging / Batunga train / Cherokee / Slipped disc / Diga diga doo / Lullaby in rhythm / Don't blame me / Blue room / Let's dance / Honeysuckle rose / Running wild / Mean to me / Memories of you / Stompin' at the Savoy / Blue and sentimental / One o'clock jump / I found a new baby / Stairway to the stars / Body and soul / Airmail special / Nice work if you can get it / Sing sing sing / Goodbye / Bugle call rag / On the sunny side of the street / 'Deed I do / Who cares / Blue skies / I want a little girl / Sometimes I'm happy / Fine romance / Harvard blues / I'm coming Virginia / Soon / Medley / Pennies from heaven / Stompin' at the Savoy / Flying home / This is my lucky day / Roll 'em / Brussels blues / When you're smiling / Happy session blues / Autumn nocturne / Oh baby / What a difference a day makes / Oh gee, oh joy / Earl / More than you know / You couldn't be cuter / I've grown accustomed to her face / Swift as the wind / Them there eyes / Room without windows / People / Benny rides again / Let's dance / No way to stop it / Memories of you / Medley / I want to be happy / Gotta be this or that / Between the devil and the deep blue sea / Body and soul / Don't get around much anymore / Sweet and lovely / After you've gone / Ten bone / St. James Infirmary / Airmail special / My baby done tol' me / Medley / Lazy afternoon / St. Louis blues / Rachel's dream / Easy living / I found a new baby / Breakfast feud / No way to stop / Sleep
MM 65095 / Jan '95 / Music Masters

☐ RARE RECORDINGS FROM YALE UNIVERSITY MUSIC LIBRARY VOL.6-10 (The King Of Swing) (5CD Set)
MM 65130 / Oct '96 / Music Masters

☐ RUNNIN' WILD (Goodman, Benny Quartet)
CDSGP 099 / Mar '94 / Prestige

☐ RUNNIN' WILD
AMSC 609 / 1 Jun '98 / Avid

☐ SMALL COMBOS 1935-1941
After you've gone / Body and soul / Who / China boy / Oh lady be good / Nobody's sweetheart / Moonglow / Dinah / Exactly like you / Sweet Sue, just you / Tiger rag / Stompin' at the savoy / Whispering / Tea for two / Runnin' wild / Avalon / Sugar / Blues in my flat / Pick-a-rib / Shivers / Rose room (in sunny roseland) / Boy meets goy (grand slam) (boy meets girl) / On the Alamo
CD 53039 / Mar '92 / Giants Of Jazz

☐ SMALL GROUPS, THE
After you've gone / Avalon / Exactly like you / Flying home / Gone with "what" wind / Good enough to keep / Limehouse blues / Moon glow / More than you know / Oh Lady be good / On the Alamo / On the sunny side of the street: *Goodman, Benny & Peggy Lee* / Opus 1/2 / Opus 3/4 / Pick-a-rib / Running wild / Sheikh of araby / Smo-o-o-o-th one / Someday sweetheart / Stardust / Sweet Georgia Brown / Wang wang blues / Wholly cats / World is waiting for the sunrise
CDAJA 5144 / Dec '94 / Living Era

☐ STOMPIN' AT THE SAVOY
King Porter stomp / Goodbye / Goody goody / Stompin' at the Savoy / These foolish things / Bugle call rag / Goodnight my love / Don't be that way / One o'clock jump / Sing sing sing
JHR 73518 / Oct '92 / Jazz Hour

☐ SWING KING
Let's dance / Don't be that way / When Buddha smiles / Down south camp meeting / You turned the tables on me / King Porter stomp / Sometimes I'm happy / Blue skies / Sugarfoot stomp / I know that you know / Why don't you do right / Perfidia / Smoke gets in your eyes / Stardust / Clarinet a la King / After you've gone / Someday sweetheart / Big John special
PAR 2029 / Sep '94 / Parade

☐ SWING SESSIONS
HCD 254 / Sep '94 / Hindsight

☐ THIS IS JAZZ
Sing sing sing (with a swing) / Flying home / Wang wang blues / Don't be that way / Running wild / King Porter stomp / Limehouse blues / Mission to Moscow / You turned the tables on me / Avalon / Memories of you
CK 64620 / May '96 / Sony Jazz

☐ TOGETHER AGAIN (Goodman, Benny Quartet)
Who cares / Dearest / Seven come eleven / I've found a new baby / Somebody loves me / I'll get by / Say it isn't so / Running wild / I got it bad and that ain't good / Four once more
09026685932 / Oct '96 / RCA Victor

☐ TRIBUTE TO BENNY GOODMAN, A (Various Artists)
NHCD 025 / Jul '96 / Nagel Heyer

☐ TRIBUTE TO BENNY GOODMAN, A (Meyer, Sabine & Bamberger Symphoniker)
CDC 72435566525 / 1 Jun '98 / EMI Classics

☐ UNDERCURRENT BLUES
Lonely moments / Whistle blues / Shirley steps out / Stealin' apples / Undercurrent blues / Shishkabop / Huckle buck / Bop hop / Trees / Dreazag / Bedlam / In the land of oo-bla-dee / Blue Lou / Fiesta time / Egg head
CDP 8320862 / Aug '95 / Capitol Jazz

☐ WHEN BUDDHA SMILES
Music Hall rag / Always / Blue skies / Down home rag / Ballad in blue / Devil and the deep blue sea / Mad house / Down South Camp meeting / Can't we be friends / Sugarfoot stomp / Big John special / Jumpin' at the woodside / Night and day / Board meeting / When Buddha smiles / Take another guess / Roll 'em / Don't be that way / Wrappin' it up / Stealin' apples / Honeysuckle rose / Zaggin' with Zig
CDAJA 5071 / May '90 / Living Era

☐ WORLD WIDE (4CD Set)
TCB 43012 / Jan '94 / TCB

☐ WRAPPIN' IT UP
AMSC 608 / 22 Sep '97 / Avid

Goodman, Dave

☐ LIVE 1996
Let it go / Little Jimi / Santa Fe / My only friend / Down the line / Hard, sad and lonely time
BCD 17009 / Nov '96 / Bear Family

Goodman, Gabrielle

☐ UNTIL WE LOVE
5140152 / Dec '94 / jMT

Goodman, Steve

☐ AFFORDABLE ART
If Jethro were here / Vegematic / Old smoothies / Talk backwards / How much tequila (did I drink last night) / When my rowboat comes in / Souvenirs / Take me out to the ballgame / Dying cub fan's last request / California promises / Watchin' Joey glow / Grand canyon song
RPJ 002CD / May '97 / Red Pajamas

☐ ARTISTIC HAIR
East St. Louis tweed / Let's give a party / Winter wonderland / Elvis imitators / Tico tico / Water is wide / Red red robin / Chicken cordon bleus / Old fashioned / City of New Orleans / Three legged man / You never even call me by my name
RPJ 001CD / May '97 / Red Pajamas

☐ BEST OF THE ASYLUM YEARS VOL.1, THE
Between the lines / Jessie's jig (Rob's romp, Beth's bounce) / Hand it to you / Death of a salesman / Still trying to care / Twentieth century is almost over / Banana republics / Two lovers / I'm attracted to you / One bite of the apple / One that got away
RPJ 006CD / May '97 / Red Pajamas

☐ BEST OF THE ASYLUM YEARS VOL.2, THE
This hotel room / Bobby don't stop / Men who love women who love men / That's what friends are for / Just lucky I guess / My old man / Video tape / Danger / Door number three / I can't sleep / You can turn to me / Spoon river
RPJ 007CD / May '97 / Red Pajamas

☐ EASTER TAPES, THE
Introduction / Red red robin / I don't know where I'm going... / Blue skies / This hotel room / I can't sleep / Banana republics / City of New Orleans / Chicken cordon bleus / It's a sin to tell a lie / Easter parade / Video tape / Big iron / Somebody else's troubles / Don't fence me in / 18 yellow roses / Splish splash / Rudolph the red nosed (Easter) reindeer / Runaway
RPJ 009CD / May '97 / Red Pajamas

☐ GATHERING AT EARL OF OLD TOWN
78067416702 / 27 Apr '98 / Drive Archive

☐ NO BIG SURPRISE (The Steve Goodman Anthology 2CD/Set)
Between the lines / Take me out to the ballgame / Go cubs go / City of New Orleans / Would you like to learn to dance / Souvenirs / Red ball jets / One that got away / Talk backwards / If she were you / Danger / You better get out while you can (The ballad of Carl Martin) / Yellow coat / Bannan republics / California promises / Bobby don't stop / My old man / This hotel room / Where's the party / I just keep falling in love / Watchin' Joey glow / Dutchman / In real life / Chicken cordon blues / I don't know where I'm goin', but I'm goin' nowhere in a hur / Is it true what they say about Dixie / Turnpike Tom / Elvis imitators / Lincoln park pirates / Wonderful world of sex / Vegematic / Dying cub fan's last request / Men who love women who love men / Auctioneer / Broken string song / Just lucky I guess / I'll fly away / It's a sin to tell a lie / Born to be wild / Teen angel / Tell Laura I love her / (Laurie) Strange things happen / You never even call me by my name / Don't let the stars get in your eyes / As time goes by
RPJ 008CD / May '97 / Red Pajamas

☐ SANTA ANA WINDS
Face on the cutting room floor / Telephone answering tape / One that got away / Queen of the road / Fourteen days / Hot tub refugee / I just keep falling in love / Big rock candy mountain / Santa Ana winds / You better get it while you can
RPJ 003CD / May '97 / Red Pajamas

☐ SOMEBODY ELSE'S TROUBLES
Dutchman / Six hours ahead of the sun / Song for David / Chicken Gordon blues / Somebody else's troubles / Loving of the game / I ain't heard you play no blues / Don't do me any favours anymore / Vegetable song / Lincoln Park pirates / Ballad of Penny Evans / Election year rag
OW 28560 / May '94 / One Way

☐ STEVE GOODMAN
I don't know where I'm going / Rainbow road / Donald and Lydia / You never even called me by my name / Mind your own business / Eight ball blues / City of New Orleans / Turnpike Tom / Yellow coat / So fine / Jazzman / Would you like to learn to dance
OW 28559 / May '94 / One Way

☐ TRIBUTE TO STEVE GOODMAN, A (Various Artists)
Souvenirs: *Prine, John* / Blues that Steve taught me: *Holstein, Ed* / Face on the cutting room floor: *Nitty Gritty Dirt Band* / Gentle on my mind: *Hartford, John* / I will not be your fool: *Bromberg, David* / Lady is a tramp: *Burns, Jethro* / I can't sleep: *Koloc, Bonnie* / California promises: *Lincoln Park Pirates & Jim Rothermel* / All over the world: *Guthrie, Arlo* / City of New Orleans: *Guthrie, Arlo* / Thanksgiving song: *Holstein, Fred* / Satisfied mmind: *Bowers, Bryan* / Angel from Montgomery: *Raitt, Bonnie & John Prine* / My old man: *Prine, John* / I don't wanna know: *Havens, Richie* / Water is wide: *Amram, David* / Cochroaches on parade: *Waller, Harry* / Dutchman: *Smith, Michael* / Please don't bury me: *Prine, John*
RPJ 004CD / May '97 / Red Pajamas

☐ UNFINISHED BUSINESS
Whispering man / Mind over matter / God bless our mobile home / Millie make some chillli / In real life / Now and then there's a fool such as I / Don't get sand in it / Dutchman / Colorado Christmas / My funny valentine
RPJ 005CD / May '97 / Red Pajamas

Goodrich, Andy

☐ MOTHERLESS CHILD
Natch'l natch'l / You must believe in Spring / Quasimodo / Reminiscing / Stranger in paradise / Serenade in black / Stablemates / Motherless child
DE 495 / Jul '97 / Delmark

Goodrick, Mick

☐ IN PAS(S)ING
Feebles, fables and ferns / In the tavern of ruin / Summer band camp / Pedal pusher / In passing
8473272 / Mar '92 / ECM

☐ RARE BIRDS (Goodrick, Mick & Joe Diorio)
RMCD 4505 / Nov '93 / Ram

☐ SUNSCREAMS (Goodrick, Mick Quartet)
RMCD 4507 / Apr '94 / Ram

Goodson, Sadie

☐ SADIE GOODSON & SAMMY RIMMINGTON (Goodson, Sadie & Sammy Rimmington)
BCD 298 / Nov '96 / GHB

Goodwin, Bill

☐ NO METHOD (Goodwin, Bill/ Hal Galper/ Billy Peterson)
FSRCD 136 / Dec '90 / Fresh Sound

Goodwin, Ron

☐ LEGEND OF THE GLASS MOUNTAIN/ ADVENTURE (2CD Set)
Legend of glass mountain / Dream of Olwen / Intermezzo / Theme from the Way to the stars / Warsaw concerto / To be loved / Spitfire prelude and fugue / Theme from limelight / Tara theme / Rhapsody on a theme from Paganini / Theme from Moulin Rouge / Cornish rhapsody / 633 squadron / Elizabethan serenade / Song of the high seas / Under the Linden tree / Trap / Girl with a dream / Those magnificent men in their flying machines / Girl from Corsica / Headless horseman / Of human bondage / Miss Marple's theme / Operation crossbow
4956212 / 10 Aug '98 / Studio 2

☐ MY KIND OF MUSIC (Goodwin, Ron & Bournemouth Symphony Orchestra)
Trap, The (London marathon theme) / Here where you are / Kojak / Hill Street Blues / Star Trek / Dynasty / Dallas / Here's that rainy day / Tribute to Miklos Rosza / Ben Hur / Red house / Four feathers / Parade of the Charioteers / Trolley song / Zip a dee doo dah / Someday my Prince will come / I wanna be like you / Little April showers / When you wish upon a star / Caravan - the girl from Corsica / Stephen Foster tribute / Oh Susanna / Swanee River / Beautiful dreamer / Camptown races / Drake 400 suite / Battle finale
CHAN 8797 / '89 / Chandos

Goofus Five

☐ GOOFUS FIVE 1926-1927, THE
Poor Papa (he's got nothin' at all) / I wonder what's become of Joe / Ya gotta know how to love / Where'd you get those eyes / Mary Lou / Someone is losin' Susan / Crazy quilt / Sadie Green the vamp of New Orleans / Heebie jeebies / Tuck in Kentucky and smile / I need lovin' / I've got the girl / Farewell blues / I wish I could shimmy like my sister Kate / Muddy water / Wang wang blues / Whisper song / Arkansas blues / Lazy weather / Vo-do-do-de-o blues / Ain't that a grand and glorious feeling / Clementine / Nothin' doe-does like it used to do-do-do / I left my sugar standing in the rain (and she melted away)
CBC 1017 / Aug '94 / Timeless Historical

Goombay Dance Band

☐ CHRISTMAS BY SEA
Silent night holy night / Mary's boy child / Lovely land / Jericho / Christmas at sea / Child of the sun / Ave Maria no morro / White Christmas / Little drummer boy / Carry the load / Sing little children / Aloho until we meet again / Riding in the sleigh / Poor boy's dream / Peace on Earth / Magical time
120002 / Oct '97 / Jingle

☐ GOOMBAY DANCE BAND VOL.1, THE
Sun of Jamaica / Aloho until we meet again / My Bonnie / King of Peru / Fly flamingo / I will return / Cherokee / Land ho / Reggae nights / Typical Jamaican mess / Long time ago / Island of dreams / Goombay dance
10082 / Oct '97 / Go On Deluxe

☐ GOOMBAY DANCE BAND VOL.2, THE
Rain / Canta mi lengua / Under the sun moon and stars / Caribbean girl / Take me home to Jamaica / Isle of Atlantic / Monkey / Montezuma / I'll be home / Mama Coco / El Bandido / Lovely land / Love and tequila / Ave Maria no morro
10092 / Oct '97 / Go On Deluxe

☐ GOOMBAY DANCE BAND VOL.3, THE
Seven tears / Eldorado / Child of the sun / Sing little children / Marrakesh / Bad bad girls / Alicia / Paradise of joy / Magician / Day after day / Conga man / Indio boy / Goombay dance band megamix
10102 / Oct '97 / Go On Deluxe

☐ GOOMBAY DANCE BAND, THE (3CD Set)
Sun of Jamaica / Aloho until we meet again / My Bonnie / Bang bang Lulu / King of Peru / Fly flamingo / I will return / Cherokee / Land ho / Reggae nights / Typical Jamaican mess / Long time ago / Island of dreams / Goombay dance / Rain / Canta mi lengua / Under the sun moon and stars / Caribbean girl / Take me home to Jamaica / Isle of Atlantic / Monkey / Montezuma / I'll be home / Mama coco / El bandido / Lovely land / Love and tequila / Ave Maria no morro / Seven tears / Eldorado / Child of the sun / Sing little children / Marrakesh / Bad bad girls / Alicia / Paradise of joy / Magician / Day after day / Conga man / Indio boy / Goombay dance band mega mix
10342 / Oct '97 / Go On Deluxe

☐ HITS COLLECTION VOL.1
10082 / Jun '97 / A-Play Collection

☐ HITS COLLECTION VOL.2
10102 / Jun '97 / A-Play Collection

☐ VERY BEST OF GOOMBAY DANCE BAND, THE
Sun of Jamaica / Aloho until we meet again / Eldorado / Seven tears / Take me home to Jamaica / Kalimba de luna / Aruba-so sweet / Queen of the island / Barbados / Sing little children / Sunshine reggae / Yellow bird / Caribbean sunshine / I see the moon
10112 / Oct '97 / Go On Deluxe

Gopalakrishan, Parur

☐ RAGA BHOOP (Gopalakrishan, Parur & Ustad Sultan Khan)
NRCD 0065 / Nov '96 / Navras

Gopalakrishnan, K.S.

☐ CARNATIC FLUTE
SM 15022 / Nov '91 / Wergo

GorJus Wrex

☐ FATHER LIAM'S IRISH MIST
Irish rover / Bucks of Oranmore / Dirty old town / Sally Gardens / Ordinary man / Ag Fas Fos / Langstrom's pony / Hard station / Ride on / From Clare to here / Homes of Donegal / Rainy night in Soho / Blackbird
CDMFP 6349 / May '97 / Music For Pleasure

Gordon, Bobby

☐ DON'T LET IT END
ARCD 19112 / Nov '94 / Arbors Jazz

☐ PLAYS BING (A Tribute To Bing Crosby)
ARCD 19172 / May '97 / Arbors Jazz

Gordon, Curtis

☐ PLAY THE MUSIC LOUDER
Rompin' and stompin' / Play the music louder / Caffeine and nicotine / Draggin' / Baby please come home / You ain't seen nothin' yet / Mobile Alabama / So tired of crying / Too young to know / I'm sittin' on top of the world / I'd do it for you / One blue moon one broken heart / Rock roll jump and jive / Out to win your heart / Don't trade / From Memphis to New Orleans / Tell 'em no / Hey mister sorrow / Cry cry / Little Bo-Peep / I'd like to tell you / Sixteen / If you tell me one more lie / Divided heart / Baby me / Please baby please / Rocky road of love / I just don't love you anymore / I wouldn't / Oh lonely heart / Greatest sin / What's a little pride / You crazy crazy moon / Where'd ja get so much of
BCD 16253 / May '98 / Bear Family

Gordon, David

☐ DOZEN A DAY (Gordon, David Trio)
Mister Sam / Solar / Zimmerfolk / Blue Pyrenees / Carol's garden / Air / Looking up / Wives and lovers / How insensitive / Czech bounce / Understand it
ZZCD 9801 / 1 Jun '98 / Zah Zah

Gordon, Dexter

☐ AFTER HOURS
SCCD 31224 / '88 / Steeplechase

☐ ART OF THE BALLAD, THE
Cheesecake / Sentimental reasons / Days of wine and roses / Star eyes / Body and soul / Those were the days / First time I ever saw your face / Some other spring / Sophisticated lady / Meditation
PRCD 110092 / Sep '98 / Prestige

☐ BACKSTAIRS (2CD Set)
Tangerine / I told you so / Skylark / Backstairs / It's you or no one / Tanya / As time goes by / Jumpin' blues
JLR 103603 / May '96 / Live At EJ's

☐ BALLADS
Darn that dream / Don't explain / I'm a fool to want you / Ernie's tune / You've changed / Willow weep for me / Guess I'll hang my tears out to dry / Body and soul
BNZ 275 / Sep '92 / Blue Note

☐ BE BOP MASTERS, THE (Gordon, Dexter & Wardell Gray)
Blow Mr. Dexter / Blow Mr. Dexter / Dexter's deck / Dexter's cuttin' out / Dexter's minor mad / Long tall Dexter / Long tall Dexter / Dexter rides again / I can't escape from you / I can't escape from you / Dexter digs in / Dexter digs in / Dell's bells / Dell's bells / One for Prez / One for Prez / Man I love / Man I love / Easy swing / Easy swing / Great lie
IGOCD 2072 / Sep '97 / Indigo

☐ BEST OF DEXTER GORDON, THE (Blue Note Years)
It's you or no one / Society red / Smile / Cheesecake / Three o'clock in the morning / Soy califa / Don't explain / Tanya
BNZ 142 / Sep '92 / Blue Note

☐ BLUE DEX (Dexter Gordon Plays The Blues)
Sticky wicket / Panther / Blue Monk / Lonesome lover blues / Jumpin' blues / Oh Karen / Gingerbread boy
PRCD 11003 / Jun '97 / Prestige

☐ BODY AND SOUL
BLCD 760118 / Feb '89 / Black Lion

☐ BOTH SIDES OF MIDNIGHT
BLCD 760103 / Dec '88 / Black Lion

☐ CHASE, THE
STB 613 / Aug '95 / Stash

☐ CITIZENS BOP (Gordon, Dexter & Wardell Gray)
BLC 760223 / Nov '97 / Black Lion

☐ CLASSICS 1943-1947
CLASSICS 999 / 1 Jun '98 / Classics

☐ COME RAIN OR COME SHINE
Doxy / Misty / For all we know / But not for me / Come rain or come shine / There will never be another you
JHR 73508 / May '93 / Jazz Hour

☐ COMPLETE SESSIONS ON DIAL, THE
Mischievious lady / Lullaby in rhythm / Chase / Chromatic abberation / It's the talk of the town / Blue bikini / I don't stand a ghost of a chance with you / Sweet and lovely / Horning in / Duel / Blues in Teddy's flat
SPJCD 130 / Apr '95 / Spotlite

☐ DADDY PLAYS THE HORN
Daddy plays the horn / Confirmation / Number four / Darn that dream / Autumn in New York / You can depend on me
CDGR 121 / Mar '97 / Charly

☐ DEXTER BLOWS HOT AND COOL
Silver plated / Cry me a river / Rhythm mad / Don't worry 'bout me / I hear music / Bonna Rue / I should care / Blowin' for Dootsie / Tenderly
CDBOP 006 / Feb '89 / Boplicity

☐ DEXTER GORDON 1943-1946
158792 / Feb '97 / Jazz Archives

☐ DEXTER RIDES AGAIN
Dexter's riff / Settin' the pace Pts 1 and 2 / So easy / Long tall Dexter / Dexter rides again / I can't escape from you / Dexter digs in / Dexter's minor mad / Blow Mr. Dexter / Dexter's deck / Dexter's cuttin' out
SV 0120 / Oct '97 / Savoy Jazz

☐ DEXTERITY (New York 1977/ Copenhagen 1967 - 2CD Set)
JWD 102303 / Oct '94 / JWD

☐ GO
Cheesecake / Guess I'll hang my tears out to dry / Second balcony jump / Love for sale / Where are you / Three o'clock in the morning
CDP 7460942 / Mar '95 / Blue Note

☐ JUMPIN' BLUES
Evergreenish / (I love you) for sentimental reasons / Star eyes / Rhythm-a-ning / If you could see me now / Jumpin' blues
OJCCD 899 / Sep '96 / Original Jazz Classics

☐ LIVE AT CARNEGIE HALL
Secret love / End of a love affair / More than you know / Blues up and down / Cheesecake
CK 65312 / 6 Apr '98 / Sony Jazz

☐ LIVE AT THE AMSTERDAM PARADISO
Fried bananas / What's new / Good bait / Rhythm-a-ning / Willow weep for me / Junior / Scrapple from the apple / Closing announcement / Introduction
LEJAZZCD 28 / Aug '94 / Le Jazz

☐ LONG TALL DEXTER
Blow Mr. Dexter / Dexter's deck / Dexter's cuttin' out / Dexter's minor mad / Long tall Dexter / Dexter rides again / I can't escape from you / Dexter digs in / Settin' the pace / So easy so easy / Dexter's riff / Dexter's mood / Dextrose index / Dextivity / Wee dot / Lion roars / After hours bop
VGCD 650117 / Oct '93 / Vogue

☐ MORE THAN YOU KNOW
SCCD 31030 / Jul '88 / Steeplechase

☐ OTHER SIDE OF 'ROUND MIDNIGHT, THE
7463972 / 1 Jun '98 / Blue Note

☐ OUR MAN IN PARIS
Scrapple from the apple / Willow weep for me / Stairway to the stars / Night in Tunisia / Our love is here to stay / Like someone to love / Broadway
BNZ 34 / Jun '87 / Blue Note

☐ REVELATION (Gordon, Dexter & Benny Bailey)
SCCD 31373 / May '96 / Steeplechase

☐ SOMETHING DIFFERENT
SCCD 31136 / Jul '88 / Steeplechase

☐ SOPHISTICATED GIANT
Laura / Moontrane / Red top / Fried bananas / You're blase / How insensitive / Diggin in/It's only a paper moon
CK 65295 / 1 Sep '97 / Sony Jazz

☐ STABLE MABLE (Gordon, Dexter Quartet)
Just friends / Misty / Red cross / So what / In a sentimental mood / Stablemates
SCCD 31040 / Oct '90 / Steeplechase

☐ TAKE THE 'A' TRAIN
But not for me / Take the 'A' train / For all we know / Blues walk / I guess I'll hang my tears out to dry / Love for sale
BLC 760133 / Oct '94 / Black Lion

☐ TOWER OF POWER
Montmartre / Rainbow people / Stanley the steamer / Those were the days
OJCCD 299 / Sep '93 / Original Jazz Classics

☐ WE THREE (Gordon, Dexter & Zoot Sims/Al Cohn)
BCD 137 / Aug '95 / Biograph

Gordon, Frank

☐ CLARION ECHOES
SNCD 1096 / '86 / Soul Note

Gordon Highlanders

☐ BAGPIPES AND DRUMS OF SCOTLAND, THE
Amazing grace / Battle on the tyne / My home in the hills / Pio braireachd / Regimental march / Route march / When the battle is over / Conundrum / Regimental company march / Reveille / Miss kirkwood / Scotland the grave
15159 / May '94 / Laserlight

☐ COCK 'O' THE NORTH
Rose of kelvingrove / Rose of kelvingrove / Ye banks and braes / Drummers fanfare / Garb of old gaul (regimental slow march) / Loch maree / Bonnie black isle / Cock o' the north (regimental quick march) / Lights out
BNA 5077 / Jan '93 / Bandleader

☐ MARCHES ECOSSAISES
824922 / Nov '90 / BUDA

Gordon, Jimmie

☐ MISSISSIPPI MUDDER 1934-1941
SOB 035182 / Feb '93 / Story Of The Blues

Gordon, Joe

☐ GORDON FAMILY, THE (Gordon, Joe & Sally Logan)
Rose of Allendale / Craigieburn woods / Band boys / Holy City / Wee toon clerk / Faraway land / Jig selection / Dark lochnagar / Medley of reels / Hunting tower / Bonnio gallows / Charness waltz / My ain folk / Dantesque / Darvol dam
CDGR 142 / Oct '92 / Ross

☐ JOE GORDON & SCOTT LA FARO (Gordon, Joe & Scott La Faro)
FSCD 1030 / Jan '93 / Fresh Sound

Gordon, Jon

☐ ALONG THE WAY
Inner urge / Empathy / Friday the 13th / Softly as in a morning sunrise / Portrait of Jenny / Just in time / Vale / Along the way / Body and soul / Just in time
CRISS 1138CD / Dec '97 / Criss Cross

☐ JON GORDON QUARTET, THE (Gordon, Jon Quartet)
CRD 316 / Mar '96 / Chiaroscuro

☐ SPARK
CRD 330 / Mar '96 / Chiaroscuro

Gordon, Kevin

☐ CADILLAC JACK'S SON
Company car / Fast train / Pauline / Lucy and Andy drive to Arkansas / Blue collar dollar / Dissatisfied / Over the levee / Looking for the killerweb / Cadillac Jack's son / Junior guitar / Evan pick up the line
SHANCD 6029 / 9 Mar '98 / Shanachie

Gordon, Michael

☐ TRANCE
4524182 / Nov '96 / Argo

☐ YO SHAKESPEARE
4432142 / Jan '95 / Argo

Gordon, Rob

☐ COMPLETE CALEDONIAN BALL (2CD Set) (Gordon, Rob & His Band)
Circassian circle / Brisk young lad / Byron strathspey / Saltire society reel / Hebridean weaving lilt / Johnnie Walker / Crammond Bridge / Silver star / Cumberland reel / New Scotia quadrille / Dundee whaler / Bannetstane / Lomond waltz / Angus reel / Belle of Bon Accord / Rab the ranter / C'est l'amour / Wind on Loch Fyne / Seton's ceilidh band / New petronella / Bonnie lass o'Bon Accord / Bank Street reel / Joe McDiarmid's jig / Broon's reel / Rothesay rant
LCDM 8005 / Dec '88 / Lismor

☐ OLD TIME AND SEQUENCE BALL
Quadrilles (patience) / Flirtation / Chrysanthemum waltz / Silver wedding waltz / Mississippi dip / Dinkie one step / Ideal schottische / Ken and Cathy Jamieson Barn dance / Marine four step / Southern two step / Stanley and Vera Carson's polka / Swedish masquerade / Foxtrots and saunters / Moonlight saunter / Heather mixture polka / Waltz cotillion (half figure) / Lancers / Waltzmaree / Honeysuckle waltz
LCDM 9014 / '89 / Lismor

Gordon, Robert

☐ ALL FOR THE LOVE OF ROCK 'N' ROLL
422506 / Mar '95 / New Rose

☐ BAD BOY
Sweet love on my mind / Worryin' kind / Bad boy / Picture of you / Torture / Crazy man crazy / Born to lose / Nervous / Uptown / Is it wrong / Need you
OW 34495 / Sep '97 / One Way

☐ BLACK SLACKS
Summertime blues / I just found out / Boppin' the blues / Picture of you / I just met a memory / Am I blue / Walk on by / Blue Christmas / Fire / Twenty flight rock / But, but / Sea cruise / Bad boy / Red cadillac and a black moustache / Uptown / Five days, five days / Are you gonna be the one / Standing on the outside of her door / Loverboy / Take me back / Too fast to live, too young to die / Born to lose / Is it wrong / Torture / Black slacks (live)
BCD 15489 / Apr '90 / Bear Family

☐ GREETINGS FROM NY CITY
422155 / Feb '97 / New Rose

☐ HUMBLER, THE (Gordon, Robert & Danny Gatton)
NCD 6842 / 19 Jan '98 / NRG

☐ LIVE AT THE LONE STAR
422156 / Feb '97 / New Rose

☐ LOST ALBUM...PLUS, THE
She's not mine anymore / It hurts so much / Run for your life / One day left / Suspicion / Movin' too slow / You girl / I found you / Signs of love / Wasting my time / Girl like you / So young so bad / If this is wrong / Blue eyes (don't run away) / Is this the way / Endless sleep / Woman (you're my woman) / Sweet surrender / It's in the bottle / Sea cruise / Fire
BCD 16251 / May '98 / Bear Family

☐ MASTERS, THE
EABCD 038 / 24 Nov '97 / Eagle

☐ ROBERT GORDON
LLR 00792 / 4 Mar '98 / LLIST

☐ ROBERT GORDON IS RED HOT
Red hot / Fool / I sure miss you / Flyin' saucer rock 'n' roll / Way I walk / Lonesome train (on a lonesome track) / I want to be free / Rockabilly boogie / All by myself / Catman / Wheel of fortune / Love baby / It's only make believe / Crazy man crazy / Worryin' kind / Nervous / Sweet love on my mind / Need you / Someday, someway / Look who's blue / Drivin' wheel / Something's gonna happen / Fire / Black slacks
BCD 15446 / Apr '89 / Bear Family

☐ ROBERT GORDON WITH LINK WRAY/ FRESH FISH SPECIAL (Gordon, Robert & Link Wray)
Red hot / I sure miss you / Summertime blues / Boppin' the blues / Sweet surrender / Flying saucers rock 'n' roll / Fool / It's in the bottle / Woman (you're my woman) / Is this the way / May I walk / Red cadillac and a black moustache / If this is wrong / Five days, five days / Fire / I want to be free / Twenty flight rock / Sea cruise / Lonesome train (on a lonesome track) / Blue eyes / Rock Billy boogie / Black slacks / Love my baby / All by myself / Nervous / Sweet love on my mind / Drivin' wheel / Someday someway / Fire (Live)
RVCD 57 / Mar '97 / Raven

☐ ROBERT GORDON WITH LINK WRAY/ FRESH FISH SPECIAL (Gordon, Robert & Link Wray)
Red hot / I sure miss you / Summertime blues / Boppin' the blues / Sweet surrender / Flyin' saucer rock 'n' roll / Fool / It's in the bottle / Woman (you're my woman) / Is this the way / Way I walk / Red Cadillac and a black moustache / If this is wrong / Five days five days / Fire / I want to be free / Twenty flight rock / Sea cruise / Lonesome train (on a lonesome track) / Blue eyes (don't run away) / Endless sleep
CDCHD 656 / Jun '97 / Ace

☐ ROCKABILLY BOOGIE
Rockabilly boogie / Love my baby / I just found out / All by myself / Black slacks / Catman / It's only make believe / Wheel of fortune / Am I blue / Walk on by / I just met a memory / Blue Christmas
OW 34496 / Sep '97 / One Way

☐ TOO FAST TO LIVE...TOO YOUNG TO DIE
Too fast to live...too young to die / Red hot / Are you gonna be the one / Black slacks / Crazy man / Born to lose / Way I walk / Love my baby / Uptown / Rock billy boogie / Red Cadillac / Woman / Am I blue / Drivin' wheel / All by myself / Sweet love on my mind / Bad boy / Fire / Twenty flight rock / Summertime blues / Lonesome train / Sea cruise / Boppin' the blues / Flying saucer rock 'n' roll / Fool / If this is wrong
74321500222 / Jun '97 / Camden

Gordon, Rosco

☐ ROSCO'S RHYTHM
T-model boogie / Decorate the counter / I wade through muddy water (dream on baby) / I love you better than I love myself / Just love me baby / Weeping blues / Do the chicken (dance with you) / Love for you baby / That's what you do to me / I found a new love / I don't like it / Hard headed woman / Shoobie oobie / Cheese and crackers / Real pretty Mama / Sally Jo / Torro / Do the bop / Nineteen years / Tired of living / If you don't love me baby / Love with me baby / Hey little girl / New Orleans LA
CPCD 8273 / Apr '97 / Charly

Gordon, Roxy

☐ SMALLER CIRCLES
Smaller circles / Andrew Gray and the ghost / Long gone Texas woman / Murder / Indians / Gods / I dreamed I saw Joe Hill last night / Willie / Santa Fe freight / Bead Mountain, Valera / Texas eagle
RGFWOWCD 031 / May '97 / Road Goes On Forever

Gore

☐ CRUEL PLACE, THE
Breeding / Cruel place / Garden of evil / Death has come
MD 7905CD / Apr '89 / Megadisc

☐ LIFELONG DEADLINE
MM1 / Mar '93 / Barooni

☐ MEST/694'3
MBMCD 07 / Feb '97 / Messback

Gore, Lesley

☐ IT'S MY PARTY (5CD Set)
Hello, young lovers / Something wonderful / It's my party / Danny / Party's over / Judy's turn to cry / Just let me cry / Misty / Cry me a river / I would / No more tears / Cry and you cry alone / I understand / Cry / Sunshine, lollipops, and rainbows / What kind of fool am I / If that's the way you want it / She's a fool / I'll make it up to you / Old crowd / I struck a match / Consolation prize / Run Bobby run / Young and foolsih / Fools rush in / My foolish heart / That's the way the ball bounces / After he takes me home (1 Voice) / After he takes me home (2 Voices) / You don't own me (Mono) / You don't own me (Stereo) / Time to go / You name it / That's the way boys are / Boys / I'm coolin', no foolin' / Don't deny it / I don't wanna be a loser / It's gotta be you / Leave me alone / Don't call me / Look of love / Wonder boy / Secret love / Maybe / Live and learn / Sometimes I wish I were a boy / Hey now / Died inside / Movin' away / It's about that time / Little girl go home / Say goodbye / You've come back / I just don't know if I can / That's the boy / All of my life / What's a girl supposed to do / Before and after / I cannot hope for anyone / I don't care / You didn't look around / Baby that's me / No matter what you do / Sunshine and lollipops / What am I gonna do with you / Girl in love / Just another fool / My town, my guy and me / Let me dream / Things we did last summer / Start the party again / I can tell / I won't love you anymore / I just can't get enough of you / Only last night / Any other girl / To know him is to love him / Young love / Too young / Will you still love me tomorrow / We know we're in love / Yeah yeah yeah that boy of mine / That's what I'll do / Lilacs and violets / Off and running / Happiness is just around the corner / Hold me tight / Cry like a baby / Treat me like a lady / Maybe now / Bubble broke / California nights / I'm going out the same way I came in / Bad / Love goes on forever / Summer and Sandy / I'm falling down / Brink of disaster / On a day like today / Where can I go / You sent me silver bells / He won't see the light / Magic colours / How can I be sure / To Sir with love / It's a happening world / Small talk / Say what you see / He gives me love (La la la) / Brand new me / I can't make it without you / Look the other way / Take good care (Of my heart) / I'll be standing by / Ride a tall white horse / 98.6 / Summer symphony / All cried out / One by one / Wedding bell blues / Got to get you into my life / Goodbye Tony (You don't own me) / Musikant (Time to go) / So sind die boys alle / Nur du allein / Hab ich das verdient / Der erste tanz / Little little liebling / Sieben girls / Tu t'en vas / Je ne sais plus / Je n'ose pas / Si ton coeur le desire / Je sais qu'en jour / C'est trop tard / Eh non / Te voila / Judy's turn to cry (Italian) / You don't own me (Italian) / Lazy day
BCD 15742 / Jun '94 / Bear Family

☐ IT'S MY PARTY (The Mercury Anthology)
Hello young lover / It's my party / Judy's turn to cry / Judy let me cry / Sunshine, lollipops and rainbows / If that's the way you want it / She's a fool / Old crowd / Consolation prize / Run Bobby run / That's the way the ball bounces / After he takes me home / You don't own me / That's the way boys are / I'm coolin', no foolin' / I don't wanna be a loser / Don't call me, I'll call you / Look of love / Wonder boy / Maybe I know / Sometimes I wish I were a boy / Hey now / Movin' away / Little girl go home / I just don't know if I can / All of my life
5325172 / Oct '96 / Mercury

☐ START THE PARTY AGAIN
RVCD 31 / Jan '94 / Raven

Gore, Martin L.

☐ COUNTERFEIT
Compulsion / In a manner of speaking / Smile in the crowd / Gone / Never turn your back on mother earth / Motherless child
CDSTUMM 67 / Apr '89 / Mute

Gore Slut

☐ ABOVE THE LISA DRUGSTORE
PSYCHOBABBLE 14 / 24 Aug '98 / Stickman

☐ THESE DAYS ARE THE QUIET KIND
PSYCHOBABBLE 008 / Jun '97 / Stickman

Gorefest

☐ CHAPTER 13
SPV 08518862 / Mar '98 / SPV

☐ EINDHOVEN INSANITY
NB 091CD / Aug '93 / Nuclear Blast

☐ ERASE
NB 231CD / Apr '97 / Nuclear Blast

☐ MINDLOSS
NB 086CD / Aug '93 / Nuclear Blast

☐ SOUL SURVIVOR
NB 143CD / Apr '96 / Nuclear Blast

Gorgoroth

☐ ANTICHRIST
MR 008CD / May '96 / Malicious

☐ DESTROYER
Destroyer / Open the gates / Devil the sinner and his journey / Om kristen og jodisk tru / Pa slagmaric langt mot Nord / Blood offer / Virginborn / Slottet I det fierne
NB 3212 / 6 Jul '98 / Nuclear Blast

☐ PENTAGRAM
TE 001CD / Oct '94 / Embassy
MR 007CD / Apr '96 / Malicious

☐ UNDER THE SIGN
MR 013CD / 27 Oct '97 / Malicious

Gories

☐ HOUSEROCKIN
EFA 11577 2 / Sep '94 / Crypt

Gorilla Biscuits

☐ START TODAY
New direction / Degradation / Forgotten / Start today / First failure / Time flies / Stand still / Good intentions / Things we say / Two sides / Competition / Cats and dogs
WB 054CD / Nov '89 / We Bite

Gorillas

☐ MESSAGE TO THE WORLD
DAMGOOD 49 / Nov '94 / Damaged Goods

Gorka, John

☐ I KNOW
RHRCD 18 / Jul '95 / Red House

☐ OUT OF THE VALLEY
Good noise / That's why / Carnival knowledge / Talk about love / Big time lonesome / Furniture / Mystery to me / Out of the valley / Thoughtless behaviour / Always going home / Flying red horse / Up until then
72902103252 / Aug '94 / High Street

☐ TEMPORARY ROAD
72902103152 / Jan '95 / High Street

Gorky's Zygotic Mynci

☐ BARAFUNDLE
Diamond dew / Barafundle bumbler / Starmoonsun / Patio song / Better rooms / Heywood lane / Pen gwag glas / Bola bola / Cursed, coined and crucified / Sometimes the father is the son / Meirion wyllt / Wizard and the lizard / Miniature kingdoms / Dark night / Hwyl fawr I pawb / Wordless song
5347692 / Apr '97 / Fontana

☐ BWYD TIME
ANKST 059CD / Apr '97 / Ankst

☐ GORKY 5
5588222 / 31 Aug '98 / Mercury

☐ INTRODUCING
5328162 / Sep '96 / Fontana

☐ MERCHED
ANKST 048CD / Apr '97 / Ankst

☐ PATIO
ANKST 055CD / Apr '97 / Ankst

☐ TATAY
ANKST 047CD / Apr '97 / Ankst

Gorl, Robert

☐ ELEKTRO (Gorl, Robert & Pete Namlock)
PK 08109 / Mar '96 / Fax

☐ WATCH THE REAL COPYCAT
EFA 122922 / Sep '96 / Disko B

Gorman, Skip

☐ GREENER PRAIRIE, A
ROUCD 329 / Oct '94 / Rounder

☐ LONESOME PRAIRIE LOVE
ROUCD 359 / May '96 / Rounder

Gorme, Eydie

☐ 20 LOVE SONGS
Sabras que te quiero / Dime / Esta tarde vi llover / Eres tu / Quiereme mucho / Tomame o dejame / Muy amigos / Hay muy pacos / Te sigo amando / Si vuel ves tu / Since I fell for you / Breaking up is hard to do / You're nobody till somebody loves you / Come in from the rain / Send in the clowns / What'll I do / God bless the child / First time / 'round midnight / But he was good for me
RMB 75025 / Jan '92 / Remember

☐ EYDIE GORME COLLECTOR'S EDITION
DVAD 6052 / Apr '95 / Deja Vu

☐ Y LOS PANCHOS
Sabras que te quiero / Dime / Esta tarde vi lover / Eres tu / Nosotros / Piel canela / Y... / Sabor a mi / Quiereme mucho / Noche de ronda / Caminito / Since I fell for you / Breaking up is hard to do / You're nobody till somebody loves you
CD 62101 / Oct '96 / Saludos Amigos

Gospel Hummingbirds

☐ TAKING FLIGHT
BPCD 5023 / Dec '95 / Blind Pig

Gospel Messengers

☐ YOU CAN LEAN ON ME
INAK 9040 / Feb '97 / In Akustik

Gospel Of The Horns

☐ SATANISTS DREAM
ENSTD 001MCD / Jul '96 / Polyphemus

Gospel Voices

☐ MAGIC GOSPEL
Wi se Lanmou (Oh happy day) / Operator / Gat away Jordan / This little light of mine / Lord I want to be a Christian / Joshua fit the battle of Jericho / Louez-Le / Freedom / Praise him / I want to be ready / Thank you Lord / When the saints
19136 / Jan '97 / Forlane

Gospellers

☐ WE'VE GOT THE POWER
VSCD 100 / Dec '95 / Vision UK

Goss, Kieran

☐ BRAND NEW STAR
DARA 3047 / 18 Aug '97 / Dara

☐ NEW DAY
DARA 3064 / Aug '97 / Dara

Gossip

☐ CHAIN REACTION
CDPG 3 / Apr '98 / Grilli

Gostanzo, Sonny

☐ SONNY'S ON THE MONEY
STCD 555 / Jan '93 / Stash

Gota

☐ IT'S SO DIFFERENT HERE
EX 3472 / Feb '97 / Instinct

Gotham Gospel

☐ BEST OF GOTHAM GOSPEL, THE
Harmonizing four / Dixie hummingbird / Echo gospel singers / Edna Gallmon Cook / Zion harmonizers / Harmony kings / Rugged cross singers
HTCD 04 / Oct '90 / Heritage

Gotohells

☐ BURNING BRIDGES
VR 334 / 20 Jul '98 / Vagrant

Gottsching, Manuel

☐ DREAM AND DESIRE
14243 / 23 Mar '98 / Spalax

☐ E2 E4
14241 / Oct '96 / Spalax

Goubert, Simon

☐ HAITI
A 7 / Apr '93 / Seventh

☐ L'ENCIERRO
A 18 / Dec '95 / Seventh

Goudreau, Barry

☐ BARRY GOUDREAU
Hard luck / Nothin' to lose / What's a fella to do / Mean woman blues / Leavin' tonight / Dreams / Life is what you make it / Sailin' away / Cold cold wind
RE 21042 / Jul '96 / Razor & Tie

Gouds Thumb

☐ GOUDS THUMB
Together / 29 / Tangerine / Beautiful local / Chemicals / Trophies / Piss pool / Apnea / El Campeon Macizo / Bottom feeder / Manny / Jesus arms / Anea electric
RR 88062 / Jul '97 / Roadrunner

Gough, David

☐ PICTURE THIS
How long / Teach me / Go ye / Good news / Highly recommended / My saviour's voice / Raise your hand / I really need you / He'll never leave you / Because of you / I'm the one / Highly recommended
DRCD 781442 / 27 Oct '97 / Doron

Gough, Orlando

☐ MESSAGE FROM THE BORDER
Saeta / Late / Currulao
09026683322 / Oct '96 / Catalyst

Gould, Morton

☐ BLUES IN THE NIGHT (Gould, Morton & His Orchestra)
Blues in the night / Birth of the blues / Solitude / That old devil moon / Nocturne / Limehouse blues / Mood indigo / St. Louis blues / Sophisticated lady / Big city blues / Moonglow / Deep purple
09026684772 / 6 Apr '98 / RCA Victor

Goulder, Dave

☐ STONE, STEAM AND STARLINGS
Clearing place / Carter / Stone on stone / These dry stone walls / Go from my window / Proper little gent / Colours / Seven summers / Friar in the well / Sally gardens / Follower / I will go with my father / Footplate cuisine
HARCD 017 / Oct '93 / Harbour Town

Gouldman, Graham

☐ GRAHAM GOULDMAN THING, THE
Impossible years / Bus stop / Behind the door / Pawnbroker / Who are they / My father / No milk today / Upstairs, downstairs / For your love / Pamela, pamela / Chestnut
EDCD 346 / Apr '92 / Edsel

Goulesco, Lido

☐ CHANTS FOLKLORIQUES TZIGANES
824412 / Nov '90 / BUDA

Goulet, Robert

☐ ROBERT GOULET
DVAD 6102 / May '95 / Deja Vu

Gourds

☐ DEM'S GOOD BEEBIE
Piss and moan blues / Caledonia / Dying of the pines / Jenny Brown / Clear night / Sweet Lil / When wine was cheap / Money honey / Honduras / Ringing dark and true / Pine tar ramparts / Makes me roll / Trampled by the sun / Web before you walk into it / I come up / All the labour
MUSA 501 / Feb '97 / Munich

☐ STADIUM BLITZER
Lament / Plaid coat / Magnolia / Stadium blitzer / LGO / Boil my strings / Coppermine / Maria / Raining in Port Arthur / Dyin' diamond / When the money comes rolling in / I ate the haggis / Cold bed / Pushed her down / Pine Island bayou / I like drinking
MUSA 503 / Feb '98 / Munich

Gourlay, James

☐ GOURLAY PLAYS TUBA (Gourlay, James & The Britannia Building Society Band)
DOYCD 028 / Apr '94 / Doyen

Gouzil, Denis

☐ LE P'TIT GROUILLOT QUI DANSE (Gouzil, Denis Groupe)
EPC 885 / Feb '92 / European Music Production

Government Issue

☐ CRASH
WB 042CD / Dec '88 / We Bite

☐ MAKE AN EFFORT
LF 114CD / Oct '94 / Lost & Found

Gov't Mule

☐ GOV'T MULE
8856115152 / 23 Feb '98 / Relativity

☐ LIVE AT THE ROSELAND BALLROOM
13012 / 23 Feb '98 / Foundation

Gowen, Alan

☐ IMPROVISATIONS (Gowen, Alan & Hugh Hopper)
Floating path / Now what exactly / Zaparoshti / Ranova / Al'Quest / Winged trilby / Six cream bombs from Beaune / Rubber daze
BP 186CD / Jul '97 / Blueprint

Gowen, Miller & Sinclair

☐ BEFORE A WORD IS SAID
Above and below / Reflexes in the margin / Nowadays a silhouette / Silver star / Fourfold / Before a word is said / Umbrellas / Fleeting glance
BP 130CD / Sep '96 / Blueprint

Goya Dress

☐ ROOMS
NUDE 5CD / May '96 / Nude

Goyeneche, Roberto

☐ TANGOS DEL SUR (Goyeneche, Roberto & Nestor Marconi)
883289 / Feb '97 / Milan Sur

Goykovich, Dusko

☐ BALKAN BLUE (2CD Set)
Simona / Yardbird suite / Medium rare / Adriatica / You've changed / Miss Bo / Nights of Skopje / Snap shot / You'd be so nice / Balkan dance / Bosna calling / Pannonia / East of Montenegro / Macedonia / Schumakya / Haze on the Danube / Ohrid / Finale
ENJ 932022 / Sep '97 / Enja

☐ BALKAN CONNECTION
Doboy / You're my everything / Bopper / Manhattan mood / Balkan blue / You don't know what love is / Handful of soul / Why not you / Nights of skopje / Nella
ENJ 90472 / Aug '96 / Enja

☐ BEBOP CITY
Sunrise in St. Petersburg / In the sign of Libra / Be bop city / Lament / Bop town / No love without tears / One for klook / Day by day / Brooklyn blues
ENJ 90152 / Jul '95 / Enja

☐ BELGRADE BLUES
HHCD 1008 / Jan '91 / Hot House

☐ SOUL CONNECTION
Soul connection / Ballad for miles / Inga / I'll close my eyes / Blues time / Adriatica / NYC / Blues valse / Teamwork song
ENJ 80442 / Mar '94 / Enja

Gozategi

☐ AINHOA
KD 441CD / Aug '97 / Elkar

☐ GOZATEGI
KDCD 405 / May '97 / Elkar

GP's

☐ SATURDAY ROLLING AROUND
Saturday rolling around / Steel guitar rag / Zimmerman blues / Together again / Pretty boy floyd / Love grows / I'm so lonesome I could cry / Penitentiary bound / Don't do it / Going, going, gone / Red apple juice / Honky tonk blues / I'm the one you need / Cut across shorty / Great balls of fire
HTDCD 53 / Mar '96 / HTD

Graae, Jason

☐ YOU'RE NEVER FULLY DRESSED WITHOUT A SMILE
VSD 5711 / Oct '96 / Varese Sarabande

Grabbers

☐ HAND YOU'RE DEALT, THE
F 021CD / Apr '97 / Fearless

Grabesmond

☐ MORDENHEIM
DPR 004CD / 15 Jun '98 / Napalm

Grabham, Mick

☐ MICK THE LAD
Sweet blossom woman / Scraunchy / You'll think of me / I won't be there / Waitin' round on you / There's ben a few since then / Let it all down / Two fifteen / Saga / On fire for you baby / Diamonds / Hit and miss / Wanderer
SJPCD 012 / Jul '97 / Angel Air

Grable, Betty

☐ PIN UP GIRL, THE (2CD Set)
Cowboy number / Snake dance / Let's k-nock k-nees / Music in my heart / Boys will be boys / What goes on here in my heart / Down Argentine way / Two dreams met / Hawaii-A / Sheik of Araby / You started something / Loveliness and love / Kindergarten conga / Hi you love / Another little dream wouldn't do us any harm / Are you kidding / I'm still crazy for you / I heard the birdies sing / Sing me a song of the islands / Down on Ami Ami Oni Oni Isle / O'Brien has gone Hawaiian / Run little raindrop run / Pan American jubilee / Cuddle up a little closer / Pretty baby / Miss Lulu from Louisville / Take it from there / Beautiful Coney Island / There's danger in a dance / Waiting at the church / My heart tells me / Sweet Rosie O'Grady / Going to the County Fair / You're my little pin up girl / Don't carry tales out of school / Once too often / Song of the very merry widow / Welcome to the Diamond Horseshoe / In Acapulco / Medley / Cooking up a show/The more I see of you / We have been around/Carolina in the morning / Powder, lipstick and rouge / I'm always chasing rainbows / Darktown strutter's ball / I can't begin to tell you
JASCD 103/4 / Apr '97 / Jasmine

Grace

☐ IF I COULD FLY
Not over yet / Down to earth / If I could fly / One day / You don't know / Orange / Love songs / You're not mine / Mineral / Skin on skin / I want to live
0630149472 / Jul '97 / Perfecto/East West

Grace

☐ GATHERING IN THE WHEAT (2CD Set)
Lunar / Driver / Buccaneer / Mullions / Square / PPiper / Architects of war / Poot / Fool / Anorak of fire / Hanging rock / Burglars / Sing something simple / Oklahoma / Wolf / Earth bites back / Court of despair / Holyman / Raindance / Roost
CYCL 065 / 17 Aug '98 / Cyclops

☐ POPPY
CYCL 044 / Nov '96 / Cyclops

☐ PULLING STRINGS & SHINY THINGS
Fool / Lean on me / Earth bites back / Every cloud has a silver lining / Architect of war / Hanging Rock / Gift
CYCL 002 / Feb '94 / Cyclops

Grace Notes

☐ RED WINE AND PROMISES
All that is good / Spirit song / Magdalen laundry / Gypsy Davey / Lies / Finistere / Red wine and promises / The light tonight / Welcome sailor / Quiet land of Erin / Witch of the westmorelands / Withered and died / I'll follow the sun
FECD 126 / 30 Mar '98 / Fellside

Grace, Teddy

☐ TURN ON THAT RED HOT HEAT
Rockin' chair swing / Turn off the moon / I want a new romance / I'm losing my mind over you / Over the rainbow / I've got rain in my eyes / Turn on that red hot heat / Rock it for me / I'm so in love / I thought about you
HEPCD 1054 / Jun '97 / Hep

Grace Thrillers

☐ CARIBBEAN RHYTHMS
GTCD 013 / 15 Dec '97 / Grace

☐ I WILL BE WITH YOU
GTCD 014 / 15 Dec '97 / Grace

Gracenotes

☐ DOWN FALLS THE DAY
GN 001CD / Jan '94 / Gracenotes

Gracie, Charlie

☐ IT'S FABULOUS
CTJCD 2 / May '95 / Cotton Town Jubilee

Graciela

☐ CON MACHITO Y SU ORQUESTA
ALCD 020 / Jul '96 / Alma Latina

Gracious

☐ ECHO
Echo / Winter / Homecoming / Cynic's gate / Autumn / Mangroove / Summer / Faith / Spring / Oil pressure
CENCD 015 / Mar '96 / Centaur

☐ GRACIOUS
REP 4060 / Aug '91 / Repertoire

☐ GRACIOUS/THIS IS GRACIOUS
Introduction / Hell / Dream / Blood red sun / Prepare to meet thy maker / What's come to be / Hold me down / Heaven / Fugue in D minor / Supercide / Arrival of the traveller / Say goodbye to love / CBS / Blue skies and adlibs
BGOCD 256 / Feb '95 / Beat Goes On

Grady Cain

☐ FACES OF CAIN
INF 80005CD / Nov '96 / Infinity

Graewe, Georg

☐ 1995 SAN FRANCISCO CONCERT, THE
10.38 / 4.30 / 5.00 / 4.05 / 7.20 / 4.50 / 3.00
CD 968 / Jun '97 / Music & Arts

☐ SATURN CYCLE
CD 958 / Dec '96 / Music & Arts

Graf, Bob

☐ BOB GRAF AT WESTMINSTER
Bernie's tune / Street of dreams / Dear old Stockholm / Funky ride / Four
DE 401 / Mar '97 / Delmark

Graff, Randy

☐ DOING SOMETHING RIGHT
VSD 5652 / Aug '96 / Varese Sarabande

Graham, Davey

☐ AFTER HOURS
RCCD 3021 / Mar '98 / Rollercoaster

☐ ALL THAT MOODY
Finger buster / Blue raga / To find the sun / Tristano etc / Anji / Travelling man / Sunshine raga / Kim / Jenra / La Morena / Preacher blues
RCCD 3022 / Apr '98 / Rollercoaster

☐ GUITAR PLAYER...PLUS, THE
Don't stop the carnival / Sermonette / Take five / How long blues / Sunset eyes / Cry me a river / Angie / 3/4 AD / Ruby and the pearl / Buffalo / Exodus / Yellow bird / Blues for Betty / Hallelujah, I love her so / Davy's train blues
SEECD 351 / Jun '92 / See For Miles

☐ TROUBADOUR
RCCD 3030 / Apr '98 / Rollercoaster

Graham, David

☐ VERY THOUGHT OF YOU, THE
West side story / Jumpin' Charlie / Slow foxtrot / Bossa nova / Let it be me / Quickstep / Love changes everything / Tango Havana / Miranda's theme / Swingin' shepherd blues / Ave Maria
OS 216 / Nov '95 / OS Digital

Graham, Larry

☐ AIN'T NO BOUT A DOUBT IT (Graham Central Station)
Your love / It's alright / I can't stand the rain / You / I know this love / It's alright / Can't stand the rain / Ain't nothing but a Warner Brothers party / Ole Smokey / Easy rider / Water luckiest people
7599263462 / Jan '96 / Warner Bros.

☐ BEST OF LARRY GRAHAM & GRAHAM CENTRAL STATION
We've been waiting / Can you handle it / It's alright / One in a million you / My radio sure sounds good to me / Is it love / Sooner or later / Your love / Jam / Hair / Now do-u-wanta dance
9362460432 / Apr '96 / Warner Bros.

Graham, Len

☐ DO ME JUSTICE
CC 37CD / Dec '94 / Claddagh

☐ YE LOVERS ALL
CC 41CD / Dec '94 / Claddagh

Graham, Peter

☐ MUSIC OF PETER GRAHAM, THE
Alderley edge / Prisms / Dimensions / Montage / Essence of time / Crimond
DOYCD 069 / Dec '97 / Doyen

Graham, Tammy

☐ TAMMY GRAHAM
7822188422 / Jul '97 / MCA

Graham-White, Susan

☐ NOT AFRAID TO FLY
BLX 10029CD / Aug '96 / Blix Street

Grainger, Porter

☐ PORTER GRAINGER 1923-1927
JPCD 1521 / Jul '96 / Jazz Perspectives

Grainger, Richard

☐ THUNDERWOOD
Silent spring / Old Whitby town / Golden Grove/ Mallaig moorings / Northern town bay / Foxhunting song / Streets of Kings Cross / Mermaid / Polly on the shore / Glasgow wedding/Far from home / Grove fisherman / Ghost of Old Solem / From Mulgrave to Eskside / Thunderwood
FSCD 27 / Aug '94 / Folksound

Gramm, Lou

☐ FOREIGNER IN A STRANGE LAND
Won't somebody take her home / Don't you know me, my friend / Better know your heart / I can't make it alone / How do you tell someone / Society's child / I wish today was yesterday / My baby / Headin' home / Watch you walk away
CDTB 065 / '88 / Thunderbolt

Grampian Police Pipe Band

☐ PIPES AND DRUMS
EUCD 1261 / Mar '94 / ARC

Grand Dominion Jazz Band

☐ GRAND DOMINION JAZZBAND VOL.2
SOSCD 1268 / Oct '93 / Stomp Off

☐ SMILES
SOSCD 1330 / Feb '98 / Stomp Off

Grand Luxe

☐ GRAND LUXE
3031732 / Jul '97 / Village Vert

Grand Mother Funck

☐ HEEBIE JEEBIES DANCE
HBR 97012CD / 16 Jul '97 / Honey Bear

Grand, Otis

☐ ALWAYS HOT (Grand, Otis & The Dance Kings)
SPCD 1019 / Oct '88 / Special Delivery

☐ ALWAYS HOT (Grand, Otis & The Dance Kings)
Love at first sight / Woke up this morning / Fix our love / Always hot / Shame shame shame / Whole lotta lovin' / Rebecca / Don't know why / Let's party / No alibi
IGOXCD 505 / Feb '97 / Indigo

☐ BLUES SESSIONS 1990-1994, THE
Beatrice, Beatrice / Young devil / Insomnia / They killed Crazy Horse / Why oh why / Blues for T-Bone / Down thru' the years / No educated woman / Chains of love / Jimmy's jump medley / Cheese and crackers / I'm the one / Sit right here
JSPCD 294 / 6 Oct '97 / JSP

☐ HE KNOWS THE BLUES
Things are getting harder to do / You hurt me / Jumpin' for Jimmy / Grand style / Real good news / SRV (My mood too) / Leave that girl / Ham / Your love pulls no punches / Swing turn / Teach me how to love you / He knows the blues
NEX CD 219 / Jul '92 / Sequel

☐ NOTHING ELSE MATTERS
NEXCD 272 / Sep '94 / Sequel

Granda, Chabuca

☐ FLOR DE LA CANELA
4301120912 / 27 Apr '98 / ANS

Grandaddy

☐ UNDER THE WESTERN FREEWAY
ABB 152CD / 13 Apr '98 / Big Cat

Granderson, John Lee

☐ HARD LUCK JOHN
Minglewood blues / Hard luck John / Flora blues / Please come back to me / Death Valley blues / Texas blues / Rock me all night long / Cold cold evening / County farm blues / Decoration day / Aching pain blues / This is your last chance / That's doggin' me / Watch out girl / One more blues / One more favour
TCD 5031 / 30 Mar '98 / Testament

Grandjean, Etienne

☐ ACCORDEON DIATONIQUE AND VIOLON
GRI 190822 / Sep '96 / Griffe

☐ CIRCUS VALSE
CD 842 / May '93 / Diffusion Breizh

☐ LA BELLE SOCIETE
BPCD 9391 / May '97 / Boucherie Productions

Grandmaster Flash

☐ GRANDMASTER FLASH VS. THE SUGARHILL GANG (2CD Set) (Grandmaster Flash & The Sugarhill Gang)
SMDCD 164 / Jul '97 / Snapper

☐ GREATEST HITS (Grandmaster Flash & Melle Mel)
White lines (don't don't do it) / Step off / Pump me up / Jesse / Beat street / Vice / Freedom / Birthday party / Flash to the beat / It's nasty (genius of love) / Message / Scorpio / Message II (survival) / New York, New York
NEMCD 622 / May '92 / Sequel

☐ GREATEST MIXES (Grandmaster Flash & The Furious Five)
White lines / Step off / Drug wars / Pump me up / Message II (Survival) / Freestyle / New York / New York / Beat Street breakdown / Message / Scratchin' / Larry's dance theme
DEEPF 015 / 19 Dec '97 / Deep Beats

☐ MORE HITS (Grandmaster Flash & The Furious Five)
Adventures of Grandmaster Flash on the wheels of steel / Message / Showdown / She's fresh / It's a shame / White lines / World war III / Hustlers convention / King of the streets / Super rappin' no.1 / New adventures of Grandmaster
DEEPM 004 / Nov '96 / Deep Beats

Grandmaster Melle Mel

☐ RIGHT NOW (Grandmaster Melle Mel & Scorpio)
Intro / On the down low / Mama / If... / Right now / When you lose a child / China white / Broke ass niggas / Smackin' rapper / New York - LA / Stupid Mutha Fuckas / Sex you / Mr. Big Stuff
0098862 RAP / 8 Sep '97 / Edel

Grandmothers

☐ DREAMS ON LONGPLAY
EFA 034032 / Apr '95 / Muffin

☐ WHO COULD IMAGINE
NETCD 53 / Nov '94 / Network

Granelli, Jerry

☐ BROKEN CIRCLE
Sign 'o' the times / Red and blue days / Washing of the water / From far away / Boogie stop shuffle / Lonnie's lament/Song of a good name / Crazy Horse's dream / Holy road / Broken circle / Dream horse leaving / Wounded knee / Crazy Horse's dream (reprise)
INT 35012 / Sep '96 / Intuition

☐ FORCES OF FLIGHT
Prelude / Prelude / Aramoana / Walking with the snake / Day / Requiem / Forces of flight / Prologue / Sound of the earth with us on it
ITMP 970061 / Apr '93 / ITM

☐ KOPUTAI
Koputai / Pillars / Haiku / I could see forever / Julia's child / In the moment
ITMP 970058 / Jan '94 / ITM

☐ NEWS FROM THE STREET
Honey boy / Big love / Rainbow's cadillac / Swamp / Sad hour / Akicita / Ellen waltzing / Brilliant corners / Blue Spanish eyes / News from the street / Little wing
VBR 21462 / 27 Apr '98 / Intuition

Graney, Dave

☐ MY LIFE ON THE PLAINS
FIRE 33020 / Oct '91 / Fire

☐ NIGHT OF THE WOLVERINE
You're just to hip, baby / Mogambo / Night of the wolverine / I'm just having one of those lives / I held the cold breeze / I remember you / Three dead passengers in a stolen second hand ford / That's the way it's gonna be / Maggie Cassidy / You need to suffer / Night of the wolverine / Out there
5321292 / May '96 / This Way Up

☐ SOFT 'N' SEXY SOUND, THE
5284162 / Sep '96 / This Way Up

☐ SOFT 'N' SEXY SOUND/1001 AUSTRALIAN NIGHTS (2CD Set)
Birds and the goats / I'm gonna live in my own big world / Apollo 69 / I'm not afraid to be heavy / Deep inside a song / Pre-revolutionary scene / Rock 'n' roll is where I hide / Salty girls / Outward bound / Scorched earth love affair / Morrison floorshow / Dandies are never unbuttoned / Night of the wolverine / You wanna be loved / You're just too hip, baby / I'm gonna live in my own big world / Birds and the goats / I'm not afraid to be heavy / Deep inside a song / Scorched earth love affair / Rock 'n' roll is where I hide
5340592 / Sep '96 / This Way Up

Granfaloon Bus

☐ ROCKET NOON
TR 30060032 / 29 Jun '98 / Trocadero

☐ SLEEPING CAR
TR 30080042 / 27 Apr '98 / Trocadero

Granger

☐ UNDERWATER HUM
SH 5712 / Oct '96 / Shanachie

Grant, Amy

☐ AGE TO AGE
In a little while / I have decided / I love a lonely day / Don't run away / Fat baby / Sing your praises to the Lord / El-Shaddai / Raining on the inside / Got to let it go / Arms of love
MYRCD 6697 / '88 / Myrrh

☐ AMY GRANT
MYRCD 6586 / '88 / Myrrh

☐ AMY GRANT IN CONCERT VOL.1
MYRCD 6668 / '88 / Myrrh

☐ AMY GRANT IN CONCERT VOL.2
MYRCD 6677 / '88 / Myrrh

☐ BEHIND THE EYES
5407602 / Sep '97 / A&M

☐ CHRISTMAS ALBUM, A
Tennessee Christmas / Hark the herald angels sing / Preiset dem Konig (Praise the King) / Emmanuel / Little town / Christmas hymn / Love has come / Sleigh ride / Christmas song / Heirlooms / Mighty fortress / Angels we have heard on high
MYRCD 6768 / '88 / Myrrh

☐ FATHER'S EYES
MYRCD 6625 / '88 / Myrrh

☐ HEART IN MOTION
Good for me / Baby baby / Every heartbeat / That's the way love is / Ask me / Galileo / You're not alone / Hats / I will remember you / How can we see that far / Hopes set high
5403212 / 15 Sep '97 / A&M

☐ HEART IN MOTION/LEAD ME ON (2CD Set)
CDA 24123 / Jul '94 / A&M

☐ HOME FOR CHRISTMAS
Have yourself a merry little Christmas / It's the most wonderful time of the year / Joy to the world / Breath of heaven (Mary's song) / O'come all ye faithful / Grown up Christmas list / Rockin' around the Christmas tree / Winter wonderland / I'll be home for Christmas / Night before Christmas / Emmanuel, God with us / Jesu joy of man's desiring
5400012 / 15 Sep '97 / A&M

☐ HOUSE OF LOVE
Lucky one / Say you'll be mine / Whatever it takes / House of love / Power / Oh how the years go by / Big yellow taxi / Helping hand / Politics of kissing / Love has a hold on me / Our love / Children of the world
5402562 / 15 Sep '97 / A&M

☐ NEVER ALONE
Look what has happened to me / So glad / Walking away with you / Family / Don't give up on me / That's the day / If I have to die / All I ever have to be / It's a miracle / Too late / First love / Say once more
MYRCD 6645 / '88 / Myrrh

☐ STRAIGHT AHEAD
MYRCD 6757 / '88 / Myrrh

☐ UNGUARDED
Love of another kind / Find a way / Everywhere I go / I love you / Stepping in your shoes / Fight / Wise up / Who to listen to / Sharayah / Prodigal
MYRCD 6806 / '88 / Myrrh

Grant, Coot

☐ GRANT & WILSON VOL.1 1925-1928 (Grant, Coot & 'Kid' Wesley Wilson)
DOCD 5563 / 21 Sep '97 / Document

☐ GRANT & WILSON VOL.2 1928-1931 (Grant, Coot & 'Kid' Wesley Wilson)
DOCD 5564 / 21 Sep '97 / Document

☐ GRANT & WILSON VOL.3 1931-1938 (Grant, Coot & 'Kid' Wesley Wilson)
DOCD 5565 / 21 Sep '97 / Document

☐ VOCAL DUET, THE (Grant, Coot & 'Kid' Wesley Wilson)
CARCD 1502 / Sep '97 / Clifford

Grant, Darrell

☐ BLACK ART
CRISS 1987CD / Sep '95 / Criss Cross

☐ NEW BOP, THE
CRISS 1106 / Dec '95 / Criss Cross

Grant, David

☐ VERY BEST OF DAVID GRANT & JAKI GRAHAM, THE (Grant, David & Jaki Graham)
Could it be I'm falling in love / Round and around / Set me free / Turn around / Rock the midnight / So excited / Love me tonight / Heaven knows / Mated / Watching you watching me / Love will find a way / Step right up / Facts of love / Stop and go / Breaking away / Where our love begins
CDGOLD 1033 / May '96 / EMI Gold

Grant, Della

☐ BLACK ROSE
RG 5803 / Feb '95 / Twinkle

☐ DAWTA OF THE DUST
RGCD 5804 / Oct '95 / Twinkle

☐ IN FINE STYLE
NGCD 556 / 10 Aug '98 / Twinkle

☐ ROOTICALLY YOURS
NGCD 542 / Feb '94 / Twinkle

Grant, Eddy

☐ BEST OF EDDY GRANT, THE
I don't wanna dance / Gimme hope Jo'anna / Electric Avenue / Walking on sunshine / Do you feel my love / Symphony for Michael opus 2 / Living on the front line / Front line symphony / Can't get enough of you / Neighbour, neighbour / I love you, yes I love you / It's our time / Romancing the stone / Till I can't take love no more / War party / Say I love you
CDMFP 6203 / Nov '95 / Music For Pleasure

☐ BEST OF EDDY GRANT, THE
DC 866122 / Mar '96 / Disky

☐ CAN'T GET ENOUGH
Do you feel my love / Time to let go / That is why / I love to truck / Can't get enough of you / Give yourself to me / I love you yes I love you / Kill 'em with kindness / California style
30122 / Oct '97 / Go On Deluxe

☐ GOING FOR BROKE
Romancing the stone / Boys in the street / Come on let me know / Till I can't take love no more / Political bassa bassa / Telepathy / Only heaven knows / Irie Harry / Rock you good / Blue wave
920412 / Jun '92 / Ice

☐ GREATEST HITS
I don't wanna dance / Gimme hope Joanna / Electric Avenue / Walking on sunshine / Do you feel my love / Symphony for Michael Opus / Living on the front line / Front line symphony / I can't get enough of you / Neighbour, neighbour / I love you, yes I love you / It's our time / Romancing the stone / Till I can't take love no more / War party / Say I love you
CDGOLD 1061 / Oct '96 / EMI Gold

☐ KILLER ON THE RAMPAGE
Electric avenue / I don't wanna dance / It's all in you / War party / Funky rock 'n' roll party / Too young to fall / Latin love affair / Another revolutionary / Drop baby drop / Killer on the rampage
30112 / Oct '97 / Go On Deluxe

☐ PAINTINGS OF THE SOUL
90202 / Mar '92 / Ice

Grant, Gogi

☐ SUDDENLY THERE'S...
PS 014CD / Feb '97 / P&S

Grant, Isla

☐ LIFE'S STORYBOOK COVER
Listen to the childern / It's been a long time / Mothers chair / God please forgive me / Mother / Keeper of my heart / Life's storybook cover / Ghosts of Culloden / There's nothing new - I'm missing you / Like leaves in the wind / Cottage in the country / Dark, deep, rolling water / Scotland you are in my heart forever / Precious Lord - please lead me / Till the day that he met you / My homeland
CDELM 4100 / Nov '96 / ELM

Grant, James

☐ SAWDUST IN MY VEINS
Pray the dawn / All her Saturdays / I can't stop bleeding / Cure for life / I don't know you anymore / Is anybody dreaming / No chicane / Hide / This is the last time / Sawdust in my veins / If you love me leave me alone
SURCD 022 / 27 Apr '98 / Survival

Grant, Julie

☐ YOU CAN COUNT ON ME
Somebody tell him / Every letter you write / So many ways / Unimportant things / When you're smiling / Lonely sixteen / Up on the roof / When you ask about love / Count on me / Then only then / That's how heartaches are made / Cruel world / Don't ever let me down / Somebody cares / Hello love / It's alright / Every day I have to cry / What what you do with my baby / You're nobody 'til somebody loves you / I only care about you / Come to me / Can't get you out of my mind / Baby baby / My world is empty without you / Giving up / 'Cause I believe in you / Lonely without you / As long as I know he's mine / Stop / When the loving ends
RPM 133 / Aug '94 / RPM

Grant Lee Buffalo

☐ COPPEROPOLIS
Homespun / Bridge / Arousing thunder / Even the oxen / Crackdown / Armchair / Bethlehem steel / All that I have / Two and two / Better for us / Hyperion and sunset / Comes to blows / Only way down
8287602 / Jun '96 / Slash

☐ FUZZY
Shining hour / Jupiter and Teardrop / Fuzzy / Wish you well / Hook / Soft wolf tread / Stars 'n' stripes / Dixie drugstore / America snoring / Grace / You just have to be crazy
8283892 / 15 Sep '97 / Slash

☐ MIGHTY JOE MOON
Lone star song / Mockingbirds / It's the life / Sing along / Mighty Joe Moon / Demon called deception / Lady Godiva and me / Drag / Last days of Tecumseh / Happiness / Honey don't think / Side by side / Rock of ages
8285412 / Aug '94 / Slash

Grant Street String Band

☐ GRANT STREET STRING BAND
Things in life / Bear song / Old crossroads / I cried again / Cash on the barrelhead / Fiddle medley / My sweet love ain't around / Say old man can you play the fiddle / Seasons of the heart / In my dear old Southern home / Once a day / Crossing the Cumberlands / Prairie lullaby
FR 103 / May '97 / Flat Rock

Grant, Tom

☐ HAVE YOURSELF A MERRY LITTLE CHRISTMAS
SH 5025 / Nov '96 / Shanachie

☐ INSTINCT
SHCD 5015 / Oct '95 / Shanachie

☐ LIP SERVICE
SHCD 5037 / Aug '97 / Shanachie

Graphite

☐ CHESNUT LOKE
AACD 020 / 15 Jun '98 / Audio Archive

☐ LIVE IN CORNWALL 1971
AACD 025 / 16 Feb '98 / Audio Archive

Grapow, Roland

☐ FOUR SEASONS OF LIFE
Prelude No.1/Presto / Winner / No more disguise / Show me the way / I remember / Dedicated to... / Bread of charity / 4 seasons of life / Finale de souvenir
SRECD 702 / Jun '97 / Reef

Grappelli, Stephane

☐ 85 AND STILL SWINGING
CDC 7549182 / Jun '94 / Angel

☐ AT THE WINERY VOL.1
You took advantage of me / So danco samba / Sheikh of Araby / Straighten up and fly right / Just in time / Talk of the town / Body and soul
CCD 4131 / Sep '86 / Concord Jazz

☐ AT THE WINERY VOL.2
You are the sunshine of my life / Love for sale / Angel's camp / Willow weep for me / Chicago / Talking a chance on love / Minor swing / Let's fall in love / Just you, just me
CCD 4139 / Jul '87 / Concord Jazz

☐ AUDIO ARCHIVE
You took advantage of me / Star eyes / Anything goes / Don't blame me / Moonlight in Vermont / Caravan / It might as well be spring / Have you met Miss Jones / Love song / Sing hallelujah
CDAA 026 / Jan '91 / Tring

☐ BACH TO THE BEATLES
CDWHL 2056 / Feb '98 / White Line

☐ BLUE SKIES (Grappelli, Stephane & Eddy Louiss)
500552 / Jan '94 / Musidisc

☐ CELEBRATING GRAPPELLI (Grappelli, Stephane & Martin Taylor)
Chicago / Gypsy / Undecided / I can't give you anything / Jive at five / Dinah / Musette for a magpie / It's only a paper moon / Years apart / Sweet Sue just you / Willow weep for me / Manoir de mes reves
AKD 094 / 16 Feb '98 / Linn

☐ CLASSICS 1935-1940
CLASSICS 708 / Jul '93 / Classics

☐ CLASSICS 1941-1943
CLASSICS 779 / Mar '95 / Classics

☐ COLLECTION, THE
How about you / Makin' whoopee / Running wild / That tune / It might as well be spring / Blue river / Someone to watch over me / Avalon / Three little words / Folks who live on the hill / You make me feel so young / This can't be love / Ain't misbehavin' / Ol' man river / Sweet georgia brown / Just a gigolo / Lady be good / Birth of the blues / Nearness of you / I can't give you anything but love / Peanut vendor / Crazy rhythm / Got the world on a string / Mean to me / Didn't we
CCSCD 274 / Oct '90 / Castle

☐ CRAZY RHYTHM
PLSCD 177 / Apr '97 / Pulse

☐ FLAMINGO (Grappelli, Stephane & Michel Petrucciani)
These foolish things / Little peace in C for U / Flamingo / Sweet Georgia Brown / I can't get started / I got rhythm / I love New York in June / Misty / I remember April / Lover man / There will never be another you / Valse du passa
FDM 365802 / Aug '96 / Dreyfus

☐ GRAPPELLI STORY, THE (Les Enregistrements Historiques De 1938 A 1992 - 2CD Set)
Stompin' at Decca / My sweet / It had to be you / Nocturne / Alexander's ragtime band / Blue ribbon rag / Oh lady be good / Stephane tune / Tiger rag / Stephane's blues / Jive bomber / Body and soul / Liza / Folks who live on the hill / Weep no more / Nuages / Nearness of you / 'S wonderful / Fascinating rhythm / Just one of those things / Lady is a tramp / I want to be happy / Dans la vie / It's only a paper moon / Flower is a lovesome thing / Minor swing / Daphne / Makin' whoopee / Pent-up house / Django / Darling Je vous aime beaucoup / Willow weep for me / How high the moon / More / Lonely street / Time after time / Misty / Shine / Lover man / I'm coming Virginia / La chanson des rues / Sweet chorus / Mon homme
5158072 / May '94 / Verve

☐ GRAPPELLI, WOODS & BELLSON (Grappelli, Stephane & Phil Woods/ Louie Bellson)
DM 15014 / Jul '96 / DMA Jazz

☐ HOT 'N' SWEET
TRTCD 179 / Jun '95 / TrueTrax

☐ I GOT RHYTHM
I saw stars / Continental / Avalon / Some of these days / After you've gone / Body and soul / Mystery Pacific / Alabamy bound / Viper's dream / Oh lady be good / Daphne / My serenade / Dinah / Noel brings the swing / I never knew / Tiger rag / Minor swing / I found a new baby
CD 6049 / Feb '97 / Music

☐ I HEAR MUSIC
I hear music / All God's chillun got rhythm / Honeysuckle rose / Do you know what it means to miss New Orleans / It's you or no one / If I were a bell / Chicago / Nuages - Daphne / La chanson des rues / Fascinating rhythm / Them their eyes / You are the sunshine of my life / I won't dance / Ol' man river / Someone to watch over me / I got rhythm / How high the moon
JHR 73586 / Apr '95 / Jazz Hour

☐ IN CONCERT (Grappelli, Stephane & McCoy Turner)
GATE 7025 / Sep '95 / Kingdom Jazz

☐ IT MIGHT AS WELL BE SWING
You took advantage of me / Star eyes / Anything goes / Don't blame me / Moonlight in vermont / Caravan / It might as well be spring / Have you met miss jones / Love song / Sing hallelujah / I didn't know what time it was
JWD 102216 / Jul '95 / JWD

☐ JAZZ MASTERS
Pennies from Heaven / Solitude / Ain't misbehavin' / Star eyes / Insensiblement / Folks who live on the hill / Nuages / Manoir de mes Reves/Daphne / Are you in the mood / Tears / Djangology / Shine / Nightingale sang in Berkeley Square / Someone to watch over me / I got rhythm
5167582 / 5 May '98 / Verve

☐ JOUE GEORGE GERSHWIN ET COLE PORTER (Plays Gershwin & Porter)
MCD 139 004 / '88 / Accord

☐ JUST ONE OF THOSE THINGS (Live At The Montreux Festival 1973)
BLCD 760180 / Apr '93 / Black Lion

☐ LA GRANDE REUNION (Grappelli, Stephane & Baden Powell)
557322 / Nov '93 / Accord

☐ LE JAZZ HOT (Grappelli, Stephane & Django Reinhardt)
I can't give you anything but love / Them there eyes / Honeysuckle rose / I've found a new baby / Night and day / Stomping at Decca / In the still of the night / China boy / My sweet / Oriental shuffle / Billets doux / Sweet chorus / Georgia on my mind / Black and white / Three little words / Limehouse blues / Swing guitars / After you've gone / Sweet georgia brown / Daphne / Nagasaki / Shine / Swing from paris / Souvenirs
300162 / Jun '98 / Hallmark

☐ LIVE 1992 (Live In Colombes)
Minor swing / Galerie des Princes / Ballade / Tears / Blues for Django and Stephane / Stella by starlight / Sweet chorus / Oh lady be good / Someone to watch over me / I got rhythm
5173922 / Mar '93 / Birdology

☐ LIVE AT THE BLUE NOTE
All God's chillun got rhythm / Night and day / I get a kick out of you / It's you or no one / I let a song go out of my heart / Honeysuckle rose / Medley / Nuages / Daphne / Blue moon / Do you know what it means to miss New Orleans / Oh lady be good / Medley / Sweet Georgia Brown
CD 83397 / May '96 / Telarc

☐ LIVE IN COPENHAGEN (Grappelli, Stephane & Joe Pass)
J33J 20041 / Aug '86 / Pablo

☐ LIVE IN LONDON
This can't be love / Flamingo / Them there eyes / After you've gone / Nuages / Tea for two
BLCD 760139 / Oct '90 / Black Lion

☐ MASTER OF VIOLIN
All of me / Star eyes / Anything goes / Caravan / Don't blame me / Moonlight in Vermont / It might as well be spring / Have you met Miss Jones
722010 / Sep '92 / Scorpio

☐ NUAGES (Grappelli, Stephane & Django Reinhardt)
Billets doux / Nuages / Exactly like you / China boy / Swing '39 / Them there eyes / St. Louis blues / Appel direct / I've found a new baby / Ultrafox / Twelfth year / Japanese sandman / I wonder where my baby is tonight / Chasing shadows / Djangology / Oh lady be good / Charleston / I'll see you in my dreams
TRTCD 148 / 26 Jan '98 / TrueTrax

☐ ONE AND ONE
How high the moon / How high the moon / I want to talk about you / Mr. p.c. / Summertime / Satin doll / I didn't know what time it was / You say you care / Yours is my heart alone / I got rhythm
MCD 9181 / Oct '93 / Milestone

☐ PARISIAN THOROUGHFARE
Love for sale / Perugia / Two cute / Parisian thoroughfare / Improvisation on prelude in E minor / Wave / Hallelujah
BLCD 760132 / Oct '94 / Black Lion

☐ PARISIAN THOROUGHFARE
After you've gone / Out of nowhere / It's only a paper moon / What a difference a day made / How high the moon / Parisian thoroughfare / I would do anything for you / 'Deed I do / As time goes by / You are the cream in my coffee / Sysmo / You're driving me crazy / It had to be you / My blue heaven / Flonville
17125 / May '97 / Laserlight

☐ PENT UP HOUSE
78067410082 / 7 Apr '98 / Drive Archive

☐ PORTRAIT OF STEPHANE GRAPPELLI, THE
Nearness of you / Tournesol / Stardust / I saw stars / There will never be another you / Memories of you / Star eyes / Paradise / Nice work if you can get it / I got rhythm / Honeysuckle rose / Honeysuckle rosew / Them there eyes
EMPRCD 567 / May '95 / Emporio

☐ REUNION (Grappelli, Stephane & Martin Taylor)
Jive at five / Willow weep for me / Drop me off in Harlem / Miraval / Jenna / Reunion / Emily / Hotel splendid / La dame du lac / I thought about you / It's only a paper moon
AKD 022 / Oct '93 / Linn

☐ SATIN DOLL
440162CD / Jul '94 / Musidisc

☐ STARDUST
Stardust / Nearness of you (take 3) / Tournesol / Greensleeves / You go to my head / Nature boy / Can't help lovin' dat man / We'll be together again / Talk of the town / Amanda / I saw stars / Greensleeves / Tournesol / Nearness of you (take 3) / Stardust
BLC 760117 / Apr '91 / Black Lion

☐ STEFF AND SLAM (Grappelli, Stephane Trio & Slam Stewart)
BB 8632 / Feb '96 / Black & Blue

☐ STEPHANE GRAPPELLI
Just one of those things / Misty / More / Them there eyes / I remember Django / Little star / Tournesol / Two cute / This can't be love / Sweet Georgia Brown / It don't mean a thing (if it ain't got that swing)
8747172 / Jul '96 / DA Music

☐ STEPHANE GRAPPELLI & JEAN-LUC PONTY (Grappelli, Stephane & Jean-Luc Ponty)
556552 / Mar '96 / Accord

☐ STEPHANE GRAPPELLI AND FRIENDS IN PARIS (2CD Set)
500762 / Sep '96 / Musidisc

☐ STEPHANE GRAPPELLI MEETS BARNEY KESSEL (Grappelli, Stephane & Barney Kessel)
BLC 760150 / Apr '91 / Black Lion

☐ STEPHANE GRAPPELLI MEETS EARL HINES
BLCD 760168 / Oct '93 / Black Lion

☐ STEPHANE GRAPPELLI WITH JEAN LUC PONTY (Grappelli, Stephane & Jean-Luc Ponty)
MCD 139 139 / '88 / Accord

☐ STEPHANE GRAPPELLI/JEAN-LUC PONTY VOL.2 (Grappelli, Stephane & Jean-Luc Ponty)
139 210 / '86 / Accord

☐ STEPHANE'S TUNE 1937-1944
158582 / Jul '96 / Jazz Archives

☐ STEPHANOVA
Tune up / Thou swell / Norwegian dance / Fulton Street samba / My foolish heart / Lover / Way you look tonight / Stephanova / Smoke rings and wine / Tangerine / Waltz for Queenie / Sonny boy
292E 6033 / Jan '90 / Concord Jazz

☐ SWEET CHORUS
BB 900 / 24 Apr '98 / Black & Blue

☐ TOGETHER AT LAST (Grappelli, Stephane & Vassar Clements)
FF 70421 / Oct '89 / Flying Fish

☐ UNFORGETTABLE CLASSICS (Grappelli, Stephane & Yehudi Menuhin/Alan Clare Trio)
Jealousy / Blue room / Fine romance / Billy / Love is here to stay / Aurore / Pick yourself up / Night and day / I can't believe that you're in love with me / These foolish things / Errol / Oh lady be good / Jermyn Street / Cheek to cheek / Lady is a tramp
CDCFP 6065 / 6 Apr '98 / Classics For Pleasure

☐ VENUPELLI BLUES (Grappelli, Stephane & Joe Venuti)
I can't give you anything but love / My one and only love / Undecided / Venupelli blues / I'll never be the same / Tea for two
LEJAZZCD 18 / Jun '93 / Le Jazz

☐ VINTAGE 1981
If I had you / I can't get started (with you) / Blue moon / But not for me / It's only a paper moon / Jamie / I'm coming Virginia / Do you know what it means to miss New Orleans / Isn't she lovely / Swing '42 / Honeysuckle rose
CCD 4169 / Nov '92 / Concord Jazz

Grapsas, Nikos

☐ FAIR MAIDEN FROM AMORGOS, A (2CD Set)
ML 48067 / 11 May '98 / Musurgia Graeca

☐ IN THE IONIAN SEAS (2CD Set)
ML 48089 / 11 May '98 / Musurgia Graeca

Grass Is Greener

☐ WOLVES A'HOWLIN'
REB 1730CD / Apr '96 / Rebel

Grass Roots

☐ 1960'S FRENCH EP COLLECTION, THE
177642 / 23 Feb '98 / Magic

☐ WHERE WERE YOU WHEN I NEEDED YOU
VSD 55112 / 28 Apr '98 / Varese Sarabande

Grass Show

☐ SOMETHING SMELLS GOOD IN STINKVILLE
Freak show / 1962 / Out of the void / Unreal world / Cavemankind / All that she wants / Talk talk talk / Make love not war / Losing touch / Love 180 / Alice / Getting you out of my head
FOODCD 20 / Jun '97 / Food

Grasshopper & The Golden Crickets

☐ ORBIT OF ETERNAL GRACE, THE
Silver balloons / Ballad of the one eyed angelfish / O-ring (baby talk) / Nickel in a lemon / Orbit of eternal grace / September fool / Univac bug track / SMPTE for the devil / NY avenue playground / Sketches of saturn (love in space) / Midnight express / NY avenue playground
BBQCD 201 / 24 Aug '98 / Beggars Banquet

Grassy Knoll

☐ GRASSY KNOLL III, THE
Beaten dog beneath the hail / Down in the happy zone / Every third thought / Blue wires / Paul has an emotional Uncle / Six to four to three / Of all possible worlds / Violent misery of everything lost / World reduced to zero / Safe / III / 112 Greene Street / Thunder ain't rain
5570872 / 5 May '98 / Antilles/Verve

☐ GRASSY KNOLL, THE
Culture of complaint / March eighteenth / Unbelievable truth / Altering the gates of the mind / Conversations with Julian Dexter / Floating above the earth / Less than one / Low / Evolution / Beauty within / Illusions of peace
5279082 / 5 May '98 / Antilles/Verve

☐ POSITIVE
5332862 / 5 May '98 / Antilles/Verve

Grateful Dead

☐ AMERICAN BEAUTY
Box of rain / Friend of the Devil / Operator / Sugar magnolia / Ripple / Brokedown palace / Till the morning comes / Attic of my life / Truckin
K2 46074 / Oct '89 / WEA

☐ ANTHEM OF THE SUN
That's it for the other one / Cryptical envelopment / Quadlibet / For tender feet / Faster we go, the rounder we get / We leave the castle / Alligator / Caution (do not stop on the tracks)
7599271732 / Feb '94 / WEA

☐ AOXOMOXOA
St. Stephen / Dupree's diamond blues / Rosemary / Doin' that rag / Mountains of the moon / China cat sunflower / What's become of the baby cosmic Charlie
7599271782 / Nov '94 / WEA

☐ ARISTA YEARS 1977-1995, THE (2CD Set)
Estimated prophet / Passenger / Samson and Delilah / Terapin station / Good lovin' / Shakedown street / Fire on the mountain / I need a miracle / Alabama getaway / Far from me / Saint of circumstance / Dire wolf / Cassidy / Feel like a stranger / Franklin's tower / Touch of grey / Hell in a bucket / West LA fadeaway / Throwing stones / Black muddy river / Foolish heart / Built to last / Just a little light / Picasso moon / Standing on the moon / Eyes of the world
078221893428 / Oct '96 / Arista

☐ BLUES FOR ALLAH
Help on the way / Slipknot / Franklin's tower / King Solomon's marbles / Music never stopped / Crazy fingers / Sage and spirit / Blues for Allah / Sand castles and glass camels / Unusual occurrences in the desert
GDCD 4001 / Feb '89 / Grateful Dead

☐ DICK'S PICKS VOL.1 (Tampa, Florida 19/12/73 - 2CD Set)
Here comes the sunshine / Big river / Mississippi half step / Weather report suite / Big railroad blues / Playing in the band / He's gone / Truckin' / Nobody's fault but mine / Jam / Other one / Jam / Stella blue / Around and around
GDCD2 4019 / Jan '96 / Grateful Dead

☐ DICK'S PICKS VOL.2 (Columbus, Ohio 31/10/71)
Dark star/Jam / Sugar magnolia / St. Stephen / Not fade away / Going down the road feeling bad / Not fade away
GDCD 4020 / Feb '96 / Grateful Dead

☐ DICK'S PICKS VOL.3 (Pembroke Pines, Florida 22/5/77 - 2CD Set)
Funiculi funicula / Music never stopped / Sugaree / Lazy lightning / Supplication / Dancin' in the streets / Help on the way / Slipknot / Franklin's tower / Samson and Delilah / Sunrise / Estimated prophet / Eyes of the world / Wharf rat / Terrapin station / (Walk me out in the) Morning dew
GDCD2 4022 / Dec '95 / Grateful Dead

☐ DICK'S PICKS VOL.4 (Fillmore East 13-14/2/70 - 3CD Set)
GDCD3 4023 / Dec '96 / Grateful Dead

☐ DICK'S PICKS VOL.5 (Oakland Auditorium Arena 26/12/79 - 3CD Set)
GDCD3 4025 / Dec '96 / Grateful Dead

☐ DICK'S PICKS VOL.6 (Hartford Civic Center 14/10/83 - 3CD Set)
Hell in a bucket / Dupree's diamond blues / Just a little light / Walkin' blues / Jack-a-roe / Never trust a woman / When I paint my masterpiece / Row Jimmy / Blow away / Playing in the band / Uncle John's band / Lady with a fan / Terrapin station / Mud love buddy jam / Drums / Space / Wheel / All along the watchtower / Stella blue / Not fade away / And we bid you goodnight / I will take you home / Goin' down the road feelin' bad / Black Peter / Around and around / Brokedown palace
GDCD3 4026 / Dec '96 / Grateful Dead

☐ DICK'S PICKS VOL.7 (Alexandra Palace 9-11/9/1974 - 3CD Set)
Scarlet begonias / Mexicali blues / Row Jimmy / Black throated wind / Mississippi half step uptown toodeloo / Beat it down the line / Tennessee Jed / Playing in the band / Weather report suite / Stella blue / Jack Straw / Brown-eyed women / Big river / Truckin' / Wood Green jam / Wharf rat / Me and my uncle / Not fade away / Dark star / Spam jam / Morning dew / US blues
GDCD3 4027 / Apr '97 / Grateful Dead

☐ DOZIN' AT THE KNICK (3CD Set)
Alabama getaway / Greatest story ever told / They love each other / Mama tried / Big river / Althea / CC rider / Tenessee Jed / Hell in a bucket / Keep your day job / Scarlet begonias / Fire on the mountain / Estimated prophet / Eyes of the world / Drums / Spinach jam / Other one / Stella blue / Sugar magnolia / US blues
GDCD3 4024 / Dec '96 / Grateful Dead

☐ EUROPE '72
Cumberland blues / He's gone / One more saturday night / Jack straw / You can win again / China cat sunflower / Sunflower / I know you rider / Brown eyed woman / Hurts me too / Ramblin' rose / Sugar magnolia / Mr. Charlie / Tennessee Jed / Truckin' / Epilogue / Prelude
7599272652 / Nov '94 / WEA

☐ FALLOUT FROM THE PHIL ZONE (2CD Set)
Dancin' in the streets / New speedway boogie / Viola lee blues / Easy wind / Mason's children / Hard to handle (yes I am) / Music never stopped / Jack-a-roe / In the midnight hour / Visions of Johanna / Box of rain
GDCD2 4052 / Jun '97 / Grateful Dead

☐ FURTHER (Various Artists)
20012 / May '97 / Hybrid

☐ GRATEFUL DEAD
Golden road (to unlimited devotion) / Beat it on down the line / Good morning little school girl / Cold rain and snow / Sittin' on top of the world / Cream puff war / Morning dew / New, new Minglewood blues / Viola Lee blues
7599271672 / Nov '94 / WEA

☐ GRATEFUL DEAD, THE
Bertha / Mama tried / Big railroad blues / Playing in the band / Other one / Me and my uncle / Big boss man / Me and Bobby McGee / Johnny B Goode / Wharf rat / Not fade away / Goin' down the road / Feelin' bad
7599271922 / Feb '93 / WEA

☐ GRATEFUL DEAD: INTERVIEW PICTURE DISC
CBAK 4039 / Apr '90 / Baktabak

☐ GRAYFOLDED
SA 1969 / Jun '97 / Swell Artifact

☐ HEARTBITS VOL.2 (Mickey & The Heartbeats)
ANT 2912 / Jun '97 / Anthology

☐ HUNDRED YEAR HALL (2CD Set)
Bertha / Me and my uncle / Next time you see me / China cat sunflower / I know you rider / Jack straw / Big railroad / Playing in the band / Turn on your lovelight / Going down the road feeling bad / One more Saturday night
GDCD2 4021 / Oct '95 / Grateful Dead

☐ IN THE DARK
Touch of grey / Hell in a bucket / When push comes to shove / West LA fadeaway / Tons of steel / Throwing stones / Black muddy river
261145 / Jul '96 / Arista

☐ INFRARED ROSES
Crowd sculpture / Parallelogram / Little Nemo in Nightland / Riverside rhapsody / Post-modern highrise table top stomp / Infrared roses / Silver apples of the moon / Speaking in swords / Magnesium night light / Sparrow hawk row / River of nine sorrows / Apollo at the Ritz
GDCD 4016 / Jan '92 / Grateful Dead

☐ INTERVIEW DISC
TELL 06 / Dec '96 / Network

☐ LIVE DEAD
Dark star / Death don't have no mercy / Feedback / And we bid you goodnight / St. Stephen / Eleven / Turn on your love / Light
K 9271812 / Jun '89 / WEA

☐ MUSIC NEVER STOPPED, THE (The Roots Of The Grateful Dead) (Various Artists)
SHCD 6014 / Oct '95 / Shanachie

☐ NIGHT OF THE GRATEFUL DEAD (Interview Disc)
OTR 1100024 / Apr '97 / Metro Independent

☐ ONE FROM THE VAULT (2CD Set)
Introduction / Help on the way / Franklin's tower / Music never stopped / It must have been the roses / Eyes of the world / King Solomon's marbles / Around and around / Sugaree / Big river / Crazy fingers / Other one / Sage and spirit / Goin' down the road feeling bad / US blues / Blues For Allah
GDCD2 4015 / May '91 / Grateful Dead

☐ RELIX BAY ROCK SHOP (Tribute To Jerry Garcia) (Various Artists)
RBRS 00098 / Jul '97 / Relix

☐ RISEN FROM THE VAULTS
DILCD 1001 / Jan '94 / Dare International

☐ SHAKEDOWN STREET
Good lovin' / France / Shakedown Street / Serengeti / Fire on the mountain / I need a miracle / From the heart of me / Stagger Lee / All new minglewood blues / If I had the world to give
251133 / Jun '91 / Arista

☐ STEAL YOUR FACE (2CD Set)
Promised land / Cold rain and snow / Around and around / Stella blue / Mississippi half step uptown toodeloo / Ship of fools / Beat it on down the line / Big river / Black throated wind / US blues / El Paso / Sugaree / It must have been the roses / Casey Jones
GDCD2 4006 / Mar '89 / Grateful Dead

☐ TERRAPIN STATION
Estimated prophet / Dancing in the street / Passenger / Samson and Delilah / Sunrise / Lady with the fan / Terrapin station / Terrapin / Terrapin transit / At a siding / Terrapin fever / Refrain
260175 / Nov '90 / Arista

☐ TRIP WITHOUT A TICKET (CD/Book Set)
262986 / Nov '97 / Sonic

☐ TWO FROM THE VAULT (2CD Set)
Good morning little schoolgirl / Dark star / Saint stephen / Eleven / Death don't have no mercy / Other one / New potato caboose / Turn on you lovelight / Morning dew
GDCD2 4018 / Apr '92 / Grateful Dead

☐ WAKE OF THE FLOOD
Mississippi half step uptown toodeloo / Row Jimmy / Here comes sunshine / Weather report / Let me sing your blues away / Stella blue / Eyes of the world
GDCD 4002 / Nov '87 / Grateful Dead

☐ WORKINGMAN'S DEAD
Uncle John's band / High time / Dire wolf / New speedway boogie / Cumberland blues / Black Peter / Easy wind / Casey Jones
K 246049 / Jun '89 / WEA

Gratz, Wayne

☐ BLUE RIDGE
Blue ridge part 1 / Blue ridge part 2 / Heart in the clouds / Sacred river / Dancing lights / Waterfall / Trail of tears / Fields are burning / Scenes of reflection / Past time / Peaks of order / Pathway to waterrock / White on white / Endless mountains
ND 61047 / May '95 / Narada

☐ FROM ME TO YOU
Here, there and everywhere / And I love her / From me to you / Michelle / In my life / If I fell / You've got to hide your love away / Girl / Do you want to know a secret / Yesterday / Norwegian wood / Long and winding road / All my loving / PS I love you / Hey Jude
ND 62811 / Aug '97 / Narada

☐ MUSIC OF THE NIGHT
Think of me / With one look / Don't cry for me Argentina / As if we never said goodbye / Music of the night / Memory / Love changes everything / I don't know how to love him / Pie Jesu / Another suitcase in another hall / All I ask of you
ND 62810 / Jun '97 / Narada

Grave

☐ AND HERE I DIE
CM 770622 / Feb '94 / Century Media

☐ DEVOLUTION
PRO 006CD / Nov '92 / Prophet

☐ HATING LIFE
CM 77105CD / Apr '96 / Century Media

☐ INTO THE GRAVE
CM 97212 / Sep '94 / Century Media

☐ SOULLESS
CM 770702 / Jun '94 / Century Media

Gravediggaz

☐ 6 FEET DEEP
GEE 1000992 / 13 Oct '97 / Gee Street

☐ NIGGAMORTIS
Just when you thought it was over (intro) / Constant elevation / Nowhere to run, nowhere to hide / Defective trip (trippin') / Two cups of blood / Blood brothers / 360 questions / 1-800 suicide / Diary of a madman / Mommy what's a gravediggaz / Bang yo head / Here comes the Gravediggaz / Graveyard chamber / Death trap / Six feet deep / Rest in peace (outro)
GEECD 14 / Jun '94 / Gee Street

☐ PICK THE SICKLE AND THE SHOVEL, THE
GEE 1000562
GEE 1000568 / 22 Sep '97 / Gee Street

Gravedigger

☐ DARK OF SUN
GUN 133CD / 4 Aug '97 / Gun

☐ KNIGHTS OF THE CROSS
Dens lo vult / Knights of the cross / Lionheart / Keeper of the Holy Grail / Inquisition / Baphomet / Battle of Bannockburn
GUN 162CD / 22 Jun '98 / Gun

☐ TUNES OF WAR
GUN 102CD / Oct '96 / Gun

☐ WITCH HUNT
NCD 002 / '88 / Noise

Gravedigger V

☐ ALL BLACK & HAIRY/THE MIRROR CRACKED
All black and hairy / Tomorrow is yesterday / No good woman / Do like me / Hate / She's a cur / Searching / She's gone / Night of the phantom / Don't tread on me / One ugly child / She got / Stoneage stomp
VOXXCD 2025 / Oct '94 / Voxx

Graveland

☐ 1000 SWORDS
A 101CD / Jun '96 / Embassy

Gravenites, Nick

☐ DON'T FEED THE ANIMALS
(Gravenites, Nick & Animal Mind)
TX 1020CD / Dec '96 / Taxim

Graverobbers

☐ SOUL PARKING
FM 02 / Nov '96 / Fundamental

Graves, Blind Roosevelt

☐ BLIND ROOSEVELT GRAVES 1929-1936
DOCD 5105 / Nov '93 / Document

Gravestone

☐ DOOMSDAY
LB 1025 / 1 Jun '98 / LB

Graveyard Rodeo

☐ ON THE VERGE
CM 770692 / Aug '94 / Century Media

Gravity Kills

☐ GRAVITY KILLS
Foward / Guilty / Blame / Down / Here / Enough / Inside / Goodbye / Never / Last / Hold
CDV 2819 / Feb '97 / Virgin

☐ MANIPULATED
TVT 59162 / Jun '97 / TVT

☐ PERVERSION
TVT 59202 / 25 May '98 / TVT

Gravity Wax

☐ LOW ENERGY PARTICULATE
ME 013 / May '97 / Mind Expansion

Gravity Wheel

☐ BULLDOGTUNAWASP
DI 0872 / 15 Jun '98 / Distance

☐ WISH
SUB 48742 / 15 Jun '98 / Distance

Gravity's Pull

☐ RADIO STATION WAGON
SH 5706 / Mar '96 / Shanachie

Gravy Train

☐ BALLAD OF A PEACEFUL MAN
REP 4122 / Aug '91 / Repertoire

☐ GRAVY TRAIN
REP 4063 / Aug '91 / Repertoire

Grawe, George

☐ MELODIE UND RHYTHMUS (Grawe, Georg Quartet)
OD 12024 / May '98 / Okka Disk

Gray, Chris

☐ FISH AND LUVCONFUSHUN
FMDCD 4 / 29 Jun '98 / Fragmented

Gray, David

☐ CENTURY ENDS, A
Shine / Century ends / Debauchery / Let the truth sing / Gathering dust / Wisdom / Lead me upstairs / Living room / Birds without wings / It's all over
CDHUT 9 / Apr '93 / Hut

☐ FLESH
What are you / Lullaby / Coming down / Falling free / Made up my mind / Mystery of love / Lullaby / New horizons / Love's old song / Flesh
CDHUT 17 / Sep '94 / Hut

Gray, Dobie

☐ DRIFT AWAY
CDCOT 106 / Jan '94 / Cottage

☐ DRIFT AWAY (The Very Best Of Dobie Gray)
RE 21122 / Aug '96 / Razor & Tie

☐ SOULFUL SOUND OF DOBIE GRAY, THE
HMNCD 022 / 3 Nov '97 / Half Moon

☐ VERY BEST OF DOBIE GRAY, THE
Drift away / I can see clearly now / Could I / Loving arms / If I ever needed you / Slip away / In crowd / Ain't that good news / We had it all / I'm only speaking my heart / Lean on me / I can live with that / It's not because we didn't try / It's over
306162 / Jan '97 / Hallmark

Gray, Glen

☐ CONTINENTAL, THE
Who's sorry now / I may be wrong / Should I / Continental / Ballin' the jack / Song of the islands / Night and day / Can't we be friends / Blue room / Man / Sunny disposish / Dixieland band / Basin street blues / Linger awhile / Chinatown, my chinatown / Blue again
HCD 261 / Oct '95 / Hindsight

☐ MOONGLOW 1930-1936 (Gray, Glen & Orchestra)
RACD 7126 / May '96 / Aerospace

☐ UNCOLLECTED 1939-1940, THE (Gray, Glen & The Casa Loma Orchestra)
Smoke rings / Wrap your troubles in dreams / Hindustan / Hour of parting / It's funny to everyone but me / Sometimes I'm happy / No name jive / Memories of you / What's the matter with me / Little brown jug / In the mood / Tuxedo junction / High society / Day in, day out / Meet me tonight in dreamland / Sassin' the boss
HCD 104 / Jan '95 / Hindsight

Gray, Henry

☐ DON'T START THAT STUFF (Gray, Henry & Short Fuse)
7422468 / Jun '98 / Last Call

Gray, Jerry

☐ STAND BY FOR MUSIC (Gray, Jerry & His Orchestra)
Desert serenade / Medley / Interview with Ginny Sims / I love Paris / Introduction to a waltz / Embraceable you / Desert serenade / When I fall in love / Interview with Jeri Southern / You'd better go now / Musicrat ramble / Gypsy in my soul / Desert serenade / How high the moon / Interview with Jane Christie / Willow weep for me / Caravan / From this moment on / Desert serenade / Blue moon / Interview with Gloria DeHaven / Somebody loves me / Crew cut / My heart stood still / Desert serenade / Interview with Mel Torme / All of you / Coronado cruise / I cover the waterfront / Desert serenade / Mountain greenery / Interview with Peggy King / Bum 'em up / It took ten days / Make yourself comfortable / Desert serenade
DAWE 85 / Jul '98 / Magic

Gray, Kellye

☐ STANDARDS
JR 001012 / Sep '92 / Justice

Gray Matter

☐ THOG
DIS 68VCD / Sep '92 / Dischord

Gray, Owen

☐ CALL ON ME
WRCD 0020 / Nov '95 / Techniques

☐ DO YOU STILL LOVE ME
FECD 24 / 29 Jun '98 / First Edition

☐ GOSPEL TRUTH VOL.1, THE
BFMCD 109 / 8 Sep '97 / Bushranger

☐ GOSPEL TRUTH VOL.2, THE
BFMCD 115 / 15 Dec '97 / Bushranger

☐ HIT AFTER HIT AFTER HIT
FECD 23 / 27 Apr '98 / First Edition

☐ LET'S GO STEADY
FECD 21 / Dec '95 / First Edition

☐ MISS WIRE WAIST
PICD 209 / Jun '95 / Body Music

☐ ON TOP
RNCD 2073 / Oct '94 / Rhino

☐ OUT IN THE OPEN
VPCD 2045 / Feb '96 / VP

☐ SOMETHING GOOD
BFMCD 105 / 24 Nov '97 / Bushranger

☐ SURELY
Surely
FECD 19 / 17 Nov '97 / First Edition

Gray, Russell

☐ SOLO
From the shores of the mighty pacific / Traumerei / Chablis / Caro nome / Fantasia on themes from Carmen / Salut d'amour / Concerto for cornet and brass bands / Bess you is my woman now / Sunshine of your smile / Aye waukin' o / Una furtiva lagrima / Song and dance / Londonderry air
QPRL 070D / Jan '95 / Polyphonic

Gray, Wardell

☐ HOW HIGH THE MOON
MCD 076 / Dec '95 / Moon

☐ MEMORIAL VOL.1
OJCCD 50 / Nov '95 / Original Jazz Classics

☐ ONE FOR PREZ
BLCD 760106 / Feb '89 / Black Lion

☐ WAY OUT WARDELL
Blue Lou / Sweet Georgia Brown / Tenderly / Just you, just me / One o'clock jump
CDBOP 014 / Jul '91 / Boplicity

Grayon, James Clare

☐ NICE WORK
SRCD 002 / Nov '96 / Stream

Greaney, Con

☐ ROAD TO ATHEA
CIC 082CD / Nov '93 / Clo Iar-Chonnachta

Great Big Sea

☐ PLAY
Ordinary day / Night Pat Murphy died / How did we get from saying I love you / Donkey riding / Haven't seen you in a long time / End of the world / General Taylor / Seagulls / Recruiting sargeant / Graveyard / My apology / Jakey's gin / Something I should know / Jolly roving tar / When I'm up (I can't get down)
COOKCD 151 / 29 Jun '98 / Cooking Vinyl

☐ UP
Run runaway / Going up / Fast as I can / Mari-mac / Dancing with Mrs. White / Something to it / Buying time / Lukey / Old black rum / Chemical worker's song / Wave over wave / Billy peddle / Nothing out of nothing / Jolly butcher / Rant and roar
COOKCD 130 / Jun '97 / Cooking Vinyl

Great British Jazz Band

☐ BRITISH JAZZ ODYSSEY, A
Riff up them stairs / KC blues / Very thought of you / Sizzle / Badger / Duke's joke / Nightingale sang in Berkeley Square / Jump / Serenade to a wealthy widow / Blues for Welshie / We fell out of love / Go Ghana / Tidy / Gypsy / Limehouse blues
CCD 79740 / Feb '97 / Candid

☐ JUBILEE
Jubilee / Jazz me blues / Original Dixieland one-step / Washboard blues / Prelude to a kiss / Idaho / Imagination / Beautiful friendship / Petite fleur / Someday sweetheart / Apex blues / All I do is dream of you / Chelsea bridge / Tiger rag
CCD 79720 / Feb '97 / Candid

Great Circle Saxophone Quartet

☐ CHILD KING DICTATOR FOOL
Stay fresh baggies / Falling from grace / Black shag / Red and green / Emma's nemesis / Hole in the sky / Now what / Thing turning (for Janet) / Blood indigo / Son of splorb / Snake tectonics / Stay fresh baggies
805162 / Jun '97 / New World

Great Guitars

☐ RETURN OF THE GREAT GUITARS, THE
Things ain't what they used to be / When lights are low / Smooth one / My funny valentine / Lady in red / Soft winds / Everie's tune / I remember you / Waltz for Wes / Seven, come eleven / Billy Bean / Nigh Roby get-a-way / On the trail
CCD 4715 / Aug '96 / Concord Jazz

☐ STRAIGHT TRACKS
I'm putting all my eggs in one basket / Clouds / Gravy waltz / Um abraco no borda / Little rock getaway / It might as well be Spring / Kingston cutie / Favela
CCD 4421 / Nov '90 / Concord Jazz

Great Jazz Trio

☐ STANDARD COLLECTION VOL.1
After you've gone / Summertime / Days of wine and roses / As time goes by / You'd be so nice to come home to / Summer knows / Georgia on my mind / Prelude to a kiss / St. Louis blues / Danny boy
MCD 0031 / Dec '95 / Limetree

☐ STANDARD COLLECTION VOL.2
Angel eyes / Autumn leaves / Black orpheus / Gone with the wind / Over the rainbow / Softly as in a morning sunrise / Misty / On Green Dolphin Street / Alone together / Dark eyes
MCD 0032 / Dec '95 / Limetree

Great Scots

☐ ARRIVE
BR 101 / 9 Mar '98 / Beatrocket

☐ GREAT LOST GREAT SCOTS ALBUM
On the road again / I ain't no miracle worker / Someone that I can't see / Don't you believe them / Ball and chain / Show me the way / Light hurts my eyes / I can do it better / Honey and wine / Lord I'm so lonely / Blue Monday / What am I to do / Run run for your life / Help myself / Ain't no miracle / You know what you can do
SC 11048 / Aug '97 / Sundazed

Great Speckled Bird

☐ GREAT SPECKLED BIRD
SPCD 1200 / Dec '94 / Stony Plain

Great Unravelling

☐ GREAT UNRAVELLING
KRS 277CD / Feb '97 / Kill Rock Stars

Great Voice Of Soul

☐ GREAT VOICE OF SOUL
CLEO 2162 / 17 Mar '98 / Cleopatra

Great White

☐ ONCE BITTEN
Lady red light / Gonna getcha / Rock me / All over now / Fast road / What do you do / Face the day / Gimme some lovin'
NSPCD 515 / Jun '95 / Connoisseur Collection

☐ ROCK ME
Once bitten twice shy / Move it / Save your love / Bitches and other women / Bitch / It's only rock 'n' roll (but I like it) / Women / Rock me / Angel song / Baby's on fire / Gonna getcha / Face the day / On the edge / Lady red light / Afterglow (of your love) / South Bay cities / Rock 'n' roll
DC 881862 / 29 Aug '97 / Disky

☐ SAIL AWAY (2CD Set)
Short overture / Mothers eyes / Cryin' / Momma don't stop / Alone / All right / Sail away / Gone with the wind / Livin' in the USA / If I ever saw a good thing / Call it rock 'n' roll / All over now / Love is a lie / Old rose motel / Babe I'm gonna leave you / Rock me / Once biten twice shy
72445110802 / Aug '94 / Zoo Entertainment

☐ SHOT IN THE DARK
RE 21102 / Jul '96 / Razor & Tie

Greater Than One

☐ G-FORCE
TORSOCD 149 / Jun '89 / Torso

Greatest Show On Earth

☐ HORIZONS/THE GOING'S EASY
Sunflower morning / Angelina / Skylight man / 1 Day of the lady / Real cool world / I fought for love / Horizons / Again and again / Borderline / Magic woman touch / Storytimes and nursery rhymes / Leader / Love magnet / Tell the story
SEECD 473 / Feb '97 / See For Miles

Greaves, John

☐ ACCIDENT
Photography / Salt / Accident / Milk / Irma / Sad emission / Wax / Ruby / Rose sob / Silence / For bearings
BP 234CD / 1 Sep '97 / Blueprint

☐ LITTLE BOTTLE OF LAUNDRY
Solitary / World tonight / Deck of the moon / Old antiquity / Rose C"est la vie / Lullaby / Almost perfect lovers / Le garcon vert / Let her go / Dedans
BP 232CD / Jun '97 / Blueprint

☐ PARROT FASHIONS
Always be new to me / How beautiful you are / Bee dream / Price we pay / Bad alchemy / Swelling valley / Rosetta's song / Dead heads duped / Jaloozy
BP 233CD / 24 Nov '97 / Blueprint

☐ SONGS
Old kinderhook / Song / Swelling valley / Green fuse / KewRhone / Eccentric waters silence / Price we pay / L'aise aux ex-sans trique / Back where we began / Gegenstand
RES 112CD / Apr '97 / Resurgence

Greco, Buddy

☐ BUDDY AND SOUL/SOFT AND GENTLE
Come rain or come shine / How long has this been going on / I'm in love / After the lights go down low / People will say we're in love / I didn't know what time it was / I'm gonna laugh you out of my life / Let me love you / But beautiful / Fly me to the moon / Just walk away / Round midnight soft and gentle / I love you love / What kind of fool am I / Nancy / My funny valentine / Then I'll be tired of you / Gigi / Angel eyes / Passing pastels / Bewitched / Moonlight in Vermont / I left my heart in San Francisco / Easy way
4840322 / Jun '96 / Columbia

☐ BUDDY GRECO
DVAD 6082 / May '95 / Deja Vu

☐ IN STYLE
Movin' on / Me and Mrs. Jones / Hungry years / Lady is a tramp / Love won't let me wait / My funny valentine / Baubles, bangles and beads / Touch me in the morning / More I see you / She loves me / You better go now / Bewitched, bothered and bewildered / Satin doll / This is all I ask / Girl talk / Teach me tonight / Legacy / Passing pastels / Neither one of us / Ready for your love / Around the world / When I fall in love
74321431582 / Oct '96 / Camden

☐ IT'S MY LIFE/MOVING ON
It's gonna take some time / October 4th 1971 / If / Power and the glory / You've got a friend / Without you / Your song / As long as she will stay / Song for you / It's my life / MacArthur park / Movin' on / Touch me in the morning / Maggi / Baby lean on me / I know where I belong / Beautiful friendship / Neither one of us (wants to be first to say go) / If I could live my life again / I could be the one / Cardboard California
C5CD 634 / Jul '98 / See For Miles

☐ MACARTHUR PARK
Around the world / Bewitched, bothered and bewildered / This is all I ask / She loves me / You better go now / Me and Mrs. Jones / Georgia road / Baubles, bangles and beads / Satin doll / Like young / My funny valentine / Girl talk / Lady is a tramp / Touch me in the morning / Legacy / Hungry years / Neither one of us / Passing pastels / Macarthur park
CYCD 71911 / Feb '97 / Celebrity

☐ ROUTE 66 (A Tribute To Nat 'King' Cole)
Gee baby ain't I good to you / Route 66 / Nature boy / I'm lost / Sweet Lorraine / Straighten up and fly right / What is this thing called love / Lush life / Smile / It's only a paper moon / Walkin' my baby back home / That's all / Moonlight in Vermont / Sweet Georgia Brown / But not for me / When I fall in love / LOVE
CYCD 1901 / Feb '97 / Celebrity

Greedsville

☐ CASINO ROYALE COLLECTION
Disco queen / Casino / Simple moonshine / Du cats / Jazz the spanish fly / Caller 38 / Stroll by the sea / It's a gas / Splash
CDBLEED 9 / Mar '94 / Bleeding Hearts

Green

☐ FOUND ON THE WAVE
Leavin' Carolina / Found on the wave / High and low / Jamie Gow's farewell to methadone / Marie Celeste / Squaddies lament / Oh Jonnie my man / Baroque daydream / Prayer for tomorrow / Rattlin' roarin' Willie / Grandad's song / Fulmer
CDLDL 1267 / Dec '97 / Lochshore

Green, Al

☐ AL
Tired of being alone / Call me / I'm still in love with you / Here I am (come and take me) / Let's stay together / Sha la la (make me happy) / LOVE Love / Look what you done for me / Love and happiness / Take me to the river / I can't get next to you / How can you mend a broken heart / I tried to tell myself / I've never found a girl / Oh me, oh my (Dreams in my arms) / You ought to be with me
AGREECD 1 / Oct '92 / Beechwood

☐ CHRISTMAS ALBUM PLUS
HILOCD 21 / Oct '95 / Hi

☐ DEEP SHADE OF GREEN, A (3CD Set)
What am I going to do with myself / One woman / Are you lonely for me baby / True love / God is standing / Tired of being alone / Let's stay together / Old time lovin' / I've never found a girl / How can you mend a broken heart / Judy / Look what you have done for me / What a wonderful thing love is / Simply beautiful / For the good times / One of these good old days / You ought to be with me / Call me / Here I am / Have you been making out OK / I'm so lonely I could cry / Funny how time slips away / So good to be here / Home again / Free at last / Unchained melody / Sha-la-la / God blessed our love / I'm hooked you / LOVE / I wish you were here / Strong as death / Could I be the one / There is love / Love sermon / I didn't know / There's no way / Together again / I'd fly away / Soon as I got home / Something / Have a good time / Nothing takes the place of you / Belle / Feels like summer / Dream / To sir with love / Up above my head / I'll be standing by / Eli's game / Silent night / People get ready / Spirit might come / On and on
HIBOOK 12 / Feb '97 / Hi

☐ DON'T LOOK BACK
Best love / Love is a beautiful thing / Waiting on you / What does it take / Keep on pushing love / You are my everything / One love / People in the world / Give it everything / Your love / Fountain of love / Don't look back / Love in motion
74321163102 / Feb '97 / RCA

☐ GREATEST HITS VOL.1
Let's stay together / I can't get next to you / You ought to be with me / Look what you done for me / Let's get married / Tired of being alone / Call me / I'm still in love with you / Here I am (come and take me) / How can you mend a broken heart
HIUKCD 425 / Feb '87 / Hi

☐ GREATEST HITS VOL.2 (Take Me To The River)
Drivin' wheel / I've never found a girl / Love and happiness / Living for you / Sha la la / LOVE Love / One woman / Take me to the river / Rhymes / Oh me, oh my (dreams in my arms) / Glory glory / Full of fire / Keep me cryin' / Belle
HIUKCD 438 / Oct '87 / Hi

☐ HI MASTERS, THE
I can't get next to you / Tired of being alone / I'm a ram / Love and happiness / Strong as death / Unchained melody / Take me to the river / LOVE / I stand accused / Have a good time / Belle / I want to hold your hand / For the good times / Funny how time slips away / Sha la la (make me happy)
HEX 35 / 3 Aug '98 / Hi

☐ LET'S STAY TOGETHER
Let's stay together / I've never found a girl / So you're leaving / It ain't no fun to me / Talk to me, talk to me / Old time lovin / Judy / What is this feelin / Tomorrow's dream / How can you mend a broken heart / La la for you
HIUKCD 405 / Jul '86 / Hi

☐ SUPREME AL GREEN, THE
Tired of being alone / I can't get next to you / Let's stay together / How can you mend a broken heart / Love and happiness / I'm still in love with you / Simply beautiful / What a wonderful thing love is / Call me / My God is real / Let's get married / Sha la la (make me happy) / Take me to the river / Love ritual / LOVE Love / I didn't know / Full of fire / Belle
HIUKCD 130 / Apr '92 / Hi

Green, Benny

☐ KALEIDOSCOPE
Kaleidoscope / Thursday's lullaby / Sexy mexy / Patience / Central park south / My girl Bill / Apricot / You're my melody / Kaleidoscope
CDP 8520372 / Feb '97 / Blue Note

Green, Brian

☐ ANTI ROAD RAGE
Jannie's theme / Candles in the sun / Astral blues / Silver rain / Thanks / Libran waltz / I'll be home / Rebirth
PLSCD 257 / 27 Oct '97 / Pulse

☐ PARTNER MASSAGE
Oh my love / When birds cease to sing / Hey girl / Can't we tell the world / Beverly Jane / Can I / Turquoise green and blue / Indian summer / Little child
3036000692 / Sep '97 / Carlton

Green, Bunky

☐ STEP HIGH (Green, Bunky Sextet)
FSRCD 301 / 5 Jan '98 / Fresh Sound

Green Day

☐ 1039/SMOOTHED OUT SLAPPY HOURS
At the library / Don't leave me / I was there / Disappearing boy / Green day / Going to Pasalacqua / Road to acceptance / Rest / Judges daughter / Paper lanterns / Why do you want him / 409 in your coffee maker / Knowledge / 1,000 hours / Dry ice / Only of you / One I want / I want to be alone
65222 / Aug '97 / Epitaph

☐ DOOKIE
Burnout / Having a blast / Chump / Longview / Welcome to paradise / Pulling teeth / Basket case / She / Sassafras roots / When I come around / Coming clean / Emenius sleepus / In the end / FOD
9362455292 / Feb '94 / Reprise

☐ INSOMNIAC
Armatage shanks / Brat / Stuck with me / Geek stink breath / Stuart and the ave / 86 / Panic song / No pride / Brain stew / Jaded / Westbound sign / Tight wad hill / Walking contradiction / Bab's uvula
9362460462 / Oct '95 / Reprise

☐ INTERVIEW DISC
SAM 7026 / Jan '97 / Sound & Media

☐ KERPLUNK
2000 light years away / One for the razorbacks / Welcome to paradise / Christie road / Private ale / Dominated love slave / One of my lies / 80 / Android / No one knows / Who wrote holden caulfield / Words I might have ate / Sweet children / Best thing in town / Strangeland / My generation
LOOKOUT 46CD / Dec '96 / Lookout
65172 / Aug '97 / Epitaph

☐ NIMROD
Nice guys finish last / Hitchin' a ride / Grouch / Redundant / Scattered / Worry rock / Desensitized / All the time / Platypus (I hate you) / Last ride in / Jinx / Haushinka / Walking alone / Suffocate / Uptight / Take back / King for a day / Good riddance / Prosthetic head
9362467942 / 13 Oct '97 / Reprise

☐ SMOOTH
LOOKOUT 22CD / Dec '96 / Lookout

Green, Earl

☐ FEEL THE FIRE
Leaving this town / You'll never change her / Turn my world around / I just got some / Borderline / Take my advice / She's sweet to me / Down home girl / Laughing to keep from crying / Feel the fire / Living without her / Sick and tired / Beauty of the night / Turn my world around (Version 2) / Nothing but heartaches / Dark days
ABACACD 002 / Jul '96 / Abacabe

Green, Grant

☐ BEST OF GRANT GREEN VOL.2, THE
Back out / Cease the bombing / Ain't it funky now / Sookie sookie / Cantaloupe woman / California green / Final connection / Windjammer
CDP 8377412 / Aug '96 / Blue Note

☐ BLUE BREAKBEATS
Ain't it funky now / Cantaloupe woman / Windjammer / Sookie Sookie / Ease back / Final countdown
4947052 / 13 Jul '98 / Blue Note

☐ CARRYIN' ON
Ease back / Hurt so bad / I don't want nobody to give me nothing / Upshot / Cease the bombing
CDP 8312472 / Mar '95 / Blue Note

☐ COMPLETE QUARTETS WITH SONNY CLARK, THE (2CD Set)
Airegin / It ain't necessarily so / I concentrate on you / Things we did last summer / Song is you / Nancy with the laughing face / Airegin / On Green Dolphin Street / Shadrack / What is this thing called love / Moon river / Gooden's corner / Two for one / Oleo / Little girl blue / Tune up / Hip funk / My favorite things / Oleo
CDP 8571942 / Aug '97 / Blue Note

☐ GRANT GREEN
Reaching out / Our Miss Brooks / Flick of a prick / One for Elena / Baby, you should know it / Falling in love with love
BLCD 760129 / May '90 / Black Lion

☐ I WANT TO HOLD YOUR HAND
I want to hold your hand / Speak low / Stella by starlight / Corcovado / This could be the start of something big / At long last love
8599622 / 10 Nov '97 / Blue Note

☐ IRON CITY
Iron city / Black Orpheus / Old man (let my people go) / Hi-heel sneakers / Motherless child / Work song
412320482 / 17 Mar '98 / Thirty Two

☐ JAZZ PROFILE
Baby's minor lope / My little suede shoes / Go down moses / Talkin' about jc / Somewhere in the night / My favourite things
CDP 8332052 / 6 Oct '97 / Blue Note

☐ LATIN BIT, THE
Mambo Inn / Besame mucho / Mama Inez / Brazil / Tico tico / My little suede shoes / Blues for Juanita / Grenada / Hey there
CDP 8376452 / Jun '96 / Blue Note

☐ LIVE AT THE LIGHTHOUSE
Intro / Windjammer / Betcha by golly wow / Fancy free / Flood in Franklin Park / Jan jan / Walk in the night
4933812 / 13 Apr '98 / Blue Note

☐ STANDARDS
You stepped out of a dream / Love walked in / If I had you / I'll remember you / You the night and the music / All the things you are / I remember you / If I had you
8212842 / 2 Feb '98 / Blue Note

☐ STREET OF DREAMS
I wish you love / Lazy afternoon / Street of dreams / Somewhere in the night
8212902 / 19 Jan '98 / Blue Note

Green Hornets

☐ FASTER THAN THE BUG ZAPPER
WIGCD 016 / 25 May '98 / Alopecia

☐ GET THE BUZZ
WIGCD 008 / Jul '96 / Alopecia

Green, Howard

☐ FORBIDDEN FRUIT
CD 431 / 6 Jul '98 / New World

Green Jelly

☐ 333
Carnage rules / Orange krunch / Pinata head / Fixation / Bear song / Fight / Super elastic / Jump jerk / Anthem / Slave boy
74321235362 / May '95 / Zoo Entertainment

Green, Jesse

☐ BEST OF JESSE GREEN, THE (Nice And Slow)
Nice and slow / Turn out the lights / I can't dance without you / Cupid / Only love (can keep us together) / Flip / In the hands of the receiver / Inside out / Make my day / Sex ooh aah / Nice and slow / You came you saw you conquered / Let's get it on / Don't let me down / Don't knock my love / You are the star
HTCD 52 / 20 Apr '98 / Hot Productions

Green, Jesse

☐ LIFT OFF
CRD 319 / Mar '96 / Chiaroscuro

☐ ROUND TRIP
BHCD 00032 / Jul '95 / Bad Habits

☐ SEA JOURNEY (Green, Jesse Trio)
CRD 328 / Nov '95 / Chiaroscuro

Green, Lee

☐ LEE GREEN VOL.1 - 1929-1930
DOCD 5187 / Oct '93 / Document

☐ LEE GREEN VOL.2 - 1930-1937
DOCD 5188 / Oct '93 / Document

Green, Lil

☐ COMPLETE RECORDED WORKS 1946-1951, THE
JPCD 1527 / Dec '97 / Jazz Perspectives

Green, Lloyd

☐ STEELS THE HITS
Misty moonlight / Ruby, don't take your love to town / My elusive dream / Crazy arms / Too much of you / There goes my everything / Take these chains from my heart / Moody river / No another time / Moon river / Feelings / My love / Little bit more / You and me / Amie / Desperado / Kiss the moonlight / Edgewater beach / Stainless steel
PLATCD 33 / Jul '92 / Platinum

Green Nuns Of The Revolution

☐ ROCK BITCH MAFIA
Cor / Thunder thighs / Conflicts / Octofunk / Ring of fire / Klunk / Rock bitch / Atomic armadillo (The Fluffening)
AFRCD 7 / 27 Oct '97 / Flying Rhino

Green On Red

☐ ARCHIVES VOL.1 (What Were We Thinking)
Green on red / La vida muerta / Gravity talks / Cheap wine / Hair of the dog / Sixteen ways / Mighty fine day / Down to the bone / Can't go home / Broken / Lonely nights / Out the back door / Loves to play the fool / Oh Carolyn / Can't drive Texas
NORMAL 194CD / Dec '97 / Normal
CORD 026 / 15 Dec '97 / Corduroy

☐ BEST OF GREEN ON RED, THE
Rock 'n' roll disease / This time around / 16 ways (live) / Fading away (live) / Hair of the dog (live) / Keith can't read / Morning blue / Zombie for love / Change (live) / Tenderloin / You couldn't get arrested / Little things in life / Two lovers (waitin' to die) / Hector's out / Baby loves her gun / Quarter / She's all mine / Frozen in my headlights / Too much fun
WOLCD 1047 / Jun '94 / China

☐ HERE COME THE SNAKES
Keith can't read / Morning blue / Broken radio / Tenderloin / DT blues / Rock 'n' roll disease / Zombie for love / Change / Way back home
WOLCD 1013 / Mar '91 / China

☐ LITTLE THINGS IN LIFE 1987-1991
Gold in the graveyard / Shed a tear (for the lonesome) / Broken radio / Rock 'n' roll disease / Good patient woman / Little things in life / Quarter / Pills and booze / We had it all / Hector's out / Zombie for love / Sixteen ways / Change / Fading away / Are you sure Hank done it this way / Hair of the dog
MCCD 037 / Sep '91 / Music Club

☐ NO FREE LUNCH
OW 30015 / Sep '94 / One Way

☐ SCAPEGOATS
Guy like me / Little things in life / Two lovers (waitin' to die) / Gold in the graveyard / Hector's out / Shed a tear (for the lonesome) / Blow fly / Sun goes down / Where the rooster crows / Baby loves her gun
WOLCD 1001 / Apr '91 / China

☐ THIS TIME AROUND
This time around / Cool million / Reverend Luther / Good patient woman / You couldn't get arrested / Quarter / Foot / Hold the line / Pills and booze / We're all waiting
WOLCD 1019 / Jul '91 / China

Green Pajamas

☐ GHOSTS OF LOVE
BCD 4033 / Jul '90 / Bomp

☐ INDIAN WINTER
GH 1059CD / Nov '97 / Get Hip

☐ STRUNG BEHIND THE SUN
CAM 005CD / 15 Sep '97 / Camera Obscura

☐ STRUNG OUT
CAM 014 / 22 May '98 / Camera Obscura

Green, Peter

☐ BANDIT
Proud Pinto / Clown / In the skies / Rubbing my eyes / Bandit / Promised land / Last train to San Antone / Lost my love / Momma don't cha cry / One woman love / Tribal dance / Just for you / Black womaan / Funky jam
74321474642 / Apr '97 / Milan

☐ BLUE GUITAR
Gotta see her tonight / Last train to San Antone / Woman don't / What'cha gonna do / Walkin' the road / Apostle / Fool no more / Loser two times / Slabo day / Crying won't bring you back
RNCD 1003 / Jun '96 / Rhino

☐ BORN ON THE WILD SIDE
ECD 3356 / 6 Jul '98 / K-Tel

☐ COLLECTION, THE (2CD Set)
RNCD 1011 / 9 Feb '98 / Rhino

☐ END OF THE GAME, THE
Bottoms up / Timeless time / Descending scale / Burnt foot / Hidden depth / End of the game
7599267582 / Jan '96 / Reprise

☐ GREEN AND GUITAR (The Best Of Peter Green)
MCCD 244 / Jun '96 / Music Club

☐ IN THE SKIES
In the skies / Slabo day / Fool no more / Funky chunk / Tribal dance / Seven stars / Just for you / Proud pinto / Apostle
RNCD 1001 / Jun '96 / Rhino

☐ KATMANDU
Dust my broom / One more night with you / Crane's train boogie / Boogie all the way / Zulu gone West / Blowing all my troubles away / Stranger's blues / Sweet sixteen / Who's that knocking / Case
100642 / May '97 / A-Play Collection

☐ LEGEND
RNCD 1009 / Nov '96 / Rhino

☐ LITTLE DREAMER
Loser two times / Momma don't cha cry / Born under a bad sign / I could not ask for more / Baby when the sun goes down / Walkin' the road / One woman love / Cryin' won't bring you back / Little dreamer
RNCD 1002 / Jun '96 / Rhino

☐ ONE WOMAN LOVE
PACD 7013 / Feb '93 / Disky

☐ RARITIES
APCD 052 / Jun '97 / Appaloosa

☐ RATTLESNAKE GUITAR (The Music Of Peter Green/2CD Set) (Various Artists)
CTC 0205 / Mar '96 / Coast To Coast

☐ ROBERT JOHNSON SONGBOOK, THE
When you got a good friend / 32-20 blues / Phonograph blues / Last fair deal gone down / Stop breakin' down blues / Terraplane blues / Walkin' blues / Love in vain blues / Ramblin' on my mind / Stones in my passway / Me and the devil blues / Honeymoon blues / Kind hearted woman blues / I believe I'll dust my broom / If I had possession over judgement day / Sweet home Chicago
SARCD 002 / 18 May '98 / Snapper

☐ SPLINTER GROUP
Hitch hiking woman / Travelling riverside blues / Look on yonder wall / Homework / Stumble / Help me / Watch your step / From 4 till late / Steady rolling man / It takes time / Dark end of the street / Going down
SARCD 101 / May '97 / Snapper

☐ TWO GREENS MAKE A BLUES (Green, Peter & Mick)
CLACD 426 / Mar '97 / Castle

☐ VERY BEST OF PETER GREEN, THE
In the skies / Slaybo day / Apostle / Loser two times / Baby when the sun goes down / One woman love / Time for me to go / Clown / Proud pinto / Bullet in the sky / Last train to San Antone / Whatcha gonna do / Woman don't / Bandit
WB 886002 / 2 Feb '98 / Disky

☐ WHITE SKY
Time for me to go / Shining star / Clown / White sky (love that evil woman) / It's gonna be me / Born on the wild side / Falling apart / Indian lover / Just another guy
RNCD 1004 / Jun '96 / Rhino

Green River

☐ DRY AS A BONE/REHAB DOLL
This town / PCC / Ozzie / Unwind / Baby takes / Searchin' / Ain't nothing to do / Queen bitch / Forever means / Rehab doll / Swallow my pride / Together we'll never / Smilin' and dyin' / Porkfist / Take a dive / One more stitch
SPCD 72 / May '94 / Sub Pop

Green, Urbie

☐ SEA JAM BLUES (Green, Urbie Quintet)
CRD 338 / May '97 / Chiaroscuro

Greenbaum, Norman

☐ PETALUMA
Grade a barn / 5 Pennies / Dairy queen / Campin' / Petaluma / Country lad / Day the well went dry / New dead shrimp blues / Crazy over you / Japanese silky
EDCD 544 / 24 Nov '97 / Edsel

☐ SPIRIT IN THE SKY (The Best Of Norman Greenbaum)
RR 4677 / 24 Nov '97 / Repertoire

☐ SPIRIT IN THE SKY/BACK HOME AGAIN
Junior Cadillac / Spirit in the sky / Jubilee / Alice Bodine / Tars of India / Power / Good lookin' woman / Milk cow / Marcy / Back home again / Rhode Island Red / Canned ham / Titfield thunder / Miss Fancy / Lucille got stealed / Circulate / Hook and ladder / Damper / I J Foxx
EDCD 470 / Feb '96 / Edsel

Greenberg, Rowland

☐ HOW ABOUT YOU
Seven up / I don't stand a ghost of a chance with you / Have you met Miss Jones / Georgia on my mind / Stella by starlight / Gone with the wind / Basin Street blues / Strike up the band / On the sunny side of the street / Taps Miller / Sweet and lovely
GECD 155 / Jan '88 / Gemini

Greenberry Woods

☐ RAPPLE DAPPLE
Trampoline / No 37 (Feels so strange) / Sentimental role / I'll send a message / Oh Christine / I knew you would / Waiting for dawn / That's what she said / Sympathy song / Adieu / Busted / More and more / Nowhere to go / Hold on
9362454952 / May '94 / WEA

Greene, Bruce

☐ FIVE MILES OF ELLUM WOOD (Old Time Kentucky Fiddle Solos)
OMC 0002 / 20 Apr '98 / One Man Clapping

Greene, Casey

☐ CASEY GREENE
LB 9713 / Jul '98 / La Brava

Greene, Jack

☐ JOLLY GREEN GIANT, THE
Ever since my baby went away / There goes my everything / All the time / What locks the door / You are my treasure / Love takes care of me / Statue of a fool / Back in the arms of love / Wish I didn't have to miss you / Whole world comes to me / If this is love / Something unseen / There's a whole lot about a woman / Makin' up his mind / Much obliged / What in the world has gone wrong with our love / Satisfaction / I need somebody bad / It's time to cross that bridge / He little thing'd her out of my arms
EDCD 515 / Mar '97 / Edsel

Greene, Lorne

☐ ON THE PONDEROSA (Lorne Green & His Western Classics)
RE 21572 / Sep '97 / Razor & Tie

Greene, Richard

☐ SALES TAX TODDLE
Drunken man's dream / Along about daybreak / Sales tax toddle / With body and soul / Done gone waltz / My little Georgia rose / I'll be sixteen next Sunday / Close by / 16 days in Georgia / Last ride / No one but my darlin' / Little rabbit
REBCD 1737 / Jul '97 / Rebel

Greenfields

☐ HOBO BY MY SIDE, A
Stay away / Broken heart / Who's that guy called Tom T Hall / Riverboat queen / Moonlight rider / San Bernardino / Come home with me tonight / Baby's gone / Rolling down / What a wonderful world / Hobo blues
BCD 15698 / Jul '93 / Bear Family

Greenfields Of America

☐ LIVE IN CONCERT
Kilkelly / Kilkelly / Reynardine / Stick to the craythur
GLCD 1096 / Aug '92 / Green Linnet

Greengate

☐ METAPHYSICAL VIBRATION
FUZ 006 / Mar '97 / Fuzzy Box
DRL 034CD / Sep '97 / Darla

Greenhouse

☐ TOMORROW THE WORLD
JUMP 011 / 16 Mar '98 / Jump Up

Greenslade

☐ BEDSIDE MANNERS ARE EXTRA
Bedside manners are extra / Pilgrims progress / Time to dream / Drum folk / Sunkissed you're not / Chalkhill
7599268662 / Jan '96 / WEA

☐ GREENSLADE
Feathered friends / English western / Drowning man / Temple song / Melange / What are you doin' to me / Sundance
7599268122 / Jan '96 / WEA

☐ SHADES OF GREEN 1972-1975
EMCD 9701 / Jul '97 / Earcotic

☐ SPYGLASS GUEST
Spirit of the dance / Little red fry up / Rainbow / Siam seesaw / Joie de vivre / Red light / Melancholic race / Theme for an imaginary western
7599268672 / Jan '96 / WEA

☐ TIME AND TIDE
Animal farm / Newsworth / Time / Tide / Catalan / Flatery stakes / Waltz for a fallen idol / Ass's ears / Doldrums / Gangsters
7599268682 / Jan '96 / WEA

Greenslade, Dave

☐ PENTATEUCH OF THE COSMOLOGY, THE
Intriot / Moondance / Beltempest / Glass / Three brides / Birds and bats and dragonflies / Nursery hymn / Minstrel / Fresco / Kashrinn / Barcarolle / Dry land / Forest kingdom / Vivat regina / Scream but not heard / Mischief / War / Lament for the sea / Miasma generator / Exile / Jubilate / Tiger the dove
BGOCD 170 / Jul '94 / Beat Goes On

Greenwich, Sonny

☐ LIVE AT SWEET BASIL
JUST 262 / Jul '92 / Justin Time

Greenwood, Lee

☐ WIND BENEATH MY WINGS
HMNCD 026 / 16 Mar '98 / Half Moon

Greer, Big John

☐ BIG JOHN'S ROCKIN' (3CD Set)
Rockin' with big john / Clambake boogie / Drinkin' wine (spo-dee-o-dee) / Long tall gal / I want ya' I need ya' / I found a dream / If I told you once / Rocking jenny jones / I'll never do that again / I've just found love / Big john's a blowin' / When you love / I'll never be free / Cheatin' / How can you forget / Red juice / It's better to be taken for granted / Once there lived a fool / A fool hasn't got a chance / Why did you go / Our wedding tune / I ain't got nothin' to lose / Little girl, don't cry / I'll never let you go / Got you on my mind / Have another drink and talk to me / Dyin' of love / I'm savin' all my lovin' / Strong red whiskey / Woman is a five letter word / I'm just another one in love with you / Let me hold you / I'm the fat man / Since you went away from me / When the roses bloom in lovers' lane / You'll never be mine / I need you / Lonesome and blue / If you let me / Tell me so / Forgive me / I guess it's all over now / You, only you / Slow and easy / Beginning to miss you / You played on my piano / Play me some loud music / Come back maybelline / Blam / Bottle it up and go / A man and a woman / Can't stand it any longer / Soon soon soon / I'm glad for your sake / Lucky, lucky me / Wait till after xmas / Will I be the one / Santa do the mambo / I'll never stop loving you / I didn't know / Lately / Don't worry about it / Ride pretty baby / Drinkin' fool / I spoke too soon / Confusion blues / Too long / Don't let me down / Will I be the one / Rhythm in the breeze / Getting mighty lonesome for you / Night crawlin'
BCD 15554 / Feb '92 / Bear Family

Greggi G

☐ HAVE BASS WILL TRAVEL
PT 611001 / May '98 / Part

Gregorio, Guillermo

☐ ELLIPSIS
HATOLOGY 511 / May '98 / Hatology

Gregory, Michael

☐ WHAT TO WHERE
Jubilee / One / Still waiting / Heart of happiness / Superstitious game / Last home at / Where / What / Falling down / Fan the flame / Slow burn (there's more) / Elan
PD 83023 / Dec '88 / Novus

Gregory, Steve

☐ BUSHFIRE
LJKCD 011 / Mar '95 / LKJ

Gregson & Collister

☐ LOVE IS A STRANGE HOTEL
For a dancer / Move away Jimmy Blue / How men are / Love is a strange hotel / Even a fool would let go / One step up / Things we do for love / (I heard that) Lonesome whistle / Same situation / Always better with you / Today I started loving you again / Most beguiling eyes
SPCD 1035 / Oct '90 / Special Delivery

☐ MISCHIEF
SPCD 1010 / Sep '87 / Special Delivery

Gregson, Clive

☐ CAROUSEL OF NOISE (Live/ Unreleased Tracks)
CGCD 9401 / May '95 / Gregsongs

☐ I LOVE THIS TOWN
FIENDCD 786 / Sep '96 / Demon

☐ PEOPLE AND PLACES
Camden town / Feathers / Mary's divorce / Gabriel / My eyes gave the game away / Medicine house / Black train coming / Box number / Blue rose / My favourite lies / Restless / Lilly of the valley / When this war is over
FIENDCD 764 / Apr '95 / Demon

Grekis, Paraskevas

☐ BOUZOUKIS
PS 65173 / Nov '96 / PlayaSound

Grenadier Guards Band

☐ BRITISH GRENADIERS, THE
British Grenadiers / Scipio / First battalion bugle call / Queens company / Second batallion bugle call / Nilimegen / Third batallion bugle call / Inkerman / Rule Brittania / Grenadiers march / Duke of York / Duke of Gloster's march / Belle isle / Portsmouth / Wargramer grenadier march / Last post / Grenadiers return / Reveille / Musick marziale
BNA 5015 / Oct '87 / Bandleader

☐ BY REQUEST (Band Of The Grenadier Guards)
BNA 5143 / 13 Apr '98 / Bandleader

☐ DRUMS AND FIFES (The 1st & 2nd Battalion Of Grenadier Guards)
British Grenadiers / Girl I left behind me / Goodbye Dolly Gray / Garry Owen / Pack up your troubles in your old kit bag / Lilliburlero / Great escape / Hazlemere / Old grey mare / Brazil / See the conquering hero comes / Scipio / Red cloak / Army and Marine / Bugle calls / Marching down the years / Potpourri / Regimental music of the 18th century / First battalion bugle call / Parade flute call / Second battalion bugle call / Drummer's call / Third battalion bugle call / Ye British Grenadiers / Flag and empire / Prussia's glory / Eton boating song / Attention / Belle Isle march / Prince Rupert's march / Duke of York / Captain Money's march / Fanfare
BNA 5003 / Nov '86 / Bandleader

☐ MARCH SPECTULAR (Bands Of The Grenadier, Coldstream & Irish Guards)
British Grenadiers / Scipio / Grenadiers march / Milanollo / Gigaro / St. Patrick's day / Let erin remember / Through bolts and bars / Army and marine / Furchtlos und treu / Red men's march / Nijmegen / Dunedin / Badenviller / Carry on / Bond of friendship / Independentia / King's troop / Luftwaffe March / Imperial echoes / Admiral of the air / Trafalgar / Frensham / Pioneer spirit / Quis separabit / Wellington / San Lorenzo / Sons of the brave / Star of St Patrick
BNA 5040 / '91 / Bandleader

☐ ON STAGE
Fanfare - stage presence / Full speed ahead / Grenadiers waltz / Overture on themes of Offenbach / Love changes everything / Carnival of Venice / Debutante / Prelude to romance / Send in the clowns / Portrait in time / Me and my girl / March and dance of the comedians / Les miserables / Spanish rhapsody fiesta / March: Atlantis / Three bavarian dances
BNA 5032 / Aug '89 / Bandleader

☐ SOUSA MARCHES/STIRRING MARCHES OF THE USA SERVICES (Grenadier Guards Band/Major Rodney Bashford)
Stars and stripes forever / El capitan / High school cadets / Washington post / Picadore / Invincible eagle / Semper fidelis / Manhattan beach / Liberty bell / Thunderer / King Cotton / Hands across the sea / Anchors aweigh / Samper paratus / She wore a yellow ribbon / West Point march / Ballad of the Green Berets / Caissons go rolling along / Marine Corps hymn / Air Corps / Commando march / Guadalcanal march / Thru' the years 1776-1969 medley
4489572 / Aug '96 / Phase 4

☐ WHEN THE GUARDS ARE ON PARADE
British grenadiers / Scorpio / Duke of York / Grenadiers return / Queen's company / Inkerman / Royal salute / Army and marine / Glorious victory / Army of the nile / Great little army / Royal standard / Steadfast and true / King's guard / National emblem / Birdcake walk / Old grenadier / Namur / Belgian gendarmes / Mareth / Line / When the guards are on parade / Bravest of the brave / On the square / Contemptibles
BNA 5104 / Mar '94 / Bandleader

☐ WORLD OF THE MILITARY BAND, THE
Imperial march / March militaire / March / March / March with honour crowned / Coronation march: crown imperial / Entry of the Boyards / Turkish march / Hungarian march / Procession of the sirdar / Radetzky march / Grand march / Grand march / March / Coronation march / March militaire / Pomp and circumstance march no.1
4529382 / Aug '97 / Decca

Grenadine

☐ NOPALITOS
SMR 23CD / Oct '94 / Simple Machines

Gretschen Hofner

☐ MARIA CALLOUS
OPIUMCD 2 / Jun '97 / Poppy

Gretsy, Alan

☐ BOBCATS RECAPTURED
JCD 258 / Dec '95 / Jazzology

Grey, Adie

☐ GRANDPA'S ADVICE
Ain't no doubt about it / It ain't the money / Daddy put your beer down / Now that he's not in love / Far away beyond these mountains / I'm with you in my dreams / Granpa's advice / Tell all the people you love / Christmas everyday / Easiest thing / Grape and the grain / My old man / If I lose my way
FIENDCD 941 / 2 Mar '98 / Demon

Grey, Al

☐ CENTER PIECE - LIVE AT THE BLUE NOTE
Diz related / South side / I wish I knew / Homage to Norman / Nascimento / SWB Blues / Lester leaps in / Bewitched, bothered and bewildered / Center piece
CD 83379 / Sep '95 / Telarc

☐ LIVE AT THE 1990 FLOATING JAZZ FESTIVAL
CRD 313 / Mar '96 / Chiaroscuro

☐ MATZOH AND GRITS
ARCD 19167 / Feb '98 / Arbors Jazz

☐ NEW AL GREY QUINTET, THE
Bluish grey / Sonny's tune / Don't blame me / Syrup and bisquits / T'ain't no use / Al's rose / Night and day / Call it whatchawanna / Underdog / Stompin' at the Savoy / Al's blues / Rue prevail / Soap gets in your eyes
CRD 305 / Oct '91 / Chiaroscuro

☐ TRULY WONDERFUL (Grey, Al & Jimmy Forrest)
STCD 552 / '92 / Stash

Grey, Jerry

☐ SOUND OFF
DAWE 73 / Oct '95 / Magic

Grey Lady Down

☐ CRIME
12.02 / All join hands / Thrill of it all / Ballad of Billy Grey / Circus of thieves / Annabez / Fugitive / I believe
CYCL 001 / Feb '94 / Cyclops

☐ FEAR
And finally / Roller coaster / Modern day cavalier / Final decree / Sliding / Usurper / Paper chains
CYCL 053 / Jul '97 / Cyclops

☐ FORCES
Paradise lost / Battlefields of counterpane / Without a trace / Cold stage / I believe / Flyer
CYCL 020 / Jun '95 / Cyclops

Grey, Michael

☐ COMPOSERS SERIES VOL.1
Allangrange garret-bruce gandy's dusty chanter (air and / Mrs. joan grey-jamie macinnis of cape breton (2\4 marches) / Katie grey's welcome from scotland-dunrovin farm (retreat / Lain ormsaig mackinnon's salute (piobaireachd) / Pipe major william livingstone-george a. walker (2\4 marche / Lain symington-blustering home (marches in compound time)
LCOM 5217 / Sep '94 / Lismor

Greyboy

☐ FREESTYLIN'
URCD 003 / Jul '96 / Ubiquity

☐ LAND OF THE LOST
URCD 012 / Jul '96 / Ubiquity

☐ TOWN CALLED EARTH
GBR 005CD / 16 Jul '97 / Greyboy

Greyboy Allstars

☐ WEST COAST BOOGALOO
GB 001CD / Jul '96 / Greyboy

Greyhound

☐ BLACK AND WHITE
Black and white / Dream lover / Stand for our rights / Jamaica rum / Sky high / Wily / Only love can win / Mango rock / Unchained melody / Hold on to your happiness / Wappadusa / Some dark city
C5CD 539 / Oct '92 / See For Miles

Grianan

☐ MAID OF EIRIN, THE
WWCD 14 / Jan '94 / West Winds

Grid

☐ 456
Face the sun / Ice machine / Crystal clear / Aquarium / Instrument / Heartbeat / Oh six one / Figure of eight / Boom / Leave your body / Fire engine red
CDV 2696 / Oct '92 / Virgin

☐ ELECTRIC HEAD
One giant step / Interference / Are you receiving / Islamatron / Traffic / Driving instructor / Beat called love / Friend of the devil / Sugar magnolia / Operator / Candy man / Ripple / Brokedown palace / Till the morning comes / Attics of my life / Truckin' / Floatation / Strange electric sun / Typical Waterloo sunset / Dr. Celine / Machine delay / This must be heaven / Beautiful and profound / Intergalactica / Central locking / First stroke
9031715572 / Sep '90 / East West

☐ EVOLVER
Wake up / Rollercoaster / Swamp thing / Throb / Rise / Shades of sleep / Higher peaks / Texas cowboys / Spin cycle / Golden dawn
74321227182 / Aug '96 / De-Construction

☐ MUSIC FOR DANCING
Floatation / Crystal clear / Boom / Figure of 8 / Rollercoaster / Texas cowboys / Swamp thing / Crystal clear (remix) / Figure of 8 (remix) / Diablo / Rollercoaster (remix)
74321276702 / Sep '95 / De-Construction

Grief

☐ AU DELA
DANCD 023 / Jan '90 / Danceteria

☐ KITTYSTRA QUATRE
DANCD 014 / Jan '90 / Danceteria

Grief

☐ COME TO GRIEF
CM 77087 / Jan '95 / Century Media

☐ TORSO
PESS 23CD / 30 Mar '98 / Pessimiser

Grief Society

☐ HOW WE USED TO LIVE
GIEXCD 001 / Nov '96 / Gentlemen In Exile

Grieg, Charlotte

☐ NIGHT VISITING SONGS
Vine leaves / Lucky in love / Gathering rushes / Bury me / Seven seas / Grey cock / Passenger / Lucy wan / Searching for lambs / Crows
HM 713 / Jul '98 / Harmonium

Grier, David

☐ FREEWHEELING
Wheeling / Shadowbrook / Old hotel rag / Angeline the baker / Bluegrass itch / Alabama jubilee / Blue midnite star / Roanoke / If I knew her name / Gold rush / Fog rolling over the Glen / New soldier's joy
ROUCD 0250 / '91 / Rounder

☐ LONE SOLDIER
ROUCD 0309 / Apr '95 / Rounder

☐ PANORAMA
Impulsive / Jeff Davis / King Wilkies run / Skeleton / Forked deer / Ticklebelly hill / Apples and oranges / Chinquapin hunting / Peartree/double file / Dead end
ROUCD 0417 / Nov '97 / Rounder

Grier, Jimmy

☐ ECHOES FROM THE COCONUT GROVE 1932
TT 421 / May '98 / Take Two

Grievous Angels

☐ NEW CITY OF SIN
BS 020CD / Jun '97 / Bloodshot

☐ ONE JOB TOWN
SP 1162CD / Oct '93 / Stony Plain

Griffett, James

☐ TROTTIN' TO THE FAIR (Irish Songs & Ballads By Sir Charles Stanford) (Griffett, James & Clifford Benson)
Chapel on the hill / Trottin' to the fair / My love's an arbutus fair / Confession / Winds of Bethlehem / Song of the bow / Jenny / Colonel Carty / Londonderry air / Blackbird and the wren / Zephyrs blest / Lament / Willow tree / Drop me a flower / Heraclitus / Blackberry time / Soft day / Merry month of May / Ploughman's whistle / Monkey's carol / Irish reel / Bold unbiddable child / Witches' charms / Fairy lough / More of Cloyne / Poison on the darts / Thief of the world / Back to Ireland
CAMEO 2001 / Nov '97 / Campion

Griffin, Buck

☐ LET'S ELOPE BABY
Pretty Lou / Girl in 1209 / You'll never come back / Stutterin' Papa / Watchin' the 7:10 roll by / Broken heart with alimony / Jessie Lee / Bow my back / Old bee tree / Every night / Party / Little Dan / Neither do I / Cochise / Go-stop-go / Bawlin' and squalin' / Let's elope baby / It don't make no never mind / Meadow lark boogie / Rollin' tears / One day after payday / Going home all alone / Twenty six steps / First man to stand on the moon / Sorry I never knew you / Lord give me strength / Next to mine / Lookin' for the green
BCD 15811 / Jun '95 / Bear Family

Griffin, Della

☐ TRAVELIN' LIGHT
Smile / Travelin' light / Out of nowhere / Some other Spring / Second time around / Easy living / Trouble in mind / Trust in me / Blue gardenia
MCD 5496 / Jul '94 / Muse

Griffin, Dick

☐ NOW IS THE TIME
Now is the time / Madrid / Multiphonic blues / Waltz my son / Queen / Peaceful thinking / Darkness of Duke / Come dance with me
CDBOP 021 / 24 Nov '97 / Boplicity

Griffin, Johnny

☐ BIG SOUL-BAND, THE (Griffin, Johnny Orchestra)
Wade in the water / Panic room blues / Nobody knows the trouble I've seen / Meditation / Holla / So tired / Deep river / Jubilation
OJCCD 485 / Oct '96 / Original Jazz Classics

☐ GRIFFIN BAGS
RW 103 / 20 Apr '98 / Reward

☐ LITTLE GIANT, THE
Catharsis / What's new / Hot sausage / Woody 'n' you / Where's your overcoat boy / Little John / 63rd Street theme / Playmates / Message / Kerry dancers / Black is the colour of my true love's hair / Green grow the rushes-o / Londonderry air
OJCCD 136 / Jun '96 / Original Jazz Classics

☐ MAN I LOVE, THE
Man I love / Hush-a-bye / Blues for Harvey / (I'm afraid) the masquerade is over / Sophisticated lady / Wee / I'll get by / Mean to me / I'll never be the same / Easy living / Foolin' myself / Without your love / Me, myself and I / Sailboat in the moonlight / Travellin' all alone / She's funny that way / Getting some fun out of life / I can't believe that you're in love with me / Back in your own backyard / You can't be mine (and someone else's too) / Say it with a kiss
BLCD 760107 / Jun '88 / Black Lion

☐ WAY OUT
Where's your overcoat, boy / Hot sausage / Sunny monday / Cherokee / Terl's tune / Little john
OJCCD 1855 / Jul '94 / Original Jazz Classics

Griffin, Kevin

☐ DOWN IN DOOLIN
OSS 109CD / Aug '97 / Ossian

Griffin, Rex

☐ LAST LETTER, THE (3CD Set)
Why should I care if you're blue / Blue eyes lullaby / Just for old times sake / Love call yodel / I don't love anybody but you / Trail to home sweet home / Let me call you sweetheart again / Mean woman blues / Dixieland sweetheart / Down in old Alabama / Everybody's tryin' to be my baby / If you call that gone goodbye / Yodelling cowboy's last song / I love you Nellie / I'm just passing through / I'm ready to reform / Walkin' blues / Old faded photograph / Sittin' on the old setee / Sweet Mama hurry home / Would you leave me alone little darling / Last love call yodel / Last letter / Over the river / Answer to the last letter / My hillbilly baby / I think I'll give up (it's all over now) / Beyond the last mile / Just partners / Lovesick blues / I love you as before / I'll never tell you that I love you / Nobody wants to be my baby / Maybe you'll think about me / You got to go to work / Old rose and a curl / Everybody's tryin' to be my baby / I'm just passin' through / I don't love anybody but you / Let me call you sweetheart / Just for old time's sake / I'm ready to reform / Walkin' blues / Old faded photograph / Trail to home sweet home / Nobody wants to be my baby / Mean woman blues / Why should I care if you're blue / I love you Nellie / Yum yum blues / Toodle-oo sweet Mama / Too good to be true / That old sweetheart of mine / Blue eyes lullaby / Yodelling cowboy's last song / Love call yodel / How can I be sure / I'm crying inside / I don't mean to mean / Thousand times or more / I'm free as the breeze / I lost again / Misery: *Griffin, Buddy* / Same tear twice: *Griffin, Buddy* / Last letter: *Griffin, Buddy* / No love, no heartaches: *Griffin, Buddy* / If you call that gone goodbye: *Griffin, Buddy* / You got to go to work: *Griffin, Buddy* / Gods of love: *Griffin, Buddy* / Shuckin' corn: *Griffin, Buddy* / High and dry: *Griffin, Buddy* / Don't talk about you love: *Griffin, Buddy* / Don't hold your breath: *Griffin, Buddy* / My Carolina mountain home: *Griffin, Buddy* / Let me walk along beside you: *Griffin, Buddy* / Just wait and see: *Griffin, Buddy* / Bartender's girl: *Griffin, Buddy* / Red rose, a bouquet or a roomful: *Griffin, Buddy*
BCD 15911 / Dec '96 / Bear Family

Griffin, Sid

☐ LITTLE VICTORIES
When I'm out walking with you / Jimmy Reed / Good times tomorrow, hard times today / Rate of exchange / I wish I was a mountain / Distant trains / Sailers and soldiers / Man who invented the blues / Monk's mood / Flak jacket / Alma Mater / Jerusalem Road
SID 007 / May '97 / Prima

Griffith, Andy

☐ JUST AS I AM (30 Favourite Old Time Hymns)
72438516662 / 31 Mar '98 / SPAW

Griffith, Grace

☐ GRACE GRIFFITH
BLX 10028CD / Apr '96 / Blix Street

Griffith, Nanci

☐ BLUE ROSES FROM THE MOONS
Everything's comin' up roses / Two for the road / Wouldn't that be fine / Battlefield / Saint Teresa of Avila / Gulf Coast highway / I fought the law / Not my way home / Is this all there is / Maybe tomorrow / Waiting for love / I'll move along / Morning train / She ain't goin' nowhere
7559620152 / Mar '97 / Elektra

☐ LAST OF THE TRUE BELIEVERS, THE
Last of the true believers / Love at the five and dime / St. Olav's gate / More than a whisper / Banks of the old Pontchartrain / Looking for the time / Goin' gone / One of these days / Love's found a shoulder / Fly by night / Wing and the wheel
CDPH 1109 / Nov '96 / Philo

☐ OTHER VOICES, OTHER ROOMS
Across the great divide / Woman of the phoenix / Tecumseh valley / Three fights up / Boots of spanish leather / Speed of the sound of loneliness / From Clare to here / I can't help but wonder where I'm bound / Do re mi / This old town / Comin' down in the rain / Ten degrees and getting colder / Morning song to Sally / Night rider's lament / Are you tired of me darling / Turn around / Wimoweh
7559614642 / 5 Jan '98 / Elektra

Griffiths, Albert

☐ WHOLE HEAP, A (Griffiths, Albert & The Gladiators)
HBCD 11554 / '88 / Heartbeat

Griffiths, Marcia

☐ AT STUDIO ONE
SOCD 1126 / Mar '96 / Studio One

☐ DREAMLAND
Dreamland / Tell me now / Truly / Mark my word / Stay / Feel like jumping / Lonesome feeling / Survival / Melody life / I've got to go back home
CDSGP 0148 / Oct '95 / Prestige

☐ INDOMITABLE
PHCD 26 / Sep '93 / Penthouse

☐ LAND OF LOVE, THE
PHCD 2045 / Jan '97 / Penthouse

☐ MARCIA
Trench town rock / It's not funny / Deep in my heart / Blue skies / True love is hard to achieve / Everywhere / Don't let me down / Cycles / Baby loves to dance / I'm leaving
DGCD 7 / Apr '89 / Germaine

☐ MARCIA GRIFFITHS
PHCD 2071 / 9 Feb '98 / Penthouse

☐ MARCIA GRIFFITHS AND FRIENDS
RNCD 2040 / Jan '94 / Rhino

☐ PUT A LITTLE LOVE IN YOUR HEART (The Best Of Marcia Griffiths)
Toil (my ambition) / Don't let me down / Put a little love in your heart / Young, gifted and black / We've got to get ourselves together / Private number / Band of gold / Pied piper / But I do / Your love / I don't care / You're mine / Help me up / First time ever I saw your face / Play me / There's no me without you / I just don't want to be lonely / Gypsy man / Sweet bitter love / When will I see you again
CDTRL 325 / Mar '94 / Trojan

☐ STEPPIN'
Steppin' out in Babylon / Where were you / Peaceful woman / Sweet bitter love / Why there is no love / Way I feel about you / I'm hurtin' inside / It's impossible / Give and you get / Where is the love
SHCD 44007 / 23 Mar '98 / Shanachie

Grifters

☐ CRAPPIN YOU NEGATIVE
185192 / May '94 / Southern

☐ EYES FULL OF GOLD
SPCD 327 / Feb '96 / Sub Pop

☐ FULL BLOWN POSSESSION
SPCD 402 / 17 Nov '97 / Sub Pop

☐ ONE SOCK MISSING
185112 / Jun '93 / Southern

Grimble Grumble

☐ GRIMBLE GRUMBLE
G$ 007CD / 23 Mar '98 / Won't Go Flat

Grimes, Carol

☐ ALIVE AT RONNIE SCOTT'S
Solitude / Never say never / Give me liberty / Wild women / Lush life / Who do you want / Where are you / Life is dangerous / Your shoes are hot / We said yes
JHCD 034 / '91 / Ronnie Scott's Jazz House

☐ LAZY BLUE EYES (Grimes, Carol & Ian Shaw)
I got it bad and that ain't good / You always miss the water (when the well runs dry) / I'm scared / Don't explain / Lush life / In a sentimental mood / Lover man / I ain't got nothin' but the blues / I cover the waterfront / I love you / Spring can really hang you up the most / Lazy blue eyes / Snake / Misty / Body and soul
CDWIK 93 / Oct '90 / Big Beat

Grimes, Tiny

☐ COMPLETE TINY GRIMES VOL.1 1944-1946, THE
BMCD 6005 / Jul '96 / Blue Moon

☐ COMPLETE TINY GRIMES VOL.2 1944-1950, THE
BMCD 6006 / Jul '96 / Blue Moon

☐ COMPLETE TINY GRIMES VOL.3 1950, THE
BMCD 6007 / Jan '97 / Blue Moon

☐ COMPLETE TINY GRIMES VOL.4 1950-1953, THE
BMCD 6008 / Jan '97 / Blue Moon

☐ COMPLETE TINY GRIMES VOL.5 1953-1954, THE
BMCD 6009 / Jan '97 / Blue Moon

☐ SOME GROOVY FOURS
Tiny's boogie woogie / Everyday I have the blues / Swinging Mama / Some groovy fours / I found a new baby / Tee mine sy / Lester leaps in / Sid West End blues / Li'l darlin' / Swinging Mama / Frankie and Johnny / Food for thought / Morgantini with mine
BB 8742 / Jan '97 / Black & Blue

☐ TINY GRIMES AND THE ROCKIN' HIGHLANDERS (Grimes, Tiny & His Rockin' Highlanders)
Call of the wild / St. Louis blues / Tiny's jump / Howlin' blues / Frankie and Johnny boogie / My baby's cool / Pert skirt / Hey Mr. J.B. / Drinking beer / Marie
KKCD 01 / Apr '89 / Krazy Kat

Grimethorpe Colliery Band

☐ BOLD AS BRASS
Red sky at night / Hogarth's hoe down / I dream of Jeannie with the light brown hair / Barney's tune / Cornet concerto / Chinese takeaway / Parade / Paris le soir / Mosaic / Stars and stripes forever / Moorside suite / Severn suite
4500232 / 17 Aug '98 / Belart

☐ CLASSIC BRASS
Florentiner march / William Tell overture / Sweet Georgia Brown / Serenade / Sugar blues / Mr. Jums / Valdres march / MacArthur Park / Gymnopedie No.1 / Mr. Lear's carnival / Misty / Procession to the Minster / Irish tune from County Derry / Finale from Faust
CDMFP 6058 / May '89 / Music For Pleasure

☐ FIREBIRD (Conducted By Ray Farr)
Midnight sleighride / On with the motley / Songs of the quay / In a sentimental mood / Pictures at an exhibition / Festive prelude / Scherzo / Berne patrol / Why did I choose you / Firebird
QPRL 010 / Oct '97 / Polyphonic

☐ FROM SONNETS TO JAZZ
Epic symphony / Unholy sonnets / Salamander / Fantasy for cornet and brass band / Refrains and cadenzas / Jazz
CHAN 4549 / 17 Sep '97 / Chandos

☐ GRIMETHORPE
CHAN 4545 / Mar '97 / Chandos

☐ MELODY SHOP, THE
Melody shop / Slaughter on 10th Avenue / Doretta's aria from La Rondine / Lezghinka / Debutante / Prelude to Act III of Lohengrin / Every time we say goodbye / Rhapsody Espana / Trumpet blues and cantabile / Adagio / Gallop from William Tell / MacArthur Park / Paganini 18th variation / Punchinello / Ave Maria / Light walk / One day in your life / Toccata
CHAN 4552 / 20 May '98 / Chandos

☐ OLD RUGGED CROSS, THE
PLSCD 194 / Apr '97 / Pulse

☐ OPERATIC EUPHONIUM (Grimethorpe Colliery Band & Kinder Children's Choir)
Celeste aida / Flower duet / Catari, catari / Largo al factotum / Duet from Don Pasquale / Evening prayer / La Donna e mobile / Marriage to Figaro / Pagageno, pagagena / Flower song / On with the motley / Quartet from rigoletto / Softly awakes my heart / Recondita armonia / Panis angelicus / Lohengrin / Oh, beloved father / Le miserere (il travatore) / You are my hearts delight / One fine day / Nun's chorus / Nessun dorma
QPRL 072D / Oct '97 / Polyphonic

☐ PAGANINI VARIATIONS FOR BRASS BAND
Raven's wood / Journey into freedom / Queen of the night's aria / Ruby Tuesday / Buster strikes back / Finale from organ symphony No. 3 / President / Girl with the flaxen hair / Blue John / Blue rondo a la Turk / Panagini variations
DOYCD 015 / May '92 / Doyen

☐ WAGNER
DOYCD 033 / Jan '96 / Doyen

☐ WHITE CHRISTMAS WITH GRIMETHORPE
White Christmas / Rockin' around the Christmas tree / Winter wonderland / Sleigh ride / Do they know it's christmas / Rudolph the red-nosed reindeer / Walking in the air / When a child is born / Midnight sleigh ride / Christmas piece / Dies natalis / Santa Claus is coming to town / Mistletoe and wine / Christmas triptych / Frosty the snowman / Holy boy / Spirit of christmas / Little drummer boy / Mary's boy child / Christmas suite
CHAN 4550 / 19 Nov '97 / Chandos

☐ WILBY
Paganini variations / Paganini variations / Masquerade / New jerusalem
DOYCD 029 / Mar '94 / Doyen

☐ YOUR 20 FAVOURITE HYMNS
For all the Saints / Old rugged cross / Lord's my shepherd / Dear lord and father of mankind / Guide me, O thou great redeemer / Amazing grace / Praise my soul the King of heaven / All in the April evening / I will sing the wondrous story / How great thou art / O worship the King / Rejoice the Lord is King / When I survey the wondrous cross / O God our help in ages past / Now thank we all our God / Fill thou my life O Lord my God / Love divine, all loves excelling / All creatures of our God and King / Day thou gavest, lord, is ended / Abide with me
PWKS 4248 / Sep '97 / Carlton

Grimetime

☐ SPIRIT OF DISGUST
KCCD 1 / Jun '94 / Kill City

Grimms

☐ ROCKING DUCK
Interruption at the Opera House / Three times corner / Sex maniac / Galatic love poem / Chairman Shankly / Italian job / Albatross ramble / Humanoid boogie / Short blues / Summer with the Monarch / Twyfords vitromant / Following you / Newly pressed suit / Eleventh hour / Conservative government figures / Brown paper carrier bag / Soul song / Rockin' duck / Songs of the stars / Right mask / Policeman's lot / Question of habit / Take it while you can / Poetic license / Masked poet / Hiss and boo / Gruesome / FX / Blab blab blab / Backwards thru space / Do chuck a mao mao
EDCD 370 / Jun '93 / Edsel

Grin

☐ GONE CRAZY
You're the weight / Boy and girl / What about me / One more time / True thrill / Beggar's day / Nightmare / Believe / Ain't for free
5407062 / Mar '97 / A&M

Grip Inc.

☐ NEMESIS
SPV 08518322 / Feb '97 / SPV

☐ POWER OF INNER STRENGTH
SPV 08576922 / Mar '96 / SPV

Grisman, David

☐ ACOUSTIC CHRISTMAS
What child is this / Santa claus is coming to town / Ancient aires and dances (respighi) / Christmas song / God rest ye merry gentlemen / We wish you a merry christmas / White christmas (dedicated to ben webster) / Flower carol (good king wenceslas) / Winter wonderland / Silent night / Auld lang syne
ROUCD 0190 / '88 / Rounder

☐ DAVID GRISMAN ROUNDER ALBUM
Hello / Sawing on the strings / Waiting on Vasser / I ain't broke but I'm badly bent / Op 38 / Hold to God's unchanging hand / Boston boy / Cheyenne / Till the end of the world rolls around / You'll find her name written there / On and on / Bob's Brewin / So long
ROUCD 0069 / '88 / Rounder

☐ DAWG '90
ACD 1 / May '97 / Acoustic Disc

☐ DAWGANOVA (Grisman, David Quintet)
Dawganova / April's wedding bossa / Barkley's bug / Caliente / Brazilian breeze / Tico Tico / El Cumbanchero / Manha de Carnaval / Nature boy
ACD 17 / Jun '97 / Acoustic Disc

☐ DAWGWOOD (Grisman, David Quintet)
ACD 7 / Jul '97 / Acoustic Disc

☐ DGQ 20 (3CD Set) (Grisman, David Quintet)
ACD 20 / Jun '97 / Acoustic Disc

☐ EARLY DAWG
SHCD 3713 / Jan '94 / Sugar Hill

☐ HERE TODAY (Grisman, David & Various Artists)
I'll love nobody but you / Once more / Foggy mountain chimes / Children are cryin' / Hot corn / Cold corn / Lonesome river / My walking shoes / Love and wealth / Billy in the lowground / Making plans / Sweet little Miss blue eyes / Going up home to live in green pastures
ROUCD 0169 / Aug '93 / Rounder

☐ HOME IS WHERE THE HEART IS
True life blues / Down in the willow garden / My long journey home / Little Willie / Highway of sorrow / Sophronie / My aching heart / Close by / Feast here tonight / Leavin' home / Little cabin home on the hill / I'm comin' back / But I don't know when / Salty Dawg blues / If I lose / Sad and lonesome day / My little Georgia rose / Foggy mountain top / I'm my own grandpa / Pretty Polly / Home is where the heart is / Nine pound hammer / Memories of mother and day / Teardrops in my eyes / House of gold
ROUCD 0251/2 / Aug '88 / Rounder

☐ NOT FOR KIDS ONLY (Grisman, David & Jerry Garcia)
ACD 9 / Jul '97 / Acoustic Disc

☐ TONE POEMS VOL.2 (The Sounds Of The Great Jazz Guitars & Mandolins) (Grisman, David & Martin Taylor)
ACD 18 / Apr '97 / Acoustic Disc

Griswalds

☐ ALL THE WAY DOWN
All the way down / Can't break away / Footstompin' / Let go / Big Daddy Cool / Aunt Nancey's bull / My love don't mean a thing / Lil' Bonnie Blue / What the fool made me do / Good, the bad, the ugly / What I say is right
JSPCD 280 / Jan '97 / JSP

Grits

☐ RARE BIRDS
CUNEIFORM 55912 / Jun '97 / Cuneiform

Grobschnitt

☐ DIE GROBSCHNITT STORY (2CD Set)
PMS 7092 / 20 Apr '98 / Repertoire

☐ GROBSCHNITT
Symphony / Modulation / Variation / Travelling / Wonderful / Sun trip / Oelberg / On the way / Battlefield / New era
RR 7093 / 20 Apr '98 / Repertoire

☐ JUMBO
Jupp / Excursion of Father Smith / Clown / Dream and reality / Sunny Sunday's sunset / Auf wiedersehen
RR 7094 / 20 Apr '98 / Repertoire

☐ ROCKPOMMELS LAND
PMS 7095WP / 22 Jun '98 / Repertoire

☐ SOLAR MUSIC-LIVE
PMS 7096WP / 22 Jun '98 / Repertoire

☐ STORY OF GROBSCHNITT, THE (2CD Set)
RR 7092 / 16 Mar '98 / Repertoire

Grodes

☐ LET'S TALK ABOUT GIRLS (Grodes/ Dearly Beloved)
BA 0010 / Feb '97 / Bacchus Archives

Grolnick, Don

☐ BLUE NOTE SESSIONS, THE (2CD Set)
Nothing personal / Tagliono / Weaver of dreams / His Majesty the baby / I want to be happy / Persimmons / Or come fog / Five bars / Heart of darkness / What is this thing called love / One bird, one stone / Nighttown Genie / Spot that man / Cost of living / Blues for pop
CDP 8571972 / Aug '97 / Blue Note

Groon

☐ REFUSAL TO COMPLY
DIS 002 / Oct '95 / FMR/Dissenter

Groop Dogdrill

☐ HALF NELSON
Lovely skin / Cocksucker's blues / Gentleman's soiree / Lifestyle / Oily rag / Southbound tuxedo / Jackie O / Gracelands / Hessus / (That) Texaco (feeling) / Salt Peter / Personal / Silver boots
MNTCD 1010 / 20 Apr '98 / Mantra

Groove Armada

☐ NORTHERN STAR
Dr Eiff / Captain sensual / Entrance to Zanzibar / At the river / Dirty listening / M 2 many / Dan solo / Pressure breakdown / What have we become / Jeanneret's groove / Pillar 13 / Bonus stitch 1 / Bonus stitch 2
TUCH 103CD / 2 Mar '98 / Tummy Touch

Groove Collective

☐ DANCE OF THE DRUNKEN MASTER
SHANCD 5045 / Jun '98 / Shanachie

☐ DANCE OF THE DRUNKEN MASTER
SH 5045 / 1 Sep '98 / Charlotte

☐ GROOVE COLLECTIVE
Restrike / Balimka / Nerd / Rahsaanasong / Ms. Grier / Whatugot / El golpe avisa / Genji monogatari / Buddha head / Saturday afternoon
9362455412 / Mar '94 / WEA

☐ WE THE PEOPLE
Jay Wrestles the Bari Constrictor / Loisaida / Lift off / Everybody (We the people) / Fly / Sneakey / I am / Caterpillar / Hide it / Anthem / Sedate / Jay wrestles the Bari Constrictor, 2 / She's so heavy (I want you) / Where are your white shoes
IMP 11632 / 8 Sep '97 / Impulse Jazz

Groove Juice Special

☐ GROOVE JUICE SPECIAL & SWEET SUBSTITUTE (Groove Juice Special & Sweet Sunstitute/Al Fairweather)
Fat and greasy / My new celebrity is you / Mama bought a chicken / Rockabye Basie / Porgy / 5 guys named Moe / Lucky Jim / Twisted / Hucklebuck / King size papa / Smoke rings / Nagasaki / Hotel Noel
LACD 83 / Jul '97 / Lake

Groove Theory

☐ GROOVE THEORY
10 minute high / Time flies / Ride / Come home / Baby love / Tell me / Hey you / Hello it's me / Good 2 me / Angel / Keep tryin' / You're not the one / Didja know / Boy at the window
4783822 / Nov '95 / Epic

Groove Thing

☐ ADVENTURE, THE
EBCD 21 / Jan '95 / Eightball

Groove Tunnel

☐ LIVEN UP
DRCD 008 / Mar '96 / Detour

Grooverider

☐ GROOVERIDER PRESENTS THE PROTOTYPE YEARS (2CD Set) (Various Artists)
Subway: *Ed Rush* / Dreams of heaven: *Codename John & Grooverider* / Threshold: *Cybotron & Dillinja* / Secrets: *John B* / Grey odyssey: *Optical* / Mute: *Matrix* / Silver blade: *Dillinja* / Deep inside: *Codename John & Grooverider* / Locust: *Ed Rush & Fierce* / Going gets tuff: *Lemon D* / Warned: *Codename John & Grooverider* / Still: *Boymerang*
4872192 / Mar '97 / Higherground

☐ GROOVERIDER'S HARDSTEP SELECTION VOL.1 (Various Artists)
KICKCD 15 / Nov '94 / Kickin'

☐ GROOVERIDER'S HARDSTEP SELECTION VOL.2 (Various Artists)
KICKCD 24 / Jul '95 / Kickin'

☐ MIXMAG LIVE VOL.2 (Grooverider/ Justin Robertson) (Various Artists)
MMLCD 002 / Jul '96 / Mixmag Live

Groovie Ghoulies

☐ APPETITE FOR ADRENOCHROME
LOOKOUT 148CD / Sep '96 / Lookout

☐ BORN IN THE BASEMENT
LOOKOUT 149CD / Sep '96 / Lookout

☐ RE-ANIMATION FESTIVAL
LK 182CD / 22 Sep '97 / Lookout

☐ WORLD CONTACT DAY
LOOKOUT 151CD / Jun '96 / Lookout

Grope

☐ DESERT STORM
PCD 029 / 29 Sep '97 / Diehard

☐ PRIMATES
RRS 941CD / Sep '95 / Lost & Found

☐ SOUL PIECES
PCD 026MCD / Apr '96 / Progress

Gross, Helen

☐ HELEN GROSS 1924-1925
DOCD 5477 / Sep '96 / Document

Gross, Henry

☐ RELEASE/SHOW ME TO THE STAGE
Juke box song / Lincoln road / Overton square / Springtime mama / Moonshine alley / Shannon / One last time / Some thing in between / Someday / Pokey / Show me to the stage / String of hearts / Painting my love songs / Come along / Help / What a sound / I can't believe / Hideaway / Showboat / If we tie our ships together
CDWIKD 104 / Apr '92 / Chiswick

Gross, Paul

☐ TWO HOUSES (Gross, Paul & David Keeley)
Two houses
SMCD 740 / 13 Jul '98 / Scorpio

Grossman, Richard

☐ EVEN YOUR EARS (Grossman, Richard Trio)
HATOLOGY 515 / May '98 / Hatology

Grossman, Stefan

☐ BEST OF THE TRANSATLANTIC YEARS, THE
Hot dogs / Cincinnati flow rag / New York City rag / Roll and tumble blues / Shake sugaree / Candyman / Morning comes / Take a whiff on me / Blues for Mr Sam / Vestapol/That's no way to get along / Those lazy blues / Blues jumped the rabbit / Teddy Roosevelt / Those pleasant days / Hi dum diddle / Bo's rag / So they say / Sound techniques recording blues / Alibi / Waterfalls / Fat man / Kokomo / Belzona blues / Orphan Sunday / Little Sally Walker
ESMCD 437 / Oct '96 / Essential

☐ BLACK MELODIES ON A CLEAR AFTERNOON
Struttin' rag / Blake's breakdown / Blues ain't dry / St Louis tickle / Working on the new railroad / Atlanta flag / Nobody's business / Haag city dance / Mables' dream / Spoonful / East Colorado blues / Little boy little boy who made your britches / Smokey mokes / Entertainer / Glory of love / Slippin' til my gal comes in partner / Harlem rag / John Henry / It won't be long / Sister Kate's syncopated dance / Silver swan / Charley James / Buck dancer's choice / Down South blues / See that girl sitting / CC rider / Powder rag / Sugarbabe / Franklin blues / Salty dog rag / King porter stomp / Bill Bailey / Delta crossroads / Faretheewell titantic
SH 98011 / Mar '98 / Shanachie

☐ NORTHERN SKIES SOUTHERN BLUES (Grossman, Stefan & Duck Baker)
Big Bill / Just a closer walk / Northern skies southern blues / Blues for the Mann / Old country rock / Hicks farewell / Jacksonville blues / M and O Blues / Back home in Indiana / Freight train / Shake sugaree / Nobody's business / Diddie wa diddie / Medley
SH 97026 / Mar '98 / Shanachie

☐ SHAKE THAT THING (Fingerpicking Country Blues Guitar)
Yazoo strut / Monkry wrench rag / Spider web blues / Crossed canoes / Death come creeping / Welsh cob blues / Square and compass / Shake that thing / Frag / Candyman / CC rider / Goose tracks / House on the hill / All my friends are gone / Drunkard's path / Kaleidoscope rag / Delia
KMCD 9501 / 23 Mar '98 / Kicking Mule

Grossman, Steve

☐ BOUNCING WITH MR. AT
Afternoon in Paris / Soultrane / Why don't I / Whims of chambers / Exemporaneous / My little suede shoes / Soul eyes / CTA
FDM 365792 / Apr '96 / Dreyfus

☐ HOLD THE LINE (Grossman, Steve Quartet)
DIW 912 / Oct '96 / DIW

☐ MY SECOND PRIME
1232462 / Nov '91 / Red

☐ REFLECTIONS (Grossman, Steve & Alby Cullaz/Simon Goubert)
500212 / Nov '93 / Musidisc

☐ SOME SHAPES TO COME
OW 30329 / Sep '94 / One Way

☐ TIME TO SMILE
415 Central Park West / Circus / I'm confessin' that I love you / Extemporaneous / This time the dreams on me / Time to smile / Till there was you / EJ's blues
FDM 365662 / Dec '94 / Dreyfus

☐ WAY OUT EAST VOL.1
1231762 / Apr '93 / Red

☐ WAY OUT EAST VOL.2
1231832 / Apr '93 / Red

Grosvenor, Luther

☐ FLOODGATES
Evesham bay / Floodgates / Best years of my life / Fullness of time / I wanna be free / Ninsky prospect / Loneliest man in town / Fire down below / Cathy
RUF 1007 / Oct '96 / Ruf

Grosz, Marty

☐ JUST FOR FUN (Grosz, Marty Quartet)
NHCD 039 / Oct '97 / Nagel Heyer

☐ LIVE AT THE LA CLASSIC (Grosz, Marty & His Orphan Newsboys)
JCD 230 / Jan '94 / Jazzology

☐ MARTY GROSZ & HIS ORPHAN NEWSBOYS
SOSCD 1225 / Oct '92 / Stomp Off

☐ MARTY GROSZ & HIS SWINGING FOOLS
CD 022 / May '96 / Nagel Heyer

☐ MARTY GROSZ & KEITH INGHAM (Grosz, Marty & Keith Ingham & Their Paswonky Serenaders)
SOSCD 1214 / Oct '92 / Stomp Off

☐ ON REVIVAL DAY (Grosz, Marty & His Sugar Daddies)
JCD 260 / Jul '96 / Jazzology

☐ SINGS OF LOVE (Grosz, Marty & Tiny Signa)
JCD 210 / Oct '93 / Jazzology

☐ SWING IT (Grosz, Marty & Destiny's Tots)
Let's swing it / Skeleton in the closet / Emaline / Old man harlem / Love dropped in for tea / Little girl / Sunrise serenade / I've got a feeling / You're foolin' / What's the use / Eye opener / Sun will shine tonight / It's been so long / I surrender dear / It's the last time / Sonny boy / High hat, a piccolo and a cane
JCD 180 / Apr '89 / Jazzology

☐ THANKS (Grosz, Marty & The Collectors' Items Cats)
JCD 310 / May '98 / Jazzology

Grotesque

☐ IN THE EMBRACE OF EVIL
BS 007CD / Nov '96 / Burning Sun

Grotewohl, Chris

☐ UNDER THE INFLUENCE
0453CD / Mar '98 / Fifth String

Grotus

☐ MASS
That's entertainment / Bad itch / White trash blues / Ebola reston / Hand to mouth / Ain't nobody's business if I do / Sick / Collect 'em all / Wild Bill / Bottom line / Back in the day
8286042 / Mar '96 / London

☐ SLOW MOTION APOCALYPSE
Up rose the mountain / Good evening / Same old sauce / Hourglass / Shivayanama / Complications / Kali yuga / Clean / Sleepwalking / Medicine / Slow motion apocalypse
VIRUS 118CD / Mar '93 / Alternative Tentacles

Ground Zero

☐ GROUND ZERO
DSA 54047 / Dec '96 / CDSA

Groundhogs

☐ BACK AGAINST THE WALL
Back against the wall / No to submission / Blue boar blues / Waiting in the shadows / Ain't no slaver / Stick to your grass / In the meantime / 54156
CDTB 111 / '91 / Thunderbolt

☐ BEST OF THE GROUNDHOGS, THE
Cherry red / Split / Mistreated / Still a fool / Split / Times / Groundhog / BDD / Strange town / You had a lesson / Rich man, poor man / Earth is not room enough / Eccentric man / Split / Amazing Grace
CDGOLD 1074 / Feb '97 / EMI Gold

☐ BLACK DIAMOND/CROSSCUT SAW
Crosscut saw / Promiscuity / Boogie withus / Fulfilment / Live a little lady / Three way split / Mean mistreater / Eleventh hour / Body talk / Fantasy partner / Live right / Country blues / Your love keeps me alive / Friendzy / Pastoral future / Black diamond
BGOCD 131 / Feb '92 / Beat Goes On

☐ BLUES OBITUARY
BDD / Daze of the weak / Times / Mistreated / Express man / Natchez burning / Light was the day
BGOCD 6 / Jan '89 / Beat Goes On

☐ FOUR GROUNDHOGS ORIGINALS (Scratching/Blues Obituary/Thank Christ/Split) (4CD Set)
Rocking chair / Early in the morning / Waking blues / Married men / No more doggin' / Man trouble / Come back baby / You don't love me / Still a fool / BDD / Daze of the weak / Times / Mistreated / Express man / Natchez burning / Light was the day / Strange town / Darkness is no friend / Soldier / Thank Christ for the bomb / Ship on the ocean / Garden / Status people / Rich man, poor man / Eccentric man / Split / Cherry red / Year in the life / Junkman / Groundhog
CDHOGS 1 / Feb '96 / Premier/EMI

☐ GROUNDHOG NIGHT
Shake for me / No more doggin' / Eccentric man / 3744 James Road / I want you to love me / Garden / Split part 1 / Split part 2 / Still a fool / I love you misogyny / Thank Christ for the bomb / Soldier / Mistreated / Me and the devil / Cherry red / Ground hog blues / Been there, done that / Down in the bottom
HTDCD 12 / Jun '93 / HTD

☐ GROUNDHOGS BEST 1969-1972
Ground hog / Strange town / Bog roll blues / You had a lesson / Eccentric man / Earth is not room enough / BDD / Split part 1 / Cherry red / Mistreated / 3744 James Road / Soldier / Sad is the hunter / Garden / Split part 4
CZ 282 / Mar '90 / EMI

☐ HOG IN WOLF'S CLOTHING, A
HTDCD 81 / 26 Jan '98 / HTD

☐ HOG WASH
I love miss ogyny / I love miss ogyny / Ringmaster / 3744 james road / Sad is the hunter / S'one song / Earth shanty / Mr. hooker, sir john / Rollin' and tumblin' / Death letter / Me and the devil / No more doggin'
BGOCD 44 / '89 / Beat Goes On

☐ HOGS ON THE ROAD
Ground hogs / Hogs in the road / Express man / Strange town / Eccentric man / 3744 James Road / I want you to love me / Split IV / Soldier / Back against the wall / Garden / Split / Waiting in the shadows / Light my light / Me and the devil / Mistreated / Ground hogs blues / Cherry red
CDTB 114 / '91 / Thunderbolt

☐ MASTERS, THE
Express man / Strange town / Eccentric man / Back against the wall / Split part 4 / Garden / Waiting in the shadows / Light my light / Me and the devil / Mistreated / Cherry red
EABCD 087 / 30 Mar '98 / Eagle

☐ NO SURRENDER
Razor's edge / 3744 James Road / Superseded / Light my light / One more chance / Garden / Split / Eccentric man / Strange town / Cherry red
HTDCD 2 / Dec '90 / HTD

☐ ON AIR 1970-1972
Garden / Eccentric man / Split / Split / Mistreated / I love Miss Oggerty / You had a lesson / Earth shanty / 3744 James road / Sad is the hunter / Split / Cherry red
SFRSCD 053 / 23 Feb '98 / Strange Fruit

☐ RAZOR'S EDGE
Razor's edge / I confess / Born to be with you / One more chance / Protector / Superseded / Moving fast standing still / I want you to love me
BP 270CD / 24 Nov '97 / Blueprint

☐ SCRATCHING THE SURFACE
Rocking chair / Early in the morning / Waking blues / Married men / No more doggin' / Man trouble / Come back baby / You don't love me / Still a fool / Oh death / Gasoline / Rock me / Don't pass the hat around
BGOCD 15 / Jul '89 / Beat Goes On

☐ SOLID
Light my light / Light my light / Sins of the father / Sad go round / Corn cob / Plea sing / Plea song / Snow storm / Joker's grave
CLACD 266 / Jun '92 / Castle

☐ SPLIT
Split / Cherry red / Year in the life / Junk man groundhog / Split (pts 2-4)
BGOCD 76 / Dec '89 / Beat Goes On

☐ THANK CHRIST FOR THE BOMB
Strange town / Darkness is no friend / Soldier / Thank Christ for the bomb / Ship on the ocean / Garden / Status people / Rich man, poor man / Eccentric man
BGOCD 67 / '89 / Beat Goes On

☐ WHO WILL SAVE THE WORLD
Earth is not room enough / Wages of peace / Body in mind / Music is the food of thought / Bog roll blues / Death of the sun / Amazing grace / Grey maze
BGOCD 77 / Apr '91 / Beat Goes On

Group 1850

☐ AGEMOS TRIP 2 MOTHER EARTH
CDP 1047DD / Nov '97 / Pseudonym

Group Called Smith

☐ SMITH
VSD 5489 / Mar '95 / Varese Sarabande

Group Home

☐ LIVIN' PROOF
Intro / Inna citi life / Livin' proof / Serious rap shit / Suspended in time / Sacrifice / Up against tha wall / 4 give my sins / Baby paw / 2 thousand / Supa star / Realness
8287252 / Mar '96 / Payday

Groupa Batuque Percussion Project

☐ SAMBA DE RUA
Wilson's intro / Jandaia / Parou al / Tabla samba / Onda leve / Mama samba / Aoyama san / Percussao livre
FARO 017CD / Aug '97 / Far Out

Groupe Kalyi Jag

☐ GYPSY SONGS OF HUNGARY
PS 65112 / Nov '93 / PlayaSound

Groves, K.C.

☐ CAN YOU HEAR IT
OMC 0006 / 20 Apr '98 / One Man Clapping

Growing Concern

☐ GROWING CONCERN, THE
GRC 003 / 16 Feb '98 / Growing Concern

Growing Movement

☐ CIRCLE OF TORTURE
WB 1107CD / Apr '94 / We Bite

Growling Mad Scientists

☐ CHAOS LABORATORY
HADSHCD 01 / Jun '97 / Hadshot Haheizart

Grown Ups

☐ MILK CARTON
SFTRI 516CD / 10 Nov '97 / Sympathy For The Record Industry

GRP All Star Big Band

☐ GRP ALL STAR BIG BAND
Airegin / Blue train / Donna Lee / Maiden voyage / Sister Sadie / Sidewinder / Seven steps to heaven / I remember Clifford / Footprints / Manteca / 'Round midnight / Spain
GRP 96722 / 25 May '98 / GRP

Grubbs, David

☐ BANANA CABBAGE
ZINC 30 / Mar '97 / Table Of The Elements

Gruberova, Edita

☐ CHILDREN'S SONGS OF THE WORLD
Poesje mauw / D'esos caballos / Si toutes les filles / Che baccan / Es klappert die muhle / Spi mladjenec / Miala kasienka / Numi numi / Tancuj tancuj / Una flor de la cantuta / Three blind mice / Aa aa alin lasta / Haragszik / Pridi ty suhajko / Yuyake koyake / Heidschi bumbeidschi / Pera ston pera kambo / L'inverno e passato / Mi jachol lassim / Sakura / Dolina dolina / Humpty dumpty / Kumbaya / Nana mara haath / Katten og killingen / Ciobanas / Schyau / Joli tambour / Ba ba vita lamm / Itsy bitsy spider / Tala al-badru 'alaina / Alle voglein
NC 706602 / Feb '94 / Nightingale Classics

Gruntz, George

☐ HAPPENING NOW (Gruntz, George Concert Jazz Band '87)
ARTCD 6008 / '88 / Hat Art

☐ MOCK-LO-MOTION
Mock-lo-motion / You should know by now / One for kids / Annalisa / Giuseppi's blues / Vodka-pentatonic
TCB 95552 / Feb '96 / TCB

☐ MPS JAZZ YEARS, THE
5335522 / Dec '96 / MPS Jazz

☐ SINS'N'WINS'N'FUNS (Gruntz, George Concert Jazz Band)
Leave on yr shoes / Reggae / Kinda Gruntzy / Rockin' in rhythm / Preacher / Trombone man / Berlin tango / Room 608 / Dimple / Yellow rose of Texas / C jam blues / Plainsong / GG Deconne
TCB 96602 / Nov '96 / TCB

Grupo ABC

☐ AMOR DE MACARADA
Grupo ABC / Que lastima / Amore de mascarada / No quiero problema / Macario / Que he de hacer / Mesie bombe / Princelda de amor
66058086 / Feb '96 / RMM

Grupo Asi-Son

☐ LLEGO EL AMOR
TCD 502 / 24 Apr '98 / Tumbao

Grupo Batuque

☐ SAMBA DE FUTEBOL
Introduction / Na cadencia do samba / Torcida do flamingo / E ruim / Ole ola / Bateria noite / Wilson canobell / Memao ronton / Brum blek blu / Sobereano / Brasiloseiros ingleses / Demorou / Candomble
FARO 023CD / 26 May '98 / Far Out

Grupo Belen De Tarma

☐ CHICHA
TUMICD 045 / '94 / Tumi

Grupo Caneo

☐ FASE IV
La rutina / Te recuerdo iqual que ayer / Sacala a bailar / Con el corazon en la mano / Mujeres divinas / Negrita / No te vayas a marchar / Aunque to amo
66058041 / Jul '94 / RMM

☐ GRUPO CANEO
RMD 80541 / 24 Mar '98 / RMM

Grupo Caribe

☐ MUSICA DE PUERTO RICO
78887220592 / 21 Apr '98 / Max Music

Grupo Chicontepec

☐ MEXICAN LANDSCAPES VOL.2
PS 65902 / Jan '92 / PlayaSound

Grupo Coca

☐ CHARANGO-QUENA CONCERT
4301120482 / 27 Apr '98 / ANS

Grupo Copagode

☐ GRUPO COPAGODE
71182 / 19 May '98 / RGE

Grupo De Capoeira Angola Pelourinho

☐ CAPOEIRA ANGOLA FROM SALVADOR, BRAZIL
SFWCD 40465 / Mar '96 / Smithsonian Folkways

Grupo Folklorico

☐ CONCEPTS IN UNITY (Grupo Folklorico & Experimental Nuevoyorquino)
CDGR 153 / May '97 / Charly

☐ LO DICE TODO
CDGR 261 / 3 Aug '98 / Charly

Grupo Los Pinos

☐ MUSICA CAMPESINA
TUMICD 056 / Mar '96 / Tumi

Grupo Mandarina

☐ DISPUESTAS A TODO
La boquita / Cada vez / Lo quiero a morir / El hueso / El falsante / Tu juego se acabo / Me nacio del alma / Mandarina mandarina / Pena solo pena
66058073 / Oct '95 / RMM

Grupo Mantaza

☐ MAMBORAMA
Intro / Intro / Noche de amor / Ayudame a vivir / Gracias mi amor por todo lo vivido / Por que / La mujer amada / Rogelio / La famosa prueba / Si tu me amaras / Amor vuelve / Sabroso casao / Salao siempre salao / Jhoana / La situacion
UCD 19076 / Jul '95 / Forlane

Grupo Merecumbe

☐ MUSIC FROM COLOMBIA, CUMBIA, MERENGUE...
EUCD 1253 / Mar '94 / ARC

Grupo Niche

☐ LO MEJOR
1385329142 / 17 Mar '98 / Caiman

☐ MAS DE LO MEJOR
1385329152 / 17 Mar '98 / Caiman

Grupo Noda De Caju

☐ MEU VICIO
RDS 1036 / 12 May '98 / RDS

Grupo Nuevo Mexico

☐ HENCHO EN CASA/CERAMICA
CSM 003 / 23 Feb '98 / CSM

Grupo Oba-Ilu

☐ SANTERIA (Songs For The Orishas)
Eleggua / Ogun / Ochosi / Babaluaye / Obbatala / Shango / Oya / Oshun / Yemaya / Elleggua
SJRCD 038 / 1 Jun '98 / Soul Jazz

Grupo Pachatusan Inkari

☐ SACRED LAND
TMGCD 1 / 21 Aug '97 / Tumi

Grupo Raices

☐ QUE VIVA LA SALSA
Se va el caiman / Asi eres tu / Dejala que se vays / Que viva la salsa / Mentiras tuyas / Cancion para ti / No me provocuas / Guaguanco pa' la calle
RMD 815922 / 7 Apr '98 / RMM

Grupo Raison

☐ TE PARACES AL AMOR
CD 0097 / Mar '96 / Egrem

Grupo Sampa Crew

☐ AROMA
BP 3001 / 12 May '98 / Eldorado

Grupo Sierra Maestra

☐ CON SALSA A CUBA
CD 0084 / Mar '96 / Egrem

Grupo Sportivo

☐ SECOND LIFE
TXCD 70006 / 10 Nov '97 / Triple XXX

Grupo Tierra De Barros

☐ POR SAN MARCOS
Noel (mess de minuit - messe de jour) / Paques / Les vepres du dimanche / La complies / La messe. les funerailles
20088 / Aug '96 / Sonifolk

Grupo Vocal Sianca

☐ MISA CRIOLLA
BMF 008 / Jan '98 / Blue Moon

Grushecky, Joe

☐ COMING HOME
Everything's going to work out right / 1945 / It's a hell of a life / Feeling better now / Gone but not forgotten / Cheap motel / I'm not sleeping / Coming home / Soul survivor / Indic's delight / Touch the rain / In our little room / Innocence is beautiful
STARC 109 / 17 Nov '97 / Big Star

☐ END OF THE CENTURY
PLR 0092 / Feb '97 / PLR

Grusin, Dave

☐ DAVE GRUSIN AND NY-LA DREAM BAND (Grusin, Dave & NY-LA Dream Band)
Shuffle city / Count down / Serengeti walk / Champ / What matters most / Three days of the condor
GRP 95012 / 25 May '98 / GRP

☐ GRUSIN COLLECTION, THE
She could be mine / Thankful 'n' thoughtful / River song / Playera / An actor's life / St. elsewhere / Serengeti walk / Mountain dance / Early a.m. attitude / Bossa baroque / On golden pond
GRP 95792 / Aug '91 / GRP

☐ HAVANA
Main title / Night walk / Cuba libre / Santa Clara suite / Los rumberos de Belen / Love theme / Hurricane country / Lost in a sweet place / Mambo lido / El conuco / Adios habana / La academia
GRP 20032 / Jan '93 / GRP

☐ ONE OF A KIND
Modaji / Heart of the lonely hunter / Catavento / Montage / Playera
GRP 95142 / 25 May '98 / GRP

☐ TWO FOR THE ROAD (A Tribute To Henry Mancini)
Peter Gunn / Dreamsville / Mr. Lucky / Moment to moment / Baby elephant walk / Two for the road / Days of wine and roses / Hatari / Whistling away the dark / Soldier in the rain
GRP 98652 / Apr '97 / GRP

Grusin, Don

☐ DON GRUSIN
Number eight / Not / Shuffle city / Cuidado / Nice going / Cowboy reggae / Kona / What a friend we have in Jesus
JMI 20102 / Nov '93 / JVC

☐ IOK-LA
Majesty / Good lookin' / Danger / Electric man / Julie Ann / Mongolia / Reggie de american babies / One more soldier / Dance / Castle
JVC 20112 / Aug '96 / JVC

Gryce, Gigi

☐ NICA'S TEMPO
Speculation / In a meditating mood / Social call / Smoke signal / You'll always be the one I love / Kerry dance / Shuffle boil / Brake's sake / Gallop's gallop / Nica's tempo
SV 0126 / Oct '97 / Savoy Jazz
CY 18057 / 13 Apr '98 / Savoy Jazz

Gryphon

☐ COLLECTION VOL.2, THE
ITEMCD 3 / 20 Apr '98 / Curio

☐ GRYPHON/MIDNIGHT MUSHRUMPS
Kemp's jig / Sir Gavin Grimbold / Touch and go / Three jolly butchers / Pastime with good company / Unquiet grave / Estampie / Astrologer / Tea wrecks / Juniper suite / Devil and the farmer's wife / Midnight mushrumps / Ploughboy's dream / Last flash of Gaberdine Tailor / Gulland Rock / Dubbel Dutch / Ethelion
ESMCD 356 / Jan '96 / Essential

☐ MIDNIGHT MUSHRUMPS
Midnight mushrumps / Ploughboys dream / Last flash of gaberdine tailor / Gulland rock / Dubbel dutch / Ethelion
ITEMCD 5 / May '95 / Curio

☐ RAINDANCE
ITEMCD 7 / May '95 / Curio

☐ RED QUEEN TO GRYPHON THREE/ RAINDANCE
Opening move / Second spasm / Lament / Checkmate / Down the dog / Raindance / Mother nature's son / Le cambriouleur est dans le mouchoir / Ormolu / Fontinental version / Wallbanger / Don't say go / (Ein klein) heldenleben
ESMCD 460 / Jan '97 / Essential

☐ TREASON
Spring song / Flash in the pantry / Snakes and ladders / Major disaster / Round and round / Falero lady / Fall of the leaf
C5CD 602 / Mar '97 / See For Miles

GTR

☐ KING BISCUIT PRESENTS...
Jekyll and Hyde / Here I wait / Prizefighters / Imagining / Hackett to bits / Spectral mornings / I know what I like / Sketches in the sun / Pennants / Roundabout / Hunter / You can still get through / Reach out (never say no) / When the heart rules the mind
KBFHCD 010 / 6 Jul '98 / King Biscuit

GTS

☐ TRACKS FROM THE DUSTSHELF
GTR 001CD / Feb '96 / GT

Guacaran, Mario

☐ LLANOS HARP
PS 65163 / May '96 / PlayaSound

Guadalquivir

☐ FLAMENCO INSTRUMENTAL
PS 65100 / Feb '93 / PlayaSound

Guana Batz

☐ GET AROUND
Every night and every day / Breakdown / Tell her / Native beat / Lady of the night / Heart of stone / Blues / Don't take this to heart / Such a night / Hot stuff / Sunsets / You're my baby
JRCD 8 / Sep '97 / Jappin' & Rockin'

☐ HELD DOWN AT LAST
Piledriver boogie / My way / See through / Batman / B side blues / Joe 96 / Train kept a rollin' / Please give me something / Devil's guitar
CDMPSYCHO 18 / 17 Nov '97 / Anagram

☐ LIVE OVER LONDON
Can't take the pressure / Rockin' in the graveyard / My way / Live for the day / Rocky road blues / See through / Loansharks / Baby blue eyes / I'm on fire / Dynamite / Rock this town / Endless sleep / King rat / Shake your moneymaker / Joe 90 / Train kept a rollin' / Please give me something / Devil's guitar / You're so fine / No particular place to go / Cave
DOJOCD 133 / Jun '93 / Dojo

☐ UNDER COVER
You're my baby / Please give me something / Bust out / My way / Slippin' in / Radio sweetheart / Shake your moneymaker / Hippy hippy shake / No particular place to go / I'm on fire / Baby blue eyes / Batman / One night / Bring my cadillac back / Rock around with Ollie Vee / Wonderous place / Lights out / Johnny B Goode / Joe 90 / Train kept a rollin' / Devils guitar (live) / Rockin' in the graveyard / Rocky road blues / Dynamite (live) / Rock this town / Endless sleep (live)
CDMPSYCHO 7 / Sep '95 / Anagram

Guano Apes

☐ PROUD LIKE GOD
Open your eyes / Maria / Rain / Crossing the deadline / We use the pain / Never born / Wash it down / Scapegoat / Bad boys / Tribute
SUPERSONIC 012CD / 18 May '98 / Gun

Guapo

☐ TOWERS OPEN FIRE
PTOOL 005 / Jun '97 / Power Tool

Guaraldi, Vince

☐ BOY NAMED CHARLIE BROWN, A (Guaraldi, Vince Trio)
Oh good grief / Pebble beach / Happiness is / Schroeder / Charlie Brown theme / Linus and Lucy / Blue Charlie Brown / Baseball theme / Freda / Fly me to the moon
FCD 8430 / Jun '96 / Fantasy

☐ CHARLIE BROWN CHRISTMAS, A
O tannebaum / What child is this / My little drum / Linus and lucy / Christmas time is here (instrumental) / Christmas time is here (vocal) / Skating / Hark the herald angels sing / Christmas is coming / Fur elise / Christmas song / Greensleeves
FCD 8431 / Nov '95 / Fantasy

☐ JAZZ IMPRESSIONS OF BLACK ORPHEUS (Guaraldi, Vince Trio)
Manha de carnaval / O nosso amor / Generique / Cast your fate to the wind / Moon river / Alma ville / Since I fell for you
OJCCD 437 / Nov '95 / Original Jazz Classics

☐ VINCE GUARALDI TRIO
Django / Fenwyck's farfel / Never never land / Chelsea bridge / Fascinating rhythm / Lady's in love with you / Sweet and lovely / Ossobucco / Three coins in a fountain / It's de-lovely
OJCCD 149 / Apr '96 / Original Jazz Classics

Guard, Charles

☐ AVENGING & BRIGHT
SH 79014 / 3 Aug '98 / Charlotte

Guardiola, Jose

☐ RECORDANDO LOS ANOS 60
5043 / Oct '96 / Divusca

Guards Division

☐ BANDS OF PARADE (Massed Bands Of Guards Division)
BNA 5063 / Jun '91 / Bandleader

☐ ON PARADE
Royal fanfare / Royal fanfare / Scarlet and gold / British grenadiers / Welsh airs and fancies / New coldstream march / Grenadiers march / Milanollo / Redetsky march / Spirit of pageantry / Guardsman / Helian' laddie / Alma march / St. patrick's day / English airs / Grenadiers waltz / Rising of the lark / Highland gathering / National anthem
3036100012 / '95 / Carlton

☐ SCARLET AND GOLD (Massed Bands Of Guards Division)
National anthem / Duke of Cambridge / Me and my girl / Slave's chorus / Radetzky march / Strauss garland / Universal judgement / Procession of the nobles / Anvil chorus / American patrol / William Tell overture / Il silenzio / Trombones to the fore / March to the scaffold / Cockles and mussels / Crown imperial
BNA 5016 / Apr '88 / Bandleader

Guarnieri, Johnny

☐ CLASSICS 1944-1946
CLASSICS 956 / Nov '97 / Classics

Guedes, Carlos

☐ CHURUN MERU (Guedes, Carlos & Desvio)
What for / Friends / Cat from Caracus / Auyantepuy / Churun meru / Caravalito / Carnaval / Spain / Americo / Theme for an angel / Soledad
INAK 30062CD / Nov '97 / In Akustik

Guedon, Henri

☐ RETROSPECTIVE (2CD Set)
FA 048 / May '96 / Fremeaux

Guem

☐ DANSE-PERCUSSIONS
LDX 274968 / Sep '93 / La Chant Du Monde

☐ GUEM & ZAKA PERCUSSION (Guem & Zaka Percussion)
LDX 2741084 / Oct '97 / Le Chant Du Monde

Guerin, Erica

☐ GET REAL
KS 034CD / Jul '97 / King Snake

Guerouabi, Hachemi

☐ LE CHAABI
AAA 119 / Oct '95 / Club Du Disque Arabe

Guerra, Marcelino

☐ RAPINDEY
Pare cochero / Arrebatadora / Guajiro / Fuiste cruelPretita / Mi manera / Que musica mas linda / Oye mi son / Busando la melodia / Pobre cantor / Maleficio / Volvi a querer / Cuando se canto bonito / Convergencia / La clave misteriosa / Sandunguera / Me vay pa'l pueblo
INT 31852 / 27 Oct '97 / Intuition

Guerrero, Tommy

☐ LOOSE GROOVES AND BASTARD BLUES
GLX 03 / 1 Dec '97 / Galaxia

Guerrero, Tony

☐ ANOTHER DAY, ANOTHER DREAM
NOVA 9137 / Jan '93 / Nova

Guerroumi, Habib

☐ ARABO-ANDALUSIAN MUSIC VOL.2
PS 65162CD / Apr '96 / PlayaSound

Guesch Patti

☐ BLONDE
132044 / Jan '97 / XIII Bis

Guesnon, George

☐ GEORGE GUESNON
AMCD 87 / Jul '96 / American Music

349

Guess Who

☐ ON TOUR
Bus rider / Clap for the wolfman / Dancin' fool / Laughing / No sugar tonight / New Mother Nature / Hand me down world / Undone / Share the land / American woman / These eyes / No time
WB 885992 / 2 Feb '98 / Disky

☐ RETROSPECTIVE, A
These eyes / Laughing / Undun / No time / American woman / No sugar tonight / New mother nature / Hand me down world / Share the land / Albert Flasher / Broken / Rain dance / Sour suite / Guns, guns, guns / Running back to Saskatoon / Follow your daughter home / Star baby / Clap for the wolfman / Dancing fool
74321133612 / Jun '97 / RCA

Guetary, Georges

☐ GEORGES GUETARY IN PARIS
Chic a chiquito / A honolulu / C'est vous mon seul amour / Le p'tit bal du sam di soir / Rosa, nina, stella / Divine melodie / Ma bella marguerite / Bolero (ravel) / Maitre pierre / Mon p'tit bouquet de fleurs / Journee de paris / Les amoureux du dimanche / Cheveux au vent / Une boucle blonde / La route fleurie / Pacifico / Valse des regrets / La polka des lampions / Dis papa / La boheme / Monsieur carnaval
CDXP 605 / Jan '89 / DRG

Gugu

☐ PRESENTS REDRUMM'S KILLA KLIQUE
64634170782 / 14 Jul '98 / CRPR

Guianko

☐ ILLAMAME "YANKO"
Temes / El amor no miente / Dime / Busco un amor / Caminaria / Y me acusas / Te quiero asi / Los ojos de ana
66058058 / Jul '95 / RMM

Guided By Voices

☐ ALIEN LANES
Salty salute / Evil speakers / Watch me jumpstart / They're not witches / As we go up we go down / (I wanna be a) Dumbcharger / Game of pricks / Ugly vision / Good flying bird / Cigarette tricks / Pimple zoo / Big chief chines restaurant / Closer you are / Auditorium / Motor away / Hit / My valuable hunting knife / Gold hick / King and Caroline / Striped white jets / Ex-supermodel / Blimps go 90 / Straw dogs / Chicken blows / Little whirl / My son cool / Always crush me / Alright
OLE 1232 / Apr '95 / Matador

☐ BEE THOUSAND
Hardcore UFO's / Buzzards and dreadful crows / Tractor rape chain / Golden heart mountain top queen directory / Hot freaks / Smothered in hugs / Yours to keep / Echos myron / Awful bliss / Mincer Ray / Big fan of pigeon / Queen of cans and jars / Her psychology today / Kicker of elves / Ester's day / Demons are real / I am a scientist / Peep-Hole / You're not an airplane
OLE 0842 / Jul '94 / Matador
SCAT 35CD / 1 Jun '98 / Scat

☐ BOX
SCT 0402 / Feb '95 / Scat

☐ MAG EARWHIG
Can't hear the revolution / Sad if I lost it / I am a tree / Old grunt / Bulldog skin / Are you faster / I am produced / Knock 'em flying / Not behind the fighter jet / Choking Tara / Hollow cheek / Portable men's society / Little lines / Learning to hunt / Finest joke is upon us / Mag earwhig / Now to war / Jane of the waking universe / Colossus crawls West / Mute in the bee-hive
OLE 2412 / May '97 / Matador

☐ PROPELLER
SCAT 49CD / 1 Jun '98 / Scat

☐ UNDER THE BUSHES, UNDER THE STARS
Man called aerodynamics / Life in finer clothing / Rhine jive click / Burning flag birthday suit / Officail ironmen rally song / Not in my airforce / System crash / Worrying song / Plantations of pale pink / Postal blowfish / Applehead / He's the uncle / Bender's bluffing muscles / Delayed reaction brats / Key losers / Catfood on the earwig / Uprooted before seeding / Don't stop now / Cooler jocks / Office of hearts / Take it to the sky / Redman and their wives / Sheetkickers / Drag days / It's like / Big boring wedding
OLE 1612 / Mar '96 / Matador

☐ VAMPIRE ON TITUS
SCAT 50CD / 1 Jun '98 / Scat

☐ VAMPIRE ON TITUS/PROPELLER
Wished I was a giant / No.2 In the model home / Expecting brainchild / Superior sector janitor / Donkey school / Dusted / Marches in orange / Sot / World of fun / Jar of cardinals / Unstable journey / E 5 / Cool off kid kiolowatt / Gleemer / Wondering boy poet / What about it / Perhaps now the vultures
OLE 0832 / Oct '94 / Matador

Guido Zen

☐ HEALTHY FUEL NAVIGATION
PNMCD 03 / 20 Apr '98 / Pik 'n' Mix

Guignolee

☐ RETOUR
GUI 1327CD / Apr '96 / Guignolee

Guilbert, Yvette

☐ LE FIACRE
Le fiacre / Madame Arthur / Ecoute dans le jardin / Enfance / Les caquets de la couchee / L'hotel de numero trois / Les ingenues / Les quatz etudiants / La soularde / A grenelle / Je suis pocharde / La pierreuse / I want yer, ma honey / Keys of heaven / A la villette / Pourquoi me bat, mon mari / Dites moi si je suis belle / Elle etait tres bien / Je m'embrouille / Le voyage a Bethlehem
PASTCD 9773 / Nov '91 / Flapper

Guild Of Ages

☐ ONE (2CD Set)
199653 / Jun '98 / Made To Measure

Guild Of Ancient Fifes & Drums

☐ BY BEAT OF DRUM
Drummer's call / Drum demonstration / English march / 1775 medley / Chester Castle / Downfall of Paris / To danton me / Rogue's march / Grenadiers march / See the conquering hero comes / Toledo / It's a long way to Tipperary / San Lorenzo / Wondermarsch / Basle drum and fife display / Der morgenstreich / Sans Gene / Come lasses and lads / Glopfgaisht / Stenlemmer / Windschi / Dtitt vars / Arabi / Guards / Der vaudois / S'laggerli
BNA 5013 / Feb '88 / Bandleader

Guildhall Symphonic Wind Ensemble

☐ GREAT BRITISH MUSIC FOR WIND BAND VOL.4
John Gay suite / Ring time / Concerto for trombone / Canyons
QPRM 127D / 15 Jun '98 / Polyphonic

Guillory, Isaac

☐ ATLANTIC YEARS 1973-1974
PRCD 005 / Dec '97 / Personal

☐ EASY...
PRCD 003 / Feb '95 / Personal

☐ LIVE
PRCD 001 / Dec '97 / Personal

☐ SLOW DOWN
PRCD 004 / Dec '97 / Personal

☐ SOLO
PRCD 002 / Dec '97 / Personal

Guillot, Olga

☐ LA MEJER CANCIONERA DE CUBA
CCD 802 / Jul '96 / Caney

Guillotine

☐ UNDER THE GUILLOTINE
NR 020CD / 19 Jan '98 / Necropolis

Guilt

☐ BARDSTWON UGLY BOX
VR 029CD / Jan '96 / Victory Europe

Guineto, Almir

☐ PES
76242 / 12 May '98 / RGE

Guinness Choir

☐ CLASSIC IRISH SONGS
CHCD 1096 / Oct '95 / Chyme

Guitar, Bonnie

☐ DARK MOON
Mr. Fire eyes / Dark moon / Open the door / Half your heart / If you see my heart dancing / Johnny Vagabond / Making believe / Down where the tradewinds blow / Letter from Jenny / There's a new moon over my shoulder / Moonlight and shadows / Carolina moon / By the light of the silvery moon / Shine on harvest moon / Moon is low / Get out and get under the moon / Moonlight on the Colorado / Moonlight and roses / It's only a paper moon / Prairie moon / Roll along Kentucky moon / Love is over / Love is done / Stand there mountain / I found you out / Love by the jukebox light / Big Mike / Very precious love / If you'll be the teacher
BCD 15531 / Feb '92 / Bear Family

Guitar Corporation

☐ ULTIMATE GUITAR COLLECTION (3CD Set)
COLBX 003 / Feb '97 / Focus

Guitar Crusher

☐ MESSAGE TO MAN (Guitar Crusher & Alvin Lee)
Heartfixing man / Long green folding friend / Message to man / Stealing a little love / Darling I miss you / Day by day / You know how to hurt a man / Do it well / Trying to fool the whole town / I wanna be with you / I can't stop loving you / Time to throw down
INAK 9034CD / Jul '97 / In Akustik

Guitar Gangsters

☐ POWER CHORDS FOR ENGLAND
Little Miss mystery / City of the damned / Bittersweet but true / Strange kind of love / All over the world / Innocent eyes / She's my kind / Radio authority / Boy like me / Playing games again / In my world / When guitars ruled the earth
CDPUNK 96 / May '97 / Anagram

☐ PROHIBITION/MONEY WITH MENACES
Nothing to shout about / Turn the tables / What did I do (this time) / That's when the razorcuts / Everybody wants to be my friend / It must be physical / Radio shakedown / It's so sad / Gotta get out of here / Long division / Endless Saturday night / Dream that dream / Seventeen again / All the worlds a television / Bad bad girl / Wild weekend / Get me out / I'm not too scared to dance / Rubber hammer / Readers wives / Yellow house / Pray all day
AHOYCD 090 / 6 Jul '98 / Captain Oi

Guitar Johnny

☐ GUITAR JOHNNY & THE RHYTHM ROCKERS (Guitar Johnny & The Rhythm Rockers)
422397 / Feb '97 / Last Call

Guitar Orchestra

☐ GUITAR ORCHESTRA
Pomp and circumstance / Stewing my wine / Fresh air / Misguided woman / Lost weekend / Ghost town / Stella / Livewire / Last chicken in the shop / Camp town / Solomon's seal
SJPCD 002 / Jan '97 / Angel Air

☐ GUITAR ORCHESTRA, THE
Really / Pernod for the bamboo man (aperitif) / First kiss / Closer to the heart / Ocean / Pernod for the bamboo man
PRKCD 6 / Jun '91 / Park

☐ INTERPRETATIONS
Africa / Fool on the hill / Space oddity / Strawberry fields forever / (Don't fear) the reaper / Stranger on the shore / Don't give up / Do it again / I am the walrus / Day in the life
PRKCD 18 / May '94 / Park

Guitar Shorty

☐ GET WISE TO YOURSELF
CDBT 1126 / Feb '96 / Black Top

☐ TOPSY TURVY
BT 1094CD / Oct '93 / Black Top

Guitar Slim

☐ CAROLINA BLUES (Guitar Slim & Jelly Belly)
Ups and down blues / Crooked wife blues / Snowing and raining / No more hard time / She's evil and mean / Mike and Jerry / Don't leave me all by myself / South Carolina blues / Crying won't make me stay / Big trouble blues / Humming bird blues / Right and wrong woman / Southern whistle blues / Jail and buddy blues / Mean girl blues / Travellin' boy's blues / Railroad blues / Yellow and brown woman / Bad acting woman / Christmas time blues / Cooking big woman / You're my honey / Early morning blues / Isabel
ARHCD 460 / 16 Mar '98 / Arhoolie

☐ THINGS THAT I USED TO DO, THE
Well I done got over it / Trouble don't last / Guitar Slim / Story of my life / Letter to my girlfriend / Reap what you sow / Later for you baby / Things that I used to do / Quicksand / Bad luck blues / Think it over / Our only child / I got sumpin' for you / Sufferin' mind / Twenty five lies / Something to remember you by
CD 52033 / May '94 / Blues Encore

Guitar Wolf

☐ MISSILE ME
Missile me / Hurricane rock / Kung fu ramone culmination tactic / Can nana fever / Midnight violence rock 'n' roll / Link Wray man / Guitar star / Racing rock / Jet rock 'n' roll / Devil stomp / Jet blues / Venus Drive
OLE 2192 / Nov '96 / Matador

☐ PLANET OF THE WOLVES
Kawasaki Z11750 / Planet of the wolves / Invader ace / Motorcycle leather boy / Far East man / Wild zero / Planet heart / Energy Joe / Jett love / (I can't get no) satisfaction / Kung Fu Ramone's passion / Let's get hurt / All through the night / Buttobase / Rumble
OLE 2482 / 22 Jun '98 / Matador

Gulabi Sapera

☐ MUSIQUE DU RAJASTHAN
Y 225213CD / Jul '95 / Silex

Gulieva, Gandab

☐ AZERBAIJAN MUGAM ANTHOLOGY VOL.8
Mugam chargah / Mugam rahab / Mugam dilkash
W 260077 / Aug '97 / Inedit

Gulliksson, Lars

☐ BUMPS AHEAD
DRCD 298 / Aug '97 / Dragon

Gullin, Lars

☐ LARS GULLIN & CHET BAKER
DRAGONCD 224 / Feb '89 / Dragon

☐ LATE SUMMER
DRCD 244 / Nov '94 / Dragon

☐ MODERN SOUNDS
DRCD 234 / Nov '94 / Dragon

☐ STOCKHOLM STREET 1959.06 VOL.4
DRCD 264 / Jun '98 / Dragon

Gullin, Peter

☐ TENDERNESS
DRAGONCD 222 / Jul '87 / Dragon

☐ TRANSFORMED EVERGREEN (Gullin, Peter Trio)
DRCD 266 / Oct '94 / Dragon

☐ UNTOLD STORY (Gullin, Peter Trio)
DRCD 315 / Feb '98 / Dragon

Gum-Nyon, Song

☐ MUSIC OF THE KAYAGUM
VICG 50182 / Mar '96 / JVC World Library

Gun

☐ 0141 632 6326
Rescue you / Crazy you / Seventeen / All my love / My sweet Jane / Come a long way / All I ever wanted / I don't mind / Going down / Alway's friends
5407232
5407222 / May '97 / A&M

☐ GALLUS
Steal your fire / Money to burn / Long road / Welcome to the real world / Higher ground / Borrowed time / Freedom / Won't back down / Reach out for love / Watching the world go by
3953832 / Mar '95 / A&M

☐ INSIDE OUT (2CD Set)
Better days / Taking on the world / Shame on you / Money (everybody loves her) / Inside out / Something to believe in / I will be waiting / Coming home / Don't believe a word / Steal your fire / Welcome to the real world / Money to burn / Borrowed time / Higher ground / Find my way / Stand in line / Word up / Don't say it's over / Stay forever / Seems like I'm losing you / Something worthwhile / Crying over you / Only one / Crazy you / I don't mind / Rescue you / Going down / Cray you / My sweet Jane / Always friends
5409242 / 10 Aug '98 / A&M

☐ SWAGGER
Stand in line / Find my way / Word up / Don't say it's over / Only one / Something worthwhile / Seems like I'm losing you / Crying over you / One reason / Vicious heart
5402542 / Jul '94 / A&M

☐ TAKING ON THE WORLD
Better days / Feeling within / Inside out / Money (Everybody loves her) / Taking on the world / Shame on you / Can't get any lower / Something to believe in / Girls in love / I will be waiting
3970072 / Mar '95 / A&M

Gun Club

☐ AHMED'S WILD DREAM
Masterplan / Walkin' with the beast / I hear your heart singin' / Another country's song / Sexbeat / Lupita screams / Go tell the mountain / Preachin' the blues / Stranger in town / Port of souls / Black hole / Little wing / Yellow eyes
527500220 / Jun '93 / Solid

☐ DEATH PARTY
890012 / May '94 / New Rose

☐ DIVINITY
527900920 / Jun '93 / Solid

☐ EARLY WARNING (2CD Set)
SFTRI 478 / 4 May '98 / Sympathy For The Record Industry

☐ FIRE OF LOVE
Sex beat / Preachin' the blues / Promise me / She's like heroin to me / For the love of Ivy / Fire spirit / Ghost on the highway / Jack on fire / Black train / Cool drink of water / Goodbye Johnny / Walking with the beast
422162 / May '94 / New Rose

☐ MOTHER JUNO
Bill Bailey, won't you please come home / Thunderhead / Lupita screams / Yellow eyes / Breaking hands / Araby / Hearts / My cousin Kim / Ports of souls
527500420 / Nov '92 / Solid

☐ PASTORAL HIDE AND SEEK
527900020 / Jun '93 / Solid

Gunjah

☐ HEREDITY
N 02082 / Feb '93 / Noise

☐ POLITICALLY CORRECT
N 02552 / May '95 / Noise

Gunk

☐ FOR GOD'S SAKE
CDBLEED 17 / Feb '96 / Bleeding Hearts

Gunn, Andy

☐ STEAMROLL
PRD 71012 / Apr '97 / Provogue

Gunn, Douglas

☐ O'CAROLAN'S FEAST (Gunn, Douglas Ensemble)
Carolan's welcome / Planxty Connor / Cupan ui eaghra / John Kelly / Sir Arthur Shaen / Madam Cole / Plearaca na ruarcach / Carolan's receipt for drinking / Madam Maxwell / Cait Ni Bhriain / Turlough Og MacDonach / Seoirse Brabston / Charles O'Connor / Thomas O'Burke / Lament for Charles MacCabe / John Nugent / Dr. Sean O'Hairt / O'Rourke's feast
CDOSS 69 / Apr '93 / Ossian

Gunn, Mike

☐ ALMARON
006 / Dec '97 / Double O

Gunn, Russell

☐ GUNN FU
Gunn fu / John Wicks / Solar / Invitation / Search / Why wonder why / Final call / Bern / Minor sweet
HCD 7003 / Jan '98 / Highnote

☐ YOUNG GUNN PLUS
60412320782 / 14 Jul '98 / Thirty Two

Gunn, Trey

☐ 3RD STAR
DGM 9606 / Aug '96 / Discipline

☐ ONE THOUSAND YEARS
Night air / Screen door and the flower girl / Killing for London / Real life / Into the wood / Gift / Take this wish / 1000 years
DGM 9302 / Sep '94 / Discipline

Gunness, Lee

☐ LEE GUNNESS & THE ECLIPSE ALLEY HEAVENLY SINGERS
BCD 354 / Jul '96 / GHB

☐ LEE GUNNESS SINGS THE BLUES
BCD 314 / Oct '93 / GHB

Guns Books & Tools

☐ GUNS BOOKS & TOOLS
SST 357CD / 24 Nov '97 / SST

Guns n' Roses

☐ APPETITE FOR DESTRUCTION
Welcome to the jungle / It's so easy / Nightrain / Out ta get me / Mr. Brownstone / Paradise city / My Michelle / Think about you / Sweet child o' mine / You're crazy / Anything goes / Rocket queen
GFLD 19286 / Oct '95 / Geffen

☐ GN'R LIES
Reckless life / Patience / Nice boys / Used to love her / Move to the city / You're crazy / Mama kin / One in a million
GFLD 19287 / Oct '95 / Geffen

☐ INTERVIEW COMPACT DISC: GUNS 'N' ROSES
CBAK 4015 / Nov '89 / Baktabak

☐ INTERVIEW DISC
SAM 7016 / Nov '96 / Sound & Media

☐ INTERVIEW, THE
SPEEK 006 / 16 Mar '98 / Talking Music

☐ SPAGHETTI INCIDENT, THE
Since I don't have you / New rose / Down on the farm / Human being / Raw power / Ain't it fun / Buick Mckane / Hair of the dog / Attitude / Black leather / You can't put your arms around a memory / I don't care about you / Look at your game girl
GFLD 19317 / 2 Feb '98 / Geffen

☐ TRUTH OR LIES THE INTERVIEW
CBAK 4077 / Feb '94 / Baktabak

☐ USE YOUR ILLUSION VOL.1
Right next door to hell / Dust and bones / Live and let die / Don't cry / Perfect crime / You ain't the first / Bad obsession / Back off bitch / Double talkin' jive / November rain / Garden / Garden of Eden / Don't damn me / Bad apple / Dead horse / Coma
GEFD 24415 / Sep '91 / Geffen

☐ USE YOUR ILLUSION VOL.2
Civil war / Fourteen years / Yesterdays / Knockin' on heaven's door / Get in the ring / Shotgun blues / Breakdown / Pretty tied up / Locomotive / So fine / Estranged / You could be mine / Don't cry / My world
GEFD 24420 / Sep '91 / Geffen

Gunshot

☐ PATRIOT GAMES
Manhunt / 25 gun salute / Gunshots history / Reign of terror / World war 3 / Radio / Day of the jackals / Bombing in 5 minutes / Patriot games / Mind of a razor / Cholo / Year 2000 / Bullets entering chest / Game over
STEAM 43CD / Jun '93 / Vinyl Solution

☐ SINGLES, THE
STEAM 92CD / Nov '94 / Vinyl Solution

☐ TWILIGHTS LAST GLEAMING
Intro / Maths and stats / Millenium / Mask of the phantasm / GS vibe / Ghetto heartbeat / Roots and reality / Die hard / True fist / Gunshot forever / Silkmaker / Return of The Gunshot / Kingpin / Untouchable / Inner space / Outro
WOWCD 51 / May '97 / Words Of Warning

Gunter, Arthur

☐ BABY LET'S PLAY HOUSE (The Best Of Arthur Gunter)
Baby let's play house / Blues after hours / Ludella / No naggin' no draggin' / Mind your own business babe / Honey babe / No happy home / Workin' for my baby / Baby can't you see / Little blue jeans woman / You're always on my mind / Baby you better listen / I want her back / Crazy me / Don't leave me now / Letter to my baby / Pigmeat / Falling in love / (Just another day) working for my baby / Story of Jesse James / She's mine, all mine / I've got a feeling something is wrong / Who will ever move you from me / Just take it easy / My baby's taking a day off / My heart's always lonesome
EXCD 3011 / Dec '96 / Ace

Gunter, Bernhard

☐ UN PEU DE NEIGE
31-GALLIUM / Dec '96 / Table Of The Elements

Gunter, Hardrock

☐ GONNA ROCK 'N' ROLL, GONNA DANCE ALL NIGHT
Birmingham bounce / Lonesome blues / Gonna dance all night / How can I believe you love me / My bucket's been fixed / Rifle belt and bayonet / Maybe baby / Birmingham bounce / Boppin' to Grandfather's clock / Beggars can't be choosers / It can't be right / Rock-a-bop baby / Whoo, I mean whee / We three / Jukebox help me find my baby / Fiddle bop / Hardrock rocks the moon (How high the moon) / Bloodshot eyes / Take away your rosy lips / Right key but the wrong keyhole / Mountain dew / I'll go chasin' women / Spring has sprung / Tico tico / Go low boogie / Bonaparte's retreat / Chattanooga sunshine boy / Dad gave my hog away / Guitar on the moon / Fallen angel / Gonna dance all night
RCCD 3013 / Aug '97 / Rollercoaster

Guo Ye

☐ RED RIBBON
TUG 1010CD / Feb '95 / Tugboat

Gupta, Buddhadev Das

☐ RAGA JAIJAIVANTI
NI 5314 / Sep '94 / Nimbus

Gurd

☐ ADDICTED
CC 035016CD / Jan '96 / Major

☐ D-FECT (The Remixes)
CM 77176CD / 29 Sep '97 / Century Media

☐ DOWN THE DRAIN
CM 77203CD / 23 Mar '98 / Century Media

Gurov, Andre

☐ NEW RAP LANGUAGE, A
JFRCD 009 / 29 Sep '97 / Jazz Fudge

☐ REVELATIONS OF WRATH
JFR 006CD / Mar '97 / Jazz Fudge

Gurtu, Shobha

☐ SHOBHA GURTU
CMPCD 3004 / 30 Mar '98 / CMP

Gurtu, Trilok

☐ BAD HABITS DIE HARD
CMPCD 80 / Mar '96 / CMP

☐ BELIEVE
CMPCD 75 / Jan '95 / CMP

☐ COLLECTION, THE
CMPCD 2501 / 6 Apr '98 / CMP

☐ CRAZY SAINTS
Manini / Tillana / Ballad for 2 musicians / Other tune / Blessing in disguise / Crazy saints / No discrimination
CMPCD 66 / Mar '96 / CMP

☐ GLIMPSE
CMPCD 85 / Feb '97 / CMP

☐ KATHAK
Ganapati / You remember this / Seven brings return / Shunyai / Who knows the mind / Kathak / Brazilian
ESC 03655 / 23 Mar '98 / ECM

☐ LIVING MAGIC
Baba / Once I wished a tree upside down / From scratch / TMNOK / Living magic / Transition / Tac, et demi
CMPCD 50 / Jun '93 / CMP

☐ USFRET
Shobarock / Shangri la-usfret / Om / Deep trl / Goose bumps / Milo
CMPCD 33 / 30 Mar '98 / CMP

Guru

☐ GURU PRESENTS THE ILL KID CLASSICS (Payday Sampler) (Various Artists)
Ill kid intro: *Bald Head Slick* / Wordplay: *Bahamadia* / Life: *Guru* / Do what pays ya: *Big Shug* / Victim of society: *Baybe* / Come clean: *Jeru The Damaja* / Who's the truest: *True Master* / Rotten apple: *Operation Ratification* / Hi energy: *Fabidden* / Momentum: *Guru & Big Shug* / Attack: *Stikken Moov* / So called friends: *Group Home* / Cup of life: *Fabidden*
8287292 / Mar '96 / Payday

☐ JAZZMATAZZ VOL.1
Intro / Loungin' / When you're near / Transit ride / No time to play / Down the backstreets / Respectful dedications / Take a look at yourself / Trust me / Slicker than most / Le bien, le mal / Sights in the city
CTCD 34 / Jun '93 / Cooltempo

☐ JAZZMATAZZ VOL.2
Intro (into the light) / Jazzalude I / New reality style / Lifesaver / Living in this world / Looking through darkness / Skit A (Interview) / Watch what you say / Jazzalude II / Defining purpose / For you / Insert A (Mental relaxation) / Medicine / Lost souls / Insert B (Mental relaxation) / Nobody knows / Jazzalude III / Hip hop as a way of life / Respect the artitect / Feel the music / Young ladies / Traveller / Jazzalude IV / Count your blessings / Choice of weapons / Something in the past / Skit B (A lot on my mind) / Revelation
CTCD 47 / Jul '95 / Cooltempo

Guru Guru

☐ BEST OF GURU GURU VOL.1, THE (Space Ship)
CLP 97162 / 24 Nov '97 / Cleopatra

☐ BEST OF GURU GURU VOL.2, THE
CLP 0077 / 6 Oct '97 / Cleopatra

☐ GURU GURU
PMS 7056 / 1 Jun '98 / Repertoire

☐ LIVE
EFA 035012 / Jan '96 / Think Progressive

☐ LIVE 1972/CONNY'S SESSION 1974 (Guru Guru & Uli Trepte)
14998 / Oct '96 / Spalax

☐ MOSHI MOSHI
EFA 035372 / Jul '97 / Think Progressive

☐ TANGO FANGO
EFA 035362 / Jul '97 / Think Progressive
PMS 7060 / 1 Jun '98 / Repertoire

☐ UFO
14296 / Oct '96 / Spalax
CD 5560052 / 16 Feb '98 / OHR

☐ ULI TREPTE - LIVE 1972/CONNY PLANK'S SESSION 1974
SPA 14998 / Oct '96 / Spalax

☐ WAH WAH
EFA 035002 / Dec '95 / Think Progressive

Gurus Of The New Millennium

☐ GURUS OF THE NEW MILLENNIUM
Sealed in stone / Guru said / Sacred heart / In our time / Show me a place / Ghosts / Sacred veil / July 11th / Nothing ever changes / Snapshots / Waiting for a sign / No fear / Freedom
GURU 7 / 6 Apr '98 / DOOB

Gus

☐ GUS
ALMCD 12 / Nov '96 / Almo Sounds

☐ PROGRESSIVE SCIENCE OF BREEDING IDIOTS FOR A DUMB SOCIETY
WRONG 14CD / Jun '95 / Wrong

Gus Gus

☐ POLYDISTORTION
Oh / Gun / Believe / Polyesterday / Barry / Cold breath '79 / Why / Rememberance / Is Jesus your pal / Purple
DADD 7005CD / Apr '97 / 4AD

Gush

☐ FROM SOUNDS TO THINGS
DRCD 204 / Apr '87 / Dragon

☐ LIVE AT FASCHING 1996
DRCD 313 / Aug '97 / Dragon

Gustafson, John

☐ GOOSE GREASE
Boogie woogie / Precious heart / Poem about a gnome / Don't care / Money dance / What's your game / Freshness / Cheap astrakhan / Goose grease
SJPCD 008 / May '97 / Angel Air

Gustafsson, Mats

☐ PARROT FISH EYE
OD 12006 / Aug '95 / Okka Disk

Gustavson, Jukka

☐ KADONNUT HAVIAMATTOMLIN
BECD 4032 / May '95 / Beta

Guthrie, Arlo

☐ ALICE'S RESTAURANT (Original Soundtrack/30th Anniversary Edition)
Alice's restaurant massacre / Chilling of the evening / Ring a round a rosy rag / Now and then / I'm going home / Motorcycle song / Highway in the wind
379592 / Aug '97 / Koch International

☐ ALICE'S RESTAURANT (Original Soundtrack)
Alice's restaurant massacre / Chilling of the evening / Ring around a rosy rag / Now and then / I'm going home / Motorcycle song / Highway in the wind
244045 / Feb '94 / Reprise

☐ AMIGO
379542 / 7 Apr '98 / Koch

☐ ARLO
379482 / Dec '97 / Koch

☐ ARLO GUTHRIE
379532 / Aug '97 / Koch International

☐ BEST OF ARLO GUTHRIE, THE
Alice's restaurant massacre / Gabriel's mother's highway ballad / Sixteen blues / Coopers lament / Motor cycle song / Coming into Los Angeles / Last train / City of New Orleans / Darkest hour / Last to leave
7599273402 / Jan '93 / Reprise

☐ HOBO'S LULLABY
379512 / Dec '97 / Koch

☐ LAST OF THE BROOKLYN COWBOYS
379522 / Dec '97 / Koch

☐ MORE TOGETHER AGAIN (Guthrie, Arlo & Pete Seeger)
RSR 0007/8 / Oct '94 / Rising Sun

☐ MYSTIC JOURNEY
379602 / 29 Jun '98 / Koch International

☐ RUNNING DOWN THE ROAD
379492 / Aug '97 / Koch International

☐ WASHINGTON COUNTY
379502 / Aug '97 / Koch International

Guthrie, Jack

☐ OKLAHOMA HILLS
Oklahoma hills / When the cactus is in bloom / Next to the soil / Shame on you / I'm branding my darlin' / With my heart / Careless darlin' / Oakie boogie / In the shadows of my heart / For Oklahoma / I'm yearning / No need to knock on my door / Shut that gate / I'm tellin' you / Chained to a memory / Look out for the crossing / Dallas darlin' / Colorado blues / Welcome home stranger / I still love you as I did in yesterday / Oklahoma's calling / Clouds rain trouble down / Answer to Moonlight / Please, oh please / I loved you once but I can't trust you now / Out of sight / I'm building a stairway to heaven / Ida Red / I told you once / San Antonio rose / You laughed and I cried
BCD 15580 / Nov '91 / Bear Family

Guthrie, Woody

☐ ASCH RECORDINGS VOL.1, THE (This Land Is Your Land)
SFWCD 40100 / May '97 / Smithsonian Folkways

☐ ASCH RECORDINGS VOL.2, THE (Muleskinner Blues)
SFWCD 40101 / Nov '97 / Smithsonian Folkways

☐ ASCH RECORDINGS VOL.3, THE (Hard Travellin')
SFWCD 40102 / 1 Jun '98 / Smithsonian Folkways

☐ BALLADS OF SACCO & VANZETTI
SFWCD 40060 / Apr '96 / Smithsonian Folkways

☐ COLUMBIA RIVER COLLECTION
Oregon trail / Roll on columbia / Newfoundland / Talking columbia / Roll columbia, roll / Columbia's waters / Ramblin' blues / It takes a married man to sing a worried song / Hard travlin' / Biggest thing that man has ever done / Jackhammer blues / Song of the coulee dam / Grand coulee dam / Washington talkin' blues / Ramblin' round / Pastures of plenty / End of my line
ROUCD 1036 / Aug '88 / Rounder

☐ DUST BOWL BALLADS
Great dust storm (dust storm disaster) / I ain't got no home / Talking dust bowl blues / Vigilante man / Dust can't kill me / Dust pneumonia blues / Pretty boy floyd / Blowin' down the road (i ain't going to be treated this w / Tom joad (part 1) / Tom joad (part 2) / Dust bowl refugee / Do re mi / Dust bowl blues / Dusty old dust (so long it's been good to know yuh)
ROUCD 1040 / '88 / Rounder

☐ DUSTBOWL BALLADS
Great dust storm (dust storm disaster) / I ain't got no home / Talking dust bowl blues / Vigilante man / Dust can't kill me / Dust pneumonia blues / Pretty Boy Floyd / Blowin' down this road (I ain't gonna be treated this way) / Tom Joad / Dust bowl refugee / Dust old dust (so long it's been good to know yuh) / Do re mi
74321578392 / 27 Apr '98 / Camden

☐ EARLY MASTERS
TCD 1017 / May '96 / Tradition

☐ GOLDEN CLASSICS VOL.2
COLCD 5098 / Aug '97 / Collectables

☐ GREATEST SONGS OF WOODY GUTHRIE VOL.1 (Various Artists)
VMD 73105 / Jan '96 / Vanguard

☐ LEGENDARY PERFORMER, A
Great dust storm / I ain't got no home / Talking dust bowl blues / Vigilante man / Dust can't kill me / Dust pneumonia blues / Pretty boy Floyd / Blowin' down this road / Tom Joad / Dust bowl refugee / Do re mi / Dust bowl blues / Dusty old dust (so long it's been good to know)
74321317742 / Feb '96 / RCA

☐ LIBRARY OF CONGRESS RECORDINGS VOL.1
ROUCD 1041 / '88 / Rounder

☐ LIBRARY OF CONGRESS RECORDINGS VOL.2
ROUCD 1042 / '88 / Rounder

☐ LIBRARY OF CONGRESS RECORDINGS VOL.3
ROUCD 1043 / '88 / Rounder

☐ LONG WAYS TO TRAVEL (Unreleased Folkways Masters 1944-1949)
SFWCD 40046 / Jun '94 / Smithsonian Folkways

☐ NURSERY DAYS
Wake up / Clean-o / Dance around / Riding in my car (car song) / Don't you push me down / My dolly / Put your finger in the air / Come see / Race you down the mountain / Howdido / Merry go round / Sleep eye / My yellow crayon / Roll on / Jiggy jiggy bum / Bubble gum
SFWCD 45036 / Dec '94 / Smithsonian Folkways

☐ PASTURES OF PLENTY - WOODY GUTHRIE TRIBUTE (Various Artists)
DJD 3207 / May '94 / Dejadisc

☐ SONGS TO GROW ON FOR MOTHER & CHILD
Grassy grass grass (grow, grow, grow) / Swimmy swim / Little sugar (little saka sugar) / Rattle my rattle / I want my milk (i want it now) / 1, 2, 3, 4, 5, 6, 7, 8 / One day old / Wash-y wash wash (warshy little tootsy) / I'll eat you, I'll drink you / Make a blobble / Who's my pretty baby (hey pretty baby) / I'll write and I'll draw / Why oh why / Pick it up y'all / Pretty and shiny-o / Needle sing / Bling-blang / Goodnight little arlo (goodnight little darlin')
SFWCD 45035 / Mar '95 / Smithsonian Folkways

☐ THIS LAND IS YOUR LAND (Guthrie, Woody & Arlo)
Howdi do / Riding in my car / Along home / Mail myself to you / This land is your land / Bling-blang / All work together / Grassey grass grass / So long, it's been good to know yuh / This land is your land / All work together
ROUCD 8050 / May '97 / Rounder

☐ VERY BEST OF WOODY GUTHRIE, THE
This land is your land / Pastures of plenty / Pretty boy Floyd / Take a whiff on me / Do re mi / Put my little shoes away / Hard travellin' / Jesus Christ / Whoopee ti yi yo / Grand coulee dam / Picture from life's other side / Talkin' hard luck blues / Philadelphia lawyer / I ain't got no home / Wreck of ol' 97 / Keep your skillet good and greasy / Dust pneumonia blues / Going down that road feeling bad / Goodnight little arlo (Goodnight little darlin') / So long (it's been good to know yuh)
MCCD 067 / Jun '92 / Music Club

☐ WE AIN'T DOWN YET - WOODY GUTHRIE'S FRIENDS (Various Artists)
DIAB 812 / Aug '94 / Diablo

☐ WOODY GUTHRIE
DVBC 92102 / May '95 / Deja Vu

☐ WOODY GUTHRIE & CISCO HOUSTON VOL.1 & 2 (Guthrie, Woody & Cisco Houston)
COLCD 5605 / Aug '97 / Collectables

☐ WORRIED MAN BLUES
COLCD 5095 / Aug '97 / Collectables

Gutierrez, Alfredo

☐ EL PALITO
TUMICD 021 / '92 / Tumi

☐ FIESTA
Los novios / Festival en guarare
12454 / Jul '95 / Laserlight

Gutierrez, Jose Luis

☐ NUCLEO (Gutierrez, Jose Luis Trio)
FSNT 039 / 1 Jun '98 / Fresh Sound New Talent

Gutterball

☐ GUTTERBALL
Trial seperation blues / Top of the hill / Lester Young / Motorcycle boy / One by one / When you make up your mind / Think it over / Falling from the sky / Please don't hold back / Preacher and the prostitute / Patent leather shoes / Blessing in disguise
OUT 1132 / Jan '94 / Brake Out

☐ TURNYOR HEDINKOV
RTS 17 / Aug '95 / Return To Sender

☐ WEASEL
OUT 1192 / Sep '97 / Brake Out

Guttermouth

☐ FRIENDLY PEOPLE
158012 / Oct '96 / Nitro

☐ LIVE FROM THE PHARMACY
158192 / 3 Aug '98 / Nitro

☐ MUSICAL MONKEY
158122 / Jul '97 / Nitro

☐ PUKE BALLS
DSR 09CD / Sep '95 / Dr. Strange

☐ RECORD FORMERLY KNOWN AS...
158072 / Sep '96 / Nitro

☐ TERI YAKIMOTO
158042 / Sep '96 / Nitro

Guttersnipe

☐ NEVER SURRENDER NEVER GIVE IN
JABSC 0016CD / 3 Aug '98 / Sidekicks

Guttormsen, Buen

☐ LJOS OG SKUGGE/SLATT OG RAGA (Guttormsen, Buen & Sahajpal)
BK 21CD / Dec '97 / Buen

Guttridge, Andy

☐ AMONGST FRIENDS
SVL 05CD / Dec '97 / Speaking Volumes

Guv'ner

☐ HARD FOR MEASY FOR YOU
No big deal / Red velvet chair / Little bitch on the phone / Bridge under water / Almond roca / Making headlines / Go to sleep / Wild couple / Touch wood / Amplituden / I will get you / Thespian girl / She dog stop
WIJ 039CD / Nov '94 / Wiiija

☐ HUNT, THE
WIJCD 1057 / Aug '96 / Wiiija

☐ IN THE FISHTANK
FISHNO 2CD / Jun '97 / Konkurrent

Guy

☐ FUTURE, THE
Her / Wanna get with U / Do me right / Teddy's jam 2 / Let's chill / Tease me tonite / Dog me out / Total control / Gotta be a leader / Future / Let's saty together / Where did the love go / Yearning for your love / Smile / Long gone / Wanna get with you
MCLD 19334 / Oct '96 / MCA

Guy, Barry

☐ GRUFFGRUFFGRUFFS (Guy/ Gustafsson/Strid Trio)
CD 1003 / Feb '98 / Music & Arts

☐ PORTRAITS
INTAKTCD 035 / Oct '94 / Intakt

Guy, Buddy

☐ ALONE AND ACOUSTIC (Guy, Buddy & Junior Wells)
Give me my coat and shoes / Big boat (buddy and junior's thing) / Sweet black girl / Diggin' my potatoes / Don't leave me / Rollin' and tumblin' / I'm in the mood / Hi heel sneakers / Wrong doing woman / Cut you loose / Sally mae / Catfish blues / My home is in the delta / Boogie chillun
ALCD 4802 / May '93 / Alligator

☐ BLUES GIANT
I smell a rat / Are you losing your mind / You've been gone too long / She is out there / Outskirts of town / When I left home
BLE 599002 / Jan '90 / Black & Blue

☐ BREAKING OUT
Have you ever been lonesome / You can make it if you try / Break out all over you / She winked her eye / I didn't know my mother had a son like me / Boogie family style / You called me in my dream / Me and my guitar / Ice around my heart
JSPCD 272 / Oct '96 / JSP

☐ BUDDY AND THE JUNIORS
Talkin' 'bout women obviously / Riffin' / Buddy's blues / Hoochie coochie man / Five long years / Rock me mama / Ain't no need
BGOCD 399 / 30 Mar '98 / Beat Goes On

☐ BUDDY GUY & JUNIOR WELLS (Guy, Buddy & Junior Wells)
MACCD 194 / Aug '96 / Autograph

☐ BUDDY GUY AND FRIENDS
She suits me to a t / You're nice and clean / Stone crazy: *Phil & Buddy Guy* / Tell me what's inside of you / Comin' on / Love is like quicksand: *Phil & Buddy Guy* / All I can do: *Sumlin, Hubert* / Smokin' dynamite: *Sumlin, Hubert* / Dollar done fell / Blue's at my baby's house / Highwayman blues: *Dawkins, Jimmy* / My way or the highway: *Guitar Shorty* / I've got a right to love my woman / I didn't know my mother had a son like me / Have you ever been lonesome / Me and my guitar / Feeling sexy: *Phil & Buddy Guy* / Texas flood: *Phil & Buddy Guy* / Have a little mercy: *Dawkins, Jimmy* / Garbage man blues: *Phil & Buddy Guy* / Shorty jumps in: *Guitar Shorty* / Ice around my heart: *Phil & Buddy Guy* / You can make it if you try / Breaking out on top: *Phil & Buddy Guy*
PDSCD 546 / Aug '96 / Pulse

☐ BUDDY'S BLUES
MCD 09374 / Jul '97 / Chess/MCA

☐ BUDDY'S BLUES 1979-1982
JSPCD 801 / Jan '98 / JSP

☐ COMPLETE CHESS STUDIO RECORDINGS, THE (2CD Set)
First time I met the blues / Stop around / I got my eyes on you / Brokened hearted blues / Let me love you baby / I got a strange feeling / Gully hully / Ten years ago / Watch yourself / Stone crazy / Skippin' / I found true love / Hard but it's fair / Baby (baby, baby, baby) / When my left eye jumps / That's it / Treasure untold / American bandstand / No lie / 100$ bill / My love is real / Buddy's boogie / Worried mind / Untitled instrumental / Moanin' / I dig your wig / My time after awhile / Night flight / Crazy love (crazy music) / Every girl I see / Too many ways / Leave my girl alone / Got to use your head / Keep it to myself / My mother / She suits me too a tee / Mother -in-law blues / Buddy's grove / Going to school / I cry and sing the blues / Goin' home / I suffer with the blues / Lip lap Louie / My time after a while / Too many ways / Keep it to myself / I didn't know my mother
MCD 09337 / Apr '97 / Chess/MCA

☐ DOUBLE DYNAMITE LIVE (Guy, Buddy & Junior Wells)
Everyday I have the blues / Leave my girl alone / I can't get no satisfaction / Messin' with the kid / Come on in this house / Lord have mercy / Buddy's blow / Out of sight / Stormy Monday blues / Junior's wail
AIM 0006CD / Sep '97 / Aim

☐ DRINKIN' TNT 'N' SMOKIN' DYNAMITE (Guy, Buddy & Junior Wells/Others)
Ah'w baby / Everything gonna be alright / How can one woman be so mean / Checking on my baby / When you see the little tears from my eyes / My younger days
NEMCD 687 / Apr '94 / Sequel

☐ FEELS LIKE RAIN
She's a superstar / I go crazy / Feels like rain / She's nineteen years old / Some kind of wonderful / Sufferin' mind / Change in the weather / I could cry / Mary ann / Trouble man / Country man
ORECD 525 / Mar '93 / Silvertone

☐ FIRST TIME I MET THE BLUES
First time I met the blues / Slop around / Let me love you baby / Got to use your head / I dig your wig / My time after a while / Stick around / No lie / Night flight / My mother / Ten years ago / Don't know which way to go / Gully hully / I got a hully / I got a strange feeling / This is the end / Broken heart / Ed blues / You sure can't do / Try to quit you baby / I got my eyes on you / Sit and cry / Untitled instrumental / Drinking muddy water
CD 52015 / '92 / Blues Encore

☐ HEAVY LOVE
Heavy love / Midnight train / I got a problem / I need you tonight / Saturday night fish fry / Had a bad night / Are you lonely for me baby / I just want to make love to you / Did somebody make a fool out of you / When the time is right / Let me show you
0591182 / 22 Jun '98 / Silvertone

☐ HOLD THAT PLANE
Watermelon man / I'm ready / You don't love me / Hello San Francisco / Hold that plane / My time after a while / Come see about me
VMD 79323 / Oct '95 / Vanguard

☐ MAN AND THE BLUES, A
Man and the blues / I can't quit the blues / Money (that's what I want) / One room country shack / Mary had a little lamb / Just playing my axe / Sweet little angel / Worry worry / Jam on a monday morning
VMD 79272 / 27 Apr '98 / Vanguard

☐ MASTERS, THE (Guy, Buddy & Junior Wells)
Buddy's blues / Blue monday / Every day I have the blues / Woman blues / Satisfaction / Messing with the kid / No use cryin' / Just to be with you / Junior's shuffle / Out of sight
EABCD 093 / 30 Mar '98 / Eagle

☐ ORIGINAL BLUES BROTHERS - LIVE (Guy, Buddy & Junior Wells)
Buddy's blues / Blue Monday / Everyday I have the blues / Woman blues / Satisfaction / Messin' with the kid / No use cryin' / Just to be with you / Junior's shuffle / Out of sight
CDBM 007 / Feb '89 / Blue Moon

☐ PLAY THE BLUES (Guy, Buddy & Junior Wells)
Man of many words / My baby left me / Come on in this house / Have mercy baby / T-bone shuffle / Poor man's plea / Messin' with the kid / This old fool / I don't know / Bad bad whiskey / Honeydripper
8122702992 / Mar '93 / Atlantic

☐ REAL DEAL, THE (Buddy Guy Live)
ORECD 538 / Mar '97 / Silvertone

☐ SLIPPIN' IN
ORECD 533 / Mar '97 / Silvertone

☐ STONE CRAZY
Slop around / Broken hearted blues / I got my eyes on you / First time I met the blues / Let me love you baby / I got a strange feeling / Hully gully / Ten years ago / Watch yourself / Stone crazy / Hard but fair / Baby (baby, baby) / When my left eye jumps / That's it no lie / Every girl I see / Leave my girl alone / She suits me to a tee / Mother in law blues / Going home / I suffer with the blues
ALCD 4723 / May '93 / Alligator

Guy Called Gerald

☐ BLACK SECRET TECHNOLOGY
JBCD 25 / Mar '95 / Juice Box

Guy, Charles Lee

☐ PRISONER'S DREAMS, THE
There goes a lonely man / This ole dog / You just don't know your man / Rich man's gold / Unhappy people / Prisoner's dream / Shackles and chains / They're all goin' home but one / Wall / Twenty one years / Folsom Prison blues / Prisoner's song "Cigarettes, whisky and will" / Send a picture of Mother / Cold gray bars / Wishin' she was here (instead of me) / Doin' my time
BCD 15581 / Apr '92 / Bear Family

Guy, Phil

☐ BREAKING OUT ON TOP
Gambler / Quicksand / Texas flood / Tina nu / Where can I go / Professor's boogie / Good thing / Stone crazy / Breaking out on top / Blues with a feeling / Winehead / Garbage man blues
JSPCD 260 / Oct '95 / JSP

☐ TINA NU
JSPCD 226 / Apr '89 / JSP

Guyger, Steve

☐ LIVE AT THE DINOSAUR
HP 330033 / 15 Jun '98 / Horseplay

Guys & Dolls

☐ THERE'S A WHOLE LOT OF LOVING
There's a whole lot of loving / You don't have to say you love me / Here I go again / Our song / Love lost in a day / All the money in the world / Starship of love / Broken dreams / I got the fire in me / I heard it on the radio / Let's all get together / Guy's 'n' Dolls / Give a little love / Love matters / Always laughing / We're all in the same boat / She's leaving home / I get around / Barbara Ann / River deep mountain high / Don't wake me while I'm sleeping
BX 4272 / Jun '96 / BR Music

Guzman, Pedro

☐ JIBARO JAZZ (The New Swing from Puerto Rico)
De aqui pa'alla / Mario brothers / Maria teina una ovejita / Mapeye montuno / Seis comerio / Guireando / Bayuya sambada / Fantasia del cuatro / Mi bella genio / Sesi antillano / Descarga machuca / Verde luz / Counting blues / Sonando con puerto rico
68949 / Apr '97 / Tropical

Guzzard

☐ ALIENATION INDEX SURVEY, THE
ARRCD 76019 / Dec '96 / Amphetamine Reptile

☐ QUICK, FAST, IN A HURRY
AMREP 037CD / Mar '95 / Amphetamine Reptile

Gwalarn

☐ A-HED AN AMZER
KMCD 10 / '91 / Keltia Musique

GWAR

☐ AMERICA MUST BE DESTROYED
Ham on the bone / Crack in the egg / Gor-gor / Have you seen me / Morality squad / America must be destroyed / Gilded lily / Poor ole tom / Rock n roll never felt so good / Blimey / Road behind / Pussy planet
398417016CD / Jun '96 / Metal Blade

☐ CARNIVAL OF SOULS
39841425CD / Apr '97 / Metal Blade

☐ HELL-O
Time for death / Americanized / Slutman city / War toy / Pure as the artic snow / Gwar theme / Ollie North / U ain't shit / Black and huge / AEIOU / I'm in love with a dead dog / World o' filth / Captain crunch / Je m'appelle J Cousteau / Bone meal / Techno's song / Rock 'n' roll party theme
398414004CD / May '96 / Metal Blade

☐ RAG NA ROCK
170012 / Oct '95 / Metal Blade

☐ RENDEZVOUS WITH RAGNAROK
3984170012 / 24 Mar '98 / Metal Blade

☐ ROAD BEHIND, THE
398414004CD / Nov '95 / Metal Blade

☐ THIS TOILET EARTH
CDZORRO 63 / Mar '94 / Metal Blade

Gwendal

☐ GLEN RIVER
345002 / Jul '96 / Melodie

☐ GWENDAL
345012 / Mar '96 / Melodie

Gwerinos

☐ DI-DIDL-LAN
SCD 2075 / Jun '95 / Sain

☐ SELLAM
SCD 2160 / Jan '98 / Sain

Gwernig, Youenn

☐ JUST A TRAVELLER
KM 49 / Sep '94 / Keltia Musique

Gwerz

☐ AUDELA
BUR CD 821 / '88 / Escalibur

☐ LIVE
GWP 001CD / Aug '93 / Gwerz

Gygafo

☐ LEGEND OF THE KINGFISHER
HBG 122/2 / Jun '97 / Background

Gypsy

☐ BAD
MRS 9744CD / 18 Aug '97 / VP

☐ BE YOURSELF
MRSCD 9643 / Jan '96 / JW

Gypsy

☐ SOUNDTRACKS
LIMB 37CD / Oct '94 / Limbo

Gypsy Kyss

☐ WHEN PASSION MURDERED INNOCENCE
972210 / May '91 / FM

Gypsy Orchestra

☐ JEWISH WEDDING
RCD 10105 / Nov '91 / Rykodisc

Gyres

☐ FIRST
Sly / Hi-fi driving / Break / Million miles / Hooligan / Are you ready / Falling down / On a roll / I'm alright / Pop cop / Downtime
SUGA 16CD / Jul '97 / Sugar

Gysin, Brion

☐ ONE NIGHT AT THE 1001 (2CD Set)
SR 142CD / 1 Jun '98 / Sub Rosa

☐ SELF PORTRAIT JUMPING
Kick / Junk / Stop smoking / Sham pain / V V V / Baboon / All those years / Dreamachine / Page 3 / Flies / I am that I am / Off the ground / Initiate / Somebody special / Door
MTM 33 / Apr '96 / Made To Measure

Gyuto Monks Of Bomdile

☐ BUDDHIST CHANT VOL.2
VICG 5040 / Jun '96 / JVC World Library

☐ FREEDOM CHANTS FROM THE ROOF OF THE WORLD
Yamantaka / Mahakala / Number 2 for Gaia
RCD 20113 / Sep '91 / Rykodisc

GZR

☐ PLASTIC PLANET
RAWCD 105 / Apr '96 / Raw Power

H

H

☐ ICE CREAM GENIUS

WENCD 016 / Feb '97 / When

H-Blockx

☐ DISCOVER MY SOUL

Try me one more time / Gimme more / Discover my soul / How do you feel / Heaven / Step back / I can't rely on you / I heard him cry / This is not America / Rainman / Duality of mind / Gotta find a way / Life is feeling dizzy / Prelude

74321402912 / Oct '96 / RCA

☐ TIME TO MOVE

Pour me a glass / Revolution / Say baby / Move / Fight the force / Little girl / Risin' high / H-Blockx / Real love / Do what you wanna do (Dave don't like it) / Go freaky / Fuck the facts / Time to fight

74321187512 / Jan '96 / RCA

H-Oilers

☐ INNOCENT CATHOLIC COMBAT WALTZ, THE

EFA 119682 / Nov '94 / Crippled Dick Hot Wax

H-Town

☐ BEGGIN' AFTER DARK

H-Town intro '94 / Sex bowl / One night gigolo / Prelude to emotion / Emotions / Cruisin' fo' honeys / Full time / 1-9800 Call Gl / Tumble and rumble / Much feeling (and it tastes great) / Beggin' after dark / Indo love / Back seat (wit no sheets) / Buss one / Baby I love ya / Rockit steady / Last record

116312 / Jan '95 / Musidisc

☐ FEVER FOR DA FLAVOR

Introduction / Can't fade da H / Treat U right / Fever for da flavor / Sex me / H-town bounce / Keepin' my composure / Interlude / Lick U up / Knockin' da boots / Won't U come back / Baby I wanna

110702 / May '95 / Musidisc

☐ LADIES EDITION

Woman's anthem intro / Don't sleep on the female / Toon girl / Die for you / Married man / Beggars can't be choosey / Ways to treat a woman / Don't hold back the rain / I sleep u I wear u / They like it slow / Special kind of fool / Natural woman / Shoo 'em up / Jezebel / Woman's world / Mindtaker / Visions in my mind / Julie rain / Woman's anthem

4891572 / 10 Nov '97 / Epic

H2O

☐ THICKER THAN WATER

Universal language / Ever ready / Talk too much / Sacred heart / Responsible / I see it in us / Go / Plus / Wake up / This time / Phone song / Thicker than water / Innocent kids / Friend

65052 / 10 Nov '97 / Epitaph

Ha Lela

☐ PABUDIMAS

ELD 003 / 2 Mar '98 / Eldethorn

Ha-Lo

☐ WELCOME TO THE FLUORESCENT ERA

EUKACD 002 / Sep '97 / Eukatech

Haas, Andy

☐ ARNHEM LAND

AVAN 048 / Sep '97 / Avant

Hab

☐ MAPOD

Gold and genetics / Tu casa / Pan / Ocra / Deff / Tfol broadcast / Niduq / Next door / Sector stp / Save the adults

DOTCD 02 / 13 Oct '97 / Dot

Habermann, Robert

☐ SALUTE TO FRANK SINATRA, A

My kind of town / All or nothing at all / I'll never smile again / Oh look at me now / Night and day / Saturday night is the lonliest night of the week / Nancy / Coffee song / Put your dreams away / Song is you / Moon was yellow / One I love belongs to somebody else / All of me / Guess I'll hang my tears out to dry / I'm a fool to want you / Birth of the blues / Lean baby / You make me feel so young / Young at heart / Look to your heart / In the wee small hours of the morning / One for my baby / Strangers in the night / Let me try again / My way

SCATCD 2 / Jun '96 / Sophisticat

Habichuela, Pepe

☐ A MANDELI

Resuene / Al aire / El dron / Guadiana / Del cerro / Mi tierra / Boabdil / A mandeli / Mandeli

HNCD 1315 / May '89 / Hannibal

Hachig, Kazarian

☐ ARMENIA ARMENIA

MCD 61452 / Jun '93 / Monitor

Hacienda

☐ NARROWED EYES

IC 0342 / 10 Aug '98 / Infracom

Hackberry Ramblers

☐ CAJUN BOOGIE

FF 629CD / Dec '93 / Flying Fish

☐ JOLIE BLONDE

ARHCD 399 / Apr '95 / Arhoolie

Hackett, Bobby

☐ BOBBY HACKETT AND HIS BAND 1952 (Hackett, Bobby Band)

STCD 6050 / Jan '97 / Storyville

☐ CLASSICS 1938-1940

CLASSICS 890 / Sep '96 / Classics

☐ LIVE AT THE ROOSEVELT GRILL VOL.1

CRD 105 / Mar '96 / Chiaroscuro

☐ LIVE AT THE ROOSEVELT GRILL VOL.2

CRD 138 / Jan '97 / Chiaroscuro

☐ MILTON JAZZ CONCERT 1963 (Hackett, Bobby & Vic Dickenson/ Maxine Sullivan)

IAJRCD 1004 / Jun '94 / IAJRC

☐ OFF MINOR (Hackett, Bobby & Jack Teagarden)

VN 162 / May '95 / Viper's Nest

☐ STRING OF PEARLS, A

Carnegie jump / Ja da / You, you and especially you / You're a sweetheart / Please be kind / Jammin' the waltz / Clementine / Don't be that way / Jungle love / Memories of you / What's the use / I don't stand a ghost of a chance with you / Ain't misbehavin' / Sunrise serenade / Embraceable you / Clarinet marmalade / Singin' the blues / String of pearls / I must have that man / At sundown / New Orleans / Skeleton jangle / When day is done

TPZ 1053 / Sep '96 / Topaz Jazz

Hackett, Steve

☐ BAY OF KINGS

Bay of kings / Journey / Kim / Marigold / St. Elmo's fire / Petropolis / Second chance / Cast adrift / Horizons / Black light / Barren land / Calmaria / Time lapse at Milton Keynes / Tales of the riverbank / Skye boat song

CAMCD 8 / 29 Sep '97 / Camino

☐ BLUES WITH A FEELING

Born in Chicago / Stumble / Love of another kind / Way down South / Blue part of town / Footloose / Tombstone roller / Blues with a feeling / Big Dallas sky / 13th floor / So many roads / Solid ground

CAMCD 13 / 29 Sep '97 / Camino

☐ CURED

Hope I don't wake / Picture postcard / Can't let go / Air-conditioned nightmare / Funny feeling / Cradle of swans / Overnight sleeper / Turn back time

CDSCD 4021 / Apr '89 / Charisma

☐ DEFECTOR

Steppes / Time to get out / Slogans / Leaving / Two vamps as guests / Jacuzzi / Hammer in the sand / Toast / Show / Sentimental

CDSCD 4018 / '89 / Charisma

☐ GENESIS REVISITED

SRECD 704 / 22 Sep '97 / Snapper

☐ GUITAR NOIR

Sierra quemada / Take these pearls / There are many sides to the night / In the heart of the city / Dark as the grave / Lost in your eyes / Little America / Like an arrow / Theatre of sleep / Walking away from rainbows / Paint your pictures / Vampyre with a healthy appetite / Tristesse / Sierra quemada / Take these pearls / In the heart of the city / Vampyre with a healthy appetite

CAMCD 12 / 13 Oct '97 / Camino

☐ MOMENTUM

Cavalcanti / Sleeping sea / Portrait of a Brazilian lady / When the bell breaks / A bed a chair and a guitar / Concert for Munich / Last rites of the innocent / Troubled spirits / Variation on a theme by Chopin / Pierrot / Momentum / Bouree / Open window / Vigil

CAMCD 10 / 13 Oct '97 / Camino

☐ PLEASE DON'T TOUCH

Narnia / Carry on up the vicarage / Racing in A / Kim / How can I / Icarus ascending / Hoping love will last / Land of 1000 autumns / Please don't touch / Voice of Necam

CDSCD 4012 / '89 / Charisma

☐ THERE ARE MANY SIDES TO THE NIGHT

Horizons / Blood on the rooftops/Cuckoo cocoon / Black light / Sky boat song / Time lapse at Milton Keynes / Beja flor / Kim / Second chance / Oh how I love you / Journey / Baroque / Walking away from rainbows / Cavalcanti / Tales of the riverbank / Vivaldi guitar concerto / Blue part of town / Ace of wands / Cinema paradiso / End of day

CAMCD 14 / 29 Sep '97 / Camino

☐ TILL WE HAVE FACES

Let me count the ways / Doll that's made in Japan / Myopia / What's my name / Rio connection / Taking the easy way out / When you wish upon a star / Duel / Matilda Smith-Williams' home for the aged / Gulf / Stadiums of the damned

CAMCD 9 / 29 Sep '97 / Camino

☐ TIME LAPSES (Live)

Camino royale / Please don't touch / Everyday / In that quiet earth / Depth charge / Jacuzzi / Steppes / Ace of wands / Hope I don't wake / Red flower of tachai blooms everywhere / Tigermoth / Tower struck down / Spectral mornings / Clocks / Angel of mons

CAMCD 11 / 13 Oct '97 / Camino

☐ TOKYO TAPES

CAMCD 15 / 27 Apr '98 / Camino

☐ VOYAGE OF THE ACOLYTE

Ace of wands / Hands of the priestess-part 1 / Tower struck down / Hands of the priestess-part 2 / Hermit / Star of Sirius / Lovers / Shadow of the Hierophant

CASCD 1111 / '87 / Charisma

Hacks-Harney, Richard

☐ SWEETMAN

EDCD 483 / Sep '96 / Edsel

Haco

☐ HACO

HACO 1 / Jun '97 / ReR/Recommended

Hada To Hada

☐ MY GERMAN LOVER

SCD 294CD / Apr '94 / Starc

Hadad, Astrid

☐ AYI (Hadad, Astrid & Los Tarzanes)

ROUCD 5066 / Nov '95 / Rounder

Haddaway

☐ ALBUM, THE

What is love / Shout / Yeah / Rock my heart / When the feeling's gone / What is love (rapino brothers-mix) / Life / Mama's house / Come back (love has got a hold on me) / Sing about love / I miss you / Life (album re-mix)

74321183202 / Aug '95 / Arista

☐ DRIVE, THE

Fly away / Breakaway / Lover by thy name / Waiting for a better world / Give it up / Catch a fire / Desert prayer / First cut is the deepest / Baby don't go / Another day without you

74321306662 / Sep '95 / Arista

Haddix, Travis

☐ BIG OLE GOODUN, A

ICH 1168CD / Jan '94 / Ichiban

☐ WHAT I KNOW RIGHT NOW

ICH 1132CD / Oct '93 / Ichiban

☐ WINNERS NEVER QUIT

Homeslice / Bag lady / She's not the kind of girl / Better than nothing / Winners never quit / Something in the milk ain't clean / Beggin' business / Abused / Someone to love / I'm mean

ICH 1101CD / Oct '93 / Ichiban

Haden, Charlie

☐ ALWAYS SAY GOODBYE (Haden, Charlie Quartet West)

Introduction / Always say goodbye / Nice eyes / Relaxin' at Camarillo / Sunset afternoon / My love and I / Alone together / Our Spanish love song / Background music / Ou es-tu mon amour / Avenue of stars / Low key lightly / Celia / Everything happens to me / Ending

5215012 / Jul '94 / Verve

☐ AS LONG AS THERE'S MUSIC (Haden, Charlie & Hampton Hawes)

Irene / Rainforest / Turnaround / As long as there's music / This is called love / Hello / Goodbye / Irene / Turnaround / As long as there's music

5135342 / Mar '94 / Verve

☐ BALLAD OF THE FALLEN

El Segardors / If you want to write me / Ballad of the fallen / Grandola vila morena / Introduction to people / People united will never be defeated / Silence / Too late / La pasionaria / La santa espina

8115462 / Sep '84 / ECM

☐ BEYOND THE MISSOURI SKY (Haden, Charlie & Pat Metheny)

5371302 / Feb '97 / Verve

☐ CLOSENESS DUETS

Ellen David / OC / For Turiya / For a free Portugal

3970002 / Mar '94 / A&M

☐ DREAM KEEPER (Haden, Charlie & The Liberation Music Orchestra)

Dream keeper / Rabo de nube / Nkosi sikelel 'I Afrika / Sandino / Spiritual / Feliciano ama / Canto del pilon / Hymn of the Anarchist women's movement

DIW 844 / Jan '92 / DIW

☐ GOLDEN NUMBER, THE

Out of focus / Shepp's way / Turnaround / Golden number

3908252 / Feb '94 / A&M

☐ HAUNTED HEART (Haden, Charlie Quartet West)

Introduction / Hello my lovely / Haunted heart / Dance of the infidels / Long goodbye / Lennie's pennies / Every time we say goodbye / Lady in the lake / Segment / Bad and the beautiful / Deep song

5130782 / Mar '92 / Verve

☐ IN ANGEL CITY (Haden, Charlie Quartet West)

Sunday at the Hillcrest / First song / Red wind / Blue in green / Alpha / Live your dreams / Child's play / Fortune's fame / Tarantella / Lonely woman

8370312 / Jul '89 / Verve

☐ LIBERATION MUSIC ORCHESTRA

Introduction / Song of the united front / El quinto regimento / Los cuatro generals (the four generals) / Ending of the first side / Song for Che / War orphans / Interlude / Circus / We shall overcome

IMP 11882 / Mar '96 / Impulse Jazz

☐ MAGICO (Haden, Charlie & Jan Garbarek/Egberto Gismonti)

8234742 / '88 / ECM

☐ MONTREAL TAPES, THE (Haden, Charlie & Geri Allen/Paul Motian)

Blues in Motian / Fiasco / First song / Dolphy's dance / For John Malachi / In the year of the dragon

5374832 / 10 Nov '97 / Verve

☐ MONTREAL TAPES, THE (Haden, Charlie & G. Rubalcaba)

5376702 / Oct '97 / Verve

☐ NIGHT IN THE CITY (Haden, Charlie & Kenny Barron)

5399612 / 6 Apr '98 / Verve

☐ STEAL AWAY (Haden, Charlie & Hank Jones)

It's me, oh lord / Nobody knows the trouble I've seen / Spiritual / Wade in the water / Swing low, sweet chariot / Sometimes I feel like a motherless child / L'amour de moi / Danny boy / I've got a robe / Steal away to jesus / We shall overcome / Go down moses / My lord, what a morning / Hymn medley

5272492 / Sep '95 / Verve

Hades

☐ AGAIN SHALL BE FREE

FMP 002 / Mar '95 / Misanthropy

Hadidjah, Idhah

☐ TONGGERET

Tonggeret / Bayu bayu / Mahoni / Hiji / Catetan / Arum / Bandung / Daun / Pulus / Keser / Bojong / Serat / Sahara

7559791732 / Jan '95 / Nonesuch

Hadjidakis, Manos

☐ BALLADS OF ATHENA STREET

MN 3909 / 11 May '98 / Musurgia Graeca

☐ MAGNUS EROTICUS

MN 0006 / 11 May '98 / Musurgia Graeca

☐ NEVER ON SUNDAY

MM 209 / 11 May '98 / Musurgia Graeca

Hadley, Jerry

☐ SONG OF NAPLES

Dicitencello vuie / Marechiare / Passione / Manella mia / Fenesta che lucive / Vurria / A Tazza e Cafe / A Vuchella / Core ngrato / O sole mio / Pecche / Silenzio cantatore / Ciove / Napule ca se ne va / Piscatore e Pusilleco / L'te vurria vasa / Maria, mari / Torna a Surriento / Addio, mia bella Napoli

09026683502 / Nov '96 / RCA Victor

Hadley, Tony

☐ HITS

Save a prayer / Slave to love / She's gone / Maybe you and I / Wonderful life / She / First cut is the deepest / Dance with me / Have you seen her / Free fallin' / Woman in chains / First of May / Love affair

5393012 / 8 Sep '97 / PolyGram TV

Haerter, Harold

☐ MOSTLY LIVE (Haerter, Harold & Dewey Redman)
Misterioso / Interlude / Cosmic / Dewey's tune / Mute / Interlude 2 / Children song / Walls bridges / I still love you / Spur of the moment / Interlude 3 / Variation on mute
8888252 / Oct '96 / Tiptoe

Hafer, Dick

☐ IN A SENTIMENTAL MOOD (Hafer, Dick Quartet)
PCD 7094 / Jul '96 / Progressive

Hafez, Abdel Halim

☐ BE AMR EL HOB 1963-1979
3105432 / 23 Feb '98 / Odeon

☐ LIVE AT THE ROYAL ALBERT HALL
3109682 / 23 Mar '98 / Odeon

☐ MAWOOD
3105092 / 23 Mar '98 / Odeon

Hafler Trio

☐ ALL THAT RISES MUST CONVERGE
KUT 5CD / May '93 / Grey Area

☐ BANG - AN OPEN LETTER
KUT 1CD / Jun '94 / Grey Area

☐ BOOTLEG
ASH 13CD / Jan '95 / Ash International

☐ FOUR WAYS OF SAYING FIVE
KUT 4CD / Oct '93 / Grey Area

☐ FUCK
TONE 3 / Oct '95 / Touch

☐ HOW TO REFORM MANKIND
TO 24 / Oct '95 / Touch

☐ INPOUTOF
KK 008CD / '88 / KK

☐ RESURRECTION (Hafler Trio & The Sons Of God)
TO 22 / Oct '95 / Touch

☐ SEVEN HOURS SLEEP
KUT 3CD / Jun '94 / Grey Area

☐ THIRSTY FISH, A
A thirsty fish / Dirty fire / A loud egg / Blind table / A hungry stone / Closed bread / An elderly testament
KUT 6CD / May '93 / Grey Area

☐ WALK GENTLY THROUGH
KUT 2CD / Jun '94 / Grey Area

Hafner, Lutz

☐ LUTZ HAFNER
MR 874804 / 8 Nov '97 / Mons

Hagalax Runedance

☐ WINDS THAT SANG MIDGARD'S FATE, THE
SAG 008CD / 22 Jun '98 / Elfinblut

Hagans, Tim

☐ HUBSONGS (Hagans, Tim & Marcus Printup)
Backlash / Happy times / Hubcap / Lament for Booker / On the que-tee / Crisis / Byrd like / Thermo / Up jumped spring / Life flight
8595092 / 8 Jun '98 / Blue Note

Hagar, Sammy

☐ ANTHOLOGY
VSOPCD 207 / Oct '94 / Connoisseur Collection

☐ BEST OF SAMMY HAGAR, THE
Red / (Sittin' on the) dock of the bay / I've done everything for you / Rock 'n' roll weekend / Cruisin' and boozin' / Turn up the music / Reckless / Trans am (highway wonderland) / Love or money / This planet's on fire / Plain Jane / Bad reputation / Bad motor scooter / You make me crazy
CDP 7802622 / 15 Sep '97 / EMI Gold

☐ BEST OF SAMMY HAGAR, THE
Red / (sittin' on) the dock of the bay / I've done everything for you / Rock 'n' roll weekend / Crusin' and boozin' / Turn up the music / Reckless / Trans am (highway wonderland) / Love or money / This planet's on fire (burn in hell) / Plain jane / Bad reputation / Bad motorscooter / You make me crazy
CDGOLD 1069 / Oct '96 / EMI Gold

☐ DANGER ZONE
Love or money / Twentieth century man / Miles from boredom / Mommy says / In the night / Iceman / Bad reputation / Heartbeat / Run for your life / Danger zone
BGOCD 281 / Jul '95 / Beat Goes On

☐ LOUD 'N' CLEAR
Rock 'n' roll weekend / Make it last / Reckless / Turn up the music / I've done everything for you / Young girl blues / Bad motor scooter / Space station no. 5
BGOCD 149 / Aug '92 / Beat Goes On

☐ MUSICAL CHAIRS
Turn up the music / It's gonna be alright kid / You make me crazy / Reckless / Try / Don't stop me now / Straight from the hip kid / Hey boys / Someone out there / Crack in the world
BGOCD 201 / May '94 / Beat Goes On

☐ NINE ON A TEN SCALE
Keep on rockin' / Urban guerilla / Flamingos fly / China / Silver lights / All American / Confession (please come back) / Young girl blues / Rock 'n' roll Romeo
BGOCD 182 / Apr '93 / Beat Goes On

☐ RED
Red / Catch the wind / Cruisin' and boozin' / Free money / Rock 'n' roll weekend / Fillmore shuffle / Hungry / Pits / Love has found me / Little star/Eclipse
BGOCD 181 / Apr '93 / Beat Goes On

☐ STREET MACHINE
Never say die / This planet's on fire / Wounded in love / Falling in love / Growing pains / Child to man / Trans am (Highway wonderland) / Feels like love / Plain Jane
BGOCD 150 / Oct '92 / Beat Goes On

☐ THROUGH THE FIRE (Hagar, Sammy/ Neil Schon/Kenny Aaronson/Michael Shrieve)
Top of the rock / Missing you / Animation / Valley of the kings / Giza / Whiter shade of pale / Hot and dirty / He will understand / My home town
RETRO 50059CD / Jan '96 / Retroactive

Hagen, Nina

☐ NINA HAGEN
Move over / Super freak family / Love heart attack / Hold me / Las Vegas / Live on Mars / Dope sucks / Only seventeen / Where's the party / Ave Maria
ACTIVCD 6 / Feb '96 / Activ

☐ REVOLUTION BALLROOM
So bad / Revolution room / Right on time / Pollution pirates / King of hearts / L'amore / Pillow talk / Berlin / I'm gonna live the life / Gypsy love / Omhaidakhandi
ACTIVCD 3 / Oct '95 / Activ

☐ STREET
Blumen fur die damen / Divine love, sex and romance / Ruler of my heart / Nina 4 president / Keep it live / Berlin / In my world / Gretchen / Erfurt and Gera / All 4 franckie
ACTIVCD 4 / Feb '96 / Activ

Hagfish

☐ HAGFISH
DON 015CD / 30 Mar '98 / Honest Don's

☐ ROCK YOUR LAME ASS
Happiness / Stamp / Flat / Bullet / Crater / Minite maid / White food / Disappointed / Plain / Buster / Trixi / Did you notice / Gertrude / Hose / Teenage kicks
8286842 / Sep '95 / London

Haggard, Merle

☐ 20 COUNTRY NO.1'S
Okie from Muskogee / I'm a lonesome fugitive / Branded man / Sing me back home / Legend of Bonnie and Clyde / Mama tired / Hungry eyes / Workin' man blues / Always wanting you / It's not love (but it's not bad) / Old man from the mountain / Everybody's had the blues / Movin' on / Roots of my raising / Fightin' side of me / Carolyn / I wonder if they ever think of me / Daddy Frank (the guitar man) / Grandma Harp / Kentucky gambler
CDMFP 6114 / Mar '94 / Music For Pleasure

☐ ALL NIGHT LONG
All night long: Haggard, Merle & Randy Travis / Honky tonk / Night-time man / I'm a white boy / Holding things together / Uncle Lem / Farmer's daughter / Man's got to give up a lot / I've done it all / Goodbye lefty / If you've got time (to say goodbye) / September in Miami / Bar in Bakersfield
D277410 / '91 / Curb

☐ COUNTRY CLASSICS
I can't stop loving you / Trouble in mind / Folsom Prison blues / Walking the floor over you / Long black limousine / Waiting for a train / San Antonio rose / Little ole wine drinker me / Today I started loving you again / She thinks I still care / Mom and Dad's waltz / Makin' believe / Blues stay away from me / You've still got a place in my heart / Green green grass of home / Moanin' the blues / (My friends are gonna be) strangers / Silver wings / I take a lot of pride in what I am / Where does the good times go
4949182 / 1 Jun '98 / EMI Gold

☐ COUNTRY LEGEND
Twinkle twinkle lucky star / If you want to be my woman / Workin' man blues / Always late / TB blues / Fulsom prison blues / Footlights / Big city / Mama tried / Brain Cloudy blues / Milk cow blues / Begging to you / Tonight the bottle let me down / What am I gonna do / Ida Red / San Antonio rose / Corine Corina / Take me back to Tulsa / Faded love: Haggard, Merle & Bonnie Owens / Maiden's prayer / Fiddle breakdown / Right or wrong / Ramblin' fever / That's the way love goes / Today I started loving you again / Okie from Muskogee / Fightin' side of me
PLATCD 358 / May '91 / Platinum

☐ HITS & MORE, THE
Okie from Muskogee / If you want to be my woman / Games people play / Workin' man blues / Corine Corina / Tonight the bottle let me down / What am I gonna do / Mama tried / That's the way love goes / San Antonio rose / Ramblin' fever / Take me back to Tulsa / Ida Red / Begging to you / Always late / Big city / Folsom Prison blues / Medley / Footlights / Today I started loving you again
HADCD 168 / May '94 / Javelin

☐ I'M A LONESOME FUGITIVE/MAMA TRIED
I'm a lonesome fugitive / All of me belongs to you / House of memories / Life in prison / Whatever happened to me / Drink up and be somebody / Someone told my story / If you want to be my woman / Mary's mine / Skid row / My rough and rowdy ways / Mixed up mess of a heart / Mama tried / Green green grass of home / Little ole wine drinker me / In the good old days (when times were bad) / I could have gone right / I'll always know / Sunny side of my life / Teach me to forget / Folsom Prison blues / Run 'em off / You'll never love me now / Too many bridges to cross over
BGOCD 328 / Mar '97 / Beat Goes On

☐ LAND OF MANY CHURCHES, THE (Haggard, Merle & Carter Family)
RE 21582 / Nov '97 / Razor & Tie

☐ MERLE HAGGARD LIVE
Mama tried / When times were good / Today I started loving you again / Chill factor / Ida red / Okie from Muskogee / Bill Cheatum / Mama's hungry eyes / Fightin' side of me / I think I'll just stay here and drink / Honky tonk night time man / Footlights / If I could only fly / Kern river / I knew the moment I lost you / This mornin' this evenin' so soon
300392 / Jun '98 / Hallmark

☐ OKIE FROM MUSKOGEE (23 Great Songs Live At Church Street Station, Florida)
Twinkle twinkle lucky star / If you want to be my woman / Workin' man blues / Always late with your kisses / TB blues / Folsom Prison blues / Footlights / Big city / Mama tried / Brain cloudy blues/Milk cow blues / Begging to you / Tonight the bottle let me down / What am I gonna do with the rest of my life / Ida red / San Antonio rose / Corrine Corrina / Take me back to Tulsa / Faded love / Fiddle breakdown / Right or wrong / Ramblin' fever / That's the way love goes / Today I started loving you again / Okie from Muskogee / Fightin' side of me
PLATCD 170 / Mar '96 / Platinum

☐ OKIE FROM MUSKOGEE
Mama tried / When times were good / Today I started loving you again / Chill factor / Ida Red / Okie from Muskogee / Bill Cheatum / Mama's hungry eyes / Fightin' side of me / I think I'll just stay here and drink / Honky tonk night time man / Footlights / If I could only fly / Kern River / I knew the moment I lost you / This mornin' this evenin' so soon
CD 6054 / Jan '97 / Music

☐ POET OF THE COMMON MAN
CURCD 040 / Apr '97 / Curb

☐ SAME TRAIN A DIFFERENT TIME
California blues / Waiting for a train / Train whistle blues / Why should I be lonely / Blue yodel No. 6 / Miss the Mississippi and you / Mule skinner blues / Frankie and Johnny / Hobo Bill's last ride / Travellin' blues / Peach pickin' time in Georgia / No hard times / Down the old road to home / Jimmie Rodgers' last blue yodel / Jimmie the kid / My rough and rowdy ways / Hobo's meditation / Mother, the Queen of my heart / My Carolina sunshine girl / My old pal / Nobody knows but me / Delta blues / Mississippi delta blues / Gambling polka dot blues
BCD 15740 / Oct '93 / Bear Family

☐ SAME TRAIN A DIFFERENT TIME (Merle Haggard Sings The Great Songs Of Jimmie Rodgers)
340512 / 1 Jun '98 / Koch

☐ SING ME BACK HOME
340542 / Nov '95 / Koch International

☐ STARS OVER BAKERSFIELD (Haggard, Merle & Buck Owens)
(my friends are gonna be) strangers / Sam hill / Sing a sad song / Please mr. d.j. / You don't have far to go / Just between the two of us / You don't even try / Slowly but surely / Down on the corner of love / House down the block / Blue love / You're for me / Please don't take her from me / It don't show on me / Why don't mommy stay with daddy and me / Three dimension love / Honeysuckle / That ain't right baby / Leavin' dirty tracks / Right after the dance
CTS 55418 / Jun '94 / Country Stars

☐ STRANGERS
(all of my friends are gonna be) strangers / Falling for you / Please mr. d.j. / You don't have far to go / Sing a sad song / Sam hill / I'm gonna break every heart I can / You don't even try / If I had left it up to you / I'd trade all of my tomorrows / Worst is yet to come / Walking the floor over you
340532 / Nov '95 / Koch International

☐ SWINGING DOORS/THE BOTTLE LET ME DOWN
340522 / Nov '95 / Koch International

☐ TRIBUTE TO MERLE HAGGARD, A (Various Artists)
CMHCD 3927 / Mar '98 / CMH

☐ TRIBUTE TO THE BEST DAMN FIDDLE PLAYER IN THE WORLD (My Salute To Bob Wills)
Brown skin gal / Right or wrong / Brain cloudy blues / Stay a little longer / Misery / Time changes everything / San Antonio rose / I knew the moment I lost you / Roly poly / Old fashioned love / Corine Corina / Take me back to Tulsa
379002 / Aug '95 / Koch

☐ TULARE DUST (The Songs Of Merle Haggard) (Various Artists)
HCD 8058 / Dec '94 / Hightone

☐ UNTAMED HAWK (5CD Set)
Sing a sad song / You don't even try / Life in prison (false start) / Life in prison / You don't have far to go / Sam Hill / Please Mr. DJ / I'd trade all of my tomorrows / Strangers / Slowly but surely / Just between the two of us / Falling for you / I wanta live again / House without love / Walking the floor over you / Worst is yet to come / Piedras negras (go home) / Singin' my heart out / Skid row / If I had left it up to you / I'm gonna break every heart I can / Stranger in my arms / If I could be him / Shade tree (fix it man) / This town's not big enough / I'll take a chance / Our hearts are holding hands / Too used to being with you / That makes two of us / Forever and ever / Wait a little longer, please Jesus / Swinging doors / Girl turned ripe / I threw away the rose / Fugitive / Loneliness is eating me alive / Someone told my story / Hang up my gloves / Longer you wait / Tonight the bottle let me down / I can't stand me / Someone else you've known / High on a hilltop / I'll look over you / No more you and me / Mixed up mess of a heart / I'm a lonesome fugitive / House of memories / All of me belongs to you / Mary's mine / If you want to be my woman / Whatever happened to me / Drink up and be somebody / Gone crazy / Some of us never learn / Branded man / You don't have very far to go / Wine take me away / If you see my baby / Somewhere between / Don't get married / My hands are tied / I made the prison band / Look over me / Long black limousine / I'll leave the bottle on the bar / Sing me back home / Son of Hickory Holler's tramp / Seeing eye dog / Will you visit me on Sundays / Home is where a kid grows up / Where does the good times go / Good times / News break / My past is present / Mom and Dad's waltz / My Ramona / Because you can't be mine / Train never stops / You still have a place in my heart / Money tree / Picture from two sides of life / Legend of Bonnie and Clyde / I started loving you again / Love has a mind of its own / Fool's castle / Is this the beginning of the end / Sunny side of my life / Run em off / I'll always know / You'll never love me now / Mama tried / In the good old days / Little ole wine drinker me / Teach me to forget / Lookin' for my mind / Green green grass of home / I could have gone right / Day the rains came / I think we're living in the good old days / Somewhere on Skid Row / Who do I know in Dallas / Folsom Prison blues / You're not home yet / Too many bridges to cross over / I take a lot of pride in what I am / I just want to look at you one more time / I'm bringin' home good news / Keep me from cryin' today / I can't hold myself in line / I'm free / It meant goodbye to me when you said hello / Who'll buy the wine / She thinks I still care / What's wrong with stayin' home / When no flowers grow / Every fool has a rainbow / Hungry eyes / Silver wings
BCD 15744 / Mar '95 / Bear Family

☐ VERY BEST OF MERLE HAGGARD, THE
I take a lot of pride in what I am / I'm a lonesome fugitive / Mama tried / Daddy Frank (the guitarman) / Sing me back home / Workin' man blues / Kentucky gambler / Holding things together / Branded man / Legend of Bonnie and Clyde / Mama's hungry eyes / Swingin' doors / Carolyn / Strangers / Bottle let me down / I think I'll just stay here and drink / Fightin' side of me / Okie from Muskogee
ECD 3099 / Jan '95 / K-Tel

☐ YESTERDAY'S WINE 1981-1988
Sing a sad song / (My friends are gonna be) strangers / My favourite memory / Big city / Are the good times really over / Yesterday's wine / Going where the lonely go / Reasons to quit / You take me for granted / Half a man / Pancho and lefty / What am I gonna do / That's the way love goes / Someday when things are good / Let's chase each other round the room / Place to fall apart / Natural high / Kern river / Friend in California / Out among the stars / Twinkle twinkle lucky stars / Chill factor / Holding things together / Workin' man blues
EDCD 549 / 6 Apr '98 / Edsel

Haggart, Bob

☐ WORLD'S GREATEST JAZZBAND (Haggart, Bob & Yank Lawson)
CDTTD 533 / Jul '94 / Timeless Traditional

Hagiopian, Richard

☐ ARMENIAN MUSIC THROUGH THE AGES
SFCD 40414 / Jun '93 / Smithsonian Folkways

☐ BEST OF ARMENIAN FOLK MUSIC
EUCD 1222 / Sep '93 / ARC

Hahn, Jerry

☐ JERRY HAHN QUINTET, THE (Hahn, Jerry Quintet)
In the breeze / My love / Dippin' snuff / Ragahantar / Ara be in
ARHCD 9011 / Jul '98 / Arhoolie

☐ TIME CHANGES
Time changes / 245 / Method / Quiet now / Blues for allyson / Oregon / Goodbye Pork Pie Hat / Hannah bear / Stolen moments / Chelsea rose
ENJ 90072 / May '95 / Enja

Hahn, John

☐ OUT OF THE SHADOWS
Rhino stomp / Captain Courageous / Outward bound / Looking glass / Warm summer rain / Cut to the chase / Let it ride / Deadly spell / Pickin' your seat / Second sight / Heat of the night / Inherit the wind
KILCD 1004 / Oct '93 / Killerwatt

Hai Karate

☐ HAI KARATE
MR 095CD / 23 Mar '98 / Man's Ruin

Haig, Al

☐ ORNITHOLOGY
PCD 7024 / Oct '91 / Progressive

Hail

☐ TURN OF THE SCREW
Another day / Honey smothered / Good luck / Sicko God / Tape hiss / Rusty old ring / Take me back / Burlesque egg / Racer hero / Tar pits / Suspended / Down the road / Star in the sky / Fifteen seconds of silence / My friend / Did you listen to this
RERHCD / Apr '91 / ReR/ Recommended

Hail Mary

☐ CRASHING DOWN
VMFM 33 / Nov '97 / Vermiform

Haines, Nathan

☐ SHIFT LEFT
5271502 / Nov '96 / Verve

Haines, Paul

☐ DARN IT
Threats that matter / There aren't these things / Curtsy / Les paramedicaux erotiques / What is going to supposed to mean / Jubilee / On the way to here and elsewhere / Funny bird song / Inexplicably / Outside the city / Poem for Gretchen Ruth / Art in heaven / Rawilpindi blues / Sticks in the mud
AMCL 10142 / Nov '93 / American Clave

Haino, Keiji

☐ 21ST CENTURY HARDY-GUIDE-Y MAN, THE
PSFD 68 / Jan '96 / PSF

☐ BOOK OF ETERNITY SET, THE
FE 036 / Nov '97 / Forced Exposure

☐ DEATH NEVER TO BE COMPLETE, A (Fushitsusha)
Just as I told you / Though it went so well / That which is becoming to me / Continuing to be / Death to be complete / Hermitage
TKCF 77014 / Jun '97 / Tokuma

☐ DRAWING CLOSE, ATTUNING... (Haino, Keiji & Derek Bailey)
TKCD 77017 / Jun '97 / Tokuma

☐ I SAID, THIS IS THE SON OF NIHILISM
ARGON 18 / Jun '97 / TOE

☐ KEEPING ON BREATHING
Where is it / My shadow / There / Wafting / Here / A code / You
TKCD 77016 / Jun '97 / Tokuma

☐ NIJIUMO
PSFD 7 / 16 Feb '98 / PSF

☐ SO, BLACK IS MYSELF
ALIENCD 3 / Jun '97 / Alien8

☐ TIME IS NIGH, THE (Fushitsusha)
Just before / My precious thing / Black cluster / Time is nigh
TKCD 77015 / Jun '97 / Tokuma

☐ VOL.2 (Haino, Keiji & Loren Mazzacane Connors)
MPK 7005CD / May '97 / Menlo Park

Hair

☐ HAIR PIECE
FLASH 002 / Jun '97 / Flashback

Haircut 100

☐ PELICAN WEST PLUS
Favourite shirts (boy meets girl) / Love plus one / Lemon firebrigade / Marine boy / Milk film / King size / Fantastic day / Baked beans / Snow girl / Love's got me in triangles / Surprise me again / Calling Captain Autumn / Boat party / Ski club / Nobody's fool / October is orange
74321100782 / Oct '92 / Arista

Hairy Chapter

☐ CAN'T GET THROUGH/EYES
SB 038 / Jun '97 / Second Battle

Haiti Cherie

☐ CREOLE - TRADITIONAL & VOODOO SONGS
995342 / Aug '93 / EPM

Haizea

☐ HONTZ GAUA
LV 006 / 16 Mar '98 / Lost Vinyl

Hajra Gipsy Orchestra

☐ EVENING OF GIPSY SONGS, AN
SOW 90129 / Sep '94 / Sounds Of The World

Hakansson, Kenny

☐ SPELAR SPRINGLEKAR
SRS 3620CD / Jul '95 / Silence

Hakim, Sadik

☐ LADYBIRD
STCD 4156 / Feb '90 / Storyville

Hakmoun, Hassan

☐ FIRE WITHIN, THE
CDT 135CD / Nov '95 / Music Of The World

☐ TRANCE (Hakmoun, Hassan & Zahar)
Bania / Only one god (Maaboud alah) / Soudan minitara (Bum bastic mix) / Challaban / Soutanbi / Soulalahoalith / Alal wahya alal (Trance mix) / Sun is gone / Soudan minitara
CDRW 38 / Aug '93 / Realworld

Hal

☐ GORILLA CONSPIRATION
PPP 121CD / Jun '97 / We Bite

Hal Al Shedad

☐ HAL AL SHEDAD
TMU 017CD / Feb '97 / Troubleman Unlimited

Halcox, Pat

☐ PAT HALCOX ALLSTARS, THE
Flintstones / Blue and sentimental / I'm gonna lock my heart and throw away the key / China boy / I wanna little girl / What's the racket / Jeepers creepers / You took advantage of me / Three four the blues / Dusk / 5 o'clock drag / Fidgety feet / Deed I do / Dr. Jazz / Mersey tunnel jazz
LACD 84 / 24 Nov '97 / Lake

☐ SONGS FROM TIN PAN ALLEY (Halcox, Pat & Friends)
JCD 186 / Oct '91 / Jazzology

Hale, Terry Lee

☐ FRONTIER MODEL
GRCD 311 / 17 Nov '97 / Glitterhouse

☐ LEAVING WEST
GRCD 399 / Dec '96 / Glitterhouse

☐ OH WHAT A WORLD
NORMAL 152CD / Mar '94 / Normal

☐ TORNADO ALLEY
GRCD 359 / May '97 / Glitterhouse

Hale, Willie

☐ VERY BEST OF LITTLE BEAVER, THE (Little Beaver)
Party down / Get into the party life / We three / Money vibrations / Listen to my heartbeat / I can dig it baby / When was the last time / Let's stick together / Wish I had a little girl like you / Groove on / Let the good times roll / Little girl blue / Joey / Party times / I feel like crying / I really love you
NEMCD 919 / Nov '96 / Sequel

Haley, Bill

☐ BEST OF BILL HALEY (Haley, Bill & The Comets)
MACCD 231 / Aug '96 / Autograph

☐ BILL HALEY
LECD 034 / May '94 / Dynamite

☐ BILL HALEY
UAE 30012 / Jan '98 / Members Edition

☐ BILL HALEY & BUDDY HOLLY (Haley, Bill/Buddy Holly)
That'll be the day: *Holly, Buddy* / I'm looking for someone to love: *Holly, Buddy* / Oh baby: *Holly, Buddy* / Tell me how: *Holly, Buddy* / Maybe baby: *Holly, Buddy* / Brown eyed handsome man: *Holly, Buddy* / Not fade away: *Holly, Buddy* / Rave on: *Holly, Buddy* / Ready teddy: *Holly, Buddy* / Peggy Sue: *Holly, Buddy* / Shake rattle and roll: *Haley, Bill* / ABC boogie: *Haley, Bill* / Rockin' through the rye: *Haley, Bill* / Thirteen women: *Haley, Bill* / Happy baby: *Haley, Bill* / Dim dim the lights: *Haley, Bill* / Razzle dazzle: *Haley, Bill* / Rock the joint: *Haley, Bill* / See you later alligator: *Haley, Bill*
ASTCD 4008 / Oct '97 / Go On Deluxe

☐ BILL HALEY & THE COMETS (Haley, Bill & The Comets)
CD 114 / Oct '94 / Timeless Treasures

☐ BILL HALEY & THE COMETS (Haley, Bill & The Comets)
Rock around the clock / Shake, rattle and roll / Abc boogie / Panic / I've got news for you / Don't mess around / See you later alligator / Wobble / This is goodbye / Train of sin / Altar of love / Helena / Saint's rock 'n' roll / Razzle dazzle / Blue comet blues / Skokiaan
12396 / Mar '95 / Laserlight

☐ BILL HALEY & THE COMETS (Haley, Bill & The Comets)
Rock around the clock / Flip, flop and fly / Skinny Minnie / Love letters in the sand / Ling ting tong / See you later alligator / Rock the joint / Saints rock 'n' roll / Shake, rattle and roll / Rock-a-beatin' boogie
399234 / Jun '97 / Koch Presents

☐ HITS COLLECTION, THE (Haley, Bill & The Comets)
Saints rock 'n' roll / Rip it up / Don't mess around with my love / Wobble / ABC boogie / Rock around the clock / Shake, rattle and roll / See you later alligator / Razzle dazzle / Panic / Helena / This is goodbye, goodbye / I've got news for you / Train of sin / Altar of love / Blue comet blues / Skokiaan a go go / Whole lotta shakin' goin' on / How many
100592 / May '97 / A-Play Collection

☐ HOUSE IS ROCKIN', THE (Comets)
House is rockin' / Lili Mae / Hey Mister Dollar / Shadow of your smile / Cafe ala rock / Buena sera / Car jam / Sixty minute man / Walking slow behind you / Shoo Sue / Later / Up above my head / Franny's medley / Bad bad Leroy Brown / Be my love tonight / Night train / Memories are sweeter / Razzle dazzle / Birth of the boogie / Crazy man crazy / Interview
RSRCD 013 / Jul '98 / Rockstar

☐ MASTERS, THE (Haley, Bill & The Comets)
Rock around the clock / Razzle dazzle / Shake rattle and roll / See you later alligator / Rip it up / Caravan / Whole lotta shakin' goin on / Real rock drive / Rock the joint / Dance with a dolly / Yes indeed / Chick safari / Farewell so long goodbye / How many / Fractured / What'cha gonna do / Blue comet blues / Skokiaan / Land of a thousand dances / Crazy man crazy / Chattanooga choo choo
EABCD 083 / 30 Mar '98 / Eagle

☐ MR. ROCK 'N' ROLL (Haley, Bill & The Comets)
(We're gonna) Rock around the clock / Saints rock and roll / Razzle dazzle / Blue comet blues / Skokiaan / Shake, rattle and roll / ABC boogie / See you later alligator / Rip it up / Caravana a go go / Whole lotta shakin' goin' on / How many
EMBCD 3401 / 29 Jun '98 / Ember

☐ ROCK AROUND THE CLOCK (Haley, Bill & The Comets)
Shake, rattle and roll / ROCK / Calling all comets / See you later alligator / Saints rock 'n' roll / Razzle dazzle / ABC Boogie / Don't knock the rock / Rip it up / Rockin' thru the rye / Birth of the boogie / Rock-a-beatin' boogie / Dim, dim the lights / Mambo rock / Rudy's rock / Skinny Minnie / Thirteen women / Corine Corina / Forty cups of coffee / (We're gonna) rock around the clock
MOCD 3015 / Feb '95 / More Music

☐ ROCK THE JOINT (Haley, Bill & The Comets)
Rocket 88 / Tearstains on my heart / Green tree boogie / Jukebox cannonball / Sundown boogie / Icy heart / Rock the joint / Dance with a dolly / Rockin' chair on the moon / Stop beatin' around the mulberry bush / Real rock drive / Crazy man crazy / What'cha gonna do / Pat-a-cake / Fractured / Live it up / Farewell, so long, goodbye / I'll be true / Ten little Indians / Chattanooga choo choo / Straight jacket / Yes indeed
RCCD 3001 / Aug '90 / Rollercoaster

☐ ROCKIN' AND ROLLIN' (Haley, Bill & The Comets)
Shake, rattle and roll / Skinny Minnie / Rip it up / See you later alligator / (We're gonna) Rock around the clock / Razzle dazzle / Crying time / Saints rock 'n' roll / Rock-a-beatin' boogie / Rock the joint / I'm walkin' / Hi-heel sneakers / Blue suede shoes / CC rider / Lawdy Miss Clawdy / Personality / Hail hail rock 'n' roll / Let the good times roll again / Battle of New Orleans / Heartaches by the number
5509552 / Mar '95 / Spectrum

☐ ROCKIN' ROLLIN' HALEY (The Decca Years & More/5CD Set) (Haley, Bill & The Comets)
(We're gonna) Rock around the clock / Thirteen women / Shake, rattle and roll / ABC Boogie / Happy baby / Dim, dim the lights / Birth of the boogie / Mambo rock / Two hound dogs / Razzle dazzle / ROCK / Rock-a-beatin' boogie / Saints rock 'n' roll / Burn that candle / See you later alligator / Paper boy / Goofin' around / Rudy's rock / Hide and seek / Hey then, there now / Tonight's the night / Hook, line and sinker / Blue comet blues / Calling all comets / Choo choo ch' boogie / Rocking little tune / Hot dog buddy buddy / Rockin' through the rye / Teenager's mother / Rip it up / Don't knock the rock / Forty cups of coffee / Miss you / You hit the wrong note Billy Goat / Rockin' rollin' rover / Please don't talk about me when I'm gone / You can't stop me from dreaming / I'm gonna sit right down and write myself a letter / Rock Lomond / Is it true what they say about Dixie / Carolina in the morning / Dipsy doodle / Ain't misbehavin' / Beak speaks / Moon over Miami / One sweet letter from you / I'll be with you in apple blossom time / Somebody else is taking my place / How many / Move it on over / Rock the joint / Me rock a hula / Rockin' Rita / Jamaica DJ / Piccadilly rock / Pretty alouette / Rockin' rollin' schnitzlebank / Rockin' Matilda / Vive la rock 'n' roll / It's a sin / Mary Mary Lou / El rocko / Come rock with me / Oriental rock / Woodenshoe rock / Walkin' beat / Skinny Minnie / Sway with me / Lean Jean / Don't nobody move / Joey's song / Chiquita Linda / Dinah / Ida, sweet as apple cider / Whoa Mabel / Marie / Eloise / Corine Corina / BB Betty / Sweet Sue, just you / Charmaine / Dragon rock / AC rock / Catwalk / I got a woman / Fool such as I / By by me / Where did you go last night / Caldonia / Shaky / Ooh, look-a-there ain't she pretty / Summer souvenir / Puerto Rican peddler / Music music music / Skokiaan / Drowsy waters / Two shadows / In a little Spanish town / Strictly instrumental / Mack The Knife / Green door / Yeah, she's evil
BCD 15506 / Oct '90 / Bear Family

☐ SEE YOU LATER ALLIGATOR (Haley, Bill & The Comets)
301374 / Dec '89 / Accord

☐ VERY BEST OF BILL HALEY & THE COMETS, THE (Haley, Bill & The Comets)
(We're gonna) Rock around the clock / Shake, rattle and roll / See you later alligator / Saints rock 'n' roll / Rock-a-beatin' boogie / Rockin' thru the Rye / Rip it up / Don't knock the rock / Mambo rock / Rudy's rock / Razzle dazzle / Skinny Minnie / ROCK / Thirteen women / ABC boogie / Birth of the boogie / Forty cups of coffee / Two hound dogs / Burn that candle / Calling all comets
MCCD 068 / Jun '92 / Music Club

Haley, Ed

☐ FORKED DEER (2CD Set)
Soundbite / Forked deer / Ida Red / Indian ate the woodchuck / Brushy run / Indian nation / Humphrey's jig / Green Mountain polka / Sourwood Mountain / Man of constant sorrow / Love somebody / Dora Dean / Soundbite / Bluegrass meadows / Cacklin' hen / Flop eared mule / Salt river / Brownlow's dream / Soundbite / Indian squaw / Dunbar / Lost Indian / Jenny Lind / Chicken reel / Cherry River rag / Cripple Creek / Done gone / Soundbite / Yellow barber / Stacker Lee / Brushy fork of John's Creek / Red apple rag / Wake up Susan / Three forks of Sandy / No corn on Tygart / Stonewall Jackson
ROUCD 1131/2 / Sep '97 / Rounder

Half Hour To Go

☐ ITEMS FOR THE FULL OUTFIT
GROW 0572 / Aug '95 / Grass

Half Japanese

☐ BONE HEAD
VIRUS 197CD / Mar '97 / Alternative Tentacles

☐ GREATEST HITS (2CD Set)
SH 21182 / Nov '96 / Safe House

☐ HEAVEN SENT
EJ 12CD / 1 Dec '97 / Emperor Jones

☐ HOT
FIRECD 047 / Jun '95 / Fire

Half Man Half Biscuit

☐ BACK AGAIN IN THE DHSS
Best things in life / D'ye ken ted moult / Reasons to be miserable - part 10 / Rod Hull is alive - why / Dickie Davies eyes / Bastard son of Dean Friedman / I was a teenage armchair honved fan / Arthur's farm / Carry on cremating / Albert Hammond bootleg / Reflections in a flat / Sealclubbing / Architecture and morality Ted and Alice / Fuckin' 'ell it's Fred Titmus / Time flies by (when you're the driver of the train) / All I want for Christmas is a Dukla Prague away kit / Trumpton riots
PROBE 008CD / 20 Oct '97 / Probe Plus

☐ BACK IN THE DHSS/THE TRUMPTON RIOTS EP
Busy little market town / God gave us life / Fuckin' 'ell it's Fred Titmus / Sealclubbing / 99% of gargoyles look like Bob Todd / Time flies by (when you're the driver of a train) / I hate Nerys Hughes / Len Ganley stance / Venus in flares / I love you because (you look like Jim Reeves) / Reflections in a flat / I left my heart in Papworth General / Trumpton riots / Architecture and morality Ted and Alice / 1966 and all that / Albert Hammond Bootleg / All I want for Christmas is a Dukla Prague away kit
PROBE 004CD / 6 Oct '97 / Probe Plus

☐ FOUR LADS WHO SHOOK THE WIRRAL
PROBE 46CD / 29 Jun '98 / Probe Plus

☐ MCINTYRE, TREADMORE AND DAVITT
Outbreak of Vitas Gerulaitis / Prag vec at the Melkweg / Christian rock concert / Let's not / Yipps (my baby got the) / Hedley verityesque / Lilac Harry Quinn / Our tune / Girlfriend's finished / With him / Everything's AOR
PROBE 030CD / 17 Oct '97 / Probe Plus

☐ SOME CALL IT GODCORE
Sensitive outsider / Fretwork homework / Faithlift / Song for Europe / Even men with steel hearts / 24.99 from Argos / Sponsoring the Mospits / Fear my wraith / Styx gig (Seen by my mates coming out of a) / Friday night and the gates are low / I, trog / Tour jacket with detachable sleeves
PROBE 041CD / Jan '97 / Probe Plus

☐ THIS LEADEN PALL
M 6ster / 4AD 3D CD / Running order squabble fest / Whiteness thy name is meltonian / This leaden pall / Turned up clocked on laid off / Improv workshop mimeshow gobshite / Thirteen Eurogoths floating in the dead sea / Whit week malarkey / Doreen / Quality janitor / Floreat inertia / Malayan jelutong / Numanoid hang glide / Footprints
PROBE 036CD / Oct '93 / Probe Plus

☐ VOYAGE TO THE BOTTOM OF THE ROAD
Shropshire lad / Bad review / Eno collaboration / Dead men don't need season tickets / Deep house victims minibus appeal / CAMRA man / PRS yearbook (Quick the drawbridge) / Tonight Matthew I'm going to be with Jesus / Song of encouragement for the orme ascent / Monmore hares running / Itma / He who would valium take / See that my bike's kept clean / Paintball coming home
PROBE 45CD / Jun '97 / Probe Plus

Half Pint

☐ 20 SUPER HITS
SONCD 0001 / Oct '90 / Sonic Sounds

☐ CLASSICS
HCD 7009 / Aug '94 / Hightone

☐ CLASSICS IN DUB
HCD 7014 / Mar '95 / Hightone

☐ ONE IN A MILLION
One in a million / One big ghetto / You lick me first / What more can I really do / Milky way / Mr. Landlord / Roots man / Pick your choice / Puchie Lou / Tell me little girl
GRELCD 74 / Sep '89 / Greensleeves

☐ VICTORY
Victory / Level the vibes / Come alive / Night life lady / She's mine / Desperate lover / Cost of living / When one gone / Mama / She's gone
RASCD 3031 / Feb '88 / Ras

Half Time Oranges

☐ ROTTERDAMNATION
RUTCD 5 / 27 Oct '97 / Rutland

Halfway House Orchestra

☐ HALFWAY HOUSE ORCHESTRA (New Orleans 1925-1928)
BDW 8001 / Jun '95 / Jazz Oracle

Halibuts

☐ CHUMMING
UPST 009 / Oct '94 / Upstart

☐ LIFE ON THE BOTTOM
Hammerhead / Caldera / Stinky / Life on the bottom / Ta-hu-wa-hu-wai / Noodles / Hombre de Palabra / Madcap / Hula scuba / Suicide Bay / Night crawler / Duck dive / Fire one / Istanbul / Summertime
UPSTART 033 / Aug '96 / Upstart

Hall & Oates

☐ ABANDONED LUNCHEONETTE
When the morning comes / Had I known you better then / Las Vegas turnaround / Stewardess song / She's gone / I'm just a kid (Don't make me feel like a man) / Abandoned luncheonette / Lady rain / Laughing boy / Everytime I look at you
7567815372 / Mar '93 / Atlantic

☐ ATLANTIC COLLECTION, THE (The Best Of Hall & Oates)
When the morning comes / Las vegas turnaround (the stewardess song) / Had I known you better then / It's uncanny / I want to know you for a long time / Lilly are you happy / I'm sorry / Goodnight and goodmorning / Fall in philadelphia / Waterwheel / You're much too soon / Past times behind / Is it a star / Beanie g and the rose tattoo / 70's scenario / Can't stop the music(he played it much too long) / Laughing boy / Lady rain / Abandoned luncheonette / I'm just a kid (don't make me feel like a man) / She's gone
8122722052 / Jul '96 / Atlantic

☐ CONCERT CLASSICS
Woman comes and goes / Don't blame it on love / Rich girl / Do what you want be what you are / It's a laugh / Sweet soul music / Serious music / Wait for me / She's gone / Pleasure beach / Bebop drop
CRANCH 7 / 14 Apr '98 / Ranch Life

☐ EARLY YEARS, THE
Per Kiomen / Past times behind / Lot of changes coming / In honour of a lady / Deep river blues / If that's what makes you happy / Provider / They needed each other / Angelina / I'll be by / Seventy
100742 / May '97 / A-Play Collection

☐ LOOKING BACK (The Best Of Daryl Hall And John Oates)
She's gone / Sara smile / Rich girl / You've lost that lovin' feelin' / Kiss on my list / Every time you go away / Private eyes / I can't go for that (no can do) / Maneater / One on one / Family man / Adult education / Out of touch / Method of modern love / Starting all over again / Back together again / So close / Everything your heart desires
PD 90388 / 11 May '98 / RCA

☐ LOT OF CHANGES COMIN'
CDSGP 0128 / Dec '94 / Prestige

☐ MARIGOLD SKY
EAGCD 011 / 8 Nov '97 / Eagle

☐ NO GOODBYES
It's uncanny / I want to know you / For a long time / Can't stop the music / Love you like a brother / Las Vegas turnaround / She's gone / Lilly (Are you happy) / When the morning comes / Beanie G and the rose tattoo / 70's scenario
7567804302 / Jul '96 / Atlantic

☐ REALLY SMOKIN'
Past times behind / Everyday's a lovely day / Rose come home / Flo gene / Seventy / I'm really smokin' / Christine / Over the mountain / Lemon road / Truly good song
CDTB 122 / Jul '93 / Thunderbolt

☐ ROCK 'N' SOUL VOL.1
Sara smile / She's gone / Rich girl / Kiss in my list / You make my dreams / Private eyes / I can't go for that (no can do) / Maneater / One on one / Wait for me / Say it isn't so / Adult education
74321289832 / Aug '95 / RCA

☐ SPOTLIGHT ON HALL & OATES
Lot of changes comin' / Drying in the sun / I'll be by / Perkiomen / Fall in Philadelphia / They need each other / Provider / Back in love again / Past times behind / Deep river blues / Goodnight and good morning / In honour of a lady / Angelina / Months, weeks, days / If that's what makes you happy
HADCD 107 / Feb '94 / Javelin

☐ WAR BABIES
Can't stop the music / He played it much too long / Is it a star / Beanie G and the rose tattoo / You're much too soon / 70's scenario / War baby son of Zorro / I'm watching you / Better watch your back / Screaming through December / Johnny Gore and the C eaters
7567814892 / Jul '96 / Atlantic

☐ WHOLE OATS
I'm sorry / All our love / Georgie / Fall in Philadelphia / Waterwheel / Lazy man / Goodnight and good morning / They needed each other / Southeast city window / Thank you for... / Lilly (are you happy)
7567814232 / Jan '93 / Atlantic

☐ WITH LOVE FROM HALL & OATES (The Best Of The Ballads)
Do what you want / Be what you are / Falling / One on one / Go solo / You've lost that loving feeling / Every time you go away / Sara smile / Nothing at all / Girl who used to be / Emptiness / It's a laugh / Have I been away too long / August day / Wait for me / Without tears / Why was it so easy
74321436622 / 2 Feb '98 / RCA

Hall, Aaron

☐ TRUTH, THE
Prologue / Do anything / Open up / Get a little freaky with me / Pick up the phone / Don't be afraid / Until I found you / You keep me crying (interlude) / Let's make love / When you need me / I miss you / Until the end of time / Epilogue
MCLD 19340 / Oct '96 / MCA

Hall, Adelaide

☐ HALL OF FAME
Ain't it a shame about Mame / Baby mine / Begin the beguine / Creole love call / Doin' as I please / Don't worry 'bout me / Drop me off at Harlem / I can't give you anything but love / I get along without you very well / I got rhythm / I have eyes / I hear a rhapsody / I poured my heart into a song / Mississippi mamma / Moon love / No souvenirs / Rhapsody in love / Shake down the stars / T'ain't what you do (it's the way that you do it) / That old feeling / Transatlantic lullaby / Who told you I cared
CDAJA 5098 / Nov '92 / Living Era

☐ HALL OF MEMORIES 1927-1939
Creole love call / Blues I love to sing (hear) / Chicago stompdown / I must have that man / Baby / Too darn fickle / Doin' what I please / Minnie the moocher / I'm red hot from harlem / I got rhythm / Strange as it seems / You gave me everything but love / Drop me off in harlem / Reachin' for the cotton moon / I'm shooting high / Say you're mine (take 4) / That old feeling / T'aint what you do (it's the way that cha do it)
CDHD 169 / Aug '90 / Happy Days

☐ RED HOT FROM HARLEM
This time it's love / You gave me everything but love / Rhapsody in love / Baby mine / I'll never be the same / I must have that man / Minnie the moocher / Too darn fickle / I'm red hot from Harlem / Doin' what I please / I got rhythm / Strange as it seems / Chlo-e / Solitude / Say you're mine / I get along without you very well / Don't worry 'bout me / T'ain't what you do (it's the way that you do it) / Shake down the stars / Who told you I cared / No souvenirs / This can't be love
PASTCD 7029 / Jan '94 / Flapper

Hall, Ben

☐ COUNTRY WAYS AND ROCKIN' DAYS (Hall, Ben & The Ramblers/Weldon Myrick)
Blue days black nights / Even tho' / Hangin' around / Crying on my shoulder / Make believe / Sleepless nights / Gunfighter's fame / Late hours / Don't ask me why / I'd give anything / All from loving you / Rose of Monterey / Drifting along with the wind / Driftwood on the river / Stormy skies / Season for love / Only 17 / That's the way dreams go / I don't wanna go home / You're here in my mind / Weeping willow / Before you begin / Johnny Law / Hiding alone / So close / Won't you be mine / I'll never be the same / I'll still be hanging around
RCCD 3004 / Oct '93 / Rollercoaster

Hall, Bob

☐ ALONE WITH THE BLUES (Hall, Bob & Tom McGuinness)
Drifting along with the blues / Jukebox shuffle / Reminiscin' / Road of no return / Sixes and sevens / Midnight hour blues / Rock this joint / Indiana avenue stomp / After hours / Runaway shoes / Blues on the downbeat / Not if I see you first / Cardboard city / Hanging out / Alone with the blues
LACD 44 / Mar '95 / Lake

☐ DOWN THE ROAD APIECE/ROLL AND SLIDE (Hall, Bob & Dave Peabody)
APCD 044 / Mar '97 / Appaloosa

Hall, Daryl

☐ SOUL ALONE
Power of seduction / This time / Love revelation / I'm in a Philly mood / Borderline / Stop loving me, stop loving you / Help me find a way to your heart / Send me / Wildlife / Money changes everything / Written in stone
4739212 / Feb '94 / Epic

Hall, Edmond

☐ CLASSICS 1937-1944
CLASSICS 830 / Sep '95 / Classics

☐ CLASSICS 1944-1945
CLASSICS 872 / Apr '96 / Classics

☐ EDMOND HALL & PAPA BUE'S VIKING JAZZBAND (Hall, Edmond & Papa Bue Viking Jazz Band)
STCD 6022 / Jan '97 / Storyville

☐ EDMOND HALL/ALAN ELSDON BAND 1966 (Hall, Edmond & Alan Elsdon)
JCD 240 / Mar '95 / Jazzology

☐ HIS LAST CONCERT
JCD 223 / Nov '96 / Jazzology

☐ JAZZ PORTRAIT
CD 14578 / Nov '95 / Complete

☐ LIVE BROADCASTS 1954 (Hall, Edmond & Ralph Sutton Group)
Checkin' with chuck / St. Louis blues / Sweet and lovely / Blues my naughty sweetie gives to me / Up jumped you with love / Black and blue / Between the devil and the deep blue sea / Honeysuckle rose / Sheik of Araby / Oh baby / Keeping out of mischief now / Basin street blues / I found a new baby / Dardenella / Tin roof blues / Love is just around the corner / I got rhythm
STCD 6052 / Jun '98 / Storyville

Hall, G.P.

☐ FIGMENTS OF IMAGINATION
FMRCD 31 / Mar '97 / Future

Hall, Gary

☐ RETURN TO THE FLAME (Hall, Gary & The Stormkeepers)
Small price to pay / Travellin' shoes / Some cry words / Red dirt roads / Dark clouds rollin' in / Claim on me / Ten days down (two to go) / Acklen Avenue / Whole world's gone crazy / Caught in the flames / First shots / Acklen Avenue
GOLDCD 003 / Apr '98 / Goldrush

☐ TWELVE STRINGS AND TALL STORIES
RTMCD 78 / Feb '96 / Round Tower

Hall, Glen

☐ BOOK OF THE HEART, THE
378172 / Feb '97 / Koch Jazz

☐ MOTHER OF THE BOOK, THE (Hall, Glen & Gil Evans)
378162 / Aug '96 / Koch Jazz

Hall, Henry

☐ HENRY HALL & THE BBC DANCE ORCHESTRA (Hall, Henry & The BBC Dance Orchestra)
Come ye back to bonnie Scotland: *Hall, Henry & His Gleneagles Hotel Band* / Mrs. Henry Hall: *Waters, Elsie & Doris* / It's just the time for dancing / Songs that are old live forever / Love / Moon country / Curly head / Phantom of a song / Rusticanella / Little Dutch mill / Viennese memories of Lehar / By the sycamore tree / OLd violin / Red sails in the sunset / Sidewalks of Cuba / Dreaming / Someday we'll meet again / Samum / I bought myself a bottle of ink / Hits of the day / Here's to the next time
PASTCD 9725 / '90 / Flapper

☐ HENRY HALL AND HIS ORCHESTRA (Hall, Henry & His Orchestra)
Teacher's pet / Proud of you / Goona Goo / One, two button your shoe / Blue moon / It's a sin to tell a lie / Honey coloured moon / Anything goes / Seeing is believing / My dance / Clouds will soon roll by / I paid for the lie that I told you / Lullaby of the leaves / Love makes the world go round / Big ship / It's the talk of the town / Leave the pretty girls alone / Making conversation / Broken record / Saddle your blues to a wild mustang / If ever a heart was in the right place / Who's afraid of the big bad wolf / Whistling Rufus / Hush, hush, hush here comes the bogey man / Teddy Bear's picnic
CDMFP 6356 / Jun '97 / Music For Pleasure

☐ MUSIC GOES ROUND AND ROUND, THE
Here's to the next time / Thank you Mr. Bach / Teddy bears' picnic / Music hath charms / Love is in the air / You took the words right out of my heart
CDEA 6008 / 15 Jun '98 / Vocalion

☐ THIS IS HENRY HALL (24 Tracks 1932-1939) (Hall, Henry & The BBC Orchestra)
It's just the time for dancing / Sun has got his hat on / Bahama mama, that tropical charmer / Underneath the arches / Teddy bear's picnic / Just an echo in the valley / Song is you / Night and day / April in Paris / Play to me, Gypsy / Wagon wheels / Radio times / Smoke gets in your eyes / Learning / Hands across the table / Man on the flying trapeze / Easter parade / Honey coloured moon / Take me back to my boots and saddle / Music goes 'round and around / One, two, button your shoe / South of the border / It's time to say 'goodnight' / Here's to the next time
CDAJA 5222 / Jun '97 / Living Era

Hall, Herb

☐ OLD TYME MODERN (Hall, Herb Quartet)
Old-fashioned love / All of me / Buddy Bolden's blues / Crying my heart out for you / Swinging down Shaw's Hall / Beale Street blues / How come you do me like you do / Willow weep for me / Do you know what it means to miss New Orleans / Sweet Georgia Brown
SKCD 23003 / Jun '93 / Sackville

Hall, Jim

☐ ALL ACROSS THE CITY (Hall, Jim Quartet)
Beija fior / Young one (for Debra) / All across the city / Something tells me / Prelude to a kiss / How deep is the ocean / Bemsha swing / REM State / Drop shot / Big blues / Jane
CCD 4384 / Sep '89 / Concord Jazz

☐ BY ARRANGEMENT (New Arrangements And Compositions By Jim Hall)
Django / Waltz for Debby / Ruby my dear / Goodbye / Art song / October song / Wendy / Wind / Whisper not
CD 83436 / Aug '98 / Telarc Jazz

☐ CIRCLES
(All of a sudden) My heart sings / Love letters / Down from Antigua / Echo / I can't get started (with you) / TC Blues / Circles / Aruba
CCD 4161 / Nov '92 / Concord Jazz

☐ CONCIERTO
Two's blues / Answer is yes / Concierto de Aranjuez / You'd be so nice to come home to / Rock skippin'
ZK 40807 / Feb '96 / Sony Jazz

☐ CONCIERTO
You'd be so nice to come home to / Two's blues / Answer is yes / Concertio de aranjuez / Rock skippin' / Unfinished business / You'd be so nice to come home to / Answer is yes / Rock skippin'
ZK 65132 / 8 Sep '97 / Sony Jazz

☐ DEDICATIONS & INSPIRATIONS
Whistle stop / Hawk / Canto nostalgico / Why not dance / Joao / Seseragi / All the things you are / Bluesography / Miro / Money / Matisse / In a sentimental mood / Street dance
CD 83365 / May '94 / Telarc

☐ JIM HALL'S THREE (Hall, Jim Trio)
Hide and seek / Skylark / Bottlenose blues / And I do / All the things you are / Poor butterfly / Three
CCD 4298 / Mar '87 / Concord Jazz

☐ PANORAMA (Live At The Village Vanguard)
Panorama / Little blues / Answer is you / Entre nous / Furnished flats / Something to wish for / No you don't / Painted pig / Here comes Jane
CD 83408 / 12 Jan '98 / Telarc

☐ SOMETHING SPECIAL
Something special / Somewhere / Down from Antigua / Steps / Deep in a dream / Where little girls play / Three / Lucky thing / Up for air / Consequently
5184452 / May '94 / Limelight

☐ TEXTURES
Fanfare / Ragman / Reflections / Quadrologue / Passacaglia / Sazanami / Circus dance
83402 / Jun '97 / Telarc Jazz

Hall, John S.

☐ BODY HAS A HEAD
BOB 104 / Nov '96 / Bob's Airport

Hall, Juanita

☐ GLORY OF LOVE, THE
ACD 053 / Jul '96 / Audiophile

Hall, Lynden David

☐ MEDICINE 4 MY PAIN
Do I qualify / Sexy cinderella / Crescent moon / There goes my sanity / 100 heart attacks / Livin' the lie / Jimmy Lee story / Yellow in blue / I wish a new / Jennifer smiles / Medicine 4 my pain
8231602 / 15 Jun '98 / Cooltempo

Hall, Marty

☐ TRIED AND TRUE
My babe / Ecoman / Easy rhythm / Stranger in my hometown / Honest I do / Hardest time / I'll provide the thrills / Moondance in Tajikistan / No respect / Trouble in mind / Rock me / You gotta go
BLU 10302 / 29 Jun '98 / Blues Beacon

Hall, Michael

☐ ADEQUATE DESIRE
DJD 3212 / Dec '94 / Dejadisc

☐ DAY
DJD 3225 / Feb '96 / Dejadisc

Hall, Pam

☐ MAGIC
VPCD 14922 / Jul '97 / VP

☐ MISSING YOU BABY
JFRCD 002 / Jul '95 / Joe Frazier

Hall, Rob

☐ OPEN UP
UGCD 010697 / Aug '97 / Future

Hall, Sandra

☐ ONE DROP WILL DO YOU
ICH 15072 / Aug '97 / Ichiban

☐ SHOWIN' OFF
ICH 1179CD / Mar '95 / Ichiban

Hall, Terry

☐ COLLECTION, THE
Gangsters / Nite club / Ghost town / Friday night, Saturday morning / Lunatics (Have taken over the asylum) / T'ain't what you do (it's the way that you do it) / Summertime / Tunnel of love / Our lips are sealed / Colourfield / Take / Thinking of you / Castles in the air / From dawn to distraction / She / Ultra modern nursery rhymes / Missing / Beautiful people
CDCHR 1974 / Nov '92 / Chrysalis

☐ HOME
Forever J / You / Sense / I drew a lemon / Moon on your dress / No no no / What's wrong with me / Grief disguised as joy / First attack the love / I don't got you
0630121232 / Dec '96 / Anxious

☐ LAUGH
Love to see you / Room full of nothing / Sonny and his sister / Happy go lucky / Ballad of a landlord / For the girl / Take it forever / Summer follows Spring / Misty water / I saw the light
CDBUBBLE 3 / 6 Oct '97 / South Sea Bubble

Hall, Tom T.

☐ BALLADS OF FORTY DOLLARS/ HOMECOMING
That's how I got to Memphis / Cloudy day / Shame on the rain / Highways / Forbidden flowers / Ain't got the time / Ballad of forty dollars / I washed my face in the morning dew / Picture of your mother / World the way I want it / Over and over again / Beauty is a fading flower / Week in the country jail / Strawberry farms / Shoe shine man / Kentucky in the morning / Nashville is a groovy little town / Margie's at the Lincoln Park Inn / Homecoming / Carter boys / Flat-footin' it / George (and the Northwoods) / I miss a lot of trains
BCD 15631 / Jul '93 / Bear Family

☐ I WITNESS LIFE/ 100 CHILDREN
Salute to a switchblade / Thankyou Connersville, Indiana / Do it to someone you love / Ballad of Bill Crump / All you want when you please / Chattanooga dog / Girls in Saigon city / Hang them all / Coming to the party / America the ugly / That'll be alright with me / Hundred children / I can't dance / I want to see the parade / Sing a little baby to sleep / Mama bake a pie (Papa kill a chicken) / Ode to half a pound of ground round / Pinto the wonder horse is dead / I hope it rains at my funeral / I took a memory to lunch / Hitch hiker / Old enough to want you
BCD 15658 / Jul '93 / Bear Family

☐ NASHVILLE STORYTELLER, THE
Mr. Bojangles / Son of Clayton Delayney / Last country song / You show me your heart / Jesus on the radio / Soldier of fortune / People as crazy as me / Six o clock news / Year Clayton Delaney died / I liked beer / I love old dogs children and watermelon wine / Great eastwest broadway onion championships / What have I got to lose / I couldn't live in Southern California / I left some kisses on the door / Old side of town / Back when gas was thirty cents a gallon / World according to Raymond / I'll go somewhere and sing my songs again
74321511962 / 1 Sep '97 / Camden

☐ OL' T'S IN TOWN
379722 / 1 Jun '98 / Koch

☐ PLACES I'VE DONE TIME
What have you got to lose / I couldn't live in Southern California / Grocery truck / Man who shot himself / Son of Clayton Delaney / Mr. Bojangles / Three sofa story / Great East Broadway onion championship of 1978 / Hat full of feathers / Gimme peace
379732 / 3 Aug '98 / Koch

☐ SOLDIER OF FORTUNE
CD 379822 / Nov '97 / Koch Country

Hall, Tony

☐ MR. UNIVERSE
American tunes / Mr. Universe / Scotland / Slow air / Slow hornpipe / Blacksmith / Stitches in the britches / Local hero / Lovely Joan / Humphrey Lyttleton / Round the horn / Jack tar / Elizabethan medley
OSMOCD 003 / Nov '95 / Osmosys

Hallberg, Bengt

☐ HALLBERG TOUCH, THE
You do something to me / Little white lies / When lights are low / Oh lady be good / Coquette / Fascinating rhythm / Sometimes I'm happy / Sonny boy / In a little Spanish town / You and the night and the music / Charleston / You brought a new kind of love to me
PHONTCD 7525 / '93 / Phontastic

☐ HALLBERG TREASURE CHEST, THE
PHONTNCD 8828 / '93 / Phontastic

☐ HALLBERG'S HAPPINESS
PHONTCD 7544 / May '95 / Phontastic

☐ HALLBERG'S HOT ACCORDION (In The Foreground)
Tiger rag / Bye bye blues / Farewell blues / St. Louis blues / Limehouse blues / Tva solroda segel / How high the moon / Sweet Sue, just you / Blue moon / Some of these days
PHONTCD 7532 / '93 / Phontastic

☐ HALLBERG'S SURPRISE
PHONTCD 7581 / Apr '88 / Phontastic

☐ HALLBERG'S YELLOW BLUES
PHONTCD 7583 / '88 / Phontastic

☐ IN A MELLOW TONE (Hallberg, Bengt & Hans Backenroth)
IKCD 5 / Feb '98 / Improkamp Musik

☐ POWERHOUSE-KRAFTVERK (Hallberg, Bengt & Arne Dommerus)
PHONTCD 7553 / '93 / Phontastic

☐ TREASURE CHEST
NCD 8828 / Apr '94 / Phontastic

☐ TWO OF A KIND (Hallberg, Bengt & Karin Krog)
My man (mon homme) / Jeepers creepers / You must believe in spring / Touch of your lips / End of the day song / I ain't here / Like that / Hallelujah, I love him so / Spring in Manhattan / Love walk right in / Dear Bix / I'm coming Virginia / Ain't nobody's business if I do
CDMR 1 / Jun '96 / Meantime

Halle Brass

☐ HALLE BRASS PLAY GREAGSON
Fanfare for europe / Equale dances / Susie's fanfare / Sonata for four trombones / Fanfare for gateshead / Brass quintet / Fanfare for a wedding 1 / Fanfare for a wedding 2 / Three dance episodes / Processional / Festival fanfare
DOYCD 038 / Feb '96 / Doyen

Hallelujahs

☐ NIKU O KURAITE CHIKAI O TATEYO
PSFD 87 / Dec '97 / PSF

Halley, David

☐ BROKEN SPELL
DOSCD 7003 / Nov '93 / Dos

Halliday, Lin

☐ DELAYED EXPOSURE
Woody 'n you / How deep is the ocean / Darn that dream / Dog ear blues / My romance / Man I love / Alone together / Serpent's tooth
DD 449 / Mar '97 / Delmark

☐ EAST OF THE SUN
All the things you are / East of the sun / I found a new baby / Indian summer / My foolish heart / Corcovado / Paradox / Ira's blues / Will you still be mine
DE 458 / Mar '97 / Delmark

☐ LIN HALLIDAY WITH IRA SULLIVAN (Halliday, Lin & Ira Sullivan)
Street of dreams / My shining hour / Sophisticated lady / Dear old Stockholm / Where or when / Over the rainbow / More I see of you / Pent-up house
DE 468 / Mar '97 / Delmark

Hallom, Gerry

☐ UNDISCOVERED AUSTRALIA VOL.2
MP 10003CD / Mar '98 / Musica Panagaea

Hallow's Eve

☐ DEATH AND INSANITY
398414059CD / Nov '96 / Metal Blade

☐ MONUMENT
Plugging to megadeth / Outer limits / Horror show / Mansion / There are no rules / Valley of the dolls / Metal merchants / Hallow's eve-routine
398414056CD / Nov '96 / Metal Blade

☐ TALES OF TERROR
Speed freak / Sheer heart attack / Rot gut / Monument (to nothing) / Painkiller / Mighty decibel / Righteous ones / No sanctuary
398414060CD / Nov '96 / Metal Blade

Hallucination Generation

☐ BLACK HOLE & BABY UNIVERSES
THPCD 98 / Feb '94 / Thunderpussy

Hallucinogen

☐ LONE DERANGER
TWSCD 1 / 1 Sep '97 / Twisted

☐ TWISTED
BFLCD 15 / 1 Sep '98 / Butterfly

Hallyday, Johnny

☐ NASHVILLE SESSIONS VOL.2
Hey baby / Tout bas, tout bas, tout bas / Shout / Quitte moi doucement / Oui, je veux / Ce n'est pas just apres tout / Les bras en croix / C'est une fille comme toil / Qui autrait dit ca / Pas cette chanson
BCD 15497 / Oct '90 / Bear Family

☐ TRIFT DIE RATTLES
Mein leben fangt erst richtig an / Lass die leute doch reden (Keep searching) / Wilde boys / House of the rising sun / Ma guitare / Ja der elefant (wap dou wap) / It's monkey time / Vieleicht bist du fur mich noch night die / J'ai un probleme
BCD 15492 / Feb '90 / Bear Family

Halo Benders

☐ DON'T TELL ME NOW
KLP 46CD / Jan '96 / K

☐ REBEL'S NOT IN, THE
KCD 81V / 26 Jan '98 / K

Halpin, Kieran

☐ MISSION STREET
Refugee from heaven / Foreigners / Mission street / Berlin calling / China rose / Heart and soul / Nothing to show for it all / Celtic myth / Salt into the wound / Farewell to pride / Chase the dragon / Rolling the dice / Child bearing child
RTMCD 31 / Jul '91 / Round Tower

Ham

☐ BUFFALO VIRGIN
TP016CD / Sep '89 / One Little Indian

Ham, Pete

☐ 7 PARK AVENUE
Catherine cares / Coppertone blues / It really doesn't matter / Live love all of your days / Would you deny / Dear father / Matted spam / No matter what / Leaving on a midnight train / Weep baby / Hand in hand / Sille veb / I know that you should / Island / Just look inside the cover / Just how lucky we are / No more / Ringside
RCD 10349 / Apr '97 / Rykodisc

Hamburg Rock Band

☐ BEST EVER ROCK COVERS, THE
Cover me / Brown sugar / You ain't seen nothing yet / Summer of '69 / Final countdown / Livin' on a prayer / Say you will / Sledgehammer / Love is a battlefield / Centrefold / Bed of roses / We will rock you / Radar love / Layla / Dirty white boy / Legs / War / 2-4-6-8 motorway
QED 224 / Nov '96 / Tring

Hamburger, Neil

☐ AMERICA'S FUNNYMAN
DC 97CD / Dec '96 / Drag City

Hamill, Claire

☐ LOVE IN THE AFTERNOON
NAGE 18CD / May '88 / Art Of Landscape

☐ OCTOBER
Island / To the stars / Please stay tonight / Wall to wall carpeting / Speedbreaker / I don't get any older / Warrior of the water / Artist / Sidney gorgeous / Crying under the bedclothes / Peaceful
BP 238CD / Mar '97 / Blueprint

☐ ONE HOUSE LEFT STANDING
When I was a child / Man who cannot see tomorrow's sunshine / Consummation / River / Where are your smiles at / Baseball blues / Urge for going / Flowers for grandma / Phoenix / Smile your blues away
BP 239CD / Jul '97 / Blueprint

☐ VOICES
NAGE 8CD / Apr '86 / Art Of Landscape

Hamilton, Andy

☐ SILVERSHINE (Hamilton, Andy & The Blue Notes)
I can't get started (with you) / Body and soul / Old folks / You are too beautiful / Andy's blues / Uncle Joe / Silvershine
WCD 025 / Oct '91 / World Circuit

Hamilton, Chico

☐ EUPHORIA
CHECD 7 / Sep '89 / Master Mix

☐ MASTER, THE
One day five months ago / Feels good / Fancy / Stu / Gengis / Conquistadores '74 / Stacy / I can hear the grass grow
CDSXE 071 / Nov '92 / Stax

☐ MY PANAMANIAN FRIEND (Hamilton, Chico & Euphoria)
1212652 / May '94 / Soul Note

☐ TRIO
1212462 / Apr '93 / Soul Note

Hamilton, Claire

☐ CELTIC HARP MOODS
Londonderry air / Riverdance / Have I told you lately / Lo, how a rose e'er blooming / Down in the Sally Gardens / Robin the hooded man / Wild mountain thyme / Flower of Scotland / Star of County Down / On your shore / An ubhal as airde / Celtic carol / Harry's Game / Patapan / Skye boat song / Carrickfergus / Shepherd moons / Noul Nouvelet / Loch Lomond / Women of Ireland / Only a woman's heart / Danny boy
3036000822 / Mar '97 / Carlton

☐ CELTIC HARP, THE
Riverdance / My lagan love / Arran boat song / Robin and the hooded man / Oxen and sheep / Wild swan / Fantaisie sur an hini a garan / She moved through the fair / Theme from 'Harry's game' / Serendipity / Lovely joan / Lord Galway's lament / Chanter / On your shore / Noel breton / Searching for lambs / Cro chinn t'saile / Aquatintes I / Lavaromp ar chapeled / Down in the sally gardens / An ubhal as airde / Women of Ireland (Theme from 'Barry Lyndon')
SUMCD 4133 / Sep '97 / Summit

☐ LOVE IS ALL AROUND (The Celtic Harp Of Claire Hamilton)
Love is all around / Lady in red / Tears in Heaven / (Everything I do) I do it for you / In the air tonight / On your shore / Killing me softly / Harry's game / Wonderful tonight / I will always love you / Take my breath away / Against all odds / LOve changes everything / Falling / Shepherd moon / Robin the hooded man / Think twice
12862 / Dec '96 / Laserlight

Hamilton, Colbert

☐ COLBERT HAMILTON & THE HELL RAZORS (Hamilton, Colbert & the Hell Razors)
Wow / Mystery train / Half hearted love / Woman love / Rock therapy / Long blonde hair / Ice cold / Long black shiny car / Nervous breakdown / Love me (the way that I love you) / I'm so high / Good rockin' tonight / I'll never let you go / Don't knock upon my door / Love me
NERCD 071 / Mar '93 / Nervous

☐ STILL TAGGIN' ALONG (Hamilton, Colbert & The Nitros)
Get out of my sight / Cruel hearted girl / Rollercoaster rock / Gaze into the crystal / Wasn't that good / Cadillac baby / Dead of night / Black magic / Get you back / New place in town / Stop / Haunted memories
JRCD 5 / Sep '97 / Jappin' & Rockin'

☐ WILD AT HEART (Hamilton, Colbert & The Nitros)
Lucille / Wild at heart / Still rockin' after all these beers / Bad reputation / Too late / Boom boom / Do you wanna rock / Abused by you / High-flyin' cat / Boogaville / Pass the bottle to the baby / Boys are back in town / Big in the world / Ninety nine girls
NERCD 076 / Mar '94 / Nervous

Hamilton, Dirk

☐ GO DOWN SWINGIN
APCD 071 / '92 / Appaloosa

☐ TOO TIRED TO SLEEP
APCD 061 / '92 / Appaloosa

☐ YEP
APCD 107 / Jun '94 / Appaloosa

Hamilton, Ed

☐ GROOVEOLOGY
Fly like an eagle / If only / On my way / Ooh child / JJ's child / April goodbyes / Souls felt / Jinda boogie / Didn't I blow your mind this time / Song for a princess
SHANCD 5047 / Jun '98 / Shanachie

☐ PLANET JAZZ
Planet jazz / 4am blues / Better days ahead / Gray day / What time is it now / South of Monterey / Life on the edge / Curtis blues / Life dreams / Race against the wind / Lullabye / Say what
CD 83387 / Apr '96 / Telarc

Hamilton, George IV

☐ AMERICAN COUNTRY GOTHIC
If I never see midnight again / My hometown / This is our love / Little country county fairs / Farmer's dream ploughed under / Never mind / I will be your friend / More about love / Heaven knows / Back up grinnin' again / Carolina sky / I believe in you
CDRR 304 / Jan '90 / Request

☐ COUNTRY BOY (The Best Of George Hamilton IV)
Abilene / Break my mind / Early morning rain / Steel rail blues / Urge for going / Canadian pacific / Second cup of coffee / Anyway / I'm, gonna be a country boy again / Both sides now / My novia scotia home / Travelin' light / 10 degrees and getting colder / Streets of london / Everything is beautiful / Carolina on my mind / She's a little bit country / West texas highway / Together alone / Rose and a baby ruth / Crystal chandeliers / Country music in my soul
74321393402 / Sep '96 / Camden

☐ GEORGE HAMILTON IV 1954-1965 (6CD Set)
Beer, wine and whiskey / Sleeping at the foot of the bed / Caribbean / Satisfaction guaranteed / Satisfied mind / Out behind the barn / Serenader's swing / It's my way / I'll always remember you / Jalopy Jane / Driftin' / Daniel Boone / Driftin' / I've got a secret / Verdict / Sam / Jamaica farewell / He's movin' on / Rose and a baby Ruth / I've got a secret / It was me / If you don't know, I ain't gonna tell you / Everybody's body / I've got a secret / Sam / Rose and a baby Ruth / If you don't, I ain't gonna tell you / If I possessed a printing press / Only one love / Everybody's body / High school romance / Everybody's body / Why don't they understand / Little Tom / Even tho' / You tell me your dream / Carolina moon / Let me call you sweetheart / When I grow too old to dream / Tell me why / Aura Lee / Girl of my dreams / Drink to me only with thine eyes / Love's old sweet song / Auld lang syne / Ivy Rose / Clementine / One heart / May I / Now and for always / House of gold / I can't help it / How can you refuse him now / Your cheatin' heart / Half as much / I could never be ashamed of you / I'm so lonesome I could cry / Cold, cold heart / (I heard that) Lonesome whistle / Wedding bells / Who's taking you to the prom / I know where I'm goin' / You win again / Take these chains from my heart / So soon / When will I know / Lucy, Lucy / House a car and a wedding ring / Two of us / Steady game / Last night we fell in love / Can you blame us / Love has come to our house / Gee / One little acre / I know your sweetheart / Tremble / Why I'm walkin' / Loneliness is all around me / Before this day ends / Wrong side of the tracks / It's just the idea / Walk on the wild side of life / That's how it goes / Can't let her see me cry / To you and yours / Three steps to the phone (millions of miles) / Ballad of Widder Jones / I want a girl / Those brown eyes / Where did the sunshine go / Baby blue eyes / Life's railway to heaven / East Virginia / Wall / If you don't, somebody else will / Rainbow / I will miss you when you go / Life is too short / China doll / Tender hearted baby / Commerce street and sixth avenue north / If you don't know I ain't gonna tell you

/ (I want to go) Where nobody knows me / Roving gambler / Oh so many years / Jimmy Brown the newsboy / Little lunch box / Come on home boy / Everglades / You are my sunshine / Last letter / If you want me to / Linda with the lonely eyes / In this very same room / Abilene / Mine / Oh so many years / Remember M, remember E, remember me / There's more pretty girls than one / You're easy to love / Fort Worth, Dallas or Houston / Fair and tender ladies / Kentucky / Candy apple red / Tag along / Little grave / Texarkana, Pecos or Houston / Truck driving man / Rose and a baby Ruth / Roll muddy river / That's alright Mama / Driftwood on the river / Let's say goodbye like we said hello / Rainbow at midnight / It's been so long darlin' / Letters have no arms / Walking the floor over you / I will miss you when you go / Half a mind / You nearly lose your mind / Fortunes in memories / Soldier's last letter / Thanks a lot / Nice place to visit / Twist of the wrist / Nice place to visit / (You don't love me) Anymore / Late Mister Jones / Write me a picture / Something special to me / I've got a secret / Slightly used / Under your spell again / Above and beyond / Excuse me (I think I've got a heartache) / Wishful thinking / I don't believe I'll fall in love today / Foolin' around / Another day, another dollar / Keep those cards and letters coming in / Under the influence of love / Big, big love / You better not do that / Long black limousine / Together again / Abilene / Three steps to the phone (millions of miles) / Rose and a baby Ruth / Fort Worth, Dallas or Houston / Before this day ends / Truck driving man / Walking the floor over you / Write me a picture / If you don't know, I ain't gonna tell
BCD 15773 / Nov '95 / Bear Family

☐ **HIDING IN THEE**
TIMED 028 / Apr '98 / Timeless Classics

Hamilton, George V

☐ **GHOST TOWN (Hamilton, George V & Nashvegas Noma)**
DFGCD 8450 / Oct '96 / Dixie Frog

Hamilton, Jeff

☐ **DYNAVIBES (Hamilton, Jeff Trio & Frits Landesbergen)**
Killer Joe / Just like SD / Cherokee / Long ago and far away / Sweet Lorraine / Close enough for love / Happy kick / Midnight sun / Tudo / Blues for Milt
MR 874794 / Jun '97 / Mons

☐ **HANDS ON (Hamilton, Jeff Trio)**
Juicy Lucy / Whisper not / Somewhere / Move / 3000 miles ago / Daahoud / To you / Spit season blues
MR 874812 / 8 Apr '98 / Mons

☐ **JEFF HAMILTON TRIO, THE (Hamilton, Jeff Trio)**
But not for me / Apple honey / Time passes on / Beshma swing / 52nd Street swing / Well you needn't / Night in Tunisia / Yesterdays / SKJ
MR 874777 / Jun '97 / Mons

Hamilton, Johnny

☐ **SWING LOW SWEET CHARIOT**
FSRCD 211 / Oct '96 / Fresh Sound

Hamilton, Scott

☐ **AFTER HOURS**
Beyond the bluebird / Woody 'n' you / Blues in my heart / Bye bye blues / What's new / You're not kind / Black velvet (Don cha go way mad) / How am I to know / Some other spring / Steeplechase
CCD 47552 / May '97 / Concord Jazz

☐ **CHRISTMAS LOVE SONG**
Christmas song / I'll be home for Christmas / Have yourself a merry little Christmas / Little drummer boy / Christmas waltz / Winter wonderland / Greensleeves (what child is this) / Santa Claus is coming to town / White Christmas / Bell carol blues / Christmas love song
CCD 47712 / 17 Nov '97 / Concord Jazz

☐ **CLOSE UP**
All of you / I remember you / Mad about you / Robbin's nest / Was I to blame for falling in love with you / Blue City / Mr. Big and Mr. Modern / Portrait of Jennie / Soft
CCD 4197 / Jun '91 / Concord Jazz

☐ **EAST OF THE SUN**
Autumn leaves / Stardust / It could happen to you / Bernie's tune / East of the sun and west of the moon / Time after time / Setagaya serenade / That's all / All the things you are / (Back home again in) Indiana
CCD 4583 / Dec '93 / Concord Jazz

☐ **GROOVIN' HIGH (Hamilton, Scott/ Ken Peplowski/ Spike Robinson)**
Blues up and down / You brought a new kind of love to me / That ole devil called love / Shine / Goof and I / What's new / I'll see you in my dreams / Groovin' high / Body and soul / Jeep is jumpin'
CCD 4509 / Jun '92 / Concord Jazz

☐ **IS A GOOD WIND WHO IS BLOWING US NO ILL**
CDD 4042 / Jul '92 / Concord Jazz

☐ **LIVE AT BRECON JAZZ FESTIVAL**
Way down yonder in New Orleans / I can't give you anything but love / My old flame / Ow / But beautiful / Fascinatin' rhythm / Nightingale sang in Berkley Square / Come rain or come shine / Blue wales
CCD 4649 / Jun '95 / Concord Jazz

☐ **MAJOR LEAGUE (Hamilton, Scott, Jake Hanna, Dave McKenna)**
Swinging at the Copper Rail / Pretty girl is like a melody / Cocktails for two / I'm through with love / Linger awhile / September in the rain / This is all I ask / It all depends on you / April in Paris
CCD 4305 / '86 / Concord Jazz

☐ **MY ROMANCE**
Abundance / Blue caper / Swingin' till the girls come home / My romance / Lullaby in rhythm / Will you still be mine / Poor butterfly / Sugarchile / Jan / Just a gigolo
CCD 4710 / Jul '96 / Concord Jazz

☐ **ORGANIC DUKE**
Jump for joy / Blue hodge / Moon mist / Paris blues / Castle rock / Just a sittin' and a rockin' / Rockin' in rhythm / Isfahan / Love you madly / Old circus train turn around blues
CCD 4623 / Nov '94 / Concord Jazz

☐ **RACE POINT**
Groove yard / Chelsea Bridge / Race point / Close enough for love / Oh, look at me now / Alone together / I've just seen her / Limehouse blues / You're my thrill / You say you care / Song is you
CCD 4492 / Jan '92 / Concord Jazz

☐ **RADIO CITY**
Apple honey / Yesterdays / I'll be around / Touch of your lips / Cherokee / Tonight I shall sleep with a smile on my face / Radio city / My ideal / Wig's blues / Remember
CCD 4428 / Aug '90 / Concord Jazz

☐ **RIGHT TIME, THE (Hamilton, Scott Quintet)**
Just in time / If I love again / Sleep / Eventide / All through the night / Skylark / Stealing port / Dropsy
CCD 4311 / Jul '87 / Concord Jazz

☐ **SCOTT HAMILTON & WARREN VACHE (With Scott's Band In New York City) (Hamilton, Scott & Warren Vache)**
CCD 4070 / Jul '96 / Concord Jazz

☐ **SCOTT HAMILTON PLAYS BALLADS**
I'll only miss her when I think of her / Dream dancing / 'round midnight / Two eighteen / Emily / In a sentimental mood / Beautiful friendship / Laura / Body and soul / Embraceable you
CCD 4386 / Sep '89 / Concord Jazz

☐ **SCOTT HAMILTON QUINTET IN CONCERT, THE (Hamilton, Scott Quintet)**
I can't believe that you're in love with me / Wrap your troubles in dreams (and dream your troubles away) / I've found a new baby / When I fall in love / Whispering / Sultry serenade / Stardust / One o'clock jump
CCD 4233 / Feb '91 / Concord Jazz

☐ **SCOTT HAMILTON VOL.2**
East of the sun and west of the moon / There is no greater love / Rough ridin' / These foolish things / I want to be happy / Everything happens to me / Love me or leave me / Blues for the players / Very thought of you / It could happen to you
CCD 4061 / Jun '94 / Concord Jazz

☐ **SECOND SET (Hamilton, Scott Quintet)**
All the things you are / Time after time / Taps Miller / All too soon / How insensitive / I never knew / For all we know / Jumpin' the blues
CCD 4254 / May '85 / Concord Jazz

☐ **TENOR SHOES**
I should care / Falling in love with love / Shadow of your smile / Nearness of you / How high the moon / Our delight / My foolish heart / OK
CCD 4127 / Apr '90 / Concord Jazz

Hamm, Stuart

☐ **KINGS OF SLEEP**
Black ice / Surely the best / Call of the wild / Terminal beach / Count zero / I want to know / Prelude in C / Kings of sleep
CDGRUB 13 / Oct '89 / Food For Thought

Hammer, Artie

☐ **ARIZONA BLUE**
GMCD 65 / Apr '98 / Gemini

☐ **JOY SPRING**
GECD 149 / Jan '89 / Gemini

Hammer, Jan

☐ **ESCAPE FROM TELEVISION**
Crockett's theme / Theresa / Colombia / Rum cay / Trial and the search / Tubbs and Valerie / Forever tonight / Last flight / Rico's blues / Before the storm / Night talk / Miami vice
MCLD 19133 / Oct '92 / MCA

Hammerhead

☐ **DUH, THE BIG CITY**
ARRCD 69012 / Mar '96 / Amphetamine Reptile

☐ **ETHEREAL KILLER**
ARRCD 36/266 / Feb '93 / Amphetamine Reptile

☐ **EVIL TWIN**
ARRCD 47 306 / Nov '93 / Amphetamine Reptile

☐ **INTO THE VORTEX**
ARR 50/323CD / Mar '94 / Amphetamine Reptile

Hammerlock

☐ **AMERICAN ASSHOLE**
MR 029 / 23 Mar '98 / Man's Ruin

Hammill, Peter

☐ **AFTER THE SHOW**
Ophelia / Shell / After the show / Stranger still / You hit me where I live / Sitting targets / Spirit / Porton down / Ain't nobody's business if I do / Sunshine / Lost and found / Sign / Just good friends / If I could
CDOVD 460 / Jan '96 / Virgin

☐ **AND CLOSE AS THIS**
Too many of my yesterdays / Faith / Empire of delight / Silver / Beside the one you love / Other old cliches / Confidente / Sleep now
CDV 2409 / Nov '88 / Virgin

☐ **BLACK BOX**
Golden promises / Losing faith in words / Jargon king / Fogwalking / Spirit / In slow time / Wipe / Flight
CDOVD 140 / Nov '88 / Virgin

☐ **CALM (AFTER THE STORM), THE**
Shell / Not for Keith / Birds / Rain 3 AM / Just good friends / (On Tuesdays she used to do) yoga / Shingle song / Faith / Dropping the torch / After the show / Stranger still / If I could / Wilhelmina / Again / Been alone so long / Ophelia / Autumn / Sleep now
CDVM 9017 / Jul '93 / Virgin

☐ **CHAMELEON IN THE SHADOW OF NIGHT**
German overalls / Slender threads / Rock and role / In the end / What's it worth / Easy to slip away / Dropping the torch / (In the) black room / Tower
CASCD 1067 / '89 / Charisma

☐ **ENTER K**
Paradox Drive / Unconscious life / Accidents / Great experiments / Don't tell me / She wraps it up / Happy hour / Seven wonders
FIE 9101 / Apr '92 / Fie

☐ **EVERYONE YOU HOLD**
Everyone you hold / Personality / Nothing comes / From the safe house / Phosphorescence / Falling open / Bubble / Can do / Tenderness
FIE 9117 / 13 Oct '97 / Fie

☐ **FIRESHIPS**
I will find you / Curtains / His best girl / Oasis / Incomplete surrender / Fireship / Given time / Reprise / Gaia
FIE 9103 / Mar '92 / Fie

☐ **FOOLS MATE**
Imperial zeppelin / Candle / Happy / Solitude / Vision / Reawakening / Sunshine / Child / Summer song (in the Autumn) / Viking / Birds / I once wrote some poems
CASCD 1037 / Oct '88 / Charisma

☐ **FUTURE NOW, THE**
Pushing thirty / Second hand / Trappings / Mousetrap (caught in) / Energy vampires / If I could / Future now / Still in the dark / Mediaevil / Motor-bike in Afrika / Cut / Palinurus (castaway)
CASCD 1137 / Nov '88 / Charisma

☐ **IN A FOREIGN TOWN**
Hemlock / Invisible ink / Sci finance (revisited) / This book / Time to burn / Auto / Vote brand X / Play's the thing / Under cover names / Smile / Time to burn (instrumental)
FIE 9108 / Mar '93 / Fire

☐ **IN CAMERA**
Ferret and featherbed / (No more) the sub-mariner / Tapeworm / Again / Faint heart and the sermon / Comet, the course, the tail / Gog magog (in bromine chambers)
CASCD 1089 / Nov '88 / Charisma

☐ **LOOPS & REELS**
Ritual speak / Critical mass / Moebius loop / Endless breath / In slow time / My pulse / Bells, The Bells
FIE 9105 / Nov '93 / Fie

☐ **LOVE SONGS**
Just good friends / My favourite / Been alone so long / Ophelia / Again / If I could / Vision / Don't tell me / Birds / (This side of) the looking glass
CASCD 1166 / Nov '88 / Charisma

☐ **NADIR'S BIG CHANCE**
Nadir's big chance / Institute of mental health / Open your eyes / Ain't nobody's business if I do / Been alone so long / Pompeii / Shingle / Airport / People you were going to / Birthday special / Two or three spectres / Burning
CASCD 1099 / Nov '88 / Charisma

☐ **NOISE, THE**
Kick to kill the kiss / Like a shot, The entertainer / Noise / Celebrity kissing / Where the mouth is / Great european department store / Planet coventry / Primo on the parapet
FIE 9104 / Mar '93 / Fie

☐ **OFFENSICHTLICH GOLDFISCH**
Offensichtlich goldfisch / Dich zu finden / Die Kalte killt den kuss / Favorit / Kaufhaus Europa / Der larm / Oase / Die prominenz kusst sich / Die tinte verlischt / Auto / Gaia / Schlaft nun
GH 70112 / Jan '95 / Golden Hind

☐ **OUT OF WATER**
Evidently goldfish / Not the man / No moon in the water / Our oyster / Something about Ysabel's dance / Green fingers / On the surface / Way out
FIE 9109 / Mar '93 / Fire

☐ **OVER**
Crying wolf / Autumn / Time heals / Alice (letting go) / This side of the looking glass / Betrayed / (On Tuesdays she used to do) Yoga / Lost and found
CASCD 1125 / Jun '91 / Charisma

☐ **PAST GO - COLLECTED**
Kick to kill the kiss / I will find you / Accidents / His best girl / Sharply unclear / Patient / Planet Coventry / Ritual mask / Noise / Gift of fire / Train time / Gaia / Your tall ship
FIE 9112 / Sep '96 / Fie

☐ **PATIENCE**
Labour of love / Film noir / Just good friends / Juenesse Doree / Traintime / Now more than ever / Comfortable / Patient
FIE 9102 / Apr '92 / Fie

☐ **PH7**
My favourite / Careering / Porton down / Mirror images / Handicap / Equality / Not for Keith / Old school tie / Time for a change / Imperial walls / Mr. X gets tense / Faculty X
CASCD 1146 / Apr '89 / Charisma

☐ **ROARING FORTIES**
Sharply unclear / Gift of fire / You can't want what you always get / Headlong stretch / Your tall ship
FIE 9107 / Sep '94 / Fie

☐ **ROOM TEMPERATURE LIVE**
Wave / Just good friends / Vision / Time to burn / Four pails / Comet, the course, the tail / Ophelia / Happy hour / If I could / Something about Ysabel's dance / Patient / Cat's eye, yellow fever (running) / Running / Skin / Hemlock / Our oyster / Unconscious life / After the snow / Way out / Future now / Traintime / Modern
FIE 9110 / Jun '95 / Fie

☐ **SILENT CORNER AND THE EMPTY STAGE, THE**
Modern / Wilhelmina / Lie (Bernini's Saint Theresa) / Forsaken gardens / Red shift / Rubicon / Louse is not a home
CASCD 1083 / Nov '88 / Charisma

☐ **SITTING TARGETS**
Breakthrough / My experience / Ophelia / Empress's clothes / Glue / Hesitation / Sitting targets / Stranger still / Sign / What I did for love / Central hotel
CDV 2203 / Oct '88 / Virgin

☐ **SKIN**
Skin / After the show / Painting by numbers / Shill / All said and done / Perfect date / Four pails / Now lover
CDOVD 344 / '89 / Virgin

☐ **SONIX**
Emmene-moi bare theme / Walk in the dark / In the Polish house / Dark matter / Hospital silence / Four to the floor / Exercise for Louis / Labyrinthe dreams / Emmene-moi full theme
FIE 9114 / Nov '96 / Fie

☐ **SPUR OF THE MOMENT (Hammill, Peter & Guy Evans)**
Sweating it out / Surprise / Little did he know / Without a glitch / Anatol's proposal / Multiman / Deprogramming Archie / Always so polite / Imagined brother / Bounced / Roger and out
CDR 102 / Mar '94 / Red Hot

☐ **STORM (BEFORE THE CALM), THE**
Nadir's big chance / Golden promises / Perfect date / Spirit / Sitting targets / Tapeworm / Ain't nobody's business if I do / Crying wolf / You hit me where I live / My experience / Breakthrough / Skin / Energy vampires / Porton down / Birthday special / Lost and found / Central hotel
CDVM 9018 / Jul '93 / Virgin

☐ **THERE GOES THE DAYLIGHT**
Sci finance (revisited) / Habit of a broken heart / Sign / I will find you / Lost and found / Planet Coventry / Empress's clothes / Cat's eye, yellow fever (running) / Primo on the parapet / Central hotel
FIE 9106 / Nov '93 / Fie

☐ **TIDES**
SIN 006 / Sep '96 / Sine

☐ **X MY HEART**
Better time / Amnesiac / Ram origami / Forest of pronouns / Earthbound / Narcissus (Bar and Grill) / Material possession / Come clean
FIE 9111 / Mar '96 / Fie

Hammond, Albert

☐ **GREATEST HITS**
Free electric band / Peacemaker / Down by the river / When I need you / Rebecca / 99 Miles from LA / It never rains in southern California / Everything I want to do / We're running out / If you gotta break another heart / Moonlight lady / These are the good old days / I'm a train / New York city here I come / Half a million miles from home / Air that I breathe
4631852 / Oct '95 / Columbia

Hammond, Beres

☐ **BERES HAMMOND**
Teeny weeny little lovin / These arms of mine / Lovely day / If only I knew / What one dance can do / She loves me now / Starting over / Someone phoned / Till you've got love / Groovy little thing
CRCD 1 / Jul '97 / Charm

☐ **BERES HAMMOND**
PHCD 2070 / 6 Apr '98 / Penthouse

☐ **EXPRESSION**
CBHB 166 / Jun '95 / Heartbeat

☐ **FROM MY HEART WITH LOVE**
RGCD 026 / Mar '94 / Rocky One

☐ **FULL ATTENTION**
CRCD 17 / 18 Aug '97 / Charm

☐ **IRIE AND MELLOW**
She loves me now / Lovely day / Starting over / Teeny weeny little lovin / Missing you for a mile / These arms of mine / If only I knew / Irie and mello / Stop your hiding / Groovy little thing / Leave it up to love / Till you've got love / Have a nice weekend / What one dance can do
RNCD 2025 / Aug '93 / Rhino

☐ LIFETIME GUARANTEE
Try if you want / Where were you / Come again / Touch and go situation / It takes you / Take a tip / Fight to defend / Left me crying / Walk away from love / Love gets stronger / Way it is / Single girl / False preacher / Come back home
GRELCD 232 / Apr '97 / Greensleeves

☐ LOVE AFFAIR, A
PHCD 14 / Jun '97 / Penthouse

☐ LOVE FROM A DISTANCE
VPCD 1480 / Mar '97 / VP

☐ MEET IN JAMAICA (Hammond, Beres & Mikey Zappow)
RNCD 2115 / Jul '95 / Rhino

☐ PUTTING UP RESISTANCE
RASCD 3230 / Aug '96 / Ras

☐ REGGAE MAX
JSRNCD 8 / Mar '97 / Jet Star

Hammond, David

☐ I AM THE WEE FALORIE MAN (Folk Songs Of Ireland)
TCD 1052 / Jul '97 / Tradition

Hammond, Doug

☐ SPACES
DIW 359 / Jul '92 / DIW

Hammond, Fred

☐ PAGES OF LIFE (Hammond, Fred & Radical For Christ)
01241431102 / May '98 / Verity

Hammond, John

☐ BIG CITY BLUES
VMD 79153 / Apr '97 / Vanguard

☐ FOUND TRUE LOVE
Found love / I hate to see you go / Fore day rider blues / Warm it up to me / Howlin' for my Darling / Hello stranger / You had too much / My mind is ramblin' / First time I met the blues / I've got to find my baby / Evolution blues / Someday baby blues
VPBCD 26 / Mar '96 / Pointblank

☐ FROGS FOR SNAKES
You don't love me / Got to find my baby / Step it up and go / Fattenin' frogs for snakes / Gypsy woman / Key to the highway / My baby left me / Louisiana blues / Mellow down easy / Your funeral and my trial / Mellow peaches / Gone so long
ROUCD 3060 / Aug '94 / Rounder

☐ GOT LOVE IF YOU WANT IT
Got love if you want it / Driftin' blues / Dreamy eyed girl / Mattie Mae / You don't love me / Nadine / No one can forgive me but my baby / You're so fine / No place to go / Preachin' blues
VPBCD 7 / Mar '92 / Pointblank

☐ HOT TRACKS
VCD 79424 / Oct '96 / Vanguard

☐ JOHN HAMMOND LIVE
I wish you would / I wish you would / Cat man blues / Custard pie / Love at first sight / I can't be satisfied / Dust my broom / Low down dog / Little school girl / Shake for me / Drop down mama / Texas tornado / Steady rollin' man / Ain't that lovin' you baby / Sail on / Wang dang doodle / Honeymoon blues / I'm movin' on
ROUCD 3074 / Feb '92 / Rounder

☐ LONG AS I HAVE YOU
Crying at daylight / Goin' away baby / So many roads so many trains / Sad to be alone / I got lucky / Lookin' for trouble / I feel so sorry / Homeless blues / Stranded / I'm gonna find my baby / Untrue blues / Don't start me talkin' / Everything's gonna be alright / Tell me mama / As long as I have you
VPBCD 44 / 15 Jun '98 / Pointblank

☐ MILEAGE
My babe / Standing around crying / Riding in the moonlight / Big 45 / Seventh son / Red hot kisses / Help me / It hurts me too / 32-20 blues / You'll miss me / Hot tamales / Diddley daddy
ROUCD 3042 / Aug '95 / Rounder

☐ NOBODY BUT YOU
Ride till I die / Sail on / Diddley daddy / Memphis town / Lost lover blues / Nobody but you / Papa wants a cookie / If I get lucky / Cuttin' out / Killing me on my feet / Mother in law blues
FF 502CD / May '93 / Flying Fish

☐ SO MANY ROADS
Down in the bottom / Long distance call / Who do you love / I want you to love me / Judgement day / So many roads, so many trains / Rambling blues / Oh yeah / You can't judge a book by the cover / Gambling blues / Baby please don't go / Big boss man
VMD 79178 / Oct '95 / Vanguard

☐ TROUBLE NO MORE
Just your fool / Who will be next / I'll change my style / Too tired / That nasty swing / Trouble blues / Love changin' blues / It's too late brother / Wild man on the loose / Homely girl / Baby how long / Fool's paradise
VPBCD 15 / Jul '93 / Pointblank

☐ YOU CAN'T JUDGE A BOOK BY THE COVER
You can't judge a book by the cover / I can't be satisfied / Midnight hour blues / I hate to see you go / My babe / Shake for me / Long distance call / My starter won't start / Southbound blues / I'm leavin' you / I live the life I love / Help me / Gambling blues
VCD 79472 / Oct '95 / Vanguard

Hammond, Jon

☐ LATE RENT
EFA 128232 / Feb '96 / Hot Wire

Hammons Family

☐ TRADITIONS OF A WEST VIRGINIA FAMILY, THE (2CD Set)
Old sledge / Camp chase / Three forks of cheat / Sugar grove blues / Turkey in the straw / Route / Fine times at our house / Yankee and markum / Sandy boys / Wilson's clog / Sugar babe / Singing birds / Old man can I have your daughter / Shaking down the acorns/Hink Cogar's deer ride / Cranberry rock / Big sciota / Greasy coat / Jimmy Johnson / Panther in the sky / Muddy roads / Bringing back the sheep / Sugar babe / Young Henerly / Parsons rock / In Scotland town / Little Omie / We're marching around the Levees / Riddles / Mercian tittery-ary-a / Jay Legg / Lonesome pines / Haunted wagon / Hard times in the Charleston jail / Ireland's green shore / When this world comes to an end / Johnny Booger / Walking in the parlor / Rocky mountain goat / Who's been here since I've been gone / Lost Indian
ROUCD 1504/5 / Feb '98 / Rounder

Hamon/Le Buhe/Marie/Vassallo

☐ GWERZIOU ET CHANTS DE HAUTE VOIX
KMRS 211CD / Feb '94 / Keltia Musique

Hampel, Gunter

☐ 8TH OF JULY 1969, THE
BIRTHCD 001 / Oct '93 / Birth

☐ CELESTIAL GLORY
BIRTHCD 040 / Oct '93 / Birth

☐ DIALOG
BIRTHCD 041 / Oct '93 / Birth

☐ HIGHER DIMENSION (Hampel, Gunter & Next Generation)
BIRTHCD 043 / Feb '98 / Birth

☐ JUBILATION
BIRTHCD 038 / Oct '93 / Birth

☐ KOLN CONCERT LIVE VOL.1 (Hampel, Gunter & Next Generation)
BIRTHCD 048 / Feb '98 / Birth

☐ TIME IS NOW
BIRTHCD 042 / Oct '93 / Birth

Hampton Callaway, Ann

☐ ANN HAMPTON CALLAWAY
Lush life / Gaze in your eyes / Perfect / I live to love you / My romance / My foolish heart / But beautiful / Like someone I love / How deep is the ocean / Here's that rainy day / All the things you are / Time for love / I've got the world on a string / Our love is here to stay / Too late now / I've got just about everything
DRGCD 91411 / Aug '92 / DRG

☐ BRING BACK ROMANCE
Music / How long has this been going on / This might be forever / My one and only / Affair to remember / Bring back romance / You can't rush spring / Out of this world / Quiet thing / There will never be another you / Where does love go / You go to my head / It could happen to you / My shining hour/I'll be seeing you
DRGCD 91417 / Sep '94 / DRG

☐ SIBLING REVELRY (Hampton Callaway, Ann & Liz Callaway)
It's today / Sweetest sound I can see / Rhythm in my nursery rhymes / My Buddy, old friend / Friendship / Meadowlark / My heart is so full of you / Nanny named Fran / Huge medley / Our time / You must believe in spring / There's a boat that's leavin' soon for New York
DRGCD 91443 / Apr '96 / DRG

Hampton, Lionel

☐ 77 VINTAGE
BB 8702 / Sep '96 / Black & Blue

☐ ALL STAR SESSIONS VOL.1 HOLLYWOOD
AMSC 611 / 15 Dec '97 / Avid

☐ ALL STAR SESSIONS VOL.2 NEW YORK
AMSC 612 / 15 Dec '97 / Avid

☐ ANTHOLOGY 1937-1944
EN 516 / Sep '95 / Encyclopaedia

☐ AT MALIBU BEACH
Flying home / Malibu swing / Autumn / Stellar PM / Breathless vibes / Short of breath
JASMCD 2535 / Jul '95 / Jasmine

☐ AT NEWPORT '78 (Hampton, Lionel All Stars)
Stompin' at the Savoy / Hamp's the champ / Flying home / On the sunny side of the street / Carnegie hall blues
CDSJP 142 / Jun '89 / Timeless Jazz

☐ AUDIO ARCHIVE
12th street rag / I'm in the mood for swing / Johnny get your horn and blow it / Don't be that way / It don't mean a thing if it ain't got that swing / Jumpin' jive / I can give you love / High society / Memories of you / Fiddle diddle / Stand by for further announcements / Rock hill special / If it's good (then I want it) / Down home jump / Shoe shiner's drag / Wizzin' the wizz / Muskrat ramble / Shufflin' at the Hollywood / Anytime at all / Sweethearts on parade
CDAA 025 / Jan '91 / Tring

☐ BASIN STREET BLUES
DM 15011 / Jul '96 / DMA Jazz

☐ BEULAH'S SISTER 1942-1949 (Hampton, Lionel Big Band)
CD 14565 / May '95 / Jazz Portraits

☐ CLASSICS 1937-1938
CLASSICS 524 / Apr '90 / Classics

☐ CLASSICS 1938-1939
CLASSICS 534 / Dec '90 / Classics

☐ CLASSICS 1939-1940
CLASSICS 562 / Oct '91 / Classics

☐ CLASSICS 1940-1941 (Hampton, Lionel & His Orchestra)
CLASSICS 624 / Nov '92 / Classics

☐ CLASSICS 1942-1944
CLASSICS 803 / Mar '95 / Classics

☐ CLASSICS 1945-1946
CLASSICS 922 / Apr '97 / Classics

☐ CLASSICS 1946
CLASSICS 946 / 21 Aug '97 / Classics

☐ CLASSICS 1947
CLASSICS 994 / 24 Apr '98 / Classics

☐ EARLY HAMP
Ramble / Moonlight blues / Charlie's idea / Over night blues / Quality shout / Stuff / Harlem / Cuttin' up / New kinda blues / California swing / Burmah girl / Gettin' ready blues / To you, sweetheart / Alboa / On a cocoanut island / You came to my rescue / Here's love in your eyes / You turned the tables on me / Sing baby sing / Sunday / California here I come
CDAFS 1011 / Oct '93 / Affinity

☐ FLYING HOME
Hot mallets / Shufflin' at the Hollywood / Central avenue breakdown / Save it pretty Mama / Dinah / Four of five times / Twelfth street rag / Chasin' with chase / Rhythm, rhythm / China stomp / Blue / Pig foot sonata / Three quarter boogie / Bouncing at the Beacon / Aint'cha comin' home / Munson street breakdown / When the lights are low / Shoe shiners drag / Ring dem bells / I've found a new baby / Singin' the blues / Flying home
RAJCD 858 / Mar '97 / Empress

☐ FOR THE LOVE OF MUSIC
Flying home / Gates groove / Gossamer wings / Don't you worry 'bout a thing / Time after time / Jazz me / Take the 'A' train / Sweet Lorraine / Another part of me / Mojazz / What a wonderful world
5305542 / Oct '95 / MoJazz

☐ HAMP IN HARLEM (Hampton, Lionel & His Jazz Giants)
CDSLP 168 / Jan '88 / Timeless Jazz

☐ HAMP'S BLUES
Airmail special / EG / Psychedelic Sally / Raunchy Rita / Fum / Ham hock blues / Ring them bells / Lion's den / Here's that rainy day / Killer Joe
17090 / Mar '97 / Laserlight

☐ HAMP'S BOOGIE WOOGIE (Hampton, Lionel & His Orchestra)
Hamp's boogie woogie no. 1 / Beulah's sister's boogie / Midnight sun / Hamp's walking boogie / Cobb's idea / Red top / Hey ba-ba-re-bop / Flying home (take 1) / Hamp's boogie woogie no. 2 / Air mail special (parts 1 and 2) / Slide hamp slide / Rockin' in rhythm (parts 1 and 2) / Flying home (take 2) / Loose wig / In the bag / Adam blew his hat / Tempo's birthday / Playboy
CD 56014 / Aug '94 / Jazz Roots

☐ I'M IN THE MOOD FOR SWING
Buzzin' round with the bees / China stomp / Everybody loves my baby / For swing / Hampton stomp / I can't get started (with you) / I'm in the mood / Jivin' the vibes / Liza / Man I love / Memories of you / My last affair / New kinda blues / Object of my affection / On the sunny side of the street / Rhythm rhythm / Ring dem bells / Running wild / Sing baby sing / Stompology / Sweet Sue, just you / Vibraphone blues / Whoa babe / You turned the tables on me
CDAJA 5090 / Feb '92 / Living Era

☐ IN VIENNA 1954 VOL.1
RST 91423 / Oct '92 / RST

☐ JAZZ GREATS
Munson Street breakdown / I've found a new baby / I can't get started / Flamenco soul / Hot Club Of Madrid serenade / Tenderly / Dinah / Tempo and swing / Jack the bellboy / Toledo blade / Bop city flamenco / Blue because of you / Jivin' with Jarvis / Central Avenue breakdown
74321499652 / 6 Oct '97 / RCA Victor

☐ JAZZ MASTERS (Hampton, Lionel & Oscar Peterson)
Jam blues / Always / Soft winds / Stardust / Je ne sais pas / Tenderly / Hallelujah / Sweethearts on parade / Date with Oscar
5218532 / 5 May '98 / Verve

☐ JAZZ MASTERS (Hampton, Lionel & His Orchestra)
Air mail special / Cherokee / Midnight sun / Vibe boogie / Glad hamp / Misty / Flying home
CDMFP 6307 / Mar '97 / Music For Pleasure

☐ JAZZ PORTRAITS
Ring dem bells / I know that you know / On the sunny side of the street / Dinah / Sheikh of Araby / Shoe shiner's drag / House of morgan / Singin' the blues / Memories of you / Dough re mi / I've found a new baby / Jivin' with Jarvis / Twelfth street rag / After you've gone / Muskrat ramble / High society / It don't mean a thing if it ain't got that swing / Drum stomp
CD 14519 / May '94 / Jazz Portraits

☐ JIVIN' THE VIBES
LEJAZZCD 1 / May '93 / Le Jazz

☐ JIVIN' THE VIBES
8464604022 / 24 Mar '98 / Special Music

☐ JUST JAZZ - LIVE AT THE BLUE NOTE (Hampton, Lionel & The Golden Men Of Jazz)
Corner pocket / Just jazz / Body and soul / God bless the child / Ring dem bells / Flyin' home
CD 83313 / Jan '93 / Telarc

☐ LIONEL HAMPTON
22707 / Feb '96 / Music

☐ LIONEL HAMPTON
Songs of the Negev / Exodus / Railroad no.1 / Wild Bill / Juice / More Juice / McGhee / Playboy theme / Hava Nagila / Lonesome nights / Wine song / How high the moon / Flying home / Mr. John / Mr. J
17068 / Jul '96 / Laserlight

☐ LIONEL HAMPTON & LARS ERSTRAND
NCD 8807 / Apr '94 / Phontastic

☐ LIONEL HAMPTON 1937-1940 (Hampton, Lionel & His Orchestra)
High society / It don't mean a thing (if it ain't got that swing) / Blue because of you / Doug-rey-mi / After you've gone / Drum stomp (crazy rhythm) / Memories of you / Sheik of araby / I've found a new baby / Jivin' with jarvis / One sweet letter from you / Four or five times / House of morgan / Sweethearts on parade / Singin' the blues (till my daddy comes home) / Dinah
15734 / Apr '94 / Laserlight

☐ LIONEL HAMPTON AND HIS JAZZ GIANTS (Hampton, Lionel & His Jazz Giants)
Sweet georgia brown / Limehouse blues / Hamp's thing / Ol' man river / Lover / Lady be good / Birth of the blues / Fox / Misty / J-m swing discoteque / Liza / Honeysuckle rose
BLE 591072 / Apr '91 / Black & Blue

☐ LIONEL HAMPTON AND HIS ORCHESTRA (Hampton, Lionel & His Orchestra)
Stompology / Ring dem bells / Shuffin' at the Hollywood / Hot mallets / I just couldn't take it baby / Rhythm rhythm / I can't get started (with you) / I surrender dear / Handful of keys / Make believe / China stomp / 12th Street rag / Ain't cha comin' home / Four of five times / I've found a new baby / Moonglow / Running wild / On the sunny side of the street / Shoe shiner's drag / Jivin' the vibes / Gin for christmas
PASTCD 9789 / May '92 / Flapper

☐ LIONEL HAMPTON IN PARIS (Hampton, Lionel & His Orchestra)
Jazz star news / Body and soul / Sweethearts on parade / La piege / Panama / Hamp swins the bells / Blues for lorraine / Jam for brigitte / What's new / Honeysuckle rose / Genevieve
CDSW 8415 / '88 / DRG

☐ LIONEL HAMPTON PRESENTS GERRY MULLIGAN (Hampton, Lionel & Gerry Mulligan)
Apple core / Song for Johnny Hodges / Blight of the fumble bee / Gerry meets Hamp / Blues for Gerry / Line for Lyons / Walking shoes / Limelight
CDGATE 7014 / Jun '87 / Kingdom Jazz

☐ LIONEL HAMPTON'S PARIS ALL STARS
September in the rain / Blue panssie / Free press oui / I only have eyes for you / Walking at the Trocadero / Real crazy / More crazy / More and more crazy / Completely crazy
74321511502 / Feb '98 / Vogue

☐ LIVE AT MUZEVAL (Hampton, Lionel Big Band)
CDSJP 120 / Mar '90 / Timeless Jazz

☐ LIVE AT THE BLUE NOTE (Hampton, Lionel & His Orchestra)
O.w. / Hamp's note / Moody's mood for love / I wish I knew / Lover / Flyin' home / Hamp's boogie woogie
CD 83308 / Oct '91 / Telarc

☐ LIVE AT THE CAVEAU DE LA HUCHETTE (European Tour 1976) (Hampton, Lionel & His Jazz Inner Circle Band)
How high the moon / Funky mama / Stardust / You are the sunshine of my life / Air mail special / Chameleon / Confessin' / Flying home / Flying home (reprise) / Happy birthday
17152 / Apr '98 / Laserlight

☐ LIVE AT THE METROPOLE CAFE (Hampton, Lionel & His Orchestra)
After you've gone / It's all right with me / Alexander's ragtime band / Rebecca, rebecca / Blues for gertie / Flying home / Mcghee / Lonesome nights (take my word) / How high the moon / Mr. john / America by night (mr. j)
HCD 242 / Feb '95 / Hindsight

☐ MADE IN JAPAN
Airmail special / Advent / Stardust / Mess is here / Interpretations, opus 5 / Minor thesis / Jodo / Valve job
CDSJP 175 / Mar '91 / Timeless Jazz

☐ MUSKRAT RAMBLE
Muskrat ramble / Fiddle diddle / Shoe shiner's drag / Johnny get your horn and blow it / Sweethearts on parade / Stand by for further announcements / Ain't cha comin' home / Denison swing / Jumpin' jive / 12th Street rag / Down home jump / Anytime at all / Wizzin' the wiz / If it's good (then I want it) / Shufflin' at the Hollywood / Don't be that way / I'm in the mood for swing / Big wig in the wigwam / I can give you love / It don't mean a thing if it ain't got that swing / High society / Rock hill special / Memories of you
GRF 090 / '93 / Tring

☐ PLAYS THE GROOVE
500682 / 21 Aug '97 / Musidisc

☐ QUINTESSENCE, THE (1930-1944/2CD Set)
FA 211 / Oct '96 / Fremeaux

☐ SMALL COMBOS 1937-1940 (Hampton, Lionel & His Orchestra)
Ring dem bells / I know that you know / On the sunny side of the street / Dinah / Sheik of araby / Shoe shiner's drag / House of morgan / Singin' the blues (till my daddy comes home) / Memories of you / Doug-rey-ml / I've found a new baby / Jivin' with jarvis / Twelfth street rag (one step) / After you've gone / Muskrat ramble / High society / It don't mean a thing (if it ain't got that swing) / Drum stomp (crazy rhythm)
CD 56058 / Mar '95 / Jazz Roots

☐ SMALL COMBOS 1937-40 (Hampton, Lionel & Friends)
CD 53050 / Mar '92 / Giants Of Jazz

☐ SONNY LESTER COLLECTION
CDC 9068 / Nov '93 / LRC

☐ STUDIO AND LIVE
Avalon / Dany boy / Cappy's blues / Louise / Vibes boogie / Dany swing / Shadow of your smile / On the sunny side of the street / In the mood / Milestone
17157 / Apr '98 / Laserlight

☐ SWINGSATION
Flying home / Royal family / In the bag / Loose wig / Flying home no.2 / Hamp's boogie woogie / Million dollar smile / Ribs and hot sauce / Blow top blues / Hey ba-ba-re-bop / Rockin' in rhythm / Airmail special / Cobb's idea / Hamp's got a duke / Midnight sun / Red top
GRP 99222 / 24 Aug '98 / GRP

☐ TEMPO AND SWING
Munson Street breakdown / I've found a new baby / I can't get started (with you) / Four or five times / Gin for Christmas / Dinah / My buddy / Swingin' the blues / Shades of jade / Till Tom special / Flying home / Save it pretty Mama / Tempo and swing / House of Morgan / I'd be lost without you: *Hampton, Lionel & Helen Forrest* / Central Avenue breakdown / Jack the bellboy / Dough re mi / Jivin' with Jarvis / Blue because of you / Martin on every block / Pig foot sonata
74321101612 / Mar '97 / Bluebird

☐ TORRID STUFF 1944-1946, THE
158902 / Jun '97 / Jazz Archives

☐ VINTAGE HAMPTON (Hampton, Lionel & His Orchestra)
Peggy's blue skylight / Apple core / Lullaby of birdland / Take the 'a' train / Midnight blues / Man I love / Blues for games / Fatha meets ganes / As long as we're here / Fables of faubus / Blues for jerry
CD 83321 / Jan '94 / Telarc

Hampton, Slide

☐ DEDICATED TO DIZ (Hampton, Slide & The Jazz Masters)
San sebastian / Lover man (oh where can you be) / Be bop / Diddy wah diddy / Tour de force / Night in tunisia / Owl (outro)
CD 83323 / Jun '93 / Telarc

☐ MELLOW-DY
CDC 9053 / Nov '92 / LRC

☐ SLIDE (Hampton, Slide Octet)
FSRCD 206 / Jul '96 / Fresh Sound

☐ WORLD OF TROMBONES
BLCD 760113 / Oct '90 / Black Lion

Hamsters

☐ HAMSTER JAM
HAMSTERCD 7 / Jul '93 / Hamsters

☐ HAMSTERS
(i wanna) make love to you / (i wanna) make love to you / Climbing the corporate ladder / In the heat of the night / Guitar bug / I wouldn't treat a dog / Slim's blues-blues for the blues / Heart of darkness / Black monday / Little fine healthy thing / Chevrolet / Sittin' on the boat dock / You'll come running back to me / Check up from the neck up
HAMSTERCD 8 / Jul '93 / Hamsters

☐ JIMI HENDRIX MEMORIAL CONCERTS VOL.1
HAMSTERCD 10 / Jul '96 / Hamsters

☐ JIMI HENDRIX MEMORIAL CONCERTS VOL.2
HAMSTERSCD 11 / May '96 / Hamsters

☐ ROUTE 666
HAMSTERCD 9 / Feb '95 / Hamsters

Hanatarash

☐ 4-AIDSADELIC
PBCD 3 / Jun '97 / Public Bath

Hancock, Butch

☐ EATS AWAY THE NIGHT
To each his own / Moanin' of the midnight train / Eileen / One kiss / Pumpkin eater / If you were a bluebird / Junkyard in the sun / Boxcars / Baby be mine / Welcome to the real world
GRCD 341 / Nov '96 / Glitterhouse
SHCD 1048 / Jan '97 / Sugar Hill

☐ JUNKYARD IN THE SUN
GR 341 / Oct '94 / Glitterhouse

☐ OWN AND OWN
Dry land farm / Wind's dominion / Diamond hill / 1981: A spare odyssey / Firewater (seeks its own level) / West Texas waltz / Horseflies / If you were a bluebird / Own and own / Fools fall in love / Yella rose / Like a kiss on the mouth / Ghost of Give-and-Take Avenue / Tell me what you want to know / Just a storm / Just tell me that / When will you hold me again
GRCD 364 / Nov '96 / Glitterhouse
SHCD 1036 / Mar '98 / Sugar Hill

☐ OWN THE WAY OVER HERE
Talkin' about this Panama Canal / Only born / Smokin' in the rain / Corona del mar / Like the light at dawn / Gift horse of mercy / Neon wind / Perfection in the mud / Only makes me love you more / Already gone / Away from the mountain
SHCD 1038 / May '93 / Sugar Hill

☐ WINDS DOMINION, THE
Sea's deadog catch / Capture rapture / Wind's dominion / Long road to Asia minor / Split and slide / Smokin' in the rain / Fighting for my life / Personal rendition of the blues / Dominoes / Once followed by the wind / Wild horses chase the wind / Own and own / Mario y Maria (cryin' statues) / Eternal triangle / Only born / Gift horse of mercy
RLT 1644D / 9 Mar '98 / Rainlight

☐ YELLA ROSE (Hancock, Butch & Marce Lacouture)
Perfection in the mud / Yella rose / Like a kiss on the mouth / Ain't no mercy on the highway / Only makes me love ya more / So I'll run / Two roads / Sharp cutting wings / Tell me what you know
RLT 1137 / Jul '98 / Rainlight

☐ YOU COULDA WALKED AROUND THE WORLD
RLT 37 / Dec '97 / Rainlight

Hancock, Herbie

☐ CANTALOUPE ISLAND
Cantaloupe island / Watermelon man / Driftin' / Blind man / What it I don't / Maiden voyage
CDP 8293312 / Jul '94 / Blue Note

☐ COMPLETE WARNER RECORDINGS, THE
2457322 / Feb '95 / Warner Bros.

☐ DIS IS DA DRUM
Call it '94 / Dis is da drum / Shooz / Melody (on the deuce by 44) / Mojuba / Butterfly / Juju / Hump / Come and see me / Rubber soul / Bo ba be ba
5281852 / Jun '95 / Mercury

☐ EVENING WITH HERBIE HANCOCK AND CHICK COREA, AN (2CD Set) (Hancock, Herbie & Chick Corea)
Someday my Prince will come / Liza / Button up / February moments / Maiden voyage / La fiesta
4772962 / Nov '94 / Columbia

☐ FEETS DON'T FAIL ME NOW
You bet your love / Trust me / Tell everybody / Ready or not / Honey from the jar / Knee deep
CK 35764 / Aug '97 / Sony Jazz

☐ FUTURE SHOCK
Rockit / Future shock / TFS / Earthbeat / Autodrive / Rough
4712372 / Jan '95 / Sony Jazz

☐ HEADHUNTERS
Chameleon / Watermelon man / Sly / Vein melter
CK 65123 / Apr '97 / Sony Jazz

☐ HEADHUNTERS/FUTURE SHOCK/ MAN CHILD (3CD Set)
Chameleon / Watermelon man / Sly / Vein melter / Rockit / Future shock / TFS / Earthbeat / Autodrive / Rough
4893462 / 1 Dec '97 / Sony Jazz

☐ IN CONCERT (2CD Set) (Hancock, Herbie & Chick Corea)
Someday my prince will come / Liza / Button up / February moment / Maiden voyage / La fiesta
C2K 65551 / 22 Jun '98 / Sony Jazz

☐ JAZZ COLLECTION, A
Liza / I fall in love too easily / Nefertiti / Someday my Prince will come / 'Round midnight / Well you needn't / Parade / Eye of the hurricane / Maiden voyage
4679012 / Nov '93 / Columbia

☐ LITE ME UP
Lite me up / Bomb / Gettin' to the good part / Paradise / Can't hide your love / Fun tracks / Motormouth / Give it all your heart
4865732 / 29 Sep '97 / Sony Jazz

☐ LIVE (Hancock, Herbie Quartet)
JD 1270 / 26 Jan '98 / Jazz Door

☐ LIVE IN NEW YORK
JD 1274 / 15 Jun '98 / Jazz Door

☐ MAIDEN VOYAGE
Maiden voyage / Eye of the hurricane / Little one / Survival of the fittest / Dolphin dance
CDP 7463392 / Mar '95 / Blue Note

☐ MANCHILD
4712352 / Jan '95 / Sony Jazz

☐ MONSTER
Saturday night / Stars in your eyes / Go for it / Don't hold it in / Making love / It all comes round
4865712 / 29 Sep '97 / Sony Jazz

☐ MR. HANDS
Spiralling prism / Calypso / Just around the corner / 4 a.m. / Shifless shuffle / Textures
4712402 / Jan '95 / Sony Jazz

☐ NEW STANDARD, THE
5277152 / Mar '96 / Verve

☐ PIANO GENIUS
Jammin' with Herbie / Herbie's blues / Rock your soul / TCB with Herbie / Soul power / Cat call
QED 076 / Nov '96 / Tring

☐ QUARTET WITH WYNTON MARSALIS
Well you needn't / 'Round midnight / Clear ways / Quick sketch / Eye of the hurricane / Parade / Sorcerer / Pee wee / I fall in love too easily
4656262 / Nov '93 / Columbia

☐ SECRETS
CK 34280 / Aug '97 / Sony Jazz

☐ SEXTANT
Rain dance / Hidden shadows / Hornets
CK 64983 / 13 Jul '98 / Sony Jazz

☐ SUNLIGHT
I thought it was you / Come running to me / Sunlight / No means yes / Good question / Magic number / Tonight's the night / Everybody's broke / Help yourself / Satisfied with love / Twilight clone
4865702 / 29 Sep '97 / Sony Jazz

☐ TAKIN' OFF
Watermelon man / Three bags full / Empty pockets / Maze / Driftin' / Alone and I
CDP 8376432 / Jun '96 / Blue Note

☐ TAKIN' OFF/INVENTIONS AND DIMENSIONS/EMPRYEAN ISLES (3CD Set)
Watermelon man / Three bags full / Empty pockets / Maze / Driftin' / Alone and I / Succotash / Triangle / Jack rabbit / Mimosa / Jump ahead / One finger snap / Oliloqui valley / Cantaloupe Island / Egg
CDOMB 009 / Oct '95 / Blue Note

☐ THIS IS JAZZ
Sorcerer / Gentle thoughts / Actual proof / Peacocks / Calypso / Maiden voyage
CK 65051 / 4 May '98 / Sony Jazz

☐ THRUST
Palm grease / Actual proof / Butterfly / Spank a lee
4865682 / 29 Sep '97 / Sony Jazz
CK 64984 / 13 Jul '98 / Sony Jazz

☐ VSOP (2CD Set)
Piano intro / Maiden voyage / Nefertiti / Introduction of players / Eye of the hurricane / Toys / Introductions / You'll know when you get there / Hang up your hang ups / Spider
486569 / 29 Sep '97 / Sony Jazz

Hancock, Keith

☐ MADHOUSE
HYCD 200107 / Feb '95 / Hypertension

Hancock, Wayne

☐ THAT'S WHAT DADDY WANTS
ELDCD 002 / 30 Mar '98 / Eldorado

☐ THUNDERSTORMS AND NEON LIGHTS
DJD 3221 / Nov '95 / Dejadisc

Hand, Frederic

☐ HEART'S SONG
MM 5018 / Oct '94 / Music Masters

☐ JAZZANTIQUA
Cantigas de Santa Maria / Rose Liz / Bachiaras / Tourdion / Lady Carey's fantasy / Chaconne / Toby and Lynn
MM 65150 / Nov '96 / Music Masters

Handala

☐ HOLOM
CD 023 / Mar '98 / Robi Droli

Handbell Ringers Of Great Britain

☐ CHRISTMAS HANDBELLS
Silent night / Jingle bells / Good King Wenceslas / We three Kings / Ave Maria / Hark what mean/ Christians awake / Hail smiling morn / Hark the herald angels sing / O little town of Bethlehem / O come all ye faithful (adeste fidelis) / I saw three ships / Born today is the child divine / Ding dong merrily on high / Away in a manger / Once in Royal David's city / Coventry carol / Christmas bells / Christmas is coming/Wassail song / Christmas candles / Zither carol / Stars watch high / Masters in the hall / Cowboy carol / Three Kings / Le jeux Noel de Robin et Marion / Hallelujah chorus / Puer nobis
4610762 / 17 Aug '98 / Belart

Handfullaflowers

☐ CAN'T STAND THE WEIGHT OF THE WORLD
SPV 08480822 / May '96 / SPV

Hands

☐ HANDS
SP 96001 / Jul '97 / Shroom

Handsome Beasts

☐ BEAST WITHIN, THE
Mr. Mescalito / Hairy legs / Way I am / Chain gang / Beast within / Rough justice / Don't hold on / Sixth day / Let it go
HMRXD 132 / Feb '90 / Heavy Metal

☐ BESTIALITY
CDMETAL 5 / Feb '97 / British Steel

Handsome Family

☐ MILK AND SCISSORS
SR 1011 / Sep '96 / Scout
SAKI 011CD / 16 Feb '98 / Saki

☐ ODESSA
SR 1004 / Jan '96 / Scout

☐ THROUGH ME FOR THE TREES
SAKI 020CD / 2 Feb '98 / Saki

☐ THROUGH THE TREES
Weightless again / My sister's tiny hands / Stalled / Where the birch trees lean / Cathedrals / Down in the ground / Giant of Illonois / Down in the valley of hollow logs / I fell / Woman downstairs / Last night I went out walking / Bury me here / My ghost
VJCD 105 / 6 Apr '98 / Loose

Handy, Captain John

☐ CAPT. JOHN HANDY & EASY RIDERS JAZZBAND
BCD 325 / Apr '94 / GHB

☐ CAPT. JOHN HANDY & HIS NEW ORLEANS STOMPERS VOL.1
BCD 41 / Aug '94 / GHB

☐ CAPT. JOHN HANDY & HIS NEW ORLEANS STOMPERS VOL.2 (Handy, Captain John & His New Orleans Stompers)
BCD 42 / Aug '94 / GHB

☐ VERY FIRST RECORDINGS
AMCD 51 / Apr '94 / American Music

Handy, John

☐ HANDY DANDY MAN
Play the musik / Lady lady / Disco samba / Everything you touch / I gotta let her know / I can tell / Handy dandy man / You live, you learn / Sing to me
INAK 8618 / Jul '97 / In Akustik

☐ JOHN HANDY QUINTET
BCD 261 / Jul '96 / GHB

☐ LIVE AT THE MONTEREY JAZZ FESTIVAL
378202 / 29 Jun '98 / Koch Jazz

☐ NEW VIEW (Handy, John New Quintet)
CD 378112 / Jul '97 / Koch Jazz

☐ NIGHT AT YOSHI'S NIGHTSPOT
BLDCD 531 / Sep '96 / Boulevard

☐ SECOND JOHN HANDY ALBUM, THE (Handy, John Quintet)
CD 378122 / Nov '97 / Koch Jazz

☐ WHERE GO THE BOATS (Handy, John & Lee Ritenour)
Right there right there / Moogie woogie / Where go the boats / Go for yourself / Hissing of summer / She just won't boogie with me / Erica / Salud to Sonny
INAK 861CD / Jul '97 / In Akustik

Hanford, Jan
☐ VESPERS
Landlocked / Delirious / Intimate / Theoria / Human response / Angels / Total truth / Denial / If I can believe what I see / Ambien II, of the five / Vespers / Dancing (moog archive 1)
AD 12CD / Dec '96 / AD

Hang Up
☐ NEVER MIND THE JERKY'S HERE'S HANG UP
NOIR 008CD / 15 Jun '98 / God Bless

Hangal, Gangubai
☐ VOICE OF TRADITION, THE
SM 15012 / Jan '91 / Wergo

Hangmen
☐ TESTED ON ANIMALS
BTCD 981 / May '98 / Bone Tone

Hangovers
☐ SLOW DIRTY TEARS
Duck song / I'm glad I'm me today / Sweetest pain / Hello pain / Soho / I feel like / Sorry / I hate you / We had a really smashing time / DrPhone / Monmsink / Monster / Sitting on top of the world
FUME 002A / 6 Apr '98 / Smoke

Hank Dogs
☐ BAREBACK
Lucky break / 18 dogs / Let go / Bareback / I'm an angel / Daddy's arms / Quality time / One from your head / Thought messages / Reunion / Sun explodes / Sea / Free spirit / Way of the soul
HNCD 1413 / 6 Apr '98 / Hannibal

Hankansson, Kenny
☐ 2117M ABOVE SEA LEVEL
SRS 4731 / Mar '96 / Silence

Hanly, Mick
☐ HAPPY LIKE THIS
RTM 61CD / Jan '94 / Round Tower

☐ WARTS AND ALL
Nothing in the can / What's his name / Don't try to cushion the blow / Fabulous thunderbirds / On vocals and guitar / Wherever you go / Joan / Warts and all / Let's not fight / Words and the bottle / Uncle John / Art and reality / My body and me / Happy to be here
RTMCD 32 / Sep '91 / Round Tower

Hanna, Fred
☐ BALLROOM CLASSICS
PHCD 541 / Jul '97 / Outlet

☐ IRISH PARTY FAVOURITES
PHCD 543 / Jul '97 / Outlet

Hanna, Jake
☐ JOINT IS JUMPIN', THE (Hanna, Jake After Hours Gang)
ARCD 19148 / 1 Jun '98 / Arbors Jazz

Hanna, Roland
☐ DUKE ELLINGTON PIANO SOLOS
In my solitude / Something to live for / In a sentimental mood / Portrait of Bert Williams / Warm valley / Isfahan / Single petal of a rose / I got it bad and that ain't good / Reflections in D / Come Sunday / Caravan
MM 5045 / Oct '94 / Music Masters

☐ GLOVE
STCD 4148 / Feb '90 / Storyville

☐ IMPRESSIONS
BB 880 / Apr '97 / Black & Blue

☐ LIVE AT MAYBECK RECITAL HALL VOL.32
Love walked in / They can't take that away from me / Softly as in a morning sunrise / Gershwin medley: Fascinating rhythm/Man I love / Let's call the whole thing off / How long has this been going on / Oleo / Lush life / This can't be love
CCD 4604 / Jul '94 / Concord Jazz

☐ PERUGIA
Take the 'A' train / I got it bad and that ain't good / Time dust gathered / Perugia / Child is born / Wistful moment
FCD 41010 / Sep '87 / Freedom

☐ REMEMBERING CHARLIE PARKER
PCD 7031 / Oct '91 / Progressive

☐ THIS TIME IT'S REAL
STCD 4145 / Feb '90 / Storyville

Hannaford Street Silver Band
☐ CHRISTMAS FLOURISH
SMCD 5175 / 7 Nov '97 / CBC

Hannah, Marcus
☐ WEEDS AND LILIES
RTS 10 / Nov '94 / Return To Sender

Hannan, Robert
☐ TRADITIONAL IRISH MUSIC PLAYED ON UILLEANN PIPES
Flood on the Holm/Miss Monahan reel / Amhran an Tae / Liz King's jig / Stay another while/College groves / Derry hornpipe / Do you want anymore/Gallowglass / Rainy day/Shaskeen / Dark woman of the Glen / Boys of Tanderagee / Jackson's morning brush / Jenny picking cockles/My love is in America / Darby Gallagher's/An Buachaillin bui / Salamanca/Jenny's welcome to Charlie / Dark Lochnagar / Rambles of Kitty/When sick is it tea you want / Curragh races/Trim the velvet / Chief O'Neill/Plains of Boyle / Pipe on the hob / Merry Blacksmith/Bonnie Kate/Gorman's reel
CC 53CD / Jan '91 / Claddagh

Hanny
☐ VOICE OF CUBA
Sexo dinero y fantasia / Derroche de amor / Ibarrena / Luna / Tu me quieres pa bien / Mil recuerdos / Polvo de luna / Noche mansa / Ojos que no ven / Uncastillo a tu magia / Coma droga poderosa
MRBCD 008 / 6 Oct '97 / Mr. Bongo

Hanoi Rocks
☐ BACK TO MYSTERY CITY
Strange boys play weird openings / Mental beat / Until I get you / Lick summer lover / Ice cream summer / Malibu beach nightmare / Tooting Bec wreck / Sailing down the years / Beating gets faster / Back to Mystery City
ESMCD 272 / Mar '95 / Essential

☐ BANGKOK SHOCKS SAIGON SHAKES
Tradegy / Stop cryin' / Lost in the city / Pretender / 11th Street kidz / First timer / Don't never leave me / Village girl / Walking with my angel / Cheyenne
ESMCD 273 / Mar '95 / Essential

☐ LEAN ON ME
Tragedy / Oriental beat / Motorvatin' / Taxi driver / Back to mystery city / Malibu beach nightmare / Life's been hard / Heart attack / Menaced by nightingales / Fast car / Shame shame shame / Rock 'n' roll / Lean on me
ESMCD 282 / Apr '95 / Essential

☐ ORIENTAL BEAT
Motorvatin' / Visitor / Sweet home suburbia / No law or order / Devil woman / Fallen star / Don't follow me / Teenage outsiders / M C Baby / Oriental beat / Bar blues
ESMCD 274 / Mar '95 / Essential

☐ SELF DESTRUCTION BLUES
Love's an injection / Dead by Xmas / Desperados / Whispers in the dark / Self destruction blues / Nothing blues / Cafe avenue / Kill city / Beer and a cigarette / Taxi driver / Problem child / I want you / Nothing new
ESMCD 271 / Mar '95 / Essential

Hanrahan, Kieran
☐ IRISH TENOR BANJO
BD 001CD / Dec '97 / Banner Discs

Hanrahan, Kip
☐ ALL ROADS ARE MADE OF THE FLESH
Buddy bolden's blues / At the same time as the subway train was pulling out of / First and last to love me (4 december) / First and last to love me (2 october)
AMCL 10292 / Aug '95 / American Clave

☐ ANTHOLOGY
AMCL 10202 / Nov '93 / American Clave

☐ DESIRE DEVELOPS AN EDGE
AMCL 1009/8 / Aug '94 / American Clave

☐ THOUSAND NIGHTS & A NIGHT, A
Shahrazade / Sitt Al Milla/Zumurrud / Jewish doctor's tale / Aziz and Azizah / Diente De Oro / Aziz and Azizah (continued) / Al-Mummum and the Arab girl by the well / Lost Prince / Princess Dunya and Taj Al-Muluk / Princess Dunya's nocturnal realization / Yemen merchant and the three different coloured woman / Jinniya who envied human suffering / Hasheater's tale / Angel Charles and the caravan of Jinns / Shahrazade and the closing of the first night of stories
AMCL 10362 / Nov '96 / American Clave

Hanrahan, Mike
☐ MIKE HANRAHAN
TUT 168 / Oct '94 / Wundertute

Hanselmann, David
☐ LET THE MUSIC CARRY ON
845158 / May '91 / FM

Hansen, Ole Kock
☐ PA EN GREN BAKKETOP
MECCACD 1002 / Nov '94 / Music Mecca

Hansen, Randy
☐ TRIBUTE TO JIMI HENDRIX, A
1890692 / Nov '92 / NMC

Hansen, Steen
☐ UNDER THE SURFACE (Hansen, Steen Quartet)
MECCACD 2042 / Oct '97 / Music Mecca

Hanshaw, Annette
☐ GIRL NEXT DOOR 1927-1932, THE
TT 408 / May '98 / Take Two

☐ LOVABLE AND SWEET
Black bottom / Six feet of Papa / Falling in love with you / Do, do, do / Everything's made for love / Ain't he sweet / Here or there / Nuthin' / You wouldn't fool me, would you / That's you, baby / Big city blues / Pagan love song / Ua like no a like (sweet constancy) / Lovable and sweet / Right kind of me / Telling it to the daisies / Little white lies / Body and soul / Would you like to take a walk / Walkin' my baby back home / Ho hum / Fit as a fiddle / Moon song / We just couldn't say goodbye / Let's fall in love
CDAJA 5220 / Apr '97 / Living Era

☐ TWENTIES SWEETHEART, THE
Black bottom / Six feet of Papa / Don't take that bottom away / Here or there / I gotta get somebody to love / Wistful and blue / What do I care / Nuthin' / I'm somebody's somebody now / I like what you like / Ain't that a grand and glorious feeling / Who-oo you-oo, that's who / Under the moon / It was only a sun shower / Who's that knocking at my door / We love it / Get out and get under the moon / There must be somebody else / Mine all mine / Thinking of you / Song is ended (but the melody lingers on)
JASMCD 2542 / May '95 / Jasmine

Hanson
☐ MIDDLE OF NOWHERE, THE
Thinking of you / Mmmbop / Weird / Speechless / Where's the love / Yearbook song / Look at you / Lucy / I will come to you / Minute wthout you / Madeline / With you in my dreams / Man from Milwaukee
5346152 / Jun '97 / Mercury

☐ SNOWED IN
Merry Christmas baby / What Christmas means to me / Little Saint Nick / At Christmas / Christmas (baby please come home) / Rockin' round the Christmas tree / Christmas time / Everybody knows the claus / Run rudolph run / Silent medley / White Christmas
5367172 / 17 Nov '97 / Mercury

☐ THREE CAR GARAGE (The Indie Recordings 1995-1996)
Day has come / Two years / I'll be thinking of you / River / Surely as the sun / Mmmbop / Soldier / Stories / Pictures / Sometimes / With you in your dreams
5583992 / 1 Jun '98 / Mercury

Hanson Brothers
☐ GROSS MISCONDUCT
No emotion / No emotion / A night without you / My girlfriend's a robot / Sabrina / Butthead / Go away / Comatose / Road pizza / No more headcheese / Duke it out / Lovesick / Jack off / Total goombah / Blitzkrieg hops / You are not for me / Bad
VIRUS 116CD / Nov '92 / Alternative Tentacles

☐ SUDDEN DEATH
K 176CD / May '97 / Konkurrent

Hanson, Mick
☐ DO YOU HAVE A NAME
Here's that rainy day / What's next / Vera cruz / I thought about you / My one and only love / My romance / Foggy day / Alfredo / There with you / Old folks / Pause for thought / Hanson is as Hanson does / Do you have a name
SPJCD 555 / May '96 / Spotlite

Hansson, Bo
☐ ATTIC THOUGHTS
SRS 3625CD / Jul '95 / Silence

☐ LORD OF THE RINGS
Leaving shire / Old forest/Tom Bombadil / Fog on the barrow downs / Black riders/Flight to the ford / At the house of Elrond/The ring goes South / Journey in the dark / Lothlorien / Shadowfax / Horns of Rohan/The Battle of Pelennor Fields / Dreams in the house of healing / Homeward bound/The scouring of the shire / Grey havens
EDCD 493 / Jun '96 / Edsel
RESCD 508 / Jul '97 / Resource

☐ MAGICIAN'S HAT
Big city / Divided reality / Elidor / Fylke / Before the rain / Findhorn's song / Playing downhill into the downs / Awakening / Wandering song / Sun (Parallel or 90 degrees) / Excursion with complications
RESCD 509 / Jul '97 / Resource

Hanyo
☐ BEYOND THE SURFACE
DC 881912 / Oct '97 / Disky

☐ INSIGHT
DC 881922 / Oct '97 / Disky

Happy Clappers
☐ GAMES
3984210312 / 24 Nov '97 / Coalition

Happy Family
☐ MAN ON YOUR STREET
Salesman / Letter from hall / Luckiest citizen / Revenge / Courier / Man on your street / A night underground / Two of a kind / March in turin / Puritans / Innermost thoughts / Mistake
GAD 214CD / 6 Jul '98 / 4AD

Happy Flowers
☐ OOF
HMS 136 2 / May '89 / Homestead

Happy Go Licky
☐ HAPPY GO LICKY
DIS 109CD / 6 Oct '97 / Dischord

Happy Mondays
☐ BUMMED
Country song / Moving in with / Mad Cyril / Fat lady wrestlers / Performance / Brain dead / Wrote for luck / Bring a friend / Do it better / Lazyitis
5200132 / Jul '95 / Factory Too

☐ LOADS
Step on / Wrote for luck / Kinky Afro / Hallelujah / Mad Cyril / Lazyitis / Tokoloshe man / Loose fit / Bob's yer uncle / Judge Fudge / Stinkin' thinkin' / Sunshine and love / Angel / Tart tart / Kuff dam / 24 hour party people
5200362 / Jul '95 / Factory Too

☐ PILLS 'N' THRILLS AND BELLYACHES
Kinky afro / God's cop / Donovan / Grandbag's funeral / Dennis and Lois / Bob's yer Uncle / Step on / Holiday / Harmony
8282232 / Jul '95 / Factory Too

☐ SQUIRREL AND G-MAN
Kuff dam / Tart tart / 'Enry / Russell / Olive oil / Weekend 5 / Little matchstick Owen / Oasis / 24 hour party people / Cob 20
5200122 / Jul '95 / Factory Too

☐ UP ALL NIGHT
CBAK 4046 / Apr '91 / Baktabak

☐ YES PLEASE
Stinkin' thinkin' / Monkey in the family / Sunshine and love / Dustman / Angel / Cut 'em loose Bruce / Theme from Netto / Love child / Total ringo / Cowboy Dave
5200262 / Jul '95 / Factory Too

Happy Traum Band
☐ BUCKETS OF SONGS
GWCD 2 / Dec '97 / Guitar

Har-Ell
☐ PAGAN MOON CHILD
EFA 009512 / Aug '95 / Nephilim

Harakami, Rei
☐ UNREST
On / More elbow / Dessert / Wreck / Rho / Pass / Vice versa / Code / Objective contents / Bioscope / Unrest
SBLCD 5024UK / 20 Apr '98 / Sublime

Haran, Mary Cleere
☐ FUNNY WORLD (Mary Cleere Hart Sings Lyrics By Hart)
VSD 5584 / Jul '95 / Varese Sarabande

Harare Dread
☐ DZIDZO
PVCD 05 / May '96 / Paxvision

Harbour Kings
☐ SUMMERCOLTS
Tattoo / Grassfires / Roads to freedom / Forsyth C / Rosemary Road / Sleepers / Searchlight / Flood dream
FIRE 33025 / Oct '91 / Fire

Hard Rain
☐ HARD RAIN
50580422 / May '97 / Semaphore

Hard Resistance
☐ ENGINE OF HATE
LF 288CD / 6 Oct '97 / Lost & Found

Hard Rubber Orchestra
☐ CRUEL YET FAIR
VICTOCD 059 / Aug '98 / Victo

Hard To Swallow
☐ PROTECTED BY THE EJACULATE OF SERPENTS
HAUS 013CD / 13 Jul '98 / Household Name

Hard Trance

☐ UNDISCOVERED
EVCD 4 / Nov '96 / Evolution

Hard-Ons

☐ YUMMY
Where did she come from / Where did she come from / Dull / Cool hand luke / Something I don't want to do / Sit beside you / Jaye's song / On and on / Ain't gonna let you go / Me or you / Spew / Fade away / Little miss evil / Wait around / Feast on flesh / Stairway to heaven
SOL 26CD / Feb '91 / Vinyl Solution

Hardcastle, Paul

☐ FIRST LIGHT
Inner changes / Sancitity / Tribal call / Source / Celestial rhythm / First light part 1 / Forest dawn / Forever dreaming / Kingdom of dreams / Nomad's flight / First light part 2 / Rush hour / Bridge / Horizons / Eden
NSPCD 516 / Jun '97 / Connoisseur Collection

☐ PAUL HARDCASTLE PRESENTS JAZZMASTERS
SPOOKCD 002 / Sep '96 / Fantom

☐ VERY BEST OF PAUL HARDCASTLE, THE
Nineteen / Don't waste my time / Just for the money / Eat your heart out / Wizzard / Foolin' yourself / Walk in the night / 40 years / Central Park / Moonhopper / Better / Earth from space / On the run / Voices of the world
CDGOLD 1040 / Jul '96 / EMI Gold

Hardcores

☐ EEDENIN POLTTAJA
AA 026 / Jul '97 / AA

☐ SANANSAATTAJAT
AA 029 / Jul '97 / AA

Hardelin

☐ UNION (Hardelin, Thore & Oline)
CCD 10005CD / Apr '95 / Musikk Distribujson

Hardeman, Rick

☐ ALL STAR RHYTHM
JCD 263 / Jun '96 / Jazzology

Harden, Wilbur

☐ MAINSTREAM 1958 (The East Coast Jazz Scene) (Harden, Wilbur & John Coltrane)
Wells Fargo / West 42nd Street / EFFPH / Snuffy / Rhodomagnetics
SV 0121 / Oct '97 / Savoy Jazz

Hardfloor

☐ BEST OF HARDFLOOR, THE (2CD Set)
Once again back / Into the nature / Mahogany roots / Dub dope / Fish 'n' chips / Ain't nuttin' but a format thing / Lost in the silver box / Yimtrop / Confess / Acperience / Fever called love: *Rising High Collective* / Circus bells: *Armani, Robert* / Is there anybody out there: *Bassheads* / Beavis at bat / Strikeout / Blue Monday: *New Order* / It's no good: *Depeche Mode* / Kangaroos and bubbles / Yeke yeke: *Mori Kante*
EYEUKCD 015 / 22 Sep '97 / Eye Q

☐ HOME RUN
HHCD 19S / Jun '96 / Harthouse

Hardie, Alastair

☐ COMPLIMENTS TO THE KING
HPMCD 002 / Jan '95 / Hardie Press

Hardie, Ian

☐ BREATH OF FRESHER AIRS, A
Mrs. Elspeth Hardie / Goat in the boat / Fiona's jig / New 19th / Mellerstain House / Knock of Braemoray / Andrew James Hardie / Cawdor wood / Palpitation reel / Mrs. Willie Wastle / Compose yourself waltz / Segs hornpipe / Macbeaths of Tulloch Castle / Invernairn two-step / Lochindorb / Lochdhu waltz / Grand slam / Horsbrugh Castle / Vivianae / Helsinki Harbour / Lethen bar / White in the heather / Suitor's waltz / Bonnie lass o'wark / Lights of balintore / Liathach / Dulsie bridge / Locked bucket / Shifting sands / Esther Stephenson of Embleton / Chatterin' teeth / Nigg rigs jig / Oystercatcher / Drumochter sun / Crown knot / Snow on the ben / Up an' doon reel / Lost village of Culbin / Tarbat ness light / Drummossie muir
CDTRAX 049 / Jan '92 / Greentrax

☐ SPIDERS WEB (Hardie, Ian & Andy Thorburn)
Tweedle dee reel / My compliments to the biochemist / Brackla waltz / Jig of the clan beag / Last farewell / Glenkinchie's compliments to Lord and Lady Macfarlane of Bea / Lime Hill / Canmembert waltz / Setting sun / Streens / 31 steps / Gallowhill reel / Torgarrow
CDTRAX 152 / 1 Mar '98 / Greentrax

Hardie, Jonny

☐ UP IN THE AIR (Hardie, Jonny & Gavin Marwick)
LDLCD 1226 / Jan '95 / Lochshore

Hardiman, Ronan

☐ SOLAS
Love song / All the way back home / Dreaming / Heaven / New lands / Take me with you / Angel / Far away / Communication / Secret world
5394382 / 16 Feb '98 / Polydor

Hardin, Andrew

☐ CONEY ISLAND MOON
RTMCD 76 / Jun '96 / Round Tower

Hardin, Eddie

☐ CIRCUMSTANTIAL EVIDENCE
Little teaser / Mine tonight / Maybe I'm amazed / That's what the lady said / Long tall Sally / California / It won't be long / Universal dream / Maybe baby / Mess of blues / Accidental instrumental / Strawberry fields forever / Isolated lady / Love is all / Move in the right place / Ressurection shuffle
SJPCD 024 / Jun '98 / Angel Air

☐ DAWN TIL DUSK
NAGE 9CD / Jul '86 / Art Of Landscape

☐ LIVE AT THE MARQUEE VOL.3 (Hardin, Eddie & Pete York)
RPM 135 / Aug '94 / RPM

☐ LIVE IN THE 70'S (Hardin, Eddie & Pete York)
Freedom suite / I care for you / Pike rides again / Find myself again / Everyone I know / Paris / My only friend will leave me in the end / Where are you now / If there's not you / Close of play / Where I'm gonna sleep tonight
SJPCD 016 / Apr '98 / Angel Air

☐ SURVIVAL
Innocent victims / Lost childhood / Seeds of suspicion / Schools of thought / Perfect survivor / Lessons to learn / Where do we go from here / Slice of paradise / Never again / Rules we can't ignore
NAGE 19CD / Sep '88 / Art Of Landscape

☐ WHEN WE WERE YOUNG
Monday afternoon / Whwn we were young / While the city sleeps / Bricks and mortar / Lost ground / Tried and tasted / One day / Taste of life / Let silence speak / For Alan
INAK 11005CD / Nov '97 / In Akustik

☐ WIND IN THE WILLOWS ROCK CONCERT, THE
Main theme / Good morning to you / I've forgotten how to smile / Fairground fantasy / Wild wood / Badger / Looking forward / Maggie's song / Piper at the gate's of dawn / Why can't we go home / Wayfarers / Life we left behind / Looking forward
SJPCD 019 / 26 Jan '98 / Angel Air

☐ WIZARD'S CONVENTION VOL.2
Hot head of steam / Zermatitus blues / Happening all the time / Here I go again / Someone sings / Talking ain't cheap / Try a little tenderness / Sultana / Brickmaker blues / Can't let you go / I think it's gonna rain today / As long as I still have you / Before we say goodbye / Lucille / What a way to spend a day
SJPCD 009 / Jun '97 / Angel Air

Hardin, Tim

☐ HANG ON TO A DREAM (The Verve Recordings/2CD Set)
Don't make promises / Green rocky road / Smugglin' man / How long / While you're on your way / It'll never happen again / Reason to believe / Never too far / Part of the wind / Ain't gonna do without / Misty roses / How can we hang on to a dream / If I were a carpenter / Red balloon / Black sheep boy / Lady came from Baltimore / Baby close it's eyes / You upset the grace of living when you lie / Speak like a child / See where you are and get out / It's hard to believe in love for long / Tribute to Hank Williams / While you're on your way / It'll never happen again / Airmobile / Whiskey, whiskey / Seventh son / Danville dame / House of the rising sun / Bo Diddley / I can't slow down / Hello baby / Rolling stone / You get a reparation / Keep your hands off her / Nobody knows you (when you're down and out) / Hoochie koochie man / So glad you're mine / You can't judge a book by its cover / She ain't home / You say you love me / How time flies / You can ruin a man / If I knew / She's up to something new / Who'll be the man / First love song
5215832 / Feb '97 / Polydor

☐ NINE
Shiloh town / Rags and old iron / Person to person / Blues on my ceiling / Fire and rain / Judge and jury / Never too far / Look our love over / Darling girl / Is there no rest for the weary / While you're on your way
SEECD 335 / Feb '97 / See For Miles

☐ SIMPLE SONGS OF FREEDOM (The Tim Hardin Collection)
Simple song of freedom / Shiloh town / Turn the page / Playing cards/The magician / First love song / Last sweet moments / If I knew / Hoboin' / Andre Johray / Southern butterfly / Bird on a wire / Midnight caller / Yankee lady / Till we meet again / I'll be home / If I knew / Thanks to Gideon
4851082 / Nov '96 / Columbia

☐ TOMORROW TODAY
RPMCD 128 / May '94 / RPM

☐ WORLD'S SMALLEST BIG BAND
RPMCD 129 / May '94 / RPM

Harding, John Wesley

☐ AWAKE
Intro / Your ghost / Window seat / Burn / It's all my fault / Sweat...tears / Poor heart / Miss Fortune / Song I wrote / Something to write / You're looking at me / You so and so / I'm staying here / Outro
ZERCD 1210 / 25 May '98 / Zero Hour

☐ NEW DEAL
JWHCD 1 / Jan '97 / Kingfisher

Harding, Mike

☐ PLUTONIUM ALLEY
Head for the hills / Cait o'ma chree / Victor jara of chile / Fiddler's elbow-dingle regatta / Christmas 1914 / Plutonium alley / Black lung blues / Wild geese / Kerry polkas / Closing time / Sangria wine
MOOCD 9 / Mar '94 / Moonraker

Hardship Post

☐ SOMEBODY SPOKE
SPCD 289 / Jul '95 / Sub Pop

Hardskin

☐ HARD NUTS AND HARD CUNTS
HOO 31CD / May '97 / Helen Of Oi
SKIP 067CD / 9 Mar '98 / Broken

Hardware

☐ RACE, RELIGION AND HATE
CDMVEST 75 / Aug '96 / Bulletproof

☐ THIRD EYE OPEN
Got a feeling / Waiting on you / What's goin' down / Love obsession / Hard look / Shake it / Walls came down / 500 Years / Tell me / Leakin'
RCD 10304 / Jun '94 / Black Arc

Hardway, James

☐ DEEPER, WIDER SMOOTHER SHIT
HEMP 3L / Jul '96 / Recordings Of Substance
HEMP 3CD / 8 Dec '97 / Recordings Of Substance

☐ RESHUFFLE AND SPIN AGAIN
HEMP 18CD / 29 Jun '98 / Recordings Of Substance

☐ WELCOME TO THE NEON LOUNGE (2CD Set)
HEMP 13CD / 23 Feb '98 / Recordings Of Substance

Hardy, Francoise

☐ COLLECTION, THE
Tous les garcons les filles / Oh oh cheri / Ton meilleur ami / J'suis d'accord / Va pas prendre un tambour / Le temps de l'amour / Je n'attend plus personne / Ce petit coeur / Je veux qu'il revienne / Le temps des souvenirs / Je changerais d'avis (se telefonado) / Il est des choses / Comme / Je ne suis la pour presonne / Ma jeunesse fout le camp / Il n'ya pas d'amour hereux
74321145202 / Apr '94 / Vogue

☐ GREATEST RECORDINGS
Tous le garcons et les filles / Le temps de l'amour / Le premier bonheur du jour / Mon amie la rose / All over the world / L'amitie / Ce petit coeur / Je ne suis la pour personne / Il est des chose / La maison ou j'ai grand / Comme / Voila
74321203912 / May '95 / Vogue

☐ IN VOGUE VOL.2
VGCD 600145 / Oct '93 / Vogue

☐ LE DANGER
CDVIR 51 / Jun '96 / Virgin

☐ LES CHANSONS D'AMOUR
472478 / Sep '96 / Flarenasch

☐ LES CHANSONS D'AMOUR
Ce petite coeur / Il n'y a pas d'amour heureux / Mon amie la rose / Tout les garcons et les filles / L'amitie / La maison ou j'ai grandi / La temps da l'amour / Il est des choses / Ma jeunesse fout le camp / Ton meilleur ami / Voila / Parlami di te / J'ai jete mon coeur / Autumn rendez-vous / La tua mano / C'est a l'amour auquel je pense / Je ne suis pas la pour personne / Le premier bonheur du jour / Comme / Find me boy / This little heart / All over the world
74321415022 / Oct '96 / Camden

☐ LES INOUBLIABLES DE...
472297 / Feb '97 / Flarenasch

☐ TOUS LES GARCONS ET LES FILLES
CD 352060 / May '93 / Duchesse

☐ YEH-YEH GIRL FROM PARIS
Tous les garcons et les filles / Ca a rate / La fille avec toi / Oh oh cheri / Le temps de l'amour / Il est tout pour moi / On se plait / Ton meilleur ami / J'ai jete mon coeur / Il est parti un jour / J'suis d'accord / C'est a la amour auquel je pense
74321264702 / May '95 / Vogue

Hardy, Hagood

☐ MOROCCO (Hardy, Hagood Sextet)
SKCD 22018 / Jun '93 / Sackville

Hardy, Jack

☐ RETROSPECTIVE
BRAM 1989072 / Nov '93 / Brambus

☐ THROUGH
BRAM 1990122 / Nov '93 / Brambus

☐ TWO OF SWORDS
422166 / May '94 / New Rose

Hardy, Rick

☐ COCKNEY FAVOURITES (18 East End Outings)
I'm Henry the eighth / Hopping down in Kent / I'm so proud that I'm a cockney / Lily of Laguna / Don't dilly dally on the way / Daisy bell / Knocked 'em in the Old Kent Road / On mother Kelly's doorstep / Milton Keynes / Gladys / She was one of the early birds / Halfway back from Southend / Sling yer hook / Harry Harry Harry / It's a great big shame / When father papered the parlour / I'm forever blowing bubbles / London medley
308902 / 11 May '98 / Hallmark

Hare

☐ PROUD TO BE LOUD
Love me to the bone / Crawling / Sorrow / Lies / Different ways / Blind / Otaku / Misery / Slum / Ready / Show me / Ice
CDMFN 215 / Feb '97 / Music For Nations

Hare, Colin

☐ MARCH HARE...PLUS
Get up the road / Bloodshot eyes / For where have you been / Find me / Underground girl / To my maker / Grannie, grannie / Alice / Nothing to write home about / New day / Cowboy Joe (saga) / Just like me / Charlie Brown's time / Fighting for peace
SEECD 261 / Sep '89 / See For Miles

Hargrove, Roy

☐ APPROACHING STANDARDS
Easy to remember / Ruby my dear / Whisper not / What's new / September in the rain / You don't know what love is / Things we did last summer / Everything I have is yours / Dedicated to you / My shining hour
01241631782 / Oct '94 / Novus

☐ COLLECTED ROY HARGROVE, THE
Wee / BHG / Ruby my dear / Heartbreaker / Night watch / Little Bennie / Milestones / My shining hour / Re-evaluation / Homelife revisited
09026687102 / Jul '98 / RCA Victor

☐ PARKER'S MOOD (Hargrove, Roy & Christian McBride/Stephen Scott Trio)
Klactoveesedstein / Parker's mood / Marmaduke / Steeplechase / Laura / Dexterity / Yardbird suite / Red cross / Repetition / Laird baird / Dewey Square / Cardboard / April in Paris / Chasin' the bird / Bongo beep / Star eyes
5279072 / Mar '96 / Verve

☐ VIBE, THE
Vibe / Caryisms / Where were you / Alter ego / Thang / Pinocchio / Milestones / Things we did last summer / Blues for booty greens / Running out of time
PD 90668 / Jun '92 / Novus

☐ WITH THE TENORS OF OUR TIME (Hargrove, Roy Quintet)
Soppin' the biscuit / When we were one / Valse hot / Once forgotten / Shade of jade / Greens at the chicken shack / Never let me / Serenity / Across the pond / Wild is love / Mental phrasing / April's fool
5230192 / Jun '94 / Verve

Haricots Rouges

☐ SANS FIL
BB 282 / Oct '96 / Black & Blue

Hariharan, A.

☐ DIVINE UNION
NRCD 0068 / Feb '97 / Navras

Harket, Morten

☐ WILD SEED
Kind of christmas card / Spanish steps / Lay me down tonight / Wild seed / Tell me what you see / Lord / East-timor / Ready to go home / Stay / Los angeles / Brodsky tune / Half in love half in hate
9362459122 / Sep '95 / Warner Bros.

Harlan Cage

☐ HARLAN CAGE
19965 / Oct '96 / Made To Measure

Harle, John

☐ TERROR AND MAGNIFICENCE
Mistress mine / Three ravens / Hunting the hare / Rosie-blood / Terror and magnificence
4526052 / Oct '96 / Argo

Harlem Gospel Singers

☐ HARLEM GOSPEL SINGERS
0028702 / Apr '95 / Edel

Harlem Hamfats

☐ HAMFAT SWING 1936-1938
158932 / Apr '97 / Blues Collection

☐ HARLEM HAMFATS VOL.1 1936
DOCD 5271 / Aug '94 / Document

☐ HARLEM HAMFATS VOL.2 1936-1937
DOCD 5272 / Aug '94 / Document

☐ HARLEM HAMFATS VOL.3 1936-1938
DOCD 5273 / Aug '94 / Document

☐ HARLEM HAMFATS VOL.4 1938-1939
DOCD 5274 / Aug '94 / Document

Harlem Jazz Camels

☐ BLUE INTERLUDE
NCD 8851 / Nov '96 / Phontastic

☐ DROP ME OFF IN HARLEM
NCD 8832 / Mar '94 / Phontastic

Harlem Spirit

☐ FUSION
FUCD 001 / May '97 / Fusion

Harlem Underground

☐ HARLEM UNDERGROUND
Cheeba cheeba / Fed up / Finger in it / Ain't no sunshine / Fed up
HUBCD 5 / Feb '96 / Hubbub

Harley, Steve

☐ BEST YEARS OF OUR LIVES (Harley, Steve & Cockney Rebel)
Introducing 'The Best Years' / Mad mad moonlight / Mr. Raffles (man it was mean) / It wasn't me / Panorama / Make me smile (come up and see me) / Back to the farm / 49th parallel / Best years of our lives / Another journey / Sebastian
CZ 385 / Feb '91 / EMI

☐ FACE TO FACE (Harley, Steve & Cockney Rebel)
7997202 / 1 Jun '98 / EMI

☐ GREATEST HITS LIVE (Harley, Steve & Cockney Rebel)
Mr. Soft / Mr. Raffles (man it was mean) / When I'm with you / Star for a week / Riding the waves (for Virginia Woolf) / Lighthouse / Best years of our life / Sweet dreams / Psychomodo / Sling it / Sebastian / Make me smile (come up and see me) / Love's a prima donna
RM 1511 / Aug '97 / BR Music

☐ HUMAN MENAGERIE (Cockney Rebel)
7947562 / 1 Jun '98 / EMI

☐ LIVE AND UNLEASHED (Harley, Steve & Cockney Rebel)
Make me smile (come up and see me) / Mr. Soft / Mr. Raffles (man it was mean) / When I'm with you / Star for a week / Riding the waves / Lighthouse / Best years of our lives / Psychomodo / Sling it / Sebastian / Love's a prima donna
QED 134 / Nov '96 / Tring

☐ MAKE ME SMILE (The Best Of Steve Harley & Cockney Rebel/2CD Set) (Harley, Steve & Cockney Rebel)
Mr. Soft / Riding the waves (for Virginia Woolf) / Irresistible / Mr. Raffles (man it was mean) / Freedom's prisoner / Hideaway / Judy Teen / Best years of our lives (live) / Make me smile (come up and see me) / If this is love (give me more) / Here comes the sun / Sebastian / Roll the dice / Understand / I believe (love's a prima donna) / Tumbling down
CDGO 2036 / Jan '97 / EMI

☐ MORE THAN SOMEWHAT (The Very Best Of Steve Harley)
Make me smile (come up and see me) / (Love) compared with you / Judy teen / Mr.Raffles / Mr.Soft / Sebastian / That's my life in your hands / Here comes the sun / All men are hungry / Best years of out lives / Star for a week / Rain in Venice / Last time I saw you / Psychomodo / Irresistible
4937642 / 23 Mar '98 / EMI

☐ ON AIR (Harley, Steve & Cockney Rebel)
SFRSCD 056 / 30 Mar '98 / Strange Fruit

☐ POETIC JUSTICE
That's my life / What becomes of the broken hearted / Two damn'd lies / Loveless / Strange communications / All in a life's work / Love minus zero-no limit / Safe / Last time I saw you / Crazy love / Riding the waves
TRACD 242 / Aug '96 / Transatlantic

☐ PSYCHOMODO, THE (Cockney Rebel)
Sweet dreams / Psychomodo / Mr. Soft / Singular band / Ritz / Cavaliers / Bed in the corner / Sling it / Tumbling down / Big big deal / Such a dream
7947552 / 1 Jun '98 / EMI

☐ STEVE HARLEY
GFS 072 / Jul '97 / Going For A Song

☐ TIMELESS FLIGHT (Harley, Steve & Cockney Rebel)
Red is a mean, mean colour / White, white dove / Understand / All men are hungry / Black or white / Everything changes / Nothing is sacred / Don't go, don't cry / Throw your soul down here / Mad mad moonlight (live)
7959272 / 1 Jun '98 / EMI

☐ YES YOU CAN
08431802 / Dec '95 / CTE

Harlingtox Angel Divine

☐ HARLINGTOX ANGEL DIVINE
LRR 6022 / Aug '97 / Laundry Room

Harman, James

☐ BLACK AND WHITE
BT 1118CD / Aug '95 / Black Top

☐ CARDS ON THE TABLE (Harman, James Band)
BT 1104CD / Jul '94 / Black Top

☐ ICEPICK'S STORY
Dirt road / Stranger blues / Leavin' for Memphis / Three way party / Got news / Drive-in life / Hollywood girls / Temporary blues / Phonebill blues / Sparks (start flyin') / Tall skinny Mama (Icepick's story) / Second voyage of Noah's ark / Walk the streets (cold and lonely) / I'm gone
MMBCD 702 / May '97 / Me & My Blues

Harman, Mark

☐ THIS 'N' THAT
Lady rock 'n' roll / Thankyou baby / Dungarees / You and I / You got your Daddy on the run / You give me heartache / You can't buy me / I guess you know by now / This 'n' that / Hold on / You'll be in my arms again / For the very last time
JRCD 12 / Sep '97 / Jappin' & Rockin'

Harmar, Jeff

☐ BECAUSE OF YOU
VSD 5831 / 16 Feb '98 / Varese Sarabande

Harmful

☐ APOPLEXY 136
EFA 152202 / 13 Oct '97 / Blu Noise

☐ HARMFUL
EFA 127902 / Dec '95 / Blu Noise

Harmonia

☐ DELUXE
POCP 2388 / 22 Jun '98 / Brain

☐ EVENTS LINE
1295700862 / Jan '97 / Materiali Sonori

☐ MUSIK VON HARMONIA
POCP 2387 / 22 Jun '98 / Brain

Harmonica Slim

☐ GET ME MY SHOTGUN
Hole in her belly / Woman 'round my door / Gun tootin' blues / Big leg woman / Bright lights big city / Coal black mare / I don't want no woman / Phone headed woman / Highway 49 / Shake for me / Drivin' wheel / San-ho-zay
FCD 5001 / Jan '98 / Fedora

Harmonizing Four

☐ 1950-1955
HTCD 29 / May '95 / Heritage

☐ I SHALL NOT BE MOVED
All things are possible / Farther along / Motherless child / Where would I go / But to the Lord / I shall not be moved / Lived and he loved me / His eye is on the sparrow / When I've done my best / Go down / Moses / Will he welcome me / I love to call his name / Pass me not / Close to thee / God will take care of you / Mary don't you weep / Faith of our fathers / My Lord what a morning / Live like Jesus / Lord's prayer
CPCD 8112 / Jul '95 / Charly

Harmony Rockets

☐ PARALYZED MIND OF THE ARCHANGEL
ABB 90CD / 20 Oct '97 / Big Cat

Harp, Everette

☐ WHAT'S GOING ON
What's going on / What's happening brother / Flying high / Save the children / God is love / Mercy mercy me / Right on / Wholy holy / Inner city blues / Inner city (reprise)
CDP 8530682 / Mar '97 / Blue Note

Harp, Sammy

☐ NOTHIN' FANCY
CDMANU 1532 / 21 Aug '97 / ODE

Harper, Ben

☐ FIGHT FOR YOUR MIND
Opression / Ground on down / Another lonely day / Please me like you want to / Gold to me / Burn one down / Excuse me Mr / People lead / Fight for your mind / Give a man a home / By my side / Power of the gospel / God fearing man / One road to freedom
CDVUS 93 / Jul '95 / Virgin

☐ WELCOME TO THE CRUEL WORLD
Three of us / Whipping boy / Breakin' down / Don't take that attitude to your grave / Waiting on an angel / Mama's got a girlfriend now / Forever / Like a king / Pleasure and pain / Walk away / How many miles must we march / Welcome to the cruel world / I'll rise / Going to see the king
CDVUS 69 / Jul '94 / Virgin

☐ WILL TO LIVE, THE
Faded / Homeless child / Number three / Roses from my friends / Jah work / I want to be ready / Will to live / Ashes / Widow of a living man / Glory and consequence / Mama's trippin' / I shall not walk alone
CDVUS 128 / May '97 / Virgin
CDVUSX 128 / 6 Apr '98 / Virgin

Harper, Billy

☐ BILLY HARPER QUINTET ON TOUR VOL.3
SCCD 31366 / Feb '96 / Steeplechase

☐ IF ONLY OUR HEARTS COULD SEE
DIW 931 / Oct '97 / DIW

☐ SOMALIA
Somalia / Thy will be done / Quest / Light within / Quest in 3
ECD 221332 / Dec '95 / Evidence

Harper, Clay

☐ EAST OF EASTER
ALT 31152 / Aug '97 / Ichiban

Harper, Don

☐ SYDNEY SUNDAY
St. Thomas / Polka dots and moonbeams / Honeysuckle Rose / Falling in love with love / Greensleeves / Sydney Sunday / Afternoon in the art gallery / Sunday morning / Them there eyes / Air on a G string / Softly as in a morning sunrise
CLGCD 024 / Jun '92 / Calligraph

Harper, Nick

☐ LIGHT AT THE END OF THE KENNEL
Hundred things / Is this really me / Shadowlands / Flying dog / Headless / Riverside
SG 094CD / Dec '94 / Sangraal
TERRCD 003 / Nov '96 / Terra Nova

☐ SEED
SRCD 095 / Jun '96 / Sangraal

☐ SMITHEREENS
QRCD 098 / 11 May '98 / Quixotic

Harper, Roy

☐ BORN IN CAPTIVITY/WORK OF HEART
Stan / Drawn to the flames / Come to bed eyes / No woman is safe / I am a child / Elizabeth / No one ever gets out alive / Two lovers in the moon / We are the people / All of us children / We are the people (reprise)
HUCD 008 / Jan '97 / Science Friction

☐ BULLINAMINGVASE
HUCD 021 / Nov '96 / Science Friction

☐ BURN THE WORLD
Burn the world (studio) / Burn the world (live)
HUCD 013 / Mar '97 / Science Friction

☐ COME OUT FIGHTING GHENGIS SMITH
Freak street / You don't need money / Ageing raver / In a beautiful rambling mess / All you need is what you have / Circle / Highgate cemetary / Come out fighting Ghengis Smith / Zaney Janey / Ballad of songwriter / Midspring dithering / Zenjam / It's tomorrow and today is yesterday / Francesca / She's the one
HUCD 006 / Jan '97 / Science Friction

☐ COMMERCIAL BREAKS
My little girl / I'm in love with you / Ten years ago / Sail away / I wanna be part of the news / Cora / Come up and see me / Fly catcher / Too many movies / Square boxes / Burn the world (part 1) / Playing prisons
HUCD 016 / Jan '97 / Science Friction

☐ DEATH OR GLORY
Death or glory / War came home / Tonight duty / Waiting for Godot / Part zed next to me / Man kind / Tallest tree / Miles remains / Fourth world / Why evening star / Cardboard city / One more tomorrow / Plough / On summer day / If I can
HUCD 012 / Oct '96 / Science Friction
HYCD 200127 / Dec '97 / Hypertension

☐ DREAM SOCIETY, THE
Songs of love / Dancing all the night / Psychopath / I want to be in love / Drugs for everybody / Come the revolution / Angel of the night / Dream society / Broken wing / These fifty years
HUCD 029 / 1 Jun '98 / Science Friction

☐ FLASHES FROM THE ARCHIVES OF OBLIVION
Commune / Don't you grieve / Twelve hours of sunset / Kangaroo blues / All Ireland / Me and my woman / South Africa / Highway blues / One man rock 'n' roll band / Another day / MCP blues
HUCD 010 / Jan '97 / Science Friction

☐ FLAT BAROQUE AND BERSERK
Don't you grieve / I hate the white man / Feeling all the saturday / How does it feel / Goodbye / Another day / Davey / East of the sun / Tom tiddler's ground / Francesca / Song of the ages / Hell's angels
HUCD 028 / 10 Nov '97 / Science Friction

☐ FLAT, BAROQUE AND BERSERK
Don't you grieve / I hate the white man / Feeling all the Saturday / How does it feel / Goodbye / Another day / Davey / East of the sun and west of the moon / Tom Tiddler's ground / Francesca / Song of the ages / Hell's angels
HUCD 3 / Oct '94 / Science Friction

☐ FOLKJOKEOPUS
Sgt. Sunshine / She's the one / In the time of water / Composer of life / One for all / Exercising some / Control / McGoohan's blues / Manana
HUCD 009 / Jan '97 / Science Friction

☐ GARDEN OF URANIUM (Descendants Of Smith)
Laughing inside / Garden of uranium / Still life / Pinches of salt / Desert island / Government surplus / Surplus liquorice / Liquorice alltime / Maile Lei / Same shoes / Descendants of Smith / Laughing inside (Demo version)
HUCD 014 / Mar '97 / Science Friction

☐ HQ
Game (parts I-V) / Game / Spirit lives / Grown ups are just silly children / Referendum / Forget me not / Hallucinating light / When an old cricketer leaves the crease
HUCD 019 / Apr '97 / Science Friction

☐ IN BETWEEN EVERY LINE
One of those days in England / Short and sweet / Referendum / Highway blues / True story / Game / One man rock 'n' roll band / Hangman
HUCD 018 / Mar '97 / Science Friction

☐ INTRODUCTION TO ROY HARPER, AN
Legend / She's the one / Tom tiddler's ground / Highway blues / Che / Hallucinating light / One of those days in England / You / Nineteen forty-eightish / Pinches of salt / Ghost dance / Tallest tree / Miles remains
HUCD 017 / Oct '96 / Science Friction

☐ LEGEND
JHD 064CD / Oct '94 / JHD

☐ LIFEMASK
Highway blues / All Ireland / Little lady / Bank of the dead / South Africa / Lord's prayer / Ballad of songwriter / Zaney Janey / Midspring dithering / Zenjam
HUCD 005 / Jan '97 / Science Friction

☐ LIVE AT LES COUSINS 1969
BP 220CD / May '96 / Blueprint

☐ LIVE AT THE BBC VOL.1
Hey Francesca / Hell's angels / She's the one / I hate the white man / It's today and today is yesterday / Don't you grieve / North country girl / Hors d'oeuvres / One man rock 'n' roll band / Same old rock / South Africa / Kangeroo blues / Forever / Twelve hours of sunset / Little lady / All Ireland
HUCD 022 / Apr '97 / Science Friction

☐ LIVE AT THE BBC VOL.2
Too many movies / MCP Blues / Forever / South Africa / Highway blues / I'll see you again / Commune / Another day / North country / Twelve hours of sunset / Me and my woman
HUCD 023 / Apr '97 / Science Friction

☐ LIVE AT THE BBC VOL.3 (John Peel/ Bob Harris)
Commune / Forever / Highway blues / I'll see you again / North country / Too many movies / Forever / North country / Twelve hours of sunset / One man rock 'n' roll band / Too many movies
HUCD 024 / Jun '97 / Science Friction

☐ LIVE AT THE BBC VOL.4
Hallucinating light / Referendum / Highway blues / Too many movies / Spirit lives / Home / Game / Grown ups are just silly children
HUCD 025 / Jun '97 / Science Friction

☐ LIVE AT THE BBC VOL.5
Hallucinating light / Spirit lives / Referendum / Another day / Cherishing the lonesome / These last days / Grown ups are just silly children / Forget me not / Same old rock / I hate the white man
HUCD 026 / Jul '97 / Science Friction

☐ LIVE AT THE BBC VOL.6
Forget me not / One of those days in England / I hate the white man / Same old rock / Twelve hours of sunset / Highway blues
HUCD 027 / Jul '97 / Science Friction

☐ LOONY ON THE BUS
No change / Playing prisons / I wanna be part of the news / Burn the world / Casualty / Cora / Loony on the bus / Come up and see me / Flycatcher / Square boxes
AWCD 1011 / Nov '88 / Awareness

☐ ONCE
Once / Once in the middle of nowhere / Nowhere to run to / Black cloud of Islam / If / Winds of change / Berliners / Sleeping at the wheel / For longer than it takes / Ghost dance
HUCD 011 / Mar '97 / Science Friction

☐ RETURN OF THE SOPHISTICATED BEGGAR, THE
China girl / Goldfish bowl / Sophisticated beggar / My friend / Big fat silver aeroplane / Blackpool / Hup hup spiral / Girlie / October the 12th / Black clouds / Mr. Station Master / Forever / Committed / Legend
CRESTCD 027 / Nov '97 / Mooncrest

☐ SOPHISTICATED BEGGAR
Goldfish bowl / Sophisticated beggar / Big fat silver aeroplane / Legend / Girlie / October 12th / Black clouds / Mr. Station Master / My friend / China girl
HUCD 007 / Jan '97 / Science Friction

☐ STORMCOCK
Hors d'oeuvres / One man rock 'n' roll band / Same old rock / Me and my woman
HUCD 004 / Apr '97 / Science Friction

☐ UNHINGED
Descendants of Smith / Legend / North Country / When an old cricketer leaves the crease / Three hundred words / Hope / Naked flame / Commune / South Africa / Back to the stones / Frozen moment / Highway blues / Same old rock
HUCD 020 / Mar '97 / Science Friction

☐ VALENTINE
Forbidden fruit / Male chauvinist pig blues / I'll see you again / Twelve hours of sunset / Acapulco gold / Commune / Magic woman / Che / North country / Forever / Home (studio) / Too many movies / Home
HUCD 015 / Jan '97 / Science Friction

Harper, Winard

☐ BE YOURSELF
Night watch / Li'l Willie / My shell / Trane stop / Last dance / Hi fly / Quiet as it's kept / Lonesome head / You're looking at me / Toku-do / Poon
4781972 / Feb '95 / Epicure

☐ TRAP DANCER
Tap dancer / Sound for sore ears / Amoretta / You don't what love is / Social call / Work song / Helen's song / Qamara / How deep is the ocean / Skylark / Blues for brown / Key west / Shorty long / Allahu akbar
SAVCD 2013 / 16 Mar '98 / Savant

Harpo, Slim

☐ BEST OF SLIM HARPO, THE
Baby scratch my back / Got love if you want it / I'm a king bee / Little queen bee (got a brand new king) / Shake your hips / Te-ni-nee-ni-nu / Buzz me baby / Buzzin' / Raining in my heart / Still rainin' in my heart / Late last night / Tip on in, Part 1 / Bobby sox baby / Don't start cryin' now / I need money (keep your alibis) / Strange love / Rock me baby / Blues hangover
CDCHM 410 / Jul '92 / Ace

☐ I'M A KING BEE
I'm a king bee / I love the life I'm livin' / Moody blues / Buzzin' / Dream girl / Got love if you want it / Wonderin' and worryin' / Strange love / You'll be sorry one day / One more day / Bobby sox baby / Late last night / Buzz me baby / Yeah yeah baby / What a dream / Don't start cryin' now / Blues hangover / My home is a prison / Please don't turn me down / Snoopin' around / Raining in my heart / That's alright baby / Lover's confession / Boogie chillun
CDCHD 510 / Oct '93 / Ace

☐ SHAKE YOUR HIPS
Shake your hips / Little queen bee (got a brand new king) / Still rainin' in my heart / I need money (keep your alibis) / What's goin' on baby / Harpo's blues / Sittin' here wonderin' / We're two of a kind / I'm gonna miss you (like the devil) / Baby scratch my back / I don't want no-one (to take me away from you) / Midnight blues / Lovin' you (the way I do) / Baby you got what I want / Your love for me is gone / I'm your bread maker, baby / Stop working blues / I'm waiting on you baby / You'll never find a love as true as mine / Little Sally Walker / I gotta stop lovin' you / Blueberry Hill / Something inside of me / Tonite I'm lonely / Man is crying / Still rainin' in my heart
CDCHD 558 / Mar '95 / Ace

☐ STING IT THEN
Star time announcement / I'm a king bee / Buzzin' / I got love oif you want it / You know I love you / Lottie Mo / Eveybody needs somebody / Big boss man / Hold me tenderly / I'll take care of you / Boogie chillun / Moody blues / Sugar coated love / Star time theme / I don't play / Rainin' in my heart / Little Liza Jane
CDCHD 658 / 24 Nov '97 / Ace

☐ TE-NI-NEE-NI-NU (The Best Of Slim Harpo)
REP 4206 / Aug '91 / Repertoire

☐ TIP ON IN
Tip on in (part 1) / Tip on in (part 2) / I'm gonna keep what I've got / I've got to be with you tonight / Mailbox blues / Te-ni-nee-ni-nu / Mohair Sam / I just can't leave you / That's why I love you / Just for you / My baby she's got it / I've been your good thing for you / Hey little Lee / Stick your chest out baby / Folsom Prison blues / Mutual friend / I've got my finger on your trigger / Price is too high / Jody man / Music's hot / You can't make it / Hippy song / Dynamite / Rock me baby / Baby please come home
CDCHD 606 / Jun '96 / Ace

Harpy

☐ HARPY
EFA 084772 / Apr '97 / Dossier

Harrell, Bill

☐ CAT CAME BACK, THE
Cat came back / Hobo Bill's last ride / Look at me and tell me / Trouble in mind / Little Maggie / Soldier's last letter / Tennessee border / Baggage coach ahead / This danged old town / It makes no difference now / Blizzard / Aren't you glad to be saved
REBCD 1742 / Jun '98 / Rebel

Harrell, Kelly

☐ COMPLETE RECORDED WORKS VOL.1 1925-1926
DOCD 8026 / Jun '98 / Document

☐ COMPLETE RECORDED WORKS VOL.2 1926-1929
DOCD 8027 / Jun '98 / Document

Harrell, Tom

☐ ART OF RHYTHM, THE
Petal's danse / Madrid / Oasis / Caribe / Doo bop / Exit in / Recitation / Las almas / Cinco quatro / Samba do amor
09026689242 / May '98 / RCA Victor

☐ FORM
Vista / Brazilian song / Scene / January spring / Rhythm form / For heaven's sake
CCD 14059 / Oct '93 / Contemporary

☐ LABYRINTH
Samba mate / Marimba song / Cheetah / Blue in one / Hot licks on the sidewalk / Majesty / Sun cycle / Darn that dream / Bear that in mind / Labyrinth
09026685122 / Oct '96 / RCA Victor

☐ SAIL AWAY
Eons / Glass mystery / Dream in June / Sail away / Buffalo wings / It always is / Dancing trees / Hope Street
CCD 14054 / Oct '93 / Contemporary

☐ STORIES
Rapture / Song flower / Mountain / Waters edge / Story / Viable blues / Touchstone
CCD 14043 / Oct '93 / Contemporary

Harrington, Jan

☐ CHRISTMAS IN NEW ORLEANS
NHRSP 4 / Nov '97 / Nagel Heyer

☐ MY GOD IS REAL
MECCACD 1042 / Feb '94 / Music Mecca

Harrington, Tim

☐ MASTER FREQUENCY
TX 51217CD / Mar '96 / Triple X

Harriott, Derrick

☐ 16 ROCKSTEADY HITS
JMC 200214 / Jul '94 / Jamaican Gold

☐ DANCEHALL TRAIN
CRCD 1016 / Mar '97 / Crystal

☐ DONKEY YEARS, THE
JMC 20012 / Apr '94 / Jamaican Gold

☐ RIDING THE MUSICAL CHARIOT
CDHB 58 / May '93 / Heartbeat

☐ SINGS ROCKSTEADY
Sock it to me / Walk the streets / Home,home,home / Tang tang festival song / Been so long / Standing in / Sitting on top / Long time / Have some mercy / Girl's alright with me / You really gotta hold on me / I'm not begging / It's alright / Close to me / Riding for a fall / Message from a black man
JMC 200213 / May '94 / Jamaican Gold

☐ SONGS FOR MIDNIGHT LOVERS
Eighteen with a bullet / Born to love you / Message from a black man / Groovy situation / Loser / Do I worry / Walk the streets / Standing in / Another lonely night / Solomon / Slave / No man is an island / Have you seen her / Since I lost my baby
CDTRL 198 / May '90 / Trojan

Harris, Anita

☐ EVERY DAY VALENTINE
Look of love / This girl's in love with you / Always something there to remind me / 24 hours from Tulsa / Whoever you are / I just don't know what to do with myself / I say a little prayer / House is not a home / Anyone who had a heart / Wives and lovers / Wishin' and hopin' / My Japanese boy / What the world needs now is love / Alfie / Walk on by / Make it easy on yourself / I'll never fall in love again / Long after tonight is all over / River deep mountain high / You've lost that lovin' feelin' / Loving you / Just loving you / Anniversary waltz
4841052 / 11 May '98 / Columbia

Harris, Barry

☐ CONFIRMATION (Harris, Barry & Kenny Barron Quartet)
Confirmation / On Green Dolphin Street / Tenderly / Embraceable you / All God's chillun' got rhythm / Body and soul / East of the sun / Oleo / Nascimento
CCD 79519 / Jan '97 / Black & Blue

☐ LIVE AT MAYBECK RECITAL HALL VOL.12
It could happen to you / All God's chillun got rhythm / I'll keep loving you / She / Cherokee / Gone again / Lucky day / It never entered my mind / Meet the flintstones / I love Lucy / Parker's mood / Would you like to take a walk
CCD 4476 / Aug '91 / Concord Jazz

Harris, Beaver

☐ BEAUTIFUL AFRICA
1210022 / May '92 / Soul Note

Harris, Bill

☐ FUNKY SITAR MAN (Harris, Bill 'Ravi' & The Prophets)
Path of the blazing sarong / Gimme some more/Hot pants / Soul makossa / I dream of Jeannie / Ravi's thing / Cissy strut / Look-a-py-py / Lost dragon of the Sahara / Pass the peas/Sex machine / Funky sitar man / Same beat
BBECD 002 / Mar '97 / Barely Breaking Even

Harris, Corey

☐ BETWEEN MIDNIGHT AND DAY
ALCD 4837 / Nov '95 / Alligator

☐ FISH AIN'T BITING
High fever blues / Frankie and Johnny / Berry Owens' blues / Take me back / Fish ain't biting / Preaching blues / Bumble bee blues / God don't ever change / 5-0 blues / Mama got worried / Worried life blues / High fever blues / Jack O'Diamonds / If you leave me / Moosemilk blues / You got to move / Clean rag
ALCD 4580 / May '97 / Alligator

Harris, Eddie

☐ BATTLE OF THE TENORS, THE (Harris, Eddie & Wendell Harrison)
Tenor madness / Wok / My shining hour / Vocalese / Eddie who / Ampedextrious
ENJ 93362 / 29 Jun '98 / Enja

☐ BEST OF EDDIE HARRIS, THE
Shadow of your smile / Freedom jazz dance / Sham time / Theme in search of a movie / Listen here / Live right now / 1974 Blues / Movin' on out / Boogie woogie / Bosa nova / Child is born / Is it in
7567813702 / Jun '93 / Atlantic

☐ EDDIE HARRIS ANTHOLOGY, THE
Exodus / Listen here / Cold duck time / Shadow of your smile / Theme in search of a movie / Sham time / Boogie woogie bosa nova / Is it in / Get on down / Funkaroma / It's alright now / 1974 Blues / Live right now / Freedom jazz dance / Yeah yeah yeah / Hey wado / Free speech / Cryin' blues / Giant steps / Without you / Mean greens / Recess / Steps up / Love for sale
8122715142 / Mar '94 / Atlantic

☐ EXODUS TO JAZZ/MIGHTY LIKE A ROSE
VJ 019 / 24 Apr '98 / Vee Jay

☐ GREATER THAN THE SUM OF HIS PARTS (2CD Set)
60412320672 / 19 May '98 / Thirty Two

☐ GREEN DOLPHIN STREET
Moon glow / Secret love / Alila / Laura / Green Dolphin Street / Fontessa / ATC / Olifant gesang
CDSPG 0221 / 16 Feb '98 / Prestige

☐ LAST CONCERT, THE
Sidewinder / Moanin' / Wade in the water / Freedom jazz dance / Work song / When a man loves a woman / Gimme some lovin' / You stole my heart
92492 / Mar '97 / Act

☐ LISTEN HERE (2CD Set)
I love you / Body and soul / God bless the child / Love for sale / Listen here / Theme in search of a movie / Exodus / Sonnymoon for two / Lover man (Oh, where can you be) / Cherokee / Ballad (for my love) / Three quarter miles / Now's the time / Straight, no chaser
R 103611 / Apr '97 / Live At EJ's

☐ LIVE IN BERLIN
Ambidextrous / La carnival / Lover / You've changed / Freedom jazz dance / Scatting unlyrically simultaneously / Airigen / Walkin' / Eddie who
CDSJP 289 / May '89 / Timeless Jazz

☐ STUDY IN JAZZ, A/BREAKFAST AT TIFFANY'S
VJ 020 / 14 Apr '98 / Vee Jay

☐ SWISS MOVEMENT (Harris, Eddie & Les McCann)
Compared to what / Cold duck time / Kathleen's theme / You got it in your soulness / Generation gap
7567813652 / Apr '94 / Atlantic

Harris, Emmylou

☐ AT THE RYMAN
Guitar town / Half as much / Cattle call / Guess things happen that way / Hard times / Mansion on the hill / Scotland / Montana cowgirl / Like strangers / Lodi / Calling my children home / If I could be there / Walls of time / Get up John / It's a hard life wherever you go/Abraham, Martin and John / Smoke along the track
7599266642 / Feb '95 / WEA

☐ BALLAD OF SALLY ROSE, THE
Ballad of Sally Rose / Rhythm guitar / I think I love him / You are my flower heart to heart / Woman walk the line / Bad news / Timberline / Long tall Sally Rose / White line / Diamond in my crown / Sweetheart of the Rodeo / K-S-O-S (Instrumental medly) / Ring of fire / Wildwood flower / Six days on the road / Swing low, sweet chariot
7599252052 / Jan '96 / WEA

☐ BLUE KENTUCKY GIRL
Sister's coming home / Beneath still waters / Rough and rocky / Hickory wind / Save the last dance for me / Sorrow in the wind / They'll never take his love from me / Every time you leave / Blue Kentucky girl / Even cowgirls get the blues
7599273922 / Jan '93 / WEA

☐ BRAND NEW DANCE
Wheels of love / In his world / Easy for you to stay / Better off without you / Brand new dance / Tougher than the rest / Sweet dreams of you / Rollin' and ramblin' / Never be anyone else but you / Red red rose
7599263092 / Oct '90 / WEA

☐ COWGIRL'S PRAYER
Ways to go / Light / High powered love / You don't know me / Prayer in open D / Crescent city / Lovin' you again / Jerusalem again / Thanks to you / I hear a call / Ballad of a runaway horse
GRA 101CD / Aug '94 / Grapevine

☐ DUETS
Price I pay / Love hurts / Thing about you / That lovin' feelin' again / We believe in happy endings / Star of Bethlehem / All fall down / Wild Montana skies / Green pastures / Gulf Coast highway / If I needed you / Evangeline
7599257912 / Aug '90 / WEA

☐ ELITE HOTEL
Amarillo / Together again / Feeling single / Seeing double / Sin City / One of these days / Till I gain control again / Here, there and everywhere / Ooh Las Vegas / Sweet dreams / Jambalaya / Satan's jewelled crown / Wheels
K 254060 / '88 / WEA

☐ LUXURY LINER
Luxury liner / Pancho and Lefty / Making believe / You're supposed to be feeling good / I'll be your San Antone Rose / C'est la vie / When I stop dreaming / Hello stranger / She / Tulsa queen
9273382 / Jun '89 / WEA

☐ PIECES OF THE SKY
Bluebird wine / Too far gone / If I could only win your love / Boulder to Birmingham / Before believing / Tonight the bottle let me down / Sleepless nights / Coat of many colours / For no one / Queen of the silver dollar
7599272442 / Feb '89 / WEA

☐ PORTRAIT (3CD Set)
Love hurts / Save the last dance for me / (you never can tell)c'est la vie / Too far gone / Before believing / Sleepless nights / Boulder to birmingham / If I needed you / Mister sandman / That lovin' you feelin' again / Boxer / Wayfaring stranger / Roses in the snow / Millworker / Blue kentucky girl / Easy from now on / Rollin' and ramblin' (the death of hank williams) / Gulf coast highway / We believe in happy endings / River for him / I still miss someone / Heartbreak hill / Love is / When I paint my masterpiece / Casey's last ride / Angel band / Heaven ain't ready for you yet / Dimming of the day / Pancho lefty / You're still on my mind / West texas waltz / Walls of time / Calling my children home / Hard times / Icy blue heart / Farther along / Pain of loving you / Sweet chariot / In my dreams / Juanita / Price you pay / Born to run / No regrets / Luxury liner / Making believe / Hello stranger / Here there and everywhere / Sweet dreams / Till I gain control again / One of these days / Everytime you leave / Beneath still waters / To know him is to love him / Angels rejoiced last night / Evangeline / To daddy / Two more bottles of wine / And I love you so / Together again / If I could only win your love / In my hour of darkness
9362453082 / Dec '96 / WEA

☐ PROFILE VOL.1 (The Best Of Emmylou Harris)
One of these days / Sweet dreams / To daddy / C'est la vie / Making believe / Easy from now on / Together again / If I could only win your love / Too far gone / Two more bottles of wine / Boulder to Birmingham / Hello stranger / You never can tell
256570 / Jun '84 / WEA

☐ PROFILE VOL.2 (The Best Of Emmylou Harris)
Blue Kentucky girl / Wayfaring stranger / Beneath still waters / Born to run / Someone like you / Mister Sandman / Pledging my love / I'm moving on / (Lost his love) On our last date / Save the last dance for me
7599251612 / Feb '94 / WEA

☐ QUARTER MOON IN A TEN CENT TOWN
Easy from now on / Two more bottles of wine / To Daddy / My songbird / Leaving Louisiana in the broad daylight / Defying / Gravity / I ain't living long like this / One paper kid / Green rolling hills / Burn that candle
9273452 / Jun '89 / WEA

☐ SPYBOY
GRACD 241 / 17 Aug '98 / Grapevine

☐ WHITE SHOES
Drivin' wheel / Pledging my love / In my dreams / White shoes / On the radio / It's only rock 'n' roll / Diamonds are a girl's best friend / Good news / Baby, better start turning 'em down / Like an old fashioned waltz
7599239612 / Jan '96 / WEA

☐ WRECKING BALL
Where will I be / Goodbye / All my tears / Wrecking ball / Goin' back to Harlan / Deeper well / Every grain of sand / Sweet old world / May this be love / Orphan girl / Blackhawk / Waltz across Texas tonight
GRACD 102 / Sep '95 / Grapevine

Harris, Gene

☐ AT LAST (Harris, Gene & Scott Hamilton Quintet)
You are my sunshine / It never entered my mind / After you've gone / Lamp is low / At last / Blues for Gene / I fall in love too easily / Some of these days / Stairway to the stars / Sittin' in the sandtrap
CCD 4434 / Nov '90 / Concord Jazz

□ BLACK AND BLUE (Harris, Gene Quartet)
Another star / Black and blue / CC rider / Hot toddy / Best things in life are free / Nobody knows you (when you're down and out) / It might as well be Spring / Blue bossa / Song is you / Will you still be mine
CCD 4482 / Oct '91 / Concord Jazz

□ BROTHERHOOD
I remember you / For once in my life / Brotherhood of man / When you wish upon a star / Sidewinder / I told you so / September song / This little light of mine / Beautiful friendship
CCD 4640 / May '95 / Concord Jazz

□ DOWN HOME BLUES (Harris, Gene & Jack McDuff)
Down home blues / J and G blues / Soft winds / Time after time / Blues for big foot / Smack dab in the middle / You don't know what love is / Stormy Monday / Cayenne blues
CCD 47852 / 10 Nov '97 / Concord Jazz

□ FUNKY GENE'S
Blues for Basie / Trouble with hello is goodbye / Old funky Gene's / Everything happens to me / Nice 'n' easy / Ahmad's blues / Bye bye blues / Children of Sanchez / Blues in Hoss's flat
CCD 4609 / Sep '94 / Concord Jazz

□ GENE HARRIS & THE PHILIP MORRIS SUPERBAND (Harris, Gene & The Philip Morris Superband)
Surrey with the fringe on top / Creme de menthe / When it's sleepy time down South / Our love is here to stay / I'm just a lucky so and so / Serious grease / Like a lover / Ol' man river / Do you know what it means to miss New Orleans / Porgy and Bess (medley) / You're my everything / There is no greater love / Things ain't what they used to be
CCD 4397 / Nov '89 / Concord Jazz

□ GENE HARRIS TRIO PLUS ONE, THE
Gene's lament / Uptown sop / Things ain't what they used to be / Yours is my heart alone / Battle hymn of the Republic
CCD 4303 / Sep '90 / Concord Jazz

□ IN HIS HANDS
Lean on me / Battle hymn of the republic / Will the circle be unbroken / Everyhting must change / Amazing grace / Lord I've tried / (Jesus keeps me) Near the cross / This little light of mine / Operator / His eye is on the sparrow / (He's got the) whole world in his hands / Granpa's hands
CCD 475582 / Jun '97 / Concord Jazz

□ IT'S THE REAL SOUL
Summertime / You don't know me / Oh lady be good / Straight, no chaser / Manage a bleu / My funny valentine / Estoril soul / That's all
CCD 4692 / May '96 / Concord Jazz

□ LIKE A LOVER (Harris, Gene Quartet)
Like a lover / Misterioso / Strollin' / Until the real thing comes along / Jeannie / I can't stop loving you / You make me feel so young / Oh, look at me now / Wrap your troubles in dreams (and dream your troubles away)
CCD 4526 / Oct '92 / Concord Jazz

□ LISTEN HERE (Harris, Gene Quartet)
His masquerade / I've got a feeling I'm falling in love / Blues for Jezebel / Lullaby / This can't be love / Don't be that way / Listen here / Sweet and lovely / Song is ended (but the melody lingers on) / To you
CCD 4385 / Sep '90 / Concord Jazz

□ LITTLE PIECE OF HEAVEN, A (Harris, Gene Quartet)
Blues in baxter's pad / Scotch and soda / Take the 'A' train / My little suede shoes / Blues for ste chapelle / Ma, he's making eyes at me / Pensativa / How long has this been going on / Old dog blues / Ode to Billy Joe / Sentimental journey
CCD 4578 / Nov '93 / Concord Jazz

□ LIVE AT THE IT CLUB
Funku pullett / I'm still sad / On Green Dolphin Street / Baby man / Love for sale / Sittin' duck / Tammy's breeze / John Brown's body
CDP 8353382 / Mar '96 / Blue Note

□ TRIBUTE TO COUNT BASIE, A (Harris, Gene All Star Big Band)
Captain Bill / Night mist blues / Swingin' the blues / When did you leave Heaven / Blue and sentimental / Riled up / (I'm afraid) the masquerade is over / Dejection blues
CCD 4337 / May '88 / Concord Jazz

□ WORLD TOUR 1990 (Harris, Gene & The Philip Morris Superband)
Airmail special / Lonely bottles / Child is born / Buhaina Buhaina / Don't get around much anymore / Lover / In the wee small hours of the morning / Tricrotism / Centerpiece / Dear blues / Nica's dream / Girl talk / Battle royal / Warm valley
CCD 4443 / Feb '91 / Concord Jazz

Harris, Greg

□ ELECTRIC
APCD 024 / Jun '94 / Appaloosa

□ ELECTRO-ACUSTIC
APCD 125 / Mar '97 / Appaloosa

□ THINGS CHANGE
APCD 047 / '92 / Appaloosa

Harris, Harold

□ AT THE PLAYBOY CLUB
VJR 502 / 5 Jan '98 / Fresh Sound

□ HERE'S HAROLD
VJR 501 / 5 Jan '98 / Fresh Sound

Harris, Jerome

□ IN PASSING
MCD 5386 / Sep '92 / Muse

Harris, Jet

□ BEYOND A SHADOW OF A DOUBT (Harris, Jet & Alan Jones/Tangent)
Beyond a shadow of a doubt / Sometimes / Thunderhawk / Uncharted island / Theme for a new day / Foot tappin' / Stormin' Norman (parts 1, 2 and 3) / Jet meets General Custer / El warthog / Twilight shadows / New world / Truckin' truckers trot / Theme from a big film / Lads / Everyone for tennis / Moonlight miraval / Wonderful landscapes / Tandoorie boogie / Sleepless walk at midnight / Khan
TANCD 002 / Mar '98 / Tangent

□ LIVE OVER ENGLAND (Harris, Jet & Tangent)
TANZRCD 1212 / Mar '98 / Tangent

□ STUDIO SESSIONS (Harris, Jet & Tangent)
Warm turn (part 1) / Stingray / FBI / Jet meets General Custer '94 / Walk don't run / Diamonds / Love me tender / Tres bon / Truckin' truckers trot / Apache / Danny boy / Warm turn (part 2)
TANCD 003 / Mar '98 / Tangent

□ TRIBUTES AND RARITIES (Harris, Jet & Alan Jones/Tangent)
Riders in the sky / Clifton lights / It's a dog's life / Apache / Theme for a new day / Crockett's theme / Stingray / Sleepless walk at midnight / Stratosfear / Warm turn / Lady in red / Equinox V / Elmer's theme
TANCD 004 / Mar '98 / Tangent

□ TWO OF A KIND (Harris, Jet & Alan Jones/Tangent)
ZRCD 1213 / 12 Jan '98 / Beat Goes On

Harris, Kim

□ IN THE HEAT OF THE SUMMER (Harris, Kim & Reggie)
FE 1412 / Nov '94 / Folk Era

□ STEAL AWAY (Harris, Kim & Reggie)
APRCD 1022 / 2 Feb '98 / Appleseed

Harris, Lafayette Jr.

□ HAPPY TOGETHER
Happy together / I'm smilin' / In the wee small hours of the morning / Getaway / You've changed / He could be perfect for me / Achern / Solace / Lady sings the blues / Sun is / Where am I / Hat's on blues
MCD 5541 / Aug '96 / Muse

Harris, Loston

□ COMES LOVE
Swinging at the haven / Moonlight in Vermont / Close your eyes / Do nothin' till you hear from me / Stompin' down broadway / Comes love / Easy listening blues / Shall we dance
N2K 10012 / 5 May '98 / N2K

Harris, M.J.

□ MURDER BALLADS (Harris, M.J. & Martyn Bates)
EEE 36 / Mar '97 / Musica Maxima Magnetica

Harris, Michael

□ WIDOR TRADITION, THE (French Organ Music From Canterbury Cathedral)
Marche Pontificale / Suite bretonne / Berceuse / Fileuse / Les cloches de perros-guirec / Suite Francaise / Variations sur un Noel Angevin / Variations sur un theme de Clement Jannequin / Prelude et Danse Fuguee
YORK CD 112 / Oct '91 / York Ambisonic

Harris, Michael

□ DEFENSE MECHANIZMS
BD 051CD / Dec '91 / Black Dragon

Harris, Mick

□ COLLAPSE (Harris, Mick & James Plotkin)
ASP 0963CD / 22 Jun '98 / Asphodel

□ OVERLOAD LADY
SR 124CD / Apr '97 / Sub Rosa

Harris, Mike

□ TOTAL STATION (Harris, Mike & Eraldo Bernocchi)
SR 137CD / 15 Jun '98 / Sub Rosa

Harris, Phil

□ ECHOES FROM THE COCONUT GROVE 1932-1933
TT 416 / May '98 / Take Two

□ THING ABOUT PHIL HARRIS, THE (The Voice Of Baloo The Bear 1931-1950)
Between the devil and the deep blue sea / Brother can you spare a dime / Buds won't bud / Darktown poker club / Darktown strutters ball / How's about it: *Harris, Phil & Leah Ray* / I got the ritz about the one I love / I wanna be a brat / Jelly bean / My kind of country / Now you've got me doing it / Old man of the mountain / One-zy two-zy / Pink elephants / River stay 'way from my door / Rose room / Some little bug / That's what I like about the South / Thing / What have we got to lose / What's the matter with Dixie / You can tell she comes from Dixie
CDAJA 5191 / Mar '96 / Living Era

Harris, R.H.

□ SHINE ON ME (Harris, R.H. & The Soul Stirrers)
By and by / I'm still living on mother's prayer / Feel like my time ain't long / Today / I have a right to the tree of life / In that awful hour / Jesus hits like the atom bomb / Shine on me / Faith and grace / Everybody ought to love their soul / Blessed by the name of the Lord / My loved ones are waiting for me (waiting and watching) / How long / Who'll be the one / Lord's my shepherd / Christ is all / By and by Pts. 1 - 3
CDCHD 415 / Nov '93 / Ace

Harris, Rhonda

□ RHONDA HARRIS
RAIN 014CD / Nov '95 / Cloudland

Harris, Richard

□ MACARTHUR PARK
HMNCD 002 / Jun '97 / Half Moon

□ WEBB SESSIONS 1968-1969, THE
RVCD 52 / Mar '96 / Raven

Harris, Rolf

□ ANIMAL MAGIC
Tie me kangaroo down sport / Maximillian mouse / Mud mud / Cat came back / Three blind mice / How much is that doggie in the window / Tit willow / Bid dog / Clock of life / Groundhog song / Six white boomers / Persian pussy cat / Wild rover / Sheepman / Kangaroo catchers / Bull dust / Dry country / Leafy Gully's shade
CDMFP 6277 / Nov '96 / Music For Pleasure

□ CAN YOU TELL WHAT IT IS YET (2CD Set)
Sun arise / One hand in my pocket / Dedicated follower of fashion / Raining on the rock / Perfect day / Bad moon rising / Ob-la-di ob-la-da / Girl like you / Hey bulldog / Fijian girl / Football crazy / Pretty flamingo / Frog went a courtin' / Rudolph the red nosed reindeer / Little robin / Sun's thing
8217802
8218802 / 20 Oct '97 / EMI

□ DIDGEREELY-DOO ALL THAT (The Best Of Rolf Harris)
Tie me kangaroo down sport / Sun arise / I've lost my Mummy / Carra barra wirra canna / Nick Teen and Al KHall / Maximillian mouse / Court of King Caractacus / Six white boomers / Jake the peg / Bid dog / Fijian girl / Hurry home / Two little boys / Jindabyne / She'll be right / Come and see my land (Jimmy my boy) / Lazy day / Yarrabangee / Northern territorian / Bargin' down the Thames / Pavlova / Raining on the rock / Stairway to heaven
CDGO 2062 / May '94 / EMI

Harris, Roy

□ RAMBLING SOLDIER, THE
Balaclava / McCafferty / Muddley barracks / Rambling soldier / I would that the wars were all done / Young recruit / Scarlet and the blue / Lass of Swansea town / Drum major / Hungry army / Banks of the Nile / Chelsea quarters
FECD 17 / Sep '97 / Fellside

Harris, Simon

□ BEATS, BREAKS AND SCRATCHES VOL.1 & 2
100 bpm (909 and 727) / 96 bpm (909 and 727) / 101 bpm (909 and 727) / 102 bpm (808) / 100 bpm (808) / 114 bpm (808) / 100 bpm (727) / 122 bpm (808 with percussion) / 122 bpm (808 no percussion) / 122 bpm (909 and 727) / 122 bpm (909) / 98 bpm (909 and 727 dumb beats) / Chime / Vibraslap / Aaagh / Fresh / Break / Screech / Thump / Flexitone / Spinback 1 / Spinback 2 / Action / Pow / Warble up / Oww / Zing / Stab / Scratch / Funky stab / Funkyroll / Crash / Snare / Clap / Radar boop / Cat screech / Gunshot / Whoosh / Radio tuning / 110 bpm (dancefloor justice) / 120 bpm (house attack - the jack zone) / 90 bpm (go go steaming and cranking) / 95 bpm (rough neck beats) / 105 bpm (rebel beats) / 113 bpm ("the loop of 88") / 98 bpm ("the loop of 87") / 104 bpm (you got soul loop) / 109 bpm (raw loop) / 104 bpm (bad young beats) / 100 bpm (raggastylee) / Screech / Woh / Stab 1 / Chaah / Hold it now / Big stab / Camera / Stab 2 / Scratch 1 / Break / Hit it / Rockit stab / Funkyroll / Dit / Stab 3 / Stab 4 / Car stab / Davey stab / Funky / Bust this / Electro krunch / Rock / Electrobark / Stab 5 / Grunt stab / Electro stab / Tom roll / Tape stop / Electro - uh / Low tom / Whistle / Magnificent / Uuh / How y'all feel / Check this out / Aah yeah / This is a test / Get on it / Laugh / Music turns me on / Ridim / You make me feel so good / Calling all cars / Go-go roll / Peeper stab / Quack / Creak / Dash / Lazer-gun / Guitar stab / Wind / Crunch
MOMIX 1/2CD / '89 / Music Of Life

□ BEATS, BREAKS AND SCRATCHES VOL.10
MOLCD 027 / Mar '93 / Music Of Life

□ BEATS, BREAKS AND SCRATCHES VOL.11
MOLCD 31 / Oct '93 / Music Of Life

□ BEATS, BREAKS AND SCRATCHES VOL.12
MOLCD 37 / Sep '95 / Music Of Life

□ BEATS, BREAKS AND SCRATCHES VOL.3 & 4
Hip house / Monster beats / Secret beats / Dopejam / Pleasure break / Deep house / Garibaldi beats / 45 rocks the spot / Scandalous riddim / Racing loop / Dancefloor drums / Southern stylet fashion / Effects and scratches / Life beats / Heavy loop / Dopin' drums / Mardi gras / Groove beats / Big beats / Hold tight / Impeach / Funky break / Compton loop / Ruff loop / Course beat / Samurai beats / Effects and scratches
MOMIX 3/4CD / '89 / Music Of Life

□ BEATS, BREAKS AND SCRATCHES VOL.7
Stop beats / Smokin' / Body beats / Number beats / Power swing / Cold sweat / Sports beats / 63. fx and scratches / Good brake / Bounce and skate / Science loop / Down beats / Funky house / Dope beat
MOMIX 7CD / Jun '91 / Music Of Life

□ BEATS, BREAKS AND SCRATCHES VOL.8
MOMIX 8CD / Nov '91 / Music Of Life

□ BEST OF BEATS, BREAKS AND SCRATCHES, THE
MOBEST 1CD / Jun '92 / Music Of Life

□ DISTURBING THE PEACE
Theme from disturbing the peace / Time / Rock right now / Ragga house (All night long) / This is serious / Don't stop the music / Shock the house / Right here, right now / Twilight / Runaway love / Ragga house
DISTURB 1CD / Nov '90 / Living Beat

□ FOR YOUR EARS ONLY
MOLCD 39 / Jan '96 / Music Of Life

Harris, Wynonie

□ EVERYBODY BOOGIE
Wynonie's blues / Here comes the blues / Baby look at you / Somebody changed the lock on my door / Gone with the wind / That's the stuff you gotta watch / Straighten him out / Young man's blues / I got a lyin' woman / Everybody boogie / Time to change your tune / Rebecca's blues / Playful baby / Young and wild / Papa tree top / Take me out of the rain / I got a lyin' woman / Everybody boogie
DE 683 / Nov '96 / Delmark

□ GOOD ROCKIN' TONIGHT
Good rockin' tonight / She just won't sell no more / Blow your brains out / I want my Fanny Brown / All she wants to do is rock / Lollipop mama / Baby, shame on you / I like my baby's pudding / Wynonie's boogie / Sittin' on it all the time / Good morning judge / I feel that old age coming on / Lovin' machine / Mr. Blues is coming to town / Quiet whiskey / Rock Mr. Blues / Bloodshot eyes / Luscious woman / Down boy down / Keep on churnin' (till the butter comes)
CDCHARLY 244 / Apr '91 / Charly

□ GOOD ROCKIN' TONIGHT
KCD 6002 / 17 Nov '97 / King

□ HERE COMES THE BLUES (The Roots Of Rock'n'Roll Vol.4)
Around the clock part 1 / Around the clock part 2 / Cock-a-doodle-doo / Yonder goes my baby / Wynonie's blues / Here comes the blues / Young man's blues / Baby look at you / She's gone with the wind / Somebody changed the lock on my door / That's the stuff you gotta watch / I gotta lyin' woman / Rebecca's blues / Everybody's boogie / Time to change your town / Playful baby / Take me out of the rain / Papa tree top / Young and wild / Good morning Corinne / Hey ba-ba-re-bop / Hey ba-ba-re-bop / In the evening / Mr. Blues jumped the rabbit / Rugged road / Come back baby / Whiskey and Jelly Roll blues
PLCD 559 / Mar '97 / President

□ WEST COAST JIVE
DD 657 / Jul '93 / Delmark

□ WOMEN, WHISKEY AND FISH TAILS
Greyhound / Deacon don't like it / Christina / Shake that thing / Don't take my whiskey away / Drinkin' sherry wine / Fish tail blues / Big old country fool / Shotgun wedding / Wine wine sweet wine / Git to gittin' baby / Mr. Dollar / Bad news baby (There'll be no rockin' tonite) / Bring it back / I don't know where to go / Man's best friend / Keep a talking / Please Louise / I get a thrill / There's no substitute for love / Mama your daughter done lied to me
CDCHD 457 / Sep '93 / Ace

Harrison, Bobby

□ SOLID SILVER
It's over / Hunter / Icelandic rock and roll / Overload / Nothing stays the same / Hot stuff / Guiding light / Highway / Victim of love / Shape I am in / Get on the right track / After the storm / Oh pretty woman
SJPCD 011 / Jun '97 / Angel Air

Harrison, Donald

□ FOR ART'S SAKE (Harrison, Donald Quintet)
So what / Nut / Softly, as in a morning sunrise / In a sentimental mood / For art's sake / Oleo / Let's go off
CCD 79501 / Feb '97 / Candid

☐ FULL CIRCLE
Force / My little suede shoes / Call me / Bye bye blackbird / Nature boy / Hold it right there / Good morning heartache / Evidence of things not seen / Infinite heart / Let's go off
66055003 / Jul '91 / Sweet Basil

☐ INDIAN BLUES
Hu-ta-nay / Indian blues / Shallow water / Ja-ki-mo-fi-na-hay / Indian red / Two way pocky way / Cherokee / Hiko hiko / Uptown ruler / Big chief / Walkin' home / Shave 'em dry: *Harrison, Donald & Dr. John*
CCD 79514 / Feb '97 / Candid

☐ NOUVEAU SWING
Nouveau swing / Bob Marley / Come back Jack / Little flowers / 81 / Sincerely your / Septembro / Cold duck / New hope / Christopher Jr / South side people / Dance hall / Duck's groove / Amazing grace
IMP 12092 / May '97 / Impulse Jazz

Harrison, Gavin

☐ SANITY AND GRAVITY
Aim / On a wave of positivity / Dog day / Place to stay / Witness (for Bobby) / Dearest blood / Sonata in H / Big news for a small day / Witness (reprise)
RES 128CD / 17 Nov '97 / Resurgence

Harrison, George

☐ ALL THINGS MUST PASS
I'd have you anytime / My sweet Lord / Wah wah / Isn't it a pity / What is life / If not for you / Behind that locked door / Let it down / Run of the mill / Beware of darkness / Apple scruffs / Ballad of Sir Frankie Crisp (Let it roll) / Awaiting on you all / All things must pass / I dig love / Art of dying / Hear me Lord / Out of the blue / It's Johnny's birthday / Plug me in / I remember jeep / Thanks for the pepperoni
CDS 7466888 / May '87 / Parlophone

☐ BEST OF DARK HORSE 1976-1989
Poor little girl / Blow away / That's the way it goes / Cockamamie business / Wake up my love / Life itself / Got my mind set on you / Crackerbox palace / Cloud 9 / Here comes the moon / Gone troppo / When we was fab / Love comes to everyone / All those years ago / Cheer down
9257262 / Oct '89 / Dark Horse

☐ BEST OF GEORGE HARRISON
Something / If I needed someone / Here comes the sun / Taxman / Think for yourself / For you blue / While my guitar gently weeps / My sweet Lord / Give me love (give me peace on earth) / You / Bangladesh / Dark horse / What is life
CDP 746 682 2 / May '87 / Parlophone

☐ CLOUD NINE
Cloud 9 / That's what it takes / Fish on the sand / Just for today / This is love / When we was fab / Devil's radio / Someplace else / Wreck of the Hesperus / Breath away from heaven / Got my mind set on you
9256432 / Sep '87 / Dark Horse

☐ DARK HORSE
Hari's on tour / Simply shady / So sad / Bye bye love / May a love / Ding dong ding dong / Dark horse / Far east man / Is it he (Jai Sri Krishna)
CDPAS 10008 / Oct '91 / Parlophone

☐ ELECTRONIC SOUNDS
Under the Mersey wall / No time or space
CDZAPPLE 02 / Oct '96 / Apple

☐ EXTRA TEXTURE (READ ALL ABOUT IT)
You / Answer's at the end / This guitar (can't keep from crying) / Ooh baby (you know that I love you) / World of stone / Bit more of you / Can't stop thinking about you / Tired of midnight blue / Grey cloudy lies / His name is legs
CDPAS 10009 / Oct '91 / Parlophone

☐ LIVE IN JAPAN
I want to tell you / Old brown shoe / Taxman / Give me love (give me peace on earth) / If I needed someone / Something / What is life / Dark horse / Piggies / Got my mind set on you / Cloud 9 / Here comes the sun / My sweet lord / All those years ago / Cheer down / Devil's radio / Isn't it a pity / While my guitar gently weeps / Roll over Beethoven
7599269642 / Jul '92 / Dark Horse

☐ LIVING IN THE MATERIAL WORLD
Give me love (give me peace on Earth) / Sue me, sue you blues / Light that has lighted the world / Don't let me wait too long / Who can see it / Living in the material world / Lord loves the one (that loves the Lord) / Be here now / Try some buy some / Day the world gets 'round / That's all
CDPAS 10006 / Oct '91 / Parlophone

☐ WONDERWALL MUSIC
Microbes / Red lady too / Table and Pakavaj / In the park / Drilling a home / Guru vandana / Greasy legs / Ski-ing / Gat kirwani / Dream scene / Party seacombe / Love scene / Crying / Cowboy music / Fantasy sequins / On the bed / Glass box / Wonderwall to be here / Singing om
CDSAPCOR 1 / Jun '92 / Apple

Harrison, Joel

☐ RANGE OF MOTION (Harrison, Joel Octet)
378412 / Jun '97 / Koch Jazz

Harrison, Lou

☐ MUSIC OF LOU HARRISON, THE
CRICD 13 / Jun '97 / CRI

☐ PORTRAIT, A (Jarreau, Al & Maria Bachmann/California SO)
4555902 / 22 Jun '98 / Decca

Harrison, Michael A.

☐ MOMENTS IN PASSION
101S 70782 / Nov '92 / 101 South

Harrison, Mike

☐ MIKE HARRISON
REP 7043 / Feb '98 / Repertoire

Harrison, Valerie

☐ GOLDEN TOUCH
WSRCD 012 / 6 Jul '98 / World Sound

Harrow

☐ PYLON OF INSANITY
N 02452 / Aug '94 / Noise

Harrow, Nancy

☐ ANYTHING GOES
ACD 142 / '91 / Audiophile

☐ LOST LADY
SN 1212632 / Oct '94 / Soul Note

☐ SECRETS
1212332 / Jan '92 / Soul Note

☐ WILD WOMEN DON'T HAVE THE BLUES
Take me back baby / All too soon / Can't we be friends / On the sunny side of the street / Wild women don't get the blues / I've got the world on a string / I don't know what kind of blues I got / Blues for yesterday
CCD 79008 / Feb '97 / Candid

Harry Crews

☐ NAKED IN GARDEN HILLS
About the author / Distopia / Gospel singer / (She's in a) bad mood / Bring me down / SOS / Man hates a man / You're it / Knockout artist / Way out / Car / Orphans
ABBCD 21 / Apr '90 / Big Cat

Harry, Deborah

☐ LIVE IN SPAIN (Harry, Deborah & Jazz Passengers)
TW 11054 / 1 Jun '98 / Crepuscule

Harry J All Stars

☐ RETURN OF THE LIQUIDATOR
CDTRD 412 / Mar '94 / Trojan

Harry Pussy

☐ RIDE A DOVE
SB 60CD / Feb '97 / Matador

☐ WHAT WAS MUSIC
SB 0602 / May '96 / Matador

Hart, Antonio

☐ HERE I STAND
Community / True friends / Flamingos / Brother nasheet / Ven devorane otra vez / Riots the voice of the unhead / Millenium / Like my own / Words don't fit in my mouth
IMP 12082 / Mar '97 / Impulse Jazz

☐ IT'S ALL GOOD
91st miracle / Great Grandmother's song / Puerto Rico / Through the clouds / Bartzology / Sounds in the street / Lunch time again / Uptown traveller / Forever in love / Cappuccini / Missin' Miles
01241631832 / Jun '95 / Novus

Hart, Billy

☐ RAH
Motional / Naaj / Renedap / Dreams / Reflections / Breakup / Reminder / Jungu
1888022 / Dec '88 / Gramavision

Hart, John

☐ BRIDGES
Under the influence / Private eyes / Rite of passion / It might as well be Spring / Urban Appalachia / Rabbit's foot / Summer wishes, Winter dreams / Dealin' and wheelin' / Zingaro / Bridges
CCD 47462 / Mar '97 / Concord Jazz

☐ HIGH DRAMA
Paradox / High drama / Blood count / I'll never be the same / Ozone / Waiting for Samuel / Luiza / Minor poet / Isfahan / Who killed Mr. Lucky
CCD 4688 / Feb '96 / Concord Jazz

Hart, Kathy

☐ TONIGHT I WANT IT ALL (Hart, Kathy & The Bluestars)
Tonight I want it all / Blue reverie / Get in / Get the money and get out / Two plays for a quarter / Good rockin' daddy / It seemed like such a good idea / Monkey ain't made outa gold
BCD 119 / Jul '91 / Biograph

Hart, Mickey

☐ AT THE EDGE
Four for Garcia / Sky water / Slow sailing / Lonesome hero / Fast sailing / Cougar run / Eliminators / Brainstorm / Pigs in space
RCD 10124 / Mar '97 / Rykodisc

☐ DAFOS (Hart, Mickey & Flora Purim/ Airto Moreira)
RCD 10108 / Dec '94 / Rykodisc

☐ MICKEY HART'S MYSTERY BOX
Where love goes (sito) / Full steam ahead / Down the road / Sandman / Next step / Look away / Only the strange remain / Sangre De Christos / Last song / John Cage is dead
RCD 10338 / Jun '96 / Rykodisc

☐ MUSIC TO BE BORN BY
RCD 0112 / Nov '91 / Rykodisc

☐ PLANET DRUM
RCD 80206 / Dec '94 / Rykodisc

☐ SUPRALINGUA (Hart, Mickey & Planet Drum)
Angola / Yabu / Endless river / Umayeyo / Secret meeting place / Tall grass / Umasha / Frog dance / Damawoo / Indoscrub / Wheel of time / Space dust
RCD 10396 / 3 Aug '98 / Rykodisc

Hart, Mike

☐ MIKE HART BLEEDS/BASHER CHALKY PONGO AND ME
Yawny morning song / Ring song / Arty's wife / Aberfan / Almost Liverpool 6 / Intro / Interlude / Pocket full of dough / Bitchin' on a train / Sing song / Jousters / Epilogue / Shelter song / Please bring back the birch for the milkman / Disbelief blues / Dance Mr. Morning Man / Joke / Nell's song / Dear Bathseeba Everdene / Influences / I have been a rover / Christmas / War, violence, heroism and such like stupidity
SEECD 419 / 10 Aug '98 / See For Miles

☐ ROLLING THUNDER
Rolling thunder / Shoshone invocation / Fletcher carnaby / Blind John / Deep, wide and frequent / Granma's cookies / Main ten / Chase / Young man / Pump song / Hangin' on
GDCD 4009 / Mar '89 / Grateful Dead

Hart Rouge

☐ BEAUPRE'S HOME
RHRCD 102 / Aug '97 / Red House

☐ INCONDITIONNEL
HYCD 200143 / Mar '95 / Hypertension

Hart, Tim

☐ SUMMER SOLSTICE (Hart, Tim & Maddy Prior)
False knight on the road / Bring us in good ale / Of all the birds / I live not where I love / Ploughboy and the cockney / Westron wynde / Sorry the day I was married / Dancing at Whitsun / Fly up my cock / Cannily cannily / Adam catched Eve / Three drunken maidens / Serving girls holiday
CRESTCD 023 / Nov '96 / Mooncrest

☐ TIM HART
Keep on travelling / Tuesday afternoon / Hillman Avenger / Lovely lady / Come to my window / Nothing to hide / Overseas / Time after time / As I go my way
BGOCD 305 / Oct '95 / Beat Goes On

Harte, Frank

☐ DAYBREAK AND A CANDLE END
Jolly young ploughboy / Roger the miller / Maid of Cabra West / In London so fair / Sarah Jane / By the hush me boys / Cockles and mussels / Charladies' ball / Holland handkerchief / Willie Taylor / I wonder what is keeping my true love / In North America / Here I am from Donegal
SPINCD 995 / Sep '97 / Spin

Hartford, John

☐ AEREO-PLAIN
Turn your radio on / Steamboat whistle blues / Back in the Goodle days / Up on the hill where they do the boogie / Boogie / First girl I loved / Presbyterian guitar / With a vamp in the middle / Symphony hall rag / Because of you / Steam powered aereo plane / Holding / Tear down the Grand Ole Opry / Leather britches / Station break / Turn your radio on
ROUCD 0366 / Sep '97 / Rounder

☐ DOWN ON THE RIVER
Here I am again in love / Bring your clothes back home / Wish I had our time again / All I got is gone away / Delta queen waltz / Old time river man / Men all want to be hobos / Right in the middle of falling for you / There'll never be another you / Little boy / General Jackson
FF 70514 / '88 / Flying Fish

☐ HARTFORD & HARTFORD
FF 566CD / Jun '94 / Flying Fish

☐ MARK TWANG
Skippin' in the Mississippi dew / Long hot summer days / Let him go on Mama / Don't leave your records in the sun / Tater Tate and Allen Mundy / Julia Belle Swain / Little cabin home on the hill Waugh Waugh / Austin minor sympathy / Lowest pair / Tryin' to do something to get your attention
FF 70020 / Oct '89 / Flying Fish

☐ ME OH MY, HOW TIME DOES FLY
FF 440CD / Jun '94 / Flying Fish

☐ MORNING BUGLE
ROUCD 03656 / Aug '95 / Rounder

☐ NOBODY KNOWS WHAT YOU DO
You don't have to do that / Don't want to be forgotten / In tall buildings / John McLaughlin / Granny wont'cha smoke some marijuana / False hearted tenor waltz / Joseph's dream / Down / Golden globe award / Sly feel / Somewhere my love / We'll meet again sweetheart / Nobody knows what you do
FF 70028 / Sep '96 / Flying Fish

☐ SPEED OF THE OLD LONG BOW, THE (A Tribute To The Fiddle Music Of Ed Haley)
Hell up coal hollar / Yellow barber / Lost Indian / Dunbar / Brushy fork of John's creek / Bonaparte's retreat / Forks of sandy / Half past four / Blackberry blossom / Pumpkin ridge / Brownlow's dream / Rebel raid / Boatman / Ida Red
ROUCD 0438 / Jun '98 / Rounder

☐ WILD HOG IN THE RED BRUSH
Squirrel hunters / Birdie / Grandmammy look at Uncle Sam / Old Virginia reel / Flannery's dream / Down at the mouth of old Stinson / Girl with the blue dress on / Wild hog in the red brush / Over the road to Maysville / Bumble bee in a jug / Bostony / Shelvin' rock / Molly put the kettle on / West Fork gals / Portsmouth airs / Coquette / Jimmy in the swamp / Lady of the lake / Natchez under the hill
ROUCD 0392 / Oct '96 / Rounder

Hartley, J.R.

☐ ALL FALL DOWN
Right person / Sometimes in the sun / All fall down / Boredom / If it gets you down / Whatcha gonna do / (Take a hold on) nothing / Acceptance song / In a hilltop village / Mind / Life is for everyone / Weak willed whinging / Something
PFE 321 / 27 Apr '98 / Profane

Hartley, Pete

☐ CLASSICS
Ave Maria / Danny boy / Killing me softly / Jesu joy of man's desiring / Lately / Air on a G string / Georgia / Nimrod / Moon dance / Bridge over troubled water / Walking in the air / And I love her / Way we were / Cavatina
CDGRS 1226 / '91 / Grosvenor

☐ JAZZ PROJECT, THE
Autumn leaves / One note samba / Body and soul / Yardbird suite / Shoddy bop / Take the 'A' train / Gypsy with spots / Mr. PC / Ninth floor taxman / Night and day / Ornithology / Night in Tunisia / Birdland / Pent-up house / Spain
CDGRS 1236 / '91 / Grosvenor

☐ MORE CLASSICS
We've only just begun / Goodbye to love / Chi mai / Lyin' eyes / Midnight train to Georgia / Aria / I shot the sheriff / Desperado / Deacon blues / Laughter in the rain / Stairway to heaven / Just the two of us / Wedding of Kevin and Claire / Nessun Dorma / Gymnopedie No.1 / Oye como va / (Everything I do) I do it for you
CDGRS 1251 / '91 / Grosvenor

Hartley, Trevor

☐ HARTICAL
JOVECD 2 / May '94 / Love Music

Hartman, Johnny

☐ ALL OF ME (Bethlehem Jazz Classics)
Blue skies / I could make you care / Tenderly / Lamp is low / While you were young / Birth of the blues / I'll follow you / I concentrate on you / Stella by starlight / I get a kick out of you / End of a love affair / All of me / Blue skies / I get a kick out of you / Birth of the blues / All of me
CDGR 137 / Apr '97 / Charly

☐ AND I THOUGHT ABOUT YOU
Mamselle / To each his own / Alone / Long ago and far away / I should care / Little girl blue / But beautiful / After you've gone / There's a lull in my life / How long has this been going on / I thought about you
CDP 8574562 / Jul '97 / Roulette

☐ I JUST DROPPED BY TO SAY HELLO
Charade / Our time / In the wee small hours of the morning / Sleepin' bee / Don't you know I care / Kiss and run / If I'm lucky / I just dropped by to say hello / Stairway to the stars / Don't call it love / How sweet it is to be in love
IMP 11762 / Oct '95 / Impulse Jazz

☐ SONGS FROM THE HEART (Bethlehem Jazz Classics)
CDGR 130 / Apr '97 / Charly

☐ THIS ONE'S FOR TED
ACD 181 / Feb '91 / Audiophile

☐ UNFORGETTABLE
Almost like being in love / Once in a while / Isn't it romantic / Our love is here to stay / More I see you / What do I owe you / Bidin' my time / Down in the depths / Fools rush in / Very thought of you / Unforgettable / Ain't misbehavin' / Today I love everybody / T'ain't no need / For the want of a kiss / Girl talk / That old black magic
IMP 11522 / Aug '95 / Impulse Jazz

Hartsman, Johnny

☐ MADE IN GERMANY (Hartsman, Johnny & The Blues Company)
Intro / That's alright / Flute juice / Cold cold feeling / I don't want no woman / Let me love you / Ain't no sunshine / Sweet Frisco blues / Flip flop and fly
INAK 9025 / Jul '97 / In Akustik

Harvest Ministers

☐ FEELING MISSION, THE
That won't wash / I've a mind / Drowning man / Temple to love / Dealing with a kid / Cleaning out the store / Only seat of power / Innopportune girl / She's buried / Modernising the new you / Mental charge / Secret way / Out of costume / Happy to abort
SETCD 019 / Apr '95 / Setanta

☐ ORBIT
Think about me more / I never raised my voice to you / Feeling mission / Stop doubting mission / Reluctant volunteer / Object of your affection / Orbit / Ballad of Lady Yarmouth / Our destines are intertwined / Don't give a cent (to the charities of hope)
SETCD 033 / Jan '97 / Setanta

Harvest Theory

☐ HARVEST THEORY
SBR 0072 / Aug '95 / Spring Box

Harvester

☐ CAMPER VAN LANDINGHAM
TR 30072 / 27 Apr '98 / Trocadero

Harvesters

☐ PEARLS BEFORE WINE
Clockwatching / Thistle and the rose / Doubt and the certainty / Cut above / Never again / Ships that pass in the night / One hit wonder / Still waters / Lavender and lilac / One step forward / Time is a thief
FSCD 41 / Jun '97 / Folksound

Harvey, Alex

☐ BEST OF THE SENSATIONAL ALEX HARVEY BAND, THE (Harvey, Alex Sensational Band)
Delilah / Cheek to cheek / Jungle rubout / Man in the jar / Weights made of lead / Sgt. Fury / Boston tea party / Next / Gamblin' bar room blues / Tomorrow belongs to me / Snakebite / School's out / Love story / Faith healer / Framed
MCCD 001 / Feb '91 / Music Club

☐ DELILAH (Harvey, Alex Sensational Band)
Delilah / Money honey / Impossible dream / Last of the teenage idols / Shake that thing / Framed / Anthem / Gamblin' bar room blues / Tomorrow belongs to me / There's no lights on the Christmas tree Mother / Cheek to cheek / Runaway / School's out / Faith healer
5506332 / Aug '94 / Spectrum

☐ GOSPEL ACCORDING TO HARVEY (2CD Set) (Harvey, Alex Band)
PILOT 045 / 20 Apr '98 / Burning Airlines

☐ LAST OF THE TEENAGE IDOLS, THE (The BBC Sessions) (Harvey, Alex Sensational Band)
PILOT 027 / Nov '97 / Burning Airlines

☐ LIVE IN GLASGOW 1993 (Harvey, Alex Band)
Faithhealer / St. Anthony / Framed / Gang bang / Amos moses / Boston tea party / Midnight moses / Vambo marble eye / Armed and ready / Delilah
JIMBO 001 / Apr '94 / Grapevine

☐ MAFIA STOLE MY GUITAR, THE (Harvey, Alex New Band)
Don's delight / Back in the depot / Wait for me Mama / Mafia stole my guitar / Shakin' all over / Whalers / Oh spartacus / Just a gigolo / I ain't got nobody
EDCD 562 / 4 May '98 / Edsel

☐ SENSATIONAL ALEX HARVEY BAND, THE (Harvey, Alex Sensational Band)
Faith healer / Delilah / Framed / Tomahawk kid / School's out / Vambo / Boston tea party / Gang bang / Gambling bar room blues / Tomorrow belongs to me / Mrs. Blackhouse / Dogs of war / Anthem / To be continued
3036001162 / Jul '97 / Carlton

Harvey, Billy

☐ MOONLIGHT THEATRE
199637 / 2 Mar '98 / Psychoactive

Harvey, Bobby

☐ CEILIDH DANCES (Harvey, Bobby & His Ceilidh Band)
CDLOC 1058 / Dec '90 / Lochshore

Harvey, Chris

☐ WHITE SAIL, THE
Biomorph / Allegiance / Paris / Secret of the screen / Liber null / Liber null / Elation sedation / Plasmate / Pixelate / Jorg / White sail
AD 15CD / Dec '96 / AD

Harvey, Clive

☐ ULTIMATE GUITAR ALBUM, THE (Harvey, Clive & Trevor Hills)
Homeward / Spanish caravan / Reunion / Blue light / Flamenco sun / Zingaro / Why / Gitane Arab / Gypsy jazz / Spain / Storm swept / Phantom wagon / Twin soul / Marooned / Blue town / Legacy
PLSCD 250 / 27 Oct '97 / Pulse

Harvey Danger

☐ WHERE HAVE ALL THE MERRYMAKERS GONE
5560002 / 3 Aug '98 / London

☐ WHERE HAVE ALL THE...
AR 006 / 26 May '98 / Arena

Harvey, Kike

☐ LA ISLA BONITA
TUMICD 048 / '95 / Tumi

☐ SALSA PACHANGA Y AMOR
TUMICD 039 / Jun '93 / Tumi

Harvey, Maxine

☐ DON'T YOU BREAK MY HEART
Don't you break my heart / Right stuff / Jut a little / That's enough / Can't hide feelings / I need your love forever / Crazy for you / I'm sorry / Get on it / Get on it
WRCD 017 / Nov '97 / World

Harvey, Mick

☐ ALTA MAREA/VATERLAND (Original Soundtrack)
IONIC 6CD / Mar '93 / The Fine Line

☐ INTOXICATED MAN
CDSTUMM 144 / Oct '95 / Mute

☐ PINK ELEPHANTS
Pink elephants / Requiem / Javanaise / Black seaweed / Comic strip / Ticket puncher / Non affair / Scenic railway / To all the lucky kids / Anthracite / Manon / I love you nor do I / Ballad of Melody Nelson / Torry Cannon / Who is in who is out / Hotel specific
CDSTUM 157 / 27 Oct '97 / Mute

Harvey's Rabbit

☐ NEW SPIRITUAL VACUUM
Happy town / Is this what you call change / My place / How life should be / Love is the law / Flowers in the sky / Jane / Whatever happened to / Your secret place / Blue cat cafe
RRAD 109 / 3 Aug '98 / Rotator

Harvison, Jon

☐ HIGH DIVING
DR 02CD / Mar '98 / Drive On

☐ LONELY AS THE MOON
D 001CD / Jul '95 / Drive On

Haryou Percussion Group

☐ HARYOU PERCUSSION GROUP
CBCD 002 / Jul '96 / Cubop

Hash

☐ BASH
Twilight ball / Ghetto / Mr. Hello / I forgot my blanket / Operation herve / 4.30 a.m. hikes / Kit and kaboodle / In the grass / Mary I wanna / Orchard moons / Travelling / I'm down / American chorus / My icy death
7559615132 / Nov '93 / Elektra

Hash Jar Tempo

☐ WELL OILED
DFR 24 / Apr '97 / Drunken Fish

Hashim, Michael

☐ BLUE STREAK, A
STCD 546 / '92 / Stash

☐ GUYS AND DOLLS
STCD 558 / Jan '93 / Stash

☐ KEEP A SONG IN YOUR SOUL
Keep a song in your soul / Get some cash for your trash / Two sleepy people / Jitterbug waltz / What did I do to be so black and blue / Fats Waller's original E flat blues / Blue turning grey over you / Prisoner of love / Honeysuckle rose
HEPCD 2068 / Nov '96 / Hep

☐ TRANSATLANTIC AIRS
Have you met Miss Jones / Love song from threepenny opera / Speak low / Corn squeezin's / Charade / Play the notes you like the loudest / My ship / Pleasures and regrets / Do everything / Born to be blue / Tickle toe
33JAZZ 023 / Jul '95 / 33 Jazz

Hasidic New Wave

☐ JEWS AND THE ABSTRACT TRUTH
KFWCD 192 / Jun '97 / Knitting Factory

☐ PSYCHO SEMITIC
Achas / AKS / Achas Ve-Achas / Hebe bop / Achas U-shtayim / Transcendence/U'Mpney Khata'Eynu / Al-Osfour Al-Majnoun / Achas Ve-Sholosh / Ve-Samakhto dub / Achas Ve-Arba / Habibi / Achas Vo-Sheysh / Blues in exile / Achas Ve-Khamesh / Men trinkt mashke
KFWCD 203 / 29 Jun '98 / Knitting Factory

Haskell, Gordon

☐ BUTTERFLY IN CHINA
Go tell Sarah / I don't remember it / Chilli chilli / Test drive / All my life / More yin than yang / Pelican pie / Wang bang world / Things we said today / Someone I knew
BP 287CD / 3 Aug '98 / Blueprint

☐ IT IS AND IT ISN'T
No meaning / Could be / Upside down / Just a lovely day / Sitting by the fire / No need / Worms / Spider / Learning not to feel / Benny / When I laugh
7567805522 / Jan '96 / Atlantic
BP 266CD / 22 Jun '98 / Blueprint

☐ IT'S JUST A PLOT TO DRIVE YOU CRAZY
BP 118CD / Jul '96 / Blueprint

☐ IT'S JUST ANOTHER PLOT TO DRIVE YOU CRAZY
VP 118CD / Jan '93 / Voiceprint

☐ SAILING IN MY BOAT
Boat trip / Born to be together / Flying home together / Lawbreaker / All since you went away / Oo la di doo da day / Time only knows / Better by far / Some other day / Zanzibar / Slow boat
VP 197CD / 20 Apr '98 / Voiceprint

☐ VOICEPRINT RADIO SESSION
VPR 001CD / Oct '94 / Voiceprint

Haskett, Chris

☐ LANGUAGE
213CD 002 / Jun '96 / 2.13.61

☐ NON FICTION (Haskett, Chris & Brandon Finley)
Lucy in the sky with dog food / L-shape / Lizzard errands / Tribute / Sly Larry's wanna b-side / Doubt of the benefit / Drill / Wheel chair waltz / Viva voice / Twin / Zadit / Neighbors say he was a quiet man / Truth is stranger / Respistory / Maybe elephants walk / Playing in Papa's clothes / Four legs in the morning / Two legs at noon / Three legs in the evening
213CD 022 / Apr '97 / 2.13.61

Haskins, Fuzzy

☐ WHOLE NOTHER/RADIO ACTIVE THANG
Tangerine green / Cookie jar / Mr. Junk man / I can see myself in you / Fuz and da boog / Which way do I disco / Love's now is forever / Sometimes I rock and roll / I'll be loving you / Right back where I started from / Not yet / I think I got my thang together / This situation called love / Gimme back (Some of the love you got from me) / Things we used to do / Woman / Sinderella / Silent day
CDSEWD 093 / Sep '94 / Westbound

Haslam, Annie

☐ ANNIE IN WONDERLAND
Introlise / If I were made of music / I never believed in love / If I loved you / Hunioco / Rockalise / Nature boy / Inside my life / Going home
7599265152 / Jan '96 / WEA

Haslam, George

☐ ARGENTINE ADVENTURES VOL.1
Tinto dreams / Ritmo catulo Castillo / Vidala para mi sombra / Los muchachos de Buenos Aires / Vidala para mi sombra / Welcome George / Las quenas de Barragan / Bailando con los raices / Affirmation
SLAMCD 304 / Oct '96 / Slam

☐ ARGENTINE ADVENTURES VOL.2
Tango libre / El subsuelo / Blues for Argentina / Monito / Kool / Blues no.9 for la plata / Incompleta
SLAMCD 307 / Jan '97 / Slam

☐ LEVEL TWO
Pastures now / Fells sunrise / Crossfield / Corner meadow / Fylde away / Moss house / In memory / Last load
SLAMCD 303 / Oct '96 / Slam

☐ SOLOS EAST WEST (Haslam, George & Lol Coxhill)
SLAMCD 308 / Sep '97 / Slam

Haslinger

☐ FUTURE PRIMITIVE
WLD 9211 / Apr '95 / Varese Sarabande

Hasni, Cheb

☐ ALA BESSE
DECLI 845295 / 3 Mar '98 / Munich

☐ CHEB HASNI
CDSB 107 / Sep '95 / Club Du Disque Arabe

☐ LATBKICHE
CDSB 103 / Sep '95 / Club Du Disque Arabe

☐ LOVER'S RAI
May God help me / That forlorn person / You ask for separation / I don't know why you are crying / Don't cry this is my destiny / My suffering was long / I know you now / I want a beautiful woman / I still have the souvenir / You the healer
ROUCD 5078 / Feb '97 / Rounder

☐ TALGHIYABEK YA GHOZAZI
CDSB 102 / Sep '95 / Club Du Disque Arabe

Hassan, Alex

☐ NOVELTY PIANO
SOSCD 1322 / Sep '97 / Stomp Off

Hassan, Chalf

☐ SONGS AND DANCES FROM MOROCCO
EUCD 1170 / '91 / ARC

Hassan, Mehdi

☐ HARPAL
IMUT 1022 / Mar '96 / Multitone

☐ HITS OF MEHDI HASSAN, THE
PMUT 019 / Aug '96 / Multitone

☐ LIVE IN LONDON VOL.1
DMUT 1183 / Mar '96 / Multitone

☐ LIVE IN LONDON VOL.2
DMUT 1184 / Mar '96 / Multitone

Hasselgard, Ake 'Stan'

☐ PERMANENT HASSELGARD, THE
Hallelujah / All the things you are / Am I blue / Lullaby in rhythm / Swedish pastry / Mel's idea
NCD 8802 / '93 / Phontastic

Hassell, Jon

☐ AKA/DARBARI/JAVA (Magic Realism)
Empire / Darbari extension
EEGCD 31 / Feb '91 / EG

☐ CITY: WORKS OF FICTION
Voiceprint / Mombasa / In the city of red dust / Ba ya d / Out of Adedara / Pagan / Tikal / Rain / Warriors
ASCD 11 / Apr '96 / All Saints

☐ DREAM THEORY IN MALAYA
Chor moire / Courage / Dream theory / Datu bintung at jelong / Malay / These times / Gift of fire
EEGCD 13 / Feb '91 / EG

☐ DRESSING FOR PLEASURE (Hassell, Jon & Bluescreen)
G-spot / Steppin' thru time / Zeitgeist / Sex goddess / Destination bakiff / Blue night / Mati / Gods they must be crazy / Buzzword / Kolo x / Club zombie / Villa narco / Personals
9362455232 / Nov '94 / Warner Bros.

☐ FLASH OF THE SPIRIT (Hassell, Jon & Farafina)
Flash of the spirit (laughter) / Night moves (fear) / Air Afrique (wind) / Out pours (kongo) / Blue (prayer) / Taboo (play) / Like warriors everywhere (courage) / Dreamworld (dance) / Tales of the near future (clairvoyance) / Vampire dances / Masque
INT 30092 / May '91 / Intuition

☐ FOURTH WORLD MUSIC (Hassell, Jon & Brian Eno)
Chemistry / Delta rain dream / Griot (over Contagious Magic) / Ba-benzele / Rising thermal / Charm
EEGCD 7 / Jan '87 / EG

☐ JON HASSEL VS. 808 STATE (Hassell, Jon & 808 State)
ASCD 17 / Apr '96 / All Saints

☐ POWER SPOT (Hassell, Jon & Brian Eno)
Power spot / Passage D E / Solaire / Miracle steps / Wing melodies / Elephant and the orchid / Air
8294662 / Oct '86 / ECM

☐ SURGEON OF THE NIGHTSKY, THE
Ravinia/Vancouver / Paris 1 / Hamburg / Brussels / Paris 2
INT 30042 / May '91 / Intuition

Hatch, Tony

☐ EASY PROJECT VOL.3, THE (The Very Best Of The Tony Hatch Orchestra) (Hatch, Tony Orchestra)
NEMCD 920 / Jan '97 / Sequel

☐ EASY PROJECT VOL.6, THE (Hatchback) (Hatch, Tony Orchestra)
You're the one / Round every corner / Beautiful in the rain / Latin velvet / Music / Crosstown commuter / I know a place / Look for a star / Herbin' / Sugar and spice / Love hustle / Who-dun-it / El Payaso / Where are you now / Brasilia mission / Return to the stars / Sole bossa nova / Bahama sound / Brazilia / Finito
NEMCD 951 / 24 Nov '97 / Sequel

☐ TONY HATCH SONGBOOK, THE (Hatch, Tony & Jackie Trent)
Downtown / Look for a star / Where are you now / Forget him / Other man's grass is always greener / Two of us / I know a place / Joanna / Call me / What would I be / Don't sleep in the subway / Sign of the times / My love / Thank you for loving me / I couldn't live without your love / Who am I / Colour my world / Opposite your smile / You're everything / Let's do it again
306632 / Jun '97 / Hallmark

Hatchard, Mike

☐ HAND-GLIDER HAS LANDED
EJL 021 / Jan '96 / Ensemble Jazz

Hatcher, Roger

☐ ROGER HATCHER COLLECTION, THE (Expansion Collector Series)
Stormy love affair / Heaven is missing an angel / Sugar Daddy / Your love is a masterpiece / All my love belongs to you / Gonna make love to somebody's old lady / I dedicate my life to you / Sweetest girl in the world / I'm gonna dedicate my song to you / Warm and tender love / Gonna rock you like a baby / She's all I got / That's when I'll stop loving you / I cried like a baby / Let your love shine on me / Caught making love
EXCDG 1 / May '96 / Expansion

Hatchett's Swingtette

☐ HATCHETT'S SWINGTETTE FEATURING STEPHANE GRAPELLI (Hatchett's Swingtette & Stephane Grapelli)
Alexander's ragtime band / Ting a ling / Beat me Daddy, eight to the bar / Playmates / Oh Johnny, Oh Johnny, Oh / Sweet potato piper / Sheikh of Araby / Oh how he misses his missus / I hear bluebirds / Wrap yourself in cotton wool / Scrub me Mama with a boogie beat / Blue ribbon rag / Twelfth Street rag / She had those dark and dreamy eyes / Scatterbrain / In the mood / I got rhythm / It's a hap-hap-happy day / Papa's in bed with his breeches on / Mind the Handel's hot / Ma, he's making eyes at me / Bluebirds in the moonlight
PASTCD 9785 / Mar '92 / Flapper

Hate Bombs

☐ HERE COMES TREBLE
36T 0004CD / Jul '97 / 360 Twist

Hate Plow

☐ EVERYBODY DIES
SPV 08453192 / 29 Jun '98 / SPV
32273CD / 30 Mar '98 / Pavement

Hate Squad

☐ PZYCHOI
GUN 129CD / Jun '97 / Gun

Hatebreed

☐ SATISFACTION IS THE DEATH OF DESIRE
VR 063CD / 10 Nov '97 / Victory

☐ UNDER THE KNIFE
GOW 002CD / 20 Jul '98 / Grapes Of Wrath

Haters

☐ CULTIVATING CALAMITY
VC 125CD / 15 Jan '98 / Vinyl Communication

☐ MIND THE GAP
VC 107 / Jan '97 / Vinyl Communication

Hatfield & The North

☐ HATFIELD AND THE NORTH
Stubbs effect / Big jobs (poo poo extract) / Going up to people and tinkling / Calyx / Son of "There's no place like Homerton" / Aigrette / Rifferama / Fol de rol / Shaving is boring / Licks for the ladies / Bossa nochance / Big jobs No.2 / Lobster in cleavage probe / Gigantic land crabs in Earth takeover bid / Other Stubbs effect / Let's eat (real soon) / Fitter Stoke has a bath
CDV 2008 / Jul '87 / Virgin

☐ ROTTERS CLUB, THE
Share it / Lounging there trying / (Big) John Wayne socks psychology on the jaw / Chaos at the greasy spoon / Yes no interlude / Fitter Stoke has a bath / Didn't matter anyway / Underdub / Mumps (Your Majesty is like a cream donut-quiet) / Mumps (lumps) / Mumps (prenut) / Mumps (your majesty is like a cream donut-loud) / Halfway between heaven and earth / Oh Len's nature / Lying and gracing
CDV 2030 / Jun '88 / Virgin

Hatfield, Juliana

☐ BECOME WHAT YOU ARE
Supermodel / My sister / This is the sound / For the birds / Mabel / Dame with a rod / Addicted / Feelin' Massachusetts / Spin the bottle / President Garfield / Little pieces / I got no idols
4509935292 / Dec '96 / East West

☐ ONLY EVERYTHING (Hatfield, Juliana Three)
My darling / Universal heart-beat / Fleur de lys / Live on tomorrow / Dumb fun / You blues / Simplicity is beautiful / Hang down from heaven / Congratulations / Ok ok / Outsider / Bottles and flowers / Dying proof / What a life
4509998862 / Dec '96 / East West

Hathaway, Donny

☐ DONNY HATHAWAY COLLECTION, A
Song for you / I love you more than you'll ever know / You were meant for me / Back together again / Where is the love / For all we know / Someday we'll all be free / Giving up / Closer I get to you / You are my heaven / What's going on / Ghetto / Young, gifted and black / You've got a friend / This Christmas
7567820922 / Apr '93 / Atlantic

☐ DONNY HATHAWAY IN PERFORMANCE
I love you more than you'll ever know / Nu-po / We need you right now / To be young gifted and black / Song for you / Sack full of dreams
7567815692 / Jan '96 / Atlantic

☐ EVERYTHING IS EVERYTHING
Voices inside / Je vous aime / I believe to my soul / Misty / Sugar Lee / Tryin' times / Thank you master / Ghetto / Young, gifted and black
8122722162 / Jul '96 / Atlantic

Hato De Foces

☐ CANTAR DE CAMINO
J 1017CD / Jun '94 / Sonifolk

Hatrix

☐ COLLISIONCOURSSE
MASSCD 040 / Nov '94 / Massacre

Haubenstock-Ramati, Roman

☐ FOR PIANO (2CD Set)
ARTCD 6196 / Mar '97 / Hat Hut

Haujobb

☐ FRAMES
CD 07622382 / Dec '96 / SPV

☐ FREEZE FRAME FACILITY
SPV 08422192 / May '95 / SPV

☐ MATRIX
08543472 / May '97 / Westcom

☐ SOLUTIONS FOR A SMALL PLANET
08543282 / Feb '97 / Humbug

Haunted

☐ HAUNTED
VCD 2012 / 16 Mar '98 / Voxx

☐ HAUNTED, THE
VOXXCD 2011 / Aug '95 / Voxx

Haunted

☐ HAUNTED, THE
Hate song / Chasm / In vein / Undead / Choke hold / Three times / Bullet hole / Now you know / Shattered / Soul fracture / Blood rust / Forensick
MOSH 197CD / 29 Jun '98 / Earache

Haunted Garage

☐ POSSESSION PARK
CDZORRO 27 / Aug '91 / Metal Blade

Hause, Alfred

☐ STRICTLY DANCING: TANGO (Hause, Alfred & Big Tango Orchestra)
Ole guapa / Ole guapa / El choclo / Tango erotico / Hernando's hideaway / Tiritomba / A media luz / Blue tango / Jalousie / Weddingbell tango / Tango notturno / La violetta / Tango bolero / When gipsy eyes are crying / Du schwarzer zigeuner / Pearlfisher tango
15340 / May '94 / Laserlight

Have Mercy

☐ HAVE MERCY
Rusty cars and lonely bars / I keep rolling / Rambling girl / Going to germany / Let yourself go / One track mind / Run molly run / It's hard being a man / Georgia rag / Let it shine on me / Walk right in / Blues never goes away / Stuff you gotta watch / Rock island line
CCD 11039 / Jan '94 / Crosscut

Havel, Vaclav

☐ TWO PRESIDENTS JAM SESSION (Havel, Vaclav & Bill Clinton)
CR 00012 / Nov '95 / Czech Radio

Haven, Alan

☐ ORGAN SPECTACULAR
Close to you / Odd couple / Finding words (to say) / Watch what happens / Caravan / Aranjuez mon amour / South to the sun / Scheherazade / Misty / Rondo alla Turca / You've lost that lovin' feelin' / Travellin' man / My man / Wave / I'll walk beside you / I (who have nothing) / I can't stop loving you / Look of love / You are the sunshine of my life / (I can't get no) satisfaction
PLSCD 248 / 27 Oct '97 / Pulse

☐ ORGAN SPECTRUM
Watch what happens / Shenandoah / One I love belongs to somebody else / How insensitive / Image / Spellbound / Tenderly / Meditation / Trust in me / Quiet nights of quiet stars / Get back / Pavanne pour une infante defunte / Flying free / Greensleeves / Exactly like you
OS 224 / Dec '96 / OS Digital

Havens, Bob

☐ IN NEW ORLEANS
Don't forget it / Good little thing / You can't get stuff no more / Love changin' blues / Savannah mama / Talkin' to your mama / East st. louis toodle-oo / A to z blues / Wee midnight hours / Brown skin woman / I keep on drinkin' / Pal of mine / Pal of mine / Honey it must be love / Sending up my timber / Sending up my timber / Lord have mercy if you please / Climbing high mountains / It's my desire / Hide me in thy bosom
BCD 126 / Jun '95 / GHB

Havens, Richie

☐ CUTS TO THE CHASE
They dance alone / Times they are a' changin / Lives in the balance / Hawk / Old love / At a glance / My father's shoes / Darkness darkness / Young boy / Fade to blue / How the nights can fly / Comin' back to me / Don't pass it up
ESMCD 397 / Sep '96 / Essential

☐ RICHIE HAVENS SINGS BEATLES AND DYLAN
RCD 20035 / May '92 / Rykodisc

Havoc Mass

☐ KILLING THE FUTURE
MASSCD 019 / Dec '93 / Massacre

Havohej

☐ DETHRONE THE SON OF GOD
CANDLE 004CD / Oct '93 / Candlelight

Hawes, Hampton

☐ AT THE PIANO
Killing me softly with his song / Soul sign eight / Sunny morning / Blue in green / When I grow too old to dream
OJCCD 877 / Aug '96 / Original Jazz Classics

☐ BLUES FOR BUD (1968)
Blues enough / Sonora / They say it's wonderful / Black forest / Spanish steps / My romance / Dangerous / Blues for Bud
BLCD 760126 / '92 / Black Lion

☐ FOUR
Four / Yardbird suite / There will never be another you / Bow jest / Sweet Sue, just you / Up blues / Like someone in love / Love is just around the corner / Thou swell / Awful truth
OJCCD 165 / May '93 / Original Jazz Classics

☐ HAMPTON HAWES TRIO VOL.1
I got rhythm / What is this thing called love / Blues the most / So in love / Feelin' fine / Hamp's blues / Easy living / All the things you are / These foolish things / Carioca
OJCCD 316 / Nov '95 / Original Jazz Classics

☐ HIGH IN THE SKY (Hawes, Hampton Trio)
FSRCD 59 / 5 Jan '98 / Fresh Sound

☐ LIVE AT MEMORY LANE 1970 (Hawes, Hampton Allstars)
FSCD 1043 / Jan '97 / Fresh Sound

☐ MONTREUX 1971 (Hawes, Hampton Trio)
FSCD 133 / Jan '91 / Fresh Sound

Hawke

☐ NAMAQUADISCO
To the discoteque / Fung / Columbo's got slow eye / Vivos en la muerte / Born under a lucky star / Stationary tornado / Lovebug / Yellow tangerine / I have her / Shnowed in
DI 0782 / 23 Mar '98 / Distance

Hawker, Sue

☐ WORD IS OUT (Hawker, Sue & Rob Koral)
How deep is the ocean / I can dream / Teach me tonight / Feel so good / On the town / Empty rooms / Cheek to cheek / Hold me tight / Travelling blues / Heroes / Traffic jam / Will you still love me tomorrow / Word is out / Tell me why
33JAZZ 030 / Jan '97 / 33 Jazz

Hawkins, Annie

☐ MARDI GRAS PARADE (Hawkins, Annie New Orleans Legacy)
PKCD 090 / Jan '98 / PEK

Hawkins, Coleman

☐ APRIL IN PARIS
Body and soul / When day is done / Bouncing with Bean / April in Paris / Angel face / I love you / There will never be another you / Little girl blue / Bean stalks again / Have you met Miss Jones
ND 90636 / Apr '92 / Bluebird

☐ AT EASE WITH COLEMAN HAWKINS
For you, for me, forevermore / While we're young, then I'll be tired of you / Mighty like a rose / At dawning / Trouble is a man / Poor butterfly / I'll get by (as long as I have you)
OJCCD 181 / Nov '95 / Original Jazz Classics

☐ AT THE OPERA HOUSE (Hawkins, Coleman & Roy Eldridge)
Bean stalkin' / Nearness of you / Time on my hands / Walker / Tea for two / Blue moon / Cocktails for two / Kerry / Bean stalkin' / I can't get started / Walker / Stuffy
5216412 / Oct '94 / Verve

☐ BEAN AND BEN 1944-1945 (Hawkins, Coleman & Ben Webster)
In the hush of the night / Out to lunch / Every man for himself / Look out, Jack / On the bean / Recollections / Flyin' Hawk / Drifting on a reed / Broke but happy / Blues on the bayou / Jumpin' with Judy / Blues on the delta / Bottle's empty / Save it pretty Mama / For lovers only / Peach Tree Street blues
HQCD 04 / Oct '90 / Harlequin

☐ BEAN AND THE BOYS
In the hush of the night / Out to lunch / Every man for himself / Look out Jack / On the bean / Recollections / Flyin' hawk / Drifting on a reed / I mean you / Bean and the boys / Bean and the boys (take 2) / Cocktails for two / You go to my head / Stasch / Trust in me / Roll 'em Pete / Skrouk / Since I fell for you / My babe
LEJAZZCD 12 / Jun '93 / Le Jazz

☐ BEAN AND THE BOYS
PRCD 24124 / Oct '93 / Prestige

☐ BEAN STALKIN' (Hawkins, Coleman & Friends)
Bean stalkin' / Stompin' at the Savoy / Take the 'A' train / Indian summer / Crazy rhythm / (Back home again in) Indiana
CD 2310933 / Jun '93 / Pablo

☐ BEAN, THE
World is waiting for the sunrise / Ill wind (you're blowing me no good) / My melancholy baby / In a mellotone / Ain't misbehavin' / Stompin' at the savoy / Midnight sun / Bean stalks again / Out of nowhere / Lucky duck / I can't get started / Ruby / And so to sleep again / Get happy / Foolin' around / Man I love
CD 53168 / Jan '94 / Giants Of Jazz

☐ BLUES WAIL (Coleman Hawkins Plays The Blues)
Juicy fruit / Blues for tomorrow / Blues wail / Soul blues / Skronk / Stealin' the bean / Foot pattin' / Blues for Ron / Pedallin'
PRCD 11006 / Jun '97 / Prestige

☐ BODY AND SOUL
Meet Dr. Foo / Fine dinner / She's funny that way / Body and soul / When day is done / Sheikh of Araby / My blue Heaven / Bouncing with Bean / Say it isn't so / Spotlite / April in Paris / How strange / Half step down please / Angel face / Body and soul / I love Paris / There will never be another you / Under Paris skies / Bean stalks again
09026685152 / Oct '96 / RCA Victor

☐ BODY AND SOUL
Rifftide / Man I love / Body and soul / Caravan / Love for sale / Love come back to me
WWCD 2018 / Mar '89 / West Wind

☐ BODY AND SOUL
TPZ 1022 / Jun '95 / Topaz Jazz

☐ BODY AND SOUL
JC 98009 / 15 Jun '98 / Jazz Classix

☐ CLASSIC YEARS, THE
Sweet Georgia Brown / Lady be good / Jamaica shout / Body and soul / Honeysuckle rose / Crazy rhythm / Out of nowhere / Lost in a fog / Lullaby / Day you came along / How come you do me like you do / My melancholy baby
CDSGP 0176 / 27 Apr '98 / Prestige

☐ CLASSICS 1929-1934
CLASSICS 587 / Aug '91 / Classics

☐ CLASSICS 1934-1937
CLASSICS 602 / Sep '91 / Classics

☐ CLASSICS 1937-1939
CLASSICS 613 / Feb '92 / Classics

☐ CLASSICS 1939-1940
CLASSICS 634 / Nov '92 / Classics

☐ CLASSICS 1943-1944
CLASSICS 807 / Mar '95 / Classics

☐ CLASSICS 1944
CLASSICS 842 / Nov '95 / Classics

☐ CLASSICS 1944-1945
CLASSICS 863 / Mar '96 / Classics

☐ CLASSICS 1945
CLASSICS 926 / Apr '97 / Classics

☐ CLASSICS 1946-1947
CLASSICS 984 / 24 Feb '98 / Classics

☐ COLEMAN HAWKINS
CD 14560 / Jul '94 / Jazz Portraits

☐ COLEMAN HAWKINS 1959-1962 (Hawkins, Coleman & Roy Eldridge/ Mickey Baker)
STCD 538 / '91 / Stash

☐ **COLEMAN HAWKINS AND BENNY CARTER (Hawkins, Coleman & Benny Carter)**
Chicago / I can't love you anymore than I do / Sweet adeline / Breeze and I / It's a wonderful world / Man I love / Forgive a fool / Passin' it around / When a congressman meets a senator don south / I can't believe that you're in love with me / I used to love you / Ill wind (you're blowing me no good) / Fish fry / Swanee river / All of me / Honeysuckle rose / Midnight / Prelude to a kiss / I heard you cried last night / On the alamo
UCD 19011 / Jun '95 / Forlane

☐ **COLEMAN HAWKINS ENCOUNTERS BEN WEBSTER (Remastered) (Hawkins, Coleman & Ben Webster)**
5214272 / Oct '97 / Verve Master Edition

☐ **COLEMAN HAWKINS MEETS THE BIG SAX SECTION (Hawkins, Coleman & The Big Sax Section)**
Ooga dooga / I've grown accustomed to your face / Thanks for the misery / Evening at Papa Joe's / There is nothing like a dame / Thanks for the misery
SV 0248 / Oct '97 / Savoy Jazz

☐ **COLEMAN HAWKINS SAMPLER**
Laura / I hadn't anyone till you / For you, for me, forevermore / Poor butterfly / Moonglow / Greensleeves
OJCX 007 / Jan '98 / Original Jazz Classics

☐ **COLEMAN HAWKINS WITH THE SECTION**
VG 650134 / Oct '92 / Vogue

☐ **COMPLETE RECORDINGS 1929-1940, THE (6CD Set)**
Hello Lola / One hour (If I could be with you one hour tonight) / Dismal Dan / Down Georgia way / Girls like you were meant for boys like me / Georgia on my mind / I can't believe that you're in love with me / Darktown strutters ball / (I'll be glad when you're dead) you rascal you / Someday sweetheart / I wish I could shimmy like my sister Kate / River's takin' care of me / Ain'tcha got music / Stringin' along on a shoe string / Shadows on the Swanee / Day you came along / Jamaica shout / Heartbreak blues / Blues rhapsody / Happy feet / I'm rhythm crazy now / Ol' man river / Minnie the moocher's wedding day / Ain't cha glad / I've got to sing a torch song / Hush my mouth / You're gonna lose your gal / Dark clouds / My Galveston gal / Georgia jubilee / Junk man / Ol' pappy / Emaline / I ain't got nobody / It sends me / On the sunny side of the street / Lullaby / Oh lady be good / Lost in a fog / I wish I were twins / I only have eyes for you / After you've gone / Some of these days / Honeysuckle rose / Hands across the table / Blue moon / Avalon / What a difference a day makes / Stardust / Chicago / Meditation / What Harlem is to me / Netcha's dream / Love cries / Sorrow / Tiger rag / It may not be true / I'm in the mood for love / I wanna go back to Harlem / Consolation / Strange fact / Original Dixieland one-step / Smiles / Something is gonna give me away / Crazy rhythm / Out of nowhere / Sweet Georgia brown / Lamentation / Devotion / Somebody loves me / Mighty like the blues / Pardon me pretty baby / My buddy / Well alright then / Blues evermore / Dear old Southland / Way down yonder in New Orleans / I know that you know / When buddha smiles / Swinging in the groove / My melancholy baby / Meet Dr. Foo / Fine dinner / She's funny that way / Body and soul / When day is done / Sheikh of araby / My blue heaven / Bouncing with Bean / Smack / I surrender dear / Dedication / Passin' it around / Serenade to a sleeping beauty / Rocky comfort / Forgive a fool / Bugle call rag / One o'clock jump / 9-20 special / Feedin' the bean
CDAFS 10266 / Sep '92 / Affinity

☐ **DESAFINADO (Hawkins, Coleman Sextet)**
Desafinado / I'm looking over a four leaf clover / Samba para bean / I remember you / One-note samba / O pato / Un abraco no bonfa / Stumpy bossa nova
MCAD 33118 / Apr '90 / Impulse Jazz
IMP 12272 / Apr '97 / Impulse Jazz

☐ **EARLY YEARS, THE**
CDSGP 0158 / Sep '95 / Prestige

☐ **GENIUS OF COLEMAN HAWKINS, THE (Remastered)**
5390652 / Oct '97 / Verve Master Edition

☐ **GENTLE HAWK**
There will never be another you / How strange / Sih sah / I love you / Angel face / I love Paris / Body and soul / It's only a paper moon / April in Paris / I surrender dear / Mon homme / Mimi / Little girl blue / Under Paris skies / Sophisticated lady / La mer / Dinner for one / Please James / Mademoiselle de Paris / Have you met Miss Jones / Body and soul
74321431592 / Oct '96 / Camden

☐ **HAWK EYES**
Hawk eyes / C'mon in / Through for the night / I never knew / La rosita / Stealin' the bean
OJCCD 294 / Feb '92 / Original Jazz Classics

☐ **HAWK FLIES HIGH, THE**
Chant / Juicy fruit / Think deep / Laura / Blue lights / Sanctity
OJCCD 27 / Oct '92 / Original Jazz Classics

☐ **HAWK IN EUROPE 1934-1937, THE**
Lullaby / Lost in a fog / Oh lady be good / Avalon / What a difference a day makes / Stardust / Meditation / Netcha's dream / Strange fact / Crazy rhythm / Honeysuckle rose / Out of nowhere / Sweet Georgia Brown / Mighty like the blues / Pardon me pretty baby / Somebody loves me / My buddy / Well alright then
CDAJA 5054 / Jul '88 / Living Era

☐ **HAWK IN PARIS, THE**
07863510592 / Jul '93 / Bluebird

☐ **HAWK RETURNS, THE**
Flight eleven / Modern fantasy / Confessin' / September song / They can't take that away from me / Should I / I'll follow my secret heart / I'll tell you later / What a difference a day makes / On my way / Last stop / Goin' down home
SV 0182 / Oct '97 / Savoy Jazz

☐ **HAWK SWINGS, THE**
Cloudy / Almost dawn / Stake out / Crosstown / Shadows
CDBOP 015 / Jul '91 / Boplicity

☐ **HAWK TALKS**
Lucky duck / I can't get started (with you) / Foolin' around / Man I love / Trust in me / Where is your heart / Wishing / Carioca / If I could be with you one hour tonight / Ruby / Sin / Midnight sun / And so to sleep again / Lonely wine
FSCD 130 / Jan '91 / Fresh Sound

☐ **HAWK TAWK**
TCD 1007 / Feb '96 / Tradition

☐ **IN A MELLOW TONE**
You blew out the flame in my heart / I want to be loved / In a mellow tone / Greensleeves / Through for the night / Until the real thing comes along / Sweetest sounds / Then I'll be tired of you / Jammin' in swingville
OJCCD 6001 / Apr '93 / Original Jazz Classics

☐ **IN CONCERT**
BS 18003 / Jul '96 / Bandstand

☐ **IN EUROPE VOL.1-3 1934-1939**
CBC 1006 / Jun '93 / Bellaphon

☐ **INTRODUCTION TO COLEMAN HAWKINS 1923-1945, AN**
4049 / Nov '97 / Best Of Jazz

☐ **JAZZ GREATS**
Body and soul / Dinah: *Hawkins, Coleman & Lionel Hampton Orchestra* / April in Paris / There will never be another you: *Hawkins, Coleman & Billy Bryers Orchestra* / Sugar foot stomp: *Hawkins, Coleman & Fletcher Henderson Orchestra* / I've got the world on a string: *Hawkins, Coleman & Henry 'Red' Allen All Stars* / Under Paris skies: *Hawkins, Coleman & Manny Albam Orchestra* / Angel face / When lights are low: *Hawkins, Coleman & Lionel Hampton Orchestra* / She's funny that way / My blue heaven: *Hawkins, Coleman All Star Octet* / Say it isn't so: *Hawkins, Coleman 52nd Street All Stars* / I love Paris: *Hawkins, Coleman & Manny Albam Orchestra* / Sweet Lorraine: *Hawkins, Coleman & Henry 'Red' Allen All Stars* / How strange / Spotlite: *Hawkins, Coleman 52nd Street All Stars*
74321499672 / Feb '98 / RCA Victor

☐ **JAZZ MASTERS**
5218562 / 5 May '98 / Verve

☐ **JAZZ TONES**
60170400062 / 14 Apr '98 / PREV

☐ **LADY BE GOOD**
Lullaby / Oh lady be good / Lost in a fog / Honeysuckle rose / Some of these days / After you've gone / After you've gone (alternative take) / I only have eyes for you / I only have eyes for you (alternative take) / I wish I were twins / I wish I were twins (alternative takes) / Hands across the table / Hands across the tables (alternate take) / Blue moon / Avalon / What a difference a day makes / Stardust / Chicago / Chicago (alternate take) / Meditation / What Harlem is to me / What Harlem is to me (alternate take) / Netcha's dream
GRF 093 / '93 / Tring

☐ **LIVE FROM THE LONDON HOUSE (Chicago 1963) (Hawkins, Coleman Quartet)**
Way you look tonight / I can't get started / Moonglow / How high the moon / Blue room / All the things you are / Honeysuckle rose
JASMCD 2521 / Nov '93 / Jasmine

☐ **MASTER, THE**
I only have eyes for you / 'S wonderful / I'm in the mood for love / Bean at the met / Flame thrower / Imagination / Night and day / Cattin' at the Keynote / On the sunny side of the street / Three little words / Battle of the saxes / Louise / Make believe / Don't blame me / Just one of those things / Hallelujah / I'm yours / Under a blanket of blue / Beyond the blue horizon / (In) a shanty in old Shanty Town
LEJAZZCD 37 / May '95 / Le Jazz

☐ **MASTERPIECES**
158712 / Apr '97 / Jazz Archives

☐ **MASTERS OF JAZZ VOL.12**
STCD 4112 / Feb '89 / Storyville

☐ **QUINTESSENCE, THE (1926-1944/2CD Set)**
FA 213 / Nov '95 / Fremeaux

☐ **RAINBOW MIST**
Rainbow mist / Woody 'n' you / Bu dee daht / Disorder at the border / Yesterdays / Feeling zero / Salt peanuts / Uptown lullaby / Pick-up boys / Porgy / Concerto for tenor / Taps miller / I can't get started / Sweet and lovely
DDCD 459 / Aug '93 / Delmark

☐ **SAVOY BROADCASTS 1940 (Hawkins, Coleman & Erskine Hawkins)**
Tuxedo junction / I'll be faithful / Whispering grass / Gin mill blues / Junction blues / Gabriel meets the Duke / Leanin' on the old top rail / Midnight stroll / Body and soul / Chant of the groove / Forgive a fool / Asleep in the deep / Can't get Indiana off my mind / Passin' it around / When a congressman meets a senator down South / I can't believe that you're in love with me
TAX 37072 / Aug '94 / Tax

☐ **SIRIUS**
Man I love / Don't blame me / Just a gigolo / One I love / Time on my hands / Sweet and lovely / Exactly like you / Street of dreams / Sugar
OJCCD 861 / Nov '95 / Original Jazz Classics

☐ **SONG OF THE HAWK**
Rhythm crazy / Oh lady be good / It sends me / Ol' man river / Heartbreak blues / Day you came along / When day is done / Sweet Georgia Brown / Out of nowhere / Passin' it around / Rocky comfort / My blue heaven / Meet Dr. Foo / Blue moon / What a difference a day makes / Bouncing with bean / He's funny that way / Fine dinner / Stardust / Love cries / I ain't got nobody
PASTCD 7032 / Jan '94 / Flapper

☐ **SOUL**
OJCCD 96 / Oct '92 / Original Jazz Classics

☐ **STANDARDS AND WARHORSES (Hawkins, Coleman & Red Allen)**
JASSCD 2 / Oct '91 / Jass

☐ **SUPREME**
Lover come back to me / Body and soul / In walked bud / Quintessence / Fine and dandy / Ow
ENJ 90092 / Apr '95 / Enja

☐ **SWINGVILLE 2001 (Hawkins, Coleman & the Red Garland Trio)**
It's a blue world / I want to be loved / Red beans and rice / Bean's blues / Blues for Ron
OJCCD 418 / Apr '93 / Original Jazz Classics

☐ **SWINGVILLE 2005 (Hawkins, Coleman All Stars)**
You blew out the flame in my heart / More bounce to the vonce / I'm beginning to see the light / Cool blue / Some stretching
OJCCD 225 / Feb '97 / Original Jazz Classics

☐ **TENOR FOR ALL SEASONS, THE (2CD Set)**
Battle hymn of the republic: *Hawkins, Coleman & Red Allen* / Frankie and Johnny: *Hawkins, Coleman & Red Allen* / When the saints go marchin' in: *Hawkins, Coleman & Red Allen* / South: *Hawkins, Coleman & Red Allen* / Won't you come home Bill Bailey: *Hawkins, Coleman & Red Allen* / Blues: *Hawkins, Coleman & Red Allen* / Maryland my Maryland: *Hawkins, Coleman & Red Allen* / Stormy weather: *Hawkins, Coleman & Red Allen* / Mean to me: *Hawkins, Coleman & Red Allen* / Lonesome road: *Hawkins, Coleman & Red Allen* / Sleepy time gal: *Hawkins, Coleman & Red Allen* / Summertime: *Hawkins, Coleman & Red Allen* / All of me: *Hawkins, Coleman & Red Allen* / Tea for two: *Hawkins, Coleman & Red Allen* / Blue Lou: *Hawkins, Coleman & Roy Eldridge* / Basin Street blues: *Hawkins, Coleman & Roy Eldridge* / Just you just me: *Hawkins, Coleman & Roy Eldridge* / Rifftide: *Hawkins, Coleman & Roy Eldridge* / I can't get started/These foolish things: *Hawkins, Coleman & Roy Eldridge* / Undecided: *Hawkins, Coleman & Roy Eldridge* / Honeysuckle rose: *Hawkins, Coleman & Roy Eldridge* / Oh lady be good: *Hawkins, Coleman & Roy Eldridge* / How high the moon/Ornithology: *Hawkins, Coleman & Roy Eldridge*
JZCL 5017 / Jul '97 / Jazz Classics

☐ **TODAY AND NOW (Hawkins, Coleman Quartet)**
Go Li'l Liza / Quintessence / Don't love me / Love song from Apache / Put on your old grey bonnet / Swingin' Scotch / Don't sit under the apple tree
IMP 11842 / Sep '96 / Impulse Jazz

☐ **WITH HENRY RED ALLEN & HORACE HENDERSON 1933/34 (Hawkins, Coleman/Henry Allen/Horace Henderson)**
Someday sweetheart / I wish I could shimmy like my sister Kate / River's takin' care of me / Ain'tcha got music / Stringin' along on a shoe string / Shadows on the Swanee / Day you come along / Jamaica shout / Heartbreak blues / Hush my mouth / You're gonna lose your gal / Dark clouds / My galveston gal / Happy feet / I'm rhythm crazy now / Ol' man river / Minnie the moocher's wedding day / Ain't cha glad / I've got to sing a torch song
HEPCD 1028 / Apr '90 / Hep

Hawkins, Dale

☐ **LET'S ALL TWIST**
Do the twist / Joanne / Going around / Someone to care / Pauline / Luky duky / Do it / What can I do / Empty shoes / Hey hey
EDCD 385 / Aug '94 / Edsel

Hawkins, Edwin

☐ **OH HAPPY DAY (Hawkins, Edwin Singers)**
TRTCD 169 / Jun '95 / TrueTrax

☐ **VERY BEST OF THE EDWIN HAWKINS SINGERS, THE (Hawkins, Edwin Singers)**
Oh happy day / His way (my way) / Lord don't move that mountain / Pray for peace / Blowin' in the wind / I believe / Jesus lover of my soul / To my father's house / Children get together / Jubilation / Whom shall I fear / I don't know how to love him / What's happening / Long way to go / Together in peace / World is going to be a better place / Precious memories / Someday / Lay down (candles in the rain)
74321558452 / 26 Jan '98 / Camden

Hawkins, Erskine

☐ **CLASSICS 1936-1938**
CLASSICS 653 / Nov '92 / Classics

☐ **CLASSICS 1939-1940**
CLASSICS 678 / Mar '93 / Classics

☐ **CLASSICS 1940-1941 (Hawkins, Erskine & His Orchestra)**
CLASSICS 701 / Jul '93 / Classics

☐ **CLASSICS 1941-1945**
CLASSICS 868 / Mar '96 / Classics

Hawkins, George Jr.

☐ **EVERY DOG**
IRS 993169 / Mar '97 / Edge Of Fluke

Hawkins, Hawkshaw

☐ **HAWK 1953-1961 (3CD Set)**
I'll trade yours for mine / Heap of lovin' / Mark round your finger / Long way / When you say yes / I'll take a chance with you / I'll never close my heart to you / Why don't you leave this town / Rebound / One white rose / I wanna be hugged to death by you / Why didn't I hear from you / Flashing lights / Waitin' for my baby / Kokomo / Ling ting tong / Pedro Gonzales Tennessee Lopez / How could anything so pretty / Car hoppin' mama / Love you steal / Oh how I cried / Borrowing / If it ain't on the menu / I gotta have you / Standing at the end of the world / I've got it again / Sunny side of the mountain / You just stood there / Dark moon / I'll get even with you / Guilty of dreaming / Are you happy / She was here / Freedom / It's easier said than done / Sensation / Ring on your finger / It would be a doggone lie / My fate is in your hands / I'll be gone / Best of company / Action / You can't find happiness that way / I don't apologise for loving you / With this pen / Thank you for thinking of me / Twenty miles from shore / Big ole heartache / Big red benson / Soldier's joy / Patanio, the pride of the plains / Alaska Lil and Texas Bill / Darkness on the face of the earth / Put a nickel in the jukebox / I can't seem to say goodbye / No love for me / You know me much too well / My story / Love I have for you / Your conscience
BCD 15539 / Aug '91 / Bear Family

Hawkins, Ronnie

☐ **FOLK BALLADS OF RONNIE HAWKINS**
Summertime / Sometimes I feel like a Motherless child / I gave my love a cherry / Brave man / Poor wayfaring stranger / Virginia bride / Mister and Mississippi / John Henry / Fare thee well / Out of a hundred / Death of Floyd Collins / Love from afar
EDCD 386 / Aug '94 / Edsel

☐ **HELLO AGAIN, MARY LOU (Hawkins, Ronnie & The Hawks)**
Mary lou / Don't start me rockin' / Girl with the dark brown hair / Lucy / Days gone by / Baby jean / Living' a life I can't afford / Mama come home / Who'll stop the rain / Making it again / Hit record / Look out time
PRD 70242 / Feb '91 / Provogue

☐ **ROULETTE YEARS, THE**
Ruby baby / Forty days / Horace / One of these days / What'cha gonna do when the creek runs dry / Wild little Willie / Mary Lou / Oh sugar / Odessa need your lovin' / My girl is red hot / Dizzy Miss Lizzy / Hayride / C riff rock / Baby Jean / Southern love / Someone like you / Hey Boba Lou / Love me like you can / You cheated, you lied / Dreams do come true / Lonely hours / Clara / Honey don't / Sick and tired / Ballad of Caryl Chessman / Summertime / You know I love you / Sexy ways / Come come / Searchin' / Honey love / I feel good / Suzie Q / Matchbox / What a party / Bo Diddley / Who do you love / Bossman / High blood pressure / There's a screw loose / Arkansas / Mojo man / Further on up the road / Nineteen years old / Cathy Jean / Mojo man take 1 / Hayride No.1 / Light in your window / My heart cries / Look for me / Love it up / Your love is what I need / Kansas City / Going to Moscow
NEDCD 266 / Oct '94 / Sequel

☐ **SINGS THE SONGS OF HANK WILLIAMS**
Cold cold heart / Hey good lookin' / Your cheatin' heart / Weary blues from waiting / They'll be no teardrops tonight / Nobody's lonesome for me / Ramblin' man / I'm so lonesome I could cry / You win again / I can't help it (if I'm in love with you) / Lonesome whistle / Jambalaya (on the bayou)
EDCD 387 / Aug '94 / Edsel

Hawkins, Screamin' Jay

☐ **AT LAST**
3027422 / 24 Feb '98 / Last Call

☐ **BEST OF ALLIGATOR WINE, THE**
Alligator wine / I put a spell on you / Feast of the mau mau / Itty bitty pretty one / Same damn thing / Deep in love / Please don't leave me / What's gonna happen on the eight day / I feel alright / It's only make believe / Poor folks / Your kind of love / Don't deceive me / All night / I don't know / Serving time / What good is it / Mountain jive / Portrait of a man / Constipation blues
MCCD 322 / Nov '97 / Music Club

☐ **BLACK MUSIC FOR WHITE PEOPLE**
Is you is or is you ain't my baby / I feel alright / I put a spell on you / I hear you knocking / Heart attack and vine / Ignant and shit / Swamp gas / Voodoo priestess / Ice cream man / I want your body / Ol' man river / Strokin'
BP 40102CD / 16 Mar '98 / Manifesto

☐ **COW FINGERS AND MOSQUITO PIE**
Little demon / You ain't fooling me / I put a spell on you / You made me love you / Yellow coat / Hong Kong / There's something wrong with you / I love Paris / Orange coloured sky / Alligator wine / Darling please forgive me / Take me back to my boots and saddle / Temptation / Frenzy / Person to person / Little demon / I put a spell on you / There's something wrong with you / Alligator wine
4712702 / Mar '92 / Legacy

☐ DON'T FOOL WITH ME
Live love or die / Because of you / Don't fool with me / Furburger / Cookie time / Rose / Tear drops / Bushman tucker / Rockin' away / Rock Australia rock
CDSGP 0358 / 17 Nov '97 / Prestige

☐ I PUT A SPELL ON YOU
Portrait of a man / Itty bitty pretty one / Don't deceive me / What's gonna happen on the 8th day / Ashes / We love / It's only make believe / Please don't leave me / I put a spell on you / I don't know / Guess who / What good is it
CPCD 8221 / Jun '96 / Charly

☐ I SHAKE MY STICK AT YOU
AIM 1031CD / Oct '93 / Aim

☐ LIVE AND CRAZY
ECD 260032 / Jan '92 / Evidence

☐ PORTRAIT OF A MAN
Little demon / I put a spell on you / Baptize me in wine / Not anymore / I hear voices / Just don't care / Ashes / There's something wrong with you / Strange / Whammy / All night / Poor folks / Your kind of love / Mountain jive / Voodoo / You put a spell on me / Portrait of a man / Ol' man river / Heart attack and vine / I don't know / Don't deceive me / Armpit no. 6 / I put a spell on you / Why I scream the blues
EDCD 414 / Jan '95 / Edsel

☐ REAL LIFE-1983
157552 / Feb '93 / Blues Collection

☐ SCREAMIN' JAY HAWKINS 1952-1955 (The Complete Gotham & Grand Recordings)
I put a spell on you / 10,000 Lincoln continental / Why did you waste my time / No hug no kiss / Take me back / Coronation jump
SJHCD 71829 / Oct '91 / Screamin' Jay Hawkins

☐ SPELLBOUND 1955-1974 (2CD Set)
Voodoo / You put a spell on me / Makaha waves / There's too many teardrops / Two can play this game / Shattered / You're an exception to the rule / I'm not made of clay / All night / Mountain jive (unissued) / I'll be there / You're all of my life to me / Well I tried / Even though / Talk about me / In my front room / This is all / What that is (unissued) / She put the whamee on me / I put a spell on you / Two can play this game (unissued) / Shattered (unissued) / You're an exception to the rule (unissued) / What that is / Feast of the Mau-Mau / Do you really love me / Stone crazy / I love you / Constipation blues / I'm lonely / Thing called woman / Dig / I'm your man / Ask him / Reprise / Please don't leave me / I want to know / I need you / My Marion / Bit it / Move me / Goodnight my love / Our love is not for three / Ain't nobody's business if I do / Take me back / Trying to reach my goal / So long
BCD 15530 / Oct '90 / Bear Family

Hawkins, Sophie B.

☐ TONGUES AND TAILS
Damn, I wish I was your lover / California here I come / Mysteries we understand / Saviour child / Carry me / I want you / Before I walk on fire / We are one body / Listen / Live and let love / Don't stop swaying
4688232 / Sep '94 / Columbia

☐ WHALER
Right beside you / Did we not choose each other / Don't don't tell me no / As I lay me down / Swing from limb to limb (my home is in your jungle) / True romance / Let me love you up / Ballad of sleeping beauty / I need nothing else / Sometimes I see / Mr. Tugboat hello
4765122 / 2 Feb '98 / Columbia

Hawkins, Ted

☐ BEST OF THE VENICE BEACH TAPES, THE
I got what I wanted / Ladder of success / Gypsy woman / He will break your heart / There stands a glass / Country roads / (Sittin' on the) dock of the bay / Crystal chandeliers / Don't ever leave me / Let the good times roll / Chain gang / San Francisco / Bring it on home to me / Green green grass of home / Part time love / North to Alaska / Quiet place / Your cheatin' heart / Too busy thinking about my baby / Blowin' in the wind / Searchin' for my baby / Just my imagination / I love you most of all
UACD 101 / Jan '97 / Unamerican Activities

☐ HAPPY HOUR
ROUCD 2033 / Jul '94 / Rounder

☐ LAST TOUR, THE
ECD 28002 / 13 Jan '98 / Evidence

☐ NEXT HUNDRED YEARS
Strange conversation / Big things / There stands the glass / Biloxi / Groovy little things / Good and the bad / Afraid / Gree-eyed girl / Ladder of success / Long as I can see the light
GED 24627 / 8 Sep '97 / Geffen

☐ WATCH YOUR STEP
Watch your step / Bring it home Daddy / If you love me / Don't lose your cool / Lost ones / Who got my natural comb / Peace and Happiness / Sweet baby / Stop your crying / Put in a cross / Sorry you're sick / Watch your step / TWA / I gave up all I had / Stay close to me
ROUCD 2024 / Jul '94 / Rounder

Hawkins, Tramaine

☐ ALL MY BEST TO YOU
Praise the name of Jesus / Potter's house / What shall I do / Goin' up yonder / All things are possible / Changed / Coming home / Highway / He loves me / Who is he / We're all in the same boat together
SPD 1429 / Aug '95 / Alliance Music

Hawks, Billy

☐ NEW GENIUS OF THE BLUES/MORE HEAVY SOUL
Got my mojo working (but it just won't work on you) / I'll wait for you baby / Got a woman / Why do things happen to me / Let me love you before you go / Wish you love / Mean woman blues / I just want to make love to you / Every time it rains / Hawk's blues / O'baby (I believe I'm losing you) / Drown in my own tears / Whip it on me / What more can I do / Heavy soul / You've been a bad girl / I'll be back / I can make it / That's your bag
CDBGPD 117 / 27 Jul '98 / Beat Goes Public

Hawkshaw, Alan

☐ GIRL IN A SPORTS CAR
Girl in a sports car / Scooter girl / Sunflower / Warm hearts / Bluebird / Midnight rhapsody / Happy rainbow / Amour / Blue note / Grange Hill / Brush off / Playmate / Flapjack / Man alone / Sky train / Man of means / Love at first sight / Beauty spot / Moody / Sheer elegance / Blue haze / Piccadilly night ride / Beat boutique / Dave Allen at large / Destination venus
HF 53CD / Jun '97 / Coliseum

☐ MYSTERIOUS UNIVERSE
HHCD 101 / Nov '97 / Hungry Hawk

Hawkwind

☐ 1999 PARTY (2CD Set)
Intro/Standing on the edge / Brainbox pollution / It's so easy / You know you're only dreaming / Veterans of a thousand psychic wars / Brainstorm / Seven by seven / Watcher / Awakening / Paradox / You'd better believe it / Psychedelic warlords (disappear in smoke) / D-rider / Sonic attack / Master of the universe / Welcome to the future
HAWKS 6 / 17 Nov '97 / EMI

☐ ACID DAZE (The Best Of Hawkwind/ 2CD Set)
RRCD 1X / May '90 / Receiver

☐ ALIEN 4
Abducted / Alien / Reject your human touch / Blue skin / Beam me up / Vega / Xenomoroph / Journey / Sputnick Stan / Kapal / Festivals / Death trap / Wastelands / Are you losing your mind
EBSCD 118 / 17 Nov '97 / Emergency Broadcast System

☐ AMBIENT ANARCHISTS (2CD Set)
SMDCD 121 / 22 Sep '97 / Snapper

☐ BEST OF FRIENDS AND FAMILY, THE
EMPRCD 547 / Nov '94 / Emporio

☐ BEST OF FRIENDS AND RELATIONS, THE
SHARP 1724CD / Nov '88 / Flicknife

☐ BRING ME THE HEAD OF YURI GAGARIN (Live At The Empire Pool - 1973)
Ga ga / Egg / Orgone accumulator / Wage war / Urban guerilla / Masters of the universe / Welcome to the future / Sonic attack / Silver machine
CDTB 101 / Dec '92 / Thunderbolt
14846
CDCRH 108 / Feb '97 / Charly

☐ BUSINESS TRIP, THE
Altair / Quark, strangeness and charm / LSD / Camera that could lie / Green finned demon / Do that / Day a wall came down / Berlin axis / Void of golden light / Right stuff / Wastelands / Dream goes on / Right to decide / Dream has ended / Future / Terra mystica
EBSCD 111 / Sep '94 / Emergency Broadcast System

☐ CHOOSE YOUR MASQUES
Choose your masques / Dream worker / Arrival in Utopia / Utopia / Silver machine / Void city / Solitary mind games / Fahrenheit 451 / Scan / Waiting for tomorrow
EBSCD 124 / 17 Nov '97 / Emergency Broadcast System

☐ CHRONICLE OF THE BLACK SWORD
Song of the swords / Shade gate / Sea king / Pulsing cavern / Elric the enchanter / Needle gun / Zarzinia / Demise / Sleep of a thousand tears / Chaos army / Horn of destiny
DOJOCD 72 / Feb '94 / Dojo

☐ CHURCH OF HAWKWIND
Angel voices / Nuclear drive / Star cannibal / Phenomeno of luminosity / Fall of Earth City / Church / Joker at the gate / Some people never die / Light specific data / Experiment with destiny / Last Messiah / Looking in the future
DOJOCD 86 / Jun '94 / Dojo

☐ DISTANT HORIZONS
EBSCD 139 / 3 Nov '97 / Emergency Broadcast System

☐ DOREMI FASOL LATIDO
Brainstorm / Space is deep / One change / Lord of the light / Down through the night / Time we left this world today / Watcher / Urban guerilla / Brainbox pollution / Lord of light / Ejection
HAWKS 3 / Mar '96 / EMI

☐ EARLY DAZE (The Best Of Hawkwind)
Hurry on sundown / Dreaming / Masters of the universe / In the egg / Orgone accumulator / Sonic attack / Silver machine
CDTB 044 / Jun '88 / Thunderbolt

☐ ELECTRIC TEPEE
LSD / Blue shift / Death of war / Secret agent / Garden pests / Space dust / Snake dance / Music of morning / Rites of netherworld / Don't understand / Sadness runs deep / Right to decide / Going to hawaii / Electric tepee
DOJOCD 244 / Jul '95 / Dojo

☐ EMERGENCY BROADCAST SYSTEM SAMPLES (Various Artists)
Camera that could lie: *Hawkwind* / Green finned demon: *Hawkwind* / Coded language: *Hawkwind* / Angels of death: *Hawkwind* / Journey: *Hawkwind* / Xenomorph: *Hawkwind* / Sonic destruction: *Hawkwind* / Rizz's radio song: *Captain Rizz* / Frenzzy: *Psychedelic Warriors* / Yassasim: *Simon House* / White zone: *Brock, Dave* / Morbius: *Spaceheads* / Brain machine: *Spaceheads* / Higher than before: *Davey, Alan*
EBSCD 119 / 24 Nov '97 / Emergency Broadcast System

☐ HALL OF THE MOUNTAIN GRILL
Psychedelic warlords (disappear in smoke) / Wind of change / D rider / Webb weaver / You'd better believe it / Hall of the mountain grill / Lost Johnny / Goat willow / Paradox / It's so easy
HAWKS 5 / Mar '96 / EMI

☐ HAWKWIND
Hurry on sundown / Reason is / Be yourself / Paranoia part 1 / Paranoia part 2 / Seeing it as you really are / Mirror of illusion / Bring it on home / Hurry on sundown / Kiss of the velvet whip / Cymbaline
HAWKS 1 / Mar '96 / EMI

☐ IN AND OUTTAKE
DOJOCD 153 / Nov '94 / Dojo

☐ IN SEARCH OF SPACE
You shouldn't do that / You know you're only dreaming / Masters of the universe / We took the wrong step years ago / Adjust me / Children of the sun / Silver machine / Seven by seven / Born to go
HAWKS 2 / Mar '96 / EMI

☐ INDEPENDENT DAYS VOL.1 & 2
Night of the hawks / Motorway city / Motorhead / Angels of death / Who's gonna win the war / Watching the grass grow / Over the top / Hurry on sundown / Kiss of the velvet whip / Kings of speed / Social alliance / Dream dancers / Dragons and fables
CDMGRAM 94 / Sep '95 / Anagram

☐ IT'S THE BUSINESS OF THE FUTURE TO BE DANGEROUS
It's the business of the future to be dangerous / Space is their (palestine) / Tibet is not China (part 1) / Tibet is not China (part 2) / Let barking dogs lie / Wave upon wave / Letting in the past / Camera that could lie / 3 or 4 Erections in the course of a night / Techno tropic zone exists / Gimme shelter / Avante
ESMCD 390 / Aug '96 / Essential

☐ LIVE CHRONICLES (2CD Set)
Songs of the sword / Dragons and fables / Narration / Sea king / Angels of death / Shade gate / Rocky paths / Narration / Pulsing cavern / Masters of the universe / Dreaming city / Choose your masques / Fight sequence / Needle gun / Zarozinia / Lords of chaos / Dark lords / Wizards of Pan Tang / Moonglum (friend without a cuase) / Elric the enchanter / Conjuration of magnu / Magnu / Dust of time / Horn of fate / Magnu / Quark strangeness and charm / Spirit of the age / Who's gonna win the war / Ghost dance / Master of the universe / Choose your masques / Lost chronicles / Tides / Wings / Void of golden light / Lives of great men / Techno tropic zone exists / Gimme shelter
CCSCD 829 / 24 Aug '98 / Castle

☐ MASTERS OF THE UNIVERSE
Masters of the universe / Brainstorm / Sonic attack / Orgone accumulator / It's so easy / Lost Johnny
CDFA 3220 / May '89 / Fame
14972 / Apr '97 / Spalax

☐ MASTERS, THE
Space is deep / Orgone accumulator / Upside down / Sonic attack / Time we left this world today / Ten seconds of forever / Brainstorm / Seven by seven / Master of the universe / Welcome to the future
EABCD 084 / 30 Mar '98 / Eagle

☐ MIGHTY HAWKWIND CLASSICS 1980-1985
Hurry on sundown / Sweet mistress of pain / King of speed (live) / Motorhead / Valium ten / Night of the hawks / Green finned demon / Dream dancers / Dragons and fables / Over the top / Free fall / Death trap
CDMGRAM 86 / Apr '92 / Anagram

☐ ONWARD FLIES THE BIRD (Live & Rare)
EMPRCD 710 / Mar '97 / Emporio

☐ OUT AND INTAKE
Turning point / Waiting for tomorrow / Cajun jinx / Solitary mind games / Starflight / Ejection / Assassins of Allah / Flight to Maputo / Confrontation / Five to four / Ghost dance
SHARP 040CD / Apr '87 / Flicknife

☐ PURPLE HAZE (Pinkwind/Hawk Fairies)
TWKCD 5 / 16 Feb '98 / Twink

☐ RARITIES (Hawkwind & Friends/ Relations)
Aimless fight: *Underground Zero* / Psychedelia lives: *Hawkwind* / Working time: *Lloyd-Langton, Huw Group* / Rainbow warrior: *Underground Zero* / Brothel in Rosenstrasse: *Moorcock, Michael Deep Fix* / Toad on the run: *Mulo, Alman Band* / Earth calling: *Hawkwind* / Changing: *Bainbridge, Harvey* / Widow song: *Calvert, Robert* / Starcruiser: *Moorcock, Michael Deep Fix* / ICU: *Inner City Unit* / I see you: *Lloyd-Langton, Huw Group* / Human beings: *Inner City Unit* / Atom bomb: *Atom God* / Phone home Elliot: *Turner, Nik*
CDMGRAM 91 / Mar '95 / Anagram

☐ RITUAL OF THE SOLSTICE
Sonic attack / Forge of vulcan / Masters of the universe / You shouldn't do that / Sonic destruction / Damnation alley / Uncle sam on mars / Silver machine / Needle gun
EBSCD 117 / 17 Nov '97 / Emergency Broadcast System

☐ SILVER MACHINE
Prelude / Silver machine / Shot down in the night / Dust of time / Psychosis / Ghost dance / You shouldn't do that / Urban guerilla / Who's gonna win the war / Fifth second of forever / Nuclear toy / Levitation / Space chase / Motorway city
5507642 / Mar '95 / Spectrum

☐ SONIC ATTACK
Sonic attack / Rocky paths / Psychosonia / Virgin of the world / Angels of death / Living on a knife edge / Coded language / Disintegration / Streets of fear / Lost chances
EBSCD 123 / 17 Nov '97 / Emergency Broadcast System

☐ SPACE RITUAL VOL.1
Earth calling / Born to go / Down through the night / Awakening / Lord of Light / Black corridor / Space is deep / Electronic no.1 / Orgone accumulator / Upside down / Ten seconds of forever / Brainstorm / Seven by seven / Sonic attack / Time we left this world today / Masters of the universe / Welcome to the future / You shouldn't do that / Masters of the Universe
HAWKS 4 / Mar '96 / EMI

☐ SPACE RITUAL VOL.2
Space / Accumulator / Upside down sonic attack / Time we left / Ten seconds of forever / Brainstorm / Seven by seven / Masters of the universe / Welcome to the future
CDTB 099 / Jan '91 / Thunderbolt
14520 / Jul '97 / Spalax

☐ STASIS (The UA Years 1971-1975)
Urban guerilla / Psychedelic warlords (disappear in smoke) / Brainbox pollution / Seven by seven / Paradox / Silver machine / You'd better believe it / Lord of light / Black corridor / Space is deep / Earth calling / Born to go / Down through the night / Awakening / You shouldn't do that
CDFA 3267 / Apr '92 / Fame

☐ TEXT OF FESTIVAL, THE (Hawkwind Live 1970-1972)
Masters of the universe / Dreaming / You shouldn't do that / Hurry on sundown / Paranoia / See it as you really are / I do it / Came home / Sound shouldn't / Improvise / Improvise...compromise / Reprise
CDTB 068 / Mar '97 / Thunderbolt

☐ TRAVELLERS AID TRUST, THE
SHARP 2045CD / Dec '88 / Flicknife

☐ UNDISCLOSED FILES - ADDENDUM
Orctone accumulator / Ghost dance / Sonic attack / Watching the grass grow / Coded language / Damned by the curse of man / Ejection / Motorway city / Dragons and fables / Heads / Angels of death
EBSCD 114 / Nov '96 / Emergency Broadcast System

☐ WELCOME TO THE FUTURE (4CD Set)
DTKBOX 82 / 26 May '98 / Dressed To Kill

☐ WELCOME TO THE FUTURE
CLEO 2202 / 21 Apr '98 / Cleopatra

☐ ZONES
Zones / Dangerous vision / Running through the back brain / Island / Motorway city / Utopia 84 / Sociat alliance / Sonic attack / Dream worker / Brainstorm
CDMGRAM 57 / Jun '88 / Anagram

☐ ZONES/STONEHENGE
SHARP 1422CD / Nov '88 / Flicknife

Hawley, Jane

☐ AS WE WALK ON THIN ICE
TX 3004CD / Jan '94 / Taxim

Hawtin, Ritchie

☐ CONCEPT 1.96
MNS 4000 / 22 Jun '98 / Minus

☐ MIXMAG LIVE VOL.20 (Various Artists)
Dry ray: *Lausen* / Quo vadis: *G-Man* / Empower: *Octave One* / Jump: *Broom, Mark* / Wipe: *Teste* / 5 Mouths: *Fred Fresh* / Basic needs: *Goio* / Substance abuse: *FUSE* / Spaz: *Plastikman* / Helicopter: *Plastikman* / Percussion electrique: *Dwarf* / Spastik: *Plastikman* / Eye trip: *Bryant, Akilah* / Boiling point: *Xtrak* / Electricity: *Naughty & Tolls* / Dollar: *Schmidt, Tobias* / Live wire: *DBX* / Venus fly trap: *Too Funk* / Cash machines: *Synchrojack* / Key follow: *Hannah, Paul* / Harz: *Sensorama* / Altes testametn: *Roman IV*
MMLCD 020 / Jul '96 / Mixmag Live

Hay, Colin James

☐ PEAKS AND VALLEYS
Into the cornfields / She keeps me dreaming / Can't take this town / Walk amongst his ruins / Hold onto my hand / Keep on walking / Dream on / Boy boy / Conversation / Melbourne song / Sometimes I wish / Go ask an old man / Sea dogs
HYCD 296166 / Feb '97 / Hypertension

☐ TOPANGA
LICD 901304 / Jan '96 / Line

☐ TRANSCENDENTAL HIGHWAY
Transcendental highway / Don't believe you anymore / My brilliant feat / Goodbye my red rose / If I go / I'm doing fine / Wash it all away / Cactus / Death row conversation / I'll leave the light on / Freedom calling / I just don't think I'll ever get over you
HYCD 298174 / Feb '98 / Hypertension

Hayden

☐ MOVING CAREFUL
SUNCD 032 / Dec '96 / Sonic Unyon

Hayden, Cathal

☐ CATHAL HAYDEN
CBM 012CD / Mar '94 / Cross Border Media

Hayes, Cathy

☐ IT'S ALRIGHT WITH ME
FSRCD 55 / 5 Jan '98 / Fresh Sound

Hayes, Clancy

☐ OH BY JINGO
Oh by jingo / Rose of Washington Square / Oriental strut / I'm comin' Virginia / Wise guy / Beale Street blues / Cakewalking babies / Tin roof blues / King Chanticleer / Michigan water blues / New Orleans stomp / My little bimbo / Tin roof blues / Rose of Washington Square / King Chanticleer / Michigan water blues / I'm comin' Virginia / New Orleans stomp
DE 210 / Jun '97 / Delmark

Hayes, Clifford

☐ CLIFFORD HAYES & THE DIXIELAND JUG BLOWERS (Hayes, Clifford & The Dixieland Jug Blowers)
Please don't holler mama / Try and treat her right / You're ticklin' me (take 1) / Love blues / Blue guitar stomp / If you can't make it easy, sweet mama / Shipwreck blues (take 3) / Barefoot stomp / Bye bye blues / Hey I am blue / Clef club stomp / Dance hall shuffle / You'd better leave me alone, sweet papa / Everybody wants my tootelum
YAZCD 1054 / Apr '91 / Yazoo

☐ CLIFFORD HAYES & THE LOUISVILLE JUG BANDS VOL.1 1924-26 (Hayes, Clifford & The Louisville Jug Bands)
JPCD 15012 / May '94 / Jazz Perspectives

☐ CLIFFORD HAYES & THE LOUISVILLE JUG BANDS VOL.2 1926-27 (Hayes, Clifford & The Louisville Jug Bands)
JPCD 15022 / May '94 / Jazz Perspectives

☐ CLIFFORD HAYES & THE LOUISVILLE JUG BANDS VOL.3 1927-29 (Hayes, Clifford & The Louisville Jug Bands)
JPCD 15032 / May '94 / Jazz Perspectives

☐ CLIFFORD HAYES & THE LOUISVILLE JUG BANDS VOL.4 1929-31 (Hayes, Clifford & The Louisville Jug Bands)
JPCD 15042 / May '94 / Jazz Perspectives

☐ FROG HOP (Hayes, Clifford Louisville Stompers)
DGF 10 / Jan '97 / Frog

Hayes, Edgar

☐ CLASSICS 1937-1938
CLASSICS 730 / Jan '94 / Classics

Hayes, Isaac

☐ BRANDED
Ike's plea / Life's mood / Fragile / Life's mood II / Summer in the city / Let me love you / I'll do anything (to turn you on) / Thanks to the fool / Branded / Soulsville / Hyperbolicsyllabicsesquedalymistic
VPBCD 24 / May '95 / Pointblank

☐ COLLECTION, THE
Shaft / Joy / Never can say goodbye / Walk on by / I stand accused / (If loving you is wrong) I don't want to be right / I just don't know what to do with myself / By the time I get to Phoenix
VSOPCD 210 / Feb '95 / Connoisseur Collection

☐ HOT BUTTERED SOUL
Walk on by / Hyperbolicsyllabicsesquedalymistic / One woman / By the time I get to Phoenix
CDSXE 005 / May '91 / Stax

☐ HOTBED
Use me / I'm gonna have to tell her / Ten commandments of love / Feel like makin' love / Hobosac and me
CDSXE 105 / Jul '94 / Stax

☐ ISAAC'S MOODS
Ike's mood / Soulsville / Joy / (If loving you is wrong) I don't want to be right / Never can say goodbye / Shaft / Ike's rap IV / Brand new me / Do your thing / Walk on by / I stand accused / Ike's rap I / Hyperbolicsyllabicsesquedalymistic / Ike's rap III / Ike's rap II
CDSX 011 / Apr '88 / Stax

☐ JOY
Joy / I love you that's all / Man will be a man / Feeling keeps on coming / I'm gonna make it (without you)
CDSXE 047 / May '92 / Stax

☐ LIVE AT THE SAHARA TAHOE (2CD Set)
Shaft / Come on / Light my fire / Ike's rap / Never can say goodbye / Windows of the world / Look of love / Ellie's love theme / Use me / Do your thing / Men / It's too late / Rock me baby / Stormy Monday blues / Type thang / First time ever I saw your face / Ike's rap VI / Ain't no sunshine / Feelin' alright
CDSXE 2053 / Jul '92 / Stax

☐ PRESENTING ISAAC HAYES
Precious precious / When I fall in love / I just wamt to make love to you / Rock me baby / Going to Chicago Blues / Misty / You don't know like I know
SCD 8596 / Jan '96 / Stax

☐ RAW AND REFINED
Birth of Shaft / Urban nights / Funkalicious / Tahoe Spring / Night before / Memphis trax / Soul fiddle / Funky junky / You make me live / Making love at the ocean / Southern breeze / Didn't know love was so good / 405
VPBCD 25 / Jul '95 / Pointblank

☐ TO BE CONTINUED
Ike's rap 1 / Our day will come / Look of love / Ike's mood / You've lost that lovin' feelin' / Runnin' out of fools
CDSXE 030 / Feb '91 / Stax

☐ WONDERFUL
Ain't no sunshine / Rolling down a mountainside / I can't help it (if I'm still in love with you) / Wonderful / Someone made you for me / Ain't that loving you (for more reasons than one) / Baby I'm a want you / Mistletoe and me / Winter snow
CDSXE 112 / Jul '97 / Stax

Hayes, Louis

☐ CRAWL, THE (Hayes, Louis Sextet)
Escape velocity / Crawl / Yesterdays / Run before the sun / Autumn in New York / Blues in five dimensions / Bushman song
CCD 79045 / Feb '97 / Candid

☐ LAUSANNE, 1977 (Hayes, Louis & Woody Shaw Quintet)
In case you haven't heard / Moontrane / Contemplation / Jean-Marie / Bilad as Sudan
TCB 02052 / Nov '96 / TCB

☐ SUPER QUARTET, THE (Hayes, Louis & Company)
Bolivia / Song is you / Up jumped spring / On your own sweet way / Chelsea Bridge / Epistrophy / Blue Lou / Fee fi fo fum
CDSJP 424 / Feb '95 / Timeless Jazz

Hayes, Martin

☐ MARTIN HAYES
Morning star/The Caoilte mountains / Paddy Fahy's jig/Sean Ryan's jig / Whistler from Rosslea/Connor Dunn's / Golden castle / Star of munster / Colliers/Johnny's wedding / Brown coffin/Good natured man / Green gowned lass / I buried my wife and danced on her grave / Rooms of Doogh / Mist covered mountain / Britches / Tommy Coen's reel/The swallow
GLCD 1127 / Jul '93 / Green Linnet

☐ THAT LONESOME TOUCH (Hayes, Martin & Dennis Cahill)
Paddy Fahy's reel / Kerfunken jig / Paul Ha'penny/Garden of butterflies/Broken pledge / Mother and child reel/Toss the feathers / John Naughton's reel/Another Paddy Fahy reel / Cat in the corner/John Naughton's jig / Old bush/The reel with the Burl / Lament for Limerick / My love is in America / Tell her I am/Gallagher's frolics / Rolling in the barrel/The morning dew / Bucks of Oranmore/Eileen Curran/Jimmy on the moor / Peggy's waltz
GLCD 1181 / Jun '97 / Green Linnet

☐ UNDER THE MOON
GL 1155CD / Jul '95 / Green Linnet

Hayes, Tommy

☐ AN RAS
LUNCD 055 / Jan '95 / Mulligan

☐ ROOM IN THE NORTH, A
OPP 001CD / Aug '97 / OPP

Hayes, Tubby

☐ 200% PROOF
CHECD 00105 / Jul '92 / Master Mix

☐ DOWN IN THE VILLAGE (Hayes, Tubby Quintet)
Johnny one note / But beautiful / Most beautiful girl in the world / Down in the village / In the night / 1st eleven
5581842 / 20 Apr '98 / Redial

☐ FOR MEMBERS ONLY (Live 1967) (Hayes, Tubby Quartet)
Dear Johnny B / This is all I ask / Dolphin dance / Mexican green / Finky minky / For members only / You know I care / Conversations at dawn / Nobody else but me / Dedication to Joy / Off the wagon / Second city steamer
CDCHE 10 / Jan '91 / Master Mix

☐ JAZZ TETE A TETE (Hayes, Tubby & Tony Coe)
PCD 7079 / Jan '94 / Progressive

☐ LATE SPOT AT SCOTT'S (Hayes, Tubby Quintet)
My man's gone now / Yeah / Quintet theme / Half a sawbuck / Angel eyes / Sausage scraper / Quintet theme
5581832 / 20 Apr '98 / Redial

☐ NIGHT AND DAY
Half a sawbuck / Spring can really hang you up the most / Simple waltz / I'm old fahioned / Night and day
JHAS 602 / Oct '95 / Ronnie Scott's Jazz House

☐ TUBBY HAYES LIVE 1969 (Hayes, Tubby Quartet)
Introduction / Off the wagon / For Heaven's sake / Vierd blues / Walkin' / Where am I going / Mainly for the Don / Grits, beans and greens
HQCD 05 / Oct '91 / Harlequin

☐ TUBBY HAYES QUARTET IN SCANDINAVIA (Hayes, Tubby Quartet)
Off the wagon / Without a song / Vierd blues / I thought about you / C minor bird / Rhythm a ning
STCD 8251 / Jun '98 / Storyville

Haymes, Dick

☐ CAPITOL YEARS, THE
It might as well be spring / More I see you / Very thought of you / You'll never know / If there is someone lovelier than you / How deep is the ocean / Nearness of you / Where or when / Little white lies / Our love is here to stay / Love walked in / Come rain or come shine / If I should lose you / You don't know what love is / Imagination / Skylark / Isn't this a lovely day (to be caught in the rain) / What's new / Way you look tonight / Then I'll be tired of you / I like the likes of you / Moonlight becomes you / Between the Devil and the deep blue sea / When I fall in love
CDEMS 1364 / Jun '90 / Capitol

☐ CLASSIC YEARS, THE
It might as well be Spring / Where or when / Breeze and I / I surrender dear / It's de-lovely / It's magic / Best things in life are free / You'd be so nice to come home to / They didn't believe me / Summertime / You send me / It had to be you / Did you ever see a dream walking / What a difference a day made / I'll be seeing you / One I love / Blue skies / To each his own
CDSGP 0214 / 26 Jan '98 / Prestige

☐ COMPLETE DUETS, THE (Haymes, Dick & Helen Forrest)
Long ago (and far away) / Look for the silver lining / It had to be you / Together / I'll buy that dream / Some Sunday morning / I'm always chasing rainbows / Tomorrow is forever / Oh what it seemed to be / You stole my heart / Gimme a little kiss, will ya, huh / 'Til we meet again / In love in vain / All through the day / Something to remember you by / Come rain or come shine / Why does it get late so early / Something old, something new
MCCD 208 / Jul '95 / Music Club

☐ FOR YOU, FOR ME, FOR EVERMORE
ACD 130 / May '95 / Audiophile

☐ IT HAD TO BE YOU
I'll never smile again / Take me / Together / You'll never know / How many times do I have to tell you / Put your arms around me honey / Where or when / Indiana / How blue the night / Long ago and far away / Amado mio / Button up your overcoat / Our waltz / Let the rest of the world go by / It can't be wrong / Minka / I never mention your name / Janie / By the old corral / In my arms / If you were the only girl in the world / I don't want to love you / It had to be you
CDMOIR 512 / Nov '95 / Memoir

☐ IT'S A GRAND NIGHT FOR SINGING
How high the moon / Fools rush in / Here comes the night / Braggin' / I'll get by / Aurora / Cherry / All or nothing at all / A sinner kissed an angel / You've changed / I've got a gal in Kalamazoo / Serenade in blue / It can't be wrong / You'll never know / Long ago (and far away) / How blue the night / Let the rest of the world go by / More I see you / I wish I knew / Love letters / Isn't it kinda fun / It might as well be Spring / That's for me / It's a grand night for singing
PLCD 546 / Aug '96 / President

☐ KEEP IT SIMPLE (Haymes, Dick & Loonis McGlohon Trio)
More I see / I get along without you very well / Little white lies / Almost like being in love / Stella by starlight / Very thought of you / I'll remember April / That's for me / It might as well be spring / Who cares / Our love is here to stay / Love walked in / You'll never know / There will never be another you
ACD 200 / Mar '95 / Audiophile

☐ MY HEART TELLS ME
I wish I knew / Easy to love / More I see you / Night is young and you're so beautiful / You make me feel so young / Come rain or shine / In love in vain / Love letters / Laura / Do you love me / They can't convince me / How deep is the ocean / Aren't you kinda glad we did / For you for me for evermore / That's for me / Isn't it kinda fun / It might as well be spring / It's a grand night for singing / Oh what it seemed to be / I'm always chasing rainbows / Some hearts sing / You are too beautiful / Another night like this / Till the end of time / My heart ntells me a lovely way to spend an evening
CDMOIR 521 / Apr '95 / Memoir

☐ SOFT LIGHTS AND SWEET MUSIC
I could write a book / There's a small hotel / Soft lights and sweet music / Penthouse serenade / Imagination / I love you / Stardust / But not for me / You're driving me crazy / You're blase / Time on my hands / Love me or leave me / I surrender dear / I never knew / Yearning / These foolish things
HCD 265 / May '97 / Hindsight

☐ STAR EYES
Star eyes / Where or when / How sweet you are / All or nothing at all / Trolley song / Over the rainbow / When I grow too old to dream / Evelina / Day by day / More I see you / I wish I knew / Dream / I love you too much / Night and day / When the red red robbin comes bob-bob-bobin' along / It might as well be spring / My foolish heart / It's magic / Lazy / Thinking of you / Nevertheless / Twenty four hours of sunshine / Best things in life are free / That lucky old sun / All the things you are / Maybe / Lovely to look at / Gypsy in my soul / They say it's wonderful / Blue skies / September song
JZCL 6004 / Feb '97 / Jazz Classics

☐ VERY BEST OF DICK HAYMES, THE
HMNCD 027 / 16 Mar '98 / Half Moon

☐ YOU'LL NEVER KNOW
You'll never know / How high the moon / Ol' man river / I'll get by / Yes indeed / Wait for me Mary / It can't be wrong / I never mention your name / How blue the night / It had to be you / Together / By the old corral / Let the rest of the world go by / Laura / More I see you / I wish I knew / Where or when / I'll buy that dream / I'll buy that drean / Night is young / It might as well be spring / It's a grand night for singing / Amada mia / You make me feel so young / For you for me for evermore
CDAJA 5232 / Sep '97 / Living Era

Haynes, Alan

☐ WISHING WELL
FOCUSCD 0256 / 5 Feb '98 / Focus

Haynes, Graham

☐ GRIOT'S FOOTSTEPS, THE
5232622 / Jan '95 / Verve

☐ TONES FOR THE 21ST CENTURY
5376922 / 15 Sep '97 / Antilles/Verve

☐ TRANSITION
5290392 / Dec '95 / Verve

Haynes, Roy

☐ HOMECOMING
Evidence / Green chimneys / You're blase / Bud Powell / Star eyes / Anniversary song
ECD 220922 / Jul '94 / Evidence

☐ MY SHINING HOUR (Haynes, Roy & Thomas Clausen's Jazzparticipants)
My shining hour / I fall in love too easily / Bessie's blues / All blues / Skylark / Rhythm-a-ning / A la blues / Bright
STCD 4199 / Mar '95 / Storyville

☐ OUT OF THE AFTERNOON (Haynes, Roy Quartet)
Moon ray / Fly me to the moon / Raoul / Snap crackle / If I should lose you / Long wharf / Some other Spring
IMP 11802 / Jan '96 / Impulse Jazz

☐ TE-VOU
Like this / If I could / Blues M45 / Trinkle twinkle / Trigonometry / Good for the soul
FDM 365692 / Nov '94 / Dreyfus

☐ TRUE OR FALSE
Limehouse blues / In a sentimental mood / Everywhere calypso / Big foot / Psalm / True or false / Played twice / Bud powell / Fee-fi-fo-fum
FRLCD 007 / Oct '92 / Freelance

Haynes, Victor

☐ OPTIMISTIC
Don't want nobody else / This is love / Turn out the light / Breakin' my heart / Respect / Optimistic / Tell me where you are / Don't stop / Do you regret / First time / Tonight / Stand up
EXCDP 7 / Nov '94 / Expansion

Haynes, Warren

☐ TALES OF ORDINARY MADNESS
Fire in the kitchen / Kiss tomorrow goodbye / Movers and shakers / I'll be the one / Blue radio / Invisible / Sister justice / Angel city / Tattoos and cigarettes / Power and the glory / Broken promise land
866912 / Oct '97 / Megaforce

Haynie, Aubrey

☐ DOIN' MY TIME
Cherokee shuffle / Dark hollow / Leavin' Rosine / Tobacco patch / Turkey in my straw / Montgomery Bell / Doin' my time / White bluff / Austin's dream / Crackerjack / Foolin' around / Forty years of trouble / Kentucky hustler / Trouble in mind
SHCD 3870 / Mar '98 / Sugar Hill

Hayride To Hell

☐ HAYRIDE TO HELL
NERCD 092 / Dec '97 / Nervous

Hays, Kevin

☐ ANDALUCIA
Agua / ANdalucia / And I love here / That's all / Mind / Chicory stick / Hart / Break / Einbahnstrasse / Con alma
8558172 / 23 Feb '98 / Blue Note

Haystack

☐ RIGHT AT YOU
OSP 001 / 27 Apr '98 / Outside Society

☐ SLAVE ME
Life / Burn out / She calms down / This is the day / Slave me / I feel fine / Object I can't control / Get it out / Alright / What's in it for me / Born beyond belief / Collector / What a way to go
CDMFN 240 / 23 Mar '98 / Music For Nations

Haystacks Balboa

☐ DETOXIFIED
AACD 024 / 16 Feb '98 / Audio Archive

Haywains

☐ GET HAPPY WITH...
Bythesea Road / Tobe's gone west / Fisherman's friends / Summer madness / I'm not really as foolish as you think / Billy Corkhill's better / Side / Kicked in the teeth / Now I've got one up on you / Emily's shop / Really (Bee) / Last pancake / Surfin' in my sleep / I wouldn't want that / Forget me not / Please don't let me get hurt / Rosanna / Boy called Burden / You laughing at me laughing at you / Boy racers a go-go
ASKCD 024 / Sep '93 / Vinyl Japan

☐ NEVER MIND MANCHESTER, HERE'S ...THE HAYWAINS
Kill karaoke / Dusty Springfield / I hate to disappoint you / New kids on the block / Your point of view doesn't count / Money-go-round / Now I've got one up on you / I'm still waiting / Always the same / Somebody loves you / Why did I ever turn you down / Bythesea road / Hold on me / Time bomb baby / Forget me not
ASKCD 014 / Mar '93 / Vinyl Japan

Hayward, Charles

☐ SUB ROSA SESSIONS, BARI OCTOBER 1996 (Hayward, Charles & David Shea/Nus)
QUANTUM 204 / Mar '97 / Sub Rosa

Hayward, Dennis

☐ 50'S IN SEQUENCE
CDTS 037 / Aug '93 / Maestro

☐ DANCING FOR PLEASURE
Bless 'em all / And the band played on / Hello hello, who's your lady friend / Ship ahoy (all the nice girls love a soldier) / My bonnie lies over the ocean / Jolly good company / Darling buds of May / Forever green / Dying swan / Jupiter / Love theme from Spartacus / Morning: Peer Gynt / One fine day / Mr. Wonderful / On a clear day (You can see forever) / Misty / Can't smile without you / I don't want to walk without you / Man I love / Can't help lovin' dat man / Nellie Dean / K-K-Katy / All by yourself in the moonlight / Dickie bird hop / Tchip tchip (birdie song) / Tonight / Lara's theme / Spanish eyes / Spanish harlem / Czardas / Sandie's shawl / Raindrops keep falling on my head / Raining in my heart / I'm confessin' that I love you / When somebody thinks you're wonderful
CDTS 034 / Aug '93 / Maestro

☐ DENNIS HAYWARD'S PARTY DANCES (2CD Set)
Barn dance / Paul Jones / Blackpool belle / Blame it on the Bossa Nova / Chanson d'amour / Island of dreams / Knees up Mother Brown / Clap clap sound / Alley cat / Agadoo / Hands up / Atmosphere / Y viva Espana / I just called to say I love you / Conga / Simon says / Birdie song / Brown girl in the ring / Rivers of Babylon / It's a holi holiday / Let's twist again / Loco-motion / Pal of my cradle days / Cokey cokey / Sailing / You'll never walk alone / We'll meet again / Fiona's polka / Lambeth walk / St. Bernard's waltz / Virginia reel / Farmer's wife / Have a drink on me / (Hands knees and) Bomps a daisy / Charleston and the black bottom / I am the music man / Chestnut tree / Sons of the sea / Match of the day / Hip hip hip hooray / Zorba's dance / Fanfare #1/2 / March of the mods / This is your life #1/2 / Sand dance / Slosh / Harry Lime / Teddy bear's picnic / Gay Gordons / Havah nagilah / Mod rock barn dance / Chord
SAV 220CD / Dec '95 / Savoy

☐ HAPPY DANCING FOR CHRISTMAS (2CD Set)
Santa Claus is coming to town / God rest ye merry gentlemen / We wish you a merry Christmas / Twelve days of Christmas / Deck the halls with boughs of holly / Good King Wenceslas / Christmas song / Have yourself a merry little Christmas / Winter wonderland / White Christmas / When a child is born / Mary's boy child / Little donkey / Do you hear what I hear / Little boy that Santa Claus forgot / Let it snow, let it snow, let it snow / I'm sending a letter to Santa Claus / Sleigh ride / Jingle bells / Midnight sleigh ride / Ding dong merrily on high / Silver bells / Away in a manger / We three kings / Silnet night / Holiday for bells / Snow coach / Snowy white and jingle bells / Here comes Santa Claus / Where did my snowman go / On Christmas island / Once upon a wintertime / I'll be home for Christmas / Fairy on the Christmas tree / Frosty the snowman / Rudolph the red nosed reindeer / O little town of Bethlehem / Jingle bell rock / Rockin' around the Christmas tree / I heard the bells on Christmas day / In the bleak mid-Winter / Christmas awake / Salute the happy morn / Angels from the realms of glory / CHRISTMAS / Caroling caroling / Santa Natale / Scarlet ribbons / Miners dream of home / Auld lang syne
SAV 199CD / Dec '95 / Savoy

☐ HAPPY DANCING VOL.1 (Hayward, Dennis Organisation)
Every little while / Dancing with my shadow / Broken doll / Glad rag doll / Peg o' my heart / She's funny that way / I don't know why / Don't blame me / White cliffs of Dover / Love is the sweetest thing / It's a sin to tell a lie / Sally / Girl of my dreams / It happened in Monterey / Where the blue of the night meets the gold of the day / I'll see you again / Chinatown, my Chinatown / Waiting for the Robert E Lee / I'm looking over a four leaf clover / Alabamy bound / Yankee doodle boy / Swanee / Can't help lovin' dat man / By the fireside / Seems to me, I've heard that song before / Two sleepy people / What more can I say / Play to me Gipsy / Goodnight Vienna / Alabama Jubilee / Is it true what they say about Dixie / California here I come / Sittin' on top of the world / Give my regards to Broadway / When the midnight choo choo leaves for Alabam' / As time goes by / It's the talk of the town / It had to be you / These foolish things / Blue room / Amapola / Marta / Mairzy doats and dozy doats / Give me five minutes more / Heart of my heart / Arm in arm together / We'll meet again / I'm a dreamer (aren't we all) / All I do is dream of you / Little on the lonely side / If I had my life to live over / Falling in love again / Carolina moon / Let the rest of the world go by / Let bygones be bygones
SAV 132CD / Mar '92 / Savoy

☐ HAPPY DANCING VOL.3
SAV 189CD / May '93 / Savoy

☐ IT'S SEQUENCE TIME VOL.1
Hello dolly/Miss Anna Belle Lee/Don't bring LuLu / Keep your sunny side up/You are my sunshine / Spread a little happiness/Smoke gets in your eyes / You are my heart's delight / Waltzing in the clouds / Sindy / All I ask of you / Always there / Tango melodica / Perhaps, perhaps, perhaps / Unforgettable/Never say goodbye / With a song in my heart/Be careful it's my heart / South of the border (Down Mexico way) / Ay ay ay / Hernando's hideaway / Whatever Lola wants (Lola gets) / Let's put out the lights and go to sleep / Shine through my dreams/My heart and I / Roses from the south / Les patineurs (skaters waltz)
SAV 177CD / Jul '92 / Savoy

☐ IT'S SEQUENCE TIME VOL.2
SAV 185CD / May '93 / Savoy

☐ LET'S DANCE (Hayward, Dennis & The Savoy Orchestra)
So tired (saunter-slow foxtrot) / Object of my affection (saunter-slow foxtrot) / Stompin' at the savoy (quickstep) / Skyliner (quickstep) / Bewitched, bothered and bewildered / Fools rush in (rumba) / Tea for two (cha-cha) / You've turned the tables on me (cha cha) / Try a little tenderness-you'll never know (foxtrot) / I'll string along with you-I'll be seeing you (foxtrot) / I'm dancing with tears in my eyes (waltz) / If I should fall in love again (waltz)
SAV 128CD / Feb '92 / Savoy

☐ MUSIC FOR CELEBRATION AND SPECIAL OCCASIONS
Fanfare / Happy birthday / Barn dance medley / Congratulations / St. Bernard waltz / Wedding march / Get me to the church / My old Dutch / Anniversary waltz / Mayfair quickstep / Balmoral blues / Modern waltz / Saunter together / Saunter medley / Tango serida / Lilac waltz medley / Stripper / Can can / Four hand star / Conga / Virginia reel / Chimes of Big Ben / Auld lang syne / Gay Gordons / Easter parade / Wish me luck / Rule Britannia / Land of hope and glory / God save the Queen
SAV 152CD / Dec '95 / Savoy

☐ RECALL
If I were a bell/This can't be love / There will never be another you / How am I to know/Time was / All or nothing at all / Beautiful lady in blue / Dream lover/I'll follow my secret heart / My boy lolipop / He's a tramp / Something stupid / Cherry pink and apple blossom white / Strangers on the shore / Strangers in the night/Tonight / Women in love / Falling in love with love / Mr. Sandman/Lady be good/Baby face / Good old bad old days/Some of these days / Softly, softly/ At the end of the day / Who's taking you home tonight / September in the rain/Pennies from heaven / Embraceable you/How about you
SAV 178CD / Jul '92 / Savoy

☐ SHALL WE DANCE VOL.2 (Hayward, Dennis & His Orchestra)
On a little street in Singapore / New York, New York / Lover / Just the way you look tonight / London by night / Hi Lili hi lo / And I love you so/How soon / Yesterday/My way / Isle of Capri / What a difference a day makes / Ecstacy / Serenata / Lover come back / Dream / Indian summer/Stormy weather / Have you ever been lonely / If ever I would leave you / Stranger in Paradise / La cucaracha / Carioca / Copacabana / Tico-tico
SAV 174CD / Jun '92 / Savoy

☐ SHOWTIME
SAV 239CD / Dec '95 / Savoy

☐ STEP BY STEP
Tears-greatest mistake of my life (waltz) / Was it a dream-memory lane (waltz) / That's my desire-sweet lorraine (foxtrot) / My jealous eyes (tango) / Besame mucho (tango) / Without a song-if I had my way (saunter) / Some enchanted evening-the shadow of your smile (rumba) / I didn't know what time it was-an affair to remember (rumb / Bring me sunshine-I'm a lonely little petunia (blues) / I'm an old cowhand-'neath the spreading chestnut tree (bl / I've got the world on a string-ain't misbehavin' (cha ch / Put your shoes on lucy-the naughty lady of shady lane (cha / Charade (waltz) / If-unless (waltz) / Little things mean a lot-my foolish heart (foxtrot) / In a little spanish town-big country (cha cha) / Mexican hat dance-it happened in monteray (cha cha)
CDTS 036 / Aug '93 / Maestro

☐ TEA DANCE VOL.2
Jeepers creepers / Be mir bist do schoen / Goody goody / Tisket-a-tasket / Don't sit under the apple tree / Undecided / Dance in the old-fashioned way / Didn't we / You'd be so nice to come home to / Wrong (it must be right) / Romanesca / Italian fiesta / Nocturn in eb / Gymnopedie No.1 / Swan / Oh my beloved daddy / Cavatina / How wonderful to know / Hey there / Yours / I won't send roses / Portrait of my love / Magic moments / Finger of suspicion / Love and marriage / I ain't got nobody / Little bit independant / Birth of the blues / My blue heaven / Room with a view / I should care / But not for me / Tango erotique / Song of the rose / Charmaine / Edelweiss / Bless you / Linger awhile / Small fry / Brother can you spare a dime / You'll never walk alone / Sleepy shores
SAV 170CD / Mar '92 / Savoy

Hayward, Justin

☐ BLUE JAYS (Hayward, Justin & John Lodge)
This morning / Remember me (my friend) / My brother / You / Nights winters years / Saved by the music / I dreamed last night / Who are you now / Maybe / When you wake up
8204912 / '88 / London

☐ CLASSIC BLUE
Tracks of my tears / Blackbird / MacArthur Park / Vincent / God only knows / Bright eyes / Whiter shade of pale / Scarborough Fair / Railway hotel / Man of the world / Forever autumn / As long as the moon can shine / Stairway to Heaven
CLACD 385 / '93 / Castle

☐ VIEW FROM THE HILL
I heard it / Broken dream / Promised land / It's not too late / Something to believe in / Way of the world / Sometimes less is more / Troubadour / Shame / Billy / Children of paradise
0607862022 / Nov '96 / CMC

Hayward, Ronnie

☐ MOVE AROUND (Hayward, Ronnie Trio)
DAGCD 7 / 10 Nov '97 / Fury

Hayworth, Rita

☐ RITA HAYWORTH
LCD 6002/3 / Jan '93 / Fresh Sound

☐ RITA HAYWORTH COLLECTOR'S EDITION
DVGH 7052 / Apr '95 / Deja Vu

Haza, Ofra

☐ KIRYA
Kirya / Innocent-a requiem for refugees / Daw da hiya / Mystery, fate and love / Horashoot - the bridge / Don't foresake me / Barefoot / Trains of no return / Take 7/8
9031761272 / Apr '92 / East West

☐ YEMENITE SONGS
Im nin' alu / Yachilvi veyachail / A salk / Galbi / Ode le 'eli / Lefelach / Ayelet chen
CDORB 006 / May '87 / Globestyle

Haze

☐ C'EST LA VIE
Roger's revenge / Don't leave me here / Fallen leaves / Load / Mairage / For whom / Hum / Gabadon
CYCL 041 / Nov '96 / Cyclops

☐ WORLD TURTLE
Ember / See her face / Ship of fools / Edge of heaven / Don't leave me here / Epitaph / Under my skin / New dark ages / Safe harbour / Autumn / Another country / Straw house / Wooden house / Stone house
CYCL 008 / Jul '97 / Cyclops

Haze

☐ HAZECOLOUR-DIA
SB 039 / Jun '97 / Second Battle

Hazel

☐ AIRIANA
CAR 22CD / Jun '97 / Candy Ass

☐ ARE YOU GOING TO EAT THAT
SPCD 144358 / Feb '95 / Sub Pop

☐ TOREADOR OF LOVE
SPCD 284 / Aug '93 / Sub Pop

Hazel, Monk

☐ BENEFIT NIGHT VOL.1
BCD 142 / Jun '96 / GHB

☐ BENEFIT NIGHT VOL.2
BCD 143 / Jun '96 / GHB

Hazeldine

☐ HOW BEES FLY
GRCD 416 / Jul '97 / Glitterhouse

Hazeltine, David

☐ HOW IT IS (Hazeltine, David Quintet)
How it is / Reasons / Pannonica / Nuit noire / Little angel / Where are you / Doxy
CRISS 1142CD / 9 Mar '98 / Criss Cross

Hazelwood, Lee

☐ COWBOY AND THE LADIES, THE (2CD Set)
LHI 97300 / 22 Jun '98 / LHI

☐ LEE HAZELWOOD AND FRIENDS
28807255 / 2 Feb '98 / Bellaphon

☐ LOVE AND OTHER CRIMES
LHI 97200 / 1 Jun '98 / LHI

☐ MANY SIDES OF LEE
CD 13505 / 1 Jun '98 / Request

☐ POET FOOL OR BUM
LHI 97100 / 1 Jun '98 / LHI

He Pepo

☐ CON ELLA
RMD 82250 / 21 Apr '98 / RMM

He Said

☐ HAIL
Pump (plus instrumental) / Shapes to escape / Kidnap yourself / I fall into your arms / Only one I / Com'era dov'era / Flagwearing / Do you mean that / Pulling 3 gs / Pale seat / Only one I / To and fro
CDSTUMM 29 / Nov '86 / Mute

☐ TAKE CARE
Watch - take care / A.b.c. dicks love / Could you / Tongueties / Screen / Not a soul / Halfway house / Get out of that rain / Hole in the sky / He said she said / A.b.c. dicks love (soft) / Suzanne / Could you (too)
CDSTUMM 57 / Sep '88 / Mute

He Said Omala

☐ MATCHING CROSSES
Here but us chickens / Liquor appears / Roaring hat seeds / Troubled mind / Oil met gravel / Idols O'varnish
OR 3001 / 14 Apr '98 / Origin

Head

☐ HEAD
Country diction / Hydrogen jukebox / Ill-tempered cavalier / Bleeding calico red / How bread is made / Black nantucket / Ben't / River's invitation / Quarter past jack / Rubber banjo / Open window / On the raga / Parsifal / Flying backwards / Fat albert in a can
VOXXCD 2061 / Jan '93 / Voxx

☐ INTOXICATOR
Walk like an angel / Stalemate / Ice cream skin / All the boyz / Party's over / Under the influence of books / Two or three things / Soakin' my pillow / Ships in the night / B'goode or be gone / You're so vain
CDV 2595 / Jul '89 / Virgin

Head & Hares

☐ HEAD & HARES
GH 1037CD / Jul '97 / Get Hip

Head, Jowe

☐ UNHINGED
OVER 35CD / Oct '94 / Overground

Head Like A Hole

☐ 13
N 02162 / Aug '94 / Noise

☐ FLIK Y'SELF OFF Y'SELF
Chalkface / Spanish goat dancer / Oily rag / Kissy kissy / Faster hooves / One pound two pound / Raw sock / Dirt eater / Pops pox 'n' vox / Spitbag / Rabbit / Nosferatoo / Theme to Nincomjool / Velvet kushin
N 02252 / Feb '95 / Noise

Head Machine

☐ ORGASM
AACD 014 / 27 Apr '98 / Audio Archive

Head, Michael

☐ MAGICAL WORLD OF THE STRANDS, THE
Queen Matilda / Something like you / And Luna / X hits the spot / Prize / Undecided (reprise) / Glynys and Jaqui / It's harvest time / Loaded man / Hocken's hey / Fontilan
CDMEGA 01 / 23 Feb '98 / Megaphone

Head, Murray

☐ BETWEEN US
951922 / Feb '97 / Pomme

☐ SAY IT ISN'T SO
Say it ain't so Joe / Boats away / Someone's rocking my dreamboat / Never even thought / Don't forget me now / Boy on the bridge / When I'm yours / She's such a drag / Silence is a strong reply / You're so taste
IMCD 83 / Feb '90 / Island

☐ SHADE
Peace of mind / Corporation corridors / (All we can do is) hold on / Not your problem / Joey's on fire / Maman / Grace / Dragonfly / Shades of the prison house
951942 / Feb '97 / Pomme

☐ VOICES
951932 / Feb '97 / Pomme

☐ WHEN YOU'RE IN LOVE
951242 / Mar '96 / Pomme

Head Of David

☐ DUSTBOWL
Tequila / El supremo / Dog day sunrise / Bugged / Great white heat / Cult of coats / Ditchwater / 108 / Roadkill / Snake domain / Grad rift faultline / Adrenicide / Pierced all over / Skin drill / Ink vine
BFFP 18CD / Apr '88 / Blast First

Head Or Tales

☐ ETERNITY BECOMES A LIE
BMCD 069 / Sep '95 / Black Mark

Head Shop

☐ HEAD SHOP
1610986 / 1 Jun '98 / Synton

Head Space

☐ OF STAR AND TIME
EBSCD 121 / 24 Nov '97 / Emergency Broadcast System

Headbutt

☐ PISSING DOWN
Sandyard / Duffle bag / Through the slides / Adding insult.... / Always scraping shit / Barbie skin
OINK 031 CD / Jan '93 / Pigboy

☐ SHOWER CURTAIN
TIRCD 001 / Apr '96 / Totem

☐ TIDDLES
DPROMCD 25 / Oct '94 / Dirter Promotions

Headcleaner

☐ I AGAINST I
Maybe tomorrow / Pass me by / Stumble and stare / Top of the world / Ordinary flight / Look inside / Signs / Nailed to the floor / Time / Bottom / Lesson to be learnt / Ideals / Utopia / All by yourself
65252 / 16 Feb '98 / Epitaph

☐ NO OFFENCE MEANT, PLENTY TAKEN
Aperetif / Oscar / Understanding / Quirk / Downer / Comet / Half life / Jack / Ampallang / Big D / Mix
118612 / Nov '95 / Musidisc UK

☐ PIGMENT OF IMAGINATION
BD 9045 / Nov '97 / Big Deal

Headcrash

☐ HEADCRASH
4509955402 / Oct '94 / Warner Bros.

Headhunter

☐ REBIRTH
CC 025050 / May '95 / Major

Headhunters

☐ RETURN OF THE HEADHUNTERS
Funk hunter / Watch R backs / Frankie and Kevin / Pee Pee Head / Premonition / Skank it up / Tip toe / Two but not too / 6/8 - 7/8 / Kwanzaa
5390282 / 15 Jun '98 / Verve

Headless Chickens

☐ HEADLESS CHICKENS EP
D 19853 / Oct '94 / Mushroom

Headman

☐ PHILADELPHIA EXPERIENCE, THE
MILL 007CD / Oct '94 / Millenium

Heads

☐ RELAXING WITH THE HEADS
HUK 001CD / Oct '96 / Headhunter

☐ TIME IS NOW
MR 097 / 11 May '98 / Man's Ruin

Heads, Hands & Feet

☐ HEADS, HANDS & FEET
I'm in need of your help / Send me a wire / Look at the world it's changing/Because you know me / Green liquor / Country boy / Tryin' to put me on / I wish you knew me / Devil's elbow / Pete might spook the horses / Everybody's hustlin'/Hang me dang me / Delaware / More you get, the more you want / Song for Suzie / Tirabad / Little bit lonely
SEECD 458 / Oct '96 / See For Miles

☐ HOME FROM HOME
Bring it all back home / Ain't gonna let it get me down / How does it feel to be right all the time / Achmed / Precious stone / Friend of a friend / Windy and warm / Who turned off the dark / Can you see me / Home from home / Make me feel much better
C5CD 633 / Oct '95 / See For Miles

☐ TRACKS
Let's get this show on the road / Safety in numbers / Road show / Harlequin / Dancer / Hot property / Jack Daniels / Rhyme and time / Paper chase / Song and dance
SEECD 459 / Oct '96 / See For Miles

Heads Up

☐ DUKE
EM 93192 / Mar '91 / Roadrunner

Headstone

☐ ON THE WINGS OF ETERNITY
TT 00392 / Jul '98 / T&T

☐ STILL LOOKING
ANT 4111 / May '97 / Anthology

Headstones

☐ 24 HOURS (EVERYDAY)
COLCD 0700 / 24 Nov '97 / Collectables

Headswim

☐ DESPITE YOURSELF
Tourniquet / Hype / Years on me / Clinging to the wreckage / Better made / Wishing I was naive / Old angel midnight / Holy Ghost / Burnt out shell of bliss / Devil in my palm / Moving on / Brother
4877262 / 18 May '98 / Epic

Healey, Jeff

☐ COVER TO COVER (Healey, Jeff Band)
Shapes of things / Freedom / Yer blues / Stop breakin' down / Angel / Evil / Stuck in the middle with you / I got the line on you / Run through the jungle / As the years go passing by / I'm ready / Communication breakdown / Me and my crazy self / Badge
74321238882 / Mar '95 / Arista

☐ FEEL THIS (Healey, Jeff Band)
Cruel little number / Leave the light on / Baby's lookin' hot / Lost in your eyes / House that love built / Evil and here to stay / Feel this / My kinda lover / It could all get blown away / You're coming home / Heart of an angel / Live and love / Joined at the heart / Dreams of love
74321120872 / Aug '95 / Arista

☐ HELL TO PAY (Healey, Jeff Band)
Full circle / I think I love you too much / I can't get my hands on you / How long can a man be strong / Let it all go / Hell to pay / While my guitar gently weeps / Something to hold on to / How much / Highway of dreams / Life beyond the sky
260815 / Aug '96 / Arista

☐ SEE THE LIGHT (Healey, Jeff Band)
Confidence man / River of no return / Don't let your chance go by / Angel eyes / Nice problem to have / Someday, someway / I need to be loved / Blue jean blues / That's what they say / Hideaway / See the light
259441 / Aug '95 / Arista

☐ VERY BEST OF THE JEFF HEALY BAND, THE (Healey, Jeff Band)
It could all get blown away / Communications breakdown / Yer blues / Stop breakin' down / Run through the jungle / Cruel little number / Shapes of things / Badge / Confidence man / Angel / House that love built / River of no return / See the light / Don't let your chance go by / Nice problem to have / While my guitar gently weeps
74321603382 / 27 Jul '98 / Camden

Healy, Jeremy

☐ FANTAZIA BRITISH ANTHEMS...SUMMERTIME (Mixed By Jeremy Healy And Sonique/2CD Set) (Various Artists)
Feel it: *Tamperer* / Deeper love: *Ruff Driverz* / Hook: *Radical Players* / Make my world go round: *Sandy B* / Dirty disco dubs: *DJ Disco* / I'm gonna love you: *Summer Junkies* / Keep slippin': *Killa Green Budds* / Disco babes from outer space: *Babe Instinct* / Funky fresh: *DJ Stew & Buddha Monks* / Song 3: *Flatback 4* / Jump and shockout: *DJ Vandan* / Distortion: *Pianoheadz* / Sounds of wickedness: *Tzant* / Windows: *SIL* / Rude boy rock: *Lionrock* / Erotic city: *Scandalous* / It's like that: *Run DMC & Jason Nevins* / Smack my bitch up: *Prodigy* / Just call: *Street Life & Dana Stovell* / Dominator: *Swimmer* / Give a little love: *Invisible Man* / Disco at the K mark: *Disco At The K Mark* / Inside: *Lamboy, Andy* / Funky grooves: *Untidy Dubs Presents* / Meet her at the love parade: *Hans G* / Twister: *Viper* / Put a spell on you: *Sonique* / You are somebody: *Full Intention* / Everybody: *Carbone, Frankie* / Deeper: *Serious Danger* / Bomb da loop: *Megablast* / To the world: *Organ* / Don't play dead: *Vapourheadz Zone*
FBA 2CD / 5 May '98 / Fantazia

☐ MIXMAG LIVE VOL.14 (Mad Hatter's Tea Party - Jeremy Healy/Brandon Block) (Various Artists)
MMLCD 014 / Jul '96 / Mixmag Live

Healy, Linda

☐ PLANT Y MOR
Dinas noddfa / Usa lan / Newid byd / Enfys yn ennis / Cariadon bosnia / Cannwyll / Tyfodd y bachgen yn ddyn / Diwrnod arall yn y ddinas / Plant y mor / Ar y ffordd / Rhydd mewn caethiwed / Llygad ebrill / Porth madryn / Colll'r tir / Glas oedd y bae
SCD 2072 / Feb '95 / Sain

Heaney, Joe

☐ COME ALL YE GALLANT IRISHMEN
CIC 020CD / Jan '90 / Clo Iar-Chonnachta

☐ FROM MY TRADITION (The Best Of Joe Heaney)
SHCD 34019 / Mar '98 / Shanachie

☐ JOE HEANEY
OSS 22CD / Dec '93 / Ossian

☐ SAY A SONG
NWARCD 001 / May '97 / Northwest

Heap, Imogen

☐ I MEGAPHONE
ALMCD 48 / 10 Aug '98 / Almo Sounds

Heap, Jimmy

☐ RELEASE ME (Heap, Jimmy & The Melody Mastg)
Release me / Love in the valley / Just to be with you / Then I'll be happy / Heartbreaker / You're in love with you / Just for tonight / Girl with a past / Lifetime of shame / You don't kiss me 'cause you love me / One that I won / Ethyl in my gas tank (no gal in my arms) / My first love affair / Love can move mountains / Conscience / I'm guilty / This song is just for you / You ought to know / I told you so / Butternut / Long John / Mingling / Heap of boogie / You're nothin' but a nothin' / That's all I want from you / I'll follow the crowd / It takes a heap of lovin' / Cry cry darlin' / You didn't have time / Let's do it just once / This night won't last forever
BCD 15617 / Apr '92 / Bear Family

Heard, Larry

☐ DANCE 2000 VOL.1
SUB 48452 / 3 Nov '97 / Distance

☐ DANCE 2000 VOL.2
Future step lesson / Evolution of mind / Give me heaven / Sunset / After hours / Motherland / Long short stay / Futuristic island life / Spinal tap / And so I dance / Gentle morning rain
DI 0732 / 3 Aug '98 / Distance

☐ ICE CASTLES
Crystal fantasy / Tryblennasense / Romantic sway / Techno-centric / Forbidden / Solitude / Carla's dance / Night images / Ice castles / Nature's bliss / Precious tears / Bongo
MECCD 002 / 7 Sep '98 / Mecca

Hearn, Kevin

☐ MOTHBALL MINT
77752112932 / 21 Apr '98 / FTCH

Heart

☐ BAD ANIMALS
Who will you run to / Alone / There's the girl / I want you so bad / Wait for an answer / Bad animals / You ain't so tough / Strangers of the heart / Easy target / RSVP
CDEST 2032 / Jul '94 / Capitol

☐ BRIGADE
Wild child / All I wanna do is make love to you / Secret / Tall, dark handsome stranger / I didn't want to need you / Night / Fallen from grace / Under the sky / Cruel nights / Stranded / Call of the wild / I want your world to turn / I love you
CDESTU 2121 / Feb '94 / Capitol

☐ DEFINITIVE COLLECTION, THE
Barracuda / Little queen / Kick it out / Dream of the archer / Cry to me / Love alive / Dog and butterfly / Straight on / Lighter touch / Nada one / Even it up / Sweet darlin' / This man is mine / Perfect stranger / Tell it like it is / How can I refuse / Allies / Johnny Moon
4805612 / 13 Jul '98 / Epic

☐ DESIRE WALKS ON
Desire / Black on black II / Back to Avalon / Woman in me / Rage / In walks the night / My crazy head / Ring them bells / Will you be there (in the morning) / Voodoo doll / Anything is possible / Avalon / Desire walks on / La mujer que hay en mi / Te quedaras (en la manana)
CDEST 2216 / Nov '93 / Capitol

☐ GREATEST HITS
Tell it like it is / Barracuda / Straight on / Dog and butterfly / Even it up / Bebe le strange / Sweet darlin' / I'm down/Long tall Sally / Unchained melody / Rock 'n' roll
4601742 / Apr '94 / CBS

☐ GREATEST HITS
Crazy on you / All I wanna do is make love to you / If looks could kill / Never / Alone / Who will you run to / Straight on / Magic man / What about love / Dreamboat Annie / Dog and butterfly / Nothin' at all / Heartless / Stranded / Will you be there in the morning / These dreams / Barracuda (live)
CDEMC 3765 / Apr '97 / Capitol

☐ HEART
If looks could kill / What about love / Never / These dreams / Wolf / All eyes / Nobody home / Nothin' at all / What he don't know / Shellshock
CDLOVE 1 / Feb '86 / Capitol

☐ INTERVIEW, THE
CBAK 4073 / Feb '94 / Baktabak

☐ LITTLE QUEEN
Little queen / Treat me well / Say hello / Cry to me / Go on cry / Barracuda / Love alive / Sylvan song / Dream of the archer / Kick it out
4746782 / Feb '97 / Columbia

☐ ROAD HOME, THE
Dreamboat Annie (Fantasy child) / Dog and butterfly / (Up on) Cherry Blossom Road / Back to Avalon / Alone / These dreams / Love hurts / Straight on / All I wanna do is make love to you / Crazy on you / Seasons / River / Barracuda / Dream of the archer
CDEST 2258 / Sep '97 / Capitol

Heart Of England Jazz Band

☐ FOLLOW YOUR HEARTS
RSCD 669 / May '98 / Raymer

Heart Of Midlothian FC

☐ HEARTS SONGS (18 Jambo Classics) (Various Artists)
Hearts song: *Nicol, Hector* / Arise Hearts: *Young, Brian / John Robertson*: *Tynecastle boys* / Hearts song: *Hearts Squad* / Corgy road: *Boys in Maroon* / We are the Hearts: *Hearts singers* / Henry Smith: *Tynecastle boys* / Hearts crazy: *1873* / 1-0: *Oh Yes* / Hearts medley: *Hearts Squad* / Hail hail jam tarts: *Jamtastics* / Hearts song: *Rayne* / C'mon the Hearts: *Rayne* / Go Jambos goal: *Rayne* / Songs of Tynecastle: *Heart Of Midlothian FC* / Marchin' thru Georgie: *Heart Of Midlothian FC* / Here we go: *Gorgie boys* / Hearts anthem: *Gorgie noise*
CDGAFFER 28 / 24 Aug '98 / Cherry Red

Heart Throbs

☐ CLEOPATRA GRIP
Tossed away / Tossed away / Big commotion / In vain / Slip and slide / Here I hide / Calavera / I wonder why / Trance / Blood from a store / Kiss me when I'm starving / White laughter
TPLP 23CD / Jun '90 / One Little Indian

☐ JUBILEE GRIP
Tiny feet / Tiny feet / Hooligan / Outside / Girl became the stairs / So far / Bright green day / Too late / Tuna / Gone
TPLP 33CD / Apr '92 / One Little Indian

☐ VERTICAL SMILE
Perry said / Perry said / Love is stretching / Incense of you / Avalanche / Brood bitch / Apple pie / Tranquilised, naked and shy / Go / Solemn child / Worser
TPLP 43CD / May '93 / One Little Indian

Heartbeats

☐ SPINNING WORLD
Ocean / Hollywood dream / All I want to do / Living in Babylon / Black mountain rag / Blue diamond mines / Signs of rain / Another day / Nine mile view of / Spinning world / They don't know you / Hand of man / Cotton eyed Joe / Power to run / Whole bunch of keys
GLCD 2111 / Jul '93 / Green Linnet

Heartdrops

☐ THIS IS
MLT 006 / Jun '97 / Melted

Heartland

☐ BRIDGE OF FOOLS
ESM 011 / 2 Mar '98 / Escape

☐ HEARTLAND III
ESM 002 / 2 Mar '98 / Escape

☐ MIRACLES BY DESIGN
ESM 029 / 4 May '98 / Escape

☐ WIDE OPEN
PM 010092 / Mar '97 / Long Island

Hearts & Flowers

☐ NOW IS THE TIME/OF HORSES, KIDS AND FORGOTTEN WOMEN
Now is the time / Save some time / Try for the sun / Rain rain / View from ward 3 / Rock 'n' roll gypsies / Reason to believe / Please / 1-2-3 Rhyme in Carnivour thyme / I'm a lonesome fugitive / Road to nowhere / 10,000 Sunsets / Now is the time for hearts and flowers / Highway in the wind / Second hand sundown queen / She sang hyms out of tune / Ode to a tin angel / When I was a cowboy / Legend of Ol' Tenbrookes / Colour your daytime / Two little boys / Extra extra
EDCD 428 / Jul '95 / Edsel

Heartsman, Johnny

☐ TOUCH, THE
Serpent's touch / Paint my mailbox blue / You're so fine / Tongue / Attitude / Got to find my baby / Butler did it / Please don't be scared of my love / Oops / Walkin' blues / Let me love you baby / Heartburn / Endless
ALCD 4800 / May '93 / Alligator

Heartworms

☐ DURING
POOF 13CD / 18 May '98 / Pop Factory

Heat

☐ GOLDFINGER
A2Z 85008CD / Sep '96 / A2Z

Heatfarm

☐ DAWN OF THE DUMB
L7 003CD / 15 Dec '97 / Lucky Seven/ Diehard

Heath Brothers

☐ AS WE WERE SAYING
Newest one / Bop agin / For seven's sake / South filthy / I'm glad there is you / Dave's haze / Daydream / Nostalgia / This is what it is
CCD 47772 / Sep '97 / Concord Jazz

Heath, Jimmy

☐ LITTLE MAN BIG BAND
Trane connections / Two friends / Voice of the saxophone / Forever Sonny / CTA / Ellington's strayhorn / Gingerbread boy / Without you, no me
5139562 / Apr '92 / Verve

☐ PICTURE OF HEALTH
60170400022 / 14 Apr '98 / PREV

☐ REALLY BIG
Big 'P' / Old fashioned fun / Mona's mood / Dat dere / Nails / On Green Dolphin Street / My ideal / Picture of Heath
OJCCD 1799 / Dec '96 / Original Jazz Classics

Heath, Ted

☐ AT CARNEGIE HALL/FIRST AMERICAN TOUR 1956-1957
8209502 / Apr '96 / Limelight

☐ BIG BAND CLASSICS VOL.2
ISCD 169 / May '98 / Intersound

☐ FROM MOIRA WITH LOVE
Folks who live on the hill / Melody in F / Clair de Lune / Our love / Liebestraum / Song of India / Look for the silver lining / Procession / Skylark / Retrospect / Bill / Nearness of you / Fourth dimension / Thou swell / September song / Memories of you / Birth of the blues / Sixteen going on seventeen / Hot toddy / Georgia on my mind / Harlem nocturne / Someone to watch over me / St. Louis blues / How high the moon / Tonight / Faithful Hussar / Blues for moderns / Our waltz / Obsession / Lush slide / Eloquence / Rhapsody for drums
CDSIV 6106 / Jul '95 / Horatio Nelson

☐ GET WITH THE SWING
Route 66 / Ad lib frolic / Out of my dreams / Best years of our lives / Them who has gets / Nightingale sang in Berkeley Square / Feudin' and fightin' / Experiment / Try a little tenderness / Open the door Richard / Mountain greenery / People will say we're in love / Watcher (knocked 'em in The Old Kent Road) / See me dance the polka / Day by day / Not so quiet please / My heart goes crazy / Bakerloo non-stop / Opus one / So would I / Twilight time / My guy's come back
PLCD 568 / 5 May '98 / President

☐ GOLDEN AGE OF TED HEATH VOL.1, THE
Opus one / Somebody loves me / Swingin' shepherd blues / My favourite things / Maria / Lullaby of Broadway / Holiday for strings / Flying home / I get a kick out of you / Jumpin' at the woodside / Man I love / Hawaiian war chant / At last / Cherokee / We'll git it / 'S Wonderful / You stepped out of a dream / Sabre dance / Blues in the night / Royal Garden blues / Moonlight in Vermont / Apple honey / Fly me to the moon / Listen to my music / Pick yourself up / Hawk talks / And the angels sing / Champ
CDSIV 6102 / Apr '93 / Horatio Nelson

☐ GOLDEN AGE OF TED HEATH VOL.2, THE
9.20 special / East of the sun and west of the moon / Intermission riff / Ad lib frolic / Girl talk / South Rampart Street Parade / American patrol / That lovely weekend / Swanee river / Artistry in rhythm / Nightingale sang in Berkeley Square / Bakerloo non stop / In the mood / I had the craziest dream / Soon amapola / I can't get started (with you) / Perdido / C jam blues / Sophisticated lady / First jump / Night and day / Poor little rich girl / Swing low, sweet chariot
CDSIV 6121 / Jul '95 / Horatio Nelson

☐ GOLDEN AGE OF TED HEATH VOL.3, THE
Let's dance / Chattanooga choo choo / Swingin' the blues / My guy's come back / Touch of your lips / Chicago / Skyliner / Nightmare / Lush slide / Serenade in blue / At the woodchoppers' ball / I've got a gal in Kalamazoo / On the sunny side of the street / I got it bad and that ain't good / Sidewalks of Cuba / After you've gone / Big John special / Chloe / Jersey bounce / Contrasts / Cotton tail / Fascinating rhythm / Snowfall / Headin' north
CDSIV 6135 / Jul '95 / Horatio Nelson

☐ GOLDEN AGE OF TED HEATH VOL.4, THE
Have you met miss jones / Tuxedo junction / I could have danced all night / Allentown jail / Send for henry / But not for me / Honky tonk train blues / At the jazz band ball / I left my heart in san francisco / St. louis blues / Ebb tide / Slaughter on tenth avenue / Mack the knife / Breeze and I / All the things you are / Night train / Manhattan serenade / Say "si si" / Blacksmith blues / In a persian market / Long john silver / Poinciana / They didn't believe me (foxtrot) / Skin deep
CDSIV 6137 / Jul '95 / Horatio Nelson

☐ IT'S SWING TIME
DAWE 82 / Jan '98 / Magic

☐ LISTEN TO MY MUSIC
East of the sun / Not so quiet please / Day by day / Twilight time / Getting nowhere / My heart goes crazy / Bakerloo non-stop / My fickle eye / Wot cher / To bed early / Any old iron / Kiss goodnight / You keep coming back like a song / So would I / My heart goes crazy / I fall in love too easily / Bells of St. Mary's / Ring dem bells / Opus one / Lullaby of Broadway / Skyliner / On the Archeson / Topeka and the Santa Fe
RAJCD 877 / Apr '97 / Empress

☐ LISTEN TO MY MUSIC VOL.1
HEPCD 52 / Jan '97 / Hep

☐ LISTEN TO MY MUSIC VOL.2 (1946-1947)
Listen to my music / Opus 1 / Hey ba ba rebop / Croeole love call / C jam blues / Anything goes / East of the sun / Lullabye of Broadway / Love will find a way / Ad lib frolic
HEPCD 57 / 16 Feb '98 / Hep

☐ TED HEATH 1935-1945
Darktown strutters ball / I want to be happy / Limehouse blues / Temptation rag / Chanson Hindooe (song of India) / Bwanga / My paradise / Stage coach / 'Deed I do / Blue champagne / You rhyme with everything that's beautiful / I've got a gal in Kalamazoo / At last / Never a day goes by / How sweet you are / First jump / Opus one / Very thought of you / Cossack patrol / My guy's come back / Twilight time
RAJCD 868 / 29 Jun '98 / Empress

☐ TED HEATH AND HIS MUSIC
Bells of St. Mary's / Oh what it seemed to be / Exactly like you / Any old iron / My baby said yes / First jump / Anything goes / I can't begin to tell you / I've found a new baby / Opus one / Knees up Mother Brown / I'll close my eyes / I can't give you anything but love / Time on my hands / Very thought of you / Symphony / Wot cher (knocked 'em in the Old Kent Road) / I dream of you / Crazy rhythm / Cossack patrol / My guy's come back / I'll never be the same
SWNCD 015 / Oct '97 / Sound Waves

☐ TED HEATH AND HIS MUSIC (Play It Again Ted)
CDMOIR 524 / Jan '98 / Memoir

☐ VERY BEST OF TED HEATH, THE
Listen to my music / Tail end Charlie / East of the sun / Swinging shepherd blues / Ad lib frolic / Chelsea / When the world was young / Fine romance / Deep night / Baby blue / On with the Don / Lullaby of Birdland / I'm gonna love that girl / Hawaiian war chant / Walkin' shoes / Sheila's theme / Hot toddy / That lovely weekend / Obsession / All the time and everywhere / Opus 1 / Lady bird
CDSIV 6150 / Jul '95 / Horatio Nelson

Heathen

☐ BREAKING THE SILENCE
Death by hanging / Goblins blade / Open the grave / Pray for death / Set me free / Breaking the silence / World's end / Save the skull
CDMFN 75 / Aug '89 / Music For Nations

Heatmiser

☐ MIC CITY SONS
Get lucky / Plainclothes man / Low flying jets / Rest my head against the wall / Fix is in / Eagle eye / Cruel reminder / You gotta move / Pop in G / Blue highway / See you later
CAR 75402 / Oct '96 / Caroline

Heaton, Angie

☐ SPARKLE
MUDCD 029 / 23 Feb '98 / Mud

Heatwave

☐ ALWAYS AND FOREVER (The Best Of Heatwave)
Boogie nights / Always and forever / Groove line / Look after love / Mind blowing decisions / Razzle dazzle / Gangsters of the groove / Jitterbuggin' / Naturally / Too hot to handle / Lettin' it loose / Posin' til closin' / Sho'nuff must be love / Hold on to the one / Mind what you find / Big guns
4840482 / May '96 / Epic

☐ BOOGIE NIGHTS
JHD 028 / Jun '92 / Tring

Heave

☐ SCARAMANGA
SCANCD 17 / Apr '96 / Radarscope

Heaven 17

☐ BEST OF HEAVEN 17, THE
(We don't need this) fascist groove thang / I'm your money / Height of the fighting (he-la-hu) / Play to win / Penthouse and pavement / Let me go / Trouble / Come live with me / Crushed by the wheels of industry / Sunset now / Flame down / This is mine / Foolish thing to do / Contenders / And that's no lie / Temptation
CDVIP 110 / Dec '93 / Virgin VIP

☐ HIGHER AND HIGHER (The Best Of Heaven 17)
(We don't need this) fascist groove thang (remix) / Let me go / Come live with me / This is mine / I'm your money / Play to win / And that's no lie / Contenders / We live so fast / Sunset now / Trouble / Height of the fighting (He-la-hu) / Penthouse and pavement / Crushed by the wheels if industry / (We don't need this) fascist groove thang / Temptation
CDV 2717 / Mar '93 / Virgin

☐ HOW MEN ARE
Five minutes to midnight / Sunset now / This is mine / Fuse / Shame is on the rocks / Skin I'm in / Flamedown / Reputation / And that's no lie
CDV 2326 / Jul '87 / Virgin

☐ LUXURY GAP
Crushed by the wheels of industry / Who'll stop the rain / Let me go / Key to the world / Temptation / Come live with me / Lady Ice and Mr. Hex / We live so fast / Best kept secret
CDV 2253 / '83 / Virgin

☐ PENTHOUSE AND PAVEMENT
(We don't need this) fascist groove thang / Penthouse and pavement / Soul warfare / Geisha boys and temple girls / Let's all make a bomb / Height of the fighting (he-la-hu) / Song with no name / Play to win / We're going to live for a very long time
CDV 2208 / Jul '87 / Virgin

☐ REMIX COLLECTION, THE
Temptation / Facist groove thang / That's no lie / Crushed by the wheels of industry / Train of love in motion / This is mine / Foolsih things to do / Play to win / Let me go / Penthouse and pavement / All come live with me
CDVIP 133 / Apr '95 / Virgin VIP

☐ RETOX/DETOX (Heaven 17 Remixed - 2CD Set)
Let me go / Let's all make a bomb / Geisha boys and temple girls / We live so fast / Come live with me / Height of the fighting / Crushed by the wheels of industry / Play to win / Let's all make a bomb / Geisha boys and temple girls / And that's no lie / Let me go / Fascist groove thang / With this ring / Penthouse and pavement / Ain't that no lie / Temptation / We live so fast / Height of the fighting / Designing Heaven / Geisha boys and temple girls
EDGCD 035 / 22 Jun '98 / Eagle

Heaven Deconstruction

☐ HEAVEN DECONSTRUCTION
December / AOAcU / Acid starngel / Improper / Drun / Riversky / F / Borea / Scories / Landing / Message / Nano pata / Lova / Light residues / Under / Numiere / Windklang
BIAS 309CD / Jan '97 / Play It Again Sam

Heavenly

☐ OPERATION HEAVENLY
WIJCD 105 / Oct '96 / Wiiija

☐ THIS IS HEAVENLY
ER 1010 / Jul '97 / Elefant

Heavenly Bodies

☐ CELESTIAL
Rains on me / Obsession / Time stands still / Con / Stars collide / Road to Maralinga / Shades of love / Cavatina / Senderoluminoso
TMCD 27 / Jun '89 / Third Mind

Heavenly Gospel Singers

☐ HEAVENLY GOSPEL SINGERS VOL.1 1935-1936
DOCD 5452 / Jun '96 / Document

☐ HEAVENLY GOSPEL SINGERS VOL.2 1936-1937
DOCD 5453 / Jun '96 / Document

☐ HEAVENLY GOSPEL SINGERS VOL.3 1938-1939
DOCD 5454 / Jun '96 / Document

☐ HEAVENLY GOSPEL SINGERS VOL.4 1939-1941
DOCD 5455 / Jun '96 / Document

Heavenly Music Corporation

☐ CONSCIOUSNESS
SR 9458 / Oct '94 / Silent

☐ IN A GARDEN OF EDEN
SR 9335 / Mar '94 / Silent

☐ LUNAR PHASE
SR 9571 / Feb '95 / Silent

Heavenly Stars

☐ OH HAPPY DAY
Old time religion / Amazing grace / I'll fly away / Swing low sweet chariot / I'm so glad / Go tell it on the mountain / Oh happy day / Battle hymn of the republic / When the saints go marching in / Just a closer walk with thee / Down by the riverside / Old rugged cross / When he calls me / Roll Jordan roll
FA 424 / Nov '97 / Fremeaux

Heaven's Gate

☐ LIVE FOR SALE
SPV 07776742 / Apr '94 / SPV

☐ LIVIN' IN HYSTERIA
0876312 / May '91 / Steamhammer

☐ PLANET E
Terminated world / Planet earth / Back from the dawn / On the edge / Children play / Rebel yell / Black religion / Animal / Noah's dream / This town ain't big enough for both of us
SPV 08518312 / Feb '97 / SPV

Heavenwood

☐ DIVA
MASSCD 106 / Jan '97 / Massacre

☐ SWALLOW
MASSCD 158 / 11 May '98 / Massacre

Heavy Balloon

☐ 32,000 POUND
LSDAZ 5001 / 15 Dec '97 / LSD

Heavy D

☐ PEACEFUL JOURNEY, A (Heavy D & The Boyz)
Now that we found love / Let it rain / I can make you go ooh / Sister sister / Don't curse / Peaceful journey / Lover's got what U need / Cuz he's alwayz around / Is it good to you / Letter to the future / Swinging with da hevster / Body and mind / Do me do me / Somebody for me
MCD 10289 / 8 Sep '97 / MCA

☐ WATERBED HEV
Big Daddy / Keep it comin' / You can get it / Waterbed hev / Shake it / I'll do anything / Don't be afraid / Justa' interlude / Can you handle it / Wanna be a player / Get fresh hev / Big Daddy
UPTD 53033 / Apr '97 / Uptown

Heavy Jelly

☐ TAKE ME DOWN TO THE RIVER
FLASH 56 / 1 Jun '98 / Flash

Heavy Pettin'

☐ BIG BANG
Born to burn / Romeo / Lonely people / This is america / Looking for love / Madonna on the radio / Don't call it love / Heaven sent / Two hearts
WKFMXD 130 / Nov '89 / FM

Heavy Shift

☐ LAST PICTURE SHOW
Double feature / Swamp monster / Rear view, earthbound / Come alive / LA nights / Steppin' out / Tango bolognese / Last picture show
ZEN 010CD / Jun '96 / Indochina

☐ UNCHAIN YOUR MIND/LIVE...
WOLCDL 1050 / Feb '95 / China

Heavy Stereo

☐ DEJA VOODOO
CRECD 185 / Sep '96 / Creation

Heavy Vegetable

☐ MONDO AQUA KITTY
HED 058 / 17 Aug '98 / Headhunter

Hecate Enthroned

☐ DARK REQUIEMS AND UNSILENT MASSACRE
BLACK 012CD / 25 May '98 / Blackend

☐ SLAUGHTER OF INNOCENCE/ REQUIEM FOR THE DYING
BLACK 004CD / Apr '97 / Blackend

☐ UPON PROMETHEAN SHORES
BLACK 002CD / Jun '96 / Blackend

Heckle

☐ COMPLICATED FUTILITY OF IGNORANCE, THE
HR 621CD / Jun '97 / Hopeless

Heckman, Thomas

☐ SPECTRAL EMOTIONS
DBMLABCD 4 / Oct '95 / Labworks

Heckstall-Smith, Dick

☐ BIRD IN WIDNES (Heckstall-Smith, Dick & John Stevens)
EFA 084302 / Jul '95 / Konnex

☐ CELTIC STEPPES
33JAZZ 027 / Mar '96 / 33 Jazz

☐ DICK HECKSTALL-SMITH QUARTET
Venerable Bede / Woza nasu / Moongoose / Baiere
CDLR 45028 / May '91 / L&R

☐ STORY ENDED, A
Future song / Crabs / Moses in the bullrushourses / What the morning was after / Pirate's dream / Same old thing / Moses in the bullrushourses (Live) / Pirates dream (Live) / No amount of loving (Live)
NEMCD 641 / Mar '93 / Sequel

(HED)pe

☐ (HED)PE
POS / Ground / Serpent boy / Firsty / Tired of sleep (TOS) / Circus / 33 / Schpamb / Ken 2012 / Bitches / Darky / Hill / Ifo
CHIP 189 / 27 Oct '97 / Jive

Hedayat, Dashiell

☐ OBSOLETE
MANTRA 075 / Sep '97 / Mantra

Hedgehog

☐ ANGELITE
VOW 064CD / 11 May '98 / Voices Of Wonder

☐ MERCURY RED
VOW 37C / Apr '94 / Voices Of Wonder

☐ PRIMAL GUTTER
VOW 034C / Dec '93 / Voices Of Wonder

☐ THORN CHORD WONDER
VOW 044CD / Jun '95 / Voices Of Wonder

Hedges, Chuck

☐ NO GREATER LOVE
There is no greater love / My old flame / Samba dees days / I'll be seeing you / I'm getting sentimental over you / Magnolia rag / I thought about you / Jitterbug waltz / I remember you / I love you / Cheek to cheek
ARCD 19121 / Nov '94 / Arbors Jazz

☐ SKYLARK
When you're smiling / Here's that rainy day / Autumn leaves / 'Round midnight / Have you met Miss Jones / Jitterbug Waltz / There will never be another you / Skylark / I found a new baby
DD 483 / Jun '97 / Delmark

☐ SWINGTET LIVE AT ANDY'S
Softly as in a morning sunrise / New Orleans / Cheek to cheek / Nuage / It's alright with me / Gambler's waltz / Breakfast feud / I don't wanna be kissed / Liza / She's funny that way / Autumn leaves / Blues (my naughty sweetie gives me)
DE 465 / Mar '97 / Delmark

Hedges, Michael

☐ AERIAL BOUNDARIES
Aerial boundaries / Bensusan / Rickover's dream / Raggamuffin / After the goldrush / Hot type / Spare change / Menage a trois / Magic farmer
01934110322 / Jan '95 / Windham Hill

☐ ROAD TO RETURN, THE
72902103292 / Jan '95 / High Street

Hedges, Ray

☐ TUBULAR BELLS VOL.1
GRF 216 / Mar '93 / Tring

☐ TUBULAR BELLS VOL.2
Sentinel / Dark star / Clear light / Blue saloon / Sunjammer / Red dawn / Bell / Weightless / Great plan / Sunset door / Tattoo / Altered state / Maya gold / Moonshine
GRF 217 / Mar '93 / Tring

Hedningarna

☐ HIPPJOKK
Hoglorfen / Navdi/fasa / Drafur och gildur / Dolkaren / Bierdna / Kina / Forshyttan / Dufwa / Vals i fel dur / Skane / Graucholorfen
SRSCD 4737 / May '97 / Silence

☐ KAKSI
Joupolle joutunut / Kruspolska / Vottikaalina / Chicago / Viktorin / Aivoton / Ful-valsen / Pal Karl / Kaivonkansi / Skamgreppet / Grodan/Widergrenen / Omas Ludvig / Kings Selma
XOUCD 101 / Oct '93 / Xource
SRS 4717 / May '97 / Silence

☐ KAKSI
2156160072 / 17 Mar '98 / Northside

☐ TRA
Tass on nainen / Min skog / Vargtimmen / Gorrlaus / Skrautval / Pornopolka / Raven / Saglaten / Tuuli / Tappmarschen / Tina Vieri
MWCD 4011 / Dec '95 / Music & Words
SRS 4712 / May '97 / Silence
2156160082 / 17 Mar '98 / Northside

Hedonist

☐ HEAD
BLUE 16CD / Oct '95 / Blue

Hefeystos

☐ PSYCHO CAFE
WLR 016CD / 6 Jul '98 / Wounded Love

Heffern, Gary

☐ PAINFUL DAYS
GRCD 362 / May '97 / Glitterhouse

Hefner

☐ BREAKING GOD'S HEART
Sweetness lies within / Sad witch / Hymn for the postal service / Love will destroy us in the end / Librarian / God is on my side / Another better friend / Love inside the stud farm / Tactile / Eloping
PURE 083CD / 6 Jul '98 / Too Pure

Hegamin, Lucille

☐ LUCILLE HEGAMIN VOL.4 1920-1926 (Alternate Takes & Remaining Titles)
DOCD 1011 / 24 Mar '98 / Document

Hegarty, Dermot

☐ CONNEMARA ROSE
Red is the rose / Whistling thief / Ballad of Patrick Furey / Connemara by the lake / If those lips could only speak / Paddy's navy / Song to remember / Boys of Barna Sraide / Shore of Lough Bran / James Connelly / Love is teasing / Danny Farrell / Avondale / Sleive na mban / Sweet Alice Ben Bolt / Dear old Donegal / Hi for the beggarman / Lakes of coolfin / Connemara Rose / I've been everywhere
3036001012 / Apr '97 / Carlton

Heid, Bill

☐ BOP RASCAL
Bop rascal / Homewood morning / Latin Larry / Bag of iku / Duff's doonk / Orange chair ballad / Phy-ops / Rhythm rascal / Like animal / Going on to Detroit
SAVCD 2009 / Jan '98 / Savant

Heidenreich

☐ DEATH GATE CYCLE
NPR 038CD / 15 Jun '98 / Napalm

Heights Of Abraham

☐ ELECTRIC HUSH
Cleric / Boogie heights / High time / Dolphins / What's the number / Olive branching / EVA / 700 channels / Sunyatta / Make love
PORK 028 / Jan '96 / Pork
0630187482
0630187489 / 10 Nov '97 / Warner Bros.
ZTT 99CD / 13 Jul '98 / ZTT

☐ HUMIDITY REPRESS
PORK 009 / 12 Jan '98 / Pork

Heimdall

☐ LORD OF THE SKY
ERO 2005 / Jul '98 / Elevate

Heinz

☐ TRIBUTE TO EDDIE
Tribute to Eddie / Hush-a-bye / I ran all the way home / Country boy / Don't you knock at my door / Summertime blues / Don't keep picking on me / Cut across shorty / Three steps to heaven / Come on and dance / Twenty flight rock / Look for a star / My dreams / I remember / Been invited to a party / Rumble in the night / I get up in the morning / Just like Eddie
RCCD 3008 / Jan '94 / Rollercoaster

Heiroglyphics

☐ THIRD EYE VISION
84732 / 20 Apr '98 / Heiro Imperium

Heiss, Frank

☐ 370 DEGREES
PLAN 9CD / 6 Oct '97 / Blue Planet

Hela Hela

☐ FILL OUT THE FORM
GRCD 017 / 23 Mar '98 / Garageland

☐ REJECTED
GRCD 020 / 23 Mar '98 / Garageland

Heldon

☐ ALLEZ TEIA
14235 / Jan '97 / Spalax

Helen Love

☐ RADIO HITS VOL.1
DAMGOOD 51CD / 15 Sep '97 / Damaged Goods

☐ RADIO HITS VOL.2
DAMGOOD 117CD / 15 Sep '97 / Damaged Goods

Helian, Jacques

☐ JACQUES HELIAN & STAN KENTON 1938-54 (Helian, Jacques & Stan Kenton)
8274172 / Jan '95 / Jazztime

Helias, Mark

☐ LOOPIN' THE COOL
Munchkins / Loop the cool / One time only / Sector 51 / Seventh sign / Penta houve / Thumbs up / Hung over easy / El baz / Pacific rim
ENJ 90492 / Feb '96 / Enja

Helicon

☐ HELICON
N 02132 / Mar '93 / Noise

Helios Creed

☐ ACTIVATED CONDITION
MR 092CD / 16 Mar '98 / Man's Ruin

☐ CHROMAGNUM MAN
EFA 084882 / 23 Mar '98 / Dossier

☐ KISS TO THE BRAIN
ARR 223CD / Nov '92 / Amphetamine Reptile

☐ NUGG THE TRANSPORT
DCD 9085 / Dec '97 / Dossier

Helium

☐ DIRT OF LUCK, THE
Pat's trick / Trizie's star / Silver angel / Baby's goin' underground / Medusa / Comet / Skeleton / Superball / Heaven / Oh the wind and rain / Honeycomb / Latin song
OLE 1242 / Apr '95 / Matador

☐ MAGIC CITY, THE
Vibrations / Leon's space song / Two oceans / Ageing astronauts / Medieval people / Queen of the fire / Lullaby of the moths / Mach 4 / Soft children / Cosmic rags / Devil's tear / Clementine / Harpsichord song / Walk away
OLE 1952 / 8 Sep '97 / Matador

☐ PIRATE PRUDE
Baby vampire made me / Wanna be a vampire too, baby / XXX / OOO / I'll get you, I mean it / Love $$$
OLE 0782 / May '94 / Matador

Helivator

☐ GASOLINE T SHIRT
ORGAN 7 CD / Mar '93 / Lungcast

Helix

☐ HALF ALIVE
Shock city psycho rock / Wrecking ball / Pusher / Big bang boom / Same room / No rest for the wicked / Dirty dog / Running wild in the 21st century / Animal house / When the hammer falls / Deep cuts the knife / Smile / Good to the last drop / Heavy metal love / Wild in the streets / Rock you
DERCD 9012 / Jun '98 / Derock

☐ IT'S BUSINESS DOING PLEASURE
CDIRS 986969 / Aug '93 / Intercord

Hell, Richard

☐ DESTINY STREET (Hell, Richard & The Voidoids)
Kid with the replaceable head / You gotta / Going going gone / Lowest common denominator / Downtown at dawn / Time / I can only give you everything / Ignore that door / Staring in her eyes / Destiny Street
ESMCD 574 / Jul '97 / Essential

☐ GO NOW
CODE 3CD / Apr '95 / Overground

Hellacopters

☐ PAYIN' DUES
JAZZ 004CD / 29 Sep '97 / White Jazz
TFCK 87142 / 27 Apr '98 / Toys Factory

☐ SUPERSHITTY TO THE MAX
JAZZ 001CD / 20 Apr '98 / White Jazz
TFCK 87143 / 27 Apr '98 / Toys Factory

Hellbastard

☐ HEADING FOR MORE DARKNESS
BFRCD 009 / 6 Jul '98 / Step 1

Hellborg, Jonas

☐ WORD, THE
Akasha / Zat / Saut e sarmad / Two rivers / Be and all became / Poets / Black rite / Cherokee mist / Miklagaard / Path over clouds
AXCD 3009 / Oct '91 / Axiom

Hellcats

☐ HOODOO TRAIN
Where the hell is Memphis / Crazy about you baby / Baby, please don't go / I did my part / When you walk in the room / Black door slam / Wall of death / I don't need / I've been a good thing (for you) / Hoodoo train / Don't fight it / Antartica / Shine / Silly whim / Love is dying / Hard time killin' floor blues / What'cha doing in the woods / Where the sirens cry
ROSE 197CD / Aug '90 / New Rose

Hellcrusher

☐ WASTELAND
BFRCD 007 / 23 Mar '98 / Bomb Factory

Hellecasters

☐ ESCAPE FROM HOLLYWOOD
Danger man / Inspector Gadget / Valley of the Pharaohs / Son becomes father / Hanging at Tom and Rita's / Axe to grind / Between twilight and dawn / Mad for mothra / Lost in Kashmir / Le journee des tziganes / Bordertown / Point in time / Major troutage
PHCD 7002 / Dec '97 / Pharaoh

☐ HELL III (New Axes To Grind)
TWPPT / Riddler's journey / Ghosts of 42nd street / Mist beyond Dehli / Almost dawn / Mad cows at ease / As we know it / Mr. Natural / Deiter's lounge / Breaking through
PHCD 7003 / Dec '97 / Pharaoh

☐ RETURN OF THE HELLECASTERS, THE
Highlander boogie / Peter Gunn / Back on terra firma / Sweet dreams / King Arthur's dream / Orange blossum special / 5 minutes to spare / Rockin' the dog / Hellecaster stomp / Passion / Help I've fallen / Menage / Hellecaster theme
PHCD 7001 / Dec '97 / Pharaoh

Hellemny, Joel

☐ LIP SERVICE
ARCD 19161 / May '97 / Arbors Jazz

Heller, Jana

☐ LAUGHING IN CRIME
Laughing in crime / Hunger / Mirror / See mystery / Mad waltzing / Innocent ways / (You could be) Somebody to love / Love is a temporary thing / Your heart can sing / Let it ride / Promise land / Light the lamp babe
CYCLECD 003 / Feb '96 / Cycle

Heller, Skip

☐ ST. CHRISTOPHER'S ARMS
St Christopher's arms / It takes one to know one / No place else to go / Crazy dangerous and blue / Gee baby ain't I good to you / O' buttermilk sky / Ti quero / Waltz for two who don't dance / Little late late show / Back of my heart / Room to room / Longer than I thought / Teller
MOUP 6019 / 16 Mar '98 / Mouthpiece

Hellkrusher

☐ BUILDINGS FOR THE RICH
Buildings for the rich / Third world exploitation / War, who needs it / Full of shit / Path to destruction / Chase is on / Sick / Conform / Dying for who / Smash the trash / Destined to die / System dictates / Threat of war / Burn a rock star / Who's system / War games / Clear the debt / Scared of change / Dead zone / Hellkrusher
CASE 004CD / Feb '93 / SMR

Hellnation

☐ YOUR CHAOS DAYS ARE OVER
POLLUTE 41CD / 12 Jan '98 / Sound Pollution

Hello

☐ NEW YORK GROOVE...THE BEST OF HELLO
New york groove / 99 ways / Seven rainy days / Machine gun hustle / Tell him / Cat is wild / Hi ho silver lining / Walking midnight / 'til you've been kissed / Star studded sham / Out of our heads / Some kind of magic / Good old usa / Do it all night / Another school day / Back seat talking / Shine on silver light / Feel this thing
MCCD 112 / Jun '93 / Music Club

Helloween

☐ BEST, THE REST, THE RARE, THE (The Collection 1984-1988)
N 01762 / Jan '92 / Noise

☐ BETTER THAN RAW
RAWCD 125 / 13 Apr '98 / Raw Power

☐ CHAMELEON
First time / When the sinner / I don't wanna cry no more / Crazy cat / Giants / Windmill / Revolution now/San Francisco / In the night / Music / Step out of hell / I believe / Longing
CDFA 3308 / Nov '94 / Fame

☐ CHAMELEON
First time / When the sinner / I don't wanna cry no more / Crazy cat / Giants / Windmill / Revolution now / In the night / Music / Step out of hell / I believe / Longing
ESMCD 412 / Aug '96 / Essential

☐ LIVE
We burn / Wake up the mountain / Sole survivor / Chance / Why / Eagle fly free / Time of the oath / Future world / Dr. Stein / Before the war / Mr. Ego / Power / Where the rain grows / In the middle of a heartbeat / Perfect gentleman / Steel tormentor
RAWCD 116 / Sep '96 / Raw Power

☐ MASTER OF THE RINGS
Irritation / Sole survivor / Where the rain grows / Why / Mr. Ego / Perfect gentleman / Game is on / Secret alibi / Take me home / In the middle of a heartbeat / Still we go
RAWCD 101 / Apr '96 / Raw Power

☐ PINK BUBBLES GO APE
Pink bubbles go ape / Kids of the century / Back on the streets / Number one / Heavy metal hamsters / Going home / Someone's crying / Mankind / I'm doin' fine - crazy man / Chance / Your turn
ESMCD 411 / Aug '96 / Essential

☐ TIME OF THE OATH
RAWCD 109 / Apr '96 / Raw Power

Helm, Bob

☐ BOB HELM & HIS JAZZ BAND
SOSCD 1310 / Nov '96 / Stomp Off

Helm, Levon

☐ AMERICAN SON
Watermelon time in Georgia / Dance me down easy / Violet eyes / Stay with me / America's farm / Hurricane / China girl / Nashville wimmin / Blue house of broken hearts / Sweet peach Georgia wine
EDCD 526 / Jun '97 / Edsel

☐ LEVON HELM
You can't win them all / Lucrecia / Even a fool would let go / I've got a bet with myself / Money / Get out your big roll daddy / Willie and the hand jive / Got song / Give a little bit / God bless 'em all
EDCD 537 / 26 Jan '98 / Edsel

☐ LEVON HELM AND THE RCO ALL STARS (Helm, Levon & The RCO All-Stars)
Washer woman / Tie that binds / You got me / Blues so bad / Sing sing sing (let's make a better world) / Milk cow boogie / Rain down tears / Mood I was in / Havana moon / That's my home
EDCD 494 / Jul '96 / Edsel

Helmet

☐ AFTERTASTE
Pure / Renovation / Exactly what you wanted / Like I care / Driving nowhere / Birth defect / Broadcast emotion / It's easy to get bored / Diet aftertaste / Harmless / (High) visibility / Insatiable / Crisis king
IND 90073 / Apr '97 / Interscope

☐ BORN ANNOYING
ARRCD 60003 / Apr '95 / Amphetamine Reptile

Helms, Bobby

☐ FRAULEIN (His Decca Recordings/2CD Set)
Tennessee rock 'n' roll / I need to know how / I don't owe you nothing / Sowin' teardrops / (Got a) heartsick feeling / Far away heart / Just a little lonesome / Fool such as I / I'm leaving now (long gone daddy) / Tonight's the night / Jingle bell rock / Captain Santa Claus / No other baby / Standing at the end of my world / My shoes keep walking back to you / New river train / Hundred hearts / Hurry baby / Sad eyed baby / Someone was already there / To my sorrow / Lonely River Rhine / Then came you / Just between old sweethearts / I can't take it like you can / My greatest weakness / Yesterday's champagne / One deep love / Once in a lifetime / Fraulein / Most of the time / My special angel / Just a little lonesome / Magic song / Sugar moon / Schoolboy crush / If I only knew / Love my lady / Plaything / Jacqueline / Living in the shadows of the past / Forget about him / I guess I'll miss the prom / Miss memory / Soon it can be told / Fool and the angel / Someone for everyone / Yesterday's champagne / Lonely River Rhine / How can you divide a little child / Borrowed dreams / You're no longer mine / My lucky day / Let me be the one / Guess we thought the world would end / Teach me
BCD 15594 / Mar '92 / Bear Family

Help Yourself

☐ HELP YOURSELF/BEWARE THE SHADOW
I must see Jesus for myself / To Katherine they fell / Your eyes are looking down / Old man / Look at the view / Paper leaves / Running down deep / Deborah / Street songs / Alabama lady / Reaffirmation / Calapso / She's my girl / Molly bake bean / American mother
BGOCD 385 / 30 Mar '98 / Beat Goes On

Helsinki Mandoliners

☐ HELSINKI MANDOLINERS
KICD 38 / Nov '95 / Kansanmusiikki Instituutti

Helsinki Philharmonic Orchestra

☐ EARQUAKE
Hansons 6th / Invocatio / Mountaineers / Ala et lolly / Prism / Night of the mayas / Aladdin / Malambo / Weapon dance / Nostalgic thoughts / Machine / Bacchanale / War dance / Can-can / Angel of light / Hekla
ODE 8942 / Oct '97 / Ondine

Helstar

☐ DISTANT THUNDER, A
King is dead / Bitter end / Abandon ship / Tyrannicide / Scorcher / Genius of insanity / Whore of Babylon / Winds of love / He's a woman, she's a man
RR 95242 / Aug '88 / Roadrunner

☐ MULTIPLES IN BLACK
MASSCD 053 / May '95 / Massacre

Heltah Skeltah

☐ NOCTURNAL
CDPTY 133 / Aug '96 / Priority/Virgin

Heltir

☐ NEUE SACHLICHKEIT
DV 024CD / Sep '95 / Dark Vinyl

Hemingway, Gerry

☐ DEMON CHASER (Hemingway, Gerry Quintet)
ARTCD 6137 / Jan '94 / Hat Art

☐ SPECIAL DETAILS (Hemingway, Gerry Quintet)
ARTCD 6084 / Jul '91 / Hat Art

Hemlock

☐ GIVE KIDS CANDY
LM 015 / Jun '97 / Liquid Meat

Hemphill, Jessie Mae

☐ FEELIN' GOOD
HMG 6502 / Aug '97 / Hightone

☐ SHE-WOLF
HMG 6508 / 2 Feb '98 / Hightone

Hemphill, Julius

☐ AT DR. KING'S TABLE (Hemphill, Julius Sextet)
805242 / Oct '97 / New World

☐ FAT MAN & THE HARD BLUES (Hemphill, Julius Sextet)
1201152 / Mar '92 / Black Saint

☐ FIVE CHORD STUD (Hemphill, Julius Sextet)
1201402 / Oct '94 / Black Saint

☐ FLAT OUT JUMP SUITE (Hemphill, Julius Quartet)
1200402 / May '92 / Black Saint

☐ LIVE FROM THE NEW MUSIC CAFE (Hemphill, Julius Trio)
CD 731 / Sep '92 / Music & Arts

☐ LIVE IN NEW YORK (Hemphill, Julius & Abdul Wadud)
1231382 / Apr '95 / Red

☐ OAKLAND DUETS (Hemphill, Julius & Abdul Wadud)
CD 791 / Jan '94 / Music & Arts

Henderson, Allan

☐ TUNING PHRASES (Henderson, Allan Trio)
6/8 marches / Strathspeys and reels / An t-eilean muileach / Bush set / 2/4 marches / Pipe set / Oran arisaig / Waltzes / Tuning phrase / Tam lin / Reels / Slow air and reel
HYCD 297170 / Feb '97 / Hypertension

Henderson, Bill

☐ BILL HENDERSON & THE OSCAR PETERSON TRIO (Henderson, Bill & Oscar Peterson Trio)
You are my sunshine / Lamp is low / All or nothing at all / I wish you love / Gravy waltz / Lot of livin' to do / I see your face before me / I've got a crush on you / At long last love / Folks who live on the hill / Baby mine / Wild is love / Where are you / Charmaine / Young and foolish / Stranger on the shore
8379372 / Mar '93 / Verve

Henderson, Bugs

☐ AT LAST
TX 1002CD / Jan '94 / Taxim

☐ FOUR TENS STRIKE AGAIN
FC 105CD / Aug '96 / Flat Canyon

☐ HAVE BLUES...MUST ROCK (Henderson, Bugs & The Shuffle Kings)
BCD 00292 / 1 Jun '98 / Burnside

☐ THAT'S THE TRUTH
TX 1013CD / Jul '95 / Taxim

☐ YEARS IN THE JUNGLE
TX 1011CD / Dec '93 / Taxim

Henderson, Chick

☐ BEGIN THE BEGUINE (1937-1940) (Henderson, Chick & The Joe Loss Band)
While a cigarette was burning / I still love to kiss you goodnight / On a little dream ranch / My prayer / Begin the beguine / By an old pagoda / Girl in the Alice Blue gown / I know now / I shall be waiting / I'll remember / It looks like rain in Cherry Blossom Lane / It's a lovely day tomorrow / May I have the next romance with you / Music maestro please / On the sentimental side / Remember me / September in the rain / Seventeen candles
CDAJA 5083 / Apr '91 / Living Era

☐ BLUE ORCHIDS
Am I for you / If you hadn't asked me to dance / Blue orchids / Greatest mistake of my life / I'm stepping out with a memory tonight / You go to my head / Mem'ry of a rose / Turning the town upside down / All the things you are / Turn the money in your pocket / Somewhere in france with you / Breeze and I / Broken hearted clown / And the angels sing / There's a new world / Until you fall in love / Until tomorrow / When I drean of home / Looking around corners for you / We'll meet again / Sierra sue / Goodnight children everywhere / Begin the beguine
CDMOIR 310 / May '95 / Memoir

☐ REMEMBER ME
Till the lights of London shine again / Serenade in blue / We'll go smiling along / Somwehere in France with you / My prayer / Black out stroll / Sweet little sweetheart / Shabby old cabby / Wish me luck as you wave me goodbye / Begin the beguine / You can't stop me from dreaming / That old feeling / You're an education / Thanks for everything / Let the curtain come down / Music maestro please / I still love to kiss you goodnight / I know how / Remember me / Small cafe by Notre Dame
PAR 2025 / Jul '94 / Parade

Henderson, Di

☐ BY ANY OTHER NAME
DHC 001 / Dec '93 / Deeaitch

Henderson, Duke

☐ GET YOUR KICKS
DD 668 / Dec '94 / Delmark

Henderson, Eddie

☐ DARK SHADOWS
El gaucho / 19th street / Goodbye / Cerulean blue / Dark shadows / Punjab / Certain vibe / Lament for Booker / Dawning dance / Water is wide
MCD 92542 / Feb '97 / Milestone

☐ THINK OF ME (Henderson, Eddie Quintet)
SCCD 31264 / Oct '90 / Steeplechase

Henderson, Fletcher

☐ CLASSIC YEARS, THE
Henderson stomp / St. Louis shuffle / Easy money / King Porter stomp / D natural blues / Variety stomp / I'm coming Virginia / Stockholm stomp / Come on baby / Jackass blues / Hop off / Money blues / Chant / Stampede
CDSGP 0193 / 27 Apr '98 / Prestige

☐ CLASSICS 1921-1923
CLASSICS 794 / Jan '95 / Classics

☐ CLASSICS 1923 (Henderson, Fletcher Orchestra)
CLASSICS 697 / Jul '93 / Classics

☐ CLASSICS 1923-1924 (Henderson, Fletcher Orchestra)
CLASSICS 683 / Mar '93 / Classics

☐ CLASSICS 1924 VOL.1
CLASSICS 647 / Nov '92 / Classics

☐ CLASSICS 1924 VOL.2
CLASSICS 657 / Nov '92 / Classics

☐ CLASSICS 1924 VOL.3
CLASSICS 673 / Nov '92 / Classics

☐ CLASSICS 1924-1925 (Henderson, Fletcher Orchestra)
CLASSICS 633 / Nov '92 / Classics

☐ CLASSICS 1925-1926 (Henderson, Fletcher Orchestra)
CLASSICS 610 / Feb '92 / Classics

☐ CLASSICS 1926-1927
CLASSICS 597 / Sep '91 / Classics

☐ CLASSICS 1927 (Henderson, Fletcher Orchestra)
CLASSICS 580 / Oct '91 / Classics

☐ CLASSICS 1927-1931
CLASSICS 572 / Oct '91 / Classics

☐ CLASSICS 1931
CLASSICS 555 / Dec '90 / Classics

☐ CLASSICS 1931-1932
CLASSICS 546 / Dec '90 / Classics

☐ CLASSICS 1932-1934
CLASSICS 535 / Dec '90 / Classics

☐ CLASSICS 1934-1937
CLASSICS 527 / Apr '90 / Classics

☐ CLASSICS 1937-1938
CLASSICS 519 / Apr '90 / Classics

☐ CROWN KING OF SWING, THE (Henderson, Fletcher Orchestra)
After you've gone / Stardust / Tiger rag / Somebody stole my gal / (I'll be glad when you're dead) you rascal you / Blue rhythm / Sugarfoot stomp / Low down on the bayou / Twelth street rag / Milenberg joys
SV 0254 / Oct '97 / Savoy Jazz

☐ FLETCHER HENDERSON & HIS ORCHESTRA (Henderson, Fletcher Orchestra)
Back in your own backyard / Rose room / Stampede / Chris and his gang / All God's chillun got rhythm / Posin' / Let 'er go / Great Caesar's ghost / If you should ever leave / Worried over you / Rhythm of the tambourine / Slumming on Park Avenue / It's wearin' me down / Trees / If it's the last thing I do / You're in love with love / Don't let the rhythm go to your head / There's rain in my eyes / Saving myself for you / What do you hear from the mob in Scotland / It's the little things that count / Moten stomp / Stealin' apples / Sing you sinners / What's your story (what's your jive)
GRF 088 / '93 / Tring

☐ FLETCHER HENDERSON 1924-1938
Christopher columbus / Moten stomp (moten swing) / Rhythm of the tambourine / Back in your own backyard / Sing you sinners / Yeah man / Big john's special / Shanghai shuffle / New king porter stomp / Big chief de sota (grand terrace swing) / Stealin' apples / Blue lou / Clarinet marmalade / Wang wang blues / I'm coming virginia / What-cha-call 'em blues / Teapot dome blues / Stampede / Singing the blues / Chinatown, my chinatown / Sugar foot stomp / Henderson stomp
CD 53179 / Nov '95 / Giants Of Jazz

☐ FLETCHER HENDERSON 1937-1938
TPZ 1004 / Jul '94 / Topaz Jazz

☐ FLETCHER HENDERSON SEXTET 1950
RST 91537 / Mar '95 / RST

☐ FLETCHER HENDERSON VOL.1 1921-1923
DOCD 5342 / May '95 / Document

☐ FLETCHER HENDERSON VOL.2 1923-1924
DOCD 5343 / May '95 / Document

☐ INTRODUCTION TO FLETCHER HENDERSON 1921-1941, AN
4019 / Mar '95 / Best Of Jazz

☐ JAZZ PORTRAITS
Moten stomp / Sing you sinners / Back in your own backyard / Rhythm of the tambourine / Christopher Columbus / Yeah man / Clarinet marmalade / Wang wang blues / I'm coming Virginia / What'cha call 'em blues / Teapot dome blues / Stampede / Big John special / Singin' the blues / Shanghai shuffle / Chinatown, my Chinatown / New King Porter stomp / Sugarfoot stomp
CD 14522 / May '94 / Jazz Portraits

☐ QUINTESSENCE, THE (1924-1936/2CD Set)
FA 219 / Oct '96 / Fremeaux

☐ STUDY IN FRUSTRATION, A (The Fletcher Henderson Story/3CD Set)
Diddy blues / Teapot dome blues / Go 'long mule / Shanghai shuffle / Copenhagen / Everybody loves my baby / How come you do me like you do / Alabamy bound / Sugar foot stomp / What-cha-call 'em blues / T.n.t. / Stampede / Jackass blues / Henderson stomp / Chant / Snag it / Rocky mountain blues / Tozo / St. louis shuffle / Whiteman stomp / I'm coming virginia / Variety stomp / St. louis blues / Goose pimples / Hop off / King porter stomp / D natural blues / Oh baby / Feeling good / I'm feeling devilish / Old black joe blues / Easy money / Come on baby / Freeze and melt / Raisin' the roof / Blazin' / Wang wang blues / Chinatown, my chinatown / Somebody loves me / Keep a song in your soul / Sweet and hot / My gal sal / Sugar foot stomp / Clarinet marmalade / Hot and anxious / Comin' and goin' / Singin' the blues / Sugar / Blue moments / New king porter stomp / Underneath the harlem moon / Honeysuckle rose / Yeah man / Queer notions / Can you take it / King porter stomp / Christopher columbus / Stealin' apples / Blue lou / Rhythm of the tambourine / Back in your own backyard / Chris and his gang / Sing you sinners / Moten stomp
C3K 57596 / Oct '94 / Columbia

☐ UNDER THE HARLEM MOON
Honeysuckle Rose / New King Porter stomp / Underneath the Harlem moon / Queer notions / Night life / Nagasaki / Rhythm crazy now / Ain't cha glad / Hocus pocus / Tidal wave / Christopher Columbus / Blue Lou / Stealin' apples / Jangled nerves / Grand Terrace rhythm / Riffin' / Shoe shine boy / Sing sing sing / Jimtown blues / Rhythm of the tambourine / Back in your own backyard / Chris and his gang
CDAJA 5067 / Mar '90 / Living Era

☐ WILD PARTY (Henderson, Fletcher Orchestra)
Hocus pocus / Phantom fantasie / Harlem madness / Tidal wave / Limehouse blues / Shanghai shuffle / Big John Special / Happy as the day is long / Down South camp meeting / Wrappin' it up / Memphis blues / Wild party / Rug cutters' swing / Hotter than 'Ell / Liza
HEPCD 1009 / Aug '94 / Hep

Henderson, Horace

☐ CLASSICS 1940-1941 (Henderson, Horace & Fletcher)
CLASSICS 648 / Nov '92 / Classics

Henderson, Ingrid

☐ LIGHT OF THE MOUNTAIN (Henderson, Ingrid & Allan)
Highland Road / Sound of Sleat / Air for Alex Henderson / Heights of Casino / Parson's farewell / Donnie Caolis of Burnbank / Strop the razor / Oran America / Solus a Bheinne / Irish jigs
CDLDL 1204 / Nov '96 / Lochshore

☐ PERPETUAL HORSESHOE (Henderson, Ingrid & Allan)
LDL 1216CD / Jun '94 / Lochshore

Henderson, Joe

☐ BALLADS AND BLUES
Lazy afternoon / La mesha / Out of the night / You know I care / Ask me now / Soulville / Portrait
CDP 8566922 / Jul '97 / Blue Note

☐ CANYON LADY
Tres palabras / Las Palmas / Canyon lady / All things considered
OJCCD 9492 / Jan '98 / Original Jazz Classics

☐ DOUBLE RAINBOW
5272222 / Mar '95 / Verve

☐ ELEMENTS (Henderson, Joe & Alice Coltrane)
Fire / Air / Water / Earth
OJCCD 913 / May '97 / Original Jazz Classics

☐ FOUR
Autumn leaves / Autumn leaves / On the trail / Stardust / Old folks / On green dolphin street / Theme
5236572 / Jan '95 / Verve

☐ JOE HENDERSON BIG BAND, THE (Henderson, Joe Big Band)
5334512 / Oct '96 / Verve

☐ JOE HENDERSON SAMPLER
Kicker / Without a song / My one and only love / Song for sinners / Crimson lake
OJCX 013 / Jan '98 / Original Jazz Classics

☐ KICKER, THE
Mamacita / Mamacita / Chelsea bridge / If / Nardis / Without a snog / O amor em paz / Mo' joe
OJCCD 465 / Nov '95 / Original Jazz Classics

☐ LUSH LIFE (The Music Of Billy Strayhorn)
Isfahan / Johnny come lately / Blood count / Raincheck / Lotus blossom / Flower is a lovesome thing / Take the 'A' train / Drawing room blues / Upper Manhattan medical group (UMMG) / Lush life
5117792 / Sep '92 / Verve

☐ MILESTONE YEARS 1967-1977, THE (8CD Set)
Mamacita / Kicker / Chelsea Bridge / If / Nardis / Without a song / Mo' Joe / O amor em paz / Tetragon / First trip / I've got you under my skin / Invitation / RJ / Waltz for Zweetie / Bead game / You don't know what love is / Unilateral / Scavenger / But not for me / Power to the people / Afro-centric / Black narcissus / Isotope / Opus one point five / Lazy afternoon / Foresight and afterthought / Caribbean fire dance / Recorda-me / Shade of jade / Isotope / 'Round midnight / Mode for Joe / If you're not part of the solution (you're part of the probl / Blue bossa / Closing theme / Gazelle / Invitation / Mind over matter / No me esqueca / Shade of jade / Round midnight / Out 'n' in / Blue bossa / Junk blues / Terra firma / Viz a viz / Foregone conclusion / Black is the colour of my true love's mind / Current events / Tress-cun-deo-la / Turned around / Song for sinners / Me among others / Bwaata / Tres palabras / All things considered / Canyon lady / Las Palmas / In the beginning there was Africa... / Air / Water / Fire / Earth / Butterfly dreams / Light as a feather / Love reborn / Summer night / Black narcissus / Hindsight and forethought / Power to the people / Other side of right / Good morning / Heartache / Amoeba / Gazelle / My cherie amour / Old slippers / Immaculate deception / Solution / Black miracle / Black narcissus / What can I say / Windows
8MCD 44132 / Nov '96 / Milestone

☐ MIRROR MIRROR
Mirror mirror / Candlelight / Keystone / Joe's bolero / What's new / Blues for liebestraum
5190922 / Apr '93 / MPS Jazz

☐ PORGY AND BESS
Intro/Jasbo Brown Blues / Summertime: *Henderson, Joe & Chaka Khan* / Here come de honeyman/They pass by singin' / My man's gone now / I got plenty o' nuttin' / Bess you got is my woman now / It ain't necessarily so: *Henderson, Joe & Sting* / I loves you Porgy / There's a boat dat's leavin' soon for New York / Oh Bess oh where's my Bess / Summertime
5390482 / Oct '97 / Verve

☐ RELAXIN' AT CAMARILLO
Y todavia la quiero / My one and only love / Crimson lake / Yes my dear / Relaxin' at camarillo
OJCCD 776 / Sep '93 / Original Jazz Classics

☐ SO NEAR, SO FAR (Musings For Miles)
Miles ahead / Joshua / Pfrancing / Flamenco sketches / Milestones / Teo / Swing Spring / Teo / Swing Spring / Circle / Side car / So near, so far
5176742 / Jan '92 / Verve

☐ STANDARD JOE, THE
1232482 / May '92 / Red

☐ STATE OF THE TENOR VOL.1 & 2
Beatrice / Friday the 13th / Happy reunion / Loose change / Ask me now / Isotope / Stella by starlight / Boo Boo's birthday / Cheryl / Y ya la quiero / Soulville / Portrait / Bead game / All the things you are
CDP 8288792 / May '94 / Blue Note

☐ STRAIGHT NO CHASER
5315612 / Jun '96 / Verve

☐ TETRAGON/IN PURSUIT OF BLACKNESS
Invitation / RJ / Bead game / Tetragon / Waltz for sweetie / First trip / I've got you under my skin / No me esqueca / Shade of jade / Gazelle / Mind over matter
CDBGPD 084 / Mar '94 / Beat Goes Public

Henderson, Joe

☐ BEST OF JOE 'MR. PIANO' HENDERSON, THE
PLSCD 284 / 1 Jun '98 / Pulse

Henderson, Mike

☐ EDGE OF NIGHT
Wouldn't lay my guitar down / Wherever you are / Nobody's fault but mine / Edge of night / Driven nails in my coffin / Take me back and try me / This property is condemned / Honky tonk vacation / You're so square / One foot in the honky tonk
DR 00042 / Dec '97 / Dead Reckoning

☐ FIRST BLOOD (Henderson, Mike & The Bluebloods)
When I get drunk / So sad to be lonesome / Hip shakin' / Pony blues / Bloody murder / Pay Bo Diddley / When the welfare turns it's back on you / Give me back my wig / How many more years / Mean mistreater
DR 00062 / Dec '97 / Dead Reckoning

Henderson, Murray

☐ WORLD'S GREATEST PIPERS VOL.4, THE
6/8 marches / Strathspeys and reels / Hornpipes / 3/4 marches / Air hornpipe and jig / 2/4 marches / Jigs / Piobaireachd / 2/4 marches / 9/8 marches / Strathspeys and reels
LCOM 5159 / May '96 / Lismor

Henderson, Ray

☐ BEST THINGS IN LIFE ARE FREE, THE (The Songs Of Ray Henderson) (Various Artists)
Here I am: *Austin, Gene* / Five foot two, eyes of blue: *California Ramblers* / Birth of the blues: *Crosby, Bing & Jack Teagarden* / I'm sitting on top of the world: *Crumit, Frank* / My dog loves your dog: *Edwards, Cliff 'Ukelele Ike'* / Button up your overcoat: *Etting, Ruth* / You're the cream in my coffee: *Etting, Ruth* / Don't bring Lulu: *Glantz, Nathan & Chick Straun* / Sunny side up: *Hamps, Johnny & His Kentucky Serenaders* / Black bottom: *Hanshaw, Annette* / Together: *Haymes, Dick & Helen Forrest* / I'm a dreamer, aren't we all: *High Hatters* / Let's call it a day: *Hutch & Harry Roy* / Life is just a bowl of cherries: Hutch / Best things in life are free: *Hylton, Jack* / If I had a talking picture of you: *Hylton, Jack & Sam Browne* / Sonny boy: *Jolson, Al* / Lucky day: *Lanin, Howard & Irving Kaufman* / Bye, bye blackbird: *Layton & Johnstone* / Magnolia: *Marvin, Johnny* / Varsity drag: *O'Neal, Zelma* / That's why darkies were born: *Robeson, Paul* / Animal crackers in my soup: *Temple, Shirley* / My song: *Vallee, Rudy* / Thrill is gone: *Vallee, Rudy*
CDAJA 5207 / Mar '97 / Living Era

Henderson, Scott

☐ ILLICIT (Henderson, Scott & Tribal Tech)
Big waves / Stoopid / Black cherry / Torque / Slidin into charlisa / Root food / Riot / Paha-sapa / Babylon / Passion dance / Just because
R 2791802 / Oct '92 / Blue Moon

Henderson, T.W.

☐ WILDERNESS YEARS, THE (Henderson, T.W. & The Blues Of Cain)
BRCD 001 / 15 Jun '98 / Bluetrack

Henderson, Wayne

☐ RUGBY GUITAR
FF 542CD / '92 / Flying Fish

☐ SKETCHES OF LIFE (Henderson, Wayne & The Next Crusade)
Strange love / We're gonna rock your sock off / Men cry too / I'll take you there / Color of love / Just because its jazz, (Don't mean ya can't dance) / Portrait of a dream / Ancestral chant / For old time's sake / Survival / I can't get started with you / Just because it's jazz (don't mean ya can't dance)
CPCD 8125 / Oct '95 / Charly

Hendon Citadel Band

☐ MARCHING WITH THE SALVATION ARMY
Starlake / Torchbearers / Bravest of the Brave / Wellingtonian / Cairo red shield / Crown of conquest / In the King's service / Roll call / Salute to America / To regions fair / Joyful news / On the news / On the king's highway / Fighting for the Lord / Fount / Victors acclaimed / Southall 100
BNA 5041 / '91 / Bandleader

Hendricks, Jon

☐ LOVE (Hendricks, Jon & Co)
Royal Garden blues / Bright moments / Willie's tune / Good of' lady / Li'l darlin' / I'll die happy / Love (Berkshire blues) / Tell me the truth / Swinging groove merchant(groove merchant) / Angel eyes / In a Harlem airshaft
MCD 5258 / Sep '92 / Muse

Hendricks, Michele

☐ CARRYIN' ON
MCD 5336 / Sep '92 / Muse

☐ KEEPIN' ME SATISFIED
MCD 5363 / Sep '92 / Muse

Hendrie, Roy

☐ DIFFERENT BLEND, A
ROYCD 5 / Dec '97 / Roy Hendrie

Hendriks, Karl

☐ BUICK ELECTRA (Hendriks, Karl Trio)
GROW 382 / Feb '95 / Grass

Hendrix, Jimi

☐ ARE YOU EXPERIENCED
Foxy lady / Manic depression / Red house / Can you see me / Love or confusion / I don't live today / May this be love / Fire / Third stone from the sun / Remember / Are you experienced / Hey Joe / Stone free / Purple haze / 51st anniversary / Wind cries Mary / Highway chile
MCD 11608 / Apr '97 / MCA

☐ AUTHENTIC PPX STUDIO RECORDINGS VOL.1 (Get That Feeling)
Get that feeling / How would you feel / Hush now / No business / Simon says / Gotta have a new dress / Strange things / Welcome home
SPV 08544222 / Jul '96 / SPV

☐ AUTHENTIC PPX STUDIO RECORDINGS VOL.2 (Flashing)
Love, love / Day tripper / Gloomy Monday / Fool for you, baby / Don't accuse me / Hornet's nest / Flashing / Odd ball / Happy birthday
SPV 08544212 / Jul '96 / SPV

☐ AUTHENTIC PPX STUDIO RECORDINGS VOL.3 (Ballad Of Jimi)
SPV 08544682 / Feb '97 / SPV

☐ AUTHENTIC PPX STUDIO RECORDINGS VOL.4 (Live At George's Club)
SPV 08544692 / Feb '97 / SPV

☐ AXIS BOLD AS LOVE
Experience / Up from the skies / Spanish castle magic / Wait until tomorrow / Ain't no tellin' / Little wing / If six was nine / You've got me floating / Castles made of sand / She's so fine / One rainy wish / Little Miss Lover / Bold as love
MCD 11601 / Apr '97 / MCA

☐ BAND OF GYPSIES
Who knows / Machine gun / Changes / Power to love / Message to love / We gotta live together
MCD 11607 / Apr '97 / MCA

☐ BBC SESSIONS, THE (2CD Set)
Foxy lady / Foxy lady / Stone free / Hey Joe / Hey Joe / Love or confusion / Foxy lady / Hey Joe / Stone free / Killing floor / Purple haze / Fire / Manic depression / Jam / I was made to love her / Ain't too proud to beg / Little Miss Lover / Driving South / Driving South / Catfish blues / Burning of the midnight lamp / Hound dog / Can you please crawl out your window / Hoochie coochie man / Driving South / Radio one / Spanish castle magic / Day tripper / Hear my train a-comin' / Hear my train a-comin' / Voodoo chile / Hey Joe/Sunshine of your love
MCD 11742 / 1 Jun '98 / MCA

☐ BLUES
Hear my train a comin' / Born under a bad sign / Red house / Catfish blues / Voodoo chile blues / Mannish boy / Once I had a woman / Bleeding heart / Jelly 292 / Electric Church Red house
5210372 / Apr '94 / Polydor

☐ COLLECTION, THE
Little wing / Purple haze / Voodoo chile (slight return) / Red house / Wild thing / Sunshine of your love / Bleeding heart / Soul food / Fire / Room full of mirrors / Psycho / Let me go / Freedom and you / Good feeling / Go go shoes / She's so shoes / Sweet thang / Win your love / Two + one goes / Voice in the wind
COL 017 / Jan '95 / Collection

☐ CROSSTOWN CONVERSATION
CBAK 4082 / Feb '94 / Baktabak

☐ DIAMOND COLLECTION, THE
3004552 / Feb '97 / Arcade

☐ EARLY YEARS, THE
Red house / Woke up this morning and found myself dead / Peoples people / Morrison's lament / Tomorrow never knows / Uranus rock / Outside woman blues / Sunshine of your love / Goodbye Bessie Mae / Soul food
DA 430052 / Nov '96 / Blueprint

☐ ELECTRIC LADYLAND
And the gods made love / Have you ever been (to Electric Ladyland) / Voodoo Chile / Crosstown traffic / Still raining, still dreaming / House burning down / All along the watchtower / Long hot summer night / Little Miss Strange / Come on (let the good times roll) / Gypsy eyes / Burning of the midnight lamp / Rainy day, dream away / 1983...(A Merman I should turn to be) / Moon, turn the tides...gently gently away
MCD 11600 / Apr '97 / MCA

☐ EXPERIENCE (Original Sountrack To The Movie Experience) (Hendrix, Jimi Experience)
CDGR 246 / 1 Jun '98 / Charly

☐ FIRST RAYS OF THE NEW RISING SUN
Freedom / Izabella / Night bird flying / Angel / Room full of mirrors / Dolly Dagger / Ezy ryder / Drifting / Beginnings / Stepping stone / My friend / Straight ahead / Hey baby (new rising sun) / Earth blues / Astro man / In from the storm / Belly button window
MCD 11599 / Apr '97 / MCA

☐ GOLD COLLECTION, THE
D2CD 03 / Dec '92 / Deja Vu

☐ GROOVE MAKER (3CD Set)
DTKBOX 81 / 26 May '98 / Dressed To Kill

☐ HOT TRIGGER
Voices / Suspicion / Free spirit / Hot trigger / Psycho / Night life / Whipper / Good times / Soul food
RTD 39700829CD / 1 Dec '97 / Institute Of Art

☐ IN FROM THE STORM (The Music Of Jimi Hendrix) (Various Artists)
And the gods made love / Have you ever been (to Electric Ladyland) / Rainy day, dream away / Wind cries Mary / Spanish castle magic / Little wing / In from the storm / Drifting / Bold as love / Burning of the midnight lamp / Purple haze / One rainy wish
74321315502 / Nov '95 / RCA Victor

☐ IN WORDS AND MUSIC (2CD Set)
OTR 1100030 / Jun '97 / Metro Independent

☐ INTERVIEW DISC
SAM 7006 / Nov '96 / Sound & Media

☐ INTROSPECTIVE
Red house / Wake up this morning and find yourself dead / Interview part one / Bleeding heart / Interview part two
CINT 5006 / Apr '91 / Baktabak

☐ JIMI HENDRIX (2CD Set)
R2CD 4003 / Jan '96 / Deja Vu

☐ JIMI HENDRIX (3CD Set)
Little wing / Voodoo chile / Purple haze / Sunshine of your love / Bleeding heart / Woke up this morning and found myself dead / Tomorrow never knows / Fire / Wild thing / Morrison's lament / Red house / Good times / Voices / Voice in the wind / Two and one goes / Let me go / Uranus rock / Outside woman blues / Room full of mirrors / Blues blues / Free spirit / Psycho / Wipe the sweat / Groove maker / Hot trigger / Night life / You got it / Suspicious / Goodbye Bessie Mae / She's a fox / Freedom and you / She's so fine / Sweet thing
KBOX 360 / Nov '96 / Collection

☐ JIMI HENDRIX (CD/CD Rom Set)
WWCDR 006 / Apr '97 / Weton-Wesgram

☐ JIMI HENDRIX AT THE MONTEREY POP FESTIVAL 1967
ITM 960008 / Sep '93 / ITM

☐ JIMI HENDRIX AT WOODSTOCK
Introduction / Fire / Izabella / Hear my train a comin' / Red house / Jam back at the house (Beginnings) / Voodoo chile / Star spangled banner / Purple haze / Woodstock improvisation / Villanova Junction / Farewell
5233842 / Aug '94 / Polydor

☐ JIMI HENDRIX BOX SET
JH 1 / Oct '92 / UFO

☐ JIMI HENDRIX COLLECTOR'S EDITION
DVBC 9032 / Apr '95 / Deja Vu

☐ JIMI HENDRIX EXPERIENCE IN 1967 (Hendrix, Jimi Experience)
JH 001 / Jul '92 / Revolver

☐ JIMI HENDRIX GOLD (2CD Set)
D2CD 4003 / Jun '95 / Deja Vu

☐ JIMI HENDRIX MUSIC FESTIVAL 1996-1997 (Various Artists)
Little wing: *Firkins, Michael Lee* / Manic depression: *Firkins, Michael Lee* / Come on (let the good times roll): *Popa Chubby* / Foxy lady: *Popa Chubby* / Up from the skies: *Popa Chubby* / Hey Joe: *Dykes, Omar* / Voodoo chile: *Trout, Walter* / Red house / Shake your moneymaker
32971092 / 2 Feb '98 / Provogue

☐ LAST EXPERIENCE, THE
CD 101 / Oct '94 / Timeless Treasures

☐ LIVE AT THE SCENE CLUB NEW YORK 1968
Red house / Wake up this morning and find yourself yourself dead / Bleeding heart / Morrison's lament / Tomorrow never knows / Outside woman blues / Sunshine of your love
ANXCD 001 / 30 Mar '98 / Mo's Music Machine

☐ LIVE IN NEW YORK
MU 5018 / Oct '92 / Musketeer

☐ NIGHT LIFE
Good feeling / Hot trigger / Psycho / Come on baby (part 1) / Come on baby (part 2) / Night life / You got it / Woke up this morning / Lime line / Peoples people / Whoa eeh
CDTB 075 / May '95 / Thunderbolt

☐ NYC 1968
MIL 6102 / 29 Jun '98 / MIL Multimedia

☐ PSYCHO
Good feeling / Hot tigger / Psycho / Come on baby / Come on baby / Night life / You got it / Woke up in the morning / Lime time / People's people / Whoa'eeh
RM 1536 / Jun '97 / BR Music

☐ PURPLE HAZE IN WOODSTOCK
ITM 960004 / Feb '94 / ITM

☐ RARE HENDRIX (Hendrix, Jimi & Lonnie Youngblood Band)
Go go shoes / Red house / Wipe the sweat / People peoples / Blue's is blues / Lime lime / Whoa ehh / She's a fox
100272 / May '97 / A-Play Collection

☐ REAL ROCK STANDARDS (2CD Set)
Little wing / Voodoo chile (slight return) / Purple haze / Sunshine of your love / Bleeding heart: *Hendrix, Jimi & Jim Morrison* / Woke up this morning and found myself dead / Tomorrow never knows: *Hendrix, Jimi & Jim Morrison* / Fire / Wild thing / Morrison's lament: *Hendrix, Jimi & Jim Morrison* / Red house / Good times / Voices / Voice in the wind / Two and one goes / Let me go / Uranus rock / Outside woman blues / Room full of mirrors
TNC 96205 / Aug '96 / Natural Collection

☐ REVENGE (A Tribute To Jimi Hendrix) (Various Artists)
Foxy lady: *Iggy Pop* / Up from the skies: *Jones, Rickie Lee* / Electric ladyland: *Bourelly, Jean-Paul* / Remember: *Harper, Ben* / Fire: *Red Hot Chili Peppers* / Purple haze: *Shamen* / Burning of the midnight lamp: *Living Color* / Voodoo chile:

Vaughan, Stevie Ray / Hey Joe dub: Kente, Ras & The Take No Prisoner Posse / Red house: Hooker, John Lee / Angel: Stewart, Rod / Crosstown traffic: Evans, Gil & His Orchestra / Little Miss Lover: Evans, Gil & His Orchestra / Message to love: Triad
682550 / May '95 / Gravity

☐ SOUTH SATURN DELTA
MCD 11684 / 27 Oct '97 / MCA

☐ STONE FREE (A Tribute To Jimi Hendrix) (Various Artists)
Purple haze: Cure / Stone free: Clapton, Eric / Spanish castle magic: Spin Doctors / Red house: Guy, Buddy / Hey Joe: Body Count / Manic depression: Seal & Jeff Beck / Fire: Kennedy, Nigel / Bold as love: Pretenders / You got me floatin': PM Dawn / I don't live today: Slash, Paul Rodgers & Band Of Gypsies / Are you experienced: Belly / Crosstown traffic: Living Color / Third stone from the sun: Metheny, Pat / Hey baby (Land of the new rising sun): MACC
9362454382 / Oct '93 / WEA

☐ SUPERSESSION
Red house / Woke up this morning and found myself dead / Peoples peoples aka bleeding heart / Morrison's lament / Tomorrow never knows / Vranus rock / Outside woman blues / Sunshine of your love / Goodbye Bessie Mae / Soul food
CD 8442002 / Jul '95 / Voiceprint

☐ TOMORROW NEVER KNOWS
Red house / Wake up this morning and find yourself dead / Bleeding heart / Morrison's lament / Tomorrow never knows / Uranus rock / Outside woman blues / Sunshine of your love
CDRIA 1000 / Sep '96 / Rialto

☐ ULTIMATE EXPERIENCE, THE
All along the watchtower / Purple haze / Hey Joe / Wind cries Mary / Angel / Voodoo chile / Foxy lady / Burning of the midnight lamp / Highway chile / Crosstown traffic / Castles made of sand / Long hot summer night / Red house / Manic depression / Gypsy eyes / Little wing / Fire / Wait until tomorrow / Star spangled banner / Wild thing
5172352 / Sep '95 / Polydor

☐ VOODOO SOUP
5275202 / May '95 / Polydor

Henke, Mel

☐ LA DOLCE HENKE
SCP 9716 / 18 Aug '97 / Scamp

Henke, Robert

☐ FLOATING POINT (Henke, Robert & Gerhard Behles)
EFA 204602 / Jul '97 / Imbalance

Henley, Don

☐ BUILDING THE PERFECT BEAST
Boys of Summer / You can't make love / Man with a mission / You're not drinking enough / Not enough love in the world / Building the perfect beast / All she wants to do is dance / Sunset grill / Drivin' with your eyes closed / Land of the living
GFLD 19267 / Feb '95 / Geffen

☐ END OF THE INNOCENCE, THE
End of the innocence / How bad do you want it / I will not go quietly / Last worthless evening / New York minute / Shangri-La / Little tin god / Gimme what you got / If dirt were dollars / Heart of the matter
GFLD 19285 / Oct '95 / Geffen

☐ I CAN'T STAND STILL
I can't stand still / You better hang up / Long way home / Ain't nobody's business if I do / Talking to the moon / Dirty laundry / Johnny can't read / Them and us / La elite / Lilah / Unclouded day
K 9600482 / Jun '89 / WEA

Hennessy, Christie

☐ BOX, THE
I've been loving you too long / In my box / Liveing the life I owe / When you give your love to one love / Can you hear me / Innocence / I am the box / Rick's cafe / World's closing in / Before the day is through / You are the girl / Glory glory / Somewhere out there / We're gonna make it together / Christmas day / Late at night / I'm going to make it on my own / I'm in this over my head / Hide away / Skipping home from school / Angel
0630146022 / Jul '96 / Celtic Heartbeat

☐ LORD OF YOUR EYES
Roll back the clouds / Out of line / I'm looking up to you / Love belongs to everyone / Love's great pretender / Where do we go from here / Sunny days / Don't go down there / Still a lonely man / Mr blue / Who rocks the cradle / I will never love again
4509975862 / Dec '96 / WEA

☐ YEAR IN THE LIFE, A
Quest / Lonely boy / Remember me / If you were to fall (and I was to fall in love with you) / Pain / Norfolk square / Vision / You can go far (if you know where you're going) / Sheila Doran / By bye love
4509919632 / Dec '96 / WEA

Hennessy, Frank

☐ THOUGHTS AND MEMORIES
Brother eagle / Jenkin's history / Keeper / Newfoundland / Valley lights / Old men and children / Mickey's song / Start and end with you / Sun's last rays / Old Camarhten oak / Fading away / Hearts on fire
SAIN 8084CD / Aug '94 / Sain

Hennessys

☐ EARLY SONGS, THE
Road and the miles / Beggar man / Ar lan y mor / Liverpool lou / Manchester rambler / Mae'n wlad I ml / Dido bendigo / Yr hen dderwen ddu / Whiskey in the jar / Newfoundland / Moliannwn / Great little trains of wales / Suo gan / Paddy lie back / A ddaw yn ol / Gresford disaster / Gypsy / Rownd yr horn / Lord lovell / Farewell to the rhondda
SCD 2044 / Feb '95 / Sain

Henning, Ann-Marie

☐ TIDAL DREAMS
DRCD 279 / Aug '97 / Dragon

Henriksen, Larsen Moe

☐ MIN VEMODS FRYD
EU 005CD / Aug '97 / Euridice

Henry, Clarence

☐ BUT I DO (Henry, Clarence 'Frogman')
Ain't got no home / It won't be long / I found a home / Baby baby please / Never never / Oh Mickey / But I do / Just my baby and me / Live it right / I want to be a movie star / Steady date / Oh why / Little Susie / You always hurt the one you love / I love you, yes I do / Lonely street / Your picture / I wish I could say the same / Standing in the need of love / Little too much / On bended knees / Jealous kind / Dream myself a sweetheart / Lost without you / Takes two to Tango / Long lost and worried / Looking back
CPCD 8007 / Feb '94 / Charly

Henry Cow

☐ LEGEND
RERHC 1 / Jun '98 / ReR/ Recommended

Henry, Joe

☐ TRAMPOLINE
Let me have it all / Bob ray / Ohio air show plane crash / Flower girl / Go with god (topless shoeshine) / Medicine / Parade / I was a playboy / Trampoline
7567926862 / Apr '96 / Atlantic

Henry, Kent

☐ SO CLOSE TO YOU
I set my sights on Jesus / So close to you / In the silence / Send your fire / Rain / Faithful God / Jump up / Freedom train
11542 / Mar '98 / Hosanna

Henry, Pauline

☐ DO OVER
Happy / Be thankful for what you got / Love hangover / Never knew love like this / Groove with you / Fools paradise / Save the overtime for me / When love calls / Sugar free / Happy (Dancehall)
4840589 / May '96 / Sony Soho2

Henry, Pierre

☐ FRAGMENTS POUR ARTAUD
3014152 / Sep '97 / Mantra

☐ GYMKHANA
MANTRA 093 / Sep '97 / Mantra

☐ L'HOMME A LA CAMERA
643250 / Dec '97 / Mantra

☐ LE LIVRE DES MORTS
MANTRA 043 / Sep '97 / Mantra

☐ MESSE DE LIVERPOOL
MANTRA 023 / Sep '97 / Mantra

☐ MESSE POUR LE TEMPS PRESENT (Metamorphose/Remix)
Psyche rock / Prologue / Psyche rock / Jericho jerk / Teen tonic / Too fortiche / Psyche rock / Too fortiche / Jericho jerk / Too fortiche / Psyche rock / Psyche rock
4562932 / 29 Sep '97 / Hi-Life

☐ MESSE POUR LE TEMPS PRESENT
Prologue / Psyche rock / Jericho jerk / Teen tonic / Too fortiche / Marche du jeune homme / La reine et les insectes / Rock electronique / Le couple / Fluidite et mobilite d'un larsen / Divinites paisibles / Balancement / Chant 1 / Eveil / Chant 2 / Etirement / Gestes / Fievre 1 / Gymnastique / Fievre 2
4566402 / 29 Sep '97 / Philips

☐ MOUVEMENT RYTHME ETU
MANTRA 024 / Sep '97 / Mantra

Henry, Vincent

☐ VINCENT
Southbound / Flintstone rock / Marcel / Make it like it was / Still the one / Big foot / No additional love / Sarah, sarah / Harbor song / Because of you
CHIP 101 / Jul '90 / Jive

Henrys

☐ CHASING GRACE
FIENDCD 784 / Sep '96 / Demon

☐ PUERTO ANGEL
Adobe abode / Get out the shovel / Bunt / One rose / Sea of tranquility / Nunc pro tunc / Dark dear heart / Look so good / Muscle beach / Radio girl / Coyote basin / Riff raff / Puerto angel
FIENDCD 769 / Apr '96 / Demon

Henry's Cat

☐ SINGS THE HITS
Barbie girl / Sweets for my sweet / Love fool / I can make you feel good / Forget-me-knots / Saturday night / Ooh aah just a little bit / TV trip / Wannabe / Funny 5 minutes / Ghostbusters / I wanna be a cowboy / Glasses / Children of the revolution / Get it on / Telegram Sam / Ride a white swan / Metal guru / Hot love / Alright / Tra la la song / Boom boom boom / Aliens / We've got it goin' on / Food food food / Kisses on the bottom / Manamana
1840664835 / 13 Jul '98 / Right Recordings

Henry's Dress

☐ BUST 'EM GREEN
SLR 054CD / Dec '96 / Slumberland

Hensley, Ken

☐ FROM TIME TO TIME
RMCCD 0195 / May '96 / Red Steel

Henson, Ronnie

☐ RONNIE HENSON
5306262 / 9 Feb '98 / Polydor

Hentchmen

☐ BROAD APPEAL
CED 257 / Nov '97 / Norton

Hepcat

☐ RIGHT ON TIME
Right on time / Can't wait / Goodbye street / Secret / Pharoah's dreams / No worries / Mama used to say / Rudies all around / Tommy's song / Nigel / Together someday / Baby blues / Open season is closed
04062 / 8 Dec '97 / Epitaph

Heppner, Ben

☐ DEDICATION
9026631042 / 10 Aug '98 / RCA

Heptones

☐ 20 GOLDEN HITS
SONCD 0021 / Apr '92 / Sonic Sounds

☐ BETTER DAYS
Suspicious mind / Crystal blue persuasion / Land of love / Oh jah / Better days / Jah bless the children / Ready baby (come on talk to me) / Everyday life / Mister do over man song / Key to her heart
RRTGCD 7715 / Jan '89 / Rohit

☐ FATTIE FATTIE
SOCD 9002 / Mar '95 / Studio One

☐ GOOD VIBES
CDSGP 048 / Jun '93 / Prestige

☐ HEPTONES VOL.1 & 2, THE
CDTRL 357 / Jul '95 / Trojan

☐ IN A DANCE HALL STYLE
MRCD 004 / 18 Aug '97 / Metronome

☐ NIGHT FOOD
Country boy / I've got the handle / Sweet talkin' / Book of rules / Mama say / Deceivers / Love won't come easy / Fatty fatty / Baby I need your lovin' / In the groove
RRCD 19 / Nov '90 / Reggae Refreshers

☐ OBSERVER STYLE
CC 2713 / Sep '94 / Crocodisc

☐ ON TOP
SOCD 0016 / Mar '95 / Studio One

☐ ON TOP
TTCD 0040 / 27 Oct '97 / Trenchtown

☐ PRESSURE
RASCD 3164 / Oct '95 / Ras

☐ RAINBOW VALLEY
CDSGP 0132 / Aug '94 / Prestige

☐ SEA OF LOVE
Be a man / Stick man / Sea of love / Tea for two / Choice of colour / Young, gifted and black / Ting-a-ling / Please be true / Get in the groove / Learn / I shall be released / Nine pounds of steel / Love won't come easy / Love me with all of your heart / You've lost that loving feeling / Joy joy
CDHB 128 / Mar '97 / Heartbeat

☐ SWING LOW
Heaven / Promise to be true / What it is / So long / I'm proud / Book of rules / Down comes the rain / Swing low, sweet chariot / You decorated my life / Pack your things
CDBS 565 / Mar '97 / Burning Sounds

☐ WONDERFUL WORLD
RNCD 2045 / Mar '94 / Rhino

Herawi, Aziz

☐ MASTER OF AFGHANI LUTES
Jhaptal-dadra / Kaharwa / Kaharwa-dadra / Charbeiti kaharwa / Kaharwa-dadra il / Ausharl / Naghma I / Mahali I / Khandan-e amaturi I / Khandan-e amaturi il / Khandan-e amaturi iil / Naghma-ye klasik in rag parl / Naghma-ye klasik in rag pilu / Mahali il / Mahali iil / Naghma il / Naghma iil
ARHCD 387 / Apr '95 / Arhoolie

Herb

☐ ON DUB
EBCD 002 / Mar '97 / Early Bird

Herbal Mixture

☐ PLEASE LEAVE MY MIND
Rock me baby / Shake it / Someone to love / Hallalujah / I'll never fall in love again / Over you baby / Please leave my mind / Love that died / Something's happening / Tailor made / Over you baby / Machines / Please leave my mind / Tailor made / Love that died / Love that died
BP 251CD / 15 Sep '97 / Blueprint

Herbaliser

☐ BLOW YOUR HEADPHONES
Opening credits / Bring it / Another mother / More styles / Ginger jumps the fence / Put it on tape / Saturday night / Intermission / Shocker zulu / Blend / Shorty's judgement / Theme from control centre / Hardcore / Mr. Chombee has the flaw / End credits / Excuse me / New and improved / Mr. Chombee has the floor / Mother (for your mind)
ZENCD 028 / Mar '97 / Ninja Tune

☐ REMEDIES
Intro / Scratchy noise / Blomp / Styles / Interloodle / Bust a nut / Herbalize it / Wrong place / Little groove / Da trax / Up / Get downs / K-doing / Chill / Real killer / Repetitive loop
ZENCD 018 / Sep '95 / Ninja Tune

Herbeck, Ray

☐ RAY HERBECK & HIS MUSIC 1940
CCD 041 / Jun '96 / Circle

Herbert

☐ AROUND THE HOUSE
Intro / So now / Around the house / Close to me / Last beat / Going round / This time / We still have (the music) / In the kitchen / Never give up / We go wrong / Bedroom jazz
GRAPHCD 001 / 6 Jul '98 / Phonography

☐ PARTS 1-3
PHONOCD 1 / Apr '96 / Phonography

Herbert, John Dale

☐ CAJUN PICKIN' (Hebert, John Dale & Tim Broussard)
Hells on fire / Little black eyes / Big Mamou / LA Blues / Last waltz / Accordion players waltz / Big wheel / Oh bye bye / Let's two step / Weekend special
SOC 90253 / Jul '96 / Cajun Sound

Herbolzheimer, Peter

☐ HIP WALK
PMS 7065 / 24 Nov '97 / Repertoire

Herborn, Peter

☐ SOMETHING PERSONAL
Last objection / Tell me your secrets / Rush hour / All along the watchtower / Music for forgotten lovers / Evidence / Blue monochrome / Falling water
8491562 / Mar '94 / jMT

Herd

☐ ANTHOLOGY
I can fly / Diary of a narcissist (I'm so pretty) / From the underworld / Sweet William / Paradise lost / Come on believe me / Mixed up minds / Sad / Fare thee well / I don't want our loving to die / Our fairy tale / On my way home / Sunshine cottage / Miss Jones / She loves me she loves me not / Something strange / Game / Beauty queen / Hanging from your loving tree / I don't wanna go to sleep again / Follow the leader / Mother's blue eyed angel / Laugh and dance and sing / Sugarloaf mountain / Understand me / Charlie Andersen / Bang
MCCD 352 / 15 Jun '98 / MCI Music

☐ FROM THE UNDERWORLD
From the underground / Paradise lost / I don't want our loving to die / I can fly / Diary of a narcissist (I'm so pretty) / Our fairy tale / Sunshine cottage / Game / Come on believe me / Miss jones / Follow the leader / Mother's blue eyed angel / On my way home / Mixed up minds / Something strange / Sad / Hangin' from your loving tree / Fare thee well / Fare thee well (instrumental reprise) / I don't wanna go to sleep again / Laugh and dance and sing / She loves me (she loves me not) / Sweet william / Sugar loaf mountain / Understand me / Bang / Charlie anderson / Beauty queen
BX 4512 / Oct '95 / BR Music

☐ VERY BEST OF THE HERD, THE
EMPRCD 801 / 18 May '98 / Emporio

Herdman, Priscilla

☐ FOREVER & ALWAYS
FF 70637 / Feb '95 / Flying Fish

☐ MOONDREAMER
Howl at the moon / Velveteen love song / 1000 pairs of pyjamas / Mid night round / While you sleep / Bluegrass boy / Stars on the water / John o' dreams / Moon and me / Lullabye (goodnight my angel) / Dreamland / All through the night
RWMCD 5401 / Jun '98 / Redwing

☐ WATER LILY, THE
CDPH 1014 / Aug '95 / Philo

Here Kitty Kitty

☐ KISS ME YOU FOOL
IT 5CD / Nov '94 / Iteration

Heresy

☐ VOICE OF FEAR
LF 191CD / Oct '96 / Lost & Found

Heretic

☐ YAYOI DREAM (2CD Set)
BELLE 96032 / Jun '97 / Belle Antique

Heritage

☐ TELL TAE ME
Acrobat-the echo / April waltz-ookpik waltz / Bonny glenshee / Duke of fife's welcome to deeside-campbell's farewell / Valse de vertoujit-valse a bargoin / Bonny udny / Fornethy house / Tell tae me / Calabrian pastorale
COMD 2051 / Feb '94 / Temple

Heritage

☐ REMORSE CODE
CDMETAL 4 / Feb '97 / British Steel

Heritage Hall Jazz Band

☐ COOKIN'
BCD 287 / Jul '93 / GHB

Herman, Jerry

☐ EVENING WITH JERRY HERMAN, AN
Mame / Shalom / Just leave everything to me / Put on your sunday clothes / Ribbons down my back / Before the parade passes by / It only takes a moment / It's today / Open a new window / Man in the moon / Gooch's song / We need a little christmas / Bosom buddies / If he walked into my life / I don't want to know / And I was beautiful / Movies were movies (the overture from mack and mabel) / I won't send roses / Time heals everything / Tap your troubles away / Hello dolly
CDSL 5173 / Jan '93 / DRG

Herman, Woody

☐ 16 CLASSIC PERFORMANCES
Golden wedding / Woodchopper's ball / Blues in the night / Las Chiapanecas / Down under / Four or five times / Woodsheddin' with Woody / Blue prelude / Yardbird shuffle / Blue frame / Fan it / Sheik of Araby / It's a blue world / Blues on parade / Blues downstairs / Amen yeah man
CWNCD 2031 / Jun '97 / Crown

☐ AMEN 1937-1942 (Herman, Woody & His Orchestra)
RACD 7108 / May '96 / Aerospace

☐ AT THE PALLADIUM HOLLYWOOD 1948/COMMODORE HOTEL NEW YORK 194 (Herman, Woody Second Herd)
STCD 8240 / Aug '97 / Storyville

☐ AT THE WOODCHOPPERS' BALL
At the woodchoppers' ball / Better get off your high horse / Blue flame / Blues downstairs / Blues in the night / Blues upstairs / Boogie woogie bugle boy / Bounce me brother with a solid four / Careless / Deep in a dream: *Herman, Woody & Connie Boswell* / Dr. Jazz / Dream valley / Fine and dandy / Frenesi / G'bye now / I'm thinking tonight of my blue eyes: *Herman, Woody & Bing Crosby* / Rumboogie / Rosetta / Sheikh of araby / Skylark / Sleepy serenade / Someone's rocking my dreamboat / String of pearls / They say: *Herman, Woody & Connie Boswell* / Whistler's mother-in-law: *Herman, Woody, Bing Crosby & Muriel Lane*
CDAJA 5143 / Nov '94 / Living Era

☐ BLOWIN' UP A STORM (2CD Set)
As long as I live / I ain't got nothing but the blues / Laura / Apple honey / I wonder / Yeah man / Happiness is a thing called Joe / Goosey gander / Kiss goodnight / Northwest passage / I've got the world on string / Good earth / Put that ring on my finger / Bijou / Gee it's good to hold you / Your father's moustache / Wild root / Blowin' up a storm / Let it snow let it snow let it snow / Atlanta GA / Welcome to my dream / Panacea / Steps / Four men on a horse / Igor / Fan it / Nero's conception / Lost weekend / Pam / Sidewalkers of Cuba / Lady McGowans dream 1 and 2 / Romance in the dark / Summer sequence / Everywhere / With someone new / Wrap your troubles / Back talk / I surrender dear / Someday sweetheart / Woodchopper's ball / Non alcoholic
CDGR 1622 / Sep '97 / Charly

☐ BLUE FLAMES
Theme: Blue flame / I say a little prayer / At the woodchoppers' ball
CDC 9049 / Nov '92 / LRC

☐ BLUES ON PARADE 1937-1941 (Herman, Woody & His Orchestra)
RACD 7122 / May '96 / Aerospace

☐ BODY AND SOUL (Herman, Woody & Lionel Hampton)
DM 15019 / Jul '96 / DMA Jazz

☐ CONCORD YEARS, THE
Things ain't what they used to be / Four brothers / 'Round midnight / It don't mean a thing if it ain't got that swing / Dolphin / Woody 'n' you / Blues for red / Perdido / Central Parkwest / Lemon drop / What are you doing the rest of your life / Battle royal
CCD 4557 / Jun '93 / Concord Jazz

☐ CREAM OF EARLY WOODY HERMAN, THE
Blues downstairs / Changing world / Herman at the Sherman / Jumpin' blues / East side kick / Big wig in the wigwam / It's a blue world / Paleface / Give a little whistle / Blues upstairs / Big morning / Jukin' / Blue ink / Farewell blues / Blues on parade / Blue prelude / Fan it / Sheikh of Araby / Blue flame / Indian boogie woogie / Dupree blues / At the woodchoppers' ball
PASTCD 9780 / Apr '92 / Flapper

☐ CROWN ROYAL (Herman, Woody & His Orchestra)
Natchel blues / Don't get around much anymore / Ready, get set, jump / Gloomy sunday / Montmartre bus ride / Aruba / Darn that dream / Crown royal / I can't get started / Grind / Off shore / Single o / Afterglow / Hermosa beach
15775 / Aug '93 / Laserlight

☐ FIRST HERD, THE
LEJAZZCD 53 / Jan '96 / Le Jazz

☐ GIANT STEPS
FCD 6099432 / Nov '86 / Fantasy

☐ HEARD WITH FRIENDS 1946-1957
EBCD 2134 / May '98 / Jazzband

☐ HERD RIDES AGAIN, THE
ECD 220102 / Jul '92 / Evidence

☐ HERMAN'S HEAT AND PUENTE'S BEAT (Herman, Woody & Tito Puente)
ECD 220082 / Jul '92 / Evidence

☐ HOLLYWOOD PALLADIUM (Herman, Woody & His Orchestra)
RST 915362 / Jun '93 / RST

☐ JANTZEN BEACH OREGON 1954
Prez conference / What is there to say / One o'clock jump / Cohn's alley / Mulligantawney / Why not / Would he / Offshore / Stardust / Hitting the bottle / Embraceable you / It happens to be me / Moten stomp / Strange / That old feeling
DSTS 1020 / Sep '96 / Status

☐ JAZZ COLLECTOR EDITION (5CD Set) (Herman, Woody/Duke Ellington/Artie Shaw)
15911 / Jan '92 / Laserlight

☐ JAZZ MASTERS
5299032 / 5 May '98 / Verve

☐ JAZZ PORTRAIT
CD 14574 / Nov '95 / Complete

☐ KEEP ON KEEPIN' ON 1968-1970 (Herman, Woody & His Thundering Herd)
Light my fire / Keep on keepin' on / Impressions on Strayhorn / Pontieo / I say a little prayer / Hush / My cherie amour / Catch that bird / I can't get next to you / Aquarius / Blues in the night / Time for love / Smiling phases / Indigenous artifact
GRP 18182 / 8 Jun '98 / Chess Jazz

☐ LAKE COMPOUNCE & JANTZEN BEACH
DSTS 1021 / Oct '96 / Status

☐ LIVE AT NEWPORT 1966
EBCD 21182 / Oct '90 / JSP

☐ LIVE AT THE PEACOCK LANE 1958
FSCD 2011 / Oct '96 / Fresh Sound

☐ LIVE IN STEREO - 1963 (Herman, Woody & The Fourth Herd)
JH 1006 / Oct '91 / Jazz Hour

☐ NORTHWEST PASSAGE VOL.2 (Herman, Woody & The First Herd)
JASSCD 625 / '91 / Jass

☐ PRESENTS A CONCORD JAM VOL.1
At the woodchoppers' ball / Rose room / Just friends / Nancy with the laughing face / Body and soul / Someday you'll be sorry / My melancholy baby / Apple honey
CCD 4142 / Aug '90 / Concord Jazz

☐ RAVEN SPEAKS, THE
Fat mama / Alone again (naturally) / Watermelon man / It's too late / Raven speaks / Summer of '42 / Reunion at Newport / Bill's blues
OJCCD 663 / Jun '94 / Original Jazz Classics

☐ READY GET SET JUMP (Herman, Woody & His Orchestra)
Ready, get set, jump / Saxy / Don't get around much anymore / Body and soul / Opus de funk / Jumpin' blue / Greasy sack blues / Make someone happy / I remember clifford / Northwest passage
JHR 73527 / May '93 / Jazz Hour

☐ THIS IS JAZZ
Woodchopper's ball / Northwest passae / 23 Red / I've got news for you / Bijou (Rhumba a la jazz) / Greasy sack blues / Goof and I / Happiness is a thing called Joe / Early autumn (Summer sequence part 4) / My favourite things / Caladonia (What makes your big head so hard) / Four brothers / Everywhere / Keen and peachy / Northwest passage
CK 65040 / May '97 / Sony Jazz

☐ THUNDERING HERD 1944, THE
JCD 621 / Feb '91 / Jass

☐ THUNDERING HERD 1945, THE
JCD 625 / Feb '91 / Jass

☐ TRIBUTE TO THE LEGACY OF WOODY HERMAN, A (Herman, Woody Orchestra)
Blue flame / Four brothers / Laura / Woodchopper's ball / Sail away / Make someone happy / Bijou / Good Earth / Woody 'n me / Lemon drop / Body and soul / Woody's whistle
NYJAM 1196 / 8 Jun '98 / Montpellier

☐ V DISC YEARS VOL.1 & 2 1944-1946, THE (Herman, Woody & His Orchestra)
Flying home / It must be jelly, 'cause jam don't shake like that / Dancing in the dawn / Happiness is a thing called Joe / Red top / Jones beachead / I can't put my arms around a memory / There are no wings on a foxhole / Apple honey / Time waits for no one / Billy Bauer's tune / Golden wedding / I've got the world on a string / Yeah man (Amen) / He's funny that way / Lover man / Your father's moustache / Don't worry 'bout that mule / 125th Street prophet / I can't put my arms around a memory / Somebody loves me / John Hardy's wife / Meshugah / He's funny that way / Secunda / Jones Beachead / Caledonia / Jackson fiddles while Ralph burns / Happiness is a thing called Joe / Mean to me / Blowin' up a storm / C Jam blues/Reprise
HEPCD 34/35 / Nov '92 / Hep

☐ V DISC YEARS, THE
HEPCD 2 / Jun '87 / Hep

☐ WILDROOT
TCD 1009 / Feb '96 / Tradition

☐ WOODCHOPPER'S BALL
Pillar to post / Sweet Lorraine / Blues on parade / Woodchopper's ball / Early Autumn / Stompin' at the Savoy / Linger in my arms a little longer / Surrender / Mabel Mabel / Steps / Four men on a horse / Igor / Fan it / Nero's conception / Heads up / Wild root / Tito meets Woody / Cha cha chick / Carioca / Summer sequence / Latin flight / New cha cha / Mambo hero / Blue stations
GRF 069 / '93 / Tring

☐ WOODCHOPPER'S BALL
Blues in the night / Herman at The Sherman / Woodsheddin' with Woody / Yardbird shuffle / Get your boots laced Papa / 'Tis autumn / Pick-a-rib / Blue upstairs / Big wig in the wigwam / Blues downstairs / At the Woodchopper's ball / Bishop's blues / Golden wedding / Hot chesnuts / Blue flame / Fur trappers ball / Down under / Blue prelude / String of pearls / Dallas blues
306682 / Jun '97 / Hallmark

☐ WOODCHOPPERS' BALL
JASSCD 621 / Aug '90 / Jass

☐ WOODSHEDDIN' WITH WOODY
Blue ink / Careless / Herman at the Sherman / Get your boots laced Papa / Jukin' / It's a blue world / East side kick / Who's dat up dere / Indian boogie woogie / Woodsheddin' with Woody / Fan it / South / Too late / Four or five times / Fort Worth jail / Blues downstairs / Blues on parade / Golden wedding / Yardbird shuffle / At the woodchoppers' ball
RAJCD 838 / Mar '97 / Empress

☐ WOODY AND FRIENDS
Caravan / I got it bad and that ain't good / Count down / Better get it in your soul / Woody 'n' you / What are you doing the rest of your life / Manteca
CCD 4170 / Jan '92 / Concord Jazz

☐ WOODY HERMAN
22706 / Feb '96 / Music

☐ WOODY HERMAN & HIS ORCHESTRA VOL.1 (Herman, Woody & His Orchestra)
JH 1014 / '92 / Jazz Hour

☐ WOODY HERMAN & HIS ORCHESTRA VOL.2 (Herman, Woody & His Orchestra)
JH 1015 / '92 / Jazz Hour

☐ WOODY HERMAN & HIS THUNDERING HERD (Herman, Woody & His Herd)
Autobahn blues / Park east / Saxy / Opus de funk / Pres conference / Stompin' at the savoy / Early autumn / Moten swing / Mother goose jumps / Sweet sue, just you / New golden wedding / Beale street blues / Celestial blues
15774 / Jul '93 / Laserlight

☐ WOODY HERMAN & ORCHESTRA 1937
CCD 95 / Apr '94 / Circle

☐ WOODY HERMAN AND HIS ORCHESTRA 1945-1947 (Herman, Woody & His Orchestra)
11087 / '88 / Laserlight

☐ WOODY HERMAN FEATURING STAN GETZ (Herman, Woody & Stan Getz)
Four brothers / Sweet and lovely / Early autumn / Cousins / Fanfare for the common man / Blues in the night / Blue serge / Blue Getz blues / Caldonia (what makes your big head so hard)
09026687022 / Mar '97 / RCA Victor

☐ WOODY HERMAN PRESENTS A GREAT AMERICAN EVENING VOL.3
I've got the world on a string / I cover the waterfront / Leopardskin pillbox hat / Avalon / Beautiful friendship / Pennies from Heaven / Wave / Caldonia
CCD 4220 / Jul '96 / Concord Jazz

☐ WOODY HERMAN VOL.1 1938-1945
158542 / Sep '96 / Jazz Archives

☐ WOODY'S GOLD STAR (Herman, Woody Big Band)
Battle royal / Woody's gold star / Mambo rockland / 'Round midnight / Great escape / Dig / Rose room / In a mellow tone / Watermelon man / Samba song
CCD 4330 / Oct '87 / Concord Jazz

Hermann, Judd

☐ HOMELESS IN THE HEART
ATD 1115 / Aug '96 / Atomic Theory

Herman's Hermits

☐ ALL THE HITS PLUS MORE
Sunshine girl / Wonderful world / Can't you hear my heartbeat / No milk today / Mrs. Brown you've got a lovely daughter / Just a little bit better / End of the world / I can take and leave your loving / I'm Henry the VIII / Sea cruise / There's a kind of hush / Something's happening / Dandy / Listen people / I'm into something good / Must to avoid / Leaning on a lamp post / I understand just how you feel / Silhouettes / Don't go out into the rain, you're going to melt / Hold on
CDSGP 0217 / Apr '97 / Prestige

☐ BEST OF THE EMI YEARS VOL.1 1964-1966, THE
I'm into something good / I'm Henery the Eighth (I am) / Silhouettes / Show me girl / Can't you hear my heartbeat / Take love, give love / Wonderful world / Mrs. Brown you've got a lovely daughter / Just a little bit better / Must to avoid / You won't be leaving / Listen people / Hold on / This door swings both ways / Leaning on a lamp-post / All the things I do for you / Little boy sad / Dial my number / George and the dragon / East west / Dandy / No milk today
CDEMS 1415 / Sep '91 / EMI

☐ BEST OF THE EMI YEARS VOL.2 1967-1971, THE
There's a kind of hush / Green Street green / Little Miss Sorrow, child of tomorrow / One little packet of cigarettes / Don't go out into the rain (you're going to melt) / Jezebel / Busy line / Museum / Rattler / I can take or leave your loving / It's nice to be out in the morning / Ooh, she's done it again / Sleepy Joe / Sunshine girl / Most beautiful thing in my life / Something is happening / My sentimental friend / Here comes the star / Years may come years may go / Bet your life I do / Lady Barbara / Oh you pretty thing
CDEMS 1416 / Feb '92 / EMI

☐ EP COLLECTION, THE
Sea cruise / Mother in law / I understand / Mrs. Brown you've got a lovely daughter / Show me girl / Silhouettes / Wonderful world / Can't you hear my heartbeat / I'm into something good / Must to avoid / I'm Henery the Eighth (I am) / Just a little bit better / Walkin' with my angel / Where were you when I needed you / Hold on / George and the dragon / All the things I do for you / Wild love / Dandy / No milk today / For love
SEECD 284 / Jan '90 / See For Miles

☐ HERMAN'S HERMITS
Heartbeat / Travelin' light / I'll never dance again / Walkin' with my angel / Dream on / I wonder / For your love / Don't try and hurt me / Tell me baby / I'm henery the eighth I am / End of the world / Mrs.Brown you've got a lovely daughter
DORIG 123 / 3 Nov '97 / EMI

☐ I'M INTO SOMETHING GOOD
HADCD 207 / Jul '96 / Javelin

☐ I'M INTO SOMETHING GOOD
I'm into something good / Wonderful world / Listen people / Dandy / Must to avoid / No milk today / Steady Eddie / God knows / Leaning on the lamp post / Silhouettes / Don't say it (if you don't) / Needles and pins / Little bit bitter / End of the world / Jezebel / Mrs. Brown you've got a lovely daughter / I'm Henry the VIII, I am / Kind of hush
PLATCD 204 / Feb '97 / Platinum

☐ VERY BEST OF HERMAN'S HERMITS, THE
I'm into something good / Silhouettes / Can't you hear my heartbeat / Wonderful world / Leaning on a lamp-post / Must to avoid / No milk today / Years may come years may go / I'm Henery the Eighth (I am) / There's a kind of hush / Dandy / Sunshine girl / Something is happening / Mrs. Brown you've got a lovely daughter / My sentimental friend / Oh you pretty things
CDMFP 6383 / 13 Oct '97 / Music For Pleasure

☐ VERY BEST OF HERMAN'S HERMITS, THE
No milk today / I'm into something good / Show me girl / Silhouettes / Wonderful world / Just a little bit better / Must to avoid / You won't be leaving / This door swings both ways / East West / Dandy / I'm Henry The VIII I am / End of the world / Mrs. Brown you've got a lovely daughter
16152 / Apr '96 / Laserlight

☐ YEARS MAY COME
Years may come, years may go / I can't take or leave your lovin' / This door swings both ways / Mrs. Brown you've got a lovely daughter / Leaning on a lampost / Must to avoid / Sleepy Joe / Something's happening / Sunshine girl / My sentimental friend / Can't you hear my heartbeat / There's a kind of hush / I'm into something good / Silhouettes / No milk today / East west / Oh you pretty things / Meet me on the corner down at Joe's cafe
BR 1352 / Dec '95 / BR Music

Hermans, Ruud

☐ BLUE HORIZON
MWCD 1004 / Aug '94 / Music & Words

Hernandez, Nilo

☐ NILO HERNANDEZ 1934-1938
HQCD 84 / Jun '97 / Harlequin

Hernandez, Patrick

☐ BEST OF PATRICK HERNANDEZ, THE (Born To Be Alive)
HTCD 64 / 20 Apr '98 / Hot Productions

Hernandez, Rafael

☐ RAFAEL HERNANDEZ 1932-1939
HQCD 68 / Jun '96 / Harlequin

Hernon, Marcus

☐ BEAL A'MHURLAIGH (Hernon, Marcus & P.J.)
CEFCD 141 / Jan '94 / Gael Linn

Hernon, Sean

☐ AN NORA BHEAG
CICD 123 / Aug '97 / Clo Iar-Chonnachta

Heroic Doses

☐ HERIOC DOSES
SPCD 432 / 3 Aug '98 / Sub Pop

Heroin

☐ DESTINATION
GRAVITY 20 / Jan '97 / Gravity

☐ SHOWING A LUMINOUS BALL
USR 001CD / Aug '95 / Cold Spring

Herold, Ted

☐ DIE SINGLES 1958-1960
Ich brauch' keinen ring / Lover doll / So schon ist nur die allererste liebe / Wunderbar wie du heut' wieder kusst / Hula rock / Dixieland rock / Dein kleiner bruder / Texas baby / Ich bin ein mann / Carolin / Hey baby / Kuss mich / Isabell / Crazy boy / Moonlight / 1:0 / Sunshine baby / Hast du funf minuten zeit / Auch du wirst gehn' / Hey little girl / Lonely / Oh so sweet / Nur sie / Wunderland
BCD 15404 / Jul '87 / Bear Family

☐ DIE SINGLES 1961-1962
BCD 15592 / Apr '92 / Bear Family

☐ HOR AUF DEIN HERZ
BCD 16291 / Jul '98 / Bear Family

Heron

☐ BEST OF HERON
Only a hobo / Lord and master / Sally Goodin / Yellow roses / Little angel / Car crash / Little boy / Goodbye / For you / John Brown / Wanderer / Great dust storm / Minstrel and a king / Winter harlequin / Smiling ladies / Love 13 (lone) / Big A / Miss Kiss / Upon reflection
SEECD 242 / Nov '88 / See For Miles

☐ HERON
SRMC 1031 / 5 Jan '98 / Siwan

Heron, Mike

☐ CONFLICT OF EMOTIONS
Torch song / Belinda / It takes my breathe away yet / Jane / Maker of islands / Transberrian express / Squeeze the minutes / Winter in China / Savage moon
UGCD 5807 / Jul '98 / Unique Gravity

☐ MIKE HERON'S REPUTATION
Down on my knees (after Memphis) / Easy street / Evie / Residential boy / Without love / Born to be gone / Angels in disguise / Wine of his song / Meanwhile the rain / One of the finest / Singing the dolphin
UGCD 5606 / Apr '98 / Unique Gravity

Herrera, Eddy

☐ LOS HOMBRES CALIENTES
74321442102 / Mar '97 / Milan

Herring Boys

☐ LUCKY NUMBER SEVEN
SPURCD 002 / Feb '97 / Spur

Herring, Vincent

☐ CHANGE THE WORLD
Change the world / Soft impressions / Rosalinda's eyes / Stranger / Zanzibar / Thirty one / Strolling / Timothy
MM 65163 / Oct '97 / Music Masters

☐ DAWNBIRD
Sound check / August afternoon / Almost always / Toku do / Dr. Jamie / Who's kidding who / Dark side of dewey
LCDI 5332 / Nov '93 / Landmark

☐ DON'T LET GO
Don't let it go / Into the midnight / Sabrosa / In the shadow of john galt / Big bertha / Unknown ideal / Liberation / Blueprint for a new tomorrow
MM 65121 / Oct '97 / Music Masters

☐ FOLKLORE (Live At The Village Vanguard)
Folklore / Theme for Dolores / Girl next door / Romantic journey / Fountainhead / Window of opportunity / This I dig of you / Mo's theme
5224302 / Mar '94 / Limelight

☐ SCENE ONE
Elation / Roused about / What is this thing called love / Almost / Running from the cookie monster / Never forget / Where or Wayne
ECD 221702 / Mar '97 / Evidence

☐ SECRET LOVE
Have you met Miss Jones / Skating in Central Park / Secret love / If you never / Autumn leaves / My foolish heart / Solar / Chelsea Bridge / And then again
8443242 / Jan '95 / Limelight

Herron, Paul

☐ DIFFERENT WORLDS
Voiceless millions / Spanish point / Connemara awakes / Summer sunsets / Lonely at the station / You've got me / Blue skies / In a song / Donegal dreams / Just down the road / Feeling great / When darkness falls / Last chance
CDTRAX 055 / Aug '92 / Greentrax

Hersch, Fred

☐ LIVE AT MAYBECK RECITAL HALL VOL.31
Embraceable you / Haunted heart / In walked Bud / You don't know what love is / If I loved you / Heartsong / Everything I love / Sarabande / Song is you / Ramblin' / Body and soul
CCD 4596 / May '94 / Concord Jazz

☐ POINT IN TIME
Point in time / You don't know what love is / As long as there's music / Spring is here / Peacocks / Infant eyes / Cat's paws / Too soon / Evidence / Drew's blues
ENJ 90352 / Oct '95 / Enja

☐ RODGERS & HAMMERSTEIN
7559794142 / Mar '97 / Nonesuch

☐ THELONIOUS (Fred Hersch Plays Monk)
'Round midnight / Crepuscule with Nellie/ Reflections / Ask me now / Five views of misterioso / Bemsha swing / I mean you / In walked Bud / Think of one / Evidence / Let's cool one / Light blue/ Pannonica / 'Round midnight reprise
7559794562 / 26 Jan '98 / Nonesuch

Hersh, Kristin

☐ HIPS AND MAKERS
Your ghost / Beestung / Teeth / Sundrops / Sparky / Houdini blues / Loon / Velvet days / Close your eyes / Me and my charms / Tuesday night / Letter / Lurch / Cuckoo / Hips and makers
GAD 4002CD / 6 Jul '98 / 4AD

☐ STRANGE ANGELS
Home / Like you / Aching for you / Cold water coming / Some catch flies / Stained / Shake / Hope / Pale / Baseball field / Heaven / Gazebo tree / Gut pageant / Rock candy brains / Cartoons
CAD 8003CD / 2 Feb '98 / 4AD

Hertfordshire Chorus

☐ FOLLOW THAT STAR (Hertfordshire Chorus & Roger Sayer)
340152 / Nov '93 / Koch

Hertz

☐ TALES
ACVCD 12 / Jan '96 / ACV

Hervieux, Gilbert

☐ ARZOUSTAFF (Hervieux, Gilbert & Jacques Beauchamp)
EOG 101CD / Nov '96 / EOG

Herwig, Conrad

☐ LATIN SIDE OF JOHN COLTRANE, THE
Blessing / Love supreme / Blue train / Afro-blue / Naima / Satellite / Africa / After the rain / Impressions / India / Drum thing / Blessing (reprise)
TCD 4003 / Nov '96 / Astor Place

Hesitations

☐ SOUL SUPERMAN
She won't come back / You'll never know / You can't bypass love / I believe to my soul / That's what love is / Soul superman / Soul kind of love / I'm not built that way / I'll be right there / Wait a minute / Soul superman No.2 / Clap your hands
SSCD 002 / Dec '96 / Goldmine

Hesperus

☐ EARLY AMERICAN ROOTS
MMCD 216 / May '97 / Maggie's Music

☐ UNICORN
DORCD 80157 / Mar '98 / Dorian

Hess, Johnny

☐ ETOILES DE LA CHANSON
8415952 / Jul '96 / Music Memoria

Hess, Nigel

☐ WIND BAND MUSIC, THE
FLYCD 105 / Oct '92 / Fly

Hession, Carl

☐ CLASSIC IRISH AIRS AND DANCE MUSIC
Morning gallop / Glenroe / Galway suite / Morgan magan / Tricast / Sliabb geal gcua / Knefsky prospect / Chestnut lane / Oyster promenade / American reels / Ace and deuce of pipering / Olaim puins / My lagan love / Trilogy / Echoes / Blackbird / Final round/Who's turn
SH 53152 / Mar '98 / Shanachie

☐ OLD TIME NEW TIME
CEFCD 173 / Aug '95 / Gael Linn

☐ TRA
CEFCD 177 / Aug '97 / Dara

Hester, Carolyn

☐ AT TOWN HALL (The Complete Concert)
Come on back / Come on in / 2.10 train / Captain, my captain / Water is wide / Carry it on / High flying bird / Three young men / Outward bound / Weaving song / Sing hallelujah / That's my song / Summertime / It takes so long / Ain't that rain / Buckeye Jim / Will you send your love / Jute mill song / What's that I hear / Where did my little boy go / Sidewalk city / I saw her / Bad girl / Playboys and playgirls
BCD 15520 / Jul '90 / Bear Family

☐ DEAR COMPANION (2CD Set)
Swing and turn jubilee / Come back baby / I'll fly away / Dear companion / Los bibilicos / Once I had a sweetheart / Galway shawl / When Jesus lived in Galilee / Dink's song / Pobre de mi / Yarrow / Virgin Mary / My love is a rider / Gregorio cortez / Simple gits / Brave wolfe / Sally free and easy / I loved a lass / This life I'm living / Pera Stous / Tumbando cana / Coo-coo / Praties they grow small / East Virginia / Come O my love / I want Jesus / That's my song / Stay not late / Amapola / Ain't that rain / Momma's tough little soldier / Lonesome tears / Everytime / Can't help but wonder where I'm bound / Ten thousand candles / Times I've had / Jute mill song / Rivers of Texas / Earl morning / Don't ask questions / Reason to believe / Blues run the game / I love my dog / Bye bye brown eyes / One in a million sunshine girl / Majhires / Outside the window / Hello you tomorrows / Penny Lane / Blues run the game / Come back baby / Los bibilicos / I'll fly away / Virgin Mary / Lonesome tears / Summertime / I want Jesus / Lonesome tears / Outside the window / Lonesome tears
BCD 15701 / Oct '95 / Bear Family

☐ FROM THESE HILLS
RGFCD 033 / Aug '96 / Road Goes On Forever

☐ TEXAS SONGBIRD (Warriors Of The Rainbow/Music Medicine)
RGFCD 019 / Aug '94 / Road Goes On Forever

☐ TRADITIONAL ALBUM, THE
RGFCD 025 / Dec '95 / Road Goes On Forever

Heuser, Andreas

☐ CONTINUUM
BEST 1086CD / May '96 / Acoustic Music

Hewerdine, Boo

☐ BAPTIST HOSPITAL
Dreamlife / Love thieves / Holywater / Worlds end / Last cigarette / Baptist hospital / Joke / Greedy / Junk / Sycamore fall / Candyfloss / Song for a friend
0630120452 / Jan '96 / Blanco Y Negro

☐ EVIDENCE (Hewerdine, Boo & Darden Smith)
All I want is everything / Reminds me (a little of you) / These chains / Out of this world / Evidence / Who, what, when, where and why / Under the darkest moon / South by South West / First chill of Winter / Love is a strange hotel / Oil on the water / Town called blue
HAVENCD 6 / Nov '95 / Haven

Hewett, Howard

☐ IT'S TIME
Crystal clear / This love is forever / Your body needs healin' / For the lover in you / I wanna know you / Say goodbye / How do I know I love you / Love of your own / Just to keep you satisfied / On and on / Call his name
EXCDP 9 / Dec '94 / Expansion

Hewitt, Ben

☐ SPIRIT OF ROCK'N'ROLL, THE
Border City callgirl / Hobnobbin' with the goblins / I wanna love you tonight / Little elfin jive / Ophelia / Because I love you / Call Mama (on the phone) / Somebody wants to love you baby / Shirley Vee / Good times and some mighty fine rock'n'roll / Florida rain / Way down on your knees / Paying for your love / Buster Brown's got the blues / Bundle of love / Good times and some mighty fine rock'n'roll
BCD 16200 / Jun '97 / Bear Family

☐ YOU GOT ME SHOOK
For quite a while / I ain't givin' up nothin' / Patricia June / You break me up / I wanna do everything for you / My search / Queen in the kingdom of my heart / Bundle of love / Whirlwind blues / You got me shook / I want a new girl / My search / Slave girl / President's Walk / Way down on your knees / I'll get over you / Can I be the one / Yesterday's dream / I need your kind of love / Together / Just to spend one day with you
BCD 16199 / Dec '97 / Bear Family

Hex

☐ BIG BANG THEORY
LABEL1CD 42 / Nov '96 / Label One

Hexedene

☐ CHOKING ON LILIES
REC 039 / 16 Mar '98 / Reconstriction

Hexenhaus

☐ EDGE OF ETERNITY
Prelude / Toxic threat / Prime evil / Home sweet home (ward sweet ward) / House of lies / A temple for the soul / Eternal nightmare (ace one) / At the edge of eternity
CDATV 13 / May '90 / Active

Heyman, Richard X.

☐ CORNERSTONE
PPCD 52707 / 16 Feb '98 / Permanent

☐ CORNERSTONE
3027402 / 24 Feb '98 / Last Call

Heymann, Ann

☐ HARPERS LAND, THE (Heymann, Ann & Alison Kinnaird)
COMD 2012 / Feb '94 / Temple

☐ QUEEN OF HARPS
Queen of harps / Ex te lux oritur / Feachain gleis / Lamentation of youths / Sir thomas brook's pavan-lord sheffield's pavan / First irish jig-holyrood measure / Hawk of ballyshannon / Temple hill reel-temple hill jigs / Lament for the harp
COMD 2057 / Oct '94 / Temple

Heyward, Nick

☐ APPLE BED, THE
CRECD 210 / 16 Feb '98 / Creation

☐ GREATEST HITS OF NICK HEYWARD AND HAIRCUT 100, THE (Heyward, Nick & Haircut 100)
Favourite shirt (boy meets girl): *Haircut 100* / Love plus one: *Haircut 100* / Fantastic day: *Haircut 100* / Nobody's fool: *Haircut 100* / Calling Captain Autumn: *Haircut 100* / Whistle down the wind: *Heyward, Nick* / Take that situation: *Heyward, Nick* / Blue hat for a blue day: *Heyward, Nick* / On a Sunday: *Heyward, Nick* / Love all day (and night): *Heyward, Nick* / Warning sign: *Heyward, Nick* / Over the weekend: *Heyward, Nick* / Laura: *Heyward, Nick* / Kick of love: *Heyward, Nick* / Goodbye yesterday: *Heyward, Nick* / Day it rained forever: *Heyward, Nick*
74321446772 / Feb '97 / Camden

Heywood, Eddie

☐ CLASSICS 1944
CLASSICS 947 / 21 Aug '97 / Classics

Heywood, Heather

☐ BY YON CASTLE WA'
Sands of the shore / Far over the forth / For a new baby / False, false hae ye been / I hae but son / Wandering piper / Jamie / Wife of Usher's well / Mistress Heywood's fancy / Dowie dens of yarrow / Some people cry / MacCrimmon's sweetheart / Corncrake among the whinnie knows / Aye waukin' o / Young watters / Paul's song / MacCrimmon's lament
CDTRAX 054 / Dec '92 / Greentrax

☐ SOME KIND OF LOVE
Sally gardens / Lord Lovat / Song for Ireland / Some kind of love / Let no man steal your thyme / Bonnie laddie ye gang by me / My bonnie moorhen / Cruel mother / Wid ye gang love
CDTRAX 010 / Oct '94 / Greentrax

Heywood, Phil

☐ LOCAL JOE
ATM 1118 / Aug '96 / Atomic Theory

Hi-Fi

☐ FEAR CITY (Hi-Fi & Roadrunners)
VE 17CD / Mar '95 / Victory

Hi-Fi's

☐ FLAT IRON YEARS (Hi-Fi's & The Roadburners)
VR 074CD / 20 Jul '98 / Victory

Hi-Five

☐ GREATEST HITS
I like the way (The kissing game) / She's playing hard to get / I can't wait another minute / I just can't handle it / Quality time / Never should've let you go / What can I say to you (to justify my love) / Unconditional love / Birthday girl / What are you doin' tonight / What was then, this is now / She said
CHIP 155 / Mar '97 / Jive

☐ KEEP IT GOIN' ON
CHIP 131 / Nov '92 / Jive

Hi-Fives

☐ AND A WHOLE LOTTA YOU
LOOKOUT 135CD / Jan '97 / Lookout

Hi-Lo's

☐ BEST OF THE COLUMBIA YEARS, THE
379262 / Feb '97 / Koch

☐ CHERRIES AND OTHER DELIGHTS
Life is just a bowl of cherries / My sugar is so refined / April snow / Lady in red / Lulu's back in town / Lazy afternoon / I could write a book / Georgia on my mind / Fascinatin' rhythm / Rockin' chair / Small fry / Back home again in indiana / You must have been a beautiful baby / Down by the sally gardens / My little grass shack
HCD 603 / Mar '94 / Hindsight

Hi-Ryze

☐ SODIUM
GPRCD 10 / Mar '95 / GPR

Hi-Speed

☐ EROIKA CON ANIMAC PLENETICO
CMDD 00022 / Jun '97 / Creative Man

Hi-Standard

☐ GROWING UP
FAT 534CD / Jan '96 / Fatwreck Chords

Hi-Tech Roots Dynamics

☐ TOKYO DUB/BERLIN DUB
TBXCD 006 / Jun '96 / Top Beat

Hiatt, John

☐ HIATT COMES ALIVE AT BUDOKAN
Through your hands / Real fine love / Memphis in the meantime / Icy blue heart / Paper thin / Angel eyes / Your Dad did / Have a little faith in me / Drive South / Thing called love / Perfectly good guitar / Feels like rain / Tennessee plates / Lipstick sunset / Slow turning
5402842 / Nov '94 / A&M

☐ LITTLE HEAD
Little head / Pirate radio / My sweet girl / Feelin' again / Graduated / Sure Pinocchio / Runaway / Woman sawwed in half / Far as we go / After all this time
CDEST 2296 / Jun '97 / Parlophone

☐ PERFECTLY GOOD GUITAR
Something wild / Straight outta time / Perfectly good guitar / Buffalo river home / Angel / Blue telescope / Cross my finger / Old habits / Wreck of the Barbie Ferrari / When you old me tight / Permanent hurt / Loving a hurricane / I'll never get over you
5401302 / Sep '93 / A&M

☐ SLOW TURNING
Drive south / Trudy and Dave / Tennessee plates / Icy blue heart / Sometime other than now / Georgia Rae / Ride along / Slow turning / It'll come to you / Is anybody there / Paper thin / Feels like rain
CDA 5206 / Aug '88 / A&M

☐ SLUG LINE/TWO BIT MONSTERS
You used to kiss the girls / Negroes were dancing / Slug line / Madonna road / (no more) dancin' in the street / Long night / Night that kenny died / Radio girl / You're my love interest / Take off your uniform / Sharon's got a drugstore / Washable ink / Back to normal / Down in front / I spy (for the f.b.i.) / Pink bedroom / Good girl, bad world / Face the nation / Cop party / Back to the war / It hasn't happened yet / String pull job / New numbers
BGOCD 176 / Jun '93 / Beat Goes On

☐ STOLEN MOMENTS
Real fine love / Seven little indians / Child in the wild blue yonder / Back of my mind / Stolen moments / Bring back your love to me / Rest of the dream / Thirty years of tears / Rock back Billy / Listening to old voices / Through your hands / One kiss
3953102 / Apr '95 / A&M

☐ WALK ON
Cry love / You must go on / Walk on / Good as she could be / River knows your name / Native son / Dust down a country road / Ethylene / I can't wait / Shredding the document / Wrote it down and burned it / Your love is my rest / Friend of mine / Mile high
CDP 8334162 / Oct '95 / Capitol

Hiatus

☐ FROM RESIGNATION...TO REVOLT
POLLUTE 12 / Mar '94 / Sound Pollution

Hibbler, Al

☐ AFTER THE LIGHTS GO DOWN LOW
7567820442 / Jun '95 / Atlantic

☐ BEST OF AL HIBBLER, THE
VSD 5930 / 19 May '98 / Varese Sarabande

☐ STARRING AL HIBBLER/HERE'S HIBBLER
After the lights go down low / I don't stand a ghost of a chance with you / You'll never know / Night and day / Pennies from Heaven / Shanghai Lil / Stella by starlight / September in the rain / Where are you / Count every star / There are such things / Where or when / Trees / Sweet slumber / Do nothin' 'til you hear from me / Very thought of you / On a slow boat to China / Because of you / What would people say / Just a kid named Joe / I hadn't anyone till you / I'll get along somehow / It's been a long long time / Town crier
JASCD 605 / Aug '96 / Jasmine

Hicken, David

☐ SHADOW OF YOUTH
CDSGP 9022 / Jun '95 / Prestige

Hickey, Ersel

☐ BLUEBIRDS OVER THE MOUNTAINS
Bluebirds over the mountain (US Version) / Hangin' around / You never can tell / Wedding / Lover's land / Goin' down that road / Love in bloom / Another wasted day / You threw a dart / Shame on me / What do you want / Due time (Incomplete) / Mighty square love affair / Teardrops at dawn / Magical love / I guess you could call it love / Lips of roses / What have I done to me / Stardust brought me you / Roll on little river (Unknown) / Don't be afraid of love / People gotta talk / I can't love another / Bluebirds over the mountain (Can version)
BCD 15676 / May '93 / Bear Family

Hickman, John

☐ DON'T MEAN MAYBE
Don't mean maybe / Salt river / Turkey knob / Birmingham fling / Sweet Dixie / Sally Goodin / Train 405 / Banjo signal / Ghost dance / Pike county breakdown / Goin' to town / Dixie breakdown
ROUCD 0101 / Feb '95 / Rounder

Hickman, Sara

☐ MISFITS
SHCD 8026 / Apr '97 / Shanachie

☐ TWO KINDS OF LAUGHTER
Two kinds of laughter / Take whatever I can get / I wear the crown / Coolness by mistake / Eight / Secret family / Look at it this way / Optimistic fool / One in our happiness / E cosi desio mem mena / Comets over Costa Rica / Let go
SHANCD 8029 / Apr '98 / Shanachie

Hickoids

☐ HICKOID HEAVEN
EFA 11340CD / Sep '93 / Musical Tragedies

Hicks, Bob

☐ FIDDLE PATCH
ROUCD 0416 / 19 Jan '98 / Rounder

Hicks, Dan

☐ RETURN TO HICKSVILLE
HIPD 40053 / 16 Feb '98 / Hippo

☐ VERY BEST OF DAN HICKS, THE (Hicks, Dan & His Hot Licks)
You got to believe / Walkin' one and only / O'reilly at the bar / Moody richard (the innocent bystander) / Flight of the fly / I scare myself / Laughing song / Canned music / I'm an old cowhand / Woe, the luck / Cowboy's dream no.19 / Lonely madman / My old timey baby / Vivando / Pay day blues / Sure beats me / Euphonius whale / It's not my time to go / Presently in the past / Sweetheart / 'long come a viper / Success / Cheaters don't win
SEECD 65 / Aug '91 / See For Miles

Hicks, Edna

☐ EDNA HICKS VOL.1
DOCD 5428 / Jul '96 / Document

Hicks, Hinda

☐ HINDA
I wanna be your lady / You think you own me / My eyes / Love reaction / If you want me / Who's saying / On and on / Move closer / Here for life / True love / When you touch me there / Truly / Child
CID 8068 / 24 Aug '98 / Island

Hicks, Joe

☐ SOMETHING SPECIAL (Hicks, Joe & Jimmy Hughes)
Team: *Hicks, Joe* / Nobody knows you (when you're down and out): *Hicks, Joe* / Train of thought: *Hicks, Joe* / Rock me baby: *Hicks, Joe* / Could it be love: *Hicks, Joe* / Rusty old halo: *Hicks, Joe* / All in: *Hicks, Joe* / Water water: *Hicks, Joe* / Ruby Dean: *Hicks, Joe* / I like everything about you: *Hughes, Jimmy* / Let 'em down baby: *Hughes, Jimmy* / I'm so glad: *Hughes, Jimmy* / Lay it on the line: *Hughes, Jimmy* / Sweet things you do: *Hughes, Jimmy* / Chains of love: *Hughes, Jimmy* / I'm not ashamed to beg or plead: *Hughes, Jimmy* / It's all up to you: *Hughes, Jimmy* / Lock me up: *Hughes, Jimmy* / What side of the door: *Hughes, Jimmy* / Peeped around yonder's bend: *Hughes, Jimmy* / Just ain't as strong as I used to be: *Hughes, Jimmy* / Did you forget: *Hughes, Jimmy*
CDSXD 098 / Jul '93 / Stax

Hicks, John

☐ BEYOND EXPECTATIONS
RSRCD 130 / Oct '94 / Reservoir

☐ GENTLE RAIN
SSCD 8062 / Jan '96 / Sound Hills

☐ HELLS BELLS
CDGR 251 / 29 Jun '98 / Charly

☐ IN CONCERT
Some other time / Some other spring / Paul's pal / Pas de trois (Dance for three) / Say it (over and over again) / Soul eyes / Take the coltrane / Oblivion
ECD 22048 / Mar '93 / Evidence

☐ LUMINOUS (Hicks, John & Elise Wood)
ECD 220332 / Sep '92 / Evidence

☐ SOME OTHER TIME
Naima's love song / Mind wine / Peanut butter in the desert / Ghost of yesterday / Some other time / With malice towards none / Dark side, light side / Night journey / After the morning / Epistrophy
ECD 220972 / Jul '94 / Evidence

☐ TWO OF A KIND (Hicks, John & Ray Drummond)
I'll be around / Take the Coltrane / Very early / Getting sentimental over you / For Heaven's sake / Come rain or come shine / Rose without a thorn / Without a song
ECD 220172 / Jul '92 / Evidence

Hicks, Taral

☐ THIS TIME
5307582 / 13 Oct '97 / Polydor

Hicksville Bombers

☐ HICKSVILLE BOMBERS, THE
RAUCD 021 / Oct '96 / Raucous

Hidalgo, Giovanni

☐ VILLA HIDALGO
Villa hidalgo / Tropica / Ianmanuel / Amunizaje / Bahia san juan / Lisl / Yuliria / Mercy, mercy, mercy / Songo pa' tl
MES 158172 / Nov '92 / Messidor

Hideaway

☐ UNABLE TO LABEL
BSCD 037 / Jan '97 / Blue Sting

Hiding In The Tall Grass

☐ COME AS YOU ARE
Ethemeral vision / Applied plant higher / Voodoo feline of larkspur lotion / Police corruption / Bored again Christian / Murderous clown / Grist for my poetry / Come as you are / United we glide / Subclout (applied plant conclusive)
TOYCD 1004 / 26 Aug '97 / Intrinsic

Hifi & the Roadburners

☐ LIVE IN FEAR CITY CHICAGO
VR 058CD / 28 Jul '97 / Victory

Higginbotham, J.C.

☐ INTRODUCTION TO J.C. HIGGINBOTHAM 1929-1940, AN
4037 / Mar '95 / Best Of Jazz

Higgins, Billy

☐ MR. BILLY HIGGINS
Dance of the clones / John Coltrane / Morning awakening / Humility / East side stomp
ECD 220612 / Nov '93 / Evidence

☐ SOWETO
1231412 / Apr '94 / Red

Higgins, Chuck

☐ PACHUKO HOP
Pachuko hop / Motor head baby / Blues and mambo / Long long time / Chuck's fever / Iron pipe / Big fat Mama / Real gone hound dog / Boyle heights / Papa Charlie / Rooster / Duck walk / Stormy / Just won't treat me rite
CDCHD 394 / Mar '92 / Ace

Higgins, Eddie

☐ BY REQUEST
SACD 104 / Oct '93 / Solo Art

☐ EDDIE HIGGINS/THE SWINGIN'EST (Higgins, Eddie/Benny Green)
VJ 015 / 24 Apr '98 / Vee Jay

☐ IN CHICAGO
SACD 124 / Aug '95 / Solo Art

☐ PORTRAIT IN BLACK AND WHITE
SSC 1072D / Feb '97 / Sunnyside

☐ PRELUDE TO A KISS
PS 010CD / Sep '95 / P&S

☐ THOSE QUIET DAYS
SSC 1052D / Jun '91 / Sunnyside

Higgins, Gary

☐ RED HASH
FLASH 65 / 20 Jul '98 / Flash

Higgs, Joe

☐ FAMILY
SHANCD 43053 / '88 / Shanachie

☐ TRIUMPH
ALCS 8313 / Aug '92 / Alligator

High

☐ HYPE
Better left untold / Healer / Sweet liberty / This is your life / Let nothing come between us / Goodbye girl / Keep on coming / Slowly happens here / Can I be / Lost and found
8283542 / Jan '93 / London

☐ SOMEWHERE SOON
Box set go / Take your time / This is my world / Rather be Marsanne / So I can see / Minor turn / Dream of dinesh / Up and down / PWA / Somewhere soon
8282242 / Oct '90 / London

High Back Chairs

☐ CURIOUSITY AND RELIEF
Share / One small step / Dream of a day / Unending / Fuj / Summer
DIS 75CD / Nov '92 / Dischord

High Country

☐ EARTHQUAKE, THE
Earthquake / That dawn the day you left me / Tears in the rain / These blues they got me / Poor wayfaring stranger / Living in the springtime / Troubles all my own / Saturday matinee / Lost yesterdays / Hundred love letters / Imitation of the blues / Big country
SCR 48 / Feb '98 / Strictly Country

High Level Ranters

☐ BONNY PIT LADDIE, THE
Hewer / Doon the waggonway / Miner's life / I wish pay Friday would come / Augengeich disaster / Collier's rant / Farewell to the Monty / Putter / Little chance / My gaffer's bait / Coal owner and the pitman's wife / Blackleg miner / Miners' lockout / South Medomsley strike / Durham lockout / Aa'm glad the strike's done / Colliers pay week / I'll have a collier / Instrumental selection / I'll make her fain to follow me / Joyful days are coming / Get her bo / Stoneman's song / Hartley calamity / Bonnie Woodha' / Banks of the Dee / Bonnie pit laddie, The (instrumental) / Bonnie pit laddie, The (vocal)
TSCD 486 / Jul '97 / Topic

☐ ENGLISH SPORTING BALLADS (High Level Ranters & Martyn Wyndham-Read)
CMBCD 002 / Apr '98 / CMB

☐ NORTHUMBERLAND FOREVER
Shew's the way to Wallington / Peacock followed the hen / Sandgate girl's lament / Elsie Marley / Bellingham boat / Lamb skinnet / Adam Buckham / Meggy's foot / Lads of North Tyne / Redesdale hornpipe / Hexhamshire lass / Breakdown / Blanchland races / Lads of Alnwick / Lamshaw's fancy / Byker hill / Whinham's reel / Nancy / Because he was a bonny lad / Salmon tails up the water / Sweet Hesleyside / Dance to your daddy / Billy boy / Nae guid luck aboot the house / Mi laddie sits ower late up / Keel row / Kafoozalum / Washing day
TSCD 483 / Jul '97 / Topic

High Llamas

☐ COLD AND BOUNCY
VVR 1000732 / 26 Jan '98 / Alpaca Park

☐ GIDEON GAYE
VVR 1001072 / 26 Jan '98 / Alpaca Park

☐ HAWAII
VVR 1001092 / 26 Jan '98 / Alpaca Park

☐ HAWAII (2CD Set)
270042 / 27 Apr '98 / Alpaca Park

☐ HIGH LLAMAS
Perry Como / Edge of the sun / Pretty boy / Hoping you would change your mind / C'mon let's go / Paint and pets / Doggy / Half face cat / Trees / Have you heard the latest news
DIAB 866 / 6 Jul '98 / Diablo

☐ SANTA BARBARA
VVR 1001082 / 26 Jan '98 / Alpaca Park

High Noon

☐ GLORY BOUND
Train of misery / Midnight shift / Rockin' wildcat / Glory bound / Too much trouble / Baby let's play house / Hold me baby / All night long / Late train / Mona Lisa / Your new flame / Who was that cat / Crazy fever / Don't have a heart left to break / Rocks me right / Feelin' no pain / Branded outlaw / Hannah Lee / Don't have a heart left to break (alt.take) / Beaumont boogie / Ain't it wrong / Havin' a whole lotta fun
GRCD 6039 / Mar '97 / Goofin'

☐ LIVE IN TEXAS AND JAPAN
Rattlesnake man / Branded outlaw / I'm not blue / When she's good / Tears keep fallin' / Rockin' wildcat / My ex is why / Devil woman / My heart cries yes / Flatland saturday night / Rock too slow / Ain't it wrong / Glory bound / Who was that cat / Stranger things / How come it / Mona Lisa
WMCD 1063 / May '97 / Watermelon

☐ STRANGER THINGS
GRCD 6060 / Nov '96 / Goofin'

High Rise

☐ DISALLOW
PSFD 78 / 16 Feb '98 / PSF

☐ DISPERSION
PSFD 26 / 16 Feb '98 / PSF

☐ HIGH RISE 2
PSFD 2 / 16 Feb '98 / PSF

High Society

☐ HIGH SOCIETY
Gotta get out of this rut / I never go out in the rain / Talk with your father / Late late train / Dancing in the moonlight / Top hat and tails / Mama said / Paper cup / Madge / I shouldn't fall in love with you / I can sing high / Walking down the strand / Private eye / Beautiful evening / All my life I gave you nothing / Powder blue / Dance till dawn
CYBVP 002CD / Jul '97 / Cyberdisk

High Strings

☐ OCEANS APART
Wagoner / Star of the County Down / Poppy leaf / Irish washerwoman / Der er solskinn I ver tone / It's only a paper moon / Ballad of Sally Ann / Soft as a whisper / Tommy Tarbukas / Greensleeves / Mrs. McLeod / Soldier's joy / Music of Spey / Walking the dug / Westphalia waltz / Stones rag / Ross Memorial Hospital / Wing Commander Donald MacKenzie / Somewhere over the rainbow / Arkansas traveller
HRMCD 003 / Feb '98 / Highlander

High Tea

☐ NEW ST. GEORGE, THE
FE 1415 / Nov '94 / Folk Era

High Tide

☐ PRECIOUS CARGO
AK 002 / 15 Jun '98 / Akarma

☐ SEA SHANTIES/HIGH TIDE
Futilist's lament / Death warmed up / Pushed, but not forgotten / Walking down their outlook / Missing out / Nowhere / Blankman cries again / Joke / Saneonymous
CZ 530 / Aug '94 / EMI

Higham, Darrel

☐ HIGH CLASS BABY
GRCD 6090 / Jul '98 / Goofin'

☐ HOWLIN' AT MY BABY
MCG 20029 / May '98 / Vampirella

☐ MOBILE CORROSION
Like a brand new man / If you can live with it / Long lonely road / Deep in the heart of Texas / I like me just fine / Second hand information / In my heart / No will will grieve / Revenue man / Country Lila Rhue / You were right I was wrong / I've been gone a long time / Don't bug me baby / Amanda's song / Travis pickin' / Life goes on / Rockin' band blues
NERCD 082 / Oct '95 / Nervous

Higher Heights

☐ TWINKLE IN A POLISH STYLEE
NGCD 537 / Jan '93 / Twinkle

Higher Intelligence Agency

☐ FREE FLOATER
Elapse / Hubble / Fleagle / Thirteen / Skank / Tortoise / Ting / Pinkgreen / UHI / Taz
RBADCD 13 / Sep '95 / Beyond

☐ POLAR SEQUENCES (Higher Intelligence Agency & Biosphere)
RBADCD 17 / Aug '96 / Beyond

Higher Than God

☐ DELIRIO CALDO
EFA 123322 / Jul '97 / Sideburn

Highland Connection

☐ GAINING GROUND
Carn na caillich / Knockdhu reel / Helsinki harbour / My tocher's the jewel / Mrs. Major L. Stewart of the island / Of java and c / Haud yer tongue Dear Sally / Campbell's roup / Seven seas hornpipe / Losing ground
CDTRAX 087 / Jan '95 / Greentrax

Highlander

☐ BORN TO BE A WARRIOR
Born to be a warrior / Journey South / Into battle / First time / I heard them cry / Run like the wind / Only one road / Homecoming / 1328 / Homeland
CDLDL 1201 / Feb '97 / Lochshore

Highlanders Regt.

☐ SPIRIT OF THE HIGHLANDS, THE
LCOM 5266 / Feb '98 / Lismor

Hightower Brothers

☐ BEST OF THE HIGHTOWN BROTHERS, THE
NASH 4004 / Feb '96 / Nashboro

Highway 101

☐ 101 SQUARED
9257422 / Sep '88 / Curb

☐ COUNTRY CLASSICS
You baby you / Home on the range / Tell me more / No chance to dance / Who's gonna love you / Last frontier / Fastest healin' broken heart / Love walks / You are what you do / I wonder where the love goes
CDMFP 6329 / Apr '97 / Music For Pleasure

☐ REUNITED (Highway 101 & Paulette Carlson)
Where'd you get your cheatin' from / Bed you made for me / Holdin' on / Hearts on the run / Setting me up / She don't have the heart to love you / Texas girl / All the reasons why / Walkin',talkin',cryin', barely beatin' broken heart / I've got your number / It must be love
NC 0101 / Nov '96 / Nashville Connection

Highway 13

☐ BEEN UP TO DEVIL'S BUSINESS
GHCD 1060 / 5 Jan '98 / Get Hip

Highway QC's

☐ COUNT YOUR BLESSINGS
Somewhere to lay my head / Everyman, woman and child / I'll trust his word / I dreamed that heaven was like this / Pray, child of god / Something on my mind / He lifted up my burdens / Count your blessings / We're working hard / Jesus I'm waiting / I heard / Great trumpet / I'll be satisfied / Amazing grace / He said / Teach me / I used to wonder / Milky white way / I'll see jesus too
CPCD 8113 / Jul '95 / Charly

Highwaymen

☐ ROAD GOES ON FOREVER, THE
Devil's right hand / Live forever / Everybody gets crazy / It is what it is / I do believe / End to understanding / True love travels a gravel road / Death and hell / Waiting for a long time / Here comes that rainbow again / Road goes on forever
CDEST 2253 / Apr '95 / Liberty

Highwoods String Band

☐ FEED YOUR BABIES ONIONS
ROUCD 11569 / Feb '95 / Rounder

Higsons

☐ IT'S A WONDERFUL LIFE
I don't want to live with monkeys / Got to let this heat out / Surrender / Dash to the shops / Lost and the lonely / (My love is) Bent (at both ends) / It goes waap / Crash / We will never grow old / Touchdown / Burn the whole thing down / Ha ha / Music to watch girls by / Push out the boat / Attack of the cannibal zombie businessmen / Clanking my bucket / I can hear voices / Do the jerk / Walk on water / 1958 / It's a wonderful life
HUX 004 / 25 May '98 / Hux

Hijack

☐ HORNS OF JERICHO, THE
Intro (Phantom of the opera) / Syndicate outta jail / Daddy rich / Back to Brixton / Airwave hijack / Hijack the terrorist group / Badman is robbin' / I had to serve you / Don't go with strangers / Brother versus brother / Paranoid schizophrenic with homicidal tendencies / Contract
7599263862 / Oct '91 / WEA

Hijas Del Sol

☐ KOTTO
Ri'oko / Sipolo / La despedida / Obe'ri / Kottto / Hoea / Kumbala / E riwey / Esa'ri / Oro negro / Experiencia / Toli kope / El nino Africano
INT 32292 / 26 May '98 / Intuition

Hildegarde

☐ DARLING, JE VOUS AIME BEAUCOUP
PASTCD 7066 / Jul '95 / Flapper

☐ DARLING, JE VOUS AIME BEAUCOUP
Darling Je vous aime beaucoup / Honey coloured moon / I believe in miracles / Listen to the german band / For me, for you / Gloomy Sunday / Isn't this a lovely day (to be caught in the rain) / Cheek to cheek / Glory of love / Hildegarde look back (Medley) / Pretty girl is like a melody / Love walked in / It's the natural thing to do / Will you remember / There's a small hotel / This year's kisses / Pennies from heaven / (I love you) for sentimental reasons / Room with a view / My ship / Saga of Jenny Pts. 1 and 2 / Lili Marlene / Goodnight angel
CDAJA 5161 / May '95 / Living Era

Hiliners

☐ BOUND FOR GLORY
DOLECD 109 / Jan '95 / Dojo

Hill & Wiltchinsky

☐ LATIN MOODS (2CD Set)
Girl from Ipanema / One note samba / Meditation / Volare / Spanish eyes / Quiet nights of quiet stars / Begin the beguine / How insensitive / Latin nights / Guantamera / Desafinado / Cubana / Wave / Agua de beber / Kiss of fire / Gift / Once I loved / Night and day / Lambada / Summer samba / Spanish harlem / Dindi / La cumparsita / Amor / On a clear day (You can see forever) / Evergreen / La bamba / Tango / Light my fire / Peal of bells / Killing me softly / Brasilia / Copacabana / Breeze from Rio / Tico tico / Perfidia
3036000122 / Jun '98 / Carlton

☐ LATIN NIGHTS
Girl from Ipanema / One note samba / Volare / Spanish eyes / Begin the beguine / Latin nights / Guantanamera / Spanish Harlem / Amor / On a clear day / Light my fire / Brasilia / Breeze from Rio / Perfidia / Lambada / Copacabana / La bamba / Summer samba
ECD 3281 / Jan '97 / K-Tel

☐ ROMANTIC GUITARS (4CD Set)
Nights in white satin / If / Walk on by / Annie's song / When I fall in love / Autumn leaves / So deep is the night / And I love her so / Girl / Faerie queen / While my guitar gently weeps / Air on a g string / Dreams / Mountains of Mourne / Melodia / This boy / Hello / First time I ever saw your face / Way we were / And I love her / Cavatina / Music of the night / Love story / Michelle / Londonderry air (Danny boy) / El noi de la mare / Fool on the hill / Romance in d / Because / As I roved out / Elvira Madigan / Romanza / Three times a lady / I know him so well / Sound of silence / Long and winding road / Walking on air / Memory / Barcarolle / I'll take you home again Kathleen / Fur Elise / Norwegian wood (this bird has flown) / Feelings / Without you / Waves / Step inside love / Minstral boy / Ave maria / Lady in red / Groovy kind of love / Greatest love of all / Windmills of your mind / Sweet sixteen / Mona Lisa / Adagio Rodrigo / For the love of Annie / Something / Here there and everywhere / You've got a friend / My love's an arbutus / Jesu joy of man's desire / Songs without words / If I fell in love with you / Gymnopedie
QUAD 012 / Nov '96 / Tring

Hill, Alex

☐ ALEX HILL 1928-1934
Parkway stomp / Mississippi wobble / She's funny that way / Shake that jelly roll / Chicago rhythm / Once or twice / Eel / Tennessee twilight / Madam dynamite / Home cooking / Stompin' 'em down / Tack head blues / Dyin' with the blues / Toogaloo shout / St.James' infirmary / Southbound / Southbound / I'm having my fun / You've had your way / Ain't it nice / Functionizin' / Song on the plow / Let's have a jubilee
CBC 1050 / 20 Apr '98 / Timeless Jazz

Hill, Andrew

☐ FACES OF HOPE
1210102 / Oct '90 / Soul Note

☐ LIVE AT MONTREUX
Snake hip waltz / Nefertisis / Come Sunday / Relativity
FCD 41023 / Dec '87 / Freedom

☐ POINT OF DEPARTURE
New monastery / Spectrum / Dedication / Flight 19 / Dedication / Refuge
7841672 / 1 Jun '98 / Blue Note

☐ SHADES
1211132 / Jan '91 / Soul Note

☐ SPIRAL
Tomorrow / Laverne / Message / Invitation / Today / Spiral / Quiet dawn
FCD 41007 / Sep '87 / Freedom

☐ STRANGER SERENADE (Hill, Andrew Trio)
1210132 / Aug '91 / Soul Note

Hill, Bertha

☐ COMPLETE RECORDED WORKS 1925-29 (Hill, Bertha 'Chippie')
DOCD 5330 / Mar '95 / Document

Hill, Buck

☐ CAPITAL HILL
MCD 5384 / Sep '92 / Muse

☐ NORTHSEA FESTIVAL (2CD Set) (Hill, Buck Quartet)
SCCD 37035 / 5 Jan '98 / Steeplechase

Hill, Dan

☐ GREATEST HITS AND MORE
341852 / Nov '95 / Koch International

☐ I'M DOING FINE
332192 / Dec '96 / Koch International

Hill, Faith

☐ IT MATTERS TO ME
Someone else's dream / You can't lose me / Room in my heart / Keep walkin' on / You will be mine / I can't do that anymore / Man's home is his castle / Let's go to vegas / Bed of roses / It matters to me
9362458722 / Aug '95 / Warner Bros.

☐ TAKE ME AS I AM
Take me as I am / Wild one / Just about now / Piece of my heart / I've got this friend / Life's too short to love like that / But I will / Just around the eyes / Go the distance / I would be stronger than that
9362453892 / Jun '94 / Warner Bros.

Hill, Joe

☐ DON'T MOURN - ORGANISE (Songs Of Labour Songwriter Joe Hill) (Various Artists)
SFCD 40026 / Nov '94 / Smithsonian Folkways

Hill, Jordan

☐ JORDAN HILL
For the love of you / You got no right / Ride / I just had to hear your voice / For the love of you (dance mix) / Remember me this way / Until the end of time / Make it right / Never should have let you go / Too much heaven / Got to be real / How many times / Slip away
7567828492 / Sep '96 / Atlantic

Hill, Michael

☐ BLOODLINES (Hill, Michael Blues Mob)
AL 4821 / Jul '94 / Alligator

☐ HAVE MERCY (Hill, Michael Blues Mob)
ALCD 4845 / Oct '96 / Alligator

☐ NEW YORK STATE OF BLUES (Hill, Michael Blues Mob)
Long hot night / Soul doin' time / Young folks blues / Papa was a rollin' stone/Mama sang the blues / Anytime anywhere / New York State of blues / Living for the city / This is my job / Up and down the stairs / Never give up on you
ALCD 4858 / Jun '98 / Alligator

Hill, Noel

☐ HILL & LINNANE (Hill, Noel & Tony Linnane)
Humours of Ballyconnell / Drunken landlady / Ryan's reel / Geese in the bog / Joe Cooley's hornpipe / Miss Monaghan / Skylark / Foxhunter / Reevey's reel / Golden keyboard / Killoran's reel / Mountain road / Anderson's reel / Carthy's / Sweeney's dream / Johnny Cope / Scotsman over the border / Tom Billy's jig / Pigeon on the gate / Daniel O'Connell / Home ruler / Kitty's wedding / Lady Ann Montgomery / Cooley's reel
TARACD 2006 / 5 May '98 / Tara

☐ IRISH CONCERTINA, THE
Last night's fun/Trip to Durrow / Boy in the bush / Kiss the maid behind the barrel/ Dublin reel / Laird of Drumblair / Pigeon on the gate/Sean sa cheo / Farewell to Ireland / Old goman's reel / Wind that shakes the barley / Taimse I'm chodladh / Wise maid/Bells of Tipperary / Gold ring/Larks in the morning / Salamanca reel / Over the moor to Maggie / Chicago reel / An draigheann / Thrush in the morning / Drunken sailor / Moving clouds/Devanny's goat/McDermott's reel
CCF 21CD / Oct '88 / Claddagh

Hill, Teddy

☐ CLASSICS 1935-1937
CLASSICS 645 / Nov '92 / Classics

☐ UPTOWN RHAPSODY
Lookie lookie here comes Cookie / Got me doin' things / When the robin sings her song again / When love knocks on your heart / Uptown rhapsody / At the rug cutter's ball / Blue rhythm fantasy / Passionette / Love bug will bite you / Would you like to buy a dream / Big boy blue / Where is the sun / Harlem, twister / Marie / I know now / Lady who couldn't be kissed / You and me that used to be / Study in brown / Twilight in Turkey / China boy / San Anton / I'm happy darling, dancing with you / Yours and mine / I'm feelin' like a million / King Porter stomp
HEPCD 1033 / Mar '92 / Hep

Hill, Tiny

☐ TINY HILL & HIS HILLTOPPERS 1943-1944
CCD 55 / Jan '94 / Circle

Hill, Tommy

☐ GET READY BABY
Ain't nothing like loving / In the middle of the morning / Can't help / Life begins at four o'clock / Oh get ready, Baby / Love words / Do me a favour / Have a little faith in me / O get ready baby / In the middle of the morning
BCD 15709 / Mar '93 / Bear Family

Hill, Vince

☐ I WILL ALWAYS LOVE YOU
I will always love you / Desperado / Love dies hard / Crying in the wind / Sweet dreams / Pray for love / When you walk through life / I want to know you / Sweet music man / Loving arms / It's not supposed to be that way / Sea of heartbreak / Always on my mind
GRCD 24 / Feb '89 / Grasmere

☐ LOVE SONGS
I will always love you / Desperado / Love dies hard / Crying in the wind / Sweet dreams / Pray for love / When you walk through life / I want to know you / Sweet music man / Loving arms / It's not supposed to be that way / Sea of heartbreak / Always on my mind
PWKM 4074 / Feb '96 / Carlton

☐ VERY BEST OF VINCE HILL, THE
Very thought of you / I only have eyes for you / Sentimental journey / Love me tender / After you've gone / Folks who live on the hill / Among my souvenirs / Old feeling / Nevertheless / I'll get by / September song / Catch a falling star / Somewhere my love / All the things you are / Roses of Picardy / Look around (and I'll find you there) / Edelweiss / Where do I begin / Close to you / I will wait for you / Spanish eyes
CDMFP 6249 / Aug '96 / Music For Pleasure

Hill, Warren

☐ SHELTER
1046770432 / May '97 / Warner Bros.

Hill, Z.Z.

☐ BRAND NEW Z.Z. HILL, THE
It ain't no use / Ha ha (laughing song) / Second chance / Our love is getting better / Faithful and true / Chockin' kind / Hold back (one man at a time) / Man needs a woman (woman needs a man) / Early in the morning / I think I'd do it / She's all I got / Raining on a sunny day / Sweeter than sweetness / Sidewalks, fences and walls / I did the woman wrong / Yours love / Laid back and easy / You and me together forever / Ain't nothin' in the news (but the blues) / Did I come back to soon (or stay away too long) / Wy whole world has ended (without you) / Cuss the wind
CDCHD 532 / Jun '94 / Ace

☐ DOWN HOME SOUL OF Z.Z. HILL, THE
Baby I'm sorry / I need someone (to love me) / Have mercy someone / Kind of love I want / Hey little girl / I found love / No more doggin' / You can't hide a heartache / That's it / Happiness is all I need / Everybody has to cry / Nothing can change this love / Set your sights higher / Steal away / You're gonna need my loving / You're gonna make me cry / Oh darling / If I could do it all over / You don't love me / You won't hurt no more / What more / You got what I need
CDKEN 099 / Sep '92 / Kent

☐ MAN NEEDS A WOMAN, A
Chokin' kind / Hold back / Man needs a woman / Early in the morning / I think I'd do it / Ha ha (laughing song) / It ain't no use / Second chance / Our love is getting better / Faithful and true
AIM 2007CD / May '97 / Aim

Hill-Louis, Joe

☐ BE BOP BOY, THE
When I am gone / Dorothy Mae / She may be yours / Keep your arms around me / Got me a new woman / I'm a poor boy / In the mood / West winds are blowin' / Little Walter's boogie / Grandmother got Grandfather told / We all gotta go sometime / Walter's boogie / Come see me / Worry you off my mind / Reap what you sow / Walter's instrumental / Hydramatic / Woman tiger / Man keep your arms around me / She may be yours (take 3) / All gotta go sometime / Shine boy
BCD 15524 / Jun '92 / Bear Family

Hillage, Steve

☐ FISH RISING
Fish / Meditation of the snake / Solar musick suite / Salmon song / Aftaglid
CDV 2031 / Jun '87 / Virgin

☐ FOR TO NEXT - AND NOT OR
These uncharted lands / Kamikaze eyes / Alone / Anthems for the blind / Bright future / Frame by frame / Waiting / Glory
CDV 2244 / Jul '90 / Virgin

☐ GREEN
Sea nature / Ether ships / Musick of the trees / Palm trees (love guitar) / Unidentified (flying being) / UFO over Paris / Leylines to Glassdom / Crystal City / Activation meditation / Glorious OM riff
CDV 2098 / Jun '90 / Virgin

☐ L
Hurdy gurdy man / Hurdy gurdy glissando / Elecktrick Gypsies / Om nama shivaya / Lunar musick suite / It's all too much
CDVIP 184 / Apr '97 / Virgin VIP

☐ LIVE HERALD
Salmon song / Dervish riff / Castle in the clouds / Light in the sky / Searching for the spark / Electric gypsies / Radiom / It's all too much / Talking to the sun / 1988 aktivator / New age synthesis (unzipping the zype) / Healing feeling / Lunar musick suite / Meditation of the dragon / Golden vibe
CDVM 3502 / Jun '90 / Virgin

☐ MOTIVATION RADIO
Hello dawn / Motivation / Light in the sky / Radio / Wait one moment / Saucer surfing / Searching for the spark / Octave doctors and the crystal machine / Not fade away (glide forever)
CDV 2777 / Jun '88 / Virgin

☐ OPEN
Day after day / Getting in tune / Open / Definite activity / Don't dither do it / Fire inside / Earthrise
CDV 2135 / Jun '90 / Virgin

☐ RAINBOW DOME MUSICK
Garden of paradise / Four ever rainbow
CDVR 1 / Jun '88 / Virgin

Hille, Sid

☐ DUNJIN'S DANCE
Dunjin's dance / Searching the quiet place / Notes from a traveller / Temple of Geha / Mombassa afrique / Little mountain / Last moment / Don't lose that number
AL 73022 / Nov '96 / A

Hille, Veda

☐ WOMEN IN (E)MOTION FESTIVAL
Driven / Precious heart / Slumber Queen / Instructions / Strange sad / With no caring / Old song / 26 years / '79 rose / Stupid polka / And birds / Driven
T&M 111 / Nov '96 / Tradition & Moderne

Hiller, Holger

☐ AS IS
Koniginnen / Sing songs / Bacillus culture / Sur la tete / Neighbours / Abacus / Gut und bose / You / Mosaik / Egg / Trojan ponies / Cuts both ways
CDSTUMM 60 / Sep '91 / Mute

☐ OBEN IM ECK
We don't write anything on paper / Or so / Tiny little cloud / Whippets / Waltz / Oben im eck (2 versions) / Warm glass / Die blatter, die blatter... / Sirtakl / 48 (achtund vierzig) / Kissen
CDSTUMM 38 / Nov '86 / Mute

Hilliard Ensemble

☐ 17TH/18TH CENTURY SONGS & CATCHES
By a bank as I lay / Tho' I am young / Lost is my quiet / We be three poor mariners / Sweeter than roses / I spy Celia / Since time so kind to us does prove / Orpheus and Euridice / Here's that will challenge all the fair / Which is the properest day to drink / Chloe found Amyntas / Here lies a woman / On thy banks gentle Stour / So well Corinna likes the joy / My man John, a riddle / Street intrigue / When the cock begins to crow
EC 33222 / Nov '96 / Saga Classics

☐ CODEX SPECIALNIK
Exordium quadruplate / Exordium quadruplate / In natalia domini / Sophia nascitur / Congaudemus / Magnum miraculum / Nibis est natus / Salve mater gracie / Christus iam surrexit / Presulem / Paraneuma eructemus / Presidiorum erogatrix / Pneuma eucaristiarum / Terrigenarum / Pulcherrima rosa / Chorus iste / Bud' buoho chvala cest / O virens virginum / Kyrie / Gloria / Tota pulchra es / Credo / Ave pura tu puella / Sanctus / Ave maria
4478072 / Apr '95 / ECM

☐ HILLIARD SONGBOOK, THE
4532592 / Oct '96 / ECM

☐ PEROTIN
8377512 / Jan '90 / ECM

Hillier, Paul

☐ PROENSA
8373602 / Apr '89 / ECM

Hillman, Chris

☐ BAKERSFIELD BOUND (Hillman, Chris & Herb Pedersen)
Playboy / Which one is to blame / Close up the honky tonks / Brand new heartache / Congratulations anyway / It's not love (but it's not bad) / He doesn't deserve you anymore / There goes my love / My baby's gone / Lost highway / Time goes so slow / Just tell me darlin' / Bakersfield bound
SHCD 3850 / Mar '98 / Sugar Hill

☐ DESERT ROSE
Why you been gone so long / Somebody's back in town / Wall around your heart / Rough and rowdy ways / Desert rose / Running the roadblocks / I can't keep you in love with me / Treasure of love / Ashes of love / Turn your radio on
SHCD 3743 / Jun '97 / Sugar Hill

☐ HILLMEN, THE (Hillmen)
Brown mountain light / Ranger's command / Sangeree / Bluegrass choppere / Barbara Allen / Fair and tender ladies / Goin' up / When the ship comes in / Fare thee well / Winsborough Cotton Mill blues / Prisoner's plea / Back road fever / Rollon muddy river
SHCD 3719 / Jun '97 / Sugar Hill

☐ LIKE A HURRICANE
Back's against the wall / Angel's cry / Sooner or later / Carry me home / Run again / Second wind / When you walk in the room / Like a hurricane / Living on the edge / Forgiveness / I'm still alive / Heaven's lullaby
SHCD 3878 / Jun '98 / Sugar Hill

☐ MORNING SKY
Tomorrow is a long time / Taker / Here today and gone tomorrow / Morning sky / Ripple / Good time Charlie's got the blues / Don't let your sweet love die / Mexico / It's happening to you / Hickory wind
SHCD 3729 / Jun '97 / Sugar Hill

☐ OUT OF THE WOODWORK (Hillman, Chris & Tony Rice/Larry Rice/Herb Pederson)
Hard times / Lord won't you help me / Somewhere on the road tonight / No one else / Street corner stranger / So begins the task / Dimming of the day / Just me and you / Do right woman / Change coming down / Story of love / Only passing through
ROUCD 0390 / Feb '97 / Rounder

☐ THREE BYRDS LAND IN LONDON (2CD Set) (Hillman, Chris & Roger McGuin/ Gene Clark)
SFRSCD 001 / Feb '97 / Strange Fruit

Hillman, Steve

☐ MATRIX
Overdrive / Matrix / Interchange / Ascendant / Sphinx dancer / Into space / Now or never / Sequent 7 / Matrix / Dawning light / Into the blue / Tritone
CYCL 011 / Jun '97 / Cyclops

☐ RIDING THE STORM
CYCL 035 / May '96 / Cyclops

Hills, Anne

☐ ANGEL OF LIGHT
FF 648CD / Nov '95 / Flying Fish

☐ DON'T PANIC
FF 608CD / Apr '94 / Flying Fish

☐ NEVER GROW OLD (Hills, Anne & Cindy Mangsen)
FF 70638 / Feb '95 / Flying Fish

Hills, Keith

☐ RECOVERY
FECD 128 / Jan '98 / Fellside

Hills, Trevor

☐ INNER PEACE
BCCD 001 / 1 Sep '97 / Blue Crystal

Hilmarsson, Hilmar Orn

☐ CHILDREN OF NATURE
T 3314 / Feb '96 / Touch

Hilton, Ronnie

☐ VERY BEST OF RONNIE HILTON, THE
Magic moments / Young and foolish / Who are we / Two different worlds / Wonder of you / Windmill in old Amsterdam / I still believe / No other love / Veni vidi vici / Around the world / Blossom fell / Stars shine in your eyes / Yellow rose of Texas / Women in love / Wonderful wonderful / I may never pass this way again / Miracle of love / World outside / Don't let the rain come down / As I love you / One blade of grass in a meadow / On the street where you live / She / Marching along to the blues / Her hair was yellow
CDMFP 6250 / Aug '96 / Music For Pleasure

Him

☐ EGG
185362 / Apr '96 / Southern

☐ HIM/THE DYLAN GROUP (Him/The Dylan Group)
BC 013 / Apr '97 / Bubblecore

☐ INTERPRETIVE BELIEF SYSTEM
EFA 012202 / Aug '97 / Word Sound Recordings

Him Kerosene

☐ RECORDER
ASR 3 / Jun '97 / Ampersand

Himber, Richard

☐ RICHARD HIMBER & HIS ORCHESTRA 1938-1940
CCD 7 / Jan '94 / Circle

Himuro

☐ NICHOYOBI
WI 014 / 1 Sep '98 / Worm Interface

Hinchcliffe, Keith

☐ CAROLAN'S DREAM
KH 001CD / Mar '94 / Ranmoor

Hinds, Donna

☐ GONE TOO FAR
FECD 18 / Jun '97 / First Edition

Hinds, Justin

☐ LOVE AND PEACE (Hinds, Justin & The Dominoes)
King Samuel / River Jordan / Botheration / Satin / Jump out the frying pan / Early one morning (holy dove) / Bail me / Turn them back / Peace and love / Never too old / After a storm / My Mama told me / Little you have / No good Rudie / On a Saturday night / Say me say / Take heed / Cock mouth kill cock / It's love you need / Oh what a feeling / You don't know / On the last days / Another heartache / Buttoo / I need your loving / Don't let me suffer / Red sun rise / Where there is life / Too late / Each day / Lonely man / Far beyond the valley / Black and white / Grow closer together / Loving pauper / Look before you leap / All I have is love / Coming home / Innocent people cry / Love is overdue / Don't go / I need your love / Rock away / Ba da / Bend down low / Sinner man / Fly little silver
CDTRL 393 / Apr '98 / Trojan

☐ SKA UPRISING (Hinds, Justin & The Dominoes)
CDTRL 314 / Mar '94 / Trojan

☐ THIS CARRY GO BRING HOME (Hinds, Justin & The Dominoes)
If it is fire you want / Sinners / Junnie / Carry go bring come / Everene / You come to drink milk / Carry go bring come (part 2) / Penny reel / Botheration / Living in the universe / Cheer up youthman
RNCD 2044 / Feb '94 / Rhino

Hines, Deni

☐ PAY ATTENTION
MUSH 24CD / 9 Mar '98 / Mushroom

Hines, Earl 'Fatha'

☐ AALBORG, DENMARK 1965
Medley: Monday date/Blues in thirds/You can depend on me / Tea for two / Medley / Shiny stockings / Perdido / Black coffee / Medley / Boogie woogie on St. Louis blues
STCD 8222 / Aug '94 / Storyville

☐ AT HOME
You are too beautiful / Love at night is out of sight / It happens to be me / Minor nothing / Moon mare / You'll never know / Cannery walk
DD 212 / Jun '97 / Delmark

☐ AT SUNDOWN
BB 8682 / Apr '96 / Black & Blue

☐ BACK ON THE STREET (Hines, Earl 'Fatha' & Jonah Jones)
CRD 118 / Nov '95 / Chiaroscuro

☐ BASIN STREET BLUES
CDCH 560 / Feb '91 / Milan

☐ BLUES AND THINGS (Hines, Earl 'Fatha' & Jimmy Rushing)
804652 / Oct '96 / New World

☐ BLUES SO LOW - 1966
Oh Lady be good / It had to be you / Black and blue / Two sleepy people / Ain't misbehavin' / Jitterbug waltz / Squeeze me / Honeysuckle rose / Epinal blues / Birth of the blues / Memphis blues / Basin Street blues / Tin roof blues / Rhapsody in blue / Shiny stockings / Sweet Lorraine / Boogie woogie on St. Louis blues / I wish you love / It's a pity to say goodnight
STCD 537 / '91 / Stash

☐ CHICAGO DATES, THE (Hines, Earl 'Fatha' & Muggsy Spanier All Stars)
My Monday date / Mood indigo / Wang wang blues / Pops blues / Apex blues / Caravan / I ain't got nobody / Mahogany hall stomp / Savoy blues / I found a new baby / Relaxin' at the touro / Bugle call rag / Ole Miss / I'm coming Virginia / It's right here for you / When the saints go marching in
STCD 6037 / Jul '98 / Citadel

☐ CLASSIC YEARS, THE
Earl / Smoke house blues / Ridin' a riff / Father's getaway / Harlem lament / Piano man / Chimes in blues / Monday date / Rosetta / Honeysuckle rose / Blues in thirds / Cavernism / Solid mama / Stowaway / Boogie woogie on St. Louis blues / Fifty-seven varieties / Weatherbird / Chicago rhythm
CDSGP 0177 / 4 May '98 / Prestige

☐ CLASSICS 1928-1932
CLASSICS 545 / Dec '90 / Classics

☐ CLASSICS 1932-1934
CLASSICS 514 / Apr '90 / Classics

☐ CLASSICS 1934-1937
CLASSICS 528 / Apr '90 / Classics

☐ CLASSICS 1937-1939
CLASSICS 538 / Dec '90 / Classics

☐ CLASSICS 1939-1940
CLASSICS 567 / Oct '91 / Classics

☐ CLASSICS 1941 (Hines, Earl 'Fatha' Orchestra)
CLASSICS 621 / Nov '92 / Classics

☐ CLASSICS 1942-1945
CLASSICS 876 / Apr '96 / Classics

☐ EARL HINES & HIS ESQUIRE ALLSTARS (Hines, Earl 'Fatha' & His All Stars)
Theme deep forest / Boogie woogie on St.Louis blues / Tin woof blues / Sleepwalking / Rosetta / Jump for joy / One o'clock jump / Ballin' the jack / You're the cream in my coffee / Love is just around the corner / Hot soup / C jam blues / Low down blues / Jumpin with symphony Sid / Piano man
STCD 8223 / Jun '98 / Storyville

☐ EARL HINES & THE DUKE'S MEN
DD 470 / Dec '94 / Delmark

☐ EARL HINES IN NEW ORLEANS 1975 (Hines, Earl 'Fatha' & Wallace Davenport/Orange Kellin)
My Monday date / Song of the islands / There'll be some changes made / Jelly roll / Tishomingo blues / One I love belongs to somebody else / Rosetta / Way down yonder in New Orleans / Someday sweetheart / Playing with the fire / Do you know what it means to miss New Orleans / Bouncing for panassie / Blues my naughty sweetie gave to me / Sugar babe / If I could be with you / Someday you'll be sorry / Moonglow / Elephant stomp
CD 53197 / Apr '98 / Giants Of Jazz

☐ FATHA
CD 14556 / Jul '94 / Jazz Portraits

☐ FATHA
TPZ 1006 / Aug '94 / Topaz Jazz

☐ FATHA JUMPS 1940-1942 (Hines, Earl 'Fatha' Orchestra)
RACD 7115 / May '96 / Aerospace

☐ FATHA'S BLUES
TCD 1028 / Aug '96 / Tradition

☐ FATHER STEPS IN
GT stomp / Jezebel / Dominick swing / Grand terrace shuffle / Father steps in / Piano man / Father's getaway / Me and Columbus / Please be kind / Goodnight, sweet dreams, goodnight / Tippin' at the terrace / XYZ / Gator swing / After all I've been to you / Mellow bit of rhythm / Ridin' a riff / Solid mama / Jack climbed a beanstalk / Ridin' and jivin' / (Back home again in) Indiana / Reminiscing at Blue Note / Riff medley
GRF 092 / '93 / Tring

☐ HINE'S TUNE (Paris 1965)
Hine's tune / One I love (belongs to someone else) / Bag's Groove / Blue turning grey over you / Don's blues / Tenderly / Boogie woogie on St. Louis blues / These foolish things / I'm a little brown bird / Que reste t'Il de nos amours / Little girl blue / You are the cream in my coffee / I can't get started (with you) / Petite laitue / Cherry / Sweet lorraine / I've got the world on a string / Body and soul / Clopin clopant / C'est si bon
FCD 101 / '88 / Esoldun

☐ HINES '74
233073 / May '87 / Black & Blue

☐ HINES SHINES
Web / Intermezzo / Dark eyes / Blues for garroway / Humoresque / Hollywood hop / A jumpin' something / It's right here for you / Savoy blues / Apex blues / When the saints go marching in / Won't you go home bill bailey / Pop's blues
17030 / May '94 / Laserlight

☐ HINES SHINES
DM 15003 / Jul '96 / DMA Jazz

☐ IN NEW ORLEANS
Someday, sweetheart / Playing with fire / Elephant stomp / Do you know what it means to miss New Orleans / Bouncing for panassie / Blues my naughty sweetie gives to me / Sugar babe / If I could be with you one hour tonight / Someday you'll be sorry / Moonglow
CRD 200 / Jan '97 / Chiaroscuro

☐ IN PARIS
500562 / 21 Aug '97 / Musidisc

☐ INTRODUCTION TO EARL HINES, AN
4047 / Jul '97 / Best Of Jazz

☐ JUST FRIENDS
Just friends / I cover the waterfront / One I love belongs to somebody else / East of the sun / Can't we talk it over / Indian summer / You made me love you / If I had you / Velvet moon
JHR 73506 / May '93 / Jazz Hour

☐ LIVE AT SARALEE'S
Once in a while / Alice blue gown / Wrap up your troubles in dreams (and dream your troubles aw / I want a little girl / Don't take your love from me / She's funny that way / So can I
15790 / Aug '92 / Laserlight

☐ LIVE AT THE NEW SCHOOL
CRD 157 / Mar '96 / Chiaroscuro

☐ MASTERPIECES VOL.14 1934-1942
MASTER 158332 / Mar '95 / Masterpieces

☐ MASTERS OF JAZZ VOL.2
STCD 4102 / '89 / Storyville

☐ ONE FOR MY BABY
BLCD 760198 / Nov '94 / Koch

☐ PIANO MAN
Blues in thirds / Boogie woogie on St. Louis blues / Cavernism / Chicago rhythm / Chimes blues / Comin' in home / Earl / Every evening / Father's getaway / Fifty seven varieties / Fireworks / Harlem lament / Honeysuckle rose / Love me tonight / Monday date / Piano man / Ridin' a riff / Rosetta / Save it pretty Mama / Skip the gutter / Smokehouse blues / Solid mama / Stowaway / Two deuces / Weatherbird
CDAJA 5131 / Oct '94 / Living Era

☐ PLAYS DUKE ELLINGTON
NW 361/362 / Aug '92 / New World

☐ PLAYS DUKE ELLINGTON (The Complete Sessions/3CD Set)
810012 / Jun '98 / New World

☐ PLAYS DUKE ELLINGTON VOL.2
805322 / Oct '97 / New World

☐ PLAYS GEORGE GERSHWIN
500522 / 21 Aug '97 / Musidisc

☐ SWINGIN' AWAY
Bright attitude / Blue lion blues / Le bijou / Don't take your love from me / Senator Sam / You can depend on me / Rosetta
BLCD 760210 / Apr '96 / Black Lion

☐ TOUR DE FORCE
When your lover has gone / Indian summer / Mack the knife / I never knew (I could love anyone like I'm loving you) / Say it isn't so / Lonesome road
BLCD 760140 / May '90 / Black Lion

☐ TOUR DE FORCE ENCORE
BLCD 760157 / '91 / Black Lion

☐ WAY DOWN YONDER IN NEW ORLEANS
My Monday date / Song of the Islands / There'll be some changes made / Jelly Roll / Tishomingo blues / One I love (belongs to somebody else) / Rosetta / Way down yonder in New Orleans / Do you know what it means to miss New Orleans / Bouncin' for panassie / If I could be with you one hour tonight / Moonglow
BCD 108 / Jul '91 / Biograph

☐ WEST SIDE STORY
West Side story medley / Close to you / Why do I love you / In my solitude / Don't get around much anymore
BLCD 760186 / Jul '93 / Black Lion

Hines, Simon

☐ SIMON HINES
Yeah yeah yeah / Way that that you feel / What difference (does it make) / Best of my love / Only fools fool around / Every little thing / Never been alone / I'm ready / Richest woman in the world / Other man / Every now and then / Call me up / Chance to love / Where do I go from here
4887122 / 15 Sep '97 / Epic

Hinn, Benny

☐ HEALING (Experience The Healing Power Of Worship)
Holy spirit thou art welcome / Lord's prayer / God can / You are my hiding place / Jehovah jireh / God is good all the time / Fill this temple / Blessed be the name of the Lord / I am the God that healeth thee / Jesus name above all names / Jesus your presence makes me whole / Glorify thy name
12042 / Mar '98 / Integrity

Hinojosa, Tish

☐ AQUELLA NOCHE
Tu que puedas, vuelvete / Cumbia, pola y mas / Manos, hueso y sangre / Reloj / La llorona / Azul cristal / Aquella noche / Historia de un amor / Una noche mas / Carlos dominguez / Samba san pedro / Malaguena salerosa / Estrellita
MRCD 156 / '91 / Munich

☐ BEST OF THE SANDIA, THE (Watermelon 1991-1992)
Toas to Tennessee / Prairie moon / Highway calls / Crazy winds and flashing yellows / Always / Aquella noche / Samba san pedro / Anos meses y dias / Una noche mas / Cumbia polka y mas / Manos huesos y sangre / De colores / Ere tu / Gracias a la vida / Building no.9 / Everything you wish / Arbolito / By the Rio Grande
WMCD 1062 / May '97 / Watermelon

☐ DESTINY'S GATE
Destiny's gate / Saying you will / What more can you say in a song / Esperate (wait for me) / Looking for my love in the pouring rain / I'm not through loving you yet / Love of mine / I want to see you again / Noche sin estrellas (night without stars) / Yesterday's paper / Baby believe
9362455662 / Jul '94 / Warner Bros.

☐ EVERY CHILD
ROUCD 8032 / Feb '96 / Rounder

☐ FRONTEJAS
Pajarillo barranquero / Malhaya la cocina / Poquita fe / Farolito / Las golondrinas / Otro vasito / Djearme Llorar / Buen amor / Polka fronterrestril / Las marias / Con su pluma en su mano / Solo tus ojos
ROUCD 3132 / Apr '95 / Rounder

☐ MEMORABILIA NAVIDENA
Abolito (little Christmas tree) / Milagro / Building / A la nantia nana / Arbolita (in English) / Cada nino/Every child / Everything you wish / Memorabilia (Honky tonker's christmas)
WMCD 1006 / Jun '93 / Watermelon

☐ TAOS TO TENNESSEE
Midnight moonlight / Prairie song / According to my heart / Taos to Tennessee / River / Amanecer / Please be with me / Crazy wind and flashing yellows / Highway calls / Who showed you the way to my heart / Let me remember / Always
MRCD 164 / '92 / Munich

Hinton, Bob

☐ MIDNIGHT RUN
RRPCD 1 / 1 Dec '97 / Rock 'n' Roe

Hinton, Eddie

☐ LETTERS FROM MISSISSIPPI
My searching is over / Sad and lonesome / Everybody needs love / Letters from Mississippi / Everybody meets Mr.Blue / Uncloudy day / I want a woman / Ting a ling ling / Wet weather man / I will always love you / It's alright / I'll come running (back to you)
ZNCD 1001 / Oct '95 / Zane

☐ VERY BLUE HIGHWAY
I love someone / Rock of my soul / Poor Ol' me / Sad Carol / Very blue highway / Call a blues physician / Good love is hard to find / Just don't know / Let it roll / How you goin' to Georgia / Standin' in / Hey Justine / Nobody but you
ZNCD 1005 / Oct '95 / Zane

Hinton, Milt

☐ BACK TO BASS-ICS (Hinton, Milt Trio)
PCD 7084 / Jun '93 / Progressive

☐ BASICALLY WITH BLUE
BB 890 / Nov '97 / Black & Blue

☐ OLD MAN TIME (2CD Set)
CRD 310 / Dec '95 / Chiaroscuro

Hip Young Things

☐ DEFLOWERED
GRCD 244 / 17 Nov '97 / Glitterhouse

☐ ROOT 'N' VARIES
GRCD 281 / 17 Nov '97 / Glitterhouse

☐ SHRUG
GRCD 347 / 17 Nov '97 / Glitterhouse
OUT 1232 / Sep '97 / Brake Out

Hipkiss, Mick

☐ ERIN'S LOVELY LEE
CMCD 061 / Dec '97 / Celtic Music

Hippos

☐ FORGET THE WORLD
VR 332CD / 20 Jul '98 / Vagrant

Hipster

☐ JAZZE JOOS
STONE 9558 / 23 Feb '98 / Yellowstone

Hipsway

☐ HIPSWAY
Honey thief / Ask the Lord / Bad thing longing / Upon a thread / Long white car / Broken years / Tinder / Forbidden / Set this day apart
8268212 / Sep '92 / Mercury

☐ SCRATCH THE SURFACE
Show me / Keepin' it together / Your love / Emerald / I'm not perfect / Handfuls of dust / Something special / Wrong about that / What makes a man loves a woman so bad / Scratch the surface / Solid gone
5541782 / Oct '97 / Spectrum

Hird Family

☐ HIRD FAMILY IN NEW ORLEANS
BCD 332 / Mar '95 / GHB

Hird, Karl

☐ KARL HIRD TRIOS
SPR 59 / Nov '96 / Australian Jazz

Hirjo

☐ TROIAD AR BED
EROCD 061 / Mar '98 / Eromi

Hiroko

☐ MOMENTS
Night in Capri / Listen to my heartbeat / Englishman in New York / Piazza in the rain / Someday in paradise / Lady moonlight / Metropolis / Hitch hiker / Blue mosque / My heart's with you / Passarada / Gone / Moment we share / Alone again
JVC 20542 / Apr '96 / JVC

Hirota, Joji

☐ RAIN FOREST DREAM
Ubiquity / Purple spring / Celebration of harvest / Malaysian image / Satellite express / Rainforest dream / Demon dance / Pacific samba
CDSDL 384 / Mar '94 / Saydisc

Hirsch & Weinstein

☐ HAIKU LINGO
RERE 139CD / Oct '95 / No Man's Land

Hirst, Clare

☐ TOUGH AND TENDER
Heavy hipsters / Tough and tender / Salsita / Beautiful(ish) / Little steps / Strollin' / Just an emotion / Rudie's blues / Mi cancion / Gallicia
33JAZZ 025 / Dec '95 / 33 Jazz

Hirt, Al

☐ AL HIRT COLLECTION, THE
RE 21482 / Nov '97 / Razor & Tie

☐ BRASSMAN'S HOLIDAY
Royal garden blues / Yellow dog blues / I can't get started / South Rampart Street Parade / Brassman's holiday / Second chance / Tin roof blues / Just a closer walk with thee / Birth of the blues / Begin the beguine / Blues in the night / Dear old Southland / Frankie and Johnny / Cornet chop suey / New Orleans / Battle hymn of the republic
HCD 608 / Jun '96 / Hindsight

☐ MASTER OF JAZZ
Tuxedo Junction / Break my mind / Deep river / Hello Dolly / I'm so lonesome I could cry / Look down that lonesome road / Stardust / When my blue moon turns to gold again / Night in Tunisia / Cotton candy / Cherry pink and apple blossom white / Moonglow / Orange blossom special / Shine / Poor butterfly / Blue eyes crying in the rain
CWNCD 2034 / Jun '97 / Crown

Hirte, Marc

☐ SECOND NATURE
BLDCD 533 / Sep '96 / Boulevard

His Hero Is Gone

☐ 15 COUNTS OF ARSON
PRANK 013CD / Feb '97 / Prank

☐ MONUMENTS TO THIEVES
PRANK 016CD / 10 Nov '97 / Prank

His Name Is Alive

☐ FORT LAKE
Glue (don't glue the world) / Everything (everything takes forever) / Waitress (the waitress) / No hiding place (no hiding place down here) / Can't (can't always be loved) / Wishing ring (wish I had a wishing ring) / Red (red haired girl) / Secret code (spirit needs a spirit tool) / Up (up your legs forever) / How it goes (how it's gotta be) / Don't make me wait (rock 'n' roll girl from rock 'n' roll ci / Last blues (last American blues)
CAD 8009CD / 22 Jun '98 / 4AD

☐ HOME IS IN YOUR HEAD
GAD 1013CD / 6 Jul '98 / 4AD

☐ LIVONIA
GAD 008CD / 6 Jul '98 / 4AD

☐ MOUTH TO MOUTH
GAD 3006CD / 6 Jul '98 / 4AD

☐ STARS ON ESP
Dub love letter / This world is not my home / Bad luck girl / What are you wearing tomorrow / Bees / What else is new list / Wall of speed / Universal frequencies / Sand that holds the lake in place / I can't live in this world anymore / Answer to rainbow at midnight / Famous goodbye king / Across the street / Movie / Last one
GAD 6010CD / 6 Jul '98 / 4AD

Hislop, Joseph

☐ SONGS OF SCOTLAND
Prelude to the loves of Robert Burns / Bonnie banks of Loch Lomond / Ye banks and braes o' bonnie Doon / Bonnie Mary of Argyle / Annie Laurie / Afton water / Land of the leal / Ariskay love lift / Island herdsmaid / Lea rig / MacGregor's gathering / Rigs O' Barley / My love is like a red red rose / Bonnie wee thing / Jessie the flower O' Dunblane / My love she's but a lassie yet / O my love's bonnie / Herding song / Island shieling song / Turn ye tae me
MIDCD 003 / Jan '95 / Moidart

Hissanol

☐ 4TH AND BACK
VIRUSUK 160CD / 10 Nov '97 / Alternative Tentacles

☐ MAKING OF HIM, THE
VIRUS 210CD / 26 Jan '98 / Alternative Tentacles

Hitchcock, Nicola

☐ BOWL OF CHALK, A
Pick up your coat / My mistake / Surf on shingle / Saddest day / Writings I hide / Down to the station / What you see is what you get / How do you feel / Strange times / Queen of the blues / Where are you now / Maire
FIENDCD 776 / May '93 / Demon

Hitchcock, Nigel

☐ SNAKERANCH SESSIONS
Speak low / Invitation / Wail / Weaver of dreams / In a sentimental mood / Donna Lee / All the things you are / Maestro / Cherokee
BBJ 1002 / 10 Nov '97 / Black Box Jazz

Hitchcock, Robyn

☐ BLACK SNAKE DIAMOND ROLE
Man who invented himself / Brenda's iron sledge / Lizard / Meat / Do policemen sing / Acid bird / I watch the cars / Out of the picture / City of shame / Love / Dancing on God's thumb / Happy the golden prince / Kingdom of love / It was the night
RSACD 819 / Feb '95 / Sequel

☐ COLLECTION, THE (Uncorrected Personality Traits)
Bass / Acid bird / Egyptian cream / Uncorrected personality traits / Heart full of leaves / Man with the lightbulb head / Queen Elvis II / She reached for a light / Airscape / My wife and my dead wife / Night ride to Trinidad / Raymond Chandler evening / Linctus house / Beautiful girl / Heaven / If you were a priest / Autumn is your last chance / City of shame / Nocturne
RSACD 957 / 26 Jan '98 / Sequel

☐ ELEMENT OF LIGHT
If you were a priest / Winchester / Somewhere apart / Ted, Woody and Junior / President / Raymond Chandler evening / Bass / Airscape / Element of light / Never stop bleeding / Lady Waters and the hooded one / Black crow knows / Crawling / Leopard / Tell me about your drugs / Can opener / Raymond Chandler evening (demo) / President (demo) / If you were a priest (demo) / Airscape (demo) / Leopard (demo)
RSACD 824 / Mar '95 / Sequel

☐ EYE
Cynthia Mask / Certainly clickot / Queen Elvis / Flesh cartoons / Chinese water python / Executioner / Linctus house / Sweet ghost of light / College of ice / Transparent lover / Beautiful girl / Raining twilight coast / Clean Steve / Agony of pleasure / Glass hotel / Satellite / Aquarium / Queen Elvis II / Clean Steve / Agony of pleasure / Ghost ship
RSACD 826 / Mar '95 / Sequel

☐ FEGMANIA
Egyptian cream / Another bubble / I'm only you / My wife and my dead wife / Goodnight I say / Man with the lightbulb head / Insect mother / Strawberry mind / Glass / Fly / Heaven / Bells of Rhymney / Dwarfbeat / Somebody / Egyptian cream (demo) / Heaven (live) / Insect mother (demo) / Pit of Souls (parts I-IV)
RSACD 822 / Mar '95 / Sequel

☐ GOTTA LET THIS HEN OUT (Hitchcock, Robyn & The Egyptians)
Listening to the Higsons / Fly / Kingdom of love / Leppo and the fly / Man with the lightbulb head / Cars she used to drive / Sounds great when you're dead / Only the stones remain / America / Heaven / My wife and my dead wife / I often dream of trains / Surgery / Brenda's iron sledge
RSACD 823 / Mar '95 / Sequel

☐ GROOVY DECAY
Night ride to Trinidad / Fifty two stations / Young people scream / Rain / America / How do you work this thing / Cars she used to drive / Grooving on an inner plane / St. Petersburg / When I was a kid / Midnight fish / It was the night / Nightride to Trinidad (disco mix) / Midnight fish (mix)
RSACD 820 / Feb '95 / Sequel

☐ I OFTEN DREAM OF TRAINS (Hitchcock, Robyn & The Egyptians)
Nocturne / Sometimes I wish I was a pretty girl / Cathedral / Uncorrected personality traits / Sounds great when you're dead / Flavour of night / Sleeping knights of Jesus / Mellow together / Winter love / Bones in the ground / My favourite buildings / I used to say I love you / This could be the day / Trams of old London / Furry green atom bowl / Heart full of leaves / Autumn is your last chance / I often dream of trains
RSACD 821 / Feb '95 / Sequel

☐ INVISIBLE HITCHCOCK (Hitchcock, Robyn & The Egyptians)
All I wanna do is fall in love / Give me a spanner Ralph / Skull, a suitcase and a long red bottle of wine / It's a mystic trip / My favourite buildings / Falling leaves / Eaten by her own dinner / Pit of souls / Trash / Mr. Deadly / Star of hairs / Messages of dark / Vegetable friends / I got a message for you / Abandoned brain / Point it at Gran / Let there be more darkness / Blues in A
RSACD 825 / Mar '95 / Sequel

☐ KERSHAW SESSIONS (Hitchcock, Robyn & The Egyptians)
Brenda's iron sledge / Veins of the queen / Lady waters and the hooded one / So you think you're in love / Bass / Sleeping with your devil mask / Open the door homer / 52 stations / Birds in perspex / If you were a priest / Acid bird / Arms of love / Superman / Tropical flesh mandala / Oceanside / Madonna of the wasps / Banana boat song / Listening to the higsons / Heaven
SFRSCD 075 / 6 Jul '98 / Strange Fruit

☐ RESPECT (Hitchcock, Robyn & The Egyptians)
Yip song / Arms of love / Moon inside / Railway shoes / When I was dead / Wreck of the Arthur Lee / Driving aloud (radio storm) / Serpent at the gates of wisdom / Then you're dust / Wafflehead
RHECD 1 / Oct '96 / RHE

☐ YOU AND OBLIVION
You've got / Don't you / Bird's head / She reached for a light / Victorian squid / Captain Dry / Mr. Rock 'n' Roll / August hair / Take your knife out of my back / Surgery / Dust / Polly on the shore / Aether / Fiend before the shrine / Nothing / Into it / Stranded in the future / Keeping still / September cones / Ghost ship / You and me / If I could look
RSACD 827 / Mar '95 / Sequel

Hitchin Post

☐ DEATH VALLEY JUNCTION
GRCD 313 / 17 Nov '97 / Glitterhouse

☐ ROADMAP
GRCD 375 / 17 Nov '97 / Glitterhouse

Hitmen DTK

☐ SURFIN' IN ANOTHER DIRECTION
842618 / May '94 / New Rose

Hitsville House Band

☐ 12 O'CLOCK STEREO
BAH 27 / Jul '96 / Humbug

Hittman

☐ HITTMAN
857568 / '88 / Steamhammer

Hives

☐ BARELY LEGAL
BHR 068CD / 29 Sep '97 / Burning Heart

hKippers

☐ GUTTED
ECCD 002 / Dec '96 / Eccentric

Ho, Chris

☐ GROWING UP
1901145712 / 21 Apr '98 / Ichiban

Ho, Fred

☐ MONKEY VOL.1 (Ho, Fred & Cindy Zuoxin Wang/Monkey Orchestra)
378152 / Oct '96 / Koch Jazz

☐ MONKEY VOL.2 (Ho, Fred & The Monkey Orchestra)
CD 378402 / Nov '97 / Koch Jazz

Hoax

☐ HUMDINGER
CRCD 27B/7 / 19 Jan '98 / Credible

☐ SOUND LIKE THIS
Lizard like me / Scaramouche / Swallow my pride / Headless chicken / Twenty ton weight / Take the money and run / Don't bust a valve / Head neck / Driving blind / Wake me up / Much too much
4509979642 / Dec '96 / Warner Bros.

☐ UNPOSSIBLE
Turn it upside down / Hungry mans blues / Got it bad / Don't let me cry / Fingers of one hand / Will be true / Fistful of dirt / Realisation dawns / Off your lead / Let it ride / Emperors new clothes
0630166392 / Nov '96 / East West

Hobbs Angel Of Death

☐ HOBBS ANGEL OF DEATH
857525 / '89 / Steamhammer

Hobbs, Steve

☐ CULTURAL DIVERSITY
Missing Carolina / On the run / Blame it on my youth / Sea breeze / Bag's groove / Coreaaah / Jane / DA / Astrud / Bernie's tune
CDSJP 375 / Mar '92 / Timeless Jazz

☐ LOWER EAST SIDE, THE
CACD 797042 / Dec '95 / Candid

☐ ON THE LOWER EAST SIDE
Amazing grace / Around and around / Sweet and lovely / Song is you / Pedra bonita / Thinking of Chet / Au privave / 18-35 (together again) / Pentachronic / But beautiful / What is this thing called love
CCD 79704 / Feb '97 / Candid

Hobex

☐ PAYBACK EP
SYM 044 / Jan '97 / Symbiotic

Hobgood, Torff

☐ UNION (Hobgood, Torff & Wertico)
NAIMCD 015 / Sep '97 / Naim Audio

Hoch Und Deutschmeister

☐ 25 JAHRE ORIGINAL HOCH UND DEUTSCHMEISTER
340012 / Apr '92 / Koch

Hochman, I.J.

☐ FUN DER KHUPE
GVCD 114 / Mar '95 / Global Village

Hock, Paul

☐ FRESH FRUIT
Fresh fruit / Barricade / Voir un ami pleurer / Sneeky / Samba for Johan Cruyff / Yvette in wonderland / Missing keys / Estate
CDSJP 343 / Oct '91 / Timeless Jazz

Hockridge, Edmund

☐ BEST OF EDMUND HOCKRIDGE, THE
No other love / By the fountains of Rome / Young and foolish / Woman in love / Long ago and far away / Moon river / S'wonderful / Way you look tonight / Tonight / They can't take that away from me / Tenement symphony / Love letters / Only a rose / Falling in love with love / I love Paris / Till there was you / I've grown accustomed to her face / Almost like being in love / I could write a book / Some enchanted evening
PLSCD 254 / 27 Oct '97 / Pulse

Hodes, Art

☐ APEX BLUES
JCD 104 / Nov '96 / Jazzology

☐ ART HODES & JOHN PETTERS HOT THREE (Hodes, Art & John Petters Hot Three)
RRCD 007 / May '98 / Rose

☐ ART HODES & THE MAGNOLIA JAZZ BAND VOL.1 & 2
BCD 171/172 / Oct '93 / GHB

☐ ART HODES TRIOS/QUARTETS
JCD 113 / Dec '97 / Jazzology

☐ FINAL SESSIONS, THE
CD 782 / May '94 / Music & Arts

☐ HODES' ART
DD 213 / Dec '94 / Delmark

☐ KEEPIN' OUT OF MISCHIEF NOW
Tennessee waltz / When your lover has gone / I'm gonna sit right down (and write myself a letter) / Saturday night function / I'm a salty dog / Makin' whoopee / Four or five times / Love for sale / CC rider / Do you know what it means / Struttin' with some barbecue / Basin street blues / Keepin' out of mischief now / Just a closer walk with thee / Preacher
CCD 79537 / Feb '97 / Candid

☐ PAGIN' MR. JELLY
Grandpa's spells / Mamie's blues / High society / Mr. Jelly lord / Buddy Bolden's blues / Pagin' Mr. Jelly / Wolverine blues / Ballin' the Jack / Pearls / Gone Jelly blues / Dr. Jazz / Oh didn't he ramble / Winnin' boy blues / Beale Street blues
CCD 79037 / Feb '97 / Candid

☐ UP IN VOLLY'S ROOM
DD 217 / Jan '93 / Delmark

Hodges, Johnny

☐ AT THE SPORTPALAST, BERLIN (2CD Set)
Take the 'A' train / In the kitchen / Mood indigo / Solitude / Satin doll / I got it bad and that ain't good / Rockin' in rhythm / Autumn leaves / Stompy Jones / C jam blues / Jeep is jumpin' / Good Queen Bess / Things ain't what they used to be / I'll get by / I let a song go out of my heart / Don't get around much anymore / Just squeeze me / Do nothin' 'til you hear from me / Rose of the Rio Grande / All of me / On the sunny side of the street / Blue moon / Perdido
CD 2620102 / Aug '96 / Pablo

☐ CARAVAN (Hodges, Johnny & Duke Ellington/Billy Strayhorn Allstars)
Frisky: *Hodges, Johnny Allstars* / Longhorn blues: *Hodges, Johnny Allstars* / Flower is a lovesome thing: *Hodges, Johnny Allstars* / Far away blues: *Hodges, Johnny Allstars* / How could it happen to a dream: *Hodges, Johnny Allstars* / Who struck John: *Hodges, Johnny Allstars* / June's jumpin': *Hodges, Johnny Allstars* / Lotus blossom: *Hodges, Johnny Allstars* / Violet blue: *Hodges, Johnny Allstars* / Searsy's blues: *Hodges, Johnny Allstars* / Taste: *Hodges, Johnny Allstars* / Let the zoomer's drool: *Hodges, Johnny Allstars* / Night walk: *Strayhorn, Billy Allstars* / She: *Strayhorn, Billy Allstars* / Happening: *Strayhorn, Billy Allstars* / Sultry serenade: *Strayhorn, Billy Allstars* / Moonlight fiesta: *Strayhorn, Billy Allstars* / Britt and butter blues: *Strayhorn, Billy Allstars* / Indian summer: *Strayhorn, Billy Allstars* / Swamp drum: *Strayhorn, Billy Allstars* / Caravan: *Ellington, Duke/Billy Strayhorn Allstars* / Hoppin' John: *Ellington, Duke Allstars* / Jumpin' with symphony Sid: *Ellington, Duke Allstars*
PCD 24103 / Aug '96 / Prestige

☐ CLASSIC SOLOS 1928-42
TPZ 1008 / Oct '94 / Topaz Jazz

☐ COMPLETE SMALL GROUP SESSIONS VOL.1 1937-1938
BMCD 1019 / Sep '95 / Blue Moon

☐ COMPLETE SMALL GROUP SESSIONS VOL.2 1939-1940
BMCD 1020 / Sep '95 / Blue Moon

☐ EVERYBODY KNOWS JOHNNY HODGES
Everybody knows / Flower is a lovesome thing / Papa knows / 310 blues / Jeep is jumpin' / Main stem / I let a song go out of my heart / Don't get around much anymore / Open mike / Stompy Jones / Mood indigo / Good Queen Bess / Little brother / Jeep's blues / Do nothin' 'til you hear from me / Ruint / Sassy cue
GRP 11162 / Jul '92 / Impulse Jazz

☐ HODGE PODGE
Jeep's blues / Rendezvous with rhythm / Empty ballroom blues / Drum elbow blues / I'm in another world / Hodge podge / Dancing on the stars / Wanderlust / Dooji wooji / Savoy strut / Rent party blues / Good gal blues / Finesse / Hometown blues / Dream blues / Sunk hollow blues
EK 66972 / Jan '95 / Sony Jazz

☐ IN A MELLOW TONE (Hodges, Johnny & 'Wild' Bill Davis)
Just squeeze me / It's only a paper moon / Taffy / Good Queen Bess / LB blues / In a mellow tone / Rockville / I'll always love you / It don't mean a thing if it ain't got that swing / Belle of Belmont
09026685972 / May '97 / Bluebird

☐ INTRODUCTION TO JOHNNY HODGES 1928-1941, AN
4010 / Mar '95 / Best Of Jazz

☐ JAZZ GREATS (Hodges, Johnny Orchestra)
I'm beginning to see the light / In a mellotone: *Hodges, Johnny & Duke Ellington Orchestra* / Passion flower / Big boy blues / Things ain't what used to be / Snibor: *Hodges, Johnny & Duke Ellington Orchestra* / Sophisticated lady: *Hodges, Johnny & Wild Bill Davis* / Good queen Bess: *Hodges, Johnny & Wild Bill Davis* / On the sunny side of the street: *Hodges, Johnny & Wild Bill Davis* / It's only a paper moon: *Hodges, Johnny & Wild Bill Davis* / That's the blues old man / Never no lament (don't get around much anymore): *Hodges, Johnny & Duke Ellington Orchestra* / Come sunday: *Hodges, Johnny & Duke Ellington Orchestra* / Isfahan: *Hodges, Johnny & Duke Ellington Orchestra*
74321556902 / Feb '98 / RCA Victor

☐ JOHNNY HODGES AND WILD BILL DAVIS, 1965 - 1966 (Hodges, Johnny & 'Wild' Bill Davis)
On the sunny side of the street / On Green Dolphin Street / Li'l darlin' / Con sould and sax / Jeep is jumpin' / I'm beginning to see the light / Sophisticated lady / Drop me off in Harlem / No one / Johnny come lately / It's only a paper moon / Taffy / Good Queen Bess / LB blues / In a mellow tone / Rockville / I'll always love you / It don't mean a thing if it ain't got that swing / Belle of the Belmont
ND 89765 / May '94 / Jazz Tribune

☐ JOHNNY HODGES PLAYS BILLY STRAYHORN
5218572 / 5 May '98 / Verve

☐ JOHNNY HODGES STORY 1926-1946, THE
158982 / Nov '97 / Jazz Archives

☐ MASTERS OF JAZZ VOL.9
Cambridge blue / Brute's roots / Bouncing with Ben / One for the duke / Walkin' the frog / Rabbit pie / On the sunny side / Good Queen Bess / Jeep is jumpin' / Things ain't what they used to be
STCD 4109 / May '89 / Storyville

☐ ON THE WAY UP
On the way up / Take 'em off, take 'em off / Jeep is jumping / Monkey on a limb / C-jam blues / On Green Dolphin Street / Con soul and sax / For jammers only / No one / Drop me off in Harlem / Johnny come lately / Big Boy blues / Sir John / Tiny bit of blues / Lil' darlin' / I'm beginning to see the light / Sophisticated lady / Very thought of you
74321523792 / 29 Sep '97 / Camden

☐ PASSION FLOWER
Daydream / Good queen Bess (takes 1 and 2) / That's the blues / Old man / Junior hop / Squaty roo / Passion flower / Thing's ain't what they used to be / Goin' out the back way / Never no lamet / Blue goose / In a mellow tone / Warm valley / After all / Giddybug gallop / I got it bad and that ain't good / Clementine / Moon mist / Sentimental lady / Come Sunday / Mood to be wooed / Rock-a-bye river
07863666162 / Aug '95 / Bluebird

☐ QUINTESSENCE, THE (2CD Set)
FA 216 / Feb '96 / Fremeaux

☐ TRIPLE PLAY
Take 'em off / Nearness of you / Monkey on a limb / Tiny bit of blues / For jammers only / On the way up / Big boy blues / Very thought of you / Fur piece / Sir John / Figurine / C jam blues
09026685922 / Oct '96 / RCA Victor

☐ USED TO BE DUKE (Hodges, Johnny Orchestra)
Used to be Duke / On the sunny side of the street / Sweet as bear meat / Madam Butterfly / Warm valley / Autumn in New York / Sweet Lorraine / Time on my hands / Smoke gets in your eyes / If you were mine / Poor butterfly / All of me / Burgundy walk / Skokiaan
8493942 / Mar '91 / Verve

Hodgson, Roger

☐ HAI HAI
Right place / My magazine / London / You make me love you / Hai hai / Who's afraid / Desert love / Land ho / House on the corner / Puppet dance
3951122 / 13 Jul '98 / A&M

☐ IN THE EYE OF THE STORM
Had a dream / In jeopardy / Lovers in the wind / Hooked on a problem / Give me love give me life / I'm not afraid / Only because of you
3950042 / 13 Jul '98 / A&M

Hoehn, Tommy

☐ TURNING DANCE, THE
FR 0071 / Jul '97 / Frankenstein

Hoenig, Michael

☐ EARLY WATER (Hoenig, Michael & Manuel Gottsching)
14536 / Jun '97 / Spalax

Hoest, Julie

☐ WHERE I'M STANDING
RER 322CD / Dec '96 / Resounding

Hoffman, Lauren

☐ MEGIDDO
Hope you don't mind / Ashram song / Lolita / Blood / Strange man / Rock star / Alive / Cannibal Ed / Build a home / Fall away / Cold and gray / Persephone
CDVUSX 131 / 15 Jun '98 / Virgin

Hoffs, Susanna

☐ SUSANNA HOFFS
8288412 / Oct '96 / London

Hofgesindt

☐ WENN'S DIE ZEIT ERLAUBT
LZ 2072 / Oct '96 / Lowenzahn

Hofners

☐ LIFE AND STUFF
Sweet Lucy Brown / Get with it / Kitchen man / Nagasaki / Walking stick / Nuages / Viola Lee blues / Live in vain / Dark end of the street / Gee baby ain't I good to you / Little red rooster / Dark was the night / Cold was the ground
LONGMAN 027CD / Sep '97 / LongMan

Hofseth, Bendik

☐ COLOURS
5376272 / 15 Sep '97 / Sonet

☐ PLANETS, RIVERS &...IKEA
5312342 / Jun '96 / Verve

Hogan, John

☐ HUMBLE MAN
Don't fight the feeling / Still got a crush on you / Walkin' in the sun / She's more to be pitied / Picture / Wreck of old no.9 / China doll / Let it be you / Humble man / I'll be gone / Something's wrong / Down by the river / Follow me / Please don't forget me
RZCD 0062 / Nov '91 / Ritz

☐ IRISH HARVEST DAY, AN
Irish harvest day / I'll buy her roses
RZCD 248 / Sep '92 / Ritz

☐ LOVING YOU
RZCD 558 / May '96 / Ritz

☐ NASHVILLE ALBUM
Till the mountains disappear / Walk through this world with me / Baby I'm lovin' you now / Morning sun and memories / I'll give my heart to you / Stepping stone / Back home again / Far away heart / I can't help it (If I'm still in love with you) / You can't take it with you when you go / Blue moon of Kentucky / Battle hymn of love / My guitar / Fallen angel
RZRCD 531 / Aug '93 / Ritz

☐ VERY BEST OF JOHN HOGAN, THE
Thank God I'm a country boy / Walk through this world with me / Irish harvest day / Cottage in the country / Your cheatin' heart / China doll / My feelings for you / Wreck of old no.9 / Turn back the years / Red river valley / Back home again / My guitar / I'll buy her roses / Brown eyes / Stepping stone / Please don't forget me / Still got a crush on you / Moonlight in Mayo / I know that you know (that I love you) / Battle hymn of love
RCD 552 / Jul '95 / Ritz

Hogan, Silas

☐ SO LONG BLUES
I'm gonna quit you pretty baby / Trouble at home blues / You're too late baby / Airport blues / Go on pretty baby / Here they are again / Lonesome la la / Roamin' woman blues / I'm goin' in the valley / Everybody needs somebody / Just give me a chance / Dark clouds rollin' / Early one morning / I'm in love with you baby / More trouble at home / Sittin' here wonderin' / So glad / Every Saturday night / Baby please come back to me / If I ever need you baby / Out and down blues / So long blues
CDCHD 523 / May '94 / Ace

Hogg, Smokey

☐ ANGELS IN HARLEM
I want a roller / Nobody treats me right / Evil mind blues / I'm through with you / What's on your mind / You better watch that jive / Goin' back to Texas / I want my baby for Christmas / Gonna leave town / I ain't gonna put you down / Every mornin' at sunrise / If it hadn't been for you / Boogie all night long / Worryin' my life away / Angels in Harlem / Born on the 13th / Crawdad / Size 4 shoe / Little fine girl / Good mornin' baby / Sure nuff
CDCHD 419 / Sep '92 / Ace

☐ CALIFORNIA BLUES (Hogg, Smokey & Lowell Fulson/John Williams/John Lee Hooker)
BLC 760224 / Nov '97 / Black Lion

Hoggard, Jay

☐ OVERVIEW
MCD 5383 / Sep '92 / Muse

☐ SOLO VIBRAPHONE
IN 1040CD / Jan '97 / India Navigation

Hogia'r Wyddfa

☐ GOREUON
Safwn yn y bwlch / Pentre bach llanber / Y gwanwyn / TYlluanod / Ddoi di gyda mi / Titw tomos las / Llanc ifanc o lyn / Teifi / Bysus bach y wlad / Tecel / Varu cymru / Wil tatw's trwy' crwyn / Ynys yr hud / Olwen / Gwaun cwm brwynog / Hwiangerddi / Hen wr ar bont y bala / Ti a dy ddoniau / Pan fyddo'r nos yn hir / Mae nhwyr y dydd
SCD 4094 / Jun '88 / Sain

Hogman, John

☐ GOOD NIGHT SISTER
SITCD 9202 / Aug '94 / Sittel

Hoirup/Legault/Quellet

☐ MELODIE
HLOCD 597 / Dec '97 / HLO

Hoj, Kirsten

☐ SPEAK LOW (Hoj, Kirsten & Soren Norbo)
MECCACD 1093 / May '97 / Music Mecca

Hokum Boys

☐ FAMOUS HOKUM BOYS VOL.2 1930-1931, THE
WBCD 012 / Jul '96 / Wolf

☐ HOKUM BOYS & BOB ROBINSON 1935-1937 (Hokum Boys & Bob Robinson)
DOCD 5237 / May '94 / Document

☐ HOKUM BOYS 1929
DOCD 5236 / May '94 / Document

Hokum Hotshots

☐ STILL IN THE GAME
Southern Whoppee blues / New KC railroad blues / Indian girl / What you're sitting on / Travelling blues / You do me anyway / Unknown blues / You don't need no religion / Badmouth / Cat's whiskers dog's bollox / Canned heat / Maybe it's the blues / Seminole blues / Tear it down
CRAPCD 01 / 3 Aug '98 / Blueprint

Holcomb, Roscoe

☐ HIGH LONESOME SOUND, THE
SWFCD 40104 / 6 Apr '98 / Smithsonian Folkways

Hold True

☐ FADE
LF 144CD / Feb '96 / Lost & Found

Holden, Lorenzo

☐ CRY OF THE WOUNDED JUKEBOX
SCD 26 / Oct '93 / Southland

Holden, Randy

☐ EARLY WORKS 1964-1966
CTCD 056 / 1 Jun '98 / Captain Trip

☐ GUITAR GOD
CTCD 028 / Jul '97 / Captain Trip

☐ POPULATION II
FLASH 007 / 16 Mar '98 / Flashback

Holder, Nick

☐ ONE NIGHT IN THE DISCO
Get up / Don't go away / Greatest dancer / Love has come / Scenic route / Zone days / Feel mighty real / Do it / Get away
K7R 009CD / Jan '97 / Studio K7

☐ STILL ON TRACK
Loungin' at Lisa's / I didn't know / Rock da house / I cried for you / Deep inside / Buscando / Rock da discotek / One nation / Plastic people
K7 018CD / 30 Mar '98 / Studio K7

Holderlin

☐ HOLDERLIN'S TRAUM
2021314 / 16 Feb '98 / OHR

Holderlin Express

☐ ELECTRIC FLIES
AD 3028CD / Nov '96 / Music Contact/ Akku Disc

☐ HOLDERLIN EXPRESS
ADCD 3025 / Jul '94 / Music Contact/ Akku Disc

Holdsworth, Allan

☐ ATAVACHRON
Non-brewed condiment / Funnels / Dominant plague / Atavachron / Looking glass / Mr. Berwell / All our yesterdays
JMS 186432 / Feb '96 / JMS

☐ HARD HAT AREA
Prelude / Ruhkukah / Low levels, high stakes / Hard hat area / Tullio / House of mirrors / Postlude
JMS 186342 / Feb '96 / JMS

☐ IOU
Things you see (When you haven't got your gun) / Where is one / Checking out / Letters of marque / Out from under / Temporary fault / Shallow sea / White line
JMS 186412 / Feb '96 / JMS

☐ IOU BAND LIVE (Holdsworth, Allan & Paul Williams)
Road games / White line / Panic station / Letter of Marque / Material real / Metal fatigue / Where is one / Things you see / Was there something
CLP 9970 / Apr '97 / Cleopatra
OM 1003CD / Jun '97 / Outer Music

☐ METAL FATIGUE
Metal fatigue / Home / Devil take the hindmost / Panic station / In-merry go-round / In the mystery
JMS 186422 / Feb '96 / JMS

☐ NONE TOO SOON
Countdown / Nuages / How deep is the ocean / Isotope / None too soon part 1 / Interlude / None too soon part 2 / Norwegian wood / Very early / San Marcos / Inner urge
JMS 186872 / Aug '96 / Cream

☐ SAND
Sand / Distance versus desire / Pud wud / Clown / 4.15 Bradford executive / Mac man
JMS 186442 / Feb '96 / JMS

☐ SECRETS
City nights / 54 Duncan Terrace / Spokes / Perila premonition / Secrets / Joshua / Maid Marion / Endomorph
JMS 186452 / Feb '96 / JMS

☐ THINGS YOU SEE, THE (Holdsworth, Allan & Gordon Beck)
JMS 186512 / Feb '96 / JMS

☐ WARDENCLYFFE TOWER, THE
Five to five / Sphere of innocence / Wardenclyffe tower / Dodgy boat / Oneipic moor / Zarabeth / Against the clock / Questions
JMS 186322 / Feb '96 / JMS

☐ WITH A HEART IN MY SONG (Holdsworth, Allan & Gordon Beck)
JMS 186642 / Feb '96 / JMS

Hole

☐ ASK FOR IT
CAROL 1470 / 20 Apr '98 / Caroline

☐ LIVE THROUGH THIS
Violet / Miss World / Plump / Asking for it / Jennifers body / Doll parts / Credit in the straight world / Softer, softest / She walks on me / I think that I would die / Gutless / Rock star
EFA 49352 / Apr '94 / City Slang
GED 24631 / Jan '95 / Geffen

☐ MY BODY THE HAND GRENADE
Turpentine / Phonebill song / Retard girl / Burn black / Dicknail / Beautiful son / 20 years in Dakota / Miss world / Old age / Softer softest / He hit me (it felt like a kiss) / Season of the witch / Drown soda / Asking for it
EFA 049952 / 29 Sep '97 / City Slang

☐ PRETTY ON THE INSIDE
Baby doll / Garbage man / Sassy / Good sister bad sister / Mrs. Jones / Berry / Loaded / Star belly / Pretty on the inside / Clouds / Teenage whore
EFA 040712 / Aug '95 / City Slang

Hole, Dave

☐ PLUMBER
Plumber / You don't have to be pretty to sing the blues / Do what you do / Is it true (part 1) / Three days out / Sign me up / Me and my guitar / New way to live / Is it true (part 2) / Wrecking yard / North west blues / Boogaloo
PRD 70462 / Mar '93 / Provogue

☐ SHORT FUSE BLUES
ALCD 4807 / May '93 / Alligator

☐ STEEL ON STEEL
PRD 70782 / Jul '95 / Provogue

☐ TICKET TO CHICAGO
PRD 71022 / Mar '97 / Provogue
ALCD 4847 / May '97 / Alligator

☐ WHOLE LOTTA BLUES
Nobody hears me crying / Short fuse blues / Quicksand / I found love / Tore down / Key to the highway / I can't be satisfied / Going down / Plumber / Berwick Road / Keep your motor runnin' / Up all night thinking / Crazy kind of woman / Blues will call your name / Counting my regrets / Travelling riverside blues
PRD 70932 / Sep '96 / Provogue

☐ WORKING OVERTIME
PRD 70562 / May '94 / Provogue

Hole In One

☐ TALES FROM THE PLANET ONCHET
700021 / Aug '96 / Essential Dance

Hole, Matt

☐ ROCKABILLY EXPRESS (Hole, Matt & The Hotrod Gang)
HOLE 002 / Jan '98 / Hole

Holi

☐ UNDER THE MONKEY PUZZLE TREE
Under the monkey puzzle tree / Right place / Five years / Meera's sigh / I need you / First impression / Lonely swan / Chandrika / Losin' my head / Green and blue
RES 105CD / Apr '97 / Resurgence

Holiday Flyer

☐ BLUE HARVEST
Blue harvest
DRL 058CD / 6 Apr '98 / Darla

Holiday, Billie

☐ 16 MOST REQUESTED SONGS
Miss Brown to you / If you were mine / These foolish things / Way you look tonight / Pennies from heaven / I can't give you anything but love / I've got my love to keep me warm / Why was I born / Carelessly / Easy living / My man / I'm gonna lock my heart (and throw away the key) / Body and soul / Gloomy Sunday / God bless the child / I'm a fool to want you
4744012 / Feb '94 / Columbia

☐ 40 GREATEST SONGS (2CD Set)
St. Louis blues / Loveless love / Let's do it / Georgia on my mind / Romance in the dark / All of me / God bless the child / Am I blue / Solitude / Jim / I cover the waterfront / Love me or leave me / Gloomy Sunday / It's a sin to tell a lie / Until the real thing comes along / Trav'lin light / Let's call the whole thing off / They can't take that away from me / Mean to me / Easy livin' / Nice work if you can get it / Can't help lovin' dat man / Back in your own back yard / You got to my head / Very thought of you / What a little moonlight can do / These foolish things / Summertime / Fine romance / Pennies from heaven / I can't give you anything but love / This is my last affair / Strange fruit / Fine and mellow / I gotta right to sing the blues / Them there eyes / Swing, brother, swing / Night and day / Man I love / Body and soul
MUCD 9507 / May '96 / Musketeer

☐ ANGEL OF HARLEM
BN 019 / Apr '98 / Blue Nite

☐ AT CARNEGIE HALL
5277772 / Oct '95 / Verve

☐ AT STORYVILLE
I cover the waterfront / Too marvellous for words / I loves you Porgy / Them there eyes / Willow weep for me / I only have eyes for you / You go to my head / He's funny that way / Billie's blues / Miss Brown to you / Lover come back to me / Ain't nobody's business if I do / You're driving me crazy
BLC 760921 / Apr '91 / Black Lion

☐ AUDIO ARCHIVE
Night and day / Hello my darling / What a little moonlight can do / I'll never fail you / Miss Brown to you / I wish I had you / Twenty four hours a day / Let's dream in the moonlight / Yankee Doodle never went to town / You're so desirable / If you were mine / Georgia on my mind / You're gonna see a lot of me / Loveless love / These 'n' that 'n' those / Please keep me in your dreams / What is this going to get us / Let's call a heart a heart / More than you know / Spreadin' rhythm around
CDAA 033 / Jun '92 / Tring

☐ BEST OF BILLIE HOLIDAY, THE
4670292 / Jan '95 / Sony Jazz

☐ BILLIE BLUES (Holiday, Billie & Her Orchestra)
I've got my love to keep me warm / Born to love / Fine romance / Where is the sun / Please keep me in your dreams / One never knows does one / One two button your shoe / Let's call a heart a heart / Billie's blues / No regrets / Did I remember / If my heart could only talk / Don't know if I'm comin' or goin' / Who wants love / Moon looks down and laughs / When a woman loves a man / Says my heart / Forget if you can / Having myself a time / I'm gonna lock my heart (and throw away the key) / I wish I had you / Under the blue jungle moon / Everything happens for the best
CD 53178 / Apr '98 / Giants Of Jazz

☐ BILLIE HOLIDAY
CD 105 / Oct '94 / Timeless Treasures

☐ BILLIE HOLIDAY
DVX 08072 / May '95 / Deja Vu

☐ BILLIE HOLIDAY (2CD Set)
R2CD 4006 / 13 Apr '98 / Deja Vu

☐ BILLIE HOLIDAY (3CD Set)
Summertime / Carelessly / Stormy weather / I'm gonna lock my heart / I've got my love to keep me warm / Fine romance / Who loves you / These foolish things / If you were mine / Let's call a heart to heart / Twenty four hours a day / Mean to me / Autumn in New York / East of the sun / I only have eyes for you / I loves you Porgy / He's funny that way / Lover man / I can't give you anything but love / That's life I guess / Gettin' some fun out of life / This is my last affair / Tenderly / Moonlight in Vermont / I got it bad and that ain't good / How deep is the ocean / It's so easy to remember / Blue moon / Sailboat in the moonlight / Do nothin' 'til you hear from me / Fine and mellow / Lover come back to me / Pennies from heaven / They can't take that away from me / My man / You let me down / Love for sale / Mood that I'm in / Me, myself and I / You go to my head / How could you / Trav'lin all alone / I don't stand a ghost of a chance with you / Detour ahead / God bless the child / It's like reaching for the moon / This year's kisses / What a little moonlight can do / Willow weep for me / Easy living / I cover the waterfront / Nice work if you can get it / No regrets / Ain't nobody's business if I do
KBOX 361 / Nov '96 / Collection
BN 302 / Dec '97 / Blue Nite

☐ BILLIE HOLIDAY GOLD (2CD Set)
D2CD 4006 / Jun '95 / Deja Vu

☐ BILLIE HOLIDAY SONGBOOK, THE
Good morning heartache / My man / Billie's blues / Don't explain / Lady sings the blues / Lover man / God bless the child / Fine and mellow / Strange fruit / Stormy blues / Travellin' light / What a little moonlight can do / I cried for you / I cover the waterfront
8232462 / Apr '86 / Verve

☐ BILLIE HOLIDAY VOL.1 1940-1941
JUCD 2014 / Mar '97 / Jazz Unlimited

☐ BILLIE HOLIDAY VOL.2 1941-1942
JUCD 2015 / Mar '97 / Jazz Unlimited

☐ BILLIE HOLIDAY WITH THE TEDDY WILSON ORCHESTRA 1935-1942 (Holiday, Billie & Teddy Wilson)
Sugar / More than you know / Love me or leave me / Mood that I'm in / It's a sin to tell a lie / You showed me the way / Carelessly / It's too hot for words / Nice work if you can get it / Moanin' low / How could you / If you were mine / Sun showers / That's life I guess / I cover the waterfront / What a night, what a moon, what a girl / Pennies from heaven / What a little moonlight can do / My man / They say / You let me down / It's like reaching for the moon / Sunbonnet blue (and a yellow straw hat) / Miss brown to you
CD 53055 / Mar '90 / Giants Of Jazz

☐ BILLIE'S BEST (Selections From 'The Complete Billie Holiday On Verve')
What a little moonlight can do / Foggy day / Come rain or come shine / Comes love / He's funny that way / Stars fell on Alabama / Gone with the wind / They can't take that away from me / East of the Sun and West of the moon / Everything I have is yours / Stormy blues / Speak low / April in Paris / I've got my love to keep me warm / Some other Spring / All the way
5139432 / May '92 / Verve

☐ BILLIE'S BLUES
1-2 Button your shoe / Let's call a heart a heart / Billie's blues / No regrets / I can't give you anything but love / This year's kisses / He ain't rhythm / Let's call the whole thing off / They can't take that away from me / Sentimental and melancholy / Way you look tonight / I'll get by / Summertime / Who wants love / He's funny that way / Now they call it swing / Nice work if you can get it / Things are looking up
MUCD 9002 / Apr '95 / Musketeer

☐ BILLIE'S BLUES
AMSC 572 / Aug '96 / Avid

☐ **BILLIE'S BLUES**
WJSCD 1005 / Jul '96 / Wolf

☐ **BILLIE'S BLUES**
Wherever you are / Georgia on my mind / Until the real thing comes / Keeps on raining / What a little moonlight can do / My man / Strange fruit / Twenty four hours a day / You're gonna see a lot of me / Let's dream in the moonlight / Let's call a heart a heart / Please keep me in your dreams / These foolish things / That's life I guess / I wish I had you / Billie's blues
CDMT 027 / Oct '96 / Meteor

☐ **CLASSICS 1933-1937 (Holiday, Billie & Her Orchestra)**
CLASSICS 582 / Oct '91 / Classics

☐ **CLASSICS 1937-1939**
CLASSICS 592 / Sep '91 / Classics

☐ **CLASSICS 1939-1940 (Holiday, Billie & Her Orchestra)**
CLASSICS 601 / Sep '91 / Classics

☐ **CLASSICS 1940-1942**
CLASSICS 680 / Mar '93 / Classics

☐ **CLASSICS 1944**
CLASSICS 806 / Mar '95 / Classics

☐ **COLLECTION, THE**
Summertime / I can't give you anything but love / Fine romance / Pennies from heaven / Mood that I'm in / That's life I guess / I've got my love to keep me warm / Carelessly / Easy living / Gettin' some fun out of life / How could you / I'm gonna lock my heart (and throw away the key) / It's like reaching for the moon / Let's call a heart a heart / Me myself and I / Mean to me / No regrets / My last affair / This year's kisses / Those foolish things / Trav'lin' all alone / Twenty four hours a day / Who loves you / You go to my head / You let me down
COL 018 / Apr '95 / Collection

☐ **COMPLETE BILLIE HOLIDAY ON VERVE 1945-1959, THE (10CD Set)**
Body and soul / Strange fruit / I cried for you / Fine and mellow / He's funny that way / Man I love / Gee baby ain't I good to you / All of me / Billie's blues / Travellin' light / He's funny that way / You better go now / You're driving me crazy / There is no greater love / I cover the waterfront / East of the Sun and West of the moon / Blue moon / You go to my head / You turned the tables on me / Easy to love / These foolish things / I only have eyes for you / Solitude / Everything I have is yours / Love for sale / Moonglow / Tenderly / If the moon turns green / Remember / Autumn in New York / My man / Lover come back to me / Stormy weather / Yesterdays / He's funny that way / I can't face the music / Blue moon / All of me / My man / Them there arms / I cried for you / What a little moonlight can do / I cover the waterfront / Billie's blues / Lover come back to me / How deep is the ocean / What a little moonlight can do / I cried for you / Love me or leave me / PS I love you / Too marvellous for words / Softly / I thought about you / Willow weep for me / Stormy blues / Say it isn't so / I've got my love to keep me warm / I wished on the moon / Always / Everything happens to me / Do nothin' 'til you hear from me / Ain't misbehavin' / Nice work if you can get it / Mandy is two / Prelude to a kiss / I must have that man / Jeepers creepers / Please don't talk about me when I'm gone / Moonlight in Vermont / Everything happens to me / When you are away dear / It had to be you / Mood that I'm in / Gone with the wind / I got it bad and that ain't good / Sun bonnet blue / I don't stand a ghost of a chance with you / I'm walkin' through Heaven with you / Just friends / Nearness of you / It's too hot for words / They say / I won't believe it / I don't want to cry anymore / Prelude to a kiss / I don't stand a ghost of a chance with you / When your lover has gone / Gone with the wind / Please don't talk about me when I'm gone / It had to be you / Nice work if you can get it / Come rain or come shine / I gotta right to sing the blues / What's new / Fine romance / I hadn't anyone till you / I get a kick out of you / Everything I have is yours / Isn't this a lovely day / Misery / Strange fruit / God bless the child / One never knows, does one / Beer barrel polka / Some of these days / My Yiddishe Momme / Lady's back in town / One never knows, does one / Travellin' light / I must have that man / Some other Spring / Lady sings the blues / Strange fruit / God bless the child / Good morning heartache / No good man / Do nothin' 'til you hear from me / Cheek to cheek / Ill wind / Speak low / We'll be together again / All or nothing at all / Sophisticated lady / April in Paris / Lady sings the blues / Ain't nobody's business if I do / Travellin' light / Billie's blues / Body and soul / Don't explain / Yesterdays / Please don't talk about me when I'm gone / I'll be seeing you / My man / I cried for you / Fine and mellow / I cover the waterfront / What a little moonlight can do / I wished on the moon / Moonlight in Vermont / Foggy day / I didn't know what time it was / Just one of those things / Comes love / Day in, day out / Darn that dream / But not for me / Body and soul / Just friends / Stars fell on Alabama / Say it isn't so / Our love is here to stay / One for my baby (and one more for the road) / They can't take that away from me / Embraceable you / Let's call the whole thing off / Gee baby ain't I good to you / Oh Lady be good / Nice work if you can get it / Willow weep for me / My man / Lover come back to me / Lady sings the blues / What a little moonlight can do / Oh lady be good / I wished on the moon / Lover man / All the way / It's not for me to say / I'll never smile again / Just one more chance / When it's sleepy time down South / Don't worry 'bout me / Sometimes I'm happy / You took advantage of me / There'll be some changes made / 'Deed I do / All of you / Baby, won't you please come home
5176582 / Jun '93 / Verve

☐ **COMPLETE COMMODORE RECORDINGS, THE (2CD Set)**
Strange fruit / Yesterdays / Fine and mellow / I gotta right to sing the blues / How am I to know / My old flame / I'll get by / I cover the waterfront / I'll be seeing you / I'm yours / Embraceable you / As time goes by / He's funny that way / Lover come back to me / Billie's blues / On the sunny side of the street
CMD 24012 / Feb '97 / Commodore Jazz

☐ **COMPLETE RECORDINGS 1933-1940, THE (8CD Set)**
Your mother's son-in-law / Riffin' the scotch / I wished on the moon / What a little moonlight can do / Miss Brown to you / Sun bonnet blue / What a night / What a moon, what a girl / I'm painting the town red / It's too hot for words / Yankee Doodle never went to town / Eeny meeny miney mo / If you were mine / These 'n' that 'n' those / You let me down / Spreadin' rhythm around / Life begins when you're in love / It's like reaching for the moon / These foolish things / I cried for you / Guess who / Did I remember / No regrets / Summertime / Billie's blues / Fine romance / I can't pretend / 1-2 Button your shoe / Let's call a heart a heart / Easy to love / With thee I swing / Way you look tonight / Who loves you / Pennies from heaven / That's life I guess / I can't give you anything but love / One never knows, does one / I've got my love to keep me warm / If my heart could only talk / Please keep me in your dreams / He ain't got rhythm / This year's kisses / Why was I born / I must have that man / Twenty four hours a day / Mood that I'm in / You showed me the way / Sentimental and melancholy / My last affair / Carelessly / How could you / Moanin' low / Where is the sun / Let's call the whole thing off / They can't take that away from me / Don't know if I'm coming or going / Sun showers / Yours and mine / I'll get by / Mean to me / Foolin' myself / Easy living / I'll never be the same / Me, myself and I / Sailboat in the moonlight / Born to love / Without your love / Getting some fun out of life / Who wants love / Travellin' all alone / He's funny that way / Nice work if you can get it / Things are looking up / My man / Can't help lovin' dat man / My first impression of you / When you're smiling / I can't believe that you're in love with me / If dreams come true / Now they call it swing / On the sentimental side / Back in your own backyard / When a woman loves a man / You go to my head / Man looks down and laughs / If I were you / Forget if you can / Having myself a time / Says my heart / I wish I had you / I'm gonna lock my heart (and throw away the key) / Any old time / Very thought of you / I can't get started (with you) / I've got a date with a dream / You can't be mine (and someone else's too) / Everybody's laughing / Here it is tomorrow again / Say it with a kiss / April in my heart / I'll never fail you / They say / You're so desirable / You're gonna see a lot of me / Hello my darling / Let's dream in the moonlight / That's all I ask of you / Dream of life / What shall I say / It's easy to blame the weather / More than you know / Sugar / You're too lovely to last / Under a blue jungle moon / Everything happens for the best / Why did I always depend on you / Long gone blues / Strange fruit / Yesterdays / Fine and mellow / I gotta right to sing the blues / Some other Spring / Night and day / Man I love / You're just a no account / You're a lucky guy / Ghost of yesterdays / Body and soul / What is this thing going to get us / Falling in love again / I'm pulling through / Tell me more / Laughing at life / Time on my hands / I'm all for you / I hear music / It's the same old story / Practice makes perfect / St. Louis blues / Loveless love
CDAFS 10198 / Jun '93 / Affinity

☐ **COMPLETE STORYVILLE CLUB SESSION, THE**
FSRCD 151 / Dec '90 / Fresh Sound

☐ **DEFINITIVE EDITION VOL.1 1936-1938, THE**
BMCD 1021 / Jul '96 / Blue Moon

☐ **DEFINITIVE EDITION VOL.2 1936-1937, THE**
BMCD 1022 / Jul '96 / Blue Moon

☐ **DEFINITIVE EDITION VOL.3 1937-1938, THE**
BMCD 1023 / Jul '96 / Blue Moon

☐ **DEFINITIVE EDITION VOL.4 1938, THE**
BMCD 1024 / Jul '96 / Blue Moon

☐ **DEFINITIVE EDITION VOL.5 1938-1939, THE**
BMCD 1025 / Jul '96 / Blue Moon

☐ **DEFINITIVE EDITION VOL.6 1939-1941, THE**
BMCD 1026 / Jul '96 / Blue Moon

☐ **DEFINITIVE EDITION VOL.7 1941-1944, THE**
BMCD 1027 / Jul '96 / Blue Moon

☐ **EARLY CLASSICS, THE**
Summertime / Sentimental and melancholy / Who loves you / Pennies from heaven / That's life, I guess / Billie's blues / When you're smiling / Carelessly / If dreams come true / Fine romance / Mood that I'm in / Let's call a heart a heart / Where is the sun / Don't know if I'm coming or going / I can't believe that you're in love with me / He's funny that way / Now they call it swing / Miss Brown to you
PASTCD 9756 / Aug '91 / Flapper

☐ **ESSENTIAL BILLIE HOLIDAY, THE**
St. Louis blues / Solitude / Man I love / Georgia on my mind / I've got my love to keep me warm / My last affair / I'll never be the same / If dreams come true / Summertime / Billie's blues / I cried for you / Mean to me / He's funny that way / My man (mon homme) / Nice work if you can get it / Night and day
4671492 / Jul '93 / Columbia

☐ **ESSENTIAL LADY DAY, THE (2CD Set)**
I wished on the moon / These foolish things / Easy to love / Way you look tonight / I can't give you anything but love / I've got my love to keep me warm / This year's kisses / Why was I born / I must have that man / I'll get by / Mean to me / Foolin' myself / Easy livin' / I'll never be the same / He's funny that way / Nice work if you can get it / I can't believe that you're in love with me / If dreams come true / You go to my head / Very thought of you / I can't get started / Say it with a kiss / More than you know / Sugar / Strange fruit / Yesterdays / Fine and mellow / Some other spring / Them there eyes / Night and day / Man I love / You're a lucky guy / Body and soul / Laughing at life / I hear music / Let's do it / Georgia on my mind / God bless the child / Jim / I cover the waterfront / Love me or leave me / Until the real thing comes along / Trav'lin light / My old flame / I'll be seeing you / On the sunny side of the street / Loverman / That ole Devil called love / Don't explain / Lover come back to me
CPCD 82642 / Dec '96 / Charly

☐ **ESSENTIAL RECORDINGS, THE**
That ole devil called love / Keeps on a rainin' / Porgy / No good man / God bless the child / What is this thing called love / My man (mon homme) / Easy living / Lover man / Good morning heartache / Ain't nobody's business if I do / You're my thrill / Solitude / There is no greater love / You better go now / Weep no more
MCCD 095 / Mar '93 / Music Club

☐ **FEEL THE BLUES**
Body and soul / Travellin' all alone / Billie's blues / Let's call the whole thing off / Sentimental and melancholy / Without your love / Under a blue jungle moon / If my heart could only talk / If you were mine / Night and day / God bless the child / These foolish things / St. Louis blues / Yesterday / I gotta right to sing the blues / Summertime
SUMCD 4005 / Nov '96 / Summit

☐ **FINE AND MELLOW 1936-1941**
IGOCD 2034 / Oct '95 / Indigo

☐ **FINE AND MELLOW 1939-1944**
Strange fruit / Yesterdays / Fine and mellow / I gotta right to sing the blues / How am I to know / My old flame / I'll get by / I cover the waterfront
CDSGP 046 / May '94 / Prestige

☐ **FINE ROMANCE, A (Billie Holiday At Her Best)**
PLSCD 204 / Apr '97 / Pulse

☐ **FIRST ISSUE (The Great American Songbook/2CD Set)**
Blue moon / Nice work if you can get it / Yesterdays / Easy to love / Prelude to a kiss / Day in, day out / I've got my love to keep me warm / Embraceable you / Our love is here to stay / Too marvellous for words / Cheek to cheek / Come rain or come shine / Let's call the whole thing off / I thought about you / Fine romance / PS I love you / Always / Do nothin' 'til you hear from me / I get a kick out of you / Say it isn't so / How deep is the ocean / Travellin' light / Remember / Stormy weather / One for my baby (and one more for the road) / But not for me / Solitude / I gotta right to sing the blues / Just one of those things / Love for sale / Foggy day / All of you / Sophisticated lady / They can't take that away from me
5230032 / Aug '94 / Verve

☐ **GITANES - JAZZ 'ROUND MIDNIGHT**
Sophisticated lady / God bless the child / Everything happens to me / Embraceable you / You go to my head / My man / These foolish things / Good morning heartache / I don't stand a ghost of a chance with you / Solitude / I must have that man / I don't want to cry anymore / Travellin' light / One for my baby (and one more for the road) / We'll be together again
8414442 / Jan '92 / Verve

☐ **GOD BLESS THE CHILD**
I don't stand a ghost of a chance (with you) / I cover the waterfront / Please don't talk about me when I'm gone / Don't explain / Now or never / Miss brown to you / He's funny that way / God bless the child
17013 / Jul '94 / Laserlight

☐ **GOD BLESS THE CHILD**
GO 3817 / 1 Dec '97 / Golden Options

☐ **GOLD COLLECTION, THE**
D2CD 06 / Dec '92 / Deja Vu

☐ **IN THE DARK**
I hear music / Time on my hands / St Louis blues / Practice makes perfect / Let's do it / Loveless love / Romance in the dark / Georgia on my mind / I'm in a low down groove / All of me / Am I blue / God bless this child / Jim / Solitude / Love me or leave me / I cover the waterfront / Wherever you are / Gloomy Sunday / It's a sin to tell a lie / Mandy is two
SUMCD 4174 / 26 Jan '98 / Summit

☐ **INTRODUCTION TO BILLIE HOLIDAY 1935-1942, AN**
4003 / Dec '93 / Best Of Jazz

☐ **JAZZ AT THE PHILHARMONIC**
Body and soul / Strange fruit / I cried for you / Fine and mellow / He's funny that way / Man I love / Gee baby ain't I good to you / All of me / Billie's blues / Travellin' light / He's funny that way / You better go now / You're driving me crazy / There is no greater love / I cover the waterfront / Nice work if you can get it / Willow weep for me / My man / Lover come back to me / Lady sings the blues / What a little moonlight can do / I wished on the moon / Lover man
5216422 / Jan '94 / Verve

☐ **JAZZ MASTERS**
What a little moonlight can do / PS I love you / Blue moon / Remember / God bless the child / Yesterdays / Lover come back to me / Some other Spring / Nice work if you can get it / Willow weep for me / All or nothing at all / Autumn in New York / Fine romance / Good morning heartache / Please don't talk about me when I'm gone / Speak low
5198252 / 5 May '98 / Verve

☐ **JAZZ MASTERS (Billie Holiday Sings Standards)**
5276502 / 5 May '98 / Verve

☐ **JAZZ PORTRAITS**
Your mother's son-in-law / Sun showers / They can't take that away from me / They say / Sugar / More that you know / I gotta right to sing the blues / Fine and mellow / Strange fruit / Yesterdays / St. Louis blues / Georgia on my mind / All of me / Let's do it / Romance in the dark / Love me or leave me / I cover the waterfront / It's a sin to tell a lie
CD 14512 / May '94 / Jazz Portraits

☐ **LADY DAY (The Best Of Billie Holiday)**
These foolish things / Summertime / Fine romance / Way you look tonight / I've got my love to keep me warm / They can't take away from me / I'll never be the same / Nick work if you can get it / Can't help lovin' that man / When you're smiling / Any old time / Very thought of you / Strange friut / Good morning heartache / Georgia on my mind / All of me / Easy living / God Bless the child / I loves you porgy / Lover man / Don't explain / You're my thrill / There is no greater love / That ole devil called love / For all we know
MOODCD 52 / 25 Aug '97 / Sony TV

☐ **LADY DAY**
BN 018 / Apr '98 / Blue Nite

☐ **LADY DAY 1934-1948 (4CD Set)**
Lost my man blues / What a little moonlight can do / Miss Brown to you / Twenty four hours a day / Yankee Doodle never went to town / If you were mine / These, that and those / You let me down / Spreadin' rhythm around / It's like reaching for the moon / These foolish things / I cried for you / Guess who / Let's call a heart a heart / Easy to love / With thee I swing / Way you look tonight / Who loves you / Pennies from heaven / That's life I guess / I can't give you anything but love / Please keep me in your dreams / Carelessly / How could you / Moanin' low / Sun showers / Mean to me / Swing brother swing / I wish I had you / I'll never fail you / You're so desirable / You're gonna see a lot of me / Hello my darling / Let's dream in the moonlight / More than you know / I gotta right to swing / I gotta right to swing the blues / Yesterdays / Strange fruit / Fine and mellow / Night and day / What is this going to get us / I'm all for you / I hear music / It's the same old story / Practise makes perfect / St Louis blues / Loveless love / Let's do it / Georgia / Romance in the dark / All of me / God bless the child / Jim / Wherever you are / Until the real thing comes along / Do nothin' 'til you hear from me / I'll get by / My old flame / I cover the waterfront / How am I to know / Embraceable you / I'm yours / I'll be seeing you / As time goes by / I love my man / He's funny that way / Lover come back to me / Don't explain / You better go now / Baby, I don't cry over you / My man
FBB 905 / 5 Dec '97 / Ember

☐ **LADY DAY AND PREZ 1937-1941 (Holiday, Billie & Lester Young)**
This year's kisses / Without your love / All of me / Me, myself and I / I'll get by / Mean to me / Sailboat in the moonlight / I'll never be the same / Getting some fun out of life / Man I love / Travellin' all alone / Time on my hands / Laughing at life / Back in your own backyard / Georgia on my mind / Let's do it / Foolin' myself / Easy living / Say it with a kiss / You can't be mine (and someone else's too) / I can't believe that you're in love with me / She's funny that way / Romance in the dark / I must have that man
CD 53006 / Mar '92 / Giants Of Jazz

☐ **LADY DAY'S 25 GREATEST HITS 1933-1944**
Back in your own backyard / Did I remember / Easy living / Fine and mellow / Ghost of yesterday / He's funny that way / I can't give you anything but love / I love my man / I must have that man / I'll get by / I'll be the same / Long gone blues / You Mother's son in law / You go to my head / What a little moonlight can do / They can't take that away from me / Them there eyes / That ole devil called love / Swing, brother, swing / Strange fruit / Some other spring / No more / My last affair / Moanin' low / Miss Brown to you
CDAJA 5181 / Jan '96 / Living Era

☐ **LADY DAY'S IMMORTAL PERFORMANCES 1933-1942 (3CD Set)**
This years kisses / Without your love / All of me / Me, myself and I / I'll get by / Mean to me / A sailboat in the moonlight / I'll never be the same (mm solo) / Getting some fun out of life / Man I love / Trav'lin' all alone / Time on my hands / Laughing at life / Back in your own backyard / Georgia on my mind / Let's do it / Foolin' myself / Easy living / Say it with a kiss / You can't be mine / I can't believe that you're in love with me / She's funny that way / Romance in the dark / I must have that man / Sugar / More than you know / Love me or leave me / Mood that I'm in / It's a sin to tell a lie / You showed me the way / Carelessly / It's too hot for words / Nice work if you can get it / Moaning low / How could you / If you were mine / Sun showers / That's life I guess / I cover the waterfront / What a night, what a moon, what a girl / Pennies from heaven / What a little moonlight can do / My man / They say / You let me down / It's like reaching for the moon / Sunbonnet blue / Miss brown to you / I got a right to sing the blues / Fine and mellow / Yesterday's / Strange fruit / Long gone blues / Swing brother, swing / St. louis blues / That's all I ask of you / Let's call the whole thing off / Summertime / Night and day / They can't take that away from me / Your mother's son-in-law / I can't pretend / Dream of life / Some other spring / Now they call it swing / I hear music / Body and soul / I wished on the moon / Ghost of yesterdays / On the sentimental side / Very thought of you / You go to my head
CDB 1204 / Apr '92 / Giants Of Jazz

☐ **LADY DAY'S IMMORTAL PERFORMANCES 1942-1957 (3CD Set)**
Cheek to cheek / Sophisticated lady / Just one of those things / Comes love / Let's call the whole thing off / They can't take that away from me / But not for me / Body and soul / Foggy day / Moonlight in vermont / I wished on the moon / Say it isn't so / One for my baby (and one more for the road) / Love is here to stay / Embraceable you / Day in, day out / Them there eyes / My man / God bless the child / Do your duty / There is no greater love / Keeps on raining / I loves you, porgy / Now or never / Deep song / Blues are brewin' / Baby I don't cry over you / Big stuff / Guilty / What is this thing called love / As time goes by / On the sunny side of the street / My old flame / I'll be seeing you / Lover come back to me / Trav'lin' light / I cover the waterfront / Billie's blues / Do nothing till you hear from me / Please don't talk about me when I'm gone / It had to be you / Love me or leave me / These foolish things / Moonglow / Autumn in new york / How deep is the ocean / Stormy blues / What a little moonlight can do / Yesterdays / I can't face the music / Easy to love / You go to my head / I cried for

you / Willow weep for me / Lover come back to me / East of the sun (and west of the moon) / Too marvellous for words (vocal george melachrino) / Tenderly / Blue moon / Solitude / I only have eyes for you / Remember

CDB 1212 / Jun '92 / Giants Of Jazz

☐ LADY IN AUTUMN (2CD Set)
Body and soul / Strange fruit / Travellin' light / All of me / There is no greater love / I cover the waterfront / These foolish things / Tenderly / Autumn in New York / My man / Stormy weather / Yesterdays / He's funny that way / What a little moonlight can do / I cried for you / Too marvellous for words / I wished on the moon / I don't want to cry anymore / Prelude to a kiss / Nice work if you can get it / Come rain or come shine / What's new / God bless the child / Do nothin' 'til you hear from me / April in Paris / Lady sings the blues / Don't explain / Fine and mellow / I didn't know what time it was / Stars fell on Alabama / One for my baby (and one more for the road) / Gee baby ain't I good to you / Lover man / All the way / Don't worry 'bout me

8494342 / Mar '91 / Verve

☐ LADY IN SATIN
I'm a fool to want you / For heaven's sake / You don't know what love is / I get along without you very well / For all we know / Violets for your furs / You've changed / Easy to remember / But beautiful / Glad to be unhappy / I'll be around / I'll be around for a love affair

CK 65144 / 6 Oct '97 / Sony Jazz

☐ LEGACY 1933-58, THE (3CD Set)
Your mother's son-in-law / I wished on the moon / What a little moonlight can do / Miss Brown to you / Saddest tale / If you were mine / These 'n' that 'n' those / You let me down / Life begins when you're in love / It's like reaching for the moon / These foolish things / Summertime / Billie's blues / Fine romance / I can't believe / Easy to love / Pennies from Heaven / That's life, I guess / I can't give you anything but love / One never knows, does one / I've got my love to keep me warm / He ain't got rhythm / This year's kisses / Why was I born / I must have that man / Mood that I'm in / My last affair / Moaning low / Where is the sun / Let's call the whole thing off / Don't know if I'm coming or going / I'll get by / Foolin' myself / Easy living / I'll never be the same / Me, myself and I / Sailboat in the moonlight / Born to love / Without your love / They can't take that away from me / Swing brother swing / I can't get started (with you) / Who wants love / Travellin' all alone / He's funny that way / My man (mon homme) / Who want's love / I can't believe that you're in love with me / When a woman loves a man / You go to my head / Having myself a time / Says my heart / Very thought of you / I cried for you / Jeepers creepers / Long gone blues / Some other Spring / Them there eyes / Night and day / Man I love / Let's do it / All of me / God bless the child / Gloomy Sunday / Until the sad thing comes along / Fine and mellow / You've changed / For all we know

4690492 / Nov '91 / Columbia

☐ LEGEND OF BILLIE HOLIDAY, THE
That ole devil called love / Lover man / Don't explain / Good morning heartache / There is no greater love / Easy living / Solitude / Porgy / My man (mon homme) / Them there eyes / Now or never / Ain't nobody's business if I do / Somebody's on my mind / Keeps on a rainin' / You're my thrill / God bless the child

MCLD 19216 / Aug '93 / MCA

☐ LOVE FOR SALE
CDSGP 0102 / May '94 / Prestige

☐ LOVE ME OR LEAVE ME (20 Classics From The First Lady Of Jazz)
Let's do it / Mandy is two / Until the real thing comes along / I cover the waterfront / Am I blue / I hear music / Loveless love / Gloomy Sunday / I'm in a low down groove / God bless the child / All of me / Romance in the dark / Wherever you are / Love me or leave me / Jim / It's a sin to tell a lie / Solitude / St. Louis blues / Practice makes perfect / Georgia on my mind

302412 / Jun '98 / Hallmark

☐ LOVE SONGS
All of me / You go to my head / Until the real thing comes along / My man / Very thought of you / Easy living / They can't take that away from me / I 've got my love to keep me warm / Them there eyes / Night and day / Man I love / Me, myself and I / Way you look tonight / If you were mine / I can't believe that you're in love with me / Let's do it

4838782 / 26 Jan '98 / Sony Jazz

☐ LOVER MAN 1940-1944
Lover man (oh where can you be) / Don't explain / Big stuff / On the sunny side of the street / Lover come back to me / That ole devil called love / No more / I love my man / Embraceable you / I'll get by / How am I to know / I'm yours / My old flame / As time goes by / Wherever you are / Solitude / Practice makes perfect / Gloomy Sunday / Until the real thing comes along / Loveless love / I'm in a low-down groove

CD 53232 / Jan '98 / Giants Of Jazz

☐ MAN I LOVE 1937-1939, THE (Holiday, Billie & Lester Young)
This year's kisses / I must have that man / I'll get by / Mean to me / I'll never be the same / Easy living / Foolin' myself / Without your love / Me, myself and I / Sailboat in the moonlight / Travellin' all alone / She's funny that way / Getting some fun out of life / I can't believe that you're in love with me / Back in your own backyard / You can't be mine (and someone else's too) / Say it with a kiss / Man I love

CD 5048 / Aug '94 / Jazz Roots

☐ MAN I LOVE, THE (Holiday, Billie & Lester Young)
This year's kisses / I must have that man / I'll get by / Mean to me / I'll never be the same (mm solo) / Easy living / Foolin' myself / Without your love / Me myself and I / Sailboat in the moonlight / Travlin' all alone / She's funny that way / Getting some fun out of life / I can't believe that you're in love with me / Sat it with a kiss / Man I love

CD 14529 / Jan '94 / Jazz Portraits

☐ MASTERPIECES 1935-1942
158182 / Mar '94 / Masterpieces

☐ MASTERS OF JAZZ
STCD 4103 / Sep '97 / Storyville

☐ MASTERS OF JAZZ (2CD Set)
R2CD 8007 / 13 Apr '98 / Deja Vu

☐ MASTERS, THE
EABCD 055 / 24 Nov '97 / Eagle

☐ MASTERS, THE (2CD Set)
EDMCD 011 / 24 Nov '97 / Eagle

☐ ME MYSELF I
219912 / Mar '95 / Milan

☐ MISS BROWN TO YOU
What a little moonlight can do / Miss Brown to you / Twenty four hours a day / Yankee Doodle never went to town / If you were mine / These n'that n'those / Spreadin' rhythm around / Let's call a heart a heart / Please keep me in your dreams / I wish I had you / I'll never fail you / You're so desirable / You're gonna see a lot more of me / Hello my darling / Let's dream in the moonlight / More than you know / Under a blue jungle moon / Night and day / What is this going to get us / Loveless love / Georgia on my mind / Romance in the dark

GRF 075 / '93 / Tring

☐ MY MAN (Holiday, Billie & Teddy Wilson Orchestra)
What a little moonlight can do / Sunbonnet blue (and a yellow straw hat) / Miss brown to you / I wished on the moon / It's too hot for words / What a night, what a moon, what a girl / If you were mine / You let me down / It's like reaching for the moon / That's life I guess / Pennies from heaven / Mood that I'm in / You showed me the way / Carelessly / Moanin' low / How could you / Nice work if you can get it / My man

CD 14536 / Jan '94 / Jazz Portraits

☐ MY MAN (Holiday, Billie & Teddy Wilson Orchestra)
What a little moonlight can do / Sunbonnet blue (and a yellow straw hat) / Miss brown to you / I wished on the moon / It's too hot for words / What a night, what a moon, what a girl / If you were mine / You let me down / It's like reaching for the moon / That's life I guess / Pennies from heaven / Mood that I'm in / You showed me the way / Carelessly / Moanin' low / How could you / Nice work if you can get it / My man

CD 56028 / Jul '95 / Jazz Roots

☐ NIGHT AND DAY
I'm gonna lock my heart / Very thought of you / I can't get started / You can't be mine / Say it with a kiss / I'll never fail you / They say / That's all I ask of you / Yesterdays / Them there eyes / Night and day / You're just a no account / Body and soul / Falling in love again / I hear music / St. Louis blues / When you're smiling / I can't believe that you're in love with me / You may call it the swing / On the sentimental side / Born to love / Without your love

RAJCD 857 / 3 Aug '98 / Empress

☐ NIGHT AND DAY
What a little moonlight can do / Miss Brown to you / Twenty four hours a day / Yankee doodle never went to town / If you were mine / These 'n' that 'n' those / Spreadin' rhythm around / Let's call a heart a heart / Please keep me in your dreams / I wish I had you / I'll never fail you / You're gonna see a lot of me / Hello, my darling / Let's dream in the moonlight / More than you know / Night and day / What is this going to get us / Loveless love / Georgia on my mind / Romance in the dark

QED 027 / Nov '94 / Tring

☐ NO REGRETS
One two button my shoe / Let's call a heart a heart / Did I remember / No regrets / I can't give you anything but love / This years kisses / He ain't got rhythm / Let's call the whole thing off / They can't take that away from me / Sentimental and melancholy / Way I look tonight / I'll get by / Summertime / Who wants love / He's funny that way / Now they call it swing / Nice work if you can get it / Things are looking up / When you're smiling / If dreams come true / Fine romance / Billie's blues

PAR 2062 / May '96 / Parade

☐ ON THE SENTIMENTAL SIDE
Practise makes perfect / Night and day / More than you know / All of me / Them there eyes / I must have that man / Time on my hands / Let's do it / Until the real thing comes along / This years kisses / Georgia on my mind / Sugar / I've got my love to keep me warm / When a woman loves a man / They don't know that I'll get by / You go to my head / I'll get by / I can't get started / On the sentimental side

PPCD 78117 / May '96 / Past Perfect

☐ PORTRAIT OF BILLIE HOLIDAY, A
GALE 409 / May '97 / Gallerie

☐ QUINTESSENCE VOL.2, THE (2CD Set)
Blues (big city blues) / It's like reaching for the moon / One never knows does one / Carelessly / How could you / They can't take that away from me / Born to love / Swing brother swing / Ain't nobody's business if I do / Say it with a kiss / I'll never be the same / My man / Can't help loving that man / I can't get started with you / You can't be mine / Here it is tomorrow again / More than you know / Long gone blues / Tell me more and more (and then some) / St. Louis blues / All of me / Gloomy Sunday / I cover the waterfront / I'm yours / Embraceable you / He's funny that way / Body and soul / Strange fruit / You better go now / Good morning heartache / No good man / I'll look around / Fine and mellow / Man I love / Gee baby ain't I good to you / Billie's blues / Trav'lin' light / Blues are a brewin'

FA 222 / 21 Aug '97 / Fremeaux

☐ QUINTESSENCE, THE (1935-1944/2CD Set)
FA 209 / Oct '96 / Fremeaux

☐ QUINTESSENTIAL VOL.1 1933-1935
Your mother's son-in-law / Riffin' the scotch / I wished on the moon / What a little moonlight can do / Miss Brown to you / Sun bonnet blue / What a night / What a moon / What a girl / I'm painting the town red / It's too hot for words / Twenty four hours a day / Yankee Doodle never went to town / Eeny meeny miney mo / If you were mine / These 'n' that 'n' those / You let me down / Spreadin' rhythm around

4509872 / Jan '95 / Sony Jazz

☐ QUINTESSENTIAL VOL.2 1935-1936
Life begins when you're in love / It's like reaching for the moon / These foolish things / I cried for you / Guess who / Did I remember / No regrets / Summertime / Bille's blue / Fine romance / I can't pretend / 1-2 Button your shoe / Let's call a heart a heart / Easy to love / With thee I swing / Way you look tonight

4600602 / Jan '95 / Sony Jazz

☐ QUINTESSENTIAL VOL.3 1936-1937
Who loves you / Pennies from Heaven / That's life I guess / I can't give you anything but love / One never knows, does one / I've got my love to keep me warm / If my heart could only talk / Please keep me in your dreams / He ain't got rhythm / This year's kisses / Why was I born / I must have that man / Mood that I'm in / You showed me the way / Sentimental and melancholy / My last affair

4608202 / Jan '95 / Sony Jazz

☐ QUINTESSENTIAL VOL.4 1937
Carelessly / How could you / Moanin' low / Where is the sun / Let's call the whole thing off / They can't take away from me / I don't know If I'm coming or going / Sun showers / Yours and mine / I'll get by / Mean to me / Foolin' myself / Easy living / I'll never be the same / My, myself and I / Sailboat in the moonlight

4633332 / Jan '95 / Sony Jazz

☐ QUINTESSENTIAL VOL.5 1937-1938
Born to love / Without your love / Getting some fun out of life / Who wants love / Travellin' all alone / He's funny that way / Nice work if you can get it / Things are looking up / My man (mon homme) / Can't help lovin' dat man / My first impression of you / When you're smiling / I can't believe that you're in love with me / If dreams come true / Now they call it swing / On the sentimental side / Back in your own backyard / When a woman loves a man

4651902 / Jan '95 / Sony Jazz

☐ QUINTESSENTIAL VOL.6 1938
4663132 / Jan '95 / Sony Jazz

☐ QUINTESSENTIAL VOL.7 1938-1939
4669662 / Jan '95 / Sony Jazz

☐ QUINTESSENTIAL VOL.8 1939-1940
4679142 / Jan '95 / Sony Jazz

☐ QUINTESSENTIAL VOL.9 1940-1942
4679152 / Jan '95 / Sony Jazz

☐ SILVER COLLECTION, THE
I wished on the moon / Moonlight in Vermont / Say it isn't so / Our love is here to stay / Darn that dream / But not for me / Body and soul / Comes love / They can't take that away from me / Let's call the whole thing off / Gee baby ain't I good to you / Embraceable you / All or nothing at all / We'll be together again

8234492 / Mar '92 / Verve

☐ SOLITUDE
East of the Sun and West of the moon / Blue moon / Easy to love / These foolish things / I only have eyes for you / Solitude / Everything I have is yours / Love for sale / Moonglow / Tenderly / If the moon turns green / Remember / Autumn in New York

5198102 / Apr '93 / Verve

☐ SONGS FOR DISTINGUE LOVERS (Remastered)
Day in day out / Foggy day / Stars fell on Alabama / One for my baby (and one more for the road) / Just one of those things / I didn't know what time it was / Let's call the whole thing off / I wished on the moon / They can't take that away from me / Body and soul / Moonlight in Vermont / Our love is here to stay

5390562 / Oct '97 / Verve Master Edition

☐ SPOTLIGHT ON BILLIE HOLIDAY
Lover man / Ain't nobody's business if I do / Billie's blues / Miss Brown to you / Good morning heartache / Why not take all of me / Do nothin' 'til you hear from me / My man / I cover the waterfront / Lover come back to me / Them there eyes / He's funny that way / You're driving me crazy / Fine and mellow

HADCD 114 / Feb '94 / Javelin

☐ STRANGE FRUIT
I gotta right to sing the blues / Fine and mellow / Yesterdays / Strange fruit / Long gone blues / Swing brother swing / St. louis blues / That's all I ask of you / Let's call the whole thing off / Embraceable you / My mother's son-in-law / I can't pretend / Dream of life / Some other spring / Now they call it swing / I hear music / Body and soul / I wished on the moon / Ghost of yesterdays / On the sentimental side / Very thought of you / You go to my head

CD 53085 / May '93 / Giants Of Jazz

☐ STRANGE FRUIT
CWNCD 2014 / Jul '96 / Javelin

☐ SUMMER OF 1949
BS 18004 / Jul '96 / Bandstand

☐ SUMMERTIME (Holiday, Billie & Her Orchestra)
Summertime / I can't pretend / Let's call the whole swing / You go to my head / Very thought of you / That's all I ask of you / Dream of life / Long gone blues / Swing brother swing / Some other spring / Night and day / Ghost of yesterdays / Body and soul / Laughing at life / Time on my hands / I hear music

CD 14539 / Jan '94 / Jazz Portraits

☐ SUMMERTIME 1936-1940
Summertime / I can't pretend / Let's call the whole thing off / On the sentimental side / Now they call it swing / You go to my head / Very thought of you / That's all I ask of you / Dream of life / Long gone blues / Swing brother swing / Some other spring / Night and day / Ghost of yesterdays / Body and soul / Laughing at life / Time on my hands / I hear music

CD 56035 / Nov '94 / Jazz Roots

☐ THIS IS JAZZ
Miss Brown to you / Easy living / These foolish things / Some other spring / I wished on the moon / For heaven's sake / This years kisses / What a little moonlight can do / Sailboat in the moonlight / Fine romance / Mean to me / Fine and mellow / My man is easy to love / Pennies from heaven / You've changed / God bless the child

CK 64622 / Oct '96 / Sony Jazz

☐ THIS IS JAZZ (Billie Holiday Sings Standards)
Them there eyes / Body and soul / Let's call the whole thing off / Time on my hands / I must have that man / Night and day / Summertime / I'm a fool to want you / I'll get by / Very thought of you / Until the real thing comes along / They can't take that away from me / Can't help lovin' dat man / More than you know / I've got my love to keep me warm / I'll never be the same / You don't know what love is / When a woman loves a man

CK 65048 / 4 May '98 / Sony Jazz

☐ TRIPLE GOLD (3CD Set)
What a little moonlight can do / All of me / Moon looks down and laughs / If I were you / Night and day / Forget if you can / Havin' myself a time / Says my heart / I wish I had you / I'm gonna lock away my heart / St. Louis blues / I can't get started / I've got a date with a dream / You can't be mine / Everybody's laughing / Here it is tomorrow again / Say it with a kiss / April in my heart / I'll never fail you / Loveless love / Falling in love again / You're a lucky guy / Ghost of yesterday / I'm pulling through / These foolish things / Tell me more and more and then some / Laughing at life / Timeon my hands / I'm all for you / I hear music / I'm in a low down groove / It's the same old story / Fine romance / Practice makes perfect / Wherever you are / Mandy is two / You're so desirable / You're gonna see a lot of me / Them three eyes / Solitude / Let's do it / Hello my darlin' / Georgia on my mind / Let's dream in the moonlight / That's all I ask of you / Dream of life / What shall I say / It's easy to blame the weather / More than you know / Sugar / You're too lovely to last / Under a blue jungle moon / Everything happens for the best / Why do I always depend on you / Long gone blues / Some other spring / Our love is different / Am I blue / God bless the child

TG 332 / 8 Sep '97 / Start

☐ TWO ON ONE: BILLIE HOLIDAY & ELLA FITZGERALD (Holiday, Billie & Ella Fitzgerald)
Night and day / Falling in love again / Fine and mellow / Man I love / Romance in the dark / All of me / This year's kisses / Georgia on my mind / Let's do it / God bless the child / Future a tasket / Undecided / My heart belongs to daddy / F.d.r. Jones / I want to be happy / Dipsy doodle / If dreams come true / Hallelujah / Bei mir bist du schoen / 't ain't what you do (it's the way that you do it)

CDTT 9 / Apr '94 / Charly

☐ ULTIMATE DIVAS
5390512 / 10 Nov '97 / Verve

☐ VOICE OF JAZZ, THE
BN 020 / Apr '98 / Blue Nite

☐ WISHING ON THE MOON (Life & Times Of Billie Holiday/Read By Annie Ross/ 2CD Set)
I wished on the moon / He ain't got rhythm / This year's kisses / Swing, brother swing / I'll get by / Easy living / Strange fruit / Some other spring / God bless the child / My sweet hunk o'trash / It ain't nobody's business if I do / My man / Lover come back to me / You've changed / For all we know

480947 / Feb '97 / Sony Jazz

Hollaender, Friedrich

☐ WENN ICH MIR WAS WUNSCHEN DURFTE (8CD Set) (Various Artists)
Jonny: Weber, Marek / Wenn der alte Motor wieder tackt: Graetz, Paul / Groschen: Ebinger, Blandine / Wenn ich mal tot bin: Ebinger, Blandine / Das ist der Hertzschlag, der zusammenhalt: Graetz, Paul / Liliput: Weber, Marek / Jonny: Waldoff, Claire / Ich tanz Charleston: Charlie's Jazz Orchester / Currendmadchen: Ebinger, Blandine / O Mond: Ebinger, Blandine / Die Hungerkunstlerin: Ebinger, Blandine / Das wunderkind: Ebinger, Blandine / Die Trommlerin als Schiessbudenfigur: Ebinger, Blandine / Ich spiel so gern mit dir Klavier: Ebinger, Blandine / Raus mit den Mannern: Waldoff, Claire / O wie praktisch: Waldoff, Claire / Hol der blaue Engel: Dietrich, Marlene / Ich bei uns so schon: Graetz, Paul / Die Herren Manner: Hesterberg, Trude / Lene Levi: Hesterberg, Trude / Bei uns um die Gedachtniscchirche: run: Revue Ensemble / Das sprichte band: Revue Ensemble / Der rote faden: Revue Ensemble / Zwei dunkle augen: Hollaender, Friedrich / Und immer noch spielen se blues: Frohlich, Carl / Nass oder trocken: Godwin, Paul / Ich tanz um die Welt mit dir: Monosson, Leo / Das nachtgespenst: Gerron, Kurt / Die Grosstadt Infanterie: Gerron, Kurt / Herr Doktor, Herr Doktor: Gerron, Kurt / Keiner weiss, wie ich bin nur du: Keller, Greta / Kitsch tango: Bois, Curt / Guck doch nicht immer nach dem Tangogeiger hin: Bois, Curt / Ich mache alles mit den beinen: Bois, Curt / Reizend: Bois, Curt / Solang wir jung sind Madame: Bois, Curt / Eine kleine sehnsucht: Mosheim, Grete / In St. Pauli bei Altona: Mosheim, Grete / Peter: Dietrich, Marlene / Jonny: Dietrich, Marlene / Der blaue Engel: Dietrich, Marlene / Ich bin die fesche Lola: Dietrich, Marlene / Nimm dich in acht vor blonden Frauen: Dietrich, Marlene / Kinder, heut' abend such ich mir was aus: Dietrich, Marlene / Ich bin von kopf bis fuss auf liebe eingestellt: Dietrich, Marlene / Wenn ich mir was wunsche: Dietrich, Marlene / Ich bin von Kopf bis fuss auf liebe eingestellt: Weintraubs Syncopators / Nimm dich in acht vor blonden Frauen: Weintraubs Syncopators / Wenn ich mir was wunschen durfte: Keller, Greta / Du hast ja eine trane im Knopfloch: George, Heinrich / Ich wunsch mir wan: Horn, Camilla / Entbehren: Roberts, Ruhmann & Sargent / Eine Liebelei, so ware es immer: Porten & Froelich / Heute nacht oder nie: Schneider & Kiepura / Guten tag liebes Gluck: Waldoff, Claire / Das ist ganz egal: Waldoff, Claire / Da ist ein kleiner Mensch: Waldoff, Claire / Was eine Frau im Frühling traumt: Dietrich, Marlene / Mein blondes Baby: Dietrich, Marlene / Jonny: Dietrich, Marlene / Wenn die beste Freundin: Dietrich, Marlene / Wo ist der Mann: Dietrich, Marlene / Leben ohne liebe kannst du nicht: Dietrich, Marlene / Kleptomanin: Dietrich, Marlene / Allein in einer grossen Stadt: Dietrich, Marlene / Ich weiss nicht zu wem ich gehore: Dietrich, Marlene / Wenn man auseinandergeht: Dietrich, Marlene / Gib acht auf dein herz: Dietrich, Marlene

ist mein baby): *Comedy Harmonists* / Ich weiss nicht, zu wem ich gehore: *Sten, Anna* / Wie hab' ich nur leben konnen ohne dich: *Harvey, Lilian* / Jonny: *Dietrich, Marlene* / Awake in a dream: *Dietrich, Marlene* / You've got that look: *Dietrich, Marlene* / Boys in the backroom: *Dietrich, Marlene* / Little Joe the wrangler: *Dietrich, Marlene* / You've got that look: *Dietrich, Marlene* / St. Moritz waltz: *Robertson, Dick Studio Orchestra* / Eski-o-lay-li-mo: *Robertson, Dick Studio Orchestra* / Desire: *Lombardo, Carmen* / My heart and I: *Crosby, Bing* / House Jack built for Jill: *Crosby, Bing* / Moonlight and shadows: *Crosby, Bing* / Paradise in waltz time: *Swarthout, Gladys* / Moonlight and shadows: *Lamour, Dorothy* / Lovelight in the starlight: *Lamour, Dorothy* / Whispers in the dark: *Crosby, Bob & His Orchestra* / Whispers in the dark: *Boswell, Connee* / Thrill of a lifetime: *Leach, Billy* / True confession: *Armstrong, Louis* / True confession: *Wain, Bea* / It's raining sunbeams: *Durbin, Deanna* / Angel: *Paramount Studio Orchestra* / You leave me breathless: *Leonard, Jack* / You leave me breathless: *Keller, Greta* / Hello, my darling: *Holiday, Billie* / You and me: *Starr, Judy* / Stolen heaven: *Wain, Bea* / Mid night: *Carter, Benny & His Orchestra* / Strange enchantment: *Lamour, Dorothy* / Sentimental sandwich: *Lamour, Dorothy* / Palms of paradise: *Lamour, Dorothy* / Moon over Burma: *Lamour, Dorothy* / Man about town: *Ambrose & His Orchestra* / Man's in the navy: *Dietrich, Marlene* / I've been in love before: *Dietrich, Marlene* / Illusions: *Dietrich, Marlene* / Black market: *Dietrich, Marlene* / Ruins of Berlin: *Dietrich, Marlene* / Falling in love again: *Holiday, Billie* / Palms of paradise: *King, Henry* / Li'l boy love: *O'Neill, Dolores* / Arise my love: *O'Neill, Dolores* / This is the moment: *Stafford, Jo* / 5000 fingers of Dr.T: *Columbia Orchestra* / Dungeon ballet: *Columbia Orchestra* / Ten happy fingers: *Rettig, Tommy* / Dream stuff: *Rettig, Tommy* / Because we're kids: *Rettig, Tommy* / Get together weather: *Conrad, Healy & Hayes* / Dressing song: *Hayes, Peter* / Because we're kids: *Simpson, Carole* / Sabrina: *Gerhardt, Charles* / Falling in love again: *Britt, May* / Wenn ich mir was wunschen durfte: *Rampling, Charlotte* / Prolog: *Hollaender, Friedrich* / Das Spukschloss im Spessart: *Hollaender, Friedrich* / Der traum auf dem baum: *Hollaender, Friedrich* / Fur sie tun wir alles: *Hollaender, Friedrich* / Kleiner Rutsch in die Vergangenheit: *Hollaender, Friedrich* / Giftmischer rumba: *Hollaender, Friedrich* / Suleika: *Hollaender, Friedrich* / Kleider machen: *Hollaender, Friedrich* / Luete: *Hollaender, Friedrich* / Schiffs blues: *Hollaender, Friedrich* / Dazu gehoren zwei: *Hollaender, Friedrich* / Das wollen wir doch mal sein: *Hollaender, Friedrich* / Empfangsgesang: *Hollaender, Friedrich* / Giftmischer rumba (reprise): *Hollaender, Friedrich* / Hoppla auf's Sofa: *Ensemble Berlin* / Festival der goldenen zwanziger: *Ensemble Berlin* / Der song vom Stottern: *Wustenhagen, Harry & Rainer Bertram* / Ich ruf sie an: *Wustenhagen, Harry & Rainer Bertram* / Totale verfremdung: *Wustenhagen, Harry & Rainer Bertram* / Etikette a la Pappritz: *Maybach, Christianne* / Die neu neurose: *Maybach, Christianne* / Das wunderkind: *Eff, Barbara* / Der Rummelplatz blues: *Eff, Barbara* / Das Berg und Talbahngefhl: *Wustenhagen, Harry* / Stroganoff: *Wustenhagen, Harry* / Der Kopf unterm arm: *Bertram, Rainer* / Mainzer spezialitaten: *Vita, Helen & Edith Hancke* / Gesang der wasserman: *Vita, Helen & Edith Hancke* / Prinzesschen: *Vita, Helen & Edith Hancke* / Rote melodie: *Kuhl, Kate* / Die zersagte Dame: *Kuhl, Kate* / Dressur: *Hesterberg, Trude* / Ach lehne deine Wange: *Hesterberg, Trude* / Zieh dich aus Petronella: *Hesterberg, Trude* / Meine schwester liebt den Buster: *Dekowa, Victor* / Seit wann blast deine Grossmama Posaune: *Dekowa, Victor* / Duett im romanischen Cafe: *Sieg, Ursula & Lore Calvies* / Die kleptomanin: *Herking, Ursula* / Die kleine Internationale: *Stephan, Ruth* / An allem sind die Juden schuld: *Stephan, Ruth* / Sex appeal: *Lion, Margo* / Das Tauentzienmadel: *Bernhardt, Christa* / Wiener Schmarrn: *Vita, Helen* / Stroganoff: *Vita, Helen* / Chanson vom falschen Zug: *Schonbock, Karl* / Der Spuk personlich: *Pauli, Christiane* / Hochste Eisenbahn: *Strietzel, Achim* / Munchausen: *Thomas, Angelika* / Circe: *Wieder, Hanne* / Jonny wenn du geburtstag hast: *Ebinger, Blandine* / Die Schnapstrine: *Ebinger, Blandine* / Ick baumle mit de Beene: *Ebinger, Blandine* / Ilse: *Ebinger, Blandine* / Drei wunsche: *Ebinger, Blandine* / Dasm madchen mit den Schwefelholzern: *Ebinger, Blandine* / Chinesisches marchen: *Ebinger, Blandine* / Die roten schuhe: *Ebinger, Blandine* / Die trommlerin: *Ebinger, Blandine* / Ein volkslied: *Ebinger, Blandine* / In den abendwind geflustert: *Ebinger, Blandine* / Das wunderkind: *Ebinger, Blandine* / Currende: *Ebinger, Blandine* / Groschenlied: *Ebinger, Blandine* / Nachtgebet: *Ebinger, Blandine* / O Mond: *Ebinger, Blandine* / Wenn ich mal tot bin: *Ebinger, Blandine* / Giftmariechen: *Ebinger, Blandine* / Wiegenlied an eine Mutter: *Ebinger, Blandine* / Kinderlied oder der fliegende Jakob: *Ebinger, Blandine* / Kitsch: *Ebinger, Blandine* / Starker Tobak: *Ebinger, Blandine* / Das Berg und Tahlbahngefhl: *Hollaender, Friedrich* / Spotterdammerung: *Hollaender, Friedrich*

BCD 16009 / Nov '97 / Bear Family

Holland

☐ SOUNDTRACK FOR SYNTHETIC VOICES

DRL 067 / 3 Aug '98 / Darla

☐ YOUR ORGASM

DRL 049 / 10 Nov '97 / Darla

Holland & Dozier

☐ VERY BEST OF HOLLAND & DOZIER, THE (Various Artists)

Why can't we be lovers / Where did we go wrong / Don't leave me starving for your love / Slipping away / If you don't want to be in my life / Lady by day / Picture never changes / Hijackin' / Don't you take me from the world outside / Baby don't leave me now / Come together / New breed kinda woman / Super woman you ain't no ordinary woman / Don't stop playing our song / Where did we go wrong / Can't get enough / I'm so glad / Why can't we be lovers

DEEPF 003 / 27 Oct '97 / Deep Beats

Holland Tunnel Project

☐ STOP AND LISTEN

Feeling good / If / La mirade / Blowin' / Park mansion / Mr. Jazz / Monireh moods / Jazz club / Latin nights / PLO

LIQ 003CD / 26 May '98 / Liquid

Holland, Dave

☐ DREAM OF THE ELDERS (Holland, Dave Quartet)

Winding way / Lazy snake / Claressence / Equality (vocal) / Ebb and flo / Dream of the edlers / Second thoughts / Equality (instrumental)

5290842 / Feb '96 / ECM

☐ EMERALD TEARS

Spheres / Combination / Under Redwoods / Flurries / Emerald tears / B40, RS4W, M236k / Solar / Hooveling

5290872 / Dec '95 / ECM

☐ EXTENSIONS (Holland, Dave Quartet)

Nemesis / Processional / Black hole / Oracle / 101 fahrenheit (slow meltdown) / Color of mind

8417782 / Oct '90 / ECM

☐ JUMPIN' IN (Holland, Dave Quintet)

Jumpin' in / First snow / Dragon and the samural / New one / Sunrise / Shadow dance / You I love

8174372 / '88 / ECM

☐ LIFE CYCLE (Solo Cello)

Inception, discovery, longing, search, resolution / Sonnet / Rune / Troubadour tale / Grapevine / Morning song / Chanson pour la nuit

8292002 / Oct '86 / ECM

☐ ONES ALL

Homecoming / Three step dance / Pork pie hat / Jumpin' in / Reminiscence / Mr. PC / Little girl I'll miss you / Cashet / Blues for CM / Pass it on / God bless the child

VBR 21482 / Jan '96 / Intuition

☐ POINTS OF VIEW (Holland, Dave Quintet)

Balance / Mr.B / Bedouin trail / Metamorphos / Ario / Herbaceous / Benevolent one / Serenade

5570202 / 6 Apr '98 / ECM

☐ RAZOR'S EDGE, THE (Holland, Dave Quintet)

Brother Ty / Vedana / Razor's edge / Blues for CM / Vortex / Five four six / Wights waits for weights / Fight time

8330482 / Oct '87 / ECM

☐ SEEDS OF TIME (Holland, Dave Quintet)

Uhren / Homecoming / Perspicuity / Celebration / World protection blues / Grid lock / Walk away / Good doctor / Double vision

8253222 / Aug '85 / ECM

☐ TRIPLICATE (Holland, Dave Trio)

8371132 / Sep '88 / ECM

Holland, Jerry

☐ FIDDLESTICKS COLLECTION, THE (1982-1992)

GLCD 1156 / Dec '95 / Green Linnet

Holland, Jools

☐ BOOGIE WOOGIE PIANO

TMPCD 022 / Oct '95 / Temple

☐ FULL COMPLEMENT

Lost chord / One more time / Together again / No ones to blame / Baby, let me hold your hand / Lady don't fall backwards / Cackophony / Movin' on / Me - U = loneliness / Blue guitar / Shake, rattle and roll / Lady don't sing

EIRSCD 1083 / Jun '96 / IRS/EMI

☐ JAZZ PIANO

TMPCD 024 / Oct '95 / Temple

☐ LIFT THE LID (Holland, Jools & His Rhythm 'n' Blues Orchestra)

3984205252 / 13 Oct '97 / Coalition

☐ RAG TIME PIANO

TMPCD 023 / Oct '95 / Temple

☐ SEX'N'JAZZ'N'ROCK'N'ROLL

Jubal's discovery / Hamster's wheel / Waiting game / Able mabel / U.j. / I, is all I ever hear / Instrumental love / Atom bomb / Rab elpmet / Scorpio rising / Well alright / Count to ten / Escaped stripe / I love a train / Wang dang doodle / Martians playing boogie woogie / Lonesome joe / Absit invidia

HF 51CD / Oct '96 / Coliseum

☐ WORLD OF HIS OWN

Architectural number / Maiden's lament / Honey dripper / Thursday in three movements / Harp solo / Biggy wiggy / Holy cow / In the heat of the night / We're through / Grand Hotel / Danger zone

EIRSCD 1082 / Jun '96 / IRS/EMI

Hollander, Rick

☐ ACCIDENTAL FORTUNE (Hollander, Rick Quartet)

Accidental fortune / My old flame / Point of the pen / I've grown accustomed to her face / Some lovely dreams / I should care / Big Stacey / Theme for Ernie / Beautiful friendship / Pull

CCD 4550 / May '93 / Concord Jazz

☐ ONCE UPON A TIME (The Music Of Hoagy Carmichael)

Skylark / Stardust / Baltimore Oriole / Georgia on my mind / Hong kong blues / Rockin' chair / Ivy / Nearness of you

CCD 4666 / Sep '95 / Concord Jazz

Holley, Major

☐ EXCUSE ME LUDWIG

BB 889 / Nov '97 / Black & Blue

☐ MULE

BB 8622 / Feb '96 / Black & Blue

Holliday, Judy

☐ HOLLIDAY WITH MULLIGAN (Holliday, Judy & Gerry Mulligan)

What's the rush / Loving you / Lazy / It must be Christmas / Party's over / It's bad for me / Suppertime / Pass that peace pipe / I gotta right to sing the blues / Summer's over / Blue prelude

CDSL 5191 / Mar '87 / DRG

Holliday, Michael

☐ 30TH ANNIVERSARY COLLECTION

Yellow rose of Texas / Gal with the yaller shoes / Love you darlin' / Keep your heart / Story of my life / Stairway of love / My heart is an open book / Palace of love / Life is a circus / For you, for you / I have waited / Steady game / Starry eyed / Dream talk / One finger symphony / Young in love / I wonder who's kissing her now / Miracle of Monday morning / Remember me / Dream boy dream / I don't want you to see me cry / Wishin' on a rainbow / Have I told you lately that I love you / Tears / I just can't win / Laugh and the world laughs with you / Just to be with you again / Drums / My last date with you

CDEMS 1509 / Feb '94 / EMI

☐ EMI PRESENTS THE MAGIC OF MICHAEL HOLLIDAY

Nothin' to do / Gal with the yaller shoes / Hot diggety / Ten thousand miles / Story of my life / In love / Stairway of love / I'll always be in love with you / Starry eyed / Skylark / Little boy lost / Have I told you lately that I love you / I wonder who's kissing her now / My house is your house / Folks who live on the hill / Yellow rose of Texas / Tears / Dear heart / Dream boy dream / Young in love / Palace of love / My last date (with you) / Old Cape Cod / Skye boat song / Rooney

CDMFP 6287 / May '97 / Music For Pleasure

☐ EP COLLECTION, THE

Runaway train / Yaller yaller gold / Darlin' Katie / Marrying for love / I'll be loving you too / Lonesome road / Just a wearyin' for you / Ramblin' man / Kentucky babe / In the good old summertime / Stairway of love / Four feather falls / Happy hearts and friendly faces / Way back home / Show me the way to go home / Side by side / Alexander's ragtime band / Just a prayer away / Careless hands / Dearest between hello and goodbye / Story of my life / I can't give you anything but love / Winter wonderland / Perfect day / Four walls / I Can't begin to tell you / Margie

SEECD 311 / Feb '91 / See For Miles

☐ TOGETHER AGAIN (Holliday, Michael & Edna Savage)

Story of my life / Arrivederci darling / Rooney / Tear fell / Tip toe through the tulips / Once / Girl in the yaller shoes / Long ago and far away / We'll gather lilacs / 'S wonderful / In the wee small hours of the morning / My house is your house / Let me be loved / Hot diggity (dog ziggity boom) / Tea for two / Catch me a kiss / I promise you / Me head in de barrel / I saw Esau / Never leave me / I'll be seeing you / Why why why / Nothin' to do / Goodnight my love

CC 252 / May '90 / Music For Pleasure

Hollies

☐ 1960'S FRENCH EP COLLECTION VOL.1 1963-1966, THE

524972 / Sep '97 / Magic

☐ 1960'S FRENCH EP COLLECTION VOL.2, THE

524982 / Sep '97 / Magic

☐ 1960'S FRENCH EP COLLECTION VOL.3 1966-1970, THE

524992 / Sep '97 / Magic

☐ 20 GREAT LOVE SONGS

Here I go again / Air that I breathe / Carrie Anne / Sorry Suzanne / I can't let go / Yes I will / Bus stop / To you my love / I'm alive / Too young to be married / Have you ever loved somebody / That's how strong my love is / Just like a woman / I can't tell the bottom from the top / Just one look / Come on back / Dear Eloise / Jennifer Eccles / What kind of boy / If I needed someone

LS 865212 / 2 Feb '98 / Disky

☐ AIR THAT I BREATHE, THE (The Best Of The Hollies)

Air that I breathe / Bus stop / Just one look / Yes I will / Look through my window / He ain't heavy, he's my brother / I can't let go / We're through / Searchin' / Stay, I'm alive / If I needed someone / Here I go again / Stop stop stop / On a carousel / Carrie Anne / King Midas in reverse / Jennifer Eccles / Listen to me / Sorry Suzanne / I can't tell the bottom from the top / Gasoline Alley bred / Hey Willy / Long cool woman in a black dress / Baby / Woman I love

CDEMTV 74 / Mar '93 / EMI

☐ AIR THAT I BREATHE, THE

Goodbye tomorrow / Too young to be married / Man without a heart / Air that I breathe / Lucy / Lonely hobo lullabye / I won't move over / Love is the thing / My island / There's always goodbye / Thanks for the memories / Be with you / Writing on the wall / Hello to romance / Amnesty / Boulder to birmingham / Harlequin / Something to live for / Satelite three

BR 1302 / May '94 / BR Music

☐ AIR THAT I BREATHE, THE (2CD Set)

I can't let go / Just one look / I can't tell the bottom from the top / Bus stop / Another night / 4th of July Ashbury Park (Sandy) / Star / My island / I'm down / Stop stop stop / Long cool woman in a black dress / Carrie Anne / Air that I breathe / Too young to be married / He ain't heavy...he's my brother / Goodbye tomorrow / Too young to be married / Man without a heart / Air that I breathe / Lucy / Lonely hobo lullabye / I won't move over / Love is the thing / My island / There's always goodbye / Thanks for the memories / Be with you / Writing on the wall / Hello to romance / Amnesty / Boulder to Birmingham / Harlequin / Something to live for / Satelite three

BS 81032 / Nov '97 / BR Music

☐ ALL THE WORLD IS LOVE

BR 1462 / Nov '94 / BR Music

☐ ANOTHER NIGHT/RUSSIAN ROULETTE/5317704/BUDDY HOLLY (4 Hollies Originals/4CD Set)

Another night / 4th Of July, Asbury Park (Sandy) / Lonely hobo lullaby / Second hand hang-ups / Machine jive / I'm down / Look out Johnny (there's a monkey on your back) / Give me time / You gave me life / Lucy / Wiggle that wotsit / Forty eight hour parole / Thanks for the memories / My love / Lady of the night / Russian roulette / Draggin' my heels / Louise / Be with you / Daddy don't mind / Say it ain't so Jo / Maybe it's dawn / Song of the sung / Harlequin / When I'm yours / Something to live for / Stormy waters / Boys in the band / Satelite three / It's in every one of us / Peggy Sue / Wishing / Love's made a fool of you / Take your time / Heartbeat / Tell me how / Think it over / Maybe baby / Midnight shifts / I'm gonna love you too / Peggy Sue got married / What to do / That'll be the day / It doesn't matter anymore / Everyday / Medley

CDHOLLIES 1 / Feb '95 / EMI

☐ ARCHIVE ALIVE (Live At King's Island, Cincinnati Ohio)

I can't let go / Just one look / Bus stop / On a carousel / Look through any window / King Midas in reverse / Wasted on the way / Teach your children / Soldier's song / Stop stop stop / Air that I breathe / Carrie Anne / Stop in the name of love / He ain't heavy he's my brother / Long cool woman in a black dress

NSPCD 518 / 29 Sep '97 / Connoisseur Collection

☐ AT ABBEY ROAD 1963-1966

Ain't that just like me / Hey what's wrong with me / Searchin' / Whole world over / Poison Ivy / Stay / Now's the time / Just one look / Keep off that friend of mine / Here I go again / Baby that's all / We're through / Come on baby / Yes I will / Nobody / I'm alive / You know he did / Look through any window / So lonely / If I needed someone / I've got a way of my own / I can't let go / Running throught the night / Bus Stop / Don't run and hide / Stop stop stop / It's you

CDABBEY 103 / 13 Oct '97 / EMI

☐ AT ABBEY ROAD 1966-1970

Pay you back with interest / On a carousel / All the world is love / Schoolgirl / Carrie Anne / Signs that will never change / King Midas in reverse / Everything is sunshine / Dear Eloise / Open up your eyes / Man with no expression / Listen to me / Do the best you can / Blowing in the wind / Sorry Suzanne / Not that way at all / He ain't heavy he's my brother / Cos you like to love me / Sign of the times / I can't tell the bottom from the top / Mad Professor Blyth / Gasoline alley / Dandelion wine / Confession of a mind

4934502 / 23 Feb '98 / EMI

☐ BEST OF THE HOLLIES, THE (Centenary Collection)

On a carousel / Stop, stop, stop / Jennifer Eccles / He ain't heavy, he's my brother / Air that I breathe / Magic woman touch / Listen to me / Pay you back with interest / We're through / Yes I will / King Midas in reverse / Gasoline Alley bred / Sandy (4th July, Asbury Park) / Purple rain / Shine silently / Baby / Mighty Quinn / Peggy Sue / Look through any window / Just like me / Mickey's monkey / Stay / Holliedaze (medley)

CTMCD 311 / Feb '97 / EMI

☐ BUTTERFLY

Dear Eloise / Maker / Would you believe / Postcard / Try it / Step inside / Away away away / Pegasus / Wish you a wish / Charlie and Fred / Elevated observations / Butterfly

BGOCD 79 / '89 / Beat Goes On

☐ CONFESSIONS OF THE MIND

Survival of the fittest / Man without a heart / Little girl / Isn't it nice / Confessions of a mind / Lady please / Frightened lady / Too young to be married / Seperated / I wanna shout

BGOCD 96 / '89 / Beat Goes On

☐ DEAR ELOISE/KING MIDAS IN REVERSE

Dear Eloise / Away away away / Maker / Pegasus / Would you believe / Wish you a wish / Postcard / Charlie and Fred / Try it / Elevated observations / Step inside / Butterfly / King Midas in reverse / Leave me / Do the best you can

CDSC 6123 / Dec '97 / Sundazed

☐ DISTANT LIGHT

What a life I've led / Look what we've got / Hold on / Pull down the blind / To do with love / Promised land / Long cool woman in a black dress / You know the score / Cable car / Little thing like love / Long dark road

BGOCD 97 / Jul '91 / Beat Goes On

☐ EP COLLECTION, THE

Woodstock / Here I go again / You know he did / What kind of boy / Baby that's all / Look through my window / What kind of love / When I'm not there / Rockin' Robin / Lucille / Memphis / Just one look / I'm alive / Come on back / We're through / I've got a way of my own / So lonely / To you my love / What'cha gonna do about it / Come on home / I can't let you go

SEECD 94 / Mar '95 / See For Miles

☐ **ESSENTIAL, THE**
(Ain't that) Just like me / Searchin' / Stay / Poison Ivy / Just one look / Here I go again / Time for love / Please don't feel too bad / Yes I will / So lonely / I'm alive / Put yourself in my place / I can't let go / Bus stop / Tell me to my face / Stop stop stop / Carrie Anne / King Midas in reverse / Away away away / Maker / Headed for a full / Lullaby to Tim / Jennifer Eccles / Sorry Suzanne / He ain't heavy he's my brother
CDMFP 6387 / 3 Aug '98 / Music For Pleasure

☐ **EVOLUTION**
Then the heartaches begin / Water on the brain / Have you ever loved somebody / Heading for a fall / Ye olde toffee shoppe / When your lights turned on / Stop right there / Lullaby to Tim / You need love / Rain on the window / Leave me / Games we play
BGOCD 80 / '89 / Beat Goes On

☐ **FOR CERTAIN BECAUSE**
What's wrong with the way I live / Pay you back with interest / Tell me to my face / Clown / Suspicious look in your eyes / It's you / High classed / Peculiar situation / What went wrong / Crusader / Don't even think about changing / Stop stop stop
BGOCD 9 / Dec '89 / Beat Goes On

☐ **HOLLIES SING DYLAN**
When the ship comes in / I'll be your baby tonight / I want you / This wheel's on fire / I shall be released / Blowin' in the wind / Quit your low down ways / Just like a woman / Times they are a changin' / All I really want to do / My back pages / Mighty Quinn
CZ 520 / Jun '93 / EMI

☐ **HOLLIES, THE**
Very last day / You must believe in me / Put yourself in my place / Down the line / That's my desire / Too many people / Lawdy Miss Clawdy / When I come home to you / Fortune teller / So lonely / I've been wrong / Mickey's monkey
DORIG 117 / 3 Nov '97 / EMI

☐ **IN THE HOLLIES STYLE**
Nitty gritty / Something's got a hold on me / Don't you know / To you my love / It's in her kiss / Time for love / What kind of boy / Too much monkey business / I thought of you last night / Please don't feel too bad / Come on home / You'll be mine / Set me free
BGOCD 8 / Oct '88 / Beat Goes On

☐ **IN THE HOLLIES STYLE (Mono/Stereo)**
Nitty gritty/Something's got a hold on me / Don't you know / To you my love / It's in her kiss / Time for love / What kind of love / What kind of boy / Too much monkey business / I thought of you last night / Please don't feel too bad / Come on home / You'll be mine / Set me free
DORIG 115 / 6 Oct '97 / EMI

☐ **LOVE SONGS (22 Of Their Most Romantic Ballads)**
I can't let go / Air that I breathe / Just one look / I can't tell the bottom from the top / Bus stop / Carrie Anne / Here I go again / Sorry Suzanne / Yes I will / To you my love / I'm alive / Come on back / Dear Eloise / Jennifer Eccles / What kind of boy / If I needed someone / You need love / King Midas in reverse / Too young to be married / Have you ever loved somebody / That's how strong my love is / Just like a woman
CDMFP 5883 / Aug '96 / Music For Pleasure

☐ **MOVING FINGERS**
Survival of the fittest / Confessions of a mind / Lady please / Too young to be married / Man without a heart / Isn't it nice / Frightened lady / Marigold Gloria swansong / Perfect lady / Housewife / Gasoline alley bred / Separated / I wanna shout / Dandelion wine / Mad Professor Blyth
CDSC 6125 / Nov '97 / Sundazed

☐ **OTHER SIDE OF THE HOLLIES...PLUS, THE**
'Cos you love me / Everything is sunshine / Signs that will never change / Not that way at all / You know he did / Do the best you can / So lonely / I've got a way of my own / Don't run and hide / Come on back / Open up your eyes / All the world is love / Whole world over / Row the boat together / Mad Professor Blyth / Dandelion wine / Baby that's all / Nobody / Keep off that friend of mine / Running through the night / Hey what's wrong with me / Blowin' in the wind
SEECD 302 / Jul '98 / See For Miles

☐ **ROMANY/WRITE ON/THE HOLLIES/A CRAZY STEAL (4 More Hollies Originals/4CD Set)**
Won't you feel good that morning / Touch / Words don't come easy / Magic woman touch / Lizzy and the Rainman / Down river / Slow down / Delaware Taggett and the Outlaw Boys / Jesus was a crossmaker / Romany / Blue in the morning / Courage of your convictions / Star / Write on / Sweet country calling / Love is the thing / I won't move over / Narida / Stranger / Crocodile woman (she bites) / My island / There's always goodbye / Falling calling / It's a shame, it's a game / Don't let me down / Out on the road / Air that I breathe / Rubber Lucy / Transatlantic Westbound jet / Pick up the pieces again / Down on the run / Love makes the world go round / Day that Curly Billy shot down Crazy Sam McGee / Writing on the wall / What am I gonna do / Let it pour / Burn out / Hello to romance / Amnesty / Caraccas / Boulder to Birmingham / Clown service / Feet on the ground
CDHOLLIES 2 / Feb '96 / Premier/EMI

☐ **SING HOLLIES**
175332 / Jul '97 / Magic

☐ **SING HOLLIES IN REVERSE (A Hollies Tribute) (Various Artists)**
ER 800118CD / Nov '97 / Eggbert

☐ **SPECIAL COLLECTION (3CD Set)**
Ain't that just like me / I'm talking about you / Lucille / Little lover / Here I go again / Don't you know / You'll be mine / We're through / Very last day / Look through any window / So lonely / I am a rock / I'm alive / Bus stop / Tell me to my face / Clown / It's you / After the fox / Stop stop stop / Carie anne / Dear Eloise / Then the heartaches begin / Pegasus / Postcard / Rain on the window / On a carousel / Have you ever loved somebody / Leave me / Listen to me / Open up your eyes / Wings / Do you believe in love / Goodbye tomorrow / He ain't heavy he's my brother / Frightened lady / Man without a heart / Isn't it nice / Gasoline alley bred / Long cool woman in a black dress / Hold on / To do with love / Little thing like love / If it wasn't for the that I love you / Day that curly Billy shot Sam McGhee / Air that I breathe / No more riders / Draggin' my heels / Daddy don't mind / Carracus / Let it pour / Soldier song / Take my love and run / Too many hearts get broken / This is it / Reunion of the heart / Find me a family / Woman I love / Purple rain
CDTRBOX 280 / 6 Oct '97 / EMI Gold

☐ **STAY WITH THE HOLLIES (Remastered)**
Talkin' about you / You better move on / Lucille / Baby don't cry / Memphis / Stay / Rockin' Robin / What'cha gonna do about it / Do you love me / It's only make believe / What kind of girl are you / Little lover / Candy man / Mr. Moonlight / You better move on / Lucille / Baby don't cry / Memphis / Stay / Rockin' Robin / What'cha gonna do about it / Do you love me / It's only make believe / What kind of girl are you / Little lover / Talkin' about you / Mr. Moonlight / Candy man
DORIG 111 / Jul '97 / EMI

☐ **WOULD YOU BELIEVE (Stereo/Mono)**
I take what I want / Hard, hard years / That's how strong my love is / Sweet little sixteen / Oriental sadness / I am a rock / Take your time / Don't you even care (what's gonna happen to me) / Fifi the flea / Stewball / I've got a way of my own / I can't let go
4951502 / 29 Jun '98 / EMI

Hollis, Mark

☐ **MARK HOLLIS**
Colour of spring / Watershed / Inside looking out / Gift / Life 1895-1915 / Westward bound / Daily planet / New Jerusalem
5376882 / 2 Feb '98 / Polydor

Hollmer, Lars

☐ **12 SIBIRISKA CYKLAR/VILL DU HORA MER**
RES 512CD / Dec '94 / Resource

☐ **LOOPING HOME**
VICTOCD 024 / Oct '94 / Victo

☐ **SIBERIAN CIRCUS, THE**
Boeves psalm / Inga pengar / Ante flottar ja te sjoss / Endlich ein zamba / Avlagsen strandvals / Starlep signs / 180 sekunder hemma / Vill du hora mer / Retsticka / Soldaten / Optimistbeat / Skar / Inte quantar / Onk kch onk kch / Skiss mellan brest och segosero / Simfageldans / Rindatrost / Spanksa trappan / Eyeliner / Karussellmusik/Utflykt med damcykel / Gitarette / Vendeltid
RESCD 502 / Jul '97 / Resource

☐ **XII SIBIRISKA CYKLAR/VIII DU HORN MER**
Avlagsen strandvals / Piano de jugugte / Hajar du idealfamiljen / Endlich ein zamba / Inga pengar / Kamelsvang / Ja ante flottar ja te sjoss / Boeves psalm / Jag vantar pa pelle / Bluesen / 44 sekunder kopt speldosa / Ung harald / Litet piano / Starlep signs / Sweet / Indojazz / Soldaten / En slags orfeo / Overgang / Baldis / Retsticka / Dragfragment / Glasmusik / Akarondo / Kuckeliku / Vill du hora mer / 180 sekunder hemma / Humanoid robottango / Finalvals
RESCD 512 / Jul '97 / Resource

Hollow

☐ **MODERN CATHEDRAL**
NB 291CD / 19 Dec '97 / Nuclear Blast

Hollow Rock String Band

☐ **TRADITIONAL DANCE TUNES**
Kitchen girl / Clog / Waltz / Dinah / Richmond cotillion / Hog eyed man / Medley / Jawbones / Betty likens / Cabin creek / Folding down the sheets / Money musk / Devil on a stump / Over the waterfall / Fiddler's drunk and the fun's all over
COCD 2715 / Jul '97 / County

Holloway, Brenda

☐ **GREATEST HITS AND RARE CLASSICS**
Every little bit hurts / Who's lovin' you / When I'm gone / Just look what you've done / You've made me so very happy / Hurt a little everyday / Starting the hurt all over again / How many times did you mean it / Operator / I'll always love you / Unchained melody / I'll be avaliable / I've been good to you / Where were you / You can cry on my shoulder / Favour for a girl / I've got to find it / Together 'till the end of the day
5544712 / 3 Aug '98 / Spectrum

Holloway, Laurie

☐ **ABOUT TIME**
Tricrotism / Teach me tonight / For you / Quinta do lago / Nothing quite like love / Good to know / S'posin' / Gettin' there / Revelation / Love for sale / I Should n' ave ever / There is no greater love / Bye bye blues
C5CD 595 / Jan '93 / See For Miles

☐ **BLUE SKIES AND OTHER VISTAS**
ELGIN 03 / Jan '97 / Elgin

☐ **SHOWTIME (Holloway, Laurie Trio)**
ELGIN 05 / Aug '97 / Elgin

Holloway, Loleatta

☐ **HOTLANTA SOUL OF LOLEATTA HOLLOWAY**
Cry to me / Go on that first plane / Part time lover, full time fool / I know where you're coming from / Mrs. So and So's daughter / I can't help myself / Just be true / Show must go on / Rainbow '71 / Casanova / We did it / Merrily / World don't owe you nothin' / Mother of shame / Bring it on up / Only a fool / So can I / (I love you) For sentimental reasons / What are you gonna do about tomorrow / Love woke me up / Help me my Lord / Our love has just got to come together / This man's arms
CDKEND 135 / Mar '96 / Kent

☐ **LOLEATTA**
Hit and run / Is it just a man's way / We're getting stronger / Dreamin' / Ripped off / Worn out broken heart / That's how heartaches are made / What now
CPCD 8063 / Nov '94 / Charly

☐ **LOVE SENSATION**
Love sensation / Dance what 'cha wanna / I'll be standing there / I've been loving you too long / Short end of the stick / My way / Long hard climb to love / Two become a crowd
CPCD 8095 / Apr '95 / Charly

☐ **RUNAWAY (The Best Of Loleatta Holloway)**
CDGR 144 / Apr '97 / Charly

Holloway, Miles

☐ **IN AT THE DEEP END (Holloway, Miles & Elliot Eastwick)**
Glide by shooting: *Two Lone Swordsmen* / Danser: *New Phunk Theory* / Space groover: *Wulf n' Bear* / Chance: *Reel Houze* / Continuum: *Laj Gloves* / Fat Dan's rub a dub: *Paper Issue No.2* / Message: *Straight Life* / Journey into happiness: *Freaks* / Piano: *Housey Doingz* / Last chance to dance: *Urban Farmers* / I love what you're doing: *Dancer* / Summer daze: *Samba Magic* / Late nighter: *Loveys, Trevor* / Northern house: *Essa*
PAGANCD 1001 / Feb '97 / Pagan

Holloway, Nancy

☐ **1960'S FRENCH EP COLLECTION, THE (2CD Set)**
174892 / Nov '97 / Magic

Holloway, Red

☐ **IN THE RED**
Chase / In my solitude / Snu fu / Gypsy / Claudia / Watermelon man / Tear in my heart / Rapture
HCD 7022 / Jun '98 / Highnote

☐ **LIVE AT THE 1995 FLOATING JAZZ FESTIVAL (Holloway, Red Quartet & Harry 'Sweets' Edison)**
Hitting the road again / River's invitation / Wave / Out of nowhere / Greazzy blues / I wish I knew / Well you needn't / This is no shit / Nica's dream / Outro vamp / Jazzspeak
CRD 348 / 8 Nov '97 / Chiaroscuro

☐ **LOCKSMITH BLUES (Holloway, Red & Clark Terry Sextet)**
Red top / Happiness is a thing called joe / Hitting the road again / Come sunday / Locksmith blues / 'round midnight / Junkman / I got it bad and that ain't good / Cotton tail
CCD 4390 / Nov '89 / Concord Jazz

☐ **RED HOLLOWAY AND COMPANY**
But not for me / Caravan / Passion flower / Blues for QM / Well you needn't / What's new / Summertime / Tokyo express
CCD 4322 / Jul '87 / Concord Jazz

Holloway, Ron

☐ **SCORCHER**
Hot house / Sidewinder / Everywhere calypso / Is that jazz / You and I / How high the moon / Red clay / Blue collar / Pulse
MCD 92572 / Oct '96 / Milestone

Holloway, Stanley

☐ **PICK OOP THA MUSKET**
Sam, pick oop tha musket / 'Alt, who goes theer / Marksman Sam / Sam's medal / Sam Small at Westminster / Up'ards / Three ha'pence a foot / 'Ole in the ark / With her head tucked underneath her arm / Lion and Albert / Song of the sea / Beefeater / Many happy returns / Gunner Joe / Beat the retreat / One each a piece all round / Sam Small's party
PASTCD 7021 / Aug '93 / Flapper

Holly, Buddy

☐ **20 GOLDEN GREATS: BUDDY HOLLY (Holly, Buddy & The Crickets)**
That'll be the day / Peggy Sue / Words of love / Everyday / Not fade away / Oh boy / Maybe baby / Listen to me / Heartbeat / Think it over / It doesn't matter anymore / It's so easy / Well alright / Rave on / Raining in my heart / True love ways / Peggy Sue got married / Bo Diddley / Brown eyed handsome man / Wishing
DMCTV 1 / Aug '93 / MCA

☐ **BUDDY HOLLY**
Peggy Sue / Rock me my baby / Ready teddy / I'm looking for someone to love / Heartbeat / Well all right / That'll be the day / Every day / Baby I don't care / Rave on / Think it over / Maybe baby / It doesn't matter anymore / I'm changing all those changes / Early in the morning / Words of love / You've got love / Oh boy / It's so easy
399541 / May '97 / Koch Presents

☐ **BUDDY HOLLY AND THE PICKS (2CD Set) (Holly, Buddy & The Picks)**
CPCD 83372 / 27 May '98 / Charly

☐ **BUDDY HOLLY/THAT'LL BE THE DAY (2CD Set)**
I'm gonna love you too / Peggy Sue / Look at me / Listen to me / Valley of tears / Ready teddy / Everyday / Mailman bring me no more blues / Words of love / Baby I don't care / Rave on / Little baby / You are my one desire / Blue days black nights / Modern Don Juan / Rock around with Ollie Vee / Ting-a-ling / Girl on my mind / That'll be the day / Love me / I'm changing all those changes / Don't come back knockin' / Midnight shift / Rock around with Ollie Vee (alternative version)
MCD 33001 / Jul '96 / MCA

☐ **DOUBLE EXPOSURE (Crickets)**
My little girl / I fought the law / Oh boy / That'll be the day / When you ask about love / Tell me how / It doesn't matter anymore / Baby my heart / Rave on / Maybe baby / Brown eyed handsome man / Teardrops fall like rain / Everyday / Think it over / More than I can say / Don't ever change / Peggy Sue / Well alright / True love ways / (They call her) La bamba / It's so easy / Love's made a fool of you
RCCD 3006 / Nov '93 / Rollercoaster

☐ **GOLDEN GREATS**
Peggy Sue / That'll be the day / Listen to me / Everyday / Oh boy / Not fade away / Raining in my heart / Brown eyed handsome man / Maybe baby / Rave on / Think it over / It's so easy / It doesn't matter anymore / True love ways / Peggy Sue got married / Bo Diddley
MCLD 19046 / Apr '92 / MCA

☐ **LEGEND LIVES, THE (15 Fantastic Guitar Instrumentals Of Classic Holly Hits) (Various Artists)**
Everyday / Heartbeat / Learning the game / That'll be the day / Listen to me / True love ways / Oh boy / Not fade away / Wishing / Raining in my heart / Peggy Sue/Peggy Sue got married / Love's made a fool of you / Fool's paradise / It doesn't matter anymore / Girl in every song
304552 / Jul '97 / Hallmark

☐ **LOVE SONGS**
True love ways / Everyday / Listen to me / You've got love / Learning the game / Send me some lovin' / Love is strange / That's what they say / Because I love you / Raining in my heart / Heartbeat / Moon dreams / Take your time (feat. wondress) / (um, oh yeah) dearest / Look at me / You're the one / Wishing / It doesn't matter any more / What to do / Words of love
MCBD 19522 / Jul '95 / MCA

☐ **NOT FADE AWAY (Remembering Buddy Holly) (Various Artists)**
Peggy Sue got married: *Holly, Buddy & The Hollies* / True love ways: *Mavericks* / Well alright: *Griffith, Nanci & The Crickets* / Midnight shift: *Los Lobos* / Not fade away: *Band & The Crickets* / Think it over: *Tractors* / Wishing: *Carpenter, Mary Chapin & Kevin Montgomery* / Oh boy: *Ely, Joe & Todd Snider* / Crying, waiting, hoping: *Stuart, Marty & Steve Earle* / It doesn't matter anymore: *Bogguss, Suzy & Dave Edmunds* / Maybe baby: *Nitty Gritty Dirt Band* / Learning the game: *Jennings, Waylon & Mark Knopfler*
MCD 11260 / Jan '96 / MCA

☐ **ORIGINAL VOICES OF THE CRICKETS, THE (Holly, Buddy & The Picks)**
True loves ways / Every day / Love me / Don't come back knockin' / Baby I don't care / Reminiscing / Peggy Sue / Well alright / Midnight shift / Blue days black nights / That's what they say / Rock-a-bye rock / Heartbeat / Girl on my mind / Ting-a-ling / I'm gonna set my foot down / It's not my fault / Rock around with Ollie Vee / You are my one desire / Because I love you / Modern Don Juan / Words / You've lost that lovin' feelin'
CDMF 088 / Mar '96 / Magnum Force

☐ **RAVIN' ON - FROM CALIFORNIA TO CLOVIS (Crickets)**
Surfin' special / Surfin' special / Lookin' all over town / I believe in you / Bring back my surfboard / Break it easy / Little hollywood girl / Rave on / I don't need a friend / My little kim ruth / Don't say you love me / It's all right with me / I'm not a bad guy / Parisian girl / Real thing / Brand new doll / A fool never learns / A fool never learns / A harlem girl / Fell in love with a face / Never ever told me / There's no better way to die / Bottom of the sea / Farewell, my bluebell / Buddy holly interview
RSRCD 002 / Apr '94 / Rockstar

☐ **SINGLES COLLECTION 1957-1961, THE (Holly, Buddy & The Crickets)**
That'll be the day / I'm looking for someone to love / Oh boy / Not fade away / Maybe baby / Tell me how / Think it over / Fool's paradise / It's so easy / Lonesome tears / Love's made a fool of you / Someone someone / When you ask about love / Deborah / Baby my heart / More than I can say / Don't cha know / Peggy Sue got married / Sweet love / I fought the law
PWKS 4205 / May '94 / Carlton

☐ **THAT'LL BE THE DAY**
You are my one desire / Blue days black nights / Modern Don Juan / Rock around with Ollie Vee / Ting a ling / Girl on my mind / Love me / I'm changing all those changes / Don't come back knockin' / Midnight shift
CLACD 309 / Jan '96 / Castle

☐ **VERY BEST OF BUDDY HOLLY, THE**
MCBD 19535 / Apr '97 / MCA

Holly Golightly

☐ **GOOD THINGS, THE**
DAMGOOD 65CD / Jun '95 / Damaged Goods

☐ LAUGH IT ALL UP
Sally go round the roses / If I could be loved by you / Mellow down easy / I can't stand it / Candy man / Look for me baby / Don't lie to me / Too much going for you / It's all over now / Troubles on my mind / Getting mighty crowded / You ain't no big thing / Sand / Hold me baby / This happens / Candle song / If I should ever leave / Mary Ann / Hold me baby / Good enough / High time / Until I find you
ASKCD 074 / 18 Aug '97 / Vinyl Japan

☐ PAINTED ON
SFTRI 474CD / Sep '97 / Sympathy For The Record Industry

☐ UP THE EMPIRE
SFTRI 506CD / 13 Feb '98 / Sympathy For The Record Industry

Hollyfaith

☐ PURRR
Bliss / Who is you / Delicacies / Watching, waiting, turning / Zero / Voodoo doll / Whatsamatta / Whirlwind / Color of blood / Needs
CRECD 163 / Aug '93 / Creation

Hollywood Brats

☐ HOLLYWOOD BRATS
Chez maximes / Another schoolday / Nightmare / Empty bottles / Courtesan / Then he kissed me / Tumble with me / Zurich 17 / Southern belles / Drowning sorrows / Sick on you
CDMRED 106 / Dec '93 / Cherry Red

Hollywood Fats Band

☐ ROCK THIS HOUSE
BT 1097CD / Jan '94 / Black Top

Hollywood Flames

☐ HOLLYWOOD FLAMES, THE
Wheel of fortune / Later / Tabarin / Wine / My confession / Sound of your voice / Crazy / Buzz buzz buzz / Ooh baby ooh / This heart of mine / Little bird / Give me back my heart / Two little bees / It's love / Your love / Frankenstein's den / Strollin' on the beach / Chains of love / Let's talk it over / Star fell / I'll get by / Just for you / Hollywood Flames / I'll be seeing you / There is something on your mind / So good / Romance in the dark / Much too much
CDCHD 420 / Sep '92 / Ace

Hollywood Joe

☐ JACK OF HEARTS
WHIT 001 / Aug '96 / Whitestone

Holman, Bill

☐ BILL HOLMAN BAND (Holman, Bill Band)
JD 3308 / Sep '88 / JVC

☐ BRILLIANT CORNERS (Holman, Bill Band)
Straight no chaser / Bemsha swing / Thelonious / 'Round midnight / Bye ya / Misterioso / Friday the 13th / Rhythm-a-ning / Ruby, my dear / Brilliant corners
JVC 90182 / Jul '97 / JVC

☐ FURTHER ADVENTURES (Holman, Bill & Netherlands Metropole Orchestra)
369032 / 29 Jun '98 / Koch Jazz

☐ VIEW FROM THE SIDE, A (Holman, Bill Band)
No joy in mudville / Any dude'll do / But beautiful / Petaluma Lu / I didn't ask / Make my day / Peacock / Tennessee waltz / View from the side
JVC 20502 / Aug '95 / JVC

Holman, Eddie

☐ EDDIE'S MY NAME
This can't be true / You can tell / I surrender / Return to me / Don't stop now / I'll cry 1000 tears / Where I'm not wanted / Hurt / Peace of mind / Never let me go / Been so long / Sexy Ed here wants a lonely girl / Eddie's my name / Sweet memories / Stay mine for heaven's sake / Free country / You know that I will / Am I a loser / I'm not gonna give up / I'll cry 1000 tears (unreleased version)
GSCD 031 / Dec '93 / Goldmine

☐ NIGHT TO REMEMBER, A
You make my life complete / Time will tell / Immune to love / This will be a night to remember / I've been singing love songs (by myself) / Where have you been all my life / Somehow you make me feel / It's over
CPCD 8061 / Nov '94 / Charly

Holman, Libby

☐ MOANIN' LOW 1927-1934
TT 415 / May '98 / Take Two

Holmes Brothers

☐ JUBILATION
Jesus is alright / Jesus is alright / Amazing grace / I'll fly away / I want jesus to walk with me / Pass me not oh gentle saviour / Will the circle be unbroken / Just a closer walk with thee / All night, all day / Do lord / Oh, how I love jesus / Power of the lord come down / A brother's prayer
CDRW 21 / Mar '92 / Realworld

☐ LOTTO LAND
TRIP 7714 / Apr '96 / Ruf

☐ PROMISED LAND
Promised land / Start stoppin' / Train song / Easy access / You're good for me / You got to go / And I love her / There's a train / Got myself together / Thank God for you / New and improved me / I surrender all
ROUCD 2142 / Feb '97 / Rounder

☐ SOUL STREET
You're gonna make me cry / You're gonna make me cry / How can I love you / Dashboard bar / Fannie mae / I found a winner / I won't hurt you anymore / Down in virginia / There goes my everything / To make a love story short / My girl josephine / Walk in the light
ROUCD 2124 / Oct '93 / Rounder

☐ WHERE IT'S AT
That's where it't at / Love is you / You can't hold on to a love that's gone / I've been a loser / Hi-heel sneakers / Worried life blues / Never let me go / Give it up / I've been to the well before / I saw the light / Drown in my own tears
ROUCD 2111 / Jun '95 / Rounder

Holmes, Chris

☐ DAN LOVES PATTI
Apiary / Cross my heart / Doot-doot / Ring / Lament / Words will fail / Jealous of the stars / Sister / Train of thought / Dan loves patti / Uneasy / I'm not telling
7567927102 / Feb '97 / Atlantic

Holmes, David

☐ LET'S GET KILLED
Listen / My mate Paul / Let's get killed / Gritty shaker / Headrush on Lafayette / Rodney Yates / Radio 7 / Parcus and Madder show / Slashers revenge / Freaknik / Caddell returns / Don't die just yet / For you
5391002 / 6 Apr '98 / Go Beat

☐ THIS FILM'S CRAP LET'S SLASH THE SEATS
No man's land / Slash the seats / Shake ya brain / Got fucked up along the way / Gone / Atom and you / Minus 61 in Detroit / Inspired by Leyburn / Coming home to the sun
8286312 / Jul '95 / Go Discs

Holmes, Richard

☐ AFTER HOURS (Holmes, Richard 'Groove')
Sweatin' / Jeannine / Minor surgery / This here / It might as well be Spring / Moose the Mooche / Groove's bag / Hallelujah, I love her so / After hours / Later / Do it my way / Secret love / Denise
CDP 8379862 / Jul '96 / Pacific Jazz

☐ BLUES ALL DAY LONG (Holmes, Richard 'Groove')
MCD 5358 / Sep '92 / Muse

☐ GROOVE'S GROOVE
Grooves groove / California blues / What a wonderful world / Misty / Walking on a tightrope / Slow blues in G / Song for my Father / My friend / Lonesome road blues / On say a joy / Danger zone is everywhere / Time has come
JHR 73585 / Apr '95 / Jazz Hour

☐ GROOVIN' WITH GROOVE (Holmes, Richard 'Groove')
Go away little girl / Young and foolish / It's impossible / You've got it bad / Choo choo / How insensitive / Red onion / No trouble on the mountain / Meditation / Good vibration / It's gonna take some time / Grooves groove
CDC 9084 / Apr '95 / LRC

☐ LEGENDS OF ACID JAZZ, THE (Holmes, Richard 'Groove')
Speak low / Blue moon / I'll remember April / Walrus / Just friends / My scenery / Healin' feelin' / CC rider / Irene Court / Castle Rock / Laura / On a clear day (you can see forever)
PRCD 24187 / 29 Jun '98 / Prestige

☐ NIGHT GLIDER (Holmes, Richard 'Groove')
500632 / Jan '97 / Musidisc

☐ SOMETHIN' SPECIAL (Holmes, Richard 'Groove')
Somethin' special / Black groove / Me and groove / Comin' through the apple / I thought I knew you / Carma / Blow the man down / Satin doll
CDP 8554522 / Mar '97 / Pacific Jazz

☐ SOUL MESSAGE (Holmes, Richard 'Groove')
Groove's groove / Dahoud / Misty / Song for my father / Things we did last summer / Soul message
OJCCD 329 / Dec '95 / Original Jazz Classics

Holmes, Rupert

☐ BEST OF RUPERT HOLMES, THE
HMNCD 037 / 22 Jun '98 / Half Moon

Holmstrom, Rick

☐ LOOKOUT
CDBT 1125 / Feb '96 / Black Top

Holocaust

☐ HYPNOSIS OF BIRDS
Hypnosis of birds / Tower / Book of seasons / Mercier and camier / Small hours / Into Lebanon / Summer tides / Mortal Mother / Cairnpapple hill / In the dark places of the earth / Caledonia
TRMCD 010 / Apr '93 / Taurus Moon

☐ SPIRITS FLY
NM 006CD / Oct '97 / Neat Metal

Holroyd, Bob

☐ FLUIDITY & STRUCTURE
In an angels footstep / African drug / Rosebud / Still / Of things lost and found / On the forest floor / Ice and sand / Fluidity and structure / Cries from the rooftop (for a free tibet) / Descent into darkness / Across the border / Dreamscape
BHCD 1001 / Jul '94 / Holroyd

☐ STAGES
BHCD 2001 / Jun '96 / Soundscape

Holst, Ivan

☐ PA FRI FUD
MECCACD 1023 / Nov '94 / Music Mecca

Holt, John

☐ 1000 VOLTS OF HOLT
Never never never / Morning of my life / Stoned out of my mind / Baby I want you / Help me make it through the night / Mr. Bojangles / I'd love you to want me / Killing me softly / You baby / Too much love / Girl from Ipanema / Which way you going, baby
CDTRL 75 / Mar '94 / Trojan

☐ 1000 VOLTS OF HOLT
RN 7007 / Sep '96 / Rhino

☐ 16 SONGS FOR SOULFUL LOVERS
I'd love you to want me / You'll never find / Too good to be forgotten / Help me make it through the night / Winter world of love / Killing me softly / If I were a carpenter / Rainy night in Georgia / I'll never fall in love again / Just the way you are / Wherever I lay my hat (that's my home) / Touch me in the morning / Love I can feel / Too much love / When I fall in love / I'll be there
PLATCD 16 / Jul '89 / Platinum

☐ 20 GOLDEN LOVE SONGS
Never never never / I'd love you to want me / Killing me softly / You will never find another love like mine / When I fall in love / I'll take a melody / Just the way you are / Too good to be forgotten / Dr. Love / Help me make it through the night / Stoned out of my mind / Touch me in the morning / I'll be lonely / Too much love / Love so right / Rainy night in Georgia / If I were a Carpenter / Everybody's talkin' / Baby don't get hooked on me / Last farewell
CDTRL 192 / May '90 / Trojan

☐ 20 GREAT HITS
Looking back / Stick by me / Lost love / Oh girl / Riding for a fall / Everybody needs love / I'll be lonely / Do you love me / Left with a broken heart / Release me / Stealing stealing / Wasted days and wasted nights / Here I come / I love my girl / Wolf and leopard / Born to lose / In the midnight hour / She want it / Homely girl / Party time
CDSGP 067 / Oct '93 / Prestige

☐ 2000 VOLTS OF HOLT/3000 VOLTS OF HOLT
Doctor love / Yester-me, yester-you, yesterday / Touch me in the morning / Keep on moving / I will / Alfie / I'll take a melody / My guiding star / On a clear day you can see forever / Peace and love / Take away my heart Teresa / For the love of you / Let's get it while it's hot / In the springtime / Till I'm gone / Let's kiss and say goodbye / Winter world of love / Oh what a day / Let's do it long / No place like home / Ungrateful lady / You will never find another love like mine
CDTRL 380 / May '97 / Trojan

☐ COLLECTION, THE
Party time / Peacemaker / Here I come / Wolf and leopard / You touch my life / In the midnight hour / Release me / Wasted days and wasted nights / Everybody needs love / Stick by me / I'm not gonna give up / Survival time part 1 / Hey love / I'll be lonely / Lost love / Oh girl / Stealing stealing / Looking back / Left with a broken heart / Born to lose / I hope we get to love in time / Riding for a fall / Hey world
COL 069 / Feb '95 / Collection

☐ FURTHER YOU LOOK, THE/DUSTY ROADS
Further you look / I sing my song / Never let me go / Saving my love / I won't come in / Just let me know / I'm a rover / Open the door / I'll be there / Memories by the score / I'll always love you / I wanna dance / Tell me why / After all / I don't mind / Not so close / I'll light your fire / You'd better take time / Dusty roads / These old memories / In the middle of the night / Make this young lady mine / I won't let you forget / Same old thing
CDTRL 388 / Sep '97 / Trojan

☐ GOLDEN HITS
RNCD 2110 / Jun '95 / Rhino

☐ GREATEST HITS OF JOHN HOLT
SOCD 1115 / Mar '95 / Studio One

☐ I WANT TO WAKE UP WITH YOU
I want to wake up with you / Before the next teardrop falls / Party time / Everybody needs love / Have you ever been in love / Ali Baba / I will always love you / I'll be lonely / I'll be there / I'll never fall in love again / I'm coming home / I'm leaving it up to you / My desire / Rainy night in Georgia / Sister Big Stuff / So long baby / Tide is high / Tonight
CD 6094 / Oct '97 / Music

☐ JOHN HOLT ARCHIVE
Baby I want you / Stealing stealing stealing / My desire / Never never never / Killing me softly with her song / Stoned out of my life / Help me make it through the night / I will / I'll be lonely / I'd love you to want me / My satisfaction / Wooden heart / Which way you going baby / Rainy night in Georgia / Tide is high / You baby / Everybody's talkin' / Doctor Love / Just the way you are / You'll never find another love like mine
RMCD 212 / Nov '97 / Rialto

☐ JOHN HOLT STORY VOL.1 & 2, THE (2CD Set)
JHCD 1/JHCD 2 / Jun '97 / Graylan

☐ JOHN HOLT STORY VOL.3 & 4, THE (2CD Set)
JHCD 3/JHCD 4 / 22 Jun '98 / Graylan

☐ KEEP ON MOVING (2CD Set)
SMDCD 222 / 10 Aug '98 / Snapper

☐ LOVE I CAN FEEL
Love I can feel / Do you want me / Make up / Love divine / Nobody else / If you let me make love to you then why can't I / Tonight / Then you can tell me goodbye / Stranger in love / It's alright / Your arms reaching out for me (too late) / My heart is gone
SOCD 9017 / Mar '95 / Studio One

☐ LOVE SONGS VOL.2
EPCD 1 / Apr '92 / Parish

☐ NEW HORIZON
CRCD 80 / 15 Dec '97 / Charm

☐ PARTY TIME (Holt, John & Dennis Brown)
SONCD 0068 / Sep '94 / Sonic Sounds

☐ PEACEMAKER
Hey love / I hope we get to love in time / Hey world / Lucy and me / Lucy and me / I'm not gonna give you up / Peacemaker / You touch my life / Survival time / Survival time
CDSGP 049 / Jun '93 / Prestige

☐ PLEDGING MY LOVE
I want to wake up with you / Everything to me / Still in chains / Just out of reach / Mr. tv man / Sometimes / Walking along / Mothers and fathers love / What's life all about / I'll be there / Riding for a fall / Pledging my love / I will always love you / Last love / Treasure of love / Looking back / Clock / Anymore / Oh girl / Tree in the meadow
RNCD 2019 / Sep '93 / Rhino

☐ PRIME OF JOHN HOLT, THE
Stick by me / Love I can feel / Last love / Riding for a fall / Hooligans change your style / On the beach / Tide is high / Pledging my love / Winter world of love / Rain from the skies / Up park camp / Just out of reach / Wear you to the ball / No man is an island / Clock / Stealin' stealin' / I'll be there / Do you love me / Rainy night i Georgia / I will always love you
MCCD 323 / Nov '97 / Music Club

☐ REGGAE CHRISTMAS ALBUM, THE
I believe in father christmas / Last christmas / Lonely this christmas / White christmas / Happy christmas (war is over) / A spaceman came travelling / When a child is born (soleado) / Santa claus is coming to town / My oh my / Blue christmas / Auld lang syne
CDTRL 230 / Nov '95 / Trojan

☐ REGGAE MAX
JSRNCD 5 / Jun '96 / Jet Star

☐ SPECIAL REQUEST TO ALL MUSIC LOVERS
JJCD 6201 / 29 Sep '97 / Channel One

☐ TIME IS THE MASTER
Time is the master / Everybody Knows / Riding For A Fall / Looking Back / Love is gone / Stick By Me / Lost Love / It May Sound Silly / Again / Oh Girl
RNCD 2002 / Jun '92 / Rhino

☐ TONIGHT AT TREASURE ISLE
RNCD 2081 / Dec '94 / Rhino

☐ TREASURE OF LOVE
SONCD 0074 / Mar '95 / Sonic Sounds

Holt, Nick

☐ NICK HOLT
WOLF 120883 / Jul '96 / Wolf

Holt, Steve

☐ CATWALK (Holt, Steve Jazz Quartet)
SKCD 22032 / Feb '94 / Sackville

☐ JUST DUET (Holt, Steve & Kieran Overs)
SKCD 22025 / Jul '93 / Sackville

Holy Barbarians

☐ CREAM
BBL 182CD / 10 Nov '97 / Beggars Banquet

Holy Body Tattoo

☐ OUR BRIEF ETERNITY
EVCD 002 / 20 Oct '97 / Ex Voto

Holy Gang

☐ FREE TYSON FREE
Free Tyson free / Get chained / Power is my life / Murder as religion / Tyson Vs Washington (FTF) / Sanity fair / Sanity (Karaoke ambient) / Sanity B
BIAS 270CD / Sep '94 / Play It Again Sam

Holy Ghost

☐ ART LUKM SUITE, THE
EFA 292842 / 3 Nov '97 / Tresor

Holy Ghost Inc.

☐ MIND CONTROL OF CANDY JONES
EFA 292562 / Oct '96 / Tresor

Holy Language

☐ CHOOSE YOUR OWN
EFA 004152 / Jul '96 / Space Teddy

Holy Modal Rounders

☐ HOLY MODAL ROUNDERS VOL.1 & 2
Blues in the bottle / Give the fiddler a dram / Cuckoo / Euphoria / Long John / Hesitation blues / Hey hey baby / Reuben's train / Mister spaceman / Moving day / Better things for you / Same old man / Hop high ladies / Bound to lose / Flop eared mule / Black eyed Susie / Sail away ladies / Clinch mountain backstep / Fishing blues / Statesboro' blues / Junko partner / Mole in the ground / Hot corn cold corn / Down the old plank road / Chevrolet six / Crowley waltz / Bully of the town / Sugar in the ground / Soldiers joy
CDWIKD 176 / 27 Jul '98 / Big Beat

☐ INDIAN WAR HOOP
10682 / 16 Feb '98 / ESP

Holy Moses

☐ NO MATTER WHAT'S THE CAUSE
SPV 8476862 / Oct '94 / SPV

☐ WORLD CHAOS
845700 / Jul '90 / SPV

Holy River Family Band

☐ HAIDA DEITIES
WILD 003 / 9 Mar '98 / Wild Places

☐ WELCOME TO RIVERHOUSE (2CD Set)
WILD 004 / 9 Mar '98 / Wild Places

Holy Terror

☐ MIND WARS
Judas reward / Debt of pain / Immoral wasteland / A fools gold-terminal humour-mind wars / Damned by judges / Do unto others / No resurrection / Christian resistance
CDFLAG 25 / Oct '88 / Under One Flag

☐ MIND WARS/TERROR AND SUBMISSION (2CD Set)
PRAGE 005CD / 30 Mar '98 / Powerage

Holywell Ensemble

☐ ENGLISH RHAPSODY, AN
BML 010 / Jan '96 / British Music

☐ HOWELLS & BRIDGE
BML 003 / Jan '96 / British Music

Holzman, Adam

☐ BIG PICTURE, THE (Holzman, Adam & Brave New World)
Toxic waste introduction / Iron curtain / Mad cow disease / Longest day / Chaos theory / Second theory / Hot zone / My game is strong / Conrad Russell / Fred Ex / Failed industrial belt
ESC 036532 / Jun '97 / Escapade

Home

☐ HOME
Dreamer / Knave / Shady Lady / Rise up / Dear Lord / Baby friend of mine / Western front / Lady of the birds
4844402 / Jul '96 / Columbia

Home

☐ HOME X
EJ 10CD / Sep '96 / Emperor Jones

Home Bru

☐ ROWIN FOULA DOON
LDL 1230C / Jul '95 / Lochshore

Home Grown

☐ THAT'S BUSINESS
BHR 045CD / Jul '96 / Burning Heart
37802CD / 29 Jun '98 / Liberation

Home Service

☐ EARLY TRANSMISSIONS
RGF 28CD / May '96 / Rgof

☐ MYSTERIES, THE
God / Creation / Serpent's dance / Cain and Abel (don't be an outlaw) / Journey to Bethlehem / Nativity, The (lay me low) / Herod / Kings / Entry to Jerusalem / Betrayal and denial (all in the morning part 1) / Arrest / Scourging (all in the morning part 2) / Trial, The (Lewk up-lewk up) / Road to Calvary / Crucifixion / Moon shines bright, (The) / We sing Hallelujah / Wonderous love / Death of Mary / Coronation of the Virgin / Lyke wyke dirge / Judgement (the wheel)
FLED 3014 / Mar '97 / Fledg'ling

☐ WILD LIFE
FLED 3001 / Apr '95 / Fledg'ling

Home T

☐ HOLDING ON (Home T & Cocoa T/ Shabba Ranks)
GRELCD 142 / Nov '89 / Greensleeves

Homelife

☐ HOMELIFE
HL 500 / 8 Jun '98 / Homelife

Homer & Jethro

☐ WEIRD WORLD OF HOMER & JETHRO, THE (America's Song Butchers)
RE 2130 / Jul '97 / Razor & Tie

Homesick James

☐ BLUES ON THE SOUTHSIDE
Woman I'm lovin' / She may be you woman / Goin' down swingin' / Homesick's shuffle / Johnny mae / Gotta move / Lonesome road / Working with homesick / Cloud is crying / Homesick's blues / Crawlin' / Stones in my passway
OBCCD 529 / Nov '92 / Original Blues Classics

☐ JUANITA
APCD 097 / Oct '95 / Appaloosa

☐ JUANITA
Juanita / My baby / Time is growin' near / Lonesome ol' train / Someday baby / Drivin' dog / Careless love / Right life / I can't hold out / Stop that thing
ECD 26085 / Mar '97 / Evidence

☐ LAST OF THE BROOMDUSTERS, THE
Early one morning / Long tall woman / Kissin' in the dark / Rockin' and rollin' / Sugar mama / Shake your money maker / Thought I heard my baby call my name / Truck drivin' woman / Crutch and cane / Woman I'm lovin/Two days before Christmas
FCD 5006 / 14 Apr '98 / Fedora

☐ ROAD ROCKIN'
MWCD 2002 / Nov '97 / Music & Words

Homler, Anna

☐ CORNE DE VACHE (Homler, Anna & Geert Waegeman/Pavel Fajt)
VICTOCD 047 / Jul '97 / Victo

Hommage Aux Aines

☐ C'EST LA FACON
HAA 1994CD / Apr '96 / Hommage

Hone, Ged

☐ SMOOTH SAILING
Let's sow a wild oat / Lover come back to me / Dance of the tamourine / Sugar / Pickings / Diga diga do / A porter's love song / Smooth sailing / Empty ballroom blues / Dr heckle and mr jibe / Nous deux / Swinging on that famous door / Ready eddy / Toledo shuffle / Just a gigolo / Changes / Hubba hubba hop
LACD 52 / Aug '95 / Lake

☐ THROWING STONES AT THE SUN (Hone, Ged & New Orleans Boys)
Smile dam you smile / Montmartre / Africa blues / Throwing stones at the sun / Tuxedo rag / Maple leaf rag / Ella Speed / I can't sleep / Streamline train / Sobbin' blues / Japansy / Blue blood blues / West End blues / Smiling the blues away / I've got a feeling I'm failing in love / Ukelele lady / Climax rag
LACD 28 / Jun '93 / Lake

Honey Boy

☐ LOVE YOU TONIGHT
RNCD 2123 / Nov '95 / Rhino

☐ REVIVAL (The Early Years Of Honey Boy)
MONCD 01 / 8 Dec '97 / Mongoose

Honey Boy Hickling

☐ STRAIGHT FROM THE HARP
CMMR 943 / Feb '95 / Music Masters

Honey Cone

☐ CONE TO THE BONE
Take my love / While you're out looking for sugar / If I can't fly / Want ads / Sunday morning people / VIP / Sittin' on a timebomb / Girls it ain't easy / Feeling's gone / My mind's on leaving but my heart won't let me go / You've made me so very happy / When will it end / Ace in the hole / Stick up / Who's it gonna be / How does it feel / Innocent till proven guilty / Are you man enough are you strong enough / One monkey don't stop no show / Day I found myself
NEMCD 968 / 1 Jun '98 / Sequel

Honey Tongue

☐ NUDE NUDES
Driver / Phone - waiting days / Like a lobster / True love / Some fun / Bedtime story / On thursdays / Big girls blouse / Let's sail away
AMUSE 012CD / Mar '95 / Playtime

Honeybunch

☐ TIME TRIALS 1987-1995
ER 1037 / 20 Oct '97 / Elefant

Honeybus

☐ AT THEIR BEST
Story / Fresher than the sweetness in water / Ceilings No. 1 / She said yes / I can't let Maggie go / Right to choose / Delighted to see you / Tender are the ashes / She sold Blackpool rock / Black mourning band / He was Columbus / Under the silent tree / I remember Caroline / Julie in my heart / Do I still figure in your life / Would you believe / How long / Scarlet lady / She's out there / Ceilings No.2 / Breaking up scene / Throw my love away / Girl of independent means / She sold Blackpool rock / How long
SEECD 264 / Jun '97 / See For Miles

Honeycombs

☐ ALL SYSTEMS GO
Colour slide / Once you know / Without you it is night / That's the way / I want to be free / How the mighty have fallen / Have I the right / Just a face in the crowd / Nice while it lasted / Me from you / Leslie anne / She's too way out / It ain't necessarily so / This too shall pass away / I can't stop / I don't love her no more / All systems go / Totem pole / Emptiness / Oo-ee train / She ain't coming back / Something I got to tell you / Our day will come / Nobody but me / There's always me / Love in tokyo / If you should / My prayer
REP 4121 / Aug '91 / Repertoire

☐ HONEYCOMBS
REP 4098 / Aug '91 / Repertoire

☐ LIVE IN TOKYO
REP 4180 / Aug '91 / Repertoire

Honeycrack

☐ PROZAIC
King of misery / No please don't go / Go away / Powerless / Genius is loose / Good, good feeling / If I had a life / I hate myself and everybody else / Animals / Samantha Pope / Paperman / Sitting at home / Parasite
4842302 / May '96 / Epic

Honeydippers

☐ BIG E BOOGIE
SHA 0112 / Feb '97 / Shattered

Honeymoon Killers

☐ SING SING (2CD Set)
SFTRI 369 / Jan '97 / Sympathy For The Record Industry

Honeymoons

☐ THIS COHERENT EXCITATION
Never forget / Flourescein / Evil / Fabrications / Dreamtime / Would you believe / Let them strive / Breathe on / Colder / Turn aside
NONSCD 54 / 29 Jun '98 / North Of No South

Honeyrider

☐ ALL SYSTEMS GO
DAMGOOD 138CD / 13 Jul '98 / Damaged Goods

Honeyshakers

☐ SKY HIGH
FLIPCD 1 / 12 Feb '98 / Real Flippy

Honeytunnel

☐ FEATURE ME
ARDCD 2 / 13 Oct '97 / Chameleon

Hongjin, Liu

☐ PIPES OF THE MINORITY PEOPLES
VICG 50172 / Mar '96 / JVC World Library

Honing, Yuri

☐ GAGARIN
Beauty of reason / Lodger / Gagarin / Nuku' alofa / On bare feet / Nelson's victory / Miradou
AL 73025 / Mar '97 / Challenge

☐ STAR TRACKS (Honing, Yuri Trio)
Isobel / True colors / Some unexpected visitors / Waltzing on the ocean / Waterloo / Body and soul / Basket case / True colors (reprise)
9920102 / Feb '97 / Via Jazz

Honky

☐ EGO HAS LANDED, THE
Who am I / Love my neighbor / Hold it / Chains / Whistler / Superfight love / Honky doodle day / Stormy weather / Eazee street / KKK / Karaoke Joe / Eleven brides of Frankeneeye / Wha ga do / Oranges and lemons / Goodnight from him
4509954552 / Mar '94 / WEA

Honolulu Mountain Daffodils

☐ ALOHA SAYONARA
Avenues and alleyways / Hurricane Marilyn / Electronic alcoholic / Drug dog girl / Rhine women and song / Farenheit 192 / Grungeda / Stigmata non starter / Psychic hit-lists victim no.8 / Slaughterhouse blues / Chien d'enfer / Celestial siren / Song of the wind surgeons / Aloha seyonara / Kramer versus Williamson / Bathtime for beelzebub / Free men of mauna loa
MISSCD 1991 / Aug '93 / Mission Discs

☐ GUITARS OF THE OCEANIC UNDERGROWTH/TEQUILA DEMENTIA
Hanging on the crosses (by the side of the road) / Wolverine / Electrified sons of Randy Alvev / Guitars of the oceanic undergrowth / Sinner's club / Black car drives south / El muerto / Final solution / Disturbo charger / (I feel like a) Francis Bacon painting / Mule brain / Collector of souls / Also sprach Scott Thurston / Death bed bimbo / Menace in the front / Tequila dementia
MISSCD 1992 / Aug '93 / Mission Discs

Honolulu Sunshine Band

☐ BLUE HAWAII
Blue Hawaii / Hilo march / Honolulu march / Sanjornara / Warchant / Aloha oe / Dreams of the island / Hawaii tattoo / Danny boy / Hawaiian island / Wailana / Yellow bird
22516 / Feb '96 / Music

Honor Role

☐ RECORDED HISTORY, THE
MRG 041CD / Apr '97 / Merge

Hood

☐ RUSTIC HOUSES FORLORN VALLEYS
S.E. rain patterns / Boer farmstead / Light reveals the place / Your ambient voice / Leaves grow old and fall and die / Diesel pioneers
WIGCD 042 / 19 Jan '98 / Domino

☐ SILENT '88
SLR 059CD / Dec '96 / Slumberland

☐ STRUCTURED DISASTERS
HAPPY 10CD / Jul '97 / Happy Go Lucky

Hood, Robert

☐ INTERNAL EMPIRE
74321247722

☐ NIGHTMARE WORLD VOL.1
CHEAPCD 2 / Oct '95 / Cheap

Hoodlum Priest

☐ BENEATH THE PAVEMENT
CPRODCD 25 / May '94 / Concrete Productions

☐ HOODLUM PRIEST
ILIGHT 007CD / 23 Feb '98 / Iris Light

Hoodoo Gurus

☐ BLUE CAVE
TVD 93455 / Oct '96 / Mushroom

Hoods

☐ NEW BLOOD
GAIN 014CD / 20 Jul '98 / Gain Ground

Hoodys

☐ D-DAY
KTR 100042 / 27 Oct '97 / K-Town

Hooka Hey

☐ FURY IN THE SLAUGHTERHOUSE
0888402 / May '91 / SPV

Hooker, Earl

☐ PLAY YOUR GUITAR, MR.HOOKER
BT 1093CD / Aug '93 / Black Top

☐ SMOOTH SLIDIN'
BB 1006 / 25 May '98 / Rhino

☐ SWEET BLACK ANGEL
MCAD 22120 / May '94 / One Way

☐ TWO BUGS AND A ROACH
ARHCD 324 / Apr '95 / Arhoolie

Hooker, John Lee

□ ALONE
I miss you so / Jesse James / Dark room / I'll never get out of these blues alive / Boogie chillun / When my first wife left me / Boom boom / One bourbon, one scotch, one beer
TBA 13009 / Aug '96 / Blues Alliance

□ ALTERNATIVE BOOGIE (Early Studio Recordings 1948-1952/3CD Set)
Come back baby / Forgive me / Streets is filled with women / Moon is rising / Whistle done blown / Turnin' gray blues / She was in Chicago / Lord taketh my baby away / Just like a woman / Throw this old dog a bone / Johnny Lee's mood / Miss Eloise, Miss Eloise / Crying all night / Welfare blues / Johnny Lee's original boogie / She left me by myself / Out the door I went / My baby she's long and tall / No mortgage on my soul / I come to you baby / I rule the den / Great disaster of 1936 / Winding highway / She quit me / How long can this go on / Can I say hello / I had a dream / Me and a woman / Throw my money around / Well I got to leave / I gotta be comin' back / I don't be welcome here / Two voice original mood / Three voice original mood / Johnny says come back / Story of a married woman / Snap them fingers boogie / Lord what more can I do / Baby, please don't go / I'm going away / Hummin' the blues / Johnny Lee and the thing / Slow down your chatter baby / I did everything / Someone to love / There's a day comin' baby / I was beggin' my baby / Nobody to talk to me / I'm gonna whip ya baby / It's a crime and a shame / I met the grindin' man / Louisiana blues for you / Long, long way from home / Sometime / TB's killin' me
CDEM 1568 / Feb '96 / Premier/EMI

□ AUDIO ARCHIVE
Dimples / Boom boom / Whiskey and wimmen / Frisco blues / Tupelo / Process / Good rockin' mama / No shoe / I'm in the mood / Dusty road / Boogie chillun / Hard hearted woman / Drug store woman / Hobo blues / Onions / Baby Lee / I'm leaving baby / Trouble blues / Little wheel / Old time shimmy
CDAA 035 / Jun '92 / Tring

□ BEST OF JOHN LEE HOOKER & CANNED HEAT, THE (Hooker, John Lee & Canned Heat)
You talk too much / Burning hell / Bottle up and go / World today / I got my eyes on you / Whiskey and wimmen / Just you and me / Let's make it / Peavine / Boogie chillen no.2
DC 871802 / Nov '96 / Disky

□ BEST OF JOHN LEE HOOKER 1965-1974, THE
MCAD 10539 / May '93 / MCA

□ BEST OF JOHN LEE HOOKER, THE
I'm in the mood / Boogie chillun / Serves me right to suffer / This is hip / House rent boogie / I'm so excited / I love you honey / Hobo blues / Crawlin' kingsnake / Maudie / Dimples / Boom boom / Louise / Ground hog blues / Ramblin' by myself / Walkin' the boogie / One bourbon, one scotch, one beer / Sugar mama / Peace lovin' man / Leave my wife alone / Blues before sunrise / Time is marching
MCCD 020 / Jun '91 / Music Club

□ BLUES BROTHER
Boogie chillun / Rollin' blues / I need lovin' / Grinder man / Women in my life / My baby's got something / Momma poppa boogie / Sailing blues / Graveyard blues / Huckle up baby / Alberta / Three long years today / Do my baby think of me / Burnin' hell / Goin' on highway / Sail on little girl, sail on / Alberta No.2 / Find me a woman / Hastings street boogie / Canal street blues / War is over (Goodbye California) / Henry's swing club
CDCHD 405 / Nov '93 / Ace

□ BOOGIE CHILLUN
Dimples / Every night / Little wheel / You can lead me baby / I love you honey / Maudie / I'm in the mood / Boogie chillun / Hobo blues / Crawlin' kingsnake / Drive me away / Solid sender / No shoes / Want ad blues / Will the circle be unbroken / I'm goin' upstairs / Boom boom / Bottle up and go / This is hip / Big legs, tight skirt / Serves me right to suffer / Your baby ain't sweet like mine
CPCD 8210 / Feb '97 / Charly

□ BOOGIE CHILLUN
Tupelo / Boogie chillun / Dimples / Drug store woman / Boom boom / Frisco blues / No shoe / I'm in the mood / Hobo blues / Baby Lee / Trouble blues / Old time shimmy / Little wheel / Whiskey and wimmen / Process / Dusty road / Send me your pillow / I'm so excited / Onions / Good rockin' mama / Thelma / Keep your hands to yourself / What do you say / Lost a good girl / Let's make it / Hard hearted woman / I'm going upstairs / I'm leaving baby
GRF 023 / '93 / Tring

□ BOOGIE MAN, THE (4CD Set)
CDDIG 5 / Feb '95 / Charly

□ BOOGIE MAN, THE
BN 021 / Apr '98 / Blue Nite

□ BOOM BOOM
Boom boom / I'm bad like Jesse James / Same old blues again / Sugar Mama / Trick bag / Boogie at Russian hill / Hittin' the bottle again / Bottle up and go / Thought I heard / I ain't gonna suffer no more / Hobo blues / I want to hug you / House rent boogie / Want ad blues / I'm so excited / Hard headed woman / I wanna walk / Onions / What do you say / She shot me down / Keep your hands to yourself / Dusty road / Send me your pillow / I want to shout / I'm leaving baby
VPBCD 12 / Oct '92 / Pointblank

□ BOOM BOOM
Boom boom / Hobo blues / I want to hug you / House rent boogie / Want ad blues / I'm so excited / Hard headed woman / I wanna walk / Onions / What do you say / She shot me down / Keep your hands to yourself / Dusty road / Send me your pillow / I want to shout / I'm leaving baby
CDSGP 066 / May '93 / Prestige

□ BOOM BOOM
Boom boom / Dimples / Whiskey and wimmen / I wanna talk / House rent boogie / No shoes / Frisco / Let's make it / Big legs tight skirts / Good rockin' mamma / Want ad blues / Nightmare / You ain't no big thing / Boogie chillun / Mamma you got a daughter / Crawlin' kingsnake
12333 / May '94 / Laserlight

□ BOOM BOOM
Tupelo / Boogie chillun / Dimples / Drug store woman / Boom boom / Frisco blues / No shoes / Hobo blues / Baby Lee / Trouble blues / Little wheel / Whisky and wimmen / Process / Send me your pillow / Good rockin' Mama / Thelma / She's mine (keep your hands to yourself) / What do you say / Lost a good girl / Let's make it / Hard headed woman / I'm going upstairs / I'm leaving
QED 067 / Nov '96 / Tring

□ BOSS, THE
MATCD 320 / Oct '94 / Castle

□ BOSS, THE
PLSCD 124 / Apr '96 / Pulse

□ BURNIN' HELL
Burning hell / Graveyard blues / Baby, please don't go / Jackson, Tennessee / You live your life and I'll live mine / Smokestack lightnin' / How can you do it / I don't want no woman if her hair ain't longer than mine / I rolled and turned and cried the whole night long / Blues for my baby / Key to the highway / Natchez fire
OBCCD 555 / Feb '93 / Original Blues Classics

□ CHILL OUT
Chill out (things gonna change) / Deep blue sea / Kiddio / Medley: Serves me right to suffer/ Syndicator / One bourbon, one scotch, one beer / Tupelo / Woman on my mind / Annie Mae / Too young / Talkin' the blues / If you've never been in love / We'll meet again
VPBCD 22 / Feb '95 / Pointblank

□ COAST TO COAST
Come back baby / Forgive me / Street is filled with women / Moon is rising / Whistle done blown / Turnin' gray blues / She was in Chicago / Lord taketh my baby away / Just like a woman / Throw this old dog a bone / Johnny Lee's mood / Miss Eloise, Miss Eloise / Crying all night welfare blues
BGOCD 363 / 26 Sep '97 / Beat Goes On

□ COLLECTION, THE (20 Blues Greats)
Dimples / I'm in the mood / Hobo blues / Boogie chillun / Boom boom / Blues before sunrise / Time is marching / Tupelo / Little wheel / Shake, holler and run / Want ad blues / Crawlin' kingsnake / Whisky and wimmen / Tease me baby / Wednesday evenin' blues / My first wife left me / Maudie / No shoes / I love you honey / Rock house boogie
CCSCD 410 / Feb '95 / Castle

□ COUNTRY BLUES OF JOHN LEE HOOKER, THE
Black snake / How long blues / Wobblin' baby / She's long, she's tall, she weeps like a willow / Pea vine special / Tupelo blues / I'm prison bound / I rowed a little boat / Waterboy / Church bell tone / Bundle up and go / Good morning little school girl / Behind the plow
OBCCD 542 / Nov '92 / Original Blues Classics

□ CRAWLING KING SNAKE 1948-1952
OCD 103 / Nov '95 / Opal

□ CREAM, THE
Hey hey / Rock steady / Tupelo / You know it ain't right / She's gone / TB sheets / Sugar mama / One room country shack / Drug store woman / I want you to roll me / Bar room drinking / Little girl / Louise / When my first wife left me / Boogie on
CPCD 8200 / Feb '97 / Charly

□ DETROIT BLUES 1950-1952 (The Gotham Titles) (Hooker, John Lee & Eddie Burns)
House rent boogie / Wandering blues / Making a fool out of me / Questionnaire blues / Real gone gal / Squeeze me baby / Feed her all night / Gangsters blues / Where did you stay last night / My daddy was a jockey / Little boy blue / How long must I be your slave / Grieving blues / Ground hog blues / Mean old train / Catfish
FLYCD 23 / Oct '90 / Flyright

□ DETROIT LION, THE
House rent boogie / I'm in the mood / Baby how can you do it / Let's talk it over / Yes, baby, baby, baby / I got the key / Four women in my life / Do my baby think of me / I'm gonna git me a woman / It hurts me so / Bluebird, bluebird, take a letter down South / Boogie chillun / Hello baby / This is 19 and 52, babe / Blues for Abraham Lincoln / Hey
FIENDCD 154 / Feb '90 / Demon

□ DIMPLES (The Best Of John Lee Hooker/Original Hit Recordings)
Dimples / Boom boom / This is hip / I'm in the mood / I love you honey / Crawlin' kingsnake / Boogie chillun / I'm mad agin / Big legs, tight skirt / I'm going upstairs / Onions / It serves me right to suffer / Send me your pillow / No shoes / I'm so excited / Hobo blues / Maudie / What do you say / She's mine / Don't look back
CDGR 151 / Apr '97 / Charly

□ DON'T LOOK BACK
Dimples / Healing game / Ain't no big thing / Don't look back / Blues before sunrise / Spellbound / Travellin' blues / I love you honey / Frisco blues / Red house / Rainy day
VPBCD 39 / Mar '97 / Pointblank

□ DON'T YOU REMEMBER ME
Stomp boogie / Who's been jivin' you / Black man blues / Poor Joe / Nightmare blues / Late last night / Wandering blues / Don't go baby / Devil's jump / I'm gonna kill that woman / Moaning blues / Numbers / Heart trouble blues / Slim's stomp / Thinking blues / Don't you remember me
CDCHARLY 245 / Oct '90 / Charly
KCD 6009 / 17 Nov '97 / King

□ ELECTRIC
Onions / Dusty road / I'm in the mood / Blues before sunrise / Baby please don't go / Hobo blues / Boom boom / Whiskey and wimmen / Time is marching / Dimples / I'm so excited / Boogie chillun / Maudie / I'm gonna kill that woman / Slim's stomp / Crawlin' king snake
CDBM 117 / Sep '96 / Blue Moon

□ ENDLESS BOOGIE
(I got) a good 'un / Pots on, gas on high / Kick hit 4 hit kix u / I don't need no steam heat / We might as well call it through / Sittin' in my dark room / Endless boogie parts 27 and 28
BGOCD 70 / Feb '90 / Beat Goes On

□ ENDLESS BOOGIE
MCD 10413 / 8 Sep '97 / MCA

□ EP COLLECTION, THE
Madman blues / You know, I know / Leave my wife alone / Down at the landing / Ground hog blues / High priced woman / Love blues / Union Station blues / Louise / One bourbon, one scotch, and one beer / Just me and my telephone / Apologise / Worried life blues / Journey / I don't want your money / Lonely boy boogie / Ramblin' by myself / Sugar Mama / It's my own fault / Women and money / Walking the boogie / Stella Mae / Let's go out tonight / Baby, please don't go
SEECD 402 / Jul '94 / See For Miles

□ ESSENTIAL COLLECTION, THE
HMNCD 019 / 3 Nov '97 / Half Moon

□ EVERYBODY'S BLUES
Do my baby think of me / Three long years today / Strike blues / Grinder man / Walkin' this highway / Four women in my life / I need lovin' / Find me a woman / I'm mad / I been done so wrong / Boogie rambler / I keep the blues / No more doggin' (aka no more foolin') / Everybody's blues / Anybody's blues / Locked up in jail / Nothin' but trouble (don't take your wife's family in) / I need love so bad / I had a good girl / Odds against me (aka backbiters and syndicators)
CDCHD 474 / Jun '93 / Ace

□ FOLK BLUES OF JOHN LEE HOOKER, THE
Black snake / How long blues / Wobblin' baby / She's long, she's tall, she weeps like a willow / Pea vine special / Tupelo blues / I'm prison bound / I rowed a little boat / Waterboy / Church bell tone / Bundle up and go / Good morning little school girl / Behind the plow
CDCH 282 / Nov '93 / Ace

□ FREE BEER AND CHICKEN
Make it funky / Five long years / 713 blues / 714 blues / One bourbon, one scotch, one beer / Bluebird / Sittin' on top of the world / (You'll never amount to anything if you don't go to) College / I know how to rock / Nothin' but the best / Scratch
BGOCD 123 / Sep '91 / Beat Goes On

□ GET BACK HOME
ECD 260042 / Jan '92 / Evidence

□ GRAVEYARD BLUES
War is over (Goodbye California) / Henry's swing club / Alberta / Street boogie / Build myself a cave / Momma poppa boogie / Graveyard blues / Burnin' hell / Sailing blues / Black cat blues / Miss Sadie Mae / Canal street blues / Huckle up baby / Goin' down highway / Sail on little girl, sail on / My baby's got something / Boogie chillun no. 2 / Twenty one boggie / Rollin' blues
CDCHD 421 / Sep '92 / Ace

□ HARD TIMES
Sally Mae / Rock with me / Hobo blues / Should've been gone / Hard times / Hooker's shuffle / I hate the day I was born
3036000962 / Mar '97 / Carlton

□ HEALER, THE
Healer / I'm in the mood / Baby Lee / Cuttin' out / Think twice before you go / Sally Mae / That's alright / Rockin' chair / My dream / No substitute
ORECD 508 / Mar '97 / Silvertone

□ HIS BEST CHESS SIDES
MCD 09391 / 23 Feb '98 / Chess/MCA

□ HOOKER 'N' THE HOGS (Hooker, John Lee & The Groundhogs)
Mai Lee / Losing you / Little girl / Lay down little dreamer / Don't be messin' with my bread / Lost everything / I cover the waterfront / I don't want nobody else / Storming on the deep blue sea / Crazy mixed up world / Seven days and seven nights / Wandering blues: Hooker, John Lee / Goin' mad blues: *Hooker, John Lee* / Black man blues: *Hooker, John Lee* / Helpless blues: *Hooker, John Lee*
IGOCD 2059 / Oct '96 / Indigo

□ HOOKER SINGS THE BLUES
I need some money / Come and see about me / I'm wanderin' / Democrat man / I want to talk about you / Gonna use my rod / Wednesday evenin' blues / No more doggin' / One of these days / I believe I'll go back home / You're leavin' me baby / That's my story
OBCCD 538 / Nov '92 / Original Blues Classics

□ HOUSE RENT BOOGIE
Mambo chillun / Time is marching / Unfriendly woman / I'm so worried baby / Baby Lee / Road is so rough / Trouble blues / Everybody rockin' / I'm so excited / Crawlin' black spider / Little fine woman / Rosie Mae / You've taken my woman / Mama you've got a daughter / House rent boogie / I'm a stranger / I'm mad again / Hard hearted woman / I wanna walk / Run on / Blues before sunrise / Onions
CPCD 8212 / Feb '97 / Charly

□ I FEEL GOOD
JEWEL 5005CD / Mar '98 / Jewel

□ I WANNA DANCE ALL NIGHT
500512 / Oct '93 / Musidisc

□ I'M IN THE MOOD
Baby Lee / Dimples / Blues before sunrise / I'm goin' upstairs / Thelma / I'm in the mood / Let's make it / Whiskey and wimmen / No shoes / Crawlin' kingsnake / Old time shimmy / Little wheel / Process / Good rockin' mama / When my first wife left me
CDSGP 027 / May '93 / Prestige

□ IF YOU MISS 'IM...I GOT 'IM
BGOCD 392 / 15 Jun '98 / Beat Goes On

□ IT SERVES YOU RIGHT TO SUFFER
Sugar mama / Decoration day / Money, that's what I want / Serves me right to suffer / Shake it baby / Country boy / Bottle up and go / You're wrong
BGOCD 335 / Dec '96 / Beat Goes On

□ JEALOUS
VPBCD 48 / 2 Mar '98 / Pointblank

□ JOHN LEE HOOKER (2CD Set)
R2CD 4007 / 13 Apr '98 / Deja Vu

□ JOHN LEE HOOKER
GFS 074 / Jul '97 / Going For A Song

□ JOHN LEE HOOKER 1948-1949
Morning blues / Boogie awhile / Tuesday evening / Miss Pearl boogie / Good business / Mercy blues / Poor Slim / We gonna make / Low down boogie / Cotton pickin' boogie / Must I make / Roll me baby / I've been down so long / Christmas time blues
KKCD 05 / Oct '90 / Krazy Kat

□ JOHN LEE HOOKER BOXSET (3CD Set)
Dusty road / My first wife left me / Maudie / Time is marching / Hug and squeeze / Blue before sunrise / Run on / That's my story / I wanna walk / Wenesday evening blues / You're leavin' me baby / I'm a stranger / Old time shimmy / No more doggin' / Solid sender / Syndicator / Tupelo / House rent boogie / Mama, you got a daughter / Tease me baby / Ground hog blues / Leave me alone / Dimples / Boom boom / Bottle up and go / Cry before I go / Back biter and syndicaters / Think twice before you go / I'm in the mood / Little wheel / Want ad blues / Whiskey and wimmen / Crawling king snake / Sugar Mama / Hobo blues / Baby Lee / I love you baby / Trouble blues / I'm so excited / She left me on bended knee / Process / Good rockin' Mama / No shoes / Send me the pillow you dream on / Onions / Frisco / Drug store woman / Let your Daddy ride / Don't you remember me / Boogie chillen
KBOX 345 / Nov '95 / Collection

□ JOHN LEE HOOKER COLLECTOR'S EDITION
DVBC 9012 / Apr '95 / Deja Vu

□ LEGENDARY JOHN LEE HOOKER, THE
Boom boom / I'm going home / House rent boogie / Hobo blues / I love you honey / One way ticket / Whiskey and wimmen / I'm mad again / I'm in the mood / SDimples / I'm so excited / Dirty groundhog / Sally Mae / No shoes / Boogie chillen / Waterfront / Big legs tight skirt
REMCD 518 / Feb '98 / Reactive

□ LEGENDARY MODERN RECORDINGS 1948-1954, THE
Boogie chillun / Sally Mae / Hoogie boogie / Hobo blues / Weeping willow boogie / Drifting from door to door / Crawlin' kingsnake / Women in my life / Howlin' Wolf / Playing the races / Let your Daddy ride / Queen bee / Wednesday evenin' blues / I'm in the mood / Tease me baby / Turn over a new leaf / Rock house boogie / Too much boogie / Need somebody / Gotta boogie / Jump me up one more time / Down child / Bad boy / Please take me back
CDCHD 315 / Apr '93 / Ace

□ LIVE AT CAFE AU GO GO
I'm bad like Jesse James / She's long, she's tall, she weeps like a willow / When my first wife left me / Heartaches and misery / One bourbon, one scotch, and one beer / I don't want no trouble / I'll never get out of these blues alive / Seven days
BGOCD 39 / Oct '88 / Beat Goes On

□ LIVE AT SUGARHILL VOL.1 & 2
I can't hold on much longer / Key to the highway / My babe / You been dealin' with the devil / Money / Run on / Matchbox / Night time is the right time / Boogie chillun / I'm gonna keep on walking / TB is killing me / This world (no man's land) / I like to see you walk / It's you I love, baby / Driftin' and driftin' / You're gonna miss me / You're nice and kind to me Lou Della / I want to get married
CDCHD 938 / Nov '93 / Ace

□ LONDON SESSIONS 1965
I don't want nobody else / Storming on the deep blue sea / I'm losing you / Go back to school, little girl / Don't be messing with my bread / Mary Lee / I cover the waterfront / Crazy mixed up world / Seven days / Little dreamer / Lost everything
NEBCD 657 / Jul '93 / Sequel

☐ MAMBO CHILLUN (Charly Blues Masterworks Vol.19)
Mambo chillun / Wheel and deal / Unfriendly woman / Time is marching / I'm so married baby / Baby Lee / Road is so rough / Trouble blues / Stop talking / Everybody rockin' / I'm so excited / I see you when you're weak / Crawlin' black spider / Little fine woman / Rosie Mae / You can lead me baby
CDBM 19 / Apr '92 / Charly

☐ MASTERS, THE
EABCD 065 / 24 Nov '97 / Eagle

☐ MASTERS, THE (2CD Set)
EDMCD 026 / 24 Nov '97 / Eagle

☐ MORE REAL FOLK BLUES
This land is nobody's land / Deep blue sea / Nobody knows / Mustang Sally and GTO / Lead me / Catfish / I can't quit you baby / Want ad blues / House rent blues
MCD 09329 / Apr '97 / Chess/MCA

☐ MR. LUCKY
I want to hug you / Mr. Lucky / Backstabbers / This is hip / I cover the waterfront / Highway 13 / Stripped me naked / Susie / Crawlin' kingsnake / Father was a jockey
ORECD 519 / Mar '97 / Silvertone

☐ NOTHING BUT THE BLUES
I feel good / Baby baby / Dazie May / Stand by / Call it the night / Going home / We are cooking / Lookin' back over my day / Roll and tumble / Bottle of wine / Baby don't do me wrong
CDBM 070 / Apr '91 / Blue Moon

☐ ONE BOURBON ONE SCOTCH ONE BEER
301342 / Apr '98 / Hallmark

☐ ORIGINAL FOLK BLUES...PLUS
Boogie chillun / Queen bee / Crawling king snake / Weeping willow boogie / Whistlin' and moanin' blues / Sally Mae / I need love so bad / Let's talk it over / Syndicator / Let your Daddy ride / Drifting from door to door / Baby, I'm gonna miss you / Cold chills / Cool little car / I wonder little darling / Jump me one more time / Lookin' for a woman / Ride till I die
CDCHM 530 / Feb '94 / Ace

☐ RARE HOOKER
House rent boogie / Wandering blues / Low down midnite boogie / Miss Lorraine / Morning blues / Talkin' boogie / Graveyard blues / I love to boogie / Do the boogie / Prison bound / Bumble bee blues / I'm so worried / I see you when you're weak / Mama you've got a daughter / Crazy about that walk / We're all god's children / My own fault / Maudie / Tupelo / I wanna walk / I wish you were here
CDGR 176 / Sep '97 / Charly

☐ REAL BLUES, THE
EMPRCD 805 / 18 May '98 / Emporio

☐ REAL FOLK BLUES
Let's go out tonight / Peace lovin' man / Stella Mae / I put my trust in you / I'm in the mood / You know, I know / I'll never trust your love again / One bourbon, one scotch, one beer / Waterfront
CHLD 19097 / Nov '91 / Chess/MCA

☐ RISING SUN COLLECTION
RSCD 001 / Apr '94 / Just A Memory

☐ SECOND CONCERT
Put your hand on your hip / Trying to survive / I won't be back no more / She left me on bended knee / You ain't too old to shift them gears / Hobo blues / I wish I could change your ways / Boogie chillen / Crawlin' king snake
TBA 130132 / Jun '97 / Blues Alliance

☐ SHAKE IT BABY (Charly Blues Masterworks Vol.45)
Shake it baby / Right time / Mai lee / I'm losin' you / Little girl go back to school / Little dreamer / Don't be messing around with my bread / Bad luck and trouble / Waterfront / No one pleases me but you / It's raining here / It's a crazy mixed up world / Seven days and seven nights
CDBM 45 / Jun '93 / Charly

☐ SIMPLY THE TRUTH
I don't wanna go to Vietnam / I wanna boogaloo / Tantalizing with the blues / I'm just a drifter / Mini skirts / Mean mean woman / One room country shack
MCAD 22136 / Oct '94 / One Way

☐ SINGS BLUES
Wandering blues / I'm gonna kill that woman / Heart trouble blues / Don't you remember me / Slim's stomp / Numbers / Nightmare blues / Moaning blues / Don't go baby / Thinking blues / Late last night / Devil's jump
EMBCD 3356 / 1 Jun '98 / Ember

☐ TANTALIZING WITH THE BLUES
Serves me right to suffer / Shake it up baby / Bottle up and go / Cry before I go / Backbiters and syndicators / Think twice before you go / I don't wanna go to Vietnam / Mini skirts / Mean mean woman / Tantalizing with the blues / I'm just a drifter / Kick hit / I'll never get out of these blues alive
MCLD 19033 / Apr '92 / MCA

☐ THAT'S MY STORY (NYC 1960)
CDCH 260 / Nov '93 / Ace

☐ THAT'S MY STORY/ FOLK BLUES OF JOHN LEE HOOKER
I need some money / I'm wanderin' / Democrat man / I want to talk about you / Gonna use my rod / Wednesday evenin' blues / No more doggin' / One of these days / I believe I'll go back home / You're leavin' me, baby / That's my story / Black snake / How long blues / Wobblin' baby / She's long, she's tall, she weeps like a willow / Pea vine special / Tupelo blues / I rowed a little boat / Waterboy / Church bell tone / Bundle up and go
CDCH 927 / '90 / Ace

☐ THAT'S WHERE IT'S AT
Teachin' the blues / Goin' to louisiana / I need you / My love comes down for you / Please don't go / I just don't know / Slow and easy / Two white horses / Feel so bad / Grinder man
CDSXE 064 / Jul '92 / Stax

☐ THIS IS HIP (The Best Of John Lee Hooker)
Dimples / Boogie chillun / I'm so excited / Sally Mae / This is hip / Moanin' blues / Big legs tight skirt / Crawlin' kingsnake / Nightmare / Baby Lee / My first wife left me / I like to see you walk / I'm in the mood / Maudie / Tupelo / Boom boom
308842 / 11 May '98 / Hallmark

☐ TRILOGY (3CD Set)
DTKBOX 90 / 6 Jul '98 / Dressed To Kill

☐ TWO ON ONE: JOHN LEE HOOKER & MUDDY WATERS (Hooker, John Lee & Muddy Waters)
Dimples / Boom boom / Maudie / Walkin' the boogie / I'm in the mood / Let's make it / Crawlin' kingsnake / Onions / Big legs, tight skirt / Everybody rockin' / Hoochie coochie man / I got my mojo working / Baby please don't go / Rollin' and tumblin' / I just want to make love to you / Mannish boy / Rolling stone / She's into something / You shook me / Baby please don't go
CDTT 3 / Apr '94 / Charly

☐ URBAN BLUES
Cry before I go / Boom boom / Backbiters and syndicators / Mr. Lucky / My own blues / I can't stand to leave you / Think twice before you go / I'm standing in line / Hot spring water / Motor city is burning / Want ad blues
BGOCD 122 / Sep '91 / Beat Goes On

☐ URBAN BLUES
MCD 10760 / 8 Sep '97 / MCA

☐ VEE JAY YEARS 1955-1964 (6CD Set)
Unfriendly woman / Wheel and deal / Mambo chillun / Time is marching / I'm so worried baby / Baby Lee / Dimples / Every night / Road is so rough / Trouble blues / Stop talking / Everybody rockin' / I'm so excited / I can see you when you're weak / Crawlin' black spider / Little find woman / Rose Mae / You can lead me baby / I love you honey / You've taken my woman / Mama / You got a daughter / Nightmare / House rent boogie / Trying to find a woman / Drive me away / I'm goin' home / Love me all the time / Lou della / Bundle up and go / Wrong doin' woman / Maudie / Tennessee blues / I'm in the mood / Boogie chillun / Hobo blues / Crawlin' kingsnake / I wanna talk / Canal street blues / I'll know tonight / I can't believe / Goin' to California / Whiskey and wimmen / Run on / Solid sender / Sunnyland / Dusty road / I'm a stranger / No shoes / Five long years / I like to see you walk / Wednesday evenin' blues / Take me as I am / My first wife left me / You're looking good to me / You're gonna miss me when I'm gone / Dirty groundhog / She loves my best friend / Sally Mae / Moanin' blues / Hobo / Tupelo / Want ad blues / Will the circle be unbroken / I'm goin' upstairs / I left my baby / Hard headed woman / I'm mad again / Process / Thelma / What do you say / Boom boom / Blues before sunrise / I lost a good girl / She's mine / I got a letter this morning / New leaf / Let's make it / Drug store woman / Old time shimmy / Onions / You know I love you / Send me your pillow / Big soul / Frisco blues / She shot me down / Take a look at yourself / Good rockin' mama / I love her / No one told me / Don't look back / One way ticket / Half a stranger / Bottle up and go / My grinding mill / I want to ramble / Sadie Mae / This is hip / Poor me / I want to shout / Love is a burning thing / I want to hug you / I'm leaving baby / Birmingham blues / I can't quit you now blues / Stop baby / Don't hold me / Bus station blues / Freight train to my friend / Talk that talk baby / Sometimes baby you make me feel so bad / You've got to walk yourself / Might fire / Big legs / Tight skirt / Flowers on the hour / Serves me right to suffer / It ain't no big thing / She left me one Wednesday / You can run / Your baby ain't sweet like mine / She's long / She's tall / You're mellow
CDREDBOX 6 / Dec '92 / Charly

☐ VERY BEST OF JOHN LEE HOOKER, THE
Boom boom / Shake it baby / Right time / Dimples / Boogie chillun / Mambo chillun / Wheel and deal / I'm so excited / Trouble blues / Everybody rockin' / Unfriendly woman / Time is marching / I see you when you're weak / I'm in the mood / Will the circle be unbroken / This is hip / Hobo blues / Solid sender
500432 / Jun '97 / Musidisc UK

☐ VERY BEST OF JOHN LEE HOOKER, THE (& Roots Of The Blues No.1 Compilation/3CD Set)
High priced woman / Leave my wife alone / Ramblin' by myself / Walkin' the boogie / Love blues / Please don't go / Down at the landing / Mambo chillun / Time is marchin' / Dimples / Every night / Crawlin' black spider / I love you honey / House rent boogie / Trying to find a woman / Maudie / I'm in the mood / Boogie Chillun / Hobo blues crawlin' kingsnake / No shoes / Dirty ground hog / Hobo blues (AKA the hobo) / I'm goin' upstairs / I'm mad again / What do you say / Boom boom / She's mine / Drug store woman / You know I love you / Send me your pillow / Don't look back / One way ticket / Bottle up and go / This is hip / Big legs / Tight skirt / It serves me right to suffer / Stella Mae / One bourbon / One scotch / One beer / Waterfront / Stack O'Lee blues / 44 Blues / Divin' duck blues / Gimme a pigfoot / Revenue man blues / Sagefield woman blues / Old times blues / Cross road blues / Harmonica blues / Easyrider / Crawling king snake / Can't you read / Bad acting women / Take a walk with me / I got a break, baby
VBCD 301 / Jul '95 / Charly

☐ VERY BEST OF JOHN LEE HOOKER, THE (2CD Set)
Mambo chillun / Time is marchin' / Dimples / Every night / Baby Lee / Crawlin' black spider / I'm so excited / Mama, you got a daughter / I love you honey / House rent boogie / Trying to find a woman / Maudie / I'm in the mood / Boogie chillun / Hobo blues / Crawlin' kingsnake / Dusty road / No shoes / My first wife left me / Moanin' blues / Dirty groundhog / Hobo blues / Tupelo / I'm going upstairs / I'm mad again / Want ad blues / What do you say / Boom boom / She's mine / Drug store woman / You know I love you / Send me your pillow / Don't look back / One way ticket / Bottle up and go / This is hip / Half a stranger / Birmingham blues / It serves me right to suffer / Big legs, tight skirt
CPCD 82422 / Oct '96 / Charly

☐ WANDERIN' BLUES
MACCD 189 / Aug '96 / Autograph

☐ WHISKEY AND WOMEN
IMP 301 / Jul '95 / Iris Music

Hooker OK

☐ HOOKER OK
SP 014 / May '97 / Sweet Pea

Hooker, William

☐ ENVISIONING (Hooker, William & Lee Ranaldo)
KFWCD 159 / Feb '95 / Knitting Factory

☐ GIFT OF TONGUES, THE (Hooker, William & Lee Ranaldo/Andrea Parkins)
KFWCD 179 / Oct '96 / Knitting Factory

☐ JOY (WITHIN) (Hooker, William & Billy Bang)
SHCD 147 / Oct '97 / Silkheart

☐ SHAMBALLA (Hooker, William & Thurston Moore/Elliott Sharp)
KFWCD 151 / Feb '95 / Knitting Factory

Hookers

☐ SATAN'S HIGHWAY
Satan's highway / Get fucked / Hometown slut / Baby you'll regret me / Back alley / Trash / Pot whore / Tear you apart / 12 gauge reaction / We don't fuck around / Take you down with me / Welcome the beast / Rock and riot / Soul taker
06402 / 16 Feb '98 / Epitaph

Hooligans

☐ LAST CALL
SKIZ 002 / Dec '96 / Skizmatic

Hooper, Johnny

☐ FAT CATS
Morning dance / Ain't no sunshine / Johnsburg Ilinois / Stranger / Summertime / Rodeo drive / Laura Grace / Just the two of us / Fat cats / Voice in the dark / Jersey girl / Can you let the musicians in
JRHCD 2 / '92 / Johnny Hooper Recordings

☐ FOR THE CITY
Pick up the pieces / Baker Street / Get here / Knock on wood / I'll be there / Move closer / Take five / Green onions / Living for the city / Easy / Saving all my love for you / I still haven't found what I'm looking for
JRHCD 3 / Jan '94 / Johnny Hooper Recordings

☐ IN THE MOOD
In the mood / American patrol / Rudy's rock / Tuxedo junction / Moonlight serenade / As time goes by / Cherokee / Take the 'A' train / Body and soul / These foolish things / Birth of the blues / Water is wide
JRHCD 5 / Dec '97 / Johnny Hooper Recordings

☐ JUKED
Harlem nocturne / My prayer / Cry me a river / Great pretender / Georgia on my mind / True love ways / Peter Gunn / Only you / Let it be me / Smoke gets in your eyes / End of the world / Somewhere / I love how you love me
JRHCD 1 / Jul '90 / Johnny Hooper Recordings

☐ MISTY
Misty / Love letters / Night train / Tequila / Unchained melody / I can't stop loving you / Breaking up is hard to do / Flamingo / When I fall in love / Love hurts / Satin doll / Yesterday
JRHCD 4 / Nov '95 / Johnny Hooper Recordings

Hoopsnakes

☐ HOOPSNAKES
MPD 6003 / Aug '96 / Mouthpiece

☐ JUMP IN AND HANG ON
MPD 6002 / Nov '94 / Flying Fish

Hoosegow

☐ MIGHTY
T&M 008 / Nov '96 / Tradition & Moderne

Hoosier Hot Shots

☐ ARE YOU READY HEZZIE
CCD 905 / Jan '94 / Circle

Hooters

☐ DEFINITIVE COLLECTION, THE
Twenty-five hours a day / Satellite / And we danced / Day by day / All you zombies / Where do the children go / Nervous night / Johnny B / Karla with AK / Fightin' on the same side / Brother don't you walk away / 500 miles / Don't knock it 'til you try it / Give the music back / Mr. Big Baboon / Shadow of Jesus
4805622 / 13 Jul '98 / Columbia

☐ HOOTERIZATION
And we danced / Nervous light / All you zombies / Satellite / Karla with a K / Where do the children go / 500 miles / Fightin' on the same side / Day by day / Lucy in the sky with diamonds / Heaven laughs / Brother don't you walk away / Johnny B / She comes in colours / Time after time / Beat up guitar
4854922 / Oct '96 / Columbia

☐ NERVOUS NIGHT
We danced / Day by day / All you zombies / Don't take my car out tonight / Nervous night / Hanging on a heartbeat / Where do the children go / South ferry road / She comes in colours / Blood from a stone
4624852 / May '94 / Columbia

Hootie & The Blowfish

☐ CRACKED REAR VIEW MIRROR
Hold my hand / Drowning / I'm goin' home / Goodbye / Not even the trees / Look away / Time / Running from an angel / Hannah jane / Let her cry / Only wanna be with you
7567826132 / Feb '95 / Atlantic

☐ FAIR WEATHER JOHNSON
Be the one / Sad caper / Tuckeris town / She crawls away / So strange / Old man and me / Earth stopped cold at dawn / Fair weather Johnson / Honeyscrew / Let it breath / Silly little pop song / Fool / Tootie / When I'm lonely
7567828862 / Apr '96 / Atlantic

Hooton 3 Car

☐ BY MEANS OF MAYBE
RSTR 010CD / 25 May '98 / Rumblestrip

☐ CRAMP LIKE A FOX
CDWOOS 2 / Apr '96 / Out Of Step

Hoover

☐ HOOVER
SLOWDIME 9CD / 2 Mar '98 / Slowdime

☐ NEW RECORDINGS
SOWDIME 09 / 23 Mar '98 / Slowdime

☐ NEW STEREOPHONIC SOUND SPECTACULAR, A
Inhaler / 2 wicky / Wardrobe / Plus profond / Barabas / Cinderella / Nr 9 / Sarangi / Someone / Revolver / Innervoice
4843892 / Jun '97 / Columbia

Hoover, Louis

☐ AND THIS IS ME
September in the rain / It's probably me / I believe in you / One for my baby / Lolita / Fly me to the moon / Mack the knife / No one ever tells you / Up the lazy river / Live love and learn / I get along without you very well / Here's that rainy day / Spend a little time / It's funny how / All of me / On my own / Night and day / ABC of love / I got it bad and that ain't good / Keep it cool
TAA 001 / 6 Jul '98 / TAA

☐ LOUIS HOOVER
ABC of love / I wanna be around / Lolita / This is all I ask / I got it bad and that ain't good / Keep it cool / Faccia di Luna / Spend a little time with her / On my own / Live, love and learn / It's funny how life can change / Should know better by now / Where in the world am I / Mack the knife
JHCD 054 / Aug '97 / Ronnie Scott's Jazz House

Hop, Lorentz

☐ HARDANGERFIDDLE
NOR 9721CD / Aug '97 / NORCD

Hope Blister

☐ SMILE'S OK
Dagger / Only human / Outer skin / Sweet unknown / Let happiness in / Is Jesus your pal / Spider and I / Hanky panky nohow
CAD 8008CD / 25 May '98 / 4AD

Hope, Bob

☐ BOB HOPE
DVGH 7102 / May '95 / Deja Vu

☐ THANKS FOR THE MEMORY (The Best Of Bob Hope)
HMNCD 033 / 22 Jun '98 / Half Moon

Hope, Elmo

☐ ALL STAR SESSIONS, THE
Weeja / Polka dots and moonbeams / On it / Avalon / Kiss for my love / Eyes so beautiful as yours / Moe jr / One mo' blues / Laberthe / Homecoming / Imagination
MCD 47037 / Jun '95 / Milestone

☐ FINAL SESSIONS, THE (2CD Set)
I love you / Night in Tunisia / Stellations / Pam / Elmo's blues / Somebody loves me / Low tide / Bird's view / Roll on / Roll on / Vi-Ann / Vi-Ann / Toothsome threesome / Grammy / Kiss for my love / Something for Kenny / Punch that
ECD 221472 / Sep '96 / Evidence

Hope, Lynn

☐ JUICY (Hope, Lynn & Clifford Scott)
Juicy / Blue and sentimental / Hang out / Stardust / Oo wee / Tenderly / Shu-ee / Very thought of you / Shockin' / Rose room / Cutie / I don't stand a ghost of a chance with you / Little landslide / Full moon / Blue lady / Sands of the Sahara / Fros-tee nite / Body and soul
CDCHARLY 280 / Oct '91 / Charly

Hopewell

☐ CONTACT
SINGE 017 / 1 Jun '98 / Burnt Hair

Hopkin, Mary

☐ EARTH SONG - OCEAN SONG
International / There's got to be more / Silver birch and weeping willow / How come the sun / Earth song / Martha / Streets of London / Wind / Water, paper and clay / Ocean song
CDP 7986952 / Jun '92 / Apple

☐ POSTCARD
Those were the days / Lord of the reedy river / Happiness runs (pebble and the man) / Love is the sweetest thing / Y blodyn gwyn / Honeymoon song / Puppy song / Inchworm / Voyage of the moon / Lullaby of the leaves / Young love / Someone to watch over me / Prince en avignon / Game / There's no business like show business / Turn turn turn (to everything there is a) / Those were the days (quelli erano giorni) / Those were the days (en aquellos dias)
CDP 7975782 / Oct '91 / Apple

☐ THOSE WERE THE DAYS
Those were the days / Goodbye / Temma harbour / Think about your children / Knock knock who's there / Whatever will be will be (Que sera sera) / Lontano degli occhi / Sparrow / Heritage / Fields of St. Etienne / Jefferson / Let my name be sorrow / Kew Gardens / When I am old one day / Silver birch / Streets of London / Water, paper and clay
CDSAPCOR 23 / Apr '95 / Apple

☐ Y CANEUON CYNNAR (The Early Recordings)
Tro tro tro / Tami / Yn y bore / Gwrandewch ar y moroedd / Pleserau serch / Draw dros y moroedd / Aderyn llwyd / Y blodyn gwyn / Rhywbeth syml / Tyrd yn ol / Yfory
SCD 2151E / Feb '97 / Sain

Hopkins, Claude

☐ CLASSICS 1932-1934
CLASSICS 699 / Jul '93 / Classics

☐ CLASSICS 1934-1935
CLASSICS 716 / Jul '93 / Classics

☐ CLASSICS 1937-1940
CLASSICS 733 / Jan '94 / Classics

☐ MONKEY BUSINESS
Three little words / Margie / King Porter stomp / Monkey business / Mandy / Honey / Church Street / Sobbin' blues
HEPCD 1031 / Jul '93 / Hep

Hopkins, David

☐ HEAR THE GRASS/ECHOES FROM THE WORLD OF BAMBOO
SM 10822 / Jun '91 / Wergo

Hopkins, Lightnin'

☐ AUDIO ARCHIVE
Just sittin' down thinking / Don't keep my baby long / Tell me pretty mama / Bad luck and trouble / Needed time / Last affair / Santa Fe blues / Someday / Jake head boogie / Glory be / Sometimes she will / Shine on moon / Have you ever loved a woman / Shake that thing / I'm leaving you now / Walk a long time / Bring me my shotgun / Just pickin' / Last night / Mojo hand
CDAA 036 / Jun '92 / Tring

☐ AUTOBIOGRAPHY IN BLUES
TCD 1002 / Feb '96 / Tradition

☐ BLUES IN MY BOTTLE
Buddy Brown's blues / Wine drinkin' spodee-o-dee / Sail on little girl, sail on / DC-7 / Death bells / Goin' to Dallas to see my pony run / Jailhouse blues / Blues in the bottle / Beans beans beans / Catfish blues / My grandpa is old too
OBCCD 506 / Nov '92 / Original Blues Classics

☐ BLUES IN MY BOTTLE/WALKIN' THIS ROAD BY MYSELF
Buddy Brown's blues / Wine drinkin' spodee-o-dee / Sail on little girl, sail on / DC 7 / Goin' to Dallas to see my pony run / Jailhouse blues / Blues in the bottle / Beans beans beans / Catfish blues / My grandpa is old too / Walkin' this road by myself / Black gal / How many more years I got to let you dog me around / Baby don't you tear my clothes / Worried life blues / Happy blues for John Glenn / Good morning little school girl / Devil jumped the black man / Coffee blues / Black Cadillac
CDCHD 930 / Mar '90 / Ace

☐ BLUES MASTERS (Hopkins, Lightnin'/ Memphis Slim)
Sad news from Korea: *Hopkins, Lightnin'* / Let me fly your kite: *Hopkins, Lightnin'* / Gone with the wind: *Hopkins, Lightnin'* / She's almost dead: *Hopkins, Lightnin'* / Ain't it a shame: *Hopkins, Lightnin'* / Crazy about my baby: *Hopkins, Lightnin'* / My Mama told me: *Hopkins, Lightnin'* / Mojo hand: *Hopkins, Lightnin'* / Shining moon: *Hopkins, Lightnin'* / Blue evening: *Memphis Slim* / No mail blues: *Memphis Slim* / You're gonna need my help someday: *Memphis Slim* / Train time: *Memphis Slim* / When Buddy comes to town: *Memphis Slim* / Train is comin': *Memphis Slim* / Question: *Memphis Slim* / Drivin' me mad: *Memphis Slim* / Never let me love: *Memphis Slim*
5541572 / 20 Apr '98 / Spectrum

☐ BRAND NEW CAR
IMP 303 / Apr '96 / IMP

☐ CALIFORNIA MUDSLIDE (AND EARTHQUAKE)
California muslide / Rosie Mae / Los Angeles Blues / Easy on your heels / New Santa Fe / Jesus will you come by here / No education / Antoinette's blues / Change my way of living / Los Angeles boogie / Call on my baby
CDCHM 546 / Nov '94 / Ace

☐ CHICKEN MINNIE
TKCD 023 / Nov '96 / Magnum America

☐ COFFEE HOUSE BLUES (Charly Blues Masterworks Vol.33)
Big car blues / Coffee house blues / Stool pigeon blues / Ball of twine / Mary Lou / Want to come home / Rolling and rolling / Devil is watching you / Please don't quit me / Coon is hard to catch / Heavy snow / Walking round in circles / War is starting again / Got me a Louisiana woman
CDBM 33 / Jan '93 / Charly

☐ COLLECTION, THE
Mojo hand / Coffee for mama / Good times / Evil hearted woman / Nothin' but the blues / Hear me talkin' / Shinin' moon / Don't wake me / Don't think cause your pretty / My little kewpie doll / Lightnin's boogie / My baby's gone / Sittin' down thinkin' / Easy on your heels / Blues for my cookie / Leave jike mary alone / Life I used to live / Rosie mae / You treat po' lightnin' wrong / California landslide / Goin' back home / Shaggy dog / Lightnin's stomp / Talk of the town / Hopkins' sky hop
COL 068 / Feb '95 / Collection

☐ COUNTRY BLUES
TCD 1003 / Feb '96 / Tradition

☐ DOUBLE BLUES
Let's go sit on the lawn / I'm taking a devil of a chance / I got tired / I asked the bossman / Just a wristwatch on my arm / I woke up this morning / I was standing on 75 highway / I'm going to build me a heaven of my own / My babe / Too many drivers / I'm a crawling black snake / Rocky mountain blues / I mean goodbye / Howling wolf / Black ghost blues / Darling do you remember me / Lonesome graveyard
CDCH 354 / Nov '93 / Ace

☐ FOREVER 1981
157792 / Feb '93 / Blues Collection

☐ FREE FORM PATTERNS
Mr. Charlie / To give me time to think / Fox chase / Mr. Ditta's grocery store / Open up your door / Baby child / Cooking's done / Got her letter this morning / Rain falling / Mini skirt
CPCD 8208 / Feb '97 / Charly

☐ GOIN' BACK HOME
Shaggy dog / Santa Fe blues / Shinin' moon / I'll be gone / Shake it baby / Goin' back home / Good times / I'm wit' it / Don't wake me / Talk of town / California landslide / Rosie Mae / Easy on your heels / Leave Jike Mary alone / You treat po' lightnin' wrong
CDSGP 090 / Nov '93 / Prestige

☐ GOLD STAR SESSIONS VOL.1
ARHCD 330 / Apr '95 / Arhoolie

☐ GOLD STAR SESSIONS VOL.2
Walkin' blues / Shining moon / Ida may / Mercy / Automobile blues / Glory b. blues (blue bird blues) / All I got is gone / Whiskey blues / European blues / What can it be / Lonesome home / Appetite blues / Lightning blues / Hammond boogie (organ boogie) / Rollin' woman blues / Jail house blues / T model blues / No mail blues / Ain't it a shame / Old woman blues / Untrue blues / Henny penny blues / Jackstropper blues / Grievance blues
ARHCD 337 / Apr '95 / Arhoolie

☐ GOOD ROCKIN' TONIGHT
Big black cadillac / Stool pigeon blues / Leave Jike Mary alone / Don't treat that man you treat me / Gonna pull a party / Coffee house blues / You treat po' Lightnin' wrong / Short haired woman / Big car blues / I heard my children crying / 'Buked and scorned / I'm gonna meet my baby somewhere / Early morning blues / Get off my toe / Foot race is on / Good rockin' tonight
CDBM 118 / Sep '96 / Blue Moon

☐ GREAT ELECTRIC SHOW AND DANCE, THE
JEWEL 5002CD / Mar '98 / Jewel

☐ HOOTIN' THE BLUES
OBCCD 571 / Jul '95 / Original Blues Classics

☐ HOUSTON GOLD
Late in the evening / Lightnin' jump / War is starting again / Got me a Louisiana woman / Born in the bottoms / Mojo hand / World's a tangle / I went to Louisiana / I feel like balling the jack / Man like me is hard to find / Go ahead / I wonder where she can be tonight / Old man / Moving out / Crying for bread
CDBM 111 / 30 Jan '98 / Blue Moon

☐ HOW MANY MORE YEARS I GOT
How many more years I got to let you dog me around / Walkin' this road by myself / Devil jumped the black man / My baby don't stand no cheatin' / Black cadillac / You is one black rat / Fox chase / Mojo hand / Mama blues / My black name / Prison farm blues / Ida Mae / I got a leak in this old building / Happy blues for John Glenn / Worried life blues / Sinner's prayer / Angel child / Pneumonia blues / Have you ever been mistreated
CDCH 409 / Nov '92 / Ace

☐ IN NEW YORK
Take it easy / Mighty crazy / Your own fault, baby, to treat me the way you do / I've had my fun if I don't get well no more / Trouble blues / Lightnin's piano boogie / Wonder why / Mister Charlie
CCD 79010 / Oct '93 / Candid

☐ LAST NIGHT BLUES (Hopkins, Lightnin' & Sonny Terry)
Rocky mountain / Got to move your baby / So sorry to leave you / Take a trip with me / Last night blues / Lightnin's stroke / Hard to love a woman / Conversation blues
OBCCD 548 / Nov '92 / Original Blues Classics

☐ LIGHTNIN'
Mojo hand / Rock me baby / Hello central / Ain't it crazy / Little and low / Hold up your head / Good times here, better down the road / Annie's boogie / My starter won't start this morning / One kind favor I ask of you / Little girl / Baby please don't go / What'd I say / I hear you calling me / Trouble in mind / Come on baby / At home blues / Take a walk / Little antoinette / Cut me out baby
ARHCD 390 / Apr '95 / Arhoolie

☐ LIGHTNIN'
Automobile blues / You better watch yourself / Mean old frisco blues / Shinin' moon / Come back baby / Thinkin' 'bout an old friend / Walkin' blues / Back to new orleans / Katie mae / Down there baby
OBCCD 532 / Nov '92 / Original Blues Classics

☐ LIGHTNIN' HOPKINS
CDSF 40019 / Aug '94 / Smithsonian Folkways

☐ LIGHTNIN' HOPKINS (1946-1960)
That mean old twister / Short haired woman / Can't get that woman off my mind / You are not going to worry my life anymore / You're gonna miss me (miss me blues) / Sugar on my mind (sugar mama) / Nightmare blues / Someday baby / Come back baby / Moon is rising (moonrise blues) / Howling wolf blues / Have to let you go / Mama's baby child / Whiskey headed woman (liquor drinkin' woman) / Shining moon / I wonder why / Papa bones boogie (buck dance boogie) / I've been a bad man (mad blues) / Corrine, corrina / Tom moore's farm / Slop
SOB 35242 / Dec '92 / Story Of The Blues

☐ LIGHTNIN' HOPKINS 1946-1960
SOB 35242CD / Apr '95 / Story Of The Blues

☐ LIGHTNIN' IN NEW YORK
Take it easy / Mighty crazy / Your own fault, baby, to treat me the way you do / I've had my fun / Trouble blues / Lightnin's piano boogie / Wonder why / Mr. Charlie
CCD 9010 / Feb '97 / Candid

☐ LIVE AT THE RISING SUN
RS 0009CD / Jul '95 / Rising Sun

☐ LONESOME DOG BLUES
Lonesome dog blues / Glory be / Sometimes she will / Shine on moon / Santa / Have you ever loved a woman / Shake that thing / I'm leaving you now / Walk a long time / Bring me my shotgun / Just pickin' / Last night / Mojo hand / Coffee for mama / Awful dreams / Black mare trot
GRF 060 / '93 / Tring

☐ LONESOME DOG BLUES (18 Blues Masterpieces)
Found my baby crying / Love me this morning / Gambler's blues / Play with your poodle / Fishing clothes / Rock me mama / Breakfast time / Lovin' arms / I'm comin' home / Ride in your new automobile / Letter to my back door / Last affair / Mr. Charlie / You're too fast / Morning blues / Wig wearing woman / Lonesome dog blues
308122 / Apr '98 / Hallmark

☐ LONESOME LIFE
Rainy days in Houston / You just gotta miss me / Pine gum boogie / Wake up the dead / How does it / Got a letter this morning / Stinking foot / Walking and walking / Good as old time religion / Born in the bottoms / Ballin' the Jack / World's in a tangle / Man like me is hard to find
CDBM 093 / Jul '92 / Blue Moon

☐ MASTERS, THE
Big black cadillac blues / Stool pigeon blues / Leave Jike Mary alone / Don't treat that man the way you treat me / Gonna pull a party / Coffee house blues / You treat po' lightnin' wrong / Short haired woman / Big car blues / I heard my children crying / 'Buked and scorned / I'm gonna meet my baby somewhere / Early morning blues / Get off my toe / Foot race is on / There's good rockin' tonight
EABCD 081 / 30 Mar '98 / Eagle

☐ MORNING BLUES (Charly Blues Masterworks Vol.8)
Found my baby crying / Letter to my (back door friend) / Fishing clothes / Morning blues / Gambler's blues / Wig wearing woman / Lonesome dog blues / Last affair / Lovin' arms / Rock me mama / Mr. Charlie (Part 1) / Mr. Charlie (Part 2) / Play with your poodle / You're too fast / Love me this morning / I'm coming home / Ride in your new automobile / Breakfast time
CD BM 8 / Apr '92 / Charly

☐ NOTHIN' BUT THE BLUES
Blues in the bottle / Catfish blues / DC-7 / Death bells / Rock me baby / Shotgun
CD 52023 / Aug '92 / Blues Encore

☐ PO' LIGHTNIN'
ARHCD 403 / Apr '95 / Arhoolie

☐ SHAKE IT BABY
Shining moon / I'll be gone / Shake it baby / Back home / Good times / What'd I say / Talk of the town / California landslide / Easy on your heels / Rosie mae / Leave jike mary alone / Don't you treat poor lightnin' wrong / Shaggy do fe blues
CWNCD 2013 / Jul '96 / Javelin

☐ SHAKE THAT THING
422173 / May '94 / New Rose

☐ SINGS THE BLUES
PCD 3056 / 27 Apr '98 / P-Vine

☐ SMOKES LIKE LIGHTNING
T model blues / Jackstropper blues / You cook alright / My black name / You never miss your water / Let's do the Susie-Q / Ida Mae / Smokes like lightning / Prison farm blues
OBCCD 551 / Jan '96 / Original Blues Classics

☐ SOUL BLUES
I'm going to build me a heaven of my own / My babe / Too many drivers / I'm a crawling black snake / Rocky mountain blues / I mean goodbye / Howling wolf / Black ghost blues / Darling, do you remember me / Lonesome graveyard
OBCCD 540 / Nov '92 / Original Blues Classics

☐ SWARTHMORE CONCERT
Baby please don't go / My black cadillac / It's crazy / Mojo hand / My babe / Short haired woman / Mean old frisco blues / Trouble in mind / Twister / Green onion / Sun goin' down / Come go home with me / I'm a stranger
OBCCD 563 / Jul '94 / Original Blues Classics

☐ TEXAS BLUES MAN
Mojo hand / Cotton / Little wail / Hurricane Betsy / Take me back, baby / Really nothin' but the blues / Guitar lightnin' / Woke up this morning / Shake yourself / California showers / Goin' out / Tom Moore blues / I would if I could / At home blues / Watch my fingers / Bud Russell blues / Cut me out baby
ARHCD 302 / Apr '95 / Arhoolie

☐ TEXAS BLUES MAN
Mojo hand / Cotton / Little wail / Hurricane betsy / Take me back baby / Really nothin' but the blues / Guitar lightnin' / Woke up this morning / Shake yourself / California showers / Goin' out / Tom moore blues / I would if I could / At home blues / Watch my fingers / Bud russell blues / Cut me out baby
CD 52005 / '92 / Blues Encore

☐ TEXAS COUNTRY BLUES (Hopkins, Lightnin' & Joel/John Henry)
ARHCD 340 / Apr '95 / Arhoolie

Hopkins, Nicky

☐ REVOLUTIONARY PIANO OF NICKY HOPKINS, THE
Mr. Big / Yesterday / Goldfinger / Don't get around much anymore / Jenni / Acapulco 1922 / You came a long way from St. Louis / Love letters / Unlonely bull / Satisfaction / Paris belles v the Ilejistry pig
4785022 / Feb '95 / Columbia

Hopkins, Rich

☐ DIRT TOWN (Hopkins, Rich & Luminarios)
OUT 1182 / Sep '97 / Brake Out

☐ DUMPSTER OF LOVE (Hopkins, Rich & Luminarios)
OUT 1212 / Aug '96 / Brake Out

☐ GLORIOUS SOUNDS OF RICH HOPKINS AND LUMINARIOS (Hopkins, Rich & Luminarios)
BLUCD 0053 / 20 Apr '98 / Blue Rose

Hopley, David

☐ SEQUENCE SELECTION
SAV 238CD / Dec '95 / Savoy

Hoppe, Michael

☐ UNFORGETTING HEART
4628625002 / 17 Mar '98 / Real Music

Hopper

☐ ENGLISH AND FRENCH
Bad kid / Placebo / Nice set up / Oh my heartless / 'Cause I rock / Someone phoned / Germolene / Ridiculous day / Four goodbyes / Interference / Homesick / English and french / Wasted / Joytown
FACD 210 / Jul '96 / Factory Too

Hopper & Sinclair

☐ SOMEWHERE IN FRANCE
VP 133CD / Dec '96 / Voiceprint

Hopper, Brian

☐ BEGGARS FARM
Long time / Story / Tomorrow won't be long / Astral plane / Sea / You're not my girl at all / Living in a building / Looking back / Thinking of me / Your lovin' man / You forever
VP 145CD / 27 Jul '98 / Voiceprint

☐ HUGE (Hopper, Brian & Kramer)
Huge / Ten mile mean streak / Tall as the Empire State Building / Terry Southern blues / Texas trombone / Only being / Celine's final breath / Einstein and Hawking / She's everything, Mr H / Waltz of the big brains / Manchester 96
BP 248CD / Apr '97 / Blueprint
KFWCD 088 / 30 Mar '98 / Knitting Factory

Hopper, Hugh

☐ 1984
MANTRA 061 / Nov '96 / Mantra
4577501042 / 27 Apr '98 / Cuneiform

☐ ALIVE (Hopper, Hugh Band)
Glider / Forget the dots / Turfschip enterprise / Double booked / Nomali / Lullaby letter bomb / Hanging around for you / Just in time / Golden section
BP 150CD / Aug '96 / Blueprint

☐ BEST SOFT
1059610 / Dec '96 / Mantra

☐ HOPPER TUNITY BOX
3012842 / Feb '97 / Culture Press

☐ MERCY DASH (Hopper, Hugh & Elton Dean/Keith Tippett/Joe Gallivan)
3012802 / Feb '97 / Culture Press

☐ MONSTER BAND (Hopper, Hugh Monster Band)
Golden section / Sliding dogs / Churchy Lily Kong / 12-8 theme / Lily Kong / Nozzles / Tecalemit / Get together
3012782 / Feb '97 / Arcade

☐ REMARK HUGH MADE, A (Hopper, Hugh & Kramer)
SHIMMY 076 / 16 Mar '98 / Shimmy Disc

Hopper, Kev

☐ SPOOMBUNG
THOOFA 1 / 18 May '98 / Thoofa

Hor

☐ FASTER MORE AGRESSIVE HOR
Burning truck / Quick fix / Tracking testing and treating the hardcore / Break ranks / Spoiled spud / Chains of despotism / Sex with recruits / Pilotless plane / Why is the hippy happy / Topless political statement / Play hurt / I thought you were supposed to be smart / Army sex / Power line paranoia / Downloaded virus / Agreed punishment
SST 347CD / 27 Oct '97 / SST

Horde

☐ HELLIG USVART
NB 1282 / Mar '95 / Nuclear Blast

Horiuchi, Glenn

☐ HILLTOP VIEW (Horiuchi, Glenn Trio/ Unit)
CD 935 / Oct '96 / Music & Arts

☐ MERCY
CD 962 / Apr '97 / Music & Arts

☐ OXNARD BEET
1212282 / Sep '92 / Soul Note

Horizon 222

☐ 3 OF SWANS
CHARRMCD 18 / Mar '94 / Charrm

☐ THROUGH THE ROUND WINDOW
HY 39100252 / Mar '94 / Hyperium

Horlen, Johan

☐ DANCE OF RESISTANCE
DRCD 260 / Oct '95 / Dragon

Horler, John

☐ GENTLE PIECE
This is my lovely day / Astra / Melancholia / Daisy / All the things you are / My funny valentine / Interlude / Gentle piece / Two bits / Solid silver / Whisper not
SPJCD 542 / Feb '97 / Spotlite

☐ LOST KEYS
I'm a fool to want you / Mood river / Abstract no.4 / Waltz / Blue in green / This is my lovely day / Lost keys / Re: Person I knew / Abstract no.2 / Mabel/ Gentle peace
CHECD 00109 / Jun '94 / Master Mix

☐ QUIET PIECE
This is my lovely day / Astra / Melancholia / Daisy / All the things you are / My funny valentine / Knterlude / Gentle piece / Two bits / Solid silver / Whisper not
SPJCD 542 / May '93 / Spotlite

Hormones

☐ WHERE OLD GHOSTS MEET
WR 1001652 / 10 Aug '98 / Banana

Horn

☐ HORNOGRAPHY
Up exe / Neither / Freaks get busy / (Do it for your girlfriend / Ful / Mirage / Short / Shadow valley / Faota / Arce / Home on Friday / Too slow for D / Something else / Villager
EVO 025CD / 3 Nov '97 / Universal Language

Horn, Jim

☐ WORK IT OUT
7599259112 / Jan '96 / WEA

Horn, Shirley

☐ HERE'S TO LIFE
Here's to life / Come a little closer / How am I to know / Time for love / Where do you start / You're nearer / Return to paradise / Isn't it a pity / Quietly there / If you love me (really love me) / Summer (Estate) / Wild is the wind
5118792 / Jan '92 / Verve

☐ I LOVE YOU, PARIS
5234862 / Dec '94 / Verve

☐ I REMEMBER MILES
My funny Valentine / I fall in love too easily / Summertime / Baby won't you please come home / This hotel / I got plenty o' nuttin' / Basin Street blues / My man's gone now / Blue in green
5571992 / 29 Jun '98 / Verve

☐ LIGHT OUT OF DARKNESS (A Tribute To Ray Charles)
Hit the road Jack / Just a little lovin' / You don't know me / Drown in my own tears / Hard hearted Hannah / Georgia on my mind / Makin' whoopee / Green / How long has this been going on / If you were mine / I got a man / Just for a thrill / Light out of darkness / Bye bye love / Sun died
5197032 / Feb '94 / Verve

☐ LOADS OF LOVE/SHIRLEY HORN WITH HORNS
Wild is love / Loads of love / My future just passed / There's a boat that's leavin' soon for New York / Ten cents a dance / Only the lonely / Second time around / Do it again / It's love / That's no joke / Love for sale / Who am I / On the street where you live / Great city / That old black magic / Mack the knife / Come dance with me / Let me love you / After you've gone / Wouldn't it be loverly / Go away little boy / I'm in the mood for love / Good life / In the wee small hours of the morning
8434542 / Apr '94 / EmArCy

☐ LOVING YOU
5370222 / Mar '97 / Verve

☐ MAIN INGREDIENT, THE
5295552 / Mar '96 / Verve

☐ SOFTLY (2CD Set)
APCD 224 / Apr '89 / Audiophile

☐ YOU WON'T FORGET ME
Music that makes me dance / Come dance with me / Don't let the sun catch you crying / Beautiful love / Come back to me / Too late now / I just found out about love / It had to be you / Soothe me / Foolin' myself / If you go / You stepped out of a dream / You won't forget me / All my tomorrows
8474822 / May '91 / Verve

Horncloud, William

☐ TRADITIONAL LAKOTA SONGS
72933761502 / 19 May '98 / CYN

Horne, Jimmy 'Bo'

☐ GIMME SOME (The Best Of The TK Years 1975-1985)
Spank / Dance across the floor / Gimme some / Get happy / (They long to be) close to you / Let me (let me be your lover) / Don't worry about it / Goin' home for love / Let's do it / Is it in / Ask the birds and the bees / Without you / I get lifted / Music to make love by / You're so good to me / Rocket in the pocket / You get me hot / I wanna go home with you / It's your sweet love
WESM 550 / 16 Mar '98 / Westside

Horne, Lena

☐ AIN'T IT THE TRUTH (Lena Horne At MGM - A Soundtrack Anthology)
Just one of those things / Spring / Ain't it the truth / Life's full of consequence / Honey in the honeycomb / Honeysuckle rose / You're indiff'rent / Jericho / Brazilian boogie / Somebody loves me / Tete a tete at tea time / Solid potato salad / Paper doll / Trembling leaf / Love / Can't help lovin' dat man / Why was I born / Bill / Where or when / Lady is a tramp / Baby come out of the clouds / If you can dream / You got looks
CDODEON 32 / 15 Sep '97 / Soundtracks

☐ BEING MYSELF
Some of my best friends / As long as I live / Autumn in New York / It's alright with me / Sleepin' bee / Imagination / How long has this been going on / After you / Willow weep for me / What am I here for
8342862 / 1 Jun '98 / Blue Note

☐ BEST OF LENA HORNE, THE
I wish I was back in my baby's arms / Love (can change the stars) / I got it bad and that ain't good / Love me or leave me / Honeysuckle rose / Poppa don't preach to me / Why was I born / Lady is a tramp / Lover man / My blue heaven / Can't help lovin' that man / From this moment on / Night and day / What'll I do / Cuckoo in the clock / At long last love / Old devil moon / Good for nothin' Joe / Take me / Nobody knows the trouble I've seen
PLSCD 119 / Dec '96 / Pulse

☐ EV'RY TIME WE SAY GOODBYE
When I fall in love / September song / I wish I'd met you / Fine romance / It could happen to you / Eagle and me / Look to the rainbow / Sing my heart / Roundabout / Joy / Ours / Close enough for love / I won't leave you again / Ev'ry time we say goodbye
QED 126 / Nov '96 / Tring

☐ FABULOUS LENA HORNE, THE (22 Hits 1936-1946)
I take to you: *Horne, Lena & Noble Sissle Orchestra* / That's what love did to me: *Horne, Lena & Noble Sissle Orchestra* / Good for nothin' Joe: *Horne, Lena & Charlie Barnet* / You're my thrill: *Horne, Lena & Charlie Barnet* / All I desire: *Horne, Lena & Charlie Barnet* / St. Louis blues: *Horne, Lena & Henry Levine/Dixieland Jazz Group* / Careless love: *Horne, Lena & Henry Levine/Dixieland Jazz Group* / Aunt Hagar's blues: *Horne, Lena & Henry Levine/ Dixieland Jazz Group* / Beale Street blues: *Horne, Lena & Henry Levine/Dixieland Jazz Group* / Don't take your love from me: *Horne, Lena & Artie Shaw* / Out of nowhere: *Horne, Lena & Teddy Wilson Orchestra* / Prisoner of love: *Horne, Lena & Teddy Wilson Orchestra* / Stormy weather / What is this thing called love / Ill wind / Mad about the boy / Moanin' low / Where or when / One for my baby and one more for the road: *Horne, Lena & Horace Henderson Orchestra* / As long as I live: *Horne, Lena & Horace Henderson Orchestra* / How long has this been going on: *Horne, Lena & Phil Moore Four* / Frankie and Johnny
CDAJA 5238 / Jun '97 / Living Era

☐ FEELIN' GOOD
On a wonderful day like today / Take the moment / I wanna be around / Feelin' good / Who can I turn to / Less than a second / Willow weep for me / Girl from Ipanema / Softly as I leave you / And I love him / Hello young lovers / Moon river / I love Paris / Never on Sunday / Somewhere / It's a mad mad mad mad world / What the world needs now is love / Let the little people talk / I get along without you very well / It had better be tonight
CDSL 8269 / Nov '95 / Music For Pleasure

☐ LA SELECTION 1936-1941
011 / Sep '93 / Art Vocal

☐ LADY AND HER MUSIC, THE
As long as I live / Good for nothin' / Where or when / Ill wind / Careless love / Beale street blues / I gotta right to sing the blues / Man I love / Prisoner of love / Captain and his men / Haunted town / You're my thrill / St Louis blues / I didn't know about you / That's what love did to me / Don't take your love from me / Stormy weather / Out of nowhere / Hagar's blues / Mad about the boy / One for my baby (and one for the road)
PASTCD 7091 / Jul '96 / Flapper

☐ LADY IS A TRAMP, THE
Why was I born / Love me of leave me / Love can change the stars / I wish I was back in my baby's arms / Good for nothing Joe / Old devil moon / I got it bad and that ain't good / Papa don't preach to me / Honeysuckle rose / Lady is a tramp / Lover man / Take me / My blue heaven / Can't help lovin' that man / From this moment on / Night and day / Cuckoo in the clock / What I'll do / At long last love / Nobody knows the trouble I've seen
CDSGP 059 / Aug '93 / Prestige

☐ LENA GOES LATIN
CDMRS 510 / '88 / DRG

☐ MASTERS, THE
EABCD 029 / 24 Nov '97 / Eagle

☐ SPOTLIGHT ON LENA HORNE
Close enough for love / Ours / Every time we say goodbye / Fine romance / Round about / September song / Joy / Eagle and me / When I fall in love / Look for the rainbow / It could happen to you / Sing my heart / Don't squeeze me / Whispering / Hesitating blues / Beale Street blues
HADCD 129 / Feb '94 / Javelin

☐ STORMY WEATHER
Stormy weather / Good for nothin' Joe / Diga diga doo / I can't give you anything but love / Mad about the boy / As long as I live / 'Deed I do / Once in a lifetime / Meantime / Silent spring / Slowin' in the wind / Best things in life are free / Lost in the stars / Now / Wouldn't it be loverly / More than you know / At long last love / Nobody knows the trouble I've seen / Blue prelude / Little girl blue / It's a rainy day / Frankie and Johnny / Lady is a tramp
GRF 062 / '93 / Tring

☐ STORMY WEATHER
I got it bad (and that ain't good) / Lover man / Love can change the stars / Honeysuckle rose / Night and day / Old devil moon / Why was I born / Poppa don't preach to me / My blue heaven / From this moment on / Love me or leave me / Lady is a tramp / Once in a lifetime / Meditation / Good for nothin' Joe / I wish I was back in my baby's arms / Can't help lovin' that man / Cuckoo in the clock / Stormy weather / Take me
300322 / Jun '98 / Hallmark

Horne, Marilyn

☐ 60TH BIRTHDAY
09026625472 / Oct '94 / RCA Victor

☐ MEN IN MY LIFE, THE
Swinging on a star / Man I love / You're just in love / Blah blah blah/Just in time / Small world / Long before I knew you / Friendship / All the things you are / In the still of the night / Some enchanted evening / I get embarrassed / All through the night / Bewitched, bothered and bewildered / All I ask of you / Little things you do together / Love walked in/Our love is here to stay
09026626472 / Nov '94 / RCA Victor

Hornsby, Bruce

☐ HARBOR LIGHTS
Harbour lights / Talk of the town / Long tall cool one / China doll / Fields of gray / Rainbow's cadillac / Passing through / Tide will rise / What a time / Pastures of plenty
07863661142 / Mar '93 / RCA

☐ HOT HOUSE
Spider fingers / White wheeled limosine / Walk in the sun / Changes / Tango king / Big rumble / Country doctor / Longest night / Hot house ball / Swing street / Cruise control
07863665842 / Aug '95 / RCA

☐ NIGHT ON THE TOWN, A (Hornsby, Bruce & The Range)
Night on the town / Fire on the cross / Across the river / Stander on the mountain / Another day / These arms of mine / Carry the water / Barren ground / Stranded on Easy Street / Lost soul / Special night
74321160012 / Sep '93 / RCA

☐ SCENES FROM THE SOUTH SIDE (Hornsby, Bruce & The Range)
Look out any window / Valley Road / I will walk with you / Road not taken / Show goes on / Old playground / Defenders of the flag / Jacob's ladder / Till the dreaming's done
ND 90492 / Nov '90 / RCA

☐ WAY IT IS, THE (Hornsby, Bruce & The Range)
On the Western skyline / Every little kiss / Mandolin rain / Long race / Way it is / Down the road tonight / Wild frontier / River runs low / Red plains
74321444212 / Feb '97 / RCA

Horny Toad

☐ THIRTEEN
Shiver / Youth / Long slow death / Fragile planet / Fire in the sky / Quicksand / Vampire ska / Eggfart / Signify / Ho / Brick / Give to me
DOMO 710132 / Apr '97 / Domo

Horo

☐ LA GRANDE BLEUE
172692 / 24 Feb '98 / Musidisc

Horo, Krachno

☐ TRADITIONAL BULGARIAN
Y 225217CD / Oct '94 / Silex

Horo, Slobo

☐ ESMA
ZENCD 2401 / Apr '95 / Rockadillo

Horovitz, Wayne

☐ 4+1 ENSEMBLE
Step aside / Up all night / Cotton club / First light / Trouble / AFAP / Exit laughing / Take me home / Calder/Snake eyes
INT 32242 / 20 Jul '98 / Intuition

☐ COLD SPELL (Horovitz, Wayne & Zony Mash)
With the space on top / Happens like that / Sex fiend / Prudence rsvp / Cold spell / Mel / Let's get mashed / Smiles / Gift / Withdrawal symptons / Daylight
KFW 201 / 24 Aug '98 / Knitting Factory

☐ WAYNE HOROVITZ & ZONY MASH (Horovitz, Wayne & Zony Mash)
KFWCD 201 / Mar '97 / Knitting Factory

Horowitz, Richard

☐ MAJOUN (Horowitz, Richard & Sussan Deyhim)
SK 62721 / 1 Sep '97 / Sony Classical

Horse

☐ SAME SKY, THE
And she smiled / Speed of the beat of my heart / Never not going to / You are / Breathe me / You could be forgiven / Don't call me / Sweet thing / Stay / Careful
CDP 7489662 / Apr '97 / EMI

Horse Latitudes

☐ HORSE LATITUDES
Oh Caroline / What is more than life / Baby don't go / Harvest days / Thrown away / Building mansions / Northern country lie / I can't stop loving you / Younger generation / Someone / There I go again
CDBRED 90 / Sep '90 / Cherry Red

Horseflies

☐ HUMAN FLY
Human fly / Hush little baby / Jenny on the railroad / Rub alcohol blues / Cornbread / Who throwed lye on my dog / I live where it's gray / Link of chain / Blueman's daughter
COOKCD 013 / Jan '97 / Cooking Vinyl

Horslips

☐ ALIENS
Before the storm / Wrath of the rain / Speed the plough / Sure the boy was green / Come Summer / Stowaway / New York wakes / Exiles / Second Avenue / Ghosts / Lifetime to pay
MOOCD 014 / Jan '95 / Outlet

☐ BEST OF HORSLIPS
My Lagan love (downtown) / Dearg doom / Green gravel / Oisin's tune / Bim Istigh ag ol / Johnny's wedding / Daybreak (opening the station) / More than you can chew / King of the fairies / Musical far East / High reel / Flower among them all
CMOD 021 / '89 / Outlet

☐ BOOK OF INVASIONS, THE
Daybreak / March into trouble / Trouble with a capital T / Power and the glory / Rocks remain / Dusk / Sword of light / Warm sweet breath of love / Fantasia (my lagan love) / King of morning, Queen of day / Sideways to the sun / Drive the cold winter away / Ride to hell / Dark
MOOCD 012 / Jan '95 / Outlet

☐ CELTIC ROCK VOL.1
Carolan's frolic / Sir Festus Burke / Carolin's frolic / Piper in the meadow / Shamrock shore / An bratach ban / Sorry to part / Denis O'Connor / Scalloway rip off / Snow and frost are all over/Paddy Fahy's / Thompson's/Cottage in the grove / King of the fairies / Crabs on the skillet / Bim istigh ag ol / Ace and deuce
CHCD 2009 / Jun '98 / Outlet

☐ CELTIC ROCK VOL.2
Trouble with a capital T / Fantasia - my Lagan love / Sideways to the sun / Man who built America / Green star liner / Long time ago / Motorway madness / Come back Beatles / High volume love / Dearg doom / Night town boy / Time to kill / Faster than the hound / Daybreak / Self defence
CHCD 2010 / Jun '98 / Outlet

☐ COLLECTION, THE
MOOCD 025 / Oct '95 / Outlet

☐ DANCEHALL SWEETHEARTS
Nightown boy / Blind can't lead the blind / Stars / We bring the Summer with us / Sunburst / Mad Pat / Blind man / King of the fairies / Lonely hearts / Best years of my life
MOOCD 007 / Jan '95 / Outlet

☐ DRIVE THE COLD WINTER AWAY
Rug muire mac do dhia / Sir Festus Burke/Carolan's frolic / Snow that melts the soonest / Piper in the meadow straying / Drive the cold winter away / Thompson's cottage to the grove / Ny kirree fo naghtey / Crabs in the skillet / Dennis O'Connor / Do'n oiche i mbeithil / Lullaby / Snow and frosts are all over / Paddy Fahey's / When a man's in love
MOOCD 009 / Jan '95 / Outlet

☐ GUESTS OF THE NATION
King of the fairies / Flower among them all / Johnny's wedding / Daybreak / Furniture / King of the morning, Queen of the day / Dearg doom / Trouble with a capital T / Man who built America / I'll be waiting / Power and the glory / Speed the plough / Long weekend / Guests of the nation
MOOCD 024 / Jan '95 / Outlet

☐ HAPPY TO MEET, SORRY TO PART
Happy to meet / Hall of mirrors / Clergy's lanentation / An bratach ban / Shamrock shore / Flower among them all / Bim istigh ag ol / Furniture / Ace and deuce of pipering / Dance to your daddy / High reel / Scalloway rip off / Musical priest / Sorry to part
MOOCD 003 / Jan '95 / Outlet

☐ HORSLIPS LIVE
Mad Pat / Blindman / Silver spear / High reel / Stars / Hall of mirrors / If that's what you want (That's what you get) / Self defence / Everything will be alright / Rakish Paddy / King of the fairies / Furniture / You can't fool the beast / More than you can chew / Dearg doom / Comb your hair and curl it / Johnny's wedding
MOOC 010 / Jan '95 / Outlet

☐ HORSLIPS STORY - STRAIGHT FROM THE HORSE'S MOUTH
High reel / Night town boy / Flower among them all / Dearg doom / Faster than the hounds / Best years of my life / Man who built America / Guests of the nation / Daybreak / Everything will be alright / Power and the glory / Sword of light / Warm sweet breath of love / Speed the plough / Trouble with a capital T / Shamrock shore / King of the fairies / High volume love / An bratach ban / Silver spear
DHCD 802 / Feb '95 / Outlet

☐ HORSLIPS, THE
High reel / Dearg doom / Man who built America / Guests of the nation / Daybreak / Power and the glory / Sword of light / Speed the plough / Trouble / King of the fairies / An Bratach Ban / Silver spear
KCD 450 / Jan '97 / Celtic Collections

☐ LIVE IN BELFAST
Trouble with a capital T / Man who built America / Warm sweet breath of love / Power and the glory / Blindman / Shakin' all over / King of the fairies / Guests of the nation / Dearg doom
MOOCD 020 / Jan '95 / Outlet

☐ MAN WHO BUILT AMERICA
Man who built America / Tonight / I'll be waiting / If it takes all night / Green star liner / Loneliness / Homesick / Long weekend / Letters from home / Long time ago
MOOCD 017 / Jan '95 / Outlet

☐ SHORT STORIES TALL TALES
Guests of the nation / Law on the run / Unapproved road / Ricochet man / Back in my arms / Summer's most wanted girl / Amazing offer / Rescue me / Life you save / Soap opera
MOOCD 019 / Jan '95 / Outlet

☐ TAIN, THE
Setanta / Meave's court / Charolais / March / You can't fool the beast / Dearg doom / Ferdia's song / Gae bolga / Cu chulainn's lament / Faster than the hounds / Silver spear / More than you can chew / Morrigan's dream / Time to kill / March
MOOCD 005 / Jan '95 / Outlet

☐ TRACKS FROM THE VAULTS
Motorway madness / Johnny's wedding / Flower among them all / Green gravel / Fairy king / Dearg doom / High reel / King of the fairies / Phil the fluter's ball / Come back Beatles / Fab four-four / Daybreak / Oisin's tune
MOOCD 013 / Jan '95 / Outlet

☐ TRADITIONAL IRISH MUSIC
My lagan love / Dearg doom / Green gravel / Oisin's tune / Bim istigh ag ol / Johnny's wedding / Daybreak / More than you can chew / King of the fairies / Musical far east / High reel / Flower among them all
MOOCD 021 / Feb '95 / Outlet

☐ UNFORTUNATE CUP OF TEA
If that's what you want (That's what you get) / Ring-a-rosey / Flirting in the shadows / Self defence / High volume love / Unfortunate cup of tea / Turn your face to the wall / Snakes' farewell to the Emerald Isle / Everything will be alright
MOOCD 008 / Jan '95 / Outlet

Horstall, Des

☐ EASY ROAD
SBDCD 1 / Oct '96 / Southbound

Horton, Big Walter

☐ ANN ARBOUR JAZZ & BLUES FESTIVAL VOL.4 (Horton, Big Walter/ King Biscuit Boys)
Little car blues: *King Biscuit Boys* / Me and the devil blues: *King Biscuit Boys* / Down so long: *King Biscuit Boys* / Cool drink of water blues: *King Biscuit Boys* / Bricks in my pillow: *King Biscuit Boys* / Sweet black angel: *King Biscuit Boys* / It's too bad: *King Biscuit Boys* / Mr. Down Child: *King Biscuit Boys* / Walter's slow blues: *Horton, Big Walter* / Hard hearted woman: *Horton, Big Walter* / Swingin' blues: *Horton, Big Walter* / That ain't it: *Horton, Big Walter* / Trouble in mind: *Horton, Big Walter* / St. Louis blues: *Horton, Big Walter* / Honeydripper (Walter jumps one): *Horton, Big Walter* / It hurts me too: *Horton, Big Walter*
NEXCD 285 / Aug '96 / Sequel

☐ BIG WALTER HORTON WITH CAREY BELL (Horton, Big Walter & Carey Bell)
Have a good time / Christine / Lovin' my baby / Little boy blue / Can't hold out much longer / Under the sun / Tell me baby / Have mercy / That ain't it / Temptation blues / Trouble in mind
ALCD 4702 / May '93 / Alligator

☐ LITTLE BOY BLUE
JSPCD 208 / Jan '88 / JSP

☐ MOUTH HARP MAESTRO
Jumpin' blues / Hard hearted woman / Cotton patch hot foot / I'm in love with you baby / What's the matter with you / Black gal / Go 'long woman / Little boy blues / Blues in the morning
CDCH 252 / Nov '93 / Ace

Horton, Johnny

☐ EARLY YEARS, THE (4CD Set)
Smoky Joe's barbecue / Devilish love light / Candy Jones / Bawlin' Baby / It's a long rocky road / Plaid and calico / Done rovin' / On the banks of the beautiful Nile / Mean mean son of a gun / Happy millionaire / My home in Shelby County / Coal smoke, valve oil and steam / Talk gobbler, talk / Rhythm in my baby's walk / Birds 'n' butterflies / Shadows on the old bayou / Go and wash those dirty feet / Words / Betty Lorraine / Somebody's rockin' my broken heart / Honky tonk Jelly Roll blues / Love and tell / I wish heartaches were strangers / Confusion / Two eyed Sunday pants / Down that river road / Egg money / Confusion / First train headin' South / Somebody's rockin' my broken heart (solo) / Honky tonk Jelly Roll blues (demo 1) / Won't you love me, love, love me / Why did it happen to me / You, you, you / Broken hearted gypsy / All for the love of a girl / My heart stopped, trembled and died / I'm a fishin' man / Where do you think you would stand / Devil made a masterpiece / Because I'm a jealous man / I'm the one that breaks in two / Train with the rhumba beat / 'Cause you're the one for me / None of you but all of me / Dark haired beauty from Cuba / Tennessee Jive / SS Lureline / I won't get dreamy eyed / Two red lips and warm red wine / I won't forget / Mansion you stole / Rest of your life / (I wished for an angel but) the devil sent me you / Shadows on the old bayou (demo recordings 1) / Somebody's rockin' my broken heart(demo rec 1) / Talk gobbler talk (demo recordings 1) / Smoky Joe's barbecue (Demo) / This won't be the first time / Child's side of life / Another women wears my wedding ring / Move down the line / Hey sweet sweet thing / No true love / Big wheels rollin' / Journey with no end / There'll never be another Mary / Devil made a masterpiece (Mercury version) / Back to my back street / You don't move me anymore baby / Ha ha and moonface / Ridin' the sunshine special / Where are you / Train with the rhumba beat / Broken hearted gypsy (Mercury Recordings) / Meant so little to you / You cry in the door of your mansion / Coal smoke, valve oil and steam (dot overdubs) / Dev'lish lovelight / Mean mean son of gun / Talk gobbler talk (dot overdubs) / Shadows on the old bayou (dot overdubs) / In my home in Shelby County (dot overdubs) / Go and wash those dirty feet (dot overdubs) / Smoky Joe's barbecue / Done rovin (briar overdubs) / It's a long rocky road (briar overdubs) / Smoky Joe's barbecue / Mean mean son of gun / Devilish lovelight / Coal smoke, valve oil and steam (briar overdubs) / Words (briar overdubs) / Shadows on the old bayou (briar overdubs) / On the banks of the beautiful Nile (briar) / In my home in Shelby County (briar overdubs) / Go and wash those dirty feet (briar overdubs) / Talk, gobbler talk (briar overdubs) / You, you, you / All for the love of a girl / Bob Sullivan stomp
BCD 16258 / Jul '98 / Bear Family

☐ JOHNNY HORTON 1956-1960 (4CD Set)
I'm a one woman / Honky tonk man / I'm ready if you're willing / I got a hole in my pirogue / Take me like I am / Sugar coated baby / I don't like I did / Hooray for that little difference / I'm coming home / Over loving you / She know why / Honky tonk mind (the woman I need) / Tell me baby I love her / Goodbye lonesome, hello baby doll / I'll do it everytime / You're my baby / Let's take the long way home / Lover's rock / Honky tonk hardwood floor / Wild one / Everytime I'm kissing you / Lonesome and heartbroken / Seven come eleven / I can't forget you / Wise to the ways of a woman / Out in New Mexico / Tetched in the head / Just walk a little closer / Don't use my heart for a stepping stone / I love you baby / Counterfeit love / Mr. Moonlight / All grown up / Got the bull by the horns / When it's springtime in Alaska / Whispering pines / Battle of New Orleans / All for the love of a girl / Lost highway / Sam Magee / Cherokee Boogie / Golden Rocket / Joe's been a gittin' there / First train headin' South / Sal's got a sugar lip / Words / Johnny reb / Ole slew foot / They shined up rudolph's nose / Electrified donkey / Same old tale crow told me / Sink the Bismarck / Ole slew foot (CD 3) / Miss Marcy / Sleepy eyed John / Mansion you stole / They'll never take her love from me / Sinking of the Reuben James / Jim Bridger / Battle of Bull Run / Snow shoe thompson / John paul jones / Comanche / Young abe lincoln / O'leary's cow / Johnny freedom / Go north / North to alaska / Rock is / Land line / Hank and joe and me / Sleeping at the foot of the bed / Old blind barnabas / Evil hearted me / Hot in the sugarcane field / You don't move me anymore baby / Gosh darn wheel / Broken hearted gypsy / Church by the side of the road / Vanishing race / Broken hearted gypsy / That boy got the habit / Hot in the sugarcane field / You don't move anymore baby (CD 4) / Church by the side of the road (CD 4) / I just don't like this kind of livin' / Take it like a man / Hank and joe and me (CD 4) / Old blind baranbas (CD 4) / Empty bed blues / Rock Island line / Shake, rattle and roll / A / Sleeping at the foot of the bed / Old dan tucker / Gosh darn wheel (CD 4) / From memphis to mobile / Back up train / Schottische in texas / My heart stopped, trembled and died / Alley gir ways / How you gonna make it / Witch walking baby / Down that river road / Big wheels rollin' / I got a slow leak in my heart / What will i do without you / Janey / Streets of dodge / Give me back my picture and you can keep the frame
BCD 15470 / May '91 / Bear Family

☐ ROCKIN' ROLLIN' JOHNNY HORTON
Sal's got a sugar lip / Honky tonk hardwood floor / Honky tonk man / I'm coming home / Tell my baby I love her / Woman I need / First train headin' South / Lover's rock / All grown up / Electrified donkey / Sugar coated baby / Let's take the long way home / Ole slew foot / Sleepy eyed John / Wild one / I'm ready if you're willing
BCD 15543 / Oct '90 / Bear Family

Horton, Pug

☐ DON'T GO AWAY
By myself / Sweetheart o'mine / I'll string along with you / Don't go away / Tipperary / Miss my lovin' time / If / Breezin' along / I can dream / Melancholy / Send a little love my way / I found a new baby
ACD 212 / Apr '94 / Audiophile

Horton, Walter

☐ HARP LEGENDS SERIES VOL.1, THE (Horton, Walter & Carey Bell)
Two old maids / 85% / Walter's shuffle / Crosscut saw / Little boy blue / Blues with a feeling / I cry for you / Second hand man / Country girl / Last night / Walter's swing / Hoochie coochie
KATCD 104 / 29 Sep '97 / Catfish

☐ LITTLE BOY BLUE
I cry for you / Lord knows I tried / Country girl / Walter's shuffle / Little boy blue / It's not easy / Two old maids / What's on your worried mind / Walter's swing
JSPCD 806 / Jun '98 / JSP

Horzu

☐ DIE RITTER DER SCHWARFELRUNDE
MOVE 7015CD / Jul '95 / Move

Hosokawa, Masahiko

☐ LIKE A SHIMMERING OF HOT AIR (2CD Set)
BELLE 96306 / Jun '97 / Belle Antique

Hoss

☐ DO YOU LEAVE HERE OFTEN
MONGO 001 / 27 Apr '98 / Mongo

Hostility

☐ BRICK
CM 77103CD / Jan '96 / Century Media

Hot Boogie Chillun

☐ SWEETS
She's gone / Leave me alone / You better / I'm coming home / Dirty old man / Fucking sweet / Dirty robber / Shot of love / Talking 'bout you / Yes or no / Have love will travel / He's waiting / Dinosaur
FCD 3045 / May '97 / Fury

Hot Chocolate

☐ COLLECTION, THE
Love is life / You could've been a lady / I believe (in love) / You'll always be a friend / Brother Louie / Rumours / Emma / Cheri babe / Disco queen / Child's prayer / You sexy thing / Don't stop it now / Man to man / Heaven is in the back seat of my cadillac
CDGOLD 1064 / Oct '96 / EMI Gold

☐ GIRL CRAZY
SE 865652 / Mar '96 / Disky

☐ GREATEST HITS
You sexy thing / It started with a kiss / Brother Louie / Girl crazy / So you win again / Put your love in me / Love is life / I'll put you together again / No doubt about it / Every one's a winner / Emma / I gave you my heart (Didn't I) / You could've been a lady / Don't stop it now / Child's prayer / What kinda boy you looking for (girl) / I believe (In love) / Are you getting enough happiness
CDEMTV 73 / 1 Dec '97 / EMI

☐ GREATEST HITS
So you win again / Put your love in me / Every one's a winner / I'll put you together again / Mindless boogie / Going through the motions / No doubt about it / Are you getting enough of what makes you happy / Love me to sleep / You'll never be so wrong / Girl crazy / It started with a kiss / Chances / What kinda boy you looking for (girl) / Tears on the telephone / I gave you my heart (didn't I)
CDMFP 6130 / Nov '95 / Music For Pleasure

☐ REST OF THE BEST OF HOT CHOCOLATE, THE
Heaven is in the back seat of my cadillac / Man to man / You could've been a lady / Rumours / Mary Anne / You'll always be a friend / Mindless boogie / Heartache no.9 / Cheri babe / Going through the motions / Blue night / Every one's a winner / You'll never be so wrong / I'm sorry / Chances / Tears on the telephone / Love me to sleep / You sexy thing (remix)
CDGO 2060 / Sep '94 / EMI

Hot Club De Norvege

☐ PORTRAIT OF DJANGO
HCRCD 83 / Feb '97 / Night & Day

Hot Club Of San Francisco

☐ HOT CLUB OF SAN FRANCISCO, THE
CCD 1006 / Jul '98 / Clarity

Hot Damn

☐ BIG FAT LOVER
HELL 41CD / Oct '97 / Hell Yeah

☐ HIGH HEELS SLUT
HELLYEAH 031CD / Sep '95 / Hell Yeah

Hot Gammes

☐ OUVERTURE
IMP 944 / Nov '96 / IMP

Hot Knives

☐ LIVE 'N' SKANKIN'
Cryin' / Alcoholic nightmare / Don't go away / Dick Barton / Turkey stomp / Doing alright / Skin up Harry / Believe it / Driving me mad / She's a lady / Liquidator / Holsten boys / Rio / WIN / Jack The Ripper / Dust of death / Double barrel / Al Capone
SKACD 104 / 22 Jun '98 / House Of Ska

☐ WAY THINGS/BLACK (Hot Knives & Liquidators)
PHZCD 82 / Sep '94 / Unicorn

Hot Pastrami

☐ WITH A LITTLE HORSERADISH ON THE SIDE
GV 158CD / May '94 / Global Village

Hot Rize

☐ HOT RIZE
Blue night / Empty pocket blues / Nellie Kane / High on a mountain / Ain't I been good to you / Powwow the Indian boy / Prayer bells of heaven / This here bottle / Ninety nine years (and one dark day) / Old Dan Tucker / Country boy rock 'n' roll / Standing in the need of prayer / Durham's reel / Midnight on the highway
FF 70206 / Sep '96 / Flying Fish

☐ RADIO BOOGIE
Radio boogie / Ain't gonna work tomorrow / Wild Bill Jones / Land of enchantment / Man in the middle / I long for the hills / Just ain't / No brakes / Walkin' the dog / Sweetest song I sing / Tom and Jerry / Gone but not forgotten
FF 70231 / 6 Oct '97 / Flying Fish

☐ RED KNUCKLES AND THE TRAILBLAZERS/IN CONCERT
Travellin' blues / Honky tonk man / Slade's theme / Dixie cannonball / I know my baby loves me / Trailblazers theme / Always late / Honky tonk song / Kansas city star / Waldo's discount donuts / Boot heel drag / Window up above / You're gonna change (or I'm gonna leave) / Long gone John from bowling green / Let me love you one more time / Goin' across the sea / My little darlin' / I've been all around this world / I'm gonna sleep with one eye open / Martha White theme / Sally Goodin / Your light leads me on / Sugarfoot rag / Intro of Red Knuckles and The Trailblazers / Texas hambone blues / Wendell's fly swatters / Oh Mona / Rank stranger / Shady grove
FF 70107 / '89 / Flying Fish

☐ SHADES OF THE PAST (Hot Rize Presents Red Knuckles & The Trailblazers) (Red Knuckles & The Trailblazers)
Travellin' blues / Honky tonk man / Slade's theme / Dixie cannonball / I know my baby loves me / Trailblazer theme / Always late / Honky tonk song / Kansas City song / Waldo's discount donuts / Boot hill drag / Window up above / You're gonna change (or I'm gonna leave) / Long gone John from Bowling Green
SHCD 3767 / Jul '88 / Sugar Hill

☐ TAKE IT HOME
Colleen Malone / Rocky road blues / Voice in the wind / Bending blades / Gone fishing / Think of what you've done / Climb the ladder / Money to burn / Bravest cowboy / Lamplighting time in the valley / Where the wild river rolls / Old rounder / Tenderly calling (Home, come on home)
SHCD 3784 / Oct '90 / Sugar Hill

☐ TRADITIONAL TIES
Hard pressed / If I should wander back tonight / Walk the way the wind blows / Hear Jerusalem moan / Frank's blues / Lost John / Montana cowboy / Footsteps so near / Leather britches / Working on a building / John Henry / Keep your lamp trimmed and burning
SHCD 3748 / Mar '89 / Sugar Hill

☐ UNTOLD STORIES
Are you tired of me darling / Untold stories / Just like you / Country blues / Bluegrass / Won't you come and sing for me / Life's too short / You don't have to move the mountain / Shadows in my room / Don't make me believe / Wild ride / Late in the day
SHCD 3756 / Mar '89 / Sugar Hill

Hot Rod Gang

☐ GO AHEAD
Rocky guys / All mixed up / Sweet love on my mind / Long gone / Pride and joy / Wished I could / Real gone rocker / Riding along / Worryin' kind / Only one / Pretty boys (we ain't no) / Uuh what a night / I'm a hobo / All by myself / Ring of fire
RUMCD 011 / Feb '92 / Rumble

Hot Strings

☐ I SAW STARS
JCD 267 / Jun '96 / Jazzology

Hot Stuff

☐ CELEBRATING EARLY JAZZ
LACD 40 / Feb '95 / Lake

Hot Toddy

☐ THREE SHEETS TO THE WIND
Hogtie's reel / Dinkies / Jenny Dang the weaver / Wing commander Donald MacKenzie / MacArthur Road / Geese in the bog / Seagull / Curlew / New rigged ship / Three sheets to the wind / Jazz's broken bridge / Alessio's / Inverness gathering / Tam Bain's lum / Auld resting chair / Carnival reel / Old grey cat / La bastringue / Waiting for the federales / Walking on the moon / Think of a name for Friday / Neil Gow's lament / Euan's tune / Captain Campbell / Sailor's wife / Kiss for nothing / Troy's wedding / Paddy's leather breeches / Wind that shakes the barley / Carol wood / Glenburnie rant / Roscoff ferry / In and out of the harbour / Atholl highlanders / Long road home / Andy Renwick's ferret / Reconciliation / Dick Gossip's reel / Midshore / Wind on the heath / Cobbler's last waltz
CDLDL 1261 / Jul '97 / Lochshore

Hot Toddy Ceilidh Band

☐ PURELY MEDICINAL
CDLOC 1092 / Apr '96 / Klub

Hot Tuna

☐ CLASSIC HOT TUNA - ACOUSTIC
REL 2075 / Aug '96 / Relix

☐ CLASSIC HOT TUNA - ELECTRIC
REL 2076 / Aug '96 / Relix

☐ DOUBLE DOSE
Winin' boy blues / Keep your lamp trimmed and burning / Embryonic journey / Killing time in the Crystal City / I wish you would / Genesis / Extrication love song / Talking about you / Funky No. 7 / Serpent of dreams / Bowlegged woman, knock kneed man / I see the light / Watch the north wind rise / Sunrise dance with the Devil / I can't be satisfied
EDCD 397 / Nov '94 / Edsel

☐ LIVE IN JAPAN (At Stove's Yokohama 20/2/97)
79241220932 / 5 May '98 / Relix

Hot Vultures

☐ VULTURAMA (The Best Of The Hot Vultures)
South coast bound / Going across the mountains / Baby whats wrong / Preachers blues / Peach picking time in Georgia / So it goes / Put your money in your shoes / Pontchartrain / Taking my time / Blues got the world by the balls / TB blues / Pretty polly / New lonesome day / I love the life I live / Black dog blues / Lone wolf blues / Handful of rain / Mistreated mama / Sky / Spring of 65 / Chattanooga papa / Write me a few of your lines / Aloha aloha what's all this ere then
WEBE 0031 / 9 Mar '98 / Weekend Beatnik

Hotel Hunger

☐ AS LONG AS
EIGEN 013CD / Dec '94 / Pingo

Hotel X

☐ ENGENDERED SPECIES
SST 304CD / Jan '95 / SST

☐ LADDERS
SST 317CD / Nov '95 / SST

☐ RESIDENTIAL SUITE
SST 301CD / Jul '94 / SST

Hothouse Flowers

☐ BORN
You can love me now / Turn up the reverb / Forever more / Born / Pop song / Used to call it love / At last / Find the time / I believe / Learning to walk
8289662 / 25 May '98 / London

Houdinis

☐ COOEE
In a sentimental mood / Breathing out of habit / Obbele Boep m Pam / Take the 'A' train / No sweet, big deal / Down under / Wrong track / Gibberish / Mood indigo
CHR 70045 / Sep '97 / Challenge

☐ HYBRID
CHR 70004 / Aug '95 / Challenge

☐ PLAY THE BIG FIVE
CHR 70027 / Nov '95 / Challenge

Houghton S

☐ POSITIVE DIRECTION
MRCC 1002 / 17 Nov '97 / Marston

☐ TRUTH
MRCCD 1008 / 17 Nov '97 / Marston

Houghton Weavers

☐ BEST OF HOUGHTON WEAVERS, THE
Ballad of Wigan Pier / Where do you go from here / We want to work / Martians have landed in Wigan / Blackpool belle / Maggie / All for me grog / Home boys home / When you were sweet sixteen / Rose of Tralee / Old miner / Mist over the Mersey / Room in the sky / Dutchman / On the banks of the roses / God must love the poor / That stranger is a friend / Will ye go lassie go / Success to the Weavers / Minguley boat song
CDSL 8272 / Sep '95 / Music For Pleasure

Houghton, Michael

☐ WORSHIP HIM ON THE SAXOPHONE
I draw near / There's a wilderness / Jesus Christ / Once again / To be in your presence / Come and see / You are beautiful beyond description / How long o Lord / He paid the price / I long for you / When peace is like a river / I will offer up my life
SPND 014 / Jun '98 / Spirit Of Praise

Houghton, Steven

☐ STEVEN HOUGHTON
Wind beneath my wings / Ain't no sunshine / You don't know me / Air that I breathe / Truly / Wonderful world / You'll never walk alone / You send me / Sorry seems to be the hardest word / We've got tonight / First time ever I saw your face
74321542592 / 17 Nov '97 / RCA

Houl Yer Whist Folk Band

☐ HISTORICAL FOLK SONGS OF ULSTER
On Boyne's red shore / William's march / My Grandfather died / Orange Maid of Silgo / Lurgan town / Biddy McDowell / Battle of Garagh / Derry's walls / Union crusade / Bleacher / Aghalee heroes / Drowning of Willie Robinson / Crimson Banner
OASCD 3005 / Apr '97 / Outlet

Houlind, Doc

☐ LIVE AT THE FEMO JAZZ 1996 (Houlind, Doc Ragtime Band & John Boutte)
MECCACD 2007 / May '97 / Music Mecca

Houmark, Karsten

☐ DAWN (Houmark, Karsten Quartet)
STCD 4211 / May '97 / Storyville

☐ FOUR (Houmark, Karsten Quartet)
Four / Again and again / Rangoon / Little man / Simple song / Blue planet / B flat for Bob / Waltz for Kenny
STCD 4197 / Mar '95 / Storyville

Houn, Fred

☐ TOMORROW IS NOW (Houn, Fred & The Afro-Asian Music Ensemble)
1211172 / Nov '93 / Soul Note

Hounslow, Keith

☐ ELATION
NEW 1033 / Nov '96 / Australian Jazz

House Band

☐ ANOTHER SETTING
GL 1143CD / Jul '94 / Green Linnet

☐ GROUNDWORK
Trip to amnesia / Diamantina drover / Anti-social worker / For the sake of example / Tornado two-step/The Cooper/The woodpecker / Joy after sorrow / War party / Cobb/Slip jig/The metric fox / Pit stands idle / Here's the tender coming / Four courts/ Fox on the prowl / Major Harrison's fedora
GLCD 1132 / Mar '94 / Green Linnet

☐ OCTOBER SONG
Tuning phrase / Zakynthos jig / Seven yellow gypsies / Three rusty swords/Dusty miller / Factory girl / Risipiti/Mairtin O'Connors / October song / War hent berc'hed / Grey funnel line / End of the world / Rock in the mountain
GLCD 1190 / May '98 / Green Linnet

☐ ROCKALL
GLCD 1174 / Aug '96 / Green Linnet

☐ STONETOWN
Skepper schotish-schotish fra lyo / Lonesome drunkards walk stonetown / Eliz iza / Sunday's best / New tobacco / Rolling waves ryans / Final trawl / Killybegs highland / Charlie O'Neils / Rond De Loudeac / Here come the weak / On the turn / Hernons / Phoenix / Geordie / Wals voor polle / Baldazka
HARCD 019 / Nov '91 / Harbour Town

☐ VERY BEST OF THE HOUSE BAND, THE
REMCD 511 / Feb '98 / Reactive

☐ WORD OF MOUTH
Walls of troy / Dusty miller-the county ground / Lady mary hays favourite scotch measure-triti putl / Wild roving / An dro d'ogham-au place de serbie / Happy one-step-green willis / From a distance / Peacock-moldavian song / Bonny light horseman-the highland brigade at magersfontein
GLCD 3045 / Oct '93 / Green Linnet

House Nation Allstars

☐ HOUSE MIX VOL.2
DST 055702813 / Nov '97 / SPV

House Of 909

☐ SOUL REBELS (Various Artists)
Slotech soul: *Slotech Soul* / Movin' on: *Future Soul Orchestra* / Deep inside: *Voices From Beyond* / Distant city: *Voices From Beyond* / Shakedown: *Shakedown* / Love of god: *Future Soul Orchestra* / Last dance: *House Of 909* / Love of god: *Future Soul Orchestra* / Main event: *House Of 909* / Life's journey: *Future Soul Orchestra* / Soul searcher: *Voices From Beyond* / Shakedown: *Shakedown* / Pussycutz: *House Of 909*
PAGANCD 1003 / 22 Sep '97 / Pagan

House Of Freaks

☐ INVISIBLE JEWEL
OUT 1172 / Sep '97 / Brake Out

House Of Love

☐ BEST OF THE HOUSE OF LOVE, THE
I don't know why I love you / Crush me / Destroy the heart / Girl with the loneliest eyes / Christine / Beatles and the Stones / Never / Shine On / Marble / Feel / Let's talk about you / Safe / You don't understand / Yer eyes / Loneliness is a gun
5583232 / 3 Aug '98 / Fontana

☐ HOUSE OF LOVE
Hanah / Shine on / Beatles and the Stones / Shake and crawl / Hedonist / I don't know why I love you / Never / Somebody's got to love you / In a room / Blind / 32nd Floor / So dest
8422932 / Jan '96 / Fontana

☐ HOUSE OF LOVE/SPY IN THE HOUSE OF LOVE (2CD Set)
Hanah / Shine on / Beatles and the Stones / Snake and crawl / Hedonist / I don't know why I love you / Never / Somebody's got to love you / In a room / Blind / Thirty second floor / Se Dest / Safe / Marble / D song '89 / Scratched inside / Phone / Put the fool down / Ray / Love II / Baby teen / Love III / Soft as fire / Love IV / No fire / Love V
5286022 / Aug '95 / Fontana

House Of Pain

☐ SAME AS IT EVER WAS
XLCD 115 / Jun '94 / XL

House Of Rhythm

☐ IN A DIFFERENT STYLE (2CD Set)
DOXOCD 264 / Jul '96 / Dojo

House, Simon

☐ YASSASIM
Yassasim / Orion / Northlands / Omedlok rides again / Laithwaite stardrive / Neuroscape / Sherwood / Oldayze
EBSSCD 115 / 24 Nov '97 / Emergency Broadcast System

House, Son

☐ DELTA BLUES (Congress Sessions From Field Recordings)
Levee camp blues / Government fleet blues / Walkin' blues / Shetland pony blues / Delta blues / Special rider blues / Low down dirty dog blues / Depot blues / American defense / Am I right or wrong / County farm blues / Pony blues / Jinx blues
BCD 118 / Jul '91 / Biograph

☐ LIBRARY OF CONGRESS SESSIONS, THE
Levee camp blues / Government fleet blues / Special rider blues / Low down dirty dog blues / Walkin' blues / Depot blues / Camp hollars
TMCD 02 / Apr '90 / Travellin' Man

☐ ORIGINAL DELTA BLUES
Death letter / Pearline / Louise Mcghee / John the revelator / Empire state express / Preachin' blues / Grinnin' in your face / Sundown / Levee camp moan / Pony blues / Downhearted blues / Motherless children / President Kennedy / Yonder comes my mother
4898912 / 20 Jul '98 / Sony Blues

☐ SON HOUSE AND THE GREAT DELTA BLUES SINGERS (1928-1930) (House, Son & The Great Delta Blues Singers)
DOCD 5002 / Feb '92 / Document

☐ SON HOUSE IN CONCERT
It's so hard / Judgement day / New York central / True friend is hard to find / Preachin' the blues / Change your mind
CDBM 020 / '91 / Blue Moon

Household Cavalry Band

☐ BEATING RETREAT
BNA 5088 / Sep '93 / Bandleader

Household Regiment Bands

☐ GUARDS IN CONCERT, THE
Royale / Capital city / La Ronde / Academic festival overture / Arrival of the Queen of Sheba / Phantom of the opera / Intermezzo / Can can for band / Cavalry of the steppes / Entry of the boyards / Les miserables / Slave's chorus / Earl of Oxford's march / Sospan fach / Star of St. Patrick / Great gate of kiev
BNA 5042 / '91 / Bandleader

Housemartins

☐ LONDON 0 HULL 4
Happy hour / Get up off our knees / Flag day / Anxious / Reverend's revenge / Sitting on a fence / Sheep / Over there / Think for a minute / We're not deep / Lean on me / Freedom / I'll be your shelter (just like a shelter)
8283472 / Jan '95 / Go Discs

☐ NOW THAT'S WHAT I CALL QUITE GOOD (Greatest Hits)
I smell winter / Bow down / Think for a minute / There is always something there to remind me / Mighty ship / Sheep / I'll be your shelter (just like a shelter) / Five get over excited / Everybody's the same / Build / Step outside / Flag day / Happy hour / You've got a friend / He ain't heavy, he's my brother / Freedom / People who grinned themselves to death / Caravan of love / Light is always green / We're not deep / Me and the farmer / Lean on me
8283442 / Jan '95 / Go Discs

☐ PEOPLE WHO GRINNED THEMSELVES TO DEATH, THE
People who grinned themselves to death / I can't put my finger on it / Light is always green / World's on fire / Pirate aggro / We're not going back / Me and the farmer / Five get over excited / Johannesburg / Bow down / You better be doubtful / Build
8283312 / Oct '92 / Go Discs

Housewreckers

☐ FOR A FEW WRECKS MORE
GRCD 6050 / Nov '96 / Goofin'

☐ WATCH OUT
GRCD 6021 / Jan '97 / Goofin'

Housey Doingz

☐ DOING IT (LIVING IT, LOVING IT, LARGIN' IT)
Poet / Brothers / Piano I / Ride / Flying saucer / Lonely tribe / Ambidextrous left / Piano II / Curly wurly / No smoke: *Matthew B* / Space bunny: *Space Bunny* / Reggae's house: *Francis, Terry* / Lonely / As you cry: *Francis, Terry* / Naff off / Naff on
PAGANCD 1002 / Jul '97 / Pagan

Housley, Chris

☐ TIME TO DANCE
SAV 184CD / May '93 / Savoy

Houston, Bee Bee

☐ HUSTLER (Houston, Bee Bee & The Highsteppers)
You think I'm your good thing / Busy Bee / Be proud to be a black man / Hustler / Break away / Things gonna get better / Never / Lovesick man / Freddy's bag / Any time / Woke up this morning / When I go out / Any time / Lovesick man / Charlie's bag / Don't take your love from me / Blues for Rupez
ARHCD 9008 / 16 Mar '98 / Arhoolie

Houston, Cisco

☐ FOLKWAYS YEARS 1944-61
SFCD 40059 / Jun '94 / Smithsonian Folkways

Houston, Clint

☐ WATERSHIP DOWN
STCD 4150 / Feb '90 / Storyville

Houston, Dudley

☐ TO THE WORLD
HRCD 005 / 17 Nov '97 / Orchid

Houston, Joe

☐ CORNBREAD & CABBAGE GREENS
Cornbread and cabbage greens / Jay's boogie / Blues after hours / Sentimental journey / Celebrity club drag / Gordon's knot / All night long / Ruth's rock / Flying home / Walkin' home / Lester leaps in / I cover the waterfront / Troubles and worries / Huggy boy radio ad / Rockin' and boppin' / She's gone / Anything / Richie's roll / Thom's tune / Teen-age hop / Well, well my love / Mambo / Shake it up / Coastin' / Midnight
CDCHD 395 / Mar '92 / Ace

Houston, Penelope

☐ BIRD BOYS
Harry Dean / Talking with you / Voices / Living dolls / Out of my life / Waiting room / Bed of lies / Wild mountain thyme / Putting me in the ground / Full of wonder / Summers of war / Stoli / Rock 'n' roll show / All that crimson
NORM 173CD / Nov '93 / Normal

☐ BIRDBOYS
Harry dean / Talking with you / Voices / Living dolls / Out of my life / Waiting room / Bed of lies / Wild mountain thyme / Putting me in the ground / Full of wonder / Summers of war / Stoll / Rock'n'roll show / All that crimson
NORMAL 173CD / Sep '97 / Normal

☐ KARMAL APPLE
NORMAL 183CD / Sep '97 / Normal

☐ SILK PURSE
RTS 2CD / Mar '94 / Return To Sender

☐ WHOLE WORLD, THE
NORMAL 153CD / Sep '97 / Normal

Houston, Thelma

☐ BEST OF THELMA HOUSTON, THE
Don't leave me this way / It's the last thing I do / Saturday night Sunday morning / Love's comin' on / Midnight moon / I wanna be in love again / Can't we try / Jumpin' jack flash / I'm here again / It's just me feeling good / Memories / I've got the devil in me / Cheap lovin' don't make me pay / Am I expecting too much / If this was the first song / Baby I love you too much / Only the beginning / And you've got me / It's a lifetime thing
5544722 / 3 Aug '98 / Spectrum

Houston, Whitney

☐ I'M YOUR BABY TONIGHT
I'm your baby tonight / My name is not Susan / All the man that I need / Lover for life / Anymore / Miracle / I belong to you / Who do you love / We didn't know / After we make love / I'm knockin'
261039 / Nov '90 / Arista

☐ PREACHER'S WIFE, THE (Original Soundtrack)
I believe in you and me / Step by step / Joy / Hold on, help is on the way / Go to the rock / I love the Lord / Who'd imagine a king / Lord is my shepherd / Somebody bigger than you and I / My heart is calling / You were loved / I believe in you and me / Step by step / Joy to the world
74321441252
07822189512 / Dec '96 / Arista

☐ WHITNEY
I wanna dance with somebody (who loves me) / Just the lonely talking again / Love will save the day / Didn't we almost have it all / So emotional / Where you are / Love is a contact sport / You're still my man / For the love of you / Where do broken hearts go / I know him so well
258141 / May '87 / Arista

☐ WHITNEY HOUSTON
How will I know / Take good care of my heart / Greatest love of all / Hold me / You give good love / Thinking about you / Someone for me / Saving all my love for you / Nobody loves me like you do / All at once
610359 / Aug '86 / Arista

Hoven Droven

☐ GROV
Slentbjenn / Timas hans / Myhrpolska / Grovhaling / Tjangel / Okynnesvals / Klarinettpolska / Grottan / Kerstins brudpolska / LP Schottis / Skvadern / Stilla / Jaintlandssangvalsen
XOUCD 114CD / May '97 / Xource

☐ HIA HIA
Hia hia amour / Farmors brudpolska / Trallpolska / Lillht green / Arepolska / Kjellingen / Kottpolska / Skogspolska / Myhrhalling / Dajmen / Hamburger / Bruvals
XOUCD 110 / May '97 / Xource

Hovercraft

☐ AKATHISIA
Quiet room / Angular momentum / Haloparidol / Vagus nerve / De-orbit burn
BFFP 135CD / Jan '97 / Blast First

Hovhannessian, Karineh

☐ MUSIC OF ARMENIA VOL.4, THE (The Kanon)
131182 / Nov '96 / Celestial Harmonies

Howard, Adina

☐ DO YOU WANNA RIDE
You got me humpin' / You can be my nigga / Let's go to da sugar shack / It's all about you / Baby come over / Coolin' in the studio / Horny for your love / My up and down / You don't have to cry / Do you wanna ride / I wants ta eat / Freak like me / If we make love tonight
7559617572 / Feb '95 / Atlantic

☐ WELCOME TO FANTASY ISLAND
Welcome to my Queendom / (Freak) And u know it / All about you / Personal freak / Crank me up / Sexual needs / Could've got away / Another level / T-shirt and panties / I'll be damned if I apologise / Don't come too fast / Take me home / Lay him down / Ain't no need / Satisfied
7559620362 / 23 Mar '98 / Mecca Don/ Elektra

Howard, Agni

☐ HIMALAYAN NIGHTS VOL.1 (Sitar And Tabla For Relaxation) (Howard, Agni & Lewis)
CSL 02 / Feb '98 / Clarity Sound & Light

☐ HIMALAYAN NIGHTS VOL.2 (Raga Omar Khayyam) (Howard, Agni & Lewis)
CSL 11 / Feb '98 / Clarity Sound & Light

Howard, Camille

☐ ROCK ME DADDY
Boogie and the blues / You don't love me / You used to be mine / Unidentified boogie / Has your love grown cold / Mood I'm in / Gotta have a little lovin' / How long can I go on like this / Cry over you / O sole mio boogie / Within this heart of mine / Boogie in G / I'm blue / Rock me Daddy / Broken memories sad and blue / I ain't got the spirit / Shrinking up fast / Easy / Money blues / Schuberts serenade boogie / You lied to me baby / Real gone Daddy
CDCHD 511 / Jan '94 / Ace

Howard, Eddy

☐ EDDY HOWARD
CCD 029 / Oct '93 / Circle

Howard, George

☐ ATTITUDE ADJUSTMENT
Watch your back / Best friend / One last time / Diana's blues / Attitude adjustment / Let's unwind / Been thinking / Whole lot of drum in you
GRP 98392 / Jan '96 / GRP

☐ DANCING IN THE SUN
Love will find a way / Dancing in the sun / Quiet as it's kept / In love / Telephone / Stay with me / Moods
GRP 96262 / 25 May '98 / GRP

☐ MIDNIGHT MOOD
Within your eyes / Exodus / Midnight mood / Africa / Silent thoughts / Still in love / Smooth / Find your way / Africa
GRP 99022 / 9 Feb '98 / GRP

☐ THERE'S A RIOT GOIN' ON
Brave and strong / Runnin' away / Time / Family affair / Smiling (you caught me) / Africa talks to you / Poet / Luv 'n' haight / Thank you for taking me to Africa
8214312 / 4 May '98 / Blue Note

☐ VERY BEST AND THEN SOME, THE
Love will follow / Baby come to me / Everything I miss at home / When summer comes / Diane's blues / Home far away / Midnight mood / Cross your mind / Find your way / Love will find a way / Miracle
GRP 98852 / 25 May '98 / GRP

Howard, Harlan

☐ ALL TIME FAVOURITE COUNTRY SONGWRITER
Busted / I fall to pieces / Heartaches by the number / Pick me up on your way down / Too many rivers / Everglades / Blizzard / Mary Ann regrets / Call me Mister In-Between / I've got a tiger by the tail / Above and beyond / I don't believe I'll fall in love today
379152 / Aug '96 / Koch International

Howard, Jason

☐ S'IO T'AMO (Great Italian Songs Of Love)
Musica proibita / Risveglio / In solitaria stanza / La seduzione / Ideale / L'ultima canzone / Nebbie / La Mattinata / Lasciati Amar / S'io t'amo / Vaga luna che inargenti / Fenesti che lucive / Pecche / Non ti scordar di me
SCD 2110 / Sep '97 / Sain

Howard, Joe

☐ JAZZ HIGHWAY 20
PS 007CD / Sep '95 / P&S

☐ SWINGIN' CLOSE IN
PS 005CD / Sep '95 / P&S

Howard, Johnny

☐ BEST OF THE DANSAN YEARS VOL.6, THE (Howard, Johnny Orchestra & Ray McVay Orchestra)
Easy to love (waltz) / True love waltz / Send in the clowns (waltz) / Just the way you are (slow foxtrot)' / All of you (slow foxtrot) / I love you samantha (slow foxtrot) / So in love (quickstep) / I get a kick out of you (quickstep) / On the street where you live (quickstep) / Pretty girl is like a melody (tango) / You do something to me (cha cha cha) / Let's do it (cha cha cha) / How deep is your love (cha cha cha) / Copacabana (samba) / It's alright with me (samba) / From this moment on (samba) / I've got you under my skin (rumba) / Night and day (rumba) / Don't cry for me argentina (rumba)
DACD 006 / Jul '92 / Dansan

☐ FOREVER DANCE (Howard, Johnny & His Orchestra)
Al no carrida (cha cha) / Guantanamera (cha cha) / I'll close my eyes (rumba) / Here's that rainy day (rumba) / Caravan (samba) / Tristeza (samba) / Go away (merengue) / Champ (jive) / Night has a thousand eyes (quickstep) / Everywhere you go (quickstep) / April in paris (foxtrot) / Romeo and juliet (foxtrot) / Hollywood (viennese waltz) / Golden earrings (tango) / What'll I do all alone (waltz) / Last waltz-auld lang syne (waltz)
CDTS 2001 / Nov '93 / Maestro

Howard, Kid

☐ LAVIDA
AMCD 54 / Oct '93 / American Music

Howard, Owen

☐ PENTAGON
CD 378572 / Nov '97 / Koch Jazz

☐ SOJOURN
378072 / Sep '96 / Koch Jazz

Howard, Rosetta

☐ ROSETTA HOWARD 1939-1947
JPCD 1514 / Dec '94 / Jazz Perspectives

Howards, Paul

☐ ELEGANCE AND DECADENCE
60233497042 / 5 May '98 / Os-Nix

Howe, Steve

☐ EARLY YEARS, THE (Howe, Steve & Bodast)
Do you remember / Beyond winter / Once in a lifetime / Black leather gloves / I want you / Tired towers / Mr. Jones / 1000 years / Nether Street / Nothing to cry for
C5CD528 / May '90 / See For Miles

☐ HOMEBREW (Unreleased Demos)
RPM 164 / Jun '96 / RPM

☐ MOTHBALLED SESSIONS 1964-1969
Maybellene / True to me / Howlin' for my baby / What to do / Leave me kitten alone / Don't know what to do / On the horizon / Stop, wait a minute / You're on your own / Why must I criticise / I don't mind / Finger poppin' / Mothballs / You never can stay in one place / Real life permanent dream / Claremount lake / Revolution / Hallucinations / Three jolly little dwarfs / My white bicycle / Kid was a killer / Come over stranger / Beyond winter / Nothing to cry for / Nether street
RPM 140 / Oct '94 / RPM

☐ MOTHBALLS
CLEO 2542 / 12 May '98 / Cleopatra

☐ QUANTUM GUITAR
Walk don't run / Collector / Light walls / Mosaic / Suddenly / Country viper / Mainland / Knights of carmelite / Paradox / Momenta / Sleep walk / Sovereigns / Totality / Solid ground / Great siege / Cacti garden / Southern accent
CSA 110 / 9 Mar '98 / Thunderbird

☐ SERAPHIM (Howe, Steve & Paul Sutin)
SPV 07689562 / Mar '96 / SPV

☐ VOYAGERS (Howe, Steve & Paul Sutin)
SPV 07689572 / Mar '96 / SPV

Howell, Carol

☐ MERRY DANCE
LCD 8008 / Aug '96 / Lizard

Howie B

☐ MUSIC FOR BABIES
Music for babies / Cry / Shag / Allergy / Away again / How to suckie / Here comes the tooth / On the way
5294642 / Mar '96 / Polydor

☐ TURN THE DARK OFF
Fizzy in my mouth/Your mouth / Hopscotch / Switch / Sore brown eyes / Take your partner by the hand: Howie B & Robbie Robertson / Limbo / Angels go bald too / Who's got the bacon / Baby sweetcorn (come here) / Butt meat
5379342 / Jul '97 / Polydor

Howie, Simon

☐ SIMON HOWIE & HIS SCOTTISH DANCE BAND
SHCD 001 / Jul '96 / Howie

Howle, Danielle

☐ ABOUT TO BURST
SMR 36CD / Jun '96 / Simple Machines

Howlin' Wolf

☐ AIN'T GONNA BE YOUR DOG (2CD Set)
Look-a-here baby / California blues / Worried all the time / Everybody's in the mood / Color and kind / Dorothy Mae / Sweet woman / Decoration day / Oh red / I'm not joking / Highway my friend / Hold your money / California blues / Stay here 'til my baby comes back / Come to me baby / So glad / Bluebird / My life / You ought to know / Nature / Walk to camp hall / Poor boy / My baby told me / Midnight blues / You can't put me out / Getting late / Wolf in the mood / My people's gone / Mama's baby / Tail dragger / Long green stuff / Joy to my soul / Poor wind that never change / Pop it to me / I had a dream / Big house / Tired of crying / Rollin' and tumblin' / More Howlin' Wolf talks / I ain't gonna be your dog no more / Woke up this morning / Ain't going down that dirt road
MCD 09349 / Apr '97 / Chess/MCA

☐ AUDIO ARCHIVE
Little red rooster / Moanin' at midnight / Down in the bottom / My life / Shake for me / Commit a crime / Back door man / You'll be mine / Highway 49 / Who's been talkin' / Goin' back home / Howlin' for my baby / Wang dang doodle / Tell me / Country sugar mama / Little baby / Hold onto your money / Spoonful / Built for comfort / Goin' down slow
CDAA 031 / Jun '92 / Tring

☐ GENUINE ARTICLE, THE (The Best Of Howlin' Wolf)
Moanin' at midnight / How many more years / I'm the wolf / Baby how long / Evil / Forty four / Smokestack lightnin' / I asked for water (she gave me gasoline) / Natchez burning / Who's been talkin' / Sittin' on top of the world / I've been abused / Howlin' for my baby (darling) / Wang dang doodle / Back door man / Spoonful / Down in the bottom / Little red rooster / I ain't superstitious / Goin' down slow / 300 pounds of joy / Killing floor / Dust my broom / Ain't goin' down that dirt road
MCD 11073 / Apr '97 / Chess/MCA

☐ HIS BEST
MCD 09375 / Jul '97 / Chess/MCA

☐ HOWLIN' AT THE SUN
Baby ride with me / How many more years / California boogie / Look a here baby / Smile at me / My baby walked off / My troubles and me / Mr. Highway man / Chocolate drop / Everybody's in the mood / Colour and kind / Bluebird / Dorothy Mae / Sweet woman (I got a woman) / Well that's alright / Decoration day / Oh red / Drinkin' CV wine / My last affair / Come back home / California blues
CPCD 8235 / Jan '97 / Charly

☐ HOWLIN' WOLF COLLECTOR'S EDITION
DVBC 9022 / Apr '95 / Deja Vu

☐ KILLING FLOOR
Highway 49 / Dust my broom / Rockin' the blues / Forty-four / Do the do / Little red rooster / All my life / I didn't mean to hurt your feelings / Howlin' for my darlin' / Commit a crime / Wang dang doodle / Built for comfort / Killing floor / Poor boy / Worried 'bout you / Going down slow
CDBM 121 / Oct '96 / Blue Moon

☐ LEGENDARY MASTERS SERIES, THE
Red rooster / Worried about you / Ain't superstitious / Goin' down slow / Commit a crime / I walked from Dallas / My mind is ramblin' / Rockin' daddy / Sittin' on top of the world / What a woman / Poor boy / Built for comfort
AIM 0003CD / 20 Oct '97 / Aim

☐ LIVE AND COOKIN' (At Alice's Revisited)
MCD 09339 / 23 Feb '98 / Chess/MCA

☐ LIVE IN CAMBRIDGE, MASS. 1966
422329 / Feb '97 / Last Call

☐ MASTERS, THE
Highway 49 / Dust my broom / Rockin' the blues / Forty four / Do the do / Little red rooster / All my life / I didn't mean to hurt your feelings / Howlin' for my darlin' / Commit a crime / Wang dang doodle / Built for comfort / Killing floor / Poor boy / Worried about you / Going down slow
EABCD 080 / 30 Mar '98 / Eagle

☐ MEMPHIS DAYS VOL.1 (Definitive Edition)
Oh red / My last affair / Come back home / California boogie / California blues / Look-a-here baby / Smile at me / My baby walked off / Drinkin' CV wine / My troubles and me / Chocolate drop / Mr. Highwayman / Bluebird blues / Color and kind / Everybody's in the mood / Dorothy Mae / I got a woman / Decoration day / Well that's alright / How many more years / Baby ride with me
BCD 15460 / Apr '89 / Bear Family

☐ MEMPHIS DAYS VOL.2 (Definitive Edition)
Baby ride with me / How many more years / Moanin' at midnight / Howlin' Wolf boogie / Wolf is at your door (howlin' for my baby) / Mr. Highwayman / Gettin' old and grey / Worried all the time / Saddle my pony / Oh red / My last affair / Come back home / Dorothy Mae / Oh red
BCD 15500 / Sep '90 / Bear Family

☐ POWER OF THE VOICE, THE
I ain't superstitious / Sittin' on top of the world / Built for comfort / Little red rooster / Highway 49 / Cause of it all / Killing floor / Brown skin woman / Sun is rising / I'm the wolf / House rockin' boogie / Dog me around / Keep what you got / My baby stole off / Crying at day break / Passing by blues / Poor boy / Commit a crime / Wang dang doodle / Do the do / Worried about my baby / Rockin' daddy
CD 52002 / '92 / Blues Encore

☐ REAL FOLK BLUES
Killing floor / Louise / Poor boy / Sittin' on top of the world / Nature / My country sugar mama (aka Sugar Mama) / Tail dragger / 300 pounds of joy / Natchez burning / Built for comfort / Ooh baby, hold me / Tell me what I've done
CHLD 19098 / Nov '92 / Chess/MCA

☐ RED ROOSTER
IMP 302 / Jul '95 / Iris Music

☐ RED ROOSTER, THE
Shake for me / Little red rooster / You'll be mine / Who's been talkin' / Wang dang doodle / Little baby / Spoonful / Goin' down slow / Down in the bottom / Back door man / Howlin' for my baby / Tell me / My baby walked off / Killing floor / Country sugar mama / My life / Goin' back home / Louise / Highway 49 / Hold onto your money / Built for comfort / I ain't superstitious / My last affair / Dorothy Mae / Commit a crime / Moanin' at midnight
GRF 026 / '93 / Tring

☐ RIDES AGAIN
House rockin' boogie / Crying at daybreak / Keep what you got / Dog me around / Moanin' at midnight / Chocolate drop / My baby stole off / I want your picture / Passing by blues / Worried about my baby / Driving this highway / Sun is rising / Riding in the moonlight / My friends / I'm the Wolf
CDCHD 333 / Oct '91 / Ace

☐ SMOKESTACK LIGHTNIN'
MCSTD 1960 / May '94 / MCA

☐ SPOONFUL
Smokestack lightnin' / Back door man / Evil / Tell me / Watergate blues / Tail dragger
CDRB 2 / Apr '94 / Charly

☐ TRIBUTE TO HOWLIN' WOLF, A (Various Artists)
Saddle my pony / Howlin' for my darling / Red rooster / Just like I treat you / Built for comfort / Ooh baby (hold me) / Ridin' in the moonlight / Back door man / Baby how long / Killing floor / Howlin' Wolf boogie / Smokestack lightnin' / Come to me baby
CD 83427 / Jul '98 / Telarc

☐ VERY BEST OF HOWLIN' WOLF, THE (& Roots Of The Blues No.3 Compilation/ 3CD Set)
Moanin' at midnight / How many more years / Wolf is at your door / Dorothy Mae / Work for your money / All night boogie / Neighbours / I'm the wolf / Baby how long / Evil / Forty four / Who will be next / Smokestack lightnin' / I asked for water (she gave me gasoline) / Natchez burning / Tell me / Sittin' on top of the world / Moanin' for my baby / I'm leaving you / I've been abused / Wang dang doodle / Back door man / Spoonful / Little baby / Down in the bottom / Shake for me / Little red rooster / You'll be mine / I ain't superstitious / Goin' down slow / Do the do / Trail dragger / Long green stuff / 300 Pounds of joy / Built for comfort / Killing floor / What a woman / Who's been talkin' / Poor boy / Rockin' Daddy / Life savers blues / Frankie / Big fat Mama blues / Blind Arthur's breakdown / Milk cow blues / Preachin' the blues / Do your duty / Brown skin girls / Back door blues / Evil hearted woman blues / Love in vain / Fox chase / I done got wise / Yancy stomp / Leaving the blues / You gonna miss me when I'm gone
VBCD 303 / Jul '95 / Charly

☐ WOLF IS AT YOUR DOOR, THE (2CD Set)
Somebody's in my home / My mind is ramblin' / I walked from Dallas / Streamline woman / Cause of it all / Do the do / Worried about you / Poor boy / Shake for me / Little red rooster / You'll be mine / Who's been talkin' / Wang dang doodle / Little baby / Spoonful / Goin' down slow / Down in the bottom / Back door man / Howlin' for my baby / Tell me / My baby walked off / Killing floor / My country sugar mama / My life / Goin' back home / Louise / Highway 49 / Hold on to your money / Built for comfort / I ain't superstitious / My last affair / Dorothy Mae / Commit a crime / Moanin' at midnight / Riding in the moonlight / Everybody's in the mood / Wolf is at your door (howlin' for my baby) / I better go now
422176 / May '94 / New Rose

Hoy, Johnny

☐ TROLLING THE HOOTCHY (Hoy, Johnny & The Bluefish)
CDTC 1151 / Apr '95 / Tonecool

☐ WALK THE PLANK (Hoy, Johnny & The Bluefish)
Love dog / You you you / AT / Honkytonk forgiveness / I'm tired / If you love me / P-man / Just another wheel / Opelousas sostan / Howlin' for my darling / Back where I belong / Rooster walk / Rocking my life away
CDTC 1166 / Apr '98 / Tonecool

☐ YOU GONNA LOSE YOUR HEAD (Hoy, Johnny & The Bluefish)
You better listen / Glad she's gone / Made for one / Another / Stand tall / Gong gong / Believer's blues / I want to see her / Mellow chick swing / Red door / Beer bellied man / I ain't got no home / Nobody else / Can't stand to sleep alone / Just to be with you
CDTC 1157 / Oct '96 / Tonecool

Hoydal, Annika

☐ OCEAN, THE
AMBIACD 3505 / Oct '97 / Ambia

HP Lovecraft

☐ HP LOVECRAFT LIVE
Wayfaring stranger / Drifter / It's about time / White ship / At the mountains of madness / Bag I'm in / I've never been wrong before / Country boy and Bleeker Street
EDCD 345 / Nov '91 / Edsel

☐ HP LOVECRAFT LIVE (11th May 1968)
SC 11008 / 22 Jun '98 / Sundazed

☐ THIS IS/HP II
10 / 22 Jun '98 / Britonic

HR

☐ ANTHOLOGY
SST 361CD / 3 Aug '98 / SST

☐ HUMAN RIGHTS
SST 117CD / Mar '88 / SST

☐ ROCK OF ENOCH
SST 274CD / May '93 / SST

☐ SINGIN' IN THE HEART
Fool's gold / Rasta time / Singin' in the heart / Treat street / Youthman sufferer / Fools gold (dub) / Don't trust no (shadows) / Youthman sufferer (dub)
SST 224CD / Sep '89 / SST

Hradistan

☐ MORAVIAN ECHOES
LT 0018 / Nov '95 / Lotos

☐ MORAVIAN SONGS AND DANCES
PS 65190 / Oct '97 / PlayaSound

Hsiao-Yueh, Tsai

☐ NAN-KOUAN VOL.1
C 559004 / Sep '93 / Ocora

☐ NAN-KOUAN VOL.2
C 560037 / Sep '93 / Ocora

☐ NAN-KOUAN VOL.3
C 560038 / Sep '93 / Ocora

☐ NAN-KOUAN VOL.4-6
C 560039/41 / Sep '93 / Ocora

Hua, Jiang Jian

☐ EARTH, THE
Jiang jiao xing / Yang guan san die / Er wuan ying yue / Hana / Murika muchibushi / Tai hu chuan / Chang yuan zong sheng / Yang guang zhao yao ze ta shiku e can / Cao yuan shang / Shima uta
JVC 90092 / May '97 / JVC World Library

Hubbard, Freddie

☐ ALL BLUES
All blues / God bless the child / Bolivia / Dear John
JWD 102217 / Apr '95 / JWD

☐ ARTISTRY OF FREDDIE HUBBARD, THE
Caravan / Bob's place / Happy times / Summertime / Seventh day
IMP 11792 / Feb '96 / Impulse Jazz

☐ BALLADS
Body and soul / But beautiful / Mirrors / Weaver of dreams / I wished I knew / Lament for booker
CDP 8566912 / Jul '97 / Blue Note

☐ BODY AND THE SOUL, THE
Body and soul / Carnival / Chocolate snake / Dedicated to you / Clarence's place / Aries / Skylark / I got it bad / Thermo
IMP 11832 / Sep '96 / Impulse Jazz

☐ BREAKING POINT
Breaking point / Far away / Blue frenzy / Blue frenzy (alt. take) / D minor mint / Mirrors / Mirrors (alt. take)
CDP 7841722 / 1 Jun '98 / Blue Note

☐ FACE TO FACE (Hubbard, Freddie & Oscar Peterson)
All blues / Thermo / Weaver of dreams / Portrait of Jennie / Tippin'
OJCCD 9372 / Nov '97 / Original Jazz Classics

☐ GOD BLESS THE CHILD
MM 65176 / Jun '98 / Music Masters

☐ HUB ART (Essence All-Stars)
HIBD 8005 / Feb '96 / Hip Bop

☐ JAZZ PROFILE
All or nothing at all / Karioka / Osie mae / Arietas / You're my everything / Hammer head / Blue frenzy / Jodo
CDP 8590712 / 6 Oct '97 / Blue Note

☐ KEYSTONE BOP VOL.2 (Friday/ Saturday)
One of another kind / 'Round midnight / Red clay / First light
PCD 241632 / Aug '96 / Prestige

☐ MINOR MISHAP
BLCD 760122 / Aug '89 / Black Lion

☐ NIGHT OF THE COOKERS VOL.1 & 2
Pensativa / Walkin' / Jodo / Breaking point
CDP 8288822 / May '94 / Blue Note

☐ OUTPOST
ENJACD 309523 / Jan '95 / Enja

☐ STRAIGHT LIFE
Straight life / Mr. Clean / Here's that rainy day
ZK 65125 / 8 Sep '97 / Sony Jazz

☐ THIS IS JAZZ
Red clay / Spirits of trane / Sky dive / In a mist / First light / Here's that rainy day
CK 65041 / May '97 / Sony Jazz

Hubbard, Ray Wylie

☐ DANGEROUS SPIRITS
CSCCD 1004 / Mar '97 / Continental Song City

Hubble

☐ MILE WIDE SMILE
HOLCD 33 / 3 Aug '98 / Holistic

Hubka, Diane

☐ HAVEN'T WE MET
Don't you know me / It's your dance / Lazy afternoon / Haven't we met / Miss Harper goes bizarre / Detour ahead / My kind of love / Favela / Everybody wants to be a cat / Thinking of you / Alone together / New cliches
AL 73128 / Jun '98 / A

Huckleberry

☐ HARD LUCK STORIES
COPPLP 7CD / 8 Jun '98 / Copper

Hucko, Peanuts

☐ TRIBUTE TO BENNY GOODMAN, A (Hucko, Peanuts/Butterfield/Erstrand)
CDTTD 513 / Jul '94 / Timeless Traditional

Huddersfield Choral Society

☐ CAROLS ALBUM, THE
O come all ye faithful (Adeste Fidelis) / Unto us is born a son / I saw three ships / Joy to the world / Away in a manger / God rest ye merry gentlemen / It came upon a midnight clear / Shepherds farewell / Good Christian men rejoice / Good King Wenceslas / Once in Royal David's City / We three kings of Orient are / In the bleak midwinter / O come, o come Emmanuel / While shepherds watched their flocks by night / First Noel / Silent night / Angles from the realms of glory / As with gladness men of old / Hark the herald angels sing / See amid the winter's snow
CDMFP 6038 / Nov '97 / Music For Pleasure

☐ CHRISTMAS CELEBRATION, A (Huddersfield Choral Society & Sellers Engineering Band)
CHAN 4530 / Nov '97 / Chandos

☐ CHRISTMAS FANTASY, A (Huddersfield Choral Society/Black Dyke Mills Band)
CHAN 4541 / Nov '97 / Chandos

Hudson, Bob

☐ INTERPLAY (Hudson, Bob Trio)
SND 0038 / Sep '97 / Sine

☐ STANDARD TIME (Hudson, Bob Trio)
SND 0021 / Sep '97 / Sine

Hudson, Dean

☐ DEAN HUDSON ORCHESTRA 1944-1950 (Hudson, Dean & His Orchestra)
CCD 13 / Mar '97 / Circle

Hudson, Keith

☐ BRAND
Image dub / National anthem dub / Feel the strain dub / Darkness dub / Highter hights dub / Leggo dub / Musicology dub / My eyes are red dub / Barrabas dub / Rub dub
CDPS 004 / Jul '95 / Pressure Sounds

☐ PICK A DUB
BAFCD 3 / Oct '94 / Blood & Fire

☐ STUDIO KINDA CLOUDY (Hudson, Keith & Friends)
CDTRL 258 / Sep '94 / Trojan

Hudson Swan Band

☐ PROSPECT LANE
LDLCD 239 / Jun '96 / Lochshore

Hue & Cry

☐ BEST OF HUE & CRY, THE
Labour of love / Looking for Linda / Under neon / Wide screen / Ordinary angel / Sweet invisibility / Peaceful face / I refuse / She makes a sound / Too shy to say / Mother Glasgow / Stars crash down
CDVIP 134 / Apr '95 / Virgin VIP

☐ JAZZ NOT JAZZ
AKD 057 / Oct '96 / Linn

☐ LABOURS OF LOVE (The Best Of Hue & Cry)
Labour of love / I refuse / Sweet invisibility / Looking for Linda / My salt heart / Violently (Your words hit me) / Strength to strength / Ordinary angel / Long term lovers of pain / She makes a sound / Widescreen / Stars crash down / Peaceful face / Man with the child in his eyes / Truth / Labour of love (7" urban edit)
HACCD 1 / Mar '93 / Circa

☐ REMOTE
Ordinary angel / Looking for Linda / Guy on the wall / Violently / Dollar William / Under neon / Only thing (more powerful than the boss) / Where we wish to remain / Sweet invisibility / Three foot blasts of fire / Remote / Family of eyes
CDVIP 187 / Apr '97 / Virgin VIP

☐ SEDUCED AND ABANDONED
Strength to strength / History city / Goodbye to me / Human touch / Labour of love / I refuse / Something warmer / Alligator man / Love is the master / Just one word / Truth
VI 874802 / Nov '96 / Disky

☐ SHOWTIME
INDELCD 7 / 27 Apr '98 / Indelible

☐ STARS CRASH DOWN
My salt heart / Life as text / She makes a sound / Making strange / Remembrance and gold / Long term lovers of pain / Stars crash down / Vera drives / Woman in time / Late in the day
CDVIP 207 / 3 Aug '98 / Virgin VIP

Hue B

☐ GOOD IN A ME, THE
CRCD 31 / Mar '94 / Charm

Hues Corporation

☐ MASTERS, THE
EABCD 039 / 24 Nov '97 / Eagle

☐ VERY BEST OF THE HUES CORPORATION, THE
Rock the boat / Rockin' soul / Love corporation / One good night together / Freedom for the stallion / Bound on a reason / Off my cloud / Family / Go to the poet / You showed me what love is / Soul salin' / Ease on down the road / No end in sight / He's my home / Gold rush / Sing to your song / Miracle maker (sweet soul shaker) / Follow the spirit / I got caught dancing again / Love's there
74321603422 / 27 Jul '98 / Camden

Huevos Rancheros

☐ DIG IN
LOUDEST 7 / Apr '95 / One Louder

☐ GET OUTTA DODGE
K 177 / 13 Oct '97 / Konkurrent

Hufschmidt, Thomas

☐ PEPILA (Hufschmidt, Thomas & Tyron Park)
BEST 1034CD / Nov '93 / Acoustic Music

Huge Baby

☐ SUPER FRANKENSTEIN
PILLMCD 5 / Aug '94 / Placebo

Huggy Bear

☐ WEAPONRY LISTENS TO LOVE
Immature adolescence / Fuck your heart / Face down / Warming rails / On the wolves tip / Erotic bleeding / Sixteen and suicide / Obesity and speed / Insecure offenders / Why am I a lawbreaker / Local arrogance
WIJ 037CD / Oct '94 / Wiiija

Hughes, Brian

☐ BETWEEN DUSK...AND DREAMING
JUST 362 / Mar '92 / Justin Time

☐ ONE 2 ONE
While the world slowly turns / One 2 one / Three graces / Nothing in this world / Here we go / Postcard from Brazil / Oh yeah / Stringbean / The way it is
VHOCD 12 / 25 May '98 / Higher Octave

☐ UNDER ONE SKY
JUST 492 / Jan '93 / Justin Time

Hughes, Brian

☐ MEASCRA (Whistle Stop)
CEFCD 178 / 11 May '98 / Gael Linn

Hughes, David

☐ 50 YARDS OF DAVID HUGHES
Dinner dance / Maldon girls / Sensitivity / Ordinary life / 50 yards / Past the stars / Hold your horses woman / David Hughes' 116th dream / Matilda / Cool BJ / Promised land / Being a poet
TFCCD 1099 / 18 May '98 / Folk Corporation

☐ ACTIVE IN THE PARISH
Millenium song / Active in the parish / Human heart / Everybody's talking about FM / Who's that (the summer of love) / Trace elements / Girls play hockey 1966 / Solid gone / Wasted / Willy Waldergrave story / State of the nation / Modest proposal
TFC 99CD / 18 May '98 / Folk Corporation

Hughes, Gary

☐ GARY HUGHES
NTHEN 040CD / 16 Feb '98 / Now & Then

☐ PRECIOUS ONES
In your eyes / Don't ever say goodbye / Colours of my life / Give my love a try / Divided we fall / Night the love died / First light / Wrecking machine / Perfect ten / This time / Heart of a woman / Precious one
FRCD 004 / 15 Jun '98 / Frontier

Hughes, Glenn

☐ BEST OF GLENN HUGHES, THE (Various Artists)
Burn: *Hughes, Glenn* / I got your number: *Hughes, Glenn* / Still the night: *Phenomena* / Surrender: *Phenomena II* / So much love to give: *LA Blues Authority* / Face the truth: *Norum, John* / Only one: *Hughes, Glenn* / Cry for love: *Liesgang, Billy* / Into the void: *Hughes, Glenn* / You keep me moving: *Hughes, Glenn* / Live and learn: *Brazen Abbot* / Lay my body down: *Hughes, Glenn* / King of the western world: *Liesgang, Billy* / Pheonix rising: *Phenomena* / Make my day: *Amen* / In your eyes: *Norum, John* / Look in your eye: *Hughes, Glenn* / Kiss of fire: *Hughes, Glenn* / Reach for the sky: *Moore, Gary* / No stranger to love: *Black Sabbath*
60234 / Nov '96 / Cargo

☐ BLUES
Boy can sing the blues / I'm the man / Here comes the rebel / What can I do for ya / You don't have to save me anymore / So much love to give / Shake the ground / Hey buddy (you got me wrong) / Have you read the book / Life of misery / Can't take away my pride / Right to live
RR 90882 / Sep '96 / Roadrunner

☐ BURNING JAPAN LIVE
SPV 08518202 / Jul '95 / SPV

☐ FEEL
CD 08589762 / Nov '95 / SPV

☐ FROM NOW ON
Pickin' up the pieces / Lay my body down / Only one / Why don't you stay / Walking on the water / Liar / Into the void / You were always there / If you don't want me to / Your love is like a fire / Homeland / From now on / Burn
RR 90072 / Sep '96 / Roadrunner

☐ GOD OF VOICE (The Very Best Of Glenn Hughes)
XRCN 2027 / 22 Jun '98 / Zero

☐ PLAY ME OUT
I got it covered / Space high / It's about time / LA cut off / Well / Solution / Your love is like a fire / Destiny / I found a woman / Smile / Getting near to you / Fools condition / Take me with you / She knows
RPM 149 / Jan '96 / RPM
CLEO 313 / 14 Jul '98 / Cleopatra

☐ WORK TAPES, THE (Hughes, Glenn & Geoffrey Downes)
Southern whoopee blues / New KC railroad blues / Travelling blues / You do me anyway / Badmouth / Cat's whisker's dog's bollocks / Canned heat / New maybe it's the blues / Seminole blues / Tear it down / Indian girl / What you're sitting on / Unknown blues / You don't need no religion
BP 285CD / 3 Aug '98 / Blueprint

Hughes, Howard

☐ CAR GOING OVER A BRIDGE
USRCD 3 / Nov '93 / Ultrasonic

Hughes, Jerry

☐ CELTIC WOMAN (Instrumentally Yours) (Hughes, Jerry & Alan Connaughton)
Orinoco flow / No frontiers / Woman's heart / Delaney's gone back on the wine / Nothing compares 2 U / After the ball / All the lies / Riverun / Teddy O'Neill / Summerfly
CHCD 030 / Apr '96 / Chart

Hughes, Joe

☐ DOWN AND DEPRESSED - DANGEROUS
NETCD 0044 / Jul '93 / Network

☐ TEXAS GUITAR MASTER-CRAFTSMAN
DTCD 3019 / Aug '88 / Double Trouble

☐ TEXAS GUITAR SLINGER
MMBCD 1 / Oct '95 / Me & My

Hughes, Spike

☐ HIS DECCA-DENTS DANCE ORCHESTRA/THREE BLIND MICE VOL.1 & 2
KCM 001/002 / Mar '95 / Kings Cross Music

☐ HIS DECCA-DENTS DANCE ORCHESTRA/THREE BLIND MICE VOL.3 & 4
KCM 003/004 / Aug '95 / Kings Cross Music

☐ SPIKE HUGHES & BENNY CARTER 1933 (Hughes, Spike & Benny Carter)
Nocturne / Someone stole Gabriel's horn / Pastorale / Bugle call rag / Arabesque / Fanfare / Sweet sorrow blues / Music at midnight / Sweet Sue just you / Air in D flat / Firebird / Music at sunrise / How come you do me like you do / Swing it / Synthetic love / Six bells stampede / Love you're not the one for me / Devil's holiday / Lonesome nights / Symphony in riffs / Blue Lou
RTR 79005 / Nov '96 / Retrieval

Hugill, Stan

☐ CHANTS PAS MARINS ANGLAIS
SCM 021 / May '93 / Diffusion Breizh

Hugo

☐ HUGO
NTHEN 036CD / 16 Feb '98 / Now & Then

Hula

☐ BEST OF HULA, THE
Fever car / Get the habit / Freeze out / Ghost rattle / Black wall blue / Big heat / Mother courage / Walk on stalks of shattered glass / Tear up / Hard stripes / Poison (Club mix) / Give me money / Cut me loose / Seven sleepers / Junshi
CDGRAM 81 / Jun '94 / Anagram

Hulbaekmo, Tone

☐ KONKYLIE
GR 4095CD / Apr '95 / Grappa

Hulett, Alistair

☐ COLD GREY LIGHT OF DAWN, THE (Hulett, Alistair & Dave Swarbrick)
Siege of Union Street / Chylde Owlett / Among proddy dogs and papes / Sons of Liberty / Suicide town / Day that the boys came down / Merchant's son / When the wee birds start leaving / Harold's best men / Swaggies have all waltzed Matilda away
MFCD 513 / 20 Apr '98 / Musikfolk

Hulkkonen, Jori

☐ SELKASAARI TRACKS
Flavatanssit / Sumthing / Blane Tudor's theme / Vinci / Mello dick track / 3rd line / Selkasaari / Cum off it / Heights
F 052CD / Feb '97 / F-Communications

☐ SPIRITS INSIDE ME, THE
Nitewalking / Aarirajoilla / 6.12 / Street near your place / You don't belong here / Red tape district / 7 nites 7 dayz / Kemi
F 089CD / 3 Aug '98 / F-Communications

Hull, Alan

☐ PIPEDREAM
Breakfast / Just another sad song / Money game / United states of mind / Country gentleman's wife / Numbers (travelling band) / For the bairns / Drug song / Song for a windmill / Blue murder / I hate to see you cry
CASCD 1069 / Feb '91 / Charisma

☐ STATUES AND LIBERTIES
TRACD 246 / Nov '96 / Transatlantic

☐ WHEN WAR IS OVER (2CD Set)
Drug song / Numbers / United states of mind / When war is over / Down on the underground / Gin and tonics all round / One more bottle of wine / Dan the plan / Dealer's choice / Winter song / Peter Brophy don't care / Squire / City song / Dan the plan / Money song / Gin and tonics all round / Golden oldies / All right on t'night / One more bottle of wine
PILOT 037 / 17 Aug '98 / Burning Airlines

Hullabaloo

☐ REGURGITATED
EFA 11381CD / Jun '93 / Musical Tragedies

Hum

☐ ELECTRA 2000
MGH 001 / 29 Sep '97 / Martians Go Home

Hum Projimo

☐ ALPENGLUH'N: SONGS FROM MURMI
EFA 112842 / Oct '95 / Glasnost

Humahuaqueno

☐ TREASURES OF INDIO MUSIC VOL.5, THE
MPCD 3028 / Jul '98 / Mariposa

Humair, Daniel

☐ EDGES
LBLC 6545 / Jan '92 / Label Bleu

☐ QUATRE FOIS TROIS
Casseroles / Helligoli / Les oignons / For flying out proud / Meditations de Thais / Huchedu / From time to time free / Bas de Lou / Huchedu / La Galinette / Kel Essouf
LBLC 661920 / 23 Feb '98 / Label Bleu

Human

☐ OUT OF THE DUST
IOU / If I could read your mind / I can't live / Hand me down / Make your light to see / Fat man's delicacy / Disguise / Lemonade / In the name / Feel
ORCD 9802 / Jun '98 / Pamplin

Human

☐ TRANSMISSION
Don't fuck with the truth / Pornocracy / Terra nostra / Insignificance / Human abattoir / Interzone / Panopticon / Simulcra / Human / Sex war / Silent minorities
CMGCD 017 / 8 Jun '98 / Communique

Human Beinz

☐ NOBODY BUT ME
Nobody but me / Foxey lady / Shamen / Flower grave / Dance on through / Turn on your lights / It's fun to be clean / Black is the colour of my true love's hair / This lonely town / Sueno / Serenade to Sarah
SEECD 327 / 8 Jun '98 / See For Miles

Human Chains

☐ HUMAN CHAINS
Freely / My Girl / Antonia / Elderberries / La la la / Grinding to the miller men / Hollyhocks / Golden slumbers / Further away / Suguxhama / Jolobe / Ikebana / Bon / Nancy D / Death
AHUM 002 / Jun '89 / Ah-Um

Human Clay

☐ U41A
Lessons of love / King of the nation / Salvation / Pain and deception / Thin line / Speed demon / U4IA / Pretender / Stand 4 the fall / Survive
CDMFN 227 / Jul '97 / Music For Nations

Human Drama

☐ 14384 DAYS LATER
TX 60009CD / 8 Dec '97 / Triple XXX

Human Instinct

☐ PINS IT IN
LW 4056 / 22 May '98 / Little Wing

Human League

☐ CRASH
Money / Swang / Human / Jam / Are you ever coming back / I need your lovin' / Party / Love on the run / Real thing / Love is all that matters
CDV 2391 / May '86 / Virgin

☐ DARE
Things that dreams are made of / Open your heart / Sound of the crowd / Darkness / Do or die / Get Carter / I am the law / Seconds / Love action (I believe in love) / Don't you want me
CDV 2192 / Oct '81 / Virgin

☐ GREATEST HITS
Don't you want me / Love action / Mirror man / Tell me when / Stay with me tonight / Open your heart / (Keep feeling) Fascination / Sound of the crowd / Being boiled / Lebanon / Love is all that matters / Louise / Life on your own / Together in electric dreams / Human / Don't you want me (Snap remix)
CDV 2792 / Oct '95 / Virgin

☐ HYSTERIA
I'm coming back / I love you too much / Rock me again and again and again..... / Louise / Lebanon / Betrayed / Sign / So hurt / Life on your own / Don't you know I want you
CDV 2315 / Jul '87 / Virgin

☐ OCTOPUS
Tell me when / These are the days / One man in my heart / Words / Filling up with heaven / Housefull of nothing / John Cleese; is he funny / Never again / Cruel young lover
4509987502 / Jan '95 / East West

☐ REPRODUCTION
Almost medieval / Circus of death / Path of least resistance / Blind youth / Word before last / Empire state human / Morale...You've lost that loving feeling / Austerity/Girl one (medley) / Zero as a limit
CDV 2133 / '87 / Virgin

☐ SOUNDTRACK TO A GENERATION
Human / Kiss the future / Together in electric dreams / Are you ever coming back / Betrayed / Hard times / Get it right this time / I need your loving / Do or die / Rebound / Soundtrack to a generation / Empire State human / Real thing / Don't you know I want you
VI 875302 / Oct '96 / Disky

☐ TRANCE LEAGUE EXPRESS (A Tribute To The Human League) (Various Artists)
CLP 9934 / Mar '97 / Hypnotic

☐ TRAVELOGUE
Black hit of space / Only after dark / Life kills / Dreams of leaving / Toyota city / Crow and a baby / Touchables / Gordon's gin / Being boiled / WXJL tonight
CDV 2160 / '87 / Virgin

Human Nature

☐ TELLIN' EVERYBODY
You got it / Whisper your name / Wishes / Something in the name / Party / Don't say goodbye / Can I do you / Sleepin' alone / September girl / Love unconditional / People get ready
4850742 / 29 Sep '97 / Epic

Human Race

☐ FOR THE SAKE OF YOUR SOUL
ZR 1997003 / Jun '98 / Z

Human Remains

☐ USING SICKNESS AS A HERO
RR 69272 / Feb '97 / Relapse

Human Waste Project

☐ E-LUX
1620672 / 16 Mar '98 / Hollywood

Humara, Walter Salas

☐ RADAR
NORMAL 193CD / Jan '96 / Normal

Humate

☐ BEST OF HUMATE, THE (Various Artists)
Love stimulation: *Humate* / Bagdad: *Paragliders* / East: *Humate & Rabbit In The Moon* / East: *Humate & Rabbit In The Moon* / 3.1: *Humate* / 3.3: *Humate* / Sound: *Humate* / Feather: *Spicelab* / 1996 (part 1): *Spicelab* / 1996 (part 2): *Humate*
EFA 628192 / Mar '97 / Superstition

Humble Pie

☐ COLLECTION, THE
Bang / Natural born bugie / I'll go alone / Buttermilk boy / Desperation / Nifty little number like you / Wrist job / Stick shift / Growing closer / As safe as yesterday / Heartbeat / Down home again / Take me back / Only you can see / Silver tongue / Every mother's son / Sad bag of Shaky Jake / Cold lady / Home and away / Light of love
CCSCD 104 / Apr '94 / Castle

☐ IMMEDIATE YEARS, THE (2CD Set)
Natural born bugie / Wrist job / Desperation / Stick shift / Buttermilk boy / Growing closer / As safe as yesterday is / Bang / Alabama 69 / I'll go alone / Nifty little number like you / What you will / Greg's song / Take me back / Sad bag of shaky Jake / Light of love / Cold lady / Down home again / Ollie Ollie / Every Mother's son / Heartbeat / Only you can see / Silver tongue / Home and away
CDIMMBOX 3 / Aug '95 / Charly

☐ KING BISCUIT PRESENTS...
Up your sleeves / 4 day creep / C'mon everybody / Honky tonk women / Stone cold fever / Blues I believe my soul / 30 days in my soul / Road runner / Hallejulah / I don't need no doctor / Hot 'n' nasty
KBFHCD 017 / 24 Aug '98 / King Biscuit

☐ NATURAL BORN BOOGIE
Natural born boogie / Sad bag of shaky jake / Heartbeat / Desperation / Big black dog / Rolling stone / 4 day creep / Light / Black coffee / I don't need no doctor
SFRSCD 066 / 27 Jul '98 / Strange Fruit

☐ PIECE OF THE PIE, A
5401792 / Apr '95 / A&M

☐ TOWN AND COUNTRY
Take me back / Sad bag of Shaky Jake / Light of love / Cold lady / Down home again / Ollie Ollie / Every mother's son / Heartbeat / Only you can see / Silver tongue / Home and away
CDIMM 020 / Feb '94 / Charly

Humblebums

☐ BEST OF THE HUMBLEBUMS, THE
PDSCD 542 / Aug '96 / Pulse

☐ NEW HUMBLEBUMS, THE/OPEN UP THE DOOR
Look over the hill and far away / Saturday round about Sunday / Patrick / Everybody knows that / Rick rack / Her father didn't like me anyway / Please sing a song for us / Joe Dempsey / Blood and glory / Coconut tree / Silk pyjamas / Good-bye-ee / My apartment / I can't stop now / Open up the door / Mary of the Mountains / All the best people do it / Steamboat row / Mother / Shoeshine boy / Cruisin' / Keep it to yourself / Oh no / Song for Simon / Harry / My singing bird
ESMCD 498 / Apr '97 / Essential

Humes, Helen

☐ BLACK CALIFORNIA
Blow blow blow / Blues a la Russ / What is this thing called love / Wake up old maid / Sad feeling / Rock me to sleep / This love of mine / He may be yours / Jam man / Slim's riff / I'm confessin' / Oxydol highball / Strollin' / Sonor / Blues mood / Skoot / I've lost your love
SV 0274 / Oct '97 / Savoy Jazz

☐ BLUE PRELUDE
TPZ 1073 / Aug '98 / Topaz Jazz

☐ CLASSICS 1927-1945
CLASSICS 892 / Sep '96 / Classics

☐ LET THE GOOD TIMES ROLL
BB 8712 / Sep '96 / Black & Blue

☐ ON THE SUNNY SIDE OF THE STREET
Alright, OK you win / If I could be with you one hour tonight / Ain't nobody's business if I do / Kansas City / I'm satisfied / Blue because of you / On the sunny side of the street / I got it bad and that ain't good
BLCD 760185 / Jul '93 / Black Lion

Hummel, Mark

☐ FEEL LIKE ROCKIN'
Georgia slop / Rockin' all the time / So darn cute / Learned my lesson (changed my ways) / Everything / Nickels and dimes / Lost in the shuffle / Bad luck blues / I'm gonna quit / Where you at / City livin' / Coast to coast / Worried mind / Last time in Florida / Third time out / When I'm not with you
FF 70634 / Nov '94 / Flying Fish

☐ HEART OF CHICAGO
My kind of baby / Rockin' at the riverside / Lost a good man / Rollin' from side to side / Tryin' to make a living / Love shock / I want your love / Peaches tree / Step back baby / But I forgive you / Out on a limb / Ready for Eddie / Drinkin' again / Living with the blues
CDTC 1158 / Feb '97 / Tonecool

☐ MARRIED TO THE BLUES
They don't want me to rock / I'm gone / Find some boogie / Rock and roll baby / Jungle scotch plaid / No buts, no maybes / Can't judge nobody / Can't live with 'em / High steppin' / Married to the blues / I got eyes / Trial by fire / Bluesman
FF 70647 / Oct '96 / Flying Fish

Hummon, Marcus

☐ ALL IN GOOD TIME
Hittin' the road / God's country USA / One of these days / Honky tonk Mona Lisa / Next step / I do / Virginia reelin' / Somebody's leaving / Bless the broken road / As the crow flies / Bridges over blue / All in good time
4810282 / Jan '96 / Columbia

Humperdinck, Engelbert

☐ 20 GREAT LOVE SONGS
After the lovin' / Can't take my eyes off you / Another time another place / Love me with all your heart / And I love you so / You are the sunshine of my life / Most beautiful girl / Help me make it through the night / Love is all / Close to you (they long to be) / Killing me softly with his song / Raindrops keep falling on my head / Can't smile without you / Leaving on a jet plane / My cherie amour / Something / Forever and ever / Without you / Everybody's talkin' / In time
LS 865542 / 2 Feb '98 / Disky

☐ AFTER DARK
Love me like we'll never love again / If I could love you more / Once in a while / I could get used to this / Healing: *Humperdinck, Engelbert & Louise Sarah Dorsey* / Answered prayers / Stay with me / Great divide / Slide a little closer / I know you hear me / There's no song like a slow song
ALPCD 100 / Mar '97 / Alpha Entertainments

☐ AND I LOVE YOU SO
12567 / Oct '95 / Laserlight

☐ BEST OF ENGELBERT HUMPERDINCK, THE
PLSCD 121 / Apr '96 / Pulse

☐ BEST OF ENGELBERT HUMPERDINCK, THE
TRTCD 219 / Jul '96 / TrueTrax

☐ COLLECTION, THE
Please release me / To all the girls I've loved before / Bella Italia / Les bicyclettes de Belsize / There goes my everything / One world / Last waltz / On the wings of a silverbird / Portofino / Spanish night is over / Under the man in the moon / I can't stop loving you / I can never let you go / Are you lonesome tonight
262540 / Feb '97 / Ariola

☐ ENGELBERT HUMPERDINCK
Lovely way to spend an evening / Far away places / I'll walk alone / My foolish heart / Very thought of you / You belong to my heart / Red sails in the sunset / You'll never know / I wish I knew / Embraceable you / I don't want to walk without you / As time goes by / Long ago and far away / Night to remember
GFS 068 / Jul '97 / Going For A Song

☐ ENGELBERT IN LOVE
Man without love / Killing me softly / Last waltz / Help me make it through the night / There goes my everything / My cherie amour / Winter world of love / Way it used to be / Something / Close to you / Am I that easy to forget / Love me tender / Release me / Quando, quando, quando (tell me when) / Most beautiful girl / Spanish eyes / Just the way you are / First time ever I saw your face / You are the sunshine of my life / And I love you so
4625592 / Feb '96 / Columbia

☐ EVENING WITH ENGELBERT HUMPERDINCK, AN (20 Love Songs)
Lovely way to spend an evening / As time goes by / Red sails in the sunset / Embraceable you / They say it's wonderful / You belong to my heart / Very thought of you / Stardust / You'll never know / I don't want to walk without you / Moonlight becomes you / Yours / My foolish heart / I'm getting sentimental over you / Harbour lights / Long ago (and far away) / More I see you / In the still of the night / I'll walk alone / I'll be seeing you
ECD 3402 / 23 Feb '98 / K-Tel

☐ FROM ENGELBERT WITH LOVE
I don't want to walk without you / Embraceable you / I wish I knew / You'll never know / Red sails in the sunset / You belong to my heart / Very thought of you / My foolish heart / I'll walk alone / Far away places / Lovely way to spend an evening / More I see you / In the still of the night / I'm getting sentimental over you / Moonlight becomes you / But beautiful / Harbour lights / They say it's wonderful / Long ago / As time goes by
100532 / May '97 / A-Play Collection

☐ GREATEST HITS
Release me / Man without love / Way it used to be / Quando, quando, quando / Everybody knows we're through / There's a kind of hush / There goes my everything / Les bicyclettes de Belsize / I'm a better man (for having loved you) / Winter world of love / My world / Ten guitars / Am I that easy to forget / Last waltz
8203672 / Jul '89 / London

☐ HIS ROMANTIC HITS
CD 3503 / Aug '94 / Cameo

☐ IN THE STILL OF THE NIGHT
In the still of the night / I'm getting sentimental over you / I'll walk alone / Moonlight becomes you / You'll never know / I don't want to walk without you / Stardust / Embraceable you / You belong to my heart / Lovely way to spend an evening / Long ago and far away / Red sails in the sunset / Far away places / My foolishy heart / Very thought of you / They say it's wonderful / Harbour lights / More I see you / Yours / As time goes by
MCCD 055 / Mar '92 / Music Club

☐ LAST WALTZ AT THE ALBERT HALL
Medley / Hello / After the loving / Medley / I just called to say I love you / I'll walk alone / Help me make it through the night / Come a little closer / Release me / Medley / Spanish eyes/Last waltz/Love is all / Medley
309072 / 13 Jul '98 / Hallmark

☐ LIVE AT THE RIVIERA LAS VEGAS
VAR 5899 / 15 Jun '98 / Varese Sarabande

☐ LIVE AT THE ROYAL ALBERT HALL
Lovely way to spend an evening / I'm so excited / Hello / After the loving / Medley / I just called to say I love you / I'll walk alone / Help me make it through the night / Follow my heartbeat / Release me / Medley / Last waltz / Love is all / If we only had love / If you love me (really love me)
PLSCD 249 / 27 Oct '97 / Pulse

☐ LIVE IN JAPAN
Intro / There's a kind of hush / All I ever need is you / Il mondo / Man without love / Stripper / Impressions / I'll be your baby tonight / Another time another place / Release me / Love is all / Without you / I can help / I never said goodbye / Last waltz / Quando quando / There goes my everything / Spanish eyes / Les bicyclettes de belsize
12657 / May '96 / Laserlight

☐ LOVE IS ALL (3CD Set)
After the lovin' / Can't take my eyes off you / Another time another place / Love me with all your heart / And I love you so / You are the sunshine of my life / You'll never walk alone(live) / Help me make it through the night / Love is all / Close to you (they long to be) / Raindrops keep fallin' on my head / Can't smile without you / Leaving on a jet plane / Release me (live) / Killing me softly with his song / My cherie amour / Something / Without you / Forever and ever / Everybody's talkin' / Sweet Marjorene / First time in my life / In time / Most beautiful girl / I can't leave a dream / Baby I'm a want you / What now my love / Man without love / Just the way you are / Can't help falling in love / I'm stone in love with you / Much greater love / Let's kiss tomorrow goodbye / Just say I love her / Those were the days / Funny familiar forgotten feelings / You light up my life / What I did for love / Love me tender / And the day begins / Here you come again / Medley
SA 872542 / Sep '96 / Disky

☐ MASTERPIECES
You are the sunshine of my life / Love me with all your heart / Killing me softly / (they long to be) close to you / My cherie amour / Raindrops keep fallin' on my head / Eternally / Another time, another place / Photograph / Something / Love is all / We made it happen / Santa lija (sogno d'amore) / Just say I love her / Everybody's talkin' / Catch me I'm falling
12329 / May '94 / Laserlight

☐ SIMPLY THE BEST - RELEASE ME
WMCD 5694 / May '94 / Disky

☐ SINGS THE CLASSICS
CCSCD 432 / Mar '95 / Castle

☐ VERY THOUGHT OF YOU, THE
Long ago and far away / Stardust / They say it's wonderful / I'll be around / But beautiful / Moonlight becomes you / I'm getting sentimental over you / In the still of the night / More I see you / I'll be seeing you / Lovely way to spend an evening / My foolish heart / Very thought of you / You belong to my heart / Red sails in the sunset / I wish I knew / Embraceable you / As time goes by
EMPRCD 908 / Jan '97 / Emporio

Humpers

☐ EUPHORIA CONFUSION ANGER AND REMORSE
Steel toad / Sneakers / Shortcut to nowhere / Devil's magic pants / Peggy Sue got buried / No you don't / Ghetto in the sky / Ten inches higher / No escape / You dirty rat / Fistful of Zen
65242 / 6 Apr '98 / Epitaph

☐ PLASTIQUE VALENTINE
64832 / Feb '97 / Epitaph

Humpff Family

☐ FATHER'S
That's what I see / Triangle / Magic journey / Can of beans / Future imperfect / Skye Bridge song / Love, death, divorce, prison, alcohol, rivers and trains / Be there / Joanie's letter / Mary's luck / Rain / Henryetta / Conduct of pigeons
IGCD 208 / Jul '94 / Iona Gold

☐ MOTHERS
Keep it down / Keep it down / I'll be your baby tonight / Hoo haa / Self pity waltz / Rattle of a simple man / In that dress / Misty again / Five years and just one day / Falling apart / Shoplifting / Teach jesus / Old film and tickets (lordy lordy) / Martha and vernon / Moby marly / Beaujolais nouveau
IRCD 019 / Oct '91 / Iona

Humphrey, Bobbi

☐ BLUE BREAKBEATS
Harlem River Drive / San Francisco lights / Smiling faces / Sometimes / Blacks and blues / My little girl / Please set me at ease
4947062 / 13 Jul '98 / Blue Note

Humphrey, Percy

☐ PERCY HUMPHREY & MARYLAND JAZZBAND
BCD 318 / Apr '94 / GHB

Humphrey, Willie

☐ NEW ORLEANS TRADITIONAL JAZZ LEGENDS
MG 9002 / Feb '95 / Mardi Gras

☐ WILLIE HUMPHREY & NORBERT SUSEMIHL (Humphrey, Willie & Norbert Susemihl)
BCD 248 / Nov '96 / GHB

Humphries, Les

☐ VERY BEST OF THE LES HUMPHRIES SINGERS, THE (Humphries, Les Singers)
Mama loo / Mexico / Clapping song / Ramba samba / God made America / Dance dance dance / Spirit of freedom / Adios auf wiedersehen / Oh happy day / To my father's house / Palma palma palma mallorca / Rock my soul
10272 / Oct '97 / Go On Deluxe

Humus

☐ HUMUS
SR 2009 / Sep '97 / Smogless

☐ MALLEUS CREASE
SR 2010 / Sep '97 / Smogless

☐ TUS OIDOS MIENTEN
SR 2008 / Sep '97 / Smogless

Huncke, Herbert

☐ FROM DREAM TO DREAM
567912 / Nov '97 / Music & Words

Hundred Years

☐ HUNDRED YEARS
H 00392 / Jul '95 / Hellhound

☐ SKYHOOK
Intuition time / Am I wrong / Mesmerized / When the day is here / Two wrong words / All man overboard / 30 Below / Dungeon hole / Liar / Fire from within / Relocation / Beds are burning / 13
N 02812 / Mar '97 / Noise

Hunger

☐ STRICTLY FROM HUNGER
AFT 010 / Jun '97 / Afterglow

Hunningale, Peter

☐ GENUINE
SAXCD 008 / 15 Dec '97 / Saxon Hit Factory

☐ MR. GOVERNMENT
Mr. Songbird / Tweet dub / Jump / Babylon / War on babylon / Mr. Government / Downing St. dub / One people / One dub / Sensi sensi
ARICD 101 / Apr '94 / Ariwa Sounds

☐ MR. VIBES
Extra classic / Heavenly / Gonna miss you / Time for love / Too late / She is not crazy / Go to make it better / Woman / Listen to your heart / Mister vibes
ARKCD 102 / Jan '93 / Arawak

☐ NAH GIVE UP
Nah give up / Trust me / Lover's affair / Thinking about you / Praises / Good and ready / Roots and culture / Sorry / Waiting on your love / Declaration of rights / Perfect lady / Baby please
DTJCD 002 / 18 May '98 / Down To Jam

☐ REGGAE MAX
JSRNCD 9 / Apr '97 / Jet Star

☐ SILLY HABITS
DTJCD 005 / 18 May '98 / Down To Jam

Hunt, Howard Slim

☐ BEST OF HOWARD SLIM HUNT & THE SUPREME ANGELS, THE (Hunt, Howard Slim & The Supreme Angels)
NASH 4506 / Feb '96 / Nashboro

Hunt, Nigel

☐ ON A COCONUT ISLAND (Hunt, Nigel Imperial Jazz Band)
PKCD 096 / Apr '98 / PEK

Hunt, Steve

☐ HEAD, HEART AND HAND
IRR 015CD / Dec '93 / Irregular

Hunt, Tommy

☐ BIGGEST MAN, THE
Biggest man / I just don't know what to do with myself / Human / Lover / New neighbourhood / She'll hurt you too / You made a man out of me / I might like it / Didn't I tell you / Make the night a little longer / This and only this / Just a little taste (of your sweet lovin') / Coming on strong / How can I be anything (without you) / Everybody's got a home but me / Words can never tell it / False alarm / I am a witness / Your man / Don't make me over / It's all a bad dream / Promised land / Paradise of broken hearts / Poor millionaire / So lonely / It's all in the game / Do you really love me / I'm wondering / Oh Lord what are you doing to me
CDKEND 145 / Apr '97 / Kent

Hunter, Alastair

☐ LORNE CHOICE (Hunter, Alastair & The Lorne Scottish Dance Band)
DACD 9716 / 20 Oct '97 / Dee-Ay

Hunter, Alberta

☐ ALBERTA HUNTER 1920'S/1930'S
JCD 6 / Jun '87 / Jass

☐ ALBERTA HUNTER VOL.1 (1921-1923)
DOCD 5422 / Jul '96 / Document

☐ ALBERTA HUNTER VOL.2 (1923-1924)
DOCD 5423 / Jul '96 / Document

☐ ALBERTA HUNTER VOL.3 (1924-1927)
DOCD 5424 / Jul '96 / Document

☐ ALBERTA HUNTER VOL.4 (1927-1946)
DOCD 5425 / Jul '96 / Document

☐ ALTERNATE TAKES 1921-1924, THE
DOCD 1006 / May '97 / Document

☐ BEALE STREET BLUES
CBCD 006 / Mar '96 / Collector's Blues

☐ CHICAGO-THE LIVING LEGENDS (Hunter, Alberta & Lovie Austin)
St. Louis blues / Moanin' low / Downhearted blues / Now I'm satisfied / Sweet Georgia Brown / You better change / C jam blues / Streets paved with gold / Gallion stomp / I will always be in love with you
OBCCD 510 / Nov '92 / Original Blues Classics

☐ SONGS WE TAUGHT YOUR MOTHER (Hunter, Alberta/Victoria Spivey/ Lucille Hegamin)
I got myself a workin' man / St. Louis blues / Black snake blues / I got a mind to ramble / You'll want my love / Going blues / You gotta reap what you sow / Arkansas blues / Got the blues so bad / Chirpin' the blues / Has anybody seen my Corine / Let him beat me
OBCCD 520 / Nov '92 / Original Blues Classics

☐ YOUNG AH, THE
JASSCD 6 / '88 / Jass

Hunter, Alfonzo

☐ BLACK A DA BERRY
Weekend thang / Blacka da berry / When you're ready / Keep it tight (interlude) / Slow motion / Crazy / Just the way (playas play) / Groove on / Would you be mine / Everything / Daddy's little baby / Rest in peace / Quiet time
CTCD 55 / Jan '97 / Cooltempo

Hunter, Charlie

☐ BING BING BING (Hunter, Charlie Trio)
Greasy granny / Wornell's Yorkies / Fistful of haggis / Come as you are / Scrabbling gor purchase / Bullethead / Bing, bing, bing, bing / Squiddlesticks / Lazy Susan / Elbo room
CDP 8318092 / Jul '95 / Blue Note

☐ READY...SET...SHANGO (Hunter, Charlie Quartet)
Ashby man / Teabaggin' / Let's get medieval / Shango / Dersu / 911 / Shango...the ballad / Thursday the 12th / Sutton
CDP 8371012 / Jun '96 / Blue Note

☐ RETURN OF THE CANDYMAN
Bongo confront / Enter the dragon / Fly like an eagle / Dope a licious / Mystic / Relaxation / Return of the candymen / Pound for pound / Grinch confront / People / Shake it / Turn me loose / Huggy bear / Of things to come
8231082 / 2 Mar '98 / Blue Note

Hunter, Ian

☐ ARTFUL DODGER, THE
Too much / Now is the time / Something to believe in / Resurrection Mary / Walk on water / 23a Swan Hill / Michael Picasso / Open my eyes / Artful dodger / Skeletons in your closet / Still the same
CIT 1CD / Jul '98 / Citadel

☐ IAN HUNTER
Once bitten twice shy / Who do you love / Lounge lizard / Boy / 3000 miles from here / Truth / Whole truth nuthin' but the truth / It ain't easy when you fall / Shades off / I get so excited
4773592 / Aug '94 / Columbia

☐ WELCOME TO THE CLUB (2CD Set)
FBI / Once bitten twice shy / Angeline / Laugh at me / All the way from Memphis / I wish I was your mother / Irene Wilde / Just another night / Cleveland rocks / Standin' in my light / Bastard / Walkin' with a mountain / All the young dudes / Slaughter on 10th Avenue / We gotta get out of here / Silver needles / Man 'o' war / Sons and daughters
CDCHR 6075 / May '94 / Chrysalis

☐ YOU'RE NEVER ALONE WITH A SCHIZOPHRENIC
Just another night / Wild east / Cleveland rocks / Ships / When the daylight comes / Life after death / Standin' in my light / Bastard / Outsider
CD25CR 03 / Mar '94 / Chrysalis

Hunter, James

☐ BELIEVE WHAT I SAY
Two can play / Way down inside / Very thought of you / It ain't funny / Turn on your love light / Let me know / I'll walk away / I wanna get old with you / Hallelujah I love her so / Believe what I say / Out of sight / Don't step on it / Hear me calling / Ain't nothing you can do
CDCHD 636 / Oct '96 / Ace

Hunter, Jim

☐ CRACK O'NOON CLUB
CRACD 14 / Mar '96 / Watercolour

☐ FINGERNAIL MOON
COMD 2047 / Feb '94 / Temple

☐ UPHILL SLIDE
COMD 2040 / Feb '94 / Temple

Hunter, Lisa

☐ FLYING
Underground / Faith / Flying / Storm / Paralyze / River / Blue / Nowhere fast / Goodbye / Water under the bridge / Overgrown / Shining through
OMC 0017 / 20 Apr '98 / One Man Clapping

☐ SOLID GROUND
Solid ground / Satisfied / Party / Breathe / Day / This road / Moonlight / Fade to black / Midnight oil / Pull from far away / Your eyes / Back on solid ground
OMC 0005 / 20 Apr '98 / One Man Clapping

Hunter, Long John

☐ BORDER TOWN LEGEND
ALCD 4839 / Feb '96 / Alligator

☐ RIDE WITH ME
BMCD 9020 / Apr '93 / Black Magic

☐ SWINGING FROM THE RAFTERS
Time and time again / I don't care / Stop what you're doing / Both ends of the world / Bugs on my window / Take it home with you / Trouble on the line / In the country / V-8 Ford / 30 days / I'm broke / Walking catfish / Locksmith man / Love prevails
ALCD 4853 / Jul '97 / Alligator

Hunter, Robert

☐ BOX OF RAIN
Box of rain / Scarlet begonias / Franklin's tower / Jack Straw / Brown eyed women / Reuben and Cerise / Space / Deal / Promontory rider / Ripple / Boys in the bar room / Stella blue
RCD 10214 / Sep '91 / Rykodisc

☐ SENTINEL
Pride of bone / Gingerbread man / Idiot's delight (excerpt) / Red dog's decoration day / Trapping a muse / Jazz / Toad in love / Rimbaud at 20 / Rain in a courtyard / Way of the ride / Sentinel / Preserpie / Poets on poets / Like a basket / Yagritz / Cocktails with Hindemith / Blue moon alley / New jungle / Full moon cafe / Tango hit palace / Exploding diamond blues / Rainwater sea / Hologomena
RCD 20265 / Nov '93 / Rykodisc

☐ TALES OF THE GREAT RUM RUNNERS
Lady Simplicity / Dry dust road / Rum runners / Maybe she's a bluebird / It must have been the roses / Standing at your door / Keys to the rain / That train / I heard you singing / Children's lament / Boys in the bar room / Arizona lightning / Mad
GDCD 4013 / May '89 / Grateful Dead

☐ TIGER ROSE
Tiger rose / Rose of Sharon / Dance a hole / Over the hills / Yellow moon / One thing to try / Wild Bill / Cruel white water / Last flash / Ariel
GDCD 4010 / Jul '90 / Grateful Dead

Hunter, Sonya

☐ FAVOURITE SHORT STORIES
NORMAL 165 / Nov '94 / Normal

☐ FINDERS KEEPERS
RTS 19 / Aug '95 / Return To Sender

☐ GEOGRAPHY
Unlikely combinations / Can two worlds collide / Middle of somewhere / Atlases / Just a job / Heart cryin' in the wind / Mama sky / Baby girl / I can't reach you / Get back on that horse / London bridges
NORMAL 160CD / Mar '94 / Normal

☐ HEADLIGHTS AND CONSTELLATIONS
EFA 121212 / 23 Mar '98 / Moll

☐ PEASANT PIE
NORM 190CD / Apr '95 / Normal

Hunter, Trevor

☐ FROM SHETLAND
DRCD 1028 / Jul '98 / Donside

Hunter, William

☐ 1982
CMCD 010 / Apr '94 / Celtic Music

☐ LEAVING LERWICK HARBOUR (Hunter, William & Violet Tulloch)
Jackie Coleman/Sally Gardens / Leaving Lerwick Harbour / Chadwicks bog / Jamie's reel / Clarence Tough / Newcastle hornpipe/Pat's reel / Caberfeidh / Randy wives of Fochabers / Carnival march / Sands of Murness / Kiwi reel / Laird o' Drumblair / De'il among the tailors / Ash plant / McGuire's welcome to Fermanagh / Alan Brown / Auld fiddler / Dumbarton Castle / Marquis of Huntley's farewell / Marquis of Tullybardine / Balkan Hills / Miller o' Hirn / Donald Stuart the piper / Weeping birches of Kilmorack / Grace Morrison of Borve / Cathie and Jim Lambie / Da grocer / Hjerdfeld / Laxo burn / Cape Breton Fiddler's welcome to Shetland / Peerie Willie / Lorna's reel
CDTRAX 106 / Apr '96 / Greentrax

☐ WILLIE HUNTER SESSIONS, THE (Hunter, William & Violet Tulloch)
Miller / Glencoe / Compliments to Dan R. MacDonald / Mairi MacLennan reel / Lament for Lowrie o' da Lea / First century reel / Leaving Glenurquhart / Laird O' Thrums / Gavin MacMillan / Lady Walpole / Batchelder's reel / Love o' da isles / Master McDermott's reel / Wee Colin Dewar / Banjo reel / Sean McGuire / Jubilee / Cape Breton visit to Shetland / Da Guizers' march / Glenfarquhar / Reested mutton / Rosemary Brown / Barmaid / Sligo maid / Rising sun / Glenmore / Brace Bridge / Out the buckthorn way / Centenary hornpipe / Faroe rum / Aandowin at da bow / Da forfeit o' da ship / Wallace and Thomas / High level / Archie Menzies / Madame Vanoni
CDTRAX 144 / 1 Oct '97 / Greentrax

Hunters

☐ COMPLETE COLLECTION, THE
BGOCD 325 / Mar '97 / Beat Goes On

Hunters & Collectors

☐ CUT
TVD 93364 / Feb '96 / Mushroom

☐ DEMON FLOWER
TVD 93401 / May '94 / Mushroom

Hunting Lodge

☐ EIGHT BALL (2CD Set)
NORMAL 61/62CD / '89 / Normal

☐ NECROPOLIS
DV 017CD / Jan '94 / Dark Vinyl

☐ WILL
DV 010CD / 22 Jun '98 / Dark Vinyl

Huntingtons

☐ HIGH SCHOOL ROCK
TNR 1103CD / 11 May '98 / Tooth & Nail

Huntley, George

☐ BRAINJUNK
TVT 551CD / Apr '96 / TVT

Huracan

☐ VOICES OF THE WIND
PV 796011 / Apr '96 / Pierre Verany

Huracanes Del Norte

☐ AIRES DE MI NORTE
5330860742 / 17 Mar '98 / Fonovisa

Hurdy Gurdy

☐ HURDY GURDY
HBG 122/11 / Apr '94 / Background

Hurleurs

☐ BAZAR
Bazar / L'air du temps / Le ballade du corbeau / Sous le vent / Je suis tout petit / Dimanche / Pigeon / Lieder / Sans nom / Les roses de saadi / Marie / La petit mort / En votre absence / Kiki l'Indien
AC 6455 / Jan '97 / Chorus

Hurley, Michael

☐ LONG JOURNEY
Long journey / Portland water / So you say / Reconciled to the blues / You got to find me / 8-ball cafe / Polynesia / Monkey on the interstate / Whiskey willey / Panama hat / Why should I have to worry / Vt ore floor / Hog of the foresaken / In the garden / Watchin' the snow
ROUCD 3011 / 16 Mar '98 / Rounder

☐ SNOCKGRASS
Midnite rounder / O my stars / Tia Marie / I'm gettin' ready to go / Watchin' the show / Autumn Slim and the fat boys / Don't treat me bad / I heard the voice of a pork chop / No home / Jole blon / I think I'll move / Goin' to Florida / You gonna look like a monkey / Sweet Lucy / Grapefruit juice blues
ROUCD 3043 / Oct '97 / Rounder

☐ WATERTOWER
HYMN 8 / Aug '97 / Fundamental

☐ WOLFWAYS
379102 / Jun '96 / Koch Veracity

Hurley, Red

☐ DANNY BOY TRILOGY
CDC 036 / Dec '97 / Ceol

Hurrah

☐ SOUND OF PHILADELPHIA
Live intro tape / Sun shines here / I'll be your surprise / Don't need food / Saturday's train / Lonely room / Hip hip / Around and around (when in rome) / If it rains / Point of perfection / Who'd've thought / Celtic (who wants to live by love alone) / Big sky / This boy / Gloria / Funny day / Walk in the park / Suffer and see / Sweet sanity / How many rivers / Miss this kiss / If love could kill / I would if I could
CREV 014CD / Sep '93 / Rev-Ola

Hurricane

☐ AMERICA'S MOST HARDCORE (Hurricane/DFL)
Hurra: *Hurricane* / Can we get along: *Hurricane* / Elbow room: *Hurricane* / Pizza man: *DFL* / America's most hardcore: *DFL* / U don't understand: *DFL* / Knuckleheadnation: *DFL* / Think about the pit: *DFL* / Smoke bomb: *DFL* / My crazy life: *DFL*
WIJ 034CD / Apr '94 / Wiiija

Hurricane

☐ SEVERE DAMAGE
Severe damage / Esat west south / Pit / Coast to coast / Japanese eyes / Ain't no love / Turn yourself around / Shaftman smack dat ass / Billionaire dreams / Mande man / 9mms and techs / Bach on set
WIJCD 1072 / 20 Oct '97 / Wiiija

Hurricane No.1

☐ HURRICANE NO.1
CRECD 206
CRECD 206L / 15 Sep '97 / Creation

Hurt, 'Mississippi' John

☐ AIN'T NOBODY'S BUSINESS
Nobody's business but mine / Angels laid him away / Baby what's wrong with you / Casey Jones / Candy man / Lonesome blues / My creole belle / Make me a pallet on your floor / Trouble I had all my days / C-H-I-C-K-E-N blues / Coffee blues / Shake that thing / Monday morning blues / Frankie and Albert / Salty dog / Spike drivers blues / Here I am, Lord, send me / Talking Casey / Hot time in The Old Town tonight / I'm satisfied / Richland woman blues
CDSGP 037 / Jan '93 / Prestige

☐ AVALON BLUES 1963
Avalon blues / Avalon blues / Spike driver blues / Salty dog / Cow hooking blues / Spanish fandango / Casey jones / Louis collins / Candy man blues / My creole belle / Liza jane (god's unchanging hand) / Joe turner blues
ROUCD 1081 / Feb '92 / Rounder

☐ COFFEE BLUES
IMP 309 / Nov '96 / IMP

☐ IMMORTAL MISSISSIPPI JOHN HURT, THE
Since I've laid my burden down / Moaning the blues / Stocktime (Buck dance) / Lazy blues / Richland woman blues / Wise and foolish virgins / Hop joint / Monday morning blues / I've got the blues and I can't be satisfied / Keep on knocking / Chicken / Stagger Lee / Nearer my God to thee
VMD 79248 / Oct '95 / Vanguard

☐ IN CONCERT
Nobody's business but mine / Angels laid him away / Baby what's wrong with you / Casey Jones / Candy man / Lonesome blues / My creole belle / Make me a pallet on the floor / Trouble I had all my days / C-H-I-C-K-E-N blues / Coffee blues / Shake that thing / Monday morning blues / Frankie and Albert / Salty dog / Spike driver's blues
CDBM 083 / Apr '91 / Blue Moon

☐ LEGEND
Trouble I've had it all my days / Pera Lee / CC rider / Louis Collins / Coffee blues / Nobody's dirty business / Do lord remember me / Monday morning blues / Let the mermaids flirt with me / Pay day / Stack o lee / Casey Jones / Frankie and Albert / Stockwell
ROUCD 1100 / Dec '97 / Rounder

☐ LIBRARY OF CONGRESS RECORDINGS, THE
FLYCD 06 / Jun '89 / Flyright

☐ MEMORIAL ANTHOLOGY VOL.1
Slidin' delta / Salty dog / Louis Collins / Stagger lee / Monday mornin' blues / Comin' home / Candy man blues / Hot time in the old town tonight / KC Jones blues / Make me a pallet on the floor / You can't come in / Joe Turner / Spanish flangdang / Lonesome am I / I shall not be moved / CC rider / Trouble blues
EDCD 381 / Feb '94 / Edsel

☐ MEMORIAL ANTHOLOGY VOL.2
Lovin' spoonful / Richland woman blues / Frankie and Albert / Creole Bell / Chicken / Let the mermaids flirt with me / Nobody's dirty business / Stop time (buck dance) / Worried blues / Avalon blues
EDCD 446 / Apr '97 / Edsel

☐ MISSISSIPPI JOHN HURT
DOCD 5003 / Feb '92 / Document

☐ SATISFIED LIVE
CWNCD 2024 / Jul '96 / Javelin

☐ TODAY
Pay day / I'm satisfied / Candy man / Make me a pallet on the floor / Talking Casey / Corinna Corinna / Coffee blues / Louis Collins / Hot time in the old time tonight / If you don't want me baby / Spike driver's blues / Beulah land
VMD 79220 / Oct '95 / Vanguard

☐ WORRIED BLUES
Lazy blues / Lazy blues / Sliding delta / Nobody cares for me / Cow hooking blues no. 2 / Talkin' casey / Weeping and wailing / Worried blues / Oh mary don't you weep / I been cryin' since you been gone
ROUCD 1082 / Feb '92 / Rounder

Hurt, Peter

☐ UMBRELLAS
Climbing / Between ourselves / So good / Les parapluies De Stoke Newington Part II / Triangle / Goat / Complications
ASCCD 10 / Jun '96 / ASC

Hurvitz, Sandy

☐ SANDY'S ALBUM IS HERE AT LAST
Child / Three hawks / All this time going by / Woman / Sun / Many different things / You'll dance alone / Tree of trees / Arch godliness of purplefull magic / Love is what I've found
EDCD 399 / Nov '94 / Edsel

Hush

☐ HUMAN
SHCD 5704 / Oct '95 / Shanachie

Hush

☐ HUSH
ESM 027 / 2 Mar '98 / Escape

Husik, Lida

☐ GREEN BLUE FIRE
Bird / Bad head day / Haunt me / Wonderland / River Ouse / Just like candy / All hands on deck / Starburst 7 / Soul of God / Dead radio
ASW 6149 / Nov '96 / Astralwerks

Husker Du

☐ CANDY APPLE GREY
Crystal / Don't want to know if you are lonely / I don't know for sure / Sorry somehow / Too far down / Hardly getting over it / Dead set on destruction / Eiffel Tower high / No promise have I made / All this I've done for you
7599253852 / Nov '92 / WEA

☐ CASE CLOSED (A Tribute To Husker Du) (Various Artists)
SRC 19 / May '94 / SPV

☐ EVERYTHING FALLS APART
From the gut / Blah blah blah / Punch drunk / Bricklayer / Afraid of being wrong / Sunshine superman / Signals from above / Everything falls apart / Wheels / Target / Obnoxious / Gravity / In a free land / What do I want / MIC / Statues / Let's go die / Amusement / Do you remember
8122711632 / Mar '93 / WEA

☐ FLIP YOUR WIG
Flip your wig / Every everything / Makes no sense at all / Hate paper doll / Green eyes / Divide and conquer / Games / Find me / Baby song / Flexible flyer / Private plane / Keep hanging on / Wit and the wisdom / Don't know yet
SST 055CD / May '93 / SST

☐ LAND SPEED RECORD
SST 195CD / Nov '88 / SST

☐ NEW DAY RISING
SST 031CD / May '93 / SST

☐ THERE'S A BOY WHO LIVES ON HEAVEN HILL (A Tribute To Husker Du) (Various Artists)
BHR 009CD / Nov '94 / Burning Heart

☐ WAREHOUSE SONGS AND STORIES
These important years / Charity, charity, prudence and hope / Standing in the rain / Back from somewhere / Ice cold ice / You're a soldier / Could you be the one / Too much spice / Friend, you've got to fall / She floated away / Bed of nails / Tell you why tomorrow / It's not peculiar / Actual condition / No reservations / Turn it around / She's a woman / Up in the air / You can live at home
7599255442 / Oct '92 / WEA

☐ ZEN ARCADE
Something I learned today / Broken home broken heart / Never talking to you again / Chartered trips / Dreams reoccuring / Indecision time / Hare krishna / Beyond the threshold / Pride / I'll never forget you / Biggest lie / What's going on / Masochism world / Standing by the sea / Somewhere / One step at a time / Pink turns to blue / Newest industry / Monday will never be the same / Whatever / Tooth fairy and the princess / Turn on the news / Recurring dream
SST 027CD / Jun '97 / SST

Husky & The Sandmen

☐ ARABIAN NIGHTS
GASCD 1 / Nov '96 / Goofin'

Husky, Ferlin

☐ FERLIN HUSKY
Convoy / Truck drivin' sun of a gun / Don't fall asleep at the wheel / Giddy up go / Truck driving blues / Drunken driving / Hello I'm a truck / Wings of a dove / Little Joe / Phantom 309 / Me and old CB
PRACD 4005 / Jun '97 / Prairie

Hussain, Zakir

☐ MAKING MUSIC (Hussain, Zakir & John McLaughlin)
Making music / Zakir / Water girl / Toni / Anisa / Sunjog / You and me / Sabah
8315442 / Jul '87 / ECM

☐ SAMBANDH
Chaturshri / Taal mela / Dhyan / Kalpana / Khand jati / Sambandh
TRS 41182 / Jul '98 / Terrascape

☐ ZAKIR HUSSAIN & THE RHYTHM EXPERIENCE (Hussain, Zakir & The Rhythm Experience)
Balinese fantasy / Nines over easy / Lineage / Def and drum / Triveni / Rapanagutan / Ryupak / Rhythm sonata in E major
MRCD 1007 / Jun '94 / Moment

Hustlers Of Culture

☐ MANY STYLES
WALLLP 007 / Aug '95 / Wall Of Sound
WALLCD 008 / Mar '96 / Wall Of Sound

Hutcherson, Bobby

☐ AMBOS MUNDOS (BOTH WORLDS)
Pomponio / Tin tin deo / Both worlds / Street song / Beep d' bop / Poema para ravel / Yelapa / Besame mucho
LCD 15222 / Nov '89 / Landmark

☐ FAREWELL KEYSTONE
Crescent Moon / Short stuff / Prism / Starting over / Rubber man / Mapenzi
ECD 220182 / Jul '92 / Evidence

☐ FOUR SEASONS (Hutcherson, Bobby & George Cables)
I mean you / All of you / Spring is here / Star eyes / If I were a bell / Summertime / Autumn leaves
CDSJP 210 / Jan '87 / Timeless Jazz

☐ MIRAGE
Nascimento / Mirage / Beyond the bluebird / Pannonica / Del Valle / I am in love / Zingargo / Ground work / Love letters / Heroes
LCD 15292 / Aug '91 / Landmark

Hutchings, Ashley

☐ ALBION JOURNEY, AN
HNCD 4802 / May '89 / Hannibal

☐ AS YOU LIKE IT (Hutchings, Ashley All Stars)
SPINCD 135 / Jan '90 / Spindrift

☐ ASHLEY HUTCHINGS BIRTHDAY BASH CONCERT
HTD 39CD / Jul '95 / HTD

☐ BATTER PUDDING FOR JOHN KEATS, A
HTDCD 62 / Jun '96 / HTD

☐ COLLECTION, THE
High level hornpipe/Uncle George's: *Sawdust Band* / Horn Fair: *Etchingham Steam Band* / Three Bampton Morris tunes: *Albion Band* / Simple melody/Faggot dance: *Albion Band* / Morris dance tunes: *Albion Country Band* / Holm's fancy/ Cuckold's all awry: *Albion Dance Band* / Sweet bird of paradise: *Albion Band* / FBI: *Big Beat Combo* / Twistin' Welsh girls: *Big Beat Combo* / Twistin' til Monday comes round: *Big Beat Combo* / Telstar: *Big Beat Combo* / LIB: *Hutchings, Ashley Dance Band* / Hayeswood reel: *Hutchings, Ashley Dance Band* / Ken's hornpipes: *Hutchings, Ashley Dance Band* / Since love was charmed away: *Hutchings, Ashley Dance Band* / Dance to the drummer's beat: *Hutchings, Ashley Dance Band* / I just got off the plane: *Hutchings, Ashley Dance Band* / Cardmouse: *Hutchings, Ashley Dance Band*
CRESTCD 030 / Apr '98 / Mooncrest

☐ GUVNOR (4CD Set)
Washington at Valley Forge / Some sweet day / You're gonna need my help / Dear landlord / College grove/Silver spear / Lay down your weary tune / Four hand reel/St. Anne's reel / Horn fair / Lament / Sailor's life / Bluebell / Six days on the road / Albion band is here again / Lost in space / Elements lament / Angelina / 3 Brampton morris tunes / We lie / Didn't he ramble / You never wanted me / Sir Patrick Spens / Morris dance tunes / Rambling sailor / Cuckoos nest / Old Slr Simon the King / High level hornpipe / Don't be an outlaw / Spirit of the dance / Lay down your waery tune / Moon shine's bright / Rose and the rock / Sweet bird of paradise / Ninety miles an hour / I just got off the plane / Rainbow over the hill / Jerusalem ridge / Memories of you / Night in the city / Marcie / Harvest home / Fair maid of Islington / Three waltzes / Y'acre of land / Boycott's bouree / By the time it gets dark / Pain or paradise / Four tunes / Moon shine's bright / Princess Royal / Down the road / It doesn't matter anymore / Loose hornpipe / Spencer the rover / Cardhouse / Brief encounters / Oak / Both sides now / Fotheringay / Mistress's health / Quaker's wife / Here we come / Holms fancy / I'm looking through you / Simple melody / Electric guitar is king / Cecil sharp show / Personent Hodie / Love gets dangerous / Pa's piano stool / Turnpike reel / Willow / Not for the want of will / Swallow your gum / Wings
HTDBX 01 / Aug '97 / HTD

☐ GUVNOR VOL.1
HTDCD 23 / Jul '94 / HTD

☐ GUVNOR VOL.2
HTDCD 29 / Mar '95 / HTD

☐ GUVNOR VOL.3
HTDCD 38 / Jul '95 / HTD

☐ GUVNOR VOL.4
HTDCD 66 / Aug '96 / HTD

☐ KICKIN' UP THE SAWDUST
La russe (medley) / Buttered peas / Hullichan jig / Wave of joy / Heel and toe polka / Tavern in the town / Double quadrille / Jumping Joan / Dorset four hand reel / Hornpipes / Speed the plough / Cumberland square eight
BGOCD 244 / Oct '94 / Beat Goes On

☐ RATTLEBONE AND PLOUGHJACK
BGOCD 353 / Jun '97 / Beat Goes On

☐ SWAY WITH ME (Hutchings, Ashley & Judy Dunlop)
RGFCD 008 / '92 / Road Goes On Forever

☐ TWANGIN' AND A TRADDIN'
FBI / Sherwood handjive / Riff raff / Telstar / Walk don't run / Duane Eddy medley / Spyder walk
HTDCD 25 / Sep '96 / HTD

Hutchinson, Frank

☐ FRANK HUTCHINSON 1926-1929 VOL.1
DOCD 8003 / Mar '97 / Document

Hutchinson, Leslie

☐ CREAM OF HUTCH VOL.1, THE (Hutchinson, Leslie 'Hutch')
I forgot the little things / Begin the beguine / Don't make me laugh / Broken hearted clown / Night and day / Dusty shoes / I need you / If I should lose you / Good night my beautiful / East of the sun and west of the moon / I couldn't believe my eyes / Turn on the old music box / You made me care / Kiss in the dark / My heart is haunted / Faithfull forever / That old feeling / Indian summer / Body and soul / I've got my eyes on you / I know now / You're just looking for romance
PASTCD 9755 / Aug '91 / Flapper

☐ CREAM OF HUTCH VOL.2, THE (Hutchinson, Leslie 'Hutch')
They say / There's rain in my eyes / I can dream can't I / Please be kind / Love walked in / Meet me down in sunset valley / Goodnight angel / In santa margherita / Have you ever been to heaven / Take me in your arms / Weep and you'll dance alone / If I didn't care / Where or when / This heart of mine / There goes my dream / Moon love / Life is nothing without music / I'm in love with the honourable mrs. so and so / Bonsoir cherie / I'll always remember / Where are you
PASTCD 7036 / Aug '94 / Flapper

☐ HUTCH SINGS COLE PORTER & NOEL COWARD (Hutchinson, Leslie 'Hutch')
Let's do it let's fall in love / I'm a gigolo / Looking at you / What is sthis thing called love / Two little babes in the wood / Night and day / Anything goes / Begin the beguine / Just one of those things / Easy to love / I've got you under my skin / It's de-lovely / Do I love you / I've got my eyes on you / You'd be so nice to come home to / Half caste woman / I'll follow my secret heart / I travel alone / Close your eyes / All I do is dream of you / I nearly let love go slipping through my fingers / Says my heart / You go to my head / Cole Porter medley (Parts one and two)
CDCHD 213 / Mar '94 / Happy Days

☐ LESLIE 'HUTCH' HUTCHINSON (Hutchinson, Leslie 'Hutch')
Heartaches / Danger ahead / I promise you / Peg o' my heart / Seems liek old times / You stepped out of a dream / Flamingo / Till stars forget to shine / Way that the wind blows / Till then / There I've said it again / Sophisticated lady / Where in the world / Absent minded moon / Sand in my shoes / Manana / But beautiful / I never loved anyone / It only happens when I dance with you / Ask anyone who knows / You do / Tree in the meadow / You keep coming back like a song / I'm confessin' / Now is the hour
CDMFP 6357 / Jun '97 / Music For Pleasure

☐ TREASURED MEMORIES (Hutchinson, Leslie 'Hutch')
Begin the beguine / All the things you are / Mist on the rivers / I've got my eyes on you / Violins and violets / Man I love / Among my souvenirs / There's a small hotel / Intermezzo / What is this thing called love / When love comes your way / Try a little tenderness / Don't make me laugh / It's a lovely day tomorrow / Shake down the stars / Should I tell you that I love you / Dusty shoes / It happens every day / Where or when / That's the beginning of the end / Let's fall in love / Cole Porter medley / Small cafe by Notre Dame / Careless / Rosita
CDAJA 5084 / Mar '92 / Living Era

Huth, Pipe Major Roger

☐ PIPER'S COMPANION, THE
RFHCD 001 / 20 Oct '97 / RFH

Hutson, Leroy

☐ BEST OF LEROY HUTSON, THE
VICP 60293 / 27 Apr '98 / Victor

☐ CLOSER TO THE SOURCE
CPCD 8310 / Aug '97 / Charly

☐ FEEL THE SPIRIT
CPCD 8275 / May '97 / Charly

☐ HUTSON VOL.1
CPCD 8280 / Jul '97 / Charly

☐ HUTSON VOL.2
CPCD 8283 / Mar '97 / Charly

☐ LOVE, OH LOVE
CPCD 8156 / Mar '96 / Charly

☐ LUCKY FELLOW (The Best Of Leroy Hutson 1973-1979)
Lucky fellow / All because of you / Where did love go / Never know what you can do (give it a try) / So in love with you / Love to hold you close / Don't it make you feel good / Ghetto '74 / In the mood / Get to this (you'll get to me) / Lovers' holiday / So nice / When you smile
CDNEW 101 / Dec '96 / Charly

☐ MAN, THE
Can't say enough about Mom / Gotta move gotta groove / Ella Weez / Give this love a try / Getto '74 / After the fight / Could this be love / Dudley Do-Right
CPCD 8128 / Oct '95 / Charly

☐ UNFORGETTABLE
Unforgettable / (You put the) funk in my life / Right or wrong / So nice / Lonely without you / More where that came from
CPCD 832 / 2 Feb '98 / Charly

☐ VERY BEST OF LEROY HUTSON VOL.1, THE (The Definitive Hits Collection)
Love the feeling / Classy lady / Ghetto '74 / So nice / All because of you / Lover's holiday / Lucky fellow / Get to this (you'll get to me) / Love to hold you close / Don't it make you feel good / Heaven right here (on earth) / More where that came from / Never know what you can do (give it a try) / Love oh love / Cool out / It's different
DEEPM 007 / Feb '97 / Deep Beats

☐ VERY BEST OF LEROY HUTSON VOL.2, THE (More Where That Came From)
Where did love go / Paradise / Closer to the source / They've got love / So much love / Don't let it get next to you / All because of you / Situations / I do I do (want to make love with you) / So in love with you / In the mood / I bless the day / I think I'm falling in love / Getting it on / After the fight / Reality / Love you down / Ella Weez
DEEPM 033 / 26 Jan '98 / Deep Beats

Hutto, J.B.

☐ HAWK SQUAT (Hutto, J.B. & His Hawks)
DD 617 / Mar '95 / Delmark

☐ HIGH AND LONESOME
High and lonesome / JB's boogie / Feel so good / Too much alcohol / Hide and seek / Laundromat blues / Coo coo baby / Walking the dog / Come back baby / Kansas City
422330 / Jan '97 / Last Call

☐ LIVE AT THE SHABOO INN 1979
422327 / Feb '97 / Last Call

☐ MASTERS OF MODERN BLUES SERIES (Hutto, J.B. & His Hawks)
TCD 5020 / Apr '95 / Testament

☐ SLIDESLINGER (Hutto, J.B. & The New Hawks)
ECD 260092 / Jan '92 / Evidence

Hutton, Betty

☐ BLONDE BOMBSHELL, THE
AEICD 005 / May '98 / AEI

Hutton, Joe

☐ NORTHUMBRIAN PIPER
EAR 15CD / Oct '94 / East Allen

Hutton, June

☐ AFTERGLOW/WARM BRANDY (Hutton, June & Dolores Gray)
Never in a million years / Gone with the wind / Until the real thing comes along / I should care / It's the talk of the town / You're getting to be a habit with me / Day by day / East of the sun / Taking a chance on love / I hadn't anyone till you / My baby just cares for me / Dream a little dream of me / Shangri-La / Penthouse serenade / Your getting to be a habit / Kiss me / How long has this been going on / Close your eyes / You go to my head / Do do do / Speak low / Don't blame me / Isn't it romantic / You're my thrill
4930632 / Jan '98 / Capitol

Hutton, Tim

☐ CONSCIOUS KIND, THE
SBZCD 005 / Dec '91 / Some Bizarre

Huub De Lange

☐ LIFE AND DEATH ON A STREET ORGAN
PAN 145CD / Dec '94 / Pan

Huun-Huur-Tu

☐ IF I'D BEEN BORN AN EAGLE
SH 64080 / Feb '97 / Shanachie

☐ ORPHANS LAMENT
SHAN 64058CD / Apr '95 / Shanachie

☐ SIXTY HORSES IN MY HERD (Old Songs & Tunes Of Tuva - Throat Singing)
SHCD 64050 / Mar '94 / Shanachie

Huxley, George

☐ SWING THAT MUSIC
JCD 239 / Mar '95 / Jazzology

Huygen, Michel

☐ BARCELONA 1992
Carvalho / Impossible love / Chase / Meeting at the hilton / Loneliness / Barcelona 1992 / Tonight
CDTB 056 / Feb '88 / Thunderbolt

☐ INTIMO
Tenderness / Light being / When I stop the time / Remoteness / El mar de la Soledad / Tempestad cerebral / Vital breath / Infinite tenderness
CDTB 092 / Sep '90 / Thunderbolt

Hwan, Kang Tae

☐ KANG TAE HWAN & SAINKHO NAMTCHYLAK LIVE (Hwan, Kang Tae & Sainkho Namtchylak)
FINCD 9301 / Apr '94 / Free Improvision Network

Hyams, Steve

☐ MISTAKEN IDENTITIES
Mistaken identites / Should have done it better / Spanish tune / Do it again / Tombstone / Lost in me / World cruise / Behind me now / Pick it up / Shuffle down easy / 1234 Kik along blues / Lonely / Stay on your own / Economic tragedy / I fall over I fall down / Dear Louise / Wavy line / Bringing in me back
SJPCD 015 / 13 Oct '97 / Angel Air

Hyatt, Walter

☐ MUSIC TOWN
SHCD 1039 / Jan '94 / Sugar Hill

Hybernoid

☐ LAST DAY
FDN 2002CD / Aug '95 / Foundation 2000

Hybirds

☐ HYBIRDS
HVNLP 20CD / 2 Mar '98 / Heavenly

Hybrid Kids

☐ HONEYMOON IN BABYLON
SPV 07745772 / Mar '96 / SPV

Hydra

☐ SPOOKY WEIRDNESS
Comfort / Dream on / Let me be your worm / Clinging vine / Nowhere over the rainbow / Custer's last grand / Butterflies / Maid of grace / Nitro / W4 syndrome
5331262 / Mar '97 / Hi-Life

Hydroplane

☐ HYDROPLANE
DRIVE 09 / Jun '97 / Drive-In

Hykes, David

☐ CURRENT CIRCULATION (Hykes, David & The Harmonic Choir)
CDCEL 13010 / Nov '92 / Celestial Harmonies

☐ CURRENT MEETINGS (Hykes, David & The Harmonic Choir)
CDCEL 14013 / Nov '92 / Celestial Harmonies

Hyla, Lee

☐ IN DOUBLE LIGHT
AVAN 015 / Sep '93 / Avant

Hyland, Brian

☐ VERY BEST OF BRIAN HYLAND
Sealed with a kiss / Warmed over kisses (left over
love) / It mary's there / I'm afraid to go home / Angel in
my heart / Tragedy / A million to one / Stay and love
me all summer / Summer job / Ginny come lately /
Lonely teardrops / Gypsy woman / Walk a lonely mile
/ I may not live to see tomorrow / I'll never stop
wanting you / Don't dilly dally sally / (the clickety
clack song) four little heels / Itsy bitsy teenie weenie
yellow polka dot bikini
MCCD 146 / Nov '93 / Music Club

Hylton, Jack

☐ CREAM OF JACK HYLTON
Rhythm like this / Trouble in Paradise / Gold diggers
song (We're in the money) / I can't remember /
Hallelujah, I'm a tramp / Stormy weather / Shadow
waltz / Dancing butterfly / With you here, and me
here / Honeymoon hotel / You're an old smoothie /
You are too beautiful / You've got me crying again /
Close your eyes / (In) a shanty in old Shanty Town /
Try a little tenderness / Ride tenderfoot ride / Good
morning / Love makes the world go round / What
goes on here
PASTCD 9775 / Feb '92 / Flapper

☐ JACK'S BACK (Hylton, Jack & His
Orchestra)
Happy days are here again / Speaking of Kentucky
days / My bundle of love / I'm looking over a four leaf
clover / World's greatest sweetheart is you /
Harmonica Harry / Gentlemen prefer blondes /
Broadway melody / Happy feet / I wanna go places
and do things / Guy that wrote 'The stein' song /
Meadow lark / Choo choo / Life is just a bowl of
cherries / Da da da / Under the ukelele tree / Hang on
to me / When day is done
CDAJA 5018 / '87 / Living Era

☐ JACK'S BACK
I won't dance / On your toes / Run rabbit run / Girls
were made to love and kiss / She's Latin from
Manhattan / Life begins at Oxford Circus
CDEA 6007 / 15 Jun '98 / Vocalion

Hyman, Dick

☐ CHEEK TO CHEEK (Hyman, Dick Trio)
ARCD 19155 / May '97 / Arbors Jazz

☐ CONCORD DUO SERIES VOL.6
(Hyman, Dick & Ralph Sutton)
I've found a new baby / I'm gonna sit right down and
write myself a letter / Always / I'm sorry I made you
cry / Everything happens to me / All of me / Sunday /
Ol' man river / Spider and the fly / World is waiting for
the sunrise / Dinah / Emaline
CCD 4603 / Jul '94 / Concord Jazz

☐ DICK HYMAN PLAYS COLE PORTER:
ALL THROUGH THE NIGHT
MM 5060 / Oct '94 / Music Masters

☐ DICK HYMAN PLAYS FATS WALLER
(Hyman, Dick & His Trio)
RR 33CD / Sep '91 / Reference
Recordings

☐ ELEGIES
GMCD 90 / May '98 / Gemini

☐ FACE THE MUSIC (A Century Of Irving
Berlin)
MM 5002 / Oct '94 / Music Masters

☐ GERSHWIN SONGBOOK: JAZZ
VARIATIONS
MM 65094 / Oct '94 / Music Masters

☐ GREAT AMERICAN SONGBOOK, THE
01612651202 / Sep '95 / Music Masters

☐ KINGDOM OF SWING & THE
REPUBLIC OF OOP BOP SH'BAM
(Jazz In July - Live At The 92nd Street)
Lester leaps in: Jazz In July / Joshua fit de battle of
jericho: Jazz In July
MM 5016 / Oct '94 / Music Masters

☐ LIVE AT THE 92ND STREET Y (Hyman,
Dick Piano Players & Significant
Others)
MM 5042 / Oct '94 / Music Masters

☐ MANHATTAN JAZZ (Hyman, Dick &
Ruby Braff)
MM 5031 / Oct '94 / Music Masters

☐ SWING IS HERE
RR 72CD / Jul '96 / Reference
Recordings

☐ THEY GOT RHYTHM (Hyman, Dick &
Derek Smith)
Jitterbug waltz / Stella by starlight / New york, new
york / I'm beginning to see the light / I got it bad and
that ain't good / Cotton tail / Strike up the band /
Softly as in a morning sunrise / I got rhythm / Sweet
georgia brown
JCD 635 / Oct '93 / Jass

Hyman, Phyllis

☐ BEST OF PHYLLIS HYMAN (The
Buddah Years)
Loving you - losing you / No one can love you more /
One thing on my mind / I don't want to lose you /
Deliver the love / Night bird gets the love / Beautiful
man of mine / Children of the world / Living inside
your love / Sweet music / Answer is you / Love is free
/ Sing a song / Soon come again / Be careful (how
you treat my love)
NEXCD 138 / Oct '90 / Sequel

☐ ONE ON ONE
HIPD 40084 / 14 Apr '98 / Hippo

☐ SWEET MUSIC
Loving you losing you / No one can love you more /
One thing on my mind / I don't want to lose you /
Deliver the love / Night bird gets the love / Beautiful
man of mine / Children of the world / Living inside
your love / Sweet music / Answer is you / Love is free
/ Sing a song / Soon come again / Be careful (how
you treat my love) / Betcha by golly wow
74321558512 / 26 Jan '98 / Camden

Hype-A-Delics

☐ MO' FUNK FOR YOUR ASS
EFA 119352 / Mar '94 / Juiceful

Hyper Go Go

☐ NATIONAL ANTHEMS
AVEXCD 32 / Apr '96 / Avex

Hyperborea

☐ SERPENTINE
SC 469 / Aug '96 / Starc

Hyperhead

☐ METAPHASIA
Making waves / Teenage mind / Terminal fear / Easy
slide / Close to hysteria / Pre-emprive counter attack
/ Ignition x 4 / Method one / Trash
CDDVN 16 / Dec '92 / Devotion

Hypermodern Jazz
2000.5

☐ HYPERMODERN JAZZ 2000.5
EFA 006732 / Apr '96 / Mille Plateau

Hypersax

☐ STEPDANCE
Stepdance / Run for fun / Sailing around Greek
islands / Princy palace / Long distance education /
Update / Song for Contessa / Red Bank NJ / Solo in
the night / Starlight / Rush hour / Rainy days / Pop
song / VIBSAX
101 2 7054 2 / Nov '92 / New Note

Hypnomen

☐ SUPER SONICO
TWINCD 34 / Nov '97 / Stupido

Hypnotone

☐ AI
Airwalk / God c.p.u. (ambient) / Sbx il / Qix /
Electraphonic / God c.p.u. / Dream beam / Quasar /
L-o-v-e / Yu-yu (f.t.d.)
CRECD 080 / May '94 / Creation

☐ HYPNOTONE
CRECD 067 / May '94 / Creation

Hypocrisy

☐ ABDUCTED
NB 133CD / Jan '96 / Nuclear Blast

☐ FINAL CHAPTER
NB 283CD / 24 Nov '97 / Nuclear Blast

☐ FOURTH DIMENSION, THE
NB 112CD / Oct '94 / Nuclear Blast

☐ INFERIOR DEVOTIES
NB 098CD / Mar '94 / Nuclear Blast

☐ MAXIMUM ABDUCTION
NB 145CD / May '96 / Nuclear Blast

☐ OBSCULUM OBSCENUM
NB 080CD / Aug '93 / Nuclear Blast

☐ OSCULUM OBSCENUM/INFERIOR
DEVOTEES/PLEASURES OF
MOLESTATION
NB 215CD / Nov '96 / Nuclear Blast

☐ PENETRALLIA
NB 164CD / Jun '96 / Nuclear Blast

Hypocrite

☐ EDGE OF EXISTENCE
OW 003CD / Jul '96 / Offworld

I

I-Compani
☐ GLUTEUS MAXIMUS
BVHAASTCD 9707 / Apr '98 / Bvhaast

☐ LUNA TRISTE
BVHAASTCD 9012 / Oct '93 / Bvhaast

☐ SOGNI D'ORO
BVHAASTCD 9404 / Oct '94 / Bvhaast

I-Cube
☐ PICNIC ATTACK
VERCD 006 / May '97 / Versatile

I Found God
☐ BEFORE HE TURNED THE GUN ON HIMSELF
OC 500022 / May '97 / Outcast

I-Gitanos
☐ AB I REISA
Ab I reisa / Fulli tschesi / Newo diwes / Mu penia / Go braucha / Deisa / Amando / Gane i mischdo / Illusioen / Enja diwes an Madrid / I bacht / Baro dewel deblesgi dei
INT 32392 / 26 May '98 / Intuition

I-Muvrini
☐ SA
3034782 / 24 Apr '98 / Arcade

I-Roy
☐ CRISUS TIME
Heart of a lion / Casmas Town / Tonight / Wrap 'n' bap 'n' / Union call / London / Roots man time / African tak / Crisus time / Equality and justice / Hypocrite back out / Musical injection / Don't touch I man locks / Satta a masagana / African herbsman / Love your neighbour / Send us little power oh jah / Moving on strong
CDFL 9015 / Jul '93 / Frontline

☐ DON'T CHECK ME WITH NO LIGHTWEIGHT STUFF (I-Roy 1972-1975)
BAFCD 16 / Jan '97 / Blood & Fire

☐ GREAT GODFATHER
RNCD 2079 / Dec '94 / Rhino

☐ KING TUBBY'S STUDIO (I-Roy & Dillinger)
LG 21116 / Oct '95 / Lagoon

☐ PRESENTING I-ROY/HELL AND SORROW
Red, gold and green / Pusher man / Black man time / Smile like an angel / Peace / Coxsone affair / Screw face / First cut is the deepest / Melinda / Tourism is my business / Tripe girl / Cow Town skank / Deep and heavy / Trouble man / Sugar candy / Monkey fashion / Black and proud / Medley mood / Jah lion jungle / Forward LA / Buck and the preacher / Dr. Phibbs / African descendent / Call on I
CDTRL 389 / Sep '97 / Trojan

☐ STRAIGHT TO I-ROY'S HEAD (Various Artists)
CC 2719 / Apr '95 / Crocodisc

I-Salonisiti
☐ CAFE VICTORIA
Los mareados / Poema valseado / Recuerdo / Coral / Romance de barrio / Uno / Payadora / Flores negras / Severina / Flor de lino / Contra bajilsmo
CDC 1695312 / Jul '86 / Harmonia Mundi

☐ AND THE BAND PLAYED ON (Music Played On The Titanic)
Comic cake walk / Destiny / El capitan / None but the lone heart / Molly on the shore / Intermezzo / Gluhwurmchen idyll / Standchen / Elite syncopations / Wiener blut / Cavatine / Everybody's doing it now / Humoresque / Pomp and circumstance / Nearer my God to thee
4583822 / 12 Jan '98 / Decca

I-Sharko
☐ I SHARKO
BCD 4053 / Apr '96 / Bomp

I-Shen Sound
☐ KING SIZE DUB
HYPOXIA 002CD / Oct '95 / Hypoxia

I-Spy
☐ PERVERSITY IS SPREADING
G7 004 / 29 Jun '98 / G7 Welcoming Committee

I Start Counting
☐ FUSED
Money / Grassnake / House / Modern sunbathing / Only after dark / Lose him / Million headed monster / Rawhide / Empty room / Car (theme from "the blessing") / Ad mans dream / Birmingham / Ra ra rawhide
CDSTUMM 50 / Jun '89 / Mute

☐ MY TRANSLUCENT HANDS
Introduction / My translucent hands / Catch that look / You and I / Lose him / Keep the sun away / Cranley Gardens / Which way is home / Letters to a friend / Still smiling / Small consolation / (There is always the) unexpected
CDSTUMM 30 / Oct '86 / Mute

I Suanatori Delle Quatro Province
☐ RACCONTI A COLORI
NT 6720 / Jan '94 / Robi Droli

I-Tara Oasului
☐ ROMANIAN FOLK MUSIC FOR WEDDINGS
ARN 64416 / 24 Apr '98 / Arion

iO
☐ 90 MINUTES IN THE EYES OF IO (i0 & Adsr)
CHEAP ONE / Apr '95 / Cheap

Ian & Sylvia
☐ END OF THE BEGINNING, THE
More often than not / Creators of rain / Summer wages / Midnight / Barney / Some kind of fool / Shark and the cockroach / Last lonely eagle / Lincoln feed me / Needle of death / Everybody has to say goodbye / Give it to the world / Jordan Station / Long Beach / Love is strange
BCD 15940 / Dec '96 / Bear Family

☐ GREATEST HITS
Early morning rain / Tomorrow is a long time / Little beggar man / Mighty Quinn / Nancy Whisky / Catfish blues / Come in stranger / French girl / Renegade / Mary Anne / You were on my mind / Four strong winds / Short grass / Southern comfort / Someday soon / Ella Speed / Circle game / 90 x 90 / Cutty Wren / Un Canadien errant / Lonely girls / Spanish is a loving tongue / This wheel's on fire
VCD 5 / 27 Jul '98 / Vanguard

☐ SO MUCH FOR DREAMING
VMD 79241 / Oct '96 / Vanguard

Ian, Janis
☐ AFTERTONES
Aftertones / I would like to dance / Love is blind / Roses / Belle of the blues / Goodbye to morning / Boy I really tried one on / This must be wrong / Don't cry / Old man / Hymn
GRACD 304 / Jan '96 / Grapevine

☐ BETWEEN THE LINES
When the party's over / At seventeen / From me to you / Bright lights and promises / In the Winter / Water colors / Between the lines / Come on / Light a tight / Tea and sympathy / Lover's lullaby
GRACD 303 / Aug '95 / Grapevine

☐ HUNGER
Black and white / On the dark side of town / Might as well be Monday / Getting over you / Searching for America / Hunger / Welcome to Acousticville / Honour them / Empty / House without a heart / Shadow
GRACD 233 / 20 Oct '97 / Grapevine

☐ JANIS IAN
Grand illusion / Some people / Tonight will last forever / Hotels and one night stands / Do you wanna dance / Silly habits / Bridge / My mama's house / Street life serenaders / I need to live alone again / Hopper painting
GRACD 306 / Jan '96 / Grapevine

☐ MIRACLE ROW
Party lights / I want to make you love me / Sunset of your life / Take to the sky / Candlelight / Let me be lonely / Slow dance romance / Will you dance / I'll cry tonight / Miracle row / Maria
GRACD 305 / Aug '95 / Grapevine

☐ NIGHT RAINS
Other side of the sun / Fly too high / Memories / Photographs / Here comes the night / Day by day / Have mercy love / Lay low / Night rains / Jenny
GRACD 307 / Jan '96 / Grapevine

☐ OLD GREY WHISTLE TEST 1976
WHISCD 008 / Mar '96 / Whistle Test

☐ PRESENT COMPANY
Seaside / Present company / See my grammy ride / Here in Spain / On the train / He's a rainbow / Weary Lady / Nature's at peace / See the river / Let it run free / Alabama / Liberty / My land / Hello Jerry / Can you reach me / Sunlight
BGOCD 165 / Nov '92 / Beat Goes On

☐ RESTLESS EYES
Under the covers / I remember yesterday / I believe I'm myself again / Restless eyes / Get ready to roll / Passion play / Down and away / Bigger than real / Dear Billy / Sugar mountain
GRACD 308 / Jan '96 / Grapevine

☐ REVENGE
GRACD 301 / May '95 / Grapevine

☐ SOCIETY'S CHILD
Society's child / Too old to go 'way little girl / Hair of spun gold / Then the tangles of my mind / I'll give you a stone if you'll throw it / Pro-girl / Younger generation blues / New Christ cardiac hero / Everybody knows / Mistaken identity / Friends again / 42nd Street / Psycho blues / She's made of porcelain / Sweet misery / When I was a child / What do you think of the dead / Look to the rain
5725912 / Jan '94 / Polydor

☐ STARS
Stars / Man you are in me / Sweet sympathy / Page nine / Thank yous / Dance with me / Without you / You've got me on a string / Applause
GRACD 302 / Jan '96 / Grapevine

☐ UNCLE WONDERFUL
GRACD 309 / Jan '96 / Grapevine

Ianescu, Ion
☐ PAN FLUTE CHRISTMAS VOL.1 (Away In A Manger) (Ianescu, Ion Ensemble)
White Christmas / Jingle bells / Do they know it's christmas / I heard the bells on Christmas day / Oh christmas tree / Medley / Little drummer boy / Oh little town of Bethlehem / O come all ye faithful (adeste fidelis) / German medley / Away in a manger / Holly and the ivy / We wish you a merry Christmas / Ave Maria
120282 / Oct '97 / Jingle

☐ PAN FLUTE CHRISTMAS VOL.2 (When A Child Is Born) (Ianescu, Ion Ensemble)
Winter wonderland / French medley / Merry christmas (war is over) / Christmas song / Winter's tale / God rest ye merry gentlemen / Medley / Silver bells / When a child is born / Joseph my dear Joseph / Twelve days of Christmas / Deck the halls / Oh du frohliche / Ding dong merrily on high
120292 / Oct '97 / Jingle

☐ PAN FLUTE CHRISTMAS VOL.3 (Mary's Boy Child) (Ianescu, Ion Ensemble)
Silent night / Mary's boy child / Mistletoe and wine / Blue Christmas / Sleigh ride / First Noel / Season of joy / Have yourself a merry little christmas / Hark the herald angels sing / Unto us a child is born / Alpenlandisches medley / Christmas is here / Rudolph the red-nosed reindeer / Auld lang syne
120302 / Oct '97 / Jingle

Iao Core
☐ ARMADILLIDIUM HONEYPAT
VC 136 / 20 Apr '98 / Vinyl Communication

Ibbotson, Daniel
☐ NEW STORIES
REEL 001CD / 24 Nov '97 / Ideal

Ibizarre
☐ WINTER AMBIENT ALBUM
0091422EXT / 12 Jan '98 / Xtravaganza

Ibrahim, Abdullah
☐ AFRICA - TEARS AND LAUGHTER (Brand, Dollar Quartet)
ENJA 30392 / 17 Oct '97 / Enja

☐ AFRICAN PIANO (Brand, Dollar)
Bra Joe from Kilimanjaro / Selby that the eternal spirit / Is the only reality / Moon / Xaba / Sunset in the blue / Kippy / Jabulani / Tintinyana
8350202 / Sep '88 / ECM

☐ AFRICAN SUN (Brand, Dollar)
African sun / Bra Joe from Kilimanjaro / Rollin' / Memories of you / Sathima / African herbs / Nobody knows the trouble I've seen / Blues for B / Gwidza / Kamalie
CDN 1008 / 27 Apr '98 / Camden

☐ ANATOMY OF A SOUTH AFRICAN VILLAGE (Brand, Dollar & Gertze/ Ntshoko)
BLC 760172 / Nov '92 / Black Lion

☐ ANCIENT AFRICA
Bra Joe from Kilimanjaro / Mama / Tokai / Ilanga / Cherry / African sun / Tintinyana / Xaba / Peace - Salaam air
SKCD 23049 / Oct '94 / Sackville

☐ BLUES FOR A HIP KING (Brand, Dollar)
Ornette's cornet / All day and all night long / Sweet Basil blues / Blue monk / Tsakwe here comes the postman / Blues for a hip king / Blues for B / Mysterioso / Just you, just me / Eclipse at dawn / King Kong / Khumbula Jane / Boulevarde East
CDN 1010 / 15 Jun '98 / Camden

☐ CAPE TOWN FLOWERS
Excursions / Eleventh hour / Kofifi blue / Chisa / Song for Aggerey / Stride / Call / African marketplaace / Joan Cape Town Flower / Maraba blue / Monk in Harlem
8888262 / May '97 / Tiptoe

☐ DOLLAR BRAND (Brand, Dollar)
Little Niles / Resolution / Which way / On the banks of Allen Waters / Knights night / Pye R squared / Mood indigo/Don't get around much anymore/Take the A train / Stride / Tintiyana / Obluega
8747112 / Jul '96 / DA Music

☐ DUKES' MEMORIES (Brand, Dollar)
233853 / '86 / Black & Blue

☐ ECHOES FROM AFRICA (Brand, Dollar)
ENJA 30472 / 17 Nov '97 / Enja

☐ FATS, DUKE AND MONK
SKCD 3049 / Mar '97 / Sackville

☐ KNYSNA BLUE
Knysna blue / You can't stop me now / Peace / Three no.1 / Kofifi / Three no.2 / Cape Town / Ask me now
8888162 / Jun '94 / Enja

☐ MANTRA MODE
8478102 / Nov '91 / New Note

☐ MEMORIES
WWCD 2029 / Apr '90 / West Wind

☐ MINDIF (Brand, Dollar)
ENJA 50732 / Jul '88 / Enja

☐ MOUNTAIN, THE (Ibrahim, Abdullah & Ekaya)
Mountain / Bra timing from Phomolong / Ehaya / Sotho blu / Tuan guru / Ntyilo ntyilo / Nelson Mendela / Wedding / Mannenberg / Cape Town
CDN 1002 / 23 Mar '98 / Camden

☐ NO FEAR, NO DIE
Calypso minor / Angelica / Meditation / Nisa / Kata / Meditation / Calypso major
8888152 / Jul '93 / Tiptoe

☐ ODE TO DUKE ELLINGTON (Brand, Dollar)
Impressions on a caravan / Ode to Duke / What really happened in the cornfield / Rose got it bad in Harlem / Solitude / In a sentimental mood / Two spirituals
WWCD 2020 / Dec '93 / West Wind

☐ PIANO SOLO
591152 / 21 Aug '97 / Musidisc

☐ REFLECTIONS (Brand, Dollar)
Honeysuckle rose / Resolution / Knight's night / Mood indigo / Don't get around much anymore / Take the 'A' train / Monk's mood / You are too beautiful / Little Niles / Pye R squared / On the banks of Allen Waters / Reflections / Which way
BLCD 760127 / May '90 / Black Lion

☐ ROUND MIDNIGHT AT MONTMARTRE (Brand, Dollar)
BLCD 76011 / Feb '89 / Black Lion

☐ TINTINYANA
Soweto is where it's at / Tintinyana / Little boy / Cherry / Bra Joe from Kilimanjaro / Shrimp boats: *Brand, Dollar* / Salaam / Just a song: *Mason, D*
CDN 1009 / 13 Jun '98 / Camden

☐ VOICE OF AFRICA, THE
Black lightning / Little boy / Black and brown cherries / Ntyilo, Ntyilo: *Davashe* / Mannenberg / Pilgrim: *Brand, Dollar*
CDN 1007 / 27 Apr '98 / Camden

☐ WATER FROM AN ANCIENT WELL
Mandela / Song for Fathima / Manenberg revisited / Tuang Guru / Water from an ancient well / Wedding / Mountain / Sameeda
8888122 / Feb '95 / Tiptoe

☐ YARONA
Nisa / Duke / Cherry / Mannenberg / African river / Tuang guru / Stardance / African marketplace / Tintinyana / Barakaat
8888202 / Jul '95 / Enja

☐ ZIMBABWE (Brand, Dollar)
ENJA 40562 / '88 / Enja

Icarus
☐ MARVEL WORLD OF ICARUS
PL 28161 / Sep '97 / Play Loud

Icarus
☐ KAMIKAZE
HEMP 16CD / 27 Apr '98 / Recordings Of Substance

Ice

☐ UNDER THE SKIN
Juggernaut kiss / Survival of the fattest / Out of focus / .357 magnum is a monster / Skyscraper / Flood / Stick insect / Implosion / Swimmer
PATH 11CD / Jul '93 / NMC

Ice

☐ SAGA OF THE ICE KING
KSCD 9596 / Jun '97 / Kissing Spell

Ice

☐ BAD BLOOD
X-1 / Snake pit / Trapped in 3 dimension / Dusted / New breed of rat / Devils / When two worlds collide
MORPH 001CD / 11 May '98 / Morpheus

Ice Age

☐ LIFE'S A BITCH
HMIXD 154 / Aug '90 / FM

Ice Cold July

☐ THERE WILL COME A DAY
SECT2 10002 / Jul '95 / Sector 2

Ice Cream Hands

☐ MEMORY LANE TRAFFIC JAM
NL 041 / 8 Jun '98 / Not Lame

Ice Cube

☐ AMERIKKKA'S MOST WANTED
Better off dead / Nigga ya love to hate / What they hittin foe / You can't fade me/JD's gaffilin / Once upon a time in the projects / Turn off the radio / Endangered species (Tales from the darkside) / Gangsta's fairytale / I'm only out for one thang / Get off my dick and tell yo bitch to come here / Drive-by / Rollin' wit' tha lench mob / Who's the mack / Amerikkka's most wanted / It's a man's world / Bomb
IMCD 230 / Sep '96 / Island

☐ BOOTLEGS & B-SIDES
Robbin' hood (cause it ain't all good) / What can I do / 24 with a L / You know how we do it / 2 n the morning / You don't wanna fuck with these / Lil ass gee / My skin is my sin / It was a good day / U ain't gonna take my life / When I get to heaven / D'Voidofpopniggafiedmegamix
IMCD 231 / Sep '96 / Island

☐ DEATH CERTIFICATE
Funeral / Wrong nigga to fuck wit / My summer vacation / Steady mobbin / Robin Lench / Givin' up the nappy dug out / Look who's burnin / Bird in the hand / Man's best friend / Alive on arrival / Death / Birth / I wanna kill Sam / Horny Lil devil / True to the game / Color blind / Doing dumb shit / Us
IMCD 232 / Sep '96 / Island

☐ KILL AT WILL
Endangered species (Tales from the darkside) / Jackin' for beats / Get off my dick and tell yo bitch to come here / Product / Dead homiez / JD gaffiliin / I gotta say what up
BRECD 572 / Mar '91 / 4th & Broadway

☐ LETHAL INJECTION
Shot / Really doe / Ghetto bird / You know how we do it / Cave bitch / Bop gun (one nation) / What can I do / Lil ass gee / Make it ruff, make it smooth / Down for whatever / Enemy / When I get to heaven
IMCD 229 / Sep '96 / Island

☐ PREDATOR, THE
First day of school / When will they shoot / I'm scared / Wicked / Now I gotta wet 'cha / Predator / It was a good day / We had to tear this MF up / Dirty mack / Don't trust 'em / Gangsta's fairytale 2 / Check yo' self / Who got the camera / Integration / Say hi to the bad guy
IMCD 228 / Sep '96 / Island

☐ WORLD IS MINE, THE
8941762 / Mar '97 / Priority/Virgin

Ice-T

☐ CLASSIC COLLECTION, THE
Ice-a-mix / Coldest rap / Killers / Ya don't quit / Six in the mornin' / Body rock / Cold wind madness / Dog 'n the wax / Icapella / Ice-o-tek
8122711702 / May '93 / Street Knowledge

☐ HOME INVASION
Warning / It's on / Ice M/F T / Home invasion / G style / Addicted to danger / Question and answer / Watch the ice break / Race war / That's how I'm livin' / I ain't new ta this / Pimp behind the wheels / Gotta lotta love / Shit hit the fan / Depths of hell / Ninety nine problems / Funky gripsta / Message to the soldier / Ain't a damn thing changed
RSYND 1 / Mar '93 / Rhyme Syndicate

☐ ICEBERG/FREEDOM OF SPEECH
Shut up / Be happy / Iceberg / Lethal weopon / You played yourself (aka the boss) / Peel their caps back / Girl tried to kill me / Black 'n' decker / Hit the deck / This one's for me / Hunted child / What ya wanna do (aka do you wanna go party) / Freedom of speech / My word is bond
9260282 / Oct '89 / Street Knowledge

☐ OG ORIGINAL GANGSTER
First impression / Ziplock / New jack hustler / Bitches 2 / Straight up nigga / OG original gangster / House / Evil E - what about sex / Fly by / Fried chicken / Lifestyles of the rich and famous / Body Count / Prepared to die / Escape from the killing fields / Tower / Ya shoulda killed me last year / Home of the bodybag / Mic contract / Mind over matter / Ed / Midnight / MVPS / Street killer / Pulse of the rhyme
7599264922 / May '91 / Street Knowledge

☐ POWER
Intro / Power / Drama / Heartbeat / I'm your pusher / LGBNAF / Syndicate / Radio suckers / Soul on ice / Outro / High rollers / Personal
9257652 / Sep '88 / Street Knowledge

☐ RETURN OF THE REAL
Pimp anthem / Where the shit goes down / Bouncin' down the stezeet / Return of the real / I must stand / Alotta niggas / Rap games hijacked / How does it feel / Lane / Rap is fake / Make the loot loop / Syndicate 4 ever / 5th / It's goin' down / They want me back in / Inside of a gangsta / Forced to do dirt / Haters / Cramp your style / Real / Dear homie
RSYND 3 / May '96 / Rhyme Syndicate

☐ RHYME PAYS
Intro / Six 'n the mornin' / Make it funky / Somebody gotta do it / 409 / I love ladies / Sex / Pain / Squeeze the trigger
7599256022 / Jan '93 / Street Knowledge

Iceberg

☐ ARC-EN-CIEL
CD 80202202 / 16 Mar '98 / Actual

☐ COSES NOSTRES
CD 80202502 / 16 Mar '98 / Actual

☐ SENTIMENTS
CD 80202402 / 16 Mar '98 / Actual

Iceburn

☐ MEDITAVOULTIONS (Iceburn Collective)
REV 042CD / Apr '96 / Revelation

Iceburn Collective

☐ POWER OF THE LION
ICE 002CD / 16 Feb '98 / Revelation

Iced Earth

☐ BURNT OFFERINGS
CM 770932 / May '95 / Century Media

☐ DARK SAGA, THE
CMCD 77131 / Jun '96 / Century Media

☐ DAYS OF PURGATORY (2CD Set)
CM 77165CD / May '97 / Century Media

☐ ICED EARTH
Iced earth / Written on the walls / Colors / Curse the sky / Life and death / Solitude / Funeral / When the night falls
8497142 / Feb '91 / Century Media

☐ SOMETHING WICKED THIS WAY COMES
CM 77214CD / 6 Jul '98 / Century Media

Icho Candy

☐ GLORY AND THE KING (Icho Candy & Jah Shaka)
SHAKACD 948 / Jul '93 / Jah Shaka

Ichor

☐ NONPLUS
EFA 112372 / May '95 / Danse Macabre

Ichu

☐ ICHU
BLR 84 023 / May '91 / L&R

Icicle Works

☐ BEST OF THE ICICLE WORKS, THE
BEGA 124CD / Aug '92 / Beggars Banquet

☐ ICICLE WORKS, THE
Chop the tree / Love is a wonderful colour / As the dragonfly flies / Lover's day / In the cauldron of love / Out of season / Factory in the desert / (Birds fly) Whisper to a scream / Nirvana / Reaping the rich harvest
BBL 50CD / Jul '88 / Beggars Banquet

☐ IF YOU WANT TO DEFEAT THE ENEMY SING HIS SONG
Hope springs eternal / Travelling chest / Sweet Thursday / Up here in the North of England / Who do you want for your love / When you were mine / Evangeline / Truck driver's lament / Understanding Jane / Walking with a mountain / Please don't let it rain on my parade / Everybody loves to play the fool / I never saw my hometown 'till I went around the world / Into the mystic
BBL 78CD / Feb '90 / Beggars Banquet

☐ SMALL PRICE OF A BICYCLE, THE
Hollow horse / Perambulator / Seven horses / Rapids / Windfall / Assumed sundowns / Saint's sojourn / All the daughters / Book of reason / Conscience of Kings
BBL 61CD / Jan '89 / Beggars Banquet

Ickes, Rob

☐ HARD TIMES
No more my land / Down in the hole / Tom Dooley / Flat lonesome / Reuben / Song for Jennifer / Look ka py py / Hard times / Ashland breakdown / One bad case of the blues / How great thou art / Uptown blues
ROUCD 0402 / May '97 / Rounder

Icon Zero

☐ VACUUM LOGIC
KFX 01CD / 17 Nov '97 / KFX

ID

☐ WHERE ARE WE GOING
FLASH 53 / 1 Jun '98 / Flash

Ida

☐ TEN SMALL PACES
SMR 54 / 22 Sep '97 / Simple Machines

Idaho

☐ THIS WAY OUT
Drop off / Drive it / Weird wood / Fuel / Still / Sweep / Glow / Taken / Crawling out / Zabo / Forever
QUIGD 7 / Jan '95 / Quigley

☐ THREE SHEETS TO THE WIND
If you dare / Catapult / Pomegranate bleeding / Shame / Stare at the sky / No one's watching / Alive again / Sound awake / Glass bottom / Get you back
CAROL 001CD / Apr '96 / Caroline

☐ YEAR AFTER YEAR
God's green earth / Skyscrape / Gone / Here to go / Sundown / Memorial day / One Sunday / Only road / Let's cheat death / Save / Year after year / Endgame
QUIGD 4 / Sep '93 / Quigley

Idee Des Nordens

☐ ELATION, ELEGANCE, EXALTATION
EFA 155832 / Apr '95 / Gymnastic

Ides Of March

☐ VEHICLE
175052 / Jul '97 / Magic

Ides Of May

☐ FEED BACK
Don't boogie on me / I feel ashamed / When a woman gets suspicious / Let's get loose / My way / Drivin' around / I get the blues so bad / Texas feedback / Dark lonely street / Drinking and thinking / She's that woman / Don't stand in my way / First time / Stealin'
TRCD 9908 / Nov '93 / Tramp

Idha

☐ MELODYINN
High over hollywood / Red balloon / From me to you / More love / Another door / Stockholm / All my loving / Hickory wind / Get undressed / Safe at home / Music carries on
CRECD 160 / Jan '94 / Creation

☐ TROUBLEMAKER
CRECD 184 / Aug '97 / Creation

Idiots

☐ IDIOTS MINI ALBUM
DIRTY 3CD / Mar '97 / Dirt

Idle

☐ EGO PARK
BD 9042 / Nov '97 / Big Deal

Idol, Billy

☐ BILLY IDOL
Come come on / White wedding / Hot in the city / Dead on arrival / Ain't nobody's business if I do / Love calling / Hole in the wall / Shooting star / It's so cruel / Congo man
ACCD 1377 / Jul '94 / Chrysalis

☐ CHARMED LIFE
Loveless / Pimping on steel / Prodigal blues / LA woman / Trouble with the sweet stuff / Cradle of love / Mark of Caine / Endless sleep / Love unchained / Right way / License to thrill
CCD 1735 / Sep '97 / Chrysalis

☐ CYBERPUNK
Wasteland / Shock to the system / Tomorrow people / Adam in chains / Neuromancer / Power junkie / Love labours on / Heroin / Shangri-La / Concrete kingdom / Venus / Then the night comes / Mother Dawn
CDCHR 6000 / Jun '93 / Chrysalis

☐ IDOL SONGS (11 Of The Best)
Rebel yell / Hot in the city / White wedding / Eyes without a face / Catch my fall / Mony mony / To be a lover / Sweet sixteen / Flesh for fantasy / Don't need a gun / Dancing with myself
BIL CD 1 / Jun '88 / Chrysalis

☐ VITAL IDOL
Dancing with myself / White wedding / Flesh for fantasy / Catch my fall / Mony mony / Love calling (dub) / Hot in the city
CCD 1502 / '86 / Chrysalis

IDOL Kings

☐ HELL NO
7019950601 / Oct '97 / Word

Idols

☐ IDOLS WITH SID VICIOUS (Idols & Sid Vicious)
422289 / Feb '97 / Last Call

Idriss, Abdel Rad

☐ YA ZEIN HOBAK
3108522 / 23 Mar '98 / Odeon

IF

☐ FUCKING CONSUMER
EFA 294692 / 16 Mar '98 / Disko B

If

☐ FORGOTTEN ROADS
NEMCD 773 / Oct '95 / Sequel

☐ IF VOL.1
I'm reaching out on all sides / What did I say about the box Jack / What can a friend say / Woman can you see / Raise the level of your conscious mind / Dockland / Promised land
EDCD 505 / Feb '97 / Edsel

☐ IF VOL.2
Sunday sad / Tarmac T Pirate and the lonesome nymphomaniac / I couldn't write and tell you / Shadows and echoes / Song for Elsa / Three days before her 25th birthday / Your city is falling
EDCD 506 / Feb '97 / Edsel

Ifan, Tecwyn

☐ SARITA
Awn ymlaen / 'Dyw hi ddim yn rhy hwyr / Chwilio am y ser / Dewines endor / Can unioni'r cam / Eco filwyr / Welaist ti'r lluniau / Anjela Duval / Sarita / Glas y dorlan / Strydoedd Gwatemala / Albatros / Bro'r twrch trwyth / Ffos y mynach
SCD 2170 / Oct '97 / Sain

Ifang Bondi

☐ DARAJA
MWCD 3009 / Jul '94 / Music & Words

Ifield, Frank

☐ ESSENTIAL COLLECTION, THE
Lucky devil / Gotta get a date / I remember you / Love sick blues / Young love / Wayward wind / Nobody's darlin' but mine / Confessin' / My blue heaven / Mule train / Don't blame me / Angry at the big oak tree / Riders in the sky / I should care / Summer is over / Paradise / Scarlet ribbons / No one will ever know / Call her your sweetheart / She taught me how to know
CDMFP 6384 / 13 Oct '97 / Music For Pleasure

☐ FIRE STILL BURNS, THE
Hearts on fire / Let me lay in your arms / Close the door / Little bit of push / Forgettin' about you / If love must go / Who am I to say / Stuck between the loving and the leaving / Let your love fall back on me / Before I'm fool enough / (I'll be your) hold me tight / Isn't it always love / (I've been) too long without you / Praised be / Hearts on fire
ODR 101 / 6 Oct '97 / Odyssey

☐ I'LL REMEMBER YOU
Just one more chance / I've got that sad and lonely feeling / Glory of love / Gone / Lonely teardrops / San Antonio rose / Heart and soul / I'm a fool to care / Wisdom of a fool / (I heard that) lonesome whistle / Any time / Before this day ends / I just can't lose the blues / In a mansion stands my love / I'll remember you
DORIG 102 / 1 Sep '97 / EMI

☐ REST OF THE EMI YEARS
Lucky devil / I remember you / She taught me how to yodel / Lovesick blues / Confessin' (that I love you) / Just one more chance / Nobody's darlin' but mine / Wayward wind / My blue heaven / Say it isn't so / Don't blame me / You came a long way from St. Louis / Summer is over / Once a jolly swagman / Botany Bay / Paradise / Wild rover / Call her your sweetheart / No one will ever know / Give me your word
CDEMS 1402 / May '91 / EMI

☐ SOMEONE TO GIVE MY LOVE TO/AIN'T GONNA TAKE NO FOR AN ANSWER
Someone to give my love to / California cotton fields / Why can't people be people / I cry my heart out for you / Country comfort / Say goodbye to Angelina / Paint the world / Silver wings / Him big top, me the clown / Don't forget I still love you / My happiness / 'Til I waltz again with you / Where is tomorrow / Count up to ten / Make up of a clown / Nearness of you / Joanne / I remember you / Sad song without words / Ain't gonna take no for an answer / Cotton Jenny / Home isn't home anymore / Excuse me friend
SEECD 439 / Mar '97 / See For Miles

Iggy Pop

☐ AMERICAN CAESAR
Character / Wild America / Mixin' the colors / Jealousy / Hate / It's our love / Plastic and concrete / Fuckin' alone / Highway song / Beside you / Sickness / Boogie boy / Perforation problems / Social life / Louie Louie / Caesar / Girls of NY
CDVUS 64 / Aug '93 / Virgin

☐ BEST OF IGGY POP LIVE, THE
Raw power / High on you / Nightclubbing / China girl / Blah blah blah / No fun / 1969 / Tv eye / Easy rider / I need somebody / 5 foot 1 / I wanna be your dog / Passenger / I got a right / Some weird sin / Real wild child / Lust for life / Search 'n' destroy
MCD 84021 / Aug '96 / MCA

☐ BLAH BLAH BLAH
Real wild child / Baby, it can't fall / Shades / Fire girl / Isolation / Cry for love / Blah blah blah / Hideaway / Winners and losers
CDMID 159 / Oct '92 / A&M

☐ BLAH BLAH BLAH/INSTINCT
Real wild child (wild one) / Baby it can't fall / Shades / Fire girl / Isolation / Cry for love / Blah-blah-blah / Hideaway / Winners and losers / Little Miss Emperor / Cold metal / High on you / Strong girl / Tom tom / Easy rider / Power and freedom / Lowdown / Instinct / Tuff baby / Squarehead
5409432 / Aug '98 / A&M

☐ BRICK BY BRICK
Home / I won't crap out / Butt town / Moonlight lady / Neon forest / Pussy power / Brick by brick / Main Street eyes / Candy / Undefeated / Something wild / Starry night / My baby wants to rock 'n' roll / Livin' on the edge of the night
CDVUS 19 / Apr '92 / Virgin

☐ CALIFORNIA BLEEDING (Iggy & The Stooges)
BCD 4069 / 1 Sep '97 / Bomp

☐ FUN HOUSE (Iggy & The Stooges)
Down on the street / Loose / TV eye / Dirt / 1970 / Fun house / LA Blues
7559606692 / Oct '93 / Elektra

☐ HEAD ON (2CD Set)
SMDCD 142 / 22 Sep '97 / Snapper

☐ HEROIN HATES YOU
OPM 2116CD / 24 Nov '97 / Other People's Music

☐ I WANNA BE A STOOGE (Various Artists)
642006 / Sep '96 / Wotre Music

☐ IDIOT, THE
Sister midnight / Nightclubbing / Fun time / Baby / China girl / Dum dum boys / Tiny girls / Mass production
CDOVD 277 / Apr '90 / Virgin

☐ IGGY POP (Interview)
3D 013 / Dec '96 / Network

☐ INSTINCT
Cold metal / High on you / Strong girl / Tom Tom / Easy rider / Power and freedom / Lowdown / Instinct / Tuff baby / Squarehead
3951982 / Dec '96 / A&M

☐ KILL CITY (Iggy Pop & James Williamson)
Kill City / Sell your love / Beyond the law / I got nothing / Johanna / Night theme / Consolation prizes / No sense of crime / Lucky moments / Master charge
BCD 4042 / Jan '93 / Bomp

☐ KILL CITY/I GOT A RIGHT (Iggy & The Stooges)
890050 / Jul '96 / Revenge

☐ KING BISCUIT PRESENTS...
Instinct / Kill city / Nineteen sixty nine / Penetration / Power and freedom / High on you / Five foot one / Johanna / Easy rider / Tuff baby / I feel alright / Winners and losers / Scene of the crime / Search and destroy / Cold metal / Squarehead / No fun / I wanna be your dog
KBFHCD 001 / 27 Apr '98 / King Biscuit

☐ LIVE 1971 & EARLY LIVE RARITIES (Iggy & The Stooges)
642011 / Sep '94 / New Rose

☐ LIVE AT THE WHISKEY-A-GO-GO (Iggy & The Stooges)
895104 / Jan '97 / Revenge

☐ LIVE CHANNEL BOSTON MA 1988
642005 / May '94 / New Rose
MIG 40/41 / Sep '97 / Revenge

☐ LIVE IN LA 1973
SMMCD 528 / 16 Mar '98 / Snapper

☐ LIVE NEW YORK RITZ 1986
642044 / May '94 / New Rose

☐ LUST FOR LIFE
Lust for life / Sixteen / Some weird sin / Passenger / Tonight / Success / Turn blue / Neighbourhood threat / Fall in love with me
CDOVD 278 / Apr '90 / Virgin

☐ MASTERS, THE
EABCD 011 / 24 Nov '97 / Eagle

☐ METALLIC KO (Iggy & The Stooges)
Raw power / Head on the curb / Gimme danger / Search and destiny / Heavy liquid / I wanna be your dog / Recital / Open up and bleed / I got nothing / Rich bitch / Cock in my pocket / Louie Louie
622322 / Apr '88 / Skydog

☐ MY GIRL HATES MY HEROIN (Iggy & The Stooges)
890028 / Jun '94 / New Rose
7890028 / Jan '97 / Wotre Music
MIG 28 / Sep '97 / Revenge

☐ NAUGHTY LITTLE DOGGIE
I wanna live / Pussy walk / Innocent world / Knucklehead / To belong / Keep on believing / Outta my head / Shoeshine girl / Heart is saved / Look away
CDVUS 102 / Feb '96 / Virgin

☐ NEW VALUES
Tell me a story / New values / Girls / I'm bored / Don't look down / Endless sea / Five foot one / How do you fix a broken heart / Angel / Curiosity / African man / Billy is a runaway
260997 / Nov '90 / Arista

☐ NIGHT OF DESTRUCTION (Iggy & The Stooges)
642100 / Jun '94 / New Rose

☐ NIGHT OF DESTRUCTION (6CD Single Set) (Iggy & The Stooges)
WM 375 / Sep '97 / Wind

☐ NUDE & RUDE (The Best Of Iggy Pop)
I wanna be your dog / No fun / Search and destroy / Gimme danger / I'm sick of you / Funtime / Nightclubbing / China girl / Lust for life / Passenger / Kill city / Real wild child / Cry for love / Cold metal / Candy / Home / Wild America
VUSCD 115 / Oct '96 / Virgin

☐ OPEN UP AND BLEED (Iggy & The Stooges)
890016 / Jul '96 / Revenge
BCD 4051 / Jan '97 / Bomp

☐ PARIS HIPPODROME 1977
893334 / Jul '96 / Revenge

☐ PARTY
Pleasure / Rock 'n' roll party / Eggs on plate / Sincerity / Houston is hot tonight / Pumpin' for Jill / Happy man / Bang bang / Sea of love / Time won't let me
253806 / Sep '89 / RCA

☐ POP MUSIC
Loco mosquito / Bang bang / Tell me a story / Pumpin' for Jill / Take care of me / I need more / I'm bored / Knocking 'em down / I snub you / Sea of love / Play it safe / Dog food / Happy man / Time won't let me / Five foot one / Angel / Girls / New values / Pleasure / Houston is hot tonight
74321415032 / Oct '96 / Camden

☐ POP SONGS
Loco mosquito / Bang bang / Pumpin' for Jill / Tell me a story / Take care of me / Mr. Dynamite / I'm bored / Sea of love / Play it safe / Endless sea / Pleasure / Five foot one / Houston is hot tonight / Dog food
262178 / Jan '92 / Arista

☐ RAW MIXES (The Complete Raw Mixes)
I got a right / No fun / 1969 / I wanna be your dog / Not right / Little doll / Fun house / Down on the street / 1970 / TV eye / Dirt / Shake appeal / Search and destroy / Raw power / I need somebody / Rubber legs / Open up and bleed / Johanna
MIG 60 / Dec '96 / Revenge

☐ RAW MIXES VOL.1 (Iggy & The Stooges)
895002 / Sep '94 / New Rose

☐ RAW MIXES VOL.2 (Iggy & The Stooges)
895003 / Sep '94 / New Rose

☐ RAW MIXES VOL.3 (Search & Destroy) (Iggy & The Stooges)
895004 / Sep '94 / New Rose

☐ RAW POWER (Iggy & The Stooges)
Search and destroy / Gimme danger / Your pretty face is going to hell / Penetration / Raw power / I need somebody / Shake appeal / Death trip
4851762 / Apr '97 / Columbia

☐ ROUGH POWER (Iggy & The Stooges)
BCD 4049 / Jan '97 / Bomp

☐ RUBBER LEGS (Iggy & The Stooges)
422351 / May '94 / New Rose

☐ SOLDIER
Loco mosquito / Ambition / Take care of me / Get up and get out / Play it safe / I'm a conservative / Dog food / I need more / Knocking 'em down (in the city) / Mr. Dynamite / I snub you
251160 / Apr '91 / Arista

☐ STOOGES, THE (Iggy & The Stooges)
1969 / I wanna be your dog / We will fall / No fun / Real cool time / Ann / Not right / Little doll
7559606672 / Oct '93 / Elektra

☐ STUDIO SESSIONS (Iggy & The Stooges)
Head on / Death trip / I got a right / Hard to beat / Cock in my pocket / Rubber legs / Johanna / Pin point eyes / Open up and bleed / Raw power
PILOT 008 / Feb '97 / Burning Airlines

☐ SUCK ON THIS
642 050 / May '93 / NMC

☐ TILL THE END OF THE NIGHT (Iggy & The Stooges)
642042 / Jun '94 / New Rose
MIG 42 / Sep '97 / Revenge

☐ TV EYE (1977 LIVE)
TV eye / Fun time / Sixteen / I got a right / Lust for life / Dirt / Nightclubbing / I wanna be your dog
CDOVD 448 / Jun '94 / Virgin

☐ WE WILL FALL (An Iggy Tribute/2CD Set) (Various Artists)
1969: *Ramone, Joey* / Search and destroy: *Red Hot Chili Peppers* / Real wild child: *Jett, Joan & The Blackhearts* / Ordinary bummer: *Adolph's Dog* / I got a right: *Misfits* / Gimme danger: *Monster Magnet* / Lust for life: *NY Loose* / Loose: *Pansy Division* / 1970: *Superdrag* / Passenger: *Lunachicks* / I'm sick of you: *Nada Surf* / Funtime: *Blanks 77* / I got nothing: *D-Generation* / Down on the street/Little doll: *County, Jayne* / Cold metal: *Sugar Ray* / Sell your love: *Extra Fancy* / Shake appeal: *7 Year Bitch* / Sixteen: *Nine Lives* / Shake appeal: *Bush Tetras* / TV eye: *Holy Bulls* / I wanna be your dog: *Jett, Joan & The Blackhearts* / We will fall: *Kaye, Lenny*
REVXD 221 / Nov '97 / Revolver
RTY 106 / Sep '97 / Royalty

☐ WILD ANIMAL (Live USA 1977)
642050 / Jul '96 / Revenge

☐ YEAR OF THE IGUANA (Iggy & The Stooges)
BCD 4063 / Mar '97 / Bomp

Iglesias, Julio

☐ 1,100 BEL AIR PLACE/STARRY NIGHT/ EMOCIONES (3CD Set)
All of you / Two lovers / Bambou medley / Air that I breathe / Last time / Moonlight lady / When I fall in love / Me va, me va / If / To all the girls I've loved before / Can't help falling in love / And I love her / Mona Lisa / Cryin' time / Yesterday when I was young / When I need you / 99 miles from LA / Vincent / If you go away / Love has been a friend to me / Me olvide de vivir / Voy a perder la cabeza por tu amor / Spanish girl / Pobre diablo / Quiereme / Preguntale / Quiereme mucho / Con una pinta asi / No vengo ni voy / Un dia tu, un dia yo
4853182 / 3 Nov '97 / Columbia

☐ 1100 BEL AIR PLACE
All of you: *Iglesias, Julio & Diana Ross* / Two lovers / Bambou medley / Air that I breathe / Last time / Moonlight lady / When I fall in love / Me va, me va / If / To all the girls I've loved before: *Iglesias, Julio & Willie Nelson*
CD 86308 / Sep '86 / CBS

☐ BEGIN THE BEGUINE
Begin the beguine / Quiereme / Me olvide de vivir / Por un poco de tu amour / Grande, grande, grande / Como tu / Guantanamera / Quiereme mucho / Hey / Un dia ty, un dia yo / Soy un truhan, soy un senor / Candilejas / El amor / 33 anos / Isla en el sol
CD 85462 / Aug '87 / CBS

☐ CRAZY
Crazy / Let it be me / Mammy blue / Fragile / Guajira/ Oye como va / When you tell me that you love me / I keep telling myself / Pelo amor de uma mulher (Por el amor de una mujer) / Caruso / Song of joy
4747382 / May '94 / Columbia

☐ DE NINA A MUJER
De nina a mujer / Volver a empezar / Despues de ti / Que nadie sepa mi sufrir / Isal en el sol / O me quieres o me dejas / Y pensar..si madam / Grande, grande, grande / Come tu
4654502 / 27 Jul '98 / Columbia

☐ JULIO
Begin the beguine / Forever and ever / Yours / La paloma / Pensami / D'abord..et puis / Never never never / Nathalie / Feelings / Hey, amor / Limelight / Rum and coca cola / Sono lo / Je nais pas change / So close to me
4510772 / 27 Jul '98 / Columbia

☐ LA CARRETERA
La carretera / Cosae de la vida / Baila morena / Derroche el ultimo / Verano / Agua dulce, agua sala / Sin exasas ni rodeos / Mal de amores / Rumbas / Vuela alto
4807042 / Jul '95 / Columbia

☐ NON STOP
Love is on our side again / I know it's over / Never never never / AE, AO / Words and music / My love (featuring Stevie Wonder) / Everytime we fall in love / Too many women / If I ever needed you (I need you now)
4609902 / Oct '95 / Columbia

☐ STARRY NIGHT
Can't help falling in love / And I love her / Mona Lisa / Crying time / Yesterday when I was young / When I need you / 99 miles from LA / Vincent / If you go away / Love has been a friend to me
4672842 / Mar '96 / Columbia

☐ TANGO
La cumparsita / El dia que me quieras / A media luz / Volver / Yira..yira / Mano a mano / El choclo / Adios / Pampa mia / Cambalanche / Uno... / Caminito / Mi buenos aires querido
4866752 / Nov '96 / Columbia

Ignatzek, Klaus

☐ ANSWER, THE (Ignatzek, Klaus Quintet)
Answer / Altered moods / Number one / With pleasure / Claudio's delight / One milestone
CCD 79534 / Feb '97 / Candid

☐ RETURN VOYAGE (Ignatzek, Klaus Jazztet)
Calling Mr. Gillespie / Return voyage / Oscar for Gigi / Jay by Jay / Un abraco do Brasil (A salute to Brazil) / Flowers around midnight / Whisper yes / Blue energy
CCD 79716 / Feb '97 / Candid

☐ SILENT HORNS (Ignatzek, Klaus Quintet)
Chasing Fats and Maggie / Morgan's message / Ballad for booker / K.D.'s loco-motion / Aproador / Quasi-modal / Waltz / Calling Mr.Gillespie / Autumn leaves
CCD 79729 / Nov '97 / Candid

Ignite

☐ BENEFIT ALBUM (Ignite/X-Acto)
ATR 005CD / 2 Mar '98 / Elevator

☐ FAMILY
LF 192CD / Jul '95 / Lost & Found

☐ IN MY TIME
LF 124CD / Feb '95 / Lost & Found

☐ SCARRED FOR LIFE
LF 104CD / Aug '94 / Lost & Found

Ignition

☐ COMPLETE SERVICES
DIS 88CD / Mar '94 / Dischord

Ignorance

☐ CONFIDENT RAT, THE
CDZORRO 17 / Feb '91 / Metal Blade

☐ POSITIVELY SHOCKING
CDZORRO 48 / Sep '92 / Metal Blade

Iha, James

☐ LET IT COME DOWN
Be strong now / Sound of love / Beauty / See the sun / Country girl / Jealousy / Lover lover / Silver string / Winter / One and two / No one's gonna hurt you
CDHUT 47 / 9 Feb '98 / Hut

Ihre Kinder

☐ LIVE 1982
14892 / 22 May '98 / Spalax

IIIrd Tyme Out

☐ LETTER TO HOME
ROUCD 0333 / Oct '95 / Rounder

☐ LIVE AT THE MAC
Introduction / White house blues / Blue moon of Kentucky / Little rabbit / What was I supposed to do / He said if I be lifted up / It's a lonesome road / Till the end / Someone took my place with you / Lord protect my soul / I ain't that broke (but I'm badbly bent) / Erase the miles / Till the end of the world rolls around / Tennessee waltz / I'm better off without you
ROUCD 0413 / May '98 / Rounder

☐ LIVING ON THE OTHER SIDE
He'll take you in / I want to stroll over heaven / I'm working on the road to Gloryland / Everybody's gonna have a wonderful time up there / Giving my soul back to him / Across the miles / When we're living on the other side / Eternity has begun / Feed me Jesus / I feel closer to Heaven / Swing low, sweet chariot / Heading for that city
ROUCD 0393 / Sep '96 / Rounder

Ijahman Levi

☐ AFRICA
Africa / To be loved by jah / Playgirl / Rise and shine / Ancient lover / Jesus selassie I keepeth my soul / Master of my mind / Africa crisis
CDJMI 400 / Dec '95 / Jahmani

☐ ARE WE A WARRIOR
Are we a warrior / Moulding / Church / Miss Beverly / Two sides of love
RRCD 25 / Nov '90 / Reggae Refreshers
CDJMI 200 / Dec '95 / Jahmani

☐ BEAUTY AND THE LION
CDJMI 2300 / 29 Sep '97 / Jahmani

☐ BLACK ROYALITIES
CDJMI 1800 / Dec '95 / Jahmani

☐ CROCODILE MAN
JMICD 2600 / 13 Jul '98 / Jahmani

☐ CULTURE COUNTRY
CDJMI 700 / Dec '95 / Jahmani

☐ ENTITLEMENT
CDJMI 1600 / Dec '95 / Jahmani

☐ FORWARD RASTAMAN
Waitin' on you / Gambler's blues / Tired of your jive / Night life / Buzz me / Sweet sixteen part 1 / Don't answer the door / Blind love / I know what you're puttin' down / Baby get lost / Gonna keep on loving you / Sweet sixteen part 2
CDJMI 800 / Dec '95 / Jahmani

☐ GEMINI MAN
CDJMI 1500 / Dec '95 / Jahmani

IJAHMAN LEVI

☐ HAILE I HYMN
Jah heavy load / Jah is no secret / Zion hut / I'm a levi / Praises in strange places / Marcus hero / Zion train
CDJMI 100 / Dec '95 / Jahmani

☐ I DO (Ijahman Levi & Madge Sutherland)
I do / My love / Call on you / Happy home / Hold on honey / Mellow music / Chariot of love / Freedom
CDJMI 600 / Dec '95 / Jahmani

☐ IJAHMAN & FRIENDS
Master ideas / Mellow music / African train / Struggling dub / Extended dub / Master dub / Struggling times / Let him go / Jah is coming
CDJMI 900 / Dec '95 / Jahmani

☐ IJAHMAN LEVI & BOB MARLEY IN DUB (Ijahman Levi & Bob Marley)
CDJMI 2200 / Dec '95 / Jahmani

☐ INSIDE OUT
CDJMI 1100 / Dec '95 / Jahmani

☐ KINGFARI
CDJMI 1400 / Dec '95 / Jahmani

☐ LILY OF MY VALLEY
CDJMI 500 / Dec '95 / Jahmani

☐ LION DUB BEAUTY
CDJMI 2400 / 29 Sep '97 / Jahmani

☐ LIVE IN PARIS 1994
CDJMI 2000 / Dec '95 / Jahmani

☐ LIVE OVER EUROPE
CDJMI 1000 / Dec '95 / Jahmani

☐ LOVE SMILES
CDJMI 1200 / Dec '95 / Jahmani

☐ MONKEY MAN
JMICD 2500 / 13 Jul '98 / Jahmani

☐ ON TRACK
CDJMI 1300 / Dec '95 / Jahmani

☐ SINGS BOB MARLEY
CDJMI 1900 / 3 Nov '97 / Jahmani

☐ TELL IT TO THE CHILDREN
CDJMI 300 / Dec '95 / Jahmani

☐ TWO DOUBLE SIX 701
CDJMI 1700 / Dec '95 / Jahmani

Ike & The Capers

☐ I'M NOT SHY TO DO
PT 619004 / Jun '98 / Part

☐ LOUD AND SILENT
PT 619003 / Oct '97 / Part

Ikeda, Royoji

☐ 0 DEGREES C
0 degrees c
TO 38 / 24 Aug '98 / Touch

☐ PLUS/MINUS
TO 30 / Nov '96 / Touch

Ikettes

☐ FINE, FINE, FINE
(He's gonna be) Fine fine fine / Can't sit down / Don't feel sorry for me / Camel walk / Blue on blue / I'm so thankful / You're trying to make me lose my mind / Sally go round the roses / Peaches and cream / Never more will I be lonely for you / Not that I recall / Your love is me / Biggest players / How come / Nobody loves me / It's been so long / Through with you / Cheater / I'm leaving you / You're still my baby / Give me a chance (try me) / Love of my man: ikettes & Venetta Fields / Living for you: Ikettes & Dee Dee Johnson / I love the way you love: Ikettes & Robbie Montgomery
CDKEN 063 / Sep '92 / Kent

Ikhwani Safaa Musical Club

☐ TAARAB MUSIC OF ZANZIBAR VOL.2
Usiji gambe / Nna zama / Pendo la wasikitisha / Nipe pee / Kanilemaza / Uki chungua / Waridi lisilo miba / Hidaya
CDORB 033 / Oct '88 / Globestyle

Ikon

☐ FLOWERS OF THE GATHERING
NRE 01CD / Apr '97 / Nightbreed

☐ MOMENT IN TIME, A
EFA 121672 / Nov '95 / Apollyon

Ile Axe

☐ BRAZILIAN PERCUSSION
PS 65059 / Nov '90 / PlayaSound

Ilium

☐ PLEXIGLASS CUBE
HEFTY 01CD / 6 Apr '98 / Hefty

Ill Wind

☐ FLASHES
AFT 012 / Jun '97 / Afterglow

Illapu

☐ RAZA BRAVA
MCD 71811 / Jun '93 / Monitor

☐ SERENO (Panpipe Instrumentals From The Andes)
Cariquima / Sol demaiz / Condorcanqui / Sereno / Chilhuanos / Paso de mulata / Bailando en Isluga / Sipassy / Cancisy / Labradores / Poblacires / O marqu waylas de cala cala / Baila campal
HEMICD 26 / Jun '97 / Hemisphere

Illdisposed

☐ FOUR DEPRESSIVE SEASONS
NB 103 / Apr '94 / Nuclear Blast

☐ HELVEDE
RRS 945CD / Sep '95 / Lost & Found

☐ RETURN FROM TOMORROW
NB 116 / Aug '94 / Nuclear Blast

☐ SUBMIT
PCD 021 / Nov '95 / Progress

Ille, Jimmy

☐ GRAND OLD CIRCUS BAND, THE
Fanfare / Caravan club / Georgia girl / Entry of the gladiators / Slim trombone / Amparita roca / Broadway one step / Trombone blues / Crimson flush / Espana / Abdullah / Teddy bears picnic / Jungle queen / Bandstand / Ringling reminiscence medley / Cantonians march / They're off / Billboard march
CD 12819 / Jan '98 / Laserlight

Illusion

☐ ENCHANTED CARESS
PL 92152 / Aug '90 / Promised Land

☐ OUT OF THE MIST / ILLUSION
Isadora / Roads to freedom / Beautiful country / Solo flight / Everywhere you go / Face of yesterday / Candles are burning / Madonna blues / Never be the same / Louis theme / Wings across the sea / Cruising nowhere / Man of miracles / Revolutionary
EDCD 369 / Mar '94 / Edsel

Illusion Of Safety

☐ WATER SEEKS IT'S OWN LEVEL
SR 9351 / Mar '94 / Silent

Illustrious

☐ NO NO NO (Illustrious GY)
I'm ugly / Take / Letters / Just another day / Dreaming / Anytime at all / Love me / So happy / Too easy / You and me / Twenty questions / Crime and punishment / Prophecy
74321157292 / Nov '93 / RCA

Iluyenkori

☐ CUBAN DRUMS
PS 65084 / Mar '92 / PlayaSound

Imachito

☐ GUAMPAMPIRO (Imachito & His Afro-Cubans)
TCD 089 / 24 Apr '98 / Tumbao

Imagination

☐ NIGHT DUBBING
Flashback / Just an illusion / Music and lights / So good, so right / Body talk / Heart 'n' soul / Changes / Burning up
BX 4302 / Jun '96 / BR Music

☐ VERY BEST OF IMAGINATION, THE
Just an illusion / Music and lights / Body talk / In and out of love / Flashback / In the heat of the night / Changes / Looking at midnight / New dimensions / State of love / Thank you my love / Shoo be doo da dabba doobee / Sunshine / Burn it up / Tell me do you want my love / One more love / All nights lovin'
BX 4182 / Apr '95 / BR Music

Imago

☐ SPIRIT DANCE, THE
DBCDA 202 / 29 Sep '97 / Dancebeat

Imai, Kazuo

☐ HOW WILL WE CHANGE
PSFD 70 / Feb '96 / PSF

Imajin

☐ IMAJIN
0518782 / 29 Jun '98 / Jive

Imbruglia, Natalie

☐ LEFT OF THE MIDDLE
Torn / One more addiction / Big mistake / Leave me alone / Intuition / Smoke / Pigeons and crumbs / Don't you think / Impressed / Wishing I was there / City / Left of the middle
74321544412 / 24 Nov '97 / RCA

Iminh-Nhuong, Nguyen

☐ ART OF THE VIETNAMESE FIDDLE, THE
ARN 60417 / 24 Apr '98 / Arion

Imlach, Hamish

☐ DEFINITIVE TRANSATLANTIC COLLECTION, THE
ESMCD 522 / 24 Nov '97 / Essential

☐ MORE AND MERRIER
CDLDL 1238 / Mar '96 / Lochshore

☐ SONNY'S DREAM
Cod liver oil and orange juice / Ballad of William Brown / Mary Anne / Reprobate's lament / Salonika / Kisses sweeter than wine / Smoker's song / Sonny's dream / If it wasn't for the union / Parcel o' rogues / I didn't raise my boy to be a soldier / Goodbye booze / D-day dodgers / Seven men of Knoydart
LCOM 7006 / May '95 / Lismor

☐ TWO'S COMPANY
CURRYCD 001 / Dec '97 / Vindaloo

Immaculate Fools

☐ KISS AND PUNCH
Little bird sing / Ready for me / Kiss and punch / No I / Tinderbox / No gods no masters / Rain song / Hard peace / Killing field / Whole world down / El emanacer
COOKCD 096 / Aug '97 / Cooking Vinyl

☐ NO GODS NO MASTERS (2CD Set)
SMDCD 146 / 27 Apr '98 / Snapper

☐ WOODHOUSE
Rain / Some of us / Ship song / Time to kill / Profit for prophets / Pass the jug / Rudy / Home / Bury my heart / Wish you were here / If you go
COOKCD 085 / Jul '97 / Cooking Vinyl

Immature

☐ JOURNEY, THE
MCAD 11668 / 29 Sep '97 / MCA

Immersion

☐ FULL IMMERSION
VWM 40 / Jun '95 / Swim

☐ OSCILLATING
WM 4CD / Sep '94 / Swim

☐ PURGE
SMTCD 002 / 10 Nov '97 / Smitten

Immolation

☐ DAWN OF POSSESSION
RC 93102 / Jan '94 / RC

☐ HERE IN AFTER
3984102CD / Jan '96 / Metal Blade

Immortal

☐ BATTLES IN THE NORTH
OPCD 027 / May '95 / Osmose

☐ BLIZZARD BEASTS
OPCD 051 / Mar '97 / Osmose

☐ PURE HOLOCAUST
OPCD 19 / Dec '93 / Osmose

Immortelle

☐ DEW SCENTED
SPV 0851826 / Mar '96 / SPV

Impact Allstars

☐ FORWARD THE BASS (Dub From Randy's 1972-1975)
Jaro / Maro / Ordinary version chapter 3 / Extraordinary version / Wire dub / Shining dub / Easy come dub / Dubwise situation / Last of the jestering / Oh jah dub / Sabotage in dub / S corner dub / Just another dub / Upbeat version / Verdict in dub
BAFCD 022 / 8 Jun '98 / Blood & Fire

Impacts

☐ DESERT ISLAND TREASURES
BA 1116CD / Mar '97 / Bacchus Archives

Impaled Nazarene

☐ LATEX CULT
OPCD 038 / Apr '96 / Osmose

☐ MOTORPENIS
OPCD 039 / Jun '96 / Osmose

☐ RAPTURE
OPCD 069 / 11 May '98 / Osmose

☐ SUOMI FINLAND
OPCD 026 / Apr '95 / Osmose

☐ TOL CORMPT NORZ NORZ NORZ
OPCD 010LTD / Nov '95 / Osmose

☐ UGRA KARMA
OPCD 018 / Apr '94 / Osmose

Impatient Youth

☐ ALL FOR FUN
LF 76CD / Nov '94 / Lost & Found

Impel

☐ OMNIDIRECTIONAL
V 141 / 15 Jun '98 / Vinyl Communication

Imperial

☐ AUX CREPUSCULES
OPCD 062 / 16 Mar '98 / Osmose

Imperial Teen

☐ SEASICK
Imperial teen / Water boy / Butch / Pig latin / Blaming the baby / You're one / Balloon / Tippy tap / Copafeelia / Luxury / Eternity
8287282 / Sep '96 / Custom

Imperials

☐ 25 GREATEST HITS (Little Anthony & The Imperials)
Tears on my pillow / Two people in the world / So much / Diary / It's not for me / Prayer and a jukebox / I'm alright / My empty room / I'm taking a vacation from love / Please say you want me / Travelling stranger / I'm on the outside (lookin' in) / Goin' out of sight out of mind / Hurt / Ten commandments of love / Better use your head / Gonna fix you good / I'm hypnotized / Yesterday has gone / Wishful thinking / Shimmy shimmy ko-ko pop
4954862 / 6 Jul '98 / EMI Gold

☐ GOIN' OUT OF MY HEAD (Little Anthony & The Imperials)
BGOCD 309 / Apr '96 / Beat Goes On

☐ WE ARE THE IMPERIALS/SHADES OF THE 40'S (Little Anthony & The Imperials)
Tears on my pillow / Over the rainbow / So much / Diary / Oh yeah / Love is a many splendoured thing / When you wish upon a star / Wishful thinking / Cha cha Henry / Travelling stranger / What did I do / Two people in the world / This love of mine / Don't get around much anymore / They say it's wonderful / If you are but a dream / Undecided / All or nothing at all / I'll never smile again / Lovely way to spend an evening / I couldn't sleep a wink last night / Ooh look a-there ain't she pretty / I've got a crush on you
WESM 556 / Feb '98 / Westside

Impious

☐ EVILIZED
BS 014CD / 25 May '98 / Black Sun

Implant Code

☐ BIODIGIT
MHCD 020 / Mar '94 / Minus Habens

Impossible

☐ SICK NOTE
BLIND 002 / 29 Jun '98 / Blunt/ Independent

Impressions

☐ ALL THE BEST
Gypsy woman / It's alright / People get ready / Talking about my baby / I'm so proud / You must believe me / Woman's got soul / I've been trying / Amen / You've been cheating / I'm the one who loves you / We're a winner / Keep on pushing / Right on time / Move on up / Mayfield, Curtis / Freddie's dead: Mayfield, Curtis / First impressions
3035900112 / Apr '96 / Carlton

☐ CHANGING IMPRESSIONS (2CD Set)
For your precious love / Come back my love / Little young lover / At the country fair / Gypsy woman / Keep on pushin' / I'm so proud / I've been trying / Amen (1970) / Fool for you / Gone away / This is my country / Seven years / Wherever he leadeth me / Choice of colours / Mighty, mighty (Spade and whitey) / (Baby) turn on to me / Check out your mind / We must be in love / Ain't got time / Times have changed / Inner city blues (make me wanna holler) / Potent love / Preacher man / Thin line / I'm a changed man (high self myself together) / If it's in you to do wrong / I'll always be here / Make a resolution / Something's mighty, mighty wrong / Sooner or later / Same thing it took / First impressions / Sunshine / Loving power / All I want to do is make you love me / Fan the fire / I don't wanna lose your love / For your precious love
CPCD 82542 / Nov '96 / Charly

☐ CHECK OUT YOUR MIND/TIMES HAVE CHANGED
Check out your mind / Can't you see / You're really something Sadie / Do you want to win / You'll be always mine / Only you / (Baby) turn onto me / Madam Mary / We must be in love / Say you love me / Stop the war / Times have changed / Inner city blues (make me wanna holler) / Our love goes on and on / Potent love / Need to belong to someone / This love's for real / Love me
NEMCD 843 / Oct '96 / Sequel

☐ COME TO MY PARTY/FAN THE FIRE
CDGR 126 / Mar '97 / Charly

☐ DEFINITIVE IMPRESSIONS, THE (28 Classic Soul Masters)
Gypsy woman / Grow closer together / Little young lover / Minstrel and queen / I'm the one who loves you / Sad, sad girl and boy / It's alright / Talking about my baby / I'm so proud / Keep on pushing / I've been trying / Girl you don't know me / I made a mistake / You must believe me / Amen / People get ready / Woman's got soul / Meeting over yonder / I need you / Just one kiss from you / You've been cheating / Since I lost the one I love / I can't satisfy / You always hurt me / I can't stay away from you / We're a winner / We're rolling on / I loved and I lost
CDKEND 923 / Oct '89 / Kent

☐ FIRST IMPRESSIONS/LOVING POWER
Sooner or later / Same thing it took / Old before my time / First impressions / Groove / I'm so glad / How high is high / Why must a love song be a sad song / Loving power / Sunshine / I can't wait to see you / If you have to ask / You can't be wrong / I wish I'd stayed in bed / Keep on trying
NEMCD 867 / Aug '97 / Sequel

☐ IMPRESSIONS/THE NEVER ENDING IMPRESSIONS
It's alright / Gypsy woman / Grow closer together / Little young lover / You've come home / Never let me go / Minsterel and queen / I need your love / I'm the one who loves you / Sad, sad girl and boy / As long as you love me / Twist and limbo / Sister love / Little boy blue / Satin doll / Girl don't you know me / I gotta keep on moving / You always hurt the one you love / That's what love will do / I'm so proud / September song / Lemon tree / Ten to one / Woman who loves me
CDKEND 126 / Aug '95 / Kent

☐ KEEP ON PUSHING/PEOPLE GET READY
Keep on pushing / I've been trying / I ain't supposed to / Dedicate my song to you / Long, long winter / Somebody help me / Amen / I thank heaven / Talking about my baby / Don't let it hide / I love you / I made a mistake / Woman's got soul / Emotions / Sometimes I wonder / We're in love / Just another dance / Can't work no longer / People get ready / I've found that I've lost / Hard to believe / See the real me / Get up and move / You must believe me
CDKEND 130 / Feb '96 / Kent

☐ MASTERS, THE
EABCD 050 / 24 Nov '97 / Eagle

☐ ONE BY ONE/RIDIN' HIGH
Twilight time / I wanna be around / Nature boy / Just one kiss from you / I want to be with you / Answer me my love / It's not unusual / Without a song / Falling in love with you / My prayer / Mona Lisa / Lonely man / Ridin' high / No one else / Gotta get away / I need to belong to someone / Right on time / I need you / Too slow / Man's temptation / That's what Mama say / Let it be me / I'm a telling you
CDKEND 152 / Jun '98 / Kent

☐ PREACHER MAN/FINALLY GOT MYSELF TOGETHER (2CD Set)
What it is / Preacher man / Simple message / Find the way / Thin line / Colour us all grey (I'm lost) / I'm loving you / If it's in you to do wrong / Finally got myself together / I'll always be here / Miracle woman / We go back a ways / Guess what I've got / Try me / Don't forget what I told you
NEMCD 866 / Jul '97 / Sequel

☐ THIS IS MY COUNTRY/YOUNG MODS' FORGOTTEN STORY
NEMCD 782 / Feb '96 / Sequel
CDGR 108 / Mar '96 / Charly

Impromptu

☐ SWEET KAFKA
Hiedeggar's lobster / Sweet Kafka / Avenue / Simply breathing / Fountain / Me and Louise / Med mig sjalv / Ginsberg / What can I say / Ten unicorns / Flay / La petite mort
RGM 194CD / Dec '94 / Red Gold Music

Impulse

☐ ONE-SIX-FOUR-ONE-SEVEN
K7R 010CD / Mar '97 / Studio K7

Impulse Manslaughter

☐ LOGICAL END
Drag / Face it / Not quite sure / Missing children / Gimme shelter / Crimson deals / No deals / Let them die / Stone dead forever / Borderline retard / Batman and the oracle of penile savage / Vomitheads / We're all bored here / Suffer in silence / Walls / They start the war / Premature evacuation / Crimes / Too late / Pills / This world / Sedation / Cheer up you fr / Kein spiel / Oatmeal il / 1987 schitzoid sam / Pattonstien's disease / Piss me off / Sack o'shit / Ratbag / Slithis / Nothing / Sedation / Chaos / Contradiction / Oatmeal
NB 013CD / Jun '89 / Nuclear Blast

Imuntzo Eta Beloki

☐ SATURNOTRIK
KD 438CD / Aug '97 / Elkar

In Aura

☐ ONE MILLION SMILES
100 degrees / This month's epic / 2-5 am / 90's itch / Virus / Desire / Sense / Soap opera / One million smiles / Las vegas leg
ORGAN 030CD / Aug '97 / Org

In Battle

☐ RAGE OF THE NORTHMEN, THE
NPR 050CD / 3 Aug '98 / Napalm

In Cahoots

☐ PARALLEL
Simmer / Parallel / Ed or Ian / Half life / Sit down / Billow
CD 004CD / Nov '96 / Voiceprint

☐ RECENT DISCOVERIES
Riffy / Trick of the light / Opener / Recent discoveries / Chez gege / Tide / Breadhead
CD 003CD / Sep '94 / Voiceprint

In Camera

☐ 13 (UNLUCKY FOR SOME)
GAD 205CD / 6 Jul '98 / 4AD

In Cold Blood

☐ HELL ON EARTH
VR 088CD / 9 Mar '98 / Victory

In Crowd

☐ NATURAL ROCK 'N' REGGAE
His majesty is coming / Born in ethiopia / Back-a-yard / We play reggae / Milk and honey / Power of the spirit / Slave ship / Baby my love / Getting cozy / Introduction little dread / Dedicated to jah / Man from new guinea / Rasta man no evil / Daughter child / Reggae groovy / Love dance / Give us more time
RNCD 2003 / Nov '92 / Rhino

☐ WE PLAY REGGAE - A TRIBUTE
3021512 / Jun '97 / Arcade
RN 7019 / May '97 / Rhino

In Flames

☐ BLACK ASH INHERITANCE
NB 251CD / 13 Oct '97 / Nuclear Blast

☐ JESTER RACE, THE
NB 168CD / Sep '96 / Nuclear Blast

☐ LUNAR STRIANS
WAR 003CD / Apr '96 / Wrong Again

☐ WHORACLE
NB 284CD / 24 Nov '97 / Nuclear Blast

In Folio

☐ IN FOLIO
Amandine / Juggling in Central Park / Varan de komodo / Nain de jardin / Bascule / Da / Onze tetes de turc / Laurent d'arabie / Visitez la belgique en autocar / 5 AM / La soupe aux choux / All blues / Spopondrilloches
JMS 186812 / Apr '96 / JMS

In Gowan Ring

☐ LOVE CHARMS
WSCD 006 / Oct '96 / World Serpent

☐ TWIN TREES, THE
Rivertime tome / One silver ring / Twin trees / Stone song III / Lady beyond the river / By moss strand and waterspathe / Cupped hands spell / Our rainbowed paradox
LUNE 002CD / Mar '97 / Lune

In My Eyes

☐ DIFFERENCE BETWEEN, THE
REV 067CD / 20 Jul '98 / Revelation

In My Rosary

☐ STRANGE EP
SPV 06519042 / Aug '95 / SPV

In Strict Confidence

☐ COLLAPSE
ZOT 177CD / 29 Sep '97 / Zoth Ommog

In The Name

☐ IN THE NAME
RS 0072942CD / Jul '98 / Rising Sun

In The Nursery

☐ AMBUSH OF GHOSTS, AN (Original Soundtrack)
After great pain / Sedation / Lipstick / Disoriented / Archaize / White robe / Cop shed / Running scene / Christian returns / Christian decides / Silk robe / Sedation 2 / Cop house / Funeral / Funeral / Dear grover / Casus belli / Syntonic / Hidden fortress / Hallucinations
TM 90382 / Mar '96 / Roadrunner

☐ ANATOMY OF A POET
TM 89762 / Mar '96 / Roadrunner

☐ ASPHALT
CORP 017CD / 27 Oct '97 / ITN Corporation

☐ DECO
CORP 014CD / May '96 / ITN Corporation

☐ DUALITY
Belle epoque / Always / Red harvest / Duality / Corruption / I thorns / Ii pulse / Iii valediction / Universe / Engraver / Mecciano
TM 91632 / Mar '96 / Roadrunner

☐ IN THE CABINET OF DR. CALIGARI
CORP 015CD / Nov '96 / ITN Corporation

☐ KODA
CORP 008CD / Jun '95 / ITN Corporation

☐ L'ESPIRIT
To the faithful / At first sight / Sesudient / Azure wings / Soeurette / Inamorata / Retaliation / Traumerei / Pearl / L'esprit / Reverie / Alluvion / Across the ruins / To the faithful (reprise)
TMCD 48 / Feb '90 / Third Mind
CORP 010CD / Jun '95 / ITN Corporation

☐ LINGUA
CORP 019CD / 27 Apr '98 / ITN Corporation

☐ PRELUDE
CORP 007CD / Jun '95 / ITN Corporation

☐ SCATTER
CORP 011CD / Jun '95 / ITN Corporation

☐ SENSE
Blue religion / Rebours / Boy behind the curtain / Temporis / Sytonic / Sense / Epigrph / Memoirs / Angelchrome / Sinistral / Sense datum / Contre coeur / Blue religion / Solitude
TM 92712 / Mar '96 / Roadrunner
CORP 018CD / 26 Jan '98 / ITN Corporation

☐ TWINS
CORP 009CD / Jun '95 / ITN Corporation

In The Woods

☐ HEART OF THE AGES
AMAZON 004CD / 3 Nov '97 / Misanthropy

☐ OMNIO
AMAZON 011CD / Jun '97 / Misanthropy

In Your Face

☐ COLLECTIVE WORKS, THE
LF 106CD / Oct '94 / Lost & Found

Inanna

☐ NOTHING
DVLR 008CD / Jun '95 / Dark Vinyl

Inca Eyeball

☐ QUATTROS SYMBOLOS
INCA 1 / 1 Dec '97 / Bentley Welcomes Careful Drivers

☐ QUATTROS SYMBOLOS
SO 10 / 23 Mar '98 / Spirit Of Orr

Incantation

☐ BEST OF INCANTATION
On the wing of a condor / Cutimy / Sacsaywaman / Dance of the flames / Sonccuiman / Noches de luna / Cacharpaya / Papel de plata / Virgins of the sun / Atahuallpa / Dolencias / Festival of Yotala / Los senors de Potasi
NAGE 100CD / May '92 / Art Of Landscape

☐ GEOGLYPH (The Very Best Of Incantation)
Dawn at Vilcabamba / Viracocha / Reunion / Santa Cruz jit / Virgins of the sun / Cacharpaya / Llaulillay / Amores hallaras / On Earth as it is in Heaven / Old thatched cabin / Condon dance/Mary and Ellen reels / Flight of the condor / Brazfest / Scarborough fair / Cutimuy / Find the child
COOKCD 148 / 22 Jun '98 / Cooking Vinyl

☐ INCANTATION
Ganado feroz / Wild / Herd / Brazfest / Reunion / Santa Cruz jit / Doina cestriana / Electric snake charmer / Llaulillay / Dawn at volcabamba / Serenading chango / Little flute player / Remembrance of Mary and Ellen / Cacharpaya shuffle
COOKCD 073 / Aug '97 / Cooking Vinyl

☐ INCANTATION CHRISTMAS
What is this fragrance / I saw three ships come sailing by / Torches / Our lady / How hard it bloweth / Solis ortus / Cardine / Virgin Mother / Holly and the ivy / In dulci jubilo / Lullay thou tiny little child / Angel Gabriel / Child divine / Shepherd's story / Spiritual / Wexford Carol / Virgin most pure / Jesus redemption omniun
3036000102 / Oct '95 / Carlton

☐ MEETING, THE
De mis huellas / Antiguos duenos de las flechas / Old thatched cabin / Canto del agua / Scarborough Fair / On earth as it is in heaven (Theme from the mission) / Phuru runas/Waya yay / El amor es un camina / Cuando / Cancion de carnival Eddi's tune / Night shadows
COOKCD 068 / Jun '94 / Cooking Vinyl

☐ PANPIPES OF THE ANDES
Amores hallaras / Cacharpaya / Papel de plata / Friends of the Andes / El pajaro madrugador / Condor dance / Sonccuiman / Dolencias / Winds on the mountain / On the wing of a condor / Sikuriadas / High flying bird
NAGE 15CD / Mar '86 / Art Of Landscape
NAGE 101CD / Oct '92 / Art Of Landscape

☐ SERGEANT EARLY'S DREAM/ GHOST DANCES
May morning dew / Sergeant early's dream / Eighteen years old / Maid of mount / Sisco/Skylark/ Richard Dwyers / Geordie / Love will you marry me/ Plains of boyle / Black is the colour of my true love's hair / Peggy Gordon / Gospel ship / Barbara Allen / Junior Crehan's / Favourite/Corney is coming / Ojo azules / Huajra / Dolencias / Papel de plata / Mis Llamitas / Sikuriadas / Ojos azules
COOKCD 069 / Feb '95 / Cooking Vinyl

Incantation

☐ DIABOLICAL CONQUEST
Impending diabolical conquest / Desercration (of the heavenly gracefulness) / Disciples of blasphemous reprisal / Unheavenly skies / United in repugnance / Shadows from the ancient empire / Ethereal misery / Unto infinite twilight / Majesty of infernal domination / Horde of bestial flames
RR 69822 / 15 Jun '98 / Relapse

☐ FORSAKEN MOURNING OF ANGELIC ANGUISH
Shadows from the ancient empire / Lusting congregation of perpetual damnation / Triumph in blasphemy / Forsaken mourning of angelic anguish / Scram bloody gore / Twisted sacrilegious journey into our darkest neurotic delir / Ibex moon / Blasphemous cremation / Essence ablaze / Blissful bloodshower
RR 69742 / 12 Dec '97 / Relapse

☐ MORTAL THRONE OF NAZARENE
Golgotha / Devoured death / Blasphemous creations / Rotting spiritual embodiment / Unholy massacre / Entrantment of evil / Christening the afterbirth / Immortal cessation / Profanation / Deliverance of horrific prophecies
RR 69052 / Jul '97 / Nuclear Blast

☐ ONWARD TO GOLGOTHA
RR 60372 / Jul '97 / Relapse

☐ TRIBUTE TO THE GOAT
ER 02CD / 22 Jun '98 / Elegy

Inch

☐ DOT CLASS C
CRGD 82071 / Feb '97 / Headhunter

Incognito

☐ BENEATH THE SURFACE
Solar fire / Labour of love / Beneath the surface / Shade of blue / Without you / Misunderstood / Hold on to me / Living against the river / She wears black / Fountain of life / Out of the storm / Dark side of the cog
5340712 / Oct '96 / Talkin' Loud

☐ BLUE MOODS
Colibri / Love is the colour / Magnetic ocean / Deep waters / L'arc en ciel de miles / Gypsy / Journey into sunlight / Sunchild / Millenium / Thinking bout tomorrow / Jcobs ladder / She wears black / Dark side of the cog
5347832 / Apr '97 / Talkin' Loud

☐ INCOGNITO REMIXED
Always there / Good love / Jump to my love / I hear my name / Giving it up / Pieces of a dream / Jacobs ladder / Everyday / Barumba / Roots / Still a friend a mine / I hear your name / Still a friend of mine
5323092 / Apr '96 / Talkin' Loud

☐ ONE HUNDRED DEGREES AND RISING
Where did we go wrong / Good love / Hundred and rising / Roots / Everyday / Too far gone / After the fall / Spellbound and speechless / I hear your name / Barumba / Millenium / Time has come / Jacob's ladder
5280002 / May '95 / Talkin' Loud

☐ POSITIVITY
Still a friend of mine / Smiling faces / Keep the fire burning / Do right / Positivity / Talkin' loud / Deep waters / Where do we go from here / Giving it up / Thinking about tomorrow
5182602 / Nov '93 / Talkin' Loud

☐ TRIBES, VIBES AND SCRIBES
Colibri / Change / River in my dreams / Don't you worry about a thing / Magnet ocean / I love what you do for me / Closer to the feeling / L'Arc en ciel de miles / Need to know / Pyramids / Tribal vibes
5123632 / 15 Sep '97 / Talkin' Loud

Incredible String Band

☐ 5000 SPIRITS OR THE LAYERS OF THE ONION
Chinese white / No sleep blues / Painting box / Mad hatter's song / Little cloud / Eyes of fate / Blues for the muse / Hedgehog's song / First girl I loved / You know that you could be / My name is death / Gently tender / Way back in the 1960's
HNCD 4438 / Jun '94 / Hannibal

☐ BE GLAD FOR THE SONG HAS NO ENDING
Come with me / All writ down / Vishangro / See all the people / Waiting for you / Song has no ending
EDCD 564 / 1 Jun '98 / Edsel

☐ BIG HUGE, THE
Maya / Greatest friend / Son of Noah's brother / Lordly nightshade / Mountain of God / Cousin caterpillar / Iron stone / Douglas Traherne Harding / Circle is unbroken
7559615482 / Jul '93 / Elektra

☐ CHANGING HORSES
Big Ted / White bird / Dust be diamonds / Sleeper's awake / Mr. and Mrs. / Creation
HNCD 4439 / Nov '94 / Rykodisc

☐ CHELSEA SESSIONS 1967, THE
Lover man / Born in your town / First girl I loved / Gently tender / Little cloud / Blues for the muse / Eyes of fate / Mad hatters song / Alice is a long time gone / See your face and know you / Frutch / Iron stone / God dog
PWMD 5003 / 9 Mar '98 / Pigs Whisker Music

☐ HANGMAN'S BEAUTIFUL DAUGHTER
Koee / Addi there / Minotaur's song / Witches hat / Very cellular song / Mercy I cry city / Waltz of the new moon / Water song / Three is a green crown / Swift as the wind / Nightfall
HNCD 4421 / Jun '94 / Hannibal

☐ HARD ROPE AND SILKEN TWINE
Maker of islands / Cold February / Glancing love / Dreams of no return / Dumb Kate / Ithkos
EDCD 368 / Jan '93 / Edsel

☐ I LOOKED UP
HNCD 4440 / Nov '94 / Rykodisc

☐ INCREDIBLE STRING BAND
Maybe someday / October song / When the music starts to play / Schaeffer's jig / Womankind / Tree / Whistle tune / Dandelion blues / How happy I am / Empty pocket blues / Smoke shovelling song / Can't keep me here / Good as gone / Footsteps of the heron / Niggertown / Everything's fine right now
HNCD 4437 / Jun '94 / Hannibal

☐ LIQUID ACROBAT AS REGARDS AIR
Talking of the end / Dear old battlefield / Cosmic boy / Worlds they rise and fall / Evolution rag / Painted chariot / Adam and Eve / Red hair / Here till here is there / Tree / Jigs / Darling belle
IMCD 130 / Jun '91 / Island

☐ NO RUINOUS FEUD
Explorer / Explorer / Saturday maybe / Jigs / Old buccaneer / At the lighthouse dance / Second fiddle / Circus girl / Turquoise blue / My blue tears / Weather the storm / Little girl
EDCD 367 / Nov '92 / Edsel

☐ WEE TAM
Job's tears / Puppies / Beyond the sea / Yellow snake / Log cabin in the sky / You get brighter / Half remarkable question / Air / Ducks on a pond
HNCD 4802 / Nov '94 / Rykodisc

Incredibles

☐ HEART AND SOUL
Heart and soul / (I love you) for sentimental reasons / Lost without you / Standing here crying / I'll make it easy / Miss Treatment / Without a word / All of a sudden / Another dirty deal / There's nothing else to say baby / Fool, fool, fool (version 1) / Stop the raindrops / I found another love / Crying heart (version 1) / Without a word / Standing here crying / Miss Treatment (45 version) / I can't get over losing your love / Fool, fool, fool (version 2)
GSCD 018 / Jul '93 / Goldmine

Incubus

☐ BEYOND THE UNKNOWN
Certain accuracy / Deceived ones / Curse of the damned cities / Beyond the unknown / Freezing torment / Massacre of the unborn / On the burial ground / Mortify
NB 039CD / Jan '91 / Nuclear Blast

☐ SERPENT TEMPTATION
RAD 124CD / Apr '96 / Radiation

Incubus

☐ ENJOY INCUBUS
You will be a hot dancer / Shaft / Take me to your leader / Version / Azwethinkweiz hilikus / Hidden bonus
4871022 / Feb '97 / Epic

☐ SCIENCE
Redefine / New skin / Idiot box / Glass / Magic medicine / Certain shade of green / Favourite things / Antigravity love song / Nebula / Deep inside / Calgon
4882616 / 6 Oct '97 / Epic

Independents

☐ STALKER, THE
ELM 021CD / 2 Mar '98 / Elevator

Index

☐ ANTHOLOGY VOL.2 (2CD Set)
INDEX 2 / 2 Feb '98 / Top Jimmy

☐ BLACK LIGHT TWILIGHT
COPCD 023 / Nov '96 / Cop International

Indicate

☐ WHELM
TO 25 / Jun '95 / Touch

Indigo

☐ CARNETS DE VOL
926642 / Feb '97 / BUDA

Indigo Girls

☐ 4.5
Joking / Hammer and a nail / Kid fears / Galileo / Tried to be true / Power of two / Pushing the needle too far / Reunion / Closer to fine / Three hits / Least complicated / Touch me fall / Love's recovery / Land of Canaan / Ghost
4804392 / Jul '95 / Epic

☐ SHAMING THE SUN
Shame on you / Get out the map / Shed your skin / It's alright / Caramia / Don't give that girl a gun / Leeds / Scooter boys / Everything in its own time / Cut it out / Burn all the letters / Hey kind friend
4869822 / May '97 / Epic

☐ SWAMPOPHELIA
Fugitive / Least complicated / Language or the kiss / Reunion / Power of two / Touch me fall / Wood song / Mystery / Dead man's hill / Fare thee well / This train revised
4759312 / May '94 / Epic

Indigo Kennedy

☐ ZET LONDON VOL.3
INGI 001CD / Jun '97 / Zet

Indo Aminata

☐ GREATEST DREAM
Love will be on your side / Dunigna colorila / Always / Leo Leo / I've waited for this love / Cruel love / When you have the greatest dream / Djeneba / Silan magninde / Follow me / Djiamma
5328812 / Nov '96 / Manifesto

Inducing The Pleasure Dreams

☐ RADIO MOOG 1996
XTC 00000011CD / Nov '96 / Apocalyptic Vision

Industrial Terror Squad

☐ TERROR DROME
35286 / Sep '96 / Industrial Strength

Inertia

☐ DEMAGNETIZED/REMAGNETIZED
NIGHTCD 021 / 3 Aug '98 / Nightbreed

☐ INFILTRATOR
EFA 125292 / Nov '95 / Celtic Circle

Infa Riot

☐ STILL OUT OF ORDER
Emergency / You ain't seen nothin' yet / Five minute fashion / Each dawn I die / Drug squad / Still out of order / Catch 22 / Power / Boot boys / Winner / Friday oh Friday / Catalogue kids / In for a riot
AHOYCD 010 / 6 Jul '98 / Captain Oi

Infections

☐ KILL...
RIPOFF 028CD / 8 Sep '97 / Rip Off

Infernal Torment

☐ BIRTHRATE ZERO
PCD 045 / 24 Nov '97 / Diehard

Inferno

☐ DEATH AND MADNESS
GTA 025 / Mar '97 / Grand Theft Auto

☐ DOWNTOWN HADES
OPCD 060CD / 2 Mar '98 / Osmose

☐ PSYCHIC DISTANCE
MASSCD 043 / Jan '95 / Massacre

☐ UTTER HELL
OPCD 044 / Oct '96 / Osmose

Infestdead

☐ HELLFUCK
IRO 26CD / 28 Jul '97 / Invasion

Infinite Wheel

☐ INFINITE WHEEL, THE
BRAINK 41CD / Oct '94 / Brainiak

Infinity

☐ NOW (Infinity & Alphonse Mouzon)
Cargo for Montreal / Just because of you / Just once / I don't know / Somehow / Utz / Fog in Frankfurt / Makin' love with you / Music till the news / Katchur / What's this
INAK 9004CD / Nov '97 / In Akustik

Infinity Project

☐ MYSTICAL EXPERIENCES
BR 005CD / Jan '96 / Blue Room Released

Infor/Mental

☐ MIND DRONE
Mind drone / Wave / Pleasuredance / Dream mode mutation / Mental journey / Frenzy / Trance induction / Infection / Dream mode mutation (mix) / Insanity / Device trigger / Ambient one
LUDDITECD 066 / Oct '93 / Death Of Vinyl

Information

☐ ARTIFACTS
BSCD 019 / 8 Jun '98 / BeatService

Ingham, Keith

☐ KEITH INGHAM & MARTY GROSZ/ COSMOPOLITES (Ingham, Keith & Marty Grosz)
SOSCD 1285 / Mar '95 / Stomp Off

☐ MOVIE SONGS 1929-1930 (Ingham-Grosz Cosmopolites)
SOSCD 1323 / Feb '98 / Stomp Off

☐ OUT OF THE PAST
SKCD 23047 / '92 / Sackville

Ingle, Red

☐ TIM-TAYSHUN
Tim-tayshun / For sentimental reasons / Song of Indians / Them durn fool things / Git up off'n the floor / Pagan ninny's keep 'er goin' stomp / Nowhere / Pearly Maude / Oh Nick-o-deemo / Gigarettes whuskey and wild wild women / Gigardust / I surrender dear / Moezart's turkey trot / Prisoner of love song / You can't be fit as a fiddle / Serutan yob / Irishman will never fight / Turn your head little darlin' / 'A' you're a dopey girl / Two dollar pistol / Girlin' and cuttin' up didoes / Pool / Comin' 'round the mountain march / Run little Eva / People are funny / Let me in / Chew tobacco rag / Git away from the wimmin'
BCD 16115 / Aug '97 / Bear Family

Ingleton Falls

☐ ABSCONDED
CHARRMCD 20 / Mar '95 / Charrm

Inglez, Roberto

☐ ROBERTO INGLEZ 1945-1947
On my way out / Os quindins de ya-ya / Chiquita banana / Green cockatoo / Brazil / Tres palabras / Autumn serenade / Rio de Janeiro / Melodies of today / Laura / Jamaican rhumba / Two silhouettes / Tico tico / Another night like this / Negra consentida / El toreador / Mam'selle / Mi vida / Chi baba / Bruca manigua / Vem vem / Ya que te vas / Shoemaker's serenade / Baia
HQCD 108 / Jan '98 / Harlequin

Ingram

☐ BEST OF INGRAM, THE
HTCD 97 / 20 Apr '98 / Hot Productions

Ingram, Adrian

☐ DUETS (Ingram, Adrian & Andy MacKenzie)
Pick yourself up / Gravy waltz / Nivram / Django's bounce / Barney's bossa / Wes mode / Kenny's groove / Mr PM / Can't buy me love / Lover man / Lullaby of birdland / Rabbit waltz
IPCD 010 / Jun '97 / Crimson

☐ SPREAD THE WORD (Ingram, Adrian & Ben Crossland Quartet)
Warm one / Seachange / Spread the word / Down at Pol's / Movin' on / Floating blue / Friday the 13th / We got it too / Peter the wolf / You don't know what love is / Ade's groove
JCCD 102 / Nov '96 / Jazz Cat

Ingram, Chris

☐ LOVING GROOVES
FECD 15 / 17 Nov '97 / First Edition

Ingram, Jack

☐ LIVIN' OR DYIN'
Nothin' wrong with that / Big time / Ghost of a man / Flutter / Rita Ballou / She does her best / Dim lights, thick smoke (and loud, loud music) / Picture on my wall / That's not me / Don't you remember / Imitation of love / Dallas / I can't leave you / Airways motel
RTD 80370 / Apr '97 / Rising Tide

Ingram, James

☐ ALWAYS YOU
Someone like you / Let me love you this way / Always you / Treat her right / Baby's born / This is the night / You never know what you've got / Too much from this heart / Sing for the children / Any kind of love
9362452752 / May '93 / Qwest

☐ POWER OF GREAT MUSIC, THE
Where did my heart go / How do you keep the music playing / Just once / Somewhere out there / I don't have the heart / There's no easy way / Get ready / Baby, come to me / Hundred ways / Yah mo be there / Remember the dream / Whatever we imagine
7599267002 / Mar '94 / Qwest

Inhaler

☐ VOLUME
LLL 2030 / Dec '96 / Seriously Groovy

Inhuman

☐ EVOLVER
EB 008CD / 11 Sep '97 / Eyeball

☐ FORESHADOW
Shadowy but immortal / Redeemer / Last whispering / Mansized heaven / Scars in your heart / Crystal / Blessing in disguise / Divinity / Lifeless seasons / Stigma
CRIDE 5 / 14 Sep '98 / Ranch Life

Iniquity

☐ SERENADIUM
RRS 953CD / Jul '96 / Progress

Inishkea

☐ PAN PIPES OF IRELAND
When you were sweet sixteen / Bunch of thyme / I'll take you home again Kathleen / Shepherd moon / Carrickfergus / Maggie / Pal of my cradle days / When Irish eyes are smiling / Molly Malone / Fields of Athenrey / Rose of Tralee / Have I told you lately / Mountains of Mourne / Leaving of Liverpool / Whiskey in the jar / Londonderry air
307602 / Jul '97 / Hallmark

Ink, Mike

☐ MASSSTAB 1:5 (M:1:5)
CD 3 / 17 Nov '97 / Profan

☐ POLKA TRAX
WAPCD 82 / Oct '96 / Warp

Ink Spots

☐ 18 HITS
KCD 5001 / Apr '97 / King

☐ BEST OF THE INK SPOTS, THE
HMNCD 001 / Jun '97 / Half Moon

☐ BLESS YOU
Bless you / If I didn't care / Whispering grass / Stop pretending / When the swallows come back to Capistrano / So sorry / Do I worry / We'll meet again / I'd climb the highest mountain / Ring, telephone, ring / That cat is high / Memories of you / My prayer / Just for a thrill / We three / Someone's rocking my dreamboat / Maybe / I'll never smile again / I'm getting sentimental over you / Coquette / Oh red / When the sun goes down
PLCD 535 / Mar '93 / President

☐ CLASSICS
Bless you / Don't get around much anymore / Ring telephone ring / So sorry / Someone's rocking my dreamboat / Do I worry / Whispering grass / Java jive / If I didn't care / I'd climb the highest mountain / When the swallows come back to Capistrano / Maybe / That cat is high / Stop pretending / With plenty of money and you / When the sun goes down / Who wouldn't love you / That's the way it is / To each his own / Everyone is saying hello again / Street of dreams / Someday I'll meet you again
RAJCD 886 / Jul '97 / Empress

☐ FABULOUS INK SPOTS, THE
Into each life some rain must fall / Cow cow boogie / I'll get by / I'm making believe / We'll meet again / Stop pretending / With plenty of money and you / Yes suh / I'm getting sentimental over you / Ring telephone ring / So sorry / Coquette / I'll never smile again (until I smile at you) / Swing high swing low / Oh Red / Don't let old age creep upon you / Street of dreams / Just for a thrill
SUMCD 4190 / 11 May '98 / Summit

☐ IF I DIDN'T CARE
GO 3823 / 1 Dec '97 / Golden Options

☐ INK SPOTS GREATEST HITS VOL.1
BMCD 3037 / Jan '97 / Blue Moon

☐ INK SPOTS GREATEST HITS VOL.2
BMCD 3038 / Jan '97 / Blue Moon

☐ INK SPOTS, THE
CD 110 / Oct '94 / Timeless Treasures

☐ JAVA JIVE
I love you truly / I love you truly / My wild irish rose / Just for a thrill / Shine on harvest moon / It's been a long, long time / When you were sweet sixteen / I've got the world on a string / Address unknown / In the shade of the old apple tree / Blueberry hill / You always hurt the one you love / In a shanty in old shanty town / Java jive
15430 / Jan '93 / Laserlight

☐ PORTRAIT OF THE INK SPOTS, A
GALE 415 / 20 Apr '98 / Gallerie

☐ SENTIMENTAL OVER YOU
HADCD 194 / Nov '95 / Javelin

☐ SWING HIGH, SWING LOW (1936-1940)
Bless you / Java jive / When the swallows come back to Capistrano / My prayer / Christopher Columbus / I'll never smile again / Stompin' at the Savoy / Whispering grass / If I didn't care / I'm getting sentimental over you / Keep away from my doorstep / Let's call the whole thing off / Maybe / Oh Red / Slap that bass / Stop pretending / Swing high swing low / That cat is high / When the sun goes down / With plenty of money and you / Yes suh / Your feet's too big
CDAJA 5082 / Apr '91 / Living Era

☐ WE FOUR (The Best Of The Ink Spots)
We three (my echo my shadow and me) / If I didn't care / Maybe / When the swallows come / I don't want to set the world on fire / Address unknown / Do I worry / So sorry / Prisoner of love / I'd climb the highest mountain / Into each life some rain must fall / Gipsy / My prayer / Puttin' and takin' / Whispering grass / Thoughtless / Ev'ry night about this time / To each his own / Don't get around much anymore / I'm beginning to the see the light / Someone's rocking my dreamboat / Until the real thing comes along / When the sun goes down / Bless you
JASMCD 2546 / Feb '98 / Jasmine

☐ WHISPERING GRASS (The Very Best Of The Ink Spots)
If I didn't care / I'll never smile again / Java jive / Stop pretending / Maybe / Your feet's too big / I don't want to set the world on fire / When the swallows come back to Capistrano / Cat is high / Whispering grass (don't tell the trees) / Someone's rocking my dreamboat / Who wouldn't love you / Christopher Columbus / Do I worry / My prayer / Slap that bass / Don't get around much more / I'm getting sentimental over you / We three / Bless you
305522 / Oct '96 / Hallmark

☐ WHISPERING GRASS
Bless you / Stop pretending / That cat is high / When the swallows come back to Capistrano / Mama don't allow it / My prayer / Whispering grass / We three (my echo, my shadow and me) / I'm getting sentimental over you / Java jive / With plenty of money and you / Keep away from my doorstep / Do I worry / I'll never smile again / Don't let old age creep up on you / Maybe / If I didn't care / Stompin' at the Savoy / Coquette / Swing high swing low / Your feet's too big / When the sun goes down
PASTCD 9757 / Aug '91 / Pearl

Inkubus Sukkubus

☐ BELLADONNA & ACONITE
ABCD 007 / Mar '96 / Resurrection

☐ BELTHANE
ABCD 11 / Oct '96 / Resurrection

☐ HEATBEAT
ABCD 005 / Apr '96 / Resurrection

☐ VAMPYRE EROTICA
ABCD 017 / 29 Sep '97 / Resurrection

☐ WYTCHES
Wytches / Queen of the May / Pagan born / Gypsy lament / Leveller / Call out my name / Conquistadors / Burning times / Song to Pan / Enchantment / Catherine / Church of madness / Rape of Maude Bowen / Dark mother / Devils
PMRCD 7 / '96 / Pagan Media

Inkuyo

☐ ANCIENT SUN - MUSIC OF THE ANDES (The Music Of the Andes)
130932 / Sep '96 / Celestial Harmonies

Inmates

☐ INMATES
892223 / May '94 / New Rose

☐ INSIDE OUT
422178 / May '94 / New Rose

☐ SILVERIO
3018322 / Feb '97 / Last Call

☐ WANTED
422460 / May '94 / New Rose

Inner Circle

☐ BAD TO THE BONE
Sweat (a la la la la long) / Shock out Jamaican style / Bad to the bone / Rock with you / Long time / Hey love / Slow it down / Living it up / Stuck in the middle / Looking for a better way / Wrapped up in your love / Bad boys / Party party / Sunglasses at nite / Tear down these walls / Down by the river / Hold on to the ridim / Why them a gwan so
9031776772 / Dec '96 / Magnet

☐ BEST OF INNER CIRCLE, THE
Rock the boat / Curfew / Duppy gunman / None shall escape the judgement / You make me feel brand new / Some guys have all the luck / Everything I own / TSOP (The sound of Philadelphia) / Westbound train / Book of rules / Natty dread / I shot the sheriff / Irie feelings / Forward Jah Jah children / Blame it on the sun / Curly locks / Your kiss is sweet / Burial / Roadblock / When will I see you again
CDTRL 318 / Mar '94 / Trojan

☐ BEST OF INNER CIRCLE, THE
We 'a' rockers / Tenement yard (live) / I've got the handle (live) / Standing firm (live) / Discipline child (live) / Stop breaking my heart / Mary mary / We come to rock you / Chips and bruises / Music machine / New age music / Everything is great / Delilah
CID 8007 / Jan '94 / Island

☐ FORWARD JAH JAH PEOPLE
Rastaman / Forward Jah Jah children / Last crusade / Lively up yourself / Funky reggae / One love
CPCD 8133 / Oct '95 / Charly

☐ ONE WAY
One way / Front and centre / Champion / Keep the faith / Love one another / Massive / Bad boys / Life / Stay with me
RASCD 3030 / Oct '87 / Ras

☐ REGGAE DANCER
Games people play / Reggae dancer / Black roses / Something so good / Signs (i can't take it) / Whip it / Only you / Alright / 24-7-365 / Broken glass / Rough boy / Walking on a rainbow / I can't imagine / Summer jammin'
4509961162 / Sep '94 / Magnet

☐ REGGAE THING
NSPCD 510 / Mar '95 / Connoisseur Collection

Inner City

☐ PARADISE
Inner city theme / Ain't nobody better / Big fun / Good life / And I do / Paradise / Power of passion / Do you love what you feel / Set your body free / Secrets of the mind
VI 874812 / Nov '96 / Disky
CDVIP 160 / Oct '96 / Virgin VIP

☐ PARADISE REMIXED
Big fun / Good life / Ain't nobody better / Do you love what you feel / What'cha gonna do with my lovin' / House fever / Paradise megamix
CDVIP 208 / 3 Aug '98 / Virgin VIP

☐ TESTAMENT '93
Good life / Pennies from heaven / Hallelujah / Praise / Follow your heart / Good life (Unity remix)
CDOVD 438 / May '93 / Virgin

Inner City Jazz Workshop

☐ INSIDE DANCING ONLY
MANU 1504 / Feb '96 / Manu

Inner City Unit

☐ NEW ANATOMY
14845 / Feb '97 / Spalax

Inner Shrine

☐ NOCTURNAL RHYMES ENTANGLED IN SILENCE
CHAOS 002CD / 13 Apr '98 / Dragonheart

Inner Swing

☐ GET IN THE SWING
TTTCD 015 / 22 Jun '98 / Hubbcap

Innes, Heather

☐ COAINEADH - SONGS FROM THE HEART
FE 099CD / Jun '94 / Fellside

Innes, Neil

☐ RE-CYCLED VINYL BLUES
Recycled vinyl blues / Angelina / Come out into the open / Prologue / Momma Bee / Lie down and be counted / Immortal invisible / Age of desperation / Topless a go-go / Feel no shame / How sweet to be an idiot / Dream on / L'amour perdu / Song for Yvonne / This love of ours / Fluff on the needle / Singing a song is easy / Bandwagon
CZ 536 / Aug '94 / EMI

Innisfree Ceoil

☐ CELTIC AIRS VOL.1
CHCD 2001 / Nov '96 / Chyme

☐ CELTIC AIRS VOL.2
CHCD 2002 / Nov '96 / Chyme

☐ CLASSIC IRISH MELODIES VOL.1 (Celtic Gold)
Dublin in the rare oul times / Riverdance / Green glens of Antrim / Woman's heart / Danny boy / Avondale / Coolin' / On Raglan road / Grace / Lonesome boatman / Cliffs of Dooneen / She moved through the fair / Banks of my own lovely Lee / Rose of Tralee / Give me your hand
CHCD 8000 / Jun '98 / Outlet

☐ CLASSIC IRISH MELODIES VOL.2 (Celtic Gold)
Isle of Innisfree / King of the fairies / Woman of Ireland / Teddy O'Neill / Roisin dubh / Mountains of Mourne / Wests awake / Meeting of the waters / Star of the county Down / Down by the Sally gardens / My Lagan love / Fields of Athenry / Carrickfergus / Town I loved so well / Snowy breasted pearl
CHCD 8001 / Jun '98 / Outlet

Innocence

☐ BELIEF
Silent voice / Let's push it / Reflections / Natural thing / Matter of fact / Higher ground / Remember the day / Moving upwards / Come together / Reprise
CCD 1797 / Oct '90 / Cooltempo

☐ BUILD
Family ties / I'll be there / Build / Looking for someone / Solitude / Family ties(Reprise) / One love in my lifetime / Promise of love / Hold on / Respect / No sacrifice / Build (reprise)
CTCD 26 / Oct '92 / Cooltempo

Innocence Mission

☐ GLOW
5403322 / 15 Sep '97 / A&M

Innocent

☐ INNOCENT
ESM 019 / 2 Mar '98 / Escape

Innocent

☐ GREETINGS FROM AFRICA (Innocent & Les Exodus Band)
Greetings from Africa / One world / Open your heart / Stay with me / Stranger / Is it true / Coming home / Back in time / Sote ni ndugu / Running
MOUP 6017 / Nov '97 / Mouthpiece

Innocents

☐ COMPLETE INDIGO RECORDINGS
Gee whiz / Please Mr. Sun / Walking along / Once in a while / Pain in my heart / Chiquita / Girl in my dreams / Because I love you / Sleeping beauty / Donna / Kathy / My baby Hully Gullys / Honest I do / Beware / I'm a hog for you / When I become a man / Two young hearts / Dee dee di oh / I believe in you / It was a tear / You got me goin' / Little blue star / I know a valley / Time makes you change / In the beginning
CDCHD 374 / Jun '92 / Ace

Inoue, Tetsu

☐ PSYCHO-ACOUSTIC
TZA 7213 / 1 Jun '98 / Tzadik

Inquisition

☐ KRANK
NMS 12555CD / 28 Jul '97 / NSM

Inquisitor

☐ WALPURGIS, SABBATH OF LUST
SHR 018CD / Jul '96 / Shiver

Insane Clown Posse

☐ CARNIVAL OF CARNAGE
Intro / Carnival of carnage / Juggla / First day out / Red neck hoe / Wizard of the hood / Guts on the ceiling / Is that you / Night of the axe / Psychopathic / Blackin' your eyes / Never had made it / Your ebel flag / Ghetto freak show / Taste
5245142 / 29 Jun '98 / Island

☐ GREAT MILENKO, THE
5244422 / 27 Oct '97 / Island

☐ RINGMASTER
Wax museum / Murder go round / Chicken huntin' / Mr. Johnson's head / Southwest song / Get off me dog / Who asked you / Dead one / For the maggots / Wagon wagon / Loons / Love songs / Bugz on my nugz / House of mirrors / Ringmaster's world
PSY 1006 / 16 Feb '98 / Psycho
5245152 / 29 Jun '98 / Island

☐ TUNNEL OF LOVE, THE
PSY 1015 / 16 Feb '98 / Psycho

Insane Jane

☐ EACH FINGER
SKYCD 5041 / Sep '94 / Sky

☐ GREEN LITTLE PILL
SKYCD 5040 / Sep '94 / Sky

Insanity Sect

☐ MANISOLA
RBADCD 15 / Feb '96 / Beyond

Insaurralde, Mirta

☐ DE IGUAL A IGUAL (Insaurralde, Mirta & Ruben Ferrero)
Duerme negrito / Que he sacado con quererte / La vieja / El dia que me quieras / Patio de naranjos / Nunca se supo porque / Vidala para mi sombra / Tierra tiembla / Homenaje a Pablo Neruda / De igual a igual
SLAMCD 502 / Oct '94 / Slam

Insekt

☐ DREAMSCAPE
Torture (rhythm pain) / Scum / Cocaine / Punisher / Dreamscape / Spiritual experience / Deceptions / Games / Knock me down / Pressure / Mask
KK 074CD / Mar '92 / KK

☐ STRESS
Perfect crime / Give me protection / Murder / Aqua death / Another bacteria / Theme from... / Stress / Bat
KK 054CD / Mar '91 / KK

☐ WE CAN'T TRUST THE INSEKT
KK 036CD / Jun '93 / KK

Inside Out

☐ SHE LOST HER HEAD
COX 032CD / Apr '92 / Meantime

Insides

☐ CLEAR SKIN
TU 7 / Feb '94 / 4AD

☐ EUPHORIA
Walking in straight lines / Bent double / Darling effect / Distractions / Relentless / Skin divers / Carly simon / Yes / Skykicking
GU 4CD / 6 Jul '98 / Guernica

Insomniacs

☐ OUT OF IT
ES 1233CD / Apr '97 / Estrus

Inspector 7

☐ ...THE INFAMOUS
RAD 700172 / 8 Sep '97 / Radical

Inspector Tuppence

☐ PARADISO
INSPEC 001 / Mar '97 / Inspec

Inspiral Carpets

☐ BEAST INSIDE, THE
Caravan / Please be cruel / Born yesterday / Sleep well tonight / Grip / Beast inside / Niagara / Mermaid / Further away / Dreams are all we have
DUNG 14CD / May '91 / Cow

☐ DEVIL HOPPING
LDUNG 25CD / Feb '94 / Cow

☐ LIFE
DUNG 008CD / Mar '90 / Cow

☐ REVENGE OF THE GOLDFISH
DUNG 19CD / Oct '92 / Cow

☐ SINGLES, THE
CDMOOTEL 3 / Sep '95 / Cow

☐ TALKING WITH THE BEAST
CBAK 4047 / Jun '91 / Baktabak

Inspirational Choir

☐ GOSPEL SONGS
Amazing grace / Rock of ages / He's got the whole world in his hands / Deep river / Every time I feel the spirit / Steal away / I've got a robe / Were you there / Old rugged cross / Old time religion / Abide with me / He's got the whole world in his hands
5501912 / Sep '94 / Spectrum

Inspirations

☐ PAN PIPE IMAGES
TCD 2819 / Mar '96 / Telstar

☐ PIANO REFLECTIONS
PMCD 7024 / Jan '96 / Pure Music

Inspirations

☐ REGGAE FEVER (Various Artists)
Mad rooster: *Willis, Lloyd & The Destroyers* / Ease up: *Inspirations* / Wet dreams: *Inspirations* / Why do we laugh at my calamities: *Inspirations* / Samfie man: *Inspirations* / Only yesterday: *Parker, Ken* / Reggae fever: *Willis, Lloyd* / Bongo nyah: *Inspirations* / Who you gonna run to: *Inspirations* / Sweet sensation: *Inspirations* / Fattie fattie: *Inspirations* / Liquidator: *Willis, Lloyd & The Destroyers* / Franco Nero: *Willis, Lloyd & The Destroyers* / Take back your duck: *Inspirations* / Niney special: *Destroyers* / Perfect born ya: *Immortals* / Rock the clock: *Gibbs, Joe* / Money raper: *Gibbs, Joe* / La la: *Inspirations* / Train is coming: *Inspirations* / Danger zone: *Destroyers* / Hijacked: *Destroyers* / Man oh man: *Inspirations* / This message to you: *Inspirations* / Frank Nero: *Destroyers* / Red red wine: *Immortals*
CDTRL 395 / 22 Apr '98 / Trojan

Instant Funk

☐ BEST OF INSTANT FUNK, THE
CDGR 159 / Aug '97 / Charly

☐ FUNK IS ON, THE
It's cool / Funk is on / Funk 'n' roll / You want my love / What can I do for you / Everybody / Can you see where I'm coming from / You're not getting older
CPCD 8097 / Apr '95 / Charly

☐ INSTANT FUNK
I got my mind made up (You can get it girl) / Crying / Never let it go away / Don't wanna party / Wide world of sports / Dark vader / You say you want me to stay / I'll be doggone
CPCD 8075 / Mar '95 / Charly

Insted

☐ BONDS OF FRIENDSHIP
LF 178CD / Sep '96 / Lost & Found

Institute Of Dubology

☐ INSTITUTE OF DUBNOLOGY & TUFFHEAD (Institute Of Dubology & Tuffhead)
LIVESTOCK 2CD / Jul '96 / Livestock

Insult

☐ MUTANT PUZZLE
SPI 021CD / Jun '95 / Spinefarm

Insult II Injury

☐ POINT OF THIS
CM 77086 / Jan '95 / Century Media

Insync

☐ ANDROID ARCHITECTS (Insync & Mysteron)
Gravity pull / Next world / Landing site / Human loop / Android architects / Science fact / Auto glide / Missing link / Dig deep / Train of thought / Naked I
TPRCD 005 / Mar '97 / 10th Planet

Intastella

☐ WHAT YOU GONNA DO
SATURNCD 1 / Oct '95 / China

Integrated Circuits

☐ PREDO
DBMLABCD 6 / Oct '95 / Labworks

Integrity

☐ SEASONS IN THE SIZE OF DAYS
VR 053CD / Jun '97 / Victory

☐ SYSTEMS OVERLOAD
VE 012CD / Aug '95 / Victory

☐ TASTE EVERY SIN
HT 004 / Jun '97 / Holy Terror

Intense

☐ LOGICAL PROGRESSION VOL.3 (2CD Set) (Various Artists)
Witness / Retro spek / Afterlife / Shara / Good times bad / Wastelands / Hemisfear / Hemisphere / She moves through: Blu Mar Ten / Alpha 7: Blame / Resolution: Tayla / Freedom: Big Bud / Sun voyage: Artemis / Remedy: Seba / Mystique: Big Bud / Get high Fiona: 2 Bob Sound System
GLRCD 003 / 27 Apr '98 / Good Looking

Intensity

☐ WASH OFF THE LIES
BTR 25 / 6 Apr '98 / Bad Taste

Intergrity

☐ WHY I NEED A BEER
WB 1135CD / Apr '96 / We Bite

Interloper

☐ AUGUR
PLKCD 5 / Jun '96 / Plink Plonk

Intermission

☐ SONG OF LOW SONGS
BVHAASTCD 9612 / Apr '98 / Bvhaast

Intermix

☐ FUTURE PRIMITIVES
SUN 49982 / Sep '96 / Mokum

International Children's Choir

☐ O HOLY NIGHT
15302 / Nov '95 / Laserlight

International Jazz Band

☐ INTERNATIONAL JAZZ BAND, THE
JCCD 3030 / Oct '97 / Jazz Crusade

International Language

☐ WHERE THE BANDS ARE
SFTRI 457 / Dec '96 / Sympathy For The Record Industry

International People

☐ INTERNATIONAL PEOPLE
EMIT 3395 / Oct '95 / Time Recordings

International Staff Band

☐ CHRISTMAS FESTIVAL IN BRASS
O come all ye faithful (adeste fidelis) / We three kings / Joy of Christmas / While sheperds watched / Carol fantasy / Staple door / Joy in Bethjlehem / Once in Royal David's city / Ding dong merrnily on high / Silent night / It came upon the midnight clear / New born babe / First nowell / I saw three ships / Away in a manger / Hark the herald sing
CDMFP 6407 / 6 Oct '97 / Music For Pleasure

International Strike Force

☐ LOVE IS
SLAMPT 41CD / Nov '96 / Slampt Underground

Interpreters

☐ BACK IN THE USSA
61422311472 / 2 Feb '98 / Freeworld

Interstate Ten

☐ SILVERLAKECREEKBELOW FORESTPRIMEVIL
WRO 12CD / 20 Jul '98 / Wrenched

Inti-Illimani

☐ ANDADAS
GL 4009CD / Oct '93 / Green Linnet

☐ CANTO DE PUEBLOS ANDINOS
MCD 71787 / Jun '93 / Monitor

☐ CANTO PARA MATAR UNA CULE
MCD 71817 / Jun '93 / Monitor

☐ DE CANTO Y BAILE
Mi chiquita / Dedica toria de un libro / Cantiga de la memoria rota / Bailando / Candidos / El colibri / El vals / La muerte no va conmigo / Danza di cala luna
MES 159362 / Apr '93 / Messidor

☐ I WILL RISK MY SKIN
Medianoche / Maria Canela / El hacha / Entre nosotros / Quien eres tu / Arriesgare la piel / Kalimba / Cumpleanos 80 de nicanor / Caramba yo soy dueno del baron / El negro bembon / Kulliacas / Canto de las estrellas
XENO 4049CD / Nov '96 / Xenophile

☐ LA NUEVA CANCION CHILENA
MCD 71794 / Jun '93 / Monitor

☐ LEJANIA
4824840512 / 14 Jul '98 / Xenophile

☐ VIVA CHILE
MCD 71769 / Jun '93 / Monitor

Inti-Raymi

☐ INCA QUENA
TUMICD 047 / '94 / Tumi

☐ INTI-RAYMI
TUMICD 009 / Dec '90 / Tumi

Intimate Orchestra

☐ TENDER MOMENTS
With you I'm born again / Crying / Suddenly / One day I'll fly away / First time ever I saw your face / Sailing / Chi mai / Cavatina / For your eyes only / Woman / Memory / All out of love / Chariots of fire / Imagine / Bright eyes / Just when I needed you most / Don't cry for me Argentina / I'm not in love / If I fell / Concierto de aranjuez
QED 175 / Nov '96 / Tring

Intini, Cosmo

☐ MY FAVOURITE ROOTS (Intini, Cosmo & The Jazz Set)
When Sunny gets blue / Powerful warrior / Round midnight / Fatherly love / My one and only love / Steps
CDSJP 339 / Aug '90 / Timeless Jazz

Into Another

☐ IGNAURUS
REV 035CD / May '94 / Revelation

☐ INTO ANOTHER
WB 083CD / Jan '92 / We Bite

☐ SEEMLESS
1620082 / Feb '96 / Hollywood

Into Paradise

☐ UNDER THE WATER
Bring me closer / Here with you / Red light / Pleasure is you / Circus came to town / Bring me closer (version) / World won't stop / Hearts and flowers / Blue moon express / Say goodnight / Beautiful day / Going home
SETCD 1 / Feb '90 / Setanta

Into The Abyss

☐ FEATHERED SNAKE, THE
EFA 112832 / Aug '95 / Glasnost

☐ MARTYRIUM
SPV 08425232 / Feb '94 / SPV

Into The Future

☐ ENDLESS JOURNEY VOL.3
FAR 413 / 23 Feb '98 / Family Affair

Intricate

☐ (VA:1)
CM 770612 / Jan '94 / Century Media

Intro

☐ INTRO
Love thang / Let me be the one / Anyhting for you / Why don't you love me / It's all about you / Ribbon in the sky / Don't leave me / Come inside / One of a kind love / So many reasons / Ecstasy of love
7567826432 / Apr '93 / Atlantic

☐ NEW LIFE
Funny how time flies / Love me better / Strung out on your lovin' / New life / My love's on the way / Somebody loves you / My song / Spending my life with you / There is a way / Feels like the first time
7567826622 / Nov '95 / Atlantic

Intro To Airlift

☐ INTRO TO AIRLIFT/JUNE PANIC (Intro To Airlift/June Panic)
SC 06 / Oct '97 / Secretly Canadian

Intruder

☐ PSYCHO SAVANT
CDZORRO 25 / Jul '91 / Metal Blade

Intuition

☐ INTUITION
FAT 002CD / Sep '93 / Fat Cat

Intveld, James

☐ JAMES INTVELD
Perfect world / Blue blue day / Cryin' over you / I'm to blame / Barely hangin' on / Samantha / Standing on a rock / My heart is achin' for you / Important words / Your lovin' / You say goodnight, I'll say goodbye / I love you
BCD 15900 / Oct '95 / Bear Family

☐ JAMES INTVELD
24911 / Sep '97 / Cich

Invaders

☐ ALL THAT'S NORMAL TURNS TO...
ELM 010CD / 2 Mar '98 / Elevator

Investigators

☐ GREATEST HITS
CRCD 73 / 15 Sep '97 / Charm

Invisbl Skratch Piklz

☐ SHIGGAR FRAGGAR SHOW
HHSR 0012 / 26 May '98 / Hip Hop Slam

Invisible Pair Of Hands

☐ DISPARATION
Inbetween times / Me me me / Disparu 2 / Strange and lovely / La Balancoire / Ship of death / Oil oil oil / Sloppy / Once upon a time / Feu d'joi
COTCD 011 / 22 Sep '97 / Cup Of Tea

Invisible String Quartet

☐ ENTOMIC
Insect flak / Traffic jam / Marsh ague / Reincarnation / 21cm band / Bee-line / Ephemera / Lagos holiday
SLAMCD 210 / Oct '96 / Slam

Invocator

☐ DYING TO LIVE
PCD 020 / Sep '95 / Progress

☐ EARLY YEARS, THE
RRS 943CD / Dec '94 / Pingo

☐ EXCURSION DEMISE
8410582 / Jan '92 / Black Mark

☐ WEAVE THE APOCALYPSE
BMCD 34 / Jul '93 / Black Mark

INXS

☐ ELEGANTLY WASTED
5346132 / Apr '97 / Mercury

☐ FULL MOON, DIRTY HEARTS
Days of rust / Gift / Make your peace / Time / I'm only looking / Please (You've got that) / Full moon, dirty hearts / Freedom deep / Kill the pain / Cut your roses down / Messenger / Viking juice
5186372 / Oct '93 / Mercury

GREATEST HITS

☐ GREATEST HITS
Mystify / Suicide blonde / Taste it / Strangest party / Need you tonight / Original sin / Heaven sent / Disappear / Never tear us apart / Gift / Devil inside / Beautiful girl / Deliver me / New sensation / What you need / Listen like thieves / Bitter tears / Baby don't cry
5262302 / Oct '94 / Mercury

☐ INXS
On a bus / Doctor / Just keep walking / Learn to smile / Jumping / In vain / Roller skating / Body language / Newsreel babies / Wishy washy
8389252 / May '90 / Mercury

☐ INXS: INTERVIEW PICTURE DISC
CBAK 4038 / Apr '90 / Baktabak

☐ KICK
Guns in the sky / New sensation / Devil inside / Need you tonight / Mediate / Loved one / Wild life / Never tear us apart / Mystify / Kick / Calling all nations / Tiny daggers
8327212 / Nov '87 / Mercury

☐ LISTEN LIKE THIEVES
What you need / Listen like thieves / Kiss the dirt / Shine like it does / Good and bad times / Biting bullets / This time / Three sisters / Same direction / One x one / Red red sun
8249572 / Jan '86 / Mercury

☐ LIVE BABY LIVE
New sensation / Mystify / Shining star / Mediate / Burn for you / This time / Suicide blonde / Never tear us apart / One x one / One thing / Stairs / Hear that sound / What you need
5105802 / Nov '91 / Mercury

☐ SHABOOH SHOOBAH
One thing / To look at you / Spy of love / Soul mistake / Here comes / Black and white / Golden playpen / Jan's song / Old world new world / Don't change
8120842 / Jul '93 / Mercury

☐ SWING, THE
Original sin / Melting in the sun / Send a message / Dancing on the jetty / Swing / Johnson's aeroplane / Love is (what I say) / Face the change / Burn for you / All the voices
8185532 / Jul '84 / Mercury

☐ WELCOME TO WHEREVER YOU ARE
Questions / Heaven sent / Communication / Taste it / Not enough time / All around / Baby don't cry / Beautiful girl / Wishing well / Back on line / Strange desire / Men and women
5125072 / Aug '92 / Mercury

☐ X
Suicide blonde / Disappear / Stairs / Faith in each other / By my side / Lately / Who pays the price / Know the difference / Bitter tears / On my way / Hear that sound
8466682 / Sep '90 / Mercury

IOFR

☐ FILE UNDER SUBCONSCIOUS
BH 005 / 20 Jul '98 / Bubblehead

Iona

☐ BEYOND THESE SHORES
WHAD 1300 / Jul '96 / What

Iona Ac Andy

☐ 100 MILES
SCD 2111 / Feb '96 / Sain

☐ CERDDED DROS Y MYNYDD
SCD 2175 / Jun '94 / Sain

☐ SPIRIT OF THE NIGHT, THE
Ni wyddost mor lwcus wyt ti (you don't know how lucky you / Gwin yr hwyrnos (spirit of the night) / Mae'r gan yn cofio pryd (the song remembers when) / Fe wnes yr oll a thi (i did it all with you) / Y ffordd adre'n ol (way back home) / Troi atat ti (I'll be seeing you) / Drain a'r rhos (the thorn upon the rose) / Awn i wario d'arian cariad (let's go spend your money) / Am reswm aeth yn angof im (for reasons I've forgotten now) / Rhan o dy fyd (part of your world)
SCD 2071 / Oct '94 / Sain

Ionatos, Angelique

☐ CHANSOMS NOMADES
088832 / 24 Feb '98 / Melodie

☐ DE LA SOURCE A LA MER
A 6222 / Feb '96 / Tempo

☐ PAROLE DE JUILLET DE ODYSSEUS ELYTIS
088532 / Jul '97 / Melodie

Iowa Beef Experience

☐ PERSONALIEN
Guilt and revenge / Hardcore fan / Cum soaked / Making the monster a snack / Pizenhead / Tools of the trade / Love muscle no.96 / Talented amature / Nonstop nacho / Dope smoking redneck...
OINK 015 CD / Jan '93 / Pigboy

Ipsen, Kjeld

☐ JAZZ CODE (Ipsen, Kjeld & Uffe Markussen)
STCD 4208 / May '97 / Storyville

IQ

☐ ARE YOU SITTING COMFORTABLY
War heroes / Drive on / Nostalgia / Falling apart at the seams / Sold on you / Through my fingers / Wurensh / Nothing at all
GEPCD 1013 / Feb '95 / Giant Electric Pea

☐ EVER
Darkest hour / Fading senses (i. after all, ii. fading senses) / Out of nowhere / Further away / Leap of faith / Came down
GEPCD 1006 / Aug '94 / Giant Electric Pea

☐ FOR EVER LIVE (2CD Set)
Wake / Darkest hour / Widow's peak / Out of nowhere / Nostalgia/Falling apart at the seams / Last human gateway / Fading senses / Thousand days / Leap of faith / Human nature / Enemy smacks / Headlong / Last human gateway / No love lost
GEPCD 1016 / 1 Jun '98 / Giant Electric Pea

☐ J'AI POLLETE D'ARNU
GEPCD 1001 / Aug '93 / Giant Electric Pea

☐ LIVING PROOF
GEPCD 1004 / Aug '93 / Giant Electric Pea

☐ NOMZAMO
No love lost / Promises (as the years go by) / Nomzamo / Still life / Passing strangers / Human nature / Screaming / Common ground
GEPCD 1012 / Oct '94 / Giant Electric Pea

☐ SUBTERRANEA (2CD Set)
Overture / Provider / Subterranea / Sleepless incidental / Failsafe / Speak my name / Tunnel vision / Infernal chorus / King of fools / Sense in sanity / State of mine / Laid low / Breathtaker / Capricorn / Other side / Unsoiled ground / Somewhere in time / High waters / Narrow margin
SPV 09528532 / Dec '97 / SPV
GEPCD 1021 / 22 Sep '97 / Giant Electric Pea

☐ TALES FROM THE LUSH ATTIC
Last human gateway / Awake and nervous / Enemy smacks / Just changing hands / Through the corridors / My baby treats me right, cause I'm a hard lovin' man all nig
GEPCD 1010 / Aug '94 / Giant Electric Pea

☐ WAKE, THE
Outer limits / Magic roundabout / Widow's peak / Headlong / Thousand days (demo) / Wake / Corners / Thousand days / Dans le Parc du chateau noir / Magic roundabout (demo)
GEPCD 1011 / Aug '94 / Giant Electric Pea

Iqulah

☐ LIVE IN SWITZERLAND
FOF 2003CD / 26 Jan '98 / Fotofon

Irakere

☐ EN VIVO
Bacalao con pan / Moja el pan / Xiomara mayoral xiomara / Taka taka-ta / La similla / Dile a catalina / Baila mi ritmo / El coco / Aguanile bonko
PSCCD 1005 / Feb '95 / Pure Sounds From Cuba

☐ EXUBERANCIA
Xiomara / El guayo de catalina / Chango / El recuentro / Samba para enrique / El guao / Brown music / Guan tan amera / Brown music (encore)
JHCD 009 / Feb '94 / Ronnie Scott's Jazz House

☐ FELICIDAD
Stella, Pete, Ronnie / La maquina del sabor / Contradanza / Anabis / Tributoa peruchin / La pastora
JHCD 014 / Jan '94 / Ronnie Scott's Jazz House

☐ GRANDES MOMENTOS
74321327212 / Nov '96 / Milan

☐ HOMENAJE A BENY MORE
MES 259042 / Feb '93 / Messidor

☐ INDESTRUCTIBLE (Irakere & Chucho Valdes)
3006036 / 1 Jun '98 / IMP

☐ IRAKERE VOL.1 (Teatro Amadeo Roldan)
EGO 145 / 14 Apr '98 / Actual

☐ IRAKERE VOL.2 (Leo Brouwer)
EGO 146 / 14 Apr '98 / Actual

☐ IRAKERE VOL.4 (Sol Exitos 1973-1978)
EGO 147 / 14 Apr '98 / Actual

☐ IRAKERE VOL.5 (Para Bailar Son Vol.5)
EGO 149 / 14 Apr '98 / Actual

☐ IRAKERE VOL.6
EGO 150 / 14 Apr '98 / Actual

☐ IRAKERE VOL.7 (Calzada Del Cerro)
EGO 151 / 14 Apr '98 / Actual

☐ IRAKERE VOL.8
EGO 152 / 14 Apr '98 / Actual

☐ LEGENDARY IRAKERE LIVE IN LONDON, THE
Bilando asi / Johana / Estela va a estallar (Stella by starlight) / Las margaritas / Lo que va a pasar / Duke
JHCD 005 / Jan '94 / Ronnie Scott's Jazz House

☐ MISA NEGRA (AFRICAN MASS)
159722 / Sep '97 / Messidor

Iration Steppas

☐ ORIGINAL DUB DAT
ISCD 005 / Jun '96 / Iration Steppas

Irazu

☐ LA FIESTA DEL TIMBALERO
Timbalero / Laura / Me voy contigo / Salseando / A Puerto padre / El son de Irazu / Si vienes te quwdas / Anoranza / Danzon del corazon / Everything happens to me
CDLR 45039 / Jan '92 / L&R

Ireland, Mike

☐ LEARNING HOW TO LIVE (Ireland, Mike & Holler)
SPCD 418 / 9 Mar '98 / Sub Pop

Irigara, Carlos Alberto

☐ NAVIDAD CRIOLLA
262063 / Oct '91 / Milan

Irini

☐ DON'T MAKE ME WISH
HIICD 023 / Jan '96 / Here It Is

Iris

☐ CROSSING THE DESERT
IRISCD 001 / Apr '97 / Blueprint

Irish Chamber Orchestra

☐ SILVER APPLES OF THE MOON
Meath pastoral / Midir's song for Etain / Windy gap / Fishamble Street-Dublin 1742 / Dance of Daemar / On the bridge at Clash / MacAnaty's reel / Dirge of Ossian / O'Carolan's concerto / Fanny Power / Planxty MacGuire / O'Carolan's farewell / Planxty Johnson / Three pieces for strings / Suite for strings / Lamento per Strumenti a Corda
BBM 1003 / 15 Jun '98 / Black Box

Irish Guards Band

☐ EMERALD ISLE (Band Of The Irish Guards)
BNA 5134 / 13 Apr '98 / Bandleader

☐ MUSIC FOR REMEMBRANCE
National anthem / March of the Royal British Legion / Heart of oak / Life on the ocean wave / Red, white and blue / Lass who loved a sailor / Great little army / WRAC march / Grey and scarlet / Old comrades / Ulster defence regiment march / Royal Air Force march past / Holyrood / Princess Royals red cross march / Boys of the old brigade / Sunset / Cwm Rhondda / Abide with me / Last post / Reveille / Eternal father strong to save / Rule Britannia / Minstrel boy / Men of Harlech / Isle of beauty / David of the white rock / Oft in the stilly night / Nimrod / Laid in earth / Solemn melody / Funeral march / O God our help in ages past / March melody / It's a long way to Tipperary / Pack up your troubles / There'll always be an England / Keep the home fires burning / Madamoiselle from Armentieres / Take me back to dear old blighty / Run rabbit run / Kiss me goodnight, Sergeant Major / Hang out the washing on the Siegfried line / Wish me good luck as you wave goodbye / Beer barrel polka / Lili Marlene / Walting Mathilda / Maple leaf forever / Maori battalion marching song
BNA 5014 / Nov '87 / Bandleader

Irish Rovers

☐ RAMBLERS AND GAMBLERS (20 All Time Irish Favourites)
Wild rover / Wild mountain thyme / I'm a rambler, I'm a gambler / Last of the Irish rovers / Unicorn / Good luck to the barleymow / Lovely isle of Innisfree / Gypsy rover / My boy Willie / Orange and the green / Liverpool Lou / Caltan weaver / Mountain tay / Turra market / Sweet Strabane / Come by the hills / Black velvet band / Whiskey on a Sunday / Star of the County Down / Rolling home to Ireland
3036001142 / Jul '97 / Carlton

Irish Soundscape

☐ CELTIC INSPIRATIONS
CDC 012 / Feb '97 / Ceol

Irish Tradition

☐ CORNER HOUSE, THE
Smash the windows-fred finn's / Smash the windows-fred finn's / In and out the harbor / Maid at the spinning wheel-the collier's jig / Hiring fair / Corner house-my maryann / Loftus jones / Spike island lassies-the humours of tulla / Dark eyed sailor / Molly on the shore-the tempest / England's motorway
GLCD 1016 / Sep '88 / Green Linnet

☐ TIMES WE'VE HAD, THE
Paddy Fahy's reel / Paddy O'Brien's reel / Shipyard apprentice / Quilty/Sault's hornpipe / Michael O'Connor / Paddy's lamentation / Festus Burke / Yellow tinker/Sally gardens / Lady fair / Happy days / Flight of wild geese / Wild rover / Lad O'Beirne's / Small hills of Offaly
GLCD 1063 / Jun '93 / Green Linnet

Irish Weavers

☐ LIVE AT BLARNEY PARK
Irish Weavers song / All for me grog / Rambles of spring / Pinch of snuff / Miss Mcleod's reel / Coolin / Dunmore lasses / Ship in full sail / Trippin' up the stairs / Whisky in the jar / Quartermaster's stores / Copperplate reel / Peter Street / O'Donovan's reel / Cork loves a stranger / Jig o'slurs / Athol highlanders / Oldest swinger in town / Lonesome boatman / Ghost of '47 / Whistling gypsy / Red Rose Cafe / My Irish Molly-O / Nation once again / Wild rover / Cockles and mussels / Boys of Fair Hill / Coming round the mountain / Irish Weavers song (play off)
GRCD 76 / Mar '96 / Grasmere

☐ WHISKEY IN THE JAR
Irish weavers song / All for me grog / Medley / Medley / Whiskey in the jar / Quartermaster's store / Medley / Cork loves a stranger / Jig o' slurs/Athol highlanders / Oldest swinger in town / Lonesome boatman / Ghost of '47 / Whistling gypsy / Red rose cafe/My Irish Molly-O / Nation once again / Medley
EMPRCD 780 / Nov '97 / Emporio

Irmin's Way

☐ OPUS DESTROY
KSCD 9569 / Jun '97 / Kissing Spell

Iron Bong

☐ BIG HITS
LOST 006 / May '97 / Lost

Iron Butterfly

☐ HEAVY
REP 4128 / Aug '91 / Repertoire

☐ IN-A-GADDA-DA-VIDA
Most anything you want / My mirage / Termination / Are you happy / In-a-gadda-da-vida / Flowers and beads
8122721962 / Jan '96 / Atlantic

☐ LIGHT AND HEAVY (The Best Of Iron Butterfly)
Iron butterfly / Possession / Unconcious power / You can't win / So lo / In-a-gadda-da-vida / Most anything you want / Flowers and beads / My mirage / Termination / In the time of our lives / Soul experience / Real fright / In the crowds / It must be love / Belda beast / I can't help but deceive you little girl / New day / Stone believer / Soldier in our own town / Easy rider (let the wind pay the way)
8122711662 / Mar '93 / Atlantic

☐ SUN AND STEEL
Sun and steel / Lightnin' / Beyond the milky way / Free / Scion / Get it out / I'm right, I'm wrong / Watch the world going by / Scorching beauty
EDCD 408 / Feb '95 / Edsel

Iron Fist

☐ MOTORSEXLE MANIA
FDN 2009CD / Jul '94 / Foundation 2000

Iron Horse

☐ DEMONS AND LOVERS
Steampacket / Auchindoon / Park no.1 / Luthier / Traveller / Anathea / Glazgo / Faith healer / Elphin knight / Demon lover / Caleo / Sleeping warrior
CDLDL 1265 / Dec '97 / Lochshore

☐ FIVE HANDS HIGH
LDL 1214CD / Aug '94 / Lochshore

☐ IRON HORSE
LDL 1202CD / Aug '94 / Lochshore

☐ THRO' WATER,EARTH & STONE
LDLCD 1206 / May '93 / Lochshore

☐ VOICE OF THE LAND
CDLDL 1232 / Sep '95 / Lochshore

Iron Lung

☐ CHASING SALVATION
PCD 043 / 29 Sep '97 / Die Hard

Iron Maiden

☐ BEST OF THE BEAST, THE
Number of the beast / Can I play with madness / Fear of the dark / Run to the hills / Bring your daughter to the slaughter / Evil that men do / Aces high / Be quick or be dead / 2 Minutes to midnight / Man on the edge / Virus / Running free / Wasted years / Clairvoyant / Trooper / Hallowed be thy name
CDEMD 1097 / Oct '96 / EMI

☐ BEST OF THE BEAST, THE (2CD Set)
Virus / Sign of the cross / Man on the edge / Afraid to shoot strangers / Be quick or be dead / Fear of the dark / Bring your daughter to the slaughter / Holy smoke / Clairvoyant / Can I play with madness / Evil that men do / Heaven can wait / Wasted years / Rime of the Ancient Mariner / Running free / 2 minutes to midnight / Aces high / Where eagles dare / Number of the beast / Trooper / Run to the hills / Hallowed be thy name / Wrathchild / Phantom of the opera / Sanctuary / Strange world / Iron Maiden
CDEMDS 1097 / Nov '96 / EMI

☐ CALL TO IRONS, A (A Tribute To Iron Maiden) (Various Artists)
Ides of March/Purgatory: *Steel Prophet* / Powerslave: *Ancient Wisdom* / Trooper: *Vital Remains* / Genghis Kahn: *Angel Corpse* / Hallowed be thy name: *Solitude Aeturnus* / Phantom Of The Opera: *New Eden* / Remember tomorrow: *Opeth* / To tame a land: *Morgion* / Strange world: *Evoken* / Rhyme Of The Ancient Mariner: *Opera 1X* / Transylvania: *Absu*
DWL 10112 / 22 Jun '98 / DWL

☐ IN PROFILE (Interview Disc)
CDINPROF 001 / Aug '97 / EMI

☐ IRON MAIDEN
Prowler / Remember tomorrow / Running free / Phantom of the opera / Transylvania / Strange world / Charlotte the harlot / Iron Maiden
CDEMS 1538 / Jul '94 / EMI

☐ KILLERS
Ides of March / Wrathchild / Murders in the Rue Morgue / Another life / Genghis Khan / Innocent exile / Killers / Prodigal son / Purgatory / Drifter
CDEMS 1536 / Jul '94 / EMI

☐ LIVE AFTER DEATH
Aces high / Two minutes to midnight / Trooper / Revelations / Flight of Icarus / Rime of the ancient mariner / Powerslave / Number of the beast / Hallowed be thy name / Iron Maiden / Run to the hills / Running free
CDEMS 1535 / Jul '94 / EMI

☐ MAIDEN OVER
3D 016 / Dec '96 / Network

☐ NO PRAYER FOR THE DYING
Tailgunner / Holy smoke / No prayer for the dying / Public enema no.1 / Fates warning / Assassin / Run silent run deep / Hooks in you / Bring your daughter... to the slaughter / Mother Russia
CDEMS 1541 / Jul '94 / EMI

☐ NUMBER OF THE BEAST
Invaders / Children of the damned / Prisoner / 22 Acacia Avenue / Number of the beast / Run to the hills / Gangland / Hallowed be thy name
CDEMS 1533 / Jul '94 / EMI

☐ PIECE OF MIND
Where eagles dare / Revelations / Flight of Icarus / Die with your boots on / Trooper / Still life / Quest for fire / Sun and steel / To tame a land
CDEMS 1540 / Jul '94 / EMI

☐ PLAYING WITH MADNESS
CBAK 4035 / Jan '92 / Baktabak

☐ POWERSLAVE
Aces high / Two minutes to midnight / Losfer words (big 'Orra) / Flash of the blade / Duellists / Back in the village / Powerslave / Rime of the ancient mariner
CDEMS 1539 / Jul '94 / EMI

☐ SEVENTH SON OF A SEVENTH SON
Moonchild / Infinite dreams / Can I play with madness / Evil that men do / Seventh son of a seventh son / Prophecy / Clairvoyant / Only the good die young
CDEMS 1534 / Jul '94 / EMI

☐ SOMEWHERE IN TIME
Caught somewhere in time / Wasted years / Sea of madness / Heaven can wait / Loneliness of the long distance runner / Stranger in a strange land / Deja vu / Alexander the great
CDEMS 1537 / Jul '94 / EMI

☐ VIRTUAL XI
Futureal / Angel and the gambler / Lightning strikes twice / Clansman / When two worlds collide / Educated fool / Don't look to the eyes of a stranger / Como estais amigos
4939152
4939922 / 23 Mar '98 / EMI

☐ X-FACTOR, THE
Sign of the cross / Lord of the flies / Man on the edge / Fortunes of war / Look for the truth / Aftermath / Judgement of heaven / Blood on the world's hands / Edge of darkness / 2 am / Unbeliever
CDEMD 1087 / Sep '97 / EMI

Iron Maiden

☐ MAIDEN VOYAGE
AACD 028 / 15 Jun '98 / Audio Archive

Iron Man

☐ BLACK NIGHT
HELL 022 / Jul '93 / Hellhound

☐ PASSAGE, THE
Fury / Unjust reform / Gargoyle / Harvest of earth / Passage / Iron warrior / Freedom fighters / Waiting for tomorrow / Time of indecision / Tony stark / End of the world
H 00222 CD / Oct '94 / Hellhound

Iron Monkey

☐ IRON MONKEY
Fink dial / Web of piss / Big loader / 666 pack / Black aspirin / Shrimp fist
MOSH 182CD / 22 Sep '97 / Earache

☐ OUR PROBLEM
Bad year / Supagorgonizer / Buff Keloid / IRMS / House anxiety / 2 Golden rules / Nine joint spiritual whip / Omi bozu
MOSH 207CD / 24 Aug '98 / Earache

Irresistable Force

☐ GLOBAL CHILLAGE
RSNCD 24 / Nov '94 / Rising High

Irvine, Andy

☐ ANDY IRVINE & PAUL BRADY (Irvine, Andy & Paul Brady)
Plains of Kildare / Lough Erne shore / Fred Finn's reel/Sailing into Walpole's marsh / Bonny woodhall / Arthur McBride / Jolly soldier / Blarney pilgrim / Autumn gold / Mary and the Soldier / Streets of Derry / Martinmas time / Little stack of wheat
GL 3201CD / Jul '94 / Green Linnet
LUNCD 008 / Dec '97 / Mulligan

☐ EAST WIND (Irvine, Andy & Davy Spillane)
Chetvorno horo / Bear's rock / Dance of suleiman / Illyrian dawn / Two steps to the bar / Pride of Macedonia / Kadana / Hard on the heels
TARACD 3027 / Apr '92 / Tara

☐ RAINY SUNDAYS, WINDY DREAMS
Come to the land of sweet liberty / Farewell to old Ireland / Edward Connors / Longford weaver / Christmas Eve / Farewell to Ballymoney / Romanian song / Paidushko horo / King Bore and sandman / Rainy Sundays
CDTUT 72141 / '88 / Wundertute

☐ RUDE AWAKENING
Never tire of the road / Raoul wallenberg / James connolly / Viva zapata / Whole damn thing / Rude awakening / Michael dwyer's escape / Douglas mawson / Alan mcclean / Love to be with you
GLCD 1114 / Apr '92 / Green Linnet

Irvine, Weldon

☐ BEST OF WELDON IRVINE VOL.1, THE
Deja vu / Bananas / Turkish bath / Walk that walk, talk that talk / Mr Clean / We getting down / Jungle juice / Music is the key
CNMDCD 01 / 16 Sep '97 / Timewarp

☐ LIBERATED BROTHER
HUBCD 12 / Oct '96 / Hubbub

☐ TIME CAPSULE
HUBCD 13 / Oct '96 / Hubbub

Irwin, Big Dee

☐ ANOTHER NIGHT WITH...BIG DEE IRWIN
Been so long / I can't help it (I'm falling in love) / Rubin Rubin / Let's try again / 'Tis farewell / And heaven was there / Everybody's got a dance but me / Swinging on a star / Another night with the boys / Happy being fat / Soul waltzing / You're my inspiration / Skeeter / Christmas song / I wish you a merry christmas / Heigh ho / I want so much to know you / It's my birthday / (You've got) personality / It's only a paper moon / Discotheque / Sun's gonna shine tomorrow / Are you really real / Mouse / You can't stop my loving you
WESM 511 / 10 Nov '97 / Westside

Is

☐ IS, THE
DMCD 1033 / Feb '92 / Demi-Monde

Isaac, Ismael

☐ TREICH FEELING
3019522 / Feb '97 / Arcade

Isaacs, Barney

☐ HAWAIIAN TOUCH
DCT 38026CD / Mar '96 / Dancing Cat

Isaacs, Barry

☐ REVOLUTIONARY MAN
ROTCD 7 / Sep '95 / Reggae On Top

Isaacs, Gregory

☐ ABSENT
GRELCD 190 / Aug '93 / Greensleeves

☐ BAD BOY LOVER MAN (2CD Set)
CPCD 82782 / Jul '97 / Charly

☐ BEST OF GREGORY ISAACS OVER THE YEARS, THE
8444172 / 8 Sep '97 / Declic

☐ BLOOD BROTHERS (Isaacs, Gregory & Dennis Brown)
RASCD 3116 / Feb '94 / Ras

☐ CALL ME COLLECT
Call me collect / Dim your lights / Guilty of loving you / Give a little love / So much love / Rude boy / Poor barry / Smokey head / Brand new me / Game called love
RASCD 3067 / Nov '90 / Ras

☐ CLASSIC HITS VOL.2
SONCD 0027 / Apr '92 / Sonic Sounds

☐ COME AGAIN DUB
RE 193CD / Nov '94 / ROIR

☐ COME CLOSER
503382 / Sep '94 / Declic

☐ COOL RULER - SOON FORWARD - SELECTION
Native woman / John Public / Party in the slum / Uncle Joe / Word of the farmer / One more time / Let's dance / Created by the father / Raving tonight / Don't pity me
CDFL 9012 / Sep '90 / Frontline

☐ COOL RULER RIDES AGAIN, THE (22 Classics From 1978-1981)
Let's dance / Permanent lover / My only lover / Gi me / Poor natty / Mr. Brown / Raving tonight / Soon forward / Front door / Tribute to wa de / Poor and clean / Fugitive / If I don't have you / Few words / I am sorry / Protection / Confirm reservation / Once ago / One more time / Hush darling / My relationship / Slave market
NSCD 017 / Jul '97 / Nascente

☐ DANCEHALL DON
SHCD 45015 / Jun '94 / Shanachie

☐ DANCING FLOOR
Dancing floor / Crown and anchor / Give it all up / Private lesson / Nobody knows / Dealing / Shower me with love / Opel ride / Chips is down / Rock me
MRCD 148 / Jul '90 / Munich

☐ DEM TALK TOO MUCH
CDTRL 355 / Jun '95 / Trojan

☐ DREAMING
CDHB 155 / Jul '95 / Heartbeat

☐ EARLY YEARS, THE
Rock away / Sweeter the victory / Sinner man / Lonely lover / Loving pauper / Promised land / Love is overdue / Bad da / Way of life / Financial endorsement / Give a hand / All I have is love
CDTRL 196 / Mar '94 / Trojan

☐ ENCORE
Out Deh / Tune in / Top ten / Private secretary / My only lover / All I have is love / Love is overdue / Can't give my love / Cool down the pace / Oh what a feeling / Addicted to you / Night nurse
CDKVL 9030 / Jan '88 / Kingdom

☐ GREGORY ISAACS & FRIENDS
SHCD 150 / Jun '94 / Shanachie

☐ GREGORY ISAACS COLLECTION, THE
RNCD 2102 / Apr '95 / Rhino

☐ HARDCORE
GSCD 70035 / Nov '92 / Greensleeves

☐ HEARTACHE AVENUE
Sorry for the man / One day soon / Dreaming / Love of my life / Heartache avenue / Penitentiary / Frenchtown comprehensive / Counterfeit lover / Juggling time / Crying over you / Sorry for the dub / Dreaming dub / Love of my dub / Heartache dub / Penitentiary dub / Frenchtown dub / Counterfeit dub / Juggling dub / Crying over dub
WRCD 009 / Nov '97 / World

☐ HEARTBREAKER
RRTGCD 7788 / Jul '90 / Rohit

☐ HOLD TIGHT
Miss Cutie Cutie / Wah dee / Hold tight / Mi no want / Tan so back / Thank you Mr. Judge / Kill them with music / Lady on the frontline / Come make love to me / Get deport / Don't go / Motherless children / I miss you
CDHB 210 / May '97 / Heartbeat

☐ I AM GREGORY
CRCD 22 / Sep '93 / Charm

☐ I AM THE INVESTIGATOR
CB 6006 / Jan '96 / Bluesilver

☐ I'LL NEVER TRUST YOU
LG 21098 / May '94 / Lagoon

☐ IOU
Too good to be true / Fall for you again / Fatal attraction / What's the matter / Can't make a slip / Report to me / I.o.u. / Express love / Hard road to travel / Break the ice / Easy life (solo cut) / Big all around (solo cut) / Jealousy
GRELCD 136 / Aug '89 / Greensleeves

☐ IRIE IRIE MAN
My number one / Willow tree / Breaking up / No speech no language / If you're feeling hot, I will cool you / Lonely days / Tumbling tears / Philistines / Can I change my mind / Border / Loving pauper / My time
RM 1537 / Aug '97 / BR Music

☐ LADY OF YOUR CALIBRE
First love / Lady of your calibre / War on poverty / Diplomatic fool's / Slapper dapper / Rude boy / Faithfully / Here by appointment / Rose in your garden / Matey
WRCD 013 / Nov '97 / World

☐ LEE PERRY PRESENTS GREGORY ISAACS
Dance with me darling / It's a shame / Don't stay away / Too young / Good luck / Put a smile on your face / Political violence / Don't make no descision / Sudden destruction / Can never change my mind / Don't try to use me girl / I've been accused / Way you're accustomed to / You'll go in silence / I've got something nice for you girl
RNCD 2030 / Dec '93 / Rhino

☐ LIVE AT THE ACADEMY
My number one / All I ask is love / My only lover / Love overdue / Storm / Mr. Brown / Slave master / Oh what a feeling / Soon forward / Sunday morning / Addicted to you / Front door / Border / Can't give my love / Cool down the pace
CDKVL 9027 / Jan '87 / Kingdom

☐ LIVE IN FRANCE
SONCD 0060 / Mar '94 / Sonic Sounds

☐ LONELY LOVER
Happy anniversary / Gi me / Tribute to Waddy / Poor and clean / Poor natty / I am sorry / Few words / Protection / Hard time / Tune in
RNCD 2047 / Mar '94 / Rhino

☐ LOOKING BACK
RASCD 3196 / Aug '96 / Ras

☐ LOVE IS OVERDUE
Love is overdue / Be careful / Another heartache / How long / Far beyond the valley / If you're in love / Financial endorsement / Dreams come true / Way she walks / Happiness come / No forgiveness / Love disguise / Sweeter the victory / How long
CDHB 98 / Aug '96 / Heartbeat

☐ LOVING PAUPER
CDTRL 396 / Jun '98 / Trojan

☐ MAXIMUM RESPECT
CDSGP 070 / Mar '94 / Prestige

☐ MEMORIES
Make love to me / Memories / Say a prayer / You keep me waiting / Spend sometime / Common sense / My apology / Love you more / Cry over me / Who will see / All in the game
112082 / Aug '95 / Musidisc UK

☐ MR. COOL
RFCD 001 / Oct '95 / Record Factory

☐ MR. ISAACS
OH 003 / Nov '95 / Ossie

☐ MR. LOVE
Mr. Brown / Word of the farmer / Black liberation struggle / Poor and clean / Slave market / Uncle Joe / Universal tribulation / Confirm reservation / Protection / Tribute to Waddy / Let's dance / One more time / John Public / Native woman / Lonely girl / If I don't have you / Poor millionaire / My only lover / Raving tonight / Hush darling / Soon forward
CDFL 9021 / Jun '95 / Frontline

☐ MY NUMBER ONE
CDHB 61 / Mar '90 / Heartbeat

☐ MY POOR HEART
HBCD 167 / Aug '94 / Heartbeat

☐ NIGHT NURSE
Material man / Not the way / Sad to know you're leaving / Hot stepper / Cool down the pace / Night nurse / Stranger in town / Objection overruled
RRCD 9 / Sep '90 / Reggae Refreshers

☐ NO INTENTIONS
VPCD 1133 / Jun '91 / RF

☐ NO LUCK
No luck / New contract / Heartache / Guilty for your love / What will your mama say / All the store are closed / Madly in love with sharon / Meet me at the same spot / We don't pet sound boys / Make a track / Village / Rock on / Don't believe in him
LG 21049 / Nov '92 / Lagoon

☐ NO SURRENDER
GVCD 2020 / Nov '92 / Greensleeves

☐ NOT A ONE MAN THING
RASCD 3145 / Jul '95 / Ras

☐ NUMBER ONE
My number one / Willow tree / Breaking up / No speech, no language / If you're feeling hot, I will cool you / Lonely days / Tumbling tears / Philistines / Can I change my mind / Border / Loving pauper / My time
CPCD 8026 / Feb '94 / Charly

☐ ONCE AGO
Tribute to Waddy / Gimme / Poor and clean / Poor Natty / I am sorry / Few words / Protection / Hard time / Hush darling / Confirm reservation / Front door / Permanent lover / My only lover / If I don't have you / Substitute / Poor millionaire / Fugitive / Once ago
CDFL 9004 / Jul '90 / Frontline

☐ OUT DEH
Good morning / Private secretary / Yes I do / Sheila / Out deh / Star / Dieting / Love me with feeling
RRCD 46 / Jul '94 / Reggae Refreshers

☐ OVER THE YEARS VOL.2
AMCD 012 / Apr '96 / African Museum

☐ OVER THE YEARS VOL.3
KPAMCD 013 / Mar '97 / African Museum

☐ PARDON ME
RASCD 3100 / Sep '93 / Ras

☐ PARDON ME (Dub Version)
504992 / May '96 / Declic

☐ PRIME OF GEGORY ISAACS, THE
Mr. Cop / My only lover / Good luck/Bad luck / Black kill black / Bring me water / Warriors / Sinner man / Lonely lover / Get ready here I come / My religion / Promise is a comfort to a fool / Slave master / Thief a man / Loving pauper / All I have is love / Dance this reggae music / Village of the underprivilege / Love light
MCCD 356 / 20 Jul '98 / Music Club

☐ PRIVATE BEACH PARTY
Wish you were mine / Feeling irie / Bits and pieces / Let off supm / No rushings / Private beach party / Better plant some loving / Got to be in tune / Special to me / Promise is a comfort
GRELCD 85 / Jul '95 / Greensleeves

☐ PRIVATE LESSON
DUBID 2CD / Sep '95 / Acid Jazz Roots

☐ RAS PORTRAITS
Private beach party / So much love / Rumours / Give in with caution / Special to me / Call me collect / Don't dis the dancehall / Nah lef the dance / Red rose for Gregory / Let off some supm / Break the ice / Intimate potential / Too good to be true / Enough is enough
RAS 3309 / Jul '97 / Ras

☐ RED ROSE FOR GREGORY
Red rose for gregory / Teacher's plight (12" promo mix) / Break the date / Rumours (12" hit mix) / Slow down / All I need is you / Rough neck (12" street mix) / Intimate potential / Me no in a dat / Closer than a brother / Mind yu dis (12" manners mix)
GRELCD 118 / Sep '88 / Greensleeves

☐ REGGAE GREATS (Gregory Isaacs Live)
Number one / Tune in / Substitute / Soon forward / Mr. Brown / Sunday morning / Oh what a feeling / Love is overdue / Top 10 / Front door / Border
5525832 / 1 Jun '98 / Spectrum

☐ REGGAE MAX
JSRNCD 3 / Mar '96 / Jet Star

☐ RESERVED FOR GREGORY
EXCD 1 / Nov '95 / Exodus

☐ SET ME FREE
VYDCD 02 / Sep '95 / Vine Yard

☐ SINNER MAN
CSAPCD 121 / Mar '96 / Connoisseur Collection

☐ SINNER MAN (2CD Set)
SMDCD 221 / 10 Aug '98 / Snapper

☐ SLUM IN DUB
CDTRL 344 / Jul '94 / Trojan

☐ SLY & ROBBIE PRESENT GREGORY ISAACS
RASCD 3206 / Dec '95 / Ras

☐ SO MUCH LOVE
JGMCD 003032 / 22 Dec '97 / Joe Gibbs

☐ SPECIAL GUEST
3021442 / Jun '97 / Arcade
RN 7016 / 23 Mar '98 / Rhino

☐ TUNE IN TO
RN 7060 / 31 Aug '98 / Rhino

☐ TWO BAD SUPERSTARS (Isaacs, Gregory & Dennis Brown)
CDTRL 335 / Mar '94 / Trojan

☐ TWO TIME LOSER
792152 / Apr '96 / Melodie

☐ UNFORGETTABLE
Unforgettable / Insecure / I'm sinking / Steal a little love / Miss celebrity / One man against the world / House of leo / After smoking my last cigarette / Half a gram of your love
RRTGCD 7736 / '88 / Rohit

☐ UNLOCKED
GRELCD 193 / Sep '93 / Greensleeves

☐ VETERANS (Isaacs, Gregory & Dobby Dobson)
PICK 002CD / 19 Jan '98 / Pickout

☐ VICTIM
VPCD 1033 / Apr '89 / VP

☐ WATCHMAN OF THE CITY
RIFWLCD 9300 / Mar '88 / Rohit

☐ WILLOW TREE
Willow tree / Breaking up / No speech, no language / Lonely teardrops / Everything is going alright / My number one / Let me be your special guest / Look before you leap / If you feeling hot, I will cool you / Happiness
JMC 200204 / Jun '94 / Jamaican Gold

☐ WORK UP A SWEAT
AMCD 010 / Feb '95 / African Museum

☐ YESTERDAY
VPCD 14942 / Jul '97 / VP

☐ YOU'RE DIVINE
RB 3002 / May '94 / Reggae Best

Isaak, Chris

☐ FOREVER BLUE
Somebody's crying / Don't leave me on my own / Forever blue / Goin' nowhere / Shadows in a mirror / End of everything / Graduation day / I believe / Changed your mind / There she goes / Things go wrong / Baby did a bad bad thing / Go walking down there
9362458452 / May '95 / Reprise

☐ HEART SHAPED WORLD
Heart shaped world / I'm not waiting / Don't make me dream about you / Kings of the highway / Wicked game / Blue spanish sky / Wrong to love you / Forever young / Nothing's changed / In the heat of the jungle
9258372 / Jun '89 / Reprise

☐ SAN FRANCISCO DAYS
San Francisco days / Beautiful homes / Round and round / Two hearts / Can't do a thing (to stop me) / Except the new girl / Waiting / Move along / I want your love / 5.15 / Lonely with a broken heart / Solitary man
9362451162 / Apr '93 / Reprise

☐ SILVERTONE
Dancin' / Talk to me / Living for your lover / Back on your side / Voodoo / Funeral in the rain / Lonely one / Unhappiness / Tears / Gone ridin' / Pretty girls don't cry / Western stars
9251562 / Dec '87 / Reprise

☐ WICKED GAME
Wicked game / You owe me some kind of love / Blue Spanish sky / Heart shaped world / Heart full of soul / Funeral in the rain / Blue Hotel / Dancin' / Nothings changed / Voodoo / Lie to me / Wicked game (instrumental)
7599265132 / Jan '91 / Reprise

Isalonisti

☐ HUMORESQUE
Souvenir / Whispering flowers / Czardas / Come away to Madrid / My sweet little friend / On the sea shore / My heart only calls to you / Humoresque / Slavonic dance No.6 / Melody in F / Syncopation / Gypsy Capriccio / Poeme / Little Viennese march / Mill in the black forest / Maiden's prayer / We wander the world / Eight in the night / When a toreador falls in love
CDC 1695132 / Oct '86 / Harmonia Mundi

Isan Slete

☐ FLOWER OF ISAN, THE
Lai lam toei sam jangwa / Hua ngawk yawk sao / Sutsanaen-noeng mode / Lam phloen / Lai pu pa lan / Toei khong / Lam doeng dong / Lai-yai mode / Lam toei thammada / Lai ngua khuen phu / Lam kio / Lai phu thai / Sutsanaen mode / Kawn lawng la / Lai an nang-sue / Imae, imae
CDORB 051 / Oct '89 / Globestyle

Isbin, Gilbert

☐ BLUE SOUNDS AND TOUCHES
Quite blue / Sueno / Tell me / In balance / Leon / Mosca Espagnola / Mar arbierto / Full moon and little bastion / Nenia / Blue 2 / Camino verde / Come into my door / Nice advance / Blue in blue / Ballad in a cave / HWYL
HWYLCD 4 / Jun '91 / Hwyl

Isbin, Sharon

☐ JOURNEY TO THE AMAZON (Isbin, Sharon & Paul Winter/Thiago de Mello)
Historia de Luar / Seis por derecho / Waltz op 8 No.4 / Hug for pixingha / Uirapuru do Amazonas / Julia Florida / El marabino / Waltz no.3 / Porro / Batucada / Lago de Janauaca / Cahmada dos ventos / Cancion de cuna / Aire de Joropo / Cochichando / Choro alegre / Cavaleiro sem armadua
0630198992 / 9 Mar '98 / Teldec Classics

Isengard

☐ HOSTMORKE
FOG 007CD / Jun '95 / Moonfog

Isfort, Tim

☐ TIM ISFORT ORCHESTRA (Isfort, Tim Orchestra)
EFA 121202 / Jul '97 / Moll

Isham, Mark

☐ AFTERGLOW
After the glow has gone / Yeses noes and in betweens / Life suspended / Hope and charity / For Charles / Yeses and noes / Undecided / Frenzy / Afterglow / Afterglow
CK 67929 / 9 Feb '98 / Sony Jazz

☐ BLUE SUN
Barcelona / Beautiful sadness / Trapeze / Lazy afternoon / Blue sun / In more than love / Miles to go before he sleeps / In a sentimental mood / Tour de chance
4813042 / 26 Jan '98 / Sony Jazz

☐ COOL WORLD
VSCD 5382 / Aug '92 / Varese Sarabande

☐ SKETCH ARTIST
VSCD 53776 / Aug '92 / Varese Sarabande

☐ TIBET
01934110802 / Sep '95 / Windham Hill

Ishii, Ken

☐ INNERELEMENT
Encoding / AFIAC / Twist of space / QF / Flurry / Garden of the palm / Pneuma / Sponge / Radiation / Loop / Fragment of yesterday / Kala / Decoding
RS 94038CD / May '94 / R&S

☐ JELLY TONES
Extra / Cocoa mousse / Stretch / Ethos 9 / Moved by air / Pause in herbs / Frame out / Endless season
RS 95065CD / 16 Feb '98 / R&S

☐ X-MIX
Fool's paradise: *United Future Organisation* / Phantom: *Renegade Soundwave* / Bumbuphone: *Fretless AZM* / Theme from the innocent: *Innocent* / Fly life: *Basement Jaxx* / NP 21: *Flare* / Mood: *Symbols & Instruments* / Gyroscope: *Strange Attractor* / Drums in a grip: *De Wulf, Frank* / Pumpin' bass manoeuvres: *Ghetto Brothers* / Dance of the naughty knights: *Jedi Knights* / Atomic moog 2000: *Coldcut* / Buckfunk discoteque: *Buckfunk 3000* / DIRR: *Flare* / Circular motion / Echo exit / No-one in the world: *Locust* / Nautilus: *Slazenger, Jake* / Squarepusher theme: *Squarepusher* / Mass: *Silent Poets*
K7 057CD / Apr '97 / Studio K7

Island

☐ PICTURES
LE 1024 / 15 Jun '98 / Laser's Edge

Island, Johnny

☐ REGGAE SOUNDS FROM JAMAICA (Island, Johnny Reggae Group)
15287 / '91 / Laserlight

Islandica

☐ SONGS AND DANCES FROM ICELAND
EUCD 1187 / Apr '92 / ARC

Isley Brothers

☐ 3 + 3
That lady / Don't let me be lonely tonight / If you were there / You walk your way / Listen to the music / What it comes down to / Sunshine (go away today) / Summer breeze / Highways of my life
4879372 / Jul '97 / Epic

☐ BEAUTIFUL BALLADS
Brown eyed girl / Hello it's me / Let's fall in love (parts 1 and 2) / You're the key to my heart / You're beside me / I once had your love (and I can't let go) / Caravan of love / All in my lovers eyes / Don't let me be lonely tonight / Make me say it again girl / Voyage to Atlantis / Choosey lover / Lay lady lay / Don't say goodnight
4805042 / May '95 / Epic

☐ BEST OF THE ISLEY BROTHERS, THE
12549 / May '95 / Laserlight

☐ BROTHER BROTHER BROTHER
Brother brother brother / Put a little love in your heart / Sweet seasons/Keep on walkin' / Work to do / Pop that thang / Lay away / It's too late / Love put me on the corner
4875122 / Jul '97 / Epic

☐ BROTHERS ISLEY, THE
I turned you on / Vacuum cleaner / I got to get myself together / Was it good to you / Blacker the berrie / My little girl / Get down off of the train / Holding on / Feels like the world
4875152 / Jul '97 / Epic

☐ COMPLETE UA SESSIONS, THE (The Legends Of Rock & Roll Series)
Surf and shout / Please please please / She's the one / Tango / What'cha gonna do / Stagger Lee / You'll never leave him / Let's go, let's go, let's go / She's gone / Shake it with me baby / Long tall Sally / Do the twist / My little girl / Open up her eyes / Love is a wonderful thing / Footprints in the snow / Who's that lady / Basement / Conch / My little girl
CDGOLD 1024 / May '96 / EMI Gold

☐ FOREVER GOLD
That lady / Live it up / Hello it's me / At your best you are love / Fight the power / For the love of you / Hope you feel better love / Highways of my life / Harvest for the world / Summer breeze
CD 32238 / 26 Jan '98 / Epic

☐ GET INTO SOMETHING
Get into something / Freedom / Take inventory / Keep on doin' / Girls will be girls / I need you so / If he can you can / I got to find me one / Beautiful / Bless your heart
4875142 / Jul '97 / Epic

☐ GIVIN' IT BACK
Ohio/Machine gun / Fire and rain / Lay lady lay / Spill the wine / Nothing to do but today / Cold Bologna / Love the one you're with
4875132 / Jul '97 / Epic

☐ GREATEST HITS
Summer breeze / That lady / Harvest for the world / Hope you feel better love / Highways of my life / Caravan of love / Who loves you better / Work to do / Between the sheets / Don't let me be lonely / For the love of you / Pride / Love the one you're with / It's a disco night
4879962 / Jul '97 / Epic

☐ LIVE
Here we go again / Between the sheets / Smooth sailin' tonight / Voyage to Atlantis / Take me to the next phase / Choosey lover / Footsteps in the dark / Groove with you / Hello it's me / Don't say goodnight (It's time for love) / Spend the night / Who's that lady / It's your thing / Shout / For the love / Fight the power / Make me say it again girl
7559615382 / Sep '93 / Elektra

☐ MISSION TO PLEASE
5242142 / May '96 / 4th & Broadway

☐ MOTOWN EARLY CLASSICS
This old heart of mine (is weak for you) / There's no love left / Seek and you shall find / Leaving here / Baby don't you do it / Stop in the name of love / I guess I'll always love you / Tell me it's just a rumour baby / Why when love is gone / Catching up on time / One too many heartaches / Nevermore / It's out of the question / Whispers (gettin' louder) / Good things / Behind a painted smile / Save me from this misery / My love is your love (forever)
5521222 / Jul '96 / Spectrum

☐ MOTOWN'S GREATEST HITS
This old heart of mine / Just ain't enough love / Put yourself in my place / I guess I'll always love you / There's no love left / It's out of the question / Take some time out for love / Whispers / Nowhere to run / Who could ever doubt my love / Behind a painted smile / That's the way love is / Tell me it's just a rumour baby / Take me in your arms / Got to have you back / Little Miss Sweetness / My love is your love (forever) / Why when the love has gone / All because I love you / I hear a symphony
5300532 / Jan '92 / Motown

☐ PACKET OF THREE VOL.8 (3CD Set) (Isley Brothers/Walter Becker & Donald Fagen/Sam & Dave)
Twist and shout: *Isley Brothers* / Time after time: *Isley Brothers* / Hold on baby: *Isley Brothers* / Snake: *Isley Brothers* / Let's twist again: *Isley Brothers* / Don't you feel: *Isley Brothers* / Nobody but you: *Isley Brothers* / Twisting with Linda: *Isley Brothers* / Spanish twist: *Isley Brothers* / Drag: *Isley Brothers* / Don't be jealous: *Isley Brothers* / This is the end: *Isley Brothers* / Let's go, let's go, let's go: *Isley Brothers* / I'm laughing to keep from crying: *Isley Brothers* / Rubber leg twist: *Isley Brothers* / I say love: *Isley Brothers* / You better come home: *Isley Brothers* / Never leave me baby: *Isley Brothers* / Brooklyn: *Becker, Walter & Donald Fagen* / Mock turtle song: *Becker, Walter & Donald Fagen* / Soul ram: *Becker, Walter & Donald Fagen* / Any world: *Becker, Walter & Donald Fagen* / You go where I go: *Becker, Walter & Donald Fagen* / This seat's been taken: *Becker, Walter & Donald Fagen* / Berry Town: *Becker, Walter & Donald Fagen* / More to come: *Becker, Walter & Donald Fagen* / Android warehouse: *Becker, Walter & Donald Fagen* / Roaring of the lamb: *Becker, Walter & Donald Fagen* / Sun mountain: *Becker, Walter & Donald Fagen* / Stone patio: *Becker, Walter & Donald Fagen* / Parker's band: *Becker, Walter & Donald Fagen* / Caves of Altimura: *Becker, Walter & Donald Fagen* / Come back baby: *Becker, Walter & Donald Fagen* / Old regime: *Becker, Walter & Donald Fagen* / Let George do it: *Becker, Walter & Donald Fagen* / I can't function: *Becker, Walter & Donald Fagen* / Brain tap shuffle: *Becker, Walter & Donald Fagen* / Ida Lee: *Becker, Walter & Donald Fagen* / Wonderful world: *Sam & Dave* / Soul sister, brown sugar: *Sam & Dave* / Dock of the bay: *Sam & Dave* / You got me hummin': *Sam & Dave* / Gimme some lovin': *Sam & Dave* / Another Saturday night: *Sam & Dave* / Cupid: *Sam & Dave* / Hold on I'm coming: *Sam & Dave* / Summertime: *Sam & Dave* / Mustang Sally: *Sam & Dave* / Good lovin': *Sam & Dave* / Land of 1000 dances: *Sam & Dave* / Satisfaction guarenteed: *Sam & Dave* / You don't know what you mean to me: *Sam & Dave* / You send me: *Sam & Dave* / Soothe me: *Sam & Dave* / Bring it on home: *Sam & Dave* / I thank you: *Sam & Dave* / Said I wouldn't tell nobody: *Sam & Dave* / You don't know like I know: *Sam & Dave*
KLMCD 308 / Nov '96 / BAM

☐ SHOUT
Shout (part 1) / Shout (part 2) / Tell me who / How deep is the ocean / Respectable / Say you love me too / Open up your heart / He's got the whole world in his hands / Without a song / Yes indeed / Ring-a-ling-a-ling / That lucky old sun / How deep is the ocean / Respectable / When the saints go marching in / Gypsy love song / St. Louis blues / (We're gonna) Rock around the clock / Turn to me / Not one minute more / I'm gonna knock on your door
BCD 15425 / Dec '88 / Bear Family

☐ SHOUT
Shout / Without a song / Respectable / Open up your heart / That lucky old sun / Yes indeed / Turn to me / Rock around the clock / St. Louis blues / He's got the whole world in his hands / Say you love me too / Ring-a-ling-a-ling / I'm gonna knock on your door / Not one minute more / Tell me who / How deep is the ocean / Gypsy love song / When the saints go marching in
74321578142 / 11 May '98 / Camden

☐ SHOUT AND TWIST WITH RUDOLPH, RONALD AND O'KELLY
Twist and shout / Nobody but me / Crazy love / Snake / Make it easy on yourself / Right now / You better come home / Twistin' with Linda / Never leave me baby / Two stupid feet / Time after time / Let's twist again / Wah watusi / I say love / Rubberleg twist / Hold on baby / I'm laughing to keep from crying / Don't you feel / Spanish twist
CDCH 928 / Apr '90 / Ace

Isotope

☐ ISOTOPE/ILLUSION
Then there were four / Do the business / Oh little fat man / Sunshine park / Bite on this / Upward curve / Retracing my steps / Windmills and waterfalls / Honkey donkey / Illusion / Rangoon creeper / Spanish sun / Edorian / Frog / Sliding dogs / Lion sandwich / Golden section / Marin county girl / Lily kong / Temper tantrums
SEECD 432 / Aug '95 / See For Miles

Isotype 217

☐ UNSTABLE MOLECULE, THE
THRILL 049CD / 5 Jan '98 / Thrill Jockey

Israel Vibration

☐ BEST OF ISRAEL VIBRATION, THE
Same song / We a de rasta / I'll go through / Give I grace / Friday evening / Ball of fire / Top control / Why worry / Crisis / Never gonna hurt
NETCD 1001 / Jan '91 / Network

☐ DUB THE ROCK
RASCD 3190 / Aug '95 / Ras

☐ FOREVER
Poor man cry / Children under the sun / Racial discrimination / Soldiers of jah army / Reggae on the river / False pretense / Be careful / Live in jah love / Red eyes / Poor man dub / Dubbin in the sunshine / Discriminatory dub
RASCD 3080 / Sep '91 / Ras

☐ FREE TO MOVE
RASCD 3231 / Sep '96 / Ras

☐ ISRAEL DUB
Dub worries / Dub of conscience / Tribute to gadman / Jah jah dub / Licks and kicks dubwise / Same dub / Weepers and mourners / Glory dub / Fire dub / Go through dub / Possibility in dub / Survival dub / Top controlling dub / Fridays blues / Graceful dub / Unconquered dub / Practise jah dub / Taxman dub
GRELCD 510 / Apr '91 / Greensleeves

☐ ISRAEL VIBRATION VOL.4
RASCD 3120 / Aug '93 / Ras

☐ LIVE AGAIN (Israel Vibration & Roots Radics)
Rockford rock / Same song / Jailhouse rocking / Rudeboy shufflin' / Never gonna hurt me again / You never know / There is no end / On the rock / Greedy dog / Racial injustice / Red eyes / Strength of my life / Licks and kicks / War
RAS 3247 / Jul '97 / Ras

☐ LIVE AT REGGAE SUNSPLASH (Israel Vibration & Gladiators)
NETCD 8925 / Nov '92 / Network

☐ ON THE ROCK
RASCD 3175 / Mar '95 / Ras

☐ PERFECT LOVE & UNDERSTANDING
NETCD 1006 / Jun '93 / Network

☐ PRAISES
Vultures / There is no end / Rumours of war / So far away / Real and right / Make it work / Jail house rocking / New wave / Try again
RASCD 3054 / Jul '90 / Ras

☐ RAS PORTRAITS
Cool and calm / We a de rasta / Same song / Jailhouse rockin' / Livity in the dub / Rudeboy shufflin' / Highway robbery / Dub of conscience / Mr. Consular Man / Falling angels / Saviour in your dub / Dub in the Middle East / Feelin' irie / Strength of my dub / Red eyes
RAS 3317 / Jul '97 / Ras

☐ RUDEBOY SHUFFLIN'
CRCDM 1 / Aug '95 / Ras

☐ SAME SONG, THE
Same song / Weep and mourn / Walk the streets of glory / Ball of fire / I'll go through / Why worry / Lift up your conscience / Prophet has arisen / Jah time has come / Licks and kicks
CDPS 003 / Jun '95 / Pressure Sounds
RASCD 3228 / Sep '96 / Ras

☐ STRENGTH OF MY LIFE
Cool and calm / Jah love me / Pay day / Greedy dog / Don't want apartheid / Perfect love and understanding / Live and give / Middle east / Strength of my life
RASCD 3037 / Dec '88 / Ras

☐ SURVIVE
LG 21115 / Oct '95 / Lagoon

☐ UNCONQUERED PEOPLE
GRELCD 148 / Jul '90 / Greensleeves

☐ VIBES ALIVE
RASCD 3091 / Nov '92 / Ras

Israel, Yoron

☐ GIFT FOR YOU, A (Israel, Yoron Connection)
FRLCD 024 / Jan '96 / Freelance

Israelites

☐ SENSI DUB VOL.8
OMCD 032 / Jun '96 / Original Music

Israelvis

☐ CHURCH OF ISRAELVIS
PRO 019 / Feb '97 / Progress

☐ EUROSIS
PRO 024 / Apr '97 / Progress

It

☐ CONCUBIA NOCTE
MASOCD 90101 / 6 Jul '98 / Materiali Sonori

☐ ERA VULGARIS NCODED - DROP 6.3
MASOCD 90078 / Jul '97 / Materiali Sonori

It

☐ ON TOP OF THE WORLD
BCKCD 1 / Jul '90 / Black Market International

It Bites

☐ BIG LAD IN THE WINDMILL
I got you eating out of my hand / All in red / Whole new world / Screaming on the beaches / Turn me loose / Cold, tired and hungry / Calling all the heroes / You'll never go to heaven / Big lad in the windmill / Wanna shout
CDV 2378 / Jul '86 / Virgin

☐ CALLING ALL THE HEROES (The Best Of It Bites)
Still too young to remember / Calling all the heroes / Strange but true / All in red / Kiss like Judas / Murder of the planet Earth / Midnight / Sister Sarah / Old man and the angel / Underneath your pillow / Screaming on the beaches / Whole new world / Yellow christian / You'll never go to heaven
CDOVD 453 / Feb '95 / Virgin

☐ EAT ME IN ST. LOUIS
Positively animal / Underneath your pillow / Let us all go / Still too young to remember / Murder of the planet earth / People of America / Sister Sarah / Leaving without you / Till the end of time / Ice melts (into water) / Charlie / Having a good day / Reprise / Bullet in the barrel
CDV 2591 / Aug '91 / Virgin

☐ ONCE AROUND THE WORLD
Midnight / Kiss like Judas / Yellow christian / Rose Marie / Old man and the angel / Hunting the whale / Plastic dreamer / Once around the world / Black December
CDV 2456 / Aug '91 / Virgin

☐ THANK YOU AND GOODNIGHT (The Best Of It Bites)
Kiss like Judas / All in red / Underneath your pillow / Murder of the planet earth / Ice melts (into water) / Yellow christian / You'll never go to heaven / Calling all the heroes / Screaming on the beaches / Still too young to remember
VGDCD 3516 / Oct '91 / Virgin

Italian Instabile Orchestra

☐ SKIES OF EUROPE
Il maestro muratore / Squilli di morte / Corbu / Meru lo snob / L'arte mistica del vasaio / Il maestro muratore (reprise) / Du du duchamp / Quand duchamp joue du marteau / Il suono giallo / Mariene e gli ospiti misteriosi / Satie satin / Masse d'urto / Fellini song
5271812 / Mar '95 / ECM

Itals

☐ BRUTAL OUT DEH
Brutal / Herbs pirate / Run baldhead run / Temptation / Action / Rastafari chariot / Truth must reveal / Give me what I want / Time will tell / Smile knotty dread
NHCD 303 / '89 / Nighthawk

☐ GIVE ME POWER
In deh / Roll river jordan / Me waan justice / Kill crime / Give me power / Make merry / Love affair / Physical pollution / Jah calling / Material gain
NHCD 307 / '89 / Nighthawk

☐ MODERN AGE
In a dis ya time / Titanic / Render love / Give this love a try / Surrender / Modern age / Crazy / Sweet memories / Together forever / Happen before the time / Almighty / In a dis ya time ska
RASCD 3180 / Jun '98 / Ras

Itch

☐ AVENUE PARADE
Superficial girl / Happy and free / Uncertain / Boy in the corner / Plain in Summer / Get up, get down / Key to life / Not my friend / Don't blame me / Never listen / Eyes across the room / Beginner's luck
DRCD 012 / Jun '97 / Detour

Ithaca

☐ GAME FOR ALL WHO KNOW, A
HBG 122/3 / Jun '97 / Background

Ito, Teiji

☐ KING UBU
TZA 7036 / 13 Jul '98 / Tzadik

Itoiz

☐ ALKOLEA
LV 013 / 16 Mar '98 / Lost Vinyl

☐ EZEKIEL
KD 4011 / 16 Mar '98 / Elkar

☐ ITOIZ
KD 4008 / 16 Mar '98 / Elkar

It's A Beautiful Day

☐ IT'S A BEAUTIFUL DAY
White bird / Hot summer day / Wasted union blues / Girl nothing eyes / Bombay calling / Bulgaria / Time is
11790 / 23 Feb '98 / SFS

☐ IT'S A BEAUTIFUL DAY/MARRYING MAIDEN
White bird / Hot summer day / Wasted union blues / Girl with no eyes / Bombay calling / Bulgaria / Time is / Don and Dewey / Dolphins / Essence of now / Hoedown / Soapstone mountain / Waiting for the song / Let a woman flow / It comes right down to you / Good lovin' / Galileo / Do you remember the sun
4894492 / 2 Feb '98 / Columbia

☐ LIVE AT THE CARNEGIE HALL
Give your woman what she wants / Hot summmer day / Angels and animals / Bombay calling / Going to another party / Good lovin' / Grand camel suite / White bird
4809702 / Aug '95 / Columbia

It's Immaterial

☐ SONG
New Brighton / Endless holiday / Ordinary life / Heaven knows / In the neighbourhood / Missing / Homecoming / Summer winds / Life on the hill / Your voice
CDSRN 27 / Apr '92 / Siren

Iturralde, Pedro

☐ NUA NOCHE EN EL CENTRAL
NDJ 2004 / 1 Jun '98 / Karonte

Itziar

☐ ITZIAR
LV 005 / 16 Mar '98 / Lost Vinyl

Ivers, Eileen

☐ EILEEN IVERS
GLCD 1139 / Apr '94 / Green Linnet

☐ KEEP IT REEL
PAG 001CD / Apr '96 / PAG

☐ SO FAR (The Eileen Ivers Collection 1979-1995)
Kerryman's daughter/Lord Gordon's / Orphan/Paul Montague's / Red haired lass/Paddy O'Brien's/The scholar / Lorraine's waltz / Sean Coughlan's/Gan ainm/Sean Coughlan's / Noisy curfew/Farewell to Erin / Flowing tide/Crock of gold/Julia Delaney's / Humours of Ballyloughlin/Knocknagow / Pachelbel's frolics / On horseback / Rights of man / Lament for Staker Wallace / Harvest
GLCD 1185 / Oct '97 / Green Linnet

☐ TRADITIONAL IRISH MUSIC
GL 1139CD / Jun '94 / Green Linnet

☐ WILD BLUE
GLCD 1166 / Feb '96 / Green Linnet

Iversen, Einor

☐ WHO CAN I TURN TO
GMCD 73 / Jan '87 / Gemini

Ives, Burl

☐ BURL IVES
Fox / Waltzing Matilda / Blue tail fly / Goober peas / Down in the valley / John Henry / Old Dan Tucker / Cowboy's lament / That's my heart strings (That's my boy) / Eerie canal / Foggy, foggy dew / Git along little doggies / Molly Malone / Mrs. McGrath / Aunt Rhody / Haul away, Joe / Prisoner's song (Midnight special) / Vive la compagnie
CD 12533 / Jun '96 / Music Of The World

☐ LITTLE BITTY TEAR, A (5CD Set)
Little bitty tear / Long black veil / Shanghai'd / Almighty dollar bill / Forty hour week / Delia / Oh my side / Lenora, let your hair hang down / Mocking bird hill / I walk the line / Drink to me only with thine eyes / Mama don't want no peas, no rice, no coconut oil / Empty saddles / Oregan trail / Home on the range / When the bloom is on the sage / My adobe hacienda / Cowboy's dream / Mexicali rose / Last round-up / Oh bury me not on the lone prairie / Jingle jangle jingle / Cool water / Tumbling tumbleweeds / Royal telephone / Holding hands for Joe / Sixteen fathoms down / What you gonna do Leroy / Brooklyn bridge / Poor little Jimmy / Thumbin' Johnny Brown / Funny way of laughing / That's all I can remember / Ninety nine / Call me Mr. In-between / I ain't comin' home tonight / How do you fall out of love / In foggy old London / Mother wouldn't do that / Bring them in / Let the lower lights be burning / Beulah land / Standing on the promises / Fairest Lord Jesus / We're marching to Zion / Sunshine in my soul / Blessed assurance / Leaning on the everlasting arms / Where he leads me / Will there be any stars / When they ring those golden bells / Same old hurt / Wishin' she was here (instead of me) / Busted / Poor boy in a rich man's town / Mary Ann regrets / Billy Bayou / Moon is high / Green turtle / Bury the bottle with me / Blizzard / It comes and goes / I'm the boss / Same old hurt (remake) / Curry road / Deepening snow / She didn't let the ink dry on the paper / Late movie / Home James / Man about town / She called me baby / My chicken run away to the bush / Baby come home to me / Roses and orchids / Lynching party / Hundred twenty miles from nowhere / Two car garage / I found my best friend in the dog pound / I'll hit it with a stick / Saskatoon, Saskatchewan / Some folks / I'll walk away smiling / There goes another pal of mine / This is your day / This is all I ask / Lower forty / Four initials on a tree / Someone hangin' round you all the time / Beautiful Annabelle Lee / Hobo jungle / Strong as a mountain / Can't you hear me / Cherry blossom song / What I want (I can never have) / Can angels fly over the Rockies / Legend of the T / Kentucky turkey buzzard / Funny little show / Hard luck and misery / Pearly shells / What little tears are made of / Short on love / Who done it / Two of the usual / Tell me / Among my souvenirs / Gater hollow / I ain't missing nobody / Catfish Bill / Time to bum again / Born for trouble / Unemployment check / Atlantic coastal line / Don't let love die / How deep is the ocean / Okeechobee ocean / My melancholy baby / Jealous / My gal Sal / By the light of the silvery moon / For me and my gal / Red sails in the sunset / Make believe / Oh how I miss you tonight / You know you belong to somebody else / Down in the Okefenokee / (I hear you) Call my name / Mr. Make-up man / River boy / Drifting and dreaming / Beyond the reef / My Isle of golden dreams / Now is the hour / Sweet Leilani / Moon of Manakoora / Song of the Islands / Keep your eyes on the hands / Hawaiian bells / Little brown girl / On the beach of Waikiki / Aloha oe / Thirty thousand feet over Denver / Betsy the cow
BCD 15667 / Jul '93 / Bear Family

☐ LITTLE BITTY TEAR, A
HMNCD 006 / Jun '97 / Half Moon

☐ MORE OF THE BEST OF BURL IVES
It makes no differenc enow / Cowboy's lament / Git along little doggies / Froggie went a-courtin' / Way oh, Santa Anna / Drunken sailor / Fox / St. John's river / On the Grand Canyon line / Down in the valley / I wonder as I wander / Sad man's song / Away Rio / Waltzing Matilda
12650 / Oct '97 / Laserlight

☐ POOR WAYFARING STRANGER
PASTCD 7090 / Mar '96 / Flapper

☐ SINGS HIS FAVOURITES
Gypsy's wedding day / Jesse James / Three crows / Cowboy's lament / Wee cooper o'Fife / Edward / Tam Pierce / Young man who couldn't hoe corn / Little McGhee / I'm goin' down the road feelin' bad / Blue tail fly / Darlin' Cory / Old Bangum / Riddle song / On top of old smokey / Swapping song / Oh Sally, my dear / Golden vanity / I'm goin' away / As I went out one morning
CBCD 007 / Sep '96 / Collector's Edition

☐ SOME OF THE BEST
I'm thinking tonight of my blue eyes / Blue tailed fly / New York girls / Venezuela / Rodger Young / I know an old lady / Jack was every inch a sailor / Goober peas / Leave her, Johnny, leave her / Lydia, the tattooed lady / Kling, kling bird (on top of the divi-divi tree) / Hush little baby / Big rock candy mountain / There is a tavern in the town
12649 / May '97 / Laserlight

☐ TIMELESS CLASSICS (Ives, Burl & The Korean Children's Choir)
Everything is beautiful / O happy day / Heaven came down / Dwelling in Beulah land / Down from His glory / I love to tell the story / I'd like to teach the world to sing / Blessed assurance / Amazing grace / At the cross / Put your hand in my hand / There is a fountain / When the roll is called up yonder / Burl's goodbye / Abide with me
TIMED 026 / Mar '98 / Timeless Classics

☐ VERY BEST OF BURL IVES, THE
Shanghaid / Little bitty tear / Pearly shells / Kentucky turkey buzzard / What little tears are made of / Big rock candy mountain / Lenora, let your hair hang down / My chicken ran away to the bush / Baby come home to me / I know an old lady / Funny way of laughing / Saskatoon, saskatchewan / Mockin' bird hill / Long black veil / I walk the line / Late movie / It comes and goes / Two car garage / Blue tail fly / This is all I ask
SOWCD 708 / May '93 / Sound Waves

☐ WELL RESPECTED MAN
Galisteo / Snowbird / Time / Real roses / Roll up some inspiration / Another day another year / Raindrops keep falling on my head / One more time billy brown / Tied down here at home / Funny way of laughing / Coming after Jimmy
CWNCD 2021 / Jul '96 / Javelin

Ivy League

☐ MAJOR LEAGUE/COLLECTOR'S IVY LEAGUE, THE (2CD Set)
What more do you want / Wait a minute / Funny how love can be / Lonely room / That's why I'm crying / Girl like you / Tossing and turning / Graduation day / Our love is slipping away / I could make you fall in love / Running around in circles / Rain rain go away / Willow tree / One day / My world fell down / When you're young / Four and twenty hours / Arrivederci baby / Suddenly things / Tomorrow is another day / Thank you for loving me / In the not to distant future / Almost grown / Floral dance / Lulu's back in town / We're having a party / Don't worry baby / Make love / Don't think twice it's alright / My old dutch / Dance to the locomation / My baby / Nancy / Lonely city / Mr.Ford's boogie / Friday / Busy doing nothing / Rock and roll medley / Humpty dumpty / Holly and the ivy league / Once in royal David's city / Good king wenceslas / Silent night
NEDCD 289 / 27 Oct '97 / Sequel

☐ THIS IS THE IVY LEAGUE
REP 4094 / Aug '91 / Repertoire

Iwamoto, Yoshikazu

☐ SHAKUHACHI FLUTE - THE SPIRIT OF THE WIND
926402 / Mar '96 / BUDA

Iwan, Dafydd

☐ CANEUON QWERIN
Moliannwn / Ar lan y mor / Y ferch o blwy' penderyn / Titrwm tatrwm / Fe drawodd yn fy meddwl / Mynwent eglwys / Harbwr corc-fflat huw puw / Rownd yr horn / Y deryn pur (gentle bird) / Ffarwel fo I dre' porthmadog / Si hei lwll / Bugeilio'r gwenith gwyn / Paid a deud / Trwy'r drysni a'r anialwch / Ffarwel I blwy llangywer
SCD 2062 / Feb '95 / Sain

☐ DALIGREDU
Draw, draw ymhell (tiger bay) / Fel yna mae hi wedi bod erioed / Can angharad / Oscar romero / Esgair llyn (fields of athenry) / Can mandela / Dal I gredu (my way) / Can I helen / Can yr aborijinl / Awely wylfa ("buachaill an eirne") / Doctor alan / Can y fam / Yr anthem geltaidd
SCD 4053 / Mar '95 / Sain

☐ YMA O HYD (Iwan, Dafydd & Ar Log)
Y wen na phyla amser / Cwm ffynnon ddu / Adlais y gog lwydlas / Tra bo hedydd / Laura Llwelyn / Ffidl yn y to / Hoffedd Gwilym/Mynydd yr heliwr/Mans o'r felin / Hoffedd Jac Nurphy / Can Wiliam / Can y medd / Per oslef / Y chwe chant a naw / Yma o hyd
SCD 2063 / Feb '95 / Sain

Izachaar, Hughie

☐ CAN'T TAKE THE PRESSURE
JWCD 012 / 3 Aug '98 / Jah Warrior

☐ PRAISE JAH
ROTCD 009 / Apr '96 / Reggae On Top

Izadi, Kamyar

☐ SANTOUR
Sur le mode Mahur / Sur le mode shur pich Daramad avaz-s reng / Sur le mode Esfahan
CP 10396 / May '97 / Cinq Planetes

J

J-Church

☐ ARBOR VITAE
Cigarettes kill / Racked / Drinking down / Church on fire / Your shirt / Without a single word / Contempt for modesty / Swallow / Switzerland / Waiting on the ground / Mr. Backrub / Stinking seas
HB 011 / Dec '96 / Honey Bear

☐ DRAMA OF ALIENATION, THE
DON 003CD / Nov '96 / Honest Don's

☐ NOSTALGIA FOR NOTHING
SKIP 037CD / Nov '95 / Broken

☐ RECESSION OF SIMULACRA, THE
JT 1019CD / Jul '95 / Jade Tree

☐ WHOREHOUSE SONGS & STATEMENTS
DAMGOOD 103CD / Sep '96 / Damaged Goods

J-Life

☐ TOMORROW'S WARRIORS PRESENT...J-LIFE
Again we begin / Fall / Music is the magic / In a sentimental mood / Deluge / Baubles bangles and beads / Dark too bright / No rest on the quest / Afro blue / In a dextrous tone / To be poor is a crime / Our dream mile
5029763002323 / 23 Mar '98 / Dune

J-Quest

☐ QUEST IS ON, THE
Given it all / Quest is on / It's gonna be alright / Brand new love / Up and down / Anything / Don't stop ya luv / From now on / Come and give it (you know what I want) / On my mind / Behind the scenes / Up and down (original mix)
5285342 / Sep '95 / Mercury

J&W Crew

☐ J&W CREW PRESENTS HIT ROCKERS OF THE 1980'S, THE (Various Artists)
JWCD 1 / Oct '96 / Heavy Beat

Jach'a Mallku

☐ ESTO ES BOLIVIA
TUMICD 064 / Feb '97 / Tumi

☐ GRAN CONDOR
TUMICD 037 / Jun '93 / Tumi

Jacinta

☐ AUTRES CHANSONS YIDDISH
C 560033 / May '92 / Ocora

☐ TANGO, MI CORAZON
MES 159112 / Jun '93 / Messidor

Jack

☐ JAZZ AGE, THE
3 O'clock in the morning / Pablo / My world vs your world / Saturday's plan / Nico's children / Lolita Elle / Cinematic / Steamin' / Love and death in the afternoon / Half cut wholly yours
PURE 072CD / 17 Aug '98 / Too Pure

Jack & The Beanstalk

☐ ...AND OTHER STORIES
PARCD 024 / Feb '97 / Parasol

Jack

☐ PIONEER SOUNDTRACKS
Of lights / Wintercomessummer / White jazz / Biography of a first son / Filthy names / I didn't mean it Marie / FU / Dress you in mourning / Hope is a liar
PURECD 055 / Jun '96 / Too Pure

Jack Fire

☐ DESTRUCTION OF SUARESILLE, THE
ESD 1213 / Sep '95 / Estrus

Jack Frost

☐ SNOW JOB
BEGL 183CD / Apr '96 / Beggars Banquet

Jack Off Jill

☐ SEXLESS DEMONS AND SCARS
24910 / Sep '97 / ICB

Jack Radics

☐ I'LL BE SWEETER
PHCD 23 / Sep '93 / Penthouse

☐ OPEN REBUKE
HBST 168CD / Aug '94 / Heartbeat

☐ RADICAL
Rough life / Rough life / Old down the tribal war / I can be so good / Who the cap fits / Baby I need your love / Ammunitio dump / Tears of a clown / One temptation / Rescue me
SHCD 45003 / Jun '93 / Shanachie

☐ SOMETHING
TOPCD 1 / Nov '92 / Top Rank

☐ TEQUILA SUNSET
SFCD 002 / Jul '95 / Sprint

☐ WHAT ABOUT ME
RN 0039 / Apr '97 / Runn

Jack Speed

☐ SURGE
Emma / Blue bossa / Tangents / Storm / Construction / With the clouds / Tone control / Fission / CTC / Froing / Fast
RS 96067CD / Jun '96 / R&S

Jack The Lad

☐ IT'S JACK THE LAD
Boilermaker blues / Back on the road again / Plain dealing / Fast lane driver / Turning into winter / Why I can't be satified / Song without a band / Rosalie / Promised land / Corny pastiche / Black cock of Wickham/Chief O'Neill's favourite / Golden rivet/ Staten Island/ The Cook in the kitchen / Lying in the water / One more dance / Make me happy
CASCD 1085 / Nov '92 / Charisma

Jackass

☐ REALITY BITES (IN SANTA BARBARA) EP
SMLX 009 / Mar '97 / Smilex

Jackie & Roy

☐ ABC-PARAMOUNT YEARS, THE
379272 / Aug '97 / Koch International

☐ EAST OF SUEZ
CCD 4149 / Jul '96 / Concord Jazz

☐ HIGH STANDARDS
I got rhythm / Stardust / Loving you / I watch you sleep / Too marvellous for words / Am I blue / Bidin' my time / Joy spring / Mine / Nobody's heart belongs to me
CCD 4186 / Nov '96 / Concord Jazz

☐ JACKIE AND ROY
Euphoria / F Y I / Oh lady be good / If I had you / 'Deed I do / I'm forever blowing bubbles / Pina colada / Gone with the wind / Once in a while / Lonely woman
SV 0218 / Oct '97 / Savoy Jazz

☐ SPRING CAN REALLY HANG YOU UP THE MOST
BLCD 760904 / Jun '88 / Black Lion

Jackie & The Cedrics

☐ GREAT 9 STOMPS SET
1+2CD 088 / 1 Jun '98 / 1+2

Jacklin, Tony

☐ SWINGS INTO
CREV 46CD / Sep '96 / Rev-Ola

Jackman, Colin

☐ ACTION TIME
CJ 0196CD / Mar '97 / Multimedia

Jackopierce

☐ BRINGING ON THE WEATHER
5402232 / 15 Sep '97 / A&M

Jacks

☐ WHY DON'T YOU WRITE ME VOL.2
Why don't you write me / Since my baby's been gone / Heaven help me / Do you wanna rock / Away / How soon / I cry / They turned the party out down at Bessie's house / Dream a little longer / Fine lookin' baby / So wrong / Wiggie waggie woo / I'm confessin' that I love you / Let's make up / If it is wrong / Annie meet Henry / My reckless heart / Why did I fall in love / I want you / You belong to me / Dancin' Dan / This empty heart / So will I / My Darling
CDCHD 535 / Apr '95 / Ace

Jackson Singers

☐ GOSPEL EMOTIONS
Storm is passing / This little light of mine / You've got to move / God has smiled on me / Over my head / Nobody knows the trouble I've seen / Put your trust in Jesus / I've decided to make Jesus my choice / Jesus said if you go / If it had not been for the Lord / Pass me not / Precious Lord
CDLR 44016 / May '92 / L&R

Jackson, Alan

☐ EVERYTHING I LOVE
Little bitty / Everything I love / Buicks to the moon / Between the devil and me / There goes / House with no curtains / Who's cheatin' who / Walk on the rocks / Must've had a ball / It's time you learned about goodbye
07822188132 / Nov '96 / Arista

☐ GREATEST HITS COLLECTION
Chattahoochee / Gone country / She's got rhythm / Midnight in Montgomery / Tall, tall trees / Chasin' that neon rainbow / I'll try / Don't rock the jukebox / Livin' on love / Summertime blues / Love's got a hold on you / (Who says) You can't have it all / Home / Wanted / I don't even know your name / Dallas / Here in the real world / Someday / Mercury blues / I'd love you all over again
07822188012 / Oct '95 / Arista

☐ HERE IN THE REAL WORLD
Ace of hearts / Blue blooded woman / Chasin' that neon rainbow / I'd love you all over again / Home / Here in the real world / Wanted / She don't get the blues / Dog river blues / Short sweet ride
260817 / Jul '90 / Arista

☐ HONKY TONK CHRISTMAS
Honky tonk christmas / Angels cried / If we make it through December / If you don't wanna see Santa Claus cry / I only want you for christmas / Merry Christmas to me / Holly jolly christmas / There's a new kid in town / Santa's gonna come in a pickup truck / Please daddy (don't get drunk this Christmas)
7822187362 / Nov '95 / Arista

☐ LOT ABOUT LIVIN', A (And A Little 'Bout Love)
Chattanoochee / She's got the rhythm (I got the blues) / Tonight I climbed the wall / I don't need the booze (To get a buzz on) / (Who says) You can't have it all / Up to my ears in tears / Tropical depression / She likes it too / If it ain't one thing (It's you) / Mercury blues
07822187112 / Jun '94 / Arista

☐ WHO I AM
Summertime blues / Livin' on love / Hole in the wall / Gone country / Who I am / You can't give up on love / I don't even know your name / Song for the life / Thank God for the radio / All American country boy / Job description / If I had you / Let's get back to me and you / Chattahoochee
74321217682 / Aug '96 / Arista

Jackson, Billy

☐ LONG STEEL RAIL
TCD 5014 / Dec '94 / Testament

☐ MISTY MOUNTAIN (Jackson, Billy & Billy Ross)
Beinn a' cheataich / Landfall / Glen of copeswood / Lass o'glenshee / Boyne water / Guidnicht and joy be wi' ye a' / Country girl and the hungarian fiddler / Tar the house / Little cascade / Geil mill / First step / Trusdar bodaich, drochaid, luideach / Na'm faighinn gille ri cheannach / For our lang bidin' here / Meudail is m'aighear s'mo ghradh
IRCD 005 / '88 / Iona

☐ WELLPARK SUITE, THE (Jackson, Billy & Ossian)
Glasgow 1885 / Dear green place changed life in the city / March of the workers / Molendinar: The spring / Brewing / Fermentation / Glasgow celebration
IRCD 008 / Aug '91 / Iona

Jackson, Bleu

☐ GONE THIS TIME
TX 1005CD / Jan '94 / Taxim

Jackson, Bull Moose

☐ BAD MAN JACKSON, THAT'S ME
Big ten inch record / Bad man Jackson, that's me / Jammin' and jumpin / We ain't got nothin' but the blues / Bull Moose Jackson blues / Honey dripper / Hold him Joe / I want a bowlegged woman / Oh John / Fare thee well / Nosey Joe / Bearcat blues / Why don't you haul off and love me / Cherokee boogie / Meet me with your black dress on / Hodge podge / Big fat mamas are back in style again / All night long / Bootsie / If you ain't lovin' (you ain't livin') / I wanna hug ya, kiss ya, squeeze ya
CDCHARLY 274 / Jan '93 / Charly

Jackson, Carl

☐ BANJO MAN (A Tribute To Earl Scruggs)
Earl's breakdown / John Henry / Grey eagle / You are my flower / Home sweet home / Careless love / Keep on the sunny side / Little darlin', pal of mine / Reuben / Ground speed / Banjo man
SHCD 3715 / Jan '97 / Sugar Hill

☐ NASHVILLE COUNTRY
Gone gone gone: *Jackson, Carl & Ricky Scaggs* / To keep your memory green: *Jackson, Carl & Sharon White/Cheryl White* / Under your spell again: *Jackson, Carl & Emmylou Harris* / Walk through the world with me: *Jackson, Carl & Emmylou Harris* / All that's left for me / Something draws me to you: *Jackson, Carl & Emmylou Harris* / When my blue moon turns to gold again: *Jackson, Carl & Emmylou Harris* / You made a memory of me: *Jackson, Carl & Sharon White/Cheryl White* / I take the chance: *Jackson, Carl & Emmylou Harris* / Before I met you: *Jackson, Carl & Ricky Scaggs* / We must have been out of our minds: *Jackson, Carl & Emmylou Harris* / Dyin' on sorrow's wine / Best we could do / Nobody's darlin' but mine
CDSD 074 / Aug '97 / Sundown

☐ SPRING TRAINING (Jackson, Carl & John Starling/The Nash Ramblers)
SHCD 3789 / Mar '89 / Sugar Hill

Jackson, Chuck

☐ ENCORE/MR. EVERYTHING
Tell him I'm not home / Blue holiday / Tomorrow / Two stupid feet / This broken heart (that you gave me) / Don't believe him, Donna / King of the Mountain / Invisible / Another day / Lonely am I / Go on Yak Yak / Getting ready for the heartbreak / Since I don't have you / I just don't know what to do with myself / I need you / I'm your man / Human / Love is a many splendoured thing / Work song / If I didn't love you / Something you've got / D-5 / Somebody new / Tears of joy
CDKEND 110 / Aug '94 / Kent

☐ GOOD THINGS
Tell him I'm not home / Beg me / I keep forgettin' / Millionaire / Hand it over / Two stupid feet / Make the night a little longer / I wake up crying / I'm your man / Castanets / Who's gonna pick up the pieces / Good things come to those who wait / I don't want to cry / Breaking point / Any other way / Any day now / Since I don't have you / They don't give medals (to yesterday's heroes) / Where do I go from here / These chains of love (are breaking me down) / What's with this loneliness / Forget about me / I just don't know what to do with myself / I can't stand to see you cry
CDKEND 935 / Aug '90 / Kent

☐ I DON'T WANT TO CRY/ANY DAY NOW
I don't want to cry / Tears on my pillow / My willow tree / In between tears / Tear of the year / I cried for you / Lonely teardrops / Don't let the sun catch you crying / Salty tears / I wake up crying / Tear / Man ain't supposed to cry / I keep forgettin' / Any day now / Just once / Same old story / What'cha gonna say tomorrow / Make the night a little longer / Who's gonna pick up the pieces / In real life / Angel of angels / Breaking point / Prophet / Everybody needs love
CDKEND 107 / Aug '93 / Kent

☐ SMOOTH SMOOTH JACKSON
I'm telling you I'm not going / I've got the need / Cover up or get ready / True believer / My memories of Marie / I don't wanna cry / Keep on ringing my bell / Changing partners / It's not unusual / Piece of rock / Smooth smooth jackson / I'm needing you, wanting you / If I were a woman / Sometimes when we touch / Beautiful woman / After the loving / Any day now / Might as well take my time / Love rights / I fell asleep / More / Carla
NEMCD 993 / 27 Oct '97 / Sequel

Jackson, Cliff

☐ CAROLINA SHOUT
Honeysuckle rose / Ain't misbehavin' / 'S wonderful / Tin roof blues / You took advantage of me / Carolina shout / I'm coming Virginia / Crazy rhythm / Beale Street blues / Someday, sweetheart / Who's sorry now
BLC 760194 / Mar '94 / Black Lion

☐ CLASSICS 1930-1945
CLASSICS 979 / 24 Feb '98 / Classics

Jackson, Cordell

☐ LIVE IN CHICAGO
BH 0003 / Jul '97 / Bughouse

Jackson, D.D.

☐ PAIRED DOWN VOL.1
Rhythm and things / Ballad for miles / Reflections / Chick-isms / Fanfare and fiesta / Subliminal messages / African dreams / For Don / Bang's dream / Easy
JUST 992 / Jul '97 / Justin Time

☐ PEACE SONG
JUST 722 / Apr '95 / Justin Time

☐ RHYTHM-DANCE
D D Blues / Nueve cancion / No boundaries / Some thoughts about you / Motion sickness / Rhythm-dance / Ayse / Dreams / Guitar song / For Mamma / Peace of mind
JUST 892 / Aug '96 / Justin Time

Jackson, David

☐ FRACTAL BRIDGE
Ecco soundbeam / Aloerotic / Three main dishes / Keystone / Wildman / Untouched by human hand / Songerie / Three kinds of rice / Hello / Ecco soundbeam reprise
FIE 9113 / Oct '96 / Fie

Jackson, Duffy

☐ FRENCH CONNECTION
Crazy rhythm / Exactly like you / Li'l darling / Like someone in love / I want to be happy / Bruno's blues / After you've / Love is here to stay / Bernie's tune / Man I love
CHECD 00119 / 20 Jul '98 / Master Mix

☐ SWING SWING SWING
MCD 9233 / Apr '96 / Milestone

Jackson, Earl

☐ BUSTIN' LOOSE (Jackson, Earl & The Jailbreakers)
POCD 016 / Oct '96 / Popcorn

Jackson, Franz

☐ SNAG IT
DD 223 / Nov '93 / Delmark

Jackson, Fred

☐ HOOTIN' AND TOOTIN'
Dippin' in the bag / Southern exposure / Preach brother / Hootin' and tootin' / Easin' on down / That's where it's at / Way down home / Stretchin' out / Mr.BJ / Egypt land / Teena / On the spot / Minor exposure / Little Fred
8218192 / 2 Feb '98 / Blue Note

Jackson, Freddie

☐ DO ME AGAIN
Don't it feel good / Love me down / Main course / It takes two / I'll be waiting for you / Don't say you love me / Do me again / Live for the moment / Second time for love / I can't take it / All over you
RE 21222 / Dec '96 / Razor & Tie

☐ DON'T LET LOVE SLIP AWAY
Nice 'n' slow / Hey lover / Don't let love slip away / Crazy (for me) / One heart too many / If you don't know me by now / You and I got a thang / Special lady / Yes I need you / It's gonna take a long, long time
RE 21212 / Dec '96 / Razor & Tie

☐ FREDDIE JACKSON STORY, THE (For Old Time's Sake)
I don't want to lose your love / I could use a little love (right now) / Look around / Second time for love / Me and Mrs Jones / Can we try / Love me down / Main course / Jam tonight / Rock me tonight (for old time's sake) / Have you ever loved somebody / You are my lady / Tasty love / Little bit more: *Jackson, Freddie & Melba Moore*
CTMCD 303 / Feb '97 / EMI

☐ GREATEST HITS OF FREDDIE JACKSON
Do me again / Rock me tonight / I don't want to lose your love / I could use a little love (right now) / Jam tonight / Nice and slow / You are my lady / Love me down / Have you ever loved somebody / Hey lover / Love is just a touch away / Tasty love / Christmas forever
CDEST 2226 / Feb '94 / Capitol

☐ HERE IT IS
Was it something / Comin' home II u / Here it is / How does it feel / Givin' my love / Paradise / Make love easy / Addictive 2 touch / I love / My family
7863 663182 / Jan '94 / RCA

Jackson, George

☐ CAIRITIONA (Jackson, George & Maggie McInnes)
IRCD 006 / '88 / Iona

Jackson, Ira

☐ GIVE HIM THE GLORY
Lord we give you praises / Clap your hands / Live the word / Your glory shines / I seek your glory / Give him the glory / Take your place / Where you are / Holy / Rejoice
IAJCD 1 / 27 Oct '97 / Jackson

Jackson, J.J.

☐ GREAT J.J. JACKSON, THE
But it's alright / Try me / That ain't right / You've got me dizzy / Change is gonna come / I dig girls / Come and see me (I'm your man) / Stones that I throw / Give me back the love / Ain't too proud to beg / Love is a hurtin' thing / Boogaloo baby / Let it out
SEECD 281 / Feb '94 / See For Miles

Jackson, Janet

☐ CONTROL - THE REMIXES
Control / When I think of you / Pleasure principle / What have you done for me lately / Let's wait awhile / Nasty
CDMID 149 / Aug '91 / A&M

☐ DESIGN OF A DECADE 1986-1996
What have you done for me lately / Best things in life are free: *Jackson, Janet & Luther Vandross* / Nasty / Control / When I think of you / Pleasure principle / Escapade / Black cat / Miss you much / Rhythm nation / Whoops now / That's the way love goes / Love will never do (without you) / Come back to me / Alright / Let's wait awhile / Runaway / Twenty foreplay
5404382
5404002
5404222 / Sep '95 / A&M

☐ JANET
Morning / That's the way love goes / You know... / You want this / Be a good boy / If / Back / This time / Go on Miss Janet / Throb / What'll I do / Lounge / Funky big band / Racism / New agenda / Love / Because of love / Wind / Again / Another lover / Where are you now / Hold on baby / Body that loves you / Rain / Anytime anyplace / Are you still up / Sweet dreams / Whoops now
CDV 2720 / May '93 / Virgin

☐ JANET REMIXED
That's the way love goes / If / Because of love / And on and on / Throb / You want this / Anytime anyplace / Where are you now / 70's love groove / What'll I do / One more chance
CDVY 2720 / Mar '95 / Virgin

☐ VELVET ROPE, THE
Interlude / Velvet rope / You / Got til it's gone / Go deep / Free xone / Memory / Together again / Online / Empty / Full / What about / Every time / Tonight's the night / I get lonely / Rope burn / Anyhting / Sad / Special / Can't be stopped
CDV 2860 / 6 Oct '97 / Virgin

Jackson, Javon

☐ BURNIN' (Jackson, Javon & Billy Pearce Quintet)
So the story goes / Mr Glenn roy / Dolo / Cocktails for two / Homestretch / Ugly beauty / Not yet
CRISS 1139CD / Dec '97 / Criss Cross

☐ GOOD PEOPLE
E'd oxum / La aguiba oxum aura da adupe / Emergency / Exotica / Good people / Diane / Flor de canela / Naaman
8566802 / 3 Nov '97 / Blue Note

☐ ME AND MR. JONES (Jackson, Javon Quartet)
CRISS 1053CD / May '92 / Criss Cross

Jackson, Jerry

☐ SHRIMP BOATS A-COMIN', THERE'S DANCIN' TONIGHT
Hey sugarfoot / Se habla espanol / Tell her Johnny said goodbye / La dee dah / You don't wanna hurt me / They really don't know you / If teardrops were diamonds / I don't play games / You might be there with him / Shrimp boats / It hurts me / Till the end of time / Blowin' in the wind / Blues in the night / Time / If I had only known / Are you glad when we're apart / Always / You're mine (and I love you) / Gone to pieces / Turn back / Wide awake in a dream / Gypsy feet / She lied
BCD 15481 / May '90 / Bear Family

Jackson, Jim

☐ COMPLETE RECORDED WORKS VOL.1
DOCD 5114 / Nov '92 / Document

☐ COMPLETE RECORDED WORKS VOL.2
DOCD 5115 / Nov '92 / Document

Jackson, Joe

☐ BODY AND SOUL
Verdict / Cha cha loco / Not here, not now / You can't get what you want / Go for it / Loisaida / Happy ending / Be my number two / Heart of ice
CDMID 118 / Oct '92 / A&M

☐ I'M THE MAN
On your radio / Geraldine and John / Kinda kute / It's different for girls / I'm the man / Band wore blue shirts / Don't wanna be like that / Amateur hour / Get that girl / Friday
CDMID 117 / Oct '92 / A&M

☐ JUMPIN' JIVE
Jumpin' with symphony Sid / Jack you're dead / Is you is or is you ain't my baby / We the cats (shall help ya) / San Francisco fan / Five guys named Moe / Jumpin' jive / You run your mouth, I'll run my business / What's the use of getting sober / You're my meat / Tuxedo junction / How long must I wait for you
5500622 / May '93 / Spectrum

☐ LOOK SHARP
One more time / Sunday papers / Is she really going out with him / Happy loving couples / Throw it away / Baby stick around / Look sharp / Fools in love / Do the instant mash / Pretty girls / Got the time
CDMID 115 / Oct '92 / A&M

☐ NIGHT AND DAY
Another world / Chinatown / TV age / Target / Steppin' out / Breaking us in two / Cancer / Real men / Slow song
CDMID 158 / Oct '92 / A&M

☐ NIGHT MUSIC
Nocturne no. 1 / Flying / Ever after / Nocturne no. 2 / Man who wrote Danny Boy / Nocturne no. 3 / Lullaby / Only the future / Nocturne no. 4 / Sea of secrets
CDVUS 78 / Oct '94 / Virgin

☐ STEPPIN' OUT (Very Best Of Joe Jackson)
Is she really going out with him / Fools in love / I'm the man / It's different for girls / Beat crazy / Jumpin' jive / Breaking us in two / Steppin' out / Slow song / You can't get what you want / Be my number two / Right and wrong / Home town / Down to London / Nineteen forever
3970522 / Sep '90 / A&M

☐ THIS IS IT (Anthology/2CD Set)
Is she really going out with him / Fools in love / One more time / Sunday papers / Look sharp / Got the time / On your radio / It's different for girls / Don't wanna be like that / Amateur hour / I'm the man / Tilt / Someone up there / One to one / Beat crazy / Biology / Jumpin' jive / What's the use of getting sober / Is she really going out with him / Another world / Breaking us in two / Chinatown / Real men / Steppin' out / Slow song / You can't get what you want / Not here, not now / Be my number two / Happy ending / Wild West / Right and wrong / Home town / Precious time / Me and you (against the world) / Down to London / Nineteen forever / Human touch
5404022 / Feb '97 / A&M

Jackson, John

☐ DON'T LET YOUR DEAL GO DOWN
Going down in georgia on a horn / Black snake moan / John henry / If hattie wants to lu, let her lu like a man / Nobody's business but mine / John's rag / Boats up the river / Rattlesnakin' daddy / Flat foot and buck dance / Bear cat blues / Reuben / Rocks and gravel / Going down the road feeling bad / Police dog blues / Don't let your deal go down / Mule skinner blues / I bring my money / John's ragtime / Red river blues / Knife blues / Trucking little baby / Blind blake's rag / Goodbye booze / Graveyard blues / Early mornin blues / You ain't no woman
ARHCD 378 / Apr '95 / Arhoolie

Jackson, John

☐ SALUTES BENNY GOODMAN (Jackson, 'Shoeless' John Quartet)
PCD 7106 / Dec '97 / Progressive

Jackson, Latoya

☐ DANCE COLLECTION
Stop in the name of love / Baby love / Baby I need your love / I can't help myself / Two lovers / Someday we'll be together / My guy / Tracks of my tears / Love child / Stop in the name of love / I'll be there / Tears of a clown
10212 / Oct '97 / Go On Deluxe

☐ MY COUNTRY COLLECTION
Fanfare/Intro / Burnin' love / So in love with you / Georgia dreamin' / I've got to be bad / Crazy / Trash like you / Another heart / Dance away these blues tonight / What you don't say / Little misunderstood / One strike you're out / Break a leg / Boots
100552 / May '97 / A-Play Collection

☐ SEXUAL FEELING
Sexual feeling / Be my lover / He's my brother / He's so good to me / Bad girl / You keep my restless heart / Playboy / You and me / You can count on me / Do the salsa / Piano man / Somewhere
304472 / Jul '97 / Hallmark

☐ SPOTLIGHT ON LATOYA JACKSON
Sexual feeling / You and me / He's my brother / Be my lover / Piano man / Restless heart / Do the salsa / Playboy / He's so good to me / Somewhere / Bad girl / You can count on me
HADCD 111 / Feb '94 / Javelin

Jackson, Lil' Son

☐ BLUES COME TO TEXAS
ARHCD 409 / Apr '95 / Arhoolie

Jackson, Mahalia

☐ DOWN BY THE RIVERSIDE
GO 3803 / 1 Dec '97 / Golden Options

☐ GOLD COLLECTION, THE (2CD Set)
R2CD 4039 / 13 Apr '98 / Deja Vu

☐ GOSPEL QUEEN
304022 / May '97 / Carlton

☐ I'M ON MY WAY
I'm on my way / Evening prayer / Joshua fit the battle of jericho / A city called heaven / Keep your hand on the plow / Lord's prayer / When the saints go marching in / My god is real (yes, god is real) / Didn't it rain / He's got the whole world in his hands / Walk over god's heaven / Go tell it on the mountain / It didn't cost very much / I'm going to live the life I sing about in my song / Nobody knows the trouble I've seen / In the upper room / I will move on up a little higher / Oh lord is it I
CD 12509 / Nov '92 / Music Of The World

☐ MAHALIA JACKSON & OTHER GREAT GOSPEL PERFORMERS 1937-1950
DOCD 5463 / Jun '96 / Document

☐ MIGHTY FORTRESS, A
Mighty fortress is our God / Be still my soul / Power in the blood / I'd rather have Jesus / Roll Jordan roll / Sweet hour of prayer / Good news / Chariot's coming / All is well / It is well with my soul / All hail the power of Jesus' name
4873912 / 2 Mar '98 / Legacy

☐ POWER AND THE GLORY, THE
Onward Christian soldiers / Holy city / Holy holy holy / In the garden / Just as I am / Rock of Ages / Lift up your heads / My country 'til of thee / Lord is my light / Jesus, Saviour pilot me / Nearer my God to thee / Abide with me
4875052 / 2 Mar '98 / Legacy

☐ QUEEN OF GOSPEL
Get away jordan / (I'm) on my way (to canaan) / I can put my trust in jesus / Said he would / He's my light / Move on up a little higher / Run all the way / Up in jerusalem / Lord's prayer / Beautiful tomorrow / Walk with me / In the upper room / I'm glad salvation is free / His eye is on the sparrow / Jesus is with me / These are they / Just as I am / How I got over / I bow my knees / Prayer changes things / Go tell it on the mountain
MCCD 122 / Aug '93 / Music Club

☐ SILENT NIGHT
Silent night / Go tell it on the mountain / Bless this house / Sweet little Jesus boy / Star stood still (Song of the nativity) / Hark the herald angels sing / Christmas comes to us all once a year / Joy to the world / O come all ye faithful (adeste fidelis) / O little town of Bethlehem / What can I give
CD 62130 / 3 Nov '97 / Columbia

Jackson, Michael

☐ BAD
Bad / Way you make me feel / Speed demon / Liberian girl / Just good friends / Another part of me / Man in the mirror / I just can't stop loving you / Dirty Diana / Smooth criminal / Leave me alone
4502902 / Sep '87 / Epic

☐ BEN
Ben / Greatest show on earth / People make the world go round / We've got a good thing going / Everybody's somebody's fool / My girl / What goes around comes around / In our small way / Shee-be-doo-be-doo-a-day / You can cry on my shoulder
5301632 / Sep '93 / Motown

☐ BEST OF MICHAEL JACKSON & THE JACKSON FIVE, THE (Jackson, Michael/Jackson Five)
I want you back: *Jackson Five* / ABC: *Jackson Five* / Love you save: *Jackson Five* / I'll be there: *Jackson Five* / Mama's pearl: *Jackson Five* / Never can say goodbye: *Jackson Five* / Got to be there: *Jackson, Michael* / Rockin' robin: *Jackson, Michael* / Ain't no sunshine: *Jackson, Michael* / Lookin' through the windows: *Jackson Five* / Ben: *Jackson, Michael* / Doctor my eyes: *Jackson Five* / We're almost there: *Jackson, Michael* / Farewell my summer love: *Jackson, Michael* / Girl you're so together: *Jackson, Michael*
5308042 / Jun '97 / PolyGram TV

☐ BIG BOY (Jackson, Michael/Jackson Five)
PLD 8122 / Jul '95 / Charly

☐ BIOGRAPHY SERIES
10011 / 3 Nov '97 / Metro Independent

☐ BLOOD ON THE DANCEFLOOR
Blood on the dance floor / Morphine / Superfly sister / Ghosts / Is it scary / Scream louder / Money / 2 Bad / Stranger in Moscow / This time around / Earth song / You are not alone / History
4875002 / May '97 / MJJ Music

☐ DANGEROUS
Jam / Why you wanna trip on me / In the closet / She drives me wild / Remember the time / Can't let her get away / Heal the world / Black or white / Who is it / Give in to me / Will you be there / Keep the faith / Gone too soon / Dangerous
4658022 / Nov '91 / Epic

☐ GOT TO BE THERE
Ain't no sunshine / I wanna be where you are / Girl don't take your love from me / In our small way / Got to be there / Rockin' robin / Wings of my love / Maria / Love is here and now you're gone / You've got a friend
5301622 / Aug '93 / Motown

☐ HISTORY PAST PRESENT AND FUTURE VOL.1 (2CD Set)
Billie Jean / Way you make me feel / Black or white / Rock with you / She's out of my life / Bad / I just can't stop loving you / Man in the mirror / Thriller / Beat it / Girl is mine / Remember the time / Don't stop till you get enough / Wanna be startin' something / Heal the world / Scream / They don't care about us / Stranger in Moscow / This time around / Earth song / DS / Money / Come together / You are not alone / Childhood / Tabloid junkie / 2 Bad / History / Little Susie / Smile
4747092 / Jun '95 / MJJ Music

☐ INTERVIEW DISC
SAM 7015 / Nov '96 / Sound & Media

☐ MOTOWN EARLY CLASSICS (Jackson, Michael/Jackson Five)
I want you back / Can you remember / Who's lovin' you / True love can be beautiful / In our small way / Goin' back to Indiana / Can I see you in the morning / I'll bet you / Rockin' Robin / People make the world go round / Doggin' around / Never can say goodbye / Lookin' through the windows / We've got a good thing going / Young folks / My little baby / (We've got) Blue skies / With a child's heart
5522242 / Jul '96 / Spectrum

☐ OFF THE WALL
Don't stop till you get enough / Rock with you / Working day and night / Get on the floor / Off the wall / Girlfriend / She's out of my life / I can't help it / It's the falling in love / Burn this disco out
CD 83468 / 27 Jul '98 / Epic

☐ THRILLER
Wanna be startin' something / Baby be mine / Girl is mine / Thriller / Beat it / Billie Jean / Human nature / PYT (pretty young thing) / Lady in my life
CD 85930 / '83 / Epic

Jackson, Millie

☐ 21 OF THE BEST (1971-1983)
Child of God / Ask me what you want / My man, a sweet man / Breakaway / It hurts so good / How do you feel the morning after / (If loving you is wrong) I don't want to be right / Loving arms / Bad risk / You can't turn me off (in the middle of turning me on) / If you're not back in love by Monday / All the way lover / Go out and get some (get it out 'cha system) / Keep the home fire burnin' / Never change lovers in the middle of the night / Kiss you all over / This is it (part 2) / It's gonna take some time this time / Do you wanna make love / Blues don't get tired of me / I feel like walking in the rain
CDSEWD 100 / Sep '94 / Southbound

☐ CAUGHT UP
(If loving you is wrong) I don't want to be right / Rap / All I want is a fighting chance / I'm tired of hiding / It's all over but the shouting / So easy going so hard coming back / I'm through trying to prove my love to you / Summer (first time)
CDSEWM 003 / Jun '89 / Southbound

☐ ESP (Extra Sexual Persuasion)
Sexercise (Parts 1 and 2) / This girl could be dangerous / Slow tongue (Working your way down) / Why me / I feel like walking in the rain / Too easy being easy / Slow tongue / You're working me
CDSEWM 093 / Apr '94 / Southbound

☐ FEELIN' BITCHY
All the way lover / Lovin' your good thing away / Angel in your arms / Little taste of outside love / You created a monster / Cheatin' is / If you're not back in love by Monday / Feeling like a woman
CDSEWM 042 / Oct '91 / Southbound

☐ FOR MEN ONLY
This is where I came in / This is it / If that don't turn you on / I wish that I could hurt that way again / Fool's affair / You must have known I needed love / Despair / Not on your life / Ain't no coming back
CDSEWM 070 / Jun '93 / Southbound

☐ FREE AND IN LOVE
House for sale / I'm free / Tonight I'll shoot the moon / There you are / Do what makes the world go round / Bad risk / I feel like making love / Solitary love affair / I'm in love again
CDSEW 032 / Aug '90 / Southbound

☐ GET IT OUTCHA SYSTEM
Go out and get some (get it out 'cha system) / Keep the home fire burnin' / Logs and thangs / Put something down on it / Here you come again / Why say you're sorry / He wants to hear the words / I just wanna be with you / Sweet music man
CDSEWM 046 / Mar '92 / Southbound

☐ HARD TIMES
Blufunkes / Special occasion / I don't want to cry / We're gonna make it / Hard times / Blues don't get tired of me / Mess on your hands / Finger rap / Mess on your hands (reprise) / Finger rap (reprise) / Feel love comin' on
CDSEWM 090 / Mar '94 / Southbound

☐ HOT, WILD, UNRESTRICTED
Hot, wild, unrestricted, crazy love / Getting to know me / Imitation of love / Love stinks / Muffle that fart / I'm waiting baby / Will you love me tomorrow / Investigative reporting / Love is a dangerous game / Sho nuff danjus
301122 / Jun '97 / Hallmark

☐ I GOT TO TRY IT ONE TIME
How do you feel the morning after / Get your love right / My love is so fly / Letter full of tears / Watch the one who brings you the news / I got to try it one time / Gospel truth / One night stand / I gotta do something about myself / In the wash
CDSEW 023 / Feb '90 / Southbound

☐ I HAD TO SAY IT
I had to say it / Loving arms / Rap / Stranger / I ain't no glory story / It's gonna take some time this time / Fancy this / Ladies first / Somebody's love died here last night / You owe me that much
CDSEWM 086 / Nov '93 / Southbound

☐ IT HURTS SO GOOD
I cry / Hypocrisy / Two-faced world / It hurts so good / Don't send nobody else / Hypocrisy (reprise) / Good to the very last drop / Help yourself / Love doctor / Now that you got it / Close my eyes / Breakaway
CDSEW 019 / Nov '89 / Southbound

☐ IT'S OVER
I can't see me without you / Don't give up on me now / Lies that we live / I just watched my love burn down / What's in it for me / You ain't killing me (the way I want to die) / Breaking up somebody's home / Missing you / When love dies / I don't want to be your friend
ICH 1502CD / Dec '95 / Ichiban

☐ JUST A LIL' BIT COUNTRY
I can't stop loving you / Till I get it right / Pick me up on your way down / Loving you / I laughed a lot / Love on the rocks / Standing in your line / Rose coloured glasses / It meant nothing to me / Anybody that don't like Millie Jackson
CDSEWM 089 / Jan '94 / Southbound

☐ LIVE AND UNCENSORED/LIVE AND OUTRAGEOUS (2CD Set)
Keep the home fire burnin' / Logs and thangs / Put something down on it / Da ya think I'm sexy / Just when I needed you most / Phuck u symphony / What am I waiting for / I still love you (you still love me) / All the way lover / Soaps / Hold the line / Be a sweetheart / Didn't I blow your mind this time / Give it up / Moment's pleasure / (If loving you is wrong) I don't want to be right / Rap / Never change lovers in the middle of the night / Sweet music man / It hurts so good / Passion / Horse or mule / Lovers and girlfriends / Don't you ever stop loving me / I had to say it / Still / Ugly men / This is it
CDSEW2 038 / Mar '91 / Southbound

☐ LOVINGLY YOURS
You can't turn me off (in the middle of turning me on) / Something 'bout you / I'll continue to love you / I can't say goodbye / Love of your own / I'll live my love for you / Body movements / From her arms to mine / Help me finish my song / I'll be rolling
CDSEWM 037 / Feb '91 / Southbound

☐ MILLIE JACKSON
If this is love / I ain't giving up / I miss you baby / Child of God / Ask me what you want / My man, a sweet man / You're the joy of my life / I gotta get away from my own self / I just can't stand it / Strange things
CDSEW 009 / Aug '89 / Southbound

☐ MOMENT'S PLEASURE, A
Never change lovers in the middle of the night / Seeing you again / Kiss you all over / Moment's pleasure / What went wrong last night / Rising cost of love / We got to hit it off / Once you've had it
CDSEWM 053 / Sep '92 / Westbound

☐ ROYAL RAPPIN'S (Jackson, Millie & Isaac Hayes)
Sweet music, soft lights and you / Feels like the first time / You never cross my mind / Love changes / I changed my mind / Do you wanna make love / If I had my way / If you had your way / You needed me
CDSEWM 059 / Jan '93 / Southbound

☐ STILL CAUGHT UP
Loving arms / Making the best of a bad situation / Memory of a wife / Tell her it's over / Do what makes you satisfied / You can't stand the thought of another me / Leftovers / I still love you (you still love me)
CDSEW 027 / Jul '90 / Southbound

☐ YOUNG MAN, OLDER WOMAN
ICH 1159CD / Feb '94 / Ichiban

Jackson, Milt

☐ AIN'T BUT A FEW OF US LEFT (Jackson, Milt & Oscar Peterson/Grady Tate/Ray Brown)
Ain't but a few of us left / Time for love / If I should lose you / Stuffy / Body and soul / What am I here for
OJCCD 785 / Jun '94 / Original Jazz Classics

☐ BAGS MEETS WES (Jackson, Milt & Wes Montgomery)
S.k.j. / Stablemates / Stairway to the stars (take 3) / Stairway to the stars (take 2) / Blue roz / Sam sack / Jingles (take 9) / Jingles (take 8) / Delilah (take 4) / Delilah (take 3)
OJCCD 234 / Apr '86 / Original Jazz Classics

☐ BAGS' BAG
Blues for Roberta / Groovin' / How are you / Slow boat to China / I cover the waterfront / Rev / Your angel / Blues for Tomi-Oka
OJCCD 9352 / Nov '97 / Original Jazz Classics

☐ BIG BAGS
Old devil moon / 'round midnight / Dream is you / You'd be so nice to come home to / Echoes / If you could see me now / Star eyes / Namesake / If I should lose you / Later than you think
OJCCD 366 / Nov '95 / Original Jazz Classics

☐ BIG THREE, THE (Jackson, Milt & Joe Pass/Ray Brown)
Pink panther / Nuages / Blue bossa / Come Sunday / Wave / Moonglow / You stepped out of a dream / Blues for Sammy
OJCCD 805 / Jul '93 / Original Jazz Classics

☐ HAREM, THE
MM 5061 / Oct '94 / Music Masters

☐ HIGH FLY (2CD Set)
Close your eyes / Here's that rainy day / Star eyes / Blues for Edith / Chicago / Time for love / Shiny stockings / Goodbye / Bye bye blackbird / Scrapple from the apple / I thought about you / High fly / If you never come to me / Li'l darlin' / Good bait
JLR 103602 / May '96 / Live At EJ's

☐ INVITATION (Jackson, Milt Sextet)
Invitation / Too close for comfort / Ruby my dear (Take 6) / Ruby my dear (Take 5) / Sealer / Poom-a-loom / Stella by starlight / Ruby / None shall wander (Take 8) / None shall wonder (Take 6)
OJCCD 260 / Sep '93 / Original Jazz Classics

☐ IT DON'T MEAN A THING IF YOU CAN'T TAP YOUR FOOT TO IT (Jackson, Milt Quartet)
Midnight waltz / Ain't that nuthin' / Stress and strain / Used to be Jackson / It don't mean a thing if it ain't got that swing / If I were a bell / Close enough for blood
OJCCD 601 / Feb '92 / Original Jazz Classics

☐ JACKSON, JOHNSON, BROWN AND COMPANY (Jackson, Milt & J.J. Johnson/Ray Brown)
Jaybone / Lament / Our delight / Bag's groove / Watch what happens / My one and only / Jumpin' blues
OJCCD 907 / Jun '97 / Original Jazz Classics

☐ JAZZ SKYLINE, THE
Lover / Can't help lovin' dat man / Lady is a tramp / Angel face / Sometimes I'm happy / What's new
SV 0173 / Oct '97 / Savoy Jazz

☐ LIVE AT THE VILLAGE GATE
Bags of blue / Little girl blue / Gemini / Gerri's blues / Time after time / Ignunt oil / Willow weep for me / All members
OJCCD 309 / May '93 / Original Jazz Classics

☐ LONDON BRIDGE, A
CD 2310932 / '93 / Pablo

☐ MEET MILT JACKSON
They can't take that away from me / Soulful / Flamingo / Telefunken blues / I've lost your love / Hearing bells / Junior / Bluesology / Bubu
SV 0172 / Oct '97 / Savoy Jazz

☐ MILT JACKSON
Wonder why / I should care / Stonewall / My funny Valentine / Nearness of you / Moonray
OJCCD 12 / Mar '92 / Original Jazz Classics

☐ MILT JACKSON & COUNT BASIE BIG BAND VOL.1 (Jackson, Milt & Count Basie Big Band)
9.20 special / Moonlight becomes you / Shiny stockings / Blues for me / Every tub / Easy does it / Lena and Lenny / Sunny side of the street / Back to the apple / I'll always be in love with you / Come back / Basie / Corner pocket / Lady in lace / Blues for Joe Turner / Good time blues / Li'l darlin' / Big stuff / Blue and sentimental
OJCCD 740 / May '93 / Original Jazz Classics

☐ MILT JACKSON & COUNT BASIE BIG BAND VOL.2 (Jackson, Milt & Count Basie)
9/20 special / Moonlight becomes you / Shiny stockings / Blues for me / Every tub / Easy does it / Lena and Lenny / Sunny side of the street / Back to the apple / I'll always be in love with you
OJCCD 741 / May '93 / Original Jazz Classics

☐ MILT JACKSON AT LONDON BRIDGE
CD 23109322 / Jul '93 / Pablo

☐ MONTREUX 1977 (Jackson, Milt & Ray Brown)
Slippery / Beautiful friendship / Mean to me / You are my sunshine / CMJ / That's the way it is
OJCCD 375 / Apr '93 / Original Jazz Classics

☐ MOSTLY MILT
Three little words / Used to be Jackson / Summer knows / Main stem / Take the 'A' train / Things ain't what they used to be / Just squeeze me (but don't tease me)
OJCCD 968 / Jul '98 / Original Jazz Classics

☐ OPUS DE JAZZ
Opus de funk / Opus pocus / You leave me breathless / Opus and interlude
SV 0109 / Oct '97 / Savoy Jazz

☐ ROLL 'EM BAGS
Conglomeration / Bruz / You go to my head / Roll 'em Bags / Faultless / Hey, Frenchy / Come rain or come shine / Fred's mood / Wild man
SV 0110 / Oct '97 / Savoy Jazz

☐ SOUL FUSION (Jackson, Milt & Monty Alexander)
Parking lot blues / Three thousand miles ago / Isn't she lovely / Soul fusion / Compassion / Once I loved / Yano / Bossa nova do marilla
OJCCD 731 / '93 / Original Jazz Classics

☐ SUNFLOWER
For someone I love / What are you doing the rest of your life / People make the world go round / Sunflower / SKJ
ZK 65131 / 8 Sep '97 / Sony Jazz

☐ THAT'S THE WAY IT IS (Jackson, Milt & Ray Brown Quintet)
Frankie and Johnny / Here's that rainy day / Wheelin' and dealin' / Blues in the basement / Tenderly / That's the way it is
MCAD 33112 / Jan '90 / Impulse Jazz

Jackson, Nicole

☐ SENSUAL LOVING
Little dab / I like / Sensual loving / Nobody but you / Tell me how you like it / Don't make me wait / Love come down / Temporary love / Make you mine / Just in case / Good thang / Sooner or later / Family
XECD 4 / Jun '95 / Debut

Jackson, P.J.

☐ P.J. JACKSON
SP 1178CD / Oct '93 / Stony Plain

Jackson, Papa Charlie

☐ PAPA CHARLIE JACKSON VOL.1 1924-1925
DOCD 5087 / '92 / Document

☐ PAPA CHARLIE JACKSON VOL.2 1924-1925
DOCD 5088 / '92 / Document

☐ PAPA CHARLIE JACKSON VOL.3 1924-1925
DOCD 5089 / '92 / Document

Jackson, Paul

☐ MR. DESTINY
SPCD 11 / Aug '95 / Spindle

Jackson, Rebbie

☐ REBBIE JACKSON COLLECTION, THE (Expansion Collector Series)
This love is forever / Friendship song / Eternal love / Open up my love / Always wanting something / Ready for love / Hey boy / Fork in the road / Tonight I'm yours / Sweetest dreams / Centipede
EXCDG 2 / Jul '96 / Expansion

☐ YOURS FAITHFULLY
What you need / Play your game / Yours faithfully / Get back to you / I don't want to lose you / You take me places / Fly away / Once in a life time love / Baby I'm in heaven / Koo koo / Centipede
4897132 / 30 Mar '98 / MJJ Music

Jackson, Rev. Charlie

☐ WAY OVER YONDER
STG 7707 / 1 Aug '97 / St. George

Jackson, Ron

☐ SONG FOR LUIS
Time in a bottle / Reminiscing / Little Nick / Memories of you / I cant' explain / Make someone happy / You / Streike up the band / Sacred love / Little Willie leaps / Visitation / Song for Luis
CHECD 00115 / Jul '96 / Master Mix

Jackson, Ronald Shannon

☐ RAVEN ROC (Jackson, Ronald Shannon Decoding Society)
DIW 862 / Sep '92 / DIW

☐ SHANNON'S HOUSE (Jackson, Ronald Shannon Decoding Society)
DIW 913 / Dec '96 / DIW

Jackson, Steve

☐ HOUSE THAT JACK BUILT, THE (Various Artists)
BDRCD 16 / Sep '96 / Breakdown

Jackson, Wanda

☐ COUNTRY CLASSICS
Jambalalaya (On the bayou) / Let's have a party / Hot dog that made him mad / Fancy satin pillows / Because it's you / I may never get to heaven / Seven lonely days / Mean mean man / Long tall Sally / Fujiyama mama / Whole lotta shakin' goin' on / Yakety yak / Right or wrong / Stand by your man / In the middle of a heartache
CDMFP 6325 / Apr '97 / Music For Pleasure

☐ PARTY
Let's have a party / What in the world's come over you / Right or wrong / I fall to pieces / Rave on / Sweet dreams / Oh boy / Breathless / Sweet nothings / It's only make believe / Stupid cupid / Raining in my heart
306062 / Jan '97 / Hallmark

☐ RIGHT OR WRONG 1954-1962 (4CD Set)
If you knew what I know / Lovin' country style / Heart / You could have had / Right to love / You can't have my love / If you don't, somebody else will / You'd be the first one to know / It's the same world (Wherever you go) / Tears at the Grand Old Opre / Don't do the things he'd do / Nobody's darlin' but mine / Wasted / I cried again / I'd rather have a broken heart / You won't forget about me / Step by step / Half as good a girl / I gotta know / Cryin' thru the night / Baby loves him / Honey bop / Silver threads and golden needles / Hot dog that made him mad / Did you miss me / Cool love / Let me explain / Don'a Wan'a / No wedding bells for Joe / Fujiyama Mama / Just queen for a day / Making believe / Just call me lonesome / Happy, happy birthday / Let me go, lover / Let's have a party / Daydreaming / Heartbreak ahead / Here we are again / I wanna waltz / I can't make my dreams understand / Moner Honey / Long tall Sally / Sinful heart / Mean mean man / Rock your baby / Date with Jerry / (Every time they play) our song / You've turned to a stranger / Reaching / I'd rather have you / Savin' my love / You're the one for me / In the middle of a heartache / Please call today / My destiny / Wrong kind of girl / Kansas City / Fallin' / Sparkling brown eyes / Hard headed woman / Baby, baby, bye bye / It doesn't matter anymore / Lonely weekends / Tweedle dee / Riot in cell block 9 / Little charm bracelet / Right or wrong / Funnel of love / Tongue tied / There's a party goin' on / Lost weekend / Man we had a party / Why I'm walkin / I may never get to heaven / Stupid cupid / Brown eyed handsome man / I cried again / Last letter / Who shot Sam / Slippin' and slidin' / My baby left me / So soon / Window up above / Sticks and stones / I don't wanta go / In the middle of a heartache / Little bitty tear / I'd be ashamed / Seven lonely days / Don't ask me why / I need you now / This should go on forever / Is it wrong / We could / You don't know baby / Before I lose my mind / Tip of my fingers / Let me talk to you / (Let's stop) Kickin' our hearts around / Between the window and the phone / If I cried every time you hurt me / I misunderstood / Let my love walk in / To tell you the truth / Greatest actor / You bug me bad / One teardrop at a time / Funny how time slips away / These empty arms / But I was lying / We haven't a moment to lose / How important can it be / Things I might've been / Little things mean a lot / Have you ever been lonely / Please love me forever / Since I met you baby / May you never be alone / Sympathy / Whirlpool / Pledging my love / What am I living for
BCD 15629 / Mar '93 / Bear Family

☐ SANTA DOMINGO (Her German Recordings)
Ich schau hinunter ins tal / Morgen, ja morgen / Oh lonesome me / Das kommt vom gluck in der liebe / Wer an das meer sein herz verliert / Wenn der abschied kommt / Ohne sterne ist der himmel leer / Doch dann kam johnny / Komm heim, mein wandersmann / Oh blacky joe / Louisiana moon / Der mond ist der freund der verliebten / Vom winde verweht / Abschiedsrosen / Addio my love / Schick ihn nicht fort, daddy / Warum gleich tranen
BCD 15582 / Apr '92 / Bear Family

☐ WANDA JACKSON: CAPITOL COUNTRY MUSIC CLASSICS
I gotta know / Silver threads and golden needles / Cool love / Don'a wan'a / Fujiyama Mama / Making believe / Let's have a party / Long tall Sally / Mean mean man / Tweedle dee / Little charm bracelet / Right or wrong / There's a party goin' on / I may never get to heaven / Slippin' and slidin' / In the middle of a

heartache / This should go on forever / (Let's stop) Kickin' our hearts around / Between the window and the phone / If I cried every time you hurt me / Slippin' / Violet and a rose / Box it came in / Blue yodel No. 6 / Because it's you / Tears will be a chaser for your wine / Both sides of the line / Girl don't have to drink to have fun / My big iron skillet / Woman lives for love / Fancy satin pillows
CDEMS 1485 / Apr '93 / Capitol

Jackson, William

☐ CELTIC SUITE FOR GLASGOW
Bird / Tree / Bell / Fish
CDTRAX 041 / Dec '90 / Greentrax

☐ CELTIC TRANQUILITY
Dove across the water / Light on a distant shore / Harvest of the fallen / Glasgow 1885 / Dear green place unchanged / Molendinar: The spring / Fermentation / Paradise valley, angels's ascent / Landfall / Fish
IR 016CD / Jun '92 / Iona

☐ HEART MUSIC
Lady Amelia Murray's strathspey / Breton march / Wauking o' the faulds / Port lennox / Strike the young harp / John Maclean of lewis / Paradise alley / Angel's ascent / Threefold flame / Air by fingal / Emigrant peak / St Kilda dance / Fair shoemaker / Rose without rue
IRCD 010 / Sep '91 / Iona

☐ INCHCOLM
AKD 037 / Mar '95 / Linn

Jackson, Willis

☐ BAR WARS
MCD 6011 / Sep '92 / Muse

☐ CALL OF THE GATORS
DD 460 / Jul '93 / Delmark

☐ PLEASE MR. JACKSON
Cool grits / Come back to sorrento / Dink's mood / Please mr. jackson / 633 knock / Memories of you
OJCCD 321 / Dec '95 / Original Jazz Classics

☐ WILLIS JACKSON WITH PAT MARTINO (Jackson, Willis & Pat Martino)
60412320622 / 27 Apr '98 / Thirty Two

Jackson, Yvonne

☐ I'M TROUBLE
I'm trouble / Sweet memories / Woman in me / She set you free / No deposit, no return / What I'd do to get your love back / Common, ordinary housewife gone bad / What'cha gonna do about it / If tears are only water / I'm walking out
BLU 10162 / Jun '94 / Blues Beacon

Jacksons

☐ 2300 JACKSON STREET
Art of madness / Nothin' (that compares 2 U) / Maria / Private affair / 2300 Jackson Street / Harley / She / Alright with me / Play it up / Midnight rendezvous / If you'd only believe
4633522 / Jul '97 / Epic

☐ AMERICAN DREAM, AN
5301192 / Jan '94 / Motown

☐ CHRISTMAS ALBUM, THE (Merry Christmas From Motown) (Jackson Five)
Have yourself a merry little Christmas / Santa Claus is coming to town / Christmas song / Up on the house top / Frosty the snowman / Little drummer boy / Rudolph the red nosed reindeer / Christmas won't be the same this year / Give love on Christmas Day / Some day at Christmas / I saw Mommy kissing Santa Claus
5501412 / Nov '96 / Spectrum

☐ DESTINY
Blame it on the boogie / Push me away / Things I do for you / Shake your body / Destiny / Bless his soul / All night dancin' / That's what you get
4688752 / Jul '97 / Epic

☐ DESTINY/TRIUMPH/VICTORY (3CD Set)
Blame it on the boogie / Push me away / Things I do for you / Shake your body (down to the ground) / Destiny / Bless his soul / All night dancin' / That's what you get (for being polite) / Can you feel it / Lovely one / Your ways / Everybody / This place hotel / Time waits for no one / Walk right now / Give it up / Wondering who / Torture / Wait / One more chance / Be not always / State of shock / We can change the world / Hurt / Body
4853192 / 3 Nov '97 / Epic

☐ GOIN' PLACES
Music's takin' over / Goin' places / Different kind of lady / Even though you're gone / Jump for joy / Heaven knows I love you, girl / Man of war / Do what you wanna / Find me a girl
4688772 / Jul '97 / Epic

☐ HISTORIC EARLY RECORDINGS (Jackson Five)
You've changed / We don't have to be over 21 (to fall in love) / Jam session / Big boy / Michael the lover / My girl / Soul jerk / Under the boardwalk / Saturday night at the movies / Tracks of my tears
CPCD 8122 / Oct '95 / Charly

☐ JACKSONS, THE
Enjoy yourself / Think happy / Good times / Keep on dancing / Blues away / Show you the way to go / Living together / Strength of one man / Dreamer / Style of life
4688772 / Jul '97 / Epic

☐ LEGEND BEGINS, THE (Jackson Five & Johnny)
Monologue / We don't have to be over 21 (to fall in love) / You've changed / Tracks of my tears / Saturday night at the movies / My girl / Stormy Monday / Big boy / Jam session / Under the boardwalk / Lonely heart / Michael the lover
306572 / Aug '97 / Hallmark

☐ LIVE
Opening/Can you feel it / Things I do for you / Off the wall / Ben Ben / This place hotel / She's out of my life / Movie and rap / Excerpts / Medley / I'll be there / Rock with you / Ovely one / Working day and night / Don't stop till you get enough / Shake your body down
4668372 / Jul '97 / Epic

☐ SOULSATION (4CD Set) (Jackson Five)
5304892 / Jul '95 / Motown

☐ TRIUMPH
Can you feel it / Lovely one / Your ways / Everybody / This place hotel / Time waits for no one / Walk right now / Give it up / Wondering who
CD 86112 / Jul '97 / Epic

☐ ULTIMATE COLLECTION (Jackson Five)
5305582 / 10 Aug '98 / Motown

☐ VICTORY
Torture / Wait / One more chance / Be not always / State of shock / We can change the world / Hurt / Body
4504502 / Jul '97 / Epic

Jackyl

☐ NIGHT OF THE LIVING DEAD
CDMFN 199 / Feb '96 / Music For Nations

Jacob, Christian

☐ MAYNARD FERGUSON PRESENTS CHRISTIAN JACOB
Remembrance / Tears of sadness / Top down / Playtime / Sergey suite / Our love is here to stay / Here's that rainy day / You don't know what love is / I've got rhythm / Still by me
CCD 47442 / Feb '97 / Concord Jazz

Jacobites

☐ HOWLING GOOD TIMES
Don't you ever leave me / Can't you see / 100 miles from here / Howling good times / Some people / Ambulance / Chelsea springtime / Older women / Margarita / Flying / Don't ever leave me (reprise)
JANIDA 004 / May '94 / Regency

☐ JACOBITES (Sudden, Nikki & Dave Kusworth)
Big store / Kissed you twice / Hurt me more / Jacobites grave / Kings and queens / Silver street / Hanging out the banners / Need a friend / Little bird / Angels in my arms / For the roses
JANIDA 001 / May '93 / Regency

☐ OLD SCARLETT
GRCD 382 / Dec '95 / Glitterhouse

Jacob's Mouse

☐ RUBBER ROOM
Kuff prang / Hawaiian vice / Public oven / James john robert / Foam face / Snivelling / Hostile / Rubber room / Club scare / Domestic / Poltergeist / Blither
WIJ 040CD / Feb '95 / Wiiija

☐ WRYLY SMILERS
Good / Dusty / Group of seven / Palace / Sag bag / Fandango widewheels / B12 Marmites / Three pound apathy / Keen apple / Lip and cheek
JCOB 001CD / Oct '94 / Wiiija

Jacob's Optical Stairway

☐ JACOB'S OPTICAL STAIRWAY
Fragments of a lost language / Naphosisous wars / Chase the escape / Fusion formula (the meetamophosis) / Majestic 12 / Solar feelings / Jacob's optical illusion / Harsh realities / Engulfing whirlpool / Quatrain 72 (Red horizon) / 20 Degrees of Taurus
RS 95079CD / 16 Feb '98 / R&S

Jacobs, Peter

☐ PIANO MUSIC OF BILLY MAYERL
PRCD 399 / Jul '92 / Priory

Jacobsen, Pete

☐ EVER ONWARD
FMRCD 12 / Apr '95 / Future

Jacquet, Illinois

☐ BOTTOMS UP
BB 893 / 24 Apr '98 / Black & Blue

☐ CLASSICS 1945-1946
CLASSICS 948 / 21 Aug '97 / Classics

☐ COMEBACK, THE
BLCD 760160 / Oct '92 / Black Lion

☐ FLYING HOME (The Best Of The Verve Years)
Speedliner / Pastel / Groovin' / Cotton tail / Boot 'em up / Bluesitis / Lean baby / Port of rico / Where are you / Heads / It's the talk of the town / Kid and the brute / Sophia / Honeysuckle rose / Stardust / Las Vegas blues / Achtung / Have you met Miss Jones / No sweat / Flying home
5216442 / Jun '94 / Verve

☐ ILLINOIS JACQUET (Jacquet, Illinois & Wild Bill Davis)
233044 / May '87 / Black & Blue

☐ ILLINOIS JACQUET
Frantic Fanny / Stella by starlight / Satin doll / Banned in Boston / Indiana (back home in Indiana) / Ydeen O / Imagination / How now / Reverie / Pucker up / Satin doll / Ydeen O / How now / Frantic Fanny / Stella by starlight
EK 64654 / Feb '96 / Sony Jazz

☐ ILLINOIS JACQUET AND ALL STAR NEW YORK BAND
JSPCD 212 / Jan '88 / JSP

☐ INTRODUCTION TO ILLINOIS JACQUET 1942-1947, THE
4055 / 24 Apr '98 / Best Of Jazz

☐ JACQUET'S STREET
Rock-a-bye basie / Broadway / Baptiste blues / Jacquet's street / Taps miller / Don't blame me / Indiana / Bottoms up / One o'clock jump / On the sunny side of the street / If you knew what it does to my heart
BLE 591122 / Oct '94 / Black & Blue

☐ JSP JAZZ SESSIONS VOL.1 (New York 1980/2CD Set) (Jacquet, Illinois All Stars/Junior Mance Trio)
Bow jest: *Jacquet, Illinois All Stars* / Limehouse blues: *Jacquet, Illinois All Stars* / G baby: *Jacquet, Illinois All Stars* / Lover come back: *Jacquet, Illinois All Stars* / I cover the waterfront: *Jacquet, Illinois All Stars* / Exactly like you: *Jacquet, Illinois All Stars* / Bow jest: *Jacquet, Illinois All Stars* / Limehouse blues: *Jacquet, Illinois All Stars* / 9-20 special: *Mance, Junior Trio* / Georgia on my mind: *Mance, Junior Trio* / Small fry: *Mance, Junior Trio* / In the evening: *Mance, Junior Trio* / I want a little girl: *Mance, Junior Trio* / Deep: *Mance, Junior Trio* / Ease on down the road: *Mance, Junior Trio* / Smoky blues: *Mance, Junior Trio* / 9-20 special: *Mance, Junior Trio* / In the evening: *Mance, Junior Trio* / I want a little girl: *Mance, Junior Trio*
JSPCD 402 / Sep '97 / JSP

☐ KID AND THE BRUTE, THE
I wrote this for the kid / Saph / Mambocito mio / Kid and the brute / September song / Jacquet's dilemma / Little Jeff / Jacquet jumps / Blue nocturne / On your toes / R u one / JATP conga / It's the talk of the town / Heads
5570962 / 20 Apr '98 / Verve

☐ LOOT TO BOOT
CDC 9034 / Jul '91 / LRC

☐ LOOT TO BOOT
Soft winds / Sweet Georgia Brown / How long / Racquet club / Loot to boot / No sweat / Blues for New Orleans / It don't mean a thing
17131 / May '97 / Laserlight

☐ MAN I LOVE, THE
BB 8652 / Apr '96 / Black & Blue

Jad Fair

☐ HONEY BEE
DRJIM 19 / Jul '97 / Dr. Jim

☐ MONARCHS
DRJIM 20 / Jul '97 / Dr. Jim

Jade

☐ JADE TO THE MAX
Don't walk away / I wanna love you / I want 'cha baby / That boy / Out with the girls / Hold me close / One woman / Give me what I'm missing / Looking for Mr. Do Right / Don't ask my neighbour / Blessed
74321148002 / Feb '96 / Giant

☐ MIND, BODY & SONG
When will I see you again / Every day of the week / Hangin' / What's going on / 5-4-3-2 (Yo' time is up) / I like the way / Do you want me / If the mood is right / Bedroom / If the lovin' ain't good / Let's get it on / It's on / There's not a man / Everything / Mind body and song
74321226052 / 1 Sep '97 / Giant

Jade Bridge

☐ AMBUSH ON ALL SIDES
Bird in flight / Calm lake and Autumn moon / Ambushed from ten sides / Thunder ends the dry season / Journey to Gusu / Horse race / Street procession / Plow is coming / Purple bamboo / Moon reflected at Second Springs / Peking Opera fantasia
HSR 0004 / Mar '97 / Henry Street

Jade Warrior

☐ BREATHING THE STORM
CDR 105 / Mar '94 / Red Hot

☐ DISTANT ECHOES
CDR 106 / Jan '94 / Red Hot

Jadis

☐ ACROSS THE WATER
Touch / In isolation / Daylight fades / Everywhere I turn / Life is all you need / World on your side / No sacrifice
GEPCD 1009 / May '94 / Giant Electric Pea

☐ MORE THAN MEETS THE EYE
Sleepwalk / Hiding in the corner / G 13 / Wonderful world / More than meets the eye / Beginning and the end / Holding your breath
GEPCD 1002 / Dec '93 / Giant Electric Pea

☐ SOMERSAULT
Live this lie / Batstein / Speechless / Losing my fear / Tomorrow always arrives / Falling away / Hear us
DMJAD 001 / Apr '97 / Dorian

Jaffe, Andy

☐ MANHATTAN PROJECTIONS (Jaffe, Andy Sextet)
STCD 549 / '92 / Stash

Jag Panzer

☐ DISSIDENT AGGRESSOR
62292CD / Nov '94 / SPV

☐ FOURTH JUDGEMENT
CM 77172CD / 25 Aug '97 / Century Media

Jager, Martin

☐ PLAYS PIANO RAGS
DOWNTOWN 9213 / Feb '98 / Downtown

Jagged Era

☐ JAGGED ERA, A
Slow motion / Addicted to your lvoe / Gotta be / Wednesday lover / Funny how / Way that you talk / Rest of our lives / I'll be right there / Redady and willing / Ain't no stoppon'
4885402 / 16 Feb '98 / Columbia

Jagger, Mick

☐ PRIMITIVE COOL
Throwaway / Let's work / Radio control / Say you will / Primitive cool / Kowtow / Shoot off your mouth / Peace for the wicked / Party doll / War baby
7567825542 / Sep '87 / East West

☐ SHE'S THE BOSS
Lonely at the top / Half a loaf / Running out of luck / Turn the girl loose / Hard woman / Just another night / Lucky in love / Secrets / She's the boss
7567825532 / Apr '92 / East West

☐ WANDERING SPIRIT
Wired all night / Sweet thing / Out of focus / Don't tear me up / Put me in the trash / Use me / Evening gown / Mother of man / Think / Wandering spirit / Hang on to me tonight / I've been lonely for so long / Angel in my heart / Handsome Molly
7567824362 / Feb '93 / East West

Jagoda, Flory

☐ GRANDMOTHER SINGS, THE (Jagoda, Flory & Family)
GV 155CD / Nov '93 / Global Village

Jagwarr, Don

☐ FADED
Intro / Bad boy / What set U from / Whose is it / Steppin' / Who do you fear / My law / Skank wit' U / Cure / RESPECT / Roll 'em up / She loves me not / Rewind (live) (Outro)
CDPTY 112 / Dec '94 / Priority/Virgin

Jah Children Invasion

☐ DANCEHALL CLASSICS VOL.1
WACKIENY 98001 / 9 Feb '98 / Wackies

☐ DANCEHALL CLASSICS VOL.2
WACKIENY 98002 / 9 Feb '98 / Wackies

Jah Lion

☐ COLOMBIA COLLY
Wisdom / Dread ina Jamdong / Hay fever / Flashing whip / Colombia colly / Fat man / Bad luck Natty / Black lion / Little Sally Dater / Sata / Soldier and police war
RRCD 47 / Jul '94 / Reggae Refreshers

Jah Messengers

☐ REGGAE TIME
HBCD 115 / May '93 / Heartbeat

Jah Red

☐ MR. BOGLE
JR 220561 / Mar '93 / Deleeuwauc

Jah Screw

☐ JAH SCREW PRESENTS DANCEHALL GLAMITY (Various Artists)
RASCD 3117 / Sep '93 / Ras

Jah Shaka

☐ AT ARIWA SOUNDS (Jah Shaka & Mad Professor)
ARICD 20 / Sep '94 / Ariwa/Shaka

☐ COMMANDMENTS OF DUB VOL.1
SHAKACD 824 / Sep '90 / Jah Shaka

☐ COMMANDMENTS OF DUB VOL.9
SHAKACD 872 / Sep '90 / Jah Shaka

☐ DISCIPLES, THE
SHAKACD 871 / Sep '90 / Jah Shaka

☐ DUB SALUTE VOL.1
SHAKACD 940 / Jul '94 / Ariwa Sounds

☐ DUB SALUTE VOL.2
SHAKACD 941 / Jul '94 / Ariwa Sounds

☐ DUB SALUTE VOL.3
SHAKACD 942 / Jul '94 / Ariwa Sounds

☐ DUB SALUTE VOL.4
SHAKACD 953 / Jul '95 / Jah Shaka

☐ DUB SALUTE VOL.5
SHAKACD 954 / Apr '96 / Jah Shaka

☐ FARI SHIP DUB (Jah Shaka & Max Romeo)
SHAKACD 989 / Nov '92 / Jah Shaka

☐ JAH CHILDREN GATHER ROUND (Jah Shaka & Prince Allah)
SHAKACD 952 / Dec '95 / Jah Shaka

☐ JAH SHAKA & THE FASIMBAS IN THE GHETTO
SHAKACD 935 / Dec '93 / Jah Shaka

☐ JAH SHAKA MEETS HORACE ANDY
SHAKA CD947 / Jul '93 / Jah Shaka

☐ MESSAGE FROM AFRICA (Jah Shaka All Stars)
SHAKACD 848 / Sep '90 / Jah Shaka

☐ NEW DECADE OF DUB (Jah Shaka & Mad Professor)
ARICD 116 / Apr '96 / Ariwa Sounds

☐ NEW TESTAMENT OF DUB VOL.2
SHAKACD 936 / Dec '93 / Jah Shaka

☐ OUR RIGHTS (Jah Shaka & Max Romeo)
SHAKACD 951 / Mar '95 / Jah Shaka

Jah Stitch

☐ LOVE AND HARMONY
Autumn season / Autumn season / Natty dread skank / Bummley shuffle / Different fashion / Love and harmony / Music hold you / No love in community / Put on your dancing shoe / Wisest dread / No dog bark / Moving away from the rest of the world
RNCD 2058 / May '94 / Rhino

☐ ORIGINAL RAGGAMUFFIN 1975-1977
Give Jah the glory / African people (3 in 1) / Raggamuffin style / Watch your step youthman / No dread can't dead / Sinners repent your soul / Judgement / Militant man / Real born African / Cool down youthman / African queen / King of the arena
BAFCD 10 / Apr '96 / Blood & Fire

Jah Thomas

☐ INA DANCEHALL STYLE (2CD Set) (Jah Thomas & Barrington Levy)
Praise God: *Jah Thomas* / Dance pon the corner / Dance with me: *Jah Thomas* / Shine eye gal / Happy birthday to you: *Jah Thomas* / Natty dread the traveller / New dress style: *Jah Thomas* / King of Kings / Advice from the doctor: *Jah Thomas* / Natty dread a de general / You no hear: *Jah Thomas* / Keep on dancing: *Jah Thomas* / Living in Jamaica: *Jah Thomas* / She nuh ready: *Jah Thomas* / Cricket lovely cricket: *Jah Thomas* / Best dress: *Jah Thomas & Errol Holt* / Mister Walker: *Jah Thomas* / Nuff boy a imitate: *Jah Thomas*
MRCD 4 / Aug '97 / Midnight Rock

☐ INNA ROOTS OF DUB (Jah Thomas & King Tubby)
RN 7026 / 8 Sep '97 / Rhino

☐ JAH THOMAS MEETS KING TUBBY IN THE HOUSE OF DUB
MRCD 1002 / Aug '96 / Majestic Reggae

☐ JAH THOMAS MEETS SCIENTIST IN DUB CONFERENCE
MRCD 1001 / Aug '96 / Majestic Reggae

☐ LYRICS FOR SALE
RNCD 2071 / Jul '94 / Rhino

Jah Warrior

☐ AFRICAN TRIBES DUB
JWCD 005 / Jun '97 / Jah Warrior

☐ DUB FROM THE HEART
Mount zion gates / Strictly yard music / Herbsman anthem / Spiral echoes / Sound boys chest / Living dub / It's a go dread / Destination revelation / Eye for a eye / Dub from the heart / Strictly yard music / Rastaman chant / Babylon shall fall / Hiding from reality
JWCD 009 / 15 Sep '97 / Jah Warrior

☐ ONE OF THESE DAYS (Jah Warrior & Naph-Tali)
Humane beings / Humane dub / What about the story / What about the dub / One of these days / One of these dubs / Visionary dream / Visionary dub / Pollution / Pollution dub / Ini culture / Culture dub / 22nd book / 22nd dub / Visionary dub / Culture dub
JWCD 008 / May '97 / Jah Warrior

Jah Wobble

☐ CELTIC POETS, THE (Jah Wobble's Invaders Of The Heart)
Dunes / Man I knew / Market rasen / Thames / Gone in the wind / Saturn / Bagpipe music / Third heaven / Star of the east / London rain
30HZCD 001 / Jun '97 / 30 Hertz

☐ HEAVEN AND EARTH
Heaven and earth / Love song / Dying over Europe / Divine Mother / Gone to Croatan / Hit me / Om namah shiva / All life is sacred (part 1) / All life is sacred (part 2)
CID 8044 / Nov '95 / Island

☐ INSPIRATION OF WILLIAM BLAKE
Songs of innocence / Lonely London / Bananas / Tyger tyger / Holy Thursday / Breathing out the world / Swallow in the world / Kings of Asia / Swallow in the world (reprise) / Bob and Harry / Angel / Gateway / Auguries of innocence
ASCD 029 / Sep '96 / All Saints

☐ LIGHT PROGRAMME, THE
Veneer / One in 7 / Night / Appearance and thing-it-itself / Nice cop: nasty cop / Magical thought / Maieusis / 15 dohs / Tranquiliser
30HZCD 003 / 13 Oct '97 / 30 Hertz

☐ PSALMS
185222 / Jul '94 / Southern

☐ REQUIEM
Requiem I / Requiem II / Requiem III / Father / Mother
30HZCD 002 / Jul '97 / 30 Hertz

☐ RISING ABOVE BEDLAM (Jah Wobble's Invaders Of The Heart)
Visions of you / Relight the flame / Bomba / Ungodly kingdom / Rising above bedlam / Erzulie / Everyman's an island / Soledad / Sweet divinity / Wonderful world
9031754702 / Sep '91 / East West

☐ TAKE ME TO GOD (Jah Wobble's Invaders Of The Heart)
God in the beginning / Becoming more like God / Whisky priests / I'm an Algerian / Amor / Amor dub / Take me to God / Sun does rise / When the storm comes / I love everybody / Yoga of the nightclub / I am the music / Bonds of love / Angels / No chance is sexy / Raga / Forever
CID 8017 / 2 Feb '98 / Island

☐ UMBRA SUMUS
Il jevedro il oblanco / Mehemda jajka bubage / Paternal kindness / Moon slowbeat part.1 / Moon slowbeat part.2 / Just a prayer / St. Mary-le-bow / I offer you everything / Organ meditation / Compound / Chela / Umbra sumus part.1 / Umbra sumus part.2 / 4 basses an organ jaki and a train / Mount Zion / Limehouse cut
30HZCD 005 / 1 Jun '98 / 30 Hertz

☐ WITHOUT JUDGEMENT (Jah Wobble's Invaders Of The Heart)
KKUK 001CD / '90 / KK

Jah Woosh

☐ AT LEGGO SOUND
OMCD 31 / Jan '96 / Original Music

☐ BEST OF JAH WOOSH, THE
Wanderer / Reaction / Crooked shank / Famine on the land / Chucky jean / This train / Liberation / Batter ears skank / Judy drowned / Pretty paul / Love brother love / Meditation (dub) / Hey daddy / Love you girl / Freedom / Jah-jah dey dey / Collie sound / Reggae in yu jeggae / Give to get / Si si si, senorita / Peace and love in the ghetto / Keep on knocking / Fire / Tickle you
RNCD 2005 / May '93 / Rhino

☐ CHALICE BLAZE
OMCD 033 / Jun '96 / Original Music

☐ DUB PLATE SPECIAL
OMCD 024 / Jan '93 / Original Music

☐ MARIJUANA WORLD TOUR
Penetrate the works of jah / Live up right / Be on the move / Mariguana world tour / No more shall I roam / I can't hide / Danger to danger / Georgie girl / Mr. tally man / Mr. biah / Music
OMCD 17 / Dec '93 / Original Music

☐ WE CHAT YOU ROC (Jah Woosh & I-Roy)
Thinking cap / Thinking cap / Deck of love / Albert classau / Red nuts and gin / Take heed / There must be a way / Chant freedom / Guns at large / Midnight version / Dr. phibbs / Reggae music / African descendant / Zion sound / Free style / Falling in love / Call on I / Riding melody
CDTRL 296 / Jul '91 / Trojan

Jahson, David

☐ NATTY CHASE
CC 2717 / Apr '95 / Crocodisc

☐ ROOTS OF DAVID
PASCD 001 / 11 Aug '97 / Pickaskill

Jaildog

☐ PUNKROCK, HIPHOP AND OTHER OBSCURE STUFF
N 02512 / Jul '95 / Noise

Jaipur Kawa Brass Band

☐ FANFARE DU RAJASTHAN
KAR 077 / 21 Aug '97 / IMP

Jairo

☐ ARGENTINA MIA...
3019502 / Feb '97 / Last Call

Jakko

☐ ARE MY EARS ON WRONG
Drowning not waving / Are my ears on wrong / Judy get down / I can't stand this pressure / Camera in your eyes / Cover up / Grown man immersed in tin tin / Shout / Sighing for the moon / Happy in the homelands / Tell her / When the taps run dry / Dangerous dreams
RES 110CD / Apr '97 / Resurgence

☐ KINGDOM OF DUST
Hands of Che Guevara / Drowning in my sleep / It's only the moon / Judas kiss
RES 101CD / Apr '97 / Resurgence

☐ MUSTARD GAS AND ROSES
Just another day / Little town / Devil's dictionary / Damn this town / Borders we traded / Perfect kiss / Saddleworth moor / Learning to cry / Handful of pearls / Then and now / Mustard gas and roses / We'll change the world
RES 103CD / Apr '97 / Resurgence

☐ ROAD TO BALLINA
RES 127CD / Jun '97 / Resurgence

Jalal

☐ FRUITS OF RAP
EFA 187052 / Feb '97 / On The One

☐ MANKIND
EFACD 0748 / Sep '93 / On-U Sound

☐ ON THE ONE
EFA 187032 / Mar '96 / On The One

Jale

☐ SO WOUND
SPCD 350 / Jun '96 / Sub Pop

Jam

☐ ALL MOD CONS
All mod cons / To be someone / Mr. Clean / David Watts / English rose / In the crowd / Billy Hunt / It's too bad / Fly / Place I love / Bomb in Wardour Street / Down in the tube station at midnight
5374192 / Jul '97 / Polydor

☐ BEAT SURRENDER
Beat surrender / Town called Malice / Pretty green / That's entertainment / Gift / Carnaby Street / Batman / In the city / All mod cons / Modern world / When you're young / Funeral pyre / Private hell / In the midnight hour
5500062 / May '93 / Spectrum

☐ DIRECTION REACTION CREATION (5CD Set)
In the city / Takin' my love / Art school / I've changed my address / Slow down / I got by in time / Away from the numbers / Batman theme / Sounds from the street / Non stop dancing / Time for truth / Bricks and mortar / All around the world / Carnaby Street / Modern world / London traffic / Standards / Life from a window / Combine / Don't tell them you're sane / In the street today / London girl / I need you (for someone) / Here comes the weekend / Tonight at noon / In the midnight hour / News of the world / Aunties and Uncles (impulsive youths) / Innocent man / David Watts / A bomb in Wardour Street / Down in the tube station at midnight / So sad about us / Night / All mod cons / To be someone (didn't we have a nice time) / Mr. Clean / English rose / In the crowd / Billy Hunt / It's too bad / Fly / Place I love / Strange town / Butterfly collector / When you're young / Smithers Jones / Eton rifles / See saw / Girl on the phone / Thick as thieves / Private hell / Little boy soldiers / Wasteland / Burning sky / Smithers Jones / Saturday's kids / Heat wave / Going underground / Dreams of children / Start / Liza Radley / Pretty green / Monday / But I'm different now / Set the house ablaze / That's entertainment / Dream time / Man in the corner shop / Music for the last couple / Boy about town / Scrape away / Funeral pyre / Disguises / Absolute beginners / Tales from the riverbank / Town called Malice / Precious / Happy together / Ghosts / Just who is the 5 o'clock hero / Trans-global express / Running on the spot / Circus / Planner's dream goes wrong / Carnation / Gift / Great depression / Bitterest pill / Pity poor Alfie / Fever / Beat surrender / Shopping / Move on up / Stoned out of my mind / War / In the city / Time for truth / Sounds from the street / So sad about us / Worlds apart / Billy Hunt / It's too bad / To be someone / David Watts / Best of both worlds / That's entertainment / Rain / Dream time / Dead End Street / Stand by me / Every little bit hurts / Tales from the riverbank / Walking in Heaven's sunshine / Precious / Pity poor Alfie / Bitterest pill / Solid bond in your heart
5371432 / 10 Nov '97 / Polydor

☐ EXTRAS
Dreams of the children / Tales from the riverbank / Liza radley / Move on up / Shopping / Smithers Jones / Pop art poem / Boy about town / Solid bond in your heart / No one in the world / And your bird can sing / Burning sky / Thick as thieves / Disguises
5131772 / Apr '92 / Polydor

☐ GIFT, THE
Happy together / Ghosts / Precious / Just who is the five o'clock hero / Trans-Global express / Running on the spot / Circus / Planner's dream goes wrong / Carnation / Town called Malice / Gift
5374222 / Jul '97 / Polydor

☐ IN THE CITY
Art school / I've changed my address / Slow down / I got by in time / Away from the numbers / Batman / In the city / Sounds from the street / Non-stop dancing / Time for truth / Takin' my love / Bricks and mortar
5374172 / Jul '97 / Polydor

☐ JAM COLLECTION, THE (2CD Set)
Away from the numbers / I got by in time / I need you (for someone) / To be someone (didn't we have a nice time) / Mr. Clean / English rose / In the crowd / It's too bad / Butterfly collector / Thick as thieves / Private hell / Wasteland / Burning sky / Saturday's kids / Liza Radley / Pretty green / Monday / Man in the corner shop / Boy about town / Tales of the river bank / Ghost / Just who is the five o'clock hero / Carnation / Great depression / Shopping
5314932 / Jul '96 / Polydor

☐ SETTING SONS
Burning sky / Eton rifles / Girl on the phone / Heatwave / Little boy soldiers / Private hell / Saturday's kids / Smithers Jones / Thick as thieves / Wasteland
5374202 / Jul '97 / Polydor

☐ SNAP
In the city / Away from the numbers / All around the world / Modern world / News of the world / Billy Hunt / English rose / Mr. Clean / David Watts / Bomb in Wardour Street / Down in the tube station at midnight / Strange town / Butterfly collector / When you're young / Smithers Jones / Thick as thieves / Eton rifles / Going underground / Dreams of children / That's entertainment / Start / Man in the corner shop / Funeral pyre / Absolute beginners / Tales from the riverbank / Town called Malice / Precious / Bitterest pill (I ever had to swallow) / Beat surrender
8217122 / Jul '97 / Polydor

☐ SOUND AFFECTS
Pretty green / Monday / But I'm different now / Set the house ablaze / Start / That's entertainment / Dreamtime / Man in the corner shop / Music for the last couple / Boy about town / Scrape away
5374212 / Jul '97 / Polydor

☐ THIS IS THE MODERN WORLD
Modern world / London traffic / Standards / Life from a window / Combine / Don't tell them you're sane / In the street today / London express / I need you for someone / Here comes the weekend / Tonight at noon / In the midnight hour
5374182 / Jul '97 / Polydor

☐ VERY BEST OF THE JAM, THE
5374232 / 13 Oct '97 / Polydor

Jam Band

☐ ROADRUNNER
JBCD 0102 / May '97 / Boyson Inc.

Jam Nation

☐ WAY DOWN BELOW BUFFALO HELL
First time / Sleeping / Awakening / Sunstroke / She moved through the fair / Mekong / Meeting of the people / Harmonix / 454 / Pre-pubescent grand prix / La visite est terminee / Prehistoric (Bone us)
CDRW 36 / Aug '93 / Realworld

Jamaaladen, Tacuma

☐ JUKEBOX
Metamorphosis / Rhythm of your mind / In the mood for mood / Naima / Time a place / Jam-all / Jukebox / Zam Zam was such a wonderful... / Solar system blues
1888032 / Dec '88 / Gramavision

Jamaica FC

☐ HAIL THE REGGAE BOYZ (Like Magic)
202 / 18 May '98 / Century

☐ TRIBUTE TO THE REGGAE BOYZ, A (Various Artists)
Jamaica land we love: *Mikey Melody* / Jah is on my side: *Tony Rebel* / Small axe: *Marley, Bob* / Reggae boyz: *Iley Dread* / Jump up for joy: *Reggie Stepper* / Black gold and green: *Riley, Jimmy* / Moving up: *Yellowman* / Win or lose: *Elliott, Paul* / Jamaica inna France: *Mega Banton* / Jamdown football: *General Trees* / Girls dem scream: *Iya Shanty* / Here come the reggae boys: *He Man* / I am a winner: *Cliff, Jimmy*
CDBRED 150 / 8 Jun '98 / Cherry Red

Jamaican Maroon Music

☐ DRUMS OF DEFIANCE
SFCD 40412 / Mar '93 / Sackville

Jamaicans

☐ BABA BOOM TIME
JMC 200231 / Oct '96 / Jamaican Gold

Jamal, Ahmad

☐ AHMAD JAMAL AND THE ASSAI QUARTET
RR 0042 / Jun '98 / Roesch

☐ AT THE PERISHING/BUT NOT FOR ME
But not for me / Surrey with the fringe on top / Moonlight in Vermont / (Put another nickel in) Music music music / No greater love / Poinciana / Woody 'n you / What's new
MCD 0918 / Apr '97 / Chess/MCA

☐ AWAKENING, THE
Awakening / I love music / Patterns / Dolphin dance / You're my everything / Stolen moments / Wave
IMP 12262 / Apr '97 / Impulse Jazz

☐ BIG BYRD (The Essence Vol.2)
5334772 / Oct '96 / Verve

☐ CHICAGO REVISITED (Live At Joe Segal's Jazz Showcase)
CD 83327 / Feb '93 / Telarc

☐ CROSS COUNTRY TOUR 1958-1961 (2CD Set) (Jamal, Ahmad Trio)
But not for me / Surrey with the fringe on top / Moonlight in Vermont / Music music music (put another nickel in) / Woody 'n' you / Poinciana / Too late now / All the things you are / Cherokee / It might as well be Spring / I'll remember April / Gone with the wind / Billy Boy / It's you or no-one / You don't know what love is / Tater pie / This can't be love / Old devil moon / Sweet and lovely / Party's over / Broadway / Snowfall / Time on my hands / Angel eyes / What is this thing called love / I'll take romance / My funny valentine / Like someone in love / Falling in love with love / Best thing for you / April in Paris / Second time around / Darn that dream
GRP 18132 / 8 Jun '98 / Chess Jazz

☐ I REMEMBER DUKE, HOAGY & STRAYHORN
My flower / I got it bad and that ain't good / In a sentimental mood / Ruby / Don't you know I care (or don't you care to) / Prelude to a kiss / Do nothin' 'til you hear from me / Chelsea bridge / I remember Hoagy / Skylark / Never let me go / Goodbye
CD 83339 / Mar '95 / Telarc

☐ LIVE AT THE PERSHING & THE SPOTLIGHT CLUB
But not for me / Surrey with the fringe on top / Moonlight in vermont / Music, music, music / No greater love / Poinciana / Woody 'n' you / What's new / You don't know what love is / A gal in calico / Ivy / Tater pie / Autumn leaves / This can't be love / Ole devil moon
JHR 73522 / Sep '93 / Jazz Hour

☐ NIGHT SONG
When you wish upon a star / Deja vu / Need to smile / Bad times / Touch me in the morning / Night song / MASH (Suicide is painless) / Something's missing in my life
5303032 / Apr '94 / Verve

☐ PRICELESS JAZZ
New rhumba / On Green Dolphin Street / Poinciana / Best thing for you / Night mist blues / Raincheck / Effendi / Concern / Misty / Whisper not
GRP 98992 / 23 Mar '98 / GRP

Jamal, Khan

☐ THINKING OF YOU
STCD 4138 / Feb '89 / Storyville

James

☐ BEST OF JAMES, THE (2CD Set)
5368982
5581732 / 23 Mar '98 / Fontana

☐ LAID
Out to get you / Sometimes / Dream thrum / One of the three / Say something / Five-O / PS / Everybody knows / Knuckle too far / Low low low / Laid / Lullaby / Skindiving
5149432 / Apr '94 / Fontana

☐ ONE MAN TALKING
CBAK 4049 / Jun '91 / Baktabak

☐ SEVEN
Born of frustration / Ring the bells / Sound / Bring a gun / Mother / Don't wait that long / Live a love of life / Next lover / Heavens / Protect me / Seven
5109322 / Feb '92 / Fontana

☐ STRIP MINE
What for / Charlie dance / Fairground / Are you ready / Medieval / Not there / Ya ho / Riders / Vulture / Strip mining
9256572 / Feb '95 / Sire

☐ STUTTER
Skullduggery / Scarecrow / So many ways / Just hipper / John Yen / Summer songs / Really hard / Billy's shirts / Why so close / Withdrawn / Black hole
7599254372 / Jul '91 / Sire

☐ WHIPLASH
Tomorrow / Lost a friend / Waltzing along / She's a star / Greenpeace / Go to the bank / Play dead / Avalanche / Homeboy / Watering hole / Blue pastures
5343542 / Feb '97 / Fontana

James Bong

☐ C'EST TRES BONG
TKCD 24 / Sep '96 / 2 Kool

James, Bob

☐ 12
No pay no play / Courtship / Moonbop / I need more of you / Ruby Ruby Ruby / Midnight / Legacy
ESMCD 466 / Jan '97 / Essential

☐ ALL AROUND THE TOWN LIVE
Touchdown / Stompin' / At the Savoy / Angela / We're all alone / Farandole / Westchester lady / Golden apple / Kari
ESMCD 449 / Nov '96 / Essential

☐ BEST OF BOB JAMES, THE
CCSCD 807 / Apr '96 / Castle

☐ BJ4
Pure imagination / Where the wind blows free / Tappan zee / Nights are forever without you / Treasure Island / El verano
ESMCD 429 / Aug '96 / Essential

☐ COOL (James, Bob & Earl Klugh)
Movin' on / As it happens / So much in common / Fugitive life / Night that love came back / Secret wishes / New York samba / Handara / Sponge / Terpsichore / San Diego stomp / Miniature
7599269392 / Sep '92 / Warner Bros.

☐ DOUBLE VISION (James, Bob & David Sanborn)
Maputo / More than friends / Moontune / Since I fell for you / It's you / Never enough / You don't know me
9253932 / Jun '86 / Warner Bros.

☐ FOXIE
Ludwig / Fireball / Zebra man / Miranda / Marco Polo / Calaban
ESMCD 464 / Jan '97 / Essential

☐ GENIE...THEMES AND VARIATIONS FROM THE TV SERIES 'TAXI', THE
Brookly heights boogie / Genie / Last chance / Ballade / Groove for Julie / Hello Nardo / Marilu / New York mellow / Night moods / Angela
ESMCD 465 / Jan '97 / Essential

☐ H
Snowbird fantasy / Shepherds song / Brighton by the sea / Walkman / Thoroughbred / Reunited
ESMCD 447 / Nov '96 / Essential

☐ HANDS DOWN
Spunky / Macumba / Shamboozie / Janus / Roberta / It's only me
ESMCD 463 / Jan '97 / Essential

☐ HEADS
Heads / We're alla lone / I'm in you / Night crawler / You are so beautiful / One loving night
ESMCD 430 / Aug '96 / Essential

☐ LUCKY SEVEN
Rush hour / Blue lick / Look alike / Big stone city / Friends / Fly away
ESMCD 446 / Nov '96 / Essential

☐ ONE
Valley of the shadows / In the garden / Soulero / Night on bald mountain / Feel like makin' love / Nautilus
ESMCD 426 / Aug '96 / Essential

☐ ONE ON ONE (James, Bob & Earl Klugh)
Kari / After glow / Love lips / Mallorca / I'll never see you smile again / Winding river
ESMCD 448 / Nov '96 / Essential

☐ PLAYIN' HOOKY
Playing with fire / Mind games / River returns / Organza / Hook, line and sinker / Glass hearts / Night sky / Do it again / Love is where / Are you ready
9362467372 / 23 Feb '98 / Warner Bros.

☐ RESTLESS
Lotus leaves / Under me / Restless / Kissing cross / Storm warning / Animal dreams / Back to Bali / Into the light / Serenissima / Awaken us to the blue
9362455362 / Mar '94 / Warner Bros.

☐ SIGN OF THE TIMES
Hypnotique / Steamin' feelin' / Enchanted forest / Unicorn / Sign of the times / Love power
ESMCD 450 / Nov '96 / Essential

☐ SWAN, THE
Swan / La delaissado / Prospero / Water music / Ensenada madness / Quietly crazy for you
ESMCD 467 / Jan '97 / Essential

☐ THREE
One mint julep / Women of Ireland / Westchester lady / Storm king / Jamaica farewell
ESMCD 428 / Aug '96 / Essential

☐ TOUCHDOWN
Angela / Touchdown / I want to thank you (very much) / Sun runner / Caribbean nights
ESMCD 431 / Aug '96 / Essential

☐ TWO
Take me to the Mardis Gras / I feel a song / Golden apple / Farandole / You're as right as rain / Dream journey
ESMCD 427 / Aug '96 / Essential

James, Boney

☐ BACKBONE
Love you all my lifetime / Bleecker street / Trinidad / Happy home / Blue / Night I fell in love / One autumn night / Just between us / Backbone
9362456112 / Feb '95 / Warner Bros.

James, Brian

☐ BRIAN JAMES
422181 / May '94 / New Rose

☐ READY TO CRACK (James, Brian & Dripping Lips)
ALIVE 029CD / 14 Apr '98 / Alive

James, Carla

☐ SACRIFICE
Sacrifice / Round and round / Love will see us through / My very first lover / Virginia's secret / Something sacred / Oh mother / Things that we all do for love / No one else will do / So what's going on / Actions speak louder
5403782 / Jul '95 / A&M

James, Colin

☐ COLIN JAMES
Five long years / Voodoo thing / Down in the bottom / Chicks 'n' cars / Why'd you lie / Hidden charms / Bad girl / Dream of satin / Three sheets to the wind / Lone wolf
CDV 2542 / Jul '93 / Virgin

☐ COLIN JAMES AND THE LITTLE BIG BAND
Cadillac baby / That's what you do to me / Sit right here / Three hours past midnight / Satellite / Surely (I love you) / Breakin' up the house / No more doggin' / Evening / Train kept a rollin' / Leading me on / Boogie twist (Part 2) / Cha shooky doo
VPBCD 18 / Jan '94 / Pointblank

☐ SUDDEN STOP
Just came back / Keep on loving me baby / Show me / Give it up / Crazy over you / T for trouble / Cross my heart / Just one love / If you lean on me / Sudden stop
CDVUS 20 / Oct '90 / Virgin

James, Danny

☐ BOOGIE IN THE MUD (Southern Swamp Guitar)
Boogie in the mud / Your gravy train came to a screeching halt / Please Mr. Sandman / Devil made me say that / That's right / No yo / Paper in my shoe / Soul and wine / Sick and tired / Lonely feeling / Intrusion / Switchit / Another day / Dark was the night / Tequila / Blue strain / Blue clouds / Crazy cat / Linda Lu / Baby you been to school / Lollypoluza / Appelousa / Peek-a-bou Lou / My river / Corpus Christi / Frosty / High camp
CDCHD 626 / Nov '96 / Ace

James, Elmore

☐ BEST OF THE EARLY YEARS, THE
Dust my broom / I held my baby last night / Baby, what's wrong / I believe / Sinful woman / Early in the morning / Hawaiian boogie / Can't stop lovin' / Make a little love / Strange kinda feeling / Please find my baby / Hand in hand / Make my dreams come true / Sho 'nuff I do / Dark and dreary / Rock my baby right / Sunnyland / Standing at the crossroads / Late hours at midnight / Way you treat me / Happy home / No love in my heart (For you) / Dust my blues / I was a fool / Blues before sunrise / Goodbye baby / Wild about you / Long tall woman
CDCHD 583 / Jun '95 / Ace

☐ CLASSIC EARLY RECORDINGS, THE (1951-1956/3CD Set)
Dust my broom / Please find my baby / Hawaiian boogie (take 1) / Hand in hand / Long tall woman / Rock my baby right / One more drink / My baby's gone / Lost woman blues / I believe / I held my baby last night / Baby what's wrong / Sinful woman / Round house boogie / Dumb woman blues / Sax-ony boogie / Kicking the blues around / I may be wrong, but I think you're wonderful / Sweet little woman / Early in the morning / Can't stop lovin' / Hawaiian boogie / Make a little love / My best friend / Make my dreams come true / Strange kinda feeling / Dark and dreary / Quarter past nine / Where can my baby be / Please come back to me (sho'nuff I do) / Session talk and sho'nuff I do / Sho'nuff I do (alternate take) / Sho'nuff I do / 1839 blues / I got a strange baby / Canton Mississippi breakdown / Standing at the crossroads / Late hours at midnight / Happy home / Sunnyland / Way you treat me / No love in my heart / Dust my blues / I was a fool / Blues before sunrise / Goodbye (baby) / So mean to me / Wild about you baby / Wild about you / Elmo's shuffle
ABOXCD 4 / Oct '93 / Ace

☐ COME GO WITH ME
Baby, please set a date / So unkind / Sunnyland train / Twelve year old boy / My kind of woman / Hand in hand / My baby's gone / Make my dreams come true / Anna Lee / Bobby's rock / Find my kinda woman / Stranger blues / Mean mistreatin' mama / I can't stop loving you / She moved / I'm worried / She done moved / My bleeding heart / Look on yonder wall / Early one morning / Strange angels / It hurts me too / Every day I have the blues / I have a right to love my baby / Standing at the crossroads
CPCD 8205 / Feb '97 / Charly

☐ CROSSROADS
Dust my broom / Look on yonder wall / Mean mistreating mama / Fine little mama / Got to move / Rollin' and tumblin' / Coming home / It hurts me too / Standing at the crossroads / Everyday I have the blues / I done somebody wrong / Pickin' the blues / Anna Lee / Sunnyland train / One way out / Sky is crying
304012 / Apr '98 / Hallmark

☐ ELMORE JAMES
Mean mistreatin' Mama / Dust my broom / Standing at the crossroads / Sky is crying / Coming home / Hand in hand / Held my baby last night / I believe / Pickin' the blues / Done somebody wrong / It hurts me too / Fine little Mama / Rollin' and tumblin' / Look on yonder wall
BN 023 / Feb '97 / Blue Nite

☐ IMMORTAL ELMORE JAMES, THE (King Of The Bottleneck Blues)
Dust my broom / Everyday I have the blues / Sky is crying / I'm worried / Coming home / Stranger blues / Fine little mama / Make my dreams come true / Early one morning / It hurts me too / Mean mistreatin' mama / Shake your moneymaker / Can't stop loving my baby / My bleeding heart / Look on yonder wall / Hand in hand / (I) done somebody wrong / Rollin' and tumblin' / Standing at the crosswords / I can't stop lovin' you
MCCD 083 / Apr '92 / Music Club

☐ KING OF THE SLIDE GUITAR, THE (The Complete Chief & Fire Sessions/3CD Set)
CPBOX 301 / Apr '97 / Charly

☐ LET'S CUT IT (The Very Best Of Elmore James)
Dust my blues / Blues before sunrise / No love in my heart / Sho' nuff I do / Standing at the crossroads / I was a fool / Sunnyland / Canton Mississippi breakdown / Happy home / Wild about you baby / Long tall woman / So mean to me / Hawaiian boogie / Mean and evil / Dark and dreary / My best friend / I believe / Goodbye baby
CDCH 192 / Nov '93 / Ace

☐ MASTER OF BLUES, THE (A Tribute To Elmore James) (Various Artists)
P 250569 / Nov '96 / Icehouse

☐ RAW BLUES POWER
Dust my broom / Look on yonder wall / It hurts me too / Coming home / Sky is crying / Standing in the crossroads / Hand in my hand / Rollin' and tumblin' / Mean mistreatin' Mama / I done somebody wrong / Pickin' the blues / I believe / My bleeding heart
CWNCD 2033 / Jun '97 / Crown

☐ SKY IS CRYING, THE (Charly Blues Masterworks Vol.12)
Sky is crying / Bobby's rock / Held my baby last night / Dust my broom / Baby please set a date / Rollin' and tumblin' / I'm worried / (I) done somebody wrong / Fine little mama / I can't stop lovin' you / Early one morning / I need you / Strange angels / She done moved / Something inside of me / Stranger blues
CDBM 12 / Apr '92 / Charly

☐ SKY IS CRYING, THE
Sky is crying / Dust my broom / Fine little Mama / Can't stop loving you / Done somebody wrong / Rollin' and tumblin' / I need you baby / Something inside me / I'm worried / Early one morning / She done moved / Strange angel / Anna Lee / Stranger blues / Look on yonder wall / Standing on the crossroads / Baby please set a date / Shake your money maker / My bleeding heart / One way out / Make my dream come true / Mean mistreatin' Mama
74321523762 / 29 Sep '97 / Camden

☐ STANDING AT THE CROSSROADS (Charly Blues Masterworks Vol.28)
Anna Lee / Stranger blues / My bleeding heart / Standing at the crossroads / One way out / Person to person / My kind of woman / So unkind / Got to move / Shake your moneymaker / Mean mistreatin' mama / Sunnyland train / My baby's gone / Find my kinda woman
CDBM 28 / Apr '92 / Charly

☐ STREET TALKIN' (James, Elmore & Jimmy Reed)
MCD 5087 / Sep '92 / Muse

James, Ethan

☐ ANCIENT MUSIC OF CHRISTMAS
Bring a torch Jeanette Isabella / From church to church/A virgin most pure/When Christ was bor / This is the truth sent from above / What lovely infant can this be/The Christmas child / Alleluya Christo lubelimus Alleluya / Balo Lammy/Three King's songs / Quem pastores Lauduere/On Christmas night / Now to conclude our Christmas mirth / Seven joys of Mary / Lullay lullay als I lay on yoolis night / Jerusalem gaude/Jesu redemptor omnium / O come O come Emmanuel / Sing we Noel/Goodnight/Christmas bells / Now we make joy / Lulajze Jezuniu/Come shepherds arise / Blessed be that maid Marie/The fleecy care / Canzone di Zampoignari
HNCD 1398 / Oct '96 / Hannibal

☐ WHAT ROUGH BEAST
EFA 121112 / Apr '95 / Moll

James, Etta

☐ BLUES IN THE NIGHT (James, Etta & Eddie 'Cleanhead' Vinson)
Kidney stew / Railroad porter blues / Something's got a hold on me / Medley: at last / Trust in me / Sunday kind of love / I just want to make love to you / Please send me someone to love / Love man / Misty
FCD 9647 / Apr '94 / Fantasy

☐ COME A LITTLE CLOSER
Out on the street again / Mama told me / You give me what I want / Come a little closer / Let's burn down the cornfield / Powerplay / Feeling uneasy / St. Louis blues / Gonna have some fun tonight / Sookie sookie
MCD 91509 / Apr '97 / Chess/MCA

☐ DEEP IN THE NIGHT
Laying beside you / Piece of my heart / Only women bleed / Take it to the limit / Lovesick blues / Strange man / Sugar on the floor / Sweet touch of love / I'd rather go blind
CDBB 9579 / Jun '96 / Bullseye Blues

☐ GENUINE ARTICLE, THE (The Best Of Etta James)
I just want to make love to you / Sunday kind of love / I just want to be loved / I'd rather go blind / Tell mama / Stormy weather / Do right woman, do right man / Security / Miss Pitiful / You got it / It's alright / I found a love / At last / All I could do was cry / Spoonful: *James, Etta & Harvey Fuqua* / Don't blame me / 842-

3089 (Call my name) / These foolish things / If I can't have you: James, Etta & Harvey Fuqua / Something's got a hold on me / Tell it like it is / WOMAN / I never meant to love him / Lovin' arms / My dearest darling
CHD 9361 / Feb '96 / Chess/MCA

☐ GOSPEL SOUL OF ETTA JAMES
KWEST 5403 / Sep '93 / Kenwest

☐ HER BEST
MCD 09367 / Jul '97 / Chess/MCA

☐ HICKORY DICKORY DOCK
Hickory dickory dock / WOMAN / My one and only / I'm a fool / Strange things happening / Hey Henry / I hope you're satisfied / Good rockin' daddy / Sunshine of love / That's all / How big a fool / Tears of joy / Pick up / Market place / Tough lover / Doin' something crazy / Be my lovey dovey / Nobody loves you (like me) / You know what I mean / Dance with me Henry / Baby baby every night / We're in love
CDCHM 680 / 30 Mar '98 / Ace

☐ LATE SHOW, THE (James, Etta & Eddie 'Cleanhead' Vinson)
Cleanhead blues / Old maid boogie / Home boy / Cherry red / Baby, what you want me to do / Sweet little angel / I'd rather go blind / Teach me tonight / Only women bleed / He's got the whole world in his hands
FCD 96552 / Apr '94 / Fantasy

☐ LIFE LOVE AND THE BLUES
Born under a bad sign / I want to ta ta you baby / Running out of lies / Inner city blues / Spoonful / Life love & the blues / Hoochie coochie gal / Cheating in the nest room / If you want to stay / Love you save may be your own / I'll take care of you / Here I am (come and take me)
01005821622 / 20 Jul '98 / Private Music

☐ LIVE FROM SAN FRANCISCO
01005821252 / Feb '95 / Private Music

☐ LOVE'S BEEN ROUGH ON ME
Rock / Cry like a rainy day / Love's been rough on me / Love it or leave it alone / Don't touch me / Hold me / If I had any pride left at all / I can give you everything / I've been loving you too long / Done in the dark
01005821402 / Apr '97 / Private Music

☐ MULTI-CULTURAL CHILDREN'S SONGS
SFWCD 45045 / Nov '95 / Smithsonian Folkways

☐ MYSTERY LADY
Don't explain / You've changed / Man I love / I don't stand a ghost of a chance with you / Embraceable you / How deep is the ocean / (I'm afraid) The masquerade is over / Body and soul / Very thought of you / Lover man / I'll be seeing you
01005821142 / Apr '94 / Private Music

☐ R & B DYNAMITE
WOMAN / Number one / I'm a fool / Strange things happening / Hey Henry / I hope you're satisfied / Good rockin' daddy / Sunshine of love / That's all / How big a fool / Market place / Tough lover / Do be my lovey dovey / Nobody loves you (like me) / Hickory dickory dock / You know what I mean / Wallflower / Baby, baby, every night / We're in love / Tears of joy / Pick-up
CDCH 210 / Nov '93 / Ace

☐ RESPECT YOURSELF
IMP 304 / Apr '96 / IMP

☐ SOMETHING'S GOT A HOLD
I just want to make love to you / If I can't have you: James, Etta & Harvey Fuqua / Spoonful / Something's got a hold on me / Street of tears / Stop the wedding / Pushover / Pay back / Two sides to every story / Baby what you want me to do / I wish someone would care / Do I make myself clear / I prefer you / I'd rather go blind / Tell mama / Security / Woman / You can leave your hat on / God's song (that's why I love mankind) / Gonna have some fun tonight
CDRB 3 / Apr '94 / Charly

☐ SOULFUL MISS PEACHES
Tell Mama / I'd rather go blind / Security / I'm loving you more everyday / Mellow fellow / In the basement / Love of my man / Same rope / I'm gonna take what he's got / Just a little bit / Steal away / I'm waiting for Charlie to come home / You got it / Almost persuaded / I got you babe / Losers weepers / All the way down / Let's burn down the cornfield / Feelin' uneasy / Out on the street again
CPCD 8017 / Feb '94 / Charly

☐ STICKIN' TO MY GUNS
Whatever gets you through the night / Love to burn / Blues don't care / Your good thing is about to end / Get funky / Beware / Out of the rain / Stolen affection / Fool in love / I've got dreams to remember
IMCD 191 / Jul '94 / Island

☐ THESE FOOLISH THINGS
Only time will tell / I want to be loved (but only by you) / Prisoner of love / How do you speak to an angel / These foolish things / You can't talk to a fool / Again / Tommorrow night / Don't take your love from me / Lover man (oh, where can he be) / Don't blame me / I won't cry anymore / Tell it like it is / Hold back the tears
MCD 09354 / Apr '97 / Chess/MCA

James Gang

☐ JAMES GANG RIDES AGAIN
Funk no. 49 / Funk no. 49 / Woman / Closet queen- gal (gather to the wind (the bomber medley) / Tend my garden / Garden gate / There's gonna be a party / Thanks / Ashes, the rain and I
BGOCD 121 / Sep '91 / Beat Goes On

☐ LIVE IN CONCERT
Stop / You're gonna need me / Take a look around / Tend my garden / Ashes, the rain and I / Walk away / Lost woman
BGOCD 120 / Sep '91 / Beat Goes On

☐ THIRDS
Walk away / Walk away / Things I could be / Dreamin' in the country / It's all the same / Midnight man / Again / White man-black man / Live my life again
BGOCD 119 / Nov '91 / Beat Goes On

☐ YER ALBUM
Take a look around / Bluebird / Stone rap / I don't have the time / Fred / Funk / Lost woman / Collage / Wrapcity in English / Stop
BGOCD 60 / Oct '90 / Beat Goes On

James, Harry

☐ 1948 - BROADCASTS (James, Harry Orchestra)
JH 1007 / Oct '91 / Jazz Hour

☐ 1964 LIVE IN THE HOLIDAY BALLROOM (James, Harry Orchestra)
Ciribiribin / Cubana chant / In a mellow tone / Sultry serenade / I'm getting sentimental over you / Koo koo / Flyin' home / Two o'clock jump / Drum solo by Buddy Rich / Malaguena Salerosa / Blues inside out / Sunday morning / My game now / Tuxedo junction / King Porter stomp / Big time / Rainbow kiss
JH 1001 / Apr '92 / Jazz Hour

☐ ALL OR NOTHING AT ALL (James, Harry & Frank Sinatra)
Ciribiribin / My buddy / Avalon / All or nothing at all / Mean to me / Melancholy mood / I found a new baby / From the bottom of my heart / Sweet Georgia Brown / To you / I poured my heart into a song / Japanese sandman / Here comes the night / Undecided / On a little street in Singapore / Let's disappear / I'm forever blowing bubbles
HCD 263 / Nov '95 / Hindsight

☐ BANDSTAND MEMORIES (James, Harry Orchestra)
Ciribiribin / Ciribiribin / Begin the beguine / Limehouse blues / Some of these days / I surrender dear / King porter stomp / Don't worry 'bout me / Star dust / Fannie may / Wishing (will make it so) / All of me / If I didn't care / Lamp is low / My love for you / Moon love / Two o'clock jump / This is no dream / When you wish upon a star / How high the moon / Alice blue gown / When the swallows come back to capistrano / Interview with harry james / Afraid to say hello / Skylark / Carnival of venice / One dozen roses / I've heard that song before / I had the craziest dream / You made me love you / Mister five by five / Strictly instrumental / A sleepy lagoon / Daybreak / I'll be with you in apple blossom time / Jump sauce / Ain't misbehavin' / Prince charming / Jalousie / Chelsea bridge / Where or when / It's been so long / Moten swing / 9.20 special / Loveless love / St. louis blues / I'll get by / On the alamo / It could happen to you / Cherry / Flatbush flanigan / Home / I'll walk alone / If I loved you / 1160 p.m. / Oh lady be good / I'm beginning to see the light / I'll buy that dream / Perdido / I'm always chasing rainbows / It's the talk of the town / Zanzibar / Deep purple / Caravan
HBCD 503 / Nov '94 / Hindsight

☐ BEST OF HARRY JAMES, THE
1509546272 / 27 Apr '98 / Intersound

☐ BIG JOHN SPECIAL 1948-1949
Big john special / Cherry / Don't cha go 'way mad / Stardust / Bluebeard blues / Slap happy / Forgotten / Body and soul / Cheek to cheek / Rank Frank / Ultra / Except February which has 28 / Hurry hurry hurry / On Moonlight Bay / Lament and Mon / Sleepy home gal / Block party / Down by the station / Bells / Things ain't what they used to be / Circus days / So tired / Two o'clock jump / Redigal jump / Six two and even
HEPCD 24 / 15 Jun '98 / Hep

☐ CLASSICS 1937-1939
CLASSICS 903 / Nov '96 / Classics

☐ CLASSICS 1939
CLASSICS 936 / Jun '97 / Classics

☐ CLASSICS 1939-1940
CLASSICS 970 / 5 Jan '98 / Classics

☐ DREAM DUO, THE (James, Harry & Betty Grable)
VJB 19482 / Nov '96 / Vintage Jazz Band

☐ GREAT HARRY JAMES, THE
How high the moon / Blue skies / Come rain or come shine / My old flame / What is this thing called love / I may be wrong (but I think you're wonderful) / Between the devil and the deep blue sea / All me / Don't get around much anymore / I cover the waterfront / Man I love / If I had you
HCD 334 / Apr '96 / Hindsight

☐ HARRY JAMES & HIS GREAT VOCALISTS
I'll get by / I don't want to walk without you / It's the dreamer in me / One dozen roses / My silent love / I had the craziest dream / I've heard that song before / I'm beginning to see the light / It's been a long, long time / I can't begin to tell you / Who's sorry now / This is always / As long as I'm dreaming / You can do no wrong / What am I gonna do about you / You'll never know
CK 66371 / Jul '95 / Columbia

☐ HARRY JAMES & HIS MUSIC MAKERS 1942-1944
VJB 1945 / May '96 / Vintage Jazz Band

☐ HARRY JAMES 1943-1946
If that's the way you want it, baby / Indiana / Body and soul / I'm satisfied / I couldn't sleep a wink last night / Rose room / All of me / Shorty George / On the sunny side of the street / Between the devil and the deep blue sea / Stardust / It's been so long / My baby just cares for me / Girl of my dreams / You go to my head / Shady lady bird
HCD 102 / Jul '96 / Hindsight

☐ HAVE TRUMPET, WILL TRAVEL
CECD 10 / Mar '96 / Collector's Edition

☐ JAZZ MASTERS
5299022 / 5 May '98 / Verve

☐ JUMP SAUCE (James, Harry & His Music Makers)
VNG 201 / Jul '94 / Viper's Nest

☐ LIVE FROM CLEARWATER VOL.1
DAWE 76 / Jul '96 / Magic

☐ LIVE FROM CLEARWATER VOL.2
DAWE 77 / Jul '96 / Magic

☐ LIVE IN CONCERT (James, Harry & His Music Makers)
Opener / King size blues / Shiny stockings / Harry's delight / Two o'clock jump / Jumpin' at the woodside / One on the house / Rockin' in rhythm / Don't get around much anymore / Tweet tweet
DBCD 03 / Jul '89 / Dance Band Days

☐ LIVE IN HI-FI AT CULVER CITY 1945 (James, Harry Orchestra)
JH 3006 / Mar '97 / Jazz Hour

☐ LIVE IN LONDON
Don't be blue / Moonglow / Opus / That's all / Charade / HJ blues / Apples / Two o'clock jump / Hits medley
JASMCD 2533 / Feb '95 / Jasmine

☐ MISTER TRUMPET (James, Harry & His Band)
Sheik of araby / And the angels sing / Sweet's fun / More than you know / Hot lips / Jazz me blues / When it's sleepy time down south / Don't be that way / Back home again in indiana / When the saints go marching in
HCD 702 / Jul '94 / Hindsight

☐ MUSIC MAKER, THE
Music makers / James Session / I cried for you / My melancholy baby / Ciribiribin / Nobody knows the trouble I've seen / I'll get by / Trumpet Rhapsody / From the bottom of my heart / Carnival of Venice / Here comes the night / Let me up / Two o'clock jump / Ol' man river / Sleepy time gal / Estrellita / Flight of the bumble bee / By the sleepy lagoon / All or nothing at all / You made me love you
RAJCD 805 / Dec '97 / Empress

☐ RARE 1940 VARSITY TITLES (James, Harry & Dick Haynes)
FLYCD 943 / Jun '95 / Flyright

☐ RAZZLE DAZZLE
Carnival of Venice / (Back home again in India) / I've heard that song before / Texas chatter / Eli-Eli / Trumpet blues and cantabile / Song of the wanderer / Back beat boogie / Duke's mixture / Record session / Concerto for trumpet / Flight of the bumble bee / Cherry / Trumpet rhapsody / Little bit of heaven / Let me up / I cried for you / Flat bush Flanagan / Sleepy time gal / Memphis blues
PASTCD 7044 / May '94 / Flapper

☐ STOMPIN' AT THE SAVOY (James, Harry Orchestra)
Bluebeard's blues / Lady was moody / Shine / Lament d'amour / King porter stomp / Roach and I / Roly poly / Stomping at the savoy / Arrival time / Snooty fruity
15771 / Jul '92 / Laserlight

☐ THERE THEY GO 1948-1949 (James, Harry Orchestra)
FSCD 2014 / Jan '97 / Fresh Sound

☐ YES INDEED
All or nothing at all: James, Harry & Frank Sinatra / Back beat boogie / Boo-woo / Ciribiribin / Everybody's laughing: James, Harry & Billie Holiday / Flash / I found a new baby / I had the craziest dream: James, Harry & Helen Forrest / Jubilee: James, Harry & Helen Humes / Just a mood / Life goes to a party / Night special / Nobody knows the trouble I've seen / One o'clock jump / Out of nowhere / Shoe shiner's drag / Spreadin' knowledge around / Sugarfoot stomp / Two o'clock jump / Woo woo / Wrappin' it up / Yes indeed: James, Harry & Dick Haynes / You made me love you / Zoom, zoom, zoom
CDAJA 5120 / Nov '93 / Living Era

James, Hilary

☐ BURNING SUN
O'er the ocean / Busy old fool / La marche des Rois / Polly Vaughan / Two sisters / Bay of Biscay / Lascia ch'io Pianga / Seeds of love / Lonesome day / Les Berceaux / March borrowed from April / Sail away
ACS 016CD / Jun '97 / Acoustics

☐ CHILDREN'S FAVOURITES - MUSICAL MYSTERY TOUR (James, Hilary & Simon Mayor)
Snowman's song / Magpie sitting on a broken chair / Parrot song / Chico the bandit / My bike / Big grey pussycat / Gypsy slimy trout / Road to Banbury / Old Dan Tucker's song / Give me a drum / Trumpet hornpipe / Fireman's song / Fat farmer / Farmyard tango / Gobble gobble gobble gobble gobble / Fuzzy Wastelot and the Right Royal rubbish dump / Australian Santa Claus / Sally Ann Johnson / Up in a big balloon
ACS 002CD / Aug '93 / Acoustics

☐ CHILDREN'S FAVOURITES FROM THE MUSICAL MYSTERY TOUR (James, Hilary & Simon Mayor)
CDACS 011 / May '98 / Acoustics

☐ LOVE, LUST AND LOSS (James, Hilary & Beryl Marriott)
ACS 029CD / May '97 / Acoustics

James, Jan

☐ COLOR OF THE ROSE
Mississipi man / To believe / Color of the rose / Come runnin' back / Down the river / Dance / Middle of fate / Shake / Treasure me / Please forgive me / Don't try to chain me down / Good woman / If I held on to you / Guilty man / Waste of my time
PRD 70862 / Feb '96 / Provogue

☐ LAST TRAIN
PRD 70702 / Feb '95 / Provogue

☐ SOUL DESIRE
PRD 70992 / Mar '97 / Provogue

James, Jimmy

☐ BEST OF JIMMY JAMES & THE VAGABONDS, THE (I'll Go Where Your Music Takes Me) (James, Jimmy & The Vagabonds)
I'll go where your music takes me / Chains of love / You don't stand a chance (if you can't dance) / Now is the time / Do the funky conga / Never had this dream before / Hey girl / I am somebody / Dancin' to the music of love / If you think that funk is junk you're drunk / Till I can't take it anymore / I can't stop my feet from dancing / Let's go disco / Disco fever / Whatever happened with the love we knew / Life
HTCD 50 / 20 Apr '98 / Hot Productions

☐ VAGABOND KING
Hi diddley dee dum dum (it's a good feeling) / I feel alright / I wanna be (your everything) / Come to me softly / This heart of mine / I wanna be your / You give me a fool for you / Ain't no big thing / Do it right / Ain't love good, ain't love proud / Don't know what I'm gonna do / I can't get back home to my baby / Hungry for love / Never like this before / Little boy blue / It's growing / Wear it on our face / Courage ain't strength / No good to cry / Four walls / Good day sunshine / Cry like a baby / (I believe) love is a doggone good thing / Everybody loves a winner / If you're gonna love me, love me / Better by far / Who could be loving you / Red red wine
NEMCD 942 / Jul '97 / Sequel

James, John

☐ SKY IN MY PIE/HEAD IN THE CLOUDS
And Sam came too / Sailor's farewell / Mammy o'mine / Easy street / Out on the rolling sea / Sky in my pie / Conquistador / Bach goes to town / Kicking up the dust / Nola / Quiet days / Weeping widow / Blap bam boom / Be mine or run / Turn your face / Georgemas Junction / Black and white rag / Head in the clouds / Slow drag / Wormwood tangle / Stranger in the world / Rags to riches / Blues for Felix / Heliotrope bouquet / Secrets in the sky / Stretching of a young girl's heart
ESMCD 358 / Jan '96 / Essential

James, Joni

☐ LET THERE BE LOVE
Let there be love / You're my everything / You're fooling someone / Am I in love / My love, my love / Purple shades / Almost always / I'll be seeing you / When we come of age / These foolish things / It's talk of the town / Too late now / In love with / That old feeling / I'm through with love / Little girl blue
JASCD 316 / Jan '95 / Jasmine

James, Josie

☐ CANDLES
Tell me / I don't wanna lose it / Candles / Looking for a man / Win your love / All over me / Take a little time / After the love / This time / Back in my arms / Cry
XECD 7 / Feb '96 / Expansion

James, Laurence

☐ THEATRE ORGAN, THE (Wurlitzer & Compton Theatre Organs) (James, Laurence/Ronald Curtis)
Whispering: Curtis, Ronald / Lullaby of the leaves: Curtis, Ronald / Alone: Curtis, Ronald / Five foot two, eyes of blue: Curtis, Ronald / Autumn concerto: Curtis, Ronald / Lover: Curtis, Ronald / Only make believe/Why do I love you: Curtis, Ronald / Caribbean honeymoon: Curtis, Ronald / Nightingale sang in Berkeley Square: Curtis, Ronald / Fairy rose: Curtis, Ronald / Top hat, white tie and tails: Curtis, Ronald / Funiculi, funicula: Curtis, Ronald / What a perfect combination: Curtis, Ronald / Over the rainbow: Curtis, Ronald / Falling in love with love: Curtis, Ronald / Bye bye blues: Curtis, Ronald / I know that you know: James, Laurence / It's the talk of the town: James, Laurence / Goody goody: James, Laurence/Roses in the dark: James, Laurence / Lazy river: James, Laurence / I know why: James, Laurence / Tuxedo junction: James, Laurence / won't dance: James, Laurence / All the things you are: James, Laurence / Alley cat: James, Laurence / Walkin' my baby back home: James, Laurence / After you've gone: James, Laurence
CDSDL 392 / Aug '91 / Saydisc

James, Paul

☐ ACOUSTIC BLUES
SP 1133CD / Oct '93 / Stony Plain

☐ ROCKIN' THE BLUES
SP 1135CD / Oct '93 / Stony Plain

James, Rick

☐ GREATEST HITS
Super freak / You turn me on / You and I / Mary Jane / Ebony eyes / Give it to me baby / Dance wit' me / Cold blooded / 17
5516392 / Sep '96 / Spectrum

James, Sian

☐ CYSGODION KARMA
Dacw 'ngharîad / Marchnad Llangollen / Mynwent eglwys / Ffarwel i ddociau lerpwl / Hiraeth am feirion / Going south / Camu nol (wrth gamu 'mlaen) / Merch ifanc o'n ben bore / Sgerbwd ar y bryn / Fy ngeneth fach / Mae'r rhod yn troi / Ev chistr 'ta laou
SAIN 4037CD / Aug '94 / Sain

☐ DI GWSG
Crac / Pan ddo'i adre' noi / Baban / Swynwr / Rhiannon / Ac'rwyt ti'n mynd / Fflyff ar nodwydd / Mae'r ffynnon yn sych / Mae'r Bore'r un mor bwsig / Fy ngeneth fach / Di gwsg / Mae'r mor yn faith
SCD 2153 / Sep '97 / Sain

☐ DISTAW
Branwen a blodeuwedd / Dy buro dl / Lloer dirion / Tincar gwynt y de / Pam na ga'l / Yr eneth glaf / Ac mae'r ffordd yn hir / Enaid ar ffo / Gwyliwch y ferch / Yr eneth gadd ei gwrthod (the rejected maiden) / Distaw
SAIN 2025CD / Aug '94 / Sain

☐ GWEINI TYMOR
Y gog lwydlas / Aderyn pur / Y gwydd / Merch ei mam / Peth mawr ydy cariad / Ei di'r deryn du / Si hei lwli / Cariad cyntaf / Deio bach / Mi fum yn gweini tymor / Mwynen merch / Ffarwel i langyelach lon / Broga bach
SCD 2145 / Feb '97 / Sain

James, Skip

☐ COMPLETE 1931 RECORDINGS
DOCD 5005 / Feb '92 / Document

☐ COMPLETE EARLY RECORDINGS, THE
Devil got my woman / Cypress grove blues / Little cow and calf is gonna die blues / Hard time killin' floor blues / Drunken spree / Cherry ball blues / Jesus is a mighty good leader / Illinois blues / How long "buck" / Four o'clock blues / 22-20 blues / Hard luck child / If you haven't any hay get on down the road / Be ready when he comes / Yola my blues away / I'm so glad / What am I to do blues / Special rider blues
YAZCD 2009 / Oct '94 / Yazoo

☐ GREATEST OF THE DELTA BLUES SINGERS
BCD 122 / '92 / Biograph

☐ SHE LYIN'
All night long / Broke and hungry / I'm so glad / Bad whiskey / Cypress grove / Catfish / Goin' away to stay / Crow jane / Devil got my woman / She lyin' / Hard time, killin' floor / Drunken spree / Black gal / Illinois blues / Worried blues / Look down the road
EDCD 379 / Nov '93 / Edsel

☐ SKIP'S PIANO BLUES
EDCD 481 / Oct '96 / Edsel

☐ TODAY
Hard times killing floor blues / Crow jane / Washington d.c. hospital centre blues / Special rider blues / Drunken spree / Cherry ball / How long / All night long / Cypress grove / Look down the road / My gal / I'm so glad
VMD 79219 / Jan '95 / Vanguard

James, Sonny

☐ YOUNG LOVE (Classic Hits Of Sonny James)
RE 21502 / Sep '97 / Razor & Tie

James, Steve

☐ AMERICAN PRIMITIVE
ANT 0030CD / Jul '94 / Antones

☐ TWO TRACK MIND
ANTCD 0024 / May '94 / Antones

James, Tommy

☐ 1960'S FRENCH EP COLLECTION, THE (2CD Set) (James, Tommy & The Shondells)
175342 / Jul '97 / Magic

☐ 25 GREATEST HITS (James, Tommy & The Shondells)
Hanky panky / Say I am (what I am) / It's only love / I think we're alone now / Mirage / I like the way / I can't take no more / Getting together / Out of the blue / Get out now / Mony mony / Somebody cares / Do something to me / Crimson and clover / Sugar on Sunday / Sweet cherry wine / Crystal blue persuasion / Ball of fire / She / Ball and chain / Church street soul revival / Draggin' the line / I'm coming home / Nothing to hide / Love song
4954842 / 6 Jul '98 / EMI Gold

☐ CRIMSON & CLOVER/CELLOPHANE SYMPHONY (James, Tommy & The Shondells)
Crimson and clover / Kathleen McArthur / I am a tangerine / Do something for me / Crystal blue persuasion / Sugar on Sunday / Breakaway / Smoky roads / I'm alive / Crimson and clover (Reprise) / Cellophane symphony / Makin' good time / Evergreen / Sweet cherry wine / Papa rolled his own / Changes / Loved one / I know who I am / Love of a woman / On behalf of the entire staff and management
NEMCD 647 / Nov '93 / Sequel

☐ HANKY PANKY/MONY MONY (James, Tommy & The Shondells)
Hanky panky / I'll go crazy / I'm so proud / Lover / Love makes the world go round / Good lovin' / Say I am / Cleo's mood / Don't throw our love away / Shake a tail feather / Soul searchin' baby / Lots of pretty girls / Mony mony / Do unto me / (I'm) Taken / Nightime (I'm a lover) / Run away with me / Somebody cares / Get out now / I can't go back to Denver / Some kind of love / Gingerbread man / 1-2-3 And I fell
NEMCD 646 / Feb '94 / Sequel

☐ IT'S A NEW VIBRATION (An Ultimate Anthology/2CD Set) (James, Tommy & The Shondells)
Hanky panky / Thunderbolt / Say I am (what I am) / It's only love (tryin' to break through) / I think we're alone now / Mirage / I like the way / Gettin' together / Real girl / Out of the area / Love's closin' in on me / Get out now / Mony Mony / One two three and I fell / Somebody cares / Do unto me / Do something to me / Crimson and clover / (I'm) taken / Sweet cherry wine / Breakaway / Crystal blue persuasion / Ball of fire / She / Radio promo / Gotta get back to you / Come to me / Ball and chain / Church street soul / Adrienne / Draggin' the line / I'm comin' home / Nothing to hide / Tell 'em Willie Boy's a-comin' / Cat's eye in the window / Love song / Celebration / Boo boo don'tcha be blue / Contact / Hold on to him / She cried / Wiggle wobble / World down on your knees / Cheater / Big time operator / We'll have a world / As we go through life / Soul serenade / Pick up / Happy
WESD 203 / 10 Nov '97 / Westside

☐ TOMMY JAMES & THE SHONDELLS (James, Tommy & The Shondells)
Mony mony / Thunderbolt / Gone gone gone / Ya ya / Love's closing in on me / Get out now / Ball and chain / Come to me / Loved one / Makin' good time / Breakaway / I'm alive
WB 885832 / 2 Feb '98 / Disky

Jamieson, Ronnie

☐ AALD NOOST
ATCD 040 / Jul '95 / Attic

Jamiroquai

☐ EMERGENCY ON PLANET EARTH
When you gonna learn / Too young to die / Hooked up / If I like it, I do it / Music of the mind / Emergency on planet Earth / Whatever it is I just can't stop / Blow your mind / Revolution 1993 / Didgin' out
4740692 / Jun '93 / Sony Soho2

☐ RETURN OF THE SPACE COWBOY
Just another story / Stillness in time / Half the man / Light years / Manifest destiny / Kids / Mr. Moon / Scam / Journey to Arnhemland / Morning glory / Space cowboy
4778132 / Oct '94 / Sony Soho2

☐ TRAVELLING WITHOUT MOVING
Virtual insanity / Cosmic girl / Use the force / Everyday / Alright / High times / Drifting along / Didjerama / Didjital vibrations / Travelling without moving / You are my love / Spend a lifetime / Funktion
4839992
4839999 / Sep '96 / Sony Soho2

Jamison, Mac

☐ HOW CAN I EXPLAIN
HBC 1218DAAD / Aug '94 / Heartbeat City

Jamma

☐ JAMMA AND FRIENDS
QRCD 003 / Dec '96 / Quartz

Jammin'Arabs

☐ NEVER BIN SURFIN'
WIGCD 018 / Jun '97 / Alopecia

Jammin' Unit

☐ DEAF, DUB AND BLIND
PLAN 4CD / Mar '97 / Blue Planet

Jams

☐ BASTARDMUSIK
TUT 72156 / Jan '94 / Wundertute

☐ FISCH
JS 004CD / Mar '98 / J Silver

Jamul

☐ JAMUL
GRC 006 / 8 Jun '98 / Growing Concern

Jan & Dean

☐ BEST OF JAN & DEAN, THE
MATCD 329 / Feb '95 / Castle

☐ BEST OF JAN & DEAN, THE
PLSCD 128 / Mar '96 / Pulse

☐ COMMAND PERFORMANCE - LIVE IN PERSON/JAN & DEAN MEET BATMAN (2CD Set)
ONE 186872 / 28 Apr '98 / One Way

☐ GREATEST HITS
Surfin' USA / Barbara Ann / Dead man's curve / I get around / Little old lady from Pasadena / Fun fun fun / California girls / Little Deuce coupe / Honolulu Lulu / Be true to your school / Surf city / New girl in school / Ride the wild surf / Drag city / Linda / Sidewalk surfin'
100702 / May '97 / A-Play Collection

☐ JAN & DEAN STORY, THE
Surf city / Dead man's curve / Ride the wild surf / Help me rhonda / Little deuce coupe / Fun, fun, fun / I get around / Sidewalk surfin' / Drag city / Little old lady from pasadena / Baby talk / Gee / We go together / There's a girl / Cindy / My heart sings / Judy / You're on my mind (crazy joe) / Clementine / Such a good nights dreaming
RNCD 1010 / Jun '93 / Rhino

☐ ORIGINAL, THE
Surf city / Little old lady from Pasadena / Dead man's curve / Drag city / Honolulu lulu / Ride the wild surf / Popsicle / Sidewalk surfin' / You really know how to hurt a guy / Linda / I found a girl / New girl in school / Batman / Tennessee / Anaheim azusa and cucamonga sewing circle book review / Fiddle around / Here they come from all over the world / Surfin' safari
TO 860162 / 2 Feb '98 / Disky

Jan & Kjeld

☐ BANJO BOY
Banjo boy / Mach doch nicht immer soviel wind / Tingelingeling mein banjo singt / Penny melodie / Banjo swing / Itsy bitsy teenie weenie / Blacky and Johnny / Traumen kann man was man will / Viele bunte lichter / Hillbilly banjo / Hello Mary Lou / Sing cowboy sing / O du lieber Augustin / Hazel bleib' da / Ginny oh Ginny / Der kaffee kommt direkt uas Brasilien / Auf meinem alten banjo / Tausen schone madchen / Kommen sie mal nach Kopenhagen / Zwei kleine Italiener / Ich druck die daumen / Sugar boy and honey baby / Lederstrumpf / Piccolina / No no mady / Icht wolt' ein madchen kussen / Hallo Dolly / Hillbilly banjo / Stasera no / Candy girl
BCD 15923 / Dec '96 / Bear Family

☐ TIGER RAG
Tiger rag / Buona sera / When the sints go marching in / Yes sir that's my baby / Grandfather's clock / When Irish eyes are smiling / Tutti frutti / Three bells / Darling Nellie Gray / Waterloo / Down by the riverside / Ballad of Tom Dooley / What you've done to me / I shall not be moved / Heartaches by the number / True true happiness / He's got the whole world in his hands / Born to late / Everybody loves Saturday night / Tell him no / When the red red robin comes bobbin' along / Can anyone explain / In the shade of the old apple tree
BCD 15924 / Dec '96 / Bear Family

☐ TINGELINGELING MY BANGO SINGS
Tingelingeling my banjo sings / Penny melody / St. Louis blues / I can't give you anything but love / Mack the knife / Some of these days / Tisket-a-tasket / Oh Susanna / O mein Papa / Freight train / Carry me back to old Virginny / You are my sunshine / Sweet Sue / Dinah / Oh Susanna / Go down Moses / I love Susi / Polly wolly doodle / Taste of honey / Got no nickel to my name / Ein kuss zum abschied / Vergiss deine tranen / Schick die andern alle weg / Entscheide dich bald
BCD 15941 / Dec '96 / Bear Family

Jan, Anne-Marie

☐ PARALLELES
KMRSCD 214 / Dec '94 / Keltia Musique

Jane

☐ AGE OF MADNESS
RR 7047 / Jun '97 / Repertoire

☐ BETWEEN HEAVEN AND HELL
PMS 7057 / Oct '97 / Repertoire

☐ GERMANIA
Germania / Rock 'n' roll / Revolution / Got no shadows / Cool and collected / Get back to you / No future / I'm so down / Driving me crazy / When I went to the scene / Southern line
PMS 7061 / 24 Nov '97 / Repertoire

☐ JANE
On my way / New man in town / Stay with me / Stop the clock / Rockin' around / Intro / Easy going / Love your life / Dynamite / Cadillac rider
RR 7062 / 24 Nov '97 / Repertoire

☐ SING NO.9
PMS 7058 / Oct '97 / Repertoire

Jane Pow

☐ LOVE IT, BE IT
Sanitized / It's on its way / Walker / Get by / Sand barrier / Shutdown / 90's / Love it, be it / Track 9 / Playpower / Morningside / Out of it / On hold / Through / Latitude / Take / Jack Boot / Warm room / Bophia Green / Fruity
SLUM 025 / Jul '93 / Slumberland

Jane's Addiction

☐ JANE'S ADDICTION
Trip away / Rock 'n' roll / I would for you / Jane says / Pigs in zen / My time / Whores / Sympathy / Chip away / 1%
7599265992 / Dec '96 / WEA

☐ KETTLE WHISTLE
Kettle whistle / Ocean size / Maceo / Hadadad / So what / Jane says / Mountain song / Slow divers / Three days / Ain't no right / Up the beach / Stop / Been caught stealing / Whores / City
9362467522 / 1 Dec '97 / WEA

☐ NOTHING'S SHOCKING
Up the beach / Had a dad / Standing in the shower / Jane Says / Thank you boys / Mountain song / Summertime rolls / Ted, just admit it / Ocean size / Idiots rule / Pigs in Zen
K9257272 / Mar '94 / WEA

☐ RITUAL DE LO HABITUAL
Stop / No one's leaving / Ain't no right / Obvious / Been caught stealing / Three days / Then she did / Of course / Classic girl
7599259932 / Feb '95 / WEA

Jang, Jon

☐ ISLAND (The Immigrant Suite No.1)
1213032 / Dec '97 / Soul Note

☐ SELF DEFENSE (Jang, Jon & the Pan-Asian Arkestra)
1212032 / Nov '92 / Soul Note

☐ TIANANMEN (Jang, Jon & the Pan-Asian Arkestra)
1212232 / Nov '93 / Soul Note

☐ TWO FLOWERS ON A STEM (Jang, Jon Sextet)
1212532 / Oct '96 / Soul Note

Janis, Conrad

☐ CONRAD JANIS & HIS TAILGATE JAZZ BAND VOL.1 (Janis, Conrad Tailgate Jazz Band)
BCD 71 / Jun '95 / GHB

☐ CONRAD JANIS & HIS TAILGATE JAZZ BAND VOL.2 (Janis, Conrad Tailgate Jazz Band)
BCD 81 / Nov '96 / GHB

Janitors Against Apartheid

☐ 1 IN 3000 NERDS CAN'T BE WRONG (Janitors Against Apartheid/One Eye Open)
DILL 016 / 2 Mar '98 / Dill

Jankowski, Horst

☐ BEST OF MR. BLACK FOREST, THE
ISCD 108 / Jun '95 / Intersound

☐ PIANO INTERLUDE
ISCD 147 / Jun '95 / Intersound

Jannah, Denise

☐ TAKE IT FROM THE TOP
Pennies from Heaven / Willow weep for me / Fragile / I've got the world on a string / I'm in a minor key today / I get along without you very well / Groovin' high / I'm a fool to want you / Sleepin' bee / My funny valentine
CDSJP 308 / Jan '92 / Timeless Jazz

Janovitz, Bill

☐ LONESOME BILLY
Girl's club / Think of all / Shoulder / Gaslight / Ghost in my piano / Strangers / My funny valentine / Peninsula / Talking to the Queen / Red balloon
BBQCD 186 / Dec '96 / Beggars Banquet

Jansch, Bert

☐ BERT AND JOHN (Jansch, Bert & John Renbourn)
East wind / Piano tune / Goodbye pork pie hat / Soho / Tic-tocative / Orlando / Red's favourite / No exit / Along the way / Time has come / Stepping stones / After the dance / Waggoner's lad / Lucky thirteen / In this game / Dissatisfied blues / Hole in the cole / Bells
HILLCD 8 / Jan '97 / Wooded Hill

☐ BERT JANSCH/IT DON'T BOTHER ME
Oh my babe / Ring a ding bird / Tinker's blues / Anti apartheid / Wheel / Man I'd rather be / My lover / It don't bother me / Harvest your thoughts of love / Lucky thirteen / As the day grows longer now / So long (been on the road so long) / Want my daddy now / 900 miles / Time has come / Soho / In this game / Dissatisfied blues
ESMCD 407 / Jul '96 / Essential

☐ BIRTHDAY BLUES/ROSEMARY LANE
Come sing me a happy song / Bright new year / Tree song / Poison / Miss Heather Rosemary Sewell / I've got a woman / Woman like you / I am lonely / Promised land / Birthday blues / Wishing well / Blues / Tell me what is true love / Rosemary Lane / M'lady Nancy / Dream, a dream, a dream / Alman / Wayward child / Nobody's bar / Reynardine / Silly woman / Peregrinations / Sylvie / Sarabanda / Bird song
ESMCD 519 / Jul '97 / Essential

☐ BLACKWATER SIDE (2CD Set)
Rosemary lane / When I get home / First time ever... / Woe is love my dear / Blackwater side / I saw an angel / Little sweet sunshine / Life depends on love / Running from home / Market song / Wishing well / Tell me what is true love / I loved a lass / It don't bother me / No exit / Bruton town / Casbah / So long (been on the road) / Tinker's blues / Courting blues / Needle of death / Oh how your love is strong / Angie / Poison / Lucky 13 / Peregrinations / Soho / Woman like you / Rambling's gonna be... / Gardener / Tic-tocative / Nobody's bar / Train song / Reynardine / Sweet child / Come back baby / Rabbit run / Strolling down the highway / Go your way my love
SMDCD 153 / May '97 / Snapper

☐ COLLECTION, THE
CCSCD 430 / Mar '95 / Castle

☐ GARDENER/ESSENTIAL BERT JANSCH 1965-71
TDEM 09 / Mar '94 / Trandem

☐ HEARTBREAK
Is it real / Up to the stars / Give me the time / If I were a carpenter / Wild mountain thyme / Heartbreak hotel / Sit down beside me / No rhyme, nor reason / Blackwater side / And not a word was said
HNCD 1312 / Jul '93 / Hannibal

☐ JACK ORION/NICOLA
Waggoner's lad / First time I ever saw your face / Jack Orion / Gardener / Nottamun town / Henry Martin / Blackwaterside / Pretty polly / Go your way my love / Woe is love my dear / Nicola / Come back baby / Little sweet sunshine / Love is teasing / Rabbit run / Life depends on love / Weeping willow / Box of love / Wish my baby was here / If the world isn't there
ESMCD 459 / Jan '97 / Essential

☐ LIVE AT THE 12 BAR
BJ 002CD / Aug '96 / Jansch

☐ MOONSHINE
Yarrow / Brought with the rain / January man / Night time blues / Moonshine / First time ever I saw your face / Ramble away / Twa corbies / Oh my Father
BJ 001CD / Jul '95 / Jansch

☐ ORNAMENT TREE, THE
Ornament tree (bonny portmore) / Banks o'sicily / Rambling boys of pleasure / Rocky road to dublin / Three dreamers / Mountain streams / Blackbird of mullamore / Lady fair / January man / Dobbins flowery vale / Road tae dundee / Tramps and hawkers
D 271365 / Nov '96 / Jansch

☐ RARE CONUNDRUM, A
St Fiacre / If you see my love / Looking for a home / Poor mouth / Cat and mouse / Three chord trick / Lost love / Daybreak / One to a hundred / Pretty saro / Doctor, Doctor / 3 AM / Curragh of Kildare / Instrumentally Irish (per's hose pipe)
CASCD 1127 / Jun '97 / Charisma

☐ ROSEMARY LANE
Tell me what is true love / Rosemary Lane / M'lady Nancy / Dream, a dream, a dream / Alman / Wayward child / Nobody's bar / Reynardine / Silly woman / Peregrinations / Sylvie / Sarabande / Bird song
HILLCD 2 / Sep '96 / Wooded Hill

☐ SKETCHES
COMD 2035 / Feb '94 / Temple

☐ THREE CHORD TRICK
Fresh as Sunday morning / Chambertin / One for Jo / Needle of death / Cluck old hen / Love anew / Lost and gone / Blues run the game / When the teardrops fell / Kingfisher / Daybreak / Doctor doctor / Curragh of Kildare / Looking for a home / Poor mouth / In the bleak midwinter
CDVM 9024 / Jul '93 / Virgin

☐ TOY BALLOON
Carnival / She moved through the fair / All I got / Bett's dance / Toy balloon / Waitin' and wanderin' / Hey doc / Sweet talking lady / Paper houses / Born and bred in old Ireland / How it all came down / Just a simple soul
COOKCD 138 / 30 Mar '98 / Cooking Vinyl

☐ WHEN THE CIRCUS COMES TO TOWN
Walk quietly by / Open road / Back home / On one around / Step around / Step back / When the circus comes to town / Summer heat / Just a dream / Lady doctor from Ashington / Steal the night away / Honey don't you understand / Born with the blues / Morning brings peace of mind / Living in the shadows
COOKCD 092 / Aug '95 / Cooking Vinyl

Jansen, Steve

☐ BEGINNING TO MELT (Medium Series Vol.1) (Jansen, Steve & Richard Barbieri/Mick Karn)
Beginning to melt / Wilderness / March of the innocents / Human agie / Shipwrecks / Ego dance / Orange asylum
MPCD 001 / Sep '96 / Medium

☐ OTHER WORLDS IN A SMALL ROOM (Jansen, Steve & Richard Barbieri)
Remains of a fragile illusion / Light years / Disturbed sense of distance / Breaking the silence / Blue lines / Way the light falls / Distant fire
MPCD 004 / Mar '97 / Medium

☐ PULSE (Jansen, Steve & Yukihiro Takahashi)
Life's like that / Choice / Wave / Memory without consequence / River dry / Prayer of gold
MPCD 7 / 3 Aug '98 / Medium

☐ SEED (Jansen, Steve & Richard Barbieri/Mick Karn)
Beginning to melt / In the black of desire / Insect tribe / Prey
MPCD 002 / Mar '97 / Medium

☐ STONE TO FLESH (Jansen, Steve & Richard Barbieri)
Mother London / Sleeper's awake / Ringing the bell backwards (pt 1 and 2) / Everything ends in darkness / Closer than I / Swim there
MPCD 003 / Sep '96 / Medium

☐ STORIES ACROSS BORDERS (Jansen, Steve & Richard Barbieri)
Long tales, tall shadows / When things dream / Lumen / Insomniac's bed / Night gives birth / Celebration / Nocturnal nightseeing / One more zombie
CDVE 908 / Jul '94 / Virgin

Janson, Claes

☐ ALL OF ME
SITCD 9209 / Mar '94 / Sittel

Jansson, Lars

☐ SADHANA
1264 / Oct '92 / Caprice

Jansson, Lena

☐ EVERYTHING I LOVE
SITCD 9206 / Jun '94 / Sittel

☐ LENA JANSSON & NILS LINDBERG BIG BAND 1983/1986 (Jansson, Lena & Nils Lindberg)
ABCD 3005 / Feb '95 / Bluebell

January's Little Joke

☐ JANUARY'S LITTLE JOKE
BUTCD 3 / Apr '97 / But

Janus Stark

☐ GREAT ADVENTURE CIGAR
Enemy lines / Panic attack / Every little counts / Floyd (What are you on) / Dynamo / White man speaks with forked tongue / Clique / New slant on nothing / 200 Dirty face / Barriers
MOSH 186CD / 11 May '98 / Earache

Janvier, Phillipe

☐ POUR LE COEUR D'UN MARINIER
KMCD 219 / Mar '96 / Keltia Musique

Jaojoby

☐ E TIAKO
LBLC 2533 / 27 Apr '98 / Indigo

☐ SALEGY
XENO 404CD / May '96 / Xenophile

Japan

☐ EXORCISING GHOSTS
Methods of dance / Swing / Gentlemen take polaroids / Quiet life / Foreign place / Night porter / My new career / Other side of life / Visions of China / Sons of pioneers / Talking drum / Art of parties / Taking islands in Africa / Voices raised in welcome, hands held in prayer / Life without buildings / Ghosts
VGDCD 3510 / Jan '85 / Virgin

☐ GENTLEMEN TAKE POLAROIDS
Gentlemen take polaroids / Swing / Burning bridges / My new career / Methods of dance / Ain't that peculiar / Nightporter / Taking islands in Africa
CDV 2180 / Jun '88 / Virgin

☐ IN VOGUE
Unconventional / Lovers on main street / Transmission / I second that emotion / All tomorrows parties / Alien / Halloween / Surburban berlin / Quiet life / Love is infectious / Fall in love with me / Adolescent sex / European son / In vogue / Life in tokyo
74321393382 / Aug '96 / Camden

☐ OIL ON CANVAS
Sons of pioneers / Cantonese boy / Visions of China / Ghosts / Voices raised in welcome, hands held in prayer / Nightporter / Still life in mobile homes / Methods of dance / Quiet life / Art of parties / Temple of dawn / Oil on canvas / Gentlemen take polaroids / Canton
CDVD 2513 / Apr '92 / Virgin

☐ TIN DRUM
Visions of China / Art of parties / Talking drum / Cantonese boy / Canton / Ghosts / Still life in mobile homes / Sons of pioneers
CDV 2209 / Jun '88 / Virgin

Japhet, Paskaal

☐ RAZANA
NDCD 002 / Jun '97 / Night & Day

Japonize Elephants

☐ LA FETE DU CLOUNE
SC 13 / 20 Apr '98 / Secretly Canadian

Jara, Victor

☐ 15 YEARS OF TRADITIONAL PORTUGUESE MUSIC
PS 65111 / Nov '93 / PlayaSound

☐ CANTO LIBRE VOL.2
MCD 71799 / Jun '93 / Monitor

☐ DEJA LA VIDA VOLAR
174392 / 1 Jun '98 / Musidisc

☐ MANIFIESTO
Te recuerdo Amanda / Canto libre / Aqui me quedo / Angelita Huenuman / Ni chichi ni limona / La plegaria a un labrador / Cuando voy al trabajo / El derecho de vivir en paz / Vientos del pueblo / Manifesto / La partida / Chile stadium
ESMCD 657 / 7 Sep '98 / Essential

☐ VIENTOS DEL PUEBLO
MCD 71778 / Jun '93 / Monitor

Jaramillo, Julio

☐ BOLEROS INOLVIDABLES
9944132212 / 3 Mar '98 / Orfeon

Jardemark, Rolf

☐ FURTHER ADVENTURES IN GUITARLAND
IGCD 067 / Aug '97 / Imogena

Jargon

☐ JARGON
LOB 10007CD / 8 Jun '98 / Lobster/Fat Wreck Chords

Jarman, Joseph

☐ AS IF IT WERE THE SEASONS (Jarman, Joseph Quartet)
DD 417 / Nov '96 / Delmark

☐ CONNECTING SPIRITS (Jarman, Joseph & Marilyn Crispell)
CD 964 / Jan '97 / Music & Arts

☐ EGWU ANWU (2CD Set)
IN 1033CD / Jun '97 / India Navigation

☐ SONG FOR JOSEPH JARMAN
Little fox run / Non-cognitive aspects of the city / Adam's rib / Song for / Little fox run
DD 410 / Mar '97 / Delmark

Jarocha, Alma

☐ SONES JAROCHOS (Music Of Mexico Vol. 1) (Jarocha, Conjunto Alma)
ARHCD 354 / Apr '95 / Arhoolie

Jarre, Jean Michel

☐ CHRONOLOGIE
4873792 / Jun '97 / Epic

☐ COMPLETE OXYGENE, THE (2CD Set)
Oxygene / Oxygene 7 / Oxygene 7 / Oxygene 7 / Oxygene 8 / Oxygene 9 / Oxygene 9 / Oxygene 9 / Oxygene 10 / Oxygene 11 / Oxygene 12 / Oxygene 13 / Oxygene in Moscow
4891562 / 24 Nov '97 / Epic

☐ CONCERTS IN CHINA (2CD Set)
Overture / Arpegiator / Equinoxe part 4 / Fishing junks at sunset / Band in the rain / Equinoxe part 7 / Orient Express / Magnetic fields III / Magnetic fields IV / Laser harp / Night in Shanghai / Last rumba / Magnetic fields II / Souvenir of China
4884392 / 29 Sep '97 / Epic

☐ DESTINATION DOCKLANDS (The London Concert)
Introduction / Overture / Revolution industrielle part 1-2-3 / Magnetic fields 2 / Oxygene IV / Computer weekend / Revolutions / London kid / Rendez-vous IV / Rendez-vous II / September / Emigrant
4881432 / 1 Sep '97 / Epic

☐ EQUINOXE
Equinoxe part 1 / Equinoxe part 2 / Equinoxe part 3 / Equinoxe part 4 / Equinoxe part 5 / Equinoxe part 6 / Equinoxe part 7 / Equinoxe part 8
4873762 / Jun '97 / Epic

☐ HONG KONG
Countdown / Chronologie / Chronologie / Hoe old are you / Equinoxe / Souvenir of China / Qu est ce que l amour / Chronologie / Chronologie / Where are you going / Oxygene / Fishing junks at sunset / Sale of the century / Digi sequencer / Magnetic fields / Band in the rain / Rendez vous / Chronologie
4881452 / 29 Sep '97 / Epic

☐ HOUSTON-LYON CITIES IN CONCERT
Oxygene part 5 / Ethnicolour / Magnetic fields part 1 / Souvenir of China / Equinoxe part 5 / Rendezvous part 2-4 / Ron's piece
4873772 / Jun '97 / Epic

☐ IMAGES (The Best Of Jean Michel Jarre)
Oxygene 4 / Equinoxe part 5 / Magnetic fields II / Oxygene 2 / Computer week-end / Equinoxe part 4 / Band in the rain / Rendezvous / London kid / Ethnicolor 1 / Orient express / Calypso 1 / Calypso 3 (fin de siecle) / Rendezvous / Moon machine / Eldorado / Globetrotter
4873782 / Jun '97 / Epic

☐ MAGNETIC FIELDS
Parts 1-5 / Last rumba
4881382 / 1 Sep '97 / Polydor

☐ MUSIC OF JEAN MICHEL JARRE, THE
Oxygene part iv / Equinox part 5 / Magnetic fields / Oxygene part 2 / Computer weekend / Equinox part 4 / Ethnicolor 1 / Moon machine / Eldorado / Globetrotter / Rendezvous / London / Band in the rain / Orient express / Calypso 1 / Calypso 3 / Rendezvous 4
306232 / Jan '97 / Hallmark

☐ ODYSSEY THROUGH O2
Odyssey overture / Oxygene 10 / Oxygene 7 / Oxygene 8 / Oxygene 8 - Hani's 303 / Odyssey phase 2 / Oxygene 8 - Sunday club / Oxygene 10 - 440 dub / Odyssey 11 / Oxygene 11 / Oxygene 12 / Oxygene 8 - Takkyu Ishino / Odyssey finale / Rendezvous '98 / Oxygene 13
4897642 / 11 May '98 / Disques Dreyfus

☐ OXYGENE
Oxygene part 1 / Oxygene part 2 / Oxygene part 3 / Oxygene part 4 / Oxygene part 5 / Oxygene part 6
4873752 / Jun '97 / Epic

☐ OXYGENE 7-13
Oxygene 7:1a / Oxygene part 1:1b / Oxyegene part 2:1c / Oxygene part 3 / Oxygene 8 / Oxygene 9:3a / Oxygene part 1:3b / Oxygene part 2:3c / Oxygene 3 / Oxygene 10 / Oxygene 11 / Oxygene 12 / Oxygene 13
4869842 / Feb '97 / Disques Dreyfus

☐ RENDEZVOUS
First rendez-vous / Second rendez-vous / Third rendez-vous / Fourth rendez-vous / Fifth rendez-vous / Last rendez-vous
4881412 / 1 Sep '97 / Epic

☐ REVOLUTIONS
Industrial revolution overture / Industrial revolution / London kid / Revolution / Revolutions / Tokyo kid / Computer weekend / September / Emigrant
4881422 / 1 Sep '97 / Epic

☐ WAITING FOR COUSTEAU
Calypso / Waiting for Cousteau
4881442 / 1 Sep '97 / Epic

☐ ZOOLOOK
Ethnicolor / Diva / Zoolook / Wooloomooloo / Zoolookologie / Blah-blah cafe / Ethnicolor II
4881402 / 1 Sep '97 / Epic

Jarreau, Al

☐ AIN'T NO SUNSHINE (A Salute To Bill Withers)
Ain't no sunshine / Lean on me / Use me / Kissing my love / Grandma's hands / You / Lonely town / Lonely street / Same love that made me laugh
CDBM 011 / Jun '88 / Blue Moon

☐ HEARTS HORIZON
All or nothing at all / So good / All of my love / Pleasure over pain / Yo jeans / Way to your heart / One way / 1 OK HI / I must have been a fool / More love / Killer love / Heart's horizon
5578512 / 3 Aug '98 / IE

☐ HEAVEN AND EARTH
What you do to me / It's not hard to love you / Blue angel / Heaven and earth / Superfine love / Whenever I hear your name / Love of my life / If I break / Blue in green (tapestry)
9031774662 / Jul '92 / Warner Bros.
5578522 / 3 Aug '98 / IE

☐ HIGH CRIME
Raging waters / Imagination / Murphy's law / Tell me / After all / High crime / Let's pretend / Sticky wicket / Love speaks louder than words / Falling
5578482 / 3 Aug '98 / IE

☐ IMPROVISATIONS
My favourite things / Stockholm sweetnin' / Sleepin' bee / Masquerade is over / Sophisticated lady / Joey / Come rain or shine / One note samba jobim, mendonca-de, hendricks / Ain't no sunshine / Lean on me / Use me / Kissing my love / Grandma's hands / You / Lonely town, lonely street / Same love that made me laugh / Livin' for you / Call me / Here I am / Let's get married / Let's stay together / You ought to be with me / Love and happiness / Tired of being alone / Look what you done for me / I'm still in love with you
CDBM 502 / Nov '96 / Blue Moon

☐ IN LONDON
Raging waters / Black and blue / I will be here for you / Let's pretend / High crime / Teach me tonight / We're in this love together
5578492 / 3 Aug '98 / IE

☐ JARREAU
Mornin' / Boogie down / I will be here for you / Save me / Step by step / Black and blue / Trouble in paradise / Not like this
5578472 / 3 Aug '98 / IE

☐ KINGS OF SOUL (Jarreau, Al & Lou Rawls)
Ain't no sunshine: *Jarreau, Al* / Lean on me: *Jarreau, Al* / Sad song: *Rawls, Lou* / Kissing my love: *Jarreau, Al* / Season of the witch: *Rawls, Lou* / Use me: *Jarreau, Al* / I love you, yes I do: *Rawls, Lou* / I want to be loved: *Rawls, Lou* / Same love that made me laugh: *Jarreau, Al* / Your good thing is about to end: *Rawls, Lou* / Grandma's hands: *Jarreau, Al* / When a man loves a women: *Rawls, Lou* / You: *Jarreau, Al* / I wonder: *Rawls, Lou* / Lonely town, lonely street: *Jarreau, Al* / Trying as hard as I can: *Rawls, Lou*
306192 / Jan '97 / Hallmark

☐ L IS FOR LOVER
Tell me what I gotta do / Says / Pleasure / Golden girl / Across the midnight sky / No ordinary romance / L is for lover / Real tight / Telepathy / Give a little more romance
5578502 / 3 Aug '98 / IE

☐ LET'S STAY TOGETHER
Let's stay together / Call me / Tired of being alone / Living for you / You ought to be with me / Let's get married / Here I am / I'm still in love with you / Ain't no sunshine / Love and happiness / Look what you've done for me / Lean on me / Same love that made me laugh / Use me / You / Grandma's hands / Kissing my love / Lonely town, lonely street
100492 / May '97 / A-Play Collection

☐ LIVING FOR YOU
Living for you / Call me / Here I am / Let's get married / Let's stay together / You ought to be with me / Love and happiness / Tired of being alone / Look what you done for me / Still in love with you
CDBM 107 / Oct '95 / Blue Moon

☐ MASQUERADE IS OVER, THE
My favourite things / Stockholm sweetnin' / Sleepin' bee / (I'm afraid) the masquerade is over / Sophisticated lady / Joey / Come rain or come shine / One note samba
CDBM 079 / Nov '89 / Blue Moon

☐ MASTERS, THE
Ain't no sunshine / Lean on me / Use me / Kissing my love / Grandma's hands / You / Lonely town lonely street / Same love that made me laugh / My favourite things / Stockholm sweetnin' / Sleepin' bee / Masquerade is over / Sophisticated lady / Joey / Come rain or come shine / One note samba
EABCD 094 / 30 Mar '98 / Eagle

☐ SPOTLIGHT ON AL JARREAU
Ain't no sunshine / Kissing my love / You / Same love that made me laugh / Rainbow in your eyes / Grandma's hands / Lonely town, lonely street / Lean on me / One good turn / We got by / Use me (till you use me up) / Loving you / Letter perfect
HADCD 115 / Feb '94 / Javelin

☐ TENDERNESS
Mas que nada / Try a little tenderness / Your song / My favorite things / She's leaving home / Summertime / We got by / Save your love for me / You don't see me / Wait for the magic / Dinosaur / Go away little girl
5578532 / 3 Aug '98 / IE

☐ TRIBUTE TO BILL WITHERS, A
CP 1001 / 11 May '98 / Rhino

Jarrett, Keith

☐ ARBOUR ZENA
Dunes / Solara march / Mirrors
8255922 / Aug '85 / ECM

☐ AT THE DEER HEAD INN
Solar / Basin Street blues / Chandra / You don't know what love is / You and the night and the music / Bye bye blackbird / It's easy to remember
5177202 / May '94 / ECM

☐ BELONGING
Spiral dance / Blossom / Long as you know you're living yours / Belonging / Windup / Solstice
8291152 / Jun '86 / ECM

☐ BOOK OF WAYS (Solo Clavichord/2CD Set)
No. 1 / No. 2 / No. 3 / No. 4 / No. 5 / No. 6 / No. 7 / No. 8 / No. 9 / No. 10 / No. 11 / No. 12 / No. 13 / No. 14 / No. 15 / No. 16 / No. 17 / No. 18 / No. 19
8313962 / Oct '87 / ECM

☐ BRIDGE OF LIGHT
Elegy / Adagio / Celebration / Song / Dance / Birth / Bridge of light
4453502 / May '94 / ECM

☐ BYE BYE BLACKBIRD (Jarrett, Keith & Jack DeJohnette/Gary Peacock)
Bye bye blackbird / You won't forget me / Butch and butch / Summer night / For miles / Straight no chaser / I thought about you / Blackbird bye bye
5130742 / May '93 / ECM

☐ CELESTIAL HAWK (For Orchestra, Percussion & Piano) (Jarrett, Keith & Syracuse Symphony)
First movement / Second movement / Third movement
8293702 / Aug '88 / ECM

☐ CHANGELESS (Jarrett, Keith & Jack DeJohnette/Gary Peacock)
Dancing / Endless / Lifeline / Ecstacy
8396182 / Oct '89 / ECM

☐ CHANGES (Jarrett, Keith & Jack DeJohnette/Gary Peacock)
Flying / Prism
8174362 / Oct '84 / ECM

☐ COMPLETE BLUE NOTE RECORDINGS, THE (6CD Set)
In your own sweet way / How long has this been going on / While we're young / Partners / No lonely nights / Now's the time / Lament / I'm old fashioned / Everything happens to me / If I were a bell / In the wee small hours of the morning / Oleo / Alone together / Skylark / Things ain't what they used to be / Autumn leaves / Days of wine and roses / Bop-be / You don't know what love is Muezzin / When I fall in love / How deep is the ocean / Close your eyes / Imagination / I'll close my eyes / I fall in love to easily / On Green Dolphin Street / My romance / Don't ever leave me / You'd be so nice to come home to / La valse bleue / Straight, no chaser / Time after time / For heaven's sake / Desert sun / How about you
5276382 / Oct '95 / ECM

☐ CONCERTS: BREGENZ
Bregenz-part 1 / Bregenz-part 2 / Untitled / Heartland
8272862 / Aug '88 / ECM

☐ CURE, THE (New York Town Hall/April 1990)
Old folks / Body and soul / Woody 'n' you / Things ain't what they used to be
8496502 / Oct '91 / ECM

☐ DARK INTERVALS
Opening / Hymn / Americana / Entrance / Parallels / Fire dance / Ritual prayer / Recitative
8373422 / Oct '88 / ECM

☐ EXPECTATIONS
Expectations / Take me back / Circular letter (for JK) / Sundance / Bring back the time when (if) / There is a road (God's River) / Common mama / Magician in you / Roussillon / Nomads
4679022 / Jan '92 / Columbia

☐ EYES OF THE HEART
Eyes of the heart / Encore (A-B-C)
8254762 / Oct '85 / ECM

☐ FACING YOU
In front / Ritooria / Lalene / My lady: my child / Landscape for future earth / Starbright / Vapallia / Semblence
8271322 / Dec '85 / ECM

☐ FORT YAWUH
If the misfits wear it / Fort Yawuh / De drums / Still life, still life
MCAD 33122 / Oct '90 / Impulse Jazz

☐ IMPULSE YEARS 1973-1974, THE (5CD Set)
(If the) misfits (wear it) / Fort Yawuh / De drums / Still life, still life / (If the) misfits (wear it) / Rich (and the poor) / Blue streak / Fullsuvollivus / Treasure Island / Yaqui Indian folk song / Le Mistral / Angels (without edges) / Sister Fortune / Death and the flower / Whistle tune / Angels (without edges) / Roads travelled, roads veiled / De drums / Melting the ice / Death and the flower / Prayer / Great bird / Prayer / In flight / Kuum / Vapallia / Backhand / Victoria
IMPD 5237 / 10 Nov '97 / Impulse Jazz

☐ IN THE LIGHT (2CD Set)
Metamorphosis / Fughata for harpsichord / Brass quintet / A pagan hymn / String quartet / Short piece for guitar and strings / Crystal moment / In the cove, in the light
8350112 / Jul '88 / ECM

☐ INVOCATIONS: THE MOTH AND THE FLAME (2CD Set)
Invocations / Moth and the flame
8254732 / Oct '85 / ECM

☐ KOLN CONCERT, THE (24 January 1975)
8100672 / '83 / ECM

☐ LA SCALA
La scala part 1 / La scala part 2 / Over the rainbow
5372682 / Jun '97 / ECM

☐ LUMINESSENCE (Music For String Orchestra & Saxophone) (Jarrett, Keith & Jan Garbarek)
Numinor / Windsong / Luminessence
8393072 / Sep '89 / ECM

☐ MY SONG
Questar / My song / Tabarka / Mandela / Journey home
8214062 / '84 / ECM

☐ MYSTERIES
Rotation / Everything that lives laments / Flame / Mysteries
MCAD 33113 / Jan '90 / Impulse Jazz

☐ MYSTERIES (The Impulse Years 1975-1976/4CD Set)
Shades of jazz / Southern smiles / Rose petals / Diatribe / Shades of jazz / Southern smiles / Rose petals / Rose petals / Rotation / Everything that lives laments / Flame / Mysteries / Everything that lives laments / Playaround / Byablue / Konya / Rainbow / Trieste / Fantasm / Yahllah / Byablue / Trieste (intro) / Rainbow / Mushi mushi / Silence / Bop be / Pyramids moving / Gotta get some sleep / Blackberry winter / Pocketful of cherry / Gotta get some sleep / Blackberry winter
IMPD 4189 / Nov '96 / Impulse Jazz

☐ NUDE ANTS (Live At The Village Vanguard/2CD Set)
Chant of the soil / Innocence / Processional / Oasis / New dance / Sunshine song
8291192 / Jun '86 / ECM

☐ PARIS CONCERT (Solo Piano/October 17th 1988/Salle Pleyel)
October 17, 1988 / Wind / Blues
8391732 / Apr '90 / ECM

☐ PRICELESS JAZZ
De drums / Silence / Blackberry winter / Bop-Be / Vapailia / Treasure Island / Byablue
GRP 98942 / 23 Mar '98 / GRP

☐ RUTA AND DAITYA
8293882 / Oct '88 / ECM

☐ SACRED HYMNS OF G.I. GURDJIEFF
Reading of sacred books / Prayer and despair / Religious ceremony / Hymn / Orthodox hymn from Asia minor / Hymn for Good Friday / Hymn for Easter Thursday / Hymn to the endless creator / Hymn from a great temple / Story of the resurrection of Christ / Holy affirming, holy denying, holy reconciling / Easter night procession / Meditation
8291222 / Jun '86 / ECM

☐ SOLO CONCERTS - BREMEN/ LAUSANNE (2CD Set)
Bremen, july 12 1973, parts 1 and 2 / Lausanne, march 20 1973
8277472 / Jul '86 / ECM

☐ SOMEWHERE BEFORE
My back pages / Pretty ballad / Moving son / Somewhere before / New rag / Moment for tears / Pout's over (and the day's not through) / Dedicated to you / Old rag
7567814552 / Mar '93 / WEA

☐ SPHERES
Spheres
8274632 / Jul '86 / ECM

☐ SPIRITS (2CD Set)
Spirits 1-26
8294672 / Oct '86 / ECM

☐ STAIRCASE (2CD Set)
Staircase / Hourglass / Sundial / Sand
8273372 / Dec '85 / ECM

☐ STANDARDS IN NORWAY
All of you / Little girl blue / Just in time / Old folks / Love is a many splendoured thing / Dedicated to you / I hear a rhapsody / How about you
5217172 / Apr '95 / ECM

☐ STANDARDS LIVE (Jarrett, Keith & Jack DeJohnette/Gary Peacock)
Stella by starlight / Wrong blues / Falling in love with love / Too young to go steady / Way you look tonight / Old country
8278272 / Feb '86 / ECM

☐ STANDARDS VOL.1 (Jarrett, Keith & Jack DeJohnette/Gary Peacock)
Meaning of the blues / All the things you are / It never entered my mind / (I'm afraid) the masquerade is over / God bless the child
8119662 / Aug '88 / ECM

☐ STANDARDS VOL.2 (Jarrett, Keith & Jack DeJohnette/Gary Peacock)
So tender / Moon and sand / In love in vain / Never let me go / If I should lose you / I fall in love too easily
8250152 / May '85 / ECM

☐ STILL LIVE (Jarrett, Keith & Jack DeJohnette/Gary Peacock)
My funny valentine / Autumn leaves / When I fall in love / Song is you / Come rain or come shine / Late lament / You and the night and the music / Someday my Prince will come / I remember Clifford
8350082 / May '88 / ECM

☐ SUN BEAR CONCERTS (Piano Solo/ Kyoto/Osaka/Tokyo/Sapporo November 1976/6CD Set)
Kyoto/November 5th 1976 / Osaka/November 8th 1976 / Tokyo/November 14th November / Sapporo/ November 18th 1976
8430282 / Oct '90 / ECM

☐ SURVIVORS' SUITE
Survivors' suite
8271312 / Dec '85 / ECM

☐ TOKYO 1996 (Jarrett, Keith & Jack DeJohnette/Gary Peacock)
It could never happen to you / Never let me go / Summer night / I'll remember April / Mona Lisa / Autumn leaves / Last night when we were young / John's Abbey / My funny Valentine
5399552 / 5 May '98 / ECM

☐ TRIBUTE (2CD Set) (Jarrett, Keith & Jack DeJohnette/Gary Peacock)
Lover man / I hear a rhapsody / Little girl blue / Solar / Sun prayer / Just in time / Smoke gets in you eyes / All of you / Ballad of the sad young man / All the things you are / It's easy to remember
8471352 / Nov '90 / ECM

☐ VIENNA CONCERT, THE (Recorded At The Vienna State Opera)
Vienna / Vienna
5134372 / Sep '92 / ECM

☐ WELL TEMPERED CLAVIER BOOK, THE (2CD Set)
8352462 / Nov '88 / ECM

☐ WORKS
Country / Riootria / Journey / Staircase (Part II) / String quartet (2nd movement) / Invocations / Nagoya (Part 2B)(Encore)
8254252 / Jun '89 / ECM

Jarrett, Winston

☐ TOO MANY BOUNDARIES
RASCD 3167 / Dec '95 / Ras

☐ TRIBUTE TO BOB MARLEY, A (Jarrett, Winston & The Righteous Flames)
OMCD 28 / Jul '94 / Original Music

☐ WISE MAN
TWCD 1001 / Apr '88 / Tamoki Wambesi

Jars Of Clay

☐ JARS OF CLAY
Liquid / Sinking / Love song for a saviour / Like a child / Art in me / He / Boy on a string / Flood / Worlds apart / Blind
ORECD 541 / Oct '96 / Silvertone

☐ MUCH AFRAID
Overjoyed / Fade to grey / Tea and sympathy / Crazy times / Frail / Five candles / Weighed down / Portrait of an apology / Truce / Much afraid / Hymn
ORECD 551 / 6 Oct '97 / Silvertone

Jarvis, Duane

☐ FAR FROM PERFECT
Far from perfect / Drive back to you / You met your match / Mr Dependability / Vanishing breed / I'm not gonna let you break my heart / Hat check girl / There is a light / Girl that's hip / Love ona ministrel's wage / Cocktail napkin / Broken clock
WMCD 1070 / 9 Mar '98 / Watermelon

Jarvis, Jane

☐ CUT GLASS
ACD 258 / Apr '93 / Audiophile

☐ JANE JARVIS' LA QUARTET
ACD 248 / '89 / Audiophile

Jasani, Viram

☐ RAGS, MALKAUNS AND MEGH (Jasani, Viram & Gurdev Singh/U.L.A. Khan)
Rag Malkauns / Rag Megh
CDSDL 377 / Mar '94 / Saydisc

Jasmine Minks

☐ JASMINE MINKS
CRECD 007 / May '94 / Creation

☐ SCRATCH THE SURFACE
CRELP 044 CD / Feb '89 / Creation

☐ SOUL STATION
Cold heart / Cold heart / Veronica / Somers town / Think / Where the traffic goes / 30 second set up / Ghost of a young man / Still waiting / Cut me deep / Ballad of johnny eye / Soul station
CRECD 112 / Sep '91 / Creation

Jason & The Scorchers

☐ CLEAR IMPETUOUS MORNING
Self sabotage / Cappucino Rosie / Drug store truck drivin' man / 2+1 = Nothing / Victory Rd / Kick me down / Everything has a cost / To feel no love / Walking a vanishing line / Tomorrow comes today / Jeremy's legend / I'm sticking with you
MR 1472 / Sep '96 / Mammoth

☐ MIDNIGHT ROADS AND STAGES SEEN
Self sabotage / My heart still stands with you / Last time around / 200 proof lovin' / This town isn't keeping you down / Good things come to those who wait / Blanket of sorrow / Broken whiskey glass / Absolutely sweet Marie / Ocean of doubt / Pray for me Mama (I'm a gypsy now) / Somewhere within / Help there's a fire / Harvest moon / If money talks / Walkin' the dog / Both sides of the line / White lies / Last blue yodel / Ezekiel's wheels/Golden ball and chain / Going nowhere / If you've got the love (I've got the time) / Still tied
5576232 / 18 May '98 / Polydor

Jason Crest

☐ COLLECTED WORKS OF JASON CREST, THE
WHCD 006 / 22 May '98 / Wooden Hill

Jaspar, Bobby

☐ BOBBY JASPAR
Seven up / My old flame / All of you / Doublemint / Before dawn / Sweet blanche / Fuzz
OJCCD 1788 / Feb '93 / Original Jazz Classics

Jasper

☐ LIBERATION
Liberation / Ain't no peace / Baby please don't go / Shelagh / Liberation interlude / Liberation interlude II / Confusion / St. Louis blues / Cutin' out / Beard / Liberation II / Finale
SEECD 438 / Apr '96 / See For Miles

Jasraj, Pandit

☐ INVOCATION
WLAES 31CD / Nov '95 / Waterlily Acoustics

☐ TABLA (Jasraj, Pandit & Shri Swapan Chaudhuri)
WRCD 1009 / Dec '94 / Koch

Javalins

☐ JAVALINS BEAT
Caroline / Mr. Chang aus Chinatown / Al Capone / Javalin's beat / Sherry / Twisting away / Hey Hey Ha Ha / Joe der Gitarrenman / Hully gully hop / Lass sie reden / Scherben / Tanz doch mit mir Swim / Jenny Jenny / Monkey walk / Be my baby / Loveliest night of the year / Es gibt kein bier aus Hawaii / Ya Ya twist / Footpatter / Git it / Sweet Georgia Brown / Twist and shout
BCD 15798 / May '94 / Bear Family

Javier

☐ HARD WAY, THE (Javier & The Str8jackers)
Intro / Shoot out / F I U Jay / Other guy / Hammer break / Real deal / Talking shit / Plain ole gangster / Pass me da 40 ounce / Talkin' shit again / Jones / Never heard rappin' / Baddest M F out da ATL / Chillin' at da crib / Candy / Players dialogue / Player style / Str8jackin' / Wildest fantasy / Outtro
ICH 1109CD / Oct '93 / Ichiban

Javors, Melissa

☐ REAL WOMAN IN ME
SPINCD 141 / Dec '97 / Spindrift

Jawbox

☐ FOR YOUR OWN SPECIAL
SWEETHEART
EFA 49322 / Mar '94 / City Slang

☐ GRIPPE
DIS 52CD / May '94 / Dischord

☐ JAWBOX
EFA 049812 / Jun '96 / City Slang

☐ NOVELTY
DIS 69CD / May '94 / Dischord

Jaworzyn, Stefan

☐ IN A SENTIMENTAL MOOD (Jaworzyn,
Stefan & Alan Wilkinson)
INCUSCD 25 / May '97 / Incus

Jay & The Americans

☐ ORIGINAL, THE
Cara mia / Come a little closer / She cried / Magic
moment / Only in America / Come dance with me /
Let's lock the door / Think of the good times / Some
enchanted evening / Sunday and me / Why can't you
bring me home / Crying / Livin' above your head /
Raining in my sunshine / When you dance /
Hushabye / Walkin' in the rain / What will my Mary
say
TO 886222 / 2 Feb '98 / Disky

Jay, Barbara

☐ JUST FRIENDS
Just friends / Speak low / East of the sun / All about
Ronnie / Come in from the rain / Nearness of you /
Willow weep for me / New York State of mind /
Stomping at the Savoy / Lady's in love with you / You
turned the tables on me / These foolish things / If
dreams come true / Man I love / Memories of you /
Smooth one / Moonglow / Goodbye
SPJCD 557 / 5 Jan '98 / Spotlite

Jay, Felix

☐ FELIX JAY AND NICOLA ALESINI (Jay,
Felix & Nicola Alesini)
HERM 1111 / 2 Mar '98 / Hermetic

☐ OTHER SUNS (Jay, Felix & Nicola
Alesini)
HERM 3333 / 2 Mar '98 / Hermetic

Jay-Z

☐ REASONABLE DOUBT
Can't knock the hustle: Jay-Z & Mary J. Blige /
Politics as usual / Brooklyn's finest: Jay-Z &
Notorious BIG / Dead presidents II / Feelin' it: Jay-Z
& Mecca / D'evils / 22 two's / Can I live / Ain't no
nigga: Jay-Z & Foxxy Brown / Friend or foe / Coming
of age: Jay-Z & Memphis Bleek / Cashmere thoughts
/ Bring it on: Jay-Z & Big Jaz/Sauce Money / Regrets
/ Can't knock the hustle: Jay-Z & Meli'sa Morgan
74321447202 / Mar '97 / Northwestside

Jayhawks

☐ HOLLYWOOD TOWN HALL
Waiting for the crowd / Crowded in the wings / Clouds /
Two Angels / Take me with you / Sister cry / Settle
down like rain / Witghita / Nevada, California /
Martin's song
74321239942 / Apr '95 / American

☐ SOUND OF LIES
Man who loved life / Think about it / Trouble / It's up
to you / Stick in the mud / Big star / Poor little fish /
Sixteen down / Haywire / Dying on a vine /
Bottomless cup / Sound of lies / I hear you cry
74321464062 / Apr '97 / American

☐ TOMORROW THE GREEN GRASS
Blue / I'd run away / Miss Williams' guitar / Two
hearts / Real light / Over my shoulder / Bad time / See
him on the streets / Nothing left to borrow / Anne
Jane / Pray for me / Red's song / Ten little kids
74321236802 / Feb '95 / American

Jays

☐ UNFORGETTABLE TIMES
JJCD 027 / Apr '96 / Channel One

Jaz Klash

☐ THRU THE HAZE
Off the edge / Intrigue (Down for whatever) / BQE /
Intoxicated / 97 / Traffic / Thru the haze / Finale / Gift
/ Party next door / One fine day
COTCD 008 / Jun '97 / Cup Of Tea

Jazayer

☐ JAZAYER (Jazayer & Ali Jihad Racy)
CDEB 2549 / May '93 / Earthbeat

Jazz Artists Guild

☐ JAZZ LIFE, THE
R and R / Black cat / Father and son / Lord, lord am I
ever gonna know / Vassarlean / Oh yeah, oh yeah
CCD 9019 / Feb '97 / Candid

☐ NEWPORT REBELS
Mysterious blues / Cliff walk / Wrap your troubles in
dreams (and dream your troubles away) / Ain't
nobody's business if I do / Me and you
CCD 9022 / Apr '87 / Candid

Jazz Butcher

☐ BEST OF DRAINING THE GLASS 1982-
1986, THE
REMCD 527 / 1 Jun '98 / Reactive

☐ BIG PLANET
CRECD 49 / May '94 / Creation

☐ CONDITION BLUE
Girls say yes / Girls say yes / Harlan / Still and all /
Monkeyface / She's a yo-yo / Honey / Shirley
maclaine / Racheland
CRECD 110 / Oct '91 / Creation

☐ CULT OF THE BASEMENT
Basement / Pineapple Tuesday / Daycare nation /
Mr. Odd / Panic in room 109 / Turtle bait / She's on
drugs / Onion field / My Zeppelin / After the
euphrates / Girl go / Sister death
CRECD 62 / May '94 / Creation

☐ ILLUMINATE (Jazz Butcher
Conspiracy)
CRECD 182 / Apr '95 / Creation

☐ WAITING FOR THE LOVE BUS
Rosemary davis world of sound / Bakersfield / Kids in
the mall-kaliningrad / Whaddya / Sweet water /
Ghosts / Baltic / Killed out / Ben / Penguins /
President chang / Angel station / Rosemary davis
world of sound (reprise)
CRECD 156 / May '93 / Creation

☐ WESTERN FAMILY
Southern Mark Smith / Shirley Maclaine / Sister
death / Still and all / Pineapple Tuesday / Angles /
Beautiful snow-white hair / She's on drugs / Girl-go /
She's a yoyo / Racheland / Everybody's talkin' /
Tugboat Captain / Over the rainbow
CRED 148 / Jan '93 / Creation

Jazz Classical Union

☐ FREE FLIGHT
Blue rondo a la turk / Pavanne for a true musical
prince (Don's song) / Chopin etude / Paganini
caprice / Racheland / Peasant dance / Bach's
groove / For Frederic and Bill / Con mucho gusto
HCD 609 / Jul '97 / Hindsight

Jazz Composer's Orchestra

☐ COMMUNICATIONS
8411242 / Nov '89 / ECM

Jazz Crusaders

☐ LIVE AT THE LIGHTHOUSE 1996
Aleluia / Blues up tight / You don't know what love is /
Miss it / 'Round midnight / Some other blues /
Scratch / Doin' that thing / Milestones
CDP 8379882 / Jul '96 / Pacific Jazz

Jazz Epistles

☐ JAZZ IN AFRICA VOL.1
Delilah / Scullery suite / Twelve times twelve / Uka-
jonga phambili / Body and soul / Scullery department /
Dollar's moods / Blues for Hughie / Love come back
to me / Vary-oo-vum / Carol's drive / Gafsa / Old devil
moon / Cosmic ray
CDN 1004 / 23 Mar '98 / Camden

☐ VERSE 1
668922 / Mar '96 / Melodie

Jazz Finger

☐ LITTLE GIRL ON THE PLANE (Who
Turned Her Doll's Head Around To
Look At Me)
MUZA 12CD / May '98 / Muzamuza

Jazz Furniture

☐ JAZZ FURNITURE
CAP 21449 / Oct '94 / Caprice

Jazz Grass Ensemble

☐ TICO BANJO
PV 758 091 / Feb '86 / Disques Pierre
Verany

Jazz Hot Ensemble

☐ JAZZ HOT ENSEMBLE
JCD 242 / Jun '95 / Jazzology

Jazz Is Dead

☐ BLUE LIGHT RAIN
ZBR 44008 / 8 Jun '98 / Decoy

Jazz Jamaica

☐ DOUBLE BARREL
Double barrel / Confucius / Monkey man / Exodus /
Chiang kai chek / Butterfly / Marcus Jnr. / Night
dreamer / Walk on by / Dewey Square / Heard it
through the grapevine
HNCD 1421 / 27 Apr '98 / Hannibal

Jazz Mentality

☐ SHOW BUSINESS IS MY LIFE
378352 / Feb '97 / Koch Jazz

Jazz Passengers

☐ CROSS THE STREET
Spirits of a flatbust / Basketballfish / Tintindeo /
Somewhere in New Jersey / My Spanish cookies /
Ghostly strange love / Little gold ring / Fathouse /
You don't know what love is / Laura / Tikkun
TWI 1012 / Apr '96 / Les Disques Du
Crepuscule

☐ IMPLEMENT YOURSELF
NW 398 / Aug '92 / New World

☐ INDIVIDUALLY TWISTED
Babble a la Roy / Maybe I'm lost / Angel eyes / Pork
chop / Aubergine / Ole / Imitation of a kiss / Jive
samba / Doncha go 'way mad / Tide is high / It came
from outer space
ESSCD 578 / Jul '97 / Essential

☐ JAZZ PASSENGERS IN LONDON
72902103282 / Mar '95 / High Street

☐ LIVE AT THE KNITTING FACTORY
KFWCD 107 / Nov '94 / Knitting Factory

☐ PLAIN OLD JOE
August 87th 1998 / Plain old Joe / 20791 peace talk
and reception / Homer B. halfsteppin / Inzane / If I
were a bell / Robbie / Blues for Helen
KFWCD 139 / 18 May '98 / Knitting
Factory

Jazz Police

☐ LONG NIGHT COMING, A
Chick's tune / Over the rainbow / Space acres / Well
you needn't / Patience / Rush / Long night coming / Back
eddy blues / Li'l darlin' / Lois lane
CDPC 748 / Oct '90 / Prestige

Jazz Posse

☐ BLUE
Antistrophy / We know who we are / Woody / Gemini
/ Crescent / Integrate / Skag / Countdown / Juke
joint / Horny / Un loco loco / Blue / Metafisico / Frog
sauce / Anna
FSCD 004 / Oct '95 / Freak Street

Jazz Steppers

☐ GET UP
CDPJA 3 / 11 May '98 / Passion Jazz

Jazz Trio

☐ 'S WONDERFUL JAZZ
'S Wonderful / Cherokee / That old feeling / You are
too beautiful / Bali Ha'i / Jitterbug waltz / You've
changed
WCD 8418 / Sep '91 / Wilson Audiophile

Jazz X

☐ PEACE AND NICENESS
XEN 006CD / Nov '96 / Funky Xen

Jazzateers

☐ I SHOT THE PRESIDENT
MA 30 / May '97 / Marina

Jazzsick

☐ JAZZSICK
EFA 120702 / Apr '95 / Hotwire

Jazztet

☐ HERE AND NOW
Tonk / Rue prevail / Richie's dilemma / Whisper not /
Just in time / Ruby my dear / In love in vain / Sonny's
back / Tonk / Sonny's back
5580522 / 20 Apr '98 / Verve

☐ MOMENT TO MOMENT
SNCD 1066 / '86 / Soul Note

☐ REAL TIME
Whisper not / Sad to say / Are you real / Autumn
leaves / Along came Betty
CCD 14034 / Jan '94 / Contemporary

JB3

☐ CLOSE GRIND
NOMU 50CD / Dec '96 / Nova Mute

JB's

☐ FUNKY GOOD TIME (The Anthology/
2CD Set)
5270942 / Aug '98 / Polydor

JC 001

☐ RIDE THE BREAK (JC 001 & DJ D'Zire)
Never again / Favourite breaks / Sea of MC's / Cupid
/ Build the mutha up / Words within words / Flow /
Ride the break / Virtual reality / All my children
4509914062 / Apr '93 / Anxious

JCB

☐ TRIP TO CAPE BRETON, A (JCB & Jerry
Holland)
Reels - Homeward bound set / 2/4 Marches - Portree
set / Crossing to Jura / Jigs - Heather ale set / Waltz -
Boo babys lullaby / Reels - Brumley brae set / 2/4
Marches - Mary MacArthur's wedding set / Slow air -
Mrs.Helen N Robertson / Jigs - Banks O'Clyde set /
Hornpipes - North shore set / Amy's waltz / Reels -
Arran Ceilidh set
CDLDL 1269 / Dec '97 / Lochshore

JD

☐ LIFE IN 1472
Intro / Turn it out / Money ain't a thing: JD & Jay Z /
Get your shit right: JD &DMX/Mad Rapper / Fresh:
JD & Slick Rick / Sweetheart: JD & Mariah Carey /
Jazzy hoes: JD & Eightball / Too short: Mr. Black &
Young Bloodz / Don't hate on me: JD & Da Brat/
Krazie Bones / Going home with me: JD & Keith
Sweat / You get dealt wit: JD & Mase/Lil Kim / Party
continues: JD & Da Brat/Usher / All that's got to go:
JD & Da Brat/La Tocha Scott / Protectors of 1472: JD
& Snoop Doggy Dog/ROC/Warren G / Lay you down:
JD & Trina/Tamara Powell / Three the hard way: JD &
Mr. Black/ROC
4897122 / 27 Jul '98 / Columbia

JD Smoothie

☐ JD SMOOTHIE
SOCD 7788 / Mar '98 / Studio One

Jean-Baptiste, David

☐ FEELING TONES
Spirit people / Murray's Montclaire blue / Cause and
effect / Copenhagen skies / You don't know what
love is / Monarchs / Feeling tones / Neuriba
cyberspace / Jitterbug waltz / No way home / Spirit
of the Sahara
CCD 79744 / 6 Oct '97 / Candid

Jeane, Deborah

☐ FLY
5679162 / Aug '96 / Music & Words

Jeanneau, Francois

☐ MALOYA TRANSIT
LBLC 6546 / Jul '92 / Label Bleu

Jeck, Philip

☐ LOOPHOLES
TO 26 / Jun '95 / Touch

☐ SURF
TO 36 / 4 May '98 / Touch

Jedi Knights

☐ NEW SCHOOL SCIENCE
May the funk be with you / Noddy Holder / One for
MAW / Science friction / Truth / Lessons / Air drums
from outer Mongolia / Human blancmange / Solina /
Afterlife
EVO 042CD / 23 Mar '98 / Universal
Language

Jeep Beat Collective

☐ ATTACK OF THE WILD STYLE
RUF 008 / Nov '96 / Ruf Beats

☐ REPOSSESSED WILDSTYLES
CLASSIC CUTS
RUF 017CD / 4 May '98 / Ruf Beats

Jefferson Airplane

☐ AFTER BATHING AT BAXTERS
Ballad of you and me and Poonell / Small package of
value will come to you shortly / Young girl Sunday
blues / Martha / Wild tyme / Last wall of the castle /
Rejoice / Watch her ride / Spare chaynge / Two
heads / Won't you try / Saturday afternoon
ND 84718 / 11 May '98 / RCA

☐ BEST OF JEFFERSON AIRPLANE, THE
Blues from an airplane / White rabbit / Somebody to
love / Ballad of you and me and Poonell / Crown of
creation / Plastic fantastic lover / Volunteers / When
the earth moves again / Aerie (gang of eagles) / Milk
train / Mexico
ND 89186 / Jan '92 / RCA

☐ CROWN OF CREATION
Lather / In time / Star track / Share a little joke /
Chushingura / If you feel / Crown of creation / Ice
cream Phoenix / Greasy heart / House at Poonell
corner
ND 83797 / 19 Jan '98 / RCA

☐ EARLY FLIGHT
High flyin' bird / Runnin' round this world / That's
alright / In the morning / JPP McStep B. blues / Go to
her / Up or down / Mexico / Have you seen the
saucers
07863674192 / 11 May '98 / RCA

☐ GOLD COLLECTION, THE (2CD Set)
R2CD 4049 / 13 Apr '98 / Deja Vu

429

☐ JOURNEY (The Best Of Jefferson Airplane)
Embryonic journey / High flyin' bird / It's no secret / Come up the years / Somebody to love / Blues from a airplane / White rabbit / Plastic fantastic lover / Aerie (gang of eagles) / Ballad of you an me and pooneil / Crown of creation / Lather / Last wall of the castle / Greasy heart / Volunteers / When the earth moves again / Triad / We can be together / Wooden ships / Milk train / Have you seen the saucers
7432140057 2 / Jan '97 / Camden

☐ LIVE AT THE MONTEREY FESTIVAL
Somebody to love / Other side of this life / White rabbit / High flying bird / Today / She has funny cars / Young girl with Sunday blues / Ballad of you and me and Pooneil
CDTB 074 / May '90 / Thunderbolt

☐ MASTERS, THE
EABCD 013 / 24 Nov '97 / Eagle

☐ SURREALISTIC PILLOW
She has funny cars / Somebody to love / My best friend / Today / Comin' back to me / Three fifths of a mile in ten seconds / DCBA-25 / How do you feel / White rabbit / Plastic fantastic lover / Embryonic journey
ND 83738 / 2 Feb '98 / RCA

☐ THROUGH THE CHAOS (Spoken Word History/2CD Set) (Kantner, Paul)
MSE 1017 / Sep '97 / Monster

☐ VOLUNTEERS
We can be together / Good shepherd / Farm / Hey Frederick / Turn my life down / Wooden ships / Eskimo blue day / Song for all seasons / Meadowlands / Volunteers
ND 83867 / 2 Feb '98 / RCA

☐ WHITE RABBIT
White rabbit / Today / It is no secret / My best friend / Don't slip away / Other side of this life / High flying bird / Somebody to love / Plastic fantastic lover / 35 of a mile in ten seconds / She has funny cars / You're so loose / What you're askin' / Would you love me / Ride / This is my life / What do you want with me / Get together
RMB 75065 / Aug '93 / Remember

Jefferson Starship

☐ DEEP SPACE
Shadowlands / Ganja of love / Dark ages / I'm on fire / Papa John / Women who fly / Gold / Light / Crown of creation / Count on me / Miracles / Lawman / Wooden ships / Somebody to love / White rabbit
ESMCD 493 / Apr '97 / Essential

☐ EARTH
Love too good / Count on me / Take your time / Crazy feelin' / Skateboard / Fire / Show yourself / Runaway / All nite long
07863668782 / Jun '97 / RCA

☐ GREATEST HITS (10 Years & Change 1979-1991) (Starship)
Jane / Find your way back / Stranger / No way out / Laying it on the line / Don't lose any sleep / We built this city / Sara / Nothing's gonna stop us now / It's not over ('til it's over) / It's not enough / Good enough
74321289902 / Aug '95 / RCA

☐ SPITFIRE
Cruisin' / Dance with the dragon / Hot water / St. Charles / Song to the sun / Don't let it rain / With your love / Switchblade / Big city / Love lovely love / Ozymandias
07863668762 / Jun '97 / RCA

☐ WE BUILT THIS CITY (The Very Best Of Starship) (Starship)
We built this city / Jane / Nothing's gonna stop us now / It's not over till it's over / Babylon / Set the night to music / Sara / Love among the cannibals / Rock myself to sleep / Hearts of the world / It's not enough / Lay it on the line / Find oyur way back / Stranger / No way out / Don't lose any sleep / Good heart
74321511912 / 1 Sep '97 / Camden

☐ WINDOWS OF HEAVEN
SPV 08529102 / 29 Jun '98 / SPV

Jefferson, Blind Lemon

☐ ALL TIME BLUES CLASSICS
8420282 / Oct '96 / Music Memoria

☐ BEST OF BLIND LEMON JEFFERSON, THE
WBJCD 016 / Jul '96 / Wolf

☐ BLIND LEMON JEFFERSON
DVBC 9072 / May '95 / Deja Vu

☐ BLIND LEMON JEFFERSON 1925-26
DOCD 5017 / Aug '91 / Document

☐ IN CHRONOLOGICAL ORDER
DOCD 5018 / Nov '93 / Document

☐ MATCHBOX BLUES (The Essential Recordings)
Got the blues / Long lonesome blues / Corinna blues / Stocking feet blues / Broke and hungry / Shuckin' sugar blues / Bad luck blues / Black snake moan / Right of way blues / Hot dogs / Rambler blues / Gone dead blues / One dime blues / Lonesome house blues / See that my grave is kept clean / Mean jumper blues / Prison cell blues / Christmas Eve blues / DB blues / Eagle eyed Mama / Peach orchard Mama / Bed springs blues
IGOCD 2075 / Apr '98 / Indigo

☐ MOANIN' ALL OVER
TCD 1011 / May '96 / Tradition

☐ SQUEEZE MY LEMON
Bad luck blues / Change my luck blues / Sunshine special / Easy rider blues / Broke and hungry / Lonesome house blues / Black snake moan / That crawling baby blues / Right of way blues / Rising high water blues / Jack O' Diamond blues / Matchbox blues / Chock house blues / One dime blues / Rabbit foot blues / Stocking foot blues / Teddy bear blues / Prison cell blues / Hangman's blues / Blind lemon's penitentiary blues / He arose from the dead / Hot dog / See that my grave is kept clean
KATCD 101 / 29 Sep '97 / Catfish

Jefferson, Carter

☐ RISE OF ATLANTIS, THE
Why / Rise of Atlantis / Wind chimes / Changing trains / Song for Gwen / Blues for wood
CDSJP 126 / Mar '91 / Timeless Jazz

Jefferson, Eddie

☐ BODY AND SOUL
See if you can get to that / Body and soul / Mercy mercy mercy / So what / There I go, There I go again / Psychedelic Sally
OJCCD 396 / Jan '94 / Original Jazz Classics

☐ JAZZ SINGER, THE (Vocal Improvisations On Famous Jazz Solos)
So what / Moody's mood for love / Sister Sadie / Lester's trip to the moon (Paper moon) / TD's boogie woogie / Now's the time / Body and soul / Workshop / Sherry / Baby girl (These foolish things) / Memphis / Honeysuckle rose / Crazy romance / Night train / NJR (I'm gone) / I've got the blues / Silly little Cynthia / Red's new dream
ECD 22062 / Oct '93 / Evidence

Jefferson, Marshall

☐ DAY OF THE ONION
EFA 019532 / Nov '96 / KTM

☐ GODFATHERS OF HOUSE SERIES VOL.1 (Marshall Jefferson Presents...Past Classics) (Various Artists)
DBM 32234 / 26 Jan '98 / Fierce

Jefferson, Thomas

☐ THOMAS JEFFERSON
Body song / Collection box / Door is still open / Learning how to fly / I'll be leaving her tomorrrow / Hole in the shoe blues / Snake in the grass / Thanks for nothing / Hoe-bus / Northern california / Easy kind of feeling / Sho' 'bout to drive me wild / Say that you love me / American lovers / Jones / Shine the light / All cried out / L.a. / One man band
EDCD 416 / Mar '95 / Edsel

Jeffrey's Accordion Band

☐ 50 WARTIME MEMORIES VOL.3
SOW 511 / May '94 / Sound Waves

Jeffries, Peter

☐ AT SWIM TWO BIRDS (Jeffries, Peter & Jono Lonie)
DFR 31 / Apr '97 / Drunken Fish

☐ ELEVATOR MADNESS
EJO 9CD / Oct '96 / Emperor Jones

Jega

☐ SPECTRUM
ZIQ 002CD / 29 Jun '98 / Planet Mu

Jekyll & Hyde

☐ HEAVENLY CREATURES
Breaking the silence / I am / King of pain / In your dreams / Jekyll and Hyde / Peace child / Holy ground / Blood on my hands / Point of no return / Legends of the fall / Everlasting / Last time / Ten years gone
ZR 1997001 / 9 Feb '98 / Z

Jel

☐ ALL THE BLINDING MENACE
KR 001 / 2 Mar '98 / Kanteen

Jelly Roll Kings

☐ OFF YONDER WALL
03102 / 17 Nov '97 / Epitaph

Jellyfish

☐ BELLYBUTTON
Man I used to be / That is why / King is half undressed / I wanna stay home / She still loves him / All I want is everything / Now she knows she's wrong / Bed spring kiss / Baby coming back / Calling Sarah
CDCUX 3 / Feb '92 / Charisma

☐ SPILT MILK
Joining a fan club / Sebrina, Paste and Plato / New mistake / Glutton of sympathy / Ghost at number one / Bye bye bye / All is forgiven / Russian hill / He's my best friend / Too much, too little, too late / Brighter day
CDCUS 20 / May '93 / Charisma

Jenkins, Billy

☐ BLUE MOON IN A FUNCTION ROOM (Jenkins, Billy & The Voice Of God Collective)
Blue of the night / Vision on / Bye bye bluebird / On the street where you live / Take five / Baby elephant walk / Ruby, don't take your love to town / Liebestraum / Pick a bale of cotton / Maria Elena / Georgia / Kalinka / Moon river
BDV 9402 / Mar '95 / Babel

☐ ENTERTAINMENT USA
BDV 9401CD / Jul '94 / Babel

☐ FIRST AURAL ART EXHIBITION (Jenkins, Billy & The Voice Of God Collective)
Brilliant / Expensive equipment / Fat people / Blues / Sade's lips / Johnny Cash / Discoboats at two o'clock / Cooking oil / Donkey droppings / Elvis Presley
VOCD 921 / Sep '92 / VOTP

☐ SAD (Jenkins, Billy & The Blues Collective)
BDV 9615 / Feb '97 / Babel

☐ SCRATCHES OF SPAIN
Monkey men / Cuttlefish / Barcelona / Benidorm motorway services / Bilbao/St.Columbus day / Cooking oil / McDonalds
BDV 9404 / Oct '94 / Babel

☐ STILL SOUNDS LIKE BROMLEY
BDV 9717 / Aug '97 / Babel

☐ TRUE LOVE COLLECTION, THE
BVD 9821 / May '98 / Babel

Jenkins, Ella

☐ AND ONE AND TWO (& Other Songs For Pre School/Primary Children)
SFWCD 45016 / Mar '96 / Smithsonian Folkways

☐ COUNTING GAMES AND RHYTHMS FOR THE LITTLE ONES
SFWCD 45029 / Dec '97 / Smithsonian Folkways

☐ EARLY EARLY CHILDHOOD SONGS (Jenkins, Ella & Lake Meadows Nursery School)
SFWCD 45015 / Oct '96 / Smithsonian Folkways

☐ HOLIDAY TIMES
SFWCD 45041 / Oct '97 / Smithsonian Folkways

☐ JAMBO (& Other Call And Response Songs/Chants)
SFWCD 45017 / Oct '96 / Smithsonian Folkways

☐ SONGS AND RHYTHMS FROM NEAR AND FAR
SFWCD 45033 / Dec '97 / Smithsonian Folkways

☐ SONGS CHILDREN LOVE TO SING (Celebrating 40 Years Of Recordings)
SFWCD 45042 / Oct '96 / Smithsonian Folkways

☐ YOU'LL SING A SONG AND I'LL SING A SONG
SF 45010CD / Dec '94 / Smithsonian Folkways

Jenkins, Gordon

☐ GORDON JENKINS COLLECTION, THE
RE 21432 / Nov '97 / Razor & Tie

Jenkins, Karl

☐ IMAGINED OCEANS
Mare Crisium / Lacus Serenitatis / Mare Vaporum / Mare Australis / Lacus Somniorum / Lacus Perevernatiae / Lacus Doloris / Mare Undarum / Palus Nebularum / Sinus Iridium / Mare Imbrium / Lacus Temporis / Lacus Lenitatis / Mare Crisium
SK 60668 / 25 May '98 / Sony Classical

Jenkins, Leroy

☐ LEGEND OF AL GLATSON, THE
Al Glatson / Brax Stone / Albert Ayler / Tuesday child / What goes around comes around
1200222 / Nov '90 / Black Saint

☐ LIFELONG AMBITIONS (Jenkins, Leroy & Muhal Richard Abrams)
1200332 / Jan '94 / Black Saint

☐ LIVE
1201222 / Sep '93 / Black Saint

Jenkins, Lillette

☐ LILLETTE JENKINS PLAYS LIL HARLEM ARMSTRONG
CRD 302 / Jan '93 / Chiaroscuro

Jenkins, Mark

☐ SPACE DREAMS VOL.1
AMPCD 015 / Feb '95 / AMP

☐ SPACE DREAMS VOL.2
AMPCD 030 / Apr '97 / AMP

Jenks, Glenn

☐ DUETS OF RAGS (Jenks, Glenn & Dan Gunstead)
SOSCD 1292 / Nov '95 / Stomp Off

Jenney, Jack

☐ STARDUST
Night is blue / High society / What is there to say / I'll get by / I've gone romantic on you / Stardust / Cuban boogie woogie / If you knew Susie
HEPCD 1045 / Mar '96 / Hep

Jennifers

☐ DRESSED FOR A DOG'S LIFE
HCCD 003 / 27 Apr '98 / Human Condition

Jennings, John

☐ BUDDY
Walking to China / It's only the rain / Do you want me now / Everybody wants me / Night will fall / Third of the world / Run run run / Another town / Willie Short / Monday night
VCD 79496 / Apr '97 / Vanguard

Jennings, Waylon

☐ ABILENE
CDSGP 0129 / Jan '95 / Prestige

☐ BACK IN THE SADDLE
HADCD 181 / Nov '95 / Javelin

☐ BEST OF WAYLON JENNINGS, THE
MUCD 3010 / Oct '94 / Musketeer

☐ BEST OF WAYLON JENNINGS, THE
74321378392 / Jul '96 / RCA

☐ CLASSIC COUNTRY COLLECTION, THE
Sally was a good ol' girl / Lorena / It's so easy / Burning memories / Don't think twice / Dream baby / Love's gonna live here / Money / Crying / White lightning / Abilene / Jole blon / Big mamou
AIM 3001CD / 20 Oct '97 / Aim

☐ CLOSING IN ON THE FIRE
ELDCD 005 / 22 Jun '98 / Ark 21

☐ CLOVIS TO PHOENIX (The Early Years)
My baby walks all over me / Stage / Another blue day / My world / Never again / Jole Blon / When sin stops / Crying / Sally was a good ole girl / Burning memories / Big mambou / Money / Don't think twice, it's alright / Dream baby / It's so easy / Lorena / Love's gonna live here / Abilene / White lightning
ZCD 2021 / Aug '95 / Zu Zazz

☐ ESSENTIAL WAYLON JENNINGS, THE
Only daddy that'll walk the line / Brown eyed handsome man / Taker / Good hearted woman / You asked me to / Amanda / Rainy day woman / Waymore's blues / Are you sure Hank done it this way / Wild side of life/It wasn't God who made honky tonk angels / Wurlitzer prize (I don't want to get over you) / Theme from Dukes of Hazard (Good ol' boys) / Storms never last: *Jennings, Waylon & Jessie Colter* / Just to satisfy you: *Jennings, Waylon & Willie Nelson* / Lucille (you won't do your daddy's will) / Never could toe the mark / America / Broken promised land / Drinkin' and dreamin' / Whatever happened to the blues
07863668572 / Aug '96 / RCA Nashville

☐ FOLK-COUNTRY
RE 821752 / 1 Sep '98 / Razor & Tie

☐ GREATEST HITS VOL.1
Lonesome, on'ry and mean / Ladies love outlaws / I've always been crazy / I'm a ramblin' man / Only daddy that'll walk the line / Amanda / Honky tonk heroes / Mamas don't let your babies grow up to be cowboys / Good hearted woman / Luckenbach, Texas (Back to the basics of love) / Texas / Are you sure Hank done it this way
ND 90304 / '90 / RCA

☐ MASTERS, THE
EABCD 025 / 24 Nov '97 / Eagle

☐ WAYMORE'S BLUES
Endangered species / Waymore's blues (part 2) / This train (Russell's song) / Wild ones / No good for me / Old timer / Up in Arkansas / Nobody knows come back and see me / You don't mess around with me
7863664092 / Oct '94 / RCA

☐ WHITE LIGHTNING
Burning memories / Big mammou / Mental revenge / White lightning / Love of the common people / Sally was a good old girl / Love's gonna live here / Jole blon / It's so easy / Lorena
15486 / Dec '94 / Laserlight

☐ WHITE LIGHTNING
MACCD 230 / Aug '96 / Autograph

☐ WHITE LIGHTNING (Jennings, Waylon/ Willie Nelson)
Don't think twice: Jennings, Waylon / Burning memories: Jennings, Waylon / Abilene: Jennings, Waylon / Money: Jennings, Waylon / Lorena: Jennings, Waylon / It's so easy: Jennings, Waylon / Dream baby: Jennings, Waylon / Crying: Jennings, Waylon / Big mamou: Jennings, Waylon / White lightening: Jennings, Waylon / Sally was a good old girl: Jennings, Waylon / Love's gonna live here: Jennings, Waylon / When sin stops: Jennings, Waylon / Jolie blond: Jennings, Waylon / Shelter of my arms: Nelson, Willie / Both ends of the candle: Nelson, Willie / Is there something on your mind: Nelson, Willie / Happiness lives next door: Nelson, Willie / Let's pretend: Nelson, Willie / Rainy day blues: Nelson, Willie
CD 6130 / Jul '98 / Music

Jenny & Carolyn
☐ FAREWELL ORKNEY
ATCD 045 / Aug '96 / Attic

Jenny Mae
☐ DON'T WAIT UP FOR ME
AW 47 / 18 May '98 / Anyway

Jensen, Ingrid
☐ HERE ON EARTH
Shiva's dance / Woodcarvings / Here on earth / Time remembered / You do something to me / Time of the barracudas / Ninety-one / Consolation / Fallin' / Avila and tequila
ENJ 93132 / Jun '97 / Enja

☐ VERNAL FIELDS
Marsh blues / Skookum spook / Vernal fields / Every time we say goodbye / I love you / Mingus that I knew / Stuck in the dark / Christiane / Be myself
ENJ 90132 / May '95 / Enja

Jensen, Kurt
☐ COPENHAGEN (A Tribute To Kid Thomas) (Jensen, Kurt New Orleans Jazz Band)
MECCACD 2028 / Oct '97 / Music Mecca

☐ JAZZ CLASSICS AND EVERGREENS (Jensen, Kurt New Orleans Trio/ Quartet)
MECCACD 2003 / May '97 / Music Mecca

Jensen, Nancy
☐ BACH NATURALLY
2236 / Aug '96 / NorthSound

Jentekor, Sandefjord
☐ PA FOLKEMUNNE
BD 7023CD / Apr '95 / Musikk Distribujson

Jepp
☐ JEPP
Superglue low / Go home early / Christy / Orbit / Barman / Tiny dancer / Guy I like / Las vegas / Bowling night / Parsons green / Young and supernatural
CDHUT 48 / 1 Jun '98 / Hut

Jericho
☐ JERICHO
REP 4058 / Aug '91 / Repertoire

Jericho Jones
☐ JUNKIES, MONKEYS AND DONKEYS
REP 4101 / Aug '91 / Repertoire

Jerks
☐ JERKS, THE
OVER 65CD / May '97 / Overground

Jerling, Michael
☐ NEW SUIT OF CLOTHES
SHCD 8010 / Dec '94 / Shanachie

Jerolamon, Jeff
☐ INTRODUCING (Jerolamon, Jeff & George Cables)
You stepped out of a dream / Dark side/light side / Straight no chaser / 'Round midnight / Quiet fire / Little B's poem / I thought about you
CCD 79522 / Feb '97 / Candid

☐ SWING THING
Midget / You go to my head / Idaho / Avalon / Seven come-eleven / Nancy with the laughing face / Evidence/Just you just me / Overtime / My heart tell me / Dark eyes / Lover come back to me
CCD 79538 / Feb '97 / Candid

Jerome, Jerry
☐ SOMETHING OLD SOMETHING NEW (2CD Set)
ARCD 19168 / Nov '97 / Arbors Jazz

Jeronimo
☐ JERONIMO
SB 044 / Oct '97 / Second Battle

Jerry's Kidz
☐ WELL FED SOCIETY
LF 294 / 27 Oct '97 / Lost & Found

Jeru The Damaja
☐ WRATH OF THE MATH
Wrath of the math / Frustrated nigga / Black cowboy / Tha bullshit / Whatever / Physical stamina / One day / Revenge of the prophet / Scientifical madness / Not tha average / Me or the papes / How I'm living / Too perverted / Ya playin' yaself / Invasion
8288462 / Oct '96 / FFRR

Jerusalem
☐ BOOK OF DAYS, THE
EFA 121782 / Jul '97 / Apollyon

Jessamine
☐ ANOTHER FICTIONALIZED HISTORY
HIST 1CD / 15 Sep '97 / Histronic

☐ DON'T STAY TOO LONG
KRANK 030CD / 10 Aug '98 / Kranky

☐ JESSAMINE
KRANK 003CD / Mar '97 / Kranky

☐ LONG ARM OF COINCIDENCE
KRANK 012CD / Mar '97 / Kranky

Jesse
☐ JESSE
SEEP 24CD / 27 Apr '98 / Rugger Bugger

Jesse, Graham
☐ REFLECTIONS
LB 9611 / Jul '98 / La Brava

Jesseyawn
☐ FOREVERMORE
HP 300011 / 15 Jun '98 / Horseplay

Jesto Funk
☐ REMIXES, THE
4893542 / 19 Jan '98 / Irma

☐ UNIVERSAL MOTHER
Universal mother (let yourself flow) / Be a warrior / Colour / Universal love: Jetsofunk & Jocelyn Brown / If you've got it you'll get it / Special love / Happy / Jetsofunk jetsofunk / Try my love / We are / Nel nome del suono / Why / Pfunk station / Earthquake / Flexion
TNL 2001032 / 18 May '98 / Irma

Jesus & Mary Chain
☐ AUTOMATIC
Here come Alice / Coast to coast / Blues from a gun / Between planets / UV ray / Her way of praying / Head on / Take it / Halfway to crazy / Gimme hell / Drop / Sunray
K 2462212 / Dec '96 / Blanco Y Negro

☐ BARBED WIRE KISSES
Kill surf city / Head / Rider / Hit / Don't ever change / Just out of reach / Happy place / Psycho candy / Sidewalking / Who do you love / Surfin' USA / Everything's alright when you're down / Upside down / Taste of Cindy / Swing / On the wall-f hole / Bo Diddley is Jesus / Here it comes again / Cracked / Mushroom
2423312 / Apr '88 / Blanco Y Negro

☐ DARKLANDS
April skies / Happy when it rains / Down on me / Deep one perfect / Fall / About you / Cherry came too / On the wall / Nine million rainy days
K 2421802 / Nov '94 / Blanco Y Negro

☐ HONEY'S DEAD
Rollercoaster / Reverence / Teenage lust / Almost gold / Catchfire / I can't get enough / Frequency / Sundown / Tumbledown / Sugar ray / Far gone and out / Good for my soul
9031765542 / Dec '96 / Blanco Y Negro

☐ MUNKI
CRECD 232 / 1 Jun '98 / Creation

☐ PSYCHO CANDY
Just like honey / Living end / Taste the floor / Hardest walk / Cut dead / In a hole / Taste of Cindy / Never understand / It's so hard / Inside me / Sowing seeds / My little underground / You trip me up / Something's wrong
2420002 / Oct '86 / Blanco Y Negro

☐ SOUND OF SPEED, THE
Snakedriver / Reverence / Heat / Teenage lust / Why'd you want me / Don't come down / Guitar man / Something I can't have / Sometimes / Write record release blues / Shimmer / Penetration / My girl / Tower of song / Little red rooster / Break me down / Lowlife / Deviant slice / Reverberation (doubt) / Sidewalking
4509931052 / Jul '93 / Blanco Y Negro

☐ STONED & DE-THRONED
Sometimes always / Between us / Dirty water / Save me / Bullet lovers / Hole / Come on / Feeling lucky / These days / You've been a friend / Everybody I know / Girlfriend / God help me / Till it shines / Wish I could / She / Never saw it coming
4509967172 / Dec '96 / Blanco Y Negro

Jesus Jones
☐ ALREADY
Next big thing / Run on empty / Look out tomorrow / Top of the world / Rails / Wishing it away / Chemical no.1 / Motion / They're out there / For moment / Addiction / Obsession and me / February
FOODCD 22 / Aug '97 / Food

☐ DOUBT
Trust me / Who, Where, Why / International bright young thing / I'm burning / Right here, right now / Nothing to hold me / Real real real / Welcome back Victoria / Two and two / Stripped / Blissed
FOODCD 5 / Feb '94 / Food

☐ LIQUIDIZER
Move mountains / Never enough / Real world / All the answers / What's going on / Song 13 / Info freako / Bring it on down / Too much to learn / What would you know / One for the money / Someone to blame
FOODCD 3 / 6 Jul '98 / EMI Gold

Jesus Lizard
☐ BLUE
I can learn / Horse doctor / Eucalyptus / Tale of two women / Cold water / And then the rain / Postcoital glow / Until it stopped to die / Soft damage / Happy snakes / Needles for teeth / Terremoto
8592662 / 20 Apr '98 / Capitol

☐ DOWN
TG 131CD / Aug '94 / Touch & Go

☐ GOAT
TG 68CD / Feb '91 / Touch & Go

☐ HEAD
TGCD 54 / Jul '93 / Touch & Go

☐ LIAR
Boilermaker / Boilermaker / Art of self-defense / Slave ship / Puss / Whirl / Rope / Perk / Zachariah / Dancing naked ladies
TG 100CD / Oct '92 / Touch & Go

☐ SHOT
Thumper / Blue shot / Thumbscrews / Good riddance / Mailman / Skull of a German / Trephination / More beautiful than Barbie / Too bad about the fire / Churl / Now then / Inamorata / Pervertedly slow
CDEST 2284 / May '96 / Capitol

Jesus Loves You
☐ MARTYR MANTRAS, THE
Generations of love / One on one / Love's gonna let you get down / After the love / I specialize in loneliness / No clause / Love hurts / Siempre te amare / Too much love / Bow down mister
CUMCD 1 / Mar '91 / More Protein

Jesus Messerschmitt
☐ JESUS MESSERSCHMITT
343752 / Sep '96 / No Bull

Jet
☐ CPH 2000
APR 017CD / Apr '97 / April

Jet Black Machine
☐ JET BLACK MACHINE
PPR 002 / Jun '96 / Phantom Power

Jet Red
☐ JET RED
CDMFN 94 / Aug '89 / Music For Nations

Jet Streams
☐ SECRET GOLDFISH, THE
MA 26 / May '97 / Marina

Jeter, Rev. Claude
☐ YESTERDAY AND TODAY
SHCD 6010 / Mar '95 / Shanachie

Jethro Tull
☐ 20 YEARS OF JETHRO TULL
Stormy Monday blues / Love story / New day yesterday / Summer day sands / Coronach / March the mad scientist / Pibroch (pee break) / Black satin / Lick your fingers clean / Overhand / Crossword / Saturation / Jack-a-Lynn / Motoreyes / Part of the machine / Mayhem / Maybe / Kelpie / Under wraps 2 / Wond'ring aloud / Dun ringill / Life's a long song / Nursie grace / Witch's promise / Teacher / Living in the past / Aqualung / Locomotive breath
CCD 1655 / Nov '89 / Chrysalis

☐ 25TH ANNIVERSARY BOX SET (4CD Set)
My Sunday feeling (remix) / Song for Jeffrey (Remix) / Living in the past (Remix) / Teacher / Sweet dream / Cross-eyed Mary / Witch's promise / Life is a long song / Bungle in the jungle / Minstrel in the gallery / Cold wind to Valhalla / Too old to rock 'n' roll, too young to die / Songs from the wood / Heavy horses / Black Sunday / Broadsword / My God / With you there to help me / Song for Jeffrey / To cry you a song / Sossity, you're a woman / Reasons for waiting / We used to know / Guitar solo / For a thousand mothers / So much trouble / My Sunday feeling / Someday the sun won't shine for you / Living in the past / Bouree / With you there to help me / Thick as a brick / Cheerio / New day yesterday / Protect and survive / Jack-a-Lynn / Whistler / My God / Aqualung / To be sad is a mad way to be / Back to the family / Passion play extract / Wind-up/Locomotive breath/Land of Hope and Glory/Wind-up / Seal driver / Nobody's car / Pussy willow / Budapest / Nothing is easy / Kissing Willie / Still loving you tonight / Beggar's farm' Passion Jig / Song for Jeffrey (Live) / Living in the past (Live)
CDCHR 6004 / Apr '93 / Chrysalis

☐ A
Crossfire / Flyingdale flyer / Working John, working Joe / Black Sunday / Protect and survive / Batteries not included / Uniform / 4 WD (low ratio) / Pine martin's jig / And further on / Bod
CCD 1301 / Jan '89 / Chrysalis

☐ AQUALUNG
Aqualung / Cross-eyed Mary / Cheap day return / Mother goose / Wond'ring aloud / Up to me / My God / Hymn 43 / Slipstream / Locomotive / Breath / Wind up
CD25CR 08 / Mar '94 / Chrysalis

☐ AQUALUNG (25th Anniversary Edition)
Aqualung / Cross eyed Mary / Cheap day return / Mother Goose / Wond'ring aloud / Up to me / My God / Hymn 43 / Slipstream / Locomotive breath / Wind up / Lick your fingers clean / Wind up / Excerpts from the Ian Anderson interview / Song for Jeffrey / Fat man / Bouree
CD25AQUA 1 / Jun '96 / Chrysalis

☐ BBC LIVE IN CONCERT
Minstrel in the gallery / This is not love / Rocks on the road / Heavy horses / Tall thin girl / Still loving you / Thick as a brick / New day yesterday / Blues jam / Jump start
SFRSCD 051 / 23 Feb '98 / Strange Fruit

☐ BENEFIT
With you there to help me / Nothing to say / Alive and well and living in / Son for Michael Collins / Jeffrey and me / To cry you a song / Time for everything / Inside / Play in time / Sossity / You're a woman
CPCD 1043 / Jun '87 / Chrysalis

☐ BEST OF JETHRO TULL, THE (2CD Set)
Song for Jeffrey / Beggar's farm / Christmas song / New day yesterday / Bouree / Nothing is easy / Living in the past / To cry you a song / Teacher / Sweet dream / Cross-eyed Mary / Mother goose / Aqualung / Locomotive breath / Life is a long song / Thick as a brick / Passion play / Skating away (on the thin ice of the new day) / Bungle in the jungle / Minstrel in the gallery / Too old to rock and roll, too young to die / Songs from the wood / Jack in the green / Whistler / Heavy horses / Dun ringill / Flyingdale flyer / Jack-a-Lynn / Pussy willow / Broadsword / Under wraps 2 / Steel monkey / Farm on the freeway / Jump start / Kissing Willie / This is not love
CDCHR 6001 / May '93 / Chrysalis

☐ BROADSWORD AND THE BEAST, THE
Beastie / Clasp / Fallen on hard times / Flying colours / Slow marching / Broadsword / Pussy willow / Watching me watching you / Seal driver / Cheerio
CCD 1380 / Apr '82 / Chrysalis

☐ CATFISH RISING
This is not love / Occasional demons / Rocks on the road / Thinking round corners / Still loving you tonight / Doctor to my disease / Like a tall thin girl / Sparrow on the schoolyard wall / Roll yer own / Gold-tipped boots, black jacket and tie
CCD 1886 / Sep '97 / Chrysalis

☐ CLASSIC CASE, A (The Music Of Jethro Tull Featuring Ian Anderson) (Palmer, David & The London Symphony Orchestra)
Locomotive breath / Thick as a brick / Elegy / Bouree / Fly by night / Aqualung / Too old to rock 'n' roll, too young to die / Teacher / Bungle in the jungle / Rainbow blues / Living in the past / War child
09026625102 / Apr '94 / RCA Victor

☐ CREST OF A KNAVE
Steel monkey / Farm on the freeway / Jump start / Said she was a dancer / Budapest / Mountain men / Raising steam / Waking edge / Dogs in the midwinter
CCD 1590 / Sep '87 / Chrysalis

☐ HEAVY HORSES
And the mouse police never sleeps / Acres wild / No lullaby / Moths / Journeyman / Rover / One brown mouse / Heavy horses / Weathercock
CCD 1175 / '86 / Chrysalis

☐ JETHRO TULL COLLECTION, THE
Acres wild / Locomotive breath / Dharma for one / Wind up / War child / Budapest / Whistler / We used to know / Beastie / Rare and precious chain / Quizz kid / Still loving you tonight / Living in the past
DC 878612 / Mar '97 / Disky

☐ LITTLE LIGHT MUSIC, A
Some day the sun won't shine for you / Living in the past / Life is a long song / Under wraps / Rocks on the road / Nursie / Too old to rock 'n' roll, too young to die / One white duck / New day yesterday / John Barleycorn / Look into the sun / Christmas song / From a dead beat to an old greaser / Bouree / Pussy willow
CCD 1954 / Sep '97 / Chrysalis

☐ LIVING IN THE PAST
Witches promise / Song for Jeffrey / Love story / Christmas song / Living in the past / Driving song / Bouree / Sweet dream / Singing all day / Witch's promise / Inside / Just trying to be / By kind permission of you / Dharma for one / Wondering again / Locomotive breath / Life is a long song / Up the 'Pool / Dr. Bogenbroom / For later / Nursie
CCD 1575 / Feb '94 / Chrysalis

☐ MINSTREL IN THE GALLERY
Minstrel in the gallery / Cold wind to Valhalla / Black satin dancer / Requiem / One white duck / O 10 equals nothing at all / Baker St. muse / Including pig me and the whore / Nice little tune / Crash barrier waltzer / Mother England reverie / Grace
CCD 1082 / '86 / Chrysalis

☐ MU - THE BEST OF JETHRO TULL VOL.1
Teacher / Aqualung / Thick as a brick / Bungle in the jungle / Locomotive breath / Fat man / Living in the past / Passion play / Skating away (on the thin ice of the new day) / Rainbow blues / Nothing is easy
ACCD 1078 / Dec '85 / Chrysalis

☐ NIGHT CAP - THE UNRELEASED MASTERS 1972-1991
First post / Animelee / Tiger toon / Look at the animals / Law of the bungle / Law of the bungle (part II) / Left right / Solitaire / Critique oblique / Post last / Scenario / Audition / No rehearsal / Paradise steakhouse / Sealion II / Piece of cake / Quartet / Silver river turning / Crew nights / Curse / Rosa on the factory floor / Small cigar / Man of principle / Commons brawl / No step / Drive on the young side of life / I don't want to be me / Broadford bazaar / Lights out / Truck stop runner / Hard liner
CDCHR 6057 / Nov '93 / Chrysalis

☐ ORIGINAL MASTERS
Living in the past / Aqualung / Too old to rock 'n' roll, too young to die / Locomotive breath / Skating away (on the thin ice of the new day) / Bungle in the jungle / Sweet dream / Songs from the wood / Witches promise / Thick as a brick / Minstrel in the gallery / Life is a long song
CCD 1515 / Apr '86 / Chrysalis

☐ REPEAT (The Best Of Jethro Tull)
Minstrel in the gallery / Cross-eyed Mary / New day yesterday / Bouree / Thick as a brick / War child / Passion play / To cry you a song / Too old to rock 'n' roll, too young to die / Glory row
CCD 1135 / Apr '86 / Chrysalis

☐ ROCK ISLAND
Kissing Willie / Rattlesnake trail / Ears of tin / Undressed to kill / Rock Island / Heavy water / Another Christmas song / Whaler's dues / Big riff and Mando / Strange avenues
CCD 1708 / Sep '97 / Chrysalis

☐ ROOTS TO BRANCHES
Roots to branches / Rare and precious chain / Out of the noise / This free will / Valley / Dangerous veils / Beside myself / Wounded, old and treacherous / At last forever / Stuck in the August rain / Another Harry's bar
CDCHR 6109 / Sep '97 / Chrysalis

☐ SONGS FROM THE WOOD
Songs from the wood / Jack in the green / Cup of wonder / Hunting girl / Ring out, Solstice bells / Velvet green / Whistler / Pibroch (cap in hand) / Fire at midnight
ACCD 1132 / '86 / Chrysalis

☐ STAND UP
New day yesterday / Jeffrey goes to Leicester Square / Bouree / Back to the family / Look into the sun / Nothing is easy / Fat man / We used to know / Reasons for waiting / For a thousand mothers
CCD 1042 / Jan '89 / Chrysalis

☐ STORM WATCH
North Sea oil / Orion / Home / Dark ages / Warm sporran / Something's on the move / Old ghosts / Dunringill / Flying Dutchman / Elegy
CCD 1238 / Jan '89 / Chrysalis

☐ THICK AS A BRICK (25th Anniversary)
Thick as a brick / Interviews
CDCNTAV 5 / Jun '97 / Chrysalis

☐ THIS WAS
My Sunday feeling / Someday the sun won't shine for you / For you / Beggar's farm / Move on alone / Serenadeto a cuckoo / Dharma for one / It's breaking me / Cat's squirrel / Song for Jeffrey / Round
CCD 1041 / '86 / Chrysalis

☐ THIS WAS/STAND UP/BENEFIT (The Originals/3CD Set)
My Sunday feeling / Someday the sun won't shine for you / Beggar's farm / Move on alone / Serenadeto a cuckoo / Dharma for one / It's breaking me / Cat's squirrel / Song for Jeffrey / New day yesterday / Jeffery goes to Leicester Square / Bouree / Back to the family / Look into the sun / Nothing is easy / Fat man / We used to know / Reasons for waiting / For a thousand mothers / With you there to help me / Nothing to say / Alive and well and living in / Son for Michael Collins / Jeffrey and me / To cry you a song / Time for everything / Inside / Play in time / Sossity / You've a woman
CDOMB 021 / 27 Jul '98 / Chrysalis

☐ THROUGH THE YEARS
Living in the past / Wind up / Warchild / Dharma for one / Acres wild / Budapest / Whistler / We used to know / Beastie / Locomotive breath / Rare and precious chain / Quizz kid / Still loving you tonight
CDGOLD 1079 / Feb '97 / EMI Gold

☐ TO CRY YOU A SONG (A Tribute To Jethro Tull) (Various Artists)
RR 88722 / Aug '96 / Roadrunner

☐ TOO OLD TO ROCK AND ROLL
Quizz kid / Crazed institution / Salamander / Taxi grab / From a dead beat to an old greaser / Bad eyed and loveless / Big dipper / Too old to rock 'n' roll, too young to die / Pied piper / Chequered flag (dead of alive)
CCD 1111 / '86 / Chrysalis

☐ UNDER WRAPS
Lap of luxury / Under wraps / European legacy / Later the same evening / Saboteur / Radio free Moscow / Nobody's car / Heat / Under wraps 2 / Paparazzi / Apologee
CCD 1461 / Sep '84 / Chrysalis

Jets

☐ ALL FIRED UP
KRYPCD 202 / Aug '91 / Krypton

☐ ONE FOR THE ROAD
KYPCD 204 / Apr '95 / Krypton

☐ STARE STARE STARE
KRYPCD 205 / Feb '97 / Krypton

Jetset

☐ BEST OF THE JETSET TOO
Count the beating hearts / (and that's the) good news / Mr. maybe / You should know by now / Make believe world of melanie bennett / Once in a lifetime / One more summer romance / Little miss rainbow / What a way to go / R.s.v.p. / Late great frank lewis / Sunday way of life / Two minute war / A million lies / Live and let love / Hard to say goodbye / Welcome to the bomb / Housewives' choice / A dead giveaway / A quick apology / Dear world / Yesterday's news
TANGCD 5 / May '93 / Tangerine

☐ BEST OF THE JETSET, THE
TANGCD 1 / Aug '92 / Tangerine

Jett, Joan

☐ I LOVE ROCK 'N' ROLL (Jett, Joan & The Blackhearts)
I love rock 'n' roll / I'm gonna run away / Love is pain / Nag / Crimson and clover / Victim of circumstance / Bits and pieces / Be straight / You're too possessive / Oh woe is me / Louie louie intro / Louie louie / You don't know what you got
4865092 / Feb '97 / Columbia

Jeune

☐ BACK TO REALITY
SR 40032 / Oct '96 / PLR

Jeunes Sonneurs

☐ CENTRAL BRITTANY
CD 437 / Mar '96 / Arfolk

Jewel

☐ PIECES OF YOU
Who will save your soul / Morning song / Painters / Amen / Angel standing by / Daddy / Don't / You were meant for me / I'm sensitive / Adrian / Pieces of you / Little sister / Foolish games / Near you always
7567827002 / Jun '96 / Atlantic

Jewish Theatre Orchestra

☐ YIDDISH FOLKSONGS (Spiritual & Traditional Music)
15185 / '91 / Laserlight

Jezebelle

☐ BAD ATTITUDE
Ain't no lady / Leave me alone / Travel on gypsy / Other side / Scandal / No mercy / Satisfaction guaranteed / Boulevard / Bum
HMRXD 148 / May '90 / Heavy Metal

JFK

☐ FOUR DAYS THAT SHOCK THE WORLD
RPM 122 / Oct '93 / RPM

Jhelisa

☐ LANGUAGE ELECTRIC
Language electric / Sending you a message / Freedom from pity / Sell me away (who will protect me from my own people) / Bete noir / That's bullshit Woody / My ego needs me tonight / Everybody jump off / Story of a musician's madness / Feeling that feeling / Live no lie
DOR 56CD / Mar '97 / Dorado

Jiani, Carol

☐ BEST OF CAROL JIANI, THE (Hit 'n' Run Lover)
HTCD 77 / 20 Apr '98 / Hot Productions

Jiddische Stikele

☐ JEWISH SONGS FROM THE PRAGUE GHETTO
9992533432 / 17 Mar '98 / SPP

Jigsaw

☐ BEST OF JIGSAW, THE (Sky High)
HTCD 71 / 20 Apr '98 / Hot Productions

Jigsy King

☐ ASHES TO ASHES
VPCD 1427 / Sep '95 / VP

☐ HAVE TO GET YOU
CRCD 19 / Jul '93 / Charm

Jiker

☐ EH FOR AN EH, AN
ELM 023CD / 2 Mar '98 / Elevator

Jim & Jesse

☐ BLUEGRASS AND MORE (5CD Set)
Stormy horizons / Gosh I miss you all the time / Flame of love / Beautiful moon of Kentucky / My empty arms / Diesel train / Voice of my darling / Uncle Will played the fiddle / Fireball / Heartaches and flowers / Sweet little miss blue eyes / Somebody loves you darlin' / She left me standing on the mountain / Don't say goodbye if you love me / Wish you knew / When it's time for the whippoorwill to sing / Grave in the valley / Blue bonnet lane / Are you missing me / Congratulations, anyway / Pickin' and a-grinnin / Stoney creek / Sixteen hundred miles from home / South bound train / Ballad of Thunder Road / Uncle Jimmy Lee / What about you / When my blue moon turns to gold again / Nine pound hammer / Little paper boy / I wonder where you are tonight / Just when I needed you / Las Cassas, Tennessee / Drifting and dreaming of you / Grass is greener / Violet and the rose / Take my ring from your finger / Why not confess / Better times a-coming / Wild Georgia boys / Cotton mill man / To the top of the world / Old time religion / Old camp meeting days / Old country church / Are you washed in the blood / It's a lonesome road / Swing low, sweet chariot / Kneel at the cross / Rock of ages / Where the roses never fade / Lord I'm coming home / This world is not my home / Where the soul never dies / Ole slew foot / Sleepy eyed John / Tell her lies and feed her candy / Y'all come / Company's coming / Stay a little longer / Rabbit in the log / Salty dog blues / Alabama / Good bunch of bisquits / Bluegrass banjo / Don't let nobody tie you down / Big hands / Dancing Molly / If you've seen one you've seen them all / Memphis / Maybellene / Johnny B Goode / Sweet little sixteen / Roll over Beethoven / Reelin' and rockin' / Brown eyed handsome man / Too much monkey business / Bye bye Johnny / Back in the USA / God moved in / I'll wear the banner / Weapon of prayer / Angel mother / Sing unto him a new song / In God's eyes / Who did, Jesus did / How much are you worth / He walks on the water / River of Jordan / Where the chilly winds don't blow / All for the love of a girl / Diesel on my tail / Truck driving man / Six days on the road / Sam's place / Ballad of Thunder Road / Lovin' machine / Hot rod race / Girl on the billboard / Give me forty acres / Tijuana taxi / Greenwich Village folksongs salesman / Pretty girls (in mini skirts) / Yonder comes a freight train / Rose City Chimes / Wildwood flower / Orange blossom special / Buckaroo / Remington ride / Sugarfoot rag / Maiden's prayer / Down yonder / Banderilla / We'll build a bridge / When the snow is on the roses / Then I'll stop goin' for you / Big job / Are you teasing me / I don't believe you've met my baby / My baby's gone / Cash on the barrelhead / Childish love / Must you throw dust in my face / When I stop dreaming / Knoxville girl / I take the chance / I'm hoping that you're hoping / Fire ball mail / Streamlined cannonball / Tennessee Central 9 / (I heard that) Lonesome whistle / Pan American / Golden rocket / Freight train in my mind / I like trains / Wabash cannonball
BCD 15716 / Sep '94 / Bear Family

☐ CLASSIC RECORDINGS (1952-1955)
I'll wash your love from my heart / Just wondering why / Are you missing me / I will always be waiting for you / Virginia waltz / Are you lost in sin / Look for me (I'll be there) / Purple heart / Airmail special / My little honeysuckle rose / Waiting for a message / Too many tears / My darling's in heaven / Two arms to hold me / Is it true / Memory of you / I'll wear the banner / My garden of love / Tears of regret / I'll see you tonight (in my dreams)
BCD 15635 / Apr '92 / Bear Family

Jimenez, Don Santiago

☐ HIS FIRST AND LAST RECORDINGS
ARHCD 414 / Apr '95 / Arhoolie

☐ MONTELONGO
SCR 44 / Aug '96 / Strictly Country

Jimenez, Fernando

☐ LA FIESTA
TUMICD 012 / Apr '90 / Tumi

Jimenez, Flaco

☐ ARIBA EL NORTE
NETCD 1008 / Aug '94 / Network

☐ AY TE DEJO EN SAN ANTONIO
ARHCD 318 / Apr '95 / Arhoolie

☐ ENTRE HUMO Y BOTELLAS
NETCD 1007 / Aug '94 / Network

☐ FLACO'S AMIGOS
La tumba sera el final / Did I tell you / Jennette / Te quiero mas / Mi primer amor / Free Mexican air force / Lucerito / Espero tu regreso / Poquita fe / Feria polka / Para toda la vida / I'm gonna love you like there is no tomorrow / Yo quisiera saber / Atotonilco
ARHCD 3027 / Apr '95 / Arhoolie

☐ FLACO'S FIRST
ARHCD 370 / Apr '95 / Arhoolie

☐ LO MEJOR DE FLACO JIMENEZ
BMPE 2 / 5 Jan '98 / Fresh Sound

☐ SAN ANTONIO SOUL
NETCD 1009 / Aug '94 / Network

☐ TEX-MEX PARTY (Jimenez, Flaco/ Santiago Jimenez Jr.)
Mis movidas: *Jimenez, Flaco* / Victoria: *Jimenez, Flaco* / Eres un encanto: *Jimenez, Flaco* / El perdido: *Jimenez, Flaco* / Que lo sepa el mundo: *Jimenez, Flaco* / La esperanza: *Jimenez, Flaco* / La Hawaiana: *Jimenez, Santiago Jr.* / De San Antonio a Penjamo: *Jimenez, Santiago Jr.* / La mujer: *Jimenez, Santiago Jr.* / El corrido de Santiago Jimenez: *Jimenez, Santiago Jr.* / Ya llegaron a la luna: *Jimenez, Santiago Jr.* / Zulema waltz: *Jimenez, Santiago Jr.*
EDCD 7041 / Jul '97 / Easydisc

☐ UN MOJADA SIN LICENCIA (Original Hits 1955-1967)
El guero polkas (polka) / Tesoro de mi alma (ranchera) / Sin fe (bolero) / Hasta la tumba (ranchera) / Mujer fatal (ranchera) / Virgencita de mi vida (ranchera) / Un mojado sin licencia (corrido) / El padre de un soldado (corrido) / Victimas de huracan beulah (corrido) / De rodillas quisiera mirarte (ranchera) / La primer noche de mayo (ranchera) / De aqui pa'l real (ranchera) / El troquero (ranchera) / Viajando en polka (polka) / Cuando mas tranquila (ranchera) / Mi borrachera (ranchera) / No me digas que te vas (ranchera) / Desvelado (ranchera) / Bajo sexto y accordeon (redova) / No te andes apasionando (ranchera) / Pa' que son pasiones (ranchera) / Ella me dijo que no (ranchera) / Alma rendida (ranchera) / No seas tonta mujer (ranchera)
ARHCD 396 / Apr '95 / Arhoolie

☐ VIVA SEGUIN
Viva sequin / La botellita / Hasta la vista / Los amores del flaco / Mi dulce amor / Horalia / Arriba el norte / Polka town / La piedrera / Viajando en polka marianela / Adios muchachos
SCR 42 / Nov '95 / Strictly Country

Jimenez, Rafael Jimenez

☐ CANTE GITANO
131122 / Aug '96 / Celestial Harmonies

Jimenez, Santiago Jr.

☐ CAMA DE PIEDRA
829462 / Jul '97 / BUDA

☐ CANCIONES DE MI PADRE
WM 1019CD / May '94 / Watermelon

☐ CORRIDOS DE LA FRONTERA
Valente quintero / El contrabando del paso / Jacinto trevino / La carga blanca / El cocoliso / Luis Martinez / Preso sin delito / Tres viudas solas / No me quiren por borracho / Juan Leyva
WMCD 1066 / May '98 / Watermelon

☐ EL MERO, MERO DE SAN ANTONIO
Ester de mi amor (polka) / Los barrandales del puente (cancion) / Pa' que andas diciendo (ranchera) / Chipina (vals) / Morena, morenita (ranchera) / California polka (polka) / Flor de dalia (mazurka) / Porque eres mujer casada (ranchera) / El alacran (cumbia) / Por quien me dejas (ranchera) / Tejano huapango (huapango) / Los huajolotes (redova) / Cada vez que cae la tarde (ranchera) / Negra ausencia (vals) / Rosa de san antonio (polka) / Mercado del paso (chotis) / El tono de mi rancho (huapango) / Por to mujer (ranchera) / Cumbia nortena (cumbia) / Atotonilco (polka) / Tienes que pagar (bolero) / Viva seguin (polka)
ARHCD 317 / Apr '95 / Arhoolie

☐ LIVE IN HOLLAND
SCR 38 / Mar '95 / Strictly Country

☐ MUSICA DE TIEMPOS PASADOS DEL PRESENTE Y FUTURO
WM 1035 / Jul '95 / Watermelon

☐ PURELY INSTRUMENTAL
Tocale otra vez / Maria te quiero / Bailar otra vez / Los caballitos / La paloma / Buenus tardes / Nuestro amor / Adios muchachos / El casino / Los arbolitos / El trenicito / Yolanda / Las copetonas / Sonando contigo / Los brinquitos / Las polkas de alemania
ARHCD 466 / Jul '98 / Arhoolie

Jimmies

☐ COUNTDOWN
SCZZ 228 / Feb '97 / Schizophonic

Jimmy & Johnny

☐ IF YOU DON'T SOMEBODY ELSE WILL
BCD 15771 / Jun '97 / Bear Family

Jinda, George

☐ BETWEEN DREAMS
SH 5020 / Mar '96 / Shanachie

☐ GEORGE JINDA & THE WORLD NEWS (Jinda, George & World News)
With a message / Springshot / Luscious Rebecca / Seven unfinished dreams / It could have been you / Snowbow / Mariella / Sheila's Caribbean skin / For miles
JVC 20142 / Nov '97 / JVC

☐ RELIABLE SOURCES (Jinda, George & World News)
Reliable sources / Behind the scenes / Storyteller / High road / Overleafing a new turn / Code of silence / Serengeti sky / Force of habit / For the rain forest
JVC 20232 / Nov '93 / JVC

Jing, Pang

☐ CLASSICAL CHINESE FOLK MUSIC (Jing, Pang & Ensemble)
EUCD 1186 / Apr '92 / ARC

Jing Ying Soloists

☐ EVENING SONG (Traditional Chinese Music)
Autumn moon / Ducks quacking / Love song of the grassland / Singing the night among fishing boats / Fishing song / Marriage of Chan Xian-Yuen / Moonlight over the spring river / Happy reunion / Bamboo song from the village / Variations on Yang City tune / Meditating on the past / Moon over Guan-Shan
CDSDL 368 / Mar '94 / Saydisc

☐ LIKE WAVES AGAINST THE SAND
Flowing streams / Suzhou scenery / Races / Love at the fair / High moon / Night / Chinese martial arts / Flower fair / Shenpadei folksong / Like waves against the sand / Bird song / Legend
CDSDL 325 / Mar '94 / Saydisc

Jinmo

☐ LIVE AT THE KNITTING FACTORY
KFWCD 129 / Feb '95 / Knitting Factory

Jivaros Quartet

☐ NEAR THE NOISE
L 8909301 / Jan '90 / Danceteria

Jive Aces

☐ BOLT FROM THE BLUE
JA 001 / Jan '98 / Jive Aces

☐ OUR KINDA JIVE
JACD 1000 / Jan '97 / Jive Aces

Jive Bunny

☐ NON STOP JUKE BOX
MCCD 239 / Mar '96 / Music Club

☐ PARTY CRAZY
MCCD 286 / Mar '97 / Music Club

☐ POP BACK IN TIME TO THE '70S (Jive Bunny & The Mastermixers)
Glam rock party / Disco flashback / 70's poptastic / Euro pop mix
MCCD 309 / 8 Sep '97 / Music Club

Jive Five

☐ OUR TRUE STORY
My true story / Do you hear wedding bells / Beggin' you please / Rain / Johnny never knew / People from another world / What time is it / When I was single / These golden rings / Girl with the wind in her hair / I don't want to be without you baby / No not again / You know what I would do / Never never / Hully gully callin' time / Hurry back
CDCH 76 / Aug '91 / Ace

Jive Turkey

☐ PERFUME EXPERIMENT
DANCD 042 / Sep '90 / Danceteria

JJB Sports Leyland Band

☐ LIGHT AS AIR
I got rhythm / Pittsburgh overture / Cute / Over the rainbow / Bohemian rhapsody / Light as air / Marching through Georgia / Colours of the wind / Kirkby Lonsdale / Concerto for flugel horn / Nightingale sang in Berkeley Square / Ticket to ride / Stardust / March of the toys / Indiana Jones and the temple of doom
QPRL 084D / Oct '97 / Polyphonic

☐ SPORTING BRASS
Grandstand / Pop looks Bach / I vow to thee my country / Olympic fanfare and theme / Mack and Mabel / Out of the blue / Champions / Gonna fly now / Summon the heroes / Nessun dorma / Trap / Abide with me / Match of the day / Capriccio Espagnol
QPRL 092D / May '98 / Polyphonic

JK

☐ SUDDENLY ONE SUMMER (JK & Co.)
AFT 18 / 16 Mar '98 / Afterglow

JK Experience

☐ JK
Off the hook / What's the word / Gina / Ain't it good to know / In the pocket / Love Jones / In my bedroom / She's got somethin' / So sorry / Say love say when / This must be love / Seduction
5571112 / 3 Aug '98 / Verve Forecast

Joan Of Arc

☐ HOW MEMORY WORKS
JT 1037CD / 25 May '98 / Jade Tree

☐ PORTABLE MODEL OF...
JT 1033CD / 1 Jun '98 / Jade Tree

Joao, Maria

☐ FABULA
5332162 / Oct '96 / Verve

Jobarteh, Pa Bobo

☐ KAIRA (Jobarteh, Pa Bobo & The Kaira Trio)
WSCD 103 / Oct '97 / Womad Select

☐ KAIRA NAATA (Jobarteh, Pa Bobo & The Kaira Trio)
WSCD 013 / Mar '98 / Womad Select

Jobim, Antonio Carlos

☐ ANTONIO BRASILIERO
So danco samba / Piano na manguiera / How insensitive / Querida surfboard / Samba de maria luiza / Forever green / Maracangalha / Maricotinha pato preto / Meu amigo radames / Blue train (trem azul) / Radames y pele / Chora coracao / Trem de ferro
4762812 / 26 Jan '98 / Sony Jazz

☐ BEST OF ANTONIO CARLOS JOBIM VOL.1, THE
Double rainbow / Wave / Someone to light up my life / How insensitive / Anos durados / Janelas abertas / Love theme from The Adventures / Pardon my english / Estrada du sol / Triste / Waters of March / Caminhos cruzados / A felicidade
12631 / May '97 / Laserlight

☐ BEST OF ANTONIO CARLOS JOBIM VOL.2, THE
Dreamer / Meditation / Once I loved / Sabia / Modinha / Bolero from 'The Adventurers' / Quiet night of quiet stars / Agua de Beber / Vivo Sonhando / Useless landscape / One note samba / Retrato em branco e preto
12632 / Oct '97 / Laserlight

☐ BLUE NOTE PLAYS JOBIM (Various Artists)
Desafinado: *Gilberto, Joao* / Waters of March: *Elias, Elaine* / Wave: *Turrentine, Stanley* / How insensitive: *Lagrene, Birelli* / O amore em paz: *Pearson, Duke* / Corcovado: *Green, Grant* / Useless landscape: *Jackson, Javon* / No more blues: *McRae, Carmen* / She's a carioca: *Turrentine, Stanley* / Se todas fossem iquais a voce: *Wilson, Jack* / Triste: *Klugh, Earl* / Girl from Ipanema: *Elias, Elaine* / Samba de uma nota so: *Gilberto, Joao*
CDP 8352832 / Mar '96 / Blue Note

☐ COMPOSER PLAYS, THE
Girl from Ipanema / O morro / Auga de beber / Dreamer / Favela / How insensitive / Corcovado / One note samba / Meditation / Jazz samba / Chega de saudade / Desafinado
8230112 / Mar '94 / Verve

☐ COMPOSER PLAYS, THE (Remastered)
5214312 / Oct '97 / Verve Master Edition

☐ DEDICATED TO ANTONIO CARLOS JOBIM VOL.1 (Various Artists)
Samba de uma nota so / Desafinado / Chega de saudade / Corcovado / Meditacao / O amor em paz / How insensitive / Outra vez (once again) / Disscissao / O Grand amor / Dreamer / Brigas, nunca maiss / So em tues bracos / So danco samba / Este seu olhar / A felicidade
CD 62083 / Jan '96 / Saludos Amigos

☐ ESTRADA BRANCA
KAR 27 / May '96 / Kardum

☐ GIRL FROM IPANEMA, THE
CD 62084 / Jan '96 / Saludos Amigos

☐ GIRL FROM IPANEMA, THE
Girl from Ipanema / Look to the sky / Antigua / Tema jazz / Caribe / Red blouse / Lamento / Carinhoso / Takatanga / Batidinha / Tide / Rockanalia / Mojave / Triste / Sue Ann / Captain bacardi / Dialogo / Wave / Remember
5405822 / Oct '96 / A&M

☐ INEDITO (2CD Set)
74321467062 / May '97 / Milan

☐ JAZZ MASTERS
Corcovado / Dreamer / So danco samba / Desafinado / Waters of March / O grande amor / Agua de beber / Double rainbow / O morro tem tem vez / How insensitive / Inutil paisasagem / Favela / Por todo minha vida / Triste / Borzeguim
5164092 / 5 May '98 / Verve

☐ JOBIM & FRIENDS (Live In Brazil 1993) (Various Artists)
5315562 / Jul '96 / Verve

☐ LES PLUS BELLES CHANSONS DE (Jobim, Antonio Carlos & Vinicus De Moraes)
KAR 073 / Apr '97 / IMP

☐ LIVE IN RIO DE JANEIRO (Jobim, Antonio Carlos & Vinicus De Moraes/ Toquinho/Miucha)
1917462 / Apr '97 / EPM

☐ SAMBA MOODS (The Music Of Antonio Carlos Jobim) (Various Artists)
Girl from Ipanema / Wave / Antigua / One note samba / Lamento / Mojave / Tema jazz / She's a carioca / Dindi / Corcavado / Red blouse / Meditation / Triste / How insensitive
307512 / Aug '97 / Hallmark

☐ STONE FLOWER
Brazil / Stone flower / God and the devil in the land of the sun / Sabia / Choro / Andorinha / Amparo / Children's games / Tereza my love
4722382 / Jan '95 / Sony Jazz

☐ TRIBUTE TO ANTONIO CARLOS JOBIM, A (Various Artists)
177192 / 24 Apr '98 / XIII Bis

Joboxers

☐ ESSENTIAL BOXERBEAT
Boxerbeat / Crosstown walk up / Curious George / She's got sex / Hide nor hair / Crime of passion / Johnny friendly / Fully booked / Not my night / Just got lucky / Don't add up / Is this really the first time (you been in love) / Dead end streets / One in a million / Some kind of heart / Strictly business / Don't keep the ladies waiting / Jealous love / Johnny friendly / She's got sex
74321393412 / Aug '96 / Camden

Jocque, Beau

☐ BEAU JOCQUE BOOGIE (Jocque, Beau & The Zydeco Hi-Rollers)
ROUCD 2120 / Jun '93 / Rounder

☐ GIT IT BEAU JOCQUE (Jocque, Beau & The Zydeco Hi-Rollers)
ROUCD 2134 / Apr '95 / Rounder

☐ GONNA TAKE YOU DOWNTOWN (Jocque, Beau & The Zydeco Hi-Rollers)
ROUCD 2150 / Sep '96 / Rounder

☐ PICK UP ON THIS (Jocque, Beau & The Zydeco Hi-Rollers)
Give it to me / Gardez donci (look at that) / Zydeco boogie woogie / Mardi gras blues / Comin' / Don't tell your mama don't tell your papa / Yesterday / Do right sometime / Hucklebuck / Pick up on this / Cher mignonne / Hi-rollers theme-low rider
ROUCD 2129 / Apr '94 / Rounder

Jodeci

☐ DIARY OF A MAD BAND
My heart belongs to you / Cry for you / Feenin' / What about us / Ride and slide / Alone / You got it / Won't waste you / In the meanwhile / Gimme all you got / Sweaty / Jodecidal hotline / Lately / Let's go through the motions / Success
MCLD 19316 / Jul '96 / MCA

☐ FOREVER MY LADY
Stay / Come and talk to me / Forever my lady / I'm still waiting / U and I / Cherish (hip hop version) / Interlude (553 - nasty) / My phone / Gotta love / Play thang / It's alright / Treat u / Xs we share
MCLD 19307 / Oct '95 / MCA

☐ SHOW, THE AFTER-PARTY, THE HOTEL, THE
Show / Bring on da funk / Room 723 / Fun 2 nite / Room 577 / S-more / After party / Get on up / Room 499 / Can we flo / Zipper / Let's do it all / Pump it back / DJ Don Jeremy / Freek 'n you / Room 454 / Time and place / Fallin' / Love U 4 life / 4 U / Good luv
MCD 11258 / Jul '95 / MCA

Jodimars

☐ LETS ALL ROCK TOGETHER
RSRCD 007 / Jan '95 / Rockstar

Joe

☐ EVERYTHING
One for me / I'm in luv / All or nothing / It's alright / (If loving you is wrong) I don't want to be right / What's on your mind / Finally back / Get a little closer / I can do it right / Everything / Baby don't stop / Do me
5188072 / Feb '94 / Vertigo

Joel, Billy

☐ 52ND STREET
Big shot / Honesty / My life / Zanzibar / Stiletto / Rosalinda's eyes / Half a mile away / Until the night / 52nd Street
CD 83181 / 1 Jun '98 / Columbia

☐ BRIDGE, THE
Running on ice / This is the time / Matter of trust / Baby grand / Big man on Mulberry street / Temptation / Code of silence / Getting closer / Modern woman
4655612 / 1 Jun '98 / Columbia

☐ COLD SPRING HARBOUR
She's got a way / You can make me free / Everybody loves you now / Why Judy why / Falling of the rain / Turn around / You look so good to me / Tomorrow is today / Nocturne / Got to begin again
4688692 / 1 Jun '98 / Columbia

☐ COMPLETE HITS COLLECTION, THE (Billy Joel's Greatest Hits 1973-1997 - 4CD Set)
Piano man / Captain Jack / Entertainer / Say goodbye / New York state of mind / Stranger / Scenes from an Italian resturant / Just the way you are / Movin' out / Only the good die young / She's always a woman / My life / Big shot / You may be right / It's still rock 'n' roll to me / Don't ask me why / She's got a way / Pressure / Allentown / Goodnight Saigon / Tell her about it / Uptown girl / Longest time / You're only human / Night is still young / Keeping the faith / An innocent man / Matter of trust / Baby grand / This is the time / Leningrad / We didn't start the fire / I go to extremes / And so it goes / Downeaster alexa / Shameless / All about soul / Lullabye / River of dreams / Make you feel my life / Hey girl / Light as a breeze / Evening of questions and answers and a little music / Scenes from an Italian resturant / Hard days night / Vienna / History through music / We didn't start the fire / River of dreams / Piano bar/ Piano man
CXK 68007 / 1 Dec '97 / Columbia

☐ FURTHER THAN HEAVEN
JHD 004 / Jun '92 / Tring

☐ GLASS HOUSES
You may be right / Sometimes a fantasy / Don't ask me why / It's still rock and roll to me / All for Leyna / I don't want to be alone / Sleeping with the television on / C'etait toi / Close to the borderline / Through the long night
4500872 / Apr '94 / CBS
4911862 / 1 Jun '98 / Columbia

☐ GREATEST HITS COLLECTION VOL.1-3, THE (3CD Set)
4912742 / 1 Jun '98 / Columbia

☐ GREATEST HITS VOL.1 & 2 (2CD Set)
Piano man / Say goodbye to Hollywood / New York state of mind / Stranger / Just the way you are / Movin' out (Anthony's song) / Only the good die young / She's always a woman / My life / Big shot / Honesty / You may be right / It's still rock and roll to me / Pressure / Allen town / Goodnight Saigon / Tell her about it / Uptown girl / Longest time / You're only human (Second wind) / Night is still young
CD 88666 / May '94 / CBS

☐ GREATEST HITS VOL.3
Keeping the faith / An innocent man / Matter of trust / Baby grand / This is the time / Leningrad / We didn't start the fire / I go to extremes / And so it goes / Downeaster Alexia / Shameless / All about soul / Lullabye / River of dreams / To ake you feel my love / Hey girl / Light as a breeze
4882362 / 20 Oct '97 / Columbia

☐ INNOCENT MAN, AN
Easy money / Innocent man / Longest time / This night / Tell her about it / Uptown girl / Careless talk / Christie Lee / Leave a tender moment alone / Keeping the faith
4663292 / 27 Jul '98 / Columbia
4911892 / 1 Jun '98 / Columbia

☐ INNOCENT MAN, AN/STORM FRONT/ THE STRANGER (3CD Set)
Easy money / Innocent man / Longest time / This night / Tell her about it / Uptown girl / Careless talk / Chritie Lee / Leave a tender moment alone / Keeping the faith / That's not her style / We didn't start the fire / Downeaster 'Alexa' / I go to extremes / Shameless / Storm front / Leningrad / State of grace / When I Rome / And so it goes / Movin' out / Stranger / Just the way you are / Scenes from an Italian restaurant / Vienna / Only the good die young / She's always a woman / Get it right the first time / Everybody has a dream
4853202 / 3 Nov '97 / Columbia

☐ INNOCENT MAN, AN/THE STRANGER (2CD Set)
Easy money / An innocent man / Longest time / This night / Tell her about it / Uptown girl / Careless talk / Christie lee / Leave a tender moment alone / Keeping the faith / Movin' out (anthony's song) / Stranger / Just the way you are / Scenes from an italian restaurant / Vienna / Only the good die young / She's always a woman / Get it right the first time / Everybody has a dream
4716042 / Jul '92 / Columbia

☐ KOHUEPT
Odoya / Angry young man / Honesty / Goodnight Saigon / Stiletto / Big man on Mulberry Street / Baby grand / Innocent man / Allentown / Matter of trust / Only the good die young / Sometimes a fantasy / Uptown girl / Big shot / Back in the USSR / Times they are a changin'
4674482 / 1 Jun '98 / Columbia

☐ NYLON CURTAIN
Allentown / Laura / Pressure / Goodnight Saigon / She's right on time / Room of our own / Surprises / Scandinavian skies / Where's the orchestra
4911882 / 1 Jun '98 / Columbia

☐ PIANO MAN
Travellin' prayer / Ain't no crime / You're my home / Ballad of Billy The Kid / Worst comes to worst / Stop in Nevada / If I only had the words (to tell you) / Somewhere along the line / Captain Jack
4879382 / Jul '97 / Columbia
CD 32002 / 1 Jun '98 / Columbia

☐ RIVER OF DREAMS
No man's land / Great wall of China / Blonde over blue / Minor variation / Shades of grey / All about soul / Lullaby (Goodnight, my angel) / River of dreams / Two thousand years / Famous last words
4738722 / 2 Feb '98 / Columbia
4911952 / 1 Jun '98 / Columbia

☐ SONGS IN THE ATTIC
Miami 2017 / Summer, highland falls / Street life serenade / Los Angelenos / She's got a way / Everybody loves you now / Say goodbye to Hollywood / Captain Jack / You're my home / Ballad of Billy The Kid / I've loved these days
CD 32364 / 1 Jun '98 / Columbia

☐ STORM FRONT
That's not her style / We didn't start the fire / Downeaster Alexa / I go to extremes / Shameless / Storm front / Leningrad / State of grace / When in Rome / And so it goes
4656582 / Mar '96 / CBS
4911942 / 1 Jun '98 / Columbia

☐ STRANGER, THE
Movin' out / Just the way you are / Scenes from an Italian restaurant / Vienna / Stranger / Only the good die young / She's always a woman / Get it right the first time / Everybody has a dream
4509142 / Jun '89 / CBS
4911842 / 1 Jun '98 / Columbia

☐ STREETLIFE SERENADE
Los Angelenos / Great suburban showdown / Root beer rag / Roberta / Entertainer / Last of the big time spenders / Street life serenade / Weekend song / Souvenir / Mexican connection
4844612 / Feb '97 / Columbia
4766112 / 1 Jun '98 / Columbia

☐ TURNSTILES
I've loved these days / Miami 2017 / Angry young man / Say goodbye to Hollywood / James / New York State of mind / Prelude / Angry young man / Summer / Highland falls / All you wanna do is dance
4746812 / 1 Jun '98 / Columbia

Joey Negro

☐ DISCO HOUSE (Mixed By Joey Negro) (Various Artists)
JAPECD 105 / Jul '95 / Escapade

☐ GET DOWN TONIGHT (Joey Negro & Doc Livingstone)
336202 / Jun '97 / Koch Dance Force

Jog, Pandit V.G.

☐ LIVE AT THE LOGAN HALL (October 1981)
Raga Kirwani - Alap / Gat composition 1 / Gat composition 2
NRCD 007 / 13 Oct '97 / Navras

☐ VIOLIN
MR 1003 / Jul '93 / Moment

Jogi, Iqbal

☐ PASSION OF PAKISTAN (Jogi, Iqbal & Party)
TCD 1045 / Mar '97 / Tradition

Johan

☐ JOHAN
SPART 54 / 15 Dec '97 / Spin Art

Johann

☐ BLOW YOUR MIND
BR 50CD / 2 Mar '98 / Blue Room

Johansen, Bjorn

☐ DEAR HENRIK
GMCD 152 / Oct '89 / Gemini

Johansen, David

☐ BUSTER'S HAPPY HOUR (Poindexter, Buster)
Breakin' up the house / Big fat mamas are back in style / Doin' what I please / Let me in / I got loaded / Saturday night fish fry / Lavender coffin / Rocket 88 / Worst beer I ever had / Who drank my beer (while I was in the rear) / Rockin' all nite long / Knock'm down whiskey / Pink champagne / Drunk / I'll die happy / Butcher pete (parts 1 and 2) / Alcohol
RSFCD 818 / Oct '94 / Sequel

Johansson, Ake

☐ SPINNING TOP, THE
DRCD 314 / Feb '98 / Dragon

Johansson, Jan

☐ FISSION (Johansson, Jan & Anders/ Shawn Lane/Mike Stern)
SHR 1118 / 24 Mar '98 / Shrapnel

☐ JAZZ PA UNGERSK/IN PLENO (Johansson, Jan & Svend Asmussen)
HE 014CD / Aug '96 / Heptagon

Johansson, Ulf

☐ BIG BAND WULF
I let a song go out of my heart / City express / In a mellow tone / I want to be happy / Ankbrand / Nuages / I won't dance / Bye bye blackbird
NCD 8820 / '93 / Phontastic

☐ TRACKIN' THE WULF
Leopard shoe / Lover come back to me / China boy / Song of Sarek / Nice work if you can get it / Moose blues / Sweet Lorraine / 2.19 Blues
NCD 8809 / Dec '94 / Phontastic

John & Mary

☐ VICTORY GARDENS
Red wooden beads / Azalea festival / Piles of dead leaves / We have nothing / Rags of flowers / I became alone / Open window / July 6th / Pram / Un Canadien errant
RCD 10203 / Jul '91 / Rykodisc

☐ WEEDKILLERS DAUGHTER, THE
Two worlds parted / Angels of stone / Your return / Clare's scarf / Cemetary ridge / Nightfall / I wanted you / One step backward / Fly me to the north / Clouds of reason / Maid of the mist / Poor murdered woman
RCD 10259 / Mar '93 / Rykodisc

John Ac Alun

☐ OS NA DDAY YFORY
SCD 2112 / Dec '95 / Sain

☐ UN NOSON ARALL
Gadael Llyn / Datod y clymau / Dy golli di / Erwau'r yd / Os oes byd / Y Cylch / Pwy fydd yma 'mhen can mlynedd / Noson Arall / Y Ddawns Olaf / Dy Gofio di / Dim ond un gusan / Cariad / Felan y fawd / Chwarelwr
SCD 2172 / Sep '97 / Sain

☐ YR WYLAN WEN CHWARELWR
Yr wylan wen / Deigryn hiraeth / Sipsi fechan (gipsy woman) / Weithiau bydd y fflam / Bod yn unig (love me tonight) / Cariad llyn / Dychwel yn ol / Hoffwn gael dy weld (i would like to see you again) / Chwarelwr (working man) / Tyrd yn ol / Un siawns / Fan acw fy ngharlad / Seren y sgrin / Bod yn rhydd (achy breaky heart) / Hwylio'r cefnfor (sailing) / Sefyll dan y lleuad (standing in the moonlight) / Y ferch o benrhyn llyn (the lovely rose of clare) / Blaenau ffestiniog / Sisial ei henw / Paid a wylo
SCD 2077 / Dec '94 / Sain

John B

☐ VISIONS (2CD Set)
NIRCD 02 / 2 Mar '98 / New Identity

John Came

☐ RHYTHMICON
CDSTUMM 140 / Jun '95 / Mute

John, Elton

☐ 17.11.70
Take me to the pilot / Honky tonk woman / Sixty years on / Can I put you on / Bad side of the moon / Burn down the mission (includes my baby left me and get back
5281652 / Oct '95 / Rocket

☐ 21 AT 33
Changing the crown / Dear God / Give me the love / Little Jeannie / Never gonna fall in love again / Sartorial eloquence / Take me back / Two rooms at the end of the world / White lady white powder
8000552 / '83 / Rocket

☐ BIG PICTURE, THE
Long way from happiness / Live like horses / End will come / I fht eriver can bend / Love's got a lot to answer for / Something about the way you look tonight / If the river can bend / Big picture / REcover your soul / January / I can't steer my heart / Wicked dreams
5362662 / 29 Sep '97 / Rocket

☐ BLUE MOVES (2CD Set)
Your starter tonight / One horse town / Chameleon / Boogie pilgrim / Cage the songbird / Crazy water / Shoulder holster / Sorry seems to be the hardest word / Out of the blue / Between 17 and 20 / Wide-eyed and laughter / Someone's final love song / Where's the shoorah / If there's a God in Heaven (what's he waiting for) / Idol / Non-existent TV series / Bite your lip (get up and dance)
5325542 / Jun '96 / Rocket

☐ BREAKING HEARTS
Restless / Slow down Georgie / Who wears these shoes / Breaking hearts / Li'l refrigerator / Passengers / In neon / Burning bridges / Did he shoot her / Sad songs
8220882 / Jun '84 / Rocket

☐ CAPTAIN FANTASTIC & THE BROWN DIRT COWBOY
Captain Fantastic and the Brown Dirt Cowboy / Tower of Babel / Bitter fingers / Tell me when the whistle blows / Someone saved my life tonight / (Gotta get a) meal ticket / Better off dead / Writing / We all fall in love sometimes / Curtains / Lucy in the sky with diamonds / One day at a time / Philadelphia freedom
5281602 / Jul '95 / Rocket

☐ CARIBOU
Bitch is back / Pinky / Dixie Lily / Solar prestige a gammon / Don't let the sun go down on me / Ticking / Grimsby / You're so static / I've seen the saucers / Stinker / Pinball wizard / Sick city / Cold highway / Step into Christmas
5281582 / May '95 / Rocket

☐ CHARTBUSTERS GOES POP
Don't forget to remember / I can't tell the bottom from the top / Young, gifted and black / Signed, sealed, delivered (I'm yours) / Natural sinner / She sold me magic / Cotton fields / Spirit in the sky / Good morning freedom / Travelling band / In the summertime / Yellow river / United we stand / My baby loves lovin' / Love of the common people / Lady D'arbanville / Snake in the grass / Up around the bend
RPM 142 / Mar '95 / RPM

☐ DON'T SHOOT ME I'M ONLY THE PIANO PLAYER
Daniel / Teacher I need you / Elderberry wine / Blues for my baby and me / Midnight creeper / Have mercy on the criminal / I'm gonna be a teenage idol / Texan love song / Crocodile rock / High flying bird / Screw you / Jack Rabbit / Whenever you're ready (we'll go steady again) / Skyline pigeon
5281542 / May '95 / Rocket

☐ DUETS (John, Elton & Various Artists)
Teardrops: *John, Elton & k.d. Lang* / When I think about love (I think about you): *John, Elton & PM Dawn* / Power: *John, Elton & Little Richard* / Shaky ground: *John, Elton & Don Henley* / True love: *John, Elton & Kiki Dee* / If you were me: *John, Elton & Chris Rea* / Woman's needs: *John, Elton & Tammy Wynette* / Don't let the sun go down on me: *John, Elton & George Michael* / Old friend: *John, Elton & Nik Kershaw* / Go on and on: *John, Elton & Gladys Knight* / Don't go breaking my heart: *John, Elton & Rupaul* / Ain't nothing like the real thing: *John, Elton & Marcella Detroit* / I'm your puppet: *John, Elton & Paul Young* / Love letters: *John, Elton & Bonnie Raitt* / Born to lose: *John, Elton & Leonard Cohen* / Duet for one: *John, Elton*
5184782 / Dec '93 / Rocket

☐ ELTON JOHN
Your song / I need you to turn to / Take me to the pilot / No shoe strings on Louise / First episode at Heinton / Sixty years on / Border song / Greatest discovery / Cage / King must die / Bad side of the moon / Grey seal / Rock 'n' roll Madonna
5281562 / May '95 / Rocket

☐ EMPTY SKY
Empty sky / Valhalla / Western Ford gateway / Hymn 2000 / Lady what's tomorrow / Sails / Scaffold / Skyline pigeon / Gulliver/It's hay chewed/Reprise / Lady Samantha / All across the heavens / It's me that you need / Just like strange rain
5281572 / May '95 / Rocket

☐ GOODBYE YELLOW BRICK ROAD
Funeral for a friend (Love lies bleeding) / Candle in the wind / Benny and the jets / Goodbye yellow brick road / This song has no title / Grey seal / Jamaica jerk off / I've seen that movie too / Sweet painted lady / Ballad of Danny Bailey (1909-1934) / Dirty little girl / All the girls love Alice / Your sister can't twist (But she can rock 'n' roll) / Saturday night's alright for fighting / Roy Rogers / Social disease / Harmony
5281592 / May '95 / Rocket

☐ HERE AND THERE (Royal Festival Hall/ Madison Square Gardens 1974) (2CD Set)
Skyline pigeon / Border song / Take me to the pilot / Country comfort / Love song / Bad side of the moon / Burn down the mission / Honky cat / Crocodile rock / Candle in the wind / Your song / Saturday night's alright for fighting / Funeral for a friend (Love lies bleeding) / Rocket man / Take me to the pilot / Benny and the jets / Grey seal / Daniel / You're so static / Whatever gets you thru the night / Lucy in the sky with diamonds / I saw her standing there / Don't let the sun go down on me / Your song / Bitch is back
5281642 / Oct '95 / Rocket

☐ HONKY CHATEAU
Honky cat / Mellow / I think I'm going to kill myself / Susie (dramas) / Rocket man / Salvation / Slave / Amy / Mona Lisas and mad hatters / Hercules / Slave (alternative version)
5281622 / Jul '95 / Rocket

☐ ICE ON FIRE (Remastered)
5584762 / Jun '98 / Rocket

☐ INTERVIEW DISC
TELL 08 / Dec '96 / Network

☐ JUMP UP
Dear John / Spiteful child / Ball and chain / Legal boys / I am your robot / Blue eyes / Empty garden / Princess / Where have all the good times gone / All quiet on the Western Front
8000372 / Jan '95 / Rocket

☐ LADY SAMANTHA
Rock 'n' roll Madonna / Whenever you're ready / Bad side of the moon / Jack rabbit / Into the old man's shoes / It's me that you need / Ho ho ho (Who'd be a turkey at Christmas) / Screw you / Skyline pigeon / Just like strange rain / Grey seal / Honey roll / Lady Samantha / Friends
8320192 / Jun '87 / Rocket

☐ LEATHER JACKETS
Leather jackets / Hoop of fire / Don't trust that woman / Go it alone / Gypsy heart / Slow rivers / Heartache all over the world / Angeline / Memory of love / Paris / I fall apart
8304872 / Nov '86 / Rocket

☐ LIVE IN AUSTRALIA (Remastered)
5584772 / Jun '98 / Rocket

☐ LOVE SONGS
Sacrifice / Candle in the wind / I guess that's why they call it the blues / Don't let the sun go down on me: *John, Elton & George Michael* / Sorry seems to be the hardest word / Blue eyes / Daniel / Nikita / Your song / One / Someone saved my life tonight / True love: *John, Elton & Kiki Dee* / Can you feel the love tonight / Circle of life / Blessed / Please / Song for Guy
5287882 / Nov '95 / Rocket

☐ MADE IN ENGLAND
Believe / Made in England / House / Cold / Pain / Belfast / Latitude / Please / Man / Lies / Blessed
5261852 / Mar '95 / Rocket

☐ MADMAN ACROSS THE WATER
Levon / Razor face / Madman across the water / Indian sunset / Holiday inn / Rotten peaches / All the nasties / Goodbye / Tiny dancer
5281612 / Jul '95 / Rocket

☐ ONE, THE (Remastered)
5584802 / Jun '98 / Rocket

☐ PLAY THE MUSIC OF ELTON JOHN (Instrumental) (Classic Rock Orchestra Of Vienna)
340322 / 1 Jun '98 / Koch

☐ RARE MASTERS (2CD Set)
Madman across the water / Into the old man's shoes / Rock me when he's gone / Slave / Skyline pigeon / Jack rabbit / Whenever you're ready (we'll go steady again) / Let me be your car / Screw you / One day at a time / Cold highway / Sick city / Ho ho ho (Who'd be a turkey at Christmas) / Step into Christmas / I saw her standing there / House of cards / Planes / Sugar on the floor / Here's to the next time / Lady Samantha / All across the havens / It's me that you need / Just like strange rain / Bad side of the moon / Rock 'n' roll Madonna / Grey seal / Friends / Michelle's song / Seasons / Variation on Michelle's song / Can I put you on / Honey roll / Reprise seasons / Four moods / I meant to do my work today (a day in the country) / Variation on friends
5143052 / Jan '93 / Rocket

☐ REG STRIKES BACK (Remastered)
5584782 / Jun '98 / Rocket

☐ ROCK 'N' ROLL MADONNA
5502132 / Mar '94 / Spectrum

☐ ROCK OF THE WESTIES
Yell help / Wednesday night / Ugly / Dan Dare (pilot of the future) / Island girl / Grow some funk of your own / I feel like a bullet (in the gun of Robert Ford) / Street kids / Hard luck story / Feed me / Billy Bones and the white bird / Don't go breaking my heart
5281632 / Jul '95 / Rocket

☐ RPO PLAYS THE MUSIC OF ELTON JOHN, THE (Royal Philharmonic Pops Orchestra)
Nikita / Your song / Goodbye yellow brick road / Easier to walk away / Sad songs (Say so much) / Blue eyes / Candle in the wind / Rocket man / I guess that's why they called it the blues / Song for Guy
EMPRCD 674 / Nov '97 / Music Club

☐ SINGLE MAN, A (Remastered)
5584742 / Jun '98 / Rocket

☐ SLEEPING WITH THE PAST (Remastered)
5584792 / Jun '98 / Rocket

☐ SOLO PIANO PLAYS THE HITS OF ELTON JOHN (Various Artists)
GRF 233 / Aug '93 / Tring

☐ SONGS OF ELTON JOHN, THE (Various Artists)
Saturday night's alright for fighting / Benny and the jets / Rocket man / Daniel / Bitch is back / Don't go breaking my heart / Don't let the sun go down on me / Crocodile rock / Goodbye yellow brick road / Your song / Honky cat / Candle in the wind / Island girl / Sorry seems to be the hardest word / Song for Guy
SUMCD 4206 / 11 May '98 / Summit

☐ TOO LOW FOR ZERO (Remastered)
5584752 / Jun '98 / Rocket

☐ TUMBLEWEED CONNECTION
Ballad of a well known gun / Come down in time / Country comfort / Son of your father / My father's gun / Where to now St. Peter / Love song / Amoreena / Talking old soldiers / Burn down the mission / Into the old man's shoes / Madman across the water
5281552 / May '95 / Rocket

☐ TWO ROOMS (A Celebration Of The Songs Of Elton John & Bernie Taupin) (Various Artists)
Border song: *Clapton, Eric* / Rocket man: *Bush, Kate* / Come down in time: *Sting* / Saturday night's alright for fighting: *Who* / Crocodile rock: *Beach Boys* / Daniel: *Wilson Phillips* / Sorry seems to be the hardest word: *Cocker, Joe* / Levon: *Bon Jovi, Jon* / Bitch is back: *Turner, Tina* / Your song: *Stewart, Rod* / Philadelphia freedom: *Hall & Oates* / Don't let the sun go down on me: *Adams, Oleta* / Madman across the water: *Hornsby, Bruce* / Burn down the mission: *Collins, Phil* / Tonight: *Michael, George*
8457492 / Oct '91 / Rocket

☐ VERY BEST OF ELTON JOHN, THE (2CD Set)
Your song / Rocket man / Honky cat / Crocodile rock / Daniel / Goodbye yellow brick road / Saturday night's alright for fighting / Candle in the wind / Don't let the sun go down on me / Lucy in the sky with diamonds / Philadelphia freedom / Someone saved my life tonight / Pinball wizard / Bitch is back / Don't go breaking my heart / Benny and the jets / Sorry seems to be the hardest word / Song for Guy / Part time love / Blue eyes / I guess that's why they call it the blues / I'm still standing / Kiss the bride / Sad songs / Passengers / Nikita / Sacrifice / You gotta love someone / I don't wanna go on with you like that / Easier to walk away
8469472 / Oct '90 / Rocket

☐ VICTIM OF LOVE
Johnny B Goode / Warm love in a cold world / Born bad / Thunder in the night / Spotlight / Street boogie / Victim of love
5128812 / Jan '95 / Rocket

John F. Kennedy Memorial Pipe Band

☐ PLAYING POPULAR IRISH MARCHES
IRB 1922CD / May '95 / Outlet

John, Little Willie

☐ 15 HITS
KCD 5004 / Apr '97 / King

☐ FEVER
Fever / I'm stickin' with you baby / Do something for me / Love, life and money / Suffering with the blues / Dinner date / All around the world / Need your love so bad / Young girl / Letter from my darling / I've got to go cry / My nerves
CDCHARLY 246 / Oct '90 / Charly

☐ SURE THINGS
Sleep / A cottage for sale / There's a difference / I'm sorry / My love is / I like to see my baby / Walk slow / Very thought of you / Heartbreak (it's hurtin' me) / Loving care / You hurt me / I'm shakin'
KCD 739 / Mar '90 / King

John, Mable

☐ STAY OUT OF THE KITCHEN
Stay out of the kitchen / Leftover love / Able Mable / Shouldn't I love him / Catch that man / Ain't giving it up / Running out / Love tornado / Bigger and better / Sweet devil / It's catching / Drop on in / That woman will give it a try / That's what my love can do / I love you more than words can say / Have your cake / Be warm to me / I taught you how / If you give up what you got (see what you lost / Don't get caught / Man's too busy / I'm a big girl now / To love what I want, and want what I love / Sorry about that / I need your love so bad
CDSXD 048 / Sep '92 / Stax

John, Michael

☐ **SINGALONG PARTY (A Collection Of All-Time Favourite Songs/2CD Set) (John, Michael Singers)**
I've got a loverly bunch of coconuts / Sweet Rosie O'Grady / On Ilkla moor baht 'at / There's a tavern in the town / John Peel / Early one morning / Little brown jug / White cliffs of Dover / Sweet Georgia Brown / Yes sir, that's my baby / Golden locket / Golden slippers / Blue tail fly / Old folks at home / Daisy, daisy / Baby face / Sunny side of the street / Comin' through the rye / Over the sea to Skye / Charlie is my darlin' / K K K Katy / I want a girl / Cockles and mussels / Last rose of summer / Minstrel boy / Goodnight Irene / Hello, hello, who's your lady friend / Finnegan's wake / Flash bang wallop / Sippin' cider / Back home / Lily of Laguna / In the shade of the old apple tree / Side by side / Come landlord / Fill the flowing bowl / Goodnight ladies / Red river valley / Ma, he's making eyes at me / Battle hymn of the republic / Poor old Joe / Marching through Georgia / If you were the only girl in the world / Something nice to say / Underneath the arches / Wi' a hundred pipers / My bonnie lies over the ocean / Loch Lomond / When I'm sixty four / Crazy / Danny boy / Harp that once / She'll be coming round the mountain / You are my sunshine / When Irish eyes are smiling / Sentimental journey / Don't dilly dally
330332 / Mar '97 / Hallmark

John Sims

☐ **PALAMINO**
SRCD 3 / 31 Aug '98 / Sorted

John Wayne Army

☐ **CLOSING TIME AT THE LAST CHANCE SALOON**
Blue is the colour / King of hell / I was betrayed / Big water / Build my gallows high / Black beat / I keep on drinking that bad moonshine / Swing for you
GCW 3 / 23 Feb '98 / Calavera

John-Krol, Louisa

☐ **ARGO**
Dunsany's hope / Hyperion / Argo / I'm not walking / Little wanderer / Inanna / Out of the eqipage / Inside the bubble / House of legend / Duncan the fiddler / Oak, ash and thorn / Healer's names
EV 0010 / Jul '97 / Evolving Discs

Johnboy

☐ **CLAIM DEDICATIONS**
TR 27CD / Aug '94 / Trance

☐ **PISTOL SWING**
TR 16CD / Jun '93 / Trance

Johnna

☐ **PRIDE**
In my dreams / I live for the night / Pride / Out of the dark / Gotta be myself / Some you win, some you lose / Treat me right / Drive me crazy / Let the spirit move you / Need you to stay tonight / Out of my head / Do what you feel
HF 50CD / Sep '96 / PWL

Johnnie & Jack

☐ **JOHNNIE AND JACK AND THE TENNESSEE MOUNTAIN BOYS (6CD Set) (Johnnie & Jack & The Tennessee Mountain Boys)**
Lord watch over my daddy / There's no housing shortage in heaven / Love in the first degree / Too many blues / This is the end / Paper boy / Sing Tom Kitty / Jolie blon / I'll be listening / This world can't stand long / Old country church / I heard my name on the radio / Turn your radio on / He will set your fields on fire / What about you / For old times sake / Just when I need you / She went with a smile / Trials and tribulations / Buried alive / I heard my saviour call / Pray together and we'll stay together / Shout / You better get down on your knees and pray / Too much sinning / Jesus hits like the atom bomb / Too far from God / Jesus remembered me / Poison love / Lonesome / I'm gonna love you one more time / Smile on my lips / Take my ring from your finger / I can't tell my heart that / Cryin' heat blues / Let your conscience be your guide / Hummingbird / How can I believe in you / You tried to ruin my name / Ashes of love / Three ways of knowing / When you want a little loving / You can't fool God / Precious memories / Shake my mothers hand for me / When the saviour reached down for me / Slow poison / But I love you just the same / Just for tonight / Don't show off / Heart trouble / Two timing blues / I've gone and done it again / Don't let the stars get in your eyes / Only one I ever loved I lost / Borrowed diamonds / Private property / SOS / Called from Potter's field / I'll live with God (to die no more) / Angel's rock me to sleep / Eastern gate / Hank Williams will live forever / South in New Orleans / You're my downfall / Winner of your heart / Don't say goodbye if you love me / Pig latin song / Love trap / Cheated out of love / From the manger to the cross / I'm ready to go / God put a rainbow in the clouds / Don't give away your bible / Crazy worried mind / Love's a pleasure not a habit in Mexico / You've got me in your power / Dynamite kisses / I loved you better than you knew / Pick-up date / I get so lonely / You're just what the doctor ordered / I ain't got time / All the time / Goodnight sweetheart, goodnight / Honey, I need you / Kiss crazy baby / Beware of it / Sincerely / Carry on / No one dear but you / We live in two different worlds / So lovely baby / Look out / Don't waste your tears / Weary moments / Dream when you're lonely / Tom cat's kittens / Feet of clay / I want to be loved / You can't divorce my heart / Baby, it's in the making / I wonder why you said goodbye / Love love love / What's the reason I'm not pleasin' you / Love fever / Live and let live / When my blue moon turns to gold again / Why not confess / Banana boat song (Day O) / Mr. Clock / Love me now / If tears would bring you back / That's why I'm leavin' / Oh boy, I love her / Baby I need you / Nothing but sweet lies / Move it on over / No one will ever know / I don't mean to cry / I wonder where you are tonight / Slowly / Wedding bells / I never can come back to you / You are my sunshine / Stop the world (and let me off) / Camel walk stroll / I've seen this movie before / Yeah / Leave our moon alone / Lonely island pearl / That's the way the cookie crumbles / Just when I needed you / With a smile on my lips / What do you know about heartaches / I wonder if you know / It's just the idea / Sailor man / Wild and wicked world / Sweetie pie / Happy, lucky love / Just like you / Dreams come true / She loves me no more / Country music has gone to town / Talkin' eyes / Lonesome night blues / Love problems / I'm always by myself when I'm alone / Smiles and tears / Uncle John's bongos / Let my heart be broken / Sweet baby / Moon is high and so am I / 36-22-36 / What do you think of her now / Bye bye love / Foolin' around / Waterloo / Little bitty tear / I overlooked an orchard / You'll never get a better chance than this
BCD 15553 / Jun '92 / Bear Family

☐ **JOHNNY & JACK WITH KITTY WELLS AT KWKH**
Raining on the mountain / Intro / Orange blossom special / White dove / Singing waterfall / Sweeping through the gate / Wake up Susan / I heard my mother weeping / My bucket's got a hole in it / This world can't stand / Cheatam country breakdown / Death of litty Kathy Fiscus / No letter in the mail today / I saw the light / Mississippi sawyer / Cotton eyed Joe / Little cabin home on the hill / Love or hate / He will set your fields on fire / It's raining on the mountain
BCD 15808 / Nov '94 / Bear Family

Johnny & The Hurricanes

☐ **DEFINITIVE COLLECTION, THE (2CD Set)**
Cross fire / Lazy / Red river rock / Buckeye / Reveille rock / Time bomb / Sand storm / Beatnik fly / Down yonder / Sheba / Rocking goose / Revival / Molly O / You are my sunshine / Ja-da / Mr. Lonely / High voltage / Old smokie / Traffic jam / Farewell farewell / Miserlou / Salvation / San Antonio rose / Come on train / Minnesota fats / Sheik of Araby / Whatever happened to Baby Jane / Greens and beans / Money honey / Shadows / Kaw-Liga / Rough road / Happy time / Cut out / Storm warning / Bam boo / Thunderbolt / Joy ride / Rock-cha / Kid / Bye bye blackbird / Teensville tonight / Mister Irving / Tom's tune / Corn pome / Milk shake / Cyclone / Travelin' / Beanbags / Rockin' T / Hot fudge / Corn bread / Catnip / 'Hep' canary / Oh du lieber augustin / James Bond theme / Hungry eye / It's a mad, mad world / That's all
CPCD 81932 / Aug '96 / Charly

☐ **MASTERS, THE**
EABCD 063 / 24 Nov '97 / Eagle

☐ **RED RIVER ROCK**
RMB 75026 / Nov '93 / Remember

Johnny & The Roccos

☐ **BOP A DEE BOP A DOO**
Open up that door / Worryin' kind / Geronimo's rock / My next door neighbour / Knee deep in the blues / Hoodoo woman / Shake shack a dooby / Cutie named judie / Crazy me / Talkin' off the wall / Blues / Ride and roll / Walkin' out on my blues / Shakin' at the norrh pole / Move it / Blue moon of Kentucky / Lonesome train / I feel like rockin' / Tight dress / Love's made a fool of you / Honey babe / Endless sleep / Got no hair / I want somebody / Bop a dee bop a doo / Tennessee zip / Baby you're playing with fire / Tell me how / Hold that dog / Pretty little mama / This thing called love
CDWIKD 174 / Sep '97 / Big Beat

☐ **GREAT SCOTS**
Crazy baby / Cat talk / Rockabilly / My baby's crazy about Elvis / Don't wake up the kids / Sneaky Pete / Stompin with the wildcats / Blue blue day / Cherokee boogie / Rock 'n' roll record girl / Holocaust boogie / My baby left me / I'm a little mixed up / Honey rush / Flying saucers / Hey little girl / Beat / Feelings of love / Southern guitar boogie / Good rockin' tonight
CDMF 091 / 27 Apr '98 / Magnum Force

Johnny Fiasco

☐ **ACID WASH VOL.2**
Phantoms / Shifted / Here I cum / Darkness / Motivate / Sweet-n-sour / Psycho drums / Walk track 2 / Get up off your ass
TRXUKCD 002 / Jun '96 / Trax UK

Johnny Hates Jazz

☐ **TURN BACK THE CLOCK**
Shattered dreams / Heart of gold / Turn back the clock / Don't say it's love / What other reason / I don't want to be a hero / Listen / Different reasons / Don't let it end this way / Foolish heart / Turn back the clock (extended) / Heart of gold (extended) / Shattered dreams (extended)
CDV 2475 / '88 / Virgin

Johnny P

☐ **BAD IN A DANCEHALL**
RRTGCD 7784 / Jul '90 / Rohit

Johnny Socko

☐ **FULL TRUCKER EFFECT**
AM 025CD / 11 May '98 / Asian Man

Johnny Violent

☐ **SHOCKER (2CD Set)**
2 kicks for yes / E heads must die / North Korea goes bang / Gotterdammerung / Destructor lives / US intervention / Hardest gabba / Kamikaze / I'm gonna fuck you / Imploding head / Happy birthday / Johnny is a bastard / Pull the trigger / Burn out
MOSH 153CD / Oct '96 / Earache

Johnny Was

☐ **SUMMER LOVERS**
CDREP 8013 / Mar '95 / Candor

Johns, Bibi

☐ **BELLABIMBA**
Night filled with echoes / Someone to kiss your tears away / Puppy love / Two faced clock / I could never be ashamed of you / I wish I was a puppet on a string / Auf Jamaika schenken abends die Maltrosen / Bella bimba / Ich habe solche Angst / Sehnsucht / Bye bye baby: *Johns, Bibi & Angele Durand* / Little rock: *Johns, Bibi & Angele Durand* / Bimbo / In Barrabana / An jedem finger zehn / Gilly gilly ossenfeffer Katzenellenbogen the sea / Carnavalito / Ro ro ro ro Robinson / Die gipsy band / Papa tanzt mambo / Nach uns die sintflut: *Johns, Bibi & Paul Kuhn* / Zwei herzen im mai / Ich mocht auf deiner hochzeit tanzen: *Johns, Bibi & Paul Kuhn*
BCD 15649 / Mar '92 / Bear Family

John's Black Dirt

☐ **PERPETUAL OPTIMISM IS A FORCE MULTIPLIER**
GROW 202 / Oct '94 / Grass

John's Children

☐ **JAGGED TIME LAPSE**
Desdemona / Remember Thomas A Beckett / It's been a long time / Arthur Green / Midsummer night's scene / Sarah crazy child / Jagged time lapse / Go go girl / Come and play with me in the garden / Perfumed garden of Gulliver Smith / Midsummer night's scene / Not the sort of girl you take to bed / Help / Casbah candy
PILOT 018 / 17 Nov '97 / Burning Airlines

☐ **LEGENDARY ORGASM ALBUM, THE**
Smashed blocked / Just what you want, just what you'll get / Killer Ben / Jagged time lapse / Smashed blocked (Live) / You're a nothing / Not the sort of girl / Cold on me / Leave me alone / Let me know / Just what you want, just what you'll get / Why do you lie / Strange affair / But she's mine
CDMRED 31 / Sep '96 / Cherry Red

☐ **SMASHED BLOCKED**
Smashed blocked / Just what you want, just what you'll get / Strange affair / But she's mine / Hippy gumbo / Jagged time lapse / Midsummer nights scene / Not the sort of girl you take to bed / Mustang Ford / Love I thought I'd found / Remember Thomas A' Beckett / Come and play with me in the garden / Daddy rolling stone / Hot rod Mama / Perfumed garden of Gulliver Smith / Sally was an angel
PILOT 012 / 18 Aug '97 / Burning Airlines

Johns, Evan

☐ **ROLLIN' THRU THE NIGHT (Johns, Evan & The H-Bombs)**
VIRUS 47CD / '92 / Alternative Tentacles

Johnson Mountain Boys

☐ **BLUE DIAMOND**
Duncan and Brady / My better days / It don't bring you back to me / Christine Leroy / See God's ark movin' / Blue diamond mines / Teardrops like raindrops / Our last goodbye / Future remains / You done me wrong / Roll on blues / There goes my love / Only a hobo / Harbor of love
ROUCD 0293 / Apr '93 / Rounder

☐ **FAVOURITES**
Tomorrow I'll be gone / Tomorrow I'll be gone / Georgia stomp / Weary hobo / God's not dead / Making up stories / Iron curtain / Let's part the best of friends / Five speed / Misery loves company / Waves on the sea / Weathered gray stone / John henry, the steel drivin' man / We'll still sing on / When I can forget / Sugarloaf mountain special / Don't throw your life away / I've found a hiding place
ROUCD 11509 / '88 / Rounder

☐ **LET THE WHOLE WORLD TALK**
Let the whole world talk / Maury river blues / Memories cover everything I own / He said if I be lifted up / Goodbye to the blues / Virginia waltz / Maybe you will change your mind / Memories that we shared / Sweeter love than yours / I'll never know / Shouting in the air / Beneath the old Southern skies
ROUCD 0225 / Aug '88 / Rounder

☐ **LIVE AT THE BIRCHMERE**
ROUCD 0191 / Oct '94 / Rounder

☐ **WORKING CLOSE**
Tomorrow I'll be gone / Misery loves company / I'm still to blame / You loved died like the rose / Call his name / Five speed / Waves on the sea / Don't throw your life away / Say you'll take me back / Day has passed / Granite hill / Are you afraid to die
ROUCD 0185 / Nov '97 / Rounder

Johnson, 'Big' Jack

☐ **'BIG' JACK JOHNSON LIVE IN CHICAGO**
EARWIGCD 4939 / Dec '97 / Earwig

☐ **WE GOT TO STOP THIS KILLIN' (Johnson, 'Big' Jack & The Oilers)**
We got to stop this killin' / Humming blues / Breakdown blues / It's the fourth of July / Lonesome road / No good cow / Cracklin' bread / Sweet home Mississippi / Black rooster / Big foot woman
MC 0033 / Nov '97 / MC

Johnson, 'Blind' Willie

☐ **DARK WAS THE NIGHT**
Let your light shine on me / God don't never change / Lord, I just can't keep from cryin' / Keep your lamp trimmed and burning / Dark was the night-cold was the ground / Nobody's fault but mine / I know his blood can make me whole / Mother's children have a hard time / Jesus make up my dying bed / If I had my way I'd tear the building down / Jesus is coming soon / Bye and bye I'm goin' to see the king / God moves on the water / You'll need somebody on your bond / Praise god I'm satisfied / When the war was on / Take your burden to the lord and leave it there / Everybody ought to treat a stranger right / Soul of a man / John the revelator
IGOCD 2024 / Sep '95 / Indigo

☐ **DARK WAS THE NIGHT**
Mother's children have a hard time / Jesus make up my dying bed / It's nobody's fault but mine / I know his blood can make me whole / Dark was the night cold was the ground / If I had my way I'd tear the building down / Bye and bye I'm goin' to see the king / Soul of a man / Lord I just can't keep from crying / Keep your lamp trimmed and burning / You'll need somebody on your bond / John the revelator / Praise God I'm satisfied / God moves on the water / Trouble will soon be over / Church I'm full saved today / Go with me to that land / When the war was on / Take your burden to the lord and leave it there / I'm gonna run to the city of refuge / Let your light shine on me / Take your stand
4898922 / 20 Jul '98 / Sony Blues

☐ **PRAISE GOD I'M SATISFIED**
Jesus make up my dying bed / Dark was the night-cold was the ground / Praise God I'm satisfied / Bye and bye I'm goin' to see the King / You're gonna need somebody on your bond / When the war was on / God moves on the water / I know his blood can make me whole / God don't never change / Rain don't fall on me / Nobody's fault but mine / Keep your lamp trimmed and burning / Jesus is coming soon / Mother's children have a hard time
YAZCD 1058 / Mar '98 / Yazoo

☐ **SWEETER AS THE YEARS GO BY**
John the revelator / You'll need somebody on your bond / Let your light shine on me / Everybody ought to treat a stranger right / Lord, I just can't keep from crying / If I had my way I'd tear the building down / If it had not been for jesus / Church, I'm fully saved today / Soul of man / I'm gonna run to the city of refuge / Can't nobody hide from god / Sweeter as the years go by / Go with me to that land / Trouble will soon be over / Take your burden to the lord and leave it there / Take your stand
YAZCD 1078 / Apr '91 / Yazoo

Johnson, Budd

☐ **BUDDY & ELLA JOHNSON 1953-1964 (4CD Set) (Johnson, Budd & Ella)**
That's how I feel about you / That's how I feel about you / Hittin' on me / Jit jit / I'm just your fool / A 12 / I never had it so good / Ain'tcha got me (where you want me) / Bring it up, van dyke / My old man / One more time / Let's start all over again (down on bended knee) / Shut your big mouth (girl) / Mush mouth / Any day now / A pretty girl (a cadillac and some money) / Ain't but one / There's no one like you / Thinking it over / If you'd say yes / It used to hurt me / Well do it / Bitter sweet / Crazy 'bout a saxophone / Send out for a bucket of beer / (gotta go) upside your head / Someday / Alright, okay, you win / If you would only say you're sorry / It's 'bout to break my heart in two / It's obdacious / Save your love for me / So good / Gone walkin' / Doot doot dow / I don't want nobody (to have my love but you) / You got it made / Bring it home to me / Buddy's boogie / Why don'tcha stop it / I'll dearly love you / Kool kitty / What a day / Goodbye baby here I go / That's what you gotta do / I still love you / Oh baby, don't you know / You'd better believe me / You're everything my heart desires / Rock on / Rockin' time / They don't want to rock no more / I've surrendered / Slide's mambo / Don't shout at me daddy / No ain't gonna let you go / Don't turn your back on me / They all say I'm the biggest fool / I cry / Baby don't you cry / Goodbye baby here I go / I don't care who knows / You'll get them blues / Stop pretending / Please mister johnson / Since I fell for you / I wonder where our love has gone / Lil' dog / Minglin' / Far cry / Lover bird / No moe / Buddy's tune / Don't fail me baby / Small taste / Baby hear my humble plea / Tuke number one / Going to new york / Have mercy on a fool / Buddy's song / Real fine frame / Walk 'em / I'm tired of cryin' over you / You better change your ways / Down yonder / Go ahead and rock / Get down on the road / Sliding horns / Come here, lovely dovey / Keeping my love for you / Buddy's rock / A woman, a lover, a friend / I'll be glad / (ha ha ha baby) the last laugh's on you / Ever so grateful / Good time man / Don't be messin' / Like you do / I gotta talk to somebody / Keep on loving you / You're the one for me
BCD 15479 / Mar '92 / Bear Family

☐ **CLASSICS 1939-1942 (Johnson, Budd Band)**
CLASSICS 884 / Jul '96 / Classics

☐ **JPJ QUARTET (Johnson, Budd & Dill Jones/Bill Pemberton/Oliver Jackson)**
STCD 8235 / May '96 / Storyville

☐ **MR. BECHET**
BB 882 / Apr '97 / Black & Blue

☐ **WALK 'EM (The Decca Sessions) (Johnson, Budd Orchestra)**
Walk 'em / Since I fell for you / Baby you're always on my mind / Boogie woogie's mother-in-law / You gotta walk that chalk line / I don't know what's troublin' your mind / Be careful (if you can't be good) / Boot man blues / 'Til my baby comes back / I'm gonna jump in the river / Talking about another man's wife / No more love / Shake 'em up / Satisfy my soul / Stormy weather / Did you see Jackie Robinson hit that ball / That's the stuff you gotta watch / They all say I'm the biggest fool / Fine brown frame / You'll get them blues / Southern echoes / When my man comes home / Please Mr. Johnson / Shufflin' and rollin'
CDCHD 623 / Jun '96 / Ace

Johnson, Bunk

☐ BUNK & LU (Johnson, Bunk & Lu Watters)
At a georgia camp meeting / Irish black bottom / Original jelly roll blues / Smokey mokes / Maple leaf rag / Memphis blues / Black and white rag / Muskrat ramble / Carless love / 2;19 blues / Girls go crazy / When I move to the sky / Ace in the hole / Ory's creole trombone / Nobody's fault but mine
GTCD 12024 / Oct '93 / Good Time Jazz

☐ BUNK JOHNSON (Johnson, Bunk & His Superior Jazz Band)
Panama / Down by the riverside / Storyville blues / Ballin' the Jack / Make me a pallet on the floor / Weary blues / Moose march / Bunk's blues / Yes Lord I'm crippled / Bunk Johnson talking
GTCD 12048 / Jul '94 / Good Time Jazz

☐ BUNK JOHNSON & HIS NEW ORLEANS BAND
DOCD 1001 / Jun '96 / Document

☐ BUNK JOHNSON & LEADBELLY (Johnson, Bunk & Leadbelly)
AMCD 46 / Oct '93 / American Music

☐ BUNK JOHNSON 1942-1945
DOCD 1010 / 28 Oct '97 / Document

☐ BUNK JOHNSON 1944-1945
AMCD 12 / Apr '94 / American Music

☐ BUNK JOHNSON AND HIS SUPERIOR JAZZ BAND
Panama / Down by the riverside / Storyville blues / Ballin' the Jack / Make me a pallet on the floor / Yes Lord I'm crippled / Weary blues / Moose march / Bunk's blues / Bunk Johnson talking
GTJCD 120482 / Jul '94 / Good Time Jazz

☐ BUNK JOHNSON PLAYS POPULAR SONGS
AMCD 15 / 27 Apr '98 / American Music

☐ IN SAN FRANCISCO
AMCD 16 / Jan '93 / American Music

☐ KING OF THE BLUES
AMCD 1 / Oct '92 / American Music

☐ LAST TESTAMENT
DD 225 / Mar '95 / Delmark

Johnson, Candy

☐ CANDY'S MOOD
BB 884 / Apr '97 / Black & Blue

Johnson, Dean

☐ ARCHIVES OF OUR LIVES
FMRCD 281295 / Apr '97 / Future

Johnson, Dean

☐ TRAINING OF THE SHOE, THE
PULCD 0151 / Sep '97 / Pulse

Johnson, Dick

☐ PLAYS ALTO SAX & FLUTE & SOPRANO SAX & CLARINET
All the things you are / I'm old fashioned / Donna Lee / Star crossed lovers / Kelly Green / When the world was young / Who cares / Kelly Blue / In a sentimental mood / Everything I love / Get out of time
CCD 4107 / Mar '92 / Concord Jazz

Johnson, Dink

☐ PIANO PLAYERS, THE (Johnson, Dink & Charlie Thompson)
AMCD 11 / Jun '93 / American Music

Johnson, Don

☐ ESSENTIAL
Tell it like it is / Voice on a hotline / Heartbeat / Other people's lives / Heartache away / What if it takes all night / Can't take your memory / Angel city / Star tonight / Lost in your eyes / Coco don't / Gotta get away / Your love is safe with me / Lonely too long / Last sound love makes / Better place
4868652 / 26 Jan '98 / Columbia

☐ HEARTBEAT
RE 821684 / 1 Jun '98 / Razor & Tie

Johnson, Earl

☐ COMPLETE RECORDED WORKS VOL.1 1927
DOCD 8005 / Apr '97 / Document

☐ COMPLETE RECORDED WORKS VOL.2 1927-1931
DOCD 8006 / Apr '97 / Document

Johnson, Eric

☐ VENUS ISLE
Venus Isle / Battle we have won / All about you / SRV / Lonely in the night / Manhattan / Camel's night out / Song for Lynette / When the sun meets the sky / Pavillion / Venus reprise
PRMDCD 11 / Sep '96 / Premier/EMI

Johnson, Freddy

☐ CLASSICS 1933-1939
CLASSICS 829 / Sep '95 / Classics

Johnson, General

☐ WHAT GOES AROUND COMES AROUND (Johnson, General & Chairmen Of The Board)
SUR 4168CD / Feb '94 / Ichiban

Johnson, George A. Jr.

☐ TURQUOISE OCEAN
Announcement / Turquoise ocean / Sittin' by a waterfall at a full moon / Teach me tonight / Beautiful kingdom / Turquoise ocean / Moment's notice / Angel eyes / Driftin' / Sittin' by a waterfall at a full moon / In the evening / I didn't know what / Turquoise ocean
AL 73097 / Dec '97 / A

Johnson, Henry

☐ MISSING YOU
All this love / Romance me / Osaka sunrise / Don't ask my neighbour / I just called / Quien para saber / Missing you / Don't go to the strangers / Flying easy / Last one / Mileslike
INAK 3029 / Nov '97 / In Akustik

☐ NEW BEGINNINGS
River / Andrea / Creepin' / Sambalea / Please send me someone to love / Flying fish / Lushlife / Tell me a bedtime story / Happiness is now / In the wee small hours of the morning / Point
101S 71382 / Jun '93 / 101 South
INAK 30192CD / Nov '97 / In Akustik

Johnson, Herman

☐ LOUISIANA COUNTRY BLUES
ARHCD 440 / May '96 / Arhoolie

Johnson, Howard

☐ ARRIVAL (Johnson, Howard & Nubia)
5239852 / May '95 / Verve

☐ GRAVITY
5310212 / Apr '96 / Verve

☐ RIGHT NOW (Johnson, Howard & Gravity)
5378012 / 15 Sep '97 / Verve

Johnson, J.J.

☐ BE BOP LEGENDS
MCD 0722 / Aug '95 / Moon

☐ BRASS ORCHESTRA
5373212 / Jul '97 / Verve

☐ GREAT KAI AND J.J. (Johnson, J.J. & Kai Winding)
This could be the start of something big / Georgia on my mind / Blue monk / Judy / Alone together / Side by side / I concentrate on you / Picnic / Trixie / Going going gone / Just for a thrill
IMP 12252 / Apr '97 / Impulse Jazz

☐ J.J. INC.
Mohawk / Minor mist / In walked horace / Fatback / Aquarius / Shutterbug / Blue 'n boogie' / Turnpike / Fatback
CK 65296 / 1 Sep '97 / Sony Jazz

☐ J.J. JOHNSON'S JAZZ QUINTETS
Jay bird / Coppin' the bop / Jay jay / Mad be bop / Boneology / Down Vernon's alley / Audobon / Don't blame me / Goof square / Bee jay / Yesterdays / Riffette
SV 0151 / Oct '97 / Savoy Jazz

☐ JAY AND KAI (Johnson, J.J. & Kai Winding)
Bernie's tune / Blues for trombones / Major / Yesterdays / Co-op / Reflections / Blues in twos / What is this thing called love / Boy next door / I could write a book / Carioca
SV 0163 / Oct '97 / Savoy Jazz

☐ TANGENCE
5265882 / May '95 / Verve

☐ THINGS ARE GETTING BETTER (Johnson, J.J. & Al Grey)
Soft winds / Let me see / Softly as in a morning sunrise / It's only a paper moon / Boy meets horn / Things ain't what they used to be / Things are getting better all the time / Don't cha hear me callin' to ya
OJCCD 745 / May '93 / Original Jazz Classics

☐ YOKOHAMA CONCERT, THE (2CD Set) (Johnson, J.J. & Nat Adderley)
Horace / Cyclops / Why not / It happens / Work song / Walkin' / Jiving / Lament / Hummin' / Melodee
2PACD 26201092 / Aug '97 / Pablo

Johnson, James

☐ BLUES COME HOME TO ROOST (Johnson, James 'Super Chikan')
Down in the delta / Well gone dry / Crystal ball eyes / Super Chikan strut / Mama / Chillen (part 1) / What it is / Captain love juice / Camel toe / White rock rooster / Bleeding from the heart / Mr. Rich man / Rockin' that caine and rollin' Mary Jane / Real you / Mama and the chillen (part 2)
R 2634 / Mar '97 / Rooster

Johnson, James 'Stump'

☐ JAMES 'STUMP' JOHNSON 1929-1933
DOCD 5250 / May '94 / Document

Johnson, James P.

☐ CAROLINA SHOUT
Steeplechase rag / Twilight rag / Carolina shout / Baltimore buzz / Gypsy blues / Harlem strut / Eccentricity / Don't mess with me / Nervous blues / Ole Miss Blues / I ain't givin' nothin' away / Muscle shoal blues / Farewell blues / Charleston
BCD 105 / Jul '91 / Biograph

☐ CLASSICS 1921-1928
CLASSICS 658 / Nov '92 / Classics

☐ CLASSICS 1928-1938
CLASSICS 671 / Nov '92 / Classics

☐ CLASSICS 1938-1942
CLASSICS 711 / Jul '93 / Classics

☐ CLASSICS 1943-1944
CLASSICS 824 / Jul '95 / Classics

☐ CLASSICS 1944 VOL.1
CLASSICS 835 / Sep '95 / Classics

☐ CLASSICS 1944 VOL.2
CLASSICS 856 / Feb '96 / Classics

☐ FEELIN' BLUE
All that I had is gone / Snowy morning blues / Chicago blues / Mournful tho'ts / Riffs / Feelin' blue / Put your mind right on it / Fare thee honey blues / You don't understand / You've got to be modernistic / Crying for the Carolines / What is this thing called love / Jingles / Go Harlem / Just a crazy song
DHDL 107 / May '95 / Halcyon

☐ HARLEM STRIDE PIANO 1921-1929
158952 / 21 Aug '97 / Jazz Archives

☐ HOT PIANO
TPZ 1048 / Jun '96 / Topaz Jazz

☐ INTRODUCTION TO JAMES P. JOHNSON 1921-1944, AN
4035 / Mar '95 / Best Of Jazz

☐ KING OF STRIDE PIANO 1918-1944
Carolina shout / Squeeze me / Ain't misbehavin' (I'm savin' my love for you) / Snowy morning blues / Honeysuckle rose / Keep off the grass / If I could be with you (one hour tonight) / Riffs / I've got a feeling I'm falling / Keepin' out of mischief now / My fate is in your hands / I'm gonna sit right down and write myself a letter / Blue turning grey over you / Over the bars / Porter's love song to a chambermaid / Jingles / What is this thing called love / You've got to be modernistic / Crying for the Carolines / Eccentricity / Down home blues / Runnin' wild medley
CD 53201 / Jan '98 / Giants Of Jazz

☐ ORIGINAL, THE
SFWCD 40812 / Nov '96 / Smithsonian Folkways

☐ RUNNIN' WILD
TCD 1048 / May '97 / Tradition

Johnson, Jeff Lee

☐ BLUE
Jungle / Everything starts right now / Little too much for Hollywood / Tryin' fire / Ain't seen Irene / Feel so fine / Love song / Blue / Black sands / You jump'd the gun again / Seems for no reason / Burn your fields on down / BHNC / Some dreams like now / Jungle
PCOM 1150 / Aug '97 / President

☐ COMMUNION
DIW 926 / Feb '98 / DIW

Johnson, Jerry

☐ EAST OF THE CITY
WRCD 1010 / 25 May '98 / Wackies

Johnson, Jimmy

☐ BAR ROOM PREACHER
ALCD 4744 / May '93 / Alligator

☐ I'M A JOCKEY
That will never do / Jockey / Engine number 9 / My ring / Highway / As the years go passing by / Black and white wall / Highway is like a woman / In the midnight hour / End of a rainbow / Look over yonder's wall
5215862 / Apr '93 / Birdology

☐ JOHNSON'S WHACKS
DD 644 / Dec '89 / Delmark

Johnson, Johnnie

☐ BLUE HANDED JOHNNIE
ECD 26017 / Feb '93 / Evidence

☐ JOHNNY B. BAD
Tanqueray / Hush oh hush / Johnny B Badde / Creek mud / Fault line tremor / Stepped in what / Can you stand it / Key to the highway / Blues no. 572 / Baby what's wrong / Cow cow blues / Movin' out
7559611492 / Sep '91 / Nonesuch

☐ ROCKIN' EIGHTY-EIGHTS (Johnson, Johnnie, Clayton Love & Jimmy Vaughn)
MBCD 1201 / Jun '93 / Modern Blues

☐ THAT'LL WORK (Johnson, Johnnie & Kentucky Headhunters)
That'll work / Sunday blues / Johnnie's breakdown / I'm not runnin' / Bumed about love / Stumblin' / Back to Memphis / Feel / I know you can / She's got to have it / Derby day special / Tell me baby
7559614762 / Aug '93 / Elektra

Johnson, L.J.

☐ BEST OF L.J. JOHNSON, THE (My Destination Is Love)
HTCD 67 / 20 Apr '98 / Hot Productions

Johnson, L.V.

☐ I GOT THE TOUCH
I got the touch / Take a little time to know her / Are you serious / I don't want to lose your love / What do you mean love ain't got nothing to do / I am missing you / I just can't get over you / Stroking kind (choking kind)
ICH 1112CD / Oct '93 / Ichiban

☐ IT'S SO COLD AND MEAN
Get him out of your system / It's so cold and mean (the drug scene) / One in a million you / Blues in the north / It's not my time / Make you mine / Steal away / How can I live without you
ICH 1050CD / Oct '93 / Ichiban

☐ UNCLASSIFIED
ICH 1137CD / May '94 / Ichiban

Johnson, Larry

☐ MIDNIGHT HOUR BLUES (Johnson, Larry & John Hammond)
Blood red river / One room country shack / Saturday evening blues / Peace breakin' people / Walking blues / Mama-less rag / Red river dam blues / Nobody's biz-ness / Midnight hour blues / When things go wrong / Tell me Mama
BCD 138 / Jul '97 / Biograph

Johnson, Laurie

☐ EASY PROJECT VOL.4, THE (...With A Vengeance) (Johnson, Laurie Orchestra)
Avengers / Top Secret / Dr. Strangelove / No Hiding Place / Beauty jungle / Doin' the raccoon / Echo Four Two / M1 / Soho / City / Limehouse / West End / Latin Quarter / Grand Central / Times Square / South beach / Seventh Avenue / Stick or twist / Drum crazy / Minor bossa nova / Dear friend / Heat wave / Twango / Winter wonderland / Hoe down / Deputy / Donkey serenade / Spring, Spring, Spring / Chaka / Sabre dance
NEMCD 935 / 24 Nov '97 / Sequel

☐ LONDON BIG BAND VOL.1 (Johnson, Laurie London Big Band)
Come rain or come shine / Isn't it romantic / Wasn't it romantic / Swanee / What makes the sunset / Mr. B / Lady is a tramp / By strauss / Someone to watch over me / From this moment on / Jeepers creepers / It could happen to you / It's easy for you to say / Embraceable you / Coasting / Avalon / Never stray / But beautiful / CTS Blues
CDSIV 6144 / Jul '95 / Horatio Nelson

☐ LONDON BIG BAND VOL.2 (Johnson, Laurie London Big Band)
CDSIV 6160 / Jul '96 / Horatio Nelson

☐ MUSIC OF LAURIE JOHNSON, THE
UKCD 2057 / Jul '92 / Unicorn-Kanchana

Johnson, Lem

☐ COMPLETE LEM JOHNSON 1940-1953, THE
BMCD 6004 / Jul '96 / Blue Moon

Johnson, Lil

☐ COMPLETE RECORDED WORKS VOL.2 1936-1937
DOCD 5308 / Dec '94 / Document

☐ HOTTEST GAL IN TOWN 1936-1937
SOBCD 35132 / Mar '92 / Story Of The Blues

☐ LIL JOHNSON & BARRELHOUSE ANNIE 1937 (Johnson, Lil & Barrelhouse Annie)
DOCD 5309 / Dec '94 / Document

☐ LIL JOHNSON VOL.1 1929-1936
DOCD 5307 / Dec '94 / Document

Johnson, Linton Kwesi

☐ BASS CULTURE
Bass culture / Street 66 / Reggae fi peach / De black petty booshwah / Inglan is a bitch / Lorraine / Reggae sounds / Two sides of silence
RRCD 26 / Nov '90 / Reggae Refreshers

☐ DREAD BEAT AND BLOOD
Dread beat and blood / Five nights of bleeding / Doun de road / Song of blood / It dread inna Inglun (for George Lindo) / Come wi goh dung deh / Man free (for Darcus Howe) / All wi doin' is defendin'
CDFL 9009 / Sep '90 / Frontline

☐ FORCES OF VICTORY
Want fi goh rave / It noh funny / Sonny's lettah / Independent intavenshan / Fite dem back / Reality poem / Forces of vicktry / Time come
RRCD 32 / Sep '91 / Reggae Refreshers

☐ IN CONCERT
SHANCD 43034/5 / '88 / Shanachie

☐ LKJ ACAPPELLA LIVE
LKJCD 016 / Oct '96 / LKJ

☐ LKJ IN CONCERT
LKJCD 03 / Mar '95 / LKJ

☐ LKJ IN DUB VOL.1
Victorious dub / Reality dub / Peach dub / Shocking dub / Iron bar dub / Bitch dub / Cultural dub / Brain smashing dub
RRCD 34 / Sep '91 / Reggae Refreshers

☐ LKJ IN DUB VOL.2
LKJCD 02 / Mar '95 / LKJ

☐ MORE TIME
LKJCD 018 / 29 Jun '98 / LKJ

☐ REGGAE GREATS
Reggae sounds / Independent intavenshan / Street 66 / Bass culture / Di great insohreckshan / It noh funny / Sonny's lettah / Reggae fi radni / Fit dem back / Making history
5528812 / Jul '97 / Spectrum

☐ TINGS AND TIMES
Story / Sense outta nansense / Tings an' times / Mi revalueshanary fren / Di good life / Di anfinished revalueshan / Dubbing for life
LKJCD 013 / Oct '95 / LKJ

Johnson, Lonnie

☐ ANOTHER NIGHT TO CRY
Another night to cry / I got news for you, baby / Blues after hours / You didn't mean what you said / Fine booze and heavy dues / I've got to get rid of you / Bow legged baby / Make love to me, baby / Lots of loving / Story about barbara / Goodbye kitten
OBCCD 550 / Nov '92 / Original Blues Classics

☐ BLUES BALLADS AND JUMPIN' JAZZ VOL.1 (Johnson, Lonnie & Elmer Snowden)
Haunted house / Memories of you / Blues for chris / I found a dream / St. louis blues / I'll get along somehow / Savoy blues / Back water blues / Elmer's blues / Jelly roll baker
OBCCD 531 / Nov '92 / Original Blues Classics

☐ BLUES BALLADS AND JUMPIN' JAZZ VOL.2 (Johnson, Lonnie & Elmer Snowden)
OBCCD 570 / Jul '95 / Original Blues Classics

☐ BLUES BY LONNIE JOHNSON
Don't ever love / No love for sale / There's no love / I don't hurt anymore / She devil / One-sided love affair / Big legged woman / There must be a way / She's drunk again / Blues 'round my door / You don't move me / You will need me
OBCCD 502 / Nov '92 / Original Blues Classics

☐ BLUES IN MY FINGERS
IGOCD 2009 / Nov '94 / Indigo

☐ COMPLETE FOLKWAYS RECORDINGS
Raise the window high / Tears don't fall no more / Long road to travel / Old rocking chair / You have my life in your hands / Lazy mood / Mister trouble / How deep is the ocean / Pouring down rain / Prisoner of love / Careless love / Juice headed baby / Teardrops in my eyes / Looking for a sweetie / I've been a fool myself / What a difference a day makes / That lonesome road / I can't believe / When you always by yourself / My mother's eyes / Summertime / CC rider / Entire family was musicians / Falling rain blues
SFWCD 40067 / Sep '94 / Smithsonian Folkways

☐ COMPLETE RECORDINGS VOL.1
BDCD 6024 / Nov '92 / Blues Document

☐ COMPLETE RECORDINGS VOL.2
BDCD 6025 / Nov '92 / Blues Document

☐ COMPLETE RECORDINGS VOL.3
BDCD 6026 / Nov '92 / Blues Document

☐ IDLE HOURS (Johnson, Lonnie & Victoria Spivey)
Darling, I miss you so: *Johnson, Lonnie* / Long time blues: *Johnson, Lonnie* / You are my life: *Johnson, Lonnie* / Oh yes, baby: *Johnson, Lonnie* / Please baby: *Johnson, Lonnie* / Leave me or love me: *Johnson, Lonnie* / Idle hours: *Johnson, Lonnie* / You have no love in your heart: *Johnson, Lonnie* / Good luck darling: *Johnson, Lonnie* / No more cryin': *Johnson, Lonnie* / I got the blues so bad: *Johnson, Lonnie* / End it all: *Johnson, Lonnie*
OBCCD 518 / Nov '92 / Original Blues Classics

☐ IN MY SOUL 1937-1946
159032 / Nov '97 / Blues Collection

☐ LOSING GAME
New orleans blues / My little kitten susie / Evil woman / What a difference a day makes / Moaning blues / Summertime / Lines in my face / Losing game / New years blues / Slow and easy / Four walls and me / You won't let me go
OBCCD 543 / Nov '92 / Original Blues Classics

☐ ME AND MY CRAZY SELF
You can't buy love / It was all in vain / Nothing but trouble / Me and my crazy self / What do you want that I've got / Pretty boy / I'm guilty / What a woman / Falling rain blues / Playing around / It's too late to cry / Seven long days / Why should I cry / Friendless blues / Happy new year darling / You only want me when you're lonely / Old fashioned love / My my baby / Just another day / What a real woman / Can't sleep anymore
CDCHARLY 266 / Mar '91 / Charly

☐ PLAYING WITH THE STRINGS
Won't don't blues / Mr. johnson's blues / Falling rain blues / Now good blues / Newport blues / Nile of genago / To do this you gotta know how / Four hands are better than two / I'm not rough / Hotter than that / Savoy blues / Playing with the strings / Stompin' em along slow / Mooche / Move over / Hot and bothered / Paducah / Stardust / Jet black blues / Blue blood blues / Sitting on top of the world / Kansas city man blues / I'm nuts about that gal / Racketeer's blues
JSPCD 335 / Dec '94 / JSP

☐ STOMPIN' AT THE PENNY (Johnson, Lonnie & Jim McHarg's Metro Stompers)
China boy / Mr. Blues walks / Dippermouth blues / Trouble in mind / Bring it home to Mam / West End blues / Stompin' at the Penny / Old rugged cross / Go go swing / My mother's eyes / Canal street blues / 14th of July / Marines' hymn
4767202 / May '94 / Legacy

☐ TOMORROW NIGHT
You will need me / I don't hurt anymore / She's drunk again / Nothing but I trouble / She devil / Little rocking chair / Trouble ain't nothing but the blues / Leave me or love me / Tomorrow night / Blues 'round my door / Workin' man blues / Jelly roll baker / End it all / Blues stay away from me / Careless love / CC rider / Clementine blues / Backwater blues / Jelly jelly / Love is the answer / Keep what you got
CD 52016 / '92 / Blues Encore

Johnson, Luther

☐ GET DOWN TO THE NITTY GRITTY (Johnson, Luther 'Georgia Snake Boy')
422255 / Feb '97 / Last Call

☐ ON THE ROAD AGAIN (Johnson, Luther 'Georgia Snake Boy')
On the road again / Back door man / Things I used to do / Catfish blues / Aces blues / You move me / Rock me baby / She moves me / You've got me running / Hoochie coochie man / Impressions from France / Mellow down easy / Little red rooster
ECD 260472 / Mar '94 / Evidence

☐ THEY CALL ME THE SNAKE (Johnson, Luther 'Georgia Snake Boy')
Woman don't lie / Take it off him and put it on me / Blues is something I'll never lose / Woman why treat me so mean / They call me the snake / Somebody loan me a dime / Slip it off your hips and move
422268 / Feb '97 / Last Call

Johnson, Luther

☐ COUNTRY SUGAR PAPA (Johnson, Luther 'Guitar Junior')
BB 9546CD / May '94 / Bullseye Blues

☐ DOIN' THE SUGAR TOO (Johnson, Luther 'Guitar Junior')
Doin' the sugar too / Flippin' and floppin' / I'm ready / I need some air / Woke up this mornin' / Hard times (have surely come) / Get on the floor / Time to make my getaway / Bad boy / You were wrong / Early in the mornin' blues / What you don't know won't hurt you / Doin' the sugar too
CDBB 9563 / Feb '97 / Bullseye Blues

☐ IT'S GOOD TO BE ME (Johnson, Luther 'Guitar Junior')
Feel so bad / Come on back to me / Deep down in Florida / I'm leaving you / If you love me like you say / Ronettes / Stealin' chicken / It's good to me / Raise your window / Next door neighbour / That's all you need / In my younger days
CDBB 9516 / Nov '92 / Bullseye Blues

☐ LUTHER'S BLUES (Johnson, Luther 'Guitar Junior')
ECD 260102 / Oct '94 / Evidence

☐ SLAMMIN' ON THE WEST SIDE (Johnson, Luther 'Guitar Junior' & The Magic Rockers)
Pretty girl (a Cadillac and some money) / She's lookin' good / Hey little girl / I ain't doin' too bad / It's good to me / Sittin' on the back seat of a Greyhound bus / Every woman needs to be loved / Stranded / Early in the morning blues / Another man / Hard times (have surely come) / Woman I love / Get up and go / Why am I treated so bad / Waiting at the station / Meet me with your black drawers on
CD 83389 / May '96 / Telarc

Johnson, Luther

☐ HOUSEROCKIN' DADDY (Johnson, Luther 'Houserocker')
I'm Mr. Luck / Bad luck blues / You could have fooled me / Fool's advice / She wants to sell my monkey / Rockin' daddy / You know I love you baby / Something you got / Don't say that no more / Things I used to do
ICH 9010CD / Nov '91 / Ichiban

☐ LONESOME IN MY BEDROOM (Johnson, Luther 'Houserocker')
ECD 260052 / Jan '92 / Evidence

☐ RETROSPECTIVES (Johnson, Luther 'Houserocker')
Rockin' daddy / Trouble blues / Big money / You could have fooled me / Pretty thing / I'm Mr. Lucky / Little car blues / She wants to sell my monkey / Cryin' and thinkin' / Fool's advice / Drivin' me crazy
ICH 1513 / 29 Jun '98 / Ichiban

Johnson, Marc

☐ BASS DESIRES
Samurai hee-haw / Resolution / Black is the colour of my true love's hair / Bass desires / Wishing doll / Mojo highway / Thanks again
8277432 / Feb '86 / ECM

☐ RIGHT BRAIN PATROL
They love me fifteen feet away / Batuki Burundi / Netcong on my mind / Right brain patrol / Heru nazel / Inside four walls / You after you / Whispers / Log o'rhythm / Light in your eye / Call
8491532 / Apr '92 / jMT

☐ SECOND SIGHT (Johnson, Marc Bass Desires)
Crossing the corpus callosum / Small hands / Sweet soul / Twister / Thrill seekers / Prayer beads / 1951 / Hymn for her
8330382 / Oct '87 / ECM

☐ SOUND OF THE SUMMER RUNNING
5392992 / 9 Feb '98 / Verve

Johnson, Margaret

☐ MARGARET JOHNSON 1923-1927
DOCD 5436 / May '96 / Document

Johnson, Mark

☐ DAYDREAM
On the sky / Blue smoke / When you were mine / Way you do the things you do / Dim the lights / Gotta do it good / Daydream / Island lullaby / You're the one / Long goodbye
JVC 20432 / Apr '95 / JVC

☐ DEEP FOCUS
I told you so / Ocean of love / Mediterranean / Deep focus / Smoke and mirrors / Don't turn away / Shades of Dre / Afrique / Tempted / And when the time comes
JVC 20582 / Oct '96 / JVC

☐ MARK JOHNSON
Overture / Exit 33 / Gift for the ages / Street samba / Come on / Mud hut / She's so funktional / Bad influence / Funky James / Hipocket / Devotional
JVC 20322 / Apr '94 / JVC

Johnson, Mark

☐ 12 IN A ROOM
NLA 022 / 29 Jun '98 / Not Lame

Johnson, Marv

☐ VERY BEST OF MARV JOHNSON, THE
Can't take another day / Paper kisses / Whole lotta shakin' in my heart / It's magic between us / Night / Something's burning my heart / Gonna fix you good (every time you're bad) / Look it's raining sunshine / Pull myself together / I'll pick a rose for my rose / Heart for sale / Better love next time / Another chance / Beware there's danger / Riding for a fall / Nothing can stop me / By hook or by crook / Come to me
3035990032 / Oct '95 / Carlton

Johnson, Mary

☐ COMPLETE RECORDED WORKS 1929-36
DOCD 5305 / Dec '94 / Document

Johnson, Merline

☐ YAS YAS GIRL 1937-1947, THE
WBJCD 006 / Jul '96 / Wolf

☐ YAS YAS GIRL VOL.1 1937-1938
DOCD 5292 / Dec '94 / Document

☐ YAS YAS GIRL VOL.2 1938-1939
DOCD 5293 / Dec '94 / Document

☐ YAS YAS GIRL VOL.3 1939-1940
DOCD 5294 / Dec '94 / Document

☐ YAS YAS GIRL VOL.4 1940-1941
DOCD 5295 / Dec '94 / Document

Johnson, Noon

☐ NOON JOHNSON & LEMON NASH 1960 (The Larry Borenstein Collection Vol.9) (Johnson, Noon/Lemon Nash)
Tiger rag: *Johnson, Noon Bazooka Band* / Exactly like you: *Johnson, Noon Bazooka Band* / Stars in the sky seem to shine: *Johnson, Noon Bazooka Band* / Jambalaya: *Johnson, Noon Bazooka Band* / Cecilia: *Johnson, Noon Bazooka Band* / Bill Bailey: *Johnson, Noon Bazooka Band* / Bourbon Street parade: *Johnson, Noon Bazooka Band* / World is waiting for the sunrise: *Johnson, Noon Bazooka Band* / Now is the hour: *Johnson, Noon Bazooka Band* / Introduction: *Johnson, Noon & Kid Thomas/'Creole' George Guesnon* / On a coconut island: *Johnson, Noon & Kid Thomas/'Creole' George Guesnon* / Should I reveal: *Johnson, Noon & Kid Thomas/'Creole' George Guesnon* / Time marches on: *Johnson, Noon & Kid Thomas/'Creole' George Guesnon* / Yakety yak/Hi yo silver: *Johnson, Noon & Kid Thomas/'Creole' George Guesnon* / Big ole mushrat: *Johnson, Noon & Kid Thomas/'Creole' George Guesnon* / Intro/Ugly child: *Nash, Lemon* / Sweet Georgia Brown: *Nash, Lemon* / Duck's yas yas: *Nash, Lemon* / Creole song: *Nash, Lemon* / Too late: *Nash, Lemon* / Rooster crowing blues: *Nash, Lemon* / Down in New Orleans: *Nash, Lemon* / Outskirts of town: *Nash, Lemon* / Stacko lee: *Nash, Lemon*
504CD 38 / 9 Mar '98 / 504

Johnson, Paul

☐ FEEL THE MUSIC
Relax with me / Little Suntin Suntin / You make me say do be do / Hear the music / About your love / Summer Heat / I wonder why / Groove
PF 056CD / Nov '96 / Peacefrog

☐ SECOND COMING
ACVCD 017 / Jun '96 / ACV

Johnson, Pete

☐ BOOGIE WOOGIE MASTER 1938-1946
158972 / Nov '97 / Jazz Archives

☐ CENTRAL AVENUE BOOGIE
Pete Kay boogie / Central Avenue drag / Margie / 66 stop / Minuet boogie / Yancy street boogie / Swanee river / Hollywood boogie / Hollywood boogie / Hollywood boogie / Hollywood boogie / Plain food blues / Plain food blues / Wiley's boogie
DD 656 / Mar '97 / Delmark

☐ CLASSICS 1938-1939
CLASSICS 656 / Nov '92 / Classics

☐ CLASSICS 1939-1941
CLASSICS 665 / Nov '92 / Classics

☐ CLASSICS 1944-1946
CLASSICS 933 / Apr '97 / Classics

☐ KING OF THE BOOGIE
CDCH 546 / Oct '91 / Milan

☐ PETE JOHNSON 1939-1947 (Live Performances/Alternate Takes)
DOCD 1009 / Dec '97 / Document

☐ PETE'S BLUES
Pete's lonesome blues / Mr. Dram meets Mr Piano / Mutiny in the dog house / Mr. Clarinet knocks twice / Page Mr Trumpet / Ben rides out / JC from KC / Pete's house warming blues / Atomic boogie / Back room blues / 1280 Stomp / I may be wonderful / Man wanted
SV 0196 / Oct '97 / Savoy Jazz

Johnson, Plas

☐ BEST OF PLAS JOHNSON, THE
WBJCD 021 / Nov '96 / Wolf

☐ POSITIVELY
Positively / Lover man (Oh where can you be) / Let's get it all together / Easy for you to say / Never more / My foolish heart / Careless love / Cottage for sale / Dirty leg blues / Sea sea
CCD 4024 / May '97 / Concord Jazz

Johnson, Puff

☐ MIRACLE
Forever more / Outside my window / All over your face / Yearning / Love between you and me / Miracle / Because of you / God sent you / True meaning of love / Come closer / Please help me I'm falling (in love with you) / Hold on to this hand
4837492 / Feb '97 / Work/Columbia

Johnson, Robb

☐ HEART'S DESIRE (Johnson, Robb & Pip Collins)
Weathering the storm / Merrie olde Englande / Tomorrow will be better / Happy song / After the rain / End of the day / Gliders for Tim / Eddie outside / Nobody but yours / Pity and mercy / Heart's desire / Sunlight on the harbour / Wall came down / Die Moorsoldaten / Bells of freedom / More than enough
IRR 014CD / Aug '93 / Irregular

☐ HELL'S KITCHEN (Johnson, Robb Roots Band)
Working on a river / U have 2 dance / Waiting for bluebirds / Cassandra's song / Room beside the sea / Motherland / Butcher's hand / Lottery land / Hell's kitchen / New moon / Permanent free zone / Armistice day / Red, white and moo
IRR 026 / Sep '96 / Irregular

☐ INTERESTING TIMES
IRR 023 / Sep '95 / Irregular

☐ INVISIBLE PEOPLE
Me and the working man / What are we waiting for / Invisible people / Martha in the mirror / Favourite story / In buttercup class we smile / Mystery / Spanish castles / Hancock in Australia / Anarchy in Hackney / Harbourtown / Tonight we dance / Last girl on the beach
IRR 029CD / Apr '98 / Irregular

☐ LACK OF JOLLY PLOUGHBOY (Johnson, Robb & Pip Collins)
Welcome to the warehouse / Wendy and Michelle / Paper poppies / House with nobody home / Shame of the nation / Dancing on a Sunday / Uncle Cyril / Mother and the motorway / Turning year / James Dean and Sameena / We rise up / Lack of jolly ploughboy / Blame the snow for falling
IRR 017CD / Oct '94 / Irregular

☐ NIGHT CAFE
IRR 025CD / May '96 / Irregular

☐ OVERNIGHT
Fairy tales in Feltham / I remember Managua / Orange class news / Last time I saw Paris / Day before the war / Vic Williams / Overnight / 17 again tonight / Tourists and casualties / Winter turns to spring / Suicide tour / Rehoused in Hounslow / Acton Town / You don't have to say goodbye
IRR 027 / Feb '97 / Irregular

☐ ROBB JOHNSON
IRR 018CD / Aug '95 / Irregular

Johnson, Robert

☐ ALL TIME BLUES CLASSICS
8420272 / Oct '96 / Music Memoria

☐ BEG BORROW OR STEAL (3CD Set)
KATCD 107 / 1 Jun '98 / Catfish

☐ BLUES OF ROBERT JOHNSON, THE (Various Artists)
Sweet home Chicago: *Shines, Johnny* / Dust my broom: *Hammond, John* / Come on in my kitchen: *Block, Rory* / 32-20 blues: *Rishell, Paul* / Walking blues: *Olsen, Kristina* / Steady rollin' man: *Hammond, John* / Hot tamales: *Hammond, John* / Crossroad blues: *Block, Rory* / Hellhound on my trail: *Block, Rory* / Kind hearted woman: *Shines, Johnny* / Terraplane blues: *Shines, Johnny* / Stones in my passway: *Brozman, Bob*
EDCD 7029 / Sep '97 / Easydisc

☐ BLUES, THE (San Antonio-Dallas 1936-1937 - 2CD Set)
FA 251 / Feb '96 / Fremeaux

☐ CROSSROAD BLUES
REMCD 504 / Feb '98 / Reactive

☐ GOLD COLLECTION, THE
D2CD 14 / Dec '92 / Deja Vu

☐ HELLHOUND ON MY TRAIL
I believe I'll dust my room / Kindhearted woman blues / Teraplane blues / 32-20 Blues / Last fair deal gone down / Ramblin' on my mind / Cross road blues / Come on in my kitchen / They're red hot / From four 'til late / Hellhound on my trail / Malted milk / Milk cow's calf blues / I'm a steady rollin' man / Stones in my passway / Sweet home Chicago / Walking blues / Stop breakin' down blues / Honeymoon blues / Little queen of spades / Me and the devil blues / Preaching blues / Love in vain
IGOCD 2017 / Mar '95 / Indigo

☐ I WENT DOWN TO THE CROSSROADS
I believe I'll dust my broom / Kind-hearted woman blues / Rambling on my mind / Sweet home Chicago / Come on in my kitchen / When you got a friend / Phonograph blues / Terraplane blues / They're red hot / 30-20 blues / Cross road blues / Dead shrimp blues / Last fair deal gone down / Walking blues / If I had possesion over judgement day / Preaching blues (up jumped the devil) / I'm a steady rollin' man / Stones in my passway
SUMCD 4194 / 11 May '98 / Summit

☐ KING OF THE DELTA
Crossroad blues / Travelling riverside blues / Walkin' blues / I believe I'll dust my broom / Hell hound on my trail / Kind hearted woman blues / Ramblin' on my mind / Stop breakin' down blues / Come on in my kitchen / 32 20 Blues / From four until late / I'm a steady rollin' man / Love in vain / Terraplane blues / When you got a good friend / Sweet home Chicago / Dead shrimp blues / Milkcow's calf blues / Preachin' blues / Little queen of spades / Malted milk / Me and the devil blues / They're red hot / Last fair deal gone
4878442 / 20 Oct '97 / Mojo Filter

☐ KING OF THE DELTA BLUES SINGERS
Crossroads blues / Terraplane blues / Come on in my kitchen / Walking blues / Last fair deal gone down / 32-20 blues / Kindhearted woman blues / If I had possession over judgement day / Preaching blues / When you got a good friend / Rambling on my mind / Stones in my passway / Traveling riverside blues / Milkcow's calf blues / Hellhound on my trail
4844192 / Sep '96 / Mastersound

☐ LOVE IN VAIN
I'm a steady rollin' man / Sweet home Chicago / Cross road blues / Kind hearted woman blues / Love in vain / Stop breakin' down blues / Me and the devil blues / Phonograph blues / Drunken hearted man / Preaching blues (up jumped the devil) / Little queen of spades / Terraplane blues
305672 / Apr '98 / Hallmark

☐ MASTERS, THE
EABCD 067 / 24 Nov '97 / Eagle

☐ ROBERT JOHNSON (2CD Set)
R2CD 4014 / 13 Apr '98 / Deja Vu

☐ ROBERT JOHNSON COLLECTOR'S EDITION
DVBC 9052 / Apr '95 / Deja Vu

☐ ROBERT JOHNSON GOLD (2CD Set)
D2CD 4014 / Jun '95 / Deja Vu

☐ ROOTS OF ROBERT JOHNSON (Various Artists)
YAZCD 1073 / Apr '91 / Yazoo

☐ TRAVELING RIVERSIDE BLUES
Kind hearted woman blues / Sweet home Chicago / Ramblin' on my mind / I believe I'll dust my broom / When you got a good friend / Come on in my kitchen / Terraplane blues / Phonograph blues / 32-20 blues / They're red hot / Crossroads blues / Walkin' blues / Preachin' blues / If I had possession over Judgement Day / I'm a steady rollin' man / Little Queen of Spades / Me and the devil blues / Stop breakin' down blues / Travellin' riverside blues / Love in vain / Milkcow's calf blues
CD 52019 / Aug '92 / Blues Encore

Johnson, Robert

☐ ALOHA FROM HAVANA (Johnson, Robert & Punchdrunks)
SE 004 / Apr '98 / Strange Edge

☐ FEELS LIKE BUZZ ALDRIN (Johnson, Robert & Punchdrunks)
SE 001 / May '97 / Strange Edge

Johnson, Robert A.

☐ CLOSE PERSONAL FRIEND
BH 006 / 2 Feb '98 / Bubblehead

Johnson, Ruby

☐ I'LL RUN YOUR HURT AWAY
I'll run your heart away / What more can a woman do / Won't be long / Love of my man / Why not give me a chance / It's not that easy / Don't play that song (You lied) / Come to me my darling / It's better to give than to receive / Keep on keepin' on / How strong is my love / Need your love so bad / Leftover love / I'd better check on myself / I'd rather fight than switch / No no no / If I ever needed love (I sure do need it now) / When my love comes down / Weak spot
CDSXD 049 / Mar '93 / Stax

Johnson, Shirley

☐ LOOKING FOR LOVE
APCD 094 / Jul '94 / Appaloosa

Johnson, Snuff

☐ WILL THE CIRCLE BE UNBROKEN
BMCD 9026 / Sep '94 / Black Magic

Johnson, Syl

☐ A SIDES, THE
Love you left behind / I wanna satisfy your every need / We did it / Back for a taste of your love / I'm yours / Let yourself go / I want to take you home (to see mama) / Take me to the river / I only have love / Star bright, star light / About to make me leave home / Fonk you / Stand by me / Mystery lady
HILOCD 06 / Mar '94 / Hi

☐ BACK IN THE GAME
Back in the game / I like your style / I can't stop / Please don't give up on me / Keep on loving me / Take me to the river / Ghetto woman / Watch what you do to me / Dipped in the water: *Johnson, Syl & Syleena Thompson* / Driving wheel / Anyway the wind blows / Clean up man / I will rise again / All of your love
DE 674 / Mar '97 / Delmark

☐ DRESSES TOO SHORT/IS IT BECAUSE I'M BLACK
Dresses too short / I can take care of business / Different strokes / Soul drippin' / Fox hunting on the weekend / Ode to soul man / Come on sock it to me / I'll take those skinny legs / Try me / Same kind of thing / I've got the real thing / Sorry 'bout dat / Is it because I'm black / Come together / Together forever / Concrete reservation / Black balloons / Walk a mile in my shoes / I'm talkin' 'bout freedom / Right on
CDKEND 148 / Aug '97 / Kent

☐ HI MASTERS, THE
Back for a taste of you / We did it / I'm yours / Don't do it / I hear the love chimes / Anyway the wind blows / Love you left behind / I want to take you home / Feelin' frisky / Let yourself go / I need a good girl go / Wind blow her back my way / You don't know me / I hate I walked away / Take me to the river
HEX 36 / 4 Aug '98 / Hi

☐ IS IT BECAUSE I'M BLACK
Come on sock it to me / Dresses too short / I can take care of business / I'll take those skinny legs / I resign / Get ready / I feel an urge / I take care of homework / Is it because I'm black / Concrete reservation / Walk a mile in my shoes / I'm talkin' 'bout freedom / Right on / Different strokes / Going to the shack / One way to nowhere / Thank you baby / One way ticket to nowhere / Kiss by kiss / Same kind of thing
CPCD 8011 / Feb '94 / Charly

Johnson, Tommy

☐ COMPLETE RECORDINGS 1928-30
WSECD 104 / Jan '94 / Wolf

☐ TOMMY JOHNSON 1928-1929
DOCD 5001 / Aug '91 / Document

Johnson, Wayne

☐ KEEPING THE DREAM ALIVE (Johnson, Wayne Trio)
Bedrock / Kite music / Occasion for Jackson / Nu blooz / Wonder mountain / Keeping the dream alive / No excuse / Tangletown / Rock runner / Portrait of a yak / Blue solanum
5302562 / Apr '94 / MoJazz

Johnson, Wilko

☐ BARBED WIRE BLUES
FREUDCD 26 / Nov '88 / Jungle

Johnson, Willie Neal

☐ BEST OF WILLIE NEAL JOHNSON & THE GOSPEL KEYNOTES, THE (Johnson, Willie Neal & The Gospel Keynotes)
NASH 4501 / Feb '96 / Nashboro

Johnsons

☐ LAZY BONES
HYMN 12 / 1 Dec '97 / Fundamental

Johnston, Bruce

☐ SURFIN' ROUND THE WORLD
Surfin' round the world / Maksha at midnight / Down under / Capetown / Biarritz / Jersey Channel Islands / Hamptons / Virginia Beach / Surf-a-nova / Hot pastrami / Mashed potatoes / Come on to... / Malibu / Surfing's here to stay / Down under / Hamptons
SC 6100 / Aug '97 / Sundazed

Johnston, Daniel

☐ 1990
Devil town / Held the hand / Some things last a long time / Don't play cards with Satan / Got to get you into my life / Funeral home / Spirit world rising / Lord give me hope / Tears, stupid tears / True love will find you in the end / Careless soul
SHIMMY 028 / 27 Apr '98 / Shimmy Disc

Johnston, Freedy

☐ CAN YOU FLY
Trying to tell you I don't know / In the new sunshine / Tearing down this place / Remember me / Wheels / Lucky one / Can you fly / Responsible / Mortician's daughter / Sincere / Down in love / California thing / We will shine
7559615872 / Sep '93 / Elektra

☐ THIS PERFECT WORLD
Bad reputation / Evie's tears / Can't sink this town / This perfect world / Cold again / Two lovers stop / Across the avenue / Gone like the water / Delores / Evie's garden / Disappointed man / I can hear the laughs
7559616552 / Jul '94 / Elektra

Johnston, Jan

☐ NAKED BUT FOR LILIES
If heaven callz / Paris / I learned (you blew me out) / Wild child / Don't be lonely / Don't make promises / Calling you / Something's in the house / Alive / Strange day
5402422 / Aug '94 / A&M

Johnston, Philip

☐ BIG TROUBLE
1201522 / Sep '93 / Black Saint

☐ MUSIC FOR FILMS
TZA 7510 / 1 Jun '98 / Tzadik

Johnston, Randy

☐ SOMEWHERE IN THE NIGHT
Dat dere / I wish I knew how it would feel to be free / Secret love / End of a beautiful friendship / Sack of woe / Somewhere in the night / Blues for the millenium / Third time around / In the wee small hours of the morning / Secret love
HCD 7007 / Jan '98 / Hightone

Johnstone, Arthur

☐ NORTH BY NORTH
North by North / Oil beneath the sea / Tinkermans daughter / Christmas 1914 / Margaret and me / Benny Lynch / Doomsday in the afternoon / Take her in your arms / Raglan Road / Crooked Jack / It's my union / Ballad of Joe Hill / Bandiera Rosa
LCOM 9039 / Apr '91 / Lismor

Johnstone, Jim

☐ TRIBUTE TO JIMMY SHAND
COMD 2039 / Feb '94 / Temple

Johnstone, Muriel

☐ RSCDS VOL.24 (Johnstone, Muriel Scottish Country Dance Band)
Scotch circle / Balquidder strathspey / Wild geese / Sailor / St. Andrew's day / Oh whistle and I'll come tae ye my lad / I canna buckle to / Hollin buss / Duke he was a bonnie beau / Campbell's are coming / Adieu mon ami / Mairrit man's favourite
RSCDSCD 012 / Jul '98 / Royal Scottish Country Dance Society

Johnstons

☐ BARLEY CORN, THE/THE JOHNSTONS
ESMCD 410 / Jul '96 / Essential

☐ COLOURS OF THE DAWN
Hello friend / Crazy Anne / Brightness she came / If I could / Angela Davis / Colours of the dawn / I'll be gone in the morning / Seems so long ago Nancy / Old man's tale
HILLCD 9 / Jan '97 / Wooded Hill

☐ GIVE A DAMN/BITTER GREEN
Give a damn / You keep going your way / Urge for going / Port of Amsterdam / Funny in a sad, sad way / Hey that's no way to say goodbye / Both sides now / Julia / Sweet Thames flow softly / I loved / I don't mind the rain on Monday / Walking out on foggy mornings / Jesus was a carpenter / Gypsy / Lord Thomas and fair Ellender / Fiddler's green / Story of Isaac / Bitter green / Penny wager / Marcie / Spanish lady / Streets of London
ESMCD 525 / Jul '97 / Essential

☐ TRANSATLANTIC YEARS
Fhir a bhata / O'Carolan's concerto / Lark in the morning / Apprentice song / You keep going your way / Urge for going / Hey, that's no way to say goodbye / Both sides now / Ye Jacobites by name / Coleraine regatta / Barleycorn / Flower of Northumberland / Fuigfidh mise'n baile sea / Story of Isaac / Bitter green / Marcie / Spanish lady / If I could / Colours of the dawn / If I sang my song / Continental trailways bus
TDEM 13 / Mar '94 / Trandem

Jolene

☐ IN THE GLOAMING
Pensacola / Wave to worrying / Exhibit / Begin 1000 / Ouisch / Recline to sensible / So selpless you / Two sisters and the lareate / 16c / Pull the weight, Virginia / Clear bottle down / 20th century pause
4344310122 / 23 Mar '98 / Sire

Jolicard, Jean-Pierre

☐ SUMMER SOLSTICE
PV 796021 / Mar '96 / Pierre Verany

Jolley & Swain

☐ BACKTRACKIN'
Autumn leaves / Walk on / Amazon / Backtrackin' / Journey / Patterns / Soul street / Lost in the night
SAK 004 / Jul '97 / Scratch

Jolliffe, Steve

☐ ALIEN
HM 1000 / Nov '96 / Atlantis

☐ TEMMENU
SIN 004 / Jun '96 / Sine

☐ ZANZI
HM 1001 / Nov '96 / Atlantis

Jolly Boys

☐ POP'N'MENTO
Mother and wife / Love in the cemetery / River come down / Ten dollars to two / Banana / Big bamboo / Ben Wood Dick / Touch me tomato / Shaving cream / Watermelon / Back to back / Nightfall
COOKCD 040 / Jun '90 / Cooking Vinyl

Jolson, Al

☐ AL JOLSON COLLECTOR'S EDITION
DVGH 7042 / Apr '95 / Deja Vu

☐ AL JOLSON VOL.3
PASTCD 7045 / Jan '96 / Flapper

☐ APRIL SHOWERS
GO 3813 / 1 Dec '97 / Golden Options

☐ AUDIO ARCHIVE
My mammy / There's a rainbow 'round my shoulder / Ma blushin' Rosie / I'm sitting on top of the world / Rock-a-bye your baby with a dixie melody / I only have eyes for you / California here I come / Let me sing and I'm happy / Swanee / When the red, red robin comes bob, bob, bobbin' along / Sonny Boy / For me and my gal / Oh you beautiful doll / You made me love you / Give my regards to Broadway / April showers / Anniversary song / After you've gone / Toot toot tootsie / Avalon
CDAA 004 / Jun '92 / Tring

☐ BEST OF AL JOLSON, THE (25 Great Songs)
CD 6038 / Sep '96 / Music

☐ BEST OF AL JOLSON, THE (20 Timeless Classics)
Rock a bye your baby with a Dixie melody / When the red red robin comes bob bob bobbin' along / Sonny Boy / April showers / Swanee / For me and my gal / By the light of the silvery moon / Avalon / About a quarter to nine / Carolina in the morning / Toot, toot, tootsie / California here I come / There's a rainbow 'round my shoulder / Waiting for the Robert E Lee / Give my regards to Broadway / Little pal / I'm in seventh heaven / Anniversary song / Let me sing and I'm happy / My Mammy
ECD 3260 / Jan '97 / K-Tel

☐ BEST OF AL JOLSON, THE
HMNCD 004 / Jun '97 / Half Moon

☐ DEFINITIVE AL JOLSON, THE (18 Timeless Classics)
April showers / Sonny boy / Mother of mine I still have you / Lazy / Hello, Tucky / You flew from the nest / There's a rainbow 'round my shoulder / Little pal / Rock a bye your baby with a dixie melody / Dirty hands dirty face / My mammy / I'm sitting on top of the world / Mr. Radio man / I'd climb the highest mountain (if I knew I'd find you) / Blue river / When the red red robin comes bob bob bobbin' along / Golden gate / I'm in seventh heaven
SUMCD 4175 / 11 May '98 / Summit

☐ FIRST RECORDINGS, THE
That haunting melody / Rum tum tiddle / Asleep in the deep (parody) / Snap your fingers (and away we go) / Brass band ephraham jones / Ragging the baby to sleep / That lovin' traumeral / Movin' that man, don't take my baby grand / My yellow jacket girl / Spaniard that blighted my life / Pullman porters' parade / You made me love you / That little german band (al jolson's la-la song) / Everybody snap your fingers with me / Back to the carolina you love / Revival day / Sister susie's sewing shirts for soldiers (take i) / Sister susie's sewing shirts for soldiers (take 2) / When the grown-up ladies act like babies (take i) / When the grown-up ladies act like babies (take 2) / Yaaka hoola hickey doola / Where did robinson crusoe go / Down where the swanee river flows / Now he's got a beautiful girl
STCD 564 / May '93 / Stash

☐ GREATEST ENTERTAINER, THE
April showers / Rock-a-bye your baby / I'm sitting on top of the world / There's a rainbow 'round my shoulder / When the red, red robin comes bob, bob, bobbin' along / Tonight's my night with baby / My mammy / Swanee / When the little red roses / Liza / Hallelujah, I'm a bum / California here I come / One I love / Golden gate / Back in your own backyard / Sonny boy
HADCD 157 / May '94 / Javelin

☐ I LOVE TO SING
JASCD 100 / Nov '95 / Jasmine

☐ JOLSON SONGBOOK, THE
Rock-a-bye your baby / Swanee / My Mammy / April showers / California here I come / Toot toot Tootsie / Sonny Boy / Let me sing and I'm happy / You made me love you / Back in your own backyard / There's a rainbow 'round my shoulder / I'm sitting on top of the world / Waiting for the Robert E Lee / Me and my shadow / Carolina in the morning / Baby face / Give my regards to Broadway / Pretty baby / Bye Bye blackbird / For me and my gal
3036200292 / Feb '97 / Carlton

☐ LET ME SING AND I'M HAPPY
Let me sing and I'm happy / Medley / Kate / Best things in life are free / Lazy / New Ashmolean marching society and students' conservatory ba / Anniversary song / When the red red robbin comes bob bob bobbin' along / I can dream, can't I / Rock a bye your baby with a dixie melody / April showers / Ma blushin' Rosie / You're wonderful / One I love belongs to somebody else / Avalon / That lucky old sun / Toot, toot, tootsie / Medley / Bye bye baby / My mammy / Rainy night in Rio / Suebonnet Sue / Pretty girl is like a melody / Linda / Swanee / My old Kentucky home / Ho time in the old time tonight / Nobody / Comedy / Oh Susanna / Medley / Comedy / Alabamy bound
RMB 75019 / Nov '93 / Remember
PARCD 004 / Jan '96 / Parrot

☐ LIVE ON THE BARRY GRAY SHOW 1948
JH 5001 / Feb '98 / Jazz Hour

☐ SALESMAN OF SONG 1911-1923
That haunting melody / Everybody snap your fingers with me / Revival day / Back to the Carolina you love / I sent my wife to the Thousand Isles / I'm saving up the means to get to New Orleans / Someone else may be there while I'm gone / Don't write me letters / Broken doll / Every little while / Wedding bells / I've got my captain working for me now / You ain't heard nothin' yet / I gave her that / Tell me / Chloe / In sweet September / O-hi-o / Yoo hoo / Angel child / Lost: a wonderful girl / Stella / You've simply got me cuckoo / That big blond mumma / Coal black Mammy of mine
PASTCD 9796 / Jul '92 / Flapper

☐ STAGE HIGHLIGHTS 1911-1925
That lovin' traumeral / Rum tum tiddle / Snap your fingers / Tha spaniard that blighted my life / You made me love you / That little german band / Sister susie's sewing shirts for soldiers / When the grown up ladies act like babies / Yaaka hula hickey dula / Where did robinson crusoe go with friday on saturd / Down where the swanee river flows / Now he's got a beautiful girl / Tillie titwillow / 'n' everything / There's a lump of sugar down in dixie / Rock-a-bye your baby with a dixie melody / Hello, central, give me no-man's land / I'll say she does / Give me my mammy / Toot toot tootsie (goo'bye) / Morning will come / I'm going south / Hello 'tucky / Keep smiling at trouble / Miami
PASTCD 9748 / Jul '91 / Flapper

☐ VERY BEST OF AL JOLSON, THE (20 Greatest Hits)
PLATCD 30 / Mar '92 / Platinum

☐ VERY BEST OF AL JOLSON, THE
There's a rainbow 'round my shoulder / Let me sing and I'm happy / Carolina in the morning / Give my regards to Broadway / Is it true what they say about Dixie / About a quarter to nine / April showers / I'm just wild about Harry / Rock-a-bye your baby / With a Dixie melody / For me and my gal / When the red, red robin comes bob, bob, bobbin' along / You made me love you / Baby face/I'm looking over a four leaf clover / My mammy / California here I come / De Campton races / Alabamy bound / Swanee / When you were sweet sixteen / I only have eyes for you / Pretty baby / I'm sitting on top of the world / Oh you beautiful doll / Toot toot tootsie goodbye / I want a girl - just like the girl that married dear old Dad / By the light of the silvery moon / Waiting for the Robert E Lee / Spaniard that blighted my life / Anniversary song
MCCD 074 / Jun '92 / Music Club

☐ WORLD'S GREATEST ENTERTAINER (Vintage Recordings 1913-1942)
My mammy / Let me sing and I'm happy / Little pal / There's a rainbow round my shoulder / I'm sitting on top of the world / When the red red robin comes a bob bob bobbin along / California here I come / April showers / Cheek to cheek / Liza (all the clouds I'll roll away) / Sonny boy / Dirty hands, dirty face / Ol' man river / Rock a bye your baby with a Dixie melody / I'll say she does / Avalon / Morning will come / Toot toot tootsie / You made me love you
QED 108 / Nov '96 / Tring

☐ YOU AIN'T HEARD NOTHIN' YET
California here I come / Sonny boy / April showers / Pasadena / When the red, red robin comes bob, bob, bobbin' along / You made me love you / I'm ka-razy for you / You ain't heard nothin' yet / Swanee / When the little red roses get the blues for you / Rock-a-bye your baby with a Dixie melody / Blue river / Used to you / Steppin' out / Spaniard that blighted my life / Golden gate / My Mammy / Miami
CDAJA 5038 / Dec '85 / Living Era

☐ YOU MADE ME LOVE YOU
Back in your own backyard / Liza (all the clouds'll roll away) / Little pal / There's a rainbow round my shoulder / April showers / I'm in seventh heaven / Tonight's my night with baby / (here I am) broken hearted / I'm sitting on top of the world / Swanee / Rock a bye your baby with a dixie melody / Sonny boy / Golden gate / Why can't you / When the red red robin comes bob bob bobbin' along / California here I come / You made me love you / Cheek to cheek / My mammy (the jazz singer - 1927)
PLCD 542 / Aug '95 / President

Jomanda

☐ NUBIA SOUL
Never / Don't deny / Just a little more time / I like it / I cried the tears / Does the music love you / Life / What you go through for love / Island / Don't fight the feelings / Kiss you / Back to you / Gotta be with you
7567805482 / Dec '93 / Atlantic

Jon

☐ SMOKE
TZ 7210 / Oct '96 / Tzadik

Jon & Vangelis

☐ BEST OF JON & VANGELIS, THE
Italian song / I'll find my way home / State of independence / One more time / Play within a play / Friends of Mr. Cairo / Outside of this (inside of that) / He is sailing / I hear you now
8219292 / Aug '84 / Polydor

☐ CHRONICLES
I hear you now / He is sailing / Thunder / Beside / Bird song / Play within a play / When the night comes / Deborah / Curious electric / Friends of Mr. Cairo / Back to school / Italian song / Polonaise / Love is
5501962 / Sep '94 / Spectrum

☐ FRIENDS OF MR.CAIRO
Friends of Mr. Cairo / Back to school / Outside of this, inside of that / State of independence / Beside / Mayflower
8000212 / Jun '88 / Polydor

☐ PAGE OF LIFE
Wisdom chain / Page of life / Money / Jazzy box / Garden of senses / Is it love / Anyone can light a candle / Be a good friend of mine / Shine for me / Genevieve / Journey to Ixtlan / Little guitar
261373 / Feb '94 / Arista

☐ PRIVATE COLLECTION
And when the night comes / Deborah / He is sailing / Polonaise / Horizon / King is coming
8131742 / '83 / Polydor

Jon B

☐ BONA FIDE
Bona fide / Simple melody / Love is Candi / Mystery 4 two / Someone to love / Time after time / Overflow / Pretty girl / Pants off / Isn't it scary / Burning for you / Gone before light / Love didn't do
4805012 / Nov '95 / 5/50 Music

☐ COOL RELAX
Shine / Bad girl / Don't say / They don't know / Can't help it / Cool relax / Are u still down / Pride and joy / I do (whatcha say boo) / Let me know / I ain't going out / Let's go / Can we get down love hurts / Tu amor / Thank you
4879202 / 15 Sep '97 / Epic

Jon Cougar Concentration Camp

☐ 'TIL NIAGRA FALLS
BYO 048CD / 6 Oct '97 / Better Youth Organisation

☐ TOO TOUGH TO DIE
LIB 27810CD / 17 Aug '98 / Liberation

Jon The Dentist

☐ PYRAMID
TECLP 24CD / Sep '96 / Truelove

Jonas Jinx

☐ CASE OF..., A
SPV 08445692 / May '95 / SPV

Jonathan Fire Eater

☐ TREMBLE UNDER BOOM LIGHTS
Search for cherry red / Make it precious / Give me daughters / Beautican / Winston Plum: Undertaker / When Prince was a kid
BLUFF 038CD / Jan '97 / Deceptive

☐ TREMBLE UNDER BOOM LIGHTS (Alternative Version)
CDHW 044 / 16 Mar '98 / Crippled Dick Hot Wax

☐ WOLF SONGS FOR LAMBS
When the curtain calls for you / Shape of things that never come / This is my room / There is no love like that / Bi-polar summer / I've changed hotels / Everybody plays the mime / These little monkeys / Station coffee / Night in the nursery / In-patient talent show
BLUFF 049CD / 29 Sep '97 / Deceptive

Jones & Leva

☐ JOURNEY HOME
She could have loved him / Nothin' for nothin' / Drunkard's lantern / Log book of love / Satan I won't be your servant no more / Sweet goodbye / Up on camp / Loving on borrowed time / Bullet in your breast / Why can't you love me / Truest love / Where did you go / Hosanna
ROUCD 0457 / Jun '98 / Rounder

Jones, Al

☐ SWIMMING POOL
I'm so happy / Angelina / Your face is pink / There goes the sun / Long time sleeping / Lady Mildred / Swimming pool / Easy life / Love and money / Percy in a hearse / You'd better get out / In a box / 7 old hats / Down again / Rock and roll / In stormy weather
WEBE 9033 / Jun '98 / Weekend Beatnik

Jones, Alan

☐ SHADOW IN TIME, A
Shadow in time (part 1) / Don't be cruel / Will you still love me tomorrow / Good rockin' tonight / Let's have a party / All shook up / Blue moon of Kentucky / Do you wanna dance / C'mon everybody / Blue suede shoes / Shadow in time / Kansas City / Songbird / Ain't no sunshine / Sleepwalk/Midnight medley / Apache wardance
VIPCD 001 / Mar '98 / VIP

Jones, Aled

☐ ALED JONES WITH THE BBC WELSH CHORUS
Away in a manger / Come unto Him / Sussex carol / O little town of Bethlehem / St. Joseph's carol / Christmas star / Ding dong merrily on high / Deck the halls with boughs of holly / Holy Boy / Jesus Christ the apple tree / Gabriel's message / Rocking / Ave Maria / My heart ever faithful / Good king Wenceslas / Hwiangerdd mair / Unto us is born a son
CDVIP 104 / Dec '94 / Virgin VIP

☐ PIE JESU
Art thou troubled / If I can help somebody / Zion hears the watchmen's voices / Jesu joy of man's desiring / Lullaby / I'll walk beside you / Crown of roses / I know that my redeemer liveth / Lausanne / God so loved the world / At the end of the day / Pie Jesu / Laudate dominum
CDVIP 107 / Nov '93 / Virgin VIP

Jones, Andrew

☐ I NEED TIME (Jones, Andrew 'Jr. Boy')
I got a stick / Hoochie Mama / I need time / These bills / Big leg, heavy brother / Blues joint / I'm with you / Jr Boy's jam / You're a dog / Gotta be foolin' you / Tribute to Freddie
JSPCD 278 / Feb '97 / JSP

☐ WATCH WHAT YOU SAY
Watch what you say / Party man / Fast woman / Memory's fading / Shuffle on / Make some changes / Little by little / Time to move on / Blues Queen / Stinky dink / Lost love blues / Soul serenade / Got to win the lottery
CDBB 9602 / Jun '98 / Bullseye Blues

Jones, Barbara

☐ FOR YOUR EARS ONLY
JMC 200216 / Jun '95 / Jamaican Gold

☐ MY LOVE
RN 7031 / 24 Nov '97 / Rhino

☐ SAD MOVIES
CDGR 118 / Mar '97 / Charly

Jones, Brad

☐ GILT FLAKE
GR 1001 / Jun '97 / Ginger

Jones, Carlo

☐ CARLO JONES & THE KASEKO SURINAM TROUBADOURS
MWCD 3011 / Jul '95 / Music & Words

Jones, Carol Elizabeth

☐ LIGHT ENOUGH TO FIND MY WAY (Jones, Carol Elizabeth & James Leva)
Someday / Cold black heart / I tell you only / Back of your hand / Black as a crow / Light enough to find my way / Nothing but gold / North Country / Smoke and mirrors / I wait alone / Love beyond / Darlin' it's too good to be true
ROUCD 0407 / Jun '97 / Rounder

Jones, Chris

☐ BLINDED BY THE ROSE
SCR 40 / Sep '95 / Strictly Country

☐ FREE MAN (Live In Concert)
Free man / Pretty Polly / Come on in my kitchen / Lover's dream / Morning light / Something wrong with you / Willin' / Mississippi kid / Middle man / Blue suede shoes / Never get enough of you / Tribute to JT / Lonesome whistle / Comes the dawn
SM 401 / Feb '98 / Strictly Music

☐ NO ONE BUT YOU (Jones, Chris & The Night Drivers)
Ribbon of darkness / No one but you / I'm not that good at goodbye / Stream of love / My baby's just like money / Sweetest love / Only my heart / Model prisoner / Close the door / In a mansion stands my love / Shaky ground / Whispering now
REBCD 1739 / 9 Mar '98 / Rebel

Jones, Curtis

☐ CURTIS JONES VOL.1 1937-1938
DOCD 5296 / Dec '94 / Document

☐ CURTIS JONES VOL.2 1938-1939
DOCD 5297 / Dec '94 / Document

☐ CURTIS JONES VOL.3 1939-1940
DOCD 5298 / Dec '94 / Document

☐ CURTIS JONES VOL.4 1941-1953
DOCD 5299 / Dec '94 / Document

☐ LONESOME BEDROOM BLUES
158312 / Apr '95 / Blues Collection

☐ TROUBLE BLUES
Lonesome bedroom blues / Whole lot of talk for you / Suicide blues / Please say yes / Weekend blues / Good woman blues / Trouble blues / Love season / Low down worried blues / Good time special / Fool blues
OBCCD 515 / Apr '94 / Original Blues Classics

Jones, Dave

☐ HAVE YOU MET MR. JONES (Jones, Dave Trio)
PARCD 507 / Feb '98 / Parrot

Jones, David

☐ BRIDGES
Bridges / I found a honky tonk angel / Let's stop living together, alone / You don't miss what you got / I'm all that I got left / Blues after sundown / Nothing lasts forever / She's got that loved on look / You're no longer mine / Tears out weigh the whiskey
ZNCD 1007 / Oct '95 / Zane

Jones, Donell

☐ MY HEART
In the hood (Playas version) / Knocks me off my feet / No interruptions / Waiting on you / I want you to know / My heart / Yearnin' / Wish you were here / All about you / You should know / Natural thang / Believe in me / In the hood / Don't cry / Onlyone you need
73008260252 / Jun '96 / Arista

Jones, Doris

☐ BEST OF DORIS JONES, THE (No Way Out)
HTCD 69 / 20 Apr '98 / Hot Productions

Jones, Ed

☐ OUT HERE
New swing / Rumplestiltskin / Silverlining / Very urgent / Indigo / Out here / Chelsea Bridge / New swing 2
ASCCD 17 / Feb '98 / ASC

☐ PIPER'S TALE
So the story goes / Returning / Long days / Piper's tale / Out in the open / Past tense / Kindred spirit
ASCCD 2 / Jun '95 / ASC

Jones, Eddie

☐ ONE STRING BLUES (Jones, Eddie 'One-String' & Edward Hazelton)
One string three-quarter banjo picker: Jones, Eddie 'One-String' / Rolling and tumbling blues: Jones, Eddie 'One-String' / Walk with me Lord: Jones, Eddie 'One-String' / Come back baby: Jones, Eddie 'One-String' / John Henry: Jones, Eddie 'One-String' / I'll be your chauffeur: Jones, Eddie 'One-String' / It's raining here: Jones, Eddie 'One-String' / Baby please don't go: Jones, Eddie 'One-String' / Dozens: Jones, Eddie 'One-String' / Mocking the train, mocking the dogs: Hazelton, Edward / Poor boy travelling from town to town: Hazelton, Edward / Hard rock is my pillow: Hazelton, Edward / Motherless children have a hard time: Hazelton, Edward / Throw a poor dog a bone: Hazelton, Edward / Red river blues: Hazelton, Edward
CDTAK 1023 / Jun '96 / Takoma

Jones, Eddie Lee

☐ YONDER GO THAT OLD BLACK DOG (Jones, Eddie Lee 'Mustright' & Family)
TCD 5023 / May '95 / Testament

Jones, Elvin

☐ AT THIS POINT IN TIME
At this point in time / Currents / Pollen / Prime element / Whims of balance / Pauke tanz / Unknighted nations / Don't cry
4933852 / 13 Apr '98 / Blue Note

☐ ELVIN
Lady Luck / Buzz-At / Shadowland / Pretty brown / Ray-El / Four on six / You are too beautiful
OJCCD 259 / Dec '96 / Original Jazz Classics

☐ HEAVY SOUNDS (Jones, Elvin & Richard Davis)
Raunchy Rita / Shiny stockings / ME / Summertime / Elvin's guitar blues / Here's that rainy day
MCAD 33114 / Jan '90 / Impulse Jazz

☐ ILLUMINATION (Jones, Elvin & Jimmy Garrison Sextet/McCoy Tyner)
Nuttin' out Jones / Oriental flower / Half and half / Aborigine dance in Scotland / Gettin' on way / Just us blues
IMP 12502 / 23 Mar '98 / Impulse Jazz

☐ IT DON'T MEAN A THING
Green chimneys / Lullaby of Itsugo village / It don't mean a thing if it ain't got that swing / Lush life / Zenzo spirit / Flower is a lovesome thing / Ask me now / Bopsy / Fatima's waltz / Change is gonna come
ENJ 80662 / Nov '94 / Enja

☐ LIVE AT PITT INN (Jones, Elvin Quartet)
Love supreme / Dear Lord / Happy birthday for 'Yuka' / Blues to Veen
4878992 / Jun '97 / Sony Jazz

☐ LIVE AT THE VILLAGE VANGUARD VOL.1
It's easy to remember / Front line / Tohryanse, tohryanse / George and me / Love supreme
LCDI 53423 / Nov '93 / Landmark

☐ LIVE IN JAPAN 1978 (Jones, Elvin Jazz Machine)
Keiko's birthday march / Bessie's blues / Antigua / EJ blues / Love supreme
KCD 5041 / Nov '92 / Konnex

☐ LOVE AND PEACE
Little rock blues / Hip Jones / Korina / For tomorrow / Sweet and lovely / Origin / House that love built
ECD 220872 / Jun '94 / Evidence

☐ ON THE MOUNTAIN
OW 30328 / Sep '94 / One Way

☐ VERY RARE
Sweet mama / Passion flower / Zange / Tin tin deo / Pitter pat / Witching hour / EJBlues / Love supreme
ECD 22053 / Jul '93 / Evidence

Jones, Etta

☐ CHRISTMAS WITH ETTA JONES
MCD 5411 / Sep '92 / Muse

☐ FINE & MELLOW/SAVE YOUR LOVE FOR ME
MCD 6002 / Sep '92 / Muse

☐ I'LL BE SEEING YOU
MCD 5351 / Sep '93 / Muse

☐ MELODY LINGERS ON, THE
Somewhere in my lifetime / A-tisket a-tasket / For sentimental reasons / What a wonderful world / What a difference a day makes / I cover the waterfront / Mr Bojangles / I apologise / I'm having a good time / Misty
HCD 7005 / Jan '98 / Highnote

☐ MY BUDDY (The Songs Of Buddy Johnson)
When my man comes home / They all say I'm the biggest fool / Save your love for me / Let's beat out some love / Baby I'm yours / Fine brown frame / I wonder where our love has gone / Please Mr. Johnson / Hittin' on me
HCD 7026 / Jun '98 / Highnote

☐ SOMETHING NICE
Through a long and sleepless night / My heart tells me / That's all there is to that / Till there was you / I only have eyes for you / Maybe you'll be there / Love is the thing / Almost like being in love / Easy living / Canadian sunset / Fools rush in (where angels fear to tread)
OJCCD 221 / Jun '95 / Original Jazz Classics

☐ SUGAR
MCD 5379 / Sep '92 / Muse

Jones, Floyd

☐ MASTERS OF MODERN BLUES SERIES (Jones, Floyd & Eddie Taylor)
TCD 5001 / Aug '94 / Testament

Jones, George

☐ ALL AMERICAN COUNTRY (18 Original Country Classics)
5525622 / Jan '97 / Spectrum

☐ BARTENDER'S BLUES
Bartender's blues / I'll just take it out on love / If you loved a liar / Ain't your memory got no pride at all / I gave it all up for you / I don't want no stranger sleepin' in my bed / I ain't got no business doin' business today / Leaving love all over the place / When your phone don't ring (it'll be me) / Julianne
RAZCD 2101 / May '96 / Razor & Tie

☐ BEST OF GEORGE JONES, THE
Why baby why / White lightning / Aching breaking heart / Tender years / Don't stop the music / Accidently on purpose / Money to burn / You're still on my mind / Slave lover / Tarnished angel / Family bible / When my heart hurts no more / You gotta be my baby / Big Harlan Taylor / Just one more / You better treat your man right / Out of control / Life to go / Who shot Sam
5544062 / 6 Apr '98 / Spectrum

☐ CLASSIC COUNTRY COLLECTION, THE
I'm ragged but right / Tender years / Things have gone to pieces / Wedding bells / Cold cold heart / Ways of the world wants of a woman / Jambalaya / Liberty / Don't you ever get tired of hurting me / On the banks of the Ponchartrain / House without love is not a home / World of forgotten people / Tarnished angel / Please don't let that woman get me / Open pit mine / Jonesy
AIM 3002CD / 20 Oct '97 / Aim

☐ COUNTRY CLASSICS
Race is on / You comb her hair / Not what I had in mind / Girl I used to know / She thinks I still care / Your heart turned left / We must have been out of our minds / Where does a little tear come from / Least of all / My tears are overdue / Running bear / You win again / I'm gonna change everything / Beggar to a king / Something I dreamed
CDMFP 6326 / Apr '97 / Music For Pleasure

☐ DON'T STOP THE MUSIC
Into my arms again / Who shot Sam / You gotta be my baby / Mr. Fool / Time lock / Candy hearts / What'cha gonna do / Vitamins l-o-v-e / Don't stop the music / Accidentally on purpose / All I want to do / Giveaway girl / Cup of loneliness / Wanderin' soul / My sweet Imogene / Likes of you / What am I worth / Boogie woogie Mexican boy / I'm with the wrong one / With half a heart / Ship of love / Honky tonk downstairs
CDCH 912 / Nov '93 / Ace

☐ DOUBLE TROUBLE (Jones, George & Johnny Paycheck)
When you're ugly like us / Along came Jones / Proud Mary / You can have her / Smack dab in the middle / Maybellene / Roll over Beethoven / Kansas City / Tutti frutti / You better move on
RAZCD 2100 / May '96 / Razor & Tie

☐ GEORGE AND TAMMY (Jones, George & Tammy Wynette)
One / Old love thing / Whatever happend to us / Will you travel down this road with me / (She's just) an old love turned memory / If God met you / Just look what we've started again / All I have to offer you is me / They're playing our song / Solid as a rock
MCD 11248 / Aug '95 / MCA

☐ GEORGE JONES & GENE PITNEY (Jones, George & Gene Pitney)
Why baby why / Someday you'll want me to want you / For me this is happy / That's all it took / I'm gonna listen to me / I'm a fool to care / She thinks I still care / Big job / I'm up to my neck in IOU's / Sweeter than the flowers / Wreck on the highway / More I saw of her / Thousand arms (five hundred arms) / I've got five dollars and it's Saturday night / Louisiana man / Drinking from the well of your love / Life to go / One has my name / Mockin' bird hill / I'd like to see me stop you / I can't stop loving you / Your old standby / Won't take long / I've got a new heartache / My shoes keep walking back to you / I really don't want to know / As long as I live / Born to lose / Don't rob another man's castle / Love bug / Y'all come
BCD 15790 / Feb '95 / Bear Family

☐ GEORGE JONES COLLECTION, THE (She Thinks I Still Care - 2CD Set)
RE 2136 / Jul '97 / Razor & Tie

☐ GOLDEN RING (Jones, George & Tammy Wynette)
Golden ring / Even the bad times are good / Near you / Crying time / I've seen better days / Did you ever / Tattletale eyes / I'll be there (if you ever want me) / If you don't, somebody else will / Keep the change
RE 21592 / Dec '97 / Razor & Tie

☐ GRAND TOUR, THE
Grand tour / Darlin' / Pass me by / She'll love the one she's with / Once you've had the best / Weatherman / Borrowed angel / She told me so / Mary don't go 'round / Who will I be loving now / Our private life
RE 21152 / Oct '96 / Razor & Tie

☐ GREATEST COUNTRY HITS OF THE SIXTIES
PWKS 4264 / Jul '95 / Carlton

☐ GREATEST HITS
He stopped loving her today / If drinking don't kill me (her memory will) / Love bug / Take me / Say it's not you / I'm a people / Tender years / She thinks I still care / When the grass grows over me / Walk through this world with me / White lightning / Window up above / I'll share my world with you / Race is on / Good year for the roses / Sometimes you just can't win / As long as I live / Accidently on purpose / Four-o-thirty three / You comb her hair / I can't get there from here / If not for you / Right won't touch a hand / Things have gone to pieces / If my heart had windows
VVC 1003 / 19 Jan '98 / Avid

☐ HIGH TECH REDNECK
High tech redneck / I've still got some hurtin' left to do / Love in your eyes / Visit / Silent partners / Tear me out of the picture / Thousand times a day / Never bit a bullet like this / Forever's here to stay / Hello darlin'
MCD 10910 / 8 Sep '97 / MCA

☐ I LIVED TO TELL
Honky tonk song / Back down to hung up on you / Billy b bad / Hundred proof memories / It ain't gonna worry my mind / Lone ranger / Tied to a stone / I'll give you something to drink about / I must have done something bad / Hello heart
MCAD 11478 / Aug '96 / MCA

☐ IN A GOSPEL WAY (2CD Set)
RE 2138 / Jul '97 / Razor & Tie

☐ IT DON'T GET ANY BETTER THAN THIS
UMD 80485 / 13 Apr '98 / Universal

☐ LIVE AT DANCETOWN USA
White lightning / Something I dreamed / Achin' breaking heart / Window up above / Bony Moronie / She thinks I still care / Ragged but right / Poor man's riches / Jolie blon / Where does a little tear come from / Big Harlan Taylor / She's lonesome again / Race is on
CDCHM 156 / May '92 / Ace

☐ LONELY STREET
Cold cold heart / Swingin' doors / Girl I used to know / Let's get together / Bridge washed out / Race is on / Heartaches and hangovers / Don't be angry / Living on easy street / Love bug / Talk back trembling lips / Ragged but right / Come sundown / Honky tonk downstairs / We must have been out of our minds / Ruby don't take your love to town / Fightin' side of me / Okie from muskogee / Blue side of lonesome / Take me / Hello darlin' / All I have to offer you (is me) / Almost persuaded / Once a day / Lonely street
CD 6104 / 29 Sep '97 / Music

☐ TENDER YEARS
Least of all / Jambalaya (on the bayou) / She's just a girl I used to know / Cold cold heart / Tender years / It's funny what a fool will do / You comb her hair / Wedding bells / Tender years / Things have gone to pieces / World's worst loser / White lightning / Once a day / Take me / You comb her hair / Things have gone to pieces / Walk through this world with me / Least of all you / Just someone I used to know / Race is on / Good year for the roses / Say it's not you / If my heart had windows / I'll share my world with you / Old brush arbors / Once a day / World's worst loser / Accidentally on purpose / I'm wasting good paper / Developing my pictures
15488 / Dec '94 / Laserlight

☐ TOGETHER AGAIN (Jones, George & Tammy Wynette)
RAZCD 2094 / Apr '96 / Razor & Tie

☐ WALK THROUGH THE WORLD WITH ME
CWNCD 2020 / Jul '96 / Javelin

☐ WAYS OF THE WORLD
Don't you ever get tired of hurting me / Open pity mind / On the banks of the old pontchartrain / House without love / Ways of the world / Please don't let that woman get me / Yes I know why / Jonesy / Old brush arbors / Liberty / Jambalaya / Cold cold heart / Ragged but right / Tarnished angel / Your tender years / Wedding bells / Things have gone to pieces / World of forgotten people / From now on all of my friends are gonna be strangers / I can't escape from you
CDSB 008 / 29 Jun '98 / Starburst

☐ WE LOVE TO SING ABOUT JESUS (Jones, George & Tammy Wynette)
We love to sing about Jesus / Old fashioned singing / He is me everything / Me and Jesus / Noah and the ark / Let's all go down to the river / Let's all sing ourselves to glory / Talkin' about Jesus / When Jesus takes his children home / Everything gonna be alright / Show him that you love him
RE 21182 / Dec '96 / Razor & Tie

Jones Girls

☐ GET AS MUCH LOVE AS YOU CAN/ KEEP IT COMIN'
(I found) that man of mine / Get as much love as you can / Nights over Egypt / Love don't ever say goodbye / ASAP / Let's be friends first (then lovers) / World will sing our song / You're breakin' my heart / Keep it comin' / Won't let you take it back / Why you wanna do that to me / You can't have my love / Better things to do / Love is comin' atcha / Ah ah ah ah / (You got the) right stuff
WESM 572 / 16 Mar '98 / Westside

Jones, Glenn

☐ GIVING MYSELF TO YOU (Greatest Hits)
RE 216622 / May '98 / Razor & Tie

☐ HERE I AM
Here I am / It's gonna be alright / Love song / Round and round / Make it up to you / Coming back to you / Give love a chance / Everything to me / Since you've been gone (a house is not a home) / Don't walk away / In you
7567825132 / Apr '94 / Warner Bros.

☐ HERE I GO AGAIN
Here I go again / I've been searchin' / Call me / Good thang / Open up your heart / Way you do / Baby, come to me / In you / Love is forever / Get it right / Say yeah
7567823522 / Dec '96 / Atlantic

Jones, Gloria

☐ VIXEN/WINDSTORM
I ain't going nowhere / High / Tell me now / Tainted love / Cry baby / Get it on (part 1) / Go now / Would you like to know / Get it on (part 2) / Drive me crazy (Disco lady) / Sailors of the highway / Stage coach
C5HCD 637 / Apr '96 / See For Miles

Jones, Grace

☐ ISLAND LIFE
Slave to the rhythm / Pull up to the bumper / Private life / La vie en rose / I need a man / My Jamaican guy / Walking in the rain / Libertango / Love is the drug / Do or die
IMCD 16 / Apr '91 / Island

☐ LIVING MY LIFE
My Jamaican guy / Nipple to the bottle / Apple stretching / Everybody hold still / Cry now - laugh later / Inspiration / Unlimited capacity for love
IMCD 18 / Jun '89 / Island

☐ NIGHTCLUBBIN'
Feel up / Walking in the rain / Pull up to the bumper / Use me / Art groupie / Libertango / I've done it again
IMCD 17 / Jun '89 / Island

☐ PORTFOLIO
Send in the clowns / What I did for love / Tomorrow / La vie en rose / Sorry / That's the trouble / I need a man
IMCD 19 / Jun '89 / Island

☐ PRIVATE LIFE (The Compass Point Years/2CD Set)
Private life / Private life / Love is the drug / Breakdown / Warm leatherette / Hunter gets captured by the game / I've done it again / Pars / Pull up to the bumper / Use me / She's lost control / She's lost control / Walking in the rain / Cry now laugh later / Nightclubbing / Apple stretching / Nipple to the bottle / My Jamaican guy / Feel up / I've seen that face before / Demolition man / Unlimited capacity for love / Ring of fire / Man around the house / Living my life / Slave to the rhythm
5245012 / 16 Jun '98 / Chronicles

☐ SLAVE TO THE RHYTHM
Jones the rhythm / Fashion show / Frog and the princess / Operattack / Slave to the rhythm / Crossing (ooh the action) / Don't cry - it's only the rhythm / Ladies and gentlemen: Miss Grace Jones
IMCD 65 / '89 / Island

☐ WARM LEATHERETTE
Warm leatherette / Private life / Rollin' stone / Love is the drug / Hunter gets captured by the game / Bullshit / Breakdown / Pars
IMCD 15 / Jun '89 / Island

Jones, Grandpa

☐ EVERYBODY'S GRANDPA (5CD Set)
It's raining here this morning / Banjo Sam / My darling's not my darling anymore / Going 'cross the sea / Groundhog / Mighty long way to travel / Make the rafters ring / All night long / Count your blessings / East bound freight train / I guess you don't remember now / I've just been gone too long / Tritzem yodel / T for Texas / Any old time / Waitin' for a train / My Carolina sunshine girl / Dear old sunny south / My little lady / Brakeman's blues / Lullaby yodel / Peach picking time in Georgia / Hobo Bill / Away out on the mountain / Roll along Kentucky moon / Waiting for a train / You and my old guitar / T for Texas / Tritzem yodel / Ladies man / Thing / I don't love nobody / Hip cat's wedding / These hills / Billy Yank and Johnny Reb / Goodbye Reb / Willi Mayberry / Sweet fern / Night train to Memphis / Rosalee / (Somewhere) somebody's waiting (for you) / Kickin' mule / Liza's up the 'simmon tree / Chicken don't roost too high / Going from the cotton fields / Tragic romance / Methodist pie / Fatal wedding / What does the deep sea say / I'm tying the leaves (so they won't come down) / Oh captain captain / Devilish Mary / Ladies man / Hip cat's wedding / Night train to Memphis / Are you from Dixie / Root hog root / Falling leaves / Here comes the champion / Banjo am the instrument / Spring time comes but once a year / Eight more miles to Louisville / Little old lady / Springtime comes but once a year / Eight more miles to Louisville / Eight more miles to Louisville / On the Jericho Road / I'll meet you in the morning / Gone home / Keep on the firing line / Just over in Gloryland / Old camp meetin' time / Empty mansion / When I get to the end of the way / Glory Land war / Turn your radio on / No tears in heaven / Lonesome train (on a lonesome track): *Jones, Grandpa & Ramona Jones* / Sandy land: *Jones, Grandpa & Ramona Jones* / Send me a red rose: *Jones, Grandpa & Ramona Jones* / Christmas roses / Christmas guest / Heart full of love / Goin' down to the river / Moon of Arizona / Steady drips of water / Everything I had going for me is gone / Don't look back / Trouble in mind / Trouble in mind / That's all this old world needs / Bill's gonna soon be home / Mountain laurel / Smoke, smoke, smoke (but not around me) / I've learned to leave that to the Lord / Old troupe dog / Sweet lips (Battle of King's Mountain) / Plans / I'll just keep living along / King of the Cannon County hills / Mountain dew / Old rattler / Old blue / Grasshopper McClain / Old Bill / Goin' down to the river / Valley of the never do no good / Four stone walls / Dollar short / Coal camp / Here I am makin' plans / Green hills of home / Are you sleeping Daddy darlin' / Nashville on my mind / Mountain man / Deep dark corner of my mind / Baby-O / My old lady / Brown girl and fair Eleanor / Four winds a-blowin' / Intro / Fix me a pallet / Dooley / Air, the sunshine and the rain / Castles in the air / Old Rattler's pup / My bonnie lies over the ocean / Rocky top / I don't love nobody / John Henry / Last ol' shevel / Southern bound / 15 cents is all I got
BCD 15788 / Jan '97 / Bear Family

Jones, Hank

☐ ARIGATO
PCD 7004 / Oct '91 / Progressive

☐ COMPASSION
BB 879 / Apr '97 / Black & Blue

☐ FAVORS
5373162 / Oct '97 / Verve

☐ HANK
Just squeeze me / In a sentimental mood / Satin doll / Prelude to a kiss / What am I here for / Do nothin' 'til you hear from me / Sophisticated lady / Oh look at me now / Alone together / Don't blame me / Gone with the wind / My heart stood still / If I had you / Very thought of you
AAJ 11003 / Jan '92 / Jazz Alliance

☐ HANK JONES QUARTET
Moonlight becomes you / Relaxin' at Camarillo / Minor contention / Sunday in savannah / Spontaneous combustion
SV 0236 / Oct '97 / Savoy Jazz

☐ HANK JONES TRIO (Jones, Hank Trio)
STCD 4180 / Jan '94 / Storyville

☐ I REMEMBER YOU
I remember you / Young no more / You took advantage of me / Love walked in / Dat dere / I'll be around / Let's fall in love / Like someone in love / Theme from jobim / It's the talk of the town / Yours is my heart alone / Come to me
BLE 233122 / Oct '94 / Black & Blue

☐ JAZZ TRIO OF HANK JONES, THE (Jones, Hank & Kenny Clarke/Wendell Marshall)
We're all together / Odd number / When hearts are young / There's a small hotel / Cyrano / Now's the time / My funny valentine / We could make such beautiful music
SV 0184 / Oct '97 / Savoy Jazz

☐ LAZY AFTERNOON
Speak low / Lazy afternoon / Intimidation / Comin' home baby / Sublime / Peedlum / Work song / Lament / Passing time / Arrival
CCD 4391 / '89 / Concord Jazz

☐ LIVE AT MAYBECK RECITAL HALL VOL.16
I guess I'll have to change my plan / It's the talk of the town / Very thought of you / Night we called it a day / Bluesette / Child is born / What is this thing called love / Oh what a beautiful mornin' / Six and four / I cover the waterfront / Memories of you / Blue monk / 'Round midnight / Oh, look at me now
CCD 4502 / Mar '92 / Concord Jazz

☐ MEETS LOUIS BELLSON AND IRA SULLIVAN
STCD 553 / '92 / Stash

☐ QUARTET - QUINTET
Almost like being in love / Evening at Papa Joe's / An' then some / Summer's gone / Don't blame me
SV 0147 / Oct '97 / Savoy Jazz

☐ SPIRIT OF 176, THE (Jones, Hank & George Shearing)
Oh look at me now / Angel eyes / I mean you / You don't know what love is / To hank jones / Minor contention / Ask me now / Triste / Take a good look / Sweet lorraine / Young no more / Lonely moments / Star eyes / Confirmation
CCD 4371 / Apr '89 / Concord Jazz

☐ URBANITY (Piano Solos)
5377492 / 22 Sep '97 / Verve Elite

Jones, Howard

☐ 12 INCH ALBUM, THE
Always asking questions / New song / What is love / Like to get to know you well / Pearl in the shell / Total conditioning
2405432 / Jul '88 / WEA

☐ BEST OF HOWARD JONES, THE
Look mama / Prisoner / Everlasting love / Lift me up / Tears to tell / Two souls / IGY / City song / What is love / New song / Pearl in the shell / Always asking questions / Things can only get better / Like to get to know you well / Life in one day / You know I love you don't you / Hide and seek / No one is to blame
4509927012 / Dec '96 / WEA

☐ CROSS THAT LINE
Prisoner / Powerhouse / Cross that line / Guardians of the breath / Wanders to you / Everlasting love / Last supper / Out of thin air / Fresh air waltz / Those who move clouds
2441762 / Mar '89 / WEA

☐ DREAM INTO ACTION
Things can only get better / Life in one day / Dream into action / No one is to blame / Look mama / Assault and battery / Automaton / Is there a difference / Elegy / Specialty / Why look for the key / Hunger for flesh
2406322 / Apr '85 / WEA

☐ HUMAN'S LIB
Conditioning / What is love / Pearl in the shell / Hide and seek / Hunt the self / New song / Don't always look at the rain / Equality / Natural / Human's lib
K 240335 2 / Jun '84 / WEA

☐ IN THE RUNNING
Lift me up / Fallin' away / Show me / Voices are back / Exodus / Tears to tell / Two souls / Gun turned on the world / One last try / City song
9031763362 / Dec '96 / WEA

☐ LIVE ACOUSTIC AMERICA
PLUCD 001 / Mar '96 / Plump

☐ ONE TO ONE
You know I love you don't you / Balance of love / All I want / Where are we going / Don't want to fight anymore / Step into these shoes / Will you still be there / Good luck bad luck / Give me strength / Little bit of snow
2420112 / Oct '86 / WEA

Jones, Hughie

☐ HUGHIE'S DITTY BAG
Champion of the seas / Marques / Coal, coal for Manchester / Christmas time odd-job man / Marco polo / Navvies' way / Fairlie duplex engine / Ellen Vannin tragedy / Stockholm tar / Shortness of sight / Grey-black stone of ffestinog / Wavertree / New York girls are pretty
FECD 081 / Jan '97 / Fellside

Jones, Ivan

☐ LEGENDS OF ACID JAZZ, THE (Jones, Ivan 'Boogaloo Joe')
Boogaloo Joe / Don't deceive me / Boardwalk blues / Dream on little dreamer / Atlantic city soul / 6.30 blues / Right on / Things ain't what they used to be / Poppin' / Someday we'll be together / Brown bag / Let it be me
PRCD 24167 / Oct '96 / Prestige

☐ MINDBENDER, THE/ MY FIRE (Jones, Ivan 'Boogaloo Joe')
Mindbender / There is a mountain / Games / Sticks and stones / Blues for Bruce / Beat goes on / Right now / Call me / Light my fire / For big Hal / St. James Infirmary / Take all / Time after time / Ivan the Terrible
CDBGPD 067 / Jun '93 / Beat Goes Public

☐ SNAKE RHYTHM ROCK/BLACK WHIP (Jones, Ivan 'Boogaloo Joe')
Hoochie coo chickie / Snake rhythm rock / First time ever I saw your face / He's so fine / Big bad midnight roller / Black whip / My love / Freak off / Daniel / Ballad of mad dogs and Englishmen / Crank me up
CDBGPD 043 / Sep '92 / Beat Goes Public

☐ SWEETBACK (Jones, Ivan 'Boogaloo Joe')
LHCD 020 / Jul '96 / Luv n' Haight

Jones, Jack

☐ BEST OF JACK JONES, THE
DSHCD 7003 / Dec '92 / D-Sharp

☐ BEST OF JACK JONES, THE
HMNCD 010 / Jul '97 / Half Moon

☐ BEWITCHED
My kind of town (Chicago is) / Along the way / She loves me / Lollipops and roses / Gypsies, the jugglers and the clowns / From Russia with love / Carioca / Feeling good / My favourite things / I don't care much / You'd better love me / Bewitched / Beautiful friendship / I must know / Afterthoughts / Mood I'm in / Julie / I will wait for you / Far away / I'm all smiles / Brother, where are you / Wives and lovers / This is all I ask / Travellin' on
3035900042 / Oct '95 / Carlton

☐ JACK JONES COLLECTOR'S EDITION
DVAD 6042 / Apr '95 / Deja Vu

☐ LIVE AT THE LONDON PALLADIUM
I had a dream / Gypsies, jugglers and clowns / Gershwin medley / Just one of those things / Child is born / Hopeless romantic / This all I ask / Falling in love / Right here waiting / Music of the night / Wives and lovers / Lady / Call me irresponsible / If / Soliloquy / Imagine / From a distance
DSHCD 7009 / Sep '93 / D-Sharp
EMPRCD 630 / Jun '96 / Emporio

☐ LIVE AT THE PALLADIUM
I had a dream / Gypsies juggers and clowns / Summertime medley / Just one of those things / Child is born / Hopeless romantic / This is all I ask / Falling in love with love / Right here waiting / Music of the night / Wives and lovers / Soliloquy / Imagine medley
3037300012 / Mar '96 / Carlton

☐ LOOK OF LOVE, THE
Look of love / She / Make it with you / If you could read my mind / Without her / God only knows / All cried out / Once in a while / It's too late / Goin' out of my head / What are you doing the rest of your life / Mean to me / You and the night and the music / For all we know
74321339442 / Jan '96 / Camden

☐ NEW JACK SWING
Every breath you take / She's leaving home / All or nothing / Dangerous mood / Have you ever loved a woman / All the days / Mack the knife / Stranger in paradise / Color of the wind / Love boat
AKD 078 / 23 Feb '98 / Linn

☐ SHE LOVES ME/THERE'S LOVE AND THERE'S LOVE
She loves me / Real love girl / Our language of love / Close your eyes / When I'm not near the girl I love / I believe in you / Lamp is low / On the other side of the tracks / Wouldn't it be loverly / My mood is you / Hit the road to dreamland / I get along without you very well / Night is young and you're so beautiful / I can't believe that you're in love with me / Young at heart / And I love her / Lovely way to spend an evening / You do something to me / Embraceable you / You made me love you / While we're young / There's love and there's love and there's love / Tenderly / True love
MCLD 19378 / 22 Jun '98 / MCA

☐ WIVES AND LOVERS/DEAR HEART
Wives and lovers / Toys in the attic / Song about love / I'm moody / Angel eyes / Fly me to the moon / Charade / I wish you love / Nina never know / Summertime promise / I see your face before me / Come rain or shine / Dear heart / You're sensational / Love is here to stay / I'll get by / You'd better love me / All the things you are / Emily / Thank heaven for little girls / I'm glad there is you / When she makes music / Someting's gotta give / You're my girl
MCLD 19364 / 23 Mar '98 / MCA

Jones, Janie

☐ I'M IN LOVE WITH THE WORLD OF JANIE JONES
Woman in white / Witches brew / Gunning for you / Go go away from me / Tickle me tootsie wootsies / High and dry / High and dry / Hammer toes / Time has come to choose / Time has come to choose / Psycho / Back on my feet again / Back on my feet again / Cross on the wall in Nashville / Charlie Smith / Nobody's perfect / Girl's song / I've never met a boy like you / Easy to remember / Take-a my tip / House of the ju ju queen: Strummer, Joe / House of the ju ju queen / Sex machine / Letter to Joe / Witches brew
RPM 177 / Jul '97 / RPM

Jones, Jim

☐ TRUST, CONTRAFUSION (Jones, Jim & The Kool Ade Kids)
CC 004 / Nov '93 / Common Cause

Jones, Jimmy

☐ ORIGINAL HANDY MAN, THE
Handy man / You got it / Part time sweetheart / Don't you just know it / Nights of Mexico / Itchin' (for love) / Snap my fingers / I told you so / Good timin' / Close your eyes / You're much too young / Ee-i-ee-i-oh / 39-21-40 shape / That's when I cried / Personal property
303172 / Jun '97 / Hallmark

Jones, Jo

☐ JO JONES TRIO (Jones, Jo Trio)
FSCD 40 / Oct '90 / Fresh Sound

Jones, Joe

☐ YOU TALK TOO MUCH (The Best Of Joe Jones)
You talk too much / Take a little walk / McDonald's daughter / Tisket-a-tasket / One big mouth (two big ears) / Here's what you gotta do / Where is my baby / To prove my love to you / Big mule / I cried for you / Just write / You talk too much (original) / I'm glad for your sake / One big mouth (original) / I love you still / Every night about eight / Tell me what's happening / Please don't talk about me when I'm gone / I need someone / Always picking on me / California sun / Because I love you / I've got a uh-uh wife / Oh gee how I cried / Indian love call / Down by the river
NEMCD 672 / Jun '94 / Sequel

Jones, Johnny

☐ AIN'T GONNA WORRY (Jones, Johnny 'Yard Dog')
4937 CD / Dec '96 / Earwig

☐ I WAS RAISED ON THE BLUES
Chip off the old block / Don't throw your love on me so strong / I was raised on the blues / Can I get an amen / Groove thing / Galloping dominoes / Herb stuffing / Sneaky suspicion / Mighty low / I done did that already / Baptism of fire
BM 9036 / Jun '98 / Black Magic

Jones, Jonah

☐ JONAH JONES STORY 1936-1945, THE
158512 / Jul '96 / Jazz Archives

Jones, Keziah

☐ AFRICAN SPACE CRAFT
African space craft / Million miles from home / Colorful world / Prodigal funk / Splash / Dear Mr. Cooper / Speech / Cubic space division / Funk 'n' circumstance / Man with the scar / Never gonna let you go / If you know
CDDLB 14 / Oct '95 / Delabel

☐ BLUFUNK IS A FACT
Wisdom behind the smile (cash) / Walkin' naked thru a bluebell field / Rhythm is love / Runaway / Where is life / Funderlying undermentals / Fringro interstellar / Free your soul / Curious kind of subconscious / Waxing and the waning / Invisible ladder / Pleasure is kisses within
CDDLB 1 / Mar '92 / Delabel

Jones, Leroy

☐ MO' CREAM FROM THE CROP
When my dreamboat comes home / Mo' cream from the crop / Sweet Lorraine / How come you do me like you do / Time for love / Bourbon street parade / Tin roof blues / Mosey roun' bring it down / Blues for ZW / New Orleans / Carnival's in town / Mood indigo / Bei mir bist du schon
4777512 / 26 Jan '98 / Sony Jazz

☐ PROPS FOR POPS
Props for pops / Struttin' with some barbecue / West End blues / Someday you'll be sorry / When it's sleepy time down south / Jeepers creepers / You must not be hearin' straight / Preacher / Ain't misbehavin' / Baby won't you please come home / What a wonderful world / Whoopin' blues / Louie's lamentation / Armstrong parade
4851412 / Oct '96 / Sony Jazz

Jones, Linda

☐ NEVER MIND THE QUALITY...FEEL THE SOUL (Live In Ohio 1970)
Introduction / If I had a hammer / That's when I'll stop loving you / For your precious love / You're so fine / I found a love
NEBCD 990 / Jul '97 / Sequel

☐ YOUR PRECIOUS LOVE
Your precious love / I do / I love you (I need you) / I've given you the best years of my life / Don't go (I can't stand to be alone) / Not on the outside / Doggin' me around / Let it be me / Hypnotised / If only we had met sooner / Fugitive from love / I'm so glad I found you / Stay with me forever / Things I've been through / When hurt comes back / I can't make it alone / Behold / Dancing in the street
NEXCD 167 / Jul '91 / Sequel

Jones, Luke

☐ COMPLETE RECORDINGS 1946-1949, THE
BMCD 6012 / Jan '98 / Blue Moon

Jones, Marti

☐ LIVE AT SPIRIT SQUARE
Intro/Hiding the boy / Inside these arms / Cliche / Tourist town / Twisted vines / Living inside the wind / I've got second sight / Any kind of lie / Read my heart / Is this the game / Follow you all over the world / Wind in the trees / Real one / If you can love somebody / Just a memory / Old friend / Second choice / Percussion solo
SHCD 5502 / Mar '98 / Sugar Hill

☐ MY LONG-HAIRED LIFE
I love the sound of breaking glass / It's not what I want / Life's a game / Black coffee in bed / Champagne and wine / Sleep of the just / Put me on top / You got what it takes / Feather on a stone / Silent partner / Songs to aging children come
SHCD 5503 / Mar '98 / Sugar Hill

Jones, Mason

☐ INTERNATIONAL INCIDENT
CHCD 31 / Aug '98 / Charnel House

Jones, Mazlyn

☐ ANGELS OVER WATER
Eden / Flying / Water and stone / Kelda / Windsmith / First light / Angels over water / Great rock / Sea of glass (II) / Glistening waters (II)
BWKD 211 / Oct '95 / Brainworks

☐ LIVE (Jones, Mazlyn & Guy Evans/Nik Turner)
Someone at the door / Twentieth century / Spirit moves / Well beyond this point / Behind the stones / Windsmith / Unseen friends / Ship to shore / It's your world
BP 250CD / Mar '97 / Blueprint

Jones, Michael

☐ AIR BORN
Air born / Summer in Chimo / Lark in the clear air / Voices in the wind
ND 61042 / Jul '94 / Narada

☐ LIVING MUSIC (2CD Set)
2438455402 / 31 Mar '98 / Narada

☐ TOUCH
Evening / Walking / Play / River / Rebirth / Longing / Storm / Grace / Delight / Touch
ND 61057 / Oct '96 / Narada

Jones, Mike

☐ OH LOOK AT ME NOW
CRD 325 / Mar '96 / Chiaroscuro

☐ RUNNIN' WILD
CRD 336 / Mar '96 / Chiaroscuro

Jones, Nic

☐ PENGUIN EGGS
Canadee-i-o / Drowned lovers / Humpback whale / Little pot stove / Courting is a pleasure / Barrack Street / Planxty Davis / Flandyke Shore / Farewell to the gold
TSCD 411 / Nov '90 / Topic

Jones, Oliver

☐ CLASS ACT, A
JUST 412 / Sep '91 / Justin Time

☐ FROM LUSH TO LIVELY (Jones, Oliver Big Band)
Way you look tonight / Why think about tomorrow / Len's den / We will love again / Swinging on a star / Jazz gavotte / Very thought of you / Tetra tetra / (Our) Love is here to stay / Should I love again / Blues for Helene
JUST 732 / Apr '96 / Justin Time

☐ HAVE FINGERS WILL TRAVEL
DGB blues / Yvonne / Street of dreams / If I were a bell / I'm thru with love / Late afternoon blues / Without a song / Charlie B / Snowy peaks / Beautiful Jayde / My romance
JUST 1022 / 17 Nov '97 / Justin Time

☐ JAZZ & RIBS LIVE AT BIDDLE'S (Jones, Oliver Trio & Charles Biddle & Bernard Primeau)
JUST 12 / May '91 / Justin Time

☐ NORTHERN SUMMIT (Mones, Oliver)
JUST 342 / Apr '91 / Justin Time

☐ REQUESTFULLY YOURS
JUST 112 / May '91 / Justin Time

Jones, Paul

☐ AMERICAN GUESTS VOL.1
JSPCD 210 / Oct '92 / JSP

☐ AMERICAN GUESTS VOL.2 (Jones, Paul Rhythm & Blues Show)
JSPCD 221 / Oct '88 / JSP

☐ COME INTO MY MUSIC BOX
Come into my music box / Weight / Tell it like it is / Baby now that I've found you / Float / Celeste / It's getting better / Pick up in the morning / How sweet is it to be loved by you / Committee / Hamburg / I'm here to nudge your mind / Wheels on fire / I'm a young boy / And the sun will shine / Dog presides / When I was six years old / You have no idea / My advice to you / I don't believe you / Aquarius / Pisces / Not before time / Shake a hand / Cats eyes
RPM 183 / 13 Jul '98 / RPM

☐ CRUCIFIX IN A HORSESHOE
REP 4196 / Aug '91 / Repertoire

☐ MY WAY
My way / Lady Godiva / It is coming closer / I can't hold on much longer / Baby tomorrow / You've got too much going for you / Very, very funny / High time / She needs company / When my little girl is smiling / Wait 'til morning comes / I can't break the news to myself
DORIG 108 / Aug '97 / EMI

☐ SOLO YEARS VOL.1, THE (My Way)
RPM 168 / Nov '96 / RPM

☐ SOLO YEARS VOL.2, THE (Love Me, Love My Friends)
RPM 169 / Nov '96 / RPM

Jones, Paul Ubana

☐ I NEED A STORM
FF 606CD / Feb '93 / Flying Fish

☐ PAUL UBANA JONES
8409422 / Sep '96 / Sky Ranch

Jones, Peter

☐ WITH TUNNELS
OZ 004 / Jan '94 / Ozone

Jones, Philly Joe

☐ BIG BAND SOUNDS
Blue gwynn / Stablemates / Carioca (El tambores) / Tribal message / Cherokee / Land of the blue veils / Philly JJ
OJCCD 1792 / Apr '97 / Original Jazz Classics

☐ MO' JOE
Mo' joe / Gone, gone, gone / Baubles, bangles and beads / Trailways express / Here's that rainy day / Lady bird
BLC 760154 / Apr '91 / Black Lion

Jones, Quincy

☐ BACK ON THE BLOCK
Prologue (2 Q's rap) / Back on the block / I don't go for that / I'll be good to you / Verb: To be / Wee b dooinit / Places you find love / Jazz corner of the world / Birdland (Inst.) / Setembro / One man woman / Tomorrow (a better you, better me) / Prelude to the garden / Secret garden
9260202 / Dec '89 / Qwest

☐ BEST OF QUINCY JONES, THE
Ai no corrida / Stuff like that / Betcha wouldn't hurt me / Dude / I'm gonna miss you in the morning / Something special / Turn on the action / Love I never had it so good / My Cherie amour / Smackwater Jack / Oh happy day / Velas / Body heat / Cry baby / There's a train leaving
5544702 / 3 Aug '98 / Spectrum

☐ BEST, THE
Ai no corrida / Betcha wouldn't hurt me / I'm gonna miss you in the morning / Body heat / Everything must change / Killer Joe / If I ever lose this Heaven / Just once / What's going on
3932002 / Feb '94 / A&M

☐ BODY HEAT
Body heat / Soul saga / Everything must change / Boogie Joe, the grinder / Everything must change / One track mind / Just a man / Along came Betty / If I ever lose this Heaven
3931912 / Feb '93 / A&M

☐ DUDE, THE
Ai no corrida / Dude / Just once / Betcha wouldn't hurt me / Something special / Razzamatazz / Hundred ways / Valas / Turn on the action
CDMID 119 / Oct '92 / A&M

☐ FREE AND EASY (Live In Sweden 1960)
Moanin / Tickle toe / I remember Clifford / Whisper not / Phantom's blues / Birth of a band / Gypsy / Ghana / Walkin' / Big red
ANC 9500 / Aug '94 / Ancha

☐ GENIUS OF QUINCY JONES, THE (Classic Jazz and Soul Arrangements)
Take five / Bossa Nova USA / Cast your fate to the wind / Exodus / Walk on the wild side / Gravy waltz / Back at the chicken shack / Watermelon man
306202 / Jan '97 / Hallmark

☐ GO WEST MAN
Dancin' pants / Blues day / Bright moon / No bones at all / Oom is blues / Be my guest / Medley / Lonodn derriere / Kings Road blues
GRP 18282 / 27 Jul '98 / Chess Mates

☐ LIVE LAUSANNE 1960 (Jones, Quincy & His Orchestra)
Cherokee / Chinese checkers / Birth of a band / I remember Clifford / Ghana / Big red / My reverie / Parisian thoroughfare / Moanin' / Soul / Midnight sun will never set / Phantom's blues / Airmail special / Airmail special (Encore)
TCB 02012 / Jul '94 / TCB

☐ PAWNBROKER, THE/THE DEADLY AFFAIR (Original Soundtracks) (Jones, Quincy & His Orchestra)
5312332 / Jun '96 / Verve

☐ Q'S JOOK JOINT
Intro / Let the good times roll / Cool Joe, mean Joe / You put a move on my heart / Rock with you / Moody's mood for love / Stomp / Reprise / Do nothin' 'til you hear from me / Is it love that we're missin' / Heaven's girl / Stuff like that / Slow jams / At the end of the day / Outro
9362458752 / Nov '95 / Qwest

☐ QUINTESSENCE
Quintessence / Robot portrait / Little Karen / Straight, no chaser / For Lena and Lennie / Hard sock dance / Invitation / Twitch
IMP 12222 / Apr '97 / Impulse Jazz

☐ SOUNDS...AND STUFF LIKE THAT
Stuff like that / Love I never had it so good / Superwoman / I'm gonna miss you in the morning / Love me by my name / Takin' it to the streets
CDMID 120 / Oct '92 / A&M

☐ WALKING IN SPACE (Jazz Heritage)
Dead end / Walking in space / Killer Joe / Love and peace / I never told you / Oh happy day
3969932 / Mar '94 / A&M

☐ WATERMELON MAN
HADCD 182 / Nov '95 / Javelin

Jones, Richard M.

☐ CLASSICS 1923-1927
CLASSICS 826 / Sep '95 / Classics

☐ CLASSICS 1927-1944
CLASSICS 853 / Feb '96 / Classics

☐ RICHARD M. JONES VOL.1 (1923-1927)
JPCD 1524 / Jul '96 / Jazz Perspectives

☐ RICHARD M. JONES VOL.2 (1927-1936)
JPCD 1525 / Jul '96 / Jazz Perspectives

Jones, Rickie Lee

☐ FLYING COWBOYS
Horses / Just my baby / Ghetto of my mind / Rodeo girl / Satellites / Ghost train / Flying cowboys / Don't let the sun catch you crying / Love is gonna bring us back alive / Away from the sky / Atlas' maker
GED 24246 / 8 Sep '97 / Geffen

☐ GHOSTYHEAD
9362465572 / Sep '97 / WEA

☐ NAKED SONGS
Chuck e's in love / Weasel and the white boy's cool / Living it up / We belong together / Autumn leaves / Stewart's coat / Altar boy / Flying cowboys / Horses / It must be love / Magazine / Skeletons / Coolsville / Young blood / Last chance texaco
9362459502 / Sep '95 / WEA

☐ PIRATES
We belong together / Living it up / Skeletons / Woody and Dutch on the slow train to Peking / Pirates / Lucky guy / Traces of western slopes / Returns
256816 / Jan '86 / WEA

☐ POP POP
My one and only love / Spring can really hang you up the most / Hi lili hi lo / Up from the skies / Second time around / Dat dere / I'll be seeing you / Bye bye blackbird / Ballad of the sad young men / I won't grow up / Love junkyard / Comin' back to me
GFLD 19293 / Oct '95 / Geffen

☐ RICKIE LEE JONES
On Saturday afternoons in 1963 / Night train / Young blood / Easy money / Last chance Texaco / Danny's all star joint / Coolsville / Weasel and the white boy's cool / Company / After hours (12 bars past midnight) / Chuck E's in love
K2 56628 / '89 / WEA

Jones, Ricky

☐ RICKY JONES
UD 53101 / 10 Oct '97 / Universal

Jones, Robin

☐ CHANGO (Jones, Robin & King Salsa)
Elugua / King Salsa theme / Vamonos Pa'l Monte / Sonando / Manteca / Controladora / Viva la vida contento / Mi songo / Mama guela / Mozambique pa'gozar / Bomba de salon / June / Tremendo / Songo for Jo / Domincian dream / Amor verdadero / Olufina / Chango
PARCD 502 / Feb '96 / Parrot

☐ DENGA/EL MAJA (Jones, Robin Quintet)
Denga / Goodbye Batucada / Urubu / Autumn / Con fuego / Zapatos amarillos / Africa revisited / El sueno / Surfaticket / My summer love / Tristeza / Šucio mambo / El maja / Santa de la luna / Oya / Atlas / Batucada da vida / Wailer / Chant Afrique / El lobo / Carica papaya
APSCD 207 / Mar '98 / Apollo Sound

Jones, Rodney

☐ ARTICULATION
Articulation / 1978 / Hard New York swing / Interlude 1 / Childville / Blues for Wes / Nereda
CDSJP 125 / Jun '91 / Timeless Jazz

Jones, Ronnie

☐ BEST OF RONNIE JONES, THE (Soul Sister)
HTCD 100 / 20 Apr '98 / Hot Productions

Jones, Salena

☐ SALENA MEETS KENNY BURRELL AND RICHIE COLE (Jones, Salena & Kenny Burrell/Richie Cole)
VG 103 / Jan '98 / Vine Gate

☐ SALENA SINGS JOBIM WITH THE JOBIMS (Jones, Salena & A. Carlos Jobim/Paulo Jobim/Daniel Jobim)
Antonio's song / Agua de beber / Useless landscape / Quiet night of quiet stars / Somewhere in the hills / Dindi / Desafinado / Girl (boy) from Ipanema / Once I loved / Meditation / One note samba / Bonita / Song of the jet / Abandoned garden
VG 102 / Oct '96 / Vine Gate

Jones, Sam

☐ CHANT, THE
Chant / Blues on down / Sonny boy / In walked Ray / Bluebird / Over the rainbow / Off-colour
OJCCD 1839 / Apr '97 / Original Jazz Classics

☐ DOWN HOME
Unit 7 / Come rain come shine / 'Round midnight / OP / Thumbstring / Down home / Strollin' / Falling in love with love
OJCCD 1864 / Apr '97 / Original Jazz Classics

☐ VISITATION
SCCD 31097 / Jul '88 / Steeplechase

Jones, Shirley

☐ ALWAYS IN THE MOOD...PLUS
Always in the mood / Do you get enough love / I'll do anything for you / Last night I needed somebody / We can work it out / Breaking up / Surrender / She knew about me / Caught me with my gaurd down / I'll do anything for you
WESM 573 / 20 Apr '98 / Westside

Jones, Spike

☐ BEST OF SPIKE JONES & HIS CITY SLICKERS, THE (Jones, Spike & His City Slickers)
Cocktails for two / William Tell overture / Chloe / My old flame / Glow worm / None but the lonely heart / Laura / Man on the flying trapeze / You always hurt the one you love / Der Fuhrer's face / Dance of the hours / Hawaiian war chant
74321135762 / May '93 / RCA

☐ COCKTAILS FOR TWO (Jones, Spike & His City Slickers)
IRS 451 / Nov '97 / IMP

☐ DIRECT OFF THE AIR 1949
HQCD 30 / Jan '95 / Harlequin

☐ JONES LAUGHING RECORDS, THE (Jones, Spike & His City Slickers)
Hawaiian war chant / My old flame / Chloe / Der Fuhrer's face / Little Bo Peep has lost sheep / Jones laughing record / Laura / Drip drip drip / Glow worm / Red wing / I'm getting sentimental over you / And the great big saw came nearer and nearer / Liebstraume / Leave your dishes in the sink Ma / Our hour / By the beautiful sea / I'm forever blowing bubblegum / Love in bloom / Behind those swinging doors / None but the lonely / Covered wagon rolled right along / Cocktails for two / My pretty girl / Hotcha cornia / Popcorn sack
AMSC 630 / Apr '98 / Avid

☐ MASTERS, THE
EABCD 040 / 24 Nov '97 / Eagle

☐ MUSICAL DEPRECIATION (Original Mono Recordings 1941-1945) (Jones, Spike & His City Slickers)
Cocktails for two / Chloe / Behind those two swingin' doors / Red wing / Covered wagon rolled right along / Clink, clink another drink / Little Bo Peep has lost her jeep / Pass the biscuits, Mirandy / Der Fuehre's face / I wanna go back to West Virginia / Hotcha cornia (black eyes) / Leave the dishes in the sink Ma / Serenade to a jerk / Holiday for strings / Blue Danube / You always hurt the one you love / Hawaiian war chant / Liebestraum / That old black magic / Nutcracker suite
CDAJA 5189 / Jan '96 / Living Era

☐ PEOPLE ARE FUNNIER THAN ANYBODY (Jones, Spike & His City Slickers)
Cocktails for two / Ill barkio / You always hurt the one you love / Blue Danube / I dream of Brownie with the light blue jeans / Hotcha cornia / Down in Jungle Town / MacNamara's band / That old black magic / I kiss your hand madame / William Tell overture / As time goes by / Old MacDonald had a farm / My two front teeth / Serenade to a jerk / Siam / Mother Goose medley / I wanna go back to West Virginia / Jones polka / Man on the flying trapeze / Barstool cowboy from Old Barstow / Clink clink another drink / People are funnier than anybody / Toot toot tootsie goodbye / Holiday for strings
AMSC 631 / Apr '98 / Avid

☐ RADIO DAYS (Jones, Spike & His City Slickers)
RMB 75017 / Nov '93 / Remember

☐ RIOT SQUAD VOL.2 (Louder & Funnier/ 1942-1945) (Jones, Spike & His City Slickers)
Blacksmith song / Moo woo woo / Don't give the chair to Buster / Big bad Bill / Red grow the roses / Casey Jones / And the great big saw came nearer / No no Nora / That's what makes the world go round / Hey Mabel / Now laugh / Three little words / At last I'm first with you / Jamboree Jones / Chloe / Trailer Annie / Mary Lou / Barstool cowboy / From old Barstow / Row row row / Toot toot tootsie goodbye / Siam
HQCD 02 / Nov '86 / Harlequin

☐ SPIKE JONES AND HIS CITY SLICKERS (Jones, Spike & His City Slickers)
Red wing / Barstool cowboy from Old Barstow / Behind those swingin' doors / Covered wagon rolled right along / Wild wild women / Clink clink another drink / Beautiful eggs / Pack up your troubles / Siam / Little bo-peep has lost her jeep / Come Jospehine in my flying machine / Pass the biscuits Mirandy / Hotcha Cornia / Der fuehrer's face / Hi neighbour / Gonna stomp them city slickers down / That / You can't say no to a soldier / Hawaiian war chant
HQCD 100 / Jan '98 / Harlequin

Jones, Steve

☐ FIRE AND GASOLINE
Freedom fighter / We're not saints / God in Louisisana / Fire and gasoline / Hold on / Trouble maker / I did U no wrong / Get ready / Gimme love / Wild wheels / Leave your shoes on / Suffragette city
MAUCD 647 / Mar '97 / Mau Mau

Jones, Stuart

☐ LIFEFORCE
CD 444 / 6 Jul '98 / New World

Jones, Thad

☐ GREAT CONCERT, THE (Jones, Thad & Mel Lewis)
COD 017 / Jun '92 / Jazz View

☐ MAD THAD
FSCD 117 / Jan '91 / Fresh Sound

☐ SWISS RADIO DAYS JAZZ SERIES VOL.4
Second race / Don't ever leave me / Waltz you swang for me / A - that's freedom / Come Sunday / Don't get sassy / Bible story / Groove merchant
TCB 02042 / Jan '95 / TCB

☐ THAD JONES AND THE DANISH RADIO BIG BAND (Jones, Thad & The Danish Radio Big Band)
STCD 4172 / Feb '90 / Storyville

Jones, Tom

☐ 20 GREAT LOVE SONGS
She's a lady / Till / Daughter of darkness / Young New Mexican puppeteer / I (who have nothing) / You've got a friend / Nothing rhymed / Ain't no sunshine / Love is in the air / Take me tonight / You've lost that lovin' feeling / Say you'll stay until tomorrow / Rescue me / Tired of being alone / Somethin' 'bout you baby I like / Til I can't take it anymore / All I ever need is you / To love somebody / My way
LS 865532 / 2 Feb '98 / Disky

☐ AT HIS BEST (2CD Set)
Delilah / Don't cry for me Argentina / On the road again / Love me tonight / Proud Mary / Let it be / Danny boy / Lady Madonna / Memphis / Long and winding road / My way / Twist and shout / I can't stop loving you / Back in the USSR / For once in my life / Can't buy me love / She's a lady / Lay down Sally / Satisfaction / Let your love flow / She believes in love / I who have nothing / Starting over / As time goes by / Cupid / Great balls of fire / I can see clearly now / Rockin' me / Oh, pretty woman / Yesterday / What's new pussycat / Georgia on my mind / Hound dog / Send in the clowns / We don't talk anymore / Honky tonk woman / Spanish eyes / Jailhouse rock / Green, green grass of home / On Broadway / Save the last dance for me
PDSCD 549 / Jul '97 / Pulse

☐ COLLECTION, THE
CCSCD 431 / Mar '95 / Castle

☐ COLLECTION, THE
It's not unusual / Spanish harlem / Detroit city / What's new pussycat / My prayer / Sixteen tons / Nearness of you / Not responsible / Loser / Lucille (live) / Cool water / This and that / I'll never let you go / Dr. Love / More / Ten guitars / If you need me / Green, green grass of home
5515202 / Aug '95 / Spectrum

☐ COLLECTION, THE
Green green grass of home / Delilah / She's a lady / Daughter of darkness / What's new pussycat / I who have nothing / I can't stop loving you / Release me / Spanish eyes / My way / Do ya think I'm sexy / Georgia on my mind / Honky tonk women / I can see clearly now / (I can't get no) Satisfaction / Proud Mary / Most beautiful girl / You're my world / Twist and shout / Una paloma blanca / We don't talk anymore / Fever / Help me make it through the night / Nights on Broadway / Send in the clowns
COL 077 / Jan '98 / Collection

☐ COMPLETE TOM JONES, THE
It's not unusual / Delilah / Kiss / I'll never fall in love again / She's a lady / Green green grass of home / Love me tonight (Alla fine della strada) / Without love (there is nothing) / Daughter of darkness / Boy from nowhere / What's new pussycat / I'm coming home / Help yourself / I who have nothing / Move closer / Detroit city / Couldn't say goodbye / Till / Something 'bout you baby I like / Young new Mexican puppeteer
8442862 / Jun '92 / London

☐ DELILAH
Delilah / You've lost that lovin' feelin' / Daughter of darkness / Help yourself / Something 'bout you baby I like / Love me tonight / Minute of your time / Without love / If I ruled the world / Kiss an angel good mornin' / Resurrection shuffle / Lodl / Polk salad annie / Raining in my heart / You've got a friend / To all the girls I've loved before
12575 / Oct '95 / Laserlight

☐ FEVER (Live/2CD Set)
Ladies night / Take me to the river / Honky tonk woman / Green green grass of home / On Broadway / Let it be / Passion / Right place wrong time / Hot legs / Sexy eyes / Bridge over troubled water / Show me / Spanish Harlem / Behind closed doors / In the midnight hour / Celebration / Knock on wood / Help me make it through the night / Higher and higher / She's a lady / Fever / I can't turn you loose / I've got to use my imagination / Georgia / Stagger Lee / Delilah / All by myself / Proud Mary / Try a little tenderness / What's new pussycat / Let your love flow / Giving it up for your love / Do ya think I'm sexy / Since I fell for you / Starting over / I'll be looking for you (it'll be me) / Rose coloured glasses / Lady Madonna / You don't have to say you love me / I who have nothing
CDN 1013 / 15 Jun '98 / Camden

☐ GOLDEN HITS
Green green grass of home / I'm coming home / I'll never fall in love again / Not responsible / Help yourself / What's new pussycat / Love me tonight / It's not unusual... / Funny familiar forgotten feelings / Detroit city / With these hands / Minute of your time / Without love / Delilah
8101922 / Jan '93 / London

☐ **GREAT SONGS OF OUR TIME**
Fever / If ever I should leave you / My way / You don't have to say you love me / Bridge over troubled water / Yesterday / Since I fell for you / Unchained melody / Spanish eyes / Over the rainbow / Save the last dance for me / If I ruled the world / Fools rush in / Danny boy / You've lost that lovin' feeling / As time goes by / Georgia on my mind / Send in the clowns
PLSCD 239 / 27 Oct '97 / Pulse

☐ **GREATEST PERFORMANCES (2CD Set)**
60412320352 / 7 Apr '98 / Thirty Two

☐ **I WHO HAVE NOTHING/SHE'S A LADY**
Daughter of darkness / I have dreamed / Love's been good to me / Lodi / Try a little tenderness / I (who have nothing) / What the world needs now is love / To love somebody / Brother can you spare a dime / See saw / She's a lady / Do what you gotta do / In dreams / Nothing rhymed / Till I can't take it anymore / Resurrection shuffle / Puppet man / It's up to the woman / Ebb tide / One night only love maker / You're my world
RR 4694 / 20 Apr '98 / Repertoire

☐ **KISS**
Kiss / What you have been missing / Move closer / After the tears / Who's gonna take you home tonight / Satisfaction / I'm counting on you / At this moment / Touch my heart / 'Til the end of time
EMPRCD 555 / Mar '95 / Emporio
100002 / May '97 / A-Play Collection

☐ **KISS**
Kiss / What you been missing / Move closer / After the tears / Who's gonna take you home tonight / Satisfaction / I'm counting on you / At this moment / Touch my heart / 'Til the end of time
QED 014 / Nov '96 / Tring

☐ **LEAD AND HOW TO SWING IT, THE**
If I only knew / Girl like you / I wanna get back with you / Situation / Something for your head / Fly away / Love is on our side / I don't think so / Lift me up / Show me / I'm ready / Changes
IND 92498 / 8 Sep '97 / Interscope

☐ **LEGENDARY TOM JONES, THE**
8445522 / Jan '96 / Deram

☐ **LIVE AT CAESAR'S PALACE**
VAR 5898 / 15 Jun '98 / Varese Sarabande

☐ **LOVE ALBUM, THE (Jones, Tom & Engelbert Humperdinck)**
DCD 5385 / Jul '94 / Disky

☐ **SENSATIONAL TOM JONES, THE (3CD Set)**
If ever I should leave you / My way / You don't have to say you love me / Bridge over troubled water / Yesterday / Since I fell for you / Unchained melody / Spanish eyes / Over the rainbow / Save the last dance for me / If I ruled the world / Fools rush in / Danny boy / You've lost that lovin' feeling / As time goes by / Georgia on my mind / Send in the clowns / Delilah / I who have nothing / Spanish harlem / I'm leaving it all up to you / Don't cry for me Argentina / Try a little tenderness / She's a lady / For once in my life / Darlin' / Satisfaction / Can't buy me love / Lay down Sally / I'll never love this way again / Daughter of darkness / I can see clearly now / Higher and higher / Great balls of fire / Pretty woman / Show me / All by myself / Stagger lee / Such a night / Ain't going to bump no more (with no fat woman) / Picture of you / Don't be cruel / Love me tonight / Proud Mary / Let it be / Gotta get you into my life / Long and winding road / I can't turn you loose / Lady Madonna / roll over Beethoven / Cupid / Breakin' up is hard to do / Without love / I thank you / We don't talk anymore / What's new pussycat / Sexy eyes / I got a woman / Hound dog / Rock 'n' roll music / On Broadway / Your my world / In the midnight hour / You are the sunshine of my life / Knock on wood / I'm walkin' / Do ya think I'm sexy
PBXCD 316 / 3 Aug '98 / Pulse

☐ **SIMPLY THE BEST - SHE'S A LADY**
WMCD 5693 / May '94 / Disky

☐ **SING FOR YOU (Jones, Tom/Englebert Humperdinck)**
Witch queen of New Orleans: *Jones, Tom* / Tired of being alone: *Jones, Tom* / Woman you took my life: *Jones, Tom* / If: *Jones, Tom* / Young New Mexican Puppeteer: *Jones, Tom* / All I ever need is you: *Jones, Tom* / You've got a friend: *Jones, Tom* / Time to get it together: *Jones, Tom* / I won't be sorry to see Suzanne again: *Jones, Tom* / Kiss an angel good morning: *Jones, Tom* / Stardust: *Humperdinck, Engelbert* / I'll be seeing you: *Humperdinck, Engelbert* / More I see you: *Humperdinck, Engelbert* / In the still of the night: *Humperdinck, Engelbert* / Moonlight becomes you: *Humperdinck, Engelbert* / But beautiful: *Humperdinck, Engelbert* / I'll be around: *Humperdinck, Engelbert* / Harbor lights: *Humperdinck, Engelbert* / They say it's wonderful: *Humperdinck, Engelbert* / Long ago (and far away): *Humperdinck, Engelbert*
RMB 75087 / Sep '96 / Remember

☐ **SINGS THE ALL-TIME HITS (3CD Set)**
What's new pussycat / I can see clearly now / Can't buy me love / Got to get you into my life / Delilah / You've lost that lovin' feeling / We don't talk anymore / Try a little tenderness / Spanish Harlem / On Broadway / Love me tonight / I can't loving you / Breaking up is hard to do / Daughter of darkness / Fools rush in / Take it to the limit / You're my world / You don't have to say you love me / Heartache tonight / Funny how time slips away / Georgia on my mind / Don't cry for me Argentina / Say you'll stay until tomorrow / Bridge over troubled waters / Green green grass of home / I write the songs / You are the sunshine of my life / Without love / Over the rainbow / As time goes by / Help me make it through the night / I'll never love this way again / Yesterday / She's a lady / All by myself / For once in my life / Such a night / I (who have nothing) / If I ever would leave you / Save the last dance for me / If I ruled the world / Release me / Send in the clowns / Unchained melody / Let it be / Long and winding road / Something 'bout you baby I like: *Jones, Tom & Rita Coolidge* / Endless love / My way
CPCD 83232 / Nov '97 / Charly

☐ **SONGBOOK (5CD Set)**
CDDIG 21 / 16 Mar '98 / Charly

☐ **THIS IS TOM JONES**
6389623 / Jun '96 / Spectrum

☐ **TOM JONES AT CAESARS PALACE**
Dance of love / Cabaret / Soul man / I (Who have nothing) / Delilah / Bridge over troubled water / My way / God bless the children / Reserrective shuffle / She's a lady / Till / I'll never fall in love again / Daughter of darkness / Love me tonight / It's not unusual / High heel sneaker / Johnny B Good / Bony Maroni / Long Tall Sally
12656 / Jun '96 / Laserlight

☐ **TOM JONES SINGS COUNTRY**
PLSCD 292 / 1 Jun '98 / Pulse

☐ **TOUCH MY HEART (3CD Set)**
She's a lady / Till / Daughter of darkness / Young New Mexican puppeteer / Try a little tenderness / After the tears / Women you took my life / At this moment / To all the girls I've loved before / If I sing you a love song / Tired of being alone / You're my world / Letter to Lucille / Whose gonna take you home / Impossible dream / Pledging my love / I (who have nothing) / You've got a friend / Nothing rhymed / Ain't no sunshine / If / Love is in the air / Venus / Proud Mary / I won't be sorry to see Suzanne again / Sugar sugar / Resurrection shuffle / All I ever need is you / Kiss an angel good morning / Anniversary sing / Memories don't leave like people do / You'll never walk alone / Take me tonight / You've lost that lovin' feelin' / Say you'll stay until tomorrow / Rescue me / Puppet man / Somethin' about you I like / Till I can't take it anymore / To love somebody / My way / Move closer / We had it all / Touch my heart / Without love / 'Till the end of time / Witch queen of New Orleans / Hit medley (live) / I'll never fall in love again/Daughter of darkness/Love me t / It's not unusual
SA 872502 / Sep '96 / Disky

☐ **ULTIMATE COLLECTION, THE (4CD Set)**
In the midnight hour / Ladies night / Take me to the river / Honky tonk woman / Green green grass of home / Proud Mary / Bridge over troubled water / Pain: *Turner, Tina* / Hot legs: *Jones, Tom & Tina Turner* / Sexy eyes / Help me make it through the night / Georgia / On broadway / Higher and higher / Please release me / Show me / Spanish Harlem / You are the sunshine of my life / What's new pussycat / Save the last dance for me / Memphis Tennessee / I can see clearly now / Right place wrong time / Passion / All by myself / She's a lady / Since I fell for you / I've got to use my imagination / Try a little tenderness / Too much too little too late: *Jones, Tom & Deniece Williams* / Do ya think I'm sexy / Turn on your lovelight / You don't have to say you love me / Rose-coloured glasses / Breaking up is hard to do / Rock 'n' roll music / You win again / I who have nothing / We don't talk anymore / Such a night / Lady Madonna / Long and winding road / Born to lose / I can't get no satisfaction / Fever / I can't turn you loose / Let it be / Delilah / You've lost that loving feeling / I write the songs / Celebration / Take it to the limit / Endless love: *Jones, Tom & Dionne Warwick* / Knock on wood: *Jones, Tom & Dionne Warwick* / Lay down Sally: *Jones, Tom & Dionne Warwick* / Let your love flow: *Jones, Tom & Dionne Warwick* / Most beautiful girl in the world: *Jones, Tom & Dionne Warwick* / Starting over: *Jones, Tom & Dionne Warwick* / I need your loving every day: *Jones, Tom & Dionne Warwick* / I'm walking: *Jones, Tom & Dionne Warwick* / For once in my life: *Jones, Tom & Dionne Warwick* / I'll be looking for you: *Jones, Tom & Dionne Warwick* / I wish I was 18 again: *Jones, Tom & Dionne Warwick* / Nine to five: *Jones, Tom & Dionne Warwick* / Late in the evening: *Jones, Tom & Dionne Warwick* / She believes in me: *Jones, Tom & Dionne Warwick* / Behind closed doors: *Jones, Tom & Dionne Warwick* / Giving it up for your love: *Jones, Tom & Dionne Warwick* / Listen to the music: *Jones, Tom & Dionne Warwick* / As time goes by: *Jones, Tom & Dionne Warwick* / I love a rainy night: *Jones, Tom & Dionne Warwick* / Funny how time slips away: *Jones, Tom & Dionne Warwick* / I know I'll never love this way again: *Jones, Tom & Dionne Warwick* / I'm leaving it up to you: *Jones, Tom & Tanya Tucker* / Stagger Lee / Without love I had nothing / Gotta get you into my life / If ever I should leave you / Love me tonight / Don't be cruel / Great balls of fire / Roll over Beethoven / I can't stop loving you / You are my world / Middle-aged crazy / Make the world go away / He stopped loving her today / My way
CDN 40014 / 17 Nov '97 / Camden

☐ **ULTIMATE PERFORMANCE**
REMCD 521 / 30 Mar '98 / Reactive

☐ **VERY BEST OF TOM JONES, THE**
8448232 / 23 Feb '98 / London

☐ **VOICE, THE**
It's not unusual / (Sittin' on the) dock of the bay / What's new pussycat / Let it be me / Green green grass of home / It's magic / Memphis Tennessee / I can't stop loving you / If you go away / Kansas City / Promise her anything / Detroit city / With these hands / I'll never fall in love again / My prayer / Love me tonight / I'm coming home
MCCD 057 / Mar '92 / Music Club

☐ **WHAT'S NEW PUSSYCAT**
What's new pussycat / Some other guy / I've got a heart / Little by little / Won't you give him (one more chance) / Bama lama bama loo / With these hands / Untrue / To wait for love is to waste your life away / I tell the sea / Rose / Endlessly / Memphis Tennessee / Kiss kiss / Once upon a time / What'cha gonna do
8205232 / Jan '93 / London

☐ **YOUNG NEW MEXICAN PUPPETEER/ BODY AND SOUL OF TOM JONES**
Witch queen of New Orleans / Tired of being alone / Woman you took my life / Young new Mexican puppeteer / All I ever need is you / You've got a friend / Time to get it together / I won't be sorry to see Suzanne again / Kiss an angel good / Running bear / Ain't no sunshine when she's gone / If loving you is wrong (I don't want to be right) / Since I loved you last / Lean on me / Letter to Lucille / Today I started loving you again / I'll share my world with you / Ballad of Billie Joe
REP 4695 / 6 Apr '98 / Repertoire

Jones, Tutu

☐ **BLUE TEXAS SOUL**
CDBB 9571 / Aug '96 / Bullseye Blues

☐ **I'M FOR REAL**
Sweet woman / I'm for real / My own fault / Excited / (Do you love) steppin' on me / She's my woman / I still love you / Too blues to be true / Stubborn woman / I'm not your fool / Outstanding
JSPCD 2112 / Jul '98 / JSP

☐ **STAYING POWER**
Daylight caught us redhanded / Milkman game / Can't leave you alone / Cant leave your love alone / After midnight / Good juice / Be good to you lady / She's so fine / You shatter my heart / Romance avenue / After loving you
CDBB 9611 / Jun '98 / Bullseye Blues

Jones, Vince

☐ **COMPLETE, THE**
If you're going to the city / Lobster / Detour ahead / Nature boy / My ideal / Big city / Blue / Don't worry about a thing / Nature of power / Since I fell for you / I put a spell on you / Dream / Not much / Budgie / Sensual item / Never let me go
INT 30902 / Nov '93 / Intuition

☐ **FUTURE GIRL**
INT 31092 / Oct '92 / Intuition

☐ **HERE'S TO THE MIRACLES**
Luncheon with the president / Here's to the miracles / America / We're still friends / Love comes back / Lost in the stars / Bye bye love / Tribute two / Can't afford to live, can't afford to die / Take a love song
INT 31982 / Feb '97 / Intuition

☐ **ONE DAY SPENT**
Detour ahead / Let's get lost / I wish you love / Since I fell for you / Afterthought / I thought about you / Time after time / Never let me go / Save your love for me / There'll never be another you
INT 30872 / Feb '92 / Intuition

☐ **TRUSTWORTHY LITTLE SWEETHEARTS**
Big city / Don't worry about a thing / Stricken by a storm / Trustworthy little sweethearts / I'm a fool to want you / Like young / My only friend / That old feeling / In an attempt to be fascinating / I didn't know what time it was / Not much / Turn around / (I'm afraid) the masquerade is over
INT 3046 2 / Mar '91 / Intuition

☐ **WATCH WHAT HAPPENS**
INT 30702 / Oct '91 / Intuition

Jones, Vivian

☐ **IJAHMAN**
IHCD 007 / Jul '95 / Imperial House

☐ **LOVE IS FOR LOVERS**
IHCD 006 / Jun '95 / Imperial House

☐ **MOMENT OF MAGIC**
IHCD 010 / 15 Dec '97 / Imperial House

☐ **REGGAE MAX**
JSRNCD 12 / Mar '97 / Jet Star

Jones, Wizz

☐ **LATE NIGHTS AND LONG DAYS (Jones, Wizz & Simeon)**
FE 091CD / Jul '93 / Fellside

☐ **VILLAGE TAPES**
TUT 72157 / Jan '94 / Wundertute

Jonny L

☐ **SAW TOOTH**
XLCD 120 / 2 Feb '98 / XL

Jonsson, Cennet

☐ **BETWEEN THE NOISE (Jonsson, Cennet & Jacob Karlzon)**
7393787970325 / Aug '97 / DB Productions

☐ **TEN PIECES**
PSCD 94 / May '97 / Phono Suecia

Jonsson, Lennart

☐ **I THOUGHT ABOUT YOU**
SITCD 9220 / Aug '95 / Sittel

Jontef

☐ **KLEZMER & YIDDISH**
EUCD 1303 / Jul '95 / ARC

Joolz

☐ **HEX**
Protection / Cat / Facade / Love is (sweet romance) / Stand / Storm / Mummy's boy / Ambition / House of dreams / Requiem / Musket fife and drum / Legend / Mad, bad and dangerous to know
CDGRAM 44 / Apr '90 / Anagram

Joos, Herbert

☐ **DAYBREAK - THE DARK SIDE OF TWILIGHT**
Why / When were you born / Leicester Court 1440 / Daybreak / Black trees / Fasten your seatbelt / Dark side of twilight
8414792 / Jan '90 / ECM

☐ **HERBERT JOOS PLAYS BILLIE HOLIDAY SONGS**
I'm a fool to want you / My man / No more / You don't know what love is / God bless the child / Don't explain / Crazy he tells me / When your lover has gone / Mood indigo
5226342 / Jan '95 / EmArCy

Jooya

☐ **JOURNEY TO PERSIA (Jooya & Saeid Faradj-Pouri)**
332652 PC09 / May '98 / Koch

Joplin, Janis

☐ **18 ESSENTIAL SONGS**
Trouble in mind / Down on me / Bye bye baby / Ball and chain / Piece of my heart / I need a man to love / Summertime / Try (just a little bit harder) / One good man / Kozmic blues / Raise your hand / Tell Mama / Move over / Mercedes Benz / Get it while you can / Me and Bobby McGee / Trust me / Half moon
4785152 / Apr '95 / Columbia

☐ **ANTHOLOGY (2CD Set)**
Piece of my heart / Summertime / Maybe / Try (just a little bit harder) / To love somebody / Kozmic blues / Turtle blues / Oh sweet Mary / Little girl blue / Trust me / Move over / Half moon / Cry baby / Me and Bobby McGee / Mercedes Benz / Down on me / Bye bye baby / Get it while you can / Ball and chain
4674052 / Jun '97 / Columbia

☐ **BLUES DOWN DEEP (The Songs Of Janis Joplin) (Various Artists)**
RUF 1018 / 15 Sep '97 / Ruf

☐ **CAN'T GO HOME AGAIN (Big Brother & The Holding Company)**
LR 104 / 9 Mar '98 / Legend

☐ **CHEAP THRILLS/PEARL/KOZMIC BLUES (3CD Set)**
Combination of the two / I need a man to love / Summertime / Piece of my heart / Turtle blues / Oh sweet Mary / Ball and chain / Move over / Cry baby / Woman left lonely / Half moon / Buried alive in the blues / My baby / Me and Bobby McGee / Mercedes Benz / Trust me / Get it while you can / Try / Maybe / One good man / As good as you've been to this / To love somebody / Kozmic blues / Little girl blue / Work me lord
4853212 / 3 Nov '97 / Columbia

☐ **CHEAPER THRILLS (Big Brother & The Holding Company)**
Let the good times roll / I know you rider / Moanin' at midnight / Hey baby / Down on me / Whisperman / Women is losers / Blow my mind / Ball and chain / Coo coo / Gutra's garden / Harry
EDCD 135 / Aug '90 / Edsel

☐ **DO WHAT YOU LOVE (Big Brother & The Holding Company)**
L 8084352 / 9 Mar '98 / Legend

☐ **FAREWELL SONG**
Tell mama / Magic of love / Misery 'n' / One night stand / Harry / Raise your hand / Farewell song / Amazing grace / Hi-heel sneakers / Catch me daddy
4844582 / Feb '97 / Columbia

☐ **GREATEST HITS**
Piece of my heart / Summertime / Try (just a little bit harder) / Cry baby / Me and Bobby McGee / Down on me / Get it while you can / Bye bye baby / Move over / Ball and chain / Everybody loves you now / Why Judy why / Falling of the rain / Turn around / You look so good to me / Tomorrow is today / Nocturne / Got to begin again
CD 32190 / May '90 / CBS

☐ **JANIS (3CD Set)**
What can drinkin' do / Trouble in mind / Hesitation blues / Easy rider / Coo coo / Down on me / Last time / All is loneliness / Call on me / Women is losers / Intruder / Light is faster than sound / Bye bye baby / Farewell song / Flower in the sun / Misery'n / Roadblock / Ball and chain / Combination of the two / I need a man to love / Piece of my heart / Turtle blues / Oh sweet Mary / Catch me daddy / Summertime / Kozmic blues / Try (just a little bit harder) / One good man / Dear landlord / To love somebody / As good as you've been to this world / Little girl blue / Work me Lord / Raise your hand / Maybe / Me and Bobby McGee / One night stand / Tell mama / Cry baby / Move over / Woman left lonely / Half moon / Happy birthday John (happy trails) / My baby / Mercedes Benz / Trust me / Get it while you can
CD 48845 / Jan '94 / Columbia

☐ **JOPLIN/HENDRIX/MORRISON (Interview Discs/3CD Set) (Joplin, Janis & Jimi Hendrix/Jim Morrison)**
55624 / Oct '97 / Laserlight

☐ **LIVE AT THE WINTERLAND 1968**
Down on me / Flower in the sun / I need a man to love / Bye bye baby / Easy rider / Combination of the two / Farewell song / Piece of my heart / Catch me daddy / Magic of love / Summertime / Light is faster than sound / Ball and chain / Down on me
4851502 / 1 Jun '98 / Columbia

☐ **LIVE AT WOODSTOCK 1969**
Raise your hand / As good as you've been to this world / To love somebody / Summertime / Try (just a little bit harder) / Cozmic blues / Can turn you loose / Work me lord / Piece of my heart / Ball and chain
ITM 960007 / Sep '93 / Koch

☐ MAGIC OF LOVE
ITM 96001 / Nov '92 / ITM

☐ PEARL
Move over / Cry baby / Woman left lonely / Half moon / Buried alive in the blues / Me and Bobby McGee / Mercedes Benz / Get it while you can / Trust me / My baby
CD 64188 / Dec '85 / CBS

☐ ULTIMATE COLLECTION, THE (2CD Set)
SONYTV 52CD / 10 Aug '98 / Sony TV

Joplin, Scott

☐ ELITE SYNCOPATION
Elite syncopations / Country club / Paragon rag / Eugenia / Cleopha / Real slow rag / Scott Joplin's new rag / Leola / Lily Queen / Chrysanthemum / Heliotrope bouquet / Reflection rag / Maple leaf rag / Ole Miss Rag / Magnetic rag / Silver swan rag
BCD 102 / Jul '91 / Biograph

☐ ENTERTAINER, THE (Classic Ragtime From Rare Piano Rolls)
Maple leaf rag / Something doing / Weeping willow rag / Entertainer / Easy winners / Pineapple rag / Solace / Gladiolus rag / Ragtime dance / Sugarcane / Crush collision march / Bethena / Combination march / Breeze from Alabama
BCD 101 / Jul '91 / Biograph

☐ ENTERTAINER, THE
SHAN 98016 / May '93 / Shanachie

☐ ENTERTAINER, THE (The Very Best Of Scott Joplin) (Rifkin, Joshua)
7559794492 / Jan '97 / Nonesuch

☐ ENTERTAINER, THE (Various Artists)
Maple leaf rag / Solace / Mexican serenade / Magnetic rag / Entertainer / Eugenia / Sycamore / Search light rag / Non pareil (none to equal) / Kismet rag / Something doing / Rosebud / Weeping willow / Gladiolus rag / Favourite / Scott Joplin's new rag / Heliotrope bouquet
SH 98015 / 23 Mar '98 / Shanachie

☐ GOLD COLLECTION, THE
D2CD 13 / Dec '92 / Deja Vu

☐ JAZZ PORTRAITS
Chrisanthemum / Scott Joplin's new rag / Something doing / Original rags / Entertainer / Maple leaf rag / Sunflower slow drag / Elite syncopations / Eugenia / Paragon rag / Euphonic sounds / Pineapple rag / Stoptime rag / Reflection rag / Cleopha / Lily Queen / Heliotrope bouquet / Country club
CD 14518 / May '94 / Jazz Portraits

☐ KING OF RAGTIME
CD 53004 / Mar '92 / Giants Of Jazz

☐ KING OF RAGTIME
Elite syncopations / Chrisanthemum / Scott Joplin new rag / Eugenia / Paragon rag / Euphonic sounds / Pineapple rag / Something doing / Original rags / Entertainer / Maple leaf rag / Sunflower slow drag / Stoptime rag / Reflection rag / Cleopha / Lily Queen / Heliotrope Bouquet / Country club / Areal slow drag / Leola
GRF 080 / Apr '93 / Tring

☐ KING OF RAGTIME (3CD Set)
Maple leaf rag / Harmony club waltz / Augustan club waltz / Peachtree rag / Swipesy cake walk / Original rags / Great crush collision march / Easy winners / Strenuous life / Ragtime dance / Elite syncopations / Little black baby / Palm leaf rag / Favorite / Cascades / Rosebud march / Sarah dear / Binks waltz / Rose leaf rag / When your hair is like the snow / Entertainer / March majestic / Weeping willow / Sycamore / Something doing / School of ragtime / Country club / Euphonic sounds / Stoptime rag / Felicity rag / Fig leaf rag / Scott joplin's new rag / Wall street rag / Paragon rag / Pineapple rag / Antoinette / Snoring sampson / Gladiolus rag / Searchlight rag / Nonpareil / Sensation / Frolic of the bears / Kismet rag / Silver swan rag / Lily queen / Highlights from 'treemonisha' / Real slow drag / Prelude to act 3 / Chrysanthemum / A breeze from alabama / I am thinking of my pickanniny days / Lovin' babe / Pleasant moments / A picture of her face / Cleopha / Leola
55542 / Oct '95 / Laserlight

☐ KING OF RAGTIME
Chrisanthemum / Scott joplin's new rag / Something doing / Original rags / Entertainer / Maple leaf rag / Sunflower slow drag / Elite syncopations / Eugenia / Paragon rag / Euphonic sounds / Pineapple rag / Stoptime rag / Reflection rag / Cleopha / Lily queen / Heliotrope bouquet / Country club
CD 56056 / Mar '95 / Jazz Roots

☐ KING OF RAGTIME WRITERS
Cascades / Strenuous life / Felicity rag / Swipsey cakewalk / Peacherine rag / Something doing / Search light / Rose leaf rag / Fig leaf rag / Rag medley no. 6 - pineapple rag / Euphonic sounds / Palm leaf rag / Kismet rag / Wall Street rag / Pleasant moments / Original rags / Sunflower slow drag / Maple leaf rag
BCD 110 / Jul '91 / Biograph

☐ MARCHES, WALTZES & RAGS
MM 67102 / Oct '94 / Music Masters

☐ PIANO RAGS OF SCOTT JOPLIN
Entertainer / Peacherine rag / Original rags / Easy winners / Strenuous life / Elite syncopations / Breeze from Alabama / Sycamore / Maple leaf rag / Sunflower slow drag / Weeping willow / Something doing / Solace / Chrysanthemum / Palm leaf rag / Cascades
EMPRCD 539 / Sep '94 / Empress

☐ PIANO RAGS, THE
CDSGP 0118 / May '94 / Prestige

☐ RAGS TO RICHES (Boriskin, Michael)
75605570282 / 26 Jan '98 / Classic FM

☐ SCOTT JOPLIN (2CD Set)
R2CD 4013 / 13 Apr '98 / Deja Vu

☐ SCOTT JOPLIN GOLD (2CD Set)
D2CD 4013 / Jun '95 / Deja Vu

☐ SCOTT JOPLIN RAGS (Eaton, Roy)
SBK 62833 / Jun '97 / Sony Classical

☐ SCOTT JOPLIN'S PIANO RAGS (Rifkin, Joshua)
7559791592 / Jan '95 / Warner Bros.

Jordan, Charley

☐ CHARLEY JORDAN VOL.1 1930-1931
DOCD 5097 / '92 / Document

☐ CHARLEY JORDAN VOL.2 1931-1934
DOCD 5098 / '92 / Document

☐ CHARLEY JORDAN VOL.3 1935-1937
DOCD 5099 / '92 / Document

Jordan, Chris

☐ TWILIGHT OF THE GODS
Pilgrims / Evening star / Grail / Dance for dead lovers / Prize / Rhinegold / Valkyrie's dream / Bride's lament
NAGE 14CD / Jun '87 / Art Of Landscape

Jordan, Clifford

☐ CLIFFORD JORDAN (Featuring Junior Cook) (Jordan, Clifford Quartet)
CRISS 1011CD / Nov '90 / Criss Cross

☐ GLASS BEAD GAMES
CDGR 245 / 27 May '98 / Charly

☐ ROYAL BALLADS (Jordan, Clifford Quartet)
CRISS 1025CD / Nov '91 / Criss Cross

Jordan, Duke

☐ DOUBLE DUKE (2CD Set)
SCCD 37039 / 5 Jan '98 / Steeplechase

☐ DUKE JORDAN'S TRIO AND QUARTET
Forecast / Sultry eve / They can't that away from me / Night in Tunisia / Summertime / Flight to Jordan / Two loves / Cu-Ba / Yesterdays / Scotch blues
CY 18060 / 13 Apr '98 / Savoy Jazz

☐ DUKE'S ARTISTRY (Jordan, Duke Quartet)
SCCD 31033 / Jul '88 / Steeplechase

☐ FLIGHT TO DENMARK (Jordan, Duke Trio)
No problem: *Jordan, Duke* / Here's that rainy day: *Jordan, Duke* / Everything happens to me: *Jordan, Duke* / Glad I met pat: *Jordan, Duke* / How deep is the ocean: *Jordan, Duke* / Green dolphin street: *Jordan, Duke* / If I did-would you: *Jordan, Duke* / Flight to denmark: *Jordan, Duke*
SCCD 31011 / Oct '90 / Steeplechase

☐ FLIGHT TO JORDAN
Flight to Jordan / Starbrite / Squawkin' / Deacon Joe / Split quick / Si Joya / Diamond stud / I should care
VGCD 650118 / Oct '93 / Vogue

☐ JORDU
VGCD 655010 / Oct '93 / Vogue

☐ ONE FOR THE LIBRARY
STCD 4194 / Aug '94 / Storyville

☐ OSAKA CONCERT VOL.1 (Jordan, Duke Trio)
SCCD 31271 / Nov '90 / Steeplechase

☐ PARIS-NEW YORK (Original Vogue Masters) (Jordan, Duke & Bud Powell)
Just one of those things / Embraceable you / Minor escamp / Scotch blues / Confirmation / Darn that dream / They can't take that away from me / Wait and see / Just one of those things / Embraceable you / Buttercup / John's abbey / Sweet and lovely / Crossin' the channel
74321457272 / May '97 / Vogue

☐ TIME ON MY HANDS (Jordan, Duke Trio)
SCCD 31232 / Jul '88 / Steeplechase

☐ TRIO & QUINTET
Forecast / Sultry eve / They can't take that away from me / Night in Tunisia / Summertime / Flight to Jordan / Two lovers / Cuba / Yesterdays / Scotch blues
SV 0149 / Oct '97 / Savoy Jazz

Jordan, Lorraine

☐ CRAZY GUESSING GAMES
LDL 1212CD / Mar '94 / Lochshore

☐ INSPIRATION
LDL 1205CD / May '93 / Lochshore

Jordan, Louis

☐ AT THE SWING CAT'S BALL 1937-1939
Gee but you're swell / Honey in the bee ball / Keep a knockin' / Doug the jitterbug / You're my meat
JSPCD 330 / Oct '91 / JSP

☐ CLASSIC RECORDINGS (9CD Set)
Toodle loo on down / So good / Away from you / Honey in the bee ball / Barnacle bill the sailor / Flat face / Keep a knockin' (but you can't come in) / Sam jones done snagged his britches in a coconut tree (inst / Doug the jitterbug / At the swing cat's ball / Jake, what a snake (instrumental) / Honeysuckle rose / 'fore day blues / But I'll be back / You ain't nowhere / You're my meat / June tenth jamboree / You run your mouth and I'll run my business / I'm alabama bound / Hard lovin' blues / You got to go when the wagon come / Lovie joe / Somebody done-hoodooed the hoodoo man / Bounce the ball (do da little um day) / Penthouse in the basement / After school swing session (swinging with symphony sid) / Oh boy, I'm in the groove / Never let your left hand know what your right hand's doin' / Don't come crying on my shoulder / Waitin' for the robert e. lee / A chicken ain't nothing but a bird / Pompton turnpike / Do you call that a buddy (dirty cat) / I know you, I know what you wanna do / Pinetop's boogie woogie (instrumental) / Two little squirrels (nuts to you) / T-bone blues / Pan pan-saint vitus dance / Saxa woogie / Brotherly love / De laff's on you / Boogie woogie came to town / John, stop teasing me / How 'bout that / Teacher (how I love my teacher) / Mama, mama blues (rusty dusty blues) / Knock me a kiss / Green grass grows all around / Mister lovingood / I'm gonna move to the outskirts of town / What's the use of gettin' sober / Chicks I pick are slender, tender and tall / I'm gonna leave you on the outskirts of town / That'll just 'bout knock me out / Dirty snake / Five guys named moe / It's a low-down shame / De laff's on you / Ration blues / Is you is or is you ain't my baby / Deacon jones / Things I want I can't get at home / How high am I / I like 'em fat like that / Truth of the matter / Hey now, let's live / Mop mop / G.i. jive / You can't get that no more / Louis' oldsmobile song / Your socks don't match / My baby said yes / My baby said yes / Your socks don't match / Buzz me / They raided the house / Caldonia boogie / Somebody done changed the lock on my door / How long must I wait for you / Don't worry 'bout that mule / Salt pork, west virginia / Paper boy / Don't worry 'bout that mule / It's so easy / Beware / Don't let the sun catch you cryin' / Choo choo ch'boogie / Ain't that just like a woman / That chick's too young to fry / No sale / If it's love you want baby, that's me / Ain't nobody here but us chickens / Let the good times roll / All for the love of lil / Texas and pacific / Jack you're dead / Reet petite and gone / Sure had a wonderful time / I know what you're puttin' down / Open the door richard / Friendship / Open the door richard / Boogie woogie blue plate / Barnyard boogie / Every man to his own profession / Early in the morning / Run joe / Look out / Beans and cornbread / Have you got the gumption / We can't agree / Chicky mo craney crow / Roamin' blues / Inflation blues / You're much too fat (and that's that) / Chug chug boogie / There'll be no days like that / Pettin' and pokin' / You're on the right track, baby / Don't burn the candle at both ends / Why'd you do it, baby / Daddy-o / Safe, sane and single / I know what I've got / You broke your promise / Pusk ka pee she pie (the saga of saga boy) / Cole slaw-beans and corn bread-onion (instrumental) / Baby's gonna go, bye bye / Heed my warning / Psycho loco (instrumental) / School days / Hungry man / Love you 'till your money's gone blues / Saturday night fish fry (part 1) / Saturday night fish fry (part 2) / Want a roof over my head / Show me how (you milk the cow) / Blue light boogie (part 1) / Blue light boogie (part 2) / Tamburitza boogie / (you dyed your hair) chartreuse / Lemonade / It's a great, great pleasure / You will always have a friend / Louisville lodge meeting / Trouble then satisfaction / Crazy baby / Life is so peculiar / I'll be glad when you're dead, you rascal you / Teardrops from my eyes / If you've got some place to go / Weak minded blues / Is my pop in there / I can't give you anything but love, baby / If you so smart, how come you ain't rich / Trust in me / Louisville lodge meeting / How blue can you get / Happy birthday boogie / May every day be christmas / Please don't leave me / Bone dry / I love that kinda carryin' on / Three handed woman / Fat sam from birmingham / Cock a doodle do / Garmoochie / There must be a way / Come and get it / Stop makin' music / Slow down / Work, baby work / Never trust a woman / All of me / There goes my heart / Lay something on the bar (besides your elbow) / Gimme gimme blues / Junco partner / Time marches on / Azure-te (paris blues) / Oil well, texas / There's nothing else that I can do / Jordan for president / Soon a baby / There's nothing else that I can do / Soon a baby / You didn't want me a baby / Man's best friend is a bed / I didn't know what time it was / It's better to wait for love / Only yesterday / Just like a butterfly that's caught in the rain / Hog wash / House party / Everything that's made of wood / I want you to be my baby / You know it too / Locked up / I gotta move / Nobody knows you when you're down and out / If it's true / Wake up jacob / Lollypop / Perdido (instrumental)
BCD 15557 / Apr '92 / Bear Family

☐ CLASSICS 1934-1940
CLASSICS 636 / Nov '92 / Classics

☐ CLASSICS 1940-1941
CLASSICS 663 / Nov '92 / Classics

☐ CLASSICS 1941-1943
CLASSICS 741 / Feb '94 / Classics

☐ CLASSICS 1943-1945
CLASSICS 866 / Mar '96 / Classics

☐ CLASSICS 1945-1946
CLASSICS 921 / Apr '97 / Classics

☐ FIVE GUYS NAMED MOE
Five guys named moe / Choo choo ch'boogie / Ain't nobody here but us chickens / Beware brother beware / Early in the morning / Saturday night fish fry / Let the good times roll / Push ka pi shee pie / Jack you're dead / What's the use of getting sober (when you're gonna get dr / Is you is or is you ain't my baby / Reet petite and gone / School days / G.i. jive / Pettin' and pokin' / Beans and cornbread / Buzz me / I know what I've got / Blue light boogie / Caldonia
MCLD 19048 / Apr '92 / MCA

☐ GOOD TIMES
Let the good times roll / Five guys named Moe / Daddy-O / Texas and the Pacific
BSTCD 9103 / May '92 / Best Compact Discs

☐ HOW 'BOUT THAT
At the swing cats ball / Small town boy / I know you, I know what you wanna do / Pompton turnpike / Honeysuckle rose / I'm gonna leave you on the outskirts of town / That'll bout knock me out / GI jive / Green grass grows all round / Caldonia boogie / Two little squirrels (nuts to you) / Ain't going nowhere / Saxa-woogie / How 'bout that / Ration blues / Is you is or is you ain't my baby / Barnacle Bill the sailor / It's a low down dirty shame / Boogie woogie came to town / You run your mouth and I'll run my business / Oh boy I'm in the groove / Sam Jones done snagged his britches / Pan pan / Brotherly love / Mama, mama blues (rusty dusty blues)
302372 / Jul '97 / Hallmark

☐ I BELIEVE IN MUSIC
ECD 260062 / Jan '92 / Evidence
BB 8762 / Feb '97 / Black & Blue

☐ INTRODUCTION TO LOUIS JORDAN, AN
4054 / 24 Feb '98 / Best Of Jazz

☐ JUMP JIVE JORDAN
Five guys named Moe / Choo choo ch' boogie / Mop mop / If you're so smart how come you ain't rich / Barnyard boogie / Fat Sam from Birmingham / Ain't nobody here but us chickens / Saturday night fish fry / Is you is or is you ain't my baby / Open the door Richard / What's the use of getting sober / Run Joe / Chartreuse / Tamburitza boogie / Hog wash / School days
MCCD 085 / Dec '92 / Music Club

☐ LIVE JIVE (Jordan, Louis & His Tympany Five)
Five guys named Moe / Buzz me / Knock me a kiss / Let the good times roll / I like 'em fat like that / Choo choo ch' boogie / On the sunny side of the street / All for the love of Lil / Safe, sane and single / Broke but happy / Texas and Pacific / Drippy drippers / Don't let the sun catch you crying / How long must I wait for you / Daddy-O / Jumping at the Jubilee / Baby that's alright for you
DATOM 4 / Jul '89 / Touch Of Magic

☐ LOUIS JORDAN & TYMPANY FIVE 1939-1944
158372 / Jul '95 / Jazz Archives

☐ LOUIS JORDAN AND CHRIS BARBER (Jordan, Louis & Chris Barber)
BLCD 760156 / '91 / Black Lion

☐ NO MOE (Louis Jordan's Greatest Hits)
Saturday night fish fry / Is you is or is you ain't my baby / Don't let the sun catch you crying / Salt Pork West Virginia / Early in the morning / Sunday / Knock me a kiss / Ain't nobody here but us chickens / Slop / Let the good times roll / Sweet Lorraine / Run Joe / Choo choo ch' boogie / I'm gonna move to the outskirts of town / Beware brothers beware / Caldonia
5125232 / Apr '92 / Verve

☐ ON FILM 1942-1948
KKCD 17 / Jun '96 / Krazy Kat

☐ PLATINUM COLLECTION, THE (2CD Set)
Buzz me / Let the good times roll / I know what you're putting down / All for the love of Lil / Reet petite and gone / Don't let the sun catch you cryin' / They raided the house / Salt pork West Virginia / No sale / How long must I wait for you / Don't worry about that mule / If it love you want baby that's me / Sure had a wonderful time / Somebody done changed that love / Reconversion blues / Beware / Texas and Pacific / Open the door Richard / It's Ain't nobody here but us chickens / Choo choo chi boogie / Caldonia boogie / That chick too young too fry / Look out / Early in the morning / Boogie woogie blue plate / Every man to his own profession / Friendship / Barnyard boogie / What's the use of getting sober / You can't get that no more / Dirty snake / Deacon Jones / Hey now let's jive / GI Jive / That'll just about knock me out / Chicks I pick are slender tender and tall / You run your mouth and I'll run my business / Honeysuckle rose / Five guys named Moe
PC 618 / 10 Nov '97 / Platinum Collection

☐ ROCK 'N' ROLL
Ain't nobody here but us chickens / Choo choo ch' boogie / Knock me a kiss / Caldonia / Let the good times roll / Is you is or is you ain't my baby / Beware brothers beware / Big Bess / Cat scratchin' / Don't let the sun catch you crying / I'm gonna move to the outskirts of town / Salt Pork West Virginia / Run Joe / Early in the morning / Morning light / Fire rock Doc / Ella Mae / Jamp / Saturday night fish fry / Got my mojo working
8382192 / Apr '89 / Mercury

☐ VERY BEST OF LOUIS JORDAN, THE
Five guys named Moe / Knock me a kiss / End of my worry / Bahama Joe / How high am I / I like 'em fat like that / Flat face / Do you call me that a buddy / Penthouse in the basement / Is you is or is you ain't my baby / You're my meat / Never let your left hand know what your right hand's doin' / Doug the jitterbug / T-bone blues / Nobody but me / GI jive
SUMCD 4035 / Nov '96 / Summit

Jordan, Montell

☐ LET'S RIDE
When you get home / Don't call me / Let's ride / Midnight rain / One last chance / Anything and everything / Body ah / Irrestible / Let's ride / Can I / Missing you / Longest night / I say yes / 4 you / I say yes
5369872 / 6 Apr '98 / Def Jam

☐ MORE TO TELL
Non-believers (interlude) / Superlover man / All I need / Tricks on my mind / Falling / What's on tonight / I say yes (interlude) / I like: *Jordan, Montell & Slick Rick* / Let me be the one / Never alone (interlude) / Never alone / Everything is gonna be alright / Bounce 2 this
5331912 / Sep '96 / Def Jam

☐ THIS IS HOW WE DO IT
My Mommy intro / Somethin' 4 da honeyz / This is how we do it / Payback / I'll do anything / Don't keep me waiting / Comin' home / Introducing shaunta / It's over / Midnight interlude / I wanna / Down on my knees / Gotta get my roll on / Close the door / Daddy's home
5271272 / May '95 / Def Jam

Jordan, Ronny

☐ ANTIDOTE, THE
Get to grips / Blues grinder / After hours / See the new / So what / Nite spice / Summer smile
CID 9988 / 2 Feb '98 / Island

☐ BAD BROTHERS (Jordan, Ronny & DJ Krush)
Jackal / Shit goes down / Love I never had it so good / So what / Season for a change / Bad brother
IMCD 8024 / Aug '94 / Island

☐ LIGHT TO DARK
Into the light / Homage / It's you / Law / Fooled / Closer than close / I see you / Downtime / Deep in your heart / Laidback / Light to dark / Last goodbye
CID 8047 / 2 Feb '98 / Island

☐ QUIET REVOLUTION, THE
Season for change / In full swing / Slam in a jam / Mr. Walker / Jackal / Come with me / Morning after / Under your spell / Tinseltown / Vanston place (00 am)
CID 8009 / 2 Feb '98 / Island

Jordan, Sass

☐ PRESENT
Q 200583 / 23 Feb '98 / Factor

☐ RACINE
Make you a believer / If you're gonna love me / You don't have to remind me / Who do you think you are / Windin' me up / I want to believe / Goin' back again / Do what you want / Cry baby / Where there's a will / Time flies
Q 2564 / 1 May '98 / Aquarius

☐ RATS
Damaged / Slave / Pissin' down / High road easy / Sun's gonna rise / Head / Ugly / I'm not / Honey / Wish / Breakin' / Give
Q 2571 / 1 May '98 / Aquarius

☐ TELL SOMEBODY
REVXD 193 / Nov '92 / FM
Q 2552 / 1 May '98 / Aquarius

Jordan, Sheila

☐ OLD TIME FEELING (Jordan, Sheila & Harvie Swartz)
MCD 5366 / Sep '92 / Muse

Jordan, Stanley

☐ BEST OF STANLEY JORDAN, THE
Jumpin' Jack / Eleanor Rigby / Lady in my life / All the children / Impressions / My favourite things / Georgia on my mind / Stairway to heaven / Flying home / Still got the blues / Over the rainbow
CDP 8315022 / Apr '95 / Blue Note

☐ BOLERO
Bolero Parts 1-6 / Always and forever / Cheleon / Betcha by golly wow / Drifting / Plato's blues / Always and forever (solo)
07822187032 / Feb '94 / Arista

Jordan, Steve

☐ HERE COMES MR. JORDAN
ACD 114 / Oct '93 / Audiophile

☐ MANY SOUNDS OF STEVE 'ESTEBAN' JORDAN, THE
La tracionera (ranchera) / El chupon (polka) / Pajarito negro (ranchero) / Falta tu amor (bolero) / Maldita tu suerte (ranchera) / Siempre hace frio (ranchera) / Hazme caso (ranchera) / Las coronelas (polka) / El castigador (ranchera) / Mujer sin alma (ranchera) / Las coronelas (polka) / Estrellita del norte (ranchera) / Midnight blues / Jamas volvere (ranchera) / El rancho grande potpuri (polka) / El corrido de jhonny el pachuco (corrido) / La pepita (polka) / Vuela la paloma (cumbia) / Together again (country) / More pretty girls than one (country)
ARHCD 319 / Apr '95 / Arhoolie

☐ RETURN OF EL PARCHE, THE
Johnny charasquis / Oaxaca / La mucura / Miedo de pederia / Yakity yak / Le sequiremos / El cascabel / El incienso / El alacran (cumbia) / Lorianna / La marcha del campesino / Chicana preciosa
ROUCD 6019 / '88 / Rounder

Jordanaires

☐ SING ELVIS'S FAVOURITE SPIRITUALS
Didn't it rain / Peace in the valley / Joshua fit de battle of Jericho / Search me lord / Dig a little deeper / You better run / Let us break bread together / Wonderful time up there / How great thou art / I'm a rollin' / Dip your fingers in some water / Roll Jordan roll / Onward christian soldiers
PWKS 4216 / Oct '94 / Carlton

☐ SONGS WE SANG WITH ELVIS
Can't help falling in love / (you're the) devil in disguise / Love me tender / Don't be cruel / Good luck charm / Return to sender / All shook up / Always on my mind / Heartbreak hotel / Teddy bear (let me be your) / That's all right (mama) / It's now or never / Are you lonesome tonight / Got a lot of living to do / Wear my ring around your neck / Jailhouse rock
WMCD 5691 / Apr '94 / Disky

Jorgensen, Knud

☐ BOJANGLES (Jorgensen, Knud & Bengt Hanson)
TMCD 002 / May '97 / Touche

☐ JAZZ TRIO
OP 8401CD / Sep '91 / Opus 3

☐ SKISS (Jorgensen, Knud Trio)
TMCD 001 / May '97 / Touche

Jormin, Anders

☐ ONCE
DRCD 308 / May '97 / Dragon

Jory, Sarah

☐ 20 CLASSIC SONGS (The Early Years)
Walk the way the wind blows / Somewhere between / I'll leave this world loving you / Just out of reach / Why me Lord / Beyond the point of no return / Let me be there / Dear God / Always have, always will / How great thou art / Jones on the jukebox / Before I'm over you / Just because I'm a woman / Faded love / It is no secret / No time at all / Funny face / Yesterday just passed my way again / Beneath still waters / Old rugged cross
RZSCD 429 / Apr '93 / Ritz

☐ 20 STEEL GUITAR FAVOURITES
Sticky fingers / Deep in the heart of Texas / Orange blossom special / Jealous heart / Under the boardwalk / Careless hands / Steel line / Way to survive / San Antonio stroll / She believes in me / Oklahoma stomp / Highway 40 blues / Rose coloured glasses / Blue jade / Cold cold heart / Three of us / In the garden / City lights / Once upon a time in the West / Remington ride
RZSCD 428 / Apr '93 / Ritz

☐ LOVE WITH ATTITUDE
RZCD 0076 / Oct '95 / Ritz

☐ NEW HORIZONS
Never had it so good / Look at us / Take your memory with you / Strings that tie you down / Darlin' / Wind beneath my wings / Orange blossom special / Mississippi / How do / Till each tear becomes a rose / You'll never get to heaven (if you break my heart) / Take a love off my mind / Heartaches by the number / Sarah's dream
RZCD 0067 / May '92 / Ritz

☐ WEB OF LOVE
Before I call it love / Even then / Candle burning / If I love you / Every time / Binding me like a chain / Web of love / When you walk in the room / Over you / Even a fool / Two sparrows in a hurricane / Who's crying now / On the way to a dream / Real slow / Stop playing with my heart
RZCD 0073 / Jul '94 / Ritz

Jo's All Stars

☐ BRIXTON CAT
CDTBL 106 / Aug '96 / Trojan

Jose, Don

☐ FLAMENCO FIESTA
Bamboleo / Amor / Welcome to my heart (La felicidad) / Ave Maria no morro / Djobi djoba / Lola from Barcelona / A mi manera (comme d'habitude) / Munira munira munira / Quando caliente el sol (love me with all of your heart) / Costa brava / Me va me va / San Jose / Tu quieres volver / Guantanamera / Maria Isabel / El Porompompero / Annabel
303362 / Jun '98 / Hallmark

Josef K

☐ ENDLESS SOUL
MA 40 / 31 Aug '98 / Marina

Joseph

☐ STONED AGE MAN
8252128 / 1 Jun '98 / EVA

Joseph, Bradley

☐ RAPTURE
Lover's return / Feel / Jewel / Healing the hollow man / Blue rock road / Robbin's Island / Stray / Stolen kiss / Gallery / Passage / Storyteller / Coastal highway / Be still
ND 63038 / Apr '97 / Narada

Joseph, David

☐ BRITISH HUSTLE (The Best Of David Joseph & Hi-Tension) (Joseph, David & Hi-Tension)
You can't hide (your love from me) / Hi-tension / Joys of life / Funktified / British hustle / There's a reason / Let's live it up (Nite people) / Latin inspiration / You're my girl / Discover / Expansions '86 expand your mind / Power and lighting / Peace on earth / You can't hide (your love from me)
5527372 / 4 May '98 / Spectrum

Joseph, Julian

☐ LANGUAGE OF TRUTH, THE
Miss Simmons / Language of truth / Don't chisel the shisel / Art of the calm / Wash house / Other side of town / High priestess / Magical one / Brothers of the bottom row / Tyrannosaurus Rex / Ode to the time our memories forgot
9031751222 / Dec '96 / East West

☐ LIVE AT THE WIGMORE HALL
All through the night / Cat / Soul eyes / Soft shoe for thad / Solo medley reality these foolish things just one / Maiden voyage / Just friends / Hard cash
0630113702 / Dec '96 / East West

☐ REALITY
Bridge to the south / Body and soul / Easy for you to say / Look out for love / Dance in a perfect world / Swingstone / Empty dream / Reality / Jean-ee-t / Creation constellation / Whispering dome / My desire
4509930242 / Dec '96 / East West

Joseph, Margie

☐ MAKES A NEW IMPRESSION/PHASE II
Women talk / Stop in the name of love / Punish me / Medicine bend / Come tomorrow / Sweeter tomorrow / Same thing / How beautiful the rain / I'm fed up / Make me believe you'll stay / Temptation's about to take your love / That other woman got my man and gone / My world is empty without you / I'll always love you / Strung out / Please don't stop loving me / I love you too much to say goodbye / Didn't have to tell me / Takin' all the love I can
CDSXD 097 / Jul '93 / Stax

Joseph, Martyn

☐ FULL COLOUR BLACK AND WHITE
GRACD 222 / May '97 / Grapevine

☐ MARTYN JOSEPH
Change your world / Gift to me / Between the raindrops / Talk about it in the morning / Everything in heaven comes apart / Home to you / If I should fall / If heaven's waiting / Condition of my heart / Cardiff bay / Carried in sunlight
4806572 / Jul '95 / Epic

☐ TANGLED SOULS
GRACD 236 / 18 May '98 / Grapevine

Josette

☐ JOSETTE
ESM 025 / 2 Mar '98 / Escape

Josetxo Goia-Aribe

☐ AUNAMENDI
TX 014CD / 1 Jun '98 / Karonte

Josey Wales

☐ COWBOY STYLE
GRELCD 198 / Feb '94 / Greensleeves

Joshi, Pandit Bhimsen

☐ IN CELEBRATION VOL.1
NRCD 0075 / Feb '97 / Navras

☐ IN CELEBRATION VOL.2
Vilambit khyal / Drut khyal / Raga shankara
NRCD 0086 / Nov '97 / Navras

☐ IN CELEBRATION VOL.3
Vilambit khyal / Drut khyal / Bhajan / Raga bhairavi
NRCD 0087 / Nov '97 / Navras

☐ RAGA BHAIRAV (Joshi, Pandit Bhimsen & Dr M. Krishna)
Alap / Drut khyal
NRCD 0088 / Nov '97 / Navras

☐ VOCAL
MR 1002 / Apr '95 / Moment

Joshua

☐ SURRENDER
Surrender love / Heart full of soul / Your love is gone / Hold on / Back to the rock / Rockin' the world / Stay alive / Loveshock / Reprise
WKFMXD 64 / Mar '86 / FM

Josi, Christian

☐ I WALKS WITH MY FEET OFF THE GROUND
Just in time / Whenever I take my sugar to tea / This time the dreams on me / Let's get lost / Sleepin' bee / Watch what happens / You've met your match / Azure te / Nightingale sang in Berkley square / Whenever that gal comes around / Gotta be this or that / Girl of my dreams / I concentrate on you / Forgetful / Birth of the blues / Party's over
CHECD 00111 / Aug '94 / Master Mix

Jouissance

☐ INFERNAL NEBULA
MHCD 019 / Jul '94 / Minus Habens

Journey

☐ CAPTURED
Majestic / Where were you / Just the same way / Line of fire / Lights / Stay awhile / Too late / Dixie highway / Feeling that way / Anytime / Do you recall / Walks like a lady / La do da / Lovin' touchin' squeezin' / Squeezin' / Wheel in the sky / Anyway you want it / Party's over
4866612 / Nov '96 / Columbia

☐ DEPARTURE
Anyway you want it / Walks like a lady / Someday soon / People and places / Pecious time / Where were you / I'm cryin' / Line of fire / Departure / Good morning girl / Stay a while / Homemade love
4866672 / Nov '96 / Columbia

☐ ESCAPE
Don't stop believin' / Stone in love / Who's crying now / Keep on running / Still they ride / Escape / Lay it down / Dead or alive / Mother, Father / Open arms
4866622 / Nov '96 / Columbia

☐ EVOLUTION
Too late / Lovin' touchin' squeezin' / City of the angels / When you're alone it ain't easy / Sweet and simple / Lovin' you is easy / Just the same way / Do you recall / Daydream / Lady Luck / Majestic
4866662 / Nov '96 / Columbia

☐ FRONTIERS
Separate ways / Send her my love / Chain reaction / After the fall / Faithfully / Edge of the blade / Troubled child / Back talk / Frontier / Rubicon
4866632 / Nov '96 / Columbia

☐ GREATEST HITS
Only the young / Don't stop believin' / Wheel in the sky / Faithfully / I'll be alright without you / Anyway you want it / (Ask) the lonely / Who's crying now / Separate ways / Lights / Lovin' touchin' squeezin' / Open arms / Girl can't help it / Send her my love / Be good to yourself
4631492 / Apr '96 / Columbia

☐ GREATEST HITS LIVE
Don't stop believin' / Separate ways (worlds apart) / After the fall / Lovin' touchin' squeezin' / Faithfully / Who's crying now / Any way you want it / Lights / Stay awhile / Open arms / Send her my love / Still they ride / Stone in love / Escape / Line of fire / Wheel in the sky
4897032 / 6 Apr '98 / Columbia

☐ INFINITY
Lights / Feeling that way / Anytime / La do da / Patiently / Wheel in the sky / Somethin' to hide / Winds of March / Can do / Open the door
4866652 / Nov '96 / Columbia

☐ JOURNEY
Of a lifetime / In the morning day / Kohoutek / To play some music / Topaz / In my lonely feeling/ conversations
4778542 / Oct '94 / Columbia

☐ RAISED ON RADIO
Girl can't help it / Positive touch / Suzanne / Be good to yourself / Once you love somebody / Happy to give / Raised on radio / I'll be alright without you / It could have been you / Eyes of a woman / Why can't this night go on forever
4866642 / Nov '96 / Columbia

☐ TIME (3CD Set)
Of a lifetime / Kohoutek / I'm gonna leave you / Cookie Duster and Nickel and Dime / For you / Velvet curtains/ Feeling that way / Anytime / Patiently / Good times / Majestic / Too late / Sweet and simple / Just the same way / Little girl / Anyway you want it / Someday soon / Good morning girl / Where you were / Line of fire / Homemade love / Natural thing / Lights / Stay awhile / Walks like a lady / Lovin' touchin' squeezin' / Dixie highway / Wheel in the sky / Party's over (Hopelessly in love) / Don't stop believin' / Stone in love / Keep on running / Who's crying now / Still they ride / Open arms / Mother, Father / La raza del sol / Only solutions / Liberty / Separate ways (Worlds apart) / Send her my love / Faithfully / After the fall / All that really matters / Eyes of a woman / Why can't this night go on forever / Once you love somebody / Happy to give / Be good to yourself / Only the young / Ask the lonely / With a tear / Into your arms / Girl can't help it / I'll be alright without you
C3K 65159 / 6 Apr '98 / Columbia

☐ TRIAL BY FIRE
Message of love / One more / When you love a woman / If he should break your heart / Forever in blue / Castles burning / Don't be down on me baby / Still she cries / Colours of the spirit / When I think of you / Easy to fall / Can't tame the lion / It's just the rain / Trial by fire / Baby I'm leaving you
4852642 / Oct '96 / Columbia

Journeyman

☐ JOURNEYMAN
NTONELP 24 / Aug '97 / Ntone

☐ NATIONAL HIJINX
National hijinx / National hijinx / Rusty beats / Spy / 50cc / Tuft ER / Sloath / Eugo lana box / Sonny / Biscuits / Dargfrog
NTONECD 024 / 29 Sep '97 / Ntone

☐ NEW IDOL SON
RED 005 / Jun '93 / Redemption

Journeymen

☐ WANDERLUST
CDLDL 1235 / Nov '95 / Lochshore

Joy Division

☐ ALL THE LYRICS (CD/Book Set)
You're no good for me / Komakino / Incubation / Incubation
SB 10 / 23 Feb '98 / Sonic Book

☐ CEREMONIAL (A Tribute To Joy Division) (Various Artists)
EFA 064982 / Mar '96 / Tess

☐ HEART AND SOUL (4CD Set)
Digital / Glass / Disorder / Day of the Lords / Candidate / Insight / New dawn fades / She's lost control / Shadow play / Wilderness / Interzone / I remember nothing / Ice age / Exercise one / Transmission / Novelty / Kill / Only mistake / Soemthing must break / Autosuggestion / From safety to where / Sound of music / Atmosphere / Dead souls / Komakino / Incubation / Atrocity exhibition / Colony / Passover / Isolation / Means to an end / Heart and soul / Twenty four hours / Eternal / Decades / Love will tear us apart / These days / Warsaw / No love lost / Leaders of men / Failures / Drawback / Interzone / Sahdowplay / Exercise one / Glass / Transmission / Dead souls / Something must break / Ice age / Walked in line / These days / Candidate / Only mistake / Chance / Love will tear us apart / Colony / As you said / Ceremony / In a lonely place / Dead souls / Only mistake / Insight / Candidate / Wilderness / She's lost control / Disorder / Interzone / Atrocity exhibition / Novelty / Auto suggestion / I remember nothing / Colony / These days / Incubation / Eternal / Heart and soul / Isolation
8289682 / 8 Dec '97 / London

☐ MEANS TO AN END, A (The Music Of Joy Division) (Various Artists)
She's lost control: *Girls Against Boys* / Day of Lords: *Honeymoon Switch* / New dawn fades: *Moby* / Transmission: *Low* / Atmosphere: *Codeine* / Insight: *Further* / Love will tear us apart: *Stanton-Miranda* / Isolation: *Starchildren* / Heart and soul: *Smith, Kendra* / Twenty four hours: *Versus* / Warsaw: *Desert Storm* / They walked in line: *Godheadsilo* / Interzone: *Face To Face* / As you said: *Tortoise*
CDHUT 29 / Oct '95 / Hut

☐ PERMANENT
Love will tear us apart / Transmission / She's lost control / Shadow play / Day of the lords / Isolation / Passover / Heart and soul / Twenty four hours / These days / Novelty / Dead souls / Only mistake / Something must break / Atmosphere
8286242 / Jun '95 / London

☐ SUBSTANCE (1977 - 1980)
She's lost control / Dead souls / Atmosphere / Love will tear us apart / Warsaw / Leaders of men / Digital / Transmission / Autosuggestion
5200142 / Jul '93 / London

Joyce

☐ DELIRIOS DE ORFEU
BOM 03CD / Jul '96 / Backbeat

☐ ESSENTIAL JOYCE 1970-1996
Caqui / Nada sera como antes / Adeus Maria Fulo / Man from the avenue / Historia do Smaba / JOYA / Pelo telefone / Pede passagem / Acorda amor / Viola fora de moda / Passarinho / Clareana / Aldeia de ogum / Banana / Feminina / Magica / Samba de gago / Beiro Rio / Docura forte/Agua e luz / Baracumbara / Curioso / Fa da bahia / Rodando a baiana
MRBCD 009 / 17 Nov '97 / Mr. Bongo

☐ TARDES CARIOCAS
Barracumbarra / Tardes cariocas / Duas ou tres coisas / Luz do chao / Curioso / Nuvem / Nacoional kid / Ela / Sour
FARO 0016CD / Jul '97 / Far Out

Joykiller

☐ 3
What it's worth / She's something else / Doorway / Ordinary / Another girl / Love you now / Your girlfriend / Supervision / Know it all / Promises / Anyone but you / Sex attack / Record collection / Make love to you / Once more
65022 / 20 Oct '97 / Epitaph

☐ JOYKILLER
864512 / Apr '95 / Epitaph

☐ STATIC
864662 / Jul '96 / Epitaph

Joyland

☐ SUN
NBX 014 / Jul '95 / Noisebox

Joyner, Bruce

☐ HOT GEORGIA NIGHTS
ROSE 129CD / Dec '87 / New Rose

Joyner, Simon

☐ CHRISTINE EP
SC 21CD / 17 Aug '98 / Secretly Canadian

Joyrider

☐ BE SPECIAL
Fabulae / Strike sparks everywhere / That tired / Said she to me / Bible blackbelt / I cursed you / Nobody home / Another skunk song / Vegetable animal mineral / I don't give in / Are you sure you're alright / Imagine dead language
PDOXCD 005 / Aug '96 / Paradox

☐ SKID SOLO
Skid solo / Chop logic / What you think of me / Learn the ropes / Whole reason / Confession / Mongoose / Tonight is stolen / Day in the sun / Growing pains / Hub of the north / Wise is nice / Devil you know / Hit for fun
5407402 / May '97 / A&M

Joystick

☐ HEAVY CHEVY
LOB 10005 / Apr '97 / Lobster/Fat Wreck Chords

JP Nystroms

☐ STOCKHOLM 1313KM
Spel nisses vals / Forsbergs polka / Matalan torpan balladi / Pojkarna pa landsvagen / Hambomazurka efter Blomqvistaru / Polska fran 1814 / Oceanangaren Titanics undergang / Sankte per / Tre broder / Kadrilj fran haparanda / Menuett fran oravais / Taitaa tulla / Lekande toner / Sa mork ar bimlen / Till havs i motorbat / Friarpolka fran Leipojarvi / Bjorn dansen
RESCD 514 / Jul '97 / Resource

☐ THA
RES 514CD / Aug '96 / Resource

JPP

☐ KAUSTINEN RHAPSODY
OMCD 53 / Dec '94 / Olarin Musiiki Oy

Jr. & His Soulettes

☐ PSYCHODELIC SOUNDS
SH 954 / Jun '97 / Shaft

JSD Band

☐ FOR THE RECORD
Sarah Jane / As I roved out / Cuckoo / Irish girl/ Musical priest / Groundhog / Johnny O'Breadislea / Sunshine hornpipe/The mountain road / Darlin' Corey / Galway races / Goin' down the road / Don't think twice / Down the road / Morrison's jig/Cooley's reel / Over and over
CDLDL 1256 / May '97 / Lochshore

☐ PASTURES OF PLENTY
Bonnie lass of Albany / Medley / Pastures of plenty / Downfall of Paris/Chanter's tune / Shake loose the border / Medley / Patrick's island / Gypsie laddie / Medley / Shady grove / Rodney's glory/An spalpeen fanach / Spanish lady
CDLDL 1274 / May '98 / Lochshore

Ju Ju Space Jazz

☐ SHLOOP
MP 11CD / 26 Jan '98 / Matsuri

Jubelklaenge

☐ 200 YEARS OF THE BAD BLEIBERG BRASS BAND
322766 / Oct '92 / Koch

Juber, Laurence

☐ LAURENCE JUBER
BEST 1081CD / Feb '96 / Acoustic Music

Jubilee All Stars

☐ SUNDAY MISCELLANY
LAKCD 009 / 15 Jun '98 / Lakota

Jubilee Gospel Team

☐ JUBILEE GOSPEL TEAM AND THE DEEP RIVER PLANTATION SINGERS (Jubilee Gospel Team & The Deep River Plantation Singers)
DOCD 5519 / Mar '97 / Document

Jubilee Hummingbirds

☐ GUILTY OF SERVING GOD (Jubilee Hummingbirds & James Carr)
God is worthy to be praised / Guilty of serving God / My soul is satisfied / He'll be there / Jesus changed me / Doin' the best I can / In the name of Jesus / Where Jesus is / Jordan river
CDCHM 611 / Jul '95 / Ace

Juck's Incorporation

☐ JUCK'S INCORPORATION VOL.1
SOCD 50109 / 2 Feb '98 / Studio One

Judah, Levi

☐ CREATION TRODDING (Nyabinghi)
ROTCD 013 / May '97 / Reggae On Top

Judas Iscariot

☐ OF GREAT ETERNITY
ER 03CD / 22 Jun '98 / Elegy

Judas Priest

☐ BEAST OF JUDAS PRIEST, THE
Dying to meet you / Never satisfied / Rocka rolla / Diamonds and rust / Victim of changes / Island of domination / Ripper / Deciever / One for the road / Dreamer deceiver / Run of the mill / Prelude / Caviar and meths / Epitaph / Tyrant / Genocide
10242 / Oct '97 / Go On Deluxe

☐ COLLECTION, THE
One for the road / Rocka rolla / Winter / Deep freeze / Winter retreat / Cheater / Never satisfied / Run of the mill / Dying to meet you / Victim of changes / Ripper / Dream deceiver / Prelude / Tyrant / Genocide / Epitaph / Island of domination
CCSCD 213 / Apr '89 / Castle

☐ CONCERT CLASSICS
Hell bent for leather / Ripper / Running wild / Living after midnight / Sinner / Beyond the realms of death / You don't have to be old to be wise / Grinder / Victim of changes / Steeler / Genocide / Tyrant / Green manalishi
CRANCH 3 / 29 Jun '98 / Ranch Life

☐ HERO HERO
Dreamer deceiver / Deceiver / Winter / Deep freeze / Winter retreat / Cheater / Diamonds and rust / Run of the mill / Genocide / Caviar and meths / Prelude / Tyrant / Rocka rolla / One for the road / Victim of changes / Dying to meet you / Never satisfied
CSAPCD 119 / Jul '95 / Connoisseur Collection

☐ JUGULATOR
SPV 08518782 / Nov '97 / SPV

☐ LIVING AFTER MIDNIGHT
Better by you, better than me / Take on the world / Green Manalishi / Living after midnight / Breaking the law / United / Hot rockin' / You've got another thing comin' / Hellion/Electric eye / Freewheel burning / Some heads are gonna roll / Turbo lover / Locked in / Johnny B Goode / Ram it down / Painkiller / Touch of evil / Night crawler
4872422 / Apr '97 / Columbia

☐ METAL WORKS 1973-1993 (2CD Set)
Hellion / Electric eye / Victim of changes / Painkiller / Eat me alive / Devil's child / Dissident aggressor / Delivering the goods / Exciter / Breaking the law / Hell bent for leather / Blood red skies / Metal gods / Before the dawn / Turbo lover / Ram it down / Metal meltdown / Screaming for vengeance / You've got another thing comin' / Beyond the realms of death / Solar angels / Bloodstone / Desert plains / Wild nights, Hot and Crazy Days / Heading out to the highway / Living after midnight / Touch of Evil / Rage / Night comes down / Sinner / Freewheel burning / Night crawler
4730502 / Oct '95 / Columbia

☐ PRIEST...LIVE
Out in the cold / Heading out to the highway / Metal gods / Breaking the law / Love bites / Some heads are gonna roll / Sentinel / Private property / Rock you all around the world / Electric eye / Turbo lover / Freewheel burning / Parental guidance / Living after midnight / You've got another thing comin'
4506392 / 2 Feb '98 / Columbia

☐ ROCKA ROLLA
One for the road / Rocka rolla / Winter / Deep freeze / Winter retreat / Cheater / Never satisfied / Run of the mill / Dying to meet you / Caviar and meths
30072 / Oct '97 / Go On Deluxe

☐ SAD WINGS OF DESTINY
Victim of changes / Ripper / Dreamer deceiver / Deceiver / Prelude / Tyrant / Genocide / Epitaph / Island of domination
30062 / Oct '97 / Go On Deluxe

☐ SIN AFTER SIN
Sinner / Diamonds and rust / Starbreaker / Last rose of summer / Let us prey / Call for the priest / Raw deal / Here come the tears / Dissident aggressor
4746842 / Feb '97 / Epic

☐ TRIBUTE TO JUDAS PRIEST VOL.1 (Various Artists)
CM 77115CD / Jun '96 / Century Media

☐ TRIBUTE TO JUDAS PRIEST VOL.2 (Various Artists)
CM 77125CD / Sep '96 / Century Media

☐ TRIBUTE TO JUDAS PRIEST, A (Various Artists)
CM 77169CD / Mar '97 / Century Media

☐ TYRANT (The Original Masters)
Rocka rolla / Run of the mill / Victim of the changes / Ripper / Prelude / Tyrant / Epitaph / Island of the domination / Diamonds and rust / One for the road / Deceiver / Dreamer deceiver / Never satisfied
EURCD 401 / 24 Aug '98 / Eureka

Judd, Cledus T.

☐ DID I SHAVE MY BACK FOR THIS
RE 82835 / 24 Mar '98 / Razor & Tie

Judd, Wynonna

☐ GREATEST HITS
No one else on earth / Making my way / Somebody to love / Change the world / Heaven help my heart / Healing / Rock bottom / To be loved by you / Father and son / Free bird / Let's make a baby king / Girls with guitars / Only love / I saw the light / She is his only need / My strongest weakness / Is it over yet / Tell me why
CURCD 041 / Apr '97 / Curb

☐ OTHER SIDE, THE (Wynonna)
CURCD 047 / 3 Nov '97 / Hit

☐ WYNONNA
What it takes / She is his only need / I saw the light / My strongest weakness / When I reach the place I'm goin' / No one else on Earth / It's never easy to say goodbye / Little bit of love (goes a long long way) / All of that love from here / Live with Jesus
4716712 / May '92 / Curb

Judds

☐ ESSENTIAL JUDDS, THE
Had a dream / John Deere tractor / Mama he's crazy / Why not me / Girls' night out / Lazy country evening / Rockin' with the rhythm of the rain / Grandpa (tell me 'bout the good old days) / Turn it loose / Sweetheart gift / Don't be cruel / Working in the coalmine / Old pictures / Guardian angels / Give a little love to me / More fun than the law allows / One little teardrop / Born to be blue / Love can build a bridge / Don't you hear Jerusalem moan
74321666802 / Feb '96 / RCA

☐ JUDDS COLLECTION, THE
CURCD 024 / May '96 / Curb

Judge

☐ NO APOLOGIES/CHUNG
LF 033CD / Apr '92 / Lost & Found

☐ WHAT WE SAID
LF 217CD / Nov '95 / Lost & Found

Judge Dread

☐ ...NEVER MIND, UP WITH THE COCK
Big 7 / Je t'aime (moi non plus) / Y viva suspenders / Dread rock/Will I what / Big 10 / Up with the cock / Lover's rock / Big 9 / Big 1 / Winkle man
QED 223 / Nov '96 / Tring

☐ 40 BIG ONES VOL.1
Lover's rock / This little piece of dinkle / Banana throat song / Confessions of a bouncer / Y'viva suspenders / Six wives of Dread / Donkey dick / Fatty dread / Oh she is a big girl now / Big 7 / Dread rock / My ding a ling / Rasta chat / Big 6 / Come outside / One eyed lodger / Belle of Snodland Town / Workers lament / Big 5 / Up with the cock / Big punk / Look a pussy / Dr. Kitch / Winkle man / Jamaica jerk off / Grandad's flannelette nightshirt / Move over darling / Will I what / Big 1 / Rudeness train / Bring back the skins / Take off your clothes / Christmas in Dreadland / Rhyme in time / What kung fu dat / Big 10 / Je t'aime / Dread's law / Trenchtown Billy / Big everything
RNCD 2001 / Jun '92 / Rhino

☐ 40 BIG ONES VOL.2
RNCD 2121 / Sep '95 / Rhino

☐ BEDTIME STORIES
Bedtime stories / J'taime / What a beautiful pair / Rudeness train / Six wives of dread / This little piece of dinkle / Last tango in snodland / Big ten / Trenchtown billy / Move over darling
RNCD 2013 / Jun '93 / Rhino

☐ BIG HITS
Big one / Rudeness is all in the mind / Big five / Je t'aime (moi non plus) / Big six / Winkle man / Big seven / Y viva suspenders / Big eight / Molly / Big nine / Come outside / Big ten / Bring back the skins / Biggest bean you ever seen / Rhyme in time / Big punk / Dreadrock / My ding a ling / Big everything
SUMCD 4088 / Jan '97 / Summit

☐ BIG ONES
CPCD 8341 / 1 Jun '98 / Charly

☐ BIG TWENTY FOUR, THE
CDTRL 333 / Feb '94 / Trojan

☐ DREAD WHITE AND BLUE
SKANKCD 012 / Jan '95 / Skank

☐ EARLY YEARS
EARLD 16 / Jan '95 / Dojo

☐ JUDGE DREAD VOL.1 & 2
LOMACD 19 / Aug '94 / Loma

☐ LAST OF THE SKINHEADS
Bring back the skins / A rhyme in time / Dread rock / Workers lament / Winkle man / Take it easy (but take it) / Come outside / Fatty dread / Y viva suspenders / Banana throat song / Bring back the skins (reprise)
RNCD 2023 / Oct '93 / Rhino

☐ SKA'D FOR LIFE
CDBM 110 / Jun '96 / Blue Moon

☐ VERY BEST OF JUDGE DREAD, THE
Big 6 / Big 7 / Big 8 / Je t'aime / Big 9 / Big 10 / Come outside / Bring back the skins / Winkle man / Y viva suspenders / Will I what / Jamaica jerkoff / Up with the cock / Lover's rock / Dread rock / Big 1
MCCD 040 / Sep '91 / Music Club

Judge Jules

☐ JOURNEYS BY DJ VOL.10 (2CD Set) (Various Artists)
JDJCD 10 / Mar '96 / JDJ

☐ SPERM BANK, THE (Various Artists)
Three minute warning: *Yum Yum* / Space grass: *Apply Within* / Livin' it up: *Yum Yum* / Headspace: *Yum Yum* / Bacchanal: *Scope* / Let me go: *Yum Yum* / Three minute warning: *Yum Yum* / Mind gap: *Yum Yum* / Inner space: *Boomerang* / So damn tuff: *Boomerang* / Free bass: *Yum Yum* / Funky cheeba: *Paradox* / Catch it: *Boomerang* / 5000 feet: *Apply Within* / Bacchanal: *Scope* / Loca motion: *Societe* / Pale drifter: *Societe* / Hypermania: *Yum Yum*
SPERM 2001 / Mar '97 / Sperm

Judith

☐ SAHARAH SEAS
AMPCD 002 / 27 Apr '98 / Resurrection

Juggernaut

☐ BLACK PAGODA
Shedding / Bitter / Decide / Difference / Green lightening / IO / Reality easel / Whisper / Make it so hard / Machine / Cry me a river / Master of pricks / Searchin' for a better high
N 02152 / Sep '94 / Noise

Juggling Suns

☐ LIVING ON THE EDGE OF CHANGE
SPV 08518942 / 3 Jul '98 / SPV

Jughead's Revenge

☐ 13 KIDDIE FAVOURITES
EFA 127222 / May '95 / Do It

☐ ELIMINATION
EFA 118722 / Mar '94 / Do It

☐ IMAGE IS EVERYTHING
158082 / Oct '96 / Nitro

☐ JUST JOINED
158162 / 30 Mar '98 / Nitro

Juhnke, Harald

☐ MIT BEIDEN HANDEN IN DEN TASCHEN
Ich glaube nicht / Von bar zu bar / Die fehler de ander'n / Mit ein paar blumen / Ich komm' mir vor / Ein whiskey zuviel / Zwischen nacht und morgen / Ich bin ich / Die wand zwischen dir und mir / Das sprachtalent / Was hast du schon davon, wenn du ein playboy bist / Beide hande in den taschen / Mr. Brown Maaison / Was nutzt das schlechte leben / Eine schoner als die an dere / Die Dolly von den folies bergere / Was mir an Paris so gefalt / Ach lass' doch bloss den blonden pianisten / Ich versetze berge / Mich nennen alle frauen cassanova / Die dame mit dem gift grunen schleier / Der schwarze Joe aus Idaho
BCD 15968 / Jul '96 / Bear Family

Juiceful Jazz

☐ BETWEEN THE CHAPTERS
EFA 127572 / Jul '95 / Juiceful

☐ STREETZ OF DESIRE
EFA 126012 / Aug '95 / Juiceful

Juicy Groove

☐ FIRST TASTE
GCR 012 / Sep '97 / GCR

Juicy Lucy

☐ BEST OF JUICY LUCY, THE
Who do you love / Midnight rider / Pretty woman / That woman's got something / Jessica / Willie the pimp/Le back and enjoy it / Changed my mind, changed my sign / Just one time / I'm a thief / Built for comfort / Mr. Skin / Mr. A. Jones / Future days / Chicago north western / Hello LA, bye bye Birmingham / Thinking of my life
NEXCD 105 / Mar '90 / Sequel

☐ BLUE THUNDER
Running blue / Fool to yourself / Win or lose / Woman of mine / Going back / Give me the news / Gin fizzer / Circle of light / Live with my blues / Lay down your arms
OM 1001CD / 3 Nov '97 / Outer Music

☐ HERE SHE COMES AGAIN
Pretty woman / Try my love / Who do you love / Voodoo child / Saturday night / Up to the tracks / Talk to me / Drug squad
HTDCD 28 / Sep '96 / HTD

☐ JUICY LUCY
OW 34433 / Nov '97 / One Way

☐ JUICY LUCY/LIE BACK AND ENJOY IT
Mississippi woman / Who do you love / She's mine / She's yours / Just one time / Chicago North Western / Train / Nadine / Are you satisfied / Thinking of my life / Built for comfort / Pretty woman / Whiskey in my jar / Hello LA, bye bye Birmingham / Changed my mind / That woman's got something / Willie the pimp / Lie back and enjoy it
BGOCD 279 / Jun '95 / Beat Goes On

☐ LIE BACK AND ENJOY IT/GET A WHIFF OF THIS
OW 34434 / Nov '97 / One Way

Juju

☐ THIS BUILDING IS ON FIRE
Home planet / New cleaner salt / Open space / Non multa (sed multum) / Off the deep end / Z head / Molehills / Plums / Jesus H / Sniff the bean
LPD 2 / 27 Jul '98 / Java

Jukon Speakers

☐ ELJEST
GRCD 014 / 23 Mar '98 / Garageland

☐ HIBERNATIONS
GRCD 004 / 23 Mar '98 / Garageland

Julian, Don

☐ HEAVEN AND PARADISE (Julian, Don & The Meadowlarks)
Heaven and paradise / Love only you / I got tore up / Untrue / Oop boopy oop / Devil or angel / Boogie woogie teenage / Blue moon / Please (say you love me) / Mine all mine / This must be paradise / Real pretty Mama / I am a believer / Big Mama wants to rock / Please love a fool / Thrill me night and day / LFMST Blues / Embarraising moments / Always and always / Doin' the cha cha / Pass the gin
CDCHD 552 / Aug '95 / Ace

Julian's Treatment

☐ TIME BEFORE THIS, A
First oracle / Coming of the mule / Phantom city / Black tower / Alda, dark lady of the outer worlds / Altarra, princess of the blue women / Second oracle / Twin suns of Centauri / Alkon, planet of Centauri / Terran / Fourth from the sun / Strange things / Time before this / Child of the night (1 and 2) / Stranger / Death of Alda / Cycles / Soldiers of time
SEECD 288 / Jan '90 / See For Miles

Julie Dolphin

☐ LIT
TIMBCD 602 / Mar '94 / Timbuktu

Julinho

☐ ACCORDEON DO BRASIL
BPE 107 / Nov '92 / Kardum

Juluka

☐ SCATTERLINGS OF JULUKA
Umfazi omdala / Impi / Siyayilanda / Zodwa / Scatterlings of africa / Unkosibomvu-the red king / December african rain / African sky blue / Walima mabele / Ibhola lethu / Sonqoba / Fever / Scatterlings of juluka
SHAKACD 2 / Sep '91 / Safari

July

☐ JULY
AFT 1004 / 2 Mar '98 / Aftermath

July, Miranda

☐ 10 MILLION MILES AN HOUR
KRS 281 / Sep '97 / Kill Rock Stars

☐ BINET-SIMON TEST, THE
KRS 296 / 22 May '98 / Kill Rock Stars

Juma, Issa

☐ SIGLAME VOL.2 (Juma, Issa & Les Wanyika)
Sigalame 2 / Money / Pole pole / Rafki uangu / Ateka / Sarah
AFRIZZ 008 / May '90 / Disc Afrique

Jumble Lane

☐ JUMBLE LANE
HBG 123/3 / Apr '94 / Background

Jumbo

☐ BEST OF JUMBO, THE (Turn On To Love)
HTCD 70 / 20 Apr '98 / Hot Productions

Jump

☐ LIVING IN A PROMISED LAND
Man who worked / Dreaming of angels / Promised man / December's moon / Promised man blues / April day / No time to kill / True to you / My magic touch / Used to the taste
CYCL 062 / 20 Apr '98 / Cyclops

☐ MYTH OF INDEPENDENCE, THE
Tower of babel / Princess of the people / On the wheel / Heaven and earth / Runaway / Keep the blues / Blind birds / Drivetime / Valediction / On my side / Shallow man
CYCL 027 / Sep '95 / Cyclops

Jump Cat Jump

☐ HOT ROCKIN'
RKCD 9601 / Nov '96 / Rockhouse

Jumpin' The Gunn

☐ SHADES OF BLUE
Cryin' blues / Green all over / Turtle blues / Crossed wires / More and more / Tired of tryin' / Shades of blue / Mind reader / Sweet Jesus / All I say to you
VPBCD 14 / Apr '93 / Pointblank

Jumping Jack Frost

☐ MIXMAG LIVE VOL.15 (Jumping Jack Frost/Randall) (Various Artists)
MMLCD 015 / Jul '96 / Mixmag Live

Junaro, Emma

☐ SI DE AMOR SE TRATA
TUMICD 015 / '92 / Tumi

Junco Partners

☐ ALMOST LIVE
DSCD 0196 / Dec '97 / Dancing Shoe

Juncosa, Sylvia

☐ NATURE
SST 146CD / Jun '93 / SST

Junction

☐ SWINSSET
RED 014CD / Jan '94 / Redemption

June

☐ I AM BEAUTIFUL
BBQCD 181 / Apr '96 / Beggars Banquet

June Brides

☐ JUNE BRIDES 1983-1986
OVER 40CD / Jan '95 / Overground

June Of 44

☐ ENGINE TAKES TO THE WATER
QS 32CD / Jun '95 / Quarter Stick

☐ FOUR GREAT POINTS
QS 54CD / 26 Jan '98 / Quarter Stick

☐ TROPICS AND MERIDIANS
QS 44CD / Jun '96 / Quarter Stick

June Panic

☐ FALL OF THE ATOM (A Thesis On Antropy)
SC 9 / 20 Apr '98 / Secretly Canadian

Jung Collective

☐ ANORAKOPHOBE
KA 002 / 23 Feb '98 / Kabal

Jungle Brothers

☐ DONE BY THE FORCES OF NATURE
Beyond this world / Feelin' alright / Sunshine / What U waitin' 4 / U make me sweat / Acknowledge your own history / Belly dancin' Dina / Good newz comin' / Done by the forces of nature / Beeds on a string / Tribe vibes / J Beez comin' through / Black woman / In dayz 2 come / Doin' our own dang / Kool accordin' 2 a Jungle Brother
7599263642 / Aug '90 / Warner Bros.

☐ J BEEZ WIT THE REMEDY
Forty below trooper / Book of rhyme pages / My Jimmy weighs a ton / Good ole hype shit / Blahbludify / Spark a new flame / I'm in love with Indica / Simple as that / All I think about is you / Good lookin' out / J Beez comin' through / Spittin wicked randomness / For the headz at company Z / Man made material
7599266792 / Jun '93 / Warner Bros.

☐ RAW DELUXE
GEE 1000282 / May '97 / Gee Street

☐ RAW DELUXE
GEE 1000280 / 11 May '98 / Gee Street

☐ STRAIGHT OUT THE JUNGLE
Straight out of the jungle / What's going on / Black is black / Jimbrowski / I'm gonna do you / I'll house you / On the run / Behind the bush / Because I like it like that / Braggin' and boastin' / Sounds of the safari / Jimmy's bonus beats
GEE 1002832 / 27 Jul '98 / Gee Street

Jungr & Parker

☐ CANADA
Canada / Nothing through the letterbox today / One step away from my heart / Nights in a suitcase / 21 years / Chosen one / Walking wounded / It's not there / You can't win 'em all / End of the line / Whatever you do / Al fresco / That's what friends are for
HARCD 023 / Oct '93 / Harbour Town

Junior Detroit

☐ TAKE OUT THE TIME
BLUS 109CD / Mar '98 / Blue Suit

Junior Gone Wild

☐ PULL THE GOALIE
TX 2011CD / Jan '94 / Taxim

☐ TOO DUMB TO QUIT
SP 1160CD / Oct '93 / Stony Plain

Junior High

☐ KILLER OF FRIENDSHIPS
MTR 365CD / 16 Mar '98 / Empty

Junior MAFIA

☐ CONSPIRACY
Intro / White chalk / Excuse me / Realms of Junior MAFIA / Players anthem / I need you tonight / Get money / I've been... / Crazaay / Backstabbers / Oof / Lyrical wizardry / Oh my Lord / Murder one / Outro
7567926142 / Sep '95 / Atlantic

Junior Varsity

☐ TAKING CARE OF YOU (Bliss Out Vol.10)
DRL 056CD / 16 Mar '98 / Darla

Junk Head

☐ ADDICTION
JUNKCD 001 / Nov '95 / Punk

Junk Monkeys

☐ BLISS
CDZORRO 51 / Aug '92 / Metal Blade

Junkera, Kepa

☐ KALEJIRA AL-BUK
KDCD 386 / May '97 / Elkar

☐ LAU ESKUTARA (Junkera, Kepa & Julio Pereira)
KD 428CD / Nov '96 / Elkar

Junkie XL

☐ SATURDAY TEENAGE KICKS
RR 87922 / 8 Dec '97 / Roadrunner

Junkster

☐ JUNKSTER
07863674672 / 11 May '98 / RCA

Junkyard Dogs

☐ GOOD LIVIN' PLATTER
SFTRI 246CD / Jun '97 / Sympathy For The Record Industry

Juno Reactor

☐ BEYOND THE INFINITE
BR 009CD / Mar '97 / Blue Room Released

☐ BIBLE OF DREAMS
BR 042CD / Jun '97 / Blue Room Released

☐ TRANSMISSIONS
NOMU 24CD / Sep '93 / Mute

Jupiter Affect

☐ JUPITER AFFECT, THE
AF 008CD / 13 Jul '98 / Aerial Flip

Jura Ceilidh Band

☐ JURA CEILIDH BAND
LDLCD 1240 / Jun '96 / Lochshore

Jurado, Damien

☐ WATERS AVES
SPCD 374 / 1 Sep '97 / Sub Pop

Jurassic 5

☐ JURASSIC 5
In the flesh / Quality control part II / Jayou / Lesson 6 / Concrete schoolyard / Setup / Action satisfaction / Sausage gut / Improvise / Blacktop beat / Without a doubt / Lesson 6 (reprise) / Cuts and scratches / Action satisfaction dub
PAN 015CD / 1 Jun '98 / Pan

Jurie, Renat

☐ ENTRE LA RIVIERA ET LA MER
Y225025 / Jun '93 / Silex

Juris, Vic

☐ MOONSCAPE
SCCD 31402 / Apr '97 / Steeplechase

☐ NIGHT TRIPPER
SCCD 31353 / Sep '95 / Steeplechase

Juryman

☐ MAIL ORDER JUSTICE (Juryman & Spacer)
Prophet and the fool / Big future / Submersible / Mail order justice / Rerun / Sunk / Night of the sun / Personnel wanted / 6 Down / Blood / Masters of the unison / No prints no trace
SSR 185 / 20 Oct '97 / SSR

Just, Andy

☐ DON'T CRY
CCD 11044 / Nov '94 / Crosscut

Juster

☐ REMEMBER THAT NIGHT
CDVEST 48 / Apr '95 / Bulletproof

Justice

☐ VIEWPOINTS
HEMP 20CD / 13 Jul '98 / Recordings Of
Substance

Justice League Of Zion

☐ DISCOVERERS
CEND 1900 / Oct '94 / Century

Justice, Jimmy

☐ WHEN MY LITTLE GIRL IS SMILING/
BEST OF JIMMY JUSTICE
I understand / Bloodshot eyes / When love has left
you / Teacher / Little bit of soap / Little lonely one /
When my little girl is smiling / If I lost your love / Ain't
that funny / One / My one sin / Spanish harlem / Write
me a letter / Dawning / Too long will be too late / Early
in the morning / Hallelujah, I love her so / World of
lonely people / I wake up crying / Little cracked bell /
Guitar player / Don't let the stars get in your eyes /
Night has a thousand eyes / Save the last dance for
me / Tell her / Folk singer / Can't get used to losing
you / Up on the roof / You're gonna need my loving /
Since you've been gone / Only heartbreaks for me /
Everything in the garden
NEXCD 241 / Jun '93 / Sequel

Juvenia 2000

☐ HOT BRASS FOR MASSES
RMD 82245 / 21 Apr '98 / RMM

JVC Force

☐ DOIN' DAMAGE
MIL 20102 / Jun '97 / MIL Multimedia

K

K-Ci & Jo Jo
☐ LOVE ALWAYS
HBI / Last night's letter / Baby come back / Just for your love / Now and forever / Don't rush / You bring me up / Still waiting / Love ballad / How many times / All my life / How could you
MCD 11613 / 27 Apr '98 / MCA

K-Group
☐ K-GROUP
HERMES 023 / 29 Sep '97 / Corpus Hermeticum

K-Hand
☐ ART OF MUSIC, THE
K7R 014CD / 25 Aug '97 / Studio K7

☐ ON A JOURNEY
K7R 001CD / Oct '96 / Studio K7

☐ READY FOR THE DARKNESS
SUB 48362 / Mar '97 / Distance

☐ SOUL
EFA 063382 / May '97 / Ausfahrt

K-Jacks
☐ DOUBLE EXPOSURE
APR 019CD / Aug '97 / April

K-Klass
☐ REMIX AND ADDITIONAL PRODUCTION BY... (Various Artists)
Question: Seven Grand Housing Authority / Mama said: Anderson, Carleen / Caught in the middle/I want you: Roberts, Juliet / Rapture: Blondie / Two can play that game: Brown, Bobby / Ruined in a day: New Order / U: Clark, Loni / Lover: Roberts, Joe / Freedom: Shiva / When: Sunscreem / What do you want from me: Knuckles, Frankie / Hideaway: De'Lacy / Love rendezvous: M-People / Come on come on: Pearl
74321342082 / Mar '96 / De-Construction

☐ UNIVERSAL
1-2-3 / Rhythm is a mystery / Let me show you / Don't stop / Underground express / What you're missing / Taking me over / La cassa / Share your love / I can take some more
CDPCSD 149 / Dec '93 / EMI

K-Passa
☐ AFTER THE HEADRUSH
QP 6651CD / Sep '94 / Que-P

Kaaos
☐ TOTAL CHAOS
LF 130 / Mar '95 / Lost & Found

Kaapana, Ledward
☐ LED LIVE SOLO
DCT 38008CD / Mar '96 / Dancing Cat

Kaasa, Anne Karin
☐ SOLEFALLSTIME
FXCD 117 / Jul '93 / Kirkelig Kultuverksted

☐ SVALANDE VIND
FXCD 103 / Jul '93 / Kirkelig Kultuverksted

Kaasinen, Sari
☐ JOUKU JOULUN ALKKAA SAA (Kaasinen, Sari & Mari)
MIPU 205CD / Dec '93 / Mipu

☐ TSIHI TSIHI (Kaasinen, Sari & Sirmakka)
14753 / Nov '96 / F

Kabalas
☐ EYE OF ZOHAR
ID 123349CD / 22 Sep '97 / Dionysus

☐ MARTINIS AND BAGELS
ID 123343CD / Oct '96 / Dionysus

Kada, Cheb
☐ FROM ORAN TO PARIS
CHCD 64029 / Jul '91 / Shanachie

Kadekaru, Rinsho
☐ FOLK SONGS OF OKINAWA
VICG 53602 / Feb '96 / JVC World Library

Kadison, Joshua
☐ PAINTED DESERT SERENADE
Jessie / Painted desert serenade / Beau's all night radio love line / Invisible man / Mama's arms / Beautiful to my eyes / Picture postcards from LA / When a woman cries / Georgia rain
SBKCD 22 / May '95 / SBK

Kadotani, Michio
☐ ROTTEN TELEPATHIES
PSFD 14 / Sep '97 / PSF

Kadura
☐ FROM THE DEPTHS OF OUTER SPACE
CHCD 26 / Jul '98 / Charnel House

Kadwaladyr
☐ LAST HERO, THE
4133CD / Aug '96 / Musea

Kaempfert, Bert
☐ 20 EASY LISTENING CLASSICS
5294922 / Apr '96 / Polydor

☐ BLUE MIDNIGHT (Good Life Music Vol.1) (Kaempfert, Bert Orchestra)
5339072 / Jun '97 / Polydor

☐ EVERGREENS (2CD Set) (Kaempfert, Bert Orchestra)
5335552 / Jun '97 / Polydor

☐ ORANGE COLOURED SKY (Good Life Music Vol.3) (Kaempfert, Bert Orchestra)
5339092 / Jun '97 / Polydor

☐ SPANISH EYES
PDSCD 522 / Sep '96 / Pulse

☐ STRANGERS IN THE NIGHT (Good Life Music Vol.2) (Kaempfert, Bert Orchestra)
5339062 / Jun '97 / Polydor

☐ SWING (Good Life Music Vol.4) (Kaempfert, Bert Orchestra)
5339082 / Jun '97 / Polydor

☐ TROPICAL SUNRISE (Good Life Music Vol.5) (Kaempfert, Bert Orchestra)
5339052 / Jun '97 / Polydor

Kaham, Bente
☐ BENTE KAHAM & DI GOJIM (Kaham, Bente & Di Gojim)
MWCD 4021 / 1 Jun '98 / Music & Words

Kahn, Brenda
☐ DESTINATION ANYWHERE
SHCD 5708 / Jul '96 / Shanachie

☐ EPIPHANY IN BROOKLYN
I don't sleep, I drink coffee instead / Mojave winters / She's in love / Madonna / Mint juleps and needles / My lover / Sleepwalking / Lost / Great divide / Madagascar / Losing time / In Indiana
SHED 004CD / Aug '93 / Ball Product

☐ OUTSIDE THE BEAUTY SALON
SHCD 5721 / Apr '97 / Shanachie
332622 / May '98 / Koch

Kahn, Si
☐ COMPANION
APRCD 1020 / Nov '97 / Appleseed

☐ GOOD TIMES & BED TIMES
No more bedtimes / Eight o'clock midnight snack / I'm not gonna go to sleep / I can't hear my parents call / Under the bed / Brush to the north / You gotta have a peanut butter song / Bark in the dark / Babysitter / Will you remember / I'm gonna stay in the bathtub 'til the soap disappears / What's that noise / Underneath the covers with my flashlight on / One glass of water / Shine on / No more bedtimes (reprise)
ROUCD 8027 / Dec '93 / Rounder

☐ I HAVE SEEN FREEDOM
FF 70578 / Jul '92 / Flying Fish

☐ I'LL BE THERE
FF 70509 / Oct '89 / Flying Fish

☐ IN MY HEART
Gone gonna rise again / Aragon Mill / Mississippi river / Farewell to Ireland / Gentle with me darling / What you do with what you've got / Last good war / Senator / Brookside strike / Luray women / Children of Poland / What will I have / Cold frosty morning / Wild rose of the mountain / Rock me, roll me / Curtains of old Joe's house / People like you / Crossing the border / Welcome to the world / Detroit December / If I live / Lady of the harbour / In my heart
PH 1169CD / May '94 / Philo
SCR 33 / Mar '97 / Strictly Country

☐ NEW WOOD
PHCD 1168 / Oct '94 / Philo

Kahr, Jim
☐ BACK TO CHICAGO
BEST 1027CD / Nov '93 / Acoustic Music

Kahvas Jute
☐ WIDE OPEN
D 19791 / Oct '97 / Festival

Kaia
☐ KAIA
CHSW 14CD / Dec '96 / Chainsaw

☐ MR. LADYMAN
MRLR 01CD / 16 Feb '98 / Mr. Ladyman

Kaikini, Dinkar
☐ MUSIC OF NORTH INDIA
C 560113 / Dec '97 / Ocora

Kailash
☐ 7 CHAKRA (Kailash & Hermann Haindl)
SM 18152 / Nov '97 / Wergo

Kaiser, Henry
☐ ACOUSTICS
VICTOCD 025 / Oct '94 / Victo

☐ DEVIL IN THE DRAIN
Sugagaki for conlon / King of the wild frontier / Dark memory / Smokestack lightnin' / Roadside picnic / Free to choose / Lost horizons / Devil in the drain / If this goes on...
SST 118CD / May '93 / SST

☐ ETERNITY BLUE
SHCD 6016 / Dec '95 / Shanachie

☐ HEARTS DESIRE
Dark star / Rivers edge / Fishin' hole / Anyone who had a heart / Losing hand / Don't let a thief steal into your heart / Number 2 Klaviertuck III / Are you experienced / Lover / Flavor bud living / Ballad of Shane Muscatel / King Harvest (has surely come) / Black light / Buried treasure / Never again
CDRECK 19 / Jan '90 / Reckless

☐ IMPROVISED VANCOUVER (Kaiser, Henry & John Oswald)
INCUS 26CD / Mar '97 / Incus

☐ LEMON FRESH TWEEZER
RUNE 45 / Dec '89 / Cuneiform

☐ OUTSIDE ALOHA PLEASURE
DEX 8 / Dec '96 / Dexter's Cigar

☐ RE-MARRYING FOR MONEY
SST 222CD / May '93 / SST

☐ SWEET SUNNY NORTH (Kaiser, Henry & David Lindley)
SH 64057 / Nov '94 / Koch

☐ SWEET SUNNY NORTH VOL.2 (Kaiser, Henry & David Lindley)
SH 64061 / Nov '96 / Shanachie

☐ TOMORROW KNOWS WHERE YOU LIVE (Kaiser, Henry & Jim O'Rourke)
VICTOCD 014 / Nov '94 / Victo

☐ WIREWORKS (Kaiser, Henry & Derek Bailey)
SHAN 5011CD / Apr '95 / Shanachie

☐ WORLD OUT OF TIME VOL.1, A (Kaiser, Henry & David Lindley)
SHAN 64041CD / '92 / Shanachie

☐ WORLD OUT OF TIME VOL.2, A (Kaiser, Henry & David Lindley)
SHAN 64048CD / Aug '93 / Shanachie

Kaisers
☐ BEAT IT UP
Watcha say / Liquorice twist / She's gonna two time / Leave my kitten alone / I just don't understand / Watch your step / She's only doggin' around / Hippy hippy shake / Don't come back / Like I do / Loopy Lu / Theme from Vengeance / (Ain't that) just like me / Don't go with him / Let's stomp / You've got to keep her underhand
NOHITCD 017 / Apr '95 / No Hit

☐ SQUAREHEAD STOMP
Alligator twist / Some other guy / Soldiers of love / Uh huh oh yeah / Don't ask me / Hipshake shimmy kitten / I'm a hog for you / Valley of the Kaisers / Peanut butter / Don't believe him / Shimmy like my sister Kate / I can tell / You won't be satisfied / That's my girl / Love potion no.9 / Money (That's what I want)
GH 1049CD / 20 Jul '98 / Get Hip

☐ WISHING STREET
TAN 001CD / 1 Dec '97 / No Hit
NOHITCD 025 / 13 Apr '98 / No Hit

Kajagoogoo
☐ VERY BEST OF KAJAGOOGOO, THE
Big Apple / Charm of a gun / Too shy / Lion's mouth / Kajagoogoo / Ooh to be aah / Never ending story / White feathers / Do I / Lies and promises / Only for love / Hang on now / Shouldn't do that / Big Apple (remix) / Too shy (12" mix)
CDGOLD 1038 / Jul '96 / EMI Gold

Kala, Musa Dieng
☐ SHAKAWTU - FAITH
SH 64072 / Oct '96 / Shanachie

Kalabra
☐ KALABRA
CAP 21525CD / Aug '97 / Caprice

Kalaf, Jerry
☐ TRIO MUSIC (Kalaf, Jerry Group)
SBCD 3018 / Jun '96 / Sea Breeze

Kalaff, Luis
☐ MERENGUE
CDHOT 638 / 1 Jun '98 / Charly

Kalahari Surfers
☐ KALAHARI SURFERS VOL.1 1980'S
RERKS 1 / Oct '96 / ReR/Recommended

Kalaniemi, Maria
☐ IHO
Lomasaevel / Green score / Slingerdansin / Surin slimat / Iho / Triolopolska / Sofias flykt / Istunpa sankys laitalla / Sade / Linjarv / Napoleon
HNCD 1396 / Jan '97 / Hannibal

Kalaschjan
☐ RURAL & URBAN TRADITIONAL MUSIC FROM ARMENIA
SM 15052 / Jan '93 / Wergo

Kaldor, Connie
☐ SMALL CAFE
Someday / What do they know / If I was to tell you / Down to a river (Alan's song) / Coyote's call / Get lucky / Choppy water (rocky marriage breakdown) / I don't care / He's running in his sleep / Old friends (Mr. Settee's song) / Prairie moon / You want that dog
CDPH 1205 / Jul '97 / Philo

Kaleef
☐ 53RD STATE OF MIND
53rd state of mind / Golden brown / I like the way / City life / Down town / Sands of time / Millennium fever / Asiatik static / Group soup / Dunk ya donuts / If you don't know me / Trials of life / Case for the prosecution / Case for the defence / Verdict / Rest in peace
UNITY 500CD / 13 Oct '97 / Unity/Eastern Bloc

☐ SEVEN DEADLY SINS (Kaliphz)
Blood in blood out / Wass the deal / Bang bang boogie / Why im ez / Knockout position / Kloud 9 / Open up your mind / Rokk on shokk on / Sx horra vylence / Citi neva sleepz / Police n thievez / Eat the world / Kashflows / Props 2 tha thru skool
8286752 / Oct '95 / Payday

Kaleidoscope
☐ BEACON FROM MARS, A
I found out / Greenwood sidee / Life will pass you by / Taxim / Baldheaded end of a broom / Louisiana man / You don't love me / Beacon from mars
EDCD 532 / Aug '97 / Edsel

☐ BERNICE
Chocolate whale / Another love / Sneakin' thru the ghetto / To know is not to be / Lulu arfin nanny / Lie and hide / Ballad of Tommy Udo / Bernice / Soft and easy / New blue ooze
EDCD 534 / Aug '97 / Edsel

☐ BLUES FROM BAGDAD
Egyptian gardens / If the night / Please / Keep your mind open / Pulsating dream / Oh death / Why try / Rampe rampe / I found out / Life will pass you by / Greenwood side / Beacon from Mars / Lie to me / Petite fleur / Banjo / Nobody / Elevator man / Hello trouble / Cuckoo / Sweet ate sweet
EDCD 375 / Aug '93 / Edsel

☐ INCREDIBLE
Lie to me / Let the good love flow / Killing floor / Petite fleur / Banjo / Cuckoo / Seven ate sweet
EDCD 533 / Aug '97 / Edsel

☐ SIDE TRIPS
Egyptian gardens / If the night / Please / Keep your mind open / Pulsating dream / Oh death / Come on in / Why try / Minnie the moocher
EDCD 531 / Aug '97 / Edsel

Kaleidoscope

☐ DIVE INTO YESTERDAY
Dive into yesterday / Mr. Small the watch repair man / Flight from Ashiya / Murder of Lewis Tollani / (Further reflections) in the room of percussion / Dear Nellie Goodrich / Sky children / Dream for Julie / Faintly blowing / Poem / Snapdragon / Story from Tom Bitz / (Love song) for Annie / If you so wish / Opinion / Jenny Artichoke / Just how much you are / Bless the executioner / Black fjord / Feathered tiger / I'll kiss you once / Do it again for Jeffrey / Music
5340032 / Feb '97 / Fontana

☐ TANGERINE DREAM
Kaleidoscope / Please excuse my face / Dive into yesterday / Mr. Small, The watch repair man / Flight from Ashiya / Murder of Lewis Tollani / Further reflections in the room / Dear nelle goodrich / Holidaymaker / Lesson perhaps / Sky children
CDTD 2165 / Jul '97 / Fingerprint

☐ TANGERINE DREAM
RR 7074 / 3 Mar '98 / Repertoire

Kaleidoscope

☐ BEATZ 'N' PIECES
PNMCD 01 / Jun '97 / Pik 'n' Mix

Kalenda Maya

☐ ARMS OF THE GOD
PCOM 1126 / Sep '92 / President

☐ PILEGRIMSREISER
FX 184CD / Aug '97 / Kirkelig Kultuverksted

Kalin Twins

☐ WHEN
Sweet sweet sugar lips / Chicken chief / Oh my goodness / Jumpin' Jack / Clickety clack / Three o'clock thrill / Spider and the fly / No money can buy / When / Forget me not / Picture of you / Zing went the strings of my heart / Walkin' to school / Momma poppa / It's only the beginning / You mean the world to me
BCD 15597 / Feb '92 / Bear Family

Kalle, Pepe

☐ GIGANTAFRIQUE
Tiembe raid pa moli / Ce chale carnaval / Marche commun / Bilala lala / Pon moun paka bouge / Ndaka ya zeke
CDORB 062 / Jul '90 / Globestyle

Kallick, Kathy

☐ CALL ME A TAXI
Call me a taxi / Thoughts of love and home / Griddle in the middle / True happy home / Close by / Burying ground / Once is enough / Send me your address from Heaven / Old time's sake / My old clinch mountain home / Stronger cup
SHCD 3856 / Mar '98 / Sugar Hill

☐ MATTERS OF THE HEART
SHCD 3820 / Jan '94 / Sugar Hill

☐ USE A NAPKIN, NOT YOUR MOM
SHCD 3833 / May '95 / Sugar Hill

Kallmann, Gunter

☐ SERENADE (Kallmann, Gunter Choir)
Elizabethan serenade / Bei walzermusick / Annabelle / Musik zum verlieben / Glocken serenade / Der reigen / Traum melodie / La montanara / Glocken klingen zu den sternen / Serenade / Oh mein Papa / Serenade / Edelweiss / Somewhere my love / La mer / My cherie amour / Romantica / Strangers in the night / Daydream / Day the rains came
CDMOIR 518 / Oct '96 / Memoir

Kalmery, So

☐ RASMI
829222 / Oct '96 / BUDA

Kaloum Star

☐ FELENKO
829332 / Jan '97 / BUDA

Kalte Farben

☐ TRUST
EFA 112352 / Dec '94 / Danse Macabre

Kalyna Krasnaya

☐ AT NARODA
SYN 189CD / Nov '95 / Syncoop

Kam

☐ KAM
7567617542 / Mar '95 / Street Knowledge

☐ MADE IN AMERICA
Pull ya hoe card / Represent / Who ridin' / Nut'n nice / Down fa mine / Keep tha peace / Intro / Trust nobody / Way'a life / That's my nigga / Givin' it up / In traffic
7559617542 / Dec '95 / Street Knowledge

☐ NEVA AGAIN
Intro / Peace treaty / Stereotype / Still got love 4 'um / Hang 'um high / Drama / Neva again / Y'all don't hear me dough / Ain't that a bitch / Holiday madness / Watts riot / Outro
7567922082 / Mar '95 / Street Knowledge

Kamelot

☐ DOMINION
Ascension / Heaven / Rise again / One day I'll win / We are not seperate / Birth of a hero / Creation / Sin / Song of Roland / Crossing two rivers / Troubled mind
N 02722 / Nov '96 / Noise

☐ SIEGE PERILOUS
N 02972 / 25 May '98 / Noise

Kamen, Michael

☐ BRAZIL
74321111242 / Jun '96 / RCA

Kamikaze Ground Crew

☐ KAMIKAZE GROUND CREW
378552 / May '98 / Koch Jazz

☐ MADAME MARIE'S TEMPLE OF KNOWLEDGE
804382 / Sep '93 / New World

☐ SCENIC ROUTE, THE
NW 400 / Aug '92 / New World

Kaminsky, Bruce

☐ ANGELS SONG
64104700202 / 14 Jul '98 / DBK

Kaminsky, Max

☐ AT THE COPLEY TERRACE 1945 (Kaminsky, Max & Pee Wee Russell)
JCD 15 / Jun '96 / Jazzology

Kamkars

☐ LIVING FIRE, THE (Live In Paris)
122157 / Feb '96 / Long Distance

☐ NIGHTINGALE WITH A BROKEN WING
Kosha hawraman / Awaz / Larzan / Bolboly bal shkaw / Amine to golakamy / Shelereh / Dekay ambar, dekay auber / Kajawa
WSCD 009 / May '97 / Womad Select

Kamoze, Ini

☐ HERE COMES THE HOTSTEPPER
Call the police / Rough / Here comes the hotstepper / Gunshot / World-a-music / Trouble you trouble me / General / Pull up the cork / Pirate / Babylon Babylon / Burnin' / I want ital
4785362 / 2 Feb '98 / Columbia

☐ ORIGINAL HOT STEPPER
RRCD 49 / Jan '95 / Reggae Refreshers

☐ SHOCKING OUT
Cool it off / Clown talking / Cone now / Boss / We run the country / Shocking out / Revolution / Girl E / Hole in the pumpkin / Spread out
GRELCD 115 / Jan '95 / Greensleeves

Kampec Dolores

☐ RAPID
RERKD 1 / Jun '98 / ReR/ Recommended

Kampfar

☐ MELLOM SKOGKLEDDE AASER
MR 011CD / 22 Sep '97 / Malicious

Kamuca, Richie

☐ JAZZ EROTICA
FSCD 500 / Feb '88 / Fresh Sound

Kamusasadi, Vumvum

☐ MUZ ANGOLA
68971 / Apr '97 / Tropical

Kanabis The Edit Assassin

☐ DIGITAL CONTACT (The First Generation)
Detroit winter / Walk under a full moon's light / Home grown (The Chatam Ontario flavour) / Blunt intermission / Circus of the confused / Peace in Detroit / Native noise interlude / Venus / Phat 107 bpm / Dee and Angel / EFW interlude / Some funk / Dedication to my Grandma
K7R 011CD / May '97 / Studio K7

Kanchay

☐ MACHU PICCHU
TUMICD 011 / Apr '90 / Tumi

Kanda Bongo Man

☐ AMOUR YOU
HNCD 1337 / Jan '89 / Hannibal

☐ KWASSA-KWASSA
Sai / Cantique / Naloti / Lowazo / Lela lela / Bedy / Liza / Lisote / Belle amie / Ebeneza
HNCD 1343 / May '89 / Hannibal

☐ NON STOP NON STOP
Iyole / Ida / Djessy / Amina / Mazina
CDORB 005 / Mar '90 / Globestyle

☐ SANGO
795372 / Apr '96 / Melodie

☐ SOUKOUS IN CENTRAL PARK
Liza / Bedy / Yesu Christu / JT / Wallow / Luta / Sai / Lela lela
HNCD 1374 / Mar '93 / Hannibal

☐ WELCOME TO SOUTH AFRICA
320052 / Apr '96 / Melodie

☐ ZING ZONG
Zing zong / Isambie / Mosali / Wallow / Monie / Yonde love me / Yesu Christu / Freres soki / Kadhi
HNCD 1366 / Jul '91 / Hannibal

Kane, Candye

☐ HOME COOKIN'
ANT 0033CD / Sep '94 / Antones

Kane, Chet

☐ TEARS FOR COLUMBIA
GRCD 315 / Sep '91 / Glitterhouse

Kane, Eden

☐ ALL THE HITS AND MORE
CDSGP 0241 / Feb '96 / Prestige

☐ HITS ALBUM, THE
MOGCD 005 / Dec '94 / Moggie

☐ WELL I ASK YOU
8209662 / Jan '96 / Deram

☐ WELL I ASK YOU (His Greatest Hits)
Well I ask you / We could have had it all / Diana / Are you lonesome tonight / I think I died and went to Heaven / Lonely weekend / Forget me not / I've ever fallen out of love / Boys cry / You and me and the night / I don't know why / Sailing ships / Pullin' me thru the bad times / Get lost / Lovin' you / Most beautiful girl in the world
308232 / 13 Oct '97 / Hallmark

Kane Gang

☐ MOTORTOWN
Motortown / Amusement park / Smalltown creed / Brother brother / Mighty day / Crease in his hat / Giving up / Don't look any further / Finer place / Respect yourself / What time is it / Spend / It's a gift / King Street man
5501952 / Mar '94 / Spectrum

Kane, Kieran

☐ KIERAN KANE
This dirty little town / He never knew what hit him / Cool me down / Bell ringing in an empty sky / Je suis tres contendre / Ramblin' man / Eight more miles / It's not love / Find somebody new / So many miles / Love's gonna live here
DR 00012 / Dec '97 / Dead Reckoning

☐ SIX MONTHS NO SUN
Table top dancer / Kill the demon / Takin' up space / In a town this size / Physical thing / Foolish as that maybe / 48 and goal / What a wonderful world / Iwonder where you are tonight / Hysteria / Six months no sun / To move my heart / Je t'aime faire l'amour
DEAR 0008 / 9 Mar '98 / Dead Reckoning

Kane, Ray

☐ PUNAHELE
DCT 38001CD / Mar '96 / Dancing Cat

Kang, Eyvind

☐ THEATRE OF MINERAL NADES
TZA 7032 / 27 Apr '98 / Tzadik

Kangaroo Moon

☐ BAGPIPES ON THE BEACH
MS 117CD / Apr '94 / MediaQuest

☐ BELONGIL
KM 02CD / Jan '96 / Kangaroo Moon

☐ KEEP THEM WARM
Keep them warm / Five fingers of the seventh wave / Bela Lughoti / Sally Sandwich / Whirlimix / Reggae reels / Open ones/Don't forget to breath/Tunes
KM 03CD / Aug '96 / Kangaroo Moon

Kankawa

☐ B III
St. Louis blues / Stone free / Hey Joe / Cat Street / Talkin' 'bout Mr. K / Impressions / Family / Tokyo intro / Tokyo / Green onions / Plant a tree, plant love
JVC 90122 / Aug '97 / JVC

Kanoute, Moussa

☐ DANCE OF THE KORA
Windswept / Courage / Ledian dance / Caribe / From the source / Pensee la vie / Happiness / I shall be released / Mosque
R 272536 / Nov '96 / Earthbeat

Kansas

☐ DEFINITIVE COLLECTION, THE
Point of know return / Carry on wayward son / What's on my mind / Icarus-borne on wings of steel / Song for America / Wall / People of the south wind / Hold on / Fight fire with fire / Play the game tonight / Tomb / Reason to be / It takes a woman's love (to make a man) / Lonely wind / Dust in the wind
4875922 / 13 Jul '98 / Epic

☐ FREAKS OF NATURE
I can fly / Desperate times / Hope once again / Black fathom / Under the knife / Need / Freaks of nature / Cold grey morning / Peaceful and warm
ESMCD 492 / Apr '97 / Essential

☐ KANSAS BOXED SET, THE
Can I tell you / Death of mother nature suite / Journey from Mariabronn / Song for America / Devil game / Incomudro-hymn to the atman / Child of innocence / Icarus / Borne on wings of steel / Mysteries and mayhem / Pinnacle / Carry on wayward son / Wall / What's on my mind / Opus insert / Magnum opus / Father Padilla meets the perfect gnat / Howling at the moon / Industry on parade / Release the beavers / Gnat attack / Point of no return / Portrait (He Knew) / Dust in the wind / Closet chronicles / People of the south wind / On the other side / Glimpse of home / Relentless / Loner / Hold on / Wheels
4893222 / 6 Apr '98 / Legacy

Kansas City Five

☐ CLASSICS 1938-1944 (Kansas City 5, 6, 7)
CLASSICS 912 / Jan '97 / Classics

Kansas City Stompers

☐ 40-ARS JUBILAEUM
MECCACD 1018 / Nov '94 / Music Mecca

☐ HAPPY JAZZ
MECCACD 1041 / Nov '94 / Music Mecca

☐ PA DANSK
MECCACD 1086 / May '97 / Music Mecca

Kante, Mory

☐ AKWABA BEACH
Yeke yeke / Deni / Inch Allah / Tama / Africa 2000 / Dia / Nanfoulen / Akwaba beach
8331192 / Apr '91 / London

Kantor, Israel

☐ UN SENOR KANTOR
4001440242 / 24 Mar '98 / ARES

KAOS

☐ INTERNATIONAL DOPE DEALERS
EFA 610032 / May '94 / Blitzvinyl

Kapa Dech

☐ KATCHUME
262602 / 1 Jun '98 / Lusafrika

Kapel, Jons Jazz

☐ LAZY 'SIPPI STEAMER
MECCACD 1019 / Nov '94 / Music Mecca

Kapelye

☐ FUTURE AND PAST
Odessa Bulgar / Yoshke furt avek / A yur nukh mayn khasene / Bessaraber khosidl / Gut purin yidn / Abe Schwartz's famous sher / In shteti Nikolaev / Vi azoy trinkt a keysor tey / Fun tashlikh / Moti der operator / Di mame iz gegangen in Mark Arayn
FF 70249 / Dec '97 / Flying Fish

450

☐ KAPELYE: ON THE AIR (Old-Time Jewish American Radio)
SHCD 67005 / Mar '95 / Shanachie

☐ LEVINE AND HIS FLYING MACHINE
Lebn zol Palestina / Oy iz dos a rebetzin / Terkishe yale v'yove tants / Levine with your flying machine / Vi bist du gevezyn far probhibition / A glezele mashke / Der shtiler Bulgar/Shpil es nokh a mol / Far nile nokh nile / Moldavian hora / Di khasene iz geven in der kazarme / Lenin um Trotsky / Oy tae s'iz git
SHANCD 21006 / May '98 / Shanachie

Kapilow, Robert

☐ GREEN EGGS AND HAM BY DR. SEUSS (Kapilow, Robert & Angelina Reaux/NJ Chamber Music Society)
389002 / Aug '96 / Koch International

Kaplan, Fred

☐ SIGNIFYIN'
BCM 7109 / Dec '97 / Blue Collar

Kaplansky, Lucy

☐ FLESH AND BONE
RHRCD 92 / Nov '96 / Red House

☐ TIDE, THE
RHRCD 65 / May '95 / Red House

Kapstad, Egil

☐ CHEROKEE
GMCD 161 / Oct '90 / Gemini

Karadjova, Nadka

☐ BULGARIAN POLYPHONY VOL.3 (Karadjova, Nadka & The Bisserov Sisters)
VICG 52332 / Mar '96 / JVC World Library

Karaindrou, Eleni

☐ MUSIC FOR FILMS
Farwell theme / Elegy for rosa / Fairytale / Parade / Return / Wandering in Alexandria / Voyage / Scream / Adagio / Rosa's song / Improvisation on farewell and waltz theme / Song / Waltz and farewell theme
8476092 / May '91 / ECM

☐ SUSPENDED STEP OF THE STORK, THE
Refugee's theme / Search - refugee's theme variation A / Suspended step / Train-car neighbourhood variation A / River / Refugee's theme symphonic variation No. 1 / Train-car neighbourhood variation B / Refugee's theme symphonic variation No. 2 / Hassaposerviko / Search - refugee's theme variation B / Waltz for the bride / Final
5115142 / Mar '92 / ECM

Kara's Flowers

☐ FOURTH WORLD, THE
Soap disco / Future kid / Myself / Oliver / Never saga / Loving the small time / To her with love / Sleepy windbreaker / Pantry Queen / My ocean blue / Captain splendid
9362465782 / 29 Sep '97 / Reprise

Karate

☐ IN PLACE
185432 / Apr '97 / Southern

☐ KARATE
185342 / Mar '96 / Southern

Karayorgis, Pandelis

☐ IN TIME (Karayorgis, Pandelis & Mat Maneri)
LABCD 002 / Oct '94 / Leo

☐ LIFT AND POISE (Karayorgis, Pandelis & Mat Maneri)
LEOLABCD 041 / Feb '98 / Leo Lab

Karelia

☐ DIVORCE AT HIGH NOON
Divorce at high noon / Love's a cliche / Say try / To his dietres / Life in a Barret Garret / Crazy irritation / Remorse at high noon / Dancing along the nekrotaphion / Devil rides hyndland / Infinite duration / Nostalgia / Tension / Bleach yours / Exaggeration / Balance yours
RR 88232 / Apr '97 / Roadrunner

Karen

☐ BETWEEN ME AND YOU
JJCD 1017 / Jan '92 / Beechwood

Kargaard, Morten

☐ COLOUR OF A MOMENT
MECCACD 2004 / May '97 / Music Mecca

Karklins, Ingrid

☐ ANIMA MUNDI
GLCD 1141 / May '94 / Green Linnet

☐ DARKER PASSION, A
Leatherwing bat / Big one/Little one / Es apkalu ozolinu/Oceans apart / Hiro/Smitten / Time/ Incredible march of the spiny lobsters / Kupla, kupla liepa auga / Crack the slab / Visas manas sikus dziesmas / Ar vilcinu riga braucu / Metenitis
GLCD 1118 / Mar '92 / Green Linnet

Karlsson, Stefan

☐ BELOW ZERO
JR 07032 / Mar '94 / Justice

☐ ROOM 292
JR 007012 / Oct '92 / Justice

Karma

☐ PAD SOUNDS
GAP 031CD / 17 Nov '97 / Groove Attack

Karma To Burn

☐ KARMA TO BURN
(Waltz of the) Playboy pallbearers / Bobbi, Bobbi, Bobbi - I'm not God / Patty Hearst's closet mantra / Mt Penetrator / Eight / Apalachian woman / Twenty four hours / Six-gun sucker punch / Thirteen six / Ma petite mort / Twin sisters and a half bottle of bourbon
RR 88622 / Feb '97 / Roadrunner

Karminski Experience

☐ ESPRESSO ESPRESSO (Various Artists)
5355472 / Aug '96 / Deram

Karn, Mick

☐ BESTIAL CLUSTER
Bestial cluster / Back in the beginning / Beard in the letterbox / Drowning dream / Sad velvet breath of summer and winter / Saday, Maday / Liver and lungs / Bones of mud
CMPCD 1002 / Jun '93 / CMP

☐ DREAMS OF REASON PRODUCE MONSTERS
First impression / Language of ritual / Buoy / Land / Three fates / When love walks in / Dream of reason / Answer
CDV 2389 / '87 / Virgin

☐ MICK KARN COLLECTORS EDITION, THE
CMPCD 1014 / 6 Apr '98 / CMP

☐ TITLES
Tribal dawn / Lost affections in a room / Passion in moisture / Weather the windmill / Saviour are you with me / Trust me / Sensitive / Piper blue
CDV 2249 / Oct '90 / Virgin

☐ TOOTH MOTHER, THE
Thundergirl mutation / Plaster the magic tongue / Lodge of skins / Gossip's cup / Feta funk / Tooth Mother / Little less hope / There was not anything but nothing
CMPCD 1008 / May '95 / CMP

Karnag

☐ PIERRE LUMIERE
BUR 867CD / Dec '97 / Escalibur

Karoli, Michael

☐ DELUGE (Karoli, Michael & Polly Eltes)
SPOONCD 16 / Mar '95 / Grey Area

Karolinka

☐ SONGS AND DANCES FROM POLAND
EUCD 1124 / '91 / ARC

Karp

☐ KARP
KLP 67CD / Apr '97 / K

☐ KARP/RYE (Karp/Rye)
TMU 026CD / 20 Oct '97 / Troubleman Unlimited

☐ SUPLEX
KLP 48CD / Oct '95 / K

Karr, Tim

☐ EVERYBODY BLEEDS
TK 001 / 20 Apr '98 / Tim Karr

Karrer, Chris

☐ DERVISH KISS
INDIGO 30542 / Dec '96 / Faruk

☐ MASK, THE
TPCD 1708016 / 2 Feb '98 / Think Progressive

☐ SUFUSTICATED
1609002 / Jun '97 / Think Progressive

Karthago

☐ SECOND STEP
941087 / 10 Nov '97 / Germanofon
PMS 7071 / 1 Jun '98 / Repertoire

Karu Nan

☐ CHIMBALOMA
TUMICD 027 / '91 / Tumi

Karukas, Gregg

☐ BLUE TOUCH
Blue touch / Azure dreaming / Cruisin' your house at midnight / Club Havana / Fly away (thinking of you) / Snaky shoes / Road back to love / Simone / Conversation / Always
5398872 / 20 Apr '98 / IE

KAS Serenity

☐ RETURN TO THE RAINBOW BRIDGE
PPP 4219 / Mar '96 / Ichiban

Kashif

☐ BEST OF KASHIF, THE
I just gotta have you (lover turn me on) / Baby don't break your baby's heart / Are you the woman: Kashif & Whitney Houston / Reservations for two: Kashif & Dionne Warwick / Love changes: Kashif & Meli'sa Morgan / Fifty ways (to fall in love): Kashif & Whitney Houston / Stay the night / Love me all over / Help yourself to my love / Dancing in the dark
262817 / Jun '92 / Arista

Kassav

☐ KASSAV VOL.3
3018842 / Jul '97 / Arcade

☐ KASSAV VOL.4
3018852 / Jul '97 / Arcade

☐ LES INOUBLIABLES DE...
472299 / Feb '97 / Flarenasch

☐ PASSEPORT
3021202 / Jul '97 / Arcade

Kastinen, Arja

☐ IRO
Amut / Kotanen / Siera / Varpa / Tisvata / Siide / Hapenet / Heutuvoa / Usmakka / Varpa / Kotanen / Prisonkka / Sihku / Tuokko / Kanna / Helve / Voli
MIPUCD 401 / May '97 / Mipu

Kastrierte Philosophen

☐ LEIPZIG DC
NORMAL 124CD / Dec '90 / Normal

Kataklysm

☐ MYSTICAL GATE OF REINCARNATION
NB 0932 / Feb '94 / Nuclear Blast

☐ SORCERY
NB 1082 / May '96 / Nuclear Blast

☐ TEMPLE OF KNOWLEDGE
NB 157CD / Jul '96 / Nuclear Blast

Katatonia

☐ DANCE OF THE DECEMBER SOULS
NFR 005 / Oct '94 / No Fashion

☐ DISCOURAGED ONES
AV 029CD / 8 Jun '98 / Avantgarde

Kater, Peter

☐ HOMAGE
March of the magic bunny / Shaman's call / Homage / Gathering / Mama sing / Gold lake / Dusk / Skyquake / River medicine / Return of the magic bunny
1390172 / May '89 / Gaia

Katharcoconsort

☐ LA DIVINA COMEDIA
21087 / Aug '96 / Sonifolk

Katharsis

☐ EARTH...HEY
CLP 9883 / Apr '97 / Cleopatra

Katie's Quartet

☐ KATIE'S QUARTET
OHCD 003 / Aug '96 / Old Hat

Katmandu

☐ CASE FOR THE BLUES, A
SARCD 007 / Apr '94 / Saraja

Kato, Ano

☐ CHTES TA KANAME
CDPAN 144 / Apr '93 / Pan

Katon, Michael

☐ BUSTIN' UP THE JOINT - LIVE
Rip it hard / Water won't boil / No more whiskey / Lucky, lucky, lucky / Love hoo doo / Rock around / Roadtested / Devil's daughter / Boogie whip / Two angels flyin' / Wake up call / Barbeque on my boogie / Get on the boogie train / Rock 'n' run
PRD 70962 / Nov '96 / Provogue

☐ GET ON THE BOOGIE TRAIN
PRD 70492 / Apr '93 / Provogue

☐ PROUD TO BE LOUD
PRD 70532 / Sep '93 / Provogue

☐ RIP IT HARD
PRD 70642 / May '94 / Provogue

☐ RUB
PRD 70792 / Mar '96 / Provogue

Katrina & The Waves

☐ KATRINA & THE WAVES/WAVES
Red wine and whisky / Do you want crying / Qu te quiero / Machine gun Smith / Cry for me / Walking on sunshine / Going down to Liverpool / Mexico / Sun won't shine / Game of love / Is that it / Tears for me / Sun Street / Lovely Lindsey / Riding shotgun / Sleep on my pillow / Money chain / Mr. Star / Love that boy / Stop trying to prove (how much of a man you is) / Red wine and whiskey
BGOCD 330 / Dec '96 / Beat Goes On

☐ VERY BEST OF KATRINA & THE WAVES, THE
Walking on sunshine / Red wine and whiskey / Do you want crying / Que te quiero / Going down to Liverpool / Machine gun Smith / Mexico / Game of love / Is that it / Tears for me / Sun street / Lovely Lindsay / I can dream about it / That's the way / Rock 'n' roll girl / (I've got a) Crush on you / Rock myself to sleep / We gotta get out of this place / Tears of a woman / I really taught me to watsui
CDEMC 3766 / Apr '97 / EMI

☐ WALK ON WATER
0630198372 / Aug '97 / East West

Katz, Dick

☐ 3 WAY PLAY
RSRCD 127 / Nov '94 / Reservoir

Katze, Nav

☐ NEVER MIND THE DISTORTION
SSR 154 / Oct '95 / SSR

Kauffeld, Greetje

☐ GREETJE KAUFFELD MIT PAUL KUHN
Leider nur eine schlechte kopie / Ruf an / Oh Charly boy / Nur wer liebt ist nie allein / Lebewohl Konny / Jeden tag da lieb' ich dich ein kleines bisschen mehr: Kauffeld, Greetje & Paul Kuhn / Jonny / Sunday melody / Benny's doodlin' band: Kauffeld, Greetje & Paul Kuhn / Der braune boy in baumwollfeld / Junge lieb im Mai / Wir konnen uns nur briefe schreiben / Musikant lass die geigen erklingen / Lieber guter alter mond: Kauffeld, Greetje & Paul Kuhn / Melodie possée / I love you: Kauffeld, Greetje & Paul Kuhn / Tanz bitte noch einmal mit mir / Blue honeymoon: Kauffeld, Greetje & Paul Kuhn / Nur am abend / Das ist so schon, das wunsch ich mir / Nur bei dir fuhl ich mich zu haus: Kauffeld, Greetje & Paul Kuhn / Wenn es nacht wird / Groschen polka: Kauffeld, Greetje & Paul Kuhn / Hey hey big boy / Kopenhagen serenade: Kauffeld, Greetje & Paul Kuhn / Komm' dach zuruck zu mir / Blonder liebling / Ich lieb' immer dur nich: Kauffeld, Greetje & Paul Kuhn / Die stunde der liebe / Ich bin immer die andere / I love you because: Kauffeld, Greetje & Paul Kuhn
BCD 16146 / Jan '97 / Bear Family

☐ MY FAVOURITE BALLADS
369022 / 1 Sep '98 / Koch Jazz

Kaufmann, Anna Maria

☐ ANNA MARIA KAUFMANN
MSPCD 9502 / Sep '95 / Mabley St.

Kaulkin, Andy

☐ SIX FOOT SEVEN AND RISING
BL 28 / Oct '96 / Bongload

Kauriga Balalaika Ensemble

☐ RUSSIAN DANCES
MCD 71789 / Jun '93 / Monitor

Kaustisen Korialla Tyylilla

☐ KAUSTISEN PARHAAT 4
KAUSP 4CD / Aug '97 / Kausp

Kava Kava

☐ SUPALUBE
DELECCD 060 / 17 Nov '97 / Delerium

☐ YOU CAN LIVE HERE
Headset / Sync / Gil / Revenge of the pseuds / Tat tvam asi / Sweal / Beat their chests / Loudest lebenstraum / In transits destined / For Uranus / Hippy bollocks / Silliness
DELECCD 024 / Apr '95 / Delerium

451

Kavana

☐ KAVANA
Crazy chance / I can make you feel good / Where are you / MFEO / Holdin' back on U / Release it / Wait for the day / Time is right / For the very first time / Protected / Jealousy / Work
CDNMS 1 / Apr '97 / Nemesis

Kavanagh, Niamh

☐ FLYING BLIND
When there's time for love / Romeo's twin / White city of lights / Let's make trouble / Miles away / I can't make you love me / Whatever it takes / Don't stop now / Flying blind / Red roses for me
74321255412 / 11 May '98 / Arista

Kavanagh, Richie

☐ AON FOCAL EILE
LYNCD 001 / Feb '97 / Wag

Kay, Arthur

☐ RARE 'N' TASTY
LOMACD 33 / Aug '94 / Loma

Kay, Fiede

☐ VOLKSSANGER AUS DEM NORDEN
EUCD 1118 / '91 / ARC

Kay Gees

☐ ESSENTIAL DANCEFLOOR ARTISTS VOL.5
You've got to / Keep on bumpin' / Get down / Masterplan / Hustle wit every muscle / Waiting at the bus stop / Cheek to cheek / I believe in music / Tango hustle / Killowatt / Killowatt/Invasion / Who's the man
DGPCD 707 / Sep '94 / Deep Beats

Kay, Janet

☐ DUB DEM SILLY
ARKCD 105 / Dec '93 / Arawak

☐ I'LL ALWAYS LOVE YOU
JFRCD 001 / Dec '93 / Joe Frazier

☐ IMMACULATE COLLECTION
So amazing / Look what love can do / Almaz / Loving you / Moving away / Kiss away / Bad, bad girl / Chariots of fire / I'd rather go blind / Closer I get to you / For the good times / Music man / Dreams of emotion / Have you ever loved somebody / Since I fell for you / One day I'll fly away / He reminds me / Trade winds / Show me the way / So good, so right / Imagine / Computer love / I want to be the one / Love won't let me wait
JANETCD 2 / Nov '93 / New Name

☐ ORCHESTRAL DUB COLLECTION
JANETCD 3 / Jul '94 / Body Music

☐ SILLY GAMES
Silly games / Imagine that / Feel no way / Rock the rhythm / Closer to you / Do you love me / Can't give it up / That night / Capricorn woman
CECD 1001 / Aug '90 / Jet Star

☐ SO AMAZING
JANETCD 01 / 5 May '98 / Body Music

☐ SWEET SURRENDER
JANETCD 5 / Jul '89 / Body Music

☐ ULTIMATE COLLECTION, THE
ARKCD 106 / Oct '95 / Arawak

Kay Yn't Seil

☐ T'MALLE SCHIP
SYNCD 164 / Jun '94 / Syncoop

Kayak

☐ ROYAL BED BOUNCER
CDP 1012DD / Jun '97 / Pseudonym

☐ SEE SEE THE SUN
Reason for it all / Lyrics / Mouldy wood / Lovely Luna / Hope for a life / Ballet of the cripple / Forever is a lonely thought / Mammoth / See see the sun
CDP 1024DD / Jun '97 / Pseudonym

Kaye, Danny

☐ ENTERTAINER EXTRAORDINARY 1941-1947
Minnie the moocher / Tchaikovsky and other Russians / Jenny / Dinah / Farming / Let's not talk about love / Fairy pipers / Babbitt and the bromide / Anatole of Paris / Frim fram sauce / Bloop bleep / Tubby tuba / Civilisation (bongo bongo bongo) / Little fiddle / Policeman's song / If you're anxious to shine / Oh by jingo / Beatin' bangin' and scratchin' / Mad dogs and Englishmen / Triplets / Ballin' the jack / Lobby number
CDAJA 5270 / Jun '98 / Living Era

☐ VERY BEST OF DANNY KAYE, THE (20 Golden Greats)
I'm Hans Christian Andersen / Inchworm / King's new clothes / Thumbelina / Ugly duckling / Wonderful Copenhagen / Tubby the tuba (parts 1 and 2) / Woody Woodpecker song / Popo the puppet / I taut I taw a puddy tat / Ballin' the Jack / Tchaikovsky / Civilization / Molly Malone / Oh by jingo, oh by gee / Candy kisses / St. Louis blues / Manic depressive parents lobby number part I and part II
MCLD 19049 / Aug '94 / MCA

Kaye, Sammy

☐ SAMMY KAYE 1944/LES ELGART 1946 (Kaye, Sammy & Les Elgart)
CCD 93 / Aug '94 / Circle

Kayirebwa, Cecile

☐ RWANDA
Rwanamiza / Tarihinda / Kana / Inkindi / Mundeke mbaririmbire / Urusamaza / Rubyiruko / Umulisa / Cyusa / Ndare / Umunezero
CDORBD 083 / Aug '94 / Globestyle

Kazan, Lainie

☐ BODY AND SOUL
MM 65126 / 1 Jul '98 / Music Masters

☐ IN THE GROOVE (Kazan, Lainie & David Benoit)
Look of love / Everything must change / You go to my head / Yesterday when I was young / Song for you
MM 65168 / 1 Jul '98 / Music Masters

Kazazian, Georges

☐ SABIL
ED 13034CD / Jul '95 / L'Empreinte Digitale

Kazda

☐ FINALLY
Your smile / Never look back / Song for my Father / Too late / I know / What have we done / Still alive / Sometimes / Vibology / Naked / Sign 'o' the times / Finally
LIP 89502 / 13 Oct '97 / Outer Music

☐ NEW STRATEGIES OF RIDING
ITM 1492 / Oct '95 / ITM

Kazjurol

☐ DANCE TARANTELLA
CDATV 12 / Sep '90 / Active

KC & The Sunshine Band

☐ BEST OF KC AND THE SUNSHINE BAND, THE
Sound your funky horn / Get down tonight / I'm your boogie man / (Shake shake shake) Your booty / Queen of clubs / That's the way (I like it) / Keep it comin' love / Please don't go / Boogie shoes / Let's go rock and roll / Give it up / Do you wanna go party / I like to do it / Shotgun shuffle / Wrap your arms around me / All I want
CDROU 5007 / Jul '90 / Roulette

☐ BEST OF KC AND THE SUNSHINE BAND, THE
That's the way I like it / Sound your funky horn / Queen of clubs / Let it go (part 1) / I'm so crazy / (Shake, shake, shake) Shake your body / Please don't go / I get lifted / Boogie shoes / Get down tonight / It's the same old song / Ain't nothin' wrong / Keep it coming love / I'm your boogie man / Baby I want your loving / Do it good
CDGOLD 1021 / May '96 / EMI Gold

☐ GET DOWN LIVE
Opening, KC, KC, KC / Give it up / Shake your booty / James Brown medley / Boogie man medley / Higher
CLACD 411 / Nov '96 / Castle

☐ GET DOWN TONIGHT
Get down tonight / That's the way (I like it) / (Shake shake shake) shake your booty / Sound your funky horn / Queen of clubs / I'm your boogie man / Give it up / Please don't go / Keep it comin' on / It's the same old song / Rock your baby / Boogie shoes / Do you wanna go party / I like to do it / Wrap your arms around me / Bonus floor fillers / That's the way (I like it) / Get down tonight
4940192 / 16 Feb '98 / EMI

☐ KC & THE SUNSHINE BAND
Let it go / That's the way (I like it) / Get down tonight / Boogie shoes / Ain't nothin' wrong / I'm so crazy 'bout you / What makes you happy / I get lifted / Let it go
MUSCD 504 / Sep '94 / MCI Original Masters

KCL Project

☐ THERE ARE MANY RIVERS TO CROSS
Octane / Listen / La liberte / Baby cry / Evolve me again / Bullet France / No retreat / Raze / In da zone / Just been searched / No retreat / JA / May 4 a day / Freeze / Lullaby / JA / Wade in the river wit me
ORCCD 4 / 8 Sep '97 / Octopus

KCM Inc.

☐ DOIN' IT FUNKY SMOOTH
Peachtowne party jam / Is it worth it / Love stepped / That love thang / Let me groove you / All 'n' all / It's all about lovin' you / Real love / Do you / Emotion
PEA 4110CD / Sep '91 / Haven

KDA

☐ JERUSATAN
RTD 3970033CD / 10 Nov '97 / Institute Of Art

Keane, Brian

☐ BEYOND THE SKY (Keane, Brian & Omar Faruk Tekbilek)
Beyond the sky / Imaginary traveller / Kolaymi / Bridge / Chargah Sirto / Your Love Is My Cure / Selemet / Strange Little Corner / Sisler / Sweet Trouble / Al Fatiha
CDCEL 13047 / Jul '92 / Celestial Harmonies

☐ SNOWFALLS
FFK 70452 / Oct '89 / Flying Fish

Keane, Conor

☐ COOLEY'S HOUSE
CKCD 01CD / Oct '94 / Conor Keane

☐ OIDHREACH
CK 002CD / Mar '98 / CK

Keane, Dolores

☐ BEST OF DOLORES KEANE, THE
TORCD 206 / 27 Oct '97 / Dara

☐ DOLORES KEANE
Sister and brother / Drag lines / Heart like a wheel / Caledonia / Mouth music / Aragon mill / Died for love / May morning dew / Lili Marlene / Foolish you
TORCD 097 / 6 Apr '98 / Dara

☐ FAREWELL TO EIREANN (Keane, Dolores & John Faulkner/Eamonn Curran)
CDTUT 724004 / Oct '89 / Wundertute

☐ LION IN A CAGE
I feel it in my bones / Lion in a cage / Room / Moorlough shore / Across the bridge / Walking on seashells / One golden rule / Island / Hold me
RTMCD 7 / Jan '94 / Round Tower

☐ LION IN A CAGE
TORCD 098 / 6 Apr '98 / Dara

☐ NIGHT OWL
FXCD 187 / Dec '97 / Kirkelig Kultuverksted

☐ NIGHT OWL
GRACD 238 / 1 Jun '98 / Grapevine

☐ SAIL OG RUA (Keane, Dolores & John Faulkner)
CEFCD 101 / Jan '94 / Gael Linn

☐ SOLID GROUND
SHCD 8007 / Mar '93 / Shanachie
DARACD 065 / Mar '95 / Dara

☐ THERE WAS A MAID
Generous lover / Bantry girl's lament / My match is made / Lord Gordon's reel / Laurel bush / Johnny and Molly / Shaskeen reel / Lament for Owen Roe O'Neill / Seven yellow gypsies / Tommy Coen's reel / There was a maid in her father's garden / Carraroe jig / Whelan's jig / Bonnie bunch of roses
CC 23CD / Nov '90 / Claddagh

☐ TIDELAND (Keane, Dolores & Rita Eriksen)
FX 175CD / Aug '97 / Kirkelig Kultuverksted

Keane, James

☐ ROLL AWAY THE REEL WORLD
Crossing the Shannon / Blooming meadows / Maud Miller's reels/The sailor's return
GLCD 1026 / '92 / Green Linnet

☐ THAT'S THE SPIRIT
GLCD 1138 / Jan '95 / Green Linnet

☐ WITH FRIENDS LIKE THESE
Welcome to Camden Town / Miss Thortons / Repeal of the union / Trip to Killavil / Lilting banshee / Collier's jig / Morning mist / Mary Macmahon's / Thady Casey's fancy / Lady Gordon / Black is the colour of my true love hair / Sean reids / Church street polkas / Hugh's polka / Hunter's purse / Flowing bowl / Tily finns / Lavalla / Strike the gay harp / Tell her / Paidin o'raifeartaigh / Turnpike gate / Killavil fancy / Boys of Ballinhinch / Na connery's / Within a mile of Dublin / Green gates / Lucy Campbell / Rights of man / Golden eagle / Paddy Taylors / First month of summer / Sporting Molly / Miss Dermont
SHANCD 78015 / 9 Mar '98 / Shanachie

Keane, Peter

☐ WALKIN' AROUND
FF 652 / Sep '96 / Flying Fish

Keane, Sean

☐ 21 IRISH ACCORDION FAVOURITES
WMCD 2001 / Sep '94 / ACL

☐ FIRE AFLAME, THE (Keane, Sean & Matt Molloy & Liam O'Flynn)
Wheels of the world / Pinch of snuff/Micho Russell's reel / Bellharbour hornpipe/Old ruined cottage in the Glen / Geese in the bog/Little fair cannavans/ Whelan's old sow / Maid of Ballingarry/Stack of barley / JB Reel/Lads of Laois/Rambling thatcher / Drunken sailor / Night fishing 30th January 1972/ Rights of man / Johnny 'Watt' Henry's reel/Jerry McMahon's reel / Pat Ward's jig/Dusty Miller / Ask my Father/Connaught heifer / Casadh na nGeanna / Ace and deuce of pipering / Eire / Sean Ryan's reel / Grand spey
CCF 30CD / Feb '93 / Claddagh

☐ GUSTY'S FROLICS
CC 17CD / Nov '95 / Claddagh

☐ JIG IT IN STYLE
Baker/Miss Mary Walker/The hawk/Marquis Of Huntley / O'Farrel's welcome to Limerick/Kitty come down from Limerick / Kiss the Maid behind the barrel / Dark Lochnagar / McLean of Pennycross/Maggie Cameron/Duntroon Castle / Maiden that jigs it in style/Girl in the big house/Alasdruim / Tennessee stud/Arkansas traveller/Miss Susan Cooper / Bereton's reel/Bucks of Oranmore / Heartbreak hotel/Cliffs of Moher / Golden eagle/Tommy Hill's favourite / Willie's single/Glen road to Carrick / Blue angel/Strike the gay harp / Willie's fling / Atlantic roar / Margaret Jackson/Reavy's reel
CCF 25CD / '90 / Claddagh

☐ TURN A PHRASE
IND 001 / May '96 / Ind

Keane, Sean

☐ ALL HEART, NO ROSES
CBM 007CD / Nov '93 / Cross Border Media

☐ NO STRANGER
GRACD 242 / 24 Aug '98 / Grapevine

Keane, Tommy

☐ PIPER'S APRON, THE
LUNCD 052 / Aug '86 / Mulligan

☐ WIND AMONG THE REEDS, THE
MMCCD 51 / Oct '95 / Maree Music

Keating, Johnny

☐ SPACE EXPERIENCE VOL.1 & 2 (2CD Set)
I feel the earth move / Unknown planet / Rocket man / Prelude to earthrise / Star trek / Space agent / Jesus Christ superstar / Upon another earth / Sound of silence / Signal to Saturn / Reach out I'll be there / Counterglow / Dreamer / Stereoskopia / Solitaire / Starcluster / Lucy in the sky with diamonds / Asteroid / Life on Mars / Earthshine
4956192 / 10 Aug '98 / Studio 2

Keatons

☐ BEIGE ALBUM, THE
FSHH 7 / Oct '94 / Dogfish

Keats

☐ KEATS
Heaven knows / Tragedy / Fight to win / Walking on ice / How can you walk away / Avalanche / Turn your heart around / Hollywood heart / Ask no questions / Night full of voices
SEECD 447 / Jul '96 / See For Miles

Keb Mo'

☐ JUST LIKE YOU
That's not love / Perpetual blues machine / More than one way home / I'm on your side / Just like you / You can love yourself / Dangerous mood / Action / Hand it over / Standin at the station / Momma / Where's my Daddy / Last fair deal gone down / Lullaby baby blues
4841172 / Jun '96 / Epic

☐ KEB MO'
Am I wrong / Come on in my kitchen / Dirty low down and bad / Don't try to explain / Kind hearted woman blues / City boy / Every morning / Tell everybody I know / Love blues / Victims of comfort / Angelina / Anybody seen my girl / She just wants to dance
4781732 / Jul '95 / Epic

Kebnekajse

☐ ELECTRIC MOUNTAIN
Barkbrodslaten / Polska fran harjedalan / Horgalaten / Eklundapolskan / Skanklat till spelman / Polska fran bingsjo / Rattvikarnas ganglat / Halling fran ekshärad / Ganglat fran dala jarna / Comanche spring
RESCD 503 / Jul '97 / Resource

Kee, John

☐ COLOUR BLIND
VTYCD 001 / Jun '94 / Verity

Keel

☐ BACK IN ACTION
DERCD 9003 / 20 Apr '98 / Derock

☐ LARGER THAN LIFE
SPV 08512102 / Aug '95 / SPV

Keel, Howard

☐ ALL TIME FAVOURITES
Hello / I've never been to me / Sometimes when we touch / Yesterday/Something / Send in the clowns / And I love you so / MacArthur Park / If / Theme from 'love story' / You needed me / Yesterday when I was young / What 50 said / This is all I ask / Always on my mind / With you I'm born again / I just called to say I love you / Just the way you are / Lady / Feelings / To all the girls I loved before / Both sides now / Memory
WB 872022 / Mar '97 / Disky

☐ BEST OF HOWARD KEEL, THE
Yesterday when I was young / Love letters / With you I am born again / Memory / Ol' man river / Make believe / If / And I love you so / Oh what a beautiful morning / Surrey with the fringe on top / People will say we're in love / Oklahoma / Softly as I leave you / Love story / Mr. Bojangles / Impossible dream / September song
JHD 014 / Jun '92 / Tring
EMPRCD 559 / Mar '95 / Emporio

☐ CLOSE TO MY HEART
There's no business like show business / O what a beautiful morning / Secret love / Surrey with the fringe on top / If I loved you / Bless your beautiful hide / Wind beneath my wings / So in love / Make believe / Love changes everything / Bring him home / Prelude into music of the night / Colours of my life / Rose Marie
CDKEEL 1 / Apr '91 / Premier/MFP

☐ ENCHANTED EVENING WITH HOWARD KEEL, A
Oklahoma medley / Some enchanted evening / This nearly was mine / I won't send roses / If ever I would leave you / La Mancha medley / You needed me / Love story / Come in from the rain / Yesterday / Something / Once upon a time / What are you doing for the rest of your life / Wave / MacArthur Park / Send in the clowns / You were always on my mind / I've never been to me / Annie get your gun medley
MCCD 006 / Feb '91 / Music Club

☐ FILM AND MUSICAL FAVOURITES
Dallas (instrumental) / Annie get your gun / If ever I would leave you / Once upon a time / Rose marie / Some enchanted evening / What are you doing for the rest of your life / Wave / This nearly was mine / Memory
15093 / May '94 / Laserlight

☐ GREAT SONGS, THE
MU 5024 / Oct '92 / Musketeer

☐ HOWARD KEEL (3CD Set)
Hello / What I did for love / Feelings / Cycles / I won't last a day without you / Both sides now / I just called to say I love you / With you I'm born again / Just the way you are / Sometimes when we touch / Way we were / To all the girls I loved before / Love the world away / Lady / Time in a bottle / Last farewell / So in love / Annie get your gun / Girl that I marry / They say it's wonderful / My defences are down / Rosemarie / Bless your beautiful hide / Send in the clowns / Showboat medley / Why do I love you / Make believe / Ol' man river / Memory / Yesterday when I was young / What 50 said / This is all I ask / And I love you so / If / Always on my mind / I've never been to me / Born again / Softly as I leave you / Oklahoma medley / Oh what a beautiful morning / Surrey with a fringe on top / People say we're in love / Some enchanted evening / This nearly was mine / I won't send roses / If ever I would leave you / La mancha medley / Don Quixote / Dulcinea / Impossible dream / You needed me / Love Story / Come in from the rain / Yesterday / Yesterday / Something / Once upon a time / What are you doing for the rest of your life / Wave / MacArthur park
HR 877092 / Oct '97 / Disky

☐ VERY BEST OF HOWARD KEEL, THE
Oklahoma medley / Some enchanted evening / You needed me / Come in from the rain / Yesterday / Something / MacArthur Park / Send in the clowns / You were always on my mind / I've never been to me / And I love you / Memory / If / Love Story / Bless your beautiful hide / Showboat medley / Born again
SUMCD 4121 / May '97 / Summit

Keelaghan, James

☐ MY SKIES
My skies / Hold your ground / I would I were / River run / Big picture / Glory bound / Kirl's piano / Hope princeton road / Orion / Abraham / Tomorrow is another day
GLCD 2112 / Jun '93 / Green Linnet

☐ RECENT FUTURE, A
GLCD 2120 / Aug '95 / Green Linnet

☐ SMALL REBELLIONS
TMCD 002 / Mar '98 / Tranquilla

Keeley, Brendan

☐ MISS YOU TONIGHT
74321506112 / 29 Sep '97 / RCA

Keen, Robert Earl

☐ BIGGER PIECE OF THE SKY, THE
So I can take my rest / Whenever kindness fail / Amarillo highway / Night right for love / Jesse with the long hair...Blow you away / Here in Arkansas / Daddy had a buick / Corpus Christie / Crazy cowboy dream / Paint the town beige
SPDCD 1048 / May '93 / Special Delivery
SHCD 1037 / Mar '98 / Sugar Hill

☐ GRINGO HONEYMOON
Think it over one time / Tom Ames prayer / Gringo honeymoon / Raven and the coyote / Lonely feeling / Merry Christmas from the family / Barbeque / Lynville train / I'm comin' home / Dreadful selfish crime
SPDCD 1051 / Oct '94 / Special Delivery
SHCD 1044 / Mar '98 / Sugar Hill

☐ LIVE ALBUM, THE
I wanna know / Torch song / Goin' down in style / If I were King / Copenhagen / I would change my life / Stewball / I'll go on downtown / Bluegrass widow / Who'll be lookin' out for me
SHCD 1024 / Mar '88 / Sugar Hill
NC 004CD / Dec '97 / New Country

☐ NO KINDA DANCER
No kinda dancer / Front porch song / Between hello and goodbye / Swervin' in my lane / Christabel / Willie / Young lovers waltz / Death of tail Fitzsimmons / Rolling by / Armadillo jackal / Lu Ann / Coldest day of Winter
SHCD 1049 / Apr '95 / Sugar Hill

☐ NO.2 LIVE DINNER
I'm going to town / Gringo honeymoon / Merry Christmas from the family / Five pound bass / Rollin' by / Sonora's death row / When the bluebonnets bloom / Think it over one time / Amarillo highway / Road goes on forever / Dreadful selfish crime / Mariano / I'm comin' home
SHCD 1051 / Mar '98 / Sugar Hill

☐ PICNIC
Undone / Over the waterfall / Levelland / I wonder where my baby is tonight / Oh Rosie / Runnin' with the night / Coming of the son and brother / Fourth of July / Then cam lo mein
07822188342 / Jul '97 / Arista Austin

☐ WEST TEXTURES
Leavin' Tennessee / Maria / Sing one for sister / Road goes on forever / Sonora's death row / Don't turn out the light / Five pound bass / It's the little things / Jennifer Johnson and me / Mariano / Love's a word I never throw around
SPDCD 1032 / Feb '90 / Special Delivery
SHCD 1028 / Mar '98 / Sugar Hill

Keenan, Brian

☐ SOLO PIANO
SACD 096 / Jun '96 / Solo Art

Keenan, Paddy

☐ NA KEEN AFFAIR
HCR 01CD / May '97 / Hot Conya

☐ POIRT AN PHIOBAIRE
CEFCD 099 / Jan '94 / Gael Linn

Keene, Tommy

☐ ISOLATION PARTY
Long time missing / Getting out from under you / Take me back / Never really been gone / World outside / Einstein's day / Battle lines / Happy when you're sad / Love dies down / Tuesday / Waiting without you / Weak and watered down / Twilights in town
OLE 2972 / 2 Mar '98 / Matador

☐ TEN YEARS AFTER
Going out again / Turning on blue / Today and tomorrow / If your heart beats alone / If you're getting married tonight / On the runway / We started over again / Good thing going / Compromise / You can't wait for time / Before the lights go down / It's now true
OLE 1772 / Feb '96 / Matador

Keene, Verill

☐ AFTERNOON AFFAIR, AN
DFCD 71259 / Nov '96 / Del-Fi

Keepers

☐ EVERY DOG IS A STAR
LCD 80010 / May '97 / Lizard

☐ LOOKING FOR A SIGN
LIZARD 80003 / Mar '95 / Lizard

Keezer, Geoff

☐ GEOFF KEEZER TRIO 1993
SKCD 2039 / Jul '96 / Sackville

☐ OTHER SPHERES
DIW 871 / Jul '93 / DIW

☐ TURN UP THE QUIET
Stompin' at the Savoy / Nearness of you / Lush life / Island palace / Madame Grenouille / Lose my breath / Rose / My shining hour / Precious one / Love dance / Bibo no Arizona
4888302 / 29 Sep '97 / Sony Jazz

Keiji, Haino

☐ ALLEGORICAL MISUNDERSTANDING
AVAN 008 / Sep '93 / Avant

Keiser, Stanley Thomas

☐ SECRET ISLAND
CCD 1008 / Jul '98 / Clarity

Keita, Mama

☐ DENILOU
NDCD 46 / 24 Apr '98 / Night & Day

Keita, Salif

☐ AMEN
Yele n na / Waraya / Tono / Kuma nyanafin / Karifa / N b'i fe / Lon
CIDM 1073 / 2 Feb '98 / Mango

☐ SORO
Wamba / Soro / Souareba / Sina / Cono / Sanni Kegniba
STCD 1020 / Mar '89 / Stern's
IMCD 243 / Mar '97 / Island

☐ SOSIE
DKMS 96001 / Jan '97 / Mellemfolkeligt

Keith, Ben

☐ SEVEN GATES - A CHRISTMAS ALBUM
Little drummer boy / Christmas time's a-coming / Silver bells / It came upon a midnight clear / O sanctissima / Greensleeves / Away in a manger / Les trois cloches / We will rock you (rocking) / Ave maria / Blue christmas
9362457732 / Nov '94 / Reprise

Keith, Bill

☐ BEATING AROUND THE BUSH
Beating around the bush / Don't let your deal go down / Cherokee shuffle / Liebestraum / Bay state bounce / Step lively / Drop in the bucket / Little old log cabin / Old hickory / Ready for the times / Bending the strings / Hornswoggled / Crab waltz
GLCD 2107 / Feb '93 / Green Linnet

☐ SOMETHING BLUEGRASS
No expectations / Green mountain hop / I'll stay around / Crazy creek / Pain in my heart / Farewell blues / Caravan / Detour / Sugarfoot rag / Jordu / Rickett's hornpipe / Auld lang syne
ROUCD 0084 / May '98 / Rounder

Keith, Toby

☐ BLUE MOON
Lonely / Every night / Closin' time at home / Woman's touch / Does that blue moon ever shine on you / Lucky me / She's perfect / She's gonna get it / Me too / Hello
5311922 / Aug '96 / A&M

☐ DREAM WALKIN'
We were in love / Dream walkin' / You don't anymore / Jackie Don Tucker (play by the rules miss all the fun) / Tired / Double wide paradise / Yet / She ran away with a rodeo clown / Strangers again / I'm so happy I can't stop crying / I don't understand my girlfriend
5348362 / 6 Oct '97 / Mercury

Kellaway, Roger

☐ ALONE TOGETHER (Kellaway, Roger & Red Mitchell)
Alone together / Just friends / I should care / I surrender dear / Blue blues / It's a wonderful world / Dear old Stockholm / Emily
DRCD 168 / Apr '89 / Dragon

☐ ART OF INTERCONNECTEDNESS, THE
You took advantage of me / Lazy 'sippi steamer goin' home / Emily / Creole love call / Sophisticated lady / Remembering you / New Orleans / Blackwall tunnel blues / Jorjana / When I grow too old to dream / I'm still in love with you / Un canto per la pace
CHR 70042 / Dec '97 / Challenge

☐ LIFE'S A TAKE (Kellaway, Roger & Red Mitchell)
If I were a bell / Mean to me / I have the feeling I've been here before / Life's a mistake / Lover man / It's a wonderful world / Take the 'A' train / Have you met Miss Jones
CCD 4551 / May '93 / Concord Jazz

☐ LIVE AT MAYBECK RECITAL HALL VOL.11
How deep is the ocean / I'm still in love with you / Love of my life / Close your eyes / New Orleans / My one and only love / Creole love call / I'm getting sentimental over you
CCD 4470 / Jul '91 / Concord Jazz

☐ PORTRAIT OF ROGER KELLAWAY
FSRCD 147 / Dec '90 / Fresh Sound

☐ ROGER KELLAWAY MEETS GENE BERTONCINI & MICHAEL MOORE (Kellaway, Roger & Gene Bertoncini/ Michael Moore)
CRD 315 / Mar '96 / Chiaroscuro

Keller, Greta

☐ THESE FOOLISH THINGS (25 Romantic Songs 1931-1938)
These foolish things / I apologise / Blues in my heart / All of me / Just friends / Faded summer love / Speak to me of love / Paradise / I don't stand a ghost of a chance with you / Say it isn't so / Zwischen heute und morgen / Die musik spielt ganz leise / Kleine melodie / Sag beim abschied / Bird on the wing / Would you / Did you mean it / They can't take that from me / Thanks for the memory / Once in a while / My fine feathered friend / You leave me breathless / So little time / Lights out / Auf wiedersehn, my dear
CDAJA 5193 / May '96 / Living Era

Kellso, Jon Erik

☐ JON ERIK KELLSO VOL.1
ARCD 9125 / Nov '94 / Arbors Jazz

☐ JON ERIK KELLSO VOL.2 (The Plot Thickens)
ARCD 19160 / Sep '97 / Arbors Jazz

Kelly Affair

☐ WELCOME TO THE KELLY AFFAIR
NL 043 / 29 Jun '98 / Not Lame

Kelly, Alan

☐ OUT OF THE BLUE
Red haired lass / Fleur de Mandragore / Gusty's frolics / Beautiful lake Ainslie / Bearhaven lassies / Trip to Dingle / Lough Isle Castle / Dancing eyes / Commodore / Spootiskerry / Far road to Sligo / Reel de Pointe-au-pic
BMM 001CD / May '97 / Black Box Music

Kelly Brothers

☐ SANCTIFIED SOUTHERN SOUL
Falling in love again / You're that great big feelin' / My love grows stronger / I've got my baby (and that's enough) / Make me glad / I'd rather have you / Counting on you / Time has made me / Got the feeling / You're the most / Love time / Can't stand it no longer / If that will hold you / How can true love be this way / Ouch oh baby / I'll be right there / Just walk on / You put your touch on me / Hanging in there / That's what you mean to me / Comin' on in / That's how I am / I got this feeling / Stop these tears / Haven't I been good to you / If it wasn't for your love / It takes you / My baby loves me
CDKEND 137 / Aug '96 / Kent

Kelly, Dave

☐ BEST OF THE 80'S
RPM 118 / Oct '93 / RPM

☐ DAVE KELLY BAND LIVE
APCD 033 / '92 / Appaloosa

☐ MAKING WHOOPEE 1979-1982 (Kelly, Dave Band)
Makin' whoopee / Hey baby / Ungrateful / Return to sender / Put your money where your mouth is / I'm into something good / Best part of breaking up / It feels right / Dawn surprise / You're gonna make me lonesome when you go / Two more bottles of wine / Red red wine / House lights / Don't cha hang up the phone / Can't win 'em all / Time after time / When I'm dead and gone / That's why / My heart in your hands / Worried man / Lights out
RPM 118 / Oct '93 / RPM

☐ STANDING AT THE CROSSROADS (Kelly, Dave Band)
One way out / When I itch / It hurts me to / Big river / Okie / Smokestack lightning / Worried man / Crossroads / Leaving / Weight / Grits and groceries / Back in the blues / To love somebody / Poor man
INAK 8807CD / Jul '97 / In Akustik

☐ WAITING FOR BESSIE (Kelly, Dave Band)
Give me my money / Come back to me / Blind man / Back in the blues / Still believe in you / Waiting for Bessie / Mais oui / Just shouldn't be that way / Love is a compromise / It isn't love / Straight line (to my heart) / Come kiss me love / Crying in the rain / Tongue tied / Foreign station / Hard to find a heart / You rocked me / Gael's blue / Glad I'm living / Ee do do qua qua
GEMCD 009 / Feb '97 / Diamond

Kelly, Ed

☐ ED KELLY & PHAROAH SANDERS (Kelly, Ed & Pharoah Sanders)
Rainbow song / Newborn / You send me / Pippin / Answer me my love / You've got to have freedom / Song for the street people / West Oakland strutt / Lift every voice / Just the two of us / Well you needn't
ECD 22056 / Jul '93 / Evidence

Kelly Family

☐ OVER THE HUMP
Why why why / Father's nose / First time / Baby smile / Cover the road / She's crazy / Ares qui / Key to my heart / Roses of red / Once in a while / Break free / Angel / Wolf / Santa Maria
CDEMC 3713 / Jun '95 / EMI

Kelly, Gene

☐ GENE KELLY
DVGH 7082 / May '95 / Deja Vu

Kelly, Jack

☐ JACK KELLY 1933-1939 (Kelly, Jack & His South Memphis Jug Band)
BDCD 6005 / '91 / Blues Document

Kelly, James

☐ TRADITIONAL IRISH MUSIC
CAP 2CD / Aug '97 / Capelhouse

☐ TRADITIONAL MUSIC OF IRELAND
SH 34014 / Apr '95 / Shanachie

Kelly, Jeff

☐ ASH WEDNESDAY RAIN
GMR 040 / 15 Jun '98 / Green Monk

Kelly, Jo Ann

☐ JUST RESTLESS (Kelly, Jo Ann Band)
APCD 028 / Feb '96 / Appaloosa

☐ STANDING AT THE BURYING GROUND (Kelly, Jo Ann & 'Mississippi' Fred McDowell)
61 Highway / Red cross store / When I lay my burden down / Evil hearted woman / I asked for whiskey, she brought me gasoline / Standing at the burying ground / Glory hallelujah / Write me a few of your lines / My baby done me wrong / Shake 'em on down / Louise / My babe / Waves of the water / Kokomo
NEBCD 851 / Aug '96 / Sequel

☐ WOMEN IN (E)MOTION FESTIVAL
T&M 110 / Dec '95 / Tradition & Moderne

Kelly, John

☐ IN THE UNIQUE WEST CLARE STYLE (Kelly, John & James)
PTICD 1041 / Oct '95 / Outlet

☐ IRISH TRADITIONAL FIDDLE MUSIC (Kelly, John & James)
PTICD 1041 / Jul '95 / Pure Traditional Irish

Kelly, Kirk

☐ GO MAN GO
SST 223CD / Jan '89 / SST

Kelly, Kris

☐ DAWN OF A NEW BEGINNING
WTCD 1097 / 9 Feb '98 / Southbound

Kelly, Luke

☐ COLLECTION, THE
CHCD 1041 / Aug '94 / Chyme

☐ IRISH FAVOURITES VOL.1 (Kelly, Luke & Dubliners)
Raglan Road / Whiskey in the jar / Donegal Danny / Old triangle / Spancil Hill / Black velvet band / Town I loved so well / Dirty old town / McAlpine's fusiliers / Song for Ireland / All for me grog / Molly Malone
CHCD 1033 / Apr '93 / Chyme

☐ IRISH FAVOURITES VOL.2 (Kelly, Luke & Dubliners)
Rare ould times / Fiddlers green / Biddy Mulligan / Avondale / Wild rover / Seven drunken nights / Finnegan's wake / Weila weila weila / Foggy dew / Lord of the dance / Johnston's motorcar / Farewell to Ireland
CHCD 1034 / Apr '93 / Chyme

☐ LUKE KELLY ALBUM, THE (Kelly, Luke & Dubliners)
Button pusher / Scorn not his simplicity / Sun is burning / Blantyre explosion / For what died the sons of Roisin / Town I loved so well / Rare ould times / Dirty old town / Foggy dew / Farewell to Carlingford / Parcel o' rogues / Bunclody / Dainty Davie / Unquiet grave
CHCD 1016 / Jul '93 / Chyme

☐ LUKE'S LEGACY (Kelly, Luke & Dubliners)
Song for Ireland / Wild rover / School days over / Monto / Joe Hill / Auld triangle / Whiskey in the jar / Raglan road / Hand me down me bible / Free the people / Peat bog soldiers / Lifeboat Mona / Springhill disaster / Gartan mothers lullaby
CHCD 1031 / May '89 / Chyme

☐ SONGS OF THE WORKERS
Joe Hill / Sun is burning / When I was a bachelor / Springhill mine disaster / Battle of the Somme / Freedom come-all-ye / Lifeboat Mona / Thirty foot trailer / Alabama '58 / Lag's song / Button pusher / School day's over / Such a parcel of rogues / High Germany / I must away now (night visiting song) / Peat bog soldiers / Blantyre explosion
CDLUKE 001 / Jun '98 / Outlet

Kelly, Nick

☐ BETWEEN TRAPEZES
CDSP 001 / May '97 / Self Possessed

Kelly, Pat

☐ BOOK OF HITS
RN 7041 / 25 May '98 / Rhino

☐ BUTTERFLIES
SONCD 0076 / May '95 / Sonic Sounds

☐ CLASSIC HITS
RNCD 2113 / Jul '95 / Rhino

☐ PORTRAIT OF A LEGEND
ANGCD 21 / Oct '93 / Angela

☐ SOULFUL LOVE (The Best Of Pat Kelly 1967-1974)
You'll want me back / Somebody's baby / Twelfth of never / Daddy's home / I'm in the mood for love / Little boy blue / You are not mine / There comes a time / Man of my word / Time has come / What am I to do / You're my everything / Dark end of the street / Since you are gone / How long (will it take) / Then you can tell me goodbye / Tammy / Prophet / Steal away / Talk about love / Where music I go / Soulful love / I wish it would rain / That special one / Best time of my life / Casanova
CDTRL 386 / Sep '97 / Trojan

☐ SREVOL
ETH 2234CD / 8 Dec '97 / Ethnic Flight

Kelly, Paul

☐ COMEDY
TVD 93343 / Jan '95 / Mushroom

☐ DEEPER WATER
TVD 93340 / Oct '95 / Mushroom

☐ GONNA STICK & STAY
BB 9523CD / May '93 / Bullseye Blues

☐ HIDDEN THINGS
D 30748 / Mar '95 / Mushroom

☐ LIVE
D 16061 / Feb '95 / Mushroom

☐ LOST
D 19467 / Mar '95 / Mushroom

☐ SONGS FROM THE SOUTH
MUSH 17CD / 12 Jan '98 / Mushroom

☐ WANTED MAN
Summer rain / God's hotel / She's rare / Just like animals / Love never runs out on time / Song from thee 16th floor / Maybe this time for sure / Ball and chain / Still picking the same sore / Everybody wants to touch me / We've started a fire / Lately / Nuhkanya
FIENDCD 758 / Aug '94 / Demon

Kelly, Sandy

☐ MUSICAL TRIBUTE TO PATSY CLINE, A
KCD 347 / Mar '94 / K-Tel

Kelly, Sean

☐ 50 SCOTTISH CELILDH ACCORDION FAVOURITES
CDSCOT 050 / Oct '95 / Outlet

☐ CELTIC JEWELS VOL.1 (A Classic Collection Of Irish Instrumental Airs & Melodies) (Kelly, Sean Ensemble)
CDIRISH 017 / Apr '97 / Outlet

☐ CELTIC TRANQUILITY (Kelly, Sean Ensemble)
CHCD 1043 / Jan '95 / Chyme

Kelly, Wynton

☐ FULL VIEW (Kelly, Wynton Trio)
I want a little girl / I thought / What a difference a day made / Autunm leaves / Don'tcha hear me callin' to ya / On a clear day (you can see forever) / Scufflin' / Born to be blue / Walk on by
OJCCD 912 / May '97 / Original Jazz Classics

☐ IT'S ALRIGHT (Kelly, Wynton Trio)
5377502 / 22 Sep '97 / Verve Elite

☐ KELLY AT MIDNITE
VJ 006 / 24 Feb '98 / Vee Jay

☐ KELLY BLUE
Kelly blue / Softly as in a morning sunrise / Green dolphin street / Willow weep for me / Keep it moving / Old clothes
911900502 / 19 May '98 / JVC

☐ KELLY GREAT
VJ 003 / 24 Feb '98 / Vee Jay

☐ LAST TRIO SESSION
DD 441 / Aug '94 / Delmark

☐ TAKIN' CHARGE
LEJAZZCD 16 / Jun '93 / Le Jazz

☐ WYNTON KELLY
VJ 011 / 24 Feb '98 / Vee Jay

☐ WYNTON KELLY INTRODUCES DONNA DRAKE (Kelly, Wynton & Donna Drake)
FSRCD 60 / 5 Jan '98 / Fresh Sound

Kelsall, Phil

☐ ALL I ASK OF YOU
Clarinet polka / All I ask of you / Waltzing in the clouds / Two hearts in waltz time / I just called to say I love you / Circus Renz / Embraceable you / I got plenty o' nuttin' / Liza / Svanee / Swanee / Dizzy fingers / Music of the night / Rouge et noir / Come to Fiona's wedding / If I can help somebody / I only have eyes for you / My melancholy baby / Poor butterfly / Romeo / Don't say goodbye / Your eyes / Love is a many splendoured thing / I'm in the mood for love / I'll see you in my dreams
GRACC 23 / May '94 / Grasmere

☐ BLACKPOOL MAGIC
Entry of the gladiators / Sanctuary of the heart / Chattanooga choo choo / You'll never know / September in the rain / Jeepers creepers / Shadows on the Seine / Russian flag / For you alone / Shuffle off to Buffalo / About a quarter to nine / Shadow waltz / Dames, young and healthy / Lullaby of Broadway / 42nd Street / Coronation scot / Dubarry waltz / Dardanella / Pied Piper / Chanson d'amour / Old fashioned way / Can't smile without you / Bless this house / Rag doll / Paradise for two / My gal's a yorkshire gal / In the twi-twi-twilight / In the shade of the old apple tree / Wonderful guy / My favourite things / Wonderful, wonderful day
GRCD 43 / '91 / Grasmere

☐ BLUE VELVET
Delicado / I dreamed a dream / Doll dance / Drigo's seranade / Chihuahua / Wind beneath my wings / Easy winners / Bluebells polka / Voices of spring / Flea market / Music from across the way / In the shadows / Meditation from Thais / Tambourin / Blue velvet / Barcarolle / I'm getting sentimental over you / I don't want to walk without you / Goodnight sweetheart / Masquerade
GRCD 47 / '92 / Grasmere

☐ CENTENARY SPECIAL
SOW 517 / Jul '94 / Sound Waves

☐ COME DANCING AT THE TOWER BALLROOM
You're driving me crazy / I wonder where my baby is tonight / Lulu's back in town / Doin' the raccoon / Anniversary waltz / When I grow too old to dream / Tammy / Charmaine / Am I blue / September song / Blue moon / Sweet and lovely / Whatever Lola wants (Lola gets) / Adios muchachos / Tower ballroom tango / Should L / Sweet and gentle / Kiss me honey, honey kiss me / Greey eyes / Sway / More than ever / Magic is the moonlight / Pierrette / Mademoiselle from Armentieres / Man who broke the bank at Monte Carlo / Wot'cher (Knocked 'em in the Old Kent Road) / Constantinople / I'm Henery the Eighth (I am) / Down forget-me-not Lane / I leave my heart in an english garden / Try a little tenderness / Moonlight bay / Chalk farm to Camberwell Green / Are we to part like this, Bill / Let me call you sweetheart / Bird in a gilded cage / Kind regards / Tiddley on pom / Morning promenade / Cindy swing / Dear hearts and gentle people / Back in your own backyard / Nice people / What can I say after I say I'm sorry / Linger awhile
GRCD 50 / '92 / Grasmere

☐ CONGRATULATIONS
GRCD 62 / Mar '94 / Grasmere

☐ DANCING THROUGH MY DREAMS (Phil Kelsall Plays The Technics SX-FA1)
Quickstep / Modern waltz / Slow foxtrot / Rhumba / Cha cha / Manana (is good enough for me) / Jersey bounce/It all depends on you / Viennese waltz / Saunter / Tango / Old tyme waltz / Bossa nova / Balmoral blues / Mayfair quickstep
GRCD 83 / Oct '97 / Grasmere

☐ DANCING TIME
Dancing time / Dancing with my shadow / Good morning / All I do is dream of you / In Marble Halls / Zigeuner / I'll see you again / Over the rainbow / I know why (and so do you) / Love me or leave me / Lonesome and sorry / Annietamento / Midnight tango / Summertime in Venice / Non Dimenticar / Till the end of time / On Green Dolphin Street / Itsy bitsy teeny weeny yellow polka dot bikini / Talk to the animals / More I see you / No can do / It's a long way to Tipperary / Pack up your troubles / When were you with last night / Just as long as the world goes 'round and around / 'Deed I do / Little Dolly Daydream / Little dutch mill / On the air / Moonlight brings memories / Rock-a-bye your baby / Buddy can you spare a dime / Puff the magic dragon / I'd like to teach the world to sing / Oh oh Antonio / I'm shy Mary Ellen / Can't we sing love's old sweet song again / One day when we were young / Wonderful world of the young / Guaglione / Namur / I love the sunshine of your smile / Jolly good company / Heartaches / I found a new baby / Dinah / Bill Bailey, won't you please come home / She'll be comin' round the mountain / When the Saints
GRCD 74 / Mar '96 / Grasmere

☐ I DO LIKE TO BE BESIDE THE SEASIDE
Oh I do like to be beside the seaside / Darling buds of May / Nights of gladness / Amazing grace / South Rampart Street Parade / At last / Goodbye blues / He loves and she loves / How long has this been going on / Our love is here to stay / Bye bye blues / Farewell blues / Soon / They all laughed / Liza / Blackpool belle / Friends for life (Amigos para siempre) / Crystal chandeliers / Crazy / Blanket on the ground / Colonel Bogey / Sprinkling tam / Parade of the tin soldiers / Holy city / Dance of comedians
GRCD 58 / Jun '93 / Grasmere

☐ MEMORIES ARE MADE OF THIS
Grasshopper's dance / Tina's toccata / Limehouse blues / Welcome to my world-what a wonderful world / Poor people of paris-the windows of paris / Snow white and the seven dwarfs (selection) / Trolley song / Down the mall (march) / Mary poppins (selection) / Love me with all your heart-love is all / Evensong / Blackpool hoedown / Windmill in old amsterdam-love me tender-memories are mad / Somebody stole my gal
GRCD 67 / Apr '95 / Grasmere

☐ MY WAY (Plays The Technics SX-FA 1)
Tritsch tratsch polka / Sailing by / Miss Chatelaine / Le cygne/The swan / Buffoon / Dear Lord and father of mankind / Salut d'amour / Mack and Mabel / Thunderbirds / Memories of Martha / Berceuse from the Dolly Suite / Bel viso polka / Folks who live on the hill/Can't help singing/I'm old fashio / Ball-scene / My way
GRCD 78 / Oct '96 / Grasmere

☐ PHIL KELSALL AT THE YAMAHA FX20
Hors d'oeuvres / I won't dance / Stepping out with my baby / Love's last word is spoken / Shadow waltz / Emmeline / Innamorata / If I didn't care / Body and soul / Unchained melody / Romance in A minor / Perhaps, perhaps, perhaps / Garden in Granada / More I see you / Amor / Cocktails for two / Tangerine / Carioca / South American way / It had better be tonight / Boogie woogie bugle boy from Company B / Dolores / Every little while / I don't want to set the world on fire / J'Attendrai / Chapel in the moonlight / Soldiers in the park / Soldiers of the Queen / Take me back to dear old blighty / Hold your hand out, naughty boy / Blame it on the Bossa Nova / Meditation / I was never kissed before / Someday my Prince will come / Say you will not forget / Love's dream after the ball / Tell me I'm forgiven / Cafe in Vienna / Whispering tango / Birth of the blues / Back home in Tennessee / Nevertheless / Music maestro please / We're gonna hang out the washing on the Siegfried Line / I've got sixpence / Five minutes more / Rolling around the world / Walking the floor / Please don't talk about me when I'm gone
GRCD 60 / Oct '93 / Grasmere

☐ PHIL KELSALL SELECTION
Shuffle off to Buffalo / About a Quarter to Nine / Shadow waltz / Dames / Coronation Scot / Catari, catari / Come back to Sorrento / Santa Lucia / Oh Maria Mari, Funiculi, Funicula / Pretty little black eyed Susie / Singin' the blues / Chicka boom / Dance of the comedians / You're driving me crazy / I wonder where my baby is tonight / Pink Lady / Paradise / Wyoming lullaby / Put me amongst the girls / Jolly good company beside the sea / When the guards are on parade / Tower Ballroom tango / Dancing with tears in my eyes / Diane / I love the moon / Garden in the rain / Rose of Washington Square / I'll string along with you / Bless 'em all / Band played on / Ash Grove / Daisy Bell / Circus Renz / My song of love / Two hearts in waltz time / Waltzing in the clouds / Choo choo samba / Braes of Strathnaver / Flea market / I dreamed a dream / Phantom of the Opera
GROSCD 1 / Oct '93 / Grasmere

☐ SEQUENCE OF DANCING FAVOURITES
I can't give you anything but love / Chicago / Hello Dolly / After you've gone / Dancing with tears in my eyes / Diane / I love the moon / Memories of you / Stars fell on Alabama / Make mine love / There's no other love / El choclo / Oh Rosalita / How wonderful to know / Always in my heart / Indian summer / A-you're adorable / One / Frenesi / Take the 'A' train / You're sixteen / Tower ballroom jive / That's my weekness now / Moonstruck / If I had a talking picture of you / Put me amongst the girls / Jolly good company beside the sea / When the guards are on parade / PS I love you / Louise / Polka dots and moonbeams / Meet me tonight in Dreamland / Three o'clock in the morning / Eton boating song / If I had my way / Glad rag doll / Broken doll / Goodbye-ee / In the good old summertime / Tulips from Amsterdam / By the side of the Zuyder Zee / Mother Machree / Keep young and beautiful / Varsity drag / Black bottom / Charleston
GRCD 39 / May '90 / Grasmere

☐ SOME ENCHANTED EVENING
Phantom of the opera / Some enchanted evening / Thoroughly modern Millie / No no Nanette / Hey there / Can't help lovin' dat man / And this is my beloved / I've got the sun in the morning and the moon at night / I whistle a happy tune / Best of times / I don't know how to love him / March of the siamese children / Out of my dreams / Girl that I marry / Waltz at Maxim's / If I loved you / Wouldn't it be loverly / Spring, spring, spring / Mame / Any dream will do / Leap year waltz / Highwayman love / Fold your wings / One flower grows alone in your garden / One alone / Indian love call / Wonderful day like today / There is nothin' like a dame / Do re mi / I could have danced all night / Oklahoma
GRCD 54 / Oct '92 / Grasmere

☐ SWINGING SLEIGH BELLS
Swinging sleigh bells / O holy night / Jingle bells-rudolph the red-nosed reindeer-let it snow let / In the bleak midwinter / I saw mommy kissing santa claus-winter wonderland / Christmas dream / It's beginning to look like christmas-christmas alphabet-p / Away in a manger / We need a little christmas-the merry christmas polka / A holly jolly christmas-here comes santa claus-frosty the s / Have yourself a merry little christmas / Jingle bell rock-rockin' around the christmas tree / Christmas song / That's what I'd like for christmas / Christmas waltz-it's the most wonderful time of the ye / Mary's boy child / Snow white christmas
GRCD 70 / Oct '95 / Grasmere

☐ THIS IS MY SONG (At The Wurlitzer Organ Of The Tower Ballroom, Blackpool)
Cherokee / Romanza / Don't be cross / Medley / Highland cathedral / Robin's return / Medley / Frasquita serenade / Peanut polka / March of the cobblers / This is my song / Medley / Autumn leaves / Kelsall kapers / Medley / Bluesette/Mood I'm in / Medley
GRCD 87 / Apr '98 / Grasmere

☐ TIME FOR DANCING
Mr. Sandman / Avalon / Crazy rhythm / Dancing with tears in my eyes / Diane / Love the moon / Memories of you / Stars fell on Alabama / Make mine love / Bewitched, bothered and bewildered / Love in bloom / Someone to watch over me / Here's that rainy day / La golondrina / Cherry pink and apple blossom white / Por favor / Skater's waltz / Spanish gypsy dance / Nagasaki / Little red monkey / One the prom prom promenade / Consider yourself / Garden in the rain / Rose of Washington Square / I'll string along with you / Girl from Ipanema / Destination love / There's no other love / El choclo / Oh Rosalita / La cumparsita / Pink Lady / Paradise / Wyoming lullaby / Little white lies / Happy feet / It's just the time for dancing / If I had my way / Glad rag doll / Broken doll / Goodbye-ee / Blees' em all / Band played on / Ash grove / Daisy bell / Tip toe through the tulips / Don't know why (I just do) / My Mammy / Scotch mist
PWKS 4210 / Aug '94 / Carlton

☐ UP, UP AND AWAY
Czardas / Anything goes/You're the top/Buddy beware / I get a kick out of you / I believe / South American Joe / Gold and silver waltz / Old rugged cross / Snowbird/Happy anniversary/I love you because / Take me home country roads / Stardust / Gimme dat ding / Diamonds are a girls' best friend / Up, up and away / Under the double eagle / Among my souvenirs/An affair to remember / You're just in love / Mack the knife / Serenade in blue / Mattinata / Ciribiribin / Hawaiian samba / Be my love/Because / Come fly with me/You make me feel so young / Lady is a tramp
GRCD 80 / Mar '97 / Grasmere

Kelsey, Rev.

☐ REV. KELSEY 1947-1951
DOCD 5478 / Sep '96 / Document

Keltz

☐ MYSTERY OF AMERGIN
Mystery of Amergin / Sineads reel / Vijays / Tune for Aidan / Leons jig / Little fiery one part 1 / Little fiery one part 2 / Garten mother's lullaby / Ginepo leer / Oak tree / Reel for Farzanch / Logan water / Blackbird
CDLDL 1247 / Jan '97 / Lochshore

☐ PRINCE OF PEACE
Gate / Siyah Chal / Mountains of Sulaymaniyyih / Exile / Garden of Ridvan / Reel of revelation / Release jig / Ascension
IRCD 024 / Jan '94 / Iona

Kelvynator
☐ REFUNKANATION
EMY 1302 / Sep '97 / Enemy

Kemener, Yann-Fanch
☐ ENEZ EUSA
L'OZ 02 / May '96 / L'Oz

☐ GWERZIOU AND SONIOU
YFK 01CD / Nov '96 / YFK

☐ ILE EXIL (Kemener, Yann-Fanch & Didier Squiban)
L'OZ 011CD / Nov '96 / L'Oz

Kemp, Gary
☐ LITTLE BRUISES
Standing in love (the still point) / Brother heart / Inexperienced man / Wasted / Little bruises / Ophelia drowning / She said / Shadowman / These are the days (born under twins) / My lady soul
4795732 / Oct '95 / Columbia

Kemp, Hal
☐ HAL KEMP & ORCHESTRA 1934-36
CCD 25 / Apr '94 / Circle

Kemp, Mike
☐ FEELING GOOD THANKS (Kemp, Mike Trio)
RRCD 1010 / May '98 / Rose

Kemp, Rick
☐ ESCAPE
What you see is what you get / Brampton to Roadhead blues / Over my head / Deep in the darkest night / Nobody put you on the train / Waiting for a miracle / Queen of light / Phoenix / Genocide / Fighting on the same side / Escape / Somewhere along the road
FECD 114 / Jan '97 / Fellside

☐ SPIES
Boundaries / Long way from paradise / Pressure's off / Hello peace / Back on your own again / Great divide / New baptism / Heart of stone / Judgement day / All in this together / Georgetown skyline
FECD 133 / Jul '98 / Fellside

Kemperle, Bagad
☐ KEJADENN
Y225023 / Jun '93 / Silex

Kendall Turner Overdrive
☐ DISPLACED LINKS
Turbine / Mechanism / Pedal stop / Sump / Cylinder / Shift / Beached driver / Dismantle
CDPSST 4 / Feb '97 / Mute

Kendall, Steve
☐ SCOTTISH COUNTRY DANCING (Kendall, Steve & The Glencastle Sound)
300792 / Jan '97 / Hallmark

☐ SHADES OF HEATHER (Kendall, Steve & The Glencastle Sound)
Waltz / Gay Gordons / Jig / Gay Gordons / Waltz / Reel / Highland Schottische / Eva three step / Two steps / Strip the willow / Circassian circle / Waltz / Gay Gordons / Polka / Hornpipe / Reel / Waltz
308912 / 11 May '98 / Hallmark

Kendrick, Graham
☐ IS ANYONE THIRSTY
Is anyone thirsty / Psalm 126 / Wake up o sleeper / How good and how pleasant / I was made for this / Knowing you / For this I have Jesus / Let me fill the room / Day of his power / Declare his glory
ALD 035 / Sep '95 / Alliance Music

☐ LAMB OF GOD
Great is the Lord / Rejoice / Let praise arise / Sing for joy in the Lord / His love endures forever / Lord have mercy / Lamb of God / My heart overflows / Think about His love / Lord thy God / Steadfast love of the Lord / Thou art worthy / Song for the nations
HMD 505 / Jan '88 / Word

☐ MEEKNESS AND MAJESTY
All heaven waits / Come and see Jesus / Stand among us / Led like a lamb / Like a candle flame / Lord, have mercy on us / Meekness and majesty / O Lord / Restore / O Lord, the clouds are gathering / Servant King / Shine, Jesus, shine / Price is paid / This is my beloved son / Who can sound the depths of sorrow
KMCD 931 / Apr '97 / Kingsway

Kendrick, Keith
☐ HOME GROUND
FECD 118 / Mar '97 / Fellside

Kendrick, Matt
☐ COMPOSITE
ICH 1166CD / May '94 / Ichiban

Kendrick, Rodney
☐ DANCE, WORLD, DANCE
Cogent / Santeria / Love is the answer / Totem / Son is / We need mercy / Little sweeter / Last day / Mr. Bruce is back
5219372 / Oct '94 / Verve

☐ LAST CHANCE FOR COMMON SENSE
5315362 / Jul '96 / Verve

Kendricks, Eddie
☐ VINTAGE '78
RE 21492 / Sep '97 / Razor & Tie

Keneally, Mike
☐ HALF ALIVE IN HOLLYWOOD (2CD Set) (Keneally, Mike & Beer For Dolphins)
TVDCD 204 / 29 Sep '97 / Third Venture

Kenickie
☐ AT THE CLUB
In your car / People we want / Spies / How I was made / Brother John / Millionaire sweeper / Robot song / Classy / Punka / Nightlife / PVC / Come out 2 nite / I never complain / Acetone / Montrose gimps it up for charity
ADISCCD 002 / Sep '97 / EMI

Kenkulian, Hrant
☐ UDI HRANT KENKILIAN
CD 4265 / Dec '94 / Traditional Crossroads

Kennedy, Brian
☐ BETTER MAN, A
Better man / For one kiss / Won't you take me home / No other words / And so I will wait for you / Life, love and happiness / Oldest dream in the world / Put the message in the box / By the mountain road / Ghost music / Wish me well
74321409132 / Oct '96 / RCA

Kennedy, Fiona
☐ MAIDEN IN HEAVEN
CD 001 / Nov '95 / Colin Campbell

Kennedy, Frankie
☐ ALTAN (Kennedy, Frankie & Mairead)
Highlandman / An Seanchaileach Gallda / Ta mo Chleamhnas a Dheanamh / Cat that ate the candle / Ceol A'Phiobaire / Tommy Peoploe's loch Altan / Danny Meehan's / Rogha an Ghabha / Sunset / Thug me Ruide / Humours of whiskey / Jimmy Lyon's Les / Citi na cumann / Con Cassidy's highland reel
GLCD 1078 / Apr '93 / Green Linnet

Kennedy, Grace
☐ ONE VOICE
EMPRCD 785 / 16 Mar '98 / Emporio

Kennedy, Joan
☐ CANDLE IN THE WIND
Trouble with love / Sometimes she feels like a man / Spanish is a loving tongue / If you want love / Some people belong together / Wild again / God's green earth / Just can't let go / I never met a liar / Candle in the window
322543 / Dec '95 / Koch International

☐ HIGHER GROUND
341072 / Dec '95 / Koch International

Kennedy, Joe
☐ FALLING IN LOVE WITH LOVE
BB 902 / 24 Apr '98 / Black & Blue

Kennedy, Nigel
☐ KAFKA
Autumn regrets / I believe in God / Transfigured night / Melody in the wind / From Adam to Eve / Fallen forest / Innig / Soleil levant sur la Seine / New road / Solitude / Breathing stone
CDEMD 1095 / Jun '96 / EMI

Kennedy, Pete
☐ LIFE IS LARGE (Kennedy, Pete & Maura)
GL 2123CD / May '96 / Green Linnet

☐ RIVER OF FALLEN STARS (Kennedy, Pete & Maura)
River of fallen stars / Same old way / Month of hours / Wall of death / Day in and day out / Winterheart / Fortune Teller Road / Stephen's green / House on fire / Run the red horses / Life goes on without you / Chelsea Embankment / Spirit compass
GLCD 2116 / Feb '95 / Green Linnet

Kennedy, Ronnie
☐ ACCORDION FAVOURITES
RZRCD 570 / Jun '98 / Ritz

☐ THOSE WERE THE DAYS
Those were the days / Dingle regatta / Irish medley / Whistling Rufus / Alpine slopes/Jacqueline waltz / Country favourites medley / Looking for a partner / Lara's theme / Scottish medley / Birdie song / Cuckoo waltz / Bluebell polka / Edelweiss
RZCD 514 / '91 / Ritz

Kennedy, Ross
☐ GATHERING STORMS (Kennedy, Ross & Archie McAllister)
CDLDL 1243 / Aug '96 / Lochshore

☐ TWISTED SINGERS (Kennedy, Ross & Archie McAllister)
CDLDL 1218 / Oct '94 / Lochshore

Kennedy, Tom
☐ BASSES LOADED
Songs for Sara / Caravan / Hey eyes / Alfred's book / Crystal / Made in New York / I'll see you / All of you / Oleo
TKM 50022 / May '96 / TKM

Kennel, Hans
☐ MYTHA
ARTCD 6110 / Aug '92 / Hat Art

☐ MYTHAHORNS VOL.2
ARTCD 6151 / Apr '95 / Hat Art

☐ STELLA
Meltdown / Moosruef / No.17 / Stella by starlight / Snobben / Varvisa / Inca Princess / Du liebe bueb vom emmital
TCB 97102 / Apr '97 / TCB

Kenney, Beverly
☐ COME SWING WITH ME
FSCD 560 / Feb '88 / Fresh Sound

Kenny & The Kasuals
☐ IMPACT
FLASH 26 / 1 Jun '98 / Flash

☐ THINGS GETTING BETTER/NOTHING BETTER TO DO
EVA 642390B39 / Nov '94 / EVA

Kenny, Emer
☐ EMER KENNY
5362282 / 13 Apr '98 / Mercury

Kenny G
☐ BREATHLESS
Joy of life / Forever in love / In the rain / Sentimental / By the time this night is over / End on the night / Morning / Even if my heart would break / G bop / Sister Rose / Year ago / Homeland / Natural ride / Wedding song / Alone
07822186462 / Mar '93 / Arista

☐ DUOTONES
You make me believe / Slip of the tongue / What does it take (to win your love) / Don't make me wait for love / Sade / Esther / Songbird / Champagne / Midnight / Three of a kind
258497 / Feb '96 / Arista

☐ G FORCE
Hi, how ya doin' / I've been missing you / Tribeca / G force / Do me right / I wanna be yours / Sunset at noon / Help yourself to my love
259059 / May '88 / Arista

☐ GRAVITY
Love on the rise / One man's poison (another man's sweetness) / Where do we take it / One night stand / Japan / Sax attack / Virgin island / Gravity / Last night of the year
74321161642 / Feb '94 / Arista

☐ GREATEST HITS
Songbird / Midnight motion / Silhouette / Going home / Dying young / Forever in love / Sentimental / Moment / Havana / Loving you / Don't make me wait for love: *Kenny G & Lenny Williams* / By the time this night is over: *Kenny G & Peabo Bryson* / All the way/ One for my baby (and one more for the road): *Kenny G & Frank Sinatra* / Everytime I close my eyes: *Kenny G & Babyface* / How could an angel break my heart: *Kenny G & Toni Braxton*
078221899123 / 1 Dec '97 / Arista

☐ KENNY G
Mercy mercy mercy / Here we are / Stop and go / I can't tell you why / Shuffle / Tell me / Find a way / Crystal mountain / Come close
259337 / Sep '95 / Arista

☐ MIRACLES - THE HOLIDAY ALBUM
Winter wonderland / White Christmas / Have yourself a merry little christmas / Christmas song / Silent night / Brahms lullaby / Greensleeves / Miracles / Away in a manger / Chanukah song / Little drummer boy / Silver bells / Spring breeze
07822187672 / Oct '95 / Arista

☐ MOMENT, THE
Moment / Passages / Havana / Always / That somebody was you / Champion's theme / Eastside jam / Moonlight / Gettin' on the step / Everytime I close my eyes / Northern lights / Innocence
07822189682 / Apr '97 / Arista

☐ MONTAGE
Songbird / I can't tell you why / Tribeca / Virgin island / I've been missing you / Uncle Al / What does it take (to win your love): *Kenny G & Ellis Hall* / Silhouette / Midnight motion / Against doctor's orders / Hi, how ya doin' / Sade / Going home / We've saved the best for last: *Kenny G & Smokey Robinson*
260621 / Apr '90 / Arista

☐ SILHOUETTE
Silhouette / We've saved the best for last / Trade winds / I'll be alright / Against doctor's orders / Pastel / All in one night / Let go / Home / Summer song
259284 / Jul '96 / Arista

Kenny, Gerard
☐ BEST OF GERARD KENNY, THE (The Singles)
I've grown accustomed to her face / You ain't pretty musical fantasy / Other woman the other man / Not just another pretty face / World full of laughter / I could be so good for you / I made it through the rain / Old friends / No mans land / Simple song / Nickels and dimes / Fantasy / Do I love you / So in love / Farewell canberra / New York New York
CDWM 114 / Jul '98 / ACL

☐ EVENING WITH GERARD KENNY, AN
Fantasy / Crime that pays / Pavement princess / Nickles and dimes / Going hollywood / You ain't pretty / Punk / Take back your heartache / Old friends / I could be so good for you / I made it through the rain / Son of a song and dance man / You're the best / Love / Ragtime / Miss otis regrets / From this moment on / I've grown accustomed to her face / Red hot radio / Other woman, the other man / D-d-dancingnew york new york / All for a dream
ACLCD 100 / Jun '95 / ACL

☐ IN LOVE
My funny valentine / Once in a while / She believes in me / If I loved you / Why did I choose you / Let it be me / One lonely voice / Where or when / All because of love / Difference is you / Love / Other woman the other man
CDWM 50 / 15 Sep '97 / ACL

☐ PLAY ME SOME PORTER PLEASE (Kenny, Gerard & Royal Philharmonic Orchestra)
Play me some Porter please / Anything goes / Night and day / Miss Otis regrets / True love / Begin the beguine / From this moment on / Every time we say goodbye / So in love / I've got you under my skin
CDWM 106 / May '92 / ACL

☐ TIME BETWEEN TIME
CDWM 110 / Aug '97 / ACL

Kenny, John
☐ FOREST RIVER OCEAN
BML 024 / Jul '98 / John Kenny

☐ VOICE OF THE CARNYX, THE
BML 016 / Feb '96 / British Music

Kenny Ken
☐ KENNY KEN PRESENTS FULL FORCE VOL.2 (2CD Set) (Various Artists)
DBM 34584 / 6 Apr '98 / Death Becomes Me

Kenny, Tony
☐ SONGS OF JOY AND INSPIRATION
CDC 037 / Dec '97 / Ceol

Kenoly, Ron
☐ HIGH PLACES (The Best Of Ron Kenoly)
Lift him up / Sing out / Praise the Lord all nations / God is able / Winna mon / Mourning into dancing / Give to the Lord / Ancient days / We're going up to high places / Let everything that has breath / Be glorified / Use me / I see the Lord / Jesus is alive / More of you
12032 / Nov '97 / Hosanna

Kenso
☐ KENSO
ARC 1003 / Jan '96 / Arc

☐ YUME NO OKA
14534 / Jul '97 / Spalax

Kenstroll
☐ MUSIQUES VIVANTES
KD 95CD / Mar '96 / Kan Dazont

Kent 3
☐ PEASANT MUSIK
SUPER 09CD / 20 Apr '98 / Super Electro

☐ STORIES OF THE NEW WEST
SUPER 08CD / May '97 / Super Electro

Kent, Stacey
☐ CLOSE YOUR EYES
More than you know / Dream dancing / Close your eyes / There's a lull in my life / It's de-lovely / There's no you / I'm old fashioned / You go to my head / Little white lies / Sleep warm / Day in, day out
CCD 79737 / May '97 / Candid

Kent, Steven

☐ FAMILY TREE (2CD Set)
COTCD 016 / 1 Jun '98 / Knock On Wood

Kent, Willie

☐ AIN'T IT NICE
Memory of you / Check it out / Worry worry / One more mile / Ain't it nice / What you're doing to me / I'm good / Ma Bea's / Come home / Feel so good / Stranded
DD 653 / Mar '97 / Delmark

☐ LONG WAY TO OL' MISS
Long way to ol' miss / Blues in my bedroom / Dirty works / It ain't right / Ain't got long to stay / My friend / Don't know much about love / Extension 309 / All my life / Ain't no love in your heart / Don't drive me away / Black night / What you doin' to me
DE 696 / Jun '97 / Delmark

☐ TOO HURT TO CRY
Too hurt to cry / Going down the road / Man and the blues / Willie Mae / Blues train / Just sitting here thinking / Good man feeling bad / This thing called love / 911 / In case we both are wrong / Night time is the right time / Countdown / All nite long
DE 667 / Mar '97 / Delmark

Kenton, Stan

☐ 18 ORIGINAL BIG BAND RECORDINGS
Hold in reserve / Four of a kind / Blues story / I understand / Between the devil and the deep blue sea / Siesta / I'm glad there is you / Mission trail / Night at the gold nugget / Peanut vendor / Fitz / Mellophobia / All the things you are / Ruben's blues / Limehouse blues / Waltz of the prophets / Tonight / Artistry in rythm
HCD 407 / Sep '92 / Hindsight

☐ 23 DEGREES NORTH, 82 DEGREES WEST (Live 1952-1953) (Kenton, Stan Orchestra)
Theme (Artistry in rhythm) and opening announcements / Works / Yesterdays / Swinghouse / Stan Kenton speaks / Gone with the wind / There will never be another you / Theme (Artistry in rhythm) and opening announcements / Love for sale / Over the rainbow / Hava Havana / Frank speaking / I'll remember April / Young blood / Street of dreams / Blue moon / Bill's blues / Lover man / Collaboration / 23 degrees North, 82 degrees West / My lady / Bill's blues
VN 1007 / Nov '96 / Viper's Nest

☐ ARTISTRY IN RHYTHM
JHR 73540 / May '93 / Jazz Hour

☐ ARTISTRY IN RHYTHM (20 Classics From His Legendary Big Band)
Artistry in rhythm / Painted rhythm / And her tears flowed like wine / Body and soul / Tampico / Scotch and water / Shoo fly pie and apple pie dowdy / Concerto to end all concertos / Eager beaver / I want a grown up man / Southern scandal / Harlem folk dance / Artistry in percussion / Easy street / Intermission riff / Willow weep for me / Opus in pastels / Artistry in boogie / Opus a dollar three-eighty / Artistry jumps
308072 / 13 Oct '97 / Hallmark

☐ ARTISTRY IN RHYTHM 1943-1947 (Kenton, Stan Orchestra)
Artistry in rhythm / Eager beaver / And her tears flowed like wine / Gotta be gettin' / Are you livin' old man / Tampico / Southern scandal / It's been a long long time / Just a sittin' and a rockin' / Painted rhythm / Shoo-fly pie and apple pan dowdy / Intermission riff / Willow weep for me / Concerto to end all concertos / Across the alley from the Alamo / Minor riff / Lovers / Theme to the west / Unison riff (the fatal apple) / Lament (for guitar) / I told ya I love ya now get out / Peanut vendor / Artistry jumps
CDAJA 5269 / Aug '98 / Living Era

☐ ARTISTRY OF STAN KENTON, THE
Eager beaver / Artistry in rhythm / Her tears flowed like wine / Balboa bash / Travellin' man / Southern scandal / Artistry jumps / Painted Rhythm / Opus in pastels / Artistry in pastels / Come back to Sorrento / Peg o' my heart / Artistry in percussion / Safranski (artistry in bass) / Ecuador / Cocktails for two / Fantasy / Concerto to end all concerto's / Artistry in bolero / Intermission riff / Are you livin' old man
CDMOIR 523 / Apr '95 / Memoir

☐ AT FOUNTAIN STREET CHURCH VOL.1
DSTS 1014 / Oct '95 / Status

☐ AT FOUNTAIN STREET CHURCH VOL.2
DSTS 1016 / Oct '95 / Status

☐ AT MARCH FIELD AIR FORCE BASE, CALIFORNIA DECEMBER 1959 (Previously Unissued Recordings) (Kenton, Stan Orchestra)
Street of dreams / I'm glad there is you / Young and foolish / Where or when / How deep is the ocean / My heart stood still / All of you / Early Autumn / Chocolate caliente / Night we called it a day / You better go now / They didn't believe me / Twilight riff / Take the 'A' train / September song/Stardust / Eager beaver/Dynaflow/Jump for Joe/Artistry in rhythm
DSTS 1011 / May '95 / Status

☐ AT THE HOLIDAY BALLROOM, CHICAGO 1962
DSTS 1018 / May '96 / Status

☐ AT THE PAVILION, HEMEL HEMPSTEAD 1973
DSTS 1017 / May '96 / Status

☐ BALLAD STYLE OF STAN KENTON
Hen I'll be tired of you / More than you know / When stars looked down / End of a love affair / Sunday kind of love / Moon song / Early autumn / How am I to know / Things we did last summer / We'll be together again / How deep is the ocean / Night we called it a day / Ill wind
CDP 8566882 / Jul '97 / Capitol Jazz

☐ BEST OF STAN KENTON, THE
Artistry in rhythm / Eager beaver / Artistry jumps / Painted rhythm / Intermission riff / Collaboration / Lover / Unison riff / Peanut vendor / Interlude / Love for sale / Laura / Twelve degrees north / Invention for guitar and trumpet / Stompin' at the Savoy / La suerte de los tontos (fortune of fools) / Waltz of prophets / Malageuna
CDP 8315042 / Apr '95 / Capitol Jazz

☐ BROADCAST TRANSMISSIONS 1941-1945
CD 883 / Sep '95 / Music & Arts

☐ CLASSICS 1940-1944
CLASSICS 848 / Nov '95 / Classics

☐ CLASSICS 1945
CLASSICS 898 / Oct '96 / Classics

☐ CLASSICS 1946
CLASSICS 949 / 21 Aug '97 / Classics

☐ EARLY CONCEPTS
LEJAZZCD 54 / Jan '96 / Le Jazz

☐ ELEGY (Kenton, Stan Orchestra)
Intermission riff / Come back to Sorrento / Dark eyes / Martha / Elegy / Artistry in rhythm / Peanut vendor / Estrellita
CDSGP 0188 / Apr '98 / Prestige

☐ FIFTIES BIRDLAND BROADCASTS, THE
EBCD 2135 / May '98 / Jazzband

☐ INNOVATIONS ORCHESTRA, THE (2CD Set)
Mirage / Conflict / Solitare / Soliliquay / Theme for Sunday / Amazonia / Lonesome road / Trajectories / Incident in jazz / Cuban episode / Evening in Pakistan / Salute / Mardi gras / In verado / Jolly rodgers / Blues in riff / Cello logy / Art pepper / Halls of brass / Maynard Ferguson / Shelly manne / June christy / House of strings / Round robin / Coop's solo / Sambo / Ennui / Samana / Coop's solo
8599652 / 8 Dec '97 / Capitol Jazz

☐ JAZZ PROFILE
Southern scandal / Just a sittin' and a rockin' / Artistry in Bolero / Machito / Harlem holiday / Evening in Pakistan / Round Robin / Street of dreams / Fascinating rhythm / Fearless finlay / Limelight / Peanut vendor / September song / Just in time / Blues story / Gloomy Sunday
CDP 8332432 / 6 Oct '97 / Blue Note

☐ LIVE AT BARSTOW 1960 (Kenton, Stan Orchestra)
DSTS 1001 / May '94 / Status

☐ LIVE AT CARTHAGE COLLEGE VOL.1 (Kenton, Stan Orchestra)
DAWE 69 / May '94 / Magic

☐ LIVE AT CARTHAGE COLLEGE VOL.2 (Kenton, Stan Orchestra)
Here's that rainy day / 2002 - Zarathustrevisited / Macarthur park / Peanut vendor / Street of dreams / Malaguena / Artistry in rhythm / Happy birthday to you / Take the 'A' train
DAWE 70 / Jun '94 / Magic

☐ LIVE AT SALT LAKE CITY VOL.1
Opener / Walking shoes / I remember you / Theme and variations / I'm glad there is you / I should care / Big chase / Artistry in rythm / Spring is here / My ideal / Love letters / Sophisticated lady / Way you look tonight / When your lover has gone / Intermission riff / Artistry in rhythm (end) / Opus in chartreuse
DAWE 56 / Feb '94 / Magic

☐ LIVE AT SALT LAKE CITY VOL.2
I get along without you very well / Tenderly / Memories of you / I married an angel / Day by day / I see your face before me / So in love / Artistry in rythm / I'm glad there is you / My ideal / Spring is here / Street of dreams / Intermission riff / Where or when / Walkin' by the river / All of you / Love for sal
DAWE 57 / Nov '92 / Magic

☐ LIVE AT SALT LAKE CITY VOL.3
DAWE 58 / Nov '92 / Magic

☐ LIVE AT THE LAS VEGAS TROPICANA
Artistry in rhythm / Bernie's tune / Tuxedo junction / Street scene / Puck's blues / This is always / Don't get around much anymore / Design for blue / Home journey / String of pearls / It's alright with me / Intermission riff / I concentrate on you / End of a love affair / You and I and George / Sentimental riff / Random riff
CDP 8352452 / Apr '96 / Capitol Jazz

☐ LIVE AT THE MACUMBA CLUB
El Congo Valiente / Fuego Cubano / Big chase / My funny valentine / Opener / I concentrate on you / I remember you / Harlem nocturne / Between the Devil and the deep blue sea / Swing house / Love for sale / Royal blue / Artistry in rhythm
DAWE 53 / Nov '91 / Magic

☐ LIVE AT THE MACUMBA CLUB - SAN FRANCISCO 1956
Walking shoes / Autumn nocturne / Artistry in rhythm / Winter in Madrid / My old flame / La suerte de los tontos (Fortune of fools) / I concentrate on you / Theme on variations / Young blood / Collaboration / Stella by starlight / Cherokee / Intermission riff / Laura / Stompin' at the Savoy / Out of nowhere
DAWE 50 / '91 / Magic

☐ LIVE AT THE SUNSET RIDGE CLUB 1976 VOL.1
DAWE 59 / ' ' / Magic

☐ LIVE AT THE SUNSET RIDGE CLUB 1976 VOL.2
DAWE 61 / Mar '93 / Magic

☐ LIVE IN 1951
EBCD 21052 / Feb '94 / Flyright

☐ LIVE IN BILOXI (Kenton, Stan Orchestra & The Four Freshmen)
Lasuerte de los tontos / I concentrate on you / Lullaby of Broadway / Nearness of you / Kingfish / Early Autumn / Love for sale / My old flame / Yesterdays / Out of nowhere / Night we called it a day / Everything happens to me / There will never be another you / So in love / With the wind and rain in your hair / Big chase
DAWE 32 / Apr '89 / Magic

☐ LIVE IN COLOGNE 1976 VOL.1
DAWE 64 / Jul '93 / Magic

☐ LIVE IN COLOGNE 1976 VOL.2
DAWE 65 / Jul '93 / Magic

☐ LONDON HILTON VOL.1 1973
DSTS 1003 / '94 / Status

☐ LONDON HILTON VOL.2 1973
DSTS 1005 / Dec '94 / Status

☐ MASTERPIECES
159182 / 1 Jun '98 / Jazz Archives

☐ MORE MELLOPHONIUM MOODS
Fly me to the moon / Foggy day / Misty / You stepped out of a dream / Reuben's blues / Magic moment / Blues story / Easy to love / Warm blue stream / Lot of livin' to do / My one and only love / Maria / Time after time / Love walked in / Like someone in love / Eager beaver/Opus in chartreuse/Dynaflow/Jump for Joe / Java junction/Tea for two / Artistry in rhythm
DSTS 1010 / Apr '95 / Status

☐ ON AIR
DSTS 1019 / Jul '96 / Status

☐ ON THE AIR (Bob Snyder Show 13th July 1952) (Kenton, Stan Orchestra)
DSTS 1022 / Nov '97 / Status

☐ ONE NIGHT STAND (Kenton, Stan Orchestra)
DAWE 66 / Dec '93 / Magic

☐ PASADENA CIVIC AUDITORIUM 1943-1944
Theme-artistry in rhythm: *Kenton, Stan Orchestra* / Begin the beguine: *Kenton, Stan Orchestra* / Do nothing 'till you hear from me: *Kenton, Stan Orchestra* / Eager beaver: *Kenton, Stan Orchestra* / You gotta talk me into it baby: *Kenton, Stan Orchestra* / Old man river: *Kenton, Stan Orchestra* / Music stopped: *Kenton, Stan Orchestra* / Ride on: *Kenton, Stan Orchestra* / Star eyes: *Kenton, Stan Orchestra* / Closing theme-artistry in rhythm: *Kenton, Stan Orchestra* / Salt lake city bounce: *Kenton, Stan Orchestra* / Shoo shoo baby: *Kenton, Stan Orchestra* / Do nothing 'till you here from me: *Kenton, Stan Orchestra* / Claire De Lune: *Kenton, Stan Orchestra* / Singing the blues: *Kenton, Stan Orchestra* / Special delivery: *Kenton, Stan Orchestra* / You betcha: *Kenton, Stan Orchestra* / Harlem folk dance: *Kenton, Stan Orchestra* / In a little Spanish town: *Kenton, Stan Orchestra* / I know that you know: *Kenton, Stan Orchestra* / I'll remember April: *Kenton, Stan Orchestra* / Five o'clock drag: *Kenton, Stan Orchestra* / Under a blanket of blue: *Kenton, Stan Orchestra* / Opus a dollar three eighty: *Kenton, Stan Orchestra*
DSTS 1023 / Jun '98 / Status

☐ PLAYS BOB GRAETTINGER CITY OF GLASS
Thermopylae / Everything happens to me / Incident in jazz / House of strings / Horn / City of glass (first movements part 1 to 4) / Orchestra / Trumpet / You got to my head / Cello / Modern opus / Reflections / Dance before the mirror / Entrance into the city
CDP 8320842 / Aug '95 / Capitol Jazz

☐ RARE RECORDINGS
15725 / Sep '92 / Laserlight

☐ RENDEZVOUS OF STANDARDS AND CLASSICS (2CD Set)
Artistry in rhythm / Eager beaver / Collaboration / Peanut vendor / Intermission riff / Concerto to end all concertos / Artistry jumps / Sophisticated lady / Begin the beguine / Lover man / Pennies from heaven / Over the rainbow / Fascinating rhythm / There's a small hotel / Shadow waltz / Tampico / Artistry in boogie / Southern scandal / Machito / Her tears flowed like wine / Minor riff / Across the valley from the Alamo / Unison riff / April in Paris / How high the moon / Crazy rhythm / I got it bad and that ain't good / You and the night and the music / Under a blanket of blue / I've got you under my skin / Autumn in New York / With the wind and rain in your hair / Memories of you / These things you left me / Two shades of autumn / They didn't believe me / Walkin' by the river / High on a windy hill / Love letters / I get along without you very well / Desiderata / This is no laughing matters / I see your face before me
CDDL 1293 / Jun '95 / Music For Pleasure

☐ STAN KENTON & HIS INNOVATIONS ORCHESTRA (Kenton, Stan Orchestra)
Spirals / Ennui / In Veradero / Shelly Manne / Conte Candoli / Art Pepper / Improvisation / Love for sale / Bob Cooper / Reflections
15770 / May '94 / Laserlight

☐ STAN KENTON & HIS INNOVATIONS ORCHESTRA/JUNE CHRISTY 1950 (2CD Set) (Kenton, Stan Innovations Orchestra & June Christy)
EBCD 2131/32 / Apr '97 / Jazzband

☐ STAN KENTON ORCHESTRA, THE (Kenton, Stan Orchestra)
Theme and variations / Fearless Finlay / I concentrate on you / My old flame / Intermission riff / La suerte de Los Tontos / Bernie's tune / SStreet scene / Out of this world
HCD 612 / Jan '98 / Hindsight

☐ STREET OF DREAMS (Kenton, Stan Orchestra & The Four Freshmen)
Send in the clowns / Rhapsody in blue / Street of dreams / Body and soul / Tiare / Too shy to say / My funny valentine
STD 1079 / Jun '95 / GNP Crescendo

☐ TRANSCRIPTION PERFORMANCES 1945-1946, THE
HEPCD 47 / Jan '97 / Hep

☐ UNCOLLECTED VOL.2 1941, THE
Congo clambake / Arkansas traveller / Shuffling the chords / Take sixteen / Opus in pastels / Reed rapture / Etude for saxophones / Tribute to flatted fifth / Quit your show / Underneath the stars / Let her go / Too soon / Hold back the dawn / Low bridge / Popocatepeil / Blue falre
HCD 124 / Apr '95 / Hindsight

Kentucky Boys

☐ FELT SO WILD
PT 612001 / Jun '96 / Part

☐ I WANT IT HOT
PT 612003 / Dec '96 / Part

Kentucky Colonels

☐ APPALACHIAN SWING
Clinch mountain backstep / Nine pound hammer / Listen to the mockingbird / Wild Bill Jones / Billy in the lowground / Lee Highway blues / I am a pilgrim / Prisoner's song / Sally Goodin / Faded love / John Henry / Flat fork
ROUSS 31CD / Aug '93 / Rounder

☐ KENTUCKY COLONELS
Clinch Mountain back-step / Nine pound hammer / Listen to the mocking bird / Wild Bill Jones / Billy in the low ground / Lee Highway / That's what you get for loving me / I am a pilgrim / Prisoner's song / Sally Goodin / Ballad of Farmer Brown / Faded love / John Henry / Flat fork
BGOCD 357 / Jul '97 / Beat Goes On

☐ LONG JOURNEY HOME
Roll on buddy / Bill Cheetham / There ain't nobody gonna miss me when I'm gone / Shuckin' the corn / Beautiful life / Get down on your knees and pray / Over in the glory land / Sally Ann / Brakeman's blues / Soldier's joy / Listen to the mockingbird / Farewell blues / Lonesome road blues / Beaumont rag / Footprints in the snow / Long journey home / In the pines / Chicken reel / Old hickory / Auld lang syne / Nola / Flat fork / Shady grove
VCD 77004 / Oct '95 / Vanguard

Kentucky Minstrels

☐ KENTUCKY MINSTRELS, THE
Banjo song medley / Holy city / White wings / Passing by / Song that reached my heart / Kentucky Minstrels plantation medley no.1 / Smilin' through / Last rose of summer / Rose of Tralee / Love's old sweet song / Carry me back to green pastures / I'll walk beside you / Bless this house / O dry those tears / Christopher Robin is saying his prayers / Homing
CDAJA 5229 / Jul '97 / Living Era

Kenyatta, Robin

☐ GHOST STORIES
ITM 970060 / Apr '91 / ITM

☐ ROBIN KENYATTA'S FREE STATE BAND
500572 / May '94 / Musidisc

☐ TAKE THE HEAT OFF ME
ITMP 970069 / Mar '92 / ITM

Kenziner

☐ TIMESCAPE
LMP 9806004CD / 8 Jun '98 / Limb

Kepone

☐ KEPONE
QS 46CD / Apr '97 / Quarter Stick

☐ SKIN
QS 33CD / Sep '95 / Quarter Stick

☐ UGLY DANCE
QS 27CD / Aug '94 / Quarter Stick

Keppard, Freddie

☐ LEGEND, THE
TPZ 1052 / Aug '96 / Topaz Jazz

☐ NEW ORLEANS GIANTS VOL.2 1922-28 (Keppard, Freddie & Ory/Dodds/carey)
152222 / Dec '93 / Hot 'n' Sweet

Kerbdog

☐ ON THE TURN
Sally / JJ's song / Didn't even try / Mexican wave / Severed / Pledge / On the turn / Secure / Lesser shelf / Pointless / Rewind / Sorry for the record
5329992 / Mar '97 / Vertigo

☐ TOTALLY SWITCHED
End of green / Dry riser / Dead anyway / Cleaver / Earthworks / Dummy crusher / Inseminator / Clock / Schism / Scram
5188662 / Apr '94 / Vertigo

Kerleo, Gwenael

☐ TERRE CELTE
KER 01CD / Nov '96 / KER

Kern, Jerome

☐ ALL THE THINGS YOU ARE (The Jerome Kern Songbook) (Various Artists)
5299072 / May '96 / Verve

☐ COMPLETE JEROME KERN SONGBOOKS, THE (All The Things You Are/A Fine Romance/Yesterdays - 3CD Set) (Various Artists)
5394412 / 10 Nov '97 / Verve

☐ FINE ROMANCE, A (The Jerome Kern Songbook) (Various Artists)
5238272 / Jan '95 / Verve

☐ GREAT MELODIES, THE (Kern, Jerome/Irving Berlin)
Smoke gets in your eyes / Fine romance / I won't dance / All the things you are / Way you look tonight / Who / Dearly beloved / Song is you / Ol' man river / Alexander's ragtime band / Puttin' on the Ritz / White Christmas / Cheek to cheek / I've got my love to keep me warm / Change partners / They say it's wonderful / Medley (tribute to Irving Berlin)
300612 / Jul '96 / Hallmark

☐ SITTING PRETTY
803872 / Aug '92 / New World

☐ TRIBUTE TO JEROME KERN, A (2CD Set) (Various Artists)
Folks who live on the hill: *Lee, Peggy* / Fine romance: *Tilton, Martha* / Last time I saw Paris: *Four Freshmen* / Way you look tonight: *Haymes, Dick* / I'm old fashioned: *Garland, Judy* / Look for the silver lining: *Brent, Tony* / Ol' man river: *Wiata, Iniate* / Yesterdays: *Stafford, Jo* / They don't believe me: *Alberghetti, Anna Maria* / Long ago and far away: *Cardinali, Roberto & the Rita Williams singers* / I still suits me: *Wiata, Iniate* / How do you like to spoon with me: *Hunt, Jan* / Why was I born: *Washington, Dinah* / Sure thing: *Simpson, Carole* / Bojangles of Harlem: *Gonella, Nat* / All through the day: *Geraldo* / Who: *Shore, Dinah* / Bill: *Laine, Cleo* / Lovely to look at: *MacRae, Gordon* / I won't dance: *Lee, Peggy* / Smoke gets in your eyes: *Hilton, Ronnie* / Song is you: *Smith, Keely* / Make believe: *Lee, Peggy* / Nobody else but me: *Laine, Cleo* / Who do I love you: *Dallas, Lorna* / Pick yourself up: *Cordell, Frank* / Can't help lovin' dat man: *Bassey, Shirley* / You were never lovelier: *Lewis, Archie* / Can I forget you: *Lewis, Archie* / You are love: *Dallas, Lorna* / Life upon the wicked stage: *Bryan, Dora* / I might fall back on you: *Bryan, Dora* / Moon love: *Silvester, Victor* / I've told every little star: *Vernon Girls* / You wouldn't be cuter: *Geraldo* / Waltz in swingtime: *Martin, Skip* / Dearly beloved: *Wilson, Nancy* / Daydreaming: *Osbourne, Tony* / All the things you are: *May, Billy* / In love in vain: *Horne, Lena*
CDDL 1290 / Jun '95 / EMI

☐ YESTERDAYS (The Jerome Kern Songbook) (Various Artists)
5333312 / May '97 / Verve

Kern, Renate

☐ DU BIST MEINE LIEBE
Kiss and shake / Die Welt ist so schon wie ein traum / Kommt nict in frage / Du bist meine liebe / Eine Welt fur uns zwei / Weine keine Abschiedstranen / Bis morgen / Ganz genau wie du / Lass den Dummen Kummer / Weinen tut so weh / An irgendeinem Tag / Du musst mir die Wahrheit sagen / Stop the beat / Damals in Napoli / Ein schlaflose nacht / Ein mann - ein wort / Lieber mal weinen im gluck / Traurigsein lohnt sich nicht / Du musst mit den Wimpern klimpern / Herbstwind / Lass doch den Sonnenschein / Meine welt ist schon / Now and then / You'll be the first one to know / I'll remember summer / Love me tonight / Happy heart
BCD 16201 / Jun '97 / Bear Family

☐ ER NAHM EIN ANDERES MADCHEN
Lieber heute gekusst / Einsamkeit / 1990 / Come on let's dance / Der wasserman / Hor auf den herz / Supermann / Silber und gold / Alle blumen brauchen sonne / Das schonste land der welt / Warum willst du weinen / Er nahm ein anderes madchen / Lass mich heute nicht allein / Auf dir lacht einmal die liebe / Geh'mit Gott / Qua la Linta / Morgen fruh, da lachst du schon wieder / Rinaldo Rinaldini / Das macht diese Welt erst richtig schon / Meine welt ist von heute an deine welt / Andiamo, amigo / Mach es wie die Sonnenuhr / Adio / Non, jene regrette rien / You'll never walk alone
BCD 16202 / Jun '97 / Bear Family

Kerosene

☐ ARRHYTHMIA
Spring / Everybody's icon / Worthless / Excess / Shame / Come alive / My friends / Everything / Mercy / So plain / Joanne / Feeling within
9362452792 / Oct '93 / WEA

Kerosene

☐ TEENAGE SECRET
CAI 2010 / 20 Apr '98 / Caipirinha

☐ WOMEN QUALITY
EFA 089212 / 1 Sep '98 / Pharma

Kerosene 454

☐ AT ZERO
SLOWDIME 11CD / 16 Mar '98 / Slowdime/Dischord

☐ CAME BY TO KILL ME
DIS 1115CD / Feb '97 / Dischord

☐ RACE
PRC 014 / 6 Oct '97 / Polyvinyl

Kerosin

☐ WHERE HAVE ALL THE FLOWERS GONE
TZ 400022 / 29 Sep '97 / Terrazone

Kerr, Alec

☐ CELTIC SOFT WINDS
CHCD 020 / May '96 / Chart

☐ ECHOES OF IRELAND (Kerr, Alec & Sandra Townsend/Brian Lynch)
Danny Boy / Carrickfergus / Moon behind the hill / Come back Paddy Reilly / Boolavogue / For Ireland I'd tell not her name / Rose of Tralee / Molly Malone / Banks of my own lovely Lee / Coulin / Sweet vale of Avoca / Mountains of Mourne / Spinning wheel / Caoineadh an spailpin / Green glens of Antrim / Noreen Bawn / Old bog road / Down by the Sally Gardens / Galway Bay / If we only had old Ireland over here / Forty shades of green / Flight of the Earls / Wind and the willows
CHCD 027 / May '96 / Chart

Kerr, Anthony

☐ NOW HEAR THIS (Kerr, Anthony Quartet)
JHCD 055 / 27 Oct '97 / Ronnie Scott's Jazz House

Kerr, Moira

☐ ALL THE BEST
Maclain of Glencoe / Where eagles fly / Skye boat song / Loch Lomond / Dark island / Banquo's walk / Sands of time / Drifting away / Mingulay boat song / Everlasting visions / Paradise for two / Cuillin
MOICD 010 / Nov '96 / Moidart

☐ BE THOU MY VISION
Be thou my vision / Who would true valour see / I vow to thee my country / Holy holy holy / Teach me, my God and King / O thou camest from above / By cool Siloam's shady rill / Stand up, stand up for Jesus / Dear Lord and Father of mankind / Immortal, invisible, God only wise / Forty days and forty nights / Breathe on me, breath of God / Alleluia, sing to Jesus / Jerusalem
CFTMCD 01 / Mar '95 / Tangmere

☐ BRAVEST HEART
Bravest heart / Corryvreckan / She moved through the fair / Only a woman's heart / Island in the mist / Queens Four Marys / Fear a bhata / For justice and honour (Rob Roy) / Safely ashore / Long black veil / House carpenter / Highlanders
CDMAYK 09 / Oct '95 / Mayker

☐ CELTIC SOUL
MacLain of Glencoe / Will ye go lassie go / Where eagles fly / Sands of time / Corryvreckan / Skye boat song / Bravest heart / Loch Lomond / Island of Tiree / Flower of Scotland / Highlanders / Mingulay / Dark Island / Farewell to Tarwathie / Skye high / Drifting away
CDMAYK 10 / May '97 / Mayker

☐ GLENCOE THE GLEN OF WEEPING
Closer to heaven / This child / Oban bay / Loch Lomond hills / Three months of the year / Glen of weeping / Glean bhaile chaoil / When I dream / Curragh of Kildare / Isle of Innisfree / Arran, the island i love / You'll be there / Glen of weeping (instrumental)
CDMAYK 1 / Nov '94 / Mayker

Kerr, Nancy

☐ STARRY GAZY PIE (Kerr, Nancy & James Fagan)
Mrs. Capron's reel/Murray's reel / Jack Orion/Rusty Jack / Turtle dove/The five fortunes / Lang stayed away/Little fishie/All the night I lay awake / Berkshire tragedy / Song of a drinking man's wife / Wrong door/Choom/The wet physician / Miles Weatherhill / Streams of lovely Nancy / Dancing on the gravel/ Pam's polka / Seven yellow gypsies / Young hunting / Branle de Bourgogne/Beyond the border / Starry gazy pie
FECD 127 / Jan '98 / Fellside

Kerr, Ron

☐ TOP LEVEL
SHIELCD 003 / Jun '98 / Shielburn Associates

Kerr, Sandra

☐ NEAT AND COMPLETE (Kerr, Sandra & Nancy)
Lads of Alnwick / Milkmaids / Wee weaver / David Malone's / James Fagan's / Shoemakker / Maid on the shore / Welcome home / Saucy Nancy / Seven yellow gypsies / Yellow haired laddie / Lovely Nancy / Great Silkie / Sheepcrook and black dog / Rusty gully / Go to Berwick Johnny / Jackie Munroe / George Collins
FECD 107 / May '96 / Fellside

Kerr, Trudy

☐ SWEET SURPRISE
UGCD 040797 / Oct '97 / FMR/Dissenter

Kerrs Pink

☐ ART OF COMPLEX SIMPLICITY
FGBG 4219AR / Jul '97 / Musea

Kersh, David

☐ IF I NEVER STOP LOVING YOU
CURCD 056 / 29 Jun '98 / Curb

Kershaw, Doug

☐ CAJUN GREATS
Cajun baby / Don't mess with my toot toot / Jambalaya (on the bayou) / Cajun boogie queen / Fiddlin' man / Louisiana man / Diggy liggy lo / Our own jole blon / Cajun joe (the bully of the bayou) / Cheated too
12474 / Jun '95 / Laserlight

☐ HOT DIGGITY DOUG
Cajun baby / Louisiana / Jambalaya / I wanna hold you / Callin' Baton rouge / My toot toot / Boogie queen / Just like you / Louisiana man / Mansion in Spain / Cajun stripper / Fiddlin' man
CDSD 066 / Oct '89 / Sundown

Kershaw, Martin

☐ ACOUSTIC DREAMS
PDSCD 531 / Aug '96 / Pulse

Kershaw, Nik

☐ COLLECTION, THE
Wouldn't it be good / I won't let the sun go down on me / Human racing / Riddle / Wide boy / Don quixote / Nobody knows / Dancing girls / One step ahead / One world / Wouldn't it be good (91 remix)
MCLD 19309 / Oct '95 / MCA

☐ WOULDN'T IT BE GOOD
Wouldn't it be good / Running scared / Radio Musicola / Wild horses / When a heart beats / LABATYD / Dancing girls / Nobody knows / Human racing / Violet to blue / Faces / Save the whale / Drum talk
PWKS 4177 / Oct '93 / Carlton

Kershaw, Rusty

☐ LOUISIANA MAN (Kershaw, Rusty & Doug)
Louisiana man / Diggy liggy lo / Cheated too / Cajun Joe / We'll do it anyway / Jolie blon / So lovely baby / Look around / Mr. Love / Going down the road / Never love again / Kaw-liga
CDSD 022 / Mar '92 / Sundown

Kershaw, Sammy

☐ LABOR OF LOVE
5363182 / 10 Nov '97 / Mercury

☐ POLITICS, RELIGION AND HER
5288932 / Aug '96 / Mercury

Kertsman, Miguel

☐ AMAZONICA (Kertsman, Miguel & Camerata Cantione Antiqua)
SK 62882 / 1 Sep '97 / Sony Classical

Kessel, Barney

☐ AQUARIUS (Music From Hair)
BLC 760222 / Nov '97 / Black Lion

☐ ARTISTRY OF BARNEY KESSEL, THE
Vickie's dream / Tenderly / 64 bars on wilshire / 'round midnight / Louisiana / Makin' whoopee / Jersey bounce / Let's cook / Sweet sue / Joy spring / Pedal point / Moving up
FCD 60021 / Oct '93 / Fantasy

☐ AUTUMN LEAVES
BLCD 760112 / Jun '88 / Black Lion

☐ BARNEY KESSEL SAMPLER
Satin doll / On a slow boat to China / Foggy day (in London Town) / Swingin' the toreador / Easy living / Mack the knife / Tenderly
OJCX 010 / Jan '98 / Original Jazz Classics

☐ GREAT GUITARS AT CHARLIE'S, GEORGETOWN (Kessel, Barney/ Charlie Byrd/ Herb Ellis)
Where or when / New Orleans / When the saints go marching in / Change partners / Opus one / Old folks / Get happy / Trouble in mind
CCD 4209 / May '94 / Concord Jazz

☐ IT'S A BLUE WORLD
JHR 73526 / May '93 / Jazz Hour

☐ JELLYBEANS (Kessel, Barney Trio)
CCD 4164 / Jul '96 / Concord Jazz

☐ LIMEHOUSE BLUES (Kessel, Barney & Stephane Grappelli)
It don't mean a thing if it ain't got that swing / Out of nowhere / Tea for two / Limehouse blues / How high the moon / Willow weep for me / Little star / Undecided
BLCD 760158 / Oct '92 / Black Lion

☐ LIVE AT SOMETIME
STCD 4157 / Feb '90 / Storyville

☐ PLAYS "CARMEN"
Swingin' the toreador / A pad on the edge of town / If you dig me / Free as a bird / Viva el toro / Flowersville / Carmen's cool / Like, there's no place like... / Gypsy's hip
OJCCD 269 / Feb '92 / Original Jazz Classics

☐ POLL WINNERS VOL.1, THE (Kessel, Barney/Ray Brown/Shelly Manne)
Jordu / Satin doll / It could happen to you / Mean to me / Don't worry 'bout me / On green dolphin street / You go to my head / Minor mood / Nagasaki
OJCCD 156 / Sep '93 / Original Jazz Classics

☐ POLL WINNERS VOL.2, THE
Be deedle dee do / Volare / Spring is here / Surrey with the fringe on top / Custard puff / When the red red robin comes bob bob bobbin' along / Foreign intrigue / Angel eyes / Merry-go-round broke down
OJCCD 607 / Feb '92 / Original Jazz Classics

☐ POOR BUTTERFLY (Kessel, Barney & Herb Ellis)
Dearly beloved / Monsieur Armand / Poor butterfly / Make someone happy / Early autumn / Hello / Blueberry Hill / I'm a lover / Brigitte
CCD 4034 / Aug '95 / Concord Jazz

☐ RED, HOT AND BLUES
CCD 14044 / Mar '95 / Contemporary

☐ SOARING
You go to my head / Get out of town / Seagull / Like someone in love / You're the one for me / Beautiful love / Star eyes / I love you
CCD 6033 / Feb '92 / Concord Jazz

☐ SOLO
Brazil / What are you doing the rest of your life / Happy little song / Everything happens to me / You are the sunshine of my life / Manha de carnaval / People / Jellybeans / Alfie
CCD 4221 / Nov '96 / Concord Jazz

☐ TO SWING OR NOT TO SWING
Begin the blues / Louisiana / Happy feeling / Embraceable you / Wail Street / (Back home again in) Indiana / Moten swing / Midnight sun / Contemporary blues / Don't blame me / Twelfth St. rag
OJCCD 317 / '93 / Original Jazz Classics

☐ YESTERDAY (Recorded Live At The Montreux Festival 1973)
BLCD 760183 / Apr '93 / Black Lion

Kessinger Brothers

☐ KESSINGER BROTHERS VOL.1 1928-1929
DOCD 8010 / Jul '97 / Document

☐ KESSINGER BROTHERS VOL.2 1929
DOCD 8011 / Jul '97 / Document

☐ KESSINGER BROTHERS VOL.3 1929-1930
DOCD 8012 / Jul '97 / Document

Kester Emeneya

☐ VIVA LA MUSICA
CDS 7007 / Jan '97 / Sonodisc

Ketama

☐ KETAMA
Sueno Ipossible / Luna, Quedate commigo / Ketama / Me lilama / Slo para dos / Domo arigato / No se si vivo o sueno / Vacio / Galuchi / Cuando salga la luna / Chupendi / Canasteros
HNCD 1336 / May '89 / Hannibal

☐ KETAMA (3CD Set)
5362842 / 1 Jun '98 / Karonte

Ketchum, Hal

☐ HITS, THE (2CD Set)
CURCD 026 / May '96 / Curb

☐ I SAW THE LIGHT
CURCD 042 / 18 May '98 / Curb

☐ PAST THE POINT OF RESCUE
Small town Saturday night / I know where love lies / Old soldiers / Somebody's love / Past the point of rescue / Five o'clock world / I miss my Mary / Don't strike a match (To the book of love) / Long day comin' / She found the place
CURCD 004 / Mar '94 / Curb

Ketting, Otto

☐ LIGHT OF THE SUN
BVHAASTCD 9105 / Oct '93 / Bvhaast

Ketty, Rina

☐ CHANSOPHONE 1936-1939
701292 / Jun '93 / Chansophone

Keun

☐ KEUN
GWP 008CD / Aug '95 / Diffusion Breizh

Kevrenn Alre

☐ LARIDONGE
CD 442 / Aug '97 / Arfolk

Kevrenn Brest Sant Mark

☐ OCEAN LIBERTY
KBSM 002CD / Nov '96 / KBSM

Key Of Life

☐ IMPRESSIONS FROM THE TOP OF THE WORLD
341122 / Apr '94 / Koch

☐ VISIONS
341112 / Apr '94 / Koch

Keyes, Colin

☐ MAGIC OF THE PIANO, THE
Carpenters medley (we've only just begun,(they long for you) / Windmills of your mind / Our world / I'll never fall in love again / Entertainer / Tribute to Nat 'King' Cole (when I fall in love, unforgettab / Birth of the blues / Passing strangers / Golden touch / TV themes medley (where everybody knows your name (theme fro / Nocturne in e flat / Wind beneath my wings / Manhattan / View from here / What are you doing the rest of your life / Memory
ECD 3084 / Jan '95 / K-Tel

Keys, Will

☐ BANJO ORIGINAL, A
Wearing of the green / Chinquapin hunting / Midnight on the water / Standing on the promises / Cat in the pear tree / Once more / Dead march / Silver bell / Eighth of January / My pretty quadroon / Snake chapman's tune / Down yonder / Cielito lindo / Texas gals / Waiting for the Robert E. Lee / Blow ye winds softly / Puncheon floor / There is a fountain / Black mountain rag / Are you from Dixie / Palms of victory / Goodbye girls I'm going to Boston
COCD 2720 / Jul '97 / County

Keystone Trio

☐ HEART BEATS
Speak low / I fall in love too easily / If I should lose you / It had to be you / How deep is the ocean / Dancin' in the dark / Bewitched, bothered and bewildered / Two hearts / Stay as sweet as you are
MCD 92562 / Dec '96 / Milestone

☐ KEYSTONE TRIO, THE
OTYOG / Times slimes / Wynton / Here's to the people / Airegin / Tell me if you love me / Silk and satin / Koko knows / Love note for Sonny
MCD 92702 / Oct '97 / Milestone

KG

☐ NATURE MORTE
F4 3 / 8 Sep '97 / Fortune 4

Khabbra, Surinder

☐ GOOD TIME
OZITCD 0026 / May '97 / Ozit

☐ KHABBRA
You blow my mind / AMG / Fire / Wrong dream / Ocean green / Don't blame me / Your favourite things / Zebra / Light the blue touch paper / I can only be me
GT 1010 / May '97 / Good Time

Khac Chi Ensemble

☐ MOONLIGHT IN VIETNAM
On the mountain top / Forest love / Quan ho folk song / T'rung stream / Mountain cave / Highland dance / Spring is coming / Cai luong folk song / Farmer's song / Spring walk / Full moon dance / Native land / Northwest folk song
HSR 0005 / May '97 / Henry Street

Khaled, Cheb

☐ KUTCHE (Khaled, Cheb & Safy Boutella)
La camel / Kutche / El lela / Baroud / Chebba / Hana hana / Chab raissi / Minuit
STCD 1024 / Mar '89 / Stern's

☐ SAHRA
Sahra / Oran marseille / Aicha / Lillah / Ouelli el darek / Detni essekra / Walou walou / Ki kounti / Wahrane wahrane / Haya haya / Mektoubi / Hey ouedi / Srati / Le jour viendra / Didi
5334052 / Mar '97 / Mango
5393232 / 27 Oct '97 / Mango

Khan

☐ EMPIRE STATE BUILDING (Khan & Walker)
82323020 / 23 Mar '98 / Harvest

☐ RADIOWAVES VOL.2 (Khan & Walker)
8844202 / 3 Nov '97 / Harvest

☐ SILENT MOVIE/SILVER SCREEN
CAI 20062 / 27 Oct '97 / Caipirinha

Khan, Ali Akbar

☐ LEGACY
Guru bandana / Hori - in Kukubh Bilawal / Tarana - in Adana / Tarana - in Bhimpalasri / Kheyal - in Gour Sarang / Dhrupad - in Sankara Bharan / Sadra / Tarana - in Milan Ki Malhar / Tara - in Bhupali / Hori - in Bhairavi / Prayer - in Bhairavi
72162 / Mar '96 / Triloka

☐ TRADITIONAL MUSIC OF INDIA
PRCD 24157 / Mar '96 / Prestige

Khan, Amjad Ali

☐ RAGA LALITADHVANI
Alap-jod-jhara / Gat
VICG 54512 / Oct '96 / JVC

Khan, Chaka

☐ CHAKA
I'm every woman / Love has fallen on me / Roll me through the rushes / Sleep on it / Life is a dance / We got the love / Some love / Woman in a man's world / Message in the middle of the bottom / I was made to love him
7599258662 / Jan '96 / Warner Bros.

☐ EPIPHANY (The Best Of Chaka Khan)
I'm every woman / What cha' gonna do for me / I know you I love you / Ain't nobody / End of a love affair / Somethin' deep / And the melody still lingers on (night in tunisia) / Never miss the water / Through the fire / Every little thing / Your love is all I know / Love me still / Everywhere / Tell me something good / I feel for you / Papillon (aka hot butterfly)
9362458652 / Nov '96 / Warner Bros.

☐ I FEEL FOR YOU
This is my night / Stronger than before / My love is alive / Eye to eye / La flamme / I feel for you / Hold her / Through the fire / Caught in the act / Chinatown
9251622 / Oct '84 / Warner Bros.

☐ LIFE IS A DANCE (The Remix Project)
Life is a dance / This is my night / Slow dancing / I'm every woman / Ain't nobody / I feel for you / I know you, I live you / Eye to eye / Fate / Million kisses / Clouds / Clouds (classic trax version)
9259462 / May '89 / Warner Bros.

☐ PERFECT FIT
7599255422 / Jan '97 / Warner Bros.

☐ WHATCHA GONNA DO FOR ME
We can work it out / What'cha gonna do for me / I know you, I live you / Any old Sunday / We got each other / Night in Tunisia / Night moods / Heed the warning / Father he said / Fate / I know you, I live you (reprise)
7599258672 / Jan '96 / Warner Bros.

☐ WOMAN I AM, THE
Everything changes / Give me all / Telephone / Keep givin' me lovin' / Facts of love / Love you all my lifetime / I want / Your love thang right / Be my eyes / This time / Woman I am / Don't look at me that way
7599262962 / Apr '92 / Warner Bros.

Khan, Nishat

☐ MEETING OF ANGELS
ARNR 1096 / Dec '96 / Amiata

☐ RAG BHIMPALASI/RAG TILAK KAMOD (Khan, Nishat & Irshad)
NI 5233 / Sep '94 / Nimbus

☐ STRING CRAFT
VICG 54522 / Oct '96 / JVC

Khan, Nusrat Fateh Ali

☐ BACK TO QAWWALI
122083CD / Apr '95 / Long Distance

☐ COMPLETE PARIS CONCERT (5CD Box Set)
C 570500 / Feb '98 / Ocora

☐ DEVOTIONAL SONGS
Allah hoo allah hoo / Yaad-e-nabi gulshan mehka / Haq ali ali haq / Ali maula ali maula ali dam dam / Mast nazroon se allah nabi jee / Ni main jogi de naal
RWMCD 2 / Nov '92 / Realworld

☐ ECSTASY (The Bally Sagoo Remixes)
Ecstasy / By the candle light / Magic touch / Heart of gold / Love comes at home / Jewel / Prayer to Allah / Star crossed
TRCD 41102 / 10 Nov '97 / Terrascape

☐ EN CONCERT A PARIS
C 570200CD / Apr '96 / Ocora

☐ FAREWELL SONG
MIL 2223 / 17 Nov '97 / MIL Multimedia

☐ GREATEST HITS
SH 64091 / Jun '97 / Shanachie

☐ IN CONCERT IN PARIS VOL.1
C558 658 / '88 / Ocora

☐ IN CONCERT IN PARIS VOL.2
C558 659 / '88 / Ocora

☐ INTOXICATED SPIRIT
SHCD 64066 / Aug '96 / Shanachie

☐ LAST PROPHET, THE
Mani madni / Sahib teri bandi / Ganj-e-shakar / Sochan dongian
CDRW 44 / Apr '94 / Realworld

☐ LIVE AT THE ROYAL ALBERT HALL
MIL 2224 / 29 Jun '98 / MIL Multimedia

☐ LIVE IN NYC (2CD Set)
MIL 2221 / 17 Nov '97 / MIL Multimedia

☐ LOVE SONGS
Woh hata rahe hain pardah / Yeh jo halka saroor hae / Biba sada dil morr de / Yaadan vichre sajan dian aiyan / Sanson ki mala / Un ke dar pen pohchne to payen
RWMCD 3 / Nov '92 / Realworld

☐ MEGASTAR
IN 5727 / Nov '97 / Interra

☐ MISSIVES FROM ALLAH
Salkhi allah / Panjabi / Jinah jinah tave / Tua gal beh / Rah hassan / Muujah haave / Surnaaja heeyve urh
MPG 74045 / Jul '97 / Movieplay Gold

☐ MUSTT MUSTT
Mustt mustt / Nothing without you (tery-bina) / Jesse's theme / Gaae / Taa deem / Grandiloquent guitar / Clearing / Tana dery na / Shadow / Avenue / Mustt mustt / Mustt mustt
CDRW 15 / Nov '90 / Realworld

☐ NIGHT SONG (Khan, Nusrat Fateh Ali & Michael Brook)
My heart, my life / Intoxicated / Lament / My comfort remains / Longing / Sweet pain / Night song / Crest
CDRW 50 / Mar '96 / Realworld

☐ NUSRAT FATEH ALI KHAN VOL.3
CDSR 003 / Aug '90 / Star

☐ NUSRAT FATEH ALI KHAN VOL.5
CDSR 017 / Aug '90 / Star

☐ ORIENTE/OCCIDENTE (Khan, Nusrat Fateh Ali & Novum Gaudium)
1295700842 / Jan '97 / Materiali Sonori

☐ QAWWALI - THE ART OF THE SUFIS VOL.1
VICG 50292 / Mar '96 / JVC World Library

☐ RAPTURE
NSCD 013 / Mar '97 / Nascente

☐ REVELATION
IN 5712 / Nov '97 / Interra

☐ SHAHBAAZ
Beh haadh ramza dhasdha / Shahbaaz qalandar / Dhyahar eh isqmeh / Jewleh lal
CDRW 16 / '91 / Realworld

☐ STAR RISE (Khan, Nusrat Fateh Ali & Michael Brook)
Sweet pain / My heart my life / Taa deem / Shadow / Longing / My comfort remains / Tracery / Lament / Tery bina
CDRW 68 / 13 Oct '97 / Realworld

☐ SUPREME COLLECTION, THE (2CD Set)
CAR 7552 / 15 Sep '97 / Caroline

Khan, Praga

☐ SPOONFUL OF MIRACLE, A (Khan, Praga & Jade 4 U)
Injected with a poison / Phantasia forever / I feel good / Give me your lovin' / Rave alert / Moonday / Travel through time / God of Abraham / Flesh and blood / Love me baby / I will survive / Love peace freedom
FILECD 439 / May '93 / Profile

Khan, Salamat Ali

☐ RAGAS GUNKALI
NI 5307 / Sep '94 / Nimbus

Khan, Steve

☐ CROSSINGS
Descargo Khanalonious / Think of one / What I'm said / Pee Wee / It's you or no-one / I love Paris / Capricorn / Melancholee / Inner urge / While my lady sleeps
5232692 / Apr '94 / Verve

Khan, Ustad Amir

☐ RAGA MANDRAGA DARBAR
DSAV 1059 / Jul '96 / Multitone

Khan, Ustad Amjad Ali

☐ LIVE 50TH BIRTHDAY CONCERT
NRCD 0070 / Feb '98 / Navras

Khan, Ustad Hafiz Ali

☐ LEGENDARY LINEAGE, THE (2CD Set)
Raga bilaskhani todi / Raga yarman kalyan / Raga desh / Raga pilu jungaia / Raga bhairav / Raga darbari
NRCD 0084 / Sep '97 / Navras

Khan, Ustad Imrat

☐ AJMER
WLAES 17CD / Nov '95 / Waterlily Acoustics

☐ EK PRAKAR KI KAUNS
NRCD 0014 / Mar '96 / Navras

☐ INDIAN MUSIC FOR SITAR AND SURBAHAR (Khan, Imrat & Sons)
LYRCD 7376 / '91 / Lyrichord

☐ LALITA
WLAES 26CD / Nov '95 / Waterlily Acoustics

☐ RAG DARBARI/RAG CHANDRA KANHRA
NI 5118 / Sep '94 / Nimbus

☐ RAG JHINJOTI/RAG PILU
NI 5195 / Sep '94 / Nimbus

☐ RAG JOG KAUNS RAGA DURGA
ED 1013 / Mar '96 / Edelweiss

☐ RAG MEGH BRIDABANI SARANG SUDH SARANG
ED 1018 / Mar '96 / Edelweiss

☐ RAG MIYA KI TODI/RAG BILASKHANI TODI
NI 5153 / Sep '94 / Nimbus

☐ RAGA MARWA
NI 5356 / Sep '94 / Nimbus

Khan, Ustad Rashid

☐ RAGAS
NRCD 0071 / Nov '96 / Navras

Khan, Ustad Sabri

☐ INDIAN SARANGI AND TABLA RECITAL (Khan, Ustad Sabri & Sawar Sabri)
EUCD 1172 / '91 / ARC

Khan, Ustad Salamat Ali

☐ BREATH OF THE ROSE
WLAES 18CD / Nov '95 / Waterlily Acoustics

Khan, Ustad Shamin Ahmed

☐ SITAR MAESTRO
Raga bhairac / Raga madhuvanti / Raga chandrakauns / Dum
NRCD 0093 / 20 Jul '98 / Navras

Khan, Ustad Sultan

☐ SARANGI INDIA
RCD 10104 / Nov '91 / Rykodisc

Khan, Ustad Vilayat

☐ UPHAAR (Khan, Ustad Vilayat & Ustad Bismillah Khan)
Alap / Gat composition
NRCD 0079 / Jul '97 / Navras

Khanum, Farida

☐ HITS OF FARIDA KHANUM, THE
PMUT 020 / Jul '96 / Multitone

Khanyile, Noise

☐ ART OF NOISE, THE
Igobondela / Izulu seliyaduma / Viva Scotch land / Mapantsula jive / Jika jika jive / Ugabuzela / Kwazamazama / USA special / Dlamini / Baba wami / Umamemeza / London Ave / Marimba jive / Groovin' jive (no. 1)
CDORB 045 / Jun '89 / Globestyle

Khao

☐ CRAZY DISEASED AND BARMY
Crazy diseased and barmy / Man / Healer teacher preacher / Darkus man / Good pain / So glad / No compromise / Supressed / Sensi / First bite
K7R 017CD / 18 May '98 / Studio K7

Khassonka Dunun

☐ TRADITIONAL MUSIC FROM MALI
PS 65187 / Jul '97 / PlayaSound

Khumalo, Sibongile

☐ LIVE AT THE MARKET THEATRE
Tsakwe/Royal blue / Umbongo / Umhome / Life is going on / Yakhalinkomo / Caution / Through the years / Mountain shade / Sekumanxa / Township medley
4913222 / 20 Jul '98 / Epic

Khumalo, Vusi

☐ FOLLOW YOUR DREAM
BW 093 / 27 Apr '98 / B&W

Kiani, Madjid

☐ TRADITION CLASSIQUE DE L'IRAN VOL.3 (Le Santour) (Kiani, Madjid & Djamchid Chemirani)
HMA 190395 / Nov '93 / Musique D'Abord

Kiani, Mary

☐ LONG HARD FUNKY DREAMS (2CD Set)
When I call your name / Till death do us disco / With or without you / Long hard funky dreams / If I see you again / Let the music play / We can be one / 100% / I imagine / Blame it on the night / I knew / Beautiful day / Memories / I give it all to you / When I call your name (Hardfloor vocal mix) / Let the music play (Perfecto vocal mix) / I imagine (Mr. Spring club mix) / 100% (Tall Paul remix) / Let the music play (Union Jack mix) / I give it all to you (Umboza mix) / When I call your name (Motiv 8 special club mix)
5345122
5345112 / Jun '97 / Mercury

Kibwe, Talib

☐ INTRODUCING
Is that so / Joy spring / Heaven scent / Hot house / Lady in white / Hi fly / Kim / Blues from Jali / Portrait of Lois Marie / Star eyes
ECD 221452 / Mar '96 / Evidence

Kick La Luna

☐ SECRET WAVES
EFA 129162 / May '96 / Turbulent

Kickback

☐ CORNERED
CM 77139CD / Nov '96 / Century Media

☐ FOREVER WAR
CM 77179CD / 27 Oct '97 / Century Media

Kicklighter, Richy

☐ IN THE NIGHT
Night after night / Without you / Under another sky / Between the worlds / Lucky / Time will tell / Tamiami / Angel
ICH 1051CD / Oct '93 / Ichiban

☐ JUST FOR KICKS
Jungle Song / In the wind / Change love / Till then / Wind in the curtains / After You're Gone / Phantoms / Now and then
ICH 1019CD / Oct '93 / Ichiban

Kid Creole

☐ BEST OF KID CREOLE & THE COCONUTS (Kid Creole & The Coconuts)
Lifeboat party / Gina Gina / Me no pop I / Off the coast of me / Don't take my coconuts / Maladie d'amour / There's something wrong in paradise / Stool pigeon / Annie I'm not your daddy / Latin music / I'm a wonderful thing, baby / Imitation / Dear Addy / Back in the field again
IMCD 216 / Mar '96 / Island

☐ PRESENTS THE KID AND I (Darnell, August & Kid Creole)
IN 10960501 / 21 Aug '97 / XIII Bis

☐ STOOL PIGEON (Kid Creole & The Coconuts)
Stool pigeon / Say hey / I'm a wonderful thing / No fish today / Dear addy / Don't take my coconuts / Table manners / Mr. softie / Lifeboat party
ST 5002 / Nov '93 / Star Collection

☐ TROPICAL GANGSTERS (Kid Creole & The Coconuts)
Annie (I'm not your daddy) / I'm a wonderful thing, baby / Imitation / I'm corrupt / Loving you made a fool out of me / Stool pigeon / Love we have / No fish today
IMCD 6 / '89 / Island

Kid Loco

☐ GRAND LOVE STORY, A
Grand love theme / Relaxin' with Cherry / Love me sweet / Bootleggers / Calling Aventura King / Sister Curare / She's my lover (a song for R.) / She Woolf daydreaming / Alone again so / Cosmic supernatural
3984208052 / 9 Feb '98 / East West/ Yellow Productions

☐ GRAND LOVE STORY, A
YP 031CD / 19 Jan '98 / Yellow

Kid Loops

☐ TIMEQUAKE
FILT 022CD / Jun '97 / Filter

Kid Million

☐ HEAVEN SMILES ON EVERY BASTARD
FBR 100 / Sep '97 / Fly By

Kid 'n' Play

☐ FACE THE NATION
It's alright y'all / Back on wax / Got a good thing going on / Next question / Face the nation / Foreplay / Slippin' / Ain't gonna hurt nobody / Give it here / Bill's at the door / Toe to toe
3368612062 / Oct '91 / WEA

Kid Rocker

☐ I'M ON A ROLL (Kid Rocker & The Phantoms)
I'm on my own / Little bugga wugga / Do you like it / Seduction / It's too late now / Don't tell me / Frank's place / Tall dark girl / Rocker / Oohh...suits you sir / I'm on a roll / Hey there Frenchie / Do what I want, when I want / Blues Mama / Gonna make me a star / You're the one / Time to say goodbye / Rock 'n' roll ah-ha / Bring her here to me
JRCD 22 / Sep '97 / Jappin' & Rockin'

Kid Sheik

☐ CLEVELAND & BOSTON 1960-1961
AMCD 69 / Aug '94 / American Music

☐ KID SHEIK & PAUL BARBARIN (Kid Sheik & Paul Barbarin)
BCD 227 / Apr '97 / GHB

☐ KID SHEIK'S SWINGSTERS 1961
AMCD 91 / Mar '97 / American Music

☐ REAL NEW ORLEANS JAZZ 1960 (Kid Sheik & Charlie Love)
When you're smiling / Waltz of the bells / Don't go 'way nobody / Sheik's blues / Corine Corina / Georgia camp meeting / Then I'll be happy / What a friend we have in Jesus / Sheikh of araby / Near the cross / Over in the glory land / Cado blues / Down in honky tonk town / Bill Bailey, Won't you please come home / Indian Sagua
504CDS 21 / Mar '98 / 504

Kidd, Carol

☐ ALL MY TOMORROWS
Don't worry 'bout me / I'm all smiles / Autumn in New York / My funny valentine / 'Round midnight / Dat dere / Angel eyes / When I dream / I thought about you / Folks who live on the hill / Haven't we met / All my tomorrows
AKD 068 / Aug '97 / Linn

☐ CAROL KIDD
Then I'll be tired of you / We'll be together / You go to my head / It isn't so good it couldn't be better / More I see you / I've grown accustomed to your face / Yes, I know when I've had it / Waltz for Debby / Never let me go / Like someone in love / Trouble is a man / I'm shadowing you / Spring can really hang you up the most / I like to recognise the tune
AKHCD 003 / Aug '90 / Linn

☐ CRAZY FOR GERSHWIN
AKD 026 / Apr '94 / Linn

☐ I'M GLAD WE MET
Lean baby / Don't go to strangers / Bad, bad Leroy Brown / I guess I'll hang my tears out to dry / Georgia on my mind / You're cheating yourself / I wish I'd met you / You're awful / Don't take your love from me / I'm a fool to want you / Please don't talk about me when I'm gone / Sometimes (not often)
AKD 017 / Nov '91 / Linn

☐ NICE WORK (If You Can Get It)
Nice work if you can get it / Havin' myself a time / Isn't it a pity / Bidin' my time / Sing for your supper / Daydream / I'll take romance / New York on Sunday / What is there to say / Mean to me / I guess I'll have to change my plan / Starting tomorrow / Confessions
AKHCD 006 / Aug '90 / Linn

☐ NIGHT WE CALLED IT A DAY, THE
How little it matters, how little we know / Where or when / I fall in love too easily / I loved him / Night we called it a day / Where are you / Glory of you / I could have told you so / I think it's going to rain today / Gloomy Sunday
AKHCD 007 / Sep '90 / Linn

☐ THAT'S ME
You don't bring me flowers / Send in the clowns / When the world was young / 'Round midnight / I can't get started / I'm always chasing rainbows / Let me sing and I'm happy / This bitter Earth / Somewhere over the rainbow / Trolley song / That's me
AKD 044 / Sep '95 / Linn

Kidd, Johnny

☐ 25 GREATEST HITS (Kidd, Johnny & The Pirates)
Shakin' all over / Please don't touch / You got what it takes / Restless / Linda Lu / Shot of rhythm and blues / I'll never get over you / Hungry for love / Always and forever / Oh boy / Fool / Send me some lovin' / Let's talk about us / Some other guy / Whole lotta woman / Your cheatin' heart / You can have her / I just want to make love to you / I can tell / I know / If you were the only girl / Feelin' / Yes sir that's my baby / Birds and the bees / Doctor Feelgood
4954802 / 6 Jul '98 / EMI Gold

☐ CLASSIC AND RARE (Kidd, Johnny & The Pirates)
I want that / So what / Feeling / Please don't touch / Restless / Let's talk about us / Birds and the bees / It's got to be you / Some other guy / Shakin' all over / I'll never get over you / Send me some lovin' / Fool / Hungry for love / Your cheatin' heart / My babe / Casting my spell / Big blon' baby
SEECD 287 / Jun '93 / See For Miles

☐ RARITIES (Kidd, Johnny & The Pirates)
I Know / Where are you / Little bit of soap / Oh boy / Steady date / More of the same / I just want to make love to you / This golden ring / Right string baby, but the wrong yo-yo / Can't turn you loose / Shakin' all over / I hate getting up in the morning / Send for that girl / Hurry on back to love / You got what it takes / Fool / Ecstacy / Shop around / Weep no more, my baby / Whole lotta woman
SEECD 120 / Jan '97 / See For Miles

☐ SHAKIN' ALL OVER (Kidd, Johnny & The Pirates)
Shakin' all over / Birds and the bees / Gotta travel on / Yes sir that's my baby / Dr. Feelgood / Feelin' / Please don't bring me down / Hurry on back to love / Jealous girl / Whole lotta woman / Your cheatin' heart / Shop around
WB 885872 / 2 Feb '98 / Disky

☐ VERY BEST OF JOHNNY KIDD & THE PIRATES, THE (Kidd, Johnny & The Pirates)
Please don't touch / If you were the only girl in the world / Feelin' / You got what it takes / Shakin' all over / Yes sir that's my baby / Restless / Hurry on back to love / Shot of rhythm and blues / I'll never get over you / Hungry for love / Always and ever / Dr. Feelgood / Whole lotta woman / Your cheatin' heart / Gotta travel on / Fool / Birds and the bees / Send me some lovin' / Some other guy
CDSL 8256 / Jul '95 / EMI

Kidjo, Angelique

☐ AYE
Agolo / Adouma / Azan nan kpe / Tatchedogbe / Djan djan / Lon lon vadjro / Houngbati / Idje idje / Yemandja / Tombo
IMCD 244 / Mar '97 / Island

☐ LOGOZO
Batonga / Tche-tche / Logozo / We-we / Malaika / Ewa ka djo / Kaleta / Eledjire / Senie / Ekoleya
CIDM 1091 / 2 Feb '98 / Mango

☐ OREMI
Introduction / Voodoo child (slight return) / Never know / Babalao / Loloye / Itche koutche / Open your eyes / Yaki yaki / Give it up / Oremi / Orubaba / No worry
CID 8070 / 8 Jun '98 / Island

Kiem

☐ YOU SHOULD TRY
CD 029 / Jul '87 / Torso

Kiermyer, Franklin

☐ KAIROS
Kairos / Kukisha m'poko / John's mode / In the house of my fathers / Baka yelli / In your presence I behold / Basheret / Elephant feast / Around the world / Epi trapezios / I turn my face towards the sun / Dream of a grandfather / Fifty years (after the liberation of Auschwitz)
ECD 221442 / Feb '96 / Evidence

☐ SOLOMON'S DAUGHTER
Three jewels / Akdemus / Peace on earth / Solomon's daughter / Birds of the Nile / If I die before I wake
ECD 220832 / May '94 / Evidence

Kiernan, Ken

☐ ERINSAGA (Kiernan, Ken & Ger MacDonald)
I am Tuan / Vision / Belgatan (our will is strong) / Tailltu's lament / Crom cruach / Dream of nuada / Battle-frenzy / My love is yours / Last battle / Erinsaga
ERCD 1 / Nov '89 / Round Tower

Kiesewetter, Knut

☐ HIS BEST SONGS
EUCD 1182 / Apr '92 / ARC

☐ SONGS UND BALLADEN (Kiesewetter, Knut Und Familie)
BCD 16024 / May '98 / Bear Family

☐ WENN WIEHNACHTEN KUMMT (Kiesewetter, Knut & Fiede Kay)
EUCD 1130 / '91 / ARC

☐ WO GEIHST DU HEN
EUCD 1117 / '91 / ARC

Kihn, Greg

☐ HORROR SHOW
Kay is the mouth of May / Noa noa / Horror show / Waterloo sunset / Come back baby / Talk of the town / JFK / Trials, troubles and tribulations / Alligator man / Beam the light / Wherever there's smoke / Vampira
CCD 716 / Nov '96 / Clean Cuts

☐ KIHNSPICUOUS TASTE (The Best Of Greg Kihn/2CD Set)
All the right reasons / Mood number / Any other woman / He will break your heart / Madison Avenue / For you / Hurt so bad / Love's made a fool of you / Politics / Secret meetings / Cold hard cash / Remember / Sorry / Rendezvous / Roadrunner / In the naked eye / For your love / Anna Belle Lee / Man who shot Liberty Valance / Break up song / Sheila / Can't stop hurting myself / Happy man / Testify / Higher and higher / Jeopardy / Love never fails / I fall to pieces / Reunited / Cherie baby / Lucky / Little red book / Another girl another planet
SMDCD 116 / 22 Sep '97 / Snapper

☐ KIHNSPIRACY (Kihn, Greg Band)
Jeopardy / Fascination / Tear that city down / Talkin' to myself / Can't love them all / I fall to pieces / Someday / Curious / How long / Love never fails / Breakup song (they don't write 'em) / Happy man / Sorry / For you / Reunited / Any other woman
HILLCD 19 / Jun '97 / Wooded Hill

☐ KING BISCUIT PRESENTS...
88004 / Dec '97 / King Biscuit

☐ MUTINY
Blood red roses / Mutiny / Sittin' on top of the world / Anniversary of my broken heart / Joshua gone Barbados / Anastasia / I wish it would rain / Not fade away Mona / Femme fatale / Shot in the dark / Subterranean homesick blues / Love of the land / Been on the job too long / Gwabi
FIENDCD 755 / Aug '94 / Demon

Kikoski, Dave

☐ PRESAGE
Hope / Hope / In the still of the night / Presage / Dirty dogs / I've got you under my skin / Doorways / A nightingale sang in berkeley square
FRLCD 011 / Oct '92 / Freelance

Kikoski, David

☐ INNER TRUST (Kikoski, David Trio)
Some other blues / Softly as in a morning sunrise / Mirical / Inner trust / You don't know what love is / Two lonely people / Once upon a summertime / We see / Old tracks / Winnies garden
CRISS 1148 / Jun '98 / Criss Cross

Kikuchi, Masabumi

☐ AFTER HOURS
Bye bye blackbird / My favourite things / Mona lisa / Soft cry / Manha de carnaval
5297472 / Mar '96 / Verve

☐ TETHERED MOON
You're my everything / Misterioso / So in love / Moniker / PS / Moor / Tethered moon
ECD 220712 / Nov '93 / Evidence

Kikuchi, Teiko

☐ TRADITIONAL MUSIC OF JAPAN
824612 / Nov '90 / BUDA

Kila

☐ MIND THE GAP
Tickelled / Feach / Finnegan / Odlum's wild oats / Tatiana / 5.30 / Juno humm / Delta / Baile bhoithin / Mind the gap / Sean deora / Ezekiel / Steps / Islandbridge
KRCD 004 / May '97 / Kila

☐ TOG E GO BOG E (Take It Easy)
Gwerzy / On taubh tuathail amach / Rusty nails / Seige of Carrickfinn International Airport / Jasmine / Oh to kiss Katie / Tog e go bog e / Crann na bpingini / Dusty wine bottle / Tip toe / Double knuckle shuffle / Rila do / Bi ann / Leanfaidh me
KRCD 005 / Jun '98 / Kila

Kilbey, Steve

☐ GILT TRIP (Kilbey, Steve & Russell)
VSC 004 / Jun '97 / Vicious Sloth

☐ NARCOSIS PLUS
VSC 005 / Jun '97 / Vicious Sloth

Kilbride

☐ KILBRIDE
TRADD 200CD / Mar '98 / Fflach

Kilbride, Pat

☐ LOOSE CANNON
GLCD 1148 / Feb '95 / Green Linnet

☐ ROCK AND MORE ROSES
COMD 2011 / Feb '94 / Temple

☐ UNDOCUMENTED DANCING
Live bait / Aires de Pontevedra / All the leaves / Hunter's house / Milestones and memories / Patrick / Unfinished revolution / Munster bacon and the jig of slurs / Wearing of the breeches / Blind Mary / Flower of Magherally / Piccadilly / Cittern jig
GLCD 1120 / Feb '91 / Green Linnet

Kilby, Cody

☐ JUST ME
Backstep / Round up / Memories of you / St. Anne's reel / El cumbanchero / Washington County / Ocoee sunrise / Monroe's hornpipe / One legged gypsy / Tune for poppy / Shenandoah breakdown / Frosty morn / Tom and Jerry
REBCD 1736 / Jul '97 / Rebel

Kilduff, Vinnie

☐ BOYS FROM BLUE HILL
LUNCD 050 / Jan '95 / Mulligan

Kilgore, Merle

☐ TEENAGER'S HOLIDAY
Ride Jesse ride / Hang doll / Everybody needs a little lovin' / Ernie / Start all over again / Tom Dooley Jr / More and more / It can't rain all the time / Seein' double, feelin' single / What makes me love you / Funny feeling / Now that you are leavin' / That's when my blues began / Teenager's holiday / Please please please / I feel guilty / Trying to find (someone like you) / Goodbye / Forty two in Chicago / Wicked city / I'll take Ginger and run away / Girl named Liz / Ain't nothin' but a man / Somethin' goin' on that I can't see / There's no food in this house / Lover's hell / Back street affair / Trouble at the tower / Love bug / I'll shake your hand
BCD 15544 / May '91 / Bear Family

Kilgore, Rebecca

☐ NOT A CARE IN THE WORLD (Kilgore, Rebecca & Dave Frishberg)
ARCD 19169 / May '97 / Arbors Jazz

Kill City Dragons

☐ KILL CITY DRAGONS
WBRCD 002 / Jan '91 / Wideboy

Kill II This

☐ ANOTHER CROSS II BARE
HR 02CD / Mar '97 / Hardware

Kill Switch Klick

☐ DEGENERATE
CLP 9928 / Mar '97 / Cleopatra

Killa Instinct

☐ ESCAPISM
MOVE 7013CD / Mar '95 / Move

Killafornia

☐ ORGANISATION
50539 / Jun '97 / Raging Bull

Killah Priest

☐ HEAVY MENTAL
GED 24971 / 9 Mar '98 / Geffen

Killarney Singers

☐ 50 FAVOURITE IRISH PUB SONGS
CDIRISH 001 / Jan '95 / Outlet

Killdozer

☐ GOD HEARS PLEAS OF THE INNOCENT
TG 139CD / Feb '95 / Touch & Go

☐ LAST WALTZ, THE
MR 065CD / 22 Sep '97 / Man's Ruin

☐ WAR ON ART
TG 82CD / '94 / Touch & Go

Killen, Louis

☐ SEAMAN'S GARLAND
KO 04CD / Mar '98 / Knock Out

Killer Bees

☐ LIVE IN BERLIN
DANCD 053 / Nov '94 / ROIR

Killer Brew

☐ KILLER BREW
MCG 20028 / May '98 / Vampirella

Killer Shrews

☐ KILLER SHREWS
EMY 1412 / Sep '97 / Enemy

Killer Tweeker Bees

☐ TWEEKER BLUES
Buyer's club / Grounds to indict / Big phoney / Tweeker blues / Erotic edge / Rat zombie / Government protects me / Pure police for now people / Rage against your mother / Now that I've solved society's problems... / Junk cool
SST 345CD / 29 Sep '97 / SST

Killermeters

☐ CHARGE
3 Minute warning / Won't let you go / All nighter / All or nothing / Which way kids / You don't love me / Short sharp shock
DRCD 017 / 27 Jul '98 / Detour

☐ METRIC NOISE (Killermeters & Soldiers Are Dreamers)
Why should it happen to me: *Killermeters* / Don't tell baby: *Killermeters* / Back in business: *Killermeters* / Cardiac arrest: *Killermeters* / Rhona: *Killermeters* / Love on the rebound: *Killermeters* / Wrong way: *Killermeters* / Can't help it: *Killermeters* / Look but don't touch: *Killermeters* / Only you (light my way): *Killermeters* / Midnight breakfast show: *Killermeters* / Open my eyes: *Killermeters* / Eight miles high: *Killermeters* / Twisted wheel: *Killermeters* / SX 225: *Killermeters* / Summertime: *Killermeters* / Cry: *Killermeters* / Which way kids: *Killermeters* / Go with the flow: *Soldiers Are Dreamers* / Tomorrow is a brighter day: *Soldiers Are Dreamers* / Midnight: *Soldiers Are Dreamers* / Dreaming my life away: *Soldiers Are Dreamers* / And I break: *Soldiers Are Dreamers* / GI Joe: *Soldiers Are Dreamers*
DRCD 013 / Apr '97 / Detour

Killers

☐ LIVE
HR 01CD / Mar '97 / Hardware

☐ NEW LIVE AND RARE (2CD Set)
Advance and be recognized / Die by the gun / Marshal law / Wrathchild / Three words / Faith healer / Murders in the Rue Morgue / Children of the revolution / Sanctuary / Phantom of the opera / City of fools / Chemical imbalance / Past due / Impaler / Protector / Menace to society / Remember tomorrow / Think brutal / Beast / Song for you
CDBLEED 23 / 11 May '98 / Bleeding Hearts

Killing Floor

☐ DIVIDE BY ZERO
REC 025 / 18 Sep '97 / Re-Constriction

Killing Joke

☐ BRIGHTER THAN A 1000 SUNS
Adorations / Sanity / Chessboards / Twilight of the moral / Love of the masses / Southern sky / Winter gardens / Rubicon / Goodbye to the village / Victory / Exile
EGCD 66 / Nov '86 / EG

☐ COURTAULD TALKS, THE
INV 004CD / Jun '97 / Invisible

☐ DEMOCRACY
BFLCD 17 / 1 Sep '98 / Butterfly

☐ FIRE DANCES
Gathering / Fun and games / Rejuvenation / Frenzy / Harlequin / Feast of blaze / Song and dance / Dominator / Let's all go (to the fire dances) / Lust almighty
EGCD 60 / '87 / EG

☐ KILLING JOKE
Requiem / War dance / Tomorrow's World / Bloodsport / Wait / Complications / SO 36 / Primitive
EGCD 57 / '87 / EG

☐ LAUGH I NEARLY BOUGHT ONE
Turn to red / Pssyche / Requiem / Wardance / Follow the leaders / Unspeakable / Butcher / Exit / Hum / Empire song / Chop chop / Sun goes down / Eighties / Darkness before dawn / Love like blood / Wintergardens / Age of greed
CDV 2693 / Oct '92 / EG

☐ NIGHT TIME
Night Time / Darkness before dawn / Love like blood / Kings and Queens / Tabazan / Multitudes / Europe / Eighties
EGCD 61 / Jan '87 / EG

☐ OUTSIDE THE GATE
America / My love of this land / Stay one jump ahead / Unto the ends of the earth / Calling / Obsession / Tiahuanaco / Outside the gate / America (mix)
EGCD 73 / May '88 / EG

☐ PANDEMONIUM
Pandemonium / Exorcism / Millennium / Communion / Black moon / Labyrinth / Jana / Whiteout / Pleasures of the flesh / Mathematics of chaos
BFLCD 9 / 1 Sep '98 / Butterfly

☐ WAR DANCE (Remix Album)
Love like blood / Savage freedom / Democracy / Four stadiums / Pandemonium / Jana / Black moon California sunshine / Intellect / White out
BFLCD 32 / 4 May '98 / Butterfly

☐ WILFUL DAYS
Are you receiving / Follow the leaders / Sun goes down / Dominator / Me or you / Wilful days / Eighties / New day / Love like blood / Madding crowd / Ecstasy / America / Change
CDOVD 440 / May '95 / EG

Killing Time

☐ BRIGHTSIDE
LF 157CD / Jul '95 / Lost & Found

Killjoys

☐ MILLION SONGS, A
D 30930 / Oct '93 / Mushroom

Killrays

☐ ON COMMON GROUND
BYE 970132 / May '97 / Bite Your Ear

☐ SPACE GIANT
LF 203CD / Nov '95 / Lost & Found

Kilmarnock Edition

☐ FROM FAR HORIZONS
MANU 1501CD / Nov '95 / Manu

Kilpatrick, Tom

☐ FIFTY SHADES OF GREEN
Come back to erin / When irish eyes are smiling / Wild colonial boy / Boys from the county armagh / Holy ground / Muirsheen durkin / Mcalpine's fusiliers / A legend in my time / Old flames / Release me / Rakes o'mallow / Boys of limerick / Teetotalers reel / Pig town / Galway bay / Rose of tralee / Leaving of liverpool / I'll tell me ma / If your irish / Dear old donegal / St. patrick's day / Seven drunken nights / Famous shamus / Larry o'gaff / Mcnamara's band / Bold o'donahue / Irish washerwoman / Mother macree / Maggie / Bunch of thyme / Irish rover / Whiskey you're the devil / Courtin' in the kitchen / Leprechaun on the blarney / Ryans rant / Peelers jacket / Forty shades of green / Love letters in the sand / Distant drums / With a shillelagh under me arm / Rakes of kildare / Rafferty's motor car / Slattery's mounted fut / Hanigan's hooley / Blackthorn stick / Catch me if you can / Golden jubilee / Danny boy / Green glens of antrim / If we only had old ireland over here / Danny boy / Irish washerwoman
CDITV 538 / Jul '91 / Scotdisc

☐ SHADES OF GREEN
PLATCD 3922 / May '94 / Platinum

☐ SHAMROCK STRAND, THE
Hello patsy fagan / O'reilly's daughter / Dicey riley / Whiskey in the jar / My wild irish rose / Rose of aranmore / Fiddle-me-bob / Roses are red / Ramblin' rose / Cold cold heart / Peter street / Six mile bridge / Wedding / Pullet / Fields of athenry / Isle of innisfree / Irish lullabye / Rose of clare / Bally mcquilty band / Kerry dances / Rocky road to dublin / Irish jaunting car / When will you marry me / New pair of shoes / Agricultural irish girl / Mick mcgilligan's daughter / Those endearing young charms / Slievenamon / Old bog road / Molly darlin' / Moonlight in mayo / Lovely leitrim / Mountain dew / Waiting for the federals / Salamanca reel / Jaky laing / Are you lonesome tonight / I just called to say I love you / It's now or never / All for me grog / Gary owen / Paddy wack / Red stockings / Humours of donnybrook / Black porter / Goodbye mick - goodbye pat / Hi for the beggarman / Sweet sixteen / I'll take you home again kathleen / Kathleen so fair and bright / Those endearing young charms
CDITV 560 / Sep '92 / Scotdisc

Kimbara Brothers

☐ TIME TO LEAVE
MMKB 9015CD / Mar '96 / Meadow Music

Kimber, Paul

☐ PECKHAM IN SPRING
Peckham in spring / Flying Joey / Must be a boon / Swing thing / Nine O'clock midnight / Slieve loughsbannagh / Ben's groove / Confidence / Happy
FMD 029 / Mar '97 / Fictional

Kimbrough, Junior

☐ ALL NIGHT LONG
Work me baby / Do the romp / Stay all night / Meet me in the city / You better run / Done got old / All night long / I feel alright / Nobody but you / Slow lightnin'
03082 / 17 Nov '97 / Epitaph

☐ DO THE RUMP (Kimbrough, Junior & The Soul Blues Boys)
Keep your hands off her / I feel good little girl / You better run / I'm so glad trouble don't last always / Done got old / Please don't leave me baby / Come on and go with me / Do the rump / I want to know what's wrong with you / Nobody but you baby / Too late baby / My mama done told me
HMG 6503 / Sep '97 / Hightone

☐ MOST THINGS HAVEN'T WORKED OUT
03092 / 17 Nov '97 / Epitaph

☐ SAD DAYS LONELY NIGHTS (Kimbrough, Junior & The Soul Blues Boys)
Sad days lonely nights / Lonesome in my home / Lord have mercy on me / Crawling king snake / My mind is rambling / Leaving in the morning / Old black Mattie / I'm in love / Pull your cloths off / I'm gonna have to leave you / Sad days lonely nights
03062 / 30 Mar '98 / Fat Possum

Kin Ping Meh

☐ KIN PING MEH VOL.1
PMS 7066 / 26 Jan '98 / Repertoire

☐ KIN PING MEH VOL.2
REP 7067 / Feb '98 / Repertoire

Kina, Shoukichi

☐ ASIA CLASSICS VOL.2 (The Best Of Shoukichi Peppermint Tea House)
Jing jing (firefly) / Hana no kajimaya (flower windmill) / Mimichiri bozu-danju kariyushi (ear cutting samura / Bash-gua suncha (the cart puller) / Subete no hito no kokoro ni hanna o (flowers for / Eternally ecstasy / I-yah hoy / Intrumental / Iyunu-pri / Haisai ojisan (hey man) / Zorba de buddha / Don-don bushi (don-don song) / Celebration / Crazy kacharsee
9362451592 / Jul '94 / Luaka Bop

Kincade, John

☐ SINGLES AND MORE, THE
MCCD 336 / 16 Mar '98 / Music Club

Kincaid

☐ GOOD CITIZENS OF THE MONTH
KC 010 / Aug '97 / Kindercore

Kind Of Jazz

☐ KIND OF JAZZ
MECCACD 2006 / May '97 / Music Mecca

Kindness Of Strangers

☐ HOPE
Kindness of strangers / Across the border / Tomorrow / Memory takes my hand / Walk away / Oh my America / Live in the world / Sunday / Day that I found love / Shelter for love / Desire / Kindness of strangers (reprise)
6544922412 / Feb '94 / East West

Kindred

☐ BOMB UP THE TOWN
GI 0052 / Mar '97 / GI Productions

Kindred, Bob

☐ HIDDEN TREASURES
74321357312 / May '96 / Milan

Kinesthesia

☐ EMPATHY BOX
CAT 022CDR
CAT 022CD / Apr '96 / Rephlex

Kinetix

☐ KINETIC ART
NCD 002 / 9 Feb '98 / Nocturnal

Kinfolk

☐ EACH AND EVERY DAY
Each and every day / Handle that shit / Trapped up in tha ghetto / Holdin' tank / Why ya wanna (lock me down) / Gotta make those endz / Deal wit tha real / Gangsta glide / Players / MsBehave / Summer again / Situation critical / Kinfolkatosis / Ya daughter gits it all / If I could / Faith / On B1/2 of nutty
74321335182 / Oct '96 / American

King, Albert

☐ ALBERT
CPCD 8327 / Nov '97 / Charly

☐ BLUES AT SUNRISE (Live At Montreux)
Don't burn the bridge (cause you might wanna come back... / For the love of a woman / I'll play the blues for you / Roadhouse blues / I believe to my soul / Blues at sunrise / Little brother (make a way)
CDSXE 017 / Nov '88 / Stax

☐ BLUES AT SUNRISE
CD 52034 / May '94 / Blues Encore

☐ BLUES AT SUNSET (Live At Wattstax 1972 & Montreux 1973)
Matchbox blues / Got to be some changes made / I'll play the blues for you / Killing floor / Angel of mercy / Matchbox blues / Watermelon man / Breaking up somebody's home / Stormy Monday
SCD 8581 / Jun '96 / Stax

☐ BLUES DON'T CHANGE, THE
Blues don't change / I'm doing fine / Nice to be nice / Oh pretty woman / King of kings / Feel the need / Firing line / Pinch paid off (Part I) / Pinch paid off (Part II) / I can't stand the rain / Ain't it beautiful
CDSXE 085 / Feb '93 / Stax

☐ BLUES FOR YOU (The Best Of Albert King)
Born under a bad sign / Killing floor / Breaking up somebody's home / Can't you see what you're doing to me / Going back to luka / Answer to the laundromat blues / That's what the blues is all about / Phone booth / I'll play the blues for you / Left hand woman (Get right with me) / Flat tire / Drowning on dry land / Pinch paid off / Sky is crying / Driving wheel / Everybody wants to go to heaven / Angel of mercy / Wrapped up in love again / Blues power / Crosscut saw
CDSXD 120 / Sep '95 / Stax

☐ CHICAGO 1978
King's bounce (instrumental) / Stormy monday blues / Born under a bad sign / Very thought of you / You're my woman / I'm your mate / Tired as a man can be / Blues at sunrise / Feel like breaking up somebody's home / Please come back to me / I'll play the blues for you
CDBL 754 / Nov '94 / Charly

☐ CROSSCUT SAW
Crosscut saw / Down don't bother me / Honey bee / Ask me no questions / I'm gonna move to the outskirts of town / They made the Queen welcome / Floodin' in California / I found love in the food stamp line / Matchbox blues / Why you so mean to me
CDSXE 076 / Oct '92 / Stax

☐ FUNKY LONDON
Cold sweat / Can't you see what you're doing to me / Funky London / Lonesome / Bad luck / Sweet fingers / Finger on the trigger / Drivin' wheel / Lovingest woman in town
SCD 8586 / Oct '96 / Stax

☐ HARD BARGAIN
Overall junction / Funk shun / You sure drive a hard bargain / You're gonna need me / As the years go passing by / Drownin' on dry land / Heart fixing business / Sky is crying / I get evil / Shake 'em down / I believe to my soul / Got to be some changes made / Albert's groove
SCD 8594 / Oct '96 / Stax

☐ I WANNA GET FUNKY
I wanna get funky / Playing on me / Walking the back streets and crying / Till my back ain't got no bone / Flat tire / I can't hear nothing but the blues / Travellin' man / Crosscut saw / That's what the blues is all about
CDSXE 081 / Jul '93 / Stax

☐ I'LL PLAY THE BLUES FOR YOU (The Best Of Albert King)
Born under a bad sign / Answer to The Laundromatt Blues / You threw your love on me too strong / Crosscut saw / I'll play the blues for you / Angel of mercy / Heart fixing business / Killing floor / Sky is crying / Going back to Iuka / Drowning on dry land / That's what the blues is all about / Left hand woman (get right with me) / Drivin' wheel / Firing line / Don't burn the bridge (cause you might wanna come back... / Can't you see what you're doing to me
CDSX 007 / Jan '90 / Stax

☐ I'LL PLAY THE BLUES FOR YOU (King, Albert & John Lee Hooker)
Born under a bad sign: *King, Albert* / Very thought of you: *King, Albert* / I worked hard: *King, Albert* / When you down: *King, Albert* / Feel good / Boom boom / Serves me right to suffer / One bourbon, one scotch, one beer / King snake
CPCD 8166 / Jun '96 / Charly

☐ I'LL PLAY THE BLUES FOR YOU/ LOVEJOY
I'll play the blues for you (parts 1 and 2) / Little brother (make a way) / Breaking up somebody's home / High cost of loving / I'll be doggone / Answer to the laundromat blues / Don't burn down the bridge ('cause you might wanna / Angel of mercy / Honky tonk woman / Bay area blues / Corina corina / She caught the katy and left me a mule to ride / For the love of a woman / Lovejoy, ill. / Everybody wants to go to heaven / Going back to iuka / Like a road leading home
CDSXD 969 / Mar '91 / Stax

☐ I'M IN A PHONE BOOTH BABY
Phone booth / Dust my broom / Sky is crying / Brother go ahead and take her / Your bread ain't done / Firing line / Game goes on / Truck load of lovin / You gotta sacrifice
CDSXE 083 / Jul '93 / Stax

☐ I'M READY (Best Of The Tomato Years/ 2CD Set)
I'm ready / Cold women with warm hearts / Cadillac assembly line / Nobody wants a loser / Ain't nothing you can do / My babe / Running out of steam / Rub my back / Real good sign / You upset me baby / Love mechanic / Call my job / Get out of my life woman / Born under a bad sign / Feeling / I get evil / Angel of mercy / Flat tyre
CPCD 82652 / Jan '97 / Charly

☐ JUST PICKIN'
MBCD 721 / Jun '93 / Modern Blues

☐ KING ALBERT
Love shock / You upset me baby / Chump chance / Let me rock you easy / Boot lace / Love mechanic / Call my job / Good time Charlie
CPCD 8233 / Oct '96 / Charly

☐ KING DOES THE KING'S THINGS (Blues For Elvis)
Hound dog / That's alright Mama / All shook up / Jailhouse rock / Heartbreak hotel / Don't be cruel / One night / Blue suede shoes / Love me tender
CDSXE 073 / Sep '92 / Stax

☐ KING OF THE BLUES GUITAR
Cold feet / You're gonna need me / Born under a bad sign / I love Luzy / Crosscut saw / You sure drive a hard bargain / Oh pretty woman / Overall junction / Funk-shun / Laundromat blues / Personal manager
7567820172 / Mar '93 / Atlantic

☐ LET'S HAVE A NATURAL BALL
MBCD 723 / Jun '93 / Modern Blues

☐ LIVE
Watermelon man / Don't burn down the bridge / Blues at sunrise / That's what the blues is all about / Stormy Monday / Kansas City / I'm gonna call you as soon as the sun goes down / Matchbox holds my clothes / Jam in a flat / As the years go passing by / Overall junction / I'll play the blues for you
CDBM 18 / Apr '92 / Charly

☐ LIVE IN CANADA
King's groove / King's jump / Watermelon man / I'm gonna move to the outskirts of town / Kansas City / Someday baby / Truckers blues / As the years go by / Rainin' in California / I'll play the blues for you / Sky is crying
CDCBL 755 / Oct '95 / Charly

☐ LIVE WIRE/BLUES POWER (Albert King Live At The Fillmore 1968)
Watermelon man / Blues power / Night stomp / Blues at sunrise / Please love me / Lookout
CDSXE 022 / Nov '89 / Stax

☐ LOST SESSION, THE
She won't gimme no lovin' / Cold in hand / Stop lying / All the way down / Tell me what true love is / Down the road I go / Money lovin' women / Sun gone down / Brand new razor / Sun gone down (take 2)
CDSXE 066 / Nov '92 / Stax

☐ MASTERS, THE
EABCD 074 / 24 Nov '97 / Eagle

☐ NEW ORLEANS HEAT
Get out of my life woman / Born under a bad sign / Feeling / We all wanna boogie / Very thought of you / I got the blues / I get evil / Angel of Mercy / Flat tire
CPCD 8211 / Feb '97 / Charly

☐ THURSDAY NIGHT IN SAN FRANCISCO (Albert King Live At The Fillmore 1968)
San-Ho-Zay / You upset me baby / Stormy Monday blues / Everyday I have the blues / Driftin' blues / I've made nights by myself / Crosscut saw / I'm gonna move to the outskirts of town / Ooh-ee baby
CDSXE 032 / Oct '90 / Stax

☐ TRUCKLOAD OF LOVIN'
Cold women with warm hearts / Gonna make it somehow / Sensation, communication, together / I'm your mate / Truckload of lovin' / Hold hands with one another / Cadillac assembly line / Nobody wants a loser
CPCD 8201 / Feb '97 / Charly

☐ WEDNESDAY NIGHT IN SAN FRANCISCO (Albert King Live At The Fillmore 1968)
Watermelon man / Why you so mean to me / I get evil / Got to be some changes made / Personal manager / Born under a bad sign / Don't throw your love on me so strong
CDSXE 031 / Sep '90 / Stax

☐ YEARS GONE BY
Wrapped up in love again / Shimmy shimmy walk / Cockroach / Killing floor / Lonely man / If the washing don't get you, the rinsing will / Drownin' on dry land / Drownin' on dry land / Heart fixing business / You threw you love on to me too strong / Sky is crying / Can't you see what you're doing to me / Cold sweat / As the years go passing by / Drownin' on dry land / Don't you lie to me / Shake 'em down / I believe to my soul / Heart fixing business / Sky is crying / You're treating me mean
CDSXD 045 / Apr '92 / Stax

King Alex

☐ HOT AS A COFFEE POT (King Alex & The Untouchables)
Hot as a coffee pot / Never do you no wrong / Grandma's sweet potato pie / Just the one that I love / Overload of love / Red cabin / I want to come back / Sweetest thing / Right all the time / Cryin' eyes / Way you do that / Weekend blues / Time is right / Some peoples do some peoples don't
BMCD 9035 / Jul '97 / Black Magic

King, B.B.

☐ AUDIO ARCHIVE
Letter / Long nights / Catfish blues / BB boogie / Evil child / Walkin' and cryin' / Sweet sixteen / Please love me / Other night blues / Everyday I have the blues / New way of driving / How blue can you get / It's my own fault / Mr. Pawnbroker / You've done lost your good thing now / Paying the cost to be the boss / I'm working on the building / Save a seat for me
CDAA 037 / Jun '92 / Tring

☐ B.B. KING SINGS SPIRITUALS
Precious Lord / Save a seat for me / Ole time religion / Swing low sweet chariot / Servant's prayer / Jesus gave me water / I never heard a man / Army of the Lord / I am willing to run all the way / I'm working on the building
DIAB 853 / 6 Jul '98 / Diablo

☐ BEST OF B.B. KING VOL.1, THE
You upset me baby / Everyday / Five long years / Sweet little angel / Beautician blues / Dust my broom / Three o'clock blues / Ain't that just like a woman / I'm King / Sweet sixteen / Whole lot of love / Mean ol' Frisco / Please accept my love / Going down slow / Blues for me / You don't know / Early every morning / Blues at sunrise / Please love me
CDCH 908 / '89 / Ace

☐ BEST OF B.B. KING, THE
Hummingbird / Cook County jail introduction / How blue can you get / Sweet sixteen / Ain't nobody home / Why I sing the blues / Thrill is gone / Nobody loves me but my mother / Caldonia
MCLD 19099 / Nov '90 / Chess/MCA

☐ BLUES COLLECTION, THE
BB boogie / New way of driving / Catfish blues / Walkin' and cryin' / How blue can you get / Mr. Pawnbroker / You've done lost your good thing now / It's my own fault baby / Paying the cost to be the boss / Sweet sixteen / Letter / Other night blues / Long nights / Evil child / Everyday I have the blues
100332 / May '97 / A-Play Collection

☐ BLUES ON TOP OF BLUES
Heartbreaker / Losing faith in you / Dance with me / That's wrong little mama / Having my say / I'm not wanted anymore / Worried dream / Paying the cost to be the boss / Until I found you / I'm gonna do what they do to me / Raining in my heart / Now that you've lost me
BGOCD 69 / '89 / Beat Goes On

☐ BLUES SUMMIT
Playin' with my friends: *King, B.B. & Robert Cray* / Since I met you baby: *King, B.B. & Katie Webster* / I pity the fool: *King, B.B. & Buddy Guy* / You shook me: *King, B.B. & John Lee Hooker* / Something you got: *King, B.B. & Koko Taylor* / There's something on your mind: *King, B.B. & Etta James* / Stormy Monday: *King, B.B. & Albert Collins* / You're the boss: *King, B.B. & Irma Thomas* / I gotta move out of this neighbourhood / Nobody loves me but my mother / Little by little: *King, B.B. & Lowell Fulson* / Everybody's had the blues: *King, B.B. & Joe Louis Walker*
MCD 10710 / Jun '93 / Chess/MCA

☐ BLUES YOU CAN USE
BN 024 / Apr '98 / Blue Nite

☐ COLLECTION, THE (20 Blues Greats)
Help the poor / Everyday I have the blues / Woke up this morning / Worry worry / Sweet little angel / How blue can you get / You upset me baby / It's my own fault / Please love me / She don't love me no more / Three o'clock blues / Fine looking woman / Blind love / You know I love you / Ten long years / Mistreated woman / Shake it up and go / Sweet sixteen / You done lost your good thing now / Outside help
CCSCD 412 / Feb '95 / Castle

☐ COMPLETELY WELL
So excited / No good / You're losin' me / What happened / Confessin' the blues / Key to my kingdom / Crying won't help you now / You're mean / Thrill is gone
MCD 11768 / 27 Jul '98 / Chess/MCA

☐ DEUCES WILD
MCD 11722 / 3 Nov '97 / Chess/MCA
MCD 11766 / 20 Apr '98 / Chess/MCA

☐ DO THE BOOGIE (B.B.King's Early 50's Classics)
Boogie woogie woman / Past day / I gotta find my baby / Woke up this morning (my baby's gone) / Please love me / Blind love / When my heart beats like a hammer / Whole lotta love / That ain't the way to do it / Everyday I have the blues / Let's do the boogie / Dark is the night (Part 1) / Dark is the night (Part 2) / Why I sing the blues / Everything I do is wrong / Woman I love / Jump with you baby / Troubles, troubles, troubles / Crying won't help you
CDCHD 916 / '89 / Ace

☐ EARLY BLUES BOY YEARS VOL.1
OCD 101 / Nov '95 / Opal

☐ EARLY BLUES BOY YEARS VOL.2
OCD 102 / Nov '95 / Opal

☐ FABULOUS B.B. KING, THE
Three o'clock blues / You know I love you / Please love me / You upset me baby / Bad luck / On my word of honor / Everyday I have the blues / Woke up this morning (my baby's gone) / When my heart beats like a hammer / Sweet little angel / Ten long years / Whole lotta love
CDFAB 004 / Aug '91 / Ace

☐ FRIENDS
Friends / I got them blues / Baby, I'm yours / Philadelphia / When everything else is gone / My song
BGOCD 125 / Sep '91 / Beat Goes On

☐ GREAT MOMENTS WITH B.B. KING
MCD 04124 / 16 Feb '98 / Chess/MCA

☐ GREATEST HITS 1951-1960
Three o'clock blues / You know I love you / Boogie woogie woman / Woke up this morning / Please love me / You upset me baby / Whole lotta love / Sneaking around / Every day I have the blues / Crying won't help you / Sweet little angel / Bad luck / I want to get married / Troubles, troubles, troubles / Please accept my love / Sweet sixteen / (I've) got a right to love my baby / My fault / You done lost your good thing now
CSAPCD 117 / Aug '94 / Connoisseur Collection

☐ GUESS WHO
Summer in the city / Just can't please you / Any other you / You don't know nothin' about love / Found what I need / Neighborhood affair / It takes a young girl / Better lovin' man / Guess who / Shoudn't have left me / Five long years
BGOCD 71 / May '90 / Beat Goes On

☐ HE'S DYNAMITE
Every day (I have the blues) / BB's boogie / New way of driving / Walkin' and cryin' / She's dynamite / Shake it up and go / My own fault / Catfish blues / Mr. Pawnbroker / Flying high / Low rider / Jump with BB / I'll survive / You're on the top / Please love me / You done lost your good thing now / You know I go for you / Past day / Other night blues / Questionnaire blues / She don't move me no more / Rock me baby / Sweet sixteen / You upset me baby
CDCHK 691 / 27 Jul '98 / Ace

☐ HEART AND SOUL (A Collection Of Blues Ballads)
Lonely and blue / Sneakin' around / You can't fool my heart / Story from my heart and soul / Don't get around much anymore / You know I love you / I'm king / Lonely lover's plea / My heart belongs to only you / Don't cry anymore / Please accept my love / Peace of mind / I was blind / On my word of honour / I'll survive / If I lost you / My reward / I am / I love you so / Key to my kingdom
CDCH 376 / Oct '92 / Ace

☐ HIS BEST (The Electric B.B. King)
MCD 11767 / 27 Jul '98 / Chess/MCA

☐ HIS BEST - THE ELECTRIC KING
Tired of your jive / BB Jones / Paying the cost to be the boss / I done got wise / Sweet sixteen / I don't want you cuttin' your hair / Don't answer the door / All over again / Think it over / Meet my happiness / You put it on me
BGOCD 37 / Oct '88 / Beat Goes On

☐ IN LONDON
Caldonia / Blue shadows / Alexis' boogie / We can't agree / Ghetto woman / Wet hayshark / Part time love / Power of the blues / Ain't nobody home
BGOCD 42 / Oct '88 / Beat Goes On

☐ INDIANOLA MISSISSIPPI SEEDS
Nobody loves me but my mother / You're still my woman / Ask me no questions / Until I'm dead and cold / King's special / Ain't gonna worry my life anymore / Chains and things / Go underground / Hummingbird
BGOCD 237 / Mar '95 / Beat Goes On

☐ KANSAS CITY 1972
CDCBL 752 / Jan '94 / Charly

☐ KING OF THE BLUES
Early every morning / Sweet little angel / Three O'clock in the morning / Ain't that just like a woman / Dark is the night (part 1) / Dark is the night (part 2) / Rock me baby / I've got a right to love my baby / Bad luck soul / Did you ever love a woman / King of guitar / You upset me baby / Get out of here / Troubles, troubles, troubles / Sweet sixteen part 1 / Sweet sixteen Part 2 / That ain't the way to do it / Ten long years / Powerhouse / Going down slow
PWKS 4211 / Mar '96 / Carlton

☐ KING OF THE BLUES (4CD Set)
Miss Martha King / She's dynamite / Three O'clock blues / Please love me / You upset me baby / Everyday I have the blues / Rock me baby / Recession blues / Don't get around much anymore / I'm gonna sit in til you give in / Blues at midnight / Sneakin' around / My baby's coming home / Slowly losing my mind / How blue can you get / Rockin' awhile / Help the poor / Stop leadin' me on / Never trust a woman / Sweet little angel / All over again / Sloppy drunk / Don't answer the door / I done got wise / Think it over / Gambler's blues / Goin' down slow / Tired of your jive / Sweet sixteen / I'm gonna do what they do to me / Lucille / Watch yourself / You put it on me / Get myself somebody / I want you so bad / Why I sing the blues / Get off my back woman / Please accept my love / Fools get wise / No good / So exited / Thrill is gone / Confessin' the blues / Nobody loves me but my mother / Hummingbird / Ask me no questions / Chains and things / Eyesight to the blind / Niji baby / Blue shadows / Ghetto woman / Ain't nobody home / I got some help I don't need / Five long years / To know you is to love you / I like to live the love / Don't make me pay for his mistakes / Let the good times roll / Don't you lie to me / Mother fuyer / Never make a move too soon / When it all comes down (I'll still be around) / Better not look down / Caldonia / There must be a better world somewhere / Play with your poodle / Darlin' you know I love you / Inflation blues / Make love to me / Into the night / Six silver strings / When love comes to town / Right time, wrong place / Many miles travelled / I'm movin' on / Since I met you baby
MCAD 410677 / Oct '92 / Chess/MCA

☐ LIVE AND WELL
Don't answer the door / Just a little love / My mood / Sweet little angel / Please accept my love / I want you so bad / Friends / Get off my back woman / Let's get down to business / Why I sing the blues
BGOCD 233 / Jun '94 / Beat Goes On

☐ LIVE AT COOK COUNTY JAIL (2CD Set)
MCD 33007 / Jul '96 / Chess/MCA

☐ LIVE AT SAN QUENTIN
Intro / Let the good times roll / Everyday I have the blues / Whole lotta lovin' / Sweet little angel / Never make a move too soon / Into the night / Ain't nobody's business if I do / Thrill is gone / Peace to the world / Nobody loves me but my mother / Sweet sixteen / Rock me baby
MCLD 19253 / Nov '94 / Chess/MCA

☐ LIVE AT THE REGAL
Everyday I have the blues / Sweet little angel / It's my own fault / How blue can you get / Please love me / You upset me baby / Worry worry / Woke up this morning / You done lost your good thing now / Help the poor
BGOCD 235 / Oct '94 / Beat Goes On

☐ LIVE AT THE REGAL
MCD 11646 / 25 May '98 / Chess/MCA

☐ LIVE IN COOK COUNTY JAIL
MCD 11769 / 27 Jul '98 / Chess/MCA

☐ LUCILLE
Lucille / You move me so / Country girl / No money no luck / I need your love / Rainin' all the time / I'm with you / Stop putting the hurt on me / Watch yourself
BGOCD 36 / Feb '89 / Beat Goes On

☐ LUCILLE AND FRIENDS
When love comes to town: *King, B.B. & U2* / Playin' with my friends: *King, B.B. & Robert Cray* / To know you is to love you: *King, B.B. & Stevie Wonder* / Caught a touch of your love: *King, B.B. & Grover Washington Jr.* / All you ever give me is the blues: *King, B.B. & Vernon Reid* / You shook me: *King, B.B. & John Lee Hooker* / Spirit in the dark: *King, B.B. & Diane Schuur* / Can't get enough: *King, B.B. & Mick Fleetwood/Stevie Nicks* / Since I met you baby: *King, B.B. & Gary Moore* / BB's blues: *King, B.B. & Branford Marsalis* / Better not look down: *King, B.B. & The Crusaders* / Frosty: *King, B.B. & Albert Collins* / Hummingbird: *King, B.B. & Leon Russell/Joe Walsh* / Ghetto woman: *King, B.B. & Friends* / Let the good times roll: *King, B.B. & Bobby Bland*
MCD 33008 / Jul '95 / Chess/MCA

☐ MY SWEET LITTLE ANGEL
My sweet little angel / Crying won't help you / Ten long years / Quit my baby / Don't look now but I've got the blues / You know I go for you / Why do everything happen to me / Worry worry / Shake yours / Please accept my love / Treat me right / Going down slow / Just like a woman / Time to say goodbye / Early every morning / You've been an angel
CDCHD 300 / Mar '92 / Ace

☐ SINGIN' THE BLUES AND THE BLUES
Please love me / You upset me baby / Everyday I have the blues / Bad luck / Three o'clock blues / Blind love / Woke up this morning (my baby's gone) / You know I love you / Sweet little angel / Ten long years / Did you ever love a woman / Crying won't help

you / Why do everything happen to me / Ruby Lee / When my heart beats like a hammer / Past day / Boogie woogie woman / Early every morning / I want to get married / That ain't the way to do it / Troubles, troubles, troubles / Don't you want a man like me / You know I go for you / What can I do
CDCHD 320 / Apr '91 / Ace

☐ SPOTLIGHT ON LUCILLE
Six silver strings / Big boss man / In the midnight hour / Into the night / My Lucille / Memory blues / My guitar sings the blues / Double trouble / Memory lane
CDCH 187 / Sep '86 / Ace

☐ SWEET LITTLE ANGEL
You upset me baby / Everyday I have the blues / Sneakin' around / Woman I love / Please accept my love / 3 o'clock blues / Save a seat for me / Sweet sixteen / Sweet little angel / Let me love you / Rock me baby / Army of the lord / I've got a right to love my baby / Well baby look at me / Please love me / Woke up this morning
305972 / Apr '98 / Hallmark

☐ TAKE IT HOME
Better not look down / Same old story / Happy birthday blues / I've always been lonely / Second hand woman / Tonight I'm gonna make you a star / Beginning of the end / Story everybody knows / Take it home
MCD 11770 / 27 Jul '98 / Chess/MCA

☐ THERE IS ALWAYS ONE MORE TIME
I'm moving on / Back in l.a. / Blue come over me / Fool me once / Lowdown / Mean and evil / Something up my sleeve / Roll roll roll / There is always one more time
MCD 10295 / 8 Sep '97 / Chess/MCA

☐ THERE MUST BE A BETTER WORLD SOMEWHERE
Victim / More, more, more / You're going with me / Life ain't nothing but a party / Born again human / There must be a better world somewhere
BGOCD 124 / Sep '91 / Beat Goes On

☐ TOGETHER FOR THE FIRST TIME (King, B.B. & Bobby Bland)
3 o'clock blues / It's my own fault / Driftin' blues / That's the way love is / I'm sorry / I'll take care of you / Don't cry no more / Why I sing the blues / Goin' down slow / I like to live the love / Don't answer the door
BGOCD 161 / Jun '94 / Beat Goes On

King Bees

☐ POLLENATIN' (King Bees & Jerry McCain/Chicago Bob Nelson)
TRCD 9927 / Dec '96 / Tramp

King, Ben

☐ CELTIC STRINGS & WINGS
IAGO 203CD / Apr '96 / Iago

King, Ben E.

☐ ANTHOLOGY (2CD Set)
There goes my baby / Dance with me / This magic moment / Lonely winds / Save the last dance for me / I count the tears / Brace yourself / Show me the way / Spanish harlem / First taste of love / Young boy blues / Stand by me / On the horizon / Here comes the night / Amor / Ectasy / Yes / Walking in the footsteps of a fool / Don't play that song (You lied) / How can I forget / Gypsy / I who have nothing / What now my love / Groovin' / That's when it hurts / Let the water run down / It's all over / River of tears / Seven letters / Record (Baby I love you) / She's gone again / Cry no more / Goodnight my love / Pleasant dreams / So much love / I swear by stars above / What is soul / Man without a dream / Tears, tears, tears / We got a thing going on / Don't take your love from me / It's amazing / Till I can't take it anymore / It ain't fair / Hey little one / Supernatural thing / Do it in the name of love / I had a love / Get it up for love / Star in the ghetto / Music trance
8122712152 / Oct '93 / Atlantic

☐ BROTHERS IN SOUL (The Best Of Ben E. King & The Drifters) (King, Ben E. & The Drifters)
Stand by me: *King, Ben E.* / Up on the roof: *Drifters* / Dance with me: *Drifters* / Don't play that song (You lied): *King, Ben E.* / On broadway: *Drifters* / This magic moment: *Drifters* / I who have nothing: *King, Ben E.* / Spanish Harlem: *King, Ben E.* / Saturday night at the movies: *Drifters* / Please stay: *Drifters* / There goes my baby: *Drifters* / Supernatural thing (Part 1): *King, Ben E.* / Under the boardwalk: *Drifters* / Save the last dance for me: *Drifters* / You send me: *Drifters* / Unchained melody: *Drifters*
ECD 3044 / Jan '95 / K-Tel

☐ COLLECTION, THE
Stand by me / Spanish harlem / Save the last dance for me / Don't play that song / I (who have nothing) / Amor / This magic moment / Young boy blues / Goodnight my love / How can I forget / It's all over / I count the tears / All of your tomorrows / Into the mystic / Love is / Only you know and I know / Poison in my mind / She does it right with nothing but her loving ways / Supernatural thing / Take me to the pilot / Beginning of it all / Travelin' woman / White moon / Love is going to get you / I guess it's goodbye
COL 055 / Jan '95 / Collection

☐ DEFINITIVE BEN E. KING ANTHOLOGY VOL.1, THE (Spanish Harlem/Classics From The Atco Masters)
Amor amor / Sway / Come closer to me / Perfida / Granada / Sweet and gentle / Perhaps, perhaps, perhaps / Frenesi / Souvenir of Mexico / Besame mucho / Love me, love me / Spanish Harlem / How often: *King, Ben E. & Lavern Baker* / Help each other romance: *King, Ben E. & Lavern Baker* / Tell Daddy / Too bad / Walking in the footsteps of a fool / Gloria Gloria / Auf wiedersehn, my dear / How can I forget
RSACD 837 / Nov '96 / Sequel

☐ DEFINITIVE BEN E. KING ANTHOLOGY VOL.2, THE (Sings For Soulful Lovers/ Classics From The Atco Masters)
My heart cries for you / He will break your heart / Dream lover / Will you love me tomorrow / My foolish heart / Fever / Moon river / What a difference a day made / Because of you / At last / On the street where you live / It's all in the game / I could have danced all night / Gypsy / I (who have nothing) / Beginning of time / What now my love / Groovin' / Don't play that song (you lied) / Stand by me / What'd I say
RSACD 838 / Sep '96 / Sequel

☐ DEFINITIVE BEN E. KING ANTHOLOGY VOL.3, THE (Don't Play That Song/ Classics From The Atco Masters)
Don't play that song (you lied) / Ecstasy / On the horizon / Show me the way / Here comes the night / First taste of love / Stand by me / Yes / Young boy blues / Hermit of misty mountain / I promise love / Brace yourself / That's when it hurts / Around the corner / What a man can do / Way you shake it / Not now, I'll tell you when
RSACD 839 / Sep '96 / Sequel

☐ DEFINITIVE BEN E. KING ANTHOLOGY VOL.4, THE (Seven Letters/Classics From The Atco Masters)
Seven letters / River of tears / I'm standing by / Jamaica / Down home / Si senor / It's all over / Let the water run down / This is my dream / It's no good for me / In the middle of the night / Don't drive me away / Where's the girl / So much love / Man without a dream / Tears tears tears / She knows what to do for me / Don't take your sweet love away
RSACD 853 / Nov '96 / Sequel

☐ DEFINITIVE BEN E. KING ANTHOLOGY VOL.5, THE (What Is Soul/Classics From The Atco Masters)
Record (baby I love you) / She's gone again / There's no place to hide / Cry no more / Goodnight my love (pleasant dreams) / Katherine / I can't break myself the news / I swear by stars above / Get in a hurry / They don't give medals to yesterday's heroes / Teeny weeny little bit / What is soul / Forgive this fool / Don't take your love from me / It's amazing / When you love someone / It ain't fair / Till I can't take it anymore / Hey little one / What'cha gonna do about it: *King, Ben E. & Dee Dee Sharp* / We got a thing going on: *King, Ben E. & Dee Dee Sharp* / Soul meeting: *Soul Clan* / That's how it feels: *Soul Clan*
RSACD 854 / Nov '96 / Sequel

☐ DEFINITIVE BEN E. KING ANTHOLOGY VOL.6, THE (Supernatural Thing/ Originals From The Atco Masters)
Supernatural thing / Supernatural thing / Your lovin' ain't good enough / Drop my heart off / Extra extra / Do it in the name of love / Happiness is where you find it / Do you wanna do a thing / Imagination / What do you want me to do / Supernatural thing / Do it in the name of love
RSACD 855 / Nov '96 / Sequel

☐ DEFINITIVE BEN E. KING ANTHOLOGY VOL.7, THE (Benny & Us/Classics From The Atco Masters) (King, Ben E. & Average White Band)
Get it up for love / Fool for you anyway / Star in the ghetto / Message / What is soul / Someday we'll all be free / Imagine / Keeping it to myself / Star in the ghetto / Star in the ghetto / Fool for you anyway / Message
RSACD 856 / Nov '96 / Sequel

☐ GREATEST HITS
Stand by me / Don't play that song / Amor / Young boy blues / Goodnight my love / Spanish harlem / How can I forget / It's all over / I (who have nothing) / Save the last dance for me / I count the tears / This magic moment
CDSGP 045 / Apr '93 / Prestige

☐ HITS COLLECTION (King, Ben E. & The Drifters)
Stand by me / Saturday night at the movies / There goes my baby / Spanish harem / Save the last dance for me / Bring it on home to me / Under the broadwalk / Supernatural thing / Sweets for my sweet / Dance with me / Don't play that song / Om broadway / Some kind of wonderful / I who have nothing
101712 / May '97 / A-Play Collection

☐ LEGENDARY BEN E. KING, THE
HADCD 180 / Nov '95 / Javelin

☐ SPANISH HARLEM/DON'T PLAY THAT SONG
CCLCD 62102 / 3 Aug '98 / Collectables

☐ STAND BY ME (The Ultimate Collection)
Stand by me / Save the last dance for me / I who have nothing / That's when it hurts / I could have danced all night / First taste of love / Dream lover / Moon river / Spanish harlem / Amor / I count the tears / Don't play that song (You lied) / This magic moment / Young boy blues / It's all in the game / Supernatural thing (part 1)
7802132 / Feb '87 / Atlantic

☐ VERY BEST OF BEN E. KING, THE
There goes my baby / Dance with me / This magic moment / Save the last dance for me / I count the tears / Spanish harlem / Stand by me / On the horizon / Amor / Young boy blues / Here comes the night / Don't play that song / How can I forget / I (who have nothing) / Supernatural thing / Do it in the name of love
8122729702 / 4 May '98 / Rhino

☐ WHAT'S IMPORTANT TO ME
It's your love (that makes me happy) / You've got all of me / Major malfunction / You still move me / She's gone again / So important to me / You can count on me / It's all right / I'm gonna be somebody
ICH 1133CD / Jan '94 / Ichiban

King, Bill

☐ MAGNOLIA NIGHTS
Amerasia / Rio grande / Magnolia nights / Emotions / Kristine / Images / Rhythm one
1390232 / May '89 / Gaia

King Biscuit Boy

☐ DOWN THE LINE
Georgia slop / Done everything I can / Mama Luchie / Neighbour, neighbour / Down the line / Hoodoo party / Route 90 / Terraplane blus / It's my soul / Necromonica / Get it right / Look out Mabel / Step back baby
NEBCD 849 / Aug '96 / Sequel

King Blank

☐ REAL DIRT, THE
Howl upside down / Blind box / Real dirt / Big pink bang / Guilty as hell / Map of pain / Shot full of holes / Killer in the rain / Uptight / Bullet proof crucifix
SITL 21CD / Nov '91 / Situation 2

King, Bob

☐ BOB KING AND THE COUNTRY KINGS
Laurel Lee / Give my love to Rose / Hey mommy / Waltz of two broken hearts / Going back to an old love affair / Why don't you leave me / My petite Marie / If the things they say are true / Be careful of stones are throw / She went without saying goodbye / Pray for me mother of mine / Let's take a fair trade / Nothing ventured nothing gained / Lonely city park / That's what's on my mind / All Canadian boy / My home by the fraser / My son calls another man daddy / Rose of ol' pawnee / I dreamed about mom last night / No parking here / Just call on me / Boy with a future / I've been dreaming / Between our hearts / It's goodbye and so long to you
BCD 15719 / Aug '93 / Bear Family

☐ JUST ME AND MY GUITAR
You and my old guitar / Little shirt my mother made for me / Patanio, the pride of the plains / Mommy please stay home with me / I'm just here to get my baby out of jail / French song / On the banks of the old pontchartrain / When the work's all done this fall / Old log cabin for sale / Driftwood on the river / Strawberry roan / Rockin' alone in an old rocking chair / I've been down that road before / Ballad of the chapeau boys / Mary Ann regrets / Memories of you / Rescue from the Moose river goldmine / When it's lamplighting time in the valley / Cat came back / Ballad of Jed Clampett / Bluest man in the town / Cowboy / Jimmie Brown / Newboy / Little Tom / Train of memories / French Canadian girl / Road paved with heartaches / It breaks a mother's heart / Once more / Coconut Joe
BCD 15718 / Aug '93 / Bear Family

King, Bobby

☐ LIVE AND LET LIVE (King, Bobby & Terry Evans)
SPCD 1016 / Apr '94 / Special Delivery

☐ RHYTHM, BLUES, SOUL AND GROOVES (King, Bobby & Terry Evans)
One way ticket to memphis / Where we gonna go from here / You're the one / We'll always be together / I fancy you / I wanna be with you / I'll be strong / I'm in love / You and me / Boogie jam
ROUCD 2101 / Dec '94 / Rounder

King, Carole

☐ FANTASY
Fantasy (beginning) / You've been around too long / Being at war with each other / Directions / That's how things go down / Weekends / Haywood / Quiet place to live / Welfare symphony / You light up my life / Corazch / Believe in humanity / Fantasy end
4879392 / Jul '97 / Epic

☐ GREATEST HITS
Jazzman / So far away / Sweet seasons / I feel the earth move / Brother brother / Only love is real / It's too late / Nightingale / Smackwater Jack / Been to Caanan / Corazon / Believe in humility
CD 32345 / Mar '91 / Epic

☐ JAZZMAN
JHD 010 / Jun '92 / Tring

☐ LIVE AT CARNEGIE HALL
Feel the earth move / Home again / After all this time / Child of mine / Carry your load / No easy way down / Song of long ago / Snow Queen / Smackwater Jack / So far away / It's too late / Eventually / Way over yonder / Beautiful / You've got a friend: *King, Carole & James Taylor* / Will you still love me tomorrow: *King, Carole & James Taylor* / Some kind of wonderful: *King, Carole & James Taylor* / Up on the roof: *King, Carole & James Taylor* / (You make me feel like) A natural woman
4851042 / Nov '96 / Epic

☐ MUSIC
Brother brother / It's going to take some time / Sweet seasons / Some kind of wonderful / Surely / Carry your load / Music / Song of long ago / Brighter / Growing away from me / Too much rain / Back to California
4844622 / Feb '97 / Epic

☐ NATURAL WOMAN (The Ode Collection 1968-1976/2CD Set)
Now that everything's been said / Hi de ho / Up on the roof / Child of mine / I feel the earth move / So far away / It's too late / Home again / Beautiful / Way over yonder / Where you lead / Will you still love me tomorrow / Smackwater Jack / Tapestry / (You make me feel like) A natural woman / You've got a friend / Music / Brother brother / It's going to take some time / Sweet seasons / Bitter with the sweet / Goodbye don't mean I'm gone / Been to Canaan / Corazon / Believe in humanity (live at Carnegie Hall) / Jazzman / Wrap around joy / Nightingale / Really Rosie / Alligators all around / There's a space between us / Only love is real / Ties that bind / You've got a friend (live) / Pocket money / This time in my life
4893212 / 6 Apr '98 / Legacy

☐ PEARLS/TIME GONE BY
Dancing with tears in my eyes / Locomotion / One fine day / Hey girl / Snow queen / Chains / Oh no not my baby / Hi de ho / Wasn't born to follow / Goin' back / Hard rock cafe / In the name of love / Morning sun / Simple things / Time gone by / You still want her / Passing of the days / Time alone / Main street saturday night / Welcome home
VSOPCD 199 / Jun '94 / Connoisseur Collection

☐ SWEET SEASON
JHD 038 / Jun '92 / Tring

☐ TAPESTRY
I feel the earth move / So far away / Beautiful / You've got a friend / Where you lead / Will you still love me tomorrow / Smack water Jack / Tapestry / It's too late / Home again / Way over yonder / (You make me feel like) a natural woman
CD 32110 / Jun '89 / Epic
4804222 / Sep '95 / Mastersound

☐ TAPESTRY REVISITED (A Tribute To Carole King) (Various Artists)
You've got a friend / (you make me feel like) a natural woman / I feel the earth move / It's too late / Tapestry / Smackwater jack / Will you love me tomorrow / Youre you lead / Way over yonder / Beautiful / Home again / So far away
7567926042 / Nov '95 / Atlantic

King, Charlie

☐ FOOD, PHONE, GAS & LODGING
FF 536CD / '92 / Flying Fish

King, Claude

☐ MORE THAN CLIMBING THAT MOUNTAIN, WOLVERTON MOUNTAIN THAT IS (5CD Set)
Flying saucers / I want to be loved / Million mistakes / Why should I / Beers and pinballs / Fifty one beers / She knows why / She's my baby / Take it like a man / So close to me / Got the world by the tail / Slow thinking heart / I think of you and me / Now that I love you / My future life will be my past / Over again / Run baby run / Not sure of you / Big river, big man / Sweet loving / Comancheros / I can't get over the way you got over me / Give me your love and I'll give you mine / Pistol packin' papa / You're breaking my heart / I'm here to get my baby out of jail / Little bitty heart / Would you care / I backed out / Wolverton mountain / This land of yours and mine / Sheepskin valley / Burning of Atlanta / Don't that moon look lonesome / I've got the world by the tail / Culpepper community / Building a bridge / What will I do / Scarlet O'Hara / Hey Lucille / Where the red red roses grow / Sixteen tons: *Platters* / Lace mantilla and a rose of red / That's what makes the world go around / Sam Hill / Big ole shoulder / Whirlpool (of your love) / When you gotta go (you gotta go) / Tiger woman / Great big tears / I won't belong in your town / Hold that tiger (tiger rag) / That's the way the wind blows / Little buddy / Come on home / Ancient history / There ain't gonna be no more / It's good to have my baby back home / Catch a little raindrop / Anna / Right place at the right time / Little things that every girl should know / Juggler / Watchman / Laura / Goodbye my love / Green green grass of home / Ruby, don't take your love to town / Almost persuaded / Ninety nine years / Parchman farm blues / Birmingham bus station / Yellow haired woman / Power of your sweet love / Beertops and teardrops / Sweet love on your mind / Green mountain / Four roses / I remember Johnny / Honky tonk man / First train headin' South / Ole slewfoot / North to Alaska / Battle of New Orleans / Sink the bismarck / All for the love of a girl / Whispering pines / When it's springtime in Alaska / House of the rising sun / Friend, lover, woman, wife / When you're twenty-one / I'll be your baby tonight / Turn it around in your mind / Mary's vineyard / Heart / Johnny Valentine / Highway lonely / Chip 'n' Dale's place / Help me make it through the night / Lady of our town / Just as soon as I get over loving you / Sweet Mary Ann / (Darlin' raise the shade) let the sun shine in / I know it's not been easy lovin' me / I know it's not been easy lovin' me / This time I'm through / He ain't country / If my heart could stop / Don't do me bad / It's such a perfect day for making love / Sometimes you lose, sometimes you win / Cotton Dan / I'll spend a lifetime loving you / Night I cried / Cry yourself a river / Sugar baby candy girl / How long would it take / Just a bum husband / Best mistake I ever made / Bucks worth of change / I wonder who she missed me with today / I sat down on a beartrap (just this morning) / It starts off good (and keeps gettin' better) / Times and things keep changing / Last days of love
BCD 15619 / Feb '94 / Bear Family

King Crimson

☐ ABSENT LOVERS (Live In Montreal 1984/2CD Set)
Entry of the crims / Larks' tongues in aspic part III / Thela hun ginjeet / Red / Matte kudasai / Industry dig me / Three of a perfect pair / Indiscipline / Satori in Tangier / Frame by frame / Man with an open heart / Waiting man / Sleepless / Larks' tongues in aspic part II / Discipline / Heartbeat / Elephant talk
DGM 9804 / 15 Jun '98 / Discipline

☐ B BOOM OFFICIAL LIVE IN ARGENTINA
Vroom / Frame by frame / Sex, sleep, eat, drink, dream / Red / One time / B'boom / Thrak / Two sticks / Elephant talk / Indiscipline / Vroom vroom / Matte kudasai / Talking drum / Lark's tongues in aspic (part 2) / Heartbeat / Sleepless / People / B'boom (Reprise)
DGM 9503 / Jul '95 / Discipline

☐ BEAT
Neal and Jack and Me / Heartbeat / Sartori in Tangier / Waiting man / Neurotica / Two Hands / Howler / Requiem
EGCD 51 / Jan '87 / EG

☐ COMPACT KING CRIMSON, THE
Discipline / Thel hun ginjeet / Matte Kudasai / Three of a perfect pair / Frame by frame / Sleepless / Heartbeat / Elephant talk / 21st century schizoid man / I talk to the wind / Epitaph / March for no reason (part of Epitaph) / Tomorrow and tomorrow (part of Epitaph) / Red / Cat food / Court of the crimson king / Return of the fire witch / Dance of the puppets
EGCD 68 / Jan '86 / EG

☐ CONCISE KING CRIMSON, THE
21st Century schizoid man / Epitaph / In the court of the Crimson King / Cat food / Ladies in the road / Starless (abridged) / Red / Fallen angel / Elephant talk / Frame by frame / Matte kudesai / Heartbeat / Three of a perfect pair / Sleepless
CDV 2721 / Oct '93 / Virgin

☐ DISCIPLINE
Elephant talk / Frame by frame / Matte Kudasai / Indiscipline / Thel hun ginjeet / Sheltering sky / Discipline
EGCD 49 / Jun '88 / EG

☐ EPITAPH (King Crimson Live In 1969/ 2CD Set)
21st Century schizoid man / In the court of the crimson king / Get thy bearings / Epitaph / Man a city / Travel weary capricorn / Mars
DGM 9607 / Apr '97 / Discipline

☐ FRAME BY FRAME (The Essential King Crimson - 4CD Set)
21st Century schizoid man / I talk to the wind / Epitaph / Moonchild / In the court of the crimson King / Peace - a theme / Cat food / Groon / Cadence and cascade / Ladies of the road / Sailor's tale / Bolero / Larks' tongues in aspic / Night watch / Great deceiver / Fracture / Starless / Red / Fallen angel / One more red nightmare / Elephant talk / Frame by frame / Matte Kudesai / Thela Hun Gingeet / Heartbeat / Waiting man / Neurotica / Requiem / Three of a perfect pair / Sleepless / Sheltering sky / Discipline / King Crimson barbershop / Get thy bearings and variations / Travel weary Capricorn / Mars / Talking drum / 21st Century schizoid man / Asbury Park / Larks' tongues in aspic part 3 / Sartori in Tangiers / Indiscipline
KCBOX 1 / Jul '95 / Virgin

☐ GREAT DECEIVER, THE (4CD Set)
Things are not as they seem / Walk on - no pussyfooting / Larks' tongues in aspic (part 2) / Lament / Exiles / Improv - a voyage to the centre of the cosmos / Easy money / Improv - providencefracture / Starless / Sleight of hand (or now you don't see it again) / Providence...continued (encore) / 21st century schizoid man / Walk off from providence / Walk on to glasgow...glasgow apollo / Sharks' lungs in lemsip / Larks' tongues in aspic (part 1) (abridged) / Book of saturday / Easy money / We'll let you know / Night watch / Improv - tight scrummy / Peace - a theme / Cat food / Penn state university / Easy money / It is for you but not for us / Acts of deception / (the magic circus, or weasels stole our fruit) / Pittsburgh, pennsylvania - stanley warner theatre / Walk on - no pussyfooting / Great deceiver / Improv - bartley butsford / Exiles / Improvdaniel dust / Night watch / Doctor diamond / Starless / Improv - wilton carpet / Talking drum / Larks' tongues in aspic (part 2) (abbreviated) / Penn state university / Applause and announcement / Improv - is there life out there / But neither are they otherwise / Toronto massey hall 24 june 1974 / Improv - the golden walnut / Night watch / Fracture / Improv - clueless and slightly slack / Zurich volkshaus / Walk on - no pussyfooting / Improv - some pussyfooting / Larks' tongues in aspic (part 1) / Improv - the law of maximum distress part one / Improv - the law of maximum distress part two / Easy money / Improv - some more pussyfooting / Talking drum
KCDIS 1 / Nov '92 / Virgin

☐ IN THE COURT OF THE CRIMSON KING
21st century schizoid man / I talk to the wind / Epitaph / Tomorrow and tomorrow (part of Epitaph) / Moonchild / Illusion / Court of the Crimson King / Return Of The fire witch / Dance of the puppets / March for no reason (part of Epitaph) / Dream
EGCD 1 / Jan '87 / EG

☐ IN THE WAKE OF POSEIDON
Peace - a beginning / Pictures of a city / Cadence and cascade / In the wake of Poseidon / Peace - a theme / Cat food / Devil's triangle / Merday Morn (part 1 of the Devil's Triangle) / Hand of Sceiron (part 2 of the Devil's Triangle) / Garden of worm (part 3 of the Devil's triangle) / Peace - an end
EGCD 2 / Jul '92 / EG

☐ LARKS' TONGUES IN ASPIC
Lark's tongues in aspic (part 1) / Book of Saturday / Exiles / Easy Money / Talking drum / Lark's tongues in aspic (part 2)
EGCD 7 / Jul '92 / EG

☐ LIZARD
Cirkus / Indoor games / Happy family / Lady of the dancing water / Lizard / Prince Rupert awakes (part 1 of Lizard) / Bolero / Battle of glass tears / Dawn song (part a of battle of glass tears) / Last skirmish (part b of Battle of Glass Tears) / Prince Rupert's lament (Part C of Battle of Glass Tears) / Big top
EGCD 4 / '88 / EG

☐ LIZARD/IN THE WAKE OF POSEIDON/ IN THE COURT OF THE... (3CD Set)
TPAK 28 / Nov '93 / Virgin

☐ NIGHT WATCH
Easy money / Lament / Book of saturday / Fracture / Night watch / Improv / Improv trio / Exiles / Improv:fright watch / Taking drum / Lrks tongues in aspic / 21st century schizoid man
DGM 9707 / 10 Nov '97 / Discipline

☐ RED
Red / Fallen angel / One more red nightmare / Providence / Starless
EGCD 15 / Jan '87 / EG

☐ SCHIZOID DIMENSION (A Tribute To King Crimson) (Various Artists)
CLP 0123 / 2 Feb '98 / Cleopatra

☐ SPACE GROOVE (2CD Set) (Projekt 2)
DGM 9801 / 13 Apr '98 / Discipline

☐ STARLESS AND BIBLE BLACK
Great deceiver / Lament / We'll let you know / Night watch / Trio / Mincer / Starless and bible black / Fracture
EGCD 12 / '87 / EG
CDVKC 6 / Jul '97 / Virgin

☐ THRAK
Vroom / Coda: marine 475 / Dinosaur / Walking on air / B'boom / Thrak / Inner garden / People / Radio I / One time / Radio II / Inner garden II / Sex, sleep, eat, drink, dream / Vroom vroom / Vroom vroom coda
KCCDY 1
KCCDX 1 / Apr '95 / Virgin

☐ THREE OF A PERFECT PAIR
Model man / Sleepless / Man with an open heart / Nuages (that which passes, passes like clouds) / Dig me / No warning / Lark's tongues in aspic (part 3) / Three of a perfect pair / Industry
EGCD 55 / Jan '87 / EG

☐ VROOOM
Vroom / Sex, sleep, eat, drink, dream / Cage / Thrack / When I say stop, continue / One time
DGM 0004 / Oct '94 / Discipline

King Curry

☐ BEYOND GOOD AND EVIL
342562 / Jun '96 / No Bull

King Curtis

☐ BEST OF KING CURTIS, THE
Night train / One mint julep / Soul twist / Soul serenade / Honky tonk / Slow drag / Hide away / Strollin' home / Sister Sadie / Tanya / Summer dream / Hung over / Bill Bailey, won't you please come home / More soul / Shake / Change is gonna come
CDP 8365042 / Aug '96 / Capitol Jazz

☐ BLUES AT MONTREUX (King Curtis & Champion Jack Dupree)
Junker's blues / Sneaky Pete / Everything's gonna be alright / Get with it / Poor boy blues / I'm having fun
7567813892 / Jan '96 / Atlantic

☐ CAPITOL YEARS 1962-1965, THE (3CD Set)
Turn 'em on / Beach party / Beautiful brown eyes / Your cheatin' heart / Tennessee waltz / Wagon wheels / High noon / Anytime / Home on the range / Night train to Memphis / I'm movin' on / Raunchy / Tumbling tumbleweeds / Walking the floor over you / Slow drag / New dance / Frisky / Alexander's ragtime band / Amorosa (Bossa Nova) / Strollin' home / Mess around / Sukiyaki / Summer dream / Do the monkey / Feel all right / Turn 'em on (Mono) / Theme from Lillies Of The Field (Amen) / More soul / Soul serenade / Honky tonk / Watermelon man / Memphis / Soul twist / Night train / Tequila / Wiggle wobble / One mint julep / Can't sit down / Swingin' shepherd blues / My last date / Hideaway / Harlem Nocturne / Java / Stranger on the shore / Melancholy serenade / Summer dream / Tanya / Hung over / Soul twine (Stereo) / Hungover / Soul twine (Mono) / Moon river / Girl from Ipanema / Sister Sadie / Something you've got / Take these chains from my heart / Let it be me / Hung over (Re-make) / Misty (Re-make) / Bill Bailey, Won't you please come home / Peter Gunn / Shake / Ain't that good news / Twistin' the night away / Good times / Send me some lovin' / Bring it on home to me / Change is gonna come / You send me / Cupid / Having a party / Chain gang / Prance / Something you've got (Overdub)
BCD 15670 / Mar '93 / Bear Family

☐ GROOVIN' WITH THE KING (The Best Of King Curtis)
Soul twist / Night train / Groovin' with the King / Midnight blue / Watermelon man / Peter Gunn / Soul serenade / Irresistible you / Big dipper / I know / Jack-o-wee / What'd I say / Wiggle wobble / Camp meetin' / Memphis
AIM 2010CD / May '97 / Aim

☐ IT'S PARTY TIME
Free for all / Easy like / Hot saxes / I'll wait for you / Party time twist / Low down / Keep movin' / (Let's do) the hully gully twist / Slow motion / Firefly / Something frantic
CDCH 262 / Nov '93 / Ace

☐ OLD GOLD/DOING THE DIXIE TWIST
Fever / Honky tonk / So rare / Tippin' in / You came a long way from St. Louis / Tuxedo junction / Hucklebuck / Lean baby / Harlem nocturne / Night train / Soft / Sweet Georgia Brown / Alexander's ragtime band / (In) a shanty in old Shanty Town / St. Louis blues / Royal garden blues / When the saints go marching in / Basin Street blues / Muskrat ramble / Up a lazy river / St. James infirmary
CDCHD 614 / Jul '95 / Ace

☐ SIMPLE SAX INSTRUMENTAL
ANGCD 020 / 13 Oct '97 / Angella

☐ SOUL TWIST (The Complete Enjoy Sessions) (King Curtis & The Knoble Knights)
CPCD 8195 / Aug '96 / Charly

☐ TROUBLE IN MIND
Trouble in mind / Jivin' time / Nobody wants you when you're down and out / Bad bad whiskey / I have to worry / Woke up this morning / But that's alright / Ain't nobody's business if I do / Don't deceive me / Deep fry
CDCHD 545 / Jul '94 / Ace

King Diamond

☐ ABIGAIL
Funeral / Arrival / Mansion in darkness / Family ghost / 7th day of July 1777 / Omens / Possession / Abigail / Black horseman
RR 87882 / 10 Nov '97 / Roadrunner

☐ CONSPIRACY
At the graves / Lies / Wedding dream / Something weird / Let it be done / Sleepless nights / Visit from the dead / Amon belongs to them / Victimised / Cremation
RR 87872 / 10 Nov '97 / Roadrunner

☐ EYE, THE
Eye of the witch / Trial / Burn / Two little girls / Into the convent / Father Picard / Behind these walls / Meetings / Insanity / 1642 / Imprisonment / Curse
RR 87862 / 10 Nov '97 / Roadrunner

☐ FATAL PORTRAIT
Candle / Jonah / Portrait / Dressed in white / Charon / Lurking in the dark / Halloween / Voices from the past / Haunted
RR 87892 / 10 Nov '97 / Roadrunner

☐ GRAVEYARD, THE
MASSDP 103 / Sep '96 / Massacre

☐ IN CONCERT 1987
Funeral / Arrival / Come to the Sabbath / Family ghost / 7th day of July 1777 / Portrait / Possession / Abigail / Candle / No presents for Christmas
RR 87842 / 10 Nov '97 / Roadrunner

☐ SPIDERS LULLABY, THE
MASSCD 062 / Jun '95 / Massacre

☐ THEM
Out from the asylum / Welcome home / Invisible guests / Tea / Mother's getting weaker / Bye bye missy / Broken spell / Accusation chair / Them / Twilight symphony / Coming home / Phonecall
RR 87852 / 10 Nov '97 / Roadrunner

☐ VOODOO
MASCD 0155
MASDP 0155 / 16 Mar '98 / Massacre

King, Diana

☐ THINK LIKE A GIRL
Think like a girl / L L Lies / Do you really want to hurt me / Love yourself / Find my way back / Mi coffee / Sweeter / I say a little prayer / Supa lova bwoy / Tenderness / New galfriend / Wicked / Still / I say a little prayer
4881162 / 3 Nov '97 / Work/Columbia

King, Don

☐ ONE-TWO PUNCH (KNOCKOUT)
ALP 49CD / 13 Oct '97 / Atavistic

King, Earl

☐ EARL'S PEARLS (The Very Best Of Earl King 1955-1960)
Those lonely lonely nights / Baby you can get your gun / Everybody got to cry / I'm packing up / Nobody cares / Little girl / My love is strong / It must have been love / I'll take you back home / Mother told me not to go / Is everything alright / These lonely lonely feelings / You can fly high / Well 'o well 'o well 'o baby / I'll never get tired / Weary silent night / Everybody's carried away / Buddy it's time to go / Don't you know you're wrong / Darling honey angel child / I can't help myself / I met a stranger / Let the good times roll / Mother's love / Baby hurry on home
WESM 520 / 10 Nov '97 / Westside

☐ GLAZED (King, Earl & Roomful Of Blues)
It all went down the drain / Your love was never there / Everybody's gotta cry sometime / Love rent / Iron cupid / Somebody's got a tail / I met a stranger / Mardi gras in the city / Those lonely lonely nights / One step beyond love
CD 1035 / '88 / Black Top

☐ HARD RIVER TO CROSS
BT 1090CD / Jun '93 / Black Top

☐ NEW ORLEANS STREET TALKIN'
It all went down the drain / Everybody's gotta cry sometime / Clairvoyant lady / Sexual telepathy / Love is the way of life / Medieval days / Time for the sun to rise / Old Mr. Bad Luck / Always a first time / Hard river to cross / No city like New Orleans
CDBTEL 7004 / May '97 / Black Top

King, Eddie

☐ ANOTHER COW'S DEAD
RR 0035 / 5 Feb '98 / Roesch

King Ernest

☐ KING OF HEARTS
I resign / I'm not the one / In the dark / Black bag blues / Better days / Long as I have you / Tell me what's the reason / Cryin' for my baby / Sadie / Forgive me
ECD 260842 / Mar '97 / Evidence

King, Evelyn

☐ FLIRT (King, Evelyn 'Champagne')
Flirt / You can turn me on / Kisses don't lie / Stop it / Hold on to what you've got / When your heart says yes / Before the date / Whenever you touch me
CDGOLD 1036 / May '96 / EMI Gold

☐ I'LL KEEP A LIGHT ON (King, Evelyn 'Champagne')
Fascinated / I think about you / I'll keep a light on / It doesn't really matter / When it comes down to it / Sweet funky thing / Lover I can love / Starchild / Love is love (All over the world) / It's not that kind of party / In it for me / Hold tight / Shame '95
XECD 1 / Jul '95 / Expansion

☐ LET'S GET FUNKY (King, Evelyn 'Champagne')
Shame / Get loose / I'm in love / High horse / I don't know if it's right / Love come down / Your personal touch / If you want my lovin' / Back to love / Betcha she don't love you / Other side of love / I need your love / Music box / Let's start all over again / Till I come off the road / Let's get funky tonight / Till midnight / I can't stand it
74321512042 / 1 Sep '97 / Camden

King Felix

☐ OWL PLANE CRASH
SR 9450 / May '94 / Silent

King Ferus

☐ MACEDONIAN WEDDING SOUL COOKING
Revisko oro / Romaniada / Kumov cocek/Olimpijski cocek / Basal ferus / Staro cunovo oro / Turska igra / Romska gajda / Stipski cocek / Romska riznica / Bugarsko K4 oro / Dada sali / Dikman / Stipski sa sa / Tikino sa sa / Kocovo oro
CDORBD 089 / May '95 / Globestyle

King, Freddie

☐ 17 HITS
KCD 5012 / Apr '97 / King

☐ BLUES GUITAR HERO (The Influential Early Sessions)
Hideaway / Lonesome whistle blues / San-Ho-Zay / I'm tore down / See see baby / Christmas tears / You've got to love her with a feeling / Have you ever loved a woman / You know that you love me / I love the woman / It's too bad things are going so tough / Sen-sa-shun / Takin' care of business / Stumble / Sittin' on the boat dock / Side tracked / What about love / Come on / Just pickin' / I'm on my way to Atlanta / In the open / (The welfare) turns its back on you / She put the whamee on me
CDCHD 454 / Aug '93 / Ace

☐ BOOGIE ON DOWN
Your move / Ain't gonna worry anymore / Hideaway / Guitar blues / Meet me in the morning / Sweet home Chicago / Boogie on down / Big legged woman / Hey baby / I'm tore down / Key to the highway / Have you ever loved a woman / Going down / Introduction / You're so good looking / Look on yonder wall / Ain't nobody's business / Big legged woman
CDBM 503 / 26 Jun '98 / Blue Moon

☐ BURGLAR
Pack it up / My credit didn't go through / I got the same old blues / Only getting second best / Texas flyer / Pulp wood / She's a burglar / Sugar sweet / I had a dream / Come on (let the good times roll)
BGOCD 137 / Apr '92 / Beat Goes On

☐ FREDDIE KING
DVBC 9062 / May '95 / Deja Vu

☐ FREDDIE KING LIVE
Big legged woman / Woman across the river / Look on yonder wall / Ain't no sunshine / Red light / Green light / We're gonna boogie / Have you ever loved a woman / Let the good times roll / Going down (encore)
CDCBL 759 / May '95 / Charly

☐ FREDDIE KING SINGS
Lonesome whistle blues / You've got to love her with a feeling / Have you ever loved a woman / It's too bad things are going so tough / You know that you love me (but you never tell me so) / You mean, mean woman (how can your love be true) / If you believe (in what you do) / Let me be (stay away from me) / Takin' care of business / I love the woman / I'm tore down / See see baby
MBCD 722 / Jun '93 / Modern Blues

☐ HIDEAWAY
See see baby / You've got to love her with a feeling / Have you ever loved a woman / Hideaway / I love the woman / Country boy / That's what you think / Lonesome whistle blues / It's too bad things are going so tough / I'm tore down / Sen-sa-shun / Side tracked / Stumble / San-ho-zay / Christmas tears / In the open / Takin' care of business / Driving sideways / Someday after awhile (you'll be sorry) / (The welfare) turns it's back on you / Let me down easy
CD 52041 / Oct '96 / Blues Encore

☐ KING OF THE BLUES
Same old blues / Dust my broom / Worried life blues / Five long years / Key to the highway / Going down / Living on the highway / Walking by myself / Tore down / Palace of the king / Lowdown in Lodi / Reconsider baby / Big legged woman / Me and my guitar / I'd rather be blind / Can't trust your neighbour / You was wrong / How many more years / Ain't no sunshine / Sky is crying / That's alright Mama / Woman across the river / Hoochie coochie man / Danger zone / Boogie man / Leave my woman alone / Just a little bit / Yonder wall / Help me through the day / I'm ready / Trouble in my mind / You don't have to go / Please send me someone to love / Gimme some lovin' / Love her with a feeling / Boogie fuck / It hurts me too / Something you got / Ain't no big deal on you / I just want to make love to you / Hide away
CDEM 1580 / Nov '95 / Premier/EMI

☐ LET'S HIDE AWAY AND DANCE AWAY
Hideaway / Butterscotch / Sen-sa-shun / Side tracked / Stumble / Wash out / San-ho-zay / Just pickin' / Heads up / In the open / Out front / Swooshy
KCD 773 / Mar '90 / King

☐ LIVE AT THE ELECTRIC BALLROOM 1974
CDBT 1127 / Mar '96 / Black Top

☐ LIVE AT THE LIBERTY HALL
Hey baby / Feeling alright / Ain't no sunshine / Going down / Have you ever loved a woman / My feeling for the blues / I love you so / Let the good times roll / Kansas City
CDBM 097 / Jul '95 / Blue Moon

☐ MY FEELING FOR THE BLUES
REP 4170 / Aug '91 / Repertoire

☐ PALACE OF THE KING
Living in the palace of the king / Please accept my love / Shake your booty baby / Mojo boogie / Big legged man / Hey baby / Look on yonder wall / Woman across the river / Have you ever loved a woman / Rock me baby
CDBM 089 / Feb '92 / Blue Moon

☐ STAYIN' HOME WITH THE BLUES
Sweet home Chicago / Farther up the road / Gambling woman blues / Sugar sweet / She's a burglar / Texas flyer / Have you ever loved a woman / Pulp wood / TV mama / Woman across the river / T'ain't nobody's biz'ness if I do / Things I used to do / You can run but you can't hide / Woke up this morning / Meet me in the morning
5528872 / Mar '98 / Spectrum

☐ TEXAS CANNONBALL
Freddie Kings with the Buggs Henderson band / Spoken introduction / Your move / Ain't gonna worry anymore / Hideaway / Guitar blues / Meet me in the morning / Boogie on down / Sweet home Chicago
CDBM 062 / Nov '90 / Blue Moon

☐ TEXAS FLYER
7956763022 / 14 Apr '98 / Multimedia

☐ TEXAS SENSATION
You've got to love her with a feeling / Hideaway / Have you ever loved a woman / Sen-sa-shun / Look ma, I'm cryin' / San-Ho-Zay / I'm tore down / Driving sideways / Takin' care of business / Someday after a while / Side tracked / You know that you love me / Teardrops on your letter / Stumble / She's put the whammy on me / Lonesome whistle blues / High rise / It's too bad (things are going so tough) / Welfare (turns its back on you) / Double eyed whammy
CDCHARLY 247 / Oct '90 / Charly
KCD 6007 / 17 Nov '97 / King

☐ THIS IS THE BLUES
IMP 701 / Nov '95 / Iris Music

King Galliard

☐ ROCKY ROAD TO DUBLIN
15370 / '91 / Laserlight

King Hash

☐ HUMDINGER
Hard as I try / I'm the one / Jessie May / Hey now / All I ever wanted was you / She's on the move / Deliver me from evil / What can I do / Leave a light on / Jack fell down / Jessie May (Reprise)
IGCD 201 / Jan '94 / Iona

King Jammy

☐ COMPUTER STYLE
792022 / Nov '92 / Ras

☐ HITS STYLE
792032 / Nov '92 / Ras

☐ ROOTS & HARMONY STYLE
792012 / Nov '92 / Ras

King, James

☐ LONESOME AND THEN SOME
ROUCD 0350 / Oct '95 / Rounder

☐ THESE OLD PICTURES
ROUCD 305 / Jan '94 / Rounder

King, Jimmy

☐ SOLDIER FOR THE BLUES (King, Jimmy & The King James Version)
Living in the danger zone / Drawers / I'm doing fine / Life is hard / I don't need nobody that don't need me / We'll be together again / Soldier for the blues / You ain't bulletproof / It takes a whole lot of money / Don't wanna go home / It ain't the same no mo' / I got sick one day
CDBB 9582 / Jul '97 / Bullseye Blues

King, Johnny

☐ MELTDOWN
Meltdoen / After six / Third rail / Quiet as it's kept / So sorry please / Jacqueline's chimes / Lady Macbeth / Wellspring / Cochabamba / For Tomorrow / Blues for Andrew Hill
ENJ 93292 / Sep '97 / Enja

☐ NOTES FROM THE UNDERGROUND
Gnosis / Notes from the underground / Soliloquy / Caffeine / Mean to me / Blow-up / Common law / Las ramblas
ENJ 90672 / Apr '96 / Enja

King, Johnny

☐ BEST OF JOHNNY KING, THE
JK 1 / 13 Oct '97 / Charlie's

King, Jonathan

☐ CREATIONS AND RELATIONS (Various Artists)
Everyone's gone to the moon / Hooked on a feeling: *King, Jonathan* / Just like a woman: *King, Jonathan* / I'll slap your face: *King, Jonathan* / Una paloma blanca: *King, Jonathan* / It only takes a minute girl: *100 Ton & A Feather* / Loop di love: *Shag* / Chick-a-boom: *33 & A Third* / Piglets: *Johnny Reggae* / It's the same old song: *Weathermen* / Lick a smurf for Christmas: *Father Abraphart & The Smurps* / Sun has got it's hat on: *Nemo* / In the mood: *Sound 9418* / I can't get no satisfaction: *Bubblerock* / Sugar sugar: *Sakkarin* / Leap up and down (wave your knickers in the air): *St. Cecilia* / It's good news week: *Hedgehoppers Anonymous* / Rubber Bullets: *10cc* / Silent sun: *Genesis* / Time warp: *London Cast*
SUMCD 4129 / Jun '97 / Summit

☐ MANY FACES OF JONATHAN KING
Everyone's gone to the moon / Let it all hang out / It's the same old song / Sugar sugar / Lazy bones / Johnny reggae / Hooked on a feeling / Flirt / Sun has got his hat on / Loop di love / (i can't get no) satisfaction / Una paloma blanca (white dove) / Chicka boom (don't ya jes love it) / It only takes a minute / When I was a star / One for you, one for me / Lick a smurp for christmas (all fall down) / I'll slap your face (entertainment usa theme)
MCCD 108 / May '93 / Music Club

King, Jonny

☐ IN FROM THE COLD
CRISS 1093CD / Sep '95 / Criss Cross

King Kong

☐ FUNNY FARM
DC 33 / Dec '96 / Drag City

☐ KINGDOM OF KONG
DC 122CD / 22 Sep '97 / Drag City

☐ ME HUNGRY
DC 67CD / Dec '96 / Drag City

King Kooba

☐ IMPERIAL SOLUTION
Release the Cracken / Wolfkub / My little phoney / Brown blood / Freakmeister / Sergio / Nearly / Elephant / White lady / Kloke / Cat's eye
SKINCD 002 / 27 Apr '98 / Second Skin

King Krab

☐ KICKING ROSE
EAR 12 / Mar '93 / Earthling

King Kurt

☐ LAST WILL AND TESTICLE 1981-1988
Destination Zululand / Zulu beat / Bo Diddley goes East / Mack the knife / Wreck-a-party-rock / Land of Ring Dang Doo / America / Goats and monkeys / Banana banana / Billy / Road to rack 'n' ruin / Slammers
DOJOCD 68 / Feb '94 / Dojo

☐ POOR MAN'S DREAM
Poor man's dream / Big black Cadillac / Howdy we're your neighbours / Too much of a good thing / Cajun weekend / Seat cover / Move on / Hey Mr. Bartender / Friends / Train kept a-rollin' / Indian bad day / Friendless Lane / Shark / First cock's crow / My business
DIAB 850 / 26 Jan '98 / Diablo

King L

☐ GREAT DAY FOR GRAVITY
Tragedy girl / Dumbest story / Tom Driver / Greedy / All hail the alien Queen / Back to loving arms / Life after you / That's how it works / Hoping they'll be open / First man on the sun / Two cars collide / Don't believe in Hollywood / Lost and found and lost again / My last cigarette
CIRCD 32 / Oct '95 / Circa

King, Lana

☐ KING AND COUNTRY
Blue bayou / I will always love you / Stand by your man / Carolina moon / He'll have to go / Desperado / Don't it make my brown eyes blue / Take these chains / Will you still love me tomorrow / Make it through the night / Rose / Amazing grace
SOV 001CD / '92 / Sovereign

King, Little Jimmy

☐ SOMETHING INSIDE OF ME
BB 9537 / Apr '94 / Bullseye Blues

King Melody

☐ COOL BREEZE
QRCD 006 / 25 May '98 / Quartz

King Memphis

☐ ASTONISHING KING MEMPHIS, THE
Crazy alien chick / Little Joe from Chicago / C'mon pretty baby / Lone star / Mr. Clean / Let it go / She hit me with a whip / 1962 ragtop / Gonna have a ball / Baby baby / You gotta pay / Walkin' my baby back home / Big hair / Red hot and ready / Gas cap / I'm mad
NERCD 086 / Jun '96 / Nervous

King Missile

☐ HAPPY HOUR
Sink / Martin Scorsese / (Why are we) Trapped / It's Saturday / Vulvavoid / Metanoia / Detachable penis / Take me home / Ed / Anywhere / Evil children / Glass / And / King Murdock / I'm sorry / Heaven / Happy hour
7567824592 / Feb '93 / WEA

☐ KING MISSILE
Love is / What if / Let's have sex / Pigs will fly / These people / Open up / Wind up toys / Delores / Tongue / Dishwasher / Socks / Bloodletting / Lies / Commercial / King David's dirge / Psalm / Happy note
7567825892 / Jun '94 / WEA

King, Morgana

☐ ANOTHER TIME, ANOTHER SPACE
MCD 5339 / Sep '92 / Muse

☐ EVERYTHING MUST CHANGE
MCD 5190 / Feb '86 / Muse

☐ SIMPLY ELOQUENT
MCD 5326 / Sep '92 / Muse

King, Nancy

☐ CLIFF DANCE (King, Nancy & Glen Moore)
JR 08032 / Jun '94 / Justice

☐ POTATO RADIO (King, Nancy & Glen Moore)
JR 008022 / Oct '92 / Justice

King Of Hearts

☐ MIDNIGHT CROSSING
IRS 993167 / Mar '97 / Edge Of Fluke

King Of Luxembourg

☐ SIR AND ROYAL BASTARD, THE
Flirt / Personality parade / Walnut whirl / Sorry / Penny was a tomboy / Chateau palmier '61 / Turbab disturbance / Battle for beauty / Queen of Luxembourg / Her eyes are a blue million miles / Virgin on the rocks / Picture of Dorian Gray / Valleri / Ruben's room / Mad / Poptines / Something for Sophia Loren / Baby / Wedding of Ramona Blair / Happy together (prelude) / Smash hit wonder / Happy together / Liar liar
ACME 16CD / 6 Oct '97 / Cherry Red

King Of The Slums

☐ BLOWZY WEIRDOS
Gone all weirdo / Smile so big / Casin' the joint / Hot pot shebeen / Keepin' it all sweet / Clubland gangs / Joy / Rimo / Mard arse / Mood on / Blowzy luv of life
CDBRED93 / Jul '91 / Cherry Red

King, Paul

☐ BEEN IN THE PEN TOO LONG/ TROUBLE AT MILL (King, Paul/King Earl Boogie Band)
Grey eyed Athena / Jean Harlow / Sugarcane / Three dog night / Whoa Buck / Clockwork machine / Candy man / I've changed my face / One legged man in a goldfish bowl / Bad storm coming / Take me back / Live your own life / Bovver blues / Plastic Jesus / If the Lord don't got you / Goin' the German / Keep your hands off my woman / Go down you murderer
SEECD 429 / Jul '95 / See For Miles

King, Pee Wee

☐ PEE WEE KING & THE GOLDEN WEST COWBOYS (7CD Set) (King, Pee Wee & The Golden West Cowboys)
That cheap look in your eye / You were the cause of it all / Texas Toni Lee / Tennessee central / Southland polka / Steel guitar rag / Hear you knockin' / Keep them cold icy fingers off of me / Don't feel sorry for me / Arkansas traveller / Out of my mind / Ten gallon boogie / Kentucky waltz / Don't forget / Jukebox blues / Chattanooga Bess / Say good mornin' Nellie / Forty nine women / Ghost and honest Joe / New York to New Orleans / I'm satisfied with you / Quit honkin' that horn / Oh Monah / Bull fiddle boogie / Tenessee waltz / Rootie tootie / Gotta climb those golden stairs / Every time I feel the spirit / Gospel boogie / Singin' as I go / Waltz of the Alamo / Whisper waltz / I lost my love (the color song) / Bonaparte's retreat / Bluegrass waltz / Alabama moon / Tennessee tears / Get together polka / Nashville waltz / Waltz of regret / Lonesome steel guitar / Cornbread, lasses and sassafras tea / Fire on the mountain / Shocking rye straw / Billy in the lowground / Devil's dream / Fisher's hornpipe / Sally Goodin / Whistling Rufus / Going back to LA / You call everybody darlin' / Battle hymn of the Republic / Black eyed Susie / When they played that old Missouri waltz / Blame it all on Nashville / Kissing dance / Rag mop / What, where and when / Birmingham bounce / We're gonna go fishin' (next Saturday night) / Cincinnati dancing pig / River road two step / Mop rag boogie / No one but you / Within my heart (la golondrina) / Helegged hilegged / You drifted / Strange little girl / Chew tabacco rag / Slow poke / You won't need my love anymore / Two roads / Railroad boogie / Makin' like a train / Crying steel guitar waltz / Ragtime Annie Lee / Slow bloke / Slow coach / Silver and gold / If and when / Busybody / I don't mind / Two-faced clock / Mighty pretty waltz / Tennessee tango / Crazy waltz / Varsoviana / San Antonio rose / My adobe hacienda / One rose (that's left in my heart) / Under the double eagle / Spanish two step / Over the waves / Screwball / Last night on the back porch / Till I waltz again with you / Gone / I'll go on alone / That's me without you / Your kisses aren't kisses anymore / Here lies my heart / Oh mis'rable love / Richochet / Dragnet / Deck of cards / Huggin' my pillow / Changin partners / Bimbo / Backward, turn backward / In a garden of roses / Red deck of cards / Keep your eye on my darling / Indian giver / Why don't you all go home / How long / Peek-a-boo waltz / Peaches and cream / I can't tell a waltz from a tango / Flying home / Woodchopper's ball / Seven come eleven / Farewell blues / Tippin' in / Melody of love / You can't hardly get them no more / Tweedle Dee / Plantation boogie / Jim, Johnny and Jonas / Nevermind / Beauty is as beauty does / Half a dozen boogie / Blue suede shoes / Tennessee dancin' doll / Ballroom baby / Catty town / Absolutely, positively / Hoot scoot / I'll be walking alone in a crowd / Sugar beet / (I tasted) tears on your lips / Catchy tune / My darlin' (we're not too young to know) / Do you remember / Congratulations Joe / Prelude to a broken heart / Unbreakable heart / Janie / Little bit about myself (a phonobiography)
BCD 15727 / Feb '85 / Bear Family

King, Peter

☐ SPEED TRAP
Mr. Silver / My man's gone now / TNK / Naima / Speed trap / Getting on
JHCD 041 / Feb '96 / Ronnie Scott's Jazz House

☐ TAMBURELLO
Dido's lament / You taught my heart how to sing / Boxer's demise / Leona / Bess, oh where's my Bess / My man's gone now / Yes or no / Imola / Ayrton / Tamburello / Theme from bartok's violin concert No.2 / Please don't ever leave me
MMCD 083 / Jul '95 / Miles Music

King Pin

☐ GOD OF LOVE
ARICD 072 / Apr '92 / Ariwa Sounds

☐ LETTER FROM JAIL
ARICD 059 / Sep '90 / Ariwa Sounds

King Pleasure

☐ GOLDEN DAYS
FSRCD 108 / 5 Jan '98 / Fresh Sound

☐ KING PLEASURE & ANNIE ROSS SING (King Pleasure & Annie Ross)
Red top / Sometimes I'm happy / What can I say after I say I'm sorry / Parker's mood / Twisted / Time was right / Jumpin' with symphony sid / This is always / Don't get scared / I'm gone / Farmer's market / Annie's lament / I'm in the mood for love / Exclamation blues / You're crying / Funk junction
OJCCD 217 / Apr '96 / Original Jazz Classics

King Prawn

☐ FIRST OFFENCE
WOWCD 46 / Dec '96 / Words Of Warning

☐ FRIED IN LONDON
WOWCD 54 / 14 Apr '98 / Words Of Warning

King, Sandra

☐ CONCERT OF VERNON DUKE, A (King, Sandra & Pat Smythe)
ACD 197 / Mar '95 / Audiophile

☐ SANDRA KING & FRIENDS
ACD 222 / Aug '94 / Audiophile

☐ SONGS OF VERNON DUKE
ACD 187 / Oct '93 / Audiophile

King, Shirley

☐ JUMP THROUGH MY KEYHOLE
GBW 007 / Nov '92 / GBW

King, Sid

☐ GONNA SHAKE THIS SHACK TONIGHT (King, Sid & The Five Strings)
Good rockin' baby / Put something in the pot boy / Drinkin' wine spoli-oli / When my baby left me / Gonna shake this shack tonight / It's true, I'm blue / Crazy little heart / Mama I want you / I like it / But I don't care / Warmed over kisses / What have ya got to lose / I've got the blues / Ooby dooby / Booger red / Twenty one / Sag, drag and fall / Blue suede shoes / Let 'er roll / Purr, kitty, purr
BCD 15535 / Mar '92 / Bear Family

King Sisters

☐ FOR YOU
For you / Just squeeze me / When the swallows come back to Capistrano / What's the use / Sophisticated lady / Everybody loves my baby / Stardust / Between the devil and the deep blue sea / At sundown / When my dreamboat comes home / Crazy rhythm / Miss Otis regrets / Red sails in the sunset / Man I love
HCD 168 / Mar '96 / Hindsight

King Sounds

☐ I SHALL SING
VZA 002 CD / Jan '94 / Viza

King, Tempo

☐ TEMPO KING 1936-1937
Bojangles of Harlem / I'll sing you a thousand love songs / Organ grinder swing / Papa tree top tall / William Tell / (I would do) anything for you / High hat, a piccolo and a cane / We can cuddle at home / You're giving me a song and a dance / Alabama barbecue / That's what you mean to me / Sweet Adeline / You've got something there / Through the courtesy of love / I was saying to the moon / One hour for lunch / To Mary, with love / Swingin' the jinx away / Keepin' out of mischief now / You turned the tables on me / Swing high swing low / Floating on a bubble / Gee but you're swell
CBC 1002 / Jan '92 / Timeless Historical

King Tubby

☐ CREATION DUB
LG 21111 / Jul '95 / Lagoon

☐ CROSSFIRE
Radication dub / Up in arms dub / Marching orders / Higher region / On the attack / Crossfire / Hard time dub / Original dub / Soundboy massacre / Thinking dub / Loving dub / Caribbean dub
LG 21050 / Nov '92 / Lagoon

☐ DANGEROUS DUB (King Tubby & Roots Radics)
Country gal dub / Loud mouth rock / Up town special / Hungry belly dub / Shepherd bush in dub / London Bridge special / Earthquake shake / Rice grain rock / Banana and yam skank / Knife and fork dubwise / King Stereo gav dub / King Tubby's hi-fi dub / Symbolic dub
GRELCD 229 / Nov '96 / Greensleeves

☐ DUB GONE 2 CRAZY (King Tubby & Prince Jammy)
BAFCD 13 / Jul '96 / Blood & Fire

☐ DUB GONE CRAZY (The Evolution Of Dub At King Tubby's 1975-79) (King Tubby & Friends)
Champion version / Satta dread dub / Real gone crazy dub / Exalted dub / Dreada version / No love version / Peace and love in the dub / Wreck up a version / Hold them in dub / Jah love rockers dub / Step it up in dub / Dub with a view / Dub to the rescue / Dub fi gwan
BAFCD 2 / May '94 / Blood & Fire

☐ DUB HITS FROM STUDIO ONE
RN 7048 / 27 Jul '98 / Rhino

☐ DUBMASTER
0445012 / 3 Nov '97 / Jet Set

☐ FIRST PROPHET OR DUB
TWCD 1012 / Dec '95 / Tamoki Wambesi

☐ FREEDOM SOUNDS IN DUB (King Tubby & The Soul Syndicate)
BAFCD 11 / May '96 / Blood & Fire

☐ GREENWICH FARM RUB A DUB (King Tubby & Scientist)
BAFCD 1001 / May '96 / Blood & Fire

☐ HERBS OF DUB (King Tubby & Jah Lloyd)
TMCD 1 / 20 Apr '98 / Teem

☐ HOUSE OF DUB (Channel One & King Tubby)
GR 006CD / May '95 / Sprint

☐ I AM THE KING VOL.1
SFCD 003 / Jul '95 / Sprint

☐ I AM THE KING VOL.2
SFCD 4 / May '95 / Sprint

☐ I AM THE KING VOL.3
SFCD 006 / Aug '96 / Sprint

☐ IN ROOTS VIBES (King Tubby & Augustus Pablo)
LG 21121 / Mar '97 / Lagoon

☐ KING TUBBY MEETS THE UPSETTER AT THE GRASS ROOTS OF DUB (King Tubby & The Upsetter)
Blood of Africa / African roots / Rain roots / Wood roots / Luke lane rock / People from the grass roots / Crime wave / No justice for the poor / 300 years at the grass roots / King and The Upsetter at Spanish town
STCD 001 / Jun '97 / Studio 16

☐ KING TUBBY MEETS VIVIAN JACKSON (King Tubby & Vivian Jackson)
YVJ 002CD / May '95 / Yabby You

☐ KING TUBBY ON THE MIX VOL.2 (Various Artists)
OMCD 023 / Jul '93 / Original Music

☐ KING TUBBY'S SOUNDCLASH VOL.1 & 2
SONCD 0012 / Jan '91 / Sonic Sounds

☐ KING TUBBY'S SPECIAL 1973-1976 (Various Artists)
CDTRD 409 / Mar '94 / Trojan

☐ KING TUBBY'S STUDIO VS. CHANNEL 1
RNCD 2126 / Nov '95 / Rhino

☐ MEGAWATT DUB (King Tubby & Lee Perry)
SH 45037 / Nov '97 / Shanachie

☐ MEMORIAL DUB
RNCD 2060 / Sep '94 / Rhino

☐ ROOTS & SOCIETY
RB 3003 / May '94 / Reggae Best

☐ RUB-A-DUB
Rub a dub / Rougher dub / Dub in waterhouse way / Digital dub / Dubbing the right / Gal a dub me / Sign of the times dub / Roaring lion dub / Ring the alarm / Dub ina foreign / Landmark dub / Dub organiser
LG 1060CD / Jun '93 / Lagoon

☐ SENSI DUB VOL.3 (King Tubby & Prince Jammy)
Black up (dub) / Sensi dub (part 3) / Free herb / Ministers (dub) / No bush (dub) / Meditation / Court house (dub) / Heavy metal
OMCD 16 / '92 / Original Music

☐ SHALOM DUB (King Tubby & The Aggrovators)
RNCD 2107 / Jun '95 / Rhino

☐ SURROUNDED BY THE DREADS AT THE NATIONAL ARENA
STCD 003 / May '93 / Studio 16

☐ UPSET THE UPSETTERS
RNCD 2037 / Nov '93 / Rhino

☐ WATER DUB
Mount zion dub / Sensimilia dub / Jah guide dub / Skanking dub / Tribal war / Don't touch dub / Wicked dub / Love up dub / Straight dub / Narrow dub / Firestick dub / Water dub
LG 21055 / Feb '93 / Lagoon

Kingdom Come

☐ BAD IMAGE
Passion departed / You're the one / Fake believer / Friends / Mad queen / Pardon the difference (but I like it) / Little wild thing / Can't resist / Talked too much / Glove of stone / Outsider
4509931482 / Feb '94 / WEA

Kingdom Folk Band

☐ RESTLESS
De'il's awa / Trooper and the maid / Star of County Down / Starry night / Rovin' journeyman / McPherson's rant / Restless / Crazy love / Clare to here / Parcel o'rogues / Cunla / Ramblin' guy / Nothing to show / Scots wha hae
RECD 518 / Dec '97 / REL

Kinglee, Fred

☐ LACHEN SIE MIT FRED KINGLEE (Kinglee, Fred & Die King Kols/Gus P. Kinglee Trio)
Meine kleine melodie (o schnibedidabedidum) / Cement mixer / Manana / Quanto le gusta (cuanto le gusta) / Das warenhaus/Der Russische salat / Schieb ab / Die samba / Sie, wenn sie mal'nen hund brauchen / Kleiner zinnsoldat / Piff-paff-boogie / Hey, ba-ba-re-bop / Wie komm ich bloss an diesem hund vorbei / La marchina / Tschagalag / Kennst du schon den rubezahl / Ei-weih / King-Kols jubilaums-mischung / Bi-bi-bitte schon/Cement mixer/Das ding / Die radiobastler / Jimmy, Johnny, Josefin' / Der herr baron / Kinglee blues (c-jam blues) / Das gibt es nur in Texas / Joachimthalerstrasse / Heimwh nach dem Kurfurstendamm / Crawel in the left / Rosalie / Dunkel war's der mond schein helle / Das warenhaus / Der Russische salat
BCD 16007 / Apr '97 / Bear Family

King's College Choir

☐ ADVENT PROCESSION WITH CAROLS
CDM 5662432 / Nov '96 / EMI Classics

☐ CAROLS
Once in royal david's city / Adam lay ybounden / Angels from the realms of glory / O little town of Bethlehem / In dulchi jublio / First Noel / I saw three ships / Whence is that goodly fragrance flowing / Quem pastores laudavere / Personet hodie / Holly and the ivy / Spotless rose / Away in a manger / While shepherds watched / My dancing day / Up good christian folk and listen / In the bleak midwinter / Ding dong / Merrily on high / Silent night / It came upon the midnight clear / Three kings / I saw a maiden / On christmas night / O come all ye faithful (adeste fidelis) / Hark the herald angel sing
CDCAROL 1 / 10 Nov '97 / EMI Classics

☐ CAROLS FROM KING'S
Once in Royal David's city / Oh Christmas night / Jesus Christ the apple tree / Adam lay-y-bounden / O little town of Bethlehem / It came upon the Midnight clear / Lamb / Cherry tree carol / God rest ye merry gentlemen / Noel nouvelet / Infant Holy / King Jesus hath a garden / While shepherds watched their flocks by night / In the bleak midwinter / Tomorrow shall be my dancing day / Three Kings / O come all ye faithful (adeste fidelis) / In dulci jubilo
CFMCD 11 / Nov '96 / Classic FM

☐ CHRISTMAS MUSIC
CDM 5662442 / Nov '96 / EMI Classics

☐ FAVOURITE CAROLS
CDM 5662412 / Nov '96 / EMI Classics

☐ FESTIVAL OF LESSONS AND CAROLS, A
CDM 5662422 / Nov '96 / EMI Classics

☐ KING'S CHRISTMAS COLLECTION (4CD Set)
CMS 5662452 / Nov '96 / EMI Classics

Kings Of Infinite Space

☐ QUEENIE
VVR 1000462 / 6 Apr '98 / V2

Kings Of Tomorrow

☐ BEGINNING, THE
Let it go / Different worlds / Gotta live my life / Expansions / Can you see the light / I'm grateful / Ancestors / I hear my calling / Rock creek / KOT anthem / Can you see the light / Time
DI 0849 / 1 Jun '98 / Distance

King's Own Royal Border Regiment

☐ BATTLE HONOURS
BNA 5075 / Feb '93 / Bandleader

King's Own Scottish Borderers

☐ SPIRIT OF SCOTLAND
CDITV 623 / Feb '97 / Scotdisc

King's Singers

☐ HERE'S A HOWDY DO
British tar / British tar / Take a pair of sparkling eyes / Ghosts' high-noon / Ah, leave me not / A wandering minstrel, I / Pirate king / Tit willow / With catlike tread / Brightly dawns our wedding day / A more humane mikado / Rising early in the morning / Patter matter (gilbert and sullivan medley) / Here's a how-de-do
09026618852 / Dec '93 / RCA Victor

☐ RENAISSANCE DESPREZ
09026618142 / Dec '93 / RCA Victor

☐ STREET SONGS (King's Singers & Evelyn Glennie)
Poor Roger / In a place far off / Prayer to the moon / Blue mist / Rainmaking with a bowstring / Broken string / Oranges and lemons / Horizons / Reaching out / Ilihubo / Mambabo / Lala mntwana / Uhambo ngesitimela / E-goli / Umdanso wasegoli / Green gravel / GilesGiles / Jenny Jones
09026631752 / May '98 / RCA Victor

Kings X

☐ DOGMAN
Dogman / Shoes / Pretend / Flies and blue skies / Black the sky / Fool you / Don't care / Sunshine rain / Complain / Human behaviour / Cigarettes / Go to hell / Pillow / Manic depression
7567825582 / Jan '94 / Atlantic

☐ EAR CANDY
Train / Mississippi moon / Lies in the sand / Fathers / Picture / American cheese / Life going by / Run / 67 / Looking for love / (Thinking and wondering) what I'm gonna do / Box / Sometime
7567828802 / May '96 / Atlantic

☐ GRETCHEN GOES TO NEBRASKA
Out of the silent planet / Over my head / Summer land / Everybody knows a little bit of something / Difference (in the garden of St. Anne's-on-the-hill) / I'll never be the same / Mission / Fall on me / Pleiades / Don't believe it (it's easier said than done) / Send a message / Burning down
7819972 / Jun '89 / Atlantic

Kingsmen

☐ 1960'S FRENCH EP COLLECTION, THE
523272 / Jul '97 / Magic

☐ JERK & TWINE TIME
You really got me / All day and all of the night / Money / Jolly green giant / Twine time / Land of 1000 dances / In crowd / Jerk / Jerktown / She's not there / Downtown / Limbo rock / In the misty moonlight / Beau and John interview
CDSC 6010 / Jan '94 / Sundazed

☐ KINGSMEN VOL.1 (Louie Louie)
Louie Louie / Waiting / Mojo workout / Fever / Money / Bent scepter / Long tall Texan / You can't sit down / Twist and shout / JAJ / Night train / Mashed potatoes / Haunted castle / Krunch / (You got) The gamma coochee
CDSC 6004 / Jan '94 / Sundazed

☐ KINGSMEN VOL.2
Kingsmen introduction / Little latin lupe lu / Long green / Do you love me / New Orleans / Walking the dog / David's mood / Something's got a hold on me / Let the good times roll / Ooh-poo-pah-doo / Great balls of fire / Linda Lou / Death of an angel / And you believed him / Give her lovin'
CDSC 6005 / Feb '94 / Sundazed

☐ KINGSMEN VOL.3
Over you / That's cool, that's trash / Jolly green giant / Don't you just know it / La do dada / Long green / Mother in law / Shout / Searchin' for love / Tall cool one / Comin' home baby / Since you been gone / It's only the dog / Wolf of Manhattan / I'll go crazy
CDSC 6006 / Jan '94 / Sundazed

☐ LIES
Lies / I can do it better / Can't you see I'm trying / Please don't fight it / Just one girl / I believe in her / Wishful thinking / You'll never walk alone / Your kind of lovin' / Harlem nocturne / It's not unusual / Turn to me / Just out of reach / Beau and John Charles interview
CDSC 6011 / Jan '94 / Sundazed

☐ LOUIE LOUIE
Louie louie / Money (that's what I want) / Little latin lupe lu / Death of an angel / Jolly green giant / Climb / Annie fanny / Give her lovin' / Long green / That's cool, that's trash / Genevieve / Killer joe / Little sally tease / Trouble / Do you love me / New orleans / Jenny take a ride / Ooh poo pah doo / Shout / Fever
CPCD 8160 / Nov '95 / Charly

☐ ON CAMPUS
Annie Fanny / Rosalie / Hard day's night / I like it like that / Stand by me / Little green thing / Climb / Sticks and stones / Peter Gunn / Sometimes / Shotgun / Genevieve / Get out of my life woman / Don't say no / My wife can't cook (mono)
CDSC 6014 / Jan '94 / Sundazed

☐ UP AND AWAY
Trouble / If I needed someone / Grass is green / Tossin' and turnin' / Under my thumb / Wild thing / (I have found) another girl / Daytime shadows / Shake a tail feather / Children's caretaker / Land of 1000 dances / Mustang Sally / Little Sally tease / Hush-a-bye / Killer Joe
CDSC 6015 / Jan '94 / Sundazed

Kingsnakes

☐ COME ON CA VA
RRHCD 004 / Mar '98 / Rock 'n' Roll House

Kingston Trio

☐ CHILDREN OF THE MORNING
FE 6017 / Aug '96 / Folk Era

☐ EP COLLECTION, THE
Across the wide Missouri / San Miguel / Greenback dollar / Take her out of pity / Ruby red / Worried man / All my sorrows / Sally / Molly Dee / Where have all the flowers gone / Tom Dooley / I'm going home / Farewell / Scarlett ribbons / Lemon tree / Sail away ladies / Unfortunate Miss Bailey / Scotch and soda / Hobo's lullaby / Turn around / Little play soldiers / Santy anno / Little boy / It was a very good year / Raspberries, strawberries
SEECD 454 / Oct '96 / See For Miles

☐ GUARD YEARS, THE (10CD/Book set)
Hard it ain't hard / Three jolly coachmen / Scotch and soda / Tom Dooley / Sloop John B / Coplas / Santo Anno / Fast freight / Bay of Mexico / Banua / Saro Jane / Wimoweh / Little Maggie / Dodi li / Tanga tika/ Toerau / Sally (don't you grieve) / Blue tattoo / Scarlet ribbons (for her hair) / When the saints go marching in / Gue gue / New York girls / Como se viene se va / Ruby red / Sally (don't you grieve) / Raspberries strawberries / Blow ye winds / MTA / Getaway John / Remember the Alamo / I bawled / Corey Corey / All my sorrows / Long black rifle / Seine / Early in the morning / Tijuana jail / Good news / Sacrlet ribbons (for her hair) / Oh Cindy / Sail away ladies / Goober peas / Haul away / Across the wide Missouri / 'Round about the mountain / Unfortunate Miss Bailey / Worried man / Wanderer / San Miguel / Rollin' stone / Oleanna / Molly Dee / E inu tatou e / Hunter / Green grasses / Green grasses / Hunter / Coo coo u / World's last authentic playboys / Bimini / Don't cry Katie / Just once around the clock / El matador / Raspberries / Farewell Adelita / With you my Johnny / With her head tucked underneath her arm / Mountains O'mourne / Tattooed lady / Home from the hill / Mangwani m'pulele / Carrier pigeon / Everglades / Escape of old John Webb / Leave my woman alone / Bad man's blunder / When I was young / This land is your land / Who's gonna hold her hand / Tattooed lady / This mornin' / South wind / Buddy better get on down / Colorado trail / Tomorrow / Goodnight my baby / Mary mild / Bye bye thou tiny little child / Round about christmas / All through the night / We wish you a merry Christmas / Follow now oh shepards / Somerset Gloucestershire wassail / Last month of the year / Go where I send thee / White snows of winter / Sing we noel / Utawena / River is wide / Speckled roan / Hard travelin' / Sea fever / Hangman / Don't you weep Mary / Blow the candle out / Come all you fair and tender ladies / Blue eyed girl / En el agua / Jug of punch / Bonny hielean' laddie / Oh yes oh / Billy goat hill / Pastures of plenty / Guardo el lobo / Mary was pretty / Run Molly run / You don't knock / Lemon tree / Wines of Madeira / Adieu to my island / You're gonna miss me / Senora / Golden spike / Razors in the air / It was a very good year / Introduction / 1st set/Saro Jane / Santo anno / Three jolly coachmen / I bawled / South coast / Dodi li / Zombie jamboree / Go where I send thee / Ruby red / Scotch and soda / Watsha / Sloop John B / Hard it ain't hard / Introduction / 2nd set/Banua / Bay of Mexico / New York girls / Scarlet ribbons (for her hair) / Shady grove / Lonesome traveler / Coplas / Fast freight / Tic tic tic (the lost watch) / Lei pakalana / Pay me my money down / Across the wide Missouri / Little Maggie / Tom Dooley / Wimoweh / When the saints go marching in / Tic tic tic (the lost watch) / Gue gue / Dorie / South coast / Wimoweh / New york girls / They called the wind Maria / Merry minuet / Shady grove/Lonesome traveler / When the saints go marching in / Banua / Three jolly coachmen / South coast / Coplas / Merry minuet / Raspberries strawberries / When the saints go marching in / Introduction by George Wein / Saro Jane / Coplas / MTA / All my sorrows / Remember the Alamo / E inu tatou e / Hard it ain't hard / Merry minuet / When the saints go marching in / Three jolly coachmen / South coast / Scotch and soda / Zombie jamboree / Kingston trio sings for 7-Up/Hunter / Oh cindy / Oh cindy / Kingston trio sings for 7-Up/Goober peas / Blow ye winds / Hunter/Oleana / Kingston trio sings for 7-Up/Corey Corey / Worried man / Kingston trio sings fro 7-Up/Molly Dee / Trio sings for 7-Up/Three jolly coachmen / Kingston trio sings for 7-Up / Scarlet ribbons / Kingston trio sings for 7-Up / MTA / Trio sings for 7-Up/Worried man / Kingston trio sings for 7-Up / Kingston trio sings for 7-Up / With you my Johny / Kingston trio sings fro 7-Up/The Hunter / Blow ye winds / Worried man / MTA / MTA / Tom Dooley / Tanga tika/Toerau / Don't cry Katie / Mountains of Mourne / Home from the hill / Mangwani m'pulele / Carrier pigeon / Run Joe / Cha cha boom: Gaurd, Dave Trio / Come back Liza: Gaurd, Dave Trio / Jamaica farewell: Gaurd, Dave Trio / Farewell: Gaurd, Dave Trio / Kisses sweeter than wine: Gaurd, Dave Trio / Lolly tu dum: Gaurd, Dave Trio / Without my lover: Gaurd, Dave Trio / Fast freight: Gaurd, Dave Trio / Without my lover / Run

Joe / Tom Dooley: *Grayson & Whitter* / Tom Dooley: *Donegan, Lonnie* / Tom Dooley Jr: *Kilgore, Merle* / Tom Duley rock: *Brooks, Clinton* / Tom Dooley rock and roll: *Hoback, Curtis* / Tom Dooley: *Nilsen Bros* / Tom Dooley: *Nilsen Bros*
BCD 16160 / Aug '97 / Bear Family

☐ LIVE AT NEWPORT 1959
Introduction / Saro Jane / MTA / All my sorrows / Remember the Alamo / E inu takou e / Hard ain't it hard / Merry little minuet / When the saints go marching in / Three jolly coachmen / South coast / Scotch and soda / Zombie jamboree
VCD 77009 / Oct '95 / Vanguard

☐ NICK, BOB & JOHN
FE 5271 / Dec '94 / Folk Era

☐ ON STAGE
Tom Dooley / Greenback Dollar / Tijuana Jail / Where have all the flowers gone / Scotch and soda / Lion sleeps tonight / Early morning rain / Baby you've been on my mind / Shape of things to come / Hard ain't it hard / I'm goin' home / Colours / Hard travellin' / Tomorrow is a long time / Roving gambler / One too many mornings / Goodnight Irene / MTA / Get away John / When the saints go marching in
STOCD 103 / Feb '97 / Start

☐ ORIGINAL, THE
Tom Dooley / Tijuana jail / Raspberries strawberries / MTA / Worried man / Coo coo u / El matador / Bad man's blunder / Everglades / Where have all the flowers gone / Scotch and soda / Jane Jane Jane / One more town / Greenback dollar / Reverend Mr.Black / Desert Pete / Ally ally oxen free / This land is your land / Scarlet ribbons (for her hair) / Seasons in the sun
TO 864342 / 2 Feb '98 / Disky

☐ SPOTLIGHT ON KINGSTON TRIO
Tom Dooley / Lion sleeps tonight / Greenback dollar / Baby, you've been on my mind / Goodnight Irene / I'm goin' home / Roving gambler / Tijuana jail / Where have all the flowers gone / Colours / MTA / Early morning rain / Shape of things to come / Tomorrow is a long time / When the saints go marching in
HADCD 106 / Feb '94 / Javelin

☐ STAY AWHILE
FE 5435 / Dec '94 / Folk Era

Kingwell, Colin

☐ ALWAYS FOR PLEASURE (Kingwell, Colin & His Jazz Bandits)
Fair and square in love / Beautiful Ohio / Vieux Carre blues / When we danced at the Mardi Gras / All I do is dream of you / In the sweet bye and bye / Did you mean it / Beg your pardon / Original Dixieland one-step / Your foolin' someone / Where could I go but to the Lord / I'll never say never again, again
LACD 59 / Mar '96 / Lake

Kinks

☐ ANIMAL KINK, AN (A Tribute To The Kinks) (Various Artists)
ANIMA 12CD / 2 Mar '98 / Animal

☐ ARTHUR OR THE DECLINE AND FALL OF THE BRITISH EMPIRE (Remastered)
ESMCD 511 / 25 May '98 / Essential

☐ DEFINITIVE COLLECTION, THE
You really got me / All day and all of the night / Stop your sobbing / Tired of waiting for you / Everybody's gonna be happy / Set me free / See my friends / Till the end of the day / Where have all the good times gone / Well respected man / Dedicated follower of fashion / Sunny afternoon / Dead end street / Waterloo sunset / Death of a clown / Autumn almanac / Suzannah's still alive / David Watts / Wonder boy / Days / Plastic man / Victoria / Lola / Apeman / Come dancing / Don't forget to dance
5164652 / Mar '97 / PolyGram TV

☐ EP COLLECTION VOL.1, THE
See my friends / I gotta move / I've got that feeling / Don't you fret / Things are getting better / Set me free / Wait till the summer comes along / Such a shame / David Watts / Lazy old sun / Death of a clown / Funny face / All day and all of the night / Louie Louie / Well respected man / It's alright / I gotta go now / You really got me / Till the end of the day / Dedicated follower of fashion / Two sisters / Situation vacant / Love me till the sun shines / Suzannah's still alive
SEECD 295 / Aug '90 / See For Miles

☐ EP COLLECTION VOL.2, THE
Long tall shorty / I took my baby home / Got love if you want it / Tired of waiting for you / Come on now / You can't win / Where have all the good times gone / Never met a girl like you before / Party line / Dandy / Sunny afternoon / Dead end street / I'm not like everybody else / Big black smoke / Session man / Fancy / This is where I belong / Sittin' on my sofa / Mr. pleasant / Waterloo sunset / Act nice and gentle / Village green / Rosie won't you please come home / I need you / What's in store for me / Long tall sally / I'm a lover not a fighter / Beautiful delilah
SEECD 329 / Sep '91 / See For Miles

☐ EVERYBODY'S IN SHOW BIZ - EVERYBODY'S A STAR
Here comes yet another day / Maximum consumption / Unreal reality / Hot potatoes / Sitting in my hotel / Motorway / You don't know my name / Supersonic rocket ship / Look a little on the sunny side / Celluloid heroes / Top of the pops / Brainwashed / Mr. Wonderful / Acute schizophrenia paranoia blues
VEL 797202 / 31 Aug '98 / Velvel

☐ FAB FORTY (The Kinks' Singles Collection 1964-1970/2CD Set)
I took my baby home / Long tall Sally / You still want me / You do something to me / You really got me / It's alright / All day and all of the night / I gotta move / Tired of waiting for you / Come on now / Everybody's gonna be happy / Who'll be next in line / I need you / Set me free / See my friends / Never met a girl like you before / Till the end of the day / Where have all the good times gone / Sunny afternoon / I'm not like everybody else / Dead end street / Big black smoke / Waterloo sunset / Act nice and gentle / Autumn almanac / Mr. Pleasant / Polly / Wonder boy / Days / She's got everything / King kong / Plastic man / This man he weeps tonight / Shangri-La / Victoria / Mr. Churchill says / Lola / Berkeley mews / Rats / Apeman
CDLIK 74 / Jan '91 / Decal

☐ FACE TO FACE (Remastered)
Party line / Rosie won't you please come home / Dandy / Too much on my mind / Session man / Rainy day in June / House in the country / Holiday in Waikiki / Most exclusive residence for sale / Fancy / Little Miss Queen of Darkness / You're looking fine / Sunny afternoon / I'll remember / I'm not like everybody else / Dead end street / Big black smoke / Mr. Pleasant / This is where I belong
ESMCD 479 / 30 Mar '98 / Essential

☐ HITS
DC 869822 / Aug '96 / Disky

☐ INTROSPECTIVE
Waterloo sunset / Lola / Apeman / Interview part one / Where have all the good times gone / Dedicated follower of fashion / You really got me / Interview part two
CINT 5005 / Apr '91 / Baktabak

☐ KINDA KINKS (Remastered)
Look for me baby / Got my feet on the ground / Nothin' in the world can stop me worryin' 'bout that girl / Naggin' woman / Wonder where my baby is tonight / Tired of waiting for you / Dancing in the street / Don't ever change / Come on now / You shouldn't be sad / Something better beginning / Ev'rybody's gonna be happy / Who'll be the next in line / Set me free / I need you / See my friends / Never met a girl like you before / Wait till the summer comes along / Such a shame / Well respected man / Don't you fret
ESMCD 483 / 30 Mar '98 / Essential

☐ KINKS (Remastered)
Beautiful Delilah / So mystifying / Just can't go to sleep / Long tall shorty / I took my baby home / I'm a lover not a fighter / You really got me / Cadillac / Bald headed woman / Revenge / Too much monkey business / I've been driving on bald mountain / Stop your sobbing / Got love if you want it / Long tall Sally / You still want me / You do something to me / I gotta go now / I've got that feeling / Louie louie / Things are getting better / It's all right
ESMCD 482 / 30 Mar '98 / Essential

☐ KINKS KONTROVERSY (Remastered)
Milk cow blues / Ring the bells / Gotta get the first plane home / When I see that girl of mine / I am free / Till the end of the day / World keeps going round / I'm on an island / Where have all the good times gone / It's too late / What's in store for me / You can't win / Dedicated follower of fashion / Sittin' on my sofa
ESMCD 507 / 30 Mar '98 / Essential

☐ LIVE AT KELVIN HALL (Remastered)
ESMCD 508 / 25 May '98 / Essential

☐ LOLA
Lola / Tired of waiting for you / Victoria / So long / Got my feet on the ground / Dancing in the street / Nothing to say / Just friends / Got to be free / Dedicated follower of fashion / Village Green Preservation Society / Tin soldier man / Don't ever change / Dead End Street / Starstruck / Holiday in Waikiki / Milk cow blues / Dandy
5507232 / Jul '95 / Spectrum

☐ LOLA VS. POWERMAN AND THE MONEY-GO-ROUND (Remastered)
ESMCD 509 / 25 May '98 / Essential

☐ MUSWELL HILLBILLIES
VEL 797192 / 31 Aug '98 / Velvel

☐ PERCY (Remastered)
ESMCD 510 / 27 Apr '98 / Essential

☐ PRESERVATION ACT VOL.1
VEL 797212 / 31 Aug '98 / Velvel

☐ PRESERVATION ACT VOL.2
VEL 797222 / 31 Aug '98 / Velvel

☐ RAY DAVIES SONGBOOK, THE (Various Artists)
I bet you won't stay: *Cascades* / Who'll be the next in line: *Sir Douglas Quintet* / Plastic man: *Katrina & The Waves* / All day and all of the night: *Stranglers* / She's got everything: *Romantics* / Scattered: *Kinks* / Lola: *Taylor, Andy* / Rosy won't you please come home: *Faithfull, Marianne* / Tired of waiting: *Little Angels* / Waterloo sunset: *Essex, David* / You really got me: *Palmer, Robert* / Days: *Costello, Elvis* / Victoria: *Fall* / Stop your sobbing: *Pretenders* / Sunny afternoon: *Geldof, Bob* / Wonder boy: *Reader, Eddi*
VSOPCD 244 / 13 Oct '97 / Connoisseur Collection

☐ REMASTERED 1964-1967 (3CD Set)
ESBCD 268 / Mar '95 / Essential

☐ SINGLES COLLECTION/WATERLOO SUNSET (2CD Set)
Long tall Sally / You still want me / You really got me / All day and all of the night / Tired of waiting for you / Everybody's gonna be happy / Set me free / See my friend / Till the end of the day / Where have all the good times gone / Dedicated follower of fashion / Well respected man / Sunday afternoon / Dead end street / Mr. Pleasant / Waterloo sunset / Death of a clown
ESSCD 592 / 29 Sep '97 / Essential

☐ SOMETHING ELSE BY THE KINKS (Remastered)
David Watts / Death of a clown / Two sisters / No return / Harry rag / Tin soldier man / Situation vacant / Love me till the sun shines / Lazy old sun / Afternoon tea / Funny face / End of the season / Waterloo sunset / Susanah's still alive / Autumn almanac / Act nice and gentle / Wonderboy / Pretty polly / Lincoln county / There's no life without love
ESMCD 480 / 30 Mar '98 / Essential

☐ TELLTALES (Interview Disc)
TELL 16 / Jun '97 / Network

☐ VILLAGE GREEN PRESERVATION SOCIETY, THE (Remastered)
ESMCD 481 / 25 May '98 / Essential

☐ YOU REALLY GOT ME
You really got me / I need you / Till the end of the day / Come on now / Long tall Sally / Cadillac / Beautiful Delilah / Everybody's gonna be happy / Things are getting better / All day and all of the night / Stop your sobbing / Don't ever change / David Watts / You still want me / Wonder where my baby is tonight / Don't you fret / Just can't go to sleep / Well respected man / I'm not like everybody else / Tired of waiting for you
5507222 / Aug '94 / Spectrum

Kinky Roland

☐ B12
Blackout / Bungee / Blast / Broadcast / Batika / Basic / Battery / Bonkas / Brazil / B movie / Betrayal / Badly
IMPCD 4 / 26 Jan '98 / More Protein

Kinlechene, Kee

☐ SONGS OF THE NAVAJO (Kinlechene, Kee & Yatza)
VICG 5334 / Jun '96 / JVC World Library

Kinleys

☐ JUST BETWEEN YOU AND ME
Just between you and me / Talk to me / You make it seem so easy / Crazy kind of love / Please / Real thing / Takin' our own sweet time / Love rules / Contradiction / Dance in the boat
4889812 / 3 Nov '97 / Epic

Kinlochard Ceilidh Band

☐ SLAINTE
Wing commander donald mckenzie-the men of ness-the drunken / Wing commander donald mckenzie-the men of ness-the drunken (/ Hector the hero (scots slow air) / Mrs. mcleod o'dunocht-the wee man from skye (canadian barn / Ireland-I'll no tell her name (irish slow air) / Margaret's waltz (scots waltz / Leaving glen affric (slow air) / Jackie colman's-joe cooley's-farewell to erin (irish reel
CDITV 601 / Mar '95 / Scotdisc

☐ SPIRIT OF FREEDOM
CDITV 622 / Mar '97 / Scotdisc

Kinnaird, Alison

☐ HARP KEY, THE
COMD 1001 / Apr '96 / Temple

☐ MUSIC IN TRUST VOL.1 (Kinnaird, Alison & The Battlefield Band)
Sweet maid of mull-macleod of mull / Frideray / Cro cinn t-saile-the kilbarchan weaver / Lady haddo / Silver darlin's / Duchess of gordon / St. kilda girl's lament-the st. kilda wedding march / Anst'er market-the east neuk of fife / Brodick castle / Dunkeld steeple-killiekrankie / Mo run gael og / Glenfinnan highland gathering-lady mackenzie of gairloch-th / Held in trust
COMD 2010 / Feb '94 / Temple

☐ MUSIC IN TRUST VOL.2 (Kinnaird, Alison & The Battlefield Band)
Laird o'brodie-danzig willie-the merchants jig / A'chlach uaine (the green stone) / I ha'e a wife-the tarbolton jig-tarbolton lodge / Massacre of glencoe / Falkland palace / Lawer's loup-miss jane fraser-mrs maule's reel / Goat fell / Farewell to glenshalloch / Fruiting branch-gledstanes' march / Pitmedden / Mote of mark-the grey mare's tail / Held in trust-peace and plenty / Fingal's weeping-the maids of kintail / Hill house-the philosopher's chair
COMD 2004 / Feb '94 / Temple

☐ QUIET TRADITION, THE (Kinnaird, Alison & Christine Primrose)
COMD 2041 / Feb '94 / Temple

☐ SCOTTISH HARP, THE
COMD 2005 / Feb '94 / Temple

Kinney, Fern

☐ CHEMISTRY (The Best Of Fern Kinney)
Groove me / If tomorrow never comes / Together we are beautiful / Easy lovin' / Under fire / Nothing takes the place of you / Boogie box / Don't make me wait / Angel on the ground / I'm ready for your love / Sweet music man / Beautiful love song / Most girls / Sun, moon, rain / Baby let me kiss you / Pipin' hot / Pillow talk
MCCD 167 / Jul '94 / Music Club

Kinsey, Big Daddy

☐ BAD SITUATION (Kinsey, Big Daddy & The Kinsey Report)
Bad situation / Treat your woman right / Slow down / Gary Indiana / Gonna make you mine / Nuclear war blues / Change your evil ways / Tribute to Muddy / You're gonna miss me / Kinsey's mood / Hard life / Sharp axe
R 2620CD / Dec '97 / Rooster

☐ CAN'T LET GO (Kinsey, Big Daddy & Sons)
CDBP 73489 / May '94 / Blind Pig

☐ I AM THE BLUES
Ode to Muddy Waters / I am the blues / Baby don't say that no more / Somebody's gonna get hooked tonight / Nine below zero / Walking thru the park / Good mornin' Mississippi / Don't you lie to me / Queen without a King / Mannish boy / Little red rooster / Got my mojo working
5191752 / May '94 / Verve

Kinsey Report

☐ EDGE OF THE CITY
Poor man's relief / I can't let you go / Got to play someday / Answering machine / Give me what I want / Full moon on Main Street / Lucky charm / Back door man / Game of love / Come to me
ALCD 4758 / May '93 / Alligator

☐ MIDNIGHT DRIVE
ALCD 4775 / May '93 / Alligator

Kipera

☐ NOUSA JA UHO 1993-1996
Vanttaut / Kylaiiello / Kaiho / Ellin Polkko / Himlens polska / Dallas / Voi ruusuni / Cihan tama maa / Ilonpito
KICD 47 / Dec '97 / Kansanmusiikki Instituutti

Kipper Family

☐ ARREST THESE MERRY GENTLEMEN
DAMCD 022 / Nov '97 / Dambuster

☐ CRAB WARS, THE
DAMCD 017 / Dec '97 / Dambuster

☐ FRESH YESTERDAY
DAMCD 020 / Dec '97 / Dambuster

☐ IN THE FAMILY WAY
DAMCD 023 / Dec '97 / Dambuster

Kipper, Sid

☐ BOILED IN THE BAG (Kipper, Sid & Dave Burland)
LERCD 2118 / Nov '97 / Leader

☐ LIKE A RHINESTONE PLOUGHBOY
LERCD 2115 / Mar '94 / Leader

Kips Bay Ceili Band

☐ DIGGING IN
You / Battle of New Orleans / Suite for Hillary / Affligem night / Talk to me / Place I am bound / Broken promises / Big dig / Boozoo goes to heaven / Crab song
GLCD 1130 / Jul '93 / Green Linnet

☐ INTO THE LIGHT
GLCD 1164 / May '96 / Green Linnet

Kirby, John

☐ BIGGEST LITTLE BAND IN THE LAND, THE (2CD Set) (Kirby, John Sextet)
It feels so good: *Kirby, John* / Effervescent blues: *Kirby, John* / Turf: *Kirby, John* / Dawn on the desert: *Kirby, John* / Anitra's dance: *Kirby, John* / Sweet georgia brown: *Kirby, John* / Drink to me only with thine eyes: *Kirby, John* / Minute waltz: *Kirby, John* / Front and center: *Kirby, John* / Royal garden blues: *Kirby, John* / Opus 5: *Kirby, John* / Fantasy impromptu: *Kirby, John* / Blue skies: *Kirby, John* / Rose room: *Kirby, John* / I may be wrong, but I think you're wonderful: *Kirby, John* / Little brown jug: *Kirby, John* / Nocturne: *Kirby, John* / One alone: *Kirby, John* / Humoresque: *Kirby, John* / Serenade: *Kirby, John* / Jumpin' in the pump room: *Kirby, John* / Milumbu: *Kirby, John* / You go your way: *Kirby, John* / Twentieth century closet: *Kirby, John* / St. Louis blues: *Kirby, John* / Hour of parting: *Kirby, John* / Temptation: *Kirby, John* / Blues petite: *Kirby, John* / On a little street in Singapore: *Kirby, John* / Chloe: *Kirby, John* / Andiology: *Kirby, John* / Can't we be friends: *Kirby, John* / Then I'll be happy: *Kirby, John* / I love you truly: *Kirby, John* / Frasquita serenade: *Kirby, John* / Sextet from 'Lucia': *Kirby, John* / Coquette: *Kirby, John* / Zooming at the zombie: *Kirby, John* / If I had a ribbon bow: *Kirby, John* / Who is Sylvia: *Kirby, John* / Molly Malone: *Kirby, John* / Barbara Allen: *Kirby, John* / Bounce of the sugar plum fairy: *Kirby, John* / Beethoven riffs on: *Kirby, John* / Double talk: *Kirby, John* / Cutting the campus: *Kirby, John*
4776352 / Jan '95 / Sony Jazz

☐ CLASSICS 1938-1939
CLASSICS 750 / Aug '94 / Classics

☐ CLASSICS 1939-1941
CLASSICS 770 / Aug '94 / Classics

☐ CLASSICS 1941-1943
CLASSICS 792 / Jan '95 / Classics

☐ CLASSICS 1945-1946
CLASSICS 964 / Nov '97 / Classics

☐ JOHN KIRBY
It feels good / Sweet Georgia Brown / Front and center / Andiology / Coquette / Zooming at the Zombie / Opus 5 / Blue skies / Jumpin' in the pump room / 20th Century closet / Blues petite / Royal garden blues / Can't we be friends / Beethoven riffs on / Rehearsin' for a nervous breakdown / Undecided / Echoes of Harlem / Blue fantasy / Revolutionary etude (Etude in C minor) / Peanut vendor / Prelude for trumpet
CD 53243 / Jun '96 / Giants Of Jazz

☐ JOHN KIRBY 1941-1944
TAX 37142 / Aug '94 / Tax

Kirby, Kathy

☐ VERY BEST OF KATHY KIRBY, THE
Secret love / Sometimes I'm happy / Dance on / Way of love / Let me go lover / I wish you love / You're the one / Havah nagilah / I want to be happy / I belong / That wonderful feeling of love / Happiness is a thing called Joe / Love me baby / Body and soul / (All of a sudden) my heart sings / Ol' man Mose / Sweetest sounds / Make someone happy / Slowly / Where in the world
5520972 / Jan '97 / Spectrum

Kirchen, Bill

☐ HOT ROD LINCOLN (Live)
HCD 8085 / Oct '97 / Hightone

☐ TOMBSTONE EVERY MILE, A
Bottle baby boogie / Tombstone every mile / Rockabilly funeral / Fool on a stool / One woman man / Lovin' cajun style / Think it over / Lover's rock / Cool lovin' baby / Secrets of love / Hole in my pirogue / Tell me the reason / Without love / No one to talk to but the blues / All tore up
BT 1109CD / Oct '94 / Black Top

Kirk

☐ MAKIN' MOVES
7467826012 / May '94 / East West

Kirk, Andy

☐ 12 CLOUDS OF JOY, THE (Kirk, Andy & Mary Lou Williams)
Bearcat shuffle / Big Jim Blues / Close to five / Corky stomp / Dunkin' a doughnut / Floyd's guitar blues / Froggy Bottom / Gettin' off a mess / In the groove / Jump Jack jump / Little Joe from Chicago / Loose ankles / Lotta sax appeal / Margie / Mary's idea / Mellow bit of rhythm / Mess-a-stomp / Moten swing / Puddin' head serenade / Steppin' pretty / Toadie toddle / Twinklin' / Walkin' and swingin' / Wednesday night hop / Wham
CDAJA 5108 / Apr '93 / Living Era

☐ CLASSICS 1929-1931
CLASSICS 655 / Nov '92 / Classics

☐ CLASSICS 1936-1937
CLASSICS 573 / Oct '91 / Classics

☐ CLASSICS 1937-1938
CLASSICS 581 / Oct '91 / Classics

☐ CLASSICS 1938
CLASSICS 598 / Sep '91 / Classics

☐ CLASSICS 1939-1940
CLASSICS 640 / Nov '92 / Classics

☐ CLASSICS 1940-1942 (Kirk, Andy & His Twelve Clouds of Joy)
CLASSICS 681 / Mar '93 / Classics

☐ INTRODUCTION TO ANDY KIRK 1929-1946, AN
4053 / 5 Jan '98 / Best Of Jazz

☐ KANSAS CITY BOUNCE (Kirk, Andy & His Twelve Clouds of Joy)
Walkin' and swingin' / Moten swing / Lotta sax apeal / Git / Froggy bottom / Bearcat shuffle / Steppin' pretty / Christofer colombus / Wednesday night hop / In the groove / Mellow bit of rhythm / Big dipper / Bear down / Twinklin' / Little joe from chicago / Mess-a-stomp / Jump jack jump / Dunkin' a doughnut / Mary's idea / Close to five / Floyd's guitar blues / Big jim blues / Fine and mellow / Little miss
BLE 592402 / Dec '92 / Black & Blue

Kirk, Rahsaan Roland

☐ ACES BACK TO BACK (4CD Set)
60412320602 / 27 Apr '98 / Thirty Two

☐ CASE OF THE THREE SIDED DREAM IN AUDIO COLOR, THE
Bye bye blackbird / Freaks for the festival / Portrait of those beautiful ladies / Echoes of primitive ohio and chili dogs / Entertainer / Freaks for the festival / Bye bye blackbird / High heel sneakers / Portrait of those beautiful ladies / Entertainer (done in the style of blues)
7567813962 / Apr '95 / Atlantic

☐ DOES YOUR HOUSE HAVE LIONS (Rahsaan Roland Kirk Anthology)
Wham bam thank you ma'am / Bye bye blackbird / If I loved you / Old rugged cross / Ain't no sunshine / Volunteered slavery / Seasons / Going home / Black and crazy blues / I say a little prayer / This love of mine / Roots / Inflated tear / Blacknuss / I love you yes I do / Portrait of those beautiful ladies / Water for Robeson and Williams / Laugh for Rory / Entertainer (done in the style of blues) / Black root / Carney and begard place / Anysha / Making love after hours / Freaks for the festival / Bye bye blackbird / Three for the festival / Bright moments
8122714062 / Feb '94 / Atlantic

☐ GIFTS AND MESSAGES (Live At Ronnie Scott's 1964)
Ronnie's intro / Bags' groove / Roland's intro / It might as well be Spring / (On a) misty night / Come Sunday / Avalon / My ship / Stritch in time / Gifts and messages / Reeling and rhyming
JHAS 606 / Sep '96 / Ronnie Scott's Jazz House

☐ INFLATED TEAR, THE
Black and crazy blues / Laugh for Rory / Many blessings / Fingers in the wind / Inflated tear / Creole love call / Handful of fives / Fly by night / Lovelievelilloqui
7567900452 / Jul '93 / Atlantic

☐ INFLATED TEAR, THE
Black and crazy blues / Laugh for Rory / Many blessings / Fingers in the wind / Inflated tear / Creole love call / Handful of fives / Fly by night / Lovellevelliloqui / I'm glad there is you
8122752072 / 20 Jul '98 / Atlantic

☐ INTRODUCING ROLAND KIRK
Call / Soul station / Our waltz / Our love is here to stay / Spirit girl / Jack the ripper
GRP 18212 / 27 Jul '98 / Chess Mates

☐ JAZZ MASTERS
Theme for the festival / Blue rol / Reeds and deeds / Hip chops / From Bechet, Fats and Byas / Berkshire blues / Nightingale sang in Berkeley Square / March on swan lake / Haunted melody / Meeting on Termini's corner / Rolando / Blues for Alice / Black diamond / You did it, you did it / Where Monk and Mingus live / Blues for C and T
5220622 / 5 May '98 / Verve

☐ KIRK'S WORK
Three for Dizzy / Makin' Whoopee / Funk underneath / Kirk's work / Doin' the sixty-eight / Too Late Now / Skater's waltz
OJCCD 459 / '93 / Original Jazz Classics

☐ RIP, RIG AND PANIC/NOW PLEASE DON'T YOU CRY, BEAUTIFUL EDITH (Kirk, Rahsaan Roland Quartet)
No tonic press / Once in a while / From Bechet, Fats and Byas / Mystical dreams / Rip, rig and panic / Black diamond / Slippery, hippery, flippery / Now please don't you cry, beautiful Edith / Blue rol / Alfie / Why don't they know / Silverlization / Fallout / Stompin' grounds / It's a grand night for swinging
8321642 / Jul '90 / EmArCy

☐ SOUL STATION
Call / Soul station / Our waltz / Our love is here to stay / Spirit girl / Jack the ripper
LEJAZZ 35 / Sep '94 / Le Jazz

☐ SOUVENIR DE MONTREUX
Pedal up / Satin doll / Improvisation / Blue rol no 2 / Volunteered slavery / Serenade to a cuckoo / Balm in gilead / Seasons
8122724532 / Jul '96 / Atlantic

☐ SWEET FIRE
My little suede shoes-groovin' high / Petite fleur-when the saints go marching in / Roller coaster-sweet fire / Love for sale-bags groove-my cherie amour / Three for the festival / Boogie man song
JHR 73579 / Jun '94 / Jazz Hour

☐ TALKIN' VERVE
5331012 / Dec '96 / Verve

☐ THIRD DIMENSION
BET 6006 / Jan '95 / Bethlehem

☐ THREE FOR THE FESTIVAL
LEJAZZCD 6 / Mar '93 / Le Jazz

☐ WE FREE KINGS
Three for the festival / Moon song / Sackful of soul / Haunted melody / Blues for Alice / We free kings / You did it, you did it / Some kind of love / My delight
8264552 / Nov '86 / Mercury

Kirk, Richard H.

☐ AGENTS WITH FALSE MEMORIES
ASH 31CD / Nov '96 / Ash International

☐ BLACK JESUS VOICE
KIRKCD 3 / Feb '95 / Grey Area

☐ ELECTRONIC EYE (2CD Set)
RBADCD 8 / Aug '94 / Beyond

☐ HIGH TIME FICTION
KIRK 2CD / Oct '94 / Grey Area

☐ IS THIS NOW (Trafficante)
Energy / This is Channel One / Bump the 45 / Vaporetti / Soul and salvation / Art of darkness / El Cid inna dub / How you know
ALPHACD 4 / 1 Jun '98 / Alphaphone

☐ NUMBER OF MAGIC, THE
WARPCD 32 / Jul '95 / Warp

☐ UGLY SPIRIT
Emperor / Confession / Infantile / Frankie machine / Hollywood babylon / Thai / Voodoo / Frankie machine (II)
KIRKCD 4 / Feb '95 / Grey Area

☐ VIRTUAL STATE
November x ray mexico / November x ray mexico / Come / Freezone / Clandestine transmission / Feeling (of warmth and beauty) / Velodrome / Soul catcher / World war three / Lagoon west
WARPCD 19 / Feb '94 / Warp

Kirkintilloch Band

☐ BRASS O' SCOTLAND
Moray firth (march) / Moray firth (march) / Wee cooper o' fyfe / Amazing grace / Ecossaise / My love is like a red, red rose / Loch lomond / Intrada, song and dance / Wee macgreegor / Love of my life / Scottish rhapsody / Eriskay love lilt / Land of the mountain and the flood / Skye boat song medley
BNA 5078 / Mar '93 / Bandleader

Kirkland, Eddie

☐ ALL AROUND THE WORLD
Shake it up / All I've got to offer / Live with it / Forty days and forty nights / Pick up the pieces / All around the world / Love don't love nobody / Country boy / There's gonna be some blues / Big city behind the sun / Someone to stand by me
DELCD 3001 / Jan '96 / Deluge

☐ HAVE MERCY
ECD 26018 / Feb '93 / Evidence

☐ IT'S THE BLUES MAN
Down on my knees / Don't take my heart / Daddy please don't cry / Have mercy on me / Saturday night stomp / I'm gonna forget you / I tried / Man of stone / I'm goin' to keep loving you / Train done gone / Something's gone wrong in my life / Baby you know it's true
OBCCD 513 / Apr '94 / Original Blues Classics

☐ SOME LIKE IT RAW
DELCD 3007 / Dec '95 / Deluge

☐ WHERE YOU GET YOUR SUGAR
DELD 3012 / Dec '95 / Deluge

Kirkland, Mike James

☐ HANG ON IN THERE
LHCD 028 / Nov '96 / Luv n' Haight

Kirkpatrick, Anton

☐ REEL OF GHOSTS
SPINCD 133 / Dec '97 / Spindrift

Kirkpatrick, Bob

☐ GOING BACK TO TEXAS
Going back to Texas / Big feet / I don't know why / Every-ree day / Schefel / I've been down so long / I got love / Old friends of mine / House calls / Sad, sad blues / Little girl / I want to see her
CD 269 / May '96 / JSP

Kirkpatrick, John

☐ EARTHLING
MWCD 4006 / Jul '94 / Music & Words

☐ FORCE OF HABIT
FLED 3007 / Feb '96 / Fledg'ling

☐ PLAIN CAPERS
Glorishears / Hammersmith flyover / Old Molly Oxford / Black Jack/Old Black Joe / Blue eyed stranger/Willow tree / Brighton camp/March past / Bobby and Joan / Monk's march/Fieldtown professional / Sweet Jenny Jones/Sherbourne jig / Lumps of plum pudding / Highland Mary / Wheatley processional / Maid of the mill/Cuckoo's nest/ William and Nancy / Buffoon/Fool's jig / Constant Billy
TSCD 458 / Aug '92 / Topic

☐ SHEEPSKINS
Last night with Archie / Three jolly black sheepskins / Mad moll - the lively jig / Over the moon / Ronnets so blue / There's no doubt about it / Beating the oak / Dick the Welshman / Todley Tome / Blue eyed stranger / Watterddy Lane / Tun dish / Maiden's prayer / Turn again Martha / Churning butter / Abram circle dance / Raddled tup / Hunting the squirrel / Zot for Joe / Four lane end / Cocking the chafer / Threepenny ha'penny treacle / Martha's comet or the evening star / Three hand reel / Green and yellow handkerchief dance / Prince of Wales / Morning star / Half a farthing candle / Hindley circle dance
MWCD 4002 / Jun '93 / Music & Words

☐ SHORT HISTORY OF JOHN KIRKPATRICK, A
TSCD 473 / Aug '94 / Topic

☐ TRANS EUROPE DIATONIQUE (Kirkpatrick, J. & R. Tessi)
Y225026 / Jun '93 / Silex

☐ WASSAIL (Traditional Celebration Of Midwinter) (Kirkpatrick, John & Rosie Cross/Georgina Le Faux)
Wassail song / Hunting the wren / Poor old horse / Sword dance song and tunes / Rattling cannister man / Stir the fire / Derby tup / Carol tunes / Holly and the ivy / Cherry tree carol / On Christmas day / King Herod and the cock / Apple tree man / Children's rhymes / Here we come a wassailing / Twelve days of Christmas / Chariots
FECD 125 / Dec '97 / Fellside

☐ WELCOME TO HELL
Step dance tunes / Golden grain/Golden hornpipe / Fields of gold / Lovely Nancy / Welcome to hell / Shropshire tunes / Accordion Joe / On the road to freedom / Fill 'em up Rosie / 49003/55005
FLED 3011 / May '97 / Fledg'ling

Kirlian

☐ CHICKEN WINGS AND BEEF FRIED RICE
EFA 122802 / '95 / Disko B

☐ PLEASURE YOURSELF
EFA 294652 / 12 Jan '98 / Disko B

Kirsti

☐ EIN STUDENT AUS UPPSALA
BCD 16236 / May '98 / Bear Family

Kirtley, Peter

☐ BUSH TELEGRAPH
Save a piece of your heart / Halfway to paradise / Bird chase bird / If the gentle rain that falls / Bush telegraph / Next year / Roman wall blues / Way of the world / Sweet talkin' blues / Let's go walkin' / Don't throw this love away / Nobody knows / Suppertime / Mrs. Bell
PLAN 013CD / Nov '97 / Planet

Kirton, David

☐ STRANGER
DK 001 / 20 Jul '98 / Birds Eye

Kirwan, Dominic

☐ BEST OF DOMINIC KIRWAN, THE
RZCD 0077 / Apr '96 / Ritz

☐ EVERGREEN
Hold me just one more time / Only couple on the floor / My happiness / Picture of you / If you're ever in my arms again / I really don't want to know / Evergreen / Absent friends / Release me / One bouquet of roses / Way love's supposed to be / Hello Mary Lou / Bless this house
RZCD 0065 / Nov '91 / Ritz

☐ IRISH FAVOURITES
Through the eyes of an Irishman / Tipperary on my mind / Irish eyes / Star of the Country Down / If we only had old Ireland over here / Sprig of Irish heather / Medley / Village of Astee / Limerick you're a lady / My Galway queen / My mother's home / Rose of Tralee / My own Donegal / Song for Ireland / Medley / Cavan girl
RZRCD 539 / Aug '94 / Ritz

☐ LOVE WITHOUT END
Like father, like son / Almost persuaded / Love letters in the sand / Straight and narrow / Just for old times sake / Stranger things have happened / Say you'll stay until tomorrow / When the girl in your arms (is the girl in your heart) / Love without end, amen / There's always me / Hand that rocks the cradle / Fool's pardon / Life is what you make it / Noreen Bawn
RZRCD 527 / Apr '93 / Ritz

☐ MUSIC'S BACK, THE
Music's back / Funny familiar feelings / You are the one / You're more than a number in my little red book / All in the game / That's what your love means to me / Young girl / I swear / When you are old / Island's in the stream / Love me tender / Needles and pins / Never too far from my mind / What more could I want from you
RZCD 0084 / 20 Oct '97 / Ritz

☐ ON THE WAY TO A DREAM
Where does love go when it dies / Tonight we just might fall in love again / Hands across the ocean / Northern lights are shining for me / On the way to a dream / Answer to everything / Our love / Someone in your eyes / We'll be together from now on / My love is like a red red rose / I won't forget you / In my sleepless nights / What am I gonna do with all this love / Thank you for being a friend
RZCD 0074 / Mar '95 / Ritz

☐ TODAY
RZCD 0071 / Oct '93 / Ritz

☐ TRY A LITTLE KINDNESS
Oh lonesome me / I'll leave this world loving you / Achin' breaking heart / Before the next teardrop falls / Try a little kindness / More than yesterday / My beautiful wife / Sea of heartbreak / Heaven knows / Heartaches by the number / Careless hands / Golden dreams / Paper roses / St. Theresa of the roses
RZCD 504 / '91 / Ritz

Kisiun

☐ BLACK FORCE DOMAIN
GUN 147CD / 6 Oct '97 / Gun

Kiske, Michael

☐ INSTANT CLARITY
Be true to yourself / Calling / Somebody somewhere / Burned out / New horizons / Hunted / Always / Time's passing by / So sick / Thanx a lot / Do I remember a life
RAWCD 112 / Sep '96 / Raw Power

Kismet

☐ WAKE UP GODS
TCCD 97232 / 16 Mar '98 / Tone Casualties

Kisor, Ryan

☐ BATTLE CRY (Kisor, Ryan Quartet)
Battle cry / It happens / Falling in love with love / I'm old fashioned / Birdlike / Sweet pumpkin / If ever I would leave you
CRISS 1145 / Jun '98 / Criss Cross

Kiss

☐ ALIVE VOL.1 (2CD Set)
Deuce / Strutter / Got to choose / Hotter than hell / Firehouse / Nothin' to lose / C'mon and love me / Parasite / She / Watchin' you / 100,000 years / Black diamond / Rock bottom / Cold gin / Rock 'n' roll all nite / Let me go rock 'n' roll
5323772 / 22 Sep '97 / Casablanca

☐ ALIVE VOL.2 (2CD Set)
Detroit rock city / King of the night time world / Ladies' room / Makin' love / Love gun / Calling Dr. Love / Christine sixteen / Shock me / Hard luck woman / Tomorrow and tonight / I stole your love / Beth / God of thunder / I want you / Shout it out loud / All American man / Rockin' in the USA / Larger than life / Rocket ride / Anyway you want it
5322382 / 22 Sep '97 / Casablanca

☐ ALIVE VOL.3
Creatures of the night / Deuce / I just wanna / Unholy / Heaven's on fire / Watchin' you / Domino / I was made for lovin' you / I still love you / Rock 'n' roll all nite / Lick it up / Forever / Take it off / I love it loud / Detroit rock city / God gave rock 'n' roll to you II / Star spangled banner
5148272 / May '93 / Casablanca

☐ CARNIVAL OF SOULS
Hate / Rain / Master and slave / Childhood's end / I will be there / Jungle / In ym head / It never goes away / Seduction of the innocent / I confess / In the mirror / I walk alone
5363232 / 27 Oct '97 / Casablanca

☐ CRAZY NIGHTS
Crazy crazy nights / Hell to hold you / Bang bang you / No no no / Hell or high water / My way / When your walls come down / Reason to live / Good girl gone bad / Turn on the night / Thief in the night
8326262 / Feb '91 / Casablanca

☐ CREATURES OF THE NIGHT
Creatures of the night / Saint and sinner / Keep me comin' / Rock 'n' roll hell / Danger / I love it loud / I still love you / Killer / War machine
5323912 / 22 Sep '97 / Casablanca

☐ DESTROYER
Detroit rock city / King of the night time world / God of thunder / Great expectations / Flaming youth / Sweet pain / Shout it out loud / Beth / Do you love me
532237827 / 22 Sep '97 / Casablanca

☐ DOUBLE PLATINUM
Strutter / Do you love me / Hard luck woman / Calling Dr. Love / Let me go rock 'n' roll / Love gun / God of thunder / Firehouse / Hotter than hell / I want you / Deuce / 100,000 years / Detroit rock city / She / Rock 'n' roll all nite / Beth / Makin' love / C'mon and love me / Cold gin / Black diamond
5323832 / 22 Sep '97 / Casablanca

☐ DRESSED TO KILL
Room service / Two timer / Ladies in waiting / Get away / Rock bottom / C'mon and love me / Anything for my baby / She / Love her all I can / Rock 'n' roll all nite
5323762 / 22 Sep '97 / Casablanca

☐ DYNASTY
I was made for lovin' you / 2000 man / Sure know something / Dirty livin' / Charisma / Magic touch / Hard times / X-ray eyes / Save your love
5323882 / 22 Sep '97 / Casablanca

☐ FIFTEEN YEARS ON (The Interview)
CBAK 4002 / Apr '88 / Baktabak

☐ GENE SIMMONS (Simmons, Gene)
5323842 / 22 Sep '97 / Casablanca

☐ GREATEST HITS
Crazy crazy nights / I was made for lovin' you / Detroit city rock / Lick it up / Hard luck woman / ACalling doctor love / Beth / Love gun / God of thunder / Sure know something / Deuce / Do you love me / Strutter / Rock and roll nite / Plaster caster / Hotter than hell / Shock me / Cold gin / Black diamond / God gave rock 'n' roll to you II
5361592 / Jun '97 / PolyGram TV

☐ GREATEST KISS
Detroit rock city / Black diamond / Hard luck woman / Sure know something / Love gun / Deuce / Goin' blind / Shock me / Do you love me / She / I was made for loving you / Shout it out loud / God of thunder / Calling Dr. Love / Beth / Strutter / Rock 'n' roll all nite / Cold gin / Plaster caster / God gave rock 'n' roll to you
5342992 / Nov '96 / Casablanca

☐ HOTTER THAN HELL
Got to choose / Parasite / Goin' blind / Hotter than hell / Let me go rock 'n' roll / All the way / Watchin' you / Mainline / Comin' home / Strangeways
5323752 / 22 Sep '97 / Casablanca

☐ INTERVIEW DISC
TELL 02 / Dec '96 / Network

☐ KISS
Strutter / Nothin' to lose / Firehouse / Cold gin / Let me know / Kissin' time / Deuce / Love theme from Kiss / 100,000 years / Black diamond
5323742 / 22 Sep '97 / Casablanca

☐ KISS (Interview)
3D 009 / Dec '96 / Network

☐ LICK IT UP
Exciter / Not for the innocent / Lick it up / All hell's breakin' loose / Fits like a glove / And on the eighth day / Dance all over your face / Gimme more / Million to one / Young and wasted
8142972 / ' / Casablanca

☐ LOVE GUN
I stole your love / Christine sixteen / Got love for sale / Shock me / Tomorrow and tonight / Love gun / Hooligan / Almost human / Then she kissed me / Plaster caster
5323812 / 22 Sep '97 / Casablanca

☐ MUSIC FROM THE ELDER
Oath / Fanfare / Just a boy / Dark light / Only you / Under the rose / World without heroes / Mr. Blackwell / Escape from the island / Odyssey / I
5323902 / 22 Sep '97 / Casablanca

☐ NUMBER ONE (Criss Cat)
MRRCD 017 / 2 Mar '98 / Megarock

☐ PAUL STANLEY (Stanley, Paul)
Tonight you belong to me / Move on / Ain't quite right / Wouldn't you like to know me / Take me away (together as one) / It's alright / Hold me touch me / Love in chains / Goodbye
5323872 / 22 Sep '97 / Casablanca

☐ PETER CRISS (Criss, Peter)
5323862 / 22 Sep '97 / Casablanca

☐ ROCK 'N' ROLL OVER
I want you / Take me / Calling Dr. Love / Ladies' room / Baby driver / Love 'em and leave 'em / Mr. Speed / See you in your dreams / Hard luck woman
5323802 / 22 Sep '97 / Casablanca

☐ SMASHES, THRASHES AND HITS
Let's put the X in sex / Crazy crazy nights / (You make me) rock hard / Love gun / Detroit rock city / I love it loud / Deuce / Lick it up / Heaven's on fire / Strutter / Beth / Tears are falling / I was made for lovin' you / Rock 'n' roll all nite / Shout it out loud
8364272 / Nov '88 / Casablanca

☐ TRIBUTE TO KISS (Various Artists)
TR 006CD / Jul '96 / Tribute

☐ UNMASKED
Is that you / Shandi / What makes the world go round / Talk to me / Naked city / Torpedo girl / Tomorrow / Two sides of the coin / She's so European / Easy as it seems
5323892 / 22 Sep '97 / Casablanca

☐ UNPLUGGED
Comin' home / Plaster caster / Goin' blind / Do you love me / Domino / Sure know something / World without heroes / Rock bottom / See you tonight / I still love you / Every time I look at you / 2000 man / Beth / Nothin' to lose / Rock 'n' roll all nite
5289502 / Mar '96 / Casablanca

☐ YOU WANTED THE BEST, YOU GOT THE BEST (The Best Of Kiss Live)
Parasite / Firehouse / Rock bottom / Rock 'n' roll all nite / I stole your love / Calling Dr. Love / Shout it out loud / Beth / Room service / Two timer / Let me know / Take me
5327412 / Jul '96 / Casablanca

Kiss It Goodbye

☐ SHE LOVES ME
REV 058CD / Apr '97 / Revelation

Kiss My Jazz

☐ DOC'S PLACE FRIDAY EVENING
KFWCD 196 / Oct '96 / Knitting Factory

☐ IN THE LOST SOULS CONVENTION
HH 97005 / 9 Feb '98 / Heaven Hotel

Kiss My Poodle's Donkey

☐ NEW HOPE FOR THE DEAD
Sacred cow / Truck / Bad hair day / Psychoman / Mood B / Gett off / See my eye / Lizard
HOT 1048CD / Feb '94 / Hot

Kissoon, Mac & Katie

☐ STAR COLLECTION
STCD 1003 / Jun '93 / Disky

☐ SWINGING SOUL OF MAC AND KATIE KISSOON
Hey you love / Pidgeon / Chirpy chirpy cheep cheep / It's a hang up world / Change it all / (I found my) freedom / True love forgives / It's all over now / Love will keep us together / Vow / Love grows (Where my Rosemary grows) / Bless me / Don't make me cry / Swinging on a star / Black skinned blue eyed boys / Sing along / Love me baby / Show me / Hey diddle diddle
C5CD538 / '89 / See For Miles

Kitachi

☐ STRONG UNIT, A (2CD Set)
Realms of dub / Heavyweight / Scratch / Spirit / Bad day / Remedy / Constructive / Stalking / Kitachi in dub / Kaos / Time out / Spirit / Scratch / Chronic / Spirit bass mix / Realms of Dub / Time out / Constructive / Spirit / Chronic / Heavyweight
CDXDOP 004 / Sep '97 / Dope On Plastic

Kitaro

☐ BEST OF KITARO VOL.1, THE
Morning prayer / Eternal spring / Oasis / Westbound / Silver moon / Four changes / Tunhuang / Scared journey II / Revelation / Silk road fantasy / Shimmering light / Everlasting road
DOMO 710582 / Jan '97 / Domo

☐ BEST OF TEN YEARS 1976-1986, THE (2CD Set)
Dawn/Rising sun / Caravansary / Shimmering horizon / Cosmic love / Theme from Silk Road / Lord of wind / Oasis / Clouds / Earth born / Aqua / Mirage / Moon star / Flight / God of thunder / Bell tower / Song for peace
DOM 0710622 / Jul '97 / Domo

☐ CIRQUE INGENIEUX (2CD Set)
Cirque ingenieux / Sarah's world / Soalr system trapeze / Tailor / Costume shop / Wall of masks / Contortionists / Winter waltz / Wizard / Galina / Underworld / Strength / Escape / Bottom of the sky / Double lira/Finale
DOMO 710222 / 6 Oct '97 / Domo

☐ ENCHANTED EVENING, AN
Mandala / Planet / Dance of Sarasvati / Silk road / Chants from the heart / Spirit of Tokyo / Kokoro / Heaven and earth
DOMO 710052 / Nov '96 / Domo

☐ GAIA ONBASHIRA
Tanne / Prayer / Misty / Gaia / Wood fairies / Satoboki / Kiotoshi
DOMO 91003 / 13 Jul '98 / Domo

☐ IN PERSON/DIGITAL
Prologue / Eternal spring / Westbound / Silver moon / Peace / Bell tower / Morning prayer / Tienshan / Four changes / Magical sand dancing
DOMO 710552 / Apr '97 / Domo

☐ KI
Revelation / Stream of being / Kaleidoscope / Oasis / Sun / Endless water / Tree / Cloud in the sky
DOMO 710572 / Apr '97 / Domo

☐ KITARO BOX SET (Original Album Collection/5CD Set)
Silk road / Bell tower / Heavenly father / Great river / Great wall of China / Flying celestial nymphs / Silk road fantasy / Shimmering light / Westbound / Time / Bodhisattva / Everlasting road / Peace / Takla Makan desert / Eternal spring / Silver moon / Magical sand dance / Year 40080 / Time travel / Reincarnation / Dawning / Tienshan / Mirage: *Kitaro & London Philharmonic Orchestra* / Flight: *Kitaro & London Philharmonic Orchestra* / Aurora: *Kitaro & London Philharmonic Orchestra* / Fire: *Kitaro & London Philharmonic Orchestra* / Spring of youth: *Kitaro & London Philharmonic Orchestra* / Simmering horizon: *Kitaro & London Philharmonic Orchestra* / Oasis: *Kitaro & London Philharmonic Orchestra* / Pilgrimage: *Kitaro & London Philharmonic Orchestra* / Jesu joy of man's desiring / Silent night / Angels we have heard on night / Joy to the world/First noel / Little drummer boy / Jingle bells / Rosa mystica / It came upon a midnight clear / God rest ye merry gentlemen / A la nanita nana / O holy night / Great spirit / Mandala / Planet / Dance of Sarasvati / Silk road / Chants from the heart / Spirit of Taiko / Kokoro / Heaven and earth
DOMO 91001 / Nov '96 / Domo

☐ KITARO'S WORLD OF MUSIC (Kitaro & Nawang Khechog)
Ocean of wisdom / Karuna / Tibet / Rhythm of Dakini / Presence / Thanksgiving to mother earth / Journey with ancients / Peace through kindness
DOMO 710042 / Jun '96 / Domo

☐ KITARO'S WORLD OF MUSIC (Kitaro & Yu-Xiao Guang)
40800 / Caravansary / Taklamakan desert / Mandala / Flying celestial nymphs / Silk road / Peace / Linden / Everlasting road
DOMO 710112 / Nov '96 / Domo

☐ KOJIKI
DOMO 710632 / Jul '97 / Domo

☐ LIGHT OF THE SPIRIT
Mysterious encounter / Sundance / Field / Light of the spirit / In the beginning / Journey of fantasy / Howling thunder / Moondance
DOMO 710612 / Jun '97 / Domo

☐ MANDALA
Mandala / Planet / Dance of Sarasvati / Scope / Chant from the heart / Crystal tears / Winds of youth / Kokoro
DOMO 810012 / Jan '97 / Domo

☐ OASIS
Morning player / Moro-rism / New wave / Cosmic energy / Eternal spring / Moonlight / Shimmering horizon / Fragrance of nature / Innocent people / Oasis
DOMO 710542 / Nov '96 / Domo

☐ PEACE ON EARTH
Jesu joy of man's desiring / Silent night / Angels we have heard on night / Joy to the world/First noel / Little drummer boy / Jingle bells / Rosa mystica / It came upon a midnight clear / God rest ye merry gentlemen / A la nanita nana / O holy night / Great spirit
DOMO 710142 / Nov '96 / Domo

☐ SILK ROAD SUITE
Tienshan / Peace / Journey / Silk road theme / Drifting sand / Fragrance of nature / Silk road fantasy / Time / Flying celestial nymphs / Silk road theme / Everlasting road / Bell tower / Sunset / Westbound / Magical sand dance
DOMO 710522 / Nov '96 / Domo

☐ SILK ROAD VOL.1
Silk Road / Bell tower / Heavenly father / Great river / Great wall of China / Flying celestial nymphs / Silk Road fantasy / Shimmering light / Westbound / Time / Bodhisattva / Everlasting Road
DOMO 710502 / Nov '96 / Domo

☐ SILK ROAD VOL.2
Peace / Takla Makan desert / Eternal spring / Silver moon / Magical sand dance / Year 40080 / Time travel / Reincarnation / Dawning / Tienshan
DOMO 710512 / Nov '96 / Domo

☐ TENKU
Tenku / Romance / Wings / Aura / Message from the Cosmos / Time travel / Legend of the road / Milky Way
DOMO 710602 / Jun '97 / Domo

☐ TUNHUANG
Lord of the wind / Fata Morgana / Sacred journey I / Lord of the sand / Tunhuang / Free flight / Mandala / Tao / Sacred journey II
DOMO 710562 / Nov '96 / Domo

☐ WORLD OF KITARO, THE (Kitaro & London Philharmonic Orchestra)
Mirage / Flight / Aurora / Fire / Spring of youth / Simmering horizon / Oasis / Pilgrimage
DOMO 710532 / Nov '96 / Domo

Kitch

☐ INCREDIBLE
JW 1018CD / Jan '96 / JW

Kitchen Radio

☐ VIRGIN SMILE
GRCD 339 / Dec '94 / Glitterhouse

Kitchens Of Distinction

☐ COWBOYS AND ALIENS
Sand on fire / Get over yourself / Thought he had everything / Cowboys and aliens / Come on now / Remember me / One of those sometimes is now / Here comes the swans / Now it's time to say goodbye / Pierced / Prince of Mars
TPCD 53 / Aug '94 / One Little Indian

☐ DEATH OF COOL
TPCD 39 / Jul '92 / One Little Indian

☐ LOVE IS HELL
TPCD 9 / May '89 / One Little Indian

☐ STRANGE FREE WORLD
TPCD 19 / Apr '91 / One Little Indian

Kitt, Eartha

☐ BACK IN BUSINESS
Back in business / Let's misbehave / Solitude / Why can't I / Ain't misbehavin' / Nearness of you / Close enough for love / Brother can you spare a dime / Angelitos negros / Moon river / Speak low / Here's to life
DRGCD 91431 / Nov '94 / DRG

☐ BEST OF EARTHA KITT, THE (Where Is My Man)
HTCD 81 / 20 Apr '98 / Hot Productions

☐ BEST OF THE FABULOUS EARTHA KITT, THE
C'est si bon (it's so good) / April in portugal / Apres moi / I want to be evil / If I love ya then I need ya if I need ya then I want you ar / Shango / My heart belongs to daddy / Uska dara / Just an old fashioned girl / Let's do it (let's fall in love) / Mack the knife / Love is a gamble / Sholem / Yellow bird / I'd rather be burnt as a witch / Santa baby
MCLD 19120 / Oct '92 / MCA

☐ EARTHA IN NEW YORK (Live At The Plaza/Ballroom New York 1975)
ITM 1493 / Mar '96 / ITM

☐ EARTHA KITT
DVAD 6092 / May '95 / Deja Vu

☐ EARTHA-QUAKE (5CD Set)
Annie doesn't live here any more / Lilac wine / I want to be evil / C'est si bon / Two lovers / Mountain high, valley low / Angelitos negros / Uska Dara / Avril au Portugal / African lullaby / Senor / Santa baby / Under the bridges of Paris / Oh John (please don't kiss me) / Let's do it / Salangadou / Sandy's tune / Smoke gets in your eyes / Blues / My heart belongs to Daddy / Lovin' spree / Somebody bad stole the wedding bell / Looking for a boy / Lonely girl / Easy does it / I wantcha round / Apres moi / Mink shmink / This year's Santa baby / Hey Jacques / Strangers in the starlight / Do you remember / Day that the circus left town / Heel / Mambo de Paree / I've got that lovin' bug itch / Dinner for one please James / My heart's delight / Freddy / Sweet and gentle / Sho-ji-jo / Nobody taught me / Nothin' for Christmas / Je cherche un homme / If I can't take it with me / Just an old fashioned girl / Mademoiselle Kitt / Oggere / No importa si menti / Lazy afternoon / There is no cure for l'amore / Lisbon Antigua / Lullaby of Birdland / Jonny / Fascinating man / Thursday's child / Le danseur de Charleston / Honolulu rock and roll / Vid kajen / Rosenkyssar / Put more wood on the fire / I'm a funny dame / Woman wouldn't be a woman / Toujour Gai / Waydown blues / Proceed with caution / Yomme, yomme / Take my love, take my love / Careless love / Beale Street blues / Hesitating blues / Memphis blues / Friendless blues / Yellow dog blues / Chantez les bas / St. Louis blues / Long gone / Steal away / Hist the window, Noah / Shango / Sholem / Torah dance / Tierra va temblar / Mack the knife / I'd rather be burned as a witch / Independent / Love is a gamble / Yellow bird / Jambo hippopotami / In the evening / Lamplight / Let's do it again / April in Portugal / Johnny with the gentle hands / Johnny with the gentle hands / Monotonous / Love is a simple thing / Bal petit bal / Overture / Dialogue : Mrs. Patterson / Mrs. Patterson / Devil scene / I was a boy / Fantasy / I wish I was a bumble-bee / Card game scene / Be good, be good, be good / Tea party scene / Tea in Chicago / My Daddy is a dandy / Finale / I can't give you anything but love / Solitude / Since I fell for you / What is this thing called love / Callete (caliente)
BCD 15639 / Oct '93 / Bear Family

☐ LIVE IN LONDON
Old fashioned girl / I want to be evil / Guess who I saw today / Could I leave you / Blues / St. louis blues / Where is my man / Ne me quitte pas / C'est si bon (it's so good) / Charleston
JHD 083 / Mar '93 / Tring

☐ MASTERS, THE
EABCD 020 / 24 Nov '97 / Eagle

☐ MY HEART BELONGS TO DADDY
Let's do it / C'est si bon / My heart belongs to daddy / I want to be evil / Just an old fashioned girl / Monotonous / Beale street blues / Lullaby of Birdland / Under the bridges of Paris / Thursday's child / St. Louis blues / Uska dara-a Turkish tale / Memphis blues / Lazy afternoon / Careless love / Lilac wine / April in Portugal / Apres moi / Day the circus left town / If I can't take it with me
743215696322 / 23 Mar '98 / Camden

☐ MY WAY - A MUSICAL TRIBUTE TO MARTIN LUTHER KING (Live At The Caravan Of Dreams, Fort Worth, Texas 1987)
Introduction (Ms. Kitt) / God bless the child / Old ship of Zion / America the beautiful / Look where God has brought us / Commentary: Ms Kitt / Old rugged cross / Abraham, Martin and John / My way
BASIC 50015 / Mar '96 / ITM

☐ SENTIMENTAL EARTHA
It is love (por amor) / Wear your love like heaven / I remember the rhymes / Paint me black angels (angelitos negros) / Catch me the wind / My sentimental friend / Once we loved / Way you are (asi eres tu) / Geneis / Hurdy gurdy man
C5LCD 628 / Sep '95 / See For Miles

☐ STANDARDS
Something may go wrong / Empty house / Life made me beautiful at forty / Smoke gets in your eyes / Yesterdays / My funny valentine / That old hotel / God bless the child / C'est si bon (it's so good) / Night and day / Autumn leaves (instrumental)
ITM 1484 / Jul '94 / Hightone

☐ THINKING JAZZ
Something may go wrong / God bless the child / You can't fool me / Empty house / Night and day / That old hotel / You'd be so nice to come home too / Smoke gets in your eyes / Life made me beautiful at forty / God bless the child (instr.) / Lullaby of birdland / My funny valentine / How many times
ITM 1477 / 26 Jan '98 / ITM

Kix
☐ SHOW BUSINESS
CDMFN 159 / Mar '95 / Music For Nations

Kjarkas
☐ A LOS 500 ANOS
4301120922 / 27 Apr '98 / ANS

☐ CANTO A LA MUJER DE MI PUEBLO
TUMICD 010 / Feb '90 / Tumi

☐ EL AMOR Y LA LIBERTAD
TUMICD 013 / Apr '90 / Tumi

☐ TECNO ANDINO
4301120932 / 27 Apr '98 / ANS

KK Null
☐ ECSTACY OF ZERO-G SEX
VC 137 / 20 Apr '98 / Vinyl Communication

☐ NEW KIND OF WATER (KK Null & Jim O'Rourke)
CHCD 6 / Jun '97 / Charnel House

Klaatu
☐ KLAATU
7920762 / 1 Jun '98 / Capitol

☐ MAGENTA LANE
SRMC 4046 / 5 Jan '98 / Siwan

Klang
☐ KLANG - WORKS FOR TAPE & TAPE INSTRUMENTS (Sonic Arts Network Collection Vol.1)
NMCD 035 / Jun '96 / NMC

Klange
☐ TIME 2/TIME 3 (Time Cubed In Time Square)
MHCD 024 / Jan '95 / Minus Habens

Klapper, Martin
☐ RECENT CROAKS (Klapper, Martin & Roger Turner)
ACTA 11 / Apr '98 / Acta

Klasse Kriminal
☐ BEST OF KLASSE KRIMINAL, THE
Generazione distruttiva / I kids devono rimanere / Non fremarti mai / Get up stand up / Scritte sopra i muri / Ci incontreremo ancora un giorno / Giusto o sbagliato / Noi non moriremo mai / Ragazzi come tu and me / Rude boys outta jail / Oi fatti un risata / Faccia a faccia / Goal / C'era un giovane che disse / Johnny too bad / Giovani skins senza una chance / Sappiamo da dove veniamo / Birra donne and cimineri / Lungo il fiume di zinola / If the kids are united
AHOYCD 076 / 3 Nov '97 / Captain Oi

☐ CI INCONTREREMO
KOCD 024 / Mar '97 / Knock Out

☐ HISTORY OF KLASSE KRIMINAL VOL.1 1985-1993, THE
KONCD 008 / Mar '97 / Knock Out

Klaw, Irving
☐ UTEK PAHTOO MOGOI (Klaw, Irving Trio)
ROCO 017CD / Jul '97 / Road Cone

Klearview Harmonix
☐ HAPPY MEMORIES VOL.1 & 2
DTCD 67 / Jul '92 / Discotex

☐ THOSE WERE THE DAYS VOL.1
DTCD 21 / May '94 / Discotex

Kleeer
☐ VERY BEST OF KLEEER, THE (Visionary Funkmasters)
Keep your body workin' / Winners / Open your mind / Get tough / Running back to you / Taste the music / De ting continues / She said she loves you / Next time it's for real / Itimate connection / Tonight / Take your heart away / Tonight's the night
8122752182 / 1 Jun '98 / Atlantic

Kleenex Girl Wonder
☐ GRAHAM SMITH IS COOLEST
MMM 71354 / 19 Jan '98 / MOC

Klein, Guillermo
☐ EL MINOTAURO
El minotauro / La manzana de las luces / Primer tango free / Lo perdido / La madre de mi hermana / Abismo / Technicolor
CCD 79706 / May '97 / Candid

Klein, Oscar
☐ MOONGLOW
CD 021 / May '96 / Nagel Heyer

☐ TIMELESS BLUES (Klein, Oscar & Karsten Grettner/Charly Antolini)
There is no greater love / Remembering Cootie / Exactly like you / Lonely harp / Franco Nero / Timeless blues / Cute / With hot lips and sticks / Dein ist mein ganzes / New Orleans memories / Jessica / Italian blues / George's chords
CDSJP 436 / Oct '96 / Timeless

Kleinow, Pete
☐ LEGEND AND THE LEGACY, THE
Spanish harlem / My back pages-peaceful easy feeling-wheels (flying medley) / Louisiana / Silver bird / Turn, turn, turn (to everything there is a season) / Hickory wind / Love is blue / Unchained melody / Maria elena / Beat the heat / Sleepy lagoon / Love of the common people / Cannon ball rag / Oklahoma rag
CDSD 076 / May '94 / Sundown

Kleinwald, Paul
☐ FROM THE HILLS
PAUL 001CD / Mar '98 / Paul Discs

Kleive, Iver
☐ KYRIE
FXCD 142 / Jan '95 / Musikk Distribujson

Klemmer, John
☐ SIMPATICO (Klemmer, John & Oscar Castro-Neves)
Bonita / My funny valentine / What's new / Picnic / Early Autumn / Moonlight in Vermont / Simpatico
JVC 90252 / Oct '97 / JVC

Kletka Red
☐ HIJACKING
TZ 7111 / Oct '96 / Tzadik

Kletter, Dana
☐ DEAR ENEMY (Kletter, Dana & Karen)
We dies in August / Meteor mom / Father song / Directions / Your mother wants to know / Sister song / Flight into Egypt / Maria Marie / Beach song / Raisins and almonds / Anna O / Blue glass
HNCD 1420 / 6 Apr '98 / Hannibal

Klezmer Conservatory Band
☐ DANCING IN THE AISLES
Freylekh jamboree / Oy s'iz gut / Farges mikh nit / Doyne/Freylekhs / Kol rina / Gimpel the fool / Mayn freylekh lid / Miserlou / Meron nign / Slow hora/ Freylekhs / Mayn Yiddishe Meydele / Freylekh fantastique / Hopkele/Dancing in the aisles / In memoriam: Yitzhak Rabin
ROUCD 3155 / Jun '97 / Rounder

☐ JUMPIN' NIGHT IN THE GARDEN OF EDEN, A
Voliner Bulgar / Mekhuteneste mayne / Mayn rue-plats / Schlof mayn kind/Zibn firtsik / Dos freylekhe shnayderl / Pearl from Warsaw / Freylekhe kneydlekh / Bay mir bistu sheyn / Der Bosfor / A brivelle der Mamen / Shalom Louis/Mazel tov / Dos geshrey fun der vilder katshke
ROUCD 3105 / '88 / Rounder

☐ KLEZMER CONSERVATORY BAND LIVE
ROUCD 3125 / Jan '94 / Rounder

☐ OY CHANUKAH
A freylekhe nakht in gan eydn / Chanukah-chanukah, the festival of lights / Khasidm tants / Celebrating in the shtetl / Der bosfor (the bosphorus) / Jewish heroines / Dona dona / Memories of klezmorim / A yingele fun polyn / Klezmorim at chanukah / Klezzified / Shlof, mayn kind-the eternal light / Bruchas / Struggle for freedom / O ir kleyne likhtelekh / Making latkes / Fayer / Dreyd song / Dreyd song / Chanukah gelt / Abi gezunt / Great yiddish poets, oy chanukah / Oy chanukah, oy chanukah
ROUCD 3102 / Oct '88 / Rounder

☐ TASTE OF PASSOVER, A (Various Artists)
Dayenu: *NEC Jewish Music Ensemble* / Der berkher: *Bikel, Theodore & NEC Jewish Music Ensemble* / Pesah a la mano: *Berkson, Judith & Rebecca Shrimpton* / Ma nishtanah: *Koenig-Plonskier, Lauren* / Sedar plate round: *NEC Children's Choir* / Freylekhe kneydlekh: *NEC Jewish Music Ensemble* / Matzoh ball demonstration: *Segal, Chaisa* / Dayenu: *NEC Jewish Music Ensemble* / Dayenu: *Solomon, Leonard* / Mose salyo de misrayim: *Berkson, Judith & Rebecca Shrimpton* / He sent a thick darkness: *NEC Orchestra/Chorus* / Dona dona: *Bikel, Theodore & NEC Jewish Music Ensemble* / Zog maran: *Berkson, Judith* / Eliyahu hanovi: *Levine, David & NEC Chorus* / Zog nit keynmol: *Bikel, Theodore & NEC Jewish Music Ensemble* / Pischu li: *NEC Gospel Choir* / Adir hu: *Berkson, Judith & NEC Medieval Music Ensemble* / Tal: *Levine, David* / Mu asapru: *Bikel, Theodore & Rebecca Shrimpton* / Quien supiese y entendiense: *Bikel, Theodore & Rebecca Shrimpton* / Ekhod mi yodea: *Bikel, Theodore & Rebecca Shrimpton* / Khad gadya: *Levine, David & NEC Jewish Music Ensemble* / Carp in the bathtub: *Bikel, Theodore*
ROUCD 3159 / Jun '98 / Rounder

Klezmer Groove
☐ TOO LOUD FOR DINNER
OOMCD 1 / Jan '95 / Oom-Cha
MSPCD 9503 / Sep '95 / Mabley St.

Klezmer Orchestra
☐ KLEZMER SUITE
SHCD 21005 / May '95 / Shanachie

Klezmorim
☐ FIRST RECORDINGS 1976-1978
ARHCD 309 / Apr '95 / Arhoolie

☐ IS GEWIJN A FOLK
EUCD 1059 / '89 / ARC

☐ JAZZ BABIES OF THE UKRAINE - LIVE
Supreme jazz baby speaks / Kishineiver / Digga dogga doo / Circus sirba / Firen / Oy tate / Moldovanke / Kramtweiss two / Disfigured / Segment X / Chase / Bulgarian boogie / Train theme / Minnie the moocher
FF 465CD / Dec '97 / Flying Fish

☐ METROPOLIS
Constantinople / Bucharest / Tuba doina / Hot dishes / Kramtweiss steps out / Good soldier / Heyser bulgar / People's dance / Moldovanke / Shryer's doina / Wild night in Odessa / Shepherd's dream
FF 70258 / Dec '97 / Flying Fish

☐ SHALOM
EUCD 1060 / '89 / ARC

KLF
☐ CHILL OUT
Brownsville turnaround on the Tex-Mex border / Pulling out of Ricardo and the dusk is falling fast / Six hours to Louisiana, black coffee going cold / Dreamtime in Lake Jackson / Madrugada eterna / Justified and ancient seems a long time ago / Elvis on the radio, steel guitar in my soul / 3am somewhere out of Beaumont / Wichita Lineman was a song I once heard / Trancentral lost in my mind / Lights of Baton Rouge pass by / Melody from a past life keeps pulling me back / Rock radio into the nineties and beyond / Alone again with the dawn coming up
TVT 7155 / Jun '97 / TVT

☐ HISTORY OF THE JAMMS (JAMMS)
TVT 4040CD / 2 Feb '98 / TVT

Klinghagen, Goran
☐ TIME AGIN
DRCD 247 / Oct '94 / Dragon

Klingonz
☐ BEST OF THE KLINGONZ, THE
DAGCD 005 / Oct '96 / Fury

☐ BOLLOX
FCD 3030 / Apr '95 / Fury

☐ FLANGE
Clones / Clones / Knacker who lives in squalor / Shocker / If u knew / I can't help being a bastard / Dangerous haircut / Tormented and gone bad / Great balls of fire / Johnny b. goode / Rockabilly rebel / Rip it up / Rock the joint / Who stole my blue suede shoes / Cry or die / Rock this town / Psycho mansion-klingstomp mix-up / Oompa loompa / Weekend on mars
FCD 3017 / Apr '95 / Fury

☐ GHASTLY THINGS
RUMCD 013 / Aug '92 / Rumble

Klug, Roger
☐ TOXIC AND 15 OTHER LOVE SONGS
Toxic / On the way to his wedding / Nothing better / She's a singer / Baby on her mind / All hacked off (an agony in three fits) / Things change / Little thing called trust / As you lay snoring next to me / Disney eyes / Dawding daughter / Where did my girlfriend go / Porcupine / Bim bam boom / Dance of the pheromones / When we're old
MG 9002 / Oct '97 / Mental Giant

Klugh, Earl
☐ BALLADS
This time / Waltz for Debby / If you're still in love with me / April fools / Rayna / Natural thing / Waiting for Cathy / Julie / Nature boy / Dream come true / Shadow of your smile / Christina
CDP 8273262 / Feb '94 / Blue Note

☐ BEST OF EARL KLUGH VOL.1, THE
Tropical legs (Wishful thinking) / Amazon (Dream come true) / Magic in your eyes / Calypso getaway / Dr. Macumba / Long ago and far away / Angelina / Heart string / Livin' inside your love / Christina (Low ride) / Wishful thinking / I don't want to leave you alone anymore
BNZ 264 / Mar '91 / Blue Note

☐ BEST OF EARL KLUGH VOL.2, THE
Crazy for you / Night drive / Goodtime Charlie's got the blues / Cabo frio / Back in Central Park / Natural thing / Jolanta / Rainmaker / Captain Caribe / Cast your fate to the wind / I'll see you again / Right from the street
BNZ 307 / Feb '93 / Blue Note

☐ BEST OF EARL KLUGH, THE
Midnight in San Juan / Brazillian stomp / Across the sand / Maybe tonight / Last song / Rainbow man / Movin' on / Traveller / Doin' it / For the love of you / One night (alone with you) / Kissin' on the beach / Masters of suspense / Jo Ann's song / One note samba
9362469812 / 13 Jul '98 / WEA

☐ CRAZY FOR YOU
I'm ready for your love / Soft stuff (and other sweet delights) / Twinkle / Broadway ramble / Calypso getaway / Rainmaker / Ballad in A / Crazy for you
CDP 7483872 / Feb '96 / Blue Note

☐ FINGER PAINTING
Dr. Macumba / Long ago and far away / Cabo frio / Keep your eye on the sparrow / Catherine / Dance with me / Jolanta / Summer song / This time
CDP 7483862 / '95 / Blue Note

☐ JAZZ MASTERS
Back in central park / Magic in your eyes / I don't want to leave you alone anymore / NAture boy / Summer song / Jamaica farewell / Lisbon Antigua / Calypso getaway / Crazy for you / Jazz masters
4934702 / 16 Feb '98 / EMI Jazz

☐ LIVING INSIDE YOUR LOVE
Captain caribe / I heard it through the grapevine / Felicia / Living inside your love / Another time another place / April fools / Kiko
CDP 7483852 / Feb '96 / Blue Note

☐ LOVE SONGS
Heart string / Laughter in the rain / Summer song / Catherine / Balladina / Alicia / Sweet rum and starlight / Mirabella / Like a lover / I'm ready for your love / Julie / Night song
CDP 8533542 / Nov '96 / Blue Note

☐ SUDDEN BURST OF ENERGY
Happy song / I'll be waiting / By the sea / Slow boat to rio / Till the end of time / Open road / I'll be waiting (reprise) / Only you / Wiggle / Maybe tonight / Sunset island
9362458842 / Mar '96 / WEA

Kluner, Kerry
☐ LIVE AT WEST END CULTURAL CENTRE (Kluner, Kerry Big Band)
JTR 84362 / Jul '92 / Justin Time

Kluster
☐ KLOPFZEICHEN
CLP 97242 / 5 Jan '98 / Cleopatra

☐ LIVE IN VIENNA VOL.1 (Zwei Osterei)
CLP 97372 / Aug '97 / Hypnotic

☐ LIVE IN VIENNA VOL.2 (Klopzeichen)
CLP 97242 / Aug '97 / Hypnotic

Klute, Martin
☐ SWING (Klute, Martin & Mark Edwards/ Paul Cavacuiti)
TCF 1731 / Apr '96 / Top Cat

KMA Productions
☐ KLEAN KLARDS
Klean kards / Blue print / Blue kards
LOCKED 003 / 27 Apr '98 / Locked On

KMFDM
☐ ANGST
RR 89872 / Jul '94 / Roadrunner

☐ KMFDM
Meglomaniac / Stary bullet / Leid und elend / Mercy / Torture / Spit sperm / Anarchy / Down and out / Unfit / Waste
4889712 / 6 Oct '97 / Dragnet
TVT 72452 / 22 Sep '97 / TVT

☐ NIHIL
IRS 993603CD / Jan '96 / Intercord

☐ WHAT DO YOU KNOW DEUTSCHLAND
CDSAW 004 / Feb '88 / Skysaw

☐ WORLD VAIOE
SBR 032 CD / May '89 / Strike Back

Knack

☐ GET THE KNACK/BUT THE LITTLE GIRLS UNDERSTAND
Let me out / Your number or your name / Oh Tara / (She's so) selfish / Maybe tonight / Good girls don't / My Sharona / Heartbeat / Siamese twins / Lucinda / That's what the little girls do / Frustrated / Baby talks dirty / I want ya / Tell me you're mine / Mr. Handleman / Can't put a price on love / Hold on tight and don't let go / Hard way / It's you / End of the game / Feeling I get / (Havin' a) Rave up / How can love hurt so much
BGOCD 248 / Dec '94 / Beat Goes On

Knauber, Carol

☐ NOW YOU'RE TALKIN'
Away with words / Bubbles, giggles and chuckles / Swinging banana shuffle / Half time / PCL / Dangerous dreams / New day / Nr 1 funk / Casey's samba / Are you still thinking (Intro) / Now you're talkin'
101S 70592 / Nov '93 / 101 South

Knepper, Jimmy

☐ CUNNINGBIRD
SCCD 31061 / Jul '88 / Steeplechase

☐ DREAM DANCING (Knepper, Jimmy Quintet)
CRISS 1024CD / May '92 / Criss Cross

☐ I DREAM TOO MUCH (Knepper, Jimmy Sextet)
SNCD 1092 / '86 / Soul Note

☐ SPECIAL RELATIONSHIP
John's bunch / Stella by starlight / Just friends / Yardbird suite / Aristocracy of Jean Lafitte / Sophisticated lady / Lester leaps / Primrose path / What is there to say / Gnome on the range / 'Round midnight / Latterday saint
HEPCD 2012 / Mar '94 / Hep

Knickerbockers

☐ DRIVING RHYTHM GUITARS, WILD SOLOS...
Lies / One track mind / I can do it better / Just one girl / I must be doing something right / Chuck Berry medley / High on love / Stick with me / Love is a bird / I love / They ran for their lives / My feet are off the ground / She said goodbye / You're bad / What does that make you / Rumours, gossip, words untrue / Comin' generation / Can't you see I'm trying / Sweet green fields / Give a little bit / Guaranteed satisfaction / Little children
CDWIKD 122 / Jan '94 / Big Beat

☐ KNICKERBOCKERISM (2CD Set)
Lies / Just one girl / I can do it better / Come on and let me / One track mind / I must be doing something right / Can't you see I'm tryin' / Please don't fight it / She said goodbye / Give a little bit / We got a good thing goin' / Is that what you want / Pad and how to use it / Playgirl / Like little children / Bite bite barracuda / Lies / Harlem nocturne / Stick with me / High on love / Rumours gossip words untrue / Love is a bird / She's gotten to me / I love / Chapel in the fields / Can you help me / Please don't love him / You're bad / Guaranteed satisfaction / Sweet green fields / What does that make you / As a matter of fact / My feet are off the ground / They ran for their lives / Come and get it / High on love
SC 11040 / Aug '97 / Sundazed

Knight, Beverley

☐ B FUNK, THE
B-funk / Moving on up / Mutual feeling / Flava of the old school / Remedy / Down for the one / Steppin' on my shoes / Promise you forever / It's your time / So happy / Cast all your cares / U've got it / In time / Goodbye innocence
DOMECD 6 / Oct '95 / Dome

☐ PRODIGAL SISTA
Made it back / Rewind (find a way) / Damn / That's alright / Awol / Sista sista / Strong hand / Greatest day / Tomorrow / Send me move me love me / Need of you / Good morning world
4962962 / 24 Aug '98 / Rhythm Series

Knight, Brian

☐ BLUE EYED SLIDE (Featuring Laurence Scott)
Pretty flower / Moving down country / Back porch / Friend in need / Wind against the trees / Trouble in mind / Take this hammer / Big road / Waiting for a train / I'm ready / How I feel / Hush puppy baby / Wee midnight hour
LMCD 022 / Dec '94 / Lost Moment

☐ FILE UNDER BLUES
CDEC 3 / Dec '94 / Blooze

Knight, Cheri

☐ KNITTER, THE
Knitter / Megalith / Down by the water / Light in the road / Last barn dance / Wishing well / That I might see / Waiting for Sara / Spellbound / Paper wings / Very last time
ESD 81122 / Jul '96 / East Side Digital

Knight, Chris

☐ CHRIS KNIGHT
UMD 80466 / 23 Feb '98 / Universal

Knight, Curtis

☐ LIVE IN EUROPE
858817 / '90 / SPV

Knight, Frederick

☐ I'VE BEEN LONELY FOR SO LONG
I've been lonely for so long / This is my song of love to you / Take me on home witcha / Friend / I let my chance go by / Your love's all over me / Pick 'um up, put 'um down / Now that I've found you / Lean on me / Trouble / Someday we'll be together
CDSXE 099 / Nov '93 / Stax

Knight, Gladys

☐ 2ND ANNIVERSARY/PIPE DREAMS (Knight, Gladys & The Pips)
Money / Street brother / Part time love / At every end there's a beginning / Georgia on my mind / You and me against the world / Where do I put his memory / Summer sun / Feel like makin' love / So sad the song / Alaskan pipeline / Pot of Jazz / I'll miss you / Nobody but you / Pipe dreams / Everybody's got to find a way / I will follow my dream
NEXCD 236 / Mar '93 / Sequel

☐ BEST OF GLADYS KNIGHT & THE PIPS 1980-1985, THE (Knight, Gladys & The Pips)
Licence to kill / Taste of bitter love / Bourgie bourgie / Love overboard / I will fight / My time / Landlord / Baby don't change your mind / Come back and finish what you started / Nobody but you / Part time love / One and only / Midnight train to Georgia / Wind beneath my wings / Try to remember (the way we were) / Best thing that ever happened to me
4720382 / '93 / Sony Music

☐ COLLECTION, THE (Knight, Gladys & The Pips)
Every beat of my heart / Letter full of tears / Lovers always forgive / Operator / Come see about me / Love like mine / Room in your heart / Before now and after then / You broke your promise / It hurts so bad / Either way I loose / Queen of tears / Get a hold of yourself / Guess who / Really didn't mean it / How do you say goodbye / I can't stand by / I want that kind of love / If ever I should fall in love / Linda / Love me again / One more lonely night / Running around / What shall I do
COL 058 / Feb '95 / Collection

☐ GLADYS KNIGHT
LECD 048 / May '94 / Dynamite

☐ GLADYS KNIGHT & THE PIPS (Knight, Gladys & The Pips)
Every beat of my heart / Room in your heart / Guess who / Letter full of tears / You broke your promise / Operator / Goodnight my love / Love me again / Come see about me / One more lonely night / I really didn't mean it / Stay away / Get a hold of yourself / Jungle love / Running around / If ever I should fall in love / I want that kind of love / I can't stand by / What shall I do / Trust in you
QED 055 / Nov '96 / Tring

☐ GREATEST HITS
Midnight train to Georgia / I've got to use my imagination / Best thing that ever happened to me / So sad the song / Come back and finish what you started / I feel a song in my heart / Love finds its own way / Baby don't change your mind / Part time love / Make yours a happy home / Nobody but you / Where peaceful waters flow / It's a better than good time / One and only / Home is where the heart face / On and on / Money / Way we were / Try to remember
74321556052 / 26 Jan '98 / Camden

☐ HIT SINGLE COLLECTABLES (Knight, Gladys & The Pips)
DISK 4506 / Apr '94 / Disky

☐ SINGLES ALBUM, THE (Knight, Gladys & The Pips)
Licence to kill / Help me make it through the night / Best thing that ever happened to me / Baby don't change your mind / Bourgie bourgie / Taste of bitter love / One and only / Just walk in my shoes / Midnight train to Georgia / Try to remember / Look of love / Part time love / Come back and finish what you started / So sad the song / Take me in your arms and love me / Love overboard / Lovin' on next to nothin' / Neither one of us
8420032 / Oct '89 / PolyGram TV

☐ THAT SPECIAL TIME OF YEAR (Knight, Gladys & The Pips)
That special time of year / Jingle bells / What are you doing New Year's Eve / This Christmas / Santa Claus is coming to town / It's the happiest time of the year / I believe / When a child is born / Lord's prayer / Let there be peace on earth (let it begin with me)
4891882 / 10 Nov '97 / Columbia

☐ ULTIMATE COLLECTION (Knight, Gladys & The Pips)
5308262 / 10 Aug '98 / Motown

☐ ULTIMATE COLLECTION, THE (Knight, Gladys & The Pips)
472122 / May '96 / Flarenasch

☐ VERY BEST OF GLADYS KNIGHT, THE
TRTCD 132 / Feb '96 / TrueTrax

☐ WAY WE WERE, THE (Knight, Gladys & The Pips)
Midnight train to Georgia / So sad the song / Baby don't change your mind / Home is where the heart is / Nobody but you / I feel a song (in my heart) / Feel like makin' love / Hold on / Little bit of love / Try to remember (the way we were) / Come back and finish what you started / Part time love / It's a better than good time / Georgia on my mind / Make yours a happy home / Best thing that ever happened to me / We don't make each other laugh anymore / Sorry doesn't always make it right
MCCD 005 / Feb '91 / Music Club

Knight, Peter

☐ NUMBER ONE (Knight, Peter & Danny Thompson)
Number 1 / Number 2
RES 108CD / Apr '97 / Resurgence

Knights

☐ KNIGHTS, THE
FLASH 66 / 1 Jun '98 / Flash

Knights Of The Occasional Table

☐ KNEES UP MOTHER EARTH
FUCD 1 / Mar '95 / Middle Earth

☐ LES ELEPHANTS DU PARADIS
MIDDL 5CD / Sep '96 / Middle Earth

☐ PLANET SWEET, THE
MIDDL 2CD / Jul '95 / Middle Earth

Knochengirl

☐ KNOCHEN=GIRL
EFA 127232 / Apr '95 / Fidel Bastro

Knopfler, Mark

☐ GOLDEN HEART
Darling pretty / Imelda / Golden heart / No can do / Vic and Ray / Don't you get it / Night in summer long ago / Cannibals / I'm the fool / Je suis desole / Ridiger / Nobody's got the gun / Done with Bonaparte / Are we in trouble now
5147322 / Mar '96 / Vertigo

☐ WAG THE DOG
Wag the dog / Working on it / In the heartland / Americna hero / Just instinct / Stretching out / Drooling national / We're going to war
5368642 / 19 Jan '98 / Vertigo

Knowles, Chris

☐ FRAME OF HARMONY
FH 0010CD / Apr '95 / Brenin

Knox, Buddy

☐ PARTY DOLL
Party doll / Rock your little baby to sleep / Somebody touched me / Lovey dovey / I think I'm gonna kill myself / Rock house / Devil woman / Ling ting tong / Maybelline / Travelin' light / Hula love / I washed my hands in muddy water / Storm clouds / I'm lookin' for someone to love / Restless / Blue levi jeans / Honky tonk man / Ooby dooby / Nebraska sunrise / Hole in the ground / Little ditty baby / Going to hollywood / Too much fun / Knock-kneed nellie / Back to new orleans / Bip bop boom / Hambone / Lotta lovin' / Kokomo island / Long lonely nights / Sweet country music / I named my little girl holly
RSRCD 004 / Apr '94 / Rockstar

Knuckledust

☐ SMASH TRADITION (Knuckledust/ Indecision)
HAUS 014CD / 18 May '98 / Household Name

Knuckles, Frankie

☐ WELCOME TO THE REAL WORLD (Knuckles, Frankie & Adeva)
Fanfare / Welcome to the real world / Too many fish / Love can change it / Keep it real / You're number one (in my book) / Passion and pain / What am I missin' / Whadda U want / Tell me why / Walkin' / Tribute / Reprise
CDVUS 82 / May '95 / Virgin

Knudsen, Hans

☐ LIVE - JUMP IN FOCUS (Knudsen, Hans Jump Band)
MECCACD 2035 / Oct '97 / Music Mecca

Knudsen, Kenneth

☐ COMPACKED
MECCACD 1008 / Nov '94 / Music Mecca

☐ I ME HIM
MECCACD 1007 / Nov '94 / Music Mecca

Knutsson, Jonas

☐ FLOWER IN THE SKY
Syskonoga / Polska efter per Johan Arnstrom, Vihelmina / Norrland / Polska efter Pekkos per, bingsjo / Take off / Hymn / Polsquette, grotesque, saquette / Vyer / Rod avgang / Flower in the sky / Arktis
92482 / Mar '97 / Act

☐ VIEWS
1426 / Jan '89 / Caprice

Kocani Orkester

☐ L'ORIENT EST ROUGE
CRAW 19 / 23 Feb '98 / Cramworld

Koch, Hans

☐ CHOCKSHUT
INTAKTCD 031 / Oct '94 / Intakt

☐ HEAVY CAIRO TRAFFIC (Koch, Hans & Martin Schutz/Fredy Studer)
Alaschaan aref albi ma 'ak / Makana / Tulli men el maschkabeia / 18, Maamal el sokar / Nightclubbing with Haschepsut / Qissa / Heavy Cairo traffic / El ghalla ghalletna / Malaib schiha / Belly button rave / Vice versa / Nubian bonus track
INT 31752 / Apr '97 / Intuition

Kochalka, James 'Superstar'

☐ MONKEY VS. ROBOT
TQ 018 / 29 Dec '97 / Tarquin

Koda, Cub

☐ JOINT WAS ROCKIN', THE (Koda, Cub & The Houserockers)
DELD 3015 / Oct '96 / Deluge

Kode IV

☐ BEST OF KODE IV
KK 149CD / Mar '96 / KK

☐ INSANE
Accelerate / Insane / Fear into power / Success / Interview / Hollywood / Electrostatisch / Disobey / Antichrist / Fight / Truth
KK 078CD / Jun '92 / KK

☐ POSSESSED
KK 052CD / Sep '90 / KK

☐ SILICON CIVILISATION
KK 109CD / Feb '95 / KK

Kodo

☐ BEST OF KODO, THE
4758732 / 10 Aug '98 / Columbia

☐ BLESSING OF THE EARTH
Zoku / Kariuta / Chonlima / Issen/oasis / Hanano / Yatai-bayashi / Ryogen-no-hi
4666302 / 10 Aug '98 / Columbia

☐ IBUKI
4899402 / 10 Aug '98 / Columbia

☐ LIVE AT THE ACROPOLIS ATHENS GREECE
4838562 / 10 Aug '98 / Columbia

Koenig, Brian

☐ WAKE UP (Koenig, Brian & The Standback Blues Band)
BLUELOONCD 027 / Jul '95 / Blue Loon

Koenig, Michael

☐ ACOUSMATRIX VOL.1 & 2 (2CD Set)
BHVAASTCD 9001/2 / Jan '92 / Bvhaast

Koerner, John

☐ BLUES, RAGS AND HOLLERS (Koerner, Ray & Glover)
RHRCD 76 / Jul '95 / Red House

☐ RAISED BY HUMANS
RHRCD 44 / Oct '95 / Red House

☐ STARGEEZER (Koerner, 'Spider' John)
RHRCD 84 / Jun '96 / Red House

Kofi

☐ FRIDAY'S CHILD
ARICD 064 / Dec '94 / Ariwa Sounds

☐ VERY REGGAE CHRISTMAS, A
Little drummer boy / Deck the halls / First noel/ Christmas song / We three kings / Hark the herald angels sing / What child is this / God rest ye merry gentlemen / O little town of Bethlehem / Silent night
7567827132 / Nov '94 / Atlantic

☐ WISHING WELL
ARICD 092 / Jan '94 / Ariwa Sounds

Koga, Miyuki

☐ DREAMIN'
My buddy / Do do do / I surrender dear / I don't know why / Blues serenade/Serenade in blue / Isn't it a lovely day / Put the blame on mame / When my sugar walks down the street / You made me love you / My melancholy baby / S'posin' / I know that you know / Let me sing and I'm happy
CCD 4588 / Feb '94 / Concord Jazz

Koglmann, Franz

☐ ABOUT YESTERDAY'S EZZTHETICS
ARTCD 6003 / Jul '88 / Hat Art

☐ CANTOS I-IV
ARTCD 6123 / Jan '94 / Hat Art

☐ L'HEURE BLEUE
ARTCD 6093 / Jan '92 / Hat Art

☐ SCHLAF SCHLEMMER, SCHLAF MAGRITTE
ARTCD 6108 / Sep '92 / Hat Art

Kohler, Wolfgang

☐ FACES (Kohler, Wolfgang Quintet)
Faces / Night has a thousand eyes / Now you know / I wished on the moon / Sketchbook / Call Paul / Mellow samba / Too much sunshine / 55/44
AL 73132 / Jun '98 / A

Koita, Oumar

☐ BAMBE KA SO
BLVD 1529 / Aug '96 / Boulevard

Koite, Habibe

☐ MUSO KO (Koite, Habibe & Bamada)
I ka barra / Muso ku / Den ko / Nanale / Fatma / Sira bulu / Ninajo / Cigarette a bana / Din din wo / Kunfe ta / Koulandian
612501 / Jul '96 / Wotre Music
MRCD 187 / Jul '97 / Munich

Kokelaere, Francois

☐ PERCUSSIONS
926952 / 5 Jan '98 / BUDA

Koken, Walt

☐ BANJONIQUE
ROUCD 0337 / Oct '94 / Rounder

☐ HEI-WA HOEDOWN
ROUCD 0367 / Nov '95 / Rounder

Koko

☐ BALFONS & AFRICAN DRUMS VOL.2 (Music From Bakino Faso)
PS 65101 / Apr '93 / PlayaSound

Kokotos, Linos

☐ SEA CLOVER
ML 0104 / 11 May '98 / Musurgia Graeca

Kokubu, Hiroko

☐ BRIDGE
Catalina Island / Rudy's dream / Bridge over troubled water / Lullaby of Takeda / Essence / Lettin' go / Keep hope alive / Baked potato man / Innocence of Spring / Our story / Pranzinzzetta
JVC 90262 / Oct '97 / JVC

☐ MORE THAN YOU KNOW
Night affair / Barcarolle / Shadow puppet / Rain dance / Lady moonlight / From shade to sunlight / What's a special evening without a little magic / I'll be with you, sometime / Great escape / Alone again
JD 3312 / Oct '88 / JVC

☐ PURE HEART
Barefoot steppin' / Luck in the rain / Smooth struttin' / Vitamina / Once and forever / Mrs. Robinson / Annabella / Weekend / It's cool / Happiest for you (for your wedding)
JVC 20422 / Mar '95 / JVC

Kol Aviv

☐ CHANTS ET DANSES D'ISRAEL
Mah tovu / El bodim kala / Suite yemenite / Ai dididdai / Bein h'har prat oumh'ar h'idekal / Hine ma tov / Chibolet basadle / Suite h'assidique / Chnei h'alilim / Ke chochana / El ginat egoz / Debka rafah / Leorh'i oukhekh / Rikoud harabbi / Debka druze / Debka kafrit / Chir Hanokdim / Im houpalnou-chevat ne'purim
ARN 64033 / '88 / Arion

Kolinda

☐ IL JU HARAMIA
199722 / Oct '93 / Hexagone

☐ OSZ
669832 / Sep '96 / Melodie

Koloc, Bonnie

☐ WITH YOU ON MY SIDE
FF 70437 / Nov '94 / Flying Fish

Kolyma

☐ SONGS OF NATURE AND ANIMALS
925662 / Aug '93 / BUDA

Komariah, Euis

☐ JAIPONGAN JAVA (Komariah, Euis & Jugala Orchestra)
Engalkeun / Bulan sapasi / Bardin / Toka toka / Seunggah / Teuteup abdi / Sinden beken / Daun pulus
CDORB 057 / Apr '90 / Globestyle

☐ SOUND OF SUNDA, THE (Komariah, Euis & Yus Wiradiredja)
Sorban palid / Salam sono / Asa tos tepang / Bulan sapasi / Campaka kambar / Duh leung / Ramalan asih / Pengkolan / Dalingding asih
CDORB 060 / Jul '90 / Globestyle

Komeda

☐ GENIUS OF KOMEDA, THE
NONS 262 / Mar '97 / Nons

☐ WHAT MAKES IT GO
Binario / It's alright baby / Curious / Cul de sac / Living things / Flabbergast / Campfire / Happyment / Our hospitality / Focus / Simple formality
NONSCD 65 / 4 May '98 / North Of No South

Komeda, Krzysztof

☐ BREAKFAST AT TIFFANY'S/BALLET ETUDES (Various Artists)
PB 00155 / Jun '98 / Power Bros.

☐ CRAZY GIRL
PB 00145 / Apr '97 / Power Bros.

☐ MEMORY OF BACH
PB 00157 / Aug '98 / Power Bros.

☐ MOJA BALLADA
PB 00161 / Aug '98 / Power Bros.

☐ NIGHTIME DAYTIME REQUIEM
PB 00159 / Aug '98 / Power Bros.

Komputer

☐ WORLD OF TOMORROW, THE
World of tomorrow / More automation / Bill Gates / Valentena / Looking down on London / Terminus interminus / Singapore / Perfect pop band / Komputer pop / Motopia / We are komputer
CDSTUMM 162 / 1 Jun '98 / Mute

Kondo, Toshinori

☐ THIS, THAT AND THE OTHER
BASIC 50007 / Jul '96 / ITM

Kondole

☐ PSYCHIC
TOPY 046CD / Dec '89 / Temple

Kone, Aicha

☐ MANDINGO LIVE FROM COTE D'IVORIE
SM 15142 / Sep '93 / Wergo

Koner, Thomas

☐ KAAMOS
EFA 006992 / 14 Apr '98 / Mille Plateau

☐ TEIMO/PERMAFROST (2CD Set)
EFA 006852 / Feb '97 / Mille Plateau

Kong

☐ EARMINED
RR 88122 / Jun '97 / Roadrunner

☐ MULTIPOETVOCALISER
Hok / Fair / P.r.o.k.o.v. / 214 / 200 max / 7\8 / Cramp / Quiet / Cows / Base / Hop
CDKTB 1 / Aug '95 / Dreamtime

☐ PUSH COMES TO SHOVE
CDKTB 17 / Feb '95 / Dreamtime

Kongos, John

☐ KONGOS
REP 4662 / 24 Nov '97 / Repertoire

☐ TOKOLOSHE MAN...PLUS
Jubilee cloud / Gold / Lift me from the ground / Tomorrow I'll go / Can someone please direct me back to Earth / Try to touch just one / Weekend lady / I would have had a good time / Come on down Jesus / Sometimes it's not enough / He's gonna step on you again / Great white lady / Higher than God's hat / Ride the lightning / Tokoloshe man
SEECD 221 / 8 Jun '98 / See For Miles

Konig, Klaus

☐ HEART PROJECT, THE
You bet / Men at work / Does money matter / Reality check / Sweet smell of success / Buy one get one free / Turn the tables / Good to know
ENJ 93382 / 24 Aug '98 / Enja

REVIEWS
Sniffing attitudes / Harry laughs / Who's that guy / Mission to the stars / Multiple choice / Matter of taste / Tuba boons / Harry laughs still / Black polo-necks / Avantgarde noise pollution / Who would have thought that / Day after
ENJ 900612 / Jul '96 / Enja

Konitz, Lee

☐ 12 GERSHWIN IN 12 KEYS (Konitz, Lee & D'Andrea, Franco)
W 3122 / Aug '92 / Philology

☐ ALONE TOGETHER (Konitz, Lee & Haden Mehldau)
Alone together / Song is you / Cherokee / What is this thing called love / 'Round love / You stepped out of a dream
8571502 / 3 Nov '97 / Blue Note

☐ CHICAGO AND ALL THAT JAZZ
My own best friend / Razzle dazzle / Loopin' de loop / Funny honey / Class / Me and my baby / Roxie / Ten percent
CDC 7971 / Nov '90 / LRC
17089 / Jan '97 / Laserlight

☐ COMPLETE MOTION (3CD Set)
I remember you / All of me / Foolin' myself / You'd be so nice to come home to / I'll remember April / You don't know what love is / These foolish things / Out of nowhere / It's you or no one / I remember you / You don't know what love is / It's all right with me / Foolin' myself / Just friends / It's you or no one / Out of nowhere / My melancholy baby / Imagination / That old feeling / I'm gettin' sentimental over you / Pennies from heaven / I'll remember April / All the things you are / Indiana / Alone together / Embraceable you / There will never be another you / What's new / Everything happens to me / Sweet and lovely / You'd be so nice to come home to / Lullaby of the leaves
5571072 / 20 Apr '98 / Verve

☐ DEARLY BELOVED (Konitz, Lee Quartet)
SCCD 31406 / Apr '97 / Steeplechase

☐ DIALOGUES (Konitz, Lee & Bert Van Den Brink)
East of the sun / Yesterdays / Kojo no Tsuki / Spring fever / Thingin' / If you could see me now / Dialogue / I love you / Moonlight in Vermont / Lover man / Cherokee
CHR 70053 / Jun '98 / Challenge

☐ DIG DUG DOG
Solar / Ruby my dear / Thingin' / I love you / You don't know what love is / Sister cheryl / Mr.88 / 88 / As time goes by / Body and soul / Gee baby ain't I good to you / I got it bad and that ain't good
4888312 / 3 Nov '97 / Sony Jazz

☐ FIGURE AND SPIRIT (Konitz, Lee Quintet)
PCD 7003 / Oct '91 / Progressive

☐ FREE WITH LEE
W 622 / Dec '95 / Philology

☐ FRIENDS
DRCD 240 / Feb '94 / Dragon

☐ FROM NEWPORT TO NICE
CD 214 W652 / May '92 / Philology

☐ I CONCENTRATE ON YOU
SCCD 31018 / Jul '88 / Steeplechase

☐ IDEAL SCENE
1211192 / ' / Soul Note

☐ IN HARVARD SQUARE
BLCD 760928 / May '97 / Black Lion

☐ JAZZ AT STORYVILLE
BLCD 760901 / Jun '88 / Black Lion

☐ JAZZ NOCTURNE
You'd be so nice to come home to / Everything happens to me / Alone together / Misty / Body and soul / My funny valentine / In a sentimental mood
ECD 220852 / Jun '94 / Evidence

☐ KONITZ
Bop goes the leesel / Easy livin' / Mean to me / I'll remember April / Skylark / Nursery rhyme / Limehouse blues
BL 760922 / Oct '93 / Black Lion

☐ KONITZ MEETS MULLIGAN (Konitz, Lee & Gerry Mulligan)
Too marvellous for words / Lover man / I'll remember April / These foolish things / All the things you are / Bernie's tune / Almost like being in love / Sextet / Broadway / I can't believe that you're in love with me / Oh lady be good / Oh lady be good
CDP 7851082 / Mar '95 / Blue Note

☐ L'AGE MUR (Konitz, Lee & Enrico Rava Quartet)
CD214W 1232 / May '98 / Philology

☐ LEE KONITZ MEETS JIMMY GIUFFRE (2CD Set) (Konitz, Lee & Jimmy Giuffre)
5277802 / Jan '97 / Verve

☐ LEE KONITZ NONET, THE (Konitz, Lee Nonet)
Fanfare / Chi chi / If you could see me now / Sometimes I'm happy / Giant steps / April/April too / Who you / Stryker's dues / Fourth dimension / Struttin' with some barbecue / Hymn too / Jazzspeak
CRD 186 / 8 Nov '97 / Chiaroscuro

LIVE AT LAREN
April / Who you / Without a song / Moon dreams / Times lie / Matrix
SNCD 1069 / '86 / Soul Note

☐ LIVE AT THE HALF NOTE
5216592 / Nov '94 / Verve

☐ LIVE IN EUROPE
COD 031 / Jul '92 / Jazz View

☐ LULLABY OF BIRDLAND (Konitz, Lee Quartet)
Lullaby of Birdland / This is always / Anthropology / Ask me know / East of the sun / Cherokee / 'Round midnight / Song is you
CCD 79709 / Feb '97 / Candid

☐ LUNASEA (Konitz, Lee & Peggy Stern)
1212492 / Sep '92 / Soul Note

☐ ONCE UPON A LINE (Konitz, Lee & Harold Danko)
500162 / Nov '93 / Musidisc

☐ OUT OF NOWHERE (Konitz, Lee & Paul Bley)
SCCD 31427 / 5 Jan '98 / Steeplechase

☐ PORTRAIT OF LEE KONITZ, A
JC 98006 / 15 Jun '98 / Jazz Classix

☐ RICHLEE (Konitz, Lee & Rich Perry)
SCCD 31440 / 1 Jun '98 / Steeplechase

☐ SATORI
Just friends / On Green Dolphin Street / Satori / Sometime ago / What's new / Hymn / Free blues
OJCCD 958 / 26 Jan '98 / Original Jazz Classics

☐ SAXOPHONE DREAMS
369002 / May '98 / Koch Jazz

☐ SPEAKIN' LOW (Konitz, Lee & R. Sellani)
W 712CD / Jul '94 / Philology

☐ STAR EYES (Konitz, Lee & Martial Solal)
HATOLOGY 518 / Jun '98 / Hatology

☐ STRINGS FOR HOLIDAY (Tribute To Billie Holiday)
But beautiful / I cried for you / Lover man / All of me / Good morning heartache / For heaven's sake / Easy living / These foolish things / For all we know
ENJ 93042 / Jul '96 / Enja

☐ SUBCONSCIOUS LEE
Progression / Tautology / Retrospection / Judy / Subconscious lee / Marshmallow / Fishin' around / Tautology / Sound lee / Rebecca / You go to my head / Ice cream Konitz / Palo alto
OJCCD 186 / Nov '95 / Original Jazz Classics

☐ TENORLEE
I remember you / Skylark / Thanks for the memory / You are too beautiful / Handful of stars / Autumn nocturne / Tangerine / Tenorlee / Lady be good / Gypsy / Tis autumn
CHCD 71019 / Mar '97 / Candid

☐ THINGIN (Konitz, Lee & Don Friedman/ Attila Zoller)
ARTCD 6174 / Feb '96 / Hat Art

☐ UNACCOMPANIED (Live In Yokohama)
PSFD 83 / May '97 / PSF

☐ VENEZIA, A (Konitz, Lee & Il Suono Improvviso)
W 532 / Nov '93 / Philology

☐ WHERE'S THE BLUES (Konitz, Lee & Mario Rusca)
Where's the blues / Beautiful love / Thingin' / Summertime / To Lee or not to Lee / On Green Dolphin Street / Autumn leaves / Anthropology / Have you met Miss Jones / I should care
CD 55303 / Dec '97 / Giants Of Jazz

☐ WILD AS SPRINGTIME
Ezz-thetic / Hairy canary / She's as wild as Springtime / Duende / It's you / Prelude no.20 / Spinning waltz / Silly samba / Hi Beck / KO / Hairy canary / Ezz-thetic
CCD 79734 / May '97 / Candid

☐ ZOUNDS (Konitz, Lee Quartet)
1212192 / Mar '92 / Soul Note

Konkhra

☐ LIVE ERASER
PCD 031 / Jul '96 / Progress

☐ SEXUAL AFFECTIVE DISORDER
NB 105CD / Mar '94 / Nuclear Blast

☐ SPIT OR SWALLOW
PCD 019 / Sep '95 / Lost & Found

☐ STRANDED
CD 7913002 / Jun '93 / Progress Red

☐ WEED OUT THE WEAK
PCD 044 / 13 Apr '98 / Diehard

Konstruktivists

☐ FORBIDDEN
OGPU 002CD / Oct '96 / Ogpu

☐ KONSTRUKTIVISTS LIVE
OGPU 001CD / Oct '96 / Ogpu

Konte, Dembo

☐ JALIOLOGY (Konte, Dembo & Kausu Kuyateh)
XENO 4036CD / Jun '95 / Xenophile

☐ KAIRABA JABI (Konte, Dembo & Kausu Kuyateh)
WEBE 9032 / Jun '98 / Weekend Beatnik

Konte, Lamine

☐ SONGS OF THE GRIOTS
VICG 50082 / Mar '96 / JVC World Library

Koobas

☐ BARRICADES
ESSEX 1004CD / 5 Jan '98 / Essex

Kooky Scientist

☐ UNPOPULAR SCIENCE
PLUS 8064CD / Jun '97 / Plus 8

Kool & The Gang

☐ ALL THE BEST
CURCD 58 / 24 Aug '98 / Curb

☐ BEST OF KOOL & THE GANG 1969-1976, THE
Funky stuff / Who's gonna take the weight / Rhyme tyme people / Hollywood swinging / Love the life you live / Give it up / Chocolate buttermilk / Jungle boogie / Let the music take your mind / Open sesame / Kool it (here comes the fuzz) / Summer madness / NT / Pneumonia / Love and understanding / Spirit of the boogie
5148222 / Jun '93 / Mercury

☐ COLLECTION, THE
Celebration / Ladies night / Victory / Big fun / Take it to the top / If you feel like dancin' / Tonight's the night / Street kids / Place for us / Hi de hi, ho de ho / Take my heart (you can have it if you want it) / Funky stuff / I sweat / Surrender / Think it over / Just friends / Fresh / Cherish
5516352 / Mar '96 / Spectrum

☐ DANCE COLLECTION
Celebration / Get down on it / Let's go dancin' (ooh la la la) / Big fun / Ladies night / Take my heart (you can have it if you want it) / In the heart / Straight ahead / Hi de hi, hi de ho / Steppin' out / Good time tonight / Fresh / Peacemaker / Emergency / Victory
8425202 / Aug '90 / Mercury

☐ GREAT AND REMIXED '91
8486042 / Jul '91 / Mercury

☐ GREATEST HITS LIVE
74321400632 / Oct '96 / Milan

☐ KOOL & THE GANG
GFS 067 / Jul '97 / Going For A Song

☐ KOOL AND THE GANG
Tonight / Emergency / Victory / Take my heart (you can have it if you want it) / Joanna / Cherish / Too hot / Unite / Ladies night / Fresh / Get down on it / Celebration / Ooh la la la (let's go dancin') / Hollywood swinging
12607 / Oct '95 / Laserlight

☐ NIGHT PEOPLE
Get down on it / Stand up and sing / Hangin' out / Morning star / Love and understanding / Be my lady / Caribbean festival / Emergency / Never give up / Good time tonight / Home is where the heart is / All she really wants to do is dance / September love / Night people
5501982 / Aug '94 / Spectrum

☐ STATE OF AFFAIRS
CURCD 21 / Jun '96 / Curb

☐ TOO HOT - LIVE HITS EXPERIENCE
Victory / Ladies night / Fresh / Take my heart / Hollywood swinging / Too hot / Joanna / Cherish / Ohh la la la (let's go dancing) / Get down on it / Celebration / Tonight / Emergency
EMPRCD 657 / Jun '96 / Emporio

☐ UNITE
(Jump up on the) Rhythm and ride / I think I love you / Love comes down / Sexy Miss / Better late than never / Heart / My search is over / Summer / Brown / Give right now / Weight / Show us the way / Unite / God will find you
74321446152 / Mar '97 / Milan

☐ UNITE
ST 5010 / Apr '95 / Star Collection

Kool Ace

☐ MACKATHERMASTATICZXONE
MRR 4212CD / Aug '95 / Ichiban

Kool G Rap

☐ 456
Blowin' up in the wind / Fast life / Ghetto knows / It's a shame / Money on my brain / Intro / 4, 5, 6 / It's a shame / Take 'em to war / Executioner style / For da brothaz
4814722 / Oct '95 / Epic

Koop

☐ SON OF KOOP
CDCOL 10002 / 15 Jun '98 / Universal

Kooper, Al

☐ REKOOPERATION
Downtime / After the lights go down low / When the spell is broken / How am I ever gonna get over you / Sneakin' round the barnyard / Soul twist-ed / Looking for clues / Honky tonk / Clean up woman / Don't be cruel / Alvino Johnson's shuffle / Johnny B Goode / I wanna little girl
8444002 / May '94 / Limelight

☐ SOUL OF A MAN (2CD Set)
MM 65113 / Jan '97 / Music Masters

☐ SUPERSESSION (Kooper, Al/Mike Bloomfield/Stephen Stills)
Alberts shuffle / Stop / Man's temptation / His holy modal majesty / Really / It takes a lot to laugh, it takes a train to cry / Season of the witch / You don't love me / Harvey's tune
CK 64608 / Jul '95 / Columbia

Kopinski, Jan

☐ GHOST MUSIC
Cemetry / House / Spahetti traffic / Slow zawsze / Station / Pool of bells / Egg ceremony / Roundfield / Spook / Station east / Marble day dream
ASCCD 19 / 9 Mar '98 / ASC

Koppes, Peter

☐ LOVE ERA/IRONY
IMM 001CD / 12 Jan '98 / Immersion

☐ WATER RITES
WW 1 / 12 Jan '98 / Worldwater

Koral, Rob

☐ WAS IT SOMETHING YOU SAID (Koral, Rob & Sue Hawker)
Yesterday's / Polka dots and moonbeams / Dance with me / Little piece of heaven / 500 Miles high / Her ways / Remember this / Horizons / I could write a book / Stay away / Crazy Sunday / Waiting for Norman / Lies / He's funny that way / I need your love so bad / Just the way things are / Was it something you said / Perdido
CHECD 00112 / Jul '95 / Master Mix

Koray, Erkin

☐ ERKIN KORAY
CD 002 / 15 Dec '97 / Istanbulplak

Korb, Kristin

☐ INTRODUCING KRISTIN KORB WITH THE RAY BROWN TRIO (Korb, Kristin & Ray Brown Trio)
Night in Tunisia / Peel me a grape / Whirlybird fever / Straight no chaser / Black Orpheus / Yeh yeh / Ain't misbehavin' / These foolish things / Funky tune for Ray / Take the 'A' train
CD 83386 / Oct '96 / Telarc

Korgis

☐ BEST OF THE KORGIS, THE
472136 / May '96 / Flarenasch

☐ KORGI'S ARCHIVE
Everybody's got to learn sometime / If I had you / All the love in the world / I just can't help it / If it's alright with you / That was my big mistake / Domestic bliss / O Maxine / Don't say that it's over / Drawn and quartered / It's no good unless you love me / Rovers return / Sticky George / Can't we be friends / Foolishness of love / Nowhere to run / Dumb waiters / Perfect hostess / Love ain't too far away / Living on the rocks
RMCD 213 / Nov '97 / Rialto

Korn

☐ KORN
Blind / Ball tongue / Need to / Clown / Divine / Faget / Shoots and ladders / Predictable / Fake / Lies / Helmet in the bush / Daddy
4780802 / Nov '95 / Epic

☐ LIFE IS PEACHY
Twist / Chi / Lost / Swallow / Porno creep / Good God / Mr. Rogers / K@#0%# / No place to Hi / Wicked / Adidas / Lowrider / Ass itch / Kill you / Twist (acapella)
4853692 / Oct '96 / Epic

Korn, Paddy

☐ BACK BEAT INSPIRED (Korn, Paddy & White Bread)
CDST 02 / Nov '95 / Stumble

Korner, Alexis

☐ ALEXIS KORNER MEMORIAL CONCERT VOL.1 (Various Artists)
IGOCD 2050 / Dec '95 / Indigo

☐ ALEXIS KORNER MEMORIAL CONCERT VOL.2 (Various Artists)
IGOCD 2051 / Dec '95 / Indigo

☐ ALEXIS KORNER'S BLUES INCORPORATED...PLUS (Korner, Alexis & Blues Incorporated)
Blue mink / Rainy Tuesday / Sappho / Preachin' the blues / Royal dooji / Captain's tiger / Anything for now / Little bit groovy / Chris Trundle's habit / Trundlin' / Taboo man / CC rider / Yogi / Navy blue
SEECD 457 / Oct '96 / See For Miles

☐ BLUES INCORPORATED
PLSCD 102 / Apr '96 / Pulse

☐ BOOTLEG HIM
She fooled me / Hoochie coochie man / Yellow dog blues / I wonder who / Dee / Oh Lord don't let them drop that atomic bomb on me / Rockin' honesty / I got a woman / Might mighty spade and whitey / Corine Corina / Operator / Love you save / Jesus is just alright / That's all / Evil hearted woman / Clay House Inn / Love is gonna go / Sunrise / Hellhound on my trail
CLACD 291 / Feb '93 / Castle

☐ I WONDER WHO
Watermelon man / Streamline train / Rock me / Come back / Going down slow / 2.19 blues / River's invitation / I wonder who / Chicken shack back home / County jail blues / Roll 'em Pete / Betty and Dupree / CC rider
BGOCD 136 / Mar '92 / Beat Goes On

☐ LIVE IN PARIS (Korner, Alexis & Colin Hodgkinson)
Blue Monday / Key to the highway / Catcoke rag / Phonograph blues / Little bitty gal blues / Sweet home Chicago / Cherry red / I got my mojo working / Gospel ship / Geneva / Working in a coalmine / Flocking with you
CDTB 109 / '91 / Thunderbolt

☐ LOST ALBUM, THE
Lend me some time / Daytime song / New orleans / Hit the road jack-working in a coalmine / Honour the young man / Road is the road / Sweet sympathy / Gambler / To whom it may concern
CDTB 162 / Nov '94 / Thunderbolt

☐ MASTERS, THE
One scotch one bourbon one beer / Stump blues / Stream line train/My babe / 32-20 blues / High-heel sneakers / Will the circle be unbroken / Mary open the door / Blue Monday / Key to the highway / Catcote rag / Phonograph blues / Little bitty gal blues / Sweet home Chicago / Cherry red / I got my mojo working / Gospelship / Geneva
EABCD 092 / 30 Mar '98 / Eagle

☐ ME
Honky tonk woman / Louise / Hammer and nails / Santa Fe blues / How long blues / Roberta / Precious lord / Honour the young man / And again / East St. Louis blues
CLACD 292 / Feb '93 / Castle

☐ NEW GENERATION OF BLUES, A
Mary open the door / Little bitty girl / Baby don't you love me / Go down sunshine / Same for you / I'm tore down / In the evening / Somethin' you got / New worried blues / What's that sound I hear / Flower
BGOCD 102 / Jul '91 / Beat Goes On

☐ ON THE MOVE
Hey good lookin' / Rosie / Blood on the saddle / Fly united / Steal away / Bluebirds fresh daily / Thief / Working in a coalmine / Rock me / Honky tonk woman / I don't know / Little bitty gal blues / Engine 143 / Louisiana blues / You got the power / Vicksburg blues / Big boss man
CCSCD 809 / Sep '96 / Renaissance Collector Series

☐ PARTY ALBUM
Things ain't what they used to be / Captain's tiger / Skipping / Spoonful / Finkless cafe / Dooji wooji / Whole mess of blues / Lining the track / Robert Johnson
CLACD 290 / Feb '93 / Castle

☐ RED HOT FROM ALEX (Korner, Alexis & Blues Incorporated)
Woke up this morning / Skipping / Herbie's tune / Stormy Monday / It's happening / Roberta / Jones / Cabbage greens / Chicken shack / Haitian fight song
HILLCD 17 / May '97 / Wooded Hill

☐ SKY HIGH (Korner, Alexis & Blues Incorporated)
IGOCD 2012 / Dec '94 / Indigo

Kornog

☐ ON SEVEN WINDS
Gavotten ar menez / Sir Aldingar / Toniou Bale / Ronds de St. Vincent / Helen of Kirkconnel / Trip to Flagstaff / Shuttle rins / Dans plinn / Gavotten / Varbishka ratchenitza
GLCD 1062 / Feb '92 / Green Linnet

☐ PREMIERE
Dans loudieg / Demon lover / Ton baleson ar rost / Dans an dro / Jesuitmont / Ton bale mur ha dans / Bonnie jean cameron / Laride-an dro / War hent kerrigouarc'h-sheriffmuir
GLCD 1055 / Feb '90 / Green Linnet

Korova

☐ DEAD LIKE AN ANGEL
NPR 047CD / 8 Jun '98 / Napalm

Korpse

☐ PULL THE FLOOD
CANDLE 005CD / May '94 / Candlelight

☐ REVIRGIN
CANDLE 014CD / Jun '96 / Candlelight

Korriganed

☐ RU HA DU
KEL 003CD / Aug '95 / Diffusion Breizh

Kosek, Kenny

☐ ANGELWOOD
Locks at Athy medley / Strictly from Dixie / Poppy's waltz / Visco City breakdown / Cemetry man / La Bataille/Booth shot Lincoln / John Morton rag / Sugar Hill / When you and I were young Maggie / Table Mountain road/Tilden / Evan's farewell / Stoney Creek
ROUCD 0362 / Feb '97 / Rounder

Koskerien

☐ EBREL
KOS96 02 / Nov '96 / KOS

Kosma

☐ UNIVERSAL
IC 018CD / Oct '96 / Infracom

Kosmic Messenger

☐ ELECTRONIC POETRY
Get down / Full moon / Eye to eye / Flash / Memories of you / I find myself / Freeky Deeky / Kosmik funk / Deathmarch / Alley cat
ELY 015CD / 10 Nov '97 / Elypsia

Kosmic Twins

☐ PSYCHO CONNECTION
DIS 009CD / Mar '94 / Disturbance

Kosmik Kommando

☐ FREQUENSEIZE (2CD Set)
CAT 010CD / May '94 / Rephlex

Kossoff, Paul

☐ BACK STREET CRAWLER
I'm ready / Time away / Molton gold / Backstreet crawler / Tuesday morning
IMCD 84 / Feb '90 / Island

☐ BLUE SOUL
Over the green hills (Part 1): *Free* / Worry: *Free* / Moonshine: *Free* / Trouble on double time: *Free* / Crossroads: *Free* / Oh I wept: *Free* / We got time: *Uncle Dog* / Oh how we danced: *Capaldi, Jim* / Stealer: *Free* / Hold on: *Kossoff/Kirke/Tetsu/Rabbit* / Catch a train: *Free* / Come together in the morning: *Free* / Molten gold / I know why the sun don't shine: *Rumbledown Band* / Tricky Dicky rides again: *Capaldi, Jim* / I'm ready / Blue soul: *Back Street Crawler*
IMCD 144 / Jul '92 / Island

☐ KOSSOFF, KIRKE, TETSU, RABBIT (Kossoff/Kirke/Tetsu/Rabbit)
Bluegrass / Sammy's alright / Anna / Just for the box / Hold on / Fool's life / Yellow house / Dying fire / I'm on the run / Colours
IMCD 139 / Aug '91 / Island

☐ LIVE AT FAIRFIELD HALLS
Band played on / Sidekick to the stars / Long way to the top / New York / Train song / Survivor / Stealing my way / All the girls are crazy / Jason blue / Rock 'n' roll junkie / Molten gold
EAMCD 035 / 30 Mar '98 / Eagle

☐ STONE FREE
Worm: *Free* / Songs of yesterday: *Free* / Mr. Big: *Free* / Time away / You and me / You've taken hold of me / Hole in the head: *Amazing Blondel* / Band plays on: *Back Street Crawler* / It's a long way down to the top: *Back Street Crawler* / Train song: *Back Street Crawler* / Stealing my way: *Back Street Crawler* / Blue soul: *Back Street Crawler* / Just for you: *Back Street Crawler* / Leaves in the wind: *Back Street Crawler* / Molten gold
3036000952 / Mar '97 / Carlton

Kossoy Sisters

☐ BOWLING GREEN (Kossoy Sisters & Eric Darling)
TCD 1065 / 12 Jan '98 / Tradition

Kostars

☐ KLASSICS WITH A K
GR 025CD / Apr '97 / Grand Royal

Kostia

☐ 10 PEBBLES
Invitation / For you / It's going to rain / American fields / Russian song / We / Interlude / Loneliness / Yarmarka / Snowy river / Home sweet home
ND 61055 / Jul '96 / Narada

Koteron, Ibon

☐ LEONEN ORROAK (Koteron, Ibon & Kepa Junkera)
KDCD 449 / May '97 / Elkar

Kotilainen, Esa

☐ AAMU JOELLA
129412 / Apr '96 / Fazer

Kottke, Leo

☐ 6 AND 12 STRING GUITAR
Driving of the year nail / Last of the Arkansas greyhound / Ojo / Crow river waltz / Sailor's grave on the prairie / Vaseline machine gun / Jack Fig / Watermelon / Jesu joy of man's desiring / Fisherman / Tennessee toad / Busted bicycle / Brain of the purple mountain / Coolidge rising
CDTAK 1024 / Apr '96 / Takoma

☐ BALANCE
Tell Mary / I don't know why / Embryonic journey / Disguise / Whine / Losing everything / Drowning / Dolores / Half acre of garlic / Learning the game
BGOCD 263 / Aug '95 / Beat Goes On

☐ BEST, THE
Machine no.11 / Cripple creek / Bourree / When shrimps learn to whistle / Bill Cheatham / Song of the swamp / Last steam engine train / Bean time / Spanish entomologist / Short stories / Hole in the day / Mona Roy / Venezuela, there you go / Monkey lust / Busted bicycle / June bug / Eggtooth / Stealing / Living in the country / Medley: Crow river waltz/ Jesu joy of man's desiring/Jack Fig / Standing in my shoes / Bumble bee / Eight miles high / Tilt blillings and the student prince / Pamela Brown / Standing on the outside / Power failure
BGOCD 277 / Jun '95 / Beat Goes On

☐ BURNT LIPS
Endless sleep / Cool water / Frank forgets / Sonora's death row / Quiet man / Everybody lies / I called back / Low thud / Orange room / Credits / Out takes from Terry's movie / Voluntary target / Burnt lips / Sand street / Train and the gate / From Terry's movie
BGOCD 259 / Dec '94 / Beat Goes On

☐ CHEWING PINE
Standing on the outside / Power failure / Venezuela, there you go / Don't you think / Regards from Chuck Pink / Monkey money / Scarlatti rip-off / Wheels / Grim to the brim / Rebecca / Trombone / Can't quite put it into words
BGOCD 148 / Mar '93 / Beat Goes On

☐ DREAMS & ALL THAT STUFF
Mona ray / When shrimps learn to whistle / Twilight property / Bill cheatham / Vertical trees medley / Constant traveler / Why ask why / Taking a sandwich to a feast / Hole in the day / Mona roy
BGOCD 132 / Nov '92 / Beat Goes On

☐ GREENHOUSE
Bean time / Tiny island / Song of the swamp / In christ there is no east or west / Last steam engine train / From the cradle to the grave / Louise / Spanish entomologist / Owls / You don't have to need me / Lost john
BGOCD 50 / Oct '90 / Beat Goes On

☐ GUITAR MUSIC
Part 2 / Available space / Side one suite / Some birds / Slang / My double / Three walls and bars / Some birds (reprise) / Perforated sleep / Strange / Little shoes / Jib's hat / Tumbling tumbleweeds / Agile / Song for the night of the hunter / All I have to do is dream / Sleepwalk
BGOCD 261 / May '95 / Beat Goes On

☐ HEAR THE WIND HOWL
Eight miles high / Pamela Brown / Cripple creek / Hear the wind howl / You tell me why / Mona Ray / Don't you think / All through the night / June bug / Grim to the brim / Poor boy / Scarlatti rip-off / Standing in my shoes / Little bit of San Antonio Rose/ America the beautiful
DC 868682 / Nov '96 / Disky

☐ ICE WATER
Morning is the long way home / Pamela brown / Good egg / Tilt billings and the student prince / All through the night / Short stories / You tell me why / You know I know you know / Born to be with you / Child should be a fish
BGOCD 146 / Jul '92 / Beat Goes On

☐ KOTTKE, LANG & FAHEY (Kottke, Leo & Peter Lang/John Fahey)
Cripple Creek: *Kottke, Leo* / Ice miner: *Kottke, Leo* / Red and white: *Kottke, Leo* / Anyway: *Kottke, Leo* / St. Charles shuffle: *Lang, Peter* / When Kings come home: *Lang, Peter* / As I lay sleeping: *Lang, Peter* / Thoth song: *Lang, Peter* / On the sunny side of the ocean: *Fahey, John* / Sunflower river blues: *Fahey, John* / Revolt of the Dyke Brigade: *Fahey, John* / In Christ there is no East and West: *Fahey, John*
CDTAK 1040 / Jun '96 / Takoma

☐ LEO KOTTKE
Buckaroo / White ape / Haysee suede / Rio Leo / Range / Airproofing / Maroon / Waltz / Death by reputation / Up tempo / Shadowland
BGOCD 257 / Oct '94 / Beat Goes On

☐ LEO KOTTKE LIVE
William Powell / Room at the top of the stairs / Airproofing / Jack gets up / Combat / Peg leg / Twilight time / Bean time / Roy Autry / Parade / I yell at traffic / Flattend brain / Little Martha / Oddball / Arms of Mary
01005821322 / Mar '96 / Private Music

☐ LIVE IN EUROPE
Train and the gate / Open country joy: Theme and adhesions / Airproofing / Tell Mary / Wheels / Up tempo / Palms blvd / Shadowland / Eggtooth / Pamela Brown / Range
BGOCD 265 / Aug '95 / Beat Goes On

☐ MUDLARK
Cripple creek / Eight miles high / June bug / Ice miner / Bumble bee / Stealing / Monkey lust / Poor boy / Lullaby / Machine no. 2 / Hear the wind howl / Bourree / Room 8 / Standing in my shoes
BGOCD 101 / Apr '91 / Beat Goes On

☐ MY FEET ARE SMILING
Hear the wind howl / Busted bicycle / Easter / Louise / Blue dot / Stealing / Living in the country / June bug / Standing in my shoes / Fisherman / Bean time / Egg tooth
BGOCD 134 / Feb '92 / Beat Goes On

☐ PECULIAROSO
Peg leg / Poor boy / Parade / Wonderland by night / World made to order / Room service / Turning into Randolph Scott (Humid child) / Porky and pale arms of Mary / Room at the stop of the stairs / Big situation / Twilight time
01005821112 / Apr '94 / Private Music

☐ STANDING IN MY SHOES
Standing in my shoes / World turning / Dead end / Vaseline machine gun / Corrina, Corrina / Realm / Cripple creek / Twice: *Kottke, Leo & Chet Atkins* / Across the street / Don't call me Ray / Itchy
1005821462 / May '97 / Private Music

☐ TIME STEP
Running all night long / Bungle party / Rings / Mr. Fonebone / Julie's house / Memories are made of this / Saginaw Michigan / I'll break out again / Wrong track / Starving / Here comes that rain again
BGOCD 255 / Apr '95 / Beat Goes On

Kotto Bass

☐ SOUKOUS FUSION
SMCD 1157 / Jan '97 / Sonima

Kotzen, Richie

☐ PROJECT (Kotzen, Ritchie & Greg Howe)
SHR 1110 / 10 Nov '97 / Shrapnel

Koun

☐ AN DRO
KMCD 59 / Feb '96 / Keltia Musique

Koutev, Philip

☐ BULGARIAN ACAPELLA (Koutev, Philip Folk Ensemble)
Kaji, kaji, Angjo / Vecherjal, Rado / Polegnala e Todora / Dumai Zlato / Dragana i slavej / Malka moma dvori mete / Dimjaninka / Dai si vasse rachizata / Stoyan ide ot grad zarigrad / Aide sanze zaide / Pilenze pee govori / Grozdanka / Protekla e voda / Prituri se planinata
JVC 53892 / Sep '96 / JVC World Library

☐ BULGARIAN POLYPHONY (Koutev, Philip Folk Ensemble)
VICG 50012 / Mar '96 / JVC World Library

☐ BULGARIAN POLYPHONY VOL.2 (Koutev, Philip Folk Ensemble)
VICG 50022 / Mar '96 / JVC World Library

Kouyate, Bassi

☐ SONGS OF BAMBARA GRIOT, MALI
926582 / Jan '97 / BUDA

Kouyate, Diaryatou

☐ GUINEA : KORA & SONG N'GABU VOL.1 (Kouyate, Diaryatou & M'Bady)
926292 / Apr '97 / BUDA

☐ GUINEA : KORA & SONG N'GABU VOL.2 (Kouyate, Diaryatou & M'Bady)
926482 / Apr '97 / BUDA

Kouyate, Famoro

☐ ASSUSU (Kouyate, Famoro & Kike)
OA 204 / Feb '94 / PAM

Kouyate, Ousmane

☐ DOMBA (Kouyate, Ousmane Band)
Djougouya / Domba / Kounady / Miriya / An' fananta lele / N'nafanta
STCD 1030 / May '90 / Stern's

Kouyate, Tata Bambo

☐ JATIGUI
Hommage a baba cissoko / Mama batchily / Goundo tandja / Ainana bah / Ahourou bocoum / Amadou traore
CDORB 042 / Jun '89 / Globestyle

Kovac, Boris

☐ FROM RITUAL NOVA I & II
RERBKCD 1 / Feb '94 / ReR/ Recommended

Koverhult, Tommy

☐ JAZZ IN SWEDEN 1983
1289 / Jan '83 / Caprice

Kovriga Balalaika Orchestra

☐ RUSSIAN FAVOURITES
MCD 71793 / Jun '93 / Monitor

Kowald, Peter

☐ TOUCH THE EARTH, BREAK THE SHELLS (Kowald, Peter & Wadada Leo Smith/Gunter 'Baby' Sommer)
FMPCD 67 / Sep '97 / Full Moon

Koxbox

☐ DRAGON TALES
BR 058CD / 24 Nov '97 / Blue Room Released

☐ LIVE FROM THE BURNING MAN
BR 031CD / Sep '97 / Blue Room Released

Kpiaye, John

☐ RED GOLD & BLUE
LJKCD 012 / Jun '94 / LKJ

Kraan

☐ LET IT OUT
941115 / 10 Nov '97 / Germanofon

Krabathor

☐ MORTAL MEMORIES
SPV 08512762 / 6 Apr '98 / SPV

☐ ORTHODOX
SPV 08412852 / May '98 / SPV

Kraftwerk

☐ AUTOBAHN
Autobahn / Kometenmelodie 1 / Kometenmelodie 2 / Mitternacht / Morgenspaziergang
CDP 7461532 / Aug '95 / EMI

☐ CAPITOL YEARS BOX, THE
CLEO 94162 / May '97 / Cleopatra

☐ COMPUTER WORLD
Pocket calculator / Numbers / Computer world / Computer love / It's more fun to compute / Home computer
CDEMS 1547 / Apr '95 / Capitol

☐ CONCERT CLASSICS
Kometenmelodie / Autobahn / Morganspaziergang
CRANCH 4 / 29 Jun '98 / Ranch Life

☐ ELECTRIC CAFE
Boing boom tschak / Techno pop / Musique non stop / Telephone call / Sex object / Electric cafe
CDEMS 1546 / Aug '95 / EMI

☐ KRAFTWERK NO.1
941001 / 23 Feb '98 / Germanofon

☐ KRAFTWERK NO.2
941002 / 23 Feb '98 / Germanofon

☐ MAN MACHINE
Robots / Spacelab / Metropolis / Model / Neon lights / Man machine
CDEMS 1520 / Apr '95 / Capitol

☐ MAN MACHINE
Robots / Spacelab / Metropolis / Model / Man machine / Die roboter / Das modell / Neon licht
CDCNTAV 4 / Jun '97 / EMI

☐ MIX, THE
Robots / Computer love / Pocket calculator / Dentaku / Autobahn / Radioactivity / Trans Europe express / Abzug / Metal on metal / Homecomputer / Musique non stop
CDEM 1408 / May '95 / EMI

☐ RADIO ACTIVITY
Geiger counter / Radioactivity / Radioland / Airwaves / Intermission / News / Voice of energy / Antenna / Radio stars / Uranium / Transistir / Ohm sweet ohm
CDEMS 1524 / Apr '95 / Capitol

☐ SHOWROOM DUMMIES
CLEO 6843CD / May '97 / Cleopatra

☐ TONE FLOAT
941000 / 5 Jan '98 / Germanofon

☐ TRANCEWERK EXPRESS VOL.2 (A Tribute To Kraftwerk) (Various Artists)
Tour De France / Pocket Calculator / Numbers / Man Machine / Kometen Melodie / Robots / Computer love / Model / Trans-Europe Express
CLP 99042 / Jan '97 / Cleopatra

☐ TRANS EUROPE EXPRESS
Europe endless / Hall of mirrors / Showroom dummies / Trans - Europe express / Metal on metal / Franz Schubert / Endless endless
CDP 7464732 / Aug '95 / EMI

Krakatu

☐ MATINALE
Matinale / Unseen sea scene / Jai ping / Rural / For Bernard Moore / Sarajevo / Shuka / Raging thirst
5232932 / Nov '94 / ECM

☐ VOLITION
Brujo / Volition / Nai / Changgo / Little big horn / Dalens ande
5119832 / May '92 / ECM

Kral, Irene

☐ WHERE IS LOVE
I like you, you're nice / When I look in your eyes / Time for love / Small world / Love came on stealthy fingers / Never let me go / Spring can really hang you up the most / Lucky to be me / Some other time / Don't look back / Where is love
CHCD 71012 / Mar '97 / Candid

Kral, Ivan

☐ NATIVE
Cry for more / Magic carpet / Maintain the rage / You can break a heart / Spirit / Dream your nights / Fight like a man / Way down below / Crazy about you
ZS 124 / Jul '92 / Special Delivery

Krall, Diana

☐ ALL FOR YOU (A Tribute To Nat 'King' Cole)
I'm an errand girl for rhythm / Gee baby ain't I good to you / You call it madness / Frim fram sauce / Boulevard of broken dreams / Baby baby all the time / Hit that jive Jack / You're looking at me / I'm thru with love / 'Deed I do / Blossom fell / If I had you
IMP 11642 / Mar '96 / Impulse Jazz

☐ LOVE SCENES
All or nothing at all / Peel me a grape / I don't know enough about you / I miss you so / They can't take that away from me / Lost mind / I don't stand a ghost of a chance with you / You're getting to be a habit with me / Gentle rain / How deep is the ocean (how high is the sky) / My love / Garden in the rain / That old feeling
IMP 12342 / Aug '97 / Impulse Jazz

☐ ONLY TRUST YOUR HEART
Is you is or is you ain't my baby / Only trust your heart / I love being here with you / Broadway / Folks who live on the hill / I've got the world on a string / Squeeze me / All night long / CRS Craft
GRP 98102 / Mar '95 / GRP

☐ STEPPING OUT
This can't be love / Straighten up and fly right / Between the devil and the deep blue sea / I'm just a lucky so and so / Body and soul / 42nd Street / Do nothin' 'til you hear from me / Big foot / Frim fram sauce / Jimmie / As long as I live
JUST 502 / Oct '96 / Justin Time

Kramer

☐ LET ME EXPLAIN SOMETHING TO YOU ABOUT ART
TZA 7119 / 15 Dec '97 / Tzadik

☐ RUBBER HAIR (Kramer & Daved Hild)
SHIMMY 087CD / 16 Mar '98 / Shimmy Disc

☐ SONGS FROM THE PINK DEATH
SHIMMYCD 502 / 16 Mar '98 / Shimmy Disc

Kramer, Billy J.

☐ AT ABBEY ROAD 1963-1966 (Kramer, Billy J. & The Dakotas)
Do you want to know a secret / I'll be on my way / I call your name / Dance with me / Sugar me / I know / I'll keep you satisfied / Little children / They remind me of you / Second to none / From a window / Every time you walk in the room / It's a mad mad world / To take her place / Under the boardwalk / It's gotta last forever / Sneakin' around / Trains boats and planes / I live to love you / Neon city / That ain't good for me / I'll be doggone / Down in the boondocks / We're doing fine / Forgive me / Listen / Take my hand
4934512 / 23 Feb '98 / EMI

☐ EP COLLECTION, THE (Kramer, Billy J. & The Dakotas)
I call your name / Bad to me / Do you want to know a secret / I'll be on my way / I'll keep you satisfied / Dance with me / It's up to you / I know / Little children / They remind me of you / Beautiful reminder / From a window / Second to none / Twelfth of never / Sugar babe / Tennessee waltz / Irresistible you / Twilight time / Cruel sea / Millionaire / Magic carpet / Humdinger / Trains and boats and planes
SEECD 422 / May '95 / See For Miles

☐ LISTEN (Kramer, Billy J. & The Dakotas)
I'll keep you satisfied / Do you want to know a secret / We're doing fine / I call your name / From a window / Second to none / Beautiful dreamer / Cruel sea / Magic carpet / I'll be on my way / Bad to me / It's up to you / Little children / Take my hand / Trains and boats and planes / Still waters run deep / Tell me girl / I know / Dance with me / Sugar babe
DORIG 110 / 3 Nov '97 / EMI

☐ VERY BEST OF BILLY J. KRAMER & THE DAKOTAS, THE (Kramer, Billy J. & The Dakotas)
I'll keep you satisfied / Do you want to know a secret / I call you name / Sneakin' around / Second to none / Bad to me / Cruel sea / Magic carpet / Oyeh / I'll be on my way / Sugar babe / It's up to you / Little children / From a window / It's mad mad world / Neon city / Trains boats and planes / It's gonna last forever / That's the way I feel / I'll be dogone / We're doing fine / Forgive me / Millionaire / Humdinger / My girl Josephine / Take my hand / San Diego / Ships that pass in the night / You can't live on memories
CDMFP 6388 / 13 Oct '97 / Music For Pleasure

Kramer, Wayne

☐ **CITIZEN WAYNE**
Stranger in the house / Back when dogs could talk / Revolution in apt. 29 / Down on the ground / Shining Mr. Lincoln's shoes / Dope for democracy / No easy way out / You don't know my name / Count time / Snatched defeat / Doing the work / Farewell to whiskey
64882 / Apr '97 / Epitaph

☐ **DEATH TONGUE**
ITEMCD 2 / Jul '92 / Curio

☐ **HARDSTUFF, THE**
E 864472 / Jan '95 / Epitaph

Krantz, Wayne

☐ **2 DRINK MINIMUM**
Whippersnapper / Dove Gloria / Shirts off / Dream called love / AFKap / Isabelle / Alliance / Secrets / Lynxpaw
ENJ 90432 / Jul '95 / Enja

☐ **LONG TO BE LOOSE**
These instrumental pieces were / Not conciously written about / Specific people, places, things or ideas / Although one began / From a little croaking sound / Friend's DAT machine makes / What they were written about / Is something I don't understand yet / But I know it when I see it / And, hopefully, so will you
ENJ 70992 / Jul '93 / Enja

☐ **SEPERATE CAGES (Krantz, Wayne & Leni Stern)**
Saturday morning / Claudine / Something is wrong in Spanish / Point falling / Nicole / King's Cross / Veronique / Keep my heart / Leave softly / Silver line / November
ALCD 1007 / Apr '97 / Alchemy

☐ **SIGNALS**
60482 / Nov '90 / Enja

Krasavik Ensemble

☐ **GRAMNITSY**
B 6843 / Mar '97 / Auvidis/Ethnic

Kraus, Peter

☐ **DIE SINGLES 1958-1960**
Sugar baby / Ich denk'an dich / Honey baby (du passt so gut zu mir) / Come on and swing / Kitty kat / Havanna love / Wunderbar wie du / Hey du bist okay / Tiger / Ich bin ja so allein / Wenn / Oh Veronika / Die jungen Jahre / Wenn du heute ausgehst / Das ist prima / OK / Cowboy Billy / Sensationell / Auf wiederseh'n und lass dir's gut ergehen / Genau wie du / Ten o'clock rock / Keine nacht kann ich schlafen / Dream face / Nobody else/Du gehorst mir
BCD 15453 / Apr '89 / Bear Family

☐ **DIE SINGLES 1960**
Susi sagt es Gabi / Doll doll dolly / Alle Madchen wollen kussen / Wenn sie dich allein lasst / Va Bene / Sag mir was du denkst / Honeymoon / Mondschein und Liebe / Ein rendezvous mit dir / Rote rosen / Ein haus in Tennessee / Blue river / Cherie, cherie / Cowboy Jenny / Rose Marie / Alles ist anders / Ausgerechnet ich / Come on and swing (live) / Basin Street blues / When the saints go marching in / Get happy / Love me or leave me / Alright, OK you win / Nobody else
BCD 15457 / Apr '89 / Bear Family

☐ **DIE SINGLES 1961-1962**
BCD 15527 / Apr '92 / Bear Family

☐ **DIE SINGLES 1962-1963**
BCD 15528 / Apr '92 / Bear Family

☐ **HERZLICHST IHR PETER KRAUS**
BCD 15478 / '88 / Bear Family

☐ **TEENAGERTRAUME, LIEBELEIEN UND SUGARBABIES (10CD Set)**
Tutti frutti / Die strasse der vergessenen / O wie gut / Susi rock / Schau keinen anderen mann an / Ten o'clock rock / Lass mich bitte nie allein / Liebelei / Teddybar / Ich will nicht wissen / Es fing so wunderbar an / Wenn teenager traumen / Mach dich schon / Hafen rock / Diana / So wie damals baby / I love you baby / Du sollst mein schicksal dein / Rosmarie / Hula baby / Mit siebzehn / Du gehorst mir / Teenager melodie: *Kraus, Peter & Micky Mann* / Ich mocht' mit dir traumen: *Kraus, Peter & Micky Mann* / Sugar baby / Ich denk an dich / Du passt so gut zu mir: *Kraus, Peter & Danny Mann* / Come on and swing / Kitty kat / Havanna love / Wunderbar wie du / Hey du bist okay / Tiger / Ich bin ja so allein / Wenn: *James Brothers* / Oh Veronika: *James Brothers* / Die jungen jahre: *James Brothers* / Wenn du heut ausgehst: *James Brothers* / Das ist prima: *James Brothers* / OK: *James Brothers* / Cowboy Billy: *James Brothers* / Sensationell: *James Brothers* / Auf wiederseh'n und lass dir's gut ergeh'n: *James Brothers* / Genau wie du: *James Brothers* / Ten o'clock rock: *James Brothers* / Keine nacht kann ich schlafen / Dream face / Nobody else / Susi sagt es Gabi / Doll doll Dolly / Alle madchen wollen kussen / Wenn sie dich allein lasst / Va bene / Sag' mir was du denkst: *Kraus, Peter & Conny Froboess* / Honey moon: *Kraus, Peter & Alice/Ellen Kessler* / Mondschein und liebe: *Kraus, Peter & Alice/Ellen Kessler* / Ein rendezvous mit dir: *Kraus, Peter & Alice/Ellen Kessler* / Rote rosen: *James Brothers* / Eine haus in Tennesse: *James Brothers* / Blue river: *James Brothers* / Cherie cherie: *James Brothers* / Cowboy Jenny: *James Brothers* / Rosemarie: *James Brothers* / Alles ist anders / Ausgerechnet ich / Come on and swing / Basin Street blues / When the saints go marchin' in / Get happy / Love me or leave me / Alright, okay you win / Ich kann dir was erzahlen: *Kraus, Peter & Alice/Ellen Kessler* / Wundervoll: *Kraus, Peter & Alice/Ellen Kessler* / Sie hat so wunderschone augen: *James Brothers* / Tiger Lilly: *James Brothers* / Jedes madchen auf erden / Von Paris bis Hawaii / Hallo Blondie / Happy baby: *Kraus, Peter & Alice/Ellen Kessler* / Ich hab' dich noch genauso lieb / Mein neuer hut / Solo tu / Blue melodie / Morgen bist du alle sargen los: *James Brothers* / Wie eine kleine lady: *James Brothers* / Das fraulein Gerda / Unsere sprache ist musik: *Kraus, Peter & Sacha Distel* / Oh so wunderbar / Twenty four hours / Everybody else but me / Mission bell / Bella bella Marie / Long long ago / Ja pense a toi / C'est toi plus belle / Comme un tigre / Par le monde: *Kraus, Peter & Alice/Ellen Kessler* / Wenn das nicht so romantisch war: *Kraus, Peter & Alice/Ellen Kessler* / Teddy: *Kraus, Peter & Alice/Ellen Kessler* / Noch ein jahr: *Kraus, Peter & Alice/Ellen Kessler* / Heute und immer my love / Farah von Haifa / Ich habe alles was ich brauche: *Kraus, Peter & Alice/Ellen Kessler* / Evelyn / Schwarze rose / Rosy oh Rosy: *James Brothers* / Beim candlelight: *James Brothers* / Ich hab' mich so an dich gewohnt: *James Brothers* / Hanna aus Havanna: *James Brothers* / Schou schou: *Twist Boys* / Twist twist: *Twist Boys* / Silver moon / Ein junges herz / Holiday lady: *James Brothers* / Komm wieder: *James Brothers* / Hallo Brigitte / Lang lang ist's her / Die ganze welt ist himmelblau / Das macht die liebe: *Kraus, Peter & Lil' Babs* / Darlin' meine liebe: *Kraus, Peter & Connie Francis* / Oh I like it: *Kraus, Peter & Connie Francis* / Heute und immer my love / Va bene / Blue melodie / Heute und immer my love / Strasse der sehnsucht / Sweety / Uns're reise fangt on / Western rose / Hande weg von den Frau'n: *Kraus, Peter & Gus Backus* / Das haben die madchen gern: *Kraus, Peter & Gus Backus* / Sonny boy sonny boy / Lorelei / Eine souvenir / Pico pico bello / Das blonde baby vom Broadway / Schenk mir einen talismann / Zucchero / Ricky ticky teeny weeny twist express: *Kraus, Peter & Gina Dobra* / Weil es so schon ist bei dir: *Kraus, Peter & Lil' Babs* / Huh a hah alter schimmel: *James Brothers* / Weit ist die welt / Cry your eyes out / Bigger the fool / She used to be mine / Cry your eyes out / Here is a heart / Ton visage, ton image / Que demandent les jeunes / Danse avec moi / Moins de vingt ans / Madchen mit herz / Dein herr Papa / Der geist von Buffalo Bill / Wer dich sieht Evelyn / Wilde rose fern in Mexico / Sonne, pizza and amore: *Kraus, Peter & Lil' Babs* / Mein liebling ist mir treu: *Kraus, Peter & Lil' Babs* / Hey Isabell: *Kraus, Peter & Lil' Babs* / Ich traum vom honey moon: *Kraus, Peter & Lil' Babs* / Schon ist die liebe: *Kraus, Peter & Lil' Babs* / Kisses in the night / Lass kein madchen lange warten / Take it easy little girl / Heidi hodi / Vergiss sie / Wenn es nacht wird am blue river / Eine die so ist wie du / Remets nous la danse / Et la, elle a dit / Les snap / J'ai beaucoup d'amour / Piccolo piccolo / 20km al giorno / 100,000 kussen / Hou je van mij / Linda Lou / Leder uur / Diane / Raunchy: *Greger, Max* / Teenager's romance: *James Brothers* / Joker: *Greger, Max* / Kewpie doll: *Berg, Jorg Maria* / Was ein mann alles kann: *Greger, Max* / Piccolissima serenata: *James Brothers* / Mit siebzehn: *Greger, Max* / Catch a falling star / Sail along silvery moon: *Greger, Max* / I love you baby / Sugartime: *Greger, Max* / When: *James Brothers* / Tequila: *Greger, Max* / Volare / Singing hills: *Greger, Max* / White sport coat / Manakoora: *Greger, Max* / Patricia: *Berg, Jorg Maria* / Vielleicht in 3, 4, 5, 6 jahren: *Greger, Max* / Hula baby / La paloma: *Greger, Max* / Buona sera / Love and kisses: *Greger, Max* / Rock around the clock / Tutti frutti / Lonely blue boy / Charly Brown / Red river rock / Brauner bar und weisse taube / Wenn teenager traumen / My happiness / Souvenirs / See you later alligator / Shake, rattle and roll / Va bene / Apache / Heartbreak hotel / Jailhouse rock / Love me tender / Itsy bitsy teenie weenie / Buona sera / Volare / Marina / Ciao ciao bambina / Twist it up America: *Kraus, Peter & Lil' Babs* / Hatt ich einen hammer: *Kraus, Peter & Lil' Babs* / Derr mann im mond/ Schwarze Rose Marie: *Kraus, Peter & Gus Backus* / Capri fischer / Ein schiff fahrt nach Shanghai / Unter einem regenschirm am abend / Wenn die Elisabeth... / Unter der roten laterne von St. Pauli / So stell ich mir die liebe vor / Mexikanische serenade / Man musst klavier spielen konnen / Du sollst mein glucksten sein / In einem kelinen cafe in Hernals / Ich nenne all frauen baby / Ich brauche keine millionen / Il nostro concerto / Cassetta in Canada / Drei munzen im brunnen / Die sussesten fruchte / Funiculi funicula / Come prima / O mia bella Napoli / O sole mio / Rumba Anna / Rosen aus Napoli / Florentinische nachte / Schau mich bitte nicht so an / Eso beso / Va bene / Am zuckerhut / Hab'n sie nicht 'ne frau fur mich / Desafinado / Amapola / Oh la la / Sweety / Bella bella Donna / Capri fischer / My golden baby / Sie sind mir so symphatisch / Zucchero / Va bene / Ich mocht' mit dir traumen: *Kraus, Peter & Conny Froboess* / Kitty kat: *Kraus, Peter & Conny Froboess* / Kuss mich: *Kraus, Peter & Vivi Bach* / Was ich will: *Kraus, Peter & Vivi Bach* / Alexander's ragtime band: *Kraus, Peter & Mina* / Las verita / Susi cacaracha / Darktown strutters ball: *Kraus, Peter & Gene Reed* / Die seidene leiter / You are my sunshine: *Kraus, Peter & Inge Bruck* / Hokus pokus: *Kraus, Peter & Inge Bruck* / Simsalabim: *Kraus, Peter & Inge Bruck* / Hokus pokus: *Kraus, Peter & Wencke Myrhe* / Verliebt verliebt: *Kraus, Peter & Wencke Myrhe* / Das alte haus von rocky doky / Und dann tanzen wir mambo / Ein kleines pferd aus holz / Teenager melodie: *Kraus, Peter & Conny Froboess*
BCD 15871 / Dec '96 / Bear Family

Krause, Bernie

☐ **AMAZON DAYS AMAZON NIGHTS WILD SANCTUARY**
9006231122 / 5 May '98 / Miramar

☐ **GORILLAS IN THE MIX**
RCD 10119 / Dec '92 / Rykodisc

☐ **OCEAN ODYSSEY (Krause, Bernie & Rodney Franklin)**
9006231042 / 7 Apr '98 / Miramar

Krause, Dagmar

☐ **SUPPLY AND DEMAND (Songs by Brecht, Weill & Eisler)**
Supply and demand (the trader's song) / Epitaph 1919 / German miserere / O falladah, die du hangest / Alabama song / Hollywood elegies / Surabaya johnny / Moritat / Matrosen tango / Lily of hell / Song of the moldau / Pavel's prison song / Easter sunday, 1935 / At potsdam 'unter den eichen' / Der song von mandelay / Benares song
HNCD 1317 / Mar '86 / Hannibal

☐ **TANK BATTLES (The Songs Of Hanns Eisler)**
Song of the whitewash / You have to pay / Ballad of the sack slingers / Perhaps song / Mankind / Song of a German mother / Bankenlied / Und endlich stirbt / Mother's hands / Genvieve: Ostern ist ball sur Seine / (I read about) tank battles / Chanson allemande / Mother Beimlein / Bettellied / Change the world - it needs it / Failure in loving / Ballad of (Bourgeois) welfare / Berlin 1919 / Rat men - the nightmare / Homecoming / To a little radio / Lied von der belebeden wirkung des geldes / Legende von der entstehung des buches Taoteking / And I shall never see again / Wise woman and the soldier
BP 138CD / May '97 / Blueprint

Krauss, Alison

☐ **EVERYTIME YOU SAY GOODBYE**
Everytime you say goodbye / Another night / Last love letter / Cluck old hen / Who can blame you / It work this time / Heartstrings / I don't know why / Cloudy days / New fool / Shield of faith / Lose again / Another day another dollar / Jesus help me stand
ROUCD 0285 / '92 / Rounder

☐ **I KNOW WHO HOLDS THE FUTURE (Krauss, Alison & The Cox Family)**
ROUCD 307 / Mar '94 / Rounder

☐ **I'VE GOT THAT OLD FEELING**
I've got that old feeling / Dark skies / Wish I still had you / Endless highway / Winter of a broken heart / It's over / Will you be leaving / Steel rails / Tonight I'll be lonely too / One good reason / That makes two of us / Longest highway
ROUCD 0275 / '90 / Rounder

☐ **NOW THAT I'VE FOUND YOU**
Baby now that I've found you / Oh Atlanta / Broadway / Everytime you say goodbye / Tonight I'll be lonely too / Teardrops will kiss the morning dew / Sleep on / When God dips his pen of love in my heart / I will / I don't believe you've met my baby / Palm of your hand / When you say nothing at all
ROUCD 0325 / Feb '95 / Rounder

☐ **SO LONG SO WRONG (Krauss, Alison & Union Station)**
ROUCD 0365 / Mar '97 / Rounder

☐ **TOO LATE TO CRY (Krauss, Alison & Various Artists)**
Too late to cry / Foolish heart / Song for life / Dusty Miller / If I give my heart / In your eyes / Don't follow me / Gentle river / On the borderline / Forgotten pictures / Sleep on
ROUCD 0235 / Aug '88 / Rounder

☐ **TWO HIGHWAYS (Krauss, Alison & Union Station)**
Two highways / I'm alone again / Wild Bill Jones / Beaumont rag / Heaven's bright shore / Love you in vain / Here comes goodbye / As lovely as you / Windy City rag / Lord don't you forsake me / Teardrops will kiss the morning dew / Midnight rider
ROUCD 0257 / '89 / Rounder

☐ **WHEN YOU SAY NOTHING AT ALL**
CRCDS 7 / Nov '95 / Rounder

Krauss, Briggan

☐ **GOOD KITTY**
KFWCD 178 / Apr '97 / Knitting Factory

Kravitz, Lenny

☐ **5**
Can we find a reason / I belong to you / Super soul finger / Thinking of you / Fly away / Live / Straight cold player / Little girl's eyes / Black velveteen / Take time / It's your life / Your my flavour / If you can't say no
CDVUS 140 / 11 May '98 / Virgin

☐ **ARE YOU GONNA GO MY WAY**
Are you gonna go my way / Believe / Come on and love me / Heaven help / Just be a woman / Is there any love in your heart / Black girl / My love / Sugar / Sister / Eleutheria
CDVUS 60 / Mar '93 / Virgin

☐ **CIRCUS**
Rock 'n' roll is dead / Circus / Beyond the 7th sky / Tunnel vision / Can't get you off my mind / Magdalene / God is love / Thin ice / Don't go and put a bullet in your head / In my life today / Resurrection
CDVUS 86 / Sep '95 / Virgin

☐ **LET LOVE RULE**
Sittin' on top of the world / Let love rule / Freedom train / My precious love / I build this garden for us / Fear / Does anybody out there even care / Mr. Cabdriver / Rosemary / Be / Blues for sister someone / Empty hands / Flower child
CDVUS 10 / May '90 / Virgin

☐ **MAMA SAID**
Fields of joy / Always on the run / Stand by my woman / It ain't over 'til it's over / More than anything in this world / What goes around comes around / Difference is why / Stop draggin' around / Flowers for Zoe / Fields of joy (reprise) / All I ever wanted / When the morning turns to night / What the fuck are we saying / Butterfly
CDVUS 31 / Apr '91 / Virgin

Kreator

☐ **OUT OF THE DARK**
N 02002 / Sep '92 / Noise

☐ **OUTCAST**
GUN 140CD / Jun '97 / Gun

☐ **RENEWAL**
N 01932 / Oct '92 / Noise

☐ **SCENARIOS OF VIOLENCE**
N 02662 / Feb '96 / Noise

Krebs, Pete

☐ **WESTERN ELECTRIC**
CSR 31 / 23 Feb '98 / Cavity Search

Kreidler

☐ **APPEARANCE AND THE PARK**
Tuesday / Il sogno di una cosa / Plus / She woke up and the world had changed / Necessity now / Good morning city / Sneak preview / Au-pair / After the preview / Coldness / Venetian blind / Cube
KIFF 011CD / 25 May '98 / Kiff SM

☐ **RESPORT**
EFA 073232 / Jun '97 / Stewardess

☐ **WEEKEND**
PIAS 556500420 / Nov '96 / Kiff SM

☐ **WEEKEND**
Traffic way / Shaun / Spat / La capital / Sand colour classic / Lio / Polaroid / Desto / Reflections / Hillwood / Telefon / La fille en beige / If / Schodringers katze
KIFF 004CD / Jun '97 / Play It Again Sam

Krekel, Tim

☐ **OUT OF THE CORNER**
APCD 083 / Jun '92 / Appaloosa

Krel

☐ **AD ASTRA**
DERNCD 11 / 3 Nov '97 / Dead Earnest

Kremer, Gidon

☐ **HOMMAGE A PIAZZOLLA**
Vardarito / Mi longa en re / Buenos Aires hora zero / Cafe 1930 / Oblivion / Esqualo / Soledad / Concierto para quintero / Celos / Le grand tango
7559794072 / May '97 / Nonesuch

☐ **LE CINEMA**
Improvviso / Nostalghia / Tamti anni prima / Rag-i-con-time / Absalom's death/Tango / Ovad (the gadfly) / Le boef sur le toit / Fantasy / Smile
0630172222 / 16 Mar '98 / Teldec Classics

Kreusch, Cornelius C.

☐ **SCOOP**
Niles / Yarum / Salif / Scoop / Imbao / Pulse / FaithPulse / Faith / Feel / Wocal / Falme / Nomad / Jafro
ACT 92552 / 23 Mar '98 / Act

Kreuz

☐ **KREUZ KONTROL**
DESCD 1 / Mar '95 / Diesel

Kreviazuk, Chantal

☐ **UNDER THESE ROCKS AND STONES**
God made me / Surrounded / Don't be good / Believer / Grace / Wayne / Imaginary friend / Hands / Disagree / Co-dependent / Green apples / Boot / Actions without love
4869372 / 4 May '98 / Epic

Krewmen

☐ **ADVENTURES OF THE KREWMEN**
LMCD 008 / Jun '97 / Lost Moment

☐ **FINAL ADVENTURES VOL.1**
Beware the moon / Arachnophobia / Presence / Lords of the night / Space crazy / Cyborg / Birth of the krewmen / Tortured life / Wrath of planet zee / Root'n toot'n hullaballoo / Forbidden planet
LMCD 023 / Apr '92 / Lost Moment

☐ **INTO THE TOMB**
LMCD 014 / Jun '97 / Lost Moment

☐ **KLASSIC TRACKS FROM 1985**
LMCD 054 / 16 Feb '98 / Lost Moment

☐ **PLAGUE OF THE DEAD**
LMCD 020 / Oct '88 / Lost Moment

☐ **POWER**
Devils lair / Devils lair / Undead / Rats / Anymore / Stone / Get lost / Two souls / Knight moves / Back to the ball
LMCD 021 / Sep '90 / Lost Moment

☐ **SINGLED OUT**
LMCD 024 / Oct '94 / Lost Moment

☐ **SWEET DREAMS**
LMCD 010 / Jun '97 / Lost Moment

Krimsky, Katrina

☐ **STELLA MALU (Krimsky, Katrina & Trevor Watts)**
Mial / Stella malu / Duogeny / Rhythm circle / Crystal morning / Song for hans / Moon beams / Villa in brazil
8335162 / Jul '88 / ECM

Krishan, Gopal

☐ DHRUPAD AND KHYAL
C 560078 / Feb '96 / Ocora

☐ NORTHERN INDIA - THE ART OF THE VICHITRA VEENA (2CD Set)
C 560048/49 / Jan '94 / Ocora

Krishnan, Ramnad

☐ SONGS OF THE CARNATIC TRADITION OF SOUTH INDIA
7559720232 / Jan '95 / Nonesuch

Krisiun

☐ APOCALYPTIC REVELATION
GUN 163CD / 17 Aug '98 / Gun

Kristian, David

☐ DAVID KRISTIAN'S CRICKLEWOOD
ALIENCD 5 / 8 Sep '97 / Alien8

Kristina, Sonja

☐ HARMONICS OF LOVE
HTDCD 34 / Apr '95 / HTD

Kristine W

☐ LAND OF THE LIVING
CHAMPCD 1029 / Jul '97 / Champion

Kristine, Liv

☐ 3AM
MASSCD 151 / 16 Mar '98 / Massacre

Kristofferson, Kris

☐ COUNTRY COLLECTION, THE
Mean old man / Shipwrecked in the eighties / They killed him / What about me / El Gavilan (the hawk) / El coyote / Anthem 84 / Heart / Old road / Love is the way / Eagle and the bear / Third world warrior / Aguila del norte / Hero / Don't let the bastards (get you down) / Love of money / Third world war / Jesse Jackson / Mal Sacate / Sandinista
5540092 / 6 Apr '98 / Spectrum

☐ LEGENDARY YEARS, THE
Me and Bobby McGee / Josie / Lover please: *Kristofferson, Kris & Rita Coolidge* / Jesus was a Capricorn / Magdalene / Living legend / Help me make it through the night / Smokey put the sweat on me / Why me / Silver tongued devil / When she's wrong / I may smoke too much / Easter Island / It's never gonna be the same again / Golden Idol / I'd rather be sorry: *Kristofferson, Kris & Rita Coolidge* / Bigger the fool / Shake hands with the Devil / Nobody loves anybody anymore / Broken freedom song / Here comes that rainbow again / Epitaph (black and blue)
KKVSOPCD 141 / Apr '90 / Connoisseur Collection

☐ NATURAL ACT (Kristofferson, Kris & Rita Coolidge)
Blue as I do / Not everyone knows / I fought the law / Number one / You're gonna love yourself in the morning / Loving her was easier (than anything I'll ever do again) / Back in my baby's arms / Please don't tell me how the story ends / Hoola hoop / Love don't live here anymore / Silver mantis
5507702 / Aug '94 / Spectrum

Kristyl

☐ KRISTYL
TITANIC 001 / Oct '97 / Titanic

Krivda, Ernie

☐ ART OF THE BALLAD, THE (Krivda, Ernie & Bill Dobbins)
378062 / Oct '96 / Koch Jazz

☐ PERDIDO (Krivda, Ernie & The Fat Tuesday Band)
378522 / May '98 / Koch Jazz

Krog, Karin

☐ GERSHWIN WITH KARRIN KROG
Who cares / How long has this been going on / That certain feeling (instrumental) / My man's gone now / Nice work if you can get it / Embraceable you / They all laughed / There's a boat that's leaving soon for new york / Someone to watch over me / Summertime / I loves you, porgy
CDMR 4 / Jun '96 / Meantime

☐ HI FLY (Krog, Karin & Archie Shepp)
Sing me softly of the blues / Steam / Daydream / Solitude / Hi fly / Soul eyes
CDMR 3 / Jun '96 / Meantime

☐ I REMEMBER YOU
I remember you / Trane / Lester's happy / Moody's mood for love / It's you or no one / Lover man / Speak low / That old feeling
MR 8 / 5 May '98 / Meantime

☐ ONE ON ONE
Blues in heart / You'd be so nice to come home to / These foolish things / But not for me / God bless the child / Just in time / Song for you / Feeling too good today / Stardust / I won't dance / Medley / Scandia skies / I was doing all right / I got the right to sing the blues / Sometimes I feel like a Motherless child / Love supreme / As you are are / Going home
MR 7 / May '97 / Meantime

☐ SOMETHING BORROWED, SOMETHING NEW
Thrill is gone / Out of this world / If I should lose you / My foolish heart / Canto mai / I get a kick out of you / All blues / Meaning of the blues / This is new / Just one of those things / I'm beginning to see the light / Every time we say goodbye / Tivoli
CDMR 2 / Jun '96 / Meantime

☐ YOU MUST BELIEVE IN SPRING (Krog, Karin & Palle Mikkelborg)
CDMR 5 / Jun '96 / Meantime

Kroke

☐ EDEN
RIEN 09CD / Dec '97 / Oriente

☐ TRIO
RIEN 04CD / Dec '97 / Oriente

Krokus

☐ TO ROCK OR NOT TO BE
SPV 08543872 / Aug '95 / SPV

Kron

☐ KRON EP
88457729 / 6 Oct '97 / Harvest

Kronos Quartet

☐ AT THE GRAVE OF RICHARD WAGNER
7559793182 / Jan '98 / Nonesuch

☐ BEST OF THE KRONOS QUARTET, THE (Celebrating 25 Years Of The Kronos Quartet)
Mai Nozipo / Asleep / String quartet no.4 / America before the war / Arioso / Ecstasy / God music / Fratres / String quartet no.5/Movement 3 / Cool wind is blowing / Adagio
7559795112 / 11 May '98 / Nonesuch

☐ BLACK ANGELS
7559792422 / Jan '98 / Nonesuch

☐ DREAMS AND PRAYERS OF ISAAC THE BLIND, THE (Kronos Quartet & David Krakauer)
Prelude, calmo, sospeso / Agitato, con fuoco, maestoso, senza misura, oscilante / Teneramenta, ruvido, presto / Calmo, sospeso, allegro pesante / Postlude, lento, liberamente
7559794442 / Apr '97 / Nonesuch

☐ EARLY MUSIC
Kyrie I / Rachel's weeping / Langdans efter byfians mats / Lachrymae antiquae / Psalom / Olmpos' pentatonic / Archtas' enharmonic / Long ge / Totem ancestor / Kyrie II / Brudmarsch fra osta / Using the apostate tyrant as his tool / Synchrony no.2 / Quod libet / Viderunt omnes / Kyrie III / Four part fantasia no.2 / O vitrus sapientie / Uleg khem / Farewell my good one forever / Collected songs where every verse is filled with grief
7559794572 / 13 Oct '97 / Nonesuch

☐ GHOST OPERA (Kronos Quartet & Wu Man)
Bach, monks and Shakespeare meet in water / Earth dance / Dialogue with 'little cabbage' / Metal and stone / Song of paper
7559794452 / Apr '97 / Nonesuch

☐ HENRYK GORECKI STRING QUARTETS NO.1 & 2
7559793192 / Jan '98 / Nonesuch

☐ HOWL USA
Howl / Sing sing / Barstow / Cold War suite
7559793722 / Jul '96 / Nonesuch

☐ HUNTING GATHERING (The Kronos Quartet Play Kevin Volans)
7559792532 / Jan '98 / Nonesuch

☐ IN FORMATION
RR 9CD / Sep '91 / Reference Recordings

☐ KRONOS QUARTET (Music Of Sculthorpe/Hendrix/Sallinen/Glass & Nancarrow)
7559791112 / Jan '87 / Nonesuch

☐ KRONOS QUARTET PERFORM PHILIP GLASS, THE
7559793562 / Jan '98 / Nonesuch

☐ NIGHT PRAYERS
7559793462 / Jan '98 / Nonesuch

☐ PIECES OF AFRICA
Mai nozipo (mother nozipo) / Mai nozipo (mother nozipo) / Tilliboyo (sunset) / Ekitundu ekisooka / Escalay (waterwheel) / Washishijay (our beginning) / White man sleeps / Kutambarara (spreading the music)
7559792752 / Jan '92 / Nonesuch

☐ RELEASED 1985-1995
Mai nozipo / Tango sensations / Amazing grace / Different trains / String quartet / Salome / Black angels / Fratres / String quartet / Cool wind is blowing / Adagio for strings / Dinner music / How it happens / Elvis everywhere / Purple haze
7559793942 / Feb '96 / Nonesuch

☐ SALOME DANCES FOR PEACE (The Kronos Quartet Plays Terry Riley/2CD Set)
7559792172 / Jan '98 / Nonesuch

☐ SHORT STORIES
7559793102 / Jan '95 / Nonesuch

☐ WHITE MAN SLEEPS (Music Of Volans/ Ives/Hassell/Coleman/Lee/Johnston & Bartok)
White man sleeps no 1 / White man sleeps no 3 / White man sleeps no 5 / Scherzo holding your own / Pano da costa (Cloth from the coast) / Lonely woman / Amazing grace
7559791632 / Jul '88 / Nonesuch

☐ WINTER WAS HARD (Sallinen/Riley/ Part/Zorn/Webern/Piazzolla/ Schnittke/Barber)
Winter was hard / Fratres / Bella by barlight / Door is ajar / Half wolf dances mad in moonlight / Forbidden fruit / Quartet No 3
7559791812 / '88 / Nonesuch

☐ WITOLD LUTOSLAWKI STRING QUARTET
7559792552 / Jan '98 / Nonesuch

Kroonenberg, Philip

☐ GROUNDED
Paradise / Candy man / Magic magicians / Louisiana / Nobody's doing a thing / Chosen / Lonesome poetry / Kid is coming / Me and my babe / Jelly / Dressed to kill / Grounded / She plays the piano / Natural causes
MRCD 192 / Jun '98 / Munich

Kropinski, Uwe

☐ AFRICAN NOTEBOOK (Kropinski, Uwe & Michael Heupel)
Addababa / Addis Hotel / Vivo Antananarivo / Zanzibar / Harare
AHO 1024 / Apr '96 / ITM

Kropotkins

☐ KROPOTKINS, THE
379242 / Sep '96 / Koch International

Krosfyah

☐ FYASIDE CHRISTMAS
KRCD 9704 / 15 Dec '97 / Kalinago

☐ ULTIMATE PARTY-PUMP ME UP
CE 001 / Apr '96 / Steel Donkey

KRS 1

☐ KRS 1
Rappaz R N dainja / De automatic: *KRS 1 & Fat Joe* / MC's act like they don't know / Ah yeah / REALITY / Free mumia: *KRS 1 & Channel Live* / Hold / Wannabemceez: *KRS 1 & Mad Lion* / Represent the real hip hop: *KRS 1 & Das EFX* / Truth / Build ya skillz: *KRS 1 & Busta Rhymes* / Out for fame / Squash all beef / Health wealth self
CHIP 165 / Mar '97 / Jive

☐ RETURN OF DA BOOM BAP
CHIP 142 / Oct '93 / Jive

Kruder & Dorfmeister

☐ DJ KICKS (Various Artists)
K7 046CD / Aug '96 / Studio K7

Krunchjam

☐ KRUNCHJAM
OME 4148CD / Feb '94 / Ichiban

Krupa, Gene

☐ CLASSICS 1935-1938
CLASSICS 754 / May '94 / Classics

☐ CLASSICS 1938
CLASSICS 767 / Aug '94 / Classics

☐ CLASSICS 1939
CLASSICS 799 / Mar '95 / Classics

☐ CLASSICS 1939-1940
CLASSICS 834 / Sep '95 / Classics

☐ CLASSICS 1940 VOL.1
CLASSICS 859 / Feb '96 / Classics

☐ CLASSICS 1940 VOL.2 (Krupa, Gene & His Orchestra)
CLASSICS 883 / Jul '96 / Classics

☐ CLASSICS 1940 VOL.3
CLASSICS 917 / Jan '97 / Classics

☐ CLASSICS 1941
CLASSICS 960 / Nov '97 / Classics

☐ DRUM BOOGIE
Drum boogie / Full dress hop / There'll be some changes made / No name jive / Boogie woogie bugle boy / Babe takes a bow / Rhumboogie / St. louis blues / Boog it / Who / Yes, my darling daughter / Tuxedo junction / Deep in the blues / Sweet georgia brown / How 'bout that mess / Blue rhythm fantasy
4736592 / Aug '93 / Columbia

☐ DRUMMER MAN
Starburst (Opening Theme) / Leave us leap / Whispering / Idaho / You go to my head / Star dust / Bolero at the Savoy / Sweet Lorriane / My ideal / Up and atom / Tea for two / How high the moon / Lyonaise potatoes and some pork chops / Gypsy mood / He's funny that way / Out you go
HCD 262 / Jun '96 / Hindsight

☐ DRUMMER'S BAND 1938-1945, THE
158592 / Jul '96 / Jazz Archives

☐ DRUMMER, THE
Drum boogie / Ta-ra-ra-boom-der-e (ta-ra-ra-boom-de-ay) / Rhythm jam / Moonlight serenade / Big do / Jam on toast / Meet the beat of my heart / My own / You're as pretty as a picture / I'm gonna clap my hands / I hope Gabriel likes my music / My old Kentucky home / You and your love / Jazz me blues / Tutti frutti / Wire brush stomp / Old black Joe / Daydreaming / Apurksody / Tropical magic / Last round-up / Blues of Israel
PASTCD 7008 / Mar '93 / Flapper

☐ DRUMMIN' MAN
Drummin' man / I know that you know / Nagasaki / Symphony in riffs / Jeepers creepers / Apurksody / Fool am I / Murdy purdy / Never felt better, never had less / Ta-ra-ra-boom-der-e / Do you wanna jump, children / Madam swings it / Georgia on my mind / Wire brush stomp / Fare thee well, annie laurie / Grandfather's clock / Bolero at the savoy / Dracula
CD 56080 / Mar '95 / Jazz Roots

☐ DRUMMIN' MAN
Drummin' man / Let me off uptown / Ball of fire / Drum boogie / After you've gone / Opus one / Lover / Massachusetts / How 'bout that mess / Rockin' chair / Rhumboogy / Apurksody / Georgia on my mind / Quiet and roll 'em / No name jive / Bolero at the Savoy / Leave us leap / Swing is here / I hope Gabriel likes my music / Sing sing sing
308862 / 11 May '98 / Hallmark

☐ DRUMS DRUMS DRUMS
MACCD 362 / 26 Jan '98 / Autograph

☐ GENE KRUPA LIVE 1946 (Krupa, Gene & His Orchestra)
JH 1039 / Feb '95 / Jazz Hour

☐ GENE KRUPA VOL.1 1946-1947 (What's This) (Krupa, Gene & His Orchestra)
(Back home again in) Indiana / My old flame / Up and atom / Wings on my shoes / Calling Dr. Gillespie / They didn't believe me / Stompin' at the Savoy / What's this / Begin the beguine / My ideal / Love's in my heart / Tea for two / Bolero at the Savoy / Leave us leap / Stardust / King Porter stomp / I'll never be the same / Wire brush stomp / Otto make that riff staccato / You go to my head / Lyonaise potatoes and some pork chops / Lover
HEPCD 26 / Aug '93 / Hep

☐ GENE KRUPA VOL.2 1946 (It's Up To You)
Blue Lou / Summertime / Hodge podge / Boogie blues / Bugle call rag / Ain't nowhere / Man I love / 10 Ritchie Drive / It's up to you / Yesterdays / Margie / Night and day / By the river Sainte Marie / These foolish things / Medley: Mood indigo/Prelude to a kiss/Solitude / Medley: In a sentimental mood/ Sophisticated Lady / I hear you screaming / Baby, won't you please come home / How high the moon / Birdhouse / It's a good day / You be you / Dear Old Southland
HEPCD 46 / May '95 / Hep

☐ GENE KRUPA VOL.3 (Hop Skip & Jump) (Krupa, Gene & His Orchestra)
All by myself / That old devil moon / Yes, yes honey / How deep is the ocean / Hop, skip and jump / Out of nowhere / What is this thing called love / Some day soon / USO / And then I looked at you / Bolero at the Savoy / King Porter stomp / Old folks at home / Idaho / Where or when / In the moon mist / Dark eyes / Sweet Lorraine / He's funny that way / (Otto make that) riff Staccato / Come to the Mardis Gras / As long as I'm dreaming / Leave us leap
HEPCD 51 / Nov '96 / Hep

☐ KRUPA & RICH (Krupa, Gene & Buddy Rich)
Buddy's blues/Bernie's tune / Gene's blues / Sweethearts on parade / I never knew / Sunday / Monster
5216432 / Mar '93 / Verve

☐ LEAVE US LEAP (Krupa, Gene & His Orchestra)
Starbust (Theme song) / Blue moon / Cry and you cry alone / I should care / Leave us leap (No.1) / Coca-Cola theme / Starburst (Theme song) / Leave us leap (No.2) / Don't take your love from me / Someday soon / Invention / Maybe baby / Moontide / Big do / Linger awhile / Leave us leap (No.3) / These foolish things / It's only a paper moon / Dark eyes / Laura / Lover / Drum boogie / Disc jockey jump
JZCL 6006 / Nov '96 / Jazz Classics

☐ MASTERPIECES VOL.13 1936-1942
158302 / Mar '95 / Masterpieces

☐ RADIO YEARS, THE
JUCD 2021 / Jul '96 / Jazz Unlimited

☐ WIRE BRUSH STOMP 1938-1941 (Krupa, Gene & His Orchestra)
RACD 7117 / May '96 / Aerospace

Kruse, Kathe

☐ LE SEXE ROUGE
EFA 153852 / Jul '97 / Todliche Doris

Kruth, John

☐ BANSHEE MANDOLIN
FF 602CD / May '93 / Flying Fish

Kryptasthesie

☐ INNER WHIRL
Flying saucers / Watching the sky / Tree / Intruder / Evening following cuttlefish / Secret power / Red shift / Chocolate Queen / Pictor HH / Then my left eye began again / Enigma / His golden guitar
DELECCD 038 / May '96 / Delerium

Ksana

☐ DIDO
39840732 / 21 Aug '97 / Blue Flame

Kuban, Ali Hassan

☐ NUBIAN MAGIC
39840952 / 21 Aug '97 / Blue Flame

Kubek, Smokin' Joe

☐ CHAIN SMOKIN' TEXAS STYLE (Kubek, Smokin' Joe Band)
Way down there / Just for a little while / Love to live the life / That's what I'll do for you / Little girl / Good understanding / Overdues / Come by here / I'm on my way / Chain smokin' / Walk with you / Soft touch / Can't quit my baby
BBCD 9524 / Jan '93 / Bullseye Blues

☐ CRYIN' FOR THE MOON
CDBB 9560 / May '95 / Bullseye Blues

☐ GOT MY MIND BACK (Kubek, Smokin' Joe Band)
Got my mind back / Got you by the tail / Can't see for lookin' / All the love there is / She's it / Let me take your picture / I'm here for you / Don't touch her / Cryin' by myself / Double or nothing
CDBB 9578 / Sep '96 / Bullseye Blues

☐ TAKE YOUR BEST SHOT (Kubek, Smokin' Joe Band & Bnois King)
Roll of the dice / Worst heartache / Take your best shot / Walk on / Spanish trace / Damn traffic / You said I love you first / One night affair / So blind / Never enough
CDBB 9600 / 27 Apr '98 / Bullseye Blues

☐ TEXAS CADILLAC (Kubek, Smokin' Joe Band)
BB 9543CD / Feb '94 / Bullseye Blues

Kubis, Tom

☐ KEEP SWINGIN' (Kubis, Tom Big Band)
SB 2090 / Sep '97 / Sea Breeze

☐ TOM KUBIS PLAYS STEVE ALLEN (Kubis, Tom Big Band)
SB 2079 / Jan '97 / Sea Breeze

Kuepper, Ed

☐ BLACK TICKET
It's lunacy / Blind girl stripper / Real wild life / All my ideas run to crime / Black ticket day / Helps me understand / There's nothing natural / Walked thin wires
HOT 1040CD / Jul '95 / Hot

☐ BUTTERFLY NET, THE
Not a soul around / At times, so emotional / Nothing changes in my house / Sometimes / Everything's fine / Also sprach / Ghost of an ideal wife / New bully in the town / Sea air / Electrical storm / What you don't know / Black ticket day / Way I made you feel / Real wild life / Always the woman pays / It's lunacy / Honey steel's gold / Everything I've got
HOT 1045CD / Mar '95 / Hot

☐ CHARACTER ASSASSINATION
By the way / Little fiddle (And the ghost of Xmas past) / Cockfighter / My best interests at heart / Take it by the hand / La di doh / I'm with you / Ill wind / So close to certainty / Good soundtrack / Ring of fire / If I had a ticket
HOT 1049CD / Aug '94 / Hot

☐ CLOUDSURFIN'
Gun runnin' / Three stigmata of James Ulmer / Last of the knucklemen / Delegatin' for the mases / Don't say you don't say / My dog killed ma gurski's cook / Thickness of two planks / Bikie groupie
HOT 1069CD / Jul '98 / Hot

☐ ELECTRICAL STORM
HOT 1020CD / Jul '95 / Hot

☐ EVERYBODY'S GOT TO
Everybody's got to / Too many clues / When there's this party / Standing in the cold, in the rain / Lonely paradise / Burned my fingers / Not a soul around / Nothing changes in my house / Spartan spirituals / No skin off your nose
HOT 1044CD / Jul '95 / Hot

☐ FRONTIERLAND
All of these things / Fireman Joe / Weepin' willow / How would you plead / MDDP Limited / Pushin' fear / Roughneck blues / Someone told me / Poor Howard
HOT 1058CD / Oct '96 / Hot

☐ HONEY STEEL'S GOLD
King of vice / Everything I've got belongs to you / Friday's blue cheer/Libertines of Oxley / Honey Steel's gold / Way I made you feel / Not too soon / Closer (but disguised) / Summer field
HOT 1036CD / Mar '95 / Hot

☐ KING IN THE KINDNESS ROOM, THE
Confessions of a window cleaner / Pissed off / Highway to hell / Messin' part II / They call me Mr Sexy / Sundown / Space pirate / Diving board
HOT 1052CD / Jul '95 / Hot

☐ LIVE
Intro / Electrical storm / Honey steel's gold / Confessions of a window cleaner / Liddle fiddle / La di doh / My best interests at heart / Weepin willow blues / When I first came to this land / Black ticket day / Poor little fool
HOT 1070CD / Jul '98 / Hot

☐ ROOMS OF THE MAGNIFICENT
Rooms of the magnificent / Also sprach the king of Euro-Disco / Sea air / Sixteen days / Without your mirror / No point in working / I am your prince / Spend five years / Show pony / Nothing you can do
HOT 1027CD / Jul '95 / Hot

☐ SERENE MACHINE
When she's done / Sleepy head (serene machine) / Who's been talkin' / It's happening before / I wish you were here / Maria peripatetica / Sounds like mysterious wind / Reasons / This hideous place / (You) don't know what to steal / You can't please everybody / Married to my lazy life
HOT 1042CD / Mar '95 / Hot

☐ SINGS HIS GREATEST HITS FOR YOU
Way I made you feel / Pissed off / Real wild life / If I had a ticket / Sleepy head / This hideous place / La di doh / It's lunacy / Highway to hell / I'm with you / Black ticket day / Everything I've got belongs to you / Confessions in paradise / I wish you were here / Sad dark eyes
HOT 1057CD / Mar '96 / Hot

☐ STARSTRUCK
Lion to your lamb / Hardhats and handbags / No.3 runaway / Rape of Cornelius / Love and happiness / Eightball / Spook / Anne 1 / Spook strain / Spring is sprung / Rachel owns the creek / Favourite angel / Wenceslas' daughter / Too many things / Angel's lament / Messin' with the tall / Diving board / Love me splendour / Christmas cake / Tom's theme / Green hat / Paul and Laurie have a party / Supermarket/ Heaven / Everybody's got to you / Pleading ignorance / International playboys vs. the third reich
HOT 1064CD / Jul '97 / Hot

☐ TODAY WONDER
Horse under water / Always the woman pays / Everything I've got belongs to you / What you don't know / I'd rather be the devil / There's nothing natural / Medley / Pretty Mary / Eternally yours / If I were a carpenter
HOT 1032CD / Mar '95 / Hot

☐ WHEELIE BIN AFFAIR, THE
Highway to hell / Edmund the confessor / Steam train / No wonder/Built for comfort / It's still nowhere / Car headlights / Chlorine vendor / Indian reservation / Cyprus grove blues / Wasn't I pissed off today sayeth bing bing the techno king / Milk cow blues / Someone's responsible / Lament for a lousy lover / Eternally yours / Romance in karaoke hell
HOT 65CD / Jul '98 / Hot

☐ WITH A KNAPSACK ON MY BACK (Live)
Sleepy head / Sam hall / Highawy to hell / All of these things / Little fiddle / Weepin' willow / I'm with you / Messin' / La di doh / Eternally yours / Crowd rain chant / Poor Howard / When I first came to this land / I'd rather be the devil / Sea air / Blind girl stripper
HOT 1066CD / Jul '98 / Hot

Kuermayr, Gunther

☐ WINDOW, THE (Kuermayr, Gunther & Jerry Bergonzi)
Moving on / Window / Tudo bem / Interlude / Departure / Back bay dreams / Walk alone / Malmo / Portrait
AL 73110 / Jun '98 / A

Kuhn, Joachim

☐ JOACHIM KUHN COLLECTION, THE
CMPCD 2503 / 1 Jun '98 / CMP

☐ KUHN/HUMAIR JENNY-CLARK COLLECTION (Kuhn, Joachim & Daniel Humair/Jenny-Clark)
CMPCD 2504 / 1 Jun '98 / CMP

☐ NIGHTLINE NEW YORK
Yvonne takes a bath / April in New York / Yvonne / Nightline / Rubber boots
INAK 869CD / Jul '97 / In Akustik

Kuhn, Josie

☐ PARADISE
RTMCD 41 / Nov '92 / Round Tower

☐ WALKS WITH LIONS
RTMCD 68 / Oct '95 / Round Tower

Kuhn, Judy

☐ JUST IN TIME
VSD 5472 / Feb '95 / Varese Sarabande

Kuhn, Paul

☐ STREET OF DREAMS (Kuhn, Paul Orchestra)
Street of dreams / Manhattan / Please don't talk about me when I'm gone / Ghost of a chance / Nancy / Come rain or come shine / How long has this been going on / Sweet and lovely / 'S wonderful / My one and only love / Stars fell on Alabama / For all we know / Broadway / I'll see you in my dreams
MR 874800 / 8 Nov '97 / Mons

Kuhn, Rolf

☐ BROTHERS (Kuhn, Rolf & Joachim)
Loverman / Express / Saturday blues / Walk / Opal / What is left / Love / Brothers / Evert time we say goodbye
VBR 21842 / Jun '96 / Vera Bra

☐ MUSIC FOR TWO BROTHERS (Kuhn, Rolf & Joachim)
My friend the Yogi / Ca. 1952 / Made in Spain / Music for two brothers / One string more / Uncle Archibald / Hip elegy in kingsize / First Frisco / Swampfire / One more bass hit
5391012 / 29 Jun '98 / MPS Jazz

Kuhn, Steve

☐ CHILDHOOD IS FOREVER (Kuhn, Steve & Aldo Romano/Steve Swallow)
CDNEW 129 / 29 Jun '98 / Charly

☐ DEDICATION
RSRCD 154 / 19 May '98 / Reservoir

☐ LIVE AT MAYBECK RECITAL HALL VOL.13
Old folks / Solar / I remember you / Autumn in New York / Meaning of the blues
CCD 4484 / Oct '91 / Concord Jazz

☐ LOOKING BACK (Kuhn, Steve Trio)
Looking back / Duke / How insensitive / Stella by starlight / Alone together / Gee baby ain't I good to you / Baubles, bangles and beads / Zingaro / Will you still be mine / Emmanuel
CCD 4446 / Feb '91 / Concord Jazz

☐ MOSTLY BALLADS
Yesterdays gardenias / Tennessee waltz / Danny boy / Don't explain / Body and soul / Emily / Airegin / How high the moon
NW 351 / May '87 / New World

☐ REMEMBERING TOMORROW
Rain forest / Oceans in the sky / Lullaby / Trance / Life's backward glance / All the rest is the same / Emmanuel / Remembering tomorrow / Feeling within / Bittersweet passages / Silver
5290352 / May '96 / ECM

☐ YEARS LATER
Gloria's theme / Upper Manhattan medical group / Years later / In a sentimental mood / Ladies in Mercedes / Good bait / Sometime ago / Silver's serenade / Born to be blue / Soul eyes
CCD 4554 / Jun '93 / Concord Jazz

Kuki

☐ EYE
19842CD / Mar '97 / Crass

Kukuruza

☐ CROSSING BORDERS
SHCD 3814 / Mar '94 / Sugar Hill

☐ ENDLESS STORY
76605625052 / 24 Mar '98 / GAD

Kula Shaker

☐ K
Hey dude / Knight on the town / Temple of everlasting light / Govinda / Smart dogs / Magic theatre / Into the deep / Sleeping Jiva / Tattva / Grateful when you're dead / 303 / Start all over / Hollow man
SHAKER 1CD / Sep '96 / Columbia

Kullman, Charles

☐ 20 UNFORGETTABLE CLASSICS
Only my song / Her name is Mary / Love here is my heart / Ah sweet mystery of life / Goodnight / For the love of you / Castles in the air / I love thee / Still as the night / Beautiful garden of roses / Serenade / Thora / World is mine tonight / On the road to Mandalay / I'm falling in love with someone / Thine alone / When you're away / Gypsy love song / Smilin' through / Ahoi so tont es weithin uber's meer
CWNCD 2038 / Jun '97 / Crown

☐ SERENADE
CDMOIR 429 / Aug '95 / Memoir

Kumar, Pramod

☐ INDIA RAGA ROUTE
ARN 64277 / Oct '94 / Arion

Kumara

☐ CONFLUENCE
White spring / Red spring / Influence / Confluence
KU 9471 / Feb '95 / CDS

Kumari, Jeena

☐ LAMBADA
Lambada / Waqt ne kiya / Ab to aaja sanam / Meray naseeb / Loat aaja / Puharte challie hoon main / Awara dil / Kheyaloon main / Khushian manian / Aja ai bahar / Neley neley ambar par / Dilhai be qarar
CDSGP 0387 / Mar '98 / Prestige

Kumo

☐ KAMINARI
Together / Butterfly / Kraken awakes / Am I (That I am) / Kick your ass / Tigerstyle / Remover of obstacles / 7 buckets / (I hear) Daruma / Hubble eyes / Armed response
PSYCD 1 / Mar '97 / Psychomat

Kunda, Jali

☐ GRIOTS OF WEST AFRICA AND BEYOND
ELLICD 3510 / May '97 / Ellipsis Arts

Kundalini Flavours

☐ REVOLUTION OF UNDOING
HIGH 2 / Nov '96 / High Strangeness

Kuni Kids

☐ CONGO SQUARE
MWCD 3003 / Jun '93 / Music & Words

Kunneke, Evelyn

☐ TALKSHOW-QUEEN
Wen ich einmal wiederkomme / Talkshow-queen / Hast du vergessen wie es ist / Egon / Lass' mich noch einmal die erde beruhr'n / 70 jahre und kein bischen leise / Ich hab das alles schon einmal geseh'n / Hundepost / Meine stadt / Hoppe hoppe reiter
CD 3565 / Aug '97 / Miami

Kunz, Charlie

☐ CHARLIE KUNZ - THE MEDLEY KING
PASTCD 9783 / Jun '92 / Flapper

☐ CHARLIE KUNZ AND THE VOCALISTS
When my dreamboat comes home / Gypsy who has never been in love / Rhythm on the range medley / Everything is rhythm medley / I'm in a dancing mood / Heart of gold / Every night at eight / It's love again medley / Goodnight my love / Here's love in your eye / It's my Mother's birthday today / All alone in Vienna / Sailing home with the tide / Have you forgotten so soon / Misty islands of the highlands / Sweet dreams sweetheart / Let's sit this one out / On a steamer coming over / Looking for a little bit of blue / There was an old woman / On tour with Charlie Kunz
PASTCD 7089 / Mar '97 / Flapper

☐ CLAP HANDS, HERE COMES CHARLIE KUNZ
Clap hands here comes Charlie / Feller that played the pianner / Solo medley / Juggler / Solo medley / He was a handsome young soldier / Solo medley of Astaire/Rogers hits / Solo medley / Life begins when you're in love / Solo medley / St. James's Park / Solo medley / Star fell out of heaven / Medley/Piccadilly pickle / I was in the mood for love / Solo medley / Intro (March winds and April showers)
PASTCD 9730 / Jan '91 / Flapper

☐ FAMOUS PIANO MEDLEYS
In the blue of evening / Heavenly music / Put your arms around me honey / Close to you / Be honest with me / If you please / Roll on tomorrow / Sunday Monday or always / With all my heart / Coming in on a wing and a prayer / In my arms / Take it from there / I never mention your name / If I had my way / Ten little men with feathers / You happen once in a lifetime / Someday we shall meet again / Pedro the fisherman / I couldn't sleep a wink last night / All of my life / Amor amor / I'll get by / Don't ask me why / Don't sweetheart me / Silver wings in the moonlight / I'd like to set you to music / Johnny zero / You rhyme with everything that's beautiful / What's the good word, Mr. Bluebird / Side by side / There are such things / Darling / I want somebody / I say / When you know you're not forgotten / Soldier boy from Caroline / Mairzy doats Dozy doats / Journey to a star / You're the rainbow / I'm sending my blessings / Pocket full o'pennies / Someday soon / I'll walk alone / Swinging on a star / Shine on victory moon / Spring will be a little late this year / Echo of a serenade / San Fernando Valley / Moonlight becomes you / I met her on Monday / Mary's a grand old name / Constantly / At last / When the lights go on again / Dearly beloved / As time goes by / Touch of Texas / Daybreak / For me and my gal / Yankee doddle boy / Love is a song / Question and answer / I've got a gal in Kalamazoo / You are my sunshine / My devotion / That's the moon my son
RAJCD 855 / Jul '97 / Empress

☐ THERE GOES THAT SONG AGAIN
PASTCD 7037 / Apr '94 / Flapper

☐ ULTIMATE COLLECTION, THE
Kentucky/Chickery chick/Let it snow / I dream of you/Ashby De La Zouche / Aren't you glad you're you / It's been a long, long time/That feeling in the moonlight / Moment I saw you/I'll buy that dream / It might as well be Spring / Mariana/On the Atcheson/Topeka and the Santa Fe / I'll close my eyes/My heart is dancing with you / Till the end of time / To bed early/Bless you/Day by day / It couldn't be true/Laughing on the outside / Coax me a little bit / So would I/To each his own/You keep coming back like a song / In love in vain/All through the day/One-zy Two-zy / You are my sunshine/My devotion / That's the moon my son/Dearly beloved / As time goes by/A touch of Texas / I'll walk alone/Swinging on a star/Shine victory moon / Mairzy doats and dozy doats/A journey to a star / You're the rainbow/You rhyme with everything thats beautiful / What's the good word, Mr. Bluebird/Side by side / Silver wings in the moonlight/I'd like to set you to music / Johnny Zero/I

couldn't sleep a wink last night / Amor amor/Roll on tomorrow / Sunday, Monday or always/With all my heart / In the blue of the evening/Heavenly music / Put your arms around me honey/Daybreak / For me and my gal/Yankee doodle boy
SWNCD 007 / Oct '97 / Sound Waves

Kunzel, Erich

☐ AMEN
CD 80315 / Aug '93 / Telarc

☐ BOND AND BEYOND
Goldfinger / James bond theme / From russia with love / Dick tracy (main theme) / Dick tracy (crime spree) /Untouchables (main theme) / Al capone / It's a long road
CD 80251 / Apr '91 / Telarc

☐ MANCINI'S GREATEST HITS (Kunzel, Erich & The Cincinnati Pops Orchestra)
CD 80183 / Aug '90 / Telarc

☐ POMP AND PIZAZZ (Kunzel, Erich & The Cincinnati Pops Orchestra)
Olympic fanfare / Towards a new life / Pomp and circumstance march no. 1 (elgar) / Epic march / Coronation march (for czar alexander iii) / Rakoczy march (liszt) / Under the double eagle march (j.f. wagner) / Entry of the gladiators / Stars and stripes forever / March medley
CD 80122 / '88 / Telarc

☐ ROUND UP
Sounds of the west / Gioacchino Rossini / Magnificent seven / Furies suite / Round up / How the west was won / Gunfight at the OK Corral / Pops Hoedown / Big country / High noon / Western medley / Silverado
CD 80141 / Apr '87 / Telarc

☐ SAILING (Kunzel, Erich & The Cincinnati Pops Orchestra)
Sailing / Great Whales / Dove / Love came for me / Wave / Under the sea / New Hampshire hornpipe / Ebb tide / Sea shanties / Beyond the sea / Lonely looking sky / Be / Dear Father / Banana boat song (Day O) / Sleepy lagoon / (Sittin' on the) dock of the bay / Sleepy shores / Margaritaville / Calypso
CD 80292 / Jul '92 / Telarc

☐ STAR TRACKS (Kunzel, Erich & The Cincinnati Pops Orchestra)
Superman (the planet krypton) / Back to the future / Warp drive / Star trek i (the klingon battle) / Star trek ii (main title) / Star trek ii - epilogue - end credits / Humpback whale song / Star trek iv (main title) / Space camp / Cocoon / Lifeforce / Return of the jedi (parade of the ewoks) / Dimensions / Right stuff
CD 80146 / '88 / Telarc

☐ VERY BEST OF ERICH KUNZEL, THE
Round up / Star Trek / Sing sing sing / Tara's theme (Gone with the wind) / Unchained melody / Nessun dorma / Little fugue in G minor / Star Wars / Batman / Grand Canyon suite / From Russia with love / Olympic fanfare / Opening sequence from Chiller / Overture to the Phantom Of The Opera / Godfather / Pink Panther / O mio babbino caro / Non-stop fast polka / Op 112 / Honor, honor, do lord / Cybergenesis / Terminator / Jurassic lunch
CD 80401 / Sep '94 / Telarc

☐ YOUNG AT HEART (Kunzel, Erich & The Cincinnati Pops Orchestra)
80245 / Oct '92 / Telarc

Kuolema

☐ NOISE NOT MUSIC
AA 031 / Jul '97 / AA

Kupper, Leo

☐ ELECTRO ACOUSTIC
POGUS 210092 / Jun '97 / Pogus

Kurnia, Detty

☐ COYOR PANON
FLTRCD 519 / Sep '93 / Flame Tree

☐ DARI SUNDA
Sorban palid / Dar der dor / Emansipasi / Bandondari / Si kabayan / Semarang solo / Asih kuring / Duriran / Mamanis / Sunayama / Hana
TUGCD 1011 / Oct '95 / Riverboat

Kursaal Flyers

☐ CHOCS AWAY/ THE GREAT ARTISTE
FOAMCD 3 / Jan '94 / On The Beach

Kustbandet

☐ IN SWEDEN
CK 83401 / Jun '94 / Kenneth

☐ OSREGN (Kustbandet In Sweden)
F and B flat 7 / Heavenly music / Stackars VI / Snofall / Hon ar en skon juvel / En liten sang om dig / Honeymooning / Osregn / Rhythm in blue / Sla dig los och ta semester / Tillie / Archipelago / Drommen / Karlek ar karlek / Regntunga skyar
CKS 3401 / Jun '94 / Kenneth

Kustomized

☐ AT THE VANISHING POINT
Handcuffs / Fingertips / Permission / Bored to death / One that got away / Hound / Amy Arrow / Camp climax / Yacky doo / You make me feel weird / Film
OLE 1872 / Mar '96 / Matador

☐ BATTLE FOR SPACE, THE
Day I had some fun / Throw your voice / Puff piece / Fifth / Gorgeous / 33 1/3 / Place where people meet / Phantasmagoria, now / La guene / Air freshner
OLE 1132 / Feb '95 / Matador

Kusworth, Dave

☐ ALL THE HEARTBREAK STORIES
Next tuesday / Always be there / Lost words / Most beautiful girl in town / One sunny morning / That girl / You never told me / Last drop of wine / What time blows away / All the heartbreak stories / I'll be your angel again
CRECD 108 / Jun '94 / Creation

Kut Klose

☐ SURRENDER
Lay my body down / Don't change / Get up on it / Do me / Lovely thang / Surrender / I like / Keep on / Giving you my love again / Sexual baby / Like you've never been done
7559616682 / Mar '95 / Warner Bros.

Kutbay, Aka Gunduz

☐ PLAYS THE TURKISH NEY
PS 65078 / Aug ' / PlayaSound

Kuti, Fela

☐ AFRO BEAT
Zombie / Chop and quench / Cross examination / Upside down / Africa - centre of the world
MPG 74024 / Jan '94 / Movieplay Gold

☐ BLACK MAN'S CRY
Zombie / Shuffering and shmiling / No agreement / Shakara / Black man's cry / Lady
SHANCD 44013 / May '98 / Shanachie

☐ BUY AMERICA (Kuti, Fela Anikulapo)
Jayen Jayen / Egbe mio / Who are you / Buy America / Fight to the finish
MPG 74036 / Jan '97 / Movieplay Gold

☐ FELA'S LONDON SCENE
STCD 3007 / Oct '94 / Stern's

☐ MR. FOLLOW FOLLOW (Kuti, Fela Anikulapo)
TRCD 40022 / Jan '97 / Terrascape

☐ MUSIC OF MANY COLOURS (Kuti, Fela & Roy Ayers)
2,000 blacks got to be free / Africa, centre of the world
MPG 74042 / Jun '97 / Movieplay Gold

☐ NO AGREEMENT (Kuti, Fela Anikulapo & Africa 70)
No agreement / Dog Eat Dog
TRCD 40032 / Jan '97 / Terrascape

☐ UNDERGROUND SYSTEM
STCD 1043 / Nov '92 / Stern's

Kuti, Fela Ransome

☐ LIVE (Kuti, Fela Ransome & Ginger Baker)
Let's start / Black man's cry / Ye ye de smell / Egbe mi o
TRCD 40012 / Jan '97 / Terrascape

Kuti, Femi Anikulapo

☐ KUTI AND THE POSITIVE FORCE
340002 / Mar '96 / Melodie

Kwak

☐ A DE VLOPE
082100 / Sep '96 / Wotre Music

☐ A LA KWAKANS
082041 / Sep '96 / Wotre Music

☐ LE GA' MECI
082079 / Sep '96 / Wotre Music

Kwan, Leonard

☐ KE ALA'S MELE
DCT 38004CD / Mar '96 / Dancing Cat

Kwenda, Forward

☐ SVIKIRO (Meditations From A Mbira Master)
SH 64095 / Aug '97 / Shanachie

Kwesi

☐ TESTIMONY
Before we get busy / Heavenly daughter / Lovely / Riot in Brixton / Ain't no need / Bluesman / Testimony / Change your life / Once in a lifetime / Before we get busy / Bridge to step 2
4879942 / 10 Nov '97 / Sony Soho2

Kweskin, Jim

☐ SIDE BY SIDE
78067417902 / 27 Apr '98 / Drive Archive

Kwest Tha Madd Ladd

☐ THIS IS MY FIRST ALBUM
Everyone always said I should start my album off with a bang / 101 things to do while I'm with your girl / Disnexone / I met my baby at VIM / Base blah (off tha head) / Lubrication / What's the reaction / Daddiez home / Kwest's theme song / Skin care / Day in the life of my asspipe / Butta-few-co / Disk and dat / 125 pennies for your thoughts / Herman's head / Bludawnmeyesneekhuz / Damn / Say my name again
74321242292 / Apr '96 / American

Kwyet Kings

☐ CHERRY PIE
SCACD 109 / Jun '97 / Screaming Apple

Kyao, Rao

☐ FLAUTAS DA TERRA
68952 / Apr '97 / Tropical

Kydd, Christine

☐ HEADING HOME
FE 093CD / Oct '93 / Fellside

Kyle, Billy

☐ CLASSICS 1937-1938
CLASSICS 919 / Mar '97 / Classics

☐ CLASSICS 1939-1946
CLASSICS 941 / Jun '97 / Classics

Kyle, Jamie

☐ BACK FROM HOLLYWOOD
NTHEN 028CD / 16 Feb '98 / Now & Then

Kynard, Charles

☐ REELIN' WITH THE FEELIN'/WA-TU-WA-ZUI
Reelin' with the feelin' / Soul reggae / Slow burn / Boogaloogin' / Be my love / Stomp / Wa-tu-wa-zui / Winter's child / Zebra walk / Something / Change up
CDBGPD 055 / Aug '93 / Beat Goes Public

Kyoma

☐ RIGHT HERE WAITING
CCD 7 / Apr '95 / Music

Kyoto Nohgaku Kai

☐ JAPANESE NOH MUSIC
LYRCD 7137 / Feb '94 / Lyrichord

Kyoto Temple Monks

☐ BUDDHIST BELLS, DRUMS & CHANTS
LYRCD 7200 / Dec '94 / Lyrichord

Kypourgos, Nikos

☐ AENIGMA EST
MS 970001 / 11 May '98 / Musurgia Graeca

Kyra

☐ HERE I AM I ALWAYS AM
Agitated / Louise / It's a stick up / Here I am here I always am / Naked / Anna K / Marieke / Ego maniac / Do things right / Organic footprints / Today is the night / Laughing song
ASKCD 071 / 18 May '98 / Vinyl Japan

Kyser, Kay

☐ KOLLEGE OF MUSICAL KNOWLEDGE
JH 1047 / Jul '96 / Jazz Hour

☐ MUSIC MAESTRO PLEASE
Stairway to the stars / You don't know how much you can suffer / So you left me for the leader of a swing band / Havin' myself a time / On the Isle Of May / Indian summer / Lost and found / Two shadows / What have you got that gets me / You're lovely Madame / Music maestro please / I'm sorry for myself / Little red fox / Let this be a warning to you baby / Deep Purple / I get along without you very well / (I gotta get some) shuteye / Sixty seconds got together / Two sleepy people / Stand by for further announcements / Mama and his dreams / Johnny Peddler
RAJCD 874 / Apr '97 / Empress

Kyss

☐ ALIVE
TRO 23CD / 15 Dec '97 / Tribute

Kyuss

☐ AND THE CIRCUS LEAVES TOWN
El rodeo / One inch man / Gloria Lewis / Jumbo blimp jumbo / Phototropic / Spaceship landing / Catamaran / Size queen / Tangy zizzle / Thee ol' boozeroony / Hurricane
7559618112 / Jun '95 / Warner Bros.

☐ BLUES FOR THE RED SUN
Thumb / Green machine / Molten universe / Fifty Million year trip (Downside up) / Thong song / Apothecarie's weight / Caterpillar march / Freedom run / 800 / Writhe / Capsized
3705613402 / Feb '93 / Warner Bros.

☐ QUEENS OF THE STONE AGE
MR 063 / 8 Dec '97 / Man's Ruin

☐ WELCOME TO SKY VALLEY
Gardenia / Asteroid / Supa scoopa and mighty scoop / 100 Degrees / Space cadet / Demon cleaner / Odyssey / Conan troutman / NO / Whitewater
7559615712 / Jun '94 / Warner Bros.

☐ WRETCH
612562 / 9 Feb '98 / Dali

477

L

L-Kage
☐ BRAZILLIANT
Showtime / Dumb dumb / Freed by your love / cascade / Half of everything / My head's on fire / Candlesoap / One day the butterfly / Loudest silence / No lullaby / She is / Spacedog / Story so far
TPLP 26 CD / Jun '93 / One Little Indian

L-Big Band
☐ DAY BY DAY
LBBCD 8 / Jul '98 / LBB

☐ ELLINGTON SACRED CONCERT
LBBCD 7 / Jan '97 / LBB

☐ LIVE WITH BLUE BIRD
LBBCD 6 / Oct '94 / LBB

L7
☐ BEAUTY PROCESS, THE
Beauty process / Drama / Off the wagon / I need / Moonshine / Bitter wine / Masses are asses / Bad things / Must have more / Non existent Patricia / Me myself and I / Lorenza Glada Alessandra
8288682 / 17 Aug '98 / Slash

☐ HUNGRY FOR STINK
Andres / Baggage / Can I run / Bomb / Questioning my sanity / Riding with a movie star / Stuck here again / Fuel my fire / Freak magnet / She has eyes / Shirley / Talk box
8285312 / 15 Sep '97 / Slash

☐ SMELL THE MAGIC
SPCD 79 / Oct '95 / Sub Pop

LA 1919
☐ GIORNI FELICI
MASOCD 90094 / 27 Oct '97 / Materiali Sonori

☐ TO PLAY (Jour Speilen)
Drumming ride / Red wire / un mondo invisibile / Donne kamikaze / Qua qua qua singing ducks / Storie del dormiveglia / Fate fagotto / Sheffield Wednesday / Hanna seppellito l'uomo sbagliato
MASOCD 90063 / May '95 / Materiali Sonori

La Argentinita
☐ DUENDE Y FIGURA
20062CD / Nov '95 / Sonifolk

☐ EL AMOR BRUJO
20090CD / Nov '96 / Sonifolk

La Bamboche
☐ LA SAISON DES AMOURS
14926 / Sep '96 / Spalax

La Barriada
☐ LA BARRIADA
74321402452 / Nov '96 / Milan

La Belle Epoque
☐ MEXICAN LANDSCAPES VOL.6
PS 65906 / Feb '93 / PlayaSound

LA Blues Authority
☐ CREAM OF THE CROP
RR 89662 / Sep '96 / Roadrunner

☐ FIT FOR A KING
Crosscut saw / Floodin' in california / Night stomp / Oh pretty woman / Down don't bother me / Sky is crying / Killing floor / I'll play the blues for you / Born under a bad sign / Wrapped up in love again / Albert's jam
RR 90492 / Sep '96 / Roadrunner

☐ HATS OFF TO STEVIE RAY
Cold shot / Empty arms / Telephone song / Lenny / Things that I used to do / Pride and joy / Crossfire / Tell me / Texas flood / Look at little sister / Blues for stevie
RR 90502 / Sep '96 / Roadrunner

☐ LA BLUES AUTHORITY
RR 91862 / Sep '96 / Roadrunner

La Bolduc
☐ SONGS OF QUEBEC 1929-1939
Y225108CD / Oct '94 / Silex

La Bottine Souriante
☐ EN SPECTACLE
MPCD 3039 / May '97 / Mille Pattes

☐ JUSQU AUX P'TITES HEURES
MPCD 2037 / Mar '96 / Mille Pattes

☐ LA MISTRINE
MPCD 2038 / Mar '96 / Mille Pattes

☐ TOUT COMME AU JOUR DE L'AN
MMPCD 2035 / Mar '96 / Mille Pattes

☐ Y'A BEN DU CHANGEMENT
MMPCD 265 / Mar '96 / Mille Pattes

La Bouche
☐ SWEET DREAMS
Forget me nots / Sweet dreams / Be my lover / Fallin in love / I'll be there / Nice 'n' slow / Where do you go / I love to love / Do you still need me / Poetry in motion / Shoo be do bee do (I like that way) / Heat is on / Mama look (I love him)
74321288882 / Mar '96 / Arista

La Calaca
☐ HUAPANGUERA
3004081 / 24 Apr '98 / IMP

La Charanga Habanera
☐ ME SUBE LA FIEBRE (Love Fever)
74321362872 / Jun '96 / Milan

La Ciapa Rusa
☐ TEN DA CHEN L'ARCHET CHE LA SUNADA L'E LONGA
MWCD 4014 / May '97 / Music & Words

La Costa Rasa
☐ AUTOPILOT
11316832 / Jul '94 / Merciful Release

La Cucina
☐ BLOOM
Through the eyes / Secrets / Devil / Who's in control / Desperado Dan / Half way to the moon / Malavita part 1 / Malavita part 2 / I nostri / Seven days / Fly away / Motivation / Picture
OSMOCD 012 / Jul '97 / Osmosis

☐ CHUCHERIA
Patagonia / Zio Pepe / Rain / Majnoon / Sucalo / Witless / Armageddon train / lato muerta / Carmen / Tour / Mare chiare / Windy windy dance night
LAC 123CD / Mar '94 / La Cucina
OSMOCD 002 / Oct '95 / Osmosys

☐ NABUMLA
Embers / Buddhas (are we) / Light shine through / Heart again / Runner / Guy Debord is sleeping / L'Americana / Villa laterno / Struggle / Question / Naked in the sunshine
OSMOCD 007 / Mar '96 / Osmosys

La Donnas
☐ SHADY LANE
No way to treat a lady / Junkman / O'Donna / Invasion / Dirty bird / Feel the pain / Death of Beewak / Long legs / Bring it on by / Counter unload / She pays the rent / Wake me / Scene's gonna get you tonight
PO 145CD / Oct '96 / Scooch Pooch
206142 / Jul '97 / Scooch Pooch

La Dusseldorf
☐ FIRST ALBUM
CTCD 064 / Jul '97 / Captain Trip

☐ INDIVIDUELLOS
CTCD 066 / Oct '97 / Captain Trip

☐ VIVA
Viva / White overalls / Rheinita / Vogel / Geld / Cha cha 2000
CTCD 065 / Jul '97 / Captain Trip

La Famille Dembele
☐ AIRA YO (La Danse Des Jeunes Griots)
ARNR 1596 / Aug '97 / Amiata

La Faro, Scott
☐ ALCHEMY OF SCOTT LA FARO, THE (Various Artists)
Too close for comfort / I've never been in love before / Time remembered / Jade vision / Variants on a theme of Thelonious Monk (criss cross) / C and D / First take / Alchemy of Scott La Faro
CD 53213 / Jan '96 / Giants Of Jazz

La Floa Maldita
☐ DEDICATION SEPERATION
EEFA 127522 / Nov '95 / Kodex

☐ L'OASIS
SPV 7625892 / Oct '96 / SPV

LA Four
☐ EXECUTIVE SUITE
Blues wellington / Amazonia / You and I / Simple invention / Entr'Acte / My funny valentine / Chega de Saudade
CCD 4215 / Nov '95 / Concord Jazz

☐ LA FOUR
Dindi / Rainbows / Rondo es pressivo / Manteca / St. Thomas / Concierto de Aranjuez
CCD 4018 / Sep '86 / Concord Jazz

☐ LA FOUR SCORES
Sundancers / Carioca hills / Allemande and the fox / Berimbau carioca / Cielo / Prelude op 28 no 4 / How insensitive / Old time rag / Manha de carnaval
CCD 6008 / Jul '88 / Concord Jazz

☐ LIVE AT MONTREUX
CCD 4100 / Jul '96 / Concord Jazz

☐ MONTAGE
Madame butterball / Syrinx / Samba for Ray / Teach me tonight / Rado's got the blues / My romance / Bachianas brasilerias No.5 / Squatty roo
CCD 4156 / Jan '95 / Concord Jazz

☐ ZACA
Zaca / You can't go home again / Child is born / O barquinho / Close ecounter for love / Pavanne op50 / Secret love
CCD 4130 / Feb '94 / Concord Jazz

La Gloria Matancera
☐ EL LIMONCITO 1948-1952
TCD 071 / Jul '96 / Tumbao Cuban Classics

☐ VENGO ARROLLANDO 1937-1949
TCD 066 / Jul '96 / Tumbao Cuban Classics

La Grand Rouge
☐ TRAVERSER DU PAYS
199732 / Oct '93 / Hexagone

La Grande Bande Des Cornemuses
☐ FAUT QU' CA BRILLE
B 6743CD / Jul '94 / Auvidis/Ethnic

LA Guns
☐ AMERICAN HARDCORE
FNA / What I've become / Unnatural act / Give / Don't pray / Pissed / Mine / Kevorkian / Hey world / Next generation / Hugs and needles / I am alive
06076862052 / Apr '97 / CMC

☐ WASTED
MLSB 002 / 1 Jul '98 / Stand Back

La India Del Oriente
☐ LA REINA DE LA GUAJIRA
CCD 9012 / Jan '98 / Fresh Sound

La Lengua Asesina
☐ HOTEL OPERA
SLR 026 / 22 Jun '98 / Smells Like

La Lugh
☐ BRIGHID'S KISS
LUGH 961CD / Mar '96 / Lughnasa

La Marienne
☐ UN BAL EN VENDEE
MRV 797CD / Nov '95 / MRV

La Mirlitanouille
☐ LA MIRLITANOUILLE 1975-1980
IG 7779CD / Aug '95 / Diffusion Breizh

La Misma Gente
☐ EL LOCO
TUMICD 030 / '92 / Tumi

La Moresca
☐ SARACENIA
RD 5033CD / Aug '96 / Robi Droli

La Morte De La Maison
☐ ARROND RED
SPV 08419592 / May '95 / SPV

La Muerte
☐ RAW
Speed, steel and gasoline / Serial killer / Black God, white devil / Hate love / Power / Wild fucker / Lucifer Sam / KKK / Couteau dans l'eau / Blood on the moon / Ecoute cette priere / Mannish boy / Shoot in your back / Kung fu fighting / Wild thing
BIAS 266CD / May '94 / Play It Again Sam

La Musgana
☐ EL DIABLO COJUELO
H 028CD / Jun '94 / Sonifolk

☐ LAS SEIS TENTACIONES
XENO 4030 / Apr '95 / Xenophile

☐ LUBICAN
GL 4010CD / Jan '94 / Green Linnet

La Negra Graciana
☐ SON JAROCHO
COCD 109 / Oct '94 / Corason

La Negra, Tona
☐ ORACION CARIBE
ALCD 023 / Jun '96 / Alma Latina

La Nina De Los Peines
☐ ART OF FLAMENCO VOL.7, THE
MAN 4856 / Oct '95 / Mandala

La Noche Celta
☐ RAMON PRADA
FA 8754CD / Nov '96 / Fono Astur

La Orquesta Del Tango De Buenos Aires
☐ LA ORQUESTA DEL TANGO DE BUENOS AIRES
74321453312 / Feb '97 / Milan Sur

La Palma
☐ SUCCES ET RARETES 1930-1936
701572 / Sep '96 / Chansophone

La Piazza
☐ MILANDE
FY 8003CD / Dec '97 / Robi Droli

La Piva Del Carner
☐ LA PEGRA A LA MATEINE
NT 6735CD / Apr '95 / Robi Droli

☐ M'HAN PRESA
FY 8001CD / Aug '97 / Robi Droli

La Rue, D.C.
☐ BEST OF D.C. LA RUE, THE (Let Them Dance)
Cathedrals / Don't keep it in the shadows / Face of love / Indiscreet / Let them dance / Do you want the real thing / Hot jungle drums and voodoo rhythm / Meter men / So much for LA
HTCD 35 / 20 Apr '98 / Hot Productions

La Secta
☐ FUZZ GOD
MRCD 119 / Jun '97 / Munster

☐ MEMORIES VOL.1
HELL 42 / Nov '97 / Munster

La Sonora Majestad
☐ LA NEGRA TOMASA
TUMICD 026 / '91 / Tumi

La Sonora Matancera
☐ EN GRANDE
TUMICD 022 / '91 / Tumi

☐ FROM CUBA TO NEW YORK
CDHOT 603 / Jun '96 / Charly

☐ LIVE ON THE RADIO 1952-1958
HQCD 79 / Sep '96 / Harlequin

☐ NOW AND FOREVER
CDHOT 634 / 16 Mar '98 / Charly

La Sonora Poncena

☐ OPENING DOORS
Bamboleo / La rumba es mia / Dejala que siga / Conga yumbambe / A la patria mia / Son matamoroscelia / La mora / Ese animal / Ese mar es mio / No me cambie camino / Cobarde / Quitate la mascara
CDHOT 514 / Sep '94 / Charly

La Souris Deglinguee

☐ LA SOURIS DEGLINGUEE
ROSE 6CD / '88 / New Rose

LA Star

☐ POETESS
Wonderous dream / NPT posse / Do you still love me / Swing to the beat / It's like that / Fade to black / My tale / It takes a real woman / Once upon a time / If you don't wanna party / NPT posse (UK remix)
FILECD 290 / Jul '90 / Profile

LA Synthesis

☐ MATRIX SURFER
PIAS 533010120 / Apr '97 / Shield

La Touche

☐ CAJUN DANCE PARTY
PLATCD 3938 / Mar '95 / Platinum

La Veillee Est Jeune

☐ JE SUIS MAL MARIE
LVJ 002CD / Apr '96 / LVJ

La Verne, Elisha

☐ HER NAME IS
ADPTCD 4 / Mar '97 / Adept

La Vienta

☐ JAZZMENCO
Tu sonrisa / Train to paris / Skeleton samfa / San miquel / Summer rain / Mecca / My desert home / Moroccan face dance / Isle of hope / Spanish invasion / Paisano / Legend of triana / Paco's night out / Shores of spain
CD 83353 / Aug '93 / Telarc

☐ NIGHT DANCE
Journey / Love for Isabel / Ariana / Tranquilo / El gato negro / Ojo caliente carnival / Beto's turn / Goodbye tomorrow / En la cueva / Promise of St Matthew / Samba loco
CD 83359 / Jun '94 / Telarc

Lab Report

☐ EXCISION
INV 082CD / 27 Oct '97 / Invisible

☐ UNHEALTHY
Open your mind / Rant / Rave / Fig.11-22 / Signal to signal / Walk in blood / Fig.x1x-1 / Fig.v111-43
CDDVN 31 / Jun '94 / Devotion

Labanda

☐ NO TODO ES SEDA
21065CD / Nov '95 / Sonifolk

LaBarbera, Joe

☐ JMOG
Game's afoot / Elvin's share / Dark ocean / Sierra Nevada / Elk the moochie / Another rainy day / Night/ Morning
SKCD 22031 / Jun '93 / Sackville

LaBeef, Sleepy

☐ I'LL NEVER LAY MY GUITAR DOWN
ROUCD 3142 / Jun '96 / Rounder

☐ LARGER THAN LIFE (6CD Set)
Baby let's play house / Don't make me go / All alone / I'm through / Lonely / All the time / All the time / Lonely / I ain't gonna take it / Little bit more / Ballad of a teenage Queen / You're so easy to love / I wish I was the moon / Ways of a woman / Home of the blues / You're the nearest thing to heaven / Guess things happen that way / Can't get you off my mind / I found out / Turn me loose / Ridin' fence / Ride on Josephine / Lonely / Just a closer walk with thee / I won't have to cross Jordan alone / Drink up and go home / Teardrop on a rose / Long time to forget / Goodnight Irene / Leave me alone with the blues / Oh so many years / Somebody's been beatin' my time / Bring around Rosie / Completely destroyed / Another mile to go / This new love / You can't catch me / Everybody's got to have somebody to love / Shame shame shame / Ain't got no home / I feel a lot more like I do now / I'm too broke to pay attention / Drinking again / Man in my position / Go ahead on / Schneider / Sure beats the heck outta' settlin' down / Too young to die / Two hundred pounds of hurt / If I go right, I'm wrong / Everyday / Man alone / Too much monkey business / Sixteen tons / Got you on my mind / Birds of all nations / Back of his hand / Asphalt cowboy / Blackland farmer / She's bringin' me down / Buying a book / Me and Bobby McGee / Boom, boom, boom / It ain't sanitary / Honey hush / Hundred pounds of lovin' / Ballad of Thunder Road / I'm ragged but I'm right / Tender years / Other side of you / Stormy Monday blues / Cool water / Mule train / Streets of Laredo / Ghost riders in the sky / Bury me not on the lone prairie / Tumbling tumbleweeds / Strawberry roan / High noon / Wagon wheels / Home on the range / There ain't much after taxes / Good rockin' boogie / Roll over Beethoven / Party doll / I'm gonna be a wheel someday / You can't have her / Mathilda / Faded love / From a Jack to a King / Send me some lovin' / You can't judge a book by it's cover / Young fashioned ways / Sittin' on top of the world / Matchbox / Corrine, Corrina / Let's turn back the years / What am I living for / Reconsider baby / Raining in my heart / Put your arms around me / Elvira / Polk salad Annie / I'm the man / Queen of the silver dollar / Long tall Texan / Stay all night, stay a little longer / Tall oak tree / Take me back to Tulsa / Blue moon of Kentucky / I'll keep on loving you / I won't have to cross Jordan alone / Just a closer walk with thee / Satisfied / Ezekiel's boneyard / I saw the light / I'll never let the Devil win / This train / I'll be somewhere listening / I feel like travelling on / Old country church / Standing in the shadows / Walk and talk with my Lord / Rock'n'roll Ruby / Big Boss man / I'm ready if you're willing / I'm coming home / I'm a one woman man / Shotgun boogie / Boogie woogie country girl / Mystery train / There is something on your mind / Jack and Jill boogie / Blues stay away from me / Honky tonk hardwood floor / Tore up / Flying saucers rock'n'roll / Red hot / Honky tonk man / My sweet love ain't around / If you don't love me someone else will / Milk cow blues / Ride, ride, ride / Are you teasing me / LaBoef's cajun boogie / Go ahead on baby / Sick and tired / Mind your own business / Lonesome for a letter / Detour / Cigarettes and coffee blues / Cut across Shorty / I'm feelin' sorry
BCD 15662 / Nov '96 / Bear Family

☐ NOTHIN' BUT THE TRUTH
Tore up over you / How do you talk to a baby / Milk cow blues / Just pickin' / Gunslinger / Ring of fire / Boogie at the Wayside Lounge / Worried man blues / Let's talk about us / My toot toot / Jambalaya / Whole lot of shakin'
ROUCD 3072 / Jul '91 / Rounder

☐ ROCKIN' DECADE, A
CPCD 8303 / May '97 / Charly

☐ STRANGE THINGS HAPPENING
Sittin' on top of the world / Playboy / Young fashioned ways / Waltz across texas / I'll be there / I'll keep on loving you / Strange things happening / Trying to get to you / You're my baby / Life turned her that way / Standing in the need of prayer / Just call me lonesome / Inside looking out / Stagger lee
ROUCD 3129 / Apr '94 / Rounder

Labelle, Patti

☐ EARLY YEARS, THE (Labelle, Patti & The Bluebells)
Sold my heart to the junkman / One phone call / Have I sinned / Academy award / Go on (This is goodbye) / Island of unbroken hearts / Impossible / Decatur street / Where are you / Down the aisle / Tear after tear / What kind of heart / Danny boy / Please hurry home / I believe / I walked right in / Itty bitty twist / When Johnny comes marching home / You'll never walk alone / Joke's on you / You will fill my eyes no more / Love me just a little / Cool water / My bridal gown / I sold my heart to the junkman
CDCHD 441 / Feb '93 / Ace

☐ GEMS
I'm in love / All this love / Right kinda lover / This world is all too good to be through / I never stopped loving you / Stay in my corner / If I didn't have you / I can't tell my heart what to do / Time will tell / Our world / Come as you are
MCD 10870 / 8 Sep '97 / MCA

☐ I SOLD MY HEART TO THE JUNKMAN
HADCD 179 / Nov '95 / Javelin

☐ SPIRIT'S IN IT/I'M IN LOVE AGAIN/ PATTI (2CD Set)
Spirit's in it / Here you come again / Love lives / I fell in love without warning / Boats against the current / Rockin' pneumonia and the boogie woogie flu / Family / Shoot him on sight / Over the rainbow / I'm in love again / Lover man (oh where can you be) / Love need and want you / If only you knew / Body language / I'll never never give up / Love bankrupt / When am I gonna find true love / Love symphony / Living double / Where I wanna be / Shy / Look to the rainbow / I can't forget you / What can I do for you / If you don't know me by now
WESD 209 / May '98 / Westside

Labeque, Katia

☐ LITTLE GIRL BLUE
We will meet again / My funny valentine / On fire / Besame mucho / Prologo / Little girl blue / Quizas quizas quizas / Volcano for hire / Turn out the stars / Summertime / La comparsa
FDM 361862 / Oct '95 / Dreyfus

Laberinto

☐ FREAKEAO
M 7034CD / 13 Apr '98 / Mascot

☐ PRIORITY
M 7023CD / Oct '96 / Mascot

Labradford

☐ LA BRADFORD
BFFP 136CD / Nov '96 / Blast First

☐ MI MEDIA NARANJA
S / P / WR / CM / G / V / P
BFFP 144CD / 13 Oct '97 / Blast First

Labyrinth

☐ RETURN TO HEAVEN DENIED
398414176CD / 20 Jul '98 / Metal Blade

Lacen, Anthony

☐ ANTHONY 'TUBA FATS' LACEN/RUE CONTI JAZZBAND/D.KELLIN
BCD 344 / Jun '95 / GHB

Lackerschmid, Wolfgang

☐ LIVE CONVERSATION
Line for Lyons / Constanchita / Waltz for Berlin / You took advantage of me / Sabada / Stefanie / Bye bye blackbird
INAK 852 / Nov '97 / In Akustik

Lacrimosa

☐ ANGST
HOS 7711CD / 27 Apr '98 / Hall Of Sermon

☐ EINSAMKEIT
HOS 7721CD / 27 Apr '98 / Hall Of Sermon

☐ INFERNO
HOS 7761CD / 27 Apr '98 / Hall Of Sermon

☐ LIVE (2CD Set)
Lacrimosa theme / Ich bin der brennende komet / Vermachtnis der sonne / Deine nahe / Tranen der sehnsucht / Siehst du mich im licht / Not every pain hurts / Schakal / Seele in not / Kabinett der sinne / Make it end / Satura / Stolzes herz / Versiegelt glanzumstromt / Versuchung / Copycat / Alles luge
HOS 7791CD / 15 Jun '98 / Hall Of Sermon

☐ SATURA
HOS 7741CD / 27 Apr '98 / Hall Of Sermon

☐ STILLE
HOS 7781CD / 27 Apr '98 / Hall Of Sermon

☐ STOLZES HERZ
HOS 771CD / 27 Apr '98 / Hall Of Sermon

Lacuna Coil

☐ LACUNA COIL
CM 77201CD / 26 Jan '98 / Century Media

Lacy, Steve

☐ 5XMONK 5XLACY
SHCD 144 / Oct '97 / Silkheart

☐ AXIEME
1231202 / Apr '93 / Red

☐ BLINKS (2CD Set)
ARTCD 6189 / Jul '97 / Hat Art

☐ CLANGS (Lacy, Steve Double Sextet)
ARTCD 6116 / Jan '94 / Hat Art

☐ COMMUNIQUE (Lacy, Steve & Mal Waldron)
1212982 / Aug '97 / Soul Note

☐ FIVE FACINGS
FMPCD 85 / May '97 / Full Moon

☐ FLAME, THE
Match / Wet spot / Gusts / Licks / Flame
1210352 / Nov '90 / Soul Note

☐ FLIM-FLAM (Lacy, Steve & Steve Potts)
ARTCD 6087 / Nov '91 / Hat Art

☐ IMAGE (DUO PERFORMANCES) (Lacy, Steve & Steve Arguelles)
AHUM 001 / Apr '89 / Ah-Um

☐ LET'S CALL THIS...ESTEEM (Lacy, Steve & Mal Waldron)
Let's call this / Monk's dream / In a sentimental mood / Snake out / Blues for Aida / Johnny come lately / What it is / Evidence / Epistrophy / Esteem
SLAMCD 501 / Oct '96 / Slam

☐ MORE MONK
1212102 / Apr '91 / Soul Note

☐ PACKET (Lacy, Steve & Irene Aebi/ Frederic Rzewski)
NA 080 / Dec '95 / New Albion

☐ REFLECTIONS (Steve Lacy Plays Thelonious Monk)
Four in one / Reflections / Hornin' in / Bye-ya / Let's call this / Ask me now / Skippy
OJCCD 63 / Sep '93 / Original Jazz Classics

☐ REMAINS
ARTCD 6102 / May '92 / Hat Art

☐ SANDS
TZA 7124 / 13 Jul '98 / Tzadik

☐ SCHOOL DAYS (Lacy, Steve & Roswell Rudd Quartet)
ARTCD 6140 / Apr '94 / Hat Art

☐ SOPRANO SAX
Day dream / Alone together / Work / Rockin' in rhythm / Little girl your daddy is calling you / Easy to love
OJCCD 130 / Nov '95 / Original Jazz Classics

☐ SPIRIT OF MINGUS (Lacy, Steve & Eric Watson)
FRLCD 016 / Oct '92 / Freelance

☐ STEVE LACY
Easy to love / Daydream / Let's cool one / Rockin in rhythm / Something to live for / Alone together / Work / Skippy / Monk's wood / Bye-ya
CD 53260 / Jan '96 / Giants Of Jazz

☐ STRAIGHT HORN OF STEVE LACY, THE
Louise / Introspection / Donna Lee / Played twice / Air / Criss cross
CCD 79007 / Feb '97 / Candid

☐ TRICKLES
Trickles / I feel a draught / Bite / Papa's midnight / Robes
1200082 / Oct '90 / Black Saint

☐ VESPERS (Lacy, Steve Octet)
1212602 / Nov '93 / Soul Note

☐ WE SEE
ARTCD 6127 / Sep '93 / Hat Art

☐ WEAL AND WOE
EM 4004 / Dec '95 / Emanem

☐ WINDOW, THE (Lacy, Steve Trio)
1211852 / Oct '90 / Soul Note

Ladae

☐ LADAE
5305422 / Jul '96 / Polydor

Ladnier, Tommy

☐ LEGENDARY NEW ORLEANS TRUMPET
159012 / 5 Jan '98 / Jazz Archives

☐ TOMMY LADNIER 1923/1939
CD 53271 / May '98 / Giants Of Jazz

☐ TRUMPET STYLIST, A
414652 / Apr '96 / Music Memoria

Ladonnas

☐ ROCK YOU ALL NIGHT LONG
Rock you all night long / Pick up the pieces / No direction / Just go / Inside / We want your money / Johnny liar liar / Perfect stranger / Hypnotised / Destruction man / That's rock 'n' roll
60432 / 24 Aug '98 / Epitaph

Lady G

☐ GOD DAUGHTER
VPCD 1436 / Oct '95 / VP

Lady June

☐ LADY JUNE'S LINGUISTIC LEPROSY
Some day silly twenty three / Reflections / Am I / Everythingsnothing / Tunion / Tourist / Bars / Letter / Mangel/Wurzel / To whom it may not concern / Optimism / Touch-downer
SEECD 350 / Jun '97 / See For Miles

Lady Lu

☐ EVERYBODY DANCE
64001440412 / 14 Jul '98 / ARES

Lady Of Rage

☐ NOTHING ROUGHNESS
INTD 90109 / 25 Aug '97 / Interscope

Lady Saw

☐ BEST OF LADY SAW, THE
VPCD 15162 / Mar '98 / VP

☐ COLLECTION, THE
DRCD 003 / 13 Oct '97 / Diamond Rush

☐ GIVE ME THE REASON
RUSHCD 1 / May '96 / Diamond Rush

☐ PASSION
VPCD 1493 / Jul '97 / VP

Ladybird

☐ BALANCE (Ladybird/Merzbow)
HW 015 / 29 Sep '97 / Human Wreckords

Ladybug Transistor

☐ BEVERLEY ATONALE
MRG 121CD / Mar '97 / Merge

Ladysmith Black Mambazo

☐ BEST OF LADYSMITH BLACK MAMBAZO, THE
SHCD 43098 / Jul '92 / Shanachie

☐ CLASSIC TRACKS
SHANCD 43074 / Oct '90 / Shanachie

☐ HEAVENLY
Inkanyesi nezazi / Yith umlilo ovuthayo / Knockin' on heaven's door / Oh happy day / People get ready / Take my hand precious Lord / Sohlabeleulu Hosana / I'll take you there / Rain rain beautiful rain / River of dreams / Jesus is my leader / Chain gang / He showed me his hands / Ilingelo Ngelakho
5407902 / Aug '97 / A&M

☐ INALA
Buya uz'ekhaya / That's why I choose you / Wahlala emnyango / Ngothandaza njalo / Kulomhlaba (thula) / Udla nge'nduku zabanye / Pauline / Isala kutshelwa / Kwashintsh's isthothobala / Uthando oluphelayo
SHANCD 43040 / Mar '89 / Shanachie

☐ INDUKU ZETHU
Mangosuthu / Induku selhu / Vukani / Kubi ukungalaeli / Ithemba lakho / Isono sami sentombi / Ingwe idla ngamabala / Umzalwane / Ifa lobukhosana / Wayabimba mfana / Watatazela / Bakhuphuka izwe lanke
SHANCD 43021 / '88 / Shanachie

☐ INKANYEZI NEZAZI
FLTRCD 502 / Aug '97 / Flame Tree

☐ JOURNEY OF DREAMS
Umusa kankulunkulu / Lindelani / Ukhalangami / Bhasobha / Hamba dompasi / Ungayoni into enhle / Amaphiko okundiza / Wayibambezeka / Ungakhowlwa rain / Amazing grace
9257532 / Aug '88 / WEA

☐ LIPH'IQINISO
Mus' ukumbulal' umuntu / Ayikh' indaw' enjengekhaya / Woza ngihambe nawe / Ekusen' emathunenI / Ubuhle beqabane / Umnjonj' asiwutholanga / Liph' iqiniso / Akesekh' engimzondayo / Abezizwe ngeke bayiqede / Isifikil' inkululeko
FLTRCD 522 / Feb '94 / Flame Tree

☐ SHAKA ZULU
Unomathemba / Hello my baby / At Golgotha / King of kings / Earth is never satisfied / How long / Home of the heroes / These are the guys / Rain rain beautiful rain / Who were you talking to
K 9255822 / Mar '94 / WEA

☐ SPIRIT OF SOUTH AFRICA, THE (The Very Best Of Ladysmith Black Mambazo)
Homeless / Hello my baby / Kangivumanga / Lelilungelo elkaho / Nomathemba / Nkosi yamakhosi / Sisesiqhingini / Zithi nqongqongo / Liph' iqiniso / Inhlelemtombi / Nansi imali / Izinto ziyavuma / Uthando olungaka / Zintombi / Awu wemadoda / Vulani amasango / Yanda yabeletha / Akehlulek'ubaba
NSCD 021 / Oct '97 / Nascente

☐ STAR AND THE WISEMAN, THE
669112 / Nov '92 / Melodie

☐ THUTHUKANI MGOXOLO - LET'S DEVELOP IN PEACE
FLTRCD 528 / Apr '96 / Flame Tree

☐ TWO WORLDS ONE HEART
Township jive / Ofana naye (nobody like him) / Bala ubhale (count and write) / Love your neighbor / Leaning on the everlasting arms / Rejoice / Hayi ngalesiskhathi (not right now) / Emhlabeni (in this world) / Isikhathi siyimal (time is money) / Ngomnyango (by the door)
7599261252 / May '90 / WEA

☐ ULWANDLE OLUNCGWELE
Izithembiso zenkosi / Limnandi izulu / Ulwandle oluncgwele / Sishuma yel'Ivangeli / Siphaum emnamlezweni / Nksoi yami ngabusinswa / Ayan qikazza amagwala / Baba no mama / Khayelihle khaya lami / Lifikile Ivangeli / Woza emthon jeni / Vukari sihambe zingelosi
SHCD 43030 / Mar '98 / Shanachie

☐ UMTHOMBO WAMANZI
SHANCD 43055 / Aug '88 / Shanachie

☐ ZULU TRADITIONAL
VICG 52302 / Mar '96 / JVC World Library

LaFarge, Peter

☐ ON THE WARPATH/AS LONG AS THE GRASS SHALL GROW
Look again to the wind / Senecas / Damn redskins / Tecumseh / Take back your atom bomb / Vision of a past warrior / Coyote / My little brother / Alaska / Custer trail of tears / Hey Mr. President / Touriste / Last words / Ballad of Ira Hayes / Johnny half breed / Radioactive Eskimo / Crimson parson / Move over, grap a 'holt / Gather round / If I could not be an Indian / Drums / White girl / I'm an Indian, I'm an alien / Stampede / Please come back, Abe-War Whoop Father
BCD 15626 / Jun '92 / Bear Family

☐ SONGS OF THE COWBOYS/IRON MOUNTAIN SONGS
Whoopee ti yi yo / Chisholm trail / Sirey peaks / Lavendar cowboy / I've got no use for the women / I ride old paint / Cowboy's lament / Yavipii Pete / When the work's all done this fall / Cowboy's dream / Black walkin' / John Strawberry Roan / Rodeo hand / Cattle calls / Stumbling / Pop Reed / Pony called Nell / Marijuana blues / Snow bird blues / Hungry blues / Avril blues / Santa Fe / Alaska 49th State / Iron mountain / Falling stars / Abraham Lincoln / Cisco Houston
BCD 15627 / Jun '92 / Bear Family

LaFave, Jimmy

☐ AUSTIN SKYLINE
BBEAT 8004 / Jan '94 / Bohemia Beat

☐ HIGHWAY TRANCE
LDCD 80002 / Sep '94 / Lizard

☐ ROAD NOVEL
You'll never know / Hold on / Vast stretches of broken heart / Into your life / Ramblin' sky / Home sweet Oklahoma / Buckets of rain / Long ago with miles between / Long time since the last time / Never put the blame / Open space / You've got that right / Big wheels / Heart of a woman / Great night
BBEA 7 / Jul '97 / Bohemia Beat
SBDCD 4 / 20 Apr '98 / Southbound

Laferriere, Marc

☐ LIVE AT THE CAVEAU DE LA HUCHETTE (1978/1979) (Laferriere, Marc Dixieland Jazz Band)
Pyramid / High society / FB blues / New resurrection / When the saints / C'est si bon chez serge / Image d'automne / Caravan / Struttin' with some barbecue / Petite fleur / Jazzap / Goldwing ramble / Lazy river / Cornet's chop suey / Plein jazz / Moulin a cafe / Moonlight serenade / Honda / Au 101 / Pilou pilou
17148 / Apr '98 / Laserlight

Lafertin, Fapy

☐ HUNGARIA (Lafertin, Fapy Le Jazz)
LJFL 2 / Nov '97 / Le Jazz

☐ SWINGING GUITARS (Lafertin, Fapy Le Jazz)
LJFL 1 / Nov '97 / Le Jazz

Laffy, Gerry

☐ MUSIC AND THE MAGIC
WKFMXD 152 / Jul '90 / FM

Lafitte, Guy

☐ LOTUS BLOSSOM (Lafitte, Guy & Wild Bill Davis)
Lotus blossom / Here's that rainy day / Colline / Ain't misbehavin' / Nature boy / Samba de orfeo / Child is born / Stuffy / Come sunday / Passion flower
BLE 591882 / Apr '91 / Black & Blue

☐ THINGS WE DID LAST SUMMER, THE
Things we did last summer / Sweet lorraine / Stephane's song / La fete au village (umbrella man) / Sweet and lovely / Tinto time / Boudouche / God bless the child / Sixteen years later, your eyes / On the trail
BLE 591922 / Apr '91 / Black & Blue

Laforet, Marie

☐ 1960'S FRENCH EP COLLECTION VOL.1, THE
174752 / Nov '97 / Magic

☐ 1960'S FRENCH EP COLLECTION VOL.2, THE
174762 / Nov '97 / Magic

☐ 1960'S FRENCH EP COLLECTION VOL.3, THE
175452 / Nov '97 / Magic

☐ MANCHESTER ET LIVERPOOL
331622 / 24 Apr '98 / Musidisc

Lag Wagon

☐ HOSS
FAT 532CD / Nov '95 / Fatwreck Chords

☐ TRASHED
FAT 5132 / Feb '94 / Fatwreck Chords

Lagaretta, Felix

☐ PUPY Y SU CHARANGA
TUMICD 033 / '93 / Tumi

Lagonia

☐ ETC, ETC
HBG 122/12 / Apr '94 / Background

Lagowski

☐ WIRE SCIENCE
TEQM 93002 / Jun '97 / TEQ

Lagrave, Jean-Francois

☐ ZOUK MALOYA
PS 65077 / Aug '91 / PlayaSound

Lagrene, Birelli

☐ BIRELLI LAGRENE & LARRY CORYELL/MIROSLAV VITOUS (Lagrene, Birelli & Larry Carlton/ Miroslav Vitous)
PSP no.2 / Berga / All the things you are / Albi / Solo no.1 / Wawe / Gloria's step / All blues
INAK 8610 / Jul '97 / In Akustik

☐ BLUE EYES
Foggy day / Witchcraft / Lady is a tramp / I've got a crush on you / My kind of town / I've got you under my skin / It's alright with me / You make me feel so young / Come fly with me / Here's that rainy day / Luck be a lady / April in Paris / Autumn in New York
FDM 365912 / 27 Apr '98 / Dreyfus

☐ LIVE (Lagrene, Birelli Ensemble)
Birelli / Minor swing / Spain / Rue De Pierre / Ornithology / Sim / Nuits de St. Germain de pres / Night of a champion / I can't give you anything but love / Moll blues
INAK 865CD / Jul '97 / In Akustik

☐ LIVE AT CARNEGIE HALL (A Tribute To Django Reinhardt)
CDJP 1040 / May '94 / Jazz Point

☐ LIVE IN MARCIAC
Softly as in a morning sunrise / Days of wine and roses / Donna Lee / Smile / Autumn leaves / Nuages / C'est si bon / Blues walk / Stella by starlight / I got rhythm
FDM 365672 / Jul '94 / Dreyfus

☐ MY FAVOURITE DJANGO
Daphne / Moppin' the bride / Babik / Melodie au creuscule / Place de brouckere / Nuages / Blues for Ike / Nuits de St. Germain des pres / Clair de lune / Troublant bolero / Solo
FDM 365742 / Oct '95 / Dreyfus

Laguna Jazz & Blues Band

☐ TIMELESS MOODS
LA 9501 / Jul '96 / Laguna

Lahawns

☐ LIVE AT WINKLES
LM 001CD / May '97 / LM

Lahiri, Bappi

☐ HEARTRAVE
FLTRCD 515 / Sep '93 / Flame Tree

Lai, Francis

☐ MAN AND A WOMAN, A
Man and a woman / Love in the rain / Intimate moments / Live for life / Bilitis / La ronde / Seduction / Solitude / Blue rose (la rose bleue) / Les unes et les autres / Whitechapel / Happy new year / African summer / Smic smac smoc / Emotion / Sur notre etoile / Par le sang des autres / Theme from 'love story'
305562 / Oct '96 / Hallmark

Laibach

☐ ALSO SPRACH JOHANN PAUL II
EFACD 204472 / Jul '97 / Robot

☐ BAPTISM, A
SUB 3306779 CD / Dec '90 / Sub Rosa

☐ JESUS CHRIST SUPERSTAR
CDSTUMM 136 / Oct '96 / Mute

☐ KAPITAL
Decade null / Everlasting in union / Illumination / Le privilege des morts / Codex durex / Hymn to the black sun / Young europa / Hunter's funeral procession / White law / Wirtschaft ist tot / Torso / Entartete welt / Kinderreich (english version) / Sponsered by mars / Regime of coincidence, state of gravity
CDSTUMM 82 / Apr '92 / Mute

☐ KRST POD TRIGLAVOM BAPTISM
CD 0019 / Aug '88 / Sub Rosa

☐ LAIBACH
EFA 131322 / Aug '95 / Nika

☐ LET IT BE
Get back / Dig a pony / Across the universe / Dig it / I've got a feeling / Long and winding road / One after 909 / Maggie Mae / For you blue
CDSTUMM 58 / Oct '88 / Mute

☐ LJUBLIANA, ZAGREB, BEOGRAD
NSK 1CD / May '93 / Grey Area

☐ MACBETH
Preludium / Agnus dei / Wutach schlucht / Die Zeit / Ohne geld / USA / 10th May 1941 / Expectans exprectavos / Coincidentia oppositorum / Wolf
STUMM 70 CD / Jan '90 / Mute

☐ MB DECEMBER 21ST 1984
Sodba veka / Ti, ki izzivas / Sila/Dokumenti / Sredi bojev / Nova akropola / Dokumenti II / Tito / Dokumenti III / Dokumenti IV
NSK 3CD / Jun '97 / Grey Area

☐ NATO
CDSTUMM 121 / Oct '94 / Mute

☐ NOVA AKROPOLA
Four personen / Nova akropola / Krvava fruda-plodna zemja / Vojna poena / Ti ki izzivas
CDMRED 67 / Mar '95 / Cherry Red

☐ OCCUPIED EUROPE NATO TOUR
NSK 2CDX / Aug '96 / Grey Area

☐ OPUS DEI
Great seal / How the west was won / Trans-national / Opus dei / Leben-tod / F I A T / Geburt einer nation / Leben heist leben
CDSTUMM 44 / Apr '87 / Mute

☐ SLOVENSKA ARKOPOLA
EFA 200252 / Aug '95 / Nika

Laibman, David

☐ RAGTIME GUITAR
Gladiolus rag / Ragtime nightingale / Contentment / Cottontail rag / Ethiopia rag / Alaskan rag / Silver swan rag / Solace - A Mexican serenade / Magnetic rag / Pleasant moments
EDCD 7026 / Feb '97 / Easydisc

Laidback

☐ INTERNATIONAL
Album tracking / Rock your world / That funky boom / Coldrock / Wobble / Knock knock / International / B-Boy nose / Hip hop loves you / Launch the raunch / Go off / Laid back attack / Wrecktify / Until the next time
BLSCD 2 / 10 Nov '97 / Bolshi

Laika

☐ AMAZING COLOSSAL BAND, THE (Laika & The Cosmonauts)
UPSTART 10 / Mar '95 / Upstart

☐ INSTRUMENTS OF TERROR (Laika & The Cosmonauts)
UPSTART 005 / Apr '94 / Upstart

☐ SILVER APPLES OF THE MOON
PURECD 042 / Oct '94 / Too Pure

☐ SOUNDS OF THE SATELLITES
Prairie dog / Breather / Out of sight and snowblind / Almost sleeping / Starry night / Bedbugs / Martinis on the moon / Poor gal / Blood and bones / Shut off / Curl up / Spooky rhodes / Dirty feet and giggles
PURECD 062 / Feb '97 / Too Pure

Laine, Cleo

☐ BEAUTIFUL THING, A
All in love is fair / Skip a long Sam / Send in the clowns / Least you can do is the best you can / They needed each other / I loves you Porgy / Until it's time for you to go / Life is a wheel / Summer knows / Beautiful thing
09026616642 / Oct '94 / RCA

☐ BLUE AND SENTIMENTAL
Lies of handsome men / I've got a crush on you / Blue and sentimental / Afterglow / Not you again / Primrose colour blue / What'll I do / Love me (if it takes you all night long) / Creole love call
09026614192 / Sep '94 / RCA

☐ CLEO AT CARNEGIE
Any place / I'm shadowing you / Crazy rhythm / Primrose colour blue / We are the music makers / You spotted snakes / Methuselah / When I was one and twenty / Sing me no song / Triboro' fair: *Dankworth, John & His Quintet* / You've got to do what you've got to do / He was beautiful / Turkish delight / Never let me go / I want to be happy
CDXP 2101 / Apr '87 / DRG

☐ CLEO'S CHOICE
RPM 160 / Apr '96 / RPM

☐ I AM A SONG
I'm gonna sit right down and write myself a letter / Early Autumn / Friendly persuasion / There is a time / Day when the world comes alive / I am a song / It might as well be Spring / Music / But not for me / Two part invention / Talk to me baby / Thieving boy / Hi-heel sneakers
09026616702 / Oct '94 / RCA

☐ RIDIN' HIGH (The British Sessions 1960-1971)
I'm gonna sit right down and write myself a letter / I'm just wild about Harry / Thieving Harry / You'll answer to me / Fear no more the heat of the sun / Woman talk / Fascinating rhythm / All gone / Little boat / Tea for two / If we lived on top of a mountain / Wintertime nights / Soliloquy / Ridin' high / Never let me go / Please don't talk about me when I'm gone
7940 / 2 Feb '98 / Koch

☐ SOLITUDE (Laine, Cleo & John Dankworth/Duke Ellington Orchestra)
Don't get around much anymore / Sophisticated lady / I'm beginning to see the light / All too soon / Take all my loves / I got it bad and that ain't good / Love call / Don't you know I care (Or don't you care to) / Solitude / Reflections / We're rockin' in rhythm / Come Sunday / September rain / Cleo's 'A' train
09026681242 / Jul '95 / RCA Victor

☐ SOMETIMES WHEN WE TOUCH (Laine, Cleo & James Galway)
Drifting dreaming / Title track / Play it again sam / Skylark / How, where, when / Fluter's ball / Consuelo's love theme / Keep loving me / Anyone can whistle / Still was the night / Lo here the gentle lark / Like a sad song
RD 83628 / Jan '87 / RCA

☐ SPOTLIGHT ON CLEO LAINE
I want to be happy / I think of you / I can dream, can't I / I've got my love to keep me warm / I got it bad and that ain't good / I'm a dreamer (aren't we all) / Popular song / I'm just wild about Harry / On a slow boat to China / Perdido / They say it's wonderful / If we lived on top of a mountain / Peel me a grape / Song without words / Fascinating rhythm / Oh Lady be good / Little boat / I cover the waterfront / Bidin' my time / Come rain or come shine / Lines to Ralph Hodgeson, Esquire / Riding high / Woman talk / I could write a book / Second time around / On a clear day (You can see forever) / Complete works / Please don't talk about me when I'm gone
8481292 / Jan '90 / Polydor

☐ VERY BEST OF CLEO LAINE, THE (2CD Set)
He was beautiful / I loves you Porgy / No one is alone / Birdsong / Solitude / Streets of London / I don't know why / Send in the clowns / Dreamsville / Gonna get through / Skylark / Creole love call / What'll I do / It don't mean a thing / You must believe in Spring /

Wish you were here (I do miss you) / Bill / Lies of handsome men / Play it again Sam / I'm gonna sit right down and write myself a letter / If / Won't you tell me why / I remember / Just a-sittin' and a-rockin' / Woman talk / Sophisticated lady / Music / Bess, you is my woman now / My man's gone now / I'm beginning to see the light / Time for farewell / Turkish delight / Born on a Friday / Thieving boy
74321432152 / May '97 / RCA Victor

☐ WORD SONGS
All the world's a stage / If music be the food of love / You spotted snakes / Winter, when icicles hang by the wall / Fear no more the heat o' the sun / It was a lover and his lass / Sigh no more ladies / Dunsinane blues / When that I was a little boy / Shall I compare thee to a summer's day / Blow, blow thou winter wind / O mistress mine, where you are roaming / Take all my loves / My love is as a fever / Who is Sylvia / Compleat works / Our revels now are ended / Lines to Ralph Hodgeson Esquire / Goe, and catche a falling starre / Bread and butter / Dr. David Mantle / Advice to a girl / O tell me the truth about love / In Tenebris 1 / Sun and fun / Song / English teeth / Viva sweet love / Mungojerrie and rumpelteazer / Thieving boy / Sing me no song
8304612 / Feb '94 / Philips

Laine, Denny

☐ MASTERS, THE (2CD Set)
EDMCD 034 / 30 Mar '98 / Eagle

☐ REBORN
SCRCD 013 / Sep '96 / Scratch

☐ ROCK SURVIVOR, THE
WCPCD 1008 / Sep '96 / West Coast

Laine, Frankie

☐ 20 GREAT TRACKS (Laine, Frankie & Friends)
That old feeling / Hambone / Tell me a story / Hey good lookin' / Up above my head / If you were mine / Way down yonder in New Orleans / I heard the angels singing / Floating down to cotton town / Rain rain rain / Sugarbush / Little boy and the old man / In the cool cool cool of the evening / Stars fell on Alabama / Juba juba jubalee / Basin Street blues / My old flame / How lovely cooks the meat / Ain't it a pity and a shame / High society
PRCDSP 301 / 10 Nov '97 / Prestige

☐ BALLADEER/WANDERLUST
Rocks and gravel / Old Virginny / Cherry red / On a Monday / Careless love / Sixteen tons / Jelly coal man / Lucy D / New orleans / Old blue / Stack of blues / And doesn't she roll / Love is where you find it / Serenade / Wagon wheels / I let her go / Misirlou / Riders in the sky / De glory road / What kind of fool am I / On the road to Mandalay / If I love again / Moment of truth / I'm gonna live till I die
4871912 / Mar '97 / Columbia

☐ BEST OF FRANKIE LAINE, THE
MU 3011 / Oct '92 / Musketeer

☐ BEST OF FRANKIE LAINE, THE
PLSCD 118 / Apr '96 / Pulse

☐ COLLECTION, THE
Rawhide / I believe / Sixteen tons / High noon (do not forsake me) / Jezebel / Your cheatin' heart / Woman in love / Answer me / Strange lady in town / Granada / Moonlight gambler / Hummingbird / There must be a reason / Don't fence me in / That lucky old sun / Jealousy / Mule train / Rain, rain, rain / On the sunny side of the street / Still water runs cool / That's my desire / Cry of the wild goose / Rose rose I love you / Wheel of fortune / You gave me a mountain
COL 039 / Apr '95 / Collection

☐ COUNTRY LAINE, A
Green green grass of home: *Kumari, Jeena* / Old dogs and children: *Kumari, Jeena* / When will I be loved: *Kumari, Jeena* / Over: *Kumari, Jeena* / I believe in love / (Let me love you) One more time / She never could dance / Let me learn to dream of you / Hummingbird / Don't fence me in / End of session blues
CDSGP 0250 / Mar '98 / Prestige

☐ DEUCES WILD/CALL OF THE WILD
Hard way / Camptown races / Luck be a lady / Get rich quick / Horses and women / Moonlight gambler / Ace in the hole / Man who broke the bank at Monte Carlo / Dead man's hand / Roving gambler / Deuces wild / Gamblin' woman / Song of the open road / North to Alaska / Swamp girl / Beyond the blue horizon / Call of the wild / On the trail / Wayfaring stranger / Tumbling tumble weeds / High road / Rollin' stone / New frontier / Girl in the wood
4810172 / Aug '95 / Columbia

☐ FRANKIE LAINE
CD 108 / Oct '94 / Timeless Treasures

☐ FRANKIE LAINE 1947 (Laine, Frankie & The Carl Fischer Orchestra)
That's my desire / I may be wrong / All of me / Two loves have I / Baby, that ain't right / It only happens once / Black and blue / Put yourself in my place, baby / But beautiful / Laughing at life / Rosetta / We'll be together again
HCD 198 / Jun '94 / Hindsight

☐ GOIN' LIKE WILDFIRE (Laine, Frankie & Jo Stafford)
Pretty eyed baby / That's the one for me / That's good, that's bad / In the cool, cool, cool of the evening / Cambella / Hey good lookin' / Ham bone / Let's have a party / Settin' the woods on fire / Piece a puddin' / Christmas roses / Chow willy / Bushel and a peck / Floatin' down to cotton town / Way down yonder in New Orleans / Basin Street blues / High society / Back where I belong
BCD 15620 / Nov '93 / Bear Family

☐ GREATEST HITS
Rawhide / Moonlight gambler / I believe / Hummingbird / Don't fence me in / Strange lady in town / Red rose I love you / There must be a reason / Answer me / Jezebel / High noon / Mule train / Jealously / Sixteen tons / Cool water / Wheel of fortune / Rain rain rain / Woman in love / Granada / Cry of the wild goose
GRF 044 / Feb '93 / Tring

☐ HITMAKER
Jezebel / Don't fence me in / Wheel of fortune / Moonlight gambler / Granada / Rose, rose I love you / Hummingbird / High noon / Sixteen tons / I believe / Jealousy / Strange lady in town / Woman in love / Rain rain rain / Cool water / Cry of the wild goose / Mule train / There must be a reason / Answer me / Rawhide
300272 / Jul '96 / Hallmark

☐ I BELIEVE
Rawhide / Jealousy / Moonlight gambler / Cry of the wild goose / Hummingbird / Don't fence me in / Strange lady in town / Rose, Rose, I love you / There must be a reason / Answer me / Jezebel / High Noon (Do not forsake me) / Mule train / Sixteen tons / Cool water / Wheel of fortune / Rain rain rain / Woman in love / Granada / I believe
CD 6055 / Jan '97 / Music

☐ INCOMPARABLE FRANKIE LAINE, THE (2CD Set)
I believe / Granada / Answer me / That's my desire / Jezebel / Rosetta / I may be wrong / All of me / Black and blue / Two loves have I / Jealousy / Shine / But beautiful / There must be a reason / That lucky old sun / Laughing at life / Your cheatin' heart / On the sunny side of the street / We'll be together again / Rain, rain, rain / Rawhide / (Ghost) Riders in the sky / Sixteen tons / Mule train / Cry of the wild goose / Cool water / Don't fence me in / Moonlight gambler / High noon / Hummingbird / It only happens once / Strange lady in town / Put yourself in my place, baby / Rose Rose I love you / Georgia on my mind / Baby, that ain't right / Don't blame me / Woman in love / Moonlight in Vermont / Wheel of fortune
MUCD 9503 / May '96 / Musketeer

☐ MAKING MEMORIES
SATCD 5001 / 4 May '98 / Satril

☐ MEMORIES IN GOLD (20 Great Hits)
Memories in gold / Jealousy / High noon / On the sunny side of the street / Mule train / Cool water / Kid's last fight / Woman in love / Georgia on my mind / Moonlight gambler / You gave me a mountain / Jezebel / That's my desire / Cry of the wild goose / I believe / Your cheatin' heart / Rawhide / That lucky old sun / Shine / We'll be together again
CDPC 5004 / Mar '92 / Prestige

☐ ON THE TRAIL
High noon / Cool water / 3.10 to Yuma / Gunfight at the OK Corral / Wanted man / Bowie knife / Mule train / Hanging tree / Along the Navajo trail / City boy / Cry of the wild goose / Rawhide / Gunslinger / Green leaves of Summer / On the trail / North to Alaska / Call of the wild / Tumbling tumbleweeds / Ghost riders in the sky / Prairie bell / Lonely man
BCD 15480 / Aug '90 / Bear Family

☐ ON THE TRAIL AGAIN
Strange lady in town / Ramblin' man / Rawhide / Champion the wonderhorse / Black gold / Where the wind blows / I let her go / Drill ye tarriers drill / El diablo / Ride through the night / Ghost riders in the sky / Beyond the blue horizon / Swamp girl / Song of the open road / My journey's end / Wagon wheels / 3.10 to Yuma / Cool water / Gunfight at the OK Corral / High noon / New frontier / Deuces wild / Moonlight gambler / Wheel of fortune / Dead man's hand / Hard way / Wayfaring stranger / Roving gambler / El diablo
BCD 15632 / Jun '92 / Bear Family

☐ RETURN OF MR RHYTHM
Sometimes I'm happy / I wish you were jealous of me / Hold me / You've changed / Sweet talk / Don't blame me / Never before / That's my desire / Singing the blues / Moonlight in vermont / S'posin' / West end blues / Someday sweetheart / What could be sweeter / Come love with me / We'll be together again
HCD 256 / May '95 / Hindsight

☐ RIDERS IN THE SKY
Riders in the sky / Rawhide / Cool water / Gunfight at the OK Corral / 3.10 to Yuma / Hummingbird / That lucky old sun / North to Alaska / Don't fence me in / Blazing saddles / Cry of the wild goose / High noon (do not forsake me) / Moonlight gambler / Wanted man / Mule train / Your cheatin' heart / Call of the wild / Along the Navajo trail / Hanging tree / Tumbling tumbleweeds
CDSGP 0248 / 26 Jan '98 / Prestige

☐ SOMETHIN' OLD, SOMETHIN' NEW
Nobody but you / Don't cry, cry baby / Send in the clowns / S'posin' / Evergreen / Lady be good / Fever / Roses of picardy / Rose ellen / Sometimes I'm happy / Fallen angel / Old enought (to be your father) / It ain't gonna be like that / This can't be love / Someday sweetheart / I'd do it over again / You've changed / Makin' whoopee / Coquette / Better to have loved / Baby, baby all the time / If I never sing another song / Time, you old gypsy man / We'll be together again
PRCDSP 300 / Jun '92 / Prestige

☐ WHEELS OF A DREAM
71493220202 / 7 Apr '98 / After 9

☐ YOUNG MASTER, THE
In the wee small hours / Heartaches / I'm confessin' / You can depend on me / I'm may be wrong / Ghost of a chance / That's my desire / Ain't that just like a woman / Texas and Pacific / On the sunny side of the street / West end blues / Black and blue / Stay as sweet as you are / Who cares what people say / Mam'selle / Sunday kind of love / Georgia on my mind / By the light of the stars / Kiss me again / Put yourself in my place / Two loves have I / Wrap you troubles in dreams / By the river Saint Marie / It only happens once / September in the rain / It ain't gonna be like that / Shine / We'll be together again
PASTCD 7826 / Apr '98 / Flapper

Laine, Paul

☐ CAN'T GET ENUFF
ESM 003 / 2 Mar '98 / Escape

Laing, Robin

☐ ANGEL'S SHARE, THE
More than just a dram / Our glens / Piper Macneil / Willie brewed a pack o' malt / Parish o' Dunkeld / Twelve and a tanner a bottle / Whiskey and women / Nancy's whiskey / De'il's awa' wi' tha exciseman / Bottle o' the best / John Barleycorn / Tell tale / Whiskey you're the devil / Tak a dram / Wee deoch an Doris
CDTRAX 137 / Jul '97 / Greentrax

☐ EDINBURGH SKYLINE
Edinburgh skyline / Burke and hare / Love is born / Union canal / Leaving today / Icarus / Ulysses / Isle of Eigg / Day by day / Andrew Lammie / Spring song / Passing time
CDTRAX 021 / 2 Feb '98 / Greentrax

☐ WALKING IN TIME
Soldier maid / Kilbowie hill / Summer of '45 / Punters / Unquiet grave / Lass O'Patie's mill / El punado de centeno / Jamie Foyers / Billy Taylor / Forth Bridge song / Loose noose / Deacon Brodie / When two hearts combine / Neil Gow lament / Calypso's Island
CDTRAX 072 / Apr '94 / Greentrax

Laka, Don

☐ DESTINY
Move on / Mamelodi / Late again / Time and space / Destiny / Sway / Tlang sekolong / Still waters / Odyssey / You will know me / No clue at all / SO long Mr
4874952 / Aug '97 / Sony Jazz

Lakatos, Roby

☐ IN GYPSY STYLE
MWCD 4010 / Jul '95 / Music & Words

Lakatos, Sandor

☐ GYPSY VIOLINS (Lakatos, Sandor & His Gypsy Band)
HMP 3903027 / Oct '94 / HM Plus/ Quintana

☐ HUNGARY - MUSIC TZIGANE
HMP 393009 / Oct '94 / HM Plus/ Quintana

Lake

☐ LAKE VOL.2
RMED 00126 / 13 Jul '98 / Renaissance

☐ LAKE/PARADISE ISLAND
RMED 0123CD / 15 Dec '97 / Renaissance

☐ OUCH
RMED 0127CD / 8 Jun '98 / Renaissance

Lake, Greg

☐ FROM THE BEGINNING (The Greg Lake Retrospective/2CD Set)
Court of the Crimson King: *King Crimson* / Cat food: *King Crimson* / Knife edge: *Emerson, Lake & Palmer* / Lucky man: *Emerson, Lake & Palmer* / From the beginning: *Emerson, Lake & Palmer* / Take a pebble: *Emerson, Lake & Palmer* / Still: *Sinfield, Pete* / Still, you turn me on: *Emerson, Lake & Palmer* / Jerusalem: *Emerson, Lake & Palmer* / Karn evil 9: *Emerson, Lake & Palmer* / I believe in Father Christmas / C'est la vie / Closer to believing / Watching over you / 21st century schizoid man / Nuclear attack / Love too much / It hurts / Retribution drive / Lie / Let me love you once / Manoeuvres / I don't know why I still love you / Touch and go: *Emerson, Lake & Palmer* / Lay down your guns: *Emerson, Lake & Palmer* / Love under fire / Money talks / Black moon: *Emerson, Lake & Palmer* / Paper blood: *Emerson, Lake & Palmer* / Affairs of the heart: *Emerson, Lake & Palmer* / Daddy: *Emerson, Lake & Palmer* / Heart of ice: *Emerson, Lake & Palmer*
ESDCD 552 / May '97 / Essential

Lake, Kirk

☐ BLACK LIGHTS
IRE 1032 / Nov '96 / Che

Lake Of Dracula

☐ LAKE OF DRACULA
GR 39CD / Jun '97 / Skingraft

Lake Of Tears

☐ GREATER ART
BMCD 49 / May '94 / Black Mark

☐ HEADSTONES
BMCD 072 / Sep '95 / Black Mark

Lake, Oliver

☐ BOSTON DUETS (Lake, Oliver & Donal Leonellis Fox)
CD 732 / Sep '92 / Music & Arts

☐ COMPILATION
R 279458 / Aug '94 / Gramavision

☐ EDGE-ING
Othello ballet suite (parts 1 and 2): *Russell, George* / Electronic organ sonata no. 1: *Russell, George*
1210142 / Oct '94 / Black Saint

☐ HEAVY SPIRITS
While pushing down turn / Owshet / Heavy spirits / Movement equals creation / Lonely blacks / Intensity
CDBLC 760209 / Apr '96 / Black Lion

☐ HOLDING TOGETHER
Trailway shake / Sad lo-uis / Hasan / Usta b / Holding together / Machine wing / Ballad
1200092 / Nov '90 / Black Saint

☐ OTHERSIDE
Gano club / Whitestone / Stand / Hymn for the old year / Weave song / Dedicated to dolphy
1889012 / Feb '89 / Gramavision

☐ ZAKI (Lake, Oliver Trio)
ARTCD 6113 / Aug '92 / Hat Art

Lakeman Brothers

☐ THREE PIECE SUITE
CRM 01CD / Jun '94 / Crapstone

Lakeside

☐ BEST OF LAKESIDE, THE
Shot of love / One minute after midnight / Given in to love / It's all the way live / Rough rider / If you like our music (Get on up and move) / Fantastic voyage / Your love is on the one / We want you (On the floor) / Say yes / Ever ready man / I want to hold your hand / Raid / Outrageous / Bulls eye
NEMCD 681 / Aug '94 / Sequel

☐ FANTASTIC VOYAGE
Fantastic voyage / Your love is on the one / I need you / Strung out / Say yes / Eveready man / I love everything you do
NEBCD 792 / Apr '96 / Sequel

☐ PARTY PATROL (2CD Set)
SMDCD 165 / 22 Sep '97 / Snapper

Lalama, Ralph

☐ CIRCLE LINE (Lalama, Ralph Quartet)
Circle line / My ideal / Giant steps / You are too beautiful / Fiesta espagnol / Dark chocolate / Homestretch / Without a song
CRISS 1132CD / Jul '97 / Criss Cross

☐ FEELIN' AND DEALIN' (Lalama, Ralph & His Manhattan All Stars)
CRISS 1046CD / May '91 / Criss Cross

☐ MOMENTUM (Lalama, Ralph Quartet)
CRISS 1063CD / Oct '92 / Criss Cross

☐ YOU KNOW WHAT I MEAN
CRISS 1097 / Apr '95 / Criss Cross

Lam, Bun-Ching

☐ CHILD GOD, THE
TZA 7031 / 2 Mar '98 / Tzadik

☐ LIKE WATER
TZA 7021 / Feb '97 / Tzadik

Lam, Kine

☐ PRAISE
SHCD 64062 / Jan '96 / Shanachie

Lama Karta

☐ TCHEUD
74321483912 / Jun '97 / Milan

☐ TIBETAN CHANTS (Buddhist Meditation)
74321327202 / Apr '96 / Milan

Lamarque, Libertad

☐ INSPIRACION 1932-1948
EBCD 72 / Jul '96 / El Bandoneon

Lamb

☐ LAMB
Lusty / God bless / Cotton wool / Trans fatty acid / Zero / Merge / Gold / Closer / Gorecki / Feela
5329682 / Sep '96 / Fontana

Lamb, Andrew

☐ PORTRAIT IN THE MIST
Air and ear painters / Negretta Mia / Light of the whirling dervish / Bohemian love affair / Portrait in the mist / Eccentricity / Morning of the black swan
DE 479 / Mar '97 / Delmark

Lamb, Annabel

☐ FLOW
Wild world / Man with no voice / Get my suitcase / Warmth of human flesh / Ain't no going back / Lee's song / Here we stand / Elisabeth / Lullaby / Freight train / Shout at the sky / Time turns
WOWCD 04 / 6 Oct '97 / Way Out West

Lamb, Barbara

☐ FIDDLE FATALE
Sally Gooden / Panhandle rag / Good woman's love / Paddy on the turnpike/gone again / Montana glide / Herman's hornpipe / So what / Foster's reel / Old French reel / I'll never be free / Katy Hill / Princess Angeline / Ducks on the Millpond (ducks with bongas)
SHCD 3810 / May '93 / Sugar Hill

☐ TONIGHT I FEEL LIKE TEXAS
Barefoot Nellie / Herman's rag / Tonight I feel like Texas / Forked deer / Riding on the rio / Satin doll / Say old man can you play the fiddle / I'll grab my saddlehorn and blow / Bill Cheatham / You done me wrong / Tennessee breakdown / Birthday waltz / Bumble bee in the gourdvine
SHCD 3860 / Mar '98 / Sugar Hill

Lamb, Natalie

☐ I'M A WOMAN (Lamb, Natalie & The Perune Jazz Band)
BCD 329 / Aug '94 / GHB

Lamb, Paul

☐ BEST OF BRITISH BLUES, THE (3CD Set) (Lamb, Paul/Ruby Turner/Stan Webb's Chicken Shack)
One more time: *Lamb, Paul & The King Snakes* / Everyday I have the blues: *Lamb, Paul & The King Snakes* / Come on everybody: *Lamb, Paul & The King Snakes* / Fine condition: *Lamb, Paul & The King Snakes* / Who do you think you are: *Lamb, Paul & The King Snakes* / Why do you treat me so: *Lamb, Paul & The King Snakes* / Texas boogie: *Lamb, Paul & The King Snakes* / I ain't asking much: *Lamb, Paul & The King Snakes* / Swing out: *Lamb, Paul & The King Snakes* / I don't need you anymore: *Lamb, Paul & The King Snakes* / Don't lose your cool: *Lamb, Paul & The King Snakes* / Good rockin' tonight: *Lamb, Paul & The King Snakes* / You can't do that: *Turner, Ruby* / There is something on your mind: *Turner, Ruby* / You're pouring water on a drowning man: *Turner, Ruby* / Me oh my: *Turner, Ruby* / Wang dang doodle: *Turner, Ruby* / Don't mess up a good thing: *Turner, Ruby* / Bring it on home to me: *Turner, Ruby* / Love like blood: *Turner, Ruby* / Ain't nobody: *Turner, Ruby* / One time around: *Turner, Ruby* / Guilty: *Turner, Ruby* / Take it as it comes: *Turner, Ruby* / That way: *Turner, Ruby* / Over the edge: *Turner, Ruby* / Rockin' good way: *Turner, Ruby* / My eyes are weeping: *Turner, Ruby* / Going up going down: *Webb, Stan & Chicken Shack* / Thrill has gone: *Webb, Stan & Chicken Shack* / Love her with a feeling: *Webb, Stan & Chicken Shack* / Look out: *Webb, Stan & Chicken Shack* / Lost the best friend I ever had: *Webb, Stan & Chicken Shack* / C.S. Opera: *Webb, Stan & Chicken Shack* / Broken hearted melody: *Webb, Stan & Chicken Shack* / Poor boy/Oh well/Poor boy: *Webb, Stan & Chicken Shack* / Dr. Brown/Reconsider baby: *Webb, Stan & Chicken Shack*
IGOBCD 003 / Dec '97 / Indigo

☐ FINE CONDITION (Lamb, Paul & The King Snakes)
One more time / Everyday I have the blues / Come on everybody / Fine condition / Who do you think you are / Why do you treat me so / Texas boogie / I ain't asking much / Swing out / I don't need you anymore / Don't lose your cool / Good rockin' tonight
IGOCD 2019 / Mar '95 / Indigo

☐ JOHN HENRY JUMPS IN (Lamb, Paul & The King Snakes)
Pillow / If the tables were turned / Sweet sweet woman / I'm packin' up / My prayer / That's no good to me / Sometimes I wonder / All because of you / Roll with it / Should be mine / Waiting on you / John Henry jumps in / Don't answer the door / Come back baby / My baby left me / Jump for it
IGOXCD 512 / Apr '98 / Indigo

☐ SHE'S A KILLER (Lamb, Paul & The King Snakes)
She's a killer / Keep on dreaming / Girl for me / Texas hop / Blackjack game / Who can it be / Just a dream / My baby she don't look like that / Whoop and holler / Reconsider baby / Wild wild women / Jump for joy / Back at the chicken shack / You're the one / John's jump
IGOXCD 503 / Jun '96 / Indigo

☐ SHIFTING INTO GEAR (Lamb, Paul & The King Snakes)
Come on everybody / Hey woman / Evening sun / Didn't do me no good / Give up giving up / Feel so good / Shifting into gear / Must be more to life than this / One more time / Snakeskin jump / I need somebody to love / Once too often
IGOXCD 504 / Feb '97 / Indigo

Lambayeque

☐ TRADITIONAL MUSIC OF PERU VOL.4
SFWCD 40469 / Dec '96 / Smithsonian Folkways

Lambchop

☐ HANK
EFA 049792 / Jul '96 / City Slang

☐ HOW I QUIT SMOKING
EFA 049692 / Jan '96 / City Slang

☐ I HOPE YOU'RE SITTING DOWN
EFA 049532 / Mar '95 / City Slang

☐ THRILLER
My face your ass / Your fucking sunny day / Hey where's your girl / Crawl away / Gloria Leonard / Thriller / Old fat robin / Superstar in France
EFA 049981 / 22 Sep '97 / City Slang

☐ WHAT ANOTHER MAN SPILLS
Interrupted / Saturday option / Shucks / Give me your love / Life #2 / Scamper / It's not alright / N.O. / I've been lonely for so long / Magnificent obsession / King of nothing never / Theme from the Neil Miller show
087112 / 7 Sep '98 / City Slang

Lambert, Gary

☐ GUITAR PICKIN' RARITIES (Lambert, Gary & Eddie Cochran)
SJCD 594 / Mar '92 / Sun Jay

Lambert, Hendricks & Ross

☐ HOTTEST NEW GROUP IN JAZZ, THE (2CD Set)
Charleston Alley / Moanin' / Twisted / Bijou / CLoudburst / Centerpiece / Gimme that wine / Sermonette / Summertime / Everybody's boppin' / Cotton tail / All too soon / Happy anatomy / Rocks in my bed / Main stem / I don't know what kind of blues I've got / Things ain't what they used to be / Midnight indigo / What am I here for / In a mellow tone / Caravan / Come on home / New ABC / Farmer's market / Cookin' at the continental / With malice toward none / Hi-fly / Home cookin' / Halloween spooks / Popity pop / Blue / Mr. PC / Preacher / Walkin' / This here (dis hyunh) / Swingin' til the girls come home / Twist city / Just a little bit of twist / Night in Tunisia
C2K 64933 / Nov '96 / Sony Jazz

Lambeth Community Youth Steel Orchestra

☐ BEST OF CARIBBEAN STEEL DRUMS
EUCD 1140 / '91 / ARC

☐ STEEL DRUMS PARTY
EUCD 1325 / Nov '95 / ARC

Lambrettas

☐ AMBIENCE
Good times / Written in neon / Total strangers / Concrete and steel / Dancing in the dark / Decent town / Ambience / Men in blue / I want to tell you / Someone talking
DOJOCD 219 / May '96 / Dojo

☐ BEAT BOYS IN THE JET AGE
Da-a-ance / Cortina MkII / London calling / Poison ivy / Leap before you look / Beat boys in the jet age / Page three / Living for today / Watch out I'm back / Don't push me / Runaround / Face to face
DOJOCD 187 / Nov '94 / Dojo

☐ BEST OF THE LAMBRETTAS, THE
DOJOCD 195 / May '95 / Dojo

☐ DEFINITIVE COLLECTION, THE (Beat Boys In The Jet Age)
CCSCD 828 / 24 Aug '98 / Castle

Lament

☐ LEVITATE
TOODAMNHY 82 / Jan '95 / Too Damn Hype

Lamond, Don

☐ DON LAMOND & HIS BIG SWING BAND/QUARTET
CCD 148 / Jun '96 / Circle

Lamond, Mary Jane

☐ BHO THIR NAN CRAOBH
O, tha mise fo ghruaimean / Air faillirinn iu / Cagaran gaolach / Domhnaill antaidh / A chuachag nam beann / He mo leannan / Bodach beag a loinean / Ho ro's toigh leam fhin thu / Cha bhi mi buan / Ba ba mo leanabh / Piuirt-a-beul / Dh'olainn deoch a laimh mo run / Oran gillean alasdair mhoir / Dan do shean ford
IRCD 045 / Mar '97 / Iona

☐ FROM THE LAND OF THE TREES
BRCD 0001 / May '95 / Macmeanmna

Lamont Cranston Blues Band

☐ HIGH FIDELITY
Play the blues / What a party / Wild women and whiskey / Blinded / You don't know / Roll with me / West side woman / Country farm / Hip cat bounce / I couldn't put you down / Hold on / Don't take me down again
ATM 1134 / Sep '97 / Atomic Theory

☐ LAMONT CRANSTON BLUES BAND
I don't wanna know / Cold winds / Two way wishin' / Love grown cold / You don't even know / Stop on by / I got designs on you / Whole lotta lovin' / Too young to die / Fever
ATM 1119 / Sep '96 / Atomic Theory

Lamothe, Rob

☐ BEING HUMAN
DCD 9838 / 13 Apr '98 / Dream Circle

☐ GRAVITY
DCD 9626 / Nov '96 / Dream Circle

Lamour, Dorothy

☐ MOON OF MANAKOORA, THE (25 Romantic Favourites)
Moonlight and shadows / Panamania / You took the words right out of my heart / Thanks for the memory / Lovelight in the starlight / Little lady make-believe / Tonight will live / On a tropic night / That sentimental sandwich / Man I love / You took me out of this world / I'm all a-tremble over you / Paradise / Sweet potato piper / Palms of paradise / Moon and the willow tree / Too romantic / I gotta right to sing the blues / It had to be you / Your kiss / This is the beginning of the end / Moon over Burma / Mexican magic / One rose that's left in my heart / Moon of Manakoora
CDAJA 5231 / Feb '97 / Living Era

Lan Doky, Niels

☐ DAYBREAK
All or nothing at all / Why / Final decision / Jet lag / Natural / Daybreak
STCD 4160 / '88 / Storyville

☐ DREAMS
Dreams / Dreams / This is all I ask / Dearest you / That's it / Loneliness / Oh well / Journey back
MCD 9178 / Oct '93 / Milestone

☐ FRIENDSHIP
Real mccoy / Endless vision / Christmas song / Confidence / KS / Point of no return / Friendship / To the limit / Center of gravity
MCD 9183 / Oct '93 / Milestone

☐ HERE OR THERE (Lan Doky, Niels Trio)
STCD 4117 / Feb '89 / Storyville

☐ TARGET, THE (Lan Doky, Niels Trio)
STCD 4140 / Feb '89 / Storyville

☐ TRUTH, THE (Live at Montmartre) (Lan Doky, Niels Trio)
STCD 4144 / Feb '89 / Storyville

Lancaster, Alan

☐ LIFE AFTER QUO
PJR 001CD / Aug '96 / Blueprint

Lancaster, Jack

☐ SKINNINGROVE BAY
CSC 7120CD / Jan '97 / Viceroy

Land, Harold

☐ MAPENZI (Land, Harold & Blue Mitchell Quintet)
CCD 4044 / Dec '90 / Concord Jazz

☐ XOCIA'S DANCE
MCD 5272 / Sep '92 / Muse

Land Of Loops

☐ BUNDLE OF JOY
UP 020CD / 16 Feb '98 / Up

Landau, Michael

☐ TALES FROM THE BULGE
I'm buzzed / Judy / Chynna / Johnny swing / Big bulge / Roodis tones / Eater / I don't care / My bulbous meathead / I'm hating
MCL 0012 / 23 Mar '98 / Smashed Hit

Landberk

☐ LONELY LAND
M&D 001 / 16 Feb '98 / Laser's Edge

Lande, Art

☐ SKYLIGHT (Lande, Art & David Samuels/Paul McCandleless)
Skylight / Dance of the silver skeezix / Duck in a colourful blanket (for here) / Chillum / Moist window/ Lawn party / Ente (to go) / Willow
5310252 / Feb '96 / ECM

Lande, Vidar

☐ FIDDLE & HARDINGER FROM ADGER, NORWAY
D 8063 / Apr '96 / Unesco

☐ SLATTER AAKHUSS
VL 001CD / Aug '96 / VL

☐ SLATTER RYSSTAD
VL 002CD / Aug '96 / VL

Landgren, Nils

☐ FOLLOW YOUR HEART
21393 / Mar '89 / Caprice

☐ GOTLAND (Landgren, Nils & Tomasz Stanko)
Den blomstertid nu kommer / Gotland / Tjelvar / Alskar barnet modernfamnen / Olu / Guldrupe / Ainbusk / Vange / Rank / Emil Kahl
92262 / Feb '96 / Act

☐ LIVE IN STOCKHOLM
Traci / Soundcheck / Impressions / Cheyenne / Simple life / Chicken / Ain't nobody / So what / Mr. M / Red horn / Yo yo
92232 / Jul '95 / Act

☐ PAINT IT BLUE (Landgren, Nils Funk Unit)
Walk tall / You dig / Why am I treated so bad / Brother Nat / Inside straight / Cannonball / Mercy mercy mercy / Mother fonk / Primitivo / After the party / Love all, serve all / Julian
92432 / Feb '97 / Act

☐ SWEDISH FOLK MODERN (Landgren, Nils & Esbjorn Svensson)
Hornlat / Vallat fran jamtland / Lapp-nils Polska / Free esbjorn / Midsommarvaka from Sweden rapsody no.1 / Morgon Mellan Fjallen / Halling / Winter's tale / Vallat fran harledalen / Gardebylaten / Visa fran leksand / Vaggvisa / Free nils
ACT 92572 / 23 Mar '98 / Act

Landis

☐ YESTERDAY'S TOMORROW...
ME 018 / 18 May '98 / Mind Expansion

Landreth, Sonny

☐ SOUTH OF 1-10
Shooting for the moon / Creole angel / Native stepson / Orphans of the motherland / Congo square / Turning wheel / South of 1-10 / Cajun waltz / Mojo boogie / C'est chaud / Great gulf wind
72445110702 / Mar '95 / Zoo Entertainment

Landry, Henri

☐ VIOLONEUX DES CANTONS DE L'EST
926432 / Jul '96 / BUDA

Land's End

☐ NATURAL SELECTION
Strictly speaking in geographical terms / From the ruins of a fallen empire / Love through the winter and blood in the spring / An emptiness that's never filled / My home / Natural selection
CYCL 047 / 29 Sep '97 / Cyclops

Landsborough, Charlie

☐ FURTHER DOWN THE ROAD
Love you every second / Loreto / Twelfth of never / Green hills are rolling still / Saints / Oh Nancy / It's raining outside / In the bleak mid-winter / Uninvited / Further down the road / God knocking on your door / I want someone to love me
RZCD 0085 / 27 Oct '97 / Ritz

☐ SONGS FROM THE HEART
I dreamed I was in heaven / Sill blue / Things that my ears can do / Walking on my memories / Song of my heart / All over but crying / One more time / You and me / Constantly / I cried / You're not the only one / Fireside dreaming / Summer country skies / Close your eyes / Lily of the valley / Still blue
RZRCD 521 / Jun '92 / Ritz

☐ WHAT COLOUR IS THE WIND
Million ways to fall / Forever friend / Dream or two / When you're not a dream / What colour is the wind / Once bitten twice shy / Throw me away / When the counting's done / Funny way to say goodbye / Song of the ocean / Dance with me / White lies and windows
RCD 542 / Sep '94 / Ritz

☐ WITH YOU IN MIND
No time at all / How do you do those things / Part of me / Shine your light / Isle of Innisfree / Down to earth / I will love you all my life / Heaven knows / If only / I say you / Irish waltz / You stand all alone
RZCD 0078 / Sep '96 / Ritz

Landstrumm, Neal

☐ BEDROOMS AND CITIES
EFA 292822 / Sep '97 / Tresor

☐ BROWN BY AUGUST
Shuttlecock / DX Serve / Index revisited / Sibling rivalry / Shake the hog / Custard tracks / Finnish deception / Home delivery / Squeeze / She-ra extra speaker
PF 040CD / Nov '95 / Peacefrog

☐ UNDERSTANDING DISINFORMATION (2CD Set)
EFA 018002 / Jul '96 / Tresor

Lane, Anita

☐ PEARL & DIRTY
CDSTUMM 81 / Sep '93 / Mute

Lane, Frankie

☐ DOBRO
CEFCD 159 / Jan '94 / Gael Linn

Lane, Gillian

☐ BEST OF GILLIAN LANE, THE
HTCD 113 / 20 Apr '98 / Hot Productions

Lane, Glenn

☐ ME & THE BLUES
ICD 50689 / 15 Jun '98 / Icehouse

Lane, Jimmy D.

☐ LONG GONE
APO 2003CD / May '97 / Analogue

Lane, Lois

☐ SENSUAL SONGS
369012 / 29 Jun '98 / Koch Jazz

Lane, Mickey Lee

☐ ROCKIN' ON...AND BEYOND
(I wanna) rock the bop / Senior class / Shaggy dog / Oo oo / (I wanna) rock the bop / Tears uncried / She cried to me / Zoo / Little girl / She don't want to / (That's how you'll know) when you're in love / Of yesterday / Yesterday / Baby what you want me to do / I'm not sure...I still want you / Bo doofus / At the sound of the gong/WMIC radio theme / Where it's rocking / Zoo / Morley trucks commercial/Move it on / Put on your leather weather baby / Coffee and toast / (Baby) I wanna be loved / Toasted love / One and one is two: *Mickey & Shonnie* / In love with love: *2 Guys & A Gal* / Frank the frog: *2 Guys & A Gal* / Hey sah-lo-ney: *2 Guys & A Gal* / Tutti frutti: *2 Guys & A Gal* / Kum ba yah: *2 Guys & A Gal* / Night cap: *2 Guys & A Gal* / Something to live on: *2 Guys & A Gal* / Recording silence with PPH: *2 Guys & A Gal*
RCCD 3014 / May '97 / Rollercoaster

Lane, Ronnie

☐ ANYMORE FOR ANYMORE (2CD Set) (Lane, Ronnie & Slim Chance)
Roll on babe / Tell everyone / Amelia Earhardt / Anymore for anymore / Bird in a gilded cage / Chicken wired / Careless love / Don't you cry for me / Gonna see the King / Silk stockings / Poacher / Poacher / How come / Done this before / Gonna see the King / How come / Roll on babe / Anymore for anymore
PILOT 015 / 26 Jan '98 / Burning Airlines

☐ ANYMORE FOR ANYMORE...PLUS (Lane, Ronnie & Slim Chance)
How come / Careless love / Don't you cry for me / Bye and bye (Gonna see The King) / Silk stockings / Poacher / Roll on babe / Tell everyone / Amelia Earhart's last flight / Anymore for anymore / Only a bird in a gilded cage / Chicken wired / Done this one before
SEECD 338 / Jun '97 / See For Miles

☐ KUSCHTY RYE (The Singles)
How come / Tell everyone / Done this one before / Poacher / Bye and bye (gonna see the King) / Roll on babe / Anymore for anymore / What went down (that night with you) / Lovely / Brother can you spare a dime / Ain't no lady / Don't try and change my mind / Well well hello (the party) / Kuschty rye / You're so right / One step / Lad's got money / Stone / Sweet Virginia
PILOT 019 / 29 Sep '97 / Burning Airlines

☐ ONE FOR THE ROAD (Lane, Ronnie & Slim Chance)
Don't try 'n' change my mind / 32nd street / Snake / Burnin' summer / One for the road / Steppin' an' reelin' (the wedding) / Harvest home / Nobody's listening / G'morning
EDCD 464 / Feb '96 / Edsel

☐ SEE ME
One step / Good ol' boys boogie / Lad's got money / She's leaving / Barcelona / Kuschty Rye / Don't tell me now / You're so right / Only you / Winning with women / Way up yonder
EDCD 492 / Jul '96 / Edsel

☐ TIN AND TAMBOURINE
Give me a penny / Tin and tambourine / You never can tell / Little piece of nothing / You're so rude / From the late to the early / How come / Winning with women / Rat's tails / Only you / Three cool cats / Richmond / Joyride (steppin' and reelin') / Nobody's listening / One for the road / Innocence lost
PILOT 046 / 13 Jul '98 / Burning Airlines

☐ YOU NEVER CAN TELL (2CD Set) (Lane, Ronnie & Slim Chance)
Ooh la la / Careless love / Flags and banners / How come / Sweet Virginia / Lovely / Anniversary / Don't try and change my mind / One for the road / Steppin' and reelin' / All or nothing / Last orders / Roll on babe / Lost/How come / You're so rude / What went down / Chicken wired / Sweet Virginia / You never can tell / Anniversary / Don't try and change my mind / Walk on by / You never can tell / Steppin' and reelin' / Ooh la la
PILOT 011 / Jun '97 / Burning Airlines

Lane, Steve

☐ EASY COME - EASY GO (Lane, Steve & Red Hot Peppers)
AZCD 14 / Nov '92 / Azure

Lanegan, Mark

☐ SCRAPS AT MIDNIGHT
Hospital roll call / Hotel / Stay / Black bell ocean / Last one in the world / Wheels / Waiting on a train / Day and night / Praying ground / Because of this
BBQCD 204 / 20 Jul '98 / Beggars Banquet

☐ WHISKEY FOR THE HOLY GHOST
SPCD 78249 / Jan '94 / Sub Pop

☐ WINDING SHEET
GR 095CD / Mar '94 / Sub Pop

Lang, Eddie

☐ BLUE GUITAR VOL.1 & 2 (Lang, Eddie & Lonnie Johnson)
BGOCD 327 / Dec '96 / Beat Goes On

☐ HANDFUL OF RIFFS, A
Eddie's twister / April kisses / Prelude / Melody man's dream / Perfect / Rainbow / Add a little wiggle / Jeannine / I'll never be the same / Church Street sobbin' blues / There'll be some changes made / Two tone stomp / Jet black blues / Blue blood blues / Bullfrog moan / Handful of riffs / Bugle call rag / Freeze and melt / Hot heels / Walking the dog / March of the hoodlums
CDAJA 5061 / May '89 / Living Era

☐ QUINTESSENTIAL EDDIE LANG 1925-1932, THE
Best black / Just the same / Wild cat / Doin' things / Put and take / Good little, bad little you / April kisses / Clementine / I'm coming Virginia / I got rhythm / Knockin' a jug / I wonder if you miss me tonight / Guitar blues / Walkin' the dog / Kitchen man / Add a little wiggle / Bench in the park / Prelude opus 3, no.2 / After you've gone / In the bottle blues / Street of dreams / Feelin' my way / Beale Street blues / I'll never be the same
CBC 1043 / 23 Feb '98 / Timeless Historical

☐ TROUBLES, TROUBLES (Lang, Eddie/ Edgar Blanchard & The Gondoliers)
ROUCD 2080 / '88 / Rounder

Lang, Jonny

☐ LIE TO ME
Lie to me / Darker side / Good morning little school girl / Still wonder / Matchbox / Back for a taste of your love / Quitter never wins / Hit the ground running / Rack 'em up / When I come to you / There's gotta be a change / Missing your love
5406402 / Jun '97 / A&M

Lang, k.d.

☐ ABSOLUTE TORCH AND TWANG (Lang, k.d. & The Reclines)
Luck in my eyes / Trail of broken hearts / Didn't I / Full moon full of love / Big big love / Walkin' in and out of your arms / Three days / Big boned gal / Wallflower waltz / Pullin' back the reins / It's me / Nowhere to stand
K 9258772 / Mar '94 / Sire

☐ ALL YOU CAN EAT
If I were you / Maybe / You're OK / Sexuality / Get some / Acquiesce / This / World of love / Infinite and unforeseen / I want it all
9362460342 / Oct '95 / Sire

☐ ANGEL WITH A LARIAT (Lang, k.d. & The Reclines)
Turn me round / High time for a detour / Diet of strange places / Got the bull by the horns / Watch your step polka / Rose garden / Tune into my wave / Angel with a lariat / Pay dirt / Three cigarettes in an ashtray
7599254412 / Aug '88 / Sire

☐ DRAG
Don't smoke in bed / Air that I breathe / Smoke dreams / My last cigarette / Joker / Valley of the dolls / Your smoke screen / My old addiction / Till the heart caves in / Smoke rings / Hain't it funny / Love is like a cigarette
9362466232 / Jun '97 / Sire

☐ EVEN COWGIRLS GET THE BLUES
Just keep me moving / Much finer place / Or was I / Hush sweet lover / Myth / Apogee / Virtual vortex / Lifted by love / Overture / Kundalini yoga waltz / In perfect dreams / Curious soul astray / Ride of bonanza jellybean / Don't be a lemming polka / Sweet little Cherokee / Cowgirl pride
9362454332 / Oct '93 / Sire

☐ INGENUE
Save me / Mind of love / Miss Chatelaine / Wash me clean / So it shall be / Still thrives this love / Seasons of hollow soul / Outside myself / Tear of love's recall / Constant craving
7599268402 / Dec '96 / Sire

☐ SHADOWLAND (The Owen Bradley Sessions) (Lang, k.d. & The Reclines)
Western stars / Lock, stock and teardrops / Sugar moon / I wish I didn't love you so / Once again around the dance floor / Black coffee / Shadowland / Don't let the stars get in your eyes / Tears don't care who cry them / I'm down to my last cigarette / Too busy being blue / Honky tonk angel's medley
9257242 / Apr '88 / Sire

Lang, Thierry

☐ THIERRY LANG
Yellow story / Comrade Conrad / Angels fly / If I should lose you / My foolish heart / Blue peach / Oliver's song / Bop boy / 'Round midnight
CDP 8562542 / Aug '97 / Blue Note

Lang, Thomas

☐ LOST LETTER Z, THE
DRYC 10012 / Sep '91 / Dry Communications

☐ OUTSIDE OVER THERE
Opening titles / Fail / Happy man / Longest song / Feels so right / Fingers and thumbs / Are you happy now / Try / Sleep with me / I will / Spirit / Injury / Out of reach / Saviour / Misunderstood / Thirst / So / Ghost of a chance / More that you expect
DRYCCD 15 / Nov '92 / Dry Communications

☐ VERSIONS
TLGCD 007 / Oct '96 / Telegraph

Lang, Tom

☐ MEDIATOR
343432 / Mar '96 / Koch International

Langa-Langa, Zaiko

☐ GRAND SUCESS DE LANGA
FLTRCD 521 / Dec '93 / Flame Tree

Langas & The Manganiars

☐ SONGS OF THE DISTANT SANDS
NRCD 0059 / Sep '96 / Navras

Lange, Katherina

☐ DAS WUNDERKIND
Abzahlen / Mignon vom kietz / Ich bin von kopf bis fuss auf liebe eingestellt / Die praktische Berlinerin / Da muss ich fliegen / Das zersagte dame / Der mann mit dem kalten blut / Currende / Abzahlen / Song der guste / Ich baumle mit de beene / Drahtseil akt / Das wunderkind / Dornroschen aus'm wedding / Das jroschenlied / Die Hungerkunstlerin / Nachtgebet / Kindertragodie / Rattenfangerlied / Es hat jeschnappt / Mit einer scheusslichen puppe / Volkslied / Oh mond / Wenn ick mal tot bin / Ich weiss nicht, zu wem ich gehore / In den abendwind jeflustert / Drei wunsche / Finale
BCD 16025 / Dec '96 / Bear Family

Langeleik, Levande

☐ LEVANDE LANGELEIK
HCD 7106 / Nov '95 / Helio

Langford, Frances

☐ GETTIN' SENTIMENTAL
I'm in the mood for love / Once in a while / Sweet someone / Is it true what they say about Dixie / Silhouetted in the moonlight / I don't want to make history / Everything you said came true / Deep shadows / I've got you under my skin / Harbour lights / You are my lucky star / Let's call a heart a heart / So do I / Speaking confidentially / Melody from the sky / Can't teach my old heart new tricks / If it's the last thing I do / So many memories / Rap tap on wood / Sweet heartache / I'm gettin' sentimental over you
CMSCD 002 / Feb '93 / Movie Stars

☐ I'M IN THE MOOD FOR LOVE
I'm in the mood for love / I feel a song coming on / Is it true what they say about Dixie / Easy to love / Rap tap on wood / Swingin' the jinx away / Was it rain / So many memories / I'm getting sentimental over you / Please be kind / At long last love / I won't tell a soul / Gipsy love song / Get out of town / Falling in love with love / Moonglow / Blue moon / When you wish upon a star / In the cool of the evening / In Waikiki / Tropical magic / Serenade in blue / Why do I love you / At last
CDAJA 5219 / Jul '97 / Living Era

☐ SWEET HEARTACHE
Kiss in the dark / Nasty man / Why do I love you / Palms of paradise / With the wind and the rain in your hair / Falling in love with love / When you wish upon a star / This can't be love / Hurry home / Serenade in blue / Neath the southern moon / Easy to love / Two dreams met / At last / You hi-de-hi-ing me / You're nearer / Little love, a little kiss / Echoes of Hawaii / Smilin' thru / Our love affair / Sweet heartache / Then you've never been blue / I'm gettin' sentimental over you / Was it rain
ROYCD 203 / Jul '96 / Flare

Langford, John

☐ SKULL ORCHARD
SF 006 / 27 Jul '98 / Sugar Free

Langheinrich, Ulf

☐ DEGREES OF AMNESIA
Invasive treatment / Severe circumstances / Running nowhere / Floating near the ground / Rome / Tissue I / Tissue II / Tissue III / Tissue IV / View down / Alluvial land / Inside pressure / Degrees of amnesia
ASP 0981CD / 9 Mar '98 / Asphodel

Langsyne

☐ LANGSYNE
REBIRTH 001 / 22 May '98 / Rebirth

Lanham, Roy

☐ SIZZLING STRINGS/THE FABULOUS GUITAR OF ROY LANHAM
Summit Ridge drive / Stomping at the Savoy / Sophisticated swing / Kerry dance / Lover / Tea for two / Air Mail special / If I had you / Slipped disc / Mellow mood / Eager beaver / Tuxedo Junction / Your heart darlin' / Holiday for strings / Roy's blues / Tuxedo Junction / We'll be together again / Brazil / In the mood / Under the Double Eagle / Brown's ferry blues / Carnival in Paris / One love / Can't we be friends
BCD 16116 / Nov '96 / Bear Family

Lanois, Daniel

☐ ACADIE
Still water / Maker / O Marie / Jolie Louise / Fisherman's daughter / White mustang II / Under a stormy sky / Where the hawkwind kills / Silium's hill / Ice / St. Ann's gold / Amazing grace
K 925969 2 / Sep '89 / Warner Bros.

☐ FOR THE BEAUTY OF WYNONA
Messenger / Brother LA / Still learning how to crawl / Beatrice / Waiting / Collection of Marie Claire / Death of a train / Unbreakable chain / Lotta love to give / Sleeping in the devil's bed / For the beauty of Wynona / Rocky world / Indian red
9362450302 / Dec '96 / Warner Bros.

Lanphere, Don

☐ DON LANPHERE AND LARRY CORYELL (Lanphere, Don & Larry Coryell)
Dragon gate / Very early / Ascending truth / Imagination / Green tutu / Spring can really hang you up the most / Sunset blues / My ideal / Beach at Nerja / Here they come, there they go / Peace
HEPCD 2048 / Dec '90 / Hep

☐ DON LOVES MIDGE (Lanphere, Don Quintet)
And the angels sing / Easy living / I remember Clifford / Try a little tenderness / Poor butterfly / I'll never be the same again / Once in a while / Old cape cod / God bless the child / Gone with the wind / Polka dots and moonbeams / Everything I have is yours / Put your dreams away / Soon / My foolish heart / There's a sweet spirit...
HEPCD 2027 / Sep '93 / Hep

☐ DON STILL LOVES MIDGE (Lanphere, Don & John Pugh)
London by night / Deep in a dream / Blues for Midge / Right to love / Just the way you are / Purple shades / That old feeling / Prelude to a kiss / Ellis in wonderland / Sinatra medley / My buddy / Gray-blue / As long as there's music / Early Autumn
HEPCD 2072 / 5 Jan '98 / Hep

☐ GO AGAIN (Lanphere, Don Sextet)
Which / Go again / Darn that dream / Shangri-La / I love you / Midges late valentine / What are you doing for the rest of your life / Maddie's dance / Music that makes me dance / Darkness on the Delta / Maestro
HEPCD 2040 / Jul '90 / Hep

☐ LOPIN' (Lanphere, Don & Bud Shank & Denny Goodhew)
I really didn't think that / Love's question / Lighten up / Time for love / Lope of a dolt / Have you met Miss Jones / Fall / El balie de la munecas (Dance of the dolls) / MK and MK
HEPCD 2058 / Sep '94 / Hep

Lansky, Paul

☐ CONVERSATION PIECES
For the moment / Chords / Now that you mention it / Same scene nine years later / Andalusia / Shadows
BRIDGE 9082 / 1 Sep '98 / Bridge

Lanterna

☐ LANTERNA
Silent hills / Down by the Seine / Turbine / 1985 / Dark spring / Passage / Colossus / End of the tunnel / Bells/Falling / Down by the Seine (drowning) / Ether net / No.7 galerie des anciennes / Dragon season / Achieving oneness / Slides / Dawn / Puerto de luna
RCD 10388 / 18 May '98 / Rykodisc

Lanz, David

☐ BELOVED
Beloved / Leaves on the seine / Madree de la tierra / Madrona / Return to the heart / First light / Courage of the wind / Summer's child / Before the last leaf falls / Reverie / Angel of hope / Cristofori's dream / Variations on a theme from pachebel's canon in D major
ND 64009 / Oct '95 / Narada

☐ BRIDGE OF DREAMS (Lanz, David & Paul Speer)
Day in the life / Into the dream / And the world falls away / Whispered in signs / Bridge of dreams / She stands on the mountain, still / Veil of fears / Reverie / Walking with Alfredo / Out of the shadows / Ode to a dark star / Song of the east (in this dream)
ND 63024 / Oct '93 / Narada

☐ CHRISTMAS EVE
ND 61046 / Oct '94 / Narada

☐ CRISTOFORI'S DREAM
Summer's child / Christofori's dream / Free fall / Spiral dance / Wings to the altair / Green into gold / Whiter shade of pale
VNDCD 1 / 11 May '98 / Virgin

☐ DESERT VISION (Lanz, David & Paul Speer)
Eagle's path / Seguaro / Desert rain / Sculptures / Canyon lands / Carlsbad / White sands / Stormlight / Tawtoma
CD 3003 / Aug '92 / Narada

☐ NATURAL STATES (Lanz, David & Paul Speer)
Miranova / Faces of the forest (part 1) / Faces of the forest (part 2) / Behind the waterfall / Mountain / Allegro 1985 / Lento 1984 / Rainforest / First light
CD 3001 / Aug '92 / Narada

☐ RETURN TO THE HEART
Return to the heart / Near the still waters of Amsterdam / Madre de la Tierra / Sounds from Koepel / Heartsounds / Manana, mi amor / Cori, Rio, Corre / Behind the waterfall/Desert rain / White shade of pale / Heart of the night / Dream of the forgotten child / Out of the darkness / Cristofori's dream / Gli uccelli di carpi / Variations on a theme / Return to the heart (reprise)
CD 4005 / Jun '92 / Narada

☐ SKYLINE FIREDANCE
CD 4001 / Aug '94 / Narada

☐ SONGS FROM AN ENGLISH GARDEN
72438454472 / 14 Jul '98 / Narada

Lanza, Mario

☐ BE MY LOVE
Be my love / Temptation / Wanting you / I'll be seeing you / With a song in my heart / Without a song / Danny boy / My wild Irish rose / And this is my beloved / Because / Only a rose / Funiculi, funicula / Come back to Sorrento / Maria Maria / O sole mio / Neapolitan love song / Arrivederci Roma / Ah sweet mystery of life / Look for the silver lining / Memories / Song is you / Ave Maria / You'll never walk alone / Serenade
GD 60720 / Mar '91 / RCA Victor

☐ BE MY LOVE (Popular Songs & Ballads)
Donkey serenade / More than you know / Loveliest night of the year / I love thee / Kiss / Softly as in a morning sunrise / Song of songs / Granada / Without a song / My song my love / Diane / Thine alone / Rosary / Ave Maria / Lord's prayer / If / They didn't believe me / Cosi cosa / Funiculi-funicula / Because you're mine / Be my love
PLATCD 148 / Mar '96 / Platinum

☐ BE MY LOVE
Be my love / Granada / Diane / My song my love / Serenade / O paradis / Marechiare / Rosary / Thine alone / Without a song / Funiculi funicula / La donna e mobile / If / Serenade / Lolita / A vuchella / Parlami D'amore mariu / Torna a surriento
302432 / Feb '98 / Hallmark

☐ CHRISTMAS WITH MARIO LANZA
Deck the halls with boughs of holly / Hark the herald angels sing / God rest ye merry gentlemen / Joy to the world / O Christmas tree / I saw three ships / It came upon the midnight clear / Ave Maria / O holy night / Virgin's slumber song / Pieta signore / First Noel / O come all ye faithful (adeste fidelis) / Away in a manger / We three kings / O little town of Bethlehem / Silent night / Guardian angels / I'll walk with God / Lord's prayer
74321411982 / Nov '97 / RCA Victor

☐ COLLECTION, THE
Ave maria / O sole mio / La donna e mobile / Joy to the world / Funiculi, funicula (denza) / Granada / Santa lucia / La spagnola / My song of love / O paradis (o paradiso) / Parliami d'amour / Rosary / A marechiare / A vuchella / Be my love / Because you're mine / Diane / Mattinata / More than you know / Serenade / Temptation / Loveliest night of the year / Vesti la giubba / Lord's prayer / There alone
COL 061 / Jun '95 / Collection

☐ DON'T FORGET ME
09026614202 / Jun '93 / RCA Victor

☐ ESSENTIAL COLLECTION, THE
Serenade / More than you know / Torna a surriento / Vogliatemi bene / Mamma mia che vo'sape / Because you're mine / Donkey serenade / Softly as in a morning sunrise / Song of songs / Loveleiest night of the year / I love thee / Ave Maria / Without a song / Catari, catari / Cosi, costa / Parig, O'Cara / Un di all azziro spazio / Une furtiva lagrima / O soave fanciulla / E lucevan le stelle / Parlami d'amore, mariu / Temptation / La donna e mobile / Kiss
PWKS 4230 / Nov '94 / Carlton

☐ FOR THE FIRST TIME/THAT MIDNIGHT KISS
Come prima / Tarantella / O sole mio / Neapolitan dance / Hofbrauhaus song / O mon amour / Mazurka / Pineapple pickers / Pagliacci - vesta la giubba / Otello - finale / Aida - grand finale / Ich liebe dich / Ave Maria / La Boheme / Che gelida manina / Mamma mia che vo'sape / I know, I know, I know / They didn't believe me / Core 'ngrato / Aida - celeste Aida
GD 60516 / Mar '91 / RCA Victor

☐ GRANADA
PLSCD 205 / Apr '97 / Pulse

☐ IN CONCERT
CD 6017 / Apr '96 / Music

☐ LEGENDARY VOICE OF MARIO LANZA, THE (2CD Set)
Serenade / Una furtiva lagrima / Catari, catari / Vogliatemi bene / Mama mia, che vo'sape / Because you're mine / Donkey serenade / Softly as in a morning sunrise / Song of songs / Loveliest night of the year / My song my love / Granada / Diane / Funiculi funicula / Thine alone / Vesti la giubba / Vuchella / La spagnola / O paradiso / Marechiare / Rosary / Lolita / If / Mattinata / They didn't believe me / Lord's prayer / Be my love / I love thee / Ave Maria / Without a song / Torna a surriento / Cosi, casa / Parigi o cara / Un di all' azzurro spazio / Temptation / E lucevan le stelle / Parlami d'amore, mariu / More than you know / La donna e mobile / Kiss
MUCD 9506 / May '96 / Musketeer

☐ LIVE IN LONDON
Introduction / Lamento di Frederico / Lasciacemi morire / Gia il sole dal gange / Tell me o blue blue sky / Introduction / Bonjour ma belle / House on the hill / E lucevan le stelle / Introduction / Mamma mia che vo' sape / Introduction / A vucchella / Marechiare / Softly as in a morning sunrise / I'm falling in love with someone / Because you're mine / Introduction / Seven hills of Rome / La donna e mobile
09026618842 / Nov '94 / RCA Victor

☐ LOVELIEST NIGHT OF THE YEAR, THE
MU 5049 / Oct '92 / Musketeer

☐ MARIO LANZA COLLECTION, THE (3CD Set)
Be my love / I'll never love you / Because you're mine / Song angels sing / Drink, drink, drink / Serenade / Loveliest night of the year / Great / La donna e mobile / Because / For you alone / Golden days / Deep in my heart / If I loved you / Yours is my heart alone / One night of love / Beloved / Beautiful love / With a song in my heart / You are my love / Call me fool / All the things you are / My song, my love / Love is the sweetest thing / Will you remember / Granada / Lolita / Temptation / Lygia / Lady of Spain / This land / Lee ah loo / Tina-lina / Boom biddy boom boom / Bayou lullaby / Lord's prayer / And here you are / Song of songs / Somewhere a voice is calling / I never knew / Ciribiribin / Wonder why / Come dance with me / O sole mio / Younger than springtime / For the first time / Never till now / Arrivederci / If you were mine / Behold / Night to remember / Love in a home / Do you wonder / Softly as in a morning sunrise / One alone / Celeste aida / Flower song / Brindisi - libiamo, libiamo / Questa o quella / Vesti la giubba / Addio all madre
GD 60889 / Mar '92 / RCA Victor

☐ MARIO LANZA LIVE
Funiculi, funicula / My song, my love / Granada / Diane / Thine alone / Vesti la giubba / Vuchella / Toselli's serenade / Because you're mine / Loveliest night of the year / O paradiso / Marechiare / Rosary / Lolita / If / Mattinata / They didn't believe me / Lord's prayer / Be my love
DATOM 2 / Apr '94 / Touch Of Magic

☐ MARIO LANZA SHOWS, THE
Introduction / Granada / Oh lady be good: *Sinatra, Ray & His Orchestra* / Serenade / Hello young lovers: *MacKenzie, Giselle* / La Fiacre: *MacKenzie, Giselle* / Because / Dizzy fingers: *Sinatra, Ray & His Orchestra* / Be my love / Funiculi, Funicula / A vucchella / Continental: *Sinatra, Ray & His Orchestra* / Fairyland: *MacKenzie, Giselle* / I'm falling in love with someone / Fiddle faddle: *Sinatra, Ray & His Orchestra* / Cock-eyed optimist: *MacKenzie, Giselle* / Torne Sorrento / Closing
OTA 101910 / Feb '97 / On The Air

☐ MY SONG OF LOVE
Because / My song of love / Granada / Dianne / Vesti la Giubba / Funiculi funicula / Thine alone / A Vucchella / Toselli's serenade / O paradiso / Marechiare / Rosary / Lolita / If / Mattinata / They didn't believe me / Lord's prayer / Be my love / Loveliest night of the year
QED 139 / Nov '96 / Tring

☐ PLATINUM COLLECTION, THE (2CD Set)
Serenade / Una furtiva lagrima / Catari catari / Voglaitemi bene / Mama mia che vo'safe / Because you're mine / Dinkey serenade / Softly as in a morning sunrise / Song of songs / Loveliest night of the year / My song my love / Granada / Diane / Funiculi funicula / Thine alone / Vesti la giubba / Vuchella / La spagnola / O paradiso / Marechiare / Rosary / Lolita / Mattinata / They didn't believe me / Lord's prayer / Be my love / I love thee / Ave Maria / Without a song / Torna a surriento / Cosi cosa / Pargi o cara / Un di all'azzurro spazio / More than you know / La donna e mobile / Kiss
PC 603 / 10 Nov '97 / Platinum Collection

☐ SERENADE
Serenade / La donna e mobile / Because you're mine / Donkey serenade / Ave Maria / My song, my love / Diane / Loveliest night of the year / Funiculi funicula / Thine alone / Granada / Vesta la giubba / A vucella / Toselli's serenade / O paradiso / A marechiare / Rosary / If / Be my love / Lord's prayer
SUMCD 4029 / Nov '96 / Summit

☐ ULTIMATE COLLECTION, THE
Be my love / Drink, drink, drink / La donna e mobile / Danny Boy / Granada / Because you're mine / Ave Maria / Valencia / Loveliest night of the year / Song of India / Because / O sole mio / Donkey serenade / Vesti la giubba / Serenade / Funiculi, funicula / Golden days / Arrivederci Roma / You'll never walk alone / Beloved / Come prima / E lucevan le stelle / Santa Lucia / I'll walk with God
74321185742 / Jan '94 / RCA Victor

☐ UNFORGETTABLE CLASSICS
MACCD 105 / Aug '96 / Autograph

☐ WITH A SONG IN MY HEART (The Love Collection)
With a song in my heart / Be my love / Because you're mine / Loveliest night of the year / Because / Temptation / Beloved / Song is you / Serenade / Lover come back to me / My wild irish rose / More than you know / Younger than springtime / September song / On the street where you live / Only a rose / Falling in love with love / And this is my beloved / My romance / This nearly was mine / All the things you are / I'll be seeing you
74321400582 / Jan '97 / Camden

☐ WITHOUT A SONG
Cose cosa / Donkey serenade / Parliamo d'amore Maria / Kiss / Recondito armante / Softly as in a morning sunrise / Una furtiva lagrima / Song of songs / Mamma mia che vo'sape / Come back to sorrento / Without a song / O sole mio / Ave maria / Perigi o cara / Vogliddemi bene, un bene piccolino / O souve funchilla / More than you know / La spagnola
MUCD 9019 / Apr '95 / Musketeer

☐ YOU'LL NEVER WALK ALONE
I'll walk with God / Trembling of a leaf / Lord's prayer / Love in a home / Somebody bigger than you and I / Through the years / Ave Maria / Without a song / Hills of home / I love thee / Rosary / Look for the silver lining / None but the lonely heart / My buddy / Guardian angels / Somewhere a voice is calling / Trees / Ave Maria / Because / Roses of Picardy / For you alone / You'll never walk alone
09026680732 / Jun '95 / RCA Victor

Lao, Molam

☐ MUSIC FROM SOUTHERN LAOS
NI 5401CD / Jun '94 / Nimbus

LaPorta, John

☐ MOST MINOR, THE (LaPorta, John Quartet)
FSRCD 208 / Oct '96 / Fresh Sound

Laptop

☐ END CREDITS
NOIR 005CDX / 1 Dec '97 / God Bless

Lara, Agustin

☐ INTERPRETA SUS CANCIONES DE AMOR
ALCD 018 / Jul '96 / Alma Latina

Lara, Roberto

☐ ARGENTINA (Guitar Of The Pampas)
LYRCD 7253 / Nov '97 / Lyrichord

Lara, Sergio

☐ RIVERWALK (Lara, Sergio & Joe Reyes)
HOMCD 45624 / 19 May '98 / Higher Octave

Laraaji

☐ DAYS OF RADIANCE
Dance no. 1 / Dance no. 2 / Dance no. 3 / Meditation / Meditation no.2
EEGCD 19 / '87 / EG

☐ FLOW GOES THE UNIVERSE
Being here / Space choir / Cave in England / Immersion / Zither dance / Mbira dance / Laughing in tongues / Deep celestial / In continuum / Silence I / Silence II / Silence III / Silence IV / Silence V
ASCD 10 / Apr '96 / All Saints

Larade, Alexandra

☐ VINI DAN TCHEW
CD 84002 / Jan '97 / Sonodisc/Atis

Lard

☐ LAST TEMPTATION OF REID, THE
VIRUS 84CD / 22 Jun '98 / Alternative Tentacles

☐ PURE CHEWING SATISFACTION
VIRUS 199CD / Jun '97 / Alternative Tentacles

Lard Free

☐ UNNAMED
14915 / Jun '97 / Spalax

Larguinho, Mathilde

☐ BEST OF FADO PORTUGUESE
EUCD 1174 / '91 / ARC

Lark

☐ 0002K
2100053 / Jun '93 / Indisc

Larkin

☐ O'CEAN
Emergence / Communitizing
ND 62812 / Aug '97 / Narada

Larkin, Kenny

☐ ART OF DANCE
SUB 48062 / Mar '96 / Distance

☐ METAPHOR
Intro / Metaphor / Nocturnal / Loop 1 / Java / Groove / Loop 15 / Catatonic part 2 / Catatonic (first state) / Loop 2 / Soul man / Symphy / Butterflies / Amethyst
RS 95954CD / Feb '95 / R&S

Larkin, Patty

☐ I'M FINE
Rescue me / Justine / Window / Dangerous / I'm fine / Pucker up / Lately / On the run / Don't want to give it up / Island of time / If I were made of metal / Caffeine / Valentine / Day to day
CDPH 1115 / Oct '88 / Philo

☐ STEP INTO THE LIGHT
PH 1103CD / Apr '94 / Philo

Larkins, Ellis

☐ LIVE AT MAYBECK RECITAL HALL VOL.22
How'd ya like to love me / Perfume and rain / Oh lady be good / I don't want to cry anymore / Blue skies / No more/God bless' The Child / I let a song go out of my heart / Spring will be a little late this year / Leave me alone / Things ain't what they used to be / When a woman loves a man/I'm through with love
CCD 4533 / Nov '92 / Concord Jazz

☐ SMOOTH ONE, A
Rose room / C.e.b. / Smooth one / Between the devil and the deep blue sea / Blues in my heart / St. louis blues / I want a little girl / Day dream
BLE 591232 / Oct '94 / Black & Blue

Larrissey, Brendan

☐ FLICK OF THE WRIST
CBM 016CD / Jul '95 / Cross Border Media

Larry Ethnic

☐ LARRY ETHNIC MEETS THE WAILERS
EMWCD 1 / 17 Nov '97 / Ethnic

Larsen, Grey

☐ GATHERING, THE
SHCD 1133 / Jan '97 / Sugar Hill

☐ ORANGE TREE, THE (Larsen, Grey & Andre Marchand)
SHCD 1136 / Apr '94 / Sugar Hill

Larsen, Morton Gunnar

☐ JELLY ROLL (Larsen, Morton Gunnar & Vernel Bagneris)
BCD 400 / Mar '97 / GHB

☐ MORTON GUNNAR LARSEN & HIS OPHELIA RAGTIME ORCHESTRA IN NEW (Larsen, Morton Gunnar Ophelia Ragtime Orchestra)
BCD 410 / Dec '97 / GHB

Larson, Nicolette

☐ NICOLETTE
Lotta love / Rumba girl / You send me / Can't get away from you / Mexican divorce / Baby, don't you do it / Give a little / Angels / Rejoiced / French waltz / Come early mornin' last in love
7599273662 / Jan '96 / WEA

Larumbe, Horacio

☐ CARNAVAL (Larumbe, Horacio Trio)
BMJ 004 / 5 Jan '98 / Blue Moon

Larval

☐ LARVAL
AVAN 055 / Sep '97 / Avant

La's

☐ LA'S
Son of a gun / I can't sleep / Timeless melody / Liberty ship / There she goes / Doledrum / Feelin' / Way out / IOU / Freedom song / Failure / Looking glass
8282022 / Nov '90 / Go Discs

Las Estrellas Caiman

☐ DESCARGA DEL MILENIO
CCD 9037 / 24 Apr '98 / Fresh Sound

Las Hermanas Mendoza

☐ JUANITA Y MARIA
ARHCD 430 / Jun '95 / Arhoolie

LaSalle, Denise

☐ HERE I AM AGAIN
Here I am again / Married, but not to each other / Share your man with me / I wanna do what's on your mind / Trying to forget / My brand on you / Stay with me awhile / Anytime is the right time / Don't nobody live here (by the name of fool) / Hit and run / We've got love / Get up off my mind / Who's the fool / Best thing I ever had
CDSEW 066 / Sep '93 / Westbound

☐ TRAPPED BY A THING CALLED LOVE/ ON THE LOOSE (2CD Set)
Man size job / What it takes to get a good woman / Harper Valley PTA / What am I doing wrong / Breaking up somebody's home / There ain't enough hate around / Your man and your best friend / Lean on me / Making a good thing better / I'm over you / I'm satisfied / Trapped by a thing called love / Now run and tell that / Heartbreaker of the year / Goody goody getter / Catch me if you can / Hung up, strung out / Do me right / Deeper I go (better it gets) / You'll lose a good thing / Keeping it coming / It's too late
CDSEWD 018 / Feb '92 / Westbound

Lascelles

☐ ROCK OIL
OERCD 003 / Jun '97 / Orange Egg

Lascelles Jams

☐ TURN OFF THE LIGHTS
JASCD 3 / Apr '97 / Sarge

Lashout

☐ DARKEST HOUR, THE
SSR 001 / Nov '94 / Stormstrike

☐ WHAT ABSCENCE YIELDS
SSR 008CD / Jul '96 / Stormstrike

Lasley, Tony

☐ LATIN MOON
M 46CD / Aug '96 / World Disc

LaSpina, Steve

☐ WHEN CHILDREN SMILE
SCCD 31419 / Nov '97 / Steeplechase

☐ WHEN I'M ALONE (LaSpina, Steve Quintet)
SCCD 31376 / Feb '96 / Steeplechase

Lassigue Bendthaus

☐ MATTER
KK 113 / Jan '94 / KK

☐ RENDER
KK 115CD / May '94 / KK

Last

☐ AWAKENING
SST 230CD / Jul '89 / SST

Last Chapter

☐ LIVING WATERS
32270 CD / 26 Jan '98 / Pavement

Last Dance

☐ TRAGEDY
EFA 121692 / Jan '96 / Apollyon

Last, David

☐ INTRODUCING DAVID LAST
Nocturne in eb / Skye boat song/Scottish soldier / Bewitched, bothered and bewildered / C'est si bon/I love Paris / Don't cry for me Argentina / Sometimes when we touch/Shenandoah / My boy lollipop / Swingin' safari / Lass of Richmond Hill / Farmer and the cowman/Alias Smith and Jones / Only you / Feelings/Music of the night / Tritsch tratsch polka / Eye level/Windmill in old Amsterdam / Unforgettable/When I fall in love / Minuet in G/ Pathetique sonata
CDTS 035 / Aug '93 / Maestro

☐ MELODIES FOR YOU
(Everything I do) I do it for you / La reve / Sailing/Red sails in the sunset / I dont't know why I love you/I love you because / Wonder of you/My own true love / Rain in spain/Viva Espana / Good the bad and the ugly / Entertainer / Dance of the hours/Nessun dorma / I dreamed a dream/Yesterday / Heartbeat / Downtown/I only want to be with you / Love me/All my love / I don't get around much anymore / Redetsky march / I walk the line/Sugartime / New world symphony / Love me forever/What now my love / Rhythm of the rain
CDTS 038 / Sep '93 / Maestro

Last Days Of April

☐ WEDDING
BTR 27 / 25 May '98 / Bad Taste

Last Delay

☐ JAIL
EFA 125332 / Oct '95 / Celtic Circle

Last Exit

☐ BEST OF LAST EXIT LIVE, THE
EMCD 110 / Feb '90 / Enemy

☐ LAST EXIT
EMY 1012 / Sep '97 / Enemy

☐ NOISE OF TROUBLE
EMY 1032 / Sep '97 / Enemy

Last Great Dreamers

☐ RETROSEXUAL
CDBLEED 10 / Oct '94 / Bleeding Hearts

Last Illusion

☐ IN A ROOTSMAN STYLE
JMF 001CD / Feb '95 / Jah Mountain Fountain

Last, James

☐ BEST FROM 150 GOLD, THE
Starparade / Hora staccato / Charmaine / Morgens um sieben (morning's at seven) / Don't cry for me Argentina / Happy music / La entrada del bilbao / Knock on wood / Ballade pour Adeline / Hppy heart / Der seinsamer hirte (the lonely shepherd) / Liechtensteiner polka / Romance for violin and orchestra / Anvil polka / Salome / Petersburger schlittenfahrt
8355622 / Oct '90 / Polydor

☐ BY REQUEST
Mornings at 7 / Elvira Madigan / Air that I breathe / Adagio from the New World Symphony / Lonely shepherd / Roses of the south / Sabre dance / Lonely bull / Tulips from Amsterdam / Seduction / Zip a dee doo dah / Spanish eyes / Valencia / That's life
8317862 / Apr '87 / Polydor

☐ CHRISTMAS ALBUM, THE
Ave verum corpus / Winter / Here I stand at your cradle / Largo / For unto us a child is born / Adagio / Largo / Christmas concerto / Thus loved God the world
5506412 / Nov '96 / Spectrum

☐ CLASSIC TOUCH
Overture marriage of Figaro / Traumerei / Eine kleine nachtmusik / Intermezzo from cavalleria rusticana / Chanson triste / Rodrigo's guitar concerto de Aranjuez / Barcarolle / In the hall of the mountain king / Adagio from the sonata pathetique no.8 / Libestraum / Elvira Madigan / Hungarian dance no.5 / Ballet music / Bolero
5500982 / Oct '93 / Spectrum

☐ GAMES THAT LOVERS PLAY
Lara's theme / Man and a woman / Games that lovers play / This is my song / What now my love / Close your eyes / I left my heart in San Francisco / Fly me to the moon / Now I know / Elizabethan serenade / Never on Sunday / Sandy's theme
8216102 / ' / Polydor

☐ IN IRELAND
Rare ould times / Rare ould times / Glenroe / Jigger / Old skibbereen / Vincent brodericks / Women of ireland / Pipe / Only our rivers / Up to the races / Blackbird / Mo ghile mear
8299272 / '88 / Polydor

☐ INSTRUMENTAL FOREVER
String of pearls / Tico tico / Granada / Brazil / St. Louis blues march / Havah nagilah / Petite fleur / Cherry pink and apple blossom white / You are my sunshine / La Bamba / Amor amor amor / Copacabana
8152502 / '89 / Polydor

☐ JAMES LAST IN SCOTLAND
Skye boat song / My love is like a red red rose / I love a lassie / Roamin' in the gloamin' / Scottish soldier / Will ye no' come back again / I belong to Glasgow / Flower of Scotland / Auld lang syne / Ye banks and braes o' bonnie Doon / Days of auld lang syne / Keel row / Barren rocks of Aden / Loch Lomond / My bonnie Mary of Argyle / Annie laurie
8237432 / Jun '85 / Polydor

☐ JAMES LAST PLAYS ANDREW LLOYD WEBBER
With one look / Jesus Christ Superstar / Memory / I don't know how to love him / Music of the night / Any dream will do / Love changes everything / Don't cry for me Argentina / Tell me on a Sunday / Take that look off your face / Phantom of the opera / Point of no return
5199102 / Nov '93 / Polydor

☐ LEAVE THE BEST TO LAST
Tell her about it / Karma chameleon / Wake me up before you go go / Heartbreaker / Take a chance on me / You can't hurry love / Uptown girl / Caribbean queen (no more love on the run) / That was yesterday / Ghostbusters / Hooray hooray it's a holi-holiday / Agadoo / I just called to say I love you / Wanderer / Easy lover / Every breath you take / You're my heart you're my soul / Super trouper / Half a minute / Do the conga / Hello / One more night / Red red wine / Live is life / Imagine
8273932 / Sep '85 / Polydor

☐ LIVE IN LONDON
Intro '78 / Tiger feet / Radar love / Jesus loves you / Bridge over troubled water / I've got you under my skin / Was ich dir sagen will / Jog dig oas / Rum and coca cola / Quando, quando, quando / South America take it away / Lonely shepherd / Larry O'Gaff / Fire on the mountain / Center amigos / Schwarze estrella / Ay ay ay / Costa brava / Eso es el amor / Star Wars / West Side story / Silly love songs / With one more look at you / Watch closely now / Love me tender / Rip it up / Don't be cruel / Jailhouse rock / Hound dog / Chicken reel / Turkey in the straw / Orange blossom special / Cockles and mussels / Daisy Daisy / Abide with me / Yes sir, I can boogie / Sorry I'm a lady / Don't leave me this way / Don't cry for me Argentina / Games that lovers play
8438092 / Nov '90 / Polydor

☐ MAKE THE PARTY LAST
Cracklin' Rosie / Rose garden / Knock three times / Banks of the Ohio / Song sung blue / Tie a yellow ribbon round the ole oak tree / Summer knows / Close to you / Soley soley / Is this the way to Amarillo / You are the sunshine of my life / Never can say goodbye / La bamba / Hava nagila / Pushbike song / What have they done to my song Ma / Joy to the world / What now my love / I don't know how to love him / In the summertime / Goodbye Sam, hello Samantha / I hear you knocking / (We're gonna) Rock around the clock / See you later alligator / Hound dog
5500332 / May '93 / Spectrum

☐ MUSIC OF JAMES LAST, THE
MACCD 240 / Aug '96 / Autograph

☐ MUSICAL STYLE OF JAMES LAST, THE (London Pops Orchestra)
Exodus theme / La bamba / You won't find another fool like me / Old fashioned way / Solitaire / Barbara Ann / Funny funny / Pushbike song / It never rains in Southern California / Help yourself / My name is Jack / La bamba / Cracklin' Rosie / Montego bay / Beautiful dreamer / Help yourself / Top of the world / Paper roses / Walk right back / Your Mama don't dance / Yellow river / Ob-la-di ob-la-da / Satisfaction / I've got you under my skin / My sweet Lord / Danny / MacArthur Park / Chitty chitty bang bang / When I'm dead and gone
QED 177 / Nov '96 / Tring

☐ POP SYMPHONIES VOL.2 (Last, James Orchestra)
5396242 / 16 Mar '98 / Polydor

☐ ROSE OF TRALEE AND OTHER IRISH FAVOURITES
Maggie / Irish stew / Coulin / Come back to Erin / Ril mhor bhaile an chalaidh / An eriskay love lilt / On the banks of my own lovely Lee / Summer in Dublin / When Irish eyes are smiling / Rose of Tralee / Londonderry air / Sweepstake / Cockles and mussels / IRELAND
8159842 / '88 / Polydor

☐ TENDERLY
(I left my heart) In San Fransisco / Air that I breathe / Fly me to the moon / I don't know how to love him / This is my song / Man and a woman / Elizabethan serenade / Close your eyes / Hey Jude / What now my love / Games that lovers play / Whiter shade of pale / Speak softly love / Lara's theme / Now I know / Romeo and Juliet / Wedding song (there is love) / Tenderly
5513192 / Mar '96 / Spectrum

☐ TWO SIDES OF JAMES LAST, THE (2CD Set)
5338822 / Nov '96 / Polydor

☐ VERY BEST OF JAMES LAST, THE
Whiter shade of pale / Bolero / From a distance / Yesterday / Granada / Mornings at seven / Penny Lane / Loneley shepherd / House of the rising sun / In the mood / Sacrifice / Viva Espana / Maggie / Roses from the South / (Everything I do) I do it for you / Games that lovers play
5295562 / Oct '95 / Polydor

Last Poets

☐ BEATS RHYME AND REVOLUTION
MCCD 311 / 8 Sep '97 / Music Club

☐ BEST OF THE LAST POETS, THE
CDNEW 105 / Mar '97 / Charly

☐ BEST OF THE PRIME TIME RHYME VOL.2
El pluribus unum / Tranquility / African slave / Beyonder / Oh my people / What will you do / Enough emotion / Unholy alliance
SP 21CD / Nov '95 / On The One

☐ CHASTISEMENT
Tribute to Obani / Jazzoetry / Black soldier / E pluribus unum / Hands off / Lone ranger / Before the white man came / Bird's word
CPCD 822 / Apr '97 / Charly

☐ DELIGHTS OF THE GARDEN (Last Poets & Bernard Purdie)
It's a trip / Ho Chi Minh / Blessed are those who struggle / Pill / Delights of the garden / Beyonder
CPCD 8191 / Sep '96 / Charly

☐ FREEDOM EXPRESS
Tough enough / Woodshed walk / Freedom express / Geronimo / Un-Holy alliance
MPG 74040 / Jan '97 / Movieplay Gold
CPCD 8329 / 2 Feb '98 / Charly

☐ HOLY TERROR
Invocation / Homesick / Black rage / Men-tality / Last rite / Talk show / Illusion of self / If only we knew / Funk / Phelhourinho
RCD 10319 / Mar '97 / Black Arc

☐ LAST POETS
Run nigger / On the subway / Niggers are scared of revolution / Black thighs / Gashman / Wake up niggers / New york, new york / Jones comin' down / When the revolution comes / Just because / Black wish / Two little boys / Suprises
CPCD 8184 / Jun '96 / Charly

☐ OH MY PEOPLE
I get movin' / This is your life / What will you do / Oh my people / Hold fast / Parting company / It's a trip / Ho chi minh / Blessed are those who struggle / Pill / Delights of the garden / (beyonder) be / Yond / Er
CPCD 8174 / Mar '96 / Charly

☐ THIS IS MADNESS
CPCD 8154 / Nov '95 / Celluloid

Last Real Texas Blues Band

☐ LAST REAL TEXAS BLUES BAND
ANT 0036 / May '95 / Antones

Last Resort

☐ BEST OF THE LAST RESORT, THE
STEPCD 010 / 8 Jun '98 / Step 1

☐ VIOLENCE IN OUR MINDS
Violence in our minds / Held hostage / Soul boys / Stormtroopers in strapdress / Resort bootboys / Red / White and blue / Rose of england / We rule ok / Rebel with a cause / Freedom / Changing / Violence in our minds / Working class kids / Johnny Baren / Horror show / Wicked woman / Right to remain silent / American faces / Last refuge / Them and us
CANCAN 003CD / 3 Nov '97 / Can Can

☐ WAY OF LIFE (Skinhead Anthems)
Freedom / Skinheads in strapress / Rebels with a cause / King of the jungle / We rule OK / Changing / Lionheart / Rose of England / Violence in our minds / Resort boot boys / Red white and blue / Stormtroopers / King of the jungle / Resort boot boys / Oi oi skinhead
AHOYCD 001 / 13 Apr '98 / Captain Oi

Last Straw

☐ ALONE ON A STONE
KSCD 9591 / Jun '97 / Kissing Spell

Lasuen, Fran

☐ WITH ESKUADRA ZARRA
AZ 001 / 1 Jun '98 / Karonte

Laswell, Bill

☐ BASELINES
CPCD 8284 / Apr '97 / Charly

☐ CITY OF LIGHT
SR 114 / Jun '97 / Sub Rosa

☐ DUB MELTDOWN (Laswell, Bill & Style Scott)
EFA 012212 / Aug '97 / Word Sound Recordings

☐ EQUATIONS OF ETERNITY (Laswell, Bill & Mick Harris/Eraldo Bernochi)
WSCD 015 / Jan '97 / Word Sound Recordings

☐ HEAR NO EVIL
Lost roads / Bullet hole memory / Illinois central / Assassin / Stations of the cross / Kingdom come
CDVE 12 / Mar '88 / Venture

☐ INTO THE OUTLANDS
Voice of thunder / Speed of light
MPG 74043 / Jun '97 / Movieplay Gold

☐ OSCILLATIONS (Remixes)
SR 122CD / 6 Oct '97 / Sub Rosa

☐ PHAT DUB VOL.1
APC 003 / Jul '97 / APC Tracks

☐ PHAT DUB VOL.2
APC 004 / Jul '97 / APC Tracks

☐ SACRED SYSTEM VOL.1
RUSCD 821 / Jul '96 / ROIR

☐ SACRED SYSTEM VOL.2
RUSCD 8233 / 1 Dec '97 / ROIR

Lateef, Yusef

☐ AFRICAN-AMERICAN EPIC SUITE
1st movement - the african as non-american / 2nd movement - transmutation / 3rd movement - love for all / 4th movement - freeddom
892142 / Jun '94 / Act

☐ BEFORE DAWN
Passion / Love is eternal / Pike's peak / Open strings / Before down / Twenty five minute blues / Chang chang chang / Constellation
5570972 / 3 Aug '98 / Verve

☐ EASTERN SOUNDS
Plum blossom / Blues for the orient / Chinq miau / Don't blame me / Spartacus (love theme) / Snafu / Purple flower / Robe (love theme) / Tree faces of balal
OJCCD 612 / Feb '92 / Original Jazz Classics

☐ JAZZ MOODS
Metaphor / Yusef's mood / Beginning / Morning / Blues in space
SV 0237 / Oct '97 / Savoy Jazz

☐ MAN WITH THE BIG FRONT YARD (3CD Set)
60412320592 / 27 Apr '98 / Thirty Two

☐ PRAYER TO THE EAST
Night in Tunisia / Endura / Prayer to the East / Love dance / Lover man
SV 0210 / Oct '97 / Savoy Jazz

Latimer

☐ LATIMER
Neolida / Kiss / Stabs the reason / Carolida / Chicken the goon / Cold front killer / Dirgesque / Hold down / Auto-redeemer / Stringbender / Poseur / Rek O Kut
WDOM 016CD / May '95 / World Domination

Latimore

☐ SWEET VIBRATIONS
Stormy Monday / Ain't nothin' you can do / Snap your fingers / Let's straighten it out / Keep the home fire burnin' / There's a redneck in the sould band / Qualified man / It ain't where you been / Something 'bout you / Sweet vibrations / I get lifted / Dig a little deeper / Long distance love
NEXCD 166 / May '91 / Sequel

Latin Playboys

☐ LATIN PLAYBOYS
Viva la raza / Ten believers / Chinese surprise / Mira / Manifold de amour / New zandu / Rudy's party / If / Same brown earth / Lagoon / Gone / Crayon sun / Pink steps / Forever nightshade Mary
8282222 / May '94 / London

Latin Quarter

☐ BRINGING ROSA HOME
SPV 08544742 / Mar '97 / SPV

☐ LONG PIG
Long pig / Better helter skelter / King for a day / Bitter to the south / Phil Ochs / More than a trace / Desert rose / Contention city / Hoopoe / Church on fire / Coming down to pray / Like a miracle / Faith and reason
CLD 91082 / Jun '95 / Cloud Nine

Latin Touch

☐ FIESTA
La senorita / Loco / Misunderstood / Fiesta / Conchita / Adios amigo / Ti me cuando / My love / Viva / Soul mate / Without you / Please tell me (illusions)
74321183242 / Feb '94 / Ariola Express

Latino Velvet
☐ CLIQUE
8536542522 / 14 Apr '98 / Lightyear

Latta, Jim
☐ CARAVAN
LB 9715 / Jul '98 / La Brava

Lattau, Kevin
☐ KEVIN LETTAU
NOVA 9135 / Jan '93 / Nova

Latte E Miele
☐ PAPILLON
SRMC 0068 / 5 Jan '98 / Siwan

☐ PASSIO SECUNDUM MATTHEUM
SRMC 0003 / 5 Jan '98 / Siwan

Latyrx
☐ LATRYX
Latryx / Say that / Quickening (the wreckoning part II) / Balcony beach / Live at 903 '94 / Muzapper's mix (aim for the flickering flame/rankin no.1) / Funky granules / Bad news / Off (with) their heads (be prompt) / Interlude (a double deuce) / Burnt pride / Scratchapella (veinte tres segundos) / Wreckoning / Burning hot in Cali on a Saturday night
SLSCD 001 / Mar '97 / Solesides

☐ MUZAPPER'S MIXES, THE
Rankin' #1 / Aim for the flickering flame / Bumpin' contraption / Lost in the feelin' / Lady don't tek no / Cloud #9 / Regions / Recalibration / Rankin #1 / Lost in the field / Lady don't tek no words / Cloud #9 / Regions / Regions dub
SLS 004CD / 18 May '98 / Solesides

Laubrock, Ingrid
☐ WHO IS IT
It happened / Piracuama / I and I / Who is it / Longe / Brasitaleiro / Underwater garden / Handle with care / A gente se ve / Conto do passaro / Com acucar com afeto
CCD 79745 / Jun '98 / Candid

Lauder, Harry
☐ I LOVE A LASSIE
I love a lassie / Roamin' in the gloamin' / Wedding of Sandy McNab / Waggle o' the kilt / O sing to me the auld Scotch songs / When I get back to bonnie Scotland / Keep right on to the end of the road / It's just like being at home / Bonnie Leezie Lindsay / I'm looking for a bonnie lass tae love me / Love makes the world a merry go round / She is my daisy / Wee Deoch an' Doris / I think I'll get wed in the summer / I like my old home town / I'm the boss of the hoose / I've loved her ever since she was a baby / Soosie MacLean
PASTCD 9719 / Oct '90 / Flapper

☐ SIR HARRY LAUDER (Britain's First Knight Of The Music Hall)
Overture - The Harry Lauder medley / I love a lassie / Will you stop your tickling jock / Breakfast in bed / Roamin' in the gloamin' / Waggle o' the kilt / Soosie Maclean / There's a wee hoose' mang the heather / I've just got off the chain / Just a wee deoch an' Doris / We parted on the shore / Keep right on to the end of the road
LCOM 5232 / May '94 / Lismor

Lauderdale, Jim
☐ PERSIMMONS
Life by numbers / Do you like it / And that's a lot / Am I only dreaming this / Don't leave your light low / Seems like you're gonna take me back / I thought we had a deal / Tears so strong / Please pardon me / Some things are too good to last / Nobody's perfect / Had a little time / That's not right babe / Optimistic messenger / Jupiter's rising
UPSTART 035 / Oct '96 / Upstart

☐ WHISPER
Goodbye song / Whisper / Sometimes / Take me down a path / She used to say that to me / In harm's way / Without you here it's not the same / It's hard to keep a secret anymore / We're gone / What do you say to that / You're tempting me / Hole in my head / I'll lead you home
07863669962 / 30 Mar '98 / RCA

Laudet, Francois
☐ MY DRUMMER IS RICH... (Laudet, Francois Big Band)
BBRC 9312 / Jan '94 / Big Blue

Laughing Clowns
☐ GHOSTS OF AN IDEAL WIFE
Crystal clear / Diabolic creature / No words of honour / Winter's way / Ghosts of an ideal wife / Only one that knows / New bully in town / It gets so sentimental / Flypaper
HOT 1013CD / Nov '93 / Hot

☐ GOLDEN DAYS WHEN GIANTS WALKED THE EARTH
Eternally yours / Theme from Mad flies, mad flies / Winter's way / Mr. Uddich-Smuddich / Holy Joe / I don't know what I want / Possessions / Eulogy / Flypaper / Every dog has it's day
HOT 1055CD / Aug '95 / Hot

Laughing Heads
☐ LAUGHING HEADS
RR 800CD / Nov '96 / Resounding

Laughing Hyenas
☐ CRAWL
TG 102CD / Oct '92 / Touch & Go

☐ HARD TIMES
TG 136CD / Feb '95 / Touch & Go

☐ MERRY GO ROUND
TG 25CD / Sep '95 / Touch & Go

Laughlin, Tim
☐ NEW ORLEANS RHYTHM
JCD 235 / Apr '94 / Jazzology

☐ NEW ORLEANS SWING
JCD 265 / Dec '95 / Jazzology

☐ SWING THAT MUSIC (Laughlin, Tim & Jack Maheu)
JCD 245 / Jun '95 / Jazzology

Laughner, Peter
☐ TAKE THE GUITAR PLAYER FOR A RIDE
Baudelaire / Rock it down / Sylvia Plath / Pledging my time / Lullaby / In the bar / Cinderlla backstreet / Only love can break your heart / Visions of Johanna / Amphetamine / Life stinks / What love is / Ain't it fun / Dear Richard / Calvary cross / Take your love away / Baby's on fire / Me and the devil blues
TK 92CD045 / Aug '94 / T/K

Laula, Carol
☐ STILL
Bad case of you / Child of mine / It's true / Gonna bu / Home to sister / Stay with me angel / Restless / Old brick wall / By the minute / White dress / Stars with my coffee
IRCD 020 / '93 / Iona

Lauper, Cyndi
☐ HAT FULL OF STARS
That's what I think / Product of misery / Who let in the rain / Lies / Broken glass / Sally's pigeons / Feels like Christmas / Dear John / Like I used to / Someone like me / Part hate / Hat full of stars
4730542 / Sep '96 / Epic

☐ NIGHT TO REMEMBER, A/SHE'S SO UNUSUAL/TRUE COLORS (3CD Set)
I drove all night / Primitive / My first night without you / Like a cat / Heading west / Night to remember / Unconditional love / Insecurious / Dancing with a stranger / I don't want to be your friend / Kindred spirit / Money changes everything / Girls just wanna have fun / When you were mine / Time after time / She bop / All through the night / Witness / I'll kiss you / She's so unusual / Yeah yeah / Change of heart / Maybe he'll know / Boy blue / True colors / Calm inside the storm / What's going on / Iko iko / Faraway nearby / 911 / One track mind
4716222 / Oct '94 / Epic

☐ SHE'S SO UNUSUAL
Money changes everything / Girls just wanna have fun / When you were mine / Time after time / She bop / All through the night / Witness / I'll kiss you / He's so unusual / Yeah yeah
4633622 / Feb '89 / Epic

☐ SHE'S SO UNUSUAL/TRUE COLORS/A NIGHT TO REMEMBER (3CD Set)
Money changes everything / Girls just want to have fun / When you were mine / Time after time / She bop / All through the night / Witness / I'll kiss you / He's so unusual / Yeah yeah / Change of heart / Maybe he'll know / Boy blue / True colors / Calm inside the storm / What's going on / Iko iko / Faraway / Nearby / 911 / One track mind / Intro / I drove all night / Primitive / My first night without you / Like a cat / Heading West / Night to remember / Unconditional love / Insecurious / Dancing with a stranger / I don't want to be your friend / Kindred spirit
4853222 / 3 Nov '97 / Epic

☐ SISTERS OF AVALON
Sisters of Avalon / Ballad of Cleo and Joe / Fall into your dreams / You don't know / Love to hate / Hot gets a little cold / Unhook the stars / Searching / Say a prayer / Mother fearless / Brimstone and fire / Lollygagging
4853702 / Feb '97 / Epic

☐ TRUE COLORS
Change of heart / Maybe he'll know / Boy blue / True colors / Calm inside the storm / What's going on / Iko iko / Faraway nearby / 911 / One track mind
4624932 / Aug '90 / Portrait

☐ TWELVE DEADLY CYNS - AND THEN SOME
I'm gonna be strong / Girls just wanna have fun / Money changes everything / Time after time / She bop / All through the night / Change of heart / True colors / What's going on / I drove all night / World is stone / Who let in the rain / That's what I think / Sally's pigeons / Hey now (girls just wanna have fun) / Come on home
4773632 / Aug '94 / Epic

Laurel Canyon Ramblers
☐ BLUE RAMBLER VOL.1
Rambler's blues / Crossroads bar / To a heart always true / This heart of mine (can never say goodbye) / Yellowhead / He said if I be lifted up / She's no angel / Jordan / Love reunited / Flatland ramble / Jesus saviour, pilot me / Roll on
SHCD 3834 / May '95 / Sugar Hill

☐ BLUE RAMBLER VOL.2
RU 4 reel / Bad case of the blues / Here today and gone tomorrow / Preachin' prayin' singin' / Hold on / Shake hands with mother again / Weasel / Whistles on the trains / Just when I needed you / Words she writes tonight / I wonder if I care as much / It won't be long / Wait a minute / RU 4 reel
SHCD 3852 / Mar '98 / Sugar Hill

Lauren, Jessica
☐ SIREN SONG
Leo rises / Fire monkey / Siren song / When you call my name / Serengeti / Just a dream / Dance for Lotte / Dangerous curves / Freefall
SJRCD 020 / Sep '94 / Soul Jazz

Laurence, Zack
☐ SINGALONG PIANO, THE (Great Medleys Of All Time Favourites)
Beatles medley / USA medley / Italian medley / Irving Berlin medley / Jolson medley / European medley / Roaring twenties medley / Moonlight medley / Winter medley / Knees up medley / Waltz medley / Soft shoe medley / Oriental medley / Fats Waller medley / Spanish medley / Vaudeville medley / Ragtime medley / London medley / Girls medley / Big band medley
304672 / Jul '97 / Hallmark

Laurent, Scott
☐ CAPOSVILLE (Laurent, Scott Band)
Madison / Paul's song / Caposville / Afraid of the ground / It always happened in the fall / Blacktop and lines / Meant to be / Waiting for me to move / You know me well / It's not the way it used to be
MRCD 1296 / Feb '97 / Club De Musique

Laurenz, Pedro
☐ MALA JUNTA 1936-1944 (Laurenz, Pedro & Pedro Maffia)
EBCD 98 / 1 Jun '98 / El Bandoneon

Lauria, Nando
☐ NOVO BRASIL
Doce morena / Thinking of recife / Just you / Tide / Shall we / Dreaming of you / Gabriel's song / Northeast wind / Don Juan / Revival
ND 63036 / Jul '96 / Narada

☐ POINTS OF VIEW
Back home / After dawn / Take two / If I fell / Cry and the smile / Saudade (longing) / Que xote (what a rhythm) / Northeast tide / Episode: Prelude / Episode
ND 63026 / Apr '94 / Narada

Laurie Accordian Orchestra
☐ SPIRIT OF SCOTLAND
CDLOC 1087 / Jun '95 / Lochshore

Laurie, Cy
☐ CHATTANOOGA STOMP (The Delving Back Series Vol.1)
Chattanooga stomp / Goober dance / Tuxedo junction / Kansas city stomp / Clarinet rondo / Minuet wobble / We shall walk through the streets of the city / Bourbon St. Parade / Perdido St. Blues / Twelfth St. Rag / Dauphjin St. blues / Canal St. Blues / Beale St Blues / Blue blood blue / There'll come a day / Keyhole blues / Don't go away nobody / Melancholy blues / St. Phillips street breakdown
LACD 61 / Jul '96 / Lake

Laury, Booker T
☐ BOOKER IN PARIS 1980
157912 / Jun '93 / Blues Collection

☐ NOTHIN' BUT THE BLUES
BB 9542CD / Feb '94 / Bullseye Blues

Lauth, Wolfgang
☐ LAUTHER
Ice nenne alle frauen baby / Est ist nur die leibe / Durch dich wird diesse welt erst schon / Bei dir war es immer so schon / Mein herz hat heut premiere / Warum bist du fortegangen / Ich werede jede nacht von ihnen traumen / Kauf dir einen bunten luftballon / Lauther / Donald / Johnnie Walker / Cool cave / I only have eyes for you / Pastels / Lauthentic / Jeb / These foolish things / Indian summer / Goofy / French fries / Can't help lovin' dat man / Chicken feet / Date on wax
BCD 15717 / May '93 / Bear Family

Lauzi, Bruno
☐ GOLDEN YEARS
74321455822 / Nov '97 / Ricordi

Lava Love
☐ WHOLE LAVA LOVE
SKYCD 2003 / Sep '94 / Sky

Lavelle, Caroline
☐ SPIRIT
Case of you / Waiting for rain / Lagan love / Sleep now (+ poem) / Island / Desire / Forget the few / Dream of picasso / Moorlough shore / Sheherazade / Turning ground
4509981372 / Mar '95 / Warner Bros.

Laverne, Andy
☐ ANDY LAVERNE PLAYS TODD DAMERON
SCCD 31372 / Feb '96 / Steeplechase

☐ FIRST TANGO IN NEW YORK
500472 / Nov '93 / Musidisc

☐ FOUR MILES (Laverne, Andy Quartet)
5361862 / 5 Jan '98 / Triloka

☐ LIVE AT MAYBECK RECITAL HALL VOL.28
Yesterdays / I loves you Porgy / Sweet and lovely / Star eyes / My melancholy baby / When you wish upon a star / Beautiful love / Turn out the stars / Moonlight in Vermont / Impression for piano / Stan Getz in Chappaqua
CCD 4577 / Oct '93 / Concord Jazz

☐ NATURAL LIVING (Laverne, Andy & John Abercrombie)
500092 / Nov '93 / Musidisc

☐ STAN GETZ IN CHAPPAQUA
SCCD 31418 / Nov '97 / Steeplechase

☐ TIME WELL SPENT
Common knowledge / There is no greater love / Cantaloupe island / On a misty night / Time well spent / I should care / Lover man / Singel petal of a rose / Fall / Blue interlude / Rhythm and blues
CCD 4680 / Feb '96 / Concord Jazz

Lavin, Christine
☐ ATTAINABLE LOVE
Attainable love / Castlemaine / Yonder blue / Sensitive new age guys / Victim/volunteer / Kind of love you never recover from / Fly on a plane / Venus kissed the moon / Moving target / Shopping cart of love:The play
CDPH 1132 / Jul '90 / Philo

☐ BEAU WOES AND OTHER PROBLEMS
CDPH 1107 / Oct '88 / Philo

☐ FUTURE FOSSILS
CDPH 1104 / '86 / Philo

☐ GOOD THING HE CAN'T READ MY MIND
Good thing he can't read my mind / Bumble bees / Santa Monica Pier / Waltzing with him / Mysterious woman / Realities / Downtown / Never go back / Eighty five degrees / Somebody's baby / Ain't love grand
CDPH 1121 / '88 / Philo

☐ LAUGH TRACKS VOL.1
SH 8022 / Nov '96 / Shanachie

☐ LAUGH TRACKS VOL.2
SH 8023 / Nov '96 / Shanachie

☐ LIVE AT THE CACTUS CAFE - WHAT WAS I THINKING
PH 1159CD / Jan '94 / Philo

☐ ON A WINTER'S NIGHT
PH 1167CD / Feb '94 / Philo

☐ PLEASE DON'T MAKE ME TOO HAPPY
SHAN 8016CD / Apr '95 / Shanachie

☐ SHINING MY FLASHLIGHT ON THE MOON
SH 8024 / Mar '97 / Shanachie

Lavitz, T
☐ MOODSWING
NOVA 9134 / Jan '93 / Nova

Law, John
☐ EXPLODED ON IMPACT (Law, John Quartet)
Couplets / Mother's lament / Pissed off tree / Kaleidoscope / Joyriding
SLAMCD 204 / Oct '96 / Slam

☐ EXTREMELY QUARTET
ARTCD 6199 / Mar '97 / Hat Art

☐ HOURS, THE
FMRCD 41 / Sep '97 / Future

☐ ONLIEST, THE (Pictures From A Monk Exhibition)
FMRCD 32 / Apr '97 / Future

Lawal, Gasper
☐ KADARA
Kadara / Iregbogbo / Irin ajo / Oyeye / Ase / Omo araye / Ola / Awo
CDORB 071 / Apr '91 / Globestyle

Lawndale

☐ SASQUATCH ROCK
SST 125CD / May '93 / SST

Lawnhurst, Vee

☐ KEYBOARD WIZARDS OF THE GERSHWIN ERA VOL.6 (Lawnhurst, Vee & Constance Mering/Muriel Pollock)
GEMMCD 9206 / Jul '98 / Pearl

Lawrence, Denise

☐ AIN'T THAT GOOD NEWS (Storyville Tickle Vol.1)
RSCD 664 / 1 Jun '98 / Raymer

☐ CAN'T HELP LOVIN' THESE MEN OF MINE
My baby just cares for me / (I want to be) Seduced / Quiney St. Stomp / Jesus on the mainline / Fish seller / Can't help lovin' that man of mine / Honky-tonk train blues / Send me to the electric chair / Cottage for sale / Iko iko / Keepin' out of mischief now / Booze and blues / Everything happens to me
LACD 60 / Apr '96 / Lake

☐ LET IT SHINE
Papa de da da / Seven golden daffodils / Way you do the things you do / Saturday night function / Mardi Gras in New Orleans / Shady green pastures / Down in Honky Tonk Town / Wasted life blues / Let your light from the lighthouse shine on me / Around the clock / New Orleans wiggle / Nice feeling
LACD 37 / Feb '95 / Lake

☐ STORYVILLE TICKLE VOL.2
RSCD 665 / Dec '97 / Raymer

Lawrence, Doug

☐ SOUL CARNIVAL
8536542632 / 12 May '98 / Lightyear

Lawrence, Steve

☐ AMALGAMATION (Lawrence, Steve & Hudson Swan)
Miss Thomson / Spirit of the Glen / Swinging the cat / Psycho magnet/Crocodile / Bill Stark's fiddle/The cottage at Camus Crois / Claypit reel / Little cascade / Kaivonkansi / Four thirty in the morning / Amalgamation/High ground jig / Bourees / Secret games / Seven hearts
CDLDL 1273 / 20 Mar '98 / Lochshore

☐ BEST OF STEVE AND EYDIE, THE (Lawrence, Steve & Eydie Gorme)
POINTCD 16265 / 24 Nov '97 / Point

☐ WE GOT US/EYDIE & STEVE SING THE GOLDEN HITS (Lawrence, Steve & Eydie Gorme)
We got us / Side by side / No two people / Darn it baby / That's love / Together / Flattery / This could be the start of something / I remember it well / Baby, it's cold outside / Two lost souls / Harmony / Cheek to cheek / I've heard that song before / I'll be with you in apple blossom time / Green eyes / I hear a rhapsody / And the angels sing / Who wouldn't love you / Bei mir bist du schon / Marie / I don't want to walk without you / I've got a gal in Kalamazoo / White Christmas / Sentimental journey
JASCD 600 / Aug '96 / Jasmine

☐ WE'LL TAKE ROMANCE (Lawrence, Steve & Eydie Gorme)
MCCD 168 / Jul '94 / Music Club

Lawrence, Syd

☐ LIVE IN DUBLIN
Evening serenade / Strike up the band / Splanky / My kind of town (Chicago is) / You're driving me crazy / Bye bye blues / Holiday for tombones / On the sunny side of the street / Sing sing sing / Skyliner / Phil the fluter's ball / Molly Malone / Galway bay / Rose of Tralee / Rakes of mallow (piper's patrol) / When Irish eyes are smiling / Elmer's tune / Too little time / Trumpet blues a cantabile / Moonlight serenade / In the mood / Irish anthem
3036100102 / Apr '96 / Pearls

☐ PLAYS THE MUSIC OF GLENN MILLER (Nice & Easy) (Lawrence, Syd Orchestra)
Moonlight serenade / Little brown jug / String of pearls / At last / I've got a gal in Kalamazoo / American patrol / Perfidia / Slumber song / Anchors aweigh / Elmer's tune / St. Louis blues / In the mood / Story of a starry night / I dream I dwelt in Harlem / Falling leaves / Pennsylvania 6-5000 / Caribbean clipper / Tuxedo junction / Stardust / Chattanooga choo choo / Frenesi / Adios
8428272 / Apr '94 / Philips

☐ SYD LAWRENCE REMEMBERS GLENN MILLER
In the mood / Pennsylvania 6-5000 / American patrol / Tuxedo junction / Serenade in blue / Perfidia / Stardust / Moonlight serenade / I've got a gal in Kalamazoo / Little brown jug / St. Louis blues / Chattanooga choo choo / Falling leaves / Frenesi
5501872 / 3 Aug '98 / Spectrum

☐ UNFORGETTABLE, THE
Evening serenade / At last / Villa / Tuxedo junction / Skylark / Chattanooga choo choo / It happened in Sun valley / String of pearls / Little brown jug / American patrol / I'll take romance / Stardust / I know why and so do you / Pennsylvania 6500 / Our love / Lover / Frenesi / St. Louis blues / In the mood / Adios
4961822 / 3 Aug '98 / Music For Pleasure

Lawrence, Tracy

☐ ALIBIS
I threw the rest away / Can't break it to my heart / We don't love here anymore / Crying ain't dying / Alibis / My second home / Don't talk to me that way / It only takes one bar (to make a prison) / Back to back / If the good die young
7567824832 / Jul '93 / Atlantic

Laws, Hubert

☐ IN THE BEGINNING
In the beginning / Restoration / Gymnopedie no.1
ZK 65127 / 8 Sep '97 / Sony Jazz

☐ LAWS OF JAZZ/FLUTE BY-LAWS
Miss thing / All soul / Black eyes peas and rice / Bessie's blues / Don't you forget it / Bimbe blue / Capers / Bloodshot / Miedo / Mean lene / No you'd better not / Let me go / Strange girl / Baila cinderella
8122716362 / May '94 / Atlantic

☐ MY TIME WILL COME
Malaguena / My time will come / It's so crazy / Shades of light / Valse / Make it last / Moonlight sonata
5184432 / May '94 / Limelight

☐ ROMEO AND JULIET
CK 34330 / Aug '97 / Sony Jazz

Laws, Ronnie

☐ DEEP SOUL
CPCD 8143 / Nov '95 / Charly

☐ HARVEST FOR THE WORLD
Prelude to the harvest / Let me down easy / At your best you are love / Who loves you better / Harvest for the world / Feel it / So you wanna stay down
8578752 / 30 Mar '98 / Blue Note

☐ SMOOTH JAZZ
Favourite love / Virgin winds (before the rainfall) / Song from Hiram / From a glance / Heart station / Imo / Love this way again / Gotta say goodbye
BN 025 / Apr '98 / Blue Nite

☐ TRIBUTE TO THE LEGENDARY EDDIE HARRIS, A
Listen here / Freedom jazz dance / Boogie woogie bossa nova / Cold duck / Sham time / I don't want no-one but you / Hip hoppin' / Compared to what
CDP 8553302 / Apr '97 / Blue Note

☐ TRUE SPIRIT
Gotta say goodbye / Love this way again / Virgin winds / From a glance / Song for Hiram / Heart station / Favorite love / Imo
CPCD 8126 / Oct '95 / Charly

Lawson, Doyle

☐ GOSPEL COLLECTION VOL.1, THE (Lawson, Doyle & Quicksilver)
SHCD 9104 / Jan '97 / Sugar Hill

☐ HEAVEN'S JOY AWAITS (Lawson, Doyle & Quicksilver)
SHCD 3760 / Dec '87 / Sugar Hill

☐ HEAVENLY TREASURES (Lawson, Doyle & Quicksilver)
SHCD 3735 / Oct '94 / Sugar Hill

☐ I HEARD THE ANGELS SINGING (Lawson, Doyle & Quicksilver)
Holy city / Stormy weather / Little mountain church house / In the shelter of his arms / I heard the angels singing / He's my guide / Little white church / City where's comes no strife / Rock of ages / I won't have to cross Jordan alone / That new Jerusalem / That home far away
SHCD 3774 / Jul '89 / Sugar Hill

☐ I'LL WANDER BACK SOMEDAY (Lawson, Doyle & Quicksilver)
A white rose / Trust each other / One way train / Dreaming / I'll wander back someday / Let us travel on / Out on the ocean / Too late / That's how I can count on you / Devil's little angel / Our last goodbye / What a wonderful saviour is he
SHCD 3769 / Mar '88 / Sugar Hill

☐ KEPT AND PROTECTED (Lawson, Doyle & Quicksilver)
I have found the way / Did you think to pray / I'll trade the old cross (for a crown) / My Lord is writing all the time / I'm not afraid of tomorrow / Kept and protected by God's love / Gloryland way / Let my life be a light / Lord I'm ready to go / Vision / Heaven's my next exit / New Jerusalem / You are my hiding place / We'll go home together on the cloud
SHCD 3867 / Mar '98 / Sugar Hill

☐ MY HEART IS YOURS (Lawson, Doyle & Quicksilver)
All in my love for you / Still got a crush on you / Move to the top of the mountain / I don't care / My heart is yours / Dreaming of you / Look for me (I'll be there) / Date with an angel / Now there's you / Between us / I'm satisfied with you / We were made for each other
SHCD 3782 / Oct '90 / Sugar Hill

☐ NEVER WALK AWAY (Lawson, Doyle & Quicksilver)
SHCD 3842 / Oct '95 / Sugar Hill

☐ ROCK MY SOUL (Lawson, Doyle & Quicksilver)
SHCD 3717 / Jan '97 / Sugar Hill

☐ THERE'S A LIGHT GUIDING ME (Lawson, Doyle & Quicksilver)
Since Jesus came into my heart / Let me tell you about Jesus / There is a God / I'm a weary pilgrim / I'm going to Heaven / Beautiful altar of prayer / Who'll be a witness / There's a light guiding me / Earth's greatest loss / I need my saviour all the time / Arm of God / Lifeboat / Calling to that other shore / There's fire down yonder
SHCD 3845 / Mar '98 / Sugar Hill

Lawson, Hugh

☐ PRIME TIME (Lawson, Hugh Trio)
Highest mountain / Blue bones / Need to smile / Duke Ellington sound of love / Rip off / I fall in love too easily / I'll keep loving you / Make me rainbows / Falling for you / Highest mountain / Need to smile
STCD 8267 / Jun '98 / Storyville

Lawson, Linda

☐ INTRODUCING LINDA LAWSON
FSRCD 16 / 5 Jan '98 / Fresh Sound

Lawson, Yank

☐ SOMETHING OLD SOMETHING NEW SOMETHING BORROWED... (Lawson, Yank Jazzband)
APCD 240 / Apr '89 / Audiophile

☐ WITH A SOUTHERN ACCENT (Lawson-Haggart Jazz Band)
JCD 203 / Feb '93 / Jazzology

☐ YANK LAWSON & BOB HAGGART (Lawson, Yank & Bob Haggart)
JCD 183 / Oct '92 / Jazzology

☐ YANK LAWSON & JOHN PETTERS DIXIELANDERS (Lawson, Yank & John Petters Dixielanders)
RRCD 1008 / May '98 / Rose

Lay Quiet Awhile

☐ DELICATE WIRE
185172 / Jun '94 / Southern

Lay, Sam

☐ LIVE (Lay, Sam Band)
AP 115 / May '97 / Appaloosa

☐ STONE BLUES (Lay, Sam Blues Band)
29 miles / Walkin' thru the park / I got wise / Short haired woman / Birmingham / Hide and seek / Jelly jelly / Red, white and blues / Shuffle master / That's alright Mama / Stone blues
ECD 260812 / Sep '96 / Evidence

Laye, Evelyn

☐ GAIETY GIRL
New moon / Lover come back to me / One kiss / Wanting you / Madame pompadour / Love me now / Blue eyes / Do I do wrong / Princess charming / Near and yet so far / Brave hearts / Love is a song / Princess awakening / Night is young / When I grow too old to dream / Paganini / My Nicolo / Love never comes too late / Nobody could love you more / Love, live forever (and rule my heart) / Bitter sweet / I'll see you again / Zigeuner / Lights up / You've done something to my heart / Let the people sing / Only a glass of champagne / Three waltzes / Forever
CDAJA 55211 / Apr '96 / Living Era

Layhe, Edgerton

☐ ROUGH AND TUMBLE
Buffalo blues / Eleanor / Why would she go / Billy can / Everybody needs something nobody knows / Teardrop whisky / Dancing down at the crossroads / The convenience reel / All the tears in Liverpool / Lonely as Los Angeles, restless as New York / I'm on your side / Six thousand shoes
FE 096CD / Jan '94 / Fellside

Layton & Johnstone

☐ ALABAMY BOUND
Anytime anywhere / Up with the lark / Wedding of the painted doll / Alabamy bound / New kind of girl with a new kind of love form / Weary river / Paddlin' Madelin' home / Turner Layton piano medley / Birth of the blues / Coquette / Hillo, 'tucky / Don't put the blame on me / Hard hearted Hannah / It all depends on you / At dawning / Medley of Layton and Johnstone successes
PASTCD 9712 / '90 / Flapper

☐ GETTING SENTIMENTAL OVER YOU
Auf wiedersehen my dear / Deep purple: Layton, *Turner* / Don't you ever cry: Layton, *Turner* / Home on the range / I wanna sing about you / I'm getting sentimental over you / It was so beautiful / I've got a feeling I'm falling in love / Love is the sweetest thing / Medley / Medley / Miracles sometimes happen: Layton, *Turner* / More than you know / Night and day / Nightfall / Nightingale sang in Berkeley Square: Layton, *Turner* / There's rain in my eyes: Layton, *Turner* / These foolish things: Layton, *Turner* / To be in love espesh'lly with you / We just couldn't say goodbye / We three: Layton, *Turner* / Where or when: Layton, *Turner* / Wind and the rain: Layton, *Turner* / Without a song
CDAJA 5111 / Jun '93 / Living Era

Layton, Eddie

☐ YOU GOTTA HAVE HEART
Bring on the Yankees / Take me out to the ball game / Jersey bounce / When the saints go marching in / My kind of town / Stormy weather / When you're smiling / You've gotta have heart
SONGCD 912 / Apr '97 / Silva Screen

Lazarus, Ken

☐ SINGS REGGAE OF THE 70'S
PKCD 61094 / Sep '94 / K&K

Lazerboy

☐ FALLEN WORLD
PROBEUP 44CD / Jul '97 / Probe Plus/Up

Lazonby, Dave

☐ WAR ALL THE TIME (Lazonby, Dave Group)
Mass / Journey to Sirius B to Earth / Bossa nova my arse / War all the time / Mass
SLAMCD 214 / Oct '96 / Slam

Lazro, Daunik

☐ PERFERIA (Lazro, Daunik & Carlos Zingaro)
IS 164 / Aug '97 / Basta/Insitu

Lazy

☐ TURNING THE WHEEL
Sweet child / Superstar / Turning the wheel / Hold my hand / Dear Father / Funny little girl / Together forever / Fly away / Come my way / Hard love / New life / I'm with you again / Lucy's baby / Overtime
SALTCD 001 / Sep '97 / Saltwater

Lazy Cowgirls

☐ LITTLE SEX AND DEATH, A
CD 12895 / 27 Oct '97 / Crypt

☐ RAGGED SOUL
EFA 115912 / Jul '95 / Crypt

☐ TAPPING THE SOURCE
1+2CD 027 / 26 Jan '98 / 1+2

Lazy K

☐ LIFE IN ONE DAY
MSS 0020CD / 20 Oct '97 / Mutant Sound System

Lazy Lester

☐ HARP AND SOUL
I done got over it / I'm a man / Dark end of the street / Bye bye baby / Alligator shuffle / Take me in your arms / Patrol wagon / Raining in my heart / Bloodstains on the wall / Five long years
ALCD 4768 / May '93 / Alligator

☐ I'M A LOVER NOT A FIGHTER
I'm a lover not a fighter / Sugar coated love / Lester's stomp / I told my little woman / Tell me pretty baby / Whoa now / I hear you knocking / Through the goodness of my heart / I love you, I need you / Late in the evening / Real combination for love / Bloodstains on the wall / You got me where you want me / I'm so tired / Patrol blues / I'm so glad / Sad city blues / If you think I've lost you / I made up my mind / Lonesome highway blues / You're gonna ruin me baby / Same thing could happen to you / Take me in your arms / You better listen to what I said
CDCHD 518 / Apr '94 / Ace

Lazy Smoke

☐ CORRIDOR OF FACES
AA 065 / 24 Nov '97 / Arf Arf

Lazy Sundays

☐ TEXTURE AND THE FLAVOUR
21107 / Jul '97 / Subterfuge

LCD

☐ MAD LOVE
CLP 9975 / Apr '97 / Cleopatra

Le Click

☐ TONIGHT IS THE NIGHT
74321528682 / 29 Sep '97 / Logic

Le Gaulois, Maurice

☐ MUSETTE ACCORDION 1895-1995
ARN 64366 / Sep '96 / Arion

Le Gop

☐ LE GOP
Y 225030CD / Dec '93 / Silex

Le Grand Blues Band

☐ LE GRAND BLUES
422430 / May '94 / New Rose

Le Jazz Non

☐ IT'S THE NEW THING
HERMES 014 / Apr '97 / Corpus Hermeticum

Le June, Iry

☐ CAJUN'S GREATEST
Grande nuit especial / Grande bosco / Duraldo waltz / I went to the dance / La valse de bayou chene / I made a big mistake / Come and get me / Donnes moi mon chapeau / Waltz of the mulberry limb / Church point breakdown / La valse du grande chemin / Jolie catin / La fitte la vove / Bayou pon pon special / La valse de cajin / Don't get married / Convict waltz / It happened to me / Parting waltz / Evangeline special / Love bridge waltz / Teche special / Calcasieu waltz / Te mone / Lacassine special
CDCHD 428 / Oct '92 / Ace

Le Maistre, Malcolm

☐ 1968 SARAJEVO EP
12032CD / Jul '95 / Unique Gravity

Le Meut, Jean

☐ PE YUVANKIZ KUHET
KM 44 / Sep '94 / Keltia Musique

Le Mystere Des Voix Bulgares

☐ LE MYSTERE DES VOIX BULGARES VOL.1
GAD 603CD / 6 Jul '98 / 4AD

☐ LE MYSTERE DES VOIX BULGARES VOL.2
GAD 801CD / 6 Jul '98 / 4AD

☐ RITUAL (Bulgarian State Television Female Choir)
7559793492 / Feb '96 / Nonesuch

Le, Nguyen

☐ 3 TRIOS
Silk / Silver / Sand / Dance of the comet / Foow / Kinderhund / Woof / Idoma / La parfum / Blue monkey / Straight no chaser
92452 / Mar '97 / Act

☐ MAGHREB AND FRIENDS
Ifrikyia / Constantine / Louanges / Yaddik Allah / Nora / Funk Rai / L'Arkha li jeya / Guinia / Nesraf
ACT 92612 / 29 Jun '98 / Act

☐ MILLION WAVES
Mille vagues / Trilogy / Be good / Mango blues / Butterflies and zebras / Little wing / El saola / Sledge / Moonshine / I feel good
92212 / May '95 / Act

☐ MIRACLES
500102 / Nov '93 / Musidisc

☐ TALES FROM VIETNAM
Wind blew it away / Black horse / Don't you go away, my friend / Trong com / Hen ho / Banyan tree song / Spring of life / Ting ning / Mangustao - part 1 / Mangustao - part 2
92252 / Feb '96 / Act

☐ ZANZIBAR
500352 / Feb '97 / Musidisc

Le Penven, Jef

☐ SYMPHONIE MOR BIHAN
BUR 876CD / Mar '98 / Escalibur

Le Pont, Jester

☐ L'ESCAPADE
MINCD 594 / Mar '96 / Minuit

Le Quintette De Cornemuses

☐ MENAGERIE
B 6795CD / Jul '94 / Auvidis/Ethnic

Le Rue, Pierre

☐ IN TWO WORLDS
GWCD 005 / Nov '95 / Weaving

Le System Crapoutchik

☐ FLOP
175032 / 23 Feb '98 / Magic

Le Thugs

☐ LABF
VIRUS 93CD / '92 / Alternative Tentacles

Lea, Barbara

☐ ATLANTA JAZZ PARTY (Lea, Barbara & Ed Polcer)
JCD 218 / Jul '93 / Jazzology

☐ DEVIL IS AFRAID OF MUSIC (Lea, Barbara & Loonis McGlohon/Dick Cary Trio)
ACD 119 / Mar '97 / Audiophile

☐ DO IT AGAIN
ACD 175 / Jun '95 / Audiophile

☐ FINE AND DANDY (Lea, Barbara & Keith Ingham)
CHR 70029 / Sep '96 / Challenge

☐ HOAGY'S CHILDREN (Lea, Barbara/ Bob Dorough/Dick Sudhalter)
ACD 291 / Apr '94 / Audiophile

☐ HOAGY'S CHILDREN VOL.2
ACD 292 / Apr '94 / Audiophile

☐ REMEMBERING LEE WILEY
ACD 125 / Jun '96 / Audiophile

☐ SONGS FROM 'POUSSE CAFE' (Lea, Barbara & Ellis Larkin)
ACD 263 / Apr '93 / Audiophile

Lea Riders Group

☐ FORGOTTEN GENERATION, THE
GRCD 032 / 13 Jul '98 / Garageland

Leach, Brian

☐ SUNRISE NEARLY KILLED ME
PARCD 005 / Dec '97 / Parasol

Leach, Tom

☐ TOM LEACH
Guitar / Confidence / Doris days / Yesterday's news / Hello friend / Ice below you / Guiatar / Guitar / Saviour / Rain, rain / Wine, cigarettes, tears / If I were you / She's coming of age / Send in the blues / Tomorrow comes / Guitar
SRRCD 027 / Jul '97 / Slow River

Leadbelly

☐ ALABAMA BOUND
Pick a bale of cotton / Whoa Buck / Midnight special / Alabamy bound / Good morning blues / Red Cross store blues / Alberta / You can't lose-a me cholly / Gray goose / Stewball / Can't you line 'em / Rock Island line / Easy rider / New York City / Roberta / On my last go round
ND 90321 / Oct '94 / Bluebird

☐ ALL TIME BLUES CLASSICS
8420322 / Oct '96 / Music Memoria

☐ COMPLETE RECORDED WORKS VOL.1 1939-1940
DOCD 5226 / Apr '94 / Document

☐ COMPLETE RECORDED WORKS VOL.2 1940-1943
DOCD 5227 / Apr '94 / Document

☐ COMPLETE RECORDED WORKS VOL.3 1943-1944
DOCD 5228 / Apr '94 / Document

☐ COMPLETE RECORDED WORKS VOL.4 1944
DOCD 5310 / Dec '94 / Document

☐ COMPLETE RECORDED WORKS VOL.5 1944-1946
DOCD 5311 / Dec '94 / Document

☐ COMPLETE RECORDED WORKS VOL.6 1947
DOCD 5568 / 21 Sep '97 / Document

☐ ESSENTIAL BLUES GREATS, THE (3CD Set) (Leadbelly/Sonny Boy Williamson/Robert Johnson)
Good morning blues: *Leadbelly* / Packin' trunk: *Leadbelly* / Death letter blues: *Leadbelly* / Roberta: *Leadbelly* / My baby quit me: *Leadbelly* / You don't know my mind: *Leadbelly* / CC rider: *Leadbelly* / Matchbox blues: *Leadbelly* / Leavin' blues: *Leadbelly* / Rock Island line: *Leadbelly* / Easy rider: *Leadbelly* / Alberta: *Leadbelly* / I'm on my last go round: *Leadbelly* / Bourgeois blues: *Leadbelly* / Gallis pole: *Leadbelly* / Can't you line 'em: *Leadbelly* / Alabama bound: *Leadbelly* / Midnight special: *Leadbelly* / Goodnight Irene: *Leadbelly* / Good morning little school girl: *Williamson, Sonny Boy* / Blue bird blues: *Williamson, Sonny Boy* / Got the bottle up and go: *Williamson, Sonny Boy* / Sugar mama blues: *Williamson, Sonny Boy* / Early in the morning: *Williamson, Sonny Boy* / Black gal blues: *Williamson, Sonny Boy* / Decoration blues: *Williamson, Sonny Boy* / Whiskey headed woman blues: *Williamson, Sonny Boy* / Lord, oh Lord: *Williamson, Sonny Boy* / Good gravy: *Williamson, Sonny Boy* / TB blues: *Williamson, Sonny Boy* / Tell me baby: *Williamson, Sonny Boy* / I have been dealing with the devil: *Williamson, Sonny Boy* / Welfare store blues: *Williamson, Sonny Boy* / My little machine: *Williamson, Sonny Boy* / Jivin' the blues: *Williamson, Sonny Boy* / Shotgun blues: *Williamson, Sonny Boy* / Million years blues: *Williamson, Sonny Boy* / Sloppy drunk blues: *Williamson, Sonny Boy* / You got to step back: *Williamson, Sonny Boy* / Ground hog blues: *Williamson, Sonny Boy* / My black name: *Williamson, Sonny Boy* / She don't love me that way: *Williamson, Sonny Boy* / What's gettin' wrong with you: *Williamson, Sonny Boy* / I believe I'll dust my room: *Johnson, Robert* / Kindhearted woman blues: *Johnson, Robert* / Terraplane blues: *Johnson, Robert* / 32-20 blues: *Johnson, Robert* / Last fair deal gone down: *Johnson, Robert* / Dead shrimp blues: *Johnson, Robert* / Ramblin' on my mind: *Johnson, Robert* / Cross road blues: *Johnson, Robert* / Come on in my kitchen: *Johnson, Robert* / They're red hot: *Johnson, Robert* / From four 'till late: *Johnson, Robert* / Hellhound on my trail: *Johnson, Robert* / Malted milk: *Johnson, Robert* / Milkcow's calf blues: *Johnson, Robert* / I'm a steady rollin' man: *Johnson, Robert* / Stones in my passway: *Johnson, Robert* / Sweet home Chicago: *Johnson, Robert* / Walking blues: *Johnson, Robert* / Stop breakin' down blues: *Johnson, Robert* / Honeymoon blues: *Johnson, Robert* / Little queen of spades: *Johnson, Robert* / Me and the devil blues: *Johnson, Robert* / Preaching blues (up jumped the devil): *Johnson, Robert* / Love in vain: *Johnson, Robert*
IGOBCD 001 / Dec '97 / Indigo

☐ GO DOWN OLD HANNAH (Library Of Congress Recordings Vol. 6)
TB blues / How long / When the train comes along / Monologue on square dances or sookey jumps / Monologue on the blues / Amazing grace / Old time religion / Stand your test in judgement / Christmas (monologue) / John henry / John hardy / Go down old hannah / Oh, something on my mind / How long / Swing low, sweet chariot / Ain't gonna study war no more / Join the band / Prayer
ROUCD 1099 / Apr '94 / Rounder

☐ GOOD MORNING BLUES
Good morning blues / Packin' truck / Death letter blues / Roberta / My baby quit me / You don't know my mind / CC Rider / Matchbox blues / Leavin' blues / Rock island blues / Easy rider / Alberta / I'm on my last go round / Bourgeois blues / Gallis pole / Can't you line 'em / Alabama bound / Midnight special / Goodnight Irene
IGOCD 2007 / Nov '94 / Indigo

☐ GOOD MORNING BLUES
TPZ 1029 / Oct '95 / Topaz Jazz

☐ GOODNIGHT IRENE
TCD 1006 / Feb '96 / Tradition

☐ GOODNIGHT IRENE
IMP 310 / Nov '96 / IMP

☐ GWINE DIG A HOLE TO PUT THE DEVIL IN
CC rider / Governor pat neff / Becky dean / Medicine man / Alberta / Old rattler / If it wasn't for dicky / Queen mary / Turn yo' radio on / Mama, did you bring any silver / Po' howard / Dance calls / Gwine dig a hole to put the devil in / Green corn
ROUCD 1045 / Feb '92 / Rounder

☐ HUDDIE LEDBETTER'S BEST
Goodnight Irene / Grasshoppers in my pillow / Eagle rocks / Rock island line / Ella speed / Backwater blues / Take this hammer / Tell me baby / Eagle rock rag / Western plain / Sweet Mary blues / On a Christmas day
BGOCD 403 / 30 Mar '98 / Beat Goes On

☐ IN THE SHADOWS OF THE GALLOWS POLE
TCD 1018 / May '96 / Tradition

☐ IRENE GOODNIGHT
New york city / Pick a bale of cotton / Midnight special / Good morning blues / Red cross store blues / Rock island line / Easy rider / Packin' trunk / Four day worry blues / Roberta / Death letter blues (part 1) / Fort worth and dallas blues / Ox drivin' blues / T.b. woman blues / My baby quit me / I'm on my last go round / Bourgeois blues / John hardy / Irene goodnight / I'm sorry mama
CD 52028 / Nov '93 / Blues Encore

☐ KING OF THE TWELVE STRING GUITAR
Packin' trunk / Becky Deem, she was gamblin' girl / Honey, I'm all out and down / Four day worry blues / Roberta / Roberta / Death letter / Death letter / Kansas city papa / Wort Worth and Dallas blues / You don't know my mind / Ox drivin' blues / Daddy I'm coming back to you / Shorty George / Yellow jacket / TB woman blues
4678932 / Nov '91 / Columbia

☐ LAST SESSIONS
SFWCD 40068 / Oct '94 / Smithsonian Folkways

☐ LEADBELLY & JOSH WHITE/PEETIE WHEATSTRAW 1924-MID 1940'S (Leadbelly & Josh White/Peetie Wheatstraw)
DOCD 5461 / Jun '96 / Document

☐ LEADBELLY LEGACY VOL.1 (Where Did You Sleep Last Night)
SFWCD 40044 / Apr '96 / Smithsonian Folkways

☐ LEADBELLY LEGACY VOL.2 (Bourgeois Blues)
SFWCD 40045 / May '97 / Smithsonian Folkways

☐ LEADBELLY LEGACY VOL.3 (Shout On)
SFWCD 40105 / 6 Apr '98 / Smithsonian Folkways

☐ LEGENDARY MASTERS SERIES, THE
COLLECT 4CD / Oct '95 / Aim

☐ LET IT SHINE ON ME
Monologue on the mourner's bench / You must have that religion, halleloo / Backslider, fare thee well / Must I be carried to the sky / Down in the valley to pray / Let it shine on me / Run sinners / Ride on / Howard hughes / When I was a cowboy / Leaving blues / Roosevelt song / No good rider / Blues about new york / Mr. hitler
ROUCD 1046 / Mar '92 / Rounder

☐ MASTERS
Matchbox blues / Bourgeois blues / Medley / My friend Blind Lemon / Can't you line 'em / John Hardy / Gallis pole / Borrow love and go / Big fat woman / Baby don't you love me no more / Bull cow / Red river blues / Alberta / Poor Howard / Kansas city papa / CC rider
CDBM 119 / Sep '96 / Blue Moon

☐ MASTERS OF THE COUNTRY BLUES (Leadbelly & 'Blind' Willie McTell)
Death letter blues: *Leadbelly* / Death letter blues part 2: *Leadbelly* / Kansas city papa: *Leadbelly* / Daddy I'm coming back to you: *Leadbelly* / Shorty George: *Leadbelly* / Yellow jacket: *Leadbelly* / TB woman blues part 1: *Leadbelly* / TB woman blues part 2: *Leadbelly* / Chainey: *McTell, 'Blind' Willie* / Murderer's home blues: *McTell, 'Blind' Willie* / Kill-it -kid rag: *McTell, 'Blind' Willie* / I got to cross de river O'Jordan: *McTell, 'Blind' Willie* / Old time religion: *McTell, 'Blind' Willie* / Will Fox: *McTell, 'Blind' Willie* / Dying crapshooters blues: *McTell, 'Blind' Willie* / Amazing Grace: *McTell, 'Blind' Willie* / Just as well get ready: Climbing high mountains, tryin' to g: *McTell, 'Blind' Willie* / King Edwards blues: AKA: Baby it must be love: *McTell, 'Blind' Willie* / Delia: *McTell, 'Blind' Willie* / Boll weevil: *McTell, 'Blind' Willie* / I got to cross the River Jordan: *McTell, 'Blind' Willie*
BCD 144 / Jun '97 / Biograph

☐ MIDNIGHT SPECIAL
Irene / Irene / Matchbox blues / Midnight special / Governor o.k. allen / Frankie and albert / Ella speed / Red river / Get up in the mornin' / You don't know my mind / I'm sorry mama / Take a whiff on me / Dekalb blues / Roberta / Careless love
ROUCD 1044 / Feb '92 / Rounder

☐ NOBODY KNOWS THE TROUBLE I'VE SEEN (Library Of Congress Recordings Vol. 5)
ROUCD 1098 / May '94 / Rounder

☐ REMAINING LIBRARY OF CONGRESS RECORDINGS VOL.1 1934-1935
DOCD 5591 / 5 Feb '98 / Document

☐ REMAINING LIBRARY OF CONGRESS RECORDINGS VOL.2 1935
DOCD 5592 / 5 Feb '98 / Document

☐ REMAINING LIBRARY OF CONGRESS RECORDINGS VOL.3 1935
DOCD 5593 / 5 Feb '98 / Document

☐ REMAINING LIBRARY OF CONGRESS RECORDINGS VOL.4 1935-1938
DOCD 5594 / 5 Feb '98 / Document

☐ REMAINING LIBRARY OF CONGRESS RECORDINGS VOL.5 1938-1942
DOCD 5595 / 5 Feb '98 / Document

☐ SINGS FOLK SONGS
SFWCD 40010 / Aug '95 / Smithsonian Folkways

☐ TITANIC, THE (Library Of Congress Recordings Vol. 4)
Blind lemon blues / Mr. tom hughes' town / Shreveport jail / Don't you love me no more / Henry ford blues / Julie ann johnson / Angola blues (so doggone soon) / Dallas and fort worth blues / Mary don't you weep / Easy, mr. tom / I ain't bothered a bit / Boll weevil / Titanic / Red cross sto' / Fo' day worry blues / Hesitation blues / Take me back / Tight like that / Sail on little girl
ROUCD 1097 / Apr '94 / Rounder

☐ TRIBUTE TO LEADBELLY, A (Various Artists)
Intro - Leadbelly / You must have that true religion / I know it was the blood / Intro - Leadbelly on the blues / Best of friends / Rock island line / Poor Howard / Baby please don't go / John Henry / Intro - Alan Lomax and Leadbelly on meter / Bourgeois blues / Redbird / In the pines (where did you sleep last night) / Kisses sweeter than wine pigmeat / Pigmeat / De grey goose / Ain't goin' down to de well no mo' / Intro - Pete Seeger / Bring me Lil' water silby / On a Monday / Midnight special / Meeting at the building / Good night Irene
TBA 130142 / Jun '97 / Blues Alliance

☐ VERY BEST OF LEADBELLY, THE
Midnight special / Sylvie / Matchbox blues / You must have that pure religion, halleloo / Fannin' street / Green corn / Bourgeois blues / When I was a cowboy / Cow cow yicky yicky yea / CC rider / Rock island line / Governor o.k. allen / De kalb blues / Leavin' blues / Roberta / Frankie and albert / Alberta / Gray goose / Careless love / Goodnight irene
MCCD 106 / May '93 / Music Club

Leadfoot

☐ BRING IT ON
RR 88332 / 29 Sep '97 / Roadrunner

Leaether Strip

☐ RETROSPECTIVE
CLP 9978 / Apr '97 / Cleopatra

☐ SELF INFLICTED
CDZOT 173 / Jul '97 / Zoth Ommog
CLP 0072 / 12 Jan '98 / Cleopatra

Leaf, Ann

☐ MIGHTY WURLITZER, THE (Leaf, Ann & Gaylord Carter)
Great day: *Carter, Gaylord* / Strike up the band: *Leaf, Ann* / You do something to me: *Leaf, Ann* / Son of the Sheik: *Leaf, Ann* / You were meant for me / Orphans of the storm / Jeannine: *Carter, Gaylord* / For heaven's sake: *Carter, Gaylord* / My romance: *Carter, Gaylord* / Charmaine: *Carter, Gaylord* / Intolerance: *Carter, Gaylord* / Phantom of the opera: *Carter, Gaylord*
NW 227 / Aug '92 / New World

Leafhound

☐ GROWERS OF MUSHROOM
Freelance fiend / Sad road to the sea / Drowned my life in fear / Work my body / Stray / With a minute to go / Growers of mushroom / Stagnant pool / Sawdust Caesar / It's going to get better
SEECD 403 / May '96 / See For Miles

League Of Gentlemen

☐ THRANG THRANG COZIMBULK
DGM 9602 / May '96 / Discipline

Leake County Revellers

☐ LEAKE COUNTY REVELLERS VOL.1 1927-1928
DOCD 8029 / 15 Jun '98 / Document

☐ LEAKE COUNTY REVELLERS VOL.2 1929-1930
DOCD 8030 / 15 Jun '98 / Document

Leal, Alamo

☐ RHYTHM OIL
ARMD 00001 / 21 Aug '97 / Armadillo

Leander, Zarah

☐ KANN DENN LIEBE SUNDE SEIN (8CD Set)
Gebundene hande / Eine frau von heut' / Merci, mon ami / Ich hab' vielleicht noch nie geliebt / Yes sir / Tiefe sehnsucht / Ich steh' im regen / Kinostar / Der wind hat mir ein lied erzahlt / Du kannst es nicht wissen / Eine frau wird erst schon durch die liebe / Drei sterne sah ich scheinen / Sag' mir nicht adieu, sag' nur auf wiedersehn / Cheri, du bist heut' so anders / Du bist genau wie die anderen / Ich bin eine stimme / Kann denn liebe sunde sein / Von der puszta will ich traumen / Lang ist's her / Ein kleiner akkord auf meinem klavier / Nur nicht aus liebe weinen / Schlafe, mein geliebter / Wo ist dein herz / Schlummerlied / Fatme, erzahl mir ein marchen / Sagt dir eine schone frau 'vielleicht' / Heut' abend lad' ich mir die liebe ein / Ein paar tranen werd' ich weinen um dich / Reite, kleiner reiter / Schiff ahoi / Du darfst mir nie mehr rote rosen schenken / Und dann tanz ich einen czardas / Er heisst Waldemar / Wen ich liebe / Ich will nicht vergessen / Ich sag' nicht ja, ich sag' nicht nein / Mein leben fur die liebe / Ich weiss, es wird einmal ein wunder geschehn / Davon geht die welt nicht unter / Blaue husaren / Einen wie dich konnt' ich lieben / So glucklich wie du und so selig wie ich / Die lustige witwe (potpourri teil 1) / Die lustige witwe (potpourri teil 2) / Frag mich nicht, ob ich dich liebe / Lass mich geh'n / Es gibt keine frau, die nicht lugt / Wenn der Hergott will / Wann wirst du mich fragen / Irgendwo, irgendwann fangt ein marchen an / Warum brauchen denn die manner soviel liebe / Du bist der, bei dem's moglich war / Servus, sagt die schone stadt der lieder / Wunderbar / Welterfolge mit Zarah Leander (teil 1) / Welterfolge mit Zarah Leander (teil 2) / Eine frau in meinem jahren / Du machst mich so nervos / Sag mir nie wieder je t'aime / Und wenn's auch sunde war / O wermeland, du schones / In meinem garten / Du glaubst doch nicht / Ich kann ganz ohne menschen sein / Var'e du / Orjanslaten mit polska / Tanzet, tanzet meine lieben madchen / Tanze aus Smaland / Du sagst, du warst der beste tanzer / Zwei tanze aus Skane / Mannertreu / Weisse weihnacht / Un desir pour toi / Le vent m'a dit une chanson / Il pleut sans treve / Ich steh' im regen / Yes sir / Ich hab eine tiefe sehnsucht in mir / Nur nicht aus liebe weinen / Kann denn liebe sunde sein / Der wind hat mir ein lied erzahlt / Davon geht die welt nicht unter / Wenn der Herrgott will / Mit roten rosen fangt die liebe meistens an / Er heisst Waldemar / Wen ich liebe / Ich kenn den Jimmy aus Havanna / Wenn die wilden rosen bluhn / Ave Maria / Drei sterne sah ich scheinen / Reite, kleiner reiter / Gebundene hande / Weil ich dich so liebe / So stell ich mir die liebe vor / Paradiesvogel / Frauen sind schwer zu durchschauen / Die alte liebe / Daran zerbricht man doch nicht / Mitternachtsblues (1 fassung) / Mitternachtsblues (2 fassung) / Warum soll eine frau kein verhaltnis haben / Schon war die zeit / Merci, mon ami, es war wunderschon / Nachts ging das telefon / Eine frau wird erst schon durch die liebe / Ein leben ohne liebe / Pardon meine damen, pardon meine herrn / Seit ich dich sah / Ein leben ohne liebe / Jose / Einsamkeit / Bleib' hier, dich furht kein weg zuruck / Nie wieder so einen wie Waldemar / Schatten der vergangenheit / Paradiesvogel / Frauen sind schwer zu durchschauen / Die rose von Nowgorod / Ein mann fur mich / Othello / Wenn du traumst / Einmal kommt die liebe / Antonius / Sag nicht adieu / Wunderbar / Mitternachtsblues / Eine frau wird erst schon durch die liebe / Wunderland bei nacht / Mir kommen tranen / Good bye, Sonny boy / Deine welt ist die kleine welt / Mitternachtslied / Antonius / Das leben ist ein roman / Othello / Kleine geige, sag adieu / Das herz einer frau / Was wissen manner von liebe / Cabaret Paris / Ich bin eine frau mir vergangenheit / Die liebe geht seltsame wege / Heinrich der achte / Ich kann den fruhling kaum erwarten / Ich kann allem wiedersteh'n / Mich hat die welt kaltgestellt / Wodka fur die konigin / Wenn am schwarzen meer / Dante / Das ist die grosse zeit / Abenteuer sind am abend teuer / Wo deine wiege stand / Einer muss da sein / Das gibt ein wiedersehn / Each time a churchbell rings / Mein herz kann lachen, mein herz kann weinen / Fragen / Adieu / Munchner g'schichten / Fenster meines lebens / Sag mir nicht adieu / Ich kenn Jimmy aus Havanna / Soll man lachen oder weinen / Liasons / Fragen / Adieu / Die kleine dinge / Ganz leise kommt die nacht / Einmal wird frieden sein / Mir kommen die tranen / Ich bin ein star / Yes sir / Drei sterne sah ich scheinen / Der wind hat mir ein lied erzahlt / Ich bin eine frau mit vergangenheit / Ich kann ganz ohne menschen sein / Wenn die wilden rosen bluhen / Nur nicht aus liebe weinen / Frauen sind schwer zu durchschauen / Warum soll eine frau kein verhaltnis haben / Ich weiss, es wird einmal ein wunder geschehn / Wenn der Herrgott will / Wunderbar / Sag mir nicht adieu / Ich kenn den Jimmy aus Havanna / Sol man lachen oder weinen / Liaisons
BCD 16016 / Apr '97 / Bear Family

Leandre, Joelle

☐ PALIMPSESTE (Leandre, Joelle & Eric Watson)
ARTCD 6103 / May '92 / Hat Art

Leandro, Edgar

☐ 16 EXITOS 2
761441524127 / 7 Apr '98 / Vedisco

Leandros, Vicky

☐ HIT SINGLES, THE
BX 5252 / 19 Jan '98 / BR Music

Lear, Amanda

☐ AMANDA LEAR
Follow me / Loving / Una notte insieme a te / Fashion pack / Speak of the devil / Peep / Everytime you touch me / On the air tonight / Dance around the room / Rien ne va plus / Time to change / Echec et mat / Ragazzino / L'ecole d'amour / Lili marlen / Alter ego
21010 / Sep '97 / Laserlight

Lears

☐ STORY SO FAR...
GH 1058CD / 20 Apr '98 / Get Hip

Leary, Timothy

☐ BEYOND LIFE WITH TIMOTHY LEARY
After life / Beyond life / While birds sing / Fifty million years / Star light: *Leary, Timothy & Dr. Fiorella Terenzi* / Eternal note: *Leary, Timothy & Liquid Mind* / Why not, why not, why not / Goodbye, goodbye / Legend of a mind: *Moody Blues* / Tale of the tribe: *Ginsberg, Allen* / Lion's mouth: *Leary, Timothy & Al Jourgensen*
5342162 / May '97 / Mouth Almighty

☐ YOU CAN BE ANYONE THIS TIME AROUND
Live and let die / You can be anyone this time around / What do you turn on when you turn on
RCD 10249 / May '96 / Rykodisc

Leary, Tom

☐ CALM WATERS
Holly in the conifer / Ragpath / Mill pond medley / Solway dawn / Mlnosegi boro / Koln Square / Dollars o'Driscoll / Polkas / Bonneville blues / Thomas' morris/Chasing the jack / Waltz for Morgan / Kingfisher / Dragonfly/The paradise place / Calm waters
SVL 03CD / Dec '97 / Speaking Volumes

Leatherface

☐ CHERRY KNOWLE
Colorado Joe/Leningrad Vlad / Animal day / This land / Ghetto / Discipline / Post war product of a fat man's wallet / Cabbage case / Right Reverand / Alright Jack / Sublime / Smile (your in a free and pleasant land) / Ghoulash / Heaven
BC 1691 / 10 Nov '97 / Bitzcore

☐ DISCOGRAPHY VOL.1
REJ 1000015 / 15 Dec '97 / Rejected

☐ DISCOGRAPHY VOL.2
REJ 1000017CD / 20 Apr '98 / Rejected

☐ LAST, THE
WIGCD 10 / Mar '94 / Domino

Leatherwolf

☐ ENDANGERED SPECIES
Spiter / Endangered species / Tonight's the night / Hook / Season of the witch / Off the track / Kill and kill again / Vagrant / Leatherwolf
HMAXD 39 / Jul '85 / Heavy Metal

Leaves

☐ 1966
422194 / May '94 / New Rose

Leaving Trains

☐ BIG JINX
SST 293CD / Jul '94 / SST

☐ FAVOURITE MOOD SWINGS (1986-1995)
SST 334CD / 3 Nov '97 / SST

☐ KILL TUNES
SST 071CD / May '93 / SST

☐ LOSER ILLUSION PART 0
SST 284CD / May '93 / SST

☐ LUMP IN MY FOREHEAD
SST 288CD / May '93 / SST

☐ ROCK'N'ROLL MURDER
SST 283CD / May '93 / SST

☐ SLEEPING UNDERWATER SURVIVORS
I love you, goodbye / Walk like a river / Suicide blues / Relapse, recover / What was left was red / Hurting word / Come / Room at the bottom / Extinction
SST 271CD / May '93 / SST

☐ TRANSPORTATIONAL D VICES
SST 221CD / Feb '89 / SST

Leavy, Hosea

☐ YOU GOTTA MOVE
You gotta move / Hey boss / Fannie Mae / Trying to get ahead / Goin' back to the country / Tore down / If you love me like you say / Born in Missouri / Going blind / Reconsider baby / When you get old / Crazy Mary
FCD 5002 / 14 Apr '98 / Fedora

Leba

☐ FORMULE EXPRESS
GLAS 42CD / 3 Nov '97 / Glastnost

Leblanc, Keith

☐ KICKIN' LUNATIC BEATS
BLCCD 12 / Oct '96 / Blanc

Lebombo

☐ KHWELA JAZZ
BVHAASTCD 9220 / Jan '93 / Bvhaast

☐ NABAKITSI
BVHAASTCD 9512 / Feb '98 / Bvhaast

Lebrijano, Juan Pena

☐ ENCUENTROS
Vivir un cuento de hadas / Dame la libertad / Las mil y una noches / Desafinado / El anillo (chibuli) / Pensamientos / Amigo mio, no / Esos ojos asesinos
CDORB 024 / Jan '89 / Globestyle

L'Echo Desluthes

☐ MUSIQUE DE HAUTE BRETAGNE
BUR 822CD / '88 / Escalibur

Leckie, Steve

☐ WHAT IT FEELS LIKE TO KILL (Leckie, Steve & The Viletones)
OPM 2119CD / 15 Jan '98 / Other People's Music

Lectroluv

☐ LECTROLUV REMIX PROJECT, THE
EBCD 4 / Jan '95 / Eightball

☐ RETURN OF LECTROLUV
PLUGCD 4
PLUGMD 4 / Apr '96 / Produce

Lecuona Cuban Boys

☐ CONGAS AND RUMBAS
CD 62014 / Apr '94 / Saludos Amigos

☐ LECUONA CUBAN BOYS
EFA 013612 / 13 Oct '97 / Ceraton

☐ LECUONA CUBAN BOYS VOL.1
HQCD 11 / '91 / Harlequin

☐ LECUONA CUBAN BOYS VOL.2 1934-1944
Cuba / Carnaval el Uruguay / La chaparrita / Mambo de jaruco / El pinero / Petrol / Rumbas de jaruco / Coctel de congas / Jose Dolores / Colibri / Bimbasaro / Tendre bolero / Patica y mondonguito / Camina pa'lante / Danza del fuego / Canto Caribe / Costa Rica / Conga de la Martinica / Tumbao / Mi ultima conga
HQCD 07 / Oct '91 / Harlequin

☐ LECUONA CUBAN BOYS VOL.3
HQCD 21 / Jul '92 / Harlequin

☐ LECUONA CUBAN BOYS VOL.4 1932-1936
HQCD 26 / Jul '92 / Harlequin

☐ LECUONA CUBAN BOYS VOL.5 1932-1946
HQCD 35 / Feb '94 / Harlequin

☐ LECUONA CUBAN BOYS VOL.6 (In Venezuela 1940)
HQCD 54 / Jun '95 / Harlequin

☐ LECUONA CUBAN BOYS VOL.7 1940-1944 (In South America)
HQCD 85 / Sep '96 / Harlequin

☐ LECUONA CUBAN BOYS VOL.8 1941-1944
Abaneque yamba / Mi negra cherie / Incertidumbre / Cuando vuelva a Paris / No quiero tu amor / La comparsa de Berlin / Guaira / Vamo Jose / Caminos cruzados / Si me pudieras / Salvaje / El gaum pam pam / Linda Chilena / Son cubano / Segun pasan los anos / Me estoy enamorando de ti / Bongo / Mi sueno y tu / Corazon para que / Cah cah le negro / Pampa
HQCD 96 / Oct '97 / Harlequin

☐ LECUONA CUBAN BOYS VOL.9 1946-1949
Baila la conga / LLa chancleta / Bongo / Cachum bambe / No me vas a enganger / Rumba bomba / Facundo / Maracas / Ahora y siempre / Ilusion / Siboney / A mi que me importa usted / Temptacion / Dark eyes / Oye mi rumba / Tipitin / Son les lecuona / Rumba tambah / Para decirte adios / Rumba blanca / Conga de jaruco / Usted
HQCD 107 / Sep '98 / Harlequin

Led Zeppelin

☐ 4 SYMBOLS
Black dog / Rock 'n' roll / Battle of Evermore / Stairway to heaven / Misty mountain hop / Four sticks / Going to California / When the levee breaks
7567826382 / Aug '97 / Atlantic

☐ BBC SESSIONS, THE (2CD Set)
You shook me / I can't quit you baby / Communication breakdown / Dazed and confused / Girl I love / What is and what should never be / Communication breakdown / Travelling riverside blues / Whole lotta love / Something else / Communication breakdown / I can't quit you baby / You shook me / How many more times / Immigrant song / Heartbreaker / Since I've been loving you / Black dog / Dazed and confused / Stairway to heaven / Going to California / That's the way / Whole lotta love / Thank you
7567830612 / 17 Nov '97 / Atlantic

☐ BIOGRAPHY SERIES
10014 / 3 Nov '97 / Metro Independent

☐ CODA
We're gonna groove / Poor Tom / I can't quit you baby / Walter's walk / Darlene / Ozone baby / Wearing and tearing / Bonzo's Montreux
7567924442 / Aug '96 / Atlantic

☐ COMPLETE STUDIO RECORDINGS, THE (10CD Set)
Good times, bad times / Babe I'm gonna leave you / You shook me / Dazed and confused / Your time is gonna come / Black mountain side / Communication breakdown / I can't quit you baby / How many more times / Whole lotta love / What is and what should never be / Lemon song / Thank you / Heartbreaker / Livin' lovin' maid (she's just a woman) / Ramble on / Moby Dick / Bring it on home / Immigrant song / Friends / Celebration day / Since I've been loving you / Out on the tiles / Gallows pole / Tangerine / That's the way / Bron-y-aur stomp / Hats off to (Roy) Harper / Black dog / Rock 'n' roll / Battle of Evermore / Stairway to heaven / Misty mountain hop / Four sticks / Going to California / When the levee breaks / Song remains the same / Rain song / Over the hills and far away / Crunge / Dancing days / D'yer mak'er / No quarter / Ocean / Achille's last stand / For your life / Royal Orleans / Nobody's fault but mine / Candy store rock / Hots on for nowhere / Tea for one / Custard pie / Rover / In my time of dying / Houses of the holy / Trampled underfoot / Kashmir / In the light / Bron-y-aur / Down by the seaside / Ten years gone / Night flight / Wanton song / Boogie with Stu / Black country woman / Sick again / In the evening / South bound saurez / Fool in the rain / Hot dog / Carouselambra / All my love / I'm gonna crawl / We're gonna groove / Poor Tom / Walter's walk / Ozone baby / Darlene / Bonzo's Montreux / Wearing and tearing / Baby, come on home / Travelling riverside blues / White summer/Black mountain side / Hey hey what can I do
7567825262 / Apr '94 / Atlantic

☐ GRAF ZEPPELIN (Interview Discs/2CD Set)
CONV 007 / Mar '97 / Network

☐ HOUSES OF THE HOLY
Song remains the same / Rain song / Over the hills and far away / Crunge / Dancing days / D'yer mak'er / No quarter / Ocean
7567826392 / Aug '97 / Atlantic

☐ IN THROUGH THE OUT DOOR
In the evening / South bound saurez / Fool in the rain / Hot dog / Carouselambra / All my love / I'm gonna crawl
7567924432 / Aug '97 / Atlantic

☐ INTERVIEW DISC
SAM 7010 / Nov '96 / Sound & Media

☐ KASHMIR (The Symphonic Led Zeppelin) (Various Artists)
Kashmir / Battle of evermore / Stairway to Heaven / Immigrant song / Friends / Going to California / Whole lotta love / All my love / Black dog / When the levee breaks
4541452 / 10 Nov '97 / Point Music

☐ LED ZEPPELIN BOX SET VOL.1 (4CD Set)
Whole lotta love / Heartbreaker / Communication breakdown / Babe I'm gonna leave you / Dazed and confused / Ramble on / Your time is gonna come / What is and what should never be / Thank you / I can't quit you baby / Friends / Celebration day / Travelling riverside blues / Hey hey what can I do / White summer/Black mountain side / Black dog / Over the hills and far away / Immigrant song / Battle of Evermore / Bron-y-aur stomp / Tangerine / Going to California / Since I've been loving you / D'yer mak'er / Gallows pole / Custard pie / Misty mountain hop / Rock 'n' roll / Rain song / Stairway to heaven / Kashmir / Trampled underfoot / For your life / No quarter / Dancing days / When the levee breaks / Song remains the same / Achille's last stand / Ten

years gone / Candy store rock / Moby Dick / In my time of dying / In the evening / Ocean / Ozone baby / Houses of the holy / Wearing and tearing / Poor Tom / Nobody's fault but mine / Fool in the rain / In the light / Wanton song / I'm gonna crawl / All my love
7567821442 / Oct '90 / Atlantic

☐ LED ZEPPELIN BOX SET VOL.2
Good times, bad times / We're gonna groove / Night flight / That's the way / Baby, come on home / Lemon song / You shook me / Boogie with Stu / Bron-y-aur stomp / Down by the seaside / Out on the tiles / Black mountain side / Moby Dick / Sick again / Hot dog / Carouselambra / South bound saurez / Walter's walk / Darlene / Black Country woman / How many more times / Rover / Four sticks / Hats off to (Roy) Harper / I can't quit you baby / Hots on for nowhere / Livin' lovin' maid (She's just a woman) / Royal Orleans / Bonzo's Montreux / Crunge / Bring it on home / Tea for one
7567824772 / Sep '93 / Atlantic

☐ LED ZEPPELIN I
Good times, bad times / Babe I'm gonna leave you / You shook me / Dazed and confused / Your time is gonna come / Black mountain side / Communication breakdown / I can't quit you baby / How many more times
7567826322 / Aug '97 / Atlantic

☐ LED ZEPPELIN II
Whole lotta love / What is and what should never be / Lemon song / Thank you / Heartbreaker / Livin' lovin' maid (she's just a woman) / Ramble on / Moby Dick / Bring it on home
7567826332 / Aug '97 / Atlantic

☐ LED ZEPPELIN III
Immigrant song / Friends / Celebration day / Since I've been loving you / Out on the tiles / Gallows pole / Tangerine / That's the way / Bron-y-aur stomp / Hats off to (Roy) Harper
7567826782 / Aug '97 / Atlantic

☐ LED ZEPPELIN: INTERVIEW PICTURE DISC
CBAK 4042 / Apr '90 / Baktabak

☐ PHYSICAL GRAFFITI
Houses of the holy / Trampled underfoot / Kashmir / Custard pie / Rover / In my time of dying / In the light / Bron-y-aur stomp / Down by the seaside / Ten years gone / Night flight / Wanton song / Boogie with Stu / Black country woman / Sick again
7567924422 / Aug '97 / Atlantic

☐ PRESENCE
Achille's last stand / For your life / Royal Orleans / Nobody's fault but mine / Candy store rock / Hots on for nowhere / Tea for one
7567924392 / Aug '97 / Atlantic

☐ REMASTERS (2CD Set)
Communication breakdown / Babe I'm gonna leave you / Good times, bad times / Dazed and confused / Whole lotta love / Heartbreaker / Ramble on / Immigrant song / Celebration day / Since I've been loving you / Black dog / Rock 'n' roll / Battle of Evermore / Misty mountain hop / Stairway to heaven / Song remains the same / Rain song / D'yer mak'er / No quarter / Houses of the holy / Kashmir / Trampled underfoot / Nobody's fault but mine / Achille's last stand / All my love / In the evening
7567804152 / Aug '97 / Atlantic

☐ SONG REMAINS THE SAME, THE (2CD Set)
Rock 'n' roll / Celebration day / Song remains the same / Rain song / Dazed and confused / No quarter / Stairway to heaven / Moby Dick / Whole lotta love
SK 289402 / Aug '97 / Swansong

☐ SONG RETAINS THE NAME VOL.1, THE (A Tribute To Led Zeppelin) (Various Artists)
Black dog: *Royal Mixxers, The & KGIG & Konan Kelly* / Living loving maid: *Hardest, Rich & Del Rays* / Down by the seaside: *Kuhlmann, Robert & Flying Boats* / Good times old times: *Kuhlmann, Robert & Flying Boats* / Four sticks: *Earwig* / Immigrant song: *Headface* / In the evening: *Twice Shy* / No quarter: *Love Ethyl* / What is a what...: *Helen Keller Plaid* / House of holly: *Fool Killers* / Rock and roll: *Tent Poles*
SAFEHOUSE 8801CD / 16 Feb '98 / Safe House

☐ SONG RETAINS THE NAME VOL.2, THE (A Tribute To Led Zeppelin) (Various Artists)
Dancing days: *Bad Livers* / Misty mountain hop: *7 Seconds* / House of the holy: *Folkadelic* / Tangerine: *When Skip Jack Tripped* / Kashmir: *Ordinaires* / When the levee breaks: *Nixon, Mojo & The Toadliquors* / Out on the tiles: *Helen Keller Plaid* / Trampled underfoot: *Hall, Michael* / Wanton song: *Whyos* / D'yer mak'er: *Alluring Strange* / Friends: *Men & Volts* / Ramble on: *Dusty Diamonds* / Misty mountain hop/Elephant walk: *Hot Joe*
SAFEHOUSE 2112CD / 30 Mar '98 / Safe House

☐ THROUGH THE YEARS (Interview Discs/2CD Set)
CONV 004 / Feb '97 / Network

☐ WHOLE LOTTA LOVE (Bootleg Zep)
Whole lotta love / Communication breakdown / Black dog / Bring it on home / Good times bad times / Living loving maid / Heartbreaker / D'yer mak'er / Ocean / Rock 'n' roll / Lemon song / Immigrant song / Dazed and confused / Live loser / Rock 'n' roll part 2 / Stairway to heaven
QED 107 / Nov '96 / Tring

Leda Trio

☐ AIRS FOR THE SEASONS
SPRCD 1036 / May '94 / Springthyme

Ledernacken

☐ BOOGALOO AND OTHER NATTY DANCERS
SBR 14CD / Oct '87 / Strike Back

☐ L
E 119302 / Dec '93 / Derriere

☐ SEX METAL
SBR 16 CD / Jan '89 / Strike Back

Ledford, Mark

☐ MILES 2 GO
5373192 / 9 Feb '98 / Verve Forecast

Ledgerwood, Leeann

☐ NOW AND ZEN (Ledgerwood, Leeann Quartet)
SCCD 31432 / 24 Feb '98 / Steeplechase

☐ YOU WISH
Robbin's row / Taisho pond / Miss Perfect / Chance / Nardis / Afterglow / You wish / Smash and grab / Terribillis / I want to talk about you
3201872 / May '92 / Triloka

Ledigo, Hugh

☐ SPEAKING FOR OURSELVES (Ledigo, Hugh Trio)
RSCD 674 / Aug '98 / Raymer

LeDonne, Mike

☐ COMMON GROUND (LeDonne, Mike Trio)
CRISS 1058CD / May '92 / Criss Cross

☐ SOULMATES (LeDonne, Mike Sextet)
CRISS 1074CD / Nov '93 / Criss Cross

LeDoux, Chris

☐ ONE MAN ROAD
One tonight / Runaway / Borderline / Old paint / Fever / Bang a drum / Ole slow foot / One ride in Vegas / Sometimes you've just gotta ride / Life is a highway / Caballo diablo / One road man
8219422 / 10 Aug '98 / EMI

Lee, Alan

☐ JAZZ AT HYDE PARK
RQCD 1511 / Nov '96 / Request

Lee, Albert

☐ ALBERT LEE & HOGAN'S HEROES - IN FULL FLIGHT
RTMCD 60 / Jan '94 / Round Tower

☐ HIDING
Country boy / Billy Tyler / Are you wasting my time / Now and then it's gonna rain / O a real good night / Setting me up / Ain't living long like this / Hiding / Hotel love / Come up and see me anytime
CDMID 121 / Oct '92 / A&M

☐ SPEECHLESS
T-Bird to Vegas / Bullish boogie / Arkansas traveller / Romany rye / Erin / Seventeenth summer / Salt creek / Cannonball
EDCD 547 / 26 Jan '98 / Edsel

☐ UNDISCOVERED (The Early Years)
Undiscovered / Long gone / Too much of nothing / Mama tried / Rocky top Tennessee / Country in Harlem / Lay lady lay / Memphis streets / Tears of rage / Victim / Tonight I'll be staying here with you / Mama come get your baby boy / That's all right mama / Best I can / Fool / Send me back to the mines / Mama tried / Fool / Six days on the road / Walkin' shoes / St.Louis / Look out Cleveland / Bullfrog / All about you / Freedom for the stallion
GEMCD 018 / 26 Jan '98 / Diamond

Lee, Alvin

☐ LIVE IN VIENNA
CDTB 171 / Oct '95 / Thunderbolt

☐ NINETEEN NINETY FOUR
Keep on rockin' / Long legs / I hear you knocking / I want you (she's so heavy) / I don't give a damn / Give me your love / Play it like it used to be / Take it easy / My baby's come back to me / Boogie all day / Bluest blues / Ain't nobody's business if I do
CDTB 150 / Mar '95 / Thunderbolt

☐ PURE BLUES
Don't want you woman / Bluest blues / I woke up this morning / Real life blues / Stomp / Slow blues in C / Wake up Mama / Talk don't bother me / Every blues you've ever heard / I get all shook up / Lost in love / Help me baby / Outside my window
CDCHR 6102 / Jul '95 / Chrysalis

☐ RETROSPECTIVE
Johnny B Goode / Help me / Good morning little school girl / Slow blues in C / Love until I die / Love like a man / One more chance / You told me / I'm going home / Jenny Jenny / Little bit of love / Truckin' down the other way
MMGV 064 / Mar '95 / Magnum Video

☐ SOLID ROCK (Lee, Alvin & Ten Years After)
Rock n roll music to the world / Detroit diesel / I'm coming on / Jenny Jenny / 50000 miles beneath my brain / Play it like it used to be / Let's shake it up / Shot in the dark / You can't win them all / Too late to urrun for cover / Baby won't you let me rock n roll you / Fight for your rights / Lets shake it up / Too late to run for cover / Fight for your right / I love you when you rock n roll me
CDCHR 6129 / 24 Nov '97 / Chrysalis

Lee, Arthur

☐ ARTHUR LEE & LOVE (Lee, Arthur & Love)
422214 / May '94 / New Rose

☐ BLACK BEAUTY & RARITIES (Lee, Arthur & Love)
EVOL 1 / Jul '97 / EVA

☐ VINDICATOR
Sad song / You can save up to 50% / Love jumped through my window / Find somebody / He said she said / Every time I look up / Everybody's gotta live / You want change for your re-run / He knows a lot of good women / Hamburger breath stinkfinger / Ol' morgue mouth / Busted feet
5406972 / Feb '97 / A&M

Lee, Ben

☐ GRANDPAW WOULD
GR 015CD / Apr '97 / Grand Royal

☐ SOMETHING TO REMEMBER ME BY
How to survive a broken heart / Deep talk in the shallow end / In the desert / New song / Eight years old / Career choice / Ketchum / Daisy / My drifting nature / 2 sisters / Month today / Bad radio today / Household name / Grammercy park hotel / End of the world / Long train ride
GR 044CD / 27 Oct '97 / Grand Royal

Lee, Bonnie

☐ SWEETHEART OF THE BLUES
DE 676 / Aug '95 / Delmark

Lee, Brenda

☐ BEST OF BRENDA LEE
Sweet nothin's / I'm sorry / Emotions / Dum dum / Fool number one / You always hurt the one you love / Will you still love me tomorrow / When I fall in love / I'll be seeing you / Speak to me pretty / Here comes that feeling / It started all over again / My colouring book / Someday you'll want me to want you / End of the world / All alone am i / Losing you / Ronettes / My whole world / Sweet impossible you / As usual / Is it true / Think / Love letters / Too many rivers / Make the world go away / Crying time / Sweet dreams / Yesterday / Always on my mind / For the good times / Feelings
MCBD 19518 / Apr '95 / MCA

☐ BEST OF BRENDA LEE, THE
MCCD 213 / Oct '95 / Music Club

☐ BRENDA LEE
Wiedersehn ist wunderschon / Kansas City / Ohne dich / Drei rote rosen bluh'n / Ich will immer auf dich warten / No my boy / Geh am gluck nicht vorbei / Am strand von Hawaii / Darling bye bye / In meinen traumen / Wo und wann fangt die liebe an / Darling was ist los mit dir / La premiere fool / Pourqui jamais moi / Sono sciocca / Nulla di me
BCD 15644 / Jun '92 / Bear Family

☐ BRENDA LEE
Sweet nothin's / Dum dum / Call me / If you love me / I'm sorry / I want to be wanted / All alone am I / As usual / Emotions / Losing you / My whole world is falling down / Is it true / Kansas City / Too many rivers / Fool No.1 / You can depend on me
12456 / Apr '96 / Laserlight

☐ COMING ON STRONG
MU 5037 / Oct '92 / Musketeer

☐ CONCERT COLLECTION
Coming on strong / Silver threads and golden needles / Johnny one time / You're the one that I want / You don't have to say you love me / Medley / How much love / All you gotta do / Your Mama don't dance / I'm sorry / Medley / Medley / Medley
PLATCD 166 / Mar '96 / Platinum

☐ EP COLLECTION, THE
Rock the bop / Weep no more baby / (If I'm dreaming) Just let me dream / Crazy talk / Speak to me pretty / Here comes that feeling / Ring-a-my-phone / Love you till I die / Rock-a-bye baby blues / Thanks a lot / All alone am I / If you love me (really love me) / I'm sorry / Georgia on my mind / I left my heart in San Francisco / Your used to be / She'll never know / Coming on strong / That's all you gotta do / Let's jump the broomstick / Stroll / Kansas City / Bigelow 6200 / Sweet nothin's / Rockin' around the Christmas tree
SEECD 425 / May '95 / See For Miles

☐ FAVOURITES
Coming on strong / Silver threads and golden needles / Johnny one time / You're the one that I want / You don't have to say you love me / Jambalaya / Is it true / My whole world / Sweet nothin's / End of the world / All alone am I / Fool no.1 / Too many rivers / How much love / That's all you gotta do / I'm sorry / Mama don't dance / Good ole acapella (soul to soul) / Old landmarks / I'll flyaway some glad morning / Operator / Up above my head / Saved / When you're smiling / You ought to be in pictures / Put on a happy face / Smile / Baby face
MUCD 9001 / Apr '95 / Musketeer

☐ GREATEST HITS
Coming on strong / Silver threads and golden needles / Johnny one time / You're the one that I want / You don't have to say you love me / Jambalaya / Is it true / My whole world is falling down / Sweet nothin's / End of the world / All alone am I / How much love / All you gotta do / You mama don't dance / I'm sorry / When you're smiling / You ought to be in pictures / Put on a happy face / Smile / Baby face / Soul to soul / Old landmarks / Some glad morning / Operator / Up above my head / Saved / Dum dum / Fool number one / Too mnay rivers
PLATCD 362 / '91 / Platinum

☐ I'M SORRY
WMCD 5570 / Oct '94 / Disky

☐ LITTLE MISS DYNAMITE (4CD Set)
Jambalaya / Bigelow 6-200 / Bigelow 6-200 / Some people / Your cheatin' heart / Doodle bug rag / Christy Christmas / I'm gonna lasso Santa Claus / Fairyland / One step at a time / Dynamite / Ain't that love / Love you till I die / One teenager to another / Rock a baby blues / Rock the bop / Ring-a-my-phone / Golden key / Little Jonah (rock on your steel guitar) / My baby likes Western guys / Papa Noel / Rockin' around the Christmas tree / Bill Bailey, won't you please come home / Heading home / Let's jump the broomstick / Hummin' the blues over you / Stroll / Rock-a-bye your baby with a dixie melody / Pretty baby / St. Louis blues / Pennies from heaven / Baby face / Ballin' the jack / Just because / Side by side / Good man is hard to find / Some of these days / Back in your own backyard / Toot toot tootsie goodbye / Sweet nothin's / (If I'm dreaming) Just let me dream / Weep no more my baby / That's all you gotta do / I want to be wanted (per tutta la vita) / Just a little / Build a big fence / Be my love again / I'm sorry / Dynamite / Love and learn / Wee Wee Willie / Jambalaya / Do I worry (yes I do) / Emotions / I want to be wanted (per tutta la vita) / No one / Crazy talk / Big chance / It's never too late / I'm learning about love / Careless, that's all / We three (my echo, my shadow and me) / If I didn't care / When my dreamboat comes home / Walkin' to New Orleans / Hallelujah I love him so / I'm in the mood for love / Swanee river rock / Pretend / If I didn't care / If you love me (really love me) / Teach me tonight / Blueberry Hill / Around the world / Fools rush in / Someone to love (The prisoner's song) / Zing went the strings of my heart / Georgia on my mind / Just another lie / When I fall in love / Cry / Will you love me tomorrow / You can depend on me / Careless, that's all / Lover come back to me / Kansas City / On the sunny side of the street / All the way / How deep is the ocean (how high is the sky) / Tragedy / Talkin' 'bout you / Tables are turning / Funny feelin' / Eventually / Dum dum / Let me be the one / Speak to me pretty / Time is not enough / Here comes that feeling / Just forget / Break it to me gently / Fool no.1 / Anybody but me / So deep / Only you (and you alone) / You've got me crying again / It's the talk of the town / You always hurt the one you love / I miss you so / I'll be seeing you / Lazy river / Send me some lovin' / Hold me / I'll always be in love with you / Organ grinder's swing / Let the four winds blow / Everybody loves me but you / Heart in hand / She'll never know / Why me / It takes one to know one / Sweet lovin'
BCD 15772 / Oct '95 / Bear Family

☐ LITTLE MISS DYNAMITE
CD 6012 / Jun '96 / Music

☐ LIVE DYNAMITE (2CD Set)
CPCD 82892 / Jul '97 / Charly

☐ ROCKIN' AROUND WITH BRENDA LEE
(If I'm dreaming) Just let me dream / Ain't that love / Bigelow 6200 / Bill Bailey, won't you please come home / Dum dum / Dynamite / Jambalaya / Let's jump the broomstick / Little Jonah (Rock on your little guitar) / Love and learn / My baby likes western guys / One step at a time / Ring-a-my-phone / Rock the bop / Rock-a-bye baby blues / Rockin' around the Christmas tree / Sweet nothin's / That's all you gotta do / Wee wee Willie's / Weep no more my baby
PWKS 4232 / Nov '94 / Carlton

☐ SINGS HER MOST BEAUTIFUL SONGS
CD 3501 / Aug '94 / Cameo

Lee, Bryan

☐ BLUES IS..., THE (Lee, Bryan & Jump Street Five)
Circles / Think / Waiting on ice / Let me down easy / It's your move / Gelle / There it is / You done me wrong / So low down / Pretty Jeanine / I worry / Blues is...
BLU 10122 / Feb '92 / Blues Beacon

☐ LIVE AT THE OLD ABSINTHE HOUSE BAR...FRIDAY NIGHT
Braille blues Daddy / Cross cut saw / Sky is crying / Ain't doing too bad / Five long years / Automobile blues / Going down / Look on yonder wall / Key to the highway / Rock me baby
JUST 1002 / 23 Feb '98 / Justin Time

☐ MEMPHIS BOUND
JUST 522 / Sep '93 / Justin Time

Lee, Bunny

☐ AGGROVATE LEE PERRY AND THE UPSETTERS (Lee, Bunny & The Aggrovators)
Badaration dub: *Aggrovators* / Dread locks rasta love dub: *Aggrovators* / Righteous people dub: *Aggrovators* / Warmonger dub: *Aggrovators* / Bad rude boy dub: *Aggrovators* / Straight to the Upsetterhead: *Aggrovators* / Straight to Lee Scratchperry head: *Aggrovators* / Aggrovator colt the game in dub: *Aggrovators* / Winning punch dub: *Aggrovators* / Golden cup dub: *Aggrovators* / Rubber dub prize dub: *Aggrovators* / Bless the cup dub: *Aggrovators* / Standing ovation dub: *Aggrovators* / Humble lion dub: *Upsetters* / Mouth murderer dub: *Upsetters* / Dub slaughterer dub: *Upsetters* / Mean dub killer dub: *Upsetters* / Straight to the Aggrovator head: *Upsetters* / Iron front war dub: *Upsetters* / Steel plate bullerproof vest dub:

Upsetters / Iron teeth killer dub: *Upsetters* / Ghetto blast dub: *Upsetters* / Upsetter murderer dub: *Upsetters* / War and peace dub: *Upsetters* / Upsetters knife edge dub: *Upsetters* / Straight to Bunny Lee's head: *Upsetters*
RN 7015 / Feb '97 / Rhino

Lee, Byron

☐ ANTHOLOGY 1964-1996
MCCD 349 / 15 Jun '98 / MCI Music

☐ BEST OF SKA VOL.1, THE (Lee, Byron & The Dragonaires)
My boy lollipop / Easy snappin' / Tell me darling / Green island / Wings of a dove / Sammy dead / Oh caroline / Oil in my lamp / Occupation / Behold / Jamaica ska
JMC 200104 / Dec '92 / Jamaican Gold

☐ BEST OF SKA VOL.2, THE (Lee, Byron & The Dragonaires)
Simmer down / Dancing mood / Puppet on a string / Carry go bring come / Eastern standard time / Riverbank / It's you / Schooling the duke / Pressure and slide / Worried over you / Ride you donkey / You won't see me
JMC 200105 / Feb '93 / Jamaican Gold

☐ BEST OF SKA VOL.3, THE (Lee, Byron & The Dragonaires)
I've got to go back home / Satisfaction / 007 (shanty town) / 54-46 (that's my number) / Girl I've got a date / Rucumbine / Wear you to the ball / Cherry oh baby / Harder they come / Life is just for living / No woman no cry
JMC 200106 / Feb '93 / Jamaican Gold

☐ CHRISTMAS IN JAMAICA (Lee, Byron & The Dragonaires)
NL 25252 / Oct '96 / Jamaican Gold

☐ JAMAICA'S GOLDEN HITS (Lee, Byron & The Dragonaires)
My boy lollipop / Easy snappin' / Tell me darling / Green island / Wings of a dove / Sammy dead / Oh Carolina / Oil in my lamp / Occupation / Behold / Jamaica ska
DYCD 3380 / Jun '96 / Dynamic

☐ JUMP UP (Lee, Byron & The Dragonaires)
D 232 / Mar '98 / Dynamic

☐ ORIGINAL BYRON LEE, THE (Lee, Byron & The Dragonaires)
KENTONE 106 / Jul '93 / Kentone

☐ PLAY DYNAMITE SKA (Lee, Byron & The Dragonaires)
JMC 200276 / Jun '93 / Jamaican Gold

☐ REGGAE BLAST OFF (Lee, Byron & The Dragonaires)
Monkey man / Elizabethan reggae / Love at first sight / Birth control
JMC 200108 / Jul '94 / Jamaican Gold

☐ REGGAE EYES
JMC 200107 / Jul '94 / Jamaican Gold

☐ REGGAE HOT SHOTS
JMC 200118 / Jul '96 / Jamaican Gold

☐ SOCA ENGINE (Lee, Byron & The Dragonaires)
DYCD 3493 / Jun '96 / Dynamic

☐ SOCA FRENZY (Lee, Byron & The Dragonaires)
DYCD 3495 / 27 Apr '98 / Dynamic

☐ SOCAROBICS (Lee, Byron & The Dragonaires)
DYCD 3494 / Jun '97 / Dynamic

☐ SOFT LEE VOL.1 (Lee, Byron & The Dragonaires)
DYCD 3423 / Oct '95 / Dynamic

☐ SOFT LEE VOL.2 (Lee, Byron & The Dragonaires)
DYCD 3456 / Sep '95 / Dynamic

☐ SOFT LEE VOL.3 (Lee, Byron & The Dragonaires)
DYCD 3460 / Sep '95 / Dynamic

☐ SOFT LEE VOL.5 (Lee, Byron & The Dragonaires)
DYCD 3489 / Jan '94 / Dynamic

☐ SOFTLEE
DY 3492 / 8 Dec '97 / Dynamic

☐ WINE DOWN (Lee, Byron & The Dragonaires)
DY 3479 / May '92 / Dynamic

Lee, Dee C.

☐ THINGS WILL BE SWEETER
CTNCD 001 / Oct '95 / Cleartone

Lee, Dino

☐ NEW LAS VEGAN, THE
ROSE 127CD / Oct '87 / New Rose

Lee, Elizabeth

☐ TEXAS BOUND
PT 617001 / Jun '96 / Part

Lee, Frankie

☐ GOING BACK HOME
BPCD 5013 / Dec '94 / Blind Pig

☐ LADIES AND THE BABIES, THE
HMG 5501 / Aug '97 / Hightone

☐ SOONER OR LATER (Lee, Frankie & the Bluzblasters)
FF 595CD / Feb '93 / Flying Fish

Lee Harvey Oswald Band

☐ BLASTRONAUT
TG 154CD / Jul '96 / Touch & Go

☐ TASTE OF PRISON
TGCD 84 / Feb '94 / Touch & Go

Lee, Jack

☐ PIPING CENTRE 1996 RECITAL SERIES VOL.1, THE (Lee, Jack & Alasdair Gillies)
Tom Wilson: *Lee, Jack* / 24th Guards Brigade at Anzio: *Lee, Jack* / Homewrecker: *Lee, Jack* / Brolum: *Lee, Jack* / High road to Linton: *Lee, Jack* / Old woman's dance: *Lee, Jack* / Biddy from Sligo: *Lee, Jack* / Michael Grey: *Lee, Jack* / 93rd at Modder River: *Lee, Jack* / Caber Feidh: *Lee, Jack* / Little cascade: *Lee, Jack* / Donella Beaton: *Lee, Jack* / Geese in the bog: *Lee, Jack* / Harry MacAleer's favourite: *Lee, Jack* / Andrew and Colin Lee: *Lee, Jack* / Big spree: *Lee, Jack* / John MacDonald of Glencoe: *Gillies, Alasdair* / Deer forest: *Gillies, Alasdair* / An t-Alltan Dubh: *Gillies, Alasdair* / Cailin mo run-sa: *Gillies, Alasdair* / Foxhunter: *Gillies, Alasdair* / Jane Campbell: *Gillies, Alasdair* / Sarah Lawrie: *Gillies, Alasdair* / Step dancer: *Gillies, Alasdair* / Lochfyneside: *Gillies, Alasdair* / Cota mor Ealasaid: *Gillies, Alasdair* / Nameless reel: *Gillies, Alasdair* / I am a poor man: *Gillies, Alasdair* / Ruidhle bean aonghais ruaidh: *Gillies, Alasdair* / MacPherson's rant: *Gillies, Alasdair* / Brenda Stubbert: *Gillies, Alasdair* / Pipe Major John Stewart: *Gillies, Alasdair* / Athole Cummers: *Gillies, Alasdair* / John MacKechnie: *Gillies, Alasdair* / Moll Roe/Drops of brandy/Gi'e us a drink of water: *Gillies, Alasdair* / Welcome the piper/Paddy be easy/The weaver: *Gillies, Alasdair* / Donald MacLennan's exercise: *Gillies, Alasdair*
COMD 2064 / Jul '97 / Temple

Lee, Jackie

☐ DUCK, THE
GSCD 011 / Feb '93 / Goldmine

Lee, Jeanne

☐ TRAVELLIN' IN SOUL TIME (Lee, Jeanne & Mal Waldron/Toru Tenda)
BVHAASTCD 9701 / Aug '97 / Bvhaast

Lee, John

☐ BAMBOO MADNESS (Lee, John & Gerry Brown)
Infinite Jones / Deliverance / Jua / Absitively posolutely / Rise on / Who can see the shadow of the moon / Bamboo madness
FCD 0001 / Nov '95 / Limetree

Lee, Julia

☐ GOTTA GIMME WHATCHA GOT
He's tall, dark and handsome / Won't you come over to my house / Come on over to my house / Trouble in mind / If it's good / Show me Missouri blues / Lotus blossom / Dream lucky blues / Julia's blues / Lies / Gotta gimme whatcha' got / When a woman loves a man / Oh Marie / I'll get along somehow / Porter's love song to a chambermaid / Have you ever been lonely / Since I've been with you / Out in the cold again / Young girl's blues / On my way out
PLCD 560 / Mar '97 / President

☐ KANSAS CITY STAR (5CD Set)
Down home syncopated / Merritt stomp / If I could be with you one hour tonight / Paseo Street / Ruff scufflin' / St. James Infirmary / He's tall, dark and handsome / Won't you come over to my house / Come over to my house / Trouble in mind / It it's good / Missouri blues / Lotus blossom / Dream lucky blues / We baby blues / I've got a crush on the fuller brush man / Two loves have I / Some of these days / St. Louis blues / Shake that thing shake it and break it / Julia's blues / Lies gotta gimme what you got / When a woman loves a man / Oh Marie / I'll get along somehow / Porter's love song / Have you ever been lonely / Since I've been with you / Out in the cold again / Young girl's blues / On my way out there / Snatch and grab it / If you hadn't gone away / Nobody knows you (when you're down and out) / Curse of an aching heart bleeding hearted blues / Living backstreet for you / You're a wise guy / Mama don't allow it / Doubtful blues / Ain't it a crime knock me a kiss / Cold hearted Daddy / My sin / When you're smiling / I was wrong / Pagan love song / All I ever do is worry / Take it or leave it / That's what I like / King size papa blues for somebody / I'm forever blowing bubbles / Breeze (blow my baby back to me) / Spinach song / Crazy world / Tell me Daddy / Christmas spirits / Until the real thing comes along / Charmaine / Lotus blosson marijuana / Sit down and drink it over / Away from you / Glory of love / Tonight's the night / My man stands out / Do you want it / It comes in like a lion / Don't come to soon / Ugly Papa / Don't save it too long / After hours waltz / You ain't got it no more / When your lover has gone / Oh chuck it (in a bucket) / Woman blues / Draggin' my heart around / It won't be long / You're gonna miss it / Can't get enough of that stuff / When a man has two women / Scream in the night / I know it's wrong / Music maestro please / Pipe dreams / When Jenny does that low down dance / If I didn't care / Lazy river / All this beef and big red tomatoes / Can't get you off my mind / I got news for you / Goin' to Chicago blues / Last call for alcohol kansas city boogie / Love in bloom / Keep 'em barefoot and busy baby / I'm through / Scat you cats / I can't see how / King size Papa / Bop and rock lullaby
BCD 15770 / Mar '95 / Bear Family

Lee, Keiko

☐ BEAUTIFUL LOVE
Beautiful love / Time for love / My romance / Summer knows / You've changed / Shadow of your smile / Don't let me be lonely tonight / I'll be around / Go away little boy / Love is all there is / If it's magic
4881942 / Aug '97 / Sony Jazz

☐ KICKIN' IT
Come back bebop - lover come back to me / Night and day / Love dance / Come rain or come shine / We'll be together again / Mr. Wonderful / Man I love / I will wait for you / How long has this been going on / God bless the child
4851352 / Sep '96 / Sony Jazz

Lee, Laura

☐ BEST OF LAURA LEE, THE (Love's Rights And Wrongs/2CD Set)
Women's love rights / I can't hold on much longer / Workin' and lovin' together / Her picture matches mine / Be careful if you can't be good / Two lonely pillows / Love and liberty / I don't want nothin' old but money / I'll catch you when you fall / Rip off / Remember me / You've got to slave me / Wedlock is padlock / If you can beat me rockin' you can have my chair / I need it just as bad as you / We've come too far to walk away / If I'm good enough tolove I'm good enough to marry / I can't make it alone / It's not what you fall for / Mirror of your soul / I need it just as bad as you / At last / Every little bit hurts / Guess who I saw today / That's how strong my love is / Since I fell for you pts.1 and 2 / When a man loves a woman / Crumbs off the table / Don't leave me starving for your love
DEEPD 025 / 27 Oct '97 / Deep Beats

Lee, Michael

☐ FIRKINS
Laughing stacks / Runaway train / Deja blues / Rain in the tunnel / Sargasso sea / 24 Grand Avenue / Cactus cruz / Space crickets / Hula hoops
RR 93992 / Aug '90 / Roadrunner

Lee, Myron

☐ AW C'MON (Lee, Myron & The Caddies)
CLCD 4439 / May '97 / Collector/White Label

Lee, Peggy

☐ AT HER BEST (2CD Set)
Love for sale / Misty / You gotta know how / Rodgers and Hart medley / Have a good time / Mr. Wonderful / Sing a rainbow / Make believe / Fever / Why don't you do right / I don't want to play in your yard / I'm not in love / Everything must change / Mack the knife / Folks who live on the hill / Lover / Here's to you / Come back to me / Moments like this / Big spender / Here and now / Misty / I go to Rio / Unforgettable / I can't stop loving you / Big bad Bill / Dreams of Summer / Train song / Fisherman's wharf / St. Louis blues / Kansas City / Goin' to Chicago / Boston beans / Basin Street blues / New York city blues / I'm not in love / Switchin' channels / Hungry years / Alright, OK, you win / What I did for love
PDSCD 543 / Jul '97 / Pulse

☐ BEST OF PEGGY LEE, THE
Lover / Black coffee / My heart belongs to daddy / It ain't necessarily so / There's a small hotel / Brown bird singing / He's a tramp / Mr. wonderful / Siamese cat song / Sing a rainbow / Somebody loves me / I don't want to play in your yard / Street of dreams / It's all right with me / It never entered my mind / Too late now / I've grown accustomed to his face / Something I dreamed last night
MCCD 157 / May '94 / Music Club

☐ BLACK COFFEE
Black coffee / I've got you under my skin / Easy living / My heart belongs to daddy / It ain't necessarily so / Gee baby ain't I good to you / Woman alone with the blues / I didn't know what time it was / When the world was young / Love me or leave me / You're my thrill / There's a small hotel
HMNCD 023 / 5 Jan '98 / Half Moon

☐ BLACK COFFEE/SEASHELLS
Black coffee / I've got you under my skin / Easy living / My heart belongs to daddy / Woman alone with the blues / I didn't know what time it was / When the world was young / Love me or leave me / It ain't necessarily so / Gee baby (ain't I good to you) / You're my thrill / There's a small hotel / Sea fever / Nine thorny thickets / Little old car / Greensleeves / Chinese love poems / Happy poems / White bitch and the sycamore / Of such is the kingdom of God / Brown bird singing / I don't want to play in your yard / Maid with the flaxen hair / Wearing of the green / Chaconde / Riddle song / Golden wedding ring
MCLD 19363 / 23 Mar '98 / MCA

☐ CHRISTMAS
I like a sleigh ride / Christmas song / Don't forget to feed the reindeer / Christmas list / Christmas carousel / Santa Claus is coming to town / Christmas waltz / Christmas riddle / Deck the halls / White Christmas / Winter wonderland / Little drummer boy / Happy holiday / Christmas spell / Toys for tots
CH 877292 / 30 May '97 / Disky

☐ CHRISTMAS ALBUM, THE
I like a sleighride (Jingle bells) / Christmas song / Don't forget to feed the reindeer / Star carol / Christmas list / Christmas carousel / Santa Claus is coming to town / Christmas waltz / Christmas riddle / Tree / Deck the halls with boughs of holly / White Christmas / Winter wonderland / Little drummer boy / Happy holiday / Christmas spell / Toys for tots
CDMFP 6149 / Oct '96 / Music For Pleasure

☐ CLOSE ENOUGH FOR LOVE
You / Easy does it / Close enough for love / A robinsong / Just one of those things / I can't resist you / Come in from the rain / In the days of our love / Through the eyes of love / Rain sometimes
CDSL 5190 / '88 / DRG

☐ EMI PRESENTS THE MAGIC OF PEGGY LEE
As time goes by / Basin Street blues / Stormy weather / Cheek to cheek / Come dance with me / Fever / Fly me to the moon / Folks who live on the hill / From now on (leave it to me) / Unforgettable / Hallelujah I love him so / Happy holiday / I am in love / I could have danced all night / I hear music / I'm a woman / Man I love / Lady is a tramp / Mack the knife / On the street where you live
CDMFP 6371 / May '97 / Music For Pleasure

☐ EXTRA SPECIAL/SOMETHIN' GROOVY
Hey look me over / When he makes music / Wailing happy / Oh you crazy moon / So what's new / Call me darling / Bucket of tears / Shining sea / Doodlin' song / Amazing / I'm gonna go fishing / Somethin' stupid / Makin' whoopee / You must have been a beautiful baby / I can hear the music / It might as well be spring / Two for the road / Release me / Sing a rainbow / No fool like an old fool / Love is here to stay / I'm gonna get it
4930652 / Jan '98 / Capitol

☐ FEVER
Fever / It's all right with me / Hallelujah I love him so / Apples, peaches and cherries / Mr. wonderful / They can't take that away from me / Alright, okay, you win / Love me or leave me / Black coffee / Sans soucl / Lover / My heart belongs to daddy / Baubles, bangles and beads / Is that all there is / Big spender / That's what a woman is for / Siamese cat song / Where can I go without you / Love letters / I'm glad there is you / I'm a woman / Swing low, sweet chariot / He needs me / Guess I'll go back home
PRS 23012 / Aug '93 / Personality

☐ FEVER (The Best Of Peggy Lee)
PLSCD 144 / Apr '96 / Pulse

☐ FEVER
GO 3812 / 1 Dec '97 / Golden Options

☐ FEVER (3CD Set)
Fever / Bewitched / Come rain or come shine / I left my heart in San Francisco / Let's fall in love / Me and my shadow / One note samba / Manana / On the street where you live / I've got the world on a string / Raindrops keep fallin' on my head / There's always something there to remind me / CC rider / Big spender / Alright OK you win / Cheek to cheek / Hallelujah I love him so / I could have danced all night / LOVE / It's a wonderful world / Something / Till there was you / I'm beginning to see the light / That's all / What are you doing the rest of your life / I'll get by / Pass me by / Music music music / My man / Days of wine and roses / You always hurt the one you love / Lady is a tramp / Mack the knife / Taste of honey / You're nobody 'til somebody loves you / Is that all there is / It's been a long time / When in Rome / There is no greater love / I'm a woman / Party's over
HR 883492 / Oct '97 / Disky

☐ FOR SENTIMENTAL REASONS (16 Tender & Romantic Hits)
Lady is a tramp / Too young / Just one more chance / Shanghai / Let there be love / He's just my kind / I'm confessin' / I gotta right to sing the blues / Oh what a beautiful morning / Love is just around the corner / September in the rain / I'm beginning to see the light / Nice work if you can get it / These foolish things / That old gang of mine / (I love you) for sentimental reasons
PLATCD 160 / Mar '96 / Platinum

☐ GOLD COLLECTION, THE (2CD Set)
R2CD 4034 / 13 Apr '98 / Deja Vu

☐ IF I COULD BE WITH YOU
If I could be with you one hour tonight / Too young / Clarinade / Shangai / Guy is a guy / Lady is a tramp / Dorsey medley / These foolish things / Just one more chance / Make the man love me
JASMCD 2534 / Jan '95 / Jasmine

☐ IN THE BEGINNING (The Legend Of Peggy Lee)
On the sunny side of the street / Blues in the night / Where or when / Why don't you do right / How deep is the ocean / Everything I love / How long has this been going on / Let's do it / Full moon / That did it Marie / Not mine / My old flame / Winter weather / I see a million people (but all I can see is you) / Shady ladybird / All I need is you / Somebody else is taking my place / Somebody nobody loves / Way you look tonight / I got it bad and that ain't good / I threw a kiss in the ocean / We'll meet again
PASTCD 7801 / Nov '96 / Flapper

☐ IT'S A GOOD DAY (Lee, Peggy & Bing Crosby)
It's a good day / Everything's movin' too fast / Baby you can count on me / Best man / I still suits me / You came a long way from... / Exactly like you / I got rhythm / Little bird told me / On a slow boat to China / Cuanta La Gusta / What is thing thing called love / He's just my kind: *Lee, Peggy* / Linger in my arms: *Lee, Peggy* / What more can a woman do/: *Lee, Peggy* / (I love you) for sentimental reasons: *Lee, Peggy* / It's all over now: *Lee, Peggy* / Nightingale can sing the blues: *Lee, Peggy* / I'll close my eyes: *Lee, Peggy* / It takes a long, long train with a red caboose: *Lee, Peggy* / Just an old love of mine: *Lee, Peggy* / Golden earrings: *Lee, Peggy* / Love, your magic spell is everywhere: *Lee, Peggy* / Top hat, white tie and tails: *Lee, Peggy & Bing Crosby/Fred*

Astaire / Isn't this a lovely day (to be caught in the rain): Lee, Peggy & Bing Crosby/Fred Astaire / They can't take that away from me: Lee, Peggy & Bing Crosby/Fred Astaire / Dearly beloved: Lee, Peggy & Bing Crosby/Fred Astaire / Catalogue: Lee, Peggy & Bing Crosby/Fred Astaire / Then I'll be happy: Lee, Peggy & Bing Crosby/Fred Astaire / Maybe you'll be there: Lee, Peggy & Bing Crosby/Fred Astaire / Cheek to cheek: Lee, Peggy & Bing Crosby/Fred Astaire / Fine romance: Lee, Peggy & Bing Crosby/Fred Astaire / Smoke gets in your eyes: Lee, Peggy & Bing Crosby/Fred Astaire / White Christmas: Lee, Peggy & Bing Crosby/Fred Astaire / Kahehameha day: Lee, Peggy & Bing Crosby/Fred Astaire / I got lucky in the rain: Lee, Peggy & Bing Crosby/Fred Astaire
PARCD 001 / Jan '96 / Parrot

☐ LATIN A LA LEE/OLE A LA LEE
Heart / On the street where you live / I am in love / Hey there / I could have danced all night / Surrey with the fringe on top / Party's over / Dance only with me / Wish you were here / C'est magnifique / I enjoy being a girl / 'Til there was you / Come dance with me / By myself / You're so right for me / Just squeeze me / Fantastico / Love and marriage / Non dimenticar / From now on / You stepped out of a dream / Ole / I can't resist you / Together wherever we go
CTMCD 111 / Mar '97 / EMI

☐ LET THERE BE LOVE
I gotta right to sing the blues / Let there be love / If I could be with you one hour tonight / These foolish things / Shanghai / Make the man love me / Lady is a tramp / It's all over now / It takes a long, long train with a red caboose / Golden earrings / I got lucky in the rain / He's just my kind / What is this thing called love / (I love you) for sentimental reasons / My last affair / Just one more chance / Love is just around the corner / Love, your magic spell is everywhere / OH what a beautiful morning / Linger in my arms a little longer
TRTCD 153 / Dec '94 / TrueTrax

☐ LET THERE BE LOVE
PLSCD 214 / Apr '97 / Pulse

☐ LET'S DO IT
Elmer's tune / My old flame / How deep is the ocean / That's the way it goes / I threw a kiss in the ocean / I got it bad and that ain't good / Shady ladybird / Let's do it / Somebody else is taking my place / We'll meet again / Full moon / All I need is you / Why don't you do right / Not a care in the world / How long has this been going on / That did it, Marie / Not mine / These foolish things (remind me of you) / Lady is a tramp / Winter weather
CD 6102 / Dec '97 / Music

☐ LISTEN TO THE MAGIC
It's a good day / I don't know enough about you / As long as I'm dreaming / I'll close my eyes / (I love you) for sentimental reasons / You and I passing by / He's just my kind / Linger in my arms a little longer baby / It's all over now / What more can a woman do / Nightingale can sing the blues / Ain'tcha never coming back / It takes a long long train with a red caboose / Just an old love of mine / Golden earrings / Ridin' high / Let there be love / I gotta right to sing the blues / Oh what a beautiful morning / What is this thing called love / Love is just around the corner / 'Deed I do / Do I love you / Just one of those things / You / I've got the world on a string / Love, your magic spell is everywhere / I got lucky in the rain
PLCD 550 / Nov '96 / President

☐ MACK THE KNIFE
TRTCD 209 / Jul '96 / TrueTrax

☐ MAN I LOVE, THE/IF YOU GO
Man I love / Please be kind / Happiness is a thing called Joe / Just one way to say I love you / That's all / Something wonderful / He's my guy / Then I'll be tired of you / My heart stood still / If I should lose you / There is no greater love / Folks who live on the hill / As time goes by / If you go / Oh love hast thou forsaken me / Say it isn't so / I wish I didn't love you so / Maybe it's because (I love you too much) / I'm gonna laugh you out of my life / I get along without you very well (except sometimes) / (I love your) gypsy heart / When I was a child / Here's that rainy day / Smile
CTMCD 105 / Jan '97 / EMI

☐ NEW COLLECTION, THE
I love being here with you / As you desire me / Witchcraft / Wind beneath my wings / So what's new / But beautiful / Lonesome road / Is that all there is / As time goes by / Just for tonight / I don't know enough about you / It's a good day / Then was then and now is now / Manana / Things are swingin' / Don't cry out loud / Best is yet to come / You fascinate me so / Touch me in the morning / Star sounds / Lover
3036001222 / 15 Sep '97 / Carlton

☐ PLATINUM COLLECTION, THE (2CD Set)
I've got to sing the blues / Let there be love / If I could be with you one hour tonight / These foolish things / Shangai / MAke the man love me / Lady is a tramp / It's all over / It takes a long long train with a red caboose / Golden earrings / I got lucky in the rain / He's just my kind / What is the thing called love / For sentimental reasons / My last affair / Just one more chance / Love is just round the corner / Love your magic spell is everywhere / Oh waht a beautiful morning / Linger in my arms a little longer / Why don't you do right / It's the sentimental thing to do / I may have been wrong (but I think you're wonderful) / All of me / I'll dance at your wedding / There'll be some changes made / You don't have to know the language / Christmad song / I can't give you anything but love baby / Lone star moon / Manana (is enough enough for me) / But beautiful / How lucky you are / Secretary song / Laroo laroo Lilli bolero / You turned the tables on me / I went down to Virginia / Nature boy / Baby don't be mad at me / Wish you were here
PC 617 / 10 Nov '97 / Platinum Collection

☐ SPOTLIGHT ON PEGGY LEE
I've got the world on a string / When a woman loves a man / I'm beginning to see the light / There is no greater love / Too close for comfort / Unforgettable / Close your eyes / If I should lose you / I'm just wild about Harry / Deep purple / It's been a long, long time / Man I love / Best is yet to come / Come rain or come shine / Fever / I wanna be around / I hear music / That's all
CDP 8285332 / Jul '95 / Capitol

☐ THESE FOOLISH THINGS
I'm confessin' / September in the rain / That old gang of mine / If I could be with you / Baby please come home / Make the man love me / These foolish things / Too young / Just one more chance / Nice work if you can get it / Lady is a tramp / Don't blame me / It never happened to me / Shanghai / Guy is a guy / I'm beginning to see the light / My last affair / Gone with the wind
300862 / Jun '98 / Hallmark

☐ THINGS ARE SWINGIN'/JUMP FOR JOY
It's a wonderful world / Things are swingin' / Alright, okay, you win / Ridin' high / It's been a long, long time / Lullaby in rhythm / Alone together / I'm beginning to see the light / It's a good, good night / You're getting to be a habit with me / You're mine, you / Life is for livin' / Jump for joy / Back in your own backyard / When my sugar walks down the street / I hear music / Just in time / Old devil moon / What a little moonlight can do / Four or five times / Music music music / Cheek to cheek / Glory of love / Ain't we got fun
CTMCD 101 / Nov '96 / EMI

☐ TOUCH OF CLASS, A
Sneakin' up on you / Come dance with me / Fever / Light of love / Till there was you / My man / Hallelujah I love him so / I'm a woman / CC rider / Mack the knife / Lady is a tramp / Alright, okay, you win / Manana / Golden earrings / Is that all there is / Pass me by
TC 862652 / 2 Feb '98 / Disky

☐ UNCOLLECTED 1948, THE
Ridin' high / Let there be love / I've got a right to sing the blues / Oh what a beautiful mornin' / It's a good day / What is this thing called love / Love is just around the corner / 'deed I do / Do I love you / Just one of those things / You / I've got the world on a string
HCD 220 / Jul '94 / Hindsight

☐ WHY DON'T YOU DO RIGHT
Elmer's tune / I see a million people but all I can see is you / I got it bad and that ain't good / My old flame / How deep is the ocean / Somebody else is taking my place / How long has this been going on / Winter weather / Blues in the night / On the sunny side of the street / Way you look tonight / We'll meet again / Full moon / Why don't you do right / Ain't goin' no place / That old feeling / What more can a woman do / You was right, baby / Waitin' for the train to come in / I don't know enough about you / Everything's movin' too fast / Linger in my arms a little longer, baby / It's a good day / It's lovin' time / It's all over now
CDAJA 5237 / May '97 / Living Era

☐ WOMAN ALONE WITH THE BLUES, A
BMCD 3034 / 5 Jan '98 / Blue Moon

Lee, Ranee

☐ LIVE AT LE BIJOU
JUST 22 / Sep '93 / Justin Time

☐ MUSICALS, THE (Jazz On Broadway)
JUST 422 / Jun '92 / Justin Time

☐ SEASONS OF LOVE
Let the flowers grow / Old folks / Early Autumn / Summer knows / 'Tis Autumn / Beautiful sight / Summer me / Winter me / Dream wish / My one and only love / Spring can really hang you up the most / Everything must change
JUST 1032 / 17 Nov '97 / Justin Time

☐ YOU MUST BELIEVE IN SWING
Secret love / Nice and easy / Angel eyes / I've got the world on a string / Au privave / My baby just cares for me / Yesterday's / Stolen moments / My romance / Fine and mellow / You must believe in spring / What is this thing called love
JUST 882 / Aug '96 / Justin Time

Lee, Riley

☐ ORIENTAL SUNRISE
NARCD 3803 / Jun '96 / Narada

Lee, Scooter

☐ HIGH TEST LOVE
STKCD 1 / 22 Sep '97 / Southern Tracks

☐ HONKY TONK TWIST
SBDCD 3 / Jul '97 / Southbound

☐ IN THE NAME OF LOVE
STKCD 2 / 17 Nov '97 / Southern Tracks

☐ MOVING ON UP
STKCD 3 / 9 Mar '98 / Southern Tracks

☐ NEW ALBUM
SBDCD 2 / Jul '97 / Southbound

Lee, Shawn

☐ DISCOMFORT
Buzz Jenkins present Shawn Lee / Cryin' blue ('til my eyes are red) / Hanging by a thread / Who do you think you are / Married / Getting closer / Real nice / December flowers / P's funky finger / Rose without a thorn / Circles / Transcendental medication / Don't let the past change the future / Porcelain china doll / I can't save you / Untitled
5327982 / Oct '96 / Talkin' Loud

Lee, Soren

☐ SOREN LEE QUARTET
New York subway waltz / Dr. Jekyll / My funny valentine / Darn that dream / Blues in the closet / Secret love / Lee meets Ray / St. Thomas / Blues for Philly Joe
CDLR 45073 / Sep '93 / L&R

Lee, Tim

☐ ALL THAT STUFF (2CD Set) (Lee, Tim 'Love')
HYMN 10 / Jun '97 / Fundamental

☐ CONFESSIONS OF A SELECTOR (Lee, Tim 'Love')
Incense: Lee, Tim / Ruffbutt: Lee, Tim / One word: Lee, Tim / Nu pholk sound: Lee, Tim / Everybody loves the jungle: Lee, Tim / Badder bongo: Lee, Tim / Java jam: Lee, Tim / Love's gonna get you: Lee, Tim / Mo' bounce: Lee, Tim / This is a story: Lee, Tim / Sugar spankin' No.2: Lee, Tim / Wack wack: Lee, Tim / At the bedside: Lee, Tim / Again son...: Lee, Tim
MBTT 007CD / Jun '97 / Tummy Touch

Lee, Tracey

☐ MANY FACEZ
UD 53036 / Apr '97 / Universal

Lee, Will

☐ OH
GOJ 60172 / 8 Jun '98 / Go Jazz

Leeb, Michel

☐ CERTAINS LEEB JAZZ
Lady is a tramp / Autumn in New York / Come rain or come shine / Can't buy me love / What's new / Fly me to the moon / Angel eyes / Teach me tonight / Moonlight in Vermont / Best is yet to come / Where or when / LA afternoon / One for my baby
FDM 365862 / Aug '97 / Dreyfus

Leech Woman

☐ 33 DEGREES
TK 421 / Illuminator / Sea shepherd / Spit / Tool / Fear and bullets / Legion / Ova / Silicon / Intolerance / Sea shepherd
VIRUS 194CD / Jun '97 / Alternative Tentacles

Leer, Thomas

☐ BRIDGE
BRIDGE 1CD / Jun '92 / Grey Area

☐ CONTRADICTIONS
Hear what I say / Mr. Nobody / Contradictions / Looks that kill / Soul gypsy / Choices / Gulf stream / Private plane / International / Kings of sham / Dry land / Don't / Letter from America / Tight as a drum / West End / All about you
CDBRED 105 / Dec '93 / Cherry Red

Lefebvre, Patrick

☐ ACCORDEAN GAVOTTE
CD 431 / Apr '95 / Diffusion Breizh

Lefevre, Raymond

☐ DEMONSTRATION
819 921 2 / '88 / Bar

Left For Dead

☐ BEATINGS FROM ORLANDO
DR 0001 / Feb '97 / Dead Records

Left Hand Frank

☐ LIVE AT THE KNICKERBOCKER CAFE
422428 / Feb '97 / Last Call

Left Hand Freddy

☐ BLUE TONIGHT (Left Hand Freddy & The Aces)
MWCD 2010 / Dec '95 / Music & Words

Left Hand Right Hand

☐ LEGS AKIMBO
TAK 10CD / Oct '96 / Tonus Kozmetica

Left Hand Solution

☐ FEVERED
NB 239CD / Apr '97 / Nuclear Blast

Leftfield

☐ BACKLOG
Not forgotten / Not forgotten (fateh's on the cast mix) / Not forgotten / More than I know (19 mix) / Not forgotten / More than I know (10k mix) / More than I know / More than I know djum djum / Difference / Difference
OUTERCD 1 / Dec '92 / Outer Rhythm

☐ LEFTISM
Release the pressure / Pressure / Afro left / Melt / Song of life / Original black flute / Space shanty / Inspection (check one) / Storm 3000 / Half fast dub / Open up / 21st Century poem
HANDCD 2 / Jan '95 / Columbia

Leftover Salmon

☐ ASK THE FISH
ATFCD 1 / Apr '96 / Bert

Leftwich, Brad

☐ SAY OLD MAN
CUY 2714CD / Aug '96 / County

Lefty Dizz

☐ AIN'T IT NICE TO BE LOVED
Cloudy weather / That's alright in the dark / I feel like jumping / Bad avenue / Ain't it nice to be loved / Look on yonder wall / Too late / Sadie / Where the hell were you when I got home
JSPCD 259 / Mar '95 / JSP

Legacy, Doug

☐ KING CAKE PARTY (Legacy, Doug & Zydeco Party Band)
King cake party / Zydeco shoes / Cakewalk into town / Crime don't pay / Evil / He hates his threads / Sweet cajun baby / Closin' time / Cakewalk / Smokey places / No self control / Ya ya
FIENDCD 206 / Jan '91 / Demon

Legal Weapon

☐ SQUEEZE ME LIKE AN ANACONDA
LRR 010 / Oct '96 / Last Resort

Legend

☐ RED BOOT ALBUM
REP 4061 / Aug '91 / Repertoire

Legend

☐ AD 1980
Legend / My heart is there / Forgotten self / Heaven sent / Advantages / Way love's meant to be / Fantasy / Behind locked doors / Inside out / Silent world / Wooden sword / AM static / Favour
ETHEL 004CD / 2 Feb '98 / Vinyl Tap

Legend

☐ LIGHT IN EXTENSION
Light in extension / Hold the flame / Nightshade / Windsong / Pipes of Pan / Chase / Lament / Evidence of autumn
PMCD 001 / '96 / Pagan Media

☐ SECOND SIGHT
Dance / New horizons / Healer / Wild hunt / Legend / I close my eyes / Mordred
PMRCD 6 / '96 / Pagan Media

☐ TRIPLE ASPECT
Cunning man / Holly King / Lyonesse / All Hallow's Eve / Triple aspect
PMRCD 9 / '96 / Pagan Media

Legend, Johnny

☐ ROCKABILLY BASTARDS (Johnny Legend's Greatest Hits)
HMG 6605 / Nov '97 / Hightone

Legenda

☐ AUTUMNAL
HOLY 025CD / Jun '97 / Holy

Legendary Blues Band

☐ KEEPING THE BLUES ALIVE
I don't wanna know / Stuck in the bottom / I love my woman / Cook me / Open your eyes / Nobody knows / Without her / What's wrong / Shake it for me / Reach way back / Steady worried man
ICH 1052CD / Oct '93 / Ichiban

☐ LIFE OF EASE
ROUCD 2029 / Oct '94 / Rounder

☐ MONEY TALKS
DOG 9107CD / May '94 / Wild Dog

☐ RED HOT 'N' BLUE
ROUCD 2035 / Oct '94 / Rounder

☐ WOKE UP WITH THE BLUES
Another mule / I woke up with the blues / Your daughter looks good to me / Honey bee / I need you so bad / Don't throw your love on me so strong / I'd like to have a girl like you / I've got to be with you tonight / You're looking good again tonight / Having a hard time
ICH 1039CD / Oct '93 / Ichiban

Legendary Pink Dots

☐ 9 LIVES TO WONDER
Madame Guillotine / On another shore / Softly, softly / Crumbs on the carpet / Hotel Z / Oasis malade / Crack in melancholy time / Siren / Angel trail / Nine shades to the circle / Terra firma welcome
BIAS 280CD / Feb '94 / Play It Again Sam

☐ ASYLUM
CDBIAS 012 / Mar '88 / Play It Again Sam

☐ CANTA MIENTRAS PUEDAS
Belladonna / I love you in your tragic beauty / Green gang / Princess coldheart / Disturbance / Grain kings / Prague spring / Triple moon salute / Joey the canary / Siren / Angel trail / Velvet resurrection / Friend
BIAS 325CD / Jul '96 / Play It Again Sam

☐ CHEMICAL PLAYSCHOOL (2CD Set)
TEKA 834 / Oct '96 / Terminal Kaleidoscope

☐ FACES IN THE FIRE
CDBIAS 001 / Aug '88 / Play It Again Sam

☐ ISLAND OF JEWELS
CDBIAS 041 / '88 / Play It Again Sam

☐ MARIA DIMENSION, THE
Disturbance / Disturbance / Thired secret / Grain kings / Ocean cried (blue murder) / Belladonna / A space between / Evolution / Cheraderama / Lilith / Fourth secret / Expresso noir / Home / Crushed velvet
BIAS 184 CD / Jan '91 / Play It Again Sam

☐ SHADOW WEAVER
Zero zero / Guilty man / Ghosts of unborn children / City of needles / Stitching time / Twilight hour / Key to heaven / Laughing guest / Prague spring / Leper colony
BIAS 225CD / Aug '92 / Play It Again Sam

☐ SHADOW WEAVER VOL.2 - MALACHAI
Joey the canary / Kingdom of the flies / Encore une fois / Wildlife estate / Pavanne / Window on the world / On the boards / We bring the day / Paris 4am
BIAS 236CD / Mar '93 / Play It Again Sam

☐ STORM CIRCLES
Love puppets / Black zone / Golden dawn / Curious day / Hanging gardens / Fifteen flies / Our lady in darkness / Apocalypse / Gladiators version
BIAS CD 1001 / Apr '89 / Play It Again Sam

☐ UNDER TRIPLE MOONS
RUSCD 8231 / Jun '97 / ROIR

Legendary Raw Deal

☐ OUTLAW MAN
Madman / Crazy lovin' / Hey lil' baby / Midnite at La Campanina (Titty Bar rock) / Devil on her mind / Jackson / Outlaw man / Broken heart / Surf slapper / Come on Lil' Mama / 4 o'clock baby / Drowning all my sorrows / Thirteen
JRCD 24 / Sep '97 / Jappin' & Rockin'

Legendary Stardust Cowboy

☐ RETRO-ROCKET BACK TO EARTH
422458 / Jan '97 / Last Call

Legende

☐ EN REVENANT DES GRANDES CHANTIERS
CDLCD 1802 / Apr '96 / Coerdelion

☐ RETOUR AUX SOURCES
CDLCD 1818 / Apr '96 / Coerdelion

Legere, Ray

☐ RIVER OF NO RETURN (Legere, Ray & Roger Williams)
Puddle jumper / Little man / Step, stomp and stumble / Contemplation / This lonesome fiddler / I've got your number / River of no return / Swing '93 / Can't keep you in love with me / Let old Mother Nature have her way / Cruisin' the autobahn / Snowy afternoon
SCR 47 / Nov '97 / Strictly Country

Legg, Adrian

☐ WAITING FOR A DANCER
RHRCD 99 / Mar '97 / Red House

Legget, Sandy

☐ DUSK TILL DAWN (Legget, Sandy & The Carseloch Ceilidh Band)
CCBCD 1 / Dec '97 / Sandy Legget

Legion

☐ DIE DATENSCHLEUDER
HY 39100982 / Apr '94 / Hyperium

☐ LEVIATHAN
DFX 024CD / Apr '97 / Side Effects

Legion Of Parasites

☐ MAN MADE FILTH
PREACH 003CD / 30 Mar '98 / Rhythm Vicar

Legrand, Michel

☐ DOUCE FRANCE (Legrand, Michel & Stephane Grappelli)
5298502 / May '96 / Verve

☐ LEGRAND GRAPPELLI (Legrand, Michel & Stephane Grappelli)
Parlez moi d'amour / C'est si bon / Les feuilles mortes / Summer of '42 / Revoir Paris / Mon legionnaire / Good life / Clopin clopant / Mon homme / What are you doing for the rest of your life / Insensiblement / Les parapluies de Cherbourg / Milou en Mai / Irma la douce / Nuages
5170282 / Mar '93 / Verve

☐ PARIS WAS MADE FOR LOVERS
Windmills of your mind / Summer of '42 / I still see you / Sea and sky: *Legrand, Michel & Dusty Springfield* / Concerto for cabs / Street where they lived / Where love begins / In love in Normandy / Place in Paris: *Legrand, Michel & Matt Monro* / Old lovers never die / On the road / Do you come here often / They simply fade away / Where love ends / Pavanne for people / Paris was made for lovers
12989 / Apr '98 / Laserlight

☐ WINDMILLS OF YOUR MIND (The Very Best Of Michel Legrand)
Summer of '42 / Where love begins / They simply fade away / Street where they lived / Old lovers never die / On the road / Windmills of your mind / Concerto for cabs / Do you come here often / In love with Normandy / Paris was made for lovers / Pavanne for people / Where love ends / Sea and sky: *Legrand, Michel & Dusty Springfield* / Place in Paris: *Legrand, Michel & Matt Monro* / I still see you (theme from 'The go between')
305572 / Oct '96 / Hallmark

Legs Diamond

☐ CAPTURED LIVE
CDMFN 137 / Jun '92 / Music For Nations

☐ WISH
CDMFN 154 / Oct '93 / Music For Nations

Leibman, Dave

☐ ELEMENTS, THE
AJ 71042 / 27 Apr '98 / Arkadia

☐ NEW VISTA
AJ 71041 / 27 Apr '98 / Arkadia

Leicester City FC

☐ FILBERT STREET BLUES (Leicester City FC/Supporters)
This is the season: *Leicester City FC 1974* / Yes we're back: *Back Five* / Oh Leicester City (calypso): *Back Five* / Follow the foxes: *Back Four* / Glory boys in blue: *Back Four* / Post horn gallop: *Back Five* / Blue army blues: *Wembley '94* / FNF rap: *Filbert Fox Songs* / Filbert Fox song: *Filbert Fox Songs* / This is the season for us: *Phil Bert & The Foxes* / Post horn gallop: *Royal Marines* / We're going up: *Blue Army* / Flowing tears: *Price, Kev & The City Strikers* / Leicester boys: *Price, Kev & The City Strikers* / At the top where we belong: *Tilbury, Steve & The Blue Team* / We're back where we belong: *Ray Nardfox* / Frank Worthington: *Joe Jordanaires* / Champions: *Leicester Lads* / Tank: *Leicester City FC 1974*
CDGAFFER 16 / Apr '97 / Cherry Red

Leich, Peter

☐ EXHILARATION
RSRCD 118 / Nov '94 / Reservoir

Leigh, Carol

☐ CAROL LEIGH & THE DUMDUSTIER STOMPERS
BCD 341 / Jun '95 / GHB

☐ CAROL LEIGH WITH ERNIE CARSON AND BOB HELM (Leigh, Carol & Ernie Carson/Bob Helm)
BCD 167 / Nov '96 / GHB

☐ YOU'VE GOT TO GIVE ME SOME
BCD 136 / Jun '96 / GHB

Leighton-Thomas, Nicki

☐ DAMNED IF I DO
BD 9822 / Aug '98 / Babeldown

Leijonhufvud, Johan

☐ HAPPY FARM (Leijonhufvud, Johan Quartet)
SITCD 9231 / May '97 / Sittel

Leila

☐ LIKE WEATHER
Something / Don't fall asleep / Underwaters / Feeling / Blue grace / Space love / Melodicore / So low amen / Misunderstood / Piano string / Won't you be my baby / Away
CAT 056CD / 23 Mar '98 / Rephlex

Leimgruber, Urs

☐ BEHIND THE NIGHT
BW 049 / Feb '96 / B&W

☐ L'ENIGMATIQUE (Leimgruber, Urs & Fritz Hauser)
ARTCD 6091 / Jun '92 / Hat Art

Leiner, Robert

☐ VISIONS OF THE PAST
Out of control / Visions of the past / Interval / To places you've never been / Aqua viva / Full moon ritual / Zenit / Dream or reality / From beyond and back / Northern dark
AMB 3925CD / Jan '94 / Apollo

Leisure Hive

☐ OUR SECRET FILMS
HIVECD 008 / 20 Jul '98 / Resurrection

Leitch, Peter

☐ ON A MISTY NIGHT
CRISS 1026CD / May '94 / Criss Cross

☐ RED ZONE
RSRCD 103 / Oct '89 / Reservoir

☐ SPECIAL RAPPORT, A
RSRCD 129 / Nov '94 / Reservoir

☐ UP FRONT
RSRCD 146 / May '97 / Reservoir

Leixapren

☐ GAITROPOS
J 1024CD / Jun '94 / Sonifolk

LeJeune, Eddie

☐ CAJUN SOUL
Le two-step a pop / Grand bosco / La valse de Samedi au soir / Don't cry my children / Le branche de murrier / Lascassine special / J'ai ete au bal / Mistake I made / Little broken heart / Love bridge waltz / Cher'ti monde / Saturday night special
HNCD 1353 / Feb '90 / Hannibal
ROUCD 6013 / Sep '97 / Rounder

☐ IT'S IN THE BLOOD
Le I'ai rencontree / Duralde waltz / Boire mon whiskey / Happy hop / Valse criminelle / Madeleine / Les conseils j'ai ecoutes / Je seras la apres t'espere / J'ai quitte ma famille dans les miseres / Teche / Fille a 'n oncle Hilaire / Reve du saoulard / Donnez moi la / J'aimerais tu viens me chercher
ROUCD 6043 / Sep '97 / Rounder

☐ LE TRIO CADIEN (LeJeune, Eddie & D.L. Menard/Ken Smith)
J'etais au bal / Traces de mon boghei / Bayou pon pon / Elle savit pas j'etais marie / Blues de Port Arthur / Valse de Kaplan / Fille de Houma / Valse a Thomas Ardoin / Eunice two-step / Les filles du Mexique / Flammes d'Enfer / Dans les Miseres / Petite fille de ville / Chere tout-toute / Mamou two-step
ROUCD 6049 / Sep '97 / Rounder

Lellis, Tom

☐ TAKEN TO HEART
Mountain flight / Taken to heart / I'm late/Alice in wonderland/You can fly / Milton's moment / Nobody does it better / Love is / My one and only love / Dukedom / It never entered my mind / It's not where you think it is / Wistful thinking
CCD 4574 / Nov '93 / Concord Jazz

Lema, Ray

☐ EURO AFRICAN SUITE (Lema, Ray & Joachim Kuhn)
925492 / Nov '92 / BUDA

☐ GREEN LIGHT
829182 / Mar '96 / BUDA

☐ NANGADEF
Kamulang / HAI 99 / Moni mambo / Boyete / Afcoeur / Nangadef / Pongi / What we need / Orchestra of the forest
CIDM 1000 / Apr '89 / Mango

☐ STOP TIME
829452 / Jun '97 / BUDA

Lemaitre, Christian

☐ BALLADE A L'HOTESSE
CD 858 / Feb '96 / Escalibur

Lembo, Kim

☐ MAMA LION
8448462 / Nov '97 / Sky Ranch

Lemercier, Valerie

☐ CHANTE
MAR 033 / 26 Jan '98 / March

Lemon, Brian

☐ BEAUTIFUL FRIENDSHIP, A (Lemon, Brian & Roy Williams Quintet)
Them there eyes / Fine and dandy / Nobody else but me / What's new / This love of mine / Comes love / Makin whoopee / One morning in May / Just friends / As time goes by / Moten swing / Up with the lark / Skylark / Beautiful friendship
ZECD 4 / Jul '97 / Zephyr

☐ BUT BEAUTIFUL
Ill wind / Old folks / Exactly like you / I thought about you / It's you or no one / But beautiful / In a sentimental mood / This can't be love / That old feeling / Gee baby ain't I good to you / I'm putting all my eggs in one basket / Blues for Suzanne / St. Thomas / My one and only love
ZECD 1 / Oct '95 / Zephyr

☐ HOW LONG HAS THIS BEEN GOING ON
Sweet Georgia Brown / How long has this been going on / Georgia on my mind / Bye bye blues / I can't get started with you / Blues in the closet / In the wee small hours of the morning / I remember you / Tenderly / When I fall in love / I've found a new baby
ZECD 5 / Mar '96 / Zephyr

☐ LEMON LOOKS BACK JUST FOR FUN (Lemon, Brian & Roy Williams)
At the jazz band ball / I hadn't anyone till you / Farewell blues / Am I blue / Jazz me blues / I never knew / On the Alamo / When day is done / When it's sleepy time down south / When your lover has gone / Cotton tail
ZECD 14 / May '97 / Zephyr

☐ OLD HANDS/YOUNG MINDS (Lemon, Brian & Alan Barnes Octet)
Limehouse blues / Polkadots and moonbeams / Mood indigo / Just one of those things / Chelsea bridge / Secret love / I gotta right to sing the blues / Willow weep for me / Someday my prince will come / After supper
ZECD 12 / Sep '96 / Zephyr

☐ OVER THE RAINBOW
Over the rainbow / Over the rainbow / What is this thing called love / White christmas / I don't stand a ghost of a chance with you / All the way / Have you met Miss Jones / Born free / When lights are low / You light up my life / Dearly beloved / Mona lisa / Secret love / I'll never stop loving you / Emily / Manha de carnival / Star eyes / For your eyes only / Straight no chaser / Way we were / Alone together / Shadow of your smile / You don't know what love is / Way you look tonight / Moon river / Days of wine and roses
ZECD 2 / Oct '95 / Zephyr

Lemon Kittens

☐ BIG DENTIST, THE
They are both dirty / Hospital hurts / Girl / Log and the pin / Nudies
BOT131 05CD / Oct '96 / Biter Of Thorpe

Lemon Pipers

☐ BEST OF THE LEMON PIPERS, THE
Green tambourine / Rice is nice / Turn around and take a look / Blueberry blue / Jelly jungle / Lonely atmosphere / Shoeshine boy / I was not born to follow / Rainbow tree / Ask me if I care / Stragglin' behind / Shoemaker of leatherwear / Square / Fifty year void / Through with you / No help from me / Everything is you / Catch me falling / Love beads and meditation / Wine and violet / Dead End Street/Half light
74321558592 / 26 Jan '98 / Camden

☐ GREEN TAMBOURINE
REP 4016 / Aug '91 / Repertoire

Lemon Sol

☐ ENVIRONMENTAL ARCHITECTURE
Sun flash / Memorandum / Natural ratio / Polymorph / Red drift / Powers of invasion / Fuse / Universal / Environmental architecture
GRCD 014 / Jul '94 / Guerilla

Lemongrass

☐ DRUMATIC UNIVERSE
INCCD 3323 / 20 Jul '98 / Incoming

Lemongrowers

☐ SEGMENTS
NBX 011 / Apr '95 / Noisebox

Lemonheads

☐ BEST OF THE LEMONHEADS, THE
Confetti / Into your arms / Mrs. Robinson / Rudderless / It's a shame about Ray / Great big no / Ride with me / My drug buddy / Big gay heart / It's about time / Outdoor type / It's all true / If I could talk I'd tell you / Hospital / Rudy with a flashlight / Into your arms / Down about it / Being around / Rick James acoustic style
7567808512 / 27 Jul '98 / Atlantic

☐ CAR BUTTON CLOTH
It's all true / If I could talk I'd tell you / Break me / Hospital / Outdoor type / Losing your mind / Knoxville girl / 6ix / One more time / C'mon Daddy / Something's missing / Tenderfoot / Secular Rockulidge
7567927262 / Sep '96 / Atlantic

☐ COME ON FEEL THE LEMONHEADS
Great big no / Into your arms / It's about time / Down about it / Paid to smile / Big gay heart / Rest assured / Dawn can't decide / I'll do it anyway / Rick James style / Being around / Favorite T / You can take it with you / Jello fund
7567825372 / Oct '93 / Atlantic

☐ CREATOR
Burying ground / Sunday / Clang bang clang / Out / Your home is where you're happy / Falling / Die right now / Two weeks in another town / Plaster caster / Come to the window / Take her down / Postcard / Live without
ESMCD 470 / Mar '97 / Essential

☐ HATE YOUR FRIENDS
Eat it / 394 / Nothing true / Second chance / Sneakyville / Amazing grace / Belt / Hate your friends / Don't tell yourself / Uhh / Fed up / Rat velvet / Fucked up
ESMCD 469 / Mar '97 / Essential

☐ IT'S A SHAME ABOUT RAY
Rockin' stroll / Confetti / It's a shame about Ray / Rudderless / Buddy / Turnpike down / Bit part / Alisons starting to happen / Hannah and Gabi / Kitchen / Ceiling fan in my spoon / Frank Mills / Mrs. Robinson
7567823972 / Feb '95 / Atlantic

☐ LICK
Mallow cup / Glad I don't know / Seven Powers / Circle of one / Cazzo di Ferro / Anyway / Luka / Come back DA / I am a rabbit / Sad girl / Ever / Strange / Mad
ESMCD 471 / Mar '97 / Essential

☐ LOVEY
Ballarat / Half the time / Year of the cat / Ride with me / Li'l seed / Stove / Come downstairs / Left for dead / Brass buttons / Door
7567821372 / Feb '93 / Atlantic

Lemper, Ute

☐ ALL THAT JAZZ (The Best Of Ute Lemper)
4589312 / 9 Feb '98 / Decca

☐ BERLIN CABARET SONGS (Lemper, Ute & Matrix Ensemble/Jeff Cohen)
Alles schwindel / Sex appeal / Peter Peter / Das gesellschaftslied / Meine beste Freundin / Ich bin ein vamp / L'heure bleue / Zieh dich aus Petronella / Raus mit den mannern / Der verflossene / Gesetzt den fall... / Ich weiss nicht / Das Lila lied / Maskulinum - femininum / Mir is heut so nach tamerlan / Eine kleine sehnsucht / Munchhausen
4526012 / Nov '96 / Entartete Musik

☐ BERLIN CABARET SONGS (English Version) (Lemper, Ute & Matrix Ensemble/Jeff Cohen)
It's all a muddle / Sex appeal / Peter Peter / Smart bet / My best friend / I am a vamp / L'heure bleue / Take it off Petronella / Away with the man / Washed up lover / Oh just suppose / I don't know / Lavender song / Maskulinim-femininum / Tamerlam / Little yearning / Oh how we wish we were kids again / Munchausen
4528492 / Jan '97 / Entartete Musik

☐ CITY OF STRANGERS
4444002 / Feb '95 / Decca

☐ CRIMES OF THE HEART
Crimes of the heart / You look just like a girl again / Sabotage / Changing with the years / Ruby / Und wenn er wiedrkommt / Wherever the dream takes me / That's the easy part / Other side of me / Small touches of you / Envie d'amour
4656762 / 5 Jan '98 / Columbia

☐ LIFE IS A CABARET
Willkommen / Mein herr / Maybe this time / Don't tell Mama / Cabaret / Non c'est rien / I dreamed a dream / One night only / Miss Celies blues / Arthur's theme / Rose
4604932 / 5 Jan '98 / Columbia

Lena, Battista

☐ BANDA SONORA
Banda 8 / Il grande cocomero / Stabat mom / Roma ovest / Il valzer del povero / Ferie diagosto / Mermaid / Valzers / Tema di pietro e ghisola
LBLC 6591 / 27 Apr '98 / Label Bleu

Lennon, Don

☐ MANIAC
MP 001 / 1 Dec '97 / M. Phillips

Lennon Family

☐ DANCE OF THE HONEY BEES
CEFCD 167 / Dec '95 / Gael Linn

Lennon, John

☐ DOUBLE FANTASY (Lennon, John & Yoko Ono)
(Just like) starting over / Kiss kiss kiss / Clean up time / Give me something / I'm losing you / I'm movin' on / Beautiful boy / Watching the wheels / I'm your angel / Woman / Dear Yoko / Every man has a woman who loves him / Hard times are over
CDP 7914252 / Jan '89 / Parlophone

☐ IMAGINE
Imagine / Crippled inside / Jealous guy / It's so hard / I don't want to be a soldier / Gimme some truth / Oh my love / How do you sleep / How / Oh Yoko
CDP 7466412 / May '87 / Parlophone

☐ IN HIS LIFE (Interview)
8048 / 17 Aug '98 / Point

☐ IN MY LIFE (3CD Set)
DTKBOX 92 / 6 Jul '98 / Dressed To Kill

☐ JOHN LENNON/PLASTIC ONO BAND
Mother / Hold on / I found out / Working class hero / Isolation / Remember / Love / Well well well / Look at me / God / My mummy's dead
CDFA 3310 / Nov '94 / Fame

☐ LENNON (4CD Set)
Give peace a chance / Blue suede shoes / Money (that's what I want) / Dizzy Miss Lizzy / Yer blues / Cold turkey / Instant karma / Mother / Hold on / I found out / Working class hero / Isolation / Remember / Love / Well well well / Look at me / God / My mummy's dead / Power to the people / Well (baby please don't go) / Imagine / Crippled inside / Jealous guy / It's so hard / Give me some truth / Oh my love / How do you sleep / How / Oh Yoko / Happy Christmas (war is over) / Woman is the nigger of the world / New York City / John Sinclair / Come together / Hound dog / Mind games / Aisumasen (I'm sorry) / One day (at a time) / Intuition / Out the blue / Whatever gets you through the night / Going down on love / Old dirt road / Bless you / Scared / Number 9 dream / Surprise surprise (sweet bird of paradox) / Steel and glass / Nobody loves you (when you're down and out) / Stand by me / Ain't that a shame / Do you want to dance / Sweet little sixteen / Slippin' and slidin' / Angel baby / Just because / Whatever gets you through the night (live) / Lucy in the sky with diamonds / I saw her standing there / (Just like) starting over / Cleanup time / I'm losing you / Beautiful boy / Watching the wheels / Woman / Dear Yoko / I'm stepping out / I don't wanna face it / Nobody told me / Borrowed time / (Forgive me) my little flower princess / Every man has a woman who loves him / Boys and girls / Grow old with me
CDS 7952202 / Oct '90 / Parlophone

☐ LENNON INTERVIEW DISC
SNECD 001 / Jun '97 / Speak 'n' Easy

☐ LENNON LEGEND
Imagine / Instant Karna / Mother / Jealous guy / Power to the people / Cold turkey / Love / Mind games / Whatever gets you through the night / No.9 dream / Stand by me / (Just like) Starting over / Woman / Beautiful boy / Watching the wheels / Nobody told me / Borrowed time / Working class hero / Happy Xmas / Give peace a chance
8219542 / 27 Oct '97 / Parlophone

☐ LIFE WITH THE LIONS (Unfinished Music No.2) (Ono, Yoko & John Lennon)
RCD 10412 / Jun '97 / Rykodisc

☐ LIVE IN NEW YORK CITY
New York City / It's so hard / Woman is the nigger of the world / Well, well, well / Instant Karma / Mother / Come together / Imagine / Cold turkey / Hound dog / Give peace a chance
CDP 7461962 / May '86 / Parlophone

☐ LIVE PEACE IN TORONTO (Plastic Ono Band)
Blue suede shoes / Money (that's what I want) / Dizzy Miss Lizzy / Yer blues / Cold turkey / Give peace a chance / Don't worry Kyoko / John John let's hope for peace
CDP 7904282 / May '95 / Apple

☐ MENLOVE AVE
Here we go again / Rock 'n' roll people / Angel baby / My baby left me / To know her is to love her / Steel and glass / Scared / Old dirt road / Nobody loves you (when you're down and out) / Bless you
CDP 7465762 / Apr '87 / Parlophone

☐ MIND GAMES
Mind games / Tight as / Aisumasen (I'm sorry) / One day (at a time) / Bring on the Lucie / Nutopian international anthem / Intuition / Out of the blue / Only people / I know (I know) / You are here / Meat city
CDP 7467692 / Aug '87 / Parlophone

☐ PLASTIC ONO BAND (Yoko Ono & The Plastic Ono Band)
RCD 10414 / Jun '97 / Rykodisc

☐ ROCK 'N' ROLL
Be bop a lula / Stand by me / Rip it up / You can't catch me / Ain't that a shame / Do you wanna dance / Sweet little sixteen / Slippin' and slidin' / Peggy Sue / Bring it on home to me / Bony Moronie / Ya ya / Just because / Ready teddy
CDP 7467072 / May '87 / Parlophone

☐ SHAVED FISH
Give peace a chance / Cold turkey / Instant karma / Power to the people / Mother / Woman is the nigger of the world / Imagine / Whatever gets you through the night / Mind games / No. 9 dream / Happy Christmas (war is over) / Give peace a chance (reprise)
CDP 7466422 / May '87 / Parlophone

☐ TESTIMONY
CDTB 095 / 2 Feb '98 / Thunderbolt

☐ TWO VIRGINS (Unfinished Music No.1) (Ono, Yoko & John Lennon)
RCD 10411 / Jun '97 / Rykodisc

☐ WALLS AND BRIDGES
Going down on love / Whatever gets you through the night / Old dirt road / What you got / Bless you / Scared / No. 9 dream / Surprise surprise (sweet bird of paradox) / Steel and glass / Beef jerky / Nobody loves you (when you're down and out) / Ya ya
CDP 7467682 / Jul '87 / Parlophone

☐ WEDDING ALBUM (Ono, Yoko & John Lennon)
RCD 10413 / Jun '97 / Rykodisc

☐ WORKING CLASS HERO (A Tribute To John Lennon) (Various Artists)
I found out: *Red Hot Chili Peppers* / I don't want to be a soldier: *Mad Season* / Steel and glass: *Candlebox* / Imagine: *Blues Traveller* / Working class hero: *Screaming Trees* / Power to the people: *Minus 5* / How do you sleep: *Magnificent Bastards* / Nobody told you: *Flaming Lips* / Well well well: *Super Eight* / Cold turkey: *Cheap Trick* / Isolation: *Sponge* / Jealous guy: *Collective Soul* / Instant karma: *Toad The Wet Sprocket* / Grow old with me: *Carpenter, Mary-Chapin* / Mind games: *Clinton, George*
6201152 / Oct '95 / Hollywood

Lennon, Julian

☐ PHOTOGRAPH SMILE
Day after day / Cold / I should have known / How many times / I don't wanna know / Crucified / Walls / Believe / Good to be lonely / Kiss beyond the catcher / And she cries / Photograph smile / Faithful / Way to your heart
MFAR 44CD / 18 May '98 / Music From Another Room

☐ SECRET VALUE OF DAYDREAMING, THE
Stick around / You get what you want / Let me tell you / I've seen your face / Coward till the end / This is my day / You didn't have to tell me / Everyday / Always think twice / I want your body
CASCD 1171 / Jul '87 / Charisma

☐ VALOTTE
Valotte / OK for you / On the phone / Space / Well I don't know / Too late for goodbyes / Lonely / Say your wrong / Jesse / Let me be
CDVIP 162 / Oct '96 / Virgin VIP

Lennon, Sean Ono

☐ INTO THE SUN
Mystery juice / Into the sun / Home / Bathtub / One night / Spaceship / Photosynthesis / Queue / Two fine lovers / Part one of the cowboy trilogy / Wasted / Breeze / Sean's theme
4945512 / 18 May '98 / Grand Royal

Lennox, Annie

☐ INTERVIEW DISC
SAM 7013 / Nov '96 / Sound & Media

☐ MEDUSA
No more I love you's / Take me to the river / Whiter shade of pale / Don't let it bring you down / Train in vain / I can't get next to you / Downtown lights / Thin line between love and hate / Waiting in vain / Something so right
74321257172 / Mar '95 / RCA

Lennox CF

☐ PICNICS & HOLIDAYS
BRAM 1989052 / Nov '93 / Brambus

Lenola

☐ SWERVING CORPSE
TPZ 004 / Oct '97 / Tappersize

Lens Cleaner

☐ WITH VOICE INSTRUMENTS
SAB 002CD / Nov '95 / Sabotage

Lenya, Lotte

☐ LENYA (11CD Set)
BCD 16019 / Jul '98 / Bear Family

Lenz, Kim

☐ KIM LENZ AND HER JAGUARS (Lenz, Kim & Her Jaguars)
Devil on my shoulder / Twinkle twinkle / Thinkin' bout you / You ain't seen nothin' / Dang good stuff / Saturday jump / I swear I was lying / Up to my old tricks again / Shake a leg / Kiss and tell baby / Ten cats down / You made a hit / Everybody's rockin'
HMG 3003 / 7 Apr '98 / Hightone

Leo, Phillip

☐ DOWN 2 EARTH
ASPCD 002 / Jul '97 / Sharma

☐ JUST 4 U
ASPCD 001 / Jul '96 / Sharma

☐ SPACE DUB
ASPCD 003 / Jul '97 / Sharma

Leo, Rodrigo

☐ THEATRUM (Leo, Rodrigo & The Vox Ensemble)
SK 63033 / 1 Sep '97 / Sony Classical

Leonard, Deke

☐ ICEBERG/KAMIKAZE
Razor blade and rattlesnake / I just can't win / Lisa / Nothing is happening / Looking for a man / Hard way to live / Broken ovation / Jesse / Ten thousand takers / Ghost of musket flat / Crosby (Second class citizen blues) / 7171 551 / Cool summer rain / Jayhawk special / Sharpended claws / Taking the easy way out / Black gates of death / Stacia / Broken glass and limejuice / April the third / Louisiana hoedown / In search of Sarah and twenty six horses / Devil's gloves
BGOCD 288 / Aug '95 / Beat Goes On

Leonard, Harlan

☐ CLASSICS 1940 (Leonard, Harlan & His Rockets)
CLASSICS 670 / Nov '92 / Classics

Leonardo

☐ LUSTRON
OMC 0013 / 20 Apr '98 / One Man Clapping

Leonhart, Jay

☐ FOUR DUKE (Leonhart, Jay & Gary Burton)
In a mellow tone / Rockin' in rhythm / C jam blues / Love you madly / Azure / Cotton tail / Creole love song / Take the 'A' train / Squeeze me / Caravan / Ishfanhan / Satin doll
CDC 9089 / Aug '95 / LRC

☐ LIFE OUT ON THE ROAD - JAZZ JOURNEY
CDSGP 0199 / Jun '96 / Prestige

☐ LIVE AT FAT TUESDAY'S (Leonhart, Jay & Friends)
Smile / Let the flower grow / Robert Frost / Lonely rider / Strangest thing / They're coming to get me / Unhappy / Momma don't you think we ought to be going / Impossible to sing and play the bass / Kentucky wild flower / Me and Lenny
8439 / Nov '93 / DRG

Leopards

☐ THEY TRIED STAYING CALM
Ju ju girl / Surf on / Motorcycle baby / Theem E / Burning / Starlings / ALways on your side / Vendetta machine / Cutting a short dog / Carried by six / Full moon flight / Derailed by mad dog / Piney's prayer / Being wowed
BENT 021CD / 15 Jun '98 / Creeping Bent

Leo's Sunshipp

☐ WE NEED EACH OTHER
Give me the sunshine / I'm back for more / Get down people / Madame Butterfly
EXCDM 2 / Sep '96 / Expansion

Leroi Brothers

☐ CHECK THIS ACTION
Are you with me baby / I can't be satisfied / Ain't I'm a dog / Big time operator / Steady with Betty / Check this action / Chicken and honey / Rockin' Daddy / Cotton pickin' / Crazy crazy lovin' / Ballad of a juvenile delinquent / Till it's too late / Arms race / Damage / Little Miss Understanding / Straight jacket / Mad about the wrong boy / Motorworld / On the third stroke / Slow patience / La la la la la loved you / Single girl / Lonesome little town / Taste of poison / High rise housewife / Talk about me / Sad about girls / Camera camera / I feel like breaking up somebody's home / Why do I / Laughin' and clownin' / If I ever had a good thing / Scarred knees / From the heart / Your love is so doggone good / We don't see eye to eye / Roadblock / Teach me to forget
ROUCD 9034 / Nov '94 / Rounder

Leroy Mafia

☐ BACK 4 GOOD
COUDCD 01 / 2 Feb '98 / Cousin

Les 4 Jeans

☐ ENTENDS TU MA BLONDE LE TONNERRE QUI GRONDE
49504CD / Nov '96 / Acousteak

Les Aborigenes

☐ SONGS AND DANCES FROM NORTH AUSTRALIA
ARN 64056 / Apr '91 / Arion

Les Angeles Prietos

☐ AGUINALDOS
PS 65160 / Feb '96 / PlayaSound

Les Ballets Africains

☐ HERITAGE
926342CD / Nov '95 / Euda

Les Calchakis

☐ FLUTES DE PAN DES ANDES
Recuerdo azul / Lima morena / Presencia lejana / Coplas de marzo / El colibri / Linda cambita / Jesusana / Cuculi / Blanca palomita / Aires de mi tierra / Sol nocturno / Amankay / Tiempo de paz / Requiem para un afilador / Uskil / Kena y siku / Sikus del titicaca / Triste tondero / Urpillay / Acuarela de sikus
ARN 64005 / '88 / Arion

☐ FLUTES DES TERRES INCAS
La pastora / El centinela et anata morena / Lejana purmamarca / La maye / Reservista purajhey / Soplo del oriente / El pastor / Sol de vilcabamba / La bocina / El sacha puma / Kacharpari / Crepusculo costeno / Tuntuneando / Kurikinga / Casi me quisiste / Himno al sol / Sanjuanero / Sonkoy / Selvas y valles / Kapullay
ARN 64002 / '88 / Arion

☐ HARPE, MARIMBA ET GUITARS LATINO-AMERICAINES
Cambai / El toro rabon / Carta a Buenos Aires / Bailecito triple / Isla saca / Nieve viento y sol / La escala / Campanas a M Nunez / Angata / La rielera / Imagenes Argentinas / Cuerdita / Joropeando / Poncho verde / Bailecito Calchaki / Concierto en la llanura / La zandunga / Lunarcito / Madrecita / Bachue
ARN 64032 / '88 / Arion

☐ MISA CRIOLLA
121482 / 5 Jan '98 / Musidisc

☐ PRESTIGE DE LA MUSIQUE LATINO-AMERICAINE
Quiero contarte / Hilanderita / Tema boliviano / Cotopaxi / Sube a nacer conmigo / Rasguido de la paz / Chimborazo / Papel de plata / El aguaceral / Kalahuayo yuyay / Si tu me olvidas / Cullaguada / Alejandra / Del otro lado del mar
ARN 64025 / '88 / Arion

Les Chiens Jaunes
☐ TRIO DE VIELLES
MB 002CD / Aug '96 / Le Micro Bleu

Les Ecoliers De Saint Genest
☐ DANCES FROM THE BERRY
B 6832CD / Aug '96 / Auvidis/Ethnic

Les Elles
☐ LES ELLES VOL.1
BP 3211 / 23 Mar '98 / Boucherie Productions

☐ LES ELLES VOL.2
BP 3212 / 23 Mar '98 / Boucherie Productions

Les Fleurs De Lys
☐ REFLECTIONS
Circles / Mud in your eye / Gong with the luminous nose / Sugar love / Hold on / Prodigal son / One city girl / Daughter of the sun / Tick tock / I can see the light / Liar / I forgive you / So come on / Hammerhead / Stop crossing the bridge / I like what I'm trying to do / Hold on / Butchers and bakers / Wait for me / Reflections of Charlie Brown / Brick by brick / I've been trying / Moondreams / So many things
BP 256CD / May '97 / Blueprint

Les Freres Guillemain
☐ BERRY BOURBONNAIS
Y 225105CD / Oct '93 / Silex

☐ HISTORICAL BAGPIPE/HURDY GURDY
Y 225105 / Oct '93 / Silex

Les Halmas
☐ PLUS ONE
IH 9601 / Jun '97 / ReR/Recommended

Les Hommes Qui Wear Espadrillos
☐ KAIRO
EFA 127922 / Dec '95 / Blu Noise

Les Irresistables
☐ LES IRRESISTABLES STORY
177462 / 5 Jan '98 / Magic

Les Joyaux De La Princesse & Regard Extreme
☐ DIE WEISSE ROSE
Tiefe sehnsucht (zu neuen ufern) / Die natur ist jetzt mit waffenkland erwacht / Jetzt aber tagts / Der reissen ninabschaumt / Rosen des lebens / Die jugend trauert (marche funebre) / Weisse blatter / Letze kampf des lebens / Die flammen entbunden / Weisse rose / Der abschied / Tiefe sensucht / Sag' mir adieu
SD 04CD / Jul '97 / New European

Les Jumeaux
☐ FEATHERCUT
CORP 013CD / Jan '96 / ITN Corporation

Les Maniacs
☐ LIVE AT BUDOKAN
STOP 09CD / Feb '90 / Danceteria

Les Mecenes
☐ SAMEDI SOIR CHEZ NANA
829172 / Mar '96 / Bleu Caraibes

Les Negresses Vertes
☐ 10 REMIXES 1987-1993
Face a la mer / Hou Mamma mia / Sous le soleil de bodega / 200 Ans d'hypocrisie / Orane / Voila l'ete / Dun de nuit / Famille heureuse / Les yeux de ton pere / Zobi la mouche / Sous le soleil de bogeda (Di moko) / Hou Mamma Mia (House mix)
CDDLB 9 / Jun '93 / Delabel

☐ FAMILLE HEUREUSE
Famille heureuse / Perpetuellement votre / Face a la mer / Belle de nuit / Get some wood / Sous le soleil de bodega / Si je m'en vais / Hou mamma mia / Infidele cervelle / La france a ses dimanches / Sang et nuit / Car c'est un blouze / Quai de jemmapes
CDDLB 2 / Feb '92 / Delabel

☐ GREEN BUS (2CD Set)
CDDLB 16 / Aug '96 / Delabel

☐ MLAH
La valse / Zobi la mouche / C'est pas la mer a boire / Voila l'ete / Orane / La faim des haricots / Les yeux de ton pere / Il / L'homme des marais / Les rablablas les roubliblis / Marcelle Ratafia / La danse des negresses vertes / Hey Maria / Le pere Magloire
CDDLB 5 / Apr '92 / Delabel

☐ ZIG-ZAGUE
Fanfaron / Tous des ouvriers / Apres la pluie / La main verte / Mambo show / Comme toujours / A quoi bon / Enfer et paradis / Bourre d'allegresse / Iza mellino/mellino / Le poete / Ivresse / Footballer du Dimanche / Tu m'as saoule
CDDLB 12 / Feb '95 / Delabel

Les Nouvelles Polyphonies Corses
☐ IN PARADISO
CD 5324532 / Feb '97 / Mercury

☐ IN PARADISU
Perdonu mio diu / Introitu / Kyrie Eleison / Gloria / Sanctus / Credo / Agnus dei / Salutaris / Tantum ergo / Subvenite / Requiem / Kyrie Eleison defunti / Dies irae / Domine offertoriu / Sanctus defunti / Agnus dei defunti / Libera me / In paradisu / Stabat mater / Dio vi salci regina
5324532 / Feb '97 / Mercury

Les Pires
☐ EN PISTE
BPCD 9421 / Dec '97 / Acousteak

☐ SAVA
562023 / Apr '96 / Bondage

Les Quatre Guitaristes De L'Apocalypso-Bar
☐ WORLD TOUR 1988
RERGQ 1 / Oct '96 / ReR/ Recommended

Les Tambours Du Bronx
☐ MONOSTRESS 225L
La Valse des Nuls / Tchi tchi ou la mort / Metropolis / Heya / Cadence 22 / Le crepuscle des Crapules / Locomotive / Monostress 225L
592048 / Nov '93 / FNAC

Les Thugs
☐ AS HAPPY AS POSSIBLE
SOL 39CD / Oct '93 / Vinyl Solution

☐ NINETEEN SOMETHING
SPCD 424 / 3 Aug '98 / Sub Pop

Les Vice Barons
☐ STEEL BLUE MOODS
NITR 009 / Feb '97 / Demolition Derby

Lesh, Lagen
☐ SEASTONES
December 1975 version / Original february 1975 version
RCD 40193 / Dec '92 / Rykodisc

Lesiman
☐ FUTURE SOUND OF LESIMAN, THE
Bagliori / Play car / Confroso / Fiaccole di pino / Controcorrente / Via nell autumno / Rolling / Moto / Messaggio / Padmina / Cottoquoi / Telescrivente / Le regole del gioco / Schegge / Direzioni / Diversioni / Traffico d'armi / Contatto umano / Motivo ricorerwete / Milano 72 / Trepido e lare giorno
ET 920CD / 27 Apr '98 / Easy Tempo

Leslie, Chris
☐ FLOW, THE
Ballydesmond/Scartaglen / Eliz Iza/Derobee de Guingamp / Aignish / Witch of the Glen / Believe me, if all those endearing young charms / Lime rock / Blackbird / Flow / Neil Gow's lament for Abercairney / Paddy Ryan's dream/Inimitable reel/The Macroom lassies / Kishmul's galley / Tune for the land of snows
BEJOCD 20 / Sep '97 / Beautiful Jo

☐ GIFT, THE
Tenpence coloured / Shaker music / Samuel's shoes/Imogen's reel / Sir John Fenwick's/John's fairy dance / No sleep for the wicked / Red haired man's wife / Eighteenth century English dances / Gow rediscovered / I wandered by a brookside / Linda's tune / Of all the ways the wind can blow / Cape Breton set / She once loved me / Buffoon/ Black joke / Highland medley
BEJOCD 5 / Jun '94 / Beautiful Jo

Less Than Jake
☐ GREASED
NIR 046 / Dec '97 / No Idea

☐ PEZCORE
AM 001 / Feb '97 / Asian Man

Lesser
☐ WELCOME TO AMERICAN EXP.
VC 127 / 19 Jan '98 / Vinyl Communication

Lessons From The Underground
☐ HARD HOUSE COLLECTION, THE
TILTCD 2 / 9 Feb '98 / Tilt

Lester Bangs
☐ JOOK SAVAGES ON THE BRAZOS (Lester Bangs & The Delinquents)
EFA 121662 / Mar '95 / Moll

Leston, Paul
☐ CARNIVAL HITS 1997
JW 124CD / Jun '97 / JW

☐ WEAKNESS FOR SWEETNESS
JW 098CD / Apr '96 / JW

Let Loose
☐ LET LOOSE
Crazy for you / Seventeen / One night stand / Way I wanna be / I love your smile / Cardboard city / Shame / Super sexy real thing / Best in me / Devotion / I believe / Love like there's no tomorrow
5260182 / Nov '94 / A&M

☐ ROLLERCOASTER
Don't change a thing / Make it with you / Take it easy / Everybody say everybody do / I wanna be your lover / Darling be home soon / Who's gonna love me now / Beautiful is what you are / Colour of your love / Need / Sweetest thing / Rollercoaster
5329552 / Sep '96 / Mercury

Let Me Dream
☐ MY DEAR
CDAR 027 / Jun '95 / Adipocre

Lethal
☐ PROGRAMMED
Fire in your skin / Programmed / Plan of peace / Another day / Arrival / What they've done / Obscure the sky / Immune / Pray for me / Killing machine
398414210CD / Nov '96 / Metal Blade

Let's Go Bowling
☐ FREEWAY LANES
AM 024CD / 27 Apr '98 / Asian Man

Lettau, Kevyn
☐ ANOTHER SEASON
Another season / Summer dreams / Morning kisses / Foundation of humanity / I've got a crush on you / Ella / You don't love me like you used to / Father, Mother / Colors of joy / Inside your love / Retrato em branco e petro / Shower the people
JVC 20302 / Mar '94 / JVC

☐ UNIVERSAL LANGUAGE
Tribute to you / Secretly begin / Universal language / Underneath / Seeing for the very first time / Our lasting love / Beatriz / Gentle flower / Three little words / Love is unconditional / Dein ist mein ganzes herz / Only trust your heart
JVC 20482 / May '95 / JVC

Letters To Cleo
☐ AURORA GORY ALICE
Big star / I see / Rim shak / Wasted / Get on with it / Here and now / From under the dust / Mellie's comin' over / Come around / Step back
WOLCD 1057 / Apr '95 / China

Leukafe, Carl
☐ WARRIOR (Leukaufe, Carl & Jodie Christian/Lin Halliday)
Airegin / Before you know it / Little warrior / Come rain or come shine / Vierd blues / Tricotism / Pannonica / Star eyes / Blues for John Gilmore / Man I love / Chant
DE 491 / Jun '97 / Delmark

Leukemia
☐ SUCK MY HEAVEN
Into the morgue / I nearly forgot / Uncarved miseria / Wandering / Sick inside / You es of ey / Everything falls apart / Memorized / Different but same
BMCD 029 / Mar '93 / Black Mark

Levallet, Didier
☐ GENERATIONS (Levallet, Didier Tentet)
EVCD 212 / Feb '94 / Evidence

Levanders, Jan
☐ MUSAIK (Levanders, Jan Octet)
DRCD 232 / Oct '94 / Dragon

Levant, Oscar
☐ PLAYS LEVANT & GERSHWIN
Gershwin: A portrait by Levant / Liza / My cousin in Milwaukee / Foggy day / Half of it dearie blues / But not for me / Rhapsody in blue / Concerto in F (third movement) / Then farewell / King and country call / Ah romantic love dream / First movement: Con ritmo / Second movement: Andantion poco mosso / Third movement: Allegro deciso / Piano concerto / Young in heart
DRGCD 13113 / Oct '94 / DRG

Level 42
☐ FOREVER NOW
Forever now / Model friend / Tired of waiting / All over you / Love in a peaceful world / Romance / Billy's gone / One in a million / Sunbed song / Talking in your sleep / Don't bother me
74321189962
LV 102CD / Sep '96 / Resurgence

☐ LEVEL 42
Turn it on / Forty three / Why are you leaving / Almost there / Heathrow / Love games / Dune tune / Starchild
8219352 / Jul '84 / Polydor

☐ LEVEL 42 REMIXES
VSOPCD 227 / Jun '96 / Connoisseur Collection

☐ LEVEL BEST
Running in the family / Sun goes down (Living it up) / Something about you / Tracie / Starchild / It's over / Hot water / Take care of yourself / Heaven in my hands / Children say / Love games / Chinese way / Leaving me now / Lessons in love / Micro kid / Take a look / To be with you again / Chant has begun
8413992 / Nov '89 / Polydor

☐ LIVE AT WEMBLEY
Heaven in my hands / To be with you again / Children say / Silence / It's over / Over there / Man / Love games / Take a look / Something about you / Running in the family / Lessons in love / Chinese way
WFRCD 005 / Apr '96 / World Famous

☐ PHYSICAL PRESENCE, A
Almost there / Turn it on / Mr. Pink / Eyes waterfalling / Kansas city milkman / Follow me / Foundation and empire / Chant has begun / Chinese way / Sun goes down (living it up) / Hot water / Love games / 88
8256772 / Jun '85 / Polydor

☐ PURSUIT OF ACCIDENTS, THE
Weave your spell / Pursuit of accidents / Last chance / Are you hearing (what I hear) / You can't blame Louis / Eyes waterfalling / Shapeshifter / Chinese way / Chinese way (extended) / You can't blame Louis (extended)
8100152 / Jun '90 / Polydor

☐ RUNNING IN THE FAMILY
Lessons in love / Children say / Running in the family / It's over / To be with you again / Two solitudes / Fashion fever / Sleepwalkers / Freedom someday
8315932 / Mar '87 / Polydor

☐ STANDING IN THE LIGHT
Micro-kid / Sun goes down (living it up) / Out of sight out of mind / Dance on heavy weather / Pharaoh's dream of endless time / Standing in the light / I want eyes / People / Machine stops
8138652 / Jun '90 / Polydor

☐ TRUE COLOURS
Chant has begun / Kansas City milkman / Seven days / Hot water / Floating life / True believers / Kouyate / Hours by the window
8235452 / '88 / Polydor

☐ TURN IT ON
Running in the family / Chinese way / Heaven in my hands / Are you hearing (what I hear) / Children say / (Flying on) The wings of love / Physical presence / Turn it on / Love meeting love / True believers / Two hearts collide / I sleep on my heart / Can't walk you home / Coup d'etat / Take care of yourself / Love games
5520182 / Mar '96 / Spectrum

☐ WORLD MACHINE
World machine / Physical presence / Something about you / Leaving me now / I sleep on my heart / It's not the same for us / Good man in a storm / Coup d'etat / Lying still / Dream crazy / Love games / Hot water / Sun goes down (living it up) (Mix) / Chinese way (US mix) / I sleep on my heart (remix) / Something about you
8274872 / Oct '85 / Polydor

Levellers
☐ BEST LIVE (Headlights, White Lines & Black Tar Rivers)
Sell out / Hope St. / Fifteen years / Exodus / Carry me / Boatman / Three friends / Men an tol / Road / One way / England my home / Battle of the beanfield / Liberty / Riverflow
WOLCDX 1074 / Aug '96 / China

☐ LEVELLERS
Warning / 100 years of solitude / Likes of you and I / Is this art / Dirty Davey / This garden / Broken circles / Julie / Player / Belaruse
WOLCD 1034 / Aug '93 / China

☐ LEVELLING THE LAND
One way / Game / Boatman / Liberty song / Far from home / Sell out / Another man's cause / Road / Riverflow / Battle of the beanfield / Fifteen years
WOLCD 1022 / Sep '91 / China

☐ MOUTH TO MOUTH
Dog train / What a beautiful day / Celebrate / Rain and snow / Far away / CCTV / Chemically free / Elation / Captain courageous / Survivors / Sail away / Too real
WOLCD 1084
WOLCDX 1084 / Aug '97 / China

☐ WEAPON CALLED THE WORD, A
World freak show / Carry me / Outside/Inside / Together all the way / Barrel of the gun / Three friends / I have no answers / No change / Blind faith / Ballad of Robbie Jones / England my home / What you know / Social insecurity / Cardboard box city / Three friends (remix)
120122 / May '90 / Musidisc UK

☐ ZEITGEIST
Hope St. / Fear / Maid of the river / Saturday to sunday / 4.am / Forgotten ground / Fantasy / PC Keen / Just the one / Haven't made it / Leave this town / Men an tol
WOLCD 1064 / Sep '95 / China

Levellers 5
☐ SPRINGTIME
PROBE 26 CD / Jul '90 / Probe Plus

Leven, Jackie
☐ CONTROL
Soft lowland tongue / Raerona / Mansion tension / Dog star / Ruins / I'm always a Prinlaws boy / Problem / Dune voices / Sleeping in bracken
COOKCD 131 / 15 Sep '97 / Cooking Vinyl

☐ FAIRYTALES FOR HARDMEN
Boy trapped in a man / Desolation blues / Extremely violent man / Old West African song / Saint Judas / Poortoun / Fear of woman / Walled covers of Ravenscraig / Sad polish song / Sexual danger / Jim o' Windygates / Mad as the mist and snow / Kirkconnell flow / Listening to crows pray / Sir Patrick Spens / Sunflower / Torture blues / Story which could be true / Scotland the brave
COOKCD 115 / Apr '97 / Cooking Vinyl

☐ FORBIDDEN SONGS OF THE DYING WEST
Young male suicide blessed by invisible woman / Some ancient misty morning / Working alone/A blessing / Leven's lament / Marble city bar / Wanderer / Exultation / Men in prison / Birds leave shadows / Stornoway girl / Silver roof / Lammermuir hills / Come back early or never of come / By the sign of the sheltered star / Scene that haunts my memory / My lord what a morning
COOKCD 090 / Sep '95 / Cooking Vinyl

☐ MYSTERY OF LOVE IS GREATER THAN THE MYSTERY OF DEATH
Clay jug / Shadow in my eyes / Call Mother a lonely field / Crazy song / Farm boy / Garden / Snow in Central Park / Looking for love / Heartsick land / Gylen Gylen / I say a little prayer / Bars of Dundee / Donna Karan / Ballad of a simple heart / Stranger on the square / Horseshoe and jug / Mary Jones' dog / So my soul can sing
COOKCD 064 / Jul '97 / Cooking Vinyl

☐ SONGS FROM THE ARGYLL CYCLE VOL.1
Stranger on the square / Walking in Argyll / Honeymoon hill / Looking for love / Grievin' at the mish nish / Ballad of a simple heart / As we sailed into Skibbereen / Some ancient misty morning / History of rain / Gylen Gylen / Fly / Crazy song
COOKCD 101 / Apr '96 / Cooking Vinyl

Levenson, Barry
☐ HEART TO HAND
Cobra days/Blue tears / Whole lotta blues / Blue stew / Late show / Royal Albert / Slippin' down / Earl's ride / Steel life / Wrong side of the blues / West side rain / Crawford's grill
STCD 8101 / Jun '98 / Storyville

Lever
☐ MUSTARD
Seep / Home / Fragment / Come what may / Drown / Hate for the sake
LJCD 005 / 10 Nov '97 / Lockjaw

Levert
☐ FOR REAL THO'
Me 'n' you / Clap your hands / Tribute song / Good ol' days / She's all that (I've been looking for) / For real tho' / Quiet storm / Do the thangs / My place (your place) / Say you will / ABC 123
7567824622 / Mar '93 / East West

Levert, Gerald
☐ FATHER SON
Wind beneath my wings / I got your back / I got you / Already missing you / Already missing you / Apple don't fall / Apple don't fall / You got your hooks in me / You got your hooks in me / I'm savin' your place / You're hurting me / Don't make me beg / You need love / Get your thing off / For the love
7559618592 / Dec '95 / East West

☐ LOVE AND CONSEQUENCES
No sense / Thinkin' about it / Point the finger / Breaking my heart / That's the way I feel about you / It's your turn / No I'm not to blame / No man's land / Men like us / Taking everything / What about me / Definition of a man / Humble me
7559622612 / 3 Aug '98 / East West

☐ LSG (Levert, Gerald & Keith Sweat/ Johnny Gill)
Door / Round and round / You got me / Where did I go wrong / My body / All the times / My side of the bed / Curious / Let a playa get his freak on / Love hurts / Drive me to tears / Where would we go
7559621252 / 9 Mar '98 / Elektra

Leverton, Jim
☐ FOLLOW YOUR HEART (Leverton, Jim & Geoffrey Richardson)
MSECD 008 / May '95 / Mouse

Levi, K.D.
☐ WE GIVE THEE THANKS
NGCD 548 / Jul '96 / Twinkle

Levi Roots
☐ FREE YOUR MIND
SBCD 01 / 19 Jan '98 / Sound Box

Leviathan
☐ RIDDLES, QUESTIONS, POETRY AND OUTRAGE
CM 77143CD / Nov '96 / Century Media

Leviev, Milcho
☐ ORACLE, THE (Live at Suntory Hall) (Leviev, Milcho & Dave Holland)
Oracle / Everybody's song but my own / Thracian flamenco / New one / Andante tranquillo / You, I love / Samba Deborah / First snow / Shoobee doobee / Warm valley
PMC 1112 / May '94 / Pan Music

Levin, Pete
☐ MASTERS IN THIS HALL
GV 794262 / Dec '90 / Gramavision

☐ PARTY IN THE BASEMENT
Bells / For a place to sleep / Party in the basement / Gone / Ragtime: Saturday night at the Last Chance / Subway / Something I said / Hunter / Complaint department / One day in the schoolyard
GV 794562 / Apr '90 / Gramavision

Levin, Tony
☐ WORLD DIARY
DGM 9601 / Jan '96 / Discipline

Levin/Gorn/Marotta
☐ FROM THE CAVES OF THE IRON MOUNTAIN
DGM 9706 / 29 Sep '97 / Discipline

Levine, Christine
☐ AWKWARD ANGEL
Sooner or later / You either like it or you don't / Parallel lines / City lights / Do you mean it / Funny things / Didn't they tell you not to talk about it / Usually the way / Sell your mother / Deceit / Beaten up again / These are the days
74321600462 / 27 Jul '98 / Boiler House

Levine, Duke
☐ COUNTRY SOUL GUITAR
DARING 3011CD / Nov '94 / Daring

☐ LAVA
Quiz show / Lovers' Lane / Manhole / Lava / Force field / Buckaroo / Far away / Fever / North of the border / Stalkin' / In the dark
DARINGCD 3028 / Jul '97 / Daring

☐ NOBODY'S HOME
Attack of the mutant guitars / Longhorn / King kamehameha blues / Stop, do not go on / When I go walkin' / Remington ride / Swamp thing / Vigilante man / Shackle hands / Nobody's home
DRCD 3005 / Jan '93 / Daring

Levine, Mike
☐ SMILEY AND ME
Our delight / When your heart's on fire smoke gets in your eyes / Stablemates / Daydream / Stompin' at the Savoy / My little brown book / Social call / Now
CCD 4352 / Feb '95 / Concord Jazz

Levitation
☐ COTTERIE
TOPPCD 001 / Jul '94 / Ultimate

Levy, Barrington
☐ 20 VINTAGE HITS
SONCD 0025 / Apr '92 / Sonic Sounds

☐ BEST OF BARRINGTON LEVY, THE
VPCD 15222 / 13 Jul '98 / VP

☐ BOUNTY HUNTER WANTED
JLCD 001 / 5 May '98 / Jah Life

☐ DIVINE
Too experienced / Silver words / Dancehall rock / Foundation / Bless my eyes / Deep in the dark / Sweet reggae music / Here I come / Darling I need your loving / Living dangerously / Don't throw it all away / Looking my love
RASCD 3124 / '95 / Ras

☐ DJ COUNTERACTION
Living dangerously / Here I come / Under mi sensi / Cool and loving / Girl I like your style / Two sounds / Don't run away / Live good / Looking my love / Why you do it / Struggler
GRECD 216 / Jun '95 / Greensleeves

☐ HERE I COME
Here I come / Do the dance / Under me sensi / Vibes is right / Real thing / Cool and loving / Struggler / Live good / Moonlight lover / Ya we deh / Give me your love / Don't run away
GRELCD 501 / May '88 / Greensleeves

☐ MAKING TRACKS
RN 7022 / Jun '97 / Rhino

☐ RAS PORTRAITS
Do the dance / Prison oval rock / Robber man / Living dangerously / Under mi sensi / Looking my love / Little children cry / Hypocrites / Vibes is right / Here I come / Mary long tongue / Please jah jah
RAS 3323 / Jul '97 / Ras

☐ REGGAE VIBES
RGCD 022 / Nov '94 / Rocky One

☐ TIME CAPSULE
RASCD 3222 / Apr '96 / Ras

Levy, Lou
☐ YA KNOW
5197002 / Jun '94 / Verve

Levy, Ron
☐ B-3 BLUES & GROOVES (Levy, Ron Wild Kingdom)
BB 9532CD / May '93 / Bullseye Blues

☐ GREAZE IS WHAT'S GOOD (Levy, Ron Wild Kingdom)
CBCD 27104 / 22 Jun '98 / Cannonball

☐ RON LEVY'S WILD KINGDOM (Levy, Ron Wild Kingdom)
I know you know I know / Chicken fried snake / So many roads / Why you stay out so late / Party in Nogales / Big town playboy / My heart's in trouble / It's hot in here / Knee squeeze / Must have missed a turn somewhere
CD 1034 / '88 / Black Top

☐ SAFARI TO NEW ORLEANS (Levy, Ron Wild Kingdom)
CD 1040 / '88 / Black Top

Lew, Benjamin
☐ LA PARFUM DU RAKI
Les versants d'un coteau / Ce qu'elle voulait que j'entende / Et tout est parti de la / Ces personnages / Les sentiment de la couleur / Le visage sale par l'ecume / La magnifique alcoolique / La parful du raki / Que de moment d'alerte / Le sol noir des faubourgs marchands / Les personnage principal est un peuple isole / Sebkha / Un mal sourd / Regardez encore
MTM 35 / May '96 / Made To Measure

☐ NEBKA (Lew, Benjamin & Steven Brown)
MTM 17 / Sep '88 / Made To Measure

Lewie, Jona
☐ HEART SKIPS BEAT
I think I'll get my hair cut / Cream Jacqueline strawberry / Stop the cavalry / Abracadabra / Louise / Seed that always dies / Heart skips beat / What have I done / You go / Guessing games / Rearranging the deckchairs on the Titanic
STIFFCD 09 / Jan '94 / Disky

☐ ON THE OTHER HAND THERE'S A FIST
Kitchen at parties / Baby she's on the street / Big shot - momentarily / Bit higher / Feeling stupid / Vous et moi / God bless whoever made you / Hallelujah Europa / On the road / I'll get by in Pittsburgh
REP 4222 / Aug '91 / Repertoire

Lewin, Hakan
☐ HAKAN LEWIN & ALDO MERISTO (Lewin, Hakan & Aldo Meristo)
SITCD 9211 / Jun '94 / Sittel

Lewis, Barbara
☐ HELLO STRANGER (The Best Of Barbara Lewis)
My heart went do dat da / My Mama told me / Puppy love / Hello stranger / Think a little sugar / Straighten up your heart / Snap your fingers / How can I say goodbye / Spend a little time / Someday we're gonna love again / Pushin' a good thing too far / Baby, I'm yours / Make me your baby / Don't forget about me / Make me belong to you / Baby, what you want me to do / I remember the feeling / I'll make him love me / Thankful for what I got / Sho' nuff (it's got to be your love)
8122716192 / Feb '92 / Atlantic

☐ MANY GROOVES OF BARBARA LEWIS, THE
Baby that's a no no / Windmills of your mind / Slip away / How can I tell / I can't break away (from your love) / Oh be my love / Just the way you are today / Anyway / But you know I love you / You made me a woman / Stars / Do I deserve it baby / Ask the lonely / Why did it take you so long / That's the way I like it
CDSXE 077 / Jul '93 / Stax

Lewis, Crystal
☐ GOLD
Not the same / Be with him / Tomorrow / For such a time as this / Lord I believe in you / Why / Dyer road / What about God / God and I / Remember who you are / Return to me / Gold
7015041650 / Apr '98 / Myrrh

Lewis, David
☐ NO STRAIGHT LINE
DJD 3215 / Aug '95 / Dejadisc

Lewis, Donna
☐ BLUE PLANET
Will love grow / I could be the one / Love him / Blue planet / Beauty and wonder / Heaven sent you / Harvest moon / Falling / Lay me down / Unforgiven / Take me home
7567831282 / 17 Aug '98 / Atlantic

☐ NOW IN A MINUTE
I love you always forever / Simone / Lights of life / Fools paradise / Silent world / Nothing ever changes / Without love / Love affection / Mother / Agenais / I love you always forever
7567827622 / Sep '96 / Atlantic

Lewis, Gary
☐ ORIGINAL, THE (Lewis, Gary & The Playboys)
This diamond ring / Count me in / Save your heart for me / Everybody loves a clown / She's just my style / Sure gonna miss her / Green grass / My heart's symphony / (You don't have to) paint me a picture / Where will the words come from / Loser / Girls in love / Jill / Sealed with a kiss / Rhythm of the rain / Needles and pins / Way way out / Tijuana wedding
TO 886212 / 2 Feb '98 / Disky

Lewis, George
☐ AT HERBERT OTTO'S PARTY
AMCD 74 / Apr '94 / American Music

☐ AT THE CLUB HANGOVER, SAN FRANCISCO 1953 VOL.1 (Lewis, George New Orleans Jazz Band)
STCD 6024 / May '97 / Storyville

☐ CLASSIC NEW ORLEANS JAZZ VOL.1
Sweet sue / Just a blues / Stompin' at the savoy / Nobody's sweetheart now / I can't give you anything but love / Rosetta / Jazz me blues / I'm gonna sit right down and write myself a letter / Just a blues / I can't give you anything but love / Blues in b flat / In the good old summertime
BCD 127 / Oct '93 / Biograph

☐ GEORGE LEWIS & BARRY MARTYN BAND
BCD 37 / Jan '94 / GHB

☐ GEORGE LEWIS & KID SHOTS (Lewis, George & Kid Shots)
AMCD 2 / Oct '92 / American Music

☐ GEORGE LEWIS & PAPA BUES VIKING JAZZ BAND
STCD 6018 / Aug '94 / Storyville

☐ GEORGE LEWIS BANDS/TRIOS/ QUINTETS
AMCD 83 / Aug '95 / American Music

☐ GEORGE LEWIS WITH KEN COLYER'S JAZZMEN 1957 VOL.1
504CD 50 / Jun '95 / 504

☐ GEORGE LEWIS WITH KEN COLYER'S JAZZMEN 1957 VOL.2
504CD 51 / Jun '95 / 504

☐ IN CONCERT MANCHESTER 1959 (Lewis, George Ragtime Band)
504CD 58 / Nov '96 / 504

☐ IN STOCKHOLM
DRAGONCD 221 / Sep '89 / Dragon

☐ JAZZ AT VESPERS
Just a little while to stay / Bye and bye / Old rugged cross / Sometimes my burden is hard to bear / Down by the riverside / Just a closer walk with thee / Lord you've been good to me / When the saints go marching in
OJCCD 1721 / Jun '94 / Original Jazz Classics

☐ JAZZ FUNERAL IN NEW ORLEANS
TCD 1049 / May '97 / Tradition

☐ JAZZ IN THE CLASSIC NEW ORLEANS TRADITION
St. Phillip's street breakdown / Salty dog / Old rugged cross / Red wing / Lou-easy-an-i-a / Careless love / Weary blues / Bill Bailey, won't you please come home / Tin roof blues / Dippermouth blues / It's a long way to Tipperary / Bugle call rag
OJCCD 1736 / Mar '94 / Original Jazz Classics

☐ OHIO UNION 1954 (2CD Set) (Lewis, George & His Jazzband)
STCD 6020/21 / Jul '96 / Storyville

☐ OXFORD SERIES VOL.1 (Lewis, George & His Ragtime Band)
AMCD 21 / Oct '92 / American Music

☐ OXFORD SERIES VOL.10
AMCD 30 / Jan '94 / American Music

☐ OXFORD SERIES VOL.11
AMCD 31 / May '95 / American Music

☐ OXFORD SERIES VOL.12
AMCD 32 / May '95 / American Music

☐ OXFORD SERIES VOL.13
AMCD 33 / Apr '97 / American Music

☐ OXFORD SERIES VOL.14
AMCD 34 / Apr '97 / American Music

☐ OXFORD SERIES VOL.2
AMCD 22 / Oct '92 / American Music

☐ OXFORD SERIES VOL.5
AMCD 25 / Apr '93 / American Music

☐ OXFORD SERIES VOL.6
AMCD 26 / Apr '93 / American Music

☐ OXFORD SERIES VOL.7
AMCD 27 / Jun '93 / American Music

☐ OXFORD SERIES VOL.8
AMCD 28 / Jun '93 / American Music

☐ OXFORD SERIES VOL.9
AMCD 29 / Oct '93 / American Music

☐ SPIRIT OF NEW ORLEANS, THE (Lewis, George & His Ragtime Band)
MECCACD 1014 / Jul '93 / Music Mecca

☐ TRIOS & BANDS
AMCD 4 / Jan '93 / American Music

Lewis, George

☐ CHANGING WITH THE TIMES
804242 / Nov '93 / New World

☐ HOMAGE TO CHARLES PARKER (Lewis, George & Anthony Davis)
1200292 / May '92 / Black Saint

☐ MONADS/TRIPLE SLOW MIX
120016 / Apr '94 / Black Saint

☐ REUNION (Lewis, George & Don Ewell)
Ida / Of all the wrongs / Whispering / Waltz you saved for me / Toot Toot Tootsie / Yes yes in your eyes / Wabash blues / Someday sweetheart / Ole miss / Bucket's got a hole in it / Ida / Of all the wrongs / Whispering / Yes yes in your eyes
DE 220 / Jun '97 / Delmark

☐ VOYAGER
AVANT 014 / Nov '93 / Avant

Lewis, Hopeton

☐ GROOVING OUT OF LIFE
Grooving out on life / Proud mary / Love is a beautiful thing / God bless whoever sent you / Funky kingston / Take it easy / Help me make it through the night / Going back to my home town / Express yourself / Joy to the world-put your hand in the hand
JMC 200109 / Sep '93 / Jamaican Gold

Lewis, Huey

☐ FORE (Lewis, Huey & The News)
Jacob's ladder / Stuck with you / Whole lotta lovin' / Hip to be square / I know what I like / I never walk alone / Power of love / Naturally / Simple as that / Doin' it all for my baby
CCD 1534 / Jul '94 / Chrysalis

☐ FOUR CHORDS & SEVERAL YEARS AGO (Lewis, Huey & The News)
Shake, rattle and roll / Blue Monday / Searching for my love / Some kind of wonderful / But it's alright / If you gotta make a fool of somebody / Mother in law / Little bitty pretty one / Good morning little school girl / Stagger lee / She shot a hole in my soul / Surely I love you / You left the water running / Your cash ain't nothin' but trash / Function at the junction / Better to have and not need / Going down slow
7559615002 / May '94 / Warner Bros.

☐ GOLD COLLECTION, THE (Lewis, Huey & The News)
Do you believe in love / Hope you loved me the way you say you do / Workin' for a livin' / Some of my lies are true / Trouble in paradise / Stop trying / Who cares / Tattoo (giving it up for love) / Only one / Change of heart / Don't make me do it / Now here's you / Whatever happened to true love
8210882 / 6 Oct '97 / EMI Gold

☐ HARD AT PLAY (Lewis, Huey & The News)
Build me up / It hit me like a hammer / Attitude / He don't know / Couple days off / That's not me / We should be making love / Best of me / Do you love me, or what / Don't look back / Time ain't money
CCD 1847 / Feb '94 / Chrysalis

☐ HEART OF ROCK AND ROLL, THE (The Best Of Huey Lewis And The News) (Lewis, Huey & The News)
Power of love / Hip to be square / Do you believe in love / If this is it / Some of my lies are true / Workin' for a livin' / Bad is bad / I want a new drug / Heart of rock and roll / Heart and soul / Jacob's ladder / Stuck with you / Trouble in paradise / Walking on a thin line / Perfect world / Small world / Back in time
CDCHR 1934 / Oct '92 / Chrysalis

☐ HUEY LEWIS & THE NEWS/PICTURE THIS/SPORTS (3CD Set) (Lewis, Huey & The News)
Some of my lies are true (sooner or later) / Don't make me do it / Stop trying / Now here's you / I want you / Don't ever tell me that you love me / Hearts / Trouble in paradise / Who cares / If you really love me you'll let me / Change of heart / Tell me a little lie / Tattoo (giving it all up for love) / Hope you love me like you say you do / Workin' for a livin' / Do you believe in love / Is it me / Whatever happened to true love / Only one / Buzz buzz buzz / Heart of rock'n'roll / Heart and soul / Bad is bad / I want a new drug / Walking on a thin line / Finally found a home / If this is it / You crack me up / Honky tonk blues
CDOMB 010 / 27 Jul '98 / Chrysalis

☐ ONLY ONE, THE (Lewis, Huey & The News)
Do you believe in love / Hope you love me like you say you do / Workin' for a livin' / Some of my lies are true / Trouble in paradise / Stop trying / Hearts / Who cares / Tattoo (giving it all up for love) / Only one / Change of heart / Don't make me do it / Now here's you / Whatever happened to true love
DC 882822 / 2 Feb '98 / Disky

Lewis, Jerry Lee

☐ 1960'S FRENCH EP COLLECTION, THE (2CD Set)
528862 / Jul '97 / Magic

☐ BEST OF JERRY LEE LEWIS, THE
Great balls of fire / Whole lotta shakin' goin' on / Drinkin' wine (spo-dee-o-dee) / Lewis boogie / Mean woman blues / You win again / Jailhouse rock / Lovin' up a storm / Pumpin' piano rock / High school confidential / Fools like me / Down the line / Breathless / Wild one / Milkshake mademoiselle / Pink pedal pushers / I could never be ashamed of you / In the mood / Let's talk about us (no. 1) / What'd I say
MCCD 081 / Sep '92 / Music Club

☐ BEST OF JERRY LEE LEWIS, THE
Heartaches by the number / Green green grass of home / Help me make it through the night / Detroit city / King of the road / I'm so lonesome I could cry / Break my mind / Sweet dreams / Reuben James / Another place another time / Before the next teardrop falls / Pick me up on your way home / What made Milwaukee famous (has made a loser out of me) / Louisiana man / Middle age crazy / I'm a lonesome fugitive / She even woke me up to say goodbye / Today I started loving you again / I forgot more than you'll never know / There stands the glass
5543792 / 20 Apr '98 / Spectrum

☐ CHANTILLY LACE
Me and Bobby McGee / There must be more to love than this / What made Milwaukee famous (has made a loser out of me) / I'm so lonesome I could cry / Heartaches by the number / I'm left, you're right, she's gone / Cold cold heart / Chantilly lace / Would you take another chance on me / He'll have to go / I love you because / For the good times / Oh lonesome me / I can't stop loving you
5501802 / Mar '94 / Spectrum

☐ COLLECTION, THE
Be bop a lula / Dixie / Goodnight Irene / Great balls of fire / High school confidential / Lewis boogie / Matchbox / Money / Sixty minute man / Ubangi stomp / Whole lotta shakin' goin' on / Wine drinkin' spo-dee-o-dee / CC rider / Good golly Miss Molly / Good rockin' tonight / Hang up my rock 'n' roll shoes / Johnny B Goode / Long gone lonesome blues / Mean woman blues / Pumpin' piano rock / Sweet little sixteen / What'd I say / Will the circle be unbroken / Let the good times roll
CCSCD 143 / Dec '90 / Castle

☐ COMPLETE SUN RECORDINGS, THE (8CD Set)
Crazy arms / End of the road / You're the only star in my blue heaven / Born to lose / Silver threads among the gold / I'm throwing rice (at the girl i love) / I love you so much it hurts / Deep Elem blues / Goodnight Irene / Goodnight Irene (undubbed master) / Honey hush / Crawdad song / Dixie / Marines' hymn / That lucky old sun / Hand me down my walking cane / You're the only star in my blue heaven (Lewis boogie) / I love you because / I can't help it / Cold cold heart / Shame on you / I'll keep on loving you / You are my sunshine / Tomorrow night / Sixty minute man / It all depends (who will buy the wine) / I don't love nobody / Whole lotta shakin' goin' on / It'll be me (alt.) / It'll be me (alt.2) / Whole lotta shakin' goin' on (master) / False start and It'll be me / Ole pal of yesterday / You win again / Love letters in the sand / Little green valley / Lewis boogie / Pumpin' piano rock / It'll be me / All night long / Old time religion / When the saints go marching in (undubbed master) / My Carolina sunshine girl / Long gone lonesome blues / Drinkin' wine spo-dee-o-dee / Singin' the blues / Keep your hands off it / Matchbox (undubbed master) / Matchbox / Ubangi stomp / Rock 'n' roll Ruby / So long I'm gone / Ooby dooby / I forgot to remember to forget (unissued) / You win again (undubbed master) / I'm feeling sorry / Mean woman blues / Turn around / Great balls of fire (movie cut) / Chatter/Great balls of fire / Why should I cry over you / Religious discussion / Great balls of fire (master) / You win again (overdubbed master) / Down the line (unissued) / Down the line (false start) / I'm sorry I'm not sorry / Down the line (master) / Sexy ways (false start) / Cool cool ways / Milkshake madamoiselle / Breathless (unissued) / Milkshake madamoiselle (false starts) / Breathless (master) / High school confidential (false start) / High school confidential (unissued) / High school confidential / Put me down (unissued) / Good rockin' tonight / Pink pedal pushers / Jailhouse rock / Hound dog / Don't be cruel / Someday / Jambalaya / Friday nights / Big legged woman / Hello hello baby / Frankie and Johnny / Your cheatin' heart / Lovesick blues / Goodnight Irene (overdubbed master) / When the saints go marching in (overdubbed master) / Matchbox (overdubbed master) / Put me down / Fools like me (undubbed master) / Carrying on (sexy ways) / Crazy heart (false start) / High school confidential (master) / Slippin' around / I'll see you in my dreams / Real wild child / Let the good times roll / Fools like me (overdubbed master) / Settin' the woods on fire (unissued) / Memory of you / Come what may / Break up / Crazy heart / Live and let live / I'll make it all up to you (false start) / Johnny B Goode / Settin' the woods on fire (false start) / Return of Jerry Lee / Break up (unissued) / I'll make it all up to you (unissued) / Break up (master) / I'll make it all up to you / I'll sail my ship alone / It hurt me so (chatter) / You're the only star in my blue heaven (unissued) / It hurt me so / Lovin' up a storm (unissued) / Big blon' baby / Lovin' up a storm / Sick and tired / Shanty town / Release me / I could never be ashamed of you (false start) / Near you (takes 1and2) / I could never be ashamed of you / Hillbilly fever / My blue heaven / Let's talk about us (false start) / Little Quennie / Home / Will the circle be unbroken / Ballad of Billie Joe / Sail away / Am I to be the one / Night train to Memphis / I'm the guilty one / Let's talk about us / Wild side of life (stereo) / Charming Billy (stereo) / Bonnie / Mexicali rose (slow) / Mexicali rose (fast) / Gettin' in the mood / In the mood / I get the blues when it rains / Don't drop it / Great speckled bird / Bonnie B / Baby, baby, bye bye / I can't help it (unissued and false starts) / Old black Joe / As long as I live (unissued) / As long as I live / What'd I say / Keep your hands off it (birthday cake) / Hang up my rock 'n' roll shoes / John Henry / What'd I say (stereo) / CC rider / When my blue moon turns to gold again (unissued) / Lewis workout / When my blue moon turns to gold again (stereo) / When I get paid / Love made a fool of me (stereo) / No more than I get (stereo) / Livin' lovin' wreck / Cold cold heart (stereo) / I forgot to remember to forget / It won't happen with me / I love you because (stereo) / Save the last dance for me / Hello Josephine / High powered woman / My blue heaven 1 (stereo) / My blue heaven 2 (stereo) / Sweet little sixteen / Ramblin' rose (master extended) / Money (stereo) / Rockin' the boat of love / Ramblin' rose / I've been twistin' / Whole lotta twistin' goin' on / I've been twistin' (stereo) / I know what it means / Sweet little sixteen / My girl Josephine (stereo) / Set my mind at ease / Waiting for a train 1 (stereo) / Waiting for a train 2 (stereo) / How's my ex treating you (stereo and unissued) / Good rockin' tonight (stereo) / Be bop a lula / My girl Josephine (stereo and unissued) / How's my ex treating you / Good golly Miss Molly (unissued) / I can't trust me (in your arms anymore) / My pretty quadroon (stereo) / Waiting for a train (unissued) / Teenage letter (stereo) / Seasons of my heart / Your lovin' ways / Just who is to blame / Just who is to blame (unissued) / Hong Kong blues / Love on Broadway (stereo) / One minute past eternity (stereo) / Invitation to your party / Invitation to your party (stereo) / I can't seem to say goodbye / Carry me back to old Virginny / Carry me back to old Virginny
BCD 15420 / Aug '89 / Bear Family

☐ COMPLETE SUN YEARS, THE (12CD Set)
Crazy arms / End of the road / I'll be me / Whole lotta shakin' goin' on / Great balls of fire / You win again / Down the line / Breathless / High school confidential / Fools like me / Return of jerry lee / Lewis boogie / Break up / I'll make it all up to you / It hurt me so / I'll sail my ship alone / Lovin' up a storm / Big blon' baby / Let's talk about us / Ballad of billy joe / Little queenie / I could never be ashamed of you / Old black joe / Baby baby bye bye / John henry / Hang up my rock and roll shoes / When I get paid / Love's made a fool of me / What'd I say / Livin' lovin' wreck / Cold cold heart / It won't happen with me / Save the last dance for me / As long as I live / Money (that's what I need) / Bonnie b / I've been twistin' / Ramblin' rose / Sweet little sixteen / How's my ex treating you / Good golly miss molly / I can't trust me (in your arms anymore) / Teenage letter / Seasons of my heart / Carry me back to old virginia / I know what it means / I get the blues when it rains / In the mood / Invitation to your party / Frankie and johnny / One minute past eternity / I can't seem to say goodbye / Waiting for a train / Big legged woman / Love on broadway / Your lovin' ways / I can't trust me (in your arms anymore) / You're the only star in my blue heaven / Born to lose / Silver threads among the gold / I'm throwing rice (at the girl I love) / I love you so much it hurts / Deep elem blues / Hand me down my walking cane / Crawdad song / Dixie / Goodnight irene / Will the circle be unbroken / Old time religion / When the saints go marching in / Turn around / That lucky old sun / I love you because / I can't help it (if I'm still in love with you) / Cold cold heart / Shame on you / I'll keep on loving you / Ole pal of yesterday / You win again / I'll sail my ship alone / Little green valley / My carolina sunshine girl / Long gone lonesome blues / You are my sunshine / Singing the blues / I forgot to remember to forget / I'll make it all up to you / Hillbilly music / I forgot to remember to forget / You win again / Jambalaya (on the bayou) / Settin' the woods on fire / I'll sail my ship alone / You're the only star in my blue heaven / Release me / Night train to memphis / Wild side of life / Mexicali rose / Great speckled bird / Your cheatin' heart / When my blue moon turns to gold again / (all around the water tank) waiting for a train / Carry me back to old virginia / Crazy arms / Someday (you'll want me to want you) / Lovesick blues / Slippin' around / I'm feeling sorry / Crazy heart / Home / Old black joe / Why should I cry over you / You can't help it / Don't drop it / I could never be ashamed of you / I'm sorry I'm not sorry / I'm the guilty one / Sixty minute man / Drinkin' wine (spo-dee-o-dee) / Honey hush / Rockin' with red (she knows how to rock me) / Cool cool ways (sexy ways) / Good rockin' tonight / Come what may / Goodnight irene / Carrying on (sexy ways) / Let the good times roll / Sick and tired / Hound dog / What'd I say / Hang up my rock and roll shoes / CC rider / My girl josephine / High powered woman / My blue heaven / Save the last dance for me / C.c. rider / Lewis boogie / I get the blues when it rains / Lewis workout / Tomorrow night / High powered woman / Sweet little sixteen / Johnny b. goode / Good golly miss molly / Goodnight irene / When the saints go marching in / I've been twistin' / Whole lotta shakin' goin' on / Matchbox / Ubangi stomp / Rock and roll ruby / Ooby dooby / Pink pedal pushers / Jailhouse rock / Hound dog / Don't be cruel / (just a shanty in old) shanty town / Friday night / Wild one (real wild child) / Johnny b. goode / Sail away / What'd I say / Rockin' the boat of love / Sweet little sixteen / Nothin' shakin' / Sittin' and thinkin' / Good rockin' tonight / Be bop a lula / My girl josephine / Mexicali rose / Hong kong blues / Ramblin' rose / My blue heaven / I forgot to remember to forget / In the mood / Mean woman blues / So long I'm gone / Love letters in the sand / Old time religion / You're the only star in my blue heaven / Ole pal of yesterday / Little green valley / I forgot to remember to forget / Goodnight irene / I'm feeling sorry / Great balls of fire / Down the line / Milkshake mademoiselle / Breathless / Whole lotta shakin' goin' on / High school confidential / Put me down / Fools like me / Wild one / Carrying on (sexy ways) / Crazy heart / High school confidential / Break up / Settin' the woods on fire / I'll sail my ship alone / I could never be ashamed of you / My blue heaven / Let's talk about us / As long as I live / Old black joe / Let's talk about us / Bonnie b / Am I to be the one / Baby baby bye bye / Bonnie b / As long as I live / What'd I say / Don't drop it / You can't help it / Milkshake mademoiselle / I've been twistin' / Sweet little sixteen / I can't trust me (in your arms anymore) / Waiting for a train / My girl josephine / I can't seem to say goodbye / I forgot to remember to forget / You're the only star in my blue heaven / Whole lotta shakin' goin' on / Breathless / It'll be me / Sixty minute man / Little green valley / It'll be me / All night long / It'll be me / Lovin' up a storm / You are my sunshine / Ooby dooby / I'm feeling sorry / Great balls of fire / Down the line / Whole lotta shakin' goin' on / You win again / It'll be me / I don't love nobody / Great balls of fire / Down the line / Breathless / High school confidential / Put me down / I'll make it all up to you / Break up / Drinkin' wine (spo-dee-o-dee) / I'll sail my ship alone / It hurt me so / Lovin' up a storm / I could never be ashamed of you / Let's talk about us / Am I to be the one / Old black joe / Baby baby bye bye / Cold cold heart / Pumpin' piano rock / Hello hello baby / I'll see you in my dreams / Memory of you / Live and let live / Near you / It all depends (on who will buy the wine) / Billy boy / My bonnie / No more than I get / Whole lotta twistin' goin' on / Set my mind at ease / My pretty squadroon / Just who is to blame / Keep your hands off it / How's my ex treating you / You're the only star in my blue heaven / Waiting for a train / Invitation to your party / Hong kong blues / Sweet little sixteen / Breathless / Ramblin' rose / When my blue moon turns to gold again / Great speckled bird / Bonnie b / Sail away / Marines' hymn / Lovin' up a storm / I'm feeling sorry / As long as I live / Great balls of fire / Down the line / Breathless / High school confidential / Break up / I'll make it all up to you / It hurt me so / Lovin' up a storm / Let's talk about us / Am I to be the one / Old pal of yesterday / Deep elem blues / Sixty minute man / I'm feeling sorry / You're the only star in my blue heaven / It'll be me / Great balls of fire / High school confidential / Carrying on / Milkshake mademoiselle / Crazy heat / Put me down / Break up / I'll make it all up to you / It hurt me so / My blue heaven / Baby baby bye bye / Bonnie / As long as I live / You can't help it / I've been twistin' / Waiting for a train / I can't trust me / I love you because / Carry me back to old virginia / High school confidential / Break up / Breathless
CDSUNBOX 4 / Feb '93 / Charly

☐ COUNTRY CLASSICS
You win again / What made Milwaukee famous (has made a loser out of me) / I can't stop loving you / Your cheatin' heart / Middle aged crazy / Mexicali rose / Bootles and barstools / Cold cold heart / Another place another time / I'll find it where I can / Careless hands / There must be more to love than this / Touching home / You are my sunshine / Thirty nine and holding / Hey good lookin' / She even woke me up to say goodbye / Will the circle be unbroken
MUCD 9018 / Apr '95 / Musketeer

☐ COUNTRY COLLECTION, THE
EABCD 057 / 24 Nov '97 / Eagle

☐ DEFINITIVE COLLECTION, THE
Great balls of fire / Lucille / What'd I say / Roll over Beethoven / Brown eyed handsome man / Down the line / Chantilly lace / Johnny B Goode / Little Queenie / Just because / High school confidential / Who's gonna play this old piano / Whole lotta shakin' goin' on / Rockin' my life away / Me and Bobby McGee / I'll make it all up to you / Mona Lisa / Sweet Georgia Brown / Drinking wine / Sweet little sixteen
SUMCD 4167 / 26 Jan '98 / Summit

☐ EP COLLECTION VOL.1, THE
Great balls of fire / Whole lotta shakin' goin' on / You win again / It'll be me / Put me down / Don't be cruel / It all depends (who will buy the wine) / Crazy arms / High school confidential / Jambalaya / When the saints go marching in / Fools like me / Livin' lovin' wreck / What I'd say / Hang up my rock and roll shoes / John henry / Money / Turn around / Teenage letter / Lovin' up a storm / I've been twistin' / Good golly miss molly / How's my ex treating you / Seasons of the heart / I can't trust me / Hello josephine / Save the last dance for me / Sweet little sixteen
SEECD 307 / Dec '90 / See For Miles

☐ EP COLLECTION VOL.2, THE
Ballad of Billie Joe / Let's talk about us / Little Queenie / I could never be ashamed of you / It won't happen with me / Cold cold heart / Baby, baby, bye bye / Old black Joe / It hurt me so / I'll sail my ship alone / Ramblin' Rose / As long as I live / When I get paid / Mean woman blues / Down the line / Breathless / I'm feeling sorry / Matchbox / Ubangi stomp / Break up / I'll make it all up to you / Big blon' baby / High school confidential / Whole lotta shakin' goin' on / Hound dog / Good rockin' tonight / Drinkin' wine spo-dee-o-dee / Great balls of fire
SEECD 397 / Mar '94 / See For Miles

☐ GREAT BALLS OF FIRE
Whole lotta shakin' goin' on / It'll be me / Lewis boogie / Drinkin' wine spo-dee-o-dee / Rock 'n' roll Ruby / Matchbox / Ubangi stomp / Great balls of fire / You win again / Mean woman blues / Milkshake madamoiselle / Breathless / Down the line / Good rockin' tonight / Jambalaya / High school confidential / Pink pedal pushers / Don't be cruel / Johnny B Goode / Break up / Big blon' baby / Lovin' up a storm / Little queenie / In the mood / What'd I say / Sweet little sixteen / Good golly Miss Molly / Be bop a lula / Teenage letter / Carry me back to old Virginny
CPCD 8206 / Feb '97 / Charly

☐ GREAT BALLS OF FIRE
Great balls of fire / Down the line / Breathless / Little Queenie / High school confidential / Lewis boogie / Let's talk about us / Lovin' up a storm / You win again / Bonnie B / What'd I say / It'll be me / In the mood / Mean woman blues / Wild one (real wild child) / Whole lotta shakin' goin' on
308772 / 11 May '98 / Hallmark

☐ GREATEST LIVE SHOWS ON EARTH, THE
Jenny Jenny / Who will the next fool be / Memphis Tennessee / Hound dog / Mean woman blues / Hi-heel sneakers / No particular place to go / Together again / Long tall Sally / Whole lotta shakin' goin' on / Little queenie / How's my ex treating you / Johnny B Goode / Green green grass of home / What'd I say (part 2) / You win again / I'll sail my ship alone / Crying time / Money / Roll over Beethoven
BCD 15608 / Nov '91 / Bear Family

☐ HEARTBREAKER
CPCD 8175 / Jun '96 / Charly

☐ HIGH SCHOOL CONFIDENTIAL
Whole lotta shakin' goin' on / Lovin' up a storm / When I get paid / Baby baby bye bye / Wild one / What'd I say / Sixty minute man / Sweet little sixteen / Hello Josephine / High school confidential / Just who is to blame / Be bop a lula / Breathless / Money / Good golly Miss Molly / Great balls of fire
SUMCD 4004 / Nov '96 / Summit

☐ **HONKY TONK ROCK'N'ROLL PIANO MAN**
My fingers do the talkin' / Why you been gone so long / Daughters of Dixie / Teenage Queen / I'm looking over a four leaf clover / I am what I am / Better not look down / Only you / Honky tonk rock 'n' roll piano man / Circumstantial evidence / I'm lookin' under a skirt / Rock 'n' roll money / Forever forgiving (alternative take no.1) / Why you been gone so long (alt. take no.3) / Get out your big roll daddy
CDCH 332 / Oct '91 / Ace

☐ **IN CONCERT**
CDSGP 0163 / Oct '95 / Prestige

☐ **IN CONCERT**
Great balls of fire / Whole lotta shakin' goin' on / Shake, rattle and roll/Flip flop and fly / Chantilly lace / What'd I say / Good Golly Miss Molly / Mona Lisa / Who's sorry now / Come on in / You win again / Honky tonk angels / Trouble in mind / Help me make it through the night / Middle age crazy / Sweet little sixteen / Think about it darlin' / High School confidential
100412 / May '97 / A-Play Collection

☐ **JERRY LEE LEWIS**
Meat man / Jailhouse rock / House of blue light / Rock 'n' roll funeral / Don't touch me / Changing mountains / Beautiful dreamer / I'm alone because I love you / Lucille / Seventeen / Mathilda / Wake up little Susie
12658 / Sep '96 / Laserlight

☐ **JERRY LEE LEWIS**
Good golly Miss Molly / High school confidential / Great balls of fire / Night train to Memphis / When the saints go marching in / Frankie and Johnny / Good rockin' tonight / Whole lotta shakin' goin' on / You win again / Jambalaya / Matchbox / Breathless / Crazy arms / Break up / What'd I say / Whole lot of twistin' / I'll make it up to you / Be bop a lula
399538 / May '97 / Koch Presents

☐ **KILLER CONCERT**
Great balls of fire / What'd I say / Lucille / Brown eyed handsome man / Hey good lookin' / Roll over Beethoven / Chantilly lace / Little queenie / Johnny B Goode / No headstone on my grave / Mexicali rose / I'll find it where I can / High school confidential / Boogie woogie country man / You are my sunshine / Meat man / Big legged woman / Rockin' my life away / Who's gonna play this old piano / Whole lotta shakin' goin' on
QED 038 / Nov '96 / Tring

☐ **KILLER HITS**
High school confidential / Great balls of fire / Big blon'baby / You win again / Drinkin' wine spo-dee-o-dee / It'll be me / Milkshake Madamoiselle / Crazy arms / I've been twistin' / In the mood / What'd I say / Breathless / Mean woman blues / Little Queenie / Down the line / That lucky old sun / Lewis boogie / Wild one / Sweet little sixteen / Let's talk about us / Lovin' up a storm / Whole lotta shakin' goin' on
PWKS 4255 / Mar '96 / Carlton

☐ **LIVE AT THE STAR CLUB, HAMBURG**
Mean woman blues / High school confidential / Money / Matchbox / What'd I say / Great balls of fire / Good golly Miss Molly / Lewis boogie / Your cheatin' heart / Hound dog / Long tall Sally / Whole lotta shakin' goin' on / Down the line
BCD 15467 / Jul '89 / Bear Family

☐ **LIVE AT THE VAPORS CLUB**
Don't put no headstone on my grave / Chantilly lace / I'll find it where I can / Drinkin' wine spo-dee-o-dee / Sweet little sixteen / Boogie woogie country man / Me and Bobby McGee / Rockin' my life away / Whole lotta shakin' goin' on / You can have her / Hey good lookin' / Will the circle be unbroken
CDCH 326 / May '91 / Ace

☐ **LIVE IN ITALY**
Rollin' in my sweet baby's arms / High school confidential / Me and Bobby McGee / Jackson / There must be more to love than this / Great balls of fire / What'd I say / Jerry Lee's rock and roll revival show / I am what I am / Whole lotta shakin' goin' on / You win again / Mona Lisa / One of those things we all go through / Hang up my rock 'n' roll shoes
CDMF 071 / Jun '89 / Magnum Force

☐ **LOCUST YEARS/RETURN TO THE PROMISED LAND (9CD Set)**
Whole lotta shakin' goin' on / Crazy arms / Great balls of fire / High school confidential / I'll make it all up to you / Break up / Down the line / Hit the road Jack / End of the road / Your cheatin' heart / Wedding bells / Just because / Breathless / He took it like a man / Drinkin' wine spo-dee-o-dee / Johnny B Goode / Hallelujah, I love her so / You went back on your word / Pen and paper / Hole he said he'd dig for me / You win again / Fools like me / Hit the road Jack / I'm on fire / She was my baby (he was my friend) / Bread and butter man / I bet you're gonna like it / Got you on my mind / Mathilda / Corine Corina / Sexy ways / Wild side / Flip flop and fly / Don't let go / Maybellene / Roll over Beethoven / Just in time / I believe in you / Herman the hermit / Baby, hold me close / Skid row / This must be the place / Rockin' pneumonia and the boogie woogie flu / Seasons of my heart / Big boss man / Too young / Danny boy / City lights / Funny how time slips away / North to Alaska / Walk right in / Wolverton mountain / King of the road / Detroit city / Ring of fire / Baby, you got what it takes / Green green grass of home / Sticks and stones / What a heck of a mess / Lincoln limousine / Rockin' Jerry Lee / Memphis beat / Urge / Whenever you're ready / She thinks I still care / Twenty four hours a day / Swinging doors / If I had it all to do over / Just dropped in / It's a hang up / Holdin' on / Hey baby / Dream baby / Treat her right / Turn on your love light / Shotgun man / All the good is gone / Another place another time / Walking the floor over you / I'm a lonesome fugitive / Break my mind / Play me a song I can cry to / Before the next teardrop falls / All night long / We live in two different worlds / What made Milwaukee famous (has made a loser out of me) / On the back row / Slippin' around / Ahe still comes around / Today I started loving you again / Louisiana man / There stands the glass / I can't have a merry Christmas, Mary / Out of my mind / I can't get over you / Listen they're playing my song / Echoes / Release me / Let's talk about us / To make love sweeter for you / Don't let me cross over / Born to lose / You belong to me / Oh lonesome me / Sweet dreams / Cold cold heart / Fraulein / Why don't you love me like you used to do / Four walls / It makes no difference now / I love you because / I'm so lonesome I could cry / Jambalaya / More and more / One has my name (the other has my heart) / Burning memories / Mom and Dad's last waltz / Pick me up on your way down / Heartaches by the number / I can't stop loving you / My blue heaven / I wonder where you are tonight / Jackson / Sweet thang / He'll have to go / You've still got a place in my heart / I get the blues when it rains / Gotta travel on / Milwaukee here I come / Crying time / Secret places / Don't take it out on me / Earth up above / Waiting for a train / Love for all seasons / She even woke me up to say goodbye / When the grass grows over me / Wine me up / Since I met you baby / Workin' man blues / Once more with feeling / In loving memories / You went out of your way (to walk on me) / My only claim to fame / Brown eyed handsome man
BCD 15783 / Nov '94 / Bear Family

☐ **MASTERS, THE (2CD Set)**
EDMCD 014 / 24 Nov '97 / Eagle

☐ **PRETTY MUCH COUNTRY**
Honky tonk heaven / She never said goodbye / That was the way it was then / Candy kisses / I am what I am / Come as you were / She sang amazing grace / Have I got a song for you / Daughters of Dixie / Send me the pillow that you dream on / She sure makes leavin' look easy / My fingers do the talkin' / Honky tonk heart / Careless hands / Honky tonk rock 'n' roll piano man / Forever forgiving
CDCH 348 / Feb '92 / Ace

☐ **RARE AND ROCKIN'**
It won't happen with me / Teenage letter / Pink pedal pushers / Hillbilly music / Deep Elem blues / You win again / I'm feeling sorry / I'm the guilty one / It hurt me so / I love you because / Cold cold heart / Whole lotta shakin' goin' on / In the mood / Great balls of fire / I forgot to remember to forget / Turn around / It all depends (who will buy the wine) / It'll be me / Sixty minute man / Lovin' up a storm / Rockin' with red / Honey hush / Hound dog / Hang up my rock 'n' roll shoes
CDCHARLY 70 / Apr '87 / Charly

☐ **ROCKIN' UP A STORM (2CD Set)**
Little Queenie / Lucille / I love you because / Break up / Crazy arms / Jailhouse rock / Matchbox / House of blue lights / Lovesick blues / Great balls of fire / That lucky old sun / Money (that's what I want) / How's my ex treatin' you / Be bop a lula / Bonnie B / Save the last dance for me / Good golly Miss Molly / Sweet little sixteen / Whole lotta shakin' goin' on / Let the good times roll / Don't be cruel / Lovin' up a storm / It'll be me / End of the road / Lewis boogie / Down the line / I've been twistin' / Good rockin' tonite / What'd I say / Livin' lovin' wreck / Wild one / Jambalaya / Sixty minute man / Hound dog / Ramblin' Rose
330142 / Jul '96 / Hallmark

☐ **SINGS THE ROCK 'N' ROLL HITS**
EABCD 056 / 24 Nov '97 / Eagle

☐ **SPOTLIGHT ON JERRY LEE LEWIS**
Hey baby / Roll over Beethoven / Boogie woogie country man/Rockin' / Sweet Georgia Brown / Just because / You win again / Sweet little sixteen / I'll find it where I can / No headstone on my grave / Whole lotta shakin' goin' on / Hadacol boogie / Middle aged crazy / Who will the next fool be / Down the line
HADCD 124 / Feb '94 / Javelin

☐ **SUN CLASSICS (4CD Set)**
Whole lotta shakin' goin' on / Great balls of fire / High school confidential / Be bop a lula / Good golly Miss Molly / Down the line / Lovin' up a storm / Wild one / Ooby dooby / End of the road / Pumping piano rock / Put me down / Don't be cruel / I'm feeling sorry / Home / Wild side of life / When my blue moon turns to gold again / I love you because / Born to lose / Jambalaya / You win again / Crazy heart / Long gone lonesome blues / Cold cold heart / I can't help it (If I'm still in love with you) / Your cheatin' heart / Big blon' baby / Rock 'n' roll Ruby / Breathless / I'm sorry I'm not sorry / Ubangi stomp / It'll be me / Milkshake Madamoiselle / Baby, baby, bye bye / Break up / It won't happen with me / Bonnie B / Livin' lovin' wreck / Your lovin' ways / Crazy arms / I'll make it all up to you / Let's talk about us / It hurt me so / As long as I live / How's my ex treating you / I can't seem to say goodbye / I'll sail my ship alone / Someday (you'll want me to want you) / Set my mind at ease / Seasons of my heart / It all depends (who will buy the wine) / Slippin' around / Night train to Memphis / Big legged woman / Rockin' with Red / Sixty minute man / I've been twistin' / Teenage letter / Mean woman blues / Drinkin' wine spo-dee-o-dee / Keep your hands off it (Birthday cake) / Money / Hound dog / Cool cool ways / Hello hello baby / I know what it means / It'll be me (alt.) / Hillbilly music / Turn around / Fools like me / I forgot to remember to forget / I can't trust me (In your arms anymore) / I'm the guilty one / Hand me down my walking cane / Crawdad song / Don't drop it / Memory of you / Crazy arms (Remake) / What I'd say / Honey hush / Tomorrow night / Carrying on (sexy ways) / Good rockin' tonight / Come what may / Hello Josephine / Little Queenie / Johnny B Goode / Hang up my rock 'n' roll shoes / Sweet little sixteen / Matchbox / CC rider / Lewis boogie / My pretty quadroon / That lucky old sun / Goodnight Irene / Will the circle be unbroken / Great speckled bird / John Henry / Frankie and Johnny / You're the only star in my blue heaven / Waiting for a train / Deep Elem blues / You are my sunshine / Carry me back to old Virginny
CDDIG 8 / Feb '95 / Charly

☐ **THAT BREATHLESS CAT**
Ragtime doodle / Meat man / Lovin' up a storm / Ubangi stomp / Rock 'n' roll ruby / Piano doodle / House of blue lights / My life would make a damn good country song / Beautiful dreamer / Autumn leaves / Pilot baby / Room full of roses / Keep a knockin' / Silver threads among the gold / Alabama jubilee / Lazy river / Mama this song's for you / Breathless / Whole lotta shakin' goin' on
STCD 2 / Feb '93 / Stomper Time

☐ **TWO ON ONE: JERRY LEE LEWIS & CARL PERKINS (Lewis, Jerry Lee & Carl Perkins)**
Whole lotta shakin' goin' on / Great balls of fire / Breathless / High school confidential / Good golly miss molly / You win again / Good rockin' tonite / Be bop a lula / Lovesick blues / What'd I say / Blue suede shoes / Honey don't / Boppin' the blues / Put your cat clothes on / Matchbox / Everybody's tryin' to be my baby / Roll over beethoven / Glad all over / Gone, gone, gone / Let the jukebox keep on playing
CDTT 5 / Apr '94 / Charly

☐ **UP THROUGH THE YEARS 1956-1963**
End of the road / Crazy arms / It'll be me / Whole lotta shakin' goin' on / You win again / Mean woman blues / Great balls of fire / Down the line / Breathless / Don't be cruel / Put me down / Break up / I'll make it up to you / I'll sail my ship alone / Lovin' up a storm / Big blon' baby / Night train to Memphis / Little Queenie / John Henry / Livin' lovin' wreck / What'd I say / Cold cold heart / Sweet little sixteen / Carry me back to old Virginny
BCD 15408 / Dec '87 / Bear Family

☐ **VERY BEST OF JERRY LEE LEWIS, THE (2CD Set)**
Whole lotta shakin' goin' on / Great balls of fire / You win again / Breathless / High school confidential / Fools like me / I'll make it all up to you / What'd I say / Cold cold heart / Invitation to your heart / One minute past eternity / I can't seem to say goodbye / Waiting for a train / Love on Broadway / Break up / I'll sail my ship alone / Lovin' up a storm / Lewis boogie / I won't happen with me / Livin' lovin' wreck / Big blon' baby / I know what it means / Milkshake mademoiselle / Hand me down my walking cane / End of the road / Wild one / Down the line / Mean woman blues / Crazy arms / Little Queenie / Hang up my rock 'n' roll shoes / Be bop a lula / It hurt me so / Good golly Miss Molly / Don't be cruel / Hound dog / Hello Josephine / CC rider / Jailhouse rock / Johnny B Goode / Money / Matchbox / Let's talk about us / How's my ex treating you / Your cheatin' heart / Teenage letter / Good rockin' tonight / Honey hush / I've been twistin' / Big legged woman
CPCD 82432 / Oct '96 / Charly

☐ **WHOLE LOTTA HITS**
CPCD 8121 / Aug '95 / Charly

☐ **WHOLE LOTTA SHAKIN'**
Whole lotta shakin' / Don't be cruel / Down the line / Let the good times roll / Jambalaya / High school confidential / Jailhouse rock / Lewis boogie / Hound dog / What'd I say / Lovin' up / Storm / Wild one / Great balls of fire / Singin' the blues / Little Queenie / Mean woman blues / Sixty minute man / Lovesick blues / Breathless / It'll be me
QSCD 6010 / Aug '93 / Charly

☐ **WORLD OF JERRY LEE LEWIS, THE**
Whole lotta shakin' goin' on / Don't be cruel / Johnny B Goode / Shake, rattle and roll / Roll over Beethoven / Sea cruise / I'm on fire / Long tall Sally / Down the line / Working man blues / Dream baby / Sweet little sixteen / Treat her right / Haunted house / Sweet Georgia Brown / I'm left, you're right, she's gone / Big blon' baby / Hound dog / Drinkin' wine spo-dee-o-dee / Great balls of fire
5520642 / May '96 / Spectrum

Lewis, Jimmy

☐ **STILL WANNA BE BLACK**
Message to the ladies / It ain't what's on the woman / There ain't no man that can't be caught / Is that any way to treat a lady / How long is a heartache supposed to last / Thank you / Go on live your life / That won't stop me from loving you / Help me understand / I got my troubles / It's never too late / Stop to start / I've got to get you back / One woman's man / When love is gone / Midnight special / Friendship only goes so far / I intend to take your place / Don't sit around / Still wanna be black
CDKEND 153 / 27 Oct '97 / Kent

Lewis, John

☐ **AMERICAN JAZZ ORCHESTRA PLAYS ELLINGTON**
Rockin' in rhythm / Ko-ko / Sepia panorama / Johnny come lately / Chloe / Warm valley / Main stem / Conga brava / Concerto for cootie / Sidewalks of new york / Bojangles / All too soon / Cotton tail / Take / Jack the bear
7567914232 / Apr '95 / Atlantic

☐ **WONDERFUL WORLD OF JAZZ**
Body and soul / I remember clifford / I should care / Afternoon in paris / If you could see me now / Stranger / Two degrees east three degrees west
7567909792 / Apr '95 / Atlantic

Lewis, Johnny

☐ **ALABAMA SLIDE GUITAR**
Hobo blues / He met me on a Thursday morning / Uncle Sam ain't no woman / Can't hardly get along / My little gal / North Carolina blues / I'm gonna quit my baby / Baby listen to me howl / You gonna miss me / Mistake in life / I got to climb a high mountain / My mother often told me / Lewis little girl done stole a black cat bone / Jumpin' jive / Poor boy / Guitar blues
ARHCD 9007 / 16 Mar '98 / Arhoolie

Lewis, Laurie

☐ **EARTH AND SKY (The Songs Of Laurie Lewis)**
Girlfriend guard your heart / Green fields / Don't get too close / Love chooses you / Texas bluebonnets / Fine line / Old friend / Maple's lament / Bear song / Light / Point of no return / Restless rambling heart / I'd be lost without you / Hills of my home / Haven of mercy / Magic light
ROUCD 0400 / Jul '97 / Rounder

☐ **LOVE CHOOSES YOU**
Old friend / Hills of home / Point of no return / I don't know why / I'd be lost without you / When the nightbird sings / Women of Ireland / Ryestraw / Light / Texas bluebonnets / Love chooses you
FF 70487 / Nov '96 / Flying Fish

☐ **OAK AND THE LAUREL, THE (Lewis, Laurie & Tom Rozum)**
ROUCD 0340 / Jul '95 / Rounder

☐ **RESTLESS RAMBLING HEART**
Bowling green / Cowgirl's song / Restless rambling heart / Cry cry darlin' / Stealin' chickens / Maple's lament / Here we go again / Green fields / Hold to a dream / I'm gonna be the wind / Haven of mercy
FF 70406 / Nov '96 / Flying Fish

☐ **SEEING THINGS**
Blue days sleepless nights / Refugee / Visualize / Kiss me before I die / Let the bird go free / Bane and balm / I'll take back my heart / Tattoo / Angel on his shoulder / Manzanar / Blackest crow
ROUCD 0428 / Jun '98 / Rounder

☐ **SINGIN' MY TROUBLES AWAY (Lewis, Laurie & Grant Street)**
Diamond Joe / Don't get too close / Rope / Beautiful bouquet / Overdrive / Heartache / When the cactus is in bloom / I wish it had been a dream / New day / Singin' my troubles away / Hell among the yearlings / Raleigh and Spencer / I miss the Mississippi and you
FF 70515 / Mar '97 / Flying Fish

☐ **TOGETHER (Lewis, Laurie & Kathy Kallick)**
Going up the mountain / Just like the rain / Is the blue moon still shining / Don't you see the train / Hideaway / Touch of the master's hand / Lost John / Maverick / That dawn the day you left me / Count your blessings / Little Annie / Don't leave your little girl all alone / Gonna lay down my old guitar
ROUCD 0318 / Feb '95 / Rounder

☐ **TRUE STORIES**
ROUCD 300 / Sep '93 / Rounder

Lewis, Lew

☐ **SAVE THE WAIL (Lewis, Lew Reformer)**
REP 4216 / Aug '91 / Repertoire

Lewis, Linda

☐ **BEST OF LINDA LEWIS, THE**
(Remember the days of) the old schoolyard / It's in his kiss / This time I'll be sweeter / Rock 'n' roller coaster / Not a little girl anymore / I do my best to impress / Baby I'm yours / May you never / Shining / You came / Come back and finish what you started / Light years away / My love is here to stay / My friend the sun / So many mysteries to find / All comes back to love / Flipped over your love / Never been done before / Can't we just sit down and talk it over / Winter wonderland
74321431562 / Oct '96 / Camden

☐ **ROCKIN' WITH LINDA (Lewis, Linda Gail)**
DECD 2001 / '96 / Deep Elem

☐ **SECOND NATURE**
TPN 3CD / Nov '95 / Turpin

☐ **WHATEVER**
Far cry / Don't come crying / Easy / Whatever / He's a diamond / Makes you wonder / Doin' the right thing / Breathing space / Last call / Light years away / Mr. Respectable / Reach for the truth / And of the sun
TPN 5CD / 27 Apr '98 / Turpin

Lewis, Margaret

☐ **LONESOME BLUEBIRD**
Shake a leg / One day, another tomorrow / Goin' to St Louie / From the cradle to the blues / Roll over Beethoven / Love is a fortune / Birmingham valley blues / You can't break my heart no more / No no never / Cheater's can't win / That's why I cry / Raggedy Ann and the player piano / There was no you / Bow wow puppy love / Dust my blues / Those lonely lonely nights / Reconsider me / You ought to see my baby / It's alright (you can go) / John De Lee (I love you) / Full grown man / Emmitt Lee / Lover's land / Baby please forgive me / Every time you turn me down / My blue eyed boy / Look what you're doing to me
CDCHD 572 / Jan '95 / Ace

Lewis, Meade 'Lux'

☐ **ALTERNATE TAKES/LIVE PERFORMANCES**
DOCD 5561 / 28 Oct '97 / Document

☐ **BARRELHOUSE PIANO**
Six wheel chaser / How long blues / Someday sweetheart / Bugle call rag / I ain't gonna give nobody none o' this jelly roll / Mike / Darktown strutters ball / Birth of the blues / Tidal boogie / Mardi Gras drag / Tishomingo blues / Jada / Basin Street blues / Fast 'A' blues / 12th Street blues / St. Louis blues
JASMCD 2536 / Mar '95 / Jasmine

☐ **BOOGIES AND BLUES**
Yancey special / Celeste blues / Mr.Freddie blues / Solitude / Melancholy / Twos and fews / Blues for tommy / Blues / Blues / Blues / Blues / Honkey tonk train blues / Bass on top / Tell your story / Jammin' in four / Edmound hall blues / Profoundly blue / Celestial express
TPZ 1069 / 27 Oct '97 / Topaz Jazz

☐ CAT HOUSE PIANO/OUT OF THE RARING 1920'S
Pittsburgh flyer / Dragon blues / Jabouti / Torpedo juice / Joe Prein's boogie / 620 boogie / Meade's mambo / San Francisco shuffle / Spooney Sam / Mama's bounce / Shooboody / Hangover boogie / Yancey's last ride / Bush street boogie
5570982 / 3 Aug '98 / Verve

☐ CLASSICS 1927-1939
CLASSICS 722 / Dec '93 / Classics

☐ CLASSICS 1939-1941
CLASSICS 743 / Feb '94 / Classics

☐ CLASSICS 1941-1944
CLASSICS 841 / Nov '95 / Classics

☐ LEWIS, AMMONS & JOHNSON 1929-1935 (Lewis, Meade 'Lux' & Albert Ammons/Pete Johnson)
PYCD 21 / Jun '96 / Magpie

☐ LEWIS, AMMONS & JOHNSON 1936-1941 (Lewis, Meade 'Lux' & Albert Ammons/Pete Johnson)
BDCD 6046 / Jun '95 / Blues Document

☐ MEADE LUX LEWIS 1939-1954
SOB 35062CD / Apr '95 / Story Of The Blues

☐ TIDAL BOOGIE
TCD 1029 / Aug '96 / Tradition

Lewis, Mel

☐ DEDICATION (Lewis, Mel & Thad Jones)
Groove merchant / Big dipper / Central Park North / Tow away zone / Quietude / Jive samba / Dedication / It only happens every time / Tiptoe / Child is born
17093 / Mar '97 / Laserlight

☐ DEFINITIVE THAD JONES VOL.1, THE (Live From The Village Vanguard) (Lewis, Mel Jazz Orchestra)
Low down / Quietude / Three in one / Walkin' about / Little pixie
MM 5024 / Oct '94 / Music Masters

☐ DEFINITIVE THAD JONES VOL.2 (Live At The Village Vanguard) (Lewis, Mel Jazz Orchestra)
Second race / Tip toe / Don't get sassy / Rhoda map / Cherry juice
MM 5046 / Oct '94 / Music Masters

☐ NEW MEL LEWIS QUINTET LIVE, THE (Lewis, Mel New Quintet)
Once I loved / Tranquilo / Pell mel / Ending shuffle
INAK 8611CD / Jul '97 / In Akustik

☐ SOFT LIGHTS AND HOT MUSIC (Classics In Jazz) (Lewis, Mel & The Jazz Orchestra)
Soft lights and sweet music / Compensation / Lester left town / It could happen to you / Off the cuff / Our love is here to stay / Little man you've had a busy day / How long has this been going on / Touch of your lips
MM 5012 / Oct '94 / Music Masters

☐ SOFT LIGHTS AND SWEET MUSIC (Lewis, Mel & The Jazz Orchestra)
50122C / Dec '94 / Music Masters

Lewis, Norma

☐ BEST OF NORMA LEWIS, THE (Maybe This Time)
Life is the reason / You've got something / (Give me back) Just a little piece of my heart / Make your own sweet music / When loving you / Maybe this time / For all we know / Fight (for the single man) / Tonight (dancing with the desperate) / Fire or ice
HTCD 46 / 20 Apr '98 / Hot Productions

Lewis, Pete

☐ SCRATCHIN' (Lewis, Pete/Jimmy Nolen/Cal Green)
Strollin' with Nolen / Louisiana hop / How fine can you be / Scratchin' / You've been goofing / Crying with the rising sun / Way you do / Big push / Raggedy blues / I can't stand you no more / After hours / Harmonica boogie / Don't leave me no more / Chocolate pork chop man / Wipe your tears / Green's blues / It hurts me too / Blast / Strawberry jam / Ooh midnight / Movin' on down the line
CDCHARLY 268 / Jun '91 / Charly

Lewis, Peter

☐ PETER LEWIS
TX 2008CD / Jul '95 / Taxim

Lewis, Philip

☐ MORE PURPLE THAN BLACK
MLSB 003 / 20 Jul '98 / Stand Back

Lewis, Ramsey

☐ COLLECTION, THE
Wade in the water / Something you got / Hard day's night / Hang on Sloopy / Ain't that peculiar / Blues for the night owl / Hi-heel sneakers / Function at the junction / Uptight (everything's alright) / Lonely avenue / Day tripper / 1-2-3 / Felicidade / Les fleurs / Caves / Since I fell for you / All my love belongs to you / He's a real gone guy / Soul man / In crowd
MOCD 3012 / Feb '95 / More Music

☐ DANCE OF THE SOUL
Baile del alma (dance of the soul) / Fragile / Sub dude / Lullaby / Portuguese love / Fire and rain / Cancion / Love's serenade / Mercy and grace / Cante hondo
GRP 99042 / 8 Jun '98 / GRP

☐ GREATEST HITS (Lewis, Ramsey Trio)
'In' crowd / My babe / Since I fell for you / Something you got / Hard day's night / Hang on sloopy / Caves / Dancing in the street / Felicidade (happiness) / Wade in the water / Ain't that peculiar / Blues for the night owl / Function at the junction / Lonely avenue / 1-2-3 / Look-a-here / High heel sneakers / Uptight (everything's alright)
MCD 06021 / Apr '97 / Chess/MCA

☐ HANG ON RAMSEY/WADE IN THE WATER
Hard day's night / All my love belongs to you / He's a real gone guy / And I love her / Movin' easy / Billy boy / Hi heel sneakers / More I see you / Satin doll / Hang on sloopy / Wade in the water / Ain't that peculiar / Tobacco road / Money in the pocket / Message to Michael / Up tight / Hold it right there / Day tripper / Mi compasion / Hurt so bad
BGOCD 396 / 3 Aug '98 / Beat Goes On

☐ IN PERSON 1960-1967 (2CD Set) (Lewis, Ramsey Trio)
Old devil moon / What's new Carmen / Bei mir bist du schon / I'll remember April / Delilah / Something you've got / Fly me to the moon / My babe / Caves / In crowd / Since I fell for you / Spartacus / You've been talkin' 'bout me baby / Come Sunday / Hard day's night / He's a real gone guy / And I love her / Movin' easy / More I see you / Satin doll / Hang on Sloopy / Dancing in the street / You don't know me / Django / Quiet nights of quiet stars / What now my love / Black Orpheus medley
GRP 18142 / 8 Jun '98 / Chess Jazz

☐ LIVE (Lewis, Ramsey Trio)
JHR 73524 / May '93 / Jazz Hour

☐ PRICELESS JAZZ
In crowd / I'll remember April / Night in Bahia / Since I fell for you / Apres vous / Maiden voyage / Delilah / Generique / Sun Goddess 2000 / Wade in the water
GRP 98982 / 23 Mar '98 / GRP

☐ SUN GODDESS
CK 33194 / Aug '97 / Sony Jazz

☐ THIS IS JAZZ
Wade in the water / Love song / Tondelayo / Waltz for Debby / There's no easy way / Blues for the night / Owl / Time for love / Brazillica / Soul sister / Spiritual / Song without words (remembering)
CK 65043 / May '97 / Sony Jazz

Lewis, Smiley

☐ SHAME, SHAME, SHAME (4CD Set)
Turn on your volume, baby / Here comes Smiley / Tee-nah-nah / Lowdown / Slide me down / Growing old / If you ever loved a woman / Dirty people / Where were you / My baby / Sad life / Bee's boogie / Don't jive me / My baby was right / Bells are ringing / Lillie Mae / You're gonna miss me / Gypsy blues / You're not the one / Gumbo blues / Ain't gonna do it / It's so peaceful / Calsonia's party / Lonesome highway / Standing on the corner / Oh baby / Big mamou / Play girl / (I love you) for sentimental reasons / Lying woman / Little Fernandez / It's music / Show me the way / Down the road / One night / Blue Monday / Rocks / Nothing but the blues / That certain door / Nobody knows / She's got me hook, line and sinker / Can't stop loving you / Baby please / Ooh la la / By the water / Too many drivers / Rootin' and tootin' / Lost weekend / Jailbird / Farewell / Please listen to me / No, no / Real gone lover / Bumpity bump / Someday you'll want me / I can't believe it / I hear you knocking / Hey girl / Down yonder we go ballin' / Come on / Queen of hearts / No letter today / Li'l Liza Jane / Mama don't like / I shall not be moved / Ain't goin there no more / Shame shame shame / Oh Red / Last night / I want to be with her / Shame, shame, shame / Tell me who / Stormy Monday blues / These bones / Goin' down the road / Sweeter words (have never been told) / Tore up / When did you leave Heaven / You are my sunshine / I'm coming down with the blues / I wake up screamin' / Tomorrow night / Go on fool / To the river / How long / Ronettes / Sometimes / Lookin' for my woman / Goin' to jump and shout / One night of sin / Sheikh of araby / Bad luck blues / Bells are ringing / School days are back again / Jump (Instrumental) / My love is gone / Walkin' the girl (Instrumental) / Oh Red / Ain't goin there no more
BCD 15745 / Nov '93 / Bear Family

Lewis, Ted

☐ IS EVERYBODY HAPPY NOW 1926-1932
TT 423 / May '98 / Take Two

Lewis, Vic

☐ CELEBRATION OF CONTEMPORARY WEST COAST JAZZ, A
CCD 79711 / Feb '97 / Candid

☐ ME AND YOU (Lewis, Vic West Coast All Stars)
Bl-you-uuz / You and the night and the music / Me and you / You're my thrill / You and me / My ideal / Between you and me and the gatepost / Somebody loves me
CCD 79739 / Jan '98 / Candid

☐ PLAY BILL HOLMAN (Lewis, Vic West Coast All Stars)
Oleo / Yesterdays / Sizzler before lunch / When I fall in love / Easter parade / As we speak / Sizzler after lunch
CCD 79535 / Jan '97 / Candid

☐ SHAKE DOWN THE STARS (The Music Of Jimmy Van Heusen) (Lewis, Vic West Coast All Stars)
Swinging on a star / But beautiful / Suddenly it's spring / I'll only miss her / Here's that rainy day / Polka dots and moonbeams / I thought about you / So would I / Shake down the stars / Collar 17
CCD 79526 / Feb '97 / Candid

☐ TRIBUTE TO STAN KENTON, A (Lewis, Vic & His Orchestra)
Hammersmith riff / Pepperpot / Man I love / Music for moderns / Design for brass / Theme for Alto / Theme for trombone / Over the rainbow / Serenade in blue / Hundred years from today / Love for sale / Where are you / Concerto to end all concertos / Heir to a chinese maiden / Cuban carnival / Porphyria's lover / Blues / For you a bone / Eindayz / Inspiration / Everywhere
VICD 567 / Jul '96 / Avid

☐ VIC LEWIS & HIS USA JAZZMEN 1938/ BRITISH JAZZMEN 1945-1947 (Lewis, Vic Jazzmen)
BALCD 1938 / Feb '98 / Baldwin

Lewis, Victor

☐ EEEYYESS
Eeeyyess / Vulnerability / Un-til / Buttercups / Alter ego / No more misunderstandings / Stamina / Here's to you baby / Shakehandre
ENJ 93112 / Apr '97 / Enja

Lewis, Walter 'Furry'

☐ FOURTH AND BEALE
Going to Brownsville / John Henry / Casey Jones / St. Louis blues / Judge Boushe blues / Just a little fun / Going back to Gary / When the saints go marchin' in / Dog named blue
5197262 / Apr '93 / Verve

☐ IN HIS PRIME (1927-29)
YAZCD 12050 / Jun '91 / Yazoo

☐ SHAKE 'EM ON DOWN
John Henry / When my baby left me / Shake 'em on down / Big chief blues / Old blue / I'm going to Brownsville / Back on my feet again / White lightning / Roberta / St. Louis blues / Baby you don't want me / Done changed my mind / Goin' to Kansas city / Judge boushay blues / Casey Jones / This time tomorrow / I will turn your money green / Frankie and Johnny / Longing blues / Long tall gal blues
CDCH 486 / Nov '93 / Ace

Lewis, Webster

☐ LIVE AT CLUB 7
Do you believe / Up on the roof / It's your thing
CR 001CD / 3 Aug '98 / Counterpoint

Lewis, Willie

☐ CLASSICS 1932-1936
CLASSICS 822 / Jul '95 / Classics

☐ CLASSICS 1936-1938
CLASSICS 847 / Nov '95 / Classics

☐ CLASSICS 1941
CLASSICS 880 / Jul '96 / Classics

Lex Talionis

☐ INTO THE SHADE
EFA 084652 / Dec '94 / Dossier

Ley, Tabu

☐ AFRICA WORLDWIDE
ROUCD 5039 / Feb '96 / Rounder

☐ BABETI SOUKOUS
Presentation / Kinshasa / Soroza / Linga ngai / Moto akokufa / Nairobi / Seli ja / I need you / Amour nala / Tu as dit que / Sentimenta / Pitie / Mosola
RWCD 5 / Jun '89 / Realworld

☐ LES ANNEES 70 (Ley, Tabu Rochereau)
CD 36562 / Jan '97 / Sonodisc

☐ MUZINA
ROUCD 5059 / Nov '94 / Rounder

Leyland DAF Band

☐ ROMANCE IN BRASS
Love changes everything / Spring / Summer night / Song of the seashore / All I ask of you / Elvira Madigan / Drink to me only with thine eyes / Can't take my eyes off you / Romance from 'The Gadfly' / Anything but lonely / Romance from 'Fair Maid of Perth' / Someone to watch over me / Serenata / Flower duet / Forgotten dreams / Fanfare, romance and finale
QPRL 043D / Jun '90 / Polyphonic

Leyland, Carl 'Sonny'

☐ BOOGIE AND BLUES
SACD 117 / Jul '96 / Solo Art

☐ FARRISH STREET JIVE
GRCD 6078 / Mar '98 / Goofin'

Leyli

☐ SPIRITUAL BELLY DANCE
EUCD 1251 / Mar '94 / ARC

Leyton, Johnny

☐ BEST OF JOHN LEYTON
Johnny remember me / Wild wind / Six white horses / Son this is she / Lone rider / Lonely city / I think I'm falling in love / Lonely Johnny / Oh lover / I don't care if the sun don't shine / (I love you) for sentimental reasons / That's how to make love / I'll cut your tail off / Land of love / Cupboard love / How will it end / It would be easy / Beautiful dreamer / Another man / Make love to me / You took my love for granted / I guess you are always on my mind / Funny man / Man is not supposed to cry / Girl on the floor above / Tell Laura I love her / On Lovers Hill / Too many late nights / Lover's lane / I'm gonna let my hair down / Don't let her go away / All I want is you / I want a love I can see
SEECD 201 / Sep '87 / See For Miles

☐ EP COLLECTION, THE
Son this is she / That's a woman / Fabulous / Voodoo woman / Wild wind / Six white horses / Thunder and lightning / Goodbye to teenage love / You took my love for granted / I don't care if the sun don't shine / Down the River Nile / Terry Brown's in love with Mary Dee / Walk with me my angel / There must be / Cupboard love / I'll cut your tail off / Beautiful dreamer / Another man / Oh lover / Lone rider / Lonely city / Lonely Johnny / On Lovers Hill / (I love you) For sentimental reasons / That's how to make love / Johnny remember me / Make love to me
SEECD 401 / Mar '94 / See For Miles

☐ JOHN LEYTON ARCHIVE
Johnny remember me / Wild wind / Six white horses / Son, this is she / Lone rider / Lonely city / I think I'm falling in love / Lonely Johnny / Oh lover / I don't care if the sun don't shine / I love you for sentimental reasons / That's how to make love / Voodoo woman / Land of love / Cupboard love / Fabulous / It would be easy / Beautiful dreamer / Another man / Make love to me
RMCD 207 / Nov '97 / Rialto

LFO

☐ ADVANCE
WARPCD 39 / Jan '96 / Warp

☐ FREQUENCIES
Intro / Lfo / Simon from sydney / Nurture / Freeze / We are back / Tan ta ha / You have to understand / El ef oh / Love is the message / Mentok / Think a moment / Groovy distortion / Track 14
WARPCD 3 / Apr '96 / Warp

Lhamo, Yungchen

☐ COMING HOME
Khyab sangye / Per rig chog sum / Heart / Ngak pai metog / Dream / Defiance / Coming home / Sky / Happiness is
CDRW 72 / 8 Jun '98 / Realworld

☐ TIBET, TIBET
CDRW 59 / Jul '96 / Realworld

Lhooq

☐ LHOOQ
Losing hand / I sit in a room / Darkness / Take me / Missile / Calling me / I don't want to know / More to life / Away bem / Peeping Tom
ECHCD 022 / 24 Aug '98 / Echo

Li Calzi, Giorgio

☐ GIORGIO LI CALZI
PHIL 672 / Oct '94 / Philology

Li He

☐ CHINESE CLASSICAL FOLK MUSIC
EUCD 1155 / '91 / ARC

Liangxing, Tang

☐ HIGH MOUNTAIN FLOWING WATER
Tianshanzhi qun / Lizu wuqu / Yangqun baixue / Meihua san long / Song wo yizhi meigueihua / Gaoshan liushui / Bawang xiejia / Xiyang xiaogu / Yizu wuqu
SHCD 6512 / Mar '98 / Shanachie

Liar Of Golgotha

☐ DWELL WITHIN THE MYSTERIOUS DARK
M 7013CD / 2 Mar '98 / Mascot

Liars In Wait

☐ SPIRITUALLY UNKNOWN
BS 008CD / Nov '96 / Burning Sun

Libana

☐ BORDERLAND
SHCD 67003 / Mar '94 / Shanachie

Liberace

☐ BEST OF LIBERACE, THE
HMNCD 035 / 22 Jun '98 / Half Moon

☐ LIBERACE REMEMBERED
Start the day with a smile / If I knew you were coming I'd have baked a cake / Rock 'n' roll waltz / I want a girl like the girl that married dear old Dad / You're just in love / If you wanna be happy / Hey Liberace / Don't ever marry for money / Tisket-a-tasket / Over the rainbow / I'll be seeing you / When Liberace winks at me
PLSCD 240 / 27 Oct '97 / Pulse

Liberation Through Hearing

☐ LIBERATION THROUGH HEARING
DELECCD 023 / Aug '94 / Delerium

Liberator

☐ FREEDOM FIGHTERS
BHR 038CD / Apr '96 / Burning Heart

☐ THIS IS LIBERATOR
BHR 047CD / Jul '96 / Burning Heart

☐ WORLDWIDE DELIVERY
BHR 076CD / 27 Apr '98 / Burning Heart

Liberman, Jeffrey

☐ THEN AND NOW
SB 034 / Jun '97 / Second Battle

Libertad, Tania

☐ TOMATE ESTA BOTELLA CONMIGO (A Tribute To Jose Alfredo Jimenez)
3145373542 / 5 May '98 / Thirsty Ear

Libertine, Eve

☐ SKATING
RH 2CD / Nov '92 / Red Herring

Liberty

☐ LIBERTY
BLIPCD 101 / Mar '94 / Urban London

Liberty Cage

☐ SLEEP OF THE JUST
Everything's different now / Fires below / Throwing stones at the sea / On her majesty's service / Swimming against the tide / One for the road / Judgement day / You make my mind stand still / Mercy of the guards / Cat and mouse affair / Murder in cell no.9
LICD 901293 / Sep '94 / Line

Libido

☐ KILLING SOME DEAD TIME
Overthrown / Supersonic daydream / Strange news / Crash out / In my shadow / Blow / Remarkably abnormal / Revolving / Molest me / Comfort / God's guest list / Magic mushroom night
FIRECD 62 / 16 Feb '98 / Fire

Library Of Congress Endangered Music Project

☐ MUSIC FOR THE GODS
Taboehgan / Taboehgan / Pedat / Genderan / Pemoengkah / Kerejing / Laghoe dindang / Meraknggila / Gambang / Kecak / Abimenijoe / Gambangan / Dandang gendis
RCD 10315 / Feb '95 / Rykodisc

Licht, Alan

☐ EVAN DANDO OF NOISE, THE
HERMES 022 / May '97 / Corpus Hermeticum

☐ MERCURY (Licht, Alan & Loren Mazzacane Connors)
ROCO 019 / 15 Dec '97 / Road Cone

Lick

☐ BREECH
INV 046CD / Jan '96 / Invisible

Lick 57's

☐ ...AND THE BAND PLAYED ON
SEMAPHORE 35954 / Nov '96 / Onefoot

Licursi, Silvana

☐ FAR FROM THE LAND OF EAGLE
LYRCD 7413 / '91 / Lyrichord

Lid

☐ IN THE MUSHROOM
Lid / Mary Agnes / Dream is over / In the mushroom / Window pain / R / You are here / Alive / Randy scouse git / For all my life
CDVILE 67 / Jun '97 / Peaceville

Liebert, Ottmar

☐ BORRASCA
Isla del sol / August moon / In the hands of love / Dancing under the moon / Twilight in Galisteo (bossa 4 Dexter) / La rosa negra / Borrasca / Bullfighter's dream / Thru the trees / Cloudless sky / La aurora / Driving 2 Madrid (B4 the storm) / Storm sings / Night in Granada / First rain / Cry of faith / Bajo la luna mix
VHOCD 7 / 25 May '98 / Higher Octave

☐ NOUVEAU FLAMENCO
Barcelona nights / Heart still beating / Women walking / 2 the night / Passing storm / Santa Fe / Surrender 2 love / Waiting 4 stars 2 fall / Road 2 her home / After the rain / Flowers of romance / Moon over trees / Shadows
VHOCD 2 / 25 May '98 / Higher Octave

Liebmann, David

☐ CLASSIC BALLADS
Out of nowhere / If I should lose you / Dancing in the dark / Skylark / Angel eyes / Stella by starlight / My funny Valentine / On green dolphin street
CCD 79512 / Feb '97 / Candid

☐ DAVID LIEBMANN & LLUIS VIDAL TRIO (Liebmann, David & Lluis Vidal Trio)
FSNT 026 / Jan '98 / Fresh Sound New Talent

☐ DAVID LIEBMANN AND LLUIS VIDAL (Liebmann, David & Lluis Vidal)
FSNT 027 / Jan '98 / Fresh Sound New Talent

☐ ENERGY OF THE CHANCE (Liebman, David & Dave Love)
Lady friends / You be you / New age / Child refugee / Scorch / Wili / Energy of the chance / Valencia / Begging for words / Better leave it alone / Slow dance
INAK 30052 / Nov '97 / In Akustik

☐ IF ONLY THEY KNEW (Liebmann, David Quintet)
If only they knew / Capistrano / Moontide / Reunion / Autumn in New York / Move on some
CDSJP 151 / Feb '91 / Timeless Jazz

☐ JOY (The Music Of John Coltrane)
After the rain / Untitled original / Alabama / India / Naima / Joy/Selflessness
CCD 79531 / Feb '97 / Candid

☐ PLAY THE MUSIC OF COLE PORTER (Liebmann, David & Steve Gilmore/Bill Goodwin)
1232362 / Apr '91 / Red

☐ QUEST VOL.2
STCD 4132 / Jul '96 / Storyville

☐ SONGS FOR MY DAUGHTERS
1212952 / Sep '95 / Soul Note

☐ TREE, THE
1211952 / Nov '91 / Soul Note

☐ VOYAGE (Liebmann, David Group)
Open eyes / Dancing in the park / When to love / Drum thing / Cut / Gravel and the bird / Maiden voyage / Yildiz
ECD 221572 / Sep '96 / Evidence

Liebzeit, Jaki

☐ NOWHERE
SPOONCD 17 / Feb '95 / Grey Area

Liedes, Anna-Kaisa

☐ KUUTTAREN KORET
OMCD 44 / Dec '93 / Olarin Musiiki Oy

☐ OI MIKSI
TUG 1099CD / Feb '95 / Tugboat

Lien, Annbjorg

☐ ANNBJORG LIEN
FXCD 88 / Jul '93 / Kirkelig Kultuverksted

☐ FELEFEBER
GR 4081CD / Dec '94 / Grappa

☐ PRISME
GR 4113CD / Nov '96 / Grappa
SHCD 64082 / Apr '97 / Shanachie

Liers In Wait

☐ SPIRITUALY UNCONTROLLED ART
DOL 007CD / Nov '92 / Dolores

Lieutenant Pigeon

☐ MOULDY OLD DOUGH
EMPRCD 782 / 16 Mar '98 / Emporio

Lieutenant Stitchie

☐ BANGARANG
SHCD 45023 / Aug '95 / Shanachie

☐ GHETTO SOLDIER
GRELCD 213 / Dec '94 / Greensleeves

☐ LIEUTENANT STITCHIE, BEENIE MAN, COBRA & FRIENDS (Lieutenant Stitchie & Beenie Man/Cobra)
RNCD 2070 / Jul '94 / Rhino

Life

☐ COCOON
NTHEN 029CD / 16 Feb '98 / Now & Then

☐ LIFE
MELLOCD 007 / 15 Dec '97 / Mellotronen

Life After Death

☐ LIFE AFTER DEATH
RS 0072952CD / 2 Mar '98 / Rising Sun

Life Force

☐ LIFE FORCE
WB 1154CD / Jun '97 / We Bite

Life Guards Band

☐ ROYAL WINDSOR (Band Of The Life Guards)
BNA 5132 / 13 Apr '98 / Bandleader

Life Of Agony

☐ SOUL SEARCHING SUN
RR 88162
RR 88165 / 15 Sep '97 / Roadrunner

☐ UGLY
RR 89242
RR 89249 / Oct '95 / Roadrunner

Life Sex & Death

☐ SILENT MAJORITY, THE
Blue velvet/we're here now / Jawohl asshole / School's for fools / Telephone call / Farm song / Fuckin' shit ass / Hey buddy / Train / Wet your lips / Tank / Raise a little hell / Guatemala / Big black bush / Rise above
7599269582 / Aug '92 / WEA

Life's Addiction

☐ INNER SHADE
Cherry red / I do believe / Jesus coming in for the kill / Like me again / End of the road / Cool cool breeze / Inner shade / Couldn't sleep last night / Ocean / Lightning strikes
8289102 / Aug '97 / FFRR

Lifesaver Laboratories

☐ TERMS AND CONDITIONS
TCCD 9718 / Sep '97 / Tone Casualties

Lifetime

☐ JERSEY'S BEST DANCERS
JT 1034CD / Jul '97 / Jade Tree

Lifter Puller

☐ LIFTER PULLER
RUNT 24 / Mar '97 / Runt

Lig

☐ BACTERIAL ACTIVITY
ABT 102CD / Jun '97 / Abstract

Ligament

☐ KIND DEEDS
FLOWCD 003 / Apr '96 / Flower Shop

Liggins, Jimmy

☐ JIMMY LIGGINS AND HIS DROPS OF JOY (Liggins, Jimmy & His Drops Of Joy)
I can't stop it / Troubles goodbye / Teardrop blues / Cadillac boogie / Move out baby / Careful love / Homecoming blues / Baby I can't forget you / Don't put me down / Nite life boogie / Mississippi boogie / Come back baby / Answer to Teardrop Blues / That song is gone / Saturday night boogie woogie man / Shuffle shock / Washboard special / That's what's knockin' me out / Hep cat boogie / I want my baby for Christmas / Train blues / Baby's boogie / Drunk / Going away / Come back home
CDCHD 306 / Oct '90 / Ace

☐ ROUGH WEATHER BLUES VOL.2 (Liggins, Jimmy & His Drops Of Joy)
Bye bye baby goodbye / Lookin' for my baby / Rough weather blues / Misery blues / Give up little girl / Lonely nights blues / Saturday night boogie woogie man / Lover's prayer / Now's the time / Sincere lover's blues / Down and out blues / Unidentified instrumental / Blues for love / Brown skin baby / Stolen love / Jumpin' and stompin' / Low down blues / Cloudy day blues / Goin' down with the sun / Dark hour blues / Pleading my cause / I'll never let you go / Railroad blues / Drunk / I'll always love you
CDCHD 437 / Jan '93 / Ace

Liggins, Joe

☐ JOE LIGGINS AND THE HONEYDRIPPERS (Liggins, Joe & His Honey Drippers)
Pink champagne / Ramblin' blues / Rag mop / Rhythm in the barnyard / Going back to New Orleans / I've got a right to cry / Honeydripper / I just can't help myself / Don't miss that train / Frankie Lee / Brand new deal in mobile / Little Joe's boogie / One sweet letter / Whiskey, gin and wine / Louisiana woman / Trying to lose the blues / Shuffle boogie blues / Rain rain rain / Flying Dutchman / Tanya / Blues for Tanya / Freight train blues / Whiskey, women and loaded dice / Big dipper / Do you love me pretty baby
CDCHD 307 / Oct '90 / Ace

Light, Allan

☐ TWO NIGHTS (Light, Allan & Loren Mazzacane)
ROCO 012CD / Feb '97 / Roadcone

Light Division

☐ BEST OF BRITISH, THE (Light Division Band & Bugles)
CDITV 640 / 6 Jul '98 / Scotdisc

☐ HORSE GUARDS PARADE (Massed Bands Of The Light Division)
Bugle calls / Light Division assembly / Advance / Sambre et meuse / Les clarions anglais / Mechanised infantry / Quick silver / Slave's chorus / Silver bugles / St. Mary / Run runaway / Light Cavalry / Keel row / Road to the Isles / Five to one / Three to one / Bugle boy / Secunderabad / Horse Guards echoes: *Massed Bands Of The Royal Air Force* / Great gate of Kiev / Fanfare Sir John Moore / Sunset / National Anthem / Light Infantry regimental march / Royal Green Jackets / No more parades today / High on a hill
BNA 5021 / Jul '88 / Bandleader

☐ LIVE AT THE ALBERT HALL
Duke of Cambridge / Marvin Hamlisch showcase / March off / Bugle feature / March on / Bugle calls / Finale from trumpet concerto / Bohemian rhapsody / St. Marys / Royal green jackets / Nightfall in camp / Crown imperial / High on a hill / Light infantry
3036100092 / Apr '96 / Pearls

☐ LIVING TRADITION, A (Band & Bugles Of The Light Division)
Silver bugles / Zorba's dance / Rifle regiment / Sir John Moore / Let's face the music and dance / Here's that rainy day / Triomphale / Concerto for clarinet / Symphonic Beatles / Gavorkna fanfare / Drigo's serenade / Bill / Sabre dance / Auld lang syne/Last post / Light division marches
BNA 5123 / Jun '96 / Bandleader

Light Of Darkness

☐ LIGHT OF DARKNESS
SB 019 / Jun '97 / Second Battle

Light Of The World

☐ BEST OF LIGHT OF THE WORLD, THE
Swingin' / Midnight groovin' / I shot the sheriff / Visualise yourself (and your mind) / I'm so happy / Time / London town / Pete's crusade / Boys in blue / Painted lady / Something for nothing / Mirror of my soul / I walk the streets alone / Dreams
MCCD 189 / Nov '94 / Music Club

☐ VERY BEST OF LIGHT OF THE WORLD, THE
Somebody help me out: *Beggar & Co* / Swingin' / Keep the dream alive / I'm so happy / Midnight groovin' / Expansions / Parisienne girl: *Incognito* / London town / Pete's crusade / Time / I shot the sheriff / Got to get your own
MOCD 3007 / Feb '95 / More Music

Lightfoot, Gordon

☐ DID SHE MENTION MY NAME/BACK HERE ON EARTH PLUS SPIN, SPIN
Did she mention my name / Wherefor and why / Last time I saw her / Black day in July / May I / Magnificent outpourings / Does your mother know / Mountains and Maryann / Pussy willows, cat tails / I want to hear from you / Something very special / Boss man / Long way back home / Unsettled ways / Long thin dawn / Bitter green / Circle is small / Marie Christine / Cold hands from New York / Affair on 8th Avenue / Don't beat me down / Gypsy / If I could / Spin, spin (New Yok remake version)
BGOCD 167 / Mar '93 / Beat Goes On

☐ EARLY LIGHTFOOT/SUNDAY CONCERT
Rich man's spiritual / Long river / Way I feel / For lovin' me / First time / Changes / Early morning rain / Steel rail blues / Sixteen miles / I'm not saying / Pride of man / Ribbon of darkness / Oh Linda / Peaceful waters / In a windowpane / Lost children / Leaves of grass / Medley: I'm not sayin'; Ribbon of darkness / Apology / Bitter green / Ballad of Yarmouth Castle / Softly / Boss man / Pussy willows, cat tails / Canadian road trilogy
BGOCD 166 / Apr '93 / Beat Goes On

☐ IF YOU COULD READ MY MIND
Minstrel of the dawn / Me and Bobby McGee / Approaching lavender / Saturday clothes / Cobwebs and dust / Poor little Allison / Sit down young stranger / If you could read my mind / Baby it's alright / Your love's return (song for Stephen Foster) / Pony man
7599274512 / Feb '92 / WEA

☐ LIGHTFOOT
If you got it / Softly / Crossroads / Minor ballad / Go go round / Rosanna / Home from the forest / I'll be alright / Song for a winter's night / Canadian railroad trilogy / Way I feel / Rich man's spiritual / Long river / For lovin' me / First time / Changes / Early morning rain / Steel rail blues / Sixteen miles / I'm not saying / Pride of man / Ribbon of darkness / Oh Linda / Peaceful waters
BCD 15576 / Apr '92 / Bear Family

☐ SUNDAY CONCERT PLUS EXTRA STUDIO CUTS
In a windowpane / Lost children / Leaves of grass / I'm not sayin and ribbon of darkness / Apology / Bitter green / Ballad of Yarmouth Castle / Softly / Boss man / Pussy willows, cat tails / Canadian railroad trilogy / Just like Tom Thumb's blues / Movin' / I'll be alright / Spin, spin (Nashville version, Tk 8) / Movin'
BCD 15691 / Mar '93 / Bear Family

☐ SUNDOWN
Somewhere USA / High and dry / Seven Island suite / Circle of steel / Is there anyone home / Watchman's gone / Sundown / Carefree highway / List / Too late for pryin'
7599272112 / Feb '92 / WEA

☐ WAY I FEEL, THE
Walls / If you got it / Softly / Crossroads / A-minor ballad / Go go round / Rosanna / Home from the forest / I'll be alright / Song for a winter's night / Canadian railroad trilogy / Way I feel
BGOCD 296 / Nov '95 / Beat Goes On

Lightfoot, Jerry

☐ BURNING DESIRE (Lightfoot, Jerry & The Essentials)
CBHCD 2002 / Mar '96 / Connor Ray

Lightfoot, Papa George

☐ GOIN BACK TO THE NATCHEZ TRACE
My woman is tired of me lyin / New mean old train / Love my baby / Goin' down that muddy road / Ah come on honey / I heard somebody crying / Take it witcha / Nighttime / Early in the morning / Walkin' / Goin' back to Natchez / Baby, please don't go / Train tune / Papa George - Talkin' about it
CDCHD 548 / Nov '94 / Ace

Lightfoot, Terry

☐ DOWN ON BOURBON STREET (Lightfoot, Terry & His Jazzmen)
Bourbon street parade / Do you know what it means to miss New Orleans / Eh la bas / When we danced at the Mardi Gras / Grandpa's spells / Closer walk with thee / Petite fleur / Chimes blues / Solace / Ole man mose / Hiawatha rag / Trouble in mind / Ice cream / Lonesome / Maryland / Ragtime music
CDTTD 581 / Mar '94 / Timeless Jazz

☐ LIVE IN LEIPZIG
Rockin' in rhythm / West End blues / Sentimental journey / Summertime / Honeysuckle rose / Ol' man Mose / Honky tonk train blues / Tuxedo junction
BLCD 760513 / May '96 / Black Lion

☐ SPECIAL MAGIC OF LOUIS ARMSTRONG, THE (Lightfoot, Terry & His Band)
Jeepers creepers / Muskrat ramble / Give me a kiss to build a dream on / You'll never walk alone / Mack the knife / Wonderful world / Hello Dolly / Tin roof blues / Dardanella / Now you has jazz / All the time in the world / Mame / Dippermouth blues / Lazy river / Faithful hussar / Cabaret / When it's sleepy time down South / Westherbird rag / Blueberry hill / Indiana
STOCD 104 / Feb '97 / Start

☐ STARDUST (Lightfoot, Terry & His Band)
At the woodchoppers' ball / Just a gigolo / Fish seller / Stardust / Bad, Bad Leroy Brown / Undecided / Gone fishin' / Jumpin' at the woodside / Frim fram sauce / Ragtime music / Black and Tan fantasy / Big noise from Winnetka / Bye and bye / Drum boogie
URCD 104 / Dec '90 / Upbeat

☐ WHEN THE SAINTS GO MARCHING IN (Lightfoot, Terry & His Band)
When the Saints go marching in / Mame / At the jazzband ball / Every lonely river / Ballad of Jesse James / Wang wang blues / When you're smiling / Muskrat ramble / John Henry / Jazz me blues / Put down the glass / Drum boogie / Mack the knife / Who's gonna play that ragtime music / River stay 'way from my door / Nobody wants to know you when you're down and out
C5MCD 566 / Apr '96 / See For Miles

Lighthouse

☐ BEST OF LIGHTHOUSE, THE (Sunny Days Again)
One fine morning / Hats off to a stranger / Little kind words / 1849 / Sunny days / Sweet lullaby / Take it slow / Broken down guitar blues / I just wanna be your friend / You girl / Silver bird / Lonely places / Pretty lady / Can you feel it / Magic's in the dancing / Good day
CAN 9002 / Oct '93 / Marquis

☐ BORN A NICE KID
ER 1033 / Aug '97 / Elefant

☐ LIGHTHOUSE LIVE
Just wanna be your friend / Take it slow / Old man / Rockin' chair / You and me / Sweet lullaby / 1849 / Eight miles high / One fine morning / Insane
CAN 9010 / Oct '93 / Marquis

Lighthouse Family

☐ OCEAN DRIVE
Lifted / Heavenly / Loving every minute / Ocean drive / Way you are / Keep remembering / Sweetest operator / What could be better / Beautiful night / Goodbye heartbreak
5237872 / Feb '96 / Wild Card

☐ POSTCARDS FROM HEAVEN
Rainland / Once in a blue moon / Question of faith / Let it all change / Sun in the night / High / Lost in space / When I was younger / Restless / Postcards from Heaven
5395162 / 20 Oct '97 / Wild Card

Lightnin' Rod

☐ HUSTLER'S CONVENTION
Sport / Spoon / Cafe black rose / Brother hominy / Grit / Coppin' some fronts for the set / Hammock's hall was big (and there was a whole lot to dig) / Bones fly from spoon's hand / Break was so loud it hushed the crowd / Four bitches is what I got / Grit's den / Shit hits the fan again / Sentenced to the chair
CPCD 8177 / Jun '96 / Charly

Lightnin' Slim

☐ BLUE LIGHTNING
Mama talk to your daughter / My baby left me this morning / It's mighty crazy / Caress me baby / I love you baby / Sky is crying / GI Slim / Help me spend my gold / My little angel child / Too close blues / I want you to love me / Bedbug blues / I'm tired waitin' baby / Ah'w baby
IGOCD 2002 / Jul '95 / Indigo

☐ HIGH AND LOW DOWN/OVER EASY (Lightnin' Slim & Whispering Smith)
Rooster blues: *Lightnin' Slim* / Things I used to do: *Lightnin' Slim* / Bad luck blues: *Lightnin' Slim* / My babe: *Lightnin' Slim* / GI blues: *Lightnin' Slim* / Oh baby: *Lightnin' Slim* / That's alright Mama: *Lightnin' Slim* / Can't hold out much longer: *Lightnin' Slim* / Good morning heartaches: *Lightnin' Slim* / Hoodoo blues: *Lightnin' Slim* / What in the world's come over me: *Smith, Whispering* / Mojo hand: *Smith, Whispering* / Way you treat me: *Smith, Whispering* / I don't need no woman: *Smith, Whispering* / Everybody needs love: *Smith, Whispering* / I know I've got a sure thing: *Smith, Whispering* / Why am I treated so bad: *Smith, Whispering* / Rock me baby: *Smith, Whispering* / Married man: *Smith, Whispering* / I know you don't love me: *Smith, Whispering* / It's all over: *Smith, Whispering* / You want to do it again: *Smith, Whispering*
CDCHD 578 / Jul '95 / Ace

☐ IT'S MIGHTY CRAZY
Rock me Mama / Bad luck / West Texas / What evil have I done / Lightnin' blues / I can't be successful / I'm him / I can't understand / Just made twenty one / Sugar plum / Goin' home / Wonderin' and goin' / Bad luck and trouble / Have you way / I'm grown / Mean old lonesome train / Rocky mountain blues / Love me Mama / I'm a rollin' stone / Hoodoo blues / It's mighty crazy / Bedbug blues / Tom Cat blues / Farming blues
CDCHD 587 / Apr '95 / Ace

☐ KING OF THE LOUISIANA SWAMP BLUES, THE
Bad luck blues / GI blues / My babe / Things I used to do / Voodoo Blues / Crazy 'bout you baby / That's all right / Good morning heartache / Rooster blues / Oh baby
AIM 2008CD / Sep '97 / Aim

☐ NOTHIN' BUT THE DEVIL
Long leanie Mama / My starter won't work / It's mighty crazy / Blues at night / I'm leavin' you baby / Feelin' awful blue / Sweet little woman / Lightnin's problems / I gonna leave / Rooster blues / GI Slim / Driftin' blues / Too close blues / My little angel child / Greyhound blues / I just don't know / Somebody knockin' / Just a lonely stranger / Cool down baby / Nothin' but the devil / Goin' away blues / I'm tired waitin' baby / Death Valley blues / Hello Mary Lee
CDCHD 616 / Mar '96 / Ace

☐ ROOSTER BLUES/LIGHTNIN' SLIM' BELL RINGER
Rooster blues / Long Leanie Mama / My starter won't work / GI Slim / Lightnin' troubles / Bedbug blues / Hoodoo blues / It's mighty crazy / Sweet little woman / Tom cat blues / Feelin' awful blues / I'm leavin' you baby / Love me Mama / She's my crazy little baby / Have mercy on me baby / Winter time blues / If you ever need me / Mean old lonesome train / Baby please come back / Love is just a gamble / Somebody knockin' / You give me the blues / Don't start me talkin' / You move me baby
CDCHD 517 / Feb '94 / Ace

☐ WINTERTIME BLUES
Mind your own business / Winter time blues / Bad luck is falling / I'm warning you baby / You're old enough to understand / I'm evil / If you ever need me / Lonely stranger aka rocky mountain blues / You give me the blues / You know you're so fine / Don't mistreat me baby / You move me baby / Strangest feelin' / Lonesome cabin blues / Don't start me talkin' / I hate to see you leave / Sittin' and thinkin' / Darlin you're the one / Baby please come back / I've been a fool for you darlin' / Can't live this life anymore / I hear my baby calling / Stranger in town / Bad luck blues
CDCHD 674 / 26 Jan '98 / Ace

Lightning

☐ LIGHTNING
ANT 3811 / Jul '97 / Anthology

Lightning Seeds

☐ CLOUD CUCKOO LAND
All I want / Bound in a nutshell / Pure / Sweet dreams / Nearly man / Joy / Love explosion / Don't let go / Control the flame / Price / God help them
CDOVD 436 / May '92 / Virgin

☐ DIZZY HEIGHTS
Imaginary friends / You bet your life / Waiting for today to happen / What if / Sugar coated iceberg / Touch and go / Like you do / Wishaway / Fingers and thumbs / You showed me / Ready or not / Fishes on the line
4866402 / Nov '96 / Epic

☐ INTERVIEW, THE
SPEEK 005 / 16 Mar '98 / Talking Music

☐ JOLLIFICATION
Perfect / Lucky you / Open goals / Change / Why why why / Marvellous / Feeling lazy / My best day / Punch and Judy / Telling tales
4772372 / Sep '94 / Columbia

☐ LIKE YOU DO (The Greatest Hits)
What you say / Life of Riley / Lucky you / You showed me / Change / Waiting for today to happen / Puke / Sugarcoated iceberg / Ready or not / All I want / Perfect / What if / Sense / Marvellous / Three lions
4890342 / 10 Nov '97 / Epic

☐ PURE LIGHTNING SEEDS
Life of Riley / Sense / Blowing bubbles / Pure / Sweet dreams / All I want / Small slice of heaven / Love explosion / Don't let go / Joy / Price / Cool place / Happy / Tingle tangle / God help them / Bound in a nutshell / Nearly man / Thinking up, looking down
CDV 2805 / Mar '96 / Virgin

☐ SENSE
Sense / Life of Riley / Blowing bubbles / Cool place / Where flowers fade / Small slice of heaven / Tingle tangle / Happy / Marooned / Thinking up, looking down
CDV 2690 / Apr '92 / Virgin

Lights Of Euphoria

☐ FAHRENHEIT
CDZOT 185 / 3 Nov '97 / Zoth Ommog

Lightsey, Kirk

☐ EVERYTHING HAPPENS TO ME (Lightsey, Kirk Trio)
CDSJP 176 / Nov '90 / Timeless Jazz

☐ FROM KIRK TO NAT (Lightsey, Kirk Trio)
CRISS 1050CD / Nov '91 / Criss Cross

☐ GOODBYE MR. EVANS (Lightsey, Kirk Trio)
New blue / In your own sweet way / From Chopin to Chopin / Medley / Four in one / Habiba / Goodbye Mr. Evans
22165 / Oct '96 / Evidence

☐ KIRK N' MARCUS (Lightsey, Kirk Quintet & Marcus Belgrave)
All my love / Loves I once knew / Windmill / Marcus' mates / Golden legacy / Lower bridge level / Lolita / Fixed wing
CRISS 1030CD / Feb '97 / Criss Cross

☐ TEMPTATION (Lightsey, Kirk Trio)
Society red / Brigette / Evidence / Temptation / Love is a many splendoured thing / Gibraltar
CDSJP 257 / Aug '90 / Timeless Jazz

Liimianarina

☐ SUPERMARKET
DC 63CD / Dec '96 / Drag City

Like A Tim

☐ YEAH RIGHT
RROOCCKK / Booming is business / Super Cooper (no freak) / Let the guitars roll / My drummachine is fine / You are too low for me / Legs / I got a blaster now all I need is a ghetto / Danger eveywhere / Starr drumming / Keep those guitars rolling / Perfect in the mind / Fun is gone / It's a fake world after all / Behind the scenes of yeah right
GEIST 003CD / 11 May '98 / Geist

L'il Brian

☐ FRESH (L'il Brian & The Zydeco Travellers)
ROUCD 2136 / Apr '95 / Rounder

Lil' Devious

☐ LIFTED
Lifted
STR 12007 / Oct '96 / Stronghouse

Lil' Ed

☐ CHICKEN, GRAVY AND BISCUITS (Lil' Ed & The Blues Imperials)
ALCD 4772 / Oct '93 / Alligator

☐ ROUGHHOUSIN' (Lil' Ed & The Blues Imperials)
ALCD 4749 / May '93 / Alligator

☐ WHAT YOU SEE IS WHAT YOU GET (Lil' Ed & The Blues Imperials)
Life is like gambling / Find my baby / Older women / Please help / Toothache / Living for today / Travellin' life / Out of the house / Upset man / Long long way from home / What you see is what you get / Bluesmobile / What am I gonna do / Packin' up
ALCD 4808 / May '93 / Alligator

Lil' Kim

☐ HARDCORE
No time / Intro in a minor / Big Momma thang: *Lil' Kim & JZ* / Spend a little doe / Take it / Scheamin' / We don't need it / Crush on you / Drugs / Player haters / Fuck you / Queen Bitch / R and B fantasies/Dreams / MAFIA land / Not tonight / Not tonight
7567927892 / 1 Sep '97 / Big Beat/ Atlantic

Lilac Time

☐ AND LOVE FOR ALL
Fields / All for love and love for all / Let our land be the one / I went to the dance / Wait and see / Honest to God / Laundry / Paper boat / Skabaskiblo / It'll end in tears (I won't cry) / Trinity / And on we go
8461902 / Jan '96 / Fontana

☐ ASTRONAUTS
In iverna gardens / In iverna gardens / Fortunes / A taste for honey / Grey skies and work things / Finistere / Dreaming / Whisper of your mind / Darkness of her eyes / Sunshine's daughter / North kensington / Madresfield
CRECD 098 / May '94 / Creation

☐ LILAC TIME, THE
Black velvet / Rockland / Return to yesterday / You've got to love / Love becomes a savage / Together / Road to happiness / Too sooner late than better / Trumpets from Montparnasse
8348352 / Jan '96 / Fontana

☐ PARADISE CIRCUS
American eyes / Lost girl in the midnight sun / Beauty in your body / If the stars shine tonight / Days of the week / She still loves you / Paradise circus / Girl who waves at trains / Last to know / Father mother wife and child / Rollercoaster song / Work for the weekend / Twilight beer hall
8386412 / Jan '96 / Fontana

Lilier

☐ BACK TO THE ROOTS (Lilier & Doc Houlind)
MECCACD 1020 / Nov '94 / Music Mecca

Lillian Axe

☐ POETIC JUSTICE
CDMFN 131 / Jul '92 / Music For Nations

☐ PSYCHOSCHIZOPHRENIA
Crucified / Deep freeze / Moonlight in your blood / Stop the hate / Sign of the times / Needle and your pain / Those who prey / Voices in my walls / Now you know / Deep blue shadows / Day that I met you / Psychoschizophrenia
CDMFN 151 / Sep '93 / Music For Nations

Lillie, Beatrice

☐ MARVELLOUS PARTY WITH BEATRICE LILLIE, A
AEICD 006 / May '98 / AEI

☐ UNIQUE INCOMPARABLE BEA LILLIE, THE
There are fairies at the bottom of our garden / I'm a campfire girl / He was a gentleman / Nicodemus / Paree / Mad about the boy / Baby doesn't know / Marvellous party / I hate spring / Trains
PASTCD 7054 / Nov '94 / Flapper

Lillie, Brian

☐ ROWBOATS (Lillie, Brian & The Squirrel Mountain Orchestra)
Sunday / My strange love / Hazel's last Christmas / Sweetheart / Carnival / Too early/too late / Squids / Flowers / Madrid / Bad advice / Best friends / Mountain / Grandpa the flyer / Thimbleful of oats / Okay / Full speed ahead / Four immeasurables
OMC 0007 / 20 Apr '98 / One Man Clapping

☐ WAKING UP IN TRAFFIC (Lillie, Brian & The Squirrel Mountain Orchestra)
Kalamazoo / Just a mile away / Alone / Bats in my bluebird house / How much can I love / Stars / Sky / Red room / Starvish / Fountain Street / Goodbye 27 / Prayer of St. Francis
OMC 0004 / 20 Apr '98 / One Man Clapping

Lilly, John C.

☐ ECCO
SR 9452 / Mar '94 / Silent

LILT

☐ FOR THE CHILDREN
ETCD 191 / Nov '90 / Alias

Lilybandits

☐ SHIFTY'S TAVERN
HYMN 9 / 16 Mar '98 / Fundamental

Lilys

☐ BETTER CAN'T MAKE YOUR LIFE BETTER
CHE 52CD / Sep '96 / Che

☐ BETTER CAN'T MAKE YOUR LIFE BETTER
3984224612 / 2 Mar '98 / Che

☐ BRIEF HISTORY OF AMAZING LETDOWNS, A
SPART 11 / 23 Feb '98 / Spin Art

☐ ECCSAME THE PHOTON BAND
SPART 43 / 23 Feb '98 / Spin Art

Limbonic Art

☐ IN ABHORRENCE DEMENTIA
ECLIPSE 008CD / 1 Dec '97 / Nocturnal Art

Limbus 4

☐ MANDALAS
14277 / 2 Feb '98 / Spalax

Limerick, Alison

☐ CLUB CLASSICS
Where love lives / Make it on my own / Come back for real love / Love come down / Time of our lives / Getting it right
74321383102 / Jul '96 / Arista

Liminal

☐ NOSFERATU
KFWCD 170 / Oct '96 / Knitting Factory

Liminal Lounge

☐ EGO DUMP
KFWCD 202 / Jul '97 / Knitting Factory

Limp Bizkit

☐ THREE DOLLAR BILL
IND 90124 / Jul '97 / Interscope

Lin, Caryn

☐ TOLERANCE FOR AMBIGUITY
Call / In the abbey of Scartaglen / No lines drawn / Little king / At the risk of the sun / Tolerance for ambiguity / In cold blood
ALCD 1010 / Apr '97 / Alchemy

Linares, Pepe

☐ MISA FLAMENCA
172462 / Mar '96 / Musidisc

Lince, Louis

☐ AT THE DOT (Lince, Louis Jelly Roll Kings)
BCD 336 / Aug '95 / GHB

☐ HOT AT THE DOT 1991 (Lince, Louis Jelly Roll Kings)
Panama / Memphis blues / Old spinning wheel / Mama's gone goodbye / One sweet letter from you / Royal telephone / Out of nowhere / Climax rag / Uptown bumps / Undecided
JRKCD 510 / Jun '96 / JRK

Lincoln Centre Jazz Orchestra

☐ THEY CAME TO SWING
Take the 'a' train / Take the 'a' train / Express crossing / Light blue / Jelly jelly / Things to come / Boy meets horn / Lost in loveliness / Back to basics / Tattooed bride
4772842 / Jan '95 / Sony Jazz

Lincoln, Abbey

☐ ABBEY IS BLUE
OJCCD 69 / Oct '92 / Original Jazz Classics

☐ IT'S MAGIC
OJCCD 205 / Feb '92 / Original Jazz Classics

☐ PEOPLE IN ME
You and me love / Natas / Dorian / Africa / People in me / Living room / Kohjoh-no-tsuki / Naturally
5146262 / Mar '94 / Verve

☐ STRAIGHT AHEAD
Straight ahead / When Malindy sings / In the red / Blue monk / Left alone / African lady / Retribution
CCD 79015 / Feb '97 / Candid

☐ TALKING TO THE SUN
ENJA 40602 / 17 Nov '97 / Enja

☐ THAT'S HIM
Strong man / Happiness is a thing called Joe / My man (mon homme) / Tender as a rose / That's him / Porgy / When a woman loves a man / Don't explain
OJCCD 85 / Oct '92 / Original Jazz Classics

☐ TURTLE'S DREAM, A
Throw it away / A turtle's dream / Down here below / Nature boy / Avec le temps / Should've been / My love is you / Storywise / Hey, lordy mama / Not to worry / Being me
5273822 / May '95 / Verve

☐ WHEN THERE IS LOVE (Lincoln, Abbey & Hank Jones)
Part of me/There are such things / When there is love / Black butterfly / Angel face / Nearness of you/Can't help singing / Close your eyes / I should care / You came a long way from St. Louis / C'est si bon / Jitterbug waltz / Time after time / You won't forget me / First came a woman
5196972 / Mar '94 / Verve

☐ WHO USED TO DANCE
5335592 / Mar '97 / Verve

Lind, Espen

☐ RED
UND 86514 / 29 Jun '98 / Universal

Lind, Ove

☐ GERSHWIN - EVERGREEN
'S wonderful / Summertime / Swanee / Embraceable you / Bidin' my time / Our love is here to stay / But not for me / Changing my tune / Of thee I sing / Somebody loves me / Someone to watch over me / Oh lady be good / Aren't you kind of glad we did / I got plenty o' nuttin' / They can't take that away from me / Strike up the band / Man I love / Nice work if you can get it / Who cares / Love is sweeping the country / I've got a crush on you / Love walked in / Foggy day / My one and only / I was doing all right / They all laughed / How long has this been going on / Let's call the whole thing off
PHONTCD 7410 / Aug '94 / Phontastic

☐ ONE MORNING IN MAY (Lind, Ove Quartet)
Just friends / Tangerine / Sky fell down / So would I / Cheek to cheek / I thought about you / Down by the old mill stream / Baby won't you please / I've got a feeling I'm falling in love / Stay as sweet as you are / I've got my eyes on you / True / One morning in May
PHONTCD 7501 / Aug '94 / Phontastic

☐ ORCHESTRA SWEDISH EVERGREENS WITH CHARLIE PARKER
PHONTCD 7408/9 / Aug '94 / Phontastic

☐ PHONTASTIC EVERGREENS VOL.1 (Lind, Ove Quartet/Sextet)
PHONTCD 7401 / Jul '96 / Phontastic

☐ PHONTASTIC EVERGREENS VOL.2 (Lind, Ove Quintet/Sextet)
PHONTCD 7403 / Jul '96 / Phontastic

☐ SUMMER NIGHT
Summer night / You leave me breathless / Say my heart / Changing my tune / Ill wind / You're a lucky guy / Oh lady be good / My cabin of dreams / You're the cream in my coffee / This heart of mine / Louise / Swinging on a star
PHONTCD 7503 / Aug '94 / Phontastic

Lindberg, John

☐ BOUNCE (Lindberg, John Ensemble)
1201922 / Mar '98 / Black Saint

☐ DIMENSION 5 (Lindberg, John Quintet)
Eleven thrice / T'wixt C and D / T'wixt C and D (part 2) / Dimension 5
1200622 / May '97 / Black Saint

☐ DODGING BULLETS (Lindberg, John & Albert Mangelsdorff & Eric Watson)
12010502 / Jan '93 / Black Saint

☐ LUMINOSITY (Hommage To David Izenzon)
CD 970 / Jul '97 / Music & Arts

☐ RESURRECTION OF A DORMANT SOUL
1201722 / Dec '96 / Black Saint

Lindberg, Nils

☐ O MISTRESS MINE
ABCD 032 / Oct '96 / Bluebell

☐ SAX APPEAL & TRISECTION
DRAGONCD 220 / Jan '89 / Dragon

☐ SAXES & BRASS GALORE
ABCD 3004 / Jun '94 / Bluebell

Lindemann, David

☐ ANCIENT EVENINGS, DISTANT MUSIC
CDSGP 9025 / Jun '95 / Prestige

☐ ETERNAL BOUNDARIES
CDSGP 9002 / Apr '95 / Prestige

Linden, Colin

☐ THROUGH THE STORM THROUGH THE NIGHT
Moon follow me home / When the carnival ends / Art of the wilderness / No rest for the wicked / Reason of the rhyme / Last time / Waiting is over / You'll be mine / Homesick in my own backyard / You are here / Devil music / Precious Lord / Sad and beautiful world
8440582 / 21 Aug '97 / Sky Ranch
FIENDCD 933 / Sep '97 / Demon

Lindgren, Erik

☐ OIL ON LINEN
AA 036 / Jul '97 / Arf Arf

Lindgren, Kurt

☐ LADY M
DRCD 189 / Oct '88 / Dragon

Lindgren, Lasse

☐ TO MY FRIENDS
DRCD 227 / Dec '88 / Dragon

Lindgren, Ole 'Fessor'

☐ BIG CITY SHUFFLE VOL.1 (Fessor's Big City Band)
MECCACD 2014 / May '97 / Music Mecca

☐ BIG CITY SHUFFLE VOL.2 (Fessor's Big City Band)
MECCACD 2015 / May '97 / Music Mecca

☐ HOT JAZZ SYNDICATE (Lindgren, Ole 'Fessor' & John Defferary)
MECCACD 2027 / Oct '97 / Music Mecca

☐ JOYFUL NOISE, A (Fessor's Big City Band)
MECCACD 1070 / May '97 / Music Mecca

Lindisfarne

☐ AMIGOS
One world / Everything changes / Working for the man / Roll on that day / You're the one / Wish you were here / Do it like this / Anyway the wind blows / Strange affair
CROCD 224 / Dec '89 / Black Crow
CLACD 384 / May '93 / Castle

☐ ANOTHER FINE MESS
Clear white light / Squire / Lady Eleanor / Meet me on a corner / Evening / City song / One world / All fall down / Winter song / This heart of mine / We can make it / Road to kingdom come / Money / Run for home / Fog on the tyne
GRACD 211
GRAVD 211 / Jul '96 / Grapevine

☐ BACK AND FOURTH
Angels at eleven / Get wise / Jukebox gypsy / King X blues / Make me want to stay / Marshall Rileys army / Only alone / Run for home / Warm feeling / Woman / You and me
CLACD 413 / Oct '96 / Castle

☐ BEST OF LINDISFARNE, THE
Meet me on the corner / Lady Eleanor / All fall down / We can swing together / Fog on the Tyne / Road to Kingdom Come / Scarecrow song / Winter song / Clear white light / January song / Down / Walk up little sister / Together forever / Alright on the night / Go back / Don't ask me
CDVIP 103 / Dec '93 / Virgin VIP

☐ BURIED TREASURES VOL.1
Buried treasures vol.1 / Red square dance / Finest hour / Together forever / Together crack - spoken word / Happy or sad / Way behind you / Behind crack - spoken word / Old peculiar feeling / True love / Love crack - spoken word / City song / Rock 'n' roll town / Swiss maid / Sporting life blues / Karen Marie / From my window / Window crack - spoken word / Run Jimmy run / Malvinas melody / Let's dance
CDVM 9012 / Nov '92 / Virgin

☐ BURIED TREASURES VOL.2
Save our ales / Ale crack / Golden apples / Try giving everything / Nothing's gonna break us now / January song / Living on the baseline / On my own I built a bridge / Bridge crack / Roll on that day / Loving around the clock / Reunion / Reunion / Friday girl / Tomorrow if I'm hungry / Hungry crack / Fog on the Tyne / Winning the games / Peter Gunn theme / Run for home
CDVM 9013 / Nov '92 / Virgin

☐ CITY SONGS
Lady Eleanor / City song / Train in G major / Fog on the Tyne / Scotch mist / Mandolin king / Poor old Ireland / Road to Kingdom Come / Lady Eleanor / Drug song / Country Gentleman's wife / Passing ghosts / Turn a deaf ear / Lady ELeanor / Scarecrow song / Meet me on the corner
PILOT 34 / 3 Aug '98 / Burning Airlines

☐ CROPREDY CONCERT, THE (Live At The Cropredy 1994)
Road to Kingdom come / All fall down / Elvis lives on the moon / City song / Lady Eleanor / Evening / Day of the jackal / We can make it / Train in G minor / Walk in the sea / Drinking song / Meet me on the corner / Run for home / Clear white light
CRESTCD 024 / 20 Oct '97 / Mooncrest

☐ DANCE YOUR LIFE AWAY
Shine on / Love on the run / Heroes / All in the same boat / Dance your life away / Beautiful day / Broken doll / Hundred miles to Liverpool
CLACD 383 / Apr '93 / Castle

☐ ELVIS LIVES ON THE MOON
Day of the Jackal / Soho Square / Old peculiar feeling / Mother Russua / Think / Spoken like a man / Heaven wails / Heeping the rage / Elvis lives on the moon / Don't leave me tonight / Demons
ESMCD 391 / Jul '96 / Essential

☐ FOG ON THE TYNE
Meet me on the corner / Alright on the night / Uncle Sam / Together forever / January song / Peter Brophy don't care / City song / Passing ghosts / Train in G major / Fog on the Tyne / Scotch mist / No time to lose
CASCD 1050 / '88 / Charisma

☐ LADY ELEANOR (2CD Set)
SMDCD 159 / Jul '97 / Snapper

☐ LINDISFARNE ARCHIVES
Meet me on the corner / Warm feeling / Clear white light / Let's dance / New Orleans / Splish splash / Lady eleanor / Love you more than I can say / Mr. Bassman / Run for home / Oh donna / Sea cruise / Fog on the tyne / Runaround sue / It'll be me / You keep a knockin' / Twist and shout / Keep your hands of my baby
RMCD 222 / Nov '97 / Rialto

☐ LINDISFARNE ON TAP (A Barrel Full Of Hits)
Run for home / Lady Eleanor / Meet me on the corner / We can make it / All fall down / Warm feeling / Winter song / Road to Kingdom come / Fog on the Tyne / Miracles / No time to lose / Running man / Elvis lives on the moon / Juke box gypsy / Dance your life away / Evening / Roll on that day / Clear white light
ESMCD 399 / Jul '96 / Essential

☐ MAGIC IN THE AIR
Lady Eleanor / Road to kingdom come / Turn a deaf ear / January song / Court in the act / No time to lose / Winter song / Uncle Sam / Wake up little sister / All fall down / Meet me on the corner / Bye-bye birdie / Train in G major / Scarecrow song / Dingley dell / Scotch mist / We can swing together / Fog on the Tyne / Clear white light
CCSCD 442 / Oct '96 / Castle

☐ NEWS, THE
Call of the wild / People say / 1983 / Log on your fire / Evening / Easy and free / Miracles / When Friday comes along / Dedicated hound / This has got to end / Good to be here
CLACD 414 / Oct '96 / Castle

☐ NICELY OUT OF TUNE
Lady Eleanor / Road to Kingdom come / Winter song / Turn a deaf ear / Clear white light part 2 / We can swing together / Alan in the river with flowers / Down / Things I should have said / Jackhammer blues / Scarecrow song / Knackers yard blues / Nothing but the marvellous is beautiful
CASCD 1025 / '88 / Charisma

☐ OTHER SIDE OF LINDISFARNE, THE
CRESTCD 020 / Jun '96 / Mooncrest

☐ RUN FOR HOME (Lindisfarne Collected)
Run for home / Marshall Riley's army / Juke box gypsy / Winter song / Train in G major / When it gets the hardest / Brand new day / Good to be here / When Friday comes along / Sunderland boys / I must stop going to parties / Dance your life away / Love on the run / Clear white light / Meet me on the corner / Elvis on the moon / Day of the jackal / Fog on the Tyne
MCCD 305 / Jun '97 / Music Club

☐ SLEEPLESS NIGHTS
Nights / Start again / Cruising to disaster / Same way down / Winning the game / About you / Sunderland boys / Love is a pain / Do what I want / Never miss the water
CLACD 382 / Mar '93 / Castle

☐ UNTAPPED AND ACOUSTIC
PRKCD 43 / 5 May '98 / Park

☐ WE CAN SWING TOGETHER
PILOT 035 / 1 Jun '98 / Burning Airlines

Lindley, David

☐ OFFICIAL BOOTLEG VOL.1 (Playing Real Good) (Lindley, David & Hani Naser)
Bon ton roulie / Ain't no way / Her mind is gone / She took off my Romeos/Pretty girl rules the world / More than Eva Braun / Play it all night long / Cottonmill blues / Rag bag / Way out West in Kansas / Tiki torches at twilight / Mercury blues
753362 / Feb '97 / Pleemhead

☐ OFFICIAL BOOTLEG VOL.2 (Playing Even Better) (Lindley, David & Hani Naser)
Jimmy Hoffa memorial building blues / Meatman / How can a poor man face such times and live / Lick the tears / Afindrafindrao / Well well well / Tijuana / Poor old dirt farmer / About to make me leave home
756762 / Feb '97 / Pleemhead

Lindner, Patrick

☐ DIE KLEINEN DINGE DES LEBENS
Die kleinen dinge des lebens / Und wenn i tanz mit dir (des is a Wahnsinn) / A bisserl Abschied gibt's halt nicht / Und wenn's Nacht wird, Gibt's a Busserl / Dein kloaner Bua / Das Gefuhl Geborgenheit / Die stimme des Herzens / Manchmal braucht man was, an des ma glaub'n kann / Einmal noch mit dir / A wirtshaus und an Kramerlad'n / Der liebe gott hat immer Zeit / Wenn i dich seh, muss i traumen
DC 868232 / Oct '96 / Disky

☐ DIE KLOANE TUR ZUM PARADIES
Die kloane tur zum paradies / Wenn d'sehnsucht a vogerl war / S'reserl vom mariental / Munchner kindl / Dann muB i hoam / Irgendwie hab i di gern / Kannst di net a bisserl freun / Arrivederci Maria Angela / Sowas liabs wie di / Zwei herzerln am birkenbaum / Immer wieder sind es lieder / Rosarot's brieaferl
DCA 876932 / Nov '96 / Disky

☐ EINE HANDVOLL HERZLICHKEIT
Die kloane aus der letzen Bank / Ich hatt / Heut nacht hab'n die sternl a pause / Du schaffst mi / Vergessen heiBt-halt immer an dich denken / Der anti-sorgen walzer / Der Mensch in dir / Wer einmal lugt / Eine Handvoll Herzlichkeit / Durfen darf ma alles / Ganseblumchen weinen nicht / LaB mei Herz a bisserl
DC 868242 / Oct '96 / Disky

☐ WEIHNACHTEN MIT
Kinder, kinder es ist winter / Weil's christkind bald Gerburtstag hat / Stille nacht / Der verlasse tannenbaum / Lasst uns mit den Hirten geh'n / Ein neues jahr / Lasst das licht in Eure Herzen / Still, still weil's kindlein schlafen will / Mandeln und zimt / Es wird scho glei dumpa / Frohliche weihnacht/kling glockchen / Weihnacht zu hause
DC 868252 / Oct '96 / Disky

Lindo, Kashief

☐ KASHIEF SINGS CHRISTMAS
CRCD 37 / Dec '94 / Charm

☐ SOUL & INSPIRATION
CRCD 45 / Jan '96 / Charm

☐ WHAT KINDA WORLD
VPCD 1504 / 29 Sep '97 / VP
CRCD 77 / 12 Jan '98 / Charm

Lindsay, Arto

☐ AGGREGATES
KFWCD 164 / Feb '95 / Knitting Factory

☐ ENVY (Lindsay, Arto & The Ambitious Lovers)
Cross your legs / Troublemaker / Pagode Americano / Nothings monstered / Crowning roar / Too many mansions / Let's be adult / Venus lost her shirt / My competition / Babu / Dora / Beberibe / Locus coruleus
CDOVD 469 / Jul '96 / Virgin

☐ MUNDO CIVILIZADO
Complicity / Q Samba / Simply beautiful / Mundo civilizado / Titles / Horizontal / Mar da gavea / Imbassai / Pleasure / Erotic city / Clown
RCD 10410 / Jun '97 / Rykodisc

☐ NOON CHILL (2CD Set)
Noon chill / Whirlwind / Simply are / Blue eye shadow / Mulata Fuzarqueria / Ridiculously deep / Anything / Gods are weak / Take my place / Daily life / Light moves away / Why compare / Auguri / Re-entry / Ambassador jr. / 3348 / Size / Channel 17
RCD 10436 / 30 Mar '98 / Rykodisc

☐ O CORPO SUTIL (The Subtle Body)
4 skies / Child prodigy / Anima animale / Este seu olhar / My mind is going / Enxugar / No meu sotaque / Unbearable / Nobody in bed / Astronauts / Sovereign
RCD 10369 / Aug '96 / Rykodisc

Lindsay, Erica

☐ DREAMER
Daydream / First movement / Walking together / Dreamer / At the last moment / Gratitude
CCD 79040 / Feb '97 / Candid

Lindsay, Reg

☐ REASONS TO RISE
LARRCD 300 / Nov '94 / Larrikin

Lindsey, Jimmy

☐ FREE HAND (Lindsey, Jimmy & His Band)
BYCD 1 / May '96 / Jim Lindsey

Lindsey, Patrick

☐ GET THE PHONK OUT OF MY FACE
SCHOOL 0012 / 3 Aug '98 / School

Lindstrom, Jack

☐ LIVE AT STAMPEN 1947-1950 & 1997 (Lindstrom, Jack Hep Cats)
TTPCD 004 / Dec '97 / True Track

Lindup, Mike

☐ CHANGES
Changes / Lovely day / Fallen angel / Spirit is free / Desire / West coast man / Judgement day / Life will never be the same / Paixao (Passion)
LV 101CD / Sep '94 / Voiceprint

Lingkungan Seni Degung Jugala

☐ GAMELAN DEGUNG
PAN 2053CD / Apr '96 / Pan

Linhart, Peter

☐ BLUE NIGHTS
EFA 120652 / Dec '94 / Hotwire

Link

☐ SEX DOWN
Club scene at GiGi's / DANCE with me / Whatcha gone do / Gimme some / I really wanna sex your body / Sex down / Sex-lude / 911 0025 / Message-lude / All night freakin' / Spill / One of a kind / I don't wanna see / Don't runaway pre-lude / Thankyou
4911282 / 6 Jul '98 / Relativity

Link 80

☐ 17 REASONS
AM 005CD / Feb '97 / Asian Man

☐ KILLING KATIE
AM 014CD / Sep '97 / Asian Man

Linka, Rudy

☐ ALWAYS DOUBLE CZECH
Coming through / Room #428 / Air Jamaica / Our drives to K1 / Man from Waikiki / Bob's tune / Secret inside / Come rain or come shine / Way back / Now this / And how are you in the mornings
ENJ 93012 / Dec '96 / Enja

☐ CZECH IT OUT
Old and new / Just on time / Uptown express / How deep is the ocean / Traveller / Welcome to the club / Folk song / At this point / Love letters
ENJ 90012 / Dec '94 / Enja

Linkchain, Hip

☐ AIRBUSTERS
House cat blues / I had a dream / Blow wind blow / Bedbug blues / On my way / Keep on searching / Gambler's blues / I'll overcome / Strain on my heart / Take out your false teeth / Bad news / Airbusters / Fugitive / Diggin' my potatoes
ECD 260382 / Sep '93 / Evidence

Links II

☐ NEW REASONS TO USE OLD WORDS
EFA 127332 / Feb '96 / Musikerhof

Linsky, Jeff

☐ ANGEL'S SERENADE
Later / Black sand / Angel's serenade / Bop bop / In out heart / Leo / Over the rainbow / Can't dance / Beautiful love / Speak low
CCD 4611 / Sep '94 / Concord Picante

☐ CALIFORNIA
Crossing / Murrietas' farwell / Samba cruz / For Elsa / Casa miguel / Second street / Pacifica / On the strand / Sonoma / Highway one / Nightfall
CCD 4708 / Jul '96 / Concord Vista

☐ PASSPORT TO THE HEART
Passport to the heart / Mornin' / Love theme from Havana / Love club / Through Love club / Through the fire / Road to Akunlal / Southern passage / Summer soft / While nature sleeps / Five reasons / Passport to the heart
CCD 47642 / Jul '97 / Concord Vista

☐ UP LATE
Armony / Besame mucho / Berimbau / Carlos / Hermosa / I didn't know what time it was / Lanikai / Monterrey / Up late / Wave
CCD 4363 / Nov '88 / Concord Jazz

Linton, Steffan

☐ UNFINISHED AFFAIR
DRCD 193 / Aug '88 / Dragon

Linx, David

☐ BANDARKAH (Linx, David & Diedrik Wissels)
Bandarkah / Gone to glory / Think about a way to stay / Let the healing begin / One last goodbye / Rekindle / I recall / Where home's at / Close / Take on that mountain / Lena
LBLC 6606 / 29 Jun '98 / Label Bleu

☐ IF ONE MORE DAY
TWI 972 / May '96 / Les Disques Du Crepuscule

Lionrock

☐ CITY DELIRIOUS
HARD 32CDX / 15 Jun '98 / Concrete

☐ INSTINCT FOR DETECTION, AN
Morning will come when I'm not ready / Straight at yer head / Peace repackaged / Death Valley clapperboard / Fire up the shoesaw / Don't take foolish / Depth / Snapshot on Pollard Street / Guide / Number nine / Bag of biros / Wilmslow Road
74321342812 / 11 May '98 / De-Construction

Lionsheart

☐ PRIDE IN FACT
CDMFN 167 / Nov '94 / Music For Nations

☐ UNDER FIRE
Lonely tonight / Had enough / World of pain / Go down / Ready or not / Blue sky / So cold / Let the children play / Can't believe / Devil's train / Dark of the night / Portrait / Living in a fantasy / Flights of angels / Stealer / Make believe / All I need / On a roll / Have mercy / Cold heart / Under fire / Going down / Good enough
CDMFN 139 / Jul '92 / Music For Nations
CDMFN 206 / 6 Apr '98 / Music For Nations

Lipovsky, Shura

☐ MOMENTS OF JEWISH LIFE
SYNCD 153 / Jun '93 / Syncoop

Lipscomb, Mance

☐ CAPTAIN CAPTAIN
Captain captain / Ain't you sorry / Night time is the right time / Mr. Tom's rag / I want to do something for you / Long tall git gun stuck on me / Rag in 'A' / Goin' up north to see my pony run / Santa fe blues / Frankie and Albert / Sentimental piece in 'G' / Farewell blues / Shorty George / Angel child / Black rat / Tom Moore's farm (take 2) / Foggy bottom blues / Heel and toe polka / Going back to Georgia / Easy rider blues / Why did you leave me / Me and my baby / Mance's talking blues / Segregation done past
ARHCD 465 / Jul '98 / Arhoolie

☐ TEXAS BLUES GUITAR
ARHCD 001 / Apr '95 / Arhoolie

☐ TEXAS SONGSTER
ARHCD 306 / Apr '95 / Arhoolie

☐ YOU GOT TO REAP WHAT YOU SOW
ARHCD 398 / Apr '95 / Arhoolie

Liquid

☐ LIQUID CULTURE
XLCD 113 / Jul '95 / XL

Liquid Hips

☐ FOOL INJECTION
EMY 1382 / Sep '97 / Enemy

☐ RAGEAHOLIC
EMY 1542 / Sep '97 / Enemy

☐ STATIC
EMY 1422 / Sep '97 / Enemy

Liquid Liquid

☐ LIQUID LIQUID
Optimo / Cavern / Scraper / Out / Lock groove in / Lock groove out / Push / Zero leg / Eyes sharp / Groupmegroup / New walk / Lub dupe / Bell head / Rubbermiro / Lock groove / Groupmegroup / Bell head / Push
MW 078CD / Aug '97 / Mo Wax

Liquid Lounge

☐ URBAN SOULSCAPE
SCAT 2CD / Jul '96 / Scat

Liquid Sound Company

☐ EXPLORING THE PSYCHEDELIC
BTR 2173 / Dec '97 / Psychout

Liquid Tension Experiment

☐ LIQUID TENSION EXPERIMENT
MAX 9023CD / 23 Mar '98 / Mascot

Liquid Z

☐ AMPHIBIC
GAMMA 002CD / 6 Oct '97 / Gamma

Liquidators

☐ LIQUIDATORS JOIN THE SKA TRAIN, THE (Various Artists)
Liquidator: Harry / All Stars / Phoenix city: Alphonso, Roland / Miss Jamaica: Cliff, Jimmy / Pressure drop: Toots & The Maytals / School moonstomp: Symarip / Guns of Navarone: Skatalites / 007: Dekker, Desmond / Shame and scandal: Tosh, Peter & The Wailers / Ethiopia: Pyramids / Johnny too bad: Slickers / Train to Skaville: Ethiopians / Monkey man: Toots & The Maytals / Rudie, a message to you: Livingstone, Dandy / It mek: Dekker, Desmond / Musical store room: Drummond, Don / Return of Django: Upsetters / Israelites: Dekker, Desmond & The Aces / Train to Rainbow City: Pyramids / Guns fever: Brooks, Baba / Double barrel: Barker, Dave & Ansell Collins / Dollar in the teeth: Upsetters / Don't be a rude boy: Rulers / Twelve minutes to go: McCook, Tommy / Rudy's dead: Pyramids
VSOPCD 136 / Jul '89 / Connoisseur Collection

Liquor Bike

☐ NEON HOOP RIDE
GROW 352 / Feb '95 / Grass

Liquor Giants

☐ EVERY OTHER DAY AT A TIME
It's raining butterflies / Beautiful Flo / What's the new mofo / Dearest darling / Kentucky lounge / I'll never mind / Medicine ball game / Multicoloured hipshake / Meaningless / It only hurts when I smile / Riverdale High / Caroline / I know I'm wrong / Summer school
OLE 2982 / 2 Mar '98 / Matador

☐ LIQUOR GIANTS
Chocolate clown / Fake love / Copycat / Cranium / 100 dollar car / Bastanchury Park / Awful good / Hideous pleasure / Hey you / Here / Jerked around / All I get / Thanksgiving in Zuma
OLE 1812 / Jun '96 / Matador

Liquorette

☐ WHEN YOU WORK I SLEEP
MUDCD 014 / 16 Feb '98 / Mud

Liquorice

☐ LISTENING CAP
Trump suite / Team player / Keeping the weekend free / Drive around / Cheap cuts / Trump suit edit / Jill of all trades / No excuses / Breaking the ice / Blew it
GAD 5008CD / 6 Jul '98 / 4AD

Liquorice Roots

☐ MELODEON
MFR 0072 / 20 Oct '97 / Mood Food

Lir

☐ MAGICO MAGICO
VELO 2003CD / Jan '94 / Cross Border Media

Lisa

☐ BEST OF LISA, THE
HTCD 109 / 20 Apr '98 / Hot Productions

Lisa Gives Head

☐ CLOSER LOOK AT THE GROUND, THE
SPV 08436262 / Mar '96 / SPV

Lisa Lisa

☐ LISA LISA & CULT JAM AND FRIENDS (Lisa Lisa & Cult Jam)
Little Jackie wants to be a star / Alice I want you just for me / Let the best hit 'em / Naughty girls (need love too) / Head to toe / Everything you take me home / I wonder if I take you home / Friends b-4 lovers / Let the beat hit 'em / I wanna have some fun / Can you feel the beat / All wanna do / Lost in emotion / Just one night / Someone to love me for me
4805652 / 13 Jul '98 / Columbia

Listening Pool

☐ STILL LIFE
Meant to be / Oil for the lamps of China / Follow where you go / Breathless / Somebody somewhere / Photograph of you / Promised the world / Blue Africa / Still life / Where do we go from here / Wild strawberries / Hand me that universe
TLGCD 002 / Feb '95 / Telegraph

Lister, Anne

☐ FLAME IN AVALON, A
HFCD 003 / Apr '96 / Hearthfire

☐ ROOT SEED THORN AND FLOWER
HFCD 04 / Mar '98 / Hearthfire

☐ SPREADING WINGS
HFCD 02 / May '93 / Hearthfire

Lister, Ayako

☐ JAPANESE KOTO, THE
EUCD 1105 / '91 / ARC

Lister, Ron

☐ BAND ON THE WALL (The Words & Music Of Ron Lister)
Dance with the wind / Mists of morning / Godman / once saw an angel / Candle in the night / Wandering man / Tears of life / Africa town / Have you ever / Love library / White rose / Dance with the wind / Deja vu
AMARA 024CD / 20 Oct '97 / Amara

☐ BLUE GENES
Have a little faith / I once had a friend / Only a woman / Friends of circumstance / Gypsy / Youth of yesterday / Devil in the dark / Frozen ground / Through the looking glass of time / Reflections / American girl / Time
AMARA 108CD / 20 Oct '97 / Amara

Listing Attic

☐ FLY LIKE AN EGO
TEC 2 / Jul '97 / Three Id Cat

Liston, Virginia

☐ VIRGINIA LISTON VOL.1 1923-1924
DOCD 5446 / May '96 / Document

☐ VIRGINIA LISTON VOL.2 1924-1926
DOCD 5447 / May '96 / Document

Litany

☐ PECULIAR WORLD
435142 / Sep '96 / Time Bomb

Lithium X-Mas

☐ BAD KARMA
LOST 007 / May '97 / Lost

Litmus Green

☐ IT MUST SUCK TO BE YOU
FLY 11CD / 16 Mar '98 / Tackle Box

Litter

☐ $100 FINE
TX 2004CD / Jan '94 / Taxim

☐ DISTORTIONS
TX 2003CD / Jan '94 / Taxim

☐ DISTORTIONS/$100 FINE
EVAB 4 / 1 Jun '98 / EVA

Little Angels

☐ TOO POSH TO MOSH
All roads lead to you / Forbidden fruit / I want love / Reach for me / Bad or just no good / Burning me / No more whiskey / Down in the night / Better than the rest / Too posh to mosh / Some kind of alien
ESMCD 398 / Jan '97 / Essential

Little Annie

☐ SHORT AND SWEET
ONUCD 16 / Jun '93 / On-U Sound

Little Anthony & The Locomotives

☐ CAN'T TAKE IT
DELCD 3005 / Mar '96 / Deluge

☐ DON'T WAIT ON ME
DELCD 3013 / Jan '96 / Deluge

Little Bob

☐ RENDEZVOUS IN ANGEL CITY
Isn't it enough / There'll never be another you / I can't wait / True love / Gimme you / Midnight crisis / As the lights go out / Keep on running / When the night falls / Never cry about the past
104 182 / Mar '90 / Musidisc

Little Buster

☐ LOOKIN' FOR A HOME (The Complete Little Buster Jubilee & Josie Sessions)
Lookin' for a home / I think I'm falling / It's loving time / All night worker / I got a good thing going / I proved I love you / But I do / I'm so lonely / Young boy blues / Cry me a river / You were meant for me / River's invitation / Whole lotta lovin' / He's gone / I knew it all the time / TCB / I love you, yes I do / I've got tears in my eyes / Just a letter / What a fool I've been / Why did it have to be me / All I could do was cry / I think I'm falling in love
NEMCD 768 / Jan '97 / Sequel

☐ RIGHT ON TIME (Little Buster & The Soul Brothers)
CDBB 9562 / Oct '95 / Bullseye Blues

Little, Booker

☐ BOOKER LITTLE AND FRIENDS
CDGR 234 / 30 Mar '98 / Charly

☐ FIRE WALTZ (Little, Booker & Eric Dolphy)
Number eight / Fire waltz / Bee vamp
ECD 220742 / Nov '93 / Evidence

☐ LIVE - THE COMPLETE CONCERT (Little, Booker & Teddy Charles Group)
COD 032 / Jul '92 / Jazz View

☐ OUT FRONT
We speak / Strength and sanity / Quiet, please / Moods in free time / Man of words / Hazy hues / New day
CCD 79027 / Feb '97 / Candid

☐ REMEMBERED LIVE AT SWEET BASIL (Little, Booker & Eric Dolphy)
Prophet / Aggression / Booker's waltz
ECD 220732 / Nov '93 / Evidence

Little Caesar

☐ TOGA TOGA TOGA (Little Caesar & The Romans)
DELFI 71262 / 6 Jul '98 / Del-Fi

Little Charlie

☐ ALL THE WAY CRAZY (Little Charlie & The Nightcats)
TV crazy / Right around the corner / Clothes line / Living hand to mouth / Suicide blues / Poor Tarzan / When girls do it / Eyes like a cat / I'll take you back / Short skirts
ALCD 4753 / May '93 / Alligator

☐ BIG BREAK, THE (Little Charlie & The Nightcats)
ALCD 4776 / May '93 / Alligator

☐ CAPTURED LIVE (Little Charlie & The Nightcats)
Tomorrow night / Run me down / Rain / Dump that chump / Ten years ago / Thinking with the wrong head / Wildcattin' / Crawlin' kingsnake / Smart like Einstein / Eyes like a cat
ALCD 4794 / Oct '93 / Alligator

☐ DELUXE EDITION (Little Charlie & The Nightcats)
Can't keep it up / Right around the corner / I beg your pardon / Don't do it / Sure seems strange / Run me down / Too close together / I feel so sorry / My next ex-wife / Clothes line / Dump that chump / I'll take you back / Booty song (I love to watch you walk away) / Gerontology / Crying won't help you
ALCD 5603 / 6 Oct '97 / Alligator

☐ DISTURBING THE PEACE (Little Charlie & The Nightcats)
That's my girl / Nervous / My money's green / If this is love / I ain't lyin' / She's talking / My last meal / Booty song / Don't boss me / V8 Ford blues / I feel so sorry / Run me down
ALCD 4761 / Apr '93 / Alligator

☐ NIGHT VISION (Little Charlie & The Nightcats)
ALCD 4812 / May '93 / Alligator

☐ STRAIGHT UP (Little Charlie & The Nightcats)
I could deal with it / I can't speak no spanish (No hablo espanol) / I'm just lucky that way / Turn my back on you / Me and my big mouth / You gonna lie / Hey gold digger / Homocide / Too close together / Gerontology / Playboy blues / Is that it / On the loose / My way or the highway
ALCD 4829 / Apr '95 / Alligator

Little Chief

☐ SPIRIT
FGUTCD 001 / Jan '94 / Futgut

Little Circus

☐ ANGEL ON YOUR PILLOW VOL.1
Angel on your pillow / I'll never let you fall / Dreamboat / Sleepy old town / Songbird / Catfish catfish / Shooting star / Tiny starfish hands / Man in the moon / Sleepyhead / Toy train / Smile upon your face / It's only the wind / Weaver
ANGELCD 1 / 10 Nov '97 / Anytime

Little Eva

☐ L-L-L-L-LITTLE EVA (The Complete Dimension Recordings)
Loco-motion / He is the boy / Some kinda wonderful / I have a love / Down home / Breaking up is hard to do / Run to her / Where do I go / Up on the roof / Will you still love me tomorrow / Keep your hands off my baby / Let's turkey trot / Old smokey loco-motion / Just a little girl / Trouble with boys / Swinging on a star / What I gotta do (to make you jealous) / Let's start the party again / Please hurt me / Christmas song / I wish you a merry christmas / Makin' with the magilla / Wake up John / Takin' back what I said / Get him / Another night with the boys / Little Eva
WESM 512 / 10 Nov '97 / Westside

☐ ORIGINAL, THE
Loco-motion / Swinging on a star / Keep your hands off my baby / Let's turkey trot / Old smokey locomation / He's the boy / Where do I go / Trouble with boys / What I gotta do / Please hurt me / Let's start the party again / Run to her / Making with the magilla / Stand by me / That's my man
TO 886242 / 2 Feb '98 / Disky

Little Feat

☐ AIN'T HAD ENOUGH FUN
Drivin' blind / Blue jean blues / Cadilac hotel / Romance without finance / Big band theory / Cajun rage / Heaven's where you find it / Borderline blues / All that you can stand / Rock 'n' roll every night / Shaketown / Ain't had enough fun / That's a pretty good love
72445110972 / Jun '95 / Zoo Entertainment

☐ AS TIME GOES BY (The Best Of Little Feat)
Dixie chicken / Willin' / Rock 'n' roll doctor / Two trains / Truck stop girl / Fat man in the bath tub / Trouble / Sailin' shoes / Spanish moon / Feats don't fail me now / Oh Atlanta / All that you dream / Long distance love / Mercenary territory / Rocket in my pocket / Texas twister / Let it roll / Hate to lose your lovin' / Old folks boogie / Twenty million things
9548322472 / Aug '93 / WEA

☐ DIXIE CHICKEN
Dixie chicken / Two Trains / Roll um easy / On Your Way Down / Kiss it off / Fool yourself / Walkin' all night / Fat man in the bathtub / Juliet / Lafayette Railroad
K 246 200 / Jul '88 / WEA

☐ DOWN ON THE FARM
Down on the farm / Six feet of snow / Perfect imperfection / Kokomo / Be one now / Straight from the heart / Front page news / Wake up dreaming / Feel the groove
K2 56667 / Jul '88 / WEA

☐ FEATS DON'T FAIL ME NOW
Rock 'n' roll doctor / Cold cold cold / Tripe face boogie / Fan / Oh Atlanta / Skin it back / Down The Road / Spanish Moon / Feats Don't Fail Me Now
256030 / Jul '88 / WEA

☐ LAST RECORD ALBUM, THE
Romance Dance / All that you dream / Long Distance Love / Day or Night / One Love / Down below the borderline / Somebody's leavin' / Mercenary Territory
K 256156 / May '88 / WEA

☐ LET IT ROLL
Hate to lose your lovin' / One clear moment / Cajun girl / Hangin' on to the good times / Listen to your heart / Let it roll / Long time till I get over you / Business as usual / Change in luck / Voices on the wind
9257502 / Aug '88 / WEA

☐ LITTLE FEAT
Snakes on everything / Strawberry flats / Truck stop girl / Brides of Jesus / Willin' / Hamburger midnight / Forty four blues / How many more years / Crack in your door / I've been the one / Takin' my time / Crazy captain Gunboat Willie
7599271892 / Dec '96 / WEA

☐ REPRESENTING THE MAMBO
Texas twister / Daily grind / Representing the mambo / Woman in love / Rad gumbo / Teenage warrior / That's her / She's mine / Feeling's all gone / Those feat'll steer ya wrong sometimes / Ingenue / Silver screen
7599261632 / Apr '90 / WEA

☐ SAILIN' SHOES
Easy to slip / Cold cold cold / Trouble / Tripe face boogie / Willin' / Apolitical blues / Sailin' Shoes / Teenage nervous breakdown / Got no shadows / Cat fever / Texas Rose Cafe
246156 / '88 / WEA

☐ TIME LOVES A HERO
Time loves a hero / Hi roller / New Delph freight train / Old folks boogie / Red streamliner / Keeping up with the Joneses / Rocket in my pocket / Missin' you / Day at the races
256349 / Jul '89 / WEA

☐ UNDER THE RADAR
SPV 08529242 / 3 Aug '98 / SPV

☐ WAITING FOR COLUMBUS
Join the band / Fat man in the bathtub / All that you dream / Oh Atlanta / Old folks' boogie / Time loves a hero / Day or night / Mercenary territory / Spanish moon / Dixie chicken / Tripe face boogie / Rocket in my pocket / Willin' / Don't Bogart that joint / Political blues / Sailin' shoes / Feats don't fail me now
7599273442 / Dec '96 / WEA

Little Georgie

☐ LIVE FROM STYLEEN'S RHYTHM PALACE (2CD Set) (Little Georgie & The Shuffling Hungarians)
QB 96662 / Jun '98 / Queen Bee Brand

Little Hatch

☐ WE'RE ALL RIGHT (Little Hatch & The Houserockers)
MB 1204 / Feb '94 / Modern Blues

Little Isidore

☐ INQUISITION OF LOVE (Little Isidore & The Golden Inquisitors)
HSAM 6061 / Nov '96 / Hy-Sam

Little Lenny

☐ ALL THE GIRLS
GVCD 1700 / Dec '95 / Ras

☐ GUN IN A BAGGY
Gun in a baggy / Fafunky man / Halla yea / Original / Healthy body / Wicked and wild / Champion bubbler / Glamity nuff / Teach reality / Diana
GRELCD 146 / Apr '90 / Greensleeves

☐ LITTLE LENNY IS MY NAME
VPCD 1172 / Nov '92 / Steely & Cleevie

Little Mike & The Tornados

☐ FLYNN'S PLACE
FF 641CD / Jul '95 / Flying Fish

Little Milton

☐ BLUES 'N' SOUL/WAITING FOR LITTLE MILTON
It's amazing / Who can handle me is you / Woman, you don't have to be so cold / Thrill is gone / Monologue 1 / That's how strong my love is / What it is / Little bluebird / Woman across the river / Behind closed doors / Sweet woman of mine / Worried dream / How could you do it to me / You're no good / Ain't nobody's business if I do / Hard luck blues
CDSXD 052 / Jun '92 / Stax

☐ BLUES IS ALRIGHT, THE
Blues is alright / How could you do it to me / Bad luck is falling / Chains and things / Walking the back streets and crying / I'd rather drink muddy water / I'm digging you / Things have got to change
ECD 260262 / Feb '93 / Evidence

☐ COMPLETE STAX SINGLES, THE
If that ain't a reason (for your woman to leave you) / Mr. Mailman (I Don't want no letter) / I'm living off the love you give / That's what love will make you do / Before the honeymoon / Walking the back streets and crying / I'm gonna cry a river / What it is / Rainy day / Lovin' stick / Who can handle me is you / Tin pan alley / Sweet woman of mine / Behind closed doors / Bet you I win / Let me back in / Let your loss be your lesson / If you talk in your sleep / How could you do it to me / Packed up and took my mind
CDSXD 106 / Jan '95 / Stax

☐ IF WALLS COULD TALK
If walls could talk / Baby I love you / Let's get together / Things I used to do / Kansas City / Poor man's song / Blues get off my shoulder / I play dirty / Good to me as I am to you / Your precious love / I don't know
MCD 09289 / Apr '97 / Chess/MCA

☐ LIVE AT WESTVILLE PRISON
DE 681 / Dec '95 / Delmark

☐ TENDING HIS ROOTS (Charly R&B Masters Vol.17)
Feel so bad / If walls could talk / Life is like that / Sweet sixteen / I can't quit you baby / I'm mighty grateful / Don't talk back / Reconsider baby / Losing hand / We're gonna make it / Stormy Monday / Blind man / I'm gonna move to the outskirts of town / Blues in the night / Did you ever love a woman / Who's cheating who / Blues get off my shoulder / Things I used to do / Don't deceive me / Grits ain't groceries
CDRB 17 / Mar '95 / Charly

Little Pattie

☐ MOMENTS LIKE THIS
LB 9613 / Jul '98 / La Brava

Little Porkchop

☐ WELCOME TO...
SFTRI 544 / 15 Jun '98 / Sympathy For The Record Industry

Little Richard

☐ 20 CLASSIC CUTS
Long tall Sally / Ready Teddy / Girl can't help it / Rip it up / Miss Ann / She's got it / Lucille / Keep a knockin' / Good golly Miss Molly / Send me some lovin' / Tutti frutti / Hey hey hey / Slippin' and slidin' / Heebie jeebies / Baby face / Jenny Jenny / By the light of the silvery moon / Ooh my soul / True fine mama / Bama lama bama loo / I'll never let you go / Can't believe you wanna leave
CDCH 195 / Jul '90 / Ace

☐ BEST OF LITTLE RICHARD, THE
Long tall Sally / Lucille / Keep a knockin' / Jenny, Jenny / Tutti frutti / Rip it up / Girl can't help it / Good golly Miss Molly / Baby face / Cherry red / Groovy little Suzy / Money honey / Without love / Talking 'bout soul / Send me some lovin' / Hound dog
CDSGP 085 / Nov '93 / Prestige

☐ BOY CAN'T HELP IT, THE
Tutti fruttl / Girl can't help it / Lucille / Good golly miss molly / Long tall sally / Rip it up / Slippin' and slidin' / Keep a knockin' / Ready teddy / She's got it / Bama lama bama loo / Send me some lovin' / Miss ann / Ohh my soul / True fine mama / Jenny jenny / By the light of the silvery moon / Baby face (foxtrot) / All around the world / Can't believe you wanna leave
QSCD 6008 / Jan '94 / Charly

☐ COLLECTION, THE
Dancing all around the world / Good golly miss molly / Baby face (foxtrot) / Tutti fruttl / Send me some lovin' / Girl can't help it / Lucille / Blueberry hill / Keep a knockin' / Rip it up / She's got it / Ooh my soul / Long tall sally / Slippin' and slidin' / Whole lotta shakin' goin' on / Going home tomorrow / Money honey / Hound dog / Lawdy miss clawdy / Short fat fanny / Cherry red / Without love / Dance what you wanna / Something moves in my heart / Jenny jenny / I don't know what you got
CCSCD 227 / Jul '89 / Castle

☐ EARLY STUDIO OUTTAKES
SJCD 565 / Sep '95 / Sun Jay

☐ EP COLLECTION, THE
Send me some lovin' / I'm just a lonely guy / Miss Ann / Oh why / Can't believe you wanna leave / She's got it / Girl can't help it / Jenny Jenny / Heebie jeebies / Slippin' and slidin' / Baby / Baby face / By the light of the silvery moon / She knows how to rock / Early one morning / Keep a knockin' / Good golly Miss Molly / All around the world / True fine mama / Kansas City / Shake a hand / Chicken little baby / Whole lotta shakin' goin' on / Rip it up / Tutti frutti / Ready teddy / Long tall Sally
SEECD 366 / Mar '98 / See For Miles

☐ EXPLOSIVE LITTLE RICHARD, THE
BGOCD 368 / 24 Nov '97 / Beat Goes On

☐ FABULOUS LITTLE RICHARD, THE
Tutti frutti / Long tall Sally / Slippin' and slidin' / Rip it up / Ready Teddy / She's got it / Jenny Jenny / Girl can't help it / Lucille / Baby face / Keep a knockin' / Good golly Miss Molly
CDFAB 001 / Aug '91 / Ace

☐ FORMATIVE YEARS, THE (1951-1953)
Get rich quick / Why did you leave me / Taxi blues / Every hour / I brought it all on myself / Ain't nothing happening / Thinking 'bout my mother / Please have mercy on me / Little Richard's boogie / Directly from my heart / I love my baby / Maybe I'm right / Ain't that good news / Rice, red beans and turnip greens / Always
BCD 15448 / Jul '89 / Bear Family

☐ FRIENDS FROM THE BEGINNING (Little Richard & Jimi Hendrix)
Whole lotta shakin' goin' on / Goodnight Irene / Keep a knockin' / Going home tomorrow / Belles stars / Tutti frutti / Lawdy Miss Clawdy / Why don't you love me / Lucille / Hound dog / Money money / Funky dish rag
EMBCD 3434 / 27 Mar '98 / Ember

☐ HERE'S LITTLE RICHARD/VOL.2/ FABULOUS LITTLE RICHARD (His 3 Original Specialty Albums/3CD Set)
Tutti frutti / True fine mama / Can't believe you wanna leave / Ready Teddy / Baby / Slippin' and slidin' / Long tall Sally / Miss Ann / Oh why / Rip it up / Jenny Jenny / She's got it / Keep a knockin' / By the light of the silvery moon / Send me some lovin' / I'll never let you go / Heebie jeebies / All around the world / Good golly Miss Molly / Baby face / Hey hey hey / Ooh my soul / Girl can't help it / Lucille / Shake a hand / Chicken little baby / All night long / Most I can offer / Lonesome and blue / Wonderin' / She knows how to rock / Kansas City / Directly from my heart / Maybe I'm right / Early one morning / I'm just a lonely guy / Whole lotta shakin' goin' on
ABOXCD 2 / Oct '90 / Ace

☐ HIS GREATEST RECORDINGS
Ready Teddy / Rip it up / Girl can't help it / I'll never let you go / Miss Ann / Good golly Miss Molly / Lucille / Keep a knockin' / Can't believe you wanna leave / Tutti frutti / Heebie jeebies / Send me some lovin' / Chicken little baby / Hey hey hey / She's got it / Long tall Sally
CDCH 109 / Jul '90 / Ace

☐ HITS COLLECTION
Long tall sally / Tutti frutti / Good golly miss molly / Jenny jenny / Lucile / Rip it up / Bama lama bama loo / Baby face / Girl can't help it / Keep a knockin' / Ready teddy / By the light of the silvery moon / She's got it / Slippin' and slidin'
101542 / May '97 / A-Play Collection

☐ KINGS OF BEAT
REP 4159 / Aug '91 / Repertoire

☐ **LITTLE RICHARD**
Whole lotta shakin' goin' on / Rip it up / Baby face / Send me some lovin' / Girl can't help it / Lucille / Ooh my soul / Jenny Jenny / Good golly Miss Molly / Tutti frutti / Long tall Sally / Keep a knockin' / Money honey / Hound dog / Groovy little Suzie / Dancing all around the world / Slippin' and slidin' / Lawdy Miss Clawdy / Short fat Fanny / She's got it
LECD 036 / May '94 / Dynamite

☐ **LITTLE RICHARD**
Keep a knockin' / Send me some lovin' / I'll never let you go / All around the world / By the light of the silvery moon / Good golly Miss Molly / Baby face / Hey hey hey / Ooh my soul / Lucille / Girl can't help it
CDCHM 131 / Jul '89 / Ace

☐ **LITTLE RICHARD**
CD 106 / Oct '94 / Timeless Treasures

☐ **LITTLE RICHARD**
Lucille / Long Tall Sally / Whole lotta shakin' goin' on / Good golly Miss Molly / Tutti frutti / Rip it up / Keep a knockin' / Ooh my soul / Jenny, Jenny / Girl can't help it / Slippin' and slidin' / She's got it / Money honey / Groovy little Suzy / Talking 'bout soul / Baby face / Blueberry Hill / Hound dog / Send me some lovin'
QED 086 / Nov '96 / Tring

☐ **LITTLE RICHARD COLLECTION**
Tutti fruttl / Good golly miss molly / Lucille / Girl can't help it / Rip it up / Jenny jenny / Long tall sally / Keep a knockin' / Hound dog / Baby face (foxtrot) / Blueberry hill / Slippin' and slidin' / Whole lotta shakin' goin' on / Cherry red / Dancin' round the world / Groovy little suzie / I don't know what you got / Money honey / Only you / Send me some lovin' / She's got it / Short fat fanny / Talkin' 'bout soul / Without love / Goodnight irene
COL 006 / Jun '95 / Collection

☐ **LUCILLE**
Lucille / Long tall Sally / Baby face / Good golly Miss Molly / Tutti frutti / Whole lotta shakin' goin' on / Money, honey / Girl can't help it / Jenny Jenny / Hound dog
15080 / Aug '91 / Laserlight

☐ **LUCILLE**
Lucille / Good golly Miss Molly / Rip it up / Girl can't help it / Send me some lovin' / I don't know what you got / Ooh my soul / Long tall Sally / Tutti frutti / Whole lotta shakin' goin' on / Ready Teddy / Keep a knockin' / She's got it / Bama Lama Bama Loo / Blueberry Hill / Hound dog
12660 / Nov '96 / Laserlight

☐ **MASTERS, THE**
EABCD 062 / 24 Nov '97 / Eagle

☐ **MASTERS, THE (2CD Set)**
EDMCD 019 / 24 Nov '97 / Eagle

☐ **NOW**
Goog golly miss molly / Tutti fruttl / Ready teddy / Lucille / Jenny jenny / Rip it up / Long tall sally / Keep a knockin' / Baby face (foxtrot) / Ooh my soul / By the light of the silvery moon / Bama lama bama loo / Girl can't help it
RNCD 1007 / Jun '93 / Rhino

☐ **RIP IT UP - THE LITTLE RICHARD MEGAMIX**
Tutti frutti / Jenny Jenny / Keep a knockin' / Girl can't help it / Long tall Sally / Good golly Miss Molly / Lucille / Ooh my Sally / Ready Teddy / Can't believe you wanna leave / Baby face / She's got it / Rip it up / Slippin' and slidin' / By the light of the silvery moon / True fine Mama / All around the world / Bama lama bama loo / Miss Ann / Send me some lovin'
ECD 3070 / Jan '95 / K-Tel

☐ **SECOND COMING, THE (2CD Set)**
Whole lotta shakin' goin' on / Hound dog / Money honey / Lawdy Miss Clawdy / Good golly Miss Molly / Groovy little Susie / Short fat Fanny / Jenny Jenny / Lucille / Long tall Sally / She's got it / Girl can't help it / Rip it up / Tutti frutti / Slippin' and slidin' / Ooh my soul / Baby face / Keep a-knockin' / Send me some lovin' / Blueberry Hill / Dance what you wanna / Dancing all around the world / Going home tomorrow / Goodnight Irene / My wheels they are slippin' all the way / Something moves in my heart / It ain't what you do / Without love / Talkin' 'bout soul / I don't know what you've got but you've got me / Cherry red / Only you / Memories are made of this / I don't know what you've got but you've got me / Cross over / You better stop / Why don't you love me / Keep a-knockin' / Belle stars / Lucille / Long tall Sally / Funky dish rag
CPCD 82442 / Nov '96 / Charly

☐ **SPECIALTY SESSIONS, THE (6CD Set)**
Shake a hand (master, take 4) / Can't believe you wanna leave (take 8) / Can't believe you wanna leave (master - probably take 8) / I got it (take 1) / I got it (take 2) / She's got it / She's got it (master) / Send me some lovin' / Send me some lovin' (take 1) / Send me some lovin' (take 9) / Hound dog (rehearsal) / Jenny, jenny (master - composite) / Good golly, miss molly (take 7) / Good golly, miss molly (take 8) / Good golly, miss molly (master -take 9) / Good golly, miss molly (take 10) / Baby face (takes 2 and 3) (false starts) / Baby face (take 4) / Baby face (master - probably take 11) / Girl can't help it (film version master - take 9) / Girl can't help it (take 10 (false start) take 11) / Girl can't help it (single master - take 12) / Send me some lovin' (master) / By the light of the silvery moon (master) / Gene nobles "royal crown" hairdressing ad / Ooh my soul (take 1) / Ooh my soul (take 3) / Ooh my soul (master) / Keep a knockin' (take 1) / Keep a knockin' (take 2) / Keep a knockin' (take 3) / Keep a knockin' (take 4) / Keep a knockin' (master - composite) / Boo hoo hoo hoo (I'll never let you go) (take 1) / Boo hoo hoo hoo (I'll never let you go) (take 2) / Boo hoo hoo hoo (I'll never let you go) (take 6) / Boo hoo hoo hoo (I'll never let you go) (master) / Good morning little schoolgirl / Ooh my soul / Ooh my soul / Ooh my soul (take 7) / Ooh my soul (take 9) / Early one morning (master) / She knows how to rock (takes 1, 2, 3 and 4) (false starts) / She knows how to rock (take 5) (false start) / She knows how to rock (master) / Whole lotta shakin' goin' on (rehearsal) / Whole lotta shakin' goin' on (master) / Bama lama bama loo (take 7) / Bama lama bama loo (master - take 10) / Poor boy paul (take 2) / Poor boy paul (take 7) / Poor boy paul (master - take 8) / Annie's back (takes 1 and 2) / Annie's back (take 3) / Miss ann (take 6) / Miss ann (take 7) / Well alright (takes 1 and 2) / Well alright (take 4) / Well alright (take 4) / Ain't that a shame-i got a woman-tutti frutti (medley)
ABOXCD 1 / Jan '92 / Ace

☐ **SPOTLIGHT ON LITTLE RICHARD**
Babyface / Tutti frutti / Long tall Sally / Keep a knockin' / Groovy little Suzie / Cherry red / Good golly miss Molly / Girl can't help it / Without love / (Sittin' on the) dock of the bay / Rip it up / Money honey / Short fat Fanny / Slippin' and slidin' / Talkin' 'bout soul / She's got it
HADCD 117 / Feb '94 / Javelin

☐ **TUTTI FRUTTI**
Tutti frutti / Slippin' and slidin' / Lucille / Send me some lovin' / She's got it / Money honey / Baby face / Rip it up / Long tall Sally / Good golly Miss Molly / Ooh my soul / Girl can't help it / Short fat Fanny / Keep a knockin' / Jenny Jenny
304292 / Jun '97 / Hallmark

☐ **VERY BEST OF LITTLE RICHARD, THE**
Rip it up / Long tall Sally / Tutti frutti / She's got it / Girl can't help it / Lucille / Jenny Jenny / Keep a-knockin' / Good golly Miss Molly / Ooh my soul / Send me some lovin' / Whole lotta shakin' goin' on / Slippin' and slidin' / It ain't whatcha do / Dancin' all around the world / Baby face
SUMCD 4019 / Nov '96 / Summit

Little River Band

☐ **DIAMANTINA COCKTAIL**
Help is on its way / Days on the road / Happy anniversary / Another runaway / Everyday of my life / Home on Monday / Inner light / Broke again / Take me home
DC 875522 / May '97 / Disky

☐ **IT'S A LONG WAY THERE**
It's a long way there / Reminiscing / Night owls / Let's dance / One for the road / Man on the run / Down on the border / Emma / I'll always call your name / Take me home / Happy anniversary / Middle man / Hard life / It's not a wonder
DC 868702 / Nov '96 / Disky

Little Roy

☐ **LONGTIME**
ONUCD 87 / Sep '96 / On-U Sound

Little Sonny

☐ **ANN ARBOR BLUES VOL.2 (Various Artists)**
Introduction/Creeper returns / They want money: *Willis, Aaron 'Little Sonny'* / Woman named trouble: *Crutcher, Betty* / Goin' down slow: *Oden, Jimmy* / Hot potatoes: *King Curtis* / Honest I do: *Reed, Jimmy* / Blues with a feeling: *Dixon, Willie* / Sad funk: *Willis, Aaron 'Little Sonny'* / No nights by myself: *Williamson, Sonny Boy* / Sweet little angel: *King, Riley B.* / Sweet sixteen: *King, Riley B.* / Interview: *Sinclair, John* / Creeper: *Willis, Aaron 'Little Sonny'* / Latin soul: *Willis, Aaron 'Little Sonny'* / Stretchin' out: *Willis, Aaron 'Little Sonny'* / Creeper returns: *Willis, Aaron 'Little Sonny'* / Interview: *Little Sonny*
NEXCD 279 / Apr '96 / Sequel

☐ **BLACK AND BLUE**
Hung up / Sonny's fever / You got a good thing / Woman named trouble / Honest I do / Wade in the water (instrumental) / Paying through the nose / Memphis B-K (instrumental) / Going home (where women got meat on their bones) / I found love / They want money
CDSXE 057 / Jul '93 / Stax

☐ **NEW KING OF THE BLUES HARMONICA/HARD GOIN' UP**
Baby, what you want me to do / Eli's pork chop / Hey little girl / Hot potato / Don't ask me no questions / Tomorrow's blues today / Back down yonder / Sad funk / Creeper returns / It's hard going up (but twice as hard coming down) / My woman is good to me / You're spreading yourself a little too thin / Day you left me / You can be replaced / Do it right now / You made me strong / Sure is good / I want you
CDSXD 968 / Jul '91 / Stax

☐ **NEW ORLEANS RHYTHM & BLUES**
BM 9023 / Feb '94 / Black Magic

☐ **SONNY SIDE UP**
Sonny side up / Positive mind / I got to find my baby / Let me love you / Ready set go / Best of the best / I'm with you all the way / Tough times never last / Next dance with you
NEXCD 276 / Jun '95 / Sequel

Little Steven

☐ **FREEDOM NO COMPROMISE**
Freedom / Trail of broken treaties / Pretoria / Bitter fruit / No more party's / Can't you feel the fire / Native American / Sanctuary
NSPCD 511 / Apr '95 / Connoisseur Collection

☐ **MEN WITHOUT WOMEN (Little Steven & The Disciples Of Soul)**
Livin' in a bed of fire / Livin' in a bed of fire / Until the good is gone / Under the gun / Save me / Princess of little italy / Forever / I've been waiting / Men without women
NSPCD 508 / Mar '95 / Connoisseur Collection

☐ **VOICE OF AMERICA**
Voice of America / Justice / Checkpoint Charlie / Solidarity / Out of the darkness / Los desaparecidos (The disappeared ones) / Fear / I am not a patriot (and the river opens for the righteous) / Among the believers / Undefeated (everybody goes home)
NSPCD 512 / Apr '95 / Connoisseur Collection

Little Suzanne

☐ **BE HERE NOW**
W 230093 / May '96 / Nettwerk

Little Walter

☐ **BLUES WITH A FEELIN' (2CD Set)**
Juke / Can't hold out much longer / Blue midnight / Fast boogie / Driftin' / Tonight with a fool / That's it / Blues with a feeling / My kind of baby / Last boogie / Come back baby / I love you so (oh baby) / Big leg mama / Mercy babe a/k/a My babe / Thunderbird / Crazy for my baby / Can't stop lovin' you / Who / Flying saucer / Teenage beat / Temperature / Shake dancer / Ah'w baby / Rock bottom / You gonna be sorry (someday baby) / Baby / My baby is sweeter / Crazy mixed up / Worried life blues / Everything's gonna be alright / Mean old Frisco / One of these mornings / Blue and lonesome / Me and Piney Brown / Break it up / Going down show / You're sweet / You don't know / I'm a business man / Chicken shack
MCD 09357 / Apr '97 / Chess/MCA

☐ **BLUES WORLD OF LITTLE WALTER**
DD 648 / Nov '93 / Delmark

☐ **CONFESSIN' THE BLUES**
It ain't right / Rocker / I got to find my baby / Lights out / One more chance with you / Crazy legs / Temperature / I got to go / Crazy mixed up world / Quarter to twelve / Confessin' the blues / Toddle / Up the line / Rock bottom / Mean old Frisco
MCD 09366 / Apr '97 / Chess/MCA

☐ **WINDY CITY BLUES (Little Walter & Otis Rush)**
It's hard for me to believe baby / May be the last time / I feel good / Otis blues / Going down slow / Walter's blues / Lovin' you all the time / Blue mood
CDBM 028 / May '91 / Blue Moon

Little Whitt

☐ **MOODY SWAMP BLUES (Little Whitt & Big Bo)**
ABP 1001 / Apr '95 / Alabama Blues Project

Little Wolf

☐ **WOLF MOON**
5363702 / 5 Jan '98 / Triloka

Littlefield, Willie

☐ **GOING BACK TO KAY CEE (Littlefield, 'Little' Willie)**
Turn the lamp down low / Last laugh blues / Monday morning blues / Striking on you baby / Blood is redder than wine / KC lovin' / Pleading at midnight / Kansas City / Midnight hour was shining / Rock-a-bye baby / Miss KC's fine / Sitting on the curbstone / Jim Wilson's boogie / My best wishes and regards / Please dont go-o-o-oh / Falling tears / Goofy dust blues / Don't take my heart little girl
CDCHD 503 / Jan '95 / Ace

☐ **I'M IN THE MOOD (Littlefield, 'Little' Willie)**
OLCD 7002 / Oct '93 / Oldie Blues

☐ **RED ONE, THE (Littlefield, 'Little' Willie)**
OLCD 7005 / Feb '98 / Oldie Blues

☐ **YELLOW BOOGIE'N'BLUES (Littlefield, 'Little' Willie)**
OLCD 7006 / Dec '94 / Oldie Blues

Littlejohn, Johnny

☐ **CHICAGO BLUES STARS**
ARHCD 1043 / Apr '95 / Arhoolie

Litton, Martin

☐ **MARTIN LITTON**
SACD 114 / Aug '94 / Solo Art

Live

☐ **SECRET SAMADHI**
Rattlesnake / Lakini's juice / Graze / Century / Ghost / Unsheathed / Insomnia and the hole in the universe / Turn my head / Gas hed goes west / Merica / Freaks / Heropsychodreamer
RAD 11590 / Mar '97 / Radioactive

☐ **THROWING COPPER**
Dam at otter creek / Selling the drama / I alone / Iris / Lightning crashes / Top / All over you / S towne / T.b.d. / Stage / Waitress / Pillar of davidson / White discussion
RAD 10997 / Oct '94 / Radioactive

Live Action Pussy Show

☐ **MONSTER LOVE**
EFA 12292 / Aug '95 / Musical Tragedies

Live Skull

☐ **POSITRACTION**
GOES ON 29CD / Mar '89 / What Goes On

Live Wire

☐ **WIRED**
ROUCD 281 / Dec '90 / Rounder

Lively Ones

☐ **SURF RIDER/SURF DRUMS**
Surfbeat / Let's go trippin' / Misirlou / Guitar man / Caterpillar crawl / Walkin' the board / Paradise cove / Goofy foot / Surf rider / Happy gremmie / Hotdoggen / Surfer's lament / Tuff surf / Rik-a-tik / Wild weekend / Bustin' surfboards / Stoked / Surfer boogie / Surf drums / Shootin' the pier / Mr. Moto / Rumble / Forty miles of bad road / Hillbilly surf
CDCHD 957 / Nov '90 / Ace

Livengood, John

☐ **CYBORG SALLY**
AMPCD 025 / Apr '95 / AMP

Liverpool Cathedral Choir

☐ **CAROLS FROM LIVERPOOL**
Maiden most gentle / Lulling her child / Gaudete, Christus natus est / On this day earth shall ring / Echo carol / Holly and the ivy / Away in a manger / Ding dong merrily on high / Little baby born at dark midnight / Christ is the flower / World's desire / Tomorrow shall be my dancing day / Spotless rose / Adam lay-y-bounden / In dulci jubilo / Noble stem of Jesse / Blessed song of God / Tyrley, tyrlow / Alleluia, a new work / Hark the herald angels sing / O come, all ye faithful / Once in Royal David's City
CDPS 386 / Nov '91 / Alpha

Liverpool FC

☐ **KOP CHOIR, THE (Liverpool's Own Football Sound) (Kop Choir)**
CDGAFFER 14 / Mar '97 / Cherry Red

☐ **YOU'LL NEVER WALK ALONE (Liverpool FC/Supporters)**
CDGAFFER 4 / Apr '96 / Cherry Red

Livgren, Kerry

☐ **INSTRUCTIONS RECONSTRUCTED**
NUMA 0003 / 1 May '98 / Numavox

☐ **TIME LINE**
RME 0101CD / 19 Jan '98 / Renaissance

Livin' Blues

☐ **BLUE BREEZE**
CDP 1044DD / Nov '97 / Pseudonym

☐ **HELL'S SESSION**
REP 4138 / Aug '91 / Repertoire

☐ **RAM JAM JOEY**
CDP 1042DD / Nov '97 / Pseudonym

☐ **WANG DANG DOODLE**
REP 4111 / Aug '91 / Repertoire

Livin' Joy

☐ **DON'T STOP MOVING**
Don't stop movin' / Follow the rules / Deep in you / Dreamer / Pick up the phone / Be original / Where can I find love / Don't cha wanna / Whenever you're lonely / Let me love you
MCD 60023 / Nov '96 / MCA

Living Color

☐ **GREATEST HITS**
Pride / Sacred ground / Visions / Love rears its ugly head / These are happy times / Release the pressure / Memories can't wait / Cult of personality / Funny vibe / WTFF / Glamour boys / Open letter to a landlord / Solace of you / Nothingness / Type / Time's up / What's your favourite colour
4810212 / Feb '97 / Epic

Living End

☐ **STIFF MIDDLE FINGER**
LRR 018 / Oct '96 / Last Resort

Living In A Box

☐ **BEST OF LIVING IN A BOX, THE**
DC 865922 / Mar '96 / Disky

☐ **COLLECTION, THE**
Living in a box / Scales of justice / So the story goes: *Living In A Box & Bobby Womack* / Love is the art: *Living In A Box & Bobby Womack* / Blow the house down: *Living In A Box & Bobby Womack* / Gatecrashing / Room in your heart / Different air / Unique / Touch sensitive / All the difference in the world / Mistaken identity / Live it up
DC 886102 / 2 Feb '98 / Disky

☐ **VERY BEST OF LIVING IN A BOX, THE**
Living in a box / Scales of justice / So the story goes / Love is the art / Blow the house down / Gatecrashing / Room in your heart / Different air / Unique / Touch sensitive / All the difference in the world / Mistaken identity / Live it up
CDGOLD 1103 / 15 Sep '97 / EMI Gold

Livingston, Carlton

☐ **EMOTIONS**
GVDCD 2025 / Jun '94 / Grapevine

Livingstone, Bill

☐ WORLD'S GREATEST PIPERS VOL.9, THE (Livingstone, Pipe Major Bill)
Clan maccoll-leaving glenurquhart (24 marches) / Bruce gandy's farewell to the iron horse-mrs macdougal (68 / Lament for the laird of annapool (piobaireachd) / Coppercliff highlanders-delvinside (24 marches) / Piobaireachd
LCOM 9045 / Jul '91 / Lismor

Lizard Music

☐ FASHIONABLY LAME
Esquire / Kill for a sprinkle / She's a very, very fat fat weirdo / Costume jewellry / Soft focus am / Goin' back to Orangeland / Routine / Jacko's book / Water / Deep in the heart of Texas / Howard's machinery / I see France / Frugal lame
WDOM 017CD / Jul '95 / World Domination

☐ LOBSTER T
WDO 0392 / Aug '96 / World Domination

Lizzy Borden

☐ LOVE YOU TO DEATH
398414089CD / Sep '96 / Metal Blade

☐ MENACE TO SOCIETY
398414090CD / Sep '96 / Metal Blade

☐ MURDERESS METAL ROADSHOW, THE
398414092CD / Sep '96 / Metal Blade

☐ TERROR RISING/GIVE 'EM THE AXE
398414091CD / Sep '96 / Metal Blade

☐ VISUAL LIES
Me against the world / Shock / Outcast / Den of thieves / Visual lies / Eyes of a stranger / Lord of the flies / Voyeur / Visions
398414095CD / Sep '96 / Metal Blade

LK

☐ GRACELESS
You / Here on in / DIA / Contracted / Chickenbone / Little killers / Car song / Harder / Now I know / Graceless
FRUCD 1002 / 18 May '98 / Fruition

LL Cool J

☐ 14 SHOTS TO THE DOME
How I'm comin' / Buckin' em down / Stand by your man / Little somethin' / Pink cookies in a plastic bag getting crushed by buildings / Straight from Queens / Funkadelic relic / All we got left is the beat / (NFA) No frontin' allowed / Back seat / Soul survivor / Ain't no stoppin' this / Diggy down / Crossroads
5234882 / Jan '96 / Def Jam

☐ ALL WORLD
I can't live without my radio / Rock the bells / I'm bad / I need love / Going back to Cali / Jingling baby / Big ole butt / Boomin' system / Round the way girl / Mama said knock you out / Back seat / I need a beat / Doin' it / Loungin' (who do you love) / Hey lover: *LL Cool J & Boyz II Men*
5341252
5343032 / Nov '96 / Def Jam

☐ BIGGER AND DEFFER
I'm bad / Get down / Bristol Hotel / My rhyme ain't done / 357 - Break it on down / Go cut creator go / Breakthrough / I need love / Ahh, let's get ill / Doo wop / On the ill tip
5273532 / Jul '95 / Def Jam

☐ MAMA SAID KNOCK YOU OUT
Boomin' system / Around the way girl / Eat 'em up L Chill / Mr. Good Bar / Murdergram (live at Rapmania) / Cheesy rat blues / Farmers boulevard (our anthem) / Mama said knock you out / Milky cereal / Jingling baby / To da break of dawn / Six minutes of pleasure / Illegal search / Power of God
5234772 / Jul '95 / Def Jam

☐ MR. SMITH
Make it hot / Hip hop / Hey lover / Doin it / Life as / I shot ya / Mr. Smith / No aerplay / Loungin / Hollis to Hollywood / God bless / Get the drop on em
5297242 / Nov '95 / Def Jam

☐ PHENOMENON
Phenomenon / Candy: *LL Cool J & Ralph Tresvant/ Ricky Bell* / Starsky and Hutch: *LL Cool J & Busta Rhymes* / Another dollar / Nobody can freak with you: *LL Cool J & Keith Sweat/LeShaun* / Hot hot hot / 4321: *LL Cool J & Redman/Method Man/Cannibus/ DMX* / Wanna get paid: *LL Cool J & Lost Boyz* / Father / Don't be late don't come too soon: *LL Cool J & Tamia*
5391862 / 13 Oct '97 / Def Jam

☐ RADIO
I can't live without my radio / You can't dance / Dear Yvette / I can give you more / Dangerous / Rock the bells / I need a beat / You'll rock / I want you
5273522 / Jul '95 / Def Jam

☐ WALKING WITH A PANTHER
Droppin' em / Smokin', dopin' / Fast peg / Clap your hands / Nitro / You're my heart / I'm that type of guy / Why do you think they call it dope / It gets no rougher / Big ole butt / One shot at love / 1-900 LL Cool J / Two different worlds / Jealous / Jingling baby / Def Jam in the motherland / Going back to Cali / Crime stories / Change your ways / Jack the ripper
5273552 / Jul '95 / Def Jam

Llan De Cubel

☐ DEVA
FA 8701CD / Jul '95 / Fono Astur

☐ IV
Cabraliega / La Molinera / Pasucais de Xuan Martin/ Munera de casu/Pasucais d'Amieva / Durme nenu / Alborada d'Amandi/Entemediu de Nemesio/ Alborada'l tigre x / Lloxana / Fandangu puntiau/ Alborada asturiana / Muneres de Tomaleo y d'os ozcos / Adios la mia vaca pinta / Pasucais d'Uvieu/ Salon de casu/Marcha nupical de villaperi
IRCD 046 / Mar '97 / Iona

☐ L'OTRU DE LA MAR
FA 8734CD / Jul '95 / Fono Astur

☐ NA LLENDE
FA 8718CD / Apr '96 / Fono Astur

Lloyd

☐ THOUGHTS FROM A DRIVEWAY
I don't wanna know / All in all / Fish on the ocean / Listening for whispers / Vapour / Mary Tyler Moore / Paper walls / Human / Mr. Warner / Forever song
ORCD 9803 / Jun '98 / Pamplin

Lloyd, A.L.

☐ BALLADS ET SHANTIES (LLoyd, A.L. & Friends)
SCM 030CD / Aug '94 / Diffusion Breizh

☐ CLASSIC A.L. LLOYD
FE 098CD / Jul '94 / Fellside

☐ OLD BUSH SONGS
LRF 354 / Aug '96 / Larrikin

Lloyd, Charles

☐ ALL MY RELATIONS
Piercing the veil / Little peace / Thelonious theonlyus / Cape to Cairo suite / Evanstide, where lotus bloom / All my relations / Hymme to the Mother / Milarepa
5273442 / May '95 / ECM

☐ CALL, THE (Lloyd, Charles Quartet)
Nocturne / Song / Dwija / Glimpse / Imke / Amarma / Figure in blue, memories of Duke / Blessing / Brother on the rooftop
5177192 / Oct '93 / ECM

☐ CANTO
Tales of Rumi / How can I tell you / Desolation sound / Canto / Machiketa's lament / M / Durga durga
5373452 / Jun '97 / ECM

☐ FISH OUT OF WATER (Lloyd, Charles Quartet)
Fish out of water / Haghia Sophia / Dirge / Bharti / Eyes of love / Mirror
8410882 / Jan '90 / ECM

☐ MOONMAN
BGOCD 393 / 24 Nov '97 / Beat Goes On

☐ NOTES FROM BIG SUR
Requim / Sister / Pilgrimage to the mountain / Sam song / Takur / Monk in Paris / When Miss Jessye sings / Pilgrimage to the mountain - part 2 surrender
5119992 / May '92 / ECM

Lloyd, David

☐ Y CANEUON CYNNAR (The Early Recordings 1940-1941)
Smilin' through / O loveliness beyond compare / Speak for me to my lady / All through the night / March of the men of Harlech / Jerusalem / England / Aberystwyth / Land of my fathers / Until / Serenade / Lovely maid in the moonlight / Bless this house / Sylvia / David of the white rock / Stars in heaven are bright / Over the stone / Cwm Rhondda
SCDC 2076 / Feb '97 / Sain

Lloyd, Floyd

☐ MEET LAUREL AITKEN (Lloyd, Floyd & Potato Five)
GAZCD 001 / '89 / Gaz's Rockin' Records

Lloyd, John

☐ BY CONFUSION (Lloyd, John Quartet)
ARTCD 6198 / Apr '97 / Hat Art

☐ PRAXIS (Lloyd, John Sextet)
FMRCD 47 / Feb '98 / FMR

☐ SYZGY (Lloyd, John Quartet)
CDLR 173 / '90 / Leo

Lloyd, Richard

☐ REAL TIME
Fire engine / Misty eyes / Alchemy / Spider talk / Lost child / No.9 / Only feeling / Soldier blue / Field of fire / Pleading / Watch yourself / Louisin Anna / Black to white
CDGR 194 / Nov '97 / Charly

Lloyd-Langton, Huw

☐ ON THE MOVE
Got your number / I could cry / Wrong streets / On the move / Move over lady / Finally finding / Farewell / Just the same / No participation / Outside the law / Lonely ma / Of the cuff
BMAC 0318S / 13 Oct '97 / BMA

Lloyd-Tucker, Colin

☐ REMARKABLE
Remarkable intro / Remarkable intro / Heart 'n' soul / Bury the hatchet / Big brass band / Love bombs / Abey see de gol' fish / House on the hill / Remarkable reprise / Dream time / Dark damp corners of despair
BAH 2 / Apr '93 / Humbug

☐ SKYSCAPING
Skyscraping / Skyscraping / Pygmy jungle / Train of thought / Greatest show / Transmission moon
BAH 8 / Jul '93 / Humbug

☐ SONGS OF LIFE, LOVE AND LIQUID
BAH 17 / Apr '96 / Humbug

Lloydie Crucial

☐ JUNGLE IN THE SUBURBS
LCCD 002 / Feb '95 / Lloydie Crucial

☐ JUNGLEMANIA VOL.1 (Lloydie Crucial & The Concrete Junglist Crew)
LCCDLP 001 / Oct '94 / Lloydie Crucial

Llwybr Llaethog

☐ MAD
ANKSTCD 065 / Jun '96 / Ankst

☐ MEWN DYB
RUSCD 8226 / Jul '96 / ROIR

Lo, Cheikh

☐ NE LA THIASS
Ne la thiass / Set / Cheikh ibra fall / Bamba sunu goorgui / Guiss guiss / Boul di tagale / Ndogal / Boxandeme / Sant Maam
WCD 046 / Oct '96 / World Circuit

Lo, Ismael

☐ DIAWAR
Jelebl / Sophia / Taar dousey / Diawar / Jalia / Adou calpe
STCD 1027 / Nov '89 / Stern's

Lo-Fidelity Allstars

☐ HOW TO OPERATE WITH A BLOWN MIND
BRASSIC 8CD / 25 May '98 / Skint

Lo-Key

☐ BACK 2 DA HOUSE
Welcome / Back 2 da howse / 26c / Don't trip on me / Getcha girlfriend / Li'l shumpin', shumpin' / Tasty / Play with me / Good ole fashion love / Turn around / Call my name / Interlude / My desire / We ain't right / Come on in
5490102 / Dec '94 / Perspective

Lo-Lite

☐ BASICS
MOTORWOLF 001 / Oct '97 / Motorwolf

Load

☐ LOAD HAVE MERCY
LE 1023 / 15 Jun '98 / Laser's Edge

Loafers

☐ COLLECTION, THE
CLP 0181 / 2 Feb '98 / Cleopatra

☐ CONTAGIOUS
Undertaker / It's so easy / Bad news / Skinhead / Z cars / Follow my leader / Everyday / She's too much / UC / Skankenstein / Livin' in a suitcase / Skankin' at the OK Corral / Postman Pat / Z cars / It's so easy / Feeling's right / Skankenstein / Average man / Summers day / Skankin' at the OK Corral / Undertaker / Living in a suitcase
SKACD 101 / 4 May '98 / House Of Ska

Loaned Finery

☐ HEYOKA
HJF 29CD / Aug '97 / Tutl

Lobato, Chano

☐ LA NUEZ MOSCA (Lobato, Chano & Pedro Bacan/Manuel Soler)
B 6840 / Oct '96 / Auvidis/Ethnic

Lobban, David

☐ STEP BY STEP VOL.5
SEQCD 005 / Jan '94 / Sound Waves

☐ STEP BY STEP VOL.7
SEQCD 007 / Jul '94 / Sound Waves

☐ WURLITZER FAVOURITES
SOW 514 / Jul '94 / Sound Waves

Lobi, Kakraba

☐ WORLD OF KAKRABA LOBI, THE
VICG 50142 / Mar '96 / JVC World Library

Lobotomy

☐ LOBOTOMY
CHAOSCD 004 / Jan '96 / Chaos

Local Area Network

☐ LOCAL AREA NETWORK
A 5 / Jun '97 / A-Musik

Local H

☐ AS GOOD AS DEAD
Manifest density (part 1) / High-fiving MF / Bound for the floor / Lovey dovey / I saw what you did and I know who you are / No problem / Nothing special / Eddie Vedder / Back in the day / Freeze dried (f)lies / Fritz's corner / OK / Manifest density (part 2)
5242022 / Mar '97 / Island

Lock, Eddie

☐ EDDIE LOCK LIVE AT THE SUNDANCE IBIZA (Various Artists)
DJ dubs: *Lock, Eddie & SMC Project/Dave Valentine/SPSF* / Work: *Self Preservation Society & Tyree Cooper* / Greasy kittens: *Impossible Beings* / Hypnotic: *Carpe Diem* / Spirit: *Lock, Eddie & SMC Project* / Gimme: *Priest* / Buzz: *Carpe Diem* / Everybody is somebody: *Flipped Out* / Rude entry: *Mind To Mind* / Turkish delight: *Lock, Eddie & SMC Project/Leah* / I do: *Shamen* / Icelation (too cold to hold): *Priest* / Small town boy: *Legato* / Dream mission: *Global Transmission* / Fiesta fiesta: *Red 5*
502043400012 / Sep '97 / Love Of Life

Lockdown

☐ DBL
HAUS 012CD / 13 Apr '98 / Household Name

Locke, Jimmy

☐ DANCETIME AT THE ORGAN VOL.3
SAV 236CD / Dec '95 / Savoy

☐ IT'S DANCE TIME
SAV 188CD / May '93 / Savoy

☐ JIMMY LOCKE PLAYS MUSIC MUSIC MUSIC
Heartaches / Amy / I'm a dreamer (aren't we all) / Little girl / I wonder who's kissing her now / True love / My mothers pearls / Memories / Foolishly yours / Yesterdays dreams / I apologise / How soon / Too young / Only you / Just loving you / Be careful it's my heart / Till / Petticoats of Portugal / From here to eternity / Return to me / In the spirit of the moment / I talk to the trees / Amapola / Strangers in the night / Oh Donna CLara / You were meant for me / Pretty baby / Heart of my heart / Breezin' along with the breeze / Someday (you'll want me to want you) / C'est magnifique / Rose of Washington Square / Whispering / Broadway melody / Is it true what they say about Dixie / Baby face / I'll always be in love with you / Under the lidden tree the one rose / When your old wedding ring was new / Pal of my cradle days / Kiss me again / Cry / If I could only make you care / Sierra Sue / Nevertheless / You were only fooling / There must be a way
SAV 171CD / Mar '92 / Savoy

☐ JIMMY'S MAGIC MELODIES
If your face wants to laugh/Follow the swallow / Three little words/Everything in rhythm with my heart / Silver wedding waltz/Last waltz of the evening / Kiss in your eyes/Memories live longer than dreams / Look for the silver lining/When did you leave heaven / My gypsy dream girl/If I didn't care / Glory of love / Rock-a-bye your baby/Have you ever been lonely / It's magic/Don't take your love from me / Love is all / Fools rush in / Cherry pink and apple blossom white/ Love me tender / Mr. Sandman/Five foot two, eyes of blue / Wait till the sun shines Nellie/I'm nobody's baby / Please/Shine through my dreams / Once in a while/Prisoner of love / Your lips are red / Isle of Capri/Echo of a serenade / Maybe/Shepherd of the hills/Home / It had to be you/Love letters in the sand
SAV 175CD / Jul '92 / Savoy

Locke, Josef

☐ HEAR MY SONG (2CD Set)
Hear my song Violetta / Soldier's dream / March of the Grenadiers / Blaze away / Goodbye / If I were a blackbird / I'll walk beside you / At the end of the day / Mother Machree / Love's last word is spoken / Cara mia / O maiden, my maiden / If I could hear somebody / You are my heart's delight / Come back to Sorrento / I'll take you home again Kathleen / Holy City / Drinking song / Santa Lucia / When you were sweet sixteen / Count your blessings / My heart and I / Goodbye / Galway Bay / Macushla / Rose of Tralee / Bard of Armagh / When it's moonlight in Mayo / How can you buy Killarney / Dear old Donegal / Isle of Innisfree / Maire my girl / Shades of old Blarney / Shawl of Galway grey
CDDL 1033 / Nov '92 / EMI

☐ HEAR MY SONG VIOLETTA (The EMI Recordings 1947-1955 - 4CD Set)
Hear my song, Violetta / Santa Lucia / Goodbye / I'll take you home again Kathleen / Holy City / Come back to Sorrento / My heart and I / Star of Bethlehem / Dear old Donegal / When you were sweet sixteen / Rose of Tralee / Count your blessings / Galway Bay / Macushla / Rosary / Ave Maria / Husha bye Rose of Killarney / Song of songs / Old Bog Road / Strange music / Bless this house / When you're in love / Soldier's dream / Beneath thy window / While the angelus was ringing / Toselli's serenade / Will the angels play their harps for me / How can you buy Killarney / Shawl of Galway grey / Lay my head beneath a rose / Silent night / O come all ye faithful (adeste fidelis) / We all have a song in our hearts / Down in the Glen / In the chapel of San Remo / Ireland must be heaven / Within this heart of mine / Festival of roses / Christopher Robin is saying his prayers / Story of the sparrows / Teddy bears' picnic / Garden where the praties grow / Eileen O'Grady / If I were a blackbird / March of the Grenadiers / You are

my heart's delight / When you talk about old Ireland / Take a pair of sparkling eyes / If I can help somebody / Keys to heaven / It is no secret / Nirvana / Dream / I'll walk beside you / Tonight beloved / At the end of the day / Charmaine / Love me little, love me long / Isle of Innesfree / Mother Machree / Wonderful Copenhagen / Love's last word is spoken / One little candle / Love me and the world is mine / It's a grand life in the army / You'll never forget about Ireland / Tear, a kiss, a smile / We'll pray for you / Shades of old Blarney / When you hear Big Ben / You're just a flower from an old bouquet / Tobermory Bay / Band of Armagh / Queen of everyone's heart / Daughter of Rose of Tralee / Rose of Slievenamon / Melba waltz / Maire my girl / When it's moonlight in Mayo / Drinking song / In the chapel in the moonlight / Cara Mia / Santo Natale / Brown bird singing / Bonnie Mary of Argyle / Blaze away / People like us / O maiden, my maiden / My mission

CDLOK 1 / Apr '96 / Premier/EMI

☐ HYMNS WE ALL LOVE

All people that on earth do dwell / When the roll is called up yonder / Old rugged cross / Lead kindly light / One love everlasting / There's a great new prospect in the sky / Onward Christian soldiers / It is no secret / Nearer my God to thee / Shall we gather at the river / Abide with me / God be with you till we meet again

DOCD 2027 / Jul '96 / Dolphin

☐ IRISH FAVORITES

Blaze away / Old bog road / Slievenamon / I'll take you home again Kathleen / Danny Boy / Little grey home in the West / Sweet sixteen / Bold gendarmes / Town I loved so well / She moved through the fair / Old house / Lovely Derry on the banks of the Foyle / On the street where you live / My way / Mountains of Mourne / Goodbye

CDIRISH 009 / Mar '97 / Outlet

☐ LET THERE BE PEACE - COLLECTED SONGS

ARANCD 601 / Nov '95 / Aran

☐ SINGALONG

In the shade of the old apple tree / My bonnie lies over the ocean / Daisy Daisy / East side, west side / Sweet Rosie O'Grady / She's only a bird in a gilded cage / In this good old summertime / If those lips could only speak / Clementine / Michael, row the boat ashore / He's got the whole world in his hands / John Brown's body / Red river valley / On top of old smokey / Beautiful brown eyes / Old faithful / Roll along covered wagon / South of the border (Down Mexico way) / Let him go, let him tarry / Ma goes Dixie / Rose of Tralee / Slaney Valley / Where the Blarney roses grow / Heaven street / Saints / Down by the Severnside / Loch Lomond / Annie Laurie / Will ye no' come back again / Oh Susanna / Beautiful dreamer / Camptown races / Quartermaster's stores / Old soldiers never die

DOCD 2026 / Nov '93 / Koch

☐ SONGS I LOVED SO WELL, THE

Blaze away march (abe holzmann) / Old bog road / Slievenamon / I'll take you home again kathleen / Danny boy / Little grey home in the west / Sweet sixteen / Bold gendarmes / Town I loved so well / She moved through the fair / Old house / Lovely derry on the banks of the foyle / On the street where you live / My way / Mountains of mourne / Goodbye

HMCD 5 / Jan '95 / Outlet

☐ TAKE A PAIR OF SPARKLING EYES

It's a grand life in the army / Take a pair of sparkling eyes / Macushla / Dear old Donegal / St. Lucia / Galway Bay / While the Angelus was ringing / Old bog road / Wonderful Copenhagen / Soldier's dream / Mother Machree / Maire my girl / Soldiers of the Queen / Shades of old Blarney / Rose of Tralee / When it's moonlight in Mayo / Toselli's serenade / Bless this house / Bard of Armagh / March of the grenadiers / Shawl of Galway grey / Tobermory bay / Isle of Innisfree / Ireland must be heaven / Ave Maria

CDP 7996402 / Jun '92 / EMI

☐ VERY BEST OF JOSEF LOCKE, THE

I'll take you home again Kathleen / Hear my song Violetta / Galway Bay / Macushla / Rose of Tralee / Bard of Armagh / When it's moonlight in Mayo / How can you buy Killarney / Marie my girl / Shawl of Galway grey / Come back to Sorrento / March of the Grenadiers / Soldier's dream / Holy city / Drinking song / Santa Lucia / When you were sweet sixteen / Count your blessings / My heart and I / Goodbye

CDMFP 6246 / Aug '96 / Music For Pleasure

Locke, Kevin

☐ FLASH OF THE MIRROR

14937 / Jun '97 / Spalax

☐ OPEN CIRCLE

14568 / Nov '97 / Spalax

Lockheart, Mark

☐ MATHERAN (Lockheart, Mark & John Parricelli)

IS 02CD / Apr '94 / Isis

Locklin, Hank

☐ MASTERS, THE

EABCD 108 / 30 Mar '98 / Eagle

☐ PLEASE HELP ME I'M FALLING (4CD Set)

Your heart is an island / Who am I to cast the first stone / You're out of step / These ruins belong to you / Good woman's love / I'm a fool / Love or spite / Why baby why / Seven or eleven / You can't never tell / Time nor tide / I don't want it / She's better than most / How much / (I'm so tired of) going home all by myself / Rich and the poor / By the sweat of my brow / Fourteen karat gold / Livin' alone / Send me the pillow you dream on / Why don't you haul off and love me / Time nor tide / I don't want it / She's better than most / Geisha girl / Fraulein / Blue grass skirt / Filipino baby / Foreign love / Lili marlene / Mexicali rose / My wild irish rose / Blue hawaii / Mademoiselle / Anna marie / Foreign love affair / First time / It's a little more like heaven / Simple things / I gotta talk to your heart / Other side of the door / Paper face / Upper room / That inner glow / Foreign car / When the band plays the blues / Border of the blues / Hiding my heart / Blues in advance / Seven days (the humming song) / Second fiddle / Please help me I'm falling / My old home town / One step ahead of my past / Toujours moi (always me) / You only want me when you're lonely / Same sweet girl / Oh how I miss you (since you went away) / Let me be the one / From here to there to you / This song is just for you / Jealous heart / One has my name (the other has my heart) / I can't stop loving you / Johnny my love (grandma's diary) / You're the reason / Keeper of the keys / Happy birthday to me / I can see an angel / Happy journey / I need you now / Welcome home, mr. blues / We're gonna go fishin' / Rudolph the red-nosed reindeer / All the world is lonely now / We live in two different worlds / Waltz of the wind / Great speckled bird / Pins and needles (in my heart) / As long as I live / Blue eyes crying in the rain / Maple on the hill / Wabash cannonball / Wreck on the highway / A precious jewel / Once more / Heading down the wrong highway / Mansion on the hill / They'll never take her love from me / I love you because / Bummin' around / Slowly / Kentucky waltz / Candy kisses / Rosalita / Wishing on a star / Flyin' south / Behind the footlights / Sweet temptation / Little bit lonesome / Ivory tower / Too close to her (and too far from you) / Followed closely by my teardrops / It keeps right on a hurtin' / You never want to love me / Wooden soldier / Kiss on the door / Galway bay / Too-ra-loo-ra-loo-ral (that's an irish lullaby) / My wild irish rose / Danny dear / Danny boy / When irish eyes are smiling / Forty shades of green / If we only had old ireland over here / Little bit of heaven / Old bog road / Kevin barry / I'll take you home again kathleen / I was coming home to you / I feel a cry coming on / Girls get prettier (everyday) / Hello heartache

BCD 15730 / Jun '95 / Bear Family

☐ SEND ME THE PILLOW YOU DREAM ON (3CD Set)

Rio Grande waltz / You've been talking in your sleep / Please come back and stay / I've got a feeling somebody's falling / I worship you / You've been talking in your sleep / Same sweet girl / Last look at Mother / One more mistake / Knocking at your door / Born to ramble / I'm lonely darling / Send me the pillow (you dream on) / Are you treating your neighbour as yourself / Fifty miles of elbow room / Crazy over you / Our love will show the way / Tho I've lost / Midnight tears / It's so hard to say I love you / Place and the time / You burned a hole in my heart / Pinball millionaire / Paper face / Come share the sunshine with me / No one is sweeter than you / Year of time / To whom it may concern / Song of the whispering leaves / Won't you change your mind / Holy train / Is there room for me / Who is knocking at my heart / Harvest is ripe (the labourers are few) / I could love you darling / Rio Grande waltz / Your house of love won't stand / Who do you think you're fooling / Sand me the pillow (you dream on) / I always lose / Stumpy Joe / I'm going to copyright your kisses / Down Texas way / Tomorrow's just another day to cry / Tell me you love me / Could you / Picking sweethearts / I like to play with your kisses / Golden wristwatch / (Sittin') alone at a table for two / I can't run away / Shadows / Red rose / Lessons in love / Let me be the one / I'm tired of bummin' around / I'll be blue til then / In the house of the Lord / Mysteries of life / Queen of hearts / Empty bottles, empty heart / Who will it be / Whispering scandal / Baby you can count me in / Let me confess / I'll always be standing by

BCD 15953 / Jan '97 / Bear Family

☐ VERY BEST OF HANK LOCKLIN, THE

Please help me I'm falling / Send me the pillow that you dream on / Baby I need you / There never was a time / Let me be the one / From here to there to you / Down on my knees / Happy birthday to me / Happy journey / These arms you push away / Night life queen / I was coming home to you / It's a little more like heaven / Geisha girl / Daytime love affair / Flying south / We're gonna go fishin'

305712 / Oct '96 / Hallmark

Lockwood, Didier

☐ NEW YORK RENDEZ-VOUS

Juggling in Central Park / Waltzy / Cousin William / Anbatoie blues / Gordon / Reminiscence / Don't drive so fast / Eastern dance / Tom Thumb

JMS 186692 / May '95 / JMS

☐ STORYBOARD

Thought of a first Spring day / Back to Big Apple / En quittant kidonk / Mathilde / Tableau d'une exposition / Serie B / Storyboard / Irremediablement / Spirits of the forest

FDM 365822 / Dec '96 / Dreyfus

Lockwood, Robert Jr.

☐ I GOT TO FIND ME A WOMAN

5374482 / 15 Sep '97 / Verve

☐ PLAYS ROBERT JOHNSON

Ramblin' on my mind / Kind hearted woman blues / Walkin' blues / I'm a steady rollin' man / Sweet home chicago / Little speed of spades / Western horizon / She is little and low / Little boy blue / Lockwood's boogie / Take a walk with me / CC rider / Sweet home chicago (take 1)

BLE 597402 / Sep '92 / Black & Blue

☐ STEADY ROLLIN' MAN

DD 630 / Jan '93 / Delmark

Loco Girasol

☐ ADIVINA ADIVINADORA

TUMICD 072 / 5 Jan '98 / Tumi

Locomotive

☐ WE ARE EVERYTHING YOU SEE

Overture / Mr. Armageddon / Now is the end, the end is when / Lay me down gently / Nobody asked me to come / You must be joking / Day in shining armour / Lovers of Augustus Abbey / Times of light and darkness / Broken heart / Rudie, a message to you / Rudi's in love / Never set me free / There's got to be a way / I'm never gonna let you go / Roll over Mary / Movin' down the line / Rudi the red nosed reindeer / White Christmas / Rudi catch the monster / My girl blue

BL 004 / Jul '97 / Shoestring

Locust

☐ MORNING LIGHT

Your selfish ways / Morning light / Just like you / I am the murderer / Jukebox heart / Folie / One way or another / No-one in the world / Clouds at my feet / Summer rain / Ancient hometown / Girl with the fairytale dream / Let me take you back / Some love will remain unsaid / Shadow play / On the horizon

AMB 7942CD / Jun '97 / Apollo

☐ TRUTH IS BORN OF ARGUMENTS

Truth is born of arguments / Penetration / I feel cold inside because of the things you say / Saturated love / When we coincide / I believe in a love I may never know / Optimist / I became overwhelmed / I am afraid of who I am / Inside I am crying / Love you cruelly gave me would not last

AMB 5940CD / Jun '95 / Apollo

☐ WEATHERED WELL

Prospero / Moist moss / Xenophobe / Weathered gate / Tamed / Still / Music about love / Lust / Fawn

AMB 3929CD / Mar '94 / Apollo

Locust Fudge

☐ ROYAL FLUSH

GRCD 370 / May '97 / Glitterhouse

Lodder, Steve

☐ ABOVE THE CLOUDS (Lodder, Steve & Mark Ramsden)

Adrift in your dreams / Retrove / Andante / Juggler / Adagio / Confluence / Flos vernalis / Saint Chappelle / Adagio and Andante / While the pulse still beats / Tumbler / Above the clouds

BREATHE 001 / Apr '96 / Breathe

Lodestar

☐ LODESTAR

Another day / Salter's ducks / Wait a minute / Representative / By halves / Better late than never / Aftertaste / Worthwhile / Soiled blood / Down in the mud / Lilac crest

TOPPCD 049 / Oct '96 / Ultimate

Lodge

☐ SMELL OF A FRIEND

Solitary / Song / Not all fathers / Smell of a friend / Match girl / Swelling valleyt / Old man's mood / Milk

RES 122CD / Dec '96 / Resurgence

Lodge, J.C.

☐ I BELIEVE IN YOU

I believe in you / I found love / Let me down easy / Too good to be true / Night work / Cool mover / Given up / You don't want my love / Together we will stay / Happy now sorry later

RRTGCD 7712 / '88 / Rohit

☐ RAS PORTRAITS

Activate me / Make it up to you / Somewhere over the rainbow / Top of the line / Love for all seasons / Can't get over losing you / You carry the swing / Love you to the max / Work with me baby / Crysis

RAS 3310 / Jun '97 / Ras

☐ SELFISH LOVER

Love's gonna break your heart / Conversations / Way up / I am in love / Sweet dreams / Cautious / Operator / Hardcore loving / Selfish love / Telephone love / Love me baby / Lonely nights / Since you came into my life

GRELCD 143 / Apr '90 / Greensleeves

☐ SOMEONE LOVES YOU HONEY

RGCD 6053 / Mar '94 / Rocky One

☐ SPECIAL REQUEST

RASCD 3168 / Jun '95 / Ras

☐ TO THE MAX

RASCD 3128 / Jan '94 / Ras

Lodge, John

☐ NATURAL AVENUE

Intro to children of rock 'n' roll / Natural Avenue / Summer breeze / Carry me / Who could change / Broken dreams, hard road / Piece of my heart / Rainbow / Say you love me / Children of rock 'n' roll / Street cafe

JS 1 / Mar '97 / Halesouth

Loeb, Chuck

☐ MOON THE STARS AND THE SETTING SUN, THE

Just us / Beneath the light / Of the moon / Hand in hand / Don't let me be lonely tonight / Stars / Above us / Shine on / While we speak / Of love and setting sun / Water runs deep

SHANCD 5038 / 9 Mar '98 / Shanachie

☐ MUSIC INSIDE, THE

SHCD 5022 / Jul '96 / Shanachie

Loeb, Lisa

☐ FIRECRACKER

GED 24946 / 16 Feb '98 / Geffen

☐ TAILS (Loeb, Lisa & Nine Stories)

It's over / Snow day / Taffy / When all the stars are falling / Do you sleep / Hurricane / Rose-colored times / Sandalwood / Alone waiting for Wednesday / Lisa listen / Garden of delights / Stay

GED 24734 / Sep '95 / Geffen

Lofgren, Nils

☐ 1 + 1 (Lofgren, Nils & Grin)

White lies / Please don't hide / Slippery fingers / Moon tears / End unkind / Sometimes / Lost a number / Hi / Hello home / Just a poem / Soft fun

4894462 / 26 Jan '98 / Columbia

☐ ACOUSTIC LIVE

You / Sticks and stones / Some must dream / Little on up / Keith don't go / Wonderland / Big tears fall / Believe / Black books / To your heart / Man in the moon / I'll arise / Blue skies / Tears on ice / All out / Mud in your eye / No mercy

FIENDCD 934 / Aug '97 / Demon

☐ ACROSS THE TRACKS (2CD Set)

SMDCD 106 / Aug '97 / Snapper

☐ ARCHIVE ALIVE (Live At The Stone Pony, Asbury Park New Jersey)

Dreams die hard / Little bit o'time / Rock 'n' roll crook / Cry tough / No mercy / Big tears fall / Anytime at all / Empty heart / Like rain / Sweet midnight / Flip ya flip / I don't wanna talk about it / Back it up / I came to dance

NSPCD 517 / 18 May '98 / Connoisseur Collection

☐ CODE OF THE ROAD

Secrets in the street / Across the tracks / Delivery night / Cry tough / Dreams die hard / Believe / Sun hasn't set on this boy yet / Code of the road / Moontears / Back it up / Like rain

CLACD 311 / '92 / Castle

☐ CRY TOUGH

Cry tough / It's not a crime / Incidentally... it's over / It's over / For your love / Share a little / Mud in your eye / Can't get closer / You lit a fire / Jailbait

3945732 / 9 Mar '98 / A&M

☐ DAMAGED GOODS

ESSCD 337 / Oct '95 / Essential

☐ DON'T WALK, ROCK (The Best Of Nils Lofgren)

Moontears / Back it up / Keith don't go / Sun hasn't set on this boy yet / Goin' back / Cry tough / Jailbait / Can't get closer / Mud in your eye / I came to dance / To be a dreamer / No mercy / Steal away / Baltimore / Shine silently / Secrets in the street / Flip ya flip / Delivery night / Anytime at all

VSOPCD 152 / Jun '90 / Connoisseur Collection

☐ FLIP

Flip ya flip / Secrets in the street / From the heart / Delivery night / King of the rock / Sweet midnight / New holes in old shoes / Dreams die hard / Big tears fall / Beauty and the beast

CLACD 312 / Nov '92 / Castle

☐ I CAME TO DANCE

5408722 / 9 Mar '98 / A&M

☐ NILS

No mercy / I'll cry tomorrow / Baltimore / Shine silently / Steal away / Kool skool / Fool like me / I found her / You're so easy / This life holds something for me

5407072 / Jan '97 / A&M

☐ NILS LOFGREN

Be good tonight / Back it up / One more saturday night / If I say it, it's so / I don't want to know / Keith don't go / Can't buy a break / Duty the sun hasn't set on / Rock 'n' roll crook / Two by two / Goin' back / Girl don't come

5407022 / Apr '97 / A&M

☐ SHINE SILENTLY

Secrets in the street / Flip ya flip / King of the rock / Delivery night / New holes in old shoes / Keith don't go / Like rain / Shine silently / I came to dance / Anytime at all / Beauty and the beast / Dreams die hard / From the heart / Sweet midnight

5507502 / Jan '95 / Spectrum

☐ SILVER LINING

Silver lining / Valentine / Walkin' nerve / Live each day / Sticks and stones / Trouble's back / Little bit o' time / Bein' angry / Gun and run / Girl in motion

ESMCD 145 / Aug '96 / Essential

☐ SOFT FUN TOUGH TEARS 1971-1979

RVCD 44 / Jun '95 / Raven

☐ STEAL YOUR HEART AWAY (The Best Of Nils Lofgren/2CD Set)

Take you to the movies / Back it up / Incidentally... it's over / If I say it, it's so / Goin' back / You're the weight / Fool like me / Duty / Steal away / Shine silently / Cry tough / No mercy / Beggar's day / Like rain / I'll cry tomorrow / Keith don't go (Ode to the Glimmer Twin) / It's not a crime / For your love / Kool skool / Rock 'n' roll crook / I came to dance / Code of the road / I found her / Moon tears / You're so easy / Baltimore / One more Saturday night / Happy / Sun hasn't set on this boy yet

5404112 / Apr '96 / A&M

Loft

☐ ONCE AROUND THE FAIR

Why does the rain / Skeleton staircase / Lonely street / Your door shines like gold / Time / Winter / Like / On a tuesday / Canal and the big red town / Up the hill and down the slope

CRECD 047 / Jun '89 / Creation

Loft Line

☐ NINE STEPS
BEST 1041CD / Nov '93 / Acoustic Music

☐ VISITORS
BEST 1085CD / Mar '96 / Acoustic Music

Loftus

☐ LOFTUS
PERISH 03CD / 16 Mar '98 / Perishable

Loftus, Caroline

☐ SUGAR
LRF 268 / Oct '93 / Larrikin

Logan, John 'Juke'

☐ JUKE RHYTHM
8409432 / Sep '96 / Sky Ranch

Logan, Johnny

☐ BEST OF JOHNNY LOGAN, THE
Hold me now / Stay / When your woman cries / I'm not in love / Helpless heart / Heartbroken man / Living a lie / Such a lady / Love letters / What's another year / Ginny come lately / Lovin' you / Love hurts / Saturday night at the movies / Take good care of my baby / Next time / When you walk in the room / Cryin' in the rain
4840472 / May '96 / Epic

☐ LIVING FOR LOVING
Living for loving / I don't want to fall in love / In London / Man with the accordion / Hey kid / Sad little woman / Carneval do Brazil / Honesty / Lonely tonight / Please please please
PZA 002CD / Feb '94 / Plaza

Logan, Willie

☐ DEDICATIONS
2001 / Burning love / Don't believe a word / Wherever I lay my hat / I shot the sheriff / 20th Century boy / Crazy little thing called love / What a wonderful world / Watching the wheels / Summertime blues / Pretty woman / Dock of the bay / Goodbye love / Voodoo Chile / True love ways
3036400052 / Apr '96 / Hallmark

Logg

☐ LOGG
You've got that something / Dancing into the stars / Something else / I know you will / Lay it on the line / Sweet to me
CPCD 8076 / Mar '95 / Charly

Logical Nonsense

☐ EXPAND THE HIVE
VIRUS 203CD / Jul '97 / Alternative Tentacles

☐ SOUL POLLUTION
VIRUS 214CD / 27 Apr '98 / Alternative Tentacles

Logsdon, Jimmy

☐ I GOT A ROCKET IN MY POCKET
Hank Williams sings the blues no more / Death of Hank Williams / It's all over but the shouting / I can't make up my mind / No longer / I'm going back to Tennessee / Midnight boogie / My sweet French baby / Good deal Lucille / Pa-paya Mama / I got a rocket in my pocket / You're gone baby / Where the Rio de Rosa flows / You ain't nothing but the blues / Love you gave to me / One way ticket to nowhere / Let's have a happy time / As long as we're together / In the Mission of St. Augustine / Where the old red river flows / That's when I'll love you the best / Midnight blues / Cold, cold rain / I'll never know / These lonesome blues / I wanna be Mama'd / (We've reached the) Beginning of the end / Road of regret
BCD 15650 / Oct '93 / Bear Family

Logue & McCool

☐ VERY BEST OF LOGUE & MCCOOL, THE
DHCD 723 / Aug '96 / Homespun

Lohan, Sinead

☐ NO MERMAID
GRACD 239 / 10 Aug '98 / Grapevine

☐ WHO DO YOU THINK I AM
DARA 186CD / Apr '95 / Dara
GRACD 209 / Oct '95 / Grapevine

Lois

☐ BET THE SKY
KLP 36CD / Nov '95 / K

☐ BUTTERFLY KISS
Davey / Narcissus / Press play and record / Staring at the sun / Valentine / Stroll always / Spray / Never last / Bonds in seconds / Sorara / Look who's sorry
KLP 15CD / Nov '95 / K

☐ INFINITY PLUS
KLP 58CD / Oct '96 / K

☐ STRUMPET
KLP 21CD / Nov '95 / K

Loitima

☐ LOITIMA
KICD 36 / Nov '95 / Kansanmusiikki Instituutti

Lo'jo

☐ MOJO RADIO
JNCD 013 / 24 Apr '98 / Night & Day

Loketo

☐ EXTRA BALL
Extra ball / Cyndl / Douce isabelle / La joie de vivre / Malou / Tcheke linha / Pardon / Mondo ry
SHCD 64028 / Jul '91 / Shanachie

Lol Interceps

☐ MUSIC FOR MOVIES
MHCD 023 / Nov '94 / Minus Habens

Loli & The Chones

☐ PS WE HATE YOU
RIPOFF 023CD / Mar '97 / Rip Off

Lolita

☐ EINE SAGE ERZAHLT...
Weisser holunder / Sieben berge / Sieben taler / Das leben ist nur fur die liebe da / Wenn im tal die veilchen wieder bluhen / Ananas / Lorena / MAmbo Lolita (die bar von Lolita) / Gold'ne Rosen / Die madchen aus Kopenhagen / Der weisse mond von Maratonga / Tadellos tadellos / Sonja dora / Corabella (das lied das Jimmy aus Jamaika) / Maria Marietta / Sudwind / Addio amigo / Mexicano / Was ein Mann alles Kann / Am strande von mindanao / Mit etwas liebe / Eine blaue Zauberblume / Melodia ba bahia / Te quiero / Mankoora / Stern van Napoli / Capitano / Manana / Caballero / Jonny / Insel der liebe / Cheerio
BCD 16203 / Nov '97 / Bear Family

☐ SEEMANN DEINE HEIMAT IST DAS MEER
Treu will ich dir bleiben / Sterne in der Tropennacht / So wird es immer sein / Traume mit mir / Bleib bei mir / La luna / Seemann (deine Heimat ist das meer) / Wenn der sommer kommt / Dei Sterne der prare / Mein schiff heisst heimwech / Sounvenir d'amour / Die wiete Welt in weiter ferne / Matrosen aus Piraus / Milord / Uber alle soeben meere / Rosen werden bluh'n / Ein strauss vergissmeinnicht / Sechnsuchht nach samoa / Und ein lied klingt durch das tal / Fur ein paar Tage / Gondoli gondola / Addio my darling by bye / For the first time / Seemann / Trauumusik / Traume van der heimat / Der jadelnde postilion / Lucki lucki polka / Wenn wir uns einmal wiedersehen
BCD 16204 / Nov '97 / Bear Family

Lolitas

☐ FUSEE D'AMOUR
ROSE 170CD / Apr '89 / New Rose

Lollipop

☐ DOG PISS ON DOG
ARRCD 74017 / Dec '96 / Amphetamine Reptile

Lollipop Shoppe

☐ JUST COLOUR
FLASH 62 / 1 Jun '98 / Flash

Lomax, Willie

☐ GIVE ME BACK MY TEETH (The Willie Lomax Blues Revue) (Various Artists)
BB 96001 / 5 Feb '98 / Big Boss

Lombardi, Carlos

☐ TANGO ARGENTINO
Nostalgias / Uno / A media luz / Garufa / El dia que me quieras / En esta tarde gris / Cambalache / Por una cabeza / Mentira / Sus ojos se cerraron / Cuesta abajo / Sombras nada mas / Yira, yira / Tomo y obligo / Donde estas corazon / Bandoneon arrabalero / Milonga sentimental / Desde el alma / Malena / Amargura / Golondrinas / Percal / Arrabal amargo / Carlos gardel / Inspiracion
SOW 90111 / Sep '93 / Sounds Of The World

Lombardo, Guy

☐ I'LL SEE YOU IN MY DREAMS (Lombardo, Guy & His Royal Canadians)
Deep purple / Boom / Faithful forever / Start the day right / Nearness of you / When the swallows come back to Capistrano / Scatterbrain / It's a hap-hap-happy day / I don't want to set the world on fire / Rainbow valley / Concerto in the park / Blues in the night / Along the Sante Fe trail / Tea for two / Hawaiian war chant / Who / Three little fishes / Cancel the flowers / Take it easy / I'll see you in my dreams / It's love love love / Goodnight sweetheart
RAJCD 851 / 1 Jun '98 / Empress

☐ LIVE AT THE WALDORF
When the saints go marchin' in / South Rampart Street Parade / Enjoy yourself / Too much mustard / Boo hoo / Cabaret / Give my regards to Broadway / Hello Dolly / Mack the knife / Silver dollar / Maple leaf rag / I want to be happy / Spanish eyes / Never on Sunday / Helena polka / Alley cat / Tarantella / Your cheatin' heart / High society / Dangerous Dan McGrew / Maria Elena / Johnson rag / Seems like old times / Show me the way to go home / Auld lang syne
CDSIV 1141 / Jul '95 / Horatio Nelson

☐ UNCOLLECTED 1950, THE (Lombardo, Guy & His Royal Canadians)
Mary lou / Snuggled on your shoulder / Pennies from heaven / I love you / Beale street blues / There'll be some changes made / This can't be love / I can't begin to tell you / Music, music, music / Nevertheless / At sundown / Embraceable you / You were meant for me / I'll walk alone / A boy from texas, a girl from tennessee / Sweet georgia brown
HCD 187 / Jan '95 / Hindsight

London

☐ PUNK ROCK COLLECTION
No time / Animal games / Reaction / Everyone's a winner / Summer of love / Us kids cold / Young / Good looking girls / Out on the skids / Speed speed / Swinging London / Everyone's a winner / Handcuffed / Friday on my mind / Siouxsie Sue
AHOYCD 077 / 3 Nov '97 / Captain Oi

London Adventist Chorale

☐ DEEP RIVER
PDSM 1 / Aug '95 / Paradisum

☐ STEAL AWAY (London Adventist Chorale & Ruby Philogene)
CDZ 5697072 / Apr '97 / EMI Classics

London After Midnight

☐ KISS
EFA 015662 / Mar '96 / Apocalyptic Vision

☐ ODDITIES
AV 024CD / 16 Mar '98 / Apocalyptic Vision

☐ PSYCHO MAGNET
EFA 015702 / Sep '96 / Apocalyptic Vision

London All Stars

☐ BRITISH PERCUSSION
BBP 440 / 26 Jan '98 / BBP

London All Stars Steel Orchestra

☐ LATIN AMERICAN HITS
EUCD 1161 / '91 / ARC

London Beat

☐ VERY BEST OF LONDON BEAT, THE
Falling in love again / 9am (the comfort zone) / I've been thinking about you / Better love / No woman no cry / You bring the sun / That's how I feel about you / I'm just your puppet on a string / Come back / She broke my heart (in 36 places) / Crying in the rain / It's in the blood / Katey / Some lucky guy / All born equal / Keeping the memories alive / Step inside my shoes / She said she loves me
74321523782 / 29 Sep '97 / Camden

London Community Gospel Choir

☐ GOSPEL GREATS
Swing low, sweet chariot / Precious Lord, amazing grace / Nobody knows the trouble I've seen / What a friend we have in Jesus / Kumbaya / Count your blessings / Love lifted me / When the saints go marching in / There is a green hill far away / Oh happy day / Old rugged cross
CDMFP 5731 / Apr '91 / Music For Pleasure

☐ OUT OF MANY ONE VOICE
Happy are the people / Found myself a reason / Every passing minute / He is worthy / It's not magic / Back in the fold / Call on him / Interlude / Feel the spirit / Teach me oh lord / Stand up
1901112 / 17 Aug '98 / EMI

London Drive

☐ AWARE
1333CD / May '96 / Infinity

London Festival Orchestra

☐ NIGHT IN VIENNA, A
MACCD 372 / 30 Mar '98 / Autograph

☐ SILENT NIGHT
CNCD 5933 / Nov '92 / Disky

London Funk Allstars

☐ FLESH EATING DISCO ZOMBIES VS THE BIONIC HOOKERS FROM MARS
Introduction / Old skool reunion / There's only one F in funk / Way out / Junkies bad trip / Allstars theme / Love is what we need / Knee deep in the beats / Never can get enough / Flesh eating disco zombies Vs the Bionic Hookers from Mars / UJ / Mad love / Chase / Give it to me raw / How to be a Ninja in one easy lesson
ZENCD 024 / Aug '96 / Ninja Tune

☐ LONDON FUNK VOL.1
Sure shot / Coolin' out / Booyakka / Six million dollar man / Listen to the beat / So good / Fetch / What's in the basket / Represent / Funky sweater / Chicago / Everybody get funky / Chun Li vs. Wah Wah Man / Wikki's revenge / Good life / Body rock / Can ya understand / Bang boogie boogie
ZENCD 016 / May '95 / Ninja Tune

London, Frank

☐ DEBT, THE
TZA 7507 / 25 Aug '97 / Tzadik

London Gabrieli Brass Ensemble

☐ UNDER THE INFLUENCE OF JAZZ
Ragtime three four / Ragtime two four / Early blues / Fastest charleston in the world / Blues from new orleans / Boogie woogie woogie / Singin' the blues / Imagination / Inner bix
CDTTD 569 / Mar '92 / Timeless Traditional

London Jazz Composers Orchestra

☐ THREE PIECES FOR ORCHESTRA
INTAKTCD 045 / May '97 / Intakt

London Jazz Orchestra

☐ DANCE FOR HUMAN FOLK (2CD Set)
HHCD 1016/17 / May '96 / Hot House

London, Jimmy

☐ JIMMY LONDON COLLECTION, THE
BETA 1004CD / Jul '96 / Beta

London, Julie

☐ ALL THROUGH THE NIGHT (Songs Of Cole Porter)
I've got you under my skin / You do something to me / Get out of town / All through the night / So in love / At long last love / Easy to love / My heart belongs to daddy / Every time we say goodbye / In the still of the night
JASCD 308 / May '94 / Jasmine

☐ AROUND MIDNIGHT/JULIE AT HOME
You'd be so nice to come home to / Lonesome road / They didn't believe me / By myself / Thrill is gone / You've gone / Goodbye / Sentimental journey / Give me the simple life / You stepped out of a dream / Let there be love / Everything happens to me / Around midnight / Lonely in Paris / Misty / Black coffee / Lush life / In the wee small hours of the morning / Don't smoke in bed / You and the night and the music / Something cool / How about me / But not for me / Party's over
CTMCD 100 / Nov '96 / EMI

☐ CALENDAR GIRL/YOUR NUMBER PLEASE
June in January / February brings the rain / Melancholy March / I'll remember April / People who are born in May / Memphis in June / Sleight ride in July / Time for August / September in the rain / This October / November twilight / Warm December / Thirteenth month / Makin' whoopee / It could happen to you / When I fall in love / It's a blue / They can't take that away from me / One for the baby / Angel eyes / Love is here to stay / More I see you / Stranger in town / Two sleepy people / Learnin' the blues
CTMCD 125 / 15 Sep '97 / EMI

☐ CRY ME A RIVER
Cry me a river / Boy on a dolphin / Saddle the wind / Must be catchin' / Come on-a my house / Broken hearted melody / Love letters / Besame mucho / Vaya con dios / I'm coming back to you / When snowflakes fall in the Summer / Say wonderful things / End of the world / Fascination / Second time around / More / Girl talk / I left my heart in San Francisco / Good life / Our day will come
CDSL 8267 / Nov '95 / Music For Pleasure

☐ CRY ME A RIVER (3CD Set)
Cry me a river / Days of wine and roses / Gone with the wind / Broken hearted melody / Love for sale / Laura / Vaya con dios / How deep is the ocean / I want to find out for myself / I'm coming back to you / Love on the rocks / Hard hearted Hannah / Little things mean a lot / June in January / All alone / End of the world / My heart belongs to Daddy / Blue moon / Guilty heart / I'll remember April / Charade / Wives and lovers / What is this thing called love / Goody goody / I left my heart in San Francisco / Why don't you do it right / Please do it again / Can't get used to losing you / Call me irresponsible / Fly me to the moon / I'm in the mood for love / Nightingale can sing the blues / Taste of honey / Girl talk / When snowflakes fall in Summer / 'S wonderful / What'll I do / September in the rain / Our day will come / More / In the still of the night / Can't help lovin' that man
HR 883412 / Oct '97 / Disky

☐ EMI PRESENTS THE MAGIC OF JULIE LONDON
Cry me a river / Boy on a dolphin / Saddle the wind / Must be catchin' / Come on-a my house / Broken hearted melody / Love letters / Besame mucho / Vaya con dios / I'm coming back to you / When snowflakes fall in the summer / Say wonderful things / End of the world / Fascination / Second time around / More / Girl talk / I left my heart in San Francisco / Good life / Our day will come
CDMFP 6375 / May '97 / Music For Pleasure

☐ END OF THE WORLD/NICE GIRLS DON'T STAY FOR BREAKFAST
End of the world / I wanna be around / Call me irresponsible / Our day will come / I left my heart in San Francisco / Fly me to the moon / Days of wine and roses / I remember you / My coloring book / Chances are / Slightly out of tune (desafinado) / Good life / Nice girls don't stay for breakfast / When I grow too old to dream / I've got a crush on you / Everything I have is yours / You made me love you / Baby, won't you please come home / I didn't know what time it was / Give a little whistle / I surrender, dear / You go to my head / There will never be another you / Mickey Mouse march
CTMCD 114 / Mar '97 / EMI

☐ JULIE IS HER NAME VOL.1 & 2
Cry me a river / I should care / I'm in the mood for love / I'm glad there is you / Can't help lovin' dat man / I love you, goodbye / Say it isn't so / It never entered my mind / Easy street / 's wonderful / No moon at all / Laura / Gone with the wind / Blue moon / What is this thing called love / How long has this been going on / Too good to be true / Spring is here / Goody goody / One I love belongs to somebody else / If I'm lucky / Hot toddy / Little white lies / I guess I'll have to change my plan / I got lost in his arms
CDP 7998042 / Oct '92 / Liberty

☐ TOUCH OF CLASS, A
Cry me a river / Saddle the wind / Love must be catchin' / Come on my house / Broken hearted melody / Love letters / Besame mucho / Vaya con dios / I'm coming back to you / When snowflakes fall in the summer / Say wonderful things / End of the world / More / I left my heart in San Francisco / Good life / Our day will come
TC 885722 / 2 Feb '98 / Disky

London Philharmonic Orchestra

☐ ABIDE WITH ME (18 Choral Masterpieces)
Pomp and circumstance / Zadok the priest / Bridal chorus / Londonderry air (Danny Boy) / Holy city / All people that on earth do dwell / Mine eyes have seen the glory / Rock of ages / Eternal father strong to save / Jerusalem / God that madest Earth and heaven / Hallelujah chorus / For unto us a child is born / For the wings of a dove / Abide with me / Brother James' air / Praise my soul the King of Heaven / God our help in ages past
3036001022 / Apr '97 / Carlton

☐ POP LEGENDS (Clark, Louis & The London Philharmonic Orchestra)
Oh pretty woman / You've lost that loving feeling / Dancing queen / Dancing in the dark / Will you still love me tomorrow / She's not there / When will I see you again / You can't hurry love / River deep, mountain high / MacArthur Park
WB 877072 / Mar '97 / Disky

☐ TORVILL & DEAN'S FIRE AND ICE
Fire and Ice: Prelude / Fire world / Ice world / Meeting / Ice court / Mask dance / Ice warriors / Skating lesson / Fire and ice(love duet) / Ambush / Lament/ war dance / Melting/battle / After the war / Dance of hope
CASTCD 7 / Nov '86 / First Night

London Sound & Art Orchestra

☐ 48 HITS FROM THE AGE OF POP VOL.1 (3CD Set)
290336 / Dec '96 / Column

☐ 48 HITS FROM THE AGE OF POP VOL.2 (3CD Set)
290337 / Dec '96 / Column

London Symphony Orchestra

☐ BEST OF CLASSIC ROCK, THE (The Ballads)
Lady in red / Don't give up / Against all odds / Groovy kind of love / Eternal flame / From a distance / Time after time / Power of love / Seperate lives / Senza una donna / I want to know what love is / Unchained melody / How am I supposed to live without you / Sailing / Hello / (Everything I do) I do it for you
4879762 / 8 Sep '97 / Columbia

☐ BEST OF CLASSIC ROCK, THE
Born in the USA / Light my fire / All right now / Living years / Purple rain / It's a sin / I want it all / I still haven't found what I'm looking for / Eloise / You're the voice / She's not there / Wind of change / Drive / Two tribes-relax / Saturday night's alright for fighting / Final countdown
4879752 / 8 Sep '97 / Columbia

☐ POWER OF CLASSIC ROCK/LIVING YEARS/COUNTDOWN (3CD Set)
Two tribes/Relax / Drive / Purple rain / Time after time / I want to know what love is / Born in the USA/ Dancing in the dark / Power of love / Thriller / Total eclipse of the heart / Hello / Modern girl / I want it all / Eternal flame / Against all odds / I still haven't found what I'm looking for / Sailing / Eloise / Smooth criminal / Clouds over aysgarth/In the air tonight / Prelude in motion/The first time / Groovy kind of love / One moment in time / Living years / Final countdown / Take my breath away / You can call me Al / Lady in red / Separate lives / It's a sin / She's not there / Don't give up / You're the voice / Golden slumbers / Carry that weight / End
4775172 / Oct '94 / Columbia

☐ ULTIMATE SYMPHONIC ROCK COLLECTION (3CD Set) (London Symphony Orchestra & London Pop Choir)
COLBX 002 / Feb '97 / Focus

London Theatre Orchestra

☐ NATIONAL ANTHEMS OF THE WORLD
God save the Queen (Great Britain) / Star spangled banner (USA) / La Marseillaise (France) / Deutschland lied (Germany) / Inno di mameli (Italy) / Mazurek dabrowskiego (Poland) / Marcha real (Spain) / Segnorizo apo tin kopsi (Greece) / Hataikvah (Israel) / O Canada (Canada) / Kiminga yowa chiyoni (Japan) / Wilhemus van nassouwe (Holland) / Scotland the Brave (Scotland) / Amthran na bh fiann (Ireland) / Land of my fathers (Wales) / European anthem (Beethoven's 9th Symphony)
EMPRCD 581 / Oct '95 / Emporio

London Trombone Quartet

☐ SOME OF OUR BEST FRIENDS
Crack up / Talk time / Until / Not doon there / See you on the 8th / Eminance / Don't go changing / Off the rails / Welcome / Lost and found / Reverse gear
ASCCD 11 / Nov '96 / ASC

London Welsh Male Voice Choir

☐ BEAUTIFUL SONG, THE (Gwyl Corau Meibion Cymry Llundain 1996)
Sailors chorus / Conspirators chorus / Sequidille / Yfory / Old woman / Ai am fod haul yn machlud / Suo gan / Love could I only tell thee / Aus der traube / Delilah / Bro aber / How green was my valley / Saint Saens organ symphony / You'll never walk alone / Soon ah will be done / Give me Jesus / Deep harmony / Mae d'eisiau di bob awr / American trilogy / Morte criste / Blaenwern
SCD 2131 / Feb '97 / Sain

☐ IN BRIGHT ARRAY ASSEMBLE (1000 Welsh Voices)
Roman war song / Soldier's farewell / Pilgrims / O Gymru / Myfanwy / Crimond / Tydi a roddaist / Rhythm of life / Rose / Love changes everything / Casatschok / Dry bones / Y nefoedd / Timeless moment / Y dref wen / Where shall I be / American triology / Finlandia / Bryn myrddin / Cwm rhondda
QPRZ 015D / Oct '97 / Polyphonic

Lone Justice

☐ LONE JUSTICE
East of Eden / After the flood / Ways to be wicked / Don't toss us away / Working late / Pass it on / Wait till we get home / Soap, soup and salvation / You are the light / Sweet sweet baby
GED 24060 / Nov '96 / Geffen

☐ SHELTER
I found love / Shelter / Reflected / Beacon / Wheels / Belfry / Dreams come true / Gift / Inspiration / Dixie storms
GED 24122 / Nov '96 / Geffen

Lone Sharks

☐ NO MESSIN'
CR 16 / Oct '97 / NOCO

Lone Star

☐ LONE STAR
She said / Lonely soldier / Flying in the reel / Spaceships / New day / Million stars / Illusions
07863666422 / Jun '96 / RCA

Lonely Stranded Band

☐ LONELY STRANDED BAND
CICD 116 / Apr '96 / Clo Iar-Chonnachta

Lonely Trailer

☐ MULTIMETEOR
MUDCD 020 / 23 Feb '98 / Mud

Lonesome Organist

☐ COLLECTOR OF CACTUS ECHO BAGS
THRILL 044CD / 11 Aug '97 / Thrill Jockey

Lonesome Pine Fiddlers

☐ WINDY MOUNTAIN
Pain in my heart / Lonesome sad and blue / Don't forget me / Will I meet Mother in Heaven / You broke your promise / I'm left alone / Nobody cares (not even you) / Twenty one years / My brown eyed darling / You left me to cry / That's why you left me so blue / I'll never make you blue / Honky tonk blues / You're so good / I'll never change my mind / Dirty dishes blues / Lonesome pine breakdown / Five string rag / Baby you're cheatin' / I'm feeling for you (but I can't reach you) / Some kinda sorry / Windy mountain / No curb service / New set of blues / There's just one you
ECD 501 / Apr '92 / Rollercoaster

Lonesome River Band

☐ OLD COUNTRY TOWN
Highway paved with pain / Highway paved with pain / Tears are blinding me / Long gone / (listen to) the old man / Who needs you / Game (i can't win) / Running hard on a broken heart / She's about trouble / Solid rock / I'll take the blame / Old lonesome welcome back
SHCD 3818 / Mar '94 / Sugar Hill

☐ ONE STEP FORWARD
When you go walking / Say I do / Sorry county blues / Southern comfort / Thank God for a mama / Flat broke and lonesome / Carolyn the teenage queen / Crossroads / Katy Daley / This lonesome song / Crazy heart / Georgia mail
SHCD 3848 / 23 Mar '98 / Sugar Hill

Lonesome Standard Time

☐ LONESOME AS IT GETS
SHCD 3839 / Oct '95 / Sugar Hill

☐ LONESOME STANDARD TIME
Lonesome standard time / Delta queen / You can't do wrong and get by / Fields of home / Lower on the hog / Castellion springs / Down the road to gloryland / Kentucky king / Little Cecil / Old river rock / Highway 40 blues / Lonesome dove / You can't take it with you when you go
SHCD 3802 / Sep '92 / Sugar Hill

☐ MIGHTY LONESOME
SHCD 3816 / Mar '94 / Sugar Hill

Lonesome Strangers

☐ LONESOME STRANGERS
HCD 8016 / Sep '94 / Hightone

Lonesome Sundown

☐ BEEN GONE TOO LONG
They call me sundown / One more night / Louisiana lover man / Dealin' from the bottom / Midnight blues again / Just got to know / Black cat bone / I betcha / You don't miss your water / If you ain't been to Houston
HCD 8031 / Jun '94 / Hightone

☐ I'M A MOJO MAN
Gonna stick to you baby / I'm a mojo man / I stood by / Don't go / Lonely, lonely me / You know I love you / Learn to treat me better / Lonesome lonely blues / I'm glad she's mine / Sundown blues / My home ain't there / What you wanna do it for / I woke up crying (oh what a dream) / When I had, I didn't need (now I need, don't have a dime) / I'm a samplin' man / Hoodoo woman blues / I'm a young man / It's easy when you know how / I got a broken heart / Don't say a word / Lost without love / Leave my money alone / My home is a prison / Lonesome whistler
CDCHD 556 / Feb '95 / Ace

Loney, Roy

☐ SCIENTIFIC BOMBS AWAY, THE (Loney, Roy & Phantom Movers)
AIM 1025CD / Oct '93 / Aim

Long Decline

☐ LONG DECLINE, THE
OVER 61CD / Apr '97 / Overground

Long Fin Killie

☐ AMELIA
British summertime / Lipstick / Kismet / Resin / Sugar helping / Ringer / Chrysler / Bigger than England / Headlines / Gold swinger / Deep house / Yawning at comets
PURECD 074 / 17 Nov '97 / Too Pure

☐ HOUDINI
Man Ray / How I blew it with Houdini / Homo Erectus / Heads of dead surfers / Montgomery / Love smothers allergy / Hollywood gem / Lamberton lamplighter / Corngold / Idiot hormone / Rockethead on mandatory surveillance / Flower carrier / Unconscious gangs of men
PURECD 047 / Jun '95 / Too Pure

☐ VALENTINO
Godiva / Pele / Kitten heels / 1,000 Wounded astronauts / Hands and lips / Valentino / Coward / Girlfriend / Matador / Cop / Cupid
PURECD 054 / May '96 / Too Pure

Long Hind Legs

☐ LONG HIND LEGS
KRS 274CD / Jan '97 / Kill Rock Stars

Long, Larry

☐ HERE I STAND: ELDERS' WISDOM, CHILDREN'S SONG (Long, Larry & Youth/Elders Of Rural Alabama)
SFWCD 45050 / Aug '96 / Smithsonian Folkways

☐ IT TAKES A LOT OF PEOPLE (A Tribute To Woody Guthrie)
FF 70508 / Oct '89 / Flying Fish

☐ RUN FOR FREEDOM/SWEET THUNDER
Run for freedom / Grandma's penny sale / It feels OK / Blue highway / Sacred black hills / Anna Mae / Michael / American hymn / Grizzly bear / Mad about the way things are / Light a candle / Your love / Road to freedom / Water in the rain / Sweet thunder / Love will lay hatred down
CDFF 655 / Jun '97 / Flying Fish

Long, P.W.

☐ WE DIDN'T SEE YOU ON SUNDAY (Long, P.W. & Reelfoot)
TG 178CD / Jun '97 / Touch & Go

Long, P.W. & Reelfoot

☐ PUSH ME AGAIN
TG 192 / 17 Jun '98 / Touch & Go

Long Ryders

☐ METALLIC BO
SID 001 / Apr '95 / Prima

☐ NATIVE SONS
I had a dream / Tell it to the judge on Sunday / Wreck of the 909 / Ivory tower / Too close to the lights / Still get by / Final wild son / (Sweet) mental revenge / Never got to meet the Mom / Fair game / Run Dusty run
DIAB 821 / Jun '96 / Diablo

☐ STATE OF OUR UNION
Looking for Lewis and Clarke / Lights of downtown / WDIA / Mason-Dixon line / Here comes that train again / Years long ago / Good times tomorrow, hard times today / Two kinds of love / You just can't ride the box cars anymore / Capturing the flag / State of my union
SID 003 / Mar '95 / Prima

☐ TWO FISTED TALES
Gunslinger man / I want you bad / Stitch in time / Light gets in the way / Prairie fire / Baby's in toyland / Long short story / Man of misery / Harriet Tubman's gonna carry me home / For the rest of my days / Spectacular fall
SID 005 / Mar '96 / Prima

Long Tall Shorty

☐ 1970'S BOY
Falling for you / Long time / If I was you / Please can you tell me / Shake / New generation / By your love / That's what I want / 1970's boy / She's all mine / I do / Can't stop moving / All by myself / By your love / 1970's boy / By your love / Win or lose / Ain't done wrong / Anti CND / Champagne charlie
MODSKACD 005 / 3 Nov '97 / Captain Mod

Long Tall Texans

☐ ACES AND EIGHTS
Notice me / Nothing left but bone / Sister / I wish / Lip service / Everyday / Bloody / (Don't go back to) Rockville / Border radio / Tomorrow today / Innocent look / Piece of your love
CDMPSYCHO 16 / Aug '97 / Anagram

☐ FEW TEXANS MORE, A
DOJOCD 262 / May '96 / Dojo

☐ IN WITHOUT KNOCKING
Poison / Rockin' Crazy / Mad About You / Saints and sinners / Gotta Go / Texas Beat / Right First Time / Rock 'n' Roll (Part 2)/Endless Sleep / My Babe / Texas Boogie / Wreckin' me / Who's Sorry Now / Your Own Way / Get Back Wet Back / Long tall Texan / Get Up And Go / Paradise / My Idea Of Heaven / Indians / Off My Mind / Bloody / Dance Of The Headhunters / Should I stay or should I go
RAGECD 109 / Aug '92 / Rage

☐ SINGING TO THE MOON
Singing to the moon / Rock Bottom Blues / Klub Foot Shuffle / Suicide At The Seaside / Winding me up / Reactor / Witch Hunting / Singing To The Moon / Axe To Grind / Smiling eyes / Alcohol / Indian Reservation / Nine Days Wonder / Senses six and seven / Alabama Song
RAGECD 108 / Apr '91 / Rage

Longfellow

☐ WE'RE HUGE IN JAPAN
300002 / 15 Jun '98 / Kung Fu

Longjian, Tan

☐ TAN LONGJIAN
OMCD 61 / Mar '96 / Olarin Musiiki Oy

Longmire, Wilbert

☐ SUNNYSIDE UP
Black is the colour / Good morning / Love why don't you find a way / Lovely day / Starflight
ESMCD 587 / 29 Sep '97 / Essential

Longoria, Valerio

☐ CABALLO VIEJO
ARHCD 336 / Apr '95 / Arhoolie

☐ TEXAS CONJUNTO PIONEER
ARHCD 358 / Apr '95 / Arhoolie

Longpigs

☐ SUN IS OFTEN OUT, THE
Lost myself / She said / Far / On and on / Happy again / All hype / Sally dances / Jesus Christ / Dozen wicked words / Elvis / Over our bodies
MUMCD 9602 / Jun '96 / Mother

Longstocking

☐ ONCE UPON A TIME CALLED NOW
CHSW 17 / 20 Oct '97 / Chainsaw

Longstone

☐ SURROUNDED BY GLASS
OCH 005LCD / 27 Apr '98 / Ochre

Longthorne, Joe

☐ I WISH YOU LOVE
Young girl / Lady blue / So deep is the night / If I only had time / Mary in the morning / Say it with flowers / Where are you now / Runaway / Over and over / True love / My funny valentine / Never say never / Walk in the room / I wish you love
CEDMC 3662 / 16 Mar '98 / EMI

☐ LIVE AT THE ROYAL ALBERT HALL
Passing strangers / Mary in the morning / If I only had time / What's going on / Unchained melody / It's not unusual / To all the girls I've loved before / Daniel / I just called to say I love you / Stand by me / This is my life / I believe I'm going to love you / Whole lotta shakin' goin' on / Great balls of fire / Life on Mars / Lady is a tramp / Perfect love / You're the first, my last, my everything / Wind beneath my wings / Born free / Portrait of my life / If I never sing another song / Somewhere
CDDPR 134 / Dec '94 / Music For Pleasure

Longview

☐ LONGVIEW
I've never been so lonesome / Lonesome old home / It's goodbye and so long to you / Southern moon / Only time can mend a broken heart / Seven year blues / Brighter mansion / Hemlocks and primroses / How will the flowers bloom / Touch of God's hand / Pale horse and his rider / Will you be faithful while I'm gone / River underground / Train that carried my girl from town
ROUCD 0386 / Sep '97 / Rounder

Look People

☐ BOOGASM
OUT 1122 / Nov '94 / Brake Out

Lookers In Clover

☐ LOOKERS IN CLOVER, THE
CAR 27CD / 20 Oct '97 / Candy Ass

Looking East

☐ LOOKING EAST
African scherzo / Reunion / Todi / Beneath the canopy / Dedication / Seven eight / Looking East / Adagio / Canary
CDLDL 1258 / Sep '97 / Lochshore

Loomis, Hamilton

☐ HAMILTON BLUES
HAMBONECD 301 / Jul '95 / Ham Bone

Loop

☐ DUAL
Collision / Crawling / Thief of fire / Thief (Motherfucker) / Black sun / Circle grave / Mother sky / Got to get it over
REACTORCD 5 / Mar '94 / Reactor

☐ GILDED ETERNITY, A
Vapour / Afterglow / Nail with burn / Blood / Breathe into me / From centre to wave / Be here now / Shot with a diamond / Nail with burn (burn out) / Arc-lite (sonar)
SITU 27CD / Feb '90 / Situation 2
BBL 27CD / Sep '95 / Beggars Banquet

Loop Guru

☐ 3RD CHAMBER
3rd Chamber parts 1-6
GURU 100CD / Nov '96 / North South

☐ AMRITA
GURU 200CD / Mar '96 / North South

☐ CATALOGUE OF DESIRES
GURU 300CD / Apr '96 / North South

☐ DUN-YA
NATCD 31 / Apr '94 / Nation

☐ IN A WORLD OF THEIR OWN (4CD Set)
GURUBOX 500CD / 1 Jun '98 / North South

☐ LOOP BITES DOG
GURU 400CD / 29 Sep '97 / North South

☐ PEEL SESSIONS, THE
SFRCD 139 / Jul '96 / Strange Fruit

Looptroop

☐ KING OF DISCO'IN
DIFCD 3 / 27 Apr '98 / Different Drummer

Loopuyt, Marc

☐ ORIENTS OF THE LUTE, THE (2CD Set)
926742 / Jun '97 / BUDA

☐ SUSPIRO DEL MORO
926252 / Mar '96 / BUDA

Loos, Charles

☐ CHARLES LOOS AND ALI RYERSON (Loos, Charles & Ali Ryerson)
EMD 89012 / May '89 / Candid

Loose

☐ ESPECIALLY FOR YOU
LAZEYE 209CD / Oct '95 / Lazy Eye

Loose Diamonds

☐ BURNING DAYLIGHT
DOSCD 7001 / May '93 / Dos

☐ NEW LOCATION
DOS 7010 / Oct '95 / Dos

Loose Ends

☐ LOOK HOW LONG
Look how long / Don't you ever (try to change me) / Time is ticking / Love's got me / Don't be a fool / Cheap talk / Love controversy / Try my love / Hold tight / I don't need to love / Symptons of love
CDVIP 186 / Apr '97 / Virgin VIP

☐ SO WHERE ARE YOU
Magic touch / New horizon / If my lovin' makes you hot / So where are you / Golden years / Hangin' on a string / Give it all you got / Sweetest pain / You can't stop the rain / Silent talking
CDV 2340 / Feb '87 / Virgin

☐ TIGHTEN UP VOL.1
Magic touch / Gonna make you mine / Hangin' on a string / Choose me (rescue me) / Little spice / Slow down / Don't worry / Love's got me / Don't be a fool / Watching you / Tell me what you want / Ooh you make me feel / Hangin' on a string (original)
DIXCD 112 / Jul '92 / 10

Lopato, David

☐ INSIDE OUTSIDE
EMY 1322 / Sep '92 / Enemy

Lopes, Carlos

☐ DREAMSVILLE
FMJXD 189 / Mar '93 / FM

Lopez, Belisario

☐ PRUEBA MI SAZON 1942-1948 (Lopez, Belisario Orquesta)
TCD 069 / Jul '96 / Tumbao Cuban Classics

Lopez De Munain Balen

☐ LABERINTOA
AZ 002 / 1 Jun '98 / Karonte

Lopez, Francisco

☐ UNTITLED 74
TECHNETIUM 43 / Jul '97 / Table Of The Elements

☐ UNTITLED MUSIC FOR GEOGRAPHY
SEDCD 024 / 17 Nov '97 / Sedimental

Lopez, Isidro

☐ EL INDIO
ARHCD 363 / Apr '95 / Arhoolie

Lopez, Israel

☐ DOS (Lopez, Israel 'Cachao')
CDGR 152 / May '97 / Charly

☐ MORE LEGENDARY DESCARGA SESSIONS (Lopez, Israel 'Cachao')
CCD 510 / Jul '96 / Caney

Lopez, Juan

☐ EL REY DE LA REDOVA
ARHCD 407 / Apr '95 / Arhoolie

Lopez, Oscar

☐ HEAT
Forgive me / Thinking of you / Senitimento / Fire and fury / Fiesta latina / Distancia / Those times / Step by step / Way I am / Flight of the flamingo / Milonguita / Morenita / My heart in Rio / Tornado de amor / Desperate love
ND 63040 / Jul '97 / Narada
VNDCD 6 / 11 May '98 / Virgin

Lopez, Trini

☐ TRINI LOPEZ
GRF 189 / Jan '93 / Tring

☐ TRINI LOPEZ
La bamba / If I had a hammer / Guantanamera / Blowin' in the wind / Adalita / America / Lemon tree / Shame and scandal / What'd I say / Bye bye blondie / Kansas City / If I had to live again / Cielito / This land is your land / Quizas, quizas, quizas / Perfidia / Gotta travel on / Down by the riverside / Marianne / When the saints go marching in / Volare / Besame mucho
399531 / Jun '97 / Koch Presents

☐ TRINI LOPEZ LIVE
America / If I had a hammer / Bye bye blackbird / Cielito Lindo / This land is your land / What'd I say / La Bamba / Granada / Bye bye Blondie / Nie meir ohne (German) / Lebewohl daisy girl / Long ago / Folk medley / Unchain my heart
BCD 15427 / May '89 / Bear Family

Lopez-Furst, Ruben

☐ ALL THE THINGS YOU ARE (Lopez-Furst, Ruben Trio)
BMJ 002 / 5 Jan '98 / Blue Moon

Lopretti, Jose

☐ CANDOMBE
CHR 70013 / Apr '95 / Challenge

Lorber, Alan

☐ LOTUS PALACE, THE (Lorber, Alan Orchestra)
Up up and away / Where / Mas que nada / Echo of the night / Lucy in the sky with diamonds / Look of love / Flute thing / Hang on to a dream / Within you without you / Roopaka dha teri dhin dhin / Serpent and the hawk / Hollow in the wind / Where / Djellaba / I heard the rain
CDWIKD 172 / May '97 / Big Beat

Lorber, Jeff

☐ MIDNIGHT
VICJ 60163 / 27 Apr '98 / Victor

☐ STATE OF GRACE
5315552 / Jul '96 / Verve Forecast

☐ WORTH WAITING FOR
Rain song / Underground / Yellowstone / Punta del este / Lost with you / Worth waiting for / High wire / Wavelength / Columbus Ave / Do what it takes / Jazzery
5179982 / Jan '94 / Verve Forecast

Lorca, Federico Garcia

☐ CANCIONES POPULARES ESPANOLAS
J 105CD / Jun '94 / Sonifolk

☐ POETRY PUT TO SONG
7996502 / Jan '95 / Hispavox

Lorca, Franco

☐ CELTIC DREAMS (Pan Pipe Tribute To Ireland)
MACCD 370 / 30 Mar '98 / Autograph

L'Orchestre Noir

☐ CANTOS
Canto / Prologue / March of angels / Te arma lucis / Down these mean streets / Man must go / Assasins and other friends / Vetus et novum / In hell's mouth / Lake of bodies - Aqua morta / In Europe / Epilogue
TURSA 013CD / Mar '97 / Tursa

Lord

☐ BEHIND THE CURTAIN OF DARKNESS
ELD 002 / 2 Mar '98 / Eldethorn

Lord Belial

☐ ENTER THE MOONLIGHT GATE
NFR 020CD / 6 Oct '97 / No Fashion

☐ KISS THE GOAT
NFR 010CD / May '95 / No Fashion

Lord Blakie

☐ RAW KAISO VOL.1 (Lord Blakie & Black Prince/Mighty Zandolie)
Introduction: Lord Blakie / Steelband clash: Lord Blakie / Maria: Lord Blakie / Mode de pussy: Lord Blakie / Calypso memory: Black Prince / Friday evening: Black Prince / One lifetime ent nuff: Black Prince / Fry balls: Black Prince / De letter: Black

Prince / Introduction to Mighty Zandolie: Mighty Zandolie / Iron man: Mighty Zandolie / Merchant of Venice: Mighty Zandolie / Whip: Mighty Zandolie / Man family: Mighty Zandolie / Stickman: Mighty Zandolie
ROUCD 5074 / Feb '98 / Rounder

Lord Creator

☐ DON'T STAY OUT LATE
VPCD 2046 / Apr '96 / VP

Lord High Fixers

☐ GROUP IMPROVISATION AND MORE
SFTRI 409CD / Sep '97 / Sympathy For The Record Industry

☐ WHEN
ANDA 199 / Feb '97 / Au-Go-Go

Lord, Jon

☐ BEFORE I FORGET
Chance on a feeling / Tender babes / Hollywood rock and roll / Bach onto this / Before I forget / Say it's alright / Burntwood / Where are you / Lady / For a friend / Pavanne / Going home
RPM 126 / Mar '94 / RPM

Lord Kitchener

☐ STILL ESCALATING
JW 055CD / Feb '94 / Soca

Lord, Mary Lou

☐ GOT NO SHADOW
OK 67574 / 26 Jan '98 / Work

Lord Of Illusion

☐ LORD OF ILLUSION
1182 / 23 Feb '98 / JMC

Lord Tanamo

☐ IN THE MOOD FOR SKA
CDTRL 313 / Mar '94 / Trojan

Lord Tariq

☐ MAKE IT REIGN (Lord Tariq & Peter Gunz)
Make it reign / We will ball / Massive heat / Sex money life or death / One life to live / Fiesta / Then and now / Startin' somethin' / Night in the Bronx / Who am I / Deja vu (uptown baby) / Keep on worldwide / Streets to da stage / Bx most wanted / Cross Bronx expressway / Precipitation / My time to go / Be my lady
4897042 / 8 Jun '98 / Columbia

Lordryk

☐ LORDRYK
VR 03CD / Apr '96 / Vroe

Lorelei

☐ EVERYONE MUST TOUCH THE...
SLR 044CD / Dec '96 / Slumberland

☐ HEADSTRONG
LDL 1213CD / Jun '94 / Lochshore

☐ PROGRESSION
CDLDL 1236 / Nov '95 / Lochshore

Lorellei

☐ SPIRITUS BREATH OF LIFE
SP 7156CD / Jul '96 / Soundings Of The Planet

Loren

☐ UP ALL NIGHT
PROCD 001 / 16 Feb '98 / Props

Lorenz, Trey

☐ TREY LORENZ
Someone to hold / Photograph of Mary / Just to be to you / Run back to me / Always in love / Wipe all my tears away / Baby I'm in heaven / It only hurts when it's love / How can I say goodbye / Find a way / When troubles come
4721722 / Dec '92 / Epic

Loretta's Doll

☐ NOCTURNAL ARCADE
World of hell / Friendly fire / David / You never knew / Nothing lasts for ever and a day / No more / One of God's miracles / Child in winter
WSCD 333 / Feb '98 / World Serpent

☐ XXI DEGREES
WSCD 004 / Oct '96 / World Serpent

L'Orient Imaginaire

☐ LABYRINTH (L'Orient Imaginaire/ Vladimir Ivanoff)
0630117562 / Jul '96 / Teldec Classics

☐ YEHUDI (Jewish Music From The Seraglio) (L'Orient Imaginaire/Vladimir Ivanoff)
0630116992 / Aug '96 / Teldec Classics

Los Activos

☐ HASTA LOS HUESOS
BB 419CD / 24 Apr '98 / Karonte

Los Alfa 8

☐ LA SALSA LLEGO
TUMICD 029 / '92 / Tumi

Los Alhama

☐ FLAMENCO
EUCD 1026 / '89 / ARC

Los Amigos

☐ SOUTH AMERICAN HOLIDAY
CNCD 5962 / Jul '93 / Disky

Los Amigos Invisibles

☐ NEW SOUND OF THE VENEZUELAN GOZADERA, THE
Guelcome / Ultra funk / Mi lindo / Sexy / Las lycras del avila / Groupie / Otra vez / Cachete a cachete / Balada de chusy / Asomacho / Ponerte en cuatro / Mango cool / Nerio compra contestadoro / Quierio desingtegrar a tu novio / El disco anal / No me pagan / Cha chaborro / Aldemaro en su camaro / New sound of the Venezuelan gozadera
9362468392 / 27 Jul '98 / Luaka Bop

Los Angeles

☐ FALL AND RISE
N 02572 / Jul '95 / Noise

Los Angeles Jazz Quartet

☐ LOOK TO THE EAST
860092 / Feb '98 / Naxos Jazz

Los Assdraggers

☐ ABBEY ROADKILL
EFA 128802 / Nov '96 / Crypt

Los Boleros

☐ LOS BOLEROS
12462 / Mar '95 / Laserlight

Los Caimanes

☐ MUSIC OF MEXICO VOL.3: LA HUASTECA (Los Caimanes & Los Caporales)
ARHCD 431 / Jan '96 / Arhoolie

Los Calchakis

☐ ART OF THE ANDEAN FLUTE, THE
ARN 60352 / 21 Aug '97 / Arion

☐ LE CHANT DES POETES REVOLTES
ARN 64374 / Nov '96 / Arion

Los Camperos De Valles

☐ EL TRUNFO
MT 007 / Jan '94 / Corason

☐ MUSE
CORA 124 / Nov '95 / Corason

Los Canarios

☐ CICLOS
SRMC 1003 / 5 Jan '98 / Siwan

Los Cenzontles

☐ CO SU PERMISO, SENORES
ARHCD 435 / Jan '96 / Arhoolie

Los Chumps

☐ PRETTY GIRLS EVERYWHERE
TX 2103CD / Jul '95 / Taxim

Los Cincos

☐ EXPERIMENTAL PROCEDURE
SFTRI 492CD / Sep '97 / Sympathy For The Record Industry

☐ FIVE DEADLY SINS
SFTRI 442CD / Jan '97 / Sympathy For The Record Industry

Los Coronas

☐ GENUINE SOUNDS
TT 002CD / 2 Mar '98 / Tritone

Los Del Rio

☐ FIESTA MACARENA
La Nina / Tocala tocala / Macarena / San sereni / No te vay as todavia / Estas pillao / Pura carroceria / Tengo tengo / El sueno de la marisma / La polvareda / La Nina / Macarena / Macarena
74321346632 / Jun '97 / RCA

Los Dos Gilbertos

☐ ESTAMOS EN TEJAS
EDCD 7042 / Jul '97 / Easydisc

Los Dug Dugs

☐ LOS DUG DUGS
PECD 470 / 19 Jan '98 / Producto

Los Gitanillos De Cadiz

☐ FLAMENCO
401982 / Aug '90 / Musidisc

Los Gusanos

☐ LOS GUSANOS
Bad day / Carve your name / Helldorado / Low / Dead man's curve / Blue sky / Burnin' / Reciprocal / Strip / Go again / Arizona / On my way out
119312 / 22 Sep '97 / Wowoka
111182 / 1 Jun '98 / Mayhem

Los Hermanos Moreno

☐ TOGETHER
Quimbombo / Hazme el amor / Sin ti no puedo vivir / Mas alla de todo / Quien como tu / Homenaje a mis colegas / Reunited / Por alguien como tu / Te quiero porqe te quiero / Maria Tomasa
66058007 / Sep '93 / RMM

Los Huertas

☐ YO QUIERO MUSICA
No quiero musica / Brillar de luna / Eviva espana / Amor de playa / Salva me / Taka takata / Ninos de la noche / Luisa / Bamboleo / Linda / Amor, amor / America
322788 / Oct '92 / Koch

Los Ileagles

☐ EL APOSTOL DE LA LUJURIA
ACD 036 / 14 Apr '98 / Avispa

Los Incas

☐ ALGERIA
824132 / Nov '90 / BUDA

☐ EL CONDOR PASA
824122 / Nov '90 / BUDA

Los Infernos

☐ PLANET KAOS
DD 0124 / Apr '97 / Dr. Dream

Los Latinos

☐ BEST OF SALSA, THE
EUCD 1125 / '91 / ARC

Los Lobos

☐ COLOSSAL HEAD
Revolution / Mas y mas / Everybody loves a train / Life is good / Manny's bones / This bird's gonna fly / Buddy ebsen loves the night time / Colossal head / Little japan / Can't stop the rain / Maricela
9362461722 / Mar '96 / Warner Bros.

☐ JUST ANOTHER BAND FROM EAST LA (2CD Set)
Volver, volver / El cuchipe / La feria de las flores / Sabor a mi / Let's say goodnight / Anseima / Will the wolf survive / Matter of time / I got to let you know / Don't worry baby / One time one night / Shakin' shakin' shakes / River of fools / Carabina. 30-30 / Tears of god / Set me free (rosa lee) / Come on let's go / La bamba / El gusto / Estoy sentado aqui / La pistola y el corazon / I wanna be like you / Someday / Down on the riverbed / Be still / Neighbourhood / I can't understand / Angel dance / Bertha / Saint behind the glass / Angels with dirty faces / Wicked rain / Kiko and the lavender moon / When the circus comes / Peace / Bella maria de mi alma / What's going on / Wrong mean theme / Blue moonlight / Politician / New zandu
8284002 / Jan '94 / Slash

☐ PAPA'S BREATH (Los Lobos & Lalo Guerrero)
942562 / Mar '95 / Music For Little People

Los Machado

☐ JIMENEZ - POETRY PUT TO SONG
7996542 / Jan '95 / Hispavox

Los Machucambos

☐ LA BAMBA
La Bamba / Mas que nada / Cuando calienta el sol / Pepito / Eso es el amor / Granada / Brazil / Con amor / Esperanza / Fio maravilha / Girl from Ipanema / Amor amor / Tres palabras / El condor pasa / Quiereme / Guantanamera / La cucaracha / Tristeza / Perfidia / Corcovado / La mama / Maria Elena / Tico-tico / Frenesie / El manisero
300052 / Aug '90 / Musidisc

☐ LIBERTARIAN SONGS FROM LATIN AMERICA
Casamiento de negros / Duerme negrito / Piedra y camino / Subo subo / Reservista purajhey / Hasta siempre comandante / Recuerdos de calahuallo / Vasija de barro / Marchinha pra Angela Davis / Pobre guajiro / Puerto Rico en el corazon / Balas / La visita / Adios al mar / Es la libertad / Cortando platano / Oda del desterrado / Te recuerdo Amanda
19152 / Apr '98 / Forlane

Los Malaguenos

☐ FLAMENCO
HMA 190965CD / Oct '94 / Musique D'Abord

Los Masis

☐ EL CORAZON DEL PUEBLO
TUMICD 062 / Nov '96 / Tumi

Los Munequitos De Matanzas

☐ CANTAR MARAVILLOSO
Oyelos de nuevo / Lo que dice el abakua / Fundamento dilanga / El marino / Mi arer / Cantar maravilloso / Arague / A los embales
CDORB 053 / Feb '90 / Globestyle

Los Naranjos

☐ RESPETA MI TAMBO
1611710112 / 17 Mar '98 / Ahi Nama

Los Paraguayos

☐ CELITO LINDO
Pajaro campana / Malaguena / La galopera / Maria elena / Cu cu ru cu cu paloma / La paloma / Besame morenita / Noche bonita / Maria dolores / Amapola / Cielito lindo / Guantanamera / Besame mucho / Noche de ronda / Alla en el rancho grande / Ramona / Valencia / Ave maria no morro
CD 3511 / Nov '95 / Cameo

☐ GUANTANAMERA & LATIN HITS
MCD 71490 / Jun '93 / Monitor

☐ MALAGUENA
Malaguena / Mexico / La galopera / Amapola / Cielito lindo / Besame mucho / Historia de un amor / Pajaro choqui / Amor, amor, amor / Maria dolores / La cumparsita / Chiquita linda / Caminito / Me voy pa'l pueblo / Ay y ay / Noche de ronda / Buenas noches mi amor / Yo te quiero mucho
CD 62005 / Oct '93 / Saludos Amigos

☐ MUSIC FROM THE ANDES
CD 12517 / Jun '94 / Music Of The World

☐ VERY BEST OF LOS PARAGUAYOS, THE
Guantanamera / La bamba / Pepito mi corazon / Besame mucho / Maria elena / Cielito lindo / La paloma / Me voy pa'l pueblo / Medley / Las mananitas / La cucaracha / El cumbanchero / La comparsita / Anahit / Solamente una vez / Amor de mis amores / Adelita / La mucura / El caiman / Ave Maria
10202 / Oct '97 / Go On Deluxe

Los Pavos Reales

☐ EARLY HITS
ARHCD 410 / Apr '95 / Arhoolie

Los Pinguinos Del Norte

☐ CONJUNTOS NORTENOS (Los Pinguinos Del Norte & Conjunto Trio San Antonio)
ARHCD 311 / Apr '95 / Arhoolie

Los Pinkys

☐ ESTA PASION
ROUCD 6064 / Feb '96 / Rounder

☐ SEGURO QUE SIL
ROUCD 6061 / Dec '94 / Rounder

Los Pleneros De La 21

☐ SOMOS BOROCUAS
HSR 0003 / Mar '96 / Henry Street

Los Quilla Huasi

☐ SONGS OF THE ANDES VOL.2
VICG 53402 / Mar '96 / JVC World Library

Los Reyes

☐ GIPSY KINGS OF MUSIC, THE
EMPRCD 504 / Apr '94 / Emporio

Los Rudiments

☐ PSYCHOSKA 1990-1993
DILL 17 / 29 Jun '98 / Dill

Los Rupay

☐ FOLKLORE DE BOLIVIA
EUCD 1001 / '91 / ARC

Los Sabandenos

☐ ATLANTIDA
68975 / Apr '97 / Tropical

Los Setenta

☐ MARFIL
5041 / Oct '96 / Divusca

Los Straitjackets

☐ LOS STRAITJACKETS
UPSTARTCD 015 / Apr '95 / Upstart

☐ VIVA
Cavalcade / Casbah / Wrong planet / Lonely Apache / Outta gear / Pacifica / Espionage / Swampfire / Lawnmower / Lurking in the shadows / Brains and eggs / Venturing out / Tsunami / Nightmare in Monte Cristo
WENCD 014 / Aug '96 / When

Los Timidos

☐ DAME UN BESITO
TUMICD 018 / '91 / Tumi

Los Tradicinales

☐ BOLEROS INEDITOS DE C PUEBLA
CUBO 002 / 1 Jun '98 / Karonte

Los Van Van

☐ AZUCAR
GLCD 4025 / Nov '94 / Green Linnet

☐ BEST OF LOS VAN VAN, THE
TUMICD 063 / Nov '96 / Tumi

☐ BEST OF LOS VAN VAN, THE
74321424372 / Jun '97 / Milan

☐ DE CUBA LOS VAN VAN WITH SALSA FORMELL
Nosotros los del Caribe / La Havana si / Si muere la tia / Por encima del nivel / Que palo / Que palo es ese / Canto la ceiba / Baila la palma real / Eso que anda
PSCCD 1003 / Feb '95 / Pure Sounds From Cuba

Los Yuras Of Bolivia

☐ MUSIC FROM THE AYMARA AND QUECHUA ANDEAN CULTURES
Quimera / Ajayu / Hilanderita / Imilla / He venido a preguntarte / Jacha sicu / Ankaturna / Khunu / Caballito blanco / Chequela / Pa ja ra jita / Sicuridas / Mama India / Tema de la mina / Yo ya me estoy yendo / Tata calamani / Mi raza / Laimes pocoata
CDE 84352 / May '97 / Meridian

Losadas

☐ PA LLORAR DE MOMENTO
NUBA 7703 / 1 Jun '98 / Nuba

Loss, Joe

☐ 50 GREAT YEARS (2CD Set)
I'll be faithful / Red sails in the sunset / Begin the beguine / Goodnight children everywhere / Thrill of a new romance / My prayer / Breeze and I / St. Mary's in the twilight / Stage coach / Tell me Marianne / Gal in calico / Man she's mine / No orchids for my lady / Put 'em in a box / Sabre dance / Ain't nobody here but us chickens / When it's evening / When you're in love / Enlloro / Flying saucer / With these hands / I wish I knew / Trumpet impromptu parts 1 and 2 / Evermore / Crazy otto rag / Why don't you believe me / Be anything / This is heaven / My heart belongs to only you / I'll always love you / My darling, my darling / Luna rossa / Got you on my mind / Wake the town and tell the people / Take care of yourself / Wishing ring / Stardust / March of the mods / Wheels / Caribbean clipper / In the mood / Love story / At the woodchoppers' ball / Sugar blues / So tired / Brazil
CDDL 1281 / Nov '94 / EMI

☐ BRITISH DANCE BANDS (3CD Set) (Loss, Joe & Nat Gonella/Harry Roy)
Sioux Sue: Loss, Joe / Deep in the heart of Texas: Loss, Joe / You again: Loss, Joe / That lovely weekend: Loss, Joe / How green was my valley: Loss, Joe / What more can I say: Loss, Joe / Hazy lazy lane: Loss, Joe / Concerto for two: Loss, Joe / For trappers ball: Loss, Joe / Baby mine: Loss, Joe / Each other beautiful: Loss, Joe / When I see an elephant fly: Loss, Joe / Daddy: Loss, Joe / You say the sweetest things: Loss, Joe / I don't want to set the world on fire: Loss, Joe / There's a land of begin again: Loss, Joe / Johnny Pedler: Loss, Joe / Cornsilk: Loss, Joe / Dance the brother with a stolid four: Loss, Joe / Purple pixie: Loss, Joe / Don't cry cherie: Loss, Joe / Georgia on my mind: Gonella, Nat / Tuxedo junction: Gonella, Nat / Big noises from Winnekta: Gonella, Nat / I understand: Gonella, Nat / At the woodchoppers ball: Gonella, Nat / South of the border (Down Mexico way): Gonella, Nat / Hep hep the jumpin' jive: Gonella, Nat / Johnson rag: Gonella, Nat / Peg o' my heart: Gonella, Nat / In the mood: Gonella, Nat / Ay ay ay: Gonella, Nat / No Mama no: Gonella, Nat / I haven't time to be

a millionaire: *Gonella, Nat* / Vox poppin': *Gonella, Nat* / Oh Buddy in my love: *Gonella, Nat* / It's a pair of wings for me: *Gonella, Nat* / Eep ipe wanna piece of pie: *Gonella, Nat* / Sunrise serenade: *Gonella, Nat* / Yes my darling daughter: *Gonella, Nat* / Plucking on the golden harp: *Gonella, Nat* / That's my home: *Gonella, Nat* / Tangerine: *Roy, Harry* / Hold your hats on: *Roy, Harry* / Oh the pity of it all: *Roy, Harry* / Humpt dumpty heart: *Gonella, Nat* / When I love I love: *Roy, Harry* / Was it love: *Roy, Harry* / Sentimental interlude: *Roy, Harry* / You bring the boogie woogie out in me: *Roy, Harry* / Greetings from you: *Roy, Harry* / Zoot suit: *Roy, Harry* / Do you care: *Roy, Harry* / When Daddy comes home: *Roy, Harry* / Darling Daisy: *Roy, Harry* / Elmer's tune: *Roy, Harry* / Madelaine: *Roy, Harry* / Chattanooga choo choo: *Roy, Harry* / Tica ti tica ta: *Roy, Harry* / It's funny to everyone but me: *Roy, Harry* / In the middle of a dance: *Roy, Harry* / Blues in the night: *Roy, Harry* / Green eyes: *Roy, Harry* / Shrine of St. Cecilia: *Roy, Harry*

EMPRESS 1001 / Jul '96 / Empress

☐ EARLY YEARS, THE
My heart belongs to daddy / In the mood / Begin the beguine / Boo hoo / Toy trumpet / Little rendezvous in Honolulu / Red sails in the sunset / Happy ending / Over my shoulder / I double dare you / Ooooo-oh boom / Let's dance at the make believe ballroom / Scene changes / South of the border (Down Mexico way) / I've got my eyes on you / You must have been a beautifel baby

GRF 101 / '93 / Tring

☐ GOLDEN SOUNDS OF JOE LOSS, THE

GS 863772 / Mar '96 / Disky

☐ IN THE MOOD
Begin the beguin / My heart belongs to daddy / In the mood / Don't sit under the apple tree / Put your arms around me honey / Wheels cha cha / Sucu sucu / Maigret theme / March of the mods / At last / American patrol / At Louis blues / Tuxedo junction / Toreando / Speak softly love / Moonlight serenade / Elmer's tune / Big ben to bow bells / Theme from the deerhunter / At the wood choppers ball

CDMFP 6393 / Jul '97 / Music For Pleasure

☐ JOE LOSS AND HIS BAND (Loss, Joe Band)
In the mood / Just a little cottage / I hear a rhapsody / Ridin' home in the buggy / Oasis / Down Forget-Me-Not Lane / Hey little hen / Honky tonk train blues / Home sweet home again / Shepherd's serenade / Blues upstairs and downstairs / Put that down in writing / Running wild / I'm nobody's baby / For all that I care / Down every street / Five o'clock whistle / Honeysuckle rose / Russian rose / You say the sweetest things / It's always you / First lullaby

PASTCD 9782 / Jun '92 / Flapper

☐ WHAT MORE CAN I SAY (Loss, Joe Band)
Sioux Sue: *Loss, Joe Band & Harry Kay/The Lost Chords* / Deep in the heart of Texas: *Loss, Joe Band & Harry Kay/The Lost Chords* / You again: *Loss, Joe Band & Bette Roberts* / That lovely weekend: *Loss, Joe Band & Chick Henderson* / How green was my valley: *Loss, Joe Band & Pat McCormack* / Oasis: *Loss, Joe Band & Chick Henderson* / What more can I say: *Loss, Joe Band & Chick Henderson* / Hazy lazy lane: *Loss, Joe Band & Bette Roberts* / Concerto for two: *Loss, Joe Band & Chick Henderson* / Fur trappers ball: *Loss, Joe Band & Chick Henderson* / Baby mine: *Loss, Joe Band & Chick Henderson* / Soft shoe shuffle: *Loss, Joe Band & Chick Henderson* / When I see an elephant fly: *Loss, Joe Band & Chick Henderson* / Daddy: *Loss, Joe Band & Bette Roberts* / You say the sweetest things: *Loss, Joe Band & Yvette Darnal* / I don't want to set the world on fire: *Loss, Joe Band & Chick Henderson* / There's a land of begin again: *Loss, Joe Band & Chick Henderson* / Johnny Peddler: *Loss, Joe Band & Bette Roberts* / Cornsilk: *Loss, Joe Band & Chick Henderson* / Bounce me brother with a solid four: *Loss, Joe Band & Chick Henderson* / Rancho pillow: *Loss, Joe Band & Chick Henderson* / Don't cry Cherie: *Loss, Joe Concert Orchestra*

RAJCD 812 / Jan '97 / Empress

☐ WORLD CHAMPIONSHIP BALLROOM DANCES (2CD Set) (Loss, Joe & His Orchestra)
Dream / I only have eyes for you / Jealousy / Singin' in the rain / We make music / Toreando / Fascination / Can't help falling in love / Brazil / Something tells me / Mamma mia / Music to watch girls by / Cavatina / Forever and ever / Waltz is for dancing / Save your kisses for me / Don't it make my brown eyes blue / Till / Don't cry for me Argentina / Sunrise sunset / Mull of Kintyre / Spanish gypsy dance / Fernando / Tea for two / Copacabana / Rivers of Babylon / Guantanamera / Is this the way to Amarillo / What's happened to Broadway / I'd like to teach the world to sing / My resistance is low / How deep is your love

CDDL 1146 / May '91 / Music For Pleasure

Loss Of Centre

☐ HUMANS LOSING HUMANITY

EFA 112862 / Jan '96 / Glasnost

Lost & Found

☐ ACROSS THE BLUE RIDGE MOUNTAINS

REBCD 1121 / Feb '96 / Rebel

☐ FOREVER LASTING PLASTIC WORDS

642420B42 / 1 Jun '98 / EVA

Lost

☐ EARLY RECORDINGS 1965-1966

AA 059 / Jul '97 / Arf Arf

Lost Boyz

☐ LEGAL DRUG MONEY
Intro / Yearn / Music makes me high / Jeeps, Lex Coups, Bimaz and Benz / Lifestyles of the rich and shameless / Renee / All right / Legal drug money / Get up / Is this da part / Straight from da ghetto / Keep it real / Channel zero / Da game / 1,2,3 / Lifestyles of the rich and shameless

UND 53010 / Jun '96 / Universal

☐ LOVE, PEACE AND NAPPINESS
Intro / Summer time / Me and my crazy world / Beats from the East / LOve, peace and nappiness / Black hoodies / So love / My crew / What's wrong / Certain things we do / Games / Get your hustle on / Tight situations / Day / Why / From my family to yours

UND 53072 / Jun '97 / MCA

Lost Breed

☐ EVIL IN YOU AND ME, THE

HELL 023CD / Jul '93 / Invisible

☐ SAVE YOURSELF
Circles / BAC (What you fear) / Gears / Going strong / 472 C.I. of death / Lease on life / Chop / Dragon of chaos / You don't need to live / Tonga slut / Simulator / Up the hill

H 00332 / Aug '94 / Hellhound

Lost Generation

☐ MIDNIGHT MEAT TRAIN

HMAXD 156 / Dec '90 / Heavy Metal

Lost Gonzo Band

☐ DEAD ARMADILLOS
Loose and on my way / Loose and on my way / Reality / People will dance / Railroad man / Take advantage of your chances / Those were the days / Fool for a tender touch / Write a song / Relief / Wilderness song / Sweet little lily / Life is the reason / Dead armadillo / Last thing I needed / Life in the pines / Ain't no way / Sexy thing / Daddy's money / I'll come knockin'

EDCD 474 / Apr '96 / Edsel

Lost Minds

☐ EXPRESS JERKY MOTIONS

DRCD 010 / Mar '96 / Detour

Lost Souls

☐ CLOSE YOUR EYES AND IT WON'T HURT

RR 88832 / Sep '96 / Roadrunner

☐ DEATHBEAT ROCK 'N' ROLL

BTCD 961 / Mar '97 / Bone Tone

☐ FRACTURE
Cavity / Demonride / Pieces / Dog dog / I'm in league with / Skinstripped / Downfall / Zero / Dead you will remain / Naked truth

NB 2942 / 26 May '98 / Nuclear Blast

☐ NEVER PROMISED YOU A ROSEGARDEN

SPV 08436192 / Oct '94 / SPV

Lost Tribe

☐ LOST TRIBE
Mythology / Dick Tracy / Procession / Letter to the editor / Eargasm / Rhinoceros / Mofungo / Space / Four directions / Fool for thought / TAthe W (Tender as the wind) / Cause and effect

01934101432 / Nov '94 / Windham Hill

☐ SOULFISH
Walkabout / Whodunit / It's not what it is / Daze of ol' / Room of life / Steel orchards / La fontaine (the fountain) / Second story / Planet rock / Fuzzy logic

72902103272 / Nov '94 / High Street

Lost Trybe

☐ LIFESTYLE

36283 / May '97 / Raging Bull

Lost Weekend

☐ LOST WEEKEND

LAST/VINTAP 1 / Jan '96 / Vinyl Tap

NTHEN 034CD / 16 Feb '98 / Now & Then

Lothar

☐ PRESENTING (Lothar & The Hand People)

OW S2117960 / Sep '94 / One Way

☐ THIS IS IT , MACHINES (Lothar & The Hand People)
Machines / Today is only yesterday's tomorrow / That's another story / Sister lonely / Sex and violence / You won't be lonely / It comes on anyhow / Wedding night for those who love / Yes, I love you / This is it / This may be goodbye / Midnight ranger / Ha (ho) / Sdrawkcab / Space hymn

SEECD 75 / May '91 / See For Miles

Lothian & Borders Police Band

☐ CENTENNIAL 1890-1990
Lothian and Borders Police centenary march / Slow air, hornpipe and jigs / March, strathspey and reel / 6/8 marches / Hornpipes / Strathspeys and reels / March medley / Drum fanfare / 2/4 marches / Slow air and jigs / Medley / March, strathspey and reel / Edinburgh City Police Pipe Band march

LCOM 5188 / Aug '96 / Lismor

Lothlorien

☐ PRIMAL EVENT, THE

BMCD 133 / 3 Aug '98 / Black Mark

Lotion

☐ NOBODY'S COOL

ABB 89CD / Jun '95 / Big Cat

☐ TELEPHONE ALBUM, THE

SPART 58CD / 16 Mar '98 / Spin Art

Lotis, Dennis

☐ BEST OF DENNIS LOTIS, THE
My resistance is low / Everything is nothing without you / Over the rainbow / All of you / Where or when / You've done something to my heart / But not for me / That lovely weekend / Dusk / How about you / No other one (can take your place) / Green grows the grass / Rich in love / That extra day / There's a time and a place / C'est la vie / Por favor / They say you're laughing at me / Sugaree / Heart

PLSCD 243 / 27 Oct '97 / Pulse

Lotti, Paolo

☐ HENDRIX (Lotti, Paolo & Harmonia)

90090 / Jun '97 / Materiali Sonori

Lotus Eaters

☐ FIRST PICTURE OF YOU, THE
First picture of you / German girl / Alone of all her sex / When you look at boys / Out on our own / Love still flows / You fill me with need / Stranger so far / Two virgins tender / Put your touch on love / Can you keep a secret / Start of the search / Signature tune

ASKCD 077 / 19 Mar '98 / Vinyl Japan

Louchie Lou

☐ DANGER-US (Louchie Lou & Michie One)
Dangerous / Party party / I knew it I blew it / Honeymoon is over / Crickets sing for Ana Maria / You'll never know (how you got me feelin') / Feel the vibes (in the air) / Kingman / Transatlantic lover / Baby I'm gonna get you / Before the night is over / Champagne and wine

ZEN 015CD / 22 Sep '97 / Indochina

☐ FREE 2 LIVE (Louchie Lou & Michie One)

WOLCD 1058 / Aug '95 / China

Loud

☐ D GENERATION
D generation / Songs for the lonely / I am the idol / Childhood times / Explosive / Black hysteria / God give me words / Infatuation / Massacre / Life on earth

WOLCD 1003 / May '91 / China

☐ PSYCHE 21

WOLCD 1026 / Jun '92 / China

Loud Family

☐ DAYS FOR DAYS
Cortex the killer / Good / There are no lions in the street / Deee-pression / Way too helpful / Mozart sonatas / Businessmen are OK / Crypto-sicko / Why don't we live in Mauritania / Sister sleep

A 1310 / 10 Aug '98 / Alias

☐ PLANTS AND BIRDS AND ROCKS AND THINGS
He do the police in different voices / Sword swallower / Aerodelira / Self righteous boy reduced to tears / Jimmy still comes round / Take me down (Too halloo) / Don't thank me all at onece / Idiot son / Some grand vision of motives and irony / Spot the setup / Inverness / Rosy overdrive / Slit my wrists / Isaac's law / Second grade applauds / Last honest face / Even you / Ballad of how you can all shut up / Give in world

A033D / Feb '93 / Alias

Loudblast

☐ CROSS THE THRESHOLD

N 02232 / Nov '93 / Noise

Loudermilk, John D.

☐ BLUE TRAIN - 1961/1962
Blue train / Mr. Jones / Language of love / Jimmie's song / Angela Jones / Bully of the beach / Rhythm and blues / What would you take for me / Great snowman / Everybody knows / Google eye / Darling Jane / Song of the lonely teen / All of this for Sally / Roadhog / He's just a scientist (that's all) / Rocks of Reno / Big daddy / Callin' Dr Casey / You just reap what you sow / Little wind-up doll / Two strangers in love / Th'wife / Bad news / Run on home baby brother / Oh how sad

BCD 15421 / Jun '89 / Bear Family

☐ IT'S MY TIME
It's my time / No playing in the snow today / Little grave / I'm looking for a world / What is it / Bubble please break / Ma Baker's little acre / Mary's no longer mine / To hell with love / Talkin' silver cloud blues / Joey stays with me / Lament of the Cherokee reservation / Jones' / You're the guilty one / Where have they gone / Little bird / Brown girl / Givin' you all my love / I chose you / Honey / That ain't all / Interstate forty / Do you / Tobacco Road

BCD 15422 / Jun '89 / Bear Family

☐ SITTIN' IN THE BALCONY
Sittin' on the balcony / A-plus in love / It's gotta be you / Teenage queen / 1000c Concrete block / In my simple way / That's all I've got / Asiatic flu / Somebody sweet / They were right / Yearbook / Susie's house / Yo yo / Lover's lane / Goin' away to school / This cold war with you / Please don't play No.9 / Angel of flight 509 / Midnight bus / Red headed stranger / Tobacco road / Happy wonderer / March of the minute men

BCD 15875 / Jun '95 / Bear Family

Loudness

☐ GHETTO MACHINE

BMCR 7017 / Sep '97 / Rooms

Loudon, Dorothy

☐ BROADWAY BABY
Broadway baby / It all depends on you / After you / It all belongs to me / Bobo's / Pack up your sins and go to the devil / Any place I hang my hat is home / I got lost in his arms / They say it's wonderful / Do it again / He was too good to me / I had myself a true love / Ten cents a dance

CDSL 5203 / Apr '87 / DRG

Loudpipes

☐ DOWN HILL BLUES

KRONH 010CD / 2 Mar '98 / Kronh

Loughrey, Johnny

☐ WORLD OF JOHNNY LOUGHREY, THE

IRBCD 2036 / Apr '98 / Outlet

Louis, Big Joe

☐ BIG 16
She was all the world to me / Back door slam / Christmas Eve 1993 / 3-6-9 / I've got to be more selective / Way I feel for you / Another married woman / Rock 'n' roll baby / Catfish / Ella Mae / Down Jamaica way / I can tell / Wine head / I took care of my homework (but Jody got my girl and gone) / Treat your daddy right / Leaving on my mind

CDCHD 622 / Feb '96 / Ace

Louis, Philippe

☐ SUNSHINE

BAH 23 / 8 Sep '97 / Humbug

Louisana Red

☐ WALKED ALL NIGHT LONG (Louisiana Red & Lefty Dizz)
First degree / Bring me my machine gun / King Bee / Stole from me / Too poor to die / Walked allnight long / Cold white sheet / I'll pay the price / Going train blues / Going down Georgia / Ever heard a church bell sound / Mary / Got a gal with a dog won't bark / Whole world

TBA 130112 / Jun '97 / Blues Alliance

Louise

☐ NAKED
Naked / In walked love / Light of my life / Best that you bring / One kiss from heaven / Thinking about you baby / Discussions / Back to love / Never too late / Goodbye to love / That's the way I like it / I'll fly away / I gave you my love

CDEMC 3748 / Jun '96 / EMI

☐ WOMAN IN ME
Arms around the world / All that matters / I pray / Let's go round again / Woman in me / Trust in you / Reminds me of you / Shut up and kiss me / Whne will my heart beat again / New York moon / Happy love / Who do you love / How you make me feel / Love will bring you back to me / Distraction / Just when I thought / Intimate / Don't be shy / Running back for more

8219032 / 6 Oct '97 / EMI

Louise, Tina

☐ IT'S TIME FOR TINA (2CD Set)
Tonight is the night / Hand across the table / Snuggled on your shoulder / Embraceable you / I'm in the mood for love / Baby, won't you say you love me / It's been a long, long time / Hold me / I wanna be loved / Let's do it / How long has this been going on / Goodnight my love

DIW 322 / Apr '90 / DIW

Louisiana Playboys

☐ SATURDAY NIGHT SPECIAL
Lafayette / Why don't we do it in the road / Cajun blues / Saturday night special / Maggie Thatcher, won't you give me a hand / Louisiana playboy's theme / Memphis / Jolie blon / Mathilda / Te petite and te meon / Accordion waltz

JSPCD 225 / Apr '89 / JSP

Louisiana Radio

☐ BAYO

343602 / May '96 / Koch International

☐ MAMA ROUX
MWCD 2011 / Aug '94 / Music & Words

☐ WULF
MWCD 2014 / Dec '95 / Music & Words

Louisiana Red

☐ ALWAYS PLAYED THE BLUES
Valerie / Down so long / Sun goes down / Leaving town / Brought up the hard way / Steel on my hand / Mambo mumbo / I'm leaving / Viviene / This little letter / Feeling inside / Hello, mean old world / Best place
JSPCD 240 / Oct '91 / JSP

☐ BLUES FOR IDA B.
JSPCD 209 / Jan '88 / JSP

☐ BLUES FOR IDA B. (Remastered)
Blues for Ida B. / Grease me / I wonder why / Love me true / Nothing but a gypsy man / Chicken licken / Little boy / Sittin' here lookin' / Love me mama / This little letter / If I had a dollar / Nothing but the blues
JSPCD 2106 / Jul '98 / JSP

☐ BLUES SPECTRUM OF LOUISIANA RED, THE
Sweet leg girl / Viviene / Soon one morning / Women that I've known / Best place / Standing like a statue / Love me mama / I wish I could lead my life again / Lamplight baby / After a while / Hello mean old world
JSPCD 803 / 9 Mar '98 / JSP

☐ LOWDOWN BACK PORCH BLUES
Ride on Red, ride on / I wonder who (alternate) / Red's dream / Workin' man blues / I'm Louisiana Red / Sweet Alesse / Keep your hands off my woman / I'm a roaming stranger / Red on red, ride on / I wonder who / Seventh son / Sad news / Two fifty three / Don't cry / Sugar hips / I'm too poor to die / Don't cry (alternate)
NEX CD 213 / Jul '92 / Sequel

☐ MIDNIGHT RAMBLER
CPCD 8168 / Jun '96 / Charly

☐ RISING SUN
RS 0006 / Oct '94 / Just A Memory

Louisiana Repertory Jazz Ensemble

☐ HOT AND SWEET SOUNDS OF LOST NEW ORLEANS
SOSCD 1140 / Jan '88 / Stomp Off

☐ LOUISIANA REPERTORY JAZZ ENSEMBLE
SOSCD 1055 / May '93 / Stomp Off

☐ LOUISIANA REPERTORY JAZZ ENSEMBLE VOL.4
SOSCD 1197 / Dec '94 / Stomp Off

Louisiana Shakers

☐ IN THE NEW ORLEANS REVIVAL STYLE
NEW 2015 / Jul '96 / Australian Jazz

☐ ONE NEW ORLEANS NIGHT
PKCD 100 / May '98 / PEK

Louisiana's LeRoux

☐ BAYOU DEGRADABLE (The Best Of Louisiana's LeRoux)
RE 21142 / Aug '96 / Razor & Tie

Louiss, Eddie

☐ EDDIE LOUISS TRIO
Nardis / Blue tempo / Hot house / No smoking / You've changed / Don't want nothin'
FDM 365012 / May '94 / Dreyfus

☐ FLOMELA
Saint Louis blues / Colchiques / Flomela / Pacha / Naissance / Comme un poisson dan le ciel / You can't see / Rene / Maxurka cacodou
FDM 365782 / May '96 / Dreyfus

☐ LOUISSIANA
IN 10951101 / 21 Aug '97 / XIII Bis

☐ MULTICOLOUR FEELING FANFARE
NTCD 105 / Nov '96 / Nocturne

☐ MULTICOLOUR FEELING FANFARE LIVE
NTCD 108 / Nov '96 / Nocturne

☐ PRESSE DE CONFERENCE (Louiss, Eddie & Michel Petrucciani)
Les grelots / Jean Philippe Herbien / All the things you are / I wrote you a song / So what / These foolish things / Amesha / Simply bop
FDM 365682 / Nov '94 / Dreyfus

☐ SANG MELE
NTCD 101 / Nov '96 / Nocturne

☐ WEBE
NTCD 109 / Nov '96 / Nocturne

Louiss, Pierre

☐ CREOLE SWING
FA 042 / Nov '95 / Fremeaux

Lounge Lizards

☐ LIVE 1979-1981
RE 136CD / Nov '94 / ROIR

☐ LIVE IN BERLIN VOL.1
Tibet / One big yes / No pain for cakes / Not a rondo / Calvin / Big heart
VBR 20442 / Sep '91 / Vera Bra

☐ LIVE IN BERLIN VOL.2
Remember / Evan's drive to Mombasa / King precious / Mr. Stinky's blues / Welcome herr Lazaro / What else is in there
VBR 20862 / Nov '92 / Vera Bra

☐ LOUNGE LIZARDS
Incident on South Street / Harlem nocturne / Do the wrong thing / Au contraire arto / Well you needn't / Ballad / Wangling / Conquest of Rah / Demented / I remember Coney Island / Fatty walks / Epistrophy / You haunt me
EEGCD 8 / Sep '90 / EG

☐ QUEEN OF ALL EARS
First and royal queen / Birds near her house / Scary children / She drove me mad / Queen of all ears / Monsters over Bangkok / Three crowns of wood / John Zorn's S and M circus / Yak / Queen repirise
SB 0015 / 18 May '98 / Strange & Beautiful

Loussier, Jacques

☐ BEST OF BACH, THE
Air on the g string (bach) / Gavotte in d major / Passachaglia in c minor bwv 582 / Vivace - concerto in c minor bwv 1062 (1st movement) / Toccata and fugue in d minor / Partita in e major bwv 1006 / Prelude no 1 / Chorale (jesu joy of man's desiring) / Minuet in g major / Allegro-adagio-presto (italian concerto) / Chorale no. 1 (sleepers, wake)
MCCD 113 / Jun '93 / Music Club

☐ BRANDENBURG CONCERTOS, THE
8440582 / Mar '91 / Limelight

☐ GREATEST BACH, THE (Loussier, Jacques Trio)
8440592 / Mar '91 / Limelight

☐ JACQUES LOISSIER PLAYS BACH
556604 / Dec '89 / Accord

☐ JACQUES LOUSSIER PLAYS BACH
Fugue No.5 in D / Italian Concerto / Pastorale in C minor / Air on a G string / Toccata and fugue in D minor / Gavotte in D / Concerto in D minor
CD 83411 / Nov '96 / Telarc Jazz

☐ PLAY BACH (2CD Set)
120512 / Nov '97 / Musidisc

☐ PULSION/SOUS LA MER
Pulsion / Caffeine / Mozart / Ludwig / Cubzac / Sous la mer / Minsk Greenwich / Madone / Birthday / Buda soupir
8440602 / Mar '91 / Limelight

☐ SATIE - GYMNOPEDIES/ GNOSSIENNES (Loussier, Jacques Trio)
CD 83431 / 1 Jun '98 / Telarc Jazz

☐ VIVALDI - THE FOUR SEASONS (Loussier, Jacques Trio)
Spring / Summer / Autumn / Winter
CD 83417 / Jun '97 / Telarc Jazz

Louvin Brothers

☐ CHRISTMAS WITH THE LOUVIN BROTHERS
RE 21542 / Nov '97 / Razor & Tie

☐ CLOSE HARMONY (8CD Set)
Alabama Alabama / Seven year blues / My love song for you / Get acquainted waltz / They've got the church outnumbered / Do you live what you preach / You'll be rewarded over there / I'll live with God (to die no more) / Rove of white / Great atomic power / Insured beyond the grave / Gospel way / Sons and daughters of God / Broadminded / Family who prays (shall never part) / I know what you're talking about / Let us travel on / I love God's way of living / Born again / Preach the gospel / From mother's arms to Korea / If we forget God / Satan and the Saint / Satan lied to me / God bless her ('cause she's my mother) / Last chance to pray / No one to sing for me / Swing low, sweet chariot / Nearer my God to thee / Make him a soldier / I can't say no / Just rehearsing / Love thy neighbour as thyself / Where will you build / Pray for me / When I stop dreaming / Pitfall / Alabama / Memories and tears / Don't laugh / I don't believe you've met my baby / Childish love / In the middle of nowhere / Hoping that you're hoping / First one to love you / I cried after you left / That's all he's asking of me / I'll be all smiles tonight / In the pines / What is home without love / Mary of the wild moor / Knoxville girl / Kentucky / Katy dear / My brother's will / Take the news to mother / Let her go God bless her / Tiny broken heart / Plenty of everything but you / Cash on the barrelhead / You're running wild / New partner waltz / I won't have to cross Jordan alone / Praying / Wait a little longer, please Jesus / This little light of mine / Steal away and pray / There's no excuse / Are you washed in the blood / Lord I'm coming home / Thankful / Take me back into your heart / Here today and gone tomorrow / We could / Tennessee waltz / Too late / Are you teasing me / Nobody's darling but mine / Don't let your sweet love die / I wonder where you are tonight / Why not confess / Making believe / Have I stayed away too long / Call me / I wish you knew / Dog sled / When I loved you / My baby's gone / She didn't even know I was gone / My baby came back / Are you wasting my time / My curly headed baby / Lorene / I wish it had been a dream / While you're cheatin' on me / If I could only win your love / You're learning / Blue from now on / Today / My heart was trampled on the street / Send me the pillow that you dream on / On my way to the show / Red hen hop / She'll get lonesome / I wonder if you know / Blue / Angels rejoiced last night / Dying from home and lost / Satan's jewelled crown / River of Jordan / I'm ready to go home / Kneeling drunkards plea / Satan is real / Christian life / Are you afraid to die / He can be found / There's is a higher power / Drunkard's doom / I see a bridge / Just suppose / Stagger / Nellie moved to town / What a change one day / Ruby's song / Last old shovel / Midnight special / Brown's ferry blues / Southern moon / Sand mountain blues / Nashville blues / Blues stay away from me / When it's time for the whippoorwill to sing / Put me on the train to Carolina / Freight train blues / Lonesome blues / Gonna lay down my old guitar / It's Christmas time / Santa's big parade / Love is a lonely street / If you love me stay away / I ain't gonna work tomorrow / I love you best of all / I can't keep you in love with me / Scared of the blues / I have found the way / He set me free / Kneel at the cross / Leaning on the everlasting arms / O why not tonight / You can't find the Lord too soon / Keep your eyes on Jesus / Almost persuaded / I feel better now / O who shall be able to stand / If today was the day / You'll meet him in the clowds / You'll meet him in the clouds (alt. take) / Away in a manger / Friendly beasts / Hark the herald angels sing / Good christian men rejoice / While shepherds watched their flocks by night / First Noel / It came upon a midnight clear / O come all ye faithful (Adeste Fidelis) / O little town of Bethlehem / Silent night / Deck the halls with boughs of holly / Joy to the world / It hurts me more the second time around / How's the world treating you / Every time you leave / Time goes slow / I died for the red, white and blue / Searching for a soldier's grave / At mail call today / Soldier's last letter / There's a star spangled banner waving somewhere / There's a grave in the wave of the ocean / Mother I thank you for the bible you gave / Seaman's girl / Robe of white / Weapon of prayer / Broken engagement / First time in life / There's no easy way / Love turned to hate / Must you throw dirt in my face / Great speckled bird / Wabash cannonball / Lonely mound of clay / Wreck on the highway / Wait for the light to shine / Low and lonely / We live in two different worlds / Precious jewel / Great judgement morning / Branded wherever I go / Not a word from home / Stuck up blues / Don't let them take the bible out of our school / I'm glad that I'm not him / Message to your heart / Thank God for my christian home / I'll never die / Price on the bottle / I've known a lady / He included me / Keep watching the sky / Now Lord, what can I do for you / Way up on a mountain / Gonna shake hands with mother over there / He was waiting at the altar / Oh Lord, my God / What would you take in exchange for my soul
BCD 15561 / Jun '92 / Bear Family

☐ RADIO FAVOURITES 1951-1957
CMFCD 009 / Jul '93 / Country Music Foundation

☐ SONGS OF THE LOUVIN BROTHERS (Various Artists)
Cash on the barrelhead: *Dreadful Snakes* / We live in two different worlds: *Skaggs, Ricky & Peter Rowan* / Are you afraid to die: *Nashville Bluegrass Band* / Make him soldier: *Whitstein Brothers* / Seven year blues: *Longview* / I'm gonna love you one more time: *Jim & Jesse/The Virginia Boys* / You're running wild: *Val, Joe & New England Bluegrass Boys* / Love and wealth: *Here Today* / Here today and gone tomorrow: *Dickens, Hazel & Johnson Mountain Boys* / My baby came back: *Lewis, Laurie & Tom Rozum* / When I stop dreaming: *McCoury, Del & The Dixie Pals* / I don't believe you've met my baby: *Moffatt, Hugh & Katy*
EDCD 7034 / Jun '97 / Easydisc

Louvin, Charlie

☐ LIVE IN HOLLAND
SCR 34 / Jul '95 / Strictly Country

☐ LONGEST TRAIN, THE
When I stop dreaming / In the pines / Cash on the barrelhead / I don't feel like dancing / Who knows where the times goes / Queen of the bayou / Are you wasting my time / Stone deaf, dumb and blind / My baby's gone / Christian life / I wanna die young (at a very old age) / Turn around
WMCD 1056 / Nov '96 / Watermelon

Lovano, Joe

☐ CELEBRATING SINATRA
I'll never smile again / Chicago / I'm a fool to want you / Imagination / I've got the world on a string / All the way / South of the border / In other words / I've got you under my skin / This love of mine / Someone to watch over me / One for my baby / Song is you
CDP 8377182 / Jan '97 / Blue Note

☐ FLYING COLORS (Lovano, Joe & Gonzalo Rubalcaba)
Flying colors / How deep is the ocean / Boss town / Bird food / Spontaneous color / Phantasm / Ugly beauty / Hot house / Gloria's step / Mr. Hyde / I love music / Along came Betty
8560922 / 19 Jan '98 / Blue Note

☐ LIVE AT THE VILLAGE VANGUARD (2CD Set) (Lovano, Joe Quartets)
Fort Worth / Birds of Springtime / I can't get started / Uprising / Sail away / Blue Note to lose / Song and dance / Lonnie's lament / Reflections / Little Willie leaps / This is all I ask / 26-2 / Duke Ellington's / Sounds of love / Sounds of joy
CDP 8291252 / Feb '96 / Blue Note

Lovaz, Iren

☐ ROSEBUDS IN A STONEYARD
8557802 / Jul '97 / Origins

Love & Rockets

☐ EXPRESS
It could be sunshine / Kundalini Express / All in my mind / Life in Laralay / Yin and Yang (the flower pot men) / Love me / All in my mind (acoustic version) / American dream
BBL 74CD / Feb '90 / Beggars Banquet

☐ HOT TRIP TO HEAVEN
BBQCD 145 / Sep '94 / Beggars Banquet

☐ SEVENTH DREAM OF TEENAGE HEAVEN
If there's a heaven above / Private future / Dog end of a day gone by / Game / Seventh dream of teenage heaven / Haunted when the minutes drag / Saudade
BBL 66 CD / Jan '89 / Beggars Banquet

☐ SWEET FA
BBL 180CD / 10 Nov '97 / Beggars Banquet

Love

☐ COMES IN COLOURS
My little red book / Can't explain / Message to pretty / Softly to me / Hey Joe / Signed DC / And more / Seven and seven is / No 14 / Stephanie knows who / Orange skies / Que vida / Castle / She comes in colours / Alone again or / And more again / Old man / House is not a motel / Daily planet / Live and let live / Laughing stock / Your mind and we belong together / August / Arthur Lee interview
RVCD 29 / Jan '93 / Raven

☐ FALSE START
Everlasting first / Flying / Gimi a little break / Stand out / Keep on shining / Anytime / Slick dick / Love is coming / Feel daddy feel good / Ride that vibration
MCAD 22029 / Apr '94 / One Way

☐ FOREVER CHANGES
Alone again or / House is not a motel / And more again / Daily planet / Old man / Red telephone / Maybe the people would be the times / Live and let live / Good humour man he sees everything like this / Bummer in the summer / You set the scene
9606562 / '89 / Elektra

☐ IFYOUBELIEVEIN (MacLean, Brian)
Barber John / Fresh hope / Kathleen / Orange skies / Strong commitment / Alone again / Tired of sitting / Blues singer / Friday's / People / Claudia / If you believe in / Orange skies / Alone again / She looks good / Old man
SC 11051 / 24 Nov '97 / Sundazed

☐ LOVE
My little red book / Can't explain / Message to pretty / My flash on you / Softly to me / No matter what you do / Emotions / You I'll be following / Gazing / Hey Joe / Signed DC / Coloured balls falling / Mushroom clouds / And more
7559740012 / Dec '93 / Elektra

☐ OUT HERE
MCAD 22030 / Apr '94 / One Way

☐ OUT THERE
I'll pray for you / Love is coming / Signed DC / I still wonder / Listen to my song / Doggone / Nice to be / Stand out / Everlasting first / Gimmi a little break / Willow willow / You are something / Love is more than words / Gather round
CDWIKD 69 / Jul '90 / Big Beat

☐ STUDIO/LIVE
MCAD 22036 / Apr '94 / One Way

Love 2 Be

☐ ALBUM
FIRMCD 8 / Oct '96 / Firm

Love 666

☐ AMERICAN REVOLUTION
AMREP 035CD / Feb '95 / Amphetamine Reptile

☐ PLEASE KILL YOURSELF SO I CAN ROCK
ARRCD 75018 / Dec '96 / Amphetamine Reptile

Love Affair

☐ EVERLASTING LOVE AFFAIR, THE
Everlasting love / Hush / 60 minutes (of your love) / Could I be dreaming / First cut is the deepest / So sorry / Once upon a season / Rainbow valley / Day without love / Tobacco Road / Tree / Handbags and gladrags / Build on love / Please stay / Tale of two
4836732 / Mar '96 / Columbia

Love As Laughter

☐ GREEKS BRING GIFTS, THE
KLP 51CD / Feb '96 / K

☐ NO.1 USA
Old gold / No.1 USA / I'm a bee / Slow blues fever / Vacation / Tonight / Puget sound sanitation / Phobias
KCD 76 / 26 Jan '98 / K

Love, Charlie

☐ CHARLIE LOVE WITH GEORGE LEWIS & LOUIS NELSON 1962 (Love, Charlie & George Lewis & Louis Nelson)
AMCD 60 / Aug '94 / American Music

Love City Groove

☐ HARD TIMES
JUMP / Let's get funky / Love city groove / Soft spot / Spice (4am jam) / Trouble / Sentence of love / Inna city love / Gonna make it alright / Collioure / Blue / Love city groove (soul mix)
SATURN 2CD / Feb '96 / Planet 3

Love Coates, Dorothy

☐ BEST OF DOROTHY LOVE COATES & THE GOSPEL HUMMINGBIRDS, THE (Love Coates, Dorothy & The Gospel Hummingbirds)
NASH 4508 / Feb '96 / Nashboro

☐ GET ON BOARD
Peace, be still / Glory to his name / I'm sealed / Get away Jordan / Rest for the weary / Deliver me / Oh my Lord / Lead me holy father / Old gospel train (the next stop is mine) / Get on board / Railroad / Plenty good room / Sometime / No hiding place / Waiting for me / Wade in the water / I wouldn't mind dying / I'll be with thee / He's calling me / Untitled instrumental / Thank you Lord for using me / These are they / 99 1/2 / That's enough
CDCHD 412 / Nov '93 / Ace

☐ VOL.1 & 2
He's calling me / One morning soon / You better run / No hiding place / When I reach my heavenly home on high / Get away Jordan / I'm sealed / That's enough / Ninety nine and a half (won't do) / Where shall I be / Jesus laid his hand on me / You can't hurry God / Jesus knows it all / You must be born again / These are they / Why not / I shall know him / Every day will be Sunday by and by / I wouldn't mind dying / Lord don't forget about me / There's a God somewhere / Just to behold his face / Am I a soldier / Heaven
CDCHD 343 / Nov '93 / Ace

Love Corporation

☐ DANCE STANCE
CRECD 199 / Jun '97 / Creation

☐ INTELLIGENTSIA
CREDCD 116 / May '94 / Creation

☐ TONES
Fleshtones / Monumental / Lovetones / Tones of incorporation / World / Palatial
CRECD 056 / May '94 / Creation

Love Decade

☐ DECADANCE
GLOBECD 3 / May '96 / All Around The World

Love Dogs

☐ I'M YO DOG
CDTC 1155 / Jun '96 / Tonecool

Love, Geoff

☐ BIG WAR MOVIE THEMES (Love, Geoff & His Orchestra)
Colonel Bogey / Lawrence of Arabia / Guns of Navarone / Battle of Britain / Longest Day / Where eagles dare / 633 Squadron / Dambusters march / Great escape / Green berets / Cavatina / Winds of war / Victory at sea extracts / We'll meet again / Is Paris burning / Reach for the Sky
CC 211 / May '88 / Music For Pleasure

☐ GOING LATIN (Love, Geoff & His Orchestra)
La Bamba / Spanish harlem / Guantanamera / Sucu sucu / Girl from Ipanema / One note Samba / South of the border (Down Mexico way) / Maria Elena / Spanish eyes / Desafinado / Breeze and I / Mexican hat dance / Temptation / La Cumparsita / Blue tango / Spider of the night / Serenta / La Paloma / Jealousy / Adios muchachos / Ecstasy
CC 270 / Aug '91 / Music For Pleasure

☐ IN THE MOOD FOR WALTZING (Love, Geoff & His Orchestra)
Falling in love with love / Ramona / Anniversary song / Always / Beautiful dreamer / I'll see you again / Fascination / My wonderful one / Charmaine / Love's last word is spoken / Love's roundabout / Now is the hour / Desert song / Around the world / When I grow too old to dream / Vaya con dios / One night of love / Lover / Edelweiss / Song / Try to remember / Ask me why I love you / Waltz of my heart / Last waltz
CC 261 / Oct '90 / Music For Pleasure

☐ MELODIES THAT LIVE FOREVER (2CD Set) (Love, Geoff & His Orchestra)
Skater's waltz / Minute waltz / Destiny / Invitation to the dance / Morning: Peer Gynt / Elizabethan serenade / Largo / Moonlight sonata / Blue Danube / Sleeping beauty / Merry widow / Tales from the Vienna Woods / Dusk / Marriage of Figaro (overture) / Enigma variations: Nimrod / Air on a G string / Clair de Lune / Jesu joy of man's desiring / Ave Maria
CDDL 1098 / Nov '92 / EMI

☐ SONGS THAT WON THE WAR (Love, Geoff Banjos)
Colonel Bogey / Sentimental journey / Lili Marlene / Good morning / You'll never know / Yours / Let the people sing / That lovely weekend / This is the army Mister Jones / Arm in arm / I'll be with you in apple blossom time / I don't want to set the world on fire
CDMFP 5887 / Feb '95 / Music For Pleasure

☐ STAR WARS/CLOSE ENCOUNTER OF THE THIRD KIND (Love, Geoff & His Orchestra)
Star Wars / UFO / Star Trek / Barbarella / Space 1999 / Also sprach zarathustra / March from things to come / Thunderbirds / Star Wars / Dr. Who / Mars, Bringer of war from The Planets / Close Encounters Of The Third Kind / Logan's Run / Flight fantastic / Star Wars / Blake Seven / Omega Man
CDMFP 6395 / Jun '97 / Music For Pleasure

☐ WHEN I FALL IN LOVE (2CD Set) (Love, Geoff Singers)
Imagine / What are you doing the rest of your life / Moon river / If / I'm stone in love with you / When I fall in love / More I see you / I only have eyes for you / It's impossible / Annie's song / Without you / My eyes adored you / First time ever I saw your face / My cherie amour / Love story / Something / Don't cry for me Argentina / Vincent / Killing me softly / Snowbird / Send in the clowns / For once in my life / Michelle / You make me feel brand new / Just the way you are / Evergreen
CDDL 1102 / May '92 / Music For Pleasure

Love Groove

☐ GLOBAL WARMING
MILL 0112 / Mar '95 / Millenium

Love Inc.

☐ LIFE'S A GAS
FIM 1021 / Sep '96 / Force Inc.

Love Interest

☐ BEDAZZLED
INVCD 025 / Feb '94 / Invisible

Love Is Colder Than Death

☐ OXEIA
HY 39100952 / Apr '94 / Hyperium

Love, Laura

☐ LAURA LOVE COLLECTION, THE
M 1182 / Mar '97 / Putumayo

Love Like Blood

☐ EXPOSURE
08545752 / Jan '96 / SPV

☐ LOVE LIKE BLOOD EP, THE
HOS 7071CD / 11 May '98 / Hall Of Sermon

☐ ODYSSEE
SPV 08445552 / Apr '94 / SPV

☐ SNAKEKILLER
HOS 7072CD / 25 May '98 / Hall Of Sermon

Love, Mary

☐ THEN AND NOW
I'm in your hands / Let me know / Because of you / I woke up / Hey stoney face / Lay this burden down / Satisfied feeling / I can't wait / Come out of the sandbox / Price / Baby I'll come / Move a little closer / More than enough love / Grace / I've gotta get you back / Talkin' about my man / Mr. Man / B Baby / Caught up / You turned my bitter into sweet / (I'm so glad) He uses me
CDKEND 109 / May '94 / Kent

Love Nut

☐ BALTIMUCHO
BIGDEAL 90542 / 20 Apr '98 / Big Deal

Love Parade

☐ LOVE IS THE MESSAGE
K7 037CD / Jul '95 / Studio K7

Love Republic

☐ IS NOTHING SACRED
ARCHO 1666 / May '95 / TEQ

Love Spit Love

☐ TRYSOME EATONE
Long long time / Believe / Well well well / Friends / Fall on tears / Little fist / It hurts when I laugh / 7 years / Sweet thing / All God's children / More than money / November 5
9362465602 / 6 Apr '98 / Maverick

Love Times Three

☐ LOVE TIMES THREE
TRI 4144CD / Feb '94 / Ichiban

Love Unlimited Orchestra

☐ BEST OF LOVE UNLIMITED ORCHESTRA, THE
5269452 / Sep '95 / Mercury

Love/Hate

☐ I'M NOT HAPPY
08518222 / Dec '95 / SPV

Loved Ones

☐ BETTER DO RIGHT
HCD 8057 / Oct '94 / Hightone

Loveless, Patty

☐ LONG STRETCH OF LONESOME ME
Party ain't over yet / To have you back again / I don't want to feel like that / High on love / Like water into wine / That's exactly what I mean / You don't seem to miss me / Too many memories / Long stretch of lonesome / Where I'm bound
4889822 / 3 Nov '97 / Epic

☐ TROUBLE WITH THE TRUTH, THE
Tear stained letter / Trouble with the truth / I miss who I was with you / Everybody's equal in the eyes of love / Lonely too long / You can feel bad / Thousand times a day / She drew a broken heart / To feel that way at all / Someday I will lead the parade
4814682 / Feb '96 / Epic

☐ WHEN FALLEN ANGELS FLY
Handful of dust / Halfway down / When the fallen angels fly / You don't even know who I am / Feelin' good about feelin' bad / Here I am / I try to think about Elvis / Ships / Old weakness (coming on strong) / Over my shoulder
4771832 / 13 Jul '98 / Epic

Lovelies

☐ TUFF OF THE TRACK
ER 1026 / Jul '97 / Elefant

Lovemongers

☐ WHIRLYGIG
WILL 048 / 12 Jan '98 / Will

Lover Speaks

☐ LOVER SPEAKS,THE
Every lover's sign / No more I love you's / Never to forget you / Face me and smile / Absent one / Love is: "I gave you everything" / This can't go on / Still faking this art of love / Tremble dancing / Of tears
3951272 / Apr '95 / A&M

Loveslug

☐ CIRCLE OF VALUES
GRCD KH / May '93 / Glitterhouse

Lovett, Eddie

☐ BEST REGGAE HITS OF EDDIE LOVETT VOL.1, THE
Too experience / Lady in red / Just when I needed you most / Shinning star / Mr. sea / Under the boardwalk / Think twice my love / Stuck on you / Do it to me one more time / Imagination / Hello / Without you / Try again / Sweet sensation
PKL 514912 / Jul '93 / K&K

☐ BEST REGGAE HITS OF...VOL.11
PKCD 33094 / Sep '94 / K&K

☐ LET'S TRY AGAIN
PKCD 33193 / Jul '93 / K&K

Lovett, Lyle

☐ I LOVE EVERYBODY
Skinny legs / Fat babies / I think you know what I mean / Hello Grandma / Creeps like me / Sonja / They don't like me / Record lady / Ain't it somethin' / Penguins / Fat girl / La to the left / Old friend / Just the morning / Moon on my shoulder / I've got the blues / Goodbye to Carolina / I love everybody
MCD 10808 / Sep '94 / MCA

☐ JOSHUA JUDGES RUTH
I've been to memphis / Church / She's already made up her mind / North dakota / You've been so good up to now / All my love is gone / Since the last time / Baltimore / Family reserve / She's leaving me because she really wants to / Flyswatterice water blues (monty trenckmann's blues) / She makes me feel good
MCAD 10475 / Mar '92 / MCA

☐ LYLE LOVETT
Cowboy man / God will / Farther down the line / This old porch / Why I don't know / If I weren't the man you wanted / You can't resist it / Waltzing fool / An acceptable level of ecstasy (the wedding song) / Closing time
MCLD 19134 / Oct '90 / MCA

☐ ROAD TO ENSENADA
Don't touch my hat / Her first mistake / Fiona / That's right (you're not from Texas) / Who loves you better / Private conversation / Promises / It ought to be easier / I can't love you anymore / Long tall Texan / Christmas morning / Road to Ensenada
MCD 11409 / Jun '96 / MCA

Lovett, Ruby

☐ RUBY LOVETT
CURCD 050 / 9 Mar '98 / Curb

Lovich, Lena

☐ FLEX
Bird song / Bird song / Angels / Night / You can't kill me / Egghead / Wonderful one / Monkey talk / Joan / Freeze / Fly / One lonely heart / O seasons, o castles / Blue
STIFFCD 21 / May '94 / Disky

☐ MARCH
Life / Wonderland / Nightshift / Hold on to love / Rage / Natural beauty / Make believe / Sharman / Vertigo / Shadow walk
ECD 280012 / Oct '95 / Evidence

☐ NO MAN'S LAND
It's you only you (mein schmerz) / Blue hotel / Faces / Walking low / Special star / Sister video / Maria / Savages / Rocky road
STIFFCD 22 / May '94 / Disky

☐ STATELESS
Lucky number / Lucky number / Sleeping beauty / Sleeping beauty / Home / Home / Too tender (to touch) / Too tender (to touch) / Say when / Say when / Tonight / Tonight / Writing on the wall / Writing on the wall / Telepathy / Telepathy / Momentary breakdown / Momentary breakdown / One in a million / One in a million / I think we're alone now / I think we're alone now / Be stiff / Be stiff / Big bird / Big bird / Fall / Fall
STIFFCD 20 / May '94 / Disky

☐ STIFF YEARS, THE
HRCD 8035 / Jan '94 / Disky

☐ VERY BEST OF LENA LOVICH, THE
Lucky number / Tonight / Say when / Be stiff / What will I do without you / Angels / Too tender / New toy / Momentary breakdown / It's you, only you / One in a million / Home / Bird song / Writing on the wall / Telepathy / I think we're alone now / Special star / Big bird / Sleeping beauty
DC 878582 / May '97 / Disky

Lovie, Robert

☐ GENERATIONS OF CHANGE
Generations of change / Buchan vet / Yellow on the broom / Drumdelgie / North East shore / Wild geese / Auld folks on the wa' / Village where I went to school / Glorious North / It's lonely in the bothy / Road and the miles to Dundee / Chapelton / MacFarlane o' the sprots o' Burnieboozie / Old house / Come a' ye tramps and hawker lads / 'Tween Tyrie and the Dour / Bonnie Aiberdein
CDGR 158 / Dec '96 / Ross

☐ NORTH EAST SHORE, THE
North east shore / Guise o'tough / Banks o'red roses / Poem / Boggyclairts / Alex Green / Auld meal mill / Butter on the bow / I aince lo'ed a lass / Alford cattle show / Prince and Jean / Band selection / Silver darlings / McGinty's meal and ale / Parting song
CDR 003 / Jan '87 / Donside

Lovin' Spoonful

☐ 1960'S FRENCH EP COLLECTION, THE (2CD Set)
517782 / Sep '97 / Magic

☐ DAYDREAM
Daydream / There she is / It's not time now / Warm baby / Day blues / Let the boy rock 'n' roll / Jug band music / Didn't want to have to do it / You didn't have to be so nice / Bald headed Lena
CLACD 194 / Aug '90 / Castle

☐ EP COLLECTION, THE
Did you ever... / Day blues / Blues in the bottle / There she is / Younger girl / Other side of this life / Sporting life / Fishin' blues / Jug band music / Loving you / Let the boy rock 'n' roll / Eyes / You baby / Butchie's tune / Wild about my lovin' / Voodoo in my basement / It's not time now / Didn't want to have to do it / Coconut grove / Do you believe in music
SEECD 229 / May '88 / See For Miles

☐ EVERYTHING PLAYING
She is still a mystery / Priscilla Millionaira / Boredom / Six o'clock / Forever / Younger generation / Money / Old folks / Only pretty, what a pity / Try a little bit / Close your eyes / Darling be home soon / Amazing air / Never going back / (Till I) run with you / Me about you
HILLCD 11 / Jan '97 / Wooded Hill

☐ HIT SINGLE COLLECTABLES
DISK 4503 / Apr '94 / Disky

☐ HUMS OF THE LOVIN' SPOONFUL
Sittin' here lovin' you / Bes' friends / Voodoo in my basement / Darling companion / Henry Thomas / Full measure / Rain on the roof / Coconut grove / Nashville cats / Four eyes
REP 4018 / Aug '91 / Repertoire

☐ SPOONFUL OF SOUNDTRAKCS, A
REP 4115 / Aug '91 / Repertoire

☐ SUMMER IN THE CITY
Daydream / Nashville cats / She is still a mystery / Didn't want to have to do it / Coconut grove / You didn't have to be so nice / Rain on the roof / Darling be home soon / Sittin' here lovin' you / On the road again / Do you believe in magic / Close your eyes / Jug band music / Summer in the city / Money / Warm baby / Night owl blues / Never going back (to Nashville)
5507362 / Jan '95 / Spectrum

☐ VERY BEST OF THE LOVIN' SPOONFUL, THE
Summer in the city / Daydream / Nashville cats / Darlin' be home soon / Younger girl / Did you ever have to make up your mind / You didn't have to be so nice / She's still a mystery / Wild about my lovin' / Darlin' companion / Never goin' back / Six o'clock / Jug band music / Lonely (Amy's theme) / Rain on the roof / Sittin' here lovin' you / Coconut grove / You're a big boy now / Boredom / Younger generation / Money / She's a lady / Pow / On the road again / Voodoo in my basement
74321558492 / 26 Jan '98 / Camden

Lovindeer

☐ JAM LIKE A JAMAICAN
TSOJ 0311962 / Oct '96 / Sound Of Jamaica

Lovsky, Fay

☐ CINEMA
Islands / Rainy day men / Steam / Sway with me / Goodnight Galileo / Underwater / Phantom conversations / Humble pie / Peppermint kisses / Automatic pilot / Fairy tales / Gentlemen and ladies / Robot / Bury the hatchet / Rembrandt
BASTA 3090422 / Sep '97 / Basta

☐ FAY LOVSKY & LA BANDE DESSINEE
Eye to eye / Unfinished business / Bad continuity / Had by you / Security pass / In the middle, in the middle / Monte Carlo guys / Champion des champignons / Underwater / Mr. Clean / Life is easy / Katzenjammer / Film noir - Danger city / Little dab'll do ya / Arirang / Big rubber ball / Esprit de l'escalier / Papa's things / Passing cloud / Rainy day men / I'm gonna walk on bye
BASTA 3090302 / Sep '97 / Basta

☐ JOPO IN MONO
Never you mind the neighbours / Yawn blues / Passi messa / Appellation controlee / Appellation non controlee / Duet for noses / Oh beebie / Passage en printemps / Jopo's bicycle / Makassar / George is my horse / Skubi Dubah
BASTA 3090322 / Sep '97 / Basta

☐ NUMBERS (Lovsky, Fay & La Bande Dessinee)
Talking talking talking / Curious and curiouser / Funny bizniz / Prairie / I don't care / Portugal / Sequoia / Morpheus / Snow / Nobody talks to me / Late nite airport / Letter to Oakland / Calm collected and cool / Food is the enemy / Empty home / Angels are among us
BASTA 3090692 / Oct '97 / Basta

☐ ORIGAMI
Ramon / Window across the street / Disney dust / Columbus Avenue / Sugar me Sam / Palmtree luxury / California daze / Don't feed the animals / Never (seem able to say goodbye) / Fuss and fight / Walk don't walk / One more time / Christmas was a friend of mine
BASTA 3090412 / Sep '97 / Basta

☐ SOUND ON SOUND CONFETTI
He don't love me anymore / Easy come, easy go / Schoolbell / Cold as ice / Maggie / Fool moon / Rude and the gang / Weather / All the same / Stay away / Esprit de l'escalier / Hong Kong nights / Crat race / Party time / Pusherman / Here's looking at you kid / Four krazy kats / Gotta stay home tonight / Never seem to be able to say goodbye / Lazy day / Safety pins / Difficult / Morpheus' arms
BASTA 3090402 / Sep '97 / Basta

Low

☐ CURTAIN HITS THE CAST, THE
Anon / Plan / Over the ocean / Mom says / Coat tails / Standby / Laugh / Lust / Stars gone out / Same / Do you know how to waltz / Prisoner / Tomorrow one
YARDCD 018 / Aug '96 / Vernon Yard

☐ LONG DIVISION
Violence / Below and above / Shame / Throw out the line / Swingin' / See-through / Turn / Caroline / Alone / Streetlight / Stay / Take
YARDCD 014 / Feb '97 / Vernon Yard

☐ ONE MORE REASON TO FORGET
INR 1040CD / 27 Jul '98 / Bluesanct Musak

☐ SONGS FOR A DEAD PILOT
KRANK 021CD / 20 Oct '97 / Kranky

Low 948

☐ PACCARISCA
KICKCD 20 / Jul '95 / Kickin'

Low, Bruce

☐ 12 UHR MITTAGS
BCD 15511 / Aug '90 / Bear Family

Low, Gary

☐ BEST OF GARY LOW, THE (I Want You)
La colegiala / Forever tonight and all my life / Non stop searching / Mi querido amor / You are a danger / Go on / Where I am / I want you / Ecuador / Get ready / Long train running
HTCD 37 / 20 Apr '98 / Hot Productions

Low Pop Suicide

☐ DEATH OF EXCELLENCE, THE
Bless my body / Almost said / Suicide ego / Zombie / Life and death / No genius / Humbled / More than this / Philo's snag / Sheep's clothing / Face to face / Tell them I was here
WDOM 012CD / Jan '95 / World Domination

☐ ON THE CROSS OF COMMERCE
Here we go / Kiss your lips / My way / Disengaged / It's easy / Your God can't feel my pain / Crush / Ride / Imagine my love / All in death is sweet
WDOM 007CD / May '94 / World Domination

Low-Fi Generator

☐ STEREO
NORMAL 207CD / Mar '97 / Normal

Lowdowns

☐ DIGGIN' A HOLE IN THE MIDDLE
168042 / 11 May '98 / Nitro

Lowe, Allen

☐ DARK WAS THE NIGHT - COLD WAS THE GROUND (Lowe, Allen & The American Song Project)
CD 811 / May '94 / Music & Arts

☐ WOYZECK'S DEATH (Lowe, Allen & Roswell Rudd)
Cold as ice / Sun on her bones / Voices in the fiddles / Misery / Beautiful sins / Hard gray sky / On thing after another / Good and beautiful murder / Woyzeck's death / Bonehead / Concentration suite
ENJ 90052 / May '95 / Enja

Lowe, Amanda

☐ SPIRAL DANCE
GRIN 941CD / Jan '95 / Grinnigogs

Lowe, Frank

☐ DECISION IN PARADISE
SNCD 1082 / Jul '86 / Soul Note

☐ FRESH
Epistrophy / Play some blues / Fresh / Mysterioso / Chu's blues
CDBLC 760214 / Apr '96 / Black Lion

☐ LIVE FROM SOUNDSCAPE (Lowe, Frank Quintet)
DIW 399CD / Jul '94 / DIW

Lowe, Jez

☐ BACK SHIFT
Back in durham gaol / Brockie lads / Galloways / Black diamonds / Bergen / Sedgefield fair / Old durham road / Chick henderson's march / Japs and english / Old bones / Cursed be the caller / High part of the town / Grey cock / Old durham waltz / Shippersea bay / Ballad of johnny collier / Honest working way
FE 089CD / Nov '95 / Fellside

☐ BAD PENNY
Another man's wife / Small coal song / Midnight mail / Dandelion clocks / Land of the living / Nearer to Nettles / Father Mallory's dance / Yankee boots / New town incident
FE 070CD / Feb '96 / Fellside

☐ BEDE WEEPS (Lowe, Jez & The Bad Pennies)
Call for the North country / These coal town days / Kid Canute / Scotty Moore's reel / Just like Moses / She'll always be freedom / Greek lightning / Dover / Delaware / Teardrop twostep / Too up and too down / Bulldog breed / Last of the widows / Mike Neville said it / Bede weeps
FE 094CD / Nov '93 / Fellside

☐ BRIEFLY ON THE STREET (Lowe, Jez & The Bad Pennies)
You can't take it with you / Famous working man / One man bound / Old hammer-head / Boonas / Soda man / Davis and Golightly / Jordan/The begging bowl / Alice / Fun without fools / Swiss reel / New moon's arms
FECD 79 / Jun '96 / Fellside

☐ GALLOWAYS/JEZ LOWE
MP 10006CD / Mar '98 / Musica Panagaea

☐ PARISH NOTICES, THE (Lowe, Jez & The Bad Pennies)
Glad rags again / Tom-tom / Propping / Sod all / Spitting cousins / Spares or repair / Limping drinker's polka / Go away Joe / Had away gan on / Parish notices / Idle time / If I had another penny
GLCD 1192 / May '98 / Green Linnet

☐ TENTERHOOKS (Lowe, Jez & The Bad Pennies)
GLCD 1161 / Jan '96 / Green Linnet

Lowe, Nick

☐ 16 ALL-TIME LOWES
American squirm / Big kick, plain scrap / Born fighter / Cruel to be kind / Heart of the city / I love the sound of breaking glass / Little Hitler / Marie Provost / Nutted by reality / Skin deep so it goes / Switchboard Susan / They called it rock / When I write the book / Without love
DIAB 801 / Oct '93 / Diablo

☐ ABOMINABLE SHOWMAN
Wish you were here / Paid the price / Saint beneath the paint / Time wounds all heals / Tanque-Rae / Around with love / Cool reaction / Chicken and feathers / We want action / Ragin' eyes / How do you talk to an angel / Man or a fall
FIENDCD 184 / Apr '90 / Demon

☐ BASHER (The Best Of Nick Lowe)
So it goes / Heart of the city / I love the sound of breaking glass / Little Hitler / No reason / Thirty six inches high / Marie Provost / Nutted by reality / American squirm / Peace, love and understanding / Cracking up / Big kick, plain scrap / Born fighter / Switchboard Susan / Without love / Love so fine / Cruel to be kind / When I write the book / Heart / Stick it where the sun don't shine / Ragin' eyes / Time wounds all heels / Tanque-rae / Maureen / Half a boy and half a man / Breakaway / She don't love nobody / Seven nights to rock / Long walk back / Rose of England / I knew the bride / Lover's jamboree
FIENDCD 142 / Aug '89 / Demon

☐ BOXED (4CD Set)
NICK 1 / Jan '94 / Demon

☐ DIG MY MOOD
Faithless lover / Lonesome reverie / You inspire me / What lack of love has done / Time I took a holiday / Failed Christian / Man that I've become / Freezing / High on a hilltop / Lead me not / I must be getting over you / Cold grey light of dawn
FIENDCD 939 / 26 Jan '98 / Demon

☐ IMPOSSIBLE BIRD
Soulful wind / Beast in me / True love travels on a gravel road / Trail of tears / Shelly my love / Where's my everything / 12-step program / Lover don't go / Drive-thru man / Withered on the vine / I live on a battlefield / 14 days / I'll be there
FIENDCD 757 / Oct '94 / Demon

☐ JESUS OF COOL
Music for money / I love the sound of breaking glass / Little Hitler / Shake and pop / Tonight / So it goes / No reason / Thirty six inches high / Marie Provost / Nutted by reality / Heart of the city
FIENDCD 131 / Oct '88 / Demon

☐ LABOUR OF LUST
Cruel to be kind / Cracking up / Big kick, plain scrap / Born fighter / You make me / Skin deep / Switchboard Susan / Endless grey ribbon / Without love / Dose of you / Love so fine
FIENDCD 182 / Apr '90 / Demon

☐ NICK LOWE AND HIS COWBOY OUTFIT
Half a boy and half a man / You'll never get me up (in one of those) / Maureen / God's gift to women / Gee and the rick and the three card trick / Hey big mouth stand up and say that / Awesome / Breakaway / Love like a glove / Live fast love hard / LAFS
FIENDCD 185 / May '90 / Demon

☐ NICK THE KNIFE
Burning / Heart / Stick it where the sun don't shine / Queen of Sheba / My heart hurts / Couldn't love you / Let me kiss ya / Too many teardrops / Ba doom / Raining / One's too many / Zulu kiss
FIENDCD 183 / Apr '90 / Demon

☐ PARTY OF ONE PLUS
FIENDCD 767 / Oct '95 / Demon

☐ PINKER & PROUDER THAN PREVIOUS
(You're my) wildest dream / Crying in my sleep / Big hair / Love gets strange / Black Lincoln Continental / Cry it out / Lover's jamboree / Geisha girl / Wishing well / Big big love
FIENDCD 99 / Mar '88 / Demon

☐ ROSE OF ENGLAND
I knew the bride / Indoor fireworks / I'm right / I can be the one you love / Everyone / Bob Skaddidle daddle / Darlin' angel eyes / She don't love nobody / Seven nights to rock / Long walk back / Rose of England / Lucky dog
FIENDCD 73 / Oct '88 / Demon

☐ WILDERNESS YEARS, THE
Fool too long / Let's go to the disco / Everybody dance / Bay city rollers we love you / Allorolla / Rollers show / Heart of the city / Halfway to paradise / Truth drug / Born a woman / Endless sleep / Shake that rat / I love my label / I don't want the night to end / So heavy / Keep it out of sight / Heart / I got a job
FIENDCD 203 / Oct '90 / Demon

☐ YOU INSPIRE ME
VEXCD 17 / 1 Jun '98 / Demon

Lower

☐ GENTLE ART OF CONDITIONING, THE
3984232952 / 15 Jun '98 / Coalition

Lower Class Brats

☐ RATHER BE HATED THAN IGNORED
GMM 137 / 20 Apr '98 / GMM

Lowercase

☐ ALL DESTRUCTIVE URGES
ARR 73016CD / Jun '96 / Amphetamine Reptile

Lowground

☐ SOUNDS FOR FREAKS
SIRE 003 / Jan '97 / Lowlands

Lowland Band & Pipers Of The Scottish Division

☐ EDINBURGH CASTLE
Scotland the brave / Bonnie black isle / Holyrood / Will ye no come back again / Pentland hills / Festoso / Edinburgh castle / Pipe set 3/4 marches / Hebrides suite / Ye banks and braes / Misty morn / Dunedin / Pipes set 6-8 marches / Garb of the old gaul / Dumbarton's drums / Regimental quick marches / Whistle o'er the lave / Blue bonnest o'er the border / Within a mile o'Edinboro' town
BNA 5115 / Oct '95 / Bandleader

Lowther, Henry

☐ ID
MRFD 97122 / Jun '98 / Village Life

LOX

☐ MONEY, POWER AND RESPECT
Yonkers tale / Livin' the life / If you think I'm jiggy / Interview / Money, power and respect: *LOX & DMX/ Lil' Kim* / Get this $ / Let's start rap over / Mad rapper / I wanna thank you / Goin' be some shit / Heist / Not to be fucked with / Set up / Bitches from Eastwick / Can't stop, won't stop: *LOX & Puff Daddy* / All for love / So right: *LOX & Kelly Price* / Everybody wanna rat / Interview / We'll always love
78612730152 / 26 Jan '98 / Puff Daddy

Loxam, Arnold

☐ ARNOLD LOXAM CELEBRATES
Celebration march / Romance / Second waltz / Hawaiian holiday / This is my mother's day / Third man theme / Jumpin' Charlie/In the pink / Audrey's melody / Spanish gypsy / Zuider Zee ballade / Mr. Snowman goes to town / Berliner Luft / Meditation / I got rhythm / Hors d'oeuvres / Cuckoo waltz / Old refrain / Amsterdam / Storm at sea / Come back to Sorrento
OS 223 / Jul '96 / OS Digital

☐ BLACKPOOL MAGIC
Beside the seaside / Blackpool walk / Blackpool bounce / So blue / Carolina moon / Wyoming lullaby / Tammy / As time goes by / I'll string along with you / Angels never leave heaven / When my dreamboat comes home / Whispering / Shepherd of the hills / Let a smile be your umbrella / If you knew Susie like I know Susie / Bye bye blackbird / Ik hou van Holland / Sing something simple / Strollin' / Love letters in the sand / Bewitched, bothered and bewildered / Neighbours / One of those songs / Cabaret / Mr. Sandman / It's party time again / Stein song / GB junior club song / Delilah / Cruising down the river / Forever and ever / I just called to say I love you / Bunch of thyme / Love changes everything / Strangers in the night / I'm confessin' that I love you / In a little Spanish town / For me and my girl / Underneath the arches / Morningtown ride / Arm in arm / White cliffs of Dover / Blackpool lights / Last mile home / Who's taking you home / Goodnight (dear goodnight) / Now is the hour / It's a pity to say goodnight / It's a lovely day today / Here's to the next time / Wish me luck as you wave me goodbye
CDGRS 1215 / '91 / Grosvenor

☐ STRANGER ON THE SHORE
Spring (excerpt) / In the news (signature tune bbc radio 2 series 'ma / Cuckoo waltz / Easter parade / Serenade to audrey / Jeepers creepers / Stranger on the shore / Whistling rufus / Summer (excerpt) / Fleetwood fisherwomen / Sobre las olas / Albatross / Stanley park / Autumn (excerpt) / October twilight / Mack the knife / Crinoline days / Promenade / Can't we sing love's old sweet song again / September song / Winter (excerpt) / Sleigh ride in alaska / December-the fairy on the christmas tree / Dance of the icicles / You made me love you
CDGRS 1240 / Feb '93 / Grosvenor

☐ WURLITZER SEASONS
Windermere march / Sunset over Morcambe bay / My darling Clementine / Grasshoppers dance / Perfect year / Dicky bird hop / Windmills of the Zuider Zee / Wear a smile / Londonderry air / End of the pier / To a wild rose / Wishing you were somehow here again / Four seasons in music / Roses of Picardy / Wurlitzer march / Narcissus / 12th Street rag / Kleine melody / Rock gospel melody
OS 212 / Jun '95 / OS Digital

Loy, Myrna

☐ I PRESS MY LIPS
NORMAL 108CD / Aug '90 / Normal

Loyde, Lobby

☐ LOBBY LOYDE & THE COLOURED BALLS (2CD Set) (Loyde, Lobby & The Coloured Balls)
8578612 / Oct '97 / Fable

Loyer, Jean-Paul

☐ LE MESSAGER
OJNABCD 01 / Apr '96 / Ojnab

Loza, Lori

☐ THIS IS LOVE
CD 52202 / Apr '96 / Salt

LSG

☐ BLACK ALBUM, THE
Train of thought / Train of thought / Go fishing / Cellular / Blaxone / Rotation / 88 / Freakz / Hellfire / Deep blue
BS 28332 / 6 Jul '98 / Superstition

☐ COLLECTED WORKS
Fragile / Netherworld / Cassiopeia / Centurion / Fontana / Microfish / Get out / Hidden sun of Venus / Novastorm / Terry's synphony / Loctrolyte
HOOJCD 005 / 26 Jan '98 / Hooj Choons

☐ LSG VOL.2
SUPER 2069CD / Dec '96 / Superstition
EFA 620692 / 22 Sep '97 / Superstition

☐ RENDEZVOUS IN OUTER SPACE
Wrong time wrong place / Lonely casseopaya / My time is yours / Can you see the yellow turtles / Miss Understanding / Sweet gravity / Sweet g (#2) / Hidden sun of Venus / Lunar orbit / Everything is / Ebter - paradise / Fontana / Reprise
SUPER 2038CD / Jun '95 / Superstition
EFA 698576 / Jul '97 / Superstition

LSO

☐ SERENITY, TRANQUILITY & PEACE
TASTE 061CD / Aug '95 / Taste

LTG Exchange

☐ LTG EXCHANGE
Waterbed / Waterbed / Saint or sinner / I like what I like / Keep on trying / Give it love / Tsen si yen yen / Trouble on the run / My love / Corazon / Young mother's love
DGPCD 725 / May '95 / Deep Beats

LTJ Bukem

☐ LOGICAL PROGRESSION SESSIONS VOL.1 (Various Artists)
Equinox: *Cedar* / Eastern promise: *Intense* / System: KMC / Cosmik: *Motive One* / Presence: *PHD & Conrad* / Emotionography: *Big Bud* / Planetary funk alert: *Seba* / Karizma: *Bio-Wire* / Inner worlds: *Artemis* / Camoflage: *Seba* / Orchestral jam: *LTJ Bukem*
GLRPS 001 / 16 Feb '98 / Good Looking

☐ LOGICAL PROGRESSION VOL.1 (Various Artists)
Demons theme: *LTJ Bukem* / Links: *Links* / Music: *LTJ Bukem* / One and only: *PFM* / Bringing me down: *Aquarius & Tayla* / Sweet sunshine: *Ills & Solo* / Danny's song: *PFM* / Vocal: *Peshay* / Cool out: *LTJ Bukem* / Western: *PFM* / Horizons: *PFM* / Alright: *Funky Technicians* / Aura: *Ills & Solo* / Drum in a grip: *Wax Doctor* / Solution: *Ills & Solo* / Untitled: *Jam Master Jay* / So long: *Seb & Lo Tek* / Pharoah: *Photek* / After hours: *DJ Trance* / Universal: *Rob* / Mind games: *DJ Crystl*
8287392
8287472 / Apr '96 / FFRR

☐ LTJ BUKEM PRESENTS EARTH VOL.1 (Various Artists)
Rhyme goes on: *Poets Of Thought* / Travelling: *Appaloosa* / Faith: *Subject 13* / Above and beyond: *PHD & Technicians* / Samba with UR: *Poets Of Thought* / Revival: *Blame* / Do what you gotta do: *Pablo* / Jamming the session: *Poets Of Thought* / Moodswings: *LTJ Bukem* / Tokyo dawn: *Doc Scott*
EARTHCD 001 / Oct '96 / Good Looking

☐ LTJ BUKEM PRESENTS EARTH VOL.2 (Various Artists)
Fictions: *Rollercone* / Cosmic interlude: *LTJ Bukem* / Artificial life: *Odyssey* / J-walkin': *Blame* / Silver dawn: *Artemis* / Flashback: *Intense* / Adrift on deep water: *Blu Mar Ten* / Senses: *DJ Addiction* / Mind games: *DJ Crystl*
EARTHCD 002 / 22 Sep '97 / Good Looking

☐ MIXMAG LIVE VOL.21 (Various Artists)
On link: *Fokus* / Source direct: *Exit 9* / Sorrow and liquid groove: *Future Bound* / Airtight: *Funky Technicians* / No mysery: *Funky Technicians* / One and only: *PFM* / Music: *LTJ Bukem* / We can change the future: *Code Of Practice* / Breathless: *Intense* / Just visiting Mars: *FBD Project* / Free la funk: *JMJ & Richie*
MMLCD 021 / Jul '96 / Mixmag Live

Luan

☐ FIRST IMPRESSIONS
ARCD 010 / May '98 / Ainm

Lubert, Philip

☐ RED LIGHTS AND LONELY FEELINGS
Maria / Lost soul / I just need to know / Lady / Blood / Fairytale / Eikosan / Les Jeux tu Joue / Highlander
XTRALUBE 001 / Jan '97 / Xtralube Productions

Lubricated Goat

☐ PADDOCK OF LOVE
BLAKCD 6 / Nov '94 / Black Eye

☐ PSYCHEDELICATESSEN
BLACKCD 11 / Mar '94 / Normal

☐ SCHADENFREUDE
BLACKCD 3 / Mar '94 / Normal

Lucas

☐ DISCOVER A WORLD OF SOUND (Lucas & Friends)
VC 118 / 8 Sep '97 / Vinyl Communication

☐ LUCACENTRIC
4509969252 / Aug '94 / Warner Bros.

Lucas & The Dynamos

☐ LOONEY TUNES
LUC 001 / Mar '98 / Lucas

Lucas, Bob

☐ RUSHSYLVANIA
BYB 001CD / Mar '98 / Bellybutton

Lucas, Carrie

☐ GREATEST HITS
Keep smilin' / Dance with you / It's not what you got but how you use it / Career girl / Show me where you're coming from / Hello stranger / Goin' in circles / Somebody said / Just a memory / Street corner symphony / Summer in the street / Rockin' for your love / I just can't do without your love
DEEPM 035 / Aug '97 / Deep Beats

Lucas, Gary

☐ BAD BOYS OF THE ARCTIC
EMY 1462 / Nov '94 / Enemy

☐ BUSY BEING BORN
TZA 7121 / 2 Mar '98 / Tzadik

☐ EVANGELINE
INDIGO 58522 / Dec '96 / Zensor

☐ GODS AND MONSTERS
EMY 1332 / Sep '97 / Enemy

☐ SKELETON AT THE FEAST
EMY 1262 / Sep '97 / Enemy

Lucas, Robert

☐ BUILT FOR COMFORT
Built for comfort / Walkin' blues / Ringing that lonesome bell / Just a kid / Blues man from LA / Hawaiian boogie / My home is a burning / Change, change / Sleeping by myself / I miss you baby / Talk to me / Come on in my kitchen
AQCD 1011 / Sep '95 / Audioquest

☐ LUKE AND THE LOCOMOTIVE
Good morning little school girl / Big man mambo / Slide on outta here / Worried about it baby / Shed a tear / Feel like going home / Don't your peaches look mellow / Meet me in the bottom / Stranger / I'm so tired / Goodbye baby
AQCD 1004 / Jul '95 / Audioquest

Lucena, Luis

☐ SELECCION DE ORO VOL.1
9132 / Oct '96 / Divusca

Lucha Libre

☐ LUCHA LIBRA & HEAVY Q CONNECTION
SUPERCD 010 / 22 Jun '98 / Tiny Superhero

Luciano

☐ BACK TO AFRICA
EXTCD 3 / Sep '94 / Exterminator

☐ DON'T GET CRAZY
CRCD 36 / Dec '94 / Charm

☐ DON'T GET CRAZY
SHRCD 6015 / Mar '96 / Sky High

☐ MESSENGER
Messenger / Life / Mama / Over the hills / Never give up my pride / Rainy days / Friend in need / How can you / Feel like moving / Carry Jah load / Guess what's happening
IJCD 3009 / Oct '96 / Island Jamaica

☐ MOVING UP
RASCD 3129 / Jan '94 / Ras

☐ ONE WAY TICKET
VPCD 1386 / 18 Aug '97 / VP
CRCD 41 / 15 Aug '97 / Charm

☐ REGGAE MAX
JSRNCD 13 / Mar '97 / Jet Star

☐ SHAKE IT UP TONIGHT
BSCD 3 / Jul '97 / Big Ship

Lucid Dream

☐ PURE PUNK
AA 003CD / Mar '97 / A13

Lucid Dreams

☐ LUCID DREAMS
EMIT 0096 / Mar '96 / Time Recordings

Lucien, Jon

☐ ENDLESS IS LOVE
Look of love / Rashida / This could be paradise / Endless is love / My special friend / Sailing / Sweet promises / Bolero / Moonchild / Frances
SHCD 5031 / Mar '98 / Shanachie

☐ MOTHER NATURE'S SON
How about you / But beautiful / You're sensational / Mother Nature's song / Mi vida / Mysteries / Once upon a time / Luna mi luna / Would you believe in me / Listen love
5148942 / Apr '94 / Verve

Lucifer's Friend

☐ LUCIFER'S FRIEND
REP 4059 / Aug '91 / Repertoire

☐ MIND EXPLODING
RR 7085 / Jul '98 / Repertoire

☐ SUMOGRIP
Get in / One way ticket to hell / You touched me / Step by step / Sheree / Intruder / Ride the sky / Get out / Heartbreaker / Don't look back / Cadillac / Rebound / Back in the track / Any day now / Free me / You touched me with your heart
ESMCD 489 / Apr '97 / Essential

☐ WHERE THE GROUPIES KILLED THE BLUES
REP 4143 / Aug '91 / Repertoire

Luckley, Stu

☐ BOX OF GOLD (Luckley, Stu & Bob Fox)
Bonny Gateshead / Two magicians / Heart like a wheel / Bold Reynard the fox / Shores of Old Blighty / Doodle let me go / Isle of Islay / Row between the cages / Sally Wheatley / Dollia / Begging / Song of the iron road / Fishing / Sally Gee
FECD 124 / Dec '97 / Fellside

Lucksmiths

☐ GOOD KIND OF NERVOUS
DRIVE 21 / 4 May '98 / Drive-In

Lucky 15

☐ COLOUR CODE WHITE
Medication through resonance / Terge / Stereo 1-5 / Monkey magic / Blue / Snowflakes in Hawaii
BU 009CD / Jun '97 / Blow Up

Lucky Bags

☐ FOOD FOR THOUGHT
FECD 112 / Feb '97 / Fellside

Lucky Dube

☐ CAPTURED LIVE
SHCD 43090 / Apr '93 / Shanachie

☐ SERIOUS REGGAE BUSINESS
CDLUCKY 10 / Nov '96 / Gallo

☐ SERIOUS REGGAE BUSINESS
Mr. DJ / Feel Irie / Together as one / Slave / Steel bars / Prisoner / Reggae strong / Oh my son (I'm sorry) / I want to know whatRemember me / House of love is / Exile / Peace perfect peace / Victims / I've got you babe / It's not easy / Different colours/One people / Back to my roots
SHANCD 45029 / May '98 / Shanachie

☐ TAXMAN
Guns and roses / Taxman / Is this the way / Take it to jah / Mirror, mirror / We love it / You've got a friend / Kiss no frog / Well fed slave/Hungry free man / Good hthings / Release me / I want to know what love is
TIMBCD 504 / Aug '97 / Timbuktu
CDLUCKY 11 / Jun '97 / Gallo

☐ TRINITY
5504792 / Apr '95 / Tabu

☐ VICTIMS
Keep on knocking / Victims / Johnny soldiers for righteousness / My world / Little heroes / You know (where to find me) / Lovers in a dangerous time / My game / Different colours-one people / Victims / Victims / Victims
FLTRCD 512 / Jul '93 / Flame Tree

Lucky Seven

☐ ONE WAY TRACK
DEL 3008 / Dec '95 / Deluge

Lucky Strikers

☐ SLIP SLIDE AND HOPE
SPV 08498812 / May '95 / SPV

Ludichrist

☐ IMMACULATE DECEPTION
WB 3034CD / Sep '93 / We Bite

☐ POWERTRIP
WB 035CD / Oct '88 / We Bite

Luecking, Juliana

☐ BIG BROAD
Oh / Fancy your hat / Gonna love a woman / 17-18-19 Grrrls / Pull the scam / Head and mouth / Come to Phoenix / Married in mid-air / Beefheart / Thanks for holding / Shiny blade / Rosita and Marita / 28 and 82 / Willy, Thelma and Kitty / Living legend / Stink / You the best / Margaret and Regina / Pretty girl / Esperanza dreams / Hide and seek / Growth spurt / Big broad / H-heart / Stick shift / Bed bath / Rescue squad / Leaf diving / To be touched / Catch
KRS 228CD / Sep '94 / Kill Rock Stars

Lukather, Steve

☐ LUKE
Real truth / Broken machine / Tears of my own shame / Love the things you hate / Hate everything about U / Reservations to live (the way it is) / Don't hang me on / Always be there for me / Open your heart / Bag o' tales / Bluebird
4873602 / Jun '97 / Columbia

Luke, Robin

☐ SUSIE DARLIN'
Well oh well oh (don't you know) / Everlovin' / Five minutes more / You can't stop me from dreaming / Who's gonna hold your hand / Susie darlin' / Part of a fool / Poor little rich boy / So alone / All because of you / Make me a dreamer / Walkin' in the moonlight / My girl / Chicka chicka honey / School bus love affair / Strollin' blues
BCD 15547 / Aug '93 / Bear Family

Lukie D

☐ CENTRE OF ATTRACTION
VPCD 1451 / Jan '96 / VP

Lull

☐ CONTINUE
RR 69492 / Feb '97 / Relapse

☐ DREAMT ABOUT DREAMING
RWK 1111 / Jun '97 / Rawkus

☐ JOURNEY THROUGH UNDERWORLDS
RKS 1112 / Feb '97 / Rawkus

☐ MOMENTS
REL 6403 / 29 Jun '98 / Release

Lullaby For The Working Class

☐ BLANKET WARM
Good morning / Honey drop the knife / Turpentine / Spreading the evening sky with cows / Boar's nest / Eskimo song duel / Three peas in a pod / Rye / Queen of the long legged insects / Drama of your life / February North 24th Street / Wounded spider / Good night
RCD 10372 / Sep '96 / Rykodisc

☐ I NEVER EVEN ASKED FOR A LIGHT
Show me how the robots dance / Irish wake / Jester's siren / Hypnotist / In honour of my / Stumbling / This is as close as we get / Sunset to the electric bill / Bread crumbs / Descent / Man vs the tide
RCD 10426 / 22 Sep '97 / Rykodisc

Lulu

☐ ABSOLUTE
DOMECD 11 / Jul '97 / Dome

☐ BEST OF LULU, THE
I'm a tiger / Boom bang-a-bang / Me the peaceful heart / Let's pretend / To Sir with love / Boy / Boat that I row / Day tripper / Love loves to love love / Take me in your arms and love me / You and I / March / To love somebody / Best of both worlds
16153 / Nov '96 / Laserlight

☐ BEST OF LULU, THE
Man who sold the world / Take your mama for a ride / Boy like you / Honey you can't take it back / Boy meets girl / Mama's little corner of the world / Make believe world / Watch that man / Man with the golden gun / My boy lollipop / Old fashioned girl / Heaven and Earth and the stars / Shout / Take your mama for a ride
WB 885542 / 2 Feb '98 / Disky

☐ EP COLLECTION, THE
Shout / Forget me baby / I am in love / Can't hear no more / That's really some good / Here comes the night / Heatwave / What's easy for two is so hard for one / Satisfied / He don't want your love anymore / Surprise surprise / Leave a little love / Chocolate ace / Not in this whole world / So in love / He's sure the boy I love / What a wonderful feeling / Tossin' and turnin' / You touch me baby / You'll never leave her / Trouble with the boys / Nothing left to do but cry / Don't answer me / Boat that I row / Let's pretend
SEECD 452 / Oct '96 / See For Miles

☐ GOLD COLLECTION, THE
Boom bang-a-bang / Boat that I row / I'm a tiger / Me the peaceful heart / Let's pretend / Boy / Love loves to love love / To sir with love / Take me in your arms and love me / Day tripper / Dreary days and nights / Best of both worlds / Morning dew / Rattler / You and I / Without him
CDGOLD 1005 / Mar '96 / EMI Gold

☐ SHOUT
DC 867412 / Aug '96 / Disky

☐ VERY BEST OF LULU, THE
Heaven and earth and the stars / Boy meets girl / Mama's little corner of the world / Man with the golden gun / Baby I don't cry / Take your mama for a ride (part one) / My boy lollipop / Honey you can't take it back / Man who sold the world / Watch that man / Old fashioned girl / Take your mama for a ride (part two) / Shout
BRCD 107 / Jan '95 / BR Music

☐ WORLD OF LULU, THE
Shout / Try to understand / Heatwave / Just one look / Call me / Don't answer me / He don't want your love anymore / That's really some good / After you / What's easy for two is so hard for one / Can't hear you no more / Trouble with boys / Here comes the night / Take me as I am / Surprise surprise / Stubborn kind of fellow / I am in love / Nothing left to do but cry / Tossin' and turnin'
5512702 / May '96 / Spectrum

Luman, Bob

☐ LORETTA
Loretta / It's a sin / If you don't love me / Love worked a miracle / Poor boy blues / Sentimental / You're welcome / Running scared / Freedom of living / Tears from out of nowhere / It's all over / Best years of my wife / Bigger man than I / Too hot to dance / I like your kind of love / Hardly anymore
CDSD 068 / Nov '89 / Sundown

Lumiere, Jean

☐ ETOILES DE LA CHANSON
882502 / Aug '93 / Music Memoria

☐ MONSIEUR CHARME
701632 / Nov '96 / Chansophone

Lumukanda

☐ ARAGLIN
NZCD 004 / Feb '94 / Nova Zembla

Luna

☐ BEWITCHED
California (all the way) / Tiger Lily / Friendly advice / Bewitched / This time around / Great Jones Street / Going home / Into the fold / I know you tried / Sleeping pill
7559616172 / Mar '94 / WEA

☐ LUNAPARK
Slide / Anesthesia / Slash your tyres / Crazy people / Time / Smile / I can't wait / Hey sister / I want everything / Time to quit / Goodbye / We're both confused
7559613602 / Aug '92 / WEA

☐ PUP TENT
Ihop / Beautiful view / Pup tent / Bobby Peru / Beggar's bliss / Tracey I love you / Whispers / City kitty / Creeps / Fuzzy wuzzy
BBQCD 194 / 18 Aug '97 / Beggars Banquet

Lunachicks

☐ BABYSITTERS ON ACID
Jan brady / Glad I'm not yew / Babysitters on acid / Makin' it / Mabel rock / Theme song / Born 2b mild / Pin eye woman 665 / Cookie core / Octopussy / Sugar luv / Complication
BFFP 52CD / Nov '89 / Blast First

☐ BINGE AND PURGE
SPV 08445432 / Mar '96 / SPV

☐ BINGE AND PURGE
SH 21072 / Nov '96 / Safe House

☐ JERK OF ALL TRADES
Drop dead / Fingerful / FDS / Light as a feather / Edgar / Dogyard / Butt plugg / Bitterness Barbie / Deal with it / Brickface and stucco / Jerk of all trades / Spoilt / Ring and run / Fallopian rhapsody / Insomnia / Why me
GK 013CD / May '97 / Go-Kart

☐ PRETTY UGLY
GK 024CD / Mar '97 / Go-Kart

Lunaire, Pierro

☐ GUDRUN
MPRCD 00 / Sep '97 / MP

Lunar Drive

☐ HERE AT BLACK MESA ARIZONA
NR 1076CD / Oct '96 / Nation

Lunasa

☐ LUNASA
Eanair / Feabhra / Marta / Aibreann / Bealtaine / Meitheamh / Iuil / Mean fomhair / Mi na samhna / Mi na nollag
LSA 001 / 19 Jan '97 / Lunasa

Lunatic Gods

☐ INHUMAN AND INSENSIBLE
POLYPH 002CD / Jul '96 / Polyphemus

Lunceford, Jimmie

☐ BABY WON'T YOU PLEASE COME HOME
Lonesome road / You set me on fire / Baby, won't you please come home / I've only myself to blame / You're just a dream / Easter parade / Blue blazes / Mixup / What is this thing called swing / Shoemaker's holiday / Ain't she sweet / Mandy / White heat / Well alright then / I love you / Oh why oh why / Who did you meet last night / You let me down / Sassin' the boss / I want the waiter / You can fool some of the people (some of the time) / Think of me, little daddy / Liza / Belgium stomp / You let me down / I used to love you (but it's all over now)
GRF 086 / '93 / Tring

☐ BLUES IN THE NIGHT (Lunceford, Jimmie & Orchestra)
T'ain't what you do (it's the way that you do it) / Blues in the night / Organ grinder swing / Margie / Le jazz hot / Uptown blues / Baby, won't you please come home / Twenty four robbers / I'm gonna move to the outskirts of town / For dancers only / Well alright then / Lonesome road / Cheatin' on me / Ain't she sweet / Mandy / Back door stuff / Harlem shout / Four or five times
CD 56013 / Sep '94 / Jazz Roots

☐ CLASSICS 1930-1934
CLASSICS 501 / Apr '90 / Classics

☐ CLASSICS 1934-1935
CLASSICS 505 / Apr '90 / Classics

☐ CLASSICS 1935-1937
CLASSICS 510 / Apr '90 / Classics

☐ CLASSICS 1937-1939
CLASSICS 520 / Apr '90 / Classics

☐ CLASSICS 1939
CLASSICS 532 / Dec '90 / Classics

☐ CLASSICS 1939-1940
CLASSICS 565 / Oct '91 / Classics

☐ CLASSICS 1940-1941 (Lunceford, Jimmie & Orchestra)
CLASSICS 622 / Nov '92 / Classics

☐ CLASSICS 1941-1945
CLASSICS 862 / Mar '96 / Classics

☐ INTRODUCTION TO JIMMIE LUNCEFORD 1934-1942, AN
4002 / Dec '93 / Best Of Jazz

☐ JIMMIE LUNCEFORD
HEPCD 1017 / Jan '91 / Hep

☐ JIMMIE LUNCEFORD & ORCHESTRA 1934-1939 (Lunceford, Jimmie & Orchestra)
Black and tan fantasy / Four or five times / Swanee river / Oh boy / Avalon / Organ grinder's swing / Harlem shout / I'll see you in my dreams / Raggin' the scale / For dancers only / Posin' / Put on your old grey bonnet / Pigeon walk / Annie laurie / Margie / Le jazz hot / Baby won't you please come home / Blue blazes / Put it away / Wham / Uptown blues / Lunceford special
BLE 592412 / Dec '92 / Black & Blue

☐ JIMMIE LUNCEFORD ORCHESTRA 1934-1942
TPZ 1005 / Aug '94 / Topaz Jazz

☐ LIVE AT JAFFERSON BARRACKS, MISSOURI (Lunceford, Jimmie & His Harlem Express)
Jeep rhythm / Blues in the night / What to do / Are you kiddin' / Holiday for strings / Let's keep smiling / Wham / Estrellita / For dancers only
HCD 221 / Sep '94 / Hindsight

☐ LIVE BROADCASTS 1936-1943 (Lunceford, Jimmie Orchestra)
JH 3004 / Mar '97 / Jazz Hour

☐ MUSIC OF JIMMIE LUNCEFORD, THE (American Jazz Orchestra)
Lunceford special / What's your story morning glory / Belgium stomp / I'm alone with you / Yard dog Mazurka / Hi spook / For dancers only / Uptown blues / Annie Laurie / Margie / I wanna hear swing songs / Organ grinder swing
8208462 / May '92 / Limelight

☐ POLISHED PERFECTION
TOPAZ 1005 / Mar '95 / Topaz/ADA

☐ POWERHOUSE SWING
Well alright / You let me down / I want the waiter / I used to love you (but it's all over now) / Belgian stomp / Think of me little Daddy / Liza / Rock it for me / I'm in an awful mood / Uptown blues / Lunceford special / Bugs parade / Blues in the groove / I got it / Chopins prelude No.7 / Swingin' in C / Let's try again / Monotony in four plats / Barefoot blues / Minnie the moocher is dead
PAR 2012 / Apr '94 / Parade

☐ QUINTESSENCE, THE (1934-1941/2CD Set)
FA 212 / Oct '96 / Fremeaux

☐ RHYTHM IS OUR BUSINESS
Rhythm is our business / Stratosphere / Unsophisticated Sue / Four or five times / Bird of paradise / I'll take the South / Hittin' the bottle / Oh boy / Best things in life are free / Muddy water / Hell's bells / He ain't got rhythm / Slumming on Park Avenue / For dancers only / Posin' / Margie / Frisco fog / What is this thing called Swing / Ain't she sweet / Life is fine
PPCD 78111 / Feb '95 / Past Perfect

☐ RHYTHM IS OUR BUSINESS
Baby, won't you please come home / Barefoot blues / Belgium stomp / Black and tan fantasy / Flaming reeds and screaming brass / For dancers only / Four or five times / Hittin' the bottle / I'm alone with you / Le jazz hot / Margie / My blue heaven / Organ grinder swing / Pigeon walk / Rhythm is our business / Shake your head / Since my best gal turned me down / Sleepy time gal / Sophisticated lady / T'ain't what you do (it's the way that you do it) / Time's a wastin' / Uptown blues / What's your story Morning Glory / While love lasts
CDAJA 5091 / May '92 / Living Era

☐ RHYTHM IS OUR BUSINESS (Lunceford, Jimmie & His Orchestra)
Organ grinder's swing / Strictly instrumental / I'm gonna move to the outskirts of town / Mood indigo / Yard dog mazurka / Posin' / Sophisticated lady / Margie / Runnin' a temperature / For dancers only / Rhythm is our business / Stratosphere / Annie Laurie / Black and tan fantasy / Twenty four robbers / Coquette / Blue prelude / Siesta at the fiesta / Knock me a kiss / Blues in the night
306312 / Jan '97 / Hallmark

☐ SWINGSATION
For dancers only / Hittin' the bottle / Avalon / He ain't got rhythm / Organ grinder's swing / My blue heaven / Rose room / Stratosphere / Miss Otis regrets / Dream of you / Stomp it off / Rhythm is our business / Runnin' wild / Four or five times / Swanee river / Oh boy / I'm nuts about screwy music / Harlem shout
GRP 99232 / 24 Aug '98 / GRP

Lydia Lunch

☐ 8-EYED SPY
ALP 75CD / 8 Sep '97 / Atavistic

☐ MATRIKAMANTRA (2CD Set)
EFA 043992 / 27 Apr '98 / CDH Wax

☐ RUDE HIEROGLYPHICS (Lydia Lunch & Excene Cervenka)
Rude hieroglyphics
RCD 10326 / Oct '95 / Rykodisc

☐ SHOTGUN WEDDING
WSP 002CD / Oct '91 / UFO

☐ TRANCE MUTATION/SHOTGUN WEDDING (2CD Set)
TWIST 2 / Jul '94 / NMC

☐ WIDOWSPEAK (The Best Of Lydia Lunch/2CD Set)
Death Valley '69: *Lydia Lunch & Sonic Youth* / Endless fall: *Lydia Lunch & Roland S. Howard* / Why don't do it in the road: *Lydia Lunch & Clint Ruin* / Some velvet morning: *Lydia Lunch & Roland S. Howard* / Four cornered room / Suicide ocean: *Lydia Lunch & Karl Blake* / No excuse: *Lydia Lunch & Lee Renaldo* / Short history of decay parts 1 and 2: *Lydia Lunch & JF Coleman/J Budenholzer* / Escape: *Lydia Lunch & Lee Renaldo* / Quiet night of murder in Greenwich Conneticut / Need to feed: *Lydia Lunch & Joseph Budenholzer* / Der Karibische western: *Lydia Lunch & Die Haut* / Twisted: *Lydia Lunch & Clint Ruin* / Past glas / Done dun: *Lydia Lunch & Roland S. Howard* / Lock your door / Diddy wah diddy: *Lydia Lunch & 8 Eyed Spy* / Run through the jungle: *Lydia Lunch & 8 Eyed Spy* / Orphans: *Lydia Lunch & Teenage Jesus* / Son of stink: *Lydia Lunch & Clint Ruin* / Still burning: *Lydia Lunch & Thurston Moore* / Tornado warnings: *Lydia Lunch & Beruit Slump* / Lady scarface
PILOT 009 / 27 Jul '98 / Burning Airlines

Lundeng, Susanne

☐ AETTESYN
FXCD 178 / May '97 / Kirkelig Kultuverksted

☐ DRAG
FX 140CD / Dec '94 / Kirkelig Kultuverksted

Lundgren, Jan

☐ CALIFORNIA COLLECTION (Lundgren, Jan & Peter Asplund Quartet)
FLCCD 148 / May '97 / Four Leaf Clover

☐ STOCKHOLM GET-TOGETHER (Lundgren, Jan Trio)
FSR 5007CD / Jul '96 / Fresh Sound

Lundsten, Ralph

☐ INSPIRATION - SWEDEN (Landscape Of Dreams)
CDM 5658842 / Mar '96 / EMI Classics

Lundy, Carmen

☐ OLD DEVIL MOON
Star eyes / When your lover has gone / Just one more chance / You're not in love / I didn't know what time it was / Flying easy / I'm worried about you baby / At the end of my rope / In a sentimental mood / Love me forever
JVC 90192 / Jul '97 / JVC

☐ SELF PORTRAIT
Spring can really hang you up the most / Better days / My favourite things / Firefly / Forgive me / These things you are to me / Triste without you / I don't want to love without you / Old friend / My ship / 'Round midnight
JVC 20472 / Nov '97 / JVC

Lundy, Curtis

☐ JUST BE YOURSELF
Jabbo's revenge / Silver's serenade / Funny (not much) / Crossroads / Never gonna let you go / Just be yourself / Ballando / Shaw 'nuff
ECD 221792 / Jul '97 / Evidence

Lung

☐ CACTII
YELLOWBIKE 003 / Jul '92 / Plastic Head

Lung Leg

☐ MAID TO MINX
POMPCD 007 / Jul '97 / Vesuvius

Lungfish

☐ ARTIFICIAL HORIZON
DIS 115CD / 11 May '98 / Dischord

☐ INDIVISIBLE
DIS 106CD / Apr '97 / Dischord

☐ PASS AND STOW
DIS 92CD / Sep '94 / Dischord

☐ RAINBOWS FROM ATOMS
DIS 78 D / Jun '93 / Dischord

☐ SOUND IN TIME
DIS 97CD / Feb '96 / Dischord

Luniz

☐ LUNATIK MUZIK
Intro / Highest niggaz in the industry / Funkin' over nuthin' / In my nature / Jus mee and U / Game / My baby Mama / Is it kool / Sad millionaire / Killaz on the payroll / Phillies / Mobb shit / Y do thugz die / Hypnotize / Handcuff your hoes / 20 bluntz a day / 11 o'clock news / Revelationz
CDVUS 136 / 10 Nov '97 / Virgin

☐ OPERATION STACKOLA
Intro / Put the lead on ya / I got 5 on it / Broke hos / Pimps, playas and hustlas / Playa hata / Broke niggaz / Operation stackola / 5150 / 900 Blame a nigga / Yellow brick road / So much drama / She's a freak / Plead guilty / I got 5 on it (Reprise) / Outro
CDVUS 94 / Mar '96 / Virgin

Lunkheads

☐ SWINGIN' SINNERS
T360 01 / May '98 / 360 Twist

Lunny, Donal

☐ DONAL LUNNY
CEFCD 133 / Jan '94 / Gael Linn

Lunsford, Bascom Lamar

☐ BALLADS, BANJO TUNES & SACRED SONGS OF NORTH CAROLINA
SFWCD 40082 / May '96 / Smithsonian Folkways

Luomakunta

☐ ROCK OK
AA 030 / Jul '97 / AA

☐ TAYSIN SYOTAVA
AA 027 / Jul '97 / AA

Lupone, Patti

☐ LUPONE LIVE (2CD Set)
I get a kick out of you / It never was you / Everything happens to me / Lush life / Ain't nobody here but us chickens / I got the sun in the morning / Dirty hands, dirty face / And his rocking horse ran away / My ship / Surabaya johnny / Calling you / Get here / Come to the supermarket in old peking / Being alive / Looking for love on broadway / Don't cry for me argentina / Sleepy man / Meadowlark (introduction) / Meadow lark / As long as he needs me / Nickel under your foot / I dreamed a dream / Anything goes / Moonshine lullaby / Heaven / Bows (heaven - reprise) / Lost in the stars
09026617972 / Jul '93 / RCA

Lurie, Evan

☐ HAPPY HERE NOW
TWI 5742 / Mar '96 / Les Disques Du Crepuscule

☐ HOW I SPENT MY VACATION
TZA 7509 / 2 Mar '98 / Tzadik

☐ PIECES OF BANDONEON
TWI 8712 / Mar '96 / Les Disques Du Crepuscule

Lurie, John

☐ FISHING WITH JOHN
Ahhh...fishing / Canoe / Beast / Arriving at Kenny's / Nana jug / Horse guitar / Fish dance / Backwards flute / Tugboat / River of men / Shark drive / Freezing guitar / Flutter / Leon's house / Revenge of fish dance / Ketchak / Struggle of man / Little / Snowmobile dismount / Ignore the giant / World of adventure / Long walk home / Fishing with John
SB 0014 / 27 Jul '98 / Strange & Beautiful

☐ MEN WITH STICKS (Lurie, John National Orchestra)
If I sleep the plane will crash / Men with sticks / Schnards live here
MTM 34 / Apr '96 / Made To Measure

Lurkers

☐ BEGGARS BANQUET PUNK SINGLES, THE
CDPUNK 94 / May '97 / Anagram

☐ FULHAM FALLOUT
Ain't got a clue / I don't need to tell her / Total war / Hey you / Shadow / Then I kicked her / Go go go / Jenny / Time of year / Self destruct / It's quiet here / Gerald / I'm on heat / Be my prisoner / Shadow / Love story / Freak show / Mass media believer / Ohh ohh I love you / Pills / We are the chaos brothers / Be my prisoner / Total war / Then I kissed her / I love the dark / Freak show
AHOYCD 073 / 3 Nov '97 / Captain Oi

☐ GOD'S LONLEY MEN
She knows / God's lonley men / Out in the dark / Cyanide / Whatever happened to Mary / Take me back to babylon / Room 309 / I'll be with you / Non contender / Seven o' clock someday / Sleep on diamonds / Bad times / Just thirteen / Countdown / Suzie is a floozie / Cyanide / New guitar in town / Little old wine drinker / Cold old night / Pick me up / Mary's coming home / New guitar in town / Little old wine drinker
AHOYCD 074 / 3 Nov '97 / Captain Oi

☐ POWERJIVE/KING OF THE MOUNTAIN
Powerjive / Lipstick and shampoo / Solitaire / Waiting for you / Things will never be the same / World of Jenny Brown / Walk like a superstar (talk like a zombie) / Go go girl / Strange desire (burn, burn, burn) / Raven's wing / I close my eyes / Lullaby / Barbara blue / Never had a beach head / Unfinished business / Going monkee again (hey hey hey) / King of the mountain (part 1) / Lucky John / King of the mountain (part 2)
CDPUNK 69 / Nov '95 / Anagram

☐ TAKE ME BACK TO BABYLON
RRCD 243 / 1 Dec '97 / Receiver

☐ THIS DIRTY TOWN
This dirty town / Frankenstein again / One man's meat / Shut out the light / Midnight hour / Drag you out / Heroin (it's all over) / Wolf at the door / Let's dance now / By the heart
CLAYCD 104 / Apr '93 / Clay

Lurssen, Gavin

☐ RESTLESS
63301444032 / 5 May '98 / Zebra

Luscious Jackson

☐ FEVER IN, FEVER OUT
Naked eye / Don't look back / Door / Mood swing / Under your skin / Electric / Take a ride / Water your garden / Soothe yourself / Why do I lie / One thing / Parade / Faith / Stardust
CDEST 2290 / Apr '97 / Grand Royal

☐ IN SEARCH OF MANNY
Let yourself get down / Life of leisure / Daughters of the kaos / Keep on rockin' it / She be wantin' it more / Bam-Bam / Satellite
ABB 46XCD / Aug '95 / Big Cat
GR 001CD / Apr '97 / Grand Royal

☐ NATURAL INGREDIENTS
City song / Deep shag / Angel / Strongman / Energy sucker / Here / Find your mind / Pele Merengue / Rock freak / Rollin' / Surprise / LP Retreat
CDEST 2234 / Aug '94 / Capitol

Lush

☐ LOVELIFE
Ladykillers / Heavenly nobodies / 50 / I've been here before / Papasan / Single girl / Ciao / Tralala / Last night / Runaway / Childcatcher / Olympia
GAD 6004CD / 6 Jul '98 / 4AD

☐ SCAR
JADCD 911 / Oct '89 / 4AD

☐ SPLIT
Light from a dead star / Kiss chase / Blackout / Hypocrite / Lovelife / Desire lines / Invisible man / Undertow / Never never / Lit up / Starlust / When I die
GAD 4011CD / Feb '96 / 4AD

☐ SPOOKY
GAD 2002CD / Feb '96 / 4AD

Lush, Connie

☐ BLUES SHOUTER
MYSCD 123 / 20 Apr '98 / Mystic

Lusher, Don

☐ JUST GOOD FRIENDS (Lusher, Don & Maurice Murphy/The Hammonds Sauce Works Band)
Londonderry air / Londonderry air / Somewhere in the night / Only love / Very thought of you / Send in the clowns / Sugar blues / Makin' whoopee / Stardust / You need me / Sun ain't gonna shine anymore / I dreamed a dream / Adagio / Up where we belong / Just the way you are / D.I. blues
DOYCD 020 / Feb '93 / Doyen

☐ TRIBUTE TO THE GREAT BANDS VOL.1 (Lusher, Don Big Band)
Peanut vendor / Take the 'A' train / I'll never smile again / Don't be that way / I've got my love to keep me warm / Kid from Red Bank / Opus one / Adios / I get a kick out of you / Early Autumn / Caravan / Two o'clock jump
CDSIV 110 / Jul '95 / Horatio Nelson

☐ TRIBUTE TO THE GREAT BANDS VOL.2 (Lusher, Don Big Band)
Trumpet blues and cantabile / Pennsylvania 6-5000 / That lovely weekend / That's right / Westlake / DL blues / Sing sing sing / April in Paris / I'm getting sentimental over you / Don't get around much anymore / Concerto to end all concertos
CDSIV 1114 / Jul '95 / Horatio Nelson

☐ TRIBUTE TO THE GREAT BANDS VOL.3 (Lusher, Don Big Band)
Carnival / Benny rides again / Song of India / Cute / Wales '87 / Moonlight serenade / At the woodchoppers' ball / Boogie woogie / Love for sale / High and mighty / Cotton tail / Tea for two
CDSIV 1125 / Jul '95 / Horatio Nelson

☐ TRIBUTE TO THE GREAT BANDS VOL.4 (Lusher, Don Big Band)
Mr. Anthony's boogie / Sunny side of the street / Continental / Isafahan / Mission to Moscow / Night in Tunisia / Apple honey / Wave / Shiny stockings / Liebestraum / String of pearls / One o'clock jump
CDSIV 1133 / Jul '95 / Horatio Nelson

Lussia

☐ FLEUR DE MANDRAGORE
422471 / May '94 / New Rose

Lussier, Rene

☐ CHANTS ET DANSES DU MONDE INANIME (Lussier, Rene & Robert Lepage)
AM 001CD / Jun '97 / Ambiances Magnetiques

☐ FIN DE TRAVAIL
AM 000CD / Jun '97 / Ambiances Magnetiques

Lustmord

☐ MONSTROUS SOUL
DFX 014CD / Oct '96 / Dark Vinyl

☐ PARADISE DISOWNED
SECD 07 / Oct '96 / Side Effects

Lutcher, Nellie

☐ BEST OF NELLIE LUTCHER, THE
Hurry on down / One I love belongs to somebody else / You better watch yourself / Bub / My mother's eyes / He's a real gone guy / Let me love you tonight / Chi-Chi-Chi Chicago / Fine and mellow / I thought about you / Kinda blue and low / Song is ended (but the melody lingers on) / Lake Charles boogie / Fine brown frame / My man (mon homme) / Chicken ain't nothing but a bird / He sends me / My new Papa's got to have everything / Come and get it / Honey / That will just about knock me out, baby / What's your alibi / Pa's not home
CDP 8350392 / Nov '95 / Capitol Jazz

☐ NELLIE LUTCHER & HER RHYTHM (4CD Set)
One I love (belongs to someone else) / Hurry on down / Lady's in love with you / You better watch yourself / Bub / Sleepy lagoon / My mother's eyes / He's a real gone guy / Let me love you tonight / Pig Latin song / Do you or don't you love me / Chi-Chi-Chi-Chicago / Loveable / Fine and mellow blues / There's another mule in your stall / I thought about you / Kinda blue and low / Reaching for the moon / Song is ended (but the melody lingers on) / So nice to see you baby / Lake Charles boogie / Fine brown frame / Humoresque / Imagine you having eyes for me / Alexander's Ragtime Band / Without a song / Wish I was in Walla Walla / Life is like that / Maid's prayer / Ditto from me to you / My man / I used to be dull / Dog fight song / Lutcher's leap / Say a little prayer for me / Cool water / Chicken ain't nothing but a bird / Princess Poo-Poo-Ly has plenty papaya / He sends me / My little boy / My new Papa's got to have everything / Come and get it honey / Little Sally Walker / To be forgotten / Darktown strutters ball / That will just about knock me out / Glad Rag doll / April in Paris / Only you / Kiss me sweet / Baby, please stop and think about me / That's aplenty / Baby, what's your alibi / I'll never get tired / For you my love / Can I come in for a second / Pa's not home / I really couldn't love you / Body and fender work / He couldn't care less / If you wanna get t'goin' / Mean to me / I want to be near you / Birth of the blues / Let the worry bird worry for you / What a difference a day made / That's how it goes / Heart of a clown / Keepin' out of mischief now / When they ask about you / How many more / Muchly verily / Whee baby / Takin' a chance on love / Takin' a chance on love / St. Louis blues / Bill Bailey, won't you please come home / Out of this world / It's been said / Blues in the night / Breezin' along with the breeze / Whose honey are you / Please come back / If I didn't love you like I do / Blue skies / Three little words / You made me love you / This can't be love / Nearness of you / It had to be you / On the sunny side of the street / Someone to watch over me / All of a sudden my heart sings / Rose coloured glasses / Ole buttermilk sky / Have you ever been lonely / Hurry on down / Let me tell you 'bout the city / If your face was as beautiful as your soul / He's a real gone guy / There's a reason / I'll never get tired / Heart of a clown / Reaching for the moon
BCD 15910 / Nov '96 / Bear Family

Lutefisk

☐ BURN IN HELL FUCKERS
BL 292 / Jan '97 / Bongload

Luter, Claude

☐ RED HOT REEDS
BCD 219 / Jul '93 / GHB

Luxon, Benjamin

☐ I LOVE MY LOVE (A Collection Of British Folk Songs) (Luxon, Benjamin & David Willison)
Jolly miller / Drink to me only with thine eyes / Foggy foggy dew / Isle of Cloy / Trees they grow so high / Died for love / Lovely Mollie / I love my love / Shooting of his dear / Down by the Sally Gardens / Old turf fire / Banks and braes / Barb'ra (H)ellen / Barbara Allen / She moved through the fair / Star of County Down / Sweet nightingale / Blow the wind southerly / British waterside / Press gang / Little Sir William / Sir Dukes went-a-fishin' / Sweet Polly Oliver / Bold William Taylor / Charlie is my darling / O Waly, Waly
CHAN 8946 / Jun '92 / Chandos

☐ TWO GENTLEMEN FOLK (Luxon, Benjamin & Friends)
Sweet nightingale / Sweet nightingale / Leaving of liverpool / She's like the swallow / Dance to your daddy / Ash grove / San francisco bay / Danny boy / White-haired cassidy / Cuckoo -leatherwing bat / Turkey in the straw / Flowers of the forest / Bold nelson - eddystone light / Waly waly / Waltzing matilda / Wabash cannonball
CD 84401 / '88 / Telarc

Luxx

☐ LUXX
64494902012 / 10 Mar '98 / Push

Luzzaschi, Luzzasco

☐ SECRET MUSIC OF LUZZASCO LUZZASCHI
CDSAR 58 / Oct '92 / Saydisc

LV

☐ GANGSTAS IN SOUTH CENTRAL
REMCD 525 / 27 Apr '98 / Reactive

Lwiro Children's Choir

☐ AFRICAN MASS
VICG 52292 / Mar '96 / JVC World Library

Ly, Mamadou

☐ MANDINKA DRUM MASTER
VPU 1001CD / May '97 / Village Pulse

Lyadrive

☐ ANOTHER TIME ANOTHER PLACE
Sign of the hunted / Dangerline / Spinning the wheel / Fools paradise / Stealaway / Lazerwind / Young lover / Another time another place / One of these days / Madame guillotine / White dress / Anytime / We've got the rock / Here comes the night
MIN 08CD / 13 Apr '98 / Minority/One

Lyall, William

☐ SOLO CASTING
Solo casting / Us / Playing in the sand / Supertrader / Reasons / Deeper you get / Maniac / Don't be silly / Take me up / Sleep
SEECD 448 / Jul '96 / See For Miles

Lycia

☐ IONIA
PRO 32 / Jan '97 / Projekt

☐ WAKE
PRO 31 / Jan '97 / Projekt

Lydon, John

☐ PSYCHO'S PATH
Grave ride / Dog / Psychopath / Sun / Another way / Dis-Ho / Take me / No and a yes / Stump / Armies / Open up / Grave ride / Sun / Psychopath / Stump
CDVUS 130 / 30 Jun '97 / Virgin

Lyle, Bobby

☐ JOURNEY, THE
7567821382 / Jan '97 / Atlantic

☐ PIANOMAGIC
7567823462 / Jan '97 / Atlantic

☐ SECRET ISLAND
7567824352 / Dec '96 / Atlantic

Lyman, Arthur

☐ BACHELOR'S DEN VOL.6
DCC 96CD / Apr '96 / DCC

☐ HAWAIIAN SUNSET
Hawaiian war chant / Sweet Leilani / Queen serenade / My Tani / Whispering reef / Song of the islands / Hi lawe / Island of golden dreams / Mapuano / Wapio / Kawohikuk-uplani / Ke kali ne au / Harbor lights / Blue Hawaii / Beyond the reef / Quiet village / Ahola-no Honolulu
RCD 50365 / Sep '96 / Rykodisc

☐ LEGEND OF PELE, THE (Sounds Of Arthur Lyman)
Pele / Fire down below / Ye isal slan / Hana Pele / Hana maui / Cumana / Scheherazade / Cubana chant / Magic Island / Tropical / Fascination / 76 Trombones
RCD 50432 / 15 Jun '98 / Rykodisc

☐ LEIS OF JAZZ
Lady is tramp / On the street where you live / Leis of jazz / Way you look tonight / How high the moon / Trigger fantasy / Lullaby of the leaves / Body and soul / My funny valentine / Gypsy in my soul / Aloha oe / Lullaby of Birdland
RCD 50431 / 23 Mar '98 / Rykodisc

☐ SONIC SIXTIES
TCD 1031 / Nov '96 / Tradition

☐ TABOO
Taboo / Katua / Ringo oiwake / Sea breeze / Miserlou / China clipper / Sim sim / Katsumi love theme / Caravan / Akaka falls / Dahil Sayo / Hilo march / Bwana A / Colonel Bogey's march / Waikiki serenade / Moon over a ruined castle
RCD 50364 / Sep '96 / Rykodisc

☐ TABOO TU
Taboo tu / Ebb tide / Babalik ka rin / Sakura / Moon of Manakoora / Jungle fantasy / Love dance / Return to paradise / Hi lili ho lo / Mangwani mpulele / Beautiful Kahana / Koni au I ka wai
RCD 50430 / 23 Mar '98 / Rykodisc

☐ WITH A CHRISTMAS VIBE
Rudolph the red nosed reindeer / Winter wonderland / Mele Kalikimaka / Mary's boy child / O' holy night / Little drummer boy / We three Kings / White Christmas / Silver bells / Sleigh ride / Christmas song / Silent night / Joy to the world
RCD 50363 / Oct '96 / Rykodisc

☐ YELLOW BIRD
Havah nagilah / Yellow bird / Bolero / Autumn leaves / Arrive derce Roma / Sweet and lovely / Bamboo tamboo / Andalusia / Adventures in paradise / Granada / September song / John Henry
RCD 50433 / 15 Jun '98 / Rykodisc

Lymon, Frankie

☐ 25 GREATEST HITS (Lymon, Frankie & The Teenagers)
Why do fools fall in love / I want you to be my girl / I'm not a know it all / I promise to remember / Who can explain / ABC's of love / Share / I'm not a juvenile delinquent / Baby baby / Teenage love / Paper castles / Out in the cold again / Goody goody / Creation of love / Bomp / Buzz buzz / Change track / My girl / Let's fall in love / Fools rush in / Diana / Please be mine / Footsteps / Little bitty pretty one / Jailhouse rock
4954792 / 6 Jul '98 / EMI Gold

☐ COMPLETE RECORDINGS (5CD Set) (Lymon, Frankie & The Teenagers)
Why do fools fall in love / Please be mine / Love is a clown / Am I fooling myself again / I'm not a know it all / Who can explain / I promise to remember / ABC's of love (Version 2) / Share / I'm not a juvenile delinquent / Baby baby / Paper castles / Teenage love / Together / You / It would be so nice / Out in the cold again / Little white lies / Begin the beguine / Love is a clown (Alt) / I want you to be my girl / I'm not a know it all (Alt) / Who can explain (Alt) / ABC's of love (Version 1) / Promise to remember (Alt) / Share (Alt) / Fortunate fellow / Love put me out of my head / Lost without your love / I'll walk alone (Without love) / Everything to me / Flip flop / Good love / Flop hop / Mama wanna rock / My broken heart / Crying / Tonight's the night / Can you tell me why / Little wiser now / What's on your mind / Love me long / He's no lover / I hear the angels cry / Wild female / Jean of the ville / Draw / Goody goody / It's Christmas once again / Only way to love / Miracle in the rain / Yours / Glow worm / Good good (Version 1) / Love is the thing / You can't be true / Fools rush in / Too young / Over the rainbow / As time goes by / Don't take your love / I don't stand a ghost of a chance with you / Goody goody (Version 2) / Creation of love / Blue moon / These foolish things / You were only fooling / Guilty / So goes my love / My girl / My baby just cares for me / Somebody loves me / Silent night / Little girl / Let's fall in love / Thumb thumb / Portable on my shoulder / Footsteps / That's the way love goes / Wake up little Susie / Short fat Fannie / Waitin' in school / Next time you see me / Jailhouse rock / Send for me / Buzz buzz buzz / Searchin' / Silouettes / It hurts to be in love / Diana / Diana (Alt) / Little bitty pretty one / Mama don't allow it / Girls were made for boys / Campus queen / No matter what you've done / Melinda / Ain't she sweet / Almost out of my mind / Rockin' tambourine / Danny Boy / Up jumped the rabbit / Before I fall asleep / Prince or pauper / What a little moonlight can do / 'Deed I do / Since the beginning of time / Pardon me please / Magic song / Kiss from your lips / Joke (Version 1) / Rainbow / Joke (Version 2) / Goody good girl / Blessed are they / I'm not to young to dream / Almost out of my mind (Version 2) / Is you is or is you ain't my baby / Lover come back to me / Change partners / So young / I put the bomp / To each his own / Teacher, teacher / Roll off / Push and pull / Sweet and lovely / Somewhere / Somewhere (Stereo) / I'm sorry / Sea breeze
BCD 15782 / Jun '94 / Bear Family

☐ ESSENTIAL RECORDINGS 1955-1961 (2CD Set)
Why do fools fall in love / Please be mine / I want you to be my girl / Im not a know it all / I promise to remember / Who can explain / ABC's of love / Share / I'm not a juvenile delinquent / Baby, baby / Teenage love / Paper castles / Love is a clown / Am I fooling myself again / Together / You / Out in the cold again / Miracle in the rain / Little white lies / It would be so nice / Fortunate fellow / Love put me out of my head / Begin the beguine / Goody goody / Creation of love / Flip flop / Everything to me / So goes my love / My girl / Footsteps / Thumb thumb / Little girl / Portable, on my shoulder / Mama don't allow it / My broken heart / Mama wanna rock / Waitin' in school / Wake up little Susie / Silhouettes / Next time you see me / Send for me / It hurts to be in love / Jailhouse rock / Diana / Buzz, buzz, buzz / Searchin' / Short fat Fannie / Little bitty pretty one / Melinda / Only way to love / No matter what you've done / Up jumped a rabbit / What a little moonlight can do / Before I fall asleep / Goody good girl / I'm not to young to dream / Tonight's the night / Crying / Little bit wiser now / Can you tell me / Change partners / So young / I put the bomp (in the bomp bomp bomp)
NEDCD 287 / Apr '97 / Sequel

☐ WHY DO FOOLS FALL IN LOVE
Why do fools fall in love / Please be mine / Love is a clown / Am I fooling myself again / I want you to be my girl / I'm not a know it all / Who can explain / I promise to remember / Abc's of love / Buzz buzz buzz / I'm not a juvenile delinquent / Baby baby / Paper castles / Teenage love / Out in the cold again / Goody goody / Creation of love / I'm not too young to dream / Portable on my shoulder / Little bitty pretty one / Little girl / Silhouettes
RMB 75034 / Nov '93 / Remember

Lynam, Ray

☐ VERY BEST OF RAY LYNAM, THE
If we're not back in love by Monday / What a lie / He stopped loving her today / You put the blue in me / You win again / Gambler / Moon is still over her shoulder / Beautiful woman / To be lovers / Mona Lisa has lost her smile / Girls, women, and ladies / Hold her in your hand / Speak softly (you're talking to my heart) / I'll never get over you / Rainy days stormy nights / I don't want to see another town
RZCD 513 / Dec '91 / Ritz

Lync

☐ REMEMBERING THE FIREBALLS PT.8
K 73CD / 22 Aug '97 / Kranky

Lynch, Brian

☐ PEER PRESSURE (Lynch, Brian Sextet)
Thomasville / Park Avenue petite / Peer pressure / Outlaw / Change of plan / Nother never
CRISS 1029CD / Nov '91 / Criss Cross

Lynch, Claire

☐ **FRIENDS FOR A LIFETIME**
Lead me on / Who do you know / Your presence is my favourite gift / Go and do the same / Paul and Peter walked / There is a fountain / God spoke his name / Friends for a lifetime / My name is Judas / He leadeth me / Somewhere above / Between the two of them / After the storm
ROUCD 0335 / Jun '98 / Rounder

☐ **MOONLIGHTER**
ROUCD 0355 / Jun '95 / Rounder

☐ **SILVER AND GOLD**
If wishes were horse / Hey lonesome / Silver and gold / Who knows what tomorrow may bring / Sweetheart, darlin' ol' mine / I'm goin' up / Death angel / Safe haven / Hitchcock railway / Out among the stars / Wednesday's child / Fair shake
ROUCD 0415 / Sep '97 / Rounder

Lynch, George

☐ **SACRED GROOVE**
Memory Jack / Love power from the Mama head / Flesh and blood / We don't own this world / I will remember / Beast part 1 / Beast part 2 / Not necessary evil / Cry of the brave / Tierra del fuego
7559614222 / Aug '93 / Elektra

Lynch, Joe

☐ **IRISH LAUGHTER IRISH TEARS**
Jug of punch / Moonshiner / Dan the man / Bank of the roses / Old rustic bridge by the mill / How are things in Glocca Morra / Old house / Wild rover no more / Finnegan's wake / Patsy McCann / Slainte jig selection / Little brown jug / Hannigan's hooley / Red rose / Rose of Tralee / Moonlight in Mayo / Temperance reel / Cruiskeen lawn / Mrs McGrath / Lisdoonvarna polka / Preab san ol / Teaching McFadden to dance / Mother McCree
307842 / Aug '97 / Hallmark

☐ **LITTLE BIT OF IRELAND, A**
MACCD 321 / Aug '96 / Autograph

Lynch, Kenny

☐ **AFTER DARK**
FRCD 100 / Jul '93 / Welfare

Lynch Mob

☐ **LYNCH MOB**
Jungle of love / Tangled in the web / No good / Dream until tomorrow / Cold is the heart / Tie your mother down / Heaven is waiting / I want it / When darkness calls / Secret
75596132212 / May '92 / Elektra

Lynch, Ray

☐ **NO BLUE THING**
No blue thing / Clouds below your knees / Here and never found / Drifted on a deeper land / Homeward at last / Evenings, yes / Fog station / A fallen temple at last / Evenings, yes / Fist City / Y'all come
01934111192 / Jan '94 / Windham Hill

☐ **NOTHING ABOVE MY SHOULDERS BUT THE EVENING**
Over easy / Her knees deep in your mind / Passion song / Ivory / Mesquite / Only an enjoyment / Vanishing gardens of Cordoba
01934111332 / Nov '93 / Windham Hill

Lynch, Tomas

☐ **CRUX OF THE CATALOGUE, THE**
LC 002CD / Apr '94 / Linecheck

Lynn, Barbara

☐ **PROMISES**
Oh baby (we've got a good thing goin') / Silly of me / Jim Dandy / That's something I can do / Dedicate the blues to me / What am I living for / There's something on your mind / Careless hands / Oh Senorita / Just a dream / Since I met you (really) (I cried at) Laura's wedding / I'm sorry I met you / To love or not to love / Don't spread it around / Jealous love / You don't have to go / Do you feel like dancin' / I've taken all I'm gonna take / What I need is love / Promises / It's better to have it / Money / Let her knock herself out / Keep on pushing your luck / All I need is your love / That's what a friend will do / You're gonna be sorry / (Don't pretend) just lay it on the line / You'll lose a good thing
BCD 16208 / Oct '97 / Bear Family

☐ **SO GOOD**
BB 9540CD / Feb '94 / Bullseye Blues

☐ **YOU'LL LOSE A GOOD THING**
You'll lose a good thing / Don't be cruel / Can't buy me love / There's something on your mind / Strange / Second fiddle girl / You better stop / Oh baby (we got a good thing goin' on) / All I need is your love / Careless hands: Lynn, Barbara & Lee Maye / Dedicate the blues to me / Lonely heartache / Letter too Mommy and Daddy / You're gonna need me / You don't sleep at night / (I cried at) Laura's wedding / You can't be satisfied / Ring telephone ring / Everybody loves somebody / Dina and Petrina / It's nothin' keep me from you / Still on my mind / Crush me / Give me a break / Heartbreaking years / People gonna talk
BCD 16207 / Oct '97 / Bear Family

Lynn, Cheryl

☐ **GOT TO BE REAL**
Got to be real / Give my love to you / All my lovin' / Star love / Shake it up / Tonight / I've got just what you need / I've got faith in you / Keep it hot / Day after day / Sleep walkin' / Believe in me / If this world were mine / Encore / It's gonna be right / Georgy Porgy
4842752 / May '97 / Columbia

Lynn, Loretta

☐ **COAL MINER'S DAUGHTER**
WMCD 5667 / Oct '94 / Disky

☐ **COAL MINER'S DAUGHTER LIVE**
Hey Loretta / Coal miner's daughter / Let your love flow / You're lookin' at country / Me and Bobby McGee / One's on the way / The pill / Out of my head and back in my bed / Somebody somewhere (don't know what he's missin' tonight) / Medley no.1 / Back in my baby's arms/She's got you / They don't make 'em like my Daddy / Your squaw is on the warpath / Spring fever / Fist city / Y'all come
CTS 55443 / Feb '97 / Country Stars

☐ **COALMINER'S DAUGHTER LIVE**
Hey Loretta / Coal miner's daughter / Let your love flow / You're looking at country / Me and Bobby McGee / Your squaw is on the warpath / Fist city / Me a long way, baby / Fist city / Spring fever / Medley / Somebody somewhere / Out of my head and back in my bed / They don't make them like my daddy anymore / Pill / You'll come / You ain't woman enough
100222 / May '97 / A-Play Collection

☐ **EVENING WITH LORETTA LYNN, AN**
MU 5069 / Oct '92 / Musketeer

☐ **GREATEST HITS**
Hey Loretta / You're looking at country / Let your love flow / We've come a long way baby / Spring fever / You squaw is on the warpath / Fist city / I fall to pieces / Walkin' after midnight / Crazy / Back in baby's arms / She's got you / Me and Bobby McGee / Somebody, somewhere / Out of my head and back in my bed / Coal miner's daughter / They don't make 'em like my daddy / One's on the way / Pill / Y'all come / You ain't woman enough / We've come a long way baby / Your squaw is on the warpath / Spring fever / Fist City / Y'all come
PLATCD 363 / '91 / Platinum

☐ **HER COUNTRY HITS SHOW**
CD 3502 / Aug '94 / Cameo

☐ **VERY BEST OF LORETTA LYNN, THE**
Coal miner's daughter / You're looking at country / Blue Kentucky girl / Wine, women and song / She's got you / One's on the way / Happy birthday / Before I'm over you / Out of my head and back in my bed / Fist city / Somebody, somewhere / Don't come a drinkin'
PLATCD 308 / Dec '88 / Platinum

☐ **VERY BEST OF LORETTA LYNN, THE**
HMNCD 013 / 3 Nov '97 / Half Moon

☐ **WOMAN OF THE WORLD (The Best Of Loretta Lynn)**
Coal miner's daughter / Don't come home a drinkin' / Rated x / Blue kentucky girl / Fist city / Love is the foundation / One's on the way / Your squaw is on the warpath / Pill / She's got you / You ain't woman enough / Trouble is paradise / Woman of the world (leave my world alone) / Hey Loretta / Out of my head and back in my bed / Somebody somewhere (don't know what he's missin' tonight)
MCCD 142 / Nov '93 / Music Club

☐ **YOU'RE LOOKIN' AT COUNTRY**
Hey Loretta / Coal miner's daughter / Let your love flow / You're lookin' at country / Me and Bobby McGee / One's on the way / Out of my head and back in my bed / Somebody somewhere / I fall to pieces / Walkin' after midnight/Crazy / Back in my baby's arms/She's got you / They don't make 'em like my daddy / One's on the way / Pill / Your squaw is on the warpath / Spring fever / Fist City / Y'all come
SUMCD 4188 / 11 May '98 / Summit

Lynn, Trudy

☐ **24 HOUR WOMAN**
ICH 1172CD / Jun '94 / Ichiban

☐ **COME TO MAMA**
Right back in the water / When somethin' is wrong with my baby / Come to Mama / When you took your love from me / One woman man / Woman's gotta have it / Do I need you (too) / Fish girl blues / Making love to me
ICH 1063CD / Oct '93 / Ichiban

☐ **RETROSPECTIVES**
Widow Winnie Brown / Dr. Feelgood / Eight days on theh road / Whole lotta leave me alones / Chilly wind / Woman's got to have it / Trudy sings the blues / Never make your move too soon / Got my mojo working / You took me as your woman / You owe it to yourself / Speak now
ICH 1515 / 29 Jun '98 / Ichiban

☐ **TRUDY SINGS THE BLUES**
Sittin' and drinkin' / Just a little bit / I can tell / Trudy sings the blues / Dr. Feelgood / Do I need you / Bring the beef home to me / Ball and chain
ICH 1043CD / Oct '93 / Ichiban

☐ **WOMAN IN ME, THE**
Woman in me / My baby can / Speak now or forever hold your peace / You owe it to yourself / Can't nothin' keep me from you / Still on my mind / I've been thinkin' / Feel you, feel me / Spare the rod (love the child)
ICH 1125CD / Oct '93 / Ichiban

Lynn, Vera

☐ **48 GOLDEN GREATS (2CD Set)**
We'll meet again / Wish me luck (as you wave me goodbye) / Bells of st. mary's / Harbor lights / Mexicali rose / Wishing (will make it so) / I'll pray for you / I shall be waiting / After a while / That lovely weekend / Be like the kettle and sing / Yours / Maybe / It's a lovely day tomorrow / A mother's prayer at twilight / I paid for the lie that I told you / Little sir echo / Goodnight wherever you are / I'll think of you / Up the wooden hills to bedfordshire / So many memories / Cinderella (stay in my arms) / Two sleepy people / Really and truly / (there'll be bluebirds over) the white cliffs of dover / A nightingale sang in berkeley square / When the lights go on again / London I love / There'll come another day / Memory of a rose / Over the hill / Goodnight children everywhere / You'll never know / Who's taking you home tonight / Only forever / Coming home / Lonely sweetheart / My own / It's a sin to tell a lie / Now it can be told / We both told a lie / First quarrel / I hear a dream (come again) / When mother nature sings her lullaby / Where your are before the rainbow / Love makes the world go round / Over the rainbow

☐ **BEST OF VERA LYNN, THE (25 Great Songs)**
(There'll be blue birds over) The white cliffs of Dover / You / Really and truly / Little King without a crown / First lullaby / Little rain must fall / Concerto for two / That autumn in old London town / White cliffs of Dover / I'll be with you / A apple blossom time / We three / Who am I / Woodpecker song / You'll never know / Who's taking you home tonight / Goodnight and God bless you / With all my heart / All the world sings a lullaby / You're breaking my heart all over again
RAJCD 820 / May '97 / Empress

☐ **COLLECTION, THE**
We'll meet again / Wishin' (will make it so) / I'll pray for you / I shall be waiting / Lonely sweetheart / It's a lovely day tomorrow / My own / Who's taking you home tonight / Mexicali rose / Harbor lights / A nightingale sang in berkeley square / I paid for the lie that I told you / Little sir echo / Its's a sin to tell a lie / Memory of a rose / Wish me luck (as you wave me goodbye) / Goodnight children everywhere / Little boy that santa claus forgot / Bells of st. mary's
COL 053 / Jun '95 / Collection

☐ **GOLDEN HITS**
Yours / Wishing (will make it so) / General's fast asleep / Harbour lights / Who's taking you home tonight / Be like the kettle and sing / It's a lovely day tomorrow / There's a new world over the skyline / Jealousy / Nightingale sang in Berkeley Square / We three (my echo, my shadow and me) / Know again / Only forever / London I love / Star fell out of Heaven / Little boy that Santa Claus forgot / Goodnight children everywhere / When the lights go on again / White cliffs of Dover / We'll meet again / Goodnight wherever you are
PASTCD 7805 / Jan '97 / Flapper

☐ **HARBOUR LIGHTS**
WMCD 5690 / May '94 / Disky

☐ **IT'S LIKE OLD TIMES**
After a while / I hope to die / Do you ever dream of / For sweetheart's everywhere / I could never tell / Symphony / How green was my valley / I couldn't sleep a wink last night / Long ago and far away / You're breaking my heart all over again / Where in the world / I had the craziest dream / Someone's rocking my dreamboat / I've heard that song before / Please think of me / It always rains before the rainbow / Who am I / It's like old times / We'll meet again
RAJCD 854 / Nov '96 / Empress

☐ **LEG DEIN GLUCK IN MEINE HANDE**
Bongiorno / Sweetheart my darling my dear / Die fontanen von rom / Addio amore / Ein bisschen gluck / Folge dem rat deines herzens / Sag nicht leb' wohl / Leg dein gluck in meine hande / Dornin dormi dorni / Wann / Sogno d'oro my darling / Grau war der tag / Blutrote rosen / Thank you danke schon / Du bist mein liebchen / Auf wiederseh'n swetheart
BCD 16181 / Feb '98 / Bear Family

☐ **LET'S MEET AGAIN**
We'll meet again / Wishing (will make it so) / Mexicali rose / I paid for the lie that I told you / Little sir echo / Who's taking you home tonight / My own / Goodnight children everywhere / Little boy that Santa Claus forgot / Little Sir Echo / Bell's of St Mary's / Harbour lights / It's a sin to tell a lie / Lonely sweetheart / Memory of a rose / When the lights go on again / London I love / Nightingale sang in Berkeley Square / Medley / I hear a dream / Medley / So rare/ You're here you're there, you're everywhere
PAR 2010 / Feb '95 / Parade

☐ **SOMETHING TO REMEMBER - WARTIME MEMORIES**
Something to remember you by / Yours / Wish me luck as you wave me goodbye / I'll pray for you / White cliffs of Dover / I shall be waiting / Over the hill / That lovely weekend / You'll never know / Who's taking you home tonight / Nightingale sang in Berkeley Square / It's a lovely day tomorrow / London I love / When they sound the last All Clear / Wishing (Will make it so) / It's a sin to tell a lie / Be like the kettle and sing / There'll come another day / Only forever / Anniversary waltz / When the lights go on again / We'll meet again
JASMCD 2541 / May '95 / Jasmine

☐ **THANK YOU FOR THE MUSIC**
PLSCD 171 / Apr '97 / Pulse

Lynne, Bjorn

☐ **THERE'S A LAND OF BEGIN AGAIN**
PASTCD 7064 / May '95 / Flapper

☐ **TRIBUTE TO VERA LYNN VOL.1, A (Sincerely Yours)**
Wish me luck as you wave me goodbye / Who's taking you home tonight / I'll pray for you / Garden in Granada / Now it can be told / First quarrel / When Mother Nature sings her lullaby / We'll meet again / Love makes the world go round / I won't tell a soul (that I love you) / Over the rainbow / I hear a dream (come again) / It always rains before a rainbow / I'll walk beside you / Wishing (will make it so) / We both told a lie / I'll think of you / I'll remember / Yours / Goodnight wherever you are / I shall be waiting / Maybe
PASTCD 9778 / Mar '94 / Flapper

☐ **TRIBUTE TO VERA LYNN VOL.2, A (It's A Lovely Day Tomorrow)**
White cliffs of Dover / Be like the kettle and sing / Goodnight children everywhere / It's a lovely day tomorrow / Only forever / There'll come another day / Anniversary waltz / London I love / Something to remember you by / Over the hill / Harbour lights / That lovely weekend / Cinderella / Mexicali rose / Jealousy / When the lights go on again / Nightingale sang in Berkeley Square / Bells of St. Mary's / It's a sin to tell a lie / I'm in the mood for love / Love bug will bite you / Heart and soul
PASTCD 7030 / Jan '94 / Flapper

☐ **VERA LYNN REMEMBERS (The Songs That Won World War 2)**
Yours / Medley / Somewhere in France with you / Medley / Medley / London pride / Nightingale sang in Berkeley Square / White cliffs of Dover / Medley / I'll be seeing you / You'd be so nice to come home to / Room five-hundred-and-four / That lovely weekend / Besame mucho / There'll always be an England / You'll never know / It had to be you / Lili Marlene / Medley / Medley / Land of hope and glory
CDEMS 1515 / May '94 / EMI

☐ **VERA LYNN REMEMBERS VOL.1**
White cliffs of Dover / Red sails in the sunset / It's a sin to tell a lie / Roll out the barrel / You'll never know / Nightingale sang in Berkeley Square / Sailing / Harbour lights / Auf wiederseh'n / Yours / From the time you say goodbye / My mother's eyes / That lovely weekend / Land of hope and glory / Coming in on a wing and a prayer / We'll meet again / Be like the kettle and sing
CDSIV 1120 / May '95 / Horatio Nelson

☐ **VERA LYNN REMEMBERS VOL.2**
CDSIV 1140 / Apr '93 / Horatio Nelson

☐ **WE'LL MEET AGAIN (The Early Years)**
Be careful it's my heart / Careless / Cinderella / Goodnight and God bless you / I had the craziest dream / I paid for the lie that I told you / I'll be with you in apple blossom time / I'll never smile again / It's a sin to tell a lie / Rosalie / Roses in December / Smilin' through / Someone's rocking my dreamboat / Something to remember you by / There'll come another day / We'll meet again / When they sound the last All Clear / When you wish upon a star / Where made me care / You'll never know / Yours
CDAJA 5145 / Oct '94 / Living Era

☐ **WE'LL MEET AGAIN**
We'll meet again / Bells of St. Mary's / Wish me luck as you wave me goodbye / Love makes the world go round / Over the rainbow / I'll walk beside you / Cinderella / Really and truly / I had the craziest dream / Two sleepy people / You'll never know / That lovely weekend / Over the hill / After a while / Coming home / When they sound the last All Clear
MUCD 9020 / Apr '95 / Musketeer

☐ **WE'LL MEET AGAIN (Her Classic Performances)**
It's a lovely day tomorrow / Goodnight children / Lonely sweetheart / Little sir echo / I'll pray for you / It's a sin to tell a lie / Mexicali rose / Nightingale sang in Berkeley square / Bells of St. Mary's / Who's taking you home tonight / Harbour lights / My own / Memory of a rose / I shall be waiting / Wishing (will make it so) / Wish me luck (as you wave me goodbye) / We'll meet again / I paid for the lie / I hear a dream / You're hear you're there you are everywhere / So rare / White cliffs of dover
305532 / Oct '96 / Hallmark

☐ **WE'LL MEET AGAIN**
GO 3816 / 1 Dec '97 / Golden Options

☐ **YOURS**
Yours / Be like the kettle and sing / Jealousy / I'll pray for you / It's a sin to tell a lie / Up the wooden hill to Befordshire / Who's taking you home tonight / Cinderella (stay in my arms) / It's a lovely day tomorrow / When the lights go on again / White Cliffs Of Dover / Harbour lights / Over the hill / With all my heart / Goodnight children everywhere
PWKS 4250 / Feb '96 / Carlton

Lynne

☐ **VOID**
Into the void / All life is one part 3 / Electroglow / Dar shan / On the edge / Truth or sanity (Part 3) / Relentless / Signals / Who knows / Nothing
CYCL 051 / Mar '97 / Cyclops

Lynne, Bjorn

☐ **DREAMSTATE**
Universe of the mind / Material matters / Now what / All life is one / Time and growth / Emptiness / Cycle / Dreaming odyssey / Mesmerized / Dark star / Sequences / Progress
CENCD 009 / Mar '95 / Centaur

☐ **WHEN THE GODS SLEPT**
Stranger on a hill pt.1 / Valley of the clouds / Forbidden desert / Alisarian's cave / Sam and Gift / Heroes return / Thief of Walaria / Gundara and Gundaree / Methydias cloudship / Battle of two stones / Betrayal in Zanzair / Stranger on a hill pt.2
CYCL 066 / 22 Jun '98 / Cyclops

Lynne, Gloria

☐ **BALLAD, THE BLUES AND THE BEAT, THE**
BMCD 3062 / Jan '98 / Blue Moon

☐ **GLORIA, MARTY AND STRINGS**
FSRCD 221 / Jul '97 / Fresh Sound

☐ **HE NEEDS ME**
FSRCD 222 / Jul '97 / Fresh Sound

☐ **I'M GLAD THERE IS YOU**
FSRCD 223 / Jul '97 / Fresh Sound

☐ **JUST IN TIME**
FSRCD 227 / Jul '97 / Fresh Sound

☐ **LONELY AND SENTIMENTAL**
FSRCD 224 / Jul '97 / Fresh Sound

☐ **MELLOW AND THE SWINGING, THE**
FSRCD 226 / Jul '97 / Fresh Sound

☐ **MISS GLORIA LYNNE**
ECD 220092 / Jul '92 / Evidence

☐ **THIS ONE'S ON ME**
This one's on me / Angel eyes / What a difference a day makes / In the wee small hours of the morning / It's autumn / While we're young / Here's that rainy day / Snowbound / Let's that rainy day / Let's fall in love / Wild is love / All day long
HCD 7015 / 16 Mar '98 / Highnote

☐ **TIME FOR LOVE, A**
MCD 5381 / Sep '92 / Muse

☐ **TRY A LITTLE TENDERNESS**
FSRCD 225 / Jul '97 / Fresh Sound

Lynnfield Pioneers

☐ **EMERGE**
Go for a ride / Add it up / Bad luck baby / Unlucky stars / Get off your feet / Last last time / Outside in / Superceded / Not for long / Cynthia / Cool calm serene / Bus / Lucite / Louis III
OLE 2422 / 3 Nov '97 / Matador

Lynott, Phil

☐ **LIZZY SONGS, THE (A Tribute To Phil Lynott) (Various Artists)**
TR 008CD / Jun '97 / Tribute

☐ **SOLO IN SOHO**
Solo in Soho / King's call / Child lullaby / Tattoo / Dear Miss Lonely Hearts / Yellow pearl / Girls / Ode to a black man / Jamaican rum / Talk in 79 / So what / Turn the hands of time
8425632 / Jul '90 / Vertigo

Lynton, Jackie

☐ **PIN-BOARD WIZARDS**
ANDCD 14 / Jun '98 / A New Day

☐ **WHY NOT TAKE ALL OF ME**
Over the rainbow / High in the sky / Wishful thinking / Don't take away your love / All of me / I'd steal / I believe / Girl in the wood / Teddy bear's picnic / Jeannie with the light brown hair / I'm talkin' 'bout you / Lawdy Miss Clawdy / Little child / Never a mention / Laura / Ebb tide / What'd I say / Three blind mice / Corrina corrina / He'll have to go / Only you / Decision / Sporting life / Answer me / I never loved a girl like you / Audrey / Ballad of Hank McCain / Did you ever hear
GEMCD 010 / Feb '97 / Diamond

Lynwood Slim

☐ **BACK TO BACK (Lynwood Slim & Junior Watson)**
Much later for you baby / Early morning blues / Just as I am / Whoopin' and hollerin' / Too late / Happy blues / Best wishes / Young and able / Tough duff / Reach for your telephone / Sittin' here drinkin' / Get on the right track
CCD 11509 / Jul '98 / Crosscut

☐ **LOST IN AMERICA**
Tried to call you / It's obadacious / Just your foot / Take me where you go / Tell me what I've done / Messin' with my bread / I'm tired / Cried last night / Ain't enough time / Atlanta blues / Got to change
BMCD 9017 / Nov '93 / Black Magic
ATM 1135 / Oct '97 / Atomic Theory

☐ **SOUL FEET**
I'm to blame / Hoy hoy hoy / I refuse / Doo nothin' 'til you hear from me / Messin' with my bread / Reach for your telephone / Things gon' change / Doo's groove / Soul feet / Nothing takes the place of you / I've been around / Bad case of love / Too poor / Wipe your tears / Look the whole world over
ATM 1121 / Oct '96 / Atomic Theory

Lynyrd Skynyrd

☐ **DEFINITIVE LYNYRD SKYNYRD, THE (3CD Set)**
Freebird (demo) / Junkie (demo) / He's alive (demo) / One more time (original) / Gimme three steps (original) / Trust (original) / Comin' home / Mr. banker (demo) / Down south junkie (demo) / Truck drivin' man (demo) / I ain't the one (demo) / Poison whisky (demo) / Tuesday gone / Tings goin' on / Freebird / Sweet home alabama / Was I right or wrong / Workin' for mca / Don't ask me no questions / Swamp music / Ballad of curtis loew / Needle and the spoon / Call me the breeze / Saturday night special / Made in the shade / Am I losin' / On the hunt / Same old blues / Double trouble / Roll gypsy roll / All I can do is write about it (acoustic) / Four walls of rainford (undubbed demo) / Gimme back my bullets (live) / Searchin' (live) / Crossroads (live) / T for texas (live) / Whisky rock a roller (live) / Ain't no good life / What's your name / Georgia peaches / What's your name / I never dreamed / I know a little / Honky tonk night time man / That smell / You got that right
MCAD 310390 / Feb '92 / MCA

☐ **FREEBIRD - THE MOVIE (Live At Knebworth 1976)**
Workin' for MCA / I ain't the one / Saturday night special / Whisky rock-a-roller / Travellin' man / Searching / What's your name / That smell / Gimme three steps / Call me the breeze / T for Texas (blue yodel no.1) / Sweet home Alabama / Free bird / Dixie
MCD 11472 / Sep '96 / MCA

☐ **GIMME BACK MY BULLETS (2CD Set)**
MCD 33002 / Jul '96 / MCA

☐ **LAST REBEL, THE**
Good lovin's hard to find / One thing / Can't take that away / Best things in life / Last rebel / Outta hell in my dodge / Kiss your freedom goodbye / South of heaven / Love don't always come easy / Born to run
7567824472 / Feb '93 / WEA

☐ **LYNYRD SKYNYRD 1991**
Smokestack lightnin' / Keeping the faith / Southern women / Pure and simple / I've seen enough / Backstreet crawler / Good thing / Money man / It's a killer / Mama (afraid to say goodbye) / End of the road
7567822582 / Jun '91 / East West

☐ **LYVE FROM STEEL TOWN (2CD Set)**
607686147 / 27 Apr '98 / CMC
SPV 08529162 / 1 Jun '98 / SPV

☐ **NUTHIN' FANCY**
Made in the shade / Saturday night special / Cheatin' woman / Railroad song / I'm a country boy / On the hunt / Am I losin' / Whiskey rock'n'roller
MCLD 19074 / Nov '92 / MCA

☐ **OLD TIME GREATS (2CD Set)**
RR 4637 / Jun '97 / Repertoire

☐ **ONE MORE FOR THE ROAD (2CD Set)**
Workin' for MCA / I ain't the one / Searching / Tuesdays gone / Saturday night special / Travellin' man / Whiskey rock'n'roller / Sweet home Alabama / Gimme three steps / Call me the breeze / T for Texas / Needle and spoon / Crossroads / Freebird
MCLDD 19139 / Dec '92 / MCA

☐ **PRONOUNCED LEH-NERD SKIN-NERD**
I ain't the one / Tuesday's gone / Gimme three steps / Simple man / Things goin' on / Mississippi kid / Poison whiskey / Freebird
MCLD 19072 / Nov '91 / MCA

☐ **SECOND HELPING**
Sweet home Alabama / I need you / Don't ask me no questions / Workin' for MCA / Ballad of Curtis Loew / Swamp music / Needle and spoon / Call me the breeze
MCLD 19073 / Oct '92 / MCA

☐ **SKYNYRDS INNYRDS**
Sweet home alabama / Swamp music / I ain't the one / Gimme three steps / Double trouble / Freebird / Truck drivin' man / Saturday night special / Workin' for mca / What's your name / That smell / Don't ask me no questions / Call me the breeze
DMCG 6046 / Apr '89 / MCA

☐ **SOUTHERN BY THE GRACE OF GOD**
Swamp music / Call me the breeze / Dixie / Freebird / Workin' for MCA / That smell / I know a little / Comin' home / You got that right / What's your name / Gimme back my bullets / Sweet home Alabama
MCLD 19010 / Apr '92 / MCA

☐ **SOUTHERN KNIGHTS (2CD Set)**
Working for MCA / Ain't the one / Saturday night special / Down south jukin / Double trouble / T For Texas / Devil in the bottle / That smell / Simple man / Whiskey rock and roller / What's your name / Gimme 3 steps / Sweet home / Freebird
SPV 08744192 / Jul '96 / SPV

☐ **STREET SURVIVORS**
What's your name / That smell / One more time / I know a little / You got that right / I never dreamt / Honky tonk night time man / Ain't no good life
MCLD 19248 / Oct '94 / MCA

☐ **TWENTY**
We ain't much different / Bring it on / Voodoo lake / Home is where the heart is / Travellin' man / Talked myself right into it / Never too late / QRR / Blame it on a sad song / Berneice / None of us are free / How soon we forget
SPV 08544392 / May '97 / SPV

☐ **VERY BEST OF LYNYRD SKYNYRD, THE**
Down south jukin' / Saturday night special / Gimme three steps / What's your name / You got that right / Gimme back my bullets / Sweet home alabama / Freebird / That smell / On the hunt / I ain't the one / Whiskey rock-a-roller / Simple man / I know a little / Tuesday's gone / Comin' home
MCLD 19140 / Jul '92 / MCA

Lyons, Jimmy

☐ **BURNT OFFERING (Lyons, Jimmy & Andrew Cyrille)**
1201302 / Jun '91 / Black Saint

☐ **GIVE IT UP (Lyons, Jimmy Quintet)**
BSR 0087 / '86 / Black Saint

☐ **JUMP UP**
ART 6139CD / Apr '94 / Hat Art

Lyres

☐ **EARLY YEARS**
EFA 11578 / Apr '97 / Crypt

☐ **LYRES LYERS**
OLE 3042 / 1 Jun '98 / Matador

☐ **NOBODY BUT ME**
TAANG 058CD / Jan '93 / Taang

☐ **ON FYRE**
ROSE 35CD / 1 Jun '98 / Matador

☐ **PROMISE IS A PROMISE, A**
Promise is a promise / Here's a heart on fyre / Every man for himself / Feel good / I'll try you anyway / Worried about nothing / Touch / Running through the night / She's got eyes that tell lie / Jagged time lapse / Knock my socks off / Sick and tired / Trying just to please / Witch
ROSE 153CD / Aug '88 / New Rose

☐ **SOME LYRES**
TAANG 82 / Aug '94 / Taang

Lytle, Johnny

☐ **LOOP/NEW & GROOVY**
Loop / More I see you / Man / Time after time / Big Bill / Possum grease / Cristo redentor / Shyster / My romance / Hot sauce / Snapper / Summertime / Selim / Shadow of your smile / Come and get it / Pulpit / Too close for comfort / Chanukah / Screamin' loud / El marcel
CDBGPD 961 / Oct '90 / Beat Goes Public

Lyttelton, Humphrey

☐ **BEANO BOOGIE (Lyttelton, Humphrey & His Band)**
Say forward I'll march / Ficklefanny strikes again / Apple honey / Do you call that a buddy / Sixth form / Beano boogie / Little king / Echoes of the jungle / Gnasher and me / Strange Mr. Peter Charles/Cop out / In swinger / Yorkville
CLGCD 021 / Jun '92 / Calligraph

☐ **DELVING BACK AND FORTH WITH HUMPH (Lyttelton, Humphrey & His Band)**
Miss Otis regrets / Workin' man blues / Mahogany hall stomp / Salty dog / South / Victory house drag / High society / Melancholy blues / Farewell blues / On treasure island / Blues for an unknown gipsy / Suffolk air / Chattanooga stomp / Low down dirty shame blues / Hopfrog / Randolph Turpin / Vox humana blues / I like to go back in the evening / Missed regrets / Working man blues
LACD 89 / Dec '97 / Lake

☐ **DELVING BACK WITH HUMPH**
Thin red line / Melancholy blues / Cakewalkin' babies / If you see me comin' / Panama / Working man blues / Fidgety feet / Weary blues / Ole Miss Rag / Vox humana / Elizabeth / Blue for Waterloo / First of many / Blues for two / High society / Royal Garden blues / Who's sorry now / Humph meets Trog / Bugle call rag / That da da strain / Sugar
LACD 72 / Feb '97 / Lake

☐ **ECHOES OF THE DUKE (Lyttelton, Humphrey & His Band & Helen Shapiro)**
Take the 'A' train / I got it bad and that ain't good / Caravan / Just squeeze me / Drop me off in Harlem / Solitude/Mood indigo / Echoes of The Duke / I ain't got nothin' but the blues / 'Cross a busy street / I let a song go out of my heart / Don't get around much anymore / It don't mean a thing if it ain't got that swing / Do nothin' 'til you hear from me / Pritti Nitti / Just a sittin' and a rockin'
CLGCD 002 / Jun '92 / Calligraph

☐ **GIGS (Lyttelton, Humphrey & His Band)**
Stanley steams in / Black butterfly / Ah mersey / Golden gumboot / Grey turning blue / Barnes bridge
CDGCD 015 / Nov '87 / Calligraph

☐ **HEAR ME TALKIN' TO YA (Lyttelton, Humphrey & His Band)**
Hear me talkin' to ya / Someone to watch over me / Madly / Blues for Zoe / Serenade to Sweden / Lord is listenin' to ya, hallelujah / Good buzz (take it from the top) / One for Al / Swinging scorpio / Beale Street blues / Moten swing / St. James infirmary / Mezzrow / I got rhythm
CLGCD 029 / Aug '93 / Calligraph

☐ **LAY 'EM STRAIGHT (Lyttelton, Humphrey & His Band)**
Lay 'em straight / Porgy / Love for sale / Some other Spring / Things ain't what they used to be / Last laugh / Song for Ruby / Zoltan's dream / Echoes of the duke / Satin doll / Ostendatious / Late night final / Bondo's blues / Only for men
CLGCD 033 / Feb '97 / Calligraph

☐ **MORE HUMPH & ACKER (Lyttelton, Humphrey & Acker Bilk)**
Senora / Sugar / Maybe / I'd climb the highest mountain / Ludo / I told you once, I told you twice / Tiz-dum, tiz-dum / Mound bayou / Bessie couldn't help it / How long has this been going on / Russian lullaby / Blues and sentimental / Maritiniquen song / Three in the morning / Last smile blues / Easter parade
CLGCD 030 / Feb '95 / Calligraph

☐ **MOVIN' AND GROOVIN'**
BLCD 760504 / Oct '90 / Black Lion

☐ **PARLOPHONES VOL.1 1949-1959, THE (Come On & Stomp Stomp Stomp) (Lyttelton, Humphrey & His Band)**
Maple leaf rag / Memphis blues / Irish black bottom / Straight from the wood / Come on and stomp stomp stomp / Careless love blues / Snake rag / Hopfrog / Ice cream / Froggie Moore / Snag it / I like to go back in the evening / Chattanooga stomp / Dallas blues / Canal street blues / Cakewalkin' babies back home / 1919 march / Trouble in mind / Panama rag / Panama rag / Low down dirty shame blues / Buddy's habit / DJC blues / On Treasure Island / Get out of here and go home
CLGCD 0351 / Jul '98 / Calligraph

☐ **PARLOPHONES VOL.2 1949-1959, THE (One Man Went To Blow) (Lyttelton, Humphrey & His Band)**
Wolverine blues / Trogs blues / Gatemouth / Suffolk air / Dormouse / Tom cat blues / Down home rag / Apex blues / One went to blow / Blues for an unknown gypsy / It makes my love come down / Hoppin' mad / Don't monkey with it / it's over now / Tia juana / Forgotten woman's blues / Chicago buzz / Out of the gallion / Old grey mare / March hare / Fidgety feet / Steppin' on the blues / Onions / Closing time / Travellin' blues
CLGCD 0352 / Jul '98 / Calligraph

☐ **ROCK ME GENTLY**
Rock me gently / Top 'n' tail / Jack the bear / My funny valentine / Frankie and Johnny / Sea-lion's siesta / Lester and Herschel / Heads or tails / Royal flush / Sidney my man / Tribal dance / If we never meet again / Lady of the lavender mist / St. Louis blues
CLGCD 026 / Sep '91 / Calligraph

☐ **TAKE IT FROM THE TOP (A Dedication To Duke Ellington)**
CDBLC 760516 / Apr '96 / Black Lion

☐ **TROGLADYTES (Lyttelton, Humphrey & Wally Fawkes)**
SOSCD 1238 / May '93 / Stomp Off

M

M

☐ FAMOUS LAST WORDS
Famous last words / Love life / Yellow magic / Smash the mirror / Neutron / Dance on the ruins / Here today gone tomorrow / To be is to buy / Eureka / Love inferno / Bridge / Guardian angel / I'm no angel
WESM 503 / 19 Jan '98 / Westside

☐ JIVE SHIKISHA (Scott, Robin & Shikisha)
Jive shikisha / Crazy Zulu / Are you ready / Masai Mara / War dance / Black connection / One man's meat / Talking drums / Jolie Africa / Jazz connection / Funky Mama / Body revolution / Mama Afrika / Afrika / Spiritual man
WESM 504 / 19 Jan '98 / Westside

☐ NEW YORK LONDON PARIS MUNICH
Pop muzik / Woman make man / Moderne man / Satisfy your love / Made in Munich / Moonlight and muzak / That's the way the money goes / Cowboys and Indians / Unite your nation / Fanfare / Cry myself to sleep / M-Factor
WESM 501 / 22 Sep '97 / Westside

☐ OFFICIAL SECRETS ACT
Transmission / Join the party / Working for the corporation / Your country needs you / Mayday / Relax / Maniac / Keep it to yourself / Abracadabra / Official secrets / Danube / Wedding dance / Mambo la / Don't believe what the papers say / Bride of fortune
WESM 502 / 22 Sep '97 / Westside

M-Man

☐ LISTEN, SING AND DANCE MY LOVE
JBF 100196 / May '96 / M-Man Productions

M-People

☐ BIZARRE FRUIT
Sight for sore eyes / Search for the hero / Open up your heart / Love rendez-vous / Precious pearl / Sugar town / Walk away / Drive time / Padlock / And finally
74321240812 / Nov '94 / De-Construction

☐ ELEGANT SLUMMING
One night in heaven / Moving on up / Renaissance / You just have to be there / Love is in my soul / Don't look any further / Natural thing / Little packet / La vida loca / Melody of life
74321166782 / Jul '96 / De-Construction

☐ FRESCO
Just for you / Fantasy island / Never mind love / Last night 10,000 / Smile / Red flower sunset / Angel st / Lonely / Rhythm and blues / Believe it / Bohemia / Avalon
743215249023 / 17 Nov '97 / M-People

☐ NORTHERN SOUL
Colour my life / How can I love you more / Inner city cruise / It's your world / Someday / Sexual freedom / Kiss it better / Tumbling down / Landscape of love / Life / Inner city dub / Colour my life (part 2) / Kiss it better / Platini / Excited / Man Smart / Colour my life (part 3) / Excited
74321117772 / Jul '96 / De-Construction

M3

☐ M-3
NAR 057CD / Dec '93 / New Alliance

Maal, Baaba

☐ BAAYA
Baayo / Mariama / Joulowo / Diahowo / Baaba / Bouyel / Yero mama / Agouyadjl / Dogata / Samba
CIDM 1061 / 2 Feb '98 / Mango

☐ LAM TORO
Yela / Toro / Daande lenol / Hamady boiro / Daniibe / Gidelam / Olel / Sy sawande / Ndelorel / Lem gt / Minuit
CIDM 1080 / 2 Feb '98 / Mango

☐ NOMAD SOUL
PALMCD 2002 / 29 Jun '98 / Palm Pictures

Maas

☐ LATITUDE
Festina / Upstate / Michigan breaks / Look at me now, falling / Esplanade / Suture / Shrift / Eurostar / Another Saturday night / Lost soul
SOMACD 7 / Apr '97 / Soma

Mabern, Harold

☐ FOR PHINEAS (Mabern, Harold & Geoff Keezer)
SKCD 2041 / Jul '96 / Sackville

☐ LOOKIN' ON THE BRIGHT SIDE (Mabern, Harold Trio)
DIW 614 / Nov '93 / DIW

☐ MABERNS' GROOVEYARD (Mabern, Harold Trio)
DIW 621 / Jan '98 / DIW

☐ PHILADELPHIA BOUND
SKCD 23051 / Oct '94 / Sackville

☐ STRAIGHT STREET (Mabern, Harold Trio)
DIW 608 / Sep '91 / DIW

Maboul, Aksak

☐ UN PEU DE L'AME DES BANDITS
Modern lesson / Palmiers en pots / Geistige nacht / I viaggi formano la gioventu / Inoculating rabies / Ce qu'on peut voir avec un bon microscope / Alluvions / Azinou crapules / Age route brra / Bosses de crosses
CRAM 002 / Apr '96 / Crammed Discs

Mabsant

☐ HUMOUR & SONG WITH MABSANT & EIRY PALFREY
SAIN 2029CD / Aug '94 / Sain

☐ MABSANT (GYDA EIRY PALFREY)
Carol y blwch / Diary / Suai'r gwynt / Child's Christmas / Ar gyfer hiddiw'r bore / Red cock / Curlews / Dear John / Y wasael / Maggie fach / Holiday memory / Ar kan y mor / Local boy/Sell out / Gwenynen / Mrs. Evans/Meanwhile Dai / Y deryn du / Blodeuwedd / Moliannwn
SCD 2029 / Oct '87 / Sain

Mabuses

☐ MELBOURNE METHOD, THE
My brilliant way / Glass of bourbon / Tongues / Keeler joins the joyce gang / Whose party is this / Rooms / Paper plane / Lynched / Picnic at the red house / Fetch the hammer / Oscar / Narc fears / She went wild
R 3132 / Apr '94 / Rough Trade

Mac Dada

☐ REGGAE HALL OF FAME
CMCD 003 / 12 Jan '98 / VP

Mac-Talla

☐ MAIRIDH GAOL IS CEOL
Boys be happy / Old hunting song / Beloved Gregor / Mouth music / Tailor's dowry / Barcelona / Brown haired Alan / Mrs. Jamieson's favourite / Mouth music / Beautiful girl / Setting a course for Lewis / Uig Brae
COMD 2054 / Feb '94 / Temple

Macabre

☐ SINISTER SLAUGHTER
NB 070CD / Jun '93 / Nuclear Blast

Macaire, Mack

☐ SOUCI Y A LA VIE
JIP 064 / Jan '96 / JIP

McAllister, Randy

☐ DIGGIN' FOR SOFA CHANGE
State of confusion / Battle cry / Sofa change / You got no right / Scary woman / I don't like it / Down in the gutter / Bob's number two / Babe and Nan's thing / Actions speak louder than words / Woman on a mission / I got it
JSPCD 297 / 21 Sep '97 / JSP

McAlmont

☐ MCALMONT
Either / Not wiser / Unworthy (edit) / Misunderstood / Is it raining / Conversation / He loves you / Worn away / It's always this way / My grey boy / They hide / Through the door / Placed aside / Unworthy / As if I'd known
CDHUT 12 / Jan '95 / Hut

McAlmont & Butler

☐ SOUND OF MCALMONT AND BUTLER, THE
Yes / What's the excuse this time / Right thing / Although / Don't call it soul / Disappointment / Debitor / How about you / Tonight / You'll lose a good thing / You do
CDHUT 32 / Nov '95 / Hut

MacAlpine, Tony

☐ EDGE OF INSANITY
Wheel of fortune / Stranger / Quarter to midnight (live solo) / Agrionia / Empire in the sky / Witch and the priest / Taker / Chopin, prelude 16, opus 28 / Edge of insanity / Raven / No place in time
RR 349706 / '89 / Roadrunner

☐ EVOLUTION
Sage / Overseas evolution / Eccentrist / Time table / Seville / Futurism / Etude no 5 opus 10 F / Powerfield / Plastic people / Sinfonia / Asturias kv 467
RR 89012 / Oct '95 / Roadrunner

☐ FREEDOM TO FLY
Ice princess / Box office poison / Salvation / Freedom to fly / Champion / Stream dream / Albania / Chopin etude no. 2 opus no. 25 / Disciples of fear / Capistrano
RR 91572 / Sep '96 / Roadrunner

☐ PREMONITION
RR 89652 / Sep '94 / Roadrunner

McAnuff, Winston

☐ ONE LOVE
CC 2716 / Apr '95 / Crocodisc

MacAskill, Paula

☐ CRYSTAL
CDRPM 0016 / May '97 / RP Media

McAuley, Jackie

☐ FRETWORK
All jokers are wild / Gone crazy on you / SOS Crumlin Road / Danger money / Lay your load on me / Kerry red / Zoom zoom / This must be love, Theresa / Johnny forty coats / When Mama got the blues / Goodnight waltz / No mans land / Gael force West
RGFCD 032 / Oct '96 / Road Goes On Forever

☐ JACKIE MCAULEY...PLUS
Turning green / Boy on the bayou / Country Joe / Cameraman Wilson and Holmes / Spanish room / One fine day / It's alright / Poor Howard / Away / Bangerine / Ruby Farm / Rockin' shoes
SEECD 315 / Jul '98 / See For Miles

McAuliffe, Marie

☐ ARK SEXTET
37859 / May '98 / Koch Jazz

McBee, Cecil

☐ ALTERNATE SPACES
IN 1043CD / Jan '97 / India Navigation

McBee, Lee

☐ 44 (McBee, Lee & The Passions)
Boogie twist / Rock this joint / 44 blues / Rooster blues / Call me / She fooled me / Get your mind out of the gutter / I been abused / Everybody loves my baby / Train fare / I'm gonna love you / Keep what you got
MMBCD 704 / Jun '98 / Me & My Blues

McBlain, John

☐ TWO CEASEFIRES AND AN ELECTION
MCCD 5001 / 11 May '98 / Quantum Mobius

McBride, Christian

☐ FAMILY AFFAIR
I'm coming home / Dream of you / Family affair / Theme from our fairy tale / Summer soft / Brown funk (for Ray) / Open sesame / Wayne's world / I'll write a song for you / Or so you thought
5575542 / 10 Aug '98 / Verve

☐ FINGERPAINTING (The Music Of Herbie Hancock) (McBride, Christian & Nicholas Payton/Mark Whitfield Trio)
Fingerpainting / Dolphin dance / Chan's song / One finger snap / Sly / Oliloqui Valley / Jane's theme / Driftin' / Chameleon / Tell me a bedtime story / Eye of the hurricane / Kiss / Speak like a child
5378562 / 15 Sep '97 / Verve

☐ GETTIN' TO IT
5239892 / Mar '95 / Verve

☐ NUMBER TWO EXPRESS
5295852 / Apr '96 / Verve

McBride, Joe

☐ GIFT FOR TOMORROW, A
Evening in Dallas / Secrets / Never be lonely / Walking in rhythm / Gift for tomorrow / Messenger / Deja vu / World to me / Everybody needs love / Reunion / You've got a friend
INAK 30252CD / Nov '97 / In Akustik

☐ GRACE
Twilight / Sunny / For all we know / Everlasting / Central expressway / Clay and ivory / Grace / Get on the right track / Need somebody to love / Chump change
INAK 30172CD / Nov '97 / In Akustik

☐ KEYS TO YOUR HEART
Highland park / Let's spend some time together / People make the world go round / It's got to be love / Chit-chat / After sunset / I can never get enough / Miracles / High steppin' / You are my lady / Squeeze play
INAK 30352CD / Nov '97 / In Akustik

McBride, Martina

☐ EVOLUTION
I'm little but I'm loud / Happy girl / Be that way / Broken wing / Wrong again / Keeping my distance / Still holding on / Whatever you say / I won't close my eyes / I don't want to see you / Some say I'm running / Here in my heart / One day you will / Valentine
7863675162 / 1 Sep '97 / RCA

☐ WAY THAT I AM, THE
Heart trouble / My baby loves me / That wasn't me / Independence day / Where I used to have a heart / Goin' to work / She ain't seen nothing yet / Life / Strangers / Ashes
74321192292 / Mar '94 / RCA

☐ WILD ANGELS
Wild angels / Phones are ringin' all over town / Great disguise / Swingin' doors / All the things we've never done / Two more bottles of wine / Cry on the shoulder of the road / You've been driving all the time / Born to give my love to you / Beyond the blue / Safe in the arms of love
07863665092 / Oct '95 / RCA

McBride, Owen

☐ LAWEESH ROCK AND OTHER SONGS
CIC 072CD / Nov '93 / Clo Iar-Chonnachta

McBroom, Amanda

☐ LIVE FROM RAINBOW & STARS, NEW YORK
September song / No fear / I love this place / Everybody wants to be Sondheim / Days of wine and roses / Time after time / I love men / Ship in a bottle / Here and now / Portrait / Rose / Carousel / Errol Flynn / Dieter's prayer / Baltimore Oriole / Breathing / My foolish heart / I can't make you love me
DRGCD 91432 / Feb '95 / DRG

Macc Lads

☐ ALE HOUSE ROCK
Piles / Alehouse rock / Back on the pies again / Tart with the heart / Vigilante shanty / Prestburt girls / Village idiot / Frogbashing / Gone fishin' / Rockweilers / Father's day / Turtles heads / Dirth glass / Thunking in the dark / Helen of fowey / Hen night
DOJOCD 250 / Mar '96 / Dojo

☐ BEER, SEX, CHIPS AND GRAVY
Lads from Macc / Beer, sex and chips 'n' gravy / Boddies / Sweaty Betty / England's glory / Blackpool / Miss Macclesfield / God's gift to women / Get weavin' / Now he's a poof / Nagasaki sauce / Saturday night / Buenos aires / Charlotte / Failure with girls / Do you love me / Dan's underpants / Twenty pints / Macc Lads party
WKFMXD 110 / Aug '89 / FM

☐ BITTER, FIT CRACK
Barrel's round / Guess me weight / Uncle Knobby / Maid of ale / Dan's big log / Got to be Gordon's / Bitter fit crack / Julie the schooly / Doctor doctor / Torremolinos / Al o'peesha
WKFMXD 100 / Feb '91 / FM
DOJOCD 155 / Nov '93 / Dojo

☐ FROM BEER TO ETERNITY
Alton Towers / Geordie girl / No sheep 'til Buxton / All day drinking / Tab after tab / Lucy Lastic / My pub / Dead cat / Lady Muck / Gordon's revenge / Pie taster / Dans round yer 'andbag / Ben Nevis / Fluffy pup / Stoppyback / Ugly women
DOJOCD 157 / May '94 / Dojo

☐ LIVE AT LEEDS (The Who?)
Sweaty Betty / Ben Nevis / Bloink / Do you love me / God's gift to women / Charlotte / Blackpool / Lads from Macc / Now he's a poof / Doctor doctor / Julie the schooly / Guess me weight / Miss Macclesfield / Fat bastard / Get weavin / Barrels' round / Dan's underpants
WKFMXD 115 / Aug '88 / FM
DOJOCD 161 / Mar '94 / Dojo

☐ ORIFICE AND A GENITAL, AN (Out-takes 1986-1991)
Eh up lets sup / Fat bastard / Baggy Anne / Head kicked in / Knutsford / No sheep 'til Buxton / Pie taster / I love Macc / Made of ale / Knock knock / Brevil brevil / Manfred Macc / Buenos Aires '90 / Fellatio Nell, son / Two stroke Eddie / Even uglier women
DOJOCD 141 / Feb '94 / Dojo
SMMCD 533 / 27 Apr '98 / Snapper

☐ TWENTY GOLDEN CRATES
No sheep 'til Buxton / Sweaty Betty / Buenos aires 91 / Beer 'n' sex 'n' chips 'n' gravy / Guess me weight / Made of ale / Ben Nevis / Blackpool / Dan's underpants / Knock knock / Gordon's revenge / My pub / Charlotte / Dead cat / Boddies / Fluffy pup / Julie the schooly / Lady muck / Miss Macclesfield / Nagasaki sauce / Barrels round / Twenty pints / Saturday night
SMMCD 525 / 29 Sep '97 / Snapper

McCafferty, Dan

☐ DAN MCCAFFERTY
Honky Tonk downstairs / Cinnamon girl / Great pretender / Boots of Spanish leather / What'cha gonna do about it / Out of time / You can't lie to a liar / Trouble / You got me hummin' / Stay with me baby / Nightingale
NEMCD 640 / Jun '94 / Sequel

McCaffrey, Frank

☐ PLACE IN MY HEART, A
Clock in the tower / Place in my heart / Day the world stood still / Drive safely darlin' / I'd rather be sorry / Annie's story / Blackboard of my heart / All alone in New York City / It's our anniversary / Give a lonely heart a home / Rose / Always Mayo
RZCD 512 / '91 / Ritz

☐ TODAY
Today / Things I wish I'd said / Silver medals and sweet memories / I wish it was me / You make me feel like a man / Forever lovers / In dreams / Wedding song / Broken wings / Lady from Glenfarn / Memories of Mayo / Sarah's smile
RZCD 0063 / Apr '91 / Ritz

☐ VERY BEST OF FRANK MCCAFFREY
It's our anniversary / Blackboard of my heart / I'll take you home again Kathleen / Ring your mother wore / Silver medals and sweet memories / Little grey home in the West / I wish it was me / Daisy a day / Place in my heart / Memories of Mayo / More than yesterday / If we only had old Ireland over here / Clock in the tower / Give a lonely heart a home / Moonlight in Mayo / My lady from Glenfarne / Things I wish I'd said / Broken wings / Day the world stood still / Wedding song
RZCD 532 / Apr '93 / Ritz

☐ YOUR SPECIAL DAY
Here's my native country / Midnight to midnight / I'm a fool / Always on my mind (forever in my heart) / Nobody's Darlin' but mine / Emigrant eyes / When your old wedding ring was new / You special day / Forty shades of green / Cr oce di oro / You're a friend of mine / Less of me / Our Lady of knock / Heart that beats in Ireland
RCD 548 / May '95 / Ritz

McCain, Jerry

☐ RETROSPECTIVES
Blues tribute / Messin' with me baby / Sue somebody / burn the crackhouse down / I've got the blues all over me / Brand new mojo / Tumblin' in the sea / Spoiled rotten to the bone / Strut your stuff / Lucy pearl / Love makin' showdown / World's on fire
ICH 1516 / 29 Jun '98 / Ichiban

☐ STRANGE KIND OF FEELIN' (McCain, Jerry 'Boogie' & Tiny Kennedy, Clayton Love)
ALCD 2701 / Oct '93 / Alligator

McCall, Darrell

☐ REAL MCCALL, THE (5CD Set)
This old heart / Excuse me (I think I've got a heartache) / Lonely River Rhine / Heart to heart talk: *McCall, Darrell & Harold Weakely* / Polka on the banjo / Fallen angel / Five brothers / North to Alaska / My kind of lovin' / My girl / Beyond imagination / What'll I do (call the zoo) / Loneliness / I gotta have you / Dear one / Up to my ears in tears / I've been known / For your sweet love / Stranger was here / I'm a little bit lonely / I can take his baby way / More than likely / Huckleberry Queen / Man can change / Hud / No place to hide / Keeping my feet on the ground / Got my baby on my mind / Step by step / Hello world / Marionette / I love you baby / I'd love to live with you again / I'd die to see you smile / Wrong kind of man / Blame me / Hurry up / Wall of pictures / Tiny ribbons / Big oak tree / Bury the bottle with me / Stranger was here / Wedding band / Hide and go cheat / New rich friend / First year / Likes of Polly / Yours and his / Don't tell my wife / Right to do wrong / Sally Bryson / Arms of my weakness / Heart of Dixie / Loser / Fiddlin' of Jacque Pierre Bordeaux / I'll break out again tonight / Mixing memories / It's the water / Rainbow at midnight / Eleven roses / Goodbye of the year / I still want you / Warm red wine (you're my sunshine) / Man you're most likely to forget / This time I won't cheat on her again / Loser never had a better friend / Here we go again / There's still a lot of love in San Antone / Texas honky tonk / Yours and his / I am love / Where is all that love you talked about / If you don't know your roses / Genuine healer of time / Never some night / Eleven roses / Champagne ladies and blue ribbon babies / Letting her be free / Face to the wall / Cold beer signs and country songs / If you don't believe I love you / She'll keep bringing all her love to me / Helpless / Pins and needles (in my heart) / Every girl I see / Waltz of the angels / I just destroyed the world / Tennessee / I come home to face the music / Are you teasing me / Sad songs and waltzes / Days when you were still in love with me / Dreams of a dreamer / It's my lazy day / It's been so long darlin' / Lily Dale: *McCall, Darrell & Willie Nelson* / Please don't leave me: *McCall, Darrell & Willie Nelson* / Half beered up and drinkin' / Weeds outlived the the roses / Old memory's arms / Down the roads of Daddy's dreams / Love didn't drive my good woman wild / Willie B / It took us all night to say goodbye / Long line of empties / I wonder which one of us is to blame / Married women / Afternoon rendezvous: *McCall, Darrell & Mona* / Just ridin' through / Sourwood Mountain / Don't wait till tomorrow / Strange little melody / Picture on the wall / Cindy / Rosewood casket / I'll cry again tomorrow / If you've got the money, I've got the time / Oh lonesome me / Heartbreak Avenue / Peace in the valley / Release me / Answer to anymore / Ages and ages ago / Under your spell again / Sweet dreams / Accidentally on purpose / Dear one / I can take his baby away / Another day, another dollar / Stranger was here / There's still a lot of love in San Antone / Helpless / It's the water / Eleven roses / Lone Star beer commercial / Coors beer commercial / Bad mouthin' / This I gotta see
BCD 15846 / Nov '96 / Bear Family

McCall, Jana

☐ JANA MCCALL
UP 049CD / May '98 / Up

McCalla

☐ HOT FROM THE SMOKE
Cause and effect / Family affair / Count all your blessings / Simmer down / Fly like an eagle / Lay you low / Ain't no sunshine / Your happiness / Let's go deeper / International love
SEA 41622 / Oct '95 / Uplands

McCallister, Don Jr.

☐ DON MCCALLISTER JR. & HIS COWBOY JAZZ REVUE
DJD 3206 / May '94 / Dejadisc

☐ DOWN IN TEXAS
Small town boy / Bluebird / I got a wheel / Ain't it funny / White freightliner / Down in Texas / Lady blues / No such pain as love / Let's go steppin' / What the cowboy's say / Steel guitar rag
AP 1312 / Dec '97 / Appaloosa

MacCallum, Hugh A.

☐ WORLD'S GREATEST PIPERS VOL.2, THE
MacNeils of Ugadale / Sweet maid of Mull / Arniston castle / Caberfeidh / Grey bob / Willie Murray / Iain Rhuadh's lament / Donald, Hugh and his dog / Rosshire volunteers / John MacFadyen of Melfort / Joe McGann's fiddle / P/M George Allan / Clan MacColl / Tulloch castle / Major D Manson / Mhairi van og (Fair young Mary) / Battle of the Somme / Archie McKinlay / Miss Ada Crawford / Captain Home / Duke of Gordon's birthday / Sleepy Maggie / Dancing feet / Tail toddle / Allan MacPherson of Mosspark / Herring wife / Lament for Mary MacLeod
LCOM 5147 / May '96 / Lismor

McCallum

☐ BIG BIGG MARKET
BIGCD 1 / Dec '94 / Mawson & Wareham

☐ TAKE ME AS I AM
RUBCD 050 / Nov '97 / Rubber

McCallum, Craig

☐ 75TH ANNIVERSARY DANCES (McCallum, Craig Scottish Dance Band)
New biggin' / Old way of Killiecrankie / Lady Susan Montgomery / Periweg / Colonel / Kelloholm jig / Mrs. Milne of Kinneff / Broadford Bay / Georgie's jig / Hay making / Mrs. Garthland's strathspey / West's hornpipe / Fyket / Sow's tail
RSCDSCD 010 / Jul '98 / Royal Scottish Country Dance Society

☐ IN A DIFFERENT LIGHT (McCallum, Craig Scottish Dance Band)
Gay Gordons / Dumbarton's drums / Pride of Erin Waltz / Canadian Barn dance / Pipe medley / Eva three step / Wild geese / Military two step / Irish reels / Highland Schottische / Circle waltz / Strip the willow / Party polka / Dashing white sergeant
CDTRAX 037 / Oct '90 / Greentrax

McCallum, David

☐ OPEN CHANNEL D
CREV 43CD / Sep '96 / Rev-Ola

McCallum, William

☐ HAILEY'S SONG
COMD 2060 / Oct '95 / Temple

☐ PIPERS OF DISTINCTION
Highland brigade depot-miss ishabel t. macdonald (68 ma / Rakes of kildare-donald maclellands tuning phrase (retreat / Crags of stirling-inveran (24 competition marches) / Groat (piobaireachd) / Duncan johnstone-jim tweedie's sea legs (hornpipes) / I got a kiss of the kings hand (piobaireachd) / Sine bhan / Turf lodge / Hen's march / Balmoral castle / Donalbane / Duke of gordon / Willie davey / Malcolm the tailor / Pigeon on the gate / Memorial bells of inveraray / He-ro-hiram / Wee man from uist / Rantin' rovin' robin
CDMON 801 / Dec '89 / Monarch

McCalmans

☐ FESTIVAL LIGHTS
Don't call me early in the morning / Pills / Far down the line / Highland road / Some hae meat / Tearing our industry down / Golden arches / Shanties / Bonnie barque the bergen / Barnyards of Delgaty / Goodnight sweetheart / Festival lights
CDTRAX 097 / Oct '95 / Greentrax

☐ FLAMES ON THE WATER
Ah'm e man at muffed it / Isle of Eigg / Devolution anthem / Farewell tae the haven / Sounding / Hawks and eagles / Siege / Who pays the piper / Festival lights / Shian Road / Men o' worth / Curtain call
CDTRAX 036 / Jul '90 / Greentrax

☐ HIGH GROUND
Cancel Marie's wedding / Lochs of the Tay / Don't sit on my Jimmy Shands / They sent a woman / Five o'clock in the morning / No one left but me / Upstairs, doonstairs / Take her in your arms / Don't waste my time / High ground / Wrecked again / White horses / Cholesterol / Libertas Ragusta
CDTRAX 138 / Aug '97 / Greentrax

☐ HONEST POVERTY
Man's a man for a' that / Single handed sailor / Your daughters and your sons / Neil Gow's apprentice / Children are running away / Kelvingrove/Paddy's leather britches/Behind the haystack / War outside/ The white collar holler / I feel like Buddy Holly / Parade / Portnahaven / 8-2-0 / Wha'll be King but Charlie / Father Mallory's dance / New Year's Eve song / Harmless
CDTRAX 067 / Sep '93 / Greentrax

☐ IN HARMONY - 30TH ANNIVERSARY COMPILATION ALBUM
Pace egging song / Sun rises bright in France / Broom / Windmills / My Johnny is a shoemaker / Smuggler / Ye Jacobites by name / Farewell to Sicily / Burn the witch / Ladies evening song / Kelty clippie / Bonnie maid of fire / Scotland / Bonnie lass o'Gala water / Mothers, daughters, wives / Rambling rover / Farewell tae the haven / Last session / Man's a man for a' that / Bound to go
CDTRAX 086 / Jan '95 / Greentrax

☐ LISTEN TO THE HEAT - LIVE
I have seen the Highlands / Town of Kiandra / Mount and go / Sister Josephine / 23rd June / Prisoner's song / Song song / Rambling Rover / Rory Murphy / First Christmas / Lakewood / Thriepmuir hornpipe / Royal Belfast / President's men / Air fa la la la lo / Sickening thank you song
CDTRAX 019 / Aug '88 / Greentrax

☐ PEACE AND PLENTY
Tullochgorum / Bells of the town / Song of the plough / Colliery gate / No you won't get me down in your mines / Black bear / Drover's lad / Top house / South Australia / Esikibo river / Blood red roses / Little Sally Rackett / Up and rin awa' Geordie / Mothers, daughters, wives / Highland road / Barratt's privateers / Men of the sea / Song for Europe / Tae the weavers gin ye gang / Leave her Johnny
CDTRAX 002 / Feb '89 / Greentrax

☐ SMUGGLER/BURN THE WITCH
Smuggler / If mother should die / Gardens / Hornpipe/Reels / Mount and go / Boatie rows/Carls O'Dysart / Flowers o'the forest / Barnyards o'Delgaty / Bar-room / No churchman am I / Silkie of Sule Skerry / Man's a man for a'that / Johnnie Cope / Skye boat song / Tammy Traddlefeet/The rising / Fare ye well ye Mormond braes / Lion / Jennie Lusswade / Farewell to Novia Scotia / Aye walkin o / Gin I were where the gaudie rins / Burn the witch / Bonnie lass o'Gala Water / Jock Stuart / March of the Cameron men / Phantom whistler/Random jig / Doon in the wee room
ESMCD 521 / Apr '97 / Essential

☐ SONGS FROM SCOTLAND
Boys that broke the ground / Tiree love song / Highland laddie / Roll the woodpile down / Hundred years ago / Westering home / Last session / All the tunes in the world / Most amazing thing of all / I will go / Widow MacKay / April waltz / Up and awa' wi' the Laverock / Scarce o'tatties / Lark in the morning / Ainster Harbour / Twa recruitin' / Sergeants / Rollin' home
CDTRAX 045 / Jul '91 / Greentrax

McCann, Eamon

☐ EVERYTHING THAT I AM
Love is blind / Small town saturday night / Hey good lookin' / Past the point of rescue / It's all over now / Don't call me, I'll call you / Everything that I am / I promised you the world / When you come to land / Can't break it to my heart / Life after you / Gift of love / Bunch of bright red roses / Mother nature's son / I'm no stranger to the rain / Only when I laugh
RCD 544 / Oct '94 / Ritz

☐ GOLD IN THE MOUNTAIN
RZRCD 554 / Mar '96 / Ritz

McCann, Jim

☐ GREATEST HITS
Galway races / Spancil hill / Easy and slow / Follow me up to Carlow / Next market day / Times have changed / Town of Ballybay / Carrickfergus / Lord of the dance / Go lassie go
CDIRISH 019 / Mar '97 / Outlet

McCann, Les

☐ BEST OF LES MCCANN, THE
Fish this week, but next week chitlins / Truth / For Carl Perkins / Vakushna / Little 3/4 time for God and co / Shout / Doreen don't cry / Big Jim / Gone on and get that church / Pretty lady / Someone stole my chitlins / Shampoo
CDP 8522162 / Aug '96 / Blue Note

☐ ON THE SOUL SIDE
Shambalala / Early riser / Black rub / Vu jade / New blues / Lift every voice and sing God Bless America / Ignominy / Children / Dippermouth / Look to your heart
5224312 / Feb '92 / Verve

☐ SOUVENIR DE MONTREUX (McCann, Les & Eddie Harris)
Step right up / Music from the seeker / Satin doll / Balm to Gedeon / Blue rot no.2 / You did it, you did it / Misty / Ragman and the junkman / Volunteered / Black boot / Cuckoo / You never can say goodbye
8122724522 / Jul '96 / Atlantic

☐ TALKIN' VERVE
Watermelon man / Beaux J Poo boo / Great city / Guantanamera / Sunny / Green green rocky road / Little freak / Red top / Compared to what / My friends / Sad little girl / La Brea / Goin' out of my head / Boo-go-loo / Colonel Rykken's southern fried chicken
5573512 / 29 Jun '98 / Verve

McCann, Phillip

☐ ALL OF THE WORLD'S MOST BEAUTIFUL MELODIES (5CD Set)
CHAN 4536 / Sep '95 / Chandos

☐ WORLD'S MOST BEAUTIFUL MELODIES VOL.5, THE (McCann, Phillip & Sellers Engineering Band)
Meditation from Thais / Salut d'amour / Suo gan / Beau soir / La calinda / Pavanne / I'll walk beside you / Clair de Lune / Exotica / On wings of song / Largo / Eriskay love lilt / Vissi d'arte / To a wild rose / Sheep may safely graze / Adagio from Symphony No. 2 / Czardas
CHAN 4532 / Aug '94 / Chandos

McCann, Susan

☐ 20 COUNTRY CLASSICS
CDC 004 / Feb '97 / Ceol

☐ BEST OF THE SIXTIES, THE
Day dream believer / My boy lollipop / Downtown / Bobby's girl / Come what may / Walking back to happiness / Lipstick on your collar / Saturday night at the movies / Stupid cupid / Calender guy / Another Saturday night / Mr. Tambourine man
TCCD 101 / Sep '97 / Irish

☐ COUNTRY GIRL
Thank God I am a country girl / When the new wears off our love / I fall to pieces / Close all the honky tonks / Queen of hearts / Radio heart / Rose garden / Before the next teardrop falls / Silver threads and golden needles / Shutters and boards / You seldom come to see me anymore / It only hurts for a little while / Sunday morning christian / There's a built-in trouble maker in every man / Out of reach of my open arms / Am I that easy to forget
CD 21212 / Nov '97 / Laserlight

☐ COUNTRY LOVE AFFAIR
Never ending love affair / Johnny lovely Johnny / Blue velvet / Forever and ever Amen / Little ole wine drinker me / Travellin' light / Let the rest of the world go by / Two broken hearts / Someone is looking for someone like you / Irish eyes / Boy in your arms / Wind in the willows / Mother's love's a blessing / Patches in heaven / How great thou art / When the sun says goodbye to the mountain
IHCD 482 / Nov '90 / Irish Heritage

☐ DIAMONDS AND DREAMS
Love me one more time / When I hear the music / Have you ever been lonely / String of diamonds / Always / You're never too old to love / He never will be mine / Loving you / I vow to thee my country / Yellow roses / Sonny's dream / Broken speed of the sound of the loneliness / Rose of my heart / Hillbilly girl with the blues / Everything is beautiful / Give me more time
IHCD 591 / Oct '91 / Irish Heritage

☐ MEMORIES
Softly, softly / String of diamonds / Whatever happened to old fashioned love / Irish memories / Dreaming of a little island / Help me make it through the night / Bus To LA / Penny arcade / If the whole world stopped loving / Once A Day / Love Has Joined Us Together / Since Johnny went away / Darlin' / Angels, Roses And Rain
IHCD 592 / Nov '92 / Irish Heritage

☐ SUSAN MCCANN'S IRELAND
TSCD 220 / Jan '95 / Outlet

☐ VERY BEST OF SUSAN MCCANN, THE
ARCD 024 / May '98 / Ainm

McCarthy

☐ ENRAGED WILL INHERIT THE EARTH, THE
Boy meets girl so what / Governing takes brains / An address to the better off / Hands off or die / What our boys are fighting for / Keep an open mind or else / We are all born creeps / Home secretary briefs the forces of law and order / I'm not a patriot but... / Throw him out he's breaking my heart / All your questions answered / New left review no.2 / Lion will lay down with the lamb / St. Francis amongst the mortals / Nobody could care less about your private lives / Can the haves use their brains / With our eye on getting their pay / Boy meets girl so what
CDMRED 148 / 27 Apr '98 / Cherry Red

☐ I'M A WALLET/BANKING, VIOLENCE & INTERNATIONAL NARCOTICS
CDMRED 138 / Feb '97 / Cherry Red

☐ THAT'S ALL VERY WELL BUT...
CDMRED 125 / Apr '96 / Cherry Red

McCarthy, Cormac

☐ PICTURE GALLERY BLUES
GLCD 2122 / Aug '95 / Green Linnet

McCarthy, Jimmy

☐ MYSTIC LIPSTICK
LUNSCD 911 / Dec '97 / Mulligan

☐ SONG OF THE SINGING HORSEMAN, THE
On my enchanted sight / Hard man to follow / Mystic lipstick / Missing you / Ride on / No frontiers / Mad lady and me / Grip of parallel / Bright blue rose / Ancient rain / Song of the singing horseman
LUNCD 053 / Jan '91 / Mulligan

☐ WARMER FOR THE SPARK (The Songs Of Jimmy McCarthy) (Various Artists)
TORCD 094 / 6 Apr '98 / Dara

McCarthy, Tommy

☐ SPORTING NELL
MMC 52CD / Dec '97 / Maree Music

McCartney, Paul

☐ ALL THE BEST
Coming up / Ebony and ivory / Listen to what the man said / No more lonely nights / Silly love songs / Let 'em in / C moon / Pipes of peace / Live and let die / Another day / Maybe I'm amazed / Goodnight tonight / Once upon a long ago / Say say say / With a little luck / My love / We all stand together / Mull of Kintyre / Jet / Band on the run
CDPMTV 1 / Nov '87 / Parlophone

☐ CHOBA B CCCP
Kansas City / Twenty flight rock / I'm in love again / Lawdy Miss Clawdy / Bring it on home to me / Lucille / Don't get around much anymore / I'm gonna be a wheel someday / That's alright Mama / Summertime / Ain't that a shame / Crackin' up / Just because / Midnight special
CDPCSD 117 / Aug '91 / Parlophone

☐ FAMILY WAY, THE (Aubut, Carl & Claudel String Quartet)
4542302 / Jun '96 / Philips

☐ FLAMING PIE
Song we were singing / World tonight / If you wanna / Somedays / Young boy / Calico skies / Flaming pie / Heaven on a Sunday / Used to be bad / Souvenir / Little willow / Really love you / Beautiful night / Great day
CDPCSD 171 / Jun '97 / Parlophone

☐ FLOWERS IN THE DIRT
My brave face / Rough ride / You want her too / Distractions / We got married / We got there / Figure of eight / This one / Don't be careless love / That day is done / How many people / Motor of love / Ou est le soleil
CDPMCOL 16 / Jun '93 / Parlophone

☐ GIVE MY REGARDS TO BROAD STREET (Original Soundtrack)
CDP 7892682 / Aug '93 / Parlophone

☐ MCCARTNEY
Lovely Linda / That would be something / Valentine's day / Every night / Hot as sun glasses / Junk / Man we was lonely / Oo you / Momma Miss America / Teddy boy / Singalong junk / Maybe I'm amazed / Kree nakoorie
CDPMCOL 1 / Apr '93 / Parlophone

☐ MCCARTNEY II
Coming up / Temporary secretary / On the way / Waterfalls / Nobody knows / Front parlour / Summer's day song / Frozen jap / Bogey music / Dark room / One of these days / Check my machine / Secret friend
CDP 7891372 / Aug '93 / Parlophone

☐ OFF THE GROUND
Off the ground / Looking for changes / Hope of deliverance / Mistress and maid / I owe it all to you / Biker like an icon / Peace in the neighbourhood / Golden earth girl / Lovers that never were / Get out of my way / Winedark open sea / C'mon people
CDP 7803622 / Feb '93 / Parlophone

☐ PAUL IS LIVE
Drive my car / Let me roll it / Looking for changes / Peace in the neighbourhood / All my loving / Robbie's bit / Good rockin' tonight / We can work it out / Hope of deliverance / Michelle / Biker like an icon / Here, there and everywhere / My love / Magical mystery tour / C'mon people / Lady Madonna / Paperback writer / Penny Lane / Live and let die / Kansas City / Welcome to soundcheck / Hotel in Benidorm / I wanna be your man / Fine day
CDPCSD 147 / Nov '93 / Parlophone

☐ PIPES OF PEACE
Pipes of peace / Say say say / Other me / Keep under cover / So bad / Man / Sweetest little show / Average person / Hey hey / Tug of peace / Through our love
CDP 7892672 / Aug '93 / Parlophone

☐ PRESS TO PLAY
Stranglehold / Good times coming / Talk more talk / Footprints / Only love remains / Press / Pretty little head / Move over busker / Angry / However absurd / Write away / It's not true / Tough on a tightrope / Feel the sun / Once upon a long ago (long version) / Spies like us
CDPMCOL 15 / Jun '93 / Parlophone

☐ RAM (McCartney, Paul & Linda)
Too many people / Three legs / Ram on / Dear boy / Uncle Albert / Smile away: *McCartney, Paul* / Heart of the country: *McCartney, Paul* / Monkberry moon delight / Eat at home / Long haired lady / Backseat of my car: *McCartney, Paul*
CDP 7891392 / Jun '93 / Parlophone

☐ STANDING STONE (A Symphonic Poem) (McCartney, Paul & LSO/John Harle/Richard Rodney Bennett)
After heavy light years / Cell growth / Human theme / He awoke startled / Crystal ship / Sea voyage / Lost at sea / Release / Subtle colours merged soft contours / Safe haven / Standing stone / Peaceful movement / Messenger / Lament / Trance / Eclipse / Strings pluck / Horns blow / Drums beat / Glory tales / Fuga / Celebration / Rustic dance / Love duet
CDC 5564842 / 13 Oct '97 / EMI Classics

☐ TUG OF WAR
Tug of war / Take it away / Always somebody who cares / What's that you're doing / Here today / Ballroom dancing / Pound is sinking / Wanderlust / Get it / Be what you see / Dress me up as a robber / Ebony and ivory
CDP 7892662 / Aug '93 / Parlophone

☐ UNPLUGGED (The Official Bootleg)
Be bop a lula / I lost my little girl / Here, there and everywhere / Blue moon of Kentucky / We can work it out / San Francisco Bay blues / I've just seen a face / Every night / She's a woman / Hi-heel sneakers / And I love her / That would be something / Blackbird / Ain't no sunshine / Good rockin' tonight / Singin' the blues / Junk
CDP 7964132 / May '91 / Parlophone

MacCaskill, Ishbel

☐ SIODA
SKYECD 006 / Jan '95 / Macmeanmna

McCaslin, Donny

☐ EXILE AND DISCOVERY
Along came Betty / Exile and discovery / Prayer for Frances / Mountain Mama / Isfahan / Tenderly / Etudes / Speak low / Bye ya
860142 / Jul '98 / Naxos Jazz

McCaslin, Mary

☐ BEST OF MARY MCCASLIN
Things we said today / Northfield / Wayward wind / Prairie in the sky / San Bernardino waltz / Dealers / Ghost riders in the sky / Cole Younger / Living without you / Circle of friends / Blackbird / Bramble and the rose / Last cannonball / Way out west / My world is empty without you / Young Westerly / Back to Salinas / Old friends
PHCD 1149 / '92 / Philo

☐ BROKEN PROMISES
PH 1160CD / May '94 / Philo

☐ OLD FRIENDS
Things we said today / Oklahoma hills / Wendigo / Way out there / Pinball wizard / My world is empty without you babe / Wayward wind / Blackbird / Don't fence me in / Old friends
CDPH 1046 / Nov '96 / Philo

☐ PRAIRIE IN THE SKY
Pass me by / Priscilla Drive / Ballad of Weaverville / Back to Silas / Ghost riders in the sky / Last cannonball / It's my time / Cornerstone cowboy / Prairie in the sky / Cole Younger / Dealers / My love
CDPH 1024 / Nov '95 / Philo

☐ WAY OUT WEST
(Waiting) music strings / Oh Hollywood / Waiting / Let it be me / Living without you / Way out west / (Down the road) down the road / San Bernardino waltz / Circle of friends / Ballad of a wanted man / Northfield / Young Westley
CDPH 1011 / Apr '98 / Philo

McCavity's Cat

☐ GENEVER CONVENTION, THE
Lady alcohol / Bar from hell / 6 1-the bullet / Dampton worm / Devil went down to georgia / Drink for 2 / Fambly / I'd rather go to hell than spend eternity with you / John wayne is big leggy / Merangue (take me back to tershcelling) / Preacher / Sinners / Thunderbird wine / Ballad of gavin shellfish
MWCD 1003 / Apr '93 / Music & Words

☐ SCRATCH
MWCD 1006 / Dec '95 / Music & Words

McClain, Sam

☐ JOY AND PAIN
Gone for good / Sledgehammer soul and down home blues / What you want me to do / Where you been so long / I'm so lonely / Forgive and forget / Lord will make a way / Long train runnin' / Soul that's been abused
CCD 11058 / Jul '98 / Crosscut

☐ KEEP ON MOVIN'
AQ 1031 / May '95 / Audioquest

McClennan, Tommy

☐ GUITAR KING 1939-1942, A
158702 / Jan '97 / Blues Collection

☐ TRAVELLIN' HIGHWAY MAN 1939-1942
You can mistreat me here / New shake 'em on down / Bottle it up and go / Boogie woogie woman / Mr. So and so blues / I love my baby / It's hard to be lonesome / Blue as I can be / Roll me baby / New highway 51
TMCD 06 / Oct '90 / Travellin' Man

McClinton, Delbert

☐ DELBERT MCCLINTON
Sun medley / Tell me about it / Weatherman / Mary Lou / Have a little faith in me / Wanderer / Just you and me / One more last chance / Lay around and love on you / He will break your heart / Outskirts of town
CURBCD 008 / Mar '94 / Curb

☐ LIVE FROM AUSTIN
Maybe someday baby / Lipstick traces / Standing on shaky ground / Sandy beaches / I wanna thank you baby / B movie boxcar blues / I've got dreams to remember / Let me be your lover / Going back to louisiana / You are my sunshine / Givin' it up for love
ALCD 4773 / May '93 / Alligator

☐ NEVER BEEN ROCKED ENOUGH
Every time I roll the dice / I used to worry / Miss you fever / Why me / Have a little faith in me / Never been rocked enough / Blues as blues can get / Can I change my mind / Cease and desist / Stir it up / Good man, good woman
CURBCD 005 / Mar '94 / Curb

☐ ONE OF THE FORTUNATE FEW
RTD 53042 / 1 Dec '97 / Radioactive

☐ VICTIM OF LIFE'S CIRCUMSTANCES/ GENUINE COWHIDE
Victim of life's circumstances / Honky tonkin' (I guess I done me some) / Two more bottles of wine / Lesson in the pain of love / Do it / Object of my affection / Ruby Louise / Real good itch / Solid gold plated fool / Morgan City fool / Troubled woman / It's love baby (24 hours a day) / Please please please / Lovey dovey / Before you accuse me / Blue Monday / I'm dyin' fast as I can / Lipstick, powder and paint / Pledging my love / One kiss led to another / (When she wants good lovin') my baby comes to me / Special love song / Let the good times roll / Love rustler / Let love come between us / Under suspicion / Some people
RVCD 65 / Feb '97 / Raven

McClure, Ron

☐ CLOSER TO YOUR TEARS
SCCD 31413 / Jul '97 / Steeplechase

☐ DREAM TEAM
SCCD 31435 / 1 Jun '98 / Steeplechase

☐ PINK CLOUD (McClure, Ron Quartet)
860022 / Jun '97 / Naxos Jazz

☐ YESTERDAY'S TOMORROW (McClure, Ron/John Abercrombie/Aldo Romano)
EPC 884 / Feb '92 / European Music Production

McCluskey Brothers

☐ AWARE OF ALL
ASKCD 013 / Jul '92 / Vinyl Japan

☐ FAVOURITE COLOURS
Perfect afternoon / Lonely satelite / Favourite colours / She said to the driver / 1000 Years / Better days / Cinder street / When the loving comes / Slip away / Passport
KF 001 CD / Jan '93 / Kingfisher

☐ WONDERFUL AFFAIR
KF 002 / Jun '96 / Kingfisher

MacColl, Angus

☐ CLAN MACCOLL, THE
2/4 marches / Seagull jigs / Reels / March/ strathspey/reel / Archie beag jigs / 6/8 marches / Strathspey/reels / Tommy Tully's air / Gaelic airs/ reel / Swallows tail reels / Gaelic air jigs
LCOM 5255 / Nov '96 / Lismor

☐ PIPING CENTRE 1996 RECITAL SERIES VOL.4, THE (MacColl, Angus & Gordon Duncan)
Rab's wedding/Mardick: *MacColl, Angus* / Medley: *MacColl, Angus* / Kelly MacColl/Margaret M. Black/ Centenary jewel: *MacColl, Angus* / Medley: *MacColl, Angus* / Medley: *MacColl, Angus* / Medley: *MacColl, Angus* / Medley: *MacColl, Angus* / Medley: *Duncan, Gordon* / Medley: *Duncan, Gordon* / Duchess of Edinburgh/93rd at Modder river: *Duncan, Gordon* / Medley: *Duncan, Gordon* / MacDougal's gathering: *Duncan, Gordon* / Crossing the minch/Clumsy lover: *Duncan, Gordon* / Medley (10): *Duncan, Gordon*
COMD 2073 / 2 Feb '98 / Temple

MacColl, Ewan

☐ BLACK AND WHITE (The Definitive Ewan MacColl Collection)
Ballad of accounting / Driver's song / My old man / Dirty old town / Black and white / Brother did you weep / Press gang / Shoals of herring / Sheath and knife / Highland muster roll / Cam ye o'er frae France / Maid gaed tae the mill / Nobody knew she was there / Looking for a job / Kilroy was here / First time ever I saw your face / Foggy dew / Joy of living
COOKCD 038 / Feb '95 / Cooking Vinyl

☐ BLOW, BOYS, BLOW (MacColl, Ewan & A.L. Lloyd)
TCD 1024 / Aug '96 / Tradition

☐ BOTHY BALLADS
OSS 101CD / Apr '94 / Ossian

☐ CLASSIC SCOTS BALLADS (MacColl, Ewan & Peggy Seeger)
TCD 1051 / Jul '97 / Tradition

☐ EFDSS & 70TH BIRTHDAY CONCERTS
Thirty foot trailer / Shoals of herring / Fish gutter's song / First time ever / White wind / Berry fields of Blair / Going to West / Invader / My old man / Spinning wheel / Joy of living / Ewan MacColl in conversation with Jim Lloyd
MASHCD 002 / Jun '96 / Cooking Vinyl

☐ JACOBITE REBELLIONS, THE
Ye Jacobites by name / Such a parcel of rogues in a nation / Will ye go to Sherriffmuir / Wae's me for Prince Charlie / Charlie is my darling / Haughs o' Cromdale / Bonnie moorhen / Johnny Cope / Cam ye o'er frae France / There's three brave loyal fellows / This is no my ain house / Piper o'Dundee / Donald MacGillavry / MacLean's welcome / Will ye no' come back again
OSS 103CD / Apr '94 / Ossian

☐ LEGEND OF EWAN MACCOLL, THE
REMCD 514 / Feb '98 / Reactive

☐ NAMING OF NAMES (MacColl, Ewan & Peggy Seeger)
Economic miracle / Just the tax for me / Grocer / Not going to give it back / Sellafield child / Bring the Summer home / Maggie went green / Nuclear means jobs / Hose hunting blues / Dracumag / Rogue's gallery / Island / We remember (naming of names)
COOKCD 036 / May '90 / Cooking Vinyl

☐ REAL MACCOLL, THE
Ye Jacobites by name / Johnny Cope / Cam ye o'er frae France / Haughs o' Cromdale / Such a parcel of rogues in a nation / Farewell to Sicily / Derek Bentley / Johnny O'Breadislee / Go down ye murderers / Van Diemen's land / Minorie / Sheep crook and black dog / Bramble briar / One night as I lay on my bed / Grey cock / Blantyre explosion / Gresford disaster / Four loom weaver / Song of the iron road / Dirty old town
TSCD 463 / May '93 / Topic

☐ SCOTTISH POPULAR SONGS
OSS 105CD / Apr '94 / Ossian

☐ SONGS OF ROBERT BURNS, THE
OSS 102CD / Apr '94 / Ossian

☐ TRADITIONAL SONGS & BALLADS
OSS 104CD / Apr '94 / Ossian

MacColl, Kirsty

☐ ELECTRIC LANDLADY
Walking down Madison / All I ever need / Children of the revolution / Halloween / My affair / Lying down / He never mentioned love / We'll never pass this way again / Hardest word / Maybe it's imaginary / My way home / One and only
CDVIP 209 / 3 Aug '98 / Virgin VIP

☐ ESSENTIAL COLLECTION, THE
STIFFCD 17 / Aug '96 / Disky

☐ GALORE (The Best Of Kirsty MacColl)
They don't know / There's a guy works down the chip shop swears he's Elvis / New England / He's on the beach / Fairytale of New York / Miss Otis regrets / Free world / Innocence / You just haven't earned it yet baby / Days / Don't come the cowboy with me Sonny Jim / Walking down Madison / My affair / Angel / Titanic days / Can't stop killing you / Caroline / Perfect day
CDV 2763 / Mar '95 / Virgin

☐ KITE
Innocence / Mother's ruin / No victims / Don't come the cowboy with me Sonny Jim / What do pretty girls do / End of a perfect day / Free world / Days / Fifteen minutes / Tread lightly / Dancing in limbo / You and me baby / You just haven't earned it yet baby / La foret de mimosas / Complainte pour ste Catherine
CDKM 1 / Apr '89 / Virgin

☐ TITANIC DAYS
You know it's you / Soho sqaure / Angel / Last day of summer / Bad / Can't stop killing you / Titanic days / Don't go home / Big boy on a Saturday night / Just woke up / Tomorrow never comes
4509947112 / Dec '96 / WEA

☐ WHAT DO PRETTY GIRLS DO
Don't come the cowboy with me sonny jim / What do pretty girls do / Don't run away from me now / Still life / There's a guy who works down the chip shop swears he's Elvis / Walk right back / Darling let's have another baby / New England / My affair / Bad / Can't stop killing you / Caroline / Free world / He's on the beach / New England
HUX 001 / 23 Feb '98 / Hux

McColley, Laurie

☐ PSEUDONYMOUS
MUDCD 022 / Oct '96 / Mud

McComb, Dave

☐ LOVE OF WILL
D 31071 / Mar '94 / Mushroom

McComiskey, Billy

☐ MAKIN' THE ROUNDS
Boogie reel-the controversial reel / Independent-rabbit in the field / Bill hoare's-mick flaherty's (reels) / O'donnell's-spellan the fiddler (hornpipes) / Eddie kelly's-miss casey's (jigs) / Wood's lamentation / Flowers of brooklyn-the palm tree (reels) / Peter murphy's-mick flaherty's (jigs) / Johnny allen's-sporting nell (reels) / Planxty davis / Windsor terrace-sault's own hornpipe (hornpipes) / Dinny delaney's-set the clock (reels) / Wandering minstrel-the millpond / Leave my way-chicago reel (reels)
GLCD 1034 / '92 / Green Linnet

McConnell, Cathal

☐ FOR THE SAKE OF OLD DECENCY (McConnell, Cathal & Len Graham)
SA 22012CD / Jan '94 / Sage Arts

McConnell, Rob

☐ BRASS IS BACK, THE (McConnell, Rob & The Boss Brass)
Strollin' / All the things you are / Love of my life / Who asked / Slow grind / Winter in Winnipeg / Days gone by / Them there eyes
CCD 4458 / May '91 / Concord Jazz

☐ BRASSY AND SASSY (McConnell, Rob & The Boss Band)
Strike up the band / Hey / Very early / Things ain't what they used to be / Scrapple from the apple / Embraceable you/Why did I choose you / Blue serge suit / Club Sirocco / Samnambles / Blues unblue
CCD 4508 / Jun '92 / Concord Jazz

☐ DON'T GET AROUND MUCH ANYMORE (McConnell, Rob & The Boss Brass)
Don't get around much anymore / Waltz you knew was blue / Once I loved / If you never came to me / Crazy rhythm / Gee baby ain't I good to you / (Back home again in) Indiana / Donna Lee / Bad and the beautiful / Robin / Back beat / Rockin' in rhythm
CCD 4661 / Aug '95 / Concord Jazz

☐ EVEN CANADIANS GET THE BLUES (McConnell, Rob & The Boss Brass)
Blue tag / Even Canadians get the blues / Clarinet black and blue / Do you mean it / Blue hodge / Sixth sense / Countless blues / Shuffle boogie swamp groove blues / O Canada
CCD 4722 / Sep '96 / Concord Jazz

☐ **JAZZ ALBUM, THE (McConnell, Rob & The Boss Brass)**
SB 2080 / Jan '97 / Sea Breeze

☐ **OUR 25TH YEAR (McConnell, Rob & The Boss Brass)**
4 BC / Imagination / What am I here for / Just tell me yes or no / Riffs I have known / TQ2 / Nightfall / Broadway / My bells / Flying home
CCD 4559 / Jun '93 / Bellaphon

☐ **OVERTIME (McConnell, Rob & The Boss Brass)**
Overtime / Touch of your lips / Stella by starlight / Hawg jawz / After you / Alone together / This may be your lucky day / Wait and see
CCD 4618 / Nov '94 / Concord Jazz

☐ **PLAY JAZZ CLASSICS (McConnell, Rob & The Boss Brass)**
Duke / Invitation / Autumn in New York / Child is born / Peace/Blue silver / Santa Claus blues / Pensativa / Day dream / Sophisticated / Lil' darlin'
CCD 47842 / 6 Oct '97 / Concord Jazz

☐ **THREE FOR THE ROAD (McConnell, Rob & Ed Bickert/Don Thompson)**
Sleepin' bee / Dream a little dream of me / Two for the road / Royal blue / Dreamsville / I'm thru with love / Seems like old times / Dream dancing / Our waltz / I don't know enough about you / Last night when we were young / Young and foolish / In the blue of evening
CCD 47652 / Apr '97 / Concord Jazz

☐ **TRIO SKETCHES (McConnell, Rob & Ed Bickert/Neil Swanson)**
Snow White / My ideal / I have dreamed / Can't we be friends / Baubles, bangles and beads / This is love of mine, this is always / Long ago and far away / I'm gonna sit right down and write myself a letter / Ornithardy / 'Deed I do
CCD 4591 / Mar '94 / Concord Jazz

McConville, Tom

☐ **CROSS THE RIVER**
Hurleys / Homes of Donegal / Tone Rowe's/Smithy's baccy tin / Caliope house / How can my poor heart / Frenchie's reel / President Garfield's reel / Johnny miner / Gold ring / Cross the river / Lark in the morning / Goodnight waltz / Overgate / Calum Donaldson/Mick Johnson's parrot/Da grocer / Wish the wars were all over / Ben's foot/Birmingham fling
OBMCD 01 / Feb '96 / Old Bridge

☐ **FIDDLER'S FANCY**
Quayside / Champion hornpipe / Cliff / Hill's no. 8 / Gateshead hornpipe / Pear tree / Cage / High level hornpipe / Flight of fancy / Hawk polka / Barber's pole / Beeswing / Lads like beer/Marquis of Waterford / Hawk / Proudlock's fancy / Fiddler's fancy / Bottle bank / Blaydon flats / Earl Grey
OBMCD 04 / Feb '96 / Old Bridge

McCoo, Marilyn

☐ **I HOPE WE GET TO LOVE IN TIME (McCoo, Marilyn & Billy Davis Junior)**
RAZCD 2098 / May '96 / Razor & Tie

McCook, Tommy

☐ **COOKIN'**
CDHR 706 / Jun '96 / Trojan

☐ **DOWN ON BOND STREET**
Inez / Yellow basket, The (a tisket a tasket) / Down on Bond Street / Wall Street shuffle / Moody ska / Real cool / Tommy's rocksteady / Soul serenade / Persian cat (in a Persian market) / Saboo / Shadow of your smile / Music is my occupation / Our man Flint / Mad mad mad / Ode to billy joe / Heatwave / World needs love / Flying home / Mary Poppins / Second fiddle
CDTRL 326 / Mar '94 / Trojan

☐ **DYNAMITE (McCook, Tommy & The Supersonics)**
RN 7050 / 13 Jul '98 / Rhino

☐ **GREATER JAMAICA (McCook, Tommy & The Supersonics)**
0444132 / 27 Oct '97 / Jet Set

McCorkle, Susannah

☐ **FROM BESSIE TO BRAZIL**
Love / People that you never get to love / Thief in the night / Waters of March / Accentuate the positive / How deep is the ocean / Lady is a tramp / Quality time / My sweetie went away / Still crazy after all these years / Adeus America / That ole devil called love / Hit the road to dreamland / You go to my head
CCD 4547 / May '93 / Concord Jazz

☐ **FROM BROADWAY TO BEBOP**
Guys and dolls / Once you've been in love / Chica chica boom chic / My buddy / It's easy to remember / Don't fence me in / One of the good guys / I don't think I'll end it all today / Moody's mood / He loves me / Friend like me / I remember Bill
CCD 4615 / Oct '94 / Concord Jazz

☐ **I'LL TAKE ROMANCE**
Beautiful friendship / My foolish heart / I'll take romance / Get out of town / It never entered my mind / Let's get lost / Spring is here / Taking a chance on love / I concentrate on you / Lover man / That old feeling / Zing went the strings of my heart / Where do you start / I thought about you
CCD 4491 / Jan '92 / Concord Jazz

☐ **LET'S FACE THE MUSIC (The Songs Of Irving Berlin)**
I'd rather lead a band / Let's face the music and dance / Isn't this a lovely day (to be caught in the rain) / Heat wave / How deep is the ocean / Medley / There's no business like showbusiness / Cheek to cheek / Love and the weather / Supper time / Medley / Better luck next time / Let yourself go / Waiting at the end of the road
CCD 47592 / Jun '97 / Concord Jazz

☐ **NO MORE BLUES**
Fascinating rhythm / Swing that music / Ballad of pearly sue / P.s. I love you / Can't take you nowhere / No more blues / Do nothing till you hear from me / Breezin' along with the blues / Don't let the sun catch you cryin' / Who cares / Sometimes I'm happy / Everything's been done before
CCD 4370 / Apr '89 / Concord Jazz

☐ **OVER THE RAINBOW (The Songs Of E.Y. 'Yip' Harburg)**
Old devil moon / Begat / If I only had a heart / Ding dong, the witch is dead / Over the rainbow / Poor you / Napoleon / What is there to say / Thrill me / Happiness is a thing called Joe / Eagle and me / Moanin' in the mornin' / Down with love / Here's to your illusions/In times like these
TJA 10033 / Dec '96 / Jazz Alliance

☐ **PEOPLE THAT YOU NEVER GET TO LOVE, THE**
No more blues / Bye bye country boy / Rain sometimes / Lady's in love with you / I have the feeling I've been here before / I won't dance / Hungry years / People that you never get to love / Call of the city / Alone too long / Foodophobia / I've grown accustomed to his face / Feeling of Jazz / I'm pulling through
TJA 100342 / Sep '97 / Jazz Alliance

☐ **SABIA**
Tristeza / Estate / Dilemma / Dreamer / Sabia / So many stars / So danco samba / Manha de carnaval / P'ra machucar meu coracao / Travessia / A felicidade
CCD 4418 / Oct '90 / Concord Jazz

☐ **SOMEONE TO WATCH OVER ME (The Songs Of George Gershwin)**
They can't take that away from me / Who cares / Someone to watch over me / It ain't necessarily so / How long has this been going on / I got rhythm / Love walked in / I loves you porgy / They all laughed / Summertime / S'wonderful / I was doing allright / I got plenty of nothin' / Will you remember me / Drifting along with the tide
CCD 47982 / 5 May '98 / Concord Jazz

☐ **SONGS OF COLE PORTER, THE**
Night and day / Anything goes / Just one of those things / It's alright with me / Weren't / From this moment on / Who wants to be a millionaire / Why don't we try staying home / You do something to me / Easy to love / Goodbye little dream, goodbye / You'd be so nice to come home to / Let's do it / Ev'rytime we say goodbye
CCD 4696 / May '96 / Concord Jazz

☐ **SONGS OF JOHNNY MERCER, THE**
At the jazz band ball / Fools rush in / I'm old fashioned / Blues in the night / My new celebrity is you / Skylark / Any place I hang my hat is my home / Talk to me baby / This time the dream's on me / Dream / How little we know / Harlem butterfly / Arthur Murray taught me dancing in a hurry / Love's got me in a lazy mood / One for my baby (and one more for the road)
TJA 10031 / Apr '96 / Jazz Alliance

☐ **THANKS FOR THE MEMORY (The Songs Of Leo Robin)**
Diamonds are a girl's best friend / My ideal / Beyond the blue horizon / It was written in the stars / My cutie's due at two to two / Thanks for the memory / Hooray for love / True blue Lou / Little girl from little rock / Hav'in myself a time / Rainy night in Rio / In love in vain / Bye bye baby
TJA 100352 / 17 Aug '98 / Jazz Alliance

McCormack, John

☐ **ACOUSTIC VICTOR/HMV RECORDINGS VOL.2 1912-1914, THE (2CD Set)**
Maire my girl / Like stars above / Take o these lips away / Masque / Asthore / Farewell Natoma / I know of two bright eyes / Eileen Alroon / Wearing of the green / Rosary / Harp that once through Tara's halls / Silver threads among the gold / I Gioielli della Madonna / At dawning / Mefistofele / Les pecheurs des perles / Mi par d'udir ancora / Nirvana / There is a flower that bloometh / My dreams / Sweet Genevieve / I'll sing thee songs of Araby / Where the river shannon flows / Silver threads among the gold / Within the garden of my heart / Dear love remember me / Manon / Molly Brannigan / Foggy dew / Low back'd car / Sospiri miei andante ove vi mando / Say au revoir but not goodbye / Mother o mine / Down in the forest / Carmen - votre mere avec moi sortait de la chapelle / I hear a thrush at eve / Goodbye
820072 / Feb '98 / Romophone

☐ **CHRISTIAN CELEBRATION, A (Favourite Hymns, Carols & Sacred Music)**
GEMMCD 9990 / Nov '92 / Pearl

☐ **COUNT JOHN MCCORMACK VOL.7**
Snowy breasted pearl / Meeting of the waters / When shall the day break in Erin / Molly Bawn / Irish emigrant / Avourneen / Killarney / Green Isle of Erin / Love thee dearest, love thee / Believe me, if all those endearing young charms / Norah the pride of Kildare / Come back to Erin / Eileen Alannah, Augus Asthore / Minstrel boy / Foggy dew / Kathleen Mavoureen / Dear little shamrock / Lily of Killarney / Once again / Wearing of the green / God save Ireland / Boys of Wexford / Nation once again / Croppy boy / Home to Athlone
OPAL CDS9847 / Aug '91 / Opal

☐ **GREEN ISLE OF ERIN**
CDC 006 / Feb '97 / Ceol

☐ **JOHN MCCORMACK**
I'll walk beside you / Green bushes / Jeannie with the light brown hair / Star of County Down / Village that nobody knows / She is far from the land / Passing by / Drink to me only with thine eyes / Sweetly she sleeps, my Alice fair / Old house / Maureen / Lass with the delicate air / Child's prayer / Harp that once thro' Tara's hall / Bard of Armagh / Terence's farewell to Kathleen / O Mary dear / Believe me / If all those endearing young charms / Ye banks and braes o' bonnie Doon / Silent moon / Meeting of the waters / Gentle maiden / Love thee, dearest, love thee / Off to Philadelphia / Oft in the stilly night
CDMFP 6358 / Jun '97 / Music For Pleasure

☐ **JOHN MCCORMACK IN AMERICAN SONG**
GEMMCD 9971 / Oct '92 / Pearl

☐ **KERRY DANCE (And Other Fine Irish Ballads)**
Come back to Erin / She is far from the land / Irish emigrant / Low backed car / My lagan loce / Kathleen Mavoureen / Killarney / Macushla / Molly Brannigan / Eileen Alannah / Mother Machree
CDCH 207 / Jun '93 / Happy Days

☐ **MINSTREL BOY, THE**
Minstrel boy / Nirvana / My dreams / Little love, a little kiss / Angel's serenade / Ave Maria / Serenata / Barcarolle / Before my window / Swans / Come, my beloved / Moonlight and roses / I look into your garden / Bird songs at eventide / By the short cut to the roses / Fairy tree / Harp that once thro' tara's halls / Once in a blue moon / Charm me asleep / Vespers / Sweetly she sleeps, my Alice fair / Song remembered / Dawning of the day / House, love, made for you and me / Old houses
CDAJA 5224 / Apr '97 / Living Era

☐ **SCOTTISH & IRISH SONGS**
Trottin' to the fair / Bonnie wee thing / My lagan love / Bonnie Mary of Argyle / Snowy breasted pearl / Turn ye to me / Wearing of the green / When the dew is falling / Low backed car / Annie Laurie / When you and I were young Maggie / Auld Scotch sangs / Irish emigrant / Maiden of morven / She moved through the fair / Ye banks and braes o' bonnie Doon / Green bushes / Song to the seals / Maureen / Star O' the country down
MIDCD 005 / Apr '95 / Moidart

☐ **SINGS IRISH SONGS**
8464604072 / 24 Mar '98 / Special Music

☐ **SONGS OF JOHN MCCORMACK**
CDIRISH 014 / Oct '95 / Outlet

☐ **WHEN IRISH EYES ARE SMILING**
Angels guard thee / Bard of Armagh / Believe me, if all those endearing young charms / Brown bird singing / Come into the garden Maud / Dear old pal of mine / Dream once again / Flirtation / Garden where the praties grow / I hear you calling me / I'll sing thee songs of Araby / Irish emigrant / Jeanie with the light brown hair / Kerry dance / Macushla / She moved through the fair / Since you went away / South winds / Star of County Down / Sunshine of your smile / Turn ye to me / Venetian song / Waiting for you / When Irish eyes are smiling / When you and I were young Maggie
CDAJA 5119 / Mar '94 / Living Era

☐ **WHERE THE RIVER SHANNON FLOWS**
Londonderry air / When Irish eyes are smiling / Garden where the praties grow / Eileen Alannah / Mother in Ireland / Ballynore ballad / Harp that once through Tara's halls / Kathleen Mavoureen / Padraic the fiddiler / Mother Machree / Bard of Armagh / My Irish song of songs / Norah O'Neale / By the short cut of the Rosses / Irish Emigrant / Snowy breasted pearl / My dark Rosaleen / Love's old sweet song / Macushla / Low back'd car / Where the River Shannon flows / Foggy dew / Rose of Tralee / Kitty my love / Star of the County Down
PASTCD 7022 / Mar '94 / Flapper

McCormick, John

☐ **COME BACK TO ERIN**
Come back to Erin / Nation once again / Boys of Wexford / Green isle of Erin / Killarney / Love thee dearest / Croppy boy / Trottin' to the fair / Savoureen deelish / My dark rosaleen / Kathleen Mavourneen / Off in the stilly night
CD 21215 / Nov '97 / Laserlight

☐ **MERCURY'S WELL**
PH 009CD / Jul '95 / Phantom

McCoury Brothers

☐ **MCCOURY BROTHERS**
ROUCD 0230 / Apr '95 / Rounder

☐ **RONNIE & ROB MCCOURY**
ROUCD 0353 / Oct '95 / Rounder

McCoury, Del

☐ **BLUE SIDE OF TOWN, THE**
Beauty of my dreams / Queen Anne's Lace / If you need a fool / Old memories mean nothing to me / Try me one more time / Before the fire comes down / Blue side of town / Seasons in my heart / That's alright mama / Make room for the blues / High on the mountain / I believe
ROUCD 0292 / '92 / Rounder

☐ **COLD HARD FACTS, THE (McCoury, Del Band)**
Cold hard facts / Blue darlin' / Smoking gun / Love is a long road / Henry Walker / Baltimore Jonny / Blackjack county chains / Hard on my heart / Snake in the house / First time she left / Loggin' man / Member of the blues
ROUCD 0363 / Oct '96 / Rounder

☐ **DEEPER SHADE OF BLUE, A**
ROUCD 303 / Jan '94 / Rounder

☐ **HIGH ON A MOUNTAIN (McCoury, Del & The Dixie Pals)**
ROUCD 0019 / Sep '95 / Rounder

☐ **I WONDER WHERE YOU ARE TONIGHT**
ARHCD 5006 / Apr '95 / Arhoolie

McCowan, Andrew

☐ **FLING TIME VOL.1**
CDMON 823 / May '95 / Monarch

☐ **FLING TIME VOL.2**
CDMON 824 / May '95 / Monarch

McCoy, Charlie

☐ **GREATEST HITS**
4658622 / Aug '90 / Monument

McCoy, Clyde

☐ **CLYDE MCCOY & HIS ORCHESTRA 1951 (McCoy, Clyde Orchestra)**
CCD 082 / Jul '96 / Circle

McCoy, Hank

☐ **MOHAWK STREET (McCoy, Hank & The Dead Ringers)**
OK 33026CD / Feb '95 / Okra

McCoy, John

☐ **BRAINSTORM**
Dreaming of the dead / Heavy metal cowboys / On and on / Outrageous / I know a place / Don't walk away / Save me / Steam train / Bad luck / Josephine / Tarot cards / Prophets of doom / List/The list continues/Zoomusic / Disillusioned / Hawaiians 2-Electrolux 1
SJPCD 026 / 7 Sep '98 / Angel Air

☐ **THINK HARD AGAIN**
Freemind / Demon rose / Loving lies / Hell to play / Heads will roll / Ride the night / Fear of the morning / Jerusalem / Oh well / Night lights / Sound of thunder / Temporary threshold shift / Because you lied / Night lights / Oh well
SJPCD 001 / Jan '97 / Angel Air

McCoy, Neal

☐ **GREATEST HITS**
Now I pray for rain / No doubt about it / Wink / City that put the country back in me / For a change / They're playin' our song / If I was a drinkin' man / You gotta love that / Then you can tell me goodbye / Shake
7567830112 / 15 Sep '97 / Atlantic

☐ **NEAL MCCOY**
Then you can tell me goodbye / Betcha' can't do that again / If it hadn't been so good / She can / Rapper's delight / Ballad of jed clampett / Going going gone / That woman of mine / Me too / I ain't complainin' / It should've happened that way / Day-o (the banana boat song)
7567829072 / Jul '96 / Atlantic

McCoys

☐ **HANG ON SLOOPY (The Best Of The McCoys)**
Meet the McCoys / Hang on sloopy / I can't explain / Fever / Sorrow / Up and down / If you tell a lie / Come on let's go / Little people / Smoky Joe's cafe / Mr. Summer / Everyday I have to cry / (You make me feel) So good / Runaway / Gaitor tails and monkey ribs / Koko / Bald headed Lena / Say those magic words / Don't worry Mother (Your son's heart is pure) / I got to go back (And watch that little girl dance) / Dynamite / Beat the clock
ZK 47074 / Jul '95 / Columbia

McCrackin, Bill

☐ **I AM THE EGGMAN**
SH 41CD / Jun '97 / Shredder

McCracklin, Jimmy

☐ **HIGH ON THE BLUES**
Double dealing / Just got to know / Stay away from that monkey / Yesterday is gone / Would man be satisfied / Like my mama / I finally got you / You're the one / Love money can't buy / Think / I got somebody / Girl stealer
CDSXE 072 / Jul '93 / Stax

☐ **MERCURY RECORDINGS, THE**
Wobble / Georgia slop / Hitched / No one to love me / (I'll be glad when you're dead) you rascal you / By myself / Doomed lover / With your love / Let's do it / Bridge / What's that (part 1) / What's that (part 2) / Folsom Prison blues
BCD 15558 / Mar '92 / Bear Family

☐ **TASTE OF THE BLUES, A**
BB 9535CD / Aug '94 / Bullseye Blues

☐ **WALK, THE (Jimmy McCracklin At His Best)**
RE 2124 / Mar '97 / Razor & Tie

McCrae, George

☐ BEST OF GEORGE MCCRAE, THE (Rock Your Baby)
Rock your baby / I ain't lyin' / Honey (I'll live my life for you) / You treat me so good / Love in motion / Nothing but love / Cut the rug / It's been so long / Let's dance (people all over the world) / Hey sexy dancer / Kiss me (the way I like it) / (You've got) my love my life my soul / Don't you feel my love / I get lifted / I can't leave you alone / Let's dance: McCrae, George & Gwen / Winners together losers apart: McCrae, George & Gwen
HTCD 30 / 20 Apr '98 / Hot Productions

☐ DO SOMETHING
343312 / Mar '96 / Koch International

☐ ROCK YOUR BABY
Rock your baby / I can't leave you alone / You got my heart / You can have it all / Look at you / Make it right / I need somebody like you / I get lifted
MUSCD 503 / Sep '94 / MCI Original Masters

☐ ROCK YOUR BABY
Rock your baby / I can't leave you alone / I get lifted / Look at you / I ain't lyin' / Honey (I'll live my life for you) / Kiss me (the way I like it) / Let's dance (people all over the world) / I need somebody like you / You can't have it all / Sing a happy song / It's been so long / You got my heart / Make it right
DC 882762 / 2 Feb '98 / Disky

McCrae, Gwen

☐ BEST OF GWEN MCCRAE, THE
Rockin' chair / For your love / It's worth the hurt / 90% of me is you / It keeps on raining / He don't ever lose his groove / Winners together or losers apart: McCrae, Gwen & George / Let your love do the talkin': McCrae, Gwen & George / You and I were made for each other: McCrae, Gwen & George / Damn right it's good / Love without sex / Starting all over again / Tonight's the night / Let's straighten it out / Love insurance / Cradle of love / Maybe I'll find somebody new / Melody of life / All this love I'm giving
NEXCD 189 / May '92 / Sequel

☐ GIRLFRIEND'S BOYFRIEND
HGCD 5 / Mar '96 / Homegrown

☐ PSYCHIC HOT LINE
GWX 42212 / Aug '96 / Ichiban

McCray, Larry

☐ DELTA HURRICANE
Delta hurricane / Adding up / Last four nickels / Soul shine / Not that much / Last hand of the night / Witchin' moon / Blue river / Hole in my heart / Three straight days of rain / Blues in the city
VPBCD 10 / May '93 / Pointblank

☐ MEET ME AT THE LAKE (McCray, Larry & The Bluegills)
Too much rooster / More walk, less talk / In a funk, in a phone booth / Hell to pay / Look around / No letter / Havoc / Never let it happen again / Moon is full / Spend it
ATM 1124 / Nov '96 / Atomic Theory

McCready, Mindy

☐ IF I DON'T STAY
What if I do / This is me / For a good time call / Cross against the moon / On the other side / Romeo / If I don't stay the night / You'll never know / Fine art of loving a woman / Only a whisper / Long long time
74321528302 / 8 Nov '97 / RCA

☐ TEN THOUSAND ANGELS
Ten thousand angels / Guys do it all the time / All that I am / Maybe he'll notice her now / Girl's gotta do (What a girl's gotta do) / Have a nice day / It ain't a party / Without love / Tell me something I don't know / Breakin' it
7863668062 / Mar '97 / BNA

McCready, Rich

☐ THAT ABOUT COVERS IT
MGO 115 / Jul '97 / MGO

McCue, Bill

☐ A' THE BEST FROM BILL MCCUE
Bonnie Scotland / Star o'Rabbie Burns / Annie Laurie / Poem (of a' the airts) / Address to the haggis / Whispering hope / If I were a rich man / Nameless lass / Auld lang syne
CDITV 587 / Oct '96 / Scotdisc

☐ COUNT YOUR BLESSINGS
Count your blessings / Softly and tenderly Jesus is calling / Where we'll never grow old / What a friend we have in Jesus / Lord's prayer / If I can help somebody / Going home / Beautiful Isle of somewhere / Shall we gather at the river / Bless this house / Whispering hope / Little drummer boy / Blessed assurance / Amazing grace
CDITV 467 / Dec '88 / Scotdisc

☐ HEART OF SCOTLAND, THE (McCue, Bill & Kinlochard Ceilidh Band)
Broadsword of Scotland / Irish reels / Ye banks and braes o' bonnie Doon / Waltz for Elizabeth / Ca' the Yowes / Military two step / Slow air / Hiking song / Jimmy Shand hornpipes / Bonnie Strathyre / Margaret's waltz / Rob Roy MacGregor / Loch Ard / Strip the willow / Christine McRichie / Whispering Hope / Amazing grace
CDITV 552 / Apr '94 / Scotdisc

☐ LUCKY WHITE HEATHER
Legend of white heather / Broadsword of scotland / Mary of argyle / March, strathspey and reel / Green grow the rushes o' / Rowan tree / 68 marches / Durisdeer / Annie laurie / This is scotland / Dark lochnagar / My name is bill mccue / Sir harry lauder selection / Culloden / Dancing in the kyle / 24 marches / My love is like a red, red rose / Star o' rabbie burns
CDITV 484 / Jul '89 / Scotdisc

☐ SCOTLAND'S ROYAL HIGHLAND SHOW
CDITV 594 / Jun '95 / Scotdisc

MacCuish, Alasdair

☐ BLACK ROSE
CDLOC 1086 / May '95 / Lochshore

☐ WEST COAST AND BEYOND
CDLOC 1093 / Jun '96 / Lochshore

McCulloch, Gordeanna

☐ IN FREENSHIP'S NAME
Shuttle rins / Bawbee birlin' / Johnny my lad / Laird o'the dainty dounby / My bonnie laddie's lang a growin' / Shepherd's wife / Skippin' barfit thro' the heather / Tam bowie / Laird o' warriston / Tail toddle / Plooman laddies / Willie's droon'd in yarrow / Laird o'drum / In freenship's name
CDTRAX 123 / Mar '97 / Greentrax

☐ SHEATH AND KNIFE
Kirk o' Birnie Bouzle / Dowie Dens o' Yarrow / Lichtbob's lassie / Will ye gang love / Bleacher lassie o' Kelvinhaugh / Yowie wi' the crookit horn / There's a herrin' in the pan / Sheath and knife / Jock since ever I saw yer face / Chevy Chase / Captain Wedderburn / Gallant weaver / Fence upon a time / Caw the yowes / Bawbie Allan / Hielan' laddie / Be kind tae yer nainsel
FECD 117 / Mar '97 / Fellside

McCulloch, Ian

☐ CANDLELAND
Flickering wall / White hotel / Proud to fall / Cape / Candleland / Horse's head / Faith and healing / I know you well / In boom / Start again
K 2462252 / Sep '89 / WEA

McCulloch, Jimmy

☐ COMPLETE (McCulloch, Jimmy & White Line)
MSCD 004 / Feb '95 / Mouse

McCurdy, Ed

☐ COWBOY SONGS
TCD 1025 / Aug '96 / Tradition

McCusker, John

☐ JOHN MCCUSKER
COMD 2059 / Apr '95 / Temple

McCutcheon, John

☐ BETWEEN THE ECLIPSE
ROUCD 0336 / Oct '94 / Rounder

☐ BIGGER THAN YOURSELF
ROUCD 8044 / Aug '97 / Rounder

☐ DOING OUR JOB (McCutcheon, John & Tom Chapin)
Well may the world go / Northfield/Pass the music on / Pastures of plenty / Our Mothers built this city / Doing my job / Every night / I don't care / Hard cider / Dead man walking / Make it right / River gonna carry me / Heaven help / Older I get / Starlight / Welcome the traveller home
ROUCD 0411 / Oct '97 / Rounder

☐ FAMILY GARDEN
Little white star / Family garden / Imaginary friend / Phobias / Baseball on the block / Family revival / How many people / Traveling in the wilderness / Watermelon / Happy adoption day / Dad's got that look / If I ran the world / Is my family
ROUCD 8026 / May '93 / Rounder

☐ FINE TIMES AT OUR HOUSE
GR 70710 / Dec '94 / Greenhays

☐ GONNA RISE AGAIN
Water from another time / Harriet tubman / Long way back to georgia / Young ones don't remember / Caught in the crossfire / Satisfied mind / Farmer is the woman / Dearest martha / Gone gonna rise again
ROUCD 0222 / Aug '88 / Rounder

☐ HOWJADOO
Cut the cake / Howjadoo / Molly and the whale / Rubber blubber whale / John henry / All god's critters / Peanut butter / Babysitter / Pap's billygoat / Here's to cheshire / Rustic dance / Father grumble / Tender shepherd
ROUCD 8009 / '88 / Rounder

☐ NOTHING TO LOSE
ROUCD 0358 / Oct '95 / Rounder

☐ SIGNS OF THE TIMES (McCutcheon, John & Si Kahn)
ROUCD 4017 / Aug '94 / Rounder

☐ SPROUT WINGS AND FLY
ROUCD 0406 / Mar '97 / Rounder

☐ STEP BY STEP
Reel a bouche / Santiago / Carolan's welcome-lord inchiquin / Frenchie's reel-denver belle / Step by step / I shall arise / Robbing peter to pay paul / Babylon is fallen / Earl eddy's favorite-snowflake breakdown / Derrota de don quixote
ROUCD 0216 / Aug '88 / Rounder

☐ SUMMERSONGS
ROUCD 8036 / Apr '95 / Rounder

☐ WINTER SOLSTICE
Christmas day, ida moarnin-un flambeau, jeanette, isabella / Erev shel shoshanim / Willie's waltz / Christmas in the trenches / Star in the east / Old christmas morning-breaking up christmas / Jesus, jesus, rest your head / For unto us a child is born / Huron carol / Detroit, december / Down in yon forest-new year's eve
ROUCD 0192 / Dec '86 / Rounder

McDade, Brian

☐ SOBW
RGFBMCD 042 / Mar '98 / Road Goes On Forever

McDaniel, Clara

☐ UNWANTED CHILD
HMG 1002 / Nov '97 / Hightone

McDaniel, Floyd

☐ LET YOUR HAIR DOWN (McDaniel, Floyd & Blues Swingers)
Raggedy ride / Blue mood / Mary Jo / Strange things happening / It don't mean a thing / I want a little girl / St. Louis blues / God bless the child / Sent for you yesterday / RM blues / Christopher Columbus / West side baby / Beale Street baby / Let your hair down / Nobody knows you when you're down and out / Why's life got to be this way / Caldonia
DE 671 / Mar '97 / Delmark

☐ WEST SIDE BABY
St. Louis blues / West side baby / Mean old world / Route 66 / Evenin' / Red top / Backwater blues / Everyday I have the blues / Every time / Sweet home Chicago / Hold it
CCD 11057 / May '98 / Crosscut

McDermott's Two Hours

☐ ENEMY WITHIN, THE
HAGCD 2 / Aug '94 / Hag

McDermott, Josie

☐ DARBY'S FAREWELL (Traditional Songs Played On Flute & Whistle)
OSS 20CD / Mar '94 / Ossian

McDermott, Kevin

☐ FAIR AND WHOLE
TULAD 002 / 7 Sep '98 / Tula

☐ FOR THOSE IN PERIL FROM THE SEA
TULAD 001 / 29 Sep '97 / Tula

☐ LAST SUPPER, THE (McDermott, Kevin Orchestra)
IGCDM 207 / Jun '94 / Iona Gold

☐ MOTHER NATURE'S KITCHEN (McDermott, Kevin Orchestra)
Wheels of wonder / Slow boat to something better / King of nothing / Diamond / Mother nature's kitchen / Into the blue / Where we were meant to be / Statue to a stone / What comes to pass / Suffocation blues / Angel / Healing at the harbour
CID 9920 / Jul '91 / Island

McDevitt, Chas

☐ FREIGHT TRAIN (McDevitt, Chas & Nancy Whisky)
Freight train / Badman Stackolee / County jail / I'm satisfied / She moved through the fair / My old man / Poor Howard / Greenback dollar / Sing sing sing / BB Blues / Deep down / Born to be with you / I want a little girl / Across the bridge / Come all ye fair and tender maidens / Sportin' life / Trottin' to the fair / Everyday of the week / Face in the rain / Goin' home / Tom Hark / It makes no difference now / Good mornin' blues / Real love / Pop pourri / Everyday I have the blues / I dig you baby / Ace in the hole / Tom Hark
RCCD 3007 / Nov '93 / Rollercoaster

MacDhonnagain, Tadhg

☐ RAIFTEIRI SAN UNDERGROUND
CICD 094 / Jan '94 / Clo Iar-Chonnachta

MacDonald, Catriona

☐ OPUS BLUE
ARADCD 103 / May '94 / Acoustic Radio

MacDonald, Fergie

☐ 21ST ALBUM - TRADITIONAL CEILIDH MUSIC
Dancing in Harris / Two button boxes / Traditional gaelic waltz / Pan/Celtic jig / Hebridean highland schottische / Na muideartaich / West highland strip the willow / Box and piob bheag / Traditional celtic reels / West highland gaelic waltz / Gay gordons / Traditional irish jigs / Box the fiddle and the pipes
CDTRAX 129 / 1 Sep '97 / Greentrax

MacDonald, Jeanette

☐ DREAM LOVERS (MacDonald, Jeanette & Nelson Eddy)
March of the grenadiers / Dream lover / Tramp tramp tramp / Love's old sweet song / Smilin' through / Soldiers of fortune / Auf weiderseh'n / Vilja / Merry widow waltz / Stout hearted men / Through the years / Dusty road / Love me tonight / Dear when I meet you / Rosary / Sun up to sun down / One hour with you / Love come back to me / At the balalaika / Sweetheart waltz / Softly as in a morning sunrise / Summer serenade
PASTCD 7824 / 25 May '98 / Flapper

☐ INDIAN LOVE CALL (MacDonald, Jeanette & Nelson Eddy)
GO 3822 / 1 Dec '97 / Golden Options

☐ VERY BEST OF JEANETTE MACDONALD, THE
SWNCD 005 / Oct '95 / Sound Waves

☐ WHEN I'M CALLING YOU (MacDonald, Jeanette & Nelson Eddy)
Ah sweet mystery of life / At the Balalaika / Beyond the blue horizon / Dear when I met you / Farewell to dreams / I'm falling in love with someone / Indian love call / Isn't it romantic / Lover come back to me / March of the grenadiers / Mounties / One kiss / One hour with you / Rose Marie / Smilin' through / Softly as in a morning sunrise / Sun up to sundown / Toreador's song / Tramp, tramp, tramp along the highway / Vilia / Waltz aria / Will you remember
CDAJA 5124 / Mar '94 / Living Era

MacDonald, John

☐ SCOTTISH ACCORDION BY THE FIRESIDE
Scottish sing-a-long / Bonny Dundee/Muckin' o'Geordie's byre/With a hundred pipers / Scottish soldier / My home / Northern light of old Aberdeen/I belong to Glasgow / Amazing grace / Scotland the brave medley / Roamin' in the gloamin/I love a lassie/Road to the Isles / It's a long way to Tipperary / Mull of Kintyre / Road and the miles to Dundee / Hail Caledonia medley / Click go the shears/On the road to Gunagai / Annie Laurie
HADCD 214 / Jun '97 / Spotlight On

☐ SINGING MOLECATCHER OF MORAYSHIRE, THE
Sleepytoun / Mains o' Fogieloan / Lord Ronald / Burns waltz / Dewy dens o' Yarrow / Bonnie hoose o' Airlie / Majuba Hill / Braes o' Balquhidder / Ploughin' match at Duffus / Haughs o' Corndale / Jacobite waltz / Farewell Tomitoul / Bonnie lassie will ye gang / Auntie Jean / Bonnie Udny / Cairngorm barn dance / Banks of Allan water / Ball o' Kirriemeer
CDTRAX 9053 / 1 Jul '98 / Greentrax

MacDonald, Kenneth

☐ SOUND OF KINTAIL FEATURING KENNETH MACDONALD
John MacColl's march to Kilbowie cottage / Col David Murray's welcome to Kintail / Tullock Castle / Piobaireacho, Donald Gruanach's / Gregory Blend and Roddy MacDonald / Boys of Glendale / I'm going home to Kintail
CDITV 460 / Oct '88 / Scotdisc

MacDonald, Pat

☐ SLEEPS WITH HIS GUITAR
ARKK 10060 / May '97 / ARKK

MacDonald, Rod

☐ BRING ON THE LIONS
BRAM 1989082 / Nov '93 / Brambus

☐ MAN ON THE LEDGE, THE
SHCD 8011 / Dec '94 / Shanachie

☐ WHITE BUFFALO
BRAM 1991292 / Nov '93 / Brambus

McDonald, Alastair

☐ HEROES AND LEGENDS OF SCOTLAND
CBNCD 019 / Sep '96 / Corban

☐ HONEST POVERTY
De'il's awa' wi' tha exciseman / Green grow the rashes / Rattlin' roarin' Willie / O wert thou in the cauld blast / Man's a man (for a' that, an' a' that) / Mary Morrison / I am a son of Mars / Ca' the ewes / Duncan Gray / We're a'noddin' / Up wi' the Carls o' Dysart / There'll never be peace till Jamie comes hame / Willie Wastle (sic a wife as Willie had) / Ay waukin o / Scots wha hae / Rantin' rovin' Robin / Such a parcel of rogues in a nation
LCOM 5250 / Feb '96 / Lismor

☐ SCOTTISH LAUGHLINES
Sam the skull / Kelty clippie / Rothesay o / Cholesterol / Mermaid's tale / Goliath of Gath / McFarlane o the Sprotts / German lairdie / Johnnie lad / Oor Gudeman / Wee cooper o'Fife / Pan drop / Auld man's mare's deid / Wee cock sparra / Ten wee wimmin' / Big Kilmarnock bunnet / Oor Hamlet / Hot asphalt / Glasgow's barraland
CBNCD 022 / Jun '98 / Corban

☐ SINGS ROBERT BURNS
LBP 2020CD / Mar '96 / Lochshore

☐ SONGS GRETNA TO GLENCOE
Gallawa' hills / Jock o'hazeldean / Barras / Kelvingrove / Rothesay o' / Will ye go lassie go / Loch lomond / Railway porter / Tramps and hawkers / Glencoe / Hie johnny cope / Skye boat song / Twa bonnie maids / Will ye no come back again
CDITV 547 / Sep '91 / Scotdisc

☐ VELVET AND STEEL
Jamie Foyers / Bruce / Bonnie Earl O'Moray / Harlaw / Seer / Lock the door / Haughs o' Cromdale / Killiecrankie / My bonnie Mary / Blue bonnets / Flodden/Floeers o' the forest / Culloden's harvest / Fyvie / Sheep and stag remain
CDTRAX 078 / Mar '95 / Greentrax

McDonald, Angus

☐ A' SIREADH SPORS
COMD 2043 / Feb '94 / Temple

☐ WORLD'S GREATEST PIPERS VOL.1, THE (MacDonald, Pipe Major Angus)
Lord MacPherson of Drumochter / Major John MacLennan / Susan MacLeod / Mrs. MacPherson of Inveran / Bobs of Balmoral / I laid a herring in saut / Fair maid of Barra / Pinney's of Scotland / Caledonian Society of London / Cameron highlanders / Banks of Allan Water / Highland brigade at Magersfontein / Road to Sham Shui Poh / Jim Tweedie's sea legs / High level / Flowers of the forest / 93rd, of Modder river / Braes of Castle Grant / Wiseman's exercise / Fiddler's joy / Smith's a gallant fireman / Laird of Drumblair / Brolum / Kalabakan / Tam bain's lum / Willie's brogues / Liverpool hornpipe / Kesh jig / Rocking the baby / Give me a drink of water / Conundrum / P/M Willie Gray's farewell to the Glasgow Police / Lament for the children
LCOM 5143 / Jun '93 / Lismor

McDonald, Country Joe

☐ CARRY ON
Picks and lasers / Lady with the lamp / Joe's blues / Hold on to each other / Stolen heart blues / Trilogy / Going home / Carry on / My last song
SHCD 8019 / Jul '96 / Shanachie

☐ CJ FISH (Country Joe & The Fish)
Sing sing sing / She's a bride / Mara / Hang on / Baby song / Hey Bobby / Silver and gold / Ochkin' round the world / Love machine / Return of sweet Lorraine / Hand of man
VMD 6555 / Jun '98 / Vanguard

☐ CLASSICS
Coyote / Love is fire / Breakfast for two / Oh jamaica / Baby baby / Copiapo / Do-wop-oh / Blood on the ice / Space patrol / U.f.o. / Get it together / Save the whales
CDWIK 108 / Jul '92 / Big Beat

☐ COLLECTORS ITEMS (The First Three EPs) (Country Joe & The Fish)
I feel like I'm fixin' to die rag / Super bird / (Thing called) love / Bass strings / Section 43 / Fire in the city: *Krug, Peter* / Johnny's gone in the war: *Krug, Peter* / Kiss my ass: *Country Joe & Grootna* / Tricky dicky: *Country Joe & Grootna* / Free some day: *Country Joe & Grootna*
NEXCD 228 / Nov '92 / Sequel

☐ ELECTRIC MUSIC FOR THE MIND AND BODY (Country Joe & The Fish)
Flying high / Not so sweet Martha Lorraine / Death sound blues / Porpoise mouth / Section 43 / Super bird / Sad and lonely times / Love / Bass strings / Masked marauder / Grace
VMCD 79244 / Oct '95 / Vanguard

☐ I FEEL LIKE I'M FIXIN' TO DIE (Country Joe & The Fish)
Fish cheer and I feel like I'm fixing to die rag / Who am I / Pat's song / Rock coast blues / Magoo / Though dream / Thursday / Eastern jam / Colors for Susan
VMD 79266 / Oct '95 / Vanguard

☐ LIVE AT THE FILLMORE WEST 1969 (Country Joe & The Fish)
Rock and soul music/Love / Here I go again / It's nice to have your love / Flying high / Doctor of electricity / Donovan's reef jam
VCD 139 / Aug '96 / Vanguard

☐ SOMETHING BORROWED SOMETHING NEW
Entertainment is my business / Who am I / Kiss my ass / Free some day / Standing at the crossroads / Your last few records didn't make it / Power plant blues / Thinking of John Fahey / Sunshine / War hero / Mourning blues / Here I go again / Hold on it's coming / Starship ride / Blues for Michael / Carry on / Got it all together
CDWIKD 180 / 27 Apr '98 / Big Beat

☐ THINKING OF WOODY GUTHRIE
Pastures of plenty / Talkin' dust bowl blues / Blowing down that dusty road / So long (it's been good to know yuh) / Tom Joad / Sinking of the Reuben James / Roll on Columbia / Pretty boy Floyd / When the curfew blows / This land is your land
VMD 6546 / Jan '97 / Vanguard

☐ TOGETHER (Country Joe & The Fish)
Rock and soul music / Susan / Mojo navigator / Bright suburban Mr. and Mrs. clean machine / Good guys/Bad guys cheer and the streets of your town / Fish moan / Harlem song / Waltzing in the moonlight / Away bounce my bubbles / Catacean / Untitled protest
VMD 79277 / Oct '95 / Vanguard

McDonald, Fergie

☐ AGUS NA MUIDEARTAICH
Ceili music / Hebridean reels / Bothan ballads (Fergie's Gaelic waltz) / Hooligan's jig / Moidart reels / Benbecula barn dance / Real Fergie jigs / Tribute to Bobby Macleod / Jig Runrig / Button box schottische / Ian MacFarlane "On the fiddle" / Jigs / Talla a'bhaile reels / Ceilidh on the croft / Isle of Skye reels / Ceol eirainn
LCOM 5222 / Oct '93 / Lismor

McDonald, Jane

☐ JANE MCDONALD
One moment in time / Twelfth of never / Do you know the way to San Jose / You're my world / How do I live / (You make me feel) like a natural woman / Wind beneath my wings / Downtown / Have I told you lately / When I fall in love / I'll never love this way again / Some you win some you lose / You don't have to say you love me / I will always love you
FMCD 001 / 13 Jul '98 / Focus

McDonald, John

☐ WELCOME TO SCOTLAND
MBPCD 7003 / 18 May '98 / Quantum Mobius

McDonald, Michael

☐ SWEET FREEDOM (The Best Of Michael McDonald)
Sweet freedom / I'll be your angel / Yah mo be there / I gotta try / I keep forgettin' / Our love / On my own / No lookin back / Any foolish thing / That's why / What a fool believes / I can let go now
2410492 / Nov '86 / WEA

☐ TAKE IT TO HEART
All we got / Get the word started / Love can break your heart / Take it to heart / Tear it up / Lonely talk / Searchin' for understanding / Homeboy / No amount of reason / One step away / You show me
7599259792 / May '90 / WEA

McDonald, Steve

☐ SONS OF SOMERLED
Introduction / Sons of somerled / Live on my warrior son / All you can know / Loch Lomond / Soldier's lament / Come to the Isle of Skye / Scotland the brave / Celtic segue / Celtic warrior / I will return / Wild mountain thyme / Per mare, per terras / Lordship of the isles / Journey of the warrior soul
9734776012 / Jul '97 / Strathan

☐ STONE OF DESTINY
Bannockburn / Fallen flowers / Lady of the loch / Oran / Boadicea / Painted men / Stone of destiny / Auld land syne / Green alba / Freedom / Harvest / Connla and the fairy maiden / Skye boat song
9734776022 / 17 Aug '98 / Strathan

MacDonnchadha, Johnny Mhairtin Learai

☐ CONTAE MHUIGHEO
CICD 013 / Dec '93 / Clo Iar-Chonnachta

McDonnell, Kate

☐ NEXT
WBGCD 0038 / Mar '98 / Waterbug

McDonough, Megon

☐ MY ONE AND ONLY LOVE
SH 5027 / Nov '96 / Shanachie

McDougall, Ian

☐ WARMTH OF THE HORN, THE
Warm / You go to my head / Like someone in love / Blue Daniel / Sixth sense / Lament / I remember you / How long has this been going on / Centerpiece / Blue skies / Mc not Mac and two L's
CCD 4652 / Jul '95 / Concord Jazz

McDougall, John

☐ WORLD'S GREATEST PIPERS VOL.8, THE
2/4 marches / Strathspeys and reels / Slow air and jigs / 6/8 marches / Strathspeys and reels / Lady Margaret MacDonald's salute / 2/4 marches / Hornpipe / Slow air and march / Strathspeys and reels / 6/8 marches / Battle of the Pass of Crieff
LCOM 5189 / Feb '97 / Lismor

MacDowell, Al

☐ MESSIAH (MacDowell, Al & Timepiece)
Messiah / Powerful one / Playing in the sand / Close to the edge / Jamming in the pyramids / Offset / Second calling / Let the music sing / Latin lady / Here we come again
GV 794512 / May '91 / Gramavision

MacDowell, Lenny

☐ FLUTE POWER
39840792 / Nov '97 / Blue Flame

☐ MAGIC FLUTE
BLR 84 027 / May '91 / L&R

McDowell, Fred

☐ AMAZING GRACE (McDowell, 'Mississippi' Fred)
TCD 5004 / Aug '94 / Testament

☐ FIRST RECORDINGS
Going down the river / 61 Highway / Wished I was in heaven sitting down / When the train comes along / Shake 'em on down / Worried mind / Woke up this morning with my mind on Jesus / You done told everybody / Keep your lamps trimmed and burning / What's the matter now / Good morning little school girl / I want Jesus to walk with me / Keep your lamps trimmed and burning / You're gonna be sorry
ROUCD 1718 / Sep '97 / Rounder

☐ GOOD MORNING LITTLE SCHOOLGIRL (McDowell, 'Mississippi' Fred)
ARHCD 424 / Apr '95 / Arhoolie

☐ LEVEE CAMP BLUES (McDowell, 'Mississippi' Fred)
TCD 6007 / 30 Mar '98 / Testament

☐ LONG WAY FROM HOME (McDowell, 'Mississippi' Fred)
Train I ride / Poor boy long way from home / Milk cow blues / John henry / Gravel road blues / Millionaire's daughter blues / Big fat mama / You drove me from your door / Sail on little girl
OBCCD 535 / Nov '92 / Original Blues Classics

☐ MISSISSIPPI BLUES (McDowell, 'Mississippi' Fred)
BLCD 760179 / Mar '93 / Black Lion

☐ MISSISSIPPI FRED MCDOWELL (McDowell, 'Mississippi' Fred)
ROUCD 2138 / Sep '95 / Rounder

☐ MY HOME IS IN THE DELTA BLUES & SPIRITUALS (McDowell, 'Mississippi' Fred & Annie Mae)
TCD 5019 / Apr '95 / Testament

☐ REAL BLUES (McDowell, 'Mississippi' Fred)
IMP 307 / Sep '96 / IMP

☐ SHAKE 'EM ON DOWN (McDowell, 'Mississippi' Fred)
Shake 'em on down / I'm crazy about you baby / John Henry / You got to move / Someday / Mercy / Lovin' blues / White lightnin' / Baby please don't go
CPCD 8165 / Apr '97 / Charly

☐ SHAKE 'EM ON DOWN
CDBB 1003 / 6 Jul '98 / Rhino

☐ STEAKBONE SLIDE GUITAR (McDowell, 'Mississippi' Fred)
TCD 1012 / May '96 / Tradition

☐ THIS AIN'T NO ROCK 'N' ROLL (McDowell, 'Mississippi' Fred)
ARHCD 441 / Sep '95 / Arhoolie

☐ WHEN I LAY MY BURDEN DOWN (McDowell, 'Mississippi' Fred & Furry Lewis)
If you see my baby / John Henry / Louise / 61 highway blues / Big fat mama / When I lay my burden down / Dankin farm / Casey Jones / Harry furry blues / Everyday in the week / Grieve my mind / Beale Street blues
BCD 130 / Jun '94 / Biograph

☐ YOU GOT TO MOVE (McDowell, 'Mississippi' Fred)
Some day baby / Milk cow blues / Train I ride / Over the hill / Goin' down to the river / I wished I were in heaven sittin' down / Louise
ARHCD 304 / Apr '95 / Arhoolie

McDuff, Jack

☐ ANOTHER REAL GOOD 'UN
Another real good 'un / Summertime / Off the beaten path / Long day blues / Rock candy / I can't get started (with you) / I cover the waterfront
MCD 5374 / Sep '92 / Muse

☐ COLOUR ME BLUE (McDuff, Jack & Friends)
Don't let the sun catch you cryin' / Mo' candy / Color me blue / Almost like being in love / Old folks / Pump it up / My funny valentine / Peddlin' / Cry me a river / Broadway
CCD 4516 / Aug '92 / Concord Jazz

☐ HEATIN' SYSTEM, THE
601 1/2 No. Poplar / Put on a happy face / Sundown / Mr. T / Jimmy Smith / In a sentimental mood / Fly away / Pink Panther / Playoff
CCD 4644 / Jun '95 / Concord Jazz

☐ HONEYDRIPPER, THE
Whap / I want a little girl / Honeydripper / Dink's blues / Mr. lucky / Blues and tonic
OJCCD 222 / Dec '95 / Original Jazz Classics

☐ HOT BARBEQUE/LIVE (AT THE FRONT ROOM) (McDuff, 'Brother' Jack)
Hot barbeque / Party's over / Briar patch / Hippy dip / 601 1/2 No. poplar / Cry me a river / Three day thang / Rock candy / It ain't necessarily so / Sanctified samba / Whistle while you work / Real good'n / Undecided
CDBGPD 053 / Apr '93 / Beat Goes Public

☐ LEGENDS OF ACID JAZZ, THE
Scufflin' / Au privave / Hallelujah time / Misconstrued / Lew's piece / Opus de Funk / Our Miss Brooks / Easy of the sun (west of the moon) / I got a woman / Hey lawdy Mama / From the bottom up / Lexington Avenue line
PRCD 24184 / 29 Jun '98 / Prestige

☐ SCREAMIN' (McDuff, 'Brother' Jack)
He's a real gone guy / Soulful drums / After hours / Screamin' / I cover the waterfront / One o'clock jump
OJCCD 875 / Jun '96 / Original Jazz Classics

☐ THAT'S THE WAY I FEEL ABOUT IT (McDuff, 'Brother' Jack)
Age of Aquarius / Blooze in G / Theme from Mission Impossible / Hat's the way I feel about it / Six am / Saturday night fish fry / Old folks / Flamingo / Moody's mood for love
CCD 47602 / Jul '97 / Concord Jazz

☐ WRITE ON CAP'N
Spec-tator / From the pulpit / Killer Joe / Room / Night in Tunisia / Captain's quarters / Billyjack / Out of my head / Goin' to the wall / Havin' a good time
CCD 4568 / Sep '93 / Concord Jazz

McDuff, Larry

☐ RE-ENTRY, THE
MCD 5361 / Sep '92 / Muse

McEachern, Malcolm

☐ MALCOLM MC EACHERN
Oh ruddier than the cherry / Lord is a man of war / Honour and arms / Arm, arm ye brave / Lord God of Abraham / Revenge, Timotheus cries / I am a roamer / O tu palermo / Le veau d'or / Sperate, O Figli...d'egitto la sui lidi / Mighty deep / On the road to Mandalay / Australian bush songs / Excelsior: *McEachern, Malcolm & Frank Titterton* / Blow, blow thou winter wind / Danny Deever / Song of the Volga boatmen / Hundred pipers / Drinking / Gendarmes duet
GEMMCD 9455 / '90 / Pearl

McElroy, Bill

☐ SLIMLINE DADDY (McElroy, Bill & The Prairie Boys)
NERCD 089 / Sep '96 / Nervous

McEntire, Reba

☐ FOR MY BROKEN HEART
For my broken heart / Is there life out there / Bobby / He's in Dallas / All dressed up / Night the lights went out in Georgia / Buying her roses / Greatest man I never knew / I wouldn't go that far / If I had only know
MCLD 19346 / Oct '96 / MCA

☐ GREATEST HITS VOL.1
Just a little love / He broke your memory last night / How blue / Somebody should leave / Have I got a deal for you / Only in my mind / Whoever's in New England / Little rock / What am I gonna do about you / One promise too late
MCLD 19177 / Mar '94 / MCA

☐ GREATEST HITS VOL.2
Does he love you / You lie / Fancy / For my broken heart / Love will find it's way to you / They asked about you / Is there life out there / Rumour has it / Walk on / Greatest man I never knew
MCD 10906 / Oct '93 / MCA

☐ IF YOU SEE HIM
UMD 80508 / 8 Jun '98 / Universal

☐ READ MY MIND
Everything that you want / Read my mind / I won't stand in line / I wish that I could tell you / She think's his name was John / Why haven't I heard from you / Still / Heart is a lonely hunter / I wouldn't want to be you / Till you love me
MCD 10994 / Jun '94 / MCA

☐ STARTING OVER
Talking in your sleep / Please come to Boston / On my own / I won't mention it again / You're no good / Ring on her finger, time on her hands / 500 miles away from home / Starting over again / You keep me hangin' on / By the time I get to Phoenix
MCD 11264 / Oct '95 / MCA

☐ WHAT IF IT'S YOU
How was I to know / Fear of being alone / What if it's you / I'd rather ride around with you / It don't matter / State of grace / Close to crazy / She's callin' it love / Just looking for him / Never had a reason to
MCD 11500 / Nov '96 / MCA

Maceration

☐ SERENADE OF AGONY, A
CD 7913004 / Jun '93 / Progress Red

McEvoy, Catherine

☐ TRADITIONAL IRISH MUSIC (McEvoy, Catherine & Felix Dolan)
CICD 117 / May '97 / Clo Iar-Chonnachta

McEvoy, Eleanor

☐ ELEANOR MCEVOY
Finding myslef lost again / Only a woman's heart / Apologise / Boundaries of your mind / For you / Go now / It's mine / Not quite love / Promises we keep / Music of it all / Leave her now / Breathing hope / Stray thoughts
GED 24606 / Jun '97 / Geffen

McEvoy, Johnny

☐ 20 GREATEST HITS (Ireland's Favourite Folk Singer)
TVCD 1 / Sep '96 / Dolphin

☐ CELEBRATION (2CD Set)
JMCD 30 / Mar '96 / Dolphin

☐ FAVOURITES
CDC 011 / Feb '97 / Ceol

☐ JOHNNY MCEVOY SINGS COUNTRY AND IRISH
PLSCD 237 / Jul '97 / Pulse

☐ SONGS OF IRELAND
Home boys home / Red is the rose / Black velvet band / Maggie / Good ship Kangaroo / Wild mountain thyme / I wish I had someone to love me / Town of ballybay / Molly,my Irish Molly / Rare ould times / Streets of New York / Travelling people / Shores of amerikkay / Bunch of thyme / Irish soldier laddie / Song for Ireland
MCBD 19520 / Apr '95 / MCA

MacEwan, Sydney

☐ FOLK SONGS AND BALLADS
Bonnie Earl O'Moray / Lark in the clear air / She moved thro the fair / O men from the fields / Dawning of the day / Mowing the barley / Silent O'Moyle / Duna / Since first I saw your face / In summertime in Bredon / Foggy dew / Pleading / Coronach / Green bushes / Banks of Allan Water / Jeanie with the light brown hair / Macishia / As I sit here / Maiden of Morven
MIDCD 007 / May '95 / Moidart

☐ GREAT SCOTTISH TENOR, THE (MacEwan, Father Sydney)
Turn ye to me / Duna / Mowing the barley / Annie Laurie / Mother of mercy / Foggy dew / Maiden of Morven
GEMMCD 9107 / May '94 / Pearl

☐ SONGS OF SCOTLAND
Road to the isles / Peat fire flame / Maighdeanan na h-airidh / Island moon / Morag bheag / Bonnie banks of Loch Lomond / Ye banks and braes o' bonnie Doon / Togorm mo phiob / When the kye come home / Rowan tree / An eriskay love lilt / Herding song / Mnhathan a ghlinne
MIDCD 002 / Jan '95 / Moidart

MacEwan, William

☐ WILLIAM MCEWAN (The Original Glasgow Street Singer-Evangelist)
Sunrise / Pull for the shore / Throw out the lifeline / I would be like Jesus / Merrily sing / Sweetest song I know / Pardoning grace / Not now but in the coming years / When the roll is called up yonder / We will talk it o'er together by and by / Old rugged cross / God be with you till we meet again / Will the circle be unbroken / My mothers hand is on my brow / Sinking sands (In loving kindness Jesus came) / He died of a broken heart / God will take care of you / I know my heavenly father knows / Someday / My ain countrie
LCOM 5235 / May '94 / Lismor

McFadden & Whitehead

☐ AIN'T NO STOPPIN' US NOW
Ain't no stoppin' us now / I've been pushed aside / I heard it in a love song / I got the love / That lets me know / Got to change / Always room for one more / Don't feel bad / I know what I'm gonna do / You're my someone / Why oh why / This is my song / Life's no good without you / Mr. music
KWEST 5406 / May '93 / Kenwest

McFadden, Charlie

☐ CHARLIE 'SPECKS" MCFADDEN 1929-1940 (McFadden, Charlie 'Specks')
BDCD 6041 / May '93 / Blues Document

McFadden, Gerry

☐ IRISH TRADITIONAL UILLEANN PIPES
PTICD 1031 / Oct '95 / Outlet

☐ UILLEANN PIPES
PTI 1031CD / Jul '95 / Pure Traditional Irish

MacFadyen, Iain

☐ CEOL MOR-CEOL BEAG
Old men of the shells / Glengarry's lament / Major General Frank Richardson / Willie MacRae of Ullapool / Braigh loch iall / Irish washerwoman / Southall / Inverary Castle / Bessie MacIntyre / Mary MacPherson of Kyle / Myles MacDonald's welcome to Skye / Leaving Ireland / Flora Cameron / Eleanor Hannah / Mrs. John MacColl / Leaving Lunga
COMD 2018 / 20 Oct '97 / Temple

☐ WORLD'S GREATEST PIPERS VOL.7, THE
March, strathspey and reel / 6/8 marches / Gaelic air and hornpipes / Jigs / 9/8 marches / Piobaireachd / 6/8 march and jig / 2/4 marches / 6/8 marches / Strathspeys and reels / Piobaireachd
LCOM 5180 / Mar '95 / Lismor

McFarland, Clinton

☐ WAKE UP
How I love you Jesus / Use me / Mighty long way / God has smiled on me / To the rock / Wake up / Remember the past / Just for me / Prayer
9261 / 27 Oct '97 / Fresh Wine

McFerrin, Bobby

☐ BANG ZOOM
Bang zoom / Rememberance / Friends / Selim / Freedom is a voice / Heaven's design / My better half / Kid's toys / Mere words
CDP 8316772 / Jan '96 / Blue Note

☐ BEST OF BOBBY MCFERRIN, THE
Don't worry be happy / Friends / Thinkin' about your body / Spain / Freedom is a voice / Drive my car / Another night in Tunisia / Blue Bossa / Turtle shoes / Good lovin' / From me to you / Bang zoom
CDP 8533292 / Nov '96 / Blue Note

☐ CIRCLESONGS
SK 62734 / Jun '97 / Sony Classical

☐ JAZZ MASTERS
Don't worry, be happy / Turtle shoes / Another night in tunisia / Even for me / Manana iguana / Drive / I hear music / Walkin' / 'round midnight
CDMFP 6303 / Mar '97 / Music For Pleasure

☐ PAPERMUSIC
SK 64600 / Jan '97 / Sony Classical

MacGabhann, Antoin

☐ AR AON BHUILE
CICD 105 / Jan '95 / Clo lar-Chonnachta

McGann, Andy

☐ ANDY MCGANN & PADDY REYNOLDS FIDDLE (McGann, Andy & Paddy Reynolds)
SHANCD 34008 / Jan '95 / Shanachie

☐ IT'S A HARD ROAD TO TRAVEL
SHCD 34011 / Jul '95 / Shanachie

☐ TRADITIONAL MUSIC OF IRELAND (McGann, Andy & Paul Brady)
SHAN 34011CD / Apr '95 / Shanachie

McGann, Eileen

☐ JOURNEYS
DRGNCD 113 / Mar '98 / Dragonwing

McGann, John

☐ UPSIDE
GLCD 2118 / Mar '95 / Green Linnet

McGarrigle, Kate & Anna

☐ DANCER WITH BRUISED KNEES
Dancer with bruised knees / Southern boys / Biscuit song / First born / Blanche comme la neige / Perrine etait servante / Be my baby / Walking song / Naufragee du tendre / Hommage a grungie / Kitty come home / Come a long way / No biscuit blues
7599259582 / Jun '94 / Warner Bros.

☐ FRENCH RECORD
Enter la jeunesse et la sagesse / Complainte pour Ste Catherine / Mais quand tu danses / Cheminant a la ville / Excursion a venise / En filant ma quenouille / La belle est etourdie / Maufragee du tendre / Avant la querre / Boire / Prends ton manteau
HNCD 1302 / Mar '97 / Hannibal

☐ HEARTBEATS ACCELERATING
Heartbeats accelerating / I eat dinner / Rainbow ride / Mother, mother / Love is / DJ serenade / I'm losing you / Hit and run love / Leave me be / St. James Hospital
261142 / Nov '90 / Private Music

☐ KATE & ANNA MCGARRIGLE
Kiss and say goodbye / My town / Blues in D / Heart like a wheel / Foolish you / Talk to me of Mendocino / Complainte pour Ste Catherine / Tell my sister / Swimming song / Jigsaw puzzle of Life / Go leave / Travelling on for Jesus
9362456772 / Jun '94 / Warner Bros.

☐ LOVE OVER AND OVER
Move over moon / Sun son (shining on the water) / I cried for us / Love over and over / Star cab company / Tu vas m'accompagner / On my way to town / Jesus lifeline / Work song / St. Valentine's day 1978 / Midnight flight
8411012 / Jul '94 / Polydor

☐ LOVE OVER AND OVER
Move over moon / Sun son (shining on the water) / I cried for us / Love over and over / Star cab company / Tu vas m'accompagner / On my way to town / Jesus lifeline / Work song / St. Valentine's day 1978 / Midnight flight / Place in your heart / Babies if I didn't have you
HNCD 1405 / 15 Sep '97 / Hannibal

☐ MATAPEDIA
Matapedia / Goin' back to Harlan / I don't know / Hang out your heart / Arbre / Jacques et Gilles / Why must we die / Song for Gaby / Talk about it / Bike song
HNCD 1394 / Sep '96 / Hannibal

McGear, Mike

☐ MCGEAR (McCartney, Mike)
Sea breezes / Norton / Have you got problems / Casket / Rainbow lady / Givin' grease a ride / What do we really want to know / Leave it / Dance the do / Sweet baby / Simply love you / Man who found God in the moon
SEECD 339 / Jun '94 / See For Miles

☐ WOMAN
Woman / Please Mr. Witness / Jolly good show / Roamin' Road / Sit down sister / Wishin' and washin' / I'm just a young man / Edward Heath / Butterscotch / Uptown downtown / Tiger
EDCD 507 / Feb '97 / Edsel

McGee, Dennis

☐ COMPLETE EARLY RECORDINGS, THE (Early American Cajun Classics)
YAZCD 2012 / Dec '94 / Yazoo

McGee, John

☐ SLINKY (McGee, John Orchestra)
CREV 047CD / Aug '97 / Rev-Ola

McGee, Kieran

☐ LEFT FOR DEAD
CCD 717 / Aug '97 / Clean Cuts

McGee, Sam

☐ GRANDAD OF THE COUNTRY GUITAR PICKERS
Sam McGee stomp / Fuller blues / Burglar bold / Dew drop / Jesse James / Ching chong / Blackberry blossom / Wheels / How great thou art / When the wagon was new / Franklin blues / Penitentiary blues / Pig ankle rag / Railroad blues / Buckdancer's choice / Black mountain rag / Wayfaring stranger
ARHCD 9009 / Nov '97 / Arhoolie

McGhee, Brownie

☐ AT THE 2ND FRET (McGhee, Brownie & Sonny Terry)
Evil hearted me / Sick man / Barking bull dog / Spread the news around / Back water blues / Custard pie / Wholesale dealin' papa / Motorcycle blues / Hand in hand / I woke up one morning and I could hardly see
OBCCD 561 / Jan '94 / Original Blues Classics

☐ BLUESVILLE VOL.5 (McGhee, Brownie & Sonny Terry)
Jump little children: *McGhee, Brownie* / Lonesome day: *McGhee, Brownie* / Killin' floor: *McGhee, Brownie* / I don't know the reason: *McGhee, Brownie* / Everyday I have the blues: *McGhee, Brownie* / I ain't gonna be your dog no more: *Terry, Sonny* / Four o'clock blues: *Terry, Sonny* / I'm gonna get on my feets afterwhile: *Terry, Sonny* / Diggin' my potatoes: *Terry, Sonny* / One monkey don't stop the show: *Terry, Sonny* / Evil hearted me: *McGhee, Brownie* / Spread the news around: *Terry, Sonny* / Custard pie: *Terry, Sonny* / Wholesale dealin' papa: *McGhee, Brownie* / Motorcycle blues: *Terry, Sonny* / Hand in hand: *Terry, Sonny* / I woke up this morning: *Terry, Sonny*
PRCD 9913 / 30 Mar '98 / Prestige

☐ BROWNIE MCGHEE 1944-1955
Watch out / Dissatisfied woman / Rum cola papa / My baby likes to shuffle / Daybreak / Doggin' blues / I'm gonna rock / Evil but kindhearted / Drinkin' wine spo-dee-o-dee
TMCD 04 / Oct '90 / Travellin' Man

☐ BROWNIE'S BLUES
Jump, little children / Lonesome day / One thing for sure / Killin' floor / Little black engine / I don't know the reason / Trouble in mind / Everyday I have the blues / Door to success
OBCCD 505 / Nov '92 / Original Blues Classics

☐ CLIMBIN' UP (McGhee, Brownie & Sonny Terry)
Gone baby gone / Tell me baby / Sittin' pretty / Bottom blues / Dissatisfied blues / Diamond ring / Way I feel / So much trouble / When it's love time / I'd love to love you / Love's a disease / My fault
SV 0256 / Oct '97 / Savoy Jazz

☐ I COULDN'T BELIEVE MY EYES (McGhee, Brownie & Sonny Terry/Earl Hooker)
Black cat bone / Brownie's new blues / Poor man blues / Tell me why / My baby's so fine / You just usin' me for a convenience / Hole in the wall / Long way from home / Don't wait for me / I'm in love with you baby / Parcel post blues / When I was drinking / I couldn't believe my eyes / Life is a gamble / Don't mistreat me / Rock Island line
BGOCD 407 / 3 Aug '98 / Beat Goes On

☐ NOT GUILTY BLUES
Picking my tomatoes / Born for bad luck / I'm calling Daisy / My barkin' bulldog blues / Let me tell you 'bout my baby / Be good to me / Step it up and go / Not guilty blues / Money spending women / Death of blind boy Fuller / Barbcue any old time / Million lonesome women / Workingman's blues / Dealing with the devil / Key to my door / I'm a black woman's man / Try me one more time / Swing soldier swing 2
CBCD 004 / 31 Jul '98 / Collector's Blues

☐ RAINY DAY
Blues had a baby / I'm going to keep on loving / Walk on / Rainy day / Christina / Don't dog your woman / Mean and evil / Wine sporty orty / Blues is truth / Bunkhouse / Kev to the highway / Blues on parade
CPCD 8167 / Jun '96 / Charly

McGhee, Howard

☐ DIAL MASTERS, THE
Intersection / Lifestream / Mop mop / Stardust / You / Stop time blues / Sleepwalker boogie / Surrender / Turnip blood / Night music / Coolie-rini / Night mist / Dorothy / High wind in Hollywood / Up in Dodo's room / Midnight at Mintons / Dialated pupils / Therodynamics / Trumpet at Tempo
SPJCD 131 / Jul '95 / Spotlite

☐ JAZZBROTHERS
In there / One for George / Island mood / Frisky / Driftin' / Queen's / Search / When Sonny gets blue / Island mood / Frisky
STCD 8266 / Feb '98 / Storyville

☐ MAGGIE
Merry Lee / Short life / Talk of the town / Bass C Jam / Down home / Sweet and lovely / Fiesta / I'm in the mood for love / Belle from Bunnycock / Lip flip / Man I love / Last word / Royal Garden blues / Mood indigo / St. Louis blues / One o'clock jump / Stormy weather / Man with a horn / Stompin' at the Savoy / Oh lady be good / Stardust / How high the moon / Don't blame me / Body and soul / Harvest time
SV 0269 / Oct '97 / Savoy Jazz

☐ MCGHEE SPECIAL
McGhee special / Sportsman's hop / Bean stalking / Ready for love / April in Paris / Rifftide / Ventura jump / Hollywood stampede / Too much of a good thing / Bean soup / Intersection / Life stream / Mop mop / Stardust / I found a new baby / Windjammer / Skylark / Be bop / Trumpet at tempo / Thermodynamics / Dial-ated pupils / Midnight at Minton's / Up in Dodo's room / High wind in Hollywood
TPZ 1062 / Feb '97 / Topaz Jazz

☐ SHARP EDGE
BLCD 760110 / Dec '88 / Black Lion

☐ SUNSET SWING (McGhee, Howard & Previn/Edison/Thompson)
BLCD 760171 / Mar '93 / Black Lion

McGhee, Stick

☐ NEW YORK BLUES (McGhee, Stick & His Spo-Dee-O-Dee Buddies)
Real good feeling: *Collins, Tom* / Heartache blues: *Collins, Tom* / Heartbreakin' woman: *Collins, Tom* / Watchin' my stuff: *Collins, Tom* / Gonna hop on down the line: *Willis, Ralph* / Do right: *Willis, Ralph* / Why'd you do it: *Willis, Ralph* / Door bell blues: *Willis, Ralph* / I'm doin' all this time (and you put me down): *McGhee, Stick* / Wiggle waggie woo: *McGhee, Stick* / Dealin' from the bottom: *McGhee, Stick* / Whiskey, women and loaded dice: *McGhee, Stick* / Little things we used to do: *McGhee, Stick* / Blues in my heart and tears in my eyes: *McGhee, Stick* / Head happy with wine: *McGhee, Stick* / Jungle juice: *McGhee, Stick* / Sad, bad, glad: *McGhee, Stick* / Six to eight: *McGhee, Stick* / Get your mind out of the gutter: *McGhee, Stick* / Double crossin' liquor: *McGhee, Stick*
CDCHD 502 / Jan '95 / Ace

McGhee, Wes

☐ BACKBEAT
Voices from exile / Long nights and banjo music / Voices from exile / Light at the end of the line / Mailman (bring me no more blues) / Contrabandistas / Ain't that lovin' you baby / (It's no use bein' a fast draw) if you can't shoot straight / Mezcal Road / This time / I feel strange / Wee freakings / Justine / (I don't wanna hang up my) rock 'n' roll shoes / Extranjero / She almost reminds me of you / Every night about this time / Here on a Saturday night / Voices from exile / Heat of the highway
RGFCD 022 / May '97 / Road Goes On Forever

☐ BORDER GUITARS
RGFCD 018 / Jul '94 / Road Goes On Forever

☐ HEARTACHE AVENUE (Classic & Unreleased Recordings 1978-1992)
RGFCD 017 / Aug '96 / Road Goes On Forever

McGillivray, James

☐ WORLD'S GREATEST PIPERS VOL.10, THE
Duncan mcgillivray, chief steward-the braemar gathering (68 / John walsh's walk-gordon macrae's favourite (hornpipes) / Ann fionghall macdonald-northern union (68 marches) / Macgregor's salute (piobaireachd)
LCOM 5216 / Oct '90 / Lismor

McGlohon, Loonis

☐ LOONIS IN LONDON 1981
Foggy day / Send in the clowns / Time for love / Where's the child I used to hold / Lazybones / Blackberry winter / Songbird / Get me to the church on time / I've grown accustomed to her face
ACD 166 / Mar '97 / Audiophile

McGlynn, Arty

☐ LEAD THE KNAVE (McGlynn, Arty & Nollaig Casey)
Lead the knave bunker hill / Brady's set / Caoineadh eoghain ruadh / Micho Russell's the yellow cow jigging the donkey / Mominsko horo / Michael Ward / Hunter's purse / Moran's return / E minor reel (lads of Laois) / Cape clear / Cottage in the grove / Barbara Needhams / Miller's maggot
MCGCD 1 / 2 Feb '98 / Ring Send

☐ MCGLYNN'S FANCY
Carolan's draught / Floating crowbar / I wish my love was a red, red rose / Peter Byrne's fancy / Blackbird / Creeping Docken / Charles O'Connor / Arthur Darley / Hills above Drumquin / Sally gardens / Sonny brogan's fancy / Brian Kiely's Delight
BERCD 011 / Nov '94 / Emerald
MCLD 19351 / Oct '96 / MCA

McGoldrick, Michael

☐ CHAMPIONS OF THE NORTH (McGoldrick, Michael & Des Donnelly)
MMRCD 801 / Dec '97 / Magnetic

☐ MORNING RORY
Jenny picking cockles/Earl's chair / Glens of Aherlow/Trip to Herve's / Copperplate/Green mountain/Controversial / History man / Knocknamoe jig/Custy's/Trip to Brittany / Peter Brown's/Mamma's pet/Sailor on the rock / My mind will never be easy/Baby Rory's slip jig / Larkin's beehive/McGann's/Amazing adventures of Dr.Moriarty / Gan ainm/Lavery's 1/Lavery's 2/ September reel / Maid of Monisco/Galway rambler / Dub reel
AUGH 01 / Nov '96 / Aughrim

McGough, Roger

☐ SUMMER WITH MONIKA
Prelude / Prologue / Epic film / I have lately learned to swim / Ten milk bottles / Big bad dark / You are so very beautiful / Sunday morning / Sky has nothing to say / Ring / Tightrope / Nobody's fool / Soup / Trench warfare / Last waltz / Porrige / Teethings / Epilogue
EDCD 508 / Feb '97 / Edsel

MacGowan, Shane

☐ CROCK OF GOLD (MacGowan, Shane & The Popes)
MACG 002CD / 27 Oct '97 / ZTT

McGowan, Geraldine

☐ RECONCILIATION
CMBCD 014 / Jan '95 / Cross Border Media

McGrattan, Paul

☐ FROST IS ALL OVER, THE
Speed the plough / Abbey reel/Primrose lass / Hare in the corn/Grainne's welcome / Sailor's return/ Chattering magpie/House on the hill / Slan le Maigh/ Tailor's twist/Mayo reels / Stone in the field/John Egan's reel/Dublin porter / Up and away/Mountain pathway/Egan's polkas / Skylark/Jenny Dang the weaver / Frost is all over/Coleman's jig/Rambling pitchfork / Johnny O'Leary's/Padraig O'Keeffe's slide / Byrne's hornpipes / Gehan's reel/Crosses of Annagh/An untitled reel / Tracey's jig/Rose in the heather/Blackthorn stick / Hardiman the fiddler/ Taim in arrears / Christmas eve/Old bush/The scholar reel / Tommy People's reel
CC 58CD / Jan '93 / Claddagh

☐ PAUL MCGRATTAN & PAUL O'SHAUGHNESSY (McGrattan, Paul & Paul O'Shaughnessy)
SPINCD 1000 / Oct '96 / Spin

☐ WITHIN A MILE OF DUBLIN (McGrattan, Paul & Paul O'Shaughnessy)
SPIN 1000CD / Aug '96 / Foetain

McGraw, Tim

☐ ALL I WANT
CURCD 16 / Sep '95 / Curb

☐ EVERYWHERE
CURCD 039 / Jun '97 / Curb

MacGregor, Hamish

☐ SCOTTISH LOVE SONGS
Bleacher Lassie / Banks o' red roses / I loved a lass / Partans in his creel / Ae fond kiss / Amang the steppin' stanes / Leaboy's lassie / Lassie of bonnie Glencoe / My love is like a red red rose / Just like another rolling stone / Ca' the yowes / Will ye no come back again
CDTT 1003 / Apr '98 / Tartan Tapes

☐ TRIP TO SCOTLAND (MacGregor, Hamish & The Blue Bonnets)
Flowers of Edinburgh/St. Kilda's wedding / Loch Lomond/Loch Ruan/Loch Maree / Pennan den / Stones of Stenness/Killiecrankie / Arniston Castle/ Inver lassies / Dark Lochnagar / Roslin Castle/ Stirling Castle/Roxburgh Castle / Kelso races/Miss Ann Cameron of Balvenie/Hoddom Castle / Banks of Loch Ness/Ben Nevis / Ye banks and the braes o' bonnie Doune/Farewell to Fuinary / Road and the miles to Dundee/Morag of Dunvegan / Glasgow hornpipe/ Inverness gathering/Perth assembly / Skye boat song / Spootiskerry/Da Scallowa lasses/Bonnie Isle of Whalsay
CDTT 1001 / Jul '97 / Tartan Tapes

McGregor, Chris

☐ GRANDMOTHER'S TEACHING
ITM 1428 / Jan '91 / ITM

☐ IN MEMORIUM (McGregor, Chris & Brotherhood Of Breath)
ITMP 970086 / Oct '95 / ITM

☐ THUNDERBOLT (McGregor, Chris & The South African Exiles)
PAMCD 405 / May '97 / Popular African Music

McGregor, Freddie

☐ ALL IN THE SAME BOAT
All in the same boat / Hungry belly pickney / Push comes to shove / Jah a the don / I'm coming home / Glad you're here with me / I don't want to see you cry / Somewhere / Mama Mama / Peace in the valley
RASCD 3014 / May '87 / Ras

☐ BIG SHIP
Big ship / Sweet lady / Peaceful man / Stop loving you / Get serious / Don't play the fool / Get united / Let me be the one / Roots man skanking / Holy Mount Zion
GRELCD 39 / May '89 / Greensleeves

☐ CARRY GO BRING COME
GRELCD 197 / Dec '93 / Greensleeves

☐ COME ON OVER
Shirley come on over / Apple of my eye / Go away pretty woman / Stand up and fight / Shortman / Are you crazy / Reggae feeling / Rhythm so nice / Natty dread / Brother man
RASCD 3002 / Apr '92 / Ras

☐ COMPILATION
RNCD 2131 / Nov '95 / Rhino

☐ EARLY YEARS (McGregor, Freddie & The Clarendonians)
RN 7004 / Sep '96 / Rhino

☐ FOREVER MY LOVE
RASCD 3160 / Aug '95 / Ras

☐ HARD TO GET
GRELCD 175 / Nov '92 / Greensleeves

☐ JAMAICAN CLASSICS VOL.1
BSCD 1 / Oct '91 / Jet Star

☐ JAMAICAN CLASSICS VOL.2
BSCD 2 / Jul '97 / Big Ship

☐ JAMAICAN CLASSICS VOL.3
BSCD 7 / Jun '96 / Big Ship

☐ LEGIT (McGregor, Freddie & Cocoa T/ Dennis Brown)
GRELCD 189 / Aug '93 / Greensleeves

☐ LIVE IN LONDON 1991
Prophecy / So many people wanna see me stop loving you / Fever / Big ship / Africa here I come / Push come to shove / I've got the handle / Loving pauper / Let him try / Baby baby babylon / Wine of violence
CPCD 8027 / Feb '94 / Charly

☐ MAGIC IN THE AIR
BSCD 5 / Aug '95 / Big Ship

☐ MASTERPIECE
Mark of the beast / Jah him never fail I / Harvest uptown famine downtown / Love was to die for: *McGregor, Freddie & Papa San* / Brandy / Spread love / Reggae ska / I feel secure / Homeward bound / I need your love / I wish there was a way / Blue skies / Darlin' darlin' baby sweet tender love / Got no time to waste / Every time you smile
GRELCD 241 / 15 Sep '97 / Greensleeves

☐ NOW
VPCD 1163 / Jun '91 / Steely & Cleevie

☐ PRESENTING FREDDIE MCGREGOR
RNCD 2136 / Apr '96 / Rhino

☐ PUSH ON
BSCD 4 / Apr '94 / Big Ship

☐ RAS PORTRAITS
Push come to shove / Go away pretty woman / Freddie / Apple of my eye / Across the border / Rastaman camp / Mama mama / Sweet child / Somewhere / Forever my love
RAS 3305 / Jun '97 / Ras

☐ REGGAE MAX
JSRNCD 7 / Mar '97 / Jet Star

☐ REGGAE ROCKERS
Lover's rock / Chant down babylon / Walls of jericho / Jah count on I / Oh no not my baby / Why did you do it / Zion chant / Rastaman camp / Do good / Brandy
RRTGCD 7714 / '89 / Rohit

☐ RUMOURS
Tin soldier / She's gone / Rumours / Graveyard in Africa / Want more loving / Stay with me tonight / Woke up smiling / If you're the one / If I should fall in love / Come on over / Who is he / Stolen legacy / Mix up and blenda / Beautiful woman / Saying goodbye
GRELCD 236 / Mar '97 / Greensleeves

☐ ZION CHANT
HB 138CD / Sep '94 / Heartbeat

McGriff, Jimmy

☐ BLUES GROOVE (McGriff, Jimmy & Hank Crawford Quartet)
Movin' upside the blues / Splanky / Frame for the blues / Lew's piece / All blues / Sermon / When I fall in love / Could be / Don't cry baby / Mercy mercy mercy
CD 83381 / Mar '96 / Telarc

☐ DREAM TEAM, THE
McGriffin / Ain't it funny how time slips away / Red hot 'n' new / Fleetwood stroll / Don't blame me / 'Tain't nobody's bizness if I do / Things ain't what they used to be
MCD 92682 / Nov '97 / Milestone

☐ ELECTRIC FUNK
Back on the track / Chris cross / Miss Poopie / Bird wave / Spear for moon dog - Part 2 / Tight times / Spinning the wheel / Funky junk
CDP 7843502 / Jan '97 / Blue Note

☐ GEORGIA ON MY MIND
Let's stay together / Shaft / What's going on / Georgia on my mind / April in Paris / Everyday I have the blues / Yardbird suite / It's you I adore / Lonesome road / Mack the knife / There will never be another you / Canadian sunset / Mr. Lucky / Moonglow / Red sails in the sunset / Secret love
CDC8513 / Nov '90 / LRC

☐ JIMMY MCGRIFF FEATURING HANK CRAWFORD (McGriff, Jimmy & Hank Crawford)
CDC 9001 / Oct '90 / LRC

☐ PULLIN' OUT THE STOPS (The Best Of Jimmy McGriff)
All about my girl / I've got a woman / Discotheque / Kiko / CC rider / Cash box / Gospel time / Where it's at / Last minute / Blue juice / Step one / Chris cross / South Wes / Black pearl / Worm / Ain't it funky now / Fat cakes
CDP 8307242 / Sep '94 / Blue Note

☐ RED BEANS
Red beans and rice / Big booty bounce / Space cadet / Alive and well / Sweet love / Love is my life / It feels so nice / Green machine / Please don't take me out / Overweight shark bait
CDC 9083 / Apr '95 / LRC

☐ SONNY LESTER COLLECTION
CDC 9070 / Nov '93 / LRC

☐ TRIBUTE TO COUNT BASIE, A (McGriff, Jimmy Big Band)
CDC 9027 / Mar '91 / LRC

☐ TRIBUTE TO COUNT BASIE, A
Hob nail boogie / Cherry point / Swingin' the blues / Lil' darlin' / Splanky / Slow but sure / Blues go away / Avenue C / Cute / Everyday
17094 / Jan '97 / Laserlight

McGuinn, Roger

☐ BORN TO ROCK AND ROLL
I'm so restless / My new woman / Draggin' / Water is wide / Same old sound / Bag full of money / Gate of horn / Peace on you / Love of the bayou / Stone (the Lord loves a rolling stone) / Lisa / Jolly Roger / Friend / Dreamland / Dixie highway / American girl / Up to me / Russian hill / Born to rock and roll
4882232 / 8 Sep '97 / Columbia

☐ LIVE FROM MARS
1620902 / Jan '97 / Polydor

☐ RETURN FLYTE VOL.1 (McGuinn, Roger & Gene Clark/Chris Hillman)
Long long time / Long long long time / Surrender to me / Backstage pass / Sad boy / Who taught the night / City / Skate date / Given' herself away / Let me down easy / Between you and me / King for a night / Turn your radio on / Angel
EDCD 358 / Dec '92 / Edsel

☐ RETURN FLYTE VOL.2 (McGuinn, Roger & Gene Clark/Chris Hillman)
Little mama / Stopping traffic / Feelin' higher / Release me girl / Bye bye baby / One more chance / Won't let you down / Street talk / Deeper in / Painted fire / Mean streets / Entertainment / Soul shoes / Love me tonight / Secret side of you / Ain't no money / Making movies
EDCD 373 / Jun '93 / Edsel

McGuinness Flint

☐ CAPITOL YEARS, THE
When I'm dead and gone / Lazy afternoon / Bondang buck / Mister mister / Heritage / I'm letting you know / Let it ride / Dream darlin' dream / Who you got to love / International / Malt and barley blues / Rock on / Happy birthday Ruthy baby / Conversation / When I'm alone with you / Fixer / Faith and gravy / Klondike / Reader to writer / Changes / Friends of mine / Piper of dreams / Jimmy's song / Sparrow / Wham bam / Back on the road again
CDGO 2070 / Oct '96 / EMI Gold

☐ LO AND BEHOLD
Eternal circle / Lo and behold / Let me die in my footsteps / Open the door Homer / Lay down your weary tune / Don't you tell Henry / Get your rocks off / Death of Emmett Till / Odds and ends / Tiny Montgomery / I wanna be your lover / Sign on the cross / Eternal circle
RVCD 62 / Oct '96 / Raven

McGuinness, Lyle

☐ ELISE ELISE (McGuinness, Lyle Band)
Elise: *McGuiness, Lyle* / What does it take: *McGuiness, Lyle* / Put the blame on me: *McGuiness, Lyle* / Yellow kimono: *McGuiness, Lyle* / Hit and run love: *McGuiness, Lyle* / You're always on my mind: *McGuiness, Lyle* / faded photographs: *McGuiness, Lyle* / Moody: *McGuiness, Lyle* / Irish eyes: *McGuiness, Lyle* / Darlin' man: *McGuiness, Lyle* / Hot lips: *McGuiness, Lyle* / Only all the time: *McGuiness, Lyle* / Acting on impulse: *McGuiness, Lyle* / At the commodore: *McGuiness, Lyle* / Fighting for the cause: *McGuiness, Lyle*
GEMCD 015 / Mar '97 / Diamond

McGuire Sisters

☐ DO YOU REMEMBER WHEN/WHILE LIGHTS ARE LOW
Do you remember when / Sometimes I'm happy / June night / All by myself / Tip toe through the tulips with me / Them there eyes / Mississippi mud / Cuddle up a little closer / Lovely mine / Does your heart beat for me / Somebody loves me / 'S wonderful / Blue skies / I'm in the mood for love / Don't take your love from me / My darling, my darling / Moonglow / Tenderly / I hadn't anyone till you / If you were only mine / Wonderful one / I'm confessin' that I love you / Moon song / Love is here to stay / Think of me kindly
JASCD 601 / Aug '96 / Jasmine

McGuire, Barry

☐ EVE OF DESTRUCTION MAN, THE
14528 / Jan '97 / Spalax

McGuire, Seamus

☐ CAROUSEL (McGuire, Seamus & Manus McGuire/Daithi Sproule)
CEFCD 105 / Jan '94 / Gael Linn

☐ MISSING REEL, THE (McGuire, Seamus & John Lee)
CEFCD 146 / Jan '94 / Gael Linn

☐ WISHING TREE, THE
GL 1151CD / Jul '95 / Green Linnet

McGuire, Sean

☐ AT HIS BEST
PTICD 1008 / Jun '98 / Outlet

☐ TRADITIONAL IRISH FIDDLE
PTICD 1006 / Jun '98 / Outlet

McGuire, Sean

☐ BROTHERS TOGETHER (McGuire, Sean & Jim)
PTICD 1055 / Apr '94 / Pure Traditional Irish

☐ CHAMPION OF CHAMPIONS
Cronin's reels / Key west / Poppy leaf / McCormack's / Coulin / Carolan's concerto / Maids of Tulla / Harvest home / High level / Strike the gay harp / Rose wood / Ned of the hill / O'Neills / Triumphal / Centenary / Planxty McGuire / Dear Irish boy / O'Rourke's boy / O'Rourke's reel / Wild Irishman / Jenny's welcome to Charlie
PTICD 1005 / Mar '97 / Pure Traditional Irish

☐ HAWKS AND DOVES
Planxty McGuire / Farl O'Gara / Liffey banks / High reels / Brian Boru / Glantan glas gweedore / Going to the well for water / Low level / Smedley's hornpipe / Dancer - Reavey's No.10 / Kerry Reel / Erin's my home / Larry O'Gaff / Jig No.3 / Maid behind the bar / Auld fiddler / Bert Murray's set reel and Lord Pottinger set / Cuckoo's nest hornpipe / End house of Connaught reel / Gypsy hornipipe / Yiddish flavoured reel / Gypsy hornpipe / An coulin / McCleod's reel / Bonny Kate / Danny boy / Humours of Westport / Andy McGann's reel
PTICD 1089 / Mar '97 / Pure Traditional Irish

☐ IRISH TRADITIONAL FIDDLING
Cronin's fancy / Tom Ward's downfall / Two reevy's / Cas an tugan / Slievenamon / Duke of Leinster and his wife / Pullet wants cock / Dairymaid / Holy land / Jackie Coleman's / Roger's fancy / Golden ring / Se fayh mo bhuartha / Two Andy McGann's / Mama's pet / Banks / Hinchie's delight / Tone rowe's
PTICD 1002 / Mar '97 / Pure Traditional Irish

☐ MASTER'S TOUCH, THE
ARCD 027 / May '98 / Ainm

☐ PORTRAIT
CMCD 048 / Dec '97 / Celtic Music

☐ TWO CHAMPIONS (McGuire, Sean & Joe Burke)
Farl O'Gara / Trim the velvet / Copper plate No.1 / Copper plate No.2 / Old grey goose / Crooked road to Dublin / Concert / Flowing tide / Galway / Dr. Gilbert / Queen of the May / Old Blackthorn / Green groves / Paddy Ryan's dream / Ballinasloe fair / Burying poteen / Cup of tea / Kesh jig / Morrison's / Cronin's / George White's fancy / Tomorrow Morning / Friendly visit / Tom Clark's fancy / Longford collector / Ships are sailing / Bird in the bush
PTICD 1014 / Mar '97 / Pure Traditional Irish

MacGuish, Alasdair

☐ ALASDAIR MACGUISH & THE BLACK ROSE CEILIDH BAND
LOC 1086CD / Jul '95 / Lochshore

Mach Kung Fu

☐ EXOTIC EXHAUST
GCS 018CD / 11 May '98 / Giant Claw

McHael, Allan

☐ NEW RIVER TRAIN
FE 1408 / Nov '94 / Folk Era

☐ OLD COUNTRY RADIO SONGS (McHael, Allan & Old Time Radio Gang)
FE 2062CD / Dec '94 / Folk Era

McHaile, Tom

☐ PURE TRADITIONAL TIN WHISTLE
PTICD 1001 / Apr '94 / Pure Traditional Irish

McHargue, Rosy

☐ OH HOW HE CAN SING
SOSCD 1253 / Jul '93 / Stomp Off

Machel

☐ CHARGE (Machel & Xtatik)
JW 154CD / 14 Apr '98 / JW

McHenry, Bill

☐ REST STOP
FSNT 033 / 1 Jun '98 / Fresh Sound New Talent

McHenry, Waltzer

☐ JAZZ IS WHERE YOU FIND IT
FSNT 021 / Jan '98 / Fresh Sound New Talent

Machete Ensemble

☐ MACHETE ENSEMBLE, THE
CDEB 2501 / May '93 / Earthbeat

Machin, Antonio

☐ 50 GRANDES EXITOS
ALCD 901 / 24 Apr '98 / Alma Latina

☐ ANGELITOS NEGROS
ALCD 502 / Nov '97 / Alma Latina

☐ ANTONIO MACHIN VOL.1 1930-1932
Adela / Suavecito / A baracoa me voy / Pobre corazon / Damelo / Se va el dulcerito / Quisiera morirme / La rosa Oriental / Oprobio / El heurfanito / Illusion China / Ojeras / Las flores de mi jardin / Buey viejo / Sigue tu senda / Triguenita / Lamento Cubano / Esperanzas muertas / Junto a un canaveral / Munequita
HQCD 24 / Oct '96 / Harlequin

☐ ANTONIO MACHIN VOL.2 1932-1933
Entre tinieblas / Don lengua / Mujer / El caramelero / Las perlas de tu boca / Cuartito Sagrado / De que te vale / Recordando a un vendedor / Lucero de mis noches / La sitiera / Asi como suena mi son / El castigador / Para que no pago o dale que ya monte / Echale salsita / El guanajo relleno / Ese hombre es un diablo / Rumba tambah: *Orquesta Antiliana* / Menealo que se empelota: *Orquesta Antiliana* / Clara / Repellito
HQCD 32 / Oct '96 / Harlequin

☐ ANTONIO MACHIN VOL.3 1933-1934
HQCD 58 / Jan '97 / Harlequin

☐ CADA NOCHE UN AMOR
ALCD 501 / Nov '97 / Alma Latina

☐ CANTA A CUBA Y SUS COMPOSITORES
CCD 803 / Jan '97 / Caney

☐ CANTA A MEXICO Y SUS COMPOSITORES
CCD 804 / Jan '97 / Caney

☐ CUARTETO MACHIN 1934-1935
Enamorado de ti / Seni / Conciencia fria / Temo despertar / Anhelo cubano / No me persigas / Flor criolla / Perversa ingratitud / El manzanero / Tu si eres buena / Al encontrarte / Justa verdad / Emocion / El viandero / No he mentido aida / Reina Afrricana / Sorpresa / La morita / Moreno / Por la cintura
HQCD 104 / Apr '98 / Harlequin

☐ DOS GARDENIAS
ALCD 504 / Nov '97 / Alma Latina

☐ ESE SOY YO
ALCD 025 / Apr '97 / Alma Latina

☐ FIEL AMIGO
ALCD 506 / Nov '97 / Alma Latina

☐ MADRECITA
ALCD 505 / Nov '97 / Alma Latina

☐ MELODIA SENTIMENTAL
ALCD 503 / Nov '97 / Alma Latina

Machin, James

☐ GUITAR AND ELECTRONICS MUSIC (Machin, James & Steve Pittis)
DPROMCD 44 / Feb '97 / Dirter Promotions

Machine Head

☐ BURN MY EYES (2CD Set)
Davidian / Old / Thousand eyes / None but my own / Rage to overcome / Death church / I'm your God now / Blood for blood / Nation on fire / Real eyes, realize, real lies / Block
RR 90165
RR 90162 / May '95 / Roadrunner
RR 90160 / Feb '97 / Roadrunner

☐ MORE THINGS CHANGE, THE
10 ton hammer / Take my scars / Struck a nerve / Down to none / Frontlines / Spine / Bay of pigs / Violate / Blistering / Blood of the zodiac / Possibility of life's destruction / My misery / Colors
RR 88605
RR 88602 / Mar '97 / Roadrunner

Machine In The Garden

☐ VEILS AND SHADOWS EP
ISOL 80022 / Feb '95 / Isol

Machines Of Loving Grace

☐ CONCENTRATION
Butterfly wings / Lilith eve / Limiter / Shake / If I should explode / Trigger for happiness / Content / Ancestor cult / Acceleration / Cheap / Albert speer / Perfect tan (bikini atoll)
4509968522 / Nov '94 / WEA

☐ GILT
0086522CTR / Apr '96 / Edel

☐ MACHINES OF LOVING GRACE
MR 00292 / Feb '92 / Mammoth

Machito

☐ BONGO FIESTA
Adios / Holiday mambo / Bongo fiesta / Mambo mucho mambo / Negro nanamboro / Ay que mate / Mambo inn / Zambia / Blem blem blem / Beerebee cum bee / Tremendo cumban / Hay que recordar / Freezelandia / Oboe mambo / Donde estabas tu / Mambo a la savoy
CD 62070 / Apr '95 / Saludos Amigos

☐ FREEZELANDIA (Machito & His Afro-Cubans)
TCD 085 / 5 Jan '98 / Tumbao Cuban Classics

☐ MACHITO & HIS AFRO-CUBANS 1948-1950
HQCD 87 / Jul '96 / Harlequin

☐ MACHITO & HIS SALSA BIG BAND/ LIVE AT NORTH SEA 1982/MACHITO (3CD Set) (Machito & His Salsa Big Band)
Elas de la rumba / Quimbobo / Piniero tenia razon / Caso perdido / Manicero / Sambia / Yerbero / Buenos noches che che / Tibri tabara / Oye la rumba / No seras mio / Dale jamon / Mambo inn / Bailan cha cha y cua guanco / Guantenanmera pensativa / Buscando la melodia / Ronnie Scott mambo / Mi cancion es para ti / Guanganco / Sopa de pichon
SJP 010 / 26 May '98 / Timeless

☐ MAMBO IN JAZZ
Tin tin deo / Wild jungle / Oyeme / Ring-a-levio / Conversation / Kenya / Minor rama / Blues a la machito / Frenzy / Congo mulence / Holiday / Cannonology / Mambo (parts 1 and 2) / Mango mangue / Okiedoke
CD 62015 / Jan '93 / Saludos Amigos

☐ RITMO PA' GOZAR (Machito & His Orchestra)
CCD 511 / Jul '96 / Caney

☐ SALSA BIG BAND 1982 (Machito & His Salsa Big Band)
Elas de la rumba / Quimbobo / Piniero tenia razon / Caso perdido / Manicero / Sambia / Yerbero
CDSJP 161 / '89 / Timeless Jazz

Machline, Norberto

☐ AIN'T MISBEHAVIN' (Machline, Norberto Trio)
BMJ 003 / Jan '98 / Blue Moon

Machlis, Paul

☐ BRIGHT FIELD, THE (Machlis, Paul & Alasdair Fraser)
CULD 107 / Jun '95 / Culburnie

☐ GREEN WOODS (Upon A Celtic Path)
4628881632 / 27 Apr '98 / Real Music

McHugh, Phil

☐ RIDE THE EARTH
3694100032 / 27 Apr '98 / Canis Major

McIlwaine, Ellen

☐ LOOKING FOR TROUBLE
SPCD 1110 / Apr '94 / Stony Plain

☐ WOMEN IN (E)MOTION FESTIVAL
Save the world / Howl at the moon / Beg for the reason / Fight the power / May this be love / Crawling kingsnake / I'm a woman / Bid you goodnight / Lean on me
T&M 112 / Jul '98 / Tradition & Moderne

MacInnes, Mairi

☐ CAUSEWAY
Clachan uaine (The green village) / Mendocino / Puirt a beul (mouth music) / Eala bhan (The white swan) / Eilidh / Cuachag nana craobh (The tree cuckoo) / Morag's na horo ghealladh (walking song) / Mairead og / Soraidh le eilean a'cheo / (Back home again in) Indiana / Tuireadh mhic criomain (MacCrimmon's lament) / Mo chridhe trom's duilich leam / Everlasting gun
LCOM 9018 / Oct '92 / Lismor

☐ THIS FEELING INSIDE
Puert a beul / Follow the light / Cum ar'naire / Come back to me / Neamhnaid gheal dochais / Sit at my table / Fraoch a ronaidh / Far from home / Fear a'bhata / Precious days / Mile marphaisg air a ghaol / Eilean m'araich / Puirt a beul / This feeling inside
CDTRAX 092 / Jul '95 / Greentrax

MacInnis, Jamie

☐ FOSGAIL AN DORUS (MacInnis, Jamie & Paul MacNeil)
Thig a staigh / DNA / Newmarket House / Paul's solo / Rothesay / Milling set / Cape Breton set / Eireann's / Gun oran binn, no canain grinn / Jamie's solo / Ian Ruadh / Electric set
IRCD 044 / Jan '97 / Iona

MacIntyre, Sandy

☐ STEEPED IN TRADITION
SMCD 9607 / Mar '98 / SM

McIntyre, Kalaparusha Maurice

☐ FORCES AND FEELINGS
Behold God's sunshine / Fifteen or sixteen / Sun spots / Ananda / Twenty-one lines / Behold God's sunshine / Ananda
DE 425 / Nov '96 / Delmark

☐ PEACE AND BLESSINGS (McIntyre, Kalaparusha Maurice Quartet)
1200372 / Oct '96 / Black Saint

McIntyre, Ken

☐ COMPLETE UA SESSIONS, THE (2CD Set)
Miss Ann / Lois Marie / Chittlin's and cavyah / Permanentity / Tip top / Kaijee / Reflections / Say what / 96.5 / Arisin' / Laura / Speak low / Cosmos / Sendai / Undulation / Turbospacey / Bootsie / New time / Naomi / Someday / Mercedes
CDP 8572002 / Aug '97 / Blue Note

☐ INTRODUCING THE VIBRATIONS (McIntyre, Ken Sextet)
SCCD 31065 / Dec '95 / Steeplechase

☐ LOOKING AHEAD (McIntyre, Ken & Eric Dolphy)
Lautir / Curtsy / Geo's tune / They all laughed / Head shakin'
OJCCD 252 / Jun '96 / Original Jazz Classics

MacIsaac, Ashley

☐ HI HOW ARE YOU TODAY
Beaton's delight / Sleepy Maggie / Rusty D-con-Struck-tion / Devil in the kitchen / MacDougall's pride / Spoonboy / What an idiot he is / Sophia's pipes / Sad wedding day / Wing-stock / Hills of Glenorchy / Brenda Stubbert
5405222 / Jun '96 / A&M

MacIsaac, Dave

☐ NIMBLE FINGERS
50399CD / Mar '98 / Factor

MacIsaac, Wendy

☐ THAT'S WHAT YOU GET
CDLDL 1266 / Dec '97 / Lochshore

Mack, Bobby

☐ RED HOT & HUMID
Black Jack / In the open / Maudie / Look watcha done / She's so fine / Phillip West / Ain't nobody's business if I do / Change my mind / All night long / Take it home
PRD 70692 / Aug '94 / Provogue

☐ SAY WHAT
By the minute / Change it / She's so fine / Treat her like a lady / Take it home / Before you accuse me / Change my mind / Give it up / Piece of my heart / 42nd street
PRD 70502 / Apr '93 / Provogue

☐ SUGAR ALL NIGHT
PRD 70812 / Feb '96 / Provogue

Mack, Craig

☐ PROJECT: FUNK DA WORLD
Project: Funk da world / Get down / Making moves with puff / That y'all / Flava in ya ear / Funk wit da style / Judgement day / Real raw / Mainline / When God comes / Welcome to 1994
78612730012 / Oct '94 / Arista

Mack, Jimmy

☐ JOY SOMETHING FOR EVERYONE
LDRCD 021 / Nov '96 / Londisc

☐ MANKIND
ORCD 008 / Jul '96 / Original Music

Mack, Leroy

☐ LEROY MACK & FRIENDS
REB 1729CD / Aug '96 / Rebel

Mack, Lonnie

☐ ATTACK OF THE KILLER V (Lonnie Mack Live)
ALCD 4786 / May '93 / Alligator

☐ HOME AT LAST
OW S2117963 / Sep '94 / One Way

☐ LONNIE MACK & PISMO
OW S2117964 / Sep '94 / One Way

☐ LONNIE ON THE MOVE
I found a love / Soul express / I've had it / Wildwood flower / Snow on the mountain / I washed my hands in muddy water / Shotgun / Sticks and stones / Jam and butter / One mint julep / Florence of Arabia / Lonnie on the move / Sa-ba-hoola / Money (that's what I want) / Dorothy on my mind / Men at play / Oh boy / Stand by me / Don't make my baby blue
CDCH 352 / Feb '92 / Ace

☐ SECOND SIGHT
Me and my car / Rock 'n' roll bones / Tough on me tough on you / Camp Washington Chili / Cincinnati / Rock people / Buffalo woman / Ain't nobody / Back on the road again / Song I haven't sung
ALCD 4750 / Oct '93 / Alligator

☐ STRIKE LIKE LIGHTNING
Hound dog man / Satisfy Susie / Stop / Long way from Memphis / Double whammy / Strike like lightning / Falling back in love with you / If you have to know / You ain't got me / Oreo cookie blues
ALCD 4739 / May '93 / Alligator

Macka B

☐ BUPPIE CULTURE
ARICD 48 / Jan '91 / Ariwa Sounds

☐ DISCRIMINATION
ARICD 098 / Jun '94 / Ariwa Sounds

☐ HERE COMES TROUBLE
Promises / Here comes trouble / Do the butterfly / Getting blacker / Don't worry / Thank you Father / Squeeze me / Reggae on the rampage / Crackpot / Rottweiler
ARICD 088 / Oct '93 / Ariwa Sounds

☐ HOLD ON TO YOUR CULTURE
Bob / Legalize the herb / Beautiful eyes / Greetings / Hold on to your culture / Give the workers / Woman / Put down the gun / Tribute to Garnett Silk
ARICD 108 / Oct '95 / Ariwa Sounds

☐ JAMAICA, NO PROBLEM
ARICD 078 / May '92 / Ariwa Sounds

☐ PEACE CUP
ARICD 068 / Jul '91 / Ariwa Sounds

☐ ROOTS RAGGA
Roots Ragga / (Get up I feel like being a) sex machine / Drink too much / Revelation time / Big mack / Devil dance / Rodney King medley / One man, one vote / Unemployment blues / Proud to be black / Back off / Buppie / Respect to the mother / Apartheid
ARICD 082 / Nov '92 / Ariwa Sounds

☐ SIGN OF THE TIMES
ARICD 028 / Feb '89 / Ariwa Sounds

☐ SUSPICIOUS
ARICD 138 / May '97 / Ariwa/Shaka

McKay, Alex Francis

☐ LIFELONG HOME, A
Rosin the bow / Duke of Athole / Earl Grey / Lady Mary Ramsey / Highland society / McGlashan jig / Coilsfield house / Christy's quickstep / Craigaillichie bridge / Welcome to your feet / Mrs Garden of Troup / Double kisses / Dunkeld hermitage / Jenny Caruthers
CDTRAX 149 / 1 Dec '97 / Greentrax
ROUCD 7020 / May '97 / Rounder

McKay, Freddie

☐ DOIN' IT RIGHT
CDGR 242 / 27 May '98 / Charly

☐ RIGHT TIME, THE
RN 7030 / 24 Nov '97 / Rhino

MacKay, Iain

☐ SEOLADH
SKYECD 07 / Sep '95 / Macmeanmna

McKay, Kris

☐ THINGS THAT SHOW
SHCD 8020 / Jul '96 / Shanachie

MacKay, Rhona

☐ CEOL NA CLARSAICH
LCOM 5130 / Oct '96 / Lismor

McKee, Maria

☐ LIFE IS SWEET
Searlover / This perfect dress / Absolutely barking stars / I'm not listening / Everybody / Smarter / What else you wanna know / I'm awake / Human carried / Life is sweet / Afterlife
GED 24819 / 8 Sep '97 / Geffen

☐ MARIA MCKEE
I've forgotten what it was in you / To miss someone / Am I the only one (who ever felt this way) / Nobody's child / Panic beach / Can't pull the wool down (over the little lamb's eyes) / More than a heart can hold / This property is condemned / Breathe / Has he got a friend for me / Drinkin' in my Sunday dress
GED 24229 / Nov '96 / Geffen

☐ YOU GOTTA SIN TO GET SAVED
I'm gonna soothe you / My lonely sad eyes / My girlhood among the outlaws / Only once / I forgive you / I can't make it alone / Precious time / Way young lovers do / Why wasn't I more grateful (when life was so sweet) / You gotta sin to get saved
GFLD 19290 / 2 Feb '98 / Geffen

McKellar, Kenneth

☐ LAND OF HEART'S DESIRE
Think on me / Old turf fire / Fairy lullaby / Ho ro my nut brown maiden / David of the White Rock / MacPherson's farewell / Land of heart's desire / Star of County Down / Ellan Vannin / Bonnie Earl O'Moray / Wee Cooper o' Fife / Old house / O' are ye sleepin' Maggie / She moved through the fair / Durisdeer / Next market day / Watching the wheat / Twa corbies / My Irish jaunting car / O' a the airts / Wee Hughie / Gortnamona
LCOM 9044 / Aug '91 / Lismor

☐ MIST COVERED MOUNTAINS OF HOME, THE
Mist covered mountains of home / Bonnie Strathyre / Nicky Tams / Oor ain fireside / O gin I were whar' gadie rins / To people who have gardens / Amazing grace / Kelvin Grove / Corn rigs / Bonnie lass o' Fyvie / O gin I were a baron's heir / Wee cock sparra / Iona boat song / Pan drap song / Flowers of the forest / Scotland the brave
LCOM 6043 / Nov '95 / Lismor

☐ SCOTTISH JOURNEY VOL.1, A
LISMOR 6037 / Jan '95 / Lismor

☐ SCOTTISH JOURNEY VOL.2, A
This is Scotland / Mingulay boat song / Island of Tiree / Hieland laddie / Corn rigs / Scots wha hae / Come o'er the stream Charlie / Royal Mile / Sing to me the old Scots songs medley / Wee cooper of Fife / Bonnie Dundee / Saturday dance / Northern lights of old Aberdeen / Nicky tams / Amazing grace / Pan drap song / Oor ain fireside / Scotland the brave
LCOM 6044 / Feb '97 / Lismor

☐ SONGS OF THE JACOBITE RISINGS VOL.1, THE
Bluebells of Scotland / Piper O'Dundee / Lewie Gordon / Cam ye by Atholl / Farewell to Glenshalloch / Ye Jacobites by name / Blackbird / Braes o'Killecrankie / Flora MacDonald's lament / Highland muster roll / Skye boat song / Ower the water to Charlie / Wae's me for Prince Charlie / Bonnets o' bonnie Dundee / Will ye no' come back again
LCOM 6028 / Aug '96 / Lismor

☐ SONGS OF THE JACOBITE RISINGS VOL.2, THE (The Laughter & The Tears)
Wah widna' fecht for Charlie / Charlie is my darling / Hey Johnny Cope / Our ain countrie / Your welcome Charlie Stuart / Kenmore's up and awa' / Come o'er the stream Charlie / Highland widow / There'll never be peace till Jamie comes hame / Wi' a hundred pipers / Twa bonnie maidens / Women are a' gane wud / Highland widows lament / Campbells are coming / Sound the pibroch / We will take the good old way / Loch Lomond
LCOM 6036 / Dec '93 / Lismor

☐ TODAY
Island of Tiree / Flower of Scotland / Braes o'Balquhidder / Old ballad (the farmer's daughter) / Northern lights of old Aberdeen / Rowan tree / Glencoe (the massacre of) / Wee place in the Highlands / Jean / Scotland again / Thou Bonnie Wood O Craigelea / Mingulay boat song / Clyde medley / Star O' rabbie burns / Mull of the cool bens / Eriskay love lilt / Ye banks and braes o' bonnie Doon
LCOM 9011 / Aug '91 / Lismor

☐ VERY BEST OF KENNETH MCKELLAR, THE
My love is like a red red rose / Skye boat song / Cockles and mussels / Wi' a hundred pipers / Stranger in paradise / Villikins and Dinah / Ye banks and braes / Serenade from the fair maid of Perth / Danny boy / Island moon / Sweet lass of Richmond Hill / There was a lad was born in Kyle / Dance to your Daddy / Twa corbies / Greensleeves / Ball of Kirriemuir / O waly waly / Last rose of summer / Bonnie labouring boy / Rising of the lark
5520952 / Jan '97 / Spectrum

McKendree Spring

☐ GOD BLESS THE CONSPIRACY
No regrets / Spock / Morning glory / Fire and rain / Susie Susie / Got no place to fall / Down by the river / Fading lady / Heart like a wheel / Hobo lady / Oh in the morning / God bless the conspiracy / Light up the skies / Man in me / What was gained
EDCD 497 / Oct '96 / Edsel

McKenna Singers

☐ 30 ALL TIME FAVOURITE SINGALONGS
MBPCD 7001 / 18 May '98 / Quantum Mobius

McKenna, Dave

☐ CELEBRATION OF HOAGY CARMICHAEL
Stardust / Riverboat shuffle / One morning in May / Moon country / Two sleepy people / Come easy, go easy love / Nearness of you / Lazybones / Sky lark / Georgia / Lazy river
CCD 4227 / May '94 / Concord Jazz

☐ CHRISTMAS IVORY
Santa Claus is coming to town / Jingle bells / Stille nacht, heilige nacht / Let it snow, let it snow, let it snow / Don't want no blues this Christmas / It came upon a midnight clear / Christmas waltz / O little town of Bethlehem/Mary's little boy child / Cantique de Noel / Silver bells / I'll be home for Christmas / Snowbound / Eggnog, some mistletoe and you / Sleigh ride / Adeste fideles / O Tannenbaum, O Tannenbaum
CCD 47722 / 17 Nov '97 / Concord Jazz

☐ CONCORD DUO SERIES VOL.2 (McKenna, Dave & Gray Sargent)
Sheikh of Araby / Girl of my dreams / Red woods in the sunset / I'm gonna sit right down and write myself a letter / Blue and sentimental / 'Deed I do / Time after time/time on my hands / Exactly like you
CCD 4552 / May '93 / Concord Jazz

☐ DAVE MCKENNA QUARTET FEATURING ZOOT SIMS (McKenna, Dave & Zoot Sims)
CRD 136 / Mar '96 / Chiaroscuro

☐ EASY STREET
Broadway / Basin Street blues / Street of dreams / Don't forget 127th street / Easy street / On Green Dolphin Street / On the street where you live / Cat's cradle / My honey's lovin' arms / When your lover is gone / Now that you're gone / After you've gone / Gone with the wind / Theodore the thumper
CCD 4657 / Jul '95 / Concord Jazz

☐ GIANT STRIDES
If dreams come true / Yardbird suite / Windsong / Dave's blues / I've got the world on a string / Love letter / Cherry / Lulu's back in town / Walkin' my baby back home / Underdog / I've found a new baby
CCD 4099 / Feb '95 / Concord Jazz

☐ HANDFUL OF STARS, A
Estrela, estrela / Stella by starlight / Star eyes / Star kissed / Handful of stars / Stardreams / Stairway to the stars / Estrellita / Stardust / Song from the stars / Swinging on a star / I've told every little star / Lost in the stars / When you wish upon a star / Stars fell on Alabama / Estrela, estrela (reprise)
CCD 4580 / Nov '93 / Concord Jazz

☐ HANGIN' OUT
Have you met Miss Jones / Just as though you were here / (Back home again in) Indiana / Splendid splinter / I'll be seeing you / Wrap your troubles in dreams (and dream your troubles away) / Easy living / Mixed emotions / When day is done / Thanks for the memories
CCD 4123 / Feb '92 / Concord Jazz

☐ MY FRIEND THE PIANO
Margie / Only trust your heart / Mean to me / Slowly / You're driving me crazy / Summer medley: guess I'll go back home this su / Indian summer / Baby, baby, all the time / Always medley: It's always you / Always / This is always
CCD 4313 / Jul '87 / Concord Jazz

☐ NO BASS HIT
But not for me / If dreams come true / Long ago and far away / Drum boogie / I love you, samaritan / I'm gonna sit right down and write myself a letter / Easy to love / Get happy
CCD 4097 / Oct '91 / Concord Jazz

☐ NO MORE OUZO FOR PUZO (McKenna, Dave Quartet)
Look for the silver lining / Smile / For you, for me, for evermore / You and I / You brought a new kind of love to me / Talk of the town / Shake down the stars / Lonesome me / No more ouzo for Puzo / I keep going back to Joe's / Talk to me / Please don't talk about me when I'm gone
CCD 365 / Jan '89 / Concord Jazz

☐ PIANO SCENE OF DAVE MCKENNA, THE
378092 / May '96 / Koch Jazz

☐ SOLO PIANO
CRD 119 / Feb '95 / Chiaroscuro

☐ SUNBEAM AND THUNDERCLOUD (McKenna, Dave & Joe Temperley)
Once in a while / Sunbeam and Thundercloud / Sunset and the mockingbird / Gone with the wind / Black and tan fantasy / I let a song go out of my heart / Lotus blossom / Tricrotism / Nightingale / I can't believe that you're in love with me / I wish I knew / I got rhythm
CCD 4703 / Jul '96 / Concord Crossover

☐ YOU MUST BELIEVE IN SWING (McKenna, Dave & Buddy DeFranco)
You must believe in swing / Invitation / Song is you / If you could see me now / Darn that dream / Autumn nocturne / Poor butterfly / Detour ahead / Anthropology / You must believe in spring
CCD 47562 / May '97 / Concord Jazz

McKenna, Joe

☐ AT HOME (McKenna, Joe & Antoinette)
Scotty wilson, donald maclellan of rothesay / Scotty wilson, donald maclellan of rothesay / Jimmy and mickie (concert waltz) / Mrs. hamilton of pencaitland (slow air) / Catherine and john fraser's diamons wedding / Mackworth-kemmel hill(slow strathspey and hornpipe) / Old scottish waltz / Gaelic reel-in the gloamin' tigh-na-gorm(gaelic reel medle / Crags of tumbledown mountain / Achill island(air) / Bluebell polka / Pierrette(veleta) / Claybraes two-step(boston two-step)
GRACC 27 / May '94 / Grasmere

☐ BEST OF JOE & ANTOINETTE MCKENNA, THE (McKenna, Joe & Antoinette)
SH 78012 / Aug '97 / Shanachie

☐ HIS ORIGINAL RECORDINGS
JMCK 1 / Nov '94 / John McKenna Society

☐ MAGENTA MUSIC (McKenna, Joe & Antoinette)
Up and away-the doran rug-the fleadh arms-jack in the box / Home in the country / Conversation / Round the house-off to the circus-escape from spiddal / Fear a'bhata / Wallfalling / End of winter / Morning after love / Dawn chorus / Tapestry
SHCD 79076 / Jun '91 / Shanachie

McKenna, Mae

☐ MIRAGE & REALITY
HYCD 200121 / Sep '93 / Hypertension

McKenna, Terence

☐ DREAM MATRIX TELEMETRY (McKenna, Terence & Zuvuya)
DELECCD 2012 / Nov '93 / Delerium

McKenna/Mendelson Mainline

☐ BLUES
FLASH 59 / 1 Jun '98 / Flash

McKennitt, Loreena

☐ ELEMENTAL
QRCD 101 / Oct '94 / Quinlan Road

☐ MASK & THE MIRROR, THE
Mystic's dream / Bonny swans / Dark night of the soul / Marrakesh night market / Full circle / Santiago / Ce he mise le ulaingt / Two trees / Prospero's speech
4509952962 / May '95 / WEA

☐ PARALLEL DREAMS
QRCD 103 / Oct '94 / Quinlan Road

☐ TO DRIVE THE COLD WINTER AWAY
QRCD 102 / Dec '94 / Quinlan Road

☐ VISIT, THE
All souls night / Bonny Portmore / Between the shadows / Lady of Shalott / Greensleeves / Tango to evora / Courtyard lullaby / Old ways / Cymbeline
9031751512 / May '95 / WEA

☐ WINTER GARDEN, A
Coventry / God rest ye merry gentlemen / Seeds of love / Snow / Good king wenceslas
0630122902 / Dec '95 / Quinlan Road

MacKenzie

☐ CAMHANACH
SKYECD 10 / Dec '97 / Macmeanmna

MacKenzie, Billy

☐ BEYOND THE SUN
NUDE 8CD / 6 Oct '97 / Nude

MacKenzie, Eilidh

☐ RAIMENT OF THE TALE, THE
COMD 2048 / Feb '94 / Temple

MacKenzie, Giselle

☐ HARD TO GET (The Best Of Giselle MacKenzie On RCA)
61774200212 / 21 Apr '98 / Collectables

MacKenzie, Kate

☐ AGE OF INNOCENCE
RHRCD 91 / Nov '96 / Red House

☐ LET THEM TALK
RHRCD 66 / May '95 / Red House

MacKenzie, Malcolm M.

☐ MACKENZIES PIPES AND BANJO (MacKenzie, Pipe Major Malcolm M.)
Maggie / Grandfather clock / Coming round the mountains / Scotch on the rocks / Gallowa' hills / Bonnie gallowa' / Scots wha hae / Take the high road / Rose of prince charlie / If you're irish come into the parlour / Dear old donegal / Macnamara's band / Irish washerwoman / Liberton polka / Royal scots polka / Flower of scotland / Pack up your troubles / It's a long long way to tipperary / Happy wanderer / Glencoe / Waters of the spey / Caller herring / Loch lomond / I love a lassie / Bluebells of scotland / Bonnie lass o' fyvie / My bonnie lies over the ocean / Make your way to stornoway / Daisy bell / Oh dear what can the matter be / Brocham lom / Keel row / High road to linton (reels) / Jock wilsons ball / Mairi's wedding / Scotland the brave / Will ye no come back again
CDLOC 1059 / Dec '90 / Lochshore

☐ MACKENZIES PIPES AND STRINGS (MacKenzie, Pipe Major Malcolm M.)
Maggie / Bunch of thyme / Silver threads among the gold / Canon in D / Annie Laurie / Rose of Tralee / Penhalonga piper / Way old friends do / MacKenzies tune / Danny boy / Scotland the brave / Isle of Arran / Mull of Kintyre / Will ye no' come back again / Amazing grace / Flower of Scotland / Bright eyes
CDLOC 1033 / Jun '87 / Lochshore

MacKenzie, Talitha

☐ SOLAS
TUGCD 1007 / Mar '94 / Riverboat

☐ SPIORAD
SH 78003 / Oct '96 / Shanachie

McKenzie, Red

☐ RED MCKENZIE 1935-1937
Murder in the moonlight (it's love in the first degree) / Let's swing it / Double trouble / That's what you think / Georgia rockin' chair / Monday in Manhattan / Every now and then / Wouldn't it be a wonder / Sing me an old fashioned song / I'm building up to an awful let-down / Don't count your kisses (before you're kissed) / When love has gone / I don't know your name (but you're beautiful) / Moon rose / I can't get started (with you) / I can pull a rabbit out of my hat / Sweet Lorraine / Wanted / I cried for you / Trouble with me is you / Farewell my love / You're out of this world / Sail along silv'ry moon / Georgianna
CBC 1019 / Aug '94 / Timeless Historical

McKeon, Gay

☐ IRISH PIPING TRADITION
GMKCD 001 / Dec '97 / Access

McKeown, Susan

☐ BONES (McKeown, Susan & Chanting House)
SNG 701CD / Nov '95 / Sheila-Na-Gig

Mackey, Steve

☐ LOST AND FOUND
BRI 9065 / Jul '96 / Bridge

Mackie Ranks

☐ LICK OUT
HCD 7001 / Aug '94 / Hightone

MacKillop, Rob

☐ FLOWERS OF THE FOREST
Chancelliours / If thy were myne own thing / Lord Aboin's aire or welcome home from London / No charme above her / Peggie I must love thee / Remember me at evening / I serve a worthie ladie / Flowers of the forrest / Canaries / I will not goe to my bed till I suld die / Adew Dundee / Six untitled pieces / Port / Port Jean Linsay / Port / Port Rorie Dall / Port Preist / I love my love in secret / Reel / Up we't Eli Eli / Tweed side / Secret kiss / Lady lie neir mee / Aur last good night / Lilt milne / Lament for the lutars
CDTRAX 155 / Jun '98 / Greentrax

McKillop, Jim

☐ TRADITIONAL IRISH FIDDLE AND PIANO (McKillop, Jim & Josephine Keegan)
PTICD 1045CD / Jul '95 / Pure Traditional Irish

McKinley

☐ MCKINLEY
BCD 00222 / May '96 / Burnside

McKinley, Ray

☐ BACK TO THE MILLER SOUND (McKinley, Ray & New Glenn Miller Orchestra)
Jeep Jockey jump / On the street where you live / Am I blue / Howdy friends / Laura / Here we go again / I'm thrilled
DAWE 46 / Nov '93 / Magic

☐ BORDERLINE (McKinley, Ray & His Orchestra)
Sand storm / Tumble bug / Hangover Square / Comin' out / I gotta right to sing the blues / Mint julep / Borderline / How by friends / Atomic era / Chief / Over the rainbow / Jiminy Crickets
SV 0203 / Oct '97 / Savoy Jazz

☐ CLASS OF '49, THE
It's only a paper moon / Blue moon / Stompin' at the savoy / Stardust / Laura / How high the moon / Lullabye in rhythm / Harlem nocturne / I gotta right to sing the blues / Don't be that way
HEPCD 4 / Dec '95 / Hep

☐ JIMINY CRICKETS
AERO 1033 / Jul '96 / Aerospace

☐ MCKINLEY TIME (McKinley, Ray & His Orchestra)
Rowdy friends / Carioca / Soon / Hard hearted Hannah / Jiminy crickets / I kiss your hand Madame / How high the moon / Along with me / Celery stalks at midnight / Pancho Maximillian Hernandez (The Best President we ever had / Blue moon / Star dest / I'm tired of waiting for you / It's only a paper moon / Laura / Stompin' at the Savoy / Tacos, enchiladas and beans / Borderline / (Where are you now) Now that I need you / Harlem nocturne / Lullaby in rhythm / Waitin' for the evenin' mail / Pete's cafe / Howdy friends
VN 1001 / Nov '96 / Viper's Nest

McKinney's Cotton Pickers

☐ CLASSICS 1928-1929
CLASSICS 609 / Oct '92 / Classics

☐ CLASSICS 1929-1930
CLASSICS 625 / Nov '92 / Classics

☐ CLASSICS 1930-1931
CLASSICS 649 / Nov '92 / Classics

☐ MCKINNEY'S COTTON PICKERS 1928-1931
Four or five times / Milenberg boys / Cherry / Stop kidding (Neckbones and saurkraut) / Nobody's sweetheart / Some sweet day / Shim-me-sha-wabble / It's tight like that / It's a precious little thing called love / Save it pretty mama / I've found a new baby / Beedle-um-bum / Plain dirt / Gee baby ain't I good to you / I'd love it / Way I feel today / Miss Hannah / Peggy / Wherever there's a will baby / Zonky / Baby won't you please come home / Cotton picker's scat / Rocky road / You're driving me crazy / Do you believe in love at first sight
CD 53220 / Apr '98 / Giants Of Jazz

McKinney, Carlos

☐ UP FRONT
You and the night and the music / Prince of jade / If I should lose you / All because of you / Mademoiselle Gregoire / Black beauty / Obelisk / Seer / Door of no return
SJL 1002 / Sep '97 / Sirocco

MacKinnon, Norman

☐ TIR NAM BEA
SILKCD 003 / Jul '98 / Norman MacKinnon

MacKinon, Maeve

☐ FO SMUAIN
SKYECD 08 / Mar '96 / Macmeanmna

MacKintosh, Iain

☐ GENTLE PERSUASION (MacKintosh, Iain & Brian McNeill/Alan Reid)
Tomorrow you're gone / Uncle Walter / Run the film backwards / My old man / It's so easy to dream / When I'm gone / January man / Farm auction / Wheelchair talking blues / Song of the pineapple rag / First you lose the rhyming / Waltzing around in the nude / Five ways to kill a man
CDTRAX 014 / Feb '97 / Greentrax

☐ RISKS AND ROSES
If I had a boat / Remember when the music / I wish I was in Glasgow / Cheeky young lad / Rats are winning / King of Rome / Flowers are red / My home town / Roses from the wrong man / Acceptable risks / Dill pickle rag / Annie McKelvie / Kilkelly / Hug song
CDTRAX 043 / Feb '91 / Greentrax

☐ STAGE BY STAGE (MacKintosh, Iain & Brian McNeil)
Plainstanes / Glasgow magistrate / Wind and rain / Sea maiden / Balkan hills / Bonny wee lassie who never said no / Holyrood house / Generations of change / Dallas domestic / Smoky mokes / Beautiful dreamer / Traveller's moon / Summer of love / Recruited collier / Tank / Cronin's / Fisherman's lilt / What you do with what you've got / Black swan / Roslin Castle / You can't take it with you when you go
CDTRAX 101 / Nov '95 / Greentrax

MacKintosh, Ken

☐ BLUES SKIES
DLD 1014 / '92 / Dance & Listen

McKnight, Brian

☐ ANYTIME
Anytime / Could / You should be mine (don't waste my time) / Show me the way back to your heart / Everytime we say goodbye / You got the bomb / Hold me / Only one for me / Til I get over you / Jam knock / When the chariot comes
5362152 / 29 Sep '97 / Talkin' Loud
5305922 / 27 Apr '98 / Polydor

☐ I REMEMBER YOU
5284302 / Aug '95 / Talkin' Loud

McKoy

☐ FULL CIRCLE
TUMCD 1 / Apr '94 / Right Track

McKuen, Rod

☐ FRENCH CONNECTION, THE
12444 / Mar '95 / Laserlight

☐ GREATEST HITS
Soldiers who want to be heroes / Doesn't anybody know my name / World I used to know / Importance of the rose / Jean / Rock gently / I'll catch the sun / Cycles / About the time / Love's been good to me / Listen to the warm / Champion charlie brown / I think of you / Amor / South america take it away / Seasons in the sun / If you go away / (the port of) amsterdam / Je vien de lion (I've been to town) / Without a worry in the world / And to each season / They're playing our song
BX 4082 / Mar '94 / BR Music

☐ ROD MCKUEN SINGS JACQUES BREL
Come, jef / If you go away / Lovers / Far west / Zangra / Song without words / (the port of) amsterdam / I'm not afraid / To you / Statue / Woman / Les bourgeois / Les amants de coeur / Seasons in the sun
BX 4072 / Mar '94 / BR Music

McKusick, Hal

☐ EAST COAST JAZZ (McKusick, Hal Quartet)
FSCD 41 / Oct '90 / Fresh Sound

McLachlan, Craig

☐ CULPRITS (McLachlan, Craig & The Culprits)
RR 88442 / Oct '96 / Roadrunner

McLachlan, Ian

☐ ISLAND HERITAGE, AN
Donald McLean's farewell / Cameron's got his wife again / March/Reels/Strathspeys / Dark Island / Ale is dear / Calum Crubach / Reels / Conundrum / Highland Harry / Jig of slurs / Devil in the kitchen / Hornpipes / Cuttie's wedding / Puirt a beul / Pipe reels
SPRCD 1022 / 16 Mar '98 / Springthyme

☐ KINGS OF THE BUTTON KEYED BOX (McLachlan, Ian & Fergie MacDonald)
From Lewis to Glencoe: *McLachlan, Ian* / Goes Irish trad: *McDonald, Fergie* / Dark island: *McLachlan, Ian* / Mouth music on button box: *McDonald, Fergie* / Jiggin' across the Minch: *McLachlan, Ian* / Iain Rhuadh's lament: *McDonald, Fergie* / Gay gordons on button box: *McLachlan, Ian* / Three jigs for three friends: *McDonald, Fergie* / Two pipe marches: *McLachlan, Ian* / Two tunes for two bonnie lasses: *McDonald, Fergie* / Gaelic waltz hebridean style: *McLachlan, Ian* / Clanranald Hotel barn dance: *McDonald, Fergie* / Old flame: *McLachlan, Ian* / Fergie's own jigs: *McDonald, Fergie* / 2/4 marches: *McLachlan, Ian/Fergie MacDonald*
LCOM 5160 / Feb '97 / Lismor

McLachlan, Sarah

☐ FUMBLING TOWARDS ECSTASY
Possession / Wait / Plenty / Good enough / Mary / Elsewhere / Circle / Ice / Hold on / Ice cream / Fear / Fumbling towards ecstasy
74321190322 / Oct '94 / Arista

☐ RARITIES B-SIDES AND OTHERS
30105 / Sep '97 / Nettwerk

McLain, 'Mighty' Sam

☐ SLEDGEHAMMER SOUL AND DOWN HOME BLUES
Slegehammer soul and down home blues / Where you been so long / Trying to find myself / Things ain't what they used to be / When the hurt is over / Pray / They call me mighty / Dancin' to the music of love / Hey Miss Bea / If you could see / Bridge of faith / Don't write me off
AQCD 1042 / Dec '96 / Audioquest

McLain, Raymond W.

☐ PLACE OF MY OWN, A
FF 597CD / Feb '93 / Flying Fish

McLain, Tommy

☐ SWEET DREAMS
Sweet dreams / Before I grow too old / Think it over / Barefootin' / I can't take it no more / Try to find another man / When a man loves a woman / After loving you / Tribute to Fats Domino / Going home / Poor me / Going to the river / Just because / Legend in my time / Together again / I thought I'd never fall in love again / So sad (to watch good love go bad) / Sticks and stones / Mu heart remembers
CDCH 285 / Jan '90 / Ace

McLaren, Malcolm

☐ DUCK ROCK
Obatala / Buffalo gals / Merengue / Punk it up / Legba / Jive my baby / Song for Chango / Soweto / World's famous / Duck for the oyster / Double Dutch
MMCD 1 / Apr '88 / Charisma

☐ LARGEST MOVIE HOUSE IN PARIS, THE
NOCD 12 / Apr '96 / No

☐ PARIS
NOMC 100 / Aug '94 / No

☐ ROUND THE OUTSIDE (McLaren, Malcolm & World Famous Supreme Team)
Operaa house / World tribe / Diva loves operaa house / Ii to be or not ii / Romeo and juliet / Wherefor art thou / Buffalo gals ii / World famous supreme team radio show / Un coche de agua negra / Aladdin's scratch
CDV 2646 / Apr '92 / Virgin

☐ WALTZ DARLING
House of the blue Danube / Waltz darling / Deep in vogue / Algernon's simply awfully good at ... / Something's jumping in your shirt / Shall we dance / Call a wave / I like you in velvet
4607362 / Jul '89 / Epic

McLaren, Nicol

☐ NOTE 'N' AWAY
SHIELCD 004 / 2 Apr '98 / Shielburn Associates

McLaughlin, Billy

☐ FINGERDANCE
Fingerdance / Blaise's ballad / Helms place / Happy archer / Breaking of the shells / While she sleeps / Hurricane Bob / Lila's healing / So long / Good wife / Stormseeker / Dreaming on a runway / Coffee break
ND 61058 / Dec '96 / Narada

McLaughlin, John

☐ ADVENTURES IN RADIOLAND (McLaughlin, John & Mahavishnu Orchestra)
Wait / Just ideas / Jozy / Half man half cookie / Florianopolis / Gotta dance / Wall will fall / Reincarnation / Mitch match / 20th Century Ltd
5193972 / Feb '93 / Verve

☐ AFTER THE RAIN
Take the coltrane / My favourite things / Sing me softly of the blues / Encuentros / Naima / Tones for elvin jones / Crescent / Afro blue / After the rain
5274672 / Jun '95 / Verve

☐ APOCALYPSE (Mahavishnu Orchestra)
4670922 / Jan '95 / Sony Jazz

☐ BEST OF SHAKTI, THE (McLaughlin, John & Shankar/Zakir Hussain)
Alap-jor-jhala / Slow gat / Madhya gat / Drut gat
MRCD 1011 / May '98 / Charlotte

☐ BEST OF THE MAHAVISHNU ORCHESTRA (Mahavishnu Orchestra)
Birds of fire / Open country joy / Wings of Karma / Sister Andrea / Dance of Maya / Meeting of the spirits / Lila's dance / Be happy
4682262 / Jan '95 / Sony Jazz

☐ BETWEEN NOTHINGNESS AND ETERNITY (Mahavishnu Orchestra)
CK 32766 / Aug '97 / Sony Jazz

☐ BIRDS OF FIRE (McLaughlin, John & Mahavishnu Orchestra)
Birds of fire / Miles beyond / Celestial terrestrial commuters / Sapphire bullets of pure love / Thousand Island park / Hope / One word / Sanctuary / Open country / Resolution
4682242 / Jan '92 / Columbia

☐ DEVOTION
Marbles / Don't let the dragon eat your Mother / Purpose of when / Dragon song / Devotion
CPCD 8232 / Dec '96 / Charly

☐ ELECTRIC DREAMS (McLaughlin, John & The One Truth Band)
Guardian angels / Miles Davis / Electric dreams / Electric sighs / Love and understanding / Desire and the comforter / Singing earth / Dark prince / Unknown dissident
4722102 / Jan '95 / Sony Jazz

☐ ELECTRIC GUITARIST
New York on my mind / Friendship / Every tear from every eye / Do you hear the voices you left behing / Are you the one / Pehnomenon / Compulsion / My foolish heart
4670932 / Jan '95 / Columbia

☐ EXTRAPOLATION
Extrapolation / It's funny / Arjen's bag / Pete the poet / This is for us to share / Spectrum / Blinky's beam / Really you know / Two for two / Peace piece
8415982 / Oct '90 / Polydor

☐ FRIDAY NIGHT IN SAN FRANCISCO (McLaughlin, John & Al Di Meola/Paco De Lucia)
Mediterranean sundance / Rio ancho / Short tales of the black forest / Frevro rasgado / Fantasia suite / Guardian angel
4890072 / 13 Oct '97 / Sony Jazz

☐ HEART OF THINGS, THE
5391532 / 10 Nov '97 / Verve

☐ INNER WORLDS
All in the family / Miles out / In my life / Gita / Morning calls / Way of the pilgrim / River of my heart / Planetary citizen / Lotus feet / Inner worlds parts 1 and 2
4769052 / Jan '95 / Sony Jazz

☐ LIVE AT THE ROYAL FESTIVAL HALL (27th November 1989) (McLaughlin, John Trio)
Blue in green / Just ideas/Jozy Florianapolis / Pasha's love / Mother tongues / Blues for LW
8344362 / Apr '90 / jMT

☐ MY GOAL'S BEYOND (McLaughlin, John & Mahavishnu Orchestra)
Goodbye pork pie hat / Something spiritual / Hearts and flowers / Phillip lane / Waltz for bill evans / Follow your heart / Song for my mother / Blue in green / Peace one / Peace two
RCD 10051 / May '92 / Rykodisc
ADC 10 / 23 Mar '98 / Douglas Music

☐ PASSION, GRACE AND FIRE (McLaughlin, John & Al Di Meola/Paco De Lucia)
Aspen / Orient blue / Chiquito / Sichia / David / Passion, grace and fire
8113342 / Jun '83 / Philips

☐ PROMISE, THE
5288282 / Mar '96 / Verve

☐ QUE ALEGRIA (McLaughlin, John Trio)
Belo Horizonte / Baba / Reincarnation / One nite stand / Marie / Hijacked / Milas repa / Que alegria / 2 willows
8372802 / Jan '92 / Verve

☐ SHAKTI & JOHN MCLAUGHLIN (McLaughlin, John & Shakti)
4679052 / Jan '95 / Sony Jazz

☐ THIS IS JAZZ
Birds of fire / Lotus feet / Love supreme / Do you hear the voices that you left behind / Guardian angel / Dark prince / Aspan / Are you the one / Dance of Maya / Until such time
CK 64971 / Oct '96 / Sony Jazz

☐ TIME REMEMBERED (John McLaughlin Plays Bill Evans)
Prologue / Very early / Only child / Waltz for Debby / Homage / My/Bells / Time remembered / Song for Helen / Turn out the stars / We will meet again / Epilogue
5198612 / Feb '94 / Verve

☐ TOKYO LIVE (The Free Spirits Featuring John McLaughlin)
One nite stand / Hijched / When love is far away / Little Miss Valley / Juju at the crossroads / Vuhovar / No blues / Mattinale
5218702 / May '94 / Philips

☐ VISIONS OF THE EMERALD BEYOND (Mahavishnu Orchestra)
4679042 / Jan '95 / Sony Jazz

☐ WHERE FORTUNE SMILES
Glancing backwards (For junior) / Earth bound hearts / Where fortune smiles / New place, old place / Hope
BGOCD 191 / Jun '93 / Beat Goes On

McLaughlin, Pat

☐ GET OUT AND STAY OUT
DOS 7012 / Oct '95 / Dos

☐ UNGLUED
DOSCD 7005 / Apr '94 / Dos

MacLean, Bryan

☐ IF YOU BELIEVE IN
Barber John / Fresh hope / Kathleen / Orange skies / Strong commitment / Alone again or / Tired of sitting / Blues singer / Friday's party / People / Claudia / If you believe in / Orange skies / Alone again or / She looks good / Old man
CDSC 11051 / May '98 / Sundazed

MacLean, Dougie

☐ BUTTERSTONE
DAMCD 002 / Dec '97 / Dambuster

☐ CRAIGIE DHU
Gin I were a baron's heir / Read for the storm / It was a' for our rightful king / High flying seagull / Edmonton airbus / Craigie Dhu / Bonnie Bessie Logan / Seanair's song / It fascinates me / Tullochgorum / Caledonia
DUNCD 001 / Feb '90 / Dunkeld

☐ DOUGIE MACLEAN COLLECTION
M 1172 / Jan '97 / Putumayo

☐ DOUGIE MACLEAN'S CALEDONIA (The Plant Life Years)
Plooboy laddies / Johnny teasie weasle / Over my mountain / Mistress MacKinley's breakfast surreals / Northern cowboy / I lo'e nae a lassie but ane / Rattlin' roarin' Willie / Mormond braes / Caledonia / Jock Stewart / Leis a lurighan / Rolling home / Mill brae / Lassies trust in providence / Bonnie Isle O'Whalsay / Ye banks and braes o' bonnie doon
OSMOCD 004 / Oct '95 / Osmosys

☐ FIDDLE
Osprey / Bob MacIntosh Atholl Arms ku-ring-gai chase / Farewell to Craigie Dhu / Tattie ball / When are you coming over / Mr. and Mrs. MacLean of Snaigow / Roy Ashby's buckny burn / One summer's morning / Ferry / Spoutwells riechip leduckie / Centre / Gin I were a baron's heir
DUNCD 002 / Oct '93 / Dunkeld

☐ INDIGENOUS
Rite of passage / Rank and roses / War / Slave's lament / Turning away / Let her go / This line is broken / Ae fond kiss / Thundering in / Eternity
DUNCD 015 / Feb '89 / Dunkeld

☐ MARCHING MYSTERY
Deepest part of me / Marching mystery / It belongs to us / All together / Holding back / Hearts can never hide / Broken wings / Land / When the people speak / Expectation
DUNCD 019 / Jul '94 / Dunkeld

☐ REAL ESTATE
Solid ground / Restless fool / Buffalo jump / Garden valley / Emmigrant / Green grow the rushes / Homeland / Mhairi bhan / Are ye sleeping, maggie / She loves me (when I try)
DUNCD 008 / Nov '92 / Dunkeld

☐ RIOF
Stepping stones / Stolen / Scythe song / Feel so near / Gneiss wind / Sfhada leam/An oidche ghemraidh / She will find me / Big river / Fragments from a mug's game / Distant son
DUNCD 021 / Aug '97 / Dunkeld

☐ SEARCH, THE
Search / Abyssal / Thermocline / Origin / Sixties vigil / Gael / Underwater vigil / Loch ness
DUNCD 011 / Nov '89 / Dunkeld

☐ SINGING LAND
Singing land / Desperate man / This love will carry / Kelphope glen / Another story / Bonnie woods o'Hatton / Other side / Tumbling down / Guillotine release / Goodnight and joy
DUNCD 004 / Oct '93 / Dunkeld

☐ SUNSET SONG
Sunset song / Burning of peesie's knapp / Kinraddie song / Cloud howe / Cirrusthe eviction / Bridge incident / Kaimes / Grey granite / Distress
DUNCD 017 / Nov '89 / Dunkeld

☐ TRIBUTE
DUNCD 020 / Nov '95 / Dunkeld

☐ WHITEWASH
Trail of the survivor / Gloomy winter / No no no / Rescue me / Dolina / Family of the mountains / Shame / Mo nighean don / Until we meet again / Little ones walk on
DUNCD 010 / Jul '90 / Dunkeld

MacLean, Joe

☐ OLD TIME SCOTTISH FIDDLE FROM CAPE BRETON ISLAND
Nancy / Inverness Strathspey and reel Margaret delight / Mabou jig / Orange and blue / Annie Golletti / Duke of Fife's birthday / Green grow the rashes / Untitled reel / Memories of Joe Maclinnis / Foxie Mary / Jig in A / Mrs Macdonald / Bonnie lass of headlake / Mr Abel banks / Twedale club / Mrs Campbell of Locknell / Fiddler's joy / Charlie hunter / Joe's hunter / Headlands march / Miller camersay / Kelvack strathspey / Old bog hole / Kitchen party medley
ROUCD 7024 / Feb '98 / Rounder

McLean, Andy

☐ ANDY'S THEME
Two hearts / Funny / Saliya / Take 5 and 6 / Please stay / Andy's theme / Is this for real / Make it last / Summer song / Early bird
CALLCD 001 / Sep '94 / Callisto

McLean, Don

☐ AMERICAN PIE
American pie / Till tomorrow / Vincent / Crossroads / Winterwood / Empty chairs / Everybody loves me / Fatima / Grave / Babylon
CDFA 3023 / May '88 / Fame

☐ DON MCLEAN
If we try / Narcissima / Dreidel / Bronco Bill's lament / Birthday song / Pride parade / More you pay (The more it's worth) / Falling through time / On the Amazon / Oh my what a shame
BGOCD 246 / Mar '95 / Beat Goes On

☐ HOMELESS BROTHER
Winter has me in its grip / La la means I love you / Homeless brother / Sunshine life for me / Legend of Andrew McCrew / Wonderful baby / You have lived / Great big man / Tangled / Crying in the chapel / Did you know
BGOCD 247 / Oct '94 / Beat Goes On

☐ PLAYIN' FAVORITES
Mule skinner blues / Bill Cheatham = Old Joe Clark / Love O love / Fool's paradise / Mountain's O'Mourne / Lovesick blues / Sitting on top the world / Ancient history / Everyday / Over the mountains / Living with the blues / Happy trails
BGOCD 21 / Apr '95 / Beat Goes On

☐ RIVER OF LOVE, THE
CURCD 19 / Nov '95 / Curb

☐ SOLO
Magdalene lane / Masters of war / Wonderful baby / Where were you baby / Empty chairs / Geordie's lost his penker / Babylon / I love you so / Mactavish is dead / Cripple creek/Muleskinner blues / Great big man / Bronco Bill's lament / Happy trails / Circus song / Birthday song / On the Amazon / American pie / Over the waterfall/Arkansas traveller / Homeless brother / Castles in the air / Three flights up / Lovesick blues / Winter has me in it's grip / Legend of Andrew McCrew / Dreidel / Vincent / Till tomorrow
BGOCD 300 / Sep '95 / Beat Goes On

☐ TAPESTRY
Castles in the air / General store / Magdalene Lane / Tapestry / Respectable / Orphans of wealth / Three flights up / I love you so / Bad girl / Circus song / No reason for your dreams
BGOCD 232 / Jun '94 / Beat Goes On

McLean, Jackie

☐ DR. JACKIE (McLean, Jackie Quartet)
Dr. jackie / Melody for melonae / Little malonae / Closing
SCCD 36005 / Oct '90 / Steeplechase

☐ JACKIE MAC ATTACK (Jackie McLean Live)
Cyclical / Song for my Queen / Dance little mandissa / Minor march / 'Round midnight / Five
5192702 / May '92 / Birdology

☐ JACKIE'S BLUES BAG (A Tribute To Jackie McLean) (Various Artists)
HIBD 8015 / Mar '97 / Hip Bop

☐ LIGHTS OUT (McLean, Jackie Quintet)
Lights out / Up 4:44 / Lorraine / Foggy day / Kerplunk / Inding
OJCCD 426 / Jun '96 / Original Jazz Classics

☐ NEW YORK CALLING
SCCD 31023 / Jul '88 / Steeplechase

☐ RHYTHM OF THE EARTH
Rhythm of the Earth / For hofsa / Sirius system / Exploreres / Oh children rise / Osyris returns / Collective expression / Dark castle
5139162 / Apr '92 / Birdology

☐ SWING SWANG SWINGIN'
What's new / Let's face the music and dance / Stablemates / I remember you / I love you / I'll take romance / 116th and Lennox
CDP 8565822 / Jun '97 / Blue Note

McLean, John

☐ MEN ARE LOVERS TOO
Life after you / Can't hold on / Time for love / Playboy / Love at first sight / Spreading rumours / Proud to be your lover / Never risk / We both belong to someone else / Dedication of love
ARICD 104 / Oct '94 / Ariwa Sounds

MacLellan, Colin

☐ WORLD'S GREATEST PIPERS VOL.11, THE
2/4 Marches / Strathspeys and reels / Retreat marches / 6/8 Marches / Slow air and jigs / March, strathspey and reel / Hornpipes / Slow air / Strathspeys and reels / Piobaireachd
LCOM 5219 / Jan '93 / Lismor

MacLellan, Elise

☐ KISS ON THE WIND
Soonhope / Spindrift/Tousie Annie / Alien road/Mrs Mac's blues / Orchardlea / Devil's teabag / Echoes of a broken heart/A touch of sarcasm / Curlylocks / Buachaille etive mor / Kiss on the wind / Cuddyburn/ Sleepless
CDLDL 1272 / 20 Mar '98 / Lochshore

MacLellan, John A.

☐ SCOTTISH BAGPIPES (MacLellan, Pipe Major John A.)
OSS 113CD / Apr '94 / Ossian

MacLennan, Ken

☐ HIGHLAND TEMPEST (MacLennan, Ken & Storm)
Tempest reel no.1 / Golden dream / Bealach na spainnteach (spaniard's pass) / Skye boat song / Laid to rest/thunder reel / She moved thro' the fair / Hornpipe suite / Scandinavian mist / Tempest reel no.2 / Highland storm
MOICD 011 / Dec '96 / Moidart

McLennan, Grant

☐ FIREBOY
BBQCD 127 / Mar '93 / Beggars Banquet

☐ HORSEBREAKER STAR
BEGA 162CD / Sep '95 / Beggars Banquet

☐ IN YOUR BRIGHT RAY
In your bright ray / Cave in / One plus one / Sea breeze / Malibu 69 / Who said love was dead / Room for skin / All them pretty angels / Comet scar / Down here / Lamp by lamp / Do you see the lights / Parade of shadows
BBQCD 192 / Jul '97 / Beggars Banquet

☐ SIMONE & PERRY
BBQ 57CD / Jun '95 / Beggars Banquet

MacLeod, Donald

☐ NEW YORK RECORDINGS 1967, THE
Cock of the North/The Campbell's are coming/ Pibroch of Donal / Devil in the kitchen/Craig-a-Bodich/Louden's bonnie Woods / Reel of Tulloch/ High road to Linton/Mrs. MacLeod of Raasay / Cronan (na Callaich)/An Island lullaby/The man from Skye / 79th's farewell to Gibraltar/The Atholl and Breadalbane Gath / Donald Dugal MacKay / Colonel Robertson/Leaving Port Askaig / Lochaber no more/ Banks of the lossie / Wee Highland laddie/Meeting of the waters/Hen's march / Irish washerwife/Pipe Major George Allan / Donald MacLellan of Rothesay/ Delvinside/Miss Proud / Invercharrow Highland gathering / All the blue bonnets over the border / Cronan na Caillach / Susan MacLeod/Thompson's dirk / Malcolm Ferguson/MacKenzie of Torridon / Mist covered mountains/My home/Mairi's wedding / Dolan's ass/Lord Panmure's march / Highland Brigade at Waterloo / Dr. Ross's 50th welcome to the Argyllshire Gathering / Pretty Dirk
LCOM 8004 / Oct '96 / Lismor

MacLeod, Doug

☐ AIN'T THE BLUES EVIL
VCD 3409 / Apr '92 / Volt

☐ NO ROAD BACK HOME
HCD 8002 / Jun '94 / Hightone

MacLeod, Jim

☐ CEILIDH
CDITV 604 / Oct '95 / Scotdisc

☐ JIM MACLEOD'S ALLSTAR SCOTTISH DANCE BAND (MacLeod, Jim Allstar Band)
Amazing grace / Scotland the brave / Bonnie Dundee / Loch Lomond / Ballad of Glencoe / Bluebell polka / Dark island / Black bear / Dashing white Sergeant
CDITV 615 / Oct '96 / Scotdisc

☐ JIM MACLEOD'S DANCE PARTY FAVOURITES
Bluebell polka / Will you save the last dance just for me / Just for old times sake / Come by the hills / Dashing white sergeant / Dashing white sergeant (encore) / Do you think you could love me again / Amazing grace / Pittenweem Jo / Shetland reels / Cruising down the river / Loch Lomond / After all these years / Gay Gordons / Gay Gordons (encore) / Leaving Dundee / Shufflin' Sammy
CD ITV 422 / Dec '86 / Scotdisc

☐ JIM MACLEOD'S HOGMANAY PARTY
Auld lang syne / Gay Gordons / Waltz / Strip the willow / Whistle and I'll dance / Bonnie lass o'Bon Accord / St. Bernard's waltz / Dashing white sergeant / My love is like a red red rose / Pipe selection / Barn dance / Crooked bawbee / Military two step
CD ITV 444 / Dec '87 / Scotdisc

☐ LAND OF MACLEOD, THE (MacLeod, Jim & His Band)
Come by the hills (song) / Welcome to my world (song) / Pipers waltz-farewell to the creeks (pipe selection) / Teach me to dance (real slow) / Canberra carousel (jim cleland (solo) / Steel away (song) / Mrs. mary prentice-tam bain's lum (selection) / Leaving dundee (song)
CDITV 548 / Aug '91 / Scotdisc

☐ PLAY SELECTED SCOTTISH COUNTRY DANCES (MacLeod, Jim & His Band)
Westminster reel / Swilcam / Sailor / Roberston's rant / Crown crourt / Burnie boozie / Earlstoun loch / Macdonald of the isles / Ladies of dunse / Porchester hall / Peggy's wedding
CDITV 491 / Oct '89 / Scotdisc

☐ ROAD AND MILES, THE (MacLeod, Jim & His Band)
Road and the miles to dundee / Loch tay boat song / Crooked bawbee lassie / Come and dance / I lo'ed nae a laddie / Muckin o' geordie's byre / Lovely banchory / Northern lights / Gordon for me / Brig o' balgownie / Bonnie kirkwall bay / Welcome to dunblane / Mairl's wedding / Deveron reel / Lonely scapa flow / March, strathspey and reel / Come to fiona's wedding / Irish rover / Kelly the boy / Wark o' the weavers / (I'd be) a legend in my time / Bonnie dundee / Midlothian pipe band / Trip to tomintoul
CDITV 583 / Nov '94 / Scotdisc

☐ SCOTTISH TOUR, A (MacLeod, Jim & His Band)
Dan macildowies reel / Alan murray's fancy / Home to the glen / Argyll grove / Aberdour bay / Clarinet polka / Today / Original / Balcombe house / Glenturret distillery / Comin' thro' the rye / My love is like a red, red rose / Lassie wi' the yellow coatie / D. morrison's seven thistles / Milladen / Scholar / Whisky on a sunday / Original
CDITV 565 / Aug '93 / Scotdisc

☐ WELCOME TO MY WORLD
Welcome to my world / Gay gordons / Scottish waltz / Steel away / March, strathspey and reel / Teach me to dance (real slow) / Slow waltz / Hebridean polka / Pipe marches / If I had to live my life over / Reel selection / If my world should end tomorrow / Eightsome reel
CDITV 461 / Nov '89 / Scotdisc

MacLeod, John

☐ MACLEOD OF DUNVEGAN
Scots wha hae / Ae fond kiss / Birlinn ghoraidh chro'bhain / Barbara Allen / Bonnie Strathyre / Mo nighean chiuin donn / Ca' the yowes / Bonnie Earl O'Moray / Ho ro mo nighean donn bhoid heach / Mary Macneil / Maiden of Morven / Cha tillmaccrimmon / Foot of Benachie / O my love is like a red red rose / Mo run geal dileas / O'er the moor / Loch Lomond / Soiriidh / Skye boat song / Tog orm mo phiob
LCOM 5206 / Mar '92 / Lismor

MacLeod, Roderick J.

☐ WORLD'S GREATEST PIPERS VOL.6, THE
Donald MacLean of Lewis / Portree Bay / Balmoral castle / John Mackenzie of Garrynahine / Stirling Castle / Farmer's daughter / Piper and the dairymaid / Be sid an gille truagh / Se siabost as boidliche leau / Donella Beaton / Turf lodge / Willie Gray's farewell to the Glasgow police / Donald MacLean's farewell to Oban / Train journey north / Crossing the Minch / Brigadier General Ronald Cheape of Tiroran / Piper's bonnet / Charlie's welcome / James MacLellan's favourite / Tenpenny bit / I ha'e a wife of my ain / Brose and butter / Grinder / Arniston Castle / Lady Mackenzie of Gareloch / Sheepwife / Broadford Bay / Mull of the mountains / Mo chuachag Laghach Thu / Irish traditional reel / Reel of Tulloch / Piobaireachd
LCOM 5177 / Aug '96 / Lismor

McLeod, Bobby

☐ GENUINE ARTICLE, THE
Highland two step / Strathspeys / Waltz / Irish two step / Pride of Erin / Party pieces / Traditional selection / Traditional polka / Waltz valeta / Dunoon barn dance / Kerrera polka / Eva three step
LCOM 5127 / Nov '96 / Lismor

McLeod, David

☐ AM I BLUE
LB 9512 / Jul '98 / La Brava

McLeod, Enos 'Genius'

☐ ENOS IN DUB
CEND 2004 / Oct '96 / Century

☐ GENIUS OF ENOS, THE
PSCD 008 / Mar '96 / Pressure Sounds

☐ GOODIES BEST
CEND 2003 / Oct '96 / Century

☐ RAM JAM PARTY
Ram jam party / Lipstick on my collar / I'm just a man / Beat of my heart / Tear drop / Satta a masagana / Tell you goodbye / Sweet sexy / Always / Dancehall style / Making love / Wish he didn't trust me so much / Puppet on a string / Woman at the house / Cash and carry / Headmistress
PRCD 606 / Sep '96 / President

McLeod, Rory

☐ ANGRY LOVE
Farewell welfare / Shirley's her name / Stop the apartheid fascists / Pauline's song / Wind is getting stronger / Angry love / Walking towards each other / Passing the pain down / Criminals of hunger
COOKCD 051 / Feb '95 / Cooking Vinyl

☐ FOOTSTEPS AND HEARTBEATS
Love like a rock (in a stormy sea) / Till I don't know who I am / Collectorman / Moments shared / Wandering fool / Take me home / Singing copper / Kind of loneliness / Mariachis love song
COOKCD 018 / Feb '95 / Cooking Vinyl

☐ KICKING THE SAWDUST
Baksheesh dance / Huge sky / Rip Van Winkle / Kicking the sawdust / Dad's dance song / Sssh baby / Interrogations and confessions / Dance of measureless love / Hug you like a mountain / In the ghetto of our love / When children starve in peacetime / Strangers / Everything is provocative / Immaculate deception / Ambitious to love you / Harmonkikas dreams / Last tree / Divorcee blues / Old brigades song / Commentator cried / Hymn for her
COOKCD 067 / Mar '94 / Cooking Vinyl

☐ LULLABY'S FOR BIG BABIES
Be my rambling woman / Big eyes / Ballad of Spitalfields market / Night watchman / Forigner forever / Grandma's grave / Tea martoonies / Come with me when I go / Looking for you / Laredo / Punchinello's confession / Body search / Long lost friend / My two feet carry me home / Horse radish / Let him go
COOKCD 125 / Jun '97 / Cooking Vinyl

☐ TRAVELLING HOME
Going song / Spring is returning-dosvedanya / Black, brown, white / Defending our homes / Cold sun shining / Compatability / Dreams we breathe through / Touchable / Sleep tonite / Farming womans war / India matea / Right mistake / Back to donegal
COOKCD 048 / Feb '95 / Cooking Vinyl

McLeod, Zan

☐ RING SESSIONS, THE (McLeod, Zan & James Kelly)
SPIN 99CD / Jan '96 / Spin

McLoughlin, Noel

☐ 20 BEST OF IRELAND
EUCD 1079 / '89 / ARC

☐ 20 BEST OF SCOTLAND
EUCD 1080 / '89 / ARC

☐ BEST OF IRELAND, THE
EUCD 1111 / '91 / ARC

☐ CHRISTMAS AND WINTER SONGS FROM IRELAND
EUCD 1086 / '91 / ARC

MacLure, Pinkie

☐ FAVOURITE
PILLCD 7 / May '95 / Placebo

☐ THIS DIRTY LIFE
Horns off / Pre dog squirm / Salvage / Leeches / A gathering of skin / Eel pout / Gluttony / Sensitive / Tasty
BND 5 CD / Feb '90 / One Little Indian

McMahan, Ken

☐ KEN MCMAHAN & SLUMPY BOY
DFGCD 8434 / Jun '96 / Dixie Frog

MacMahon, Tony

☐ I GCNOC NA GRAI (MacMahon, Tony & Noel Hill)
CEFCD 114 / Jan '94 / Gael Linn

☐ TONY MACMAHON
SHCD 34006 / May '93 / Claddagh

☐ TRADITIONAL IRISH ACCORDION
CEFCD 033 / Jan '94 / Gael Linn

McMahon, Charlie

☐ TJIJILATJILA
SPX 405CD / Nov '97 / Les Disques Du Crepuscule

McManus, Ross

☐ ELVIS' DAD SINGS ELVIS
Blue suede shoes / Suspicious minds / All shook up / Don't cry daddy / It's now or never / Hound dog / (Let me be your) teddy bear / In the ghetto / Heartbreak hotel / Love me tender / If I can dream / Jailhouse rock
306602 / Jun '97 / Hallmark

McManus, Tony

☐ POURQUOIS QUEBEC
Medley / Tune for Frankie/An phis fluich / Medley / Port na bPucai/Crooked road/Paddy Taylor's / 70th year / Medley / Catherine Kelley's/Sunset / Sean o' Duibhir a ghleanna / Dance of suleiman / Medley / Annan waters
CDTRAX 151 / 2 Feb '98 / Greentrax

☐ TONY MCMANUS
Doherty's / Return to Milltown / Tommy Peoples / Sweetness of Mary / Piper's bonnet / Emigrant's farewell / Flanagan Brothers jig / Dermot Byrnes / Miss Sarah Mcfadyen / Jackie Coleman's / Millner's daughter / Rakish Paddy / Connor Dunn's / Breizh / Duck / Seagull / Humours of Barrack Street / Letterkenny blacksmith / Ar bhruach na laoi / Snowy path / Harper's chair / Gavotte de marcel / Dans fisel / Hector the hero / Girls at Martinfield / Johnstown reel / What a wonderful world / Charlie Hunter's / Humours of Tulla
CDTRAX 096 / Dec '95 / Greentrax

MacMaster, Buddy

☐ JUDIQUE ON THE FLOOR
ACD 9020 / Mar '98 / Sea Cape

MacMaster, Natalie

☐ COMPILATION, A
CDTRAX 140 / Jul '97 / Greentrax

☐ FIT AS A FIDDLE
John Campbell's/Miss Ann Moir's birthday / Lady Georgina Campbell/Angus on the turnpike/ Sheehan's reel / My Dungannon sweetheart/ Scaffies Cairet/Juniper jig / Carnival march / Miller of Drone/MacKinnon's brook / Lucy Campbell/Annie is my darling/Gordon Cote/Bird's nest / Man behind the bar/Nancy's waltz / Compliments to Sean Maguire / President Garfield/Miss Watt/Casa Loma Castle / O'r the moor among the heather / Traditional/Lady Mary Ramsay / Jenny Dang the weaver/Lassies of Stewarton/Garfield Vale / Jean's reel / I'll always remember you / Girls at Martinfield/ Bennets favorite/Greenfields of Glentow / Counselor's/Rakes of Kildare/The lark in the morning / Lass of Carrie Mills/Lennox's love to Blantyre / Archie Menzies/Reichwall Forest / If ever you were mine / MacNeil's of Ugadale / MacLaine of Loch Buie/Colville's rant/Pibroch O'Donal Dhu
NMAS1972CD / Jul '95 / CBC Maritimes
CDTRAX 141 / Jul '97 / Greentrax
ROUCD 7022 / Mar '97 / Rounder

☐ MY ROOTS ARE SHOWING
Hey Johnny Cope / Willie Fraser / Boys of the lake / Wildcat / Balmoral Highlander / Shakin's o' the pocky / Captain Keeler / E Flat set / Glad you made it Howie / Close to the floor / Jigs / Queen of the West / A' chuthag / Glencoe dance set
CDTRAX 163 / 1 Jun '98 / Greentrax

☐ NO BOUNDARIES
Honeysuckle set / My friend Buddy / Fiddle and bow / Reel Beatrice / Paddy LeBlanc's set / Silver wells / Drunken piper / Catharsis / Where's Howie / Bill Crawford's set / Beaumont rag / Autograph / Rev Archie Beaton
ROUCD 7023
CDTRAX 142 / Aug '97 / Greentrax

MacMathuna, Padraic

☐ HIVES OF HONEYED SOUND
CEFCD 157 / Jan '94 / Gael Linn

McMeen, El

☐ IRISH GUITAR ENCORES
Danny boy / Danny boy / My mary of the curling hair / My Mary of the curling hair / Castle of Dromore / Castle of dromore / Blarney pilgrim jig / Blarney pilgrim jig / Inisheer air / Inisheer air / One morning in may-boys of the ould brigade (medley) / One morning in May/Boys of the ould brigade / Sheebeg and sheemore / Sheebeg and sheemore / Humours of ballyloughlin jig / Humours of Ballyloughlin jig / Will ye go lassie go / Will ye go lassie go / Song for ireland / Song for Ireland / Bridget Cruise 3rd air / Bridget cruise 3rd air / Gypsy rover / Gypsy rover / Eleanor Plunkett / Eleanor plunkett / Carolan's receipt / Carolan's receipt / Bridget Cruise 4th air / Bridget cruise 4th air / Carolan's no. 179 / Carolan's no. 179 / Carolan's cottage / Carolan's cottage
SHCD 97017 / Mar '98 / Shanachie

☐ OF SOUL AND SPIRIT
Not alone for mighty empire / In the bleak mid-winter / Be thou my vision/Amazing grace / Be still my soul / Fairest Lord Jesus / Bring a torch Jeannette Isabella / Irish meditation 1 / Away in a manger / Let us break bread together/Kumbaya / In Christ there is no East or West/This is my father's world / Irish meditation 2 / Of the father's love begotten / O for a thousand tongues/Praise to the Lord / Onward Christian soldiers / Irish meditation 3
SH 97012 / 23 Mar '98 / Shanachie

McMillan, James

☐ CRESCENTE MOON
Savoy remix no.1 / Coppin' the bop / Winterset / Swing low sweet Cadillac / Love me pretty baby / Dexter's riff / Five spot after dark / Almost like being in love / Softly as in a morning sunrise
CY 78846 / Oct '97 / Savoy Jazz

☐ SAVOY VS QUIET MONEY (The Rematch)
Recardo bossa nova / Hank's shout / Caribbean cutie / Barbados / Surf ride / You better go now / Nostalgia / Night in Tunisia / Bohemia after dark
CY 78959 / Oct '97 / Savoy Jazz

☐ UP ALL DAY UP ALL NIGHT
Quiet money time / Deliberate / Quiet money vibe / If I were a bell / You made it happen / Interlude / Change in rhythm / Not to forget / Music's now my inspiration / Explain yourself / Make sure you're sure
CY 78859 / Oct '97 / Savoy Jazz

McMurdo, Dave

☐ FIRE AND SONG (2CD Set) (McMurdo, Dave Jazz Orchestra)
SK2CD 5004 / Dec '97 / Sackville

☐ LIVE AT MONTREAL BISTRO (McMurdo, Dave Jazz Orchestra)
SKCD 22029 / Jun '93 / Sackville

McMurty, James

☐ IT HAD TO HAPPEN
Paris / Peter Pan / For all I know / No more buffalo / 12 o'clock whistle / Sixty acres / Be with me / Wild man from Borneo / Stancliff's lament / Jaws of life
SHCD 1058 / Mar '98 / Sugar Hill

McNabb, Ian

☐ HEAD LIKE A ROCK
Fire inside my soul / You must be prepared to dream / Child inside a father / Still got the fever / Potency / Go into the light / As a life goes by / Sad strange solitary catholic mystic / This time is forever / May you always
IMCD 233 / Sep '96 / Island

☐ MERSEYBEAST
Merseybeast / Affirmation / Beautiful old mystery / Love's young dream / Camaraderie / Don't put your spell on me / Heydays / Little bit of magic / You stone my soul / Too close to the sun / They settled for less than they wanted / I'm a genius / Available light / Merseybeast (reprise)
5242152 / Apr '96 / This Way Up

☐ MERSEYBEAST/NORTH WEST COAST (2CD Set)
Merseybeast / Affirmation / Beautiful old mystery / Love's young dream / Camaraderie / Don't put your spell on me / Heydays / Little bit of magic / You stone my soul / Too close to the sun / They settled for less than they wanted / I'm a genius / Avaliable light / Merseybeast
5242402 / May '96 / This Way Up

☐ TRUTH AND BEAUTY
(I go) My own way / These are the days / Great dreams of heaven / Truth and beauty / I'm game / If love was like guitars / Story of my life / That's why I believe / Trip with me / Make love to you / Presence of the one
5143782 / Jan '93 / Phonogram

McNally, James

☐ EVERYBREATH
Black is the colour / Woman's heart / I still haven't found what I'm looking for / Bandia/Homes of Donegal/Island / Everybreath you take / Mo gra / Song for Ireland/Coming home / Irish boy / Fairytale of New York / Lonesome boatman 2000 / Foggy dew / Raglan road / Isle of Innisfree / Sheas mo chroa / Belfast child / Saviour
74321443722 / Jul '97 / RCA

McNally, John

☐ EVERGREENS
Galway bay / When Irish eyes are smiling / If I only had time / Danny boy / Bless this house / He ain't heavy he's my brother / I'll walk with God / Morning has broken / Mary in the morning / Song of joy / I believe / May each day / He'll have to go / Impossible dream / Croppy boy / I'll take you home again Kathleen / You light up my life / And I love her / You don't bring me flowers / Evergreen
EMPRCD 561 / Mar '95 / Emporio

McNally, Larry John

☐ VIBROLUX
DIGIT 5679152 / Jun '96 / Dig It

MacNamara, Mary

☐ TRADITIONAL MUSIC FROM EAST CLARE
Cailleach an airgid / Kerfunten jig / Rolling in the barrel / Tap room / Earl's chair / Humours of Tullycrine / Mikey Callaghan's / Pigeon on the gate / Lad O'Beirne's / John Naughton's / Reel with the birl / Paddy Lynn's delight / Connie Hogan's / Kitty goes milking / Killavil jig / Have a drink with me / Toss the feathers / Boys of Ballisodare / Fisherman's lilt / My love is in America / Rooms of Doogh / Walls of Liscarroll / Caoilte mountains / Green gowned lass / John Naughton's jigs / McGreevy's favourite / Miss McGuinness / Sweetheart reel / Maghera mountain / Huomours of Castlefin / Glen of Ahelow / Killarney boys of pleasure
CC 60CD / Oct '94 / Claddagh

MacNamara, Paddy

☐ IRISH PARTY
Macnamara's band / Black velvet band / Jigs / Kathleen / Danny boy / Mick mcgilligan's ball / Too-ra-loo-ra-loo-ral (that's an irish lullaby) / Irish rover / Mother machree / Muirsheen durkin
SOW 90124 / Apr '94 / Sounds Of The World

MacNamara, Pat

☐ TWO SIDES OF PAT MAC, THE
GTDCD 006 / Jan '95 / GTD

McNamara, Keiko

☐ KEIKO IN SWEDEN (McNamara, Keiko Trio)
Heisei I / Lush life/Yesterdays / Heisei II / Skylark / Cubano chant / Our love is here to say / Round midnight / Shu-mo-ku / Heisei III
SRCD 503 / 9 Mar '98 / Jazzizit/Solna

McNaughtan, Adam

☐ LAST STAND AT MOUNT FLORIDA
Dear green place / Cholesterol / You've got to get your folios done / Scottish song / Soor mulk cairt / Shy lover / Old man Noah / Green belongs to Glasgow's folk / Weaver's lament / Coming hame / My grandfather's socks / Thomas Muir of Huntershill / Erchie Cathcairt / Twin-towered stand
CDTRAX 120 / Sep '96 / Greentrax

McNaughton's Vale Of Atoll Pipe Band

☐ LIVE 'N' WELL
Il paco grande / Showaco set / Inveran set / MacCrimmon will never return set / Gargoyles set / Dugald NcColl's farewell to France set / Nameless piobaireachd set / Molendinar - The Wellpark Suite Set / Maclain of Glencoe / Smeceno horo set / Bu deonach leam tilleadh set / Steam train to Mallaig / Eileen Mary Connolly set / Il Paco grande (Encore)
CDTRAX 111 / Jul '96 / Greentrax

McNaughton, Virginia

☐ MUSIC
Tender / Diver / Unfinished business / 'Til hell freezes over / Senseless thing / Without words / Flight of fancy / Protector / If we are ever / Some faces / Dead mens fingers
CDMI 7001 / 13 Oct '97 / GMG

McNeely, 'Big' Jay

☐ BLUES AT DAYBREAK (McNeel, Big Jay & C. Rannenberg)
BEST 1018CD / Nov '93 / Acoustic Music

McNeely, James

☐ LIVE AT MAYBECK RECITAL HALL VOL.20
There will never be another you / Zingaro / Bye ya / 'Round midnight / Touch / All the things you are / Body and soul / Breaking up breaking out
CCD 4522 / Sep '92 / Concord Jazz

☐ PLOT THICKENS, THE
MCD 5378 / Sep '92 / Muse

☐ RAIN'S DANCE
SCCD 31412 / Jul '97 / Steeplechase

MacNeil, Flora

☐ CRAOBH NAN UBHAL
COMD 1002 / Jan '94 / Temple

MacNeil, Rita

☐ FLYING ON YOUR OWN
Flying on your own / Neon city / She's called Nova Scotia / Baby baby / Leave her memory / Fast train to Tokyo / Everybody / Used to you / Loser (when it comes to love) / Realised your dreams
8434232 / Jul '92 / Polydor

☐ HOME I'LL BE
5112772 / Jul '92 / Polydor

☐ REASON TO BELIEVE
Walk on through / Two steps from broken / City child / Doors of the cemetary / Reason to believe / When the loving is through / Causing the fall / Music's going round again / Sound your own horn / Working man / Good friends
D 5177793 / Oct '94 / LPO

☐ WORKING MAN (The Best Of Rita MacNeil)
5178612 / Sep '90 / Polydor

McNeil, John

☐ EMBARKATION (McNeil, John Quintet)
SCCD 31099 / Oct '95 / Steeplechase

☐ THINGS WE DID LAST SUMMER
SCCD 31231 / Jul '88 / Steeplechase

McNeill, Brian

☐ BACK O' THE NORTH WIND, THE (Tales Of The Scots In America)
Back o' the North wind / Entail / Strong women rule us with their tears / Rock and the tide / Destitution road / Muir and the master builder / Atlantic reels / Best o' the barley / Ewen and the gold / Drive the golden spike / Lang Johnnie More / Steel man / Bridal boat
CDTRAX 047 / Sep '91 / Greentrax

☐ BUSKER AND THE DEVIL'S ONLY DAUGHTER, THE
COMD 2042 / Feb '94 / Temple

☐ HORSES FOR COURSES
CDTRAX 071 / Mar '94 / Greentrax

☐ MONKSGATE
Queen of slutswillie is a bonny lad / Flowers of the thorn / Master crowley's reelbobby casey's reel / Rowley burnroxburgh castle / Planxty charles cooteplanxty hugh o'donnell / Monksgate / Hag at the spinning wheel / Eclipsethe mathematician
CDTRAX 062 / May '93 / Greentrax

☐ NO GODS
No gods and precious few heroes / Miss Michison regrets / Any Mick'll do / Drover's road / Breton wedding march / Trains and my grandfather / Tommy Sheridan's / Annie Lawson / Jocky's treble tops / Assynt crofters / Montrose / Inside the whale / Princess Augusta / Fighter / Alison Hargreaves / Veillon's / Young master Haigh / Steady as she goes / Bring back the wolf
CDTRAX 098 / Dec '95 / Greentrax

☐ NO GOODS
TRAX 098CD / Mar '96 / Greentrax

☐ UNSTRUNG HERO
Lift your glass to the landlady / Peter Calver's favourite / Steeple reel / Butterfly chain / Angela Morrison's pavanne / White dress / Foggy banks of Haines / Boys that broke the ground / Ortiguera / Tall ships in their prime / Ivory reel / Miss Susan Feddersen / Quill / Belle-ile / Crookhill / Laverock song / Heron / Molly's roses / Hamish Henderson's refusal / Blue jay and a Cardinal / Bothkennar / Down the road to Galloway / Catherine Jane's polka
COMD 2017 / 20 Oct '97 / Temple

McNeir, Ronnie

☐ DOWN IN THE NEIGHBOURHOOD
Intro / Down in the neighbourhood / Interlude / Save the children / Baby you're wrong / Substance abuse / Traitors / Part time lover
XECD 11 / 27 Oct '97 / Expansion

☐ LOVE SUSPECT
Love suspect / Lately / Summertime medley / Sexy Mama / Everybody's in a hurry / I'll be loving you / Follow your heart / Tying to keep my heart / Please come and be with me
EXCDP 1 / Jun '93 / Debut

☐ RARE MCNEIR
Baby I know / Different kind of love / Lonely superstar / Southern pearl / Ain't no woman like my baby / This is my prayer / I want to thank you / Strong for each other / Good side of your love / Your best friend and me / I'll come running back / Remember baby / I got someone
ATCD 024 / Aug '95 / ATR

McNerney, Steve

☐ SHE'S A FUNNY BLOKE (McNerney, Steve & Changing Man)
DOMCD 008 / Mar '97 / Public Domain

Macorlan, Pierre

☐ CHANSONS DU QUAI DES BRUMES (Macorlan, Pierre & Monique Morelli)
984332 / Nov '97 / EPM

McPartland, Marian

☐ AT THE FESTIVAL
I love you / Willow weep for me / Windows / In the days of our love / Cotton tail / Here's that rainy day / On green dolphin street / Oleo
CCD 4118 / Oct '94 / Concord Jazz

☐ AT THE HICKORY HOUSE
I hear music / Tickle toe / Street of dreams / How long has this been going on / Let's call the whole thing off / Lush life / Mad about the boy / Love you madly / Skylark / Ja da / I've told every little star / Moon song
JASCD 312 / Aug '95 / Jasmine

☐ FROM THIS MOMENT ON
From this moment on / Emily / Sweet and lovely / Ambiance / You and the night and the music / If you could see me now / Lullaby of the leaves / There is no greater love / Polka dots and moonbeams
CCD 4086 / Aug '91 / Concord Jazz

☐ GREAT BRITAINS (McPartland, Marian & George Shearing)
It might as well be Spring / Gypsy in my soul / Strike up the band / Our love is here to stay / Love for sale / Yesterdays / All the things you are / Sweet and lovely / When darkness falls / So rare / Bop's your uncle / Sophisticated lady / Buccaneer's bounce / Cozy's bop / Have you met Miss Jones
SV 0160 / Oct '97 / Savoy Jazz

☐ IN MY LIFE
CCD 4561 / May '94 / Concord Jazz

☐ JUST FRIENDS
Jeepers creepers / I've got a crush on you / Some time ago / It's you or no one / Just friends / Twilight world / Lullaby of the leaves / Chrysalis / Gone with the wind / There will never be another you / Lady be good / When the Saints go marching in
CCD 48052 / 13 Jul '98 / Concord Jazz

☐ LIVE AT YOSHI'S NITESPOT
Like someone in love / In a sentimental mood / Pretty woman / Come rain or shine / Shine / Straight, no chaser / Silent pool / Steeplechase / Pensativa / Bemsha swing / Warm valley / If I should lose you / Turn around
CCD 4712 / Jul '96 / Concord Crossover

☐ LOOKING FOR A BOY (McPartland, Marian & Barbara Carroll/Adelaide Robbins)
Great day / Everything but you / Gentleman is a dope / Looking for a boy / You stepped out of a dream / Dancing on the ceiling / Liza / September song / Laura / Embraceable you / Barbara's Carroll / Puppet that dances be-bop
SV 0226 / Oct '97 / Savoy Jazz

☐ MARIAN MCPARTLAND IN CONCERT
Gypsy in my soul / These foolish things / Get happy / Strike up the band / Foggy day / Lady is a tramp / I've got the world on a string / Manhattan / Aunt Hagar's blues / Four brothers / Once in a while
SV 0202 / Oct '97 / Savoy Jazz

☐ MARIAN MCPARTLAND PLAYS THE MUSIC OF ALEC WILDER
Jazz waltz for a friend / Why / While we're young / Lullaby for a lady / Inner circle / I'll be around / Trouble is a man / Homework / Where are the good companions / It's so peaceful in the country
TJA 10016 / Oct '92 / Jazz Alliance

☐ PERSONAL CHOICE
I hear a rhapsody / Meditation / In your own sweet way / Sleepin' bee / I'm old fashioned / When the sun comes out / Tricrotism / Melancholy mood
CCD 4202 / Mar '87 / Concord Jazz

☐ PIANO JAZZ (McPartland, Marian & Dave Brubeck)
St. Louis blues / Thank you / Duke / In your own sweet way / One moment worth years / Summer song / Free piece / Polytonal blues / Take five
TJA 12001 / Jun '93 / Bellaphon

☐ PIANO JAZZ (McPartland, Marian & Teddy Wilson)
TJA 12002 / Jul '93 / Jazz Alliance

☐ PIANO JAZZ (McPartland, Marian & Dizzy Gillespie)
Con alma / In a mellow tone / On the alamo / Manteca / For Dizzy / Lullaby of the leaves / 'Round midnight / Portrait of Diz / Night in Tunisia
TJA 12005 / Feb '94 / Jazz Alliance

☐ PIANO JAZZ (McPartland, Marian & Eubie Blake)
Betty Washboard rag / Valse Marion / Song for Marian (Margaret) / You're lucky to me / Charlston rag / Dream rag / For the last time call me sweetheart / Stars and stripes forever / Falling in love with someone / Kiss me again / St. Louis blues / I'm just wild about Harry / Little gypsy sweetheart
TJA 12006 / Mar '94 / Jazz Alliance

☐ PIANO JAZZ (McPartland, Marian & Dick Wellstood)
Ain't misbehavin' / Medley / Lulu's back in town / 'Deed I do / Gee baby ain't I good to you / Detour ahead / Fine and dandy
TJA 12007 / May '94 / Jazz Alliance

☐ PIANO JAZZ (McPartland, Marian & Barbara Carroll)
Too soon / My man's gone now / This time the dream's on me / Imagination / Old friends / Marbara / There will never be another you
TJA 12008 / Jun '94 / Jazz Alliance

☐ PIANO JAZZ
Snapper / Come Sunday / There'll be other times / Mumbles / Simple waltz / Michelle / Memories of you / Wham
TJA 12009 / Aug '94 / Jazz Alliance

☐ PIANO JAZZ (McPartland, Marian & Bobby Short)
Mood indigo / Nobody's heart / Experiment / 'Round midnight / I guess I'll have to change my plan / Just one of those things / Reflections in D / My shining hour / It don't mean a thing if it ain't got that swing
TJA 12010 / Sep '94 / Jazz Alliance

☐ PIANO JAZZ (McPartland, Marian & Dick Hyman)
Carousel memories / Relax / Handful of keys / Gone with the wind / Body and soul / Flower is a lovesome thing / This time the dream's on me / Delicate balance / Skylark / Lover come back to me
TJA 12012 / Nov '94 / Jazz Alliance

☐ PIANO JAZZ (McPartland, Marian & Red Richards)
Have you met Miss Jones / What a wonderful world / Tangerine / Hundred years from today / Keepin' out of mischief now / Echoes of spring / Someday you'll be sorry / Talk of the town / Running wild
TJA 12011 / Oct '94 / Jazz Alliance

☐ PIANO JAZZ (McPartland, Marian & Stanley Cowell)
Top of your head blues / Stella by starlight / 'Round midnight / Juan Valdez / Watergate blues / Equipoise / You took advantage of me / God bless the child / Cherokee
TJA 12013 / Feb '95 / Jazz Alliance

☐ PIANO JAZZ (McPartland, Marian & Mercer Ellington)
C Jam blues / Kinda dukish / Caravan / Prelude to a kiss / Chelsea bridge / Moon mist / Thing's aint' waht they used to be / Portrait of Mercer Ellington / Solitude
TJA 12014 / Feb '95 / Jazz Alliance

☐ PIANO JAZZ (McPartland, Marian & Benny Carter)
Easy money / Faraway / Blues in my heart / Lonely woman / Only trust your heart / Evening star / Kiss from you / Key largo / Summer serenade / When lights are low
TJA 12015 / Feb '95 / Jazz Alliance

☐ PIANO JAZZ (McPartland, Marian & Milt Hinton)
Milt's rap (MH solo) / All the things you are / My one and only love (Duet) / Joshua / Willow weep for me / Old man time (duet) / These foolish things / Stranger in a dream / How high the moon
TJA 12016 / Apr '95 / Jazz Alliance

☐ PIANO JAZZ (McPartland, Marian & Jack DeJohnette)
Freddie freeloader / I loves you Porgy / It could happen to you / Alice in wonderland / Ambiance / Blue in green / Silver hollow / Mr. PC
TJA 12018 / May '95 / Jazz Alliance

☐ PIANO JAZZ (McPartland, Marian & Jess Stacy)
Dancing fool / Lover man / Oh baby / Keepin' out of mischief now / Improv in A minor / Autumn of New York / I would do most anything for you / Moon mist / Heavy hearted blues / St. Louis blues
TJA 12017 / May '95 / Jazz Alliance

☐ PIANO JAZZ (McPartland, Marian & Kenny Burrell)
Listen to the dawn / 'Round midnight / I'm old fashioned / All too soon / Don't worry 'bout me / Spring can really hang you up the most / I'm just a lucky so and so / Raincheck
TJA 12021 / Aug '95 / Jazz Alliance

☐ PIANO JAZZ (McPartland, Marian & Amina Claudine)
B I / Mood indigo / Windows / So what / Call him / Do you wanna be saved / Free impro / Have mercy upon us / Portrait of Amina / Sonnymoon for two
TJA 12022 / Oct '95 / Jazz Alliance

☐ PIANO JAZZ (McPartland, Marian & Henry Mancini)
Two for the road / Meggie's theme / Pink Panther / Mr. Lucky / Dreamsville / Charade / Baby elephant walk / Moon river / Days of wine and roses
TJA 12024 / Dec '95 / Jazz Alliance

☐ PIANO JAZZ (McPartland, Marian & Roy Eldridge)
Fast booie / Ball of fire / Une petite laitue / Rockin' chair / I want a little girl / Indian summer / M and R Blues
TJA 12025 / Feb '96 / Jazz Alliance

☐ PIANO JAZZ (McPartland, Marian & Oscar Peterson)
Old folks / Place St Henri / Like someone in love / Body and soul / Emily / Take the 'A' train / Falling in love with love / Willow creek / Cotton tail
TJA 12028 / Apr '96 / Jazz Alliance

☐ PIANO JAZZ (McPartland, Marian & Jay McShann)
Vine Street boogie / Georgia on my mind / 'Deed I do / Living back street for you / My chile / Tain't nobody's bizness if I do / What's your story morning glory / Confessin' the blues / Oh lady be good
TJA 12030 / Jun '96 / Jazz Alliance

☐ PIANO JAZZ (McPartland, Marian & Charles Brown)
These blues / All my life / Is you is or is you ain't my baby / Drifting blues / There is no greater love / 'Round midnight / Sweet slumber / Joyce's boogie / Seven long days
TJA 12032 / Sep '96 / Jazz Alliance

☐ PIANO JAZZ (McPartland, Marian & Les McCann)
Every time I see a butterfly / Prince of peace / Marian and Les together / Just squeeze me / My funny valentine / With these hands / Bill Evans / Why / Compared to what
TJA 12031 / Oct '96 / Jazz Alliance

☐ PLAYS THE BENNY CARTER SONG BOOK
When lights are low / I'm in the mood for swing / Kiss from you / Key largo / Another time another place / Summer serenade / Doozy / Lonely woman / Only trust your heart / Evening star / Easy money
CCD 4412 / Jun '90 / Concord Jazz

☐ PLAYS THE MUSIC OF BILLY STRAYHORN
Intimacy of the blues / Isfahan / Lotus blossom / Raincheck / Lush life / UMMG / Flower is a lovesome thing / Take the 'A' train / Daydream / After all
CCD 4326 / Oct '87 / Concord Jazz

☐ PLAYS THE MUSIC OF MARY LOU WILLIAMS
Scratchin' the gravel / Lonely moments / What's your story Morning Glory / Easy blues / Threnody (a lament) / It's a grand night for swingin' / In the land of Oo-Bla-Dee / Dirge blues / Koolbonga / Walkin' and swingin' / Cloudy / My blue heaven / Mary's waltz / St. Martin de Porres
CCD 4605 / Jul '94 / Concord Jazz

☐ PORTRAIT OF MARIAN MCPARTLAND
Tell me a bedtime story / It never entered my mind / No trumps / Wind flower / I won't dance / Spring can really hang you up the most / Matrix / Time and time again
CCD 4101 / Oct '91 / Concord Jazz

☐ SENTIMENTAL JOURNEY, A (McPartland, Marian & Jimmy)
Royal garden blues / Sentimental journey / Blue prelude / Dinah / Basin Street blues / When you wish upon a star / Avalon / Perdido / Willow weep for me / I'm gonna sit right down and write myself a letter / Polka dots and moonbeams / Wolverine blues
TJA 10025 / Oct '94 / Jazz Alliance

☐ SILENT POOL (McPartland, Marian & Strings)
For Dizzy / Twilight world / Stranger in a dream / Delicate balance / Ambiance / Silent pool / Castles in the sand / Melancholy mood / Threnody / Time and time again / There'll be other times / With you in mind
CCD 47452 / Feb '97 / Concord Jazz

McPeak Brothers

☐ BOTTOM LINE
72232101592 / 14 Apr '98 / Copper Creek

McPhatter, Clyde

☐ BEST OF CLYDE MCPHATTER, THE
I can't stand up alone / Seven days / Treasure of love / Rock and cry / I'm lonely tonight / Without love (there is nothing) / Deap sea ball / Just to hold my hand / My island of dreams / No matter what / Come what may / Lovey dovey / I'm not worthy of you / Lover's question / Thirty days / You went back on your word / Little girl / No love like her love / Long lonely nights / Since you've been gone
RSACD 812 / Oct '94 / Sequel

☐ LOVE BALLADS
Heartaches / Come what may / Rock and cry: *McPhatter, Clyde & Ruth Brown* / That's enough for me / I gotta have you / Just to hold my hand / Long lonely nights / When you're sincere / No matter what / No love like her / You'll be there / Love has joined us together: *McPhatter, Clyde & Ruth Brown* / Go yes go / Let me know / Just give me a ring / I can believe
RSACD 802 / Nov '96 / Sequel

MacPhee, Catherine-Anne

☐ CANAN NAN GAIDHEAL
Hi rivio ra ill o / Nighean nan geug taladh / Puirt a buel / Soiridh leis a' bhreacan ur / Iomair thusa, choinnich chridhe / Ca' nan gaidheal / 'S fliuch an oidhche / Onan an Ioiaire / Cearcall a' chuain / Ataireach ard
CDTRAX 009 / May '93 / Greentrax

☐ CHI MI'N GEAMHRADH (I SEE WINTER)
Chi mi'n geamhradh / Chaidh mo dhunnchadh dha'n bheinn / Oh hi ri lean / Bidh clann ulaidh / Mile marbhphaisg air a' ghaol / Seathan bu deonach leam tilleadh / 'S muladach mi 's mi air m'aineol / Bothan airigh am braigh rainneach / Tha na h-uain air an tulaich / Na libh o ho I
CDTRAX 038 / Apr '91 / Greentrax

☐ SINGS MAIRI MHOR
Nuair bha mi og / Coinneamh nan croiteran / Eilean a cheo / Soraidh leis an nollaig uir / Soraidh le eilean a'cheo / Oran beinn / Camanachd glaschu / Oran sarachaidh / Clach agus mairi / Luchd na beurla / Mar a tha / Faistneachd agus / Beannachd di na caidheil
CDTRAX 070 / Jun '94 / Greentrax

McPhee, Joe

☐ AT WBAI'S 1971 (McPhee, Joe & Survival Unit 11)
ARTCD 6197 / Feb '97 / Hat Art

☐ LINEAR B (McPhee, Joe PO Music)
ARTCD 6057 / Dec '91 / Hat Art

☐ MEETING IN CHICAGO, A (McPhee, Joe & Ken Vandermark/Kent Kessler)
OD 12016 / May '98 / Okka Disk

☐ OLD EYES AND MYSTERIES (McPhee, Joe PO Music)
ARTCD 6047 / Apr '92 / Hat Art

☐ SWEET FREEDOM - NOW WHAT
ARTCD 6162 / Sep '95 / Hat Art

McPhee, Tony

☐ BLEACHING THE BLUES
When you're down / All your women / There's a light / Went in like a lamb / When your man has gone / Many times / All last night / When you're walking down the street / Meeting of the minds / Bleaching the blues / If I had possession / Love in vain / Floatin' bridge / Terraplane blues / Little red rooster
HTDCD 72 / Apr '97 / HTD

☐ FOOLISH PRIDE
Foolish pride / Every minute / Devil you know / Masquerading / Time after time / On the run / Took me by suprise / Whatever it takes / Been there, done that / I'm gonna win
HTDCD 10 / Sep '96 / HTD

☐ ME AND THE DEVIL/I ASKED FOR WATER SHE GAVE ME GASOLINE
Rollin' and tumblin' / Duckin' and dodgin' / Death letter / Elevator woman / Make me a pallat / Heartstruck sorrow / When you got a good friend / Me and the devil / You better mind / Hard time killing floor / Same thing on my mind / Broke down engine / Arkansas woman / No more doggin' / Buy you a diamond ring / Oh death / She's gone / Factory blues / Boogie woman / Nervous / Crazy with the blues / Lord I feel tired / Gasoline / Rock me / London's got the blues / Love's in vain / Dust my blues / Built my hopes too high / Don't pass the hat around / When my woman is with me / I'm so tired
BGOCD 332 / 27 Apr '98 / Beat Goes On

☐ SLIDE T.S. SLIDE
Reformed man / Mean disposition / Slide to slide / From a pawn to a King / Tell me baby / Hooker 'n' The Hogs / Someday baby / Driving duck / No place to go / Me and the devil
HTDCD 26 / Sep '96 / HTD

☐ WHO SAID CHERRY RED (McPhee, Tony & The Groundhogs)
Rocking chair / Man trouble / Married men / BDD / Times / Natchez burning / Status people / Rich man, poor man / Darkness is no friend / Junkman / Year in the life / Sad is the hunter / Earth shanty / Mr. Hooker Sir John
IGOCD 2058 / Oct '96 / Indigo

MacPherson, Donald

☐ MASTER PIPER, THE
LCDM 9013 / '90 / Lismor

MacPherson, Fraser

☐ ELLINGTON 1987
SKCD 22043 / Jan '97 / Sackville

☐ ENCORE (MacPherson, Fraser Quartet)
JTR 84202 / Jan '94 / Justin Time

☐ IN THE TRADITION (MacPherson, Fraser Quintet)
Louisiana / Why am I blue / Struttin' with some barbecue / Hundred years from today / Constantly / When it's sleepy time down South / Desolation blues / You're lucky to me / If you could see me now / Dream of you / Ol' Bill's blues
CCD 4506 / May '92 / Concord Jazz

MacPherson, Sandy

☐ I'LL PLAY TO YOU
I'll play to you / Vilia / Dancing on the ceiling / Room with a view / My heart stood still / June night on Marlow Reach / Was it a dream / Wonderful one / Till we meet again / It's a lovely day tomorrow / Who's taking you home tonight / Over the rainbow / Humoresque / Nobody knows the trouble I've seen / O Peter go ring-a-dem bells / Swing low, sweet chariot / Desert song / One flower / One alone / Can't help lovin' dat man / Why do I love you / Ol' man river / There's a boy coming home on leave / In an old Dutch garden / Woodpecker's song / Totem Tom / Indian love call / Rose Marie / Merry widow waltz / Dancing my way to heaven / Over my shoulder / When you've got a little springtime in your heart / March of the Bowmen / Oh Mama Mia / You made me care / My Capri serenade / Riff song / Waltz duet / Foreign legion / 'Tis me O Lord / Deep night / I got a robe / I've got no strings / Little wooden head / Give a little whistle / Carissima / Starlight / I do like to be beside the seaside / I've got to sing a torch song / Keep smiling / Oh Mr. Porter / Rhapsody in blue
RAJCD 861 / 29 Jun '98 / Empress

McPherson, Charles

☐ CHARLES MCPHERSON
Viper / I can't get started / Shaw'nuff / Here's that rainy day / Never let me go / Suddenly / I believe in you / Epistrophy / Luminessence
PCD 24135 / Nov '95 / Prestige

☐ FIRST FLIGHT OUT
Lynn grins / Lizabeth / Blues for Chuck / Nostalgia in Times Square / Well you needn't / Seventh Dimension / Goodbye Pork Pie Hat / Deep night / Portrait / Karen / My funny valentine / First flight out
AJ 0113 / Jan '95 / Arabesque

McQuade, Victor

☐ KEY IMPRESSIONS
7017505506 / Mar '98 / Word

McRackins

☐ BACK TO THE CRACK
LOUDEST 20 / Oct '96 / One Louder

☐ BEST FRIEND
SH 40 / Jan '97 / Shredder

☐ LIVE IN MADRID
LOUDEST 26 / 12 Jan '98 / One Louder

McRae, Carmen

☐ BEST OF CARMEN MCRAE, THE
Like a lover / I have the feeling I've been here before / Man I love / Would you believe / Child is born / Star eyes / Miss Otis regrets / Too close for comfort / Old folks / Dindi / Ain't nobody's business if I do
CDP 8335782 / Nov '95 / Capitol Jazz

☐ BLACK MAGIC 'LIVE'
Black magic / Last winter / New york state of mind / Underneath the apple tree / Thou swell / Send in the clowns / I just can't wait to see you / How long has this been going on / If I were a bell / My foolish heart / Secret love / Body and soul / 'tis autumn / Bye bye blackbird / End of a beautiful friendship
JHR 73558 / Oct '92 / Jazz Hour

☐ CARMEN MCRAE
Straighten up and fly right / Inside a silent tear / Imagination / Right to love / All the things you are / It takes a whole lot of human feeling / I fall in love too easily / Hey john / Where are the words / Nice work if you can get it / You are the sunshine of my life / You and I / Masquerade
15745 / Apr '94 / Laserlight

☐ CARMEN MCRAE (Bethlehem Jazz Classics)
CDGR 129 / Apr '97 / Charly

☐ CARMEN MCRAE LIVE
Black magic / Superwoman (where were you when I needed you) / Underneath the apple tree / Thou swell / Send in the clowns / I just can't wait to see you / How long has this been going on / If I were a bell / My foolish heart / Secret love / I concentrate on you
CDGATE 7001 / Sep '88 / Kingdom Jazz

☐ CARMEN MCRAE SINGS LOVER MAN (& Other Billie Holiday Classics)
Them there eyes / Yesterdays / I'm gonna lock my heart (and throw away the key) / Strange fruit / Miss Brown to you / My man / I cried for you (now it's your turn to cry over me) / Lover man / Trav'lin' light / Some other Spring / What a little moonlight can do / God bless the child / If the moon turns green / Christmas song
CK 65115 / Jun '97 / Sony Jazz

☐ COLLECTED CARMEN MCRAE, THE
Dear Ruby / Still we dream / It's magic / Dedicated to you / Poor butterfly / Misty / Tenderly / Don't explain / Lover man / I'm pulling through / My old flame / If you were mine / It's like reaching for the moon
09026687132 / Jul '98 / RCA Victor

☐ EVERYTHING HAPPENS TO ME
Nice work if you can get it / Do nothing till you hear from me / Everything a good man needs / Body and soul / Them there eyes / My funny valentine / No more blues / Everything happens to me / Upside down / Take 5 / Besame mucho / New york state of mind / Don't misunderstand me / Ain't misbehavin'
JHR 73582 / Dec '94 / Jazz Hour

☐ GREAT AMERICAN SONGBOOK, THE
Satin doll / At long last love / If the moon turns green / Day by day / What are you doing the rest of your life / I only have eyes for you / Easy living / Days of wine and roses / It's impossible / Sunday / Song for you / I cried for you / Behind the face / Ballad of Thelonious Monk / There's no such thing as love / Close to you / Three little words / Mr. Ugly / It's like reaching for the moon / I thought about you
7567813232 / Jun '93 / Atlantic

☐ I'LL BE SEEING YOU (2CD Set)
Something to live for / Speak low / But beautiful / Midnight sun / Good morning heartache / I don't stand a ghost of a chance with you / We'll be together again / Star eyes / Whatever Lola wants (Lola gets) / Lush life / Until the real thing comes along / You don't know me / Skyliner / Party's over / East of the sun and west of the moon / Dream of life / Perdido / Exactly like you / I'm through with love / I'll see you again / Invitation / Bye bye blackbird / Flamingo / Oh yes, I remember Clifford / If I were a bell / Any old time / What's new / Night we called it a day / Please be kind / Thrill is gone / My myself / Do you know why / More I see you / When your lover has gone / If I could be with you one hour tonight / I only have eyes for you / I'm glad there is you / Ain't misbehavin' / I'll be seeing you
GRP 2647 / Aug '95 / GRP

☐ IN CONCERT
DM 15020 / Jul '96 / DMA Jazz

☐ IT TAKES A WHOLE LOT OF HUMAN FEELING
CDGR 170 / Jul '97 / Charly

☐ MASQUERADE IS OVER, THE
CDSGP 0183 / May '96 / Prestige

☐ PRICELESS JAZZ
Bye bye blackbird / My funny valentine / Flamingo / You took advantage of me / How long has this been going on / Love is a simple thing / Every time we say goodbye / Nice work if you can get it / I'm putting all my eggs in one basket / My man's gone now / Speak low / East of the sun / Exactly like you / Something to live for / I'm glad there is you / How little we know
GRP 98972 / 23 Mar '98 / GRP

☐ SONG TIME
HCD 602 / Sep '96 / Hindsight

☐ VELVET SOUL
Nice work if you can get it / It takes a whole lot of human feeling / I fall in love too easily / Hey John / Where are the words / Straighten up and fly right / Inside a silent tear / Imagination / Right to love / All the things you are / You're mine you / You and I / How could I settle for less / Good life / Sunshine of my life / Exactly like you / There will come a time / (I'm afraid) the masquerade is over
CDC 7970 / Nov '90 / LRC

☐ YOU'D BE SO EASY TO LOVE (The Finest Of Carmen McRae - The Bethlehem Years)
BET 6018 / Jan '95 / Bethlehem

☐ YOU'RE LOOKING AT ME
I'm an errand girl for rhythm / Beautiful moons ago / Frim fram sauce / Come in and out of the rain / How does it feel / If I had you / I can't see for lookin' / Sweet Lorraine / You're lookin' at me / Just you, just me
CCD 4235 / Sep '86 / Concord Jazz

MacRae, Gordon

☐ BEST OF GORDON MACRAE, THE
Dear hearts and gentle people / Mule train / Sunshine of your smile / Younger than Springtime / Lover's waltz / On Rosary Hill / My Buick, my love and I / If someone had told me / How do you speak to an angel / Face to face / Be my little baby bumble bee / By the light of the silvery moon / Beela note / Who are we / People will say we're in love / Surrey with the fringe on top / Woman in love / I've grown accustomed to her face / Sound of music / If ever I would leave you
CDSL 8275 / Nov '95 / Music For Pleasure

☐ BEST THINGS IN LIFE ARE FREE/ MOTION PICTURE SOUNDSTAGE
Best things in life are free / Button up your overcoat / It all depends on you / Sonny boy / Just a memory / One more time / Birth of the blues / Together / You try somebody else / Without love / You're the cream in my coffee / Best things in life are free / Singin' in the rain / Dancing in the dark / You're a sweetheart / Cabin in the sky / Hooray for love / Love is a many splendored thing / Jealousy / Pennies from heaven / Laura / Easy to love / Flirtation walk / Goodnight sweetheart
4930662 / 19 Jan '98 / Capitol

Macrocosmica

☐ AD ASTRA
NOIR 004CD / 17 Nov '97 / God Bless

McShane, Ian

☐ FROM BOTH SIDES NOW
Avalon / Fool (if you think it's over) / This guy's in love with you / I'd really love to see you tonight / From both sides now / I don't mind / I'm not in love / I could have been a sailor / Drive / Every breath you take / Reason to believe / Little in love / Shadow of your smile
5176192 / Nov '92 / PolyGram TV

McShann, Jay

☐ AFTER HOURS
After hours / Kansas city blues / How long blues / Staggers / Vognporten boogie / Ace in the hole / Yardbird waltz / Man from Muskogee / Diblin' and dablin' / Fore day rider / Tain't nobody business / Doo wah doo / Hot biscuits / Cherry red / Jumpin' with McShann
STCD 8279 / Mar '98 / Storyville

☐ AIRMAIL SPECIAL
SKCD 23040 / '88 / Sackville

☐ AT CAFE DES COPAINS
SKCD 22024 / Jun '93 / Sackville

☐ BEST OF FRIENDS (McShann, Jay & Al Casey)
'Deed I do / One o'clock jump / Going to Kansas City / One sweet blues / How deep is the ocean / Anything / Hello little girl / Honky tonk train blues / Oh lady be good / Casey's shuffle / Stroll / Mess of trouble / Noodlin' / Al's theme
JSPCD 291 / Jul '97 / JSP

☐ CLASSICS 1941-1943
CLASSICS 740 / Feb '94 / Classics

☐ CLASSICS 1944-1946
CLASSICS 966 / Jan '98 / Classics

☐ CONFESSIN' THE BLUES
BB 8672 / Apr '96 / Black & Blue

☐ GOING TO KANSAS CITY (McShann, Jay & The All Stars)
Doggin' around / Hootie's ignorant oil / Blue and sentimental / Hootie's in hutchinson / Say forward, I'll march / Four day rider / Moten swing
NW 358 / '88 / New World

☐ JUST A LUCKY SO 'N' SO
SKCD 3035 / Jul '96 / Sackville

☐ LAST OF THE WHOREHOUSE PIANO PLAYERS
CRD 306 / Mar '96 / Chiaroscuro

☐ MAN FROM MUSKOGEE, THE
Vine Street boogie / Staggers / Yardbird waltz / My Chile / Confessin' the blues / Moten swing / Man from Muskogee / Blues for an old cat / I ain't mad at you / Do wah doo / Dexter blues
SKCD 3005 / Jul '96 / Sackville

☐ MISSOURI CONNECTION, THE (McShann, Jay & John Hicks)
RSRCD 124 / Nov '94 / Reservoir

☐ MY BABY WITH BLACK DRESS ON
New hootie blues / Evenin' / But not for Hootie / Stardust / Georgia on my mind / My Chile / I just picked it out of the sky / Body and soul / All of me / Cherry red / Vine street boogie / Yardbird waltz / Hands off / I'll see you in my dreams / Jazzspeak
CRD 345 / 6 Jul '98 / Chiaroscuro

☐ PARIS ALL STAR BLUES (A Tribute To Charlie Parker) (McShann, Jay Kansas City Band)
Jumpin' blues / Moten swing / I'm just a lucky so and so / Lonely boy blues / Parker's mood / Say forward, I'll march / Tender touch / Swingin' the blues / Have you ever had the blues / Sebastian / Vine street boogie / Hootie blues
8208332 / May '91 / Limelight
MM 5052 / Oct '94 / Music Masters

☐ SOME BLUES
CRD 320 / Mar '96 / Chiaroscuro

☐ SWINGMATISM (McShann, Jay & Don Thompson/Archie Alleyne)
SKCD 23046 / Jun '93 / Sackville

☐ VINE STREET BOOGIE
My chile / Hootie blues / Satin doll / I'm beginning to see the light / Vine Street boogie / Confessin' the blues / Yardbird waltz / Hootie's ignorant oil
BLCD 760187 / Jul '93 / Black Lion

McShee, Jacqui

☐ ABOUT THYME
Jabalpur / Lovely Joan / Thyme / Factory girl / Would you / Little voices (Leah's song) / Sandalwood down to Kyle / Indiscretion / Don't turn on the light / Wife of Usher's well
GJSCD 012 / Jul '95 / GJS

☐ PASSE AVANT (McShee, Jacqui Pentangle)
House carpenter / Nightingale / Gypsy countess / Way it is / Jardin d'amour / We'll be together / Edsong / Lagan love / Midnight dance / Just for you
PRKCD 46 / 27 Jul '98 / Park

McTell, 'Blind' Willie

☐ 1927 - 1935
Scarey day blues / Scarey day blues / Ticket agent blues / Experience blues / It's a good little thing / Atlanta strut / Southern can mama / God don't like it / Painful blues / Razor ball / Cold winter day / Stole rider blues / B and o blues no. 2 / My baby's gone
YAZCD 1037 / Apr '91 / Yazoo

☐ BLIND WILLIE MCTELL VOL.1 1927-1931
DOCD 5006 / Feb '92 / Document

☐ BLIND WILLIE MCTELL VOL.2 1931-1933
DOCD 5007 / Feb '92 / Document

☐ LAST SESSION
Baby, it must be love / Baby, it must be love / Don't forget it / Kill it kid / That will never happen no more / Goodbye blues / Salty dog / Early life / Beedle um bum / A married man's a fool / A to z blues / Wabash cannonball / Pal of mine / Kill it kid / Broke down engine blues
OBCCD 517 / Nov '92 / Original Blues Classics

☐ LIBRARY OF CONGRESS RECORDINGS - 1940
BDCD 6001 / '91 / Blues Document

☐ PIG 'N' WHISTLE RED
BCD 126 / May '93 / Biograph

☐ STATESBORO BLUES
IGOCD 2015 / Feb '95 / Indigo

McTell, Ralph

☐ BEST OF RALPH MCTELL, THE
TRTCD 206 / Feb '96 / TrueTrax

☐ BLUE SKIES, BLACK HEROES
TPGCD 10 / Dec '94 / Leola

☐ BOY WITH A NOTE, THE
Son of the sea wave (overture) / Meet the detctive (introductory narration) / Summer girls / Slim lover (narration) / Irish girl / Fitzroy (narration) / Slip shod tap room dance (soho so what) (narration) / These soho streets (narration) / No grown mans land (narrated by nerys hughes) / Milk for one (storm in a tea cup) / Leaving for the states (narration) / Wonderful country (a proposition of propositions) / Caitlin's dream (summerbird's are leaving) (perfomed by m / Certain tide (narration) (performed by bob kingdom) / Continuing investigations (narration) / Get me a doctor / Tunnels "never end" in sight (narration) / I miss you most of all / Naked at the station (narration) / Cradled in the rocking boat
TPGCD 11 / Dec '94 / Leola

☐ COMPLETE ALPHABET ZOO, THE
RGFCD 016 / Jan '94 / Road Goes On Forever

☐ DEFINITIVE TRANSATLANTIC COLLECTION, THE
Nanna's song / Mermaid and the seagull / I'm sorry I must leave / Eight frames a second / Streets of London / Mrs. Adlam's angels / England 1914 / Last train and ride / Fairground / Spiral staircase / Michael in the garden / Clown / Father forgive them / I've thought about it / Factory girl / Kew Gardens / Silver birch and weeping willow
ESMCD 527 / 24 Nov '97 / Essential

☐ GREATEST HITS
CD 845008 / Jan '94 / Bluebird

☐ RALPH, ALBERT AND SYDNEY
First song / Grande affaire / Big tree / Michael in the garden / Dry bone rag / Zimmerman blues / Maginot waltz / Five knuckle shuffle / When I was a cowboy / Let me down easy / Naomi / Sylvia / Streets of London / Sweet mystery / Winnie's rag / Waltzing Matilda
OLA 16E1CD / Dec '97 / Leola

☐ SAND IN MY SHOES
TRACD 119 / Apr '96 / Transatlantic

☐ SILVER CELEBRATION
Summer girls / Girl from the hiring fair / Barges / Michael in the garden / Tequila sunset / Bridge of signs / Song for martin / Throw out a line and dream / Setting / From clare to here / Mr. connaughton / Hands of joseph / Stranger to the seasons / Weather the storm / Ferryman / Streets of london
08431822 / Dec '95 / CTE

☐ SLIDE AWAY THE SCREEN
Love grows (Where my Rosemary grows) / One heart / Gold in California / Van nuys, cruise night / London apprentice / Traces / Heroes and villains / Harry / Autumn / Promises / White dress / Save the last dance for me
RGFCD 021 / Sep '94 / Road Goes On Forever

☐ SONGS FOR SIX STRINGS VOL.2
Gypsy / Mrs. Adlam's angels / Mermaid and the seagull / Lovin' I crave / Factory girl / From Clare to here / Red and gold / Summer girls / Fingerbuster / Near enough / Proposal / Slip shod tap room dance / Old brown dog / Girl from the hiring fair / Setting / First and last man / Affairs of the heart / Response / When did you leave heaven / Great dreams of heaven
OLA 15B2CD / Feb '97 / Leola

☐ SPIRAL STAIRCASE
Streets of London / Mrs. Aalam's angels / Wino and the mouse / England 1914 / Last train and ride / Fairground / Spiral staircase / Kind hearted woman blues / Bright and beautiful things / Daddy's here / Rizraklaru / (My) baby keeps staying out all night long / Terminus
HILLCD 5 / Sep '96 / Wooded Hill

☐ SPIRAL STAIRCASE (2CD Set)
Summer come along / Terminus / Michael in the garden / Nanna's song / Last train and ride / Wino and the mouse / Clown / Willoughby's farm / Mermaid and the seagull / Eight frames a second / Wait until the snow / Hesitation blues / England 1914 / Girl on a bicycle / Mrs Adlam's angel / Granny takes a trip / Blind Blake's rag / Spiral staircase / Father forgive them / All things change / Streets of London / Factory girl / Bright and beautiful things / Father forgive them / Michael in the garden / I've thought about it / Blues in more than 12 bars / Rizraklaru / Factory girl / Siver birch and weeping willow / Louise / Too tight drag / Kew gardens / Fairground / Sleepy time blues / Daddy's here / Morning dew / I'm sorry I must leave
SMDCD 151 / May '97 / Snapper

☐ STREETS
Streets of London / You make me feel good / Grande affaire / Seeds of Heaven / El progresso / Red apple juice (trad) / Heron song / Pity the boy / Interest on the loan / Jenny Taylor - Je n'tais la / Lunar lullaby
TPGCD 12 / Apr '95 / Leola

☐ STREETS OF LONDON (The Best Of Ralph McTell)
PLSCD 164 / Apr '97 / Pulse

McTells

☐ WHAT HAPPENS NEXT
Expecting Joe / Trash can man / Everytime / Uncle Joe / All the time / Villiers Street / Buffalo / Jesse Rae / That / Sweetly breathing / Never look down / Francis said / Fridge freezer / This afternoon / Shadders / Secret wish / Everything heaven sent you / Theme / Back of my hand / Of only if / It happens / Side by side / Snowy white / Right way round / Rotten / Take the car / Virginia MC / Sometimes
ASKCD 040 / Jun '94 / Vinyl Japan

McVay, Ray

☐ GEORGE GERSHWIN COLLECTION, THE
HMNCD 020 / 3 Nov '97 / Half Moon

McWilliams, Brigette

☐ TAKE ADVANTAGE OF ME
Set up / Cherish this love / Baby don't play me / Take advantage of me / No groove sweatin' (A funky space reincarnation) / Gotta be down / It's on / I get the job done / That's on me / Blankets of playboys / You got someth'n I want / (Don't let me catch you) slippin' / I'm ready
CDVUS 77 / Jul '94 / Virgin

☐ TOO MUCH WOMAN
Dawn / Morning / Actions (speak louder than words) / It's your life / Through it all / Dusk / Fire / Don't wanna stay / Too much woman / Better off without you / Wishing / Writing a letter / Fire / It's morning...again / Through it all
CDVUS 137 / 3 Nov '97 / Virgin

Mad Caddies

☐ DUCK AND COVER
Road rash / Gentleman / No hope / Macho nachos / Monkeys / Econo line / Joust / Betty / Apathetic / Popcorn / Medium unwell
FAT 576CD / 17 Aug '98 / Fatwreck Chords

Mad Cow Disease

☐ TANTRIC SEX DISCO
My death squad / Craw / As good a place as any / Goatsucker / Exit / White dove / Annie Leiboritz version / Keep smiling / Elevator (going down) / Unicycle / Plague song / Epic departure
118052
118042 / Sep '95 / Musidisc

Mad Doctor X

☐ HIP HOP EXPERIMENT ESCAPES FROM THE LAB
Mad(e) in London / I like my beats hard / Bounce / Dirty old man / Realism / Believe in your stealth / Mean machine
FUNKRCD 005 / Aug '96 / Ninja Tune

☐ PICNIC WITH THE GREYS (2CD Set)
FNTCD 2 / 27 Oct '97 / Freshanova

Mad Jocks

☐ TAKE JOCK AND PARTY (Mad Jocks & Jockmaster BA)
Auld lang syne / Christmas cracker / No lager / Vicar / Jock party mix / Brigadier / Zorba's dance / Religious experience / Here we go again / Kennel talk / Jock jack mix / Pensioners / Guaglione / Daddy's tales / Auld lang syne
CDSKM 1 / Nov '96 / SMP

Mad Lads

☐ BEST OF THE MAD LADS, THE
So nice / Make room / Seeing is believing / Make this young lady mine / Love is here today / Cry baby / By the time I get to Phoenix / Gone the promise of yesterday / Did my baby call / No strings attached / These old memories / I forgot to be your lover / I'm so glad I fell in love with you / Let me repair your heart
CDSXE 114 / Jul '97 / Volt

☐ THEIR COMPLETE EARLY VOLT RECORDINGS
Don't have to shop around / I want someone / Come closer to me / I'm learning / (You're) My inspiration / Michael (The lover) / You mean so much to me / Land of 1000 dances / Nothing can break through / She's the one / Get out of my life / Sugar sugar / Tear-maker / What will love tend to make you do / I want a girl / Patch my heart / For these simple reasons / I don't want to lose your love / Mr. Fix it / Whatever hurts you / No time is better than right now / Please wait until I'm gone / Candy / Cloudburst
CDSXD 111 / Jun '97 / Stax

Mad Lion

☐ REAL LOVER
VPCD 1402 / Mar '95 / VP

Mad Parade

☐ CAT BITTEN TONGUE
LF 256CD / Dec '96 / Lost & Found

☐ CLOWN TIME IS OVER
LRR 025 / Mar '97 / Last Resort

☐ CRAWL
LF 208CD / Apr '96 / Lost & Found

☐ THIS IS LIFE
LF 166CD / Aug '95 / Lost & Found

Mad Professor

☐ ADVENTURES OF A DUB SAMPLER, THE
ARICD 033 / Oct '92 / Ariwa Sounds

☐ AT CHECKPOINT CHARLIE
DANCD 089 / Jul '97 / Danceteria

☐ BEYOND THE REALMS OF DUB
AFRICD 003 / Jan '91 / Ariwa Sounds

☐ BLACK LIBERATION DUB VOL.1
Psychological warfare / Black liberation dub / Riot in Capetown / Slavery 21st century / Freedom must be taken / Chip on the slave master shoulder / When revolution comes / Black skin white minds / Tribal dub / Dub in D minor / Medicine doctor / Colonial mentality
ARICD 095 / Mar '94 / Ariwa Sounds

☐ BLACK LIBERATION DUB VOL.2 (Anti-Racist Dub Broadcast)
Anti-racist dub broadcast / Dangerous escapades of dub / King Jimmy's dub / Basking in colonialism / Petty bourgeois dub / Pandora's box / Battle of Ciskei / Buthelezi trump card / Lion's domain / Rough rough dub / Legacy of Mussolini / Ethnic cleansing dub
ARICD 100 / Sep '94 / Ariwa Sounds

☐ BLACK LIBERATION DUB VOL.3 (Evolution Of Dub)
Harder than babylon / No man's land / Kunte 96 / Solar system / Kathmandu dub / Cultural explosion / Gringo dread / Cosmic ray / Village gossip / Atonement dub / Kiwi culture
ARICD 110 / Apr '96 / Ariwa Sounds

☐ BLACK LIBERATION VOL.4 (Under The Spell Of Dub)
ARICD 121 / 15 Sep '97 / Ariwa Sounds

☐ DUB ME CRAZY VOL.1
ARICD 001 / Mar '97 / Ariwa Sounds

☐ DUB ME CRAZY VOL.12 (Dub Maniacs On The Rampage)
ARICD 075 / Oct '92 / Ariwa Sounds

☐ DUB ME CRAZY VOL.3 (The African Connection)
ARICD 005 / Aug '94 / Ariwa Sounds

☐ DUB ME CRAZY VOL.9 (Science & The Witchdoctor)
Anansi skank / Blue ball fire / Cry of thee old higue / Coming of the obeahe man / Witch's brew / Mistaken identity / Natural fact / Jumbie umbrella / Bacoo in the bottle / Bohra seed / Holokoko dub
ARICD 045 / May '89 / Ariwa Sounds

☐ DUB YOU CRAZY WITH LOVE
ARICD 124 / Feb '97 / Ariwa Sounds

☐ FEAST OF YELLOW DUB, A
Dose of diseases / Some hot, hot girls / Bit of ready made sauce / Some hot, hot boys / Some wild western peppers / One nasty ex-President / Some army slop / One pretty girl / Virgin / Some memories
RAS 3069CD / Nov '97 / Ras

☐ IN A RUB A DUB STYLE
Dubbing Jah / Bad man dubbing / Lighting dub / Cruel dub / Classic dub / True skank / Wicked skank / Skanking girl / Wolf skank / Skanking princess
CDBM 105 / Jun '95 / Blue Moon

☐ IT'S A MAD MAD MAD MAD PROFESSOR
CRMCD 1 / Jun '95 / CRS
ARICD 105 / Jun '96 / Ariwa Sounds

☐ JAH SHAKA MEETS MAD PROFESSOR AT ARIWA SOUNDS (Mad Professor & Jah Shaka)
ARICD 020 / Sep '94 / Ariwa Sounds

☐ LOST SCROLLS OF MOSES, THE
African Hebrew chant / African Hebrew dub / Land of Canaan / Moses in the bullrushes / Jordan crossing / Fire on Mount Sinai / Dub on Mount Sinai / Amorites dub / Dead Sea scrolls / Subversive literature / Bogle soca / Los Lomas
ARICD 087 / Jul '93 / Ariwa Sounds

☐ MAD PROFESSOR CAPTURES PATO BANTON (Mad Professor & Pato Banton)
Mad professor captures pato banton / Gwarn (go on) / Nuff kind of dread / King step / Give me oil / My opinion
ARICD 023 / Oct '94 / Ariwa Sounds

☐ PSYCHEDELIC DUB
Cool running mandela / Go deh nelson, go deh / In king david's style / Don't drink the piss / 1990 arwia style / Psychedelic dub / Bammie' riff / Raging storm / Open troppen / Man from senegal
ARICD 057 / Sep '90 / Ariwa Sounds

☐ RAS PORTRAITS
Dub science / Beyond the realms dub / Zion / Holokoko dub / Sistren Version / Buccaneer's cove / Rasta chase / Hi-jacked to Jamaica / Cool runnings Mandela / Fire on Mt.Sinai / Black skin white minds / Anti rascist broadcast / Harder than Babylon
RAS 3329 / Jul '97 / Ras

☐ TRUE BORN AFRICAN DUB
ARICD 073 / May '92 / Ariwa Sounds

☐ WHO KNOWS THE SECRET OF THE MASTER TAPE
ARICD 021 / Aug '94 / Ariwa Sounds

Mad Pudding

☐ DIRT AND STONE
Indian reels / Dirt and stone / Toast part 1 / Toast part 2 / Dewy dells of Yarrow / Crazy Creek set / Patchwork / Air / Dance of the hungry panda / Hey to the pipes / Ploughman's son / Heather Bonn / Service / Spanish lady / Brandon Town / Big John McNeil
IRCD 040 / Aug '96 / Iona

Mad River

☐ MAD RIVER
Merciful monks / High all the time / Amphetamine gazelle / Eastern light / Wind chimes / War goes on / Julian Hush
EDCD 140 / Mar '85 / Edsel

☐ PARADISE BAR AND GRILL
Harfy magnum / Paradise bar and grill / Love's not the way to treat a friend / Leave me stay / Copper plates / Equinoxe / They bought sadness / Revolution's in my pockets / Academy cemetry / Cherokee queen
EDCD 188 / May '86 / Edsel

Mad Sin

☐ AMPHIGORY
Amphigory / Eat yourself (survivor type) / Body snatchers / Alien bug / Buried alive / Vampire slut / 1999 / Paranoid brain / Your death is my delight / Tornado / You better run / Rockin' bones
FCD 3019 / Oct '96 / Fury

Madam Crain

☐ PUNK BABY FROM MARS (Madam Crain & Warhorn)
X 09827 / 6 Jul '98 / Casual Tonalities

Madame Christine

☐ REAL EXPERIENCE
SUNCD 006 / May '93 / Sunvibe

Madball

☐ BALL OF DESTRUCTION
CMCD 77130 / May '96 / Century Media

☐ DEMONSTRATING MY STYLE
RR 88752 / Jun '96 / Roadrunner

☐ LOOK MY WAY
Look my way / Moment of truth / Cut off / Temptation or restraint / Waste of time / False threats / Pushin' me / Walk away / Our family / Lesson of life / All I can take / Been there done that
RR 88072 / 15 Jun '98 / Roadrunner

☐ SET IT OFF
Set it off / Lockdown / New York City / Never had it / It's time / CTYC / Across your face / Down by law / Spit on your grave / Face to face / Smell the bacon / Get out / World is mine / Friend or foe
RR 89912 / Aug '94 / Roadrunner

Madden & Harris

☐ FOOL'S PARADISE
VSC 001 / 24 Nov '97 / Vicious Sloth

Madden, Glyn

☐ CHRISTMAS WISHES
Winter wonderland / Silver bells / Fist Noel / I'm walking in the air / In the bleak midwinter / God rest ye merry gentlemen / Rudolph the red nosed reindeer / I saw Mommy kissing Santa Claus / Ave Maria / O little town of Bethlehem / Silent night / Frosty the snowman / Once in Royal David's City / Christmas tree with its candles gleaming / Dance of the snowmen / Sleigh ride / Have yourself a merry little Christmas / Christmas song / Ding dong merrily on high / White Christmas / O come all ye faithful (Adeste fidelis) / Jingle bells / Here we come a-wassailing / I heard the bells on Christmas day / O little one sweet / We wish you a merry Christmas
CDGRS 1221 / '91 / Grosvenor

☐ TICO TICO
Take the 'a' train / Till I loved you (love theme from goya - pops orch / All that my heart can hold / Tristeza / Water fountain / Tico tico / Somewhere out there / On my own / Ai no corrida / I won't last a day without you / Swing street / La chanson d'orphee / Go (before you break in my heart) / Girl from ipanema / Up where we belong / Root beer rag / Over the rainbow / Green dolphin street
CDGRS 1234 / Feb '93 / Grosvenor

☐ ZWEI NACHTS IN EINER GROSSEN STADT
Thunderbirds (dramatic tv theme) / At the dance (theatre organ) / Till I loved you (love theme from goya - pops orch / Hot points (accordion novelty) / Standchen serenade (brass band cornet solo) / Hello dolly (honky tonk jazz band) / Water fountain / Nessun dorma (none shall sleep tonight-orchestral) / Zing went the strings of my heart (come dancing) / Hora staccato (novelty orchestra) / Splanky (big band) / Rondo alla turca (mozart) (mixed style) / Peanut polka (novelty theatre organ) / Prisoners chorus (nabucco-james last style) / Two for the road (pops orchestra) / Light cavalry (cavalerie legere-orchestral) / Zwei nachts in einer grossen stadt (glen miller st / Entry of the gladiators (march of triumph-military
CDGRS 1250 / Feb '93 / Grosvenor

Madden, Joanie

☐ SONG OF THE IRISH WHISTLE
HS 11060 / Mar '96 / Hearts Of Space

☐ WHISTLE ON THE WIND
GL 1142CD / Aug '94 / Green Linnet

Madder Rose

☐ TRAGIC MAGIC
7567830092 / Jun '97 / Atlantic

Madding Crowd

☐ I HATE FLIES
FETMC 1 / Mar '95 / Fuller's Earth

Maddox Brothers

☐ AMERICA'S MOST COLOURFUL HILLBILLY BAND VOL.1 (Maddox Brothers & Rose Maddox)
ARHCD 391 / Apr '95 / Arhoolie

☐ AMERICA'S MOST COLOURFUL HILLBILLY BAND VOL.2 (Maddox Brothers & Rose Maddox)
ARHCD 437 / Sep '95 / Arhoolie

☐ MOST COLOURFUL HILLBILLY BAND IN AMERICA, THE (4CD Set) (Maddox Brothers & Rose Maddox)
I'll make sweet love to you / Take these shackles from my heart / Cocquito of Laredo / Wedding blues / Empty mansions / Little Willie Waltz / Hiccough song / Green grow the lilacs / No help wanted / Hearts and flowers / Will there be any stars in my crown / Just over the stars / I'm a little red caboose (on the choo choo train of love) / These wasted years / Nightingale song / I'd rather die young (than grow old without you) / Kiss me quick and go / On Mexico's beautiful shores / I won't stand in your way / Wooin' we will go / Life that you've led / Kiss me like crazy / Just one more time / Second choice / Beautiful bouquet / Kiss from your lips / My child has a billy goat / Time is spring / Breathless love / Hasty baby / There's no right way to do me wrong / Birthday card song / You won't believe this / Forever yours / I could never stop loving you / Fountain of youth / Marry me again / Poor little heartbroken Rose / I wonder if I can lose the blues this way / Waltz of the pines / I've got four big brothers (to look after me) / I gotta get my baby / Rusty old halo / No more time / Wild wild young men / Hoot owl melody / There was a teardrop / I'm gonna be loved tonight / Words are so easy to say / Wild wind / Hummingbird / When the sun goes down / I'll find her / It's a dark dark place / Away this side of heaven / I wish you would / Let this be the last time / Old black choo choo / Tall man / Hey little dreamboat / Burrito Joe / False hearted / By the sweat of my brow / Ugly and slouchy / Paul Bunyan love / Death of rock 'n' roll / Your sweet mean heart / I'll go steppin' too / Did you ever come home / Looky there over there / Let those brown eyes smile at me / Take a gamble on me / Tomorrow land / Old man blues / 1234 Anyplace Road (Somewhere USA) / Love is strange / Short life and its troubles / My life with you / Dig a hole / Let me love you / Donkey song / Stop whistlin' wolf / Way with God is so beautiful / Keep on talking (tell him everything) / Precious memories / I saw the light / Someone to care / Dear Lord take my hand / He leadeth me / Keep on talking (tell him everything) / How can you refuse him now / No one knows (what faith can do) / Take my hand precious Lord / Swing low sweet chariot / Bringing in the sheaves
BCD 15850 / Mar '98 / Bear Family

☐ ON THE AIR: THE 1940'S (Maddox Brothers & Rose Maddox)
Cowboy has to yell / Let me ride my pony down the sunset trail / Once I had a darling Mother / Hold that critter down / I'm talking about you / I'm going to the hoedown / Small town Mama / Mama please stay home with me / If you ain't got the do-re-mi / I might have known / I'll reap my harvest in Heaven / Don't hang around me anymore / Sinner's prayer is never answered / Girl I love don't pay me no mind / Write me sweetheart / I'm a handy man to have around / I've rambled around / Gathering flowers for the master's bouquet / I couldn't believe it was true / KTRB theme/Regal Pale Beer ad / Goldrush is over / Almost / Too old to cut the mustard / Breathless love / Walkin' in my sleep / Introduction by Fred and Rose / Fried potatoes / Nobody's love is like mine / Meanest man in town / Freight train boogie / KTRB theme out
ARHCD 447 / Nov '96 / Arhoolie

Maddox, Rose

☐ $35 & A DREAM
ARHCD 428 / Apr '95 / Arhoolie

☐ ONE ROSE, THE (4CD Set)
What makes me hang around / Bill Cline / Gambler's love / Lies and alibis / Custer's last stand / I lost today / Live and let live / My little baby / Philadelphia lawyer / Tramp on the street / Gathering flowers for the master's bouquet / I'm happy every day I live / Sally let your bangs hang down / Whoa sailor / On the banks of the old Ponchartrain / Honky tonkin' / At the first fall of snow / Why don't you haul off and love me / Chocolate ice cream cone / Move it on over / Shining silver, gleaming gold / Down down down / Please help me, I'm falling / Johnny's last kiss / Philadelphia lawyer / Johnny's last kiss / Wait a little longer, please Jesus / Empty mansions / Great speckled bird / This world is not my home / That glory bound train / Drifting too far from the shore / When I take my vacation in heaven / How beautiful heaven must be / I'll reap my harvest in heaven / Smoke, fire and brimstone / Will the circle be unbroken / Kneel at the cross / There's better times a comin' / I want to live again / Kissing my pillow / Dime a dozen / Loose talk / Mental cruelty / Conscience I'm guilty / Read my letter once again / Tall men / Early in the morning / There ain't no love / What am I living for / Stop the world (and let me off) / Jim Dandy / North to Alaska / Lonely Street / Gotta travel on / Just one more time / Don't tell me your troubles / There ain't no love / Your kind of lovin' won't do / Take me back again / Fool me again / Long journey home / From a beggar to a Queen / Let's pretend we're strangers / If you see my baby / Let those brown eyes smile at me / When the sun goes down / Alone with you / My life has been a pleasure / Curly Joe / Here we go again / Long black limousine / White lightning / Uncle Pen / Footprints in the snow / Blue moon of Kentucky / My rose of old Kentucky / Molly and Tenbrooks / Rollin' in my sweet baby's arms / Cotton fields / Each season changes you / Old crossroad is waitin' / I'll meet you in church Sunday morning / Down down down / Lonely teardrops / Sing a little song of heartache / Tie a ribbon in the apple tree / George Carter / Let me kiss you for old times / I don't hear you / Down to the river / Somebody told somebody / Sweethearts in heaven / We're the talk of the town / Back street affair / No fool like an old fool / I won't come in while he's there / Silver threads and golden needles / Bluebird let me tag along / That's a mighty long way to fall / Stand up fool / Silver threads and golden needles / Great pretender / Tia Lisa Lynn / Lonely one / Big Ball in Cowtown / Wabash cannonball / I'll always be loving you / Mad at the world / Big big day tomorrow / Cotton wood road / Down to the river (live)
BCD 15743 / Oct '93 / Bear Family

☐ ROSE OF THE WEST COUNTRY
ARHCD 314 / Apr '95 / Arhoolie

Maderna, Bruno

☐ OBOE CONCERTOS
BVHAASTCD 9302 / Oct '94 / Bvhaast

Madness

☐ 7
Cardiac arrest / Shut up / Sign of the times / Missing you / Mrs. Hutchinson / Tomorrows dream / Grey day / Pac-a-mac / Promises, promises / Benny bullfrog / When dawn arrives / Opium eaters / Day on the town
CDOVD 135 / Nov '89 / Virgin

☐ ABSOLUTELY
Baggy trousers / Embarrassment / ERNIE / Close escape / Not home today / On the beat Pete / Solid gone / Take it or leave it / Shadow of fear / Disappear / Overdone / In the rain / You said / Return of the Los Palmas 7
CDOVD 134 / Nov '89 / Virgin

☐ BUSINESS, THE (The Definitive Singles Collection/3CD Set)
Prince / Madness / One step beyond / Mistakes / Nutty theme / My girl / Stepping into line / In the rain / Night boat to Cairo / Deceives the eye / Young and the old / Don't quote me on that / Baggy trousers / Business / Embarrassment / Crying shame / Return of the Los Palmas 7 / That's the way you do it (aka odd jobman) / My girl (demo version) / Swan lake / Grey day / Memories / Shut up / Town wih no name / Never ask twice (aka airplane) / It must be love / Shadow on the house / Cardiac arrest / In the city / House of fun / Don't look back / Driving in my car / Terry Wogan jingle / Animal farm / Riding on my bike / Walking with Mr. Wheeze / Our house (stretch mix) / Tomorrow's just another day / Madness / Wings of a dove / Behind the eight ball / One's second thoughtlessness / Sun and the rain / Fireball XL5 / Visit to Dracstein castle / Michael Caine / If you think there's something / One better day / Guns / Victoria gardens / Sarah / Yesterday's men / All I knew / It must be love (live) / Uncle Sam / David Hamilton jingle / Inanity over Christmas / Please don't go / Sweetest girl / Jennie / Tears you can't hide / Call me / Waiting for the ghost train / One step beyond (Italian version) / Maybe in another life / Seven year scratch / Release me / Carols on 45 / National anthem
MADBOX 1 / Dec '93 / Virgin

☐ COMPLETE MADNESS
Embarrassment / Shut up / My girl / Baggy trousers / It must be love / Prince / Bed and breakfast man / Night boat to Cairo / House of fun / One step beyond / Cardiac arrest / Grey day / Take it or leave it / In the city / Madness / Return of the Los Palmas 7
HITCD 1 / Jul '86 / Virgin

☐ DIVINE MADNESS
Prince / One step beyond / My girl / Night boat to Cairo / Baggy trousers / Embarrassment / Return of the Los Palmas 7 / Grey day / Shut up / It must be love / Cardiac arrest / House of fun / Driving in my car / Our house / Tomorrow's just another day / Wings of a dove / Sun and the rain / Michael Caine / One better day / Yesterday's men / Uncle Sam / Waiting for the ghost train
CDV 2692 / Feb '92 / Virgin

☐ HEAVY HEAVY HITS
Grey day / Sweetest girl / Michael Caine / Embarrassment / Night boat to Cairo / House of fun / Yesterday's men / It must be love / Driving in my car / (Waiting for the) ghost train / Uncle Sam / Shut up / Cardiac arrest / Our house / My girl / Sun and the rain / Baggy trousers / Wings of a dove / Tomorrow's just another day / One better day / Return of the Los Palmas 7 / Prince / One step beyond
CDV 2862 / 1 Jun '98 / Virgin

☐ IT'S MADNESS
House of fun / Don't look back / Wings of a dove / Young and the old / My girl / Stepping into line / Baggy trousers / Business / Embarrassment / One's second thoughtlessness / Grey day / Memories / It must be love / Deceives the eye / Driving in my car / Animal farm
CDVIP 105 / Mar '94 / Virgin VIP

☐ IT'S MADNESS TOO
Prince / Madness / One step beyond / Mistakes / Return of the Los Palmas 7 / Night boat to Cairo / Shut up / Town with no name / Cardiac arrest / In the city / Our house / Walking with Mr. Wheeze / Tomorrow's just another day / Victoria Gardens / Sun and the rain / Michael Caine
CDVIP 117 / Jun '94 / Virgin

☐ KEEP MOVING
Keep moving / Michael Caine / Turning blue / One better day / March of the gherkins / Waltz into mischief / Brand new beat / Victoria gardens / Samantha / Time for tea / Prospects / Give me a reason
CDOVD 191 / Nov '89 / Virgin

☐ MAD NOT MAD
I'll compete / Yesterday's men / Uncle Sam / White heat / Mad not mad / Sweetest girl / Burning the boats / Tears you can't hide / Time / Coldest day
JZCD 1 / Jul '87 / Zarjazz

☐ MADNESS, THE
Nail down the days / What's that / I pronounce you / Oh / In wonder / Song in red / Nightmare nightmare / Thunder and lightning / Beat the bride / Gabriel's horn / Eleventh hour / Be good boy / Flashings / 4BF
CDV 2507 / Aug '91 / Virgin

☐ MADSTOCK
One step beyond / Prince / Embarrassment / My girl / Sun and the rain / Grey day / It must be love / Shut up / Driving in my car / Bed and breakfast man / Close escape / Wings of a dove / Our house / Night boat to Cairo / Madness / House of fun / Baggy trousers / Harder they come
8283672 / Nov '92 / Go Discs

☐ ONE STEP BEYOND
One step beyond / My girl / Night boat to Cairo / Believe me / Land of hope and glory / Prince / Tarzan's nuts / In the middle of the night / Bed and breakfast man / Razor blade alley / Swan lake / Rockin' in AB / Mummy's boy / Chipmunks are go
CDOVD 133 / Apr '90 / Virgin

☐ ONE STEP BEYOND/ABSOLUTELY/ RISE AND FALL (3CD Set)
One step beyond / My girl / Night boat to cairo / Believe me / Land of hope and glory / Prince / Tarzan's nuts / In the middle of the night / Bed and breakfast man / Razor blade alley / Swan lake / Rockin' in a flat / Mummy's boy / Madness (surprise track - not listed on sleeve) / Chipmunks are go / Rise and fall / Tomorrow's just another day / Blue skinned beast / Primrose hill / Mr. speaker gets the word / Sunday morning / Our house / Tiptoes / New delhi / That face / Calling cards / Are you coming (with me) / Madness (it's all in the mind) / Baggy trousers / embarrassment / E.r.n.i.e. / Close escape / Not home today / On the beat pete / Solid gone / Take it or leave it / Shadow of fear / Disappear / Overdone / In the rain / You said / Return of the los palmas
TPAK 8 / Oct '90 / Virgin

☐ RISE AND FALL
Rise and fall / Tomorrow's just another day / Blue skinned beast / Primrose hill / Mr. Speaker gets the word / Sunday morning / Our house / Tiptoes / New Delhi / That face / Calling cards / Are you coming (with me) / Madness
CDOVD 190 / Nov '89 / Virgin

☐ TRIBUTE TO MADNESS, A (Various Artists)
My girl: *Skanker* / Michael Caine: *Gordon* / Prince: *Crocked Beat* / Nightboat to Cairo: *Tick tocks* / House of fun: *Skalatones* / One: *Ducksoup* / Bed and breakfast man: *Stiff Breeze* / Disappear: *Agent Bulldog* / Our house: *Poblers United* / Madness: *Dr. Ring Ding* / In the rain: *Skanksters*
TR 016CD / 6 Apr '98 / Tribute

☐ UTTER MADNESS
Our house / Driving in my car / Michael Caine / Wings of a dove / Yesterday's men / Tomorrow's just another day / I'll compete / Waiting for the ghost train / Uncle Sam / Sun and the rain / Sweetest girl / One better day / Victoria gardens
JZCD 2 / Nov '86 / Zarjazz

Madonna

☐ BEDTIME STORIES
Survival / Secret / I'd rather be your lover / Don't stop / Inside of me / Human nature / Forbidden love / Love tried to welcome me / Sanctuary / Bedtime story / Take a bow
9362457672 / Oct '94 / Maverick

☐ BIOGRAPHY SERIES
10018 / 3 Nov '97 / Metro Independent

☐ EROTICA
Erotica / Fever / Bye bye baby / Deeper and deeper / Where life begins / Bad girl / Waiting / Thief of hearts / Words / Rain / Why's it so hard / In this life / Did you do it / Secret garden
9362450312 / Oct '92 / Sire

☐ FIRST ALBUM, THE
Lucky star / Borderline / Burning up / I know it / Holiday / Think of me / Physical attraction / Everybody
9238672 / Oct '84 / Sire

☐ GIVE IT TO ME
Give it to me / Shake / Get down / Time to dance / Wild dancing / Let's go dancing / Cosmic / On the street
RM 1549 / Jun '97 / BR Music

☐ I'M BREATHLESS
He's a man / Sooner or later / Hanky panky / I'm going bananas / Cry baby / Something to remember / Back in business / More / What can you lose / Now I'm following you / Vogue
7599262092 / May '90 / Sire

☐ IMMACULATE COLLECTION (Best Of Madonna)
Holiday / Lucky star / Borderline / Like a virgin / Material girl / Crazy for you / Into the groove / Live to tell / Papa don't preach / Open your heart / La Isla Bonita / Like a prayer / Express yourself / Cherish / Vogue / Justify my love / Rescue me
7599264402 / Nov '90 / Sire

☐ INTERVIEW COMPACT DISC: MADONNA
CBAK 4019 / Nov '89 / Baktabak

☐ INTERVIEW DISC
TELL 01 / Dec '96 / Network

☐ INTERVIEW DISC - LIVE TO TELL
DIST 006 / Jun '96 / Disturbed

☐ LIFE AND TIMES OF MADONNA, THE (2CD Set)
OTR 1100035 / Jun '97 / Metro Independent

☐ LIKE A PRAYER
Like a prayer / Love song / Promise to try / Dear Jessie / Keep it together / Act of contrition / Express yourself / Till death do us part / Cherish / Oh Father / Spanish eyes
K 925844 2 / Mar '94 / Sire

☐ MATERIAL GIRL (Royal Philharmonic Orchestra Plays The Music Of Madonna) (Royal Philharmonic Orchestra)
True blue / La isla bonita / Papa don't preach / Like a prayer / Crazy for you / This used to be my playground / Borderline / Into the groove / Like a virgin / Holiday / Material girl / Who's that girl
MCCD 353 / 20 Jul '98 / Music Club

☐ RAY OF LIGHT
Drowned world (substitute for love) / Swim / Ray of light / Candy perfume girl / Skin / Nothing really matters / Sky fits heaven / Shanti/Ashtangi / Frozen / Power of goodbye / To have and not to hold / Little star / Mer girl
9362468472 / 2 Mar '98 / Maverick

☐ SALUTE TO MADONNA (Various Artists)
Like a virgin / Into the groove / Angel / Justify my love / Express yourself / Holiday / Human nature / Borderline / Papa don't preach / Dress you up / Deeper and deeper / Like a prayer / Vogue / La isla bonita / Bedtime story / True blue
306782 / May '97 / Hallmark

☐ SOMETHING TO REMEMBER
I want you: *Madonna & Massive Attack* / I'll remember / Take a bow / You'll see / Crazy for you / This used to be my playground / Live to tell / Love don't live here anymore / Something to remember / Forbidden love / One more chance / Rain / Oh father / I want you (orchestral): *Madonna & Massive Attack*
9362461002 / Nov '95 / Maverick

☐ TRUE BLUE
Papa don't preach / Open your heart / Love makes the world go round / Jimmy Jimmy / La Isla Bonita / True blue / Where's the party / Live to tell / White heat
K 9254422 / Mar '94 / Sire

☐ WILD DANCING (Madonna & Otto Van Wernherr)
DS 2301 / May '96 / BR Music

☐ WOW (Madonna & Otto Van Wernherr)
DS 2302 / May '96 / BR Music

☐ YOU CAN DANCE
Spotlight / Holiday / Everybody / Physical attraction / Over and over / Into the groove / Where's the party / Holiday (dub) / Into the groove (dub) / Over and over (dub)
9255352 / Feb '95 / Sire

Madou, Cora

☐ SUCCES ET RARETES 1926-1935
701612 / Nov '96 / Chansophone

Madre

☐ MESMERISMO
SR 002CD / 23 Feb '98 / Resurrection

Madsen, Katrine

☐ DREAM DANCING
MECCACD 2044 / Jan '98 / Music Mecca

☐ I'M OLD FASHIONED (Madsen, Katrine Swing Quintet)
MECCACD 1095 / May '97 / Music Mecca

Madura

☐ MUSIQUE SAVANTE (Music From Indonesia)
C 560083 / Dec '95 / Ocora

Mady, Kasse

☐ FODE
Fode / Malo magnl / Laban djoro / Siran mogoye / Djina / Den te san
STCD 1025 / Mar '89 / Stern's

Maeror Tri

☐ EMOTIONAL ENGRAMM
ILIGHT 005CD / 3 Nov '97 / Iris Light

Maerz, Marion

☐ ER IST WIEDER DA
Er ist wieder da / Terry / Liebe auf den ersten Blick / Andy / Er und ich / Mister boyfriend / Blau, blau, blau / Wie soll es weitergehn / Versprich mir nicht zuviel / Wenn das kein zufall ist / Da gehoren zwei dazu / Ich hab einen guten freund gehabt / Wer die liebe sucht / So fing es an / Auf, auf und davon / Weit, weit, weit / Klopf auf holz / Bis ans ende aller tage / Wenn du da bist / Sugar, sugar / Nur du / Falt ein stern zur welt / Mach nicht tur zu / Nichts als sorgen macht er mir / Hinter flas / Wir halten zusammen / Du bist genau wie die andern / Nur beim abschied nicht weinen / Du wirst schon seh'n was du davon hast / Round and round
BCD 15964 / Jul '96 / Bear Family

Maes, Christian

☐ TILTED HOUSE (Maes, Christian & Sandi Miller)
KM 43CD / Feb '94 / Keltia Musique

Mafia & Fluxy

☐ REVIVAL HITS VOL.3
MFCD 009 / Mar '97 / Mafia/Fluxy

Magadini, Pete

☐ BONES BLUES (Magadini, Pete Quartet)
Old devil moon / Freddie freeloader / Poor butterfly / Solar / I remember Clifford / What a time we had / Bones blues / Freddie freeloader no. 2
SKCD 24004 / Jun '93 / Sackville

☐ NIGHT DREAMS (Magadini, Pete Quintet)
Friendly imposition / Exchanging love / Sunny side / Giant steps / Carolyn / Shutterbug / In a sentimental mood / Stablemates
CDSJP 317 / Aug '91 / Timeless Jazz

Magazine

☐ MAGIC, MURDER AND THE WEATHER
About the weather / So lucky / Honeymoon killers / Vigilance / Come alive / Great man's secrets / This poison / Naked eye / Suburban Rhonda / Garden
CDV 2200 / '88 / Virgin

☐ PLAY
Give me everything / Song from under the floorboards / Permafrost / Light pours out of me / Model worker / Parade / Thank you (falettinme be mice elf agin) / Because you're frightened / Twenty years ago / Definitive gaze
CDV 2184 / '88 / Virgin

☐ RAYS AND HAIL 1978-1981 (The Best Of Magazine)
Shot by both sides / Definitive gaze / Motorcade / Light pours out of me / Feed the enemy / Rhythm of cruelty / Back to nature / Permafrost / Because you're frightened / You never knew me / Song from under the floorboards / I want to burn again / About the weather / Parade
CDVM 9020 / Jul '94 / Virgin

☐ REAL LIFE
Definitive gaze / My tulpa / Shot by both sides / Recoil / Burst / Motorcade / Great beautician in the sky / Light pours out of me / Parade
CDV 2100 / '88 / Virgin

☐ SCREE (Rarities 1976-1981)
My mind ain't so open / Touch and go / Goldfinger / Give me everything / I love you big dummy / Rhythm of cruelty / TV baby / Book / Light pours out of me / Feed the enemy / Twenty years ago / Shot by both sides / In the dark / Operative
CDOVD 312 / Jul '90 / Virgin

☐ SECONDHAND DAYLIGHT
Feed the enemy / Rhythm of cruelty / Cut out shapes / Talk to the body / I wanted your heart / Thin air / Back to nature / Believe that I understand / Permafrost
CDV 2121 / '88 / Virgin

Magellan

☐ IMPENDING ASCENSION
Estadium Nacional / Waterfront weirdos / Songsmith / Virtual reality / No time for words / Storms and mutiny / Under the wire
RR 90572 / Jun '93 / Roadrunner

☐ TEST OF WILLS
RR 88172 / Jun '97 / Roadrunner

Maggies

☐ HOMESICK
CMRD 01 / 30 Mar '98 / Chickenman

Magi

☐ WIN OR LOSE
FLASH 51 / Nov '97 / Flash

Magic

☐ ENCLOSED
FLASH 44 / Jul '97 / Flash

Magic Affair

☐ OMEN (The Story Continues)
Communication / Omen III / In the middle of the night / Homicidal / Fire / Water of sin / Under the sea / Carry on / Make your mind up / Give me all your love / Wonderland / Thin line
CDEMC 3686 / Sep '97 / EMI

Magic Carpet

☐ MAGIC CARPET
MC 1001CD / Oct '96 / Magic Carpet

☐ ONCE MOOR
MC 1004CD / Dec '96 / Magic Carpet

Magic Dick

☐ BLUESTIME (Magic Dick & Jay Geils)
NETCD 51 / '95 / Network

☐ LITTLE CAR BLUES (Magic Dick & Jay Geils)
ROUCD 3141 / Aug '96 / Rounder

Magic Dirt

☐ FRIENDS IN DANGER
HUK 004CD / 29 Jun '98 / Headhunter

☐ MAGIC DIRT
38203422 / 6 Oct '97 / Subway

☐ SPARROW
ANDA 211CD / 22 Sep '97 / Au-Go-Go

☐ YOUNG AND FULL OF THE DEVIL
ANDA 237CD / 15 Jun '98 / Au-Go-Go

Magic Malik

☐ MAGIC MALIK
176542 / 24 Feb '98 / Musidisc

Magic Mixture

☐ THIS IS MAGIC MIXTURE
FLASH 61 / 1 Jun '98 / Flash

Magic Mushroom Band

☐ FRESHLY PICKED
EYECD 7 / Feb '93 / Magick Eye

☐ SPACED COLLECTION, THE
CLP 9949 / Apr '97 / Cleopatra

☐ SPACED OUT
EYECDLP 6 / Aug '94 / Magick Eye

Magic Sam

☐ BLACK MAGIC (Magic Sam Blues Band)
DD 620 / Mar '95 / Delmark

☐ GIVE ME TIME
DD 654 / Sep '91 / Delmark

☐ MAGIC BLUES GENIUS
CWNCD 2016 / Jul '96 / Javelin

☐ MAGIC SAM LEGACY, THE
I feel so good / Lookin' good / Walkin' by myself / Hoochie coochie man / That ain't it / That's all I need / What have I done wrong / I just want a little bit / Everything's gonna be alright / Keep on doin' what you're doin' / Blues for Odie Payne / Easy baby / Keep on lovin' me baby
DE 651 / Jul '97 / Delmark

☐ MAGIC TOUCH
BT 1085CD / May '93 / Black Top

☐ WEST SIDE SOUL (Charly Blues Masterworks Vol.29)
All your love / Love me with a feeling / Everything gonna be alright / Look watcha done / All night long / All my whole life / Easy baby / Twenty one days in jail / Love me this way / Magic rocker / Roll your moneymaker / Call me if you need me / Every night about this time / Blue light boogie / Out of bad luck / She belongs to me
CDBM 29 / Apr '92 / Charly

Magic Slim

☐ BLACK TORNADO (Magic Slim & The Teardrops)
Jealous man / Wake me up early / Still a fool / Black tornado / Playin' with my mind / I can't trust my woman / Magic boogie / You've got bad intentions / Crazy woman / Young man's blues / It's alright / Love like I wanna
BPCD 5046 / Jun '98 / Blind Pig

☐ CHICAGO BLUES SESSION (Magic Slim & The Teardrops)
WOLF 120870 / Jul '96 / Wolf

☐ GRAVEL ROAD (Magic Slim & The Teardrops)
Cold women with warm hearts / Gravel road / Hard to handle / Bad luck is fallin' / Pretty girls everywhere / Further on up the road / Mustang sally / Prisoner of love / Before you accuse me / Please don't waste my time / Slim's hideaway
BPCD 73690 / Nov '96 / Blind Pig

☐ HIGHWAY IS MY HOME
ECD 260122 / Dec '97 / Tramp

☐ MAGIC SLIM LIVE VOL.2
STCD 8040 / Aug '97 / Storyville

☐ RAW MAGIC (Magic Slim & The Teardrops)
ALCD 4728 / May '93 / Alligator

☐ SCUFFLIN' (Magic Slim & The Teardrops)
Think / Hole in the wall / Scufflin' / Down in Virginia / I'm not the same person / Just before you go / I'm gonna send you back to Georgia / Room 109 / I need lovin' / I'm gonna get you babe / Lookin' for a lover / Can't get no grindin'
BPCD 5036 / Nov '96 / Blind Pig

Magical Power Mako

☐ BLUE DOT
BELLE 95131 / Nov '97 / Belle Antique

☐ NO GOVERNMENT AFTER REVOLUTION
BELLE 97390 / Nov '97 / Belle Antique

Magical Strings

☐ BELL OFF THE LEDGE
Mummer's dance / Bell off the ledge / By the island knoll / Lullaby for a soul's journey / Lament for merlin / Kora reminisence / Rolling wave / Maid at the spinningwheel / Bonny kate-corofin reel / Song of love / Paddy's rambles / Longing for ireland / Everlasting peace
FF 70631CD / Apr '94 / Flying Fish

☐ CROSSING TO SKELLIG
FF 531CD / '92 / Flying Fish

☐ ISLANDS CALLING
Ferry to Islesboro / Malagasy greeting / Warm island / Holy Island / Jamaican port o' call / Twilight over cove / Winter into Spring / Bahamian Time / Moussa's Kora / Dance of the Valiha / Father Dollard's hornpipe / Farewell
935282 / Nov '96 / Earthbeat

Magick A

☐ LEMON SAAB AND A BOOK
APR 027CD / 19 Jan '98 / April

Magick Brothers

☐ LIVE AT THE WITCHWOOD
BP 107CD / Feb '97 / Blueprint

Magick Lantern Cycle

☐ CHIMAERA
DURTRO 015CD / Oct '96 / Durtro

Magid, Yakov

☐ LEKHAYM YIDN
MU 3101762 / Dec '93 / Multisonic

Maglio, Juan 'Pacho'

☐ EL LEGENDARIO 1927-1930
EBCD 86 / Apr '97 / El Bandoneon

Magma

☐ 1001 CENTIGRADES
REX 6 / Apr '91 / Rex

☐ ATTAHK
Last seven minutes / Spiritual / Rinde / Lirik necronomicus kant / Maahnt / Dondai / Nono
CPCD 8170 / Apr '96 / Charly

☐ INEDITS
REX 19 / Jun '97 / Seventh

☐ KOMPILA
REX 20 / Nov '97 / Seventh

☐ LES VOIX - CONCERT 1992
AKT 1 / Nov '92 / AKT

☐ MAGMA (2CD Set)
REX 4/5 / Mar '93 / Seventh

☐ MAGMA LIVE
Kohntark / Kobah / Lihns / Khat / Mekanik zain
CPCD 8171 / Jun '96 / Charly

☐ MEKANIK KOMMANDOH
AKT 10 / Nov '97 / AKT

☐ MYTHS AND LEGENDS 1969-1972
REX 14 / Mar '93 / Seventh

☐ OPERA DE RHEIMS 1976 (3CD Set)
AKT 9 / Jan '97 / AKT

☐ RETROSPEKTIW VOL.3
REX 15 / Mar '93 / Seventh

☐ SIMPLES
REX 11 / Aug '98 / Seventh

☐ UDU WUDU
Udu wudu / Weidorje / Troller tanz / Soleil d'ork / Zombies / De futura
CPCD 8169 / Apr '96 / Charly

Magna Carta

☐ IN CONCERT
HTDCD 69 / Dec '96 / HTD

☐ MAGNA CARTA
Times of change / Daughter daughter / Old John Parker / I am no more / Ballad of Francis Alabadeleio / Spinning wheels of time / Romeo Jack / Mid Winter / Shades of grey / Emily thru the window pane / Sea and sand / 7 o'clock hymn
HTDCD 68 / Dec '96 / HTD

Magnapop

☐ HOT BOXING
Slowly slowly / Texas / Lay it down / Here it comes / Piece of cake / Free mud / Leo / Crush / Ride / In the way / Idiot song / Get it right / Emergency / Skinburns
BIAS 251CD / Feb '94 / Play It Again Sam

☐ MAGNAPOP
Garden / Guess / Ear / Thirteen / Spill it / Chemical / Favourite writer / Complicated / Merry
BIAS 220CD / Jul '92 / Play It Again Sam

☐ RUBBING DOESN'T HELP
This family / I don't care / Open the door / Come on inside / Down on me / An apology / My best friend / Juicy fruit / Firebrand / Cherry bomb / Radio waves / Snake / Dead letter
BIAS 321CD / May '96 / Play It Again Sam

Magnarelli, Joe

☐ ALWAYS THERE (Magnarelli, Joe & Quintet/Sextet)
I'm old fashioned / Allison's welcome / I fall in love too easily / JJ Burnside blues / Always there / Rahsah / Waltz for Auntie Marie / Put on a happy face
CRISS 1141CD / 9 Mar '98 / Criss Cross

☐ WHY NOT
CRISS 1104 / Oct '95 / Criss Cross

Magnetic Fields

☐ CHARM OF THE HIGHWAY STRIP, THE
Lonely highway / Long vermont roads / Born on a train / I have the moon / Two characters in search of a country song / Crowd of drifters / Fear of trains / When the open road in closing in / Sunset city / Dustbowl
SETCD 021 / Aug '95 / Setanta

☐ GET LOST
With whom to dance / Smoke and mirrors / All the umbrellas in London / Why I cry / Save a secret for the moon / Don't look away / Love is lighter than air / Desperate things you made me do / You and me and the moon / Village in the morning / Famous / When you're old and lonely / Dreaming moon
SETCD 023
SETCD 023L / Mar '96 / Setanta

Magnetic North

☐ MILLER'S JIG, THE
YDW 005CD / Aug '97 / YDW

Magnificent VII

☐ LIVE AT THE HILTON
ARCD 19123 / Nov '94 / Arbors Jazz

☐ NEWPORT BEACH SESSION, THE
ARCD 19129 / 1 Jun '98 / Arbors Jazz

Magnog

☐ MAGNOG
KRANK 010CD / Mar '97 / Kranky

☐ MORE WEATHER (2CD Set)
KRANK 022 / 17 Nov '97 / Kranky

Magnolia Jazz Band

☐ CHRISTMAS WITH THE MAGNOLIA JAZZ BAND
BCD 420 / Jan '97 / GHB

☐ MAGNOLIA ANYTIME
BCD 220 / Aug '95 / GHB

Magnolias Milan

☐ 2K
BBPTC 68 / Jul '97 / Black Bean & Placenta Tape Club

Magnum

☐ ARCHIVE
Sea bird / Stormbringer / Slipping away / Captain America / Master of disguise / Without your love / Find the time / Everybody needs / Kingdom of madness / Lights burned out / Word / True fine wine
JETCD 1005 / Feb '98 / Jet

☐ CHASE THE DRAGON
Lights burned out / We all play the game / Teacher / Spirit / Soldier of the line / On the edge of the world / Walking the straight line / Sacred hour
WKFMXD 112 / Jun '88 / FM
CLACD 222 / '91 / Castle

☐ COLLECTION, THE
Great adventure / Back to earth / Spirit / All that is real / Soldier of the line / Battle / So far away / Word / Everybody needs / On the edge of the world / Invasion / Changes / All of my life / One night of passion / Teacher / Hold back your love / Kingdom of madness / Firebird / If I could live forever
CCSCD 272 / Oct '90 / Castle

☐ ELEVENTH HOUR, THE
Prize / Great disaster / Vicious companions / One night of passion / Word / Road to paradise / Breakdown / So far away / Hit and run / Young and precious souls
WKFMXD 111 / Jun '88 / FM
CLACD 223 / '91 / Castle

☐ FIREBIRD
Back to earth / Prize / So far away / Hit and run / Lights burned out / Soldier of the line / Changes / Foolish heart / All of my life / Great adventure / Invasion / Kingdom of madness / Universe / Firebird
5507372 / Jun '95 / Spectrum

☐ FOUNDATION
In the beginning-kama, the god of love and disire / Baby rock me / Universe / Kingdom of madness / All that is real / Bringer / Invasion / Lords of chaos / All come together / Soldier of the line / On the edge of the world / Spirit / Sacred hour / Walking the straight line / We all play the game / Teacher / Lights burned out / Prize / Breakdown / Great disaster / Vicious companions / So far away / Hit and run / One night of passion / Word / Young and precious souls / Road to paradise / Just like an arrow / Soldier of the line / Changes / Sacred hour / Great adventure / How far jerusalem / Spirit / Word / Prize / Kingdom of madness / How far jerusalem / Just like an arrow / On a storyteller's night / Before first light / Les morts dansant / Endless love / Two hearts / Steal your heart / All england's eyes / Last dance / Great adventures / Changes / Battle / If I could live forever / Reborn / So cold the night / Foolish heart / Staying alive / Firebird / All of my life
WKFMBXD 145 / Apr '90 / FM

☐ KEEPING THE NITE LITE BURNING
Prize / Heart broken busted / Foolish heart / Onely nights / Start talking love / Only a memory / Need a lot of love / Maybe tongiht / One night of passion / Wihtout your love / Shoot / Soldier of the line
JETCD 1006 / Feb '98 / Jet

☐ KINGDOM OF MADNESS
In the beginning / Baby rock me / Universe / Kingdom of madness / All that is real / Bringer / Invasion / Lords of chaos / All come together
CLACD 126 / '86 / Castle
WKFMXD 118 / Jan '89 / FM

☐ MAGNUM ARCHIVES
How far Jerusalem / Just like an arrow / Les morts dansant / Kingdom of madness / Prize / Soldier of the line / All of my life / Foolish heart / Start talking love / Word / Changes / On a story teller's night / Spirit / Lights burned out / Sacred hour
RMCD 217 / Nov '97 / Rialto

☐ MAGNUM VOL.2
Great adventure / Changes / Battle / If I could live forever / Reborn / So cold the night / Foolish heart / Stayin' alive / Firebird / All of my life
CLACD 125 / Mar '87 / Castle
WKFMXD 119 / Jan '89 / FM

☐ MIRADOR
Just like an arrow / Soldier of the line / Changes / Sacred hour / Great adventure / Lights burned out / In the beginning / How far Jerusalem / Spirit / Word / Prize / Kingdom of madness / If I could live forever / Lords of chaos / Storyteller's night
WKFMXD 106 / Nov '87 / FM

☐ ON A STORYTELLER'S NIGHT
How far Jerusalem / Just like an arrow / Before first light / On a storytellers night / Les morts dansant / Endless love / Two hearts / Steal your heart / All England's eyes / Last dance
WKFMXD 34 / May '85 / FM
JETCD 1007 / Feb '98 / Jet

☐ SLEEP WALKING
Stormy weather / Too much to ask / You're the one / Flood / Broken wheel / Just one more heartbreak / Every woman, every man / Only in america / Sleepwalking / Prayer for a stranger / Long ride
CDMFN 143 / Oct '92 / Music For Nations

☐ STRONGHOLD (2CD Set)
RRDCD 007 / Jun '97 / Receiver

☐ UNCORKED (The Best Of Magnum)
Just like an arrow / Kingdom of madness / Soldier of the line / All England eyes / Without your love / True fine love / Before first light / All of my life / Master of disguise / Endless love / How far Jerusalem / Foolish heart / Captain America / Steal your heart / Maybe tonight / Word / Changes / Last dance
JETCD 1008 / Feb '98 / Jet

☐ VINTAGE MAGNUM
How far Jerusalem / Two hearts / On a storyteller's night / All England's eyes / Just like an arrow / Les morts dansant / Last dance / Kingdom of madness / Foolish heart / Endless love / Prize / Soldier of the line / One night of passion / Lonely nights / Start talking love / Lights burned out
EMPRCD 596 / Oct '95 / Emporio

Magoo

☐ CLOSE CONTINENTAL DNA
NBX 036 / 20 Apr '98 / Noisebox

☐ SOATERAMIC SOUNDS OF MAGOO, THE
CHEM 012CD / Apr '97 / Chemikal Underground

Magpie Lane

☐ JACK-IN-THE-GREEN
May song / Mother Goose/The priest and his boots/ Hopkinson's favourite / In Sheffield Park / Thame fair / Flowers of Edinburgh / Rosebud in June / Jack-in-the-green/Jack's alive / Sheepstealer / Quickstep at the battle of Prague/Welch's polka / Northill May song/Cuckoo's nest / Seeds of love / Just as the tide was flowing / Banks of the Lea / Font Whatlings polka/Galloway girth / Two ravens / Mayer's song/ The Rochdale coconut dance/Three around three
BEJOCD 22 / Jul '98 / Beautiful Jo

☐ OXFORD RAMBLE, THE
Magpie Lane / As I walked through the meadows / First of May / Oxford city / Oxfordshire Damosel / John Barleycorn / Johnny so long/Eynsham poaching song / Old Molly Oxford / Boar's head carol / Oxford scholar / Great Tom is cast / Old Tom of Oxford/Bonny Christ church bells / Astley's ride / Oxford ramble / Trunkles / Near Woodstock town / Double lead through / Princess Royal / Husbandman and servingman / Banbury Bill/As I was going to Banbury / Adderbury medley / May Day carol
BEJOCD 3 / Jun '94 / Beautiful Jo

☐ SPEED THE PLOUGH
Carter's health / Regent's fete/Sir Roger de Coverley / Green bushes / Highwayman outwitted / Jockey to the fair / Bonny at Morn / Davy, Davy, knick-knack / Poor old horse / Kempshott hunt/Death of the fox / Swaggering Boney / Painful plough / Fool's jig / Mistress's health / Girl with the blue dress on/Swiss boy / Bushes and briars / Reading summer dance / Beverly maid and the tinker / Turtle dove/Bobbing Joe / Shepherd's song / Shooter's hornpipe / Bill Brown / Streets of Oxford / We're all jolly fellows that follow the plough / Speed the plough
BEJOCD 4 / Jun '94 / Beautiful Jo

Magraw, Dean

☐ SEVENTH ONE
RHRCD 116 / 6 Apr '98 / Red House

Maguire, Sean

☐ GREATEST HITS
Good day / Somewhere to love / You to me are everything / Take this time / Suddenly / Now I've found you / Don't pull your love / Lean on me / Love by candlelight / Sun shines from you / Count on me / Party zone / Stay / Devotion / Good day / You to me are everything
4951632 / 1 Jun '98 / EMI Gold

☐ SPIRIT
Good day / Treat me / You to me are everything / If you really care / I'll be good for you / If I surrender / Now I've found you / Your love / Don't pull you love / Sweet town / Where do broken hearts go / Make it right
CDPCSD 169 / Jun '96 / Parlophone

Magus

☐ TRAVELLER
95042 / 23 Feb '98 / IEV

Mah Damba

☐ NYARELA
710735 / 21 Aug '97 / Melodie

Mahaleo

☐ MAHALEO (Music From Madagascar)
PS 65157 / Oct '95 / PlayaSound

☐ TADIDIKO
088772 / 5 Jan '98 / Melodie

Maharaj, Pandit Kishan

☐ LIVE TABLA SOLO RECITAL, A
NRCD 0051 / Jul '96 / Navras

Maharishi Mahesh Yogi

☐ MAHARISHI MAHESH YOGI
Love / Untapped source of power that lies within
BGOCD 331 / Dec '96 / Beat Goes On

Maher, Tony

☐ IRISH TRANQUILITY
HCD 009 / Apr '95 / GTD

Mahieddine

☐ MAHIEDDINE
AAA 138 / Dec '96 / Club Du Disque Arabe

Mahlathini

☐ BEST OF MAHLATHINI & THE MAHOTELLA QUEENS, THE
Madlamini / Lilileza mililileza / I'm in love with a rastaman / Makhomabaji / Josefa / Marabi-yo / Thokozile / Won't you please sing along / Melodi yalla / Sengikala Ngiyabaleka / Reya dumedisa / Jive motella / Thutswane basadi / Music of our soul
CDN 1006 / 27 Apr '98 / Camden

☐ LION ROARS, THE (Mahlathini & The Mahotella Queens)
SHCD 43081 / Jun '91 / Shanachie

☐ STOKI STOKI (Mahlathini & The Mahotella Queens)
SH 64068 / Aug '96 / Shanachie

Mahogany Hall Stompers

☐ MAHOGANY HALL STOMPERS
SOSCD 1221 / Oct '92 / Stomp Off

Mahogany Rush

☐ CHILD OF THE NOVELTY
REP 4029 / Aug '91 / Repertoire

☐ DRAGONFLY (The Best Of Frank Marino & Mahogany Rush) (Marino, Frank & Mahogany Rush)
RE 21052 / Jul '96 / Razor & Tie

☐ LEGENDARY MAHOGANY RUSH, THE (Child Of The Novelty/Maxoom/ Strange Universe)
Look outside / Thru the milky way / Talking 'bout a feelin' / Child of the novelty / Makin' my wave / New rock and roll / Changing / Plastic man / Guit war / Chains of (s)pace / Maxoom / Buddy / Magic man / Funky woman / Madness / All in your mind / Blues / Boardwalk lady / Back on home / New beginning / Tales of the Spanish warrior / King who stole (The universe) / Satisfy your soul / Land of 1000 nights / Moonlight lady / Dancing lady / Once again / Tryin' anyway / Dear music / Strange universe
CDWKM2 149 / Jul '95 / Big Beat

☐ STRANGE UNIVERSE
REP 4028 / Aug '91 / Repertoire

Mahogany, Kevin

☐ DOUBLE RAINBOW
All blues / Confirmation / Save that time / Double rainbow / Our love remains / Dat dere / Little butterfly (Pannonica) / My dungeon shook / Since I fell for you / Three little words / Duke Ellington's sound of love / No one knows what love holds in store (two degrees east, thr / Bring it on home
ENJ 70972 / Jul '93 / Enja

☐ SONGS AND MOMENTS
Coaster / West coast blues / City lights / Night flight / Next time you see me / Songs and moments / Caravan / My foolish heart / Red top / Jim's ballad / Take the 'A' train / When I fall in love
ENJ 80722 / Oct '94 / Enja

☐ YOU GOT WHAT IT TAKES
Baby you got what it takes / Stockholm sweetnin' / Just in time / Sophisticated lady / Route 66 / Here's the rainy day / Yardbird suite / My funny valentine / Old times sake / BG's groove / God bless the children / Little Sherri / Please send me someone to love
ENJ 90392 / Oct '95 / Enja

Mahotella Queens

☐ PUTTING ON THE LIGHT (Mahotella Queens & Mahlathini)
Umthakathi / Uyagiyaumahlathini / Umoya / Imbodlomane / Izulungelami / Duduzile / Sithunyiwe / Ukohhliwe / Dolly swidilami / Thina siyakhanyisa / Gabi gabi / Bantwanyana
HNCD 4415 / Jul '93 / Hannibal

☐ WOMEN OF THE WORLD
Women of the world / Mbube / Africa / Dilika town hall / Malaika / Kukhona intombi / I shall be released / Homeless / Thoko / I'm not your good time girl / Amabhongo / Don't be late for heaven / Sabolana / Isilingo sesoka
FLTRCD 510 / Jun '93 / Flame Tree

Mai Rouge

☐ TAKE IT OR LEAVE IT
SPRAYCD 303 / Dec '97 / Making Waves

Mai Tai

☐ ESSENTIAL COLLECTION, THE
EMPRCD 804 / 18 May '98 / Emporio

Maids Of Gravity

☐ FIRST SECOND, THE
Half awake / Don't you disagree / Light you gave / No room / Another one / Golden harm / Can't lose / Looks the same / Islands / Live and die / In the days / It don't have to be
VYD 019 / Mar '97 / Vernon Yard

☐ STRANGE CHANNEL
Your ground / Slave and rule / Moonspiders / Taste / In other words
CDVUSM 85 / Apr '95 / Virgin

Maiguashca, Mesias

☐ READING CASTANEDA
WER 20532 / Mar '98 / Wergo

Mailhes, Rene

☐ GOPALINE (Mailhes, Rene Trio)
IMP 922 / Nov '95 / Iris Music

Main

☐ CORONA
HERTZ 1 / Jun '95 / Beggars Banquet

☐ DELIQUESCENCE
Particle suspension / Phase space / Outer corona / Carrier wave / Cavitation / Valency
BBQMCD 196 / 25 Aug '97 / Beggars Banquet

☐ FIRMAMENT VOL.3
BBQMCD 179 / Nov '96 / Beggars Banquet

☐ FIRMAMENT VOL.4
BBQMCD 202 / 18 May '98 / Beggars Banquet

☐ HERTS SERIES, THE
HERT 16CD / Jan '96 / Beggars Banquet

☐ MAIN
HSRTZ 3 / Aug '95 / Beggars Banquet

☐ NEPER
HERT 26 / Nov '95 / Beggars Banquet

Main Ingredient

☐ AFRODISIAC
379922 / Mar '98 / Koch

☐ I JUST WANNA LOVE YOU
I just wanna love you / Surrender / Nothing's too good for my baby / Never give up on love / Just say you will / When we need it bad / Meant to be in love / I can't go for that
8412492 / Mar '90 / Polydor

Main Source

☐ FUCK WHAT YOU THINK
Diary of a hit man / Only the real survive / What you need / Merrick Boulevard / Down low / Intermission / Where we're coming from / Hellavision / Fuck what you think / Set it off / Scrach and kut 94
CDPITCH 002 / Mar '94 / Wild Pitch

Main Stream Power Band

☐ MEMORIES IN SWING
Music makers / Flight of the foo birds / In a persian market / Empty roads / Sailor's boogie / Way down yonder in New Orleans / Fantail / Down South camp meetin' / Soho beat / Main stream boogie / Lovely rose / When the saints go marching in / Bakerloo non-stop / Splanky / Memories in swing / Wrappin' it up / Jumping duck / Hampstead Saturday night / Merry go round / Hot pink / Saxes on fire / What's the trouble / If dreams come true / Play bounce
MONTCD 001 / May '96 / Montpellier

Mainer, J.E.

☐ RUN MOUNTAIN
ARHCD 456 / Feb '97 / Arhoolie

Mainesthal

☐ OUT TO LUNCH
CDZOT 117 / Aug '94 / Zoth Ommog

Mainieri, Mike

☐ AMERICAN DIARY, AN
Somewhere / King Kong / Piano sonata (vivace) / Piano sonato No 1 / Town meeting / Overture to the school for scandal / Hudson river valley / Sometimes I feel like a Motherless child / Song of my people / In the gloaming / Out of the cage / In the universe of Ives
NYC 60152 / Jul '95 / NYC

☐ COME TOGETHER
Come together / She's leaving home / Here, there and everywhere / And I love her / Michelle / Something / Eleanor Rigby / Norwegian wood / Blackbird / Within you without you / Yesterday
NYC 60042 / Jun '93 / NYC

☐ LIVE AT SEVENTH AVENUE SOUTH
Tee bag / Flying colours / Song for Seth / Bullet train / Sara's touch / Bamboo / Crossed wires
NYC 60222 / Jun '96 / NYC

☐ MAN BEHIND BARS
ESP / Trinary motion / Push-pull / Equinox / Satyr dance / Momento No 1 / Nearness of you / Momento No 2 / All the things you are / Binary motion
NYC 60192 / Dec '95 / NYC

☐ WANDERLUST
Bullet train / Sara's touch / Crossed wires / Flying colours / L'image / Bamboo / Wanderlust
NYC 60022 / Oct '92 / NYC

☐ WHITE ELEPHANT
Peace of mind / Jones / Battle royal / Look in his eyes / White elephant / Easy on / Animal fat / Monkey
NYC 60082 / Oct '94 / NYC

☐ WHITE ELEPHANT VOL.2
More to love / Broadway Joe / Dreamsong / Gunfighter / Right back / Sunshine clean / Save the water / Auld lang syne / Field song / Battle royal
NYC 60112 / Feb '96 / NYC

Mainliner

☐ MAINLINER SONIC
100252 / May '97 / Charnel House

☐ SONIC
CHCD 25 / Jul '98 / Charnel House

Mainstream Power Band

☐ DATE WITH SWING, A (Mainstream Power Band & Heinz Schonberger)
Since my best gal turned me down / A date with swing / Mayfair swing / Oh babe maybe someday / Gentle move / Whirly bird / You're a heavenly thing / Big ben bounce / Indiana (back home again in indiana) / Trombones preferred / Cute / Music hall rag / Swing is in the air / Pony tail / Lover's leap / Alexander's playmobil / Scattin' at the kit kat / Clap your hands / Stomp it off / Scuttlebutt / Road to swing / March of the commanders / Highway boogie / On the verge
MONTCD 002 / Jan '97 / Montpellier

☐ HOLIDAY FOR SWING
Holiday for swing / Ev'rything is jumpin' / New bond street / Introduction to a waltz / Big bear / Scool / Study in brown / Silver lining / One foot in the groove / Oh, so good / Crisp and clean / Flag waver / Highlight in swing / Jumping jack / Any old time / Lush slide / Walking together / Send for henry / Free wheeling / Easy to say / Follow your heart / Bag-a-bones / Starlight / Camptown swing
MONTCD 003 / Nov '96 / Montpellier

Maipu

☐ MUSIC FROM THE ANDES
Correvuela / Vuelvo / Rin / La pulga / Porfiada fe / La nostalgica / La barca / Paine / Rengueando / Callejero / Telares
15496 / Jan '94 / Laserlight

Maisonneuve, Arnaud

☐ OUILET MEN DEULAGAD
RSCD 222 / Jul '96 / Keltia Musique

Maitre, Pandit Kamalesh

☐ TABLA TARANG - RAGAS ON DRUMS (The World's Musical Traditions No.10)
SFWCD 40436 / Mar '96 / Smithsonian Folkways

Maixa Ta Ixiar

☐ MANTALGORRI
KD 467CD / Dec '97 / Elkar

Majella

☐ SPINNING WHEEL, THE (24 Traditional Irish Favourites) (Majella & The Don Lowes Orchestra)
I know where I'm going / Leaving of Liverpool / Merskeen durkin / Song of Derry / Will ye go lassie go / She moves through the fair / Whiskey in the jar / Green glens of Antrim / Old maid in the garret / Connemara cradle song / Courtin' in the kitchen / Forty shades of green / Wild colonial boy / Irish soldier laddie / Galway boy / If we only had old Ireland over here / Rose of Tralee / It's Heaven around Galway Bay / Mountains of Mourne / Mary from Dungloe / Danny boy / Hanningan's hooley
306862 / Jul '97 / Hallmark

Majestic

☐ NO WORDS, NO MISUNDERSTANDINGS
EFA 125172 / Sep '95 / Celtic Circle

Majic Ship

☐ COMPLETE RECORDINGS
GF 107 / 15 Dec '97 / Gear Fab

☐ MAJIC SHIP
FLASH 56 / Oct '97 / Flash

Majik J

☐ SLOW MOTION
Subway / Gemini / Third eye / Stationary / Silicon valley / Organised crime / Slow motion / Mermaids / Chakara / Kindred spirit
INFRACD 001 / 23 Feb '98 / Infa Red

Major Accident

☐ CLOCKWORK HEROES
AHOYCD 016 / 9 Mar '98 / Captain Oi

☐ CRAZY TORTURED TUNES
LOMACD 43 / May '96 / Loma

☐ MASSACRED MELODIES/A CLOCKWORK LEGION
Schizophrenic / Standing on the sidelines / Last night / Psycho / People / Terrorist gang / War boots / Mr. Nobody / Self appointed hero / That's you / Brides of the beast / Classified information / Middle class entertainment / Clockwork legion / Respectable / Twisted mind / Affliction / Cue the dead / Leaders of the dead / Clockwork toys / Sorry (we can't help you) / Fight to win / Vendetta
AHOYCD 027 / 8 Jun '98 / Captain Oi

Major Lance

☐ BEST OF MAJOR LANCE, THE
BGOCD 369 / 24 Nov '97 / Beat Goes On

☐ LIVE AT THE TORCH
Hey hey / I wanna make up / My girl / Um um um um um um / Beat / Ain't no soul / Investigate / Monkey time
CDXELV 1 / 1 Jun '98 / Elevate

Major Stars

☐ ROCK REVIVAL
TW 1044CD / 30 Mar '98 / Twisted Village

Major Worries

☐ BABYLON BOOPS
792082 / Apr '93 / Jammy's

Majumdar, Ronu

☐ REVERIE
NRCD 0073 / Feb '97 / Navras

Makai

☐ MILLENIUM
PCD 01 / 7 Jul '98 / Precision

Make Up

☐ AFTER DARK
DIS 105CD / Feb '97 / Dischord

☐ IN MASS MIND
DIS 113CD / 16 Mar '98 / Dischord

☐ LOVE LIVE
DIS 99CD / Apr '96 / Dischord

☐ SOUND VERITE
KLP 64CD / Mar '97 / K

Makeba, Miriam

☐ BEST OF MIRIAM MAKEBA & THE SKYLARKS, THE (Makeba, Miriam & The Skylarks)
Uthando luyaphela / Table mountain / Miriam and spokes phatha phatha / Mtshakasi / Ndimsbone dluca / Makoti / Ndidliwe zintaba / Inkomo zodwa / Sindiza ngecadillacs / Nomalungelo / Kutheni sithandwa / Vula amasango / Owakho / Baya ndi memeza / Yini madoda / Ekoneni / Uyadela
CDN 1001 / 23 Mar '98 / Camden

☐ FOLK SONGS FROM AFRICA
Click song / Retreat song / Mbube / Suliram / Olilili / Amampondo / Nomeva / Pole mze / Saduva / Iyaguduza / Kilimanjaro / Qhude / Dubula / Umhome / Kwedini / Maduna / Lakutshn ilanga / Mayibuye
CD 12514 / Jun '94 / Music Of The World

☐ LIVE FROM PARIS AND CONAKRY
Kilmandjaro / I shall sing / Kulala / Malaika / Jolinkomo / Measure the valley / Ring bell / Pata pata / I'mm you'mm we'mm / U shaka / Tonados del media noche / Malcolm X / Tutu Maramba / Amampondo / West wind / Mas que nada / Forbidden games / Ngoma kurila / Congas / I phin dlela / Tutu marmamba
DRGCD 5234 / Jul '96 / DRG

☐ WELELA
Amampondo / African sunset / Diju de galinha / A luta continua / Soweto blues / Welela / Hapo zamani / Pata pata / Saduva / Africa
8382082 / May '89 / Philips

Makem, Tommy

☐ CLASSIC GOLD (Makem, Tommy & Liam Clancy)
TF 1010 / Oct '94 / Third Floor

☐ COLLECTION, THE (Makem, Tommy & Liam Clancy)
TFCB 1009CD / Oct '94 / Third Floor

☐ DUTCHMAN, THE (Makem, Tommy & Liam Clancy)
SHCD 52005 / May '93 / Shanachie

☐ FROM THE ARCHIVES
SHCD 52040 / Mar '95 / Shanachie

☐ IN CONCERT (Makem, Tommy & Liam Clancy)
TF 1002 / Oct '94 / Third Floor

☐ LARK IN THE MORNING, THE (Makem, Tommy & Liam Clancy)
TCD 1001 / Feb '96 / Tradition

☐ REUNION (Makem, Tommy & The Clancy Brothers)
TF 5009 / Oct '94 / Third Floor

☐ SONG TRADITION, THE
Long woman's grave / Canny auld lad / Galway city / Peace and justice / Bold fisherman / Sweet Dromintee / Maid of Ballydoo / Men of no conscience / Darkley weaver / Maid of fivey / Golden vanity / Lough Tay boat song / Uncle Dan / Ships of war / Newry town / Captain Farrell
SHANCD 5245 / Jun '98 / Shanachie

☐ SONGS OF TOMMY MAKEM, THE
TCD 1054 / Jul '97 / Tradition

☐ TOMMY MAKEM'S CHRISTMAS
SHCD 52041 / Nov '96 / Shanachie

Makers

☐ HIP-NOTIC/SHOUT ON
SFTRI 470CD / May '97 / Sympathy For The Record Industry

☐ HUNGER
ES 1232CD / Mar '97 / Estrus

☐ PSYCHOPATHIA SEXUALIS
ES 1248CD / 8 Jun '98 / Estrus

☐ SHOUT ON
SFTRI 470 / Jun '97 / Sympathy For The Record Industry

Makowicz, Adam

☐ **CONCORD DUO SERIES VOL.5 (Makowicz, Adam & George Mraz)**
Don't ever leave me / 400 West d-flat / Where is love / Anything goes / Mito / Say it isn't so / Culebra / Concordance / I loves you Porgy / Cherokee
CCD 4597 / Jun '94 / Concord Jazz

☐ **HANDFUL OF STARS, A (Makowicz, Adam & Jack DeJohnette/George Mraz)**
Satin wood / Just in time / Opalescence / Somebody loves me / Bye bye blues / Past tense / Handful of stars / Adam's waltz / What is this thing called love / I'm old fashioned / Falling / Jazzspeak
CRD 209 / 8 Nov '97 / Chiaroscuro

☐ **MUSIC OF JEROME KERN, THE (Makowicz, Adam Trio)**
All the things you are / Way you look tonight / Who / Song is you / I won't dance / Ol' man river / Long ago and far away / Smoke gets in your eyes / Yesterdays / Dearly beloved / I'm old fashioned
CCD 4575 / Nov '93 / Concord Jazz

☐ **MY FAVOURITE THINGS (The Music Of Richard Rodgers)**
Where or when / I didn't know what time it was / Surrey with the fringe on top / My favourite things / Lady is a tramp / This can't be love / My funny valentine / My romance / Lover / It might as well be spring / Have you met Miss Jones
CCD 4631 / Feb '95 / Concord Jazz

☐ **SOLO ALBUM - ADAM IN STOCKHOLM**
Blues for Stockholm / Scandinavia / 'Round midnight / Castle Hotel / I surrender dear / Yesterdays / Snowflower / Body and soul / Song for Tung / Summertime
5178882 / Jan '94 / Verve

Makulis, Jimmy

☐ **GITARREN KLINGEN LEISE DURCH DIE NACHT**
Gitarren klingen leise durch die Nacht / Addio mein blondes Madel / Tahiti / Das wunder einer Sternenacht / Ein boot, eine Mondnacht und du / Nachts in Rom / Am Lido wartet eine Gondel / Weites Land / Sweetheart guitar / Das Tal der weissen rose / Ich habe im leben nur dich / Keiner weiss wohin / Maro, Maro / Weil ich weiss, dass wir uns wiedersehn / Horst du das lied aus alter zeit / Der bunte Hochzeitswagen / Traumen van der Sudsee / Eine Insel aus Traumen geboren / Lebe wohl, du blume von Tahiti / Der wind hat sich gedreht / Bald kommt der tag / Gold im sonnenschein / Vaya con dios / Aloha oe / Fontana di Trevi (Es war wie ein Marchen) / So kommt ein Stern in der nacht
BCD 15922 / May '96 / Bear Family

Malach, Bob

☐ **AFTER HOURS**
Gaslight / Stop start / All or nothing at all / Jody Grind / Stockholm sweetnin' / Big P / 12 more bars to go / Fair weather / Edda
GO 60312 / 24 Aug '98 / Go Jazz

Malachy, Doris

☐ **IRISH PUB SING-ALONG VOL.1 (33 Favourite Songs)**
O'Brien has no place to go / Do you want your aul' lobby washed down / Catch me if you can / Back to Castlebar / Lovely Leitrim / Old Dungannon road / Among the Wicklow hills / Isle of Inisfree / Lovely Irish eyes / Shores of Lough Neagh / Noreen bawn / Treat my daughter kindly / Little country town in Ireland / Where the grass grows the greenest / Pretty little girl from Omagh / Wild rover / Shores of Amerikay / Moonshiner / Rambles of spring / Donegal Danny / Boys of Killybegs / County of Tyrone / Any Tipperary town / Slievenamon / Mursheen durkin / Irish rover / Patsy Fagan / Ballybunion by the sea / 21 years / Cottage on the borderline / Cliffs of Dooneen / Bunch of thyme / Town I loved so well
CDPUB 020 / Jun '98 / Outlet

☐ **IRISH PUB SING-ALONG VOL.2**
CDPUB 021 / Jun '98 / Outlet

Malaise

☐ **FIFTY TWO WAYS**
MEMO 015CD / Jan '97 / Nightbreed

Malaria

☐ **REVISITED**
DANCD 083 / Jul '97 / Danceteria

Malavoi

☐ **DIAMOND COLLECTION, THE**
3004402 / Feb '97 / Arcade

Malayev, Ilyas

☐ **AT THE BAZAAR OF LOVE (Timeless Central Asian Maqam Music) (Malayev, Ilyas Ensemble)**
SH 64081 / Feb '97 / Shanachie

Malcahy, Mick

☐ **MICK MULCAHY AND FRIENDS**
CEFCD 143 / Jan '94 / Gael Linn

Malcoda

☐ **CASCADE**
WDM 10053 / 22 Jun '98 / World Domination

Malcolm X

☐ **ROOTS OF DUB VOL.3, THE**
DTCD 25 / Apr '96 / Discotex

Malcolm, James

☐ **ROHALLION**
Battle of Waterloo / Amulree / Gorbals melody / Skye cuckoo rag / Sierra whoosh / Vinney den / Tam O'Shanter / Dream / Cycles / Billy won't come back to Edinburgh
CDTRAX 150 / 1 Apr '98 / Greentrax

☐ **SCONEWARD**
Scotch blues / Neptune / Losin' auld reeki / Wild geese / Scotlandshire / Achiltibuie / Lochs of the Tay / Wisest fool / Noran water / Barrenlands / Grandfathers / Party / Flowers of Edinburgh
CDTRAX 083 / Mar '95 / Greentrax

Malevolent Creation

☐ **ETERNAL**
CDVEST 52 / Mar '96 / Bulletproof

☐ **IN COLD BLOOD**
PM 32258CD / Jun '97 / Pavement
SPV 08453182 / 1 Sep '98 / SPV

Mali Rain

☐ **ARMADILLO**
STONE 032CD / 25 May '98 / 3rd Stone

☐ **ELECTRONIC MUSIC FOR THE MIND AND BODY**
In the presence of angels / Cove / Hagakure / Pin points / Talia / Alhambra / Pelicula / Tundra / Minch / Be dark / All of my life
STONE 033CD / 30 Mar '98 / 3rd Stone

☐ **FORECAST FOR STORMS**
Forecast for storms / Koan / Sentinel / Via Dolorosa / Khat / Statikat / Cove / Pende / Optimist castle / Basking / Octane / Pulse
STONE 024CD / 30 Mar '98 / 3rd Stone

☐ **WE SHALL RETURN TO THE SEA**
Basking / Arp-aht / Statikat / Simms / Tranquility bass / Canopy / Callow Hill 508 AM / Peyostasia / Octane / Koan
STONE 017CD / 30 Mar '98 / 3rd Stone

Malicorne

☐ **BALANCOIRE ENFEU**
BPCD 9331 / Feb '96 / Boucherie Productions

☐ **EN PUBLIC**
BPCD 9311 / Feb '96 / Boucherie Productions

☐ **L'EXTRAORDINAIRE**
BPCD 9301 / Feb '96 / Boucherie Productions

☐ **LE BESTIAIRE**
BPCD 9321 / Feb '96 / Boucherie Productions

☐ **LEGENDE: DEUXIEME EPOQUE**
Le Prince D'Orange / Le ballet des coqs / Compagnons qui roulez en provence / La mule la conduite / Pierre De Grenoble / Vive la lune / La dance des dames / La Chasse Gallery / La nuit des sorcieres / Dormeur / L'ecolier assassin / Beau charpentier / Quand le cypes
HNCD 1360 / Jul '91 / Hannibal

☐ **VOX**
BPCD 9291 / Feb '96 / Boucherie Productions

Malie

☐ **DANCE MUSIC FROM TONGA**
PANCD 2011 / May '93 / Pan

Malika

☐ **TARABU (Music From The Swahili Of Kenya)**
SH 64089 / Jun '97 / Shanachie

Malinga, Joe

☐ **ITHI GQI (Malinga, Joe Group)**
BRAM 1990112 / Nov '93 / Brambus

Malinverni, Pete

☐ **THIS TIME**
RSRCD 147 / May '97 / Reservoir

Malkowsky, Liselotte

☐ **ALLES STEHT IN DEN STERNEN**
Ausgerechnet du Durch Paris da fliesst die Seine / Ruggediguh / Ein Ziguener ist mein Herz / In der cafetaria von Milano / Ach konnt ich einmal an der reeling steh'n / In deiner Koje hangt ein bildt von mir / Das meer / Bis ans ende der welt / Wirst du mich auch nicht vergessen / Amigo / Egal cherie / Wenn ein ziguener weint / Wie sich die zeiger weiterreh'n / Das ganze jahr bluh'n keine rosen / Ein schiff kommt ubers meer / Der alte hein / In Santa Cruz steht ein haus / Alter kapitan / Du felsht mir all die stunden / Das lied vom Abschied / Alles steht in den sternen / Wohin du acuch geh'n wirst / Jenny / Joe / Man sagt Adieu
BCD 16134 / Oct '97 / Bear Family

☐ **SONNTAGNACHT AUF DER REEPERBAHN**
Sonntagnacht auf der Reeperbahn / Der alte Seemann kann nachts nicht sclafen / Auf dem Meeresgrunde / Meine stille liebe ist Elbe / Marju, gruss mir mein St. Pauli / Geht ein Schiff in see / Eine einsame harmonika / Fang' keine liebe mit Matrosen an / Das rote Licht an backbord / Das Herz von St. Pauli / Er war in Hamburg / Eine kleiner Akkordeonspieler / Jim spiele harmonika / Was macht der seeman, wenn er sehnsucht hat / Warum zahlen die Matrosen nachts die Sterne / Ein Herz und eine Rose / Schone insel Hawaii / Ja wenn das Meer nicht war / Mein schiff hab' gute Reise / In der bar 'Zum gold'nen anker' / Auf St. Pauli spielt der Jonny Mundharmonika / Ein seemann bleibt nicht zu hause / Wenn die schiffe den hafen verlassen / Fahr mich in die Ferne, mein blonder Matrose / Seemann, komm' doch nach haus' / Der alte Matrose
BCD 15955 / May '96 / Bear Family

Malkuri

☐ **TRADITIONAL MUSIC OF THE ANDES**
SP 7143CD / Aug '96 / Soundings

Mallan, Peter

☐ **SCOTLAND IN SONG**
Bonnie gallowa' / Annie laurie / Sweet afton / Ye banks and braes / Ballochmyle / Star o'rabbie burns / Down in the glen / Fishin' song / Dark lochnagar / Skye boat song / I love a lassie / Roamin' in the gloamin / Keep right on to the end of the road / Eriskay love lilt / Farewell my love / Scotland the brave / My ain folk
CDLOC 1088 / Jul '95 / Lochshore

Mallett, David

☐ **FOR A LIFETIME**
For a lifetime / Sweet Tennessee / My old man / Some peace will come / Night on the town / Hometown girls / This city life / Lost in a memory of you / Light at the end of the tunnel / Summer of my dreams
FF 70497 / Jul '89 / Flying Fish

☐ **OPEN DOORS AND WINDOWS**
FF 70291 / Feb '95 / Flying Fish

☐ **PARALLEL LIVES**
I hate to see this town go down / Summer of my dreams / Closer to truth / I picture you / You say the battle is over / Introduction to Phil Brown / Phil Brown / Snowbound / Garden song / After the fall / Like this / Daddy's Oldsmobile / Fifty years / My old man / Nothin' but a long goodbye / Parallel lives
CDFF 670 / Nov '97 / Flying Fish

Mallku De Los Andes

☐ **ON THE WINGS OF THE CONDOR**
TUMICD 004 / '86 / Tumi

Malmkvist, Siw

☐ **HARLEKIN**
BCD 15661 / Oct '93 / Bear Family

☐ **LIEBESKUMMER 1961-1968**
BCD 15660 / Oct '93 / Bear Family

Malmquist, Dan Gisen

☐ **NATTLJUS**
Nattljus / Spegling / Speldosan / Motvals / Glasskapet / Sorg / Pavag / Gycklaren / Fallande angel / Gryningen / Kluring / Svanen / Kneppolskan / Festen ar over
XOUCD 116 / May '97 / Xource

☐ **VATTENRINGER**
RES 516CD / Jul '97 / Resource

Malmsteen, Yngwie

☐ **CONCERTO SUITE**
PCCY 01211 / 22 Jun '98 / Canon

☐ **FACING THE ANIMAL**
Braveheart / Facing the animal / Enemy / Sacrifice / Like an angel / My resurrection / Another time / Heathens from the north / Alone in paradise / End of my rope / Only the strong / Poison in your veins / Air on a theme
CRIDE 2 / 11 May '98 / Dream Catcher

☐ **FIRE AND ICE**
Perpetual / How many miles to babylon / Cry no more / Teaser / Dragonfly / No mercy / Leviathan / C'est la vie / Final curtain / Golden dawn / All I want is everything / I'm my own enemy / Forever is a long time / Fire and ice
7559611372 / Feb '92 / Elektra

☐ **INSPIRATION (2CD Set)**
CDMFN 200 / Oct '96 / Music For Nations

☐ **MAGNUM OPUS**
Vengeance / No love lost / Tomorrows gone / Only one / Die without you / Overture 1622 / Voodoo / Cross the line / Time will tell / Fire in the sky / Amber dawn / Cantabile
CDMFN 188 / Jul '95 / Music For Nations

☐ **MARCHING OUT (Malmsteen, Yngwie & Rising Force)**
Prelude / I'll see the light tonight / Don't let it end / Disciples of hell / I'm a viking / Overture 1383 / Anguish and fear / On the run again / Soldier without faith / Caught in the middle / Marching out
8257332 / Aug '85 / Polydor

☐ **ODYSSEY (Malmsteen, Yngwie & Rising Force)**
Rising force / Hold on / Heaven tonight / Dreaming (tell me) / Bite the bullet / Riot in the dungeons / Deja vu / Crystal ball / Now is the time / Faster than the speed of light / Krakatau / Memories
8354512 / Mar '96 / Polydor

☐ **RISING FORCE**
Black star: *Malmsteen, Yngwie & Rising Force* / Far beyond the sun / Now your ships are burned / Evil eye / Icarus' dream suite / As above so below: *Malmsteen, Yngwie & Rising Force* / Little savage / Farewell
8253242 / May '88 / Polydor

☐ **YNGWIE MALMSTEEN COLLECTION, THE**
Black star / Far beyond the sun / I'll see the light tonight / You don't remember, I'll never forget / Liar / Queen in love / Hold on / Heaven tonight / Deja vu / Guitar solo / Spanish castle magic / Judas / Making love / Eclipse
8492712 / Mar '96 / Polydor

Malone, J.J.

☐ **HIGHWAY 99**
Black nights / Daddy rolling stone / Highway 99 / Biscuit bakin' woman / Sail on / Killing floor / Old fashioned blues / They call it the crawl / Long way from San Antone / Mary Anne / Automobile blues / Sittin' here thinkin'
FCD 5003 / Jan '98 / Fedora

Malone, Michelle

☐ **BENEATH THE DEVIL MOON**
VEL 79703 / 6 Jul '98 / Velvel

☐ **NEW EXPERIENCE**
SKYCD 5025 / Sep '94 / Sky

Malone, Russell

☐ **SWEET GEORGIA PEACH**
IMP 12752 / 24 Aug '98 / Impulse Jazz

Maloney, Bunny

☐ **SINGS OLDIES IN A REGGAE**
HM 501172 / Sep '95 / Mudies

Malope, Rebecca

☐ **FREE AT LAST (South African Gospel)**
Mmele Wajeso (Kebophelo) / Uhlal'ekhona / Kojabula / Take my hand / Buyani / Emadleweni / In his hands / Umoya wam ngegazi lemvana / I'll bide my time / Vuselela / I'll be free / Shwele baba
HEMICD 27 / Jun '97 / Hemisphere

Malouma

☐ **DESERT OF EDEN**
Y habbi / Magrhrour / Eden / Ya malhba / Outhrouki / Hara / Rasm / Soura / Ayam zaman / Fa fa fa fa / Habbi haybeytov / Chikh m'backe / El vabiz
SHANCD 64088 / 9 Mar '98 / Shanachie

Malta

☐ **CINEMATRIX**
Aphrodite / EOS / Danae / Cassandra / Donky King / Donky queen / Shaista / Blackjack / P S I luv you / Whiter shade of pale
JVC 90222 / Aug '97 / JVC

☐ **HIGH PRESSURE**
High pressure / Touch / Only name missing is... / Exotic bird / Over-night trip / Secret island / My summer love / Feel the heat / Splashing angel / Stranger in paradise / Quiet stars
JD 3303 / Jul '88 / JVC

☐ **MY BALLADS**
JD 3315 / May '89 / JVC

☐ **OBSESSION**
Sentimental morning / Obsession / 101 freeway / Looking for you / Lucky seven / Reflections / When you wish upon a star / Time and tide / Not yet / Sweet dreams
JD 3310 / Oct '88 / JVC

☐ **UK UNDERGROUND**
Songs for my father / Nica's dream / So what / Moanin' / Crisis / Sidewinder / Along came Betty / Les liaisons dangereuses / 'Ascenseur pour L'echafaud' Generique / Donna Lee / Brother Mason / London funktion / Half Moon street
JVC 90042 / Aug '96 / JVC

Maltese

☐ **COUNT YOUR BLESSINGS**
Blessed are the strong / Hell walks laughing / Rain / Scream out / Count your blessings / Borrowed time / Too late / Blessed are the strong (reprise)
CDATV 21 / Jul '92 / Active

Mam

☐ **FLAMMES**
829492 / 21 Aug '97 / BUDA

Mama Sana

☐ MUSIC FROM MADAGASCAR
SHCD 65010 / May '95 / Shanachie

Mamangakis, Nikos

☐ EXCURSION
ML 3552 / 11 May '98 / Musurgia Graeca

Mamas & The Papas

☐ BEST OF THE MAMAS & THE PAPAS, THE
MCBD 19519 / Apr '95 / MCA

☐ CREEQUE ALLEY
MCLD 19124 / Sep '94 / MCA

☐ ELLIOTT, PHILLIPS, GILLIAM, DOCHERTY
California dreamin' / Dedicated to the one I love / Even if I could / Once there was a time I thought / You baby / In crowd / I saw her again / Did you ever want to cry / John's music box / Too late / Go where you wanna go / Midnight voyage / Creeque alley / Strange young girls / Dancing bear / No salt on her tail / My cart stood still / Dream a little dream of me: Mama Cass / California earthquake / Somebody groovy / Sing for your supper / Free advice / String man / I can't wait
VSOPCD 119 / Jul '88 / Connoisseur Collection

☐ EP COLLECTION, THE
California dreamin' / Somebody groovy / Monday, Monday / In crowd / I saw her again / Go where you wanna go / Look through my window / Trip, stumble and fall / Dedicated to the one I love / Free advice / Straight shooter / Get a feeling / Hey girl / You baby / Even if I could / I call your name / Words of love / Dancing in the street / I can't wait / That kind of girl
SEECD 333 / Aug '97 / See For Miles

☐ GOLDEN GREATS
Dedicated to the one I love / Monday, Monday / Look through my window / California dreamin' / I call your name / My girl / Dream a little dream of me: Mama Cass / Go where you wanna go / Got a feelin' / I saw her again / Words of love / Twelve thirty / Dancing in the street / Glad to be unhappy / Creeque alley / Midnight voyage / Spanish Harlem / You baby / Do you wanna dance / Twist and shout / Safe in my garden / California earthquake
MCLD 19125 / Jul '92 / MCA

☐ HITS OF GOLD
California dreamin' / Dedicated to the one I love / Monday, Monday / I saw her again / Creeque alley
MCLD 19050 / Apr '92 / MCA

☐ MAMAS & THE PAPAS
GFS 070 / Jul '97 / Going For A Song

☐ VERY BEST OF MAMAS & PAPAS, THE
Monday, Monday / California dreamin' / Dedicated to the one I love / Creeque alley / It's getting better / Straight shooter / Spanish Harlem / Twelve thirty / Go where you wanna go / I saw her again / People like us / My girl / California earthquake / For the love of Ivy / Got a feelin'
PLATCD 302 / Dec '88 / Platinum

Mambo

☐ MAMBOS QUE HICIERON HISTORIA
995202 / Aug '93 / EPM

Mambo Macoco

☐ MAMBO MACOCO WITH TITO PUENTE AND HIS ORCHESTRA (Mambo Macoco & Tito Puente Orchestra)
TCD 018 / Dec '92 / Fresh Sound

Mambossa

☐ MAMBOSSA
BOM 06CD / Jul '96 / Bomba

Mamduko

☐ MUNDIALISTAS
TUMICD 020 / '92 / Tumi

Mami, Cheb

☐ PRINCE OF RAI, THE
Dertfik confiance (nakara) / Ralia mahboubit galbi / Ana mazel / Lella rani ensaaf el mektoub / Tayo tayo adiani / Douni el bladi
SH 64013 / Mar '98 / Shanachie

Mammoth

☐ XXXL
White mammoth on the M1 / Fatman / Dressed to kill / All the days / Can't take the hurt / Always and forever / Do what you want to / Working for the man / Catcher in the rye / Hope you find it / Monster mania
SJPCD 006 / Apr '98 / Angel Air

Mamouchka

☐ NEW TSAREVITCH
177232 / 24 Apr '98 / Musidisc

Mamu

☐ TOWNSHIP BOY
What a lie / Soweto so where to / Mpoho / We don't buy from town / Love / Township boy / Today someone died / Prologue/monologue / Don't bother me / War is declared
KAZ CD 9 / Nov '89 / Kaz

Man

☐ 2OZ OF PLASTIC WITH A HOLE IN THE MIDDLE
Prelude / Storm / It is as it must be / Spunk box / My name is Jesus Smith / Parchment and candles / Brother Arnold's red and white striped tent
SEECD 273 / Nov '89 / See For Miles

☐ ALL'S WELL THAT ENDS WELL
Let the good times roll / Welsh connection / Ride and the view / Hard way to live / Born with a future / Spunkrock / Romain
PNTVP 103CD / 4 May '98 / Point

☐ BACK INTO THE FUTURE
Night in dad's bag / Just for you / Back into the future / Don't go away / Ain't their fight / Never say nups to nepalese / Saspan fach (by the gwalia male choir) / C'mon / Jam up jelly tight / Oh no not again (spunk rock 73)
BGOCD 211 / Nov '93 / Beat Goes On

☐ BE GOOD TO YOURSELF AT LEAST ONCE A DAY
C'mon / Keep on crinting / Bananas / Life on the road
BGOCD 14 / Jul '89 / Beat Goes On

☐ CALL DOWN THE MOON
Call down the moon / If I were you / Dream away / Blackout / Man with the X-ray eyes / Heaven and hell / Girl is trouble / Drivin' around / Burn my working clothes
PNTVP 116CD / 3 Aug '98 / Point

☐ CHRISTMAS AT THE PATTI
Welcome to the party / Boogaloo babe / My way / Jambalaya / Jingle bells/Run run Ruldolph / Mona / Eddie Waring / Life on the road / Shuffle
PNTVP 110CD / 8 Sep '97 / Point

☐ DAWN OF MAN (2CD Set)
SMDCD 124 / Jul '97 / Snapper

☐ DEFINITIVE COLLECTION, THE (2CD Set)
And in the beginning / Sudden life / Empty room / Puella puella / Love / Erotica / Blind man / And castles rise in children's eyes / Don't just stand there (come out in the rain) / Missing pieces / Future hides it's face / Prelude/Storm / It is as it must be / Spunk box / My name is Jesus Smith / Parchment and candles / Brother Arnold's red and white striped tent / (You're gonna) hurt yourself / Have I offended the girl / My love come home / If you walk away / 98.6 / Stubborn king of fellow / Royal blue summer sunshine day / Make up your mind / Patter people / Green grass / When Jezamine goes / Cave of clear light / This world is my world / Painting the time
CCSCD 832 / 24 Aug '98 / Essential

☐ DO YOU LIKE IT HERE
Angel easy / All good clean fun / We're only children / Many are called but few get up / Manillo / Love your life
PNTVP 107CD / 13 Oct '97 / Point

☐ FRIDAY 13TH
PNTVP 106CD / 13 Oct '97 / Point

☐ GREASY TRUCKERS PARTY
Spunkrock / Angel easy / Andy Dunkley
PNTVP 104CD / Jul '97 / Point

☐ LIVE AT THE PADGET ROOMS, PENARTH
BGOCD 365 / 26 Sep '97 / Beat Goes On

☐ LIVE IN LONDON
7171-551 / Hard way to die / Breaking up once again / Life on the road / Day and night / Someone is calling / Many are called but few get up / Brazilian cucumber meets Deke's new nose
PNTVP 101CD / Jul '97 / Point

☐ LIVE OFFICIAL BOOTLEG
EFA 035052 / Apr '97 / Think Progressive

☐ MAXIMUM DARKNESS
7171-551 / Codine / Babe I'm gonna leave you / Many are called but few get up / Bananas
BGOCD 43 / Nov '91 / Beat Goes On

☐ OFFICIAL BOOTLEG, THE
C'mon / Mad on her / Even visionaries go blind / Chinese cut / Wings of mercury / Slide guitar intro to... / Ride and view / Feather on the scales of justice / Bananas
PNTVP 109CD / 4 May '98 / Point

☐ REVELATION
And in the beginning / Sudden life / Empty room / Puella, puella (woman, woman) / Love / Erotica / Blind man / And castles rise in children's eyes / Don't just stand there (come out of the rain) / Missing pieces / Future hides its face
REP 4024 / Aug '91 / Repertoire

☐ RHINOS, WINOS AND LUNATICS
Taking the easy way out again / Thunder and the lightning kid / California silks and satins / Four day louise / Intro / Kerosene / Scotch corner / Exit
BGOCD 208 / Oct '93 / Beat Goes On

☐ SLOW MOTION
Hard way to die / Grasshopper / Rock and roll you out / You don't like us / Bedtime bone / One more chance / Rainbow eyes / Day and night
BGOCD 209 / Oct '93 / Beat Goes On

☐ TALK ABOUT A MORNING
DRESS 600 / 1 Jun '98 / Dressed To Kill

☐ TO LIVE FOR TO DIE
Spunk box / Conscience / Storm / Would the christians wait five minutes / Alchemist of the mind / Daughter of the fireplace / Scholar of consciousness
PNTVP 108CD / 13 Apr '98 / Point

☐ WELSH CONNECTION
Ride and the view / Out of your head / Love can find a way / Welsh connection / Something is happening / Car toon / Born with a future
PNTVP 102CD / Jul '97 / Point

Man 2 Man

☐ BEST OF MAN 2 MAN, THE (Male Stripper)
HTCD 88 / 20 Apr '98 / Hot Productions

Man = Mouse

☐ HEROIC COUPLET
Fuck the lottery / I don't care what you say, think or do / Hex / Spin / Towards tomorrow / Testify / Rejecting the authority of Vedas / England's glory, my shame / Blowhole / No extra track / You're going down with the Mackems
HOVE 1CD / Dec '94 / Stereophonic Hovesound

Man Called Adam

☐ APPLE
BLRCD 7 / Oct '91 / Big Life

☐ DUENDE
THECD 111 / 29 Jun '98 / Other

Man Is The Bastard

☐ SUM OF MEN
VFMCD 9 / Apr '96 / Vermiform

Man Or Astro Man

☐ DESTROY ALL ASTRO MEN
ESD 1215 / Jul '95 / Estrus

☐ EXPERIMENT ZERO
LOUDEST 12 / Apr '96 / One Louder

☐ INTRAVENOUS TELEVISION CONTINUUM
LOUDEST 8 / Jul '95 / One Louder

☐ IS IT
ESD 129 / Jul '95 / Estrus

☐ LIVE TRANSMISSIONS FROM URANUS
LOUDEST 6 / Mar '95 / One Louder

☐ MADE FROM TECHNETIUM
LOUDEST 25 / 8 Sep '97 / One Louder

☐ PROJECT INFINITY
ES 1221CD / Jul '95 / Estrus

☐ WHAT REMAINS INSIDE A BLACK HOLE
ANDA 191 / Jan '97 / Au-Go-Go

☐ YOUR WEIGHT ON THE MOON
LOUDEST 4 / Aug '94 / One Louder

Man Parrish

☐ BEST OF MAN PARRISH, THE
HTCD 110 / 20 Apr '98 / Hot Productions

Man Will Surrender

☐ MAN WILL SURRENDER
CR 019CD / Jul '96 / Conversion

Man With No Name

☐ EARTH MOVING THE SUN
Vavoom / Seratonin sunrise / Camouflage / Own the world / First day (horizon) / Treacle / Possessed / Parallel universe / Spaghettification / Tarantula / Breech
3984229752 / 20 Jul '98 / Perfecto/East West

☐ MOMENT OF TRUTH
DICCD 125 / Feb '96 / Beggars Banquet

Man, Wu

☐ CHINESE TRADITIONAL AND CONTEMPORARY MUSIC (Man, Wu & Ensemble)
Xiyang xiaogu / Niao tou lin / Han'gong qiuyue / Xiao ou'an zhou / Shimian maifu / Yang'guan san die / Run / CAGE IV / Gu yun san die
NI 5477 / Mar '96 / Nimbus

☐ SOLO PIPA (Man, Wu & Ensemble)
Dengyue jiaohui (lanterns and moon competing in brilliance) / Wuwn yiyun (ancient melodies of wulin) / Bawang xie jia (the tyrant removes his armour) / Chen su (chen and su dynasties) / Xu la (sounds of nature) / Yu'er gao (the moon on high) / Dian (the points)
NI 5368 / Mar '95 / Nimbus

Manahedji, Behnam

☐ MASTER OF THE PERSIAN SANTOOR
SM 15082 / Feb '94 / Wergo

Manasseh

☐ SHINING (Manasseh & The Equaliser)
DUBIDCD 6 / Aug '96 / Acid Jazz

Manbreak

☐ COME AND SEE
Ready or not / Kop karma / Morning / News of the world / Wasted / It's on / God's never heard of you / City life / Round and round / Cuts up / Future days / Is everyone still asleep
TPLP 84CD / 10 Nov '97 / One Little Indian

Mance, Junior

☐ AT THE VILLAGE VANGUARD (Mance, Junior Trio)
Looptown / Letter from home / Girl of my dreams / 63rd street theme / Smokey blues / 9.20 special / Bingo domino / You are too beautiful
OJCCD 204 / Jan '97 / Original Jazz Classics

☐ FOR DANCERS ONLY (Mance, Junior & Martin Rivera)
SKCD 3031 / Dec '97 / Sackville

☐ JUBILATION
SKCD 22046 / Jan '97 / Sackville

☐ JUNIOR MANCE QUARTET PLAY THE MUSIC OF DIZZY GILLESPIE (Mance, Junior Quintet)
SKCD 23050 / Feb '93 / Sackville

☐ JUNIOR MANCE SPECIAL
SKCD 23043 / Oct '92 / Sackville

☐ SMOKEY BLUES (Mance, Junior Trio)
9.20 special / Georgia on my mind / Small fry / In the evenin' / I want a little girl / Deep / Ease on down the road / Smokey blues
JSPCD 219 / Jul '88 / JSP

☐ TRIO BLUE MANCE (Mance, Junior Trio)
CRD 331 / Mar '96 / Chiaroscuro

Manchester City FC

☐ BLUE MOON (A Tribute To Manchester City Football Club) (Various Artists)
Alan Ball: *Kinky Singers* / Dancing in the Kippax: *Freshies* / Manchester City medley: *Sidebottom, Frank* / Boys in blue: *Manchester City FC* / Me balls burst: *Syndicate* / Up the balls: *Syndicate* / Blue city: *Harmony Blend* / Kinnel Tommy: *Bangor, Ed* / Blue moon: *Barmy Army* / We're back: *Brock, Ronnie* / Sugar sugar: *Lee, Francis & Friends* / Cinnamon stick: *Lee, Francis & Friends* / Make me an island: *Ball, Alan & Friends* / Manchester football double: *Lord Kitchener Fitzroy Band* / Playing for city: *Universal*
CDGAFFER 21 / 17 Nov '97 / Cherry Red

Manchester United FC

☐ COME ON YOU REDS (20 Manchester United Classics) (Various Artists)
MULPCD 001 / 1 Jun '98 / MCI Music

☐ FOOTBALL CLASSICS - MANCHESTER UNITED (Various Artists)
Manchester United calypso / Red Devils / Ryan Giggs we love you / George Best - Belfast boy / I love George Best / Echoes of the cheers / Manchester United football double / United, Manchester United / Look around / Yellow submarine / Oh what a lovely morning / Storm in a teacup / Precious memories / Congratulations / Never be alone / Chirpy chirpy cheep cheep / Love again, live again / Saturday afternoon at the football / Raindrops keep falling on my head / Munich air disaster - Flowers of Manchester
MONDE 16CD / Apr '95 / Cherry Red

☐ GLORY GLORY MAN UNITED
United united: *Stretford End Boys* / We will stand together / Red devils: *Georgie Boys* / Ryan Giggs we love you: *Rainbow Choir* / Le diable rouge: *Stretford End Boys* / United / Look around / Yellow submarine / Oh what a lovely morning / Storm in a teacup / Precious memories / Congratulations / Never be alone / Chirpy chirpy cheep cheep / Love again live again / Saturday afternoon (at the football) / Raindrops keep falling on my head / Glory glory Man Utd / We're the most united team in the land / Belfast boy: *Fardon, Don*
EMPRCD 629 / Jun '96 / Emporio

Manchester Vineyard

☐ I LONG FOR YOU
Here I am / I long for you / You are there / I trust in you / Be free / Lord send me / Clean heart / More love more power / Blessed be the name / Nothing else matters / Draw me close / Spirit song
SPND 013 / Apr '98 / Spirit Of Praise

Manchild

☐ POWER AND LOVE/FEEL THE PHUFF
CDGR 128 / Mar '97 / Charly

Mancini, Henry

☐ BEST OF HENRY MANCINI, THE
Breakfast at Tiffany's / Pink Panther / Days of wine and roses / Moon river / Shot in the dark / Love story / Raindrops keep fallin' on my head / Mr. Lucky / Peter Gunn / Experiments in terror / Windmills of your mind / Dream a little dream of me / Love is a many splendoured thing / By the time I get to Phoenix / Charade / Shadow of your smile / Evergreen / Midnight cowboy / Till there was you / Summer knows / Baby elephant walk / Hatari / Blue satin / Moment to moment
74321476762 / Apr '97 / Camden

☐ IN THE PINK
Pink Panther theme / Moon river / Days of wine and roses / Baby elephant walk / Theme from Hatari / Charade / Thorn birds theme / Blue satin / Two for the road / My lucky / Theme from the Molly Maguires / Moment to moment / As time goes by / Shot in the dark / Misty / Love Story / Pennywistle jig / (Everything I do) I do it for you / Moonlight sonata / Tender is the night / Theme from Mommie Dearest / Raindrops keep falling on my head / Crazy world / Mona Lisa / Peter Gunn / Unchained melody / Summer knows / Experiment in terror / Windmills of your mind / Til there was you / Speedy gonzales / Sweetheart tree / Love theme from Romeo and Juliet / Dream a little dream of me / Lonesome / Pie in the face polka / Love is a many splendoured thing / By the time I get tp Phoenix / Dear heart / Charade (opening tides) / Shadow of your smile / One for my baby (and one more for the road) / Breakfast at Tiffany's / That old black magic / Evergreen / Midnight cowboy
74321242832 / Nov '95 / RCA

☐ MARTINIS WITH MANCINI
Playboys theme / Moon river cha cha / Brief and breezy / Something loose / Mambo Parisienne / Lightly Latin / Raindrops in Rio / Something for sellers / Oddball / Old College try cha cha / Mister Lucky goes latin / Everybody blow / It had better be tonight / No-cal sugar loaf / Bijou / Your father's feathers / Megeue / Chaser / Beat / Loose caboose
07863675382 / 2 Feb '98 / RCA

☐ MASTERS, THE
EABCD 019 / 24 Nov '97 / Eagle

☐ MERRY MANCINI CHRISTMAS, A
Little drummer boy / Jingle bells / Sleigh ride / Christmas song / Winter wonderland / Silver bells / Frosty the snowman / Rudolph the red nosed reindeer / White Christmas / Carol for another Christmas / Silent night / O holy night / O little town of Bethlehem / God rest ye merry gentlemen / Deck the halls with boughs of holly / Hark the herald angels sing / We three kings of Orient are / O come all ye faithful (Adeste Fidelis) / Joy to the world / It came upon a midnight clear / Away in a manger / First Noel
ND 81928 / Nov '96 / Arista

☐ ROMANTIC MOMENTS
VSD 5530 / Nov '94 / Varese Sarabande

☐ SHOTS IN THE DARK (A Henry Mancini Tribute) (Various Artists)
DOCD 2113 / Jan '97 / Del-Fi

Mandala

☐ LIVE FROM VENUS
MANCD 111 / May '96 / Mandala

Mandala Jati Ensemble

☐ GAMELAN SEMARPEGULINGAN
VICG 50252 / Feb '96 / JVC World Library

Mandalaband

☐ EYE OF WENDOR, THE
Eye of Wendor / Florians song / Ride to the city / Almar's tower / Like the wind / Tempest / Dawn of a new day / Departure from Carthillias Elsethea / Witch of Waldow wood / Silesandre / Aenord's lament / Funeral of the king / Coronation of Damien
RPM 105 / Jul '93 / RPM

☐ MANDALABAND
Om mani padme hum (in four movements) / Determination / Song for a king / Roof of the world / Looking in
EDCD 343 / Feb '92 / Edsel

Mandalay

☐ EMPATHY
VVR 1001292 / 23 Mar '98 / V2

Mandators

☐ POWER OF THE PEOPLE
CDBH 156 / Apr '94 / Heartbeat

Mandel, Harvey

☐ BABY BATTER
Baby batter / One way street / Freedom ball / Hank the ripper / Midnight sun / Morton grove Mama / El stinger
BGOCD 252 / Feb '95 / Beat Goes On

☐ PLANETARY WARRIOR
LTY 54215 / Sep '97 / LTY

☐ SHANGRENADE
BGOCD 410 / 17 Aug '98 / Beat Goes On

☐ SNAKE, THE
Divining rod / Pegasus / Lynda Love / Peruvian flake / Snake / Unoino / Ode to the owl / Levitation / Bite the electric eel
BGOCD 398 / 24 Nov '97 / Beat Goes On

☐ SNAKES AND STRIPES
CCD 1013 / Jul '98 / Clarity

Mandingo

☐ LO MEJER DE LA SALSA VENEZOLANA
EUCD 1258 / Mar '94 / ARC

☐ WATTO SITTA
CPCD 8153 / Nov '95 / Celluloid

Mandinka

☐ INDEPENDENCE
VICP 5646 / Jun '96 / JVC World Library

Mando & The Chili Peppers

☐ ON THE ROAD WITH ROCK 'N' ROLL
I love to eat chili in Chile / South of the border / Don't say goodnight / Swingin' baby / I'm walkin' the floor over you / Cherry pie / This is true love / Congo mombo / San Antonio rose / Why can't it be / There's a new moon over my shoulder / Harbour lights / Beg your pardon / Candy kisses / Baby baby I can't believe / Someday (you'll want to make me want you) / Boppin' the rock / Maybellene
CDCHD 683 / 27 Apr '98 / Ace

Mandolin Allstars

☐ MANDOLIN ALLSTARS
ACS 027CD / Aug '95 / Acoustics

Mandragore

☐ MANDRAGORE
PS 65202 / Jun '98 / PlayaSound

Mandrill

☐ COMPOSITE TRUTH
CCLCD 60052 / 4 Aug '98 / Collectables

☐ JUST OUTSIDE OF TOWN
CCLCD 60062 / 4 Aug '98 / Collectables

☐ MANDRILL
Mandrill / Warning blues / Symphonic revolution / Rollin' on / Peace and love / Movement - Birth, Now, Time, Encounter, Beginning / Chutney
CCLCD 60022 / 3 Aug '98 / Collectables

Mandroid

☐ ELECTRO FREAKS REHAB CLINIC
Electro freaks rehab clinic / Analogue addict / Funky brother / Computer controlled / Jammin' on my old piano / Android / Battle theme / Subsonic tendencies / Rogue missile / Retrospect / Linear phase / Jammin' on my old piano
BRK 8CD / 6 Apr '98 / Breakin'

Mandukhai Ensemble

☐ MANDUKHAI ENSEMBLE OF MONGOLIA
PS 65115 / Nov '93 / PlayaSound

Mandville-Greeson, Liz

☐ LOOK AT ME
4938 CD / Dec '96 / Earwig

Mane, Malang

☐ BALANTA BALO (Talking Wood Of Casamance)
VPU 1006CD / May '97 / Village Pulse

Manegarm

☐ NORDSTJARNANS TIDSLADER
D 00057CD / 22 Jun '98 / Displeased

Maneri, Joe

☐ BLESSED (Maneri, Joe & Mat)
At the gate / There are no doors / 61 joys / From loosened soil / Five fantasies / Never said a mumblin' word / Is nothin' near / Body and soul / Race you home / Gardenias for gardeners / Outside the whole thing / Blessed
5573652 / 15 Jun '98 / ECM

☐ DAHABENZAPPLE
ARTCD 6188 / Dec '96 / Hat Art

☐ IN FULL CRY (Maneri, Joe Quartet)
Coarser and finer / Tenderly / Outside the dance hall / Kind of birth / Seed and all / Pulling the boat in / Nobody knows the trouble I've seen / In full cry / Shaw was a good man / Lift / I feel like a motherless child / Prelude to a kiss
5370482 / Aug '97 / ECM

☐ THREE MEN WALKING (Maneri, Joe & Joe Morris/Mat Maneri)
Calling / What's new / Bird's in the Belfry / If not now / Let me tell you / Through the glass / Three men walking / Deep paths / Diuturnal / Fevered / Gestalt / To Anne's eye's / Arc and point / For Josef Schmid
5310232 / Apr '96 / ECM

Manet, Raghunath

☐ MUSIC AND DANCE (2CD Set)
FA 414 / Oct '96 / Fremeaux

☐ PONDICHERY
FA 419 / Jun '97 / Fremeaux

Manfila, Kante

☐ KANKAN BLUES (Manfila, Kante & Balia Kalia)
OA 201 / Feb '94 / PAM

☐ N'NA NIWALE: KANKAN BLUES VOL.2
PAM 402CD / Mar '94 / PAM

☐ NI KANU
Ni kanu / Fenko / Akadi / Koufenko / Akassa / Djanfa / L'unite / Foya / Denko / N'tesse / Dinyiya
CDEMC 3705 / Sep '97 / EMI

Manfred Mann

☐ 20 YEARS OF MANFRED MANN'S EARTHBAND (Manfred Mann's Earthband)
Blinded by the light / Joybringer / Somewhere in Africa / You angel you / Questions / For you / California / Tribal statistics / Davy's on the road again / Runner / Mighty quinn / Angels at the gate
BOMME 1CD / Nov '90 / Cohesion

☐ 5-4-3-2-1 (Manfreds)
Handbags and gladrags / One in the middle / Sha-la-la / Little red book / Just like a woman / Semi-detached suburban Mr. James / Mighty Quinn / Ragamuffin man / My name is Jack / If you gotta go / Come tomorrow / Hubble bubble / Pretty flamingo / Do wah diddy diddy / Oh no not my baby / You gave me somebody to love / Ha ha said the clown / Fox on the run / 5-4-3-2-1
743215666325 / 23 Mar '98 / Camden

☐ AGES OF MANN
5-4-3-2-1 / Pretty flamingo / Do wah diddy diddy / Sha la la / If you gotta go, go now / Oh no not my baby / Come tomorrow / My name is Jack / One in the middle / I put a spell on you / Just like a woman / Poison Ivy / Mighty quinn / Semi-detached suburban Mr. James / Ha ha said the clown / Raggamuffin man / Hubble bubble (toil and trouble) / There's no living without your loving / You gave me somebody to love / Got my mojo working / With God on our side / Fox on the run
5143262 / Sep '95 / PolyGram TV

☐ ANGEL STATION (Manfred Mann's Earthband)
Don't kill it Carol / You angel you / Hollywood town / Belle of the earth / Platform end / Angels at the gate / You are / I am / Waiting for the rain / Resurrection
COMMECD 4 / Nov '90 / Cohesion

☐ ASCENT OF MANN, THE (2CD Set)
Just like a woman / I wanna be rich / Trouble and tea / Each and every day / Smemi detached surburban Mr. James / Morning after the party / Box office draw / Let it be me / All I wanna do / Vicar's daughter / I love you / Autumn leaves / Feeling so good / Mohair Sam / Love bird / Brown and Prter's meat exporters lorry / Its dso easy falling / Now and then thing / Another kind of music / Ha ha said the clown / Eastern street / Funniest gig / Miss JD / By request Edwin Garvey / Sunny / Wild thing / A 'B' side / Last train to Clarksville / Budgie / So long Dad / Please Mrs. Henry / Mighty quinn / Sunshine superman / Big Betty / As long as I have loving / Each other's company / Sweet pea / My name is Jack / Sleeply hollow / Harry the one man band / Sitting alone in the sunshine / Dealer dealer / Everyday another hair turns grey / Fox on the run / Country dancing / Up the junction / I think it's gonna rain today / There is a man / Cubist town / One way / Too many people / Ragamuffin man
5348062 / Jun '97 / Fontana

☐ AT ABBEY ROAD 1963-1966
Why should we not / Brother Jack / Without you / Cock a hoop / Now you're needing me / 54321 / Hubble bubble / Ain't that love / Do wah diddy diddy / What are you gonna do / Sha la la / John Hardy / Come tomorrow / What did I do wrong / Oh no not my baby / What am I doing wrong / What am I to do / One in the middle / I can't beleive what you say / If you gonna go go now / Stay around / That's all I ever want from you baby / I can't believe what you say / That's all I ever want from you / Pretty flamingo / You're standing by / You gave me somebody to love / Poison ivy
CDABBEY 101 / 13 Oct '97 / EMI

☐ CHANCE (Manfred Mann's Earthband)
Lies (through the 80's) / One the run / For you / Adolescent dream / Fritz the blank / Stranded / This is your heart / No guarantee / Heart on the street
COMMECD 9 / Nov '90 / Cohesion

☐ EP COLLECTION, THE
5-4-3-2-1 / Cock-a-hoop / Without you / Groovin' / Do wah diddy diddy / Can't believe it / One in the middle / Watermelon man / What am I to do / With God on our side / There's no living without your loving / Tired trying, bored of lying, scared of dying / I can't believe what you say / That's all I ever want from you baby / It's getting late / Machines / She needs company / Tenessee waltz / When will I be loved / I got you babe
SEECD 252 / Oct '94 / See For Miles

☐ FIVE FACES OF MANFRED MANN
Smokestack lightning / Don't ask me what I say / Sack o' woe / What you gonna do / Hoochie coochie man / I'm your kingpipn / Down the road apiece / I've got my mojo working / It's gonna work out fine / Mr. Anello / Untie me / Bring it to Jerome / Without you / You've got to take it
DORIG 121 / Jul '97 / EMI

☐ FOUR MANFRED MANN ORIGINALS (4CD Set)
Do-wah-diddy diddy / Don't ask me what I say / Sack o' woe / What you gonna do / Hoochie coochie man / Smokestack lightning / Got my mojo working / It's gonna work out fine / Down the road apiece / Untie me / Bring it to Jerome / Without you / Sha la la / Come tomorrow / She / Can't believe it / John Hardy / Did you have to do that / Watermelon man / I'm your kingpin / Hubble bubble (toil and trouble) / You've got to take it / Groovin' / Dashing away with the smoothing iron / My little red book / Oh no, not my baby / What am I to do / One in the middle / You gave me somebody to love / You're for me / Poison ivy / Without you / Brother Jack / Love like yours (don't come knocking every day) / I can't believe what you say / With God on our side / Pretty flamingo / Let's go get stoned / Tired of trying, bored with lying, scared of dying / I put a spell on you / It's getting late / You're standing by / Machines / Stay around / Tennessee waltz / Driva man / Did you have to do that
CDMANFRED 1 / Feb '96 / Premier/EMI

☐ GLORIFIED MAGNIFIED (Manfred Mann's Earthband)
Meat / Look around / One way glass / I'm gonna have you all / Down home / Our friend George / Ashes to the wind / Wind / It's all over now / Baby blue / Glorified magnified
MFMCD 11 / Nov '93 / Cohesion

☐ GOOD EARTH, THE (Manfred Mann's Earthband)
Give me the good earth / Launching place / I'll be gone / Earth hymn (parts 1 and 2) / Sky high / Be not too hard
MFMCD 12 / Nov '93 / Cohesion

☐ GROOVIN' WITH THE MANFRED'S (The Manfred Mann R&B Album)
Groovin' / Can't believe it / What you gonna do / Don't ask me what I say / Hoochie coochie man / Smokestack lightning / I'm your kingpin / Bring it to Jerome / Without you / Let's go get stoned / Watermelon man / I put a spell on you / Driva man / Call it stormy Monday / What did I do wrong / Got my mojo working / Down the road apiece / Watch your step / LSD / One in the middle / Did you have to do that / Sticks and stones / Cock-a-hoop / Way you do the things you do / You've got to take it / Hubble bubble (toil and trouble)
CDEMS 1601 / Oct '96 / EMI

☐ LIVE IN BUDAPEST (Manfred Mann's Earthband)
Spirits in the night / For you / Lies (through the 80's) / Redemption song / Demolition man / Davy's on the road again / Blinded by the light / Mighty Quinn
COMMECD 10 / Nov '90 / Cohesion

☐ MANFRED MANN CHAPTER THREE VOL.1 (Manfred Mann Chapter 3)
MFMCD 14 / Feb '94 / Cohesion

☐ MANFRED MANN CHAPTER THREE VOL.2 (Manfred Mann Chapter 3)
MFMCD 15 / Feb '94 / Cohesion

☐ MANFRED MANN'S EARTHBAND (Manfred Mann's Earthband)
California coastline / Captain Bobby Stout / Sloth / Living without you / Tribute / Please Mrs. Henry / Jump sturdy / Prayer / Part time man / Up and leaving
COMMECD 6 / Nov '90 / Cohesion

☐ MANN ALIVE (2CD Set) (Manfred Mann's Earthband)
MLIVE 1 / 8 Jun '98 / Cohesion

☐ MANN MADE
Since I don't have you / You're for me / Look away / Adominable snowman / Watch your step / Call it stormy Monday / I really do believe / Hi Lili hi low / Way you do the things you do / Bare hugg / You don't know me / LSD / I'll make it up to you
DORIG 119 / 6 Oct '97 / EMI

☐ MESSIN' (Manfred Mann's Earthband)
Messin' / Buddah / Cloudy eyes / Get your rocks off / Sad joy / Black and blue / Mardi Gras day
COMMECD 7 / Nov '90 / Cohesion

☐ NIGHTINGALES AND BOMBERS (Manfred Mann's Earthband)
Spirits in the night / Countdown / Time is right / Cross fade / Visionary mountains / Nightingales and bombers / Fat Nelly / As above so below
COMMECD 8 / Nov '90 / Cohesion

☐ PRETTY FLAMINGO
Do wah diddy diddy / 5-4-3-2-1 / Hubble bubble (toil and trouble) / Sha la la / Got my mojo working / Stormy Monday blues / If you gotta go, go now / Pretty flamingo / Oh no not my baby / Come tomorrow / You gave me somebody to love / Since I don't have you / One in the middle / Hi lili hi lo
16140 / Sep '96 / Laserlight

☐ ROARING SILENCE, THE (Manfred Mann's Earthband)
Blinded by the light / Singing the dolphin through / Waiter, there's a yawn in my ear / Road to Babylon / This side of paradise / Starbird / Questions
COMMECD 2 / Nov '90 / Cohesion

☐ SINGLES IN THE SIXTIES
54321 / Hubble bubble, toil and trouble / Do wah diddy diddy / Sha la la / Come tomorrow / Oh no not my baby / My little red book / One in the middle / If you gotta go, go now / There's no living without your loving / Pretty flamingo / You gave me somebody to love / Just like a woman / Semi-detached suburban Mr. James / Ha ha said the clown / Sweet pea / So long Dad / Mighty Quinn / Up the junction / My name is Jack / Fox on the run / Ragamuffin man
BX 5152 / Oct '97 / BR Music

☐ SOFT VENGEANCE (Manfred Mann's Earthband)
GRACD 213 / Jun '96 / Grapevine

☐ SOLAR FIRE (Manfred Mann's Earthband)
COMMECD 1 / Nov '90 / Cohesion

☐ SOMEWHERE IN AFRICA (Manfred Mann's Earthband)
Tribal statistics / Eyes of Nostradamus / Third world service / Demolition man / Brothers and sisters / To Bantustan (Africa suite) / Koze kobenini / Lalela, redemption song (no kwazulu) / Somewhere in Africa
COMMECD 5 / '90 / Cohesion

☐ SPOTLIGHT (Manfred Mann's Earthband)
MFMCD 013 / Sep '92 / PolyGram TV

☐ UP THE JUNCTION
Up the junction / Sing songs of love / Walking around / Up the junction / Love theme / Up the junction / Just for me / Love theme / Sheila's dance / Belgravia / Wailing horn / I need your love / Up the junction / Sleepy hollow
RPM 189 / 17 Aug '98 / RPM

☐ VERY BEST OF MANFRED MAN, THE
Do wha diddy diidy / 54321 / Sha la la / Hubble bubble / If you gotta go go now / Oh no not my baby / Bare hugg / Got my mojo working / Hoochie coochie man / Smokestack lightning / Pretty flamingo / You gave me somebody to love / Don't ask me what I say / I'm your kingpin / It's gonna work out fine / Hi lili hi lo / Stormy monday blues / Abominable snowman / Since I don't have you / Come tomorrow
CDMFP 6381 / 3 Aug '98 / Music For Pleasure

☐ WATCH (Manfred Mann's Earthband)
COMMECD 3 / Nov '90 / Cohesion

☐ WORLD OF MANFRED MANN, THE
Mighty Quinn / Ha ha said the clown / Vicar's daughter / Semi-detached suburban Mr. Jones / I wanna be rich / My name is Jack / A 'B' side / Fox on the run / It's so easy falling / Ragamuffin man / Trouble and tea / Box office draw / Sweet pea / Up the junction / Feeling so good / So long Dad / Each other's company / Just like a woman
5523572 / Apr '96 / Spectrum

Mangalam

☐ FUNKY CLASSICAL INDIAN MUSIC
Twisted sara / Alex / Five it up / Anjneyar / Rainy sara / Dee I / Deetune Kedar / Jhaan
8888272 / Jun '97 / Tiptoe

Mangas, Yiorgos

☐ YIORGOS MANGAS
Tsifteteli rok / Roumaniko / Autoschediasmos / Ibon / Chorepste / Ta chrysa dactyla / Yia tous anthropous pou agapao / Skaros / To diko mou
CDORB 021 / Jul '90 / Globestyle

Mangelsdorff, Albert

☐ WIDE POINT, THE/TRILOGUE/LIVE IN MONTREUX (Three Originals/2CD Set)
Up and down man / Mayday Hymn / Oh horn / I mo take you to the hospital and cut your liver out / Mood indigo / Wide point / For Peter / Trilogue / Zores Mores / Foreign fun / Accidental meeting / Ant steps on an elephant's toe / Dear Mr. Palmer / Mood azur / Stay on the carpet / Rip off
5192132 / Apr '94 / MPS Jazz

Mangione, Chuck

☐ A&M GOLD SERIES
Feels so good / Hill where the Lord hides / You're the best there is / Fun and games / Cannonball run / Land of make believe / Give it all you got / Hide and seek / Children of Sanchez / Chase the clouds away / Bellavia / Doin' everything with you / Maui waui
3970752 / Mar '94 / A&M

Mango Jam

☐ FLUX
SHCD 5710 / Sep '96 / Shanachie

Mangual, Jose Jr.

☐ TRIBUTE TO CHANO POZO VOL.2, A
MIC 921 / Nov '96 / Fresh Sound

Mangwana, Sam

☐ GALO NEGRO
79024801402 / 19 May '98 / Putumayo

Manhattan Jazz Quintet

☐ FUNKY STRUT
Swing street / Hot grits / Mercy mercy mercy / Sister Sadie / Song for my Father / Funky strut / Foxy little thang
66055006 / Oct '91 / Sweet Basil

☐ MY FAVOURITE THINGS
My favourite things / No groovin' allowed / You'd be so nice to come home too / Pina colada / What's cooking / Recado bossa nova
K32Y 6210 / Sep '88 / Electric Bird

Manhattan New Music Project

☐ MOOD SWING
1212072 / Apr '93 / Soul Note

Manhattan Project

☐ DREAMBOAT
Dreamboat / Cape Town ambush / Misty / Depth / I remember / Sacrifice / Someday my Prince will come / I didn't know what time it was / Alluding to
CDSJP 327 / Aug '90 / Timeless Jazz

Manhattan Transfer

☐ BEST OF THE MANHATTAN TRANSFER, THE
Tuxedo Junction / Boy from New York City / Twilight zone / Body and soul / Candy / Four brothers / Birdland / Gloria / Trickle trickle / Operator / Java jive / Nightingale sang in Berkeley Square
2508412 / Aug '84 / WEA

☐ BOP DOO WOP
Unchained melody / Route 66 / My cat fell in the well / Duke of Dubuque / How high the moon / Baby come back to me / Safronia B / Heart's desire / That's the way it goes
7567812332 / Mar '93 / WEA

☐ BRASIL
Soul food to go / Zoo blues / So you say / Capim / Metropolis / Hear the voices / Agua / Jungle pioneer / Notes from the underground
7567818032 / Mar '93 / WEA

☐ COMING OUT
Don't let go / Zindy Lou / Chanson d'amour / Helpless / Scotch and soda / Speak up mambo / Cuentame / Poinciana / SOS / Popsicle toes / It wouldn't have made any difference / Thought of loving you
7567815022 / Mar '93 / WEA

☐ DOWN IN BIRDLAND
Trickle trickle / Gloria / Operator / Helpless / Ray's rockhouse / Heart's desire / Zindy Lou / Mystery / Baby come back to me (morse code of love) / Route 66 / Java jive / Chanson d'amour / Foreign affairs / Smile again / Spice of life / Speak up Mambo / Soul food to go (Sina) / So you say (Esquinas) / Boy from New York City / Twilight zone / Twilight tone / Four brothers / Bee blop blues / Candy / Gal in Calico / Love for sale / On a little street in Singapore / Tuxedo junction / That cat is high / Body and soul / Meet Benny Bailey / Sing joy spring / To you / Down south camp meeting / Until I met you / Why not / Another night in Tunisia / Capim / Nightingale sang in Berkley Square / Birdland (Vocal)
8122710532 / Jan '94 / WEA

☐ EXTENSIONS
Birdland / Wacky dust / Nothin' you can do about it / Coo coo-u / Body and soul (Eddie and the bean) / Twilight zone (part 1) / Twilight zone (part 2) / Trickle trickle / Shaker song / Foreign affair
7567815652 / Mar '93 / WEA

☐ LIVE
Four brothers / Rambo / Meet Benny Bailey / Airegin / To you / Sing joy Spring / Move / That's killer Joe / Duke of Dubuque / Gloria / On the boulevard / Shaker song / Ray's rockhouse
7567817232 / Oct '87 / WEA

☐ MANHATTAN TRANSFER
Tuxedo Junction / Sweet talking guy / Operator / Candy / Gloria / Clap your hands / That cat is high / You can depend on me / Blue champagne / Occapella / Heart's desire
7567814932 / '87 / WEA

☐ MECCA FOR MODERNS
On the Boulevard / Boy from New York City / Smile again / Wanted dead or alive / Spies in the night / Corner pocket / Confirmation / Kafka / Nightingale sang in Berkeley Square
7567814822 / Mar '93 / WEA

☐ PASTICHE
Four brothers / Gal in Calico / Love for sale / Je voulais (te dire que je t'attends) / On a little street in Singapore / In a mellow tone / Walk in love / Who, what, when, where and why / It's not the spotlight / Pieces of dreams / Where did our love go
8122718092 / Jan '95 / WEA

☐ TOUCH OF CLASS, A
Chicken bone bone / I need a man / You're a viper / Fair and tender ladies / Rosianna / Sunny disposish / Java jive / One more time around / Rosie / Guided missiles / Roll Daddy roll
TC 877002 / 2 Feb '98 / Disky

Manhattans

☐ DEDICATED TO YOU/ FOR YOU AND YOURS
Follow your heart / That new girl / Can I / Boston monkey / I've got everything but you / Manhattan stomp / Searchin' for my baby / Our love will never die / I'm the one love forgot / What's it gonna be / Teach me (the Philly dog) / Baby I need you / I call it love / I betcha / Sweet little girl / There goes a fool / Alone on New Year's Eve / All I need is your love / I wanna be / When we're made as one / Call somebody please / For the very first time / It's that time of year / Baby I'm sorry
CDKEND 103 / Jun '93 / Kent

Mani, Alamelu

☐ GENIUS OF TYAGARAJA, THE
Srikiantha Niyeda / Raghuvira / Varasikhi Vahana / Vinave o Manasa / Graha pala maeme / Sriramya chita / Saketa / Parulanu vedanu / Mrudubhashana / Daya juchuta / Paritapamu / Sri tulasamma / Samiki sari / Mummurtulu / Verevare nive gati
NRCD 0077 / 6 Jul '98 / Navras

Manic Eden

☐ MANIC EDEN
NTHEN 015CD / 16 Feb '98 / Now & Then

Manic Hispanic

☐ MENUDO INCIDENT
DD 010 / 24 Nov '97 / Dr. Dream

Manic Street Preachers

☐ EVERYTHING MUST GO
Elvis impersonator: Blackpool Pier / Design for life / Kevin Carter / Enola alone / Everything must go / Small black flowers that grow in the sky / Girl who wanted to be God / Removables / Australia / Interiors (song for Willem De Kooning) / Further away / No surface all feeling
4839302 / May '96 / Epic

☐ GENERATION TERRORISTS
Slash 'n' burn / Nat West-Barclays-Midland-Lloyds / Born to end / Motorcycle emptiness / You love us / Love's sweet exile / Little baby nothing / Repeat (stars and stripes) / Tennessee / Another invented disease / Stay beautiful / So dead / Repeat (UK) / Spectators of suicide / Damn dog / Crucifix kiss / Methadone pretty / Condemned to rock 'n' roll
4710602 / Jun '92 / Columbia

☐ GOLD AGAINST THE SOUL
Sleepflower / From despair to where / La tristesse durera (scream to a sigh) / Yourself / Life becoming a landslide / Drug drug druggy / Roses in the hospital / Nostalgic pushead / Symphony of tourette / Gold against the soul
4740642 / Sep '96 / Columbia

☐ HOLY BIBLE
Yes / Ifwhiteamericatoldthetruthforonedayitsworld wouldfallapart / Of walking abortion / She is suffering / Archives of pain / Revol / 4st 7lb / Faster / This is yesterday / Die in the summertime / Intense humming of evil / PCP / Mausoleum
4774212 / Feb '97 / Columbia

☐ INTERVIEW, THE
SPEEK 002 / 16 Mar '98 / Talking Music

☐ MANIC STREET PREACHERS INTERVIEW 1991
MSPCD 1 / May '96 / Total

Manifold

☐ CHESTERFIELD SUITE
MILE 6 / Oct '97 / Trans Siberian

Manigat, Eval & Tchaka

☐ CREOLITE
68989 / 24 Apr '98 / Tropical

Manilla Road

☐ CIRCUS MAXIMUS
BDCD 53 / Oct '92 / Black Dragon

Manilow, Barry

☐ BARRY (Live In Britain)
It's a miracle / Old songs medley / Stay / Beautiful music / I made it through the rain / Bermuda Triangle / Break down the door / Who's been sleeping in my bed / Copacabana / Could it be magic / Mandy / London - we'll meet again / One voice
261320 / Apr '91 / Arista

☐ GREATEST HITS
Ships / Some kind of friend / I made it through the rain / Put a quarter in the jukebox / One voice / Old songs / Let's hang on / Memory / You're looking hot tonight
258552 / May '88 / Arista

☐ GREATEST HITS
Mandy / Can't smile without you / Looks like we made it / Tryin' to get the feeling again / I made it through the rain / Read 'em and weep / Somewhere in the night / Lonely together / Stay / If I should love again / I write the songs / One voice (live) / Bermunda triangle / Hey mambo / I wanna do it with you / Let's hang on / Some kind of friend / Copacabana (1993 remix) / I'm your man / Could it be magic
74321175452 / Apr '96 / Arista

☐ LIVE ON BROADWAY
Sweet life / It's a long way up / Brooklyn blues / Memory / Upfront / God bless the other 99 / Mandy / It's a miracle / Some good things never last / If you remember me / Do like I do / Best seat in the house / Gonzo hits medley / If I can dream
353785 / Feb '90 / Arista

☐ MANILOW MOODS (20 Instrumental Versions Of Barry Manilow's Classic Hits) (Evolution)
Mandy / Trying to get the feeling again / It's a miracle / I don't want to walk without you / Ships / I made it through the rain / I wanna do it with you / Even now / Ready to take a chance again / Looks like we made it / Bermuda triangle / Can't smile without you / Old songs / Could it be magic / One voice / New York city rhythm / Somewhere in the night / Weekend in New England / Copacabana / I write the songs
3036000752 / Mar '97 / Carlton

☐ SINGING WITH THE BIG BANDS
Sentimental journey / And the angels sing / Green eyes / I should care / On the sunny side of the street / All or nothing at all / I'm getting sentimental over you / I'll never smile again / Don't get around much anymore / I can't get started (with you) / Chattanooga choo choo / Moonlight serenade / Don't sit under the apple tree / I'll be with you in apple blossom time / Where does the time go
07822187712 / Oct '94 / Arista

☐ SONGS 1975-1990, THE
I write the songs / One voice / Old songs / Don't want to walk without you / Some good things never last / Somewhere down the road / When I wanted you / Stay / Even now / Read 'em and weep / Somewhere in the night / I made it through the rain / Daybreak (live) / Please don't be scared / Looks like we made it / Mandy / If I should love again / All the time / Copacabana / Keep each other warm / Weekend in New England / Lonely together / Can't smile without you / Trying to get the feeling again / Could it be magic / Brooklyn blues / Who needs to dream / Ready to take a chance again / If I can dream
353868 / Jun '90 / Arista

☐ SONGS TO MAKE THE WHOLE WORLD SING
Please don't be scared / One that got away / Keep each other warm / Once and for all / When the good times come again / In another world / My moonlight memories of you / Little travelling music please / Some good things never last / You begin again / Anyone can do the heartbreak
259927 / May '89 / Arista

☐ SUMMER OF '78 (Love Songs Of The 70's)
Summer of '78 / Interlude - Love's theme / Reminiscing / I go crazy / When I need you / Air that I breathe / Bluer than blue / We've got tonite / I'd really love to see you tonight / Sometimes when we touch / Never my love / Just remember I love you
7822188092 / Nov '96 / Arista

Manly, Gill

☐ DETOUR HEAD
PARCD 505 / Dec '94 / Parrot

Mann, Aimee

☐ I'M WITH STUPID
Long shot / Choice in the matter / Sugarcoated / You could make a killing / Superball / Amateur / All over now / Par for the course / You're with stupid now / That's just what you are / Frankenstein / Ray / It's not safe
GED 24951 / Oct '95 / Geffen

☐ WHATEVER
I should've known / Fifty years after the fair / 4th of July / Could've been anyone / Put me on top / Stupid thing / Say anything / Jacob Marley's chain / Mr. Harris / I could hurt you now / I know there's a word / I've had it / Way back when
GFLD 19319 / Jul '96 / Geffen

Mann, Carl

☐ MONA LISA (4CD Set)
Gonna rock and roll tonight / Rockin' love / Mona Lisa (master) / Foolish one / Rockin' love (master) / Pretend / I can't forget you / Some enchanted evening / I'm coming home / South of the border (Down Mexico way) / Ain't got no home / If I ever needed you / Island of love / Walkin' and thinkin' / Baby I don't care / I'm bluer than anyone can be / Wayward wind / Born to be bad / If I could change you / When I grow too old to dream / Mountain dew / Mona Lisa (alt.) / Look at that moon / Rockin' love (alt.) / Too young / Take these chains from my heart / I can't forget you (undubbed) / South of the border (Down Mexico way) / Kansas City / Today is Christmas / Crazy fool / Blueberry Hill / I'll always love you darlin' / Ain't you got no lovin' for me / Then I turned and walked slowly away / Serenade of the bells / It really doesn't matter now / Sentimental journey / Born to be bad (undubbed) / I love you, I adore you / Are you teasing me / Stop the world (and let me off) / I don't care / I'm walking the dog / Ubangi stomp / Don't let the stars get in your eyes / Long black veil / Canadian sunset / Even tho' / Chinatown, my Chinatown / Because of you / Till the end of forever / Mexicali rose / Hey doll baby / Vanished / Down to my last forgive you / Blue river / Yesterday is gone / Burnin' holes in the eyes of Abraham Lincoln / German town / She was young / Paying for the crimes / Met her in Alaska / Funny way of gettin' over someone else / When the leaves turn brown / Everyday grows sweet with the wine / More to life / Going to church with mama / It really matters / Toast to a fool / I'm married friend / My favorite bunch of roses / Ballad of Johnny Clyde / Cheatin' time / Keep feeding her the wine / Let's turn back the pages / If I ever love again / Make a man want to / Neon lights / I'm just about out of my mind / It's not the coffee that's keeping me awake / No easy way to say goodbye / Back lovin' / Annie over time / I've got feelings too / Twilight time / Eighteen yellow roses / Belly rubbin' country soul / Tennemonk, Georgia / She loves to love for the feeling / Love died a long time ago / Darling of Atlanta / Country was the song / Second guessing / One last goodbye / On the back streets of Dallas / Tripping on teardrops / I love you too much
BCD 15713 / Aug '93 / Bear Family

☐ ROCKIN' MANN
Mona Lisa / Foolish one / Rockin' love / Pretend / Some enchanted evening / I can't forget you / Look at that moon / Take these chains from my heart / Too young / South of the border / Kansas City / Wayward wind / Ain't got no home / Blueberry Hill / I'll always love you darling / Baby I don't care / I don't care / Ubangi stomp / I'm comin' home / Born to be bad / Ain't you got no lovin' for me / Don't let the stars get in your eyes / When I grow too old to dream / Mountain dew / If I could change you / Even tho' / Because of you / Long black veil
CPCD 8234 / Nov '96 / Charly

Mann, Dany

☐ SEXIE HEXY
BCD 15483 / '88 / Bear Family

Mann, Geoff

☐ IN ONE ERA
Piccadilly square / I wouldn't lie to you / Kingdom come / Afterwards / For God's sake / Green paper snow / My soul / Slow one / Creation / Dance / Gethsemane / Waves / Flowers
CYCL 004 / Jun '97 / Cyclops

☐ MINISTRY OF THE INTERIOR (Mann, Geoff Band)
Bashan beef (babylon babe) / What's in a name / Down here / Smile / Dayspring / This is your doing
CDGRUB 21 / Sep '91 / Food For Thought

☐ PEACE OFFERING
CYCL 042 / Nov '96 / Cyclops

Mann, Herbie

☐ AFRO JAZZIAC
Herbie's buddy / Perido / Baubles bangles and beads / Give a little whistle / Here's Pete / Theme from theme from / Nancy with the laughing face / Morning after / African five / Bacao / Calypso John / Carabunta / Answer me / Love chant / To Birdland and hurry / Afro jazziac / Ring a levio
CDSGP 0397 / Jul '98 / Prestige

☐ AT THE VILLAGE GATE
Comin' home baby / Summertime / It ain't necessarily so
7567813502 / Mar '93 / Atlantic

☐ BEST OF HERBIE MANN, THE
Comin' home baby / Memphis underground / Philly dog / Man and a woman / This little girl of mine
7567813692 / Mar '93 / Atlantic

☐ DEEP POCKET
Down in the corner / Knock on wood / Moanin' / When something is wrong with my baby / Papa was a rollin' stone / Sunny / Mercy mercy mercy / Go home / Amazing grace
KOKO 1296 / Sep '94 / Kokopelli

☐ EPITOME OF JAZZ
BET 6011 / Jan '95 / Bethlehem

☐ EVOLUTION OF MANN, THE (2CD Set/ The Herbie Mann Anthology)
Baghdad/Asia minor / Sawa sawa de / This little girl of mine / Comin' home baby / One note samba / Blues walk / Gymnopedie / I love you / Soul guajira / Mushi mushi / Feeling good / Philly dog / Memphis underground / Claudia pie / Muscle shoals nitty gritty / Yesterday's kisses / Push push / Hold on I'm comin' / In memory of Elizabeth Reed / Mellow yellow / Hijack / Lugar comun (Common place) / Draw your breaks / Cricket dance / Birdwalk / Aria / Dona primeira / Amazing grace
8122716342 / May '94 / Atlantic

☐ FLAMINGO VOL.2 (Mann, Herbie Quartet)
BET 6007 / Jan '95 / Bethlehem

☐ FLUTE SOUFFLE (Mann, Herbie & Bobby Jaspar)
Tel aviv / Somewhere else / Let's march / Chasin' the Bird
OJCCD 760 / Apr '93 / Original Jazz Classics

☐ HERBIE MANN PLAYS (Bethlehem Jazz Classics)
CDGR 133 / Apr '97 / Charly

☐ HERBIE MANN-SAM MOST QUINTET, THE (Mann, Herbie & Sam Most)
BET 6008 / Jan '95 / Bethlehem

☐ JAZZ MASTERS
5299012 / 5 May '98 / Verve

☐ JUST WAILIN'
Minor groove / Blue echo / Blue dip / Gospel truth / Jumpin' with Symphony Sid / Trinidad
OJCCD 900 / Sep '96 / Original Jazz Classics

☐ LOVE AND THE WEATHER (Mann, Herbie Orchestra)
BET 6009 / Jan '96 / Bethlehem

☐ MEMPHIS UNDERGROUND
Memphis underground / New Orleans / Hold on I'm comin' / Chain of fools / Battle hymn of the Republic
7567813642 / Sep '95 / Atlantic

☐ NIRVANA (Mann, Herbie & Bill Evans)
Nirvana / Gymnopedie / I love you / Willow weep for me / Lover man / Cashmere
7567901412 / Jun '95 / Atlantic

☐ OPALESCENCE
Dona Palermeira / Comin' home baby / Song for Lea / Bahia de tadas as contas / Dry land / Two rivers (Do oiapoque ao chui) / Sir Charles Duke / Number fifty-five / Calling you
KOKO 1298 / Sep '94 / Kokopelli

☐ PEACE PIECES
Peri's scope / Funkallero / Interplay / Turn out the stars / We will meet again / Blue in green / Waltz for Debby / Very early / Peace piece
KOKO 1306 / Feb '96 / Kokopelli

☐ YARDBIRD SUITE
Yardbird suite / Here's that man / One for Tubby / Squire's parlor / Who knew / Opicana
SV 0193 / Oct '97 / Savoy Jazz

Mann, John

☐ ASPECTS OF MUSIC
All the world's a stage / My heart and I / Annen polka / Kiss me / Romantica / Lost chord / Me and my girl / Love makes the world go round / Leaning on a lamp-post / Lambeth walk / Sun has got his hat on / Music in May / Czardas / Non, je ne regrette rien / L'accordeoniste / Hymne a l'amour / Funiculi, funicula / Melody of love / My blue heaven / Happy days and lonely nights / Bells are ringing / Ave Maria / Mistakes / Where is your heart (Moulin Rouge) / Gigi / Waltz at Maxim's / Night they invented champagne / Thank heavens for little girls / I remember it well / Parisians, I'll be seeing you
CDGRS 1232 / '91 / Grosvenor

☐ EVERGREENS
Medley: Our Gracie Fields / Medley: De Sylva Brown and Henderson / Medley: Rodgers and Hammerstein / Intermezzo from Cavalleria Rusticana / Thunder and lightning polka / Dolores / Song of paradise / Blue tango / Brown bird singing / Post horn gallop / Medley: Off to the sea / Medley: Minstrel magic
CDGRS 1263 / Mar '95 / Grosvenor

☐ THAT'S ENTERTAINMENT
And all that jazz / Dreaming ballerina / La cumparsita / Marigold / My curly headed baby / Nicola / Summer in Venice / My foolish heart / Amor amor / Narcissus / It had to be you / Hello Dolly / Walking my baby back home / Any dream will do / Vienna / Neapolitan serenade / Flirtation waltz / Temptation rag / Grasshoppers dance / Catari, catari / Roses of Picardy / Windows of Paris / Bye bye blues
PLATCD 3918 / Apr '93 / Platinum

☐ VIENNA CITY OF MY DREAMS
CDGRS 1254 / Feb '93 / Grosvenor

Mann, Woody

☐ HEADING UPTOWN
SHCD 8025 / Apr '97 / Shanachie

☐ STAIRWELL SERENADE
BEST 1072CD / Aug '95 / Acoustic Music

☐ STORIES
GR 70724 / Nov '94 / Greenhays

Manna

☐ 5:1
AMB 8945CDX / 16 Mar '98 / Apollo

☐ MANNA
From heaven / Secret life of bass / Mr. Echo (go to hell) / Eat it, weave it and wear it / Kelham's island / Transport of delight / Lonely tones
AMB 5937CD / Jan '95 / Apollo

Manne, Shelly

☐ ALIVE IN LONDON
Three on a match / Once again / Big oak basin / Illusion / Don't know
OJCCD 773 / Jan '94 / Original Jazz Classics

☐ AT THE BLACK HAWK VOL.1 (Manne, Shelly & His Men)
Summertime / Our delight / Poinciana / Blue Daniel / Blue Daniel (alternate version) / Theme: A gem from Tiffany
OJCCD 656 / Apr '93 / Original Jazz Classics

☐ AT THE BLACK HAWK VOL.2 (Manne, Shelly & His Men)
OJCCD 657 / Mar '93 / Original Jazz Classics

☐ AT THE BLACK HAWK VOL.3 (Manne, Shelly & His Men)
OJCCD 658 / Mar '93 / Original Jazz Classics

☐ AT THE BLACK HAWK VOL.4 (Manne, Shelly & His Men)
OJCCD 659 / Mar '93 / Original Jazz Classics

☐ AT THE BLACK HAWK VOL.5 (Manne, Shelly & His Men)
OJCCD 660 / Mar '93 / Original Jazz Classics

☐ DEEP PEOPLE (Manne, Shelly & Bill Russo)
Pooch McGooch / Count on Rush Street / All of me / It don't mean a thing if it ain't got that swing / Deep purple / Princess of evil / Slightly brightly / Ennui / Gloomy Sunday / Vignette / Esthete on Clarke Street / S'posin' / Cathy / Cookie / Strange fruit
SV 0186 / Oct '97 / Savoy Jazz

☐ MY FAIR LADY (Manne, Shelly/Andre Previn/Leroy Vinnegar)
Get me to the church on time / I've grown accustomed to her face / Ascot gavotte / With a little bit of luck / On the street where you live / Wouldn't it be loverly / Show me / I could have danced all night
OJCCD 336 / Jan '92 / Original Jazz Classics

☐ PERK UP
Perk up / I married an angel / Seer / Come back / Yesterdays / Drinking and driving / Bleep / Bird of paradise
CCD 4021 / Aug '95 / Concord Jazz

☐ PLAY PETER GUNN (Manne, Shelly & His Men)
Peter Gunn / Floater / Sorta blue / Brothers / Soft sounds / Fallout / Slow and easy / Brief and breezy / Dreamsville / Profound gass
OJCCD 9462 / Aug '98 / Original Jazz Classics

☐ SHELLY MANNE & HIS FRIENDS (Manne, Shelly & His Friends)
Tea for two / How high the moon / When we're alone / On the sunny side of the street / Time on my hands / Moonglow / Them there eyes / Sarcastic lady / Night and day / Flamingo / Steps steps up / Steps steps down
OJCCD 240 / Oct '92 / Original Jazz Classics

☐ SWINGING SOUNDS (Manne, Shelly & His Men)
Dart game / Bea's flat / Parthenia / Un poco loco / Bernie's tune / Doxy / Slan / Gem from Tiffany
OJCCD 267 / Jan '97 / Original Jazz Classics

☐ WEST COAST SOUND VOL.1, THE (Manne, Shelly & His Men)
Grasshopper / La mucura / Summer night / Afrodisia / You and the night and the music / Gazelle / Sweets / Spring is here / Mallets / You're getting to be a habit with me / You're my thrill / Fugue
OJCCD 152 / Feb '93 / Original Jazz Classics

Mannheim Steamroller

☐ CHRISTMAS
Deck the halls with boughs of holly / We three kings / Bring a torch, Jeannette, Isabella / Coventry carol / Good king Wenceslas / Wassail, wassail / Carol of the birds / I saw three ships / God rest ye merry Gentlemen / Stille nacht
AGCD 1984 / Nov '94 / American Gramophone

☐ FRESH AIRE CHRISTMAS, A
Hark the herald trumpets sing / Hark the herald angels sing / Veni veni Emmanuel / Holly and the ivy / Little drummer boy / Still, still, still / Lo how a rose e'er blooming / In dulci jubilo / Greensleeves / Carol of the bells / Traditions of Christmas / Cantique de noel (o holy night)
AGCD 1988 / Nov '94 / American Gramophone

☐ FRESH AIRE VOL.1
AGCD 355 / Dec '88 / American Gramophone

☐ FRESH AIRE VOL.2
AGCD 359 / Dec '88 / American Gramophone

☐ FRESH AIRE VOL.3
AGCD 365 / Dec '88 / American Gramophone

☐ FRESH AIRE VOL.4
AGCD 370 / Dec '88 / American Gramophone

☐ FRESH AIRE VOL.5
AGCD 385 / Dec '88 / American Gramophone

☐ FRESH AIRE VOL.6
AGCD 386 / Dec '88 / American Gramophone

Manning, Barbara

☐ 1212
Fireman / Evil plays piano / Evil craves attention/Our son/10X10 / Trapped and drowning / End of the rainbow / Blood of feeling / Rickity tikity tin / Syain on the sun / Isn't lonely lovely / That kid / First line (seven the row) / Marcus Leid / Stammtisch
OLE 2212 / Jun '97 / Matador

☐ ONE PERFECT GREEN BLANKET
NORMAL 138CD / Mar '94 / Normal

Manning, Matt

☐ WALTZIN' AN ANGEL
RTMCD 80 / Oct '96 / Round Tower

Manning, Roger

☐ ROGER MANNING
Busy body blues (E5th Street blues) / Take back the night / No. 19 blues (pearly blues no.3) / Hitchhiker's blues no.2 (pearly blues no.3) / Traitors / Radical blues / Speaker phone / Persia blues / Unrequited / Waterloo blues / Subway blues / Waterloo calling/ Parade account / Pacifica blues / Dallas blues / Serious blues (no.18 blues) / Tompkins Square blues no.99 / Gallows pole / Sub folk
SH 5718 / Feb '97 / Shanachie

Mannsfield, Rodney

☐ LET'S GET IT ON
Dance for me / I adore you / I can't live / Let me know / How can this be / Are you ever coming back / I wanna get it on / Nobody else / No way / Call me
XECD 2 / Sep '96 / Expansion

Mano Negra

☐ KING OF BONGO
Bring the fire / King of bongo / Don't want you no more / Le bruit du frigo / Letter to the censors / El jako / It's my heart / Madman's dead / Out of time man / Madame Oscar / Welcome in occident / Furious fiesta / Fool / Paris la nuit
CDVIR 5 / Jul '91 / Virgin

☐ PUTA'S FEVER
Man negra / Rock 'n' roll band / King kong five / Soledad / Sidi hbibi / Rebel spell / Peligro / Pas assez de toi / Magic dice / Mad house / Guayaquil City / Voodoo / Patchanka / La rancon du succes / Devil's call / Roger Cageot / El sur / Patchuko hop
CDV 2608 / Jan '90 / Virgin

Manola, Pirko

☐ KUSSE IM MONDSCHEIN (Manola, Pirko & Wyn Hoop)
BCD 16235 / May '98 / Bear Family

Manolin

☐ PARA MI GENTE
74321401372 / Sep '96 / Milan
1611710022 / 17 Mar '98 / Ahi Nama

Manone, Wingy

☐ CLASSICS 1927-1934
CLASSICS 774 / Aug '94 / Classics

☐ CLASSICS 1934-1935
CLASSICS 798 / Mar '95 / Classics

☐ CLASSICS 1935-1936
CLASSICS 828 / Sep '95 / Classics

☐ CLASSICS 1936
CLASSICS 849 / Nov '95 / Classics

☐ CLASSICS 1936-1937
CLASSICS 887 / Jul '96 / Classics

☐ CLASSICS 1937-1938
CLASSICS 952 / Nov '97 / Classics

☐ COLLECTION VOL.1, THE
COCD 03 / Jan '89 / Collector's Classics

☐ SWINGIN' AT THE HICKORY HOUSE (His 24 Greatest)
San Sue strut: *Arcadian Serenaders* / Fidgety feet: *Arcadian Serenaders* / Cat's head: *Manone, Joe 'Wingy' Harmony Kings* / Wailin' blues: *Cellar Boys* / Shake that thing: *Barbecue Joe & His Hot Dogs* / Tar paper stomp: *Barbecue Joe & His Hot Dogs* / In the slot: *Manone, Wingy Orchestra* / Never had no lovin': *Manone, Wingy Orchestra* / Panama blues: *New Orleans Rhythm Kings* / Tin roof blues: *New Orleans Rhythm Kings* / Royal Garden blues: *Manone, Wingy Orchestra* / Blues have got me: *Manone, Wingy Orchestra* / Swing brother swing: *Manone, Wingy Orchestra* / Isle of Capri: *Manone, Wingy Orchestra* / Swingin' at the Hickory House: *Manone, Wingy Orchestra* / Dallas blues: *Manone, Wingy Orchestra* / Sweet Lorraine: *Manone, Wingy Orchestra* / Oh say can you swing: *Manone, Wingy Orchestra* / Loch Lomond: *Manone, Wingy Orchestra* / Limehouse blues: *Manone, Wingy Orchestra* / Dinner for the Duchess: *Manone, Wingy Orchestra* / Mama's gone goodbye: *Manone, Wingy Orchestra* / Shake the blues away: *New Orleans Buzzards* / Where can I find a cherry: *Manone, Wingy & His Cats*
CDAJA 5241 / Jul '97 / Living Era

☐ WINGY MANONE AND HIS CATS
FLYCD 945 / Jul '96 / Flyright

☐ WINGY MANONE COLLECTION VOL.4 1935-1936
Every little moment / Black coffee / Sweet and slow / Lulu's back in town / Let's swing it / Little door, little lock, little key / Love and kisses / Rhythm is our business / From the top of your head / Takes two to make a bargain / Smile will go a long, long way / I'm gonna sit right down and write myself a letter / Every now and then / I've got a feelin' you're foolin' / You're my lucky star / I've got a note / I'm shooting high / Music goes 'round and around / You let me down / I've got my fingers crossed / Rhythm in my nursery rhymes / Old man mose / Broken record / Please believe me
COCD 20 / Nov '94 / Collector's Classics

Manouri, Olivier

☐ CUMPARSITA - TANGOS (Manouri, Olivier & E. Pascualla)
Y225212 / Jun '93 / Silex

Manowar

☐ ANTHOLOGY
VSOPCD 235 / Apr '97 / Connoisseur Collection

☐ HELL OF STEEL, THE (The Best Of Manowar)
Fighting the world / Kings of metal / Demon's whip / Warriors prayer / Defender / Crown and the ring / Blow your speakers / Metal warriors / Black wind, fire and steel / Hail and kill / Power of thy sword / Herz aus stahl / Kingdom come / Master of the wind
7567805792 / Feb '92 / Atlantic

☐ LOUDER THAN HELL
Return of the warlord / Brothers of metal / Gods made heavy metal / Courage / Number 1 / Outlaw / King / Today is a good day to die / My spirit lives on / Power
GED 24925 / Nov '96 / Geffen

☐ TRIUMPH OF STEEL
Achilles, agony and ecstacy in eight parts / Metal warriors / Ride the dragon / Spirit of the cherokee / Burning / Power of sword / Demon's whip / Master of the wind
7567824232 / Oct '92 / Atlantic

Manring, Michael

☐ THONK
Big fungus / Snakes got legs / Monkey businessman / Disturbed / On a day of many angels / My three moons / Cruel and unusual / Bad hair day / Adhan / You offered only parabolas / Enormous room
72902103222 / Feb '94 / High Street

Man's Ruin

☐ WHO YOU CALLIN' CRACKER
GMM 140B / 20 Apr '98 / GMM

Mansfield, Jayne

☐ BUSTS UP LAS VEGAS
MISS 005 / 1 May '98 / Missing/Marginal

Manson, Charles

☐ COMPLETE STUDIO RECORDINGS, THE
GM 05CD / Jan '97 / Grey Matter

☐ FAMILY JAMS (2CD Set) (Manson Family)
ARO 002CD / May '97 / Aoroa

☐ LIVE AT SAN QUENTIN
GM 01CD / Jan '97 / Grey Matter

Manson, Jean

☐ COUNTRY GIRL (2CD Set) (Manson, Jeane)
3008272 / Feb '97 / Arcade

Mansour, Ahmad

☐ TUMBLEWEED
591032 / Nov '97 / Musidisc

Mansun

☐ ATTACK OF THE GREY LANTERN
Chad who loved me / Mansun's only love song / Taxloss / You, who do you hate / Wide open space / Stripper vicar / Disgusting / She makes my nose bleed / Naked twister / Egg shaped Fred / Dark Mavis
CDPCS 7387 / Jun '97 / Parlophone

Mansurov, Malik

☐ AZERBAIDJAN
926962 / 24 Feb '98 / BUDA

Mantaray

☐ REDS AND THE BLUES, THE
Know where to find you / I don't make promises / Always tomorrow / Look after myself / Just a ride / Something special / Everybody looks the same / Rise above it all / Blackburn / Behind the clouds / Patient man / Don't believe in me
5342052 / May '97 / Fontana

Mantas

☐ WINDS OF CHANGE
Hurricane / Desperado / Sionara / Nowhere to hide / Deceiver / Let it rock / King of the rings / Western days / Winds of change
NEATCD 1042 / Jan '96 / Neat

Mantilla, Ray

☐ HANDS OF FIRE (Mantilla, Ray Space Station)
1231742 / Apr '93 / Red

☐ SYNERGY (Mantilla, Ray Space Station)
1231982 / Apr '94 / Red

Mantler, Karen

☐ FAREWELL
Farewell / Mister E / Brain dead / Arnold's dead / I'm his boss / My life is hell / Help me / Bill / Con Edison / I hate money / Beware
5315572 / Jul '96 / Watt

☐ GET THE FLU (Mantler, Karen & Her Cat Arnold)
Flu / I love Christmas / Let's have a baby / My organ / Au lait / Waiting / Call a doctor / Good luck / I'm not such a bad guy / Mean to me
8471362 / Nov '90 / ECM

☐ MY CAT ARNOLD
839 093 2 / Jun '89 / ECM

Mantler, Michael

☐ ALIEN
8276392 / Dec '85 / ECM

☐ HAPLESS CHILD, THE
Sinking spell / Object-lesson / Insect god / Doubtful guest / Remembered visit / Hapless child
8318282 / Jul '87 / ECM

☐ I SEARCH FOR AN INNOCENT LAND
5270922 / Jul '95 / ECM

☐ LIVE
Preview - no answer / Slow orchestra piece no.3 (Prisonniers) / For instance / Slow orchestra piece no.8 (A l'abattoir) / When I run / Remembered visit / Slow orchestra piece no.6 / Hapless child / Doubtful guest
8333842 / Oct '87 / ECM

☐ MANY HAVE NO SPEECH
Introduction / Just as someone / Ce qu'a de dis / Alles scheint rand / Imagine / In the end / Vieil allec / Rien nul / Tant de temps / En face / Chaque jour / Pss / En cadence / Something there / Connrade / Den atemt au getauscht / Al'anattoir / And what
8355802 / Jul '88 / ECM

☐ SCHOOL OF UNDERSTANDING, THE (2CD Set)
Prelude / Introductions / First lesson / News / Love begins / War / Pause / Understanding / Health and poverty / Love continues / Platitudes / Intolerance / Love ends / What's left to say / What is the word
5379632 / 17 Nov '97 / ECM

Mantovani

☐ ALL TIME FAVOURITES (Mantovani & His Orchestra)
MU 5010 / Oct '92 / Musketeer

☐ ALL TIME FAVOURITES (2CD Set) (Mantovani Orchestra)
Tango / Zigeunerweisen / Hungarian dance No.5 / Solveig's song / Schon rosmarin / Ave Maria / Spanish dance / Tristesse op 10-3 etude in E major / Largo / Barcarolle / Meditation / Air on the G string / Clair De Lune / Song of India / None but the lonely heart / Slavonic dances no.2 in E minor / Chanson du matin / On wings of song / Come Prima / Stardust / Anima e core / Sunrise sunset / Over the rainbow / Lovely way to spend an evening / Andalucia / Limelight / Amapola / Three coins in a fountain / Smoke gets in your eyes / I left my heart in San Francisco / Autumn leaves / Tonight / Malaguena / Swedish rhapsody / La vie en rose / Jalousie
330402 / Mar '97 / Hallmark

☐ CHANSON D'AMOUR (Mantovani Orchestra)
PLSCD 208 / Apr '97 / Pulse

☐ CHARMAINE (Mantovani Orchestra)
Charmaine / Blue Danube / Cara mia / Moulin rouge / Moon river / Ziguenereisen / Student prince serenade / Greensleeves / Some enchanted evening / Around the world / Summertime in Venice / Granada / Estrelita / Catari (cor 'ngrato) / La mer / Love is a many splendoured thing
309122 / 13 Jul '98 / Hallmark

☐ CHRISTMAS
First Noel / Good King Wenceslas / O Holy night / God rest ye merry gentlemen / Nazareth / Holly and the ivy / Midnight waltz / O little town of Bethlehem / White Christmas / O tannenbaum / Toy waltz / O come all ye faithful (Adeste fidelis) / Mary's boy child / O thou that tellest good tidings / Skater's waltz / Silent night
5501432 / Nov '96 / Spectrum

☐ CHRISTMAS ALBUM, THE (Mantovani Orchestra)
God rest ye gentlmen / Canticle Noel / Jesu joy of man's desiring / O tannenbaum / Hark the herald angels sing / Little drummer boy / Holly and the ivy / Silent night / Ding dong merrily on high / Good king Wenceslas / Sleigh ride / Jingle bells / Christmas song / Let it snow / Winter wonderland / Santa Claus is coming to town / O come all ye faithful (adeste fidelis) / Rudolph the red-nosed reindeer
120052 / Oct '97 / Jingle

☐ CLASSIC MELODIES
Spanish dance no.5 / Solveig's song / Ave Maria / Etude no.3 / Barcarolle / Schon Rosemarin / On wings of song / Slavonic dance no.2 / Hungarian dance no.5 / Tango in D / Air on a G string / Claire de lune / Song of India / Meditation from Thais / None but the lonely heart / Largo from Xerxes / Chanson du matin
12574 / Dec '96 / Laserlight

☐ CLASSICAL LOVE THEMES (3CD Set)
September morn / How deep is your love / Music box dancer / Blue bayou / She believes in me / With you I'm born / Theme from 'mahogany' / She needed me / Broken hearted me / Scarborough fair / Heartbreaker / Hurt so bad / It goes like it goes / Midnight blue / You are the sunshine of my life / You've got a friend / She's always a woman / Touch me in the morning / My love / Chanson d'amour / Tomorrow / Scarborough fair '80 / Winter takes it all / Don't want to walk without you / Somewhere in the night / Still / I honestly love you / You're the one love / Send one your love / Whiter shade of pale / Bye bye love / First time I ever saw your face / Plaisir d'amour / Skaters waltz, the (les patineurs) (waldteufel) / La mer / Theme from 'new york, new york' / Way we were / Copocabana / You don't bring me flowers / Manhattan skyline / I'll never love this way again / Don't cry out loud / Evergreen / Mull of kintyre / Just the way you are / Annie's song / You make me feel brand new / Nobody does it better / Let it be me / Weekend in new england / Without you / Killing me softly / She's out of my life / Rose / Love's theme / Pieces of dreams / Long and winding road / Look what they've done to my song ma / Theme from rocky / Macarthur park / Nights in white satin / Don't cry for me argentina / Eres tu / You light up my life / Can't smile without you / When I need you / What I did for love / One / I write the songs / O tannenbaum / Time for us / Greensleeves '80
MBSCD 430 / Nov '93 / Castle

☐ ESSENTIAL MANTOVANI (3CD Set)
Theme from "superman" / Long ago and far away / Espana / Give my regards to broadway / Take the 'a' train / Tea for two / Mexican hat dance / Slaughter on tenth avenue / Yellow rose of texas / Belle of the ball / On my own / Charmaine / Love is a many splendored thing / Some enchanted evening / I've grown accustomed to her face / Summertime in venice / Merry widow waltz (lehar) / Cavatina / Autumn leaves / Love me tonight / Elizabethan serenade / Shadow of your smile / Big country / Three coins in the fountain / Sound of music / Impossible dream / Deep purple / More / What are you doing the rest of your life / Entertainer / Send in the clowns / For once in my life / Charmaine / Somewhere my love / Swedish rhapsody / Valencia / Carnival of venice / Tzena, tzena, tzena / Flamingo / Midnight cowboy / Colours of my life / Old songs / Will we ever know each other / La mer / Begin the beguine / Tenderly / Live and let die / Song of skye
TFP 023 / Nov '92 / Tring

☐ GOLDEN AGE OF MANTOVANI, THE
Siboney / Woman in love / Amazing grace / Candy man / Nessun Dorma / Italian Medley / I'll get By / Good life / Zorba the Greek / Ben Hur / Tara's Theme / Ay ay ay / Tie A Yellow Ribbon / People / Cara mia / Elizabethan serenade / For All We Know / Green Cockatoo / Big Country / Legend Of The Glass Mountain / Yellow rose of Texas / Sweetest sounds / Dream of Olwen / Trolley Song
CDSIV 6128 / Jul '95 / Horatio Nelson

☐ GOLDEN HITS VOL.2
Tonight / Andalucia / Jealousy / La vie en rose / Smoke gets in your eyes / I left my heart in San Francisco / Limelight / Over the rainbow / Amapola / Malaguena / Sunrise, sunset / Anema e core / Lovely way to spend an evening / Come prima / Stardust
12573 / Sep '96 / Laserlight

☐ GREATEST HITS (Mantovani Orchestra)
MACCD 157 / Aug '96 / Autograph

☐ INTERNATIONAL HITS (Mantovani Orchestra)
Autumn leaves (french version) / Londonderry air / Amazing grace / Tales from the vienna woods / Tritsch-tratsch polka / Carnival of venice / Barber of seville (overture) / Big country (main title) / Czardas / Swedish rhapsody / Greensleeves / Die fledermaus overture (johann strauss ii)
PWK 079 / Jan '89 / Carlton

☐ LATINO CONNECTION
Cielito lindo / Be mine tonight / La paloma / Siboney / Maria elena / Perfidia / Tico tico / Besame mucho / Blue tango / Blue sky (blauer himmel) / El relicario / Adios / Green cockatoo / Spanish gypsy dance / Quizas, quizas, quizas / Adios muchachos / La cumparsita / Vaya con dios
12307 / Apr '94 / Music Of The World

☐ LOVE ALBUM, THE (20 Romantic Favourites)
Some enchanted evening / Very thought of you / I can't stop loving you / April love / It's impossible / My cherie amour / Shadow of your smile / Lovely way to spend an evening / Love is all / Charmaine / Hello, young lovers / Man and a woman / Dear heart / For all we know / She / I will wait for you / And I love you so / What are you doing the rest of your life / Spanish eyes / More
PLATCD 14 / Dec '88 / Platinum

☐ LOVE THEMES, THE
Charmaine / Love story / For once in my life / Shadow of your smile / If I loved you / Love letters / Stardust / Long ago and far away / Some enchanted evening / Embraceable you / Moon river / Tenderly / When I fall in love / Most beautiful girl / And I love you so / Till there was you / Way you look tonight / Love me with all your heart / Nearness of you / You are beautiful / Tea for two / Lover / Till / I have dreamed / September song / I wish you love / My prayer / Very thought of you
CDSIV 6101 / Jul '95 / Horatio Nelson

☐ MAGIC OF MANTOVANI
DCD 5301 / Dec '93 / Disky

☐ MANTOVANI ORCHESTRA (Mantovani Orchestra)
Superman / Memory / I just called to say I love you / Medley / Medley / Canon / Nessun dorma / Medley / Chariots of fire / Flamingo / Midnight cowboy / Colours of my life / La mer / Begin the beguine / Tenderly / Live and let die
QED 059 / Nov '96 / Tring

☐ NOBODY DOES IT BETTER (Mantovani Orchestra)
MACCD 153 / Aug '96 / Autograph

☐ ROMANTIC MELODIES (Mantovani Orchestra)
DCD 5392 LM/VM / Apr '94 / Disky

☐ SERENADE
Around the world / Elizabethan serenade / Stardust / Old fashioned way / As time goes by / Anniversary waltz / And I love you so / Blue Danube / Very thought of you / Walk in the Black Forest / Stranger in paradise / Londonderry air / Spanish eyes / Swedish rhapsody
5500172 / May '93 / Spectrum

☐ TENDERLY (Mantovani Orchestra)
Flamingo / Midnight cowboy / La mer / Begin the beguine / Send in the clowns / Song of Skye / Autumn leaves / Some enchanted evening / Love is a many splendoured thing / Deep purple / Swedish rhapsody / What are you doing the rest of your life / Tenderly / Colours of my life / Three coins in the fountain / Charmaine
PWK 031 / '88 / Carlton

☐ VERY BEST OF MANTOVANI, THE
4600392 / 16 Mar '98 / Decca

☐ VINTAGE MANTOVANI (Mantovani & His Tipica Orchestra)
Raggamuffin / Fete in Santa Lucia / Have you forgotten so soon / Madame, you're lovely / You're laughing at me / Spider of the night / No more you / In a German beer-garden / September in the rain / Aromas mendocinas / Marcay / Eto nutche / Traumerei / Romany / Speak to me of love / Smoke gets in your eyes / Her name is Mary / Rose dreams / Nothing lives longer than love / Serenade / Ten pretty girls
PASTCD 9724 / Nov '90 / Flapper

☐ WAY WE WERE, THE
PDSCD 510 / Sep '97 / Pulse

Mantra

☐ PAINTED RED
ABCD 016 / 29 Sep '97 / Resurrection

Mantra, Michael

☐ SONIC ALTAR
SR 9449 / Mar '94 / Silent

Manu Lann Huel

☐ CADOU
RS 209CD / May '94 / Keltia Musique

Manual Scan

☐ PLAN OF ACTION (The Best Of Manual Scan)
FUN 003 / Jul '97 / Snap

Manuel

☐ GOLDEN SOUNDS OF MANUEL & THE MUSIC OF THE MOUNTAINS, THE (Manuel & The Music Of The Mountains)
GS 863552 / Mar '96 / Disky

☐ MANUEL AND HIS MUSIC OF THE MOUNTAINS (Manuel & The Music Of The Mountains)
Concerto de Aranjuez / Love theme / Strangers in the night / Stardust / Spanish Harlem / Moon river / Stranger on the shore / Una paloma blanca / Besame mucho / Cuando calienta el sol / Moonlight serenade / Cavatina
WB 885582 / 2 Feb '98 / Disky

☐ REFLECTIONS/CARNIVAL (2CD Set) (Manuel & The Music Of The Mountains)
Theme from a summer place / Romance / Bali ha'I / Till / Fools rush in' / None but the lonely heart / Reflections / Ebb tide / Baia / Moon river / Intermezzo / Moonglow / Mascara negra / How insensitive / Honeymoon song / Zambesi / Summertime in Venice / La mer / White rose of Athens / Guantanamera / Rodrigo's guitar concerto de Aranjuez / Mantilla / Angelito's negros / Come closer to me / Mosaic theme
4956222 / 10 Aug '98 / Studio 2

Manuel, Juan

☐ CORAZON DE BACHATA
71385329112 / 12 May '98 / Caiman

Manuel, Manny

☐ ES MI TIEMPO
RMD 82222 / 27 Apr '98 / RMM

Manuela Y La Major Salsa

☐ CANTO MI CORAZON
SABCD 947 / 5 Jan '98 / Fresh Sound

Manusardi, Guido

☐ COLORED PASSAGES (Manusardi, Guido & Garzone/Lockwood/Gullotti)
RMCD 4504 / Nov '93 / Ram

☐ TOGETHER AGAIN (Manusardi, Guido & Red Mitchell)
1211812 / Nov '91 / Soul Note

☐ VILLAGE FAIR, THE
1213312 / Mar '98 / Soul Note

Manuskript

☐ DIVERSITY OF LIFE, THE
ABCD 12 / Oct '96 / Resurrection

☐ I CAN'T BELIEVE
ABCD 008 / Jul '96 / Resurrection

Manzanera, Phil

☐ 801 LIVE
Lagrima / TNK (Tomorrow never knows) / East of Asteroid / Rongwrong / Sombre reptiles / Baby's on fire / Diamond head / Miss Shapiro / You really got me / Third uncle
EGCD 26 / '87 / EG

☐ GUITARISSIMO
La Escena / Criollo / Diamond head / You are here / Rude awakening / Listen now / Big dome (part 2) / Caracas / Lagrima / Europe 70-1 / Island / That falling feeling / Big dome (part 1) / City of light / Initial speed
EGCD 69 / '87 / EG

☐ LIVE AT MANCHESTER UNIVERSITY (Manzanera & 801)
TNK (Tomorrow Never Knows) / Flight 19 / Listen now / Law and order / Diamond head / Out of the blue / Remote control / Miss Shapiro / You really got me
EXVP 2CD / 15 Jun '98 / Expression

☐ LIVE AT THE KARL MARX THEATRE (Manzanera, Phil & Moncada)
Yo te queria Maria / Mama Hue / Yolanda/Pablo Milanes / Caimán no come caiman / Mi canto sube / Cantar el son de Cuba / Southern cross / Astrud / Musica / Corazon corazon
EXVP 4CD / 15 Jun '98 / Expression

☐ MAINSTREAM (Quiet Sun)
Bargain classics / Mummy was an asteroid, Daddy was a non-stick kitchen utensil / RFD / Rongwrong / Sol caliente / Trot / Trumpets with motherhood
BP 246CD / Mar '97 / Blueprint

☐ MANZANERA AND MACKAY (Manzanera, Phil & Andy Mackay)
Black gang chine / Free yourself / Built for speed / Many are the ways / I can be tender / Dreams of the East / Sacrosanct / Every king of stone / Men with extraordinary / Safe in the arms of love / Forgotten man
EXVP 5CD / Feb '97 / Expression

☐ MANZANERA COLLECTION, THE (2CD Set)
Tomorrow never knows / Over you / Out of the blue / Fat lady of Limbourg / Impossible guitar / Charlie / Take a chance with me / Frontera / Diamond head / Needle in a camel's eye / Miss Shapiro / End / Gun / Europe 70-1 / Leyenda / Frontera 91 / Southern cross / Sphinx / Amazona / Million reasons why / Fifth wheel / It's just love / Talk to me / Suzanne / Blackgang Chine / Lorelei / Criollo / Mama hue / Corazon Corazon / Flor de azalea / Espiritu
CDVDM 9033 / May '95 / Virgin

☐ MILLION REASONS WHY, A
Million reasons why / Tambor / Great leveller / Astrud / Southern cross / Blood brother / Guantanamera / Rich and poor / Dance (break this trance) / Verde / De Fidel / Vencermos
EXVP 1CD / Apr '97 / Expression

☐ ONE WORLD (Manzanera, Phil & John Wetton)
It's just love / Keep on loving yourself / You don't have to leave my life / Suzanne / Round in circles / Do it again / Every trick in the book / One world / Can't let you go / Have you seen her tonight / Talk to me
BP 241CD / Mar '97 / Blueprint

☐ SOUTHERN CROSS
EXPCD 1 / Oct '90 / Expression

Manzarek, Ray

☐ LOVE LION (Manzarek, Ray & M. McClure)
SHAN 5006CD / Oct '93 / Shanachie

Manzi, Homero

☐ HOMENAJE A LOS POETAS DEL TANGO
EBCD 78 / Jul '96 / El Bandoneon

Mao Tse Tung Experience

☐ ARMOURER
RTD 19519092 / Nov '94 / Our Choice

Mapfumo, Thomas

☐ CHIMURENGA (African Spirit Music) (Mapfumo, Thomas & The Blacks Unlimited)
WSCD 104 / Oct '97 / Womad Select

☐ CHIMURENGA FOREVER (The Best Of Thomas Mapfumo)
Serevende / Mhondoro / Vanhu vetama / Nyoka musango / Hanzvadzi / Nyarara mukadzi wangu / Zvenyika / Hondo / Ndave kuende / Shumba / Zvandivringa / Hwa hwa
CDEMC 3722 / Oct '95 / Hemisphere

Maphis, Joe

☐ FLYING FINGERS
Flying fingers / Lorrie Ann / Guitar rock 'n' roll / Randy Lynn rag / Sweet fern / Twin banjo special / Fire on the strings / Bully of the town / Town Hall shuffle / Floggin' the banjo / Tennessee two step / Katy Warren breakdown / Bye, bye: *Maphis, Joe & Larry Collins* / Early American: *Maphis, Joe & Larry Collins* / Rockin' gypsy: *Maphis, Joe & Larry Collins* / Hurricane: *Maphis, Joe & Larry Collins* / Short recess / Moonshot / Del Rio / Mavajo (war party) / Jubilo / Marching through Georgia / Water baby boogie / Black sombrero
BCD 16103 / Jan '97 / Bear Family

☐ LIVE AT THE TOWN HALL 1958-1961
RFDCD 16 / Jan '97 / Country Routes

Mar-Keys

☐ BACK TO BACK (Mar-Keys/Booker T. & MG's)
Introduction / Green onions / Red beans and rice / Tic-tac toe / Hip hug-her / Philly dog / Grab this thing / Last night / Gimme some lovin' / Booker-loo / Outrage
7567903072 / Feb '93 / Atlantic

☐ GREAT MEMPHIS SOUND, THE
Honey pot / Plantation Inn / I've been loving you too long / Cleo's back / Grab this thing / Philly dog / Walking with the Duke / Girl from Ipanema / In the mood / Dear James
7567823392 / Jul '93 / Atlantic

Mara

☐ DON'T EVEN THINK
SSMCD 042 / May '94 / Sandstock

☐ IMMIGRI (Mara & Jalal)
BARBARITY 016 / Jun '97 / Barbarity

Marachi Sol

☐ MEXICO LINDO
EUCD 1249 / Mar '94 / ARC

Maraire, Dumisani

☐ CHAMINUKA
CDC 208 / Jun '93 / Music Of The World

☐ SHONA SPIRIT (Maraire, Dumisani & Ephat Mujuru)
T 136 / Aug '96 / Music Of The World

Maralung, Alan

☐ BUNGGRIDJ-BUNGGRIDJ: WANGGA SONGS FROM NORTHERN AUSTRALIA
New song / Bushfire / Ibis / Green frog / Jabiru / Brolga / Garranan / Minmin kight
SFCD 40430 / Jan '94 / Smithsonian Folkways

Marascia

☐ ATOMICI
UCD 003 / Mar '96 / Undercontrol

☐ REWORKED
ICDIG 001 / Sep '96 / Illegal Gathering

Marbele, Aurulus

☐ SEBENE DANCE
JIP 51 / Jan '96 / JIP

Marble Orchard

☐ ADVENTURES IN MUTATION
SGCD 6 / Sep '97 / September Gurls

Marble Valley

☐ SAUCKIEHALL STREET
ECHO 140CD / 29 Sep '97 / Echo Static

Marbles

☐ PYRAMID LANDING
SPART 53CD / Feb '97 / Spin Art

Marc, Julian

☐ BEACH SAMBA
5331412 / Aug '96 / PolyGram TV

Marcano, Neville

☐ GROWLING TIGER OF CALYPSO, THE
War / Senorita panchita / Parrot / Money is king / Bury Boula for me / War / Train blow / When I dead bury me clothes / Rose of Caracus / Getting along with the Calypso music / Atomic energy calypso / Senorita panchita
ROUCD 1717 / Feb '98 / Rounder

Marcano, Pedro

☐ PEDRO MARCANO 1935-1940
HQCD 86 / Jun '97 / Harlequin

Marce Et Tumpak

☐ ZOUK CHOUV
Gren-n lanmou / Chien cho / Zouk chouv / Lans difou / Lese woule
CDORB 035 / May '89 / Globestyle

Marcello, Melis

☐ FREE TO DANCE
1200232 / Oct '94 / Black Saint

Marcels

☐ MARCELS COMPLETE COLPIX SESSIONS, THE
Blue moon / Goodbye to love / Loved her the whole week through / Peace of mind / I'll be forever loving you / Most of all / Sunday kind of people / Two people in the world / Sweet was the wine / Fallen tear / Over the rainbow / Crazy bells / Tetter totter love / Hold on / Footprints in the sand / You are my sunshine / Find another fool / Summertime / Flower pot / Heartaches / Allright, okay, you win / My love for you / Don't cry for me this xmas / Merry twistmas / Twistin' fever / My melancholy baby / Really need your love / Don't turn your back on me / That old black magic / Give me back your love / Tell them about it / Baby where y'been / I wanna be the leader / Friendly loans / Blue heartaches / Lollipop baby / One last kiss / Honestly sincere
NEDCD 264 / Nov '93 / Sequel

March,'Little' Peggy

☐ ICH DENK ZURUCK AN DIE ZEIT
Ich denk zuruck an die Zeit / Gib mir deine hand / Mein baum / Carmen aus Sevilla / Ich schau in deine augen / Sing, wenn du glucklich bist / Lieben ist schoner als traumen / Sonne und Wein / Hey Jude / Die Stadt im Meer / Ich geh mit dir / Eleanor Rigby / Die schonsten Zeiten der Erinnerung / Nie war diese Welt so schon / Kinder ohne Sonne / Zeig mir den Weg ins Gluck / Frag mich nie danach / Auf wiedersehen und gute nacht / Amerika nein sagt sich so leicht / Chim chim cheree / Ganz Paris traumt von der liebe / Der Weg in die Seligkeit / Superstar
BCD 15969 / Nov '96 / Bear Family

☐ IN DER CARNABY STREET
BCD 15967 / Jun '96 / Bear Family

☐ MEMORIES OF HEIDELBERG
Memories in Heidelberg / Antwort weiss ganz allein der wind / Tausend steine: *March, 'Little' Peggy & Benny Thomas* / Lass mich nie allein / Romeo und Julia / Fallt der regen in das meer / Spar dir deine dollar / Mississippi shuffle boat / Ender der zwanziger jahre / Es war hochste eisenbahn / Bahama lullaby / Telegramm aus Tennessee / Das ist musik fur mich / Ein zigeuner ohne geige / Wedding in my dreams / Du, du, du gehst mir im kopf herum / Die sonne kommt ja wieder / Hey (das ist musik fur dich) / Ich frage die zigeunerin / Weil die liebe zaubern kann / Der mond scheint schon / Mr. Giacomo Puccini / 1969 (weil es so schon war) / Male nicht den teufel an die wand / Yesterday waltz / Canale grande / Wiedersehn
BCD 15602 / Nov '91 / Bear Family

☐ MIT SIBZEHN HAT MAN NOCH TRAUME
Mit siebzehn hat man noch traume / Wer die junge liebe kennt / Er schoss mir eine rose / Liebesbriefe / Es fallt ein stern / Wenn der silbermond / Hee, hee, hey hey / Sweetheart, schenk ir einen ring / Ich hab'ein herz zu verschenken / Du bist der mann nach meinen herzen / Lady music / Ja, oh ja / Der sommerwind / Immer wieder kommst du-ich bin ein cowgirl / Hundert jahre und noch mehr / Lass mir meine traume / Das gluck lasst sich zeit / Sechs tage lang / Little john / Deine weltist meine welt / Hello boy / Bei dem dudel di del / Die schonen stunden gehn schnell vorbei / Das gluck vergeht / Ein boy wie du / Der schuster macht schone schuhe / Goodbye, goodbye, goodbye / Spiel nicht mit meiner liebe / Bobby kusst wunderbar / Tino
BCD 15536 / Mar '91 / Bear Family

March Violets

☐ BOTANIC VERSES
FREUDCD 42 / Sep '93 / Jungle

Marchand, Erik

☐ ERIK MARCHAND
Y 225043CD / Oct '94 / Silex

Marclay, Christian

☐ RECORDS 1981-1989
ALP 62CD / Aug '97 / Atavistic

Marcondes, Caito

☐ PORTA DO TEMPLO
Toada / Santa clara / Upa neguinho / Oyukoumene / Ciranda / Lamento sertanejo / Miguel de carrinho novo / Fato consumado / Passarim / Ginga / Romaria / Ponteio
ACT 50162 / 27 Apr '98 / Act

Marconi, Nestor

☐ UN BANDONEON DE BUENOS AIRES
74321453292 / Feb '97 / Milan Sur

Marcotulli, Rita

☐ NIGHT CALLER
LBLC 6551 / Jan '93 / Label Bleu

☐ WOMAN NEXT DOOR, THE
Le cinema est la cinema / Les 400 coups / Songs of innocence / Songs of experience / Escape / Masse di memoria / Musique en jeu / Les enfants s'ennuient le dimanche / Antoine Doinel / Arpeggio E fuga / Japanese mistress / Que reste-T-Il / Fragment (of the third kind)
LBLC 6601 / 29 Jun '98 / Label Bleu

Marcovicci, Andrea

☐ LIVE FROM LONDON
3787750232 / 27 Apr '98 / Cabaret

Marcucci, Alfredo

☐ TIMELESS TANGO
CCS 10997 / 3 Aug '98 / Channel Classics

Marcus, Hannah

☐ FAITH BURNS
NORMAL 214CD / Nov '97 / Normal

☐ RIVER OF DARKNESS
NORMAL 178CD / Mar '96 / Normal

Marcus, Michael

☐ INVOLUTION
Israel / Quadrophonics / Legend of Hale Bopp / Soultrane / Man from Lovejoy / Off minor / Sacred law / Dear Lord / Surfer girl / Involution
JUST 1162 / 27 Jul '98 / Justin Time

☐ REACHIN'
Picnic in blue / Constant / Reachin' / Forgotten paradise / Psalm walk / Along the line / Into Nowhersville / Stritch 'n' / With you in mind / Feels like home
JUST 872 / Aug '96 / Justin Time

☐ UNDER THE WIRE
60642 / Apr '91 / Enja

Marcus, Steve

☐ 201
4722082 / Nov '92 / Sony Jazz

Marcy Playground

☐ MARCY PLAYGROUND
Poppies / Sex and candy / Ancient wall of flowers / Saint Joe on the school bus / Clock of elvenkind / Sherry Fraser / Gone crazy / Opium / One more suicide / Dog and his master / Shadow of Seattle / Vampires of New York
85335692 / 27 Apr '98 / EMI

Marden Hill

☐ LOST WEEKEND, THE (A Marden Hill Collection)
Masque / Oh Constance / Bachus is back / Curtain / Satellite / Execution / Our man in... / Come on (superpimp) / Long drive / Summertime / Spanish slalom / Bardot / Arrival / Sugarplums
CDMRED 149 / 22 Jun '98 / Cherry Red

Mardones, Benny

☐ STAND BY YOUR MAN
CURCD 030 / Nov '96 / Hit

Marduk

☐ DARK ENDLESS
NFR 003 / Oct '94 / No Fashion

☐ GLORIFICATION
OPCD 043 / Oct '96 / Osmose

☐ HEAVEN SHALL BURN WHEN WE ARE GATHERED
OPCD 40 / Jul '96 / Osmose

☐ LIVE IN GERMANY
OPCD 054 / Jun '97 / Osmose

☐ NIGHTWING
OPCD 064 / 30 Mar '98 / Osmose

☐ OPUS NOCTURNE
OPCD 028 / Jan '95 / Osmose

Marginal Man

☐ IDENTITY
DIS 013CD / 6 Oct '97 / Dischord

Margitza, Rick

☐ GAME OF CHANCE
Good question / August in Paris / 13 bar blues / Careless / Blades run / Bird shit (for Charlie Parker) / Jazz prelude no.9 / No minor affair / Cidade vazia / Game of chance
CHR 70044 / Jul '97 / Challenge

☐ HANDS OF TIME
CHR 70021 / Sep '95 / Challenge

Margo

☐ IRELAND ON MY MIND
I would like to see you again / Poverty / Tribute to Packie Bonner / Tipperary far away / Born in Ireland / Consider the children / Little town on the Shannon / Man from the glen / Rented room / Little white house / Ireland on my mind / How far is heaven
RZRCD 516 / Apr '92 / Ritz

☐ NEW BEGINNINGS
You'll remember me / Eyes of a child / Back in baby's arms / Irish harvest day / Home is where the heart is / Infamous angel / Memories of Mayo / I'll forgive and I'll try to forget / Pick me up on your way down / Paper mansions / If I kiss you / To my children I'm Irish / Sitting alone / Friends
RZCD 540 / Aug '94 / Ritz

Margolin, Bob

☐ DOWN IN THE ALLEY
ALCD 4816 / Nov '93 / Alligator

☐ MY BLUES AND MY GUITAR
ALCD 4835 / Nov '95 / Alligator

☐ UP AND IN
Window / Alien's blues / Imagination / She and the devil / Blues for bartenders / Why are people like that / Goin' back out on the road / Up and in / Coffee break / 'Bout out / Not what you said last night / Long ago and far away / Just because / Later for you
ALCD 4851 / May '97 / Alligator

Margy, Lina

☐ ETOILES DE LA CHANSON
882402 / Aug '93 / Music Memoria

Maria, Tania

☐ BEST OF TANIA MARIA, THE
I don't go / Made in New York / I do I love you / Valeu / Bronx / Tanoca Vignette / Chuleta / Please don't stay / O bom e / Ca c'est bon / Marguerita / 210 West
CDP 7986342 / Jun '93 / World Pacific

☐ BLUESILIAN
Yes, is the way to go / Eric's blues / Zaza / Bluesilian / Feeling the air / Rebordosa / All alone together / Please me / If I could change / From my window / Oxala
TKM 50032 / May '96 / TKM

☐ COME WITH ME
Sangria / Embraceable you / Lost in Amazonia / Come with me / Sementes, graines and seeds / Nega / Euzinha / It's all over now
CCD 4200 / Jul '95 / Concord Picante

☐ EUROPE
Funky tamborine / Chuleta / I can do it / Senso unico / O bom e / She's outrageous / Bom bom bom (Chi chi chi)
NNCD 1003 / May '97 / New Note

☐ LOVE EXPLOSION
Funky tambourine / It's all in my hands / You've got me feeling your love / Love explosion / Bela la bela / Rainbow of your love / Deep cove view / Pour toi
CCD 4230 / Dec '86 / Concord Jazz

☐ NO COMMENT
Pelham melody / Liqued groove / Keep in mind / Desire / Marvin my love / Who knows / Jack Hammer / Gotcha / Fanatic / Bali / Something for now
TKM 50012 / May '95 / TKM

☐ OUTRAGEOUS
Dear Dee Vee / Confusion / She's outrageous / Bom bom bom / Happiness / Amei demais / Ta tudo cetto / I can do it / Minha Moe / Happiness / Granada
CCD 4563 / Aug '93 / Concord Picante

☐ PIQUANT
Yatra-ta / It's not for me to say / Triste / Chicl'ete com banana / Lemon cuica / Super happy / Comecar de novo / Vem pra roda
CCD 4151 / Jul '88 / Concord Jazz

☐ REAL TANIA MARIA-WILD, THE
Yatra - ta / A cama na varanda / Vem pra roda / Come with me / Funy tamborine / 2 a.m. / Sangria
CCD 4264 / Nov '86 / Concord Jazz

☐ TAURUS
CCD 4175 / Oct '87 / Concord Picante

Maria-Jose

☐ ETOILES DE LA CHANSON
882412 / Aug '93 / Music Memoria

Mariachi Azteca

☐ BEST OF MARIACHI AZTECA, THE
EUCD 1119 / '91 / ARC

Mariachi Cobre

☐ XXV ANIVERSARIO 1971-1996
150222 / Aug '96 / Celestial Harmonies

Mariachi Jalisco

☐ SINGS TO THE HOMELAND
ARN 64342 / Feb '96 / Arion

Mariachi Reyes Del Aserradero

☐ SONES FROM JALISCO
CO 108 / Feb '94 / Corason

Mariachi Sol

☐ CU CU RRU CU CU PALOMA
EUCD 1246 / Nov '93 / ARC

Mariano, Charlie

☐ 70 (Mariano, Charlie & Friends)
Il Piacere / Everybody's song / Deep river / Rabou abou kabou / Crystal bells / Seva la murga
VBR 21492 / Feb '94 / Vera Bra

☐ ALTO SAX...FOR YOUNG MODERNS (Mariano, Charlie, Quartet)
Johnny one note / Very thought of you / Smoke gets in your eyes / King for a day / Darn that dream / Floormat / Blues / I heard you cry last night
BET 6013 / Jan '95 / Bethlehem

☐ BOSTON DAYS 1954 (Mariano, Charlie Quintet)
FSRCD 207 / Nov '94 / Fresh Sound

☐ CHARLIE MARIANO PLAYS
BET 6012 / Jan '95 / Bethlehem

☐ ENJOY
ISCD 168 / May '98 / Intersound

☐ FRIENDS (Mariano, Charlie & Stephen Diez)
ISCD 121 / '91 / Intersound

☐ FROM ME TO YOU
ISCD 148 / Jun '95 / Intersound

☐ IT'S STANDARD TIME VOL.1 (Mariano, Charlie & Tete Montoliu Trio)
FSR 5021CD / Jan '98 / Fresh Sound

☐ IT'S STANDARD TIME VOL.2 (Mariano, Charlie & Tete Montoliu Trio)
FSR 5022CD / Jan '98 / Fresh Sound

☐ JYOTHI
Voice solo / Vandanam / Varshini / Saptarshi / Kartik / Bhajan
8115482 / Aug '86 / ECM

Marias, Gerard

☐ EST
HOP 200001 / May '94 / Label Hopi

Marie, Donna

☐ FEEL GOOD
LDRCD 023 / 1 Dec '97 / Londisc

☐ REGGAE LOVE MUSIC VOL.1
PICD 202 / Jun '97 / Pioneer

Marie, Teena

☐ GREATEST HITS
I'm a sucker for your love / Don't look back / Behind the groove / I need your lovin' / Square biz / It must be magic / Ballad of Cradle Rob and me / Portugese love / Aladdin's lamp / Irons in the fire / I'm gonna have my cake (and eat it too) / Yes indeed / Deja vu (I've been there before) / Opus III (does anybody care)
5525462 / 4 May '98 / Spectrum

☐ STAR CHILD
Lovergirl / Help youngblood get to the freaky party / Out on a limb / Alibi / Jammin' / Star child / We've got to stop (meeting like this) / My Dear Mr.Gaye / Light
7464395282 / Feb '85 / Epic

Marienthal, Eric

☐ EASY STREET
5373382 / May '97 / IE

☐ ERIC MARIENTHAL COLLECTION
Oasis / Hustlin' / Sun was in my eyes / Written in the wind / Brazilian dream / That's the way / Walk through the fire / Where are you / Hold on my heart / Where you belong / Street dance / Legenda
GRP 98532 / Feb '97 / GRP

Marilla

☐ SWEET SOUNDS OF CHRISTMAS, THE
Ding dong merrily on high / Once in royal David's city / O come all ye faithful (adeste fidelis) / When a child is born / Away in a manger / Drummer boy / Do you hear what I hear / In the bleak mid Winter / Angels we have heard on high / O little town of Bethlehem / It came upon the midwinter clear / Silent night / Mary's boy child / O holy night
MLM 114 / Dec '96 / One Stop

Marillion

☐ AFRAID OF SUNLIGHT
Gazpacho / Cannibal surf babe / Beautiful / Afraid of sunrise / Out of this world / Afraid of sunlight / Beyond you / King
CDEMD 1079 / Jun '95 / EMI

☐ B'SIDES THEMSELVES
Grendel / Charting the single / Market square heroes / Three boats down from the Candy / Cinderella search / Lady Nina / Freaks / Tux on / Margaret
CZ 39 / Jul '88 / EMI

☐ BEST OF BOTH WORLDS, THE (2CD Set)
Script for a jesters tear / Market square heroes / He knows you know / Forgotten sons / Garden party / Assassing / Punch and Judy / Kayleigh / Lavender / Heart of Lothian / Incommunicado / Warm wet circles / That time of the night (the short straw) / Sugar mice / Uninvited guest / Easter / Hooks in you / Space / Cover my eyes (pain and heaven) / No one can / Dry land / Waiting to happen / Great escape / Alone again in the lap of luxury / Made again / King / Afraid of sunlight / Beautiful / Cannibal surf babe
CDEMC 3761 / Feb '97 / EMI

☐ BRAVE
Bridge / Living with the big lie / Runaway / Goodbye to all that / Wave / Mad / Opium den / Slide / Standing in the swing / Hard as love / Hollow man / Alone again in the lap of luxury / Now wash your hand / Paper lies / Brave / Great escape / Last of you / Falling from the moon / Made again
CDEMD 1054 / Feb '94 / EMI

☐ CLUTCHING AT STRAWS
Hotel hobbies / Warm wet circles / That time of the night / Going under / Just for the record / White Russian / Incommunicado / Torch song / Slainte Mhath / Sugar mice / Last straw
CZ 214 / '89 / EMI

☐ COLLECTION, THE
Grendel / He knows you know / Jigsaw / Punch and Judy / Cinderella search / Kayleigh / Lavender / Lady Nina / Torch song
CDGOLD 1058 / Oct '96 / EMI Gold

☐ FUGAZI
Assassing / Punch and Judy / Jigsaw / Emerald lies / She chameleon / Incubus / Fugazi
CDEMC 3682 / May '94 / EMI

☐ FUGAZI (The Best Of Both Worlds Remasters Series/2CD Set)
Assassing / Punch and Judy / Jigsaw / Emerald lies / She chameleon / Incubus / Fugazi / Cinderella dearch / Assassing / Three boats down from the candy / Punch and Judy / She chameleon / Emerald lies / Incubus
4933692 / 2 Mar '98 / EMI

☐ HOLIDAYS IN EDEN (The Best Of Both Worlds Remasters Series/2CD Set)
Splintering heart / Cover my eyes / Party / No one can / Holidays in Eden / Dry land / Waiting to happen / This town / Rakes progress / 100 nights / Sympathy / How can it hurt / Collection / Cover my reyes / Sympathy / I will walk on water / You don't need anyone / No one can / Party / This town / Waiting to happen / Eric / Epic
4933722 / 2 Mar '98 / EMI

☐ MADE AGAIN (Live)
Splintering heart / East / No one can / Waiting to happen / Cover my eyes / Space / Hooks in you / Beautiful / Kayleigh / Lavender / Afraid of sunlight / King / Bridge / Living with the big lie / Runaway / Goodbye to all that / Wave / Mad / Opium den / Slide / Standing in the swing / Hard as love / Hollow man / Alone again in the lap of luxury / Now wash your hands / Paper lies / Brave / Great escape / Last of you / Falling from the moon / Made again
CDEMD 1094 / Mar '96 / EMI

☐ MISPLACED CHILDHOOD
Pseudo-silk kimono / Kayleigh / Lavender / Bitter suite / Heart of Lothian / Waterhole / Lords of the backstage / Blind curve / Childhood's end / White feather
CDEMC 3684 / May '94 / EMI

☐ REAL TO REEL/BRIEF ENCOUNTER (2CD Set)
Assasing / Incubus / Cinderella search / Emerald lies / Forgotten sons / Garden party / Market square heroes / Lady Nina / Freaks / Kayleigh / Fugazi / Script for a jester's tear
CDEM 1603 / Jun '97 / EMI

☐ SCRIPT FOR A JESTER'S TEAR
He knows you know / Web / Garden party / Chelsea Monday / Forgotten sons / Script for a jester's tear
CDGOLD 1012 / Mar '96 / EMI Gold

☐ SCRIPT FOR A JESTER'S TEAR (Remastered/2CD Set)
Script for a jester's tear / He knows you know / Web / Garden party / Chelsea Monday / Forgotten sons / Market square heroes / Three boats down from the candy grendel / Chelsea Monday / He knows you know / Charting the single / Market square heroes
REMARIL 001 / 29 Sep '97 / EMI

☐ SCRIPT FOR A JESTER'S TEAR/ FUGAZI/MISPLACED CHILDHOOD (The Originals/3CD Set)
Script for a jester's tear / He knows you know / Web / Garden party / Chelsea Monday / Forgotten sons / Punch and Judy / Jigsaw / Emerald lies / She chameleon / Incubus / Fugazi / Pseudo silk kimono / Kayleigh / Lavender / Bitter suite / Heart of Lothian / Waterhole (Expresso Bongo) / Lords of the backstage / Blind curve / Childhood's end / White feather
CDOMB 015 / 27 Jul '98 / EMI

☐ SEASON'S END (Remastered/2CD Set)
King of sunset town / Easter / Uninvited guest / Seasons end / Holloway girl / Berlin / After me / Hooks in you / Space / Uninvited guest / Bell in the sea / Release / King of sunset town / Holloway girl / Seasons end / Uninvited guest / Berlin / Bell in the sea
REMARIL 005 / 29 Sep '97 / EMI

☐ TALES FROM THE ENGINE ROOM (This Strange Engine Remixed) (Marillion & The Positive Light)
Estonia / Memory of water / This strange engine / One fine day / Face 1004 / 80 days
EAGCD 033 / 22 Jun '98 / Eagle

☐ THIS STRANGE ENGINE
Man of a thousand faces / One fine day / 80 Days / Estonia / Memory of water / An accidental man / Hope for the future / This strange engine
RAWDP 121
RAWCD 121 / Apr '97 / Raw Power

Marilyn Manson

☐ ANTICHRIST SUPERSTAR
Irresponsible hate anthem / Beautiful people / Dried up tied up and dead to the world / Tourniquet / Little Horn / Cryptorchid / Deformography / Wormboy / Mister superstar / Angel with the scabbed wings / Kinderfeld / Antichrist superstar / 1996 / Minute of decay / Reflecting God / Man that you fear
IND 90086 / Oct '96 / Interscope

☐ GET YOUR GUN
INTDM 95902 / Dec '96 / Interscope

☐ INTERVIEW SESSIONS
CHAT 2 / 3 Nov '97 / Chatback

☐ LUNCHBOX
INTDM 95806 / Dec '96 / Interscope

☐ PORTRAIT OF AN AMERICAN FAMILY
Prelude (the family trip) / Organ grinder / Cake and sodomy / Lunchbox / Cyclops / Get your gunn / Dope hat / Misery machine / My monkey / Snake eyes and sissies / Sweet tooth / Dogma / Wrapped in plastic
IND 92344 / Jul '96 / Interscope

☐ SMELLS LIKE CHILDREN
Hands of small children / Diary of a dope fiend / Shitty chicken gang bang / Kiddie grinder / Sympathy for the parents / Sweet dreams (are made of this) / Everlasting cuntsucker / Fuck frankie / I put a spell on you / May cause discolouration of the urine or feces / Scab, guns and peanut butter / Dance of the dope hats / White trash / Dancing with the one-legged... / Rock 'n' roll nigger
IND 92641 / Aug '96 / Interscope

☐ SMELLS LIKE WHITE TRASH (CD Interview Booklet)
UFOCD 15BX
UFOCD 15 / 3 Nov '97 / UFO

Marine Girls

☐ LAZY WAYS/BEACH PARTY
Place in the sun / Leave me with the boy / Falling again / Love to know / Different light / Sunshine blue / Second sight / Don't come back / That fink, jazz-me-blues boy / Fever / Shell island / Lazy ways / Such a thing / You must be mad / In love / Fridays / Tonight / Times we used to spend / Flying over russia / Tutti lo sanno / All dressed up / Honey / Holiday song / He got the girl / Day - night dreams / Promises / Silent red / Dishonesty / 20,000 leagues / Marine girls
CDMRED 44 / Aug '88 / Cherry Red

Mariner

☐ AMPHIBIAN
15096995312 / 27 Apr '98 / Intersound

Maring, Wil

☐ OCEAN FROM HOME, AN
Things will be better next year / Easy / Pal I left behind / It's raining / Christmas in my hometown / Old mill valley / Bucky's present / Ocean from home / Waiting and wondering / Old eight by forty / Eight more miles to Louisville / Bottomlands
BCD 16233 / Nov '97 / Bear Family

Marini, Giovanna

☐ DEPARTURES (Twenty Years After The Death Of Pier Paolo Pasolini) (Marini, Giovanna Vocal Quartet)
Il galeone / Il mio prino incontro con Pier Paolo Pasolini / Mi pesa andar lontano / E adesso / Miserere di Santu Lussurgiu / Amour mi amour/ Dansa di narcis / Pauli/Madonuta / Stornelli e Discanti all cepranese / Montefiori dall'aso / Stabermater / Eccoci bella mia buongiorno / Calpastevano mosaico / Si lui la vole / Sono arrivati i barbari / El di de la me muart / Lied / Lamento per la morte di Pasolini / Biva biva
Y 225065 / Jan '97 / Silex

☐ PASOLINI PARTENZE (Marini, Giovanna Vocal Quartet)
Y 225065CD / May '97 / Silex

Marino

☐ AFTER FOREVERS GONE
Northern sky (part 1) / Jasmine / El Salvador / Look into the sun / After forever's gone / Fishermen (part II) / Borderline / Ian's garden / Did I say that / Northern sky (part II) / Present light / Northern sky (part III)
WKFMCD 139 / Mar '90 / FM

☐ BLUES FOR LOVERS
Angel of mercy / Sanctify my soul / Lovers forever (jan's theme) / Angel of mercy part 2 (lovers become one) / Blissed out in havana / Alone in the dark / Sanctified part 2 (sweet seduction) / Blues for lovers
WKFMXD 167 / Mar '91 / FM

Marino, Frank

☐ WORLD ANTHEM (Marino, Frank & Mahogany Rush)
4894452 / 26 Jan '98 / Columbia

Marion

☐ PROGRAM, THE
8289942 / 24 Aug '98 / London

☐ THIS WORLD AND BODY
Fallen through / Sleep / Let's all go together / Wait / Only way / I stopped dancing / All for love / Toys for boys / Time / Vanessa / Your body lies / My children
8286952 / Feb '96 / London

Marionettes

☐ AVE DEMENTIA
Heaven and hell / Damien / Ave dementia / She said / Like Christabel / Love is / Play dead / Obsession
AVECD 001 / 15 Dec '97 / Flicknife
DARK 005CD / 2 Mar '98 / Darkend

☐ MEPHISTO'S MOB
Z 910062 / May '93 / Jungle

☐ RISE
Rise / Monster / Sickness / Temptation / Fall / Absolution / One day at a time / I / Death of a friend / Speed / Rise
BACCYCD 005 / 15 Dec '97 / Community

☐ RISE/BOOK OF SHADOWS (2CD Set)
DARK 006CD / 2 Mar '98 / Darkend

Mariteragi, Marie

☐ TUAMOTU AND BORA BORA ISLANDS
S 65817CD / Apr '95 / Manuiti

Maritime Crew

☐ HURRAH FOR OUR CAPTAIN
CDMANU 1533 / Jul '97 / ODE

Marjane, Leo

☐ CHANSOPHONE 1937-1942
701282 / Jun '93 / Chansophone

☐ HER FAVOURITE MOVIE SONGS
995702 / Jul '96 / EPM

MARK B MAIN SECTION R.E.D. CD CATALOGUE

Mark B
☐ UNDERWORLD CONNECTION
JFRCD 008 / Jul '97 / Jazz Fudge

Mark, Jon
☐ CELTIC STORY, A
WCL 11002 / May '94 / White Cloud

☐ SUNDAY IN AUTUMN, A
WCL 110032 / May '95 / White Cloud

Mark Of Cain
☐ BATTLESICK
213CD 010 / Feb '97 / 2.13.61

Mark T
☐ GARDEN OF LOVE, THE
FSCD 20 / '92 / Folksound

Mark-Almond Band
☐ NIGHTMUSIC
WCL 110262 / Sep '96 / White Cloud

Markamaru
☐ RAICES INCAS
4301120942 / 5 May '98 / ANS

Marketts
☐ BATMAN
EVAB 36 / 16 Mar '98 / EVA

Markopoulos, Yannis
☐ BRIGHTNESS
ML 0186 / 11 May '98 / Musurgia Graeca

Markowitz, Phil
☐ TAXI RIDE
70317600312 / 21 Apr '98 / Passage

Marks, Evan
☐ THREE DAY WEEKEND
5376902 / 9 Feb '98 / Verve Forecast

Marks, Louisa
☐ BREAKOUT
BFMCD 101 / Jan '97 / Bushranger

Marks, Roger
☐ C'EST MAGNIFIQUE (Marks, Roger Armada Jazzband)
RSCD 676 / Jul '98 / Raymer

Markus, Ben
☐ RABBLE WITHOUT A CAUSE (Markus, Ben Band)
SPRAYCD 307 / Nov '97 / Making Waves

Marley Booker, Cedella
☐ AWAKE ZION
DANCD 067 / Jun '97 / Danceteria

Marley, Bob
☐ 36 REGGAE SONGS (2CD Set)
Duppy conqueror / Trench Town rock / Lively up yourself / Rainbow country / Sun is shining / Soul almighty / All in one / Can't you see / Chances are / Hammer / Mellow mood / Mr. Brown / Reaction / Soon come / There she goes / Touch me / It's alright / Stop the train / Rebel's hop / Natural mystic / Treat you right / 400 years / Corner stone / Soul captive / African herbsman / Do it twice / Back out / No sympathy / No water / Small axe / Soul shakedown party / Try me / Brain washing / Caution / Don't rock my boat / I gotta keep on moving
TNC 96202 / Aug '96 / Natural Collection

☐ AFRICA (Marley, Bob & The Wailers)
TDCY 6006 / 22 Jun '98 / TDK

☐ AFRICAN HERBSMAN
Lively up yourself / Small axe / Keep on moving / Duppy conqueror / Trenchtown rock / African herbsman / Fussing and fighting / All in one / Stand alone / Don't rock the boat / Put it on / Sun is shining / Kaya / 400 years / Riding high / Brain washing
CDTRL 62 / Mar '94 / Trojan

☐ ALL THE HITS
RRTGCD 7757 / Apr '91 / Rohit

☐ AUDIO ARCHIVE
CDAA 047 / Jun '92 / Tring

☐ BABYLON BY BUS (Marley, Bob & The Wailers)
Positive vibration / Funky reggae party / Exodus / Rat race / Lively up yourself / Rebel music / War / No more trouble / Stir it up / Concrete jungle / Kinky reggae / Is this love / Heathen / Jamming
TGDCD 1 / Jan '94 / Tuff Gong

☐ BEST OF BOB MARLEY, THE (1968-1972)
Trenchtown rock / Don't rock the boat / Kaya / Soul shakedown party / Cheer up / Keep on moving / Try me / Lively up yourself / All in one / Soul rebel / Duppy conqueror / Keep on skanking / Caution / Mr. Brown
CSAPCD 107 / Jun '90 / Connoisseur Collection

☐ BEST OF THE WAILERS (Marley, Bob & The Wailers)
444032 / Jan '97 / Rhino

☐ BEST, THE
Natural mystic / Kinky reggae / Go tell it on the mountain / Sun is shining / Back out / Soon come / Do it twice / Stop the train / Small axe / Rebel's hop / Soul almighty / Kaya / Duppy conqueror / Trench town rock / Can't you see
15499 / Nov '92 / Laserlight

☐ BOB MARLEY (The Great Legend Of Reggae)
Soul rebel / Caution / Treat me right / How many times / There she goes / Mellow mood / Tell me / Hammer / Touch me / Chances are / More axe / You can't do that to me / Corner stone / Reaction / No sympathy / Keep on skanking / Soul shakedown party / Try me / Wisdom / African herbsman / No water / Brainwashing / All in one / It's alright / Thank you lord / Adam and Eve / Brand new second hand / Jah is mighty / This train / Turn me loose / Mr. Brown / My cup
24336 / Nov '96 / Laserlight

☐ BOB MARLEY (4CD Set)
Trench town rock / Medley (Bend down low, Nice time, One love, Simmer down, It / Soul rebel / Try me / It's alright / No sympathy / No water / Reaction / Rainbow country / Natural mystic / There she goes / Mellow mood / Treat you right / Chances are / Hammer / Touch me / Soul shakedown party / Stop that train / Caution / Soul captives / Go tell it to the mountain / Can't you see / Soon come / Cheer up / Back out / Do it twice / Keep on moving / Don't rock my boat / Put it on / Fussing and fighting / Duppy conqueror / Small axe / Riding high / Kaya / African herbsman / Stand alone / Sun is shining / Mr. Brown / 400 years / Lively up yourself / Soul almighty / My cup / Corner stone / Brain washing / Rebel's hop / You can't do that to me / How many times
QUAD 004 / Nov '96 / Tring

☐ BOB MARLEY (CD/CD Rom Set)
WWCDR 004 / Apr '97 / Weton-Wesgram

☐ BOB MARLEY & THE WAILERS ARCHIVES (Marley, Bob & The Wailers)
Run for cover / More axe / (Don't) rock me boat / Rainbow country / Kaya / Dreamland / All in one / Memphis / Dracula / Keep on skanking / Turn me loose / Dream / Stand alone / One in all / Try me / I gotta (keep moving) / Fussing and fighting / African herbsman
RMCD 223 / Nov '97 / Rialto

☐ BOB MARLEY 50TH ANNIVERSARY (Various Artists)
CDTAL 800 / Jan '96 / Trojan

☐ BOB MARLEY AND THE WAILERS (Upsetter Record Shop Pt.1) (Marley, Bob & The Wailers)
LG 21040 / Aug '92 / Lagoon

☐ BOB MARLEY AND THE WAILERS (Upsetter Record Shop Pt.2) (Marley, Bob & The Wailers)
LG 21044 / Aug '92 / Lagoon

☐ BOB MARLEY ARCHIVE
Mr. Brown / Soul rebel / Duppy conqueror / Four hundred years / Try me / African herbsman / Keep on moving / Fussing and fighting / Stand alone / My cup / Put it on / Sun is shining / Rebel's hop / Brand new secondhand / Cornerstone / No water / Jah is mighty / Riding high / Brainwashing / Dreamland
RMCD 206 / Nov '97 / Rialto

☐ BOB MARLEY COLLECTION, THE (3CD Set)
Don't rock my boat / Soul shakedown party / There she goes / Stop the train / Mellow mood / Caution / Treat you right / Soul almighty / Sun is shining / Chances are / Kaya / Back out / Hammer / Lively up yourself / Cheer up / Mr. Brown / Riding high / Rainbow country / Small axe / Soul captives / Kinky reggae / Can't you see / Natural mystic / Soon come / Trenchtown rock / No sympathy / Do it twice / Keep on moving / My cup / Put it on / Fussing and fighting / Corner stone / African herbsman / No water / Stand alone / Brain washing / Rebel's hop / Go tell it to the mountains / All in one / 400 years / Duppy conqueror / Soul rebel / You can't do that to me / Touch me / Try me / How many times / Memphis / It's alright
TFP 010 / Nov '92 / Tring

☐ BRISBANE AUSTRALIA 1979 (Marley, Bob & The Wailers)
KECH 5012 / 22 Jun '98 / A-In-Co

☐ BURNIN' (Marley, Bob & The Wailers)
Get up stand up / Hallelujah time / I shot the sheriff / Burnin' and lootin' / Put it on / Small axe / Pass it on / Duppy conqueror / One foundation / Rastaman chant
TGLCD 2 / Jan '94 / Tuff Gong

☐ BUSTIN' OUT OF TRENCH TOWN (2CD Set)
SMDCD 108 / Jul '97 / Snapper

☐ CATCH A FIRE
Concrete jungle / 400 years / Stop the train / Baby we got a date / Rock it baby / Kinky reggae / No more trouble / Midnight ravers
TGLCD 1 / Jan '94 / Tuff Gong

☐ COLLECTION, THE
COL 024 / Apr '95 / Collection

☐ COLLECTION, THE (3CD Set) (Marley, Bob & The Wailers)
African herbsman / Mr. Brown / Soul almighty / Stand alone / Small axe / Rebel's hop / No sympathy / Keep on moving / Soul rebel / Brand new second hand / Chances are / Stop that train / Hammer / Wisdom / This train / Touch me / Caution / Thank you lord / Rainbow country / Lively up yourself / Natural mystic / Kaya / My cup / Put it on / Cheer up / Can't you see / Treat you right / Soul shakedown party / Tell me / Duppy conqueror / Mellow mood / You can't do that to me / Soon come / How many times / Go tell it on the mountain / Don't rock the boat
390572 / Aug '97 / Hallmark

☐ COMPLETE WAILERS 1967-1972, THE (3CD Set) (Marley, Bob & The Wailers)
22110022 / 17 Mar '98 / JAD

☐ CONFRONTATION (Marley, Bob & The Wailers)
Chant down Babylon / Buffalo soldier / Jump Nyabinghi / Mix up, mix up / Give thanks and praises / Blackman redemption / Trench town / I know / Stiff necked fools / Rastaman live up
TGLCD 10 / Jan '94 / Tuff Gong

☐ DORTMUND GERMANY 1980 (Marley, Bob & The Wailers)
KECH 5013 / 22 Jun '98 / A-In-Co

☐ DOWN SOUTH MIAMI (Marley, Bob & The Wailers)
KECH 5004 / 22 Jun '98 / A-In-Co

☐ DREAMS OF FREEDOM (Ambient Translations Of Bob Marley In Dub)
5244192 / 3 Nov '97 / Axiom

☐ EARLY COLLECTION (Marley, Bob & The Wailers)
Wings of a dove / Do you remember / Love and affection / Donna / It hurts to be alone / Do you feel the same way / Dancing shoes / I'm still waiting / I made a mistake / One love / Maga dog / Nobody knows / Lonesome feeling / Let him go / Lonesome track / I'm going home
4679542 / Oct '95 / Columbia

☐ EXODUS (Marley, Bob & The Wailers)
Natural mystic / So much things to say / Guiltiness / Heathen / Exodus / Jamming / Waiting in vain / Turn your lights down low / Three little birds / One love - people get ready
TGLCD 6 / Jan '94 / Tuff Gong

☐ GOLD COLLECTION, THE (2CD Set)
R2CD 4048 / 13 Apr '98 / Deja Vu

☐ IN MEMORIAM (3CD Set)
CDTAL 400 / Mar '94 / Trojan

☐ IN THE BEGINNING
Soul shakedown party / Adam and Eve / Brand new secondhand / Cheer up / This train / Jah is mighty / Caution / Thank you Lord / Keep on skanking / Wisdom / Stop the train / Mr. Chatterbox / Turn me loose
CDTRL 221 / Mar '94 / Trojan

☐ INTERVIEW DISC
SAM 7022 / Nov '96 / Sound & Media

☐ JAMAICAN SINGLES VOL.1
60012 / Nov '95 / Declic

☐ JAMAICAN SINGLES VOL.2 (Dub Versions)
60022 / Nov '95 / Declic

☐ KAYA (Marley, Bob & The Wailers)
Easy skanking / Is this love / Sun is shining / Satisfy my soul / She's gone / Misty morning / Crisis / Kaya / Running away / Time will tell
TGLCD 7 / Jan '94 / Tuff Gong

☐ KEEP ON MOVING
Keep on moving / Soul almighty / Small axe / Soul shakedown party / Go tell it on the mountain / Soon come / Can't you see / Cheer up / Do it twice / Back out / Soul captive
EMPRCD 700 / 8 Sep '97 / Emporio

☐ LEE PERRY SESSIONS, THE
Lively up yourself / Small axe / Trenchtown rock / Sun is shining / Kaya / African herbsman / Brainwashing / Mr. Brown / Try me / No sympathy / Duppy conqueror / Stand alone / Fussing and fighting / Rebel's hop / Soul almighty / It's alright / Don't rock the boat / Put it on / All in one / Keep on moving
CPCD 8009 / Oct '93 / Charly

☐ LEGEND (Marley, Bob & The Wailers)
Is this love / Jamming / No woman, no cry / Stir it up / Get up and stand up / Satisfy my soul / I shot the sheriff / One love / Buffalo soldier / Exodus / Redemption song / Could you be loved / Want more
BMWCDX 1 / May '91 / Tuff Gong

☐ LEGEND IN SAX
AACD 88 / Jun '95 / A&A Productions

☐ LEGENDARY BOB MARLEY, THE (3CD Set)
Trench Town rock / Rebels hop / Soul shake down / Mr. Brown / My cup / Fussin' and fightin' / Treat you right / Reaction / Soul almighty / You can't do that to me / Riding high / Duppy conquerer / Sun is shining / Rainbow country / Chances are / Stop that train / Kaya / Mellow moods / Soul captives / Put it on / Can't you see / All in one / How many times / Hammer / Caution / Try me / Small axe / Brain washing / African Herbsman / Touch me / 400 years / Lively up yourself / Go tell it to the mountain / Don't rock my boat / Soul shake down party / Soul rebel / Cheer up / Corner stone / Stand alone / It's alright / Do it twice / Keep on moving / Back out / Soon come / Natural mystic / No sympathy / No water
101162 / May '97 / A-Play Collection

☐ LIVE (Wailers)
SUB 48482 / Jun '97 / Melting Pop

☐ LIVE AT THE LYCEUM (Marley, Bob & The Wailers)
Trenchtown rock / Burnin' and lootin' / Them belly full (But we hungry) / Lively up yourself / No woman, no cry / I shot the sheriff / Get up stand up
TGLCD 4 / Jan '94 / Tuff Gong

☐ LIVE IN AUSTRALIA 1979 (Marley, Bob & The Wailers)
MECI 35101/2 / 27 Apr '98 / Crown

☐ LIVELY UP YOURSELF
Soul shakedown party / Lively up yourself / Riding high / It's alright / Reaction / My cup / Can't you see / No water / Trenchtown rock / No sympathy / Stop the train
CDSGP 056 / May '93 / Prestige

☐ LIVELY UP YOURSELF
Soul shakedown party / Stop that train / Caution / Soul captives / Go tell it on the mountain / Can't you see / Soon come / Cheer up / Back out / Do it twice / Keep on moving / Don't rock my boat / Put it on / Fussing and fighting / Duppy conqueror / Small axe / Riding high / Kaya / African herbsman / Stand alone / Sun is shining / Mr. Brown / 400 years / Lively up yourself
QED 005 / Apr '96 / Tring

☐ LIVELY UP YOURSELF
Soul shakedown / Put it on / Fussin' and fightin' / Kaya / Lively up yourself / Trench Town Rock / Soul rebel / Soul captives / Natural mystic / There she goes / Mellow mood / Treat you right / Hammer / You can't do
PLATCD 132 / Feb '97 / Platinum

☐ LIVELY UP YOURSELF
Lively up yourself / Go tell it to the mountain / Don't rock my boat / Soul shake down party / Soul rebel / Cheer up / Corner stone / Stand alone / It's alright / Do it twice / Keep on moving / Back out / Soon come / Natural mystic / No sympathy / No water
100062 / May '97 / A-Play Collection

☐ MAJESTIC WARRIORS (Wailers)
3640022 / Oct '91 / A&M

☐ MARLEY FAMILY ALBUM (Various Artists)
HBCD 160 / Feb '95 / Heartbeat

☐ MARLEY MAGIC (Live In Central Park At Summerstage/2CD Set) (Various Artists)
Lion in the morning: *Marley, Julian* / Me name Jr Gong/Crazy bald heads: *Marley, Damian 'Jr. Gong'* / Same old story: *Marley, Julian* / Searching: *Marley, Damian 'Jr. Gong'* / Babylon cookie jar: *Marley, Julian* / Love and inity: *Marley, Damian 'Jr. Gong'* / Exodus: *Marley, Julian* / We need love: *Yvad* / Music is the food of love: *Yvad* / No peace: *Yvad* / Freedom: *Yvad* / So much things to say: *Marley, Rita* / Good girls culture: *Marley, Rita* / That's the way: *Marley, Rita* / Harambe: *Marley, Rita* / To love somebody: *Marley, Rita* / Guava jelly/No woman no cry: *Marley, Rita* / Jammin'/Lively up yourself: *Marley, Rita* / Natty dread: *Marley, Ziggy & The Melody Makers* / Positive vibration: *Marley, Ziggy & The Melody Makers* / Stir it up: *Marley, Ziggy & The Melody Makers* / Get up stand up: *Marley, Ziggy & The Melody Makers* / Water and oil: *Marley, Ziggy & The Melody Makers* / Sun is shining: *Marley, Ziggy & The Melody Makers* / Free like we want to be: *Marley, Ziggy & The Melody Makers* / Could you be loved: *Marley, Ziggy & The Melody Makers*
HBECD 20603 / May '97 / Heartbeat

☐ MIAMI USA 1980 (Marley, Bob & The Wailers)
KECH 5011 / 22 Jun '98 / A-In-Co

☐ NATTY DREAD (Marley, Bob & The Wailers)
Lively up yourself / No woman, no cry / Them belly full (but we hungry) / Rebel music / So jah say / Natty dread / Bend down low / Talkin' blues / Revolution
TGLCD 3 / Jan '94 / Tuff Gong

☐ NATURAL MYSTIC
AVC 506 / Dec '92 / Avid

☐ NATURAL MYSTIC
Trench town rock / All in one / Soul rebel / Try me / It's alright / No sympathy / No water / Reaction / Rainbow country / Natural mystic / There she goes / Mellow mood / Treat you right / Chances are / Hammer / Touch me
QED 030 / Nov '96 / Tring

☐ NATURAL MYSTIC - THE LEGEND LIVES ON
Natural mystic / Easy skanking / Iron Lion Zion / Crazy baldheads / So much trouble in the world / War / Africa unite / Trenchtown rock / Keep on moving / Sun is shining / Who the cap fits / One drop / Roots, rock, reggae / Pimpers paradise / Time will tell
BMWCD 2 / May '95 / Tuff Gong

☐ NEVER ENDING WAILERS, THE (Wailers)
RASCD 3501 / Feb '94 / Ras

☐ ONE DAY OF BOB MARLEY (Marley, Bob & The Wailers)
TDCY 6004 / 22 Jun '98 / TDK

☐ ONE LOVE (Various Artists)
5320622 / Jul '96 / Antilles/New Directions

☐ ONE LOVE/ROOTS VOL.2
CDBM 052 / Mar '95 / Blue Moon

☐ PLATINUM COLLECTION, THE (2CD Set)
African herbsman / Don't rock my boat / Stand alone / Cheer up / Mellow mood / Duppy conqueror / Reaction / Brain washing / Rebel's hop / 400 years / Back out / Small axe / Lively up yourself / Fussing and fighting / Do it twice / Hammer / Mr. Brown / Kaya / Put it on / Trenchtown rock / My cup / Caution / All in one / Natural mystic / Chances are / Corner stone / Can't you see / Treat you right / Riding high / Soon come / Soul rebel / Go tell it on the mountain / Soul captive / It's alright / No sympathy / Rainbow country / How many times / Keep on moving / No water / Try me
PC 614 / Jul '97 / Platinum Collection

☐ POWER
Redder than red / My cup (I've got to cry) / Power and more power / Hypocrites / Thank you Lord / Mr. Chatterbox / Soul almighty / Nice time / Try me (I've got the action) / Mellow mood / Redder than red / My cup (I've got to cry) / Power and more power / Hypocrites / Thank you Lord / Mr. Chatterbox / Hey happy people / Nice time / Try me (I've got the action) / Mellow mood
MOCD 3014 / Nov '96 / More Music

☐ RARITIES VOL.1, THE (Marley, Bob & The Wailers)
Shocks of mighty / All in one / Copasetic / More axe / Axe man / Duppy conquer / Zig zag / Run for cover / Picture on the wall version 3 / Picture on the wall version 4 / Man to man / Nicoteen / Rock my boat / Like it like this
JMC 200229 / May '96 / Jamaican Gold

☐ RARITIES VOL.2, THE (Marley, Bob & The Wailers)
Dreamland / Dreamland version 2 / Jah is mighty / Turn me loose / Second hand / Second hand, part 2 / Brand new second hand / Love life / Keep on moving / Keep on skanking / Mr. Brown / Mr. Brown Version / Send me that love
JMC 200230 / May '96 / Jamaican Gold

☐ RASTAMAN (2CD Set)
Soul shakedown party / Caution / Do it twice / Back out / Try me / Corner stone / No water / Soul almighty / I made a mistake / Let him go / I'm going home / Nobody knows / Wings of a dove / Soul captive / Don't rock my boat / Stand alone / Love and affection / One love / Mega dog / Donna / Lonesome feeling / It hurts to be alone / Who feels it / Dancing shoes / Lonesome talk / Ten commandments of love / Chances are
CDBM 501 / Sep '95 / Blue Moon

☐ RASTAMAN VIBRATION (Marley, Bob & The Wailers)
Positive vibration / Roots, rock, reggae / Johnny was / Cry to me / Want more / Crazy baldheads / Who the cap fits / Night shift / War / Rat race
TGLCD 5 / Jan '94 / Tuff Gong

☐ REACTION
Reaction / I gotta keep on moving / Put it on / Go tell it on the mountain / Can't you see / Cheer up - good times are comin' / Don't rock the boat / Fussing and fighting / Memphis / African herbsman / Stand alone / Sun is shining / Brain washing / Mr. Brown / All in one / Soul rebel / Try me / Caution / No sympathy / It's alright
PWK 072 / Sep '88 / Carlton

☐ REAL SOUND OF JAMAICA (Marley, Bob & The Wailers)
Concrete jungle / Satisfy my soul / Rainbow country / Put it on / Don't rock my boat / Keep on movin' / Redder than red / Power and more power / Hypocrites / Thank you Lord / Mellow mood / Soul rebels / Reaction / Try me / Soul almighty
74321440032 / Apr '97 / Milan

☐ REBEL MUSIC (Marley, Bob & The Wailers)
Rebel music / So much trouble in the world / Them belly full (But we hungry) / Rat race / War / Roots / Slave driver / Ride natty ride / Crazy baldheads / Get up stand up / No more trouble
TGLCD 11 / Jan '94 / Tuff Gong

☐ REBEL REVOLUTION (2CD Set) (Marley, Bob & The Wailers)
Small axe / My cup / Keep on moving / Try me / Don't rock the boat / 400 Years / Put it on / Cornerstone / Fussing and fighting / No water / Duppy conqueror / Reaction / Memphis / Soul almighty / It's alright / Riding high / Soul rebel / Kaya / African herbsman / Satisfy my soul / Stand alone / Rebels hop / Sun is shining / Love life / Brain washing / Mr. Brown / Long long winter
JMC 200277 / May '96 / Jamaican Gold

☐ REGGAE ROOTS
901622 / '91 / FM

☐ RIDING HIGH (Marley, Bob & The Wailers)
CPCD 8029 / Feb '94 / Charly

☐ ROOTS OF A LEGEND (2CD Set) (Marley, Bob & The Wailers)
Duppy conqueror / Try me / Keep on skanking / Small axe / Kaya / Brain washing / Put it on / Fussing and fighting / Mr. Brown / No sympathy / Lively up yourself / Fussing and fighting / More axe / Corner stone / Riding high / Trench Town rock / Turn me loose / It's alright / Sun is shining / Caution / Stand alone / Stand alone / 400 years / All in one / Duppy conqueror / Soul shakedown party / Adam and Eve / Brand new second hand / Soul rebel / My cup / No water / Reaction / African herbman / Stop the train / There she goes / How many times / Rebel hop / Chances are / Hammer / Treat me right / Cheer up / Touch me / Rainbow country / Soon come / Long, long winter / Mellow mood / Soul almighty / Don't rock the boat / Keep on movin' / Memphis
CPCD 82462 / Nov '96 / Charly

☐ ROOTS VOL.1
I made a mistake / Let him go / I'm going home / Nobody knows / Wings of a dove / Soul captives / Don't rock my boat / Stand alone / Soul shakedown party / Caution / Do it twice / Back out / Try me / Corner stone / No water / Soul almighty
MM 008 / 29 Jun '98 / MagMid

☐ ROOTS VOL.2 (One Love)
One love / Love and affection / Mega dog / Donna / Lonesome feeling / It hurts to be alone / Who feels it / Dancing shoes / Lonesome talk / Ten commandments of men / Soul rebel / Chances are
CDBM 1052 / '89 / Blue Moon

☐ SATISFY MY SOUL
Satisfy my soul / Soul rebels / Concrete jungle / Soul almighty / Redder than red / My cup (I've got to cry) / Don't rock my boat / Try me (I've got to cry) / Thank you Lord / Nice time / Try me / (I've got the action) / One love / Love life / Rainbow country / Long long winter / Corner stone / Reaction / It's all right / No water can quench my thirst / Keep on moving / Put it on
CD 6074 / Apr '97 / Music

☐ SIMMER DOWN AT STUDIO ONE (Marley, Bob & The Wailers)
CDHB 171 / May '95 / Heartbeat

☐ SONGS OF FREEDOM (3CD Set)
Judge not / One cup of coffee / Simmer down / I'm still waiting / One love / Put it on / Bus dem shut (pyaka) / Mellow mood / Bend down low / Hypocrites / Stir it up / Nice time / Thank you Lord / Hammer / Caution / Back out / Soul shakedown party / Do it twice / Soul rebel / Sun is shining / Don't rock the boat / Small axe / Duppy conqueror / Mr. Brown / Screwface / Lick samba / Trenchtown rock / Craven choke puppy / Guava jelly / Acoustic medley / High tide or low tide / Slave driver / No more trouble / Concrete jungle / Get up stand up / Rastaman chant / Burnin' and lootin' / Iron lion zion / Lively up yourself / Natty dread / I shot the sheriff / No woman, no cry / Who the cap fits / Jah live / Crazy baldheads / War / Johnny was / Rat race / Jammin' / Waiting in vain / Exodus / Natural mystic / Three little birds / Running away / Keep on moving / Easy skanking / Is this love / Smile Jamaica / Time will tell / Africa unite / Survival / One drop / One dub / Zimbabwe / So much trouble in the world / Ride natty ride / Babylon system / Coming in from the cold / Real situation / Bad card / Could you be loved / Forever loving Jah / Rastaman live up / Give thanks and praise / One love/People get ready (12" mix) / Why should I / Redemption song
TGCBX 1 / Sep '92 / Tuff Gong

☐ SOUL ALMIGHTY (Natural Mystic II)
Try me / Touch me / Soul almighty / Do it twice / Back out / Cheer up / Put it on / Kaya / Fussin' and fightin' / Corner stone / African herbman / No water / Stand alone / Rebels hop / All in one / Duppy conqueror / 400 years / You can't do that to me / How many times
AVC 563 / Dec '95 / Avid

☐ SOUL ALMIGHTY (The Formative Years)
ANANCD 001 / Jun '96 / Anansi

☐ SOUL CAPTIVE (Marley, Bob & The Wailers)
RB 3010 / Nov '94 / Reggae Best

☐ SOUL OF THE GONG (Bob Marley's Greatest Hits) (Various Artists)
RNCD 2134 / Feb '96 / Rhino

☐ SOUL OF THE GONG IN DUB (Bob Marley's Greatest Hits In Dub) (Various Artists)
RNCD 2135 / Feb '96 / Rhino

☐ SOUL REBEL
EMPRCD 698 / Apr '97 / Emporio

☐ SOUL REBEL (Marley, Bob & The Wailers)
Soul rebel / There she goes / Treat me right / Put it on / Tell me / How many times / Mellow mood / Chances are / Hammer / Touch me
306542 / Jun '97 / Hallmark

☐ SOUL REVOLUTION VOL.1 & 2 (2CD Set) (Marley, Bob & The Wailers)
Keep on moving / Don't rock my boat / Fussing and fighting / Put it on / Memphis / Soul rebel / Riding high / Kaya / Stand alone / African herbsman / Brain washing / Mr. Brown
CDTRD 406 / Mar '94 / Trojan

☐ STOP THAT TRAIN
Stop that train / Kaya / Mellow moods / Soul captives / Put it on / Can't you see / All in one / How many times / Hammer / Caution / Try me / Small axe / Brain washing / African herbsman / Touch me / 400 years
100072 / May '97 / A-Play Collection

☐ SURVIVAL (Marley, Bob & The Wailers)
So much trouble / Africa unite / Babylon system / Ride Natty ride / One prop / Fighting against ism and skism / Top ranking / Wake up and live / Survival / Zimbabwe
TGLCD 8 / Jan '94 / Tuff Gong

☐ TALKIN' BLUES (Marley, Bob & The Wailers)
Talkin' blues / Burnin' and lootin' / Kinky reggae / Get up, stand up / Slave driver / Walk the proud land / You can't blame the youth / Rastaman chant / Am-a-do / Bend down low / I shot the sheriff
TGLCD 12 / Feb '91 / Tuff Gong

☐ TRENCH TOWN ROCK
Trench Town rock / Rebels hop / Soul shake down / Mr. Brown / My cup / Fussin' and fightin' / Treat you right / Riding high / Soul almighty / You can't do that to me / Riding high / Duppy conqueror / Sun is shining / Rainbow country / Chances are
101202 / May '97 / A-Play Collection

☐ TRIBUTE TO BOB MARLEY VOL.1, A (Various Artists)
CDTRL 332 / Mar '94 / Trojan

☐ TRIBUTE TO BOB MARLEY VOL.1, A (Various Artists)
RNCD 2089 / Feb '95 / Rhino

☐ TRIBUTE TO BOB MARLEY VOL.2, A (Various Artists)
CDTRL 341 / May '94 / Trojan

☐ TRIBUTE TO BOB MARLEY VOL.2, A (Various Artists)
RNCD 2117 / Sep '95 / Rhino

☐ TRIBUTE TO BOB MARLEY VOL.3, A (Various Artists)
(Marley's gone) his songs live on: *Hibbert, Toots* / Bend down low: *Groovers* / I'm still waiting: *Edwards, Jackie* / Mellow mood: *Gaytones* / Simmer down: *Clarke, Johnny* / Hypocrites: *Campbell, Al* / You poured sugar on me: *Smith, Ernie* / Duppy conqueror: *Lazarus, Ken* / My sympathy (400 years): *Upsetters* / Natty dread: *Shervington, Pluto* / No woman no cry: *Clarke, Johnny* / War: *Jarrett, Killerman* / I shot the sheriff: *Shervington, Pluto* / Time will tell: *Clarke, Johnny* / Talking blues: *Maroons* / Guava jelly: *Fab Five Inc.* / Easy skanking: *Clarke, Johnny* / I'm still waiting: *Brown, Dennis* / (Marley's gone) his songs live on: *Hibbert, Toots*
CDTRL 372 / Sep '96 / Trojan

☐ TRIBUTE TO BOB MARLEY, A (Various Artists)
CC 2709 / Apr '94 / Crocodisc

☐ TRIBUTE TO BOB MARLEY, A (An All Star Tribute To The Reggae Legend) (Various Artists)
Buffalo soldier: *Thomas, Ruddy* / I shot the sheriff: *Blues Busters* / Nice time: *Dunkley, Errol* / Soul rebel: *Max Romeo* / Bend down low: *Clarke, Johnny* / Get up stand up: *Mafia & Fluxy* / Could you be loved: *Thomas, Ruddy* / Put it on: *Aggrovators & The Wailers* / Jammin': *Spence, Michael* / Thank you lord: *Max Romeo* / No woman no cry: *Clarke, Johnny* / Small axe: *Hammond, Beres & Zappow* / Is this love: *Thomas, Ruddy* / Hypocrites: *Campbell, Al* / Simmer down: *Aggrovators & The Wailers* / Exodus: *Mafia & Fluxy* / Stir it up: *Edwards, Jackie* / Redemption song: *Frazer, Dean*
ECD 3296 / Feb '97 / K-Tel

☐ TRUE ROOTS
74321533992 / 8 Nov '97 / Camden

☐ UPRISING (Marley, Bob & The Wailers)
Coming in from the cold / Real situation / Bad card / We and them / Work / Zion train / Pimpers paradise / Could you be loved / Forever loving Jah / Redemption song
TGLCD 9 / Jan '94 / Tuff Gong

☐ VERY BEST OF THE EARLY YEARS (Marley, Bob & The Wailers)
Trenchtown rock / Lively up yourself / Soul almighty / Wisdom / Caution / Cheer up / Thank you lord / Stop the train / This train / Small axe / More axe / Don't rock my boat / Keep on moving / Brand new secondhand / Kaya / Turn me loose / Sun is shining / Keep on skanking
MCCD 033 / Sep '91 / Music Club

☐ WAILING WAILERS AT STUDIO ONE (Marley, Bob & The Wailers)
CDHB 172 / May '95 / Heartbeat

☐ WAILING WAILERS, THE (Wailers)
SOCD 1001 / Aug '94 / Studio One

☐ WISDOM (2CD Set) (Marley, Bob & Peter Tosh)
SMDCD 220 / 10 Aug '98 / Snapper

Marley, Damian

☐ MR. MARLEY (Marley, Damian 'Jr. Gong')
Trouble / Love and inity / 10,000 chariots / Old war chant / Party time / Kingston 12 / Keep on grooving / Searching (so much bubble) / One more cup of coffee / Julie / Me name Jr Gong / Mr. Marley
HBECD 20602 / May '97 / Heartbeat

Marley, Julian

☐ LION IN THE MORNING
Loving clear / Blossoming and blooming / Lion in the morning / Now you know / Babylon cookie jar / Same old story / Attack back / Arm your soul / Ease these pains / When the sun comes up / Got to be
HBECD 20601 / May '97 / Heartbeat

Marley, Kymani

☐ LIKE FATHER LIKE SON
RN 7001 / Aug '96 / Rhino

Marley, Rita

☐ HARAMBE
SHANCD 43010 / Nov '87 / Shanachie

☐ WE MUST CARRY ON
I know a place / Serious time / Who colt the game / So much things to say / To love somebody / Earth runnings / Bus dem shut (bredda pyaka) / Dem a fight (freedom) / Just one more morning / Special rhythm
SHCD 43082 / Jun '91 / Shanachie
322573 / Apr '97 / Koch International

☐ WHO FEELS IT KNOWS IT
SHANCD 43003 / '87 / Shanachie

Marley, Ziggy

☐ CONSCIOUS PARTY
Conscious party / Tumblin' down / Who a say / Have you ever been to hell / Lee and Molly / Tomorrow people / We propose / What's true / Dreams of home / We a guh some weh / New love
CDV 2506 / Mar '88 / Virgin

☐ FALLEN IS BABYLON (Marley, Ziggy & The Melody Makers)
Fallen is Babylon / Everyone wants to be / People get ready / Postman / Brotherly sisterly love / Born to be lively / Long winter / I remember / Day by day / Five days a year / Notice / Diamond City / Jah bless / People get ready (remix)
7559620322 / Jul '97 / Elektra

☐ JAHMEKYA (Marley, Ziggy & The Melody Makers)
Raw riddin' / Kozmik / Rainbow country / Drastic / Good time / What conquers defeat / First night / Wrong right wrong / Herbs an' spices / Problem with my woman / Jah is true and perfect / Small people / So good, so right / Namibia / New time and age / Generation
CDVIP 210 / 3 Aug '98 / Virgin VIP

☐ JOY AND BLUES (Marley, Ziggy & The Melody Makers)
Joy and blues / Brothers and sisters / There she goes / Talk / Rebel in disguise / X marks the spot / Head top / African herbsman / World so corrupt / Garden / Mama / This one
CDVUS 65 / Jul '93 / Virgin

☐ ONE BRIGHT DAY
Black my story (not history) / One bright day / Who will be there / When the lights gone out / Problems / All love / Look who's dancing / Justice / Love is the only law / Pains of life / Ur-ban music / Give it all you got / When the light's gone out (Jamaican style)
CDVIP 211 / 3 Aug '98 / Virgin VIP

Marlo, Clair

☐ BEHAVIOUR SELF
WLD 9208 / Apr '95 / Varese Sarabande

Marmalade

☐ ALL THE HITS PLUS MORE
I see the rain / Lovin' things / Wait for me Mary Ann / Ob la di ob la da / Baby make it soon / Reflections of my life / Rainbow / My little one / Cousin Norman / Back on the road / Radancer / Falling apart at the seams / Heavens above / I gave up / I listen to the heart / What are you gonna do / Best of my love / Good luck to you
CDSGP 0218 / 10 Nov '97 / Prestige

Marmarosa, Dodo

☐ DIAL MASTERS
Deep purple / Bird lore / Midnight at Mintons / High wind in Hollywood / Tone paintings II / Dodo's dance / Dary departs / Tea for two / Dilated pupils / Up in Dodo's room / Tone paintings I / Bopmatism / Trade winds / Cosmo Street
SPJCD 128 / Feb '96 / Spotlite

☐ DODO LIVES
Moose / Summertime / Don't blame me / Mellow mood / Deep purple / Boyd meets Stravinsky / Yardbird suite / Dodo's bounce / Smooth sailing / Dodo's lament
TPZ 1058 / Sep '97 / Topaz Jazz

☐ PITTSBURGH 1958
UPCD 2744 / Nov '97 / Uptown

Marocana

☐ CELTIC MYSTERIES
PLSCD 282 / 1 Jun '98 / Pulse

☐ TESTAMENT
Testament / Arab zenith / First light / Blue town / Evocation / Marooned / Desert uprising / Memories / Betrayal / 1000 years / New dawn / Slaves of time / Crucifixion
MDMCD 004 / Nov '95 / Moidart

Marohnic, Chuck

☐ COPENHAGEN SUITE (Marohnic, Chuck Quartet)
SCCD 31408 / Apr '97 / Steeplechase

☐ MANY MANSIONS
Speak like a child / All the things you are / Goal in mind / Autumn leaves / Somewhere in the middle / Ascesis / Many mansions / How deep is the ocean / Ralph's piano waltz / Oleo
AL 73127 / Jun '98 / A

☐ PAGES OF STONE (Marohnic, Chuck, David Friesen & Joe Labarbera)
ITMP 970064 / Apr '92 / ITM

Marone, Boy

☐ HEY
262562 / 1 Jun '98 / Lusafrika

Maroon Dogs

☐ NATURE INTENDED
All of my lifetime / Goldtown / Special beauty / Go today / You've got me to blame / Forever more / Not taking sides / You got sunshine / Didn't want me / Waiting for whem / Heart and soul / Empty stages
RCCD 6001 / Jul '98 / Rollercoaster

Maroon Town

☐ HIGH AND DRY
Thatchers children / Woman say no / Pound to the dollar / Man in the street / Average man / Nostalgia / Fire / Welcome / Travelling light / Possee / Thatcher's children
SKACD 103 / 22 Jun '98 / House Of Ska

Marqua Y Su Combo

☐ SABOR TROPICAL
TUMICD 016 / '91 / Tumi

Marques, Fernando

☐ VERSAS Y TROVAS
7432144812 / Jun '97 / Milan

Marquet, Alain

☐ CLARINET JOY (Marquet, Alain & Reimer von Essen)
SOSCD 1259 / Jul '93 / Stomp Off

☐ HOP SCOT BLUES
SOSCD 1229 / Nov '92 / Stomp Off

Marra, Michael

☐ CANDY PHILOSOPHY
Land of golden slippers / Don't look at me / Johnny Hallyday (Je vous salue) / True love (something no one should ever be without) / Violin lesson / To beat the drum / Painters painting paint / King Kong's visit to Glasgow / Guernsey kitchen porter / Australia instead of stars / O fellow man / This evergreen bough
ECLCD 9309 / Jan '96 / Eclectic

☐ GAELS BLUE
Mincing wi' Chairlhi / Racing from Newburgh / Angus man's welcome to Mary Stuart / King George III's return to sanity / General Grant's visit to Dundee / Black babies / Monkey hair / Altar boys / Gael's blue / Happed in mist
ECLCD 9206 / Jan '96 / Eclectic

☐ ON STOLEN STATIONERY
Margaret Reilly's arrival at Craiglockhart / Wise old men of Mount Florida / Under the ullapool moon / Rats / Hamish / Harmless / Neil Gow's apprentice / Humphrey Kate's song / Like another rolling stone / Here come the weak / Bawbee birlin' / O penitence
ECLCD 9104 / Jan '96 / Eclectic

☐ PAX VOBISCUM (In Concert)
ECLCD 9616 / Jul '96 / Eclectic

Marriott, Beryl

☐ WEAVE THE MIRROR
Big strong lad herding the goats/High road to Linton / Phantasy in fives/Searching for lambs/Bold fisherman / Cam ye by athol/Laird O'Drumblair/ Glengarry's march / Whelan's jig/Morrison's jig/ McFadden's favourite/Smokey hous / Jenny Nettles/Give me your hand/March of the King of Laoise / Dance of the kings of man/Gillie Callum / Y deryn pur / Bridget cruise/Carolan's cup / Kid on the mountain / Lochaber no more / Carolan's welcome / Black nag/Nonsuch
WRCD 016 / Jan '92 / Woodworm

Marriott, Steve

☐ 30 SECONDS TO MIDNIGHT
Knocking on your door / All or nothing / One more heartache / Um um um um um song / Superlungs my supergirl / Get up stand up / Rascal you / Life during wartime / Phone call away / Clapping song / Shakin' all over / Gypsy woman
CLACD 386 / Mar '93 / Castle

☐ ALL STARS
Over you / Midnight rollin' / Times they are a-changin' / Wonderful world / Where're you going tonight / Factory girl / Soldier / Where're you going tonight / Things you do / Ruthy / Gimme some lovin' / Soldier / Vagabond lady / Midnight rollin' / Wham bam thank you Mam / Nobody but you
PILOT 022 / Aug '97 / Burning Airlines

☐ DINGWALLS 6.7.84
Whatcha gonna do about it / Fool for a pretty face / Shame on you / Bad moon rising / Cockney rhyme / All shook up / Fixer / All or nothing / Five long years / Thirty days in the hole / Don't need no doctor / Big train stop at memphis / Walkin' the dog
MAUCD 609 / Sep '91 / Mau Mau

☐ INTERPRETATIONS (Documentary/ Live)
OTR 1100023 / Jun '97 / Metro Independent

☐ LIVE
RRCD 251 / 2 Feb '98 / Receiver

☐ LIVE AT THE PALACE (Marriott, Steve & A Packet Of Three)
OTR 1100020 / Jun '97 / Metro Independent

☐ MARRIOTT ANTHOLOGY, THE (Interview/2CD Set)
OTR 1100021 / Jun '97 / Metro Independent

☐ SCRUBBERS
CD 0029 / Nov '97 / Barsa

Marrow, Lee

☐ BEST OF LEE MARROW, THE
ZYX 204582 / 15 Jun '98 / ZYX

Mars

☐ '78 RE-ISSUE
ALP 48CD / Apr '97 / Atavistic

Mars Accelerator

☐ I AM THE SOUTH POLE
RXR 007CD / Nov '96 / RX Remedy

Mars, Johnny

☐ KING OF THE BLUES HARP
Horses and places / Rocket 88 / Johnny's groove / Desert island / I'll go crazy / Imagination / Mighty Mars / Cash ain't nothing / If I had a woman
JSPCD 217 / Jul '88 / JSP

☐ LIFE ON MARS
Born under a bad sign / Don't start me talkin' / Back door man / Steal away / Standing in line / Hot lips boogie / I can't take a jealous woman / Get on up / Desert island / Keep on swinging
BGOCD 159 / Oct '93 / Beat Goes On

Marsala, Joe

☐ CLASSICS 1936-1942
CLASSICS 763 / Jun '94 / Classics

☐ CLASSICS 1944-1945
CLASSICS 902 / Nov '96 / Classics

Marsalis, Branford

☐ BEAUTYFUL ONES ARE NOT YET BORN, THE
Roused about / Beautyful ones are not yet born / Xavier's lair / Gilligan's Isle / Cain and Abel / Citizen Tain / Dewey baby / Beat's remark
4688962 / Jan '95 / Columbia

☐ CRAZY PEOPLE MUSIC
Spartacus / Dark knight / Wolverine / Mr. Steepee / Rose petals / Ransom abstract (diddle it) / Ballad of Chet Kincaid (hikky burr)
4668702 / 26 Jan '98 / Columbia

☐ DARK KEYS, THE (Marsalis, Branford Trio)
Dark keys / Hesitation / Thousand autumns / Sentinels / Lykeif / Judas Iscariot / Blutain / Schott happens
4866682 / Nov '96 / Sony Jazz

☐ I HEARD YOU TWICE THE FIRST TIME
Brother trying to catch a cab / (On the East side) blues / BB's blues / Rib tip Johnson / Mabel / Sidney in da haus / Berta Berta / Stretto from the ghetto / Dance of the Hei Gui / Road you choose / Simi valley blues
4721692 / Jul '93 / Columbia

☐ RANDOM ABSTRACT
Yes and no / Crescent city / Broadway fools / Lonjellis / I thought about you / Lonely woman / Steep's theme
4687072 / Jan '95 / Sony Jazz

☐ ROYAL GARDEN BLUES
Swingin' at the haven / Dienda / Strike up the band / Emanon / Royal Garden blues / Shadows / Wrath of Tain
4687042 / Jan '95 / Sony Jazz

☐ SCENES IN THE CITY
No backstage pass / Scenes in the city / Solstice / Waiting for Tain / No sidestepping / Parable
4684582 / Jan '95 / Sony Jazz

☐ TRIO GP
Housed from Edward / Three little words / UMMG / Doxy / Stardust / Random abstract (Tain's rampage) / Nearness of you / Makin' whoopee / Gut bucket steepy / Makin' whoopee / Peace
4651342 / 26 Jan '98 / Sony Jazz

Marsalis, Ellis

☐ CLASSIC MARSALIS, THE
Monkey puzzle / Whistle stop / After / Dee Wee / Twelve's it / Yesterdays / Magnolia triangle / Little joy / Swinging at the Haven / 'Round midnight / Night in Tunisia
CDBOP 016 / Apr '93 / Boplicity

☐ LOVED ONES (Marsalis, Ellis & Branford)
Delilah / Maria / Lulu's back in town / Miss Otis regrets / Angelica / Stella by starlight / Louise / Bess, you is my woman now / Liza / Nancy / Laura / Alice in wonderland / Sweet Lorraine / Dear Dolores
4836242 / Mar '96 / Sony Jazz

☐ NIGHT AT SNUG HARBOR, NEW ORLEANS, A
Introduction / Nothin' but the blues / Call / After / Some monk funk / I can't get started / Jitterbug / Very thought of you / Night in Tunisia
ECD 221292 / Sep '95 / Evidence

☐ PIANO IN E - SOLO PIANO
Hallucinations / Django / Jitterbug waltz / Nica's dream / So in love / Fourth autumn / Zee blues
CD 2100 / May '91 / Rounder

☐ TWELVE'S IT (Marsalis, Ellis Trio)
Twelve's it / Syndrome / Homecoming / Mozartin' / Orchid blue / Friendships / Surrey with the fringe on top / I've grown accustomed to her face / Tell me / All good intentions / Zee blues / Party's over
CK 69123CD / 15 Jun '98 / Sony Jazz

☐ WHISTLE STOP
Whistle stop / Dee wee / Moment alone / Magnolia triangle / Mozartin' / Cry again / Cochise / Li'l boy man / Monkey puzzle / After / Beautiful old ladies / Little joy / When we first met
4745552 / Apr '94 / Columbia

Marsalis, Wynton

☐ AMERICAN HERO, AN
One by one / My funny valentine / 'Round midnight / ETA / Time will tell / Blakey's theme
CDGATE 7018 / Nov '86 / Kingdom Jazz

☐ BLACK CODES (From The Underground)
Black codes / For wee folks / Delfeayo's dilemma / Phryzzian march / Aural oasis / Chambers of Tain / Blues
4687112 / Feb '94 / Columbia

☐ BLOOD ON THE FIELDS (3CD Set)
Calling the Indians out / Move over / You don't hear no drums / Market place / Soul for sale / Plantation coffle / March / Work song (blood on the fields) / Lady's lament / Flying high / Oh we have a friend in Jesus / God don't like ugly / Juba and a O'Brown squaw / Follow the drinking gourd / My soul fell down / Forty lashes / What a fool I've been / Back to basics / I hold out my hand / Look and see / Sun is gonna shine / Will the sun come out / Sun is gonna shine / Chant to call the Indians out / Calling the Indians out / Follow the drinking gourd / Freedom is in the trying / Due North
CXK 57694 / Jun '97 / Sony Jazz

☐ BLUE INTERLUDE
4716352 / Jan '95 / Sony Jazz

☐ CARNAVAL
Variations on Le Carnaval de Venise / Grand Russian fantasia / Debutante / Believe me, if all those endearing young charms / Moto perpetuo / 'Tis the last rose of Summer / Flight of the bumble bee / Napoli / Variations on a Neapolitan song / Fantasie brillante / Sometimes I feel like a Motherless child / Valse brillante
MK 42137 / Apr '87 / CBS

☐ CITI MOVEMENT (Griot New York/2CD Set) (Marsalis, Wynton Septet)
4730552 / 26 Jan '98 / Sony Jazz

☐ CRESCENT CITY CHRISTMAS CARD
Carol of the bells / Silent night / Hark the herald angels sing / Little drummer boy / We three kings of Orient are / Oh tannenbaum / Sleigh ride / Let it snow, let it snow, let it snow / God rest ye merry gentlemen / Winter wonderland / Jingle bells / O come all ye faithful (Adeste Fidelis) / 'Twas the night before Christmas
4658792 / Dec '89 / CBS

☐ FIRST RECORDINGS WITH ART BLAKEY
Angel eyes / Bitter dose / Wheel within a wheel / Gypsy / Jody
CDGATE 7013 / Oct '87 / Kingdom Jazz

☐ GOLD COLLECTION, THE (2CD Set)
R2CD 4041 / 13 Apr '98 / Deja Vu

☐ HOT HOUSE FLOWERS
Stardust / Lazy afternoon / For all we know / When you wish upon a star / Django / Melancholia / Hot house flowers / Confession
4687102 / Feb '94 / Columbia

☐ IN GABRIEL'S GARDEN (Marsalis, Wynton & English Chamber Orchestra/ Anthony Newman)
SK 66244 / Jul '96 / Sony Classical

☐ IN THIS HOUSE, ON THIS MORNING (2CD Set) (Marsalis, Wynton Septet)
4745522 / Apr '94 / Columbia

☐ J MOOD
J mood / Presence that lament brings / Insane asylum / Skain's domain / Melodique / After / Much later
4687122 / Jan '95 / Sony Jazz

☐ JOE COOL'S BLUES (Marsalis, Wynton & Ellis)
Linus and Lucy / Buggy ride / Peppermint Patty / On Peanuts playground / Oh good grief / Wright Brothers rag / Charlie Brown / Little Red Haired Girl / Pebble Beach / Snoopy and Woodstock / Little birdie / Why Charlie Brown / Joe Cool's blues
4782502 / May '95 / Sony Jazz

☐ LIVE AT BUBBA'S 1980 (2CD Set) (Marsalis, Wynton & Art Blakey's Jazz Messengers)
JWD 102311 / Oct '94 / JWD

☐ LIVE AT BUBBA'S JAZZ RESTAURANT VOL.1
DM 15012 / Jul '96 / DMA Jazz

☐ LIVE AT BUBBA'S JAZZ RESTAURANT VOL.2
DM 15013 / Jul '96 / DMA Jazz

☐ LIVE IN SWING TOWN (Marsalis, Wynton Septet)
JD 1290 / 2 Mar '98 / Jazz Door

☐ LONDON CONCERT, THE
SK 57497 / Jan '96 / Sony Classical

☐ MAJESTY OF THE BLUES, THE
Majesty of the blues (Puheeman strut) / Hickory dickory dock / New Orleans function / Death of jazz / Premature autopsies (sermon) / Oh, but on the third day (happy feet blues)
4651292 / Jan '95 / Sony Jazz

☐ MARSALIS STANDARD TIME
Caravan / April in Paris / Cherokee / Goodbye / New Orleans / Soon all will know / Foggy day / Song is you / Memories of you / In the afterglow / Autumn leaves
4510392 / Oct '87 / CBS

☐ MASTER OF TRUMPET
One by one / My funny valentine / 'Round midnight / ETA / Time will tell / Blakey's theme / Jody
722008 / Sep '92 / Scorpio

☐ MIDNIGHT BLUES
Party's over / You're blase / After you've gone / Glad to be unhappy / It never entered my mind / Baby won't you please come home / Guess I'll hang my tears out to dry / I got lost in her arms / Ballad of the sad young men / Spring will be a little late this year / My man's gone now / Midnight blues
CK 68921 / 18 May '98 / Sony Jazz

☐ MY IDEAL
My funny valentine / Bitter dose / Jodl / Wheel within a wheel / Gypsy / Soulful mr timmons / My ideal / Blakey's theme
JHR 73562 / Oct '92 / Jazz Hour

☐ PORTRAIT
SK 44726 / Jan '96 / Sony Classical

☐ SOUL GESTURES IN SOUTHERN BLUE VOL.1 (Thick In The South)
4686592 / Jan '95 / Sony Jazz

☐ SOUL GESTURES IN SOUTHERN BLUE VOL.2 (Uptown Ruler)
4686602 / Jul '94 / Columbia

☐ SOUL GESTURES IN SOUTHERN BLUE VOL.3 (Levee Low Moan)
4686582 / Jan '95 / Sony Jazz

☐ THINK OF ONE
Think of one / Knozz-Moe-King / Fuschia / My ideal / What is happening here (now) / Bell ringer / Later / Melancholia
4687092 / Feb '94 / Columbia

☐ TIME WILL TELL
One by one / Angel eyes / Round 'bout midnight / Ata / Time will tell / Moanin' / Free for all / Blakey's theme
JHR 73561 / Oct '92 / Jazz Hour

☐ WYNTON MARSALIS
Father time / I'll be there when the time is right / RJ / Hesitation / Sister Cheryl / Who can I turn to / Twilight / Knozz-Moe-King / Just friends / Knozz-moe-king (Interlude) / Juan / Cherokee / Delfeayo's dream / Chambers of Tain / Au privave / Do you know what it means to miss New Orleans / Juan (Skip Mustaad) / Autumn leaves / Skain's domain / Much later
4687082 / Nov '93 / Columbia

☐ WYNTON MARSALIS STANDARD TIME VOL.1
4687132 / Jan '95 / Sony Jazz

☐ WYNTON MARSALIS STANDARD TIME VOL.2 (Intimacy Calling)
4682732 / Jan '95 / Sony Jazz

☐ WYNTON MARSALIS STANDARD TIME VOL.3 (The Resolution Of Romance)
4668712 / Jan '95 / Sony Jazz

Marscape

☐ MARSCAPE
OZ 0052 / Jun '96 / Ozone

Marsden, Bernie

☐ AND ABOUT TIME TOO
You're the one / Song for Fran / Love made a fool of me / Here we go again / Still the same / Sad clown / Brief encounter / Are you ready / Head the ball
RPM 152 / Oct '95 / RPM

☐ GREEN AND BLUES
ESSCD 324 / Nov '95 / Essential

☐ LOOK AT ME NOW
Look at me now / So far away / Who's foolin' who / Always love you so / Behind your dark eyes / Byblos shack / Thunder and lightnng / Can you do it / After all the madness
RPM 153 / Oct '95 / RPM

Marsden, Gerry

☐ TRIBUTE TO LENNON AND McCARTNEY, A
Pipes of peace / Yellow submarine / Fool on the hill / Silly love songs / Yesterday / Woman / Ebony and ivory / Let it be / Long and winding road / My love / With a little luck / Imagine / It's for you / Love / You've got to hide your love away / Just like starting over / Mull of Kintyre / Give peace a chance
ECD 3138 / Jan '95 / K-Tel

Marsh, Hugh

☐ BEAR WALKS, THE
Versace / My brother / At the top of the hill (a double left) / San calimero / La carezza / Znefu for y'all / Big fun / Bear walks / Laura with the laughing eyes / Doctor is out
VBR 20112 / Dec '90 / Vera Bra

Marsh, Josephine

☐ JOSEPHINE MARSH
JMCD 001 / Feb '96 / Josephine Marsh

Marsh, Warne

☐ DUO - LIVE AT THE SWEET BASIL 1980 (Marsh, Warne & Red Mitchell)
FSCD 1038 / Nov '94 / Fresh Sound

☐ NEWLY WARNE
STCD 4162 / Feb '90 / Storyville

☐ TWO DAYS IN THE LIFE OF...
STCD 4165 / Feb '90 / Storyville

☐ UNISSUED COPENHAGEN STUDIO RECORDINGS, THE (Marsh, Warne Trio)
STCD 8278 / May '97 / Storyville

Marshal, King Wasiu Ayinde

☐ TALAZO FUJI MUSIC PARTY
Fuji collections / Talazo / Ultimate / Consolidation / Eyo / Series
WSCD 101 / Jul '97 / Womad Select

Marshall & The Shooting Stars

☐ AIRMAIL SPECIAL
(In) a shanty in old Shanty Town / Hey Mr. Cottonpicker / Frankie and Johnny / Fat gal / I love you so much it hurts / Well now dig this / Them there eyes / Five foot two, eyes of blue / I'm getting sentimental over you / Airmail special / Honestly / Rattle shakin' daddy
JRCD 9 / Sep '97 / Jappin' & Rockin'

Marshall Law

☐ LAW IN THE RAW
NM 008CD / Oct '97 / Neat Metal

☐ MARSHALL LAW
Armageddon / Under the hammer / Rock the nation / Marshall law / Hearts and thunder / Screaming / We're hot / Feel it / System X / Future shock / When will it end
HMRXD 138 / Dec '89 / FM

Marshall, Amanda

☐ AMANDA MARSHALL
Let it rain / Birmingham / Fall from grace / Dark horse / Beautiful goodbye / Sitting on top of the world / Last exit to Eden / Trust me this is love / Let's get lost / Promises
4837912 / Jul '96 / Epic

Marshall, Brian

☐ TEXAS POLISH ROOTS (Marshall, Brian & His Tex-Slavik Playboys)
Helena polka / Panni matka / Chappell Hill Drive / Going home / Tatusio waltz / Clear water / 4-step / Z padla z wisne / John Mushinski's waltz / Rose garden polka / Chappell Hill special / Martha polka / Na weselu polka / Kuba's wedding waltz / Moravia polka / Walking cane waltz / In the barn waltz / Czum czi rum czum polka / Galicia waltz / Siwi kon / Beczka waltz
ARHCD 464 / Jul '98 / Arhoolie

Marshall, Evan

☐ IS THE LONE ARRANGER
ROUCD 0338 / May '95 / Rounder

Marshall, John

☐ BODYWORK (Marshall, John & Theo Travis/Mark Wood)
Scoping / Speed / Eyes like the sun / Gonzo / Ozymandias / B-Line / Brainstorming / Quiet / Olinda / Sand dance / No hard angel / Bodywork
33JAZZ 036 / Feb '98 / 33 Jazz

☐ KEEP ON KEEPING ON (Marshall, John Quintet)
You / Waltz for Birks / Nobody else but me / All through the night / Thrill is gone / Keep on keepin' on / That ole devil called love / Houston St. beat / Off minor / Theme of Kareem
MR 874774 / Jun '97 / Mons

☐ LIVE FOR TODAY
Let's hope our love is not a mistake / On my way to Memphis / Johnny's jam / Live for today / Jodi man / Not like this before / 4 o'clock in the morning / Dave's CC groove / Love to play them blues / Crazy 'bout my woman / Sweetest thing I know
JSPCD 2104 / Feb '98 / JSP

Marshall, Larry

☐ I ADMIRE YOU
HBCD 57 / Dec '92 / Greensleeves

☐ THROW MI CORN
OMCD 29 / Sep '94 / Original Music

Marshall, Mike

☐ GATOR STRUT
ROUCD 0208 / Aug '88 / Rounder

Marshall, Peter

☐ CHANNEL ONE REVISITED
TBXCD 002 / Oct '95 / Top Beat

Marshall, Wayne

☐ 90 DEGREES AND RISING
90 degrees / Hump tonight / King of sex and soul / Sexual thing / Your G-spot / Kinky sex / Shake it / Touch and kiss you / Goodie goodie / Slow down / Love life satisfaction / So bad / For those who've got the juice / Juice me
SOULCD 31 / Jun '94 / Soultown

☐ BLESSED IS THE CHILD
EWCD 003 / May '95 / Teams

☐ CENSORED
SOULCD 34 / Dec '94 / Soultown

☐ DOUBLE X-POSURE
SOULCD 42 / Feb '96 / Soultown

Marshes

☐ FLEDGLING
BC 1706 / Feb '97 / Blitzcore

☐ POX ON THE TRACKS
DSR 63CD / Nov '97 / Dr. Strange

Marshmallow Overcoat

☐ MARSHMALLOW OVERCOAT
36T 0002CD / Jul '97 / 360 Twist

Martains

☐ LOW BUDGET STUNT KING
ALLIED 057CD / Nov '95 / Allied

Martel, Johnny

☐ JAZZVILLE 4AM
PS 016CD / Jan '98 / P&S

Martell, Lena

☐ FEELINGS (The Best Of Lena Martell)
One day at a time / Don't cry for me Argentina / Nevertheless (I'm in love with you) / Let me try again / Old fashioned way / Running bear / Call collect / Old rugged cross / Danny come home / Six weeks every summer / Movin' on / Until it's time for you to go / Pledging my love / Love letters / Why did I choose you / Make the world go away / Everybody get together / Feelings / Call / Four and twenty hours / Forever in blue jeans
TRTCD 131 / Oct '94 / TrueTrax

☐ ONE DAY AT A TIME (The Best Of Lena Martell)
One day at a time / Movin' on / Until it's time for you to go / Pledging my love / Love letters / First time ever I saw your face / Make the world go away / Running bear / Call collect / Old rugged cross / Danny come home / Six weeks every summer / Stay away from the apple tree / Everybody get together / Hillbilly hoedown / Feelings / Call / Four and twenty hours / Forever in blue jeans / I'm gonna be a country girl again / Help me make it through the night / (It looks like) I'll never fall in love again
PLSCD 169 / Feb '97 / Pulse

☐ SONGS OF LIFE
MACCD 373 / 30 Mar '98 / Autograph

Martha, Istvan

☐ WIND RISES, THE
RERSD 1 / Jun '98 / ReR/ Recommended

Marthely, J.P.

☐ MARTHELOI (Marthely, J.P. & P. St. Eloi)
CD 84707 / Jan '97 / Sonodisc

Marti, Virgilio

☐ SALUDANDO A LOS RUMBEROS
Saludando a los rumberos / Mucho cante / Todos vuelven / El panuelito / Inyere / La mula / Odiame / Quimeras
CCD 9006 / 5 Jan '98 / Fresh Sound

Martignon, Hector

☐ FOREIGN AFFAIR
Benitez sez / Foreign affair / My one and only love / La propuesta / Some day my spring will come / Blues for Leticia / Sorrindo / Prelude no.8 in Eb minor / Unwritten postcards / New morning mambo / As heard
CCD 79746 / Apr '98 / Candid

☐ PORTRAIT IN WHITE AND BLACK
Teorema / Gabriela / She said she was from Sarajevo / Portrait in white and black / Coqueteos / Laura / Colombaiao / Noviembre / Susurro y cumbia / La puerta / Hell's kitchen / Sarabande / La candelaria / Tomorrow's past / You and the night and the music
CCD 79727 / Jul '97 / Candid

Martika

☐ MORE THAN YOU KNOW (The Best Of Martika)
I feel the earth move / More than you know / Toy soldiers / Water / Martika's kitchen / Love... thy will be done / Coloured kisses / Cross my heart / Temptation / Don't say u love me / Safe in the arms of love / More than you know / I feel the earth move / Toy soldiers / Love... thy will be done
4885812 / 8 Sep '97 / Columbia

Martin, Alex

☐ EVENTUAL EXTREMES
PAGCD 002 / 3 Aug '98 / Pagoda

Martin, Anne

☐ CO...
WWAVECD 001 / Feb '98 / White Wave

Martin, Billie Ray

☐ DEADLINE FOR MY MEMORIES
Hands up and amen / Running around town / Still waters / Deadline for my memories / Imitation of life / I try / True moments of my world / We shall be true / I don't believe / Space oasis / You and I (keep holding on) / Your loving arms / Big tears and make-up
0630121802 / Jan '96 / Magnet

Martin Circus

☐ EN DIRECT DU ROCK 'N' ROLL CIRCUS
175432 / 23 Feb '98 / Magic

Martin, Carl

☐ MARTIN, BOGAN & ARMSTRONG/ OLD GANG OF MINE (Martin, Carl & Ted Bogan/Howard Armstrong)
FF 003CD / Feb '93 / Flying Fish

Martin, Carl

☐ CARL MARTIN 1930-1936/WILLIE BLACKWELL 1941 (Martin, Carl & Willie Blackwell)
DOCD 5229 / Apr '94 / Document

☐ CROW JANE BLUES
TCD 6006 / Dec '97 / Testament

Martin, Claire

☐ DEVIL MAY CARE
Devil may care / Victim of circumstance / If love were all / Devil's gonna git you / By myself / Close enough for love / Can't give enough / Sun was falling from the sky / October thoughts / On thin ice / Save your love for me
AKD 021 / Apr '93 / Linn

☐ MAKE THIS CITY OURS
Make this city ours tonight / Another night / How deep is the ocean / Bye bye country boy / Empty bed / Could this be the one / No moon at all / Summer (estate) / Anyplace I hang my hat is a home / Collagen lips / Gettin' high
AKD 066 / Mar '97 / Linn

☐ OFFBEAT
Offbeat / Buy and sell / Come back to me / I'll close my eyes / Monk's new tune / I do it for your love / Worth the wait / Wishful thinking / Comes love / Would you believe / Lost in his arms / Something real / Make sure you're sure / Some other time
AKD 046 / Nov '95 / Linn

☐ OLD BOYFRIENDS
When the sun comes out / Close as pages in a book / Partners in crime / Chased out / Moon ray / Old boyfriends / Out of my continental mind / I've got news for you / Wheelers and dealers / I was telling him about you / Gentleman friend / Killing time
AKD 028 / Sep '94 / Linn

☐ WAITING GAME, THE
You hit the spot / Be cool / This funny world / Better than anything / If you could see me now / Some cats / Four AM / People that you never get to love / Tight / Everything happens to me / Key to your Ferrari
AKD 018 / Mar '92 / Linn

Martin, Daisy

☐ DAISY MARTIN & OZIE MCPHERSON 1921-1926 (Martin, Daisy & Ozie McPherson)
DOCD 5522 / Mar '97 / Document

Martin, Dean

☐ 20 GREAT LOVE SONGS
That's amore / I've got my love to keep me warm / Pretty as a picture / In Napoli / Kiss / June in January / Hit the road to dreamland / Young and foolish / Return to me / Imagination / Let me go lover / There's my lover / Come back to Sorrento / I have but one heart / You're nobody till somebody loves you / Love me my love / Dream a little dream of me / Goodnight sweetheart / Write to me from Naples / How do you speak to an angel
LS 886332 / 2 Feb '98 / Disky

☐ ALL THE HITS 1948-1963
That certain party / Powder your face with sunshine (smile, smile, smile) / I'll always love you / If / You belong to me / That's amore / Love me love me / Sway / I'd cry like a baby / Money burns a hole in my pocket / Memories are made of this / Standing on the corner / Innamorata / Watching the world go by / Return to me / Volare / Angel baby / On an evening in roma / Sam's song / From the bottom of my heart (dammi, dammi, dammi)
PRS 23015 / Jan '94 / Personality

☐ ALL THE HITS 1964-1969
Everybody loves somebody / Door is still open to my heart / You're nobody till somebody loves you / You'll always be the one I love / Send me the pillow you dream on / (remember me) I'm the one who loves you / Houston / I will / Somewhere there's a someone / Come running back / A million and one / Nobody's baby again / (open up the door) let the good times in / Lay some happiness on me / In the chapel in the moonlight / Little ole wine drinker me / In the misty moonlight / You've still got a place in my heart / Not enough indians / I take a lot of pride in what I am
PRS 23016 / Jan '94 / Personality

☐ BEST OF DEAN MARTIN, THE
CPCD 8150 / Nov '95 / Charly

☐ BEST OF DEAN MARTIN, THE (1962-1968 Reprise Recordings)
CDGR 106 / Jan '96 / Charly

☐ BEST OF DEAN MARTIN, THE (3CD Set)
Memories are made of this / That's more (that's love) / Come back to Sorrento / Cha cha cha d'amour / Angel baby / I've got my love to keep me warm / Kiss / Please don't talk about me when I gone / Dream a little dream of me / All I do is dream of you / Things we did last summer / How do you speak to an angel / Young and foolish / Standing on the corner / That lucky old Sun / I napoli / Volare (nel blu dipinto du blue) / Write to me from Naples / Dream / Hey brother pour the wine / Buona sera / June in January / Hit the road to dreamland / Imagination / Let me go lover / Every street's a boulevard / There's my lover / Long long ago / In the cool of the evening / Just one more chance / Two sleepy people / Me 'n' you 'n' the moon / Return to me / Baby it's cold outside / Rio bravo / Goodnight sweetheart / I have but one heart / You nobody 'til somebody loves you / When you're smiling / Under the bridges of Paris / Somebody loves you / You can't love 'em all / Pretty as a picture / You was / Love me my love / Night train to Memphis / On an evening in Roma / Watching the world go by
CDTRBOX 288 / 6 Oct '97 / EMI Gold

☐ CAPITOL YEARS 1950-1962, THE (2CD Set)
Memories are made of this / Powder your face with sunshine (smile smile smile) / You was: *Martin, Dean & Peggy Lee* / Dreamy old New England moon / I'm gonna paper all my walls with your love letters / I'll always love you (day after day) / Solitaire / Night train to Memphis / Pretty as a picture / Oh Marie / You belong to me / Susan / Peanut vendor / I'm yours / That's amore / I'd cry like a baby / Hey brother, pour the wine / Every street's a boulevard (in old New York): *Martin, Dean & Jerry Lewis* / I'll gladly make the same mistake again / Open up the doghouse (two cats are coming in): *Martin, Dean & Nat 'King' Cole* / Carolina in the morning / In Napoli / Inamorata / I'm gonna steal you away: *Martin, Dean & The Nuggets* / Only trust your heart / Beau James / Good mornin' life / Return to me / Volare / On an evening in Rome / All I do is dream of you / Medley / My guiding star / Until the real thing comes along / Ain't that a kick in the head / Just in time / Be an angel / Non dimenticar / Somebody loves you / It's 1200 miles from Palm Springs to Texas
PRDFCD 2 / Aug '96 / Capitol

☐ DEAN MARTIN
DVGH 7092 / May '95 / Deja Vu

☐ DEAN MARTIN SINGS COUNTRY
Send me the pillow that you dream on / Green green grass of home / Crying time / (Remember me) I'm the one who loves you / Little ole wine drinker, me / Lay some happiness on me / Born to lose / Detroit city / My heart cries for you / In the misty moonlight / You've still got a place in my heart / First thing every morning (and the last thing every night) / Detour / I take a lot of pride in what I am / Where the blue and lonely go / Little green apples
CTS 55438 / May '96 / Country Stars

☐ DINO (The Golden Years 1962-1973/ 4CD Set)
Face in a crowd / Everybody loves somebody / Door is still open to my heart / Send me the pillow you dream on / (Remember me) I'm the one who loves you / Houston / I will / Somewhere there's a someone / Come running back / Million and one / Shades / Nobody's baby again / (Open up the door) let the good times in / Lay some happiness on me / In the chapel in the moonlight / Little ol' wine drinker me / You've still got a place in my heart / April again / That old time feelin' / Five card stud / Not enough Indians / Gentle on my mind / I take a lot of pride in what I am / She's a little bit country / Get on with your livin' / My shoes keep walking back to you / I'm gonna change everything / Crying time / Once a day / Ain't gonna try anymore / Any time / I'll hold you in my heart (till I can hold you in my arms ag / Candy kisses / Middle of the night is my cryin' time / Detour / Bouquet of roses / Nobody but a fool / Make it rain / If you ever get around to loving me / Pride / Just a little lovin' / You're the reason I'm in love / Sneaky little side of me / If I ever get back to Georgia / One cup of happiness (and one peace of mind) / Hammer and nails / Down home / Everybody but me / Bumming around / Blue, blue day / Ramblin' rose / You're nobody till somebody loves you / I don't know why (I just do) / Blue moon / Smile / Corrine Corrina / Born to lose / Release me / My heart cries for you / It keeps right on-a hurtin' / Wallpaper roses / Hey good lookin' / What a difference a day made / Guess who / South of the border / Poor people of Paris / Things we did last summer / In a little Spanish town / I love Paris / La paloma / C'est si bon / Wedding bells / In the misty moonlight / Everybody loves somebody / I'll be seeing you / Singin' the blues / I can't help it (if I'm still in love with you) / Tips of my fingers / He's got you / Things / I'm so lonesome I could cry / You better move on / Take these chains from my heart / Where the blue and lonely go / Clinging vine / My heart is an open book / I walk the line / Room full of roses / My

woman, my woman, my wife / Together again / Detroit city / Walk on by / Shutters and boards / Georgia sunshine / Kiss the world goodbye / Honey / Here we go again / For the good times / By the time I get to Phoenix / For once in my life

CDDIG 19 / Oct '97 / Charly

□ GOLD COLLECTION, THE (2CD Set)
R2CD 4052 / 13 Apr '98 / Deja Vu

□ GREAT GENTLEMEN OF SONG, THE
All I do is dream of you / Please don't talk about me when I'm gone / Things we did last summer / Mean to me / Wrap your troubles in dreams (and dream your troubles away) / Imagination / Sleepy time gal / You're nobody till somebody loves you / Someday (you'll want me to want you) / June in January / I can't believe that you're in love with me / Dream a little dream of me / Just in time / Cuddle up a little closer / Lovely mine / Until the next thing comes along / Hit the road to dreamland / Goodnight sweetheart

CDP 8320982 / Aug '95 / Capitol

□ ITALIAN LOVE SONGS/CHA CHA DE AMOR
Just say I love her / Arriverderci Roma / My heart reminds me / You're breaking my heart / Non dimenticar / Return to me / Vieni su / On an evening in Roma / Pardon / Take me in your arms / I have but one heart / There's no tomorrow / Somebody loves you / My one and only love / Love (your spell is everywhere) / I wish you love / Cha cha d'amour / Hundred years from today / I love you much too much (I love you) for sentimental reasons / Let me love you tonight / Amor / Two loves have I / If love is good to me

CTMCD 108 / Jan '97 / EMI

□ MEMORIES ARE MADE OF THIS (3CD Set)
Memories are made of this / That's amore / Come back to Sorrento / Cha cha cha d'amour / Angel baby / I've got my love to keep my warm / Kiss / Please don't talk about me when I'm gone / Dream a little dream of me / All I do is dream of you / Things we did last summer / How do you speak to an angel / Young and foolish / Standing on the corner / In Napoli / That lucky old son / Volare (nel blu dipinto di blu) / Dream / Hey, brother pour the wine / Buona sera / June in January / Hit the road to dreamland / Imagination / Let me go lover / Every street's a boulevard / There's my lover / Long long ago / Martin, Dean & Nat 'King' Cole / In the cool cool of the evening / Just one more chance / Two sleepy people: Martin, Dean & Line Renaud / Me 'n' you 'n' the moon / Return to me (rittorna a me) / Baby it's cold outside / Rio bravo / Goodnight sweetheart / I have but one heart (O Marenariilo) / You're nobody till somebody loves you / When you're smiling / Under the bridges of Paris / Somebody loves you / You can't love them all / Pretty as a picture / You was with Peggy Lee / Love me, my love / Night train to Memphis / On a evening in Roma / Watching the world go by

SA 872662 / Sep '96 / Disky
HR 883302 / Oct '97 / Disky

□ MEMORIES ARE MADE OF THIS (8CD Set)
Which way did my heart go / All of me / I got the sun in the morning / Sweetheart of sigma chi / Oh Marie / Walkin' my baby back home / Santa Lucia / Hold me / Memory lane / Louise / One foot in heaven / Night is young and you're so beautiful / Money song / Certain party / Tarra ta larra ta tar / Once in love with Amy / You was: Martin, Dean & Peggy Lee / Powder your face with sunshine / Absence makes the heart grow fonder / Have a little sympathy / Johnny get your gun / Dreamy old England moon / Three wishes / Just for fun / My own my only all / Lucky old sun / Vieni su / Rain zing a zing a zing boom / I'm gonna paper all my walls with your love / Musrat ramble / I don't care if the sun don't shine / Choo'n'gum / Be honest with me / I still get a thrill / Bye bye blackbird / Happy feet / Baby obey me / I'll always love you / Darktown strutters ball / I'm in love with you: Martin, Dean & Margaret Whiting / Don't rock the boat dear: Martin, Dean & Margaret Whiting / Tonda Wanda huy / Who's sorry now / Wham bam thank you ma am / Peddler's serenade / If / Beside you / I love the way you say goodnight / You and you're beautiful eyes / We never talk must we just / How'd ya like your eyes / In the cool cool cool of the evening / Bonne nuit / Luna mezzo mare / Pennies from heaven / Go go go go / Awc'mon / Hangin' around with you / Solitaire / My heart has found a home / Bella bimbo / Sailors polka / I ran all the way home / Meanderin' / As you are / Lue smoke / Night train to Memphis / Until / Oh boy oh boy oh boy oh boy oh boy / Come back to Sorrento / Never before / When you're smiling / Won't you surrender / All I have to give you / Pretty as a picture / I passed your house / Bet I cha / You belong to me / Kiss / What could be more beautiful / Little did we know / Susan / Peanut vendor / I know a dream when I see / Second chance / Hominy grit / Just one more chance / I'm yours / With my eyes wide open I'm dreaming / There's my lover / Girl named Mary and a boy named Bill / Who's your little zis / I feel like a feather in a breeze / I feel a song comin' on / Til I find you / Don't you remember / If I could sing like Bing / Love me love me / That's amore / You're the right one / If I cry like a baby / Where can I go without you / If I should love again / Christmas blues / Hey brother pour the wine / Money burns a hole in my pocket / Moments like this / That's what I like / I want you / How do you speak to an angel / Ev'ry street's a boulevard / Money burns a hole in my pocket / That's what I like / Belle from Barcelona / Sway / Under the bridges of Paris / Peddlar man / I never had a chance / Confused / One more time / Try again / I'll gladly make the same mistake again / Open up the doghouse: Martin, Dean & Nat 'King' Cole / Long long ago: Martin, Dean & Nat 'King' Cole / Mississippi mud / When it's sleepy time down south / Carolina moon / Way down yonder in New Orleans / Just a little bit south of North Carolina / Georgia on my mind / Waiting for the Robert E Lee / Carolina in the morning / Let me go lover / Naughty lady of shady lane / Mambo Italiano / That's all I want from you / Young and foolish / Basin street blues / Is it true what they say about Dixie / Dinah / Alabamy bound / Chee chee oo chee / In Napoli / That's all I want from you / Young and foolish / Basin Street Blues / Lady with the big umbrella / I like them all / Love is all that matters / Simpatico / Ridin' into love / Relax-ay-voo / Two sleepy head: Martin, Dean & Line Renaud / I know your mother loves you / Memories are made of this: Martin, Dean & The Easy Riders / Change of heartWhen you pretend: Martin, Dean & The Easy Riders / You look so familiar / You look so familiar / Innamorata / Song forSong in the air / My one my only baby / All / Here's to love / Baby obey me / Singin a

vagabound song / I'll always love you / Santa Lucia / Toda wanda hoy / You amd your beautiful eyes / Tarra ta larra ta lar / Bailin' the jack / I'm in the mood for love / Today tomorrow forever / Sailors polka / Old calliope / Never before / Parachute jump / Big blue sky / I know a dream when I see one / Keep a little dream handy / Who's your little who zis / With my eyes wide opening I'm dreaming / I feel a song coming on / Girl named Mary a boy / I feel like a feather in the breeze / Just one more chance / I don't care if the sun don't shine / You hit the spot / Whta have you done for me lately / San domingo / When somebody thinks you're wonderful / Song of the enchilada man / What would you do without me / Everybody loves somebody / Sweetheart / Tie a yellow ribbon round the old oak tree / Red roses for a blue lady / Welcome to my world / Release me / We'll sing in the sunshine / Singing the blues / King of the road / Birds and the bees / Make the world go away / Money / Every street's a boulevard in New York / It's a big wonderful world / Hey punchinello / Relax-ay-voo / I know your mother loves you / Love is all that matters / Face the music simpatico / I like to hike / these chains from my heart / Artists and models / When you pretend / Look so familiar / Lucky song / Inammorata / When you pretend

BCD 15781 / Nov '97 / Bear Family

□ RETURN TO ME (8CD Set)
Look / Mississippi dreamboat / Standing on the corner / Street of love (Rue de mon amour) / Watching the world go by / Pardners: Martin, Dean & Jerry Lewis / Test of time / Me 'n' you / 'n the moon / Wind the wind / I'm gonna steal you away / Bamboozled / Give me a sign / captured / I know I can't forget / I never had a chance / It looks like love / Let's be friendly / Just kiss me / Day in the country / Hollywood or bust / Man who plays the mandolino / Nevertheless (I'm in love with you) / I can't give you anything but love / It's easy to remember / Pretty baby / Sleepy time gal / For you / Maybe / Once in a while / I don't know why (I just do) / Object of my affection / Only forever / You've got me crying again / Money is a problem / You I love / Ten thousand bedrooms / Only trust your heart / Beau jamin / Promise her anything (but give her love) / Tricche tracche (the tree-kay trah-kay) / Write to me from Naples / Good mornin' life / Makin' love ukelele style / Cheatin' on me / Return to me / Buona sera / Forgetting you / Tu sei bella / Angel baby / It's 1200 miles from Palm Springs to Texas / You were made for love / Once upon a time (it happened) / Outa my mind / Magician / Volare (nel blu dipinto di blu) / Rio brava / It takes so long (to say goodbye) / On an evening in Roma (sott'er celo de Roma) / My rifle my pony and me / Dream / Dream a little dream of me / Goodnight sweetheart / Cuddle up a little closer / Sleep warm / Let's put out the lights (and go to sleep) / Brahm's lullaby / Goodnight my love / Wrap your troubles in dreams (and dream your troubles away) / All I do is dream of you / Hit the road to dreamland / Sogni d'oro / Napoli / You can't love 'em all / How sweet is / Off again on again / Humdinger / I ain't gonna lead this / Things we did last summer / Winter wonderland / White Christmas / Canadian sunset / Winter romance / June in January / It won't cool off / I've got my love to keep me warm / Out in the cold again / Baby it's cold outside / Rudolph the red-nosed reindeer / Let it snow let it snow let it snow / Professor professor / Napoli / (Love is a) career / Who was that lady / My guiding star / Overture / It's a perfect relationship: Martin, Dean & Judy Holliday / Do it yourself / It's a simple little system / Better than a dream: Martin, Dean & Judy Holliday / I met a girl / Just in time: Martin, Dean & Judy Holliday / Drop that name: Martin, Dean & Judy Holliday / That party's over: Martin, Dean & Judy Holliday / Midas touch: Martin, Dean & Hal Linden / I'm going back: Martin, Dean & Judy Holliday / Someday (you'll want me to want you) / On the street where you live / I'm grown accustomed to her face / Imagination / (It will have to do) Until the real thing comes along / I'm gonna paper all my walls when I'm gone / You're nobody 'til somebody loves you / Ain't that a kick in the head / Mean to me / Just in time / Cuddle up a little closer / You made me love you / You're the right one / Bella bella bambina / Giuggiola / Sparklin' eyes / Let me know / Be an angel / Hear my heart (sente le coure) / All in a nights work / Story of life (all this is mine) / Bella bimbo / There's no tomorrow (o sole mio) / Return to me / Non dimenticar (don't forget) / I have but one heart (o marenariello) / You're breaking my heart (mattinata) / On an evening in Roma / Pardon / Just say I love her / Take me in your arms / My heart reminds me / Vieni su / Love your spell is everywhere / Cha cha cha d'amour / Amor / Two loves have I / If love is good to me / (I love you) for sentimental reasons / Somebody loves you / Hundred years from today / Wind the world / Bella bimbo / love / If love is good to me / (I love you) for sentimental reasons / Somebody loves you / Mumblin / How i love you

CPCD 81992 / Aug '96 / Charly

□ SLEEP WARM
Sleep warm / Hit the road to dreamland / Dream / Cuddle up a little closer / Sleepy time gal / Goodnight sweetheart / All I do is dream of you / Let's put out the lights / Dream a little dream of me / Wrap your troubles in dreams (and dream your troubles away) / Goodnight my love / Brahms lullaby

PRMCD 3 / Apr '96 / Premier/EMI

□ TOUCH OF CLASS, A
Memories are made of this / Return to me / Baby it's cold outside / Standing on the corner / Cha cha cha d'amore / Angel baby / Volare / Kiss / Please don't talk about me when I'm gone / That's amore / How do you speak to an angel / Hey brother pour the wine / Bridges of Paris / Young and foolish / June in January / Let me go lover / Under the bridges of a stranger / Beautiful brown eyes

TC 886292 / 2 Feb '98 / Disky

□ VERY BEST OF DEAN MARTIN, THE
Return to me / Angel baby / Rio bravo / I've got my love to keep me warm / Baby, it's cold outside / Buona sera / That's amore / Goodnight sweetheart / Volare / Write to me from Naples / Memories are made of this / June in January / Come back to Sorrento / Hey brother pour the wine / Cha cha cha d'amour / I have but one heart

CDMFP 6032 / Sep '88 / Music For Pleasure

4932842 / 12 Jan '98 / EMI Gold

□ WELCOME TO MY HEART
28707257 / 16 Mar '98 / Bellaphon

Martin, Emile

□ EMILE MARTIN
BCD 317 / Oct '93 / GHB

Martin, George

□ BEATLES TO BOND AND BACH, THE
REP 4142 / Aug '91 / Repertoire

□ IN MY LIFE (Various Artists)
Come together: McFerrin, Bobby & Robin Williams / Hard days night: Hawn, Goldie / Day in the life: Beck, Jeff / Here there and everywhere: Dion, Celine / Because: Mae, Vanessa / I am the walrus: Carrey, Jim / Here comes the sun: Williams, John / Being for the benefit of Mr. Kite: Connolly, Billy / Pepperland suite: Martin, George / Golden slumbers: Collins, Phil / Friends and lovers: Martin, George / In my life: Connery, Sean

ECHCD 020 / 16 Mar '98 / Echo

Martin, Helene

□ CHANTE LES POETES
983862 / Sep '96 / EPM

□ LUCIENNE DESNOUES PAR H MARTIN
983922 / Feb '97 / EPM

Martin, Janis

□ FEMALE ELVIS, THE
Drug store rock 'n' roll / Will you Willyum / Love and kisses / My boy Elvis / Crackerjack / Bang bang / Ooby dooby / Barefoot baby / Good love / Little bit / Two long years / All right baby / Billy boy my billy boy / Let's elope baby / Love me love / Love me to pieces / William / Here today and gone tomorrow / Teen street / Hard times ahead / Cry guitar / Just squeeze me / One more year to go / Blues keep calling / Please be my love / I don't want anymore / Half loved / My confession / I'll never be free

BCD 15406 / Jul '87 / Bear Family

Martin, Jim

□ MILK AND BLOOD
SPV 08518742 / Apr '98 / SPV

Martin, Jimmy

□ JIMMY MARTIN & THE SUNNY MOUNTAIN BOYS (5CD Set) (Martin, Jimmy & The Sunny Mountain Boys)
Save it save it / Chalk up another one / I like this boo / They didn't know the difference (but I did) / 20 Vision / That's how I account you / Before the sun goes down / Skip, hop and wobble / You'll be a lost ball / Hitparade of love / Grand ole opry song / I'm the boss (of this here house)

BCD 15959 / May '98 / Bear Family

□ SINGLES, THE
You was: Lee, Peggy & Dean Martin / That lucky old sun / Night train to Memphis / In the cool, cool, cool of the evening / Kiss / There's my lover / When you're smiling / Pretty as a picture / How do you speak to an angel / Every street's a boulevard: Martin, Dean & ...

Jerry Lewis / Long long ago / Let me go, lover / Under the bridges of Paris / Two sleepy people: Martin, Dean & Line Renaud / Young and foolish / Just one more chance / Standing on the corner / Me 'n' you 'n' the moon / You can't love 'em all / I wish you love

CDMFP 6129 / Sep '94 / Music For Pleasure

□ SINGS THE ALL TIME GREATEST HITS (2CD Set)
Little ole wine drinker me / Raindrops keep fallin' on my head / Turn the world around / For once in my life / Everybody loves somebody / Sweetheart / Tie a yellow ribbon round the old oak tree / Red roses for a blue lady / Welcome to my world / Release me / We'll sing in the sunshine / Singing the blues / King of the road / Birds and the bees / Make the world go away / Give me the roses now / Prayer bell of heaven / Moonshine hollow / Give me your hand / Undo what's been done / Deep river / What was I supposed to do / I can, I will, I do believe / There was a love / Poor little bull frogs / Steppin' stones / There ain't nobody gonna miss me / Little angels in heaven / Pretending I don't care / Leavin' town / Don't give your heart to a rambler / God guide our leader's hand / Train 45 / Mr. Engineer / This world is not my home / Drink up and go home / Lord I'm coming home / Goodbye / Pray the clouds away / Give me the roses now / Prayer bell of heaven / Moonshine hollow / Give me your hand / Stormy waters / What would you give in exchange / Shut in's prayer / Beautiful life / Little white church / Old man's drunk again / Hey someone / Tennessee / Widow maker / I'm thinking tonight of my blue eyes / Red river valley / John Henry / Truck driving man / There's more pretty girls than one / Six days on the road / Truck driver's queen / I'd rather have America / Little Robin / There's better times a coming / Guitar picking president / It takes one to know one / Sunny side of the mountain / Snow white grave / Poor Ellen Smith / Shenandoah waltz / Coming back but I don't know when / In the pines / Last song / Sweet Dixie / Wild indian / Run boy run / Theme time / Orange blossom special / I can't quit cigarettes / Lost highway / Good things out weigh the bad / Summer's come and gone / Fraulein / You're gonna change for I'm gonna leave) / Tennessee waltz / Little Maggie, she's so sweet / Big country / Little red rooster / Crow on the banjo / You are my sunshine / Going up dry branch / Living like a fool / Union county / Uptown blues / Goin' ape (over you) / Steal away somewhere and die / Freeborn man / Losing you / Just and old standby / Slowly / Lonesome prison blues / Shackles and chains / Doin' my time / Milwaukee here I come / Arab bounce / (I've got my) Future on ice / Midnight rambler / Between fire and water / Singing all day / Lift your eyes to Jesus / Shake hands with Mother again / When the saviour reached down for me / Help thy brother / My Lord keeps a record / I'd like to be sixteen again / I cried again / Chattanooga dog / Mary Ann / I buried my future / Just plain yellow / Fly me to Frisco / Grave upon the green hillside / Lost to a stranger / Beautiful brown eyes

BCD 15705 / Sep '94 / Bear Family

□ YOU DON'T KNOW MY MIND
ROUCD 5521 / Dec '90 / Rounder

Martin, Juan

□ ANDALUCIAN SUITES, THE
Evocation de la invasion arabe ad 711 / La feria / Alborada / Gitanos / Guadalquivir / Sevilla / Cordoba / Triana / Linares / Jerez / El tajo de ronda / Cadiz / Malaga / Noche en los jardines de granada / Moron de la frontera

CDFV 01 / Jun '91 / Flamencovision

□ GUITARRA FLAMENCA
31837 / Oct '96 / Divusca

□ LUNA NEGRA
CDFV 02 / May '93 / Flamencovision

□ MUSICA ALHAMBRA
FVRPM 0042 / Nov '96 / Flamencovision

□ PICASSO PORTRAITS
Harlequin / Desire caught by the tail / Three musicians / Sleeping girl / Self portrait / Actionado / Girls of Algiers / Weeping woman / Piccador

CDFV 03 / Apr '94 / Flamencovision

Martin Luther Lennon

□ MUSIC FOR A WORLD WITHOUT LIMITATIONS
NL 0039 / Feb '97 / Not Lame

Martin, Marilyn

□ MARILYN MARTIN
Body and the beat / Night moves / Too much too soon / Turn it on / Thank you / One step closer to you / Beauty or the beast / Move closer / Dream is always the same / Here is the news

7567802112 / Jan '96 / Atlantic

Martin, Mary

□ DECCA YEARS 1938-1946, THE
379062 / Nov '95 / Koch International

Martin, Mel

□ PLAYS BENNY CARTER
Kiss from you / Hello / Zanzibar / When lights are low / Summer serenade / Souvenir / Another time, another place / Wonderland / Only trust your heart

ENJ 90412 / Jul '95 / Enja

Martin, Mick

□ GOOD REACTION (Martin, Mick Bluesrockers)
Good reaction / Back talking baby / Lovehound / Can't get enough / I don't care / Don't give up on me / I don't play games / Got to see someone / You're right / Make her mine / Been burned

JSPCD 299 / Apr '98 / JSP

□ LONG DISTANCE CALL (Martin, Mick Bluesrockers)
Long distance call / I'm the blues man / Dog bite your hide / I'll drink no more wine / Ocean of diamonds / Sophronie

DTCD 3038 / Apr '97 / Double Trouble

Martin, Moon

☐ SHOTS FROM A COLD NIGHTMARE/ ESCAPE FROM DOMINATION
Hot nite in Dallas / Victim of romance / Nite thoughts / Paid killer / Cadillac walk / Bad case of lovin' you / Hands down / All I've got to do / You don't care about me / She's a pretender / I've got a reason / She made a fool of you / Dreamer / Gun shy / Hot house baby / Feeling's right / Rolene / No chance / Dangerous / Bootleg woman
EDCD 432 / Jul '95 / Edsel

☐ STREET FEVER/MYSTERY TICKET
EDCD 433 / Oct '95 / Edsel

Martin, Nicholas

☐ HAPPY DAYS ARE HERE AGAIN (At The Wurlitzer Organ)
Happy days are here again / I wonder where my baby is tonight / Smile / Smiling through / Busy line / Very thought of you / Cherokee
GRCD 49 / '92 / Grasmere

Martin, Philip

☐ ANOTHER CANTERBURY TALE
CD 02 / Aug '97 / Balancing Act

Martin, Ricky

☐ A MEDIO VIVIR
Fuego de noche / Nieve de dia / Maria / Te extrano / Te olvido te amo / Donde estaras / Volveras / Revolucion / Somos la semilla / Como decirte adios / Bombom de azucar / Corazon / Nada es impposible
4798827 / 29 Sep '97 / Columbia

Martin, Sallie

☐ PRECIOUS LORD (Martin, Sallie Singers)
Precious Lord / That's what he done for me / Old ship of Zion / Own me as a child / Search my heart / God is moving / Let me cross over / There's not a friend / No one ever cared / God is here / I need him / Nothing but the grace of God / He's in my heart / Seeking for me / Let Jesus come into my heart / When he comes / Keep me Jesus / Closer to Jesus / I was glad when they said to me / Jesus I love you
CPCD 8116 / Jul '95 / Charly

☐ THROW OUT THE LIFELINE (Martin, Sallie Singers & Cora Martin)
God is a battle axe / Didn't it rain / I'll make it somehow / Oh yes, he set me free / He's able to carry me through / Oh what a time / Throw out the lifeline / Eyes hath not seen / Good old way / Jesus is waiting / Great day / I know it's well with my soul / Jesus said / I called the Lord and got an answer / There is a fountain filled with blood / It's a long, long way / I'm bound for the promised land / Hold to God's unchanging hand / Ain't that good news / (There is no sorrow) that heaven cannot heal / I'm getting nearer to my Lord / Every once in a while / One of these mornings / Thy servant's prayer / On the other side / He put his trust in me / I know that he cares for me / Lord I need you every day of my life
CDCHD 481 / Jul '93 / Ace

Martin, Tony

☐ LEGENDARY SONG STYLIST
MACCD 359 / 26 Jan '98 / Autograph

☐ SOMETHING IN THE AIR
Rainbow on the river / Star fell out of heaven / It's love I'm after / Where the lazy river goes by / Afraid to dream / By a wishing well / My sweetheart / That week in Paris / When did you leave Heaven / Loveliness of you / Sweetheart let's grow old together / There's something in the air / Mist is over the moon / You're slightly terrific / Song of old Hawaii / This may be the night / So do I / World is mine tonight
CMSCD 004 / '88 / Movie Stars

☐ THIS MAY BE THE NIGHT
By a wishing well / Cancel the flowers / Donkey serenade / Dream valley / Flamingo / I hadn't anyone till you / Island of Maui Hula / Just let me look at you / Last time I saw Paris / Marching along with time / My sweetheart / Now it can be told / One love affair / Rhythm of the waves / Song of old Hawaii / That week in Paris / This may be the night / 'Tis Autumn / Too beautiful to last / Where in the world / You couldn't be cuter / You stepped out of a dream
CDAJA 5099 / Dec '92 / Living Era

Martinez, Baldo

☐ NO PAIS DOS ANANOS
KAR 7758 / 1 Jun '98 / Karonte

Martinez, Narciso

☐ FATHER OF TEX MEX CONJUNTO (1948-1960)
ARHCD 361 / Apr '95 / Arhoolie

Martinez, Nigel

☐ SO GOOD
EXCDP 18 / 18 May '98 / Expansion

Martinez, Pepe

☐ ART OF FLAMENCO VOL.8, THE (1923-1984)
MAN 4865 / Feb '96 / Mandala

Martino, Al

☐ 20 GREAT LOVE SONGS
Spanish eyes / What now my love / Here in my heart / I love you because / Speak softly love / Can't help falling in love / I started loving you again / I can't help it (if I'm in love with you) / My cherie / Can't take my eyes off you / Walking in the sand / Let it be me / If I were a carpenter / Never my love / This guy's in love with you / True love / Unchained melody / Shadow of your smile / No other arms no other lips / Have I told you lately that I love you
LS 862622 / 2 Feb '98 / Disky

☐ AL MARTINO
Spanish eyes / Red roses for a blue lady / My way / Hey Mama / Sweet Caroline / Everybody's talkin'
16114 / May '94 / Laserlight

☐ AL MARTINO IN CONCERT
Fly me to the moon-let's get away from it all / Fools rush in / How deep is the ocean / Let's face the music - dancing in the dark / Speak softly love / Here in my heart / Granada / Granada vamp
CDPT 841 / Feb '91 / Prestige

☐ COLLECTION, THE
It had to be you / All of me / Three little words / I've got you under my skin / When your lover has gone / That old feeling / Baby won't you please come / Makin' whoopee / Without a word of warning / Why do I love you / All or nothing at all / Summertime / Our concerto / Sunday
308222 / 13 Oct '97 / Hallmark

☐ CONCERT COLLECTION
Song is you / I have but one heart / Cuando cuando cuando / Feelings / More I see you / Somewhere my love / Mary in the morning / Spanish eyes / Strangers in the night / To the door of the sun / Man without love / Because you're you / I love you more and more everyday / Painted tainted rose / Speak softly love / End of the line / I've got to be me / Can't help falling in love with you / Volare
PLATCD 152 / Mar '96 / Platinum

☐ GREATEST HITS
Song is you / I have but one love / Cuando cuando cuando / Feelings / More I see you / Somewhere my love / Mary in the morning / Spanish eyes / Strangers in the night / As long as you're with me / Lonely is a man without love / I love you because / I love you more and more every day / Wild and lovely rose / Speak softly love / End of the line / Come into my life / I've got to be me / Can't help falling in love / Volare
PLATCD 364 / '91 / Platinum

☐ HITS OF AL MARTINO, THE
Here in my heart / Spanish eyes / Granada / Wanted / Story of Tina / Now (before another day goes by) / Mary in the morning / White rose of Athens / Man from Laramie / Volare / Painted tainted rose / To the door of the sun / Rachel / I won't last a day without you / Take my heart / I love you because
CDMFP 6030 / Jul '88 / Music For Pleasure

☐ LIVE IN CONCERT
Quando quando quando / You will be my music / Song is you / You will be my music / I have but one heart / Feelings / More I see you / Some where my love / Mary in the morning / Spanish eyes / Strangers in the night / To the door of the sun / Man without love / I love you because / I love you more and more everybody / Painted tainted rose / Speak softly love / End of the line / Come into my life / I've gotta be me / Can't help falling in love / Volare
EMPRCD 634 / Jun '96 / Emporio

☐ QUANDO QUANDO QUANDO
WMCD 5695 / Oct '94 / Disky

☐ SPANISH EYES
MU 5063 / Oct '92 / Musketeer

☐ SPANISH EYES
Now / Say you'll wait for me / Way paesano / There'll be no teardrops tonight / Wanted / Give me something to go with the wine / No one can change destiny / I still believe / No one but you / Not as a stranger / Don't go to strangers / Snowy, snowy mountains / To please my lady / Small talk / Somebody else is taking my place / What now my love / Melody of love / Spanish eyes / My love forgive me / You belong to me
CDMFP 6176 / Nov '95 / Music For Pleasure

☐ SPANISH EYES
Spanish eyes / Quando quando quando / Feelings / More I see you / Somewhere my love (Lara's theme) / Mary in the morning / This song is you / Strangers in the night / Can't help falling in love / I love you because I love you more and more each day / Volare / Lonely is a man without love / I've got to be me / Come into my life / End of the line / Speak softly love / Painted tainted love
CD 6067 / Apr '97 / Music

☐ SPANISH EYES (Live)
Spanish eyes / Strangers in the night / You will be my music/The song is you / Quando, quando, quando / Speak softly love / Can't help falling in love / Mary in the morning / Feelings / Volare (nel blu dipinte di blu) / More I see you / Somewhere my love / I've gotta be me / Lonely is a man without love / Come into my life / I love you because you're you / I love you more and more every day
100712 / May '97 / A-Play Collection

☐ THIS IS MY SONG (3CD Set)
Volare (nel blu dipinto di blu) / Here in my heart / Can't take my eyes off you / Wanted / Now / Granada / White rose of Athens / Walking in the sand (and the seasons come and go) / Unchained melody / Story of Tina / Don't go to strangers / Melody of love / Mary in the morning / Man from Laramie / Always together / Can't help falling in love / Spanish eyes / I won't last a day without you / Speak softly love / My cherie / Never my love / No other arms, no other lips / Rachel / No one but you / Love is blue / I love you because / Give me something to go with the wine / Painted tainted rose / Have I told you lately that I love you / Way Paesano / Tears and roses / I can't help it if I'm still in love with you / To the door of the sun / Take my heart / Vaya con dios / What now my love / Shadow of my smile / True love / I still believe / This guy's in love with you / Somebody else is taking my place / There'll be no teardrops tonight / I started loving you again / To please my lady / Small talk / If I were a carpenter / You belong to me / Let it be me
SA 872822 / Sep '96 / Disky

☐ TOUCH OF CLASS, A
Here in my heart / Take my heart / Now / Rachel wanted / Story of Tina / Spanish eyes / Summertime / Man from Laramie / Painted, tainted rose / Tears and roses / Mary in the morning / Volare / Always together / Love is blue / Vaya con dios
TC 862642 / 2 Feb '98 / Disky

Martino, Pat

☐ ALL SIDES NOW
Too high / Two of a kind / Progression / I'm confessin' (that I love you) / Ellipsis / Ayako / Two days old / Outrider / Never and after
CDP 8376272 / Aug '97 / Blue Note

☐ DESPERADO
Blackjack / Dearborn walk / Oleo / Deperado / Portrait of Diana / Express
OJCCD 397 / Apr '93 / Original Jazz Classics

☐ EAST
East / Close your eyes / Park Avenue petite / Lazy bird
OJCCD 248 / May '97 / Original Jazz Classics

☐ STONE BLUE
Uptown blue / Stone blue / With all the people / 13 to go / Boundaries / Never say goodbye / Mac tough / Joyous lake / Two weighs out
8530822 / 3 Aug '98 / Blue Note

☐ WE'LL BE TOGETHER AGAIN
60412320712 / 19 May '98 / Thirty Two

Martins, Carlos

☐ PASSAGEM
Sofia / Mali m'blue baaba / Duo / A Espera / Working blues / Round trip / Passado presente / I trust on you / Sophisticated lady / Naif
ENJ 90732 / May '97 / Enja

Martins, Vasco

☐ ISLAND OF THE SECRET SOUNDS
669752 / Mar '96 / Melodie

Martland, Steve

☐ MARTLAND - FACTORY MASTERS
Babi Yar / Drill / Crossing the border / Principia / American invention / Re-mix / Shoulder to shoulder
09026683982 / Nov '95 / Catalyst

☐ PATROL
Danceworks (4 dances) / Principia / Patrol (3 movements)
09026626702 / Sep '94 / Catalyst

Marton, Tolo

☐ MY PLACE IS CLOSE TO YOU
Certitude of laundromats / Alpine valley / See what you've done to me / Music lady / Plains of joy / Rainy day / Back to my youth / I don't wanna be alone / My place is close to you / Wake up / Pinto creek
PRD 70922 / May '96 / Provogue

Martve Boys Choir

☐ GEORGIAN POLYPHONY VOL.2
VICG 50042 / Mar '96 / JVC World Library

Martyn, Barry

☐ BARRY MARTYN
SKCD 23056 / Jun '94 / Sackville

☐ ON TOUR
BCD 255 / Aug '94 / GHB

☐ SOPHISTICATED SLIDE (Martyn, Barry & Mike Owen/Freddy John)
JCD 282 / Dec '97 / Jazzology

☐ VINTAGE BARRY MARTYN
BCD 75 / Apr '97 / GHB

Martyn, Jean

☐ BLACKPOOL TOWER, THE WURLITZER AND ME
Oklahoma selection / Red River valley/Nut rocker / Rule Brittania/A life on the ocean wave/Anchors aweigh / Sailor's hornpipe/Skye boat song/Lead us heavenly father / We are sailing / Wurli bird / Somewhere over the rainbow / California, here I come/Mammy / Toot toot Tootsie/Goodbye / Blackpool Belle / Under the Double Eagle / What a friend we have in Jesus/And it can be / Will your anchor hold/Old rugged cross / Blessed assurance/ How great thou art / You're a lady / Way you look tonight/Dream / Radetsky march / Breeze and I/ September in the rain / Tenderly/Sentimental over you / When day is done
CDGRS 1294 / Feb '97 / Grosvenor

Martyn, John

☐ AND
Sunshine's better / Suzanne / Downward pull of human nature / All in your favour / Little strange / Who are they / Step it up / Carmine / She's a lover / Sunshine's better
8287982 / Jul '96 / Go Discs

☐ APPRENTICE, THE
Live on love / Look at that gun / Send me one line / Hold me / Apprentice / River / Income town / Deny this love / UPO / Patterns in the rain
HYCD 101101 / Sep '93 / Hypertension
INDELCD 1 / 27 Apr '98 / Indelible

☐ BLESS THE WEATHER
Go easy / Bless the weather / Sugar lump / Walk to the water / Just now / Head and heart / Let the good things come / Back down the river / Glistening Glyndebourne / Singin' in the rain
IMCD 135 / Jul '91 / Island

☐ CHURCH WITH ONE BELL, A
ISOM 3CD / 23 Mar '98 / Independiente

☐ COOLTIDE
Hole in the rain / Annie says / Jack the lad / Number nine / Cure / Same difference / Father Time / Call me / Cooltide
HYCD 200116 / Jul '97 / Hypertension

☐ ELECTRIC JOHN MARTYN, THE
Johnny too bad / Certain surprise / Sweet little mystery / Dancing
IMCD 66 / '89 / Island

☐ FOUNDATIONS
IMCD 180 / Mar '94 / Island

☐ GLORIOUS FOOL
Couldn't love you anymore / Amsterdam / Hold on my heart / Perfect hustler / Hearts and keys / Glorious fool / Never say never / Pascanel (get back home) / Didn't do that / Please fall in love with me / Don't you go
2292530642 / 10 Nov '97 / WEA

☐ GRACE AND DANGER
Some people are crazy / Grace and danger / Lookin' on / Johnny too bad / Sweet little mystery / Hurt in your heart / Baby please come home / Save some for me / Our love
IMCD 67 / '90 / Island

☐ HIDDEN YEARS, THE
ARTFULCD 2 / Jan '97 / Artful

☐ INSIDE OUT
Fine lines / Eibi gheal chiuin ni chearbhaill / Ain't no saint / Outside in / Glory of love / Look in / Beverley / Make no mistake / Ways to cry / So much in love with you
IMCD 172 / Mar '94 / Island

☐ LIVE AT LEEDS
Outside in / Solid air / Make no mistake / Bless the weather / Man in the station / I'd rather be the devil / My baby girl / You can discover / So much in love with you / Clutches / Mailman
OW 107CD / 24 Aug '98 / Blueprint

☐ LONDON CONVERSATION
Fairytale lullaby / Sandy Grey / London conversation / Ballad of an elder woman / Cocaine / Run honey run / Back to stay / Rollin' home / Who's grown up now / Golden girl / This time / Don't think twice, it's alright
IMCD 134 / Jun '91 / Island

☐ NO LITTLE BOY/COULDN'T LOVE YOU MORE (2CD Set)
Lonely love / Couldn't love you more / Sweet little mystery / Head and heart / Could've been me / One day without you / Over the hill / Fine lines / May you never / One world / Ways to cry / Angeline / Man in the station / Solid air / Never let me go / Solid air / Ways to cry / Could've been me / I don't want to know / Just now / One day without you / Sweet little mystery / Pascanel / Sunday's child / Head and heart / Fine lines / Bless the weather / Man in the station / One world / Rock salt and nails / Hole in the rain
BP 278CD / 9 Feb '98 / Blueprint

☐ ONE WORLD
Dealer / One world / Smiling stranger / Big muff / Couldn't love you anymore / Certain surprise / Dancing / Small hours
IMCD 86 / Feb '90 / Island

☐ PHILENTROPY
Make no mistake / Don't want to know / Root love / Lookin' on / Hung up / Johnny too bad / Sunday's child / Smiling stranger
BP 275CD / 24 Nov '97 / Blueprint

☐ PIECE BY PIECE
Nightline / Lonely lover / Angeline / One step too far / Piece by piece / Serendipity / Who believes in angels / Love of mine / John Wayne
IMCD 68 / Nov '89 / Island

☐ REST OF THE BEST, THE
ARTFULCD 13 / 30 Mar '98 / Artful

☐ ROAD TO RUIN, THE (Martyn, John & Beverley)
Primrose Hill / Parcels / Auntie Aviator / New day / Give us a ring / Sorry to be so long / Tree green / Say what you can / Road to ruin
IMCD 165 / Mar '93 / Island

☐ SAPPHIRE
Over the rainbow / You know / Watching her eyes / Acid rain / Sapphire / Fisherman's dream / Mad dog days / Climb the walls / Coming in on time / Rope souled
IMCD 164 / Mar '93 / Island

☐ SNOOO
She's a lover / All in your favour / Step it up / Little strange
BP 276CD / 24 Nov '97 / Blueprint

☐ SOLID AIR
Over the hill / Don't want to know / I'd rather be the devil / Go down easy / Dreams by the sea / May you never / Man in the station / Easy blues / Solid air
IMCD 85 / Feb '90 / Island

☐ STORMBRINGER (Martyn, John & Beverley)
Go out and get it / Can't get the one I want / Stormbringer / Sweet honesty / Woodstock / John the baptist / Ocean / Traffic light lady / Tomorrow time / Would you believe me
IMCD 131 / Jun '91 / Island

☐ SUNDAY'S CHILD
One day without you / Lay it all down / Root love / My baby girl / Sunday's child / Spencer the rover / Clutches / Message / Satisfied mind / You can discover / Call me crazy
IMCD 163 / Mar '93 / Island

☐ SWEET LITTLE MYSTERIES (The Island Anthology/2CD Set)
Bless the weather / Head and heart / Glistening Glyndebourne / Solid air / Over the hill / Don't want to know / I'd rather be the devil / May you never / Fine lines / Make no mistake / One day without you / Lay it all down / Root love / Sunday's child / Spencer the rover / You can discover / Call me crazy / Couldn't you love me more / Certain surprise / Dancing / Small hours / Dealer / One world / Some people are crazy / Lookin' on / Johnny too bad / Sweet little mystery / Hurt in your heart / Baby please come home / Sapphire / Fisherman's dream / Angeline / Send me one line / Eibhli ghail chuin ni chearbaill
CRNCD 4 / Jun '94 / Island

☐ TUMBLER, THE
Sing a song of summer / River / Goin' down to Memphis / Gardener / Day at the sea / Fishin' blues / Dusty / Holto train / Winding boy / Fly on home / Kuckledy crunch and slipledge slee song / Seven black roses
IMCD 173 / Mar '94 / Island

☐ VERY BEST OF JOHN MARTYN, THE
ARTFULCD 4 / Apr '97 / Artful

☐ WELL KEPT SECRET
Could've been me / You might need a man / Hung up / Gun money / Never let go / Love up / Changes her mind / Hiss on the tape / Back with a vengeance / Livin' alone
2292530632 / 10 Nov '97 / WEA

Martyr Whore

☐ ROSEYDOLVET BALLET
EFA 121612 / Aug '95 / Apollyon

Martyrium

☐ MARTYRIUM
MRCD 002 / Jul '95 / Modern Invasion

Marusia, Sergei

☐ RUSSIAN GYPSY SONGS
MCD 71565 / Jun '93 / Monitor

Marvaless

☐ FEARLESS
72438456752 / 21 Apr '98 / AWOL

Marvelettes

☐ ULTIMATE COLLECTION
5308562 / 13 Jul '98 / Motown

☐ VERY BEST OF THE MARVELETTES, THE
Make it right / Blame it on yourself / Ride the storm / Secret love affair / Right away / For the rest of my life / Just in the nick of time / Bad case of nerves / My wheel of fortune / When you're young and in love / Pushing too hard / Time has a new meaning / Holding on with both hands / We're gonna stay in love / You're my remedy / All things abide / Special feeling / Universal love
3035990022 / Oct '95 / Carlton

Marvellous Caine

☐ GUN TALK
SUBBASE CD3 / Nov '95 / Suburban Base

Marvin & Johnny

☐ CHERRY PIE
Cherry pie / Tick tock / Forever / Kiss me / Sugar / Dear one / Honey girl / Little honey / Vip vop / Kokomo / Sometimes I wonder / Baby, won't you marry me / I love you, yes I do / Butter ball / Sugar Mama / Oh me oh my / Sweet dreams / Will you love me / I wanna / Let me know / Ain't that right / Sweet potato / Wonderful, wonderful one / Yes I do / Tell me darling / Have mercy Miss Percy / Have mercy Miss Percy (Take 1)
CDCHD 509 / Feb '94 / Ace

☐ FLIPPED OUT
Wine woogie / Old man's blues / Dream girl / As long as you're satisfied / My baby won't let me in / Sun was shining / Baby doll / I'm not a fool / Jo Jo / Honey / How long she been gone / If I should lose you / Boy loves girl / School of love / I want lovin' / Day in, day out / What's the matter / Flip / Hunter Hancock radio ad / Mamo mamo / Ding dong baby / Tell me darling / Yak yak woman / Pretty one / Bye bye my baby
CDCHD 385 / May '92 / Ace

Marvin, Brett

☐ ALIAS TERRY DACTYL & THE DINOSUARS (Marvin, Brett & The Thunderbolts)
Sae side shuffle / Little red caboose / Take your money / Shave 'em dry / I'm coming / Eyesight to the blind / Highway 61 / Southbound lane / Calcutta got better / Thoughts on you / Ball and chain / Love in jest / On a Saturday night / Going round the world
C5CD 671 / 10 Aug '98 / See For Miles

Marvin, Greg

☐ I'LL GET BY
Ding dong the witch is dead / Our angel / Devil's dream / I'll get by / Over the rainbow / How deep is the ocean / Old faithful / 317 East 32nd / Tuesday / Yesterdays / I'm with you
CDSJP 347 / Oct '91 / Timeless Jazz

Marvin, Hank

☐ ANOTHER SIDE OF HANK MARVIN
Don't talk / Slow down / Janine / Tahlia take your time / China town / Captain Zlogg / Trouble with me is you / Oh Suzie / Night nurse / Go Jimmy / Then I found love / Life line / Just another heartbreak / Hawk and the dove / Where do you go when you dream / Invisible man / Leila (Danny's got a song) / Don't answer / Stardom / Rainy day goodbye / 99 days / All alone with friends
5545172 / 6 Jul '98 / Spectrum

☐ HANK MARVIN AND JOHN FARRAR (Marvin, Hank & John Farrar)
So hard to live with / Music makes my day / Skin deep / If I rewrote yesterday / Galadriel (spirit of starlight) / Love oh love / Help me onto your wagon / Small and lonely light / You never can tell / Nobody cares / Lord how it's hurting
SEECD 322 / Jul '91 / See For Miles

☐ HANK MARVIN GUITAR SYNDICATE
New Earth / Have you never been mellow / St. Louis blues / I've got you under my skin / Syndicated / Ebb tide / Bird of beauty / Thunder thumbs and lightnin' licks / Flamingo / Silvery rain / You are everything
SEECD 289 / Apr '93 / See For Miles

☐ HANK PLAYS CLIFF
5294262 / 15 Sep '97 / Polydor

☐ HANK PLAYS HOLLY
Peggy Sue / It's so easy / Raining in my heart / Oh boy / Peggy Sue got married / Listen to me / Wishing / Well...all right / It doesn't matter anymore / That'll be the day / Brown eyed handsome man / Everyday / Rave on / True love ways / Maybe baby / Not fade away / Heartbeat
5337132 / Nov '96 / PolyGram TV

☐ HANK PLAYS LIVE (Live At The Birmingham Symphony Hall)
Live and let die / Devil woman / Summer holiday / Foot tapper / Living doll / Pipeline / Medley / Sleepwalk / Atlantis / Savage / Young ones / Travellin' light / Eleanor Rigby / Guitar tango / Hound dog / Mystery train / Wonderful land / Theme from the Deer Hunter (Cavatina) / Rise and fall of Flingel Bunt / Apache / Move it
5374282 / 15 Sep '97 / PolyGram TV

☐ HEARTBEAT
Heartbeat / Oxygene / Mrs. Robinson / Space oddity / Achy breaky heart / I will always love you / Crying game / Cable beach / Wonderful land / Hot rox / Rocket man / Take five / Wichita lineman / Live and let die / Crying / Limited slip
5542272 / Oct '97 / Spectrum

☐ INTO THE LIGHT
We are the champions: Marvin, Hank & Brian May / Pipeline: Marvin, Hank & Duane Eddy / Sylvia / Jessica / Another day in paradise / Everybody wants to rule the world / Don't know much / Road train / Sumiko / Into the light / (Everything I do) I do it for you / Rikki don't lose that number / Scirocco / Moontalk / Tailspin / Steel wheel
5542262 / Oct '97 / Spectrum

☐ MARVIN, WELCH & FARRAR (Marvin, Hank & Bruce Welch/John Farrar)
You're burning bridges / Thousand conversations / Brownie Kentucky / My home train / Silvery rain / Throw down a line / Baby I'm calling you / Faithful / Mistress Fate and Father Time / Take her away / Wish you were here / Mr. Sun / Strike a light
SEECD 324 / 8 Jun '98 / See For Miles

☐ SECOND OPINION (Marvin, Hank & Bruce Welch/John Farrar)
Black eyes / Tiny robin / Simplify your head / Ronnie / Far away falling / Let's say goodbye / Lonesome mole / Thank heavens I've got you / Lady of the morning / Time to care / Come back nature / All day, all night blues / Song of yesterday
SEECD 325 / 8 Jun '98 / See For Miles

☐ TWANG (A Tribute To Hank Marvin) (Various Artists)
Apache: *Blackmore, Ritchie* / FBI: *May, Brian* / Wonderful land: *Iommi, Tony* / Savage: *Stevens, Steve* / Rise and fall of Fingel Bunt: *Marvin, Hank* / Midnight: *Green, Peter Splinter Group* / Spring is nearly here: *Young, Neil & Randy Bachman* / Atlantis: *Knopfler, Mark* / Frightened city: *Frampton, Peter* / Dance on: *Urban, Keith* / Stingray: *Summers, Andy* / Stranger: *Fleck, Bela*
PRMDCD 25 / Mar '97 / Premier/EMI

☐ WOULD YOU BELIEVE IT... PLUS
Aquarius / Born free / This guy's in love with you / Tokyo guitar / Chameleon / Lara's theme / Big Country / Love and occasional rain / Georgia on my mind / Windmills of your mind / Sacha / High sierra / Evening comes / Wahine / Morning star / Sunday for seven days / Boogatoo / Would you believe it / Midnight cowboy / Goodnight Dick
SEECD 210 / May '89 / See For Miles

Marx, Bill

☐ MY SON THE FOLK SWINGER/JAZZ KALEIDOSCOPE
VJ 021 / 24 Apr '98 / Vee Jay

Marx, Richard

☐ FLESH AND BONE
Fool's game / You never take me dancing / Touch of heaven / What's the story / Can't lie to my heart / Until I find you again / My confession / Surrender to me / Eternity / What's wrong with that / Image / Too shy to say / Talk to ya later / Breathless / Miracle
CDEST 2294 / 15 Sep '97 / Capitol

☐ GREATEST HITS
Don't mean nothing / Endless summer nights / Now and forever / Should've known better / Angelia / Hold on to the nights / Angel's lullaby / Take this heart / Satisfied / Until I find you again / Hazard / Way she loves me / Keep coming back / Children of the night / Touch of heaven / Right here waiting
8219142 / 9 Feb '98 / Capitol

☐ PAID VACATION
Way she loves me / One more try / Silent scream / Nothing to hide / Whole world to save / Soul motion / Now and forever / Goodbye / Hollywood / Heaven's waiting / Nothing left behind us / What you want / One man / Miami 2017 / Baby blues
CDESTU 2208 / Feb '94 / EMI

Marxer, Marcy

☐ JUMP CHILDREN
Jump children / Beautiful day / Chickery chick / Grandpa's farm / 10 cats down / Pop goes the weasel / Hush little baby / Start / If you're happy / Use your own two feet / January, february, march... / Ride 'em high-the cowpoke dance / Rock-a-bye boogie / Skinnamirink / Time to sleep
ROUCD 8012 / '88 / Rounder

☐ VOICE ON THE WIND (Marxer, Marcy & Fink & Cathy)
ROUCD 0408 / Mar '97 / Rounder

Marxman

☐ TIME CAPSULE
ZCDKR 5 / Nov '96 / More Rockers

Mary Beats Jane

☐ MARY BEATS JANE
Neighbourhood psycho / This life / Old / Grind / Blood and oil / War on society / Wasted / Blind / I don't care / Hollowhead / Porno / Corn / Gunshot / Cxxx cxxx report
MCD 11135 / Oct '94 / MCA

Mary Jane

☐ HAZY DAYS
SGCD 10 / Sep '97 / September Gurls

Maryland Jazzband

☐ MARYLAND JAZZ BAND
BCD 358 / Nov '96 / GHB

Marzipan & Mustard

☐ FUSE
MILL 061CD / 11 May '98 / Millenium

Mas Optica

☐ CHOOSE TO SEE MORE
IRS 972234 / 6 Oct '97 / Intercord

Masaoka Orchestra

☐ WHAT IS THE DIFFERENCE BETWEEN STRIPPING AND PLAYING
VICTOCD 058 / Jul '98 / Victo

Maschinenzimmer 412

☐ NACHT DURCH STIMME
DVLR 007CD / Mar '95 / Dark Vinyl

Mase

☐ HARLEM WORLD
8612730172 / 27 Oct '97 / Puff Daddy

Masekela, Hugh

☐ AFRICAN BREEZE
Don't go lose it baby / African breeze / Rainmaker (Motla le pula) / It's raining / Grazing in the grass / Wimoweh / Lady / Politician / Joke of life / Ritual dancer / Zulu wedding / Run no more
MOCD 3013 / Feb '95 / More Music

☐ AFRICAN BREEZE
Don't go lose it baby / Motla le pula / African breeze / Seven riffs of Africa / Lion never sleeps, Isikhokhyana / Grazing in the grass / Joke of life / Lady / U-Dwi / Coal train / Zulu wedding / Run no more / Tonight
EMPRCD 656 / Jun '96 / Emporio

☐ BEATIN' AROUN' DE BUSH
Steppin' out / Ngena-ngena (instrumental) / Ngena (acapella) / Batsumi (mayibuye i Afrika) / Rock with you / Polina / Languta / Sekunjalo / U-mama / Beatin' aroun' de bush
PD 90686 / Jul '92 / Novus

☐ BLACK TO THE FUTURE VOL.1
Mama ndoro / Boy's doin' it / Ashiko / Chileshe / JJC/ JJD / Song of love / Khawuleza / Child of the earth / Excuse me baby please / Strawberries / Nina / Bokone
4894772 / 9 Feb '98 / Sony Jazz

☐ HOPE
Abangoma / Uptownship / Mandela (Bring him back home) / Grazin in the grass / Lady / Until when / Languta / Nomali / Market place / Ntyilo ntyilo (The love bird) / Ha le se (The dowry song) / Stimela (coaltrain)
3202032 / Feb '94 / Triloka

☐ LASTING IMPRESSIONS OF OOGA BOOGA, THE
Bajabula bonke / Dzinorabiro / Unhlanhia / Cantelope island / U-owi / Masuenada / Abangoma / Mixolydia / Con mucho carino / Where are you going / Mocolo / Bo Masekela / Unohila
5316302 / Aug '96 / Verve

☐ NOTES OF LIFE
Mama / Heart breaker / Moments of love / Father of our nation / Whooh Africa / No more cryin' / Talking thoughts / Bone thru the nose / Baby ngiya ku thanda / Somebody is stealin' my car / Thank you Madiba
4844502 / Jul '96 / Sony Jazz

☐ STIMELA
Languta / Child of the earth / Ha lese le di khanna / Coincidence / Bajabula bonke (the healing song) / Grazing in the grass / If there's anybody out there / Mace and grenades / Felicidade / African secret society / Been such a long time / Stimela (coaltrain)
VSOPCD 200 / Jun '94 / Connoisseur Collection

Mashu

☐ ELEPHANTS IN YOUR HEAD
Used to / Chariot / Sea beyond / Jus de peche / Elephant / Bell and clay / Passage thru NW / Afaiu / Chariot repriese
VP 188CD / May '97 / Voiceprint

Maslak, Keshavan

☐ EXCUSE ME MR. SATIE (Maslak, Keshavan & Katsuyuki Itakura)
CDLR 199 / Oct '94 / Leo

☐ MOTHER RUSSIA
CDLR 177 / '90 / Leo

☐ NOT TO BE A STAR (Maslak, Keshavan & Paul Bley)
1201492 / Sep '93 / Black Saint

Maslon, Jimmie Lee

☐ SALACIOUS ROCKABILLY CAT
HMG 6606 / Dec '97 / Hightone

Mason

☐ HARBOUR
GRC 017 / 8 Jun '98 / GRC

Mason, Allison

☐ ISIM SKISM
NGCD 549 / Jul '96 / Twinkle

Mason, Barbara

☐ OH HOW IT HURTS
Oh how it hurts / I don't want to lose you / Happy girl / For your love / Peace of mind / Dreams really come true / Ain't got nobody / Forever / Gee whizz / Poor girl in trouble / (I can feel your love) slipping away / Take it easy / You better stop it / Don't ever go away / Game of love / If you don't love me (tell me) / I do love you / Tried so hard / Is it me / I need your love (I need love) / Think about it / Just you and me / Dedicated to you / I'll keep on loving you / Lonely too long / I'm not good for you
BCD 16206 / Oct '97 / Bear Family

☐ VERY BEST OF BARBARA MASON, THE
NEMCD 680 / May '96 / Sequel

☐ YES I'M READY
Yes I'm ready / Come to me / You got what it takes / Misty / Something you got / Come see about me / Sad sad girl / Got to get you off my mind / Keep him / Girls have feelings too / Moon river / Trouble child / Bobby is my baby / Change me if you can / Hello baby / You can depend on me / You'll lose a good thing / Don't ever want to lose your love / You're the one / Dedicated to the one I love / You never loved me (at all) / Half a love / Crowd is there / Tighten up / Going out of my head / Groovin' / Misty / More yes I'm ready / Sad sad girl / I need love / Oh how it hurts
BCD 16205 / Oct '97 / Bear Family

Mason, Ian

☐ AT FARNHAM MALTINGS (Mason, Ian & Rod Mason)
BCD 335 / Aug '95 / GHB

Mason, Phil

☐ HERE'S TO YOU (Mason, Phil New Orleans All-Stars)
Tears / Dardanella / Waiting for the robert e. lee / Feeling drowsy / Crawl / Swing low, sweet chariot / Jump in the line / Kitchen man / Cornet chop suey / Oh peter / Sensation / Freight train blues / One morning in may / Sweet sue / One hour mama / Tailgate ramble / Keeping out of mischief now / Walking with the king / He'll have to go
LACD 41 / Mar '95 / Lake

☐ PHIL MASON & NEW ORLEANS ALL STARS
BCD 315 / Apr '94 / GHB

☐ SPIRITUALS AND GOSPELS (Mason, Phil New Orleans All-Stars)
Sing on / Let God abide / Precious Lord / Nobody knows the trouble I've seen / Storm is passing over / Lilly of the valley / It is no secret / In the garden / Sweet fields / We shall not be moved / Just a closer walk with thee / When I move to the sky / We shall walk through the streets of the city / Higher ground / Over in the gloryland / When the saints go marching in
LACD 64 / Jun '96 / Lake

☐ WEST INDIES BLUES (Mason, Phil New Orleans All-Stars & Christine Tyrrell)
June night / Over the waves / West Indies blues / Picking on your baby / I'm putting all my eggs into one basket / I want a big butter and egg man / Davenport blues / What the Lord has done for me / Short dress gal / Light from the lighthouse / You've got the right key but the wrong keyhole / Yacka hula hickey dula / Lazy bones / Fidgety fingers / Amazing Grace / Royal telephone / Algiers strut
LACD 93 / 9 Mar '98 / Lake

☐ YOU DO SOMETHING TO ME (Mason, Phil New Orleans All-Stars & Christine Tyrrell)
I wish I were in Dixie / Jersey lightning / My curly headed baby / You do something to me / Bugle call rag / Gulf coast blues / Dreaming the hours away / Mahogany Hall stomp / That teasin' rag / When I grow too old to dream / Sheikh of Araby / My silent love / In the mood / Fair and square / Squeeze me / High society
LACD 33 / Jan '95 / Lake

Mason, Rod

☐ STRUTTIN' WITH SOME BARBECUE
BLCD 760511 / Jun '94 / Black Lion

Mason, Steve

☐ CONCEPTION VESSEL ONE
EXGCD 001 / Jun '97 / Experience Grooves

☐ IN THE MIX VOL.4
EXGCD 003 / 6 Jul '98 / Experience Grooves

Mason-Dixon Hobos

☐ MESSERS
PT 604001 / Jun '96 / Part

Masonics

☐ DOWN AMONG THE DEAD
SFTR 1530CD / 6 Apr '98 / Sympathy For The Record Industry

Masonna

☐ FREQUENCY LSD
ALIENCD 007 / 30 Mar '98 / Alien8

☐ HYPER CHAOTIC
V 001 / Feb '97 / V

☐ SPECTRUM RIPPER
CSR 17CD / 2 Mar '98 / Cold Spring

Masqualero

☐ AERO
Aero / Science / Venise / Printer / Balet / Return / Bee gee
8357672 / Jul '88 / ECM

☐ RE-ENTER
Re-enter / Li'l Lisa / Heimo gardsjenta / Gaia / Little song / This is no jungle in Baltimore / Find another animal / Stykkevis og delt
8479392 / May '91 / ECM

Mass

☐ MASS
PLE 11022 / Jun '98 / Paratactile

Mass Psychosis

☐ FACE
341912 / Nov '95 / No Bull

Massacre

☐ KILLING TIME
CDGR 249 / 1 Jun '98 / Charly

Massengill, David

☐ COMING UP FOR AIR
FF 590CD / Apr '94 / Flying Fish

☐ RETURN, THE
PLUCD 5 / Jun '96 / Plump

Massey, Cal

☐ BLUES TO COLTRANE
Blues to Coltrane / What's wrong / Bakai / These are soulful days / Father and son
CCD 79029 / Feb '97 / Candid

Massey, Zane

☐ BRASS KNUCKLES
DD 464 / Aug '94 / Delmark

☐ SAFE TO IMAGINE
Blues for Awliya / Lady Charlotte / Telekinetics / Sun of son / Saminiego / Quiet dawn / Myra's maya / Things have got to change
DE 487 / Jun '97 / Delmark

Massive Attack

☐ BLUE LINES
Safe from harm / One love / Blue lines / Be thankful for what you've got / Five man army / Unfinished sympathy / Daydreaming / Lately / Hymn of the big wheel
WBRCD 1 / Jun '91 / Wild Bunch

☐ MEZZANINE
Angel / Risingson / Teardrop / Inertia creeps / Exchange / Dissolved girl / Man next door / Black milk / Mezzanine / Group 4 / Exchange
WBRCD 4
WBRCDX 4 / 20 Apr '98 / Wild Bunch

☐ NO PROTECTION (Massive Attack & The Mad Professor)
Radiation ruling the nation / Bumper ball dub / Trinity dub / Cool monsoon / Eternal feedback / Moving dub / I spy / Backward sucking
WBRCD 3 / Feb '95 / Wild Bunch

☐ PROTECTION
Protection / Karmacoma / Three / Weather storm / Spying glass / Better things / Euro child / Sly / Heat miser / Light my fire
WBRCD 2 / Sep '94 / Wild Bunch

Masso, George

☐ JUST FOR A THRILL
Summer night / Child is born / You brought a new kind of love to me / Soft lights and sweet music / Just for a thrill / Love walked in / Touch of your lips / I remember you / That old feeling / Half of it dearie blues / Sleepin' bee / Fred
SKCD 22022 / Jun '93 / Sackville

☐ LET'S BE BUDDIES (Masso, George & Dan Barrett)
ARCD 19127 / Nov '94 / Arbors Jazz

☐ MASSO/POLCER/NEW YORK ALLSTARS 1992-1993 (Masso, George Allstars & Ed Polcer/New York Allstars)
CD 008 / May '96 / Nagel Heyer

☐ SHAKIN' THE BLUES AWAY (Masso, George & Brian Lemon/Roy Williams)
Lester leaps in / Love is just around the corner / My funny valentine / Shakin' the blues away / Keepin' out of mischief / I've got it bad and that ain't good / Stompin' at the Savoy / There is no greater love / Up a lazy river / Watch what happens / By George / This is all I ask / Sometimes I'm happy
ZECD 6 / May '97 / Zephyr

☐ THAT OLD GANG OF MINE
ARCD 19173 / Nov '97 / Arbors Jazz

☐ WONDERFUL WORLD OF GEORGE GERSHWIN, THE (Masso, George Allstars)
CD 001 / May '96 / Nagel Heyer

Master

☐ MASTER
NB 040 / Jan '91 / Nuclear Blast

☐ ON THE 7TH DAY GOD CREATED MASTER
NB 054CD / Feb '92 / Nuclear Blast

Master Musicians Of Jajouka

☐ JOUJOUKA BLACK EYES
SR 87 / Jan '96 / Le Coeur Du Monde

☐ MASTER MUSICIANS OF JAJOUKA
GCD 3000 / Jan '98 / Genes

Master P

☐ MP DA LAST DON
Soldiers, riders and G's / Till we dead and gone / Thinkin' 'bout U / So many souls deceased / Get your paper / Ride / Goodbye to my homies / Ghetto love / Hot boys and girls / Welcome to my city / Ghetto life / Let's get 'em / Family business / Gangsta B / Snitches / Rock-a-bye haters / Ghetto's got me trapped / Dear Mr. President / Da last Don / More 2 life / Mama raised me / Let my 9 get 'em / Eternity / War wounds / Black and white / These streets keep me rollin' / Reverse the game / Make em say uhh no.2 / Thug girl
CDPTYX 152 / 27 Jul '98 / Priority/Virgin

Mastermind

☐ MASTERMIND VOL.1
CYCL 037 / 29 Sep '97 / Cyclops

☐ MASTERMIND VOL.2 (Brainstorm)
1st Futility / Code of honor / Wake up America / William Tell overture / Resurrection / Tormented heart / Hammer of fate / Aspirations / Prelude / Ride of the Valkyrie / Nowhere in sight / Firefly / Resolution / Dance of the demons / From the ashes / Breakdown
CYCL 052 / Apr '97 / Cyclops

☐ TRAGIC SYMPHONY
Tiger tiger / Power and the passion / All the king's horses / Tragic symphony / Sea of tears / Nothing left to say / Into the void
CYCL 026 / Jul '95 / Cyclops

☐ UNTIL ETERNITY
CYCL 043 / Oct '96 / Cyclops

Master's Apprentices

☐ HANDS OF TIME
RVCD 13 / Dec '97 / Raven

Masters At Work

☐ HELTER SKELTER VOL.2 (3CD Set) (Various Artists)
Hustlers in hardcore: *DJ Demo* / Coming on strong: *Slam & Charly B* / Crazy knowledge: *SLAM* / You belong to me: *Kingsize & Eternity* / Jump around: *Slippery Project* / Muzik: *Happy Rollers* / Your mine: *DJ Demo* / Deep in the underground: *DJ Demo* / Funfair: *Force & Styles* / Freedom: *DJ Fade* / My dreams: *Sub Ace* / Power of love: *Q-Tex* / Distant skies: *Unique* / One: *OMG* / Equazion 9: *Q-Tex* / Feelin' fine: *Unique* / Cutting deep: *Force & Styles* / Images of you: *Quest* / Sailaway: *Bang* / Be good to yourself: *Jhal* / Sub dub: *Seduction* / Killer: *DJ Sy & DJ Demo* / In effect: *DJ Red Alert* / I'll be there: *Jhal* / Vampire: *Choose One* / It's an 'ardcore thing: *2 MC's* / Love is: *Voodoo Posse & Jocelyn Brown* / Rush hour: *DJ Magical* / Shooting star: *Bang* / Virtual: *Elevate* / Seasons of love: *Vinyl Groover & Brisk* / Into my mind: *DJ Destiny* / Total control: *Sound Assassins* / Rainfall: *Vinyl Groover & Brisk* / Bright eyes: *Vinyl Groover & Edy C* / Let off the love: *Smith Brothers* / My mind can't work: *Daniel* / Can you feel the force: *Choci* / That emotion: *Smith Brothers* / Warriors: *Vandalize* / Ultra funky: *Ultra Sonic* / Progressive attack: *DJ Energy* / Breaking up: *Daniel* / Just feel it: *Choci* / Energy: *DJ Gollum* / Quatro: *Electric Fruit Orchestra* / Wanna play house: *Code 21* / See you at the streetparade: *Re-Move* / Tripwire: *D-Factor* / Air attack: *M-Zone* / Synergy: *Bounce* / D-Trance: *Gary D* / Plasma man: *M-Zone*
CDHSR 005 / 8 Jun '98 / Helter Skelter

☐ MASTERWORKS (Masters At Work - The Essential Kenlou House Mixes) (Various Artists)
I can't get no sleep: *Masters At Work* / Only love can break your heart: *St. Etienne* / Beautiful people: *Tucker, Barbara* / Buddy: *Cherry, Neneh* / Voices in my mind: *Voices* / Photograph of Mary: *Lorenz, Trey* / My love: *Masters At Work* / We can make it: *Sole Fusion* / Moonshine: *Kenlou* / Can't play around: *Brown, Kathy* / Souffles H: *Mondo Grosso* / I like: *Shanice* / Bounce: *Kenlou*
HARMCD 001 / Sep '95 / Harmless

Masters Hammer

☐ RITUAL
OPCD 031 / Feb '95 / Osmose

☐ SLAGRY
KRONH 03CD / Feb '96 / Osmose

Masters Of Ikuta Ryu

☐ SOUL OF THE KOTO VOL.2, THE
LYRCD 7433 / Nov '97 / Lyrichord

Masters, Frank

☐ FRANKIE MASTERS
CCD 048 / Oct '93 / Circle

☐ FRANKIE MASTERS & HIS ORCHESTRA 1947 (Masters, Frank Orchestra)
CCD 063 / Jul '96 / Circle

Masters, Sammy

☐ EVERYBODY DIGS SAMMY
ID 123555CD / 23 Mar '98 / Dionysus

Masterson, Declan

☐ END OF THE HARVEST
CEFCD 148 / Jan '94 / Gael Linn

☐ FIONNUISCE
FR 961CD / Dec '97 / Fairwater

☐ TROPICAL TRAD
Tropical trad / Down the back lane/Kit O'Mahony's / Ravelled Hank of Yarn/Picking the spuds/London jig / Kildare fancy/Jimmy Reilly's / Young Tom Ennis/King of the pipers / Aisling gheal / Mistress/John Kelly's / When you go home/Caterpillar / Jack Rowe's/The gooseberry bush / Lady Gethin / Munster bank/The mile bush / Hazel woods / Boys of the town/James Kelly's/Bernie Cunnion's jig / Conor Tully's/Chattering magpie / Hibernian/Contentment is wealth/Katie's fancy / Cambar lassies/Crowley's/James Kelly / Full moon/Trail of tears/Keep her going
SCD 1093 / Jan '94 / Starc

Masuda, Mikio

☐ BLACK DAFFODILS
JVC 90302 / 19 Jan '98 / JVC

☐ SMOKIN' NIGHT
JD 3313 / Oct '88 / JVC

Matadors

☐ WHAT'S WRONG WITH MODERNY
RT 019 / Sep '97 / Roto

Matata

☐ FEELIN' FUNKY
Wanna do my thing / Return to you / Good good understanding / Gettin' together / I believed her / Good samaritan / I feel funky / I don't have to worry / Something in mind / I want you / Love is the only way / Gimme some lovin / Talkin' talkin
PCOM 1134 / Mar '94 / President

☐ WILD RIVER
Wild river / Beautiful burra / Mayo mayo / Jungle warrior / Wowo wowo / I need somebody / Vuana Africa / Pigha yako / Mosala tokosalaka / You've gotta find me / Maendeleo yakenya / Ulimwengu
PCOM 1133 / Mar '94 / President

Matchbox

☐ GOING DOWN TOWN
Get up and get out / Going down town / Stealing hearts / Nothing to do but rock 'n' roll all day / She's hot / Can't get over you / Roller skating Sally / Flip flop floosie / Shooting gallery / Think you took my loving and run / Hot love / This is where I'm getting off
CDSJ 570 / May '98 / Sun Jay

☐ MATCHBOX LIVE
PEPCD 102 / Jan '95 / Pollytone

☐ SHADES OF GENE
Dance in the street / In my dreams / Got my eyes on you / Summertime / Everybody's talkin' 'bout Gene / Wedding bells / Ain't misbehavin' / Right here on Earth / Woman love / Be bop a lula / Lonesome fugitive / Git it / Sure fire way / Rocky road blues
PEPCD 108 / Mar '95 / Pollytone

Matchbox 20

☐ YOURSELF OR SOMEONE LIKE YOU
Real world / Long day / 3am / Push / Girl like that / Back 2 good / Damn / Argue / Kody / Busted / Shame / Hang
7567927212 / 13 Apr '98 / Atlantic

Matching Mole

☐ BBC RADIO 1 IN CONCERT
Instant pussy / Litheing and graceing / Marchides / Part of the dance / Brandy as benge
WINCD 063 / Jun '94 / Windsong

☐ LITTLE RED BOOK
Starting in the middle of the day / Marchides / Nan's true hole / Righteous rumba / Brandy as in Benj / Gloria gloom / Flora fidgit / Smoke signal
4714892 / Mar '97 / Columbia

Mateo & Matos

☐ NEW YORK RHYTHMS
Change up the groove / Release the rhythm / Summer groove / Journey beyond / Mama / Don't let it go / Happy feelin' / Keep on dancin' / Nice and slow
GUCD 002 / 27 Oct '97 / Glasgow Underground

Matera

☐ SAME HERE
INV 092CD / 13 Oct '97 / Invisible

Material

☐ BEST OF MATERIAL, THE
CDNEW 117 / 16 Mar '98 / Charly

☐ LIVE FROM SOUNDSCAPE
DIW 389 / Feb '94 / DIW

☐ MEMORY SERVES
Memory serves / Disappearing / Upriver / Metal test / Conform to the rhythm / Unauthorised / Square dance / Silent land
CPCD 8285 / Apr '97 / Charly

☐ ONE DOWN
Take a chance / I'm the one / Time out / Let me have it all / Come down / Holding on / Memories / Don't lose control / Busting out
CPCD 8282 / Jan '97 / Charly

☐ SEVEN SOULS
Ineffect / Seven souls / Soul killer / Western lands / Deliver / Equation / End of words
5349052 / 15 Sep '97 / Mercury

☐ TEMPORARY MUSIC
OAO / White man / On sadism / Process/Motion / Discourse / Slow murder / Secret life / Reduction / Heritage / Dark things / Detached / Ciquiri
MPG 74044 / Jul '97 / Movieplay Gold
CPCD 8286 / May '97 / Charly

Mateu, Jaque

☐ DE VILLAVICENCIO
21044CD / Jun '94 / Sonifolk

Mathers, Peter

☐ SUNDANCE
MPCD 3001 / Jul '98 / Mariposa

Matheson, Karen

☐ DREAMING SEA
SURCD 020 / May '98 / Survival

Matheson, William

☐ SCOTTISH TRADITION VOL.16 (Gaelic Bards & Minstrels)
CDTRAX 9016 / Feb '94 / Greentrax

Mathews, Tony

☐ CONDITION: BLUE
I really got the blues today / White powder / Coming home to you / Uncle Joe / Lovely Linda / Ann Marie / Laid off / Let me know when you're comin' / Changes
HMG 5502 / Aug '97 / Hightone

Mathey

☐ CLEPO
087882 / Jan '97 / Lusafrika

Mathieson, Robert

☐ BIG BIRL, THE
LCOM 5262 / Feb '98 / Lismor

☐ EBB-TIDE (Mathieson, Pipe Major Robert)
LCOM 9038 / Oct '90 / Lismor

☐ GRACE NOTES (Mathieson, Pipe Major Robert)
Hornpipes / Air and jigs / March, strathspey and reel / Galician dance / Irish reels and hornpipe / Mazurka / Air and jigs / Dance and jig / Hornpipes / Slip jig and Viennese waltz / Jigs / Airs and reels
LCOM 5171 / Oct '92 / Lismor

Mathieu, Mireille

☐ CHANTE PIAF
4509940242 / Apr '97 / Carrere

Mathis, Johnny

☐ CELEBRATION (The Anniversary Album)
You saved my life / Wonderful, wonderful / It's not for me to say / Chances are / When a child is born / Too much, too little, too late / Last time I felt like this / Stop, look, listen (to your heart) / With you I'm born again / Three times a lady / She believes in me / I will survive / Evergreen / When I need you / Sweet surrender / How deep is your love / We're all alone / Misty / I'd rather be here with you / If it's magic
4674522 / Oct '90 / CBS

☐ GLOBAL MASTERS
Bye bye Barbara / Call me irresponsible / April love / Laura / Shangri-La / Dream dream dream / When you wish upon a star / Beyond the blue horizon / Limehouse blues / Touch of your lips / More / Granada / After the storm / Hello Dolly / Manhattan / On a wonderful day / Sweetheart tree / Danny boy / Lovers in New York / Something's coming / On a clear day / So nice / Music that makes me dance / Somewhere my love
4871182 / May '97 / Columbia

☐ HITS OF JOHNNY MATHIS, THE
Misty / Love story / Time for us / Twelfth of never / Look of love / This guy's in love with you / When will I see you again / I'm stone in love with you / Killing me softly / Me and Mrs. Jones / First time ever I saw your face / Do you know where you're going to / Moon river / Feelings / How deep is your love / When a child is born
4679532 / 27 Jul '98 / Columbia

☐ LOVE SONGS
Man and a woman / Feelings / Help me make it through the night / How deep is your love / I'll never fall in love again / I'm stone in love with you / I only have eyes for you / Killing me softly with her song / Mandy / Misty / Twelfth of never / First time (ever I saw your face) / Most beautiful girl / Way we were / Too much, too little, too late: *Mathis, Johnny & Deniece Williams* / When I need you / When will I see you again / Where do I begin (love story) / With you I'm born again / Without you / You are the sunshine
4781712 / Sep '96 / Columbia

☐ MERRY CHRISTMAS
Winter wonderland / Christmas song / Sleigh ride / Blue Christmas / I'll be home for Christmas / White Christmas / O holy night / What child is this / First Noel / Silver bells / It came upon a midnight clear / Silent night
4814382 / 3 Nov '97 / Columbia

☐ PERSONAL COLLECTION (4CD Set)
99 Miles from LA / Certain smile / Lovely smile / Way to spend an evening / Man and a woman / Ride on a rainbow / Time for us / All alone am I / All the thing you are / All through the night / I think that's what I'll do / Arianne / Baia / Betcha by golly wow / By myself / Chances are / Clopin clopant / Don't blame me / El amar y el querer / Evie / Feelings / Friends in love / Gina / Happy / Heavenly / I had the craziest dream / I have a love / I heard a forest praying / I look at you / I married an angel / I'm coming home / It's not for me to say / I've grown accustomed to her face / Laura / Let me be the one / Life is a song worth singing / Live for life / Long ago and far away / Love / Love look away / Love won't let me wait / Maria / Misty / Moonlight becomes you / More than you know / One / One day in your life / Photograph / Prelude to a kiss / Small world / Smile / Someone / Something to live for / Speak softly love / Spring is here / Best of everything / Island / Last time I felt like this / Twelfth never / There goes my heart / Theme from summer of '42 / Tonight / Too much too little too late / Toyland / Warm / Warm / We're all alone / What will my Mary say / What'll I do / When a child is born / When I'm with you / When sunny gets blue / Wild is the wind / With you I'm born again / Wonderful / Yellow roses on her gown / You belong to me / You set my heart to music / You'll never know
CD 489320 / 1 Dec '97 / Columbia

☐ RAINDROPS KEEP FALLING ON MY HEAD/LOVE STORY (2CD Set)
Man and a woman / Odds and ends / Jean / Everybody's talkin' / Bridge over troubled water / Raindrops keep falling on my head / Honey come back / Watch what happens / Something / Alfie / Midnight cowboy / Love story / Rose garden / Ten times forever more / It's impossible / I was there / What are you doing the rest of your life / We've only just begun / Traces / For the good times / My sweet lord / Loss of love
4775942 / Oct '94 / Columbia

☐ THAT'S WHAT FRIENDS ARE FOR (Mathis, Johnny & Deniece Williams)
You're all I need to get by / Until you come back to me / You're a special part of my life / Ready or not / Me for you, you for me / Your precious love / Just the way you are / That's what friends are for / I just can't get over you / Touching me with love
4879512 / Jul '97 / Columbia

☐ ULTIMATE HITS COLLECTION
Wonderful wonderful / It's not for me to say / When sunny gets blue / Chances are / Twelfth of never / Wild is the wind / Certain smile / Misty / Brazil / Maria / Stranger in paradise / Stardust / I'm coming home / Sweetheart tree / Love theme from Romeo and Juliet / Too much too little too late / Friends in love / 99 Miles from LA
4910512 / 22 Jun '98 / Legacy

☐ WARM/SWING SOFTLY
Warm / My one and only love / Baby baby baby / Handful of stars / By myself / I've grown accustomed to her face / Then I'll be tired of you / I'm glad there is you / What'll I do / Lovely things you do / There goes my heart / While we're young / You hit the spot / It's de lovely / Get me to the church on time / Like someone in love / You'd be so nice to come home to / Love walked in / Heart of mine / To be in love / Sweet Lorraine / Can't get out of this mood / I've got the world on a string / Easy to say (but so hard to do)
4898032 / 23 Mar '98 / Columbia

Matipo Pyramid

☐ AOTEAROA
MPP 001 / Jan '97 / Matipo Pyramid

Matire

☐ MATIRE
DOMCD 015 / Apr '95 / Dominator

Matlock, Glen

☐ WHO'S HE WHEN HE'S AT HOME
CRECD 191 / May '96 / Creation

Matlubeh

☐ TURQUOISE OF SAMARKAND, THE
LD 122039 / Sep '96 / Long Distance

Matmos

☐ MATMOS
VAGUE 001 / Aug '97 / Vague Terrain

☐ QUASI OBJECTS
VAGUE 02 / 6 Apr '98 / Vague Terrain

Matos, Bobby

☐ CHANGO'S DANCE
CBCD 001 / Jul '96 / Cubop

☐ FOOTSTEPS
CBCD 005 / Nov '96 / Cubop

☐ SESSIONS
God of the crossroads / Chameleon / Cafe con bagels / Mi guaguanco / Creator has a master plan / Chameleon / Ayo / Afro Cubismo / Bembe/Promised land / Chameleon / Groovin' / Guiro Elegua
CBCD 011 / 24 Aug '98 / Cubop

Matrimony

☐ KITTY FINGERS
KRS 270CD / Aug '97 / Kill Rock Stars

Matsui, Keiko

☐ FULL MOON AND SHRINE
60863177752 / 7 Apr '98 / ULG

Matt Bianco

☐ BEST OF MATT BIANCO, THE
Don't blame it on that girl / Yeh yeh / Sneaking out the back door / Half a minute / Dancing in the street / Fire in the blood / Wap bam boogie / Good times / More than I can bear / Get out of your lazy bed / Matt's mood / Just can't stand it / Whose side are you on / Say it's not too late / Nervous / We've got the mood
9031725902 / Dec '96 / WEA

☐ WHOSE SIDE ARE YOU ON
More than I can bear / No no never / Half a minute / Matt's mood / Get out of your lazy bed / It's getting late / Sneaking out the back door / Riding with the wind / Matt's mood II / Whose side are you on / Big Rosie / Other side
2404722 / Aug '84 / WEA

Mattea, Kathy

☐ LOVE TRAVELS
Love travels / Sending me angels / Patiently waiting / If that's what you call love / Further and further away / 455 rocket / I'm on your side / Bridge / All roads to the river / End of the line / Beautiful fool
5328992 / Jan '97 / Mercury

☐ READY FOR THE STORM (Favourite Cuts)
Rock me on the water / Last night I dreamed of loving you / Nobody's gonna rain on our parade / Ready for the storm / I will / Standing knee deep in a river (Dying of thirst) / Untasted honey / Mary did you know / Asking us to dance / Few good things remain / Summer of my dreams / Late in the day
5280062 / Apr '95 / Mercury

☐ WALKING AWAY A WINNER
5188522 / May '94 / Mercury

Matthew's Southern Comfort

☐ ESSENTIAL COLLECTION, THE
HMNCD 014 / 3 Nov '97 / Half Moon

☐ MATTHEW'S SOUTHERN COMFORT/ SECOND SPRING
BGOCD 313 / Jun '96 / Beat Goes On

Matthews, Dave

☐ BEFORE THESE CROWDED STREETS (Matthews, Dave Band)
Pantala naga pampa / Rapunzel / Last stop / Don't drink the water / Stay (wasting time) / Halloween / Stone / Crush / Dreaming tree / Pig / Spoon
07863676602 / 5 May '98 / American

☐ CRASH
So much to say / Two steps / Crash into me / Too much / # 41 / Say goodbye / Drive in drive out / Let you down / Lie in our graves / Cry freedom / Tripping billies / Proudest monkey
7863669042 / Jul '96 / RCA

☐ UNDER THE TABLE AND DREAMING
Best of what's around / What would you say / Satellite / Rhyme and reason / Typical situation / Dancing nannies / Ants marching / Lover lay down / Jimi thing / Warehouse / Pay for what you get / No 34
07863664492 / Mar '95 / RCA

Matthews, David

☐ AMERICAN PIE (Matthews, David Trio & Gary Burton)
American pie / Mr. Tambourine man / My back pages / Sound of silence / Sunny / Como en Vietnam / Taste of honey / Moonlight melody
66055005 / Jul '91 / Sweet Basil

Matthews, Eric

☐ IT'S HEAVY IN HERE
SPCD 312 / 20 Apr '98 / Sub Pop

☐ LATENESS OF THE HOUR, THE
Ideas that died that day / My morning parade / Pair of cherry / To clear the air / Yes everyone / Everything so real / Becomes dark blue / Pleasent kind / Gilded cages / Since the wheel free / Festival fun / No gnashing teeth
SPCD 404 / 6 Apr '98 / Sub Pop

Matthews, Iain

☐ DARK SIDE, THE
WM 1025 / Oct '94 / Watermelon

☐ EXCERPTS FROM SWINE LAKE
Something mighty / Horse left in the rain / Dance of fate / Trail of the survivor / Changes / Cave in / Heroes / Touching the fleece / Even if it kills me / Sight unseen / Where the big dogs run / Break a window
FIENDCD 942 / Mar '98 / Demon

☐ GOD LOOKED DOWN
WMCD 1055 / Sep '96 / Watermelon

☐ JOURNEYS FROM GOSPEL OAK
Things you gave me / Tribute to Hank Williams / Met her on a plane / Do right woman, do right man / Knowing the game / Polly / Mobile blue / Bride 1945 / Franklin Avenue / Sing me back home
CRESTCD 004 / Mar '91 / Mooncrest

☐ NIGHT IN MANHATTAN
TX 2001CD / Dec '93 / Taxim

☐ ORPHANS & OUTCASTS
CDL 102 / Jun '94 / Dirty Linen

☐ PURE AND CROOKED
Like dominoes / Mercy Street / Hardly innocent mind / Rains of '62 / New shirt / Bridge of Cherokee / Busby's babes / Say no more / Perfect timing / Out of my range / This town's no lady
WMCD 1029 / Dec '94 / Watermelon

Matthews, Jessie

☐ DANCING ON THE CEILING
Dancing on the ceiling / When you've got a little springtime in your heart / It's love again / Gangway / Everything's in rhythm with my heart / Your heart skips a beat / One little kiss from you / When you gotta sing you gotta sing / Tony's in town / By the fireside / Head over heels in love / Lord and Lady Whoozis / One more kiss and then goodnight / Let me give my happiness to you / Tinkle tinkle tinkle / Just by your example / I'll stay with you / Three wishes / May I have the next romance with you / Looking around corners for you / Souvenir of love / My river
CDAJA 5063 / Jul '89 / Living Era

☐ MY HEART STOOD STILL
My heart stood still / Got to dance my way to heaven / There's that look in your eyes again / It's love again / Trusting my luck / Looking around corners for you / Gangway / May I have the next romance with you / Head over heels / One more kiss / Three wishes / By the fireside / I'll stay with you / Dancing on the ceiling / Hold my hand / Let me give my happiness to you / One little kiss from you / Everything's in rhythm with my heart / Tony's in town / I nearly let love go slipping through my fingers / When you gotta sing, you gotta sing / Just by your example
PASTCD 9746 / Aug '91 / Flapper

Matthews, Julie

☐ SUCH IS LIFE
RGFCD 030 / Mar '96 / Road Goes On Forever

Matthews, Ronnie

☐ AT CAFE DES COPAINS
SKCD 22026 / Jun '93 / Sackville

☐ DARK BEFORE THE DAWN
DIW 604 / Jun '91 / DIW

☐ LAMENT FOR LOVE
DIW 612 / Jan '93 / DIW

☐ SELENA'S DANCES
In a sentimental mood / My funny valentine / Stella by starlight / Selena's dance / Body and soul / There is no greater love / Blue bossa / Fee fi fo fum
CDSJP 304 / Aug '90 / Timeless Jazz

☐ SHADES OF MONK
SSCD 8064 / Jan '96 / Sound Hills

☐ SONG FOR LESLIE
RED 1231622 / Aug '95 / Red

Matthews, Wall

☐ COLOUR OF DUSK, THE (Songs Set To Poems By Dolores Kendrick) (Matthews, Wall & Aleta Greene)
Jenny in love / Ndzeli in passage/Jenny in love / Jenny in tears/Jenny in love / Leah in freedom / Prunella's picnic/Jenny in love / Tildy's prayer / Julia carrying water / Lucy sleeps with Master Muford / Slightly coloured lady / Harriet in mid air / Prayin' ground / Canticle of a black lady
CCD 715 / Nov '96 / Clean Cuts

☐ GATHERING THE WORLD
Where the rainbow ends / Go down old Hannah / Night waterman / Pastures of plenty / Clementine / Gathering of the world / She comes from the sea / Ada / Whale
CCD 712 / Nov '96 / Clean Cuts

☐ HEART OF THE WINTER, THE
Oh Holy night / Joy to the world/Here we come a-wassailing / We three Kings of Orient are / Greensleeves / Carol of the bells / Little drummer boy / O come o come Emmanuel / Sing we Noel / Hark the herald angels sing/Decks the halls/Angels we have h / Good King Wenceslas/I saw three ships / God rest ye merry gentlemen/Masters in the hall / O little town of Bethlehem / First Noel/Silent night / Jingle bells
CCD 710 / Nov '96 / Clean Cuts

☐ RIDING HORSES
Traveller / Rain tin / Maybe next year / Riding horses / Clowns / Old woman / Evening watch / By the fire light / Lion's tooth / Cloak of sorrow / Across the universe / I don't know what to say to you but I love you / Fol de rol / Lover of night / Stolen child
CCD 709 / Nov '96 / Clean Cuts

Matthews, Wendy

☐ LILY
Friday's child / Walk away / TKO / Mother can't do / Quiet art / Day you went away / If only I could / Homecoming song / Face of Appalachia / Naming names / Inexorably yours
4509905472 / Mar '93 / East West

Mattlar, Marja

☐ LUMI
829322 / Feb '97 / BUDA

Matto Congrio

☐ MATTO CONGRIO
F 1031CD / Jun '94 / Sonifolk

Mattsson, Dag

☐ DON'T FORCE THE LEVEL
FLCCD 152 / Oct '97 / Four Leaf Clover

Matutina Noctem

☐ ANIMA MEAM
CDAR 042 / 8 Dec '97 / Adipocre

Matveinen, Liisa

☐ OTTILIA
OMCD 55 / Mar '96 / Olarin Musiiki Oy

Maubuissons

☐ TREONVEL TRANSIT
MB 194CD / Nov '96 / MB

Mauger, Jacques

☐ SHOWCASE FOR TROMBONE
DOYCD 027 / Nov '93 / Doyen

Maulidi & Musical Party

☐ MOMBASA WEDDING SPECIAL
Mkufu / Hukomi mpelelezi / Shuga dedi / Mume ni moshi wa koko / Fadhila kama kukopa / Vishindo vya mashua / Ukiondoka mpenzi / Hasidi
CDORBD 058 / May '90 / Globestyle

Maupin, Bennie

☐ DRIVING WHILE BLACK (Maupin, Bennie & Patrick Gleeson)
Smiling faces / Riverside drive / Work / Lookout / Driving while black / Bank float / Miles to go / In re: Nude orbit / Vutu
INT 32422 / 20 Jul '98 / Intuition

Maure, Hector

☐ SOBRE EL PUCHO
EBCD 99 / 1 Jun '98 / El Bandoneon

Mauriat, Paul

☐ ESCAPADES
3019362 / Apr '97 / Arcade

☐ LOVE IS BLUE (Best Collection)
3019352 / Apr '97 / Arcade

☐ PAUL MAURIAT ORCHESTRA, THE (Mauriat, Paul Orchestra)
Love is blue / She / Love story / If you go away / Somethin' stupid / Ebony and ivory / Feel like making love / Come back to Sorrento / Summer place / Jeux interdits / Man and a woman / This is my song / Don't cry for me Argentina / My way / Mamy blue / Summer knows / La mer / Malaguena / Bridge over troubled water / Way we were
5542242 / Oct '97 / Spectrum

☐ SOUNDTRACKS
3019372 / Apr '97 / Arcade

Maurinier, Charles

☐ ZOUK POWER
MCD 51349 / '91 / Sonodisc

Maurizia, Leon

☐ MAURIZIA, LEON & BASILIO (Maurizia, Leon & Basilio)
KD 165CD / Aug '97 / Elkar

Maurizio

☐ MAURIZIO
EFA 222222 / Jun '97 / M

Mauro, Jose

☐ OBNOXIUS
CDRSQ 1 / Feb '96 / Quartin

Mauro, Renata

☐ BALLADS
RTCL 805CD / Jul '96 / Right Tempo

Mauro, Turk

☐ UNDERDOG, THE
All God's children got rhythm / Underdog / Turkquoise / Jazz leif / Zoot and Al / Until it's time for you to go / My buddy / Until it's time for you to go / For all we know / Jazz leif / All God's children / Underdog
STCD 8265 / 9 Mar '98 / Storyville

Mausardi, Guido

☐ ALLA STUDIO 7 (Mausardi, Guido Trio)
RTCL 808CD / Jul '96 / Right Tempo

Mause

☐ TEEN RIOT GUNTHER - STRACKTURE
EFA 692922 / Aug '97 / Morbid

Mavericks

☐ FROM HELL TO PARADISE
Mr. jones / End of the line / Excuse me (i think I've got a heartache) / This broken heart / I got you / From hell to paradise / A better way / Forever blue / Hey good lookin' / Children
MCAD 10544 / 16 Feb '98 / MCA

☐ MAVERICKS, THE
HIPD 40113 / 30 Jun '98 / Hippo

☐ SONGS FOR ALL OCCASIONS
Foolish heart / One step away / Here comes the rain / Missing you / All you ever do is bring me down / My secret flame / Writing on the wall / Loving you / If you only knew / I'm not gonna cry for you / Something stupid / Blue moon
MCD 11344 / Oct '95 / MCA

☐ TRAMPOLINE
UMD 80456 / 2 Mar '98 / Universal

☐ WHAT A CRYING SHAME
There goes my heart / What a crying shame / Pretend / I should have been true / Things you said to me / Just a memory / All that heaven will allow / Neon blue / O what a thrill / Ain't found nobody / Losing side of me
MCLD 19353 / Apr '97 / MCA

Max Polo

☐ ELEVATION ZERO
ACCD 018 / Nov '96 / ACV

Max Romeo

☐ CROSS OR THE GUN
TZ 018 / Apr '94 / Tappa

☐ MCCABEE VERSION
SONCD 0078 / May '95 / Sonic Sounds

☐ ON THE BEACH
Nothing takes the place of you / Party night / I'm still waiting / Since I met you baby / Lost love / My heart is gone / On the beach / That lucky old sun / What am I living for / My secret love / Set me free / Ten commandments / Israelites / Before the next tear drops
LG 21042 / Feb '93 / Lagoon

☐ WET DREAM
Wet dream / Day dream / Rent man / Two people / Pussy watchman / My dickie / There's a man in your life / Sometimes / Chi chi bud / Chi chi bud version / Fowl thief / Mr. chatterbox / Macabee version / Music book / Stick by me / Let the power fall / Holla zion
CC 2705 / Aug '93 / Crocodisc

Maxeen

☐ DIARY, THE
SOULCD 35 / Jan '96 / Soultown

Maxi Jazz

☐ ORIGINAL GROOVE JUICE VOL.1 (Maxi Jazz & The Soul Food Cafe)
REVCC 012 / Jul '96 / Revco

Maximalist

☐ WHAT THE BODY DOESN'T REMEMBER
SUBCD 00826 / '89 / Sub Rosa

Maximum Penalty

☐ INDEPENDENT
IJT 003 / Mar '97 / Idjit

☐ SUPERLIFE
Believe / Overdue / Too little too late / Among friends / 70's boxxx / Heartless / Hate / Life jacket / Mood swings / Could you love me / East side story / Identify / Immaculate conception / For what it's worth / No more Monday's
VEL 79782 / 25 May '98 / Velvel

Maximum Style

☐ STYLIN'
74321476752 / May '97 / RCA

Maxwell

☐ EMBRYA
Gestation:Mythos / Everwanting:To want you to want / I'm you:You are me and we are you / Luxury:Cococure / Drowndeep:Hula / Matrimony:Maybe you / Arroz con pollo / Know these things shouldn't you / Submerge:Til we become the sun / Gravity:Pushing to pull / Eachhoureachsecondeachminuteeachday / Of my life / Embrya
4894202 / 22 Jun '98 / Columbia

☐ MAXWELL UNPLUGGED
Suite urban theme / Mello sumthin / Lady suite / This womans work / Whenever wherever whatever / Ascension / Gotta get closer / Til the cops come knockin'
4882922 / Jul '97 / Columbia

☐ MAXWELL'S URBAN HANG SUITE
Urban theme / Welcome / Sumthin' sumthin' / Ascension (don't ever wonder) / Dancewitme / Til the cops come knockin / Whenever wherever whatever / Lonely's the only company / Reunion / Suitelady / Suite theme
4836992 / Feb '97 / Columbia

Maxwell House

☐ MAXWELL HOUSE VOL.1
Sparticus / River Karnack / Brogal frets / Hilton box / Blossom cod / Cats phat / Window in the mix
PF 052CD / Sep '96 / Peacefrog

☐ MAXWELL HOUSE VOL.2
Arena of the odd / Stuck up pylons / Almulantarah / In time with nine / Mild flowers / Dream / Tony's movement one / Mid heaven express / Tony's phones / Odd
PF 067CD / Apr '97 / Peacefrog

Maxwell Street Klezmer Band

☐ YOU SHOULD BE SO LUCKY
SH 67006 / May '96 / Shanachie

Maxwell, David

☐ MAXIMUM BLUES PIANO
Blues don't bother me / Breakdown on the bayou / After hours / Sister Laura Lee / Down at PJ's place / Honky tonk train / Heart attack / Deep into it / Walk the walk / Manhattan wax (boppin' wit da chippies) / Take me on home
CDTC 1160 / Jun '97 / Tonecool

Maxx

☐ TO THE MAXIMUM
PULSE 15CD / Jul '94 / Pulse 8

May, Billy

☐ BEST OF BILLY MAY VOL.1, THE
AERO 1013 / Jul '96 / Aerospace

☐ BEST OF BILLY MAY VOL.2, THE (May, Billy & His Orchestra)
AERO 1014 / Jul '96 / Aerospace

☐ GIRLS AND BOYS ON BROADWAY/ SWEETEST SWINGIN' SOUNDS OF...
Girls against the boys / My darling, my darling / If I were a bell / Where did we go / Out / Guys and dolls / Rich butterfly / Heart / Old fashioned girl / Till there was you / Girls and boys / I've never been in love / I gotta have you / No strings / Sweetest sounds / Love makes the world go / Nobody told me / Loads of love / Maine / Eager beaver / Look no further / Orthadox fool / La la la / Man whose has everything / Be my host
CTMCD 118 / Jun '97 / EMI

☐ SORTA MAY/ SORTA DIXIE (May, Billy & His Orchestra)
Thou swell / Blues in the night / Chicago / All you want to do is dance / You go to my head / Soon / In a Persian market / Just one of those things / You're the top / Donkey serenade / Deep purple / They didn't believe me / Oh, by jingo / South Rampart Street Parade / Down home rag / Sugar foot strut / Sheik of Araby / Sorta blues / Panama / Riverboat shuffle / Five foot two / Eyes of blue (has anybody seen my gal)
STD 1051 / '87 / Creative World

May, Brian

☐ ANOTHER WORLD
Space / Business / China belle / Why don't we try again / On my way up / Cyborg / Guv'nor / Wilderness / Slow down / One rainy wish / All the way from Memphis / Another world
4949732 / 1 Jun '98 / Parlophone

☐ LIVE AT THE BRIXTON ACADEMY
Back to the light / Driven by you / Tie your mother down / Love token / Headlong / Love of my life / Let your heart rule your head / Too much love will kill you / Since you've been gone / Now I'm here / Guitar extravaganza / Resurrection / Last horizon / We will rock you / Hammer to fall
CDPCSD 150 / Jan '94 / Parlophone

May, Brian

☐ THEMES AND DREAMS AND LOVE SONGS
HADCD 190 / Nov '95 / Javelin

May, Brother Joe

☐ BEST OF BROTHER JOE MAY, THE
NASH 4507 / Feb '96 / Nashboro

☐ LIVE 1952-1955
God leads his children along / I'm a child of the king / Move on up a little higher / He's waiting for me / Old ship of Zion / Vacation in heaven / Jesus is real to me / All of my burdens (ain't that good news) / He's the one / I want Jesus on the road I travel / How I got over / Hold to God's unchanging hand / By and by when I get home / Speak, Lord Jesus / He'll understand and say well done
CDCHD 565 / Mar '94 / Ace

☐ THUNDERBOLT OF THE MIDDLE WEST
Old ship of zion (live) / WDIA plug / Search me lord / How much more of life's burden can we bear / In that day / I'm gonna live the life I sing about in my songs / Day is past and gone / Do you know him / I just can't keep from cryin' sometime / I want Jesus on the road I travel / Precious Lord / What do you know about Jesus / Our father / I'll make it somehow / Your sins will find you out / Remember me / I claim Jesus first / It's a long, long way / Don't forget the name of the lord / He'll understand and say Well Done / I'm happy working for the Lord / Grow closer / Jesus knows / Vacation in heaven / Going home
CDCHD 466 / Mar '93 / Ace

May, Derrick

☐ INNOVATOR (2CD Set)
TMT 2CD / 8 Jun '98 / R&S

May, Mark

☐ TELEPHONE ROAD HOUSTON TX (May, Mark & The Agitators)
ICD 50690 / 15 Jun '98 / Icehouse

May, Simon

☐ NEW VINTAGE
CDART 102 / Oct '94 / ARC

May, Tina

☐ CHANGE OF SKY (May, Tina & Nikki Iles)
Come rain or come shine / On the dunes / Black coffee / For Jan / You must believe in spring / Timeless place / Still we dream / My one and only love / Change of sky
33JAZZ 039 / 20 Apr '98 / 33 Jazz

☐ FUN (May, Tina Quartet)
33JAZZ 013CD / Jun '93 / 33 Jazz

☐ IT AIN'T NECESSARILY SO
It ain't necessarily so / Maestro / Rosy glow / Chelsea bridge / They can't take that away from me / Wanting to be home / Les feuilles mortes / Solitude / Writers block
33JAZZ 017 / May '95 / 33 Jazz

☐ JAZZ PIQUANT (May, Tina & Tony Coe)
N'oublie jamais / Clopin clopant / Nuages / Que reste-il / I love Paris/C'est magnifique / Anouman / C'est si bon / A tu vois mu mere / Sous le ciel de Paris / April in Paris
33JAZZ 042 / 29 Jun '98 / 33 Jazz

☐ NEVER LET ME GO (May, Tina Quartet)
33JAZZ 005CD / Jun '93 / 33 Jazz

☐ TIME WILL TELL
Stolen moments / Only time will tell / 'Round midnight / Do nothin' 'til you hear from me / I'd rather be in Hippodelphia / Where is love / Look of love / Hawk-man / After the love has gone / What's new
33JAZZ 029 / May '96 / 33 Jazz

May, Tom

☐ RIVER AND THE ROAD
FE 1420 / Dec '94 / Folk Era

Maya

☐ CROSS OF SILENCE
MAYACD 1 / May '95 / Maya

Mayafra Combo

☐ MAYAFRA
RTCL 802CD / Jul '96 / Right Tempo

Mayall, John

☐ 1982 REUNION CONCERT, THE
OW 30008 / Apr '94 / One Way

☐ BANQUET IN BLUES, A
MCAD 22075 / Apr '94 / One Way

☐ BARE WIRES (Mayall, John & The Bluesbreakers)
Bare wires suite / Where did I belong / Start walking / Open a new door / Fire / I know now / Look in the mirror / I'm a stranger / No reply / Hartley quits / Killing time / She's too young / Sandy
8205382 / Jun '88 / London

☐ BLUES BREAKERS (Mayall, John & Eric Clapton)
All your love / Hideaway / Little girl / Another man / Double crossin' time / What'd I say / Key to love / Parchman farm / Have you heard / Ramblin' on my mind / Steppin' out / It ain't right
8000862 / Aug '90 / Deram

☐ BLUES FOR THE LOST DAYS
Dead city / Stone cold deal / All those heroes / Blues for the lost days / Trenches / One in a million / How can you live like that / Some other day / I don't mind / It ain't safe / Sen-say-shun / You are for real
ORECD 547 / Apr '97 / Silvertone

☐ BLUES FROM LAUREL CANYON
Vacation / Walking on sunset / Laurel Canyon home / 2401 / Ready to ride / Medicine man / Somebody's acting like a child / Bear / Miss James / First time alone / Long gone midnight / Fly tomorrow
8205392 / Jan '88 / Deram

☐ BLUESBREAKER
John lee boogie / Lost and gone / Road show / Why worry / Baby what you want me to do / Mama talk to your daughter / Big man / Reaching for a mountain / Mexico city
307802 / Apr '98 / Hallmark

☐ CROSS COUNTRY BLUES
OW 30009 / Apr '94 / One Way

☐ CRUSADE (Mayall, John & The Bluesbreakers)
Oh pretty woman / Stand back baby / My time after awhile / Snowy wood / Man of stone / Tears in my eyes / Driving sideways / Death of JB Lenoir / I can't quit you baby / Streamline / Me and my woman / Checkin' up on my baby
8205372 / Jun '88 / Deram

☐ HARD CORE PACKAGE, A
MCAD 22071 / Apr '94 / One Way

☐ HARD ROAD, A (Mayall, John & The Bluesbreakers)
Hard road / It's over / You don't love me / Stumble / Another kinda love / Hit the highway / Leaping Christine / Dust my blues / There's always work / Same way / Supernatural / Top of the hill / Some day after a while (you'll be sorry) / Living alone
8204742 / Jul '89 / London

☐ LAST OF THE BRITISH BLUES, THE
Tucson lady / Parchman farm / There's only now / Teaser / Hideaway / Bear / Lonely birthday / Lowdown blues / It must be there
MCAD 22074 / Apr '94 / One Way

☐ LOTS OF PEOPLE (Live In LA 1976)
MCAD 22073 / Apr '94 / One Way

☐ NEW YEAR, NEW BAND, NEW COUNTRY (Live In LA 1976)
MCAD 22072 / Apr '94 / One Way

☐ NOTICE TO APPEAR
MCAD 22070 / Apr '94 / One Way

☐ POWER OF THE BLUES, THE (2CD Set)
CPCD 83052 / Sep '97 / Charly

☐ RETURN OF THE BLUESBREAKERS
AIM 1004CD / Oct '93 / Aim

☐ ROADSHOW BLUES
Why worry / Road show / Mama talk to your daughter / Big man / Lost and gone / Mexico City / John Lee Boogie / Reaching for a mountain / Baby, what you want me to do
CDTB 060 / Oct '88 / Thunderbolt

☐ SENSE OF PLACE, A (Mayall, John & The Bluesbreakers)
I want to go / Send me down to Vicksburg / Sensitive kid / Let's work together / Black cat moan / All my life / Congo square / Without her / Jacksborn highway / I can't complain / Sugarcane
IMCD 167 / Mar '93 / Island

☐ SPINNING COIN
ORECD 537 / Mar '97 / Silvertone

☐ STORMY MONDAY
Oh pretty woman / Sitting in the rain / Long gone midnight / No reply / Hartley quits / Jenny / Room to move / They call it Stormy Monday / Don't pick a flower / Thinking of my woman / Don't waste my time / Plan your revolution / Took the car / Time's moving on
5507172 / Sep '94 / Spectrum

☐ TURNING POINT
Laws must change / Saw Mill Gulch Road / I'm gonna fight for you JB / So hard to share / California / Thoughts about Roxanne / Room to move
BGOCD 145 / Jun '92 / Beat Goes On

☐ WAKE UP CALL
Mail order mystics / Maydell / I could cry / Wake up call / Loaded dice / Undercover agent for the blues / Light the fuse / Anything I can say / Nature's disappearing / I'm a sucker for love / Not at home / Ain't that lovin' you baby
ORECD 527 / Apr '93 / Silvertone

Mayaula Mayoni

☐ TO DO ONE'S BEST (Mayaula Mayoni & Tpok Jazz)
NG 025 / Jan '97 / Ngoyarto

Mayer, John

☐ ASIAN AIRS (Mayer, John Indo-Jazz Fusions)
Chakkar / Megha / Yaman / Song before sunrise / Pilu / Bear / Jhaptal / Mela / Asian airs
NI 5499 / Nov '96 / Nimbus

Mayerl, Billy

☐ BILLY MAYERL
Hop-o-my-thumb / Nimble fingered gentleman / Baby's birthday party / Harp of the winds / Marigold / Over she goes (selection) / Parade of the sandwich board men / Joker / Bats in the belfry / Green tulips / Railroad rhythm / Mistletoe / Billy mayerl's savoy havana memories / Ace of spades / Ten cents a dance / Phil the fluter's ball / Willow moss-moorish idol-fantail-whirligig (aquarius suite)
PASTCD 7053 / Oct '94 / Flapper

☐ BILLY MAYERL FAVOURITES
In my garden / Hop-o-my thumb / Four aces suite / Ten cents a dance / Jasmine / Mignonette / Limehouse blues / Eskimo shivers / All-of-a-twist / Sing you sinners / Millionaire kid medley / Chopsticks / Puppets suite no 3 / Nimble fingered gentleman / Ace of spades / Balloons / Aquarium suite / Desert song medley / Anytime's the time to fall in love / Match parade
CDGRS 1265 / Jun '93 / Grosvenor

☐ VERSATILITY OF BILLY MAYERL
Golliwog / Judy / Punch / Honky tonk - A rhythmical absurdity / Sweet nothin's / Wistaria / Personal course in modern syncopation / Rag doll / Sennen Cove / Wedding of the painted doll / Old fashioned girls / He loves and she loves / It don't do nothing but rain / Drink to me only with thine eyes / Rainbow / Chopsticks / Masculine women, feminine men / Lay me down to sleep in Carolina / I ain't got nobody / Toodle-oo-sal / Hire purchase system / When lights are low in Cairo / More we are together
PASTCD 9708 / '90 / Flapper

Mayes, Sally

☐ OUR PRIVATE WORLD
VSD 5529 / Mar '95 / Varese Sarabande

Mayfair Laundry

☐ SCRUB
My dear Watson / Wait and see / Lovely feet / Wonderful wonder / Bucket brigade / Bridge / Farewell my circus / Wish you were here / Lift the flower
ORCD 9725 / May '98 / Pamplin

Mayfield, Curtis

☐ BACK TO THE WORLD
Back to the world / Future shock / Right on for the darkness / Future song (love a good woman, love a good man) / If I were a child again / Can't say nothin' / Keep on trippin'
MPG 74029 / Jan '94 / Movieplay Gold
CPCD 8040 / Jun '94 / Charly

☐ BACK TO THE WORLD (2CD Set)
NEMCD 967 / 27 Jul '98 / Sequel

☐ BBC RADIO 1 IN CONCERT
Superfly / It's alright / I'm so proud / Billy Jack / Freddie's dead / People get ready / We've gotta have peace / Homeless / Move on up / Invisible / (Don't worry) If there's a hell below, we're all gonna go
WINDCD 052 / Jan '94 / Windsong

☐ BEST OF CURTIS MAYFIELD, THE
Move on up / Give me your love / Never stop loving me / Tripping out / Soul music / Right combination / Hard times / So in love / Freddie's dead / (Don't worry) if there's a hell below, we're all gonna go / Future shock
SUMCD 4119 / May '97 / Summit

☐ BEST OF CURTIS MAYFIELD, THE
VICP 60292 / 27 Apr '98 / Victor

☐ CURTIS
(Don't worry) If there's a hell below, we're all gonna go / Other side of town / Wild and free / Makings of you / Miss Black America / Move on up / We the people who are darker than blue / Give it up
MPG 74026 / Jan '94 / Movieplay Gold
CPCD 8036 / Jun '94 / Charly

☐ CURTIS (The Very Best Of Curtis Mayfield)
Move on up / Get down / Give it up / Little child running wild / Pusherman / Freddies dead / Give me your love / Eddie you should know better / No thing on me (cocaine on me) / Superfly / People get ready / Right on for darkness / Don't worry (if there's a hell) / Wild and free
CURTISCD 1 / 1 Jun '98 / Beechwood

☐ CURTIS IN CHICAGO
Superfly / For your precious love / I'm so proud / Preacher man / If I were a child again / Duke of Earl / Love oh love / Amen
CPCD 8046 / Sep '94 / Charly

☐ CURTIS LIVE (2CD Set)
Mighty mighty / I plan to stay a believer / We've only just begun / People get ready / Star and stare / Check out your mind / Gypsy woman / Makings of you / We the people who are darker than blue / (Don't worry) If there's a hell below, we're all gonna go / Stone junkie / We're a winner
CPCD 8038 / Jun '94 / Charly
MPG 74176 / Mar '94 / Movieplay Gold

☐ CURTIS MAYFIELD
Move on up / Soul music / In your arms again (shake it) / Do do wap is strong in here / Hard times / So in love / You are, you are / Pusherman / Never stop loving me / Tripping out / Ain't no love lost / Superfly / Freddie's dead / This year / Give me your love / (Don't worry) If there's a hell below, we're all gonna go
12364 / May '94 / Laserlight

☐ CURTIS MAYFIELD'S CHICAGO SOUL (Various Artists)
You can't hurt me no more: *Opals* / What would you do: *Jackson, Walter* / I'm the one who loves you: *Major Lance* / I can't work no longer: *Butler, Billy & The Enchanters* / Good times: *Chandler, Gene* / Monkey time: *Major Lance* / Patty cake: *Artistics* / (I've got a feeling) You're gonna be sorry: *Butler, Billy & The Enchanters* / Think nothing about it: *Major Lance* / Nevertheless (I love you): *Butler, Billy & The Enchanters* / It's all over: *Jackson, Walter* / Found true love: *Butler, Billy & The Enchanters* / You'll want me back: *Major Lance* / That's what mama say: *Jackson, Walter* / Gotta get away: *Butler, Billy & The Enchanters* / Funny (not much): *Jackson, Walter* / You're gonna be sorry: *Opals* / Gonna get married: *Major Lance*
4810292 / Jan '96 / Columbia

☐ CURTIS/GOT TO FIND A WAY (2CD Set)
(Don't worry) if there's a hell below we're all gonna go / Other side of town / Wild and free / Makings of you / Miss Black America / Move on up / We the people who are darker than blue / Give it up / Love me (right in the pocket) / So you don't love me / Prayer / Mother's son / Cannot find a way / Ain't no love lost
NEMCD 965 / 27 Jul '98 / Sequel

☐ DEFINITIVE COLLECTION, THE (2CD Set)
(Don't worry) if there's a hell below, we're all gonna go / Get down / Give it up / We got to have peace / Beautiful brother of mine / Move on up / Superfly / Freddie's dead / Future shock / If I were only a child again / Kung fu / To be invisible / Sweet exorcist / Billy Jack / So in love / Mothers' son / Only you babe / Soul music / Party night / I'm gonna win your love / Need someone to love / Do wap is strong in here / Short eyes/Freak free free free / Do it all night / This year / You're so good to me / Between you baby and me / Tripping out / Something to believe in / Love's sweet sensation / Baby it's you / Homeless / Do be down
CPCD 81892 / Oct '96 / Charly

☐ DO IT ALL NIGHT
Do it all night / No goodbyes / Party party / Keeps me loving you / In love, in love, in love / You are, you are
CPCD 8050 / Sep '94 / Charly

☐ ESSENTIAL CURTIS MAYFIELD, THE (2CD Set)
SMDCD 105 / 22 Sep '97 / Snapper

☐ GET DOWN TO THE FUNKY GROOVE
Get down / Superfly / Freddie's dead / Move on up / Wild and free / (Don't worry) If there's a hell below, we're all gonna go / Little child runnin' wild / Pusherman / If I were only a child again / Beautiful brother of mine / Now you're gone / Keep on trippin' / Right on for the darkness
CPCD 8034 / Feb '95 / Charly

☐ GIVE GET TAKE AND HAVE
In your arms again / This love is sweet / P.s. I love you / Party night / Get a little bit (give, get take and have) / Soul music / Only you babe / Mr. welfare you
CPCD 8070 / Jun '94 / Charly

☐ GIVE IT UP (The Best Of The Curtom Years 1970-1977)
Wild and free / Move on up / Mighty mighty (spade and whitey) / We got to have peace / Never say you can't survive / If I were only a child again / Billy Jack / Superfly / We the people who are darker than blue / Underground / Back to the world / Keep on keeping on / People get ready / Give it up
MCCD 314 / 6 Oct '97 / Music Club

☐ GOT TO FIND A WAY
Love me (right in the pocket) / So you don't love me / Prayer / Mother's son / Cannot find a way / Ain't no love lost
CPCD 8048 / Sep '94 / Charly

☐ GROOVE ON UP
CPCD 8043 / Jun '94 / Charly

☐ HEARTBEAT
Tell me, tell me / What is my woman for / Between you baby and me / Victory / Over the hump / You better stop / You're so good to me / Heartbeat
CPCD 8071 / Jun '94 / Charly

☐ I'M SO PROUD (A Jamaican Tribute To Curtis Mayfield) (Various Artists)
It's all right: *Morgan, Derrick* / Keep on pushing: *Lloyd & Glen* / Queen majesty: *Techniques* / My voice is insured for half a million dollars: *Alcapone, Dennis* / Dedicate my song to you: *Jamaicans* / Gypsy woman: *Uniques* / Rocksteady time: *Progressions* / I'm so proud: *White, Joe* / Little boy blue: *Kelly, Pat* / Man's temptation: *Brown, Noel 'Bunny'* / He will break your heart: *Silvertones* / My woman's love: *Uniques* / That's what love will do: *Gaylads* / Long long winter: *Marley, Bob & The Wailers* / Soulful love: *Kelly, Pat* / Closer together: *Smith, Slim* / I've been trying: *Heptones* / I gotta keep on moving: *Marley, Bob & The Wailers* / Queen Majesty: *Chosen Few* / Gypsy man: *Griffiths, Marcia*
CDTRL 376 / May '97 / Trojan

☐ LIVE IN EUROPE
Intro / Freddie's dead / We gotta have peace / People get ready / Move on up / Back to the world / Gypsy woman / Pusherman / We've only just begun / When seasons change / (Don't worry) If there's a hell below, we're all gonna go
CPCD 8178 / Mar '96 / Charly

☐ LOVE IS THE PLACE/HONESTY
NEMCD 783 / Mar '96 / Sequel

☐ MAN LIKE CURTIS, A
Move on up / Superfly / (Don't worry) If there's a hell below, we're all gonna go / You are, you are / Give me your love / Never stop loving me / Tripping out / Soul music / This year / Ain't no love lost / Pusherman / Freddie's dead / Do do wap is strong in here / Hard times / In your arms again (Shake it) / So in love
MUSCD 007 / Nov '92 / MCI Music

☐ MASTERS, THE
EABCD 054 / 24 Nov '97 / Eagle

☐ MASTERS, THE (2CD Set)
EDMCD 009 / 24 Nov '97 / Eagle

☐ MOVE ON UP
Move on up / Pusherman / Get down / Future shock / Superfly / We got to have peace / Beautiful brother of mine / Can't say nothin' / Freddie's dead / Kung Fu / So in love / (Don't worry) If there's a hell below, we're all gonna go / If I were only a child again
APH 102802 / Apr '96 / Audiophile Legends

☐ MOVE ON UP
Move on up / Love to keep you in mind / In your arms again (Shake it) / Power for the people / Eddie you should know better / Soul music / Superfly / Makings of you / Hard times / Ain't no love lost / Keeps me loving you / Miss Black America
306532 / May '97 / Hallmark

☐ NEVER SAY YOU CAN'T SURVIVE
Show me / Just want to be with you / When we're alone / Never say you can't survive / I'm gonna win your love / All night long / When you used to be mine / Sparkle
CPCD 8049 / Sep '94 / Charly

☐ NEW WORLD ORDER
New world order / Oh so beautiful / Let's not forget / Girl I find stays on my mind / Got dang song / It was love that we needed / No one knows about a good thing (you don't have to / Just a little bit of love / We people who are darker than blue / Here but I'm gone / I believe in you / Back to living again / Ms martha
9362463482 / Feb '97 / Warner Bros.

☐ PEACE, LOVE AND UNDERSTANDING (3CD Set)
NXTCD 286 / Mar '97 / Sequel

☐ PEOPLE GET READY (Live At Ronnie Scott's)
Little child runnin' wild / It's alright / People get ready / Freddie's dead / Pusherman / I'm so proud / We've gotta have peace / Billy Jack / Move on up / To be invisible
CLACD 329 / '93 / Castle

☐ ROOTS
Get down / Keep on keeping on / Underground / We got to have peace / Beautiful brother of mine / Now you're gone / Love to keep you in my mind
MPG 74027 / Jan '94 / Movieplay Gold
CPCD 8037 / Jun '94 / Charly

☐ ROOTS/SWEET EXORCIST (2CD Set)
Get down / Keep on keeping on / Underground / We got to have peace / Beautiful brother of mine / Now you're gone / Love to keep you in mind / Ain't got time / Sweet exorcist / To be invisible / Power to the people / Kung fu / Suffer / Make me believe in you
NEMCD 966 / 27 Jul '98 / Sequel

☐ SHORT EYES (Original Soundtrack)
Do wap is strong in here / Back against the wall / Need someone to love / Heavy dude / Short eyes / Break it down / Another fool in love / Father confessor
CPCD 8183 / Jun '96 / Charly

☐ SOMETHING TO BELIEVE IN
Love me love me now / Never let me go / Tripping out / People never give up / It's alright / Something to believe in / Never stop loving me
CPCD 8073 / Jun '94 / Charly

☐ SUPERFLY (Original Soundtrack)
CPCD 8039 / Jun '94 / Charly

☐ SUPERFLY (Original Soundtrack/2CD Set)
CDNEW 1302 / 29 Jun '98 / Charly

☐ SUPERFLY/SHORT EYES (Original Soundtracks)
Little child runnin' wild / Pusherman / Freddie's dead / Junkie chase / Give me your love / Eddie you should know better / No thing on me / Think / Superfly / Do do wap is strong in here / Back against the wall / Need someone to love / Heavy dude / Short eyes / Freak freak free free free / Break it down / Another fool in love / Father confessor
NEMCD 964 / 1 Jun '98 / Sequel

☐ SWEET EXORCIST
Ain't got time / Sweet exorcist / To be invisible / Power to the people / Kung fu / Suffer / Make me believe in you
CPCD 8047 / Sep '94 / Charly

☐ TAKE IT TO THE STREETS
Homeless / Got to be real / Do be down / Who was that lady / On and on / He's a fly guy / Don't push / I mo git U sucka
CPCD 8179 / Apr '96 / Charly

☐ THERE'S NO PLACE LIKE AMERICA TODAY
Billy Jack / When seasons change / So in love / Jesus / Blue monday people / Hard times / Love to the people
CPCD 8069 / Jun '94 / Charly

☐ TRIBUTE TO CURTIS MAYFIELD, A (Various Artists)
Choice of colors: *Knight, Gladys* / It's alright: *Winwood, Steve* / Let's do it again: *Repercussions & Curtis Mayfield* / Billy Jack: *Kravitz, Lenny* / Look into your heart: *Houston, Whitney* / Gypsy woman: *Springsteen, Bruce* / You must believe me: *Clapton, Eric* / I'm so proud: *Isley Brothers* / Fool for you: *Marsalis, Branford & The Impressions* / Keep on pushing: *Campbell, Tevin* / Making of you: *Franklin, Aretha* / Woman's got soul: *King, B.B.* / People get ready: *Stewart, Rod* / (Don't worry) If there's a hell below, we're all gonna go: *Walden, Narada Michael* / I've been trying: *Collins, Phil* / I'm the one who loves you: *Wonder, Stevie* / Amen: *John, Elton & The Sounds of Blackness*
9362455002 / Feb '94 / WEA

☐ TRIPPING OUT
Get a little bit (give, get take and have) / Just want to be with you / Between you baby and me / This year / Soul music / All night long / Suffer / Love sweet sensation / Move on up (single version) / Tripping out (single version) / I'm so proud (live) / Something to believe in / I'm gonna win your love / You're so good to me / Right combination / Ain't no love lost / Love me, love me now
CPCD 8065 / Nov '94 / Charly

☐ VERY BEST OF CURTIS MAYFIELD, THE
CCSCD 806 / Apr '96 / Castle

Mayfield, Percy

☐ MEMORY PAIN
Please send me someone to love / Strange things happen / Two hearts are greater than one / Big question / My blues / Nightless lover / How deep is the well / Ruthie Mae / My heart / Lonesome highway / Lonely one / I ain't gonna cry no more / Memory pain / You are my future / Kiss tomorrow goodbye / Advice (For men only) / I need love so bad / Does anyone care for me / It's good to see you baby / Sugar mama - Peachy papa / You were lyin' to me / Voice within / Please believe me / Diggin' the moonglow / Hit the road Jack
CDCHD 438 / Jan '93 / Ace

☐ POET OF THE BLUES
Please send me someone to love / Prayin' for your return / Strange things happening / Life is suicide / What a fool I was / Lost love / Nightless lover / Advice (for men only) / Cry baby / Lost mind / I dare you baby / Hopeless / Hunt is on / River's invitation / Big question / Wasted dream / Louisiana / Bachelor blues / Get way back / Memory pain / Loose ups / You don't exist anymore / Nightmare / Baby, you're rich / My heart is cryin'
CDCHD 283 / Oct '90 / Ace

Mayhams, Norridge
☐ NORRIDGE MAYHAMS & THE BLUE CHIPS 1936 (Mayhams, Norridge & The Blue Chips)
DOCD 5488 / Nov '96 / Document

Mayhem
☐ DE MYSTERIIS DOM SATHANAS
ANTIMOSH 006CD / Mar '94 / Deathlike Silence

☐ DEATHCRUSH
ANTIMOSH 003CD / Oct '96 / Deathlike Silence

☐ TRIBUTE TO EURONYMOUS (Various Artists)
NR 009CD / Sep '96 / Necropolis

☐ WOLF'S LAIR ABYSS
I am the labyrith / Fall of the seraphs / Ancient skin / Symbols of bloodswords
AMAZON 012CD / 3 Nov '97 / Misanthropy

Mayhew, Virginia
☐ NINI GREEN
Yes or no step and go / Good morning heartache / Voyage / Nini Green / Maybe someday / Time alone / Blue green and brown / Invitation / Jazzspeak
CRD 351 / 8 Nov '97 / Chiaroscuro

Mayko
☐ RASA BHAVA
SR 9606 / Feb '97 / Silent

Mayock, Emer
☐ MERRY BITS OF TIMBER
KEY 121CD / Nov '96 / Key

Mayoiga
☐ HIMEKAMI
21089 / Aug '96 / Sonifolk

Mayor, Simon
☐ ENGLISH MANDOLIN, THE
St. Paul's suite 1 / Molly on the shore / Nell Gwyn / Three English folk tune settings / Musick's handmaid / Capriol suite
ACS 025CD / Jul '95 / Acoustics

☐ MANDOLIN ALBUM, THE
Jump the gun/Reelin' over the rooftops / Two seagulls call from my Birch Tree / Maple flames / Arrival of the Queen Of Sheba / Exchange / When summer comes again / Concerto for Mandolin / Villanelle / Tune for a mop fair / Jericho waltz / Wheelin' and dealin' / Sarabande / Double / Mosstrooper medley
ACS 012CD / May '97 / Acoustics

☐ MANDOLIN TUTOR
ACS 028CD / Sep '97 / Acoustics

☐ MANDOLINQUENTS (Mayor, Simon Quintet)
ACS 034CD / Nov '97 / Acoustics

☐ NEW CELTIC MANDOLIN
Carolan's frolics / Dark and slender boy / Neil Gow's lament for Abercarney / Dance of the waterboatmen / Mrs. Murray of Abercarney / Butterfly / Waynsboro / Farewell to the shore / Ymdaith gwyr dyfnaint / Athol highlanders/Barren rocks of Aden / Little Molly-o / Bottom of the punch bowl / Wasp reels
ACS 035CD / 30 Mar '98 / Acoustics

☐ SECOND MANDOLIN ALBUM, THE
Hungarian dance no.1 / Buttermere waltz / Huppings / Finale spirituoso / Three part invention / Pipped at the post / Two days in Tuscany / Great bear / Concerto for two mandolins / Old man of the mountain / Sonata / Hornpipe / Dead sea dances
ACS 014CD / Jul '97 / Acoustics

☐ WINTER WITH MANDOLINS
I saw three ships / Ballades / All hallows dance / La rejouissance / Song of the birds / Gabriel's message (the angel gabriel from heaven came') / Toss the pancake / German cradle song / Past three o'clock / God rest ye swinging gentlemen / When the birds fly / Mad as a march hare / Hail smiling morn / Biscay carol / Christmas candle
ACS 015CD / Aug '95 / Acoustics

Mayor, Violaine
☐ DANSE AVEC LES FEES
VM 01CD / Nov '96 / Hent Telenn

Mays, Bill
☐ CONCORD DUO SERIES VOL.7 (Mays, Bill & Ed Bickert)
Sometime ago / Taking a chance on love / Gee baby ain't I good to you / On the trail / Quietly / Do nothin' 'til you hear from me / Crazy she calls me / Bick's bag
CCD 4626 / Nov '94 / Concord Jazz

☐ ELLINGTON AFFAIR, AN
I'm just a lucky so and so / Satin doll / Something to live for / My azure / Don't you know / Dancers in love / Single petal of a rose / Passion flower / Little African flower / Wig wise / Daydream / I let a song go out of my heart
CCD 4651 / Jul '95 / Concord Jazz

☐ LIVE AT MAYBECK RECITAL HALL VOL.26
Nightingale sang in Berkeley Square / I wish I knew / Stompin' at the Savoy / Boardwalk blues / Lush life / I'm confessin' that I love you / Guess I'll hang my tears out to dry / Jitterbug waltz / Thanksgiving prayer / Why did I choose you / Never let me go / Grandpa's spells
CCD 4567 / Aug '93 / Concord Jazz

☐ MAYS IN MANHATTAN
Manhattan / Summer in Central Park / UMMG (Upper Manhattan Medical Group) / New York state of mind / All across the city / Sunday in New York / 317 E. 32nd St. / Autumn in New York / '39 World's fair
CCD 4738 / Dec '96 / Concord Jazz

Mays, Lyle
☐ SWEET DREAMS
Feet first / August / Chorinho / Possible straight / Hangtime / Before you go / Newborn / Sweet dreams
GFLD 19194 / Mar '93 / Geffen

Maysa
☐ TOM JOBIM POR MAYSA
DM 30502 / 14 Apr '98 / Discmedi

Maytals
☐ ORIGINALS, THE
CDGR 252 / 29 Jun '98 / Charly

Mayte
☐ CHILD OF THE SUN
Child of the sun / In your gracious name / If I love U 2nite / Rhythm of your heart / Ain't no place like u / House of brick / Love's no fun / Baby don't cry / However much u want / Mo' better / If I love u 2nite / Most beautiful boy in the world
0061622NPG / Jul '97 / Edel

Maytones
☐ BROWN GIRL IN THE RING
CDTRL 363 / Oct '95 / Trojan

☐ FUNNY MAN
JMC 200206 / Nov '93 / Jamaican Gold

☐ LOVER MAN
Lover man / Ready baby / People are changing / Jah is the master / How long / Show us the way / No ease up / Never gonna run away / One awy / Judgement day / Serious world / Who feel it / Don't show off / Take your time
RN 7027 / 25 Aug '97 / Rhino

☐ LOVING REGGAE
Let it be me / Loving reggae / Funny man / Serious love / Billy Goat / Ital Queen / Cool you up / As long as you love me / One way / Contiquros / Take your time / Come along / Baby give me the right loving / Ready baby / Zion land / Do good / Africa we want to go / De dey wid di money / Lover man / Holy ground / Be careful / Don't show off / Boat to Zion
CDGR 127 / Apr '97 / Charly

☐ MADNESS VOL.2
MJRCD 01 / 1 Dec '97 / Mr. Jordan

Mayweather, George
☐ WHUP IT, WHUP IT (Mayweather, George 'Earring')
CDTC 1147 / May '94 / Tonecool

Maze
☐ ANTHOLOGY (2CD Set)
While I'm alone / Lady of magic / Working together / Golden time of day / Feel that you're feelin' / Lovely inspiration / Southern girl / Joy and pain / Happy feelings / Reason / Running away / Before I let go / Love is the key / Never let you down / I wanna thank you / Your own kind / Back in stride / Too many games / I wanna be with you / When you love someone
CTMCD 332 / Aug '97 / Capitol

☐ BACK TO BASICS
Nobody knows what you feel inside / Love is / Morning after / Laid back girl / What goes up / In time / All night long / Don't wanna lose your love / Twilight
9362452972 / Sep '93 / Warner Bros.

☐ CAN'T STOP THE LOVE (Maze & Frankie Beverly)
Back in stride / Can't stop the love / Reaching down inside / Too many games / I want to feel I'm wanted / Magic / Place in my heart
8181722 / 1 Jun '98 / Capitol

☐ GOLDEN TIME OF DAY (Maze & Frankie Beverly)
Travelling man / Song for my mother / You're not the same / Working together / Golden time of day / I wish you well / I need you
7576432 / 1 Jun '98 / Capitol

☐ JOY AND PAIN (Maze & Frankie Beverly)
Changing times / Look in your eyes / Family / Roots / Joy and pain / Southern girl / Happiness
RE 2092 / Jun '96 / Razor & Tie

☐ MAZE (Maze & Frankie Beverly)
Time is on my side / Happy feelin's / Color blind / Lady of magic / While I'm alone / You / Look at California
7912442 / 1 Jun '98 / Capitol

☐ MAZE LIVE IN NEW ORLEANS
You / Changing times / Joy and pain / Happy feelin's / Southern girl / Look at California / Feel that you're feelin / Look in your eyes / Running away / Before I let you go / We need love to live / Reason
CUTLEGCD 1 / Jul '95 / Beechwood

☐ SILKY SOUL
Silky soul / Can't get over you / Just us / Somebody else's arms / Love's on the run / Change our ways / Songs of love / Mandela / Midnight / Africa
K 9258022 / Mar '94 / WEA

☐ WE ARE ONE (Maze & Frankie Beverly)
Love is the key / Right on time / Your kind of way / I want to thank you / We are one / Never let you down / I love you so much / Metropolis
8576062 / 1 Jun '98 / Capitol

Maze Of Torment
☐ FORCE, THE
CR 6503CD / Jun '97 / Corrosion

Mazelle, Kym
☐ GOLD COLLECTION, THE
Woman of the world / No one can love you more than me / Useless (I don't need you now) / Don't scandalize my name / Love strain / Never in a million years / Was that all it was / If it's love you want / Skin I'm in / Crazy 'bout the man / This love will never die / Wait / Just what it takes / Got to get you back
CDGOLD 1018 / Mar '96 / EMI Gold

Mazeltones
☐ LATKES & LATTES
GV 159CD / May '94 / Global Village

Mazetier, Louis
☐ ECHOES OF CAROLINA (Mazetier, Louis & Francois Rilhac)
SOSCD 1218 / Oct '92 / Stomp Off

☐ IF DREAMS COME TRUE (Mazetier, Louis & Neville Dickie)
SOSCD 1289 / Nov '95 / Stomp Off

Mazey Fade
☐ SECRET WATCHERS BUILT THE WORLD
Dumb cripple tag / Red bloodied / Touchdown / I'll give you a name / Gastronomy (bad version) / Inside my blush / 1,999.2 / Anastesia / Porcelain heads / Flouridation / Pacemakers
WIGCD 009 / Apr '94 / Domino

Mazinga Phaser
☐ ABANDINALLHOPE
ID 011 / 27 Apr '98 / Idol

☐ CRUISING IN THE NEON
MAZPHA 007 / May '97 / Womb Tunes

Mazur, Marilyn
☐ CIRCULAR CHANT (Mazur, Marilyn & Pulse Unit)
Circular chant / Celldance / Louise / Pulsens sang / Gong piece 1 / Reeds duo / Amulu / Chordal piece / Gong piece 2 / Green bones / Balophone tune / Circular chant
STCD 4200 / Mar '95 / Storyville

☐ FUTURE SONG
First dream / Saturn song / When I go to the mountain / Urstro / Rainbow birds / Aina's travels / Rainbow birds / Well of clouds / Rainbow birds / Seventh dream
VBR 21052 / Aug '92 / Vera Bra

☐ SMALL LABYRINTHS
World of gates / Drum tunnel / Electric cave / Dreamcatcher / Visions in the wood / Back to the dreamfrog mountain / Creature talk / See there / Valley of fragments / Enchanted place / Castle of air / Holey
5336792 / Mar '97 / ECM

Mazurek, Robert
☐ BADLANDS (Mazurek, Robert/Eric Anderson)
Arthur's seat / Angel eyes / Badlands / Deep purple / Kay's birthday / Evert time we say goodbye / Edinburgh nights / Stranger in paradise / I fall in love to easily / Nomad
HEPCD 2065 / Jun '95 / Hep

☐ GREEN AND BLUE (Mazurek, Robert & Eric Alexander)
Streets of Raith/Uptown / 5000 miles away / White river / In walked boom / Green and blue / Black river / Skylark / Other place
HEPCD 2067 / Jan '97 / Hep

☐ MAN FACING EAST
Manaus / Pretty blue butterfly / Flora's house / Tenderly / Man facing east / Roselis / Freddies blues / I wish I knew / Dragoon blue
HEPCD 2059 / Sep '94 / Hep

☐ PLAYGROUND (Mazurek, Robert & Chicago Underground)
Blow up / Flamingos dancin' on luminescent moonbeams / Boiled over / Le sucoer velours / Compnents changes / Palyground / Jeff's new idea / Inner soul of H / Whitney / Ostinato
DE 503 / 9 Mar '98 / Delmark

Mazzacane-Connors, Loren
☐ CALLODEN HARVEST
ROCO 018 / 15 Dec '97 / Road Cone

☐ HELL, HELL, HELL
TLS 003CD / Apr '97 / Lotus Sound

☐ IN PITTSBURGH
DEX 7CD / Dec '96 / Dexter's Cigar

☐ POSSIBLE DAWN, A
HATN 801 / Mar '98 / Hat Noir

Mazzarella, Mike
☐ DIARY OF A MAD ROOK
NL 040 / 13 Jul '98 / Not Lame

Mazzy, Jimmy
☐ HALFWAY TO HEAVEN (Mazzy, Jimmy & Eli Newberger/Joe Muranyi)
SOSCD 1319 / Mar '97 / Stomp Off

☐ SHAKE IT DOWN (Mazzy, Jimmy & Eli Newberger)
SOSCD 1109 / Jan '97 / Stomp Off

Mazzy Star
☐ AMONG MY SWAN
Disappear / Flowers in December / Rhymes of an hour / Cry, cry / Take everything / Still cold / All your sisters / I've been let down / Roseblood / Happy / Umbilical / Look on down from the bridge
CDEST 2288 / Nov '96 / Capitol

☐ SO TONIGHT THAT I MIGHT SEE
Fade into you / Bells ring / Mary of silence / Five string serenade / Blue light / She's my baby / Unreflected / Wasted / Into dust / So tonight that I might see
CDEST 2206 / Sep '97 / Capitol

Mbango, Charlotte
☐ CHARLOTTE MBANGO VOL.3
CD 54681 / '91 / Sonodisc

Mbarga, Prince Nico
☐ AKI SPECIAL
ROUCD 11545 / May '88 / Rounder

Mbaye, Jimi
☐ DAKAR HEART
SH 64094 / Aug '97 / Shanachie

M'boom
☐ COLLAGE
Circles / It's time / Jamaican sun / Street dance / Mr. Seven / Quiet place
SNCD 1059 / '86 / Soul Note

Mbuli, Mzwakhe
☐ CHANGE IS PAIN
Many years ago / Behind the bars / Drumbeats / Now is the time / Change is pain / Day shall dawn / Ignorant / Triple M / What a shame / I have travelled / Spear has fallen / Last struggle / Ngizwa ubgina bguzwa usajako / Sisi bayasinyanyisa
PIR 3 CD / Sep '88 / World Circuit

MC 900ft Jesus
☐ HELL WITH THE LID OFF
Greater God / UFO's are real / I'm going straight to heaven / Talking to the spirits / Place of lonliness / Real black angel / Shut up / Spaceman / Too bad
NETCD 015 / Feb '90 / Nettwerk

☐ ONE STEP AHEAD OF THE SPIDER
New moon / But if you go / If I only had a brain / Stare and stare / Buried at sea / Tiptoe through the inferno / Garacias pepe / New Year's eve / Bill's dream / Rhubarb
74321242312 / Mar '95 / American

MC Det
☐ OUT OF DET
Stick up / So simple / Can't sample det / Freeform reality / We nuh ease up / Abducted / Junglist massive / Elevate / Can U feel / Dub plate special / Amber / Nuclear det / Hands clappin' / Let me recommend / Tonic's reality
SOURCD 005 / Jul '96 / SOUR

MC Duke
☐ ORGANISED RHYME
Organised rhyme / We go to work / Free / Throw your hands in the air / I'm riffin' / Miracles / For the girls / Gotta get your own / Running man / Alternative argument
DUKE 1CD / Nov '89 / Music Of Life

MC Eiht
☐ LAST MAN STANDING
Under attack / Who's the man / King of pimpish / Me and my bitch / Anything u want / Can I get mine / Hangin' / Compton 4 death / When all hell breaks loose / Tha business / Hubtouchables / On top of all that / Tough guyz / Return fire / Got cha humpin' / Hit the floor
4888272 / 5 Jan '98 / Epic

MC Hammer

☐ FAMILY AFFAIR (2CD Set)
78009120002 / 30 Jun '98 / Oakland

☐ FUNKY HEADHUNTER, THE
Oaktown / It's all good / Somethin' for the OG's / Don't stop / Pumps and a bump / One mo time / Clap yo' hands / Break 'em off somethin' propa / Don't fight the feeling / Goldie in me / Sleepin' on a master plan / It's all that / Funky headhunter / Pumps and a bump reprise (bump Teddy bump) / Help Lord (won't you come) / Do it like this / Heartbreaka (is what they call me)
74321188622 / Mar '94 / RCA

☐ GREATEST HITS
U can't touch this / Too legit to quit / Turn this mutha out / Pray / Addams groove / Do not pass me by / Here comes the Hammer / Have you seen her / Gaining momentum / Pump it up (here's the news) / They put me in the mix
CTMCD 300 / Feb '97 / Capitol

MC Lyte

☐ BAD AS I WANNA B
Keep on keepin' on / Everyday / Cold rock a party / Have u ever / Trg / Zodiac / Keep on keepin' on / Two seater / Druglord superstar / One on one
7559617812 / Aug '96 / Elektra

☐ BADDER THAN BEFORE (The Remix Album)
Cold rock a party / Everyday / TRG / One on one / Druglord superstar / Have U ever / Keep on keepin' on / Two seater / Zodiac / Cold rock a party / Anthology mega mix / Two seater / I'm leaving U
7559621222 / 10 Nov '97 / Elektra

☐ SEVEN AND SEVEN
In my business / Too fly / This MC / Top billin' / Give me what I want / Woo woo (freak out) / Playgirls play / Put it on you / Propa / It's all yours / I can't make a mistake / Want what I got / Party goin' on / Break it down / Closer / Radio nightmare / My time / Assaholic anonymous / King of rock / Better place
7559623072 / 17 Aug '98 / East West

MC Solaar

☐ PARADISIAQUE
Intro / Gangster moderne / Zoom / Dakota / Les temps changent / Les boys bandent / Wonderbra / Protege tibia / Paradisiaque / Tournicotic / Le sens de la vie / Illico presto / Daydreamin' / Les pensees sont des flowers / Le 11eme choc / Quand le soleil devient froid
5337692 / Jun '97 / Talkin' Loud

☐ PROSE COMBAT
Aurade / Obsolette / Nouveau Western / A la claire fontaine / Superstarr / La concubine de l'hemoglobine / Devotion / Temps mort / L'nmiaccd htck72kpdp / Sequelles / Dieu ait son ame / A dix de mes disciples / La paim justifie les moyene / Relations humaines / Prose combat
5212892 / Apr '94 / Talkin' Loud

MC5

☐ AMERICAN RUSE, THE
NERCD 2001 / Feb '95 / Total Energy

☐ BABES IN ARMS
Shakin' street / American ruse / Skunk (sonically speaking) / Tutti frutti / Poison / Gotta keep movin' / Tonite / Kick out the jams / Sister / Future now / Gold / I can only give you everything / One of the guys / I just don't know / Looking at you
RE 122CD / Nov '94 / ROIR
RUSCD 8236 / 26 Jan '98 / ROIR

☐ BACK IN THE USA
Tutti frutti / Tonight / Teenage lust / Let me try / Looking at you / High school / Call me animal / American ruse / Shakin' street / Human being lawnmower / Back in the USA
8122710332 / Mar '93 / Atlantic

☐ HIGH TIME
Sister Anne / Baby won't ya / Miss X / Gotta keep movin' / Future/now / Poison / Over and over / Skunk (sonically speaking)
8122710342 / Mar '93 / WEA

☐ ICE PICK SLIM
ALIVECD 8 / Feb '97 / Alive

☐ LIVE DETROIT 68/69
Intro / Come together / I want you right now / I believe / Come on down (High rise) / It's a man's man's man's world / Looking at you / Fire of love
895050 / Nov '94 / New Rose

☐ POWER TRIP
ALIVE 005CD / Oct '94 / Alive

M'Carver, Kimberly

☐ BREATHE THE MOONLIGHT
Silver wheeled pony / Whistle down the wind / Cryin' wolf / Borrowed time / Only in my dreams / Jose's lullaby / Springtime friends / My way back home to you / Carnival man / Serious doubt / Texas home
CDPH 1129 / '90 / Philo

☐ INHERITED ROAD
CDPH 1179 / Dec '94 / Philo

MD 45

☐ CRAVING, THE
Hell's motel / Day the music died / Fight hate / Designer behaviour / Creed / My town / Voices / Nothing is something / Hearts will bleed / No pain / Roadman
CDEST 2286 / Jun '96 / Capitol

MDC

☐ HEY COP, IF I HAD A FACE LIKE YOURS
MDC 812 / Mar '92 / R Radical

☐ METAL DEVIL COKES
WB 3110CD / Apr '94 / We Bite

☐ MILLIONS OF DAMN CHRISTIANS
WB 3022CD / Sep '93 / We Bite

☐ MILLIONS OF DEAD COPS
Business on parade / Dead cops / America's so straight / Born to die / Corporate deathburger / I remember / Violent rednecks / John Wayne was a nazi / Dick for brains / I hate work / My family is a little weird / Greedy and pathetic / Church and state / Kill the light / American achievements
WB 3109CD / Apr '94 / We Bite

☐ MORE DEAD COPS
WB 3033CD / Sep '93 / We Bite

☐ SHADES OF BROWN
WB 3112CD / Apr '94 / We Bite

☐ SMOKE SIGNALS
WB 3155CD / Oct '96 / We Bite

Me First

☐ AWFUL FRIENDLY
SKIP 64CD / Oct '97 / Broken

Me First & The Gimme Gimmes

☐ HAVE A BALL
FAT 554CD / 16 Mar '98 / Fatwreck Chords

Mead, Steven

☐ EUPHONY (Mead, Steven & Royal Northern College Of Music Brass Band)
Euphonium concerto / Carrickfergus / Euphony / Aubade / Return to Sorrento / Euphonium music / Nappoli / Midnight euphonium / Better world
QPRL 082D / Dec '96 / Polyphonic

☐ WORLD OF THE EUPHONIUM VOL.1, THE
Sonata in F / Partita Op 89 / Vocalise / Soliloquy IX / Fantasy for euphonium / Variations for ophicleide / Sonata euphonica / Apres un reve / Weber's last waltz / Heart to heart / Barcarolle / New carnival of Venice
QPRZ 014D / Jul '92 / Polyphonic

☐ WORLD OF THE EUPHONIUM VOL.2, THE
Concert gallop / Solo de Concurse / Fantasia / Swan / Fantasie contertante / Song for Ina / Ransomed / Libesfreud / Largo elegaico / Panache / Two Faure duets / Ball of fire / Horo staccato
QPRZ 017D / Oct '97 / Polyphonic

☐ WORLD OF THE EUPHONIUM VOL.3, THE
Song of the brother / Flight / Romance / Party piece / Song of the seashore / Fantasy variations / Sonata for euphonium / Im tiefsten walde / When you wish upon a star / Notturno / Concerto per flicorno basso
QPRZ 019D / Oct '97 / Polyphonic

Meade, Tyson

☐ MOTORCYCLE CHILDHOOD
ECHO 100 / Apr '97 / Echo Static

Meadows, Marion

☐ BODY RHYTHM
My cherie amour / Be with you / South beach / Later on / Get involved / One more chance / Kool / Marion's theme / Wanna be loved by you / Body rhythm / Deep waters / Summer's over / Lift
07863666232 / Aug '95 / Novus

☐ FORBIDDEN FRUIT, THE
Red lights / Always on my mind / Asha / Forbidden fruit / Whenever your heart wants to song / You will never know what you're missing / Back2back / Save the best for last / Somewhere island / Comin' home to you / Nocturnal serenade
01241631672 / Mar '94 / Novus

Mean Cat Daddies

☐ GHOST OF YOUR LOVE
Sally-Ann / Just a memory / Sign of the times / Why do I cry / Drivin' all night / I can tell / Decision time / Tell me / Am I the one / Ghost of your love / Midnight cruise / Losing game / Waiting for you / This is the end
NERCD 079 / Oct '94 / Nervous

Mean Red Spiders

☐ DARK HOURS
Love in a bottle / Live and let live / Arms open wide / Just can't stop / Feel so bad / Drunken fool / Dangerous game / Heaven above / Teacher / Happy on my own / Murder my baby / Love won't save you now / Sure can't hide / Lie and cheat you blind / No more work song / Coming back for more / Call me long distance
GBCD 1 / 22 Sep '97 / Gray Brothers

Mean Season

☐ GRACE
NA 024CD / Jul '96 / New Age

Meanies

☐ GANGRENOUS
EFA 123012 / Mar '94 / Vince Lombard

Meantime

☐ WELCOME: MOTHER EARTH
Crusin' the hood / Lugnut / Down by the farm intro / Down by the farm / Tortoise shell sky / Detour / Two in one / Welcome Mother Earth
JUST 802 / Aug '96 / Justin Time

Meantime

☐ UNSOPHISTICATED
SPV 08056822 / Sep '94 / Wolverine

Meanwhile

☐ REMAINING RIGHT
RAD 001CD / Jun '95 / Nuclear Blast

Measles

☐ SEVERAL FACES OF THE MANSHARK, THE
CMSR 341 / 26 May '98 / Standard

Meat Beat Manifesto

☐ 99%
BIAS 180CD / May '90 / Play It Again Sam

☐ ORIGINAL FIRE
INTD 90127 / Jun '97 / Nothing

☐ SATYRICON
Postsounds / Mindstream / Drop / Original control (version 1) / Your mind belongs to the state / Circles / Sphere / Brainwashed this way/Zombie/That shirt / Original control (version 2) / Euthanasia / Edge of no control (part 1) / Edge of no control (part 2) / Untold stories / Son of Sam / Track 15 / Placebo
BIAS 202CD / Aug '92 / Play It Again Sam

☐ SUBLIMINAL SANDWICH
Sound innovation / Nuclear bomb / Long periods of time / 1979 / Future worlds / What's your name / She's unreal / Phone calls from the dead / Asbestos lead asbestos / Mass producing hate / Radio mellotron / Assasinator / Cancer / We done / Transmission / No purpose no design / Addiction / Lucid dream
BIAS 302CD
BIAS 302CDX / May '96 / Play It Again Sam

☐ VERSION GALORE
Radio babylon (space children intro) / Radio babylon (version galore) / Psyche out (sex skank strip down) / Psyche out (version 1) / Psyche out (dub) / Radio babylon / Psyche out
BIAS 192CD / Feb '91 / Play It Again Sam

Meat Katie

☐ OFF THE BONE
KSRCD 5 / 17 Aug '98 / Kingsize

Meat Loaf

☐ ALIVE IN HELL
Bat out of hell / You took the words right out of my mouth / Two out of three ain't bad / Modern girl / Rock 'n' roll mercenaries / Paradise by the dashboard light / Blind before I stop / Midnight at the lost and found / Piece of the action / Bad attitude / Surf's up
PMCD 7002 / Oct '94 / Pure Music

☐ BAD ATTITUDE
Bad attitude / Modern girl / Nowhere fast / Surf's up / Piece of the action / Jumping the gun / Cheatin' in your dreams / Don't leave your mark on me / Sailor to a siren
259049 / Dec '93 / Arista

☐ BAT OUT OF HELL
You took the words right out of my mouth / Heaven can wait / All revved up and no place to go / Two out of three ain't bad / Bat out of hell / For cryin' out loud / Paradise by the dashboard light / Praying for the end of time / Man and woman / Dead ringer for love
4804112 / Jul '95 / Epic

☐ BAT OUT OF HELL VOL.2 (Back Into Hell)
I'd do anything for love (But I won't do that) / Life is a lemon and I want my money back / Rock 'n' roll dreams come through / It just won't quit / Out of the frying pan (and into the fire) / Objects in the rear view mirror may appear closer... / Wasted youth / Everything louder than everything else / Good girls go to heaven (bad girls go everywhere) / Back into hell / Lost boys and golden girls
CDV 2710 / Aug '93 / Virgin

☐ BLIND BEFORE I STOP
Execution day / Rock 'n' roll mercenaries / Getting away with murder / One more kiss (night of the soft parade) / Blind before I stop / Burning down / Standing on the outside / Masculine / Man and a woman / Special girl / Rock 'n' roll here
257741 / Dec '93 / Arista

☐ COLLECTION, THE
Bat out of hell / Bad attitude / One more kiss (Night of the soft parade) / Execution day / Jumpin' the gun / Sailor to a siren / Modern girl / Special girl / Standing on the outside / Cheatin' in your dreams / Masculine / Rock 'n' roll mercenaries
74321152182 / Sep '93 / Ariola Express

☐ DEAD RINGER
Peel out / I'm gonna love her for both of us / More than you deserve / I'll kill you if you don't come back / Read 'em and weep / Nocturnal pleasure / Dead ringer for love / Everything is permitted
CD 83645 / Nov '87 / Epic

☐ DEAD RINGER/MIDNIGHT AT THE LOST AND FOUND (2CD Set)
Peel out / I'm gonna love her for both of us / More than you deserve / I'll kill you if you don't come back / Read 'em and weep / Nocturnal pleasure / Dead ringer for love / Everything is permitted / Razor's edge / Midnight at the lost and found / Wolf at your door / Keep driving / Promised land / You never can be too sure about the girl / Priscilla / Don't you look at me like that / If you really want to / Fallen angel
4784862 / Mar '95 / Epic

☐ DEAD RINGER/MIDNIGHT AT THE LOST AND FOUND/BAT OUT OF HELL (3CD Set)
Peel out / I'm gonna love her for the both of us / More than you deserve / I'll kill you if you don't come back / Read 'em and weep / Nocturnal pleasure / Dead ringer for love / Everything is permitted / Razor's edge / Midnight at the lost and found / Wolf at your door / Keep driving / Promised land / You never can be too sure about the girl / Priscilla / Don't you look at me like that / If you really want to / Fallen angel / Bat out of hell / You took the words right out of my mouth / Heaven can wait / All revved up with no place to go / Two out of three ain't bad / Paradise by the dashboard light / For crying out loud / Dead ringer for love
4886742 / 3 Nov '97 / Epic

☐ DEFINITIVE COLLECTION, THE
Paradise by the dashboard light / Paradise / Let me sleep on it / Praying for the end of time / Bat out of hell / You took the words right out of my mouth / Two out of three ain't bad / Heaven can wait / Dead ringer for love / Read 'em and weep / I'm gonna love her for both of us / More than you deserve / Peel out / Everything is permitted / Razor's edge / If you really want to / Don't you look at me like that / Fallen angel / I love you so I told you a lie: *Meat Loaf & Ted Nugent*
4805672 / 13 Jul '98 / Epic

☐ HITS OUT OF HELL
Bat out of hell / Read 'em and weep / Midnight at the lost and found / Two out of three ain't bad / Dead ringer for love / Modern girl / I'm gonna love her for both of us / You took the words right out of my mouth / Razor's edge / Paradise by the dashboard light
4504472 / Mar '91 / Epic
4504479 / 13 Jul '98 / Epic

☐ LIVE AND KICKING
Bat out of hell / Two out of three ain't bad / Modern live / Blind before I stop / Piece of the action / Rock 'n' roll mercenaries / Paradise by the dashboard light / Masculine / Took the words / Midnight at the lost and found / Bad attitude / Medley: Johnny B Goode/ Slow down/Jailhouse rock/Blue suede
74321339422 / Jan '96 / Camden

☐ LIVE AT WEMBLEY
Blind before I stop / Rock 'n' roll mercenaries / Took the words / Midnight at the lost and found / Modern girl / Paradise by the dashboard light / Two out of three ain't bad / Bat out of hell / Masculine / Johnny B Goode/Slow down/Jailhouse rock/Blue suede shoes
258599 / 1 Sep '97 / Arista

☐ MEAT LOAF & FRIENDS
Paradise by the dashboard light / Holding out for a hero: *Tyler, Bonnie* / You took the words right out of my mouth / We belong to the night: *Foley, Ellen* / Bad for good: *Steinman, Jim* / What's the matter baby: *Foley, Ellen* / Two out of three ain't bad / Faster than the speed of night: *Tyler, Bonnie* / Dead ringer for love / Night out: *Foley, Ellen* / Total eclipse of the heart: *Tyler, Bonnie* / Left in the dark: *Steinman, Jim*
4724192 / Oct '94 / Epic

☐ MIDNIGHT AT THE LOST AND FOUND
Razor's edge / Midnight at the Lost and found / Wolf at your door / Keep driving / Promised land / You never can be too sure about the girl / Priscilla / Don't you look at me like that / If you really want to / Fallen angel
4503602 / Jan '94 / Epic

☐ PRIMECUTS
Modern girl / Getting away with murder / Bat out of hell / Surf's up / Blind before I stop / Bad attitude / Jumpin' the gun / Two out of three ain't bad / Paradise by the dashboard light (live) / Rock 'n' roll mercenaries
260363 / Dec '89 / Arista

☐ ROCK 'N' ROLL HERO
Bad attitude / Sailor to a siren / One more kiss / Jumpin' the gun / Special girl / Modern girl / Masculine / Don't leave your mark on me / Rock 'n' roll mercenaries / Cheatin' in your dreams / Blind before I stop / Piece of the action / Rock 'n' roll hero / Paradise by the dashboard light / Bat out of hell
74321393362 / Jun '96 / Camden

☐ WELCOME TO THE NEIGHBOURHOOD
When the rubber meets the road / I'd lie for you (and that's the truth) / Original sin / 45 seconds of ecstasy / Runnin' for the red light (I gotta life) / Fiesta de Las Almas Perdidas / Left in the dark / Not a dry eye in the house / Amnesty is granted / If this is the last kiss (let's make it last all night) / Martha / Where angels sing
CDV 2799 / Oct '95 / Virgin

Meat Puppets

☐ MONSTERS
Attacked by monsters / Light / Meltdown / In love / Void / Touchdown king / Party till the world obeys / Flight of the fire weasel / Strings on your heart / Like being alive
SST 253CD / Oct '89 / SST

☐ NO JOKE
Scum / Nothing / Head / Taste of the sun / Vampires / Predator / Poison arrow / Eyeball / For free / Cobbler / Inflatable / Swet ammonia / Chemical garden
8286652 / 15 Sep '97 / London

☐ TOO HIGH TO DIE
Violet eyes / Never to be found / We don't exist / Severed Goddess head / Flaming heart / Shine / Backwater / Roof with a hole / Station / Things / Why / Evil love / Comin' down / Lake of fire
8284842 / Feb '94 / London

Meat Purveyors

☐ SWEET IN THE PANTS
BS 026 / 22 May '98 / Bloodshot

Meatfly

☐ FATNESS
DISC 1CD / '92 / Vinyl Japan

Meathead

☐ MEATHEAD AGAINST THE WORLD (Various Artists)
Introoutofthisworld / Large Amerikan jaw: Meathead / Schweinhund: Cop Shoot Cop / Filler: Meathead / Black room: Zeni Geva / Digraceland: Meathead / Cancer beat: Babyland / Godbastardgod: Meathead / Digraceland: Meathead / Possible end, 47: Meathead / Tigress of Babylon: Pain Teens / Godbastardgod: Meathead / Schweinhund: Cop Shoot Cop / Large Amerikan Jaw: Meathead
WHIP 023 / Dec '96 / Submission

☐ PROTECT ME FROM WHAT I WANT
Would u / Feel like / Pool / Let it out-hit me / Wipeout / Rotula / Pianola / Broken spine / My money / Timoti / Gravida code / Wipe out all their pain / Canterbury
DY 00232 / May '97 / Dynamica

Meatlocker

☐ TRIANGLE OF PAIN
PRLCD 7913011 / Apr '95 / Progress Red

Meatmen

☐ CRIPPLED CHILDREN SUCK
TG 59 CD / Feb '91 / Touch & Go

☐ EVIL IN A LEAGUE WITH SATAN
GKCD 028 / Nov '97 / Go-Kart

☐ WAR OF THE SUPERBIKE
GK 022CD / Oct '96 / Go-Kart

Mecano

☐ AIDALAI
El fallo positivo / El uno, el dos, el tres / Bilando salsa / El 7 Septiembre / Naturaleza muerta / 1917 / Una rosa es una rosa / El lago artificial / Tu / Dalai Lama / El peon del rey de negras / JC Sentia
261786 / Nov '91 / Ariola

Mecca Normal

☐ EAGLE AND THE POODLE, THE
Breathing in the dark / Her ambition / Revival of cruelty / Rigid man in an ice age / When you build a house without doors / Prize arm / Mrs. McGillvary / Now that you're here / Kingdom without weather / Cave in / Drive at / Peach-a-vanilla / When you know
OLE 1862 / Apr '96 / Matador

☐ SITTING ON SNAPS
Vacant night sky / Something to be said / Crimson dragnet / Frozen rain / Only heat trapped / Inside your heart / Alibi / Pamela makes waves / Bepo's room / Cyclone / Gravity believes
OLE 1122 / Feb '95 / Matador

☐ WHO SHOT ELVIS
Medieval man / Who shot Elvis / Excalibur / Orbit / Step into my sphere / Way of love / All about the same thing / OK here we go / Don't heal me like a dog just to break me like a horse / In Canada
OLE 2452 / 6 Oct '97 / Matador

Meco

☐ BEST OF MECO, THE
Star Wars theme/Cantina / Empire strikes back medley / Close Encounters / Wizard Of Oz / Star Trek medley / Topsy / Meco's theme/3W57 / Moondancer / Spooky / Can you read my mind / Werewolf (loose in London) / Star Wars / Other galactic funk / Asteroid field/Finale
5532552 / Mar '97 / Mercury

Mecolodians

☐ JOE BAIZA/RALPH GORODETZSKY/ TONY CICERO
EMY 1472 / Sep '97 / Enemy

Medalark 11

☐ MEDALARK 11
Cute / Smoke / Coffee / Throw down a rope / Metalark / Snake / Socket / Call your name / Diving / Querelcia / Big sharp
CRECD 145 / Dec '93 / Creation

Medallions

☐ SPEEDIN'
Speedin' / Magic mountain / I wonder wonder wonder / Letter / Dance and swing / Dear and darling / Push button automobile / Lover's prayer / Edna / '59 Volvo / Unseen / Ticket to love / I'm in love with you / Buick '59 / Behind the door / Don't shoot baby / I want a love / My Mary Lou / For better or for worse / Give me the right / Telegram / Rocket ship / Did you have fun / Coupe de ville baby / Shedding tears for you
CDCHD 536 / Mar '96 / Ace

Medardo Y Su Orquesta

☐ LA BODA
TUMICD 032 / '92 / Tumi

Medeski, John

☐ COMBUSTICATION (Medeski, John & Billy Martin/Chris Wood)
Sugarcraft / Just like I pictured it / Start/stop / Nocturne / Hey hee hi ho / Whatever happened to Gus / Latin shuffle / Everyday people / Coconut boogaloo / Church of logic / No ke anu ahiahi / Hypnotized
4930112 / 3 Aug '98 / Blue Note

Media Form

☐ BEAUTY REPORTS
SOHO 18CD / Nov '94 / Suburbs Of Hell

Mediaeval Baebes

☐ SALVA NOS
Salve Virgo virginum / Now springes the spray / Ah si mon moine / Adam lay ibounden / Foweles in the frithe / So treiben wir den winter aus / Coventry carol / Gaudete / Adult lullaby / Veni, veni / Salva nos / Verbum caro / Lo here my hert / Binnorie o binnorie / This ay nicht / Miri it is
CDVE 935 / 17 Nov '97 / Venture

Medicine

☐ HER HIGHNESS
All good things / Wash me out / Candy Candy / Feel nothing at all / Fractured smile / Farther down / Aarhus / Seen the light alone / Heads
74321287572 / Nov '95 / American

☐ SHOT FORTH SELF LIVING
One More / Aruca / Defective / Short happy life / 5ive / Sweet Explosion / Queen of tension / Miss Drugstore / Christmas Song
CRECD 142 / Oct '92 / Creation

Medicine Ball

☐ SCIENCE SECRET STARS
SGCD 5 / Sep '97 / September Gurls

Medicine Drum

☐ SUPERNATURE
646344000223 / 11 May '98 / Abstract

Medicine Head

☐ MEDICINE HEAD LIVE
RMCCD 0201 / Aug '96 / Red Steel

☐ NEW BOTTLES OLD MEDICINE
When night falls / Ooee baby / Next time the sun comes round / This love of old / Home's odyssey / Oh my heart in to peace / Do it now / Be it as we are / Fire under the mountain / Two men now / Crazy about you baby / Goin' home / His guiding hand / Walkin' blues / Pictures in the sky / Natural sight / Just like Tom Thumb's blues / Blue suede shoes / To train time
SEECD 411 / Oct '94 / See For Miles

☐ TIMEPEACE (BOOM, HOWL AND MOAN)
RMOCD 0201 / Sep '95 / Red Steel

Medicine Rain

☐ NATIVE
MACDL 945 / Nov '96 / Resurrection

Medicine Wheel

☐ IMMORAL FABRIC
HGCD 0955 / 15 Jun '98 / High Gain

Meditation Dub

☐ MEDITATION DUB
WRCD 15 / Oct '92 / Techniques

Meditation Singers

☐ GOOD NEWS
My soul looks back and wonders / Ain't that good news / You don't know how blessed you are / He's alright with me / Remember me / One river to cross / Know the day is over / Make a step in the right direction / Day is past and gone / I'm saying yes / I'm determined to run this race / Do you know Jesus / Promise to meet me there / Until I reach my heavenly home / He made it all right / Jesus is always there / Too close to heaven / God is good to me / WDIA plug / My soul looks back in wonders
CDCHD 465 / Mar '93 / Ace

Meditations

☐ DEEPER ROOTS
HBCD 158 / Jun '94 / Heartbeat

☐ FOR THE GOOD OF MAN
Mr. Vulture man / Roots man party / Tin sardin / Wallah up / For the good of man / Bourgeois game / Dem a fight / Man no better than woman / Woman woman / Rocking in America
GRELCD 114 / Aug '88 / Greensleeves

☐ NO MORE FRIEND
No more friend / Forcing me / Jack on top / Mother love / Book of history / Carpenter rebuild / Fuss and fight / Slick chick / Talk of the town / Big city
GRELCD 52 / Aug '95 / Greensleeves

☐ RETURN OF THE MEDITATIONS
HBCD 130 / Nov '92 / Heartbeat

Medium Cool

☐ IMAGINATION
How long has this been going on / That old feeling / I fall in love too easily / Look for the silver lining / My foolish heart / Like someone in love / Let's get lost / My buddy / Imagination / Little girl blue
COOKCD 055 / Apr '93 / Cooking Vinyl

Medlow, Junior

☐ THRILL FOR THRILL
LIZARD 80006 / Aug '95 / Lizard

Mednick, Lisa

☐ ARTIFACTS OF LOVE
DJD 3209 / May '94 / Dejadisc

Medulla Nocte

☐ CONVERSATION ALONE
HAUS 017CD / 22 Jun '98 / Household Name

Medusa Cyclone

☐ MEDUSA CYCLONE
3G 11 / Jun '97 / Third Gear

☐ MR. DEVIL
3G 22 / 24 Aug '98 / Third Gear

Meek, Joe

☐ I HEAR A NEW WORLD (Meek, Joe & The Blue Men)
RPM 103 / Jan '92 / RPM

☐ INTERGALACTIC INSTROS (Various Artists)
Night of the vampire: Moontrekkers / Just for chicks: Ramblers / Oo la la: Jay, Peter & The Jaywalkers / Red rocket: Laverne, Roger & The Microns / Hatahiai: Moontrekkers / Green jeans: Fabulous Flee Rekkers / West point: Checkmates / Keep moving: Sounds Incorporated / Spook walks: Spooks / Lawrence of Arabia: Tornados / Pinto: Stonehenge Men / Bogey man: Tornados / Totem pole: Jay, Peter & The Jaywalkers / Saxon way cry: Saxons / Union pacific: Original Checkmates / Cerveza: Fabulous Flee Rekkers / Melodie d'amore: Moontrekkers / Take it away: Ramblers / Big feet: Stonehenge Men / There's something at the bottom of the well: Moontrekkers / Dodge city: Ramblers / Order of the keys: Sounds Incorporated / Spy: Original Checkmates / Sunday sunset: Moontrekkers / Jaywalker: Jay, Peter & The Jaywalkers / You are my sunshine: Fabulous Flee Rekkers / John Brown's body: Moontrekkers / Poet and peasant: Jay, Peter & The Jaywalkers / Telstar: Tornados / Exodus: Tornados / Czardas: Tornados / Telstar demo: Meek, Joe
GEMCD 002 / Oct '96 / Diamond

☐ JOE MEEK - THE PYE YEARS VOL.2 (304 Holloway Road) (Various Artists)
Pocket full of dreams and eyes full of tears: Gregory, Iain / Night you told a lie: Gregory, Iain / Who's the girl: Jay, Peter / Bittersweet love: Riot Squad / Try to realise: Riot Squad / When love was young: Rio, Bobby & the Revelles / Happy talk: Saints / Midgets: Saints / Parade of the tin soldiers: Saints / Baby I go for you: Blue Rondos / What can I do: Blue Rondos / May your hearts stay young forever: Reader, Pat / Goodness knows: Wayne, Ricky & the Off-Beats / Baby I like the look of you: London, Peter / Fickle heart: Garfield, Johnny / Stranger in paradise: Garfield, Johnny / As time goes by: Dean, Alan & His Problems / Cool water: Cameron, Chick Ted Group & The D.J.'s / Rescue me: Wayne, Ricky / It can happen to you: Conrad, Jess / There and Bach again: Cook, Peter / Sing C'est la vie: Collins, Glenda / I'm not made of clay: Rio, Bobby / My saddest day: Austin, Reg / Two timing baby: Carter-Lewis & The Southerners / Tell me: Carter-Lewis & The Southerners
NEXCD 216 / Feb '93 / Sequel

☐ JOE MEEK COLLECTION, THE (Hidden Gems Vol.1)
GEMCD 022 / 24 Aug '98 / Diamond

☐ JOE MEEK STORY VOL.5, THE (The Early Years) (Various Artists)
Georgia's got a moon: Miller, Betty / Robin Hood: Miller, Gary / Cry me a river: Ryan, Marion / Rhythm and blues: Winston, Eric / 16 Tons: Hockridge, Edmund / Sugarfree: Lotis, Dennis / Garden of eden: Miller, Gary / Love is strange: Donegan, Lonnie / Bye bye love: Fraser, Johnny / Freight train: Seeger, Peggy / Wild eyes and tender lips: Hicks, Colin & The Cabin Boys / Land of make believe: Davis, Jackie / Story of my life: Miller, Gary / Mule skinner blues: Donegan, Lonnie / Cerveza: Wainer, Cherry / Weekend: Price, Red Band / Charlie Brown: Ellington, Ray / Venus: Valentine, Dickie / Yashmak: Arnaz, Chico / Allentown jail: Roza, Lita / Hold back tomorrow: Miki & Griff / What do you want to make those eyes at me for: Ford, Emile & The Checkmates / Dear Daddy: Clark, Petula / Mr Blue: MacBeth, David / This love I have for you: Fortune, Lance
NEMCD 882 / Mar '97 / Sequel

☐ LET'S GO WITH JOE MEEK'S GIRLS (Various Artists)
RPM 166 / Jun '96 / RPM

☐ RGM RARITIES VOL.1 (The Joe Meek Collection) (Various Artists)
It matters not: Douglas, Mark / In the night: Lee, Jamie & The Atlantics / Other side of the track: Cristo, Bobby & The Rebels / Heart's ice cold: Charles, Don / Can't you hear my heart: Rivers, Danny / Angel face: Temple, Gerry / Fool such as I: Kaye, Davy / They were wrong: Carson, Chad / I'm waiting for tomorrow: Rivers, Danny / Angel of love: Charles, Don / In my way: Kaye, Davy / Don't want to know: Cox, Michael / Movin' in: Rivers, Danny & The Rivermen / Dear one: Victor, Tony / Louisiana marna: Lennon, Jimmy & The Atlantics / It's my way of loving you: Charles, Don / All the stars in heaven: Kaye, Davy / Seventeen come Sunday: Temple, Gerry / Hey there cruel heart: Cavell, Andy / Striped purple shirt: Klein, Alan / Stop picking on me: Carson, Chad / In this lonesome old house: Cox, Michael / We're gonna dance: Rivers, Danny & The Rivermen / Upside down: Douglas, Mark / No more tomorrows: Temple, Gerry / Little girl in blue: Lee, Jamie & The Atlantics / Walk with me my angel: Charles, Don / Three coins in the sewer: Klein, Alan
GEMCD 012 / Jun '97 / Diamond

☐ RGM RARITIES VOL.2 (The Beat Group Era/The Joe Meek Collection) (Various Artists)
That's my plan: Beat Boys / Third time lucky: Beat Boys / You're holding me down: Beat Boys / I gotta buzz: Buzz / Sticks and stones: Checkmates / Right girl for me: Chris, Peter & The Outcasts / I've got you out of my mind: Cristo, Bobby & The Rebels / Singin' the blues: Eddie, Jason & The Centremen / True to you: Eddie, Jason & The Centremen / Whatcha gonna do: Eddie, Jason & The Centremen / Come on baby: Eddie, Jason & The Centremen / Man's gotta stand tall: Four Matadors / I don't love her no more: Hotrods / Ain't coming back no more: Hotrods / Too far out: Impac / Kansas City: Jay, Peter & The Jaywalkers / I love to see you strut: John, David & The Mood / Bring it to jerome: John, David & The Mood / Diggin' for gold: John, David & The Mood / She's fine: John, David & The Mood / Summer without the sun: Kingsley, Charles Creation / SStill in love with you: Kingsley, Charles Creation / Wishing well: Kingsley, Charles Creation / Boys and girls: Parker, Benny & The Dynamics / Bluebirds over the mountain: Joey, Shade & The Night Owls / Every once in a while: Shakeouts / Who told you: Starr, Freddie & the Midnighters / It's shakin' time: Starr, Freddie & the Midnighters
GEMCD 016 / Jul '97 / Diamond

☐ WORK IN PROGRESS
RPM 121 / Oct '93 / RPM

Meeks, Carl

☐ JACKMANDORA
Jackmandora / Tuff scout / Born and grow yah / Bad minded people / Come a dance / Haul and pull selector / Girl is right / Raw born rub-a-dub / We rule dance-hall / Now is the time
GRELCD 132 / Jul '89 / Greensleeves

Mega Banton

☐ FIRST POSITION
VPCD 1343 / Jan '94 / VP

☐ NEW YEAR, NEW STYLE (Mega Banton & Friends)
SHCD 45020 / Dec '94 / Shanachie

☐ SHOWCASE (Mega Banton & Ricky General)
BSCCD 17 / Dec '93 / Black Scorpio

Mega City Four

☐ INSPIRINGLY TITLED - THE LIVE ALBUM
Thanx / Shivering sand / Props / Messenger / Stop / Revolution / Words that say / Callous / Lipscar / Peripheral / Clown / Open / What you've got / Don't want to know if you are lonely / Who cares / Finish
MEGCD 2 / Nov '92 / Big Life

☐ MAGIC BULLETS
Perfect circle / Drown / Rain man / Toys / Iron sky / So / Enemy skies / Wallflower / President / Shadow / Underdog / Greener / Speck
MEGCD 3 / May '93 / Big Life

☐ SEBASTOPOL RD
Ticket collector / Scared of cats / Callous / Peripheral / Anne Bancroft / Prague / Clown / Props / What's up / Vague / Stop / Wasting my breath
MEGCD 1 / Feb '92 / Big Life

☐ SOULSCRAPER
FIRECD 54 / Mar '96 / Fire

Mega Drums

☐ LAYERS OF TIME
Ancient feelings / Layers of time / Olua / Mahakal / Bardo / Tschung mori / Parabao / Ga ma la / Gecko's in bahia
INT 31732 / Sep '96 / Intuition

Mega,Tom

☐ FOR YOU ONLY
ITM 001485 / Dec '93 / ITM

Megadeth

☐ CRYPTIC WRITINGS
Trust / Almost honest / Use the man / Mastermind / Disintegrators / I'll get even / Sin / Secret place / Have cool, will travel / She-wooolf / Vortex / FFF
CDEST 2297 / Jun '97 / Capitol

☐ PEACE SELLS...BUT WHO'S BUYING/SO FAR, SO GOOD, SO WHAT/RUST (The Originals/3CD Set)
Wake up dead / Conjuring / Peace sells / Devil's Island / Good morning / Bad omen / I ain't superstitious / My last words / Black Friday / Into the lungs of hell / Set the world afire / Anarchy in the UK / Mary Jane / 502 / In my darkest hour / Liar / Hook in mouth / Holy wars...the punishment due / Hangar 18 / Take no prisoners / Five magics / Poison was the cure / Lucretia / Tornado of souls / Dawn patrol / Rust in peace...Polaris
CDOMB 019 / 27 Jul '98 / Capitol

☐ YOUTHANASIA
Reckoning day / Train of consequences / Addicted to chaos / Tout le monde / Elysian fields / Killing road / Blood of heroes / Family tree / Youthanasia / I thought I knew it all / Black curtains / Victory / No more Mr. Nice Guy / Breakpoint / Go to hell / Angry again / Ninety nine ways to die / Paranoid / Diadems / Problems
CDEST 2244 / Oct '94 / Capitol

Megakronkel

☐ MEGAKRONKEL
K 148D / Mar '93 / Konkurrel

Megashira

☐ ZERO HOUR
IC 0262 / Jun '97 / Infracom

Megora

☐ WAITING
SPV 08496742 / Dec '94 / SPV

Mehldau, Brad

☐ NEW YORK - BARCELONA CROSSING (Mehldau, Brad & Mario Rossi)
FSNT 031 / Jan '98 / Fresh Sound New Talent

Mehta, Narsinh

☐ DEVOTIONAL SONGS VOL.1
Naaraatananum naam / Nirajhane ganganabamaan / Mehulo gaje / Naagaar nandajinaa laal / Gori taare traajude / Raat rahe jaahre / Dyaan dhar / Bholi re bharavaadan / Jal kamal / Jaagine joun to / Padhao re popat / Vaishnav jan
NRCD 0062 / Mar '98 / Navras

☐ DEVOTIONAL SONGS VOL.2
Jaagane jaadava / Naanun sarakhun / Kesarbhina kahaanji / Vaa vaaya ne / Maalan laave / Praan thaki / Naan re daan maage / Jaago re / Jashodaa taaara / Ahkil brahmaandmaan / Naachataan naachtaan / Halave halave / Chaal ramiye / Vaari jaaun
NRCD 0063 / Mar '98 / Navras

☐ DEVOTIONAL SONGS VOL.3
Je game jagat / Raamsabhaamaan / Paachhali raatanaa / Bhootal bhakti / Maari hoondi / Praataha havu / Ramjiham ramjiham / Jyaan lagi aatmaatava / Sukhduku manamaan / Evaa re amo / Ame mahiyaaran / Gori taaraa nepoor / AAjani ghadi
NRCD 0064 / Mar '98 / Navras

Meices

☐ DIRTY BIRD
8286812 / Jan '96 / London

☐ GREATEST BIBLE STORIES EVER TOLD
EFA 113822 / Sep '94 / Empty

☐ TASTES LIKE CHICKEN
That good one / Good one / Daddy's gone to California / All time high / Light 'em up / Slide / Until the weekend / Lettuce is far out / Big shitburger / Untruly / Hopin' for a ride / Now / That other good one / Don't let the soap run out / Alex put something in his pocket / Pissin' in the sink / Number one
BLUFF 013CD / Feb '95 / Deceptive

Mejia, Miguel Aceves

☐ SUS GRANDES EXITOS VOL.2
ALCD 022 / Jul '96 / Alma Latina

☐ SUS GRANDES EXITOS VOL.3
ALCD 024 / Jul '96 / Alma Latina

Mekon

☐ WELCOME TO TACKLETOWN
Phatty's lunchbox / Freestyle / Rock 'n' roll / Revenge of the Mekon / Hook link / Mr Sophistication / Welcome to tackletown / Mekon Vs Artery / Broken synth lead / Skool's out / Agent mekon
WALLCD 006 / May '97 / Wall Of Sound

Mekons

☐ DEVIL'S RATS AND PIGGIES (A Special Message From Godzilla)
QS 66CD / Aug '97 / Quarter Stick

☐ ME
QS 53CD / 26 May '98 / Quarter Stick

☐ MEKONS
Snow / St. Patrick's day / DP Miller / Institution / I'm so happy / Chopper squad / Business / Trimden grange explosion / Karen / Corporal chalkie / John Barry / Another one
CDMGRAM 76 / Feb '94 / Cherry Red

☐ PUSSY, KING OF THE PIRATES (Featuring Kathy Acker)
QS 36CD / Feb '96 / Quarter Stick

☐ RETREAT FROM MEMPHIS
QS 26CD / Jun '94 / Quarter Stick

☐ ROCK 'N' ROLL
Memphis, Egypt / Club Mekon / Only darkness has the power / Ring o'roses / Learning to live on your own / Cocaine Lil / Empire of the senseless / Someone / Amnesia / I am crazy / Heaven and back / Blow your tuneless trumpet / Echo / When darkness falls
BFFP 40CD / '89 / Blast First

Mel & Kim

☐ FLM
FLM / Showing out / Respectable / Feel a whole lot better / I'm the one who really loves you / More than words can say / System / From a whisper to a scream / Who's gonna catch you / Showing out (remix) / Respectable (remix)
CDGOLD 1006 / Mar '96 / EMI Gold

Mel & Tim

☐ GOOD GUYS ONLY WIN IN THE MOVIES
Good guys only win in the movies / Forget it I've got it / I've got puredee / Feeling bad / Groovy situation / Backfield in motion / Caught you in the act / I found that I was wrong / Mail call time / Ain't love wonderful / Do right baby / Never on time / We've got the groove to move you / I'm the one / Put an extra plus to your love
SC 6078 / Aug '97 / Sundazed

☐ STARTING ALL OVER AGAIN
Don't you mess with my money, my honey or my woman / Starting all over again / I may not be what you want / Carry me / Free for all / Heaven knows / Wrap it up / What's your name / I'm your puppet / Too much wheelin' and dealin' / Forever and a day / It's those little things that count / Same folks / Yes we can-can
CDSXE 078 / Jan '93 / Stax

Melanie

☐ BBC LIVE IN CONCERT
SFRSCD 035 / 29 Sep '97 / Strange Fruit

☐ BEST OF MELANIE, THE
Ruby Tuesday / Brand new key / Animal crackers / Mr. Tambourine man / Baby day / Beautiful people / Save the night / Lay down (candles in the rain) / Close it all / What have they done to my song Ma / Lay lady lay / Some day I'll be a farmer / Good book / Peace will come / Gardens in the city / Nickel song / Pebbles in the sand / Tell me why
MCCD 011 / Feb '91 / Music Club

☐ BORN TO BE
In the hour / Bo Bo's party / Momma momma / Animal crackers / Close to it all / I'm back in town / Mr. Tambourine man / Really loved Harold / Christopher Robin / Merry Christmas
C5CD 582 / Apr '92 / See For Miles

☐ FOUR SIDES OF MELANIE, THE
Somebody loves me / Beautiful people / In the hour / I really loved Harold / Johnny boy / Any guy / I'm back in town / What have they done to my song Ma / Lay down (candles in the rain) / Peace will come / Good book / Nickle song / Babe rainbow / Mr. Tambourine man / Carolina in my mind / Ruby Tuesday / Lay lady lay / Christopher Robin / Animal crackers / I don't eat animals / Leftover wine
HILLCD 10 / Jan '97 / Wooded Hill

☐ FROM WOODSTOCK TO THE WORLD (2CD Set)
Brand new key / Long long time / Beautiful people / Lay down / Peace will come / Look what they've done to my song / Ruby Tuesday / Babe rainbow / Close to it all / Ring around the moon / Ring the living bell / Nickel song / Summer of love / Good book / Estate sale / Alexander Beetle / I don't eat animals / Purple haze / Silence is King / Christopher Robin / Arrow / These nights / Something warm / Look what they've done to my song
24337 / Nov '96 / Laserlight

☐ GOOD BOOK, THE
Good book / Babe rainbow / Sign on the window / Saddest thing / Nickel song / Isn't it a pity / My father / Chords of fame / You can go fishin / Birthday of the sun / Prize
C5CD 597 / Feb '93 / See For Miles

☐ HIT SINGLE COLLECTABLES
DISK 4505 / Apr '94 / Disky

☐ RUBY TUESDAY
Mr. Tambourine man / Beautiful people / Carolina in my mind / Lay lady lay / Kansas / My bonny lies over the ocean / Someday I'll be a farmer / Nickel song / Happy birthday / Ruby Tuesday / What have they done to my song Ma / Somebody loves me / Tell me why / Candles in the rain / Leftover wine / Brand new key / Stop, I don't wanna hear it anymore / Peace will come
5507512 / Jan '95 / Spectrum

☐ UNPLUGGED
Ruby Tuesday / Look what they've done to my song / Brand new key / Beautiful people / Freedom knows my name / Lay down (candles in the rain) / Ballerina / Peace will come / Sun and moon / Life will not go away / Babe rainbow / Ring around the moon / Arrow / Close to it all / Long long time / Purple haze
DC 879982 / May '97 / Disky

☐ VERY BEST OF MELANIE, THE
Ruby Tuesday / Brand new key / Nickel song / What have they done to my song Ma / Beautiful people / Any guy / Close to it all / Mr. Tambourine man / Baby day / I don't eat animals / Lay lady lay / In the hour / Pebbles in the sand / Save the night / Gardens in the city / Christopher Robin / Good book / Carolina on my mind / Somebody loves me / Leftover wine / Lay down (candles in the rain) / Peace will come (according to my plan)
74321558502 / 26 Jan '98 / Camden

Meldonian, Dick

☐ DICK MELDONIAN & SONNY IGOE BIG BAND 1980-1982 (Meldonian, Dick & Sonny Igoe)
CCD 73 / Nov '96 / Circle

☐ DICK MELODIAN TRIO (Meldonian, Dick Trio)
JCD 164 / Aug '94 / Jazzology

☐ SWING ALTERNATE (Meldonian, Dick & Orchestra)
CLCD 150 / Mar '90 / Circle

☐ SWING OF ARR. OF GENEROLA (Meldonian, Dick & Orchestra)
CCD 150 / Oct '91 / Circle

☐ YOU'VE CHANGED (Meldonian, Dick Quartet)
PCD 7052 / Jun '93 / Progressive

Melek-Tha

☐ ASTRUM ARGENTINIUM
CDAR 032 / Apr '96 / Adipocre

Melford, Myra

☐ ALIVE IN THE HOUSE OF SAINTS (Melford, Myra Trio)
ARTCD 6136 / Nov '93 / Hat Art

☐ ELEVEN GHOSTS (Melford, Myra & Han Bennink)
HATOLOGY 507 / Dec '97 / Hatology

☐ JUMP
EMY 1152 / Sep '97 / Enemy

☐ NOW AND NOW (Melford, Myra Trio)
EMY 1312 / Sep '97 / Enemy

Melis, Efisio

☐ LAUNEDDAS
RD 5025CD / Mar '96 / Robi Droli

Mellencamp, John

☐ AMERICAN FOOL (Mellencamp, John Cougar)
Can you take it / Hurts so good / Jack and Diane / Hand to hold on to / Danger list / Can you fake it / Thundering hearts / China girl / Close enough / Weakest moments
8149932 / '88 / Mercury

☐ BEST THAT I COULD DO 1978-1988, THE
Jack and Diane / ROCK in the USA / Hurts so good / I need a lover / Ain't even done with the night / Crumblin' down / Pink houses / Authority song / Lonely ol' night / Small town / Paper in fire / Cherry bomb / Check it out / Without expression
5367382 / 5 Jan '98 / PolyGram TV

☐ CHESTNUT STREET INCIDENT (Mellencamp, John Cougar)
American dream / Oh pretty woman / Jailhouse rock / Dream killin' town / Supergirl / Chestnut Street revisited / Good girls / Do you believe in magic / Twentieth Century Fox / Sad lady / Chestnut street
SMMCD 513 / 23 Feb '98 / Snapper

☐ DANCE NAKED
5224282 / 15 Sep '97 / Mercury

☐ HUMAN WHEELS
5180082 / 15 Sep '97 / Mercury

☐ JOHN COUGAR
Little night dancin' / Miami / Do you think that's fair / Welcome to Chinatown / Pray for me / Small paradise / Great midwest / I need a lover / Sugar Marie / Taxi dancer
8149952 / Jan '86 / Mercury

☐ KID INSIDE, THE (Mellencamp, John Cougar)
Kid inside / Take what you want / Cheap shot / Sidewalks and streetlights / R Gang / American son / Gearhead / Young genocides / Too young to live / Survive
SMMCD 510 / 23 Feb '98 / Snapper

☐ LONESOME JUBILEE, THE
Paper in fire / Down and out in paradise / Check it out / Real life / Cherry bomb / We are the people / Empty hands / Hard times for an honest man / Hot dogs and hamburgers / Rooty toot toot
8324652 / Jul '92 / Mercury

☐ MR. HAPPY GO LUCKY
Overture / Jerry / Key West intermezzo / Just another day / This may not be the end of the world / Emotional love / Mr. Bellows / Full catastrophe / Circling around the moon / Large world turning / Jackamo Road / Life is hard
5328962 / Oct '96 / Mercury

☐ SCARECROW
Rain on the scarecrow / Grandmas's theme / Small town / Minutes to memories / Lonely ol' night / Face of the nation / Justice and independence '85 / Between a laugh and a tear / Rumbleseat / You've got to stand for something / ROCK in the USA / Kind of fella I am
8248652 / Nov '85 / Mercury

☐ UH-HUH
Crumblin' down / Pink houses / Authority song / Hurts so good / Thundering hearts / Warmer place to sleep
8144502 / Oct '91 / Mercury

☐ WHENEVER WE WANTED
Love and happiness / Now more than ever / I ain't never satisfied / Get a leg up / Crazy ones / Last chance / They're so tough / Melting pot / Whenever we wanted / Again tonight
5101512 / Oct '91 / Mercury

Meller, Raquel

☐ LA VIOLETERA
BMCD 7604 / 5 Jan '98 / Fresh Sound

☐ LAS PRIMERAS GRABACIONES
BMCD 7606 / 1 Jun '98 / Blue Moon

☐ SUCCES ET RARETES 1926-1932
701562 / Sep '96 / Chansophone

Melling, Steve

☐ UN LOCO POCO
What is this thing called love / Prelude to a kiss / Night and day / In a monochrome / Leona / Janas delight / Eronet / Un poco loco / Wise one / Some other time
JHCD 045 / Feb '96 / Ronnie Scott's Jazz House

Mellow Candle

☐ SWADDLING SONGS
Heaven Heath / Sheep season / Silversong / Poet and the witch / Messenger birds / Dan the wing / Reverend Sisters / Break your token / Buy or beware / Vile excesses / Lonely man / Boulders on my grave
SEECD 404 / May '96 / See For Miles

☐ VIRGIN PROPHET
KSCD 9520 / Jun '97 / Kissing Spell

Mellow Fellows

☐ STREET PARTY
I've got to find a way / Street party / I've got a feeling / Feels like rain / Drivin' wheel / We'll be friends / Don't turn your heater down / Since I fell for you / Last night / Me and my woman / Broad daylight
ALCD 4793 / May '93 / Alligator

Mellstock Band

☐ CAROLS & DANCES OF HARDY'S WESSEX
CDSDL 360 / Oct '92 / Saydisc

☐ SONGS OF THOMAS HARDY'S WESSEX (With Sally Dexter/Julie Murphy/Ian Giles/Andy Turner)
Foggy dew / Jockey to the fair/Dame Durden / Mistletoe bough / Cupid's garden / Queen Eleanor's confession / Spotted cow / Seeds of love / Barley mow / Prentice boy / I have parks, I have hounds / Break o'the day / Sheepshearing song / Tailor's breeches / Downhills of life / I wish I wish / Joan's ale / Outlandish knight / Such a beauty I did grow / Banks of Allan Water / King Arthur had three sons / Light of the moon
CDSDL 410 / Mar '95 / Saydisc

☐ TENANTS OF THE EARTH
WGS 281CD / Nov '96 / Wild Goose

☐ THOMAS HARDY READINGS (Readings/Poetry & Music) (Mellstock Band & Alan Bates)
Swiss boy / Downfall of Paris / Rejoice ye tenants of the Earth / Wounded Hussar / Time to remember the poor / Sweet Jenny Jones
NTCD 012 / 15 Jun '98 / Droffig

Melly, George

☐ ANYTHING GOES
PLSCD 112 / Mar '96 / Pulse

☐ BEST OF GEORGE MELLY LIVE, THE
LCD 7019 / Jul '95 / D-Sharp

☐ BEST OF GEORGE MELLY, THE
I can't give you anything but love / I'm gonna sit right down and write myself a letter / It's a sin to tell a lie / Ain't misbehavin' / Georgia / Someday you'll be sorry / Rockin' chair / Everybody loves my baby / My very good friend the milkman / Nobody's sweetheart / Lazy river / Tain't what you do / St. louis blues / Squeeze me in / After you've gone / Don't get around much anymore / Honeysuckle rose / Lazy bones / Shimmy like my sister kate / Making whoopee / Sweet georgia brown / Way down yonder in new orleans / Yellow dog blues / There'll be some changes made / Sweet lorraine / Baby won't you please come home
KAZCD 22 / Jul '92 / Kaz

☐ BEST OF GEORGE MELLY, THE
Anything goes / Oh Chubby, stay the way you are / House of the rising sun / Porter's love song / Nobody knows you (When you're down and out) / Hard hearted Hannah / Puttin' on the ritz / I ain't got nobody / Someday sweetheart / Route 66 / September song / Maybe not at all / It had to be you / Wrap your troubles in dreams (and dream your troubles away) / Chicago (That toddling town) / I hate a man like you / Sundown mamma / I don't want to set the world on fire
TRTCD 160 / Dec '94 / TrueTrax

☐ HOT DOG MAN, THE
Glory of love / Nuts / Crazy rhythm / My honey's lovin' arms / Living on my own / Frankie and Johnny / Take me for a buggy ride / Waiter and the porter / Sweet substitute / Salty dog / I wish I were twins / You call it joggin' / Riverboat shuffle / (I wanna) hot dog
303192 / Jun '97 / Hallmark

Melochita

☐ LIBERTAD
LPCD 8901 / Nov '97 / Fresh Sound

☐ MI SON SABROSON
1004CD / Nov '96 / Fresh Sound

Melodia, Luiz

☐ DECISAO
ML 51011 / 14 Apr '98 / Musica Latina

Melodian Pops Orchestra

☐ TIJUANA TRUMPET
Pan pot dixie / O sole mio / Mextet / Bossa nova scotia / Taste of honey / Pedro Smith / Ghost of influence / Little zab / Bell and the bugle / Soft waving with a tik / Guantanamera / Furlough for two / Arena Santa Monica / Tijuana sleigh ride / Trouble spot / Studying for elephant / Last train to Tampico / Down the road a piece / EL tora bravo / Rambling swallow
302562 / Jun '98 / Hallmark

Melodians

☐ GREATEST HITS
RN 7056 / 10 Aug '98 / Rhino

☐ RIVERS OF BABYLON (The Best Of The Melodians 1967-1973)
You don't need me / I'll get along without you / You have caught me / Let's join hands together / Come on little girl / Little nut tree / You are my only love / Swing and dine / I could be a King / Sweet Rose / It comes and goes / Ring of gold / You've got it / Personally speaking / When there is you / Everybody brawlin' / Sweet sensation / It's my delight / Day seems too long / Say darling say / Rivers of Babylon / It took a miracle / Your destiny / Lock love away / Passion love / Black man kingdom come
CDTRL 387 / Sep '97 / Trojan

☐ SWING & DINE
HBCD 129 / Nov '92 / Heartbeat

Melodie E Canzoni

☐ ERIK SATIE
NT 6717 / Jan '94 / Robi Droli

Melt Banana

☐ SCRATCH OR STITCH
GR 34CD / May '96 / Skingraft

Melting Euphoria

☐ INSIDE GARDENS OF MIND
CLEO 0089 / 13 Jul '98 / Cleopatra

☐ INSIDE THE GARDENS OF THE MIND
CLP 0089 / 6 Oct '97 / Cleopatra

Melton, Barry

☐ SALOON YEARS
SR 1994CD / Dec '97 / Saloon

☐ SONGS OF THE NEXT GREAT DEPRESSION
OW 34506 / Sep '97 / One Way

Melusine

☐ FRANCE FOLK
B 6833CD / Aug '96 / Auvidis/Ethnic

☐ VOIX CONTREVOIX
140192 / Mar '96 / Musidisc

Melvin, Brian

☐ NIGHT FOOD
Ain't nothin' but a party / Don't forget the bass / Night food / Zen turtles / For Max / Polly wanna rhythm / Primalass / Warrior / Continuum
CDSJP 214 / '88 / Timeless Jazz

Melvin, Harold

☐ IF YOU DON'T KNOW ME BY NOW (The Best Of Cabaret) (Melvin, Harold & The Bluenotes)
Cabaret / Love I lost / If you don't know me by now / Don't leave me this way / I'm weak for you / Everybody's talkin' / Hope that we can be together soon / Keep on lovin' you / Tell the world how I feel about cha baby / I miss you / Satisfaction guaranteed / Yesterday I had the blues / Yesterday / Wake up everybody / Where are all my friends / Bad luck
4805092 / May '95 / Epic

☐ SATISFACTION GUARANTEED (The Best Of Harold Melvin & The Blue Notes) (Melvin, Harold & The Bluenotes)
Don't leave me this way / Satisfaction guaranteed / Love I lost / Wake up everybody / Hope that we can be together soon / You know how to make me feel so good / Be for real / Nobody could take your place / Bad luck / Where are all my friends / Keep on loving you / Tell the world about how I feel about cha baby / To be true / I'm searching for a love / To be free to be who we are / If you don't know me by now
4720392 / Jul '92 / Epic

☐ SOUND OF PHILADELPHIA LIVE IN LONDON (Melvin, Harold & The Bluenotes/Three Degrees/Billy Paul)
Introduction/Love I lost: *Melvin, Harold & The Bluenotes* / If you don't know me by now: *Melvin, Harold & The Bluenotes* / Hope that we can be together soon: *Melvin, Harold & The Bluenotes* / Don't leave me this way: *Melvin, Harold & The Bluenotes/Billy Paul* / Wake up evrybody: *Melvin, Harold & The Bluenotes/Billy Paul* / Me and Mrs Jones: *Melvin, Harold & The Bluenotes/Billy Paul* / TSOP (The Sound Of Philadelphia): *Three Degrees* / My simple heart: *Three Degrees* / Medley: *Three Degrees* / Woman in love: *Three Degrees* / Dirty ol' man: *Three Degrees* / When will I see you again: *Three Degrees* / Love train
QED 016 / Nov '96 / Tring

☐ WAKE UP EVERYBODY (Melvin, Harold & The Bluenotes)
If you don't know me by now / Love I lost / Satisfaction guaranteed / Where are all my friends / Bad luck / Hope that we can be together soon / Wake up everybody / You know how to make me feel so good / Be for real / Nobody could take your place / Keep on lovin' you / To be true / I'm searching for love / To be free to be who we are / Do it any way you wanna
RMB 75086 / Mar '96 / Remember

Melvins

☐ HONKY
ARRCD 81024 / Apr '97 / Amphetamine Reptile

☐ HOUDINI
Hooch / Night goat / Lizzy / Goin' blind / Honey bucket / Hag me / Set me straight / Sky pup / Joan of arc / Teet / Copache / Pearl bomb / Spread eagle beagle
7567825322 / Sep '93 / Atlantic

☐ LIVE AT THE FUCKER CLUB
AMREP 072CD / 3 Aug '98 / Amphetamine Reptile

☐ LYSOL
TUP 422 / Nov '92 / Tupelo

☐ OZMA
BR 16 / 20 Apr '98 / Boner

☐ PRICK
ARRCD53 333 / Sep '94 / Amphetamine Reptile

☐ SINGLES 1-12
BOOMBA 003CD / 8 Jun '98 / Boomba

☐ STAG
Bit / Hide / Bar-x-the rocking m / Bloat / Black bock / Tipping the lion / Cotton mouth / Bertha / Captain pungent / Skin horse / Lacrimosa / Sterilized / Buck owens / Soup / Goggles / Yacob's lab
7567828782 / Jul '96 / Atlantic

☐ STONER WITCH
Skweetis / Roadbull / Goose freight train / Lividity / June bug / Shevil / Magic pig detective / At the stake / Queen / Revolve / Sweet willy rollbar
7567827042 / Nov '94 / Atlantic

Melys

☐ RUMOURS AND CURSES
Achilles heel / Diwifr / Acid queen / Painfully thin / Hatchepsut / Fade away (for the last time) / Lemming / When you put Leonard Cohen on / Ambulance chaser / Misunderstand me / Hope you cry yourself to sleep / Martryoshka
KOLD 102CD / 15 Jun '98 / Arctic

Members

☐ SOUND OF THE SUBURBS (A Collection Of The Members' Finest)
Handling the big jets / Sally / GLC / Offshore banking business/Pennies in the pound / Soho a go-go / Muzak machine / Rat up a drainpipe / Sound of the suburbs / Phone-in show / Brian was / Killing time / Clean men / Romance / Flying again / Solitary confinement / Chelsea nightclub / Gang war / Police car
CDOVD 455 / Feb '95 / Virgin

Members Only

☐ MEMBERS ONLY WITH NELSON RANGELL (Members Only & Nelson Rangell)
MCD 5332 / Sep '92 / Muse

☐ TOO
MCD 5348 / Sep '92 / Muse

Membranes

☐ BEST OF THE MEMBRANES, THE
Ice age / Fashionable junkies / Muscles / High St. yanks / Man from moscow / Kafka's dad / Spike Milligan's tape recorder / Myths and legends / Shine on pumkin moon / I am fish eye / Mr. Charisma brain / Everything's brilliant / Kennedy '63 / Spaceships / Everyone's going triple bad acid yeah / Time warp 1991 / Love your puppy / Electric storm / Tatty seaside town / Voodoo chile
CDMGRAM 112 / Jun '97 / Anagram

☐ WRONG PLACE AT THE WRONG TIME
CCON 001CD / Jul '93 / Constrictor Classics

Memento Mori

☐ APOCALYPSE VOL.6
BMCD 124 / 24 Nov '97 / Black Mark

☐ LIFE, DEATH AND OTHER MORBID TALES
BM 051CD / Aug '94 / Black Mark

Memorandum

☐ ARS MORIENDI
EFA 01556CD / Sep '96 / Apocalyptic Vision

Memphis Horns

☐ MEMPHIS HORNS
Take me to the river / Fa fa fa fa fa (Sad song) / I've been loving you too long / Somebody have mercy / Break the chain / Holding on to love / I'm just another soldier / Rumours / Rollercoaster / You don't miss your water / Desire in your eyes
CD 83344 / Jul '95 / Telarc

Memphis Jug Band

☐ MEMPHIS JUG BAND
Lindberg hop / On the road again / Stealin' stealin' / Insane crazy blues / K.c. moan / Cocaine habit blues / Newport news blues (take 1) / Whitewash station blues / Old folks started it / Everybody's talking about sadie green / Memphis jug blues (take 1) / Gator wobble / Little green slippers / Taking your place / Sometimes I think I love you / Memphis boy blues / Aunt caroline dyer blues / What's the matter / Oh ambulance man / Beale street mess around / She stays out all night long / You may leave but this will bring you back / Forth street mess around
YAZCD 1067 / Apr '91 / Yazoo

☐ MEMPHIS JUG BAND 1932-1934, THE
BDCD 6002 / '91 / Blues Document

☐ MEMPHIS JUG BAND VOL.1
DGF 15 / Dec '97 / Frog

☐ MEMPHIS JUG BAND VOL.2
DOCD 5022 / Nov '93 / Document

☐ MEMPHIS JUG BAND VOL.2
DGF 16 / Dec '97 / Frog

☐ MEMPHIS JUG BAND VOL.3
DGF 18 / Jun '98 / Frog

Memphis Minnie

☐ ANTHOLOGY 1929-1944
EN 520 / Sep '95 / Encyclopaedia

☐ HOT STUFF
Hot stuff / I hate to see the sun go down / Memphis minnie-jitis / Frankie / She put me outdoors / I don't want that junk outta you / Biting bug blues / Moonshine / Chicksaw train blues / Down by the riverside / I called you this morning / Man you won't give me no money / Keep on sailing / It's hard to be mistreated / New bumble bee / Me and my chauffeur blues / Good morning / Ice man
CBCD 2 / 1 Jun '98 / Collector's Blues

☐ IN MY GIRLISH DAYS
Down home girl / Night watchman blues / Kid man blues / Broken heart / Lake michigan / Kissing in the dark / World of trouble / Conjur man / Moaning blues / I'm so glad / I'm not a bad gal / Looking the world over / Me and my chaffeur blues / In my girlish days / Boyfriend blues / Nothing in rambling / My baby don't want me no more / Moonshine / Joe louis strut / I'm talking about you / Bumble bee / Friso town
CD 52036 / May '94 / Blues Encore

☐ ME AND MY CHAUFFER 1935-1946
158822 / Feb '97 / Blues Collection

☐ MEMPHIS MINNIE & KANSAS JOE (Memphis Minnie & Kansas Joe)
DOCD 5031 / Nov '93 / Document

☐ QUEEN OF THE BLUES, THE
When the levee breaks / Where is my good man / Joiliet bound / Drunken barrelhouse blues / He's in the ring / Joe Louis strut / New Orleans stop time / Blues everywhere / Please don't stop me / Has anyone seen my man / I'd rather see him dead / Call the fire wagon / Bad outside friends / Lonesome shack / Pig meat on the line / Looking the world over / When you love me / Love come and go / Fashion plate daddy / Killer driller blues
4878452 / 20 Oct '97 / Mojo Filter

☐ QUEEN OF THE BLUES, THE (2CD Set)
Frisco town / Can I do it for you / I never told a lie / Don't want no woman / Memphis Minnie-jitis blues / Plymouth rock blues / Georgia skin blues / New bumble bee blues / Frankie Jean / What's the matter with the mill / Crazy cryin' blues / Today today blues / Soo cow soo / Too late / Drunken barrelhouse blues / Chickasaw train blues / Squat it / Moaning the blues / Weary woman blues / Doctor doctor blues / New Orleans stomp time / I'm a bad luck woman / Caught me wrong again / It's hard to be mistreated / I'd rather see him dead / Black widow stinger / Poor and wandering woman blues / Worried baby blues / Nothing in rambling / Ma Rainey / This is your last chance / I'm not a bad gal / Don't turn the card / Looking the world over / It was you baby / I am sailin'
FA 259 / Nov '97 / Fremeaux

Memphis Nighthawks

☐ MEMPHIS NIGHTHAWKS & THE CHICAGO RHYTHM KINGS, THE (Memphis Nighthawks & Chicago Rhythm Kings)
CYG 1001 / Sep '97 / Frog

Memphis Pilgrims

☐ MECCA
REL 2077 / Aug '96 / Relix

Memphis Roots

☐ GOOD NOISE (The Best Of Western Line Dancing)
Good noise / Elvira / Any way the wind blows / One step forward / Je suis contendre / Tempted / Haunted heart / Land of enchantment / There goes my heart / Gone country / All you ever do is bring me down / Cajun moon / Boys and me / Poor boy blues / Bring it on down to my house
3036000442 / Jun '98 / Carlton

Memphis Slim

☐ 4.00 BLUES
4.00 Blues / Trouble in mind / Worried life blues / Cow cow blues / Lonesome in my bedroom / Diggin' my potatoes / In the evening / Blue and disgusted / Miss Ida Bea / I'll take her to Chicago / Lonesome / Cold blooded woman / One man's mad / Let the good times roll creole / What is the mare rack / Pigalle love / Four walls / It's been too long / Big Bertha / I'm lost without you / I'll just keep on singing the blues / True love
GRF 059 / '93 / Tring

☐ ALL KINDS OF BLUES
Blues is trouble / Grinder man blues / Three in one boogie / Letter home / Churnin' man blues / Two of a kind / Blacks / If you see Kay / Frankie and Johnny Boogie / Mother earth
OBCCD 507 / Nov '92 / Original Blues Classics

☐ ALONE WITH MY FRIENDS
Highway 51 blues / I feel so good / Rock me Momma / Goin' down slow / Sittin' on top of the world / Sunnyland train / Goin' down to the river / I just want to make love to you / I can hear my name a-ringin' / Going back to my plow
OBCCD 581 / Oct '96 / Original Blues Classics

☐ AUX TROIS MAILLETZ (Memphis Slim & Willie Dixon)
Rock 'n' rolling the house / Baby please come home / How make you do me like you do / Way she loves a man / New way to love / African hunch with a boogie beat / Shame / Pretty girls / Baby baby baby / Do de do / Cold blooded / Just you and I / Pigalle love / All by myself
5197292 / Mar '94 / Verve

☐ BABY PLEASE COME HOME (Memphis Slim & Willie Dixon In Paris) (Memphis Slim & Willie Dixon)
Rock 'n' rolling the house / Baby please come home / How come you do me like you do / Way she loves a man / New way to love / African hunch with a boogie beat / Shame pretty girls / Baby baby baby / Do de do / Cool blooded / Just you and I / Pigalle love / All by myself
OBCCD 582 / Oct '96 / Original Blues Classics

☐ BLUE THIS EVENING
BLCD 760155 / '91 / Black Lion

☐ BLUEBIRD RECORDINGS 1940-1941, THE
Beer drinkin' woman / You didn't mean me no good / Grinder man blues / Empty room blues / Shelby County blues / I see my great mistake / Old Taylor / I believe I'll settle down / Jasper's gal / You got to help me some / Two of a kind / Whiskey store blues / Maybe I'll loan you a dime / Me, myself and I / Whiskey and gin blues / You gonna worry too / This life I'm livin' / Caught the old coon at last / Don't think that you're smart / Lend me your love
07863667202 / Feb '97 / Bluebird

☐ BROKEN SOUL BLUES
BGOCD 373 / 12 Jan '98 / Beat Goes On

☐ COMPLETE RECORDINGS 1940-1941, THE
158032 / Jun '93 / Blues Collection

☐ DIALOGUE IN BOOGIE (Memphis Slim & Philippe Lejeune)
Rockin' / EEC boogie / C'est normal, c'est normand / Jefferson county blues / Fourth and beale / This is the way I feel / Three, two, one boogie / Midnite tempo / Cooky boogie / C and L boogie
157112 / Feb '93 / Blues Collection

☐ I AM THE BLUES
CDSGP 080 / Jan '95 / Prestige

☐ LIFE IS LIKE THAT
Life is like that / Nobody loves me / Sometimes I feel like a Motherless child / Pacemaker boogie / Harlem bound / Darling / I miss you so / Lend me your love / Cheatin' around / Letter home / Now I got the blues / Grinder man blues / Don't ration my love / Slim's boogie / Little Mary / Mistake in life / Messin' around with the blues / Midnight jump
CDCHARLY 249 / Oct '90 / Charly

☐ LIVE AT THE CAVEAU DE LA HUCHETTE (Paris 1977)
Rockin' the house / Misery / Mean old Frisco / Baby please come home / What is the blues / Didn't we baby / Animal in me / Boogie woogie / Big fat mama / Too late now / I'm lost without you / May be wrong / Little lonely girl / New York getaway / All by myself / Christina / You won't let me go / Every day / Come back / Wish me well / Headed for Nashville / Rack em' back Jack / Yackety yack / Three and one boogie / Shake rattle and roll / Something in your mind / My babe / Next time you see me / Bye bye blues
17151 / Sep '97 / Laserlight

☐ MEMPHIS HEAT (Memphis Slim & Canned Heat)
Back to Mother Earth / Trouble everywhere I go / Black cat cross my trail / Mr. Longfingers / Five long years / When I was young / You don't know my mind / Boogie duo / Down the big road / Whizzle wham / Paris
5197252 / Feb '94 / Verve

☐ MEMPHIS SLIM
DVBC 9082 / May '95 / Deja Vu

☐ MEMPHIS SLIM USA
Born with the blues / Just let it be me / Red haired boogie / Blue and disgusted / New key to the highway / I'd take her to Chicago / Harlem bound / El capitan / I just landed in your town / John Henry / I believe I'll settle down / Bad luck and trouble / Late afternoon blues / Memphis Slim USA
CCD 79024 / Feb '97 / Candid

☐ MOTHER EARTH
OW 30007 / Jul '94 / One Way

☐ RAINING THE BLUES
Beer drinking woman / Teasing the blues / IC Blues / Baby doll / Just blues / Blue and disgusted / Blue brew / Rack 'em back Jack / Motherless child / Brenda / When your dough roller is gone / Hey slim / Darling I miss you so / Lonesome traveller / No strain / Don't think you're smart / Raining the blues / You're gonna need my help one day / Angel child / Fast and free / My baby left me / Lucille / Nice stuff
CDCH 485 / Nov '93 / Ace

☐ REAL FOLK BLUES
My baby / Trouble trouble / Slim's blues / Tiajuana / I guess I'm a fool / Really got the blues / Feeling low / For a day / Mother Earth / Blues for my baby / What is the mare rack / Having fun
MCD 09270 / Apr '97 / Chess/MCA

☐ ROCKIN' THE BLUES
Gotta find my baby / Come back / Messin' around / Sassy Mae / Lend me your love / Guitar cha cha / Stroll on little girl / Rockin' the house / Wish me well / Blue and lonesome / My gal keeps me crying / Slim's blues / Steppin' out / Mother Earth / What's the matter / This time I'm through
CDBM 21 / Apr '92 / Charly

☐ STEADY ROLLIN' BLUES
Mean mistreatin' mama / Soon one morning / Steady rolling blues / Celeste's boogie / Big legged woman / Rock me baby / Goin' down slow / Sweet root man / Mr. freddie boogie / Three woman blues
OBCCD 523 / Nov '92 / Original Blues Classics

☐ TRAVELLING WITH THE BLUES
Memphis boogie / St. Louis blues / Santa Fe blues / Chicago new home of the blues / Chicago house / Rent party blues / Arkansas road house blues / Midnight jump / Goodbye blues / Reminiscin' with the blues / Good rockin' blues / Blues confession / Boogie woogie / Blues made up / Worries all the time
STCD 8021 / Mar '95 / Storyville

☐ TRIBUTE TO BIG BILL BROONZY
I feel so good / Rockin' chair blues / Baby gone / Cow cow blues / Miss Ida B / Forty-four blues / Trouble in my mind / Worried life blues / Don't want my rooster crowin' after the sun goes down / Lonesome in my bedroom / Diggin' my potatoes / In the evening
CCD 79023 / Feb '97 / Candid

Memphis Willie B

☐ HARD WORKING MAN BLUES
OBCCD 578 / Jan '96 / Original Blues Classics

MEN

☐ I FEEL
CDRPM 0011 / Mar '97 / RP Media

☐ I FEEL
I feel / Thrills of my life / Have I done enough to be trusted / You will never know / You got to be positive / He said... / I'm really sorry / Your market value
MENCD 3 / 8 Dec '97 / MEN

Men At Large

☐ ONE SIZE FITS ALL
Let's talk about it / Holiday / Don't cry / First day / Funny feeling / Do ya / Will you marry me / I wanna roll / Good things don't last / Better off by myself / I'm in a freaky mood / Feet wet
7567924592 / 5 Jan '98 / Atlantic

Men At Work

☐ BUSINESS AS USUAL
Who can it be now / I can see it in your eyes / Down under / Underground / Helpless automaton / People just love to play with words / Be good Johnny / Touching the untouchables / Catch a star / Down by the sea
4508872 / Apr '94 / Epic

☐ CARGO
Dr. Heckyll and Mr. Jive / Overkill / Settle down my boy / Upstairs in my house / No sign of yesterday / It's a mistake / Highwire / Blue for you / I like to / No restrictions
4746832 / Feb '97 / Columbia

☐ CARGO/BUSINESS AS USUAL (2CD Set)
Dr. Heckyll and Mr. Jive / Settle down my boy / Upstairs in my house / No sign of yesterday / It's a mistake / Highwire / Blue for you / I like to / No restrictions / Who can it be now / I can see it in your eyes / Down under / Underground / Helpless automaton / People just love to play with words / Be good Johnny / Touching the untouchables / Catch a star / Down by the sea
4610232 / Jul '92 / Columbia

☐ CONTRABAND (The Best Of Men At Work)
Who can it be now / It's a mistake / Hard luck story / Still life / Underground / Upstairs in my house / I live to / High wire / Maria / Be good Johnny / Dr. Jheckyll and Mr. Jive / Overkill / Man with two hearts / Snakes and ladders / Down by the sea
4840112 / Jul '96 / Columbia

☐ DEFINITIVE COLLECTION, THE
Down under / Who can it be now / I can see it in your eyes / Down by the sea / Be good Johnny / People just love to play with words / Underground / Touching the untouchables / Catch a star / Overkill / It's a mistake / Dr. Heckyll and Mr. Jive / Upstairs in my house / No sign of yesterday / Blue for you / Everything I need / Man with two hearts / Children on parade / Snakes and ladders
4875622 / 20 Jul '98 / Columbia

Men They Couldn't Hang

☐ BIG SIX PACK, THE
VEXCD 15 / Jun '97 / Demon

☐ FIVE GLORIOUS YEARS
ORECD 509 / Nov '89 / Silvertone

☐ HOW GREEN IS THE VALLEY
Gold strike / Ghosts of Cable Street / Bells / Shirt of blue / Tiny soldiers / Parted from you / Gold rush / Dancing on the pier / Going back to Coventry / Rabid underdog / Parade
MCLD 19075 / Nov '92 / MCA

☐ MAJESTIC GRILL (The Best Of The Men They Couldn't Hang)
Ironmasters / Ghosts of cable street / Shirt of blue / Scarlet ribbons / Crest / Colours / Island in the rain / Rosettas / Dog's eyes owl meat and man chop / Map of Morocco / Dennis Law and Ali McGraw / Australia / Eye / Our day / Nightbird / Green fields of France
FIENCD 940 / 2 Mar '98 / Demon

☐ NEVER BORN TO FOLLOW
FIENDCD 788 / Oct '96 / Demon

☐ NIGHT OF A THOUSAND CANDLES
Day after / Jack Dandy / Night to remember / Johnny come home / Green fields of France / Iron masters / Hush little baby / Walkin' talkin' / Kingdom come / Scarlet ribbons
DIAB 839 / 24 Nov '97 / Diablo

☐ WELL HUNG
Crest / Crest / You're the one / Home fires / Going back to coventry / Colours / Ironmasters / Lobotomy, gets 'em home / Man in the corner shop / Australia / Night to remember / Scarlet ribbons (for her hair)
CDAFTER 10 / Mar '91 / Fun After All

Menace

☐ GLC - RIP
GLC / Insane society / Screwed up / I need nothing / Electrcutioner / Young ones / Live for today / Tomorrow's world / Carry no banners / I'm civilised / Last year's youth
AHOYCD 017 / 3 Nov '97 / Captain Oi

Menace To Society

☐ PURE AND UNCUT
TX 51234CD / Oct '96 / Triple X

Menano, Antonio

☐ ARQUIVOS DO FADO
HTCD 31 / Jun '95 / Heritage

Menard, D.L.

☐ SWALLOW RECORDINGS, THE (Menard, D.L. & Austin Pitre)
Louisiana aces special: *Badeaux & The Louisiana Aces* / Back door: *Badeaux & The Louisiana Aces* / I can't forget you: *Badeaux & The Louisiana Aces* / She didn't know I was married: *Badeaux & The Louisiana Aces* / Bachelor's life: *Badeaux & The Louisiana Aces* / Valse de Jolly Rodgers: *Badeaux & The Louisiana Aces* / Miller's cave: *Menard, D.L.* / Water pump: *Menard, D.L.* / It's too late you're divorced: *Menard, D.L.* / Riches of a musician: *Menard, D.L.* / Vail and the crown: *Menard, D.L.* / I can live a better life: *Badeaux & The Louisiana Aces* / Rebecca Ann: *Badeaux & The Louisiana Aces* / Two step de bayou teche: *Pitre, Austin* / Opelousas waltz: *Pitre, Austin* / Two step a tante adele: *Pitre, Austin* / Rainbow waltz: *Pitre, Austin* / Rene's special: *Pitre, Austin* / Grand mamou blues: *Pitre, Austin* / Flumes d'enfer: *Pitre, Austin* / Chinaball blues: *Pitre, Austin* / Le pauvre hobo: *Pitre, Austin* / Pretty rosie cheeks: *Pitre, Austin* / Don't shake my tree: *Pitre, Austin* / La valse d'amour: *Pitre, Austin* / Jungle club waltz: *Pitre, Austin* / J'ai coiner a ta porte: *Pitre, Austin* / Chataigner waltz: *Pitre, Austin*
CDCHD 327 / Jul '91 / Ace

Menche, Daniel

☐ VENT
ORHOLD 5 / 6 Jul '98 / Touch

Menck, Ric

☐ BALLAD OF RIC MENCK, THE
SHINEUS 16 / 24 Nov '97 / Summershine

Mendelssohn, Felix

☐ FELIX MENDELSSOHN & HIS HAWAIIAN SERENADERS 1940-1945 (Mendelssohn, Felix & His Hawaiian Serenaders)
HQCD 93 / Apr '97 / Harlequin

Mendes Brothers

☐ TORRI DI CONTROL
3001801 / 24 Feb '98 / IMP

Mendes, Jose

☐ SELECAO DE OURO 20 SUCESSOS
3304725072 / 14 Apr '98 / Copacabana

Mendes, Sergio

☐ BRASILEIRO
Fanfarra / Magalenha / Indiado / What is this / Lua soberana / Sambadouro / Senhoras do amazonas / Kalimba / Barabare / Esconjuros / Pipoca / Magano / Chorado
7559613152 / May '92 / Elektra

☐ DANCE MODERNO
P 630991CD / Apr '97 / Rare Brazil

☐ OCEANO
Rio De Janeiro / Trilhos urbanos / Holografico olodu / Anos dourados / Madalena / Puzzle of hearts / Capivara / Anjo de mim / Vale da ribeira / Maracatudo / Los aveux / Un oceano silenzi
5328022 / Oct '96 / Verve

☐ VERY BEST OF SERGIO MENDES & BRASIL '66, THE (2CD Set) (Mendes, Sergio & Brasil '66)
Mas que nada / So many stars / Viola / With a little help from my friends / Wichita lineman / Batacuda / Dois dias / Easy to be hard / Roda / Some time ago / Masquerade / Fool on the hill / You stepped out of a dream / Moanin' / Salt sea / For me / Stillness / Cinnamon and clove / Going out of my head / Look who's mine / Like a lover / Ye-me-le / Day tripper / Viramundo / Wave / What the world needs now / For what it's worth / Where are you coming from / Chelsea morning / Lost in paradise / Joker / Night and day / Scarborough Fair/Canticle / Tim-Dom-Dom / Pretty world / Righteous life / Look of love / One note samba / Agua de beber / Cancao do nosso amor / Empty faces / Triste / Norwegian wood / Bim-Bom / So danco samba / Sometimes in winter / Constant rain / Pradizer Adeus
5407522 / 18 May '98 / A&M

Mendoza Line

☐ LIKE SOMEONE IN LOVE
KC 020CD / 20 Jul '98 / Kindercore

Mendoza, Celeste

☐ LA REINA DEL GUAGUANCO
Papa ogun / Estas acabando / Recordare / Mi rumba echando candela / Yo le llamo vivir / A ti na ma / Que me castigue dios / Muere la luz / Carinto ven / Lo que vale mi querer / Si yo fuera / En la cumbre
PSCCD 1009 / Feb '95 / Pure Sounds From Cuba

Mendoza, Lydia

☐ FIRST QUEEN OF TEJANO MUSIC
ARHCD 392 / Apr '96 / Arhoolie

☐ LA GLORIA DE TEXAS
ARHCD 3012 / Apr '95 / Arhoolie

Mendoza, Victor

☐ IF ONLY YOU KNEW
Para gozar un poquito / If only you knew / Siempre caliente / Terri by the sea / Snow samba / At the tortilla factory / Cancao da noite / Santa Fe
CDLR 45019 / Nov '90 / L&R

Mendoza, Vince

☐ JAZZ PANA (Mendoza, Vince & Arif Mardin)
El vito cante / Tangos / Entre tinieblas / Tanguillo / Soy gitano / Buleria / Suite fraternidad / El vito en gran tamano
92122 / Apr '94 / Act

☐ SKETCHES
Pavanne (pour une infante defunte) / Sketches (part 1) / Sketches (part 2) / Sketches (part 3) / Sketches (part 4) / Sketches (part 5) / Sketches (part 6) / Sketches (part 7) / Sketches (part 8)
892152 / Jul '94 / Act

Menezes, Margareth

☐ LUZ DOURADA
Vou mandar / Black show / Luz dourada / Vai mexer / Novos rumos / Mar de amor / Raca negra / Desabalada / Club de brown benjor / Ate rir o mar / Olho do farol / Chegar a Bahia
5195372 / Jan '94 / Verve

Mengelberg, Misha

☐ DUTCH MASTERS (Mengelberg, Misha/Steve Lacy/George Lewis)
1211542 / Mar '92 / Soul Note

☐ MISHA MENGELBERG (Live At Angelica)
AI 010 / Jun '98 / ReR/Recommended

☐ NO IDEA
DIW 619 / Sep '97 / DIW

☐ ROOT OF THE PROBLEM, THE
HATOLOGY 504 / Nov '97 / Hatology

☐ WHO'S BRIDGE
DIW 036 / May '95 / DIW

Mengo, Jerry

☐ BIG BAND CLASSICS VOL.3 (Mengo, Jerry & Attilio Donadio)
ISCD 170 / May '98 / Intersound

Mengual, David

☐ TRIBUTE TO THELONIOUS MONK, A (Mengual, David Monkiana)
FSNT 019 / Jan '98 / Fresh Sound New Talent

Menhaden Countrymen

☐ WON'T YOU HELP ME TO RAISE 'EM
GV 220CD / Nov '93 / Global Village

Menis

☐ TEMPORARY INSANITY
KRCD 005 / 16 Feb '98 / Koyote

Menke, Frl.

☐ HOHE BERGE
BCD 16252 / May '98 / Bear Family

Men's Recovery Project

☐ GOLDEN TRIUMPH OF NAKED HOSTILITY
VMFM 40CD / 16 Mar '98 / Vermiform

Menswear

☐ NUISANCE
125 West 3rd Street / I'll manage somehow / Sleeping in / Little Miss Pin Point Eyes / Daydreamer / Hollywood girl / Being brave / Around you again / One / Stardust / Piece of me / Stardust (Reprise)
8286762 / Mar '96 / Laurel

Mental Crypt

☐ EXTREME UNCTION
BMCD 134 / 16 Feb '98 / Black Mark

Mental Hippie Blood

☐ MENTAL HIPPIE BLOOD
SPV 08476752 / Oct '94 / SPV

Mental Overdrive

☐ PLUGGED
LDO 001CD / Sep '96 / Love OD Communications

Mentallo

☐ BURNT BEYOND RECOGNITION (Mentallo & The Fixer)
SPV 08543582 / 1 Jun '98 / SPV

Mentallo & The Fixer

☐ WHERE ANGELS FEAR TO TREAD
CDZOT 108 / Mar '94 / Zoth Ommog

Mentally Damaged

☐ PUNK GRUNK
SPV 08456802 / Oct '94 / Wolverine

Mentaur

☐ DARKNESS BEFORE DAWN
CYCL 033 / Jan '97 / Cyclops

Menuhin, Yehudi

☐ MENUHIN & GRAPPELLI PLAY BERLIN/KERN/PORTER (Menuhin, Yehudi & Stephane Grappelli)
Cheek to cheek / Isn't this a lovely day (to be caught in the rain) / Piccolino / Change partners / Top hat, white tie and tails / I've got my love to keep me warm / Heatwave / Way you look tonight / Pick yourself up / Fine romance / All the things you are / Why do I love you / I get a kick out of you / Night and day / Looking at you / Just one of those things / My funny valentine / Thou swell / Lady is a tramp / Blue room
CDM 769 219 2 / Feb '88 / EMI

☐ MENUHIN AND GRAPPELLI PLAY 'JEALOUSY' (& Other Great Standards) (Menuhin, Yehudi & Stephane Grappelli)
Jealousy / Tea for two / Limehouse blues / These foolish things / Continental / Nightingale sang in Berkeley Square / Sweet Sue, just you / Skylark / Laura / Sweet Georgia Brown / I'll remember April / April in Paris / Things we did last summer / September in the rain / Autumn leaves / Autumn in New York / Button up your overcoat
CDM 769 220 2 / Mar '88 / EMI

☐ MENUHIN AND GRAPPELLI PLAY GERSHWIN (Menuhin, Yehudi & Stephane Grappelli)
Fascinating rhythm / Summertime / Nice work if you can get it / Foggy day / 'S wonderful / Man I love / I got rhythm / They all laughed / Funny face / Oh lady be good
CDM 769 218 2 / Mar '88 / Angel

☐ STRICTLY FOR THE BIRDS (Menuhin, Yehudi & Stephane Grappelli)
Nightingale sang in Berkeley Square / Lullaby of Birdland / When the red, red robin comes bob, bob, bobbin' along / Skylark / Bye bye blackbird / Coucou / Flamingo / Dinah / Rosetta / Sweet Sue, just you / Once in love with Amy / Laura / La route du roi / Sweet Georgia Brown
CDCFP 4549 / Sep '97 / Classics For Pleasure

Menzies, Ian

☐ GREAT BRITISH TRADITIONAL JAZZBANDS VOL.9 (Menzies, Ian & His Clyde Valley Stompers)
Roses of picardy / Beale St. Blues / Gettysburg march / Swinging seamus / Ace in the hole / Sailing down chesapeake bay / In a Persian market / There'll be a hot time in the old town tonight / Mack the knife / World is waiting for the sunrise / Scotland the brave / Salty dog / Fish man / Royal garden blues / Irish black bottom / Yellow dog blues / Just a closer walk with thee / Tres moutarde
LACD 79 / Apr '97 / Lake

Meow

☐ GOALIE FOR THE OTHER TEAM
OUT 1202 / Sep '97 / Brake Out

Mephisto

☐ SUBTERRANEAN SOUND, THE
SSR 162CD / Feb '96 / SSR

Mephisto Waltz

☐ CROCOSMIA
EFA 15564 / Apr '93 / Gymnastic

☐ ETERNAL DEEP, THE
CLEO 63082 / Apr '94 / Cleopatra

☐ TERROR REGINA
CLEO 92592 / Mar '94 / Cleopatra

Mephistopheles

☐ LANSCAPE SYMPHONIES
CDAR 040 / 8 Dec '97 / Adipocre

Mera

☐ HUNGARIAN FOLK MUSIC FROM TRANSYLVANIA
SYN 188 / Nov '95 / Syncoop

Merauder

☐ MASTER KILLER
CM 77104CD / Nov '95 / Century Media

Mercer, Johnny

☐ MORE OF THE BEST
I'm an old cowhand / Jawa jive / Jamboree Jones / Fare thee well to Harlem: *Mercer, Johnny & Jack Teagarden* / Accentuate the positive / Conversation while dancing: *Mercer, Johnny & Jo Stafford* / Steamboat Bill / GI jive / Small fry: *Mercer, Johnny & Bing Crosby* / Goody goody / One for my baby (and one for the road) / It's great to be alive: *Mercer, Johnny & Jo Stafford*
12628 / Apr '98 / Laserlight

☐ MY HUCKLEBERRY FRIEND
DRGCD 5244 / May '96 / DRG

☐ PARDON MY SOUTHERN ACCENT
Watch a darkie dance / You took advantage of me / Dr. heckle and mr. jibe / Fare-thee-well to harlem / Christmas night in harlem / Pardon my southern accent / Here come the british / Lord I give you all my children / Bathtub ran over again / I've got a note / Eeny meeny miney mo / I'm building up to an awful let down / Murder of j b markham / Last night on the back porch / Bob white / Jamboree jones / Small fry / Mr. gallagher and mr. shean / Cuckoo in the clock / Sent for you yesterday and here you come today / Show your linen, miss richardson / Mister meadowlark
CDHD 203 / Aug '93 / Happy Days

☐ SONGWRITER SERIES VOL.3 (Old Music Master) (Various Artists)
PASTCD 7094 / Jun '96 / Flapper

☐ STARS SALUTE JOHNNY MERCER, THE (Tribute To A Songwriting Legend) (Various Artists)
That old black magic: *Eckstine, Billy* / Goody, goody: *Goodman, Benny Orchestra* / Day in, day out: *McRae, Carmen* / GI jive: *Jordan, Louis & His Tympany Five* / Trav'lin light: *Holiday, Billie* / Jeepers creepers: *Bennett, Tony & Count Basie* / Arthur Murray taught me dancing in a hurry: *Dorsey, Jimmy Orchestra* / Laura: *Sinatra, Frank* / Dearly beloved: *Richards, Ann* / Lazy bones: *Carmichael, Hoagy* / Accentuate the positive: *Mercer, Johnny* / Cuckoo in the clock: *Horne, Lena* / Blues in the night: *Herman, Woody Orchestra* / Bernadine: *Boone, Pat* / Out of this world: *Connor, Chris* / Fools rush in: *Miller, Glenn Orchestra* / Skylark: *O'Day, Anita* / I'm an old cowhand: *Crosby, Bing* / Dream: *Washington, Dinah* / Moon river: *Butler, Jerry*
305842 / Oct '96 / Hallmark

☐ SWEET GEORGIA BROWN
By the river sainte marie / Sugar / Sweet georgia brown / When the bloom is on the sage / Margie / Sweet lorraine / Someday sweetheart / Back home again in indiana / I can't get the one I want / Lulu's back in town / Gee baby, ain't I good to you / Button up your overcoat / I never knew / Louisville lou / Love is just around the corner / Crazy rhythm
HCD 152 / Nov '95 / Hindsight

☐ TOO MARVELLOUS FOR WORDS (The Songs Of Johnny Mercer) (Various Artists)
Too marvelous for words: *Crosby, Bing & Jimmy Dorsey Orchestra* / Out of breath and scared to death of you: *Arden, Victor & Phil Ohman Orchestra* / Lazybones: *Mills Brothers* / I'm an old cowhand: *Crosby, Bing & Jimmy Dorsey Orchestra* / Jeepers creepers: *Mills Brothers* / You must have been a beautiful baby: *Crosby, Bing & Bob Crosby Orchestra* / And the angels sing: *Goodman, Benny Orchestra & Martha Tilton* / Fools rush in: *Sinatra, Frank & Tommy Dorsey Orchestra* / Mister Meadowlark: *Crosby, Bing & Johnny Mercer/Victor Young Orchestra* / Waiter and the porter and the upstairs maid: *Martin, Mary & Bing Crosby/Jack Teagarden Orchestra* / This time the dream's on me: *Miller, Glenn Orchestra* / Tangerine: *Dorsey, Jimmy Orchestra* / Blues in the night: *Shore, Dinah & Leonad Joy/RCA Victor Orchestra* / That old black magic: *Miller, Glenn Orchestra & Skip Nelson/The Modernaires* / Skylark: *Shore, Dinah & Rosario Bourdon/RCA Victor Orchestra* / I'm old fashioned: *Astaire, Fred & John Scott Trotter Orchestra* / Old music master: *Mercer, Johnny & Jack Teagarden/Paul Whiteman Orchestra* / Dearly beloved: *Astaire, Fred & John Scott Trotter Orchestra* / One for my baby and one more for the road: *Horne, Lena & Horace Henderson Orchestra* / Accentuate the positive: *Crosby, Bing and Andrews Sisters/Vic Schoen Orchestra* / Laura: *Haymes, Dick & Victor Young Orchestra* / On the Atchison Topeka and the Santa Fe: *Garland, Judy & Lennie Hayton Orchestra* / Come rain or come shine: *Haymes, Dick & Helen Forrest/Victor Young Orchestra* / Hit the road to dreamland: *Whiting, Margaret & Freddie Slack Orchestra*
CDAJA 5230 / Sep '97 / Living Era

☐ TOO MARVELLOUS FOR WORDS (The Johnny Mercer Songbook) (Various Artists)
I remember you: *Parker, Charlie* / Out of this world: *Mulligan, Gerry Concert Jazz Band* / Too marvellous for words: *Young, Lester* / Come rain or come shine: *Evans, Bill* / Mandy is two: *Getz, Stan* / Jeepers creepers: *Carter, Benny* / Satin doll: *Hodges, Johnny* / That old black magic: *Garner, Erroll* / Tangerine: *Hawkins, Coleman & Ben Webster* / Charade: *Jones, Quincy* / Laura: *Byas, Don* / I'm old fashioned: *Peterson, Oscar* / Skylark: *Motian, Paul* / Day in day out: *Gibbs, Terry Big Band* / When the world was young: *Getz, Stan* / Days of wine and roses: *Henderson, Joe*
5571402 / 26 May '98 / Verve

☐ TRAV'LIN' LIGHT (The Johnny Mercer Songbook) (Various Artists)
5554022 / 9 Feb '98 / Verve

Merceron, Mariano

☐ YO TENGO UN TUMBAO 1940-1946
TCD 064 / Jul '96 / Tumbao Cuban Classics

Mercey, Larry

☐ FULL SPEED AHEAD
Full speed ahead / You always come through for me / She feels like a new man tonight / You'll find me where you are / True blue / There's gotta be a better way than this / When's momma comin' home / Hold that thought / If I could live my love over / You're still in these crazy arms of mine
322544 / Jul '91 / Koch

Merchant

☐ EARLY YEARS
JW 1016CD / Oct '96 / JW

Merchant, Natalie

☐ OPHELIA
Ophelia / Life is sweet / Kind and generous / Frozen Charlotte / My skin / Break your heart / King of May / Thick as thieves / Effigy / Living / When they ring them golden bells
7559621962 / 1 Jun '98 / Elektra

☐ TIGERLILY
Carnival / Letter / River / Seven years / Where I go / Jealousy / Cowboy romance / I may know the word / San andreas fault / Wonder / Beloved wife
7559617452 / Jun '95 / Elektra

Merciless

☐ TREASURES WITHIN, THE
Treasures within / Mind possession / Darkened clouds / Book of lies / Perish / Shadows of fire / Lifeflame / Act of horror / Branded by sunlight
CDATV 26 / Jun '92 / Active

☐ UNBOUND
NFR 007 / Oct '94 / No Fashion

Merciless

☐ LEN OUT MI MERCY
ANXCD 1 / Jun '95 / Annex

Mercouri, Melina

☐ MELINA MERCOURI
ML 0031 / 11 May '98 / Musurgia Graeca

Mercury Rev

☐ BOCES
Meth of a rockette's kick / Meth of a rockette's kick / Bronx cheer / Boys peel out / Downs are feminine balloons / Something for joey / Snorry mouth / Hi-speed boats / Continuous drunks and blunders / Girlfren
BBQCD 140 / May '93 / Beggars Banquet

☐ YERSELF IS STEAM/LEGO IS MY EGO
BBQCD 125 / Nov '92 / Beggars Banquet

Mercury Rising

☐ BUILDING ROME
Cathedrals / Building Rome / Occurence of tomorrow / Narrow door / Lesser of men / Renaissance / Think
N 02922 / 20 Apr '98 / Noise

☐ UPON DEAF EARS
Upon deaf ears / Light to grow / Halfway to forever / Minute man / Zeros and ones / It's war / Prayer / Where fear ends
N 02782 / Feb '97 / Noise

Mercury, Freddie

☐ BARCELONA (Mercury, Freddie & Montserrat Caballe)
Barcelona / Fallen priest / Golden boy / Guide me home / Overture piccante / La japonaise / Ensueno / Guid me home / How can I go on
8372772 / Oct '88 / Polydor

☐ MAN FROM MANHATTAN, THE (Mercury, Freddie & Brian May & Eddie Howell)
Man from manhattan (original) / Man from manhattan (original) / Drink her away / Man from manhattan (revisited)
BUD 002CD / Feb '95 / Voiceprint

Mercyful Fate

☐ BEGINNING, THE
Doomed by the living dead / Corpse without soul / Nuns have no fun / Devil eyes / Curse of the pharoahs / Evil / Satan's fall / Black masses
RR 87712 / 10 Nov '97 / Roadrunner

☐ BELLWITCH
398417027CD / Feb '97 / Metal Blade

☐ DEAD AGAIN
398414159CD / 15 Jun '98 / Metal Blade

☐ DON'T BREAK THE OATH
Dangerous meeting / Nightmare / Desecration of souls / Night of the unborn / Oath / Gypsy / Welcome princess of hell / To one far away / Come to the Sabbath
RR 87692 / 10 Nov '97 / Roadrunner

☐ MELISSA
Evil / Curse of the pharoahs / Into the coven / Sound of the demon bell / Black funeral / Satan's fall / Melissa
RR 87702 / 10 Nov '97 / Roadrunner

☐ RETURN OF THE VAMPIRE
Burning the cross / Curse of the pharaos / Return of the vampire / On a night of full moon / A corpse without soul / Death kiss / Leave my soul alone / M.d.a. / You asked for it
RR 91842 / May '92 / Roadrunner

☐ TIME
398417028CD / Feb '97 / Metal Blade

Mercyless

☐ COLOURED FUNERAL
CM 770542 / Nov '93 / Century Media

Merdy Girl

☐ TWIST HER
NL 13CD / Oct '96 / No Life

Mere Dead Men

☐ STACKS STILETTOS MAKE UP AND MOHICANS
HSI 010CD / 8 Jun '98 / High Society

Meridian

☐ SUNDOWN EMPIRE
Descent into solitude / Dreams unveiled / Call / This masquerade / Hiding / Surreal embrace / Athanasia / Revelations in black / Wail in weep / Messiah / Children / Gatekeeper
CDMFN 210 / Dec '96 / Music For Nations

Meridian Arts Ensemble

☐ EAR MIND I
Lumpy gravy / Marqueson's chicken / King kong / Pygmy twylyte / Jungry freaks daddy / Black page / Sanctity / Moo shu wrap rap / Fanfare for nothing / Sleepless / MAE we strut / Crunch / Brass quintet / Dr J. Geyser / Lullaby / Skunk funk
CCS 11898 / 1 Sep '98 / Channel Classics

☐ PRIME MERIDIAN
CCS 8195 / 3 Aug '98 / Channel Classics

☐ TAXIN/BARBER/RADZYNSKI/ SAMPSON/ROBLES
CCS 9496 / Jul '96 / Channel Classics

Merino Brothers

☐ VALLENTINO DYNAMOS
De mi vida una ilusion / Acompaname a sufrir / Mal procedimiento / La democracia / Riquezas de la vida / Minutos felices / Ese soy yo / Maria Elena / Noches de desvelos / Mi padre el campesino
CDORB 049 / Nov '89 / Globestyle

Merkin

☐ MUSIC FROM MERKIN MANOR
GF 109 / 9 Feb '98 / Gear Fab

Merlino, Benito

☐ SONGS OF SICILY AND THE AEOLIAN ISLANDS
926862 / Jan '98 / BUDA

Merlons Of Nehemiah

☐ CANTONEY
EFA 113952 / Jan '94 / Musical Tragedies

☐ ROMANOIR
EFA 122222 / Apr '95 / Musical Tragedies

Merman, Ethel

☐ AMERICAN LEGENDS
I get a kick out of you / Heatwave / Make it another old fashioned, please / Blow, Gabriel, blow / But not for me / You're the top / Hot and happy / Down in the depths on the ninetieth floor / It's delovely / I'll pay the check / Marching along with time / Friendship / You're the top
12741 / May '97 / Laserlight

☐ I GET A KICK OUT OF YOU
You're the top / It's de-lovely / Hey good lookin' / Ridin' high / Red hot and blue / Eadie was a lady / I get a kick out of you / How deep is the ocean / Satan's little lamb / An earful of music / Lady in red / You're a builder upper / I gotta right to sing the blues / It's the animal in me / A lady needs a chance / Down in the depths / My mother would love you / Let's be buddies / I've still got my health / Make it another old-fashioned please / I'll follow you / Something for the boys
PASTCD 7056 / Jan '95 / Flapper

☐ LEGENDARY SONG STYLIST
MACCD 361 / 26 Jan '98 / Autograph

Mermen

☐ GLORIOUS LETHAL EUPHORIA, A
7567926342 / Mar '96 / Warner Bros.

Merricks

☐ IN SCHWIERIGKEITEN
EFA 155462 / Apr '95 / Sub Up

☐ SOUND OF MUNICH, THE
EFA 155502 / Jun '97 / Sub Up

Merrill, Helen

☐ BLOSSOM OF STARS
My romance / Willow weep for me / What is this thing called love / Autumn leaves / You'd be so nice to come home to / All of you / Misty Summertime / In a mellow tone / Quand tu dors pres de moi / 'S wonderful / We are not alone
5146522 / Feb '94 / EmArCy

☐ BROWNIE
5223632 / Dec '94 / Verve

☐ CLEAR OUT OF THIS WORLD
Out of this world / Not like this / I'm all smiles / When I grow too old to dream / Some of these days / Maybe / Tender thing is love / Soon it's gonna rain / Willow weep for me
5106912 / Jun '92 / EmArCy

☐ COLLABORATION (Merrill, Helen & Gil Evans)
Summertime / Where flamingoes fly / Dream of you / I'm a fool to want you / Troubled waters / I'm just a lucky so and so / People will say we're in love / By myself / Any place I hang my hat is home / I've never seen / He was too good to me / New town is a blue town
8342052 / Apr '93 / EmArCy

☐ DREAM OF YOU
People will say we're in love / By myself / Any place I hang my hat is home / I've never seen / He was too good to me / New town is a blue town / You're lucky to me / Where flamingos fly / Dream of you / I'm a fool to want you / I'm just a lucky so and so / Troubled waters / Alone together / Glad to be unhappy / This is my night to cry / How's the world treating you
5140742 / Feb '93 / EmArCy

☐ HELEN MERRILL WITH CLIFFORD BROWN/GIL EVANS (Merrill, Helen & Clifford Brown/Gil Evans)
Don't expain / You'd be so nice to come home to / What's new / Falling in love with love / Yesterdays / Born to be blue / 'S wonderful / He was too good to me / I've never seen / I'm a fool to want you / Troubled waters / By myself / People will say we're in love / You're lucky to me / Dream of you
8382922 / Jan '93 / EmArCy

☐ JUST FRIENDS (Merrill, Helen & Stan Getz)
Cavatina / It never entered my mind / Just friends / It don't mean a thing if it ain't got that swing / Baby ain't I good to you / It's not easy being green / If you go away / Yesterdays / Music maker
8420072 / Apr '93 / EmArCy

☐ OUT OF THIS WORLD
Out of this world / Not like this / I'm all smiles / When I grow too old to dream / Some of these days / Maybe / A tender thing is love / Soon it's gonna rain / Willow weep for me
5106912 / Feb '92 / Philips

Merry Pranksters

☐ RUMPUS ROOMS, THE (2CD Set)
NOZACD 01 / Apr '96 / Ninebar

MerryThoughts

☐ PSYCHOCULT
SPV 08561392 / May '97 / SPV

Mersey-Sippi Jazz Band

☐ MERSEY TUNNEL JAZZ
Jersey lightning / Aunt Hagar's blues / Black and tan fantasy / Emporer Norton's hunch / Chicago buzz / Blue's doctor / West coast shout / Sidewalk blues / Saturday night function / Ostrich walk / Tres moutarde / Weatherbird rag / Kansas city stomps / Bienville blues / Duff Campbell's revenge / My journey to the sky / Hop frog / If I had you / Cataract rag / I'm gonna sit right down and write myself a letter
LACD 85 / 29 Sep '97 / Lake

Merseybeats

☐ MERSEY SOUNDS
HADCD 202 / Jul '96 / Javelin

☐ VERY BEST OF THE MERSEYBEATS, THE
I think of you / Don't let it happen to us / Wishin' and hopin' / I love you, yes I do / I stand accused / Last night (I made a little girl cry) / Long tall Sally / It would take a long long time / Milkman / It's love that really counts / Fortune teller / Mr. Moonlight / Hello young lovers / He will break your heart / Really mystified / Good good lovin' / Don't turn around / See me back / Jumping Jonah / All my life
5521022 / Jan '97 / Spectrum

Mertens, Wim

☐ AFTER VIRTUE
TWICD 825 / Sep '88 / Les Disques Du Crepuscule

☐ ALLE DINGHE (3CD Set)
TWI 9432 / Mar '96 / Les Disques Du Crepuscule

☐ BEST OF WIM MERTENS, THE
TWI 1051 / Jan '98 / Les Disques Du Crepuscule

☐ DIVIDED LOYALTIES (2CD Set)
It serves you right / What's mine is yours / Letter of intent / Quotable lines / How about it / How about what / Now you see it, now you don't
TWI 1004 / Feb '95 / Les Disques Du Crepuscule

☐ EDUCES ME
TWICD 808 / Sep '88 / Les Disques Du Crepuscule

☐ EPIC THAT NEVER WAS
Circular breathing / Multiple 12 / Land beyond the sunset / Voo outro / Humility / La femme de nulle part / Iris / Kanaries/Night creature / Belly of an architect / Close cover
TWI 9832 / Apr '94 / Les Disques Du Crepuscule

☐ FOR AMUSEMENT ONLY
Insert coin / Deluxe / 8 ball / Mystik / Fireball / Invader / Dog in / Gorf
TWI 048CD / Jul '88 / Les Disques Du Crepuscule

☐ GAVE VAN NIETS (3CD Set)
De blik omhoog / Ofwel daar, Ofwel Hier / Van wie je alles verwacht / Do komst van een ander / Buiten het oog / Zie niet / Hoor niet / Wees niet / Altijd haast / Waar ik heers / Schillen / Schorsen / Alles gisteren / Het lied / Restorica
TWI 1005 / Feb '95 / Les Disques Du Crepuscule

☐ INSTRUMENTAL SONGS
TWICD 666 / Dec '86 / Les Disques Du Crepuscule

☐ INTEGER VALOR
TW 11052 / 1 Jun '98 / Crepuscule

☐ JARDIN CLOS
TWI 1020 / Oct '96 / Les Disques Du Crepuscule

☐ JEREMIADES
Kaf / Kof / Mem / Alef / Gimel / Jod
TWI 1019 / Jun '95 / Les Disques Du Crepuscule

☐ MAN WITH NO FORTUNE/WITH A NAME TO COME
TWICD 748 / Nov '86 / Les Disques Du Crepuscule

☐ MAXIMIZING THE AUDIENCE
TWI 4802 / '89 / Les Disques Du Crepuscule

☐ MOTIVES FOR WRITING
TWI 8262 / '89 / Les Disques Du Crepuscule

☐ RECULER POUR MIEUX SAUTER (3CD Set)
Plus grandes les parts du mort / Plus grandes les parts de vie / Trouver les repos / Les saisons qui apportent / Tout / Ce qui arrive / Ce qui se produit / Ce qui a lieu / Le vrai / Le heros / Le cas / Le propos / La mesure
TWI 1006 / Feb '95 / Les Disques Du Crepuscule

☐ SHOT AND ECHO
Their duet / His own thing / Watch over me / One who matters / Silver lining / Shot one / We'll find out / Let him go / Wandering eyes
TWI 9502 / May '93 / Les Disques Du Crepuscule

☐ SIN EMBARGO
TW 11050 / Nov '97 / Les Disques Du Crepuscule

☐ SOURCES OF SLEEPLESSNESS (2CD Set)
TWI 9412 / Mar '96 / Les Disques Du Crepuscule

☐ STRATEGIE DE LA RUPTURE
TWI 9562 / Mar '96 / Les Disques Du Crepuscule

☐ WHISPER ME
01934111412 / Sep '95 / Windham Hill

☐ YOU'LL NEVER BE ME (2CD Set)
No - men / Chasms / Leaps / Laid back / Wo - men
TWI 1003 / Feb '95 / Les Disques Du Crepuscule

Merton, Johnny

☐ PARTY HITS NON-STOP (Merton, Johnny Party Sound)
Let's twist again / Roll over Beethoven / Rock 'n' roll music / Hound dog / Twist and shout / Baby come back / Black is black / Hippy hippy shake / Bend me shape me / Back in the USSR / Massachussetts / San Francisco / Air that I breathe / All I have to do is dream / California dreamin' / Keep on running / Hey tonight / Girls, girls, girls / Fox on the run / Whiskey in the jar / Relax / Like a virgin / Super trouper / Final countdown / Mr. Vain / Sing hallelujah / Don't talk just kiss / Rhythm is dancer / It's my life
333304 / Dec '95 / Music

Merton Parkas

☐ COMPLETE MOD COLLECTION, THE
CDMGRAM 111 / May '97 / Anagram

Merzbow

☐ 1930
TZA 7214 / 1 Jun '98 / Tzadik

☐ AKASHA GULVA
ALIENCD1 / Nov '96 / Alien8

☐ ECONOBONDAGE
DISTEMPER 1 / Nov '97 / Distemper

☐ HYBRID NOISEBLOOM
VC 113 / Jun '97 / Vinyl Communication

☐ LIVE AT 20000V 30/9/95
BBPTCX 1 / Dec '97 / Black Bean & Placenta Tape Club

☐ LOVES EMIL BEAULIEAU
PURE 45 / Jun '97 / Pure

☐ MERZBOW/BASTARD NOISE (Merzbow/Bastard Noise)
RR 9646 / Nov '96 / Release

☐ OERSTED
VC 104CD / Oct '96 / Vinyl Communication

☐ RAINBOW ELECTRONICS VOL.2
DEX 6 / Dec '96 / Dexter's Cigar

☐ RECTAL ANARCHY (Merzbow/Gore Beyond)
Punks not Dead Kennedys rectal anarchy / Chaos disorder rectal anarchy / Pretty vacant panty rectal anarchy / Love me Suicidal Tendencies rectal anarchy / Sunlight path rectal anarchy / Between nothingness and eternity rectal anarchy / Split crotch disorder rectal anarchy / Snatch punk rectal anarchy / Pussy poking disorder chaos anarchy rectal anarchy / In tight disorder rectal anarchy / Tits 4 chaos rectal anarchy / Finger friggin' in grind rectal anarchy / Melon and mounds rectal mosh anarchy / There way all the mosh rectal anarchy / Say ah punks rectal anarchy / That takes balls rectal anarchy / Ski meat funky rectal anarchy / Jeff Stryker super star rectal anarchy / Horse named rectal anarchy / Heritage banner dictate passion hate rectal anarchy / Force dead face apathy under the rectal anarchy / London calling chaos damnation action violent anarchy / Parricide blaze of socialized rectal anarchy / Agent orange country war feast rectal anarchy / Release from agony state of processsion rectal anarchy / Morbid shit confusion anarchy / Violent rectal anarchy / Manta size shit body pollution hate rectal anarchy / Up her shit emotion disregarded qrectal anarchy / He can fly them against cruel no harm shit rectal anarchy
RR 69622 / May '97 / Relapse

☐ SCUMTRON
House of kaya: *O'Rourke, Jim* / Eat beat eat: *O'Rourke, Jim* / Elephants memory: *Panasonic* / Anmon: *Rehberg & Bauer* / Micromedley: *Haswell, Russell* / Ecobondage: *Autechre* / Eat beat eat 1 / Untitled: *Gunter, Bernhard*
BFFP 138CD / Jun '97 / Blast First

☐ SPACE METALIZER
ALIENCD 4 / 24 Nov '97 / Alien8

☐ SPIRAL HONEY
WIP 004 / Oct '96 / Work In Progress

☐ TINT
VC 110CD / Jun '97 / Vinyl Communication

☐ VENEREOLOGY
Ananga-ranga / Kloken phantasie / I lead you / Towards glorious times / Slave new desert
RR 69102 / Jul '97 / Relapse

Mesa Music Consort

☐ SPIRITS OF THE WILD
TTCD 131 / Mar '96 / Talking Taco

Meshuggah

☐ CONTRADICTIONS COLLAPSE
Paralyzing ignorance / Erroneous manipulation / Abnegating cecity / Internal evidence / Qualms of reality / We'll never see the day / Greed / Choirs of devastation / Cadeverous mastication
NB 049CD / Jun '96 / Nuclear Blast

☐ DESTROY ERASE IMPROVE
NB 121DCD / May '95 / Nuclear Blast

☐ NONE
NB 102CD / Jun '95 / Nuclear Blast

☐ TRUE HUMAN DESIGN
NB268CD / 25 Aug '97 / Nuclear Blast

Mess Of Booze

☐ STAATSFEIND NR.1
PT 615001 / Jun '96 / Part

Message

☐ FINE LINE
ESM 032 / 6 Jul '98 / Escape

Messano, Bobby

☐ DOMINION ROADS (Messano, Bobby & NBO)
D 2249412 / 3 Aug '98 / Ichiban

Messaoud, Bellemou

☐ LE PERE DU RAI
Rire zarga ouana / Andi probleme / Chanson pour lekip / Khla darumha khalia / Musique instrumental / Harai harai ouama / Lala habibi ouah / Hada raykoum / Meha ouyel I bet / Lhalia darl
WCD 011 / May '89 / World Circuit

Messenger 45

☐ SIGNS AND SYMBOLS
NHM 40220 / 13 Apr '98 / Northern Heights

Messer, Michael

☐ MOONBEAT
APCD 123 / Nov '95 / Appaloosa

☐ SLIDEDANCE (Messer, Michael Band)
336452 / 29 Jun '98 / Koch International

Messiah

☐ 21ST CENTURY JESUS
Age of the machine / Beyond good and evil / Defiance / There is no law / Temple of dreams / Creator / Peace and tranquility / Thunderdome / Destroyer / I feel love / 20,000 hardcore members / Desire
4509943932 / Dec '93 / WEA

Messiah

☐ PSYCHOMORPHIA
N 01803 / '91 / Noise

☐ ROTTEN PERISH
N 01952 / Jul '92 / Noise

☐ UNDERGROUND
N 02442 / Jun '94 / Noise

Messina, Jim

☐ WATCHING THE RIVER RUN
Follow your dreams / Watching the river run / Whispering waters / I Mexican minutes / Listen to a country song / Child's claim to fame / Kind woman / You better don't dance / Your mama don't dance / Angry eyes / Peace of mind
FIENDCD 935 / Aug '97 / Demon

Messina, JoDee

☐ I'M ALRIGHT
CURCD 054 / 16 Mar '98 / Curb

Mestisay

☐ LA ROSA DE LOS VIENTOS
Sulema / Fado de mar / Donde te Lleva/El Corazon / Son del tronquillo / La flor de Guinea / La Rosa de Los Vientos / Canta Machin / Olvidarme de querer / Canciones del sur / Asi / Estrella y ana / Sangueo
INT 32072 / Aug '97 / Intuition

Meta

☐ SONGS AND DANCES FROM HUNGARY
EUCD 1068 / '89 / ARC

☐ WINTER AND CHRISTMAS SONGS FROM HUNGARY
EUCD 1085 / '91 / ARC

Metal Church

☐ HANGING IN THE BALANCE
SPV 08562170 / May '94 / SPV

Metal Molly

☐ SURGERY FOR ZEBRA
Flipper / Poolbell / Pvc / Orange / Small supernova / Superskunk / Autumn colours / Silver / Monday is queer / 60,000 brill buildings and rising / Round / Zebra
ORECD 544 / Nov '96 / Silvertone

Metal Sound

☐ METAL SOUND
503412 / Apr '95 / Declic

Metal Spark

☐ CORROSIVE
BR 065CD / 13 Jul '98 / Blue Room Released

Metallica

☐ AND JUSTICE FOR ALL
Blackened / Eye of the beholder / Shortest straw / Frayed ends of sanity / Dyes eve / And justice for all / One / Harvester of sorrow / To live is to die
8360622 / Oct '88 / Vertigo

☐ BAY AREA THRASHERS
Hit the lights / Seek and destroy / Motorbreath / Phantom lord / Mechanix / Jump in the fire / Metal militia
CRANCH 1 / 14 Apr '98 / Ranch Life

☐ BAY AREA THRASHERS, THE (Interview/2CD Set)
OTR 1100060 / Aug '97 / Metro Independent

☐ INTERVIEW DISC
SAM 7012 / Nov '96 / Sound & Media

☐ INTERVIEW SESSIONS
CHAT 13 / 11 May '98 / Chatback

☐ **KILL 'EM ALL**
Hit the lights / Four horsemen / Motorbreath / Jump in the fire / Pulling teeth (Anasthesia) / Whiplash / Phantom lord / No remorse / Seek and destroy / Metal militia
8381422 / May '89 / Vertigo

☐ **LOAD**
Ain't my bitch / 2X4 / House that Jack built / Until it sleeps / King nothing / Hero of the day / Bleeding me / Cure / Poor twisted me / Wasting my hate / Mama said / Thorn within / Ronnie / Outlaw thorn
5326182 / Jun '96 / Vertigo

☐ **MASTER OF PUPPETS**
Battery / Master of puppets / Thing that should not be / Welcome home (Sanitarium) / Disposable heroes / Leper messiah / Orion / Damage Inc
8381412 / May '89 / Vertigo

☐ **METAL MILITIA (A Tribute To Metallica) (Various Artists)**
Disposable heroes / Leper messiah / For whom the bell tolls / Fight fire with fire / Battery / Escape / Motorbreath / Thing that should not be / Damage Inc / Eye of the beholder / Fade to black
BS 01CD / Feb '95 / Dolores

☐ **METALLIC-ERA (Various Artists)**
Let it loose: *Savage* / Sucking my love: *Diamond Head* / Killing time: *Sweet Savage* / Am I evil: *Diamond Head* / Blitzkrieg: *Blitzkrieg* / Prince: *Diamond Head* / Crash course in brain surgery: *Budgie* / Wait: *Killing Joke* / Breadfan: *Budgie* / So what: *Anti Nowhere League*
NM 013CD / 18 May '98 / Neat Metal

☐ **METALLICA**
Enter sandman / Sad but true / Holier than thou / Unforgiven / Wherever I may roam / Don't tread on me / Through the never / Nothing else matters / Of wolf and man / God that failed / My friend of misery / Struggle within
5100222 / Aug '91 / Vertigo

☐ **METALLICA: INTERVIEW COMPACT DISC**
CBAK 4016 / Nov '89 / Baktabak

☐ **METALLICA: INTERVIEW COMPACT DISC VOL.2**
CBAK 4053 / Apr '92 / Baktabak

☐ **PLAYS METALLICA BY FOUR CELLOS (Apocalyptica)**
5327072 / Sep '96 / Vertigo

☐ **RE-LOAD (Interview Disc)**
DIST 007 / 9 Feb '98 / Disturbed

☐ **RE-LOAD**
Fuel / Memory remains / Devil's dance / Unforgiven II / Better than you / Carpe diem baby / Prince charming / Bad seed / Where the wild things are / Slither / Low man's lyric / Attitude / Fixxxer
5364092 / 17 Nov '97 / Vertigo

☐ **RIDE THE LIGHTNING**
Fight fire with fire / Ride the lightning / For whom the bell tolls / Fade to black / Trapped under ice / Escape / Creeping death / Call of Ktulu
8381402 / May '89 / Vertigo

☐ **TRIBUTE TO METALLICA VOL.2, A (Various Artists)**
TR 001CD / Apr '96 / Tribute

Metamatics

☐ **METAMATICS PRODUCTION, A**
CLR 429CD / Apr '97 / Clear

Metamora

☐ **GREAT ROAD, THE**
SHCD 1134 / Jan '97 / Sugar Hill

☐ **METAMORA**
SHCD 1131 / May '95 / Sugar Hill

Metcalfe, Bridget

☐ **IN YOUR EYES**
Martini please / Time / Cooper's calling / Whispered dreams / Everything happens to me / I didn't know what time it was / (I can't) let this one go / One single girl / In your eyes / Moon and sand / Seventh samba / Every time we say goodbye
AMBCD 20997 / Sep '97 / Amber

Meteors

☐ **BASTARD SONS OF A ROCK 'N' ROLL DEVIL**
HELLRAISER 001CD / Jan '97 / Hellraiser

☐ **BEST OF THE METEORS, THE**
Voodoo rhythm / Graveyard stomp / Wreckin' crew / Mutant rock / Hills have eyes / Johnny remember me / When a stranger calls / I don't worry about it / I'm just a dog / Stampede / Fire, fire / Hogs and cuties / Bad moon rising / Rhythm of the bell / Surf city / Go Buddy go / Don't touch the bang bang fruit / Swamp thing / Rawhide / Surfin' on the planet zorch / Somebody put something in my drink / Please don't touch / Chainsaw boogie / Madman roll / Who do you love
CDMGRAM 66 / Sep '93 / Anagram

☐ **FROM ZORCH WITH LOVE (The Very Best Of The Meteors)**
Voodoo rhythm / Graveyard shift / Wreckin' crew / Mutant rock / Hills have eyes / Johnny remember me / When a stranger calls / I don't worry about it / Stampede / Michael Myers / Fire fire / Rhythm of the bell / Go buddy go / Repo man / Don't touch the bang bang fruit / Swamp thing / Rawhide / Surfin' on the planet Zorch / Somebody put something in my drink / Chainsaw boogie / Hell ain't hot enough for me / Kattle slut / You don't know me very well / Straight down to hell / Slow down you grave robbing bastard
CDMPSYCHO 17 / 8 Dec '97 / Anagram

☐ **GRAVEYARD STOMP (The Best Of The Meteors 1981-1988)**
Voodoo rhythm / Graveyard stomp / Wreckin' crew / Sick things / Blue sunshine / Mutant rock / Hills have ears / Michael Myers / Bad moon rising / Fire fire / Power of steel / Eat the baby / Rhythm of the bell / Surf city / Go Buddy go / Somebody put something in my drink / Don't touch the bang bang fruit / Corpse grinder
REMCD 513 / Feb '98 / Reactive

☐ **IN HEAVEN**
In Heaven / Shout so loud / Earwigs in my brain / In the cards / Attack of the zorch men / Crazed / Get off my cloud / Love you to death / Teenagers from outer space / Maniac / Into the darkness / Death dance / Psycho for your love / Room / Rockabilly psychosis
EDCD 509 / Feb '97 / Edsel

☐ **INTERNATIONAL WRECKERS VOL.2 (The Lost Tapes Of Zorch)**
Shout so loud / Death dance / Michael Myers / Sweet love on my mind / I'm just a dog / Stampede / Kit boy / Hills have eyes / Long blond hair / Graveyard stomp / Ain't gonna bring me down / Hoover rock / Love you to death / In the cards / Rockhouse / When a stranger calls / I ain't ready / Maybe tomorrow
RRCD 230 / Oct '96 / Receiver

☐ **LIVE STYLES OF THE SICK AND SHAMELESS**
Ex-men boogie / Wipeout / Rattlesnakin' daddy / Mutant rock / Maniac / Blue sunshine / Mind over matter / These boots / Lil' red riding hood / Hill have eyes / Wild thing / I go to bed with the undead / Voodoo rhythm / I ain't ready / Wreckin' crew / Lonesome train (on a lonesome track) / Rock bop / Ain't gonna bring me down / Graveyard stomp
SUMCD 4109 / Mar '97 / Summit

☐ **LIVE, LEARY AND FUCKING LOUD**
Wipeout / Maniac rockers from hell / Lonesome train (on a lonesome track) / I ain't ready / Ain't gonna bring me down / Sick things / Crazy lovin' / When a stranger calls / Rawhide / I don't worry about it / Voodoo rhythm / You crack me up / Mutant rock / Graveyard stomp / Wreckin' crew / Long blonde hair
DOJOCD 213 / Jun '95 / Dojo

☐ **MUTANT MONKEY AND THE SURFERS FROM ZORCH**
Swamp thing / Electro II (the revenge) / Side walk psycho / I'm invisible man / She's my baby again / Surfin' on the planet Zorch / Spine bender / Dance crazy baby / Rawhide / Oxygen dog / Yellow zone / Meet me in the morgue
CDMPSYCHO 12 / Feb '97 / Anagram

☐ **ONLY THE METEORS ARE PURE PSYCHOBILLY**
Voodoo rhythm / Graveyard stomp / Wreckin' crew / Sick things / Blue sunshine / Mutant rock / Hills have eyes / Fire, fire / Power of steel / Eat the baby / Rhythm of the bell / Sure city / Go buddy go / Somebody put something in my drink
SUMCD 4089 / Jan '97 / Summit

☐ **SEWERTIME BLUES**
Ain't taking a chance / So sad / Here's Johnny / Mind over matter / Acid and psyam / Sewertime blues / Return of Ethel Merman / Deep dark jungle / Never get away / I bury the living / Vibrate / Surf city / Go Buddy go / Midnight people / Low livin' daddy / Your worst nightmare / Wildkat ways / Repo man / Don't touch the bang bang fruit / Crack me up / Shaky shaky / Psycho kat / Let's go / Revenge of the el trio los bastados
CDMPSYCHO 3 / Apr '95 / Anagram

☐ **STAMPEDE/MONKEY BREATH**
Ex man boogie / Power of steel / Hoover rock / Kit boy / Maybe tomorrow / Electro / Stampede / Just a dog / In too deep / Cecil drives a combine harvester / Michael Myers / Only a fury in my heart / Hogs and cuties / Alligator man / Rhythm of the bell / You're out of time / Ain't gonna bring me down / Night of the werewolf / Take a ride / Just the three of us / Meat is meat / Jobba's revenge
CDMSPSYCHO 9 / Oct '95 / Anagram

☐ **TEENAGERS FROM OUTER SPACE**
Voodoo rhythm / Maniac rockers from hell / My daddy is a vampire / You can't keep a good man down / Graveyard stomp / Radioactive kid / Leave me alone / Dog eat robot / Walter Mitty blues / Just the three of us / Blue sunshine / Insight / Attack of the zorch men / Jupiter stroll / Another half hour till sunrise / Island of lost souls / Napoleon solo / Get me to the world on time
CDWIK 47 / May '86 / Big Beat

☐ **UNDEAD, UNFRIENDLY AND UNSTOPPABLE**
Razor back / Disneyland / My kind of rockin' / Lonesome train (on a lonesome track) / Johnny God / I go to bed with the undead / Out of the attic / Brains as well / Charlie Johnny Rawhead and me / Lies in wait / Surf mad pig / Please don't touch
CDMPSYCHO 2 / Apr '95 / Cherry Red

☐ **WELCOME TO THE WRECKIN' PITT**
RRCD 217 / Apr '96 / Receiver

☐ **WRECKIN' CREW**
Wreckin' crew / Scream of the mutants / Hills have eyes / Mutant rock / I don't worry about it / Zombie noise / Rattlesnakin' Daddy / When a stranger calls / Blue sunshine / Sick things / Wild things / I'm not mad/Get off my cloud / Insane / I ain't ready / Johnny remember me
DOJOCD 121 / Apr '93 / Dojo

Meters

☐ **CRESCENT CITY GROOVE MERCHANTS**
Riddle song / Big chief / Come together / Tell me what's on your mind / Gossip / All I do every day / Trip / Meters jam / Bo diddley / It's too late / People get ready / Stretch your rubber band / Groovy lady
CPCD 8066 / Nov '94 / Charly

☐ **FUNDAMENTALLY FUNKY**
CPCD 8044 / Jun '94 / Charly

☐ **FUNKY MIRACLE**
Look-ka py py / 9 till 5 / Cissy strut / I need more time / Pungee / Ease back / Cardova / Yeah you're right / Tippi-toes / Chicken strut / Sassy lady / Little old money maker / Rigor mortis / Live wire / A message from the meters / Hey last minute / My last affair / Darling darling darling / Go for yourself / Sophisticated cissy / Here comes the meterman / Mob / Funky miracle / Ride your pony / Art / Dry spell / Thinking / Handclapping song / Britches / Liver splash / Joog / Same old thing / 6v6 la / Sehorns farm / Sing a simple song / Stormy / Ann / Oh, calcutta
CDNEV 2 / Mar '91 / Charly

☐ **GOOD OLD FUNKY MUSIC**
Look-ka-py-py / Seahorn's farm / Art / Ease back / Cissy strut / Message from the Meters / Thinking / Good old funky music / Live wire / Stretch your rubber band / Doodle-opp / Tippi toes / Rigor mortis / Nine to five / Sophisticated Cissy / Chicken strut / Here come the metermen / Darling darling / Dry spell / Ride your pony
ROUCD 2104 / Dec '94 / Rounder

☐ **ORIGINAL FUNKMASTERS, THE**
Sophisticated Sissy / Funky miracles / Look-ka py py / Ease back / Ride your pony / Stormy / Dry spell / Cissy strut / Tippi toes / Chicken strut / I need more time / Live wire / Handclapping song / Message from The Meters / Here comes The Metermen
CPCD 8229 / Sep '96 / Charly

Metheny, Pat

☐ **80-81 (2CD Set)**
Goin' ahead / Two folk songs / Bat / Turn around / Open / Pretty scattered / Everyday I thank you
843 169 2 / Oct '90 / ECM

☐ **AMERICAN GARAGE**
(Cross the) Heartland / Airstream / Search / American garage / Epic
8271342 / Dec '85 / ECM

☐ **AS FALLS WICHITA, SO FALLS WICHITA FALLS (Metheny, Pat & Lyle Mays)**
As falls Wichita, so falls Wichita Falls / September 15th / It's for you / Estupenda graca
8214162 / Jul '85 / ECM

☐ **BLUE ASPHALT (Metheny, Pat Group)**
JD 1223 / 26 Jan '98 / Jazz Door

☐ **BRIGHT SIZE LIFE**
Bright size life / Sirabhorn / Unity village / Missouri incompromised / Midwestern nights dream / Unquity road / Omaha celebration / Round trip-Broadway blues
8271332 / Dec '86 / ECM

☐ **FIRST CIRCLE (Metheny, Pat Group)**
Forward march / Yolanda / You learn / First circle / If I could / Tell it all / End of the game / Mas alla (beyond) / Praise
8233422 / Nov '84 / ECM

☐ **IMAGINARY DAY**
Imaginary day / Follow me / Into the dream / Story within the story / Heat of the day / Across the sly / Roots of coincidence / Too soon tomorrow / Awakening
9362467912 / 13 Oct '97 / Warner Bros.

☐ **IN CONCERT**
JD 1231 / 26 Jan '98 / Jazz Door

☐ **NEW CHAUTAUQUA**
New chautauqua / Country poem / Long ago child / Fallen star / Hermitage / Sueno con Mexico / Daybreak
8254712 / Aug '85 / ECM

☐ **OFFRAMP**
Barcarolle / Are you going with me / Au lait / Eighteen / Offramp / James / Bat (part 2)
8171382 / Sep '84 / ECM

☐ **PAT METHENY GROUP (Metheny, Pat Group)**
San Lorenzo / Phase dance / Jaco / Aprilwind / April joy / Lone jack
8255932 / Aug '88 / ECM

☐ **PAT METHENY/PAUL WERTICO/ GREGG BENDIAN/DEREK BAILEY (3CD Set) (Metheny, Pat & Paul Wertico/Gregg Bendian/Derek Bailey)**
KFWCD 197 / May '97 / Knitting Factory

☐ **QUARTET**
Introduction / When we were free / Montevideo / Take me there / Seven days / Oceania / Dismantling Utopia / Double blind / Second thought / Mojave / Badland / Glacier / Language of time / Sometimes I see / As I am
GED 24978 / Jan '97 / Geffen

☐ **QUESTION AND ANSWER (Metheny, Pat/Dave Holland/Roy Haynes)**
Solar / Question and answer / H and H / Never too far away / Law years / Change of heart / All the things you are / Old folks / Three flights up
GFLD 19197 / Mar '93 / Geffen

☐ **REJOICING**
Lonely woman / Tears inside / Humpty dumpty / Blues for Pat / Rejoicing / Story from a stranger / Calling / Waiting for an answer
8177952 / Jun '84 / ECM

☐ **ROAD TO YOU, THE**
Have you heard / First circle / Road to you / Half life of absolution / Last train home / Better days ahead / Naked moon / Beat 70 / Letter from home / Third wind / Solo from More travels
GED 24601 / Jul '93 / Geffen

☐ **SECRET STORY**
Above the treetops / Facing west / Cathedral in a suitcase / Finding and believing / Longest summer / Sunlight / Rain river / Always and forever / See the world / As a flower blossoms (I am running to you) / Antonia / Truth will always be / Tell her you saw me / Not to be forgotten (our final our)
GEFD 24468 / Jul '92 / Geffen

☐ **SIGN OF 4, THE (3CD Set)**
Study in scarlet (1 to 9) / Evidently / Untidy habits / Rule of three / Strange story / Aurora / Tracks / Break in the chain / One object / Euclid / Fortune / Poisoned arrows / Trichinopoly / Ransom / Antecedents / In quest of a solution
KFW 197 / 20 Apr '98 / Knitting Factory

☐ **STILL LIFE TALKING (Metheny, Pat Group)**
Minuano / So may it secretly begin / Last train home / It's just talk / Third wind / Distance / In her family
GFLD 19196 / Mar '93 / Geffen

☐ **TRAVELS (2CD Set) (Metheny, Pat Group)**
Are you going with me / Fields, the sky / Goodbye / Phase dance / Straight on red / Farmer's trust / Extradition / Goin' ahead / As falls Wichita, so falls Wichita Falls / Travels / Song for Bilbao / San Lorenzo
8106222 / Aug '86 / ECM

☐ **UNITY VILLAGE**
JD 1246 / 26 Jan '98 / Jazz Door

☐ **WATERCOLORS**
Watercolors / Icefire / Lakes / River Quay / Florida Greeting song / Legend of the fountain / Sea song
8274092 / Feb '86 / ECM

☐ **WE LIVE HERE**
Here to stay / And then I knew / Girls next door / To the end of the world / We live here / Episode d'azur / Something to remind you / Red sky / Stranger in town
GED 24729 / Jan '95 / Geffen

☐ **WORKS**
Sueno con Mexico / (Cross the) Heartland / Travels / James / It's for you / Everyday I thank you / Goin' ahead
8232702 / Jun '89 / ECM

Method Man

☐ **TICAL**
Tical / Biscuits / Bring the pain / All I need / What the blood clot / Meth vs. Chef / Sub-crazy / Release yo'delf / PLO style / I get my thang in action / Mr. Sandman / Stimulation / Method man / I'll be there for you/You're all I need to get by: *Method Man & Mary J. Blige*
5238392 / Dec '94 / Def Jam

Metri

☐ **METRI**
SAHK 0006 / Apr '94 / Sahko

Metroshifter

☐ **METROSHIFTER, THE**
CR 021CD / Jul '96 / Conversion

☐ **RETURN TO ROCK**
DOG 051CD / Nov '97 / Doghouse

Metrotone

☐ **LESS YOU HAVE THE MORE YOU ARE, THE**
WORM 21CD / 20 Jul '98 / Earworm

Metsanvaki

☐ **KAAPIOVIERAAT**
MVAKI 01CD / Mar '98 / Metsanvaki

Metura, Philip

☐ **SENTIMENTAL LOVE**
LM 60732 / '91 / Melodie

Metz, Henrik

☐ **HENRIK METZ, FREDRIK LUNDIN & NIELS PEDERSON (Metz, Henrik & Fredrik Lundin/Niels Pederson)**
MECCACD 1024 / Oct '93 / Music Mecca

Meurkens, Hendrik

☐ **CLEAR OF CLOUDS**
Samba for Claudio / Clear of clouds / Seu acalento / Mambo inn / Estate / Chega de saudade/To Brenda with love / Hesitation / Beauty and the priest / You go to my head / Joe's donut / Allan's theme
CCD 4531 / Nov '92 / Concord Picante

☐ DIG THIS SAMBA (Meurkens, Hendrik & Manfredo Fest)
Samba novo / Brazilian Dorian dream / Madison Square / Tristeza de nos dois / One for Manfredo / A ilha / Dig this samba / Caminhos cruzados / Frajola / Madalena / Seu acalento
CCD 79747 / Apr '98 / Candid

☐ OCTOBER COLORS
October colors / Who did it / In motion / Night in the afternoon / Brigas, nunca mais / Footprints / Chorinho no 1 / Summer in San Francisco / Tranchan / High tide
CCD 4670 / Nov '95 / Concord Jazz

☐ POEMA BRASILEIRO
Her smile / Boa Noticia / Desperar jamais / Chelsea nocturne / Angel eyes / Saindo de mim / Felicidade / Peach (Chorinho No.4) / One note samba / Passarin / Manhattan samba
CCD 4728 / Sep '96 / Concord Picante

☐ QUIET MOMENTS
Afternoon / Sophisticated lady / Secret love / Quiet moments / Strollin' / Time for love / Beautiful friendship / My one and only love
ECD 22214 / 14 Jul '98 / Evidence

☐ SAIL ALONG (Meurkens, Hendrik & Stefan Diez Group)
ISCD 167 / May '98 / Intersound

☐ SLIDIN'
Come rain or come shine / Have you met Miss Jones / Slidin' / Cottage / Bolero para paquito / All of you / Stolen moments / Fortuna / Tribute / Voyage / Once was / Talking trout
CCD 4628 / Jan '95 / Concord Jazz

☐ VIEW FROM MANHATTAN, A
Meet you after dark / Whisper not / Park Avenue South / Speak low / Naima / Prague in March / Monster and the flower / Body and soul / Madison Square / Moment's notice / Child is born
CCD 4585 / Dec '93 / Concord Jazz

Meuross, Reg

☐ GOODBYE HAT, THE
RTMCD 75 / Feb '96 / Round Tower

Meves, Carol

☐ NATURAL FLUTE, THE
2685 / Aug '96 / NorthSound

Mevlevi Ensemble

☐ WHEREVER YOU TURN IS THE FACE OF GOD
WLAES 50CD / Feb '96 / Waterlily Acoustics

Mexican Mariachi Band

☐ MARIACHI FROM MEXICO
15284 / '91 / Laserlight

Mexico 70

☐ DUST HAS COME TO STAY, THE
Wonderful lie / Just like we never came down / What's in your mind / Sacred heart / I feel fine / Drug is the love / All day long / Find someone else to play Misty / For you / Always by your side / Queen of swords / You make it worse / Make it right / Kenton's lane
CDBRED 101 / Jun '92 / Cherry Red

Meyer, Liz

☐ WOMANLY ARTS
SCR 37 / Dec '94 / Strictly Country

Meyer, Peter 'Banjo'

☐ JAZZ PARTY
CD 009 / May '96 / Nagel Heyer

Meyer, Richard

☐ LETTER FROM THE OPEN SKY, A
SHCD 8012 / Dec '94 / Shanachie

Meyers, Augie

☐ FINALLY IN LIGHTS (Meyers, Augie Western Head Band)
Release me / Deep in the heart of Texas / Cryin' out loud / It's alright / My friend / Sky high / Deed to Texas / Miller's cave / Don't let me / Baby baby
EDCD 555 / 1 Jun '98 / Edsel

☐ LIVE AT THE LONGNECK (Meyers, Augie Western Head Band)
Introduction / High Texas rider / Hello Mary Lou / You win again / Hen pecked polka / Dusty roads / Today I started loving you again / Memories / Hokey pokey / Long tail cat / Come on baby
EDCD 554 / 1 Jun '98 / Edsel

☐ MY MAIN SQUEEZE
Open up your heart / Sittin' up at nite / Kep pa so / Lover please / Velma from Selma / To nothing at all / La ronda / Going down to Mexico / Matilda / Did I tell you / Just because / Come back home
EDCD 556 / 1 Jun '98 / Edsel

☐ WHITE BOY
MWCD 2019 / Dec '95 / Music & Words

Meza, Lisandro

☐ AMOR LINDO
TUMICD 017 / '91 / Tumi

☐ CUMBIAS COLOMBIANAS
TUMICD 046 / '94 / Tumi

Mezcal Jazz Unit

☐ IGNALINA
591332 / 21 Aug '97 / Musidisc

Mezcla

☐ FRONTERAS DE SUENOS
La Guagua / Fronteras de Suenos / La mulata de Caramelo / Ikiri adda / Rio quibu / Vivir para ver / Como una campana de cristal / Muros transparentes / Ando buscando uno amor
INT 30472 / Feb '91 / Intuition

Mezquida, Allen

☐ GOOD THING, A
378222 / Aug '96 / Koch Jazz

Mezzoforte

☐ RISING
Check it in / Take off / Happy hour / Waves / Blizzard / Solid / Northern comfort / Fiona rising / Check it out
ZYX 100232 / Nov '96 / ZYX

Mezzrow, Mezz

☐ CLASSICS 1928-1936 (Mezzrow, Milton 'Mezz')
CLASSICS 713 / Jul '93 / Classics

☐ CLASSICS 1936-1939 (Mezzrow, Milton 'Mezz')
CLASSICS 694 / May '93 / Classics

☐ MEZZROW/BECHET QUINTET/ SEPTET VOL.1 (Mezzrow-Bechet Quintet & Septet)
STCD 8212 / May '93 / Storyville

☐ MEZZROW/BECHET QUINTET/ SEPTET VOL.2 (Mezzrow-Bechet Quintet & Septet)
STCD 8213 / May '93 / Storyville

☐ MEZZROW/BECHET QUINTET/ SEPTET VOL.3 (Mezzrow, Milton 'Mezz')
STCD 8214 / May '93 / Storyville

☐ MEZZROW/BECHET QUINTET/ SEPTET VOL.4 (Mezzrow, Milton 'Mezz')
STCD 8215 / May '93 / Storyville

☐ MILTON 'MEZZ' MEZZROW 1933-1945 (Mezzrow, Milton 'Mezz')
Perdido street stomp / House party / Jelly roll / Bowin' the blues / Old school / Gone away blues / De luxe stomp / Rosetta / Who / Royal garden blues / Everybody loves my baby / I ain't gonna give nobody none o' this jellyroll / Revolutionary blues / Swingin' for Mezz (careless love) / Swing session's called to order / Hot club stomp / Blues in disguise / Mutiny in the parlour / Panic is on / Apologies / 35th and calumet / Dissonance
CD 53686 / Apr '98 / Giants Of Jazz

MFG

☐ NEW KIND OF WORLD
20802 / 12 Jan '98 / Phonokol

Mhlongo, Busi

☐ BABHEMU
Izinziswa / Ting-tingu (Cash dispenser) / Unomkhubulwane (African angel) / Umenthisi (Matches) / Shosholoza (Keep going) / Mfazonga phesheva (Woman from abroad) / Ujantshi (Rails) / Ntandane (Orphan)
STCD 1053 / Mar '94 / Stern's

Mhoireach, Anna

☐ INTO INDIGO
Finbarr Saunders: Campbell, Rory / Gaol na h-oige, na goisidich: Campbell, Rory / Tar the house / Medley / Zeto the bubbleman / Medley / Tarruing teann an crios / Medley / Ballivanich / Medley / Miss Campbell of Sheerness / Medley / Medley / Medley
CDLDL 1249 / Mar '97 / Lochshore

☐ OUT OF THE BLUE
CDLDL 1219 / Nov '94 / Lochshore

MI22

☐ WHATEVER IT IS
Whatever it is / Hit me with your rhythm / You fade away / Letter (brev fra ditte) / Moonlight bright / Still remember / Exit 5 / Game is over / Too late / Talkin' loud / Jamboree / Deal with it
STCD 4222 / Dec '97 / Storyville

Miaabal, Robert

☐ SONG CARRIER
MTI 1295 / Aug '96 / MTI

Miah, Shahjahan

☐ MYSTICAL BAUL SONGS OF BANGLADESH
AUW 260039 / Feb '93 / Auvidis/Ethnic

Miasma 1195

☐ EMIT 1195
EMIT 1195 / Mar '95 / Time Recordings

Mic Force

☐ IT AIN'T OVER
MOVE 7009CD / Apr '94 / Move

Mic Geronimo

☐ VENDETTA
Nothin' move but for the money / Vendetta / Survival / Life lessons / For tha family / Street life / Be like mic / Unstoppable / Single life / Thimgs ain't what they used to be / How you been / Usual suspects
4894672 / 5 Jan '98 / Epic

☐ VENDETTA
TVT 49302 / 4 Nov '97 / TVT

Micaelli, Jacky

☐ CORSICA SACRA
Agnus dei / Lamentu di Ghjesu / Kyrie / Perdono mio dio / Stabat mater / Tota pulchra / L'amica / Sanctus / Adoriamo / Lodi al sepolcro / Dio vi salvi regina / Misere mini mei
B 6842 / Jan '97 / Auvidis/Ethnic

Micastro, Michelle

☐ ON MY OWN
VSD 5810 / 16 Feb '98 / Varese Sarabande

Michael, George

☐ FAITH
Faith / Father figure / I want your sex / One more try / Hard day / Hand to mouth / Look at your hands / Monkey / Kissing a fool / Last request (I want your sex, pt 3)
4600002 / Nov '87 / Epic

☐ INTERVIEW DISC
SAM 7024 / Jan '97 / Sound & Media

☐ KYMAERA (The Music Of George Michael) (Various Artists)
Jesus to a child / Hand to mouth / Kissing a fool / Strangest thing / Different corner / Club tropicana / Careless whisper / Move on / Mother's pride / Older / Cowboys and angels / Faith / Last Christmas
CDSGP 0391 / 27 Apr '98 / Prestige

☐ LISTEN WITHOUT PREJUDICE VOL.1
Praying for time / Freedom 90 / They won't go when I go / Something to save / Cowboys and angels / Waiting for that day / Mothers pride / Heal the pain / Soul free / Waiting (Reprise)
4672952 / Sep '90 / Epic

☐ MUSIC OF GEORGE MICHAEL, THE (Royal Philharmonic Orchestra)
MCCD 338 / 16 Mar '98 / Music Club

☐ OLDER
Jesus to a child / Fastlove / Older / Spinning the wheel / It doesn't really matter / Strangest thing / To be forgiven / Move on / Star people / You have been loved / Free
CDV 2802 / Apr '96 / Virgin

☐ OLDER AND UPPER
Jesus to a child / Fastlove / Older / Spinning the wheel / It doesn't really matter / Strangest thing / To be forgiven / Move on / Star people / You have been loved / Free / Fastlove / Spinning the wheel / Strangest thing / You know what I want to do / Safe
CDVX 2802 / 1 Dec '97 / Aegean

Michael, Walt

☐ HAMMERED DULCIMER RETROSPECTIVE
Prince William/Salt Creek/Temperance reel / Black nag / Southwind / Little rabbit / Cuckoo's nest / Fly around my pretty little Miss / Farewell to whiskey/ Bluegrass minor / Hawks and eagles / Sons of Jubal / Gentle maiden / Golden slippers / Snowblind / Grey cat on the Tennessee farm/Rockingham Cindy / Arran boat / Fanny power
CDFF 673 / Jun '98 / Flying Fish

☐ MUSIC FOR HAMMERED DULCIMER
EP 101 / Mar '94 / Eastwick Productions

☐ STEP STONE
FF 70480 / Apr '94 / Flying Fish

Michel, Matthieu

☐ ESTATE
Leaving / Never let me go / Moon princess / It could be worse / Estate / Round trip / Sail away / Caruso / On the spot / Moment to moment
TCB 95802 / Dec '95 / TCB

Michelle, Yvette

☐ MY DREAM
Way I feel / Summer lover / All I really want / Crazy / Everyday and everynight / Let's stay together / Only want to be with you / Something in my way / In my dreams / First time / We can get down / I'm not feeling you / DJ keep playing / I'm not feeling you
74321504652 / 6 Oct '97 / RCA

Michigan & Smiley

☐ DOWNPRESSION (Michigan, Papa & General Smiley)
Downpression / Natty heng on in deh / Come when Jah call you / Ghetto man / Jah army / Diseases / Living in a babylon / Jah know / Arise / Come on black people
GRELCD 42 / Aug '95 / Greensleeves

☐ RUB-A-DUB STYLE
HBCD 3512 / May '92 / Heartbeat

☐ STEP BY STEP
JJCD 81 / 17 Aug '98 / Channel One

☐ SUGAR DADDY
RASCD 3004 / Nov '92 / Ras

Michigan State University

☐ TRIBUTE
Original fantasie / Night in June / From the shores of the mighty Pacific / Rhapsody / Beautiful Colorado / Concertino / Fanrasia di concerto / Estrellita / Atlantic Zephyrs / Believe me, if all those endearing young charms / Flower Song / Auld lang syne
QPRM 118D / Aug '92 / Polyphonic

Michiru, Monday

☐ DELICIOUS POISON (Michiru, Monday & The Paradox Band)
5376412 / Jul '97 / Verve

☐ MERMAID
5575152 / 29 Jun '98 / EmArCy

Mickey & Ludella

☐ BEDLAM A GO-GO
That look that you gave to me / I believed your lies / Stop and listen / Ain't nobody's friend / I'm afraid they're all talkin about me / Tell me / Surfin' snow matador / Bedlam a go-go / Bring it back / Do I expect to much / Standing next to the railway track / We're gonna get married / I'm on the way down / She's drunk / Well now
ASKCD 052 / Jan '96 / Vinyl Japan

Mickey & Sylvia

☐ LOVE IS STRANGE (2CD Set)
Forever and a day / Se de boom run dun / I'm so glad / Rise Sally rise / Seems like just yesterday / Peace of mind / No good lover / Love is strange / Walkin' in the rain / Two shadows on your window / Who knows why / In my heart / I'm going home / Two shadows on your window / There oughta be a law / Dearest / Where is my honey / Too much weight / Let's have a picnic / New idea on love / Say the word / Love will make you fail in school / I gotta be home by ten / Love is a treasure / Loving you darling / I'm working at the five and dime / Shake it up / There'll be no backin' out / Summertime / Rock and stroll room (take 1) / Rock and stroll room (take 12) / It's you love / True, true, love / Bewildered / Oh yeah Uh huh / To the valley / Mommy out de light / Gonna work out fine / What would I do / Sweeter as the days goes by / I'm glad for your sake / I hear you knocking / Love lesson / This is my story / Baby you're so fine / Love is the only thing / Dearest / From the beginning of time / Fallin' in love / Gypsy / Yours / Let's shake some more
BCD 15438 / May '90 / Bear Family

☐ WILLOW SESSIONS
Love is strange / He gave me everything / Love drops / Hucklebuck / Baby you're so fine / Mickey's blues / Anytime / Darling (I miss you so) / Walking in the rain / I'm guilty / Loving you darling / Sylvia's blues / Since I fell for you / Love is the only thing / I can't help it / Our name (alternative take) / Because you do it to me / Soulin' with Mickey and Sylvia
NEM 763 / Jan '96 / Sequel

Mickey & The Heartbeats

☐ HARTBITS
ANT 25 / Dec '97 / Anthology

Microdisney

☐ BIG SLEEPING HOUSE (A Collection Of Choice Cuts)
Horse overboard / Loftholdingswood / Singer's Hampstead home / She only gave in to her anger / Gale force wind / I can't say no / Angels / Mrs. Simpson / Armadillo man / And he descended into hell / Rack / Big sleeping house / Back to the old town / Send Herman home / Town to town / Begging bowl
CDOVD 452 / Feb '95 / Virgin

☐ CLOCK COMES DOWN THE STAIRS, THE
CREV 41CD / May '96 / Rev-Ola

☐ EVERYBODY IS FANTASTIC
CREV 40CD / May '96 / Rev-Ola

☐ LOVE YOUR ENEMIES
CREV 42CD / May '96 / Rev-Ola

Microscopic 7

☐ TAKE THE Z TRAIN
378632 / 29 Jun '98 / Koch Jazz

Microstoria

☐ INIT DING
EFA 006672 / Oct '95 / Mille Plateau

☐ MICROSTORIA
THRILL 035CD / Oct '96 / Thrill Jockey

☐ REPROVISERS
EFA 006872 / Mar '97 / Mille Plateau

☐ REPROVISERS
THRILL 042 / Jun '97 / Thrill Jockey

☐ SND
EFA 006752 / Jun '96 / Mille Plateau

Microwave Dave

☐ NOTHIN' BUT THE BLUES (Microwave Dave & The Nukes)
DFGCD 8448 / Jul '96 / Dixie Frog

Micus, Stephan

☐ ATHOS
5232922 / Sep '94 / ECM

☐ DARKNESS AND LIGHT
Part 1 / Part 2 / Part 3
8472722 / Dec '90 / ECM

☐ EAST OF THE NIGHT
East of the night / For Nobuko
8256552 / Mar '88 / ECM

☐ GARDEN OF MIRRORS
Earth / Passing cloud / Violeta / Flowers in chaos / In the high valleys / Gates of fire / Mad bird / Night circles / Words of truth
5371622 / Aug '97 / ECM

☐ LISTEN TO THE RAIN
For Abai and Togshan / Dancing with the morning / Listen to the rain / White paint on silver wood
8156142 / '88 / ECM

☐ OCEAN
Part 1 / Part II / Part III / Part IV
8292792 / Jun '86 / ECM

☐ TILL THE END OF TIME
Till the end of time / For wis and ramin
5137862 / '88 / ECM

☐ TO THE EVENING CHILD
Nomad song / Yuko's eyes / Young moon / To the evening child / Morgenstern / Equinox / Desert poem
5137802 / Sep '92 / ECM

☐ TWILIGHT FIELDS
Part 1 / Part 2 / Part 3 / Part 4 / Part 5
8350852 / Feb '88 / ECM

☐ WINGS OVER WATER
Part 1 / Part 2 / Part 3 / Part 4 / Part 5 / Part 6
8310582 / Aug '88 / ECM

Middle Of The Road

☐ ALL THE HITS PLUS MORE
Chirpy chirpy cheep cheep / Sacramento / Tweedle dum tweedle dee / Kailakee kailako / Union silver / Soley soley / Bottoms up / Will you still love me tomorrow / Talk of all the USA / On this land / Samson and Delilah / Yellow boomerang / Tweedle dee tweedle dum / Chirpy chirpy cheep cheep
CDSGP 0357 / 3 Nov '97 / Prestige

☐ MIDDLE OF THE ROAD
295594 / Dec '92 / Ariola

☐ TODAY
Midnight blue / Samson and Delilah / Love takes prisoners / Sacramento / Dance with me / South America / Soley Soley / Turn on your radio / Chirpy chirpy cheep cheep / Tweedle dee - Tweedle dum / Kailakee Kailakoe / Fall / One kiss
399368 / Jun '97 / Koch Presents

Middlesbrough FC

☐ UP THE BORO (20 Boro Classics) (Various Artists)
Bryan Robson's red 'n' white army: *International Strike Force* / Archie Stephens' birthday party: *Shrug* / Mission from Todd: *Shrug* / Power game: *Stapleton, Cyril* / Up the Boro: *1st Division* / Men of iron: *Middlesbrough FC* / Boro's coming to Wembley: *McCoy, Danny* / We're coming through: *McCoy, Danny* / We are Teeside: *Middlesbrough FC* / Willie's reggae: *Dale, Ray Fine Band* / Let's dance: *Middlesbrough FC & Chris Rea/Bob Mortimer* / It's only a game: *Clough, Brian & Friends* / Wembley: *Dale, Ray Hip Hop Band* / Juninho jest: *Mannion* / Riverside red: *Mannion* / Tranmere Rovers: *Mannion* / Come on Boro: *Red Sky* / Old Ayresome: *Riverside Ramblers* / Boro shirt: *Riverside Ramblers* / We're the Boro: *Borozone*
CDGAFFER 23 / 6 Apr '98 / Cherry Red

Middleton, Arthur

☐ HARMONICA FAVOURITES
CDR 012 / Oct '89 / Donside

Middleton-Pollock, Marilyn

☐ DOLL'S HOUSE, A
FE 086CD / Feb '87 / Fellside

☐ RED HOT AND BLUE
Don't try your jive on me / Don't try your jive on me / Black and tan fantasy / Bugle boy march / Iv'e got ford engine movements in my hips / Come back sweet papa / Buddy, can you spare a dime / Harlem bound / Once in a while / When I take my sugar to tea / That lovin' rag / Indian summer / Wa wa wa / Kiss me sweet / Saturday night function / Devil's gonna get you
LACD 42 / Jan '95 / Lake

☐ THOSE WOMEN OF THE VAUDEVILLE BLUES
Miss Jenny's blues / Aggravatin' papa / Handyman / Barrelhouse blues / It's tight like that / Moanin' the blues / Mighty tight woman / Trouble in mind / Hot time in the old town / Last journey blues / Wild women don't get the blues / Dark man / I got a mind to ramble / St. Louis blues / Women don't need no mens / Nobody knows you (when you're down and out) / Some of these days
LACD 18 / Feb '91 / Lake

Midget

☐ JUKEBOX
Invisible balloon / Ben wants to be a secret agent / Day of your life / Magic lamp / You cope / One who should save me / All fall down / On the run / Canada / Guy like me / Optimism / Way things turn out
TINYCD 9 / 8 Jun '98 / Radarscope

☐ TOGGLE SWITCH, THE
ANDA 203 / Mar '97 / Au-Go-Go

Midi Rain

☐ ONE
STEAM 56CD / Jul '94 / Vinyl Solution

Midler, Bette

☐ BETTE MIDLER
Skylark / Drinking again / Breaking up somebody's home / Surabaya Johnny / I shall be released / Optimistic voices / Lullaby of broadway / In the mood / Uptown / Da doo ron ron / Twisted / Higher and higher
7567827792 / Jan '94 / Atlantic

☐ BETTE OF ROSES
In this life / To comfort you / I know this town / Bottomless / To deserve you / Bed of roses / Last time / I believe in you / It's too late / As dreams go by / Perfect kiss
7567828232 / Nov '95 / Atlantic

☐ DIVINE MADNESS
Stay with me / Fire down below / Big noise from winnetka / Paradise / You can't always get what you want / Shiver me timbers / I shall be released / Chapel of love / Boogie woogie bugle boy / Summer (the first time) / E street shuffle / My mother's eyes / Leader of the pack
7567827812 / Jun '94 / Atlantic

☐ EXPERIENCE THE DIVINE BETTE MIDLER (The Greatest Hits Of Bette Midler)
Hello in there / Do you want to dance / From a distance / Chapel of love / Only in Miami / When a man loves a woman / Rose / Miss Otis regrets / Shiver me timbers / Wind beneath my wings / Boogie woogie bugle boy / One for my baby (and one more for the road) / Friends / In my life
7567824972 / Oct '93 / Atlantic

☐ SOME PEOPLE'S LIVES
One more round / Some people's lives / Miss Otis regrets / Spring can really hang you up the most / Night and day / Girl is on to you / From a distance / Moonlight dancing / He was too good to me/Since you stayed here / All of a sudden / Gift of love
7567821292 / Sep '90 / Atlantic

Midnight Choir

☐ MIDNIGHT CHOIR
Talk to me / Don't turn out the light / Gypsy rider / What am I worth to you / Turning of the tide / Hearts gone wild / Mercy on the street / Rock bottom / Lonesome drifter / Lift me up
119742 / Sep '96 / Musidisc UK

Midnight Configuration

☐ DIGITAL INTERFEARENCE
NIGHTCD 019 / 16 Mar '98 / Nightbreed

☐ FUNERAL NATION
NIGHTCD 015 / 4 Aug '97 / Nightbreed

☐ GOTHTEC
NIGHTMCD 001 / Mar '94 / Nightbreed

Midnight Oil

☐ 10,9,8,7,6,5,4,3,2,1/RED SAILS IN THE SUNSET/BLUE SKY MINING (3CD Set)
Outside world / Only the strong / Short memory / Read about it / Scream in blue / US forces / Power and the passion / Maralinga / Tinlegs and tin mines / Somebody's trying to tell me something / When the generals talk / Best of both worlds / Sleep / Minutes to midnight / Jimmy Sharman's boxers / Bakerman / Who can stand in the way / Kosiusko / Helps me help you / Harrisburg / Bells and horns in the back of beyond / Shipyards of New Zealand / Blue sky / Stars of Warburton / Bedlam bridge / Forgotten years / Mountains of Burma / King of the mountain / River runs red / Shakers and movers / One country / Antarctica
4886752 / 3 Nov '97 / Columbia

☐ 20000 WATTS RSL
What goes on / Power and the passion / Dreamworld / White skin black heart / Kosciuszko / Dead heart / Blue sky mine / Us forces / Beds are burning / One country / Truganini / King of the mountain / Hercules / Surf's up tonight / Back on the borderline / Don't wanna be the one / Forgotten years
4888662 / 3 Nov '97 / Columbia

☐ BLUE SKY MINING
Blue sky mining / Stars of Warburton / Bedlam bridge / Forgotten years / Mountains of Burma / King of the mountain / River runs red / Shakers and movers / One country / Antarctica
465653 2 / Sep '93 / Columbia

☐ BREATHE
Underwater / Surf's up tonight / Common ground / Time to heal / Sins of omission / One too many / Times / Star of hope / In the rain / Bring on the change / Home / E-beat / Barest degree / Gravelrash
4854029 / Oct '96 / Columbia

☐ DIESEL AND DUST
Beds are burning / Put down that weapon / Dreamworld / Arctic world / Warakuma / Dead heart / Woah / Bullroarer / Sell my soul / Sometimes
4600052 / May '88 / CBS

☐ MIDNIGHT OIL
Powderworks / Head over heels / Dust used and abused / Surfing with a spoon / Run by night / Nothing lost, nothing gained
4509022 / Feb '94 / CBS

☐ REDNECK WONDERLAND
4899712 / 3 Aug '98 / Columbia

☐ SCREAM IN BLUE
Scream in blue / Read about it / Dreamworld / Brave faces / Only the strong / Stars of Warburton / Progress / Beds are burning / Sell my soul / Sometimes / Hercules / Powderworks / Burnie
41714532 / May '92 / Columbia

Midnight Star

☐ BEST OF MIDNIGHT STAR, THE
I've been watching you / Hot spot / Feels so good / Playmates / Scientific love / Headlines / Don't rock the boat / I won't let you be lonely / Wet my whistle / Curious / Let's celebrate / Operator / Midas touch
NEMCD 682 / Nov '94 / Sequel

☐ HEADLINES
Searching for love / Headlines / Get dressed / Stay here by my side / Midas touch / Close encounter / Engine no.9 / Dead end / Headlines / Engine no.9
NEBCD 786 / Jul '96 / Sequel

☐ MIDNIGHT STAR (2CD Set)
SMDCD 169 / 22 Sep '97 / Snapper

☐ NO PARKING ON THE DANCE FLOOR
Electricity / Night rider / Feels so good / Wet my whistle / No parking (on the dance floor) / Freak-a-zoid / Slow jam / Play mates
NEBCD 787 / Jul '96 / Sequel

☐ VERY BEST OF MIDNIGHT STAR, THE
Headlines / Midas touch / Freakazoid / Operator / Engine No. 9 / Electricity / No parking on the dancefloor / Make it last / Slow jam / Luv u up / Wet my whistle / Victory / Money can't buy you love / Work it out / Snake in the grass / Heartbeat
CCSCD 805 / Sep '95 / Renaissance Collector Series

☐ VICTORY/PLANETARY INVASION
Victory / Move me / Make time (to fall in love) / Hot spot / You can't stop me / Be with you / Operator / Body snatchers / Scientific love / Let's celebrate / Curious / Planetary invasion / Can you stay with me
DEEPM 030 / Aug '97 / Deep Beats

Midnight Sunrise

☐ BEST OF MIDNIGHT SUNRISE, THE (On The House)
HTCD 63 / 20 Apr '98 / Hot Productions

Midori

☐ SECRET OF THE PANPIPES
CD 447 / 6 Jul '98 / New World

Midwinter

☐ AT THE SIGHT OF THE APOCALYPSE DRAGON
BDP 002 / 22 Sep '97 / Black Diamond

Miel, Melinda

☐ KISS ON A TEAR, A
NORM 161CD / Mar '94 / Normal

☐ LAW OF THE DREAM, THE
NORMAL 113CD / Mar '94 / Normal

Migenes Johnson, Julia

☐ LIVE AT OLYMPIA
CDCH 503 / Mar '90 / Milan

Mighty Baby

☐ JUG OF LOVE, A
FLASH 58 / 1 Jun '98 / Flash

☐ MIGHTY BABY
Egyptian tomb / Friend you know but never see / I've been down so long / Same way from the sun / House without windows / Trials of a city / I'm from the country / At a point between fate and destiny / Only dreaming / Dustbin full of rubish / Understanding love / My favourite day / Saying for today
CDWIKD 120 / Feb '94 / Big Beat

Mighty Bop

☐ AUTRES VOIX AUTRES BLUES
YP 013ACD / Nov '96 / Yellow

☐ LA VAGUE SENSORIELLE
YP 008ACD / Jul '96 / Yellow

Mighty Clouds Of Joy

☐ BEST OF THE MIGHTY CLOUDS OF JOY, THE
HMNCD 034 / 22 Jun '98 / Half Moon

☐ POWER
In God's will / Have you told him lately / We will stand / He saw me / I'm ready / I've been in the storm to long / What a wonderful God / Hold on / Nearer my God to thee / Hour of the holy ghost
CDK 9147 / Aug '95 / Alliance Music

Mighty Diamonds

☐ BEST OF MIGHTY DIAMONDS, THE
MDRP 001CD / Jul '97 / Hitbound

☐ BUST OUT
Screechie 'cross the border / Cool it / Africans / I need a roof / Bogle / Love me girl / Hotter the battle / In de dance again / Tell the heathen / Declaration of rights / Came, saw and conquered / Fight fire with fire
GRELCD 188 / Aug '93 / Greensleeves

☐ GET READY
Schoolmate / Another day another raid / Tonight I'm gonna take it easy / Idiers' corner / Cannot say you didn't know / Sensimillia / My baby / Get ready / Up front / Modeller
GRELCD 112 / Jun '88 / Greensleeves

☐ HEADS OF GOVERNMENT
PHCD 2046 / Oct '96 / Penthouse

☐ LIVE (Mighty Diamonds & Mutabaruka)
GCD 8926/27 / Jan '98 / Genes

☐ LIVE IN EUROPE
Party time / Country living / Mr. Botha / Have mercy / I need a roof / My baby / Puttin' on the Ritz / Real enemy / I don't mind / Right time / Africa / Keep on moving / Heavy load
GRELCD 124 / Feb '89 / Greensleeves

☐ MAXIMUM REPLAY
GCCD 0382 / 11 May '98 / Gone Clear

☐ MIGHTY DIAMONDS MEETS DON CARLOS & GOLD AT CHANNEL 1 STUDIO (Mighty Diamonds & Don Carlos)
JJ 084085 / Jun '94 / Jet Star

☐ PAINT IT RED
RASCD 3114 / Jun '93 / Ras

☐ RAS PORTRAITS
Gone bad / Bodygaurd / Posse are you ready / Knock knock / Corrupt cop / Anti-crack / This time / Putting up the ritz / Kick up rumpus / Gold digger
RAS 3326 / Jul '97 / Ras

☐ REAL ENEMY
Real enemy / Gang war / Play girl / Babylon is dangerous / Dem a worry / Free Africa / Right feelin' / I say no / Mr. Botha / Chant down war
GRELCD 102 / Sep '88 / Greensleeves

☐ REGGAE STREET
SHANCD 43004 / May '90 / Shanachie

☐ RIGHT TIME
Right time / Why me black brother why / Shame and pride / Gnashing of teeth / Them never love poor Marcus / I need a roof / Go seek your rights / Have mercy / Natural natty / Africa
SHANCD 43014 / Jan '84 / Shanachie

☐ STAND UP TO YOUR JUDGE
JJCD 020 / Apr '96 / Channel One

Mighty House

☐ LOVE THE SEA IS BLUE
CDGOLD 1 / May '96 / Mighty House

Mighty Lemon Drops

☐ ROLLERCOASTER (The Best Of The Mighty Lemon Drops 1986-1989)
Happy head / Into the heart of love / My biggest thrill / Inside out / Other side of you / Out of hand / Like an angel / Fall down (like the rain) / Splash #1 (now I'm home) / Beautiful shame / Rollercoaster / In everything you do / Uptight / Shine / Where do we go from (heaven) / Count me out / Something happens / Sympathise with us / Now she's gone
CDCHRM 103 / Feb '97 / Chrysalis

Mighty Loverboy

☐ CASSAVA MAN
TRCD 6103 / May '97 / Taso

Mighty Mellow

☐ FOLK FUNK PSYCHEDELIC EXPERIENCE
STONE 9559 / 23 Feb '98 / Yellowstone

Mighty Mighty Bosstones

☐ DEVIL'S NIGHT OUT
Devil's night out / Howwhywuz, Howwhyyam / Drunks and children / Hope I never lose my wallet / Haji / Bartender's song / Patricia / Cave / Do something crazy / Little bit ugly
RR 93582 / 1 Jun '98 / Roadrunner

☐ DEVILS NITE OUT
TAANG 044CD / 11 May '98 / Taang

☐ DON'T KNOW HOW TO PARTY
5148362 / 29 Jun '98 / Mercury

☐ LET'S FACE IT
5344722 / 5 Jan '98 / Big Rig

☐ MORE NOISE AND OTHER DISTURBANCES
TAANG 060CD / 11 May '98 / Taang

☐ QUESTION THE ANSWERS
5228452 / 29 Jun '98 / Mercury

☐ SKA CORE THE DEVIL
5145512 / 29 Jun '98 / Mercury

☐ WHERE'D YOU GO
Where'd you go / Sweet emotion / Enter Sandman / Do something crazy / Ain't talkin' 'bout love
TAANG 048CD / 11 May '98 / Taang

Mighty Pat

☐ BEST OF THE MIGHTY PAT VOL.1, THE
MPCD 1 / 15 Jun '98 / Mighty Pat

Mighty Ryeders

☐ HELP US SPREAD THE MESSAGE
LHCD 017 / Jul '96 / Luv n' Haight

Mighty Sparrow

☐ EXPLODES INTO CALYPSO TIME
Obeah wedding / Bongo / Lion and donkey (rematch) / Wood in the fire / Congo man / Dan is the man (in the van) / Sparrow dead / Sell the pussy / Same time, same place / Carnival woman / Du du yemi / Miss universe / Idi Amin / Soca man / Rose / Madam dracula
SEECD 446 / Jul '96 / See For Miles

☐ SALVATION WITH SOCA BALLADS
BLSCD 1017 / Feb '94 / Soca

☐ SUPREME SERENADER
BLS 1022CD / 27 Apr '98 / BLS

Mika Vainio

☐ ONKO
TO 34 / 10 Nov '97 / Touch

Mikami, Kan

☐ ARASHI AME ARASHI
PSFD 67 / Aug '98 / PSF

☐ TOGE NO SHONIN (Merchant On The Pass)
PSFD 84 / May '97 / PSF

Mike & Rich

☐ EXPERT KNOB TWIDDLERS
CAT 027CD / Jun '96 / Rephlex

Mike & The Mechanics

☐ BEGGAR ON A BEACH OF GOLD
Beggar on a beach of gold / Another cup of coffee / You've really got a hold on me / Mea Culpa / Over my shoulder / Someone always hates someone / Ghost of sex and you / Web of lies / Plain and simple / Something to believe in / House of many rooms / I believe (when I fall in love it will be forever) / Going, going... home
CDV 2772 / Mar '95 / Virgin

☐ LIVING YEARS, THE
Nobody's perfect / Seeing is believing / Nobody knows / Poor boy down / Blame / Don't / Black and blue / Beautiful day / Why me / Living years
CDV 2825 / Feb '97 / Virgin

☐ MIKE & THE MECHANICS HITS
All I need is a miracle / Over my shoulder / Word of mouth / Living years / Another cup of coffee / Nobody's perfect / Silent running / Nobody knows / Get up / Time and place / Taken in / Everybody gets a second chance / Beggar on a beach of gold
CDV 2797 / Feb '96 / Virgin

☐ MIKE AND THE MECHANICS
Silent running / All I need is a miracle / Par avion / I believe (when I fall in love) / Revolution / Take the reins / You are the one / Call to arms / Taken in
CDV 2824 / Feb '97 / Virgin

Mike & The Mellotones

☐ LIVE MAGIC
Not fade away / Love gone sour / Louise / Careless rooster blues / Louisiana nights / Travelin' blues / So glad to have you / Song for a friend / I'd hate you if I didn't love you / Love don't love nobody
LCD 80007 / Nov '96 / Lizard

Mike Ink

☐ GOLDEN
STUDIO 001 / Apr '97 / Studio One

Mike Stuart Span

☐ TIMESPAN
WHCD 003 / Mar '97 / Wooden Hill

Mikey Dread

☐ AFRICAN ANTHEMS
Saturday night style / Industrial spy / Headline news / Mikey Dread in action / Resignation dub / Technician selection / Comic strip / Pre-dawn dub / Operator's choice
ABB 108CD / Apr '96 / Big Cat

☐ BEST SELLERS
Quest for oneness / Break down the walls / Goodbye / Industrial spy / Wake up call (instrumental with dub) / Warrior style / S.w.a.l.k. / Barber saloon - haircut / Choose me / Jah jah love / Sunday school / Positive reality / Enjoy yourself / Roots and culture / Knock knock / My religion (live)
RCD 20178 / Aug '91 / Rykodisc

☐ BEYOND WORLD WAR III
Break down the walls / Jah jah love (in the morning) / Jumping master / Israel (12 tribe) styles / Warrior stylee / Money dread / Rockers delight / Mental slavery / World war III
ABB 109CD / Apr '96 / Big Cat

☐ DUB PARTY
RUSCD 8208 / Jul '95 / ROIR

☐ PAVE THE WAY
HBCD 31 / Oct '95 / Heartbeat

Mikey General

☐ I'M JUST A RASTA MAN
EXTCD 6 / Sep '97 / Exterminator

☐ XTERMINATOR
Sinners / I'm going home / Women of Israel / Tired of it / I'm wondering / I know I love you / New name / I'll never be / Rastaman have to be strong / Black and comey / Deh pon derm / Many have fallen
CRCD 43 / Sep '95 / Charm

Mikey Roots

☐ PRAISE AND HONOUR
Uncle Tom / Plastic City / Give thanks and praise / Praise and honour / I'm alive / Life at the top / We a watch dem / Jesus Jesus Jesus / Paradise / Girl you turn me on / Sweet reggae music / The master / Girl of my mind) / Great is Jah / Life is for real
SPV 0855212 / Aug '96 / SPV

Mikey Spice

☐ ALL ABOUT YOU
So much things to say / Goodbye to you / Lady / Where do love go / All about you / I will stand tall / Rock you / I can't get over you / Give thanks and praise / Baby / Lucky girl to love you / You make me / Let's work it out: Mikey Spice & Luciano
RASCD 3192 / Nov '96 / Ras

☐ BORN AGAIN
VPCD 1465 / Feb '96 / VP

☐ CLOSE THE DOOR
Way you are / What the world need now / Close the door / Deeper and deeper / Am I losing you / Can't get enough / Loving you / Baby come back / Real good men / Sunday morning / Winter of a loving heart / Be my friend
CRCD 52 / Jan '96 / Charm

☐ HAPPINESS
RN 0042 / Apr '95 / Runn

☐ IT'S ALL ABOUT TIME
FHCD 1 / Mar '97 / Firehouse

☐ JAH LIFTED ME
VPCD 1488 / Apr '97 / VP

☐ SO MUCH THINGS TO SAY
BSCD 6 / Oct '96 / Big Ship

☐ TOE 2 TOE (Mikey Spice & Garnet Silk)
CRCD 66 / Jun '97 / Charm

Miki & Griff

☐ BEST OF MIKI & GRIFF, THE
PLSCD 227 / Jul '97 / Pulse

☐ LITTLE BITTY TEAR
Little bitty tear / When I stop dreaming / Even the bad times are good / Cryin' time / Have I told you lately / Streets of london / Shelly's winter love / For the good times / Oh, so many years (I loved you) / I recall a dream / Among my souvenirs / I wanna stay here / Rockin' alone / Hold back tomorrow / Blowin' in the wind
SSLCD 203 / Jun '95 / Savanna

☐ VERY BEST OF MIKI & GRIFF, THE
Hold back tomorrow / Rockin' alone / Last thing on my mind / Take me home country roads / Little bitty tear / All I have to do is dream / Tennessee waltz / It comes and goes / Crystal chandeliers / I wanna stay here / When I grow too old to dream / Crying time / For the good times / I'll have to say I love you, in a song / Streets of london / Blowin' in the wind / Annie's song / Top of the world / You're my best friend / One day at a time
SOW 702 / May '94 / Sound Waves

Mila Et Loma

☐ TAHITI: BELLE EPOQUE VOL.2
S 65809 / Jul '92 / Manuiti

Milagro Saints

☐ MILAGRO SAINTS
MFR 0092 / 24 Aug '98 / Mood Food

Milan, Emma

☐ SERENATA PORTENA
3026722 / 5 Jan '98 / Arcade

Milanes, Pablo

☐ ADEMAS LA SALSA
74321401842 / Feb '97 / Milan

☐ ANIVERSARIO
74321401852 / Feb '97 / Milan

☐ CANTOS DE AMOR Y DESAMOR
74321434702 / Feb '97 / Milan

☐ DE TODO PARA BAILAR (Milanes, Pablo & Adalberto Alvarez/Isaac Delgado)
74321401822 / Feb '97 / Milan

☐ EL GUERRERO
74321402862 / 11 May '98 / Milan

☐ IDENTIDAD
74321402852 / Feb '97 / Milan

☐ PROPOSICIONES
74321401832 / Feb '97 / Milan

Milder, Joakim

☐ STILL IN MOTION
DRCD 188 / Jan '88 / Dragon

☐ WAYS
DRCD 231 / Jan '89 / Dragon

Miles, Anthony

☐ CRYSTAL HEALING
CD 226 / 6 Jul '98 / New World

☐ EVEN WOLVES DREAM
CD 251 / 6 Jul '98 / New World

☐ EVENING STILLNESS
CD 439 / 6 Jul '98 / New World

☐ SANCTUS
CD 294 / 6 Jul '98 / New World

Miles, Buddy

☐ HELL AND BACK (Miles, Buddy Express)
Born under a bad sign / Change / All along the watchtower / Let it be me / Come back home / Be kind to your girlfriend / Decision / Nothing left to lose
RCD 10305 / Jun '94 / Black Arc

☐ TRIBUTE TO JIMI HENDRIX, A
Bad bad misses / Knock on wood / Red house / Come together / Peter Gunn / Take higher / Superstition / Life is what you make it
IRSCD 993013 / Nov '94 / Intercord
SPV 03442072 / Feb '97 / Hengest

Miles, Butch

☐ COOKIN'
CD 020 / May '96 / Nagel Heyer

☐ LIVE (Miles, Butch & Kansas City Big Band)
MECCACD 1013 / Nov '94 / Music Mecca

Miles, Floyd

☐ GOIN' BACK TO DAYTONA
Same thing / Goin' back to Daytona / Mean heartbreaker / No life at all / Oh, Mary / Two against them all / All the love I can / Samson and Delilah / That's why I'm here tonight / Love on the rocks
FIENDCD 752 / Jun '94 / Demon

Miles, Gerry

☐ GERRY MILES (Miles, Gerry & Alan Licht/Keijo Haino)
ALP 71CD / Mar '97 / Atavistic

Miles, Josie

☐ JOSIE MILES VOL.1 1922-1924
DOCD 5466 / Jul '96 / Document

☐ JOSIE MILES VOL.2 1924-1925
DOCD 5467 / Jul '96 / Document

Miles, Lizzie

☐ LIZZIE MILES
AMCD 73 / Feb '95 / American Music

☐ LIZZIE MILES VOL.1 1922-1923
DOCD 5458 / Jun '96 / Document

☐ LIZZIE MILES VOL.2 1923-1928
DOCD 5459 / Jun '96 / Document

☐ LIZZIE MILES VOL.3 1928-1929
DOCD 5460 / Jun '96 / Document

Miles, Lynn

☐ SLIGHTLY HAUNTED
CDPH 1190 / Mar '96 / Philo

Miles, Robert

☐ 23AM
Introducing / New flower / Everyday life / Freedom / Full moon / Awakening / Maresias
74321541132 / 24 Nov '97 / De-Construction

☐ DREAMLAND
Children / Fable / Fantasya / Landscape / In my dreams / Princess of dreams / In the dawn / Red zone
74321429742 / 11 May '98 / De-Construction

Milestone

☐ HERE THERE AND EVERYWHERE
ELS 10 / Sep '97 / Elastic

Milk & Honey Band

☐ ROUND THE SUN
Tin cans / Not heaven / Another perfect day / Out of nowhere / Tea / Round the sun / Pie view / Puerto / My hands / Light / Raining / Bird song
R 3572 / Oct '94 / Rough Trade

Milkshakes

☐ 107 TAPES (Early Demos & Live Recordings)
Pretty baby / Ruhrge beat / Well well / I want you / Flat foot / I say you lie / Beautiful country 81 / Don't love another / Mumble the peg / You did her wrong / Red monkey / Let's stomp / Eaten more honey / Tell me where's that girl / Girl called mine / Little Queenie / Jaguar / Cadillac / Black sails (in the moonlight) / Sit right down and cry / She tells me she loves me / Soldiers of love / Monkey business / Let me love you / El Salvador / Boys
ASK 008CD / '91 / Vinyl Japan

☐ 19TH NERVOUS SHAKEDOWN
It's you / Please don't tell my baby / Shed country / Pretty baby / Don't love another / Another midnight / Seven days / Black sails (in the moonlight) / Cadalina / You did her wrong / Shimmy shake / Hide and scatter / El Salvador / Jaguar / General Belgrano / Klansmen kometh / Brand new Cadillac / Love can lose / Little Bettina / I'm the one for you / Let me love you / Quiet lives / Wounded knee / I'm needing you / Red monkey / Ambassador of love / Can't seem to love that girl / Casandra / Green hornet / Out of control
CDWIKD 939 / Jul '90 / Big Beat

☐ 20 ROCK'N'ROLL HITS OF THE 50'S & 60'S
Hippy hippy shake / Rip it up / I'm gonna sit right down and cry over you / Say mama / Peggy Sue / Jaguar and the thunderbirds / Comanche / I'm talking about you / Sweet little sixteen / Money (that's what I want) / Carol / Boys / Something else / Some other guy / Who do you love / Jezebel / Hidden charms / Little Queenie / Ya ya twist / I wanna be your man
CDWIKM 20 / Mar '91 / Big Beat

☐ AFTER SCHOOL
SCRAG 10CD / Apr '97 / Hangman's Daughter

☐ MILKSHAKES REVENGE, THE
Let me love you / I want you / If I saw you / Graveyard woods / Boys / Little girl be good / Pipeline / She tells me loves me / Little girl (mumble the peg) / Every girl I meet / One I get / Baby what's wrong
HOG1 / Sep '94 / Hangman's Daughter

☐ STILL TALKIN' BOUT
ASK 010CD / Nov '92 / Vinyl Japan

☐ TALKING 'BOUT - MILKSHAKES
She'll be mine / Pretty baby / After midnight / Bull's nose / Shed country / Don't love another / Tell me where's that girl / Can't cha see / Love you the whole night through / Nothing you can say or do / I say you lie
SCRAG 4CD / Jul '95 / Hangman's Daughter

Milky Way

☐ MILKY WAY
Minimal samba / Out of brooklyn / Cruisin' / Ofra haza / Cool wave / Milky way / Ice palace / Mysterious bookshop / Overture / Kolotek / Destiny
CDLR 45012 / Jun '89 / L&R

Milky Wimpshake

☐ BUS ROUTE TO YOUR HEART
SLAMPT 48CD / May '97 / Slampt Underground

Milladoiro

☐ AS FADAS DE ESTRANO NOME
Polca dos campaneiros / O nosso tempo / Vals de libunca / Foliada de berducido / Alala das marinas / Foliada de santirso / Xota para aida / Brincadeiro / As fadas de estrano nome / Danza e contradanza de darbo / Aires de pontevedra / Invernia / O voo da pomba / Danza de alberllos / Clumsy lover
GLCD 3118 / Mar '97 / Green Linnet

☐ GALICIA NO TEMPO
GLCD 3073 / Feb '93 / Green Linnet

☐ GALLAECIA FVLGET
DM 1003CD / Aug '96 / Discmedia

Millar Brass Ensemble

☐ WORLD ANTHEMS VOL.1
USA / UK / Canada / Italy / Argentina / South AFrica / Ukraine / India / Hungary / France / China / Slovakia / Czech Republic / Venezuela / Egypt / Russia / Spain / Trinidad and Tobago / Jordan / Belgium / Ireland / Greece / Chile / Finland / Kenya / South Korea / Israel / Denmark / Bulgaria / Brazil / Japan / Monaco / Latvia / Mexico / New Zealand / Ethiopia / Sweden / Poland / Lithuania / Taiwan / Indonesia / Germany / Estonia / Netherlands / Norway / Austria / Turkey / Australia
DE 3199 / Jul '96 / Delos

Millencolin

☐ FOR MONKEYS
BHR 056CD / Apr '97 / Burning Heart

☐ LIFE ON A PLATE
BHR 033CD / Apr '97 / Burning Heart

☐ SAME OLD TUNES
BHR 019CD / Apr '97 / Burning Heart

☐ SKAUCH
BHR 016CD / Oct '94 / Burning Heart

☐ STORY OF MY LIFE
BHR 032CDS / Apr '97 / Burning Heart

☐ TINY TUNES
BHR 019CD / Feb '95 / Burning Heart

Millenium Project

☐ MILLENIUM PROJECT, THE
Shades of youth / Glide / Sweet / Portal / Take me away / Marine drive march / Adventures of the junky munkey
MFCD 006 / 23 Feb '98 / Mo' Funk

Millennium

☐ 21ST CENTURY BEBOP
REVCC 014 / Nov '96 / Revco

Millennium

☐ BEGIN
CREV 052CD / 15 Dec '97 / Rev-Ola

Miller, Al

☐ COMPLETE RECORDED WORKS 1927-36
DOCD 5306 / Dec '94 / Document

☐ WILD CARDS
I don't play / Stuck in Chicago / Seventy-four / Long grey mare / Can't stay here no more / Special way / Deal the cards / Red top boogie / Fallin' rain / I had a dream / Jockey blues / Big 'C' blues / Blues for John Littlejohn / Sittin' here thinkin'
DE 675 / Mar '97 / Delmark

Miller Bros.

☐ MILLER BROTHERS BAND, THE
CLCD 2853 / Jul '97 / Collector/White Label

Miller, Buddy

☐ POISON LOVE
HCD 8084 / Dec '97 / Hightone

☐ YOUR LOVE AND OTHER LIES
HCD 8063 / Aug '95 / Hightone

Miller, Byron

☐ GIT WIT ME
NOVA 9029 / Jan '93 / Nova

Miller, Cercie

☐ DEDICATION
ST 580 / Jun '94 / Stash

Miller, Dave

☐ FINGER PICKING RAGS AND OTHER DELIGHTS
Sweet Georgia Brown / Stagger Lee / God bless the child / Cheap wine / Chattanooga choo-choo / Inflation blues / Bicycle built for two/Sidewalks of New York / Air on a G string / Too tite rag / Pitschel Players theme / Amtrak shuffle / Blue prelude / Take it on the run / Nice work if you can get it / Son of Diddie / Birth of the blues / Shelley's swing / Fleabites / Little fugue / Hey Jude / Boys from Blue Hill
KMCD 3904 / Jul '97 / Kicking Mule

Miller, Domenic

☐ FIRST TOUCH
ARNR 0197 / 15 Jun '98 / Amiata

Miller, Ed

☐ AT HOME WITH THE EXILES
Pittenween Jo / Darling Allie / John McLean march / Blood upon the grass / Bottle o'the best / Mistress / Yellow on the broom / Jute Mill song / Crooked Jack / Broom o'the cowdenknowes / Generations of change / Man's man / At home with the exiles / Tak a dram
CDTRAX 089 / Jul '95 / Greentrax

☐ EDINBURGH RAMBLER, THE
Home away from home / Rigs o' the rye / Manchester (Edinburgh) rambler / Muir the master builder / Room for us all in the dance / Freewheelin' now / Same old story / Shearin' no for you / Silver darlins/I hae laid a herrin' in saut / Scots wha hae / Teacher's rant / Green and the blue / Devil made Texas / Irish washerwoman / Lads o' duns / Duns dings a'
CDTRAX 164 / Jun '98 / Greentrax

Miller, Frankie

☐ BBC LIVE IN CONCERT
Free and safe on the road / Play something sweet (Brickyard blues) / It takes a lot to laugh, it takes a train to cry / With you in mind / Rock / Be good to yourself / Fool in love / Jealous guy / I can't break away / Double heart trouble / Stubborn kind of fellow / Falling in love / Goodnight sweetheart / Woman to love / When I'm away from you / When something is wrong with my baby / Darlin' / Ain't got no money
WINDCD 054 / Feb '94 / Windsong

☐ BEST OF FRANKIE MILLER, THE
Darlin' / When I'm away from you / Be good to yourself / I can't change it / Highlife/Brickyard blues / Fool in love / Have you seen me lately Joan / Love letters / Caledonia / Stubborn kind of fellow / Devil gun / Hard on the levee / Tears / I'm ready / Shoo-rah shoo-rah / Double heart trouble / So young, so young
CDCHR 1981 / Feb '94 / Chrysalis

☐ LOVE LETTERS
DC 864322 / Mar '96 / Disky

Miller, Frankie

☐ SUGAR COATED BABY
Sugar coated baby / Love me now / Living doll / This lonely heart / Power of love / I don't know / I won't forget / I'm still in love with you / I'm gettin' rid of you / You just had / Bare foot blues / I'm only wishin' / I'm so blue I don't know what to do / I dreamed you were here last night / Baby we're really in love / I can't run away / I'd still want you / I don't know what to tell my heart / Hey where ya goin' / You'll never be true / It's no big thing to me / What have I ever done / Paid in full / My wedding song to you / You're going to cry on my shoulder again / You don't show me much / What you do from now on / Paint, powder and perfume / Day by day / I don't know why I love you
BCD 15909 / May '96 / Bear Family

Miller, Gary

☐ BEST OF GARY MILLER, THE
PLSCD 286 / 1 Jun '98 / Pulse

Miller, Glenn

☐ ABBEY ROAD RECORDING
AMSC 575 / Aug '96 / Avid

☐ AMERICAN PATROL VOL.2 (Miller, Glenn Orchestra)
DAWE 55 / Nov '93 / Magic

☐ ARMY AIR FORCE BAND 1943-1944, THE
St. Louis blues march / Peggy, the pin-up girl / Speak low / Tail-end Charlie / Anvil chorus / Oh what a beautiful morning / There are Yanks / Everybody loves my baby / Enlisted mens mess / I'll be around / There'll be a hot time in the town of Berlin / People will say we're in love / Pearls on velvet / Poinciana / It must be jelly, 'cause jam don't shake like that / Jeep jockey jump / Victory polka
ND 86360 / Jun '88 / Bluebird

☐ ARMY AIRFORCE ORCHESTRA VOL.2
DAWE 78 / Jul '96 / Magic

☐ AT MEADOWBROOK 1939 (Miller, Glenn Orchestra)
Moonlight serenade / Little brown jug / Blue rain / Oh johnny oh johnny oh / In an old Dutch garden / Tiger rag / Love with a capital you / Bugle call rag / Blue moonlight / Indian summer / Why couldn't it last last night / This changing world / I just got a letter / On a little street in Singapore / Faithful to you / Farewell blues / Moonlight serenade (theme and fadeout)
DAWE 34 / Sep '89 / Magic

☐ AUDIO ARCHIVE
Moonlight serenade / Pennsylvania 6-5000 / Don't sit under the apple tree / In the mood / St. Louis blues march / Little brown jug / Anvill chorus / My blue heaven / Sun valley jump / Sunrise serenade / Chattanooga choo choo / Indian summer / Tuxedo junction / Pin ball Paul / Song of the Volga boatmen / Woodpecker song / Begin the beguine / Over there / String of pearls / Slumber song
CDAA 011 / Jun '92 / Tring

☐ BATTLE OF THE BANDS (Miller, Glenn & Tommy Dorsey)
I'm getting sentimental over you / Moonlight serenade / Boogie woogie / In the mood / Indian summer / You and I: *Miller, Glenn & Tommy Dorsey/ Frank Sinatra* / You and I: *Miller, Glenn & Tommy Dorsey/Ray Eherle* / Imagination: *Miller, Glenn & Tommy Dorsey/Ray Eherle* / Imagination: *Miller, Glenn & Tommy Dorsey/Frank Sinatra* / Fools rush in (where angels fear to tread) / Fools rush in (where angels fear to tread): *Miller, Glenn & Tommy Dorsey/ Frank Sinatra* / I'll never smile again: *Miller, Glenn & Tommy Dorsey/Frank Sinatra* / I'll never smile again / Our love affair: *Miller, Glenn & Tommy Dorsey/Ray Eherle* / Our love affair: *Miller, Glenn & Tommy Dorsey/Frank Sinatra* / Stardust: *Miller, Glenn & Tommy Dorsey/Frank Sinatra* / Stardust / String of pearls / Opus one
09026687232 / 10 Aug '98 / RCA Victor

☐ BBC BIG BAND PLAYS GLENN MILLER (BBC Big Band)
In the mood / American patrol / I've got a gal in Kalamazoo / Little brown jug / Chattanooga choo choo / Pennsylvania 6-5000 / String of pearls / Anvil chorus / Moonlight serenade / Tuxedo junction / Don't sit under the apple tree / Song of the Volga boatmen / Begin the beguine / St. Louis blues
QED 138 / Nov '96 / Tring

☐ BEST OF GLENN MILLER, THE
Moonlight serenade / Hallelujah / In a sentimental mood / Back to back / Jumpin' drive / In the mood / Chattanooga cho cho / Happy in love / Serenade in blue / Don't sit under the apple tree / Moonlight cocktail / Pensylvania 6-5000
DCD 5333 / Dec '93 / Disky

☐ BEST OF GLENN MILLER, THE
MACCD 178 / Aug '96 / Autograph

☐ BEST OF GLENN MILLER, THE
In the mood / American patrol / String of pearls / Tuxedo junction / Take the 'A' train / King Pavior stomp / Sun valley jump / Old black magic / Rhapsody in blue / I got rhythm / Little brown jug / Don't sit under the apple tree / I've got a girl in Katamazoo / Pennsylvania 65000 / Chattanooga choo choo / Beat me Daddy, eight to the bar / St. Louis blues / Georgia on my mind / In a sentimental mood / Moonlight serenade
CD 601 / Apr '97 / Music

☐ BEST OF GLENN MILLER, THE (The Lost Recordings/The Secret Broadcasts)
In the mood / Army air corps song: *Desmond, Johnny* / Music stopped: *Desmond, Johnny* / Snafu jump / Summertime / Victory polka: *Glee Club* / Moonlight serenade / Mission to Moscow / Oh, what a beautiful mornin': *Desmond, Johnny & The Crew Chiefs* / Caribbean clipper / Jeanie with the light brown hair / Beat me Daddy, eight to the bar / String of pearls / Anvil chorus / Speak low: *Desmond, Johnny* / Tuxedo junction / Stealin' apples / Jeep jockey jump / Poinciana: *Desmond, Johnny & The Crew Chiefs* / Song of the volga boatmen / American patrol / Little brown jug
75605522902 / 8 Sep '97 / Happy Days

☐ BEST OF GLENN MILLER, THE
Moonlight serenade / Hallelujah / In a sentimental mood / Back to back / Jumpin' jive / In the mood / Chattanooga choo choo / Happy in love / Serenade in blue / Don't sit under the apple tree / Moonlight cocktail / Pensylvania 6-5000
399233 / Jun '97 / Koch Presents

☐ BEST OF THE BIG BANDS, THE
Blues serenade / Moonlight on the Ganges / I got rhythm / Sleepy time gal / Community swing / Time on my hands / My fine feathered friend / Humoresque / Doin' the jive / Silhouetted in the moonlight / Every day's a holiday / Sweet stranger / Don't wake up my heart / Why'd ya make me fall in love / Sold American / Dippermouth blues
4716562 / Jun '92 / Columbia

☐ BIG BAND BASH
Moonlight serenade / Pennsylvania 6-5000 / American patrol / Tuxedo junction / I've got a gal in Kalamazoo / String of pearls / Song of the Volga boatmen / Perfidia / In the mood / Chattanooga choo choo / St. Louis blues march / Anvil chorus / Johnson rag / My melancholy baby / Sun valley jump / Sunrise serenade / Jumpin' jive / Farewell blues / Little brown jug / Hallelujah / Under a blanket of blue
CD 53024 / Mar '90 / Giants Of Jazz

☐ BIG BAND FAVOURITES
BN 028 / Apr '98 / Blue Nite

☐ BROADCAST VERSIONS 1938-1942 (Miller, Glenn Orchestra)
JH 1004 / Feb '91 / Jazz Hour

☐ CANDLELIGHT MILLER
Moonlight serenade / Stairway to the stars / Indian summer / Careless / It's a blue world / When you wish upon a star / Danny boy / Fools rush in (where angels fear to tread) / Nearness of you / Nightingale sang in Berkely Square / You stepped out of a dream / It's always you / I guess I'll have to dream the rest / Moonlight cocktail / Serenade in blue / At last / Moonlight becomes you / Rhapsody in blue
09026687162 / 12 Jan '98 / RCA Victor

☐ CHATTANOOGA CHOO CHOO (The No.1 Hits)
Wishing (will make it so) / Stairway to the stars / Moon love / Over the rainbow / Man with the mandolin / Blue orchids / In the mood / Careless / Tuxedo junction / When you wish upon a star / Woodpecker / Imagination / Fools rush in / Blueberry Hill / Song of the Volga boatmen / You and I / Chattanooga choo choo / Elmer's tune / String of pearls / Moonlight cocktail / Don't sit under the apple tree / I've got a gal in Kalamazoo / That old black magic
ND 90584 / Oct '91 / Bluebird

☐ CHESTERFIELD SHOWS 1942, THE (Miller, Glenn Orchestra)
JH 1028 / Feb '93 / Jazz Hour

☐ CLASSIC GLENN MILLER, THE (2CD Set) (Miller, Glenn Orchestra)
Moonlight serenade / Sunlight serenade / Wishing (will make it so) / Lady in love with you / Stairway to the stars / Little brown jug / Moon love / Over the rainbow / Man with the mandolin / Blue orchids / My prayer / Careless / When you wish upon a star / Indian summer / Tuxedo Junction / Woodpecker song / Imagination / Shake down the stars / Say it / Slow freight / Fools rush in / Nearness of you / Pennsylvania 6-5000 / When the swallows come back to Capistrano / Adios / In the mood / Blueberry Hill / Five o'clock whistle / Nightingale sang in Berkeley Square / Along the Santa Fe trail / Song of the Volga boatmen / I dreamt I dwelt in Harlem / Perfidia / You and I / Chatanooga choo choo / I know why (and so do you) / Elmer's tune / String of pearls / White cliffs of Dover / Moonlight cocktail / Skylark / Don't sit under the apple tree / American patrol / I've got a gal in Kalamazoo / At last / Serenade in blue / Dearly beloved / Moonlight becomes you / That old black magic / Juke box Saturday night
CPCD 82492 / Oct '96 / Charly

☐ CLASSIC YEARS, THE (Miller, Glenn Orchestra)
CDSGP 092 / Oct '93 / Prestige

☐ COLLECTION, THE
In the mood / Pennsylvania 6-5000 / Chattanooga choo choo / Kalamazoo / String of pearls / Song of the volga boatman / Tuxedo junction / Serenade in blue / Moonlight serenade / I'm getting sentimental over you / American patrol / Little brown jug / Anvil chorus / Boogie woogie / Sunrise serenade / I dreamt I dwelt in harlem / Little man who wasn't there / Chestnut tree / April in paris / Georgia on my mind / Sun valley jump / King's march / Glenn island line / Bugle call rag / Flying home
COL 025 / Apr '95 / Collection

☐ COMMEMORATION 1944-1994
OVCCD 002 / May '94 / Satellite Music

☐ COMPLETE GLENN MILLER 1938-1942, THE (13CD Set) (Miller, Glenn Orchestra)
My reverie / By the waters of Minnetonka / King Porter stomp / Shut eye / How I'd like to be with you in Bermuda / Cuckoo in the clock / Romance runs in the family / Chestnut tree / And the angels sing / Moonlight serenade / Lady's in love with you / Wishing (will make it so) / Three little fishes (Itty bitty poo) / Sunrise serenade / Little brown jug / My last goodbye / But it don't mean a thing / Pavanne / Running wild / To you / Stairway to the stars / Blue evening / Lamp is low / Rendezvous time in Paris / We can live on love / Cinderella / Moon love / Guess I'll go back home / I'm sorry for myself / Back to back / Sliphorn jive / Oh you crazy moon / Ain't cha comin' out / Day we meet again / Wanna hat with cherries / Solid American / Pagan love song / Ding dong the witch is dead / Over the rainbow / Little man who wasn't there / Man with the mandolin / Starlit hour / Blue orchids / Glen Island special / Love with a capital you / Baby me / In the mood / Wah (re-bop-boom-bam) / Angel in a furnished room / Twilight interlude / I want to be happy / Farewell blues / Who's sorry now / My isle of golden dreams / My prayer / Blue moonlight / Basket weaver man / Melancholy baby / (Why couldn't it last) last night / Out of space / So many times / Blue rain / Can I help it / I just got a letter / Bless you / Bluebirds in the moonlight / Faithful forever / Speaking of Heaven / Indian summer / It was written in the stars / Johnson rag / Ciribiribin / Careless / Oh Johnny oh Johnny oh / In an old Dutch garden / This changing world / On a little street in Singapore / Vagabond dreams / I beg your pardon / Faithful to you / Gaucho serenade / Sky fell down / When you wish upon a star / Give a little whistle / Missouri waltz / Beautiful Ohio / What's the matter with me / Say si si / Fhumba jumps / Stardust / My melancholy baby / Let's all sing together / Rug cutter's swing / Woodpecker song / Sweet potato piper / Too romantic / Tuxedo junction / Danny boy / Imagination / Shake down the stars / I'll never smile again / Starlight and music / Polka dots and moonbeams / My my / Say it / Moments in the moonlight / Hear my song Violetta / Sierra Sue / Boog it / Yours is my heart alone / I'm stepping out with a memory tonight / Alice blue gown / Wonderful one / Devil may care / April played the fiddle / Fools rush in / I haven't time to be a millionaire / Slow freight / Pennsylvania 6-5000 / Bugle call rag / Nearness of you / Mr. Meadowlark / My blue heaven / When the swallows come back to Capistrano / Million dreams ago / Blueberry Hill / Cabana in Havana / Be happy Angel child / Call of the Canyon / Our love affair / Crosstown / What's your story Morning Glory / Fifth Avenue / I wouldn't take a million / Handful of stars / Old black Joe / Yesterthoughts / Falling leaves / Shadows on the sand / Goodbye little darlin' goodbye / Five o'clock whistle / Beat me Daddy, eight to the bar / Ring, telephone, ring / Make believe ballroom time / You've got me this way / Nightingale sang in Berkeley Square / I'd know you anywhere / Fresh as a daisy / Isn't that just like love / Along the Santa Fe trail / Do you know why / Somewhere / Yes my darling daughter / Stone's throw from heaven / Helpless / Long time no see baby / You are the one / Anvil chorus (parts 1 and 2) / Frenesi / Mem'ry of a

rose / I do, do you / Chapel in the valley / Prairieland lullaby / Ida, sweet as apple cider / Song of the Volga boatmen / One I love (belongs to somebody else) / You stepped out of a dream / I dreamt I dwelt in Harlem / Sun Valley jump / What that man is dead and gone / Spirit is willing / Little old church in England / Perfidia / It's always you / Spring will be so sad (when she comes this year) / Airminded executive / Below the equator / Boulder buff / Bogglie woggle piggy / Chattanooga choo choo / I know why / Don't cry cherie / Cradle song / Sweeter than the sweetest / I guess I'll have to dream the rest / Take the 'A' train / Peek-a-boo to you / Angels came thru / Under blue Canadian skies / Cowboy serenade / You and I / Adios / It happened in Sun Valley / I'm thrilled / Kiss polka / Delilah / From one love to another / Elmer's tune / Says who, says you, says I / Orange blossom lane / Dear Arabella / Man in the moon / Ma-ma-Maria / This time the dream is on me / Dreamsville / Ohio / Papa Niccolini / Jingle bells / This is no laughing matter / Humpty dumpty heart / Everything I love / String of pearls / Baby mine / Long tall mama / Daydreaming / Moonlight sonata / Slumber song / White cliffs of Dover / We're the couple in the castle / It happened in Hawaii / Moonlight cocktail / Happy in love / Fooled / Keep 'em flying / Chip off the old block / Story of a starry night / At the President's birthday ball / Angels of mercy / On the old assembly line / Let's have another cup of coffee / Skylark / Dear Mom / When the roses bloom again / Always in my heart / Shhh, it's a military secret / Don't sit under the apple tree / She'll always remember / Lamplighter's serenade / When Johnny comes marching home / American patrol / Soldier, let me read your letter / Sleep song / Sweet Eloise / I've got a gal in Kalamazoo / Serenade in blue / At last / Lullaby of the rain / Knit one, purl two / That's sabotage / Conchita, Marquita, Lolita, Pepita, Rosita, Juanita Lopez / Hummingbird / Yesterday's gardenias / Dearly beloved / Moonlight mood / Caribbean clipper / Here we go again / That old black magic / Moonlight becomes you / Jukebox Saturday night / It must be jelly, 'cause jam don't shake like that / I'm old fashioned / Pink cocktail for a blue lady / Rainbow rhapsody / Sleepy town train / Rhapsody in blue / Mr. Meadlowlark / Beat me daddy, eight to the bar / Anvil chorus (part 2)

ND 90600 / Nov '91 / Bluebird

☐ **DANCE TIME USA 1939-1940 (Miller, Glenn Orchestra)**
Slumber song / Song of the Volga boatmen / You walk by / There I go / Oh so good / Stone's throw from Heaven / I dreamt I dwelt in Harlem / Moonlight serenade / Beer barrel polka / Cinderella / Back to back / Pagan love song / Dippermouth blues / Moon love / Guess I'll go back home / Moon is a silver dollar / Heaven can wait / Bugle call rag / Sometime
DAWE 51 / Nov '93 / Magic

☐ **DECEMBER 25TH 1943 (Miller, Glenn & The Army Airforce Orchestra)**
JH 1041 / Feb '95 / Jazz Hour

☐ **DEFINITIVE COLLECTION VOL.1, THE (2CD Set)**
MAK 105 / 1 Dec '97 / Avid

☐ **DEFINITIVE COLLECTION VOL.2, THE (2CD Set)**
MAK 106 / 1 Dec '97 / Avid

☐ **DEFINITIVE COLLECTION, THE**
Moonlight serenade / Hallelujah / In a sentimental mood / Back to back / Jumpin jive / In the mood / Chattanooga choo choo / Happy in love / Serenade in blue / Don't sit under the apple tree / Moonlight cocktail / Pensylvania 6-5000 / Johnson rag / St Louis blues / My prayer / Anchors aweigh / I've got a girl in Kalamazoo / Woodpecker song / I know why / Medley (my melancholy baby, moon love, stomping at the Savoy
ECD 3112 / Jan '95 / K-Tel

☐ **EARLY YEARS, THE**
DHDL 129 / Oct '96 / Magic

☐ **ESSENTIAL GLENN MILLER ORCHESTRA, THE**
4715582 / Jan '95 / Sony Jazz

☐ **ESSENTIAL GLENN MILLER, THE**
Moonlight serenade / Wishing / Sunrise serenade / Little brown jug / Running wild / Stairway to the stars / Moon love / Over the rainbow / My isle of golden dreams / In the mood / Indian summer / It's a blue world / Gaucho serenade / When you wish upon a star / Say si si / Stardust / Tuxedo junction / Danny Boy / Imagination / Fools rush in / Pennsylvania 6-5000 / Nearness of you / When the swallows come back to Capistrano / Million dreams ago / Nightingale sang in Berkley Square / Along the Santa Fe trail / Yes my darling daughter / Anvil chorus / Song of the Volga boatmen / Perfidia / Chattanooga choo choo / I know why / You and I / Adios / Elmer's tune / String of pearls / White cliffs of Dover / Moonlight cocktail / Skylark / Always in my heart / Don't sit under the apple tree / American patrol / I've got a gal in Kalamazoo / Serenade in blue / At last / Old black magic / Jukebox Saturday night
07863766520 / Apr '95 / Bluebird

☐ **ESSENTIAL WARTIME RECORDINGS**
MCCD 249 / Jun '96 / Music Club

☐ **FRESH AS A DAISY (Miller, Glenn Orchestra)**
Cabana in Havana / Fresh as a daisy / Stardust / Sweeter than the sweetest / Don't cry cherie / Blue moonlight / Farewell blues / Who's sorry now / I dreamt I dwelt in Harlem / Let's have another cup of coffee / It was written in the stars / My melancholy lullaby / All I do is dream of you / Blue orchids / Blue rain / Wonderful one / Twilight interlude / Pagan love song / Running wild / Ciribiribin / My Isle of golden dreams / In the mood
RAJCD 841 / May '98 / Empress

☐ **GLENN MILLER (4CD Set)**
American patrol / Serenade in blue / That old black magic / You and I / Moonlight cocktail / Under a blanket of blue / Perfidia / Stardust / At last / Adios / Elmer's tune / Little man who wasn't there / This time the dream's on me / Everything I love / Skylark / There'll be bluebirds over the white cliffs of Dover / I dreamt I dwelt in Harlem / Starlit hour / Danny boy / I've got a gal in Kalamazoo / Moonlight serenade / Sunrise serenade / Don't sit under the apple tree with anyone else but me / Lady's in love with you / Anvil chorus / Indian summer / I got rhythm / Blue skies / Johnson rag / St. Louis blues / Pennsylvania 6-5000 / String of pearls / I know why / One o'clock jump / Farewell blues / Caribbean clipper / On a little street in Singapore / Hop / In the mood / My melancholy baby / Little brown jug / Tuxedo junction / I wan't to be happy / My blue heaven / I wanna hat with cherries / Begin the beguine / Say it / Dearly beloved / Song of the Volga boatmen / Perfidia becomes you / It must be jelly / Fools rush in / Chattanooga choo choo / You are always in my heart / And the angels sing / When Johnny comes marching home / Running wild / Slip horn jive / Seven-o-five / Falling leaves
QUAD 007 / Dec '96 / Tring

☐ **GLENN MILLER (CD/CD Rom Set)**
In the mood / Chatanooga choo choo / Tuxedo Junction / Kalamazoo / Song of the Volga boatman / Pennsylvania 6-5000 / Moonlight serenade / Little brown jug / String of pearls / American patrol / Anvil chorus / I dreamt I dwelt in Harlem / Serenade in blue / April in Paris / Sunrise serenade / Starlit hour / Sun valley jump
WWCDR 003 / Apr '97 / Weton-Wesgram

☐ **GLENN MILLER**
In the mood / Sunrise serenade / American patrol / My melancholy baby / Anvil chorus / Stardust / Juke box Saturday night / String of pearls / Johnson rag / I've got a gal in Kalamazoo / Moonlight serenade / Song of the Volga boatmen / Sun Valley jump / I know why / St. Louis blues march / Chattanooga choo choo / Pennsylvania 6-5000 / Perfidia
399529 / May '97 / Koch Presents

☐ **GLENN MILLER (Miller, Glenn & His Orchestra)**
In the mood / Elmer's tune / Blue velvet / Chatanooga choo choo / Pennsylvania 6-5000 / Serenade in blue / Caribbean clipper / Little brown jug / At last / Sun valley jump / Moonlight cocktail / Everybody loves my baby / Canadian sunset
4874452 / 29 Sep '97 / Sony Jazz

☐ **GLENN MILLER 1943-1944**
PHONTCD 9307 / Aug '94 / Phontastic

☐ **GLENN MILLER AND HIS AMERICAN BAND 1945**
DAWE 72 / Dec '94 / Magic

☐ **GLENN MILLER AND HIS ARMY AIR FORCE ORCHESTRA 1944**
DAWE 62 / Jul '93 / Magic

☐ **GLENN MILLER ARMY AIR FORCE BAND 1943-1944, THE**
Anvil chorus / Stormy weather / Jukebox Saturday night / Jeep jockey jump / All the things you are / Song of the Volga boatmen / With my head in the clouds / I hear you screaming / Long ago and far away / Cherokee / Peggy and the pin-up girl / In the mood / Holiday for strings / String of pearls / Don't be that way
ND 89767 / Jun '94 / Jazz Tribune

☐ **GLENN MILLER COLLECTOR'S EDITION**
DVX 8022 / Apr '95 / Deja Vu

☐ **GLENN MILLER GOLD (2CD Set)**
D2CD 4001 / Jun '95 / Deja Vu

☐ **GLENN MILLER LIVE 1940**
TAX 37042 / Aug '94 / Tax

☐ **GLENN MILLER ORCHESTRA, THE**
Moonlight serenade / Sunrise serenade / Don't sit under the apple tree / Bugle call rag / Anvil chorus / Moonlight cocktail / Indian summer / Sun Valley jump / Farewell blues / Under a blanket of blue / Penfida / Stardust / At last / St. Louis blues march / Adios / Little brown jug / American patrol / Tuxedo junction / Slumber song / My blue heaven / Blues in my heart / Begin the beguine / Everybody loves my baby / Over there / Song of the Volga boatmen / Enlisted mens blues / It must be jelly, 'cause jam don't shake like that / Rainbow rhapsody / Londonderry air / I've got a gal in Kalamazoo / Pennsylvania 6-5000 / String of pearls / April in Paris / Little man who wasn't there / Georgia on my mind / Baby me / Chestnut tree / Kings march / I dreamt I dwelt in Harlem / Starlit hour / Glenn Island line / That old black magic / In the mood / Serenade in blue / Pin ball Paul / Chatanooga choo choo / String of pearls / Blue champagne / When Johnny comes marching home / Jeanie with the light brown hair / Serenade in blue / In a sentimental mood / Elmer's tune / Seven-o-five / Falling leaves / Caribbean clipper / My love for you / Lover / Woodpecker song / Hallelujah
TFP 017 / Nov '92 / Tring

☐ **GLENN MILLER VOL.1**
Moonlight serenade / St. louis blues / Rhapsody in blue / Londonderry air / American patrol / Little brown jug / Jeannie with the light / Serenade in blue / Georgia on my mind / Tchaikovsky's piano concert / In a sentimental mood / I've got a gal in kalamazoo / In the mood / Tuxedo junction / String of pearls / At last
15701 / Apr '97 / Laserlight

☐ **GLENN MILLER VOL.2**
15712 / Apr '94 / Laserlight

☐ **GLENN MILLER'S GI'S IN PARIS**
How high the moon / Stompin' at the Savoy / S'wonderful / Blue skies / You're driving me crazy / On the sunny side of the street / Hommage a Fats Waller / Don't blame me / Pennies from heaven / Stealin' Smack's apples / After you've gone / China boy
CBC 1051 / 27 Jul '98 / Timeless Historical

☐ **GLENN MILLER'S MEN IN PARIS (Various Artists)**
STD 1 / Nov '95 / Starlite

☐ **GLENN MILLER/DUKE ELLINGTON/ BENNY GOODMAN (2CD Set) (Miller, Glenn & Duke Ellington/Benny Goodman)**
MAK 104 / Nov '94 / Avid

☐ **GOLD COLLECTION, THE**
D2CD 01 / Dec '92 / Deja Vu

☐ **GOLD COLLECTION, THE (2CD Set)**
R2CD 4001 / 13 Apr '98 / Deja Vu

☐ **GREAT INSTRUMENTALS 1938-1942 (Miller, Glenn Orchestra)**
RTR 79001 / May '96 / Retrieval

☐ **GREATEST HITS**
In the mood / String of pearls / Pennsylvania 6-500 / Chattanooga choo choo / Tuxedo junction / Little brown jug / I've got a gal in Kalamazoo / American patrol / Moonlight serenade / Don't sit under the apple tree / Serenade in blue / Song of the Volga boatmen
74321339352 / Jan '96 / Camden

☐ **GREATEST HITS LIVE 1940-1942 (Miller, Glenn Orchestra)**
DLWE 1 / Nov '93 / Magic

☐ **GREATEST HITS OF GLENN MILLER, THE**
GO 3809 / 1 Dec '97 / Golden Options

☐ **HANDFUL OF STARS 1940, A**
DAWE 71 / '94 / Magic

☐ **HIS GREATEST BAND (Miller, Glenn & The Army Airforce Orchestra)**
3037300042 / May '97 / Carlton

☐ **I SUSTAIN THE WINGS VOL.2 (USA 1943) (Miller, Glenn & The Army Airforce Orchestra)**
DAWE 67 / Jan '94 / Magic

☐ **IN REAL HI-FI STEREO 1941 (Miller, Glenn Orchestra)**
JH 1042 / Feb '95 / Jazz Hour

☐ **IN THE DIGITAL MOOD (Miller, Glenn Orchestra)**
In the mood / Chattanooga choo choo / American patrol / String of pearls / Little brown jug / I've got a gal in Kalamazoo / Tuxedo Junction / St. Louis blues march / Pennsylvania 6-5000 / Moonlight serenade
GRP 95022 / 25 May '98 / Universal

☐ **IN THE MOOD**
In the mood / Pennsylvania 6-5000 / Moonlight serenade / American patrol / Sunrise serenade / Jumpin' jive / Tuxedo junction / Anvil chorus / Chattanooga choo choo / Johnson rag / String of pearls / St. Louis blues march / I've got a gal in Kalamazoo / Song of the Volga boatmen / Perfidia / Little brown jug / My melancholy baby / Serenade in blue
CD 56006 / Aug '94 / Jazz Roots

☐ **IN THE MOOD**
In the mood / Pennsylvania 6-5000 / Moonlight becomes you / Sunrise serenade / Moonlight serenade / Elmer's tune / Jukebox Saturday night / Tuxedo junction / Chattanooga choo choo / Caribbean clipper / Moonlight cocktail / American patrol / I got a gal in Kalamazoo / Danny Boy / Serenade in blue / String of pearls / At last / Going home / I know why / Don't sit under the apple tree
MUCD 9010 / Apr '95 / Musketeer

☐ **IN THE MOOD**
TRTCD 192 / Jun '94 / TrueTrax

☐ **IN THE MOOD**
String of pearls / Pennsylvania 6-5000 / Moonglow / Slaughter on 10th avenue / Moonlight serenade / American patrol / Sentimental journey / Little brown jug / Anvil chorus / Elmer's tune / Begin the beguine / Flag waver / In the mood / Chattanooga choo choo / Don't sit under the apple tree / Get happy / Swing low sweet chariot\
100612 / May '97 / A-Play Collection

☐ **IN THE MOOD**
BN 026 / Apr '98 / Blue Nite

☐ **IN THE MOOD 1939-1940**
Blueberry Hill / Bugle call rag / Careless / Danny Boy / Imagination / In the mood / Indian summer / It's a blue world / Moonlight serenade / My My / Nearness of you / Out of space / Pennsylvania 6-5000 / Rug cutters' swing / Say it / Slow freight / Stairway to the stars / Stardust / Sunrise serenade / Tuxedo junction / Wishing / Woodpecker song
CDAJA 5078 / Apr '91 / Living Era

☐ **INTRODUCTION TO GLENN MILLER 1935-1942, AN**
4033 / Jul '96 / Best Of Jazz

☐ **JAZZ COLLECTION (2CD Set)**
Moonlight serenade / St.Louis blues / American patrol / Little brown jug / Serenade in blue / In the mood / Tuxedo junction / String of pearls / At last / Is you is or is you ain't my baby / Great day / Sun valley jump / I got rhythm / My blue heaven / Tisket a tasket / Solitude / Here we go again / Jeep jockey jump / Over there / Peggy the pin up girl / Georgia on my mind / In a sentimental mood / Jeannie with the light brown hair / Woodpecker / Moon love / Stardust / Anchors aweigh / Caribbean clipper / Glen Island special / Perfidia
24 367 / Nov '97 / Laserlight

☐ **JAZZ GREATS**
In the mood / Moonlight serenade / Tuxedo junction: *Hurley, Clyde & Dale McMickle/Chummy MacGregor* / Chattanooga choo choo: *Beneke, Tex & Texas Modernaires/Paul Kelly* / String of pearls / When you wish upon a star / That old black magic: *Nelson, Skip & The Modernaires* / Moon love: *Eberle, Ray* / Little brown jug / Sunrise serenade / Pennsylvania 6-5000 / I've got a gal in Kalamazoo: *Beneke, Tex & Texas Modernaires/Marion Hutton* / American patrol / Don't sit under the apple tree: *Beneke, Tex & Texas Modernaires/Marion Hutton* / King Porter stomp
74321499782 / 6 Oct '97 / RCA Victor

☐ **JAZZ PORTRAITS (Miller, Glenn Orchestra)**
In the mood / Pennsylvania 6-5000 / Moonlight serenade / American patrol / Sunrise serenade / Jumpin' jive / Tuxedo junction / Anvil chorus / Chattanooga choo choo / Johnson rag / String of pearls / St. Louis blues march / I've got a gal in Kalamazoo / Song of the Volga boatmen / Perfidia / Little brown jug / My melancholy baby / Serenade in blue
CD 14502 / May '94 / Jazz Portraits

☐ **L'INCONTOURNABLE**
3014642 / Apr '97 / Arcade

☐ **LEGEND LIVES ON, THE (The Civilian Orchestra 1938-1941/4CD Set)**
Theme / Moonlight serenade / Butcher boy / Don't wake up my heart / Cowboy from Brooklyn / My best wishes / I know that you know / On the sentimental side / On the Alamo / Dipsy doodle / Theme / Moonlight serenade / Sold American / Please come out of your dream / Poinciana / Lady's in love with you / Wishing / Pavanne / And the angels sing / King Porter stomp / Moon is a silver dollar / Sometime / Hold tight / Moonlight serenade / Glen island special / Lamp is low / Jumpin' jive / My blue heaven / Runnin' wild / Moonlight serenade / I've got no string / Theme, Moonlight Serenade / Woodpecker song / Sweet and lovely / Sierra Sue / Very thought of you / Blue evening/Tiger rag / Boog It / Anchors aweigh / Moonlight serenade / Let's all sing together / Say it / On the Alamo / Fools rush in / Slow freight / Woodpecker song / By the waters of Minnetonka / Runnin' wild / Solitude / On the Alamo / King Porter stomp / Wham / Solid as a Stonewall Jackson / Jeannie with the light brown hair / I never took a lesson in my life / I want to be happy / Farewell blues / Fifth avenue / Sophisticated lady / Isn't it romantic / Shadows on the sand / Blue prelude / Moonlight serenade / Midnight on the Nile / Shadows on the sand / Limehouse blues / Handful of stars / Crosstown / Tiger rag / In a sentimental mood / Beat me daddy / Eight to the bar / Bugle woogie / High on a windy hill / Goin' home / You walk by / Georgia on my mind / Morning after / In the mood / Moonlight serenade / Sun valley jump / Chattanooga choo-choo / It happened in sun valley / Spirit is willing / I know why / Measure for measure / Whatcha' know, Joe / Are you Rusty Gate / Love song hasn't been sung / Just a little bit north of south Carolina / Here we go again / Song of the Volga boatmen / Hereafter / Moonlight serenade/Jingle bells / Nobody ever wants me / Sun valley jump/Moonlight serenade
FBB 902 / 27 Oct '97 / Ember

☐ **LEGEND, THE**
Jeep jockey jump / Symphony / Rhapsody in blue / Seven-o-five / Killarney / I've got a heart filled with love / Wabash blues / Everybody loves my baby / In the mood / There'll be a hot time in the town of Berlin / Speak low / Keep 'em flying / Moonlight serenade / Why dream / Here we go again / Fellow on a furlough / Passage interdit / Little brown jug / Deep purple / Jukebox Saturday night / Now I know / Bubble bath / Closing time
DBCD 01 / Oct '87 / Dance Band Days

☐ **LEGENDARY PERFORMER, A**
Moonlight serenade / Sunrise serenade / Little brown jug / Danny boy / Tuxedo junction / My melancholy baby / Pennsylvania / So you're the one / Sentimental me / Song of the Volga boatmen / Jack and Jill / String of pearls / Stardust / Everything I love / Jingle bells / In the mood / Chattanooga choo choo / At last / Moonlight cocktail / I've got a gal in Kalamazoo / Jukebox Saturday night
ND 90586 / Oct '91 / Bluebird

☐ **LIVE 1938/39 PARADISE RESTAURANT NEW YORK (Miller, Glenn Orchestra)**
Lovelight in the starlight / How'd ya like to love me / You leave me breathless / Please come out of your dream / What have you got that get's me / Room with a view / Wait until
DAWE 42 / '89 / Magic

☐ **LIVE AT CAFE ROUGE 1940 (Miller, Glenn Orchestra)**
JH 1037 / Feb '95 / Jazz Hour

☐ **LIVE AT THE HOLLYWOOD PALLADIUM 1946**
Sun valley jump / Try a little tenderness / Woodchuck song / There's a small hotel / Blue skies / Don't be a baby, baby / Troop movement / If you were the only girl in the world / Juke box saturday night / These foolish things / Anvil chorus / Jeep jockey jump / Anybodys love song / I've got the sun in the morning / Falling leaves / Come rain or come shine / Here we go again / Texas tex / Cynthia's in love / I hear you screamin' / Moonlight serenade
CD 53200 / Aug '95 / Giants Of Jazz

☐ **LIVE FROM MEADOWBROOK BALLROOM 1939 VOL.2**
DAWE 81 / Jul '97 / Magic

☐ **LIVE IN HI-FI, GLEN ISLAND 1939 (Miller, Glenn Orchestra)**
JH 1012 / '91 / Jazz Hour

☐ **LOST RECORDINGS VOL.1, THE (Conducted By Glenn Miller - 1944) (American Band Of The Allied Expeditionary Force)**
In the mood / Stardust / Song of the Volga boatmen / Long ago and far away / Is you is or is you ain't my baby / American patrol / Summertime / Tuxedo junction / Begin the beguine / Anvil chorus / Here we go again / My heart tells me / String of pearls / Stormy weather / Poinciana / All I do is dream of you / Where or when / Cow cow boogie
CD 53288 / Jul '97 / Giants Of Jazz

□ LOST RECORDINGS VOL.2, THE (Conducted By Glenn Miller - 1944) (American Band Of The Allied Expeditionary Force)
Stardust / Farewell blues / I've got a heart filled with love (for you dear) / Caribbean clipper / Smoke gets in your eyes / Little brown jug / Holiday for strings / Tail end Charlie / Begin the Beguine / Everybody loves my baby / Jeep jockey jump / Great day / All the things you are / Swing low, sweet chariot / Body and soul / Beat me daddy, eight to the bar / Get happy / Moonlight serenade
CD 53289 / Jul '97 / Giants Of Jazz

□ LOST RECORDINGS, THE
In the mood / Stardust / Song of the Volga boatmen / Long ago and far away / Is you is or is you ain't my baby / Great day / Summertime / Tuxedo junction / Begin the beguine / Anvil chorus / Poinclana / American patrol / Here we go again / My heart tells me / String of pearls / Stormy weather / Little brown jug / Where or when / Cow cow boogie / Holiday for strings / All I do is dream of you / Farewell blues / I've got a heart filled with love / Dear / Caribbean clipper / Smoke gets in your eyes / Tail end Charlie / Everybody loves my baby / Jeep jockey jump / All the things you are / Swing low, sweet chariot / Body and soul / Beat me Daddy, eight to the bar / Eight to the bar / Get happy / Moonlight serenade
CDHD 4012 / Feb '95 / Happy Days

□ MAGIC OF GLENN MILLER (4CD Set)
CDDIG 14 / Apr '95 / Charly

□ MAJOR GLENN MILLER ARMY AIRFORCE OVERSEAS ORCHESTRA (Miller, Glenn Orchestra)
Flying home / Long ago and far away / Moonlight serenade / I can't give you anything but love / Symphony / Cherokee / Laura
DAWE 47 / Nov '93 / Magic

□ MARVELLOUS MILLER MAGIC (2CD Set)
String of pearls / I've got a gal in Kalamazoo / In the mood / Tuxedo junction / Wishing / Moon love / I dreamt I dwelt in Harlem / Juke box Saturday night / Stairway to the stars / My blue heaven / Elmers tune / Skylark / I know why / Sunrise serenade / Pennsylvania 6-5000 / Little brown jug / Rainbow rhapsody / Blueberry Hill / Serenade in blue / Adios / Don't sit under the apple tree / American patrol / Fools rush in / At last / Moonlight cocktail / Nightingale sang in Berkeley Square / Song of the Volga Boatmen / Over the rainbow / Take the 'A' train / When you wish upon a star / It's a blue world / Long tall mama / You and I / Stardust / Chattanooga choo choo / Slow freight / Danny Boy / Old black magic / Rhapsody in blue / Moonlight serenade
330022 / Jul '96 / Hallmark

□ MEMORIAL ALBUM, THE
UAE 34092 / 27 Apr '98 / Memorial Album

□ MEMORIAL FOR GLENN MILLER VOL.2
King's march / Tuxedo Junction / All the things you are / April in Paris / American patrol / Song of the Volga boatmen / Night and day / Baby me / Georgia on my mind / Dream / Over the rainbow / Running wild / Stormy weather / Man I love / Lady is a tramp / Adios / Tisket-a-tasket
139 005 / Dec '86 / Accord

□ MEMORIAL FOR GLENN MILLER VOL.3
139 218 / Dec '86 / Accord

□ MILLER MAKES IT HAPPEN
Little brown jug / Anvil chorus / Blueberry Hill / Sliphorn jive / Johnson rag / Perfidia / King Porter stomp / My blue Heaven / Sun Valley jump / Caribbean clipper / It's a blue world / Bugle call rag / Blue moonlight / Everything I love / Glen Island special / When Johnny comes marching home / Happy in love / Blues in the night
307112 / 13 Oct '97 / Hallmark

□ MISSING CHAPTERS VOL.1 (American Patrol)
Sun valley jump / Pearls on velvet / With my head in the clouds / Speak low / Here we go again / Rhapsody in blue / Dipsy doodle / String of pearls / Cherokee / Music stopped / It must be jelly / Songs my Mother taught me / Stompin' at the Savoy / Poinciana / Tail-end Charlie / Summertime / Song of the Volga boatmen / Oh what a beautiful morning / Suddenly it's Spring / Honeysuckle rose / Stardust / Anvil chorus
AMSC 556 / Dec '95 / Avid

□ MISSING CHAPTERS VOL.2 (Keep 'Em Flying)
Bubble bath / Blue Danube / Everybody loves my baby / Blues in the night / In the mood / In the gloaming / Over there / Stormy weather / Victory polka / Tuxedo junction / I love you / Holiday for strings / Jeanie with the light brown hair / Enlisted men's mess / Now I know / Guns in the sky / Don't be that way / All through the night / Put your arms around me / Moondreams / Keep 'em flying / All the things you are / Music makers / Squadron song
AMSC 557 / Dec '95 / Avid

□ MISSING CHAPTERS VOL.3 (All's Well Mademoiselle)
Moonlight serenade / 705 / Sweet Lorraine / Tuxedo junction / Jeannie with the light brown hair / Begin the beguine / Blue rain / Down the road apiece / Great day / Jerry's Aachen back / Anchors aweigh / Song of the Volga boatmen / Little brown jug / Parachute jump / Wham / Mission to Moscow / Git along song / What is this thing called love / Time alone will tell / All's well Madamoiselle / Hog snortin' romp / I sustain the wings / I'll see you again / Londonderry air / Way you look tonight / I'll be seeing you / I sustain the wings
AMSC 558 / Dec '95 / Avid

□ MISSING CHAPTERS VOL.4 (The Red Cavalry March)
Moonlight serenade / Song of the Volga boatmen / Laura / Get happy / Drink to me with thine eyes / There goes that song again / Music makers / Farewell blues / Red cavalry march / I've got sixpence / String of pearls / Trolley song / Shoo shoo baby / Time alone will tell / My guy's come back / Everybody loves my baby / Moonlight serenade / Here we go again / I'll be seeing you / Swing low, sweet chariot / Poinciana / Moonlight serenade
AMSC 559 / Dec '95 / Avid

□ MISSING CHAPTERS VOL.5 (The Complete Abbey Road Recordings)
Moonlight serenade / In the mood / Stardust / Song of the Volga boatmen / Long ago and far away / Is you is or is you ain't my baby / Great day / Moonlight serenade / American patrol / Summertime / Tuxedo junction / Now I know / Begin the beguine / Anvil chorus / Moonlight serenade / Hre we go again / My heart tells me / String of pearls / Stormy weather / Poinciana / Moonlight serenade
AMSC 560 / Dec '95 / Avid

□ MISSING CHAPTERS VOL.6 (Blue Champagne)
Army Air Corps/I sustain the wings / Sun valley jump / Suddenly it's Spring / All through the night / I love you / Take it easy / Blue Hawaii / Juke box Saturday night / Pearls on velvet / There are Yanks / I sustain the wings / My ideal / Holiday for strings / Goin' home / Dipsy doodle / Speak low / It must be jelly / Annie Laurie / In the mood / In an 18th century drawing room / Guns in the sky / Deep purple / Oh what a beautiful morning / Now I know / Put your arms around me honey / Blue champagne / Snafu jump / Army Air Corps song
AMSC 561 / Dec '95 / Avid

□ MISSING CHAPTERS VOL.7 (S'wonderful)
I sustain the wings / In the mood / My heart tells me / Holidays for strings / Victory polka / Wigan pier wiggle / Going my way / Everybody loves my baby / Song and dance / Long long ago / Music stopped / Dipsy doodle / Blues in my heart / Eyes and ears of the world / Waiting for the evening mail / She's funny that way / 9.20 Special / S'wonderful / You, fascinating you / Sleepy town train / I heard you screamin'
AMSC 588 / Mar '97 / Avid

□ MISSING CHAPTERS VOL.8 (Get Happy)
Song and dance / Somebody's wrong / Whatcha know Joe / I dream of you / Plain and fancy blues / Moonlight serenade / In the mood / More and more / Get happy / Old black Joe / Someone to love / Here we go again / My prayer / Her tears flowed like wine / Schubert's serenade / Some other time / Little brown jug / Under a blanket of blue / No compris / With my head in the clouds / I sustain the wings / Spring will be a little late this year / I dream of Jeannie with the light brown hair / Lover come back to me
AMSC 589 / Mar '97 / Avid

□ MISSING CHAPTERS VOL.9
In the mood / Dearly beloved / Caribbean clipper / Star eyes / Tuxedo junction / I'll be around / Jeep jockey jump / Speak low / Along the Santa Fe trail / Long ago and far away / There'll be a hot time in the town of Berlin / Tail end Charlie / Shoo shoo baby / Chattanooga choo choo / Wham (rebop boom bam) / GI jive / Oh Wisconsin / After you've gone / Notre Dame victory march / Breakin' in a pair of shoes / Oh lady be good / Shine on harvest moon / King Porter stomp / Makin' whoopee / I'm confessin' that I love you / Blue skies / I'll remember April
AMSC 635 / 22 Jun '98 / Avid

□ MOOD SWINGS
Moonlight serenade / Serenade in blue / Chattanooga choo choo / It happened in Sun Valley / American patrol / Bugle call rag / I've got a gal in Kalamazoo / Spirit is willing / Tuxedo junction / I know why / At last / String of pearls / Measure for measure / Pennsylvania 6500 / Sun Valley jump / In the mood
SUMCD 4017 / Nov '96 / Summit

□ MOONLIGHT COCKTAIL (Miller, Glenn & Ray Eberle)
Too romantic / Imagination / Danny boy / Say it / Hear my song violetta / Pennsylvania 6-5000 / Sierra Sue / Devil may care / Bugle call rag / Nearness of you / Moonlight cocktail / Story of a starry night / Sleep song / Serenade in blue / At last / Beethoven's moonlight sonata / Who's sorry now / Out of space / One I love / Brahms cradle song / Slow freight / Blue orchids
CDMOIR 309 / Apr '95 / Memoir

□ MOONLIGHT COCKTAIL
American patrol / Serenade in blue / That old black magic / Bugle call rag / Moonlight cocktail / Under a blanket of blue / Perfidia / Stardust / At last / Adios / April in Paris / Little man wasn't there / Georgia on my mind / Baby me / Chestnut tree / Kings march / I dreamt I dwell in Harlem / Starlit hour / Glen island line / Rainbow rhapsody / Londonderry air / Kalamazoo
GRF 271 / Apr '93 / Tring

□ MOONLIGHT COCKTAIL
American patrol / Serenade in blue / That old black magic / You and I / Moonlight cocktail / Under a blanket of blue / Perfidia / Stardust / At last / Adios / Elmer's tune / Little man who wasn't there / This time the dream's on me / Everything I love / Skylark / White cliffs of Dover / I dreamt I dwelt in Harlem / Starlit hour / Londonderry air / I've got a gal in kalamazoo
QED 218 / Nov '96 / Tring

□ MOONLIGHT SERENADE
Moonlight serenade / King Porter stomp / Little brown jug / In the mood / Tuxedo junction / Pennsylvania 6-5000 / String of pearls / Elmer's tune / Chattanooga choo choo / Don't sit under the apple tree / American patrol
ND 90626 / Apr '92 / Bluebird

□ MOONLIGHT SERENADE
Moonlight serenade / Wham / Sunrise serenade / Ciribiribin / Bluebirds in the moonlight / My prayer / Little brown jug / Nearness of you / Fresh as a daisy / Blueberry Hill / Booglie wooglie piggy / When the swallows come back to Capistrano / Boulder buff / Handful of stars / Kiss polka / I know why / Chattanooga choo choo / It happened in Sun Valley / Let's have another cup of coffee / Story of a starry night / Don't sit under the apple tree / Jukebox Saturday night / Adios
CDHD 210 / Feb '97 / Happy Days

□ MOONLIGHT SERENADE
Moonlight serenade / Little brown jug / Sunrise serenade / Pin ball Paul / Indian summer / Woodpecker song / Pennsylvania 6-5000 / Slumber song / Chatanooga choo choo / String of pearls / Don't sit under the apple tree / My blue heaven / In the mood / Sun Valley jump / Farewell blues / Tuxedo junction / Blues in my heart / Begin the beguine / Anvill chorus / St. Louis blues march / Everybody loves my baby / Over there / Song of the Volga boatmen / Enlisted mens' Miss / It must be jelly, 'cause jam don't shake like that
GRF 076 / Apr '93 / Tring

□ MOONLIGHT SERENADE
Moonlight serenade / Pennsylvania 6-5000 / Johnson rag / Blue orchids / American patrol / Moonlight cocktail / Little brown jug / Frenesi / Elmer's tune / Slip horn jive / Don't sit under the apple tree / String of pearls / Chattanooga choo choo / Take the 'A' train / Perfidia / Tuxedo Junction / Nightingale sang in Berkeley Square / Boulder buff / Story of a starry night / At last / Serenade in blue / I've got a gal in Kalamazoo / In the mood
PPCD 78116 / Feb '95 / Past Perfect

□ MOONLIGHT SERENADE
BN 027 / Apr '98 / Blue Nite

□ ON THE AIR
Pennsylvania 6-5000 / My isle of golden dreams / Booglie wooglie piggy / Tuxedo junction / People like you and me / Bless you / Fresh as a daisy / Limehouse blues / Woodpecker song / Sweet and lovely / Sierra Sue / Very thought of you / Blue evening / Keep 'em flying / Jingle bells / Introduction to a waltz / Five o'clock whistle / Here we go again / St. Louis blues / I've got no strings / Handful of stars / Baby me / Blueberry hill / Chattanooga choo choo / Song of the Volga boatmen / Everybody loves my baby / Rumba jumps
AVC 550 / Jun '95 / Avid

□ ON THE RADIO 1939-1941 (Miller, Glenn Orchestra)
DAWE 63 / Sep '93 / Magic

□ ORIGINAL GLENN MILLER & HIS ORCHESTRA, THE (Miller, Glenn Orchestra)
When Johnny comes marching home / Man with the mandolin / American patrol / Sweet Eloise / Chip off the old block / My blue heaven / Sweet potato piper / Wishing / My, my / Let's have another cup of coffee / Over the rainbow / Boog it / Chattanooga choo choo / Alice blue gown / Wonderful one / Day we meet again / Boulder buff / Frenesi / Booglie wooglie piggy / I know why / Anvil chorus
PASTCD 7011 / Apr '93 / Flapper

□ PORTRAIT OF GLENN MILLER, A
GALE 410 / May '97 / Gallerie

□ RETURN TO THE CAFE ROUGE
DAWE 38 / '89 / Magic

□ SECRET BROADCASTS (3CD Set)
I sustain the wings / Mission to Moscow / Army Air Corps song/Music stopped: *Desmond, Johnny* / Long tall mama / Blue Danube / I've got a heart filled with love (for you dear): *Desmond, Johnny & The Crew Chiefs* / Summertime / Caribbean clipper / Army Air Corps song/Irresistible you: *Desmond, Johnny & The Crew Chiefs* / Out waltz / Everybody loves my baby / Along the Santa Fe trail / Keep 'em flying / Songs my mother taught me / Over there: *Crew Chiefs* / Pearls on velvet / My blue heaven / Here we go again / Moon dreams: *Desmond, Johnny & The Crew Chiefs* / Oh lady be good / Begin the beguine / Caprice Viennois / Tuxedo junction / Squadron song: *Desmond, Johnny & The Crew Chiefs/The Glee Club* / Stompin' at the Savoy / Swing low, sweet Chariot / I sustain the wings / I sustain the wings / Bubble bath / Way you look tonight / Going my way: *Desmond, Johnny* / Snafu jump / Rhapsody in blue / Oh, what a beautiful mornin': *Desmond, Johnny & The Crew Chiefs* / In the gloamin' / In the mood / Suddenly it's Spring: *Desmond, Johnny* / Dipsy doodle / Stardust / There'll be a hot time in the town of Berlin: *McKinley, Ray & The Crew Chiefs/Glee Club* / Blue is the night / Tail-end Charlie / I love you: *Desmond, Johnny* / American patrol / All the things you are / Put your arms around me honey: *Desmond, Johnny & The Crew Chiefs* / Lovely way to spend an evening: *Desmond, Johnny & The Crew Chiefs* / 7-0-5 (Seven-o-five) Goin' home / Don't be that way / With my head in the clouds: *Desmond, Johnny & The Crew Chiefs* / Farewell blues / Anvil chorus / I sustain the wings / I sustain the wings / Stealin' apples / Army Air Corps song/Fellow in a furlough: *Desmond, Johnny* / Cherokee / Stormy weather / Guns in the sky: *Desmond, Johnny & Ensemble* / Jeanie with the light brown hair / Music makers / Summertime / It must be jelly ('cause jam don't shake like that) / Holiday for strings / Victory Polka: *Glee Club* / String of pearls / Moonlight serenade / Speak low: *Desmond, Johnny* / Sun valley jump / Annie Laurie / Enlisted men's mess / Poinciana: *Desmond, Johnny & The Crew Chiefs* / Song of the Volga boatmen / All through the night / 9.20 Special / Now I know: *Desmond, Johnny* / Jeep jockey jump / Goodnight wherever you are: *Desmond, Johnny & The Crew Chiefs* / I sustain the wings
75605525002 / Nov '96 / Happy Days

□ SINGALONG PARTY
String of pearls / Song of the Volga boatmen / Chatanooga choo choo / Pennsylvania 6-5000 / Don't sit under the apple tree / American patrol / Sun valley jump / Little brown jug / In the mood / Tuxedo junction / St. Louis blues / My blue heaven / Anvil chorus / Over there / Indian summer / Moonlight serenade / Miller's megamix / Swingalong megamix
GRF 152 / '93 / Tring

□ SPIRIT IS WILLING 1939-1942, THE
King Porter stomp / Slip horn jive / Pagan love song / Glen island special / I want to be happy / Farewell blues / Johnson rag / Rug cutter's swing / Slow freight / Bugle call rag / My blue heaven / I dreamt I dwelt in Harlem / Sun valley jump / Spirit is willing / Boulder buff / Take the 'A' train / Long tall Mama / Keep 'em flying / Caribbean clipper / Here we go again / Rainbow rhapsody / Rhapsody in blue
07863665292 / Apr '95 / Bluebird

□ SPOTLIGHT ON GLENN MILLER & THE DORSEY BROTHERS (Miller, Glenn & Dorsey Brothers)
Boogie woogie: *Dorsey, Tommy* / Moonlight serenade: *Miller, Glenn* / String of pearls: *Miller, Glenn* / Amapola: *Dorsey, Jimmy* / Little brown jug: *Miller, Glenn* / Chattanooga choo choo: *Miller, Glenn* / Green eyes: *Dorsey, Jimmy* / In the mood: *Miller, Glenn* / Serenade in blue: *Miller, Glenn* / I'm getting sentimental over you: *Dorsey, Tommy* / Over the rainbow: *Miller, Glenn* / Song of India: *Dorsey, Tommy* / So rare: *Dorsey, Jimmy* / I've got a gal in Kalamazoo: *Miller, Glenn* / Sunrise serenade: *Miller, Glenn*
HADCD 128 / Feb '94 / Javelin

□ STRING OF PEARLS, A
Little brown jug / Sunrise serenade / In the mood / I'm sitting on top of the world / Jumpin' jive / Moonlight Bay / String of pearls
BSTCD 9107 / May '92 / Best Compact Discs

□ STRING OF PEARLS, A
Always in my heart / American patrol / At last / Chip off the old block / Don't sit under the apple tree / Elmer's tune / Humpty Dumpty heart / I guess I'll have to dream the rest / It must be jelly, 'cause jam don't shake like that / I've got a gal in Kalamazoo / Jukebox Saturday night / Lamplighter's serenade / Let's have another cup of coffee / Moonlight cocktail / Moonlight becomes you / Serenade in blue / Skylark / Story of a starry night / String of pearls / Sweet Eloise / Take the 'A' train / That old black magic / This is no laughing matter / When Johnny comes marching home
CDAJA 5109 / Jun '93 / Living Era

□ STRING OF PEARLS, A
PLSCD 113 / Apr '96 / Pulse

□ STRING OF PEARLS, A
MACCD 222 / Aug '96 / Autograph

□ SUN VALLEY SERENADE/ ORCHESTRA WIVES
BMCD 7001 / Jan '95 / Blue Moon

□ SUNSET SERENADE (22/11/41) (Miller, Glenn Orchestra)
Intro / Tuxedo junction / Dreamsville Ohio / Chattanooga choo choo / I know why / It happened in Sun Valley / Everything I love / V Hop / In a sentimental mood / I guess I'll have to dream the rest / Do you care / Tschaikovsky's piano concerto / Till reveille / I don't want to set the world on fire / Papa Niccolini / In the mood / Close
JH 1002 / Apr '90 / Jazz Hour

□ SUNSET SERENADE (8/11/41) (Miller, Glenn Orchestra)
JH 4001 / Dec '97 / Jazz Hour

□ SUNSET SERENADE (29/11/41) (Miller, Glenn Orchestra)
JH 4002 / Dec '97 / Jazz Hour

□ SUNSET SERENADE (3/1/42) (Miller, Glenn Orchestra)
JH 4003 / Dec '97 / Jazz Hour

□ SUNSET SERENADE/CAFE ROUGE 1941
JH 1021 / Feb '93 / Jazz Hour

□ SUSTAINING REMOTE BROADCASTS VOL.1 & 2, THE (2CD Set) (Miller, Glenn Orchestra)
Moonlight serenade: *Miller, Glenn & His Orchestra* / I never knew (I could love anybody like I'm loving you): *Miller, Glenn & His Orchestra* / This can't be love: *Miller, Glenn & His Orchestra* / What have you got that gets me: *Miller, Glenn & His Orchestra* / Change partners: *Miller, Glenn & His Orchestra* / When paw was courtin' maw: *Miller, Glenn & His Orchestra* / Why doesn't somebody tell me these things: *Miller, Glenn & His Orchestra* / Without you on my mind: *Miller, Glenn & His Orchestra* / Down South camp greetin': *Miller, Glenn & His Orchestra* / Moonlight serenade: *Miller, Glenn & His Orchestra* / Lady's in love with you: *Miller, Glenn & His Orchestra* / Twilight interlude: *Miller, Glenn & His Orchestra* / Dong dong the witch is dead: *Miller, Glenn & His Orchestra* / Bugle call rag: *Miller, Glenn & His Orchestra* / Moonlight serenade: *Miller, Glenn & His Orchestra* / Moonlight serenade: *Miller, Glenn & His Orchestra* / Pennsylvania 6-5000: *Miller, Glenn & His Orchestra* / Call of the canyon: *Miller, Glenn & His Orchestra* / Gentleman needs a shave: *Miller, Glenn & His Orchestra* / Handful of stars: *Miller, Glenn & His Orchestra* / Moonlight serenade: *Miller, Glenn & His Orchestra* / On, brave old army team: *Miller, Glenn & His Orchestra* / When the swallows come back to Capistrano: *Miller, Glenn & His Orchestra* / Down for the count: *Miller, Glenn & His Orchestra* / Glenn Miller speaks: *Miller, Glenn & His Orchestra* / Slumber song: *Miller, Glenn & His Orchestra* / Lady's in love with you: *Miller, Glenn & His Orchestra* / Rendezvous time in Paree: *Miller, Glenn & His Orchestra* / (Hep hep) the jumpin' jive: *Miller, Glenn & His Orchestra* / Farewell blues: *Miller, Glenn & His Orchestra* / Moonlight serenade: *Miller, Glenn & His Orchestra* / Moonlight serenade: *Miller, Glenn & His Orchestra* / Glen island special: *Miller, Glenn & His Orchestra* / Why couldn't it last last night: *Miller, Glenn & His Orchestra* / Wham (re bop boom bam): *Miller, Glenn & His Orchestra* / Indian summer: *Miller, Glenn & His Orchestra* / King porter stomp: *Miller, Glenn & His Orchestra* / It's a blue world: *Miller, Glenn & His Orchestra* / I wanna hat with cherries: *Miller, Glenn & His Orchestra* / My blue heaven: *Miller, Glenn & His Orchestra* / Moonlight serenade: *Miller, Glenn & His Orchestra* / Moonlight serenade: *Miller, Glenn & His Orchestra* / Johnson rag: *Miller,*

Glenn & His Orchestra / Gaucho serenade: *Miller, Glenn & His Orchestra* / Boog it: *Miller, Glenn & His Orchestra* / Sky fell down: *Miller, Glenn & His Orchestra* / I want to be happy: *Miller, Glenn & His Orchestra* / Starlit hour: *Miller, Glenn & His Orchestra* / Glenn Miller speaks: *Miller, Glenn & His Orchestra* / Tuxedo junction: *Miller, Glenn & His Orchestra* / Too romantic: *Miller, Glenn & His Orchestra* / Glenn Miller speaks again: *Miller, Glenn & His Orchestra* / My my: *Miller, Glenn & His Orchestra*
JZCL 5011 / Nov '96 / Jazz Classics

☐ SWING ALONG PARTY
String of pearls / Song of the Volga boatmen / Chattanooga choo choo / Pennsylvania 6-5000 / Don't sit under the apple tree / American patrol / Sun valley jump / Little brown jug / In the mood / Tuxedo junction / St. Louis blues / My blue heaven / Anvil chorus / Over there / Indian summer / Moonlight serenade / Medley 1 / Medley 2
QED 100 / Nov '96 / Tring

☐ SWINGING MR. MILLER
It happened in Sun Valley / When Johnny comes marching home / American patrol / I got a gal in Kalamazoo / Ida, sweet as apple cider / Song of the Volga boatmen / Sun valley jump / Frenesi / Five o'clock whistle / Beat me Daddy, eight to the bar / Yes my darling daughter / Pennsylvania 6-5000 / My blue heaven / Caribbean clipper / Old black magic / Jukebox Saturday night / It must be jelly, 'cause jam don't shake like that / Pagan love song / Glen island special / Take the 'A' train / Tuxedo junction / Wonderful one
RAJCD 807 / Apr '97 / Empress

☐ TRIPLE GOLD (3CD Set)
In the mood / Nearness of you / Boogie woogie piggie / Crosstown / Five o'clock whistle / Nightingale sang in Berkely square / Yes my darling daughter / Dearly beloved / When you wish upon a star / Skylark / That old black magic / Along the Sante Fe trail / Falling leaves / Sweet eloise / When the swallows came back to Capistrano / Shake down the stars / Indian summer / American patrol / Last night / I guess I'll have to dream the rest / Tuxedo junction / Anvil chorus / Moonlight mood / This time the dream's on me / Handful of stars / It's a blue world / Gaucho serenade / Careless / Pennsylvania 6-5000 / Devil may care / Boog it / In an old Dutch garden / Moon love / Blue orchids / Our love affair / It must be jelly / Everything I love / My prayer / Runnin' wild / Wishing / Chattanooga choo choo / Moonlight becomes you / Always in my heart / Say si si / Slow freight / I'll never smile again / Man with the mandolin / Perfidia / Stairway to the stars / Speaking of heaven / Bluebirds in the moonlight / Don't sit under the apple tree / Changing world / I dreamt I dwelt in Harlem / Say it / Ooh what you said / My reverie / I'm stepping out with a memory tonight / I've got a girl in Kalamazoo / Adios
TG 334 / 8 Sep '97 / Start

☐ TWO ON ONE: GLENN MILLER & BENNY GOODMAN (Miller, Glenn & Benny Goodman)
Moonlight serenade / In the mood / Tuxedo junction / Chattanooga choo choo / String of pearls / Little brown jug / Pennsylvania 6-5000 / Don't sit under the apple tree / I've got a gal in kalamazoo / Sunrise serenade / King porter stomp / Down south camp meeting / Sugar foot stomp / One o'clock jump / Christopher columbus / Bugle call rag / Stompin' at the savoy / Goody goody / Goodbye / Sing, sing, sing
CDTT 10 / Apr '94 / Charly

☐ ULTIMATE GLENN MILLER, THE
In the mood / Little brown jug / Sliphorn jive / My prayer / Tuxedo junction / Fools rush in / Pennsylvania 6-5000 / Blueberry Hill / Song of the Volga boatmen / Perfidia / Chattanooga choo choo / I know why / Adios / String of pearls / Skylark / Don't sit under the apple tree / American patrol / Serenade in blue / I've got a gal in Kalamazoo / St. Louis blues march / At last / Moonlight serenade
74321131372 / Feb '93 / RCA

☐ UNFORGETTABLE GLENN MILLER, THE
Moonlight serenade / Little brown jug / In the mood / Pennsylvania 6-5000 / Don't sit under the apple tree / Sunrise serenade / Chattanooga choo choo / Tuxedo junction / American patrol / I've got a gal in kalamazoo / Stardust / St. Louis blues march / Serenade in blue / Perfidia / Juke box Saturday night / String of pearls
74321578012 / 11 May '98 / RCA

☐ VERY BEST OF GLENN MILLER, THE
74321511892 / 1 Sep '97 / Camden

☐ VERY BEST OF GLENN MILLER, THE (Hits And Rarities)
In the mood / Little brown jug / Tuxedo junction / Chattanooga choo choo / Blue skies / Anvil chorus / Woodpecker song / Sun valley jump / I got rhythm / I know why (and so do you) / Moonlight serenade / My blue heaven / Don't sit under the apple tree / Song of the Volga boatman / I've got a gal in Kalamazoo / String of pearls / Fools rush in (where angels fear to tread) / In a sentimental mood / American patrol / Pennsylvania 6-5000
301192 / Feb '98 / Hallmark

Miller, Herb

☐ REMEMBER GLENN MILLER (Miller, Herb Orchestra)
Sun Valley jump / I'm thrilled / Johnson rag / Angel divine / Bugle call rag / Quiet nights of quiet stars / Long tall mama / Slumber song / Caribbean clipper / Remember Glenn Miller / Anchors aweigh / Days of wine and roses / Here we go again / Skylark / I dreamt I dwelt in Harlem
CDPT 504 / Jan '94 / Prestige

Miller, Jacob

☐ I'M JUST A DREAD
RGCD 6016 / Mar '94 / Rocky One

☐ JACOB MILLER MEETS FATMAN RIDDIM SECTION
CC 2715 / Apr '95 / Crocodisc

☐ MIXED UP ROOTS
CC 2707 / Jan '94 / Crocodisc

☐ NATTY CHRISTMAS (Miller, Jacob & Ray-I)
Wish you a merry Christmas: *Miller, Jacob* / Ahameric temple: *Ray-I* / Silver bells: *Miller, Jacob* / Natty no Santa Claus: *Ray-I* / All I want for ismas / On the twelve day of ismas: *Miller, Jacob* / Deck the halls
RASCD 3103 / Nov '92 / Ras
DREAD 331032 / Dec '97 / Dread Beat

☐ REGGAE GREATS (Miller, Jacob & Inner Circle)
Shaky girl / Tenement yard / Suzy Wong / Sinners / Healing of the nation / 80,000 careless Ethiopians / I've got the handle / Tired fe lickweed in a bush / Roman soldiers of Babylon / Standing firm / All night 'til daylight / Forward Jah Jah children
5527382 / Jul '97 / Spectrum

☐ WHO SAY JAH NO DREAD
GRELCD 166 / Jul '97 / Greensleeves

☐ WITH THE INNER CIRCLE BAND & AUGUSTUS PABLO
Curfew / Forward jah jah children / Ala-ala-bama / Ell's move / Have some mercy / Westbound train / Curly locks / Curly lock's dub / All night till daylight / Fire a go burn / Gun trade / Meet me tonight / None shall escape the judgement / Can you handle it / You make me feel brand new
LG 21053 / Nov '92 / Lagoon

Miller, Jerry

☐ LIFE IS LIKE THAT (Miller, Jerry Band)
MRSCD 004 / Jun '97 / Messaround

Miller, Julie

☐ BLUE PONY
HCD 8079 / Jun '97 / Hightone

☐ INVISIBLE GIRL
SPARK 7037CD / Feb '95 / Spark

☐ MEET JULIE MILLER
MYRRH 5610CD / Feb '95 / Myrrh

☐ ORPHANS AND ANGELS
MYRRH 7616CD / Jan '95 / Myrrh

Miller, June

☐ WHEN LIFE HURTS
GMICD 066 / May '96 / Spark

Miller, Luella

☐ LUELLA MILLER & LONNIE JOHNSON
DOCD 5183 / Oct '93 / Document

Miller, Marcus

☐ BEST OF MARCUS MILLER, THE
VICP 60153 / 27 Apr '98 / Victor

☐ LIVE AND MORE
Intro / Panther / Tutu / Funny (all she needs is love) / Strange fruit / Summertime / Maputo / People make the world go round / Sophie / Jazz in the house
FDM 365852 / Mar '97 / Dreyfus

☐ SUN DON'T LIE, THE
Panther / Steveland / Rampage / Sun don't lie / Scoop / Mr. Pastorius / Funny (all she needs is love) / Moons / Teen town / Ju Ju / King is gone (for miles)
FDM 365602 / Aug '93 / Dreyfus

☐ TALES
Blues / Tales / Eric / True geminis / Rush over / Running through my dreams / Erhiopia / Strange fruit / Visions / Brazilian rhyme / Forevermore / Infatuation / Tales (reprise) / Come together
FDM 365712 / Apr '95 / Dreyfus

Miller, Max

☐ CHEEKY CHAPPIE AT HIS BEST, THE
New kind of old fashioned girl / Cheeky chappie picks from the white book and the blue book / Stringing along with you / Sitting in the old armchair / Hiking song / All good things come to an end / Why should the dustman get it all / Impshe / Backscratchers / Down in the valley / Mary from the dairy / When we go on our honeymoon / I thought we came here to pick some flowers / All because I rolled my eyes / Cheeky chappie concludes / Ophelia / At the bathing parade / Julietta / You can't blame me for that
SWNCD 010 / 15 Sep '97 / Sound Waves

☐ CHEEKY CHAPPIE...PLUS
Lulu / Lulu (Reprise) / She said she wouldn't / Doing all the nice things / With a little bit of luck / Influence / Mother Brown story / There's always someone worse off than you
C5LCD 613 / Sep '94 / See For Miles

☐ MAX AT THE MET/THAT'S NICE MAXIE
Mary from the dairy / Hearts and flowers / Be sincere (Introduction) / Fan dancer (Oh dear what can the matter be) / Mary Ann (The five year plan) / Twin sister / Tit bits / Passing the time away / Be sincere / Girls I like / Hikin / Josephine / On the banks of The Nile / Market song
C5LCD 598 / Sep '94 / See For Miles

☐ MAX MILLER VOL.1 (The Cheeky Chappie At The Holborn Empire/ Finsbury Park 1938-1939)
Max with the band / Max on stage - Holborn Empire / Max on stage - Holborn Empire / Max on stage - Finsbury Park Empire
PASTCD 9714 / '90 / Flapper

☐ MAX MILLER VOL.2 (The Pure Gold of Music Hall)
Julietta / Love bug will bite you / Max with the forces: *Miller, Max & Jean Carr* / Confessions of a cheeky chappy / Woman improver / Weeping willow / You can't blame me for that / Backscratcher / Impshe / Max the auctioneer / Girl next door / How the so-and-so can I be happy / Do re mi / Everything happens to me / At the bathing parade / No, no, no
PASTCD 9736 / Feb '91 / Flapper

☐ THERE'LL NEVER BE ANOTHER/THE ONE AND ONLY
Mary from the dairy / When we go on our honeymoon / Cheeky chappie tells a few / I thought we came here to pick some flowers / All because I rolled my eyes / Girls who work where I work / Every Sunday afternoon / New kind of old fashioned girl / From the white book / And the blue book / Is there no end to his cleverness / What Ju Ju wants Ju Ju must have / Stringing along with you / Sitting in the old armchair / Hiking song / Doh-re-me / No, no, no / Cheeky chappie tells some / Passing the time away / About etiquette and manners / Cheeky chappie tells some more / Down where the rambling roses grow / I don't like the girls / All good stuff lady / Mary Ann
C5LCD 631 / Feb '96 / See For Miles

Miller, Mulgrew

☐ COUNTDOWN, THE
LCD 15192 / Apr '89 / Landmark

☐ GETTING TO KNOW YOU
Eastern joy dance / Second thoughts / Sweet Sioux / Getting to know you / Whisper / Didn't we / Fool on the hill / I don't know how to love him / If I should lose you / Nandhi
01241631882 / Feb '96 / Novus

☐ KEYS TO THE CITY/WORK
60412320552 / 7 Apr '98 / Thirty Two

☐ WINGSPAN
LCD 15152 / Jul '88 / Landmark

Miller, Ned

☐ FROM A JACK TO A KING
From a jack to a king / Parade of broken hearts / Turn around / Lights in the street / Old mother nature and old father time / Roll o' rollin' stone / One among the many / Man behind the gun / Another fool like me / Magic moon / Sunday morning tears / Big love / Old restless ocean / Invisible tears / Do what you do do well / Dusty guitar / Just before dawn / Go on back you fool / Dark moon / Cold grey bars / My heart waits at the door / Big lie / Heart without a heartache / Billy Carino / Cry of the wild goose / Long shadow / Mona Lisa / Stage coach / You belong to my heart / King of fools / Girl across the table
BCD 15496 / Feb '91 / Bear Family

Miller, Pat

☐ RADIO DAYS (Miller, Pat & Mike Edwards)
NEW 1006 / Nov '96 / Australian Jazz

Miller, Paul D.

☐ VIRAL SONATA
Prologue / Indra's net / Morphic interlude / Invisual ocean / Striated interlude no.1 / Necrologue / Striated interlude no.2 / City on the edge of forever / Zona rosa / Colophon / Striated interlude no.3 / Primary inversion / Striated interlude no.4 / Epilogue
EFA 709762 / Aug '97 / Asphodel
ASP 0976CD / 26 Jan '98 / Asphodel

Miller, Pete

☐ HOMAGE TO CATATONIA
BA 1123CD / 16 Feb '98 / Bacchus Archives

Miller, Phil

☐ CUTTING BOTH WAYS
Green and purple extract / Hic haec hoc / Simple man / Eastern region / Hard shoulder / Figures of speech / Green and purple
RUNE 11 / Dec '89 / Cuneiform

☐ DIGGING IN
RUNE 34 / Oct '90 / Cuneiform

☐ IN CAHOOTS - LIVE IN JAPAN
No holds barred / Bass motives / Speaking to Lydia / Truly yours / Second sight / Green and purple extract / Digging in extract
CD 2CD / Jun '93 / Crescent Discs

☐ SPLIT SECONDS
And thus far / Final call / Dada soul / Truly yours / Double talk / I remain / Your 2 / Foreign bodies
CDRECK 8 / Mar '89 / Reckless

Miller, Punch

☐ ICON
AMCD 52 / May '95 / American Music

☐ PUNCH MILLER
Ice cream / Icried for you / Sugar blues / Royal garden blues / Dippermouth blues / Darktown strutters ball / St James infirmary / Some of these days / All of me / Basin street blues / Milenburg joys / Sister Kate / 12th street rag / Casey Jones / You can depend on me / Tiger rag / Bill Bailey / Baby won't you please come home
504CD 40 / Mar '98 / 504

☐ PUNCH MILLER 1925-1930
JPCD 1517 / May '95 / Jazz Perspectives

☐ PUNCH MILLER'S NEW ORLEANS BAND 1957 (Larry Borenstein Vol.5) (Miller, Punch New Orleans Band)
I ain't gonna give nobody none of my jelly roll / You rascal you / Linda Muger (you never say yes) / Sheik of Araby / Snag it / Baby won't you please come home / Some of these days / Darktown strutter's ball / I cried for you / Sister Kate / Royal garden blues / Exactly like you / St. James infirmary / All of me / Happy birthday to Larry / When the saints go marching in
504CD 34 / Mar '98 / 504

Miller, Robyn

☐ MYST
Planetarium / Treegate / Un-finale / Bonus tracks / Tower / Mechanical age / Last message / Fortress ambience part.1 / Fortress ambience part.2 / Mechanical mystgate / Sirrus' cache / Compass rose / Temple of Achenar / Selentic mystgate / Finale / Fireplace theme / Early scientific mystgate / Myst island / Channelwood age / Above stoneship / Achenar's theme-Stoneship age / Original un-finale / Selentic age / Shipgate / Myst theme / Sirrus' theme-Stoneship age / Achener's theme-Mechanical age / Achenar's cache / Achenar's theme-Channelwood age / Finale / Mechanical age / Stoneship age
CDVUS 143 / 4 May '98 / Virgin

☐ RIVEN
Moeity prison / Catherine's theme / Bonus track / Fissure / Gehn's theme / Jungle totem / Catherine's freedom / Catherine's prelude / Temple / Red cave / Link / Moeity theme / Moeity caves / Village entrance theme / Survey island theme / Gateroom / Boat ride / Artus' theme / Wahrk room / Gehn speaks
CDVUS 142 / 16 Mar '98 / Virgin

Miller, Rodger

☐ BINARY SYSTEM (Live At The Idea Room) (Miller, Rodger & Larry Dersch)
Fish laughs at his own commands / Peerd rail se / Plate glass / Tornado / Moon dance / Machete hackers boogie woogie / Abruption / What's up Ched Voogis / Djinn / Binary mechanics / Turbo wheel / Tibet / Last oak king
SST 349CD / 29 Sep '97 / SST

Miller, Rodney

☐ AIRPLANG
Sail away ladies/Waynesboro / Erin/Soulmate / Hangman's reel / In Christ there is no east or west/ Salimony waltz / Contrazz/Old Joe / Dancing bear / Elvira/Asher / Nancy's waltz/Dark island / Fair Jenny / Cotton Eyed Joe
CMCD 075 / Jul '97 / Celtic Music
ROUCD 0193 / May '97 / Rounder

☐ ALL ROUND COLLECTION OF JIGS REELS AND AIRS
VOY 342CD / Mar '98 / Voyager

☐ GREASY COAT
SA 1301CD / Apr '94 / Sage Arts

Miller, Roger

☐ BEST OF ROGER MILLER, THE
MATCD 327 / Feb '95 / Castle

☐ BEST OF ROGER MILLER, THE
PLSCD 126 / Apr '96 / Pulse

☐ BEST OF ROGER MILLER, THE
King of the road / Loving her was easier (than anything I'll ever do again) / Green green grass of home / Jody and the Kid / Train of life / Ruby don't take your love to town / Heartbreak hotel / Home / Less and less / Tall tall trees / Invitation to the blues / When two world's collide / World so full of love / Dang me / Engine no.9 / Kansas city star / Little green apples / Only Daddy that'll walk the line / Husbands and wives / Me and Bobby McGee / Billy Bayou / England swings / Walking in the sunshine
5543722 / 6 Apr '98 / Spectrum

☐ DANG ME (Greatest Hits)
Dang me / Dang me / Can't rollerskate in a buffalo herd / Release me / Don't we all have the right to be wrong / My uncle used to love me but she died / My elusive dreams / When two worlds collide / Me and bobby mcgee / Billy bayou / England swings
15479 / Aug '94 / Laserlight

☐ KING OF THE ROAD
You're part of me / Fair Swiss maiden / Every which a way / It happened just that way / I get up early in the morning / I catch myself crying / I'll be somewhere / Little green apples / I know who it is (and I'm gonna tell on him) / But I love you more / If you want me too / Burma shave / You don't want my love / Sorry Willie / You can't do me that way / When two worlds collide / Lock, stock and teardrops / Trouble on the turnpike / Hey little star / Footprints in the snow / Hitch hiker / Dang me / King of the road / Chug-a-lug / Engine no.9 / Kansas City star / England swings / Do wacka do / One dyin' and a buryin'
BCD 15477 / Feb '90 / Bear Family

☐ KING OF THE ROAD
Engine engine no.9 / England swings / Kansas city star / King of the road / Dang me / Chug-a-lug / Husbands and wives / Walking in the sunshine / My uncle used to love me but she died / When two worlds collide / You can't rollerskate in a buffalo herd / Me and Bobby McGee / Please release me / In the summertime / Last word is lonesome / My elusive dreams / Everything's coming up roses / Do-wacka-do / Billy Bayou / Burning bridges
PLATCD 216 / Feb '97 / Platinum

☐ KING OF THE ROAD
King of the road / Dang me / Engine engine no.9 / Everything's coming up roses / Kansas city star / My elusive dreams / Please release me / Chug-a-lug / One dyin' and a buryin' / Billy Bayou / When two worlds collide / Burni / Do-wacka-do / England

swings / In the summertime (you don't want my love) / Me and Bobby McGee / My uncle used to love me but she died / Walkin' in the sunshine / You can't rollerskate in a buffalo herd / Husbands and wives / Last word in lonesome is me / Little green apples
308652 / 20 Apr '98 / Hallmark

☐ MASTERS, THE
EABCD 030 / 24 Nov '97 / Eagle

☐ VERY BEST OF ROGER MILLER, THE
King of the road / Dang me / Me and Bobby McGee / Husbands and wives / In the summertime / When two worlds collide / Kansas city star / Do-wacka-do / Last word in lonesome is me / Engine engine no.9 / Chug a lug / You can't roller skate in a buffalo herd / My elusive dreams / Heartaches by the number / Burning bridges / Billy Bayou / Walking in the sunshine / England swings
SUMCD 4140 / Sep '97 / Summit

☐ WORLD OF ROGER MILLER, THE
King of the road / Engine / Kansas City star / England swings / Little green apples / Dang me / Husbands and wives / Boeing Boeing 707 / Chug-a-lug / (You had a) do-wacka-do / You can't roller skate in a buffalo herd / My Uncle used to love me but she died / Walkin' in the sunshine / Me and Bobby McGee / By the time I get to Phoenix / Gentle on my mind / Ruby, don't take your love to town / Everybody's talking
5511112 / May '96 / Spectrum

Miller, Roger

☐ ELEMENTAL GUITAR
SST 318CD / Aug '95 / SST

☐ OH
We grind open (in) / Meltdown man / Chinatown samba / Firetruck / Cosmic battle / You son of a bitch / War bolts / Fun world reductions / Space is the place / Forest / Kalgastak
NAR 097 / Mar '94 / New Alliance

☐ UNFOLD (Miller, Roger Exquisite Corpse)
SST 307CD / Sep '94 / SST

Miller, Sing

☐ BLUES, BALLADS & SPIRITUALS
MG 9006 / Feb '95 / Mardi Gras

Miller, Steve

☐ ABRACADABRA (Miller, Steve Band)
Keeps me wondering why / Something special / Give it up / Never say no / Things I told you / Young girl's heart / Goodbye love / Abracadabra / Cool magic / While I'm waiting
EAMCD 044 / 1 Jun '98 / Eagle

☐ BOOK OF DREAMS (Miller, Steve Band)
Threshold / Jet airliner / Winter time / Swingtown / True fine love / Wish upon a star / Jungle love / Electro lux imbroglio / Sacrifice / Stake / My own space / Babes in the wood
EAMCD 042 / 1 Jun '98 / Eagle

☐ BRAVE NEW WORLD (Miller, Steve Band)
7912462 / 1 Jun '98 / Capitol

☐ CHILDREN OF THE FUTURE
7912452 / 1 Jun '98 / Capitol

☐ CIRCLE OF LOVE (Miller, Steve Band)
Heart like a wheel / Get on home / Circle of love / Baby wanna dance: *Miller, Steve* / Macho city
EAMCD 043 / 1 Jun '98 / Eagle

☐ FLY LIKE AN EAGLE (Miller, Steve Band)
Blue odyssey / Dance, dance, dance / Fly like an eagle / Mercury blues / Rock 'n' me / Serenade / 2001 / Sweet Marie / Take the money and run / Wild mountain honey / Window / You send me
EAMCD 041 / 1 Jun '98 / Eagle

☐ ITALIAN X-RAYS (Miller, Steve Band)
Radio 1 and 2 / Italian X Rays / Daybreak / Shangri-La / Who do you love / Harmony of the spheres / Bongo bongo / Out of the night / Golden opportunity / Hollywood dream / One in a million
EAMCD 045 / 1 Jun '98 / Eagle

☐ JOKER, THE (Miller, Steve Band)
Sugar babe / Mary Lou / Shu ba da du ma ma ma / Your cash ain't nothin' but trash / Joker / Lovin' cup / Come on in my kitchen / Evil / Something to believe in
CDP 7944452 / Sep '96 / Capitol

☐ NUMBER 5
8296862 / 1 Jun '98 / Capitol

☐ SAILOR (Miller, Steve Band)
Song for our ancestors / Dear Mary / My friend / Living in the USA / Quicksilver girl / Lucky man / Gangster of love / You're so fine / Overdrive / Dime-a-dance romance
7944492 / 1 Jun '98 / Capitol

☐ STEVE MILLER BAND LIVE (Miller, Steve Band)
Gangster of love / Rock 'n' me / Livin' in the USA / Fly like an eagle / Jungle love / Joker / Mercury blues / Take the money and run / Abracadabra / Jet airliner
EAMCD 046 / 1 Jun '98 / Eagle

☐ WIDE RIVER (Miller, Steve Band)
Wide river / Midnight train / Blue eyes / Lost in your eyes / Perfect world / Horse and rider / Circle of fire / Conversation / Cry cry cry / Stranger blues / Walks like a lady / All your love (I miss loving)
EAMCD 053 / 1 Jun '98 / Eagle

☐ YOUR SAVING GRACE (Miller, Steve Band)
Little girl / Just a passin' fancy in a midnite dream / Don't let nobody turn you around / Baby's house / Motherless children / Last wombat in Mecca / Feel so glad / Your saving grace
7944482 / 1 Jun '98 / Capitol

Millican

☐ VAYA CON DIOS (The Best Of Millican & Nesbitt) (Millican & Nesbitt)
Vaya con dios / Old lamplighter / Paper roses / Near you / My happiness / Moonlight and roses / Ramona / Distant drums / Someday (you'll want me to want you) / Mexicali rose / Far away places / I'll be with you in apple blossom time / So tired / You'll never know / You always hurt the one you love / I don't know why (I just do) / Heartaches / Dear hearts and gentle people / Yours / Anniversary waltz / Que sera, sera / Unchained melody / I have loved you girl (but not like this before) / For old times sake
PLSCD 244 / 27 Oct '97 / Pulse

Millinder, Lucky

☐ BACK BEATS
Swingin' in E flat / African lullaby / Dancing dogs / Back beats / Spitfire / Harlem heat / Trouble in mind / Slide Mr. Trombone / Ride Red Ride / Rock Daniel / Big fat Mama / Shout sister shout / Apollo jump / Rock me / Let me off uptown / That's all / I want a tall skinny Papa / Savoy / Mason flyer / Little John special / Shipyard social function / Hurry hurry / Who threw the whiskey in the well / All the time
TPZ 1056 / Oct '96 / Topaz Jazz

☐ CLASSICS 1941-1942
CLASSICS 712 / Jul '93 / Classics

Million

☐ ELECTRIC
SPV 08511162 / 29 Jun '98 / SPV

Millman, Jack

☐ FOUR MORE (Millman, Jack Quartet/Quintet)
FSRCD 217 / Jan '97 / Fresh Sound

Mills Blue Rhythm Band

☐ BLUE RHYTHM
HEPCD 1008 / Aug '92 / New Note

☐ CLASSICS 1931
CLASSICS 660 / Nov '92 / Classics

☐ CLASSICS 1931-1932
CLASSICS 676 / Mar '93 / Classics

☐ CLASSICS 1934-1936
CLASSICS 710 / Jul '93 / Classics

☐ CLASSICS 1936-1937
CLASSICS 731 / Jan '94 / Classics

☐ INTRODUCTION TO MILLS BLUE RHYTHM BAND 1931-1937, AN
4009 / Mar '95 / Best Of Jazz

☐ RHYTHMS SPASM
Cabin in the cotton / Minnie the moocher's wedding day / Growl / Might sweet / Rhythm spasm / Swanee lullaby / White lightning / Wild waves / Sentimental gentlemen from Georgia / You gave me everything but love / Ol' yazoo / Reefer man / Jazz cocktail / Smoke rings / Ridin' in rhythm / Weary traveller / Buddy's Wednesday outing / Harlem after midnight / Jazz martini / Feelin' gay / Break it down / Kokey Joe / Love's serenade
HEPCD 1015 / Jun '93 / Hep

Mills Brothers

☐ BOARD OF DIRECTORS, THE/ANNUAL REPORT (Mills Brothers & Count Basie)
(Up a) lazy river / I may be wrong but I think you're wonderful / Release me / I want to be happy / Down down down / Whiffenpoof song / I dig rock and rock music / Tiny bubbles / December / Let me dream / April in Paris / Gentle on my mind / Cherry / You never miss the water til the well runs dry / Glow worm / Sent for you yesterday / Sunny / I'll be around / Cielito lindo / Blue and sentimental / Everyday
MCLD 19366 / 23 Mar '98 / MCA

☐ CHRONOLOGICAL VOL.2
Old man of the mountains / Dirt dishin' daisy / I can't give you anything but love / My honey's lovin' arms / That's georgia / Swing it sister / Jungle fever / Money in my pockets / I've found a new baby
JSPCD 302 / Apr '89 / JSP

☐ CHRONOLOGICAL VOL.3
Put on your old grey bonnet / Sleepy head / Lazy bones / Sweet georgia brown / Miss otis regrets / Some of these days / Limehouse blues / Lulu's back in town / Since we fell out of love
JSPCD 303 / Apr '89 / JSP

☐ CHRONOLOGICAL VOL.4
Sweet and slow / Old fashioned love / Shoe shine boy / Solitude / Swing is the thing / When lights are low / Pennies from heaven / Carry me back to old virginny / Old folks at home
JSPCD 304 / Oct '88 / JSP

☐ CLASSICS
Put another chair at the table / Meet me tonight in Dreamland / Don't be a baby, baby / There's no-one but you / I'll be around / I wish / I'm afraid to love you / Till then / Flat foot floogie / Organ grinder's swing / Jeepers creepers / Swanee river / Georgia on my mind / Shine / In the shade of the old apple tree / Caravan / It don't mean a thing / Paper doll / Smoke rings / I guess I'll get the papers / Boog it / Too many irons in the fire
RAJCD 883 / Jul '97 / Empress

☐ DARLING NELLY GRAY 1936-1940
Cherry / Dedicated to you / Boog it / Flat foot floogie / My walking stick / Big boy blue / Darling nellie gray / Carry me back to old virginny / Rockin' chair swing / W.p.a. / In the shade of the old apple-tree / Marie / Old folks at home / Swing for sale / Love bug will bite you / Long about midnight / Swing is the thing / Song is ended
CD 56072 / Jul '95 / Jazz Roots

☐ FOUR GUYS AND A GUITAR
BMCD 3039 / Jan '98 / Blue Moon

☐ I'VE FOUND A NEW BABY 1932-1934
Put on your old grey bonnet / Sleepy head / I've found a new baby / Doin' the new low down / Jungle fever / Diga, diga doo / Swing it sister / My honey's lovin' arms / Dirt dishin' daisy / Git along / I can't give you anything but love / Smoke rings / Fiddlin' joe / Money in my pockets / Anytime, anyday, anywhere / That's georgia / Lazy bones / Out for no good
CD 56057 / Jul '95 / Jazz Roots

☐ JAZZ PORTRAIT VOL.1
CD 14584 / Nov '95 / Complete

☐ JAZZ PORTRAIT VOL.2
CD 14587 / Nov '95 / Complete

☐ JAZZ PORTRAIT VOL.3
CD 14577 / Nov '95 / Complete

☐ LA SELECTION 1931-1938
012 / Sep '93 / Art Vocal

☐ MEET THE BIG BANDS
BMCD 2014 / 5 Jan '98 / Blue Moon

☐ MILLS BROTHERS MEET ARMSTRONG (Mills Brothers & Louis Armstrong)
BMCD 3056 / Apr '97 / Blue Moon

☐ MILLS BROTHERS VOL.1 1931-1934
Sweet georgia brown / Sweet georgia brown / Tiger rag / I've found a new baby / Doin' the new low down / Chinatown, my chinatown / Bugle call rag / Diga, diga do / It don't mean a thing (if it ain't got that swing) / Old man of the mountain / Dinah / Shine / My honey's lovin' arms / Nobody's sweetheart / I heard / Life is just a bowl of cherries / Rockin' chair / St. louis blues / Out for no good / Coney island washboard / Dirt dishin' daisy / Git along / I can't give you anything but love / Fiddlin' joe / Nagasaki / My gal sal / Money in my pockets
CD 53086 / May '92 / Giants Of Jazz

☐ MILLS BROTHERS VOL.2, THE
Sweet Sue, just you / Goodbye blues / How 'm I doin', hey-hey / Baby, won't you please come home / (I'll be glad when you're dead) you rascal you / Tiger rag / My romance / Old man of the mountains / Anytime, anyday, anywhere / That's Georgia / Jungle fever / Swing it, sister / Smoke rings / I heard / Put on your old grey bonnet / Sleepy head / Lazybones / Old-fashioned love / Miss Otis regrets / Sweeter than sugar / Ida, sweet as apple cider / Limehouse blues / Shuffle your feet / Bandana babies / My little grass shack in Kealakekua Hawaii
CD 53273 / Jun '96 / Giants Of Jazz

☐ MILLS BROTHERS VOL.3, THE
Rockin' chair swing / Love bug will bite you / Big boy blue: *Mills Brothers & Ella Fitzgerald* / Dedicated to you: *Mills Brothers & Ella Fitzgerald* / Rhythm saved the world / Solitude / Lulu's back in town / Sweet and slow / Shoe shine boy / London rhythm / Swing is the thing / 'Long about midnight / Pennies from heaven / Swing for sale / Sweet Lucy Brown / Song is ended / Don't be afraid to tell your Mother / Since we fell out of love / Moanin' for you / What's the reason (I'm not pleasin' you) / Caravan / Little old lady / When lights are low / I found the thrill again
CD 53276 / Feb '97 / Giants Of Jazz

☐ MILLS BROTHERS VOL.4 1937-1940
Flat foot floogie / My walking stick / Song is ended / Organ grinder's swing / Let me dream / Caravan / Carry me back to old Virginny / Darling Nellie Gray / In the shade of the old apple tree / Old folks at home / Funiculi' funicula' / Asleep in the deep / Side kick Joe / Julius Ceasar / Cherry / Marie / Boog it / WPA / Lambeth walk / Yam / Just a kid named Joe / Sixty seconds got together / Elder Eatmore's sermon on throwing stones / Elder eatmore's sermon on generosity
CD 53279 / Jul '97 / Giants Of Jazz

☐ MILLS BROTHERS, THE
Swing is the thing / Stardust / Shoe-shine boy / Nagasaki / Flat foot floogie / Window washing man / How did she look / Boog it / When you were sweet sixteen / (I'll be glad when you're dead) you rascal you / It don't mean a thing if it ain't got that swing / Caravan / Georgia / Jeepers creepers / Organ grinder swing / Lazybones / FDR Jones / My Gal Sal / Sleepy time gal / Shine / Smoke rings / London rhythm
PASTCD 7049 / May '94 / Flapper

☐ SWEETER THAN SUGAR
Tiger rag / Old-fashioned love / Fiddlin' Joe / Smoke rings / I've found a new baby / Chinatown, my Chinatown / Lazybones / Diga diga doo / Nagasaki / Sweeter than sugar / Miss Otis regrets / Ida, sweet as apple cider / Rockin' chair / Some of these days / Sweet Georgia Brown / Nobody's sweetheart
CDAJA 5032 / Feb '87 / Living Era

☐ TIGER RAG 1931-1932
Chinatown, my chinatown / Bugle call rag / Tiger rag / It don't mean a thing (if it ain't got that swing) / Dinah / Shine / Old man of the mountain / I heard / St. louis blues / Coney island washboard / Life is just a bowl of cherries / Nobody's sweetheart / You rascal you / Baby won't you please come home / How'm I doin', hey-hey / Goodbye blues / Sweet sue, just you / Loveless love
CD 56050 / Nov '94 / Jazz Roots

☐ VERY BEST OF MILLS BROTHERS, THE
HMNCD 021 / 3 Nov '97 / Half Moon

Mills, Chris

☐ EVERY NIGHT FIGHT FOR YOUR LIFE
SF 005 / 27 Jul '98 / Sugar Free

Mills, Jeff

☐ JEFF MILLS LIVE AT THE LIQUID ROOM, TOKYO (Various Artists)
Utopia: *Mills, Jeff* / Extremist: *Mills, Jeff* / Life cycle: *Mills, Jeff* / Untitled A: *Mills, Jeff* / 19: *Mills, Jeff* / Changes of life: *Mills, Jeff* / Ax-009: *Mills, Jeff* / Detached: *Mills, Jeff* / Loop 3: *Mills, Jeff* / Untitled B: *Mills, Jeff* / Growth: *Mills, Jeff* / Casa: *Mills, Jeff* / Magneze: *Surgeon* / Move: *Surgeon* / Start it up: *Beltram, Joey* / Gameform: *Beltram, Joey* / Step to enchantment: *Milsart* / Work that body: *DJ Funk* / Run (UK): *DJ Funk* / Play with the voice in USA: *Vannelli, Joe T.* / Clementina: *Wicked Wipe* / Overkill: *Circuit Breaker* / Wet floor: *Traxmen* / Nocturnal: *Young, Claude* / Bad boy: *Advent* / 187 Skillz: *DJ Skull* / Strings of life: *Rhythm Is Rhythm* / Extra: *Ishii, Ken* / Avion: *Wild, Damon* / Intro: *X-120* / Suspense: *H&M* / Other side: *Shadow* / Flowerchild: *Morgan, Dan* / Bazetoya: *Hell & Jonzon*
REACTCD 077 / May '96 / React

☐ OTHER DAY, THE
Solarized / Gamma player / Sleeping giants / I9 / Time out of mind / Growth / Gateway of zen / Medusa / Man from tomorrow / Spider formation / Childhood / Humana / Inner life
REACTCD 105 / May '97 / React

☐ PURPOSE MAKER
Dancer / Casa / Bells / Reverting / Alarms / Outsiders / Cubango / Medicine man / Paradise / Masterplan / Fly guy / Fuzz dance / Tango / Captivate
PMW 9801 / 22 Jun '98 / Purpose Maker
REACTCD 126 / 25 May '98 / React

☐ WAVEFORM TRANSMISSION VOL.1
EFA 01742CD / Feb '93 / Tresor

☐ WAVEFORM TRANSMISSION VOL.3
74321227172 / Jul '97 / Tresor
EFA 292762 / 9 Feb '98 / Tresor

Mills, Stephanie

☐ PERSONAL INSPIRATIONS
I had a talk with God / Sweepin' through the city / He cares / In the morning time / Everything you touch / Everybody ought to know / Power of God / People get ready / He cares (reprise) / I'm gonna make you proud
GCD 2123 / Jul '95 / Alliance Music

Milltown Brothers

☐ VALVE
When it comes / Turn off / Killing all the good men, Jimmy / Pictures (Round my room) / Turn me over / Trees / Sleepwalking / Falling straight down / Crawl with me / Someday / It's all over now baby blue / Cool breeze
5401322 / Apr '95 / A&M

Milsap, Ronnie

☐ ESSENTIAL RONNIE MILSAP, THE
Stranger things have happened / She keeps the home fires burning / Nobody likes sad songs / Any day now / Woman in love / Cowboys and clowns / Snap your fingers / He got you / Where do the nights go / Stranger in my house / All is fair in love and war / Happy, happy birthday baby / (There's) no getting over me / Make no mistake, she's mine / How do I turn you on / I wouldn't have missed it for the world / Why don't you spend the night / Lost in the Fifties tonight / Don't you ever get tired / Turn that radio on
74321665342 / Feb '96 / RCA

☐ NIGHT THINGS
(After sweet memories) play born to lose again / Who'll turn out the lights (in your world) / Daydreams about night things / I'm no good at goodbyes / Just in case / Remember to remind me (I'm leaving) / Borrowed angel / Love takes a long time to die / Lying here / I'll be there (if you ever want me)
7990 / 2 Feb '98 / Koch

Milteau, J.J.

☐ J.J. MILTEAU LIVE
192007 / Sep '95 / Saphir

Milton, Richie

☐ COMING BACK FOR MORE (Milton, Richie & The Lowdown)
When baby don't wanna play / It's getting harder / Wise to your jive / You wanna take a mile / Free from loving you / Salty water / Bottle and the blues / Find another man / Coming back for more / Rollit over again / Leave a light in your window / Wassamatta couch potata / You gotta run / How come baby
IGOXCD 510 / Feb '98 / Indigo

□ STRAIGHT AHEAD, NO STOPPIN' (Milton, Richie & The Lowdown)
Dressed to kill / Straight ahead no stoppin' / Bluest man alive / Wasn't that love / Long come your man / Prisoner of love / Love city / Forever in my mind / Boogie woogie country girl / Caldonia / Messed up in your love / Mo' killin' the lowdown
RTCD 017 / Jul '95 / Right Track
IGOCD 2083 / Feb '98 / Indigo

Milton, Roy

□ ROY MILTON VOL.1 (Milton, Roy & His Solid Senders)
Milton's boogie / RM blues / True blues / Camille's boogie / Thrill me / Big fat mama / Keep a dollar in your pocket / Everything I do is wrong / Hop, skip and jump / Porter's love song to a chamber maid / Hucklebuck / Information blues / Where there is no love / Junior jives / Bartender's boogie / Oh babe / Christmas time blues / It's later than you think / Numbers blues / I have news for you / T town twist / Best wishes / So tired / Night and day I miss you / Blue turning grey over you
CDCHD 308 / Oct '90 / Ace

□ ROY MILTON VOL.2 (Groovy Blues) (Milton, Roy & His Solid Senders)
Groovy blues / Rhythm cocktail / On the sunny side of the street / Little boy blue / Pack your sack Jack / Roy rides / Cryin' and singin' the blues / Unidentified shuffle blues / I want a little girl / My blue heaven / T'ain't me / Junior jumps / Sympathetic blues / Oh Marie / Waking up baby / Playboy blues / Bye bye baby blues / Don't you remember baby / One O'clock jump / Marie / Unidentified novelty song No.1 / That's the one for me / Cold blooded woman / Short, sweet and snappy / I stood by
CDCHD 435 / Jan '93 / Ace

□ ROY MILTON VOL.3 (Blowin' With Roy) (Milton, Roy & His Solid Senders)
Coquette / Song is ended (but the melody lingers on) / Them there eyes / When I grow too old to dream / What's the use / Train blues / LA Hop / Blue skies / If you don't know / Along the navajo trail / You mean so much to me / New year's resolution / I've had my moments / Ol' man river / Everything I do is wrong / There is something missing / My sweetheart / Believe me baby / Blowin' with Roy / Thelma Lou / Sad feeling / Practice what you preach / If you love me baby / Blues ain't news / Cool down
CDCHD 575 / Jul '94 / Ace

Milverton Trio

□ TIME TO MOVE, A
LOTCD 4307 / 1 Jun '98 / Loose Tie

Milwaukee Slim

□ LEMON AVENUE
BLUELOONCD 016 / Jul '95 / Blue Loon

Mimani Park Orchestra

□ SUNGI
PAM 403 / Dec '94 / PAM

Mimir

□ MIMYRIAD
STREAMLINE 1001 / 3 Nov '97 / Streamline

Mimms, Garnet

□ CRY BABY/WARM AND SOULFUL
For your precious love / Cry to me / Nobody but you / Until you were gone / Baby don't you weep / Anytime you need me / Runaway lover / Cry baby / Don't change your heart / Quiet place / So close / Wanting you / I'll take good care of you / Looking for you / It won't hurt (half as much) / It was easier to hurt her / Thinkin' / Prove it to me / More than a miracle / As long as I have you / One girl / There goes my baby / It's just a matter of time / Little bit of soap / Look away / I'll make it up to you
BGOCD 268 / Apr '95 / Beat Goes On

Min, Jung Jung

□ SIMCHONGGA
VICG 50192 / Mar '96 / JVC World Library

Min, Xiao Fen

□ SPRING RIVER FLOWER MOON NIGHT
ASP 0974CD / 22 Jun '98 / Asphodel

□ WITH SIX COMPOSERS
AVANT 21 / Aug '98 / Avant

Minafra, Pina

□ NOCI ... STRANI FRUTTI (Minafra, Pina & Reijseger/Bennik)
CDLR 176 / '90 / Leo

Minales, Pablo

□ ANTOLOGIA
68968 / Jul '97 / Tropical

Mind Doctors

□ ON THRESHOLD OF REALITY
KSCD 9597 / Jun '97 / Kissing Spell

Mind Funk

□ PEOPLE WHO FELL FROM THE SKY
CDMFN 182 / Mar '95 / Music For Nations

Mind Odyssey

□ NAILED TO THE SHADE
GUN 165CD / 17 Aug '98 / Gun

□ SCHIZOPHENIA
RS 0082062CD / Jul '98 / Rising Sun

Mind Over Midi

□ ICE ACOUSTIK
BSCD 016 / 2 Feb '98 / BeatService

Mind Over Rhythm

□ WINTER SUN
Time's up / Skyclad / Mongoose / Sniper / Refugee / Kitchen sync / Mojo fly / Winter sun / Ebe's campfire stories
RUMBLE 015CD / Jul '97 / Rumble

Mind Pilots

□ NO ORDINARY PLANET
No ordinary planet / Cruel world / Waiting for you / Bad for you / Wrong side / Another love / Heart of stone / Sleepwalking / Shoot the moon
TERRCD 0012 / Jun '98 / Terra Nova

Mind Riot

□ PEAK
GOD 012CD / May '95 / Godhead

Mindbomb

□ TRIPPIN' THRU THE MINEFIELD VOL.1
RUF 009CD / Nov '96 / Ruf Beats

□ TRIPPIN' THRU THE MINEFIELD VOL.2
RUFCD 010 / Nov '96 / Ruf Beats

Mindfeed

□ TEN MILES HIGH
IOMCD 022 / 1 Jun '98 / InsideOut

Mindheavy Mustard

□ CHEMICALS, CIGARETTES AND LA WOMEN
Bitterness / Complication / Cocaine / Say it / Auto pilot / Chemicals / Interwine / Adopted / Co-pilot / Off ramp / Razor blade / Bungalow / Sing-a-long pizza / Nicole Eggert
N 02482 / Sep '96 / Noise

Mindjive

□ CHEMICALS
BHR 040CD / Apr '96 / Burning Heart

□ MINDJIVE
BHR 020CD / Feb '95 / Burning Heart

Mindless Drug Hoover

□ TOP BANANA
Theme from hoover / Sorry about the shag / Reefer song / Suicide is dangerous / Prune / Murder is fun / Don't take ecstacy / Pancreas / Boxing ring of love / Fluff / Fuck off / Rust / Fag stealer / Booze and drugs hell / Buy my record / Where is Claire / Digital silence / Ring / Ansaphone
DVNT 013CD / 29 Jun '98 / Deviant

Mindrot

□ DAWNING
Dawning / Anguish / Burden / Withersoul / Forlorn / Internal isolation / Across vast oceans
RR 69252 / 26 Jan '98 / Relapse

□ SOUL
Dissipate / Nothing / Suffer / Incandescence / Cold skin / In silence / Clemency / Despair
RR 69672 / 18 May '98 / Relapse

Mindset

□ MINDSET
Shed the skin / 2am / Cosmic Charles / Shoe shine boy / Ihateyoudon'tleaveme / Nosebleed / Sleeping pills / If the devil wore Adidas / Great unwashed / Delilah / Home grown God / Monster in the closet / Psycho sound wave / Faced
N 02732 / Mar '97 / Noise

Mindstore

□ LIGHTENING THE LOAD
Doubled sided walk / Make a sound / Single day / Mindstore / PC streets / Moon riser / Nutmunch / Falling for your love / Buck funk / We are sleeping
INT 845286 / 3 Nov '97 / Alternation

Mindstorm

□ LOVE GOES BLIND
PRS 10292 / Sep '91 / Provogue

Mineo, Attileo

□ MAN IN SPACE WITH SOUNDS
SUBCD 4 / 15 Dec '97 / Subliminal
SUB 0042 / 6 Jul '98 / Subliminal

Mineral

□ POWER OF FAILING
CRC 18CD / 23 Mar '98 / Crank

Ming-Yeuh Ling, David

□ DIALOGUE WITH THE OCEAN
68920 / Jul '97 / Tropical

□ DREAM OF THE BUTTERFLY
68928 / Jul '97 / Tropical

Minger, Pete

□ LOOK TO THE SKY
(I'm afraid) the masquerade is over / Night has a thousand eyes / Make someone happy / Falling in love with love / Soon / Moose the mooche / Like someone in love / Blue 'n' boogie / I hear a rhapsody / Look to the sky
CCD 4555 / Jun '93 / Concord Jazz

Mingus Big Band

□ LIVE IN TIME
Number 29 / Dianne/Alice's wonderland / Boogie stop shuffle / Sue's changes / This subdues my passion / Children's hour of dream / Baby take a chance with me / So long Eric / Moanin' Mambo / Chair in the sky / E's flat, ah's flat too / Shoes of the fisherman's wife are some jive-ass slippers / Us is two / Man who never sleeps/East coasting / Wednesday night prayer meeting
FDM 365832 / Feb '97 / Dreyfus

Mingus, Charles

□ AT BOTTOM LINE (Mingus Dynasty Band)
WWCD 2060 / Jan '91 / West Wind

□ BLACK SAINT AND THE SINNER LADY, THE
Solo dancer / Group and solo dancers / Single solos and group dance / Trio and group dancers / Group dancers freewoman / Duet solo dancers / Stop, look and listen / Sinner Jim Whitney / Heart's beat and shades in physical embraces / Stop, look and sing songs of revolutions / Saint and sinner join in merriment on battle front / Group and solo dance of love / Pain and passioned revolt then / Farewell my beloved
IMP 11742 / Nov '95 / Impulse Jazz

□ BLUES AND ROOTS
Wednesday night prayer meeting / Cryin' blues / Moanin' / Tension / My Jelly Roll soul / E's flat ah's flat too
7567813362 / Mar '93 / Atlantic

□ BLUES AND ROOTS
Wednesday night prayer festival / Cryin' blues / Moanin' / Tensions / Mr. Jelly Roll Soul / E's flat ah's flat too / Wednesday night prayer meeting / Tensions / Mr. Jelly Roll Soul / Eh's flat ah's flat too
81227522052 / 20 Jul '98 / Atlantic

□ CHANGES ONE
Remember rockefeller at Attica / Sue's changes / Devil blues / Duke Ellington's sound of love
8122714042
8122714032 / Jul '96 / Atlantic

□ CHANGES TWO
Free cell block F tis Nazi USA / Orange was the colour of her dress, then silk blue / Black bats and poles / Duke Ellington's sound of love / For Harry Carney
8122710422 / Jul '96 / Atlantic

□ CHARLES MINGUS
Caroline Keikki Mingus / It might as well be Spring / Peggy's blue skylight / Duke Ellington's sound of love / What is this thing called love / Fables of Faubus / Slop / So long Eric / Farewell blues / Just for laughs part 1
BN 029 / Feb '97 / Blue Nite

□ CHARLES MINGUS AND FRIENDS (2CD Set)
Jump monk / ESP / Ecclusiastics / Eclipse / Us is two / Taurus in the arena of life / Mingus blues / Little royal suite / Strollin' / I of hurricane Sue / E's flat, ah's flat too / Ool-ya-koo / Portrait / Don't be afraid, the clown's afraid too
C2K 64975 / Nov '96 / Sony Jazz

□ CHARLES MINGUS AT CARNEGIE HALL
7567813952 / Jun '95 / Atlantic

□ CLOWN, THE
Haitian fight song / Clown / Reincarnation of a lovebird / Blue cee
7567901422 / Dec '96 / Rhino

□ COMPLETE 1959 SESSIONS, THE (Mingus Ah-Um/Mingus Dynasty & Bonus Tracks/3CD Set)
Better git it in your soul / Goodbye pork pie hat / Boogie stop shuffle / Self portrait in three colours / Open letter to Duke / Bird calls / Fables of Fabuos / Pussy cat dues / Jelly roll / Pedal point blues / GG train / Girl of my dreams / Slop / Diane / Song with orange / Gunslinging bird / Things ain't what they used to be / Far wells / Mill valley / Mood indigo / Put me in that dungeon / Strollin' / Better git it in your soul / Bird calls / Jelly roll / Song with orange / Diane / New now know how / New now know how
C3K 65145 / 22 Jun '98 / Sony Jazz

□ COMPLETE DEBUT RECORDINGS 1951-1958, THE (12CD Set)
What is this thing called love / Darn that dream / Yesterdays / Body and soul / Blue moon / Blue tide / Darn that dream / Jeepers creepers / Jeepers creepers / Portrait / Portrait / I've lost my love / I've lost my love / Extra sensory perception / Extra sensory perception / Precognition / Make believe / Paris in blue / Montage / Day dream / Day dream / Rhapsody in blue / Rhapsody in blue / Jet / Jet / You go to my head / Can you blame me / You and me / Be bopper / Cupid / Drum conversation / I've got you under my skin / Embraceable you / Sure thing / Cherokee / Hallelujah / Lullaby of Birdland / Wee Allen's alley / Hot house / Night in Tunisia / Perdido / Salt peanuts / All the things you are / 52nd Street theme / Perdido / Salt peanuts / All the things you are / 52nd Street theme / Wee Allen's alley / Hot house / Night in Tunisia / Bass-ically speaking / Bass-ically speaking / Bass-ically speaking / Bass-ically speaking / Wee dot (blues for some bones) / Stardust / Move / I'll remember April / Now's the time / Trombosphere / Ow / Chazzanova / Yesterdays / Kai's day / Pink topsy / Miss Bliss / Blue tide / Pink topsy / Eclipse / Eclipse / Opus 1 / Opus 1 / (Teapot) walkin' / Like someone in love / I can't get started / Spontaneous combustion / Theme / Split kick / This time the dream's on me / Zootcase / Santa Claus is coming to town / Pendulum at falcon's lair / Jack the fieldstalker / Stockholm sweetnin' / Low and behold / Elusive / Chazzanova / I'll remember April / Bitty ditty / Sombre intrusion / You don't know what love is / Like someone in love / Peace of mind / Lament / Jeep is jumpin' / Git up from there / Lament / One more / I can't get started / More of the same / Get out of town / One more / Get out of town / Ensenada / Machajo / Cherokee / Seven moons / Seven moons / All the things you are / All the things you are / Cherokee / Nature boy / Alone together / There's no you / Easy living / Edge of love / Makin' whoopee / Fanny / Portrait / Jump Monk / Serenade in blue / Percussion discussion / Work song / Septemberly / All the things you C# / I remember April / Love chant / Foggy day / Drums / Haitain fight song / Lady Bird / Jump Monk / All the things you C(#2) / Drums / Drums / I'll remember April / Foggy day / Portrait of Bud Powell / Haitian fight song / Love chant / Lady Bird / What is this thing called love / Latter day Saint / Cunningbird / Jumpin' blues / Masher / Latter day Saint / Latter day Saint / Masher / Latter day Saint / Untitled original blues / Stella by starlight / Stella by starlight / Untitled original composition / Untitled original composition / Autumn in New York / Autumn in New York / Long ago and far away / Long ago and far away / Long ago and far away / Untitled original blues / Joldi / Joldi / Untitled percussion composition
12DCD 4402 / Nov '96 / Debut

□ COMPLETE TOWN HALL CONCERT, THE
Freedom / Osmotin / Epitaph (pt 1) / Peggy's blue skylight / Epitaph (pt 2) / My search / Portrait / Duke's choice (Don't come back) / Please don't come back from the moon / In a mellow tone / Epitaph
CDP 8283532 / Jul '94 / Blue Note

□ CONCERTGEBOUW AMSTERDAM APRIL 1964 VOL.1
087112 / Sep '95 / Ulysse

□ CONCERTGEBOUW AMSTERDAM APRIL 1964 VOL.2
087122 / Sep '95 / Ulysse

□ CUMBIA & JAZZ FUSION
Cumbia jazz fusion / Music for 'todo modo' / Wedding march slow waltz [take 12] / Wedding march slow waltz [take 9]
8122717852 / Sep '94 / Atlantic

□ DEBUT RARITIES VOL.2
What is this thing called love / Blue moon / Blue tide / Jeepers creepers / Daydream / Rhapsody in blue
OJCCD 1808 / Apr '93 / Original Jazz Classics

□ DEBUT RARITIES VOL.3
OJCCD 1821 / Apr '93 / Original Jazz Classics

□ EAST COASTING (Mingus, Charles Sextet)
Memories of you / East coasting / West Coast ghost / Celia / Conversation / Fifty First Street blues
CDGR 120 / Mar '97 / Charly

□ FINAL WORK, THE
DM 15007 / Jul '96 / DMA Jazz

□ GOODBYE PORK PIE HAT
JHR 73516 / '91 / Jazz Hour

□ GREAT CONCERT - PARIS 1964
500072 / Nov '93 / Musidisc

□ GUNSLINGING BIRDS (Mingus Big Band)
Gunslinging birds / Reincarnation of a lovebird / O P / Please don't come back from the moon / Fables of Faubus / Jump monk / Noon night / Hog callin' blues / Started melody
FDM 365752 / Jul '95 / Dreyfus

□ HIS FINAL WORK
Just for laughs / Peggy's blue skylight / Caroline Keikki Mingus / Fables of Faubus / Duke Ellington's sound of love / Farewell farewell / So long Eric / Slop / It might as well be spring
CDGATE 7016 / Oct '87 / Kingdom Jazz

□ IN A SOULFUL MOOD
MCCD 201 / May '95 / Music Club

□ IN YOUR SOUL
Better git it in your soul / Wednesday night prayer / Folk forms no.2 / Prayer for passive resistance / What love / I'll remember April
SUMCD 4162 / 23 Feb '98 / Summit

☐ JAZZ COMPOSER'S WORKSHOP
Purple heart / Gregorian chant / Eulogy for Rudy Williams / Tea for two / Smog LA / Level seven / Transeason / Rose Geranium / Getting together
SV 0171 / Oct '97 / Savoy Jazz

☐ JAZZ EXPERIMENTS OF CHARLES MINGUS
BET 6016 / Jan '95 / Bethlehem

☐ JAZZ WORKSHOP
VGCD 650132 / Oct '93 / Vogue

☐ JAZZICAL MOODS (Mingus, Charles & John LaPorta)
What is this thing called love / What is this thing called love / Minor intrusion / Abstractions / Thrice upon a theme / Four hands / Spur of the moment-echonitus
OJCCD 1857 / Apr '93 / Original Jazz Classics

☐ LIVE AT BIRDLAND 1962
COD 028 / Mar '92 / Jazz View

☐ LIVE AT THE TTB PARIS VOL.1 (Big Band Charlie Mingus)
1211922 / Nov '93 / Soul Note

☐ LIVE AT THE TTB PARIS VOL.2 (Big Band Charlie Mingus)
1211932 / Nov '93 / Soul Note

☐ LIVE AT THE VILLAGE VANGUARD (Mingus Dynasty Band)
STCD 4124 / Feb '90 / Storyville

☐ MINGUS
MDM / Stormy weather / Lock 'em up
CCD 79021 / Feb '97 / Candid

☐ MINGUS AH UM
Better git it in your soul / Goodbye Pork Pie Hat / Boogie stop shuffle / Self portrait in three colours / Open letter to Duke / Bird calls / Fables of Faubus / Pussy cat dues / Jelly roll
4504362 / Oct '93 / Columbia

☐ MINGUS AT ANTIBES
Wednesday night prayer meeting / Prayer for passive resistance / What love / I'll remember April / Folk forms 1 / Better git it in your soul
7567905322 / Mar '93 / Atlantic

☐ MINGUS AT CARNEGIE HALL
C jam blues / Perdido
8122722852 / Mar '96 / Atlantic

☐ MINGUS AT THE BOHEMIA
OJCCD 45 / Oct '92 / Original Jazz Classics

☐ MINGUS DYNASTY
Slop / Diane / Song with orange / Gunslinging birds / Things ain't the way they used to be / Far wells / Mill valley / New now, know how / Mood indigo / Put me in that dungeon
4729952 / Feb '94 / Columbia

☐ MINGUS IN EUROPE VOL.2
ENJA 30772 / 17 Nov '97 / Enja

☐ MINGUS MOVES
Canon / Opus 4 / Moves / Flowers for a lady / Newcomer / Opus 3 / Big Alice / Call
8122714542 / Jul '96 / Atlantic

☐ MINGUS PLAYS PIANO
Myself when I am real / I can't get started (with you) / Body and soul / Roland Kirk's message / Memories of you / She's just Miss Popular hybrid / Orange was the colour of her dress, then silk blue / Meditations for Moses / Old portrait / I'm getting sentimental over you / Compositional theme story
IMP 12172 / Apr '97 / Impulse Jazz

☐ MINGUS REVISITED
Take the 'A' train / Prayer for passive resistance / Eclipse / Mingus fingus no.2 / Weird nightmare / Do nothin' 'til you hear from me / Bemoanable lady / Half mast inhibition
8264962 / Feb '97 / Verve

☐ MINGUS THREE
Yesterdays / Back home blues / I can't get started / Hamp's new blues / Summertime / Dizzy moods / Laura
CDP 8571552 / Jul '97 / Roulette

☐ MINGUS, MINGUS, MINGUS, MINGUS, MINGUS
II BS / I x love / Celia / Mood indigo / Better git it in your soul / Theme for Lester Young / Hora decubitus
MCAD 39119 / Jun '89 / Impulse Jazz

☐ MODERN JAZZ SYMPOSIUM OF MUSIC AND POETRY (Bethlehem Jazz Classics)
CDGR 131 / Apr '97 / Charly

☐ MYSTERIOUS BLUES
Mysterious blues / Wrap your troubles in dreams (and dream your troubles away) / Body and soul / Vassarlean / Reincarnation of a love bird / Me and you blues / Melody for the drums
CCD 79042 / Feb '97 / Candid

☐ NEW TIJUANA MOODS
Dizzy moods / Ysabel's table dance / Los mariachis (the street musicians) / Flamingo / Tijuana gift shop
09026685912 / Oct '96 / RCA Victor

☐ NOSTALGIA IN TIMES SQUARE (Mingus Big Band '93)
Nostalgia in Times Square / Moanin' / Self portrait in three colours / Don't be afraid... / Duke Ellington's Sound of love / Mingus fingers / Weird nightmare / Open letter to Duke / Invisible lady / Ecclusiastics
FDM 365592 / Aug '93 / Dreyfus

☐ OH YEAH
Hog callin' blues / Devil woman / Wham bam thank you ma'am / Ecclusiastics / Oh Lord don't let them drop that atomic bomb on me / Eat that chicken / Passion of a man
7567906672 / Mar '93 / Atlantic

☐ ORANGE
MCD 078 / Dec '95 / Moon

☐ PARIS 1947
Parkeriana / Meditations for integration / Orange was the colours of the dress, then blue silk
CD 56047 / Nov '94 / Jazz Roots

☐ PARIS 1964
LEJAZZCD 19 / Jun '93 / Le Jazz

☐ PARIS 1967 VOL.2 (Mingus, Charles & Sonny Stitt)
So long Eric / Parkeriana
LEJAZZCD 38 / May '95 / Le Jazz

☐ PARIS TNP OCTOBER 1970
087312 / Sep '95 / Ulysse

☐ PASSIONS OF A MAN (The Complete Atlantic Recordings/6CD Set)
Pithecanthropus erectus / Foggy day / Love chant / Profile of Jackie / Laura / When your lover has gone / Just one of those things / Blue greens / Clown / Passions of a woman loved / Blue Cee / Tonight at noon / Reincarnation of a lovebird / Haitian fight song / E's flat ah's flat too / My jelly roll soul / Tensions / Moanin' / Cryin' blues / Wednesday night prayer meeting / Eh's flat ah's flat too / My jelly roll soul / Tensions / Wednesday night prayer meeting / Prayer for passive resistance / Better git hit in your soul / Wednesday night prayer meeting / Folk forms / What love / I'll remember April / Devil woman / Ecclusiastics / 'Old' blues for Walt's Torin / Peggy's blue skylight / Hog callin' blues / Oh lord don't let them drop that atomic bomb on me / Passions of a man / Wham bam thank you ma'am / Invisible lady / Eat that chicken / Interview
8122728712 / 8 Dec '97 / Atlantic

☐ PITHYCANTHROPUS ERECTUS
7567814562 / Jul '96 / Atlantic

☐ PLUS MAX ROACH (Mingus, Charles & Max Roach)
Drums / Haitian fight song / Ladybird / I'll remember April / Love chant
OJCCD 440 / Sep '93 / Original Jazz Classics

☐ PRESENTS CHARLES MINGUS
Folk forms No.1 / Original Faubus fables / What love / All the things you could be by now if Sigmund Freud's wife..
CCD 79005 / Feb '97 / Candid

☐ QUE VIVA MINGUS (Mingus Big Band)
Cumbia and jazz fusion / Tijuana gift shop / Moods in mambo / Los Mariachis / Far Wells Mill valley / Dizzy moods / Slippers / Love chant / Eat that chicken (paella) / Ysabel's table dance
FDM 365932 / 23 Feb '98 / Dreyfus

☐ REINCARNATION (Mingus Dynasty Band)
SNCD 1042 / '86 / Soul Note

☐ REINCARNATION OF A LOVE BIRD
Reincarnation of a love bird / Wrap your troubles in dreams / Body and soul / Bugs / R and R
CCD 79026 / Feb '97 / Candid

☐ REVENGE
32002CD / May '96 / Thirty Two

☐ RIGHT NOW: LIVE AT THE JAZZ WORKSHOP
New fables / Meditation
OJCCD 237 / Sep '93 / Original Jazz Classics

☐ THIS IS JAZZ
Better git it in your soul / Goodbye Pork Pie Hat / Fables of faubus / Self portrait in three colours / Slop / Song with orange / Gunslinging bird / Far Wells, Mill Valley / New now, know how / Shoes of the fisherman's wife are some jive ass slippers / Please don't come back from the moon
CK 64624 / May '96 / Sony Jazz

☐ THREE OR FOUR SHADES OF BLUE
Better git it in your soul / Goodbye Pork Pie Hat / Noddin ya head blues / Three or four shade of blues / Nobody knows
7567814032 / Mar '93 / Atlantic

☐ TOWN HALL CONCERT
So long Eric / Praying with Eric
OJCCD 42 / Sep '93 / Original Jazz Classics

☐ WEDNESDAY NIGHT PRAYER MEETING
Better git it in your soul / Wednesday night prayer meeting / Wednesday night prayer meeting / Folk forms no.2
306662 / Jun '97 / Hallmark

☐ WONDERLAND
Nostalgia in Times Square / I can't get started (with you) / No private income blues / Alice's wonderland
CDP 8273252 / Feb '94 / Blue Note

Minh Doky, Christian

☐ APPRECIATION
STCD 4169 / Feb '90 / Storyville

☐ SEQUEL, THE
Fall / Certified / Message / Alone / Sequel / Falling in love with love / Brother / Let's pretend
STCD 4175 / Feb '90 / Storyville

Minimal Compact

☐ DEADLY WEAPONS/NEXT ONE IS REAL
CRAM 3032 / Nov '88 / Crammed Discs

☐ FIGURE ONE CUTS
CRAM 055 / Oct '87 / Crammed Discs

☐ LOWLANDS FLIGHT
MTM 10CD / '88 / Made To Measure

☐ MINIMAL COMPACT LIVE
CRAM 061 / Nov '88 / Crammed Discs

☐ ONE PLUS ONE BY ONE
CRAM 1521 / Nov '88 / Crammed Discs

☐ RAGING SOULS
CRAM 042 / '88 / Crammed Discs

Minimal Man

☐ HUNGER IS ALL SHE'S EVER KNOWN/ MOCK HONEYMOON
BIAS 071CD / '90 / Play It Again Sam

Ministry

☐ FILTH PIG
Reload / Filth pig / Crumbs / Useless / Lava / Dead guy / Face / Brick windows / Game show / Lay lady lay / Reload (edit)
9362458382 / Jan '96 / WEA

☐ LAND OF RAPE AND HONEY
Stigmata / Missing / Deity / Golden dawn / Destruction / Land of rape and honey / You know what you are / Flashback / Abortive / Hizbollah / I prefer
7599257992 / Nov '92 / WEA

☐ LIVE - IN CASE YOU DIDN'T FEEL LIKE SHOWING UP
Missing / Deity / So what / Burning inside / Thieves / Stigmata
7599262662 / Nov '92 / WEA

☐ MIND IS A TERRIBLE THING TO TASTE, THE
Thieves / Never believe / Breathe / Burning inside / Cannibal song / So what / Test / Dream song / Faith collapsing
7599260042 / Mar '94 / WEA

☐ PSALM 69
NWO / Just one fix / TV II / Hero / Jesus built my hotrod / Scarecrow / Psalm 69 / Corrosion / Grace
7599267272 / Dec '96 / WEA

Ministry Of Ska

☐ RARIN' TO GO
Skankin' with the torreadores / Rarin' to go / Saint / Ras / Dangerman / Skaty / Rawhide / Tell William / Condoms / Head 'em up, move 'em out / Norman / Skanking with the torreadores
FLEGCD 6 / Jun '96 / Future Legend

Ministry Of Terror

☐ FALL OF LIFE
FDN 2011CD / Jun '95 / Foundation 2000

Mink Deville

☐ CABRETTA/RETURN TO MAGENTA
Venus of Avenue D / Little girl / One way street / Mixed up, shook up girl / Gunslinger / Can't do without it / Cadillac walk / Spanish stroll / She's so tough / Party girls / Guardian angel / Soul twist / Train lady / Rolene / Desperate days / Just your friends / Steady drivin' man / Easy slider / I broke that promise / Confidence to kill
RVCD 59 / Oct '96 / Raven

☐ CABRETTA/RETURN TO MAGENTA/ LE CHAT BLEU (3CD Set)
Venus of Avenue D / Little girl / One way street / Mixed up / Shook up girl / Gunslinger / Can't do without it / Cadillac Walk / Spanish stroll / She's so tough / Party girl / Guardian angel / Soul twist / A-train lady / Rolene / Desperate days / Just your friends / Steady drivin' man / Easy slider / I broke that promise / Confidence to kill / This must be the night / Savoire faire / That world outside / Slow drain / You just keep holding on / Lipstick traces / Just to walk that little girl home / Turn you every way but loose / Bad boy / Heaven stood still
CDOMB 013 / 27 Jul '98 / EMI

☐ CENTENARY COLLECTION, THE (The Best Of Mink Deville)
Venus of Avenue D / Little girl / One way street / Mixed up / Shook up girl / Gunslinger / Cadillac walk / Spanish stroll / Guardian angel / Soul twist / 'A' train lady / Rolene / Desperate days / Just your friends / I broke that promise / This must be the night / Savoir faire / Slow drain / You just keep holding on / Mazurka / Just to walk that little girl home
CTMCD 333 / 8 Sep '97 / EMI

☐ LE CHAT BLEU
This must be the night / Savoir faire / That world outside / Slow drain / You just keep holding on / Lipstick traces / Bad boy / Mazurka / Just to walk that little girl home / Heaven stood still
WM 339002 / Jun '93 / Wotre Music

☐ RETURN TO MAGENTA
Just your friends / Soul twist / Train lady / Rolene / Desperate days / Guardian angel / Steady drivin' man / Easy slider / I broke that promise / Confidence to kill
WM 339003 / Jun '93 / Wotre Music

☐ SPANISH STROLL
RVCD 32 / Jun '93 / Raven

Mink Stole

☐ EATS HEAD
SPV 07745582 / Jul '94 / SPV

Minnelli, Liza

☐ COLLECTION, THE
Cabaret / Look of love / On a slow boat to China / Man I love / Stormy weather / Leavin' on a jet plane / Liza / Everybody's talkin'/Good morning starshine / Come rain or come shine / Love story / Love for sale / Can't help lovin' dat man / I will wait for you / Nevertheless (I'm in love with you) / For no one / Macarthur Park / Lazybones / God bless the child / Maybe this time / How long has this been going on
5518152 / 3 Aug '98 / Spectrum

☐ LIVE AT CARNEGIE HALL
CD 85502 / '88 / Telarc

☐ RESULTS
I want you now / Losing my mind / If there was love / So sorry, I said / Don't drop bombs / Twist in my sobriety / Rent / Love pains / Tonight is forever / I can't say goodnight
4655112 / Oct '89 / Epic

☐ TOUCH OF CLASS, A
Blue moon / It's just a matter of time / Maybe this time / I knew him when / If I were in your shoes / Maybe soon / Meantime / Travelin' life / Don't ever leave me / Together wherever we go / Try to remember / I who have nothing / I'll build a stairway to paradise / Looking at you / Hello Dolly / Chicago medley
TC 883682 / 2 Feb '98 / Disky

Minogue, Aine

☐ BETWEEN THE WORLDS
Exile / O'Carolan / Silence / Grove / Mai bhan ni chuilionain / Between the worlds / Fyvie Castle / Rosemary faire / Parting / Jezebel carol / Across the universe / Sleep song
09026684862 / 6 Oct '97 / RCA Victor

Minogue, Dannii

☐ GIRL
All I wanna do / Disrememberance / Heaven can wait / You're all I need / So in love with yourself / It's amazing / Moving up / Everybody changes underwater / Dreaming / Coconut
3984205492 / 8 Sep '97 / Eternal

Minogue, Kylie

☐ INTERVIEW COMPACT DISC: KYLIE & JASON (Minogue, Kylie & Jason Donovan)
CBAK 4026 / Nov '89 / Baktabak

☐ KYLIE MINOGUE
Confide in me / If I was your lover / Where is the feeling / Put yourself in my place / Dangerous game / Automatic love / Where has the love gone / Falling / Time will pass you by
74321227492 / Jun '96 / De-Construction

☐ KYLIE MINOGUE
Too far / Cowboy style / Some kind of bliss / Did it again / Breathe / Say hey / Drunk / I don't need anyone / Jump / Limbo / Through the years / Dreams
74321517272 / 16 Mar '98 / De-Construction

☐ TOO FAR
74321587152 / 3 Aug '98 / De-Construction

Minor Forest

☐ CONSTITUENT PARTS 1993-1996
THRILL 034CD / Oct '96 / Thrill Jockey

☐ FLEMISH ALTRUISM
THRILL 34CD / Jul '97 / Thrill Jockey
RUNT 27 / Mar '97 / Runt

☐ ININDEPENDENCE
THRILL 058CD / 17 Aug '98 / Thrill Jockey

Minor Threat

☐ COMPLETE DISCOGRAPHY
DISCHORD 40 / Mar '90 / Dischord

Minott, Sugar

☐ 20 SUPER HITS
SONCD 0009 / Oct '90 / Sonic Sounds

☐ AFRICAN SOLDIER
Mandela / In a time like this / Chant them down / Africa is calling / Easy come, easy go / Play me nah play / Jah work to do / African soldier / Vibes / Apartheid (that nuh right)
HBCD 49 / '88 / Heartbeat

☐ BREAKING FREE
RAS 3176 / Aug '96 / Ras

☐ CHANNEL ONE COLLECTION
SMCD 1 / Feb '96 / Channel One

☐ COLLECTION, THE
All kind a style / Musical murder / Lovers rock medley / Power of love / I am a man / Let love come in / Keep the crowd coming / Forever in love / We rule rythem / Hot fe the riddim / Play this rub a dub / Gone away / Freedom for the people / Mind what you say / No turning back / Love we know / Teach the youth the truth / Got to live in love / Lets make things right / Rocking from dust to dawn
RN 7011 / 20 Apr '98 / Rhino

☐ COLLECTORS COLLECTION VOL.1
CDHB 206 / Aug '96 / Heartbeat

☐ EASY SQUEEZE
WRCD 007 / Jun '97 / World

☐ GOOD THING GOING
Good thing going / High up above / Never my love / House on a hill / My sister / Jasmine / Life without money / Lonely days / Walk on by / Family affair
HBCD 13 / Aug '88 / Heartbeat

☐ GOOD THING GOING
CDSGP 0146 / Jul '95 / Prestige

☐ HERBMAN HUSTLING
So she hot / Herbman hustling / Dance hall business / All gone / Give Jah the key / Dance hall we deh / Ghetto living / Far away / Uptown girl / Rock of ages / Hard time pressure / Come back baby / Palavin spree / Nice it up / New love / Easy squeeze
CDHB 212 / Apr '98 / Heartbeat

☐ INNA REGGAE DANCE HALL
Victim of society / Nah follow nuh fashion / Hard time rock / All day and night / Four wheel wheelie / You've got the love / War and crime / Down the line / Nuh know it like me / Run come / Rhythmatic / Inna rub a dub
HBCD 29 / Jul '88 / Heartbeat

☐ INTERNATIONAL
RASCD 3197 / 5 May '98 / Ras

☐ JAH MAKE ME FEEL SO GOOD
EXTCD 4 / Mar '97 / Exterminator

☐ NICE IT UP (The Very Best Of Sugar Minott)
VPCD 15152 / 5 May '98 / VP

☐ RAS PORTRAITS
Ain't nobody move me / Sprinter stayer / Run things / Herbsman hustling / Dancehall fever / Devil's pickney / Gun gang / Ramdance master / International herbalist / A just rasta / Break free / Rub-a-dub sound / Heads of conference
RAS 3319 / Jul '97 / Ras

☐ REGGAE LOVE SONGS
Good thing going / Lovers rock / Lonely days / Now we know / Just don't wanna be lonely / Make it with you / Missing you / Show me that you love me / Girl is in love / Sandy / You've lost that loving feeling / Never too young / Can you remember / House is not a home
CD 6064 / Apr '97 / Music

☐ REGGAE MAX
JSRNCD 16 / Jun '97 / Jet Star

☐ SHOWDOWN VOL.1 (Minott, Sugar & Frankie Paul)
78249700160 / Apr '95 / Channel One

☐ SHOWDOWN VOL.2 (Minott, Sugar & Frankie Paul)
JJCD 160 / 18 May '98 / Channel One

☐ SLICE OF THE CAKE
HBCD 24 / '88 / Heartbeat

☐ SUGAR MINOTT STORY, THE
UPTCD 25 / Jul '97 / Uptempo

☐ TOUCH OF CLASS, A
JMCD 001 / Mar '91 / Jammy's

☐ WITH LOTS OF EXTRA
78249700120 / Apr '95 / Channel One

Minstrels Of Annie Street

☐ ORIGINAL TUXEDO RAG
SOSCD 1272 / Apr '94 / Stomp Off

Mint 400

☐ INTERCOMFORT
HIPCD 16 / Jun '96 / Backs

Mint Condition

☐ DEFINITION OF A BAND
Intro / Change your mind / You don't have to hurt no more / Gettin' it on / What kind of man would I be / Let me be the one / Definition of a band / Ain't hookin' me up enough / Funky weekend / I want it again / On and on / Never that you'll never know / Asher in Rio interlude / Raise up / On and on / Sometimes / Missing / If it wasn't for your love - dedication
5490282 / Jun '97 / Polydor

☐ MINT CONDITION
5490392 / 15 Jun '98 / Perspective

Mint Juleps

☐ ONE TIME
Don't let your heart / Don't let your heart / Jimmy mack / Rhythm and blues / Drip drop / Mumblin' boy / Da doo ron ron / I'm so sorry / Ain't the got nerve / One bad stud / Move in closer / I don't need your love / Stand by me / Shout
STIFFCD 15 / Jan '94 / Disky

☐ WOMEN IN (E)MOTION FESTIVAL
T&M 104 / Nov '94 / Tradition & Moderne

Minton, Phil

☐ TWO CONCERTS (Minton, Phil & John Butcher)
FMPOWN 90006 / Jan '98 / Full Moon

Minty

☐ OPEN WIDE
Procession / Minty / That's nice / Plastic bag / Useless man / Homage / Manners mean / King size / Hold on / Nothing / Homme aphrodite / Dream / Art / Jeremy
CAN 2CD / Jul '97 / Candy

Mintzer, Bob

☐ LIVE AT THE BERLIN JAZZ FESTIVAL
BASIC 50003 / Jun '96 / ITM

Minucci, Chieli

☐ IT'S GONNA BE GOOD
Undercovers / Endless summer / Dreams / So far away / Cool town / Follow you follow me / Gift / Baci / It's gonna be good / Beginnings / On the border / Kama sutra
JVC 90322 / Apr '98 / JVC

☐ JEWELS
Courageous cats / Phat city / Only you / Sitting in limbo / Hideaway / Dig the dirt / Mountains / Realm of the senses / Moment of love / Jewels
JVC 20442 / May '95 / JVC

☐ RENAISSANCE
Big sky country / Renaissance / Cause we've ended as lovers / Come as you are / Anything and everything / Shine / In your arms / Spirit / Sun will always shine / Cacoutra / Leilani / Mixomelodia / Reunion / Faith
JVC 20562 / Jun '96 / JVC

Minus 5

☐ MY CHARTREUSE OPINION
162127 / Dec '97 / Hollywood

☐ OLD LIQUIDATOR
GRCD 350 / 17 Nov '97 / Glitterhouse

Minus, Rich

☐ BORDERLINE BLUES
422432 / Feb '97 / New Rose

☐ COLLECTION, THE
422231 / Feb '97 / New Rose

☐ RICH MINUS 3
422497 / Feb '97 / New Rose

Minute By Minute

☐ DON'T MESS WITH FIRE
Don't mess with fire / Long hot night / A million miles away / Short Avenue / Go back to sleep / Black and blue / I'll be back / It'll be all right on the night / Tijuana holiday / Three times your age / Homesick / Katie's love
SRH 803 / Feb '97 / Start

Minutemen

☐ 3 WAY TIE (FOR LAST)
Price of paradise / Lost / Big stick / Political nightmare / Courage / Hve you ever seen the rain / Red and the black / Spoken word piece / No one / Stories / What is it / Ack ack ack / Just another soldier / Situations at hand / Hittin' the bong / Bermuda
SST 058CD / Feb '86 / SST

☐ BALLOT RESULT
Little man with a gun in his hand / Political song for michael jackson to sing / I felt like a gringo / Jesus and tequila / Courage / King of the hill / Bermuda / No one / Mr. robot's holy orders / Ack ack ack / History lesson (part two) / This ain't no picnic / Cheerleaders / Time / Cut / Split red / Shit you hear at parties / Hell (second take) / Tour-spiel / Take our test / Punch line / Search / Bob dylan wrote propaganda songs / Badges / Tension / If reagan played disco / No no no to draft and war-joe mccarthy's ghost
SST 068CD / May '93 / SST

☐ BUZZ OR HOWL UNDER THE INFLUENCE OF HEAT
SST 016CD / May '93 / SST

☐ DOUBLE NICKELS ON THE DIME
SST 028CD / Oct '87 / SST

☐ FAT
SST 214CD / Nov '88 / SST

☐ INTRODUCING THE MINUTEMEN
SST 363CD / 3 Aug '98 / SST

☐ POLITICS OF TIME
SST 277CD / May '93 / SST

☐ POST-MERSH VOL.1
SST 138CD / May '93 / SST

☐ POST-MERSH VOL.2
SST 139CD / May '93 / SST

☐ POST-MERSH VOL.3
SST 165CD / May '93 / SST

☐ PROJECT MERSH
SST 034CD / May '93 / SST

☐ PUNCH LINE, THE
SST 004CD / May '93 / SST

☐ WHAT MAKES A MAN START FIRES
SST 014CD / May '93 / SST

Minxus

☐ PABULUM
Minxus / Silk purse / I know you want to stop / Pabulum / Falcon contract / Vultura / Wonderful pair / Get / I live on sand / Monkey theme / Liberty bodice / Fecund girls / Sunshine / X Y Zoom / Ever since forever
PURECD 043 / Jan '95 / Too Pure

Mion, Philippe

☐ LEONE
IMED 9632 / Jun '97 / Diffunzioni Musicali

Mioritza

☐ SONGS AND DANCES FROM ROMANIA
EUCD 1070 / '89 / ARC

Miracle Mile

☐ CANDIDS
CDMM5 / 6 Jul '98 / Miracle

Miracle Workers

☐ ANATOMY OF A CREEP
TX 51156CD / Feb '96 / Triple X

☐ INSIDE OUT
Go now / That ain't me / Inside out / You'll know why / Another guy / Love has no time / I'll walk away / 535 / Tears / Already gone / Hey little bird / Mystery girl / One step closer to you
VOXXCD 2031 / '94 / Voxx

Mirageman

☐ THRILLING
Raptus / El paso / Hashish / La coruna / Thrilling / Hypnosis / Crimen / Gulp / Obesession / Paprika / Cicinatti / Michigan / Tuscon / Katawa
4892292 / 24 Nov '97 / Irma La Douce

☐ THUNDER AND LIGHTING
4892282 / 24 Nov '97 / Irma La Douce

Miranda

☐ PHENOMENA
SUB 48372 / Feb '97 / Distance

Miranda Sex Garden

☐ FAIRYTALES OF SLAVERY
CDSTUMM 120 / May '94 / Mute

☐ IRIS
Lovely Joan / Falling / Fear / Blue light / Iris
CDSTUMM 97 / May '92 / Mute

Miranda, Carmen

☐ BRAZILIAN BOMBSHELL, THE
LEGEND CD 6005 / Dec '92 / Fresh Sound

☐ BRAZILIAN BOMBSHELL, THE (23 Hits 1939-1947)
Mama eu quero / Bambu bambu / South American way / Co co co co co co co ro / Touradas em Madrid / I yi yi yi yi (I like you very much) / Chica chica boom chic / Cae cae / Alo alo / Arca de noe / Weekend in Havana / Man with the lollipop song / Rebola a bola / When I love I love / Ella diz que tem / Nao tem dou a chupeta / Manuelo / Chattanooga choo choo / Tic tac do meu coracao / O passo du kanguru / Boneca de pixe / Upa upa / Tico tico / Matador: Miranda, Carmen & The Andrews Sisters / Cuanto le gusta: *Miranda, Carmen & The Andrews Sisters*
CDAJA 5342 / Mar '98 / Living Era

☐ CARMEN MIRANDA
883723 / May '97 / Milan

☐ CARMEN MIRANDA VOL.1
HQCD 33 / Oct '93 / Harlequin

☐ CARMEN MIRANDA VOL.2 1930-1945
Iaia ioio / Pra voce gostar de mim / Quero ver voce chorar / Dona balbina / Cuidado hein / Malandro / Moleque indigidesto / Um pouquinho / Na batacada da vida / Mamae nao quer / Elogio da raca / Pra quem sabe dar valor / Amor amor / Eu quero casar com voce / Minha deusa partiu / Balance / Minha terra tem palmeiras / Boneca de piche / Salada mista / A pensoa da dona stella / Cuidado com a gaita do avry / Voltei pro morro / Tici tico no fuba
HQCD 94 / Oct '97 / Harlequin

☐ SOUTH AMERICAN WAY
South American way / Mama eu tuero (I want my mama) / I yi yi yi yi (I like you very much) / Chica chica boom chic / Weekend in Havana / When I love I love / Chattanooga choo choo / Manuelo / O passo du kanguru / Bambu bambu / Cae cae / Turadas em madrid / Tic tac do meu coracao / Co co co co ro / Cuanto Lagusta / Wedding samba
JASCD 317 / Nov '93 / Jasmine

Miranda, Marcia

☐ UNBOUNDED
JMC 1143CD / Mar '97 / JMC

Miranda, Marlui

☐ 2 IHU KEWERE: REZAR
Canto de entrada / Kyrie / Gloria / Aleluia / Credo / Ofertorio / Pai nosso / Agnus dei / Comunhao / Acao de gracas / Canto final
ACT 50182 / 17 Nov '97 / Act

☐ TODOS OS SONS
Tchori Tchori / Pame Daworo / Tche nane / Naumu / Awina/Ijain Je E' / Araruna / Mena Barsaa / Bep / Festa da flauta / Yny maj Hyrynh / Hirigo / Wine merewa / Meko merewa / Ju parana / Kworo kango / Mito - Metumji laren / 15 variacoes de Hai Nai Hai
ACT 50052 / Aug '97 / Act

Mireille

☐ MIREILLE & JEAN SABLON/PILLS & TABET (2CD Set) (Mireille & Jean Sablon)
FA 043 / Feb '96 / Fremeaux

Mirrors Over Kiev

☐ NORTHERN SONGS
Jane's farewell / Midnight sky / Rolling in the hay / By your side / Arrows in your eyes / All his women / My cheatin' heart / Scars are healing / Northern song / Dance you through / Hang down your head
RRACD 014 / Sep '91 / Run River

Mirwais

☐ MIRWAIS
ROSE 235 CD / Feb '91 / New Rose

Mirza

☐ ANADROMOUS
DRL 043CD / Jul '97 / Darla

Misanthrope

☐ 666 THEATRE BIZARRE
HOLY 016CD / Nov '95 / Holy

☐ MIRACLES TOTEM TABOO
HOLY 006CD / Jul '94 / Holy

☐ VARIATION ON INDUCTIVE THEORIES
HOLY 002CD / May '94 / Holy

☐ VISIONNAIRE
HOLY 027CD / 13 Oct '97 / Holy

Mischo, R.J.

☐ COOL DISPOSITION (Mischo, R.J. Red Hot Blues Band)
(Everybody's) in the mood / I should be dead / Cold hearted woman / Get your money / Second wind / Love my baby / Taste of my own medicine / Main Street strut / Little village / A-OK / Don't bring a friend / Skinny woman / High maintainance woman / Dangerous boy / Travellin' all day
CCD 11055 / Jun '97 / Crosscut

☐ READY TO GO (Mischo, R.J. & Teddy Morgan Band)
She's murder / Rockin' the mule / You're sweet / Kidstuff / Had my fun / Forty days / Baby I don't care / RJ's jump / Change your way / I got to find my baby / McCabe's 88's / Can't get nothing / Evil / Lightnin' blues
ATM 1126 / Feb '97 / Atomic Theory

Misconduct

☐ ANOTHER TIME
BTR 019CD / 25 Aug '97 / Bad Taste

Miscreant

☐ DREAMING ICE
WAR 004CD / Apr '96 / Wrong Again

Misery

☐ WHO'S THE FOOL
SKULD 020CD / Jan '97 / Skuld

Misery Index

☐ MISERY INDEX
MIS 001 / Jan '97 / Misery Index

Misery Loves Company

☐ HAPPY
Happy / Strain of frustration / This is no dream / Private hell / Kiss your boots / Sonic attack
MOSH 151CD / 1 Sep '97 / Earache

☐ MISERY LOVES COMPANY
My mind still speaks / Kiss your boots / Need another one / Sonic attack / This is no dream / Happy / Scared / I swallow / Private hell / Only way / Two seconds
MOSH 133CD / 1 Sep '97 / Earache

☐ NOT LIKE THEM
It's all yours / A million lies / Prove me wrong / Owe you nothing / Complicated game / Taste it / Deny everything / Them nails / Infected / Feed the creep / Not the only one / Nothing remains
MOSH 184CD
MOSH 184CDL / 6 Oct '97 / Earache

Misfits

☐ AMERICAN PSYCHO
Abominable Dr. Phibes / American psycho / Speak of the devil / Walk among us / Hunger / From hell they came / Dig up her bones / Blacklight / Resurrection / This island Earth / Crimson ghost / Day of the dead / Haunting / Mars attacks / Hate the living, love the dead / Shining / Don't open til Doomsday
GED 24939 / May '97 / Geffen

☐ EARTH AD (Earth AD/Die Die My Darling)
PL9CD 02/3 / Jan '97 / Plan 9/Caroline

☐ EVILIVE
20 eyes / Night of the living dead / Astro zombies / Horror business / London dungeon / Nike a go go / Hate breeders / Devil's whorehouse / All hell breaks loose / Horror hotel / Ghouls night out / We are 138
PL9CD 08 / Mar '97 / Plan 9/Caroline

☐ HEAVEN ON EARTH (A Tribute To The Misfits) (Various Artists)
TR 004 / 1 Jun '98 / Tribute

☐ HELL ON EARTH (A Tribute To The Misfits) (Various Artists)
TR 004CD / Dec '96 / Tribute

☐ LEGACY OF BRUTALITY
PL9CD 06 / Jan '97 / Plan 9/Caroline

☐ MISFITS BOX SET (4CD Set)
CDCAR 7529 / Jan '97 / Caroline

☐ MISFITS COLLECTION VOL.1
Bullet / Horror business / Teenager's from Mars / Night of the living / Where eagles dare / Vampira / Skulls / I turned into a martian / Eyes / Violent world / London dungeon / Ghoul's night out / Halloween / Die die my darling / Mommy, can I go out and kill tonight
PL9CD 1 / Jan '97 / Plan 9/Caroline

☐ MISFITS COLLECTION VOL.2
CAROL 75152 / Jan '97 / Caroline

☐ STATIC AGE
Static age / TV casualty / Some kinda hate / Last caress / Return of the fly / Hybrid moments / We are 138 / Teenagers from mars / Come back / Angelfuck / Hollywood Babylon / Attitude / Bullet / Theme for a Jackal / She / Spinal remains / In the doorway
CAROL 75202 / Jul '97 / Caroline

☐ VIOLENT WORLD (A Tribute To The Misfits) (Various Artists)
She: *Snapcase* / Astro zombies: *Pennywise* / 20 eyes: *Shades Apart* / TV casualty: *Tanner* / Where eagles dare: *Therapy* / London dungeon: *Prong* / Death comes ripping: *108* / Mommy, can I go out and kill tonight: *Bouncing Souls* / Ghouls night out: *Goldfinger* / Horror business: *Deadguy* / All hell breaks loose: *Sick Of It All* / Last caress: *NOFX* / Earth AD: *Earth Crisis* / Return of the fly: *Farside*
CAROL 006CD / Feb '97 / Caroline

Misha

☐ CONNECTED TO THE UNEXPECTED
Si kuku ni ta kuja / Thoughts the rain / 1 and the 9 / Black ballet / Poet in the trash can / Who are you / Electrified / Donde estan mis zapatos / Moon over my ami / Smooth / Moonlight serenade
JVC 20552 / Jun '96 / JVC

Mishra, Rajan Sajan

☐ RAGAS, DESI AND SHUDDH BHAIRAVI
NRCD 0057 / May '96 / Navras

Mishra, Sanjay

☐ BLUE INCANTATION (Mishra, Sanjay & Jerry Garcia)
My meditation / Monsoon / For Julia / Allegro / Clouds / Passage of time / Self portrait / Bach in time / Nocturne / Before summer rain
RCD 10409 / Apr '97 / Rykodisc

Misia

☐ FADO (Garras Dos Sentidos)
Garras dos sentidos / Da vida quero os sinais / Nao me chamem pelo nome / Danca de magoas / Sete luas / Estatua falsa / Sou de vidro / Nenhuma estrela caiu / Litania / Fado do retorno
3984227312 / 9 Mar '98 / Erato

Misiani, Daniel Owino

☐ PINY OSE MER/THE WORLD UPSIDE DOWN (Misiani, Daniel Owino & Shirati Band)
Isabella Muga / Rose Akoth / Margret Odero / Piny Ose Mer / Makuru bor / Otieno anyango / Wuoth iye tek / Dora Mamy
CDORB 046 / Jul '89 / Globestyle

Misra, Pandit Lalmani

☐ MUSIC OF PANDIT LALMANI MISRA, THE
D 8627 / Feb '96 / Unesco

Miss Alans

☐ LEDGER
WD 352 / Aug '96 / World Domination

Miss Angie

☐ 100 MILLION EYEBALLS
Trampoline / Life life life / In your hands / Free / Satisfied / Sun / 100 million eyeballs / Lift my eyes up / Bullfrogs and butterflys
7017024613 / Nov '97 / Myrrh

Miss Bliss

☐ MISS BLISS
MDR 10CD / Jul '97 / Meltdown

Miss Jones

☐ MISS JONES...THE OTHER WOMAN
5309492 / 10 Aug '98 / Polydor

Miss Lou

☐ YES M'DEAR
SONCD 0079 / Nov '95 / Sonic Sounds

Miss Murgatroid

☐ METHYL ETHYL KEY TONES
WOE 24 / Nov '93 / Worrybird

Miss World

☐ MISS WORLD
First female serial killer / Nine steps to nowhere / Watch that man weep / Blow / What a wonderful world / British pharmaceuticals / Highway of dead roads / Mother Mary / Speak / Troubled blood / Love is the whole of the law / Thief inside / Dead flowers
4509903522 / Nov '92 / Anxious

Missing Brazilians

☐ WARZONE
ONUCD 18634 / Aug '97 / On-U Sound

Mission

☐ BLUE
SMEECD 002 / Jun '96 / Equator

☐ CARVED IN SAND
Amelia / Into the blue / Butterfly on a wheel / Sea of love / Deliverance / Grapes of wrath / Belief / Paradise (will shine like the moon) / Hungry as the hunter / Lovely
8422512 / Jan '90 / Mercury

☐ CHILDREN
Beyond the pale / Wing and a prayer / Heaven on earth / Tower of strength / Kingdom come / Breathe / Shamera Kye / Black mountain mist / Heat / Hymn (for America)
8342632 / Feb '88 / Mercury

☐ CHILDREN/CARVED IN SAND (2CD Set)
Amelia / Into the blue / Butterfly on a wheel / Sea of love / Deliverance / Grapes of wrath / Breathe / Child's play / Shamera Kye / Black mountain mist / Dream on / Heat / Hymn for America / Beyond the pale / Wing and a prayer / Fabienne / Heaven on earth / Tower of strength / Kingdom come / Belief / Paradise (will shine like the moon) / Hungry as the hunter / Lovely
5286052 / Aug '95 / Mercury

☐ FIRST CHAPTER, THE
Over the hills and far away / Serpent's kiss / Crystal ocean / Dancing barefoot / Like a hurricane / Naked and savage / Garden of delight / Wake / Tomorrow never knows / Wishing well
8325272 / May '88 / Mercury

☐ GRAINS OF SAND
Hands across the ocean / Grip of disease / Divided we fall / Mercenary / Mr. Pleasant / Kingdom come / Heaven sends you / Sweet smile of mystery / Love / Bird of passage
8469372 / Oct '90 / Mercury

☐ NEVERLAND
Raising cain / Sway / Lose myself in you / Swoon / Afterglow (reprise) / Stars don't shine without you / Celebration / Cry like a baby / Heaven knows / Swim with the dolphins / Neverland (vocal) / Daddy's going to heaven now
SMEECD 001 / Feb '95 / Equator

☐ SONGS FROM THE WASTELAND (A Tribute To The Mission) (Various Artists)
REC 041 / 23 Feb '98 / Reconstriction

☐ SUM AND SUBSTANCE (The Best Of The Mission)
Tadeusz / Serpent's kiss / Stay with me / Wasteland / Severina / Tower of strength / Beyond the pale (7" version) / Kingdom come / Butterfly on a wheel / Deliverance / Into the blue / Never again / Like a child again / Tower of strength / Beyond the pale / Forever more
5184472 / Jan '94 / Mercury

Mission Of Burma

☐ FORGET
TAANG 24CD / Nov '92 / Taang

Mississippi Heat

☐ LEARNED THE HARD WAY
VR 101 / 5 Feb '98 / Van Der Linden

☐ STRAIGHT FROM THE HEART
VR 100 / 5 Feb '98 / Van Der Linden

☐ THUNDER IN MY HEART
VR 102 / 5 Feb '98 / Van Der Linden

Mississippi Sheiks

☐ MISSISSIPPI SHEIKS VOL.1 1930
DOCD 5083 / '92 / Document

☐ MISSISSIPPI SHEIKS VOL.2 1930-1931
DOCD 5084 / '92 / Document

☐ MISSISSIPPI SHEIKS VOL.3 1931-1934
DOCD 5085 / '92 / Document

☐ MISSISSIPPI SHEIKS/CHAPMAN BROTHERS VOL.4 1934-1936
DOCD 5086 / '92 / Document

☐ STOP AND LISTEN
Stop and listen blues / Lonely one in this town / World is going wrong / She ain't no good / Sitting on top of the world / Too long / That's it / Bootleggers' blues / Somebody's got to help you / Jail bird love song / Shooting high dice / Tell me to do right / Sales tax / Livin' in a strain / Sweet maggie / She's crazy about her lovin' / Please baby / I've got blood in my eyes for you / Kind treatment / He calls that religion
YAZCD 2006 / May '98 / Yazoo

Mist Of Thyme

☐ BRAVEHARP
Loch Lomond / Dark island / Caledonia / Skye boat song / Ye banks and braes / Road and the miles to Dundee / My love is like a red, red rose / Ae fond kiss / Amazing grace / Auld lang syne/Will ye no come back again / Flower of Scotland / Wild mountain thyme / Northern lights of Old Aberdeen / Always Argyll / Island waves
RECD 511 / Jan '98 / REL

Mistakes

☐ MISTAKES, THE
TVCD 203 / Apr '96 / Third Venture

Mistinguett

☐ EMPRESS OF THE MUSIC HALL, THE
995732 / Jul '97 / EPM

☐ MISTINGUETT 1926-1931
124 / Nov '92 / Chansophone

Misty In Roots

☐ CHRONICLES (The Best Of Misty In Roots)
Food clothes and shelter / Live up / Follow fashion / Earth / Wondering wanderer / Wise and foolish / Musi-o-tunya / Poor and needy / Dreadful dread / Peace and love / West livity / Bail out / Ireation / Economical slavery / Salvation / Rich man / Jah bless africa
KAZCD 903 / Jun '94 / Kaz

☐ EARTH
KAZCD 601 / Aug '95 / Kaz

☐ FORWARD
Fiesta / Midas touch / Hawks on the street / Save a thought / Forward / Jah see Jah know / Envy us / Look before you leap / Feelings / Sinner
KAZCD 900 / Aug '91 / Kaz

☐ JAH SEES...JAH KNOWS (2CD Set)
Food, clothes and shelter / Live up / Follow fashion / Earth / Wondering wanderer / Wise and foolish / Musi o tunya / Poor and needy / Dreadful dread / Peace and love / West livity / Bail out / Ireation / Economical slavery / Salvation / Rich man / Jah bless Africa / Introduction / Man kind / Ghetto of the city / How long Jah / Oh wicked man / Judas Iscariote / See them ah come / Sodom and Gomarrah
SMDCD 107 / May '97 / Snapper

☐ LIVE AT THE COUNTER EUROVISION
Introduction / Mankind / Ghetto of the city / How long Jah / Oh wicked man / Judas Iscariot / See them a-come / Sodom and Gomorrah
KAZCD 12 / Jun '90 / Kaz

☐ MUSI O TUNYA
KAZCD 602 / Aug '95 / Kaz

☐ WISE AND FOOLISH
KAZCD 603 / Aug '95 / Kaz

Misunderstood

☐ BEFORE THE DREAM FADED
Children of the sun / My mind / Who do you love / Unseen / Find a hidden door / I can take you to the sun / I'm not talking / Who's been talkin' / I need your love / You don't have to go / I cried my eyes out / Like I do / Crying over love
CDBRED 32 / Sep '96 / Cherry Red

☐ BROKEN ROAD
When the prophet comes / Child / Carry me far / Peace of mind / Children of the sun / I unseen / Smile on me / No survivors / Queen of madness / No survivors / Let us influence you / Broken road / Mona
CDMRED 147 / 9 Mar '98 / Cherry Red

☐ GOLDEN GLASS
Never had a girl like you before / Golden glass / I don't want to discuss it / Little red rooster / You're tuff enough / Flamingo music / Freedom / Keep on running / I'm cruising
GET 4CD / Sep '97 / Get Back

☐ LEGENDARY GOLD STAR, THE/ GOLDEN GLASS
Blues with a feeling / Who's been talking / You got me dizzy / You don't have to go / Goin' to New York / Shake your money maker / I just want to make love to you / I'm not talking / Never had a nice girl / Golden glass / I don't want to discuss it / Little red rooster / Tuff enough / Freedom / Keep on running / I'm cruising
CDBRED 142 / Mar '97 / Cherry Red

Mitchell's Christian Singers

☐ MITCHELL'S CHRISTIAN SINGERS VOL.1 1934-1936
DOCD 5493 / Nov '96 / Document

☐ MITCHELL'S CHRISTIAN SINGERS VOL.2 1936-1938
DOCD 5494 / Nov '96 / Document

☐ MITCHELL'S CHRISTIAN SINGERS VOL.3 1938-1940
DOCD 5495 / Nov '96 / Document

☐ MITCHELL'S CHRISTIAN SINGERS VOL.4/WRIGHT BROTHERS GOSPEL SI (Mitchell's Christian Singers/Wright Brothers Gospel Singers)
DOCD 5496 / Nov '96 / Document

Mitchell, Blue

☐ BIG SIX
Blues march / Big six / There will never be another you / Brother 'ball / Jamph / Sir john / Promenade
OJCCD 615 / Nov '95 / Original Jazz Classics

☐ BLUE SOUL
Minor vamp / Head / Way you look tonight / Park avenue petite / Top shelf / Waverley street / Blue soul / Polka dots and moonbeams / Nica's dream
OJCCD 765 / Jun '94 / Original Jazz Classics

☐ DOWN WITH IT
Hi-heel sneakers / Perception / Alone, alone, alone / March on Selma / One shirt / Samba de Stacy
CDP 8543272 / Feb '97 / Blue Note

☐ OUT OF THE BLUE
Blues on my mind / It could happen to you / Boomerang / Sweet cakes / Missing you / When the saints go marching in / Studio b
OJCCD 667 / Nov '95 / Original Jazz Classics

☐ SMOOTH AS THE WIND
Smooth as the wind / But beautiful / Best things in life are free / Peace / For Heaven's sake / Nearness of you / Blue time / Strollin' / For all we know / I'm a fool to want you
OJCCD 871 / Aug '96 / Original Jazz Classics

Mitchell, Bobby

☐ YOU ALWAYS HURT THE ONE YOU LOVE (2CD Set)
I'm crying / Rack 'em back / I'm a young man / Angel child / Wedding bells are ringing / Meant for me / One Friday morning / 4 x 11 = 44 / Baby's gone / Sister Lucy / I cried / I wish I knew / I'm in love / Try rock 'n' roll / I fell for you / You are my angel / No no no / I try so hard / Goin' round in circles / I've got my fingers crossed / How long (must I wait) / Sixty four hours / You always hurt the one you love / I love to hold you (more and more) / I would like to know / I'm gonna be a wheel someday / You better go home / You're going to be sorry / Hearts of fire / Well I done got over it / Just say you love me / Send me your picture / You're doing me wrong / There's only one of you / Mama don't allow / When we first met / I'll fiddle while you cry / Oh yeah / My Southern belle / Got to call that number / I never knew what hit me / I don't want to be a wheel no more / Walking in circles / You got the nerve
BCD 15961 / Jan '97 / Bear Family

Mitchell, Chad

☐ VIRGO MOON
SCD 91590 / Dec '94 / Folk Era

Mitchell, Guy

☐ 20 GREATEST HITS
My truly fair / Chick a boom / Pretty little black eyed susie / Sparrow in the tree top / My heart cries for you / Call Rosie on the phone / Singin' the blues / Knee deep in the blues / Roving kind / There's a pawn shop on the corner in Pittsburg, Pennsylvania / Feet up pat him on the po po / Music music music / She wears red feathers / My shoes keep walking back / Cuff of my shirt / Sippin' soda / Cloud lucky seven / Rock-a-billy
300372 / Jul '96 / Hallmark

☐ 20 GREATEST HITS
CDSGP 0279 / Jun '97 / Prestige

☐ BEST OF ALL, THE (18 Greatest Hits)
My truly fair / Chick-a-boom / Pretty little black eyed Sue / Sparrow in the tree top / Side by side / My heart cries for you / Call Rosie on the phone / Singin' the blues / Heartaches by the number / Pittsburg Pennsylvania / Feet up (pat him on the po po) / Music music music / She wears red feathers / My shoes keep walking back / Cuff of my heart / Sippin' soda / Cloud lucky seven / Rock-a-billy
PLATCD 161 / Mar '96 / Platinum

☐ BEST OF GUY MITCHELL, THE
Singin' the blues / Roving kind / Cut of my shirt / She wears red feathers / Chicka boom / Belle, belle my liberty belle / Rock-a-billy / My truly, truly fair / Feet up (pat him on the po-po) / Look at that girl / Sparrow on the treetops / My heart cries for you / Pittsburgh, Pennsylvania / There's always room at my house / Crazy with love / Cloud lucky seven / Dime and a dollar / Heartaches by the number / Knee deep in the blues / Christopher Columbus / Pretty little black eyed Susie / Sippin' soda / Day of jubilo / Call Rosie on the phone
4840392 / May '96 / Columbia

☐ BEST OF GUY MITCHELL, THE (Singing The Blues)
My truly truly fair / Chicka boom / Pretty little black-eyed Susie / Sparrow in the tree top / Side by side / My heart cries for you / Call Rosie on the phone / Singing the blues / Knee deep in the blues / Roving kind / Heartaches by the number / There's a pawnshop on the corner in Pittsburgh Pennsylvania / Feet up (pat him on the po-po) / Music music music / She wears red feathers / My shoes keep walking back to you / Cuff of my shirt / Sippin' soda
SUMCD 4180 / 11 May '98 / Summit

☐ CLASSIC ALBUM, THE (2CD Set)
KCD 7000 / Apr '97 / King

☐ GUY MITCHELL
GRF 237 / Aug '93 / Tring

☐ HEARTACHES BY THE NUMBER
Heartaches by the number / Miracle of love / Rockabilly / Singin' the blues / Notify the FBI / Same old me / Sunshine guitar / My shoes keep walking back to you / Sweet stuff / Hoot owl / Knee deep in the blues / Take me back baby / Because I love you / Pittsburgh, Pennsylvania / Roving kind / My heart cries for you / Dime and a dollar / My truly, truly fair / House of the swinging bamboo / Sparrow on the tree-top / Christopher Columbus / Belle belle, my liberty belle / Ninety nine years / Pretty little black eyed Susie / Unless
BCD 15454 / May '90 / Bear Family

☐ SINGING THE BLUES
My truly, truly fair / Knee deep in the blues / Cloud lucky seven / Music music music / She wears red feathers / Roving kind / Pretty little black-eyed Susie / Pittsburgh Pennsylvannia / Chicka boom / Heartaches by the number / Singin' the blues / Side by side / Sparrow in the treetop / My shoes keep walking back to you / Sippin' soda / Rock-a-billy / Cuff of my shirt / Rosie on the 'phone / My heart cries for you / Feet up
QED 058 / Nov '96 / Tring

☐ SINGING THE BLUES
Singing the blues / Chick-a-boom / Pretty little black eyed Susie / Sparrow in the tree top / Side by side / My heart cries for you / Call Rosie on the phone / My truly fair / Knee deep in the blues / Roving kind / Heartaches by the number / There's a pawn shop on the corner in Pittsburgh Pennsylvania / Feet up (pat him on the po po) / Music music music / She wears red feathers / My shoes keep walking back / Cuff of my shirt / Sippin' soda / Cloud lucky seven / Rock-a-billy
CD 6090 / Aug '97 / Music

Mitchell, Joni

☐ BLUE
All I want / My old man / Little green / Carey / Blue / California / This flight tonight / River / Case of you / Last time I saw Richard
244128 / Jan '87 / Reprise

☐ CHALK MARK IN A RAINSTORM
My secret place / Number one / Lakota / Tea leaf prophecy / Dancing clown / Cool water / Beat of black wings / Snakes and ladders / Recurring dream / Bird that whistle
GFLD 19199 / Aug '93 / Geffen

☐ CLOUDS
Tin angel / Chelsea morning / I don't know where I stand / That song about the Midway / Roses blue / Gallery / I think I understand / Songs to ageing children come / Fiddle and the drum / Both sides now
K2 44070 / Jan '88 / Reprise

☐ COURT AND SPARK
Court and spark / Help me / Free man in Paris / People's parties / Same situation / Car on a hill / Down to you / Just like this train / Raised on robbery / Trouble child / Twisted
2530022 / May '83 / Asylum

☐ DOG EAT DOG
Good friends / Fiction / Three great stimulants / Tax free / Smokin' / Dog eat dog / Shiny toys / Ethiopia / Impossible dreamer / Lucky girl
GED 24074 / Nov '96 / Geffen

☐ FOR THE ROSES
Banquet / Cold blue steel and sweet fire / Barangrill / Lesson in survival / Let the wind carry me / For the roses / You see sometime / Electricity / You turn me on, I'm a radio / Blonde in the bleachers / Woman of heart and mind / Judgement of the moon and stars
253007 / Dec '87 / Asylum

☐ GHOSTS
OTR 1100027 / Jun '97 / Metro Independent

☐ HEJIRA
Coyote / Amelia / Furry sings the blues / Strange boy / Hejira / Song for Sharon / Black crow / Blue motel room / Refuge of the roads
2530532 / Oct '87 / Asylum

☐ HISSING OF SUMMER LAWNS, THE
In France they kiss on Main Street / Jungle line / Edith and the kingpin / Don't interrupt the sorrow / Shades of scarlet conquering / Hissing of summer lawns / Boho dance / Harry's house / Sweet bird / Shadows and light
253018 / Dec '87 / Asylum

☐ HITS
Urge for going / Chelsea morning / Big yellow taxi / Woodstock / Circle game / Carey / California / You turn me on, I'm a radio / Raised on robbery / Help me / Free man in Paris / River / Chinese cafe / Come in from the cold / Both sides now
9362463262 / Oct '96 / Reprise

☐ JONI MITCHELL
I had a King / Michael from the mountains / Night in the city / Marcie / Nathan La Franeer / Sisotowbell Lane / Dawntreader / Pirate of penance / Song to a seagull / Cactus tree
244051 / '87 / Reprise

☐ LADIES OF THE CANYON
Morning Morgantown / For free / Conversation / Ladies of the canyon / Willy / Arrangement / Rainy night house / Priest / Blue boy / Big yellow taxi / Woodstock / Circle game
K 244085 / Jul '88 / Reprise

☐ MINGUS
Happy birthday / God must be a boogie man / Funeral / Chair in the sky / Wolf that lives in Lindsey / Is a muggin' / Dry cleaner from Des Moines / Lucky / Goodbye Pork Pie Hat / Sweet sucker dance / Coin in the pocket
253091 / '88 / Asylum

☐ MISSES
Passion play / Nothing can be done / Case of you / Beat of black wings / Dog eat dog / Wolf that lives in Lindsay / Magdalene laundries / Impossible dreamer / Sex kills / Reoccuring dream / Harry's house / Arrangement / For the roses / Hejira (travelling)
9362463582 / Oct '96 / Reprise

☐ NIGHT RIDE HOME
Night ride home / Passion play / Cherokee Louise / Windfall (Everything for nothing) / Slouching towards Bethlehem / Come in from the cold / Nothing can be done / Only joy in town / Ray's dad's Cadillac / Two grey rooms
GED 24302 / 8 Sep '97 / Geffen

☐ TURBULENT INDIGO
Sunny Sunday / Sex kills / How do you stop / Turbulent indigo / Last chance lost / Magdalene laundries / Not to blame / Borderline / Yvette in English / Sire of sorrow (Job's sad song)
9362457862 / Oct '94 / Asylum

☐ WILD THINGS RUN FAST
Chinese cafe / Unchained melody / Wild things run fast / Ladies man / Moon at the window / Solid love / Be cool / Baby I don't care / You dream flat tires / Man to man / Underneath the streetlight / Love
GFLD 19129 / Jul '92 / Geffen

Mitchell, Kevin

☐ I SANG THE SWEET REFRAIN
CDTRAX 108 / Apr '96 / Greentrax

Mitchell, Prince Phillip

☐ LONER
While the cat's away / Starting from scratch / Come to bed / Can't nobody love you better than me / Never let her down / Nothing hurts like love / You did what you had to do / Loner / She's a party animal
ICH 1110CD / Oct '93 / Ichiban

Mitchell, Red

☐ ALONE TOGETHER
DRAGONCD 168 / Jan '88 / Dragon

☐ BIG TWO VOL.1, THE (Mitchell, Red & Warne Marsh Duo)
STCD 8257 / Jun '98 / Storyville

☐ BIG TWO VOL.2, THE (Mitchell, Red & Warne Marsh)
Hot house / Undertow / Loverman / Tea for two / Gone with the wind / Ornithology / It could happen to you / Easy living / I'm getting sentimental over you / Background music / Scrapple from the apple
STCD 8257 / Jun '98 / Storyville

☐ EVOLUTION
DRCD 191 / Jan '89 / Dragon

☐ MITCHELL/KELLAWAY/MILDER (Mitchell, Red & Roger Kellaway/ Joakim Milder)
DRCD 219 / Oct '94 / Dragon

☐ VERY THOUGHT OF YOU, THE
DRAGONCD 161 / Jan '89 / Dragon

Mitchell, Roscoe

☐ 3 X 4 EYE
120050 / Apr '94 / Black Saint

☐ HEY DONALD
DE 475 / Oct '95 / Delmark

☐ LIVE AT THE KNITTING FACTORY (Mitchell, Roscoe & The Sound Ensemble)
1201202 / May '92 / Black Saint

☐ SONGS IN THE WIND
VICTOCD 011 / Nov '94 / Victo

☐ SOUND
Ornette / Sound 1 / Little suite / Ornette / Sound 2
DE 408 / Nov '96 / Delmark

☐ SOUND SONGS (2CD Set)
Let's get ready to rumble / They all had new clothes / Messenger in traffic / Fallen heroes / Full frontal saxophone / Down at the pond / 4.50 express / Meeting / For Lester B / Near and far / Song for percussion and bamboo sax / Play / Garden / Night / On the country road / Side one / Other side / Side two / First sketches of Leola / Appear and disappear / Dream machine / For Madeline / Closer
2DE 493 / Jul '97 / Delmark

☐ THIS DANCE IS FOR STEVE MCCALL (Mitchell, Roscoe & The Note Factory)
1201502 / Nov '93 / Black Saint

Mitchell, Ross

☐ ALL NIGHT LONG (Mitchell, Ross Band/Singers)
Shall we dance (quickstep) / Taking a chance on love-be careful it's my heart (quickste / Together hand in hand (waltz) / Onedin line (theme) (waltz) / Without a song (foxtrot) / Manhattan (foxtrot) / Perhaps, perhaps, perhaps (tango) / Florentina tango (tango) / I just want to dance with you (cha cha cha) / Volare (cha cha cha) / Under the sea (samba) / All night long (samba) / Memory (rumba) / One day in my life (rumba) / Rock around the clock (jive) / Bandstand boogie (jive)
DLD 1037 / May '93 / Dance & Listen

☐ BAM-BOOM
Hello it's good to see you- the night has a thous / It don't mean a thing (if it ain't got that swing) / Things we did last summer (waltz) / Who's taking you home to-night-last waltz (waltz) / Our love is here to stay (foxtrot) / Getting to know you (foxtrot) / Tango cubana (tango) / I feel pretty (v. waltz) / Pata pata (cha cha) / Eso es el amor (cha cha) / Maria bonita (cha cha) / It's in his kiss (shoop, shoop song) (cha cha) / I go to rio (samba) / Ease de tension (samba) / One moment in time (rumba) / Till I loved you (rumba) / Mexico (the battle of new orleans) (jive) / House of bamboo (mambo) / Mexico (extended version) (jive)
DLD 1023 / '92 / Dance & Listen

☐ BEST OF THE DANSAN YEARS VOL.2, THE (Mitchell, Ross Band/Singers)
Rainbow connection (waltz) / My foolish heart (waltz) / Come back to sorrento (waltz) / Hernando's hideaway (tango) / At last (slow foxtrot) / Let's do it (let's fall in love) (slow foxtrot) / Gal in calico (foxtrot) / Top hat, white tie and tails (quick step) / Let's teach the world to dance (quickstep) / Strike up the band (quickstep) / Chattanooga choo choo (cha cha cha) / You're the top (cha cha) / Wouldn't it be loverly (cha cha cha) / Eso beso (samba) / Quando, quando, quando - tequila (samba) / Bali ha'i (rumba) / Carnival-shadow of your smile (rumba) / Breeze and I (rumba) / Opus one (jive) / Be bop 'n' boogie (jive)
DACD 002 / Jul '92 / Dansan

☐ BEST OF THE DANSAN YEARS VOL.3, THE (Mitchell, Ross Band/Singers)
Cavatina (waltz) / Watching the night (waltz) / With you I'm born again (waltz) / Just an old fashioned girl (tango) / Whatever lola wants (lola gets) (tango) / On a slow boat to china (slow foxtrot) / Younger than springtime (slow foxtrot) / Dancing on the ceiling (slow foxtrot) / Continental (quickstep) / Best of times (quickstep) / Zing went the strings of my heart (quickstep) / Everybody likes to cha cha cha (cha cha cha) / Pepito (cha cha cha) / It's cha cha (cha cha cha) / Peanut vendor (samba) / Breakin' down (samba) / Half a minute (samba) / I just called to say I love you (rumba) / Moving south (rumba) / Frankie (jive)
DACD 003 / Jul '92 / Dansan

☐ CFD VOL.6
DLD 1062 / Dec '95 / Dance & Listen

☐ DON'T STOP
Don't stop / Smile to smile / What'll I do / Lullaby / Way you look tonight / Heaven can wait / Blue tango / Sixties melody / Dangado lambada / Baila conmigo / Wheels / Coeur de loup / Soul limbo / We kiss in a shadow / Sacrifice / Ain't nobody here but us chickens / Konk a donk-blame it on the bossa nova
DLD 1016 / '92 / Dance & Listen

☐ GO DANCING
DLD 1028 / Jul '92 / Dance & Listen

☐ MERRY CHRISTMAS (Mitchell, Ross Band/Singers)
Sleigh ride-here comes santa / Frosty the snowman-santa claus is coming to town / Christmas bride / What child is this / Christmas song / Have yourself a merry little christmas-just look around / Rudolph the red-nosed reindeer / I saw mommy kissing santa claus / White christmas / Winter wonderland / Rockin' around the christmas tree / I wish it could be christmas every day
DLD 1006 / Jul '92 / Dance & Listen

☐ OPENING NIGHT (Mitchell, Ross Band/ Singers)
Opening night (quickstep) / I'm in a dancing mood (quickstep) / Sam (waltz) / Lovers' waltz (waltz) / Fly me to the moon (foxtrot) / Time medley (foxtrot) / Adios muchachos (tango) / Talk to the animals (cha cha cha) / Oye como va (cha cha cha) / Samba with me (samba) / De rabbit (samba) / Amigos para siempre (rumba) / Best of my love (rumba) / Pick a bale o'cotton (jive) / Penny whistle (jive) / Mambo italiano (mambobossa nova) / Pick a bale o'cotton (extended version) (jive)
DLD 1031 / May '93 / Dance & Listen

☐ RAINBOW COLLECTION, THE
DLD 1004 / Jul '92 / Dance & Listen

☐ ROSS MITCHELL PRESENTS CFD
DLD 1027 / May '92 / Dance & Listen

☐ STANDARD AND LATIN DANCES
Walking on sunshine (quickstep) / You can't hurry love (quickstep) / I wonder why (waltz) / If you don't know me by now (waltz) / Never let her slip away (foxtrot) / Any dream will do (foxtrot) / Pretty woman (tango) / Always and forever (v.waltz) / Loco in acapulco (cha cha cha) / September (cha cha cha) / Use it up and wear it out (samba) / That's the way (i like it) (samba) / My one temptation (rumba) / Save the best for last (rumba) / Everybody needs somebody (jive) / Why do fools fall in love (jive)
DLD 1042 / Nov '93 / Dance & Listen

☐ STAR REQUESTS (Mitchell, Ross Band/Singers)
I won't dance / Tap your troubles away / Desert song / Kisses in the dark / Fascination / Wish upon a star / Jealousy / Star / Tea for two / Brazil / Shall we dance / All I ask of you / I won't send roses / Wake up little Susie
DLD 1003 / Oct '88 / Dance & Listen

☐ ZING VOL.1 (Mitchell, Ross Band/ Singers)
Get happy / Stepping out with my baby / Grey panther swing / Dancing like lovers / True love / I can dream can't I / Moonlight serenade / La coqueta (the flirt) / New fangled tango / Carousel waltz / Once upon a dream / Elmer's tune / Laughter in the rain / Feline fine / Happy talk / Bamboleo / Happy ever after / I'm getting sentimental over you / Wind beneath my wings / La corrida / Foot tapper / Reet petite
DLD 1010 / '92 / Dance & Listen

☐ ZING VOL.2 (Mitchell, Ross Band/ Singers)
Baubles, bangles and beads / Dancing in the dark / London by night / Where is your heart / Swingin' down the lane / One / Rain in Spain / Wrap your troubles in dreams (and dream your troubles away) / Sway / Zambesi / Quand tu chantes / If I loved you / With a song in my heart / Trickle trickle
DLD 1002 / Apr '88 / Dance & Listen

Mitchell, Sam

☐ ART OF THE BOTTLENECK GUITAR, THE
Ambidextrous march / Travelling riverside blues / (Baby let me) follow you down / Laguna luna / Paddlin' Madeline / Nobody's fault but mine / Earl blue / Sunshine in Houston / Dark was the night cold was the ground / Crossroads blues / Livingstone blues / Let me play it first / Cat's eyes / Jubilee jamboree / Motherless children / Two step swing thing / Hellbound on my trail / Come onin in my kitchen / Pile driver / Hambone / Rainy day blues / Part time love / Sophisticated slide / Dirty dozen
SH 98007 / Mar '98 / Shanachie

Mitchell, Waddie

☐ WADDIE MITCHELL LIVE
Old spinning wheel / Typical / Goat on a rope / Old nighthawk / Blood sweat and steers / Sentence / Bill Cheatham / Owl critic / Sounds a cowboy hears / Cross-eyed bull / Walkin' man / Red River valley / Piddlin' Pete / Swedish waltz / No second chance
SHANCD 6030 / Apr '98 / Shanachie

Mitchell, Warren

☐ ALF GARNETT'S MUSIC HALL
At Trinity church / Old rustic bridge by the mill / I live in Trafalgar Square / Gilbert the filbert / Down the road / Bill Bailey / In the twi-twi-twilight / If it wasn't for the 'ouses in between / It's a great big shame / Every little while / When father papered the parlour / Hold your hand out naughty boy / Let's all go down the strand / Honeysuckle and the bee / My grandfather's clock
306592 / May '97 / Hallmark

Mitchell, Willie

☐ HI MASTERS, THE
That driving beat / 20-75 / Louie Louie / Champion / Mercy / Ooh baby you turn me on / 30-60-90 / Who's making love / Everything is gonna be alright / Bad eye / Buster Browne / Soul serenade / At the woodchoppers ball / Sunshine of your sunshine / Papa's got a brand new bag
HEX 37 / 4 Aug '98 / Hi

☐ SPARKLE
Sparkle / Reaching out / Honey bear / Midnight rhapsody / Give the world more love / Sugar candy / Expressions / Happy hour
C5CD517 / Jun '88 / See For Miles

☐ WALKIN' WITH WILLIE
RCCD 3009 / Jun '94 / Rollercoaster

Mitchum, Robert

☐ CALYPSO
Jean and Dinah / From a logical point of view / Not me / What is this generation coming to / Tic tic tic / Beauty is only skin deep / I learn a merengue, mama / Take me down to lover's row / Mama look a boo boo / Coconut water / Matilda Matilda / They dance all night
CREV 037CD / Jul '95 / Rev-Ola

☐ THAT MAN
You deserve each other / Walker's woods / Wheels (it's rollin' time again) / In my place / Ballad of Thunder Road / That man right there / Litle ole wine drinker me / Ricardo's mountain / Sunny / They dance all night / Matilda Matilda / Coconut water / Boo Boo (shut your mouth go away) / Mama look / Take me down to lovers row / Meremgue, Mama / I learn A / Beauty is only skin deep / Tic, tic, tic (lost watch) / What is this generation coming to / Not me / From a logical point of view / Jean and dinah / Gotta travel on / Whip-poor-will / Little white lies
BCD 15890 / Jun '95 / Bear Family

Mithotyn

☐ IN THE SIGN OF THE RAVENS
IR 28CD / 28 Jul '97 / Invasion

Mitra, Rhona

☐ COME ALIVE (AKA Lara Croft)
Getting naked / Making love / Naked / Getting naked / Beautiful day / Beautiful day / Come alive / Tashina / Really real / Feel myself / Rock your own world / Interactive track
4948720 / Jun '98 / Naked

Mittoo, Jackie

☐ EVENING TIME
SOCD 8014 / Mar '95 / Studio One

☐ IN AFRICA
QRCD 004 / 29 Sep '97 / Quartz

☐ KEEP ON DANCING
CSCD 8020 / Mar '96 / Studio One

☐ KEYBOARD LEGEND
SONCD 0073 / Apr '95 / Sonic Sounds

☐ SHOWCASE VOL.3
JIMCD 4957 / Jun '95 / A&A Productions

☐ TRIBUTE TO JACKIE MITTOO
CDHB 189190 / Aug '95 / Heartbeat

Mixed Emotions

☐ BEST OF MIXED EMOTIONS, THE
You want love (Maria, Maria) / It's over now / One way love / Bring back (sha na na) / Changin' light of love / Love is so easy now / Just for you / Sweetheart-darlin'-my dear / Children of a lesser paradise / Chiquitita Renita / I never give up / Sentimental song / Over the limit / Close to heaven now
DC 871102 / Nov '96 / Disky

Mixman

☐ EARLY DUB TAPES, THE
BLKMCD 011 / Oct '94 / Blakamix

☐ NEW DIMENSIONS DUB
BLKCD 002 / Sep '92 / Blakamix

☐ SEEK AND YOU WILL FIND - THE DUB PIECES
BLKCD 16 / Nov '95 / Blakamix

Mixmaster G-Flexx

☐ WE SHINE
8536542512 / 21 Apr '98 / Lightyear

Mixmaster Mike

☐ ANTI THEFT DEVICE
Ultra intro / Ill shit / Unidentifried / Supa wyde laces / Billie klubb / Sektor one / Rebel enforcer / Sektor two / Jack knyfe / Radiation / Sektor three / Well wicked / Deeportashun / All pro / Vyce gripp / Gang tackle / Sektor four / Anti theft device / Astronaut / Mean dirty killer / Government secret / Can of kick ass / Sektor five / Surprize packidge / Fur coat / Sektor six / Sloh beat / Electrocute / Black level clearance / Sektor seven / One minute massacre
ASP 0985CD / 27 Jul '98 / Asphodel

Mixmaster Morris

☐ DREAMFISH VOL.2 (Mixmaster Morris & Pete Namlock)
PW 016 / Nov '95 / Fax

Mixon, Donovan

☐ LOOK MA, NO HANDS
W 1122 / Sep '93 / Philology

Miyati, Kohachiro

☐ SHAKUHACHI, THE JAPANESE FLUTE
7559720762 / Jan '95 / Nonesuch

Mizarolli, John

☐ MESSAGE FROM THE 5TH STONE
No magic love / Granny did it / Ain't nobody gonna bring me down / Message from the 5th stone / Lost your love my love / Wake up and live / Is mamma the president / Menopause / Mama never told you
INAK 867 CD / '88 / In Akustik

Mizell Brothers

☐ SKY HIGH (The Best Of The Mizell Brothers) (Various Artists)
Peace of mind: *Allen, Rance* / Street lady: *Byrd, Donald* / Shifting gears: *Byrd, Donald* / Think twice: *Byrd, Donald* / New York Times: *Humphrey, Bobbi* / Starborne: *Hammond, Johnny* / Love so far away: *Byrd, Donald* / Music is my sanctuary: *Bartz, Gary* / Uno esta: *Humphrey, Bobbi* / Truth is marching: *Allen, Rance* / Change (makes you want to hustle): *Byrd, Donald* / Boogie oogie oogie: *Taste Of Honey*
4939942 / 11 May '98 / Blue Note

Mizpah

☐ THIS GLORIOUS DAY
5679202 / 1 Jun '98 / Music & Words

MJG

☐ NO MORE GLORY
UD 53105 / 17 Nov '97 / Universal

MJT & 3

☐ MAKE EVERYBODY HAPPY
VJ 009 / 24 Apr '98 / Vee Jay

☐ MJT & 3
VJ 002 / 24 Feb '98 / Vee Jay

MK

☐ REMIXED REMADE REMODELLED
ACTIVCD 10 / 4 Aug '97 / Activ

☐ SURRENDER (MK & Alana)
Crazy, crazy / Always / Only you / Almost gave up / Burning / Love changes / Surrender / MK Apella / Reality / Precious jewels / Games / Hot stuff
ACTIVCD 2 / Jun '95 / Activ

MK Ultra

☐ THIS IS THIS
13318162 / Jul '94 / Merciful Release

MLO

☐ IO
RSNCD 16 / Apr '94 / Rising High

☐ PLASTIC APPLE (3CD Set)
DJ Food's sonic soup / New generation / Samarkand / Garden / Samarkand / Two voyages / Out of the blue / Gun crazy / New generation / Sleeper / Dreamlab / Blowpipe / Samarkand / Two voyages / One beat too many / Out of the blue / Garden / Long and winding / New generation / Aqua / Birds 'n' flutes 'n' shit
SUCD 5 / Oct '96 / Aura Surround Sounds

MN8

☐ FREAKY
Tuff act to follow / Dreaming / Freaky / I'll give you my everything / Baby I surrender / Beautiful body / It's all on you / Shake it / This heart / I promise / Keep it in the family / Talk to you
4852992 / Nov '96 / Columbia

Mnemonic

☐ WEAPONS
APR 008CD / Aug '96 / April

Mo, Billy

☐ MISTER RHYTHM KING
Swing Methusalem / Buona Sera / Oh Marie / Gonggonza / Ding dong / Darling du weisst ja / Regenbogen blues / La Paloma / Habe mitleid / Mary my girl / Oh Jennilie / Billy boy / Tatalee / Mister Rhythm King / Nevada swing / Das fraulein Gerda / Salambuli / You are my sunshine / Smoke like it hot / Baby / Golden River / Dickie Doo / Dolly Doo / Lass mich rein Barberina / Susie / Pinguin jive / Ay, ay, ay / Mitternachts blues / Ich kauf mir lieber einen Tirolerhut
BCD 15966 / May '96 / Bear Family

Mo Rag's Marauders

☐ NOO VOL.2
LCOM 5256 / Nov '96 / Lismor

Mo Thugs

☐ FAMILY SCRIPTURES VOL.2 (Family Reunion)
Mo thug intro / Mighty mighty warrior / Heart of it / Queen / Riot / All good / Ghetto cowboy / Believe / Urban souljah / Ain't said no names / Mo thuggin' / You don't own me / Ride with a palya / Pimpin' ain't easy / U don't own me / Otherside / Otherside outro
4898522 / 3 Aug '98 / Relativity

Moahni Moahna

☐ TEMPLE OF LIFE
RS 0072912CD / Jul '98 / Rising Sun

☐ WHY
RS 0072922CD / 2 Mar '98 / Rising Sun

Moal, Gildas

☐ AN DISPUT (Moal, Gildas & Rene Chaplain)
CD 438 / Sep '96 / Arfolk

Moaning

☐ BLOOD FROM STONE
NFR 018CD / 13 Oct '97 / No Fashion

Moaning Wind

☐ VISIONS OF FIRE
CR 6502CD / Jun '97 / Corrosion

Mob

☐ MOB, THE
Maybe I'll find a way / Once a man, twice a child / (I'd like to see) more of you / Lost / Give it to me / For a little while / Goodtime baby / I dig everything about you / Love's got a hold on me / Back on the road again / Savin' my love for you / Everyday people / Love power / Make me yours / All I need / I feel the earth move / Money (that's what I want) / Where you lead / Two and two together / Uh-uh-uh-uh-uh-uh

NEMCD 724 / May '95 / Sequel

Mob

☐ LET THE TRIBE INCREASE
Youth / Crying again / Witch hunt / Shuffling souls / No doves fly here / I hear you laughing / Mirror breaks / Stay / Another day, another death / Cry of the morning / Dance on (you fool) / Raised in a prison / Slayed / Our life, our world / Gates of hell / I wish / Never understood / Roger
SEEP 012CD / Oct '95 / Rugger Bugger

Mob 47

☐ GARANTEART MANGEL
DISTCD 022 / Nov '95 / Distortion

Mobb Deep

☐ HELL ON EARTH
Animal instinct: *Mobb Deep & Ty Nitty/Gambino* / Drop a gem on 'em / Bloodsport / Extortion: *Mobb Deep & Method Man* / More trife life / Man down: *Mobb Deep & Big Noyd* / Can't get enough of it: *Mobb Deep & General C* / Nightime vultures: *Mobb Deep & Chef Raekwon* / GOD part 3 / Get dealt with / Shook ones part 1 / Front lines (hell on earth) / Give it up fast: *Mobb Deep & Nas/Big Noyd* / Still shinin' / Apostles warning
74321425582 / Nov '96 / Loud

☐ INFAMOUS MOBB DEEP, THE
Start of your ending / Survival of the fittest / I for Ai (your beef is mines) / Give up the Gods (just step) / Temperature's rising / Up North trip / Trife life / QU - hectic / Right back at you / Cradle to the grave / Drink the pain away (situations) / Shook ones / Party over
07863664802 / 2 Feb '98 / Loud

Mobido, Askia

☐ WASS REGGAE
STCD 1060 / May '96 / Stern's

Mobile Mob Freakshow

☐ DEATHTRIP 2000
NOX 008CD / 24 Nov '97 / Noxious

Mobley, Bill

☐ TRIPLE BILL (Mobley, Bill Sextet)
Prelude / 49th Street / I concentrate on you / Mulgrew's motif / I love it when you dance that way / Three gifts / They say it's wonderful / Panon impressions / I didn't know what time it was
ECD 221632 / Sep '96 / Evidence

Mobley, Hank

☐ BEST OF HANK MOBLEY, THE
Avila and Tequila / Funk in deep freeze / Fin de l'affaire / Take your pick / This I dig of you / Smokin' / Recado bossa nova / No room for squares / Turnaround / 3rd time around
CDP 8370522 / Apr '96 / Blue Note

☐ JAZZ MESSAGE OF HANK MOBLEY, THE
There'll never be another you / Cattin' / Madeline / When I fall in love / Budo / I married an angel / Jazz message (freedom for all)
CY 18058 / 13 Apr '98 / Savoy Jazz

☐ JAZZ MESSAGE VOL.1, THE
There'll be another you / Cattin' / Madeline / When I fall in love / Budo / I married an angel / Jazz message
SV 0133 / Oct '97 / Savoy Jazz

☐ JAZZ MESSAGE VOL.2, THE
That's blues / Doug's minor B, OK / B for BB / Blues no. 2 / Space flight
CY 18063 / Jun '98 / Savoy Jazz

☐ REACH OUT
Reach out I'll be there / Up over and out / Lookin' east / Goin' out of my head / Good pickings / Beverly
8599642 / 10 Nov '97 / Blue Note

Moby

☐ AMBIENT
My beautiful blue sky / Heaven / Tongues / J breas / Myopia / House of blue leaves / Bad days / Piano and string / Sound / Dog / 80 / Lean on me
ATLASCD 002 / Oct '93 / Arctic

☐ ANIMAL RIGHTS (2CD Set)
CDSTUMM 150
LCDSTUMM 150 / Sep '96 / Mute

☐ END OF EVERYTHING, THE (Voodoo Child)
CDIDIOT 1 / Jul '96 / Mute

☐ EVERYTHING IS WRONG (2CD Set)
Hymn / Feeling so real / All that I need is to be loved / Let's go free / Everytime you touch me / Bring back my happiness / What love / First cool hive / Into the blue / Anthem / Everything is wrong / God moving over the face of the waters / When it sl'd like to die
CDSTUMM 130
LCDSTUMM 130 / Mar '95 / Mute
XLCDSTUMM 130 / Jan '96 / Mute

☐ HYMN
CDMUTE 161 / May '94 / Mute

☐ I LIKE TO SCORE
Novio / James Bond Theme / Go / Ah ah / I like to score / Oil / New dawn fades / God moving over the face of the waters / First cool hive / Nash / Love theme / Grace
CDSTUMM 168 / 10 Nov '97 / Mute

☐ MIXMAG LIVE VOL.7 (Moby/Slam) (Various Artists)
MMLCD 007 / Jul '96 / Mixmag Live

☐ STORY SO FAR
Ah ah / I feel it / Everything / Mercy / Help me to believe / Go / Yeah / Drop a beat (the new version) / Thousand / Slight return / Go (subliminal mix unedited version) / Stream
ATLASCD 001 / Jul '93 / Equator

Moby Grape

☐ LIVE AT INDIGO RANCH
SFS 04880 / 2 Mar '98 / SFS

☐ MOBY GRAPE
Hey Grandma / Mr. Blues / Fall on you / 8.05 / Come in the morning / Omaha / Naked, if I want to / Someday / Ain't no use / Sitting by the window / Changes / Lazy me / Indifference
SFS 04805 / 23 Feb '98 / SFS

☐ MOBY GRAPE 1983
SFS 04830 / 2 Mar '98 / SFS

☐ VINTAGE - THE VERY BEST OF MOBY GRAPE (2CD Set)
Hey grandma / Mr. Blues / Fall on you / 8.05 / Come in the morning / Omaha / Naked, if I want to / Rounder / Someday / Ain't no use / Sitting by the window / Changes / Lazy me / Indifference / Looper / Sweet ride / Bitter wind / Place and the time / Miller's blues / Big / Skip's song / You can do anything / Murder in my heart / For the judge / Can't be so bad / Just like Gene Autry / Foxtrot / He / Motorcycle Irene / Funky tunk / Rose coloured eyes / If you can't learn from your mistakes / Ooh mama ooh / Ain't that a shame / Trucking man / Captain Nemo / What's to choose / Going nowhere / I am not willing / It's a beautiful day today / Right before my eyes / Truly fine citizen / Hoochie / Soul stew / Seeing
4839582 / Jun '96 / Columbia

☐ WOW/GRAPE JAM
SFS 04801 / 23 Feb '98 / SFS

Mocket

☐ BIONIC PARTS
PNMV 10 / 24 Nov '97 / Punkinmyvita

☐ FANFARE
KLP 70CD / 13 Oct '97 / K

Mockingbirds

☐ MOCKINGBIRDS
HTIG 0999 / 1 Dec '97 / Htig
NLL 002 / 29 Jun '98 / Not Lame

Moco, Maio

☐ PORTUGAL NOVO
PS 65071 / May '91 / PlayaSound

MOD

☐ DEVOLUTION
Land of the free / Devolution / Repent / Angry man / Resist / Crash 'n' burn / Supertouch / Rock tonite / Behind / Running / Time bomb / Unhuman race
CDMFN 163 / Jun '94 / Music For Nations

☐ DICTATED AGRESSION
CDMFN 201 / May '96 / Music For Nations

☐ LOVED BY THOUSANDS HATED BY MILLIONS
Noize / Aren't you hungry / Spandex enormity / Aids / Hate tank / Goldfish / Surfin USA / Surfs up / Mr. Oofus / No glove no love / True colours / Livin in the city / Get up and dance / Rhymestein / Irresponsible / Rally (NYC) / Ballad of Dio / Bubble butt / Short but sweet / Ode to Harry / Vents / Theme song / Bonanza / Buckshot blues / Dublin seals / US Dreams / He's dead Jim / Get the boot
CDVEST 66 / Oct '95 / Bulletproof

Model 500

☐ DEEP SPACE
Milky Way / Orbit / Flow / Warning / Astralwerks / Starlight / Last transport (to Alpha Centauri) / I wanna be there / Lightspeed
RS 95066CD / 2 Mar '98 / R&S

Modern Art

☐ ALL ABOARD THE MIND TRAIN
GAAS 2501 / 16 Feb '98 / Acme

Modern English

☐ AFTER THE SNOW
I melt with you / Tables turning / Carry me down
GAD 206CD / 6 Jul '98 / 4AD

☐ MESH AND LACE
Sixteen days / Just a thought / Move in light / Grief / Token man / Viable commercial / Black houses / Dance of devotion (love song)
GAD 105CD / 6 Jul '98 / 4AD

☐ RICOCHET DAYS
Rainbow's end / Machines / Spining me round / Richochet days / Hands across the sea march / (sousa) / Blue waves / Heart / Chapter 12 / Chapter 12 (twelve inch mix) / Ringing in the change / Reflection / Breaking away
GAD 402CD / 6 Jul '98 / 4AD

Modern Folk Quartet

☐ AT CHRISTMAS
FE 1404 / Nov '94 / Folk Era

Modern Jazz Quartet

☐ 2 DEGREES EAST 3 DEGREES WEST
VN 161 / May '95 / Viper's Nest

☐ 40TH ANNIVERSARY CELEBRATION
Bag's groove / All the things you are / Cherokee / (Back home again in) Indiana / Come rain or come shine / Willow weep for me / Memories of you / Blues for Juanita / There will never be another you / Easy living / Django / Dance that dream / Billie's bounce
7567825382 / Feb '93 / Atlantic

☐ ARTISTY OF THE MODERN JAZZ QUARTET
La ronde / Rose of the rio grande / Queen's fancy / Delauney's dilemma / In a sentimental mood / Stopper / Almost like being in love / No moe / Django / One bass hit / Milano / Ralph's new blues / I'll remember april / Concorde / Softly as in a morning sunrise
FCD 60016 / Oct '93 / Fantasy

☐ BEST OF MODERN JAZZ QUARTET, THE
Valeria / Le cannet / Nature boy / Watergate blues / Connie's blues / Reunion blues / Echoes
CD 24054232 / Apr '94 / Pablo

☐ BLUES ON BACH
Regret / Blues in B flat / Rise up in the morning / Blues in A minor / Precious joy / Blues in C minor / Don't stop this train blues in H / Tears from the children
7567813932 / Mar '93 / Atlantic

☐ CONCORDE
Ralph's new blues / All of you / I'll remember April / Gershwin melodies / Concorde
OJC20 0022 / Sep '98 / Original Jazz Classics

☐ DJANGO
Queen's fancy / La ronde suite / Django / One bass hit / Milano / Delauney's dilemma
OJCCD 57 / Feb '92 / Original Jazz Classics
OJC20 0572 / Sep '98 / Original Jazz Classics

☐ ECHOES/TOGETHER AGAIN
CD 2312142 / Oct '92 / Pablo

☐ IN A CROWD
Pyramid / In a crowd / Mean to me / Winter tale / Bag's groove / I should care / Sheriff
DM 10025 / 15 Jun '98 / Douglas Music

☐ LAST CONCERT, THE
Softly as in a morning sunrise / Cylinder / Summertime / Travellin' blues / One never knows, does one / Bag's groove / Confirmation / Round midnight / Night in Tunisia / Golden striker / Skating in Central Park / Django / What's new
7567819762 / Apr '98 / Atlantic

☐ LONGING FOR THE CONTINENT
Animal dance / Django / England's carol / Bluesology / Bag's groove / Sketch 3 / Ambiquite / Midsummer
CDC 7678 / Nov '90 / LRC

☐ LOOKING FOR THE CONTINENT
Animal dance / Django / England's carol / Bluesology / Bag's groove / Sketch / Ambiquite / Midsummer
17077 / Jan '97 / Laserlight

☐ MJQ BOX, THE (Concorde/Django/ 3CD Set)
Ralph's new blues / All of you / I'll remember April / Gershwin medley / Softly as in a morning sunrise / Concorde / Django / One bass hit / La ronde suite / Queen's fancy / Delauney's dilemma / Autumn in New York / Ballad for Me / Milano / All the things you are / La ronde / Vendome / Rose of the Rio Grande / Opus de funk / I've lost your love / Buhaina / Soma
3PRCD 7711 / Nov '96 / Prestige

☐ MJQ FOR ELLINGTON
It don't mean a thing (if it ain't got that swing) / Come Sunday / For Ellington / Prelude to a kiss / Rockin' in rhythm / Jack the bear / Maestro EKE / Ko-ko / Sepia panorama
7567909262 / Mar '93 / Atlantic

☐ MODERN JAZZ QUARTET (Modern Jazz Quartet & Milt Jackson Quintet)
All the things you are / All the things you are / Vendome / Rose of the rio grande / Opus de funk / I've lost your love / Buihaina / Soma
OJCCD 125 / May '93 / Original Jazz Classics

☐ QUARTET, THE
Softly as in a morning sunrise / Love me pretty baby / Autumn breeze / Milt meets Sid / Moving nicely / D and E blues / Heart and soul / True blues / Bluesology / Yesterdays / 'Round midnight / Between the devil and the deep blue sea
SV 0111 / Oct '97 / Savoy Jazz

☐ SPACE
Visitor from Venus / Visitor from Mars / Here's that rainy day / Dilemma / Adagio from Concierto de Aranjuez
CDSAPCOR 10 / Oct '96 / Apple

☐ TOGETHER AGAIN (Live At The Montreux Jazz Festival 1982)
Django / Cylinder / Martyr / Really true blues / Odds against tomorrow / Jasmine tree / Monterey mist / Bag's new groove / Woody 'n' you
CD 2308244 / Jun '93 / Pablo

☐ TOPSY THIS ONE'S FOR BASIE
Reunion blues / Nature boy / Topsy / D and E blues / Valeria / Milano / Le cannet
CD 2310917 / Apr '94 / Pablo

☐ UNDER THE JASMINE TREE
Blue necklace / Three little feelings (parts 1, 2 and 3) / Exposure / Jasmine tree
CDP 7975802 / Oct '91 / Apple

Modern Klezmer Quartet

☐ HORA AND BLUE
GV 156CD / May '94 / Global Village

Modern Whigs

☐ RAPED BY THE COPS
LOST 012CD / Sep '97 / Lost

Modernaires Orchestra

☐ TRIBUTE TO GLENN MILLER VOL.1, A
ROSSCD 66212 / Feb '89 / Ross

☐ TRIBUTE TO GLENN MILLER VOL.2, A
ROSSCD 66222 / Feb '89 / Ross

☐ TRIBUTE TO GLENN MILLER VOL.3, A
ROSSCD 66152 / Feb '89 / Ross

Modernist

☐ OPPORTUNITY KNOX
8215352 / 3 Nov '97 / Harvest

Modest Mouse

☐ LONESOME CROWDED WEST, THE
UP 044CD / 16 Feb '98 / Up

Modest Proposal

☐ CONTRAST
BAR 999D / Mar '93 / Barooni

Modesty Blaise

☐ MODERN GUITARS WITH AMPLIFICATION
SAVAGE 003 / 27 Oct '97 / Savage Bee

Mods

☐ TWENTY TWO MONTHS
OPM 2106CD / Oct '96 / Other People's Music

Modugno, Paolo

☐ LE BALA ET LA MOUCHE
NT 6732 / Aug '96 / New Tone

Moebius

☐ DOUBLE CUT (Moebius & Beerbohm)
SKYCD 3091 / May '95 / Sky

☐ OTHER PLACES (Moebius & Neumer/ Engler)
EFA 035422 / 23 Feb '98 / EFA

☐ RASTAKRAUT PASTA/MATERIAL (Moebius & Plank)
SKYCD 32/105-106 / Jun '97 / Sky

Moelwyn Male Voice Choir

☐ COR Y MOELWYN A SEINDORF YR OAKELEY (Moelwyn Male Voice Choir & Oakeley Silver Band)
Y ddau wladgarwr / Llygaid duon / Boadicea / Take me home / Solitaire / Nant y mynydd / Bro aber / Emyn noswyl / When the saints go marching in / Cariad sydd o'n cwmpas / Lion King / Where shall I be / O sole mio / Salm 23 / Young Amadeus / Tyddyn Iiwyn / Finlandia
SCD 2108 / Oct '97 / Sain

Moen, Don

☐ LET YOUR GLORY FALL
For all you've done / We've come to bless your name / My love and my light / Because we believe / God is here / Be still my soul / I live to know you / Deeper in love / More of you / Let your glory fall / Hallelujah to the lamb / May your presence go with us
11522 / Nov '97 / Hosanna

Moer, Paul

☐ PLAYS THE MUSIC OF ELMO HOPE (Moer, Paul Trio)
FSR 5008CD / Jul '96 / Fresh Sound

Moffatt, Hugh

☐ DANCE ME OUTSIDE (Moffatt, Hugh & Katy)
It's been decided / We'll sweep out the ashes in the morning / On the borderline / I don't believe you've met my baby / Dance me outside / Right over me / La Luna / Making new / Walking on the moon / Dark end of the street
PH 1144CD / '92 / Philo

☐ HEART OF A MINOR POET
WM 1047CD / Aug '96 / Watermelon

☐ LIVE AND ALONE
BRAM 1991182 / Nov '93 / Brambus

☐ LOVING YOU
When you held me in your arms / Mama Rita / Old flames (can't hold a candle to you) / Words at twenty paces / Slow movin' freight train / No stranger to the blues / Loving you / Tomorrow is a long time / Carolina star / Jack and Lucy / Roll with weather
PH 1111CD / '88 / Philo

☐ WOGNUM SESSIONS, THE (Moffatt, Hugh Trio)
SCR 32 / Dec '94 / Strictly Country

Moffatt, Katy

☐ CHILD BRIDE
Child bride / In a moment / Lonely avenue / Look out it must be love / Playin' fool / We ran / You better move on / Anna / Settin' the woods on fire
PH 1133CD / '90 / Philo

☐ MIDNIGHT RADIO
RTMCD 81 / Jun '96 / Round Tower

☐ WALKIN' ON THE MOON
Walkin' on the moon / I'm sorry darlin' / If anything comes to mind / Papacita (Mama Rita) / Mr. Banker / Borderline / Fire in your eyes / I'll take the blame / Hard time on Easy street / I know the difference now
RTM 59CD / Jun '97 / Round Tower

Moffett, Cody

☐ EVIDENCE
CD 83343 / Oct '93 / Telarc

Mofungo

☐ BUGGED
SST 191CD / May '93 / SST

Mogel

☐ SCREAM
KAMEL 016 / Oct '96 / Kamel

Mogensen, Anders

☐ AQUITAINE (Mogensen/Frisk Quartet)
Mr. JT / Virtual mind / Blues conclave / Trane bird / Aspasia / Aquitaine / Spaceship in the tale of bop / Leo bop
STCD 4216 / Dec '97 / Storyville

Moggsway

☐ EDGE OF THE WORLD
Change brings a change / All out of luck / Gravy train / Fortune town / Halfway / Down to move from myself / Mother Mary / House of pain / It's a game / History of gray / Abebe / Pisa na barata
RR 88042 / Jul '97 / Roadrunner

Mogwai

☐ KICKING A DEAD PIG
Like Herod / Helicon 2 / Summer / Gwai on 45 / Cheery wave from stranded youngsters / Like Herod / Mogwai fear Satan / R u still in 2 it / Tracy / Mogwai
EYEUKCD 019 / 18 May '98 / Eye Q

☐ KICKING A DEAD PIG (US Issue - 2CD Set)
TWA 13CD / 8 Jun '98 / Jetset

☐ MOGWAI YOUNG TEAM
Yes I am a long way from home / Like Herod / Katrien / Radar maker / Tracy / Summer / With portfolio / R U still in 2 it / Cheery wave from stranded youngsters / Mogwai fear satan
CHEM 018CD / 27 Oct '97 / Chemikal Underground

☐ TEN RAPID
TWA 05CD / Jun '97 / Jetset

Mohead, John

☐ LULA CITY LIMITS
OKRATONE 4961 / Aug '95 / Okratone

Moher

☐ OUT ON THE OCEAN
CBMCD 013 / Jan '95 / Cross Border Media

Mohiuddin, Dagar Zia

☐ RAGA YAMAN
NI 5276 / Sep '94 / Nimbus

Moholo, Louis

☐ BUSH FIRE (Moholo, Louis & Evan Parker Quintet)
OGCD 009 / May '97 / Ogun

☐ VIVA LA BLACK
OGCD 006 / Sep '94 / Ogun

Moiseyev Dance Co.

☐ RUSSIAN FOLK DANCES
MCD 71310 / Jun '93 / Monitor

Moist Fist

☐ MOIST FIST
RR 1212 / Jul '93 / Rise

Moistboyz

☐ MOISTBOYZ VOL.1
GR 004CD / Apr '97 / Grand Royal

☐ MOISTBOYZ VOL.2
It ain't rude / Secondhand smoker / Lazy and cool / Rock, stock and barrel / Man of the year / American made and duty free / Crank / Powervice / Keep the fire alive / Good morning America
GR 037CD / 16 Mar '98 / Grand Royal

Moity, Francoise

☐ OPENING NIGHT
829372 / Feb '97 / BUDA

Mojave 3

☐ ASK ME TOMORROW
Love songs on the radio / Sarah / Tomorrow's taken / Candle song 3 / You're beautiful / Where is the love / After all / Pictures / Mercy
GAD 5013CD / 6 Jul '98 / 4AD

Mojo

☐ TRA MOR
Dial y dail / Rhy hwyr / Byd yn bwysicach na dyn / Chwilio am yr hen fflam / Tro ar ol tro / Chwilio am dy galon / Dawnsio o flaen dy delyn / Gwyr y craig / Sefyll yn f'unfan / Daw'fr cyflawn yn rhydd / Eiliad mewn einioes / Pan fo'r cylch yn cau / Byd mewn crud / I sycharth yn ol
SCD 2137 / Nov '96 / Sain

Moke

☐ SUPERDRAG
Sleepy head / Down / My desire / Hide and seek / Wheel in motion / Another weekend / Mislaid the key / Powercut / Water
DOR 068CD / 20 Apr '98 / Dorado

Mokenstef

☐ AZZ IZZ
Be in the rain / Just be gentle / Azz izz / He's mine / Don't go there / Stop callin' me / It happens / Laid back / Let him know / It goes on / I got him all the time
5273642 / Sep '95 / Def Jam

Mola, Tony

☐ BRAGADA
Pega pega / Tribal / Abracadabra / Vem benzinho / Amem / Som / Tem dende / Baby volta pra mim / De gray / Abebe / Pisa na barata
BJAC 50062 / Sep '97 / Blue Jackel

Molard, Patrick

☐ AR BAZ VALAN
KMCD 87 / 1 Jun '98 / Keltia Musique

☐ ER BOLOM KOH (Molard, Patrick & Y. Le Bihan)
GWP 007CD / Jul '95 / Diffusion Breizh

☐ PIOBAIREACHD
GWP 003CD / Aug '93 / Gwerz

Mole, Miff

☐ SLIPPIN' AROUND VOL.1
DGF 19 / Jun '98 / Frog

Moleque De Rua

☐ STREET KIDS OF BRAZIL
Pregoes do Rio / Rap do moleque / Louco e triste / Zumbi / Nao vou pagar pra ser boiada / Dor de dente / Herodes / O sosia / Filosofia do bom malandro / Assaltar papai noel / Ze do Brazil / Ensaio geral
MOL 91002 / Aug '96 / Cramworld

Molest

☐ MILKFISH
PCD 023 / Nov '95 / Progress

Moller, Ale

☐ HASTEN OCH TRANAN
AMCD 732 / May '96 / Amigo

☐ VIND
Klavaheilagt / Skalhallingar / Gauketrail/ Vigstadmoin / Lugum leik / Jakup lom / Mikaelidagen/Kladdlaten / Finn hanses ganglat / Tre stromningar / Fodelsedagsvisan/Gratlaten / Fars lilla / Liabekken/Gammelhusin/Sylfest mork / Mans nerhole / Munnharpevals / Gjermundhalling / Drang jerkpolska / Jubelskagget / Kopmanpolska / Guns brudvals / Havamal
XOU 106CD / May '97 / Xource

Molloy, Matt

☐ CONTENTMENT IS WEALTH (Molloy, Matt & Sean Keane)
Gorman's-the dawn-mrs. creehan's reel / Mcgettrick's-mcdonagh's-tommy gunn's / Gillan's apples-up and about in the morning / Kitty in the lane-captain kelly-the green mountain / Caislean an oir-the new century / Gooseberry bush-the limestone rock / London lasses-farewell to ireland-the piper's despair / Sword in the hand-the providence reel-the old bush / George white's favourite-the virginia reel / Vincent campbell's-the swaggerin' jig-the holly bush / Dargai-the marquis of huntley-the mathematician / Golden keyboard-mayor harrison's fedora / Seamus ennis' jig-connie o'connell's / Dowd's no.9-the first month of spring-the reconciliation
GLCD 1058 / Jun '93 / Green Linnet

☐ HEATHERY BREEZE
SHAN 79064CD / Aug '93 / Shanachie

☐ MATT MOLLOY
LUNCD 004 / Aug '94 / Mulligan

☐ SHADOWS ON STONE
Morning thrush / Crib of perches/Carmel Mahoney Mulhaire's / Wind in the woods / Garret Barry's jig/ Paddy Rafferty's favourite / Mulvihill's/Wallop the spot / Mason's apron / Fig for a kiss/Poll Ha'penny/ Merry sisters / Chinese lake reflections / Music of the seals / Banshee / Sirius reel / Humours of Max / Babbling brook / Galway piper/Sligo polka / Skylark/ Finbar Dwyer's
CDVE 930 / May '97 / Venture

☐ STONY STEPS
McFadden's favourite / Boys of the town / City of Savannah / Primrose lass mullinger races / Parting of friends / Stony steps/Michael Dwyers's favourite / Mrs. Kenny's barndance / Paddy Murphy's wife / Jig of slurs / O Rathaille's grave / Miss Mcguiness/Reel of mullinavat / Frank Roche's favourite / Johnny 'Watt' Henry's favourite / Gravel walk / Slip jig
CCF 18CD / May '88 / Claddagh

Molly Hatchet

☐ DEVIL'S CANYON
Down from the mountain / Rolling thunder / Devil's canyon / Heartless land / Never say never / Tatanka / Come hell or high water / Look in your eyes / Eat your heart out / Journey / Dreams I'll never see
SPV 08544352 / Aug '96 / SPV

☐ LIGHTNING STRIKES TWICE
SPV 08544342 / Dec '96 / SPV

☐ NO GUTS NO GLORY
What does it matter / Ain't even close / Sweet dixie / Fall of the peacemakers / What's it gonna take / Kinda like love / Under the gun / On the prowl / Both sides
4736932 / Feb '97 / Epic

☐ SILENT REIGN OF HEROES
SPV 08529222 / 29 Jun '98 / SPV

Moloko

☐ I AM NOT A DOCTOR
Flipside / Knee deepen / Blink / Stylophone / Downsized / Sorry / Sing it back / Pretty bridges / Be like you / Caught in a whisper / Dr. Zee / ID / Tatty narja / Over my head / Should've been could've been
ECHCD 021
ECHCX 021 / 31 Aug '98 / Echo

Moloney, Kevin

☐ BRIDGING THE GAP (Moloney, Kevin & Sean)
MOL 001CD / Aug '97 / MOL

Moloney, Mick

☐ 3 WAY STREET (Moloney, Mick & Eugene O'Donnell & Seamus Egan)
Mulholland's fancy (polka) / Mulholland's fancy (polka) / Gan ainm-emily's reel (air and hornpipe) / Oilean mannan (the isle of man)-brighid of nock (air and hor / Mrs. kenny's-the donegal barn dance (barn dances) / Uncle dan mccann / Planxty hugh o'donnell (set dances) / Maid of mount kisco-dowd's no.9 (reels) / Rambling boy-sprig of shillelah (reels) / Man with a cap / John doherty's-crowley's-emily's (reels) / Sally gardens / Four provinces (flings) / Galbally farmer / Margaret mary robinson (air and waltz)
GLCD 1129 / Jul '93 / Green Linnet

☐ MICK MOLONEY WITH EUGENE O'DONNELL (Moloney, Mick & Eugene O'Donnell)
Joseph Baker / John Dwyer's reel/Lasses of Castlebar / Killin's fairy hill / Limerick rake / Clar hornpipe/Pride of Moyvane/Humours of Newcastle West / Blackthorn stick/Poet Carney / Bantry girl's lament / Fairie's hornpipe / Winnie Greene's reel/ Boston boys / John of dreams / Kilkenny races / Sean Reid's reel/Toss the feathers / Paddy O'Brien's jig/King of the pipers / Irish maid
GLCD 1010 / Oct '88 / Green Linnet

☐ STRINGS ATTACHED
My love is in America/Lisdoonvarna reel / Arthur Darley's reel/Over the hills to Runbush / Munster grass/Peacock's feathers / Gooseberry bush/ Charlie Mulvihill's reels / Loftus Jones / Dunmore lassies/McFadden's handsome daughter / Off to Puck Fair / Ricky's white fence/Top of the stairs / Bush on the hill / Bellharbour reel / Miss Lyon's fancy / Tom of the hill / Jackson's morning brush/Paddy Reynold's dream / Coyle's pono reels
CDGL 1027 / Oct '88 / Green Linnet

☐ THERE WERE ROSES
Ballad of Jack Dolan / Allastromm's/Julia Clifford's / Drimin Donn Dilis (Dear brown cow) / Redican's mother/Gan ainm/Blast of wind / Almost every circumstance / I will leave this town / There were roses / Fair haired cassidy/Paddy Gavin/Priest's boots / Commodore/Charleston reel / Mickey dam / Harvey Street hornpipe/Birds/O'Connor's frolics / Here I am from Donegal
GLCD 1057 / Oct '88 / Green Linnet

☐ UNCOMMON BONDS (Moloney, Mick & Eugene O'Donnell)
St. Brendan's fair Isle / Road to Dunmore / Bow legged tailor/Galway jig/April fool/O'Lochlainn's / Miss Fogarty's christmas cake / Sean McGlynn's mazurka / Bonny blue-eyed Nancy / O'Hara, Hughes, McCreesh and Sands / Blackbird and hen/ Keane's farewell to Nova Scotia / Mary in the morning / Farewell my gentle harp / Muldoon the solid man / Curlew's reel/Derry reel/Hanly's / Bay of Biscay
GLCD 1053 / Oct '88 / Green Linnet

Molsky, Bruce

☐ BIG HOEDOWN (Molsky, Bruce & Big Hoedown)
Sugar babe / Five miles out of town / Pretty saro / Half past four / Wagoner's lad / Shove the pig's foot a little bit further into the fire / John Henry / Rocky mountain / Paddy won't you drink some good old cider / Robert's serenade / Old paint / We'll all go to Heaven when the devil goes blind / Shady grove / Train on the island/Golden chain tree / Blue tail fly / Clyde's hiccups
ROUCD 0421 / Jul '97 / Rounder

☐ LOST BOY
ROUCD 361 / Feb '96 / Rounder

Molton, Flora

☐ UNITED STATES - GOSPEL (Molton, Flora & Eleanor Ellis)
C 580053 / May '94 / Ocora

Molvaer, Nils Petter

☐ KHMER
Kymer / Tion / Access/Song of sand i / On stream / Platonic years / Phum / Song of sand ii / Exit
5377982 / 2 Mar '98 / ECM

Moment

☐ MOD GODS
TANGCD 10 / Mar '96 / Tangerine

Moments

☐ MOMENTS TO REMEMBER (Every Hit & More/2CD Set)
Not on the outside / Sunday / I do / I'm so lost / Lovely way she loves / Love on a two-way street / If I didn't care / All I have / I can't help it / That's how it feels / Lucky me / To you with love / Thanks a lot / Just because he wants to make love (don't mean he loves you) / My thing / Gotta find a way / Sexy mama / Sho 'nuff boogie / What's your name / Girls / Sweet sweet lady / Dolly my love / Jack in the box / Look at me (I'm in love) / Nine times / With you / (We) don't cry out loud / I don't wanna go / Oh I could have loved you / It don't rain in my backyard / Just to spend some time / Gonna keep you busy / Sleep won't come / More than that / So in love / We finally found us / If you could be my sweet baby / Lady in blue / I may be right, I may be wrong / I've got to keep my head
DEEPD 021 / Apr '97 / Deep Beats

Momus

☐ 20 VODKA JELLIES
CDMRED 133 / Sep '96 / Cherry Red

☐ CIRCUS MAXIMUS
Lucky like St. Sebastian / Lesson of Sodom / John The Baptist Jones / King Solomon's song and mine / Little Lord Obedience / Day the circus came to town / Rape of Lucretia / Paper wraps rock / Rules of the game of quoits
ACME 2CD / Jun '97 / El

☐ HIPPOPOTAMOMUS
Hippopotamomus / I ate a girl right up / Michelin man / A dull documentary / Marquis of sadness / Bluestocking / Ventriloquists and dolls / Painter and his model / A monkey for sallie / Pornography / Song in contravention
CRECD 097 / May '94 / Creation

☐ HOLD BACK THE NIGHT
Trust me, I'm a doctor / Right hand heart / Lord of the dance / Lifestyles of the rich and famous / How do you find my sister / Don't stop the night / Amongst women only / Guitar lesson / Cabriolet / Shaftesbury avenue / Hairstyle of the devil
CRECD 052 / Nov '89 / Creation

☐ MONSTERS OF LOVE
Morality is vanity / Ballad of the barrel organist / Third party, fire and theft / Hotel marquis de sade / Murderers, the hope of women / What will death be like / Eleven executioners / Gilda / Hairstyle of the devil / Monsters of love
CRECD 059 / May '94 / Creation

☐ PHILOSOPHY OF MOMUS
Toothbrushead / Madness of Lee Scratch Perry / It's important to be trendy / Quark and Charm, the robot twins / Girlish boy / Yokohama Chinatown / Withinity / K's diary / Virtual Valerie / Red pyjamas / Cabinet of Kuniyoshi Kaneko / Slide projector lie detector / Microworlds / Complicated / I had a girl / Philiosophy of Momus / Loneliness of lift music / Paranoid acoustic seduction machine / Sadness of things
CDBRED 119 / May '95 / Cherry Red

☐ PING PONG
Ping pong with a Hong Kong king kong / His majesty the baby / My pervert doppleganger / I want you but I don't need you / Professor Shaftenberg / Shoesize of the angel / Age of infomation / Sensation of orgasm / Anthem of shibuya / Lolitapop dollhouse / Tamagotchi press officer / Space jews / Kindly friend the censor / Animal that desires / How to get and stay famous / 2PM
SATYR 001 / 3 Nov '97 / Satyricon

☐ POISON BOYFRIEND
CRECD 021 / Apr '88 / Creation

☐ SLENDER SHERBERT (Readings Of My Early Years)
Complete history of sexual jealousy / Guitar lesson / Closer to you / Homosexual / Charm of innocence / Lucky like St Sebastian / I was a maoist intellectual / Lifestyles of the rich and famous / Angels are voyeurs / Hotel Marquis De Sade / Gatecrasher / Hairstyle of the devil / Bi shonen / Angels reprise
CDBRED 123 / Oct '95 / Cherry Red

☐ TENDER PERVERT
Angels are voyeurs / Love on ice / I was a maoist intellectual / Homosexual / Bishonen / Ice king / In the sanatorium / Charm of innocence / Angels are voyeurs (reprise) / Right hand heart
CRECD 036 / Nov '88 / Creation

☐ TIMELORDS
CRECD 151 / Oct '93 / Creation

☐ ULTRACONFORMIST (Live Whilst Out Of Fashion)
Sinister themes / Last of the window cleaners / Ladies understand / Cape and stick gang / Ultraconformist / Mother In Law / La catrina / Cheques in the post / Spy on the moon / Forests
MONDE 3CD / Jun '97 / Cherry Red

☐ VOYAGER
Cibachrome blue / Virtual reality / Vocation / Conquistador / Spacewalk / Summer holiday 1999 / Afterglow / Trans siberian express / Voyager / Momutation 3
CRECD 113 / Jun '92 / Creation

Mona Lisa

☐ 11-20-79
5242442 / Jul '96 / 4th & Broadway

Monaco

☐ MUSIC FOR PLEASURE
What do you want from me / Shine / Sweet lips / Buzz gum / Blue / Junk / Billy bones / Happy Jack / Tender / Sedona
5372422 / Jun '97 / Polydor

Monastery

☐ MONASTRY/ANARCHUS (Monastery/ Anarchus)
SLAP 152 / Mar '93 / Slap A Ham

Monastyr

☐ NEVER DREAMING
MN 03CD / Jan '95 / Nuclear Blast

Mondo Grosso

☐ INVISIBLE MAN
99 2135 / Jul '96 / Ninetynine

☐ LIVE AND REMIXED
99124CD / Nov '96 / Ninetynine

☐ MARBLE
99 2125 / Jul '96 / Ninetynine

☐ MONDO GROSSO
99 2122 / Jul '96 / Ninetynine

Mondo Topless

☐ 50,000 DOLLAR HAND JOB
36T 0001CD / Jul '97 / 360 Twist

Mondonga, Lomani

☐ LA PLEINE LUNE DES ELEPHANTS
AT 8009 / Apr '97 / Night & Day

Money, Eddie

☐ SHAKIN' WITH THE MONEY MAN
86223 / Nov '97 / CMC

Money Mark

☐ MARK'S KEYBOARD REPAIR
Pretty pain / No fighting / Ba ba ba boom / Have clav will travel / Don't miss the boat / Sunday garden Blvd / Insects are all around us / Scenes from / Poet's walk / Spooky / Cry / Flute / Hand in your head / That's for sure / Stevie / Time lapse / Sly / Sometimes / Latin
MW 034CD / Aug '95 / Mo Wax

☐ PUSH THE BUTTON
Push the button / Too like you / Monkey dot / Tomorrow will be like today / Poor shakes / Bossa nova 101 / Rock in the rain / Crowns / All the people / Underneath it all / I don't play piano / Destroyer / Hand in your head / Trust / Maybe I'm dead / Dha teen ta / Powerhouse / Harmonics of life
MW 090CD
MW 090CDS / 4 May '98 / Mo Wax

☐ THIRD VERSION
Sometimes you gotta make it alone / Revolt of the octopi / Slow flames / Hard ass / From the beginning to the end / Function / World lesson / Inner laugh / Grade / Mark's keyboard repair
MW 043CD / Mar '96 / Mo Wax

Monger, Eileen

☐ LILTING BANSHEE, THE (Airs & Dances For Celtic Harp)
King of the fairies / Lilting banshee / O South wind / Great high wind / Wild geese / Bonnie Portmore / Morning dew / Ivy leaf / Limerick's lamentation / Give me your hand / Neil Gow's lament / Farewell to Craigie Dhu / Fingal's cave
CDSDL 348 / Mar '94 / Saydisc

Moniars

☐ EVEN GRANNY WAS DANCING
CRAICD 062 / Feb '96 / Crai

☐ Y GORAU O DDAU FYD
CRAICD 045 / Dec '94 / Crai

Monica

☐ BOY IS MINE, THE
Boy is mine / Angel of mine / Inside / For you I will / First night / I keep it to myself / Street symphony / Ring da bell / Misty blue / Gon' be fine / Cross da room
07822190112 / 13 Jul '98 / Rowdy

☐ MISS THANG
Miss Thang / Don't take it personal (just one of dem days) / Like this and like that / Get down / With you / Skate / Angel / Woman in me / Tell me if you still care / Let's straighten it out / Before you walk out of my life / Now I'm gone / Why I love you so much / Never can say goodbye / Forever always
75444370062 / Sep '95 / Rowdy

Monifah

☐ MO'HOGANY
UND 53155 / 10 Aug '98 / Universal

Monk, Meredith

☐ BOOK OF DAYS
Early morning melody / Dawn / Traveller 4 / Churchyard entertainment / Afternoon melodies / Field/Clouds / Dusk / Eva's song / Evening / Travellers / Jewish storyteller/Dance/Dream / Plague / Madwoman's vision / Cave song
8396241 / Apr '90 / ECM

☐ DO YOU BE
Scared song / I don't know / Window in 7's / Double fiesta / Do you be / Panda chant 1 / Memory song / Panda chant 11 / Quarry lullaby / Shadow song / Astronaut anthem / Wheel
8317822 / Jul '87 / ECM

☐ DOLMEN MUSIC
Gotham lullaby / Travelling / Biography / Tale / Dolmen music
8254592 / Oct '85 / ECM

Monk, T.S.

☐ MONK ON MONK
Little rootie tootie / Crepuscule with Nellie / Boo boo's birthday / Dear Ruby / Two timer / Bright Missisippi / Suddenly / Ugly beauty / Jackie-ing
N2KE 10017 / 3 Oct '97 / N2K

Monk, Thelonious

☐ 5 BY MONK BY 5
Jackie-ing / Straight no chaser / Played twice (take 3) / Played twice (take 1) / Played twice (take 2) / I mean you / Ask me now
OJCCD 362 / Feb '92 / Original Jazz Classics

☐ ALONE IN SAN FRANCISCO
Blue monk / Ruby my dear / Round lights / Everything happens to me / You took the words right out of my heart / Bluehawk / Pannonica / Remember / There's danger in your eyes, cherie / Reflections / There's danger in your eye's, cherie (take 1)
OJCCD 231 / Feb '92 / Original Jazz Classics

☐ AND THE JAZZ GIANTS
Bemsha swing / Crepuscule with Nellie / Nutty / I mean you / Pea eye / In walked Bud / Little Rootie Tootie / Played twice / San Francisco holiday
FCD 60018 / Apr '94 / Fantasy

☐ ART OF THE BALLAD, THE
Ruby my dear / Tea for two / Round midnight / Smoke gets in your eyes / I surrender / Crepuscule with Nellie / Mood indigo / Pannonica / Monk's mood / Sweet and lovely / I'll let a song go out of my heart / April in Paris / Ruby my dear
PRCD 110122 / Sep '98 / Prestige

☐ AT THE BLACKHAWK
Let's call this / Four in one / I'm getting sentimental over you / San francisco holiday (worry later) / 'round midnight / Epistrophy (closing theme) / Epistrophy (complete) / Evidence
OJCCD 305 / Feb '92 / Original Jazz Classics

☐ AT TOWN HALL
Thelonious (complete version) / Friday the 13th / Monk's mood / Little rootie tootie / Off minor / Crepuscule with nellie / Little rootie tootie (encore)
OJCCD 135 / Feb '92 / Original Jazz Classics

☐ BEST OF THELONIOUS MONK, THE
Thelonious / Ruby my dear / Well you needn't / April in Paris / Monk's mood / In walked Bud / 'Round midnight / Evidence / Misterioso / Epistrophy / I mean you / Four in one / Criss cross / Straight no chaser / Ask me now / Skippy
BNZ 261 / Mar '91 / Blue Note

☐ BIG BAND AND QUARTET IN CONCERT (2CD Set)
Bye-ya / I mean you / Evidence / Epistrophy / When it's darkness on the delta / Played twice / Misterioso / Light blue / Oskat / Four in one
4768982 / Aug '94 / Columbia

☐ BLUE MONK
Hackensack / Light blue / Evidence / Blue monk / Jackie-ing / Ruby my dear
JHR 73501 / Sep '93 / Jazz Hour

☐ BLUE MONK (Blue Note Plays Monk's Music) (Various Artists)
Bemsha swing: *Peterson, Ralph Trio* / Reasons for living / Canine blues from make of two hearts / Rocky mount: *Tracey, Stan Octet* / Doug and carol from the gift / Monk's dream: *Young, Larry* / Monk in wonderland: *Moncur, Grachan III* / Hero from hell and high water / Dr green and a mother's death from loves labor lo / Blue Monk: *Tyner, McCoy & Bobby Hutcherson* / Hell and high water from hell and high water / 'Round midnight: *Evans, Gil* / Shep arrives from the healers / Round midnight: *Gonzales, Babs & Jimmy Smith* / Epistrophy: *Taylor, Art* / Hold on from hell and high water / It came upon a midnight clear / Straight no chaser: *Three Sounds* / Theme from er (tv version) / Well you needn't: *Rubalcaba, Gonzala* / Hat and beard: *Dolphy, Eric* / Shattered glass from hell and high water / Raul dies from the healers / Carter see you next fall from everything old is n / Healing hands / Goodbye baby susie from fever of unknown origin / Theme from er / Dr lewis and renee fro the birthday party
CDP 8354712 / Oct '95 / Blue Note

☐ BRILLIANT CORNERS (Monk, Thelonious & Sonny Rollins)
Brilliant corners: *Monk, Thelonious* / Ba-lue bolivar ba-lues-are: *Monk, Thelonious* / Pannonica: *Monk, Thelonious* / I surrender dear: *Monk, Thelonious* / Bemsha swing: *Monk, Thelonious*
OJCCD 26 / Feb '92 / Original Jazz Classics

☐ COMPLETE RIVERSIDE RECORDINGS 1955-1961, THE (15CD Set)
It don't mean a thing if it ain't got that swing / Sophisticated lady / I got it bad and that ain't good / Black and tan fantasy / Mood indigo / I let a song go out of my heart / Solitude / Caravan / Liza / All the clouds'll roll away / Memories of you / Honeysuckle rose / Darn that dream / Tea for two / You are too beautiful / Just you, just me / Ba-lue Bolivar ba-lues are / Pannonica / Pannonica / Brilliant corners / Bemsha swing / I surrender dear / I don't stand a ghost of a chance with you / I don't stand a ghost of a chance with you / I should care / I should care / I should care / 'Round midnight / Round midnight / April in Paris / I'm getting sentimental over you / Monk's mood / Monk's mood / Functional / Functional / All alone / Crepuscle with Nellie / Crepuscule with Nellie / Blues for tomorrow / Off minor / Off minor / Abide with me / Crepuscule with Nellie / Crepuscule with Nellie / Epistrophy / Epistrophy / Well you needn't / Well you needn't / Ruby my dear: *Monk, Thelonious & Coleman Hawkins* / Ruby my dear: *Monk, Thelonious & John Coltrane* / Nutty / Trinkle tinkle / Straight no chaser / Straight no chaser / Rhythm-a-ning / I mean you / I mean you / I mean you / Round midnight / Decidedly / Decidedly / Sweet and lovely / Coming on the Hudson / In orbit / One foot in the gutter / Trust in me / Let's cool one / Pea eye / Argentia / Moonlight fiesta / Buck's business / Flugelin' the blues / Very near blues / Evidence / Blues five spot / In walked Bud / Epistrophy / Nutty / Blue five spot / Let's cool one / In walked Bud / Misterioso / Epistrophy / I walked Bud / Blue Monk / Unidentified solo piano / Bye-ya / Epistrophy / Round midnight / Bye-ya/Epistrophy / Light blue / Coming on the Hudson / Rhythm-a-ning / Just a gigolo / Blue Monk / Evidence / Epistrophy / Rhythm-a-ning / Monk's mood / Friday the 13th / Little rootie tootie / Off minor / Thelonious / Crepuscule with Nellie / Little rootie tootie / Played twice / Played twice / Straight no chaser / Ask me now / I mean you / Jackie-ing / Round lights / Pannonica / Blue Monk / Ruby my dear / There's danger in your eyes Cherie / Cherie / There's danger in you eyes cherie / Everything happens to me / Reflections / Remember / Bluehawk / You took the words right out of my heart / San Francisco holiday / Just you, just me / Round midnight / San Francisco holiday / I'm getting sentimental over you / Evidence / Epistrophy / Epistrophy / Four in one / Let's call this / Round midnight / San Francisco holiday / Four in one / Epistrophy / Well you needn't / Crepuscule with Nellie / Jackie-ing / Body and soul / Off minor / April in Paris / I mean you / Rhythm-a-ning / Just a gigolo / Hackensack / Epistrophy / I'm getting sentimental over you / Jackie-ing / Body and soul / Straight no chaser / Crepuscule with Nellie / Bemsha swing / San Fransisco holiday / Rhythm-a-ning / Epistrophy
RCD 0222 / Nov '96 / Riverside

☐ COMPOSER, THE
'Round midnight / Bemsha swing / Rhythm-a-ning / Reflections / Straight no chaser / Brilliant corners / Ruby my dear / Well you needn't / Blue monk / Criss cross / Crepuscule with Nellie
4633382 / Jan '95 / Sony Jazz

☐ ESSENTIAL THELONIOUS MONK, THE
4685712 / Jan '95 / Sony Jazz

☐ EVIDENCE
Rhythm-a-ning / Ruby my dear / Bright Mississippi / 'Round midnight / Evidence / Jackie-ing / Stuffy / Blue monk
FCD 105 / Jan '88 / Esoldun

☐ GENIUS OF MODERN MUSIC VOL.2
Carolina moon / Hornin' in / Skippy / Let's cool one / Suburban eyes / Evonce / Straight no chaser / Nice work if you can get it / Monk's mood / Who knows / Ask me now / Four in one / Criss cross (alt. take) / Eronel / Ask me now (alt. take) / Willow weep for me / Skippy (alt. take) / Hornin' in (alt. take) / Sixteen (first take) / Sixteen (second take) / I'll follow you
CDP 7815112 / Mar '95 / Blue Note

☐ GREATEST HITS, THE
Well you needn't / Misterioso / Bemsha swing / 'Round midnight / Epistrophy / Ruby / My dear / Crepuscule / Blue monk / Straight / No chaser
CK 65422 / 26 Jan '98 / Sony Jazz

☐ IN ACTION (Monk, Thelonious Quartet)
Light blue / Coming on the hudson / Rhythm-a-ning / Epistrophy / Blue monk / Evidence / Epistrophy (theme) / Blues five spot / In walked bud / Epistrophy (theme)
OJCCD 103 / '92 / Original Jazz Classics

☐ IN ITALY
Jackie-ing / Epistrophy / Body and soul / Straight no chaser / Beshma swing / San Francisco holiday / Crepuscule with Nellie / Rhythm-a-ning
OJCCD 488 / Apr '93 / Original Jazz Classics

☐ IN JAPAN 1963 (Monk, Thelonious Quartet)
Evidence / Blue monk / Just a gigolo / Bolivar blues / Epistrophy
PRCDSP 202 / Aug '93 / Prestige

☐ INTERPRETATIONS OF MONK, VOL.1 (2CD Set)
Spoken introduction by Nat Hentoff / Crepuscule with nelli / I mean you / Ask me now / Gallop's gallop / Blue monk / Four in one / Ruby my dear / Light blue / Bye / Ya / Pannonica / Off minor / Epistrophy
378382 / Oct '97 / Koch Jazz

☐ IT'S MONK'S TIME
Lulu's back in town / Memories of you / Stuffy turkey / Brake's sake / Nice work if you can get it / Shuffle boil
4684052 / Jan '95 / Sony Jazz

☐ JAZZ MASTERS
'round midnight / Misterioso / In walked bud / April in paris / Evidence / Well you needn't / Straight no chaser / Ruby my dear / Epistrophy / Monks mood
CDMFP 6300 / Mar '97 / Music For Pleasure

☐ JAZZ PORTRAITS
'Round midnight / Thelonious / Off minor / Well you needn't / Ruby my dear / Epistrophy / Evidence / Mysterioso / Ask me now / Criss cross / Straight no chaser / Hornin' in / Let's cool one / Little rootie tootie / Monk's dream / Bemesha swing / Reflections / Let's call this
CD 14510 / May '94 / Jazz Portraits

☐ LIVE AT THE IT CLUB (2CD Set)
Blue Monk / Well you needn't / 'Round midnight / Rhythm-a-ning / Blues five spot / Bemsha swing / Evidence / Nutty / Epistrophy / Straight no chaser / Teo / I'm getting sentimental over you / Misterioso / Gallop's gallop / Ba-lue Bolivar Ba-lues-are / Bright Mississippi / Just you just me / All the things you are / Epistrophy
C2K 65288 / 6 Apr '98 / Sony Jazz

☐ LIVE AT THE JAZZ WORKSHOP (2CD Set)
4691832 / Jan '95 / Sony Jazz

☐ LIVE AT THE VILLAGE GATE
60170400092 / 14 Apr '98 / PREV

☐ LONDON COLLECTION VOL.1
Trinkle tinkle / Crepuscule with Nellie / Darn that dream / Little rootie tootie / Meet me tonight in dreamland / Nice work if you can get it / My melancholy baby / Jackie-ing / Lover man / Blue sphere
BLCD 760101 / Jun '88 / Black Lion

☐ LONDON COLLECTION VOL.2
BLCD 760116 / Oct '94 / Black Lion

☐ LONDON COLLECTION VOL.3
BLCD 760142 / Oct '90 / Black Lion

☐ MEMORIAL ALBUM
'round midnight / I want to be happy / Black and tan fantasy / Brilliant corners / Epistrophy / Ruby my dear / Nutty / I mean you / Little rootie tootie / Jackie-ing
MCD 47064 / Oct '93 / Milestone

☐ MISTERIOSO
4684062 / Jan '95 / Sony Jazz

☐ MONK
4684072 / Jan '95 / Sony Jazz

☐ MONK ALONE (Complete Columbia Solo Studio Recordings 1962-1968/ 2CD Set)
Body and soul / Just a gigolo / Don't blame me / Nice work if you can get it / Memories of you / Sweetheart of all my dreams / I surrender dear / Sweet and lovely / Everything happens to me / I should care / North of the sunset / These foolish things (remind me of you) / I hadn't anyone 'til you / Dinah / I'm confessin' (that I love you) / Monk's point / Ask me now / Ruby my dear / 'Round midnight / Between the devil and the deep blue sea / This is my story this is my song / Introspection / Darn that dream / Body and soul / Body and soul / Don't blame me / Sweetheart of all my dreams / Sweet and lovely / Everything happens to me / Everything happens to me / I hadn't anyone 'til you / Dinah / I'm confessin' (that I love you) / Ask me now / Everything happens to me / Introspection / Ruby my dear
C2K 65495 / 8 Jun '98 / Sony Jazz

☐ MONK AND ROLLINS (Monk, Thelonious & Sonny Rollins)
Friday 13th / Work / Nutty / Way you look tonight / I want to be happy
OJCCD 59 / Feb '92 / Original Jazz Classics

☐ MONK IN COPENHAGEN (Monk, Thelonious Quartet)
STCD 8283 / May '97 / Storyville

☐ MONK IN FRANCE
OJCCD 670 / '93 / Original Jazz Classics

☐ MONK QUINTET
We see / Smoke gets in your eyes / Locomotive / Hackensack / Let's call this / Think of one (take 2) / Think of one (take 1)
OJCCD 16 / Feb '92 / Original Jazz Classics

☐ MONK'S BLUES
Let's cool one / Reflections / Rootie tootie / Just a glance at love / Brilliant corners / Consecutive seconds / Monk's point / Trinkle tinkle / Straight no chaser / Blue Monk / 'Round midnight
4756982 / Feb '94 / Columbia

☐ MONK'S DREAM (1952-1956) (Monk, Thelonious Quartet)
Monk's dream / Body and soul / Bright Mississippi / Five spot blues / Bolivar blues / Just a gigolo / Bye ya / Sweet and lonely
4600652 / Jan '95 / Sony Jazz

☐ MONK'S MUSIC
Abide with me / Well you needn't / Ruby my dear / Epistrophy / Crepuscule with Nellie
OJCCD 842 / eeb '92 / Original Jazz Classics
OJC20 084 / Sep '98 / Original Jazz Classics

☐ MULLIGAN MEETS MONK (Monk, Thelonious & Gerry Mulligan)
'Round midnight / Rhythm-a-ning / Sweet and lonely / Decidedly / Straight no chaser / I mean you
OJCCD 301 / Oct '92 / Original Jazz Classics

☐ NONET LIVE, THE
LEJAZZCD 7 / Mar '93 / Le Jazz

☐ PIANO SOLO 1954 (Original Vogue Masters)
'Round midnight / Evidence / Smoke gets in your eyes / Well you needn't / Reflections / Wee see / Eronel / Off minor / Hackensack
74321429242 / Apr '97 / Vogue

☐ ROUND MIDNIGHT
'Round midnight / Off minor / Mysterioso / Criss cross / Hornin' in well / You needn't / Ruby my dear / Let's cool one / Straight no chaser / Ask me now / Thelonious / Evidence / Epistrophy / Monk's dream / Little rootie tootie / Reflections / Blue monk / Let's call this / Bemesha swing / Rhythm-a-ning
CD 56022 / Aug '94 / Jazz Roots

☐ SAN FRANCISCO HOLIDAY
In walking bud / Blue monk / Rhythm-a-ning / Bye-ya-epistrophy / San francisco holiday / Four in one / Epistrophy / Jacjie-ing / April in paris
MCD 9199 / Oct '93 / Milestone

☐ SOLO MONK
4712482 / Jan '95 / Sony Jazz

☐ STANDARDS
4656812 / Jan '95 / Sony Jazz

☐ STRAIGHT NO CHASER
Locomotive / I didn't know about you / Straight, no chaser / Japanese folk song / Between the devil and the deep blue sea / We see / This is my story, this is my song / I didn't know about you / Green chimneys
CK 64886 / Sep '96 / Sony Jazz

☐ SWEET AND LOVELY
MCD 079 / Dec '95 / Moon

☐ THELONIOUS HIMSELF
April in paris / I don't stand a ghost of a chance with you / Functional / I'm getting sentimental over you / I should care / All alone / Monk's mood / 'Round midnight
OJCCD 254 / Feb '92 / Original Jazz Classics

☐ THELONIOUS MONK (2CD Set)
STCD 8255/6 / Dec '97 / Storyville

☐ THELONIOUS MONK & JOHN COLTRANE (Monk, Thelonious & John Coltrane)
Ruby my dear / Trinkle tinkle / Nutty / Functional / Off minor / Epistrophy
OJC20 0392 / Sep '98 / Original Jazz Classics

☐ THELONIOUS MONK SAMPLER
It don't mean a thing (if it ain't got that swing) / Honeysuckle rose / Memories of you / Way you look tonight / Hackensack / Mood indigo
OJCX 002 / Jan '98 / Original Jazz Classics

☐ THELONIUS MONK & JOHN COLTRANE (Monk, Thelonious & John Coltrane)
Ruby my dear: *Monk, Thelonious* / Trinkle tinkle: *Monk, Thelonious* / Off minor: *Monk, Thelonious* / Nutty: *Monk, Thelonious* / Epistrophy: *Monk, Thelonious* / Functional: *Monk, Thelonious*
OJCCD 392 / Feb '92 / Original Jazz Classics

☐ THIS IS JAZZ
'Round midnight / Well you needn't / Bemsha swing / Ruby my dear / Straight no chaser / Blue Monk / Rhythm-a-ning / Monk's dream / Misterioso / Epistrophy
CK 64625 / May '96 / Sony Jazz

☐ TRIO AND BLUE MONK VOL.2
CDJZD 009 / Nov '91 / Prestige

☐ UNDERGROUND
Ugly beauty / Raise four / Boo boo's birthday / Easy street / Green chimneys / In walked bud
4600662 / Jan '95 / Sony Jazz

☐ UNIQUE, THE
Invitation / Lover come back to me / September song / Will you still be mine / I love paris / Tropicville / Moonlight in vermont / Bye bye blues / Manuel's mambo / All the things you are / Blues from havana
OJCCD 642 / Feb '92 / Original Jazz Classics

Monkees

☐ BIRDS, BEES & THE MONKEES
Daydream believer / We were made for each other / Dream world / Auntie's municipal court / Tapioca tundra / I'll be back up on my feet / P o box 9847 / Poster / Lady's baby / Girl I left behind me / P o box 9847 / I'm gonna try / Alvin / Zor and zam / Valleri / Magnolia simms / Writing wrongs
4509976562 / Dec '94 / Warner Bros.

☐ CHANGES
Oh my my / It's got to be love / You're so good to me / Ticket on a ferry ride / Acapulco sun / Tell me love / I love you better / Do you feel it too / Lady jane / Do it in the name of love / Time and time again / I never thought it peculiar / Midnight train / All alone in the dark / 99 pounds
4509976572 / Dec '94 / Warner Bros.

☐ HEADQUARTERS
You just may be the one / I can't get her off my mind / I'll spend my life with you / Forget that girl / Shades of gray / Band 6 / Girl I knew somewhere / All of your toys / Randy scouse git / Early morning blues and greens / No time / Zilch / Sunny girlfriend / Mr webster / Nine times blue / Jericho / Peter gunn's gun / For pete's sake / You told me / Pillow time
4509976622 / Jan '95 / Warner Bros.

☐ INSTANT REPLAY
Man without a dream / Don't listen to linda / Through the looking glass / Just a game / Don't wait for me / Me without you / Through the looking glass / Me without you / St matthew / Smile / Rosemarie / Carlisle wheeling / Someday man / Shorty blackwell / Tear drop city / While I cry / You and i / I won't be the same without her / Girl I left behind me
4509976612 / Jan '95 / Warner Bros.

☐ JUST US
ARTFULCD 6 / Jan '97 / Artful

☐ MONKEES PRESENT..., THE
Little girl / Monkees present radio promo / Mommy and daddy / Listen to the band / Calico girlfriend samba / Pillow time / Oklahoma backroom dancer / Mommy and daddy / French song / Listen to the band / Ladies and society / Looking for the good times / Never tell a woman yes / Bye bye baby bye bye / Good clean fun / If I knew
4509976602 / Dec '94 / Warner Bros.

☐ MONKEES TALK DOWNUNDER (Interviews)
RVCD 38 / Nov '97 / Raven

☐ MONKEES' GREATEST HITS, THE
PLATCD 05 / '88 / Platinum

☐ MONKEES, THE
Last train to clarksville / (theme from) the monkees / Saturday's child / Tomorrow's gonna be another day / Take a giant step / Papa gene's blues / (theme from) the monkees / I don't think you know me / I can't get her off my mind / Gonna buy me a dog / Sweet young thing / I'll be true to you / Let's dance on / This just doesn't seem to be my day / I wanna be free
4509976552 / Dec '94 / Warner Bros.

☐ MORE OF THE MONKEES
She / When love comes knockin' / Mary Mary / Hold on girl / Your Auntie Grizelda / Look out (here comes tomorrow) / Kind of girl I could love / Day we fell in love / Sometime in the morning / Laugh / I'm a believer
4509976582 / Dec '94 / Warner Bros.

☐ PISCES, AQUARIUS, CAPRICORN & JONES LTD.
Salesman / Words / Cuddly toy / Pleasant valley sunday / Door into summer / Star collector / Daily nightly / Love is only sleeping / Door into summer / Salesman / Goin' down / Star collector / Don't call on me / Daily nightly / Peter percival patterson's pet pig porky / What am I doing hangin' 'round / Hard to believe / She hangs out / Love is only sleeping
4509976632 / Jan '95 / Warner Bros.

☐ POOL IT
Heart and soul / I'd go the whole wide world / Long way home / Secret heart / Gettin' in / I'll love you forever / Every step of the way / Don't bring me down / Midnight / She's movin' in with Rico / Since you went away / Counting on you
8122721542 / Nov '95 / Rhino

Monkey Beat

☐ SHAKE
LUCKY 79207 / Mar '95 / Lucky Seven

Monkey Business

☐ IN A TIME LIKE THIS
Much too much / Bad Daddy B / Money / Conga bop / Let your body go / No time / Love your neighbour / Tea for two / In a time like this
ME 000292 / Oct '95 / Soulciety

Monkey Island

☐ MERE PRAWNS TO ME
ULR 001 / Feb '97 / Ultra Recordings

Monkey Mafia

☐ LIVE AT THE SOCIAL VOL.2 (Mixed By John Carter) (Various Artists)
Supa: *Dope, Kenny & The Mad Racket* / He ya hey: *Budha Baboons* / Gucci dance live: *Sam The Beast* / I'm the magnificent: *Special Ed* / *Real McCoy* (ah ah ah): *Rankin' Don* / Play wit fire: *Yard Boy Ten* / Bells of NY: *Slo Moshun* / That other hop hop track: *Bitch* / Here comes the hotstepper: *Kamoze, Ini* / A buen a ting: *DJ Doubles* / Ain't nothin' to it: *K-9 Posse* / Program: *Morales, David & The Bad Yard Club/Papa San* / Yeah: *Audioweb* / Come togther: *Transplant* / Request the style: *Top Cat* / Peckings: *Balistic Brothers* / Opus Vol.2: *Bass Bin Twins* / Revenge of the Mekon: *Mekon & Mad Frankie Fraser* / Everybody thinks I'm high: *DJ Voodoo & The Liquid Method* / Sine eye: *Ragga Twins* / Assault 1: *Melting Pot* / Carry go bring home: *McGregor, Freddie* / Say Party: *Shut Up & Dance* / Mr. Loverman: *Shabba Ranks*
HVNLP 15CD / Aug '96 / Heavenly

☐ SHOOT THE BOSS
HVNLP 21CD / 5 May '98 / Heavenly

Monkey See

☐ MONKEY SEE
TKCF 45018 / 2 Mar '98 / Escape

Monkhouse

☐ CAKEY PIG
DAMGOOD 55CD / Apr '95 / Damaged Goods

☐ DEAD ROOM/GLUE BAG (Monkhouse & Striknien DC)
REJ 1000003 / Aug '96 / Rejected

☐ FINAL INDIGNITY
REJ 1000006 / Dec '96 / Rejected

Monks

☐ SUSPENDED ANIMATION
Don't want no reds / Suspended animation / Don't bother me I'm a Christian / James Bondage / Grown ups / Oxford street / Cool way to live / Go / I can do anything you like / Plastic Max / King dong / Space fruit / Gold and silver / Lost in romance / Slimy gash / Beast in cages / Ann Orexia / Cybernetic sister
CYBVP 001CD / Jul '97 / Cyberdisk

Monks Of Bodnath Monastery

☐ TIBETAN RITUAL
Rituel du soir
PS 65183 / May '97 / PlayaSound

Monks Of Melleray Abbot

☐ MUSICAL MEDITATIONS FROM MOUNT MELLERAY
ARCD 029 / May '98 / Ainm

Monks Of Zhihuasi Temple

☐ BUDDHIST MUSIC OF THE MING DYNASTY
VICG 52592 / Mar '96 / JVC World Library

Monne, Joan

☐ SON SONG
FSNT 010 / Feb '96 / Fresh Sound New Talent

Mono

☐ FORMICA BLUES
Life in mono / Silicone / Slimcea girl / Outsider / Disney town / Blind man / High life / Playboys / Penguin freud / Hello Cleveland
ECHCD 017 / Aug '97 / Echo

☐ FORMICA BLUES (2CD Set)
Life in mono / Silicone / Slimcea girl / Outsider / Disney town / Blind man / High life / Playboys / Penguin freud / Hello Cleveland / Slimcea girl / Silicone / High life / Life in mono
ECHDD 017 / 27 Jul '98 / Echo

Mono Men

☐ BENT PAGES
ANDA 215CD / May '97 / Au-Go-Go

☐ HAVE A NICE DAY MOTHERFUCKER
ES 1234CD / 8 Sep '97 / Estrus

☐ LIVE AT TOM'S
ES 108CD / Jun '95 / Estrus

☐ STOP DRAGGIN' ME DOWN
ESCD 1R / Sep '94 / Estrus

☐ WRECKAGE
ESD 123 / Sep '94 / Estrus

Mono Puff

☐ UNSUPERVISED
Guitar was the case / Unsupervised, I hit my head / Don't break the heart / Nixon's the one / To serve mankind / Don't I have the right / Careless Santa / So long, mockingbird / Dr. Kildare / Hello hello / What bothers the spaceman / Devil went down to Newport / Distant antenna
RCD 10360 / Jun '96 / Rykodisc

Monochrome Set

☐ BLACK & WHITE MINSTRELS 1975-1979
CDMRED 118 / Jan '95 / Cherry Red

☐ CHAPS (2CD Set)
SMDCD 134 / 22 Sep '97 / Snapper

☐ CHARADE
Overture / Forevever young / Clover / Snow girl / My white garden / Her pain / Little noises / Crystal chamber / Girl / Angie / Talking about you / (I've got) No time (for girls) / Christine / Tilt
CDBRED 102 / Jan '93 / Cherry Red

☐ DANTE'S CASINO
ASK 004CD / '92 / Vinyl Japan

☐ ELIGIBLE BACHELORS
Jet set junta / I'll cry instead / On the 13th day / Cloud 10 / Mating game / March of the eligible bachelors / Devil rides out / Fun for all the family / Midas touch / Ruling class / Great barrier riff
SUMCD 4096 / Feb '97 / Summit

☐ GOOD LIFE, THE
He's Frank / Martians go home / Straits of Malacca / Sugar plum / B-I-D spells bid / Alphaville / Heaven can wait / Goodbye Joe / Strange boutique / Strange boutique (reprise) / Jacob's ladder / Wallflower / Apocalypso / Mr. Bizarro / I'll cry instead / Espresso / 405 lines / Eine symphonie des grauns / Monochrome Set
MONDE 8CD / Oct '92 / Richmond

☐ HISTORY 1978-1996
CDBRED 128 / May '96 / Cherry Red

☐ LIVE 1990
NINETY 4 / Jun '93 / Code 90

☐ MISERE
Milk and honey / Pauper / Dr. Robinson / Achilles / Leather jacket / Someone has been sleeping / Handsome boy / Ethereal one / UFO 10 / Integrate me / Twang 'em high
CDBRED 114 / May '94 / Cherry Red

☐ TOMORROW WILL BE TOO LONG
Monochrome Set (I presume) / Lighter side of dating / Expresso / Puerto Rican fence climber / Tomorrow will be too long / Martians go home / Love goes down the drain / Ici les enfants / Etcetera stroll / Goodbye Joe / Strange boutique / Love zombies / O come all ye faithful (Adeste fidelis) / 405 lines / B-I-D spells bid / RSVP / Apocalypso / Karma suture / Man with the black moustache / Weird, wild, wonderful world of Tony Potts / In love, Cancer
CDOVD 458 / Feb '95 / Virgin

☐ TRINITY ROAD
Flame dials / All over / April dance affair / Bliss / Bar Madiera / Hob's end / Golden apples of the sun / Worst is yet to come / Two fits / Albert bridge / Hula honey / Snake-fingers / Mousetrap / Kissy kissy / I love Lambeth
CDBRED 122 / Sep '95 / Cherry Red

☐ VOLUME, CONTRAST, BRILLIANCE...
Eine symphonie des grauns / Jet set junta / Love zombies / Silicon carne / Ruling class / Viva death row / Man with the black moustache / He's Frank / Fun for all the family / Lester leaps in / Ici les enfants / Fat fun / Alphaville / Avanti
CDBRED 47 / May '93 / Cherry Red

☐ WESTMINSTER AFFAIR
Jet set junta / Cast a long shadow / Ruling class / Lester leaps in / Mating game / On the 13th day / March of the eligible bachelors / Devil rides out / Fun for all the family / Andiamo / Cowboy country / JDHANEY / Noise / Eine symphonie des grauns / Viva death row / Jacob's ladder / Ici les enfants / Avanti
ACME 17 CD / Aug '88 / El

Monolake

☐ HONG KONG
EFA 503042 / 24 Nov '97 / Chain Reaction

Monolith

☐ TALES OF THE MACABRE
Morbid curiosity / Sleep with the dead / Misery / Undead burial / Devoured from within / Locked in horror / Catalogue of carnage / Maceration
SOL 036CD / Mar '93 / Vinyl Solution

Monomorph

☐ ALTERNATIVE FLUID
DIS 016CD / Sep '94 / Disturbance

Monorchid

☐ WHO PUT OUT THE FIRE
TG 190CD / 29 Jun '98 / Touch & Go

Monotonic

☐ ELECTRALUX
HUK 002CD / Jun '97 / Headhunter

Monro, Matt

☐ HOLLYWOOD AND BROADWAY
Look for small pleasures / Stranger in paradise / Impossible dream / Apple tree / I'll only miss her when I think of her / Come back to me / Hello Dolly / Sunrise sunset / Walking happy / If she walked into my life / Put on a happy face / Till the end of time / Charade / Green leaves of summer / Second time around / Everybody's talkin' / Shadow of your smile / I've grown accustomed to her face / Chattanooga choo choo / Pretty Polly
CDMFP 6137 / Oct '94 / Music For Pleasure

☐ LOVE IS THE SAME ANYWHERE
Love is the same anywhere / Jeannie / Let's face the music and dance / Such is my love / Thing about love / Come sta / Cheek to cheek / I'll dream of you / April fool / Mirage / There are no words for love / No one will ever know
DORIG 103 / 1 Sep '97 / EMI

☐ LOVE SONGS (2CD Set)
Softly as I leave you / Portrait of my love / Somewhere / From Russia with love / On days like these / Michelle / Speak softly love / My love and devotion / This time / Can this be love / When love comes along / I will wait for you / Time after time / Love walked in / And we were lovers / Time for love / Till then my love / With these hands / Let's face the music and dance / When I fall in love / Autumn leaves / Sweet Lorraine / Stardust / Didn't we / My kind of girl / And you smiled / Eye level theme / Cheek to cheek / Love is a many splendored thing / How little we know / Skylark / I have dreamed / Girl I love / I'm glad there is you / I'll take romance / Strangers in the night / Walk away / One day / Unchained melody / In the arms of love / Man and a woman / Hello young lovers / You light up my life / Maria / I've grown accustomed to her face / Precious moments / Let there be love / Real live girl / September song / You're sensational / All my loving / I get along without you very well / Fools rush in / In other words (fly me to the moon) / If you go away
CDTRBOX 256 / Jan '97 / Music For Pleasure

☐ MATT MONRO SINGS (2CD Set)
I have dreamed / Who can I turn to / My friend, my friend / Love is a many splendoured thing / It's a breeze / Without the one you love / Once in every long and lonely while / All my loving / If this should be a dream / How soon / Exodus / Here and now / Friendly persuasion / Start living / Stardust / Small fry / How little it matters, how little we know / Nearness of you / Georgia on my mind / Skylark / One morning in May / I get along without you very well / Memphis in June / I guess it was you all the time / Blue orchids / Rockin' chair / You're sensational / Love walked in / Yesterday / Alfie / Hello, young lovers / Michelle / Softly as I leave you / Here, there and everywhere / Somewhere / From Russia with love
CDDL 1072 / May '91 / Music For Pleasure

☐ MATT SINGS MONRO (Monro, Matt Jr. & Matt Monro Sr.)
We're gonna change the world / Did it happen / More / You and me against the world / You've made me so very happy / For all we know / He ain't heavy, he's my brother / If i never sing another song / Long and winding road / On days like these / I'll never fall in love again / I close my eyes and count to ten / Jean / Didn't we
CDMFP 6279 / Nov '96 / Music For Pleasure

☐ MOMENT TO MOMENT (3CD Set)
Portrait of my love / My kind of girl / Yesterday / For mama / Why not now / Alfie / Cheek to cheek / Let's face the music and dance / Spring is here / Laura / Nearness of you / Green leaves of summer / Softly as I leave you / Sweet Lorraine / Everybody's talkin' / How little we know / Born free / Gonna build a mountain / Walk away / And you smiled / When love comes along / Didn't we / Hello dolly / Autumn leaves / Ebb tide / Shadow of your smile / For all we know / Love is a many splendoured thing / April fool / Moment to moment / Come sta / Here and now / Unchained melody / From Russia with love / My love and devotion / Without you / Georgia on my mind / Strangers in the night / With these hands / Sunrise sunset / Fools rush in / Fly me to the moon / Maria / Spanish eyes / If you go away (no me dejes) / You've made me so very happy / Answer me / My way
SA 871692 / Sep '96 / Disky
HR 883262 / Oct '97 / Disky

☐ SOFTLY AS I LEAVE YOU
Born free / On days like these / Walk away / Softly as I leave you / Michelle / Who can I turn to / Love is a many splendoured thing / From Russia with love / One morning in May / For all we know / I have dreamed / All my loving / Stardust / Portrait of my love / Nearness of you / Unchained melody / Hello, young lovers / Alfie / September song
CDMFP 6003 / Oct '87 / Music For Pleasure
4939842 / 16 Mar '98 / EMI Gold

☐ THIS IS (2CD Set)
Portrait of my love / Walk away / Time after time / Cheek to cheek / On a wonderful day like today / For once in my life / Laura / Girl I love / Choose / On days like these / Born free / Why not now / Moment to moment / Singin' in the rain / When Sunny gets blue / This is the life / You're gonna hear from me / Party's over / Who can I turn to / Softly as I leave you / From Russia with love / My kind of girl / Days of wine and roses / Precious moments / Ten out of ten / As long as she needs me / One day / Happy / Sweet Lorraine / Can this be love / Yesterday / Michelle / If she should come to you / You and me against the world / I'm glad I'm not young anymore / This way Mary / Happening / What to do / My love and devotion / Speak softly love
CDDL 1257 / Jan '94 / Music For Pleasure

☐ THIS IS THE LIFE/HERE'S TO MY LADY
I'm glad there's you / This is the life / You're gonna hear from me / I'll take romance / Strangers in the night / On a clear day (you can see forever) / Sweet Lorraine / My best girl / On a wonderful day like today / Merci cherie / Honey on the vine / When Joanna loved me / Real live girl / When sunny gets blues / Laura / People / Here's to my lady / Good life / You've got possibilities / Rain sometimes / Sweet talkin' Hannah / Nina never knew
CTMCD 107 / Jan '97 / EMI

☐ THROUGH THE YEARS
As long as I am singing / Fools rush in / Ethel baby / Ebb tide / Hava nagila / Fly me to the moon / Good life / Autumn leaves / Did it happen / Mira / Let me sing a happy song / Spring is here / Spanish eyes / If you go away (no me dejes) / Come sta / Roses and roses / You've made me so very happy / My way / This is all I ask / Party's over
CDEMS 1544 / Feb '95 / EMI

☐ TIME FOR LOVE, A
Portrait of my love / Softly as I leave you / Why not now / Can this be love / My kind of girl / When love comes along / Without you / Speak softly love / Wednesday's child / I will wait for you / Time after time / Love walked in / And we were lovers / Time for love / With these hands / Answer me / Till then my love / Man and a woman / On days like these / Didn't we / Alguien Canto (The music played) / Be my love / In the arms of love / You light up my life
CDMFP 6070 / Aug '89 / Music For Pleasure

☐ VERY BEST OF MATT MONRO, THE
Born free / Softly as I leave you / From Russia with love / On days like these / Walk away / Around the world / My love and devotion / Michelle / On a clear day (You can see forever) / Somewhere / Impossible dream / Gonna build a mountain / Who can I turn to / Portrait of my love / Speak softly love / My kind of girl / For mama / Yesterday / This time / We're gonna change the world
CDMFP 5568 / Aug '96 / Music For Pleasure

Monroe, Bill

☐ BLUEGRASS 1950-1958 (4CD Set)
Bluegrass ramble / New muleskinner blues / My little Georgia rose / Memories of you / I'm on my way to the old home / Alabama waltz / I'm blue, I'm lonesome / I'll meet you in church Sunday morning / Boat of love / Old fiddler / Uncle Pen / When the golden leaves begin to fall / Lord protect my soul / River of death / Letter from my darling / On the old Kentucky shore / Rawhide / Poison love / Kentucky waltz / Prisoner's song / Swing low, sweet chariot / Angels rock me to sleep / Brakeman's blues / When the cactus is in bloom / Sailors plea / My Carolina sunshine girl / Ben Dewberry's final run / Peach pickin' time in Georgia / Those gamblers blues / Highway of sorrow / Rotation blues / Lonesome truck driver's blues / Sugar coated love / You're drifting away / Cabin of love / Get down on your knees and pray / Christmas time's a coming / First whippoorwill / In the pines / Footprints in the snow / Walking in Jerusalem / Memories of Mother and Dad / Little girl and the dreadful snake / Country waltz / Don't put it off till tomorrow / My dying bed / Mighty pretty waltz / Pike County breakdown / Wishing waltz / I hope you have learned / Get up John / Sittin' alone in the moonlight / Plant some flowers by my grave / Changing partners / Y'all come / On and on / I believed in you darling / New John Henry blues / White House blues / Happy on my way / I'm working on a building / Voice from on high / He will set your fields on fire / Close by / Blue moon of Kentucky / Wheel hoss / Cheyenne / You'll find her name written there / Roanoke / Wait a little longer, please Jesus / Let the light shine down on me / Used to be / Tall timbers / Brown County breakdown / Fallen star / Four walls / Good woman's love / Cry cry darlin' / I'm sitting on top of the world / Out in the cold world / Roane Country prison / Goodbye old pal / In despair / Molly and tenbrooks / Come back to me in my dreams / Sally Jo / Brand new shoes / Lonesome road / I saw the light / Lord build me a cabin / Lord lead me on / Precious jewel / I'll meet you in the morning / Life's railway to heaven /

I've found a hiding place / Jesus hold my hand / I am a pilgrim / Wayfaring stranger / Beautiful life / House of gold / Panhandle country / Scotland / Gotta travel on / No one but my darlin' / Big mon / Monroe's hornpipe
BCD 15423 / Jul '89 / Bear Family

☐ BLUEGRASS 1959-1969 (4CD Set)
When the phone rang / Tomorrow I'll be gone / Dark as the night, blue as the day / Stoney lonesome / Lonesome wind blues / Thinking about you / Come go with me / Sold down the river / Linda Lou / You live in a world all your own / Little Joe / Put my rubber doll away / Seven year blues / Time changes everything / Lonesome road blues / Big river / Flowers of love / It's mighty dark to travel / Bluegrass / Little Maggie / I'm going back to old Kentucky / Toy heart / Shady grove / Nine pound hammer / Live and let live / Danny boy / Cotton fields / Journey's end / John Hardy / Bugle call rag / Old Joe Clark / There was nothing we could do / I was left on the street / Cheap love affair / When the bees are in the hive / Big ball in Brooklyn / Columbus / Stockade blues / Blue Ridge mountain blues / How will I explain about you / Foggy river / Old country Baptising / I found the way / This world is not my home / Way down deep in my soul / Drifting too far from the shore / Going home / On the Jericho road / We'll understand it better / Somebody touched me / Careless love / I'm so lonesome I could cry / Jimmie brown the newsboy / Pass me not / Gloryland, way / Farther along / Big Sandy river / Baker's breakdown / Darling Corey / Cindy / Master builder / Let me rest at the end of the day / Salt Creek / Devil's dream / Sailor's hornpipe / Were you there / Pike county breakdown / Shenandoah breakdown / Santa Claus / I'll meet you in church Sunday morning / Mary at the home place / Highway of sorrow / One of God's sheep / Roll on Buddy roll on / Legend of the Blue Ridge mountains / Last old dollar / Bill's dream / Louisville breakdown / Never again / Just over in the Gloryland / Fire on the mountain / Long black veil / I live in the past / There's an old old house / When my blue moon turns to gold again / I wonder where you are tonight / Turkey in the straw / Pretty fair maiden in the garden / Log cabin in the lane / Paddy in the turnpike / That's alright Mama / It makes no difference now / Dusty Miller / Midnight on the stormy deep / All the good times are past and gone / Soldier's joy / Blue night / Grey eagle / Gold rush / Sally Goodin / Virginia darlin' / Is the blue moon still shining / Train 45 / Kentucky mandolin / I want to go with you / Crossing the Cumberlands / Walls of time / I haven't seen Mary in years / Fireball male / Dead march / Cripple creek / What about you / With body and soul / Methodist preacher / Walk softly on my heart / Tall pines / Candy gal / Going up Caney / Lee wedding tune / Bonnie / Sweet Mary and the miles between
BCD 15529 / Feb '91 / Bear Family

☐ BLUEGRASS 1970-1979 (4CD Set)
McKinley's march / Texas gallop / Road of life / It's me again Lord / Beyond the gate / I will sing for the glory of God / Kentucky waltz / Girl in the blue velvet band / Lonesome moonlight waltz / Tallahassee / Summertime is past and gone / Rocky road blues / Mule skinner blues / Katy hill / Poor white folks / Old grey mare come tearing out / Kiss me waltz / Jenny Lynn / Heel and toe polka / Milenburg joys / Sweetheart you done me wrong / Banks of the Ohio / Tall pines / Mother's only sleeping / Foggy mountain top / Love please come home / What would you give in exchange / When the golden leaves begin to fall / Walls of time / My old Kentucky and you / Mule skinner blues / You won't be satified that way / Uncle pen / Blue moon of Kentucky / Ole slewfoot / Sweet little miss blue eyes / Please be my love / I wish you knew / Train 45 / Bonny / When my blue moon turns ot gold again / Hit parade of love / Mary Ann / Sunny side of the mountain / Freeborn man / Tennessee / Rollin' in my sweet baby's arms / Feudin' banjos / Ballad of Jed Clampett / I wonder where you are tonight / Orange blossom special (instrumental) / Fiddler roll call / Down yonder / Soldier's joy / Grey eagle / Swing low, sweet chariot / Clinging to a saving hand / Show me the way / Jerusalem ridge / Ashland breakdown / Mary Jane, won't you be mine / Old old house / Watson's blues / Thank God for Kentucky / Reasons why / Weary traveller / My cabin in Caroline / No place to pillow my head / My sweet blue eyed darling / Monroe's blues / First whippoorwill / Lucky lady / My Louisiana love / Christmas time's a coming / Texas blue-bonnet / Sunset trail / My sweet memory / She's young and I'm growing old / Blue goose / My Florida sunshine / Wabash cannonball / Hard times have been here (but they've gone) / Six feet under the ground / Who's gonna shoe your pretty little feet / Jake Satterfield / Muddy waters / Corine Corina / Have a feast here tonight / Golden river / I'm going back to Old Kentucky / Those memories of you / Intro (Watermelon hangin) / John Henry / Dog house blues / Old mountaineer / Little cabin home on the hill / Orange blossom special / Molly and the Tenbrooks medley: Little Magggie, Train 45 / Little girl and the dreadful snake / In despair / Y'all come
BCD 15606 / Apr '94 / Bear Family

☐ BLUEGRASS BREAKDOWN (Monroe, Bill & His Bluegrass Boys)
Bluegrass breakdown / No letter in the mail / Uncle Pen / Orange blossom special / Footprints in the snow / I saw the light / Shady grove / Muleskinner blues / Shenandoah breakdown / Prison song / Blue moon of Kentucky / Can't you hear me calling / Nine pound hammer
PRACD 4003 / Jun '97 / Prairie

☐ OFF THE RECORD VOL.1 (Live Recordings 1956-1969) (Monroe, Bill & His Bluegrass Boys)
SF 40063CD / Nov '94 / Smithsonian Folkways

☐ OFF THE RECORD VOL.2 (Live Duets From 1963-1980) (Monroe, Bill & Doc Watson)
Foggy mountain top / What would you give in exchange for your soul / Watson's blues / Soldier's joy / Where is my sailor boy / You won't be satisfied that way / Kentucky mandolin / East tenessee blues / Midnight on the stormy deep / Lonesome moonlight waltz / Banks of the ohio / Fire on the mountain / Chicken reel / Turkey in the straw / Memories of you / Have a feast here tonight / Paddy on the turnpike
SFWCD 40064 / Aug '95 / Smithsonian Folkways

☐ TRUE LIFE BLUES (The Songs Of Bill Monroe - An All Star Tribute) (Various Artists)
Molly and tenbrooks / True life blues / I'm on my way back to the old house / Highway of sorrow / Old Ebenezer Scrooge / Memories of you / Rawhide / Can't you hear me callin' / Letter from my darling / Sittin' alone in the moonlight / Big mon / Get down on your knees and pray / Used to be / Scotland / Travellin' this lonesome road / Heavy traffic ahead / Little cabin home on the hill
SHCD 2209 / Mar '98 / Sugar Hill

Monroe Mustang

☐ PLAIN SWEEPING THEMES FOR THE UNPREPARED
TR 68CD / 13 Jul '98 / Trance

Monroe, Marilyn

☐ COLLECTION, THE
I wanna be loved by you / Diamonds are a girl's best friend / My heart belongs to daddy / Lazy / I'm thru with love / Some like it hot / Fine romance / When I fall in love / Specialisation / After you get what you want you don't want it / Kiss / One silver dollar / Heatwave / I'm gonna file my claim / When love goes wrong, nothing goes right / She acts like a woman should / Down in the meadow / Two little girls from little rock (duet j. russell) / Running wild / Do it again / Anyone can see I love you / You'd be surprised / River of no return / Every baby needs a da-da-daddy / Bye bye baby
COL 042 / Mar '95 / Collection

☐ DIAMOND COLLECTION, THE
WWRCD 6002 / Jun '95 / Wienerworld

☐ DIAMONDS ARE A GIRL'S BEST FRIEND
CDGFR 135 / Jun '92 / Tring

☐ ESSENTIAL RECORDINGS, THE
I wanna be loved by you / Diamonds are a girl's best friend / Some like it hot / I'm gonna file my claim / You'd be surprised / She acts like a woman should / Fine romance / Bye bye baby / Do it again / Running wild / When love goes wrong / Lazy / I'm through with love / River of no return / Heatwave / Kiss / My heart belongs to daddy / Little girl from Little Rock / Happy birthday Mr. President
MCCD 062 / '92 / Music Club

☐ GOLD COLLECTION, THE (2CD Set)
R2CD 4035 / 13 Apr '98 / Deja Vu

☐ KISS
You'd be surprised / River of no return / I wanna be loved by you / When I fall in love / Bye bye baby / Diamonds are a girl's best friend / One silver dollar / I'm gonna file my claim / When love goes wrong, nothing goes right / After you get what you want you don't want it / Runnin' wild / Specialisation / My heart belongs to daddy / Two little girls from little rock / Heat wave / Kiss
CD 3555 / Mar '96 / Cameo

☐ MARILYN MONROE
DVGH 7072 / May '95 / Deja Vu

☐ MARILYN MONROE
I wanna be loved by you / Two little girls from Little Rock: *Monroe, Marilyn & Jane Russell* / I'm gonna file my claim / My heart belongs to Daddy / Runnin' wild / Fine romance / You'd be surprised / Diamonds are a girl's best friend / Bye bye baby / I'm through with love / Specialisation: *Monroe, Marilyn & Frankie Vaughan* / Heatwave / Do it again / When love goes wrong, nothing goes right: *Monroe, Marilyn & Jane Russell* / After you get what you want, you don't want it / River of no return / Lazy / Kiss / When I fall in love / Happy Birthday Mr. President
399534 / May '97 / Koch Presents

☐ PORTRAIT: MARILYN MONROE
I wanna be loved by you / Diamonds are a girl's best friend / Little girl from Little Rock / When love goes wrong / Bye bye baby / My heart belongs to Daddy / I'm gonna file my claim / River of no return / Do it again / Kiss / You'd be surprised / This is a fine romance / I'm through with love / Heatwave / Running wild / Lazy / Happy birthday Mr. President
PLATCD 3905 / Dec '88 / Platinum

☐ SOME LIKE IT HOT
Diamonds are a girl's best friend / Man chases a girl / Every baby needs a da da daddy / Happy birthday Mr. President / Incurably romantic / Down in the meadow / Some like it hot / I found a dream / Anyone can see I love you / Specialization / Heatwave / Ladies of the chorus / When I fall in love / Let's make love / Bye bye baby / Fine romance / One silver dollar / That old black magic / There's no business like show business / I wanna be loved by you
HADCD 153 / May '94 / Javelin

Monroe, Vaughan

☐ THERE I'VE SAID IT AGAIN (Monroe, Vaughan Orchestra)
Racing with the moon / There I go / We could make such beautiful music / It's only a paper moon / Did you ever see a dream walking / Sleepy lagoon / There I've said it again / Last time I saw Paris / I'll see you in my dreams / Moonlight and roses / Blue moon / It's my lazy day / Drifting and dreaming / My devotion / Rum and Coca Cola / Sinner kissed an angel / Life can be beautiful / Tangerine / Things we did last summer / Moonglow / All the time / Very thought of you / G'bye now / Dream
CDMOIR 525 / Apr '98 / Memoir

☐ VAUGHAN MONROE 1943 (Monroe, Vaughan Orchestra)
CCD 045 / Jun '96 / Circle

☐ VAUGHAN MONROE 1943-1944 (Monroe, Vaughan Orchestra)
CCD 116 / Jun '96 / Circle

☐ VAUGHAN MONROE 1944-1945
6224741652 / 27 Apr '98 / Circle

☐ VAUGHAN MONROE ORCHESTRA 1944-1945 (Monroe, Vaughan Orchestra)
CCD 165 / May '98 / Circle

Monster Magnet

☐ 25...TAB
CAROL 1471 / Sep '97 / Caroline

☐ DOPES TO INFINITY
Dopes to Infinity / Negasonic teenage warhead / Look to your orb for warning / All friends and kingdom come / Ego, the living planet / Blow 'em off / Third alternative / I control, I fly / King of Mars / Dead Christmas / Theme from Masterburner / Vertigo / Forbidden planet
5403152 / Feb '95 / A&M

☐ POWERTRIP
5409082 / 1 Jun '98 / A&M

☐ SPINE OF GOD
GR 0172 / Jun '92 / Glitterhouse
CAROL 1718 / Oct '97 / Caroline

Monster Truck Five

☐ BREAKER
SFTRI 511CD / 8 Dec '97 / Sympathy For The Record Industry

Monsterland

☐ AT ONE WITH TIME
At one with time / Jane Wiedlin used to be a Go-Go / Your touch is uncomfortable to me / Chewbacca / Blank / Girlfriend on drugs
959282 / Mar '94 / Seed

☐ DESTROY WHAT YOU LOVE
Insulation / Rid of you / Lobsterhead / Nobody loves you / Car on fire / Twice at the end / At one with time / Fish eye / Crashing teenage crush / Angel scraper / Bursitis
142362 / Nov '93 / Seed

Monstertruckfive

☐ COLUMBUS OHIO
SFTRI 367CD / Aug '95 / Sympathy For The Record Industry

Monstrosity

☐ IMPERIAL DOOM
NB 055CD / Feb '92 / Nuclear Blast

☐ MILLENNIUM
NB 208CD / Nov '96 / Nuclear Blast

Montague Orchestra

☐ MELODIES FOR LOVERS
MACCD 365 / 30 Mar '98 / Autograph

Montana

☐ GIVE
SCCD 03 / 11 May '98 / Scenario

Montana, Dick

☐ DEVIL LIED TO ME, THE (Montana, 'Country' Dick)
7422511 / Nov '96 / Last Call

Montanas

☐ YOU'VE GOT TO BE LOVED (Singles A's And B's)
All that is mine can be yours / How can I tell / That's when happiness began / Goodbye little girl / Ciao baby / Anyone there / Take my hand / Top hat / You've got to be loved / Difference of opinion / Step in the right direction / Someday / You're making a big mistake / Run to me / Roundabout / Mystery / Let's ride / I need to fly / Hold on / Sammy / Tear drops / You've got me wrong girl / One thing or the other / One thing or the other / Hold / Difference of opinion
NEMCD 994 / 27 Oct '97 / Sequel

Montand, Yves

☐ A PARIS
Mon manage a moi / L'assasin du mimanche / Rue Lepic / Planter cafe / Le Galerien / Grands boulevards / C'est si bon / Les routiers / Aparis / Le cocher de fiacre / Les familles mortes / Le Gamin de Paris
DRGCD 5574 / 26 May '98 / DRG

☐ BATTLING JOE
995892 / 24 Apr '98 / EPM

☐ SONGS OF PARIS
MCD 61535 / Jun '93 / Monitor

Montaro, Francisco

☐ STRICTLY BALLROOM - CHA CHA (Montaro, Francisco Ensemble)
Mr. Lucky / 'Til there was you / Por favor / Patricia / Teach me tonight / Guantanamera / Sway / Dansaro yellow days (la mentira) / I just called to say I love you
QED 145 / Nov '96 / Tring

☐ STRICTLY BALLROOM - FAVOURITES (Montaro, Francisco Ensemble)
Mr. Lucky / Frenesi / Copy cabana / All my lovin' / Blue Tango / I only have eyes for you / Miami Beach Rhumba / Blue Danube waltz / Begin the beguine / Matilda
QED 154 / Nov '96 / Tring

☐ STRICTLY BALLROOM - FOX TROT (Montaro, Francisco Ensemble)
I only have eyes for you / April in Paris / Our love is here to stay / All the things you are / It had to be you / Entertainer / Sweet Caroline / After the lovin' / Morning train / Michelle
QED 148 / Nov '96 / Tring

☐ STRICTLY BALLROOM - LATIN (Montaro, Francisco Ensemble)
Marina / Begin the beguine / Preciosa / Matilda / Manha de carnival / How insensitive / Mary Ann medley / Wedding samba / Tico tico / Espana cani
QED 151 / Nov '96 / Tring

☐ STRICTLY BALLROOM - MAMBO (Montaro, Francisco Ensemble)
Asi mambo / Mambo inn / Tequila / Mas que nada / Come a little bit closer / St. Thomas / Say si si / Frenesi / Mambo jambo / Karma chameleon
QED 150 / Nov '96 / Tring

☐ STRICTLY BALLROOM - RHUMBA (Montaro, Francisco Ensemble)
Miami Beach Rhumba / Siboney / Flamingo / Besame mucho / Que reste-t-il / And I love her / If / Serenata / Speak low / Cherish
QED 152 / Nov '96 / Tring

☐ STRICTLY BALLROOM - SAMBA (Montaro, Francisco Ensemble)
Anna / Delicado / Quando quando / Samba de orpheu / Copy cabana / Brazil / El cambanchero / One note samba / Amor / It had better be tonight
QED 146 / Nov '96 / Tring

☐ STRICTLY BALLROOM - TANGO (Montaro, Francisco Ensemble)
Blue Tango / Orchids in the moonlight / Softly as in a morning sunrise / La paloma / Jalousie / No other love / Tango of roses / Adios muchachos / Hernandos hideaway / La cumparsita
QED 149 / Nov '96 / Tring

☐ STRICTLY BALLROOM - TRIPLE SWING (Montaro, Francisco Ensemble)
Honky tonk / Kansas City / Leroy Brown / Work song / I'm getting sentimental over you / All my lovin' / On the sunny side of the street / Walk between the raindrops / Wake me up before you go go / I ain't got nobody/just a Gigolo
QED 153 / Nov '96 / Tring

☐ STRICTLY BALLROOM - WALTZ (Montaro, Francisco Ensemble)
Petite waltz / Blue Danube waltz / Somewhere my love / French waltz medley / Baubles bangles and beads / Hello young lovers / Do I hear a waltz / Girl next door / Moon river / Could I have the dance
QED 147 / Nov '96 / Tring

Montbel, Eric

☐ CHABRETAS, LES CORNEMUSES A MIROIRS DU LIMOUSIN
ALCD 156 / Nov '96 / Al Sur

☐ L'ART DE CORNEMUSE VOL.1
ARN 60347 / Feb '97 / Arion

Monte Cazazza

☐ POWER VERSUS WISDOM
DFX 015CD / Apr '97 / Side Effects

Monte, Marisa

☐ GREAT NOISE, A
Arrepio / Magla Malabaris / Chuva no Brejo / Cerebro eletronico / Tempos modernos / Maraca / Panis et circencis / De noi te na Cama / Beija eu / Give me love / Aindo me lembro / A Menina Danca / Danca de Soliao / Ao meu redor / Bem de leve / Segue o seco / Xote das meni nas
CDP 8533532 / Nov '96 / Metro Blue

☐ ROSE AND CHARCOAL
Maria de Verdade / Na Estrada / Ao meu redor / Seque o seco / Pale blue eyes / Danca da Solidao / De Mais / Ninguem / Alta noite / O Ceu / Bern leve / Balanca pema / Enquanto isso / Esta melodia
CDP 8300802 / Oct '94 / Blue Note

Montego Joe

☐ MONTEGO JOE
PRCD 24139 / Jul '93 / Prestige

Monteiro, Alcimar

☐ VAQUEJADAS BRASILEIRAS
829162 / Feb '96 / BUDA

Montepulciano

☐ YOU'RE ALWAYS WELCOME AT CLUB MONTEPULCIANO
CIAOCD 10 / 3 Aug '98 / Ciano

Montero, Germaine

☐ GERMAINE MONTERO: SINGS
LDX 274959/60 / Mar '93 / La Chant Du Monde

Monterose, J.R.

☐ LITTLE PLEASURE, A (Monterose, J.R. & Tommy Flanagan)
RSRCD 109 / Dec '94 / Reservoir

Montez, Chris

☐ LET'S DANCE
Let's dance / You're the one / It takes two / Tell me (it's not over) / No no no / Monkey fever / I feel like dancing / Rock 'n' blues / Chiquita mia / He's been leading you on / In an English town / Say you'll marry me / Shoot that curl / Let's do the limbo / All you had to do (was tell me) / It's not puppy love / My baby loves to dance / Love me / I ran / Some kinda fun
MOCD 3008 / Feb '95 / More Music

☐ LET'S DANCE (The Monogram Sides)
Let's dance / No no no / Some kinda fun / It takes two / I ran / It's not puppy love / Shoot that curl / My baby loves to dance / All you had to do (was tell me) / Rockin' blues / Chiquita Mia / You're the one / Let's do the limbo / Tell me (it's not over) / I feel like dancing / He's been leading you on / In an English town (in a Turkish town) / Monkey fever / Say you'll marry me / Love me
CDCH 369 / Mar '92 / Ace

☐ LET'S DANCE AND HAVE SOME KINDA FUN
REP 4152 / Aug '91 / Repertoire

Montez, Manuelo

☐ STRICTLY DANCING: PASODOBLES (Montez, Manuelo Orchestra)
15334 / May '94 / Laserlight

Montgomery Brothers

☐ GROOVE YARD
Back to back / Groove yard / If I should lose you / Delirium / Just for now / Doujie / Remember
OJCCD 139 / Jun '96 / Original Jazz Classics

Montgomery, Buddy

☐ LIVE AT MAYBECK RECITAL HALL VOL.15
Since I fell for you / Man I love / Cottage for sale / Who cares / Night has a thousand eyes / How to handle a woman / What'll I do / You've changed / Money blues / By myself / This time I'll by sweeter / Soft winds / My lord and master/Something wonderful
CCD 4494 / Jan '92 / Concord Jazz

☐ SO WHY NOT
LCD 15182 / Apr '89 / Landmark

Montgomery, Field Marshall

☐ LIVE IN CONCERT (Montgomery, Field Marshall Pipe Band)
MGBCD 4001 / 11 May '98 / Mobius

Montgomery, James

☐ OVEN IS ON, THE (Montgomery, James Band)
CDTC 1145 / May '94 / Tonecool

Montgomery, John Michael

☐ JOHN MICHAEL MONTGOMERY
Cowboy love / Just like a rodeo / Long as I live / Holdin' on to something / It's what I am / Heaven sent me you / No man's land / High school heart / Sold (the grundy county auction incident) / I can love you like that
7567827282 / Apr '95 / Warner Bros.

☐ KICKIN' IT UP
Be my baby tonight / Full time love / I swear / She don't need a band to dance / All in my heart / Friday at five / Rope the moon / If you've got skin / Oh how she shines / Kick it up
7567825592 / Feb '92 / Warner Bros.

Montgomery, Little Brother

☐ BAJEZ COPPER STATION
BLU 10022 / Jun '93 / Blues Beacon

☐ CHICAGO - THE LIVING LEGENDS
Home again blues / Up the country blues / Saturday night function / Michigan water blues / Sweet daddy (your mam's done gone mad) / Prescription for the blues / 44 Vicksburg / Trouble in mind / Riverside boogie / Oh daddy blues / Somethin' keep worryin' me
OBCCD 525 / Apr '94 / Original Blues Classics

☐ GOODBYE MISTER BLUES
DD 663 / May '94 / Delmark

☐ LITTLE BROTHER MONTGOMERY 1930-1936
DOCD 5109 / Nov '92 / Document

☐ LITTLE BROTHER MONTGOMERY 1930-1954
BDCD 6034 / Apr '93 / Blues Document

☐ TASTY BLUES
Tasty blues / Santa fe / How long brother / Pleading blues / No special rider / Brother's boogie / Sneaky pete blues / Something keeps worrying me / Cry, cry baby / Satellite blues / Deep fried / Vicksburg blues
OBCCD 554 / Jan '94 / Original Blues Classics

Montgomery, Marian

☐ FOR THE LOVE OF MERCER VOL.1
ELGIN 01 / Jan '97 / Elgin

☐ FOR THE LOVE OF MERCER VOL.2
ELGIN 02 / Jan '97 / Elgin

☐ I GOTTA RIGHT TO SING
In the dark / 'Deed I do / Love dance / People will say we're in love / That old black magic / You came a long way from St. Louis / Mean to me / Ol' man river / Georgia on my mind / Yesterday's wine / I gotta right to sing the blues / He's my guy / Lady is a tramp
JHCD 003 / Jan '94 / Ronnie Scott's Jazz House

☐ MAKIN' WHOOPEE (Montgomery, Marian & Mart Rodgers Manchester Jazz)
Way down yonder in New Orleans / You took advantage of me / Mean to me / Shake it and break it / Kansas City Man blues / If I ever cease to love / I get the blues when it rains / Sobbin' blues / Dinah / After you've gone / Then it changed / Canal Street blues / My melancholy baby / You're a sweetheart / I'm crazy 'bout my baby / Makin' whoopee / Froggie Moore / Love me or leave me / Riverboat shuffle
OWSCD 2602 / May '93 / Bowstone

☐ MELLOW
Where or when / Dancing in the dark / I've got you under my skin / Long ago and far away / I thought of you last night / Never let me go / When the world was young / Speak low / It's not over / Skylark / Ill wind / Secret love / Why can't you behave / I guess I'll hang my tears out to dry / Remind me / I got lost in his arms / Why did I choose you
C5HCD 594 / Aug '96 / See For Miles

☐ NICE AND EASY (Montgomery, Marian & Richard Rodney Bennett)
Ain't no sunshine / It amazes me / Man I love / Loads of love / I wonder what became of me / Partners in crime / In the wee small hours of the morning / Summertime / Nice work if you can get it/Easy to love / But not for me / Blues in the night / If you can't keep the one you love / Bye bye blackbird
JHCD 011 / Jan '94 / Ronnie Scott's Jazz House

☐ SOMETIMES IN THE NIGHT
Man I love / Somebody loves me / Just in time / People that you never get to love / My foolish heart / Maybe (if he knew me) / Tell me softly / You're the best love / I don't want to walk without you / But love (that's another game) / Very thought of you / You've come a long way from St Louis / Not funny / Tender trap / You are my lucky star / Sometimes in the night
C5CD 532 / May '89 / See For Miles

☐ THAT LADY FROM NATCHEZ
ACD 296 / Dec '97 / Audiophile

Montgomery, Roy

☐ NOW THE RAIN SOUNDS LIKE LIFE IS FALLING THROUGH IT
DFR 41 / 13 Apr '98 / Drunken Fish

☐ TEMPLE IV
KRANK 009 / Mar '97 / Kranky

Montgomery, Wes

☐ ALTERNATIVE, THE
Born to be blue / Come rain or come shine / Fried pies / Besame mucho / Way you look tonight / Stairway to the stars / Jingles / Back to back / Movin' along / Body and soul / Tune up
MCD 47065 / Jul '94 / Milestone

☐ ARTISTRY OF WES MONTGOMERY, THE
'Round midnight / Four on six / Klactoveesedstein / Says you / Remember / Cotton tail / Jingles / Cariba / Tune up / Dearly beloved / Freddie the freeloader
FCD 60019 / Oct '93 / Fantasy

☐ BODY AND SOUL
Sonny boy / Wes easy blues / Solo ballad in A major / Gone with the wind / Broadway / Body and soul / I'll remember April / Here's that rainy day / Words from Wes
JHAS 604 / May '96 / Ronnie Scott's Jazz House

☐ BOSS GUITAR
Besame mucho / Dearly beloved / Days of wine and roses / Trick bag / Canadian sunset / Fried pies / Breeze and I / For Heaven's sake
OJCCD 261 / Feb '92 / Original Jazz Classics

☐ BUMPIN' (Remastered)
5390622 / Oct '97 / Verve Master Edition

☐ CALIFORNIA DREAMIN'
8278422 / Mar '97 / Verve

☐ COMPLETE RIVERSIDE RECORDINGS, THE (12CD Set)
'Round midnight / Satin doll / Satin doll / Missile blues / Missile blues / Jingles / Whisper not / End of a love affair / Too late now / Ecaroh / Yesterdays / Airegin / West Coast blues / Four on six / D natural blues / In your own sweet way / Mister Walker / Polka dots and moonbeams / Gone with the wind / Sack o' woe / Work song / Scrambled eggs / Pretty memory / Fall out / My heart stood still / Mean to me / Violets for your furs / I've got a crush on you / Compulsion / Terrain / Klactoveesedstein / Ursula / West Coast blues / Don't explain / Lolita / Chant / Azule serape / Never will I marry / Yours is my heart alone / Au privare / Au privare / Tune up / Tune up / Body and soul / Body and soul / Body and soul / Sandu / So do it / So do it / Movin' along / Moin' along / Movin' along / I don't stand a ghost of a chance with you / Says you / Doujie / Doujie / Just for now / Groove yard / Heart strings / Remember / Delirium / Back to back / Back to bock / If I should lose you / If I should lose you / Doujie / Somethin' like Bags / I'm just a lucky so and so / Cotton tail / Twisted blues / I wish I knew / Repetition / While we're young / One for my baby (and one more for the road) / Darn that dream / Darn that dream / And then I wrote / Double deal / No hard feelings / Love walked in / Love walked in / Lois Ann / Enchanted / Love for sale / Stranger in paradise / Mambo in chimes / Mambo in chimes / Lamp is low / Blue Roz / Jingles / Jingles / Stairway to the stars / Stairway to the stars / Stablemates / Stablemates / Sam Sack / Sam Sack / SKJ / SKJ / Delilah / Delilah / Come rain or come shine / Born to be blue / Blue 'n' boogie / Cariba / SOS / Come rain or come shine / Born to be blue / Full house / Cariba / Blue 'n' boogie / SOS / I've grown accustomed to her face / In the wee small hours of the morning / Pretty blue / Girl next door / Girl next door / God bless the child / God bless the child / My romance / Prelude to a kiss / Prelude to a kiss / All the way / Somewhere / Tune up / Tune up / Tune up / Baubles, bangles and beads / Baubles, bangles and beads / Trick bag / Trick bag / Days of wine and roses / Canadian sunset / Dearly beloved / For Heaven's sake / Besame mucho / Fried pies / Fried pies / Breeze and I / Moanin' / Dreamsville / Freddie Freeloader / Movin' along / Mi cosa / For all we know / Way you look tonight / Way you look tonight / Yesterday's child / Geno / Dangerous / Lolita / Blues riff / Blues riff / Moanin'
12RCD 44082 / Nov '96 / Riverside

☐ ENCORES VOL.1 (Body & Soul)
Body and soul / So do it / Movin' along / Doujie / Blue Roz / Stablemates / Sam Sack / SKJ
MCD 9252 / Aug '96 / Milestone

☐ ENCORES VOL.2 (Blues 'n' Boogie)
Born to be blue / Blue 'n' boogie / Cariba / Girl next door / God bless the child / Prelude to a kiss / Tune-up / Baubles, bangles and beads / Trick bag / Movin' along
MCD 92612 / Mar '97 / Milestone

☐ FINGERPICKIN'
Sound carrier / Bud's beaux arts / Back to back / Lois Ann / All the things you are / Fingerpickin' / Stranger in Paradise / Baubles, bangles and beads / Not since Ninevah
CDP 8379872 / Jul '96 / Pacific Jazz

☐ FULL HOUSE (Montgomery, Wes & Johnny Griffin)
Full house / I've grown accustomed to her face / Blue 'n' boogie no.2 / Cariba / Come rain or come shine / SOS / Come rain or come shine / SOS / Born to be blue
OJCCD 106 / Feb '92 / Original Jazz Classics
OJC20 1062 / Sep '98 / Original Jazz Classics

☐ FULL HOUSE
LEJAZZCD 13 / Jun '93 / Le Jazz

☐ FUSION
All the way / Pretty blue (take 2) / Pretty blue (take 1) / In the wee small hours of the morning / Prelude to a kiss / Girl next door / My romance / God bless the child / Tune up (take 5) / Tune up (take 2) / Tune up (take 4) / Somewhere / Baubles, bangles and beads
OJCCD 368 / Feb '92 / Original Jazz Classics

☐ GUITAR ON THE GO (Montgomery, Wes Trio)
Way you look tonight (alternate take) / Way you look tonight / Dreamsville / Geno / Missile blues / For all we know / Fried pies / (Unidentified solo guitar)
OJCCD 489 / Apr '93 / Original Jazz Classics

☐ INCREDIBLE JAZZ GUITAR
Airegin / D-Natural blues / Polka dots and moonbeams / Four on six / West coast blues / In your own sweet way / Mr. Walker / Gone with the wind
OJC20 0362 / Sep '98 / Original Jazz Classics

☐ JAZZ MASTERS
Goin' out of my head / Impressions / My one and only love / Tequila / Bumpin' / What the world needs now is love / No blues / Shadow of your smile / Caravan / Bumpin' on sunset / Twisted blues / Oh you crazy moon / Con alma / Thumb
5198262 / 5 May '98 / Verve

☐ JAZZ MASTERS
Billie's bounce / Leila / Stompin' at the savoy / Stranger in paradise / Renie / Wes' tune / Summertime / Montgomeryland funk / Baubles, bangles and beads / Hymn for carl
CDMFP 6302 / Mar '97 / Music For Pleasure

☐ LIVE IN EUROPE
CD 214 W972 / Feb '92 / Philology

☐ MOVIN' ALONG
Movin' along / Tune up / I don't stand a ghost of a chance with you / Sandu / Body and soul / So do it / Says you
OJCCD 89 / Feb '92 / Original Jazz Classics

☐ MOVIN' WES
West coast blues / Caravan / Movin' Wes / Moca flor / Matchmake / Theodora / In and out / Born to be blue / People / Phoenix love theme
8100452 / Mar '89 / Verve

☐ MOVIN' WES (Remastered)
5214332 / Oct '97 / Verve Master Edition

☐ PORTRAIT OF WES
Freddie the freeloader / Lolita / Blues riff / Blues riff (take 8) / Dangerous / Yesterday's child / Moanin' / Moanin' (take 7)
OJCCD 144 / Feb '92 / Original Jazz Classics

☐ ROUND MIDNIGHT
Four on six / Girl next door / Mr. Walker / Here's that rainy day / 'Round midnight / Impressions
LEJAZZCD 34 / Sep '94 / Le Jazz

☐ STRAIGHT NO CHASER
BS 18002 / Jul '96 / Bandstand

☐ TWISTED BLUES (Montgomery, Wes Quartet)
Jingles / Twisted blues / Girl next door / Impressions / Here's that rainy day / Four on six
JHR 73569 / Nov '93 / Jazz Hour

☐ ULTIMATE WES MONTGOMERY, THE
5397872 / 16 Mar '98 / Verve

☐ WES MONTGOMERY SAMPLER
Polka dots and moonbeams / Body and soul / One for my baby / Blues riff / Come rain or come shine / Four on six
OJCX 006 / Jan '98 / Original Jazz Classics

☐ WES MONTGOMERY TRIO, THE (Montgomery, Wes Trio)
'Round midnight / Yesterdays / End of a love affair / Whisper not / Ecaroh / Satin doll / Missile blues / Too late now / Jingles
OJCCD 342 / Feb '92 / Original Jazz Classics

Month Of Birthdays

☐ THESE THINGS THAT WE DO
SUB 13 / 18 Sep '97 / Subjugation

Montifiore Cocktail

☐ RACCOLTA NO.1
4881961 / 16 Jul '97 / Irma

Montoliu, Tete

☐ BODY AND SOUL
CDBLC 760212 / Apr '96 / Black Lion

☐ BODY AND SOUL (Montoliu, Tete Trio)
CDG 813 / Nov '96 / Helix

☐ CATALONIAN NIGHTS VOL.1 (Montoliu, Tete Trio)
SCCD 31433 / 24 Feb '98 / Steeplechase

☐ EN EL SAN JUAN
NM 15690CD / Apr '97 / Fresh Sound

☐ INTERPRETA A SERRAT
FSRCD 228 / 24 Apr '98 / Fresh Sound

☐ IT'S ABOUT BLUES TIME
FSRCD 305 / Jan '98 / Fresh Sound

☐ LUNCH IN LA
15365 / 14 Apr '98 / N.Medios

☐ MAN FROM BARCELONA, THE (Montoliu, Tete Trio)
Concierto de Aranjuez / Stella by starlight / Easy living / Autumn leaves / For you my love / Tune up / I fall in love too easily / Django / When lights are low / Please, I like to be gentle / Night in Tunisia
CDSJP 368 / Feb '92 / Timeless Jazz

☐ MOMENTOS INOLVIDABLES DE UNA VIDA
FSR 6001CD / 24 Apr '98 / Fresh Sound

☐ MUSIC I LIKE TO PLAY VOL.3
1212302 / Jan '92 / Soul Note

☐ MUSIC I LIKE TO PLAY VOL.4 (Soul Eyes)
1212502 / Jan '93 / Soul Note

☐ SONGS FOR LOVE
ENJA 20402 / 17 Nov '97 / Enja

☐ TETE
SCCD 31029 / Jul '88 / Steeplechase

☐ TETE EN LA TROMPETILLA
SRPD 27003 / Nov '97 / Fresh Sound

☐ TOOTIE'S TEMPO
SCCD 31108 / Jul '88 / Steeplechase

☐ TRIO LIURE JAZZ (Montoliu, Tete Trio)
CDG 812 / Nov '96 / Helix

Monton, Jose Luis

☐ AROMA
Aroma / Mi nina de Cali / Me sabe a mar / Agui / A solas / Pozo amargo / Nubes / Acuerdate
B 6854 / Jan '98 / Auvidis/Ethnic

Montoya, Carlos

☐ AIRES FLAMENCOS
Malaguena / Sevillanas / Granadinas / Tanguillo-zambrilla / Bulerias / Soleares / Rondena / Bolero malorquin-castilla-galicia / Seguiriya / Fandango de huelva y verdiales / Peteneras del cafe de chinitas / Farruca / Solea-bulerias por solea / Malaguenas boleras
CD 12510 / Nov '92 / Music Of The World

☐ FLAMENCO
TCD 1008 / Feb '96 / Tradition

☐ GOLD COLLECTION, THE (2CD Set)
R2CD 4050 / 13 Apr '98 / Deja Vu

Montoya, Coco

☐ JUST LET GO
Fear no evil / What's done is done / Just let go / My side of the fence / Cool like dat / Do what you want to do / Give it to a good man / Hard love / Beginner at the blues / Mother and daughter / Nothing's too good for my baby / Never seen you cry this way before / Sending me angels
BPCD 5043 / 6 Oct '97 / Blind Pig

☐ YA THINK I'D KNOW BETTER
BLPCD 5033 / Sep '96 / Blind Pig

Montoya, Ramon

☐ ART OF FLAMENCO VOL.4, THE
MAN 4840CD / Apr '95 / Mandala

Montreal Jubilation Gospel Choir

☐ CAPPELLA, A
Lord I know I've been changed / There is a balm in Gilead / Ezekiel saw de wheel / Deep river / In that great gettin' up morning / Swing low, sweet chariot / Soon ah will be done
BLU 10142 / Nov '92 / Blues Beacon

☐ GLORY TRAIN
10082 / Mar '91 / Blues Beacon

☐ HAMBA EKHAYA (GOIN' HOME)
Processional medley / Jesus lover of my soul / Nkosi Sikelel' iAfrika / Impipi / Amavaka / Wembulalin / Hamba Ku Jesu / Imbizo / Ingwe / Ngubani omemezayo / Ayimale / Babethandaza / Amazing Grace / Highway to heaven
JUST 962 / 17 Nov '97 / Justin Time

☐ JUBILATION - JOY TO THE WORLD
JUST 542 / Feb '94 / Justin Time

☐ JUBILATION VOL.2
10062 / Mar '91 / Blues Beacon

Montrose, J.R.

☐ MESSAGE, THE
FSRCD 7001 / Jul '97 / Fresh Sound

Montrose, Jack

☐ JACK MONTROSE SEXTET, THE (Montrose, Jack Sextet)
Listen hear / Bewitched bothered and bewildered / Some good fun blues / Fools rush in / Speakeasy / Credo / Pretty / That old feeling / Meet Mr. Gordon / Modus operandi / What a difference a day makes / Onion bottom / Tea for two / Two can play / For Sue / Love is here to stay / Two can play
4931612 / 18 May '98 / Pacific Jazz

Montrose, Ronnie

☐ CONCERT CLASSICS (Gamma & Ronnie Montrose)
Ready for action / Thunder and lightning / Razor king / Wish I was / I got the fire / Open fire / Fight to the finish / I'm alive / (So you wanna be a) rock and roll star / No tears
CRANCH 5 / 13 Jul '98 / Ranch Life

Monty

☐ NAPOLEON COMPLEX, THE
Napoleon complex / Don't make me love you / Angel delight / 89 St. James' Square / Time machine / Love me to death / Haunted / Lion in Windsor / Kensington girl / All my birthdays / So non e vero (e bon trovato)
BAH 29 / Oct '96 / Humbug

☐ TYPICAL SCORPIO, A
Mr. Inconsistent / I'm Spartacus / Will I ever learn / Understanding Alfie / Ah Voodoo / Baby octopus / Moving the goalposts / Signorina / Come into my parlour / Can you do the mashed potato / Marianne / Say the word / Apple for the teacher / Bitten by the lovebug
BAH 6 / Oct '93 / Humbug

Monty's Sunshine Jazz Band

☐ LIVE AT THE BP STUDIENHAUS
Over in Gloryland / Savoy blues / Memphis blues / I wish I was in Peoria / Put on your old grey bonnet / In the sweet bye and bye / BP march / You are my sunshine / Papa de da da / Joe Avery's place / Melancholy blues / Going home / When I grow too old to dream
TTD 620 / 27 Jul '98 / Timeless Traditional

☐ YOU ARE MY SUNSHINE
You are my sunshine / Peoria / Yellow dog blues / Just a little while to stay here / Wildcat blues / Mama / Magnolia's wedding day / Hindustan / In the sweet bye and bye / Lover / Black cat on the fence / Far away blues / Sweet Georgia brown / Glory of love / Curse of an arching heart / Till we meet again
CDTTD 609 / Jun '97 / Timeless

Monumentum

☐ IN ABSENTIA CHRISTI
AMAZON 007CD / 3 Nov '97 / Misanthropy

Mooch

☐ 3001
TASTE 44CD / Nov '94 / Taste

☐ POST VORTA
TASTE 48 / Jan '95 / Taste

☐ STARHENGE
TASTE 057CD / Aug '95 / Taste

Mood

☐ DOOM
Esoteric manuscripts / Info for the streets / He is the DJ hi-tek / Karma / Vision / Tunnel bound / Nuclear hip-hop / Another day / Secret pt.1 / Peddlers of doom / Millennium / Babylon the great / Peace infinity / Secrets of the sand / Illuminated sunlight / Industry lies / No ordinary brother / Cincinnati / Insights
TVT 44302 / 6 Oct '97 / TVT/Blunt
COTCD 020 / 20 Jul '98 / Cup Of Tea

Mood Six

☐ BEST OF MOOD SIX, THE
Hanging around / She's too far / Rain falls on Mary / It's your life / Plastic flowers / Party time / Victim / I wanna destroy you / What have you ever done / Intruder / Contemporary scene / When the time comes / Voice of reason / Game show / I saw the light / You could be my soul / I'll keep holding on / Mad about the boy / Flowers and boxes / Look at me now / Shake some action / Somebody
CDMRED 141 / Mar '97 / Cherry Red

Moodie

☐ EARLY YEARS, THE
MMCD 1052 / Jul '94 / Moodie

Moodorama

☐ BASEMENT MUSIC
SD 022CD / 22 Jun '98 / Stereo Deluxe

Moods, J.

☐ GENTLE ONES, THE (Moods, J. Quartet)
Calimero / Dark princess / Gentle ones / Daroewalla's dwarf / Divine intervention / Another fine mess / After Tony / Introduction for bass and tenor sax / Baba yaga
AL 73123 / Jun '98 / A

Moods Orchestra

☐ HOLDING BACK THE YEARS
MACCD 329 / Aug '96 / Autograph

☐ NIGHTS IN WHITE SATIN
MACCD 331 / Aug '96 / Autograph

☐ POWER OF LOVE, THE
MACCD 330 / Aug '96 / Autograph

☐ WOMAN IN LOVE, A
MACCD 328 / Aug '96 / Autograph

Moodswings

☐ LIVE AT LEEDS
Tabla motown / Crunch / Back to basics / Hozanna / Spiritual high (part iii) / Brutal / Mood swings
74321186312 / Feb '94 / Arista

☐ MOODFOOD
Spiritual high / Moodswings overture / Problem solved / Thailand / Wombtones / Skinthieves / Rainsong / 100% total success / Microcosmic / Hairy piano / Throw off the shackles / Spiritual high (state of independence)(reprise)
74321111702 / 11 May '98 / Arista

☐ PSYCHEDELICATESSEN
Lifeforce in a pizza / Crysmile / Undistracted / Dancing is important / Together as one (luminous) / Great sound of letting go / Sugarush / Destruction and destroy / Indian drug carpet / Spore / Redemption song (oh happy day) / Horrozontal / Vibratonik / Okinawa / Hinkenlooper's eclipse / God knows what I want / Happy piano
74321442172 / May '97 / Arista

Moody Blues

☐ BIOGRAPHY SERIES
10023 / 3 Nov '97 / Metro Independent

☐ CAUGHT LIVE AND FIVE
8201612 / Jan '97 / London

☐ EVERY GOOD BOY DESERVES FAVOURS
Procession / Story in your eyes / Our guessing game / Emily's song / After you came / One more to live / Nice to be here / You can never go home / My song
8201602 / '86 / London

☐ GREATEST HITS
Your wildest dreams / Voice / Gemini dream / Story in your eyes / Tuesday afternoon (Forever Afternoon) / Isn't life strange / Nights in white satin / I know you're out there somewhere / Ride my see-saw / I'm just a singer (in a rock 'n' roll band) / Question
8406592 / Jan '90 / London

☐ IN WORDS AND MUSIC
OTR 1100025 / Jun '97 / Metro Independent

☐ LIVE AT RED ROCKS
Overture with excerpts / Late lament / Tuesday afternoon (Forever afternoon) / For my lady / Lean on me (Tonight) / Lovely to see you / I know you're out there somewhere / Voice / Your wildest dreams / Isn't life strange / Other side of life / I'm just a singer (in a rock 'n' roll band) / Nights in white satin / Question / Ride me see-saw
5179772 / Mar '96 / Polydor

☐ LONG DISTANCE VOYAGER
Voice / Talking out of turn / Gemini dream / In my world / Meanwhile / 22,000 days / Nervous / Painted smile / Reflective smile / Veteran cosmic rocker
8201052 / '86 / London

☐ ON THE THRESHOLD OF A DREAM
In the beginning / Lovely to see you / Dear diary / Send me no wine / To share our love / So deep within you / Never comes the day / Lazy day / Are you sitting comfortably / Dream / Have you heard (part 1) / Voyage / Have you heard (part 2)
8201702 / '86 / London

☐ OTHER SIDE OF LIFE
Your wildest dreams / Talkin talkin / Rock 'n' roll over you / I just don't care / Running out of love / Other side of life / Spirit / Slings and arrows / It may be a fire
8291792 / Jan '90 / Polydor

☐ SUR LA MER
I know you're out there somewhere / Want to be with you / River of endless love / No more lies / Here comes the weekend / Vintage wine / Breaking point / Miracle / Love is on the run / Deep
8357562 / Mar '96 / Polydor

☐ TIME TRAVELLER
5164362 / Sep '94 / Polydor

☐ VERY BEST OF THE MOODY BLUES, THE
Go now / Tuesday afternoon / Nights in white satin / Ride my see-saw / Voices in the sky / Question / Story in your eyes / Isn't life strange / I'm just a singer / Blue guitar / Steppin' on a slide zone / Forever Autumn / Voice / Gemini dream / Blue world / Your wildest dreams / I know you're out there somewhere
5358002 / Sep '96 / PolyGram TV

☐ VOICES IN THE SKY
Ride my see-saw / Talking out of question / Driftwood / Never comes the day / I'm just a singer (in a rock 'n' roll band) / Gemini dream / Voice / After you came / Question / Veteran cosmic rocker / Isn't life strange / Nights in white satin
8201552 / Apr '91 / London

Moody Boyz

☐ PRODUCT OF THE ENVIRONMENT
Shango / Pigmy song / Fight back / Head in the sky / Elite presents this / Just out of Africa / July / Glich / Shango (Black dog) / Ogdon / Elite dubs the snooze the sequel / Funny thing happened to me on Wednesday
GRCD 013 / Jul '94 / Guerilla

☐ RECYCLED EP
GREP 006CD / Jul '94 / Guerilla

Moody, James

☐ AT THE JAZZ WORKSHOP
Bloozey / Jazz twist / One for Nat / Bunny Boo / Moody flooty / It might as well be Spring / Disappointed / Sister Sadie / Little Buck / Home fries / 'Round midnight / Stablemates / Moody's mood for love
GRP 18152 / 8 Jun '98 / Chess Jazz

☐ BLUES AND OTHER COLOURS
Main stem / Everyone needs it / Savannah calling / Statement / Gone are the days / Feeling low / You got to pay / Old folks
OJCCD 954 / 26 Jan '98 / Original Jazz Classics

☐ DON'T LOOK AWAY NOW
Don't look away now / Darben the Redd Foxx / Easy living / Hey Herb where's Alpert / Hear me / When I fall in love / Last train from Overbrook
OJCCD 9252 / Jan '98 / Original Jazz Classics

☐ FEELIN' IT TOGETHER
Anthropology / Dreams / Autumn leaves / Wave / Morning glory / Kriss kross
412320452 / 17 Mar '98 / Thirty Two

☐ MOODY'S MOOD FOR LOVE
Foolin' the blues / Plus eight / I'm in the mood for love / Phil up / You go to my head / Billie's bounce / Stardust / Mean to me
GRP 18232 / 27 Jul '98 / Chess Mates

☐ MOODY'S PARTY
Birthday tribute / Groovin' high / It might as well be spring / Parker's moon / Eternal triangle / Polka dots and moonbeams / Benny's from heaven / Be bop
CD 83382 / Oct '95 / Telarc

Moody Marsden Band

☐ TIME IS RIGHT, THE
ESDCD 225 / Sep '94 / Essential

Moodyman

☐ MAHOGANY BROWN
Radio / Sunshine / On the run / MEANDJB / Mahogany brown / Me and my peoples eyes / Stoneodenjoe / Joy / Black Sunday
PF 074CD / 20 Apr '98 / Peacefrog

Moom

☐ TOOT
Prelude / Sally / Astronaught / Void is clear / Babbashagga / Higher the sun / Crocodillian suite / Waiting for the sphere eye / I can't remember the sixties
DELECD 035 / Jul '95 / Delerium

Moon & The Banana Tree

☐ NEW GUITAR MUSIC FROM MADAGASCAR
SH 64074 / Dec '96 / Shanachie

Moon, Keith

☐ TWO SIDES OF THE MOON
Crazy like a fox / Solid gold / Don't worry baby / One night stand / Kids are alright / Move over Ms. L / Teenage idol / Backdoor Sally / In my life / Together / US Radio spot / I don't suppose / Naked man / Do me good / Real emotion / Teenage idol / Together rap
REP 4635 / 10 Nov '97 / Repertoire

Moon Lay Hidden Beneath A Cloud

☐ AMARA TANTA TYRI
ART 2CD / Oct '96 / Arthur's Round Table

☐ MOON LAY HIDDEN
ART 1CD / Oct '96 / Arthur's Round Table

☐ NEW SOLDIER, A
ART 3CD / Oct '96 / Arthur's Round Table

☐ SMELL OF BLOOD BUT VICTORY, THE (2CD Set)
ART 11CD / Apr '97 / Arthur's Round Table

Moon Lore

☐ SPHERES BENEATH THE HEAVENS
MR 11CD / 22 Sep '97 / Malicious

Moon Seven Times

☐ SUNBURNT
Further / Through the roses / Nashville / Thirteen days / What you said / Bug collection / Neither luminary / Some of them burn / Montgomery L / You look past me / Fat dog / Full moon
RR 89112 / Jul '97 / Roadrunner

Moonboot Oz

☐ MUSIC FROM THE PSYCHEDELIC CAFE
ARDCD 1 / May '97 / Chameleon

Moon'doc

☐ GET MOONED
341342 / Oct '96 / No Bull

☐ MOON'DOC
342052 / Oct '95 / No Bull

Moondog

☐ FAT LOT OF GOOD
BETCD 002
BETCD 002L / Jun '96 / Better

Moondogg

☐ MOONDOGG
Caribea / Lullaby / Tree trail / Death when you come to me / Big cat / Frog bog / To a sea horse / Dance rehearsal / Surf session / Tree against the sky / Tap dance / Ooo debut / Drum suite / Street scene
OJCCD 1741 / May '93 / Original Jazz Classics

☐ MORE MOONDOGG
Queen elizabeth whistle and bamboo pipe / Conversation and music at 51st st. and 6th avenue / Hardshoe ray malone / Tugboat toccata / Autumn / Seven beat suite / Oo solo / Rehearsal of violeeta's barefoot dance / Oo solo / Ostrich feathers played on drum / Oboe round / Chant / All is loneliness / Sextet / Fiesta piano solo / Moondog monologue / Up broadway / Perpetual motion / Gloving it / Improvisation / Ray malone softshoe / Two quotations in dialogue / 58 in two shades / Moondog's theme / In a doorway / Duet / Trimbas in quarters / Wild wood / Trimbas in eighths / Organ rounds
OJCCD 1781 / Jun '93 / Original Jazz Classics

Mooney, Claire

☐ DRAWING BREATH SKETCHING DREAMS
RED 002CD / Apr '95 / Red

Mooney, Gordon

☐ OVER THE BORDER
COMD 2031 / Feb '94 / Temple

Mooney, John

☐ AGAINST THE WALL
Sacred ground / Doggone thing / Sweat 'n' bone / Broken mould / Late on in the evening / Three sides / Bitter pill / You told me / One step forward / Somebody been missing somebody (too long)
RUF 1019 / 29 Sep '97 / Ruf

☐ DEALING WITH THE DEVIL
Mighty / Dead or alive / Trouble / Junky Heaven / You never can tell / Later / Is it any wonder / Over my shoulder / Are you waiting for me / Intuition / William's lamentation / Myopia / I'm ready
T&M 007 / Nov '96 / Tradition & Moderne

☐ TRAVELLIN' ON (Mooney, John & Bluesiana)
CCD 10032 / May '93 / Crosscut

Moonglows

☐ GREATEST HITS
MCD 09379 / Jul '97 / Chess/MCA

Moonkyte

☐ COUNT ME OUT
MERLIN 005 / 27 Apr '98 / Merlin

Moonlight Serenaders

☐ COLE PORTER ALBUM, THE
Who wants to be a millionaire / Friendship / Anything goes / It's de lovely / Let's do it lets fall in love / Love for sale / All of you / I love Paris / Ev'ry time I say goodbye / Begin the beguine / I've got you under my skin / I get a kick out of you / What is this thing called love / I concentrate on you / Easy to love / Did you ever / Just one of those things / From this moment on
307772 / Aug '97 / Hallmark

☐ STARDUST MEMORIES (Hits Of The 1930's/1940's)
Change partners / Night and day / Cheek to cheek / Let's face the music and dance / Way you look tonight / You're the top / Zing went the strings of my heart / Nice work if you can get it / We're in the money / I've got a gal in Kalamazoo / In the mood / Chattanooga choo choo / Moonlight serenade / Boogie woogie bugle boy / Don't sit under the apple tree / White cliffs of Dover / Easter parade / Trolley song
PWKM 4038 / Feb '96 / Carlton

Moonshake

☐ BIG GOOD ANGEL
Two trains / Capital letters / Girly loop / Seance / Flow / Helping hands
PURECD 022 / May '93 / Too Pure

☐ EVA LUNA
Wanderlust / Tar Baby / Seen and not heard / Bleach and salt water / Little Thing / City Poison / Sweetheart / Spaceship Earth / Beautiful Pigeon / Mugshot Heroine
PURECD 016 / Sep '92 / Too Pure

☐ SOUND YOUR EYES SHOULD FOLLOW
PURECD 033 / Apr '94 / Too Pure

Moonshine Willy

☐ BOLD DISPLAYS OF IMPERFECTION
BS 018 / 19 Jan '98 / Bloodshot

☐ PECADORES
BS 005 / 19 Jan '98 / Bloodshot

Moonspell

☐ IRRELIGIOUS
CMCD 77123 / Jul '96 / Century Media

☐ SECOND SKIN EP
CM 77189CD / 20 Oct '97 / Century Media

☐ SIN/PERCADO
CM 77190CD / 26 Jan '98 / Century Media

☐ UNDER THE MOONSPELL
CDAR 021 / Jan '97 / Adipocre

☐ WOLFHEART
CM 77112CD / Jan '96 / Century Media

Moonstone

☐ BEST OF MOONSTONE, THE
Out of the ballgame / You're sending me delirious / Stop when the light is on red / Summer on the beach / Love in the first degree / Meet me halfway / Spring summer autumn winter / Visitors / (I can't believe it) It's a miracle / My love will last forever / It's the dream of a lifetime / Love and pain / Voice of freedom
HTCD 62 / 20 Apr '98 / Hot Productions

Moorcock, Michael

☐ NEW WORLD FAIR, THE
DOJOCD 88 / May '95 / Dojo

Moore, Aaron

☐ HELLO WORLD
Hello world / What did you do to me / I just called / You got good business / Keep lovin' me / I feel alright again / Why you so mean to me / So long / Security / Searching for love / I once was lost / Castle Rock boogie / Lonely blues / True love is like that / It's all over
DE 695 / Jun '97 / Delmark

Moore, Abra

☐ SING
BBEA 4 / Aug '95 / Bohemia Beat

☐ STRANGEST PLACES
Four leaf clover / Don't feel like cryin' / Strangest places / Happiness / Never believe you know / Say it like that / Your faithful friend / All I want / In the light of it all / Keeps my body warm / Guitar song / Summer's ending
07822188392 / 27 Oct '97 / RCA

Moore, Alex

☐ FROM NORTH DALLAS TO THE EAST SIDE (Moore, 'Whistlin' Alex)
ARHCD 408 / Apr '95 / Arhoolie

☐ WHISTLIN' ALEX MOORE - 1929-1951 (Moore, 'Whistlin' Alex)
DOCD 5178 / Oct '93 / Document

☐ WIGGLE TAIL
Wiggle tail / Everybody have a good time / Chasin' rainbows / Newest blue bloomer blues / Elephant brain man / More alex / Mistreatin' woman / Knockin' on my door / My daily nutrition / Lonesome / Neglected woman
ROUCD 11559 / '88 / Rounder

Moore, Anthony

☐ FLYING DOESN'T HELP
Judy get down / Ready ready / Useless moments / Lucia / Caught being in love / Timeless strange / Girl it's your time / War / Just us / Twilight, Uxbridge Rd
VP 177CD / Oct '94 / Voiceprint

☐ OUT
Stitch in time / Thousand ships / River / Please go / You tickle / Lover of mine / Johnny's dead / Dreams of his laughter / Driving blind / Pilgrim / Catch a falling star / Wrong again
VP 165CD / 27 Apr '98 / Voiceprint

☐ REED WHISTLE AND STICKS
BP 281CD / 10 Aug '98 / Blueprint

Moore, Brew

☐ NO MORE BREW (Moore, Brew Quartet)
It could happen to you / Manny's tune / No more brew / Blue monk / Special brew / I remember you / Samba de orfeu / Straight no chaser
STCD 8275 / Jun '98 / Storyville

☐ SVINGET 14
BLCD 760164 / Oct '93 / Black Lion

Moore, Chante

☐ LOVE SUPREME, A
Intro / Searchin' / This time / My special perfect one / I'm what you need / Your love's supreme / Old school lovin' / Free/Sail on without your love / I want to thank you / Mood / Thank you for loving me / Soul dance / Am I losing you / Thou shalt not
MCD 11197 / 8 Sep '97 / MCA

Moore, Christy

☐ AT THE POINT - LIVE
GRACD 203 / Jan '95 / Grapevine

☐ COLLECTION VOL.1 1981-1991, THE
Ordinary man / Mystic lipstick / Lakes of Ponchartrain / City of Chicago / Faithful departed / Don't forget your shovel / Delirium tremens / Knock song / Messenger boy / Lisdoonvarna / Voyage / Missing you / Night visit / Biko drum / Time has come / Easter snow / Bright blue rose / Reel in the flickering light / Nancy Spain / Ride on
903173512 / Sep '91 / WEA

☐ COLLECTION VOL.2, THE
GRACD 234 / 17 Nov '97 / Grapevine

☐ GRAFFITI TONGUE
GRACD 215 / Sep '96 / Grapevine

☐ IRON BEHIND THE VELVET (Moore, Christy & Friends)
Patrick was a gentleman / Sun is burning / Morrissey and the Russian sailor / Foxy devil / Three reels / Trip to Jerusalem / Three reels / Patrick's arrival / Gabriel McKeon's / Dunlavin Green / Joe McCann
TARACD 2002 / Apr '95 / Tara

☐ KING PUCK
Before the deluge / Two Conneeleys / Lawless / Yellow furze woman / Guiseppe / Sodom and Begorra / Johnny Connors / King Puck / Away ye broken heart / Me and the rose
ATLASCD 003 / Oct '93 / Equator

☐ LIVE IN DUBLIN (Moore, Christy/Donal Lunny/Jimmy Faulkner)
Hey Sandy / Boys of Barr Na Sraide / Little mother / Clyde's bonnie banks / Pretty boy Floyd / Bogey's bonnie banks / Crack was ninety in the Isle of Man / Black is the colour of my true love's hair / One last cold kiss
TARACD 2005 / Feb '95 / Tara

☐ PROSPEROUS
Raggle taggle Gipsies / Tabhair dom do lamh / Dark eyed sailor / I wish I was in England / Lock hospital / James Connolly / Hackler from Grouse Hall / Tribute to Woody / Ludlow massacre / Letter to Syracuse / Spancillhill / Cliffs of Dooneen / Rambling Robin
TARACD 2008 / Feb '95 / Tara

☐ RIDE ON
City of Chicago / Vive la quinte brigada / Song of wandering aengus / Mcilhatton / Lisdoonvarna / Wicklow hills / Sonny's dream / Dying soldier / El Salvador / Back home in Derry / Least we can do
2292404072 / Jul '95 / WEA

☐ SMOKE AND STRONG WHISKEY
Welcome to the cabaret / Fairytale of new york / Scapegoats / Aisling / Bunning times / Smoke and strong whiskey / Whacker humphries / Blackjack country chains / Green island / Encore
CM 00022 / May '91 / Newberry

☐ UNFINISHED REVOLUTION
Biko drum / Natives / Metropolitan Avenue / Unfinished revolution / Other side / Messenger boy / On the bridge / Suffocate / Derby day / Dr. Vibes / Pair of brown eyes
2292421342 / Jul '95 / WEA

☐ VOYAGE
Mystic lipstick / Voyage / Mad lady and me / Deportees club / Night visit / All for the roses / Missing you / Bright blue rose / Farewell to pripchat / Muscha God help her / First time ever I saw your face / Middle of the island
2292461562 / Jul '95 / WEA

Moore, Dorothy

☐ SONGS TO LOVE BY
4802131012 / 24 Mar '98 / SZO

Moore, Gary

☐ AFTER HOURS
Cold day in hell / Don't you lie to me / Story of the blues / Since I met you baby / Separate ways / Only fool in town / Key to love / Jumpin' at shadows / Blues is alright / Hurt inside / Nothing's the same
CDV 2684 / Mar '92 / Virgin

☐ AFTER THE WAR
After the war / Speak for yourself / Livin' on dreams / Led clones / Running from the storm / This thing called love / Ready for love / Blood of emeralds / Messiah will come again / Dunluce
CDVIP 212 / 3 Aug '98 / Virgin VIP

☐ AFTER THE WAR/RUN FOR COVER/ WILD FRONTIER (3CD Set)
TPAK 18 / Nov '91 / Virgin

☐ BALLADS AND BLUES (1982-1994)
Always gonna love you / Still got the blues / Empty rooms / Parisienne walkways / One day / Separate ways / Story of the blues / Crying in the shadows / With love (remember) / Midnight blues / Falling in love with you / Jumpin' at shadows / Blues for Narada / Johnny boy
CDV 2738 / Nov '94 / Virgin

☐ BLUES ALIVE
Cold day in hell / Walking by myself / Story of the blues / Oh pretty woman / Separate ways / Too tired / Still got the blues / Since I met you baby / Sky is crying / Further on up the road / King of the blues / Parisienne walkways / Jumpin' at shadows
CDVX 2716 / May '93 / Virgin

☐ BLUES FOR GREENY
If you be my baby / Long grey mare / Merry go round / I loved another woman / I need your love so bad / Same way / Supernatural / Driftin' / Showbiz blues / Love that burns / Looking for somebody
CDV 2784 / May '95 / Virgin

☐ CORRIDORS OF POWER
Don't take me for a loser / Always gonna love you / Wishing well / Gonna break my heart again / Falling in love with you / End of the world / Rockin' every night / Cold hearted / I can't wait until tomorrow
CDV 2245 / Jul '85 / Virgin

☐ DARK DAYS IN PARADISE
One good reason / Cold wind blows / I have found my love in you / One fine day / Like angels / What are we here for / Always there for tomorrow / Where did we go wrong / Business as usual / Dark days in paradise
CDV 2826 / May '97 / Virgin

☐ G-FORCE (G-Force)
You / White knuckles / Rockin' and rollin' / She's got you / I look at you / Because of your love / You kissed me sweetly / Hot gossip / Woman's in love / Dancin'
CLACD 212 / Feb '91 / Castle

☐ LOOKING AT YOU (2CD Set)
Nuclear attack / Dirty fingers / Dancin' / Really gonna rock / She's got you / Hiroshima / I look at you / Kidnapped / Because of your love / Lonely nights / Woman's in love / You kissed me sweetly / Rest in peace / White knuckles / Rockin' and rollin' / Don't let me be misunderstood / Bad news / Run to your Mama / Hot gossip / Back on the streets / Run to your Mama / Dancin' / She's got you / Parisienne walkways / Nuclear attack / Dallas warhead / You / You
SMDCD 123 / May '97 / Snapper

☐ ROCKIN' EVERY NIGHT (Live In Japan)
Rockin' every night / Wishing well / I can't wait until tomorrow / Nuclear attack / White knuckles / Rockin' and rollin' / Back on the streets / Sunset
XIDCD 1 / Jun '88 / 10

☐ RUN FOR COVER
Out in the fields / Reach for the sky / Run for cover / Military man / Empty rooms / Nothing to lose / Once in a lifetime / All messed up / Listen to your heartbeat / Out of my system
DIXCD 16 / Feb '86 / 10

☐ STILL GOT THE BLUES
Moving on / Oh pretty woman / Walking by myself / Still got the blues / Texas strut / All your love / Too tired / King of the blues / As the years go passing by / Midnight blues / That kind of woman / Stop messin' around
CDV 2612 / Mar '90 / Virgin

☐ VICTIMS OF THE FUTURE
Murder in the skies / All I want / Hold on to love / Law of the jungle / Victims of the future / Teenage idol / Shape of things to come / Empty rooms
DIXCD 2 / Jun '88 / 10

☐ WALKWAYS
Don't let me be misunderstood / Hot gossip / Really gonna rock tonight / Back on the streets / Dallas warhead / Parisienne walkways / Nuclear attack / Run to your Mama / Woman's in love / Kidnapped / Dirty fingers / Dancin' / White knuckles/Rockin' and rollin' / Hiroshima
5507382 / Sep '94 / Spectrum

☐ WE WANT MOORE
Murder in the skies / Shape of things to come / Victims of the future / Cold hearted / End of the world / Back on the streets / So far away / Empty rooms / Don't take me for a loser / Rockin' and rollin'
GMDLD 1 / Apr '92 / 10
CDVIP 213 / 3 Aug '98 / Virgin VIP

☐ WILD FRONTIER
Over the hills and far away / Wild frontier / Take a little time / Loner / Friday on my mind / Strangers in the darkness / Thunder rising / Johnny boy / Wild frontier / Over the hills and far away (12" version) / Crying in the shadows
DIXCD 56 / Feb '87 / 10

Moore, Glen

☐ DRAGONETTI'S DREAM
Oxeye / Beautiful swan lady / If you can't beat em, beat em / Red and black / Dragonetti's dream / Jade visions / Walcott's pendulum / Enter the king / Vertebra / Travels with my foot / Put in a quarter / Burning fingers / Fat horse / Four queasy pieces / Appalachian dance
VBR 21542 / Feb '96 / Vera Bra

Moore, Grace

☐ ONE NIGHT OF LOVE
CDMOIR 424 / Sep '94 / Memoir

Moore, Hamish

☐ BEES KNEES, THE (Moore, Hamish & Dick Lee)
Thunderhead / Easy club reel / Rumblin' brig / Boatman Bill / Iain McGhee's Romanian boots / Birnam triangle / Nigheann dubh alainn / Teapot jig / Rock and Wee Pickle tow / Bannocks of Beremeal / Song for Julie / Thoir a nall ailean thugam / Jenny's chickens / Jenny dang the weaver / Maggie's reel / Slippit bar / Paddy in the sauna / Slow hare / Mongoose in the Byre / Bee's knees / Staten island / Trip to Pakistan / Anne's tune / Buccleuch Street / Famous ballymoate
HARCD 014 / '90 / Harbour Town

☐ FAREWELL TO DECORUM (Moore, Hamish & Dick Lee)
Third movement of a concerto for bagpipes and jazz orchestra / Autumn returns / Galician jigs / Cat's pyjamas, The/The Mental blockade / Farewell to Nigg / Resolution No. 9 / Ye banks and braes/Malts on the optics/Farewell to decorum / Round dawn / Forest lodge/Primrose lass/Miss Girdle / Monster / 12.12.92 (A march for democracy) / Freedom come all ye
CDTRAX 063 / Sep '93 / Greentrax

☐ STEPPING ON THE BRIDGE
King George IV strathspey / King's reel / Blue bonnets / Margaret MacLachlan / Back of the change house / Lucy Campbell / Go immediatley / High road to Linton / Father John MacMillian of Barra / Sprig of ivy / St Josephs / Mrs. Gregor's search / Cameron's strathspley / Crippled boy / Helen Black of Inveran / Dal nahas ag / Sparks rant / Drose and butter / Stumpie
CDTRAX 073 / Jul '94 / Greentrax

Moore, Johnny B.

☐ 911 BLUES
WOLF 120873 / Jul '96 / Wolf

☐ LIVE AT BLUE CHICAGO
Rollin' and tumblin' / Turn on your love light / Same thing / Sweet little angel / All my whole life / Back door friend / All of your love / Mean mistreater / You can't lose what you never had / If you don't put nothin' in it / Straight from the shoulder / Boogie chillen'
DE 688 / Jun '97 / Delmark

☐ TROUBLED WORLD
Troubled world / Keep it to yourself / Sittin' here thinkin' / I'm going upside your head / Things that I used to do / Why you wanna do me like that / Stoop down baby / Broke your promise / Walkin' through the park / Think twice / It's too late brother
DE 701 / Jun '97 / Delmark

Moore, Kid Prince

☐ KID PRINCE MOORE
DOCD 5180 / Oct '93 / Document

Moore, Melba

☐ THIS IS IT
This is it / Lean on me / I am his lady / Must be dues / Greatest feeling / Living free / Long and winding road / Way you make me feel / I don't know no one else to turn to / One less morning / Free / Stay awhile / Make me believe in you / Natural part of everything / Brand new / Promised land / Standing right here / Ain't no love lost / Blood red roses / Play boy scout
74321558522 / 26 Jan '98 / Camden

Moore, Merrill E.

☐ BOOGIE MY BLUES AWAY (2CD Set)
Rock rock ola / House of blue lights / Big bug boogie / Saddle boogie / Corine Corina / Red light / Bartender's blues / Hard top race / Nola boogie / Bell bottom boogie / Doggie house boogie / Sweet Jenny Lee / Fly right boogie / It's a one-way door / Snatchin' and grabbin' / I think I love you too / Ten ten am / Yes indeed / Five foot two, eyes of blue / Cow cow boogie / Boogie my blues away / Rock Island line / King Porter stomp / Cooing to the wrong pigeon / She's gone / Down the road apiece / Gotta gimme whatcha got / Nursery rhyme blues / Buttermilk baby / Barrel house Bessie / Tuck me to sleep in my old Kentucky home / Music music music / Sun Valley walk / Lazy river / (Back home again in) Indiana / South / (In) a shanty in old Shanty Town / Sweet Georgia Brown / Nobody's sweetheart / Jumpin' at the woodside / Somebody stole my gal / Moore blues / Sentimental journey
BCD 15505 / Sep '90 / Bear Family

Moore, Michael

☐ BERING (Moore, Michael Trio)
RAMBOY 11 / Apr '98 / Ramboy

☐ CHICOUTIMI
RAMBOY 6 / Oct '94 / Ramboy

☐ CONCORD DUO SERIES VOL.9
I remember you / Just me, just me / If I loved you / Limehouse blues / Come Sunday / Ain't she sweet / I should care / Zoot's suite / All the things you are / Old new waltz / Seven, come eleven / Liebst du um schonheit / Cotton tail / Deep summer music
CCD 4678 / Dec '95 / Concord Jazz

☐ PLAYS GERSHWIN
Summertime / Love walked in / Shall we dance / Embraceable you / He loves, she loves / But not for me / 'S Wonderful / Foggy day / They all laughed / I've got a crush on you / Someone to watch over me / Who cares
CHECD 00110 / Mar '95 / Master Mix

Moore, Monette

☐ MONETTE MOORE VOL.1 1923-1924
DOCD 5338 / May '95 / Document

☐ MONETTE MOORE VOL.2 1924-1932
DOCD 5339 / May '95 / Document

Moore, Ralph

☐ 623 C STREET (Moore, Ralph Quartet)
Un poco loco / Christina / Black diamond / It never entered my mind / Cecilia / 623 C street / Deceptacon / Speak low
CRISS 1028CD / Jun '98 / Criss Cross

☐ ROUND TRIP
RSRCD 104 / Oct '89 / Reservoir

☐ WHO IT IS YOU ARE (Moore, Ralph Quartet)
Skylark / Recado bossa nova / But beautiful / Testifyin' / Sunday in New York / Yeah you / After your call / Some other time / Esmerelda / Delightful deggy / Since I fell for you
CY 75778 / Oct '97 / Savoy Jazz

Moore, Rebecca

☐ ADMIRAL CHARCOAL'S SONG
KFWCD 162 / Feb '95 / Knitting Factory

Moore, Rudy Ray

☐ GOOD OLE BIG ONES
Fast black / Silent George / Good ole big ones / He can give it / Hell of a blow job / Period / Black topping / White beans / Sack of nookie and others / Dirty dozens, Hercules / Catch me some nuts / Grow by the minute / St. Peter and Bro. rap
CDPS 002 / Nov '95 / Pulsar

Moore, Scotty

☐ GUITAR THAT CHANGED THE WORLD, THE
Hound dog / Loving you / Money honey / My baby left me / Heartbreak hotel / That's alright Mama / Milk cow blues / Don't / Mystery train / Don't be cruel / Love me tender / Mean woman blues
4809662 / Aug '95 / Epic

Moore, Seamus

☐ WINNING DREAM, THE
Fagan's wake / Cobble fighter / West of the old river shannon / Breathalyser song / Second-hand trousers / Blind / Rocking the baby / Turf footing / Winning dream / Whiskey in me tae / Teenager in 1968 / Cottage on the hill / Transit van / Fiddle / Take me back to castlebar / Pothole song
HRCD 1030 / Apr '94 / Hazel

Moore, Thomas

☐ DREAMER IN RUSSIA
Molenie o lybuvi (Prayer for love) / Michael Michael / Lake of Ponchartrain / Schlar / Fog in Monterey / No clouds / Sonya and Amy in Grey / Crooked road / Believe me Sligo
SUNCD 2 / '90 / Sound

☐ GORGEOUS AND BRIGHT
SCD 1294 / Feb '95 / Starc

Moore, Thurston

☐ BAREFOOT IN THE HEAD (Moore, Thurston & Jim Sauter/Don Dietrich)
FE 015 / Dec '96 / Forced Exposure

☐ KLANGFARBENMELODIE
HERMES 011 / Apr '97 / Corpus Hermeticum

☐ PIECE FOR JETSUN DOLMA
VICTOCD 045 / Mar '97 / Victo

☐ PILLOW WAND (Moore, Thurston & Nels Cline)
LB 011CD / Jul '97 / Little Brother

Moore, Tina

☐ TINA MOORE
Never gonna let you go / All I can do / Waiting / At last / Love don't feel like love / Nobody better / Tell me how you like to be done / Colour me blue / Follow your heart / Never without love / Never gonna let you go / Never gonna let you go
74321522652 / 22 Sep '97 / Delirious

Moore, Vinnie

☐ OUT OF NOWHERE
CDMFN 194 / Feb '96 / Music For Nations

Moorefield, Virgil

☐ TEMPERATURE IN HELL IS OVER 3000 DEGREES, THE
TZA 7026 / 6 Oct '97 / Tzadik

Moorish, Lisa

☐ I'VE GOT TO HAVE IT ALL
8287502 / Aug '96 / Go Beat

Moose

☐ HONEY BEE
Uptown invisible / Meringue / Mondo cane / You don't listen / Joe courtesy / Asleep at the wheel / I wanted to see you to see if I wanted you / Around the warm bend / Stop laughing / Dress you the same / Hold on
BIAS 260CD / Oct '93 / Play It Again Sam

☐ LIVE A LITTLE, LOVE A LOT
Play God / Man who hanged himself / First balloon to Nice / Rubdown / Poor man / Eve in a dream / Old man time / Love on the dole / So much love so little time / Last of the good old days / Regulo 7
BIAS 320CD / Feb '96 / Play It Again Sam

☐ XYZ
Soon is never soon enough / I'll See You In My Dreams / High Flying Bird / Screaming / Friends / XYZ / Slip and slide / Little Bird / Don't Bring Me Down / Polly / Whistling Song / Everybody's talkin' / River is nearly dry / Live At The Happy Moustache / Early Morning Rain / Moon Is Blue
CDHUT 005 / Aug '92 / Hut

Mooseheart Faith

☐ CORONAL MASS EJECTION
SGCD 18 / 15 Jun '98 / September Gurls

☐ COSMIC DIALOGUES
SGCD 4 / Sep '97 / September Gurls

☐ GLOBAL BRAIN
SGCD 9 / Sep '97 / September Gurls

☐ MAGIC SQUARE OF THE SUN
SGCD 19 / 15 Jun '98 / September Gurls

MOP

☐ FIRST FAMILY FOR LIFE
Billy skit / Breakin' the rules / 4 alarm blaze: *MOP & Teflon/Jay-Z* / Blood sweat and tears / Down 4 whateva: *MOP & OC* / Facing off / My kinda nigga: *MOP & Heather B* / I luv: *MOP & Freddie Foxx* / Salute: *MOP & Gangstarr* / Ride with us / Handle Ur bizness / Fly nigga hill figga / What the future holds / Downtown swinga / Fame skit / Brooklyn/Jersey get wild / New York salute
4898532 / 10 Aug '98 / Relativity

Moped, Johnny

☐ BASICALLY (Studio Recordings/Live At The Roundhouse 19th Feb '78)
No one / VD boiler / Panic button / Little Queenie / Maniac / Darling, let's have another baby / Groovy Ruby / 3D time / Wee wee / Make trouble / Wild breed / Hell razor / Incendiary device / Somethin' else / Groovy Ruby (Live) / VD boiler (Live) / Little Queenie (Live) / Wee wee (Live) / Panic button (Live) / Make trouble (Live) / Somethin' else (Live) / Incendiary device (Live) / Hard lovin' man (Live) / Wild breed (Live) / Hell razor (Live) / Starting a moped / Groovy Ruby / It really digs / Mystery track
CDWIKD 144 / Sep '95 / Chiswick

Moped Lads

☐ KICKED OUT '77
NV 44CD / Oct '96 / Nasty Vinyl

Moradi, Shahmirza

☐ MUSIC OF LORESTAN
NI 5397 / Sep '94 / Nimbus

Moraes, Angel

☐ HOT 'N' SPYCY - THE ALBUM
SUB 17D / Jun '96 / Subversive

☐ NEW YORK IN THE MIX VOL.1
SUB 5D / Nov '95 / Subversive

Moraito

☐ FLAMENCO VIVO COLLECTION (Morao Y Oro)
Feria fel caballo / Alameda vieja / Bulerianido / Bronce / Musica en el aire / Terremoto / Rompeserones / Ventorrillo de la union / Mercado persa
AUB 6772 / Feb '93 / Auvidis/Ethnic

Morales, Noro

☐ BROADCASTS & TRANSCRIPTIONS 1942-1948
HQCD 78 / Nov '96 / Harlequin

Moran, Paul

☐ SMOKIN' B-3
BASL 004 / 31 Aug '98 / Baseline

Morath, Max

☐ LIVING A RAGTIME LIFE
SACD 110 / Jul '93 / Solo Art

☐ REAL AMERICAN FOLK SONGS
SACD 120 / Mar '95 / Solo Art

Moravenka Band

☐ MUSIC FOR PLEASURE
VA 0039 / Nov '95 / Musicvars

Moraz, Patrick

☐ OUT IN THE SUN
Out in the sun / Rana batucada / Nervous breakdown / Silver screen / Tentacles / Kabala / Love hate sun rain you / Time for a change
CDOVD 445 / May '94 / Virgin

☐ STORY OF I, THE
Impact / Warmer hands / Storm / Cachaca / Intermezzo / Indoors / Best years of our lives / Descent / Incantation (procession) / Dancing now / Impressions (the dream) / Like a child in disguise / Rise and fall / Symphony in the space
CDOVD 446 / May '94 / Virgin

Morbid Angel

☐ ABOMINATIONS
Invocation-chapel of ghouls / Unholy blasphemies / Angel of disease / Azagthoth / Gate-lord of all fevers and plague / Hell spawn / Abominations / Demon seed / Welcome to hell
MOSH 048CD / 1 Sep '97 / Earache

☐ ALTARS OF MADNESS
Visions from the darkside / Chapel of ghouls / Maze of torment / Damnation / Bleed for the devil
MOSH 011CD / 1 Sep '97 / Earache

☐ BLESSED ARE THE SICK
Intro / Fall from grace / Brainstorm / Rebel lands / Doomsday celebration / Day of suffering / Blessed are the sick-leading the rats / Thy kingdom come / Unholy blaspheming / Abomination / Desolate ways / Ancient ones / In remembrance
MOSH 031CD / 1 Sep '97 / Earache

☐ COVENANT
Rapture / Pain divine / World of shit / Vengeance is mine / Lion's den / Blood on my hands / Angel of disease / Sworn to black / Nar mattaru / God of emptiness
MOSH 081CD / 1 Sep '97 / Earache

☐ DOMINATION
Dominate / Where the slime live / Eyes to see, ears to hear / Melting / Nothing to fear / Dawn of the angry / This means war / Caesar's Palace / Dreaming / Inquisition (burn with me) / Hatework
MOSH 123CDSL / 1 Sep '97 / Earache

☐ ENTANGLED IN CHAOS
Immortal rites / Blasphemy of the holy ghost / Sworn to the black / Lord of all fevers and plague / Blessed are the sick / Days of suffering / Chapels of ghouls / Maze of torment / Rapture / Blood on my hands / Dominate
MOSH 167CD / Nov '96 / Earache

☐ FORMULAS FATAL TO THE FLESH
Heaving Earth / Prayer of hatred / Bil ur-sag / Nothing is not / Chambers of dis / Disturbance in the great slumber / Umulamahri / Hellspawn (the rebirth) / Covenant of death / Hymn to a gas giant / Invocation of the continual one / Ascent through the spheres / Hymnos rituales de guerra / Trooper
MOSH 180CD / 23 Feb '98 / Earache

Morbid Saint

☐ SPECTRUM OF DEATH
GCI 89803 / Jun '92 / Plastic Head

Morbius

☐ ALIENCHRIST
CYBERCD 16 / May '95 / Cyber

Morcheeba

☐ BIG CALM
Sea / Shoulder holster / Part of the process / Blindfold / Let me see / Bullet proof / Over and over / Friction / Diggin' in a watery grave / Fear and love / Big calm
ZEN 017CDX
ZEN 017CD / 16 Mar '98 / Indochina

☐ WHO CAN YOU TRUST
Moog island / Trigger hippie / Post houmous / Tape loop / Never an easy way / Howling / Small town / Enjoy the wait / Col / Who can you trust / Almost done / End theme
ZEN 009CD / Apr '96 / Indochina

Mordred

☐ FOOLS GAME
CDNUK 135 / May '89 / Noise

☐ NEXT ROOM, THE
N 02112 / Aug '94 / Noise

More, Benny

☐ BAILA MI SON
CCD 506 / Jul '96 / Caney

☐ BOLEROS DE ORO
Mi amor fugaz / No te atrevas / Preferi perderte / Mi corazon lloro / Corazon rebelde / Dolor y perdon / Por que pensar asi / No puedo callar / Fiebre de ti / Y te encontre / Que me hace dano / Como fue / Esta noche corazon / Mucho corazon
CD 62103 / Oct '96 / Saludos Amigos

☐ CARICIAS CUBANA
SON 035 / Jul '95 / Iris Music

☐ EL BARBARO DEL RITMO
Te quedaras / Encatidando de la vida / En el tiempo de la colonia / Oh vida / Locas por el mambo / Mi chiquita / Barbaro del ritmo / A media noche / Cinturita / Corazon rebelde / El bobo de la yuca / Me voy pa'el / Pueblo
PSCCD 1004 / Feb '95 / Pure Sounds From Cuba

☐ VOZ Y OBRA
74321283412 / Jun '96 / Milan

More Fiends

☐ TOAD LICKIN'
Fatty humps / Yellow spades / Slug juice / Vinyl grind / Y.our a.ss k.icked / 4 aliens on ice / Yo asphalt head / Big tea party (I'm gonna have one) / Lizard tail / Lust / Dodge the bullet / More friends / Wild west philly / Confusion is a blessing / Vinyl grind / Eb and flow show / Slug juice / Everything's an omen / Time-warp bio-feedback amphetamine nightmare / Watch yr back / Flash of frustration / Mad at everyone / Clear to me
SR 330290CD / Dec '90 / Semaphore

More Rockers

☐ DUB PLATE SELECTION VOL.1
ZCDKR 1 / Feb '95 / More Rockers

More Tequila

☐ COUNTRY LINE DANCE COLLECTION, THE
PLSCD 274 / 2 Mar '98 / Pulse

Moreau, Jean

☐ JEAN MOREAU
I'm losing my mind / Life is fleeting / Skin, Leon / Nothing happens anymore / Ask for me, I prefer / Lazy blues / Life of leisure / Man to love / Clockmaker / Neither too soon, nor too late / Lies / Love out of focus / I'll never tell you that I'll love you forever / All blue / I once had a friend / Words about nothing / Anonymous / Farewell to life / You bother me / Sometimes red sometimes blue / Le Tourbillon
DRGCD 5567 / Aug '96 / DRG

Moreira, Airto

☐ FORTH WORLD (Moreira, Airto & Forth World)
JH CD 026 / Sep '92 / Ronnie Scott's Jazz House

☐ OTHER SIDE OF THIS, THE
RCD 10207 / Jun '92 / Rykodisc

☐ TRIBAL ETHNO DANCE
BW 092 / 27 Apr '98 / B&W

Morel, George

☐ ARE YOU READY TO PLAY (Morel Inc)
ZYX 204532 / 15 Jun '98 / ZYX

Moreland, Ace

☐ I'M A DAMN GOOD TIME
ICH 9014CD / Jun '94 / Ichiban

Morellos

☐ CRAZY RHYTHM
Manoir des mes reves / Jeepers Creepers / Crazy rhythm / Embraceable you / Bolero / Buona sera / Bonjour mon amour / Pennies from heaven / Paper moon / Zing went the strings
33JAZZ 028 / Aug '96 / 33 Jazz

Moreno, Antonita

☐ CARRETERA DE ASTURIAS
9175 / Oct '96 / Divusca

Moreno, Buddy

☐ BUDDY MORENO ORCHESTRA 1947-1949 (Moreno, Buddy Orchestra)
CCD 49 / Nov '96 / Circle

Moreno, Tutti

☐ TENDIDO (Moreno, Tutti & Friends & Joyce)
F 006CD / Jul '96 / Far Out

☐ TOCANDO, SENTINDO, SUANDO (Playing, Feeling, Sweating) (Moreno, Tutty & Joyce)
Magica / Algo sobre nos / Pricesinha / Costelaco / Pega leve / Pianco / GB / Camaleao
FARO 006 / Aug '96 / Far Out

Moreton, Ivor

☐ NIMBLE FINGERS (Moreton, Ivor & Dave Kay)
Aurora / It always rains before a rainbow / Ridin' home on the buggy / That lovely weekend / Sand in my shoes / Do you care / Wrap yourself in cotton wool / Shepherd serenade / Elmer's tune / Sailor with the navy blue eyes / Baby mine / When I love / Deep in the heart of Texas / Tica ti tica ta / Tomorrow's sunrise / I don't want to walk without you / Flamingo / Someone's rocking my dreamboat / Arm in arm / Time was / In an old dutch garden / Lamplighter's serenade/Sometimes/Somebody else is taking my / Where in the world/Always in my heart/Soft shoe shuffle / Jersey bounce / Three little sisters / Tell me teacher / Only you / Idaho / It costs so little / Mean to me / Time on my hands / If I had you / Be careful it's my heart / Love is a song/Here you are / Love is a song / Here you are / This is worth fighting for / You walked by / Loveliest / Whispering grass / Three dreams/There's a harbour of dreamboats / Where's my love/Lady who don't believe in love/Keep an eye on / Why don't you fall in love with me/All our tomorrows / Hit the road to dreamland/I spy/Let's get lost / I can't hear you anymore / I haven't time to be a millionaire / We'll go smiling along / All over the place/Maybe/Where was I / All the things you are/Blueberry Hill/Sierra Sue / In the blue hills of Maine / Zoot suit / When your old wedding ring was new
RAJCD 822 / May '97 / Empress

Moretti, Dan

☐ SAXUAL
Waiting for the call / Hot summer night / Just a matter of time / Midnight layer cake / First love / Cru-cre coroso / Keepin' up the magic / Serenade / Tune for Tina / Be my quest
PAR 2019CD / Apr '94 / PAR

Morgan, Carlos

☐ FEELIN' ALRIGHT
UMD 81054 / 30 Mar '98 / Universal

Morgan, Cindy

☐ LOVING KIND, THE
In the garden / March / Loving kind / Last supper / Devil man / Can you hear me / Only way / Hard heart / Whipping / Higher / Take my life / Alive and well / Praise the King
7019962602 / Mar '98 / Word

Morgan, Denroy

☐ I'LL DO ANYTHING FOR YOU
VPRD 6224 / 30 Mar '98 / VP

☐ SALVATION
HMGCD 01 / 1 Jun '98 / 71 Productions

Morgan, Derrick

☐ 21 HITS SALUTE
SONCD 0077 / May '95 / Sonic Sounds

☐ BLAZING FIRE
PHZCD 80 / Nov '93 / Unicorn

☐ CLASSICS OF YESTERDAY
HRCD 200 / Sep '96 / Hop

☐ DERRICK MORGAN AND OWEN GRAY (Morgan, Derrick & Owen Gray)
RN 7051 / 27 Jul '98 / Rhino

☐ DERRICK TOP - THE POP
TRRCD 03 / 16 Feb '98 / Trybute

☐ I AM THE RULER
Teach my baby / Hop / Forward march / Housewives' choice / Gypsy woman / Blazing fire / No raise no praise / Look before you leap / I found a Queen / Don't you worry / It's alright / Got you on my mind / You never miss your water / I am the ruler / I want to go home / Conquering ruler / Gimme back / Tears on my pillow
CDTRL 300 / Mar '94 / Trojan

☐ ROCKSTEADY
RNCD 2103 / Apr '95 / Rhino

☐ SKA MAN CLASSICS
CDBH 170 / Nov '95 / Heartbeat

☐ TIME MARCHES ON
Time marches on / Fatman / You're a pest / I wish I were an apple / Love not to brag / Lover boy / Do the beng beng / Father Killam / Bad luck on me / Ain't that crazy / Tears on my pillow / Lagga head / That crazy feeling / Conquering ruler / Top the pop / Rudies don't fear / Just the deputy / Moon hop
CDHB 153 / Jul '97 / Heartbeat

Morgan, Frank

☐ BEBOP LIVES (Morgan, Frank Quintet)
What is this thing called love / Parker's mood / Well you needn't / Little Melonae / Come Sunday / All the things you are / Night in Tunisia
CCD 14026 / Apr '94 / Contemporary

☐ BOP (Morgan, Frank & The Rodney Kendrick Trio)
Milano / Well, you needn't / KC blues / Night in Tunisia / Blue monk / Half Nelson / Cover man / 52nd Street theme
CD 83413 / Mar '97 / Telarc Jazz

☐ DOUBLE IMAGE (Morgan, Frank & George Cables)
All the things you are / Virgo / Blues for Rosalinda / After you've gone / Helen's song / Love dance / Love story / I told you so / Blue in green
CCD 14035 / Apr '94 / Contemporary

☐ LISTEN TO THE DAWN
Listen to the dawn / Grooveyard / Remembering / Little waltz / It might as well be spring / When joanna loved me / I didn't know about you / Goodbye
5189792 / Aug '94 / Antilles/New Directions

☐ LOVE, LOST AND FOUND
Nearness of you / Last night when you were young / What is this thing called love / Skylark / Once I loved / I can't get started with you / It's only a paper moon / My one and only love / Someday my prince will come / All
CD 83374 / Oct '95 / Telarc

☐ YARDBIRD SUITE (Morgan, Frank Quartet)
Yardbird suite / Night in Tunisia / Billie's bounce / Star eyes / Scrapple from the apple / Skylark / Cheryl
CCD 14045 / Apr '94 / Contemporary

Morgan, George

☐ CANDY KISSES (9CD Set)
All I need is some more lovin' / Candy kisses / Rainbow in my heart / Please don't let me love you / Silver river / Don't make me sorry / Put all your lovin' on a cookie jar / Room full of roses / I love everything about you / Ring on your finger / Cry baby heart / Why in heaven's name / Shoe is on the other / Wedding dolls / Greedy fingers / Angel mother / Lucky seven / You wind the bride / So far / Warm hands, cold heart / Don't be afraid to love me / I know you'll never change / Pardon me for being a fool / D-Á-R-L-I-N-G / Somebody robbed my beehive / I love no one but you / Broken candy heart / I wish I may, I wish I might / Tennessee hillbilly ghost / Waltzing by the Ohio / My heart keeps telling me / Fresh red apple cheeks / My baby lied to me / Strangers in the night / Mansion over the hilltop / Cry of the lamb / You're a little doll / Almost / Every little thing rolled into one / Be sure you know / Whistle my love / One woman's prayer / Believe / Pardon of broken hearts / Will the angel let me play / Can you trust me again / You're the only one / Withered roses / You love me just enough to hurt me / Grapevine swing / Ain't love grand / Lovers' quarrel / Honky tonk street / Most of all / Every prayer is a flower / How many times / I passed by your window / Lonesome waltz / I'll furnish the shoulder you cry on / Half hearted / Look what followed me home tonight / No one knows it better than me / Love, love, love / First time I told you a lie / It's been nice / Walking shoes / I think I'm going to cry / Sweetheart / Cheap affair / So lonesome / I'd like to know / Shot / Shot in the dark / Best mistake / Wither thou goest / Oceans of tears / Oh, gentle shepherd / You don't have to walk alone / Lonesome record / Ever so often / Little pioneer / She's back in town / Jesus savior pilot me / Stay away from my baby / Take a look at yourself / Send for my baby / Now you know / There goes my love / Way of a hopeless love / Perfect romance / Can't be dreaming / Don't cry, for you I love / Sweet, sweet lips / Tears behind the smile / Don't knock it / Our summer vacation / It always ends too soon / Late date / My house is divided / It's a sin / One rose / Where I love / Another place in the sun / Now heaven / I'm not afraid / Loveable you / Rockabilly bungalow / Come away from his arms / I'm in love again / Touch of your sweet lips / It was all in your mind / Little dutch girl / Last thing I want to know / You're the only green man / Only one minute more / Day will come / Mother Machree / Smilin' thru / Mighty like a rose / Beautiful dreamer / Galway Bay / Memories / Danny Boy / Rosary / Old refrain / Across the wide Missouri / Dear little boy of mine / Every day of my life / Don't you know me / You're no good / I love no one but you and love today / I can hear my heart break / Have you ever been untrue / Blue snowfall / Beyond my heart / Macht michts / Where is my love / Speedball / Would you believe / Whose memory are you / All right / One dozen roses / You're not home yet / Back again / Just like a fool / We could / Almost all the time / In

your eyes / Your lonely nights are over / Just out of reach / Sin and silver / Slipping around / I love you so much it hurts / Country boy - city girl / Just your conscience / Too busy saying goodbye / Tears and roses / Dear John / Happy endings / Please help me / I'm falling / Slowly / How can we plan the future / Beginning of the end / Eyes of the world / I'm thinking tonight of my blue eyes / I'll call you Charlie / Yesterday's roses / Bouquet of roses / Teardrops on the roses / Petal from a faded rose / Convict and the rose / Roses / Violet and a rose / Roses are red / By the river of the roses / Picture that's new / Bring your roses to her now / Red roses for a blue lady / It's all coming home to you but me / Not from my world / Saving all my love / Home is where the heart is / No man should hurt as bad as I do / There goes my world / Married / Wheel of hurt / Speak well of me
BCD 15851 / Jul '96 / Bear Family

☐ ROOM FULL OF ROSES
RE 21092 / Oct '96 / Razor & Tie

Morgan, Greg

☐ SPIRIT OF LIGHT VOL.1
Spirit of light
SLAMCD 221 / Oct '96 / Slam

Morgan Heritage

☐ ONE CALLING
One bingi man / Come and arise / One calling / Prison cell / Trodding to Zion / Down with you / Wicked seeking hiding place / Give we a licence: Morgan Heritage & Denroy Morgan / God is god / Oh Israel / Goodbye / Warning to wicked man / Why do we / Greensleeves
GRELCD 244 / 27 Oct '97 / Greensleeves

☐ PROTECT US JAH
VPCD 1485 / Apr '97 / VP

☐ PROTECT US JAH
ANACD 002 / Jul '97 / Anansi

Morgan, Lee

☐ AT THE LIGHTHOUSE 70 (Morgan, Lee Quintet)
FSRCD 140 / Dec '90 / Fresh Sound

☐ BLUE BREAKBEATS
Sidewinder / Cornbread / Caramba / Nite flite
4947042 / 13 Jul '98 / Blue Note

☐ CARAMBA
Caramba / Suicide city / Cunning Lee / Soulita / Helen's ritual / Baby's smile
CDP 8533582 / Nov '96 / Blue Note

☐ CHARISMA
Hey chico / Somethin' cute / Rainy night / Sweet honey bee / Murphy man / Double up
8599612 / 10 Nov '97 / Blue Note

☐ EXPOOBIDENT
Expoobident / Easy living / Triple threat / Fire / Just in time / Hearing / Lost and found / Terrible 'T' / Mogie / I'm a fool to want you / Running brook / Off spring / Bess
LEJAZZCD 39 / May '95 / Le Jazz

☐ EXPOOBIDENT
VJ 008 / 24 Feb '98 / Vee Jay

☐ HERE'S LEE MORGAN
VJ 005 / 24 Feb '98 / Vee Jay

☐ INTRODUCING LEE MORGAN
Hank's shout / Nostalgia / Bet / Softly as in a morning sunrise / PS I love you / Easy living / That's all
SV 0116 / Oct '97 / Savoy Jazz

☐ LAST SESSION
Capra black / In what direction are you heading / Angela / Croquet ballet / Inner passions out
4934012 / 13 Apr '98 / Blue Note

☐ LIVE AT THE LIGHTHOUSE (3CD Set)
Introduction / Beehive / Absolutions / Peyote / Speedball / Nommo / Neophilia / Something like this / I remember Britt / Aon / Yunjanna / 416 East 10th Street / Sidewinder
CDP 8352282 / May '96 / Blue Note

☐ SIDEWINDER
Sidewinder / Totem pole / Gary's notebook / Boy what a night / Hocus pocus
CDP 7841572 / Mar '95 / Blue Note

☐ STANDARDS
This is the life / God bless the child / Blue gardenia / Lot of livin' to do / Somewhere / If I were a carpenter / Blue gardenia
8232132 / 2 Feb '98 / Blue Note

☐ TAKE TWELVE (Morgan, Lee Quintet)
Raggedy Ann / Waltz for Fran / Lee sure time / Little spain / Take twelve / Second's best
OJCCD 310 / Apr '93 / Original Jazz Classics

☐ TRIBUTE TO LEE MORGAN (Various Artists)
Lion and the wolf / Sidewinder / Ceora / Speedball / You don't know what love is / Kozo's waltz / Yama / Ca-lee-so / Search for the new land
NYC 601062 / Jul '95 / NYC

☐ WE REMEMBER YOU
FSCD 1024 / Oct '93 / Fresh Sound

Morgan, Lorrie

☐ GREATER NEED
Soldier of love / I just might be / Greater need / Steppin' stones / I can buy my own roses / Don't stop in my world / By my side / Reading my heart / Good as I was to you / She walked beside the wagon / Back among the living
7863668472 / Jul '96 / RCA

☐ GREATEST HITS
7863665082 / Jul '95 / RCA

☐ SHAKIN' THINGS UP
Shakin' things up / One of those nights tonight / You can't take that / Go away / Crazy from the heat / I'm not that easy to forget / I've enjoyed as much of this as I can stand / Finishing touch / You'd think he'd know me better / Maybe I love me tomorrow / In a perfect world
7863674992 / 15 Sep '97 / RCA

Morgan, Meli'sa

☐ DO YOU STILL LOVE ME (The Best Of Meli'sa Morgan)
RE 21132 / Jul '96 / Razor & Tie

Morgan, Mike

☐ AIN'T WORRIED NO MORE (Morgan, Mike & The Crawl)
BT 1102CD / Apr '94 / Black Top

☐ LET THE DOGS RUN (Morgan, Mike & Jim Suhler)
BT 1106CD / Oct '94 / Black Top

☐ LOWDOWN AND EVIL (Morgan, Mike & The Crawl/Jim Suhler)
I don't want you hangin' around / She's taking me to Heaven / Lowdown and evil / Frankie's blues / Where'd you get your sugar from / Looky here / I just want to get to know you / I'm worried / You ain't like you used to be / Blue cat blues / I gotta leave / I ain't worried no more / Kiss me baby / Should've done better
MMBCD 703 / Jun '97 / Me & My Blues

☐ ROAD, THE (Morgan, Mike & The Crawl)
Road / Bad luck and trouble / No more clouds / You're gonna miss me to / Born to boogie / Wino II / I'm blue / Cold wind / You did me a favour / No money down / Alexandria VA
CDBT 1143 / 16 Mar '98 / Black Top

Morgan, Pamela

☐ COLOUR OF AMBER (Morgan, Pamela & Anita Best)
AMBERCD 9008 / Mar '98 / Amber

Morgan, Russ

☐ 22 ORIGINAL BIG BAND RECORDINGS (Morgan, Russ & His Orchestra)
Does your heart beat for me / Just as though you were here / Way down yonder in new orleans / Sweet elouise / In the mood / Goodbye my lady love / You're a natural / Fine and dandy / Moonlight and shadows / I must see annie tonight / Woodpecker song / You got me / Could be / Don't let julia fool ya / With the wind and rain in your hair / Boo hoo / Johnson rag / Isle of capri / Hurry home / Say it with a kiss / What do you know about love / So long (closing theme)
HCD 404 / Oct '92 / Hindsight

Morgan, Sonny

☐ COCO DE MER (Morgan, Sonny & Seychellois)
Reggae creole / L'echo des isles / A la creole / Island way of life / Koz mwan / Femme napa marie / Coco de mer / La digue / Gros Claire / Aroa / Libre pou choisir / Tropical girls / Mahe island
MISSCD 1990 / Aug '93 / See For Miles

Morgan, Tudur

☐ BRANWEN
O Eire/Llongau ddaeth/Efnisien/Wedi'r wledd / Ffarwel i'r marian / Hiraeth am Feirion / Cefnfor Erin / Bryniau Iwerddon / Damhsa tara / Ar Iannau Llinon / Gwern / Drudwy Branwen/Hiraeth / Cenad Aber Menai / Bendigeidfran a brwydrau Erin / Ffarwel Erin / Alaw'r Alaw / Llongau aeth / Hedd i'r Gymru / Cnwd delwyf i Gymru'n ol / Yr eneth glaf / Titrwm tatrwm / Suo gan / Bryniau Wicklow / Mil harddach wyt / Nae 'nghariad i'n fenws
SCD 4074 / Feb '95 / Sain

Morgana Lefay

☐ FATA MORGANA
BMCD 128 / 8 Jun '98 / Black Mark

☐ PAST, PRESENT, FUTURE
BMCD 084 / Nov '95 / Black Mark

☐ SANCTIFIED
BMCD 063 / Mar '95 / Black Mark

☐ SECRET DOCTRINE, THE
BMCD 42 / May '94 / Black Mark

Morgane

☐ BLUES AND CHANSONS DE DANIELLE MESSIA
KM 47CD / Jan '95 / Keltia Musique

Morganelli, Mark

☐ SPEAK LOW (Morganelli, Mark & The Jazz Forum All Stars)
Speak low / Dreams / Blues for Ian / When I fall in love / Summertime / Opus 15 / Lamb kurma / Child is born / Jolly jumper
CCD 79054 / Feb '97 / Candid

Morganistic

☐ FLUIDS AMNIOTIC
INMCD 1 / Nov '94 / GPR

Morgen

☐ MORGEN
EVAB 20 / Sep '97 / EVA

Morgion

☐ AMONG MAJESTIC RUIN
Relic of a darkened past / In ashen tears (thus I cry) / Travesty / Basking under a blacksun dawning / Invalid prodigy
RR 69242 / Mar '97 / Relapse

Morgoth

☐ CURSED
CM 97192 / Sep '94 / Century Media

☐ ETERNAL FALL & RESURRECTION ABSURD
CM 97082 / Sep '94 / Century Media

☐ FEEL SORRY FOR THE FANATIC
CM 77119CD / Oct '96 / Century Media

☐ ODIUM
8497492 / Jun '93 / Century Media

Morgual

☐ PARODY OF THE MASS
NPR 046CD / 22 Jun '98 / Napalm

Moria Falls

☐ EMBRACE
Tearing at the heartstrings / Falling down / Crime of passion / Heaven bound / No one to talk to / Portraits / Walk away / Justify / End game
VRCDMF 004 / 17 Aug '98 / Cyclops

Morin, Christian

☐ ESQUISSE
3052 / Nov '92 / Deesse

Morissette, Alanis

☐ INTERVIEW CD
UFOMMW 3CD / Nov '96 / UFO

☐ INTERVIEW DISC
SAM 7027 / Jan '97 / Sound & Media

☐ JAGGED LITTLE PILL
All I really want / You oughta know / Perfect / Hand in my pocket / Right through you / Forgiven / You learn / Head over feet / Mary Jane / Ironic / Not the doctor / Wake up / You oughta know (version) / Your house
9362459012 / Jun '95 / Maverick

☐ PILL (Interview Disc)
CONV 002 / Feb '97 / Network

Moritz, Christoph

☐ YELLOW SIX
Green country / Yellow six / Spin / Welcome / Listen from behind / Blue world / Skyline / Brainland / Il conte / Song for Alex / Stop thinking / Half moon
101 S 7053 2 / Nov '92 / New Note

Moriyama, Takeo

☐ LIVE AT LOVELY
DIW 820 / Mar '97 / DIW

Mork Gryning

☐ RETURN FIRE
NFR 022CD / 13 Oct '97 / No Fashion

☐ TUSEN AR HAR GATT
NFR 012CD / Jan '96 / No Fashion

Morley, David

☐ TILTED
AMB 8948CDX / 19 Jan '98 / Apollo

Morley, Michael

☐ PAVILLION OF FOOLS
BHC 004CD / Jul '97 / Black Halo

Morlocks

☐ UGLIER THAN YOU'LL EVER BE
VCD 2071 / Nov '97 / Voxx

Morly Grey

☐ ONLY TRUTH, THE
FLASH 52 / 1 Jun '98 / Flash

Mormos

☐ GREAT WALL OF CHINA
14540 / Jul '97 / Spalax

☐ MAGIC SPELL OF MOTHER'S WRATH
14541 / Jul '97 / Spalax

Morning Again

☐ AS TRADITION DIES SLOWLY
REV 070CD / 6 Jul '98 / Revelation

Morning Glories

☐ FULLY LOADED
SCANCD 06 / Oct '95 / Radarscope

☐ LET THE BODY HANG
HED 069 / Jun '97 / Headhunter

Morohas, Hiroshi

☐ TIME NOTE
PIAS 533010320 / Jun '97 / Shield

Morphew, Jason

☐ TRANSPARENT
BING 009 / Apr '97 / Ba Da Bing

Morphine

☐ B SIDES AND OTHERWISE
Have a lucky day / All wrong / I know you / Bo's veranda / Mile high / Shame / Down love's tributaries / Kerouac / Pulled over the car / Sundayafternoonweightlessness / Virgin bride / Mail / My brain
RCD 10387 / 22 Sep '97 / Rykodisc

☐ BUENA
RCD 51035 / Mar '94 / Rykodisc

☐ CURE FOR PAIN
Dawna / Buena / I'm free now / All wrong / Candy / Head with wings / In spite of me / Thursday / Cure for pain / Mary won't you call my name / Let's take a trip together / Sheila / Miles Davis' funeral
RCD 10262 / Mar '97 / Rykodisc

☐ GOOD
Good / Saddest song / Claire / Have a lucky day / You speak my language / You look like rain / Do not go quietly unto your grave / Lisa / Only one / Test tube baby/Shoot'm down / Other side / I know you
RCD 10263 / Jun '97 / Rykodisc

☐ LIKE SWIMMING
Lilah / Potion / I know you / Early to bed / Wishing well / Like swimming / Murder for the money / French fries with pepper / Empty box / Eleven o'clock / Hanging on a curtain / Swing it low
RCD 10362 / Mar '97 / Rykodisc

☐ THURSDAY
RCD 1036 / May '94 / Rykodisc

☐ YES
Honey white / Scratch / Radar / Whisper / Yes / All your way / Super sex / I had my chance / Jury / Sharks / Free love / Gone for good
RCD 10320 / Mar '97 / Rykodisc

Morphogenesis

☐ CHARIVARI MUSIC
PD 902 / Jun '97 / Paradigm

Morris, Audrey

☐ LOOK AT ME NOW
ACD 297 / Sep '97 / Audiophile

Morris, Bill

☐ DADDY WHAT'S A TRAIN
CREEK 302CD / Mar '98 / Ivy Creek

Morris, Butch

☐ CONDUCTS BERLIN SKYSCRAPER (2CD Set)
FMPCD 92/93 / Jun '98 / Full Moon

☐ DUST TO DUST
804082 / Jun '91 / New World

☐ TESTAMENT (A Conduction Collection/10CD Set)
804782 / Dec '95 / New World

Morris, Danny

☐ STORM SURGE (Morris, Danny Band)
NMC 9717 / 19 Mar '98 / New Moon

Morris, Joe

☐ LIKE RAYS (Morris, Joe Trio)
Photon / New fire / Within reach / Like rays / So as to touch / Life stuff / Parlance / I can live with that / Hand signals / From dreams / Levitate
KFWCD 224 / 27 Jul '98 / Knitting Factory

☐ SYMBOLIC GESTURE
SN 1212042 / Oct '94 / Soul Note

☐ YOU AND ME (Morris, Joe Quartet)
1213042 / Jul '97 / Soul Note

Morris, Lynn

☐ BRAMBLE AND THE ROSE (Morris, Lynn Band)
Blue skies and teardrops / Coat of many colours / Engineers don't wave from trains anymore / Why tell me why / Love grows cold / Bramble and the rose / I'll pretend it's raining / Hey porter / New patches / My younger days / Red line too Shady Grove / Heartstrings
ROUCD 0288 / Feb '92 / Rounder

☐ LYNN MORRIS BAND (Morris, Lynn Band)
My heart skips a beat / You'll get no more me / Adams county breakdown / Black pony / Come early morning / Help me climb that mountain / Kisses don't die / Handyman / What was I supposed to do / If lonely was the wind / Don't tell me stories / Valley of peace
ROUCD 0276 / '90 / Rounder

☐ MAMA'S HAND
ROUCD 0328 / Oct '95 / Rounder

Morris On

☐ MORRIS ON
Bean setting / Shooting / I'll go and enlist for a sailor / Princess Royal / Cuckoo's nest / Morris off / Morris call / Greensleeves / Nutting girl / Old woman tossed up in a blanket / Shepherd's hey / Trunkles / Staines morris / Lads a bunchum / Young Collins / Vandals of Hammerwich / Willow tree
HNCD 4406 / Jan '87 / Hannibal

Morris, R.B.

☐ TAKE THAT RIDE
World owes me / Ridin' with O'Hanlon / They say there's a time / Hell on a poor boy / Take time to love / Ballad of Thunder Road / Take that ride / Roy / Dog days / Pot hole street / Bottom of the big black hull / Glory dreams
OBR 016CD / May '97 / Oh Boy

Morris, Sarah Jane

☐ BLUE VALENTINE
JHCD 038 / Apr '95 / Ronnie Scott's Jazz House

Morris, Sonny

☐ BLUES FOR THE GOOD OLD BOYS (Morris, Sonny & The Delta Jazz Band)
Do what Ory say / Black cat on a fence / Yellow dog blues / Dr. Jazz / Sensation rag / Dallas rag / Hiawatha rag / Blue for the good old boys / Girls go crazy / Silver birches / Joe Avery's piece / In the gloaming / Trombonium
LACD 63 / Jul '96 / Lake

☐ GLORYLAND (Morris, Sonny & The Delta Jazz Band)
PKCD 024 / Jul '96 / PEK

☐ SONNY MEETS PAT (Morris, Sonny & The Delta Jazz Band/Pat Halcox)
Bogalusa strut / Bugle boy march / One sweet letter from you / Poor little green bean / Climax rag / There's yes, yes in your eyes / Tin roof blues / Panama rag / You took advantage of me / Flee as a bird/Didn't he ramble / Home
LACD 81 / Jun '97 / Lake

☐ SPIRIT LIVES ON, THE (Morris, Sonny & The Delta Jazz Band)
Yaaka hula hickey dula / Hesitation blues / While we danced at the Mardi Gras / Canal street blues / Dusty rag / If I had my life to live over / When you and I were young Maggie / I can't escape from you / Barefoot boy / Sometimes my burden is so hard to bear / Mandy, make up your mind / Give me a june night / Wabash blues / Looks like a big time tonight
LACD 46 / Apr '95 / Lake

Morris, Thomas

☐ CLASSICS 1923-1927
CLASSICS 823 / Jul '95 / Classics

☐ WHEN A 'GATOR HOLLERS (Thomas Morris 1926)
Lazy drag / Jackass blues / Charleston stampede / Georgia grind / Ham gravy / Who's dis heah stranger / When a 'gator hollers, folks say it's a sign of rain / My baby doesn't squawk / King of the Zulus / South Rampart Street blues / Blues for the Everglades / PDQ blues / Mess / Chinch
DGF 1 / May '95 / Frog

Morrisey, Louise

☐ WHEN I WAS YOURS
I couldn't leave you if I tried / He thinks I still care / Old flames / Blue eyes cryin' in the rain / Oh what a love / I still love you / Night Daniel O'Donnell came to town / When I was yours / Tipperary on my mind / Rose of Allendale / Hills of Killinaule / Green willow / Slievenamon / Roses and violets / Amazing grace
RZCD 508 / '91 / Ritz

☐ YOU'LL REMEMBER ME
Just in case / Out of sight out of mind / Waltzing with you tonight / That's the way to my heart / Come back Paddy Reilly to Ballyjamesduff / Precious memories / Don't say goodbye / You'll remember me / I'd live my life over you / You make me feel like a woman / I'll bet my heart on you / Getting over getting over you / Heaven I call home / Hills I used to roam
RZCD 546 / Nov '94 / Ritz

Morrison, Alexander

☐ SCOTTISH MEMORIES
CDLOC 1089 / Jun '95 / Lochshore

Morrison, Cliff

☐ KNOW PEAKING
TWCD 44851 / 1 Jun '98 / Focus Move

Morrison, Fred

☐ BROKEN CHANTER, THE
Reels / Strathspeys and reels / Jigs / Hornpipes / Malcolm Ferguson / Irish reels / Polkas / 2/4 Marches / Jigs / Hector the hero / Strathspeys and reels / Piobaireachd
LCOM 5223 / Sep '93 / Lismor

Morrison, Frieda

☐ FLYING BY THE SUN
BLR 101 / May '97 / Smiddy Made

Morrison, Junie

☐ WESTBOUND YEARS
Junie / Tightrope / Walt's first trip / Place / When we do / Johnny Carson samba / Loving arms / Junie II / Not as good as you should / Cookies will get you / Freeze / Super J / Granny's funky rolls royce / Junie III / Surrender / Suzie / Super gorouge / Suzy Thundertussy / Spirit J Junie's ultimate departure
CDSEWD 064 / Apr '94 / Westbound

Morrison, Mark

☐ ONLY GOD CAN JUDGE ME (Verse I Chapter II)
Headlines / Who's the mack / Lord's prayer / Only God can judge me / NEC '96 / Mac life / Lisa at lunchtime / Blackstabbers / Lord's prayer
0630195392 / 15 Sep '97 / WEA

☐ RETURN OF THE MACK
Home / Crazy / Let's get down / Get high with me / Moan and groan / Return of the mack / I like / Trippin' / Tears for you / Horny / I really love you / Crazy / Home
0630145862 / Apr '96 / WEA

Morrison, Peter

☐ LAND OF THE EAGLE
Land of the eagle / Ae fond kiss / Crinan canal / Hundred pipers / Culloden's harvest / Roses of Prince Charlie / Caledonia / Muckin' o' Geordie's byre / Mary Morrison / Bonnie Well's O'Wearie / Niel Gow's farewell to whiskey / Marching medley
CDGR 155 / Jul '96 / Ross

☐ TOAST TO THE MUSIC OF SCOTLAND, A
Toast is music / There was a lad / Roamin' in the gloamin' / Wee Deoch an' Doris / I love a lassie / My love is like a red red rose / Calling me home / Man's a man for a' that / Lass I lo'v ye dearly / Bonnie lass O'Ballochmyle / Dancing in Kyle / Of a the airts / Think on me / Hail Caledonia
LCOM 6015 / Aug '96 / Lismor

Morrison, Van

☐ ASTRAL WEEKS
Astral weeks / Beside you / Sweet thing / Cyprus Avenue / Young lovers do / Madame George / Ballerina / Slim slow rider
7599271762 / Jan '95 / Warner Bros.

☐ AVALON SUNSET
Whenever God shines his light / Contacting my angel / I'd love to write another song / Have I told you lately that I love you / Coney island / I'm tired Joey Boy / When will I ever learn to live in God / Orangefield / Daring night / These are the days
8392622 / May '89 / Polydor

☐ BANG MASTERS
Brown eyed girl / Spanish rose / Goodbye baby (baby goodbye) / Ro ro Rosey / Chicka boom / It's alright / Send your mind / Smile you smile / Back room / Midnight special / TB sheets / He ain't give you none / Who drove the red sports car / Beside you / Joe Harper saturday morning / Madame George / Brown eyed girl (alternate take) / I love you (the smile you smile)
4683092 / Mar '92 / Legacy

☐ BEAUTIFUL VISION
Celtic ray / Northern music / Dweller on the threshold / Beautiful vision / Aryan mist / Across the bridge where angels dwell / Vanlose stairway / Scandinavia / Cleaning windows
5375422 / 6 Apr '98 / Polydor

☐ BEST OF VAN MORRISON VOL.1, THE
Whenever God shines his light: *Morrison, Van & Cliff Richard* / Jackie Wilson said (I'm in Heaven when you smile) / Brown eyed girl / Bright side of the road / Have I told you lately that I love you / Moondance / Here comes the night / Domino / Gloria / Baby please don't go / And it stoned me / Sweet thing / Warm love / Wild night / Cleaning windows / Did ye get healed / Dweller on the threshold / Queen of the slipstream / Wonderful remark / Full force gale / Brown eyed girl
5374592 / 6 Apr '98 / Polydor

☐ BEST OF VAN MORRISON VOL.2, THE
Real real gone / When will I ever learn to live in God / Sometimes I feel like a Motherless child / In the garden / Sense of wonder / Carrickfergus / Coney island / Enlightenment / Rave on, John Donne / Don't look back / It's all over now baby blue / One Irish rover / Mystery / Hymns to the silence / Evening meditation
5177602 / Jan '93 / Polydor

☐ BLOWIN' YOUR MIND
Brown eyed girl / He ain't give you none / TB Sheets / Spanish rose / Goodbye baby (baby goodbye) / Ro ro Rosy / Who drove the red sports car / Midnight special
4804212 / Jun '95 / Mastersound

☐ BROWN EYED BEGINNINGS (2CD Set)
79567666642 / 27 Apr '98 / Multimedia

☐ BROWN EYED GIRL
Brown eyed girl / Goodbye baby (baby goodbye) / Ro Ro Rosey / Back room / Midnight special / He ain't give you none / Who drove the red sports car / Joe Harper Saturday morning / Madame George / Spanish rose / Chick-a-boom / Smile you smile / It's alright / TB Sheets / Beside you / I love you (the smile you smile) / Send your mind
APH 102805 / Apr '96 / Audiophile Legends

☐ BROWN EYED GIRL
Brown eyed girl / He ain't give you none / TB sheets / Spanish rose / Goodbye baby (baby goodbye) / Ro Ro Rosey / Who drove the red sportscar / Midnight special / Beside you / It's alright / Madame George / Send your mind
GUV 1 / 16 Mar '98 / Squire

☐ COMMON ONE
Haunts of ancient peace / Summertime in England / Satisfied / When heart is open / Wild honey / Spirit
5375412 / 6 Apr '98 / Polydor

☐ DAYS LIKE THIS
Perfect fit / Russian roulette / Raincheck / You don't know me / No religion / Underlying depression / Songwriter / Days like this / I'll never be free / Melancholia / Ancient highway / In the afternoon
5273072 / Jun '95 / Polydor

☐ ENLIGHTENMENT
Real real gone / Enlightenment / So quiet in here / Avalon of the heart / See me through / Youth of 1,000 summers / In the days before rock 'n' roll / Start all over again / She's a baby / Memories
8471002 / Oct '90 / Polydor

☐ HARD NOSE THE HIGHWAY
Snow in San Anselmo / Warm love / Hard nose the highway / Wild children / Great deception / Bein' green / Autumn song / Purple heather
5374522 / Jun '97 / Polydor

☐ HEALING GAME, THE
Rough God goes riding / Fire in the belly / This weight / Waiting game / Piper at the gates of dawn / Burning ground / It once was my life / Sometimes we cry / If you love me / Healing game
5371012 / Mar '97 / Polydor

☐ HIS BAND & STREET CHOIR
Domino / Crazy face / Give me a kiss / I've been working / Call me up in Dreamland / I'll be your lover too / Blue money / Virgo clowns / Gypsy queen / Sweet Jannie / If I ever needed someone / Street choir
7599271882 / Oct '93 / Warner Bros.

☐ HOW LONG HAS THIS BEEN GOING ON
5291362 / Dec '95 / Verve

☐ HYMNS TO THE SILENCE (2CD Set)
Professional jealousy / I'm not feeling it anymore / Ordinary life / Some peace of mind / So complicated / I can't stop loving you / Why must I always explain / Village idiot / See me through / Take me back / By his grace / All Saints Day / Hymns to the silence / On Hyndford Street / Be thou my vision / Carrying a torch / Green mansions / Pagan streams / Quality Street / I must be you / I need your kind of love
8490262 / Sep '91 / Polydor

☐ INARTICULATE SPEECH OF THE HEART
Higher than the world / Connswater / River of time / Celtic swing / Rave on John Donne / Inarticulate speech of the heart / Irish heartbeat / Street only knew your name / Cry for home / Inarticulate speech of the heart / September night
5375432 / 6 Apr '98 / Polydor

☐ INTO THE MUSIC
Bright side of the road / Full force gale / And the healing has begun / Steppin' out queen / Troubadors / Rolling hills / You make me feel so free / Angelou / It's all in the game / You know what they're writing about
5375402 / 6 Apr '98 / Polydor

☐ IRISH HEARTBEAT (Morrison, Van & The Chieftains)
Star of County Down / Irish heartbeat / Ta mo chleamhnas deanta / Raglan Road / She moved through the fair / I'll tell me ma / Carrickfergus / Celtic ray / My lagan love / Marie's wedding
5375482 / 6 Apr '98 / Polydor

☐ IT'S TOO LATE TO STOP NOW (2CD Set)
Ain't nothin' you can do / Warm love / Into the mystic / These dreams of you / I believe in my soul / I've been working / Help me / Wild children / Domino / I just want to make love to you / Bring it on home to me / St. Dominic's preview / Take your hand out of my pocket / Listen to the lion / Here comes the night / Gloria / Caravan / Cyprus Avenue
5374532 / Jun '97 / Polydor

☐ LIVE AT THE GRAND OPERA HOUSE BELFAST
Into the mystic / Inarticulate speech of the heart / Dweller on the threshold / It's all in the game / You know what they're writing about / She gives me religion / Haunts of ancient peace / Full force gale / Beautiful vision / Vanlose stairway / Rave on John Donne / Rave on John Donne / Northern muse / Cleaning windows
5375442 / 6 Apr '98 / Polydor

☐ MASTERS, THE
EABCD 051 / 24 Nov '97 / Eagle

☐ MOONDANCE
Stoned me / Moondance / Crazy love / Caravan / Into the mystic / Come running / These dreams of you / Brand new day / Everyone / Glad tidings
246040 / Jan '86 / Warner Bros.

☐ NEW YORK SESSIONS 1967 (2CD Set)
SMDCD 103 / 22 Sep '97 / Snapper

☐ NEW YORK SESSIONS 1967, THE (2CD Set)
Brown eyed girl / He ain't give you none / TB sheets / Spanish rose / Goodbye baby (baby goodbye) / Ro ro Rosey / Who drove the red sportscar / Midnight special / Beside you / It's alright / Madame George / Send your mind / Smile you smile / Back room / Joe Harper Saturday morning / Chick-a-boom / I love you (the smile you smile) / Brown eyed girl / Jam session
PILOT 006 / Feb '97 / Burning Airlines

☐ NIGHT IN SAN FRANCISCO, A (2CD Set)
Did ye get healed / It's all in the game/Make it real one more time / I've been working / I forgot that love existed / Vanlose stairway/Trans-Euro train/Fool for you / You make me feel so free / Beautiful vision / See me through/Soldier of fortune/Thankyou falettinmebemicel / Ain't that lovin' you baby / Stormy Monday/Have you ever loved a woman/No rollin' blues / Help me / Good morning little school girl / Tupelo honey / Moondance/My funny valentine / Jumpin' with symphony Sid / It fills you up / I'll take care of you/It's a man's man's man's world / Lonely avenue/4 o' clock in the morning / So quiet in here/ That's where it's at / In the garden/You send me/ Allegheny / Have I told you lately that I love you / Shakin' all over/Gloria
5212902 / Apr '94 / Polydor

☐ NO GURU NO METHOD NO TEACHER
Got to go back / Oh the warm feeling / Foreign window / Town called Paradise / In the garden / Tir na nog / Here comes the knight / Thanks for the information / One Irish rover / Ivory tower
5375462 / 6 Apr '98 / Polydor

☐ NO PRIMA DONNA (A Tribute To Van Morrison) (Various Artists)
You make me feel so free: *O'Connor, Sinead* / Queen of the slipstream: *Kennedy, Brian* / Coney Island: *Neeson, Liam* / Crazy love: *Wilson, Cassandra* / Bright side of the road: *Hothouse Flowers* / Irish heartbeat: *Kennedy, Brian & Shana Morrison* / Full force gale: *Costello, Elvis* / Tupelo honey: *Coulter, Phil Orchestra* / Madame George: *Faithfull, Marianne* / Friday's child: *Stansfield, Lisa*
5233682 / Jul '94 / Polydor

☐ PAYIN' DUES (The Best Of The 1965 Studio Recordings/2CD Set)
Brown eyed girl / He ain't give you none / TB Sheets / Spanish rose / Goodbye baby (baby goodbye) / Ro ro Rosy / Who drove the red sports car / Midnight special / Beside you / It's alright / Madame George / Send your mind / Smile you smile / Back room / Joe Harper Saturday morning / Chicka boom / I love you (The smile you smile) / Brown eyed girl / Twist and shake / Shake and roll / Stomp and scream / Scream and holler / Jump and thump / Drivin' wheel / Just ball / Shake it Mable / Hold on George / Big royalty check / Ring worm / Savoy Hollywood / Freaky if you got this far / Up your mind / Thirty two / All the bits / You say France and I whistle / Blow in your nose / Nose in your blow / La mambo / Go for yourself / Want a Danish / Here comes dumb George / Chickee coo / Do it / Hang on groovy / Goodbye George / Dum dum George / Walk and talk / Wobble / Wobble and ball
CPCD 80352 / Aug '96 / Charly

☐ PERIOD OF TRANSITION, A
You gotta make it through the world / It fills you up / Eternal Kansas City / Joyous sound / Flamingoes fly (heavy connection) / Cold wind in August
5374572 / Jun '97 / Polydor

☐ PHILOSOPHER'S STONE, THE (2CD Set)
Really don't know / Ordinary people / Wonderful remark / Not supposed to break down / Laughing in the wind / Madame Joy / Bright side of the road / I'm ready / Street theory / Real real gone / Showbusiness / For Mr. Thomas / Crazy Jane on God / Song of a being a child / High spirits / Contemplation Rose / Don't worry about tomorrow / Try for sleep / Lover's prayer / Drumshanbo hustle / Twilight zone / Foggy mountain top / Naked in the jungle / There there child / When I deliver / John Henry / John Brown's body / I have finally come to realise / Flamingoes fly / Stepping out Queen part 2
5317892 / 15 Jun '98 / Polydor

☐ POETIC CHAMPIONS COMPOSE
Spanish Steps / Mystery / Queen of the slipstream / I forgot that love existed / Sometimes I feel like a Motherless child / Celtic excavation / Someone like you / Alan Watts blues / Give me my rapture / Did ye get healed / Allow me
5375472 / 6 Ap '98 / Polydor

☐ SENSE OF WONDER, A
Tore down a' La Rimbaud / Ancient of days / Evening meditation / Master's eyes / What would I do / Sense of wonder / Boffyflow and Spike / If you only knew / Let the slave
5375452 / 6 Apr '98 / Polydor

☐ ST. DOMINIC'S PREVIEW
Jackie Wilson said (I'm in heaven when you smile) / Gypsy / I will be there / Listen to the lion / St. Dominic's preview / Redwood tree / Almost Independence Day
5374512 / Jun '97 / Polydor

☐ TB SHEETS
He ain't give you none / Beside you / It's all right/For sentimental reasons / Madame George / TB Sheets / Who drove the red sports car / Ro Ro Rosy / Brown eyed girl
4678272 / May '91 / Columbia

☐ TOO LONG IN EXILE
Too long in exile / Big time operators / Lonely avenue / Ball and chain / In the forest / Till we get the healing done / Gloria / Good morning little school girl / Wasted years / Lonesome road / Moody's mood for love / Close enough for jazz / Before the world was made / Medley: I'll take care of you
5192192 / Jun '93 / Polydor

☐ TUPELO HONEY
Wild night / Straight to your heart like a cannonball / Old old Woodstock / Starting a new life / You're my woman / Tupelo honey / I wanna roo you / When that evening sun goes down / Moonshine whisky
5374502 / 6 Apr '98 / Polydor

☐ VAN MORRISON SONGBOOK, THE (Various Artists)
Cleaning windows: *Whitfield, Barrence & Tom Russell* / Jackie Wilson said (I'm in heaven when you smile): *Dexy's Midnight Runners* / I shall sing: *Garfunkel, Art* / Madame George: *Energy Orchard* / Angeliou: *Deacon Blue* / I wanna roo you: *Hawn, Goldie* / Have I told you lately: *Emilio* / Brown eyed girl: *Steel Pulse* / Tupelo honey: *Springfield, Dusty* / Irish heartbeat: *Connolly, Billy* / Moondance: *McFerrin, Bobby* / My lonely sad eyes: *McKee, Maria* / Sweet thing: *Waterboys* / Mercy, mercy, mercy/ Vanlose stairway: *Fame, Georgie & The Blue Flames* / Gloria: *Eddie & The Hot Rods*
VSOPCD 233 / Mar '97 / Connoisseur Collection

☐ VEEDON FLEECE
Fair play / Linden Arden stole the highlights / Who was that masked man / Streets of Arklow / You don't pull no punches but you don't push the river / Bulbs / Cul de sac / Comfort you / Come here my love / Country fair
5374562 / Jun '97 / Polydor

☐ WAVELENGTH
Kingdom Hall / Checking it out / Natalia / Venice USA / Lifetimes / Wavelength / Santa Fe: Beautiful obsession / Hungry for your love / Take it where you find it
5374582 / Jun '97 / Polydor

Morrison, William

☐ PIPERS OF DISTINCTION
MON 821CD / Oct '94 / Monarch

☐ PIPING CENTRE 1996 RECITAL SERIES VOL.3, THE (Morrison, William/ Dr. Angus MacDonald)
Arthur Bignold of Lochrosque: *Morrison, William* / Abercairney Highlanders: *Morrison, William* / Champion of the seas: *Morrison, William* / Donald MacLennan's tuning phrase: *Morrison, William* / Judge's dilemma: *Morrison, William* / Dorothy MacCormick: *Morrison, William* / Alistair and Tricia's wedding: *Morrison, William* / Sandy Clarke: *Morrison, William* / MacPhedran's strathspey: *Morrison, William* / O'er the moor and among the heather: *Morrison, William* / Brathan Castle: *Morrison, William* / Old reel: *Morrison, William* / Hey I will follow thee: *Morrison, William* / Periwig: *Morrison, William* / Malcolm the tailor: *Morrison, William* / Dancing feet: *Morrison, William* / Finlay MacDonald's welcome to Bornish: *Morrison, William* / Atholl cummers: *Morrison, William* / John Morrison of Assynt House: *Morrison, William* / Johnnie Ross/ Craigard: *Morrison, William* / Michael Martin MP for Stirling: *Morrison, William* / Creagorry blend: *Morrison, William* / On tour in Cape Breton: *Morrison, William* / Boneshaker: *Morrison, William* / Cameronian rant: *Morrison, William* / Casc na Cisean: *MacDonald, Dr. Angus* / Heights of Cassino: *MacDonald, Dr. Angus* / Roderick MacDonald: *MacDonald, Dr. Angus* / An t-seann chailleach: *MacDonald, Dr. Angus* / Brenda Stubbert's reel: *MacDonald, Dr. Angus* / Port Mairi Alastair Raonghaill: *MacDonald, Dr. Angus* / Aodainn strathbhain: *MacDonald, Dr. Angus* / Inspector Campbell Ness: *MacDonald, Dr. Angus* / Tubular peat: *MacDonald, Dr. Angus* / Kilbowie cottage: *MacDonald, Dr. Angus* / Delvinside: *MacDonald, Dr. Angus* / Stornaway castle: *MacDonald, Dr. Angus* / Johnny Allan MacDonald: *MacDonald, Dr. Angus* / Sud mar chuir mi'n geamhradh tharam: *MacDonald, Dr. Angus* / Togail a bhuntata: *MacDonald, Dr. Angus* / MacFarlane's rant: *MacDonald, Dr. Angus* / Frances MacKenzie/Sydney CB: *MacDonald, Dr. Angus* / When night is falling: *MacDonald, Dr. Angus* / Crossing the minch: *MacDonald, Dr. Angus* / I laid a herring in salt: *MacDonald, Dr. Angus* / Fhir a dhireas am bealach: *MacDonald, Dr. Angus* / Sister's reel: *MacDonald, Dr. Angus* / Woman of the house: *MacDonald, Dr. Angus* / Cape Breton fiddler's welcome to Shetland: *MacDonald, Dr. Angus*
COMD 2070 / 20 Oct '97 / Temple

Morriss, Amy

☐ WITHIN THE SOUND OF YOUR VOICE
It has to be you / In the name of Jesus / Underneath all the stars / Within the sound of your voice / Rain falls / Defenceless / Wonder
701702561X / Oct '97 / Myrrh

Morrissey

☐ BONA DRAG
Piccadilly palare / Interesting drug / November spawned a monster / Will never marry / Such a little thing makes such a big difference / Last of the famous international playboys / Ouija board, ouija board / Hairdresser on fire / Everyday is like Sunday / He knows I'd love to see him / Yes, I am blind / Luckylisp / Suedehead / Disappointed
CDCLP 3788 / Mar '94 / HMV

☐ MALADJUSTED
Maladjusted / Alma matters / Ambitious outsiders / Trouble loves me / Papa Jack / Ammunition / Wide to receive / Roy's keen / He cried / Satan rejected my soul
CID 8059 / Aug '97 / Island

☐ SOUTHPAW GRAMMAR
Teachers are afraid of the pupils / Reader meet author / Boy racer / Operation / Dagenham Dave / Do your best and don't worry / Best friend on the payroll / Southpaw
74321299532 / Aug '95 / RCA

☐ SUEDEHEAD (The Best Of Morrissey)
Suedehead / Interesting drug / Boxers / Last of the famous international playboys / Sunny / Tomorrow / Interlude / Everyday is like Sunday / Hold on to your friends / My love life / Our Frank / Picadilly Palare / Ouija board, ouija board / You're the one for me, fatty / We hate it when our friends become successful / Pregnant for the last time / November spawned a monster / More you ignore me, the closer I get / That's entertainment
CDEMC 3771 / 15 Sep '97 / EMI

☐ SUEDEHEAD (The Best Of Morrissey/ Special Edition)
Suedehead / Interesting drug / Boxers / Last of the famous international playboys / Sunny / Tomorrow / Interlude / Everyday is like Sunday / Hold on to your friends / My love life / Our Frank / Picadilly Palare / Ouija board, ouija board / You're the one for me, fatty / We hate it when our friends become successful / Pregnant for the last time / November spawned a monster / More you ignore me, the closer I get / That's entertainment / Striptease with a difference / Will never marry / Oh phoney / November the second
CDEMCX 3771 / 8 Sep '97 / EMI

☐ VAUXHALL AND I
Now my heart is full / Spring heeled Jim / Billy Budd / Hold on to your friends / More you ignore me, the closer I get / Why don't you find out for yourself / I am hated for loving / Lifeguard sleeping, girl drowning / Used to be a sweet boy / Lazy sunbathers / Speedway
CDPCSD 148 / Mar '94 / HMV

☐ YOUR ARSENAL
You're gonna need someone on your side / Glamorous glue / We'll let you know / National front disco / Certain people I know / We hate it when our friends become successful / You're the one for me fatty / Seasick, yet still docked / I know it's gonna happen someday / Tomorrow
CDCSD 3790 / Jul '92 / HMV

Morrissey, Bill

☐ FRIEND OF MINE (Morrissey, Bill & Greg Brown)
PH 1151CD / May '93 / Philo

☐ NIGHT TRAIN
PH 1154CD / Jan '94 / Philo

Morrissey, Dick

☐ IT'S MORRISEY MAN
St. Thomas / Cherry blue / Bench in the park / Sancticity / Mildew / Puffing Billy / Gurney was here / Happy feet / Where is love / Dancing in the dark / Willow weep for me / Jellyroll
5587012 / 3 Aug '98 / Redial

☐ THERE AND BACK (Morrissey, Dick Quartet)
JHAS 607 / Feb '97 / Ronnie Scott's Jazz House

Morriston Orpheus Choir

☐ 60 YEARS OF SONG
Rhyfelgrch gwyr Harlech (march of the men of Harlech) / Way you look tonight / Morte Criste (When I survey the wondrous cross) / Memory / How great thou art / Bugeilio'r gwenith gwyn / Did those feet in ancient time (Jerusalem) / Speed your journey (va pensiero from Nabucco) / Old rugged cross / In my Father's house / Drinking song / You'll never walk alone / Gwahoddiad / Amazing grace / Llanfair / Myfanwy
CDPR 133 / Feb '95 / Premier/MFP

☐ ALWAYS ON MY MIND
Morte christie (When I survey the wonderous cross) / Always on my mind / Just a closer walk with thee / Non nobis, domine / Y nefoedd / Nidaros / Rhythm of life / Give me Jesus / When I fall in love / Where could I go but to the Lord / Sound an alarm / There is a balm in gilead / My wish for you / Cwm rhondda
GRCD 59 / Jun '93 / Grasmere

☐ CHRISTMAS FROM THE LAND OF SONG
Have yourself a merry little Christmas / Joy to the world / When a child is born / Ding dong merrily on high / Silent night / God rest ye merry gentlemen / Do they know it's Christmas / Saviour's day / Mistletoe and wine / Happy Christmas (war is over) / Hark the herald angels sing / Winter wonderland / Holly and the ivy / Deck the halls with boughs of holly / See amid the winter's snow / Child this day is born / O little town of Bethlehem / Good King Wenceslas / Away in a manger / We three Kings / I saw three ships / O come all ye faithful (Adeste Fidelis) / White Christmas
CDXMAS 1 / Dec '94 / Premier/MFP

☐ LAND OF MY FATHERS
Land of my fathers (Hen wlad fy nhadau) / It's now or never / Moonlight and memory / Funiculi, funicula / Gloria / Be still my soul / Where shall I be / By babylon's wave / Aberystwyth / Calon lan / Onward, ye peoples / Sanctus / Arwelfa / Do you hear the people sing / I dramed a dream / Master of the house / On my own / Drink with me / Empty chairs at empty tables
GRCD 40 / Sep '90 / Grasmere

☐ LET'S FACE THE MUSIC
Tribute to the USA / Non ti scordar di me / True love / Let's face the music and dance / Very best time of year / Nos a bore / In the spirit / Memories of Martha / La vergine degli angeli / I bob un sy'n Ffyddion / Smilin' through / Flower that shattered the stone / They led my Lord away / Jesus Christ Superstar medley
GRCD 81 / Mar '97 / Grasmere

☐ MORRISTON ORPHEUS CHOIR & FRIENDS
Cwm Rhondda (Guide me O thou great redeemer) / Wynwbwn 'fory pan ddan (Let's face the music and dance) / Cymru fach / Nessun dorma / Bugeilio'r Gwenith Gwyn / Llanfair / Ceidward y goleudy / Law yn llaw / Un ydym ni / Finlandia / Y nefoedd / Ni cherdd'n unig fyth (You'll never walk alone)
CDMFP 6213 / Feb '96 / Music For Pleasure

☐ MYFANWY
Myfanwy / With a voice of singing / Kula serenade / High on a hill / Ave verum corpus / Come back to Sorrento / Old rugged cross / Love could I only tell thee / Roll Jordan roll / Scarborough Fair / My little Welsh home / We'll gather lilacs / How soon / Gloria in excelsis / Amazing grace / Eli Jenkin's prayer / Speed your journey / Battle hymn of the Republic / Little drummer boy
CDMFP 6027 / Jul '88 / Music For Pleasure

☐ YOU'LL NEVER WALK ALONE
Dies irae / Let it be me / Anvil chorus / Miserere / Rise up shepherd and follow / You'll never walk alone / Cymru fach / Creation's hymn / Old folks at home (Swanee river) / Li'l Liza Jane / My hero / Martyrs of the arena
GRACC 7 / May '94 / Grasmere

Morrow, Buddy

☐ NIGHT TRAIN
AERO 1034 / Jul '96 / Aerospace

Mors Syphilitica

☐ MORS SYPHILITICA
EFA 01568CD / Sep '96 / Apocalyptic Vision

Morse, Ella Mae

☐ BARRELHOUSE BOOGIE AND BLUES (5CD Set)
Cow cow boogie: Morse, Ella Mae & Freddie Slack / He's my guy: Morse, Ella Mae & Freddie Slack / Mister five by five: Morse, Ella Mae & Freddie Slack / Thrill is gone: Morse, Ella Mae & Freddie Slack / Old Rob Roy: Morse, Ella Mae & Freddie Slack / Get on board little chillun: Morse, Ella Mae & Freddie Slack / Shoo shoo baby / No love no nothin' / Solid potatoe salad / Milkman keep those bottle quiet / Why shouldn't I / Boogie blues / Tess's torch song / Invitation to the blues / Patty cake man / Patty cake man / Hello Suzanne / Take care of you for me / Ya' betcha / Captain Kidd / Jumpin' Jack / Rip van winkle / Buzz me / House of blue lights / Hey Mr. Postman / Your conscience tells me so / Pig foot Pete / That's my home / Mister fine / Merry ha-ha / Pine Top Schwartz / Hoodle addle / Get off it and go / Old Shank's mare / Little further down the road apiece / Early in the morning / Bombo B. Bailey / On the sunny side of the street / Tennessee Saturday night / Sensational / Love ya like mad / Old spider fingers / Love me or leave me / Blacksmith blues / Am I in love / Okie boogie / Organ grinder's swing / It's so exciting / Sleeping at the foot of the bed / Okie boogie / I'm hog tired over you: Morse, Ella Mae & Tennessee Ernie Ford / False hearted girl: Morse, Ella Mae & Tennessee Ernie Ford / Here comes the blues / Male call / Song is for you / You've taken an unfair advantage of me / Greyhound / Jump back honey / Boucin' ball / Find a man for me mama / Good / You for me / Guy who invented kissin' / I'm a rich woman / Big mamou / Big mamou / Big mamou / 'ta'ain't whatcha do / Carioca / Is it any wonder / Forty cups of coffee / Oh you crazy moon / It ain't necessarily so / Have mercy baby / Money honey / Rock me all night long / Daddy daddy / I love you yes I do / 5-10-15 hours / How can you leave a man like this / It's raining tears from my eyes / It's you I love / Happy habit / Dedicated to you / Lovey dovey / Goodnight sweetheart / (We've reached) the point of no return / Give a little time to your lover / Bring back my baby / All I need is you / Livin' livin' / Won't you listen to me baby / Smack dab in the middle / Afraid / Heart full of hope / Yes yes I do / Razzle dazzle / Ain't that a shame / Piddily patter patter / Seventeen / Birmingham / Occasional man / Singing-ing-ing / When boy kiss girl (it's love) / Give me love / Once you've been lovers / What good it'll do me / Down in Mexico / I'm gonna walk / Rock and roll wedding / Coffee date / Put your arms around me honey / You ought to be mine / Mister memory maker / Long time ago / Ac-ecnt-tchu-ate the positive / I'm gonna sit right down and write myself... / My funny valentine / Baby won't you please come home / Rockin' and rollin' / Sway me / I'm hog tired over you / I'm gone / Jersey bounce / Heart and soul / When my sugar walks down the street / I can't get started
BCD 16117 / Aug '97 / Bear Family

Morse, Lee

☐ MUSICAL PORTRAIT 1925-1951, A
TT 420 / May '98 / Take Two

Morse, Steve

☐ STRESSFEST
Stressfest / Rising power / Eyes of a child / Nightwalk / Brave new world / Four minutes to live / Easy way / Glad to be / Delicate business / Live to ride
72902103482 / Jun '96 / High Street

☐ STRUCTURAL DAMAGE (Morse, Steve Band)
Sacred ground / Good to go / Dreamland / Barbary Coast / Smokey Mountain Drive / Slice of time / Native dance / Just out of reach / Rally cry / Foreign exchange / Structural damage
72902103322 / Feb '96 / High Street

Morta Skuld

☐ DYING REMAINS/AS HUMANITY FADES
CDVILE 60 / May '95 / Peaceville

☐ FOR ALL ETERNITY
Bitter / For all eternity / Vicious circle / Justify / Tears / Germ farm / Second thought / Bleeding heart / Crawl inside / Burning daylight
CDVILE 57 / Oct '95 / Peaceville

☐ SURFACE
32272 CD / 26 Jan '98 / Pavement

Mortal

☐ DECO
Moroccan dip / Rouen / Minus one / Mentor / Test drive / Chrysler / Luxor
08543632 / 2 Feb '98 / Westcom

Mortal Constraint

☐ LEGEND OF DEFORMATION, THE
GLA 112692 / Apr '94 / Glasnost

Mortals

☐ LAST TIME AROUND
ES 1228CD / Sep '96 / Estrus

Mortem

☐ DEMON TALES
MRCD 004 / 1 Sep '97 / Merciless

☐ DEVIL SPEAKS IN TONGUES, THE
MRCD 007 / 17 Aug '98 / Merciless

Mortician

☐ HACKED UP FOR BARBECUE
RR 69522 / Feb '97 / Relapse

☐ HOUSE BY THE CEMETERY
Intro/Defiler of the dead / Barbaric cruelties / World domination / Driller killer / House by the cemetery / Procredtion (of the wicked) / Scum / Gateway to beyond / Flesheaters / Noturam demondo
RR 69332 / Jul '97 / Relapse

☐ ZOMBIE APOCALYPSE
Devoured alive / Incinerated / Zombie apocalypse / Slaughterhouse / Hell on earth / Fuck off death / Horrified / Charred corpses / Dissected / Blood harvest
RR 69692 / 13 Apr '98 / Relapse

Mortification

☐ BLOOD WORLD
NB 1182 / May '95 / Nuclear Blast

☐ ENVISION EVANGELENE
NB 159CD / Jul '96 / Nuclear Blast

☐ MORTIFACTION
NB 101CD / Mar '94 / Nuclear Blast

☐ POST MOMENTARY AFFLICTION
NB 082 / Nov '93 / Nuclear Blast

☐ POST MOMENTARY AFFLICTION/ SCROLLS OF THE MONOLITH
NB 214CD / Nov '96 / Nuclear Blast

☐ PRIMITIVE RHYTHM MACHINE
NB 134CD / Aug '95 / Nuclear Blast

Mortimer, Harry

☐ HARRY MORTIMER - A TRIBUTE IN MUSIC (Various Artists)
Cossack / Yeoman of the guard / Three jolly sailormen / Shipbuilders / Trumpet voluntary / Relaxation / Force of destiny / Medallion / Grandfather's clock / Jesu joy of man's desiring / Alla hornpipe / All in the April evening / Life divine / Praise my soul
QPRL 050D / Oct '97 / Polyphonic

Morton, Benny

☐ CLASSICS 1934-1945
CLASSICS 906 / Nov '96 / Classics

Morton, Eddy

☐ TATTERDEMALION
MM 014CD / Nov '96 / New Mountain

Morton, Jelly Roll

☐ ANTHOLOGY 1926-1939
EN 515 / Sep '95 / Encyclopaedia

☐ BLUES AND STOMPS FROM RARE PIANO ROLLS
Jelly Roll blues / Mr. Jelly Lord / London blues / Sweet man / Grandpa's spells / Stratford hunch / Shreveport stomp / Tom cat blues / King Porter stomp / Midnight mama / Tin roof blues / Dead man blues / Pep / Naked dance
BCD 111 / Jul '91 / Biograph

☐ CHICAGO DAYS 1926-1927
158942 / 21 Aug '97 / Jazz Archives

☐ CHICAGO TO NEW YORK 1927-1928
159162 / 1 Jun '98 / Jazz Archives

☐ CLASSIC YEARS, THE
CDSGP 0174 / Feb '96 / Prestige

☐ CLASSICS 1923-1924
CLASSICS 584 / Oct '91 / Classics

☐ CLASSICS 1924-1926
CLASSICS 599 / Sep '91 / Classics

☐ CLASSICS 1926-1928
CLASSICS 612 / Feb '92 / Classics

☐ CLASSICS 1928-1929
CLASSICS 627 / Nov '92 / Classics

☐ CLASSICS 1929-1930
CLASSICS 642 / Nov '92 / Classics

☐ CLASSICS 1930-1939
CLASSICS 654 / Nov '92 / Classics

☐ CLASSICS 1939-1940
CLASSICS 668 / Nov '92 / Classics

☐ COMPLETE JELLY ROLL MORTON'S RED HOT PEPPERS
MM 30380 / Apr '91 / Music Memoria

☐ COMPOSITIONS OF JELLY ROLL MORTON, THE (Various Artists)
Froggie Moore / London (Cafe) Blues / Kansas city stomps / Milenberg joys / Granpa's spells / Chicago breakdown / King Porter stomp / Dead man blues / Black bottom stomp / Sidewalk blues / Schreeveport stomp / Midnight Mama / Windy city blues (Stomp) / Wild man blues / Jelly roll blues / Jungle blues / New King Porter stomp / Sweetheart O'mine / Wolverine blues / Shoe shiner's drag / Pearls / Original Jelly Roll blues
CBC 1027 / Aug '96 / Timeless Jazz

☐ DOCTOR JAZZ
JHR 73521 / '91 / Jazz Hour

☐ DOCTOR JAZZ (His Greatest Recordings)
Ballin' the Jack / Black bottom stomp / Burnin' the iceberg / Chant / Deep Creek / Dirty, dirty, dirty / Dr. Jazz / Don't you leave me here / Freakish / Grandpa's spells / King Porter stomp / Low gravy / Mama Nita / Mamie's blues / Michigan water blues / Mint Julep / Mournful serenade / Pearls / Ponchatrain blues / Seattle hunch / Shreveport stomp / Tia Juana / Turtle twist / Winin' boy blues / Wolverine blues
CDAJA 5125 / Mar '94 / Living Era

☐ DOCTOR JAZZ
Doctor Jazz / Pearls / High society / Climax rag / Beale St. blues / Ballin' the jack / Red hot peppers / Black bottom stomp / Mint julep / Jersey Joe / Mushmouth shuffle / Gambling Jack / Oh didn't he ramble / Wolverine blues / Original Jelly Roll blues / Wild man blues / Kansas City stomps / Grandpa's spells / Strokin' away / Low gravy / Smilin' the blues away / Try me out / Shreveport
74321500212 / Jun '97 / Camden

☐ INTRODUCTION TO JELLY ROLL MORTON 1926-1939, AN
4008 / May '94 / Best Of Jazz

☐ JAZZ GREATS (Morton, Jelly Roll & His Red Hot Peppers)
Black bottom stomp / Dead man blues / Pretty Lil / Wild man blues / Doctor jazz / Sidewalk blues / Steamboat stomp / Turtle twist / Burnin' the iceberg / Red hot pepper: Morton, Jelly Roll Orchestra / Smokehouse blues: Morton, Jelly Roll Orchestra / Original Jelly Roll blues / Pearls / Georgie swing / Shreveport stomp / Deep creek / Kansas city stomps
74321499682 / Feb '98 / RCA Victor

☐ JELLY ROLL MORTON
RTR 79002 / Nov '95 / Retrieval

☐ JELLY ROLL MORTON 1923/24
King Porter stomp / New Orleans joys / Grandpa's spells / Kansas city stomp / Wolverine blues / Pearls / Tia Juana / Shreveport stomp / Froggie Moore / Mamanita / Jelly roll blues / Big foot ham blues / My gal / Muddy water blues / Steady roll / Fish tail blues / High society / Weary blues / Tiger rag
MCD 47018 / Jun '93 / Milestone

☐ JELLY ROLL MORTON VOL.4 (Alternative Takes)
Chant / Sidewalk blues / Dead man blues / Someday sweetheart / Grandpa's spells / Original Jelly Roll blues / Mournful serenade / Pearls / Georgia swing
JSPCD 324 / Apr '91 / JSP

☐ JELLY ROLL MORTON VOL.4 1928-29
152132 / Oct '93 / Hot 'n' Sweet

☐ LAST SESSIONS
Sporting house rag (perfect rag) / Original rags / Crave / Naked dance / Mister Joe / King porter stomp / Winin' boy blues (wineing boy) / Animule dance / Buddy Bolden's blues / Naked dance / Don't you leave me here / Mamie's blues / Michigan water blues / Sweet substitute / Panama / Good old New York / Big lip blues / Why / Get the bucket / If you knew / Shake it / Dirty, dirty, dirty / Swinging the elkes / Mama's got a baby / My home is a Southern town
CMD 14032 / Feb '97 / Commodore Jazz

☐ LIBRARY OF CONGRESS RECORDINGS (3CD Set)
Original quadrille / Tiger rag / Panama / My jelly lord / Miserere / Hyena stomp / Animule ball (in 2 parts) / Demonstration of scat / CC rider / New orleans funeral (extract) / Discourse on jazz (extracts) / Kansas city stomp (parts 1 and 2) / Demonstration of breaks / Darktown strutters' ball / Example of slower type of jazz music / Randall's rag / Maple leaf rag (st louis) in 2 parts / Maple leaf rag (new orleans) in 2 parts / King porter stomp-you can have it / Mamanita / Spanish swat / New orleans blues / La paloma / Creepy feelings (parts 1 and 2) / Crave / Fickle fay creep / Aaron harris / Georgia skin game / Pearls / Pep / Ain't misbehavin' / Jungle blues / Imitation of tony jackson's style / Pretty baby / Mamie desdoumes blues / Game kid / Buddy carter's honky tonk number / Number played against benny frenchy-all that I ask / Wolverine blues / Low down blues / Michegan water blues / This murder ballad / Winin' boy blues / Winin' boy blues / Salty dog / Miserere / Alabama bound (parts 1 and 2) / Sweet peter / State and madison / Freakish / My gal sal / King porter stomp / Original jelly roll blues / Here is the way of the bands would play 'stars and / Buddy bolden's legend / Creole song / If you don't shake / Levee man blues / Naked dance / I hate a man like you / Honky tonk blues (pts 1 and 2) / If I was whisky and you was a duck
CDAFS 10103 / Oct '92 / Affinity

☐ LIBRARY OF CONGRESS RECORDINGS 1938 VOL.1 (Kansas City Stomp)
ROUCD 1091 / Jan '94 / Rounder

☐ LIBRARY OF CONGRESS RECORDINGS 1938 VOL.2 (Anamule Dance)
ROUCD 1092 / Jan '94 / Rounder

☐ LIBRARY OF CONGRESS RECORDINGS 1938 VOL.3 (The Pearls)
ROUCD 1093 / Jan '94 / Rounder

☐ LIBRARY OF CONGRESS RECORDINGS 1938 VOL.4 (Winin' Boy Blues)
ROUCD 1094 / Jan '94 / Rounder

☐ LIBRARY OF CONGRESS RECORDINGS VOL.1
SACD 11 / Jul '93 / Solo Art

☐ MR. JELLY LORD
Dr. Jazz / Original Jelly Roll blues / Mr. Jelly Lord / Beale Street blues / Oh, didn't he ramble / High society / I thought I heard Buddy Holden say / Kansas city stomp / Shoe shiner's drag / Shreveport stomp / Turtle twist / Georgia swing / Wild man blues / Black bottom stomp / Cannonball blues / Wolverine blues / Boogaboo / Grandpa's spell
CD 56017 / Aug '94 / Jazz Roots

☐ OH DIDN'T HE RAMBLE
CDSGP 065 / Aug '93 / Prestige

☐ PIANO ROLLS, THE
7559793632 / Jul '97 / Nonesuch

☐ QUINTESSENCE, THE (1923-1940/2CD Set)
FA 203 / Oct '96 / Fremeaux

☐ RED HOT PEPPERS, NEW ORLEANS JAZZMEN & TRIOS
Oh, didn't he ramble / West End blues / High society / I thought I heard Buddy Bolden say / Kansas city stomp / Shoe shiner's drag / Deep creek / Chant / Original Jelly Roll blues / Mr. Jelly Lord / Shreveport stomp / Turtle twist / Beale Street blues / Georgia swing / Wild man blues / Black bottom stomp / Grandpa's spells / Dr. Jazz / Cannonball blues / Wolverine blues / Boogaboo / Winin' boy blues / Ballin' the Jack
CD 53018 / Jun '88 / Giants Of Jazz

☐ SWEET & HOT
TPZ 1003 / Jul '94 / Topaz Jazz

Morton, Mandy

☐ MAGIC LADY (Morton, Mandy & Spriguns)
ENG 1011 / Apr '94 / English Garden

Morton, Pete

☐ COURAGE, LOVE AND GRACE
HARCD 029 / Apr '95 / Harbour Town

☐ MAD WORLD BLUES
Mad world blues / Songbird / Kurdistan / It is what it is / Down to earth / John barleycorn (intro) / John barleycorn / People who go under / Patriotic claptrap / Malnutrition at standing rock / Keys to love / Crazy man / Katie
HARCD 018 / Oct '93 / Harbour Town

☐ ONE BIG JOKE
Prisoner / Simple love / Water from the houses of our fathers / First day / Little boy's room / Another train / Lucy / Old grey moon / One big joke / Girls like you / River of love / Somewhere in love / Live your life
HARCD 004 / Oct '93 / Harbour Town

☐ URBAN FOLK VOL.1 & 2 (Morton, Pete & Roger Wilson/Simon Edwards)
Love's trainee / Fox / Hey Joe / Lord Randall / Absent love / Old Joe Clark/The Louisiana two step / Della / Bleak mist / Rambleaway / False bride / Shadow of an absent friend / It takes a lot to laugh, it takes a train to cry / Running outta lovin' / When you see those flying saucers / Little musgrave / Goodbye my love / Belly boys / Cuckoo's nest / O' Reilly / Swimming song / None so fair / Love hurts / Derwentwater's farewell
HARCD 032 / Mar '97 / Harbour Town

Morwells

☐ DUB ME (Morwell Unlimited & King Tubby)
Sky ride / Bald head / Morwell's star / Jah star / John Bull / Lightning and thunder / Pegasus rock / Morwell's theme / Concord / Jungle shuffle / Swing and dub / Morpheus special / Ethiopians special / Stepping in HQ
BAFCD 018 / May '97 / Blood & Fire

Mosalini, Juan Jose

☐ BORDONEO Y 900
Bordoneo Y 900 / Lo que vendra / Alma de bohemio / Don goyo / Al maestro con nostagias / Retrato a julio ahumada / De contrapunto / Ojos negros / Danzarin / Adios nonino / Fuego lento / Bien al mango / Dominguera / La bordona / Tres Y dos / Cabulero
LBLC 2507 / Nov '95 / Indigo

☐ LA BORDONA (Mosalini, Juan Jose/ Gustavo Beytelmann/Patrice Caratini)
La bordona / El choclo / Cardo y malvon / Nocturna / La cumparsita / Inspiracion / Palomita blanca / Contrajeando la cumparsita / Inspiracion / Palomita blanca
LBLC 6548 / Jan '92 / Label Bleu

Mosby, Curtis

☐ ON THE WEST COAST AND IN LONDON (Mosby, Curtis & Henry Starr)
BDW 8003 / Nov '96 / Jazz Oracle

Mosca, Sal

☐ CONCERT, A
From here / Co-play / Pay line / All of it / Give a rag a ride / Prelude to a kiss / Murph / Lennie bird / That time / All the music you ever heard / Key of Dee / Bio express / Bits of wits / Fine fettle / Dreams / Family song / Fantacid
JR 8CD / Sep '97 / Jazz

Moscheles, Gary

☐ SHAPED TO MAKE YOUR LIFE EASIER
SSR 171CD / Nov '96 / SSR

Moschos, Aristidis

☐ DULCIMER JOURNEYS
ML 4842 / 11 May '98 / Musurgia Graeca

Moscow Sax Quintet

☐ JAZZNOST TOUR
AJ 71161 / 27 Apr '98 / Arkadia

Moses, Bob

☐ DEVOTION
1211732 / Dec '96 / Soul Note

☐ EAST SIDE (Moses, Bob & Billy Martin)
ITM 1415 / '89 / ITM

☐ STORY OF MOSES
1887032 / May '89 / Gaia

Moses, Pablo

☐ MISSION, THE
Will power / Brain wash / He was bad / Tick tock / One shot / Too much / Never seen / You got a spell / Stand off back off / These are the days / Live up woman / Mission
RASCD 3158 / Jul '95 / Ras
111962 / Jun '97 / Musidisc UK

☐ REVOLUTIONARY DREAM
I love I bring / Be not a dread / Give I fe I name / Come mek we run / Revolutionary dream / Where am I / I man a grasshopper / Corrupted man / Blood money / Lonely singer
198832 / Feb '94 / Musidisc UK

Mosher, David

☐ SYCAMORE TREE
HERM 001CD / Mar '98 / Hermit

Moskowitz, Joseph

☐ ART OF THE CYMBALOM, THE
ROUCD 1126 / Mar '96 / Rounder

Mosley, Rev. W.M.

☐ REV. W.M. MOSLEY 1926-1931
DOCD 5480 / Sep '96 / Document

Moss, Anne Marie

☐ TWO FOR THE ROAD (Moss, Anne Marie & Vivian Lord)
STCD 554 / '92 / Stash

Moss, Buddy

☐ ATLANTA BLUES LEGEND
Hurry home / Red river / Pushin' it / Comin' home / How I feel today / That'll never happen no more / Oh lawdy mama / I'm sitting on top of the world / Kansas City / It was in the weary hour night / Chesterfield / I've got to keep to the highway / Come on round to my house / Step it up and go / Everyday seems like Sunday / I got a woman don't mean me no good / Betty and dupree / Every day every day
BCD 139 / Jun '97 / Biograph

☐ BUDDY MOSS 1930-1941
I'm on my way down home / Diddle da diddle / She looks so good / She's coming back some cold rainy day / Bye bye mama / Unfinished business / I'm sittin' here tonight / Joy rag / You need a woman / Who stole de lock / Tampa strut / Jealous hearted man / Mistreated boy
TMCD 05 / Oct '90 / Travellin' Man

☐ BUDDY MOSS VOL.1 1933
DOCD 5123 / Oct '92 / Document

☐ BUDDY MOSS VOL.3 1935-1941
DOCD 5125 / Oct '92 / Document

Moss, Danny

☐ BIRDLAND, HAMBURG (Moss, Danny Quartet & Jeanie Lambe)
CD 019 / May '96 / Nagel Heyer

☐ SWINGIN' AFFAIR, A (Danny Moss Meets Buddah's Gamblers)
CD 034 / Aug '97 / Nagel Heyer

☐ THA GOOD (Moss, Danny & Jack Jacobs)
PCD 7018 / Aug '94 / Progressive

☐ WEAVER OF DREAMS (Moss, Danny Quartet)
CD 017 / May '96 / Nagel Heyer

Moss, David

☐ MY FAVOURITE THINGS
INTAKTCD 022 / Mar '92 / Intakt

☐ TEXTURE TIME
INTAKTCD 034 / Oct '94 / Intakt

Moss Icon

☐ LYBURNUM
VMFM 013CD / May '97 / Vermiform

Moss, Paul

☐ ROSES AND DIAMONDS (Moss, Paul Group)
Roses and diamonds / Let Peremsky dream / Survivors / Ballet of the bored / Breakfast / Eye on clouds / To Nevsky / Even this is serving my time / Babushka's Odessa tale / Your warm overcoat
ASCCD 22 / 29 Jun '98 / ASC

Mosser, Jonell

☐ AROUND TOWNES
WH 3308CD / Aug '96 / Winter Harvest

Mossman, Mike

☐ GRANULAT (Mossman, Mike & Daniel Schnyder)
1232402 / Nov '91 / Red

☐ MAMA SOHO
Ronita's fantasy / Bossanita / All things you are / Mama Soho / Yvelyse's dance / Brokenhearted / No peeking / My sentiments / Firewalk strut
TCB 9810 / 26 May '98 / TCB

Motards

☐ SATURDAY NIGHT SPECIAL
MTR 358CD / 22 Sep '97 / Empty

Motels

☐ LITTLE ROBBERS
Where do we go from here / Suddenly last summer / Isle of you / Trust me / Monday shut down / Remember the nights / Little robbers / Into the heartland / Tables turned / Footsteps
OW 19342 / 15 Jun '98 / One Way

Moten, Bennie

☐ CLASSICS 1923-1927 (Moten, Bennie Kansas City Orchestra)
CLASSICS 549 / Dec '90 / Classics

☐ CLASSICS 1927-1929
CLASSICS 558 / Oct '91 / Classics

☐ CLASSICS 1929-1930
CLASSICS 578 / Oct '91 / Classics

☐ CLASSICS 1930-1932
CLASSICS 591 / Sep '91 / Classics

☐ INTRODUCTION TO BENNIE MOTEN 1923-1932, AN
4027 / Nov '95 / Best Of Jazz

Mother

☐ WATAMANU
SIXXCD 5 / Nov '96 / Six6

Mother Carey's Chickens

☐ I'LL TELL ME MA
MCC 010694CD / Aug '94 / MCC Music

Mother Destruction

☐ HAGAZUSSA
SR 001CD / 20 Jul '98 / Schwarz Rock

Mother Earth

☐ PEOPLE TREE
Institution man / Jesse / Stardust bubblegum / Mr. Freedom / Warlocks of the mind / Dragster / Find it / People tree / Apple green / Time of the future / Saturation 70 / Illusions / Trip down brain lane
JAZIDCD 083 / Feb '94 / Acid Jazz

☐ STONED WOMAN
JAZIDCD 048 / May '92 / Acid Jazz

☐ STONED WOMAN/YOU HAVE BEEN WATCHING (2CD Set)
SMDCD 171 / 22 Sep '97 / Snapper

Mother Fucker 666

☐ MOTHER FUCKER 666
GH 777CD Æ2 Mar '98 / Get Hip

Mother Hips

☐ BACK TO THE GROTTO
Hey Emilie / Portrero Road / Run around me / Chum / Back to the grotto / This is a man / Precious opal / Two young queens / Stephanie's for LA / Figure 11 / Hot lunch / Turtle bones
74321254512 / Jul '95 / American

☐ PART TIMER GOES FULL
Shut the door / Stoned up the road / Mona Lisa / Poison / Afternoon after afternoon / Magazine / Are you breathing / Petfoot / Sunshine feel / Tehachapi / Beat carousel / Bad Marie / Been lost once / Trunk box
74321289772 / Nov '95 / American

☐ SHOOTOUT (ON 22ND AVENUE)
I can't sleep at all / Mother Hips / Honey dew / Collected some nerve / Single spoon / So much more to learn / Transit / Wind / Shootout on 22nd Avenue / Two river blues / Engagement ring / Whiskey on a southbound / Picture of him / Emergency exit / Super winners
74321403052 / Feb '97 / American

Mother Love Bone

☐ STARDOG CHAMPION
This is Shanrila / Stardog champion / Holy roller / Bone china / Come bite the apple / Stargazer / Heartshine / Captain Hi-top / Man of golden words / Capricorn sister / Gentle groove / Mr. Danny Boy / Crown of thorns / Thru fade away / Mindshaker meltdown / Half ass monkey boy / Chloe dancer / Crown of thorns / Lady Godiva blues
5141772 / Jul '92 / Polydor

Mother May I

☐ SPLITSVILLE
Poison dart / Teenage Jesus / Painted on / Something better / Birthday wish / Disk and Jane / Meet you there / In a box / Never ending riddle / In between / Bastard / All the way in
4782032 / Nov '95 / Columbia

Mother Station

☐ BRAND NEW BAG
Put the blame on me / Love don't come easy / Spirit in me / Black beauty / What's on your mind / Stranger to my soul / Show you the way / Hangin' on / Somebody else will / Love me / Fool for a pretty face / Heart without a home
7567923662 / Oct '94 / Warner Bros.

Mother Superior

☐ MOTHERSHIP HAS LANDED, THE
SPV 08545892 / May '97 / SPV

Motherlight

☐ BOBAK, JONS & MALONE
MER 004 / 23 Mar '98 / Merlin

Mother's Army

☐ PLANET EARTH
USG 10182 / 23 Mar '98 / USG

Mother's Finest

☐ BEST OF MOTHER'S FINEST, THE (Not Yer Mothers Funk)
RE 2137 / Jul '97 / Razor & Tie

Moths

☐ HERON'S DAUGHTER
KSCD 9470 / Jun '97 / Kissing Spell

Motian, Paul

☐ CONCEPTION VESSEL
Georgian bay / Ch'I energie / Rebica / Conception vessel / American Indian:Song of sitting bull / Inspiration from a Vietnamese lullaby
5192792 / Jun '93 / ECM

☐ DANCE
5192822 / Jul '94 / ECM

☐ FLIGHT OF THE BLUE JAY (Motian, Paul Electric Bebop Band)
9100092 / Dec '97 / Winter & Winter

☐ IT SHOULD'VE HAPPENED A LONG TIME AGO (Motian, Paul Trio)
It should've happened a long time ago / Fiasco / Conception vessel / Introduction / India / In the year of the dragon / Two women from padua
8236412 / Apr '85 / ECM

☐ JACK OF CLUBS (Motian, Paul Quintet)
SN 1124 / '86 / Soul Note

☐ LE VOYAGE
Folk song for Rosie / Abacus / Cabla/Drum music / Sunflower / Le voyage
5192832 / Mar '94 / ECM

☐ LIVE IN TOKYO
From time to time / Shakalaka / Kathelin Gray / Hoax / Mumbo jumbo / Bird song / Move V1 / Two women from Padua / It is / Bird song
8491542 / Oct '91 / jMT

☐ PAUL MOTIAN & THE ELECTRIC BEBOP BAND
Shaw nuff / I waited for you / Dance of the infidels / Darn that dream / Hot house / Dizzy atmosphere / Scrapple from the apple / Monk's dreams
5140042 / Jan '93 / jMT

☐ PAUL MOTIAN ON BROADWAY VOL.2
Good morning heartache / You and the night and the music / Moonlight becomes you / But not for me / Bess, oh where's my Bess / I got rhythm / All the things you are / Nice work if you can get it / It might as well be spring / Look to the rainbow / Body and soul
8344402 / May '90 / jMT

☐ PSALM (Motian, Paul Band)
Psalm / White magic / Boomerang / Fantasm / Mandeville / Second hand / Etude / Yahllah
8473302 / Mar '92 / ECM

☐ REINCARNATION OF A LOVEBIRD
Split decision / Ask me now / Two bass hit / Be bop
5140162 / Mar '95 / jMT

☐ SOUND OF LOVE
9100082 / Oct '97 / Winter & Winter

☐ TRIBUTE
Victoria / Tuesdays ends Saturdays / War orphans / Sod house / Song for Che
51928122 / Nov '93 / ECM

☐ TRIO 2000 + ONE
9100322 / Jul '98 / Winter & Winter

☐ TRIOISM (Motian, Paul Trio)
It should've happened a long time ago / Cosmology / Blue midnight / Congestion / Monica's garde / Jack of clubs / Play / In remembrance of things past / Zabel / Endgame
5140122 / Jun '94 / jMT

☐ YOU TOOK THE WORDS OUT OF MY HEART (Live At The Village Vanguard)
5140282 / Apr '96 / jMT

Motion

☐ BEST OF MOTION, THE
HTCD 112 / 20 Apr '98 / Hot Productions

Motion Control

☐ DIGITS
BSCD 017 / 18 May '98 / BeatService

Motions

☐ IMPRESSIONS OF WONDERFUL
CDP 1004DD / Jun '97 / Pseudonym

Motley Crue

☐ DECADE OF DECADENCE 1981-1991
Live wire / Piece of your action / Shout at the devil / Looks that kill / Home sweet home / Smokin' in the boys room / Girls, girls, girls / Wild side / Dr. Feelgood / Kickstart my heart / Teaser / Rock 'n roll junkie / Primal scream / Angela / Anarchy in the UK
7559612042 / Oct '91 / Elektra

☐ DECADENT DISCUSSION
CBAK 4031 / Mar '92 / Baktabak

☐ DOCTOR FEELGOOD
Same old situation / Slice of your pie / Rattlesnake shake / Kickstart my heart / Without you / T.n.t. (Terror 'n go away mad / Dr. Feelgood / Sticky sweet / Time for a change / T 'n' T (Terror 'n Tinseltown) / Dr. Feelgood
9608292 / Sep '89 / Elektra

☐ GENERATION SWINE
Find myself / Afraid / Flush / Generation swine / Confessions / Beauty / Glitter / Anybody out there / Let us prey / Rocketship / Rat like me / Shout at the devil '97 / Brandon
7559619012 / Jun '97 / Elektra

595

☐ MOTLEY CRUE
Power to the music / Uncle Jack / Hooligan's holiday / Misunderstood / Loveshine / Poison apples / Hammered / Till death do us part / Welcome to the numb / Smoke the sky / Droppin' like flies / Drift away
7559615342 / Mar '94 / Elektra

☐ THEATRE OF PAIN
City boy blues / Fight for your rights / Use it or lose it / Smokin' in the boys room / Louder than hell / Keep your eye on the money / Home sweet home / Tonight (we need a lover) / Save our souls / Raise your hands to rock
9604182 / Jul '86 / Elektra

Motley, Frank

☐ BEST OF WASHINGTON DC R'N'B, THE (Motley, Frank & TNT Tribble)
Duel trumpet blues / Bow wow wow / That's alright with me / Herbert's jump / Hurricane lover / Movin' man / Fat man / Groove / Good mama / Half a pint of whiskey / Oh babe / Red hot boogie / Long gone / Annie's boogie
FLYCD 32 / Apr '91 / Flyright

Motor City Mass Choir

☐ SHOUT IN THE HOUSE
Use me / Worthy you are worthy / You are holy / Great is thy faithfulness / We are marching / Battle is the Lord's / Ain't gonna let no rock / Give thanks / God will make a way / No eye has seen / In his presence / We behold you
11412 / Oct '97 / Hosanna

Motor Totemist Guild

☐ ARCHIVE ONE
NML/MTG 1 / Jun '97 / ReR/ Recommended

Motorbass

☐ PANSOUL
Fabulous / Ezio / Flying fingers / Les ondes / Neptune / Wan dence / Genius / Pariscyde / Bad vibes / Off
DIF 001CD / Oct '96 / Different

Motorhead

☐ ACE OF SPADES
Ace of spades / Bite the bullet / Chase is better than the catch / Dance / Fast and loose / Fire, fire / Hammer / Jailbait / Live to win / Love me like a reptile / We are the road crew / Shoot you in the back
ESMCD 312 / Aug '96 / Essential

☐ ACES (The Best Of Motorhead)
Ace of spades / Louie Louie / Bomber / Iron fist / No class / Overkill / I'm the doctor / Go to hell / Bang to rights / Lemmy goes to the pub / America / Speed freak / Sex and outrage / I've got mine / All the aces / Dirty love / Please don't touch / Motorhead / Chase is better than the catch / Deaf forever
SELCD 502 / Mar '98 / Castle Select

☐ ALL THE ACES
CCSCD 427 / May '95 / Castle

☐ ANOTHER PERFECT DAY
Back at the funny farm / Shine / Dancing on your grave / Rock it / One track mind / Another perfect day / Marching off to war / I got mine / Tales of glory / Die you bastard / Turn you around again / Hoochie coochie man / (Don't need) religion
ESMCD 438 / Sep '96 / Essential

☐ BOMBER
Dead men tell no tales / Lawman / Sweet revenge / Sharp shooter / Poison / Stone dead forever / All the aces / Step down / Talking head / Bomber
ESMCD 311 / Aug '96 / Essential

☐ BORN TO LOSE - LIVE TO WIN (The Best Of Lemmy) (Various Artists)
It's alright: *Rockin' Vickers* / Watcher: *Hawkwind* / Lost Johnny: *Hawkwind* / Iron horse: *Motorhead* / Leavin' here: *Motorhead* / Motorhead: *Motorhead* / Louie Louie: *Motorhead* / Dead men tell no tales: *Motorhead* / Stay clean: *Motorhead* / Ace of spades: *Motorhead* / Please don't touch: *Headgirl* / Motorhead (live): *Motorhead* / Stand by your man: *Williams, Wendy O. & Lemmy* / Night of the hawks: *Hawkwind* / Count down: *Jarvinen, Albert Band* / Blue suede shoes: *Lemmy & The Upsetters* / Paradise: *Lemmy & The Upsetters*
VSOPCD 206 / Oct '94 / Connoisseur Collection

☐ COLLECTION, THE (Bear Trap)
Motorhead / Overkill / Talking head / Rock it / Iron fist / I got mine / Steal your face / We are the road crew / Swaggletooth / Stay clean / Iron horse / One track mind / Speedfreak / Loser / (Don't need) religion / Stone dead forever / Sweet revenge / Capricorn / Love me like a reptile / Ace of spades
CCSCD 237 / Mar '90 / Castle

☐ FROM THE VAULTS
Too late too late (live) / Dead men tell no tales (live) / Leaving here (live) / Stone dead forever (live) / Dirty love / Over the top (live) / Under the knife / Remember me I'm gone / Turn you round again / Under the knife / Bomber / Don't do that / Masterplan / No class / Stand by your man
NEXCD 136 / Nov '90 / Sequel

☐ IRON FIST
Iron fist / Heart of stone / I'm the doctor / Go to hell / Loser / Sex and outrage / America / Shut it down / Speed freak / Don't let them grind ya down / (Don't need) religion / Bang to rights
ESMCD 372 / Aug '96 / Essential

☐ KEEP US ON THE ROAD
Motorhead / Vibrator / Keep us on the road / Watcher / Iron horse / Leaving here / On parole / I'm your witchdoctor / Train kept a rollin' / City kids / White line fever
CDRIA 1001 / Sep '96 / Rialto

☐ KING BISCUIT PRESENTS...
Back at the funny farm / Tales of glory / Marchin' off to war / Iron horse/Born to lose / Another perfect day / Shine / I got mine / Interview with Lemmy
KBFHCD 002 / Apr '98 / King Biscuit

☐ LIFELINES (The Complete Collection) (Rockin' Vickers)
I go ape / Someone like me / Zing went the strings of my heart / Stella / It's alright / Stay by me / Dandy / I don't need your kind / Baby never say goodbye / I just stand there / Say Mama / Shake, rattle and roll / What's the matter Jane / Little Rosey
RETRO 803 / Jul '95 / RPM

☐ LIVE
Motorhead / Vibrator / Keep us on the road / Watcher / Iron horse / Leaving here / On parole / I'm your witchdoctor / Train kept a rollin' / City kids / White line fever
JHD 081 / Mar '93 / Tring

☐ MOTORHEAD
Motorhead / Vibrator / Lost Johnny / Iron horse / Born to lose / White line fever / Keep us on the road / Watcher / Train kept a rollin' / City kids / Beer drinkers and hell raisers / On parole / Instro / I'm your witch doctor
CDWIK 2 / Jun '88 / Chiswick

☐ MOTORHEAD
GFS 073 / Jul '97 / Going For A Song

☐ MOTORHEAD ARCHIVES
Treat me nice / Ace of spades / Fire fire / Fast and loose / Sharpshooter / Waltz of the vampire / Fun on the farm / Dirty love / Bastard / You ain't gonna live forever / Step down / Jailbait / Godzilla akimbo / Louie louie / Bomber / Road crew
RMCD 221 / Nov '97 / Rialto

☐ MOTORHEAD LIVE AND LOUD
Motorhead / I'll be your sister / Keep us on the road / Louie louie / Love me like a reptile / Vibrator / Iron horse / Watcher / Ace of spades / Fast and loose / Leavin' here / Tear you down / Train kept a rollin' / On parole / City kids / Road crew
EMPRCD 575 / Jul '95 / Emporio

☐ MOTORHEAD VOL.1 - ACES HIGH
Stone dead forever / All the aces / Poison / Ace of spades / Live to win / America / Jailbait / Please don't touch / Iron fist / Go to hell / Don't let 'em grind ya down / Dance / Heart of stone / I got mine / Tales of glory / Overkill
5507242 / Aug '94 / Spectrum

☐ NO REMORSE
Ace of spades / Motorhead / Jailbait / Stay clean / Too late too late / Killed by death / Bomber / Iron fist / Shine / Dancing on your grave / Metropolis / Snaggletooth / Overkill / Please don't touch / Stone dead forever / Like a nightmare / Emergency / Steal your face / Louie Louie / No class / Iron horse / We are the road crew / Leaving here / Locomotive / Under the knife / Under the knife / Masterplan / No class / Stand by your man
ESDCD 371 / Sep '96 / Essential

☐ NO SLEEP 'TIL HAMMERSMITH
Ace of spades / Stay clean / Metropolis / Hammer / Iron horse / No class / Overkill / We are the road crew / Capricorn / Bomber / Motorhead
ESMCD 313 / Aug '96 / Essential

☐ NO SLEEP AT ALL
Dr. Rock / Dogs / Built for speed / Deaf forever / Killed by death / Traitor / Ace of spades / Eat the rich / Just coz you got the power / Overkill / Stay clean / Metropolis
ESMCD 558 / Jul '97 / Essential

☐ ON PAROLE (Remastered)
Motorhead / On parole / Vibrator / Iron horse/Born to lose / City kids / Watcher / Leaving here / Lost Johnny / Fools / On parole / City kids / Motorhead / Leaving here
CDGO 2072 / Feb '97 / EMI Gold

☐ ORGASMATRON
Deaf forever / Nothing up my sleeve / Ain't my crime / Claw / Mean machine / Built for speed / Ridin' with the driver / Dr. Rock / Orgasmatron / On the road / Steal your face / Claw
ESMCD 557 / Jul '97 / Essential

☐ OVERKILL
Overkill / Stay clean / (I won't) Pay your price / I'll be your sister / Capricorn / No class / Damage case / Tear ya down / Metropolis / Limb from limb
ESMCD 310 / Aug '96 / Essential

☐ OVERNIGHT SENSATION
CD 08518302 / Nov '96 / SPV

☐ PROTECT THE INNOCENT 1975-1992 (4CD Set)
On parole / Leaving here / White line fever / Motorhead / Beer drinkers and hell raisers / City kids / Louie Louie / Tear ya down / Overkill / Too late, too late / No class / Like a nightmare / Stay clean / Metropolis / Bomber / Over the top / Dead men tell no tales / Stone dead forever / All the aces / Ace of spades / Dirty love / Please don't touch: *Motorhead & Girlschool* / Jailbait / We are the roadcrew / Chase is better than the catch / Train kept a rollin' / Motorhead / Hammer / Capricorn / Iron horse / Iron fist / Remember me, I'm gone / Heart of stone / America / Don't let 'em grind ya down / Stand by your man / I got mine / Turn you round again / Tales of glory / Shine / Hoochie coochie man / Dance on your grave / Another perfect day / Snaggletooth / Under the knife / Under the knife / Deaf forever / On the road / Steal your face / Orgasmatron / Dr. Rock / Rock 'n' roll / Dogs / Eat the rich / Wolf / Cradle to the grave / Just 'cos you got the power / Killed by death / Built for speed / Traitor / One to sing the blues / Deadman's hand / Eagle rock / Shut you down / I ain't no nice guy / You better run
ESBCD 562 / Aug '97 / Essential

☐ ROCK 'N' ROLL
Rock 'n' roll / Eat the rich / Black heart / Stone deaf in the USA / Wolf / Traitor / Dogs / All for you / Boogeyman / Cradle the the grave / Just 'cos you got the power
ESMCD 556 / Jul '97 / Essential

☐ SACRIFICE
SPV 08576942 / Dec '96 / SPV

☐ SINGLES COLLECTION, THE
CLP 203 / 20 Apr '98 / Cleopatra

☐ STONE DEAD FOREVER
RRCD 238 / Feb '97 / Receiver

☐ TAKE NO PRISONERS (2CD Set)
Overkill / Stay clean / No class / Bomber / All the aces / Dead men tell no tales / Please don't touch / Ace of spades / Iron fist / Don't need religion / Another perfect day / I got mine / Shine / Killed by death / Deaf forever / Orgasmatron / Rock 'n' roll / Eat the rich / Dirty love / We are the road crew / Fast and loose / Shoot you in the back / Bastard / Stone dead forever / Love me like a reptile / Louie Louie / Jailbait / Tear ya down / Sharpshooter / Motorhead / Leaving here / Train kept a rollin' / On parole / City kids / White line fever
SMDCD 127 / May '97 / Snapper

☐ WE'RE MOTORHEAD AND WE'RE GONNA KICK YOUR ASS
CD 08576942 / Nov '96 / Steamhammer

Motorpsycho

☐ ANGELS AND DAEMONS AT PLAY (3CD Set)
PBMEGA 007 / Jun '97 / Stickman
PSYCHOBABBLE 007CD / Mar '97 / Stickman

☐ BLISSARD
INDIGO 39022 / Nov '96 / Indigo
PSYCHOBABBLE 003 / Apr '97 / Stickman

☐ TRUST US (2CD Set)
PSYCHOBABBLE 012CD / 30 Mar '98 / Stickman

Motors

☐ AIRPORT (The Motors' Greatest Hits)
Dancing the night away / Sensation / Airport / Metropolis / Love and loneliness / Forget about you / Emergency / Tenement steps / Today / Freeze / That's what John said / You beat the hell outta me / Soul redeemer / Cold love / Time for make up / Love round the corner / Here comes the hustler
CDVM 9032 / Jan '95 / Virgin

Mott The Hoople

☐ ALL THE YOUNG DUDES
All the young dudes / Honaloochie boogie / All the way from Memphis / Roll away the stone / Golden age of rock 'n' roll / Foxy foxy / Saturday gig / She's a star / Yesterday / Forgotten dreams / Steamer / Yes
RM 1547 / Apr '97 / BR Music

☐ BALLAD OF MOTT, THE (A Retrospective/2CD Set)
Rock 'n' roll Queen / Walkin' with a mountain / Waterlow / Sweet Angeline / All the young dudes / Momma's little jewel / One of the boys / Sucker / Sweet Jane / Sea diver / Reach for love/After lights / Ballad of Mott The Hoople / Drivin' sister / Violence / Rose / I wish I was your mother / Honaloochie boogie / All the way from Memphis / Whizz kid / Hymn for the dudes / Golden age of rock 'n' roll / Rest in peace / Marionette / Crash street kidds / Born late '58 / Roll away the stone / Where do you all come from / Henry and the H-bomb / Foxy foxy / Saturday gigs / Lounge lizard / Through the looking glass / American pie
4744202 / Jun '96 / Columbia

☐ DRIVE ON
By tonight / Monte Carlo / She does it / I'll tell you something / Stiff upper lip / Love now / Apologies / Great white wail / Here we are / It takes one to know one / I can show you how it is
4872372 / Mar '97 / Columbia

☐ GREATEST HITS
All the way from Memphis / Honaloochie boogie / Hymn for the dudes / Born late '58 / All the young dudes / Roll away the stone / Ballad of Mott the Hoople / Golden age of rock 'n' roll / Foxy foxy / Saturday gigs
CD 32007 / Apr '89 / CBS

☐ MOTT
All the way from Memphis / Whizz kid / Hymn for the dudes / Honaloochie boogie / Violence / Drivin' sister / Ballad of Mott the Hoople / I'm a Cadillac / El camino dolo roso / I wish I was your mother
4674022 / Mar '95 / Columbia

☐ MOTT THE HOOPLE
Dear Louise / Hot footin' / World cruise / Brother soul / 1-2-3-4 Kickalong blues / Wild in the streets
SEACD 7 / May '93 / See For Miles

☐ MOTT THE HOOPLE
GFS 065 / Jul '97 / Going For A Song

☐ MOTT THE HOOPLE/MAD SHADOWS
You really got me / At the crossroads / Laugh at me / Backsliding fearlessly / Rock 'n' roll Queen / Rabbit food and Toby time / Half moon bay / Wrath and roll / Thunderbuck ram / No wheels to ride / You are one of us / Walkin' with a mountain / I can feel / Threads of iron / When my minds gone
EDCD 361 / Jan '93 / Edsel

☐ ORIGINAL MIXED UP KIDS (The BBC Sessions 1970-1971)
WINCD 084 / Jul '96 / Windsong

☐ PHILADELPHIA 1972
PILOT 005 / Apr '97 / Burning Airlines

☐ SHOUTING AND POINTING
Shouting and pointing / Collision course / Storm / Career (No such thing as rock 'n' roll) / Hold on you're crazy / See you again / Too short (I don't care) / Broadside outcasts / Good times
4894922 / 26 Jan '98 / Columbia

☐ WALKING WITH A MOUNTAIN (The Best Of Mott The Hoople 1969-1972)
Rock 'n' roll queen / At the crossroads / Thunderbuck ram / Whiskey woman / Waterlow / Moon upstairs / Second love / Road to Birmingham / Black scorpio (momma's little jewel) / You really got me / Walkin' with a mountain / No wheels to ride / Keep a knockin' / Midnight lady / Death may be your Santa Claus / Darkness darkness / Growing man blues / Black hills
IMCD 87 / Jun '90 / Island

Mould, Bob

☐ BLACK SHEETS OF RAIN
Black sheets of rain / One good reason / Hanging tree / Hear me calling / Disappointed / It's too late / Stop your crying / Last night / Out of your life / Sacrifice / Let there be peace
CDVUS 21 / Apr '92 / Virgin

☐ BOB MOULD
CRECD 188 / Apr '96 / Creation

☐ POISON YEARS
Black sheets of rain / It's too late / Stop your crying / Out of your life / Hanging tree / Sacrifice / Wishing well / See a little light / All those people know / Compositions for the young and old / If you're true / Poison years / Brasilia crossed with Trenton / Shoot out the lights
CDVM 9030 / May '94 / Virgin

☐ WORKBOOK
Sunspots / Wishing well / Heartbreak a stranger / See a little light / Poison years / Sinners and their repentances / Brasilia crossed with Trenton / Compositions for the young and old / Lonely afternoon / Dreaming, I am whichever way the wind blows
CDVUS 2 / Jul '89 / Virgin

Moulin, Marc

☐ SAM SUFFY
CR 003CD / Apr '97 / Counterpoint

Mound City Blues Blowers

☐ CLASSICS 1935-1936
CLASSICS 895 / Oct '96 / Classics

☐ MOUND CITY BLUES BLOWERS 1935-1936
What's the reason I'm not pleasin' you / She's a Latin from Manhattan / You've been taking lessons in love / (Back home again in) Indiana / Red sails in the sunset / I'm sittin' high on a hilltop / On Treasure Island / Thanks a million / Eeny meeny miney Mo / Little bit independent / I'm shootin' high / I've got my fingers crossed / High Society / Muskrat ramble / Broken record / Music goes 'round and around / I'm gonna sit right down and write myself a letter / Mama don't allow it / Rhythm in my nursery rhymes / I hope Gabriel likes my music / You hit the spot / Spreadin' rhythm around / Saddle your blues to a wild mustang / Wah-hoo / I'm gonna clap my hands
CBC 1018 / Aug '94 / Timeless Historical

Moundanda, Antoine

☐ GEANT
Retraite / M'sangou / Kouelohele / Bako / Kesse Kesse / Havachibora / Liwa / Wali ti mbi / Cheu / Mancongo
LBLC 2541 / 23 Feb '98 / Indigo

Mounsey, Paul

☐ NAHOO
Passing away / Alba / Journeyman / Dalmore / Stranger in a strange land / As terras baixas da / Hollanda / From ebb to flood / I will go / My faithful fond one / Illusion
IRCD 029 / Jan '95 / Iona

☐ NAHOO TOO
IRCD 050 / Feb '98 / Iona

Mount Pilot

☐ HELP WANTED LOVE NEEDED CARETAKER
Drop D blues / Rain / 3 years in October / Boulevard / County swing / Taken all I've got / Cretin / Im gone / Gyspy queen / Been forgotten / Funeral train / Walk alone / Arkansas ambush
DRCD 7029 / Mar '98 / Doolittle

Mount Shasta

☐ PUT THE CREEP ON
GR 013CD / Apr '94 / Skingraft

☐ WATCH OUT
GR 52CD / 6 Apr '98 / Skingraft

☐ WHO'S THE HOTTIE
GR 31CD / May '95 / Skingraft

Mountain

☐ BEST OF MOUNTAIN, THE
Never in my life / Taunta (Sammy's tune) / Nantucket sleighride / Roll over Beethoven / For Yasgur's farm / Animal trainer and the toad / Mississippi Queen / Kings Chorale / Boys in the band / Don't look around / Crossroader
4663352 / Aug '90 / CBS

☐ CLIMBING
Mississippi queen / Theme for an imaginary western / Never in my life / Silver paper / For Yasgur's farm / To my friend / Laird / Sittin' on a rainbow / Boys in the band
4721802 / Feb '95 / Columbia

☐ FLOWERS OF EVIL
Flowers of evil / King's chorale / One last cold kiss / Crossroader / Pride and passion / Mississippi queen
BGOCD 113 / Jun '97 / Beat Goes On

☐ OVER THE TOP (2CD Set)
Blood of the sun / Long red / Blind man / Dreams of milk and honey / Southbound train / Never in my life / Silver paper / For yasgur's farm / To my friend / Sittin' on a rainbow / Stormy Monday / Waiting to take you away / Don't look around / Taunta (Sammy's tune) / Nuntucket sleighride (To Owen Coffin) / You can't get you away / Animal trainer and the toad / My lady / Travellin' in the dark (To EMP) / Great train robbery / Flowers of evil / One last cold kiss / Crossroader / Roll over Beethoven / Back where I belong / Bardot damage / Shimmy on the footlights / Talking to the angels
4848982 / Jun '96 / Columbia

☐ ROAD GOES ON FOREVER, THE (Mountain Live)
Long red / Waiting to take you away / Crossroader / Nantucket sleigh
BGOCD 111 / Jun '97 / Beat Goes On

☐ TWIN PEAKS
Never in my life / Imaginary western / Blood of the sun / Guitar solo / Nantucket sleigh ride / Nantucket sleigh ride / Crossroader Mississippi queen / Silver paper / Roll over Beethoven
4721832 / 26 Jan '98 / Columbia

Mountain Ash Band

☐ HERMIT, THE
DORIS 2 / Jan '96 / Vinyl Tap

Mountain Bus

☐ SUNDANCE
EVA 32 / 1 Jun '98 / EVA

Mountain Goats

☐ BEAUTIFUL RAT SUNSET
SHR 99 / Dec '96 / Shrimper

☐ FULL FORCE GALESBURG
EJ 11CD / 10 Nov '97 / Emperor Jones

☐ NINE BLACK POPPIES
EJ 02CD / Nov '95 / Emperor Jones

☐ SWEDEN
SHR 68CD / Dec '96 / Shrimper

Moura, Paulo

☐ ALMA BRASILEIRA
ML 51022 / 14 Apr '98 / Musica Latina

☐ CARIMBO DO MOURA
ML 51024 / 14 Apr '98 / Musica Latina

☐ GAFIEIRA ETC & AL
CDGR 203 / Nov '97 / Charly

☐ PIXINGUINHA (Moura, Paulo & Os Batutas)
Ainda me rocordo / Segura ele / Proezas de solon / Cochichandon / Ingenuo / Lamentos / Carinhoso / Misura e manda / Batuque na cozinha / Oito batutas / Pele telefone / Rosa / Naquele tempo / Vou vivendo / Um a zero / Urubu malandro
BJAC 50192 / 24 Aug '98 / Blue Jackel

☐ RIO NOCTURNES
Guadeloupe / Capricornio / Rio nocturne / Baleias / Jumento elegante / Barbara's vatapa / Sereia do leblon / Mulatas / Tumbalele / Concierto brasitalian / Tarde de chuva / Casamento em xaxei
158162 / Aug '92 / Messidor

☐ TEMPOS FELIZES
ML 51023 / 14 Apr '98 / Musica Latina

Mourn

☐ MOURN
RISE 10CD / Jun '95 / Rise Above

Mourning

☐ GREETINGS FROM HELL
FDN 2005CD / Jul '93 / Foundation 2000

Mourning Phase

☐ MOURNING PHASE
KSCD 9440 / Jun '97 / Kissing Spell

Mourning Reign

☐ MOURNING REIGN, THE
BR 102CD / 9 Mar '98 / Beatrocket

Mourning Sign

☐ ALIENOR
GOD 015CD / Jun '95 / Godhead

☐ MOURNING SIGN
GOD 016CD / Oct '95 / Godhead

☐ MULTIVERSE
GOD 022CD / Jan '97 / Godhead

Mouse & The Traps

☐ FRATERNITY YEARS, THE
Public execution / Maid of sugar, maid of spice / Nobody cares / Cryin' inside / I'm a man: St. John, Chris / Lie, beg, borrow and steal / I've got her love: St. John, Chris / I am the one / Like I know you do / Sometimes you just can't win / All for you / Do the best you can / Look at the sun / You don't love me (you don't care): St. John, Chris / Promises promises / I satisfy / Requiem for Sarah / LOVE love / Ya ya / Good times / Hand in hand / You are my sunshine / I wonder where the birds fly / Mohair Sam / As far as the sea: St. John, Chris
CDWIKD 171 / May '97 / Big Beat

☐ PUBLIC EXECUTION
EVAB 15 / 1 Jun '98 / EVA

Mouse

☐ LADYKILLER
FID 35 / 15 Dec '97 / Fid

Mouse On Mars

☐ AUTODITACKER
Sui shop / Juju / Twirt shoeblade / Das tamagnochi / Dark FX / Scat / Tux and damask / Sehnsud / X-files / Scnick schnack melt made / Rodio / Maggots hell wings
PURECD 070 / Aug '97 / Too Pure

☐ IAORA TAHITI
Stereomission / Kompod / Staurday night world / Cup fieber / Schunkel / Gocard / Kanu / Bib / Schlecktron / Preprise / Pap Antoine / Omnibuzz / Hallo / Die innere orange
PURECD 048 / Aug '95 / Too Pure

☐ VULVA LAND
PURECD 036 / Jun '94 / Too Pure

Mousetrap

☐ CEREBRAL REVOLVER
GROW 0032 / Jul '93 / Grass

☐ LOVER
GROW 0232 / Jun '94 / Grass

Mouskouri, Nana

☐ MAGIC OF NANA MOUSKOURI, THE
Only love / White rose of Athens / Never on a Sunday / Yesterday / Amazing grace / Try to remember / Power of love / Bridge over troubled water / Only time will tell / Morning has broken / And I love you so / Ave Maria / Love me tender / Nights in white satin / Song for liberty / Lonely shepherd
8364927 / Sep '88 / Philips

☐ PASSPORT
Amazing grace / And I love you so / Bridge over troubled water / Cu-cu-rru-cu-cu-paloma / Day is done / Enas mithos / Four and twenty hours / I have a dream / If you love me / Last rose of Summer / Loving song / Milisse Mou / My friend the sea / Never on Sunday / Odos oniron / Over and over / Plaisir d'amour / Seasons in the sun / Try to remember / Turn on the Sun / White rose of Athens
8307642 / Jul '93 / Mercury

☐ RETURN TO LOVE
5345732 / May '97 / Mercury

Mouth Music

☐ BLUE DOOR GREEN SEA
TRECD 209 / Jul '98 / Triple Earth

☐ MODI
TRECD 111 / Feb '95 / Triple Earth

☐ MOUTH MUSIC
Bratach bana / Mor a' cheannaich / Chi mi na morbheana / Mile marbh'aisg a'ghaol / Froach a ronaigh / Co ni mire rium / Martin Martin / I bhi a da / Air fair a lail o
TRECD 109 / Aug '90 / Triple Earth

☐ MOVE ON/COLOUR OF MY LOVE
TEMCD 113 / Jul '98 / Triple Earth

☐ SHORELIFE
TRECD 113 / Oct '94 / Triple Earth

Mouthpiece

☐ WHAT WAS SAID
NA 020CD / Jul '96 / New Age

Mouzon, Alphonse

☐ MIND TRANSPLANT
Mind transplant / Snowbound / Carbon dioxide / Ascorbic acid / Happiness is loving you / Some of the things people do / Golden rainbows / Nitroglycerin / Real thing
RPM 116 / Sep '93 / RPM

☐ MORNING SUN
I'm glad that you're here / When Linda smiles / Lullaby for little alphonse / To Mom with love / Tell me / Morning sun / If tomorrow comes / Just because of you / Do I have to / Space invaders
TENAC 92102 / Aug '97 / Tenacious

☐ NIGHT IS STILL YOUNG
Protocol / Daddy's blues / Daddy's little girl / Promise kept / Waltz for Emma / To drum or not to drum / What are you doing later on / Seduction / Night is still young / Slammin' / Just another Samba / Undulation / Africa
TENAC 92112 / Mar '97 / Tenacious

☐ SKY IS THE LIMIT, THE
Why don't you break it / Jean-Pierre / Do you wanna dance / Making love with you / Come and see what I've got / Sky is the limit / Starting all over again / Rock 'n' roll waltz / Don't break my funk / Old friends / Night for love / One more time / I'm glad that you're here
TENAC 92082 / Aug '97 / Tenacious

Move

☐ BBC SESSIONS, THE
You'd better believe me / Night of fear / Stop get a hold of myself / Kilroy was here / Walk on the water / I can hear the grass grow / Morning dew / Flowers in the rain / So you wanna be a rock 'n' roll star / Stephanie knows who / Cherry blossom clinic / Hey grandma / Fire grandma / Weekend / It'll be me / Useless information / Kentucky woman / Higher and higher / Long black veil / Wild tiger woman / Piece of my heart / Blackberry way / Going back / California girls / Christian life
SFRSCD 069 / 20 Jul '98 / Strange Fruit

☐ BEST OF THE MOVE, THE
Blackberry Way / Curly / Yellow rainbow / I can hear the grass grow / Fire brigade / Hey Grandma / Kilroy was here / Night of fear / Feel too good / Brontosaurus / Flowers in the rain / Walk upon the water / Stephanie knows who / Turkish tram conductor blues / Useless information / Weekend / Cherry blossom clinic revisited / So you want to be a rock 'n' roll star
MCCD 009 / Feb '91 / Music Club

☐ BEST OF THE MOVE, THE
REP 4686 / Oct '97 / Repertoire

☐ LOOKING ON
REP 4692 / Feb '98 / Repertoire

☐ MESSAGE FROM THE COUNTRY
Message from the country / Ella James / No time / Don't mess up / Until your Mama's gone / It wasn't my idea to dance / Minister / Ben Crawley steel company / Words of Aaron / My Marge
BGOCD 238 / Jun '94 / Beat Goes On

☐ MOVE, THE
CUCD 15 / Oct '94 / Disky

☐ MOVE, THE
REP 4690 / Feb '98 / Repertoire

☐ MOVE, THE
MCCD 345 / 20 Apr '98 / Music Club

☐ MOVEMENTS (30th Anniversary Anthology/3CD Set)
Night of fear / Disturbance / I can hear the grass grow / Wave the flag and stop the train / Yellow rainbow / Kilroy was here / Lemon tree / Weekend / Walk upon the water / Flowers in the rain / Useless information / Zing went the strings of my heart / Girl outside / Fire brigade / Mist on a monday morning / Cherry blossom clinic / Hey grandma / Disturbance / Wild tiger woman / Blackberry way / Something / Curly / This time tomorrow / Hello suzie / Beautiful daughter / Second class / Wild tiger woman blues / Curly where's your girly / Something / Vote for me / Looking in / Turkish tram conductor blues / What / When Alice comes back to the farm / Open up said the world at the door / Brontosaurus / Lightning never strikes twice / So you want to be a rock and roll star / Stephanie knows who / Something else / It'll be me / Piece of my heart / Too much in love / (Your love keeps lifting me) higher and higher / Sunshine help me
WESX 302 / 13 Oct '97 / Westside

☐ SHAZAM
REP 4691 / Feb '98 / Repertoire

Move D

☐ EXPLORING THE PSYCHEDELIC LANDSCAPE (Move D & Peter Namlook)
PK 08121 / Dec '96 / Fax

Mover

☐ MOVER
Kick the beam / Move over / Junk / Samba diablo / Tricolore / Stand / We got it going on / Bite the bullet / Classic no.9 / Let's bond / Stay gold
MOVE 004CD / 25 May '98 / Superior Quality

☐ ORIGINAL RECIPE
MR 068CD / May '97 / Man's Ruin

Movietone

☐ DAY AND NIGHT
Sun drawing / Blank like snow / Useless landscape / Summer nights of the acacias / Crystallisation of salt at night
WIGCD 036 / 22 Sep '97 / Domino

☐ MOVIETONE
PUNK 10CD / Nov '95 / Planet

Moving Cloud

☐ MOVING CLOUD
GLCD 1150 / Feb '95 / Green Linnet

Moving Hearts

☐ DARK END OF THE STREET
229250144 / May '95 / WEA

☐ LIVE HEARTS
2292402302 / May '95 / WEA

☐ STORM, THE
Lark / Storm / Tribute to Peardar O Donnell / Titanic / Finore / May morning dew
BUACD 892 / Feb '89 / Son

Moving Sidewalks

☐ FLASH
AFT 2 / Sep '97 / Afterglow

Moving Targets

☐ BRAVE NOISE
Failing / Brave noise / Nothing changes and things are going by / Car crash / Seperate hearts / Instrumental / In the way / 2500 club / Into the forest / June 7th / Through the door / Lights
TAANG 030CD / Jan '93 / Taang

☐ FALL
TG 93042 / May '91 / Roadrunner

☐ TAKE THIS RIDE
TAANG 73CD / Jun '93 / Taang

Moviola

☐ GLEN ECHO AUTOHARP
SO 7 / Feb '97 / Spirit Of Orr

☐ YEAR YOU WERE BORN
AW 040 / Dec '96 / Anyway

Mowatt, Judy

☐ BLACK WOMAN
Strength to go through / Concrete jungle / Slave queen / Put it on / Zion chant / Black woman / Down in the valley / Joseph / Many are called / Sisters chant
GRELCD 111 / Jul '88 / Greensleeves

☐ LOVE IS OVERDUE
Sing our own song / Love is overdue / Try a little tenderness / Long long time / Rock me / Get up and chant / Screwface / Hold dem jah / One more time / Who is he
GRELCD 103 / Jul '87 / Greensleeves

☐ ONLY A WOMAN
SHANCD 43007 / '88 / Shanachie

☐ WORKING WONDERS
SHANCD 43028 / Aug '85 / Shanachie

Mowrey, Dude

☐ DUDE MOWREY
07822186782 / Jul '94 / Arista

Moxham, Stuart

☐ CARS IN THE GRASS (Moxham, Stuart & The Original Artists)
My criteria / Hello world / Return to work / Tug of love / Night by night / Soft eject / Against creating war / God knows / Appropriate response / Cars in the grass / Drifting west
ASKCD 035 / Mar '95 / Vinyl Japan

☐ SIGNAL PATH (Moxham, Stuart & The Original Artists)
Over the sea / Between edits / Her shoes (are right) / Knives (always fall) / Broken heart blues / It says here / No one road / That's my love / I wonder why / Remember / It took you / Mutual gaze / Yeah x 3 / Unit of desire
FGAO 015 / Mar '93 / Feel Good All Over

Moxy

☐ SELF DESTRUCTION
PACE 001EX / Dec '97 / Pacemaker

Moxy Fruvous

☐ BARGAINVILLE
Stuck in the 90's / Drinking song good night irene / River valley / Video bargainville / Lazy boy / Fell in love / Gulf war song / Laika / Bittersweet / Darlington darling / King of spain / Morphee / My baby loves a bunch of authors / B j don't cry / Spiderman
4509931342 / Apr '94 / WEA

Moyet, Alison

☐ ALF
Love resurrection / Honey for the bees / For you only / Invisible / Steal me blind / All cried out / Money mile / Twisting the knife / Where hides sleep
4838362 / 27 Jul '98 / Columbia

☐ RAINDANCING
Weak in the presence of beauty / Ordinary girl / You got me wrong / Without you / Sleep like breathing / Is this love / Blow wind blow / Glorious love / When I say (no giveaway) / Stay
4501522 / Mar '90 / Columbia

☐ SINGLES
First time I ever saw your face / Only you / Nobody's diary / Situation / Love resurrection / All cried out / Invisible / That ole devil called love / Is this love / Weak in the presence of beauty / Ordinary girl / Love letters / It won't be long / Wishing you were here / This house / Falling / Whispering your name / Getting into something / Ode to boy II / Solid wood
4806632 / May '95 / Columbia

☐ SINGLES/LIVE (2CD Set)
First time ever I saw your face / Only you / Nobody's diary / Situation / Love resurrection / All cried out / Invisible / That ole devil called love / Is this love / Weak in the presence of beauty / Ordinary girl / Love letters / It won't be long / Wishing you were here / This house / Falling / Whispering your name / Getting into something / Ode to boy II / Solid wood / Getting into something / Chain of fools / Love letters / All cried out / Dorothy / Falling / Ode to boy / Is this love / Nobody's diary / Whispering your name / There are worse things I could do
4806339 / Apr '96 / Columbia

Mr. B

☐ SHINING THE PEARLS
BP 71886 / Dec '95 / Blind Pig

Mr. Barth

☐ MY OLD BLUES SUITS
PLUMPCD 101 / Mar '97 / Plumphouse

Mr. Big

☐ BIG, BIGGER, BEST
Addicted to that rush / Rock 'n' roll over / Green-tinted sixties mind / To be with you / Just take my heart / Daddy, brother, lover, little boy / Wild world / Colorado bulldog / Nothing but love / Promise her the moon / Take cover / Where the wind blows / Seven impossible days / Not one night / Unnatural / Stay together
7567806852 / Apr '97 / East West

☐ BUMP AHEAD
Colorado bulldog / Price you gotta pay / Promise her the moon / What's it gonna be / Wild world / Mr. Gone / Whole world's gonna know / Nothing but love / Temperamental / Ain't seen love like that / Mr. Big
7567824952 / Sep '93 / Atlantic

☐ HEY MAN
Trapped in toyland / If that's what it takes / Take cover / Little mistake / Fool us today / Mama d / Dancin' right into the flame / Out of the underground / Jane doe / Goin' where the wind blows / Chain / Where do I fit in
7567806482 / Feb '96 / Atlantic

☐ LEAN INTO IT
Daddy / Brother / Lover / Little boy / Alive and kickin' / Green tinted sixties mind / CDFF-Lucky this time / Voodoo kiss / Never say never / Just take my heart / My kinda woman / Little loo loose / Road to ruin / To be with you
7567822092 / Apr '91 / Atlantic

☐ LIVE - MR BIG
Daddy, brother, lover, little boy (the electric drill song) / Alive and kickin' / Green tinted sixties mind / Just take my heart / Road to ruin / Lucky this time / Addicted to that rush / To be with you / Thirty days in the hole / Shy baby / Baba O'Riley
7567805232 / Nov '92 / Atlantic

☐ MR. BIG
Addicted to that rush / Wind me up / Merciless / Had enough / Blame it on my youth / Take a walk / Big love / How can you do what you do / Anything for you / Rock 'n' roll over
7819902 / Jul '89 / Atlantic

Mr. Bloe

☐ GROOVIN' WITH MR. BLOE
Groovin' with Mr. Bloe / Straight down the line / Smokey Joe / Mighty mouse / Land of 1000 dances / Dancing machine / Chicken feed / If you've gotta make a fool of somebody / Sugar sugar / Doo-di-dog-dad / Ja da / Curried soul
5526362 / Feb '97 / Spectrum

Mr. Bungle

☐ DISCO VOLANTE
Everyone I went to High School with is dead / Chemical marriage / Carry stress in the jaw / Desert search for techno Allah / Violenza domestica / After school special / Phlegmatics / Ma meeshka mow skwoz / Bends / Backstrokin' / Platypus / Merry go bye bye
8286942 / 17 Aug '98 / Slash

☐ MR. BUNGLE
Quote, unquote / Slowy growing deaf / Squeeze me macaroni / Carousel / My ass is on fire / Hypnotic / Again / Stand tall / Sea / on fire / Girls of porn / Love is a fist / Dead goon
8282762 / Sep '91 / Slash

Mr. C

☐ FANTAZIA DJ COLLECTION VOL.3 (Various Artists)
FANTA 10CD / Mar '97 / Fantazia

☐ X-MIX VOL.6 (Electronic Storm) (Various Artists)
K7 044CD / Apr '96 / Studio K7

Mr. Doo

☐ PRESENTS THE DOO EXPERIENCE
FILERCD 418 / Nov '91 / Profile

Mr. Electric Triangle

☐ KOSMOSIS IN DUB
TKCD 38 / Sep '96 / 2 Kool

Mr. Epp

☐ RIDICULING THE APOCALYPSE
SUPER 06 / Nov '96 / Super Electro

Mr. Fox

☐ MR. FOX/THE GIPSY
Join us in our game / Hanged man / Gay goshawk / Rip Van Winkle / Mr. Trill's song / Little woman / Salisbury plain / Ballad of Neddy Dick / Leaving the dales / Mr. Fox / Gipsy / Aunt Lucy Broadwood / House carpenter / Elvira Madigan / Dancing song / All the good times
ESMCD 433 / Oct '96 / Essential

Mr. Gloria's Head

☐ DARLING'S OUT OF COCKTAIL
ALIVE 0026 / Nov '96 / Bomp

Mr. Gone

☐ LOOKING AT THE FUTURE IN THE REARVIEW MIRROR
Equation: boogie / Mosquito coast '94 - '96 / Les cinq notes magiques / Is it modern interlude 2 / I love Paris interlude 3 / Looking at the future in the rearview mirror / La pomme d'Adam / Souvenirs sapphique / No disrespect interlude 1 / I love jazz / That's an earthquake / Les cinq notes magiques
IBCD 8 / Apr '97 / Internal Bass

Mr. Hageman

☐ TWIN SMOOTH SNOUTS
STAR 5CD / Dec '96 / Starlight

Mr. Hate

☐ FRAGMENTS
USG 10132 / 20 Apr '98 / USG

Mr. Mister

☐ BROKEN WINGS
Broken wings / Hunters of the night / Black/white / Kyrie / Is it love / Uniform of youth / Stand and deliver / Healing waters / Something real / Tube / Control / Watching the world / Power over me / Man of a thousand dances / Run to her / Welcome to the real world
743215695929 / 23 Mar '98 / Camden

Mr. President

☐ NIGHTCLUB, THE
3984207352 / 20 Apr '98 / WEA

☐ UP 'N' AWAY
Up'n away / Up 'n away / I'll follow the sun / 4 on the floor / I believe / On my mind / Outro / Keep it up / I would die for you / Gonna get along (without you now) / Close to your heart / Sweet lies / Easy come easy go / Never leave me / Close to you / Intro
4509997002 / Jun '95 / East West

☐ WE SEE THE SAME SUN
Intro / Coco jamboo / Side to side / Goodbye, lonely heart / I give you my heart / Love below me / Show me the way / Olympic dreams / You can get it / Don't you ever stop / Turn it up / I love the way you love me / I love to love / Where the sun goes down / Outro
0630149462 / Jul '97 / East West

Mr. Quimby's Beard

☐ OUT THERE
DMCD 1035 / 24 Nov '97 / Demi-Monde

Mr. Review

☐ MR. REVIEW/SPY EYE (Mr. Review/ Spy Eye)
PHZCD 81 / Nov '94 / Unicorn

Mr. So & So

☐ COMPENDIUM
Closet skeletons / Missionary / Bolton-eeny-noo / Tick a box / Primrose days / Sixes and sevens / Hobson the traveller
CYCL 114 / Jul '97 / Cyclops

☐ PARAPHERNALIA
PMCD 004 / '96 / Pagan Media

Mr. Spats

☐ DREAM PATROL
NOVA 8913 / Jan '93 / Nova

Mr. T Experience

☐ ALTERNATIVE IS HERE TO STAY
LOOKOUT 126CD / Sep '95 / Lookout

☐ BIG BLACK BUGS BLEED BLUE BLOOD
LOOKOUT 145CD / May '97 / Lookout

☐ EVERYONE'S ENTITLED TO THEIR OWN OPINION
LOOKOUT 39CD / Jul '95 / Lookout

☐ LOVE IS DEAD
LOOKOUT 134CD / Jan '96 / Lookout

☐ OUR BODIES
LOOKOUT 80CD / Jul '95 / Lookout

☐ REVENGE IS SWEET AND SO ARE YOU
LK 180CD / 8 Sep '97 / Lookout

Mr. Z

☐ DOT'S POLKATAINMENT
TCD 1034 / Nov '96 / Tradition

Mraz, George

☐ BOTTOM LINES
Three views of a secret / San Felice / Christina / Lisa Marie / Mr. Pastorius / Little waltz / Strange blues / Goodbye porkpie hat / Falling grace
MCD 92722 / Jan '98 / Milestone

☐ JAZZ
Moonlight in Vermont / Cinema paradiso (love theme) / Infant eyes / Happy saint / Foolish door / Your story / Spring is here / Pepper / Time remembered / Peacocks / Cinema paradiso (reprise)
MCD 92482 / Mar '96 / Milestone

☐ MY FOOLISH HEART
Alice in wonderland / Sunday's song / Picturesque / Passion flower / Icicles / Ask me now / Blue in green / Robo bop / My foolish heart / Haunted heart
MCD 92622 / Jan '98 / Milestone

Mrs. Mills

☐ EP COLLECTION, THE
Bobbikins / Popcorn / Broken doll / I wonder where my baby is tonight / Birth of the blues / I can't give you anything but love / Underneath the arches / Heartaches / My very good friend the milkman / Pennies from heaven / Goodnight sweetheart / Show me the way to go home
SEECD 332 / Sep '91 / See For Miles

MSB & Dosezero

☐ CONTROL REMOTO 2.0
EFAO 15652 / Mar '96 / Apocalyptic Vision

Mseleku, Bheki

☐ BEAUTY OF SUNRISE
5318682 / Jul '97 / Verve

☐ CELEBRATION
WCD 028 / Apr '92 / World Circuit

☐ MEDITATIONS
Meditations (suite in nine movements) / Meera ma (divine mother)
5213372 / Jan '95 / Verve

☐ TIMELESSNESS
5213062 / Feb '94 / Verve

MT

☐ LORD HAVE MERCY ON MY SOUL
FILECD 465 / Mar '96 / Profile

MTA

☐ BY THE BULLET OR THE BALLOT
MIA 002CD / Sep '94 / MIA

Mu

☐ BAND FROM A LOST CONTINENT, THE (2CD Set)
XMCD 1
SC 11037 / Jun '97 / Sundazed

☐ BEST OF MU, THE
CDRECK 4 / Oct '89 / Reckless

MU330

☐ CHUMPS ON PARADE
AM 008CD / Jun '97 / Asian Man

☐ CRAB RANGOON
AM 016CD / Sep '97 / Asian Man

☐ PRESS
AM 007CD / May '97 / Asian Man

Mua, Boua Zou

☐ MUSIC OF THE HMONG PEOPLE OF LAOS
ARHCD 446 / Apr '96 / Arhoolie

Muckafurgason

☐ TOSSING A FRIEND
DER 363CD / 6 Jul '98 / Deep Elm

Mucky Pup

☐ ACT OF FAITH
CM 9731 CD / Jul '92 / Century Media

☐ ALIVE AND WELL
SPV 08489222 / Dec '96 / SPV

☐ CAN'T YOU TAKE A JOKE
Knock knock / Nazichizm / Caddy killer / M.b. (ballad of the moron bros.) / Innocent's / Daddy's boy (theme song) / F..... / U - nothing / A.i.d.s. / Life 4 def / Laughing in your face / Woody / Bushpigs / Mr. presidents / l.r.s. / Shmbluh
RR 95532 / Feb '93 / Roadrunner

☐ FIVE GUYS IN A REALLY HOT GARAGE
SPV 08544022 / Jan '96 / SPV

☐ LEMONADE
CM 77058 / Jan '94 / Century Media

☐ NOW
Hippies hate water / Three dead gophers / Jimmy's / Baby / She Quieffed / Feeling sick / Headbangers balls and 120 minutes / My hands, your neck / Face / Hotel Penitentiary / Mucky pumpin' beat / I know nobody / Walkin' with the devil / Yesterdays / To be lonely
RO 93402 / Feb '93 / Roadrunner

Mud

☐ DYNAMITE
Crazy / Hypnosis / Dynamite / Tiger feet / Cat crept in / Rocket / Lonely this christmas / Secrets that you keep / Oh boy / Moonshine sally / One night / L-l-lucy / Show me you're a woman / Shake it down / Hide on the tiles / Lean on me / Under the moon of love / Blue moon / Tallahassee lassie / Let's have a party
BX 4212 / Jul '94 / BR Music

☐ DYNAMITE
SE 865642 / Mar '96 / Disky

☐ GOLD COLLECTION, THE
Dynamite / Tiger feet / Cat crept in / Secrets that you keep / Oh boy / Blue moon / Hippy hippy shake / Tallahassee lassie / Living doll / Diana / End of the world / One night / Crazy / Hypnosis / Moonshine Sally / Rocket
CDGOLD 1003 / Mar '96 / EMI Gold

☐ OH BOY
Oh boy / Do you love me / Hippy hippy shake / Blue moon / Living doll / Tallahassee lassie / Let's have a party / I love how you love me / Diana / Medley
WB 885852 / 2 Feb '98 / Disky

☐ SINGLES 1967-1978 (2CD Set)
REP 4657 / 24 Nov '97 / Repertoire

Mud

☐ TRAIN TO FOREVER
DIS 1095CD / Mar '97 / Radiopaque

Mudane

☐ SEED
BMCD 075 / Jun '95 / Raw Energy

Mudboy

☐ NEGRO STREETS AT DAWN (Mudboy & The Neutrons)
422469 / May '94 / New Rose

☐ THEY WALK AMONG US (Mudboy & The Neutrons)
379132 / Nov '95 / Koch International

Mudhoney

☐ EVERY GOOD BOY DESERVES FUDGE
Generation genocide / Let it slide / Good enough / Something so clear / Thorn / Into the drink / Broken hands / Who you drivin' now / Move out / Shoot the moon / Fuzzgun '91 / Pokin' around / Don't fade IV / Check out time
SPCD 105 / Jan '94 / Sub Pop

Mueller, Tommy

☐ IT'S ALL ABOUT TIME
63828702012 / 14 Apr '98 / DENW

Muffin Men

☐ MULM
EFA 034082 / Jul '94 / Muffin

☐ PLAY UNCLE FRANK LIVE
EFA 034172 / Jan '97 / Muffin

☐ SAY CHEESE AND THANKYOU
EFA 034022 / Jan '94 / Muffin

Muffins

☐ 185
CUNEIFORM 55013 / Jun '97 / Cuneiform

Muffs

☐ MUFFS, THE
Lucky guy / Saying goodbye / Everywhere I go / Better than me / From your girl / Not like me / Baby go round / North pole / Big mouth / Every single thing / Don't waste another day / Stupid jerk / Another day / Eye to eye / I need you / All for nothing
9362452512 / Aug '93 / Warner Bros.

Mugam Ensemble

☐ AZERBAIJAN - LAND OF FLAMES (Mugam Ensemble Jabbar Karyagdy)
PANCD 2012 / Oct '93 / Pan

Mugar

☐ KABILY TOUSEG (Celtic Arabic Fusion)
345022 / 24 Feb '98 / Melodie

Muhammad, Abu Al-Ila

☐ ABU AL-ILA MUHAMMAD
AAA 114 / Oct '95 / Club Du Disque Arabe

Muhammad, Idris

☐ BLACK RHYTHM REVOLUTION/ PEACE AND RHYTHM
Express yourself / Soulful drums / Super bad / Wander / By the red sea / Peace / Rhythm / Brother you know you're doing wrong / Don't knock my love / I'm a believer
CDBPGD 046 / Oct '92 / Beat Goes Public

☐ KABSHA
Kabsha / I want to talk to you / Little feet / GCCCG Blues / Soulful drums / St. M / Kabsha (Alternate take) / GCCG Blues
ECD 220962 / Jul '94 / Evidence

Mujician

☐ JOURNEY, THE
RUNE 42 / Dec '87 / Cuneiform

Mujuru, Ephat

☐ RHYTHMS OF LIFE
LYRCD 7407 / '91 / Lyrichord

Mukherjee, Budhaditya

☐ RAG BAGESRI/RAG DES
NI 5268 / Sep '94 / Nimbus

☐ RAG RAMKALI/RAG JHINJOTI
NI 5221 / Sep '94 / Nimbus

Muki

☐ CABIN FEVER
Spring / Jahbar / Ki juice / Esc / Nite lite / Full scope / Shine / Runner / Concord
MNTCD 1007 / 6 Jul '98 / Mantra

Muld, Sorten

☐ SORTEN MULD
INT 33 / May '96 / Inter Music

Muldaur, Maria

☐ FANNING THE FLAMES
Home of the blues / Somebody was watching over me / Trust in my love / Stand by me / Well, well, well / Fanning the flames / Heaven on earth / Brotherly love / Talk real slow / Stop running from your own shadow / Can't pin yo' spin on me / Strange and foreign land
CD 83394 / Nov '96 / Telarc Jazz

☐ MARIA MULDAUR
Any old time / Midnight at the oasis / My Tennessee mountain home / I never did sing you a love song / Work song / Don't you feel my leg / Walking one and only / Long hard climb / Three dollar bill / Vaudeville man / Mad mad mad
7599272082 / Sep '93 / Reprise

☐ MEET ME AT MIDNIGHT
BT 1107CD / Oct '94 / Black Top

☐ SOUTHLAND OF THE HEART
Ring me up / Get up get ready / Southland of the heart / Latersville / Think about you / There's a devil on the loose / Fool's paradise / One short life / If I were you / Someday when we're both alone / Blues gives a lesson
CD 83423 / Mar '98 / Telarc

☐ SWEET & SLOW
SP 1183CD / Oct '93 / Stony Plain

Muldrow, Ronald

☐ DIASPORA
ENJACD 80862 / May '95 / Enja

☐ FACING WES
On the fritz / Facing wes / Andrea / Granite green / Oliver's moments / Our day will come / Minus mingus / Cryin' blues / Little white lies / Three quarter miles
KOKO 1311 / Aug '96 / Kokopelli

☐ GNOWING YOU (Muldrow, Ronald Trio)
Quasimodal / Deaceleration / Soleshia / Georgia Ann / Growing you / Polka dots and moonbeams / Little Wes
CDLR 45047 / Feb '92 / L&R

Mule

☐ IF I DON'T SIX
QS 29CD / Sep '94 / Quarter Stick

☐ MULE
QS 15 CD / Feb '93 / Quarter Stick

Mulhall, Eamon

☐ BOY SOPRANO
PLSCD 283 / 1 Jun '98 / Pulse

Mullens

☐ MULLENS, THE
GH 1062CD / Nov '97 / Get Hip

Mullican, Moon

☐ MOON'S ROCK
Moon's rock / Jenny Lee / Pipeliner blues / Sweet rockin' music / That's me / Cush cush ky yay / Writing on the wall / Wedding of the bugs / Nobody knows but my pillow / My love / I'm waiting for the ships that never come in / You don't have to be a baby to cry / I'll sail my ship alone / I was sorta wonderin' / Every which a way / I don't know why (I just do) / Sweeter than the flowers / Leaves mustn't fall / Anything that's part of you / Early morning blues / My baby's gone / Colinda / Make friends / Cajun coffee song / Quarter mile rows / Just to be with you / I'll pour the wine / Fools like me / Big big city / Mr. Tears / She once lived here / This glass I hold
BCD 15607 / Apr '92 / Bear Family

☐ MOONSHINE JAMBOREE
Hey Mr. Cotton Picker / Leaving you with a worried mind / What's the matter with the mill / Pipeliner blues / Triflin' woman blues / Nine tenths of the Tennessee River / Cherokee boogie / All I need is you / I'll sail my ship alone / Good deal Lucille / Moonshine blues / Rocket to the moon / Downstream / I done it / Goodnight Irene / Rheumatism boogie / Well oh well / Don't ever take my picture down / Lonesome hearted blues / It's a sin to love you like I do / I'm gonna move home and bye and bye / I left my heart in Texas / I'll take your hat right off my rack
CDCHD 458 / Sep '93 / Ace

Mulligan, Gerry

☐ COMPLETE GERRY MULLIGAN & BEN WEBSTER SESSIONS, THE (Remastered/2CD Set) (Mulligan, Gerry & Ben Webster)
5390552 / Oct '97 / Verve Master Edition

☐ CONCERT IN THE RAIN
EBCD 2129 / Jun '96 / Jazzband

☐ DRAGONFLY (Mulligan, Gerry Quartet)
Dragonfly / Brother blues / I'm not rappaport / Backstage / Little glory / Art of trumpet / Listening to Astor / Ninth life / Underneath a pale blue moonlight / Start all over again
CD 83377 / Feb '96 / Telarc

☐ DREAM A LITTLE DREAM
Nobody else but me / Home (when shadows fall) / Dream a little dream / I'll be around / They say it's wonderful / Real thing / Here's that rainy day / Georgia on my mind / My funny valentine / As close as pages in a book / My shining hour / Walking shoes / Song for Strayhorn
CD 83364 / Nov '94 / Telarc

☐ GERRY MEETS HAMP (Mulligan, Gerry & Lionel Hampton)
Apple core / Song for johnny hodges / Blight of the fumble bee / Gerry meets hamp / Blues for gerry / Line for lyons / Walking shoes / Limelight / Fables of faubus
JHR 73555 / Jan '93 / Jazz Hour

☐ GERRY MULLIGAN & CONCERT JAZZ BAND
5233422 / 5 May '98 / Verve

☐ GERRY MULLIGAN MEETS BEN WEBSTER (Mulligan, Gerry & Ben Webster)
Chelsea Bridge / Cat walk / Sunday / Who's got rhythm / Tell me when / Go home / In a mellotone / What is this thing called love / For Bessie / Fajista / BLues in B flat
8416612 / Aug '90 / Verve

☐ GERRY MULLIGAN/ASTOR PIAZZOLLA 1974 (Mulligan, Gerry & Astor Piazzolla)
556642CD / Aug '94 / Accord

☐ GERRY MULLIGAN/PAUL DESMOND QUARTET (Mulligan, Gerry & Paul Desmond)
Blues in time / Body and soul / Stand still / Line for Lyons / Wintersong / Battle hymn of the republican / Fall out / Tea for two / Wintersong / Lover
5198502 / Mar '94 / Verve

☐ IDOL GOSSIP (Mulligan, Gerry & His New Sextet)
CRD 155 / Mar '96 / Chiaroscuro

☐ IMMORTAL CONCERTS
I may be wrong, but I think you're wonderful / Gold rush / Makin' whoopee / Laura / Soft shoe / Nearness of you / Love me or leave me / Bernie's tune / Walking shoes / Five brothers / Lullaby of the leaves / Limelight / Come out wherever you are / Moonlight in Vermont / Lady is a tramp / Bark for Barksdale
CD 53020 / Jun '88 / Giants Of Jazz

☐ IN CONCERT (Mulligan, Gerry Quartet)
RTE 760463 / May '95 / RTE/Europe 1

☐ IN CONCERT WITH EUROPE 1 (19/11/60 - 2CD Set) (Mulligan, Gerry Concert Jazz Band)
RTE 15052 / 3 Aug '98 / Charlotte

☐ JAZZ GREATS (Mulligan, Gerry Quartet)
I may be wrong / Gold rush / Makin' whoopee / Laura / Soft shoed / Nearness of you / Love me or leave me / Bernie's tune / Walkin' shoes / Moonlight in Vermont / Lady is a tramp / Bark for Barksdale
74321556912 / Feb '98 / RCA Victor

☐ JERU
Get out of town / Here I'll stay / Inside impromptu / Blue boy / You've come home / Lonely town / Capricious
4736852 / Nov '93 / Columbia

☐ LIMELIGHT
DM 15016 / Jul '96 / DMA Jazz

☐ LIVE IN STOCKHOLM 1957
Come out wherever you are / Birth of the blues / Moonlight in Velmont / Lullaby of the leaves / Open country / I can't get started (with you) / Frenesi / Baubles, bangles and beads / Yardbird suite / Walkin' shoes / My funny valentine / Blues at the roots / Introduction / Bernie's tune
MCD 0462 / Nov '93 / Moon

☐ LONESOME BOULEVARD
Rico Apollo / I heard the shadows dancing / Lonesome boulevard / Curtains / Ring around a bright star / Splendor in the grass / Good neighbour / Thelonious / Wallflower / Flying Scotsman / Etude for Franca
3970612 / Mar '94 / A&M

☐ MULLIGAN
Jeru / Festive minor / Rose room / North Atlantic run / Taurus moon / Out back of the barn
17081 / Jan '97 / Laserlight

☐ MULLIGAN IN THE MAIN (Newport Jazz Festival July 3rd/6th 1958)
NCD 8814 / '93 / Phontastic

☐ MULLIGAN SONGBOOK, THE
Four and one more / Crazy day / Turnstile / Sextet / Disc jockey jump / Venus de Milo / Revelation / Mayreh / Preacher / Good bait / Bags' groove
CDP 8335752 / Jan '96 / Pacific Jazz

☐ NEWS FROM BLUEPORT (Mulligan, Gerry & Art Farmer)
As catch can / Baubkes, bangles and beads / News from blueport / Walkin' shoes / Spring is sprung / Blueport / Moonlight in vermont / Utter chaos
JHR 73577 / May '94 / Jazz Hour

☐ ORIGINAL MULLIGAN QUARTET (With Chet Baker/2CD Set) (Mulligan, Gerry Quartet)
Disc happy / 'S wonderful / Godchild / Dinah / She didn't say yes, she didn't say no / Bernie's tune / Lullaby of the leaves / Utter chaos / Aren't you glad you're you / Frenesi / Nights at the turntable / Freeway / Soft shoe / Walkin' shoes / Aren't you glad you're you / Get happy Poinciana / Makin' whoopee / Cheery motel / My old flame / Love me or leave me / Swinghouse / Swinghouse / Jeru / Utter chaos / Darn that dream / Darn that dream / I may be wrong / I may be wrong / I'm beginning to see the light / I'm beginning to see the light / Nearness of you / Tea for two / Five brothers / I can't get started / Ide's side / Funhouse / My funny valentine / Love me or leave me
4944072 / 20 Jul '98 / Pacific Jazz

☐ PARAISO (Mulligan, Gerry & Jane Duboc)
CD 83361 / Oct '93 / Telarc

☐ PARIS 1954/LA 1953 (Mulligan, Gerry Quartet)
Soft shoes / Five brothers / Lullaby of the leaves / Limelight / Come out wherever you are / Motel / My funny valentine / Turnstile / Speak low / Ladybird / Love me or leave me / Swing house / Varsity drag / Half Nelson
VG 655616 / Nov '92 / Vogue

☐ PLEYEL CONCERT 1954 VOL.1 (Original Vogue Masters) (Mulligan, Gerry Quartet)
Bernie's tune / Presentation of the musicians / Walkin' shoes / Nearness of you / Motel/Utter chaos / Love me or leave me / Soft shoe / Bark for Barksdale / My funny valentine / Turnstile/Utter chaos / I may be wrong / Five brothers / Gold rush / Makin' whoopee
74321429232 / Apr '97 / Vogue

☐ PLEYEL CONCERT 1954 VOL.2 (Original Vogue Masters) (Mulligan, Gerry Quartet)
Lady is a tramp / Laura / Motel / Five brothers / Lullaby of the leaves / Nearness of you / Limelight / Come out come out wherever you are / Makin' whoopee / Love me or leave me / Laura / Line for Lyons / Moonlight in Vermont / Bark for Barksdale / Utter chaos
74321429222 / Apr '97 / Vogue

☐ QUARTETS, THE
Five brothers / Motel / Love in New Orleans / My funny valentine / Four for three / Walkin' shoes / Marguerite / Festive minor / Darn that dream / As catch can / Jive at five / News from Blueport / Getting sentimental over you / Just in time / Open country
HCD 611 / Jan '98 / Hindsight

☐ SHADOW OF YOUR SMILE (Mulligan, Gerry Quartet)
MCD 003 / Sep '89 / Moon

☐ SOFT LIGHTS AND SWEET MUSIC (Mulligan, Gerry & Scott Hamilton)
Soft lights and sweet music / Gone / Do you know what I see / I've just seen her / Noblesse / Ghosts / Port of Baltimore blues
CCD 4300 / Jan '87 / Concord Jazz

☐ STOCKHOLM 1959 (Mulligan, Gerry Quartet)
TAXCD 3711 / Jan '93 / Tax

☐ SWISS RADIO DAYS JAZZ SERIES VOL.9 (Mulligan, Gerry Quartet)
Utter chaos and presentation / Open country / Love in New Orleans / Seventeen mile drive / Subterranean blues / Spring is sprung / Darn that dream / Blueport
TCB 02092 / 27 Apr '98 / TCB

☐ SYMPHONIC DREAMS (Mulligan, Gerry Quartet)
Entente / Sax chronicles / Song for Strayhorn / Sax chronicles / K4 Pacific
SION 18130 / Jul '97 / Sion

☐ THANK YOU GERRY (Mulligan, Gerry All Star Tribute Band)
AJ 71191 / 27 Apr '98 / Arkadia

☐ THIS IS JAZZ
Line for Lyons / Festive minor / As catch can / What is there to say / You've come home / Bernie's tune / Utter chaos / My funny valentine / Lullabye de Mexico
CK 64972 / Oct '96 / Sony Jazz

☐ WALKING SHOES
BS 18008 / Jul '96 / Bandstand

☐ WALKING SHOES 1959/NEW YORK 1977 (2CD Set)
JWD 102310 / Oct '94 / JWD

☐ WHAT IS THERE TO SAY (Mulligan, Gerry Quartet)
What is there to say / Just in time / News from blueport / Festive minor / My funny valentine / As catch can / Blueport / Utter chaos
4756992 / Feb '94 / Columbia

Mulligan, Mick

☐ MEET MICK MULLIGAN & GEORGE MELLY (Mulligan, Mick & George Melly)
Young and healthy / Button up your overcoat / All I do is dream / I'm crazy 'bout my baby / All of me / Rocking chair / Bei mir bist du schon / There'll be some changes made / Girl of my dreams / Ace in the hole / Alexander's ragtime band / Oh you beautiful doll / Muscrat ramble / Sweet Lorraine / When you're smiling / After you've gone / I'll see you in my dreams / Mama don't allow
LACD 66 / Aug '96 / Lake

Mulligan, Neil

☐ LEITRIM THRUSH
SCD 1037 / Aug '97 / Spring

Mullins, Rob

☐ 5TH GEAR
NOVA 8810 / Jan '93 / Nova

☐ JAZZ JAZZ
NOVA 8918 / Jan '93 / Nova

☐ ONE NIGHT IN HOUSTON
Polka dot dress / Very blue / Quick call the note police / Jazz man / One night in Houston / Plus three / Quiet fire / Holiday / Too cold
AQCD 1020 / Sep '95 / Audioquest

☐ TOKIO NIGHTS
NOVA 9026 / Jan '93 / Nova

Mulo, Alman

☐ AFRODIZIAC DREAMTIME (Mulo, Alman Band)
TASTE 41CD / Nov '93 / Southern

☐ DIAMONDS AND TOADS (Mulo, Alman Band)
TASTE 46 / Jan '95 / Taste

☐ ORISHA (Mulo, Alman Band)
TASTE 37 / Jan '95 / Taste

Mulqueen, Ann

☐ MO GHRASA THALL NA DEISE (Memorable Songs In The Munster Tradition)
CIC 080CD / Jan '93 / Clo Iar-Chonnachta

Multiphonic Ensemble

☐ KING OF MAY
SR 128 / 20 Oct '97 / Sub Rosa

Multiplex

☐ MACHINE HUNTER
KKT 001CD / 1 Dec '97 / KK

Mulvihill, Brendan

☐ FLAX IN BLOOM, THE
Flax in bloom/Honeymoon / Crabs in the skillet / Concertina/The circus / Lament for O'Donnell / John Grady's downfall/The flogging reel / Pigeon on the gate/Miss Monahan's reel / Dr. O'Neill's reel / Home ruler / Brigade / Fermoy lassies/Bunker hill / Hardiman's fancy/Billy Rush's own / First house in Connaught/Dairy maid
GLCD 1020 / Feb '93 / Green Linnet

☐ MORNING DEW, THE (Mulvihill, Brendan & Donna Long)
Morning dew/Grants / Brian Maguire/Thomas Judge/The broken pledge/McGlinchey's/Th / Rathlin Island / Shandon bells/Boys of the town/ Rakes of Clonmel/Girls of / Festus Burke/John Drury / An ceileabrad caoine / Morgan Magan/Greig's pipes / Mrs. Judge / Down the broom/Joseph Bank / Kean and Colonel O'Hara/Flaggon reel/Dublin lasses
GLCD 1128 / Jul '93 / Green Linnet

Mumbleskinny

☐ HEAD ABOVE WATER
SECT2 10011 / Jul '95 / Sector 2

Mumps

☐ FATAL CHARM
ER 80011CD / Dec '97 / Eggbert

Mumy, Bill

☐ DYING TO BE HEARD
RMED 1997CD / Nov '97 / Renaissance

Munarriz, Valeria

☐ TANGO
Melodia de arrabal / Melodia de arrabal / Milonga para el domingo / Nostalgias / Ciudades / El candombe / Sueno de juventud / Balada para mi muerte / Milonga de mis amores / Volver
MES 159172 / Feb '93 / Messidor

Mundane

☐ FEEDING
HYPSD 1055CD / 15 Jan '98 / Hypnotic

Munde, Alan

☐ BLUE RIDGE EXPRESS
Blue ridge express / Peaches and cream / Leather britches / Remington ride / Darcy farrow / Tennessee wagoner / Dear old dixie / Meloon's tune / Paddy on the turnpike / Earl of broadfield / Sail away ladies / Munde's child / Sleepy eyed john / I don't love nobody / Train to mexico / Sally johnson / Hank's lonesome cowdawg blues / Doc's riverboat reel / Sabrosa / Sockeye
ROUCD 0301 / Apr '94 / Rounder

☐ FESTIVAL FAVOURITES REVISITED
Hot burrito breakdown / Molly bloom / Clinch mountain backstep / Doug's tune / Shenandoah valley breakdown / Santa claus / Buffalo gals (texohomanew mexiline gals) / Liberty / John hardy / Salt creek / Sally goodin / Girl I left behind / Bill cheatham / Cripple creek / Devil's dream / Little rock getaway / Dusty miller / No title yet blues / Earl's breakdown / Billy boy
ROUCD 0311 / Apr '93 / Rounder

☐ WELCOME TO WEST TEXAS (Munde, Alan & Joe Carr)
Oklahoma flats / Yellow rose / Used to be / Keep a light on in the window / Wildflower moon / Jenny's desire / San Jancito farewell / When the cottonwoods are yellow / Dust drought and depression / Border baby boogoe Polka / Trial of the century / Dos coranzones / Please play the Tennessee waltz/Tennessee waltz / Welcome to West Texas
CDFF 669 / Apr '98 / Flying Fish

Mundell, Hugh

☐ AFRICA MUST BE FREE BY 1983
Let's all unite / My mind / Africa must be free by 1983 / Why do blackmen fuss and fight / Book of life / Run revolution come / Day of judgement / Jah will provide / Ital sip
GRELCD 94 / May '90 / Greensleeves

☐ BLACK MAN FOUNDATION
SHANCD 43012 / Jun '85 / Shanachie

☐ MUNDELL
Jacqueline / Rasta have the handle / Going places / Red, gold and green / Tell I a lie / Twenty four hours a day / Jah music / Your face is familiar
GRELCD 36 / Jul '97 / Greensleeves

Mundy

☐ JELLY LEGS
Reunion / Pardon me / Life's a cinch / Song for my darlin' / Gin and tonic sky / Blown away / To you I bestow / Stone / Springtown / Sisters / Arrow of gold / Private paradise / Mundy in wonderland
MUNDY 3CD
MUNDY 3CDS / Oct '96 / Epic

Munequitos De Matanzas

☐ LIVE IN NEW YORK
2616700262 / 31 Mar '98 / QBA

Mungo Jerry

☐ ALL THE HITS PLUS MORE
Wild love / Open up / Sugar mama / Baby jump / Just can't say goodbye / Long legged woman dressed in black / Alright, alright, alright / Put a little love in your letter / Duke street stomp / In the summertime / Lady rose / You don't have to be in the army to fight in the war / Mighty man / Feels like I'm in love / Pushbike song / We're ok
CDPT 002 / Jun '92 / Prestige

☐ BEST OF MUNGO JERRY, THE
Lana / It's a secret / Hello Nadine / Let's get started / Forgotten land / Drum song / In the summertime / Lady Rose / Somebody stole my wife / Alright, alright / Long legged woman / Sugar Mama / That's my baby / Angel Mama / I'm gonna bop till I drop / Rockin' on the road / Baby jump / You don't have to be in the army to fight the war / Open up / Wild love
4776449 / 11 May '98 / Columbia

☐ BEST OF MUNGO JERRY, THE (Alright, alright, alright)
In the summertime / Baby jump / Open up / John B. Badde / Lady Rose / Little Miss Hipshake / Long legged woman dressed in black / Mighty man / Don't stop / Alright alright alright / Somebody stole my wife / You don't have to be in the army to fight in the war / Maggie / Wild love / Hey Rosalyn / Northcote arms / Gonna bop till I drop / Have a whiff on me / Summer's gone
MCCD 292 / May '97 / Music Club

☐ ELECTRONICALLY TESTED
She rowed / I just want to make love to you / In the summertime / Somebody stole my wife / Baby jump / Follow me down / Memoirs of a stockbroker / You better leave that whisky alone / Coming back to you
REP 4179 / Aug '91 / Repertoire

☐ GREATEST HITS
In the summertime / Wild love / Baby jump / Mighty man / Another bad day / Callin' / Long legged woman dressed in black / Lady Rose / Alright, alright, alright / Open up / Feels like I'm in love / Keep me up all night / Hello Nadine / You don't have to be in the army to fight in the war
399360 / Jun '97 / Koch Presents

☐ IN THE SUMMERTIME
In the Summertime / Wild love / Summer's gone / Alright alright alright / Hey Rosalyn / Long legged woman / Dressed in black / Baby jump / On a Sunday / Open up / Lady Rose / Going down the dusty road / You don't have to be in the army to fight the war
REP 4177 / Aug '91 / Repertoire

☐ IN THE SUMMERTIME
In the summertime / Mighty man / Lady rose / Maggie / Alright alright alright / Baby jump / Have a whiff of me / Say goodnight / Johnny b. badde / On a sunday / Open up / You better leave that whiskey alone / Somebody stole my wife / You don't have to be in the army to fight the war / It's a secret / Hello nadine
21021 / Sep '97 / Laserlight

☐ IN THE SUMMERTIME
SELCD 526 / 27 Jun '98 / Castle Select

☐ MUNGO JERRY/ELECTRONICALLY TESTED
Baby let's play house / Johnny B Badde / San Francisco Bay blues / Sad eyed Joe / Maggie / Peace in the country / See me / Movin' on / My friend / Mother fucker boogie / Tramp / Daddie's brew / She rowed / I just want to make love to you / In the summertime / Somebody stole my wife / Baby jump / Follow me down / Memoirs of a stockbroker / You better leave that whiskey alone / Coming back to you when the time comes
BGOCD 286 / Oct '96 / Beat Goes On

☐ SUMMERTIME
In the summertime / Baby jump / Lady Rose / Alright alright alright / Wild love / My girl and me / Maggie / Johnny B Badde / Don't stop / Long legged woman dressed in black / All dressed up and no place to go / I don't wanna go back to school / Baby let's play house / Gonna bop till I drop / Brand new car / Somebody stole my wife / Sweet Mary Jane / Too fast to live, too young to die
5507492 / Jan '95 / Spectrum

☐ VERY BEST OF MUNGO JERRY, THE
In the summertime / Hello Nadine / Alright, alright, alright / Baby jump / Snakebite / All I wanna do / Heartbreak avenue / Girl like you / Red leather and chrome / Sugar in the bowl / Jesse James / Remember me / Rock 'n' roll-rock 'n' roll / Right on / Lady Rose / Long legged dressed in black / Open up / It's a secret / Let's get started / Forgotten land
SUMCD 4090 / Jan '97 / Summit

☐ VERY BEST OF MUNGO JERRY, THE
In the summertime / Alright, alright, alright / Dancing in the street / Rocking on the road / Mighty man / It's a secret / Dance rave / Red leather and chrome / Forgotten land / Open up / Girl like you / Maggie / Bottle of beer / Baby jump
100622 / May '97 / A-Play Collection

☐ YOU DON'T HAVE TO BE IN THE ARMY/ BOOT POWER (2CD Set)
You don't have to be in the army to fight the war / Ella speed / Pigeon stew / Take me back / Give me love / Hey Rosalyn / Northcote arms / There's a man going round taking names / Simple things / Keep your hands off her / On a sunday / That old dust storm / Open up / She's gone / Lookin' for my girl / See you again / Demon / My girl and me / Sweet Mary Jane / Lady Rose / Dusty road / Brand new car / 46 an' on
BGOCD 292 / Oct '96 / Beat Goes On

Munoz, Rafael

☐ RAFAEL MUNOZ VOL.1
Macafu / Ensueno / Agapito / Fiel adoracion / El timbal magico / Enojo / El hueso de maria / Mi loca tentacion / Cantalicio / Eres mala / Anoranza / El chivo la mastico / Claro de luna / La conga del 39 / No muevas la cintura / Por que te quiero / El sueno de macafu / Deseos / Vacilando
HQCD 97 / 3 Sep '97 / Harlequin

☐ RAFAEL MUNOZ VOL.2
Preparate Juan Jose / A la guerra yo no voy / Esperanza / La reina del palmar / Sin ti / Mi abuelita no quiere / Bembeteo no mas / Falsa mujer / Inconsolable / Pa'lante es pa'lla / Rumbamba / Olvidame / No me mires asi / Petalos de rosa / No olvido tu querer / Sigue como eres / Mi ilusion eres tu / Sandunguera / Di corazon / Sapo sapo japones
HQCD 110 / Apr '98 / Harlequin

Munroe, Hamish

☐ LOCAL HERO
CDGR 164 / May '98 / Ross

Munros

☐ CELTIC SUNSET
Rabbie burns trilogy (my love is a red red rose/ rosebud) / Maid of the loch / Whiskey in the jar / Amazing grace / Come o'er the stream Charlie / Danny boy / Celtic sunrise / Hill / Lord Lavat's lament / Hasten and come with me / My home / Auld lang syne / She moves thru' the fair / Rosebud
4914482 / 3 Aug '98 / Columbia

☐ LONE PIPER, THE
Scots wha'e / Ae fond kiss / Glengarry's lament / Lord Lovat's lament / Ye banks and braes / Abide with me / Morag of Dunvegan / El Alemain / Amazing grace / Auld lang syne / Dark island / My home / Skye boat song / Highland cathedral / Hasten and come with me / Scottish soldier / Flower of Scotland
VTCD 185 / 8 Jun '98 / Virgin

Munyon, David

☐ ACRYLIC TEEPEES
GRCD 393 / Nov '96 / Glitterhouse

☐ CODE NAME: JUMPER
GRCD 307 / May '97 / Glitterhouse

Munzer, Fritz

☐ STRAIGHT OFF (Munzer, Fritz Sound Express)
ISCD 112 / Oct '91 / Intersound

Muppets

☐ CHRISTMAS TOGETHER, A (Denver, John & Muppets)
Twelve days of christmas / Have yourself a merry little christmas / Peace carol / Christmas is coming / A baby just like you / Deck the hall with boughs of holly / When the river meets the sea / Little saint nick / Noel christmas eve, 1913 / Christmas wish / Silent night, holy night / We wish you a merry christmas
MCCDX 007 / Nov '94 / Music Club

☐ KERMIT UNPIGGED (Various Artists)
74321233382 / Oct '94 / BMG Kidz

Mur, Mona

☐ WARSZAW
SPLCD 1 / Jul '92 / Solid Pleasure

Muranyi, Joe

☐ JOE MURANYI WITH THE ORIENT DIXIELAND JAZZ BAND
JCD 266 / Jun '96 / Jazzology

Murata, Yoichi

☐ DOUBLE EDGE
Return of prodigal son / Some skunk funk / Wrecker / Good-bye pork pie hat / Squib cakes / Shuffling jazzmen / Reflections / Freedom jazz dance / Manteca / Sweet Henry
JVC 90052 / Aug '96 / JVC

☐ WHAT'S BOP (Murata, Yoichi & Solid Brass)
Be bop - what's the matter / Teen town / Snapping turtle / Ponta march / Acute angles / Three views of a secret / Bring back / High old time / Come Sunday / Port to port
JVC 90162 / Aug '97 / JVC

Murcott, Dominic

☐ SLAPPER
RMCD 005 / 3 Nov '97 / Ready Made

Murder City Devils

☐ MURDER CITY DEVILS
DIECD 001 / 1 Sep '97 / Sub Pop

Murder Inc.

☐ MURDER INC
INVCD 013 / Feb '94 / Invisible

Murderer's Row

☐ MURDERER'S ROW
A2Z 85012CD / Jul '96 / A-Z

Murk

☐ MIAMI DEEP (The Essential Mixes)
HURTCD 005 / 19 Jan '98 / Harmless

Murmur

☐ SEXPOWDER 2000 VOLTS
RAIN 013CD / Apr '95 / Cloudland

Murphy, Column

☐ IRISH DRUM, THE
CEFCD 175 / Mar '96 / Gael Linn

Murphy, David Lee

☐ GETTING OUT THE GOOD STUFF
Every time I get around you / Road you leave behind / She's really something to see / Genuine rednecks / 100 years too late / Born that way / Breakfast in Birmingham / Getting out the good stuff / I've been a rebel (and it don't pay) / Pirates cove
MCAD 11423 / Jun '96 / MCA

☐ WE CAN'T ALL BE ANGELS
UMD 80422 / 10 Oct '97 / Universal

Murphy, Dennis

☐ MUSIC FROM SLIABHRA LUCHRA
RTE 183CD / Jan '95 / RTE/Europe 1

Murphy, Donal

☐ SLIABH NOTES (Murphy, Donal & Matt Cranitch/Tommy O'Sullivan)
CBMCD 018 / Jul '96 / Cross Border Media

Murphy, Elliott James

☐ 12
422244 / May '94 / New Rose

☐ AFFAIRS ETC.
422237 / May '94 / New Rose

☐ CHANGE WILL COME
422239 / May '94 / New Rose

☐ IF POETS WERE KING
422240 / May '94 / New Rose

☐ LIVE HOT POINT
422241 / May '94 / New Rose

☐ MILWAUKEE
ROSE 99CD / Nov '86 / New Rose

☐ PARIS-NEW YORK
422401 / May '94 / New Rose

☐ PARTY GIRLS/BROKEN POETS
DJD 3201 / May '94 / Dejadisc

Murphy, Jeanette

☐ BITING
OCEAN 212 / 11 May '98 / Ocean

Murphy, Jimmy

☐ SIXTEEN TONS ROCK'N'ROLL
Sixteen tons rock'n'roll / My gal Dottie / Grandpaw's cat / Baboon boogie / I'm looking for a mustard patch / Put some meat on them bones / Here Kitty Kitty / Sweet sweet lips (unissued) / Electricity / Big mama blues / That first guitar of mine / Love that satisfies / Educated fool / Rambling heart / We live a long, long time / Mother where is your daughter
BCD 15451 / Sep '90 / Bear Family

Murphy, Maggy

☐ LINKIN' O'ER THE LEA
VT 134CD / Aug '96 / Veteran Tapes

Murphy, Mark

☐ BEAUTY AND THE BEAST
VGCD 600606 / Jan '93 / Vogue

☐ JAZZ STANDARDS
60412320632 / 19 May '98 / Thirty Two

☐ RAH
Angel eyes / On green dolphin street / Stoppin the clock / Spring can really hang on to you / No tears for me / Out of this world / Milestones / My favourite things / Doodlin' / L'il darlin' / Twisted
OJCCD 141 / Jun '95 / Original Jazz Classics

☐ SONG FOR THE GEESE
You go to my head / Sugar / Baltimore oriole / Do it again / (Baby) it's just talk / You're blase / Song for the geese / Everybody loves me / Lament / I remember / We two / I wish you love
74321448652 / 6 Oct '97 / RCA Victor

Murphy, Matt

☐ WAY DOWN SOUTH
Way down south / Big 6 / Gonna be some changes made / Big city takedown / Buck's boogie / Thump tyme / Matt's guitar boogie / Low down and dirty / Gimme somma dat / Blue walls
ANTCD 0013 / Mar '91 / Antones

Murphy, Matt 'Guitar'

☐ BLUES DON'T BOTHER ME, THE
RR 0037 / 5 Feb '98 / Roesch

Murphy, Maurice

☐ LIGHTER SIDE OF MAURICE MURPHY
Concerto for trumpet / A brown bird singing / Georgia on my mind / Spanish eyes / Marianne / Tico tico / Don't it make your dreams eyes blue / Charivari / Sunshine of your smile / Virtuosity / Misty / My love is like a red, red rose / Way we were / Love on the rocks / Solitaire / People
DOYCD 007 / Oct '91 / Doyen

Murphy, Pat J.

☐ BYGONE DAYS
CDC 009 / Feb '97 / Ceol

Murphy, Peter

☐ CASCADE
BBL 175CD / 10 Nov '97 / Beggars Banquet

Murphy, Phil

☐ TRIP TO CULLENSTOWN, THE
(Murphy, Phil, John & Pip)
Flogging reel/Kathy jones/The honeymoon / Shores of Lough Gowna/Humours of Kesh / Wexford and Bannow Bay hornpipes / Pete's polka/The happy polka / Micky the moulder/Tatter Jack Welsh / Shepherd's love dream / Kitty come over/The mug of brown ale / Ballygow reel / Trip to Cullenstown / Congress/The heather breeze/Earl's chain / Lakes of Kincora/Cronin's hornpipe / Mummer's jigs / Pete Bate's hornpipe/Joe Kearne's favourite / Ballygow polka / Wistful lover / Kerry hills / King of Clans/Castlekelly / Listowel polka
CC 55CD / Nov '92 / Claddagh

Murphy, Rose

☐ I WANNA BE LOVED BY YOU
3038352 / 1 Jun '98 / Arcade

☐ LIVE IN CONCERT 1982
EQCD 7002 / Jan '95 / Equinox

☐ ROSE MURPHY
ACD 70 / Jul '96 / Audiophile

Murphy, Turk

☐ BEST OF TURK MURPHY, THE
MMRCCD 2 / Jul '93 / Merry Makers

☐ CONCERT IN THE PARK (Murphy, Turk Jazz Band)
MMRCD 12 / Jul '96 / Merry Makers

☐ ITALIAN VILLAGE 1952-53 (Murphy, Turk Jazz Band)
MMRCD 11 / Aug '95 / Merry Makers

☐ LIVE AT CARSON HOT SPRINGS (Murphy, Turk Jazz Band)
SFTJFCD 101 / May '98 / Merry Makers

☐ OZ TURK PLUS (2CD Set)
BAC 072 / Dec '97 / Bilarm

☐ SAN FRANCISCO JAZZ (Murphy, Turk Jazz Band)
MMRCCD 3 / Jun '88 / Merry Makers

☐ SAN FRANCISCO JAZZ VOL.2 (Murphy, Turk Jazz Band)
CMMRC 115 / Jun '88 / Merry Makers

☐ TURK MURPHY AND HIS SAN FRANCISCO JAZZ BAND (Murphy, Turk San Francisco Jazz Band)
BCD 91 / Oct '93 / GHB

☐ TURK MURPHY AND HIS SAN FRANCISCO JAZZ BAND VOL.2
BCD 92 / Jan '93 / GHB

Murphy, Walter

☐ BEST OF WALTER MURPHY, THE (A Fifth Of Beethoven)
HTCD 105 / 20 Apr '98 / Hot Productions

Murphy, Willie

☐ HUSTLIN' MAN BLUES (Murphy, Willie & The Angel-Headed Hipsters)
MU 1 / Apr '97 / Muff Ugga

☐ MONKEY IN THE ZOO
Keep on rocking the boat / World is a neighbourhood / Kamikaze / I just wanna be / Open letter / Time (is running out) / Midnight hour / Great balls of fire / Monkey in the zoo
ATM 1125 / May '97 / Atomic Theory

Murrain

☐ FAMINE, THE
MAB 003CD / Jul '93 / MAB

Murray, Anne

☐ BEST OF ANNE MURRAY SO FAR, THE
Snowbird / Now and forever (you and me) / Danny's song / Nobody loves me like you do / Love song / Time don't run out on me / You won't see me / Just another woman in love / You needed me / Little good news / I just fall in love again / Somebody's always saying goodbye / Broken hearted me / Could I have this dance / Daydream believer / Another sleepless night / Shadows in the moonlight / Blessed are the believers / Make love to me / Over you
CDP 8311582 / Jul '95 / EMI

☐ CROONIN'
Old cape cod / Wayward wind / Secret love / Fever / When I fall in love / Allegheny moon / You belong to me / Born to be with you / True love / Teach me tonight / Cry me a river / Make love to me / Hey there / It only hurts for a little while / I'm confessin' /I'm a fool to care / Wanted / I really don't want to know / Moments to remember
CDEMC 3672 / Mar '94 / EMI

☐ THERE GOES MY EVERYTHING
HADCD 183 / Nov '95 / Javelin

Murray, David

☐ ACOUSTIC OCTFUNK
SSCD 8051 / Apr '94 / Sound Hills

☐ BALLADS FOR BASS CLARINET (Murray, David Quartet)
DIW 880 / Jan '94 / DIW

☐ BODY AND SOUL (Murray, David Quartet)
1201552 / Nov '93 / Black Saint

☐ CHILDREN
BSR 0089 / '86 / Black Saint

☐ CREOLE
Gete / Flor na paul / Guadelupe / Soma tour / Savon de toilette / Gansavn'n / Mona / Guadeloupe after dark / Tonte vontarde
JUST 1152 / 27 Jul '98 / Justin Time

☐ DARK STAR (The Music Of The Grateful Dead)
Shakedown Street / Sampson and Delilah / Estimated prophet / China doll / One more Saturday night / Should have been
TCD 4002 / Jul '96 / Astor Place

☐ DAVID MURRAY BIG BAND
DIW 851 / Nov '91 / DIW

☐ DEATH OF A SIDEMAN (Murray, David Quintet)
DIW 866 / Feb '93 / DIW

☐ FLOWERS FOR ALBERT (2CD Set) (Murray, David & Low Class Conspiracy)
IN 1026CD / Jun '97 / India Navigation

☐ FO DEUK REVUE
Blue muse / Evidence / One world family / Too many hungry people / Chant africain / Abdoul aziz sy / Village urbaine / Thilo
JUST 942 / Jun '97 / Justin Time

☐ FOR AUNT LOUISE
DIW 901 / Dec '95 / DIW

☐ HEALERS, THE (Murray, David & Randy Weston)
1201182 / ' / Black Saint

☐ HOME (Murray, David Octet)
Home / Santa Barbara and Crenshaw / Follies / Choctaw blues / Last of the hipmen / 3-D family
BSRCD 055 / Sep '85 / Black Saint

☐ HOPE SCOPE (Murray, David Octet)
1201392 / Apr '91 / Black Saint

☐ I WANT TO TALK ABOUT YOU (Murray, David Quartet)
1201052 / Sep '89 / Black Saint

☐ INTERBOOGIEOLOGY
Namthinl's shadow / Blues for david / Interboogieology
1200182 / Nov '90 / Black Saint

☐ LIVE AT SWEET BASIL VOL.1 (Murray, David Big Band)
BSRCD 085 / '86 / Black Saint

☐ LIVE AT SWEET BASIL VOL.2 (Murray, David Big Band)
BSRCD 0095 / '86 / Black Saint

☐ LIVE AT THE LOWER MANHATTAN OCEAN CLUB
IN 1032CD / Jan '97 / India Navigation

☐ LONG GOODBYE, THE (A Tribute To Don Pullen) (Murray, David Quartet)
DIW 930 / Sep '97 / DIW

☐ LOVE AND SORROW
DIW 921 / Feb '97 / DIW

☐ MING (Murray, David Octet)
Fast life / Hill / Ming / Jasvan / Dewey's circle
BSRCD 045 / Sep '85 / Black Saint

☐ MODERN PORTRAIT OF LOUIS ARMSTRONG, A (Murray, David, Cheatham, Loren Schoenburg, Allen Lowe)
STCD 563 / May '93 / Stash

☐ MORNING SONG (Murray, David Octet)
Morning song / Body and soul / Light blue / Jitterbug waltz / Off season / Duet
BSRCD 075 / Sep '85 / Black Saint

☐ MURRAY'S STEPS (Murray, David Octet)
BSR 0065 / '86 / Black Saint

☐ PICASSO (Murray, David Octet)
DIW 879 / Jan '94 / DIW

☐ REAL DEAL (Murray, David & Milford Graves)
DIW 867 / Jan '93 / DIW

☐ REMEMBRANCES (Murray, David Quintet)
DIW 849 / Nov '91 / DIW

☐ SANCTUARY WITHIN, A
1201452 / Nov '92 / Black Saint

☐ SHAKILL'S WARRIOR VOL.1 (Murray, David Quartet)
DIW 850 / Nov '91 / DIW

☐ SHAKILL'S WARRIOR VOL.2
DIW 884 / Oct '94 / DIW

☐ TENORS (Murray, David Quartet)
DIW 881 / Jan '94 / DIW

☐ TIP, THE
DIW 891 / Mar '95 / DIW

☐ WINDWARD PASSAGES (Murray, Dave & Dave Burrell)
1201652 / Dec '97 / Black Saint

Murray, Diedre

☐ FIRESTORM (Murray, Diedre & Fred Hopkins)
VICTOCD 020 / Nov '94 / Victo

☐ STRINGOLOGY (Murray, Diedre & Fred Hopkins)
1201432 / May '94 / Black Saint

Murray, Keith

☐ ENIGMA
CHIP 172 / Nov '96 / Jive

☐ MOST BEAUTIFULLEST THING IN THE WORLD, THE
Live from New York / Sychosymatic / Dip dip di / Most beautifullest thing in the world / Herb is pumpin' / Sychoward / Straight Loonie / Danger / Get lifted / How's that / Chase / Take it to the streetz / Bom bom zee / Countdown / Escapism / Most beautifullest thing in this world
CHIP 159 / Mar '97 / Jive

Murray, Martin

☐ DARK HORSE, A
CBM 021CD / Nov '96 / Cross Border Media

Murray, Pauline

☐ PAULINE MURRAY & THE INVISIBLE GIRLS (Murray, Pauline & The Invisible Girls)
Screaming in the darkness / Dream sequence 1 / European eyes / Shoot you down / Sympathy / Time slipping / Drummer boy / Thundertunes / When will we learn / Mr. x / Judgement day / Visitor / Animal crazy / Searching for heaven
PILOT 002 / Mar '97 / Burning Airlines

Murray, Ruby

☐ EMI PRESENTS THE MAGIC OF RUBY MURRAY
Heartbeat / Mr. Wonderful / Little white lies / Have you ever been lonely / When Irish eyes are smiling / Let him go, let him tarry / Goodbye Jimmy goodbye / Knock on any door / Passing stranger / Dear old Donegal / I'll come when you call / Nevertheless (I'm in love with you) / Softly softly / Danny boy / Let him go lover / Honestly I do / Evermore / Make him jealous / Two kinds of tears / Galway Bay / How can you buy Killarney / O'Malley's tango / Smile / Happy days / Lonely nights / Mountains of Mourne
CDMFP 6293 / May '97 / Music For Pleasure

☐ WHEN IRISH EYES ARE SMILING/ IRISH AND PROUD OF IT
CTMCD 110 / Mar '97 / EMI

Murrell, Christopher

☐ GOSPELS & SPIRITUALS (Murrell, Christopher & Robert Irving)
NHRSP 3 / Jul '96 / Nagel Heyer

Mursal, Maryam

☐ JOURNEY, THE
Lei lei / Kufilaw / Somali udilda ceb / Sodewou / Hamar / Qax / Nin han / Fejigno
CDRW 70 / 16 Mar '98 / Realworld

Musafir

☐ GYPSIES OF RAJASTHAN, THE
39850062 / Nov '97 / Blue Flame

Musavi, Mohammad

☐ NEY OF MOHAMMAD MUSAVI, THE
926452 / Sep '96 / BUDA

Muscadine

☐ BALLAD OF HOPE NICHOLLS, THE
Alice in Indieland / Popsicles for Mommy / Southern belle / Mon petit chou / Nalexis dakota / She doesn't want me / Saltwater suntan / Mr.Music / Wind up doll / Well / Dignity
4344310032 / 23 Mar '98 / Sire

Muschalle, Frank

☐ BATTIN' THE BOOGIE
DOCD 7000 / Mar '97 / Document

Musci, Roberto

☐ DEBRIS OF A LOA
LOW 009 / 30 Mar '98 / Lowlands

☐ LOSING THE ORTHODOX PATH (Musci, Roberto & Giovanni Venosta/ Massimo Mariani)
VICTOCD 049 / Jul '97 / Victo

☐ MESSAGES AND PORTRAITS (Musci, Roberto & Giovanni Venosta)
RERMVCD / Jan '93 / ReR/ Recommended

☐ NOISE, A SOUND, A (Musci, Roberto & Giovanni Venosta)
RERMVCD 2 / Oct '96 / ReR/ Recommended

Muse

☐ INNOCENT VOICES
3031282 / Jul '97 / Arcade

Muses Rapt

☐ SPIRITUAL HEALING
Spiritual healing / Ancient sounds of gods / Angel and the wave / Enchanted forest / Return of the travellers / ...an the sensities will be kings / Warriors of temperance / Carazon de fuego
BFLCD 29 / 11 May '98 / Butterfly

Mushroams

☐ ICH ZAHLE TAGLICH MEINE SORGEN
Ich zahle taglich meine Sorgen / Motorbiene / Rote lippen soll man kussen
BCD 15999 / Nov '96 / Bear Family

Mushroom

☐ EARLY ONE MORNING
LW 2043 / 2 Mar '98 / Little Wing

Mushroom

☐ ALIVE AND IN FULL BLOOM
IRCD 001 / 16 Feb '98 / In Betweens

Music De Madrid

☐ LA FOILE DE LA SPAGNA
HM 90 1050 / Oct '88 / Harmonia Mundi

Music Emporium

☐ MUSIC EMPORIUM
FLASH 54 / 1 Jun '98 / Flash

Music Inc.

☐ MUSIC INC. (Music Inc. & Big Band)
CDGR 227 / 16 Mar '98 / Charly

Music Machine

☐ TURN ON THE MUSIC MACHINE
Talk talk / Trouble / Cherry, Cherry / Taxman / Some other drum / Masculine intuition / People in me / CC rider / Wrong / 96 tears / Come on in / Hey Joe
REP 4154 / Aug '91 / Repertoire

Music Makars

☐ JIG FOR JOY
EWO 002CD / 2 Apr '98 / Etienne Ozorak

Music Revelation Ensemble

☐ CROSSFIRE
DIW 927 / Jan '98 / DIW

☐ IN THE NAME OF
DIW 885 / Oct '94 / DIW

Musica De La Tierra

☐ INSTRUMENTAL & VOCAL MUSIC VOL.2
CDC 207 / Jun '93 / Music Of The World

Musica Electronica Viva

☐ LEAVE THE CITY
14968 / Jun '97 / Spalax

☐ SOUND POOL, THE
14969 / 23 Mar '98 / Spalax

Musica Transonic

☐ MUSICA TRANSONIC & KEIJI HAINO
PSFD 98 / Jul '98 / PSF

☐ WORLD OF MUSICA TRANSONIC, THE
PSFD 91 / Jul '97 / PSF

Musicians Of The Nile

☐ CHARCOAL GYPSIES
Bitnadini tani lih / Eb'at Djawaben / Sq Al-Manadl / Mawwal-doha / Rais al-bahr / Al-ward Al-foll / Ramla / Salamat / Walla zaman
CDRW 63 / Nov '96 / Realworld

Musicians Union Band

☐ MUSICIANS UNION BAND, THE
Poor misguided woman / In my room / City ride / Caroline belle / Bad boy / Your man / Put your trust in the Lord / Sugar lipped Sal / My babe / Let the circle be unbroken / Elvis lives / Heartbreak hotel / Love me tender / One night / Jailhouse rock / Beggar man / Funky / Shake your moneymaker / Put your trust in the Lord / Part 2 / Yes it must be Spring / Side step
SJPCD 010 / Jul '97 / Angel Air

Muskrats

☐ YOUNG AND RESTLESS
NERCD 091 / Oct '97 / Nervous

Musselwhite, Charley

☐ ACE OF HARPS
Blues overtook me / She may be your woman / River hip mama / Leaving your town / Hello pretty baby / Mean ol' Frisco / Kiddio / Yesterdays / Hangin' on / My road lies in darkness
ALCD 4781 / May '93 / Alligator

☐ HARMONICA ACCORDING TO CHARLEY MUSSELWHITE, THE
BPCD 5016 / Dec '94 / Blind Pig

☐ IN MY TIME
ALCD 4818 / Mar '94 / Alligator

☐ MELLOW DEE
Hey Miss Bessie / Need my baby / I'll get a break / Peach orchard mama / Ask me nice / Come back baby / Comin' home baby / Baby, please don't go / Lotsa poppa / Steady on your trail / Can't you see what you're doing to me / Christo redemptor
CCD 11013 / Nov '88 / Crosscut

☐ MEMPHIS CHARLEY
ARHCD 303 / Apr '95 / Arhoolie

☐ ROUGH NEWS
Both sides of the fence / I sat and cried / Sleepwalk / Natural born lover / Darkest hour / Harlem nocturne / Drifting boy / Rough dried woman / Feel it in your heart / Rainy highway / Clarksdale boogie / Rough news
VPBCD 42 / Apr '97 / Pointblank

☐ SIGNATURE
Make my getaway / Blues got me again / Mama long legs / 38 special / It's gettin' warm in here / What's new again / Hey Miss Bessie / Me and my baby and the blues / Catwalk / Cheatin' on me
ALCD 4801 / May '94 / Alligator

☐ STAND BACK (Here Comes Charley Musselwhite's South Side Band)
Baby will you please help me / No more lonely nights / Cha cha the blues / Christo redemptor / Help me / Chicken shack / Strange land / 39th and Indiana / My baby / Early in the morning / 4 pm / Sa day
VMD 79232 / Oct '95 / Vanguard

☐ STONE BLUES (Musselwhite, Charley Blues Band)
My buddy buddy friends / Everything's gonna be alright / My baby's sweeter / Clay's tune / Gone and left me / Cry for me baby / Hey baby / Juke / She belongs to me / Bag gloom brews
VMD 79287 / Oct '95 / Vanguard

☐ TAKING CARE OF BUSINESS
Louisiana fog / Takin' care of business / Big legged woman / Riffin' / Leavin' / Just a little bit / Fell on my knees / Directly from my heart / Fat city
CDTB 172 / Nov '95 / Thunderbolt

☐ TENNESSEE WOMAN
VMD 6528 / 27 Apr '98 / Vanguard

Musso, Robert

☐ TRASONIC
AW 013CD / Dec '96 / Ambient World

Musso, Vido

☐ LOADED (Musso, Vido & Stan Getz)
Moose in a caboose / Moose on the loose / My Jo-Ann / Vido in a jam / Bassology / Spellbound / Jam mego / Jam session at Savoy / Sweet Miss / Loaded / Grab your axe Max / Always
SV 0227 / Oct '97 / Savoy Jazz

Mussolini Headkick

☐ BLOOD ON THE FLAG
WD 6663CD / Oct '90 / World

Mussolini, Romano

☐ SOFT AND SWING
RTCL 809CD / Jul '96 / Right Tempo

Mustafa, Melton

☐ BOILING POINT (Mustafa, Melton Orchestra)
Boiling point (3 in 1 blues) / Blind love blues / Bridging the gap / Some kind of blues / I can sing / Easy as it goes / A night at El Morocco) / Upsy Daisy / Let it be known / Where there's smoke / Swinging my lady / Gift of knowledge (El don del conocimiento)
CCD 14075 / Jul '96 / Contemporary

Mustang Ford

☐ CHATTERBOX
SISSY 004 / May '97 / Sticksister

Mustang Lightning

☐ MUSTANG LIGHTNING
422499 / May '94 / New Rose

Mustapha, Sabah Habas

☐ JALAN KOPO
3814620202 / 27 Apr '98 / Omnium

Mustard Plug

☐ EVIL DOERS BEWARE
HR 6202 / Jun '97 / Hopeless

Mustard Seeds

☐ MUSTARD SEEDS
87902IDE / May '96 / Edel

Mutabaruka

☐ BLAKK WI BLAK..K..K
You and yourself / Great queens of afrika / Dispel the lie / I am de man / People's court / Mad reality / Letter to congress (is it because wi blakk) / Wind of time / Blakk wi blakk / Ecology poem / Junk food / I don't have a color problem
322574 / Oct '91 / Koch

☐ CHECK IT
ALCD 8306 / Aug '92 / Alligator

☐ MELANIN MAN
SHCD 45013 / Apr '94 / Shanachie

☐ MYSTERY UNFOLDS, THE
Leaders speak / Dub poem / Revolutionary words / My great shun / Old cut bruk / Bun dung Babylon / Mustery unfolds / Dis poem / Famine injection / Eyes of liberty / Walkin' on gravel / Voice
SHANCD 43037 / Aug '87 / Shanachie

☐ OUT CRY
SHANCD 43023 / Nov '87 / Shanachie

☐ ULTIMATE COLLECTION, THE
GRELCD 224 / May '96 / Greensleeves

Mute Beat

☐ MUTE BEAT IN DUB
RUSCD 8227 / Sep '96 / ROIR

Mute Drivers

☐ EVERYONE
I'm counting the days / Company chairman / Amsterdam / Government man / Hey mikhail / Holes in my shoes / House of cards / All is quiet / Pwa / Firing squad / Suicide / Honey child / Holy moses / Prime minister
BND 4CD / Feb '90 / One Little Indian

Muthspiel, Christian

☐ MUTHSPIEL - PEACOCK - MUTHSPIEL - MOTIAN (Muthspiel, Christian & Wolfgang/Gary Peacock/Paul Motian)
Jodler / Chill out honey pie / Eight slash eight / Hanne / Mupemo / One for Igor / After all / Gnome's run / (Grand) canon
5196762 / Mar '94 / Amadeo

☐ OCTET OST VOL.1
Introitus / VII / Interlude / II / Interlude / II continues / Interlude / VII / Interlude / I / Interlude / IV / X / Interlude / III / Interlude / XIV / Extroitus
5133292 / May '94 / Amadeo

☐ OCTET OST VOL.2 (Indirect View Of Beauty)
Part one / Song nine / Part two
5218232 / May '94 / Amadeo

Muthspiel, Wolfgang

☐ BLACK AND BLUE (Muthspiel, Wolfgang Sextet)
Dance / North shore / Swords crossing / Duet / Miles / Square 1 / Rules of the game / Visions / Bliss and other short stories
5176532 / May '94 / Amadeo

☐ PERSPECTIVE
5334662 / Nov '96 / Amadeo

☐ PROMISE, THE
TG / Sonic presence of David Lee / My funny valentine / Promise / No luck in Paris / New York was another story / La Nevada / End of the day / Trackings
8470232 / May '94 / Amadeo

☐ TIMEZONES (Muthspiel, Wolfgang Trio)
My hill / Chip / Asleep (for Christine) / Introduction / Everything happens to that dog / On the edge / Singing beach / Timezones / Blue morning rays (for Menga)
8390132 / May '94 / Amadeo

Mutiny

☐ AFTERSHOCK 2005
Growl / It's all good / No choice / Passion / Tickin' like a time bomb / Rock the boat / Desires / Moments
RCD 10334 / Feb '96 / Black Arc

Mutter

☐ HAUPTSACHE MUSIK
EFA 047032 / Jul '94 / DEG

☐ ICH SCHANE MICH GEDANKEN ZU HAB
EFA 047012 / Jul '94 / DEG

Mutton Birds

☐ ENVY OF ANGELS
Straight to your head / She's been talking / Trouble with you / April / Like this train / Another morning / Ten feet tall / Come around / Crooked mile / While you sleep / Inside my skin / Envy of angels
CDVIR 55 / Jun '97 / Dindisc

☐ NATURE
Nature / Dominion Road / Anchor me / Heater / Giant friend / Your window / White valient / In my room / Thing well made / Queen's English / There's a limit / Too close to the sun
CDVIR 39 / Sep '95 / Dindisc

Mutton Gun

☐ MUTTONGUN 111
Rain rain / Turkey / Better / Demon honey / End of it all / Bullet for a guide / Good bad dog / Turquoise blue / Chucky bear / Young / Thought for the day / Enter the hogger / Summer in the city
KOKOPOP 005CD / Feb '94 / Kokopop

Mutukudzi, Oliver

☐ NDEGA ZVANGU
SHAVAC 008 / 3 Mar '98 / Music & Words

Muzsikas

☐ BLUES FOR TRANSYLVANIA
Old song from somogy / Legenyes from kalotaszeg / My lord, my lord / Szapora / Outlaw song / Dawn song from bodonkut / On my way to kolozsvar town / Cimbalmos from bonchida / Kati-kata / Old wedding song / Time is autumn
HNCD 1350 / Feb '90 / Hannibal

☐ KETTO
MRCD 175 / Sep '95 / Munich

☐ MARAMAROS (The Lost Jewish Music Of Transylvania)
Hasid wedding dances / Rooster is crowning / Dance from maramures / Lamenting song / Anne Maamini / I have just come from gyula / Farewell to Saturday evening / Jewish dance from Szaszregan / Hat ein jid ein wejbele / Jewish csardas series from szek / Hassid dance / Greeting of the bride / Haneros halelu / Farewell to the guests
HNCD 1373 / Mar '93 / Hannibal

☐ MORNING STAR (Muzsikas & Marta Sebestyen)
Wedding in Fuzes village / Song from Madocsa / Roun dance of Gyimes / My mother's rosebush / Oh, the road is long / If I were a rose / Trouble trouble / Cry only on Sundays / Oh evening star farewell to soldiers
HNCD 1401 / Sep '97 / Hannibal

☐ PRISONER'S SONG, THE (Muzsikas/Marta Sebestyen)
Rabnota / Eddig veneta / Azt gondoltam, eso esik / Hidegen fujnak a szelek / Bujdosodal / Repuli madar, repuli / Regen volt / Soka lesz / Szerlem, szerelem / En szak azt csodalom / Element a madarka
HNCD 1341 / Jan '89 / Hannibal

Muzur, Virgil

☐ MASTER OF THE ROMANIAN FIDDLE, THE
B 6821CD / Aug '96 / Auvidis/Ethnic

MX 80

☐ DAS LOVE BOAT
ALP 56CD / Apr '97 / Atavistic

☐ HARD ATTACK/BIG HITS EP
Man on the move / Kid stuff / Fascination / Summer '77 / PCB's / Crushed ice / Theme from checkmate / Facts/facts / You're not alone / Civilised/Semi pers / Afterbirth/Aftermath / Boy trouble/Girl trouble / Myonga von bontee / SCP / You turn me on / Train to loveland / Till death do us part / Tidal wave
ALP 30CD / Apr '97 / Atavistic

☐ I'VE SEEN ENOUGH
ALP 67CD / Apr '97 / Atavistic

☐ OUT OF CONTROL
ALP 32CD / Apr '97 / Atavistic

MXPX

☐ LIFE IN GENERAL
TND 1060CD / 13 Apr '98 / Tooth & Nail

☐ ON THE COVER
TND 1044CD / 13 Apr '98 / Tooth & Nail

☐ POKINATCHA
TND 1014CD / 13 Apr '98 / Tooth & Nail

☐ TEENAGE POLITICS
TND 1032CD / 13 Apr '98 / Tooth & Nail

My Bloody Valentine

☐ ISN'T ANYTHING
Soft as snow / Lose my breath / Cupid come / You're still in a dream / No more sorry / All I need / Feed me with your kiss / Sueisfine / Several girls galore / You never should / Nothing much to lose / I can see it
CRECD 040 / Nov '88 / Creation

☐ LOVELESS
Only shallow / Loomer / Touched / To here knows when / When you sleep / I only said / Come in alone / Sometimes / Blown a wish / What you want / Soon
CRECD 060 / Nov '91 / Creation

My Dad Is Dead

☐ EVERYONE WANTS THE HONEY
EJ 16CD / 13 Oct '97 / Emperor Jones

☐ FOR RICHER, FOR POORER
EJ 01CD / Nov '95 / Emperor Jones

☐ SHINE(R)
EJ 5CD / Jun '96 / Emperor Jones

My Drug Hell

☐ THIS IS MY DRUG HELL
VTONECD 001X / May '97 / Voltone

My Dying Bride

☐ ANGEL AND THE DARK RIVER (2CD Set)
CDVILE 50 / Apr '96 / Peaceville

☐ AS THE FLOWER WITHERS
CDVILE 32 / Apr '95 / Peaceville

☐ LIKE GODS OF THE SUN
Like Gods of the sun / Dark caress / Grace unhearing / Kiss to remember / All swept away / For you / It will come / Here in the throat / For my fallen angel
CDXVILE 65

☐ STORIES, THE
Symphonaire internus et spera empyrium / God is alone / De sade soliloquay / Thrash of naked limbs / Le cerf malade / Gather me up forever / I am the bloody earth / Transcending (Into the exquisite) / Crown of sympathy
VILE 045CD / Oct '94 / Peaceville

TRINITY
☐ TRINITY
Symphonaire infernus / Thrash of naked limbs / I am the bloody earth / God is alone / Le cerf malade / Sexuality of bereavement / De sade soliloquy / Gather me up forever / Crown of sympathy
CDVILE 46 / Sep '95 / Peaceville

☐ TURN LOOSE THE SWANS
Sear me MCMXC111 / Songless bird / Snow in my hand / Crown of sympathy / Turn loose the swans / Black God
CDVILE 39 / Mar '95 / Peaceville

My Friend The Chocolate Cake
☐ BROOD
D 31136 / Mar '95 / Mushroom

☐ GOOD LUCK
TVD 93462 / Aug '96 / Mushroom

☐ REVIEW
MUSH 4CD / Jul '97 / Mushroom

My Life In Rain
☐ SLOWBURN
ALLIED 081CD / Jan '97 / Allied

☐ THIS BAND IS KILLING ME
ALLIED 091CD / 10 Nov '97 / Allied

My Life Story
☐ GOLDEN MILE
12 reasons why I love her / Suited and booted / Marriage blister / Strumpet / Claret / Mr. Boyd / King of kissingdom / I dive (unanswered questions and questionable answers) / You can't uneat the apple / Sparkle / April 1st / November 5th / Duchess
CDPCSY 7386 / 18 Aug '97 / Parlophone

☐ MORNINGTON CRESCENT
Forever / Girl a girl b boy c / Checkmate / Under the ice / Motorcade / Penthouse in the basement / Angel / Up the down escalator / Funny ha ha / You don't sparkle (in my eyes) / Triumphant / Bullets fly
4933752 / 26 Jan '98 / Parlophone

My Own Victim
☐ BURNING INSIDE
CM 77105CD / Jan '96 / Century Media

☐ MY OWN VICTIM
CM 770822 / Mar '95 / Century Media

☐ WEAPON
CM 77205CD / 2 Mar '98 / Century Media

My Sister's Machine
☐ WALL FLOWERS
Inside of me / Broken land / This is fear / Steamy swamp thang / Feed / Empty room / Sixteen ways to go / Enemy / I slip away / Burn / Mockingbird / Cracking new ground
3705615122 / Jul '93 / WEA

My Solid Ground
☐ MY SOLID GROUND
SB 035 / Jun '97 / Second Battle

Mya
☐ MYA
INTD 90166 / 13 Jul '98 / Interscope

Myaz, Benjy
☐ INTIMATE RELATIONSHIP
VPCD 1495 / May '97 / VP

Myers, Amina Claudine
☐ SALUTES BESSIE SMITH
CDLR 103 / Feb '89 / Leo

☐ WOMEN IN (E)MOTION FESTIVAL
T&M 102 / Nov '94 / Tradition & Moderne

Myers, Billie
☐ GROWING PAINS
UND 53100 / 20 Apr '98 / Universal

Myers, Dave
☐ YOU CAN'T DO THAT
Please don't leave me / Dave's boogie guitar / You can't do that / Elevate me mama / Reconsider baby / Ting a ling / Oh baby / Legs up / Going home tomorrow / Chattanooga shoe shine / You can't love me that way / Love by the pound / Stone cold fox / Blues in Mexico
CDBT 1142 / 16 Mar '98 / Black Top

Myers, Hazel
☐ HAZEL MEYERS VOL.1
DOCD 5430 / Jul '96 / Document

Myers, Louis
☐ I'M A SOUTHERN MAN
TCD 5026 / Aug '95 / Testament

Myles, Alannah
☐ ALANNAH MYLES
Still got this thing / Black velvet / Lover of mine / If you want to / Who loves you / Love is / Rock this joint / Kickstart my heart / Just one kiss / Make love
7819562 / Nov '89 / Atlantic

☐ ARRIVAL
ELDCD 001 / 3 Nov '97 / Eldorado
ARKK 10018 / 24 Mar '98 / ARKK

☐ ROCKING HORSE
Our world our times / Make me happy / Sonny say you will / Tumbleweed / Livin' on a memory / Song instead of a kiss / Love in the big town / Last time I saw William / Lies and rumours / Rocking horse
7567824022 / Nov '92 / WEA

Myles, Heather
☐ JUST LIKE OLD TIMES
Love lyin' down / Why I'm walkin' / Changes / Rum and rodeo / Make a fool out of me / Other side of town / Just like old times / Stay out of my arms / I love you, goodbye / Lovin' the bottle / One good reason why / Playin' in the dirt
FIENDCD 717 / Apr '92 / Demon

☐ SWEET LITTLE DANGEROUS
Read you and wrong (introduction) / Gonna have love / Other side of town / Sweet little dangerous / If the truth hurts / True love won't let you down / Lovin' the bottle / When the tingle becomes a chill / Love me a little longer / Rum and rodeo / Worried wife blues / Changes / Walk through this world with me / Cadillac cowboy
FIENDCD 772 / Feb '96 / Demon

☐ UNTAMED
And it hurts / Just leave me alone / When you walked out on me / Cadillac cowboy / Until I couldn't have you / Indigo moon / It ain't over / Begging to you / How could she / Coming back to me / Gone too long / Untamed
FIENDCD 763 / Jan '95 / Demon

Mylett, Peter
☐ SOMETHING OLD SOMETHING NEW
FRCD 030 / Oct '94 / Foam

Mynediad Am Ddim
☐ MYNEDIAD AM DDIM 1974-1992
Wa MacSpredar / P-Pendyffryn / Arica / Beti Wyn / Fi / Liwch y glo / Padi / Mi ganaf gan / Ceidwad y goleudy / Ynys Llanddwyn / Mynd yn bell i ffwrdd / Y gwrthodedig / Yn y dre / Hi yw fy ffrind / Mae'r byd yn wag / Cofio dy wyneb / Pappagio's / Gwaed i'r llwch / Can y cap / Wini / Casa eroti / Y storu wir
SCD 2003 / Feb '95 / Sain

Mynta
☐ FIRST SUMMER
XOUCD 117 / May '97 / Xource
61868500032 / 5 May '98 / MMEL

☐ NANDUS DANCE
Nandu's dance / Tarana / Tove / What's the bag dad / Kamala / Sounds / Hey-ho / She survived / Emma / Indian summer / Faroe islands
XOUCD 107 / Nov '93 / Xource

Myopia
☐ SONGS OF NO IMPORTANCE
KNEK 2 / 13 Apr '98 / Kuro Neko

Myracle Brah
☐ LIFE ON PLANET EARTSNOT
NL 044 / 29 Jun '98 / Not Lame

Myrick, Gary
☐ TEXAS GLITTER AND TOMBSTONE TALES (Myrick, Gary & Havana 3am)
BCD 00242 / Sep '96 / Burnside

Myrna Loy
☐ IMMERSCHON
NORM 158CD / Nov '93 / Normal

Myron
☐ LET'S GO DISTORTION KIDS
LIQ 005CD / Jun '97 / Liquid

Myron
☐ DESTINY
We can get down / So fly / Destiny / Come around / See you cry / So damn much / Heavenly girl / Give my all to you / Hit it / Eastside girl / You're my everything / Angel / Destiny
5244792 / 10 Aug '98 / Island Black Music

Myster-Me
☐ LET ME EXPLAIN (Myster-Me & DJ 20/ 20)
What's the word / Can't fuck with the record / If ever / Playtime's over / Unsolved mysterme / Myster Master / Call me Myster / Happy like death / Whatever whatever / Peepin' the wreck / Hoodie down / Under the influence
GEECD 15 / Jul '94 / Gee Street

Mysteries Of Life
☐ FOCUS ON THE BACKGROUND
FLT 108 / Mar '97 / Flat Earth

Mysteries Of Science
☐ EROTIC NATURE OF AUTOMATED UNIVERSE, THE
IAE 005CD / Jul '95 / Instinct Ambient Europe

Mystery Machine
☐ 10 SPEED
W 230098 / Oct '95 / Nettwerk

☐ GLAZED
Shaky ground / Everyone's alright / Valley song / Ride / Stay high / Hooked / Floored / Hi-test / Invitation / Salty / Underground / Broken / Slack / Stain master
NET 043CD / Mar '93 / Nettwerk

☐ HEADFIRST INTO EVERYTHING
YTV / Gleam / Wake up pill / Doubter / Doubt is all you know / I'm not anything / What I want / Drone / Teenage drag / Fool / Ditch / Mad / Bring you down
301222 / 8 Jun '98 / Nettwerk

Mystic Astrologic
☐ FLOWERS NEVER CRY
Factory endeavour / Factory endeavour / Antagonizing friend / Barnyard philosophy / Flowers never cry / Geometry alley / October sunshine / Le vent / Publicly inclined (to blow her mind) / Yesterday girl / M.a.c.b. theme / Sunbeams and rainbows / I think I'll just lie here and die / Gaberdene square / Ah ha ha ha / Krystalyze / Today / Yellow room / Authors / It's strong / Only time / Oatmeal quicksand
DOCD 1993 / Jul '91 / Drop Out

Mystic Charm
☐ SHADOWS OF THE UNKNOWN
SHR 008CD / Aug '95 / Shiver

Mystic Revealers
☐ JAH WORKS
RASCD 3123 / Sep '93 / Ras

RAS PORTRAITS
☐ RAS PORTRAITS
Space and time / Remember Romeo / Saw you smiling / Righteous / Religion / Religion dub / We and dem / Got to be a better way / Space and dub / Dem problem / Mash down apartheid / World War Three
RAS 3328 / Jul '97 / Ras

☐ SPACE AND DUB
RASCD 3173 / Apr '96 / Ras

☐ SPACE AND TIME
RASCD 3170 / Aug '95 / Ras

☐ YOUNG REVOLUTIONARIES
RAS 3226 / Mar '96 / Ras

Mystic Siva
☐ MYSTIC SIVA
MR 1 / Jul '97 / Mystic

Mystic Tide
☐ SOLID SOUND/SOLID GROUND
DR 1006 / Jun '97 / Distortions

Mystics
☐ MYSTICS MEET THE JARMELS (Mystics/Jarmels)
Hush-a-bye: Mystics / All through the night: Mystics / It's only a paper moon: Mystics / Star crossed lovers: Mystics / Don't take the stars: Mystics / (I begin) to think of you again: Mystics / Let me steal your heart away: Mystics / Adam and Eve: Mystics / Little bit of soap: Jarmels / One by one: Jarmels / Come on girl (it's time to smile again): Jarmels / Way you look tonight: Jarmels / Gee oh gosh: Jarmels / Loneliness: Jarmels / You don't believe a word I say: Jarmels / White cliffs of Dover: Mystics / Sunday kind of love: Mystics / So tenderly: Mystics / Again: Mystics / Darling I know now: Mystics / Over the rainbow: Mystics / Blue star: Mystics / Goodbye Mr. Blues: Mystics / She loves to dance: Jarmels / Keep your mind on me: Jarmels / Why am I a fool for you: Jarmels / Little lonely one: Jarmels / Red sails in the sunset: Jarmels / I'll follow you: Jarmels / Little bug: Jarmels
CDCH 929 / 23 Mar '98 / Ace

Mystics
☐ MYSTICS
RRAD 114 / 14 Sep '98 / Rotator

Mystifier
☐ GOETIA
OPCD 16 / Nov '93 / Osmose

☐ IF THE WORLD IS SO GOOD (THAT WHO MADE IT DOESN'T LIVE HERE ANYMORE)
OPCD 042CD / Sep '96 / Osmose

Mystik
☐ PERPETUAL BEING
MASSCD 028 / Apr '94 / Massacre

Myth Science
☐ LOVE IN OUTER SPACE
KFWCD 183 / Oct '96 / Knitting Factory

Mythos
☐ CONCRETE CITY
14571 / 2 Feb '98 / Spalax

☐ DREAMLAB
SPALAX 14206 / Nov '96 / Spalax

☐ PAIN AMPLIFIER
EOR 0002 / Feb '95 / Evil Omen

☐ STRANGE GUYS
14570 / Sep '97 / Spalax

Mythra
☐ DEATH AND DESTINY
CDMETAL 16 / 13 Oct '97 / Anagram

N

N2 Deep

☐ BACK TO THE HOTEL
FILERCD 427 / May '92 / Profile

N-Trance

☐ ELECTRONIC PLEASURE
What is your pleasure / Electronic pleasure / Stayin' alive / I will take you you there / (Just) Let it go / Set you free / Softly (Dragging me down) / Do you wanna rock / Gimme 1 2 3 4 5 / Turn up the power / I don't wanna lose your love again / That's all we need
GLOBECD 2 / 3 Aug '98 / All Around The World

☐ HAPPY HOUR
GLOBECD 8 / 15 Jun '98 / All Around The World

☐ MIND OF THE MACHINE
GLOBECD 5 / Nov '97 / All Around The World

N-Tyce

☐ ALL DAY EVERYDAY
TCD 2945 / 8 Jun '98 / Telstar

Na Casaidigh

☐ 1691
CEFCD 154 / Jan '94 / Gael Linn

Na Fili

☐ PURE TRADITIONAL MUSIC OF IRELAND
PTICD 1010 / Apr '94 / Pure Traditional Irish

Na Firein

☐ NA FIREIN
CEFCD 162 / Jan '94 / Gael Linn

Na Lua

☐ CONTRADANZAS
GCDF 1002CD / Apr '95 / Sons Galiza

☐ ONDAS DO MAR DE VIGO
DF 006CD / Aug '97 / Do Fol

☐ OS TEMPOS SON CHEGADOS
DF 007CD / Aug '97 / Do Fol

☐ PELIQUEIRO
SGF 1021CD / Apr '95 / Sons Galiza

Naa, D.K.

☐ GIFTY
CD 4398 / May '96 / Gifty

Naam, Fong

☐ JAKAJAN (Music From New Siam)
NI 5486 / Aug '96 / Nimbus

☐ NANG HONG SUITE
NI 5332 / Sep '94 / Nimbus

☐ SLEEPING ANGEL, THE
NI 5319 / Sep '94 / Nimbus

Nabat

☐ NATI PER NIENTE
BB 023CD / Oct '96 / Banda Bannot

Nada

☐ CELMETRA
CC 006CD / Oct '94 / Common Cause

Nada Surf

☐ HIGH/LOW
Popular / Plan / Sleep / Psychic caramel / Stalemate / Hollywood / Zen brain / Icebox / Treehouse / Deeper well
7559619132 / Oct '96 / Elektra

Nadine

☐ BACK TO MY SENSES
GRCD 418 / 23 Mar '98 / Glitterhouse

Naftule's Dream

☐ SEARCH FOR THE GOLDEN DREYDL
TZA 7118 / 27 Oct '97 / Tzadik

Nagflar

☐ VITTRA
WAR 008CD / Apr '96 / Wrong Again

Nagle, Paul

☐ EARTHSHAPER
AMPCD 034 / Apr '97 / AMP

Naglfar

☐ DIABOLICAL
WAR 0005CD / 25 May '98 / War

Nagourney, Jan

☐ THREE AND ONE
Tadd's delight / Byrd in hand / Gregory is here / Dancing on the ceiling / In the wee small hours of the morning / Split kick / Three and one / Thanks for Hanks / Juicy Lucy / We're all together / Koolin' on the street
LICD 3168 / Jan '97 / Liphone

Naif

☐ WAITING IS OVER
ZYX 204262 / Jan '97 / ZYX

Nail, Jimmy

☐ BIG RIVER
Big river / I think of you / Can't hold on / Right to know / Love / What kind of man am I / Something that we had / What's the use / Hands of time / I wonder
0630128232 / Nov '95 / East West

☐ CROCODILE SHOES VOL.1
Crocodile shoes / Cowboy dreams / Only one heart / Love will find someone for you / Bitter and twisted / Dragons / Don't wanna go home / Between a woman and a man / Angel / Once upon a time / Calling out your name
4509985562 / Nov '94 / East West

☐ CROCODILE SHOES VOL.2
My buddy / Until the day I die / Just can't win / Running man / Gentle's lament / I refuse to lie down / Still I dream of it / I'm a troubled man / Blue roses / Fear no evil / Country boy
0630169352 / Nov '96 / East West

☐ GROWING UP IN PUBLIC
Ain't no doubt / Reach out / Laura / Waiting for the sunshine / Real love / Only love (can bring us home) / Wicked world / Beautiful / I believed / Absent friends
4509901442 / Dec '94 / East West

☐ NAIL FILE, THE
Love don't live here anymore / Ain't no doubt / Crocodile shoes / Cowboy dreams / Big river / Country boy / Blue roses / On this night of a thousand stars / Running man / Love / Once upon a time / Dragons / Absent friends / Calling out your name / Show me heaven / Black and white
3984207392 / 6 Oct '97 / East West

☐ TAKE IT OR LEAVE IT
That's the way love is / Airwaves / Walk away / Your decision today / Ladies and gentlemen of South Africa / Rain burns / Same again / Further on / One more day / Love don't live here anymore
CDVIP 111 / Nov '93 / Virgin VIP

Nailbomb

☐ POINT BLANK
Wasting away / Vai toma no cu / 24 hour bullshit / Guerrillas / Blind and lost / Sum of your achievements / Cockroaches / For f's sake / World of shit / Exploitation / Religious cancer / Shit pinata / Sick life
RR 90552 / Jul '95 / Roadrunner

Naing, Kyaw Kyaw

☐ PAT WAING (The Magic Drum Circle Of Burma)
Saddan ai thar / Ma Bay dar / Shwe ka nyar / Hiyat pan khway nwe / Shwe maung than/Aung Bar zay / Oat aw than aye / Tay htat kwet sun / Ah pay ah you / Pat waing let swan pya / Sein chew kyar nyaung
SHANCD 66005 / Apr '98 / Shanachie

Naive, Steve

☐ IT'S RAINING SOMEWHERE
KFWCD 198 / 27 Jul '98 / Knitting Factory

Najjad, Nasser Rasngad

☐ IN A PERSIAN GARDEN
LYRCD 7434 / Nov '97 / Lyrichord

Najma

☐ ATISH
TRECD 108 / Nov '93 / Triple Earth

☐ FORBIDDEN KISS
SH 64063 / Aug '96 / Shanachie

☐ QAREEB
Neend koyi / Har sitani aap ka / Zikar hai apna mehfil mehfil / Karcon na yad magar / Jane kis tarjha / Dil laga ya tha
TRECD 103 / Nov '93 / Triple Earth

Nakagawa, Masami

☐ PRELUDE FOR AUTUMN
1st movement from symphony no. 40 / Venetianisches gondellied / Prelude no 8 / Variations on a theme by haydn / 'la meneuse de tortues d' or" / 2nd movement from symphony no. 5 / "foreign lands and people" / Siciliano / 4th movement from symphony no. 1
JD 3304 / Jul '88 / JVC

☐ TOUCH OF SPRING
Violin concerto in d minor / Piano sonata in a minor k331 / Apres un reve op. 7-1 / 3rd movt. from symphony no. 6 in f maj. op. 68 / Liebestraume nocturne no. 1 / Siciliano for flute and guitar / Tambourin / Intermezzo for flute and guitar / Etude op.2 no.1 in c sharp minor (scriabin)
JD 3311 / Oct '88 / JVC

Nakai, R. Carlos

☐ DESERT DANCE (The Spirit Of The Native American)
130332 / Dec '95 / Celestial Harmonies

☐ ISLAND OF BOWS
CRCD 7018 / Mar '96 / Canyon

☐ KOKOPELLI'S CAFE
CR 7013CD / Nov '96 / Canyon

☐ SPIRIT HORSES
CRCD 7014 / Mar '96 / Canyon

Nakamoto, Mari

☐ WHAT IS LOVE
I could write a book / If I were a bell / Whisper not / All of me / All too soon / In a mellow tone / Speak low / Easy to love / What is this thing called love / You don't know what love is
JVC 90082 / 24 Nov '97 / JVC

Naked Aggression

☐ GUT WRINGING MACHINE
GRL 005CD / 1 Jun '98 / Grilled Cheese

☐ NAKED REGRESSIONS
SKIP 70CD / 1 Jun '98 / Broken

Naked City

☐ ABSINTHE
AVAN 004 / Jan '94 / Avant

☐ BLACK BOX (2CD Set)
TZA 73122 / Feb '97 / Tzadik

☐ GRAND GUIGNOL
AVANT 002 / Jan '93 / Avant

☐ HERETIC - JEUX DES DAMES CRUELLES
AVANT 001 / Aug '92 / Avant

☐ RADIO
AVAN 003 / Jan '94 / Avant

Naked Ear

☐ ACOUSTIC GUITAR DUOLOG
BEST 1022CD / Nov '93 / Acoustic Music

Naked Funk

☐ EVOLUTION ENDING
PUSSYCDLP 010 / 6 Jul '98 / Pussy Foot

Naked Ray Gun

☐ ALL RISE
HMS 045CD / Jul '88 / Homestead

☐ LAST OF THE DEMOHICANS
DYS 21 / 19 Jan '98 / Dyslexic

☐ THROB THROB
HMS 008CD / 16 Mar '98 / Homestead

Naked Rhythm

☐ FATBOX
MASSCD 038 / Nov '94 / Massacre

Namanax

☐ AUDIOTRONIC
Return of the deadly mantis / Immune / Aquanax / Tomb of the seagull / Giggling winds
RR 69632 / 1 Sep '97 / Relapse

Namlook, Pete

☐ 2350 BROADWAY 3 (Namlook, Pete & Tetsuo Inuoe)
PW 025CD / Feb '96 / Fax

☐ 4 SEASONS
SEA 00 / Oct '96 / Fax

☐ DARK SIDE OF THE MOOG VOL.4 (Namlook, Pete & Bill Laswell)
PH 08112 / Apr '96 / Fax

☐ DARK SIDE OF THE MOOG VOL.5 (Namlook, Pete & Bill Laswell)
PK 08123CD / Dec '96 / Fax

☐ DREAMFISH (Namlook, Pete & Mixmaster Morris)
AW 012CD / Oct '96 / Ambient World

☐ ELECTRONIC MUSIC CENTRE
PK 08119 / Oct '96 / Fax

☐ JET CHAMBER
PK 08115CD / May '96 / Fax

☐ KOOLFANG VOL.2 (Namlook, Pete & David Monfang)
PK 08106CD / Jan '96 / Fax

☐ NAMLOOK ATOM
PK 08107CD / Jan '96 / Fax

☐ NAMLOOK XI
PK 08113CD / May '96 / Fax

☐ OUTLAND VOL.2 (Namlook, Pete & Bill Laswell)
PW 028CD / Apr '96 / Fax

☐ OZOONA (Namlook, Pete & Gordon)
PW 030 / Sep '96 / Fax

☐ PSYCHONAVIGATION VOL.2 (Namlook, Pete & Bill Laswell)
PW 024CD / Nov '95 / Fax

☐ SHADES OF ORION
PW 029CD / May '96 / Fax

☐ SULTAN
PW 027CD / Apr '96 / Fax

☐ TIME VOL.2 (Namlook, Pete & Tetsuo Inuoe)
PW 032CD / Dec '96 / Fax

Namyslowski, Zbigniew

☐ KUJAVIACK GOES FUNKY
PBR 33859 / Aug '95 / Power Bros.

☐ ZBIGNIEW NAMYSLOWSKI QUARTET
PBR 33861 / Oct '95 / Power Bros.

Nanaco

☐ LOVE IS A DRUG
HYD 10012 / Jun '96 / CDS

Nancy Boy

☐ PROMOSEXUAL
BENDCD 001 / Oct '95 / Equator

Nancy Vandal

☐ DEBRIEFING ROOM, THE
FNARR 73 / 12 Aug '97 / Half Arsed

Nannini, Gianna

☐ LATIN LOVER
811 669 2 / '88 / Ricordi

☐ PUZZLE
813 387 2 / '88 / Ricordi

Naos

☐ MELANCHOLIA
NIHIL 15CD / Aug '96 / Cacophonous

Napalm

☐ CRUEL TRANQUILITY
Mind melt / AOA / Shake it off / Gag of steel / Devastation / Combat zone / Immoral society / Attack on America / Reanimate / Act of betrayal / Nightmare administrator / Practice what you preach / Kranked up and out
857565 / Jun '89 / Steamhammer

☐ ZERO TO BLACK
847622 / Nov '90 / Steamhammer

Napalm Death

☐ BOOTLEGGED IN JAPAN
Antibody / My own worst enemy / More than meets the eye / Hung / Greed killing / Suffer the children / Mass appeal madness / Cursed to crawl / Glimpse into genocide / I abstain / Lucid fairytale / Plague rages / Cold forgiveness / Control / Diatribes / Life / Siege of power / If the truth be known / Unchallenged hate / Nazi punks fuck off / From enslavement to obliteration / Kill / Scum / Ripe for the breaking
MOSH 209CD / 22 Jun '98 / Earache

☐ BREED TO BREATHE (CD/Rom)
Breed to breathe / All intensive purposes / Stranger now / Bled dry / Time will come / Suffer the children / Breed to breathe / Biography
MOSH 185CD / 17 Nov '97 / Earache

☐ DEATH BY MANIPULATION
MOSH 051CD / 1 Sep '97 / Earache

☐ DIATRIBES
Greed killing / Glimpse into genocide / Ripe for the breaking / Cursed to crawl / Cold forgiveness / My own worst enemy / Just rewards / Dogma / Take the strain / Corrosive elements / Placate, sedate, eradicate / Diatribes / Take the stain
MOSH 141CD / Jan '96 / Earache

☐ FEAR EMPTINESS DESPAIR
Twist the knife (slowly) / Hung / Remain nameless / Plague rages / More than meets the eye / Primed time / State of mind / Armageddon X 7 / Retching on the dirt / Fasting on deception / Throwaway
MOSH 109CD / 1 Sep '97 / Earache

☐ FROM ENSLAVEMENT TO OBLITERATION
Evolved as one / It's a MAN's world / Lucid fairytale / Private death / Unchallenged hate / Uncertainty blurs / Vision / Retreat to nowhere / Display to me / From enslavement / Blind to the truth / Emotional suffocation / Practice what you preach / Mentally murdered / Worlds apart
MOSH 008CD / Sep '97 / Earache

☐ HARMONY OF CORRUPTION
MOSH 019CD / 1 Sep '97 / Earache

☐ INSIDE THE TORN APART
Breed to breathe / Birth in regress / Section / Reflect on conflict / Down in the zero / Inside the torn apart / If systems persist / Prelude / Indispose / Purist realist / Low point / Lifeless alarm / Time will come / Bled dry / Ripe for the breaking
MOSH 171CD
MOSH 171CDL / Jun '97 / Earache

☐ PEEL SESSIONS, THE (13.9.87/8.3.88)
Kill / Prison without walls / Dead part 1 / Deceiver / Lucid fairytale / In extremis / Extremis / Blind to the truth / Negative approach / Common enem6y / Obstinate direction / Life / You suffer / Multi-national cooporations / Instinct of survival / Stigatised / Parasites / Moral crusade / Worlds apart / MAD / Divine death / C 9 / Control / Walls / Raging in hell / Conform or die / SOB
SFPMCD 201 / '89 / Strange Fruit

☐ SCUM
Multinational corporations / Instinct of survival-the kill / Scum-caught...in a dream / Polluted minds-sacrificed / Siege of power-control / Born on your knees / Numan garabage / You suffer / Life7-prison without walls / Point of no return / Negative approach-success7 / Deceiver-c.s.-parasites / Pseudo death-divine death / As the machine rolls on / Common enemy-moral crusade / Stigmatized-m.a.d.-dragnet
MOSH 003CD / 1 Sep '97 / Earache

☐ UTOPIA BANISHED
Discordance / I abstain / Dementia access / Christening of the blind / World keeps turning / Idiosyncratic / Aryanisms / Cause and effect / Juidical slime / Distorting the medium / Got time to kill / Upward and uninterested / Exile / Awake (to a life of misery) / Contemptuous
MOSH 053CD / 1 Sep '97 / Earache

Napoleon, Phil

☐ LIVE AT NICK'S
JCD 39 / Nov '96 / Jazzology

Narayan, Aruna

☐ SARANGI
NI 5447 / Nov '95 / Nimbus

Narayan, Brij

☐ RAGA LALIT/RAGA BAIRAGI BHAIRAV (Narayan, Brij & Zakir Hussain)
NI 5263 / Sep '94 / Nimbus

Narayan, Pandit Ram

☐ RAG BHUPAL TORI/RAG BATDIP
NI 5119 / Sep '94 / Nimbus

☐ RAG LALIT
NI 5183 / Sep '94 / Nimbus

☐ RAG SHANKARA/RAG MALA IN JOGIA
NI 5245 / Sep '94 / Nimbus

Narcotica

☐ DRUG FREE AMERICA
Narcotica / Sewers of paradise / Fear and adrenalin / Baby doll / Ransacking the earthnet / Soap opera and Brown / Drop zone / Baby doll (Reprise)
CDKTB 21 / Jul '95 / Dreamtime

Nardini, Nino

☐ NO.7 POP (Nardini, Nino & Le Pop Riviera Group)
RM 7CD / 25 May '98 / Rotunda

Nardini, Peter

☐ SCREAMS & KISSES
Don't know / Light up the sky / Wid became an astronaut / And I will fly / She said, O, is that right / Kiss from Wishaw cross / Another star / Zak Anderson / Double take / You're like a rock / Don't shut the door ma / River without you
ECLCD 9307 / Jan '96 / Eclectic

Nardo Ranks

☐ COOL AND HUMBLE
CDHB 183 / Aug '95 / Heartbeat

Narell, Andy

☐ DOWN THE ROAD
01934101392 / Sep '95 / Windham Hill

☐ LONG TIME BAND, THE
Bacchanal / Jenny's rooms / De long time band / You the man / Play one for Keith / Groove town / Dance class / Canboulay / De long time band (conclusion)
01934111722 / Oct '95 / Windham Hill

Narholz, Gerhard

☐ HAPPY SIXTIES, THE (Narholz, Gerhard Orchestra)
ISCD 172 / May '98 / Intersound

Narnia

☐ AWAKENING
NB 303CD / 26 Feb '98 / Nuclear Blast

Narnia

☐ ASLAN IS NOT A TAME LION
NAR 1 / 15 Jun '98 / NA

Nas

☐ ILLMATIC
Genesis / NY State of mind / Life's a bitch / World is yours / Half time / Memory lane (sittin' in da park) / One love / One time 4 your mind / Represent / It ain't hard to tell
4759592 / Feb '97 / Columbia

☐ IT WAS WRITTEN
Intro / Message / Street dreams / I gave you power / Watch dem niggas / Take it in blood / Nas is coming / Affirmative action / Set up / Black girl lost / Suspect / Shootouts / Live nigga rap / If I ruled the world (imagine that)
4841962 / Jul '96 / Columbia

Nascimento, Milton

☐ ANGELUS
Seis horas da tarde / Estrelada / De um modo geral / Angelus / Coisas de minas / Hello goodbye / Sofro calado / Clube da Esquina No.2 / Meu veneno / Only a dream in Rio / Qualquer coisa a haver com o paraiso / Vera cruz / Novena / Amor amigo
9362454992 / Jul '94 / Warner Bros.

☐ CLUBE DA ESQUINA VOL.1
Tudo que voce podia ser / Cais / O trem azul - part esp: Lo borges / Saidas e bandeiras no.1 - part esp: Beto guedes / Nuvem cigana / Cravo e canela / Dos cruces / Um girassol da cor de seu cabelo - part esp: Lo borges / San Vincente / Estralas - part esp: Lo Borges / Clube da Esquina no. 2 / Paisagem da Janela - part esp: Lo Borges / Me deixz em pas - part esp:: Alaide Costa / Os povos / Saidas e bandeiras no.2 - part esp: Beto guedes / Um gosto de sol / Pelo amor de deus / Lilia / Trem de doido - part esp: Lo Borges / Nada sera como antes - part esp: Beto Guedes / Ao que vai nascer
CDEMC 3702 / Mar '95 / EMI

☐ CLUBE DA ESQUINA VOL.2 (2CD Set)
Credo / Nascente / Ruas da cidade / Paiuxao e fe / Casmiento de Negros / Olho d'agua / Canoa, canoa / O que foi feito devera (De Vera) / Misterios / Pao e agua / E dai (A Queda) / Cancao Amiga / Cancion por la unidad Latinoamericana / Tanto / Dona Olimpia / Testamento / A sede do peixe (Para o que nao tem solucao) / Leo / Maria Maria / Meu Menino / Toshiro / Reis e rainhas do Maracatu / Que bom, amigo
CDEM 1550 / Mar '95 / Hemisphere

☐ MILAGRE DOS PEIXES
Os escravos de jo / Carlos, Lucia, Chico e Tiago / Milagre dos peixes / A chamada / Cade-canto:Nico e Telo / Pablo no 2 / Tema dos deuses / Hoje e dia de el-ray / Ultima sessao de musica / Sacramento / Pablo-canto:Nico
INT 30082 / Sep '96 / Intuition

☐ MILTON NASCIMENTO
Panis angelicus / Vera cruz / Que bom amigo (it's so good my friend) / Paula e bebeto (paula and bebeto) / Veja esta cancao (see this song) / Bola de meia bola de gude (stickball and marbles) / Milagre dos peixes suite (miracle of the fishes / Simples (simple) / Coracao de estudante (a student's heart) / Eu sei que vou te amar (i know I'll love you) / Cancao da america (unencounter) / Estrelada / O cio da terra (the earth in heat)
9362462482 / Jun '96 / Warner Bros.

Nascimento, Toninho

☐ ADORADA ESTRELA GUIA
A beleza du amor / Tropicana / Zoraide / Men curacao e quem diz / Ladeira / Segredos de mulher / Daqui algum tempo / Adorada estrela guia / Passarinho cantador / Samba de avias / Morro velho
TCB 03022 / '96 / TCB

Nash, Johnny

☐ BEST OF JOHNNY NASH, THE
I can see clearly now / Dream lover / Hold me tight / There are no more questions than answers / Let's be friends / Cupid / Reggae on Broadway / Let's move and groove together / Guava jelly / What a wonderful world / Stir it up / Ooh what a feeling / Loving you / Tears on my pillow (I can't take it) / All I have to do is dream / Halfway to paradise
4688592 / Feb '96 / Columbia

☐ I CAN SEE CLEARLY NOW
I can see clearly now / Let's be friends / Cream puff / Reggae on Broadway / Wonderful world / Ooh what a feeling / Birds of a feather / Cupid / Tears on my pillow / Guava jelly / That woman / Dream lover / There are more questions than answers / All I have to do is dream / Nice time / You got soul / My merry go round / Halfway to paradise / Stir it up
4653062 / May '89 / Epic

Nash, Lewis

☐ RHYTHM IS MY BUSINESS
Let me try / 106 Nix / Sing me a song everlasting / My shining hour / Sabuku / Omlette / When you return / Monk's dream / Danuelle's waltz / Pranayama
ECD 22041 / Mar '93 / Evidence

Nash, Orville

☐ GIT ALONG
FCD 3052 / Oct '97 / Fury

Nashville All-Stars Country Band

☐ AFTER THE RIOT IN NEWPORT
Relaxin' / Nashville to Newport / Opus de funk / Wonderful / 'Round midnight / Frankie and Johnny / Riot-chorus
BCD 15447 / Jun '89 / Bear Family

☐ COUNTRY ALL THE WAY
Most beautiful girl / Oh lonesome me / Rocky mountain high / There's a heartache following me / Snowbird / Rhinestone cowboy / Take these chains from my heart / Jolene / Have I told you lately that I love you / Last train to San Fernando / From a Jack to a king / Release me / Welcome to my world / Adios amigos / It's four in the mornin' / Your cheatin' heart / Heartaches by the number / Make the world go away
306612 / May '97 / Hallmark

Nashville Bluegrass Band

☐ BOYS ARE BACK IN TOWN, THE
Get a transfer to home / Long time gone / Big river / Hard times / Connie and Buster / Don't let our love die / I'm rollin' through this unfriendly world / Rock bottom blues / Diamonds and pearls / Ghost of Eli Renfro / Weary blues from waiting / Big cow in Carlisle / Dark as the night, blue as the day / Boys are back in town
SHCD 3778 / Jul '90 / Sugar Hill

☐ HOME OF THE BLUES
SHCD 3793 / Jan '97 / Sugar Hill

☐ IDLE TIME
Idle time / Old devil's dream / Two wings / I closed my heart's door / All I want is you / Angeline the baker / Little Maggie / Last night I dreamed of loving you / No one but my darling / My Lord heard Jerusalem when she moaned / Old timey risin' damp / Train carryin' Jimmie Rodgers home
ROUCD 0232 / Aug '88 / Rounder

☐ MY NATIVE HOME
ROUCD 0212 / Jul '93 / Rounder

☐ TO BE HIS CHILD
Goodnight the Lord's coming / Every humble knee must bow / No hiding place / You're drifting away / Hold fast to the right / Child enters life / To be his child / Gospel plow / Are you afraid to die / I'll be rested / Old Satan / New born soul
ROUCD 0242 / Aug '88 / Rounder

☐ UNLEASHED
SHCD 3843 / Oct '95 / Sugar Hill

☐ WAITIN' FOR THE HARD TIMES TO GO
Back trackin' / Waitin' for the hard times to go / Kansas City railroad line / Open pit mine / Train of yesterday / Father I stretch my arms to thee / When I get where I'm goin' / Waltzing's for dreamers / I ain't goin' down / We decided to make Jesus our choice / On again off again / Soppin' the gravy
SHCD 3809 / May '93 / Sugar Hill

Nashville Playboys

☐ ELVIS LINE DANCE SONGBOOK, THE
TROUBLE / Don't be cruel / Promised land / Burning love / Jailhouse rock / Mess of blues / She's not you / Moody blue / I'm left you're right she's gone / All shook up / Little sister / I can help / Good luck charm / Guitar mabn / Stuck on you / Teddy bear / Way down / I need your love
303601342 / 13 Jul '98 / Hallmark

Nashville Pussy

☐ LET THEM EAT PUSSY
AMREP 069CD / 23 Mar '98 / Amphetamine Reptile

Nashville Voices

☐ NEW COUNTRY HITS
Summertime blues / Summertime blues / Rock bottom / Thinkin' problem / My love / Heart won't lie / Come on come on / One night a day / I swear / No doubt about it / Foolish pride / I take my chances / Indian outlaw / Maverick / Man in love with you / Standing knee deep in a river (dying of thirst)
12504 / Jun '95 / Laserlight

Nastasee

☐ TRIM THE FAT
SPV 08544122 / May '96 / SPV

☐ ULE TIDE
SPV 08544132 / Mar '98 / SPV

Nasty, Billy

☐ RACE DATA ETA (2CD Set)
AVEXCD 55 / Jun '97 / Avex

Nasty Savage

☐ INDULGENCE/ABSTRACT REALITY
398414064CD / Nov '96 / Metal Blade

☐ NASTY SAVAGE
398414063CD / Nov '96 / Metal Blade

Nasum

☐ INHALE/EXHALE
This is / Masked face / Digging in / Time to act / Disdain and contempt / I see lies / Inhale/exhale / Too naked to distort / There's no escape / Rest is over / Disappointed / Lagg om / You're obsolete / Tested / Shapeshifter / Feed them kill them skin them / When science fails / Closing in / World that you made / System has failed again / For what cause / Fullmated / Screwed / Shaping the end / New firing squad / New sign of improvement / My philosophy / I'm not silent / Breathing furnace / Information is free / Burning inside / Request for guidance / Grey / Worldcraft / It's never too late / Du ar bevaked / Blinded / Can du lach
RR 69842 / 13 Jul '98 / Relapse

Natas

☐ DELMAR
MR101 / 13 Jul '98 / Man's Ruin

Nathan & Zydeco Cha Cha's

☐ CREOLE CROSSROADS
ROUCD 2137 / Oct '95 / Rounder

☐ FOLLOW ME CHICKEN
ROUCD 2122 / Aug '93 / Rounder

☐ I'M A ZYDECO HOG
ROUCD 2143 / Aug '97 / Rounder

Nathanson, Roy

☐ COMING GREAT MILLENNIUM, THE (Nathanson, Roy & Anthony Coleman)
KFWCD 119 / Oct '92 / Knitting Factory

☐ I COULD'VE BEEN A DRUM (Nathanson, Roy & Anthony Coleman)
TZA 7113 / Feb '97 / Tzadik

☐ LOBSTER & FRIEND (Nathanson, Roy & Anthony Coleman)
KFWCD 147 / Feb '95 / Knitting Factory

Nation

☐ WITHOUT REMORSE
NTHEN 038CD / 16 Feb '98 / Now & Then

Nation Of Ulysses

☐ 13 POINT PROGRAM...
Spectra sonic sound / Look out soul is back / Today I met the girl I'm going to marry / Ulythium / A kid who tells on another kid is a dead kid / Cool senior high school (fight song) / Diptheria / Aspirin kid / Hot chocolate city / P. power / You're my miss washington, d.c. / Target u.s.a. / Love is a bull market / Sound of young america / Channel one ulysses / Atom bomb
DIS 57CD / Feb '97 / Dischord

☐ PLAYS PRETTY FOR BABY
DIS 71VCD / Oct '92 / Dischord

National Health

☐ DS AL CODA
Flanagan's people / Toad of toad hall / Portrait of a shrinking man / Tales of a damson knight / Black hat / TNTFX / Feel a night coming on / Arriving twice / Shining water
BP 129CD / Sep '96 / Blueprint

☐ MISSING PIECES
VP 113CD / Nov '96 / Voiceprint

☐ NATIONAL HEALTH
Tenemos roads / Brujo / Borogroves / Elephants
CDCRH 113 / Feb '97 / Charly
14827 / Jun '97 / Spalax

☐ OF QUEUES AND CURES
Bryden 2 step (for amphibians) / Collapso / Squarer for Maud / Dreams wide awake / Binoculars / Phlakaton / Bryden 2 step (for amphibians)
CDCRH 117 / Feb '97 / Charly

National Heroes

☐ ONCE AROUND THE SUN
FFR 016 / Apr '96 / Freek

Native Colours

☐ ONE WORLD
Pumpkin's delight / Freedom / Girlie's world / Highest mountain / Reflections in D / One world / Nature boy / I'm glad there is you / Orion's belt / Time was
CCD 4646 / Jun '95 / Concord Jazz

Native Son

☐ CROSSFIRE
RMCCD 0192 / Aug '96 / Red Steel

☐ NO MAN'S LAND
RMCCD 0194 / Aug '96 / Red Steel

☐ SOLID GROUND
RMCCD 0191 / Jul '96 / Red Steel

Natural Acoustic Band

☐ BRANCHING IN
SRMC 1040 / 5 Jan '98 / Siwan

Natural Born Groovers

☐ GROOVEBIRD SYSTEM, THE
ZYX 204372 / Jul '97 / ZYX

Natural Four

☐ BEST OF NATURAL FOUR, THE
You bring out the best in me / Try love again / Can this be real / What's happening here / It's the music / Count on me / Love that really counts / Love's society / Get it over with / Nothing beats a failure (but a try) / Heaven right here on earth / How have you been / Love's so wonderful / Free / Eddie you should know better
CDGR 2717 / 24 Aug '98 / Charly

☐ HEAVEN RIGHT HERE ON EARTH
CPCD 8155 / Mar '96 / Charly

☐ NATURAL FOUR
Can this be real / You bring out the best inme / Try love again / You can't keep running away / This is what's happening now / Love that really counts / Try to smile / Love's society / Things will be better tomorrow
CPCD 8127 / Oct '95 / Charly

☐ NIGHT CHASER
CPCD 8309 / 16 Mar '98 / Charly

Natural Language

☐ NATURAL LANGUAGE
We are learning about blue / At the White House / I am not part of nature / Le repos du stable / Blasted with ecstasy / Rubber hammer / Nervous velvet / Sylvanshine / Not going gently
EMIT 0098 / 14 Apr '98 / Emit

Nature & Organisation

☐ BEAUTY REAPS THE BLOOD OF SOLITUDE
DURTRO 021CD / Oct '96 / Durtro

Naturel, Gilles

☐ NATUREL
Feeling of jazz / Trusting / Nice reed / Little world / Ray's blues / Trois bornes / I had a dream
JMS 186762 / Mar '96 / JMS

Naturists

☐ FRIENDLY ISLANDS
Shaving cream / Boogie 2 shoes / Green green grass of home / Mavis Riley / Mission impossible / Lost in Tonga
ACTIVE 001CD / Jan '94 / Interactive

Naundorf, Frank

☐ FRANK NAUNDORF & BAND
BCD 316 / Apr '94 / GHB

Navarro, Fats

☐ AT THE ROYAL ROOST VOL.1 (Navarro, Fats & Tadd Dameron)
COD 010 / Mar '92 / Jazz View

☐ AT THE ROYAL ROOST VOL.2 (Navarro, Fats & Tadd Dameron)
COD 025 / Jun '92 / Jazz View

☐ BE BOP BOYS, THE (Navarro, Fats & Sonny Stitt/Bud Powell)
Be bop in pastel / Fool's fancy / Bombay / Ray's idea / Serenade to a square / Good kick / Seven up / Blues in be bop / Boppin' a riff / Fatboy / Everything's cool / Webb city / Calling Dr. Jazz / Fracture / Maternity / Stealin' trash / Just a mystery / Red pepper / Spinal / Hollerin' and screamin'
IGOCD 2071 / Sep '97 / Indigo

☐ COMPLETE BLUE NOTE & CAPITOL RECORDINGS, THE (2CD Set) (Navarro, Fats & Tadd Dameron)
Chase / Chase / Squirrel / Squirrel / Our delight / Our delight / Dameronia / Dameronia / Jahbero / Jahbero / Lady Bird / Lady Bird / Symphonette / Symphonette / I think I'll go away / Sid's delight / Casbah / John's delight: *Dameron, Tadd & Miles Davis* / What's new: *Dameron, Tadd & Miles Davis* / Heaven's doors are wide open: *Dameron, Tadd & Miles Davis* / Focus: *Dameron, Tadd & Miles Davis* / Skunk: *McGhee, Howard & Fats Navarro Sextet* / Boperation: *McGhee, Howard & Fats Navarro Sextet* / Boperation: *McGhee, Howard & Fats Navarro Sextet* / Skunk: *McGhee, Howard & Fats Navarro Sextet* / Double talk: *McGhee, Howard & Fats Navarro Sextet* / Double talk: *McGhee, Howard & Fats Navarro Sextet* / Bouncing with Bud: *Powell, Bud & Fats Navarro* / Dancing with Bud: *Navarro, Fats & Bud Powell* / Bouncing with Bud: *Navarro, Fats & Bud Powell* / Wall: *Navarro, Fats & Bud Powell* / Dance of the infidels: *Navarro, Fats & Bud Powell* / Dance of the infidels: *Navarro, Fats & Bud Powell* / 52nd Street: *Navarro, Fats & Bud Powell* / Steekin' apples: *Goodman, Benny & Fats Navarro*
CDP 8333732 / Oct '95 / Blue Note

☐ IN THE BEGINNING....BE-BOP
Mr. Dues / Saxon / O-Go-Mo / Oh Kai / Blue brew / Brew blue / More brew / No more brew / Spinal / Red pepper / Just a mystery / Maternity
SV 0169 / Oct '97 / Savoy Jazz

☐ MEMORIAL
Serenade to a square / Good kick / Seven up / Blues in be-bop / Boppin' a riff / Fat boy / Everything's cool / Webb City / Be bop carol / Tadd walk / Gone with the wind / That someone must be you
SV 0181 / Oct '97 / Savoy Jazz

☐ NOSTALGIA
Nostalgia / Barry's bop / Be bop romp / Fats' blows / Dextivity / Dextrose / Dexter's mood / Index / Stealing trash / Hollerin' and screamin' / Fracture / Calling Dr. Jazz
SV 0123 / Oct '97 / Savoy Jazz

Navarro, Jorge

☐ FASCINATING RHYTHM (Navarro, Jorge Trio)
BMJ 001 / Jan '98 / Blue Moon

Navarro, Jose Angel

☐ MIEL
ASHECD 2002 / Nov '96 / Ashe

Navigator

☐ NOSTALGIE
SFO 32CD / 27 Jul '98 / Swarf Finger

Nawazish, Shabnu

☐ TAMANNA
DMUT 1188 / Mar '96 / Multitone

Naylor, Oliver

☐ OLIVER NAYLOR 1924-1925
High society / Oh Johnny, please don't, Mom Ma / Ringelberg blues / Hugo (I go where you go) / She wouldn't do what I asked her to / I've got a cross eyed Papa (but he looks straight at me) / You / 31st Street blues / Ain't that hateful / Twilight rose / So I took the $50,000 / Driftwood / Say say Sadie / Susquehanna home / You and I / Take me / Bye bye baby / Headin' for Louisville / Carolina stomp / Sweet Georgia Brown / Slowin' down blues
RTR 79008 / Feb '97 / Retrieval

Nazareth

☐ 2XS
Love leads to madness / Boys in the band / You love another / Gatecrash / Games / Back to the trenches / Dream on / Lonely in the night / Preservation / Take the rap / Mexico
CLACD 217 / Feb '91 / Castle

☐ AT THE BBC (2CD Set)
Called her name / Fool about you / Hard living / Goin' down / Razamanaz / Broken down angel / Night woman / Too bad too sad / Turn on your receiver / Bad bad boy / Shapes of things / Silver dollar forger / Glad when you're dead / Jet lag / Dear John / Morning dew / Vigilante man / Paper sun / Woke up this morning / Boogie / Road ladies / Hair of the dog / Teenage nervous breakdown / This flight tonight / Love hurts / Expect no mercy
SRDCD 707 / 13 Jul '98 / Reef

☐ CATCH, THE
Party down / Ruby Tuesday / Last exit Brooklyn / Moondance / Love of freedom / This month's messiah / You don't believe in us / Sweetheart tree / Road to nowhere / Do you think about it
ESMCD 499 / 29 Sep '97 / Essential

☐ CHAMPIONS OF ROCK
CR 867112 / Mar '96 / Disky

☐ CINEMA
Cinema / Juliet / Just another heartache / Other side of you / Hit the fan / One from the heart / Salty salty / White boy / Veteran's song / Just another heartache
ESMCD 500 / 29 Sep '97 / Essential

☐ CLOSE ENOUGH FOR ROCK 'N' ROLL
Telegram / Vicki / Homesick again / Vancouver shakedown
ESMCD 618 / 30 Mar '98 / Essential

☐ EXERCISES
I will not be led / Cat's eye, apple pie / In my time / Woke up this morning / Called her name / Fool about you / Love now you're gone / Madelaine / Sad song / 1692 (Glencoe massacre)
CLACD 220 / Feb '91 / Castle

☐ EXPECT NO MERCY
All the king's horses / Expect no mercy / Gimme what's mine / Gone dead train / Kentucky fried blues / New York broken toy / Place in your heart / Revenge is sweet / Shot me down / Busted
ESMCD 619 / 30 Mar '98 / Essential

☐ FOOL CIRCLE, THE (Remastered)
Dressed to kill / Another year / Moonlight eyes / Pop the silo / Let me be your leader / We are the people / Every young man's dream / Little part of you / Cocaine / Victoria / Every young man's dream / Big boy / Juicy Lucy / Morning dew
ESMCD 623 / 1 Jun '98 / Essential

☐ FROM THE VAULTS
Friends / If you see my baby / Hard living / Spinning top / Love hurts / Down / My white bicycle / Holy roller / Railroad boy / You're the violin / Good love / Greens / Desolation road / Heart's grown cold / Razamanaz / Hair of the dog / Talkin' to one of the boys / Morning dew / Juicy Lucy / On the run
NEMCD 639 / Mar '93 / Sequel

☐ GREATEST HITS VOL.1
Razamanaz / Holy roller / Shanghai'd in Shanghai / Love hurts / Turn on your receiver / Bad bad boy / This flight tonight / Broken down angel / Hair of the dog / Sunshine / My white bicycle / Woke up this morning / Morning dew / Love now your gone / Carry out feelings / I want to do everything for you / Expect no mercy
ESMCD 369 / Oct '96 / Essential

☐ GREATEST HITS VOL.2
Whatever you want babe / May the sunshine / Star / Hearts grown cold / Holiday / Tush / Love hurts / Cocaine / Dressed to kill / Morgentau / Love leads to madnes / Dream on / Milk and honey / Where are you now / This month's messiah / Ruby Tuesday / Just another heartache / Veteran's song / Piece of my heart / Winner on the night / This flight tonight / Tell me that you love me / Let me be your dog
ESMCD 597 / 24 Aug '98 / Essential

☐ HAIR OF THE DOG
Hair of the dog / Miss Misery / Guilty / Changing times / Beggar's day / Rose in the heather / Whisky drinkin' woman / Please don't Judas me / Love hurts / Railroad boy
ESMCD 550 / May '97 / Essential

☐ LOUD 'N' PROUD
Go down fighting / Not faking it / Turn on your receiver / Teenage nervous breakdown / Free wheeler / This flight tonight / Child in the sun / Ballad of Hollis Brown / This flight tonight / Go down fighting / Ballad of Hollis Brown
ESMCD 379 / Sep '96 / Essential

☐ MALICE IN WONDERLAND
Holiday / Showdown at the border / Talkin' to one of the boys / Heart's grown cold / Fast cars / Big boy / Talkin' 'bout love / Fallen angel / Ship of dreams / Turning a new leaf
ESMCD 617 / 30 Mar '98 / Essential

☐ MOVE ME
Let me be your dog / Can't shake these shakes / Crack me up / Move me / Steamroller / Stand by your beds / Rip it up / Demon alcohol / You had it comin' / Bring it on home to mama / Burning down
ESMCD 503 / May '97 / Essential

☐ NAZARETH
Witchdoctor woman / Dear John / Empty arms, empty heart / I had a dream / Red light lady / Fat man / Country girl / Morning dew / King is dead
CLACD 286 / Jun '92 / Castle

☐ NO JIVE
Hire and fire / Do you wanna play house / Right between the eyes / Everytime it rains / Keeping our love alive / Thinking man's nightmare / Cover your heart / Lap of luxury / Rowan tree / Tell me that you love me / Cry wolf / Tell me that you love me / This flight tonight
ESMCD 502 / 29 Sep '97 / Essential

☐ NO MEAN CITY (Remastered)
Just to get into it / May the sunshine / Simple solution / Star / Claim to fame / Whatever you want babe / Wha's in it for me / No mean city / May the sunshine / Whatever you want babe / Star
ESMCD 622 / 1 Jun '98 / Essential

☐ PLAY 'N' THE GAME
Somebody to roll / Down home girl / Flying / Waiting for the man / Born to love / I want to do everything for you / I don't want to go on without you / Wild honey / LA girls
CLACD 219 / Feb '91 / Castle

☐ RAMPANT
Silver dollar forger / Glad when you're gone / Loved and lost / Shanghai'd in Shanghai / Jet lag / Light my way / Sunshine / Shapes of things / Space safari / Down
ESMCD 551 / May '97 / Essential

☐ RAZAMANAZ
Razamanaz / Alcatraz / Vigilante man / Woke up this morning / Night woman / Bad bad boy / Sold my soul / Too bad, too sad / Broken down angel / Hard living / Spinning top / Woke up this morning / Witchdoctor woman
ESMCD 370 / Sep '96 / Essential

☐ SINGLES COLLECTION, THE
Broken down angel / Bad bad boy / This flight tonight / My white bicycle / Out of time / Shanghai'd in Shanghai / Love hurts / Hair of the dog / Holy roller / Carry out feelings / You're the violin / Somebody to roll / I don't want to go on without you / Gone dead train / Place in your heart / May the sunshine / Star / Dressed to kill / Morning dew / Games / Love leads to madness
CCSCD 280 / Dec '90 / Castle

☐ SNAKES AND LADDERS
We are animals / Lady luck / Hang on to a dream / Piece of my heart / Trouble / Key / Back to school / Girls / Donna, get off that crack / See you, see me / Helpless / Winner on the night
ESMCD 501 / May '97 / Essential

☐ SNAZ
Telegram / Razamanaz / I want to do everything for you / This flight tonight / Beggar's day / Every young man's dream / Heart's grown cold / Java blues / Cocaine / Big boy / So you want to be a rock 'n' roll star / Holiday / Let me be your leader / Dressed to kill / Hair of the dog / Expect no mercy / Shapes of things / Love hurts / Morning dew / Juicy Lucy / On your way
ESMCD 531 / May '97 / Essential

☐ SOUND ELIXIR
All nite radio / Milk and honey / Whipping boy / Rain on the window / Back room boy / Why don't you read the book / I ran / Rags to riches / Local still / Where are you now
CLACD 218 / Feb '91 / Castle

Nazeri, Sharam

☐ NOWRUZ
58395CD / Apr '96 / World Network

Nazgul

☐ NAZGUL, THE
PSCD 0005 / 5 Jan '98 / Psi-Fi

☐ TOTEM
VAMP 7495CD / Jan '96 / Vampire

Nazia & Zoher

☐ CAMERA
Camera / Camera / Mehrbanl / Walaval / Tali de thullay / Camera dance mix / Nasha / Pyar ka geet / If you could read my mind / Mama papa / Dil ki lagl / Kyoun
TIMBCD 500 / Sep '92 / Timbuktu

NCE Engine

☐ GRAVITY WELL
SH 1872203 / Nov '95 / Interfere Chrome

Ndai Ndai

☐ EN CONCERT
MW 3013CD / Nov '96 / Music & Words

Ndegeocello, Me'shell

☐ PEACE BEYOND PASSION
Womb / Way / Ecclesiastes free my heart / Mary magdalene / Leviticus faggot / Makes me wanna holler / Tear and a smile / Bittersweet / Stay / Who is he and what is he to you / God shiva / Deuteronomy niggerman
9362460332 / Jun '96 / Maverick

☐ PLANTATION LULLABIES
Plantation lullabies / I'm diggin' you (like an old soul record) / If that's your boyfriend (he wasn't last night) / Shoot'n up and gett'n high / Dred loc / Untitled / Step into the projects / Soul on ice / Call me / Outside your door / Picture show / Sweet love / Two lonely hearts (on the subway)
9362457542 / Jul '94 / Maverick

Ndere Troupe

☐ KIKWABANGA
PAN 2016CD / Oct '93 / Pan

N'Dour, Youssou

☐ BEST OF YOUSSOU N'DOUR
Set / Shakin' the tree: *N'Dour, Youssou & Peter Gabriel* / Sinebar / Medina / Lion - Gaiende / Toxiques / Fenene / Miyoko / Bamako / Fakastalu / Bes / Hey you / Macoy / Immigres bitim rew / Xale rewmi / Kocc barma
CDV 2773 / Oct '94 / Virgin

☐ GAINDE (N'Dour, Youssou & Yande Codou Sene)
53891 / Mar '96 / World Network

☐ GUIDE (WOMMAT)
Leaving / Old man / Without a smile / Mame bamba / Seven seconds / How are you / Generations / Tourista / Undecided / Love one another / Life / My people / Oh boy / Silence / Chimes of freedom
4765082 / Feb '97 / Columbia

☐ HEY YOU (The Essential Collection 1988-1990)
Lion / Hey you / Fenene / Sinebar / Fakastalu / Set / Bes / Miyoko / Shakin' the tree / Immigres/Bitim rew / Medina / Sabar / Bamako / Toxiques / Macoy
NSCD 018 / Jul '97 / Nascente

☐ LION, THE
Lion / Gaiende / Shakin' the tree / Kocc barma / Bamako / Truth / Old tucson / Macdy / My daughter (sama doom) / Bes
CDV 2584 / Jun '89 / Virgin

☐ SET
Set / Alboury / Sabar / Toxiques / Sinebar / Medina / Miyoko / Xale rewmi / Fenene / Fakastalu / Hey you / Oneday / Ay chono la
CDV 2634 / Sep '90 / Virgin

NDR Big Band
☐ BRAVISSIMO VOL.2
Blues for Alice / Come Sunday / Piano groove / Carpet ride / O vos omnis / Old fairy tale / Love for tale / Round about midnight / My funny Valentine / After you've gone / Mosher / Red horn / Go
ACT 925992 / 27 Apr '98 / Act

☐ MAGIC NIGHT
ISCD 164 / Jul '96 / Intersound

Neal & Leandra
☐ ACCIDENTAL DREAMS
RHRCD 85 / May '96 / Red House

☐ HEARTS AND HAMMERS
RHRCD 62 / Jul '95 / Red House

Neal, Kenny
☐ BAYOU BLOOD
ALCD 4809 / May '93 / Alligator

☐ BIG NEWS FROM BATON ROUGE
ALCD 4764 / Apr '93 / Alligator

☐ DELUXE EDITION
Caught in the jaws of a vise / That knife don't cut no more / Outside looking in / Hoodoo moon / Truth hurts / Caught your back door man / Evalina / Baby bee / Neal and prey / Any fool will do / Lightning's gonna strike / Morning after / Son I never knew / Howling at the moon / Change my way of livin' / Believe in yourself
ALCD 5604 / 6 Oct '97 / Alligator

☐ DEVIL CHILD
ALCD 4774 / May '93 / Alligator

☐ HOODOO MOON
ALCD 4825 / Nov '94 / Alligator

☐ WALKING ON FIRE
Look but don't touch / Truth hurts / I put my trust in you / Blues stew / Morning after / IOU / My only good thing / I been missing you too / Caught in the jaws of a vice / Things to get better / Walking on fire / Bad luck card
ALCD 4795 / May '93 / Alligator

Neal, Raful
☐ LOUISIANA LEGEND
ALCD 4783 / May '93 / Alligator

Neale, Dan
☐ FANCY DOG'S ROCKIN' CHRISTMAS (Neale, Dan 'Fancy Dog')
Santa Claus is coming to town / Sleigh ride / Winter wonderland / Frosty the snowman / Reindeer boogie / White Christmas / Let it snow / Hark the herald angels sing / Jingle bells / Run run Rudolph / Christmas time is here / Rudolph the red nosed reindeer / Hava negala/We three kings medley / Jingle bell rock / Holly jolly Christmas
MOUP 6016 / Oct '97 / Mouthpiece

Neanders Jazzband
☐ OH DIDN'T HE RAMBLE
MECCACD 1027 / Nov '94 / Music Mecca

Near Castlegar
☐ IN JANUARY
SHR 72 / Dec '96 / Shrimper

Neary, Paddy
☐ MUSICAL GEMS
Scotland the brave-hundred pipers-cock of the north / Maggie / Grannie's heilan hame / Ballinakelly reel / Dumbarton's drums-the green hills of tyrol / Eriskay love lilt-on the banks of my own lovely lee / Amazing grace-mist covered mountain / Irish washerwoman / When irish eyes are smiling-rose of tralee-londonderry air / Bluebells of scotland / Come back to erin / Miss mcleod's reel
CDITV 512 / Oct '90 / Scotdisc

Nebula
☐ NEBULA
TP 001 / 23 Feb '98 / Tee Pee

Necessary Evils
☐ SPIDER FINGERS
ITR 045CD / Jun '97 / In The Red

Neckbeard
☐ PLEASURE STEWARD
NB 001 / Nov '97 / MK Ultra

Neckbones
☐ SOULS ON FIRE
Dead and kids / Souls on fire / It ain't enough / Don't ya leave me / Hit me / Keep driving / Crack Whore blues / Dolly / Superstar Chevrolet / You can't touch her / Skronky tonk / Art school drop out / Love ya rock 'n' roll / Can't drive you / Shouldn't call your man a fool / Gambling
03042 / Aug '97 / Fat Possum

Necromandus
☐ OREXIS OF DEATH
AACD 013 / 15 Jun '98 / Audio Archive

Necromantia
☐ ANCIENT PRIDE
OPMCD 048 / Mar '97 / Osmose

☐ CROSSING THE FIERY PATH
OPCD 021 / Feb '94 / Osmose

☐ SCARLET EVIL WITCHING BLACK
OPCD 036 / Nov '95 / Osmose

Necronomicon
☐ TIPS ZUM SELBSTMORD
LW 1049 / 2 Mar '98 / Little Wing

Necrophobic
☐ NOCTURNAL SILENCE
BMCD 40 / Aug '93 / Black Mark

Necropolis
☐ END OF THE LINE
NM 021CD / Oct '97 / Neat Metal

Nectarine
☐ STERLING BEAT
GROW 0342 / May '95 / Grass

Nectarine No.9
☐ FRIED FOR BLUE MATERIAL
Stacey Keach dada message bag / Strychnine vinaigrette / Adidas Francis Bacon / Walter Travis / Central deli Davis Jnr. / Boneless chops / Starthing / Friends of the cult sixties pop / Burnt nylon carseat cover flavour / Fuzzy dice mahlersdog / Port of Mars / South of an imaginary line / Subtitles for the blind drunk / Soon be over / Michaelanglo
BENT 035CD / 27 Apr '98 / Creeping Bent

☐ NIAGARA FALLS
SALD 214 / 1 Jun '98 / Shake The Record Label

Need
☐ NEED, THE
CHSW 19 / 20 Oct '97 / Chainsaw

Needs, Lyndon
☐ GUITAR CRAZY
CRCD 02 / Jul '98 / Nervous

Neel, Johnny
☐ COMIN' ATCHA LIVE
BIGMO 10272 / Aug '95 / Big Mo

Neely, Don
☐ DON NEELY AND HIS ROYAL SOCIETY JAZZ ORCHESTRA (Neely, Don & His Royal Society Jazz Orchestra)
MMRCCD 6 / Feb '94 / Merry Makers

☐ DON'T BRING... (Neely, Don & His Royal Society Jazz Orchestra)
SOSCD 1250 / May '93 / Stomp Off

☐ IF I HAD YOU (Neely, Don & His Royal Society Jazz Orchestra)
MMRCCD 15 / Feb '98 / Merry Makers

☐ ROLL UP (Neely, Don & His Royal Society Jazz Orchestra)
CCD 147 / Aug '95 / Circle

Nefertiti
☐ FROM 18TH DYNASTY
FILERCD 421 / Nov '91 / Profile

Negative FX
☐ NEGATIVE FX/LAST RITES (Negative FX/Last Rites)
TAANG 005CD / 11 Aug '97 / Taang

Negativland
☐ ESCAPE FROM NOISE
SST 133CD / May '93 / SST

☐ FREE
SEELAND 009 / Jun '93 / Seeland

☐ GUNS
SST 291CD / May '93 / SST

☐ HAPPY HEROES
SEELAND 018 / 11 May '98 / Seeland

☐ HELTER STUPID
Prologue / Helter stupid / Perfect cut
RECDEC 29 / Jul '93 / Rec Rec
SST 252CD / May '93 / SST

☐ LETTER U & THE NUMBER 2, THE
RECDEC 51 / Jul '93 / Rec Rec

Negazione
☐ BEHIND THE DOOR
WB 05051CD / '90 / We Bite

☐ LITTLE DREAMER
WB 030CD / '89 / We Bite

☐ LO SPIRITO CONTINUA
TVOR 04CD / Jan '92 / Plastic Head

☐ WILD BUNCH
846113 / Aug '90 / SPV

Neglect
☐ END IT
WB 21132 / Oct '94 / We Bite

☐ FOUR YEARS OF HATE (2CD Set)
GG 006CD / Dec '96 / Gain Ground

Negra, Pata
☐ BLUES DE FRONTORA
Bodas de sangre / Blues de la frontera / Pasa la vida / Yo me quedo en sevilla / How high the moon / Camaron / Calle betis / Lindo gatito / Lunatico
HNCD 1309 / May '89 / Hannibal

Negrete, Jorge
☐ SUS GRANDES EXITOS VOL.3
ALCD 021 / Jul '96 / Alma Latina

Negro Problem
☐ POST MINSTREL SYNDROME
AF 0007 / Dec '97 / Aerial Flip

Negrocan
☐ MEDIA MUNDO
DEPE 01CD / Jul '96 / Deep South

Neighb'rhood Childr'n
☐ LONG YEARS IN SPACE
Feeling zero / Long years in space / Up down turn around world / Changes brought to me / Please leave me alone / Hobbit's dream / Chocolate angel / Patterns / Happy child / Happy world of Capistran K / She's got no identification / Can't buy me love / That's what's happening / Sunday afternoon / Feeling zero / Little black egg / Tomorrow's gone / Over the rainbow / Louie, Louie / I need love / Yesterday's thoughts / Woman think / Long years in space / Behold the lilies
SC 11041 / 20 Jul '98 / Sundazed

Neil
☐ NEIL'S HEAVY CONCEPT ALBUM
Hello vegetables / Hole in my shoe / Heavy potato encounter / My white bicycle / Neil the barbarian / Lentil nightmare / Computer alarm / Wayne / Gnome / Cosmic jam / Golf girl / Bad karma in UK / Our tune / Ken / End of the world cabaret / God save the Queen / Floating / Hurdy gurdy man / Paranoid mix / Amoeba song
4509948522 / Jan '94 / WEA

Neil, Alan
☐ STEPPING OUT VOL.1
DLD 1025 / '92 / Dance & Listen

☐ STEPPING OUT VOL.2
Red sails in the sunset-oh my pa-pa (saunter) / Your cheatin' heart-take these chains from my heart (saunt / Janita-kevana (tango) / La morenita-jennifer tango (tango) / Breeze and i-stranger in paradise (rumba) / Echo of serenade-you belong to my heart (rumba) / Blame it on the bossa nova-when mexico gave up the rhumba (/ Island in the sun-yellow bird (bossa nova) / Mother of mine-my dad (waltz) / Waiting for sheila-daddy's little girl (waltz) / September in the rain-september song (foxtrot) / We'll gather flaco-red roses for a blue lady (foxtrot) / Beautiful sunday-ten guitars (rock beat) / Red river rock-snoopy versus the red baron (rock beat)
DLD 1032 / Mar '93 / Dance & Listen

Neil, Fred
☐ EVERYBODY'S TALKIN'
Dolphins / I've got a secret / That's the bag I'm in / Badi-da / Faretheewell (fred's tune) / Everybody's talkin' / Everything happens / Sweet cocaine / Green rocky road / Cynicrustpetefredjohnraga
CREV 021CD / Jan '94 / Rev-Ola

Neil, Vince
☐ EXPOSED
Look in her eyes / Sister of pain / Can't have your cake / Edge / Can't change me / Fine, fine wine / Living is a luxury / You're invited but your friend can't come / Gettin' hard / Forever
9362452602 / Apr '93 / Warner Bros.

Neill, Ben
☐ GOLDBUG
Tunnel vision / Dark gift / Route me out / Freezer burn / Lookinglast / Shirt waste / Goldbug / It's only money / Syntonic / Blue maroon
5570852 / 15 Jun '98 / Antilles/Verve

☐ TRIPTYCAL
5331842 / Mar '97 / Antilles/Verve

Neill, Casey
☐ CASEY NEILL
APRCD 1019 / 3 Aug '98 / Appleseed

Neither Neither World
☐ ALIVE WITH THE TASTE OF HELL
WSCD 011 / Oct '96 / World Serpent

☐ MADDENING
DVLR 010CD / Nov '95 / Dark Vinyl

Nekromantik
☐ FAIRY CATCHER
DBCD 001 / 23 Feb '98 / Resurrection

Nekromantix
☐ BROUGHT BACK TO LIFE
INTCD 009 / May '95 / Nervous

☐ CURSE OF THE COFFIN
NERCD 063 / '91 / Nervous

☐ DEMONS ARE A GIRL'S BEST FRIEND
RMD 96042 / Dec '96 / Record Music

☐ HELLBOUND
TBCD 2001 / Mar '93 / Tombstone

Nell, Bob
☐ WHY I LIKE COFFEE
804192 / Sep '92 / New World

Nelson
☐ IMAGINATOR
VICP 5817 / May '97 / Victor
VSD 1009 / 7 Apr '98 / Varese Sarabande
8800719 / 26 Jan '98 / CNR

☐ SILENCE IS BROKEN, THE
VICP 60174 / 1 Jun '98 / Victor

Nelson
☐ DE UN SIGLO AL OTRO (Nelson Y Sus Estrellas)
LPCD 8903 / Nov '97 / Fresh Sound

Nelson, Bill
☐ AFTER THE SATELLITE SINGS
Deeply dazed / Tomorrow yesterday / Flipside / Streamliner / Memory babe / Skull baby cluster / Zoom sequence / Rocket to Damascus / Beautiful nudes / Old goat / Squirm / Wow it's Scootercar Sexkitten / Phantom sedan / Ordinary idiots / V-ghost / Blink agog
RES 114CD / 3 Aug '98 / Blueprint

☐ BLUE MOONS AND LAUGHING GUITARS
Ancient guitars / Girl from another planet / Spinnin' around / Shaker / God man slain / Dead we wake with the upstairs drum / New moon rising / Glory days / Wishes / Angel in my system / Wings and everything / Boat to forever / Invisible man and the unforgettable girl / So it goes / Fires in the sky / Dream ships set sail
CDVE 912 / Aug '92 / Venture

☐ BUDDHA HEAD
My philosophy / Killing my desires / Buddha head / Way / Big river / Karma kisses / We will rise / Signs and signals / Lotus in the stream / Enlightenment / Clarity / Duality / Perfect world / Heart has its reasons / Sun will rise / Big illumination / Life as we know it
POPU 004CD / Mar '97 / Populuxe

☐ CONFESSIONS OF A HYPERDREAMER (2CD Set)
Sun at six windows / Bird ornaments / My favourite atom / Girl I never forgot / Circle the world in a paper canoe / Queer weather / Astro-coaster / Brutal Tinkerbell / Waltz at the end of the world / Secret agent at Science Park / Twentieth century / Aura hole / Radiant nature knows not the workers sorrow / Essoldo stripshow / Rain and neon / Candyland / Birds and blue stuff / Radiated robot men / Coney Island / Weird critters / Golden satellites / Brotherhood of sleeping car porters / Quarter moons and stars / Wonder story / Cool blue heaven / Far too flip / Realm rider / Angels in Arcadia
POPBOXCD 1 / Jan '97 / Populuxe

☐ CRIMSWORTH
Crimsworth
RES 104CD / Apr '97 / Resurgence

607

☐ DEEP DREAM DECODER
Things to come / God bless me / Rise (above these things) / Snowing outside / It's all true / Head full of lights and a hat full of haloes / Girls I've loved / Amazing things / Deep dream decoder / Dissolve / Year 44 (the birthday song) / Wing and a prayer / Dreamnoise and angel / Tired eyes / Golden girl / Spark
POPU 005CD / Jun '97 / Populuxe

☐ ELECTRICITY MADE US ANGELS
Begin to burn / Heaven's happy hemisphere / God in her eyes / Float away / Big blue day / Sweet is the mystery / If wishes were horses / Fair winds and flying boats / Ocean over blue / River of love / This is destiny / Wonders never cease / Nothing yet / God thundered boy / She sends me
POPU 003CD / Feb '97 / Populuxe

☐ NORTHERN DREAM
SM 777CD / Mar '96 / Blueprint

☐ PRACTICALLY WIRED
Roses and rocketships / Spinning planet / Thousand fountain island / Piano 45 / Pink buddha blues / Kid with cowboy tie / Royal ghosts and great fires / Her presence in flowers / Big noise in Twanagton / Tiny little thing / Wild blues sky / Every moment infinite / Friends from heaven / Eternal for a-ton / Soapland
ASCD 022 / 23 Feb '98 / All Saints

Nelson, Bob

☐ BACK TO BOGALUSA
Leave the young girls alone / Came home this morning / When I had (I didn't need) / Going home / Sugar Mama / Sawmp jump / Wilma Jean / Everybody needs somebody / Been down so long / Short haired woman / Back to Bogalusa / It's a shame
KS 028 / May '98 / King Snake

☐ JUST YOUR FOOL (Nelson, 'Chicago' Bob & The Shadows)
HMG 6506 / Aug '97 / Hightone

Nelson, David

☐ LIMITED EDITION (Nelson, David Band)
DNB 95001 / Jun '97 / Icenine

Nelson, Grant

☐ RIDE THE UNDERGROUND (Mixed By Grant Nelson/Norris 'Da Boss' Windross/2CD Set) (Various Artists)
Saved my life: *Edwards, Todd* / Oye como va: *Puente, Tito* / Closer: *Mood II Swing* / Hallelujah: *Chandler, Kerri* / Got myself together: *Nelson, Grant* / In and out of my life: *Dantzler, Tonja* / Goin' round: *D'Bora* / 4 you: *4th Measure Men* / Inside your mind: *GOD Ltd.* / Part 4: *Morels Grooves* / Anytime: *Nu Birth* / Vol.1: *Cover Ups* / Deep inside: *Hard Drive* / Pleasuredome: *Soul II Soul* / Groovers track: *Federation X* / Long time coming: *Bump & Flex* / Everybody: *Mousse T* / Nothing better: *Colourblind* / Murder track: *Delgado, Mike* / Step to me: *Nelson, Grant* / Right before my eyes: *N&G* / Movin' on: *Pender, Debbie* / Love bug: *Ramsey & Fen* / Kung foo: *187 Lockdown* / Hyper funk: *Antonio* / Get happy: *Underground Solution* / Too late: *Thompson, Carroll* / Sincere/Guilty: *Cole, MJ* / Sweet sensations: *Peekay* / I keep: *N&G* / Belo: *Heartists* / Spend the night: *Lewis, Danny J.* / Beautiful people: *Tucker, Barbara* / Bizzi's party: *Bizzi* / Baby: *Y-Tribe* / It's my house: *New Horizon* / Say what: *Paolo & Rodriguez* / Spirit of the sun: *Fontana, Lenny* / R U sleeping: *Indo* / You make me wanna: *Usher* / Desire: *Dem 2* / My desire: *Amira*
SOLIDCD 014 / 1 Jun '98 / Solid State

Nelson, Louis

☐ LOUIS NELSON BIG FOUR VOL.1
BCD 25 / Jun '96 / GHB

☐ LOUIS NELSON BIG FOUR VOL.2
BCD 26 / Jun '96 / GHB

Nelson, Oliver

☐ AFRO AMERICAN SKETCHES (Nelson, Oliver Orchestra)
Message / Jungleaire / Emancipation blues / There's a yearnin' / Going up North / Disillusioned / Freedom dance
OJCCD 1819 / Jun '96 / Original Jazz Classics

☐ BLUES AND THE ABSTRACT TRUTH
Stolen moments / Hoedown / Cascades / Yearnin' / Butch and butch / Teenie's blues
MCAD 5659 / Nov '91 / Impulse Jazz

☐ JAZZ MASTERS
5276542 / 5 May '98 / Verve

☐ MEET OLIVER NELSON
Jams and jellies / Passion flower / Don't stand up / Ostinato / What's new / Booze blues baby
OJCCD 227 / Nov '95 / Original Jazz Classics

☐ MORE BLUES AND THE ABSTRACT TRUTH
Blues and the abstract truth / Blue o'mighty / Mr. Broadway / Midnight blue / Critic's choice / One for Bob / Blues for Mr. Broadway / Goin' to Chicago blues
IMP 12122 / Apr '97 / Impulse Jazz

☐ SCREAMIN' THE BLUES
Screamin' the blues / March on, march on / Drive / Meetin' / Three seconds / Alto-itis
OJCCD 80 / Nov '95 / Original Jazz Classics

☐ STRAIGHT AHEAD (Nelson, Oliver & Eric Dolphy)
OJCCD 99 / Nov '95 / Original Jazz Classics

Nelson, Ozzie

☐ HEAD OVER HEELS IN LOVE
HCD 259 / Oct '95 / Hindsight

☐ NELSON TOUCH, THE (25 Band Hits 1931-1941) (Nelson, Ozzie & Harriet)
It's gonna be you / Dream a little dream of me / Yes suh / Got you where I want you (Right in my arms) / By a waterfall / Oh Susanna, dust off that old pianna / Rigamarole / About a quarter to nine / Swamp fire / And them some / Tiger rag / But where are you / Wave-a-stick blues / Our penthouse on third avenue / Subway / Roses in December / Says my heart / Ramblin wreck from Georgia tech / That sly old gentlemen from Featherbed Lane / Yours for a song / I want the waiter with the water / I'm looking for a guy who plays alto and baritone and double / Jersey jive / Swingin' on the golden gate / Central Avenue shuffle
CDAJA 5197 / Jun '96 / Living Era

☐ OZZIE NELSON
CCD 027 / Oct '93 / Circle

Nelson, Phyllis

☐ BEST OF PHYLLIS NELSON, THE
I like you / Don't stop the train / Move closer / In a Cadillac / It's tonight / Happy to see you / Somewhere in the city / Reachin' / Explosive combination / Make believe that we're sixteen / Take me nowhere / I don't know / Then came you / Land of make believe / Chemical reaction
HTCD 61 / 20 Apr '98 / Hot Productions

Nelson, Portia

☐ LET ME LOVE YOU (The Songs Of Bart Howard)
Beautiful woman / On the first warm day / Thank you for the lovely summer / One love affair / Fly me to the moon / Be my all / Let me love you / Never kiss / If you leave Paris / It was worth it / Year after year / Music for lovers
DRGCD 91442 / Dec '95 / DRG

☐ LOVE SONGS FOR A LATE EVENING
Gentleman is a dope / Get out of town / My ship / Just love / Once in a blue moon / Come away with me / Love for sale / No lover / If love were all / Who wants to fall in love / My love is a wanderer / One life to live / Remind me / Autumn leaves / By Strauss / Down in the depths / Nobody's heart / While we're young / Out of this world / All in fun / One look at you / Alone with me / It's alright with me / Take care of yourself
DRGCD 91451 / 20 Apr '98 / DRG

☐ THIS LIFE
Confession of a New Yorker / It's the little things / Gentle love / I don't smoke / I never planned to love you / Let me be the music / Pieces / Decisions / Grittin' over the blues / Pony, pony / Love on the rocks / Such a man / As I remember him / Autobiography in five short chapter / This life / Make a rainbow
DRGCD 91445 / May '96 / DRG

Nelson, Red

☐ RED NELSON 1935-1947
OTCD 6 / Jul '95 / Old Tramp

Nelson, Rick

☐ 25 GREATEST HITS
Hello Mary Lou / Travellin' man / Milk cow blues / Be bop baby / Stood up / Believe what you say / My bucket's got a hole in it / Poor little fool / Lonesome town / I got a feeling it's late / There's good rockin' tonight / Shirley Lee / Boppin' the blues / Down the line / Whole lotta shakin' goin' on' / Tryin' to get to you / If you can't rock me / My babe / Trying to get to you / I'm in love again / Summertime / Lucky star / Congratulations / You are the only one / It's all in the game
4954872 / 6 Jul '98 / EMI Gold

☐ ALL MY BEST
Travellin' man / Hello Mary lou / Poor little fool / Stood up / You are the only one / It's late / You know what I mean / Young world / Lonesome town / I got a feeling / Just a little too much / Believe what you say / It's up to you / Waitin' in school / Never be anyone else but you / Don't leave me this way / Fools rush in / Teenage idol / I'm walkin' / Mighty good / Sweeter than you / Garden party
CDMF 081 / Mar '92 / Magnum Force

☐ ANTHOLOGY (2CD Set)
CPCD 82902 / Jul '97 / Charly

☐ BEST ALWAYS/LOVE AND KISSES
I'm not ready for you yet / You don't know me / Ladies choice / Lonely corner / Only the young / Mean old world / I know a place / Since I don't have you / It's beginning to hurt / By blue heaven / How does it go / When the chips are down / Love and kisses / I catch myself crying / Love is where you find it / Try to remember / Our funny way / Liz / Say you love me / More / Raincoat in the river / Come out dancin' / I should have loved you more / I paid for loving you
CDCHD 669 / 23 Feb '98 / Ace

☐ BEST OF RICKY NELSON, THE (Nelson, Ricky)
Stood up / Waitin' in school / Be bop baby / Never be anyone else but you / Lonesome town / Poor little fool / It's late / Hello mary lou (goodbye heart) / Young world / Believe what you say / Just a little too much / It's up to you / Teenage idol / Young emotions / Travelin' man
MATCD 328 / Feb '95 / Castle

☐ BEST OF RICKY NELSON, THE (Nelson, Ricky)
PLSCD 127 / Mar '96 / Pulse

☐ BEST OF THE LATER YEARS 1963-1975, THE
I got a woman / String along / Gypsy woman / Everytime I see you smiling / Fools rush in / For you / Hey there little miss tease / Very thought of you / I wonder (if your love will ever belong to me) / Love is the sweetest thing / There's nothing I can say / I'm talking about you / Truck drivin' man / Night train to Memphis / Mystery train / Don't blame it on your wife / For emily whenever I may find her / Stop by my window / She belongs to me / Hello Mary lou goodbye heart / I'm walkin' / Look at mary / Feel so good (feel so fine) / Garden party / I don't want to be lonely tonight / Rock and roll lady
CDCHD 671 / Sep '97 / Ace

☐ BRIGHT LIGHTS AND COUNTRY MUSIC/COUNTRY FEVER
Truck drivin' man / You just can't quit / Louisiana man / Welcome to my world / Kentucky means paradise / Here I am / Bright lights and country music / Hello walls / No vacancy / I'm a fool to care / Congratulations / Night train to Memphis / Take a city bride / Funny how time slips away / Bridge washed out / Big Chief Buffalo Nickel / Mystery train / Things you gave me / Take these chains from my heart / (I heard that) lonesome whistle blow / Walkin' down the line / You win again / Salty dog
CDCHD 670 / Jun '98 / Ace

☐ EP COLLECTION, THE
I'm in love again / Baby I'm sorry / Boppin' the blues / There goes my baby / Your true love / Stood up / Down the line / Don't leave me this way / If you can't rock me / Stop sneakin' around / Hello Mary Lou, goodbye heart / Lucky star / Young world / Mad mad world / It's up to you / Have I told you lately that I love you / Never be anyone else but you / I can't help it / Someday / Poor little fool / It's late / There's good rockin' tonight / I'm feelin' sorry / You tear me up / Believe what you say
SEECD 483 / Aug '97 / See For Miles

☐ ESSENTIAL COLLECTION, THE (Nelson, Rick & The Stone Canyon Band)
HMNCD 031 / 22 Jun '98 / Half Moon

☐ FOR YOUR SWEET LOVE/SINGS FOR YOU
For your sweet love / Gypsy woman / You don't love me anymore (and I can tell) / Everytime I see you smiling / Pick up the pieces / String along / One boy too late / Everytime I think about you / Let's talk the whole thing over / I got a woman / What comes next / I will follow you / For you / Fools rush in / Down home / That same old feeling / You're free to go / I rise I fall / That's all she wrote / Legend in my time / Just take a moment / Hello Mister Happiness / Hey there little Miss Tease / Nearness of you
CDCHD 667 / 29 Sep '97 / Ace

☐ GARDEN PARTY
Let it bring you along / Garden party / So long Mama / I wanna be with you / Are you really real / I'm talking about you / Nightime lady / Flower opens gently by / Don't let your goodbye stand / Palace guard
WMCD 5696 / Oct '94 / Disky

☐ GARDEN PARTY/WINDFALL (Nelson, Rick & The Stone Canyon Band)
Let it bring you along / Garden party / So long Mama / I wanna be with you / Are you really real / I'm talking about you / Nighttime lady / Flower opens gently by / Don't let your goodbye stand / Palace guard / Legacy / Someone to love / How many times / Evil woman child / Don't leave me here / Wild nights in Tulsa / Lifestream / One night stand / I don't want to be lonely tonight / Windfall
BGOCD 333 / Nov '96 / Beat Goes On

☐ GREATEST HITS
MU 5019 / Oct '92 / Musketeer

☐ GREATEST HITS
Hello Mary Lou / Garden party / Fools rush in / Travellin' man / Poor little fool / Lonesome town / It's late / Never be anyone else but you / Teenage idol / I'm walkin' / Young world / I got a feeling / Mighty good / Don't leave me this way / You know what I mean / Believe what you say / Waitin' in school / Stood up / Just a little too much / It's up to you / Sweeter than you / You are the only one
100202 / May '97 / A-Play Collection

☐ HELLO MARY LOU (GOODBYE HEART) (The Best Of Rick Nelson)
Hello Mary Lou (goodbye heart) / Never be anyone else but you / Be bop baby / Stood up / I got a feeling / Someday (you'll want me to want you) / Poor little fool / Waitin' in school / It's late / Lonesome town / Sweeter than you / Have I told you lately that I love you / You are the only one / Mighty good / Yes sir that's my baby / Just a little too much / Everlovin' / (It's a) young world / It's up to you / Travellin' man / If you can't rock me / Young emotions / Today's teardrops / Wonder like you
CZ 560 / Feb '96 / Premier/EMI

☐ IN CONCERT (From Chicago To LA)
Stood up / Waitin' in school / I got a feeling / Travellin' man / Hello Mary Lou / Garden party / You know what I mean / That's alright mama / Believe what you say / Milk cow blues boogie / Never be anyone else but you / Fools rush in / It's up to you / Poor little fool / It's late / Honky tonk woman / My bucket's got a hole in it / Boppin' the blues / Lonesome town
CDMF 083 / Jan '92 / Magnum Force

☐ LIVE
Hello mary lou (goodbye heart) / Travellin' man / Fools rush in / Never be anyone else but you / It's up to you / Boppin' the blues / That's all right (mama) / Honky tonk woman / Garden party / Milk cow blues boogie
15178 / Aug '91 / Laserlight

☐ LIVE AT THE ALADDIN
Garden party / Poor little fool / My bucket's got a hole in it / Last time around / Milkcow blues / She belongs to me / Lonesome town / Travelling man / Hello Mary Lou / It's late / Merry Christmas baby / Mystery train
CDMF 078 / Feb '91 / Magnum Force

☐ ORIGINAL, THE (Nelson, Ricky)
Poor little fool / Stood up / Someday / Be true to me / Thank you darling / Young world / Have I told you lately (that I love you) / Never be anyone else but you / Teenage idol / Be bop baby / It's up to you / Just a little too much / Wonder like you / Young emotions / I got a feeling / It's late / Sweeter than you / Believe what you say
TO 860142 / 2 Feb '98 / Disky

☐ POOR LITTLE FOOL
GFS 089 / Nov '97 / Going For A Song

☐ RICK NELSON & THE STONE CANYON BAND VOL.1
If you gotta go, go now / I shall be released / She belongs to me / Easy to be free / California / Anytime / Down along the bayou country / This train / Life / Love minus zero-no limit / Gypsy pilot / Garden party / Legacy / Lifestream / Wild nights in tulsa / One night stand / Try (try to fall in love) / Louisana belle / Rock and roll lady / Fade away
EDCD 417 / Mar '95 / Edsel

☐ RICK NELSON & THE STONE CANYON BAND VOL.2 (Nelson, Rick & The Stone Canyon Band)
Hello Mary Lou / I'm walkin' / Believe what you say / Violets of dawn / Red balloon / Louisiana man / Easy to be free / We've got a long way to go / Sweet Mary / Look at Mary / Mr Dolphin / How long / Reason why / Just like a woman / Honky tonk women / Feels so good / Night time lady / Palace guard / I'm talking about you / Windfall / Don't leave me here
EDCD 521 / Apr '97 / Edsel

☐ ROCKIN' WITH RICK
Travellin' man / Hello Mary Lou / Poor little fool / Garden party / Young world / Don't leave me this way / I'm walkin' / Lonesome town / Just a little too much / You are the only one / Stood up / Waitin' in school / I got a feeling / You know what I mean / That's alright mama / Believe what you say / Milk cow blues / It's late / Boopin' the blues / Fools rush in
CPCD 8004 / Oct '93 / Charly

☐ ROCKIN' WITH RICKY
Mighty good / Milk cow blues / If you can't rock me / Be bop baby / Good rockin' tonight / It's late / Waitin' in school / Shirley Lee / There goes my baby / Boppin' the blues / I got a feeling / My babe / Stood up / Down the line / One of these mornings / Your true love / Ain't nothin' but love / Believe what you say / My bucket's got a hole in it / Whole lotta shakin' goin' on / I'm in love again / You tear me up / You'll never know what you're missin' / Just a little too much / You're so fine / Break my chain / Oh yeah I'm in love / Stop sneakin' around / I'll make believe / Today's teardrops / Poor loser / I've been thinkin'
CDCHD 85 / Apr '96 / Ace

☐ VERY THOUGHT OF YOU, THE/ SPOTLIGHT ON RICK
My old flame / Just a little bit sweet / Loneliest sound / You'll never fall in love again / Very thought of you / I don't wanna love you / I'll get you yet / I wonder (if your love will ever belong to me) / Be my love / I love you more than you know / Love is the sweetest thing / Dinah / I'm a fool / I tried / I'm talking about you / Yesterday's love / Happy guy / From a distance / Stop, look and listen / Don't breathe a word / That's why I love you like I do / In my dreams / Just relax / Live and learn
CDCHD 668 / 24 Nov '97 / Ace

☐ WINDFALL (Nelson, Rick & The Stone Canyon Band)
LICD 9012730 / Nov '96 / Line

Nelson, Sandy

☐ BEAT THAT DRUM/BE TRUE TO YOUR SCHOOL
You name it / Shuckin' / Turf rider / Here we go / Puttin' it on / Diddley walk / Lonesome drums / Rockin' party / Drummin' good time / Viva Nelson / Alexes / Wiggle walk / Be true to your school / School days / High school USA / Hey little girl (in the High School sweater) / Waitin' in school / Teen march / Cheer leader / School's out / Rock around the clock / Charley Brown / Moments to remember / Graduation day
C5HCD 650 / Aug '96 / See For Miles

☐ COUNTRY STYLE/TEENAGE HOUSE PARTY
North wind / Wolverton mountain / Battle of New Orleans / Geisha girl / On a honky tonk hardwood floor / Bimbo / Waterloo / Wild side of life / Tijuana jail / Fraulein / Four walls / Chew tobacco rag / House party rock / Hearts of stone / Let the four winds blow / Tweedle dee / Let the good times roll / Feel so good / Day train / Night train / Limbo rock / Dumplins / Teenage party
C5HCD 649 / Aug '96 / See For Miles

☐ DRUMMIN' UP A STORM/ COMPELLING PERCUSSION
Castle rock / Sandy / I'm in love again / All night long / C jam blues / Here we go again / All around the world with drums / Tub thumpin' / Drummin' up a storm / Civilization / And then there were drums / Alexes / Chicka boom / Jump time / Drums - For drummers only / Drums - For strippers only
C5HCD 641 / Jun '96 / See For Miles

☐ GOLDEN HITS/BEST OF THE BEATS
Live it up / Splish splash / Kansas City / Early in the morning / Rock house / Walking to New Orleans / What'd I say / Honky tonk / Bony Moronie / I'm gonna be a wheel someday / I want to walk you home / Be bop baby / Let's go / Yakety yak / Yakety yakety / My wife can't cook / Stagger Lee / All shook up / Don't be cruel / La bomba bossa nova / Wiggle wobble / Ooh pooh pah doo / Willy and the hand jive / Stood up / Mother In Law
C5HCD 648 / Aug '96 / See For Miles

☐ KING OF DRUMS (His Greatest Hits)
Teen beat / There were drums / In beat / Cool operator / Ooh-poo-pah-doo / Freak beat / Big noise from the jungle / You name it / Blues theme / Let there be drums / Mr. John Lee (parts 1 and 2) / Swamp beat / Quite a beat / Drum stuff / Let there be drums and brass / Drums are my beat / Teen beat '65 / Gimme some skin / Drum stomp / Drums a go go / Drummin' up a storm / Soul drums / Live it up / Kitty's theme
SEECD 423 / Jul '95 / See For Miles

☐ LET THERE BE DRUMS/DRUMS ARE MY BEAT
Slippin' and slidin' / Tequila / My girl Josephine / Big noise from Winnetka / Let there be drums / Bouncy / Birth of the beat / Quite a beat / Get with it drum roll / My blue heaven / Hawaiian war chant / Caravan / Drums are my beat / Day drumming / Drum stomp / Hum drum / Topsy / City
C5HCD 640 / Jun '96 / See For Miles

☐ ROCK 'N' ROLL DRUM BEAT
Day train / Slippin' and slidin' / Willie and the hand jive / All night long / My girl Josephine / All shook up / Sandy / Alexis / Let's go / City / Linda Lu / Bullfrog / Bony Moronie / Tough beat / Yakety yak / La bamba bossa nova / Jivin' around / Don't be cruel (to a heart that's true) / Flip / Be bop baby / Live it up / Dumplin's / Wiggle wobble / Limbo rock / School day / In the mood / Charlie Brown / My wife can't cook / I'm gonna be a wheel someday / Let there be drums
CDCHD 586 / Oct '95 / Ace

☐ TEEN BEAT/HE'S A DRUMMER BOY
Teen beat / Jivin' around / Funny face / Wiggle / Rainy day / Drum party / In the mood / Alexes / Lost dreams / I'm walkin' / Boom chicka boom / Party time / Cool operator / Feel beat / Linda Lou / Bullfrog / Tough beat / Raunchy / Jive talk / Jumpin' jungles / Flip / Big noise from the jungle / Walkin' to Hartford / Tim tam
C5HCD 639 / Jun '96 / See For Miles

Nelson, Shara

☐ FRIENDLY FIRE
Rough with the smooth / Movin' on / Poetry / I fell (so you could catch me) / Footprint / Between the lines / After you / Exit 1 / Friendly fire / Keeping out the cold / Segabeats
CTCD 48 / Sep '95 / Cooltempo

☐ WHAT SILENCE KNOWS
Nobody / Pain revisited / One goodbye in ten / Inside out / Chance / Uptight / Down that road / Thoughts of you / How close / What silence knows
CTCD 35 / Sep '93 / Cooltempo

Nelson, Steve

☐ COMMUNICATIONS (Nelson, Steve Quartet)
CRISS 1034CD / Nov '90 / Criss Cross

Nelson, Tracy

☐ HOMEMADE SONGS/COME SEE ABOUT ME
God's song / I've been there before / Ice man / Summer of the silver comet / Tightrope / You don't need to move a mountain / She's taking my part / Friends of a kind / Sounds of the city / Suddenly / Come see about me / Done got over / Holiday / It's growing / Walk away / Tears / Hold on I'm coming / See saw / River's invitation / You're my world
FF 70052 / Sep '96 / Flying Fish

☐ I FEEL SO GOOD
ROUCD 3133 / Feb '95 / Rounder

☐ IN THE HERE AND NOW
ROUCD 3123 / Jun '93 / Rounder

☐ MOVE ON
ROUCD 3143 / Aug '96 / Rounder

Nelson, Willie

☐ 20 OF THE BEST
Funny how time slips away / Night life / My own peculiar way / Hello walls / Mr. Record man / To make a long story short (she's gone) / Good times / She's still gone / Little things / Pretty paper / Bloody Mary morning / What can you do to me now / December days / Yesterday's wine / Me and Paul / Goodhearted woman / She's not for you / It should be easier now / Phases and stages / Circles, cycles and scenes
ND 89137 / Mar '91 / RCA

☐ ALL OF ME
Stardust / All of me / What a wonderful world / Moon river / Mona Lisa / Georgia on my mind / South of the border / Without a song / I'm confessin' (That I love you) / I'm gonna sit down and write myself a letter / Harbour lights / You'll never know / Autumn leaves / To each his own / Who's sorry now / Some enchanted evening / September song / Over the rainbow
4878732 / 26 Jan '98 / Columbia

☐ ALWAYS ON MY MIND
Will you remember mine / Some other time / I hope so / Is there something on your mind / Broken promises / Blame in on the times / Face of a fighter / Shelter of your arms / End of understanding / Home is where you're happy / And so will you my love / Waiting time / No tomorrow in sight / Everything but you / Happiness lives next door / Right from wrong / I'll go away / I'll stay around / Always on my mind
SUMCD 4007 / Nov '96 / Summit

☐ ALWAYS ON MY MIND
CD 6096 / 29 Sep '97 / Music

☐ AUGUSTA (Nelson, Willie & Don Cherry)
My way / Augusta / One for the road / Red sails in the sunset / Try a little tenderness / Tangerine / I love you for sentimental reasons / Prisoner of love / Tenderly / Maybe you'll be there / Don't go to strangers / Night life / Rainy day blues
CDSD 080 / 24 Oct '97 / Sundown

☐ BEST OF WILLIE NELSON, THE
Georgia on my mind / Help me make it through the night / Highwayman / Don't get around much anymore / Someone to watch over me / For the good times / Mamas don't let your babies grow up to be cowboys / Good hearted woman / Blue eyes crying in the rain / Mona Lisa / Stardust / City of New Orleans / As time goes by / Moonlight in Vermont / Amazing grace / Lovin' her was easier (than anything I'll ever do) / Always on my mind
4840412 / May '96 / Columbia

☐ BEST OF WILLIE NELSON, THE
74321378402 / Jul '96 / RCA

☐ BEST OF WILLIE NELSON, THE (Funny How Time Slips Away)
Fire and rain / Me and Paul / Crazy arms / Night life / Funny how time slips away / Hello walls / If you can touch her at all / Yesterday's wine / Help me make it through the night / Good times / Mountain dew / You ought to hear me cry / One in a row / She's not for you / San Antonio rose / Once more with feeling / I'm a memory / Pretty paper / Sweet memories / Little things / Laying my burdens down / Party's over
74321487272 / May '97 / Camden

☐ CHRISTMAS ALBUM
Away in a manger / Deck the halls / It came upon a midnight clear / Joy to the world / First Noel / O little town of Bethlehem / O come all ye faithful (adeste fidelis) / We wish you a merry Christmas / Silent night / Pretty paper
1200012 / Oct '97 / Jingle

☐ CLASSIC AND UNRELEASED COLLECTION, A
Rosetta / Walkin' / So much to do / Stay all night (stay a little longer) / Slow down old world / Slow down old world / Whiskey river / Sister's coming home / I saw the light / I'm so ashamed / I gotta have something I ain't got / I hope so / Who do I know in dallas / Suffering in silence / Face of a fighter / Things to remember / Healing hands of time / December day / Any old arms won't do / Moment isn't very long / Shelter of your arms / Why are you picking on me / Lumberjack / No place for me / Sugar moon / Move it on over / Good hearted woman / Funny how time slips away / She thinks I still care / No love around / Bloody mary morning / (how will I know) I'm falling in love again / Me and paul / Crazy / My bucket's got a hole in it / Mind your own business / I'm so lonesome I could cry / Truck driving man / I'm gonna sit right down and write myself a letter / My cricket and me / Both ends of the candle / Under the double eagle / Night life / Party's over / I'll sail my ship alone / If it's wrong to love you / Till the end of the world / It should be easier now / I'll keep on loving you / My son calls another man daddy / Why should we try anymore / They'll never take her love from me / Why don't you love me / House is not a home / Jimmy's road / Who'll buy my memories / Will you remember mine / Struttin' with some barbeque / I'll take what I can get / I'm a fool to care / Bloody mary morning take me back to tulsa / After the fire is gone
8122714622 / Jan '96 / WEA

☐ CLASSIC COLLECTION (23 Of His Best)
Country Willie / Healing hands of time / Shelter of your arms / Things to remember / Night life / I can't find the time / Is there something on your mind / Face of a fighter / Broken promises / Suffer in silence / You wouldn't cross the street to say goodbye / Both ends of the candle / Any old arms won't do / Ghost / I didn't sleep a wink / Home is where you're happy / Why are you picking on me / Happiness lives next door / Everything but you / I'm gonna lose a lot of teardrops / Building heartaches / Half a man
AIM 3003CD / Sep '97 / Aim

☐ COLLECTION, THE
You'll always have someone / I'm building heartaches / Things to remember / Home is where you're happy / You wouldn't cross the street to say goodbye / Any old arms won't do / Everything but you / Face of a fighter / Go away / I can't find the time / I feel sorry for him / I just don't understand / I'll stay around / I'm going to lose a lot of teardrops / Is there something on your mind / Let's pretend / No tomorrow in sight / Pride wins again / Right from wrong / She's not for you / Last letter / Waiting time / What can you do to me now / Why are you picking on me / Will you remember mine
COL 026 / Oct '95 / Collection

☐ COUNTRY CLASSICS
Country Willie / Willingly / Mr. Record man / Crazy / Hello walls / There's gonna be love at my house tonight / Touch me / Funny how time slips away / Cold war with you / Half a man / You took my happy away / Last letter / Seasons of my heart / I'll walk alone / I hope so / River boy / Take me as I am (or let me go) / Undo the right / Columbus stockade blues / There'll be no teardrops tonight
4949222 / 1 Jun '98 / EMI Gold

☐ COUNTRY LOVE SONGS
Home is where you're happy / I let my mind wonder / I can't find the time / You'll always have someone / December days / Suffering in silence / I feel sorry for him / Blame it on the time / I just don't understand / Shelter of my arms / Any old arms won't do / Slow down old world / I didn't sleep a wink / And so will you my love / Things to remember / One step beyond / Undo the wrong / Healing hands of time / Why are you picking on me / You wouldn't cross the street to say goodbye
100342 / May '97 / A-Play Collection

☐ ESSENTIAL WILLIE NELSON, THE
Me and Paul / Yesterday's wine / December day / Bloody Mary morning / Healing hands of time / Darkness on the face of the earth / Funny how time slips away / Family bible / My own peculiar way / Mr. Record Man / I gotta get drunk / Hello walls / Sweet memories / Night life / Waltz across Texas / Party's over / Some other world / Goin' home / Once more with feeling / Phrases, stages, circles, cycles and scenes
74321665902 / Feb '96 / RCA

☐ FACE OF A FIGHTER
MU 5067 / Oct '92 / Musketeer

☐ FACE OF A FIGHTER
And so will you my love / Will you remember mine / Home is where you're happy / I hope so / Some other time / Is there something on your mind / Broken promises / Waiting time / Face of a fighter / No tomorrow in sight / Everything but you / Shelter of your arms / Happiness lives next door / End of understanding / Go away / Blame it on the times / Right from wrong / I'll stay around
300042 / Jul '96 / Hallmark

☐ GOLD
GOLD 032 / Aug '96 / Gold

☐ GREATEST HITS
Railroad lady / Heartaches of a fool / Blue eyes cryin' in the rain / Whiskey river / Goodhearted woman / Georgia on my mind / If you've got the money, I've got the time / Look what thoughts will do / Uncloudy day / Mamas don't let your babies grow up to be cowboys / My heroes have always been cowboys / Help me make it through the night / Angel flying too close to the ground / I'd have to be crazy / Faded love / On the road again / Heartbreak hotel / If you could touch her at all / Till I gain control again / Stay a little longer
4714122 / '92 / Columbia

☐ HEARTACHES
Touch me / Half a man / I hope so / Any old arms won't do / End of understanding / Healing hands of time / Last letter / Shelter of your arms / Ashamed / Suffer in silence / Face of a fighter / Building heartaches
CDSGP 052 / Apr '93 / Prestige

☐ HOW GREAT THOU ART
FA 9605CD / Aug '96 / Fine Arts

☐ IS THERE SOMETHING ON YOUR MIND
Ghost / Let's pretend / I'm gonna lose a lot of teardrops / Wastin' time / Go away / No tomorrow in sight / New way to cry / Broken promises / I let my mind wander / December days / I can't find the time / I didn't sleep a wink / You wouldn't cross the street to say goodbye / Suffering in silence / I feel sorry for him / You'll always have someone / I just don't understand / Building heartaches / Pages / Is there something on your mind / Face of a fighter / I hope so / Everything but you / Moment isn't very long / Some other time / Shelter of my arms / Blame it on the times / End of an understanding / One step beyond
GRF 032 / Feb '93 / Tring

☐ LEGEND BEGINS, THE
Some other time / I hope so / Will you remember mine / Is there something on your mind / Everything but you / Moment isn't very long / Blame it on the times / Face of a fighter / Shelter of my arms / End of understanding
CDMF 086 / Nov '92 / Magnum Force

☐ LOVE SONGS
To all the girls I've loved before / Blue skies / Let it be me / Tenderly / Harbour lights / Mona Lisa / To each his own / Over the rainbow / Seven Spanish angels / Georgia on my mind / Bridge over troubled water / Without a song / Unchained melody / That lucky old sun / In my mother's eyes / Always on my mind
4674512 / 27 Jul '98 / Columbia

☐ MASTERS, THE
EABCD 033 / 24 Nov '97 / Eagle

☐ MOONLIGHT BECOMES YOU
December days / Moonlight becomes you / Afraid / Heart of a clown / Please don't talk about me when I'm gone / Everywhere you go / Have I stayed away too long / Sentimental journey / World is waiting for the sunrise / You'll never know / I'll keep on loving you / You just can't play a sad song on a banjo / You always hurt the one you love / Someday (you'll want me to want you) / In God's eyes
4759452 / 13 Jul '98 / Columbia

☐ MY SONGS
EABCD 027 / 24 Nov '97 / Eagle

☐ NASHVILLE WAS THE ROUGHEST... (8CD Set)
King of a lonely castle / (There'll be) someone waiting for you / To make a long story short / I never cared for you / You left me a long long time ago / I feel that old feeling / King of a lonely castle / Pretty paper / What a merry Christmas this could be / Healing hands of time / Talk to me / Whisky walzer / Little darling / Permanently lonely / Healing hands of time / Ashamed / She's not for you / Are you sure / Night life / Mr. Record man / Healing hands of time / Funny how time slips away / My own peculiar way / One day at a time / It should be easier now / darkness on the face of the earth / Buddy / Hello walls / So much to do / Within your crowd / Did I ever love you / And so will you my love / I just can't let you say goodbye / Down to our last goodbye / Fraulein / I love you because / I'd trade all of my tomorrows (for just one yesterday) / Making believe / Home in San Antone / Don't you ever get tired (of loving me) / Columbus stockade blues / Seasons of my heart / Heartaches by the number / Go on home / My window faces the south / San Antonio rose / I'm still not over you / San Antonio rose / Columbus stockade blues / He sits at my table / Wonderful yesterday / Party's over / One in a row / Make way for a better man / Did I ever love you / I just can't let you say goodbye / Down to our last goodbye / Wonderful yesterday / Party's over / One in a row / Have I stayed away too long / Some other world / If it's wrong to love you / Have I told you lately that I love you / You made me live love and die / Born to lose / What now my love / Lovin' lies / Teach me to forget / Tender years / Mansion on the hill / Something to think about / Blackjack county chain / Don't say love or nothing / You ought to hear me cry / I don't feel anything / Hold me tighter / I'll stay around / Moment isn't very long / Ghost / No tomorrow in sight / There goes a man / Go away / Once alone / End of understanding / To make a long story short (she's gone) / Suffer in silence / Truth number one / When I don't have you / Someday you'll call my name / Wild memories / December day / Pages / Little things / Good times / She's still gone / Sweet memories / Johnny one time / Jimmy's road / Bring me sunshine / I let my mind wonder / I just don't understand / I just dropped by / Local memory / Natural to be gone / Love has a mind of it's own / I'll walk alone / It will come to pass / My own peculiar way / Message / That's all / Any old arms won't do / Johnny one time / Jimmy's road / Bring me sunshine / Bloody merry morning / Pins and needles (in my heart) / Everybody's talkin' / Crazy arms / I gotta get drunk / Wabash cannon ball / One has my name (the other has my heart) / Who do I know in Dallas / Both sides now / It could be said that way / Once more with feeling / Following me around / Minstrel man / Where do you stand / When we live again / If you could see what's going through my mind / Happiness lives next door / I've seen that look on me (a thousand times) / I don't feel anything / Laying my burdens down / How long have you been there / Senses / Sunday mornin' comin' down / What can you do to me now / Losers song / I can cry again / Fire and rain / I'm a memory / That's why I love her so / If you could see what's going through my mind / Losers song / Yours love / Kneel at the feet of Jesus / Today I started loving you again / I'm so lonesome I could cry / Will you remember / Wonderful future / Wake me when it's over / Help me make it through the night / Rainy day blues / If you really loved me / Words don't fit the picture / What do you want me to do / Stay away from lonely places / Good hearted woman / Home is where you're happy / My kind of girl / I'd rather you didn't love me / Undo the right / One step beyond / I want a girl / Country Willie / You left a long long time ago / London / Who'll buy me memories / No love around / Come on home / Mountain dew / Dallas / San Antonio / Streets of Laredo / Who put all my ex's in Texas / Hill country theme / Waltz across Texas / Travis letter / Remember the Alamo / Texas in my soul / There's a little bit of everything in Texas / Beautiful Texas / Where's the show/Let me be a man / In God's eyes / Family bible / It's not for me to understand / These are difficult times/Remember the good times / Summer of roses / December day / Yesterday's wine / Me and Paul / Goin' home / Phases stages circles cycles and scenes / Pretend I never happened / Sister's coming home / Down at the corner beer joint / I'm falling in love again / Chet's tune / Poor old ugly Gladys Jones / Introduction / Bo Powell/Willie introduces band / Mr. Record man/Hello walls/One day at a time / Last letter/Half a man / I never cared for you / Yesterday / Touch me / Something to think about / I just can't let you say goodbye / How long is forever / Night life / Oppurtunity to cry/Permanently lonely / My own peculiar way / I love you because / I'm still not over you / There'll be no teardrops tonight
BCD 15831 / May '98 / Bear Family

☐ NIGHTLIFE
Night life / Right from wrong / Waiting time / I'll stay around / Broken promises / Happiness lives next door / Ghost / I'm gonna lose a lot of teardrops / Go away / Pride wins again / No tomorrow in sight / New way to cry
15485 / May '94 / Laserlight

☐ OLD TIME RELIGION (Nelson, Willie & Bobby Nelson)
Just a little walk with jesus / Just a little walk with jesus / Where the soul never dies / Lily of the valley / I'll fly away / Are you washed in the blood / Where he leads me / Old time religion / Revive us again / Sweet bye and bye / When we all get to heaven
12114 / May '93 / Laserlight

☐ ONE STEP BEYOND
I let my mind wander / December days / I can't find the time / I didn't sleep a wink / You wouldn't cross the street to say goodbye / Suffering in silence / I feel sorry for him / You'll always have someone / I just don't understand / Pages / Any old arms won't do / Slow down old world / Healing hands of time / And so will you my love / Things to remember / One step beyond / Undo the wrong / Home is where you're happy / Why are you picking on me / I hope so
CDSB 011 / 3 Aug '98 / Starburst

☐ ORIGINAL OUTLAWS (Nelson, Willie & Waylon Jennings)
Crying / Ghost / Sally was a good old girl / Let's pretend / Abilene / I'm gonna lose a lot of teardrops / It's so easy / Waiting time / Love's gonna live here / Go away / Don't think twice / No tomorrow in sight / Dream baby / New way to cry / Lorena / Broken promises / Burning memories / Let my mind wander / White lightning / Moment isn't very long / Big mamou / I can't find the time / Money / I feel sorry for him
QED 116 / Nov '96 / Tring

☐ OUTLAW REUNION (Nelson, Willie & Waylon Jennings)
Some other time: *Nelson, Willie* / Is there something on your mind: *Nelson, Willie* / Broken promises: *Nelson, Willie* / End of our understanding: *Nelson, Willie* / Home is where you're happy: *Nelson, Willie* / Waiting time: *Nelson, Willie* / I'll stay around: *Nelson, Willie* / Happiness lives next door: *Nelson, Willie* / Sally was a good old girl: *Jennings, Waylon* / White lightning: *Jennings, Waylon* / Love's gonna live here: *Jennings, Waylon* / Burning memories: *Jennings, Waylon* / Don't think twice: *Jennings, Waylon* / Lorena: *Jennings, Waylon* / Dream baby: *Jennings, Waylon* / It's so easy: *Jennings, Waylon*
ECD 3344 / May '97 / K-Tel

☐ PEACE IN THE VALLEY (Nelson, Willie & Willie Nelson Jr.)
PLMCD 052158 / Nov '94 / Promised Land

☐ REUNION (Can't Get The Hell Out Of Texas) (Offenders)
Can't get the hell out of Texas / Linda on my mind / I'm so ashamed / Daybreak / Walk me to the door / Sleepwalk / Are you sure this is where you want to be / She's not for you / I know I love you / There she goes / Hey good lookin' / Rainy day blues
BCD 16124 / Oct '97 / Bear Family

☐ REVOLUTIONS IN TIME (3CD Set)
Time of the preacher / Blue eyes crying in the rain / If you've got the money I've got the time / Uncloudy day / Always late with your kisses / Georgia on my mind / Blue skies / Whiskey river / Stay a little longer / Mr. Record Man / Loving her was easier / Mammas don't let you babies grow up to be cowboys / It's not supposed to be that way / On the road again / Angel flying too close to the ground / Mona Lisa always on my mind / Last thing I needed the first thing this morning / Party's over / Summertime: *Nelson, Willie & Leon Russell* / Faded love: *Nelson, Willie & Ray*

Price / Pancho and lefty: Nelson, Willie & Merle Haggard / Old friends: Nelson, Willie & Roger Miller/ Ray Price / In the jailhouse again: Nelson, Willie & Webb Pierce / Everything's beautiful (in it's own way): Nelson, Willie & Dolly Parton / Take it to the limit: Nelson, Willie & Waylon Jennings / To all the girls I loved before: Nelson, Willie & Julio Iglesias / How do you feel about foolin' around: Nelson, Willie & Kris Kristofferson / Seven Spanish angels: Nelson, Willie & Ray Charles / Hello walls: Nelson, Willie & Faron Young / I'm movin' on: Nelson, Willie & Hank Snow / Highwayman: Nelson, Willie & J. Cash/W. Jennings/K. Kristofferson / Slow movin' outlaw: Nelson, Willie & Lacy J Dalton / Are there any more real cowboys: Nelson, Willie & Neil Young / They all went to Mexico: Nelson, Willie & Carlos Santana / Half a man: Nelson, Willie & George Jones / Texas on a Saturday night: Nelson, Willie & Mel Tillis / Heartland: Nelson, Willie & Bob Dylan / Nobody slides my friend / Little old fashioned karma / Harbour lights / Without a song / Good time Charlie's got the blues / City of New Orleans / Who'll buy my memories / Write your own songs / Forgiving you was easy / Me and Paul / When I dream / My own peculiar way / Living in the Promiseland / There is no easy way (but there is a way) / Buttermilk sky / Horse called music / Nothing I can do about it now / Is the better part over / Ain't necessarily so / Still is still moving to me
C3K 64796 / 1 Dec '97 / Columbia

☐ SHOTGUN WILLIE
Shotgun Willie / Whiskey river / Sad songs and waltzes / Local memory / Slow down old world / Stay all night (stay a little longer) / Devil in a sleepin' bag / She's not for you / Bubbles in my beer / You look like the devil / So much to do / Song for you
7567814262 / Mar '93 / WEA

☐ SINGS THE COUNTRY HITS
EABCD 016 / 24 Nov '97 / Eagle

☐ SINGS WILLIE NELSON
Let's pretend / I can't find the time / Healing hands of time / Things to remember / A moment isn't very long / Any old arms won't do / Slow down old world / One step beyond / You'll always have someone / I just don't understand / I feel sorry for him / I'm building heartaches / Why are you picking on me / I didn't sleep a wink / You wouldn't cross the street to say / Goodbye / Suffering in silence
308052 / 15 Sep '97 / Hallmark

☐ SIX HOURS AT PEDERNALES
Nothings changed / Chase the moon / Are you sure / Party's over / We're not talking anymore / Turn me loose / Once your past the blues / It won't be easy / Stray cats, cowboys and girls of the night / Best worst thing / It should be easier now / My own peculiar way
SORCD 0084 / Oct '94 / D-Sharp
30102 / Oct '97 / Go On Deluxe

☐ SPIRIT
5342422 / May '96 / This Way Up

☐ SPOTLIGHT ON WILLIE NELSON
I just don't understand / I didn't sleep a wink / Blame it on the times / I let my mind wander / Shelter of my arms / And so will you my love / Home is where you're happy / I feel sorry for him / Slow down old world / Why are you picking on me / Any old arms won't do / Broken promises / I can't find the time / Things to remember / You always have someone / One step beyond
HADCD 132 / Feb '94 / Javelin

☐ TEATRO
5245482 / 7 Sep '98 / Island

☐ WILLIE NELSON
295047 / Oct '94 / Ariola

☐ WILLIE NELSON
Let's pretend / I'm gonna lose a lot of teardrops / Go away / No tomorrow in sight / New way to cry / Broken promises / I let my mind wander / I can't find the time / I didn't sleep a wink / Building heartaches / Pages / Is there something on your mind / Face of a fighter / I hope so / Everything but you / Moment isn't very long / Some other time / Blame it on the times / End of understanding / One step beyond
QED 068 / Nov '96 / Tring

☐ WILLIE NELSON COLLECTION, THE
Shelter of my arms / Face of a fighter / Things to remember / Moment isn't very long / Blame it on the times / Building heartaches / Undo the right / Will you remember mine / Any old arms won't do / Slow down old world / And so will you my love / Why are you picking on me / I hope so / Everything but you / Healing hands of time / No tomorrow in sight / One step beyond / Go away
ECD 3073 / Jan '95 / K-Tel

Nembrionic

☐ INCOMPLETE
D 00051CD / 17 Aug '98 / Displeased

Nembrionic Hammerdeath

☐ BLOODCULT
D 00052CD / 10 Nov '97 / Displeased

Nemesis

☐ PEOPLE WANT BASS
FILECD 461 / May '95 / Profile

☐ TEMPLE OF BOOM
Temple of boom / Nemesis on the premises / Deep up on it / Cantfiguritout / Big, the bad, the bass / Get ya flow on / Str8jackin' / Hard from birth / Parkin' lot on Dixon / Go Ron C / Brand new team / Cloud 7
FILECD 441 / Jun '93 / Profile

Nemesis

☐ NEMESIS
RTD 3970021CD / 10 Nov '97 / Institute Of Art

Nemeth, Yoska

☐ GYPSY KINGS (Nemeth, Yoska & Paul Toscano)
Les deus guitares / Je vous al aimee / Cocher vite chez yar / Czardas / Le chant de l'alouette / Fascination / Le temps de cerises / Suite hongroise / Cocher, ralentis tes chevaux / Romance et czardas hongroises / Airs populaires roumains / Confidences de roses rouges / Joue jusqu'au matin / Beltz scha stil / Reviens / Souika hora / Petites clochettes monotones / L'ame des violons / Romance et danse caucasiennes
300062 / Aug '90 / Musidisc

Nemirovski, Bielka

☐ DE LA MER BLANCE A LA MER NOIRE
8558392 / Jul '97 / Origins

Nena

☐ DEFINITIVE COLLECTION, THE
Nur getraumt / 99 luftballons / Leuchtturm / Fragezeichen / Irgendwie irgendwo irgendwann / Vollmond / Rette mich / Feuer und flamme / Wunder gescheh'n / Ich bleib' im bett / Lass mich dein pirat sein / Haus der drei sonnen / Tokyo / Manchmal ist ein tag / Du kennst die liebe nicht / Mondsong / Unerkannt durchs marchenland / Bongo girl
4837152 / 20 Jul '98 / Epic

Nenes

☐ AKEMODORO UNAI
Akemodoro / Shima Yakara / Chimugukuru / Tsubasa o yasumeni kimasenka / Hei wa no ryuka / Kuduchi / 3rd of March / Zampa / Nasake shirazuya / Erabu no komoriuta / Akemodoro
CDORBD 096 / 27 Jul '98 / Globestyle

Neolithic

☐ PERSONAL FRAGMENT
CDAR 028 / Jun '95 / Adipocre

Neon Hearts

☐ BALL AND CHAIN
OVER 64CD / Jul '97 / Overground

Neon Judgement

☐ ALASKA HIGHWAY
BIAS 167 CD / Jun '90 / Play It Again Sam

☐ DAZSOO
KK 177CD / 25 May '98 / KK

☐ FIRST JUDGEMENTS
CDBIAS 070 / Sep '87 / Play It Again Sam

Neos

☐ INDEFINITA ATMOSPHERA
SC 304CD / 16 Oct '97 / Schema

Neotropic

☐ 15 LEVELS OF MAGNIFICATION
NW37th / Laundry / La centinela / Laundry / 15 levels of magnification / Weeds / Nana / Nincompoop / Electric bud / CCTV / Neotropic / Beautiful pool / Regents park / Your turn to wash up / Aloo gobi / Frozen hands
NTONECD 017 / Sep '96 / Ntone

Neptunas

☐ LET THEM EAT TUNA
SFTRI 536 / 22 Jun '98 / Sympathy For The Record Industry

Neptune Towers

☐ CARAVANS TO EMPIRE ALGOL
FOG 002 / Dec '94 / Moonfog

☐ TRANSMISSIONS FROM EMPIRE ALGOL
FOG 008CD / Nov '96 / Moonfog

Neptune, John Kaizan

☐ TOKYOSPHERE
JD 3316 / May '89 / JVC

Nerell, Loren

☐ LILEN DEWA
DFX 026CD / May '97 / Side Effects

Nerem, Bjarne

☐ BJARNE NAREM & AL GREY
GMCD 162 / Oct '88 / Gemini

☐ EVERYTHING HAPPENS TO ME
GMCD 71 / Jan '89 / Gemini

☐ HOW LONG HAS THIS BEEN GOING ON
GMCD 72 / Jan '90 / Gemini

☐ MOOD INDIGO
GMCD 159 / Jan '90 / Gemini

☐ MORE THAN YOU KNOW
When your lover has gone / Everything I have is yours / Easy to love / Autumn nocturne / Miss Mopay / More than you know / Gone with the wind / Cabin in the sky / Emaline
GMCD 156 / Jan '88 / Gemini

☐ THIS IS ALWAYS
GMCD 147 / Mar '89 / Gemini

Nerf Herder

☐ NERF HERDER
MY 8052CD / Sep '96 / My Records
07822189542 / Jul '97 / Rhythm King

Nerious Joseph

☐ GUIDANCE
FADCD 023 / Nov '92 / Fashion

☐ REJOICE
CRCD 64 / Mar '97 / Charm

Nerney, Declan

☐ PART OF THE JOURNEY
Part of the journey / With this ring / In your arms / I really don't want to know / Anna from Fernangh / You in the morning / Lovely Derry on the banks of the Foyle / Honky tonk girl / Blue side of lonesome / Born to hang / Half as much / Cottage on the borderline / Tonight we just might fall in love again / Love me
RCD 549 / Jul '95 / Ritz

☐ WALKIN' ON NEW GRASS
Walkin' on new grass / Among the Wicklow hills / I found my girl in the USA / Give an Irish girl to me / North to Alaska / Just call me lonesome from now on / Stand at your window / Crazy dreams / Tipperary on my mind / Never again will I knock on your door / I still miss someone / I'd rather love and lose you / World of our own / Molly Bawn
RZRCD 526 / Apr '93 / Ritz

Nero Circus

☐ HUMAN PIGS
GOD 018CD / Jul '95 / Godhead

Nero's Acolytes

☐ ALBATROCITY
Blonde in black / Low point x / If if if / Cloning by numbers / Venus in furs / Nightmare trip III / Sex kills II / Fetch a gaoler / High flyer no safety net / Monster mash / Inner space / Join the system / Insatiable / Blinded by delight / Triggerman / My roots are wheels / Kiss of death / Remember me this way
EXIT 001CD / May '97 / Exoteric

Nerve

☐ CANCER OF CHOICE
Coins / Fragments / Oil / Rage / Closedown / Water / Seed / Dedalus / Trust / Waters / Thirties
BIAS 261CD / Oct '93 / Play It Again Sam

Nervous

☐ SON OF THE GREAT OUTDOORS
GRACD 214 / Aug '96 / Grapevine

Nervous Fellas

☐ BORN TO BE WILD
Suck my poison / Stop shaking them / Luger / L'homme a la moto / Hope you never see my woman cry / My split / Go home / Don't get down / Little john / Young boys wild boys / Ride and die / Baby's gone / Rock'n'roll haunts my blues / Family ties
NERCD 055 / '90 / Nervous

Nervous Project

☐ BACK TO BASICS
DBMLABCD 8 / Mar '96 / Labworks

Nesby, Ann

☐ I'M HERE FOR YOU
Let the rain fall / I'm still wearing your name / If you love me / Invitation / (What a) Lovely evening / I'll do anything for you / String interlude / Thrill me / Hold on / In the spirit / This weekend / Can I get a witness / I'm here for you / I'll be your everything / Let old memories be / Lord how I need you
5490222 / May '96 / Perspective

Nesmith, Michael

☐ AND THE HITS JUST KEEP ON COMING (Nesmith, Michael & Countryside Band)
AWCD 1027 / Nov '91 / Awareness

☐ INFINITE RIDER
AWCD 1031 / Mar '92 / Awareness

☐ LISTEN TO THE BAND
Silver moon / Listen to the band / Different drum / Some of Shelly's blues / Mama Nantucket / Harmony constant / Grand ennui / Bonaparte's retreat / Little red rider / Lady of the valley / First national rag / Keys to the car / Two different roads / Nevada fighter / I fall to pieces / Rainmaker / Calico girlfriend / Nine times blue / I've just begun to care (propinquity) / Conversations / Joanne / Beyond the blue horizon
74321523772 / 29 Sep '97 / Camden

☐ LOOSE SALUTE (Nesmith, Michael & The First National Band)
Silver moon / I fall to pieces / Thanx for the ride / Dedicated friend / Conversations / Tengo amore / Listen to the band / Bye bye bye / Lady of the valley / Hello lady
AWCD 1024 / Mar '91 / Awareness

☐ MAGNETIC SOUTH (Nesmith, Michael & The First National Band)
Calico girlfriend / Nine times blue / Little red rider / Crippled lion / Joanne / First national rag / Mama Nantucket / Keys to the car / Hollywood / One rose / Beyond the blue horizon
AWCD 1023 / Mar '91 / Awareness

☐ MASTERS, THE
EABCD 105 / 30 Mar '98 / Eagle

☐ NEVADA FIGHTER (Nesmith, Michael & The First National Band)
Grand ennui / Propinquity (I've begun to care) / Here I am / Only bound / Nevada fighter / Texas morning / Tumbling tumbleweeds / I looked away / Rainmaker / Rene
AWCD 1025 / Mar '91 / Awareness

☐ NEWER STUFF, THE
AWCD 1014 / Apr '89 / Awareness

☐ OLDER STUFF, THE
AWCD 1032 / Mar '92 / Awareness

☐ TANTAMOUNT TO TREASON
Mama Rocker / Lazy lady / You are my one / In the afternoon / Highway 99 with Melange / Wax minute / Bonaparte's retreat / Talking to the wall / She thinks I still care
AWCD 1026 / Sep '91 / Awareness

Ness, Marilla

☐ ABBA MY FATHER
Alleluia my father / Father in my life I see / Peace is flowing like a river / Yahweh is the God of my salvation / Light in you / I will never forget you my people / Fill my house / Abba my father / Freely / Turn your eyes upon Jesus / Jesus how lovely you are / Our father / Lord have mercy / What colour is the wind / Our God reigns
MLM 116 / 19 Jan '98 / Merciful Love Music

☐ COME BACK TO ME
Close to you / Do not be afraid / When I feel the touch / Jesus take me as I am / Oh the word of my Lord / Resting place / Spirit of the Lord / Only a shadow / Worship the Lord / O Lord you're beautiful / Lord I love you / Holy is his name / How great thou art
MLM 106 / 19 Jan '98 / Merciful Love Music

☐ FROM WHERE I STAND
Make my heart your dwelling place / Breathe on me holy one / Lord you are more precious / I exalt thee / Wind was cold / As gentle as silence / Only have to close my eyes / Maranatha / Cup of life outpoured / Abba Father let me be / Isn't he beautiful / Jesus, Jesus, Jesus / From where I stand / Jesus the healer / Take our bread / Rise from the dreams of time / We see the Lord
MLM 118 / 19 Jan '98 / Merciful Love Music

☐ HE TOUCHED ME
Holy Spirit we welcome you / Lay your hands / Lift up heads / I love you Lord / He touched me / He is Lord / Sweet heart of Jesus / Lord you are so precious / You are near / With a clean heart / This is Holy Ground / Sing of a girl / Jesus name above all names / Pierce my ear / Oh Lord your tenderness / Here I am Lord
MLM 101 / 19 Jan '98 / Merciful Love Music

☐ HEART OF LOVE
Loving you gently Lord / How can I keep from singing / Tender mercy / Jesus you are Lord / Communion song / One bread one body / Heart of love / Father we love you / Come to the water / To do your will / You are here / As the deer / Walk in the light
MLM 110 / 19 Jan '98 / Merciful Love Music

☐ HOLY ONE OF ISRAEL
Peace like a river / Lamb of God / Abide with me / Open your eyes / See his glory / Reign in me / Mary most Holy / Lord you are the holy one / Alleluia he is coming / All heaven declares / When I look into your holiness / Such love / Walk humbly with your God / I lift my hands / For you and me / Make us one Lord
MLM 104 / 19 Jan '98 / Merciful Love Music

☐ LOVE MUST BE THE REASON
Be still / Jesus we enthrone you / Majesty / Transfiguration / I will be with you / What kind of love is this / I am the bread of life / Make me a channel / My God loves me / I am with you forever / Just like you promised / Worthy are you O Lord / Sweet sacrament divine / There is love / Be not afraid
MLM 112 / 19 Jan '98 / Merciful Love Music

☐ SORROWFUL WOMAN
As I kneel before you / Behold I see the virgin / Hail Mary / Mary most Holy / New Lourdes hymn / Sorrowful woman / Hail Queen of Heaven / Sing of a girl / Magnificat / O purest of creatures / Mother of peace / O Mary when our God chose you
MLM 108 / 19 Jan '98 / Merciful Love Music

☐ SWEET SOUNDS OF CHRISTMAS
Ding dong merrily on high / Once in Royal David's city / O come all ye faithful / When a child is born / Away in a manger / Drummer boy / Do you hear what I hear / In the bleak midwinter / Angels we have heard on high / O little town of Bethlehem / It came upon the midnight clear / Silent night / Mary's boy child / O holy night
MLM 114 / 19 Jan '98 / Merciful Love Music

Netherworld

☐ NETHERWORLD
HNF 025CD / Mar '97 / Head Not Found

Network

☐ BEST OF NETWORK, THE
WEN 006 / 20 Apr '98 / Wenlock

Network

☐ PERIHELION
HOS 7031CD / 27 Apr '98 / Hall Of Sermon

Networks 3

☐ INTELLIGENT COMPILATION, AN
K7 047CD / Sep '96 / Studio K7

Netzer, Effi

☐ FESTIVAL OF JEWISH SONGS, A (Netzer, Effi Singers)
TCD 1060 / 13 Oct '97 / Tradition

☐ HAVA NAGILA
EUCD 1052 / '89 / ARC

Neu

☐ 1972 LIVE
CTCD 045 / Dec '97 / Captain Trip

☐ CHA CHA 2000 (Live In Tokyo/2CD Set)
CTCD 100/101 / 8 Jun '98 / Captain Trip

☐ DIE WITH DIGNITY
CTCD 098 / 8 Jun '98 / Captain Trip

☐ HOMAGE TO NEU, A (Various Artists)
CLP 300 / 22 Jun '98 / Cleopatra

☐ LA NEU DUSSELDORF
CTCD 051 / Jun '97 / Captain Trip

☐ LA NEU ZEELAND LIVE 1997
CTCD 086 / 2 Feb '98 / Captain Trip

☐ NEU 1975
941030 / 22 May '98 / Germanofon

☐ NEU VOL.1
Hallogallo / Sonderangebot / Weissensee / Jahresuberlick Im Gluck / Negativland / Lieber honig
941025 / 16 Feb '98 / Germanofon

☐ NEU VOL.2
941026 / 5 Jan '98 / Germanofon

☐ NEU VOL.4
CTCD 020 / Dec '97 / Captain Trip

☐ REMBRANDT
CTCD 087 / 27 Apr '98 / Captain Trip

NEUK

☐ STATE OF MIND
BRC 101CD / Jul '95 / Black Mail

Neumann, Alberto

☐ PERPETUAL TANGO VOL.1
926302 / Feb '96 / BUDA

☐ PERPETUAL TANGO VOL.2
926512 / Jul '96 / BUDA

Neumann, Drew

☐ EYE SPY (2CD Set)
TCCD 9724 / 15 Jun '98 / Tone Casualties

Neumann, Gunter

☐ AUFNAHMEN AUS DEN JAHREN 1948-1964 (8CD Set)
BCD 16005 / Dec '97 / Bear Family

☐ GUNTER NEUMANN UND SEINE INSULANER
Insulaner lied / Die Klatschdamen am Kurfurstendamm / Keene Strumpfe / Aber Gamaschen / Wie wird man ein star / Herr Kummer telefoniert / Breitwand rhapsodie / Frau Mode ist ein seltsam launisch Kind / Genosse und die volkseigene musik / Theater parodien / Seh'n se, das ist Berlin
BCD 16028 / 24 Nov '97 / Bear Family

Neumeier & Hollinger

☐ MEET THE DEMONS OF BALI
035382 / 23 Feb '98 / EFA

Neumeier & Schweizer

☐ EURO MASTERS OF INNOVATION
CTCD 068 / 15 Dec '97 / Captain Trip

Neuro

☐ ELECTRIC MOTHERS OF INVENTION
3BTTCD 2 / Nov '93 / 3 Beat

Neuronium

☐ CHROMIUM ECHOES
Prelude / Chromium echoes / Neutron age
CDTB 057 / Jul '89 / Thunderbolt

☐ FROM MADRID TO HEAVEN
Intro / Part 1 / Part 2 / Part 3 / Part 4
CDTB 2064 / '89 / Thunderbolt

☐ NUMERICA
500 years / Deep illness of love / Promenade / Power of your smile / Numerica / Maze extreme limits / Au revoir
CDTB 082 / Apr '90 / Thunderbolt

☐ SUPRANATURAL
When the goblins invade Madrid / Digitron / Priorite absolue / Europe is Europe / Sundown at Tanah Lot
CDTB 055 / Mar '88 / Thunderbolt

Neuropolitique

☐ BEYOND THE PINCH
ELEC 33CD / Jun '97 / New Electronica

☐ NOMENCLATURE (2CD Set)
Factory junction / Can't get off the slide / Mind you don't slip / Gene pools / No feet on stage / Remote phrases / Artemis / In the mix / Menage a trois / 1494 backslash 48207 / Large spoon / Mind mirror / Idiotic lantern / Neu arena / Express triangle / Fusion neu / Report / Ad nauseum / 1492 backslash 48207 / Box / Faze / Wide / 365 Fellatio / Animated data
ELEC 29CD / Jun '96 / New Electronica

Neurosis

☐ SOULS AT ZERO/ENEMY OF THE SUN (2CD Set)
CDMFN 234 / 20 Oct '97 / Music For Nations

☐ THROUGH SILVER IN BLOOD
ICR 002CD / Jun '96 / Iron City
CDMFN 235 / 20 Oct '97 / Music For Nations

Neurotica

☐ SEED
71899128002 / 21 Apr '98 / NTM

Neutral Milk Hotel

☐ IN THE AEROPLANE OVER THE SEA
King of carrot flowers / In the aeroplane over the sea / Two headed boy / Fool / Holland 1945 / Communist daughter / Oh comely / Ghost / 10 / Two headed boy
BRRC 10192 / 1 Jun '98 / Blue Rose

☐ ON AVERY ISLAND
FIRECD 53 / Sep '96 / Fire

Neutron 9000

☐ WALRUS
FILERCD 407 / May '91 / Profile

Neuwirth, Bob

☐ BACK TO THE FRONT
Eye on the road / Annabelle Lee / Private eye / Beauty / Heartaches / Pretend / Turn it around / Venice beach / Lucky / Akron / For PB
380092 / 1 Sep '98 / Koch

☐ LOOK UP
WM 1050CD / Aug '96 / Watermelon

Neven

☐ TWIN CYCLES
LOW 007 / Jul '96 / Lowlands

Neverland

☐ SURREAL WORLD
ESM 007 / 2 Mar '98 / Escape

Nevermore

☐ IN MEMORY
CM 77121CD / Jul '96 / Century Media

☐ POLITICS OF ECSTACY, THE
CM 77132CD / Nov '96 / Century Media

Nevil, Robbie

☐ C'EST LA VIE
Just a little closer / Dominoes / Limousines / Back to you / C'est la vie / Wot's it to ya / Walk your talk / Simple life / Neighbours / Look who's alone tonight
NSPCD 513 / Apr '95 / Connoisseur Collection

Neville Brothers

☐ BROTHERS KEEPER
Brother blood / Steer me right / Sons and daughters / Jah love / Witness / Sons and daughters (reprise) / Bird on the wire / Brother Jake / Fearless / Fallin' rain / River of life / My brother's keeper / Mystery train
3953122 / Aug '90 / A&M

☐ FAMILY AFFAIR, A (A History Of The Neville Brothers/2CD Set)
Over you: *Neville, Aaron* / Funky miracle: *Meters* / Little girl from the candy store: *Neville, Art* / Show me the way: *Neville, Aaron* / Sophisticated cissy: *Meters* / I'm waiting at the station: *Neville, Aaron* / My baby don't love me anymore: *Neville, Art* / 6V6 love: *Meters* / Ride your pony: *Meters* / Wrong number: *Neville, Aaron* / Cardova: *Meters* / I need some Art: *Neville, Art* / How could I help but love you: *Neville, Aaron* / Cissy strut: *Meters* / Humdinger: *Neville, Aaron* / That rock 'n' roll beat: *Neville, Art* / Chicken strut: *Meters* / Don't cry: *Neville, Aaron* / All these things: *Neville, Art* / Britches: *Meters* / Even though (reality): *Neville, Aaron* / Get out of my life: *Neville, Aaron* / Darling don't leave me this way: *Neville, Art* / Live wire: *Meters* / House on the hill (rock 'n' roll hootenanny): *Neville, Art* / Dry spell: *Meters* / Humdinger: *Neville, Art* / Tippi-toes: *Meters* / Hook, line and sinker: *Neville, Art* / For everybody there's a girl: *Neville, Aaron* / *Art: Meters* / Same old thing: *Meters* / You won't do right: *Neville, Art* / Everyday: *Neville, Aaron* / Sweet little mama: *Neville, Aaron* / Pains in my heart: *Neville, Art* / Joog: *Meters* / Tell it like it is: *Neville, Aaron* / Hercules: *Neville, Aaron* / I'm gonna put some hurt on you: *Neville, Art* / Make me strong: *Neville, Aaron* / Kook-ka py py: *Meters* / All those things: *Neville, Aaron* / Ease back: *Meters* / Bo Diddley: *Neville, Art* / Heartaches: *Neville, Aaron* / Been so wrong: *Neville, Aaron* / Message from the Meters: *Meters* / Going home: *Neville, Aaron* / Dance your blues away: *Neville, Charles*
CPCD 82482 / Nov '96 / Charly

☐ FAMILY GROOVE
Fly like an eagle / One more day / I can see it in your eyes / Day to day thing / Line of fire / Take me to heart / It takes more / Family groove / True love / On the other side of paradise / Let my people go / Saxafunk / Maori chant / Good song
3971802 / Apr '92 / A&M

☐ FIYO ON THE BAYOU
Hey pocky away / Sweet honey dripper / Fire on the Bayou / Ten commandments / Sitting in limbo / Brother John / Iko iko / Mona lisa / Run Joe
CDMID 187 / Jan '94 / A&M

☐ LIVE AT TIPITINA'S VOL.2
Wishin' / Rock 'n' roll medley / All over again / Everybody's got to wake up / Dance your blues away / Little Liza Jane / Wildflower / My girl / Riverside / Saib's groove / Pocky way / Doo wop medley / Rockin' pneumonia and the boogie woogie flu / Something you got / I know / Everybody loves a lover
CLACD 347 / Jun '94 / Castle

☐ LIVE ON PLANET EARTH
Shake your tambourine / Voodoo / Dealer / Junk man / Brother Jake / Sister Rosa / Yellow moon / Her African eyes / Sands of time / Congo Square / Love the one you're with/You can't always get what you want / Let my people go/Get up stand up / Amazing Grace / One love/People get ready/Sermon
5402252 / Apr '95 / A&M

☐ MITAKUYE OYASIN OYASIN
Love spoken here / Sound / Holy spirit / Soul to soul / Whatever you do / Saved by the grace of your love / You're gonna make your Momma cry / Fire on the mountain / Ain't no sunshine / Orisha dance / Sacred ground
5405212 / May '96 / A&M

☐ NEVILLE-IZATION
Fever / Woman's gotta have it / Mojo Hannah / Tell it like it is / Why you wanna hurt my heart / Fear, hate, envy, jealousy / Caravan / Big chief / Africa
DIAB 840 / 24 Nov '97 / Diablo

☐ TELL IT LIKE IT IS
Tell it like it is: *Neville, Aaron* / Over you: *Neville, Aaron* / That rock 'n' roll beat: *Neville, Art* / For every boy there's a girl: *Neville, Aaron* / I'm waiting at the station: *Neville, Aaron* / House on the hill (rock 'n' roll hootenanny): *Neville, Art* / How many times: *Neville, Aaron* / How could I help but love you: *Neville, Aaron* / All these things: *Neville, Art* / Cry me a river: *Neville, Aaron* / Speak to me: *Neville, Aaron* / Hook, line and sinker: *Neville, Art* / Mardi Gras mambo: *Hawketts* / Cardova: *Meters* / Funky miracle: *Meters* / Ride your pony: *Meters* / Struttin' on Sunday: *Neville, Aaron* / Make me strong: *Neville, Aaron* / Heartaches: *Neville, Art* / Show me the way: *Neville, Aaron* / Wrong number: *Neville, Aaron* / You won't do right: *Neville, Art* / Get out of my life: *Neville, Aaron* / Hercules: *Neville, Aaron*
MCCD 022 / May '91 / Music Club

☐ UPTOWN
Whatever it takes / Forever...for tonight / You're the one / Money back guarantee (my love is guaranteed) / Drift away / Shek-a-na-na / Old habits die hard / I never needed no one / Midnight key / Spirits of the world
DC 883842 / 2 Feb '98 / Disky

☐ WITH GOD ON OUR SIDE (2CD Set)
Ten commandments of love / I owe you one / Change is gonna come / Bells / Will the circle be unbroken / Sitting in limbo / Yellow moon / Fearless / Brother Jake / Love the one you're with/You can't always get what you want / Bird on a wire / Fallin' rain / Louisiana 1927 / Mona Lisa / Ave Maria / That's the way she loves / Song of Bernadette / Close your eyes / Ain't no way / Feels like rain / Don't go, please stay / Don't fall apart on me tonight / Betcha by golly, wow / My brother, my brother / La vie dansante / True love / On the other side of paradise / Let my people go/Get up stand up / Take me to heart / With you in mind / One more day / Amazing grace / O holy night / Lord's prayer / With god on our side
5406912 / Jun '97 / A&M

☐ YELLOW MOON
My blood / Yellow moon / Fire and brimstone / Change is gonna come / Sister Rosa / With God on our side / Wake up / Voodoo / Ballad of Hollis Brown / Will the circle be unbroken / Healing chant / Wild injuns
3952402 / Apr '95 / A&M

Neville, Aaron

☐ GRAND TOUR
Don't take away my heaven / I owe you one / Don't fall apart on me tonight / My brother, my brother / Betcha by golly / Song of bernadette / You never can tell / Bells / These foolish things / Roadie song / Ain't no way / Grand tour / Lord's prayer / Ronnie-o
5401002 / Jan '94 / A&M

☐ HERCULES
Over you / Show me the way / How could I help but love you / Get out of my life / Wrong number / I'm waiting at the station / I found another love / How many times / Hey little Alice / Let's live / Tell it like it is / Struttin' on Sunday / Make me strong / Hercules / Been so wrong / Cry me a river / Greatest love / One fine day / All these things / Performance
CPCD 8016 / Feb '94 / Charly

☐ MAKE ME STRONG
Struttin' on Sunday / Hercules / Make me strong / All these things / Baby I'm a want you / Performance / Mojo Hannah / Greatest love / One fine day / Tell it like it is / Cry me a river / Been so wrong / Speak to me / Wild flower / Feelings / Nadie / For the good times / She's on my mind
CPCD 8213 / Jun '96 / Charly

☐ ORCHIDS IN THE STORM
For your precious love / Ten commandments of love / This is my story we belong together / Earth angel / Pledging my love
8122709562 / May '95 / Rhino

☐ TATTOOED HEART
Can't stop my heart from loving you (The rain song) / Show some emotion / Everyday of my life / Down into muddy water / Some days are made for rain / Try (a little harder) / Beautiful night / My precious star / Why should I fall in love / Use me / For the good times / In your eyes / Little thing called life / Crying in the chapel
5403492 / May '95 / A&M

☐ TO MAKE ME WHO I AM
Say what's in my heart / Just to be with you / Sweet Amelia / To make me who I am / First time ever I saw your face: *Neville, Aaron & Linda Ronstadt* / Yes I love you / Your sweet and smiling eyes / I can't change the way you don't feel / Please remember me / What did I do (to deserve you) / God made you for me / Lovely lady dressed in blue
5407842 / 13 Oct '97 / A&M

Neville, Art

☐ HIS SPECIALTY RECORDINGS 1956-58
Please believe me / Standing on the highway / Please don't go / When my baby went away / Please listen to my song / Lover's song / Oooh-baby / Whiffenpoof song / Oooh-wee baby / Let's rock / Back home to me / Zing zing / Cha dooky-doo / That old time Rock 'N' Roll / Arabian love call / Rockin' pneumonia and the boogie woogie flu / What's going on / Belle amie / Dummy / I'm a fool to care
CDCHD 434 / Jan '93 / Ace

☐ KEYS TO THE CRESCENT (Neville, Art & Eddie Bo/Charles Brown/Willie Tee)
ROUCD 2087 / Sep '91 / Rounder

☐ MARDI GRAS ROCK 'N' ROLL
Zing zing / Oooh-wee baby / Bella Mae / I'm a fool to care / Cha dooky-doo / Back home to me / What's going on / Old time rock 'n' roll / Rockin' pneumonia and the boogie woogie flu / Bring it on home to me / Dummy / Let's rock / Arabian love call / Please listen to my song / Whiffenpoof song
CDCHD 188 / Oct '90 / Ace

Neville, Charles

☐ CHARLES NEVILLE & DIVERSITY (Neville, Charles & Diversity)
Diverse / Summertime / Woman's place / Baluba / Ladies / Samba de orpheus / God bless the child / Jamaica John / Nyomba / Moose the mooche / Jitterbug waltz / Jiminy Syndicate
17045 / Jul '96 / Laserlight

Neville, Charmaine

☐ IT'S ABOUT TIME
Playing on the front porch / Rocket V / Barbecue Bess / Two to mars / Dance / Softly as in a morning sunrise / Staurday night fish fry / Don't stop the carnival / Right key but the wrong keyhole
ME 000392 / Oct '95 / Soulciety

Neville, Cyril

☐ FIRE THIS TIME, THE (Neville, Cyril & The Uptown Allstars)
CD 08544112 / Jul '96 / SPV

Neville, Ivan

☐ IF MY ANCESTORS COULD SEE ME NOW
CD 08544102 / Jul '96 / SPV

☐ THANKS
CD 08544092 / Jul '96 / SPV

New & Used

☐ 2ND
KFWCD 163 / Feb '95 / Knitting Factory

☐ NEW AND USED
KFWCD 125 / Nov '92 / Knitting Factory

New Age Radio

☐ SURVIVAL SHOW
MANCD 1999 / Nov '95 / Mandala

New Age Steppers

☐ MASSIVE HITS VOL.1
ONUCD 10 / May '94 / On-U Sound

New Bad Things

☐ ENNUI GO
POP 005 / Apr '97 / Pop Secret
DRL 039 / May '97 / Darla

New Black Eagle Jazz Band

☐ CHRISTMAS WITH THE NEW BLACK EAGLE JAZZ BAND
Tannenbaum / Blue Christmas / Let it snow / Santa Claus is coming to town / O holy night / God rest ye merry gentlemen / All I want for Christmas is my two front teeth / Jingle bell rock / It came upon a midnight clear / Winter wonderland / White Christmas / Silent night / Jingle bells
DARINGCD 3025 / Sep '96 / Daring

New Bomb Turks

☐ AT ROPE'S END
Scapegoat soup / Snap decision / Ally smile / So long silver lining / Veronica Lake / Defiled / Bolan's crash / Raw law / Minimum wages of sin / At rope's end / Common cold shoulder / Aspirin aspirations / Streamline yr skull
65152 / 23 Mar '98 / Epitaph

☐ DESTROY OH BOY
E 11560D / Apr '93 / Crypt

☐ INFORMATION HIGHWAY REVISITED
EFACD 115852 / Oct '94 / Crypt

☐ PISSING OUT THE POISON
EFA 115982 / Oct '95 / Crypt

☐ SCARED STRAIGHT
64792 / Aug '96 / Epitaph

New Bushbury Mountain Daredevils

☐ BUSHBURY MOUNTAIN
Colours / Fisher's clock / Faith healer / Won't come back again / That's the way of the world / Bushbury Mountain / Catch me if I fall / Thinking about you / If you're leaving the door's over there / London Road / If only for the day / That's what friends are for / First three chords / Falling for the angel in your eyes / You decide my love / Clarice's waltz
MM 010CD / Sep '97 / Mountain Music

☐ PEACE AND JUSTICE
Best thing / Ghost train / Harvest before the rain / Peace and justice / Barefoot in the city / What am I doing here / Always another way / Reel thing / Far away / Black as any crow / Ballad of Albion / Wall around your heart / Walking just the same / One more time / End of the day
ENI 101CD / Sep '97 / Enigma

☐ URBAN HILLBILLY
Urban hillbilly / Homeland / Born in the right time / Town called Hope / Our country / Man who's got no name / You ain't the only one / Going home / Cold down in Dalmeny / Rebecca's heart / King of my own country
EN 1105CD / Sep '97 / Enigma

New Celeste

☐ CELTIC CONNECTION, THE
Music for a found harmonium / I once loved a lass / Wiggly jig / When a man's in love / Don't think about me / Celtic connection suite / Julie / Fare thee well sweet Mally
LCOM 9036 / Oct '90 / Lismor

☐ IT'S A NEW DAY
Banks of Ayr / Stumblin' and stottin' / Lasher / Posie / Scottish brawl / Reconnected / It's a new day / 70 Years / Caber / Polkadotty / Davie and Jeannie / Dance of Los / Randan / Prove yourself, yourself
IRCD 033 / Jul '96 / Iona

New Christs

☐ BORN OUT OF TIME
LRR 020 / Sep '97 / Lance Rock

New College Choir

☐ NATIVITAS (A Celebration Of Peace)
I wonder as I wonder / Adam lay y-bounden / Alma redemptoris / Angel Gabriel / Ave Maria / Spotless rose / There is no rose / As I walked down the road at set of sun / Once in royal David's city / Stille nacht / Sing lullabye / Gloria sei dir gesungen / O magnum mysterium / In duci jubilo / O jesulein suss / While shepherds watched their flocks / Quem vidistis pastores / Shepherds shake off / O come all ye faithful (adeste fidelis) / Videntes stellam / Rocking / Here is the little door / Hark the herald angels sing
0630193502 / 17 Nov '97 / Erato

New Cool Collective

☐ MORE SOUL JAZZ LATIN FLAVOURS NINETIES VIBES
AL 73118 / Feb '98 / Club 802

☐ SOUL JAZZ LATIN FLAVOURS NINETIES VIBE
AL 73087 / Jun '97 / Club 802

New Dawn

☐ THERE'S A NEW DAWN
809972 / 16 Feb '98 / Synton

New Departures Quintet

☐ NEW DEPARTURES QUINTET, THE
HHCD 1010 / Mar '95 / Hot House

New Dylans

☐ AMERICAN WAY, THE
RHRCD 75 / Jul '95 / Red House

☐ WARREN PIECE
RHRCD 61 / Oct '95 / Red House

New Edition

☐ CANDY GIRL
Gimme your love / She gives me a bang / Is this the end / Pass the beat / Popcorn love / Candy girl / Ooh baby / Should have never told me / Gotta have your lovin' / Jealous girl
8101442 / Sep '96 / London

☐ GREATEST HITS VOL.1
MCD 10434 / 8 Sep '97 / MCA

☐ HOME AGAIN
Oh, yeah, it feels so good / Hit me off / You don't have to worry / Tighten it up / Shop around / Hear me out / Something about you / Try again / How do you like you're love served / One more day / I'm still in love with you / Thankyou / Home again
MCD 11480 / Aug '96 / MCA

New Electric Warriors

☐ NEW ELECTRIC WARRIORS
Running / Battle torn heroes / She's no angel / Grind and heat / Feel the power / Hard man / Firing on all eight / If I were king / Rock and roll are four letter words / Chain reaction / Holding back your love / Workin' nights / Still on the outside / Hit / Bedtime
CDMETAL 13 / Sep '97 / Anagram

New FADS

☐ LOVE IT ALL
These foolish things / Life is an accident / Left right / Every once in a while / Why waste your love / Monday it is / Saxophone / What I feel / PSV / Kill my instincts / Souvenir
BIAS 285CD / Jan '95 / Play It Again Sam

☐ PIGEONHOLE
BIAS 185CD / Nov '90 / Play It Again Sam

New Grass Revival

☐ BARREN COUNTRY
FF 70083 / Mar '97 / Flying Fish

☐ LIVE
SHCD 3771 / Jan '97 / Sugar Hill

☐ ON THE BOULEVARD
SHCD 3745 / Jan '97 / Sugar Hill

☐ TOO LATE TO TURN BACK NOW
Lonesome and a long way from home / With care from someone / High lonesome sound / Rainbow bridge / Watermelon man / Fly through the country / Red man blues
FF 70050 / 6 Oct '97 / Flying Fish

☐ WHEN THE STORM IS OVER/FLY THROUGH THE COUNTRY
Skippin' in the Mississippi dew / Good woman's love / Glory / All night train / Fly through the country / This heart of mine / Dancer / When she made laughter easy / Doin' my time / These days / Four days of rain / White freightliner blues / Sail to Australia / When the storm is over / And he says "I love you" / Vamp in the middle / Like a child in the rain / Tennessee wagoner / Colly Davis / Crooked smile
FF 032CD / Feb '97 / Flying Fish

New Islanders

☐ CARIBBEAN DREAMS
CNCD 5956 / Jul '93 / Disky

New Japan Philharmonic Orchestra

☐ MUSIC OF THE WORLD (National Anthems)
Germany / France / United Kingdom / Netherlands / Belgium / Luxembourg / Austria / Italy / Spain / Portugal / Norway / Sweden / Denmark / Finland / Switzerland / Liechenstein / Andorra / Monaco / Ireland / Iceland / Estonia / Latvia / Lithuania / Poland / Czech Republic / Slovakia / Hungary / Romania / Yugoslavia / Slovenia / Croatia / Bosnia / Bulgaria / Macedonia / Greece / Canada / United States Of America / Mexico / Costa Rica / Jamaica / Brazil / Chile / Argentina / Russia / Belarus / Ukraine / Moldova / Georgia / Armenia / Azerbaidjan / Kazakhstan / Uzbekistan / Kyrgyz Republic / Japan / Korea / China / Mongolia / Turkey / Cyprus / Israel / Iran / India / Australia / New Zealand / Algeria / South Africa
4566562 / 9 Feb '98 / Philips

New Jazz Wizards

☐ GOOD STUFF
SOSCD 1244 / May '93 / Stomp Off

New Jersey Kings

☐ PARTY TO THE BUS STOP
JAZIDCD 033 / Jul '92 / Acid Jazz

☐ STRATOSPHERE BREAKDOWN
JAZIDCD 123 / Nov '95 / Acid Jazz

New Kingdom

☐ PARADISE DON'T COME CHEAP
Mexico or bust / Horse latitudes / Infested / Unicorns were horses / Kickin' like Bruce Lee / Shining armour / Paradise don't come cheap / Co-pilot / Big 10 1/2 / Valhalla soothsayer / Animal / Half asleep / Terror mad visionary
GEECD 18 / Jul '96 / Gee Street

New Lost City Ramblers

☐ NEW LOST CITY RAMBLERS 1958-1962, THE
Colored aristocracy / Hopalong Peter / Don't let your deal go down / When first into this country / Sales tax on the women / Rabbit chase / Leaving home / How can a poor man stand such times and live / Franklyn D Roosevelt's back again / I truly understand you love another man / Old fish song / Battleship of Maine / No depression in heaven / Dallas rag / Bill Morgan and his gal / Fly around my pretty little Miss / Lady from Carlisle / Brown's ferry blues / My long journey home / Talking hard luck / Teetotals / Sal got a meatskin / Railroad blues / On some foggy mountain top / My sweet farm girl / Crow black chicken
SFCD 40036 / '91 / Smithsonian Folkways

☐ NEW LOST CITY RAMBLERS 1963-1973, THE
John Brown's dream / Riding on that train / Titanic / Don't get trouble in your mind / Cowboy waltz / Shut up in the mines of coal creek / Private John Q / Old Johnny Brooker won't do / I've always been a rambler / Automobile trip through Alabama / Who killed poor Robin / My wife died on Saturday night / Little satchel / Black bottom strut / Cat's got the measles / Dog's got the whooping cough / Dear Okie / Smoketown strut / Little girl and the dreadful snake / Fishing creek blues / '31 depression blues / Black Jack daisy / Victory rag / Little carpenter / On our turpentine farm / Parlez - nous a' boire / Valse du bamboucheur / Old Joe bone
SFCD 440040 / '92 / Smithsonian Folkways

☐ OLD TIME MUSIC
Introduction / Leather britches / Free little bird / My name is John Johanna / Jesse James / Bow down / Stone's rag / Gold watch and chain / Worried man blues / Little darlin' pal of mine / Wildwood flower / Sally Johnson / Little birdie / Sail away ladies / Pretty little Miss out in the garden / Lost John / Chilly winds / Wish I was a single girl again / Waterbound / Needle case / Roll on Buddy / Bowling green / San Antonio rose / Old gospel ship / Train 45 / Oh death / Weapon of prayer / Black jack Davy / This world is not my home
VCD 77011 / Oct '95 / Vanguard

☐ OUT STANDING IN THE FIELD
SF 40040CD / Aug '93 / Smithsonian Folkways

☐ THERE AIN'T NO WAY OUT
SFWCD 40098 / Aug '97 / Smithsonian Folkways

New Mind

☐ FORGE
08543442 / Mar '97 / Westcom

☐ FRACTURED
MA 442 / Nov '93 / Machinery

New Model Army

☐ B SIDES AND ABANDONED TRACKS
Heroin / Adrenalin / Nosense / Trust / Brave new world / RIP / Brave new world II / Ten commandments / Courage / Lights go out / Prison / Curse / Ghost of your father / Modern times / Drummy B / Marry the sea / Sleepwalking / Heroin (mix)
CDEMC 3688 / Sep '94 / EMI

☐ GHOST OF CAIN, THE
Hunt / Lights go out / Fifty first State / All of this / Poison Street / Western dream / Love songs / Heroes / Ballad / Master race
CDFA 3237 / '94 / Fame

☐ HISTORY
No rest / Better than them / Brave new world / Fifty first state / Poison street / White coats / Stupid questions / Vagabonds / Green and grey / Get me out / Purity / Space / Far better thing / Higher wall / Adrenalin / Luurstaap
CDP 7989542 / Sep '96 / EMI

☐ IMPURITY
Get me out / Space / Innocence / Purity / Whirlwind / Marrakesh / Lust for power / Bury the hatchet / Eleven years / Lurhstap / Before I get old / Vanity
CDFA 3273 / 7 Jul '98 / EMI Gold

☐ NO REST FOR THE WICKED
Frightened / Ambition / Grandmother's footsteps / Better than them / My country / There is no greater love / No rest / Young, gifted and skint / Drag it down / Shot 18 / Attack
CDGOLD 1019 / Mar '96 / EMI Gold

☐ RAW MELODY MEN
Whirlwind / Charge / Space / Purity / White coats / Vagabonds / Get me out / Lib Ed / Better than them / Innocence / Love songs / Lurhstap / Archway towers / Smalltown England / Green and grey / World
CDFA 3296 / May '93 / Fame

☐ SMALL TOWN ENGLAND (2CD Set)
SMDCD 129 / Jul '97 / Snapper

☐ STRANGE BROTHERHOOD
EAGCD 021 / 14 Apr '98 / Eagle

☐ THUNDER AND CONSOLATION
I love the world / Stupid questions / 225 / Inheritance / Green and grey / Ballad of Bodmin Pill / Family life / Vagabonds / 125 mph / Archway towers / Charge / Chinese whispers / Nothing touches / White coats
CDFA 3257 / Aug '91 / Fame

New Musik

☐ FROM A TO B
Straight lines / Sanctuary / Map of you / Science / On islands / This world of water / Living by numbers / Dead fish (don't swim home) / Adventures / Safe side
4773532 / Aug '94 / GTO

New Noakes

☐ THROUGH GREEN AND PLEASANT LANDS
Second season / First season / Through green and pleasant lands / Easter ballad / Fourth season / Pax latinus / Anti-clockwise / Autumn (A piece for Charlotte)
33JAZZ 004CD / May '95 / 33 Jazz

New Order

☐ BEST OF NEW ORDER, THE
True faith '94 / Bizarre love triangle / 1963 / Regret / Fine time / Perfect kiss / Shellshock / Thieves like us / Vanishing point / Run / Round and round / World (price of love) / Ruined in a day / Touched by the hand of God / Blue Monday '88 / World in motion
8285802 / Aug '95 / Factory

☐ BLUE ORDER - A TRANCE TRIBUTE TO NEW ORDER (Various Artists)
CLP 9985 / Jun '97 / Cleopatra

☐ NEWSPEAK (Interview)
3D 015 / Dec '96 / Network

☐ REST OF NEW ORDER, THE
World / Blue Monday / True faith / Confusion / Touched by the hand of God / Bizarre love triangle / Everythings gone green / Ruined in a day / Regret / Temptation / Age of consent
8286612
8286572 / Aug '95 / Factory

☐ SUBSTANCE 1987 (2CD Set)
Ceremony / Everything's gone green / Temptation / Blue Monday / Confusion / Thieves like us / Perfect kiss / Subculture / Shellshock / State of the nation / Bizarre love triangle / True faith / Procession / Mesh / Hurt / In a lonely place / Beach / Confused / Murder / Lonesome tonight / Kiss of death / Shame of the nation / 1963
5200082 / 29 Jun '98 / Factory

New Order

☐ DECLARATION OF WAR
422252FC031 / Nov '94 / Fan Club

New Orleans Blue Serenaders

☐ NEW ORLEANS BLUE SERENADERS
BCD 221 / Jan '93 / GHB

New Orleans CAC Jazz Orchestra

☐ MOOD INDIGO
Don't get around much anymore / New Orleans / Bye bye blackbird / Sometimes I'm happy / I'm just a lucky so and so / Spring can really hang you up the most / I love Paris / Lost mind / Let's get lost / Mood indigo / Everyday I have the blues / Stormy Monday / Not trustworthy
ROUCD 2145 / Feb '97 / Rounder

New Orleans Classic Jazz Orchestra

☐ BLOWIN' OFF STEAM
SOSCD 1223 / Oct '92 / Stomp Off

New Orleans Jazz Wizards

☐ JAMBALAYA
Jambalaya / In the sweet bye and bye / Love song of the nile / I'm going to sit right down and write myself a letter / River stay away from my door / China boy / I don't want to walk without you / St Jmes infirmary / Let the rest of the world go by / Darktown strutters ball / Tin roof blues / Stumbling / When my dreamboat comes home / Saints
504CD 55 / Mar '98 / 504

☐ JAMBALAYA 1995
504CDS 55 / Jul '96 / 504

New Orleans Joymakers

☐ NEW ORLEANS JOYMAKERS
BCD 353 / Nov '96 / GHB

New Orleans Klezmer All Stars

☐ BIG KIBOSH
SH 6026 / Oct '97 / Shanachie

New Orleans Nightcrawlers

☐ FUNK CITY
Bud's delights / Pick up the pieces / Royal flush / Heavy Henry / Auz / Imperial march (of The Nightcrawlers) / Purple gazelle / Crawlin' / Chicken / Reply / Funky Liza
ROUCD 2154 / Oct '97 / Rounder

☐ NEW ORLEANS NIGHTCRAWLERS
ROUCD 2147 / Aug '96 / Rounder

New Orleans Ragtime Orchestra

☐ CREOLE BELLES
Creole belles / Black and white rag / Purple rose of Cairo / War cloud / Maple leaf rag / High society / Entertainer / Ragtime dance / New Orleans hop scop blues / My Maryland / Chrysanthemum / Panama / Wall Street rag / Love will find a way / Rubber plant rag / You can have it, I don't want it / Tickled to death / Junk man rag / Winin' boy blues / St. Louis tickle / Hindustan / Ethiopia / Red pepper / Pickles and peppers
ARHCD 420 / Apr '95 / Arhoolie

New Orleans Rhythm Kings

☐ INTRODUCTION TO THE NEW ORLEANS RHYTHM KINGS 1922-1935, AN
4050 / Nov '97 / Best Of Jazz

☐ NEW ORLEANS RHYTHM KINGS AND JELLY ROLL MORTON (New Orleans Rhythm Kings & Jelly Roll Morton)
Eccentric / Farewell blues / Discontented blues / Bugle call rag / Panama / Tiger rag / Livery stable blues / Oriental / Sweet lovin' man / That's a plenty / Shimmeshawabble / Weary blues / That Da DA strain / Wolverine blues / Maple leaf rag / Tin roof blues / Sobbin' blues / Marguerite / Angry / Clarinet / Marmalade / Mr. Jelly Lord / London blues / Milenberg joys / Mad
MCD 47020 / Jan '93 / Milestone

New Orleans Saxophone Ensemble

☐ NEW NEW ORLEANS MUSIC VOL.2 (New Orleans Saxophone Ensemble & Improvising Arts Quintet)
ROUCD 2066 / '88 / Rounder

New Orleans Spiritualettes

☐ I BELIEVE
FA 418 / Feb '97 / Fremeaux

New Phunk Theory

☐ JUST A PHASE
Killer picture / Mezzophunk / Dancer / Shoot the shit / Singled out / Phunk theory theme / No more TV / Honey falls / 0191 / Drummed Out / Shoot the dub
PAPCD 003 / 27 Jul '98 / Paper

New Race

☐ FIRST AND THE LAST, THE
NER 3013 / Oct '97 / Total Energy

New Radiant Storm King

☐ SINGULAR NO ARTICLE
Correct liar / Barium springs / Founder's day / Occidental florist / Carry my chin / Secrets to better skin / Right scream / Pocket Greek chorus / Miranda / Leftover blues / Contentedly / Era died
RQTZ 008 / 20 Apr '98 / Rainbow Quartz

New Riders Of The Purple Sage

☐ MARIN COUNTY LINE
Till I met you / Llywelyn / Knights and queens / Green eyes a flashing / Oh what a night / Good woman likes to drink with the boys / Turkeys in a straw / Jasper / Echoes / Twenty good men / Little Miss Bad / Take a red
MCAD 22107 / Apr '94 / One Way

☐ NEW RIDERS OF THE PURPLE SAGE
I don't know you / What'cha gonna do / Portland woman / Henry / Dirty business / Glendale train / Garden of Eden / All I ever wanted / Last lonely eagle / Louisiana lady
MCAD 22108 / Apr '94 / One Way

☐ WASTED TASTERS 1971-1975
Henry / Glendale train / Lousiana lady / I don't know you / Last lonely eagle / I don't need no doctor / Contract / Rainbow / Sweet lovin' one / Dim light thick smoke / She's no angel / Sutter's mill / Sailin' / Panama red / Lonesome LA cowboy / Kick in the head / Teradrops in my eyes / Hello mary lou / Dead flowers / You angel you / Singing cowboy / I heard you been layin' my old lady / Farewell Angelina
RVCD 36 / May '94 / Raven

☐ WHO ARE THOSE GUYS
MCAD 22109 / Apr '94 / One Way

New Salem Witch Hunters

☐ COLONIAL CELLAR
GH 1056CD / 6 Apr '98 / Get Hip

New Scorpion Band

☐ WHY, SOLDIER, WHY (Songs Of Battles Lost & Won)
Female drummer / On board a '98' / Jacky Tar / Lord Nelson's hornpipe / Why, soldier, why / Over the hills and far away / Gentleman soldier / High barbaree / Bony crossing the Rhine / Soldier's joy / Bold Nelson's praise / Balaclava / St. Helena march / Dark-eyed sailor / Dolphin / Tommy
SAMPPCD 402 / Aug '96 / Soundalive

New Seekers

☐ ANTHEMS (Their Greatest Hits)
You won't find another fool like me / Circles / Runaway / I get a little sentimental over you / Power of love / Forever in my mind / Never ending story of love / I'd like to teach the world to sing / What have they done to my song ma / Shambala / Beg steal or borrow / I wanna go back / Pinball wizard - see me, feel me / Stay / Come softly to me / Anthem
300682 / Jul '96 / Hallmark

☐ COLLECTION, THE
Beg, steal or borrow / Beg, steal or borrow / You won't find another fool like me / Look what they have done to my song ma / Pinball wizard-see me, feel me / Never ending song of love / Circles / I get a little sentimental over you / Come softly to me / I wanna go back / Yesterday / California dreamin' / Just an old fashioned love song / A perfect love / Forever on my mind / Anthem / Little street cafe / World I wish for / Runaway / All over the world / Power of love / Shambala / Come the day / Last thing on my mind / Stay
COL 037 / Mar '95 / Collection

☐ GREATEST HITS
I'd like to teach the world to sing / Come softly to me / You won't find another fool like me / Morning has broken / What have they done to my song Ma / Circles / I get a little sentimental over you / Your song / Beg, steal or borrow / Nevertheless (I'm in love with you) / Day by day / Georgy girl / Just an old fashioned love song / Goodbye is just another word / Pinball wizard / See me, feel me / Goin' back / Never ending song of love
8453982 / May '91 / Polydor

☐ WORLD OF THE NEW SEEKERS, THE
I'd like to teach the world to sing / Beg, steal or borrow / Come softly to me / You won't find another fool like me / Friends/With a little help from my friends / Pinball wizard/See me, feel me / Nevertheless (I'm in love with you) / Brother Love's travelling salvation show / Circles / Beautiful people / One / Never ending song of love / Goodbye is just another word / Dance dance dance / What have they done to my song Ma / Melting pot / Something in the way he moves / Brand new song / Greatest song I've ever heard / I get a little sentimental over you
5520802 / May '96 / Spectrum

New Shtetl Band

☐ JEWISH AND BALKAN MUSIC
GVM 121CD / Jul '95 / Global Village

New Sweet Breath

☐ SHOTGUN DOWN AN AVALANCHE
BTO 005 / Jul '97 / Big Top

New Tradition

☐ AR CAHAINS AR CEDL
CDLOC 1090 / Jun '95 / Lochshore

New Vaudeville Band

☐ WINCHESTER CATHEDRAL
Winchester Cathedral / Tap your feet / Whatever happened to Phyllis Puke / Holiday Inn / Nightingale sang in Berkeley Square / I was Lord Kitchener's valet / Peek-a-boo / I wonder who's kissing her now / Finchley Central / If I had a talking picture of you / 14 lovely women / Shine on harvest moon / There's a kind of hush / Sadie Moonshine / That's all for now sugar baby / Green Street green
308192 / 13 Oct '97 / Hallmark

☐ WINCHESTER CATHEDRAL
Winchester cathedral / Finchley central / Peek-a-boo / Amy / I was lord kitchener's valet / Green street green / Holiday inn / I wonder who's kissing her now / Sadie moonshine / If I had a talking picture of you / Lili Marlene / Nightingale sang in Berkley Square / So tired / Whispering / Oh Donna Clara / Tap your feet (and go bo-de-do-de-do) / Whatever happened to Phyllis Puke / 14 lovely women / Rosie / That's all for now sugar baby / Reflections / Shirl / Diana goodbye / Shine on harvest moon
C5CD 558 / 10 Aug '98 / See For Miles

New Wet Kojak

☐ NASTY INTERNATIONAL
TG 164CD / Aug '97 / Touch & Go

☐ NEW WET KOJAK
TG 144CD / Oct '95 / Touch & Go

New Winds

☐ DIGGING IT HARDER FROM AFAR
VICTOCD 028 / Nov '94 / Victo

☐ POTION
VICTOCD 053 / Feb '98 / Victo

New World

☐ TOM TOM TURN AROUND
Tom tom turn around / Kara kara / Sister Jane / But not afraid to dream / Sleep in the sun / Lord of the dance / Rooftop singing / Rose garden / Morning has broken / Sitting in the sun / Yesterday's gone / Old Shep / Sally's a lady / Killing me softly with her song / Something's wrong / If you could read my mind / Living next door to alice / Do you wanna dance
DC 865712 / Mar '97 / Disky

New York Allstars

☐ COUNT BASIE REMEMBERED VOL.1
NHCD 031 / Mar '97 / Nagel Heyer

☐ COUNT BASIE REMEMBERED VOL.2
NHCD 041 / Jan '98 / Nagel Heyer

☐ NEW YORK ALLSTARS PLAY THE MUSIC OF LOUIS ARMSTRONG, THE
When it's sleepy time down South: *Armstrong, Louis* / Mabel's dream: *Armstrong, Louis* / Sugar foot stomp: *Armstrong, Louis* / Big butter and egg man: *Armstrong, Louis* / Cornet chop suey: *Armstrong, Louis* / Wild man blues: *Armstrong, Louis* / Potato head blues: *Armstrong, Louis* / Muskrat ramble: *Armstrong, Louis* / Savoy blues: *Armstrong, Louis* / Sruttin' with some barbecue: *Armstrong, Louis* / Basin street blues: *Armstrong, Louis* / Weather bird: *Armstrong, Louis* / Medley: *Armstrong, Louis* / Swing that music: *Armstrong, Louis* / If I could be with you: *Armstrong, Louis* / Mack the knife: *Armstrong, Louis* / Faithful hussar: *Armstrong, Louis* / Ole miss: *Armstrong, Louis* / Mabel's dream: *Armstrong, Louis* / When it's sleepy time down South: *Armstrong, Louis*
CD 029 / Jan '97 / Nagel Heyer

☐ NEW YORK ALLSTARS VOL.1
CD 002 / May '96 / Nagel Heyer

☐ NEW YORK ALLSTARS VOL.2
CD 003 / May '96 / Nagel Heyer

New York Band

☐ GRANDES EXITOS
Si tu no estas / Maria / Y tu no estas / Ay Mama / El cibaeno / Dame Vida / Chim pun callao / Corazon de azucar / Que no me adivina / Mambo mix / Que beuno bvaila usted / Ponte el sombrero / Muevelo / El lloron / Pelotero / El caravine / Jala jala / Dancing mood / Nadie como tu
66058069 / Sep '95 / RMM

New York City Gay Men's Chorus

☐ LOVE LIVES ON
VC 7596632 / Jan '95 / Virgin Classics

New York Composers Orchestra

☐ FIRST PROGRAM IN STANDARD TIME
804182 / Sep '92 / New World

☐ MUSIC BY EHRLICH, HOLCOMB, HOROVITZ & WIESELMAN
NW 397 / Aug '92 / New World

New York Connection

☐ ALONG CAME JONES
Three card Molly / Summary / Intimidation / Allen's alley / Shadowland / Child is born / Three in one / Wise one
SJL 1003 / 18 May '98 / Sirocco

New York Dolls

☐ LIPSTICK KILLERS
Bad girl / Looking for a kiss / Don't start me talkin' / Don't mess with cupid / Human being / Personality crisis / Pills / Jet boy / Frankenstein
RE 104CD / Nov '94 / ROIR

☐ LIVE IN PARIS 1974
RSR 7006 / 27 Apr '98 / Red Star

☐ NEW YORK TAPES 1972-1973
622572 / Mar '96 / Skydog

☐ PARIS BURNING
622562 / Mar '96 / Skydog

☐ RED PATENT LEATHER
Girls / Downtown / Pirate love / Personality crisis / Pills / Something else / Daddy rollin' stone / Dizzy Miss Lizzy
422253 / May '94 / New Rose

☐ ROCK 'N' ROLL
Courageous cat theme / Trash / Personality crisis / Babylon / Looking for a kiss / Lone star queen / Vietnamese baby / Lonely planet boy / Frankenstein / Private world / Chatterbox / Bad girl / Don't mess with cupid / Subway train / Who are the mystery girls / Stranded in the jungle / It's too late / Puss 'n' boots / Jet boy / Human being
5221292 / Oct '94 / Mercury

☐ TEENAGE NEWS
RS 7006 / 6 Oct '97 / Red Star

☐ TOO MUCH TOO SOON
8342302 / Jan '94 / Mercury

New York Hardbop Quintet

☐ ROKERMOTION
Rokermotion / Strike / More than you know / Hip Naz / El-Cee / Little Jake / Est of the sun / Wan
TCB 96352 / Nov '96 / TCB

New York Jazz Collective

☐ I DON'T KNOW THIS WORLD WITHOUT DON CHERRY
860032 / Jun '97 / Naxos Jazz

New York Loose

☐ YEAR OF THE RAT
1620492 / Sep '96 / Polydor

New York Pro Musica Antiqua

☐ ENGLISH MEDIEVAL CHRISTMAS CARDS
TCD 1056 / 13 Oct '97 / Tradition

New York School

☐ NEW YORK SCHOOL, THE
ARTCD 6101 / Sep '92 / Hat Art

New York Swing

☐ PLAYS JEROME KERN
Song is you / I dream too much / Why do I love you / Smoke gets in your eyes / Can't help lovin' dat man / Sure thing / Pick yourself up / Bill / Yesterdays / Why was I born / I'm old fashioned / All the things you are / Remind me / Nobody else but me
CDC 9082 / Apr '95 / LRC

New York Voices

☐ SIMON SAYS (The Songs Of Paul Simon)
Baby driver / Cecilia / One man's ceiling is another man's floor / So long / Frank Lloyd Wright / Loves me like a rock / Me and Julio down by the school yard / St. Judy's comet / Punky's dilemma / Overs / Mother and child reunion / I do it for you love / Still crazy after all these years / Why don't you write me / Old friends/ Bookends
09026688722 / 6 Apr '98 / RCA Victor

New Zealand Maori Chorale

☐ NEW ZEALAND SINGS
VPS 488 / Sep '96 / Viking

Newborn, Phineas Jr.

☐ HARLEM BLUES
Harlem blues / Sweet and lovely / Little girl blue / Ray's idea / Stella by starlight / Tenderly / Cookin' at the continental
OJCCD 662 / Oct '96 / Original Jazz Classics

☐ NEWBORN TOUCH, THE
Walkin' thing / Double play / Sermon / Diane / Blessing / Groove yard / Blue Daniel / Hard to find / Pazmuerte / Be deedle dee doo / Good lil' man
OJCCD 270 / May '97 / Original Jazz Classics

☐ SOLO
Stompin' at the Savoy / Easy living / How high the moon / Breeze and I / Nature boy / Days of wine and roses / Confirmation / Might as well be Spring / Love me or leave me / Temptation
CDLR 45020 / Feb '91 / L&R

☐ TIVOLI ENCOUNTER (Newborn, Phineas Trio)
STCD 8221 / Aug '97 / Storyville

☐ WORLD OF PIANO, A
Cheryl / Manteca / Lush life / Daahoud / Oleo / Juicy Lucy / For Carl / Cabu
OJCCD 175 / Apr '96 / Original Jazz Classics

Newcastle United FC

☐ **TOON ARMY TUNES (A Tribute To Newcastle United FC) (Various Artists)**
Black 'n' white / We will follow united / Home Newcastle / Never been defeated / Harry Geordie medley / Blaydon races / Howay the lads 93 / Toon toon army / Andy Cole song / United, Newcastle united / Thank you mention from the team / Head over heals in love / Move on down / Fog on the Tyne / Geordie boys / Santa is a Geordie
CDGAFFER 3 / Nov '95 / Cherry Red

Newcomen, Tommy

☐ **SCOTTISH TOUR**
Scottish medley / Reel time / Two steps / Dundee medley / Scottish marches / Highland medley / Scottish waltzes / Rabbie Burns medley / Highland reels / Irish medley / Slow waltzes / Scottish marches / Scottish waltzes / Scottish jigs / Northern lights medley / Country medley / Medley
A-ONECD 030 / Apr '98 / A-One

Newcomer, Carrie

☐ **ANGEL AT MY SHOULDER, AN**
PH 1163CD / Apr '94 / Philo

☐ **BIRD OR THE WING, THE**
CDPH 1183 / May '95 / Philo

☐ **MY FATHER'S ONLY SON**
Crazy in love / Tracks / These are the moments / You can choose / My father's only son / I'm not thinking of you / Up in the attic / Closer to you / Bearing witness / Madness you get used to / Rooms my mother made / Amelia almost
CDPH 1203 / Oct '96 / Philo

☐ **MY TRUE NAME**
I should've known better / When one door closes / What kind of love is this / This long / Moon over Tuscan / Razor's edge / Take it around again / My true name / Something worth fighting for / Just a little hand / One good turn / Close your eyes / Length of my arms
CDPH 1223 / 9 Mar '98 / Philo

☐ **VISIONS AND DREAMS**
CDPH 1193 / Nov '95 / Philo

Newell, Jeff

☐ **JACK THE RIPPER**
78116498062 / 14 Jul '98 / IGM

Newell, Martin

☐ **BOX OF OLD HUMBUG, A (2CD Set)**
BAH 33 / 8 Sep '97 / Humbug

☐ **GREATEST LIVING ENGLISHMAN, THE**
Goodbye dreaming fields / Before the hurricane / We'll build a house / Greatest living Englishman / She rings the changes / Home counties boy / Street called prospect / Christmas in suburbia / Straight to you, boy / Jangling man / Green-gold girl of summer
BAH 10 / Feb '97 / Humbug

☐ **OFF WHITE ALBUM**
BAH 25 / Apr '96 / Humbug

Newley, Anthony

☐ **ONCE IN A LIFETIME (The Anthony Newley Collection)**
RE 21452 / Sep '97 / Razor & Tie

☐ **VERY BEST OF ANTHONY NEWLEY, THE**
Personally / Why / Do you mind / If she could come to you / Strawberry fair / And the Heaven's cried / Pop goes the weasel / Bee bom / What kind of fool am I / D-darling / That noise / My blue angel / Lifetime of happiness / I'll walk beside you / I've waited so long / I guess it couldn't happen to a nicer guy / Young only yesterday / Girls were made to love and kiss / You are too beautiful
5520902 / Jan '97 / Spectrum

☐ **WHAT KIND OF FOOL AM I**
Candyman / Too much woman / Why / Rainbows / Do you mind / Way that I did / Bee bom / Nearly wonderful / Who can I turn to / White boy / Autumn / What kind of fool am I / Remember / Centrefold / If I were a rich man / Do you love me / Make 'em laugh / Puttin' on the ritz / They can't take that away from me / Thank heaven for little girls
3036400122 / May '96 / Carlton

Newlydeads

☐ **NEWLYDEADS, THE**
800062 / Aug '97 / Mutiny

☐ **REBOUND**
MUTINY 12 / 18 May '98 / Mutiny

Newman, Chris

☐ **FRETWORK**
Pass the pick / Down the wind / Riverside / Fretwork / Hook olle storpolska / Arctic goose / Artic goose / Albatross waltz / Tom McConville's idea/Arthur's rover/Black cat reel / Astronomer's gaze / Where's the bar / Mallard's minuet / Off the hook/Last resort / Water on the moon / Tell her lies and feed her candy / Old Joe Clark / Skinner set / Dance of dawn / Last call
OBMCD 11 / 11 May '98 / Old Bridge

Newman, Colin

☐ **A - Z**
I've waited for ages / And jury / Alone / Order for order / Image / Life on deck / Troisieme / S-S-S Star eyes / Seconds to last / Inventory / But no / B
BBL 20CD / Sep '88 / Beggars Banquet

☐ **BASTARD**
Sticky / May / Slowfast (falling down the stairs with a drumkit) / Without / G-deep / Spaced in / Spiked / Orange house and the blue house / Turn
WM 3 / Jul '97 / Swim

☐ **COMMERCIAL SUICIDE**
CRAM 045 / Oct '86 / Crammed Discs

☐ **IT SEEMS**
CRAM 058 / May '88 / Crammed Discs

☐ **PROVISIONALLY ENTITLED THE SINGING FISH/NOTTO**
Fish / Reprise / Lorries / Don't bring reminders / You me and happy / We meet under tables / Safe / Truculent yet / 5/10 / 123 beep beep / NotTo / Indians / Remove for improvement / Blue jay way / We means we starts / NotTo / You and your dog / HCTFR / No doubt / Grace you know
GAD 108/2CD / 6 Jul '98 / 4AD

Newman, David

☐ **BLUE HEAD (Newman, David 'Fathead' Quintet)**
Strike up the band / Blue head / Willow weep for me / Blues for David / What's new / Eyewitness blues
CCD 79041 / Feb '97 / Candid

☐ **STILL HARD TIMES (Newman, David 'Fathead')**
Shana / One for my baby (and one more for the road) / To love again / Still hard times / Please send me someone to love
MCD 5283 / Sep '92 / Muse

Newman, Denny

☐ **NOAH'S GREAT RAINBOW**
NM 002 / Jul '95 / New Blue

Newman, Jackie

☐ **COMPLETE RECORDED WORKS**
DOCD 5351 / Jun '95 / Document

Newman, Jimmy C.

☐ **BOP A HULA/DIGGY LIGGY LO (2CD Set)**
You didn't have to go / Cry cry darlin' / Can I be right / Your true and faithful one / What will I do / I'll always love you darlin' / Once again / Let me stay in your arms / Night time is cry time / Diggy liggy lo / You don't want me to know / Do you feel like I feel about you / Daydreaming / Dream why do you hurt me so / Crying for a pastime / Angel have mercy / Blue darlin' / Let me stay in your arms / I thought I'd never fall in love again / God was so good / Let's stay together / What will I do (unissued) / I've got you on my mind / Seasons of my heart / Come back to me / I wanta tell all the world / Yesterday's dreams / Let the whole world talk / Honky tonk tears / Last night / No use to cry / Way you're living is breaking my heart / What a fool I was to fall for you / Fallen star / I can't go on this way / Need me (unissued) / Sweet kind of love / Need me / Cry cry darlin' / You're the idol of my dreams / Step aside shallow water / Bop a hula / Carry on / With tears in my eyes
BCD 15469 / Sep '90 / Bear Family

☐ **CAJUN COUNTRY MUSIC OF A LOUISIANA MAN, THE**
Cry cry darling / Daydreamin' / Blue darlin' / Let me stay in your arms / God was so good / I thought I'd fall in love again / Seasons of my heart / Fallen star / Come back to me / Last night / Everybody's dying for love / Alligator man / Bayou talk / DJ for a day / City of angels / Back in circulation / Artificial rose / Back pocket money / Dropping out of sight / Louisiana saturday night / Blue lonely winter / Born to love you / Tibby Dough and his Cajun band / Louisiana man
EDCD 572 / 4 Aug '98 / Edsel

Newman, Joe

☐ **AT THE ATLANTIC**
Summertime / Airmail special / I can't get started (with you) / When you're smiling / Caravan / Liza / Stardust
NCD 8810 / '93 / Phontastic

☐ **GOOD 'N' GROOVY (Newman, Joe Quintet)**
AM romp / Li'l darlin' / Molasses / To rigmor / Just squeeze me / Loop-d-loop
OJCCD 185 / Jun '96 / Original Jazz Classics

☐ **HANGIN' OUT (Newman, Joe & Joe Wilder)**
Midgets / Here's that rainy day / Duet / Battle hymn of the Republic / Secret love / You've changed / Lypso mania / He was too good to me
CCD 4262 / Feb '92 / Concord Jazz

☐ **I FEEL LIKE A NEWMAN**
BLCD 760905 / Jun '88 / Black Lion

Newman, June

☐ **WEST COAST BLUES (Newman, June & Gary Lee)**
RQCD 1510 / May '96 / Request

Newman, Michael

☐ **CANTOS DE ESPANA (The Songs Of Spain/The Music Of Isaac Albeniz) (Newman, Michael & Laura Oltman)**
Cantos de Espana / Six album leaves / Rumores de la caleta malaguena / Zambra granadina / Spanish suite / Improvisacion / Serenata Espanola / Asturie
MM 67181 / Oct '97 / Music Masters

☐ **LAMENTS AND DANCES (Music From The Folk Traditions) (Newman, Michael & Laura Oltman)**
MM 67145 / Oct '97 / Music Masters

☐ **TANGO SUITE (Romance For Two Guitars) (Newman, Michael & Laura Oltman)**
MM 7071 / Oct '97 / Music Masters

Newman, Paul

☐ **FRAMES PER SECOND**
TR 65CD / 26 Jan '98 / Trance Syndicate

Newman, Randy

☐ **BEST OF RANDY NEWMAN, THE (Lonely At The Top)**
Love story / Living without you / I think it's going to rain today / Mama told me not to come / Sail away / Simon Smith and the amazing dancing bear / Political science / God's song (that's why I love mankind) / Rednecks / Birmingham / Louisiana 1927 / Marie / Baltimore / Jolly coppers of parade / Rider in the rain / Short people / I love LA / Lonely at the top / My life is good / In Germany before the war / Christmas in Capetown / My old Kentucky home
2411262 / Jun '87 / WEA

☐ **GOOD OLE BOYS**
Rednecks / Marie / Guilty / Every man a king / Naked man / Back on my feet again / Birmingham / Mr. President (have a pity on the working man) / Louisiana 1927 / Kingfish / Wedding in Cherokee county / Rollin'
9272142 / Sep '89 / WEA

☐ **LITTLE CRIMINALS**
Baltimore / I'll be home / In Germany before the war / Jolly coppers on parade / Kathleen / Old man on the farm / Rider in the rain / Short people / Sigmund Freud's impersonation of Albert Einstein In America / Texas girl at the funeral of her father / You can't fool the fat man
K 256404 / Jan '88 / WEA

☐ **TROUBLE IN PARADISE**
I love LA / Same girl / My life is good / Real emotional girl / Miami / Song for the dead / I'm different / There's a party at my house / Take me back / Mikey's / Blues / Christmas in capetown
7599237552 / May '94 / Warner Bros.

Newman, Todd

☐ **TEMPORARY SETBACK**
BIR 037 / Jan '97 / Barber's Itch

Newman, Tom

☐ **ASPECTS**
NAGE 7CD / '86 / Art Of Landscape

☐ **BAYOU MOON**
NAGE 2CD / Feb '86 / Art Of Landscape

☐ **FINE OLD TOM**
Sad sing / Nursery rhyme / Song for SP / Will you be mine in the morning / Alison says / Day of the Percherons / Suzie / Poor Bill / Superman / Ma song / Penny's whistle boogie / She said she said / Ma song / Superman / Oh Susie / Poor Bill / She said she said
BP 166CD / Jun '97 / Blueprint

☐ **HOTEL SPLENDIDE**
VP 195CD / Feb '97 / Voiceprint

☐ **LIVE AT THE ARGONAUT**
Don't treat your woman bad / Kentucky / It don't come easy / Entropy / Gamblin' man / For the old times / Tales from Brendan's beard / Roving gambler / Draught guinnes / Paperback writer / Give a little take a little / Aeigough
VP 168CD / Feb '95 / Voiceprint

☐ **OZYMANDIAS**
Dying civilisation / Cycle for moving dunes / Ozymandias / Cenotaph / Song abstracted / Missing peace / Reprise
BP 192CD / 6 Oct '97 / Blueprint

☐ **SNOW BLIND (Newman, Tom & Friends)**
Fire and brimstone / Mysterious woman / Nowhere to go / For old times / When the levee breaks / Honey I need / I beg of you / Sleep / Don't treat your woman bad / She said yeah
RFCDX 006 / 20 Jul '98 / Blueprint

Newport Jazz Festival All Stars

☐ **BERN CONCERT '89**
I want to be happy / Jeep's blues / Just a gigolo / I'm just a lucky so and so / Johnny come lately / Blue and sentimental / In a sentimental mood / Jumpin' at the woodside
CCD 4401 / Jan '90 / Concord Jazz

☐ **EUROPEAN TOUR**
Tickle toe / Mood indigo / Love me or leave me / These foolish things / Take the 'A' train / Things ain't what they used to be / Through for the night
CCD 4343 / May '88 / Concord Jazz

Newport Rebels

☐ **JAZZ ARTISTS GUILD**
Mysterious blues / Cliff walk / Wrap your troubles in dreams (and dream your troubles away) / Ain't nobody's business if I do / Me and you
CCD 79022 / Feb '97 / Candid

Newsome, Sam

☐ **SAM I AM (Newsome, Sam Quintet)**
CRISS 1056CD / May '92 / Criss Cross

Newton

☐ **SOMETIMES WHEN WE TOUCH**
DMINCD 52 / 13 Oct '97 / Dominion

Newton, Abby

☐ **CROSSING TO SCOTLAND**
Catskill mountain air/Wagon wheel notch / Drunk at night dry in the morning / Loftus Jones / Tune for Mairead and Anna Ni Mhaonaigh / Sister Jean / Tarbolton lodge / Crossing to Ireland / Earl of Dalhousie's happy return to Scotland / Da full rigged ship/Da new rigged ship / Independence trail / Heroes of Longhope / O'Carolan's draught / Medley / Gin ye kiss my wife I'll tell the minister / Catskill mountain air / Tune for / Here we go again
CUL 110CD / 2 Feb '98 / Culburnie

Newton, Adi

☐ **FILM**
ARCD 007 / Aug '97 / Anterior Research

Newton, Anney

☐ **NEW HORIZONS (Newton, Anney & The Relics)**
REL 001CD / Jul '95 / Relic

Newton, David

☐ **12TH OF THE 12TH (A Jazz Portrait Of Frank Sinatra)**
My kind of town (Chicago is) / I've got the world on a string / I fall in love too easily / Witchcraft / Lady is a tramp / This is all I ask / It's nice to go trav'ling / Violets for your furs / All or nothing at all / You make me feel so young / All the way / Twelfth of the twelfth / Only the lonely / Saturday night is the loneliest night of the week / In the wee small hours of the morning
CCD 79728 / Feb '97 / Candid

☐ **DNA**
DNA / Julia / Highwire / Where is the one / Feet on the ground / Garden of dreams / Ablution / Scribe / We'll be together again
CCD 79742 / 6 Oct '97 / Candid

☐ **EYE WITNESS**
Ol' blues eyes / Bedroom eyes / Angel eyes / Eye witness / Soul eyes / Stars in my eyes / Eye of the hurricane / My mother's eyes
AKD 015 / Nov '91 / Linn

☐ **IN GOOD COMPANY (Newton, David Trio)**
Get lost / Blessed land / Teach me tonight / June time / My romance / There's a small hotel / Sugar cake / Remark you made / Older and wiser / When will I see you
CCD 79714 / Feb '97 / Candid

☐ **RETURN JOURNEY**
AKD 025 / Apr '94 / Linn

☐ **VICTIM OF CIRCUMSTANCE**
Wishful thinking / Night we called it a day / Katy's song / It never entered my mind / Victim of circumstance / One and only / Please come home / Way you look tonight
AKD 013 / Feb '91 / Linn

Newton, Frankie

☐ **CLASSICS 1937-1939**
CLASSICS 643 / Nov '92 / Classics

Newton, Juice

☐ **COUNTRY CLASSICS**
It's a heartache / Let's keep it that way / Any way you want me / Sunshine / Angel of the morning / All I have to do is dream / Queen of hearts / Sweetest thing (I've ever known) / Heart of the night / I'm gonna be strong / Love's been a bit hard on me / Break it to me gently / Come to me: *Newton, Juice & Silver Spur* / Love like yours: *Newton, Juice & Silver Spur* / Hey baby: *Newton, Juice & Silver Spur*
CDMFP 6327 / Apr '97 / Music For Pleasure

Newton, Lauren

☐ **18 COLOURS (Newton, Lauren & Joelle Leandre)**
CDLR 245 / May '97 / Leo

Newton, Mark

☐ **LIVING A DREAM**
Sugar coated love / Last song / High plateau / Monrosine / Fast as I can crawl / God has a place / Pretty Polly / Chain of memories / When we're gone / I've just seen the rock of ages / Midnight rider / Amazing Grace
REBEL 1744 / Jun '98 / Rebel

Newton-John, Olivia

☐ BACK TO BASICS (The Essential Collection 1971-1992)
If not for you / Banks of the Ohio / What is life / Take me home country roads / I honestly love you / Have you never been mellow / Sam / You're the one that I want / Hopelessly devoted to you / Summer nights / Little more love / Xanadu / Magic / Suddenly / Physical / Rumour / Not gonna be the one / I need love / I want to be wanted / Deeper than a river
5126412 / Jul '92 / Mercury

☐ BACK WITH A HEART
UMD 80487 / 18 May '98 / Universal

☐ COUNTRY GIRL
Love song / Banks of the old Ohio / If not for you / If you could read my mind / Lullaby / It's so hard to say goodbye / Winterwood / What is life / Changes / Living in harmony / If we only have love / Take me home country road / I love you honestly I love you / Music makes my day / Rosewater / Let me be there / Please Mr. Please / Air that I breathe / If you love me (let me know) / Have you never been mellow
4949702 / 25 May '98 / EMI

☐ EMI COUNTRY MASTERS (2CD Set)
Love song / Banks of the Ohio / Me and Bobby McGee / If not for you / Help me make it through the night / If you could read my mind / In a station / Where are you going to my love / Lullaby / No regrets / If I gotta leave / Would you follow me / If / It's so hard to say goodbye / Winterwood / What is life / Changes / Everything I own / I'm a small and lonely light / Just a little too much / Living in harmony / Why don't you write me / Angel of the morning / Mary Skeffington / If we only have love / My old man's got a gun / Maybe then I'll think of you / Amoureuse / Take me home country roads / I love you, I honestly love you / Music makes my day / Heartbreaker / Leaving / You ain't got the right / Feeling best / Rose water / Being on the losing end / If we try / Let me be there / Country girl / Loving you ain't easy / Have love will travel / Hands across the sea / Please Mr. please / Air that I breathe / Loving arms / If you love me (Let me know) / Have you never been mellow
CDEM 1503 / Aug '93 / EMI

☐ GAIA (One Woman's Journey)
DSHCD 7017 / Feb '95 / D-Sharp

☐ GAIA (One Woman's Journey)
Trust yourself / No matter what you do / No other love / Pegasus / Why me / Don't cut me down / Gaia / Do you feel / I never knew love / Silent run / Not gonna give in to it / Way of love
30082 / Oct '97 / Go On Deluxe

☐ SINGLES, THE
TVD 93361 / 22 May '98 / Festival

Newtown Grunts

☐ DAY OF THE JACKEY
SHAG 014 / 22 Dec '97 / Flotsam & Jetsam

Newtown Neurotics

☐ 45 REVOLUTIONS PER MINUTE
FREUDCD 31 / Feb '94 / Jungle

☐ BEGGARS CAN BE CHOOSERS
Lean on me / Life in their hands / Get up and fight / Living with unemployment / No respect
DOLECD 111 / Jan '95 / Dojo

☐ PUNK SINGLES COLLECTION
Hypocrite / You said no / When the oil runs out / Oh no / Kick out the Tories / Mindless violence / Licensing hours / No sanctuary / Blitzreig bop / Hypocrite / I remember you / Suzi is a heartbreaker / Fools / Living with unemployment / Airstrip / My death / Never thought / Screaming / Stand by me / Mind of Valerie / Sect / Never thought
CDPUNK 91 / Mar '97 / Anagram

Next

☐ RATED NEXT
Intro / Too close / Butta love / My place / Penetration / You are my high / I still love you / Stop drop and roll / Represent me / Next experience: *Next & Adina Howard/Castro* / Problems: *Next & Coffee Brown* / Do you think about me / Admit the rat / Sexitude / Taste so good / Phone sex / Rock on
07822189732 / 6 Oct '97 / Arista

Next Step Up

☐ HEAVY (The Return Of Next Step Up)
GAIN 013CD / 17 Nov '97 / Gain Ground

Nexus

☐ WORLD PERCUSSION MUSIC (Nexus & Peter Sadlo)
315572 / May '97 / Koch Classics

NFL Horns Project

☐ TRIANGLE BELOW CANAL STREET
IBCD 4 / Feb '97 / Internal Bass

Ng La Banda

☐ BEST OF NG LA BANDA, THE
74321424392 / Jun '97 / Milan

☐ ECHALE LIMON
3006038 / 1 Jun '98 / IMP

Nganasan

☐ SHAMANIC SONGS OF SIBERIAN ARCTIC
925642 / Jun '93 / BUDA

Ni Bheaglaoich, Eilin

☐ MILE DATH/A CLOAK OF MANY COLOURS
CIC 079CD / Jan '92 / Clo Iar-Chonnachta

Ni Bheaglaoich, Seosaimhin

☐ UNDER THE SUN
CEFCD 170 / Dec '95 / Gael Linn

Ni Bhrolchain, Deirbhile

☐ SMAOINTE
CEFCD 147 / Jan '94 / Gael Linn

Ni Chathasaigh, Maire

☐ CAROLAN ALBUMS: THE MUSIC OF TURLOUGH O'CAROLAN (Ni Chathasaigh, Maire & Chris Newman)
Carolan's draught / John O'Connor / Colonel John Irwin (Planxty Irwin) / Hewlwtt / Maire Dhall / Lord Inchiquin / Morgan Magan / Si beag si mor / Princess Royal / John Drury (Planxty Drury) / Fanny Power / Carolan's concerto / Maurice O'Connor / Constantine Maguire / Mr. O'Connor / Robert Jordan / Bridget Cruise / Frank Palmer / Grace Nugent / George Brabazon / Kean O'Hara / Madam Judge / Eleanor Plunkett / Baptist Johnston
OBMCD 06 / Apr '94 / Old Bridge

☐ LIVE IN THE HIGHLANDS (Ni Chathasaigh, Maire & Chris Newman)
Turkey in the straw / Gander in the pratie hole/ Donnybrook boy/Queen of the rushes / Thugamar fein an Samhradh linn / Unknown title/Wellington's reel / Eleanor Plunkett / Acrobat/Bonnie banchory/ Millbrae / Roisin dubh / Humours of Ballyloughlin / A shaighdiuirin a chroi (Dear soldier of my heart)/ Blackbird / Salt creek / Taimse I'm Chodladh / Sore point / Stroll on
OBMCD 08 / Oct '95 / Old Bridge

☐ LIVING WOOD, THE (Ni Chathasaigh, Maire & Chris Newman)
Caitlin ni aedha/The sport of the chase / Lady Dillon / Fiddler's dream/Whiskey before breakfast / Fare thee well lovely Mary / Walsh's hornpipe/The peacock's feather / Flax in bloom/Lough Allen/ McAuliffe's / Beating around the bush / An paistin fionn/La valse d'Hasperren / Charlie Hunter's/ Peggy's leg/Fogarty's jig / Cuach mo londubh bui/ The Virginia / Mairead's mazurka / Bob McQuillan's/ Sonny Brogan's / Moynihan's polkas
CROCD 221 / Mar '94 / Black Crow
OBMCD 07 / '95 / Old Bridge

☐ NEW STRUNG HARP, THE
Charles O'Conor/Father Hanly / O ho Nighean, e ho Nighean / Madam Maxwell / Pullet/The volunteer / An Speic Seoigheach / Humours of Ballyloughlin / Hindero horo / Bantry girls' lament / Gander in the Pratie Hole/The queen of the rushes / Carolan's farewell to music / Fisherman's hornpipe/The cuckoo's nest / Boys of Malin/Old oak tree / Planxty Sudley
COMD 2019 / Sep '97 / Temple

☐ OUT OF COURT (Ni Chathasaigh, Maire & Chris Newman)
Out of court / Harper's chair / Cherry blossom / Will you meet me tonight on the shore / Frieze breeches / Lady Gethin / Sore point / Graf spee / Tuirne mhaire / Eclipse/Hurricane / Old bridge / Wild geese / Lakes of Champlain / Stroll on
OBMCD 03 / '91 / Old Bridge

Ni Dhomhnaill, Caitlin

☐ SEAL MO CHUARTA
CIC 070CD / Nov '93 / Clo Iar-Chonnachta

Ni Dhomhnaill, Maighread

☐ NO DOWRY
CEFCD 152 / Jan '94 / Gael Linn

Ni Dhomhnaill, Triona

☐ TRIONA
CEFCD 043 / Jan '92 / Gael Linn

Ni Fhearraigh, Aoife

☐ AOIFE
CEFCD 172 / May '97 / Gael Linn

Ni Mhaonaigh, Mairead

☐ CEOL ADUAIDH (Ni Mhaonaigh, Mairead & Frankie Kennedy)
CEFCD 102 / Jan '94 / Gael Linn

Ni Riain, Noirin

☐ CAOINEADH NA MAIGHDINE
CEFCD 084 / Jan '94 / Gael Linn

☐ DARKEST MIDNIGHT, THE
STAA 322CD / Mar '98 / Sounds True

☐ STOR AMHRAN
OSS 7CD / Mar '95 / Ossian

☐ VOX DE NUBE (Ni Riain, Noirin & Monks Of Glenstal Abbey)
CEFCD 144 / Jan '94 / Gael Linn

Ni Uallachain, Padraigin

☐ BENEATH THE SURFACE
CEFCD 174 / Feb '97 / Gael Linn

Niacin

☐ HIGH BIAS
High bias / Birdland / Slapped silly / Montuno / Revenge / Cool to the touch / Darkside / It's the little things / Soul diversion / Who cares if it's raining / Hang me upside down
SCD 90172 / 8 Jun '98 / Stretch

☐ NIACIN
No man's land / Clean-up crew / Do a little dirty work / I miss you (like I miss the sun) / One less worry / Three feet back / Bullet train blues / Hell to pay / Alone on my own little island / For crying out loud / Klaghorn / Spring rounds / Spring rounds squared / Pay dirt / Fudgesicle
SCD 90112 / Feb '97 / Stretch

Niblock, Phill

☐ YOUNG PERSON'S GUIDE TO PHILL NIBLOCK, A
BFFP 102CD / Jul '97 / Blast First

Nice & Smooth

☐ AIN'T A DAMN THING CHANGED
5234782 / Jan '96 / RAL

☐ JEWEL OF THE NILE
Return of the hip hop freaks / Sky's the limit / Let's all get down / Doin' our own thang / Do whatcha gotta / Old to the new / Blunts / Get fucked up / Save the children / Cheri
5233362 / Nov '94 / Island

Nice

☐ AMERICA
CD 12334 / Apr '94 / Laserlight

☐ AMERICA - THE BBC SESSIONS
RRCD 224 / Jul '96 / Receiver

☐ ARS LONGA VITA BREVIS (Remastered)
Daddy, where did I come from / Little Arabella / Happy Freuds / Intermezzo from Karelia suite / Don Edito el Gruva / Ars longa vita brevis / Brandenburger
ESMCD 646 / 3 Aug '98 / Essential

☐ ELEGY
Third movement / America / Hang on to a dream / My back pages
CASCD 1030 / Feb '91 / Charisma

☐ FIVE BRIDGES SUITE
Fantasia (1st bridge, 2nd bridge) / Chorale (3rd bridge) / High level fugue (4th bridge) / Finale / Intermezzo from Karelia suite / Pathetique (symphony no.6 3rd movement) / Country pie/ Brandenburg concerto No. 6 / One of those people
CASCD 1014 / Feb '91 / Charisma

☐ IMMEDIATE YEARS, THE (3CD Set)
Flower kings of flies / Thoughts of Ememrlist Davjack / Bonnie K / Rondo / War and peace / Tantalising Maggie / Dawn / Cry of Eugene / America / Diamond hard blue apples of the moon / Daddy / Where did I come from / Azrael / America 2nd ammendment / Little Arabella / Happy freuds / Intermezzo / Brandenburger / Don Edito El Gruva / First movement / Third movement (acceptance brandenburger) / Fourth movement (denial) / Coda / Extension to the big note / Azrael revisited / Hang on to a dream / Diary of an empty day / For example / Rondo (69) / She belongs to me / First movement (awakening) / Second movement (realization)
CDIMMBOX 2 / Aug '95 / Charly

☐ NICE (Remastered)
Azrael revisited / Hang on to a dream / Diary of an empty day / For example / Rondo 69 / She belongs to me / Hang onto a dream (mono) / Diary of an empty day (mono)
ESMCD 645 / 3 Aug '98 / Essential

☐ THOUGHTS OF EMERLIST DAVJACK
Flower kings of flies / Thoughts of Emerlist Davjack / Bonnie K / Rondo / War and peace / Tantalising Maggie / Dawn / Cry of Eugene
CDIMM 010 / Feb '94 / Charly

☐ THOUGHTS OF EMERLIST DAVJACK (Remastered)
Flower king of flies / Thoughts of Emerlist Davjack / Bonnie K / Rondo / War and peace / Tantalising Maggie / Dawn / Cry of Eugine / Thoughts of Emerust Davjack (mono) / Azrail (angel of death) / Diamond hard blue apples of the moon
ESMCD 647 / 3 Aug '98 / Essential

Nicholas, Albert

☐ ALBERT NICHOLAS & ALAN ELSDON BAND VOL.1 (Nicholas, Albert & Alan Elsdon Band)
JCD 259 / Jul '96 / Jazzology

☐ ALBERT NICHOLAS & ALAN ELSDON BAND VOL.2 (Nicholas, Albert & Alan Elsdon Band)
JCD 269 / Nov '96 / Jazzology

☐ BADEN 1969 (Nicholas, Albert & Henri Chaix Trio)
SKCD 2045 / Jan '97 / Sackville

☐ LIVE IN COPENHAGEN 1954
Fidgety feet / Tin roof blues / Tears / Basin street blues / Lulu's back in town / Dippermouth blues / Room rent blues / Royal garden blues / Winin' boy blues / Rose room / Ostrich walk / Black and blue / I found a new baby / Weary blues
STCD 5522 / 9 Mar '98 / Storyville

☐ NEW ORLEANS-CHICAGO CONNECTION (Nicholas, Albert & Art Hodes Quartet)
Digga digga do / Winin' boy blues / Song of the wanderer / Ain't misbehavin' / Blues my naughty sweetie gave to me / Anah's blues / Lover come back to me / Etta / I'm comin' Virginia / Rose room / Nick warms up / Rose room / I'm comin' Virginia / Lover come back to me / Winin' boy blues / Digga digga do / Careless love / Song of the wanderer / Ain't misbehavin' / Blues my naughty sweetie gave to me / Etta
DE 207 / Jun '97 / Delmark

Nicholas, John

☐ THRILL ON THE HILL
ANTCD 0032 / Dec '94 / Antones

Nicholls, Billy

☐ UNDER ONE BANNER
EXPCD 3 / Nov '90 / Expression

Nicholls, Gillie

☐ SPIRIT TALK
SPINCD 152 / Jul '94 / Spindrift

Nichols, Herbie

☐ COMPLETE BLUE NOTE RECORDINGS, THE
Third world / Third world / Step tempest / Dance line / Blue chopsticks / Double exposure / Double exposure / Cro-magnon nights / Cro-magnon nights / It didn't happen / Amoeba's dance / Brass rings / Brass rings / 2300 skidoo / 2300 skiddo / Shuffle Montgomery / It didn't happen / Crisp day / Shuffle Montgomery / Gig / Applejackin' / Hangover triangle / Lady sing the blues / Chit chatting / House party starting / Gig / Furthermore / Furthermore / 117th street / 1117th street / Sunday stroll / Nick at T's / Furthermore / Terpsichore / 'Orse at safari / Applejackin' / Applejackin / Mine / Mine / Trio / Trio / Spinning song / Spinning song / Riff primitif / Riff primitif / Query / Query
CDP 8593522 / 6 Oct '97 / Blue Note

☐ LOVE IS PROXIMITY (Nichols, Herbie Project)
1213132 / Mar '97 / Soul Note

Nichols, Keith

☐ DUKE AND JOHNSON TUNES (Nichols, Keith & His Cotton Club Orchestra)
SOSCD 1320 / Feb '98 / Stomp Off

☐ SYNCOPATED JAMBOREE
SOSCD 1234 / Oct '92 / Stomp Off

Nichols, Nichelle

☐ DOWN TO EARTH
CREV 045CD / Feb '97 / Rev-Ola

Nichols, Red

☐ 1929 RECORDINGS (Nichols, Red & Jack Teagarden)
Dinah / On the Alamo / Somebody to love me / Get happy / Smiles / They didn't believe / Rose of Washington Square / That da da strain / Sally won't you come back / New Yorkers
TAXS 52 / Aug '94 / Tax

☐ BATTLE HYMN OF THE REPUBLIC (Nichols, Red & His Five Pennies)
JCD 90 / Mar '97 / Jazzology

☐ ON EDISON 1924-1927
BDW 8007 / May '98 / Jazz Oracle

☐ RADIO TRANSCRIPTIONS 1929-1930 (Nichols, Red & His Five Pennies)
CD 1011 / Nov '96 / IAJRC

☐ RED NICHOLS & HIS FIVE PENNIES/ DOTTIE O'BRIEN (Nichols, Red & His Five Pennies/Dottie O'Brien)
DAWE 84 / Jul '98 / Magic

☐ RED NICHOLS 1936/WILL OSBORNE 1934 (Nichols, Red & Will Osborne)
CCD 110 / Apr '94 / Circle

☐ RHYTHM OF THE DAY (Nichols, Red & His Five Pennies)
Rhythm of the day / Buddy's habit / Boneyard shuffle / Alexander's ragtime band / Alabama stomp / Hurricane / Cornfed / Mean dog blues / Riverboat shuffle / Eccentric / Feeling no pain / Original Dixieland one-step / Honolulu blues / There'll come a time / Harlem twist / Alice blue gown / Corine Corina / Oh Peter, you're so nice / Waiting for the evening mail / Sweet Sue, just you
CDAJA 5025 / Feb '87 / Living Era

Nicholson, Gimmer

☐ CHRISTOPHER IDYLLS
CD 9204 / Dec '94 / Lucky Seven

Nick, Michael

☐ DIS TANZ (Nick, Michael Trio & Dave Liebman)
TE 009 / Jan '97 / BUDA

Nickel Bag

☐ 12 HITS AND A BUMP
USG 120092 / Apr '97 / USG

☐ MAS FEEDBACK
LG 0022 / 10 Dec '97 / Lizard

Nicki

☐ KLEINE WUNDER
Manchmoi glaubn's i war a star / Nur mit dir mit dir des war mei leben / Anders als die anderen / Doch wie's mal var vergiss i nie / Mehr von dir / Dann denk i du warst bei mir / Auf amoi / Einsam ohne di / I bin a bayriches cowgirl / Wenn teenager traumen / Des muss liebe sei
DC 868282 / Oct '96 / Disky

☐ WEIHNACHTEN MIT
Heilig abend is nimma weit / Weihnachtstraum d'liab is vom himmi kumma / Drobn im himmi herrscht hochbetried / Es wird scho glei dumpa / Winterwunderland / Heidschi bumbeidschi / Leise rieselt der schnee / Weihnacht wie in der kinderzeit / Susse die glocken nie klinga / Mei schonster traum / Susser die glocken nie klinga
DC 868272 / Oct '96 / Disky

Nicks, Stevie

☐ OTHER SIDE OF THE MIRROR
Rooms on fire / Long way to go / Two kinds of love / Oh my love / Ghosts / Whole lotta trouble / Fire burning / Cry wolf / Alice / Juliet / Doing the best I can (Escape from Berlin) / I still miss someone
CDEMD 1008 / Feb '94 / EMI

☐ STREET ANGEL
Blue denim / Greta / Street angel / Docklands / Listen to the rain / Destiny / Unconditional love / Love is like a river / Rose garden / Maybe love / Just like a woman / Kick it / Jane
CDEMC 3671 / May '94 / EMI

☐ WILD HEART
Stand back / I will run to you / Nothing ever changes / Sable on blond / Beauty and the beast / Wild heart / If anyone falls / Gate and garden / Night bird / Enchanted
CDGOLD 1017 / Mar '96 / EMI Gold

Nico

☐ CAMERA OBSCURA
Camera obscura / Tanaore / Win a few / My funny valentine / Das lied von einsanen madchens / Fearfully in danger / My heart is empty / Into the arena / Konig
BBL 63CD / Mar '96 / Beggars Banquet

☐ CHELSEA GIRL
Fairest of the seasons / These days / Little sister / Winter song / It was a pleasure then / Chelsea girl / I'll keep it with mine / Somewhere there's a feather / Wrap your troubles in dreams (and dream your troubles away) / Eulogy to Lenny Bruce
8352092 / Apr '94 / Polydor

☐ CHELSEA GIRL LIVE
CLEO 61082 / May '94 / Cleopatra

☐ CHELSEA LIVE
Tananore / One more chance / Procession / My heart is empty / Janitor of lunacy / Sphinx / You forget to answer / Fearfully in danger / Sixty forty / All tomorrow's parties / Purple lips / Femme fatale / Saeta / End
SEECD 461 / Oct '96 / See For Miles

☐ DO OR DIE
RE 117CD / Nov '94 / ROIR

☐ DRAMA OF EXILE
Genghis Khan / Purple lips / One more chance / Henry Hudson / Heroes / Waiting for the man / Sixty forty / Sphinx / Orly flight
SEECD 449 / Aug '96 / See For Miles

☐ END, THE
It has not taken long / Secret side / You forgot to answer / Innocent and vain / Valley of the kings / We've got the gold / End / Das lied der Deutschen
IMCD 174 / Mar '94 / Island

☐ FATA MORGANA 1988 (Nico's Last Concert) (Nico & The Faction)
SPV 08496202 / Sep '96 / SPV

☐ HEROINE
My heart is empty / Procession / All tomorrow's parties / Valley of the kings / Sphinx / We've got the gold / Mutterlein / Afraid / Innocent and vain / Frozen warnings / Fearfully in danger / Tananore / Femme fatale
CDMGRAM 85 / 24 Aug '98 / Anagram

☐ LIVE IN TOKYO
My heart is empty / Purple lips / Tananore / Janitor of lunacy / You forget to answer / 60-40 / My funny valentine / Sad lied von einsannen madchens / All tomorrow's parties / Femme fatale / End
DOJOCD 50 / May '95 / Dojo

☐ MARBLE INDEX
Prelude / Lawns of dawns / No one is there / Ari's song / Facing the wind / Julius Caesar (memento hodie) / Frozen warnings / Evening of light / Roses in the snow / Nibelungen
7559610982 / Apr '91 / WEA

Nico Demus

☐ DANCEHALL GIANT
49007 CD / Mar '97 / Positive Beat

Nicol, John

☐ JOHN NICOL
LB 9714 / Jul '98 / La Brava

Nicol, Ken

☐ LIVING IN A SPANISH TOWN
Midnight cowboy / Last night in Paris / Should've known better / Credit card blues / Living in a Spanish town / Last chances / I'd rather be with you / Down on the island / One more night / This time it's me / Jigs and reels / Back out of love / Same old lang syne
PLAN 012CD / Nov '97 / Planet

Nicolai, Giancarlo

☐ GIANCARLO NICOLAI TRIO
CDLR 164 / Aug '97 / Leo

Nicole

☐ MAKE IT HOT
Time is now / Seventeen / In da street / Traffic jam / Curiosity / Make it hot / Prelude (I can't see) / I can't see / Nervous / Pressure / Boy you should listen / Eyes better not wander / Radio DJ / Silly love song / Raise your frown / Borrowed time / Testing our love (suga)
7559622092 / 24 Aug '98 / Gold Mind/ East West

Nicolette

☐ DJ KICKS (Various Artists)
It's yours: *Doc Scott* / Never not: *Katze, Nav* / Nightbreed: *Bolland, C.J.* / Java bass: *Shut Up & Dance* / Suicide: *Alec Empire* / Migrant: *Palace Of Pleasure* / Phyzical: *Roni Size* / Ventolin: *Aphex Twin* / Pound your ironing board: *Mike Flowers Pops & Slang* / I woke up: *Nicolette* / Lash the 90ties: *Alec Empire* / Original nuttah: *UK Apachi & Shy FX* / Severe trauma: *Critical Mass* / Burning: *DJ Krust* / Pillow: *Ohm Square* / 70+ DF: *Horn* / Basses playin' loud: *TAGG* / Single ring: *Nicolette* / Sweat: *Shizuo* / Bastards: *Shut Up & Dance* / Too busy to live: *Oge* / You, them and maybe us: *Grammatix* / Angry dolphin: *Plaid* / Walhalla's gate: *Aquastep* / Bless to kill: *Mark NRG* / All day (DJ Kicks): *Nicolette*
K7 054CD / Mar '97 / Studio K7

☐ LET NO-ONE LIVE RENT FREE IN YOUR HEAD
Don't be afraid / We never know / Song for Europe / Beautiful day / Always / Nervous / Where have all the flowers gone / No government / Nightmare / Judgement day / You are Heaven sent / Just to say peace and love / No government / Don't be ashamed (don't be afriad)
5326342 / Oct '96 / Talkin' Loud

☐ NOW IS EARLY
No government / Dove song / Single minded vocal / I woke up / Waking up / O si nene / It's only to be expected / Wicked mathematics / Single ring / School of the world / Udi eqwu
SUADCD 1 / Apr '92 / Shut Up & Dance
K7R 016CD / 20 Oct '97 / Studio K7

Niden Div.187

☐ IMPERGIUM
NR 016CD / 27 Oct '97 / Necropolis

Niebla, Eduardo

☐ MEDITERRANEO (Niebla, Eduardo & Adel Salameh)
Mediterraneo / Andalucia / Gardens of the heart / Oasis
TUGCD 1012 / Apr '96 / Riverboat

☐ POEMA (Niebla, Eduardo & Antonio Forcione)
CDJP 1035 / Sep '93 / Jazz Point

Niehaus, Lennie

☐ PATTERNS
FSR 5013CD / Nov '97 / Fresh Sound

Niekku

☐ NIEKKU
OMCD 11 / Dec '93 / Olarin Musiiki Oy

Nielson Chapman, Beth

☐ SAND AND WATER
Colour of roses / Beyond the blue / All the time in the world / Sand and water / Fair enough / Seven shades of blue / Happy girl / No one knows but you / Heads up for the wrecking ball / Say goodnight
9362465212 / 1 Dec '97 / Reprise

Niemack, Judy

☐ BLUE BOP
FRLCD 009 / Oct '92 / Freelance

☐ HEARTS DESIRE (Niemack, Judy & Kenny Barron)
STCD 548 / '92 / Stash

☐ LONG AS YOU'RE LIVING
Long as you're living / Waltz for debby / Maestro / Good bye pork pie hat-i remember clifford / Caribbean fire dance / Island / Monk's dream / You've taken things too far / To welcome the day / Out of this world / Daahoud / Infant eyes
FRLCD 014 / Oct '92 / Freelance

☐ MINGUS, MONK & MAL (Niemack, Judy & Mal Waldron)
FRLCD 021 / May '95 / Freelance

☐ STRAIGHT UP
FRLCD 0018 / Apr '93 / Freelance

Nieves, Tito

☐ DALE CARA A LA VIDA
RMD 82171 / 24 Mar '98 / RMM

Nifelheim

☐ DEVIL'S FORCE
NR 022CD / 15 Jun '98 / Necropolis

Nig

☐ HEIST
DC 30CD / 16 Feb '98 / Drag City

Night Ark

☐ IN WONDERLAND
5344712 / Aug '97 / EmArCy

Night In Gales

☐ THUNDERBEAST
Intruder / Darkzone anthem / Perihelion / Crystalthorn's call / Feverfeast / Shadowchamber / Thunderbeast / I am the dungeon god / Blackfleshed / Dustcrown / Stormchild / Heralds of starfall from ebony skies
NB 3282 / 27 Jul '98 / Nuclear Blast

☐ TOWARDS THE TWILIGHT
NB 243CD / Jun '97 / Nuclear Blast

Night Ranger

☐ ROCK IN JAPAN '97
XRCN 2004 / 22 Jun '98 / Zero

☐ SEVEN
CMC 186257 / 13 Jul '98 / CMC
SPV 08518172 / 1 Sep '98 / SPV

Night Shadows

☐ NIGHT SHADOWS VOL.1 (R&B Period)
52156000032 / 10 Nov '97 / Hot Trax

☐ NIGHT SHADOWS VOL.2 (Little Phil Era)
52156000062 / 10 Nov '97 / Hot Trax

Night Sun

☐ MOURNIN'
SB 041 / Jun '97 / Second Battle

Night Trains

☐ CHECKMATE
Blow out / Takin' a stroll / Release the chain / Miles away / Take the cash / Hang on to that cove / On your toes / Hot and cool / Bongo breakdown / In the crowd / Checkmate / Street chase
CDBGP 1033 / Feb '91 / Beat Goes Public

☐ LOADED
JAZIDCD 018 / Jun '92 / Acid Jazz

☐ SLEAZEBALL
Sure can't go to the moon / Hold on for the truth / Lonely road / On my own / Love is the teacher / Move on out together / What good is love / Smoky's clown / International way / Lovesick / Sleazeball
JAZIDCD 098 / Apr '94 / Acid Jazz

Nightcrawlers

☐ LET'S PUSH IT
Push the feeling on / Surrender your love / Don't let the feeling go / Should never (fall in love) / Just like before / Lift me up / World turns / Let's push it / I like it / All over the world
74321309702 / Sep '95 / Arista

☐ LET'S PUSH IT FURTHER (The 12" Mixes) (Nightcrawlers & John Reid)
Push the feeling on / Keep on pushing our love / Surrender your love / Let's push it / Lift me up / Should I ever (fall in love) / Don't let the feeling go / Surrender your love (Wand's crunchy nut mix) / Let's push it (Motiv 8 bump 'n' boost vocal) / Push the feeling on (Argonaut's smokin' hot mix)
74321390432 / Aug '96 / Arista

Nightfall

☐ ATHENIAN ECHOES
HOLY 014CD / Oct '95 / Holy

☐ EONS AURA
HOLY 009CD / Mar '95 / Holy

☐ LESBIAN SHOW (2CD Set)
HOLY 028CD
HOLY 028BOX / 13 Oct '97 / Holy

☐ MACABRE SUNSETS
HOLY 004CD / Jun '94 / Holy

☐ PARADE INTO CENTURIES
HOLY 001CD / Feb '95 / Holy

Nighthawk, Robert

☐ MASTERS OF MODERN BLUES SERIES (Nighthawk, Robert & Houston Stackhouse)
TCD 5010 / Dec '94 / Testament

☐ RARE CHICAGO BLUES RECORDINGS (From The Collection Of Norman Dayron) (Nighthawk, Robert & His Flames Of Rhythm)
Goin' down to ell's / Mr. bell's shuffle / Time have come / Yakity yak / Nighthawk shuffle / Take it easy baby / Maxwell street medley / Burning heat / I need love so bad / Excerpts from interview-kansas city
ROUCD 2022 / Sep '91 / Rounder

Nighthawks

☐ BACKTRACK
CDVR 036 / '88 / Varrick

☐ BEST OF THE NIGHTHAWKS, THE
GCD 4140/45 / Jan '98 / Genes

☐ HARD LIVING
CDVR 022 / '88 / Varrick

☐ JACKS AND KINGS
GCD 4120/25 / Jan '98 / Genes

☐ LIVE
GCD 4110 / Jan '98 / Genes

☐ LIVE IN EUROPE
CCD 11014 / Nov '88 / Crosscut

☐ OPEN ALL NITE
GCD 4105 / Jan '98 / Genes

☐ PAIN AND PARADISE
Trouble comin' every day / Shade tree mechanic / Same thing / Soul of a man / High temperature / Pain and paradise / Is love enough / Trouble on the way / I told you so / Snap it
BIGMO 1030 / Oct '96 / Big Mo

☐ ROCK THIS HOUSE
BIGMO 1023 / Jul '94 / Big Mo

☐ SIDE POCKET SHOT
GCD 4115 / Jan '98 / Genes

☐ TIMES FOUR
GCD 4130/35 / Jan '98 / Genes

Nighthawks At The Diner

☐ FOOL'S TANGO
King in yellow / Fool's tango / You invented me / Sunday afternoon / Dreamtime intermission / Killing sparrows / For better and for worse / Intel R inside / Won't say goodbye / Paul Wilson GR
AL 73092 / Jul '97 / A

Nightingale

☐ BREATHING SHADOW
BMCD 66 / May '95 / Black Mark

Nightingale, Mark

☐ DESTINY
I'm old fashioned / My foolish heart / Song is you / Solitude / Don't mention the blues / Destiny / Whisper not / What is this thing called love
MR 874293 / Jun '97 / Mons

Nightlife Unlimited

☐ BEST OF NIGHTLIFE UNLIMITED, THE
HTCD 111 / 20 Apr '98 / Hot Productions

Nightmare Lodge

☐ NEGATIVE PLANET
MHCD 022 / Jun '94 / Minus Habens

Nightmare Visions

☐ SUFFERING FROM ECHOES
HNF 013CD / Feb '96 / Head Not Found

Nightmares On Wax

☐ SMOKERS DELIGHT
WARPCD 36 / Sep '95 / Warp

☐ WORD OF SCIENCE, A
Nights interlude / Case of funk / Coming down / Stop (crack) / Biofeedback / Mega donutz / Playtime / Aftermath / Fun / Back into time / Dextrous / B.w.t.m. / Sal / E.a.s.e. / How ya doin'
WARPCD 4 / Apr '96 / Warp

Nightnoise

☐ DIFFERENT SHORE, A
Call of the child / For Eamonn / Falling apples / Busker on the beach / Morning in Madrid / Another wee niece / Different shore / Mind the dresser / Clouds go by / Shuan
01934111662 / Aug '95 / Windham Hill

☐ SHADOW OF TIME
One little nephew / March air / Shadow of time / Silky flanks / Water falls / Fionnghuala (mouth music) / Nigh in that land / This just in / For you / Sauvie island / Rose of Tralee / Three little nieces
01934111302 / Nov '93 / Windham Hill

☐ WHITE HORSE SESSIONS
Silky flanks / Shadow of time / Jig of sorts / Shaun / Do we / Murrach na gealaich (Murdo of the moon) / Hugh / Moondance / Crickets wicket / Night in that land / At the races / Heartwood
01934111952 / Mar '97 / Windham Hill

☐ WINDHAM HILL RETROSPECTIVE, A
19A / Toys not ties / Timewinds / Hugh / Cricket's wicker / Kid in the cot / Something of time / Swan / Bleu / At the races / Hourglass / End of the evening / Nollaig / Bridges / Bring me back a song
01934111112 / Jan '95 / Windham Hill

Nightowls

☐ AT THE CHARLESTON BALL
GBMR 28 / May '98 / GBM

Nightsky Bequest

☐ UNCOUNTED STARS, UNFOUNDED DREAMLANDS
POLYPH 004CD / Jul '96 / Polyphemus

Nightstick

☐ BLOTTER
Workers of the world unite / Some boys / Set the controls for the heart of the sun / Mommy, what's a funkadelic / Blotter / Fellating the dying Christ
RR 69512 / Mar '97 / Relapse

☐ ULTIMATUM
Cut it off then kill it / United snakes / Pentagon / Pig in shit / 4 more years / August 6 1945 / Dream of the witche's sabbath / He is dead wrong / Live at Mama Kin's
RR 69772 / 9 Mar '98 / Relapse

Nightwing

☐ MY KINGDOM COME
LIR 00123 / Mar '97 / Long Island

☐ NATURAL SURVIVORS
NM 009CD / Oct '97 / Neat Metal

Nightwish

☐ ANGELS FALL FIRST
Elvenpath / Beauty and the beast / Carpenter / Astral romance / Angels fall first / Tutankhamen / Nymphomaniac fantasia / Know why the nightingale sings / Lappi
SPI 47CD / 30 Mar '98 / Spinefarm

Nigra Nebula

☐ LIFE AFTER LIFE
EFA 125222 / Sep '95 / Celtic Circle

Nihon No Oto Ensemble

☐ TRADITIONAL JAPANESE
B 6784 / Oct '94 / Auvidis/Ethnic

Nika

☐ STATE OF GRACE
110242 / Nov '93 / Musidisc

Nikola

☐ BALKAN TRADITIONAL (Nikola & Friends)
HMA 1903007CD / Aug '94 / Musique D'Abord

Niks Project

☐ FUTURE MUSEUM
BVHAASTCD 9705 / Apr '98 / Bvhaast

Nil 8

☐ HAL LE LUJAH
BOOK 2CD / Nov '93 / Worrybird

Nile

☐ AMONGST THE CATACOMBS OF NEPHREN-KA
Smashing the antiu / Barra edinazzu / Kudurru maqlu / Serpent headed mask / Ramses bringer of war / Stones of sorrow / Die rache krieg lied der assyriche / Howling of the jinn / Pestilence and iniquity / Opening of the mouth / Beneath the eternal oceans of sand
RR 69835 / 15 Jun '98 / Relapse

Nile, Willie

☐ ARCHIVE ALIVE
ACH 80009 / Jul '97 / Archive

Nils

☐ BLUE PLANET
D 2249522 / 3 Aug '98 / Ichiban

Nilsson

☐ WHISPER
Shalom / I am so small / Beautitudes / Before you were born / Whisper / It is well / Your love calls / God is watching / Total eclipse / Abba father / All the days of my life / Sheep may safely graze / Doxology
7019968600 / Apr '98 / Everland

Nilsson, Erik

☐ ALONE ON A STRANGE PLANET
7393787970394 / Aug '97 / DB Productions

Nilsson, Harry

☐ ALL THE BEST
Without you / Everybody's talkin' / Mother nature's son / It's been so long / Good old desk / Without her / Mournin' glory story / Mr. Richland's favourite song / Mr. Bojangles / She's leaving home / Lullaby in ragtime / Makin' whoopee / Cuddly toy / River deep, mountain high / Little cowboy / As time goes by
MCCD 129 / Sep '93 / Music Club

☐ AS TIME GOES BY (The Complete Schmilsson In The Night)
Intro / Lazy moon / For me and my gal / It had to be you / Always / Makin' whoopee / You made me love you / Lullaby in ragtime / I wonder who's kissing her now / What'll I do / Nevertheless (I'm in love with you) / This is all I ask / I'm always chasing rainbows / Make believe / Trust in me / It's only a paper moon / Thanks for the memory / Over the rainbow / As time goes by
74321416362 / Jan '97 / Camden

☐ BEST OF NILSSON, THE
74321223152 / Aug '94 / RCA

☐ EVERYBODY'S TALKIN' (The Very Best Of Harry Nilsson)
Everybody's talkin' / Without you / Me and my arrow / Without her / All I think about is you / Coconut / I guess the Lord must be in New York City / Mr. Bojangles / Spaceman / Little cowboy / Cuddly toy / Puppy song / Moonbeam song / Blanket for a sail / Mr. Richland's favourite song / Cowboy / Mucho mungo / Mother Nature's son / 1941 / Joy / I'll be home / Subterranean homesick blues
74321476772 / Apr '97 / Camden

☐ LITTLE TOUCH OF SCHMILSSON IN THE NIGHT
For me and my gal / It had to be you / Lazy moon / Always / Makin' whoopee / You made me love you / Lullaby in ragtime / I wonder who's kissing her now / What'll I do / Nevertheless / This is all I ask / As time goes by
ND 90582 / Aug '91 / RCA

☐ MASTERS, THE
EABCD 041 / 24 Nov '97 / Eagle

☐ NILSSON SCHMILSSON
Gotta get up / Driving along / Early in the morning / Moonbeam song / Down / Let the good times roll / Jump into the fire / Without you / I'll never leave you
ND 83464 / Oct '87 / RCA

☐ PUSSY CATS
Many rivers to cross / Subterranean homesick blues / Don't forget me / All my life / Old forgotten soldier / Save the last dance for me / Mucho mucho/Mt Elga / Loop de loop / Black sails (In the moonlight) / (We're gonna) Rock around the clock
07863505702 / Aug '96 / RCA

☐ SIMPLY THE BEST
WMCD 5706 / Oct '94 / Disky

☐ VERY BEST OF NILSSON VOL.1 (Without Her, Without You)
Over the rainbow / Without her / Cuddly toy / Wailing of the willow / Everybody's talkin' / I guess the Lord must be in New York City / Mother Nature's son / Puppy song / Mournin' glory story / Daddy's song / Maybe / Down to the valley / Life line / River deep, mountain high / Moonbeam song / Without you / Mucho mungo / Mount Elga / Subterranean homesick blues
ND 90520 / Nov '90 / RCA

☐ VERY BEST OF NILSSON, THE
74321486592 / Aug '97 / RCA

Nimal

☐ VOIX DE SURFACE
RECDEC 31 / Oct '93 / Rec Rec

Nimitz, Jack

☐ CONFIRMATION (Nimitz, Jack Quartet)
FSR 5006CD / Jul '96 / Fresh Sound

Nimmons, Phil

☐ ATLANTIC SUITE, THE (& Suite PEI/ Tributes - 2CD Set)
SK2CD 5003 / Dec '97 / Sackville

Nimoy, Leonard

☐ HIGHLY ILLOGICAL
CREV 017CD / Sep '93 / Rev-Ola

Nimrod

☐ NIMROD
SCRATCH 22 / Feb '97 / Scratch

Nimsgern, Frank

☐ FRANK NIMSGERN (Nimsgern, Frank & Chaka Khan/Billy Cobham)
Last Summer / Just another way out / Catch the time / Take me away / Pretty secrets / Don't you think it's alright / Latin jokes / Pat's prelude / On the trip / Spring
890012 / Feb '91 / Lipstick

☐ FUNKY SITE
Funky site / Beautiful day / Seal of love / No words / On your own / Race of hearts / Body and soul / Now here / Next day / Tell me again / Snakedance / Road dream / Here's my plan
INAK 9047 / Nov '97 / In Akustik

☐ STREET STORIES
Show me the way / Good news / We need tomorrow / Better here and now / So nize / En quittant / You're the one / Who's in the house / Street stories / Rough moods / Brazil / Stories from the past
INAK 9013CD / Nov '97 / In Akustik

☐ TRUST
Symbol of trust / Sound of deliverance / I told you / Trust / Wind and fire / Toys / Let's get it together / Break free / Don't worry / Hope / Wings / Cold fire / Elements / Soul trouble / Jump the rail / Sound of deliverance
INAK 9031CD / Nov '97 / In Akustik

Nin, Khadja

☐ SAMBOLERA
Sambolera mayi son / Sina mali, sina deni (free) / Wale watu / Mama Lusiya / Save us / Mwana wa mama / Leo Leya / M'barik fall / Soul le charme / Rosy / Bwana C
74321360482 / Jan '97 / BMG

Nine

☐ CLOUD NINE
FILECD 469 / Sep '96 / Profile

☐ NINE LIVEZ
FILECD 460 / Mar '95 / Profile

Nine

☐ KISSED BY MISANTHROPE
JABSCO 012CD / 22 Jun '98 / Sidekicks/Burning Heart

☐ LISTEN
Without questioning / Common ground / Drying well / Silence / For me to define / Unprotected / Reflection / Everything / Fail
STAR 52172 / 8 Sep '97 / Startracks
JABSCO 011CD / 27 Apr '98 / Burning Heart

Nine Below Zero

☐ BACK TO THE FUTURE
Soft touch / Bad town / Down in the dirt again / On the road again / Sweet little contessa / Mama talk to your daughter / Jump back baby / Another kinda love / One way street / Ain't coming back / Three times enough / Don't point your finger / Eleven plus eleven / Egg on my face / Sugar beet / Wipe away your kiss / Can't say yes, can't say no
WOLCD 1040 / Feb '94 / China

☐ ICE STATION ZEBRO
5404302 / Mar '96 / A&M

☐ LIVE IN LONDON
IGOCD 2023 / Jun '95 / Indigo

☐ OFF THE HOOK
Soft touch / Bad town / Work shy / Down in the dirt again / Jump back baby / She gives me the shakes / Satellite blues / Fire down below / Blue moon fever / Another kinda love / Goodbye cherry red
WOLCD 1028 / Sep '92 / China

☐ ON THE ROAD AGAIN
On the road again / No more the blues / Kiddio / Much too much / Doin' fine / Mama talk to your daughter / Cold cruel heart / Sweet little contessa / Hard goin' up (twice as hard coming down) / Sioux's shoes / Bird
WOLCD 1014 / Apr '91 / China

☐ WORKSHY
WOKCD 2027 / Sep '92 / China

Nine Inch Nails

☐ DISTURBED (Interview Disc)
DIST 001 / Mar '96 / Disturbed

☐ DOWNWARD SPIRAL, THE
Mr. Self destruct / Piggy / Heresy / March of the pigs / Closer / Ruiner / Becoming / I do not want this / Big man with a gun / Warm place / Eraser / Reptile / Downward spiral / Hurt
CID 8012 / Mar '94 / Island

☐ FIXED
Gave up / Wish / Happiness in slavery / Throw this away / First fuck / Screaming slave
IMCD 8005 / Dec '92 / Island

☐ FURTHER DOWN THE SPIRAL
Piggy (Nothing can stop me now) / Art of destruction (part 1) / Self destruction / Heresy / Downward spiral / Hurt / At the heart of it all / Ruiner / Eraser (Denial, realization) / Self destruction, final
IMCD 8041 / May '95 / Island

☐ INTERVIEW SESSIONS (Reznor, Trent)
CHAT 7 / 23 Feb '98 / Chatback

☐ PRETTY HATE MACHINE
Head like a hole / Terrible lie / Down in it / Sanctified / Something I can never have / Kinda I want to / Sin / That's what I get / Only time / Ringfinger
CID 9973 / Sep '91 / Island

☐ TRENT REZNOR INTERVIEW
RVCD 260 / 4 May '98 / Quantum Rockview

Nine Lives

☐ COMMON TRAP
BD 95001 / Jul '96 / Black Dog

☐ ROUNDABOUT
NERCD 093 / 27 Feb '98 / Nervous

Nine Pound Hammer

☐ HAYSEED TIMEBOMB
EFA 11583 2 / Sep '94 / Crypt

Ninefinger

☐ NINEFINGERED
TDH 019 / Feb '97 / Too Damn Hype

Niney The Observer

☐ BLOOD AND FIRE 1971-1972 (Niney & Friends)
Blood and fire / Brimstone and fire / Psalm 9 to keep in mind / Fire bunn / Aily and ailaloo / Reggaematic / Beardman / Keep on pushing / Ital correction / Rascal man / Rasta wagon man / When jah speak / Groming of jah / Message of the ungodly / In the gutter / Hiding by the riverside / 1234567 Jive it up / Observing the avenue / Everyday music / Swinging along / Mud and water / Lightning and thunder / My baby has gone / You must believe in me
CDTRL 263 / Dec '97 / Trojan

☐ FREAKS
HBCD 99 / Mar '95 / Heartbeat

☐ HERE I COME AGAIN VOL.1
RN 7003 / Sep '96 / Rhino

☐ NINEY THE OBSERVER
14807 / Jun '97 / Spalax

☐ OBSERVER ATTACK DUB
RUSCD 8209 / Jul '95 / ROIR

☐ TURBO CHARGE
CDHB 85 / May '91 / Rounder

Ninjaman

☐ BOOYAKKA BOOYAKKA
Disarm them / Go put it down / This girl is mine / Lighter / Education '94 / Gun fi bun / How master God world a run / Mi easy / Leff him / Reality (Part 2) / 'Pon mi mind / Woman a "U" ways / Matie / Sweeter ways
GRELCD 201 / Mar '94 / Greensleeves

☐ BOUNTY HUNTER
VYDCD 013 / Jul '96 / Vine Yard

☐ DON BAD MAN, THE
SONCD 0040 / Feb '93 / Sonic Sounds

☐ HARDCORE KILLING
GRELCD 191 / Sep '93 / Greensleeves

☐ HOLD ME (LIKE A M16)
Discipline child / Lou Lou / One black rat / Donkey mile / Lead me home / Walk that road / Vintage memories / Coming in hot / Kecke and kotch / On the road again
113822 / Jul '95 / Musidisc

☐ HOLLOW POINT BAD BOY
Bad boy nuh cub scout / Nuh badda trust dem / Tiger no dead / World dance / Write your will / Hold me / Whap dem bubba / Bad publicity
GRELCD 207 / Aug '94 / Greensleeves

☐ NOBODY'S BUSINESS BUT MY OWN
SHCD 45007 / May '93 / Shanachie

☐ ORIGINAL FRONT TOOTH, GOLDTOOTH, GUN-PON-TOOTH DON GORGON
GRELCD 181 / Feb '93 / Greensleeves

☐ RUN COME TEST
RASCD 3118 / Sep '93 / Ras

☐ TING A LING (SCHOOL PICKNEY)
GRELCD 176 / Nov '92 / Greensleeves

☐ WHAT A SHAME
What a shame / Warzone / New Jamaica / Two roads / Thank you Lord / Dem no like it / Bring dem all / Right hand / Bible a go through / Nice and slow
119912 / Sep '96 / Musidisc UK

Ninnghizhidda

☐ BLASPHEMY
IR 036CD / 20 Jul '98 / Invasion

Nipa

☐ GHANA A CAPELLA
925692 / Jun '93 / BUDA

Nirvana

☐ BARK AND THE BITE, THE (Interview Disc)
DIST 003 / Mar '96 / Disturbed

☐ BIOGRAPHY SERIES (Cobain, Kurt)
10012 / 3 Nov '97 / Metro Independent

☐ BLEACH
Blew / Floyd the barber / About a girl / School / Love Buzz / Paper cuts / Negative creep / Scoff / Swap meet / Mr. Moustache / Sifting / Big cheese / Downer
GFLD 19291 / Oct '95 / Geffen

☐ FROM THE MUDDY BANKS OF THE WISHKAH
Intro / School / Drain you / Aneurysm / Smeels like teen spirit / Been a son / Lithium / Sliver / Spank thru / Scentless apprentice / Heart-shaped box / Milk it / Negative creep / Polly / Breed / Tourette's / Blew
GED 25105 / Sep '96 / Geffen

☐ IN UTERO
Serve the servants / Scentless apprentice / Heart shaped box / Rape me / Frances Farmer will have her revenge on Seattle / Dumb / Very ape / Milk it / Pennyroyal tea / Radio friendly unit shifter / Tourette's / All apologies / Gallons of rubbing alcohol flow through the strip
GED 24536 / Sep '93 / Geffen

☐ INCESTICIDE
Dive / Sliver / Been a son / Turnaround / Molly's lips / Son of a gun / (New wave) Polly / Beeswax / Downer / Mexican seafood / Hairspray queen / Aero Zeppelin / Big long now / Aneurysm
GED 24504 / 8 Sep '97 / Geffen

☐ INTERVIEW DISC
TELL 07 / Dec '96 / Network

☐ INTERVIEW DISC
SAM 7008 / Nov '96 / Sound & Media

☐ KURT COBAIN (Interview Disc)
12827 / Oct '97 / Laserlight

☐ KURT COBAIN EXPOSE (2CD Set) (Cobain, Kurt)
OTR 1100039 / Jun '97 / Metro Independent

☐ NEVERMIND
Smells like teen spirit / In bloom / Come as you are / Breed / Lithium / Polly / Territorial pissings / Drain you / Lounge act / Stay away / On a plain / Something in the way
DGCD 24425 / Aug '91 / Geffen

☐ SINGLE BOX SET (6CD Singles Set)
Smells like teen spirit / Drain you / Even in his youth / Aneurysm / Come as you are / Endless nameless / School / Drain you (live) / Lithium / Been a son / Curmudgeon / D7 / In bloom / Sliver / Polly / Heart shaped box / Milk it / Marigold / All apologies / Rape me / Moist vagina
GED 24901 / Nov '95 / Geffen

☐ TRIBUTE TO NIRVANA, A (Various Artists)
TR 002CD / Jul '96 / Tribute

☐ UNPLUGGED IN NEW YORK
About a girl / Come as you are / Jesus doesn't want me for a sunbeam / Man who sold the world / Pennyroyal tea / Dumb / Polly / On a plain / Something in the way / Plateau / Oh me / Lake of fire / All apologies / Where did you sleep last night
GED 24727 / Oct '94 / Geffen

Nirvana

☐ BLACK FLOWER
Black flower / I believe in magic / It happened two Sundays ago / Life ain't easy / Pentecost Hotel / World is cold without you / We can make it through / Satellite jockey / Excerpt from The blind and the beautiful / June / Tiny goddess / Illinois / Tres tres bien / Love suite
EDCD 378 / Oct '93 / Edsel

☐ LOCAL ANAESTHETIC
REP 4109 / Aug '91 / Repertoire

☐ ORANGE & BLUE
EDCD 485 / Jun '96 / Edsel

☐ SECRET THEATRE
Girl in the park / Girl in the park / All through the night / Suspect sunday / Indiscreet harlequin / Bad boy / Dali / Jacqueline / Rio de janeiro / Waterfall / Radio ufo / Crazy hotel / 24 kisses / Electric money / Baby let me play ball / Rainbow chaser / Pascale / Tiny goddess / Restless wind / Habemus de loca / Girl from roxyville
EDCD 407 / Jan '95 / Edsel

☐ TRAVELLING ON A CLOUD
Rainbow chaser / Pentecost hotel / Tiny Goddess / Girl in the park / Melanie blue / You can try it / Trapeze / Satellite jockey / Wings of love / Show must go on / Touchables (All of us) / We can help you / Oh what a performance / Darling darlane
5109742 / Jul '92 / Island

Nissen, Peter

☐ PETER NISSEN
BCD 348 / Nov '96 / GHB

Nite Flyte

☐ 30,000 FEET
Cruise control / Coast to coast / 30,000 feet / Freefall / Here to eternity / 4am / Tuned in - spaced out / Professional widow / No bars held / Coast to coast
CDPJA 2 / 3 Nov '97 / Passion

Nite Life

☐ AS THE NIGHT MOVES THE SINGING J
SUNCD 005 / May '93 / Sunvibe

☐ ORIGINAL SING J, THE
OWCD 1093 / 15 Sep '97 / One World

Nitrate

☐ ACID STUKER
DBMLABCD 9 / Sep '96 / Labworks

Nitrogen

☐ INTOXICA (2CD Set)
ALPHACD 1 / Dec '96 / Alphaphone

Nitschky, Morten

☐ MUSIK TIL DIGTE (Nitschky, Morten Kvartet)
ASPCD 3502 / May '97 / Ambia

Nitty Gritty

☐ JAH IN THE FAMILY
BDCD 005 / Nov '92 / Blacka Dread

☐ TRIALS AND CROSSES (Tribute To Nitty Gritty) (Various Artists)
VPCD 1304 / Aug '93 / VP

☐ TURBO CHARGED
Gimme some of you something / Turbo-charged / Ram up the dance / Key to your heart / Rub-a-dub a kill you / Amazing grace / Cry cry baby / Down in the ghetto / Don't want to lose you / Hog in a minty
GRELCD 514 / May '92 / Greensleeves

Nitty Gritty Dirt Band

☐ ALIVE/RARE JUNK
Crazy words crazy tune / Buy for me the rain / Candy man / Foggy mountain breakdown / Rock me baby / Fat boys (can make it in Santa Monica) / Alligator man / Crazy words, crazy tune / Goodnight my love pleasant dreams / Reason to believe / End of your line / Willie the weeper / Hesitation blues / Sadie Green the vamp of New Orleans / Collegiana / Dr. Heckle and Mr. Jibe / Cornbread and lasses / Number and a name / Mournin' blues / These days
BGOCD 245 / Mar '95 / Beat Goes On

☐ ALL THE GOOD TIMES
Sixteen tracks / Fish song / Jambalaya / Down in Texas / Creepin' round your back door / Daisy / Slim Carter / Hoping to say / Baltimore / Jamaica say you will / Do you feel it too / Civil war trilogy / Diggy liggy lo
BGOCD 93 / Dec '90 / Beat Goes On

☐ BANG BANG BANG
UMD 80507 / 11 May '98 / Universal

☐ COUNTRY CLASSICS
Battle of New Orleans / I have to do is dream / Bayou jubilee / Sally was a guddun / Rave on / Mr Bojangles / Honky tonkin' / House at pooh corner / Some of shelly's blues / Moon just turned blue / Make a little magic / American dream / Hey good lookin' / Slim carter / Diggy liggy id
CDMFP 6328 / Apr '97 / Music For Pleasure

☐ DREAM
BGOCD 311 / Apr '96 / Beat Goes On

☐ HOLD ON
Fishin' in the dark / Joe knows how to live / Keepin' the road hot / Blue Ridge Mountain girl / Angelyne / Baby's got a hold on me / Dancing to the beat of a broken heart / Oh what a love / Oleanna / Tennessee
7599255732 / Feb '95 / Warner Bros.

☐ PURE DIRT
Buy for me the rain / It's raining here in long beach / Dismal swamp / Tide of love / Holding / Call again / You're gonna' get it in the end / Shadow dream song / Song to Jutta / Teddy bears picnic / Truly right / Put a bar in my car / Candy man / I'll search the sky
BGOCD 243 / Sep '94 / Beat Goes On

☐ RICOCHET
Teddy bears picnic / Happy fat annie / Coney island washboard / I'll never forget what's her name / Ooh po pi do girl / Put a bar in my car / It's raining here in long beach / Search the sky / Call again / Tide of love / Truly right / Shadow dream song
BGOCD 284 / Oct '95 / Beat Goes On

☐ STARS AND STRIPES FOREVER
Jambalaya / Dirt band interview / Cosmic cowboy Part 1 / Aluminium record award / Fish song / Mr. Bojangles / Vassar Clements interview / Listen to the mockingbird / Sheikh of Araby / Resign yourself to me / Dixie hoedown / Cripple creek / Mountain whippoorwill / Honky tonkin' / House at Pooh corner / Buy for me the rain / Oh boy / Teardrops in my eyes / Glocoat blues / Stars and stripes forever / Battle of New Orleans / It came from the 50's / My true story / Diggy liggy lo
BGOCD 128 / Jul '90 / Beat Goes On

☐ UNCLE CHARLIE AND HIS DOG TEDDY
Some of Shelly's blues / Rave on / Livin' without you / Uncle Charlie interview / Mr. Bojangles / Clinch Mountain breakdown / Propinquity / Cure / Opus 36 / Clementi / Chicken reel / Travellin' mood / Billy in the lowground / Swanee river / Randy Lynn rag / Santa Rosa / Prodigal's return / Yukon railroad / House at Pooh Corner / Jesse James / Uncle Charlie / Uncle Charlie interview / End / Spanish fandango
BGOCD 22 / Apr '90 / Beat Goes On

☐ WILL THE CIRCLE BE UNBROKEN (2CD Set)
DC 870432 / Aug '96 / Disky

☐ WILL THE CIRCLE BE UNBROKEN VOL.2 (Nitty Gritty Dirt Band/Various Artists)
Life's railway to heaven / Grandpa was a carpenter / When to get my rewards / Don't you hear Jerusalem moan / Little mountain church house / And so it goes / Mary danced with soldiers / Riding alone / I'm sitting on top of the world / Lovin' on the side / Lost river / Bayou jubilee / Blueberry Hill / Turn of the century / One step over the line / You ain't goin' nowhere / Valley road / Will the circle be unbroken / Amazing grace
BGOCD 400 / 30 Mar '98 / Beat Goes On

Nitzer Ebb

☐ BELIEF, THE
Hearts and minds / For fun / Control im here / Captivate / Twa / Blood money / Shame / Drive / Without belief / K.i.a. drive without belief / K.i.a. / Control im here (s.d.i. mix) / Without belief (inst)
CDSTUMM 61 / Oct '88 / Mute

☐ BIG HIT
CDSTUMM 118 / Mar '95 / Mute

☐ EBBHEAD
Reasons / Lakeside drive / I give to you / Sugar sweet / Djvd / Time / Ascend / Godhead / Trigger happy
CDSTUMM 88 / Sep '91 / Mute

☐ SHOWTIME
Getting closer / Nobody knows / One man's burden / All over / My heart / Lightning man / Rope / Hold on / Fun to be had
CDSTUMM 72 / Feb '90 / Mute

☐ THAT TOTAL AGE
Fitness to purpose / Violent playground / Murderous / Smear body / Let your body learn / Let beauty loose / Into the large air / Join in the chant / Alarm / Join in the chant (metal mix) / Fitness to purpose ' / Murderous (instrumental)
CDSTUMM 45 / May '87 / Mute

Nivens

☐ SHAKE
DANCD 022 / Jan '90 / Danceteria

Nix, Bern

☐ ALARMS AND EXCURSIONS (Nix, Bern Trio)
804372 / Sep '93 / New World

Nix, Don

☐ GONE TOO LONG/SKYRIDER
Goin' thru another change / Feel a whole lot better / Gone too long / Backstreet girl / Rollin' in my dreams / Yazoo city jail / Harpoon Arkansas turnaround / Forgotten town / Demain / Skyrider / Nobody else / Maverick woman blues / Do it again / Long tall Sally / I'll be in your dreams / On the town again / All for the love of a woman
DIAB 805 / Feb '94 / Diablo

Nix, Rev. A.W.

☐ REV. A.W. NIX VOL.1 1927-1928
DOCD 5328 / Mar '95 / Document

☐ REV. A.W. NIX/REV. EMMETT DICKINSON VOL.2 1928-1931 (Nix, Rev. A.W. & Rev. Emmett Dickinson)
DOCD 5490 / Nov '96 / Document

Nixon, Hammie

☐ TAPPIN' THAT THING
HMC 6509 / 30 Mar '98 / Hightone

Nixon, Mojo

☐ HORNY HOLIDAYS (Nixon, Mojo & The Toadliquors)
422427 / May '94 / New Rose

☐ WHEREABOUTS UNKOWN
422052 / May '95 / Last Call

No Authority

☐ KEEP ON
Don't stop / Up and down / Girlfriend / Why / Please don't break my heart / Keep on / One more time / If you want me / Never let you go / I like it
4895342 / 4 May '98 / Epic

No Comment

☐ EYES
SPV 07784712 / Jul '94 / SPV

No Doubt

☐ BEACON STREET COLLECTION, THE
Open the gate / Total hate 95 / Stricken / Greener pastures / By the way / Snakes / That's just me / Squeal / Doghouse / Blue in the face
BS 03 / Apr '97 / Beacon Street

☐ INTERVIEW SESSIONS
CHAT 16 / 1 Dec '97 / Chatback

☐ INTERVIEW, THE
SPEEK 003 / 16 Mar '98 / Talking Music

☐ NO DOUBT
IND 92109 / 25 May '98 / Interscope

☐ TRAGIC KINGDOM
Spiderwebs / Excuse me Mr. / Just a girl / Happy now / Different people / Hey you / Climb / Sixteen / Sunday morning / Don't speak / You can do it / World go 'round / End it on this / Tragic kingdom
IND 90003 / Jul '96 / Interscope

No Empathy

☐ GOOD LUCK MAKES ME
JFR 040CD / 23 Mar '98 / Johann's Face

No For An Answer

☐ THOUGHT CRUSADE, A/FACE THE NATION (No For An Answer/Carry Nation)
FLY 002 / Oct '96 / Tackle Box

No Fraud

☐ NO FRAUD
Resist the urge for power / Search / Open / Smoke the bone / Hard to the core / Aggression / L.i.f.e. / Failure / Don't let me grow old / Thinking of you / Wastecase / Intro / Nothing left inside / Suicidal maniac / It's all economic / Changes
MIND 003CD / Jul '91 / Nuclear Blast

No Fun At All

☐ AND NOW FOR SOMETHING COMPLETELY DIFFERENT
JABSC 003CD / Apr '97 / Burning Heart

☐ BIG KNOCKOVER
BHR 066CD / 9 Oct '97 / Burning Heart

☐ EP'S GOING STEADY
BHR 077CD / 27 Apr '98 / Burning Heart

☐ NO STRAIGHT ANGLES
BHR 011CD / Aug '95 / Burning Heart

☐ OUT OF BOUNDS
BHR 013CD / Oct '95 / Burning Heart

☐ STRANDED
BHR 023CD / May '95 / Burning Heart

☐ VISIONS
BHR 003CD / Aug '95 / Burning Heart

No ID

☐ ACCEPT YOUR OWN BE YOURSELF
Heat / Fate or destiny / We orck like so / State to state / We like to rock so / I'm thinkin' / Mega live (that's the joint) / Sky's the limit / Dreams / Real weight / Jump on it / Gem / Original man / Pray for sinners / Two steps behind
4886642 / 22 Sep '97 / Epic

No Innocent Victim

☐ NO INNOCENT VICTIM
TOL 9802CD / 8 Jun '98 / Tolerance

No Lesson Learned

☐ ONE MORE SURRENDER
LF 269CD / May '97 / Lost & Found

☐ PERSONAL
LF 305CD / 25 May '98 / Lost & Found

No Man

☐ DAMAGE THE ENEMY
NAR 043CD / May '93 / New Alliance

No Man

☐ CAROLINA SKELETONS
STONE 037CD / 24 Aug '98 / 3rd Stone

☐ DRY CLEANING RAY
Dry cleaning Ray / Sweetside silver night / Jack the
sax / Diet mothers / Urban disco / Punished for being
born / Kightlinger / Evelyn (Song of slurs) / Sicknote
STONE 035CD / 16 Mar '98 / 3rd Stone

☐ FLOWERMIX
Angeldust / Faith in you / All I see / Natural neck /
Heal the madness / You grow more / Beautiful
(version) / Sample / Why the noise / Born simple
HIART 002 / Oct '96 / Hidden Art

☐ FLOWERMOUTH
Angel gets caught in the beauty trap / You grow more
beautiful / Animal ghost / Soft shoulders / Shell of a
fighter / Teardrop fall / Watching over me / Simple /
Things change
TPLP 67CD / Jun '94 / One Little Indian

☐ HEAVEN TASTE
Long day full / Babyship blue / Bleed / Road / Heaven
taste
HIART 001 / Oct '96 / Hidden Art

☐ WILD OPERA
Radiant city / Pretty genius / Infant phenomenon /
Sinister jazz / Housewives hooked on heroin /
Librtino libretto / Taste my dream / Dry cleaning ray /
Sheep loop / My rival Trevor / Time travel in Texas /
My revenge on Seattle / Wild opera
STONE 027CD / 30 Mar '98 / 3rd Stone

No Man Is Roger Miller

☐ WIN INSTANTLY
Run water, run water / Run water, run water / Calling
the animals / Scratch / This is not a photograph /
Promised land / Quarry / Renegades / Voluptuous
airplanes
SST 243CD / Jul '89 / SST

No Means No

☐ 0+2=1
VIRUS 98CD / Oct '91 / Alternative
Tentacles

☐ DANCE OF THE HEADLESS
BOURGEOISIE
VIRUS 215CD / 29 Jun '98 / Alternative
Tentacles

☐ DAY EVERYTHING BECAME
ISOLATED AND DESTROYED, THE
Day everything became nothing / Dead souls /
Forget your life / Beauty and the beast / Brother rat /
What slayde says / Dark ages / Junk / And that's sad
/ Small parts isolated and destroyed / Victory /
Teresa give me that knife / Real love / Lonely
VIRUS 62/63CD / Jan '89 / Alternative
Tentacles

☐ IN THE FISHTANK
FIRSTFISH 1CD / May '97 / Konkurrent

☐ LIVE AND CUDDLY
VIRUS 97CD / '92 / Alternative
Tentacles

☐ MAMA
WRONG 001CD / Nov '92 / Wrong

☐ NO MEANS NO PRESENTS: MR
WRIGHT & MR WRONG
WRONG 13 / Oct '94 / Wrong

☐ SEX MAD
Sex mad / Dad / Obsessed / No fucking / She beast /
Dead Bob / Long days / Metronome / Revenge / Self
pity
VIRUS 56CD / '92 / Alternative
Tentacles

☐ SMALL PARTS ISOLATED AND
DESTROYED
VIRUS 63CD / '88 / Alternative
Tentacles

☐ WHY DO THEY CALL ME MR. HAPPY
Land of the living / River / Machine / Madness and
death / Happy bridge / Kill everyone now / I need you
/ Slowly melting / Lullaby / Cats, sex and nazis
VIRUS 123CD / May '93 / Alternative
Tentacles

☐ WORLDHOOD OF THE WORLD AS
SUCH
VIRUS 171CD / Nov '95 / Alternative
Tentacles

☐ WRONG
VIRUS 77CD / Oct '89 / Alternative
Tentacles

No Mercy

☐ MY PROMISE
Where do you go / Kiss you all over / Don't make me
live without you / When I die / Please don't go /
Bonita / My promise to you / D'yer mak'er / Missing /
This masquerade / In and out / Who do you love /
How much I love you / Part of me / Where do you go
74321466902 / May '97 / Arista

No More Heroes

☐ RATS, RAVENS AND MEN IN BLACK
77283CD / 6 Jul '98 / Fliptop

No Neck Blues Band

☐ LETTER FROM THE EARTH (2CD Set)
YODSOUND 1 / Apr '97 / Father Yod/
Sound

No No Diet Bang

☐ RAZZIA
1991252 / Nov '93 / Brambus

No One Is Innocent

☐ UTOPIA
Black garden / Invisible / Chile / Nomenklatura /
Radio 101 / Le poison / Women / Amere / Autobahn
babies / Two people / Ce que nous savons / Inside /
Pinecrest solution / Neuromatrix
5243372 / Mar '97 / Island

No Redeeming Social Value

☐ ROCKS THE PARTY
SFT 12 / 26 May '98 / Striving For
Togetherness

No Safety

☐ LIVE AT THE KNITTING FACTORY
KFWCD 149 / Feb '95 / Knitting Factory

☐ SPILL
KFWCD 127 / Nov '94 / Knitting Factory

☐ THIS LOST LEG
RECDEC 25 / Oct '93 / Rec Rec

No Secrets In The Family

☐ PLAY AND STRANGE LAUGHTER
RECDEC 23 / Oct '93 / Rec Rec

No Sports

☐ RIDDIM ROOTS AND CULTURE
DM 300022 / 8 Jun '98 / Deshima

No Talents

☐ WE ARE THE NO TALENTS
SKIP 062CD / 8 Sep '97 / Broken

No Think

☐ THINKING ANIMALS
Dirt king / Choice / Discrimination / No think /
Science dream / Continue of dead noise / Thinking
animals
FIST 7X / Jun '98 / Discipline

No Use For A Name

☐ DAILY GRIND, THE
FATCD 507 / Sep '93 / Fatwreck Chords

☐ LECHE CON CARNE
FAT 522 / Mar '95 / Fatwreck Chords

☐ NRA YEARS
CDHOLE 013 / 13 Oct '97 / Fatwreck
Chords

No Wings Fins Or Fuselage

☐ NO WINGS FINS OR FUSELAGE
LLL 2040 / 13 Oct '97 / Saucer

No.1 De No.1

☐ DAKAR SOUND VOL.6
2002969 / Jan '97 / Dakar Sound

Noa

☐ BOTH SIDES OF THE SEA
61868500042 / 5 May '98 / MMEL

Noakes, Rab

☐ STANDING UP
I've hardly started / I wish I was in England / What do
you want the girl to do / Solid gone / Love is a gamble
/ Downtown lights / Gently does it / Blue dream /
Psycho killer / Deep water / Open all night / Niel
young's apprentice / Goodbye to all that / Lenny Bruce
/ When this bloody war is over / Remember my name
/ Absolutely sweet Marie
MDMCD 003 / Oct '94 / Moidart

Noble, Liam

☐ CLOSE YOUR EYES
FMRCD 25 / Oct '95 / Future

Noble, Ray

☐ HMV SESSIONS VOL.1 1930-1934, THE
(Noble, Ray & His Orchestra)
Goodnight sweetheart / You're driving me crazy /
Time on my hands / I'm telling the world she's mine /
Lady of Spain / Fiesta: Noble, Ray & His Orchestra/Al
Bowlly
CDEA 6009 / 15 Jun '98 / Vocalion

☐ RAY NOBLE 1941 (Noble, Ray & His
Orchestra)
CCD 126 / Aug '94 / Circle

☐ VERY THOUGHT OF YOU, THE (Noble,
Ray & Al Bowlly)
After all, you're all I'm after / Bugle call rag / By the
fireside / Close your eyes / Dinah / Don't say
goodbye / Double trouble / Down by the river /
Goodnight sweetheart / I'll string along with you /
Lazy day / Love is the sweetest thing / Love looked
out / Mad about the boy / Maybe I love you too much /
Oceans of time / Soon / Time on my hands / Very
thought of you / Way down yonder in New Orleans /
We've got the moon and sixpence / When you've got
a little springtime in your heart / Where am I / You
ought to see Sally on Sunday / You're more than all
the world to me
CDAJA 5115 / May '94 / Living Era

☐ VERY THOUGHT OF YOU, THE
Very thought of you / Love is the sweetest thing /
Spanish eyes / Dreaming a dream / Slumming on
Park Avenue / By the fireside / Top hat, white tie and
tails / I used to be colour blind / Medley / That's what
life is made of / Let yourself go / Basin Street blues /
Oh you nasty man / Change partners / Love locked
out / Goodnight sweetheart / Medley / Medley
PAR 2032 / Oct '94 / Parade

Noble Rot

☐ REAL LUST FOR LIFE
BMCD 52 / May '94 / Black Mark

Noble, Steve

☐ BUD MOON (Noble, Steve & Oren
Marshall/Steve Buckley)
PPPCD 002 / May '97 / Ping Pong

☐ FLATHEAD REUNION (Noble, Steve &
Oren Marshall/Davey Williams)
PPPCD 001 / Oct '97 / Ping Pong

Nobodys

☐ GREATASSTITS
HR 628CD / 22 May '98 / Hopeless

☐ SMELL OF VICTORY, THE
HR 622CD / Jul '97 / Hopeless

Nock, Mike

☐ IN OUT AND AROUND (Nock, Mike
Quartet)
Break time / Dark light / Shadows of forgotten / Gift /
Hadrian's wall / In, out and around
CDSJP 119 / Jun '91 / Timeless Jazz

☐ NOT WE BUT ONE (Nock, Mike Trio)
860062 / Jun '97 / Naxos Jazz

☐ ONDAS
Forgotten love / Ondas / Visionary / Land of the long
white cloud / Doors
8291612 / Aug '86 / ECM

☐ OZBOPPIN'
Ozboppin' / Philosphers / Five'll getcha / Exile /
Snafu / Dreamtime visitor / Come Sunday /
Emperor's clothes / End of a love affair
860192 / Jul '94 / Naxos Jazz

Noctes

☐ PANDEMONIC REQUIEM
NFR 025CD / 11 May '98 / No Fashion

Nocturnal Emissions

☐ DROWNING IN A SEA OF BLISS
TO 4 / Oct '95 / Touch

☐ SONGS OF LOVE AND REVOLUTION
DV 019CD / May '95 / Dark Vinyl

☐ VIRAL SHREDDING
DV 011CD / Sep '95 / Dark Vinyl

Nocturnal Rites

☐ IN A TIME OF BLOOD AND FIRE
MRRCD 032 / Nov '96 / Dark Age Music

☐ TALES OF MYSTERY AND
IMAGINATION
CM 77208CD / 13 Apr '98 / Century
Media

Nocturne, Johnny

☐ SHAKE 'EM UP (Nocturne, Johnny
Band)
BBCD 9553 / Nov '94 / Bullseye Blues

☐ WAILIN' DADDY (Nocturne, Johnny
Band)
Wailin' / Just a dream / Let's ball / Baby, I'm doin' it /
Howling at midnight / Blues has got me / Candy / I've
got a feeling / I'm a fool to want you / No, I ain't gonna
let you go / Rebop jump
BBCD 9526 / Jun '93 / Bullseye Blues

☐ WILD AND COOL
Lemon twist / New kind of mambo / Tu ma qui te /
Don't get around much anymore / Hey Mister Jessie
/ Pound of blues / At my front door / By the river Ste.
Marie / Cha-bootie / After the lights go down low /
Little slam
CDBB 9586 / Apr '98 / Bullseye Blues

Nod

☐ MAGNETIC ANOMALY
SLR 025 / 8 Jun '98 / Smells Like

Node

☐ NODE
Clock / Olivine / Slapback / Levy / Propane
DVNT 005CD / Oct '95 / Deviant

Noferini, Stefano

☐ FROM HERE TO THE MOON
ACVCD 016 / Jun '96 / ACV

NOFX

☐ I HEARD THEY SUCK...LIVE
FATCD 528 / Dec '96 / Fatwreck Chords

☐ LONGEST LINE
FAT 503CD / Dec '96 / Fatwreck Chords

☐ MAXIMUM ROCK 'N' ROLL
MYSTICCD 180 / Oct '94 / Mystic

☐ S & M AIRLINES
E 86405CD / Nov '92 / Epitaph

☐ SO LONG AND THANKS FOR ALL THE
SHOES
180 degrees / I'm telling him / Dad's bad news /
Falling in love / Kill rock stars / Punk rock elite /
Murder the government / Stuck in the k-hole agin /
Desperation's gone / All outta angst / Champs
Elysees / Quart in session / Mono syllabic girl / Eat
the meek
65182 / 3 Nov '97 / Epitaph

Nogenja Jazz Soloist Ensemble

☐ REGNI
PSCD 93 / May '97 / Phono Suecia

Nogueras, Jose

☐ TIEMPO NUEVO
66058077 / Dec '95 / RMM

Noirin Ni Riain

☐ SOUNDINGS
OSSCD 88 / Dec '94 / Ossian

Noise & Paradox

☐ NOISE & PARADOX
NOZACD 8 / 13 Oct '97 / Ninebar

☐ TRANSMOGRAPFICATION
NOZACD 09 / 26 May '98 / Ninebar

Noise Addict

☐ MEET THE REAL YOU
GR 024CD / Apr '97 / Grand Royal

☐ YOUNG AND JADED
GR 005CD / Apr '97 / Grand Royal

Noise Annoys

☐ FIRST STEP
EFA 11841CD / Jul '93 / Vince Lombard

Noise Box

☐ BEGINNING, THE
CLP 99272 / Jul '97 / Cleopatra

☐ MONKEY ASS
SPV 08422202 / Jun '95 / SPV

Noise Unit

☐ DECODER
EFA 084662 / May '95 / Dossier

☐ DRILL
08543372 / Feb '97 / Westcom

☐ STRATEGY OF VIOLENCE
CLEO 94752 / Aug '95 / Cleopatra

Noiseaddict

☐ YOUNG AND JADED
I wish I was him / My song / Meat / Pop queen /
Back in your life / Don't leave
WIJ 035CD / Apr '94 / Wiiija

Noitarega

☐ NOITAREGA
40040CD / Jun '94 / Sonifolk

Nolan, Anthony

☐ CLASSIC IRISH MELODIES
CHCD 040 / Oct '96 / Chart

Nolan, Col

☐ NOLAN'S GROOVE
LB 9601 / Jul '98 / La Brava

Nolan Irie

☐ WORK SO HARD
People can you hear me / People's dub / Work so hard / Dub like nails / Irie feelings / Dub feelings / Because of dub / Turn it up / Dub it up / Never give it up / Just dub it up / Beware, the coming is nigh / Beware, the dub is nigh / Educated dub
ARICD 81 / Nov '93 / Ariwa Sounds

Noland, Patrick

☐ PIANO GATHERING LIGHT
NAIMCD 011 / May '97 / Naim Audio

Noland, Terry

☐ HYPNOTIZED
Hyopnotized / Ten little women / Come marry me / Oh baby look at me / Don't do me this way / Oh Judy / Sugar drop / Guess I'm gonna fall / There was a fungus among us / Everyone but one / One sweet kiss / Crazy dream / Let me be your hero / Puppy love / Patty baby / Teenage teardrops / Forever loving you / You and I / Leave me alone / My teenage heart / She's gone (master) / Ten little women / Hypnotized / World's a rockin' / Heartless woman / She's gone / That ain't right / Hound dog
BCD 15428 / Feb '90 / Bear Family

Nolans

☐ BEST OF THE NOLANS, THE
In the mood for dancing / Attention to me / Don't love me too hard / Gotta pull myself together / Don't make waves / Sexy music / Thank you for the music / Every little thing / Simple case of loving you / I'm never gonna let you break my heart again / If it takes me all night / Let's make love / God knows / Dragon fly / Chemistry / Who's gonna rock you / Every home should have one / Touch me in the morning / Crashing down / Spirit, body and soul
4840442 / May '96 / Epic

☐ I'M IN THE MOOD FOR DANCING
I'm in the mood for dancing / Attention to me / Don't love me too hard / Chemistry / Dragonfly / Crashin' down / Sexy music / Gotta pull myself together / Every home should have one / Who's gonna rock you / Spirit, body and soul / Don't make waves
QED 029 / Nov '96 / Tring

☐ I'M IN THE MOOD FOR DANCING
I'm in the mood for dancing / Attention to me / Don't love me too hard / Chemistry / Dragonfly / Crashin' down / Sexy music / Gotta pull myself together / Every home should have one / Who's gonna rock you / Spirit, body and soul / Don't make waves
101152 / May '97 / A-Play Collection

☐ VERY BEST OF THE NOLANS, THE
Somebody loves you / That's what friends are for / I'm in the mood for dancing / Who's gonna rock you / Dragonfly / Chemistry / Every home should have one / Gotta pull myself together / Out of control / Don't love me too hard / Attention to me / Don't make waves / Crashing down / Run to you / Sexy music / Spirit, body and soul / Almaz / Unchained melody
SUMCD 4062 / Nov '96 / Summit

Nolet, Jim

☐ WITH YOU
KFWCD 150 / Feb '95 / Knitting Factory

Nomad

☐ QUATUOR VOCAL
TE 011 / Jun '97 / EPM

Nomad, Naz

☐ GIVE DADDY THE KNIFE, CINDY (Nomad, Naz & The Nightmares)
Nobody but me / Action woman / Wind blows your hair / Kicks / Cold turkey / She lied / I had too much to dream last night / Trip / I can only give you everything / I can't stand this love, goodbye / Do you know I know / Just call me Sky
CDWIKM 21 / Jun '88 / Big Beat

Nomads

☐ MADE IN JAPAN
1+2CD 086 / 26 Jan '98 / 1+2

☐ POWERSTRIP
(I'm) out of it / Bad vibes / Better off dead / I don't know/I don't care / Sacred / Just lost / Kinda crime / Dig up the hatchet / Robert Johnsong / In the doghouse / Glad to be in your past / Blind spot
RTD 1578082 / Jun '94 / World Service

Nomicon

☐ NOMICON/SARNATH (Split CD) (Nomicon/Sarnath)
SHR 011CD / Aug '95 / Shiver

Nomos

☐ I WON'T BE AFRAID ANYMORE
GRACD 205 / Apr '95 / Grapevine

☐ SET YOU FREE
GRACD 230 / Aug '97 / Grapevine

Non

☐ BLOOD AND FAME
Fire in the organism / Make red / Sunset / Taste of blood / Kingdom come / King of beast / Dark shadows / Pillar of silence / Storm / Cruenta voluptas / Secret garden, secret fire / Only one / Rise below / And if thou will, remember / Operation carnival / Rise / If I will remember / Inside out / Carnis vale
CDSTUMM 32 / Jan '87 / Mute

☐ GOD AND BEAST
God and beast / Between Venus and Mars / Millstones / Coming forth / Law / Lucifer the morning star / Out out out / Phoenix / Total war
CDSTUMM 158 / 3 Nov '97 / Mute

☐ IN THE SHADOW OF THE SWORD
World on fire / Love and loves murder / Fire in the organism-vengeance / Scorched earth / Invocation / Abraxas
CDSTUMM 113 / Oct '92 / Mute

☐ MIGHT!
CDSTUMM 139 / Oct '95 / Mute

Non Serviam

☐ NECROTICAL
IR 037CD / 20 Jul '98 / Invasion

Non-Fiction

☐ IT'S A WONDERFUL LIE
085518242 / Jan '96 / SPV

Nonce

☐ WORLD ULTIMATE
74321254522 / Oct '95 / RCA

Nonet, Arnaud

☐ KAMALA (Nonet, Arnaud Mattei)
CDLLL 147 / Aug '93 / La Lichere

Nonex

☐ NONEX
SD 019CD / 22 Jun '98 / Stereo Deluxe

Nonoyesno

☐ DEPSHIT ARKANSAS
NB 0942 / Feb '94 / Nuclear Blast

Nookie

☐ SOUND OF MUSIC, THE
RIVETCD 5 / Mar '95 / Reinforced

Noonan, Carol

☐ ABSOLUTION
CDPH 1176 / Sep '95 / Philo

☐ NOONAN BUILDING AND WRECKING (Noonan, Carol Band)
PH 1196CD / Aug '96 / Philo

☐ ONLY WITNESS, THE
Don't be afraid / Emery Lane / Steadfast / Taillights fade / Queen Jane / Not coming home / Under my eyes / Break her heart / Only witness / Unknown thing
CDPH 1209 / Sep '97 / Philo

Noone, Jimmie

☐ APEX OF NEW ORLEANS JAZZ, THE (His 25 Greatest)
Play that thing: *Powers, Ollie Harmony Syncopators* / Messin' around: *Cookie's Gingersnaps* / Here comes the hot tamale man: *Cookie's Gingersnaps* / I know that you know: *Noone, Jimmie Apex Club Orchestra* / Four of five times: *Noone, Jimmie Apex Club Orchestra* / Every evening: *Noone, Jimmie Apex Club Orchestra* / Apex blues: *Noone, Jimmie Apex Club Orchestra* / Monday date: *Noone, Jimmie Apex Club Orchestra* / Blues my naughty sweetie gives to me: *Noone, Jimmie Apex Club Orchestra* / Oh sister ain't that hot: *Noone, Jimmie Apex Club Orchestra* / King Joe: *Noone, Jimmie Apex Club Orchestra* / Some rainy day: *Noone, Jimmie Apex Club Orchestra* / Chicago rhythm: *Noone, Jimmie Apex Club Orchestra* / I got a misery: *Noone, Jimmie Apex Club Orchestra* / I lost my gal from Memphis: *Noone, Jimmie New Orleans Band* / San: *Noone, Jimmie Apex Club Orchestra* / Way down yonder in New Orleans: *Noone, Jimmie New Orleans Band* / Blues jumped a rabbit: *Noone, Jimmie New Orleans Band* / Sweet Georgia Brown: *Noone, Jimmie New Orleans Band* / New Orleans hop scop blues: *Noone, Jimmie Orchestra* / Keystone blues: *Noone, Jimmie Orchestra* / Clambake in B flat: *Capitol Jazz Band* / Muskrat ramble: *Ory, Kid Creole Jazz Band* / Sugarfoot stomp: *Ory, Kid Creole Jazz Band*
CDAJA 5235 / Apr '97 / Living Era

☐ CLASSICS 1923-1928
CLASSICS 604 / Sep '91 / Classics

☐ CLASSICS 1928-1929 (Noone, Jimmie & Friends)
CLASSICS 611 / Feb '92 / Classics

☐ CLASSICS 1929-1930
CLASSICS 632 / Nov '92 / Classics

☐ CLASSICS 1930-1934
CLASSICS 641 / Nov '92 / Classics

☐ CLASSICS 1934-1940
CLASSICS 651 / Nov '92 / Classics

☐ COLLECTION VOL.1, THE
COCD 06 / Nov '92 / Collector's Classics

☐ COMPLETE RECORDINGS VOL.1 (3CD Set)
Lonesome and sorry / Baby o' mine / My blue heaven / Miss Annabelle Lee / I know that you know / Sweet Sue, just you / Four or five times / Every evening I miss you / Ready for the river / Forevermore / Oh sister ain't that hold / I ain't got nobody / Apex blues / Monday date / Blues my naughty sweetie gives to me / King Joe / Sweet Lorraine / Some rainy day / It's tight like that / Let's sow a wild oat / She's funny that way / St. Louis blues / Chicago rhythm / I got a misery / Wake up chill'un, wake up / Love me or leave me / Anything you want / Birmingham Bertha / Am I blue / My daddy's rock me / Ain't misbehavin' / That rhythm man / Off time / S'posin' / True blue / Through / Satisfied / I'm doin' what I'm doin' for love / He's a good man to have around / My melancholy baby / After you've gone / Love / El rado scuffle / Deep trouble / Crying for the Carolines / Have a little faith in me / Should I / I'm following you / When you're smiling / I lost my gal from Memphis / On revival day / I'm drifting back to dreamland / Virginia Lee / So sweet / San
CDAFS 10273 / Oct '92 / Affinity

☐ INTRODUCTION TO JIMMIE NOONE 1923-1940, AN
4034 / Jul '96 / Best Of Jazz

Noone, Peter

☐ I'M INTO SOMETHING GOOD
WMCD 5630 / Oct '94 / Disky

☐ PETER NOONE SINGS HITS OF HERMAN'S HERMITS
MU 5021 / Oct '92 / Musketeer

Noordhoek, Tineke

☐ GAMES (Noordhoek, Tineke & Camilla Clauson-Kaas)
MECCACD 2043 / Oct '97 / Music Mecca

Nooten, Pieter

☐ SLEEPS WITH THE FISHES (Nooten, Pieter & Michael Brook)
Several times I / Searching / Choice / After the call / Finally ii / Instrumental / Suddenly ii / Suddenly I / Clouds / Finally I / Several times ii / Equal ways / These waves / Times / Several times iii
GAD 710CD / 6 Jul '98 / 4AD

Nora

☐ NORA
HABITCD 002 / Oct '95 / Habit

Norbo, Soren

☐ SOREN NORBO & JOAKIM MILDER (Norbo, Soren & Joakim Milder)
MECCACD 2012 / May '97 / Music Mecca

Nord Express

☐ CENTRAL
SLR 057CD / May '97 / Slumberland

☐ NORD EXPRESS
SLR 051CD / Dec '96 / Slumberland

Nord Rundfunk Bigband

☐ BRAVISSIMO
Cat / Blue monk / Voodoo chile / Sagma / Night in Tunesia / Take the 'A' train / Supraconductivity / Sister Sadie / Mood indigo / Django / Descent / Country roads
92322 / Jun '96 / Act

Nordenstam, Stina

☐ AND SHE CLOSED HER EYES
Little star / Viewed from the spire / When debbie's back from texas / And she closed her eyes / Something nice / So this is goodbye / I see you again / Murder in the mairyland park / Hopefully yours / Proposal / Fireworks / Crime
4509938982 / Dec '96 / East West

☐ DYNAMITE
Under your command / Dynamite / Almost a smile / Mary Bell / Man with the gun / Until / This time John / CQD / Down desire avenue / Now that your leaving
0630182402 / Apr '97 / East West

☐ MEMORIES OF A COLOR
Memories of a color / Return of Alan Bean / Another story girl / His song / He watches her from behind / I'll be cryin' for you / Alone at night / Soon after Christmas / Walk in the dark
4509907672 / Dec '96 / East West

Nordes

☐ CRUZ DE PEDRA
20054CD / Dec '94 / Sonifolk

Nordic All Women Big Band

☐ SOMEWHERE IN TIME
MECCACD 1048 / Nov '94 / Music Mecca

Nordine, Ken

☐ COLORS
ASP 0954CD / 22 Jun '98 / Asphodel

☐ DEVOUT CATALYST
I love a groove / Mr. slick / Inside of is / Aging young rebel / Quatrains of thought / Spread eagle and the final page / Thousand bing bangs / Cracks in the ceiling / Ways of the meek / Movie / Zodiac uprising / Last will
GDCD 4017 / Feb '92 / Grateful Dead

Nordstrom, Inger

☐ I'LL LET YOU MAKE IT UP TO ME
CDSGP 0145 / Jul '96 / Prestige

Nordstrom, Nils

☐ UR UPP LANDSKT (Nordstrom, Nils & Ann-Christine Granfors)
AW 9CD / Aug '96 / Tongang

Noreaga

☐ NORE
PENCD 3077 / 13 Jul '98 / Tommy Boy

Noren, Fredrik

☐ JAZZ IN SWEDEN 1980
1211 / Feb '87 / Caprice

Nori, Samul

☐ RECORD OF CHANGES
CMPCD 3002 / 30 Mar '98 / CMP

Noris, Gunter

☐ DANCE WITH ME
Dirty mambo / Night dance / Tango negro / Corrida / Rainbow melody / Rock 'n' roll forever / Leipziger jive / Babloo you / Cha cha cubana / Viva la samba / Midnight in Munich / Animation / Brandenburger schwung / Furstenberg fantasie / Swinging Berlin / Frohliches meissen
12712 / May '96 / Laserlight

☐ HOLIDAY DANCING (Noris, Gunter & His Gala Big Band)
EDL 29172 / Dec '95 / Savoy

☐ TANZE MIT MIR IN DEN MORGEN (Noris, Gunter & His Gala Big Band)
EDL 29142 / Dec '95 / Savoy

☐ WE PLAY REQUESTS VOL.1
Quickstep in catsby / Exercise jive / Flic flac fox (quickstep) / Dance and dream (slow foxtrot) / Slowly to heaven (slow foxtrot) / Midnight waltz / Darf ich bitten (waltz) / Tango erotique / Tango negro / Montags waltzer / Walzer fur nicola (viennese waltz) / Happy dancer (cha-cha-cha) / Pinacolada (cha cha) / Echo cha-cha / Samba banana / Jamaican samba / Rumba sangria / Rumba romantica (rumba) / Exercise jive / Rock and roll forever (jive) / Corrida (paso doble)
WRCD 5001 / Oct '95 / WRD

Norma

☐ HARP AND THE DONKEY, THE
RERNORMA 1 / Jan '98 / ReR/ Recommended

Norma Jean

☐ NATURAL BLONDE KILLERS
HSICD 003 / 8 Jun '98 / High Society

Normal

☐ NORMAL 1977-1984
AR 05 / 20 Apr '98 / Airlines

Norman, Charlie

☐ CHARLIE NORMAN 1943-1947
ANC 9704 / Dec '97 / Ancha

☐ PAPA PIANO
NCD 8830 / Jun '94 / Phontastic

Norman, Jessye

☐ CHRISTMAS ALBUM OF THE YEAR, THE (In The Spirit - Songs For Christmas)
Angels from the realms of glory / First Noel / It came upon a midnight clear / Away in a manger / O come little children / Of the Father's love begotten / Mary had a baby / Lo' how a rose e'er blooming / Puer natus / Ave Maria / Noel nouvelet / Christmas garland / Balade du Jesus-Christ / Silent night / Balm in Gilead / O come all ye faithful (adeste fidelis)
4549852 / Nov '96 / Philips

Normand, Carla

☐ JUST YOU (Normand, Carla & The New Deal Jazz Band)
ACD 244 / Apr '93 / Audiophile

Normansell, Amanda

☐ AS LOVE IS MY WITNESS
I must have been a fool / Ever fallen in love with someone / We ran out of time / As love is my witness / I spent a lifetime / Don't come back this time / Only love / I didn't think it would hurt / One more night of loving you / This is the life / Now I know / I still believe in you / Hopeless wishing
ITSCD 2 / 8 Dec '97 / It's Music

Normansson, Carina

☐ ANGLAR
AWCD 17 / Mar '98 / Tongang

Norovbanzad, Namdzilin

☐ URTIIN DUU
JVC 53942 / Sep '96 / JVC World Library

Norris, Ken

☐ MODERN FOLKLORE
829382 / Feb '97 / BUDA

Norris, Walter

☐ DRIFTING
ENJACD 20442 / 17 Nov '97 / Enja

☐ HUES OF BLUES
Fontessa / Serenata / Hues of blues / I want to be happy / I can't get started / Backbone mode / Have you met Miss Jones / Spider web / Orchids in green / Afterthoughts
CCD 4671 / Nov '95 / Concord Jazz

☐ LIVE AT MAYBECK RECITAL HALL VOL.4
Song is you / 'Round midnight / Waltz for Walt / Best thing for you / Darn that dream / Scrambled / Modus vivendi / It's always Spring / Body and soul
CCD 4425 / Aug '90 / Concord Jazz

☐ SUNBURST (Norris, Walter Quartet)
Sunburst / What's new / Naima / Stella by starlight / Never should it ever end / So in love
CCD 4486 / Nov '91 / Concord Jazz

Norrlatar

☐ RAVN
Smaflamskan / En lohtua loyva / Lapp-Nilspolska / Ust Awarm / Nabbskotaget fran norr / Vals fran Alvik / Polska efter Fritz Sandberg / Sytamestani rakastan / Mikaels polska / Ravn
XOUCD 105 / May '97 / Xource

☐ SIGN OF THE RAVEN
Ruts lilla / Silbaatno / Dans kring kuddens kudde / Shottis fran lulea / Karin och kalle / Sarisuando / Vackra norskan / Visa fran erkheikki / Algen / Ko over sarek / Sepan salli / Visa fran kieksiaisvaara / Tukkipoika / Sermiliik / Valurei / Na del twin
RESCD 506 / Jul '97 / Resource

Norte, Marisela

☐ NORTE/WORD
NAR 062CD / May '93 / New Alliance

North Sea Gas

☐ CALEDONIAN CONNECTION
Killiecrankie / Yellow on the broom / Fields of athon rye / Ringsend rose / Montrose / Alamo / Irish rover / Lads o the fair / Steal away / Kirk douglas ghoullie / Loch lomond / Black velvet band / Wild rover / Flower of scotland
CDITV 483 / Jul '89 / Scotdisc

☐ KELTIC HERITAGE
Ballad of st. ann's reel / St. ann's reel / If wishes were fishes / Battles over / Gypsy rover / Liberty / Broadford bay / Hawks and eagles / Whip jamboree / Sweet eleanor / Dirty old town / Wark o' the weavers / Flowers o'edinburgh / Andy renwick's ferret / Rolling home / Will ye no come back again
CDITV 541 / Sep '91 / Scotdisc

☐ POWER OF SCOTLAND, THE
Sound the pibroch / Carrickfergus / Mason's apron / Heiland harry / Black jack davey / Spanish lady - blackthorn stick / Final trawl / Lord of the dance / Hieland laddie / Whiskey on a sunday / Rattlin' roarin' willie - the kesh jig / Rolling hills of the borders / Mingulay boat song / Leezie lindsay / I wish I was hunting / I'll tell me ma-green gates-the barren rocks of aden
CDITV 607 / Oct '95 / Scotdisc

☐ SCHIEHALLION
Mally Leigh / Coshieville / Gypsy laddie o's / Come ye by Atholl / Dark island / Schiehallion / Lads among the heather / Mothers daughters wives / Haugh's o' Cromdale / Westering home / Shoals of herring / Troy's wedding march / I'm a river / Loch Tay boat song / Uist tramping song / Bound to go
CDITV 629 / 27 Oct '97 / Scotdisc

Northeast Winds

☐ IRELAND BY SAIL
FE 2054 / Dec '94 / Folk Era

☐ NORTHEAST WINDS ON TOUR
FE 1403 / Nov '94 / Folk Era

Northern Cree Singers

☐ COME & DANCE
CRCD 6246 / Aug '96 / Canyon

☐ HONOUR EAGLE FEATHER
72933762692 / 19 May '98 / CYN

Northern Jazz Orchestra

☐ GOOD NEWS
LACD 38 / Sep '94 / Lake

Northern Lights

☐ CAN'T BUY YOUR WAY
Can't buy your way / My only love / Light-house / When the time had fully come / September's end / Rainmaker / City on a hill / Take you back again / Heartache tonight / Shake this feeling / Jubilation / Anger and tears / On the edge
FF 70593 / Mar '97 / Flying Fish

☐ LIVING IN THE CITY
RHRCD 94 / Sep '96 / Red House

☐ TAKE YOU TO THE SKY
Northern rain / Hold watcha got / Roseville fair / Early morning riser / Let it roll / T for Texas / Winterhawk / Home brew fever / April snow / Souvenirs / Back on my mind again / Bourree/Borealis blues
FF 70533 / Nov '96 / Flying Fish

☐ WRONG HIGHWAY BLUES
FF 70632 / Nov '96 / Flying Fish

Northern Lights Orchestra

☐ ORCHESTRAL POPS COLLECTION (Hits Of The 1960's And 1970's)
Nights in white satin / Can't help falling in love / House of the rising sun / You're my world / Anyone who had a heart / Angel of the morning / My guy / Don't let the sun catch you crying / Somewhere / You don't have to say you love me / Moon river / Make it easy on yourself / Rose garden / Tears of a clown / Air that I breathe / Everything I own / Make it with you / Nothing rhymed / She / When will I see you again / Love is in the air / Love on the rocks / Baby I'm a want you / Thornbirds
300472 / Feb '98 / Hallmark

Northern Picture Library

☐ ALASKA
Untitled / Into the ether / Catholic Easter colours / Glitter spheres / Insecure / Dreams and stars and sleep / Lucky / LSD icing / Truly madly deeply / Isn't it time you faced the truth / Untitled / Skylight / Of traffic and the ticking / Lucky (reprise) / Monotone
ASKCD 023 / Oct '93 / Vinyl Japan

Northern Uproar

☐ YESTERDAY TOMORROW TODAY
HVNCD 19 / 25 Aug '97 / Heavenly

Northrop, Kate

☐ ROOTS & WINGS
BRAM 1992342 / Nov '93 / Brambus

Northup, Harry E.

☐ HOMES
NAR 120CD / Nov '95 / New Alliance

Northwind

☐ SISTER BROTHER LOVER
AACD 007 / 27 Apr '98 / Audio Archive

Norton, Ricky

☐ LITTLE SISTER
ARN 001 / Dec '96 / Antea

Norum, John

☐ FACE IT LIVE 1997
SHR 1117 / 24 Mar '98 / Shrapnel

Norvell, Congo

☐ ABNORMALS ANONYMOUS
TWA 08CD / Nov '97 / Jetset

Norvo, Red

☐ DANCE OF THE OCTOPUS
Knockin' on wood / Honeysuckle rose / Blues in E flat / Gramercy square / Music goes 'round and around / I got rhythm / Oh Lady be good
HEPCD 1044 / Aug '95 / Hep

☐ FORWARD LOOK, THE (Norvo, Red Quintet)
Rhee waahnee / Forward look / Between the Devil and the deep blue sea / Room 608 / For Lena and Lennie / Cookin' at the Continental
RR 8CD / Sep '91 / Reference Recordings

☐ JIVIN' THE JEEP
It all begins and ends with you / A porter's love song to a chambermaid / I know that you know / Picture me without you / It can happen to you / Now that summer has gone / It's live I'm after / Peter piper / When is a kiss not a kiss / Thousand dreams of you / Smoke dreams / Slumming on park avenue / I've got my love to keep me warm / Remember / Liza / I would do anything for you / Jivin' the jeep / Everyone's wrong but me / Posin' / Morning after / Do you ever think of me
HEPCD 1019 / Dec '87 / Hep

☐ LIVE FROM THE BLUE GARDENS: JANUARY 1942 (Norvo, Red & His Orchestra)
MM 65090 / Oct '94 / Music Masters

☐ MOVE
Move / I can't believe that you're in love with me / I'll remember April / September song / Zing went the strings of my heart / I've got you under my skin / I get a kick out of you / If I had you / Godchild / This can't be love / Cheek to cheek / Swedish pastry
SV 0168 / Oct '97 / Savoy Jazz

☐ ON DIAL
Hallelujah / Get happy / Slam slam blues / Congo blues
SPJCD 127 / Apr '95 / Spotlite

☐ RED NORVO WITH TAL FARLOW & CHARLES MINGUS (Norvo, Red & Tal Farlow/Charles Mingus)
I can't believe that you're in love with me / Time and tide / Little white lies / Prelude to a kiss / Move / September song / I'm yours / I get a kick out of you / Zing went the strings of my heart / Cheek to cheek / Night and day / Godchild / Mood indigo / If I had you / 'Deed I do / I'll remember April / This can't be love / I've got you under my skin / Swedish pastry / Have you met Miss Jones
SV 0267 / Oct '97 / Savoy Jazz

☐ RED NORVO'S FABULOUS JAM SESSION
Hallelujah / Congo blues / Slam slam blues
STB 2514 / Sep '95 / Stash

☐ ROCK IT FOR ME
Tears in my heart / Worried over you / Clap hands, here comes Charlie / Russian lullaby / Always and always / I was doing all right / 'S Wonderful / Our love is here to stay / Serenade to the stars / More than ever / Weekend of a private secretary / Please be kind / Jeannie, I dream of lilac time / Tea time / How can you forget / There's a boy in Harlem / Says my heart / Moonshine over Kentucky / Rock it for me / After dinner speech / If you were in my place (What would you do)
HEPCD 1040 / Sep '94 / Hep

☐ WIGWAMMIN'
Daydreaming (all night long) / Cigarette and a silhouette / (I've been) savin' myself for you / You leave me breathless / Put your heart in a song / Wigwammin' / Sunny side of things / How can I thank you / Garden of the moon / Just you, just me / Now it can be told / Jump jumps here / I haven't changed a thing / Love is where you find it / I used to be colour blind / Tisket-a-tasket / This is madness (to love like this) / Who blew out the flame / You're a sweet little headache / I have eyes / St Louis blues / You must have been a beautiful baby / Have you forgotten so soon
HEPCD 1050 / Jan '97 / Hep

Nosferatu

☐ RISE
Gathering / Rise / Dark angel / Her heaven / Lucy is red / Lament / Alone / Vampyres cry / Crysania / Siren / Away / Close
POSSCD 006 / May '93 / Possession

Nostramus

☐ EARTHLIGHTS
HEMP 5CD / Jun '97 / Recordings Of Substance

Nosy Parker

☐ NOSY PARKER
FLASH 69 / 20 Jul '98 / Flash

Not Available

☐ RESISTANCE IS FUTILE
LF 268CD / May '97 / Lost & Found

Not Even The TV

☐ NOT EVEN THE TV
ANA 001 / Oct '96 / Anathema

Not Sensibles

☐ INSTANT PUNK CLASSICS
(I'm in love with) Margaret Thatcher / Little boxes / Garry Bushell's band of the week / Death to disco / Coronation Street hustle / Lying on the sofa / Instant classic / Girl with scruffy hair / Freedom / King Arthur / Ploppy / I am a clone / Sick of being normal / (Love is like) Banging my head against a brick wall / Because I'm mine / Wrong love / Blackpool rock / Daddy won't let me love you song / Don't wanna work anymore / I thought you were dead / I make a balls of everything I do / Teenage revolution / I am the bishop / Telephone rings again
CDPUNK 38 / Aug '94 / Anagram

Notations

☐ NOTATIONS
It's all right (This feeling) / Take it slow / Bill's breakup homes / Make me twice the man / There I go / Since you've been gone / It only hurts for a little while / I'm losing / Make believin' / Think before you stop / Superpeople
CDGR 191 / Oct '97 / Charly

Notenstock

☐ LIVE IN VIENNA 1993
590952 / Nov '97 / Musidisc

Notes, Freddie

☐ MONTEGO BAY (Notes, Freddie & The Rudies)
CDTRL 349 / Sep '95 / Trojan

Nothing

☐ SUSPICIOUSLY HIGH
ER 1042 / 1 Dec '97 / Elefant

Nothing Painted Blue

☐ POWER TRIPS DOWN LOVERS' LANE
White bicycles / Peace dividend / Block Colors / Officer Angel / Campaign Song / Register / Storefronts / Unscheduled Train / Epistemophelia / Smothered / Scapegoat / Few / Rock 'n' roll friend / Undeserving
KOKOPOP 001CD / Aug '93 / Kokopop

Notorious BIG

☐ LIFE AFTER DEATH (2CD Set)
Life after death / Somebody's gotta die / Hypnotize / Mad rapper / Kick in the door / Lovin' you tonight / Last day / Dice / I love the dough / What's beef / BIG / I'm coming out (more money) / Niggaz bleed / Story to tell / Notorious thugs / Interlude / Missing you / Another man / Cali (interlude) / Going back to Cali / 10 crack commandments / Playa hater / Interlude / Nasty boy / Interlude / Sky's the limit / World is filled / Interlude / My downfall / Long kiss goodnight / You're nobody
78612730112 / 9 Feb '98 / Puff Daddy

☐ LIFE AFTER DEATH
Hypnotize / Notorious BIG / I love the dough / BIG interlude / Miss U / Mo money mo problems / Playa hater / Another / Ten crack commandments / Sky's the limit / Going back to Cali / You're nobody ('til somebody kills you) / Lovin' you tonight
786127301922 / 24 Nov '97 / Puff Daddy

☐ READY TO DIE
Intro / Things done changed / Gimmie the loot / Machine gun funk / Warning / Ready to die / One more change / Me (interlude) / What / Juicy / Everyday struggle / Me and my / Big poppa / Respect / Friend of mine / Unbelievable / Suicidal thoughts
78612730002 / May '97 / Arista

Notre-Dame D'Argentan Benedictine Monks Choir

☐ REX PACIFICUS
74321333272 / Sep '96 / Milan

Notre-Dame De Triors Benedictine Monks Choir

☐ GAUDE ET LAETARE
74321333262 / Sep '96 / Milan

Notting Hillbillies

☐ MISSING...PRESUMED HAVING A GOOD TIME
Railroad worksong / Bewildered / Your own sweet way / Run me down / One way gal / Blues stay away from me / Will you miss me / Please baby / Weapon of prayer / That's where I belong / I feel like going home
8426712 / May '97 / Vertigo

Nottingham Forest FC

☐ YOU REDS (20 Forest Favourites) (Various Artists)
We've got the whole world in our hands: *Nottingham Forest & Paper Lace* / You can't win them all: *Clough, Brian & J.J. Barrie* / Brian: *Fat & Frantic* / Nottingham Forest: *Blakwell, Vic & Supporters* / Marching to Munich: *Karl & The Heidelburgers* / You'll never walk alone: *Anderson, Viv & Trevor Francis* / Nottingham Forest is my rock 'n' roll: *Helle, Njaal* / Who'll win the European cup: *Medium Wave Band* / Magic in Madrid: *Shandy, Tristam* / Come on you Forest: *Fans* / Forest fire: *Strikers* / Nottingham Forest is my soul: *Helle, Njaal* / Do it cos you like it: *Fashanu, Justin* / We reign supreme: *Blott, Geoff & The Nottingham Boys* / You reds: *Resistance 77* / Psycho: *Merry Men* / Sorted for Clough: *Give Us A Kiss* / Robin Hood: *Cortez, Hector & His Formation* / Road to Nottingham: *Richards, Josh* / It's only a game: *Clough, Brian & J.J. Barrie/Friends*
CDGAFFER 8 / 23 Mar '98 / Cherry Red

Nottingham Harmonic Choir

☐ CHRISTMAS CAROLS
O little town of Bethlehem / O come all ye faithful (adeste fidelis) / God rest ye merry gentlemen / Silent night / Hark the herald angels sing / While shepherds watched their flocks / Good King Wenceslas / We wish you a merry Christmas / Twelve days of Christmas / Torches / Christmas is coming / Of the Father's heart begotten / Personent hodie / O come, O come, Emmanuel / Holly and the ivy
XMAS 001 / Nov '96 / Tring

Notts. Alliance

☐ OUT OF THE DARKNESS
RMB 003CD / Aug '97 / RMB

Notwist
☐ 12
COM 10032162 / Jun '97 / Community

Nouthong Phimvilayphone
☐ VISIONS OF THE ORIENT (Music From Laos)
ARNR 0195 / Oct '97 / Amiata

Nova Bossa Nova
☐ JAZZ INFLUENCE
AJ 71241 / 27 Apr '98 / Arkadia

Nova Ghost Sect Tet
☐ LIFE ON URANUS
Oriki oshum / Uncle Willies Iron river boogie / Jack Nife / Oriki oya / Ntu the 9th wonder / Life on Uranus / Mentat's mix / Makikoshun gateway / A ra kiss / Reaching for a star / Ursa minor
AL 73109 / Jun '98 / A

Nova, Heather
☐ BLOW
Sugar / Maybe an angel / Blessed / Mother tongue / Talking to strangers / Shaking the doll
ABB 57CD / 10 Aug '98 / Big Cat

☐ SIREN
VVR 1001872 / 8 Jun '98 / V2

Novak Seen
☐ NOVAK SEEN
SPV 08545832 / Jun '96 / SPV

Novalis
☐ BANISHED BRIDGE
RR 7050 / Jun '97 / Repertoire

☐ BRANDUNG
REP 7069 / 15 Dec '97 / Repertoire

☐ NOVALIS
PMS 7063 / 10 Nov '97 / Repertoire

☐ SOMMERABEND
PMS 7079 / 26 Jan '98 / Repertoire

Novello, Ivor
☐ GIRL I KNEW, THE (The Music Of Ivor Novello & Jerome Kern) (Dallas, Lorna)
Glamourous night / London old dear London / Englishman in love / Waltz of my heart / Waltz in swing time / If only he'd looked my way / All things you are / Matter in minutes / In the heart of the dark / Girl I knew / Nuts in May / Dark music / Left all alone again blues/Have you forgotten me blues / Josephine / My life belongs to you/Love made the song / You are love/Look in my heart / Night may have its sadness/Look for silver lining
HCD 1501 / Feb '98 / Harbinger

☐ MARILYN HILL-SMITH SINGS IVOR NORVELLO (Hill-Smith, Marilyn & Chandos Concert Orchestra/Stuart Barry)
Some day my heart will awake / Primrose / Love is my reason / Dark music / Little damozel / When the gyspy played / On such a night as this / Fly home little heart / Keep the home fires burning (til the boys come home) / Music in May / Violin began to play / Spring of the year / My dearest dear / Finder please return / Look in my heart / When I curtsied to the King / We'll gather lilacs / Fairy laughter / Glamorous night / Why is there ever goodbye
FBCD 2006 / 18 Mar '98 / Flyback

November 67
☐ WELCOME TO THE REVOLUTION
HNRCD 6 / 25 May '98 / Hengest

November's Doom
☐ AMID ITS HALLOWED MIRTH
AV 010 / Feb '95 / Avantgarde

Novembre
☐ WISH IT WOULD
POLYPH 001CD / Jun '95 / Polyphemus

Novick, Billy
☐ REMEMBERING YOU
DARINGCD 3018 / Oct '95 / Daring

Novocaine
☐ FRUSTRATION NO.10
FIREMCD 61 / Jan '97 / Fire

☐ NERVOUS DISPOSITION
Walls / Mother/father / Awake / Bittersoul / Stoneface / Frustration no.10 / Pondlife / Million miles / Sorry (scum like me) / Boring git / Waiting / Analyse / Horses / She knows nothing
FIRECD 67 / Aug '97 / Fire

Now
☐ ACME 143
FO 26CD / Apr '97 / Fearless

Nowomowa
☐ WASTED LANDS, THE
NAGE 20CD / '88 / Art Of Landscape

NRA
☐ IS THIS FOR REAL
BC 1708 / Oct '96 / Blitzcore

☐ SURF CITY AMSTERDAM
BC 1711CD / 29 Jun '98 / Bitzcore

NRBQ
☐ GOD BLESS US ALL
Introduction / Crazy like a fox / Here comes terry / Every boy, every girl / In the mood / Sitting in the park / She got the house / Down at the zoo / Me and the boys / Mouthwaterin' / Success / 12 bar blues / God bless us all / Get rhythm / They loved it / Shake, rattle and roll / I gotta go, babe
ROUCD 3108 / '88 / Rounder

☐ HONEST DOLLAR
Ridin' in my car / Batman / That I get back home / Ain't it good / Amy's theme / Tennessee / Deep in the heart of texas / Green lights / Wacky tobacky / New tune / Lucille / 1-2-3 / I love air conditioning / Never take the place of you / Dummy song / Dummy song / It's a sin to tell a lie
RCD 10240 / Jul '92 / Rykodisc

☐ MESSAGE FOR THE MESS AGE
Over your head / Don't bite the head / Designated driver / Everybody thinks I'm crazy / Spampinato / Advice for teenagers / Everybody's smokin' / Little bit of bad / Big dumb jukebox / Ramona / Nothin' wrong with me / Better word for love / Girl scout cookies
RSFCD 800 / Oct '96 / Sequel

☐ TAP DANCIN' BATS
Captain Lou / I don't think of / You got it / Rats in my room / Bog goodbyes / Tex / Trouble at the henhouse / Ain't it alright / Pretty thing / Dry up and blow away / Dough got low / Tapdancin' bats
ROUCD 3066 / Feb '98 / Rounder

☐ TOKYO
I want you bad / Rain at the drive-in / Crazy girl / Just ain't fair / Ramona / Green lights / Ain't it all right / Everybody thinks I'm crazy / Blues stay away from me / Miracles / Little floater / I love her, she loves me / RC Cola and a Moon pie / If I don't have you / Me and the boys / You and I and George / Want you to feel good too
ROUCD 3146 / Feb '97 / Rounder

☐ UNCOMMON DENOMINATORS
Me and the boys / Still in school / People / Want you to feel good too / Only you / Feel you around me / Howard johnson's got his ho-jo workin' / Wacky tobacky / Miss moses / Captain lou / Trouble at the henhouse / Don't she look good / Doctor's wind / I don't think of... / Rc cola and moon pie / Beverly / It was a accident / Ridin' in my car / Definition of love
ROUCD 11506 / '88 / Rounder

☐ YOU'RE NICE PEOPLE YOU ARE
You're nice people you are / Encyclopedia / Always safety first / Music lesson / There's a girl there's a boy / Next stop Brattleboro / Spider / Keep looking for tumbleweeds Danny / It's St. Patrick's day / We're walking / Plenty of somethin' / You're nice people you are / Sleep
ROUCD 8045 / Jul '97 / Rounder

NRG Ensemble
☐ BEJAZZO GETS A FACELIFT
AFP 73CD / 14 Apr '98 / Atavistic

☐ THIS IS MY HOUSE
Hyperspace / Cut flowers / Whirlwind / Bullseye witness / Bustanut / Burnt toast / Straight time / In the middle of Pennsylvania
DE 485 / Jun '97 / Delmark

Nu Civilisation
☐ NU CIVILISATION
STEAM 77CD / Feb '94 / Vinyl Solution

Nu Colours
☐ NU COLOURS
Special kind of lover / Desire / Yes I will / Back together / Do you wanna go back (to when) / I pray / You gave me more / (You) Took me to heaven / Heart's a messenger / Don't mind waiting / Tomorrow love / Joy / Thinking about you / Special kind of lover (C and J RNB mix)
5317512 / Sep '96 / Wild Card

Nu Philly Groove
☐ NU PHILLY GROOVE, THE
ITM 1494 / Oct '95 / ITM

Nu Troops
☐ MIGRATIONS
Transmigration / Goree island / Hamattan / Place to place / Asante / 741 / Ode to Ama / Incentricity / Papa Dayie / Pinocchio
DUNECD 01 / Apr '97 / Dune

Nu Yorican Soul
☐ NU YORICAN SOUL
Runaway / MAW Latin blues / Gotta new life / It's alright I feel it / Jazzy Jeff's theme / Roy's scat / You can do it (baby) / Shoshana / I am the black gold of the sun / Nervous track / Nautilus (Mawtilus) / Mind fluid / Sweet tears / Habriendo El Dominate
5344602
5344512 / Feb '97 / Talkin' Loud

Nu Yorican Symphony
☐ NU YORICAN SYMPHONY LIVE AT THE KNITTING FACTORY
KFWCD 138 / Feb '95 / Knitting Factory

Nubiles
☐ MINDBLENDER
LS 01 / 5 May '98 / Lime Street

Nuclear Assault
☐ ASSAULT AND BATTERY
Happy days / Enter darkness / Leaders / Hang the pope / Radiation sickness / Hypocrisy / Behind glass walls / No time / Sadam / Preaching to the deaf / Hang the pope / Ping / Torture tactics / Fight to be free / Trail of tears / Ping again / Butt fuck
RRCD 244 / 29 Sep '97 / Receiver

☐ OUT OF ORDER
CDFLAG 64 / Sep '91 / Under One Flag

Nucleus
☐ ELASTIC ROCK/WE'LL TALK ABOUT IT LATER
Elastic rock / Striation / Taranaki / Twisted track / Crude blues / Crude blues part two / 1916 (Battle of boogaloo) / Torrid zone / Stonescape / Earth mother / Speaking for myself, personally / Persephones jive / Song for the bearded lady / Sun child / Lullaby for a lonely child / We'll talk about it later / Oasis / Ballad of Joe Pimp / Easter 1916
BGOCD 47 / Mar '94 / Beat Goes On

Nugent, Laurence
☐ TRADITIONAL IRISH MUSIC ON FLUTE & TIN WHISTLE
SH 78001 / Jun '96 / Shanachie

☐ TWO FOR TWO
McDermott's/The home ruler / Scully Casey's/Willie Johnson's/Ryan's / Sean O Duibhir a' gleanna / Dans en dro / Unknown/Chris Droney's/Sean McCusker's / Old hag you have killed me/Pride of Erin/The monument / Hector the hero / Within a mile of Dublin/Emmet's reel/Francie Quinn's / Paddy on the binge/The pint rustler / Cape clear / Mother's delight/Lad O'Beirne's/Eileen Curran / Return home/Tommy Poeples / Tom Moyland's frolic/Willie Clancy's/McGlynns / Down the back lane/Porttown harbour/Jim Donoghue's / Banks of the Suir/Lois na banriona / Smell of the bog/The wind that shakes the barley/Emmet's dou
SHANCD 78014 / May '98 / Shanachie

Nugent, Ted
☐ GREAT GONZOS (The Best Of Ted Nugent)
Cat scratch fever / Just what the doctor ordered / Free for all / Dog eat dog / Motor city madness / Paralysed / Stranglehold / Baby, please don't go / Wango tango / Wang dang sweet poontang
4712162 / Feb '97 / Epic

☐ LIVE AT HAMMERSMITH ODEON
Stormtroopin' / Just what the doctor ordered / Free for all / Dog eat dog / Cat scratch fever / Need you bad / Paralyzed / It don't matter / Wang dang sweet poontang / Stranglehold / Motor City madness / Gonzo
4851052 / May '97 / Columbia

☐ ON THE EDGE
Dr. Slingshot / Night time / You talk sunshine, I breathe fire / Scottish tea / Good natured Emma / Prodigal man / Missionary Mary / St. Philip's friend / Journey to the centre of the mind / Flight of the byrd / Baby, please don't go / Inside the outside / Loaded for bear / On the edge
CDTB 097 / '91 / Thunderbolt

☐ OVER THE TOP
Down on Philips escalator / Surrender to your kings / Gimme love / For his namesake / I'll prove I'm right / Conclusion/Journey / To the centre of the mind / Migration / Lovely lady / Mississippi murderer / Let's go get stoned / It's not true / Ivory castles / Colours / Over the top
CDTB 120 / May '91 / Thunderbolt

☐ SPIRIT OF THE WILD, THE
Thighraceous / Wrong side of town / Tooth fang claw / Fred bear / Hot or cold / Heart soul / Just do it like this / Spirit of the wild / Kiss my ass / Primitive man / Lovejacker / I shoot back
7567826112 / Jun '94 / Atlantic

Nulisch, Darrell
☐ BLUESOUL
HPR 511CD / 19 Mar '98 / Higher Plane

Null
☐ TERMINAL BEACH
MNF 13 / Feb '97 / Manifold

Numan, Gary
☐ BEST OF GARY NUMAN 1984-1992, THE
I can't stop / Berserker / Skin game / I still remember / Machine and soul / Empty bed, empty heart / Are 'friends' electric / Your fascination / This disease / Miracles / Child with the ghost / Strange charm / London times / Time to die / America / My dying machine
EMPRCD 666 / Sep '96 / Emporio

☐ BLACK HEART
CP 1004 / 6 Apr '98 / Rhino

☐ EXILE
EAGCD 008 / 20 Oct '97 / Eagle

☐ GARY NUMAN ARCHIVE VOL.1
Are friends electric / Me I disconnect from you / U got the look / Berserker / God film / We are glass / Poison / Creatures / Cars / Call out the dogs / God only knows / Down in the park / You need the mystery to bed / My shadow in vain / Love isolation / Generator
RMCD 205 / Nov '97 / Rialto

☐ GARY NUMAN ARCHIVE VOL.2
In a glass house / Confession / Down in the park / Tricks / Rumour / I die you die / Sleep room / My breathing / This is love / We need it / Emotion / Time to die / I can't stop / Here I am / Need
RMCD 225 / Nov '97 / Rialto

☐ GREATEST HITS (Numan, Gary & Tubeway Army)
Cars / I die: You die / Are 'friends' electric / Down in the park / We are glass / Bombers / We take mystery (to bed) / She's got claws / Complex / Music for chameleons / That's too bad / This wreckage / Warriors / Love needs no disguise / This boys and heroes / Sister surprise / Stormtrooper in drag
5311492 / Mar '96 / PolyGram TV

☐ MIX, THE
CLEO 1922 / 14 Apr '98 / Cleopatra

☐ NUMA YEARS, THE (5CD Set)
Berserker / This is new love / Secret / My dying machine / Cold warning / Pump it up / God film / Child with the ghost / Hunter / Empty bed empty heart / Here am I / She cries / Rumours / This ship comes apart / Call out the dogs / This disease / Your fascination / Miracles / Pleasure skin / Creatures / Tricks / God only knows / I still remember / We need it / Anthem / No shelter / Puppets / Fear / My breathing / Unknown and hostile / Sleeproom / New thing from London Town / I can't stop / Strange charm / Need / This is love / Survival / Faces / Time to die / River / Mistasax / Machine and soul / Generator / Skin game / Poison / I wonder / Emotion / Cry / U got the look / Love isolation / Hanoi / Dark mountain / Hauntings / 1999 / Cry baby / Wonder eye / Pray / Deadliner / Question of faith / Desire / Scar / Love and napalm / You walk in my soul / Magic / Bleed / Seed of a lie / Play like God / Whisper of truth / Metal beat / Absolution
EAGBX 025 / 22 Jun '98 / Eagle

☐ PEEL SESSIONS, THE (Gary Numan/ Tubeway Army - 29.5.79) (Numan, Gary & Tubeway Army)
Cars / Airlane / Films / Conversation / Me, I disconnect from you / Down in the park / I nearly married a human
SFPMCD 202 / '89 / Strange Fruit

☐ PLEASURE PRINCIPLE, THE (Remastered)
BBL 10CD / 22 Jun '98 / Beggars Banquet

☐ RANDOM 2
Metal / Dans le parc (down the park) / I die you die / Cars / Cars / Warriors / Are friends electric / Remember I was vapour / We are glass / Films / Iceman comes
BBQCD 197 / 9 Mar '98 / Beggars Banquet

☐ REPLICAS (Tubeway Army)
Me, I disconnect from you / Are friends electric / Machman / Praying to the aliens / Down in the park / You are in my vision / Replicas / It must have been years / I nearly married a human
MUSCD 509 / May '95 / MCI Original Masters

☐ REPLICAS (Remastered) (Tubeway Army)
BBL 7CD / 22 Jun '98 / Beggars Banquet

☐ STORY SO FAR, THE (3CD Set)
RRXCD 505 / Jul '96 / Receiver

☐ TELEKON (Remastered)
BBL 19CD / 22 Jun '98 / Beggars Banquet

☐ TUBEWAY ARMY (Remastered) (Tubeway Army)
BBL 4CD / 22 Jun '98 / Beggars Banquet

Numb
☐ BLOOD MERIDIAN
KK 165CD / 13 Oct '97 / KK

☐ CHRISTMEISTER
Is this life / No pay today / So called friends / Matchbox car / Rich kid / (ain't no-one gonna) take my soul away / One and only / Halfway home / Lazy girls / Stay / Pimp / Take a day for a day / My baby / No. 1 / Smell the sweat / Another weary day
KK 146 / Apr '96 / KK

☐ DESIRE/BLIND
K 164 / 18 May '98 / KK

☐ FIXATE
KK 094 / Feb '94 / KK

☐ WASTED SKY
KK 126CD / Nov '94 / KK

Number 9

☐ SMOKIN' COUNTRY ROCKIN' BLUES
Swinging Daddy / Tables have turned / Wanted man / Stay away / She's a sin / Break for the border / I love you just the same / Where's Robin / Time / Country boy / One monkey dont' stop no show / I'm hanging up my heart for you / High sheriff of Calhoun Parrish / Lay lady lay / You can have her / On the road again
JRCD 16 / Sep '97 / Jappin' & Rockin'

Number One Cup

☐ WRECKED BY LIONS
Ease back down / Backlit / Chisel / Paris / Bright orange / Fireball sun / Black choppers cry / Astronaut / Waiting on the lions / Maybe there's a thread / Tree song / Concordia / Malcolm's X-ray picnic / Flickers and flames / So inclined / Three miles from talent
BRRC 10132 / Jun '97 / Blue Rose

Nuncira, Chuco

☐ LA FUERZA MAYOR
TUMICD 019 / '92 / Tumi

Nunes, Clara

☐ CLARA NUNES COM... VIDA
Morena de Angola / Peixe com coco / Na linha do mar / Coisa da Antiga / Nacao / Viola de Penedo / Ijexa (Filhos de Gandhi) / Conto de Areia / Sem companhia / Coracao Leviano / A flor da Pele / As forcas da natureza / Amor perfeito / Menino Deus
CDEMC 3744 / Feb '96 / Hemisphere

Nunez, Carlos

☐ BROTHERHOOD OF STARS
Brotherhood of stars / Dawn / Two shores / Black shadow / Moonlight piper / Cantigueiras / Galician carol / Dancing with Rosina / Lela / Flight of the Earls / Rainmaker's air / Para Vigo me voy
74321453752 / May '97 / RCA Victor

Nunez, Gerardo

☐ AS MELHORES
ATR 21185 / 12 May '98 / Atracao

☐ JUCAL
F 001 / 1 Jun '98 / Karonte

Nunez, Joseito

☐ CON LA ORQUESTA DE BELISARIO LOPEZ 1937-1940 (Nunez, Joseito & Belisario Lopez)
TCD 063 / Jul '96 / Tumbao Cuban Classics

Nuns

☐ FOUR DAYS IN A HOTEL ROOM
EFA 122012 / Feb '94 / Musical Tragedies

Nunu

☐ KLEZMO-COPTER
Lomir sich iberbetn / Frejlechs / Djurdjev dan/ Ederlezi / KalamatianosMoyde ani / Di lustign chossidn / Djelem djelem / Der hejser bulgar / Bavno pomasschko / Moja mala nema mane / Ale vasserlech flisn avek / Sto e ludo son sonilo / Baj mir bistu schejn / Ich hob dich zuvil lib / Bajtsche mir ois a finfunzwanziger
8888282 / Sep '97 / Tiptoe

Nurock, Kirk

☐ REMEMBERING TREE FRIENDS
378582 / May '98 / Koch Jazz

Nurse With Wound

☐ 150 MURDEROUS PASSIONS
UD 009CD / Oct '96 / United Dairies

☐ ACTS OF SENSELESS BEAUTY
Either open or unsound / Bloodclot / Window of possible organic development / Entertainer / Some magic powers
UD 100CD / Jul '97 / United Dairies

☐ CHANCE MEETING
UD 001CD / Oct '96 / United Dairies

☐ CRUMB DUCK (Nurse With Wound & Stereolab)
UD 059CD / Oct '96 / United Dairies

☐ HOMOTOPY FOR MARIE
UD 013CD / Oct '96 / United Dairies

☐ LARGE LADIES
UD 038CD / Oct '96 / United Dairies

☐ LIVE AT THE BAR MALDOROR
UD 034CD / Oct '96 / United Dairies

☐ MERZBILDSCHWET
UD 004CD / Oct '96 / United Dairies

☐ MISSING SENSE, A (Nurse With Wound & Organum)
Missing sense / Swansong / Dada
UD 042CD / Oct '97 / United Dairies

☐ ROCK 'N' ROLL STATION
UD 039CD / Oct '96 / United Dairies

☐ SOLILOQUY FOR LILLITH (2CD Set)
UD 035CD / Oct '96 / United Dairies

☐ SPIRAL INSANA
Sea armchair / Migration to the head / Earthwork / Red period / This lady is for burning / Chasing the carrot / Sugarland / There's always another illusion / Stewing the red herring / Mourning smile / Pulse interplay / View from Lammas Tower / Swallowhead / Fitching / Wrong sucker / All that's left over / Forever chasing the carrot / Terminal song / Ship of the dead / Obituary obligations / Nihil
UD 073CD / Oct '97 / United Dairies

☐ SUCKED ORANGE, A
Paradise lost / Internal torment II / Autopsy / Stillborn / Deviated instinct / Resurrection encore / Doom / Means to an end / Confessor / Uncontrolled / Talion / Laws of retaliation / Electro hippies / Freddy's revenge / Toranaga / Dealers in death
UD 032CD / Dec '89 / United Dairies

☐ SUGAR FISH DRINK
UD 036CD / Oct '96 / United Dairies

☐ SYLVIA AND BABS
UD 072CD / Oct '96 / United Dairies

☐ THUNDER PERFECT MIND
UD 040CD / Oct '96 / United Dairies

☐ TO THE QUIET MEN...
UD 003CD / Oct '96 / United Dairies

☐ WHO CAN I TURN TO STEREO
UD 049CD / Jan '97 / United Dairies

Nus

☐ VERTICAL ANGELS, THE
SR 102 / May '96 / Sub Rosa

Nutmeg

☐ GHETTO'S CHILD
50571 / Jun '97 / Raging Bull

Nuttin' Nyce

☐ DOWN FOR WHATEVER
CHIP 160 / Aug '95 / Jive

Nuttso

☐ BETRAYAL
4360221012 / 31 Mar '98 / PRDE

Nuuk Posse

☐ KAATAQ
SR 108CD / Oct '96 / Sub Rosa

NWA

☐ EFIL4ZAGGIN
Real niggaz don't die / Niggaz 4 life / Protest / Appetite for destruction / Don't drink that wine / Alwayz into something / To kill a hooker / One less bitch / Findum fuckum and flee / Automobile / She swallowed it / I'd rather fuck you / Approach to danger / 1-900 2 Compton / Dayz of wayback
BRCD 562 / Apr '91 / 4th & Broadway

☐ STRAIGHT OUTTA COMPTON
Straight outta Compton / Fuck tha police / Gangsta gangsta / If it ain't ruff / Parental discretion iz advised / Express yourself / I ain't tha 1 / Dopeman / Compton's 'n the house / 8 ball / Something like that / Quiet on the set / Something 2 dance 2
BRCD 534 / Aug '89 / 4th & Broadway

Nwe, U Yee

☐ SANDAYA
Sanda kein na yi / Htan tara tay shin basin taung than / Than yoe / Phone moe thun long / Sandaya let swan pya / Mae zar taung che / Nyoo nyoo sign sign / Kyon kyon paing tha / Zayar kan ahla bagyi
SHANCD 66007 / Apr '98 / Shanachie

Ny'a

☐ EMBRACE
NAP 4220 / Mar '96 / Ichiban

Nyah Fearties

☐ GRANPA CREW
NYAH 942 / Feb '95 / Danceteria

Nyberg, Lina

☐ CLOSE
TMCD 004 / Sep '97 / Touche

Nygaard

☐ NO HURRY
ROUCD 267 / Dec '90 / Rounder

Nygaard, Scott

☐ DREAMER'S WALTZ
ROUCD 0397 / Jun '96 / Rounder

Nyhus, Sven

☐ BERGROSA
MASTER 702CD / Jul '93 / Master

NYJO

☐ 47 FRITH STREET (National Youth Jazz Orchestra)
Sweet London bridge / Whole thing / El rey pedro / Roxy beaujolais / Not really / In the hour before dawn / Kosher horses / Late night blues / London / New in London / Headche / 47 Frith Street / Will ye no come back again
JHCD 058 / 27 Apr '98 / Ronnie Scott's Jazz House

☐ ALGARHYTHMS (National Youth Jazz Orchestra)
Praia do vau / Bom dia, roseira / Quinto do lago / Faro way / Cartaz de rua / Portimao / Adeus tristeza / Cai fora / Montes de alvor / Holiday affair / East of the sun / Albufeira / Play off
NYJCD 017 / Sep '96 / NYJO

☐ BIG BAND CHRISTMAS (National Youth Jazz Orchestra)
Deck the halls with boughs of holly / Silent night / Christians awake / Maryland, my Christmas tree / In the bleak midwinter / At Christmas / I saw six ships / My dancing day / Wenceslas squared / Away in a manger / Thirst, The - No ale / O come all ye faithful (Adeste Fidelis) / Christmas blues / Take five kings / I left my heart in Royal David's City / Holly and the ivy / Hark the herald angels sing
NYJCD 009 / Aug '94 / NYJO

☐ COOKIN' WITH GAS (National Youth Jazz Orchestra)
Beyond the Hatfield Tunnel / Hot gospel / Step on the gas / Mr. B.G. / Be gentle / Behind the gasworks / Cookin' with gas / 'S Wonderful / We care for you / Big girl now / Gasanova / Afterburner / Water babies / Heat of the moment
NYJCD 010 / Apr '95 / NYJO

☐ COTTONING ON (National Youth Jazz Orchestra)
Sea island samba / Miss Malfatti, I presume / Cottoning on / Lady can tell / One for Oscar / Tenor each way / Blues for Duke / Be gentle / Night is a pup / Night slide / Gasbag blues
NYJCD 016 / Dec '95 / NYJO

☐ GIANTS OF, THE (National Youth Jazz Orchestra)
NYJVC 901 / Apr '95 / NYJO

☐ HALLMARK (National Youth Jazz Orchestra)
Hallmark / I have been here before / Blood orange / Adeus Tristeza / Samba for Cheryl / Have you seen them cakes / U-Turn / Suits me / While the cat's away / Reepicheep / Tara's Tuesday / Castle's in Spain
NYJCD 015 / Apr '95 / NYJO

☐ IN CONTROL (National Youth Jazz Orchestra)
High speed gas / Willow, green willow / El sid / Groovin' with gas / You were marvellous, darling / Miles away / In control / 50,000 flies can't be wrong / Villamoura / Off shore peers / Gas mark 2 / Don't drink on an empty head
JHCD 037 / Mar '95 / Ronnie Scott's Jazz House

☐ LOOKING FORWARD, LOOKING BACK (National Youth Jazz Orchestra)
Shadow of doubt / Way with words / Just a breath away / Let the loving begin / Wait and see / Time and again and again / It's over / Looking forward / Looking back / Blues to you, too (we're history) / I was hoping / No way / That's that / As long as there are summers / Too late / It's my chance to get even / New in london
NYJCD 012 / Apr '95 / NYJO

☐ MALTESE CROSS (National Youth Jazz Orchestra)
NYJCD 008 / Apr '95 / NYJO

☐ MERRY CHRISTMAS AND A HAPPY NEW YEAR (National Youth Jazz Orchestra)
We wish you a merry Christmas / O come, o come / Bethlehem lift off / While shepherds watched their flocks by night / Midnight clear / My gift to you / Noel nouvelet / OLTOB / Christmas song / Angels from the second storey / Childsotnes / Winter snow / It's Christmas / Twelve bars of Christmas / Auld land syne
NYJCD 014 / Aug '94 / NYJO

☐ PORTRAITS (National Youth Jazz Orchestra)
Blues at the bull / Woody / Basie / Dizzy / Duke / Bird / Quincy / Monk / Duke II / Kenton / Point of no return / Come on the blues / Royal flush / Southern horizons
HHCD 1007 / May '95 / Hot House

☐ REMEMBRANCE (National Youth Jazz Orchestra)
Remembrance (for Jim) / Remembrance (for Chrish and Eamonn) / Remembrance (for Kenny and Charlie) / Remembrance (for Valery) / I'll never forget / Half steps / Snakes and ladders / Long hot summer / Rodeo / Yessica / Take the CandA train / Almost there / Give up
NYJCD 011 / Apr '95 / NYJO

☐ THESE ARE THE JOKES (National Youth Jazz Orchestra)
Still doing the trick with the horse, Madam / First time I've seen dead people smoke (Smokey eyes) / Keep looking young-hang around with old people / Chef's rash has cleared up nicely / Much too much / No hair just a red head / Are we keeping you up sir / Roxy beaujolais / Audient was on its foot / Watching the traffic lights change / Don't go to her
JHCD 024 / Jan '94 / Ronnie Scott's Jazz House

☐ THIS TIME LIVE AT THE CLUB (National Youth Jazz Orchestra)
Lift off / Waiting for Morgan / Half steps / Yessica / Have you seen them cakes / Almost there / Looking forward / I have been here before / Beyond the Hatfield Tunnel / Aardvark
JHCD 049 / Jun '97 / Ronnie Scott's Jazz House

☐ UNISON IN ALL THINGS (National Youth Jazz Orchestra)
For starters / In a daze / You'd think I'd learn / Along came Benny / Dearly beloved / I wasn't looking for love / Unison in all things / Eyes down / Reprieve / Never the twain / How can you believe in love / Atropus / Blues for Mike / For starters
NYJCD 018 / Feb '97 / NYJO

☐ VIEW FROM THE HILL, A (National Youth Jazz Orchestra)
Marston Pedigree / Flight of the heart / View from the hill / Don't try and argue with me / Norwich Union / Riffin' the griffin / Ballad for Anne Boleyn / Fleet / Samba deeze, samba doze / Someone / Luton Hoo / Astra Brazilia
JHCD 044 / Jan '96 / Ronnie Scott's Jazz House

☐ WITH AN OPEN MIND (National Youth Jazz Orchestra)
Cheese'n'Carrots / Revenge of the Amoebae / With an open mind / Remembrance for Jim / Aardvark / Syrup of Phiggs / Fly to me / Midnight oil / Going Dutch
NYJCD 007 / Apr '95 / NYJO

☐ WITH ONE VOICE (National Youth Jazz Orchestra)
Overdue dues blues / With one voice / Composite motion / Tinker's tune / Have you met Paul Jones / Magen's bay / Don't mention the blues / LBG / If you should change your mind / Big girl now / Guarachamos / For starters
NYJCD 019 / 2 Feb '98 / NYJO

Nylons

☐ ONE SIZE FITS ALL
RR 349926 / '88 / Roadrunner

☐ SEAMLESS
RR 349856 / '89 / Roadrunner

Nyman, Michael

☐ CONCERTO ALBUM, THE
Double concerto for saxophone and cello / Concerto for harpsichord and strings / Concerto for trombone and orchestra
CDC 5564872 / 13 Oct '97 / EMI Classics

☐ ESSENTIAL (Nyman, Michael Band)
Chasing sheep is best left to shepherds / Eye for optical theory / Garden is becoming a robe room / Prawn watching / Time lapse / Fish beach / Wheelbarrow walk / Knowing the ropes / Miserere paraphrase / Memorial / Stroking / Synchronising / Miranda
4368202 / Jan '93 / Decca

☐ KISS AND OTHER MOVEMENTS, THE
Kiss / Nose list song / Tano between the lines / Images were introduced / Water dances (making a splash)-1 Stroking / Water dances (making a splash)-2 Gliding / Water dances (making a splash)-3 Synchronising
EEGCD 40 / Jan '87 / EG

☐ LIVE
In Re Don Giovanni / Bird list / Queen of the night / Water dances - dipping / Water dances - stroking / Upside down violin - Slow/Faster/Faster still / Piano - concert suite
CDVE 924 / Oct '94 / Virgin

☐ SUIT AND THE PHOTOGRAPH, THE
CDC 5565742 / 4 May '98 / EMI Classics

☐ TIME WILL PRONOUNCE
Self-laudatory hymn of Inanna and her omnipotence / Time will pronounce / Convertability of lute strings / For John cage
4402822 / Jun '93 / Decca

Nyman, Monica

☐ SPRICKAN MELLAN VARLDARNA (Nyman, Monica Kvintett)
IGCD 065 / May '97 / Imogena

Nyolo, Sally

☐ TRIBU
087952 / Nov '96 / Melodie

Nyro, Laura

☐ ELI AND THE THIRTEENTH CONFESSION
Luckie / Lu / Sweet blindness / Poverty train / Lonely women / Eli's comin' / Timer / Stoned soul picnic / Emma / Woman's blues / Once it was alright now (Farmer John) / December's boudoir / Confession
4872402 / Mar '97 / Columbia

☐ **STONED SOUL PICNIC (The Best Of Laura Nyro/2CD Set)**
Wedding bell blues / Blowin' away / Billy's blues / Stoney end / And when I die / Lu / Eli's comin / Stoned soul picnic / Timer / Emmie / Confession / Capt. St. Lucifer / Gibsom Street / New York tendaberry / Save the country / Blackpatch / Upstairs by a chinese lamp / Beads of sweat / When I

was a freeport and you were the main drag / I met him on a Sunday / Bells / Smile / Sweet blindness / Money / Mr. Blue / Wilderness / Mother's spiritual / Woman of the world / Louise's church / Broken rainbow / To a child / Lite a flame (the animal rights song) / And when I die / Save the country

4851092 / Feb '97 / Legacy

☐ **TIME AND LOVE (The Music Of Laura Nyro) (Various Artists)**
Time and love: Snow, Phoebe / Stoned soul picnic: Sobule, Jill / Buy and sell: Vega, Suzanne / When I think of Laura Nyro: Siberry, Jane / Stoney end: Chapman, Beth Nielsen / Eli's coming: Germano, Lisa / Wedding bell blues: Roches / And when I die:

Sweet Honey In The Rock / Save he country: Cash, Rosanne / He's a runner: Brooke, Jonathan / Poverty train: Larkin, Patty / Sweet blindness: Cole, Holly / Upstairs by a chinese lamp: Stern, Leni / Woman's blue: Bryant, Dana

TCD 4007 / Jun '97 / Astor Place

O

O

□ NIGHTMARCIA
5396272 / 15 Jun '98 / Polydor

□ OLENTO
EFA 501122 / Oct '96 / Sahko

□ TULKINTA
EFA 501132 / May '97 / Sahko

O-Level

□ DAY IN THE LIFE OF GILBERT & GEORGE, A
There's a cloud over Liverpool / I helped Patrick McGoohan escape / Odd man out / Apologise / We're not sorry / Sometimes good guys don't follow trends / Storybook beginnings / Sun never sets / Dressing up for the cameras / He's a professional / John Peel march / East Sheen revisited / Pseudo punk / O Level / We love Malcolm / Leave me / Everybody's on revolver tonight / Stairway to boredom / Many unhappy returns / I love to clean my polaris missile / Don't play God with my life / East Sheen
CREV 005CD / Nov '92 / Rev-Ola

Oakenfold, Paul

□ ALL STAR BREAKBEATS VOL.2 (Bust A Groove)
MOLCD 34 / Jun '94 / Music Of Life

□ PAUL OAKENFOLD LIVE IN OSLO (2CD Set) (Various Artists)
GU 004CD / Jun '97 / Boxed

□ PERFECTION - A PERFECTO COMPILATION (Mixed Live By Paul Oakenfold) (Various Artists)
Embracing the sunshine: BT / Tripping the light fantastic: BT / Loving you more: BT / I want to live: Grace / I dream: Tilt / Believe in me: Quiver / Not over yet: Grace / Passion: Jon Of The Pleased Wimmin / Dreams: Wild Colour / Sing it: Mozaic / Floor-essence: Man With No Name / Sun: Virus / Reach up: Perfecto All Stars
0630123482 / Oct '95 / Perfecto/East West

Oakey, Philip

□ PHIL OAKEY/GIORGIO MORODER (Oakey, Philip & Giorgio Moroder)
Why must the show go on / In transit / Goodbye bad times / Brand new love (take a chance) / Valerie / Now / Together in electric dreams / Be my lover now / Shake it up
CDVIP 214 / 3 Aug '98 / Virgin VIP

Oakley, Pete

□ GHOST IN THE CITY
FE 103CD / Mar '95 / Fellside

Oasis

□ (WHAT'S THE STORY) MORNING GLORY
Hello / Roll with it / Wonderwall / Don't look back in anger / Hey now / Might say / Cast no shadow / She's electric / Morning glory / Champagne supernova
CRECD 189 / Oct '95 / Creation

□ (WHAT'S THE STORY) MORNING GLORY (4CD Single Set/Interview Disc)
CREMG 002 / Nov '96 / Creation

□ (WHAT'S THE STORY) MORNING GLORY (Interview)
CREMG 001 / Nov '96 / Creation

□ BE HERE NOW
D'you know what I mean / My big mouth / Magic pie / Stand by me / I hope I think I know / Girl in the dirty shirt / Fade in-out / Don't go away / Be here now / All around the world / It's gettin better (man) / All around the world
CRECD 219 / 21 Aug '97 / Creation

□ BE THERE THEN (Interview)
OTR 1100068 / 3 Nov '97 / Metro Independent

□ BIOGRAPHY SERIES
10017 / 3 Nov '97 / Metro Independent

□ DEFINITELY MAYBE
Rock 'n' roll star / Shakermaker / Live forever / Up in the sky / Columbia / Supersonic / Bring it on down / Cigarettes and alcohol / Digsy's dinner / Slide away / Married with children
CRECD 169 / Aug '94 / Creation

□ DEFINITELY MAYBE SINGLES BOX (4CD Singles/Interview Disc)
CREDM 002 / Nov '96 / Creation

□ GETTING HIGH (Interview Discs/2CD Set)
CONV 001 / Feb '97 / Network

□ INTERVIEW DISC
SAM 7023 / Nov '96 / Sound & Media

□ MORNING GLORY (The Oasis Story/ 2CD Set)
OTR 1100040 / Jun '97 / Metro Independent

□ OASIS INTERVIEW
UFOMWW 11CD / Sep '96 / UFO

□ ROYAL PHILHARMONIC ORCHESTRA PLAYS THE MUSIC OF OASIS, THE (Royal Philharmonic Orchestra)
Roll with it / Live forever / Rock 'n' roll star / Cigarettes and alcohol / Shakermaker / Up in the sky / Don't look back in anger / Wonderwall / Supersonic / She's electric / Some might say / Champagne supernova
MCCD 320 / 6 Oct '97 / Music Club

□ SALLY CAN WAIT (Interview Discs/2CD Set)
CONV 006 / Feb '97 / Network

Oatts, Dick

□ ALL OF THREE
SCCD 31422 / Nov '97 / Steeplechase

□ STANDARD ISSUE
SCCD 31439 / 1 Jun '98 / Steeplechase

Obadia, Hakki

□ IRAQI JEWISH/IRAQI MUSIC
GV 147CD / May '94 / Global Village

O'Baoill, Sean

□ CEOLTA GAEL
OSS 2CD / Nov '90 / Ossian

O'Beirne, Gerry

□ HALF MOON BAY
BEIRNE 01CD / Mar '98 / Beirne

Obenda

□ OBENDA (Obenda & The Sunshine Kids)
NOTP 1CD / Dec '97 / NOTP

Oberlin, Russell

□ ENGLISH MEDIEVAL SONGS
LEMS 8005 / Aug '94 / Lyrichord

□ ENGLISH POLYPHONY
LEMS 8004 / Aug '94 / Lyrichord

□ FRENCH ARS ANTIQUA, THE
LEMS 8007 / Aug '94 / Lyrichord

□ LAS CANTIGAS
LEMS 8003 / Aug '94 / Lyrichord

□ NOTRE DAME ORGANA
LEMS 8002 / Aug '94 / Lyrichord

□ TROUBADOUR/TROUVERE SONGS
LEMS 8001 / Aug '94 / Lyrichord

Obermayer, Gilles

□ CONTRACTION
G 004CD / Apr '95 / Musikk Distribujson

Oberon

□ MIDSUMMER NIGHT'S DREAM, A
AACD 012 / 27 Apr '98 / Audio Archive

Obey, Chief Ebenezer

□ GET YOUR JUJUS OUT
Ose olorum oba / Sisi ba millionaire lo / Ile ti ya / Koseni tomo ojo ola / To ba je tere / Erawa oloyon momo / Awa eve iwoyl / What god has joined / E ma se lo-rinain
RCD 20111 / Aug '91 / Rykodisc

□ JUJU JUBILATION
Edumare a dupe / Ab anije enia / Babu lukudi / Ma ba e lo / O ba won yo / Ki oloriburuku enia / Paga / Ori mi ma jeki nmo osi / Nigba ewe / A gbere wa de America / Ladies and gentlemen / I am black and proud / Nostologi / Ojeje / Operation feed the nation
724382350422 / 19 Jan '98 /
Hemisphere

Obituary

□ BACK FROM THE DEAD
Threatening skies / By the light / Inverted / Platonic diseases / Download / Rewind / Feed on the weak / Lockdown / Pressure point / Back from the dead / Bullituary
RR 88312 / Apr '97 / Roadrunner

□ CAUSE OF DEATH
Infected / Chopped in half / Dying / Cause of death / Turned inside out / Bodybag / Circle of the tyrants / Find the arise / Memories remain
RR 87672 / 17 Nov '97 / Roadrunner

□ DEAD
Download / Threatening skies / By the light / Chopped in half / Body bag / Turned inside out / Dying / Cause of death / I'm in pain / Rewind / Till death / Kill for me / I don't care / Back from the dead / Final thoughts / Slowly we rot
RR 87552 / 27 Apr '98 / Roadrunner

□ END COMPLETE, THE
I'm in pain / Back to one / Dead silence / In the end of life / Sickness / Corrosive / Killing time / End complete / Rotting ways
RC 92012 / Sep '96 / Roadrunner

□ END COMPLETE, THE (Remastered)
I'm in pain / Back to one / Dead silence / In the end of life / Sickness / Corrosive / Killing time / End complete / Rotting ways / I'm in pain (live) / Killing time (live)
RR 87412 / 8 Jun '98 / Roadrunner

□ SLOWLY WE ROT
Internal bleeding / Godly beings / Til death / Slowly we rot / Immortal visions / Gates to hell / Words of evil / Suffocation / Intoxicated / Deadly intentions / Bloodsoaked / Stinkupuss
RR 87682 / 17 Nov '97 / Roadrunner

□ WORLD DEMISE
RR 89952 / Sep '96 / Roadrunner

□ WORLD DEMISE (Remastered)
Don't care / World demise / Burned in / Redefine / Paralysing / Lost / Solid state / Splattered / Final thoughts / Boiling point / Set in stone / Kill for me / Infected / Godly beings / Body bag
RR 87402 / 8 Jun '98 / Roadrunner

Oblivians

□ PLAY 9 SONGS WITH MR. QUINTRON
EFACD 12892 / Jun '97 / Crypt

Oblivion, Greg

□ HEAD SHOP (Oblivion, Greg & The Tip Tops)
SFTRI 513CD / 23 Mar '98 / Sympathy For The Record Industry

Oblivions

□ POPULAR FAVOURITES
EFA 128762 / Jul '96 / Crypt

□ SOUL FOOD
EFA 115892 / Feb '95 / Crypt

Obmana, Vidna

□ RIVER OF APPEARANCE, THE
PRO 65 / Oct '96 / Projekt

□ WELL OF SOULS (2CD Set) (Obmana, Vidna & Steve Reich)
PRO 60 / Oct '96 / Projekt

Obo

□ DIAMOND LOSER
SDW 0392 / 3 Mar '98 / Shadow

O'Briain, Garry

□ SONGS FOR ALL AGES (O'Briain, Garry & Padraigin Ni Uallachain)
CEFCD 166 / Jan '95 / Gael Linn

O'Brien, Daniel

□ BRILLIANT NEW DISASTER
Medicate / Good day / Mount carmal / Brilliant new disaster / Pretty as hell / Powder / Winter sunset / Because / Way things go / One minute on a cloud / Too late
199621 / 16 Mar '98 / Made To Measure

O'Brien, Dermot

□ BEST OF DERMOT O'BRIEN, THE (2CD Set)
Girl from Clare / Castlebar / Rare ould times / Nancy Spain / Donegal Danny / Waterford girls / Jock Stewart / County Mayo / Lisdoonvarna polka / Lakes of Sligo / Maggie / I will love you / Road to Malin Moor / Eileen / Old Claddagh ring / Boys of Killybegs / Sleeve gallon braes / Nora / Connemara rose / Farewell to Galway / Katy Daly / Turfman from Ardee / Home boys home / Boys of Bawn / Galway shawl
PLSCD 218 / Feb '97 / Pulse

□ WHERE THE THREE COUNTIES MEET
Farewell to Galway / Sailing home / Where the three counties meet / Ould claddagh ring / Home boys home / Come to the bower / I'm goin' home / Connemara rose / Slieve Gallion Braes / My ould tambourine / Boys of Killybegs / World goes round / Gypsy boy / County Leitrim Queen / Galway shawl / Nora / Holy ground / My Eileen / Road to Malinmore / Song of an Irish husband / Three leaf shamrock
3036001092 / Jun '97 / Carlton

O'Brien, Hod

□ OPALESSENCE
Opalessence / Touchstone / Bits and pieces / Joy road / Handful of dust / Blues walk / Detour ahead / Joy road (take 1)
CRISS 1012CD / Apr '92 / Criss Cross

□ RIDIN' HIGH
RSRCD 116 / Nov '94 / Reservoir

O'Brien, Kelly

□ TRADITIONAL MUSIC OF IRELAND (O'Brien, Kelly & Sproule)
SHAN 34014CD / Apr '95 / Shanachie

O'Brien, Mick

□ MAY MORNING DEW, THE
ACM 101CD / Nov '96 / ACM

O'Brien, Mollie

□ TELL IT TRUE
If I live / At ain't love / Northern cross / Lark in the morning / Alaska / Never get off the ground / Sign your name / Having myself a time / Bollweevil holler / Henhouse blues / Moonlight ain't no use to me / When I set out for glory
SHCD 3846 / Mar '98 / Sugar Hill

O'Brien, Paddy

□ BANKS OF THE SHANNON (O'Brien, Paddy & Seamus Connolly)
GLCD 3082 / Dec '93 / Green Linnet

□ STRANGER AT THE GATE
Mountain meadow-the highlander who kissed his granny / Trip to sligo-daithi sproules (double jigs) / Coachman's whip-the foxhunters' chorus (reels) / Lady lyle-liz carroll's (strathspey and reel) / Stranger at the gate-miss ratray (reels) / Wounded hussar / Miss hutton-miss johnson of pilworth (strathspey and reel) / Jimmy powers' favourite-the luck of the toss (slip jigs) / Paddy fahy's-miss patterson's slippers (reels) / John brady's-garrett barry's (double jigs) / Colonel rodney-the reel of bogie (reels) / Golden eagle-ed reavy's reel (reels) / Lament from eoin rhua-the march of the gaelic order / Dr. gilbert's white-guys dolan's (reels) / Tiny the trooper-the girls of knockagow (jigs) / Miller of draughin-the humours of castlefin (reels)
GLCD 1091 / Feb '90 / Green Linnet

□ SUNNYSIDE
Keep on the sunny side / Loreena / Close to you / Little town on the Shannon / My wedding band (is a halo of gold) / My lovely Leitrim Shore / Devil woman / Will you think of you / Knock at my window love / She's mine / There goes my everything / Truck driving man / Everybody's reaching out for someone / Sweethearts in heaven / New attraction / She taught me how to yodel
HM 051CD / Mar '90 / Harmac

O'Brien, Rich

□ SEASONS ROADS AND FACES
SH 6024 / Nov '97 / Shanachie

O'Brien, Sean

□ 50 IRISH ACCORDION FAVOURITES, VOL.1
PADDYCD 1 / Apr '98 / Sharpe

□ 50 IRISH ACCORDION FAVOURITES, VOL.2
PADDYCD 3 / Apr '98 / Sharpe

O'Brien, Tim

□ AWAY OUT ON THE MOUNTAIN (O'Brien, Tim & Mollie)
SHCD 3825 / Oct '94 / Sugar Hill

☐ HARD YEAR BLUES
Good deal Lucille / Cora is gone / Land's end / Cabin in gloryland / High road / Cotton tail / Hard year blues / Honky tonk hardwood floor / Evening / Back up and push / Queen of hearts / Twelve gates to the city
FF 70319 / Nov '96 / Flying Fish

☐ ODD MAN IN
Fell in love (and I can't get out) / One way street / Circles around you / Handsome Molly / Lonely at the bottom too / Like I used to do / Lone tree standing / Love on hold / Flora, lily of the west / Hold to a dream / That's what I like about you / Every tear has a reason why / Hungry eyes / Romance is a slow dance
SHCD 3790 / Jul '91 / Sugar Hill

☐ OH BOY O'BOY (O'Brien, Tim & The O'Boys)
Church steeple / When I paint my masterpiece / Heartbreak game / Time to learn / Perfect place to hide / Run mountain / Good woman bad / Few are chosen / Shadows to light / Farmer's cursed wife / Johnny don't get drunk/Rye straw / He had a long chain on
SHCD 3808 / May '93 / Sugar Hill

☐ RED ON BLONDE
Senor (tales of Yankee power) / Tombstone blues / Farewell Angelina / Wicked messenger / Father of night / Subterranean homesick blues / Everything is broken / Man gave names to all the animals / Masters of war / Oxford Town / Maggie's farm / Forever young / Lay down your weary tune
SHCD 3853 / Mar '98 / Sugar Hill

☐ REMEMBER ME (O'Brien, Tim & Mollie)
Looking for the stone / If I had my way / Floods of south Dakota / Shut de do / Stagger lee / Remember me / Somebody the blues / Do right to me baby / That's the way to treat your woman / Motherless children / Pilgrim of sorrow / Hush while the little ones sleep / Out in the country
SHCD 3804 / Jul '92 / Sugar Hill

☐ ROCK IN MY SHOE
SHCD 3835 / Jul '95 / Sugar Hill

☐ TAKE ME BACK (O'Brien, Tim & Mollie)
Leave that liar alone / Sweet sunny South / I loved you a thousand ways / Just someone I used to know / Down to the valley to pray / Wave the ocean, wave the sea / Your long journey / When the roses bloom in Dixieland / Unwed fathers / Nobody's fault but mine / Papa's on the housetop / Dream of the miner's child / Christ was born in Bethlehem
SHCD 3766 / Aug '96 / Sugar Hill

☐ WHEN NO ONE'S AROUND
Kick me when I'm down / River of blood / One drop of rain / When you come back down / Out on the rolling sea / I like the way you cook / How come I ain't dead / Love and laughter / Love is pleasin' / Think about last night / Don't be surprised / First days of fall / When there's no one around
SHCD 3866 / Mar '98 / Sugar Hill

O'Brien-Moran, Jimmy

☐ SEAN REID'S FAVOURITE
PPP 001CD / May '97 / Piping Pig

O'Bryant, Jimmy

☐ JIMMY O'BRYANT VOL.1 1924-1925
JPCD 1518 / May '95 / Jazz Perspectives

☐ JIMMY O'BRYANT VOL.2 1923-1931 (O'Bryant, Jimmy & Vance Dixon)
JPCD 1519 / May '95 / Jazz Perspectives

Obsessed

☐ LUNAR WOMB
H 00152 / Jan '92 / Hellhound

Obsession Quintet

☐ BULGAROIDE TRIBU
DP 96013CD / Aug '96 / Mustradem

OC

☐ JEWELZ
Intro / My world / War games / Can't go wrong / Chosen one / Dangerous / Win the g / Far from yours / Stronjay / MUG / Crow / You and yours / Hypocrite / It's only write / Jewelz
5243992 / Aug '97 / London

Ocal, Burhan

☐ OTTOMAN GARDEN
ED 13044 / Jan '97 / L'Empreinte Digitale

O'Callaghan, Pep

☐ TOT JUST
FSNT 017 / Jan '98 / Fresh Sound New Talent

O'Canainn, Thomas

☐ UILEANN PIPES AND SONG
PTICD 1035 / Oct '95 / Pure Traditional Irish

Ocarina

☐ SONG OF OCARINA
DSHLCD 7020 / Aug '95 / D-Sharp

O'Cathain, Darach

☐ DARACH O CATHAIN
SHCD 34005 / May '93 / Claddagh

☐ TRADITIONAL IRISH UNACCOMPANIED SINGING
CEFCD 040 / Jan '94 / Gael Linn

Occasional Word

☐ YEAR OF THE GREAT LEAP SIDEWAYS, THE
Open the box / Eternal truth, man / Thoroughly British affair / Clock clock / I'm so glad / Barnyard suite / Girl behind me / Missed my times / Evil venus tree / Eine steine knack muzak / Trixie's song / Train set / Sweet tea song / Nuts and bolts / Internal truth, woman / Playground that fought back / Skin diver / Mrs. Jones / Hortensia / Close the box
SEECD 420 / May '95 / See For Miles

Occasionals

☐ BACK IN STEP
Grand march / Boston two-step / Flying Scotsman / Hesitation waltz / Jacky tar two step / Circassion circle / Lombard waltz / Baden / Hullichan's jig / Duke of Perth / Russian ballet / Friendly waltz / Haymakers / Gypsy tap / Southern rose waltz / Drops of brandy / Call of the pipers / Orcadian strip the willow
CDTRAX 107 / Jul '96 / Greentrax

☐ FOOTNOTES: THE COMPLETE SCOTTISH CEILIDH DANCE
Gay gordons / Eva three step / St. Bernard's waltz / Dashing white sergeant / Military two step / Canadian barn dance / Pride of Erin waltz / Strip the willow / Britannia two step / Waltz country dance / Cumberland square eight / Highland schottische / Swedish masquerade / Virginia reel / Foula reel / Veleta waltz / Eightsome reel / Last waltz
IRCD 021 / Jan '93 / Lismor

Occult

☐ ENEMY WITHIN, THE
FDN 2011CD / Jun '96 / Foundation 2000

☐ PREPARE TO MEET THY DOOM
FDN 2010CD / Jun '94 / Foundation 2000

Ocean

☐ GOD'S CLOWN
3034842 / 24 Feb '98 / Mantra

☐ SILVER
DHR 1 / Mar '94 / Doll's House

Ocean 11

☐ GOOD, THE BAD AND THE UGLY, THE
ATY 003CD / Apr '97 / A To Y

Ocean, Billy

☐ LOVE REALLY HURTS WITHOUT YOU
Love really hurts without you / Emotions in motion / On the run (the battle is over) / Whose little girl are you / He ain't as black as he is painted / What's gonna happen to our love / Wild beautiful woman / Light up the world with your sunshine / Can you feel it / Eye of a storm / Hungry for love / Super woman super lover
QED 114 / Nov '96 / Tring

☐ LOVE REALLY HURTS WITHOUT YOU
Love really hurts without you / Emotions in motion / On the run (the battle is over) / Whose little girl is you / He ain't black as he's painted / On the run (battle is over) / What's gonna happen to our love / Wild beautiful woman / Light up the world with sunshine / Can you feel it / Eye of the storm / Hungry for love / Super woman, super lover / On the run (the battle is over)
100192 / May '97 / A-Play Collection

☐ LOVER BOY
Loverboy / Let's get back together / Promise me / Without you / Long and winding road / It's never too late to try / Here's to you / Caribbean queen (no more love on the run) / Stand and deliver / Colour of love / There'll be sad songs (To make you cry) / If I should lose you / Showdown / Because of you
5501182 / Oct '93 / Spectrum

Ocean Blue

☐ BENEATH THE RHYTHM AND SOUND
Peace of mind / Sublime / Listen it's gone / Either or / Bliss is unaware / Ice skating at night / Don't believe everything you hear / Crash / Cathedral bells / Relatives / Emotions ring
9362453692 / Sep '93 / Sire

Ocean Colour Scene

☐ MARCHIN' ALREADY
MCD 60048 / 15 Sep '97 / MCA

☐ MARCHIN' ALREADY
MCD 60053 / 27 Apr '98 / MCA

☐ MOSELEY SHOALS
Riverboat song / Day we caught the train / Circle lining your pockets / Fleeting mind / 40 past midnight / One for the road / It's my shadow / Policeman and pirates / Downstream / You've got it bad / Get away
MCD 60008 / Apr '96 / MCA

☐ OCEAN COLOUR SCENE
Talk on / How about you / Giving it all away / Justine / Do yourself a favour / Third shade of green / Sway / Penny pinching rainy heaven days / One of those days / Is she coming home / Blue deep ocean / Reprise
5122692 / Jan '96 / Fontana

Oceanic

☐ THAT ALBUM BY OCEANIC
Is this the end / Insanity / Heavenly feel / Wicked love / Ignorance / Controlling me / Strut / Using me / Give this love some meaning / Moments in time / Insanity / Wicked love
GOODCD 1 / May '92 / Dead Dead Good

O'Ceannabhain, Tomas

☐ FONN LE FONN
SC 2032 / Jul '98 / Blue Sun

Ocho

☐ TORNADO
Mamey Colorao / Tornado / Way we were / Sneakin' up behind you / Majnabuca / Mode 1 / Mode 2 / Mode 3 / Mode 4
USCDTOR 1 / Nov '96 / Universal Sound

Ochoa, Callixto

☐ SALSA CUMBIA VALLENATO (Ochoa, Callixto & Las Vibraciones)
TUMICD 036 / '94 / Tumi

Ochoa, Rafael

☐ HARPS OF VENUZUELA (Ochoa, Rafael & Rafael Aponte)
PS 65083 / Mar '92 / PlayaSound

Ochs, Phil

☐ ALL THE NEWS THATS FIT TO SING
One more parade / Thresher / Talking Vietnam / Lou Marsh / Power and the glory / Celia / Bells / Automation song / Ballad of William Worthy / Knock on the door / Talking Cuban crisis / Bound for glory / Too many martyrs / What's that I hear
HNCD 4427 / Apr '94 / Hannibal

☐ BROADSIDE TAPES VOL.1, THE
SFWCD 40008 / Mar '95 / Smithsonian Folkways

☐ GREATEST HITS
One way ticket home / Jim Dean of Indiana / My kingdom for a car / Boy in Ohio / Gas station women / Chords of fame / Ten cents a coup / Bach, Beethoven, Mozart and me / Basket in the pool / No more songs
EDCD 201 / Jul '90 / Edsel

☐ I AIN'T MARCHING ANYMORE
I ain't marching anymore / In the heat of the summer / Draft dodger rag / That's what I want to hear / That was The President / Iron lady / Highway man / Links on the chain / Hills of West Virginia / Men behind the guns / Talking Birmingham jam / Ballad of the carpenter / Days of decision / Here's to the state of Mississippi
HNCD 4422 / Apr '94 / Hannibal

☐ LAST AMERICAN TROUBADOUR, THE (2CD Set)
Cross my heart / Flower lady / Outside of a small circle of friends / Pleasures of the harbor / Crucifixion / Tape from California / White boots marching in a yellow land / Half a century high / Joe Hill / War is over / William BYeates vists Lincoln Park and escapes unscathed / Here's to the state of Richard Nixon / Scorpion departs but never returns / Doesn't Lenny live here anymore / Rehearsals for retirement / I kill therefore I am / Bells / Highwayman / Another age / There but for fortune / One way ticket home / Jim Dean of Indiana / My kingdom for a car / Gas station women / Chords of fame / No more songs / Mona Lisa / I ain't marchin' anymore / School days / Power and the glory / Kansas City bomber / Bwatue / Niko Mchumba Ngombe / Changes
5407282 / Aug '97 / A&M

☐ LIVE AT NEWPORT
Ballad of Edgar Evers / Talking of Birmingham jam / Power and the glory / Daft dodger rag / I ain't marching / Links on the rain / Talking Vietnam blues / Cross your heart / Half a century high / Is there anybody here / Party / Pleasure of the harbour
VCD 77017 / 27 Jul '98 / Vanguard

O'Connell, Helen

☐ SWEETEST SOUNDS, THE
Sweetest sounds / Taking a chance on love / Fly me to the moon / Tangerine / September in the rain / I can't believe that you're in love with me / Beautiful friendship / Embraceable you / Autumn leaves / Moon river / Green eyes / Just in time / Not mine / When the sun comes out / Witchcraft / Amapola
HCD 251 / Aug '94 / Hindsight

O'Connell, Maura

☐ ALWAYS
TFCB 5011CD / Oct '94 / Third Floor

☐ BLUE IS THE COLOUR OF HOPE
Still hurts sometimes / I would be stronger than that / Love to learn / Bad news (at the best of times) / Sunnyshine day / First you cry / So soft your goodbye / It don't bring you / Blue train / To be the one
9362450632 / Jan '95 / WEA

☐ JUST IN TIME
Scholar / If you love me / Feet of a dancer / Isle of Malachy / New Orleans / Water is wide / Leaving Neidin / Crazy dreams / Love's old sweet song / Another morning / I will / Just in time
CDPH 1124 / '90 / Philo

☐ MAURA O'CONNELL
Living in these troubled times / God only knows / Send this whisper / Lovers at last / Till the right one comes along / I don't know how you do it / Saw you running / All of me / Love is on a roll / Spend the night with you / My Lagan love
TFCB 5007CD / Oct '94 / Third Floor

☐ STORIES
Blue chalk / Hit the ground running / Love divine / Poetic justice / Stories / Half moon bay / This town can't get over you / Rainmaker / Shotgun down the avalanche / Ordinary day / If I fell / Wall around you heart
HNCD 1389 / Oct '95 / Hannibal

☐ WANDERING HOME
West coast of Clare / I hear you calling / Down the moor / Teddy O'Neill / Shades of Gloria / Irish blues / Down where the drunkards roll / A Stor Ma Chroi / Down by the Sally Gardens / Dun Do Shuil / Singer's house
HNCD 1410 / Jun '97 / Hannibal

O'Connell, Moloney

☐ KILKELLY (O'Connell, Moloney & Keane)
GLCD 1072 / Feb '92 / Green Linnet

O'Connell, Robbie

☐ CLOSE TO THE BONE
Gay old hag / William Hollander / Week before Easter / Earl of Murray / Waterford waltz / With Kitty I'll go for a waltz / Torn petticoat/The rambling pitchfork / I know where I'm going / Bobby's britches / Sliabh na mBan / Ferrybank piper / Ham Sunday
GLCD 1038 / Oct '88 / Green Linnet

☐ LOVE OF THE LAND, THE
Love of the land / Keg of brandy / Early riser / Full moon over Managua / Land of Liberty / Road to Dunmore / Two nations / Last of the Gleemen / You're not Irish
GLCD 1097 / Nov '92 / Green Linnet

☐ NEVER LEARNED TO DANCE
Love knows no bounds / American lives / Galileo / Winning side / Turning of the tide / Hard to say goodbye / Man from Connemara / When the moon is full / Old man of the mountain / Mistress / So near / Singer
GLCD 1124 / May '93 / Green Linnet

O'Connor, Cavan

☐ SMILIN' THROUGH
Rose of tralee / One alone / Danny boy / In the still of the night / Vagabond song / Hear my song Violetta / Could you be true to eyes of blue / God will remember / Little village green / Marie / My heart is always calling you / Put a little springtime / Shannon river / Smilin' through / Star and the rose / Star of County Down / Take me back to dear old Ireland / There's something in your eyes / When it's springtime in old Ireland / Without you / Would you take me back again / You, me and love
CDAJA 5085 / Mar '97 / Living Era

☐ VAGABOND OF SONG, THE
PLATCD 35 / Mar '95 / Platinum

☐ VERY BEST OF THE SINGING VAGABOND, THE
I'll take you home again kathleen / Kathleen mavourneen / Lullaby of the leaves / When a pal bids a pal goodbye / My song goes round the world / Love's roses / Rose of tralee / Without you / Starlight serenade / Fool with a dream / God will remember / Song o' my heart / Day-break / Alone / Desert song / Song of paradise / Singing vagabong song / White cliffs of dover / There's a blue haze on the mountains / You, me and love / Down the lane to home sweet home / I'm only a strolling vagabond
SWNCD 001 / May '95 / Sound Waves

O'Connor, Charles

☐ ANGEL ON THE MANTLEPIECE
ALZO 1CD / Jul '95 / Ritual

O'Connor, Des

☐ CHRISTMAS WITH DES O'CONNOR
PLSCD 267 / 29 Sep '97 / Pulse

☐ VERY BEST OF DES O'CONNOR, THE
Careless hands / One two three O'Leary / When you're smiling / Everybody's talkin' / Raindrops keep fallin' on my head / For the good times / You always hurt the one you love / Your cheatin' heart / Didn't we / I pretend / Dream a little dream of me / With love / Anytime / Dick-a-dum-dum / Tips of my fingers / I'll go hopping / Lonliness (No sono Maddelena) / Something / All I need is you / Heartaches / Try to remember / Red roses for a blue lady / My thanks to you
CDMFP 6248 / Aug '96 / Music For Pleasure

O'Connor, Gerry

☐ LA LUGH (O'Connor, Gerry & Eithne Ni Uallachain)
Mal bhan ni Chilleannain/Destitution / Sterling Tom/ Tommy Bhetty's hornmmpipe / One morning in May / Wedding jig/Aunt Lizzie's jig / Liostail me le Sairsint / Shetland bus / Donellan set / Road to Clady / Mummer's march/The Water Ouzel / Rosebuds in summer / Launching the boat / Draw near my wayward Darling / On Brigid's eve / Boy in his pants/ Big John's jig / Emigrant's farewell / Drogheda lassies/The Donegal traveller/Lisa Ornstein's reel
CCF 29CD / Jun '93 / Claddagh

☐ TIME TO TIME
LUNCD 051 / Sep '86 / Mulligan

O'Connor, Hazel

☐ LIVE IN BERLIN
D-days / Runaway / Blackman / Spancil Hill / Tell me why / Hanging around / Will you / Eighth day / Calls the tune / If only / Reach / Driftwood
SRH 804 / Feb '97 / Start

O'Connor, Mark

☐ CHAMPIONSHIP YEARS 1975-1984, THE
Grey eagle / Clarinet polka / Dusty Miller / I don't love nobody / Wednesday night waltz / Herman's rag / Sally Goodin / Sally Johnson / Yellow rose waltz / Tom and Jerry / Billy in the lowground / Herman's rag / Allentown polka / Brilliancy / Black and white rag / Tom and Jerry / Clarinet polka / Dill pickle rag / Grey eagle / Leather britches / Don't let the deal go down / Golden eagle hornpipe / I don't love nobody / Brilliancy / Tug boat / Grey eagle / Beaumont rag / Hell among the yearlings / Bill Cheatham / Sally Goodin / Herman's rag / Choctaw / Westphalia waltz / Black and white rag / Herman's hornpipe / Dill pickle rag / Sally Ann / Clarinet polka / Arkansas traveller / Jesse polka
CMFCD 015 / Jan '93 / Country Music Foundation

☐ HEROES
9362452572 / Feb '94 / WEA

☐ MARKOLOGY
Dixie breakdown / Markology / Kit's waltz / Fluid drive / Blackberry blossom / Pickin' the wind / Banks of the Ohio / Berserkeley / On top of the world
ROUCD 009 / Aug '93 / Rounder

☐ RETROSPECTIVE
Dusty miller / Dreamer's waltz / Pickin' in the wind / Tom and jerry / Dixie breakdown / Beserkeley / On top of the world / Dixie breakdown / Soft gyrations / Dark rain / Ease with the breeze / Peaches 'n' cream / Misty moonlight waltz / Wild fiddler's rag / Floating bridge of dreams / Rose among thorns / Thanks and goodbyes / Empty hall into the walls of mandoness
ROUCD 11507 / '88 / Rounder

☐ SOPPIN' THE GRAVY
Soppin' the gravy / Misty moonlight waltz / College hornpipe / Calgary polka / Morning star waltz / Tennessee Wagoner / Yellow rose waltz / Medley / Jesse polka / Dawn waltz / Wild fiddler's rag / Over the rainbow
ROUCD 0137 / '92 / Rounder

O'Connor, Martin

☐ CHATTERBOX
DARACD 052 / Oct '93 / Dara

☐ CONNACHTMAN'S RAMBLES
LUNCD 027 / Feb '95 / Mulligan

☐ PERPETUAL MOTION
Fandango / Rags to rock'n'roll / Happy hours / Carnival of Venice / Perpetual motion / Ebra polka / Emerald blues / Cajun medley / Beau St. Waltzes / Bulgarian jig / Sophie for Sofia / Midnight on the water / Hound dog
CCF 26CD / '90 / Claddagh

O'Connor, Sinead

☐ AM I NOT YOUR GIRL
Why don't you do right / Bewitched, bothered and bewildered / Secret love / Black coffee / Success has made a failure of our home / Don't cry for me Argentina / I wanna be loved by you / Gloomy Sunday / Love Letters / How insensitive / Don't cry for me Argentina (Inst)
CCD 1952 / Sep '92 / Ensign

☐ I DO NOT WANT WHAT I HAVEN'T GOT
Feel so different / I am stretched on your grave / Three babies / Emperor's new clothes / Black boys on mopeds / Nothing compares 2 U / Jump in the river / You cause as much sorrow / Last day of our acquaintance / I do not want what I haven't got
CCD 1759 / Mar '90 / Ensign

☐ LION AND THE COBRA, THE
Jackie / Mandinka / Jerusalem / Just like u said it would b / Never get old / Troy / I want your (hands on me) / Drink before the war / Just call me Joe
CCD 1612 / Oct '87 / Ensign

☐ SO FAR (The Best Of Sinead O'Connor)
Herpone / Mandinka / Jackie / Troy / Nothing compares 2 U / I am stretched on your grave / Emperor's new clothes / Last day of our acquaintance / Success has made a failure of our home / Thank you for hearing me / Fire on Babylon / John I love you / Perfect Indian / You made me the thief of your heart / Empire / This is a rebel song
8215812 / 10 Nov '97 / Chrysalis

☐ UNIVERSAL MOTHER
Speech extract / Fire on Babylon / John I love you / My darling child / Am I a human / Red football / All apologies / Perfect Indian / Scorn not his simplicity / All babies / In this heart / Tiny grief song / Famine / Thank you for hearing me
CDCHEN 34 / Sep '94 / Ensign

Octagon Man

☐ EXCITING WORLD OF...
TRONCD 5X / Nov '95 / Electron Industries

October Faction

☐ SECOND FACTIIONALISATION
SST 056CD / May '93 / SST

October Meeting 1991

☐ ANATOMY OF A MEETING
BIMHUIS 004 / Aug '97 / Bvhaast

Octopus

☐ RESTLESS NIGHT...PLUS
River / Summer / Council plans / Restless night / Thief / Queen and the pauper / I say / John's rock / Rainchild / Tide / Girlfriend / Laugh at the poor man
SEECD 328 / Aug '97 / See For Miles

Octopus

☐ FROM A TO B
Your smile / Everyday kiss / If you want to give me more / King for a day / Adrenalina / Instrumental 1 / Jealousy / Magazine / From A to B / Instrumental 2 / Saved / Wait and see / Theme from Joy Pop / Night song / In this world
FOODCD 18 / Sep '96 / Food

Octoscope

☐ OCTOPHOBIC
CLP 9968 / Apr '97 / Cleopatra

O'Day, Anita

☐ ANITA O'DAY 1975
STCD 4147 / Feb '90 / Storyville

☐ ANITA O'DAY SINGS THE WINNERS
Take the 'A' train / Tenderly / Night in Tunisia / Four / Early Autumn / Four brothers / Sing sing sing / My funny valentine / Frenesi / Body and soul / What's your story Morning Glory / Peanut vendor / Whisper not / Blue champagne / Stompin' at the Savoy / Hershey Bar / Don't be that way / Peel me grape / Star eyes
8379392 / Apr '90 / Verve

☐ ANITA O'DAY SWINGS COLE PORTER
Just one of those things / Love for sale / You'd be so nice to come home to / Easy to love / I get a kick out of you / All of you / Get out of town / I get you under my skin / Night and day / It's de-lovely / I love you / What is this thing called love / You're the top / My heart belongs to Daddy / Why shouldn't I / From this moment on / Love for sale / Just one of those things
8492662 / Mar '91 / Verve

☐ BIG BAND YEARS, THE
Georgia on my mind / Just a little bit south of north Carolina / Slow down / Green eyes / Let me off uptown / Kick it / Stop the red light's on / Walls keep talking / Skylark / Bolero at the Savoy / Thanks for the boogie ride / That's what you think / Massachusetts / Murder he says / I'm going mad for a pad / And her tears flowed like wine / I want a grown up man / Memories of you / Opus 1 / Did you ever get that feeling in the moonlight / Boogie blues / Chickery chick / In the middle of May / Tea for two / Harriet
PLCD 547 / Aug '96 / President

☐ HIGH STANDARDS
CDSL 5209 / Jan '89 / DRG

☐ I GET A KICK OUT OF YOU
Song for you / Undecided / What are you doing the rest of your life / Exactly like you / When Sunny gets blue / It had to be you / Opus one / Gone with the wind
ECD 22054 / Jul '93 / Evidence

☐ JAZZ MASTERS
5276532 / 5 May '98 / Verve

☐ L'ART VOCAL 1941-1945
700192 / Jul '97 / L'Art Vocal

☐ LET ME OFF UPTOWN
Georgia on my mind / Just a little bit South of North Carolina / Slow down / Green eyes / Let me off uptown / Kick it / Stop, the red light's on / Watch the birdie / Walls keep talking / Skylark / Bolero at the Savoy / Thanks for the boogie ride / Pass the bounce / Harlem on parade / That's what you think / Massachusetts / Murder he says / Opus one / Boogie blues / That feeling in the moonlight / Tea for two / Harriet
TPZ 1046 / Jul '96 / Topaz Jazz

☐ MEETS THE BIG BANDS
MCD 0472 / Nov '93 / Moon

☐ ONCE UPON A SUMMERTIME
Sweet Georgia Brown / Love for sale / 'S Wonderful / Tea for two / Once upon a summertime / Night and day / Anita's blues / They can't take that away from me / Boogie blues / Girl from Ipanema / Is you is or is you ain't my baby / Nightingale sang in Berkeley Square
JASMCD 2531 / Feb '95 / Jasmine

☐ PICK YOURSELF UP
I'm with you / Don't be that way / Rock 'n' roll waltz / Let's face the music and dance / Getaway and the chase / I never had a chance / Stompin' at the Savoy / Your picture's hanging crooked on the wall / Pick yourself up / We laughed at love / I'm not lonely / Stars fell on Alabama / Sweet Georgia Brown / Let's face the music and dance / Stars fell on Alabama / I won't dance / Man with a horn / I used to be colour blind / There's a lull in my life / Let's begin
5173292 / Jun '93 / Verve

☐ RULES OF THE ROAD
Rules of the road / Black coffee / Detour ahead / Shaking the blues away / Music that makes me dance / As long as there's music / Sooner or later / What is a man / Here's that rainy day / It's you or no one / I told ya I love ya, now get out
CD 2310950 / Apr '94 / Pablo

O'Day, Molly

☐ MOLLY O'DAY AND THE CUMBERLAND MOUNTAIN FOLKS
Tramp on the street / When God comes and gathers his jewels / Black sheep returned to the fold / Put my rubber doll away / Drunken driver / Tear stained letter / Lonely mound of clay / Six more miles / Singing waterfall / At the first fall of snow / Matthew twenty four / I don't care if tomorrow never comes / Hero's death / I'll never see sunshine again / Too late, too late / Why do you weep dear willow / Don't forget the family prayer / I heard my mother weeping / Mother's gone but not forgotten / Evening train / This is the end / Fifteen years ago / Teardrops falling in the snow / With you on my mind / If you see my saviour / Heaven's radio / When my time comes to go / Don't sell Daddy anymore whiskey / Higher in my prayers / Travelling the highway home / It's different now / When the angels rolled the stone away / It's all coming true / When we see our Redeemer's face
BCD 15565 / Jun '92 / Bear Family

Odd Toot

☐ BAMPOT
HEMP 8CD / Jul '97 / Recordings Of Substance

Oddsods

☐ SCALLYWAGS AND SCOUNDRELS
Sam Hall / Johnny I hardly knew you / Belfast mill / Peeking pup waltz / World turned upside down / All for me grog / Boys of the blue hill/Corn hornpipe / Johnny jump up / Man you don't meet everyday / I'm missing you / Hewletts/Princess Royale / Red is the rose / Maids when you're young / Star of the County Down/Tenpenny Bit / Weile weile / Last but one / Spontaneous bananas
FSCD 46 / Dec '96 / Folksound

Oden, Jimmy

☐ JIMMY ODEN 1932-1948
SOB 35082CD / Apr '95 / Story Of The Blues

☐ ST. LOUIS JIMMY ODEN VOL.1 1932-1944
DOCD 5234 / May '94 / Document

☐ ST. LOUIS JIMMY ODEN VOL.2 1944-1955
DOCD 5235 / May '94 / Document

Odessa Balalaikas

☐ ART OF THE BALALAIKA, THE
7559790342 / Jan '95 / Nonesuch

Odessa Express

☐ BABEL
SYNCD 159 / Jun '94 / Syncoop

Odetta

☐ AT THE GATE OF HORN
TCD 1063 / 12 Jan '98 / Tradition

☐ CHRISTMAS SPIRITUALS
Rise up shepherd and follow / What month was Jesus born in / Mary had a baby, yes Lord / Somebody talking 'bout Jesus / Virgin Mary had one son / Go tell it on the mountain / Shout for joy / Poor little Jesus / O Jerusalem / Ain't that a-rockin' / If anybody asks you / Beautiful star / Children go where I send thee
VMD 79079 / Oct '96 / Vanguard

☐ ESSENTIAL, THE
If I had a hammer / When I was a young girl / Gallows poet / God's a gonna cut you down / John Riley / All the pretty little horses / Prettiest train / Meetin' at the building / No more auction block for me / Hold on / Sometimes I feel like a motherless child / Ain't no grave can hold my body down / He had a long chain on / He's got the whole world in his hands / Take this hammer / Ox driver's song / What month was Jesus born in / Timber
VCD 43/44 / 27 Apr '98 / Vanguard

☐ ODETTA AND THE BLUES
Hard, oh Lord / Believe I'll go / Oh papa / How long blues / Hogan's alley / Leavin' this morning / Oh, my babe / Yonder come the blues / Make me a pallet on the floor / Weeping willow blues / Go down sunshine / Nobody knows you (when you're down and out)
OBCCD 509 / Nov '92 / Original Blues Classics

☐ ODETTA AT THE TOWN HALL
VMD 2109 / Jan '96 / Vanguard

☐ SINGS BALLADS AND BLUES
TCD 1004 / Feb '96 / Tradition

☐ TIN ANGEL (Odetta & Larry Mohr)
John henry / Old cotton fields at home / Frozen logger / Run come see jerusalem / Old blue / Water boy / Santy ana / I was born about 10,000 years ago-the biggest thing / Car-car song / No more cane on the brazos / Pay day at coal creek / I've been 'buked abd I've been scorned / Rock island line / Another man don' gone / Children go where I send thee / I know where I'm going / He's got the whole world in his hands / Timber / Timber / Wade in the water
OBCCD 565 / Jul '94 / Original Blues Classics

☐ WOMEN IN (E)MOTION FESTIVAL
T&M 101 / Nov '94 / Tradition & Moderne

Odium

☐ SAD REALM OF THE STARS, THE
ECLIPSE 010CD / 17 Aug '98 / Nocturnal Art

Odom, Andrew

☐ FEEL SO GOOD (Odom, Andrew 'Big Voice' & Magic Slim/Lucky Peterson)
Feel so good / I made up my mind / Mother In Law Blues / Woke up this morning / Memo blues / Bad feeling / You say that you love me baby / Reconsider baby
ECD 260272 / Feb '93 / Evidence

O'Donnell, Daniel

☐ BOY FROM DONEGAL, THE
Donegal shore / Old rustic bridge / Galway bay / Forty shades of green / My side of the road / 5000 miles from Sligo / Old bog road / Slievenamon / Noreen Bawn / Ballyhoe
IHCD 04 / Oct '89 / Irish Heritage

☐ CHRISTMAS WITH DANIEL
Silent night / Memory of an old Christmas card / Silver bells / C-H-R-I-S-T-M-A-S / White Christmas / When a child is born / Rockin' around the Christmas tree / Christmas song / Christmas long ago / Gift / Christmas time in Inisfree / Snowflake / I saw Mommy kissing Santa Claus / Pretty paper
RZBCD 704 / Nov '94 / Ritz

☐ CLASSIC COLLECTION
RZBCD 705 / Oct '95 / Ritz

☐ DANIEL O'DONNELL IRISH COLLECTION
RZCD 0080 / Jul '96 / Ritz

☐ DATE WITH DANIEL O'DONNELL - LIVE, A
I just wanna dance with you / Whatever happened to old fashioned love / Somewhere between / Follow your dream / You're the reason / Love in your eyes / Minute you're gone / Little things / My Irish country home / Isle of Innisfree / I need you / Never ending song of love / Wedding song / My Donegal shore / Stand beside me / Old rugged cross / How great thou art / Pretty little girl from Omagh / My shoes keep walking back to you / Rose of Tralee / Our house is a home / Mountains of Mourne / Roses are red/ Moonlight and roses
RZBCD 702 / Oct '93 / Ritz

☐ DON'T FORGET TO REMEMBER
I don't care / Old loves never die / I wonder where you are tonight / Don't be angry / Roses are red / Before I'm over you / Take good care of her / Pretty little girl from Omagh / Green willow / Don't let me cross over / Good old days / Pat Murphy's meadow / I just can't make it on my own
RZCD 105 / Dec '87 / Ritz

☐ ESPECIALLY FOR YOU
Singin' the blues / Lover's chain / You're the first thing I think of / Someday / There'll never be anyone else / Travelling light / Old broken hearts / Leaving is easy / She goes walking through my mind / Come back paddy reilly to Ballyjamesduff / Sweet forget me not / Silver threads among the gold / It comes and goes / Guilty / Happy years
RZBCD 703 / Oct '94 / Ritz

☐ FAVOURITES
Bed of roses / Excuse me / Geisha girl / Home sweet home / Home is where the heart is / Forever you'll be mine / Streets of Baltimore / Bringing Mary home / Banks of my own lovely Lee / Green hills of Sligo
RZCD 0052 / Apr '90 / Ritz

☐ FOLLOW YOUR DREAM
I need you (intro) / Stand Beside Me / Eileen / Pretty Little Girl From Omagh / Destination Donegal / Medley / Medley / Wedding song (Ave Maria) / Irish country home / Ramblin' Rose / I just want to dance with you / Medley / Medley / White River stomp / Our House Is A Home / Never Ending Song Of Love / Rockin' alone in an old rocking chair / Standing Room Only / Welcome home / Love in your eyes / You send me your love / Turkey In The Straw / I Need You / Medley / Reprise / How Great Thou Art
RZBCD 701 / Nov '92 / Ritz

☐ I BELIEVE
Everything is beautiful / I believe / Wonderful world / I can see clearly now / I have a dream / Greatest love / Little peace / Way old friends do / Rivers of Babylon / Any dream will do / Song for the world / When I was a child / Beyond the great divide / Special absent friends / Love, hope and faith / Give a little love / Desiderata
RZBCD 710 / 27 Oct '97 / Ritz

☐ I NEED YOU
Sing me an old Irish song / I need you / From a jack to a king / Lovely rose of Clare / Stand beside me / Irish eyes / Dear old Galway town / Three leaf shamrock / Veil of white lace / Kickin' each others hearts around / Medals for mothers / Wedding bells / Snowflake / Your friendly Irish way / Lough Melvin's rocky shore / I love you because
RZCD 104 / Jun '87 / Ritz

☐ LAST WALTZ, THE
Here I am in love again / We could / Last waltz of the evening / When only the sky was blue / Heaven with you / You know I still love you / Talk back trembling lips / Shelter of your eyes / When we get together / Ring of gold / Fool such as I / Memory number one / Look both ways / Little patch of blue / Marianne
RZCD 0058 / Oct '90 / Ritz

☐ SONGS OF INSPIRATION
RZBCD 709 / Oct '96 / Ritz

☐ TIMELESS (O'Donnell, Daniel & Mary Duff)
RZBCD 707 / Mar '96 / Ritz

☐ TWO SIDES OF DANIEL O'DONNELL, THE
Green glens of Antrim / Blue hills of Breffni / Any Tipperary town / Latchyco / Home town on the Foyle / These are my mountains / My Donegal shore / Crying my heart out over you / My old pal / Our house is a home / Your old love letters / Twenty one years / Highway 40 blues / I wouldn't change you if I could
RZCD 500 / '91 / Ritz

☐ VERY BEST OF DANIEL O'DONNELL, THE
I need you / Never ending song of love / Don't forget to remember / Country boy like me / She's no angel / Stand beside me / Eileen / Pretty little girl from Omagh / Danny boy / Wedding song / My Donegal shore / Letter from the postman's bag / Three bells / Our house is a home / Loved ones goodbye / Home is where the heart is / Old rugged cross / You send me your love / Take good care of her / Standing room only
RZBCD 700 / Oct '91 / Ritz

O'Donnell, Eugene

☐ FOGGY DEW, THE (O'Donnell, Eugene & James MacCafferty)
Foggy dew / Wild rose of the mountain-the gentle maiden / De bharr an cnoch-sean o duibhir an gleanna / Da slockit light / An coulin agus an tsean coulin / Lord mayo / Lament for the death of rev. archie beaton-thios cois ma fa / Eugene o'donnell / Donal mor / Bogay house / Derry air
GLCD 1084 / Feb '91 / Green Linnet

☐ SLOW AIRS & SET DANCES
Downfall of Paris / Scotsman over the border / Lodge Road / Da auld resting chair/Derry hornpipe / Barney Brallaghan/Ride a mile / Celtic lament / Planxty O'Donnell / Jockey to the fair / Hunt / I won't see you anymore, my dear / Three sea captains / Bonny lass o'Bon Accord / Hurry the jug / Humours of Bandon/ Planxty Maggie Brown / Planxty Drury
GLCD 1015 / Oct '88 / Green Linnet

O'Donnell, Peter

☐ SHAKESPEARE BLUES
QMCD 001 / Jun '94 / Bareface

O'Dowd, Barry

☐ 20 IRISH FAVOURITES
MBPCD 7004 / 11 May '98 / Quantum Mobius

☐ 20 IRISH PARTY SONGS (O'Dowd, Barry & The Shamrock Singers)
If your Irish come into the parlour / With my shillelagh under me arm / Galway Bay / Peggy O'Neil / Unicorn / Isle of Innisfree / Did your mother come from Ireland / Too-ra-loo-ra-loo-ra / Dear old Donegal / Little bit of heaven / It's a great day for the Irish / Stone outside Dan Murphy's door / My wild Irish rose / Goodbye Johnny / When Irish eyes are smiling / I'll take you home again Kathleen / Danny boy / Phil the fluter / How can you buy Killarney / MacNamara's band
MBPCD 7002 / 18 May '98 / Quantum Mobius

O'Dowda, Brendan

☐ IRISH FAVOURITES
CDMFP 6346 / May '97 / Music For Pleasure

O'Duffy, Michael

☐ GOLDEN VOICE OF IRELAND, THE
PLSCD 289 / 1 Jun '98 / Pulse

Odyssey

☐ BEST OF ODYSSEY, THE
ECD 3386 / 18 Sep '97 / K-Tel

☐ GREATEST HITS
Going back to my roots / Inside out / Magic touch / Oh no not my baby / Weekend lover / Don't tell me, tell her / Use it up and wear it out / Hang together / It will be alright / Follow me (play follow the leader) / Easy come, easy go / When you love somebody / If you're looking for a way out / Native New Yorker
ND 90436 / Mar '90 / RCA

☐ GREATEST HITS
Native New Yorker / Use it up and wear it out / Hang together / It will be alright / Lucky star / I got the melody / Ever lovin' Sam / Going back to my roots / Inside out / Magic touch / Oh no not my baby / Weekend lover / Don't tell me tell her / Follow me / Easy come easy go / When you love somebody / If you're looking for a way out
74321511952 / 1 Sep '97 / Camden

☐ ROOTS
Joy (I know it) / You can't take it away / Going back to my roots / Before we say hello / Laughing and smiling / Sing / Joy (I know it)
307312 / Jun '97 / Hallmark

Odyssey

☐ ODYSSEY
TB 103 / Jul '97 / Tim's Brain

Odyssey Band

☐ REUNION
No other option / Channel 1 / Running man / I believe in you / Online junkie / I am / Iam: Ulmer, James 'Blood' & The Odyssey Band / Love dance / Where did all the girls come from / Alham du allah
KFWCD 220 / 18 May '98 / Knitting Factory

Oe, Tatsuye

☐ ENCOUNTER WITH (Captain Funk)
RLCD 01 / 20 Jul '98 / Reel Musiq

Oedo Sukeroku Taiko

☐ DRUMS OF TOKYO, THE
PS 65191 / Nov '97 / PlayaSound

O'Farrell, Chico

☐ CUBAN BLUES (The Chico O'Farrell Sessions/2CD Set)
5332562 / Jan '97 / Verve

O'Farrell, Sean

☐ ALWAYS
Way love ought to be / Eighteen yellow roses / She's good at loving me / I'd love you to want me / Those brown eyes / Soldier's tale / Every road leads back to you / Judy / Champion of 403 Mulberry Drive / Baby don't you know / Always / Do you know how much I love you / Longing to hold you again / Still
RCD 535 / Oct '93 / Ritz

☐ SONGS JUST FOR YOU
When the girl in your arms (is the girl in your heart) / This song is just for you / Love without end, Amen / Galway shawl / Walk on by / Nobody's child / Wanted / Billy can't read / Two loves / Straight and narrow / You would do the same for me / Hey pretty lady / Crystal chandeliers / Missing him
RCD 541 / Jun '94 / Ritz

Ofcro Tribe

☐ SPORADIC SPIRO GYRA
EBSCD 125 / 24 Nov '97 / Emergency Broadcast System

Off Broadway

☐ FALLIN' IN
PM 32257CD / 23 Sep '97 / Pavement

Offer, Cullen

☐ FEATHER MERCHANT
PCD 7091 / Jun '93 / Progressive

☐ STRIKE UP THE BAND (Offer, Cullen Quartet)
PCD 7104 / Jun '96 / Progressive

☐ SWINGIN' TEXAS TENOR, THE
PCD 7086 / Jun '93 / Progressive

Offering

☐ PARIS THEATRE DEJAZET 1987 (2CD Set)
AKT 11 / May '98 / AKT

Offermans, Wil

☐ DAILY SENSIBILITIES
BVHAASTCD 9206 / Oct '87 / Bvhaast

Offs

☐ CALIFORNIAN SKAPUNK PIONEERS
LF 282CD / 6 Oct '97 / Lost & Found

Offspring

☐ IXMAY ON THE HOMBRE
64872 / Feb '97 / Epitaph

☐ NITRO
158032 / Oct '95 / Epitaph

☐ OFFSPRING
Jennifer lost the war / Elders / Out on patrol / Crossroads / Demons / Beheaded / Tehran / Thousand days / Blackball / I'll be waiting / Kill the president
864602 / Nov '95 / Epitaph

☐ SMASH
864322 / May '94 / Epitaph

Offworld

☐ ANOTHER PLANET
CRECD 203 / Jul '96 / Creation

Oficina De Cordas

☐ PERNAMBUCO'S MUSIC
NI 5398 / Oct '94 / Nimbus

O'Flaharta, John Beag

☐ AN LOCHAN
CIC 084CD / Nov '93 / Clo Iar-Chonnachta

☐ AN TANCAIRE - FICHE AMHRAN 1980-1990
CIC 025CD / Jan '91 / Clo Iar-Chonnachta

☐ TA AN WORKHOUSE LAN
CICD 093 / Dec '93 / Clo Iar-Chonnachta

☐ WINDS OF FREEDOM
CICD 106 / Jan '95 / Clo Iar-Chonnachta

O'Flynn, Liam

☐ BRENDAN VOYAGE (O'Flynn, Liam & Orchestra)
TARACD 3006 / Oct '89 / Tara

☐ FINE ART OF PIPING, THE
CMCD 054 / Dec '97 / Celtic Music

☐ GIVEN NOTE, THE
O'Farrell's welcome to Limerick / O'Rourke's/The Merry sisters/Colonel Fraser / Come with me over the mountain / Smile in the dark / Farewell to Govan / Joyce's tune / Green island/Spellan the fiddler / Foliada de Elvina / Ag taisteal na Blarnan / Rambler / Aherlow jig / Smith's a gallant fireman / Romeo's exile / Rocks of Bawn / Cailin na gruage doinne / Teno un amor na / Alborada - Unha noite no Santo Cristo
TARACD 3034 / Oct '95 / Tara

☐ OUT TO ANOTHER SIDE
Foxchase / Wild geese / Dean's pamphlet / Gynt at the gate / Winter's end / After Aughrim's great disaster / Blackwells / Ar Bhruach na laoi / Lady Dillon / Dollards and The Harlequin hornpipes / Sean O Duibhir a Ghleanna
TARACD 3031 / Aug '93 / Tara

☐ PIPER, THE
TARACD 3037 / 26 May '98 / Tara

Oforia

☐ DELIRIOUS
BFLCD 26 / 1 Sep '98 / Butterfly

OG Funk

☐ OUT OF THE DARK
Me and my folks / Funk is in the house / Funkadelic groupie / Music for my brother / I've been alone / I wanna know / Don't take your love from me / Outta the dark / Angie
RCD 10303 / Jun '94 / Black Arc

Ogada, Ayub

☐ EM MANA KUOYO
Obiero / Dala / Wa Winjigo Ero / Thum Nyatiti / Kronkrohino / 10% / Ondiek / Kothbiro / En Mana Kuoyo
CDRW 42 / May '93 / Realworld

Ogden, Nigel

☐ DOWN WITH THE CURTAIN
Down with the curtain / Selection / Call me madam / Westminster waltz / Legend of the Glass Mountain / April in Portugal / Portuguese washerwomen / My prayer / Tampico / On my own / I dreamed a dream / Lingering lovers / Ballet Egyptian themes / How deep is your love / 'S wonderful / Lady is a tramp / Who / Moving South / Moving out / I'm getting sentimental over you / Deed I do / Georgia on my mind / Coronation Scot / Valse triste / New era
OS 225 / Dec '96 / OS Digital

☐ MUSIC FOR ALL
When the saints go marching in / Border ballad / Mulligan musketeers / Tritsch tratsch polka / Sweet and low / Kalinka / Liberty bell / Going home / Dam busters march / Bobby Shaftoe / Sailing / Storm at sea / Strawberry fair / Bells of St. Mary's / Tydi a roddiast / Jerusalem / Finlandia / Morte criste
OS 211 / Jan '95 / OS Digital

☐ SENTIMENTAL JOURNEY/TRIBUTE TO REGINALD DIXON
Royal Air Force march past / I'll string along with you / You'll never know / Polly / Smile smile smile / Certain smile / Morning, Noon and night / I can't tell a waltz from a tango / Val suzon / Under the linden tree / I kiss your hand, Madame / Spitfire prelude / Cole Porter classics / Sentimental journey / Somebody stole my gal / Why did she fall for the leader of the band / Solitude / Saddle your blues to a wild mustang / Rosalie / I double dare you / Oh ma ma / I love to whistle / You're an education / I won't dance / Lovely to look at / Smoke gets in your eyes / Little girl / As time goes by / When I take my sugar to tea / Happy feet / Manhattan / Boo hoo / Marching with the organ
OS 214 / Aug '95 / OS Digital

☐ SUNDAY CELEBRATION, A
Fanfare / March in A / Jesu joy of man's desiring / Prelude in classic style / Steal away / Faith / Prelude / Pie Jesu / I'll walk with God / O for the wings of a dove / Sanctuary of the heart / Scherzetto on St. George / St. George's Day / Big blue planet / Star of God / Elegy / Intermezzo/Easter Hymn / Chorale prelude on Crimond / Lost chord
OS 221 / Jul '96 / OS Digital

☐ THROUGH THE DECADES - 1950'S
OS 236 / 29 Jun '98 / Bandleader

☐ THROUGH THE DECADES - 1970'S
OS 238 / 29 Jun '98 / Bandleader

☐ WURLITZER CELEBRATION
Beyond the blue horizon / Valse romantique / Pizzicato polka / Celebration march / How are things in Glocca Morra / Art deco / Three piece suite / Duo / In a clock store / Shadow waltz / At the sign of the swingin' cymbal / Love everlasting / Minuet / Paean / Whistler and his dog / Dusk / Waterloo march / Tell me I'm forgiven / Gymnopedie / Eric coates fantasia
OS 206 / Mar '94 / OS Digital

Ogeret, Marc

☐ CHANTS DE MARINS
983772 / Mar '96 / EPM

O'Grada, Conal

☐ TOP OF COOM, THE
CCF 27CD / Jan '91 / Claddagh

Oh Romeo

☐ BEST OF OH ROMEO, THE
HTCD 96 / 20 Apr '98 / Hot Productions

O'Hara, Betty

☐ HORNS APLENTY
Euphonics / Stardust / My heart stood still / Pigeon toed Joad / It don't mean a thing (if it ain't got that swing) / You stepped out of a dream / Alligator crawl / Sleeping bee / Medley from 'On the town' / If dreams come true
DD 482 / Jun '97 / Delmark

O'Hara, Helen

☐ NIGHT IN IRELAND, A
CD 450 / 6 Jul '98 / New World

☐ SOUTHERN HEARTS
CD 212 / 6 Jul '98 / New World

O'Hara, Mary

☐ BEAUTIFUL MUSIC OF MARY O'HARA, THE
Lord of the dance / Danny boy / Last rose of summer / In an english country garden / Bunch of thyme / My lagan / Going home / Perhaps love / She moved through the fair / Messenger / One day at a time / Willie's gane to Melville castle / Roisin dubh / Scent of the roses / Scarborough Fair / Never saw the roses / Memory / Quiet land of Erin
MCCD 070 / Jun '92 / Music Club

☐ COLLECTION, THE
Kitty of coleraine / Haigh didil dum / Famine song / Down by the glenside / Roisin dubh / Gartan mother's lullaby / An crann ubhall / Frog song / Maidrin ruadh / Silent, o'moyle / Luibin o luth / Jackets green / Dia luain dia mairt / Parting / I will walk with my love / Cucuin a chuaichin / Leprauchan / Oro mo bhaidin / Down by the sally gardens / Na leanbhai i mbeithil / Wexford mummer's song / She didn't dance / She lived beside the anner / Seoithin seo / Farewell but whenever
COL 072 / Mar '95 / Collection

☐ DOWN BY THE GLENSIDE (The Songs Of Ireland)
TCD 1055 / Jul '97 / Tradition

O'Hara, Mary Margaret

☐ MISS AMERICA
To cry about / Year in song / Body's in trouble / Dear darling / New day / When you know why you're happy / My friends have / Help me lift you up / Keeping you in mind / Not be alright / You will be loved again
379192 / Sep '96 / Koch International

O'Heanai, Seasamh

☐ O' MO DHUCHAS (From My Tradition)
CEFCD 051 / Jul '97 / Gael Linn

Ohia

☐ SONGS
HAPPY 14 / 20 Apr '98 / Happy Go Lucky

Ohio Express

☐ OHIO EXPRESS
REP 4017 / Aug '91 / Repertoire

Ohio Players

☐ BEST OF THE OHIO PLAYERS, THE
Love rolercoaster / Who'd she coo / Sweet sticky thing / Feel the beat (everybody disco) / Body vibes / Skintight / I want to be free / Good luck charm / FOPP / Merry go round / Far East Mississippi / OHIO / Magic trick / Time slips away / Funk-O-Nots / Fire / Jive turkey
5543222 / 20 Apr '98 / Spectrum

☐ ECSTASY
Ecstasy / You and me / (Not so) sad and lonely / (I wanna know) do you feel it / Black cat / Food stamps y'all / Spinning / Sleep talk / Silly Billy / Short change
CDSEW 026 / Feb '90 / Westbound

☐ FUNK ON FIRE (The Mercury Anthology/2CD Set)
5281022 / Aug '98 / Mercury

☐ OHIO PLAYERS
Over the rainbow / Lonely street / Street party / Summertime / Bad bargain / Man that I am / Find someone to love / Cold, cold world / Here today and gone tomorrow / Mother in law / Stop lying to yourself / Tell me why / You don't mean it / Trespassing / I've got to hold on / It's a crying shame / Soupbone / Soul party / Thing called love / My neighbours / I gotta get away / Love slips through my fingers / Being the man that I am / Lonely streets at midnight
GRF 045 / Apr '93 / Tring

☐ OL' SCHOOL
Skin tight / Ol' school / Pain / Skin tight / Sweet sticky thing / Thank you / I wanna be free / Love rollercoaster / Fire / Megamix
ESMCD 443 / Oct '96 / Essential

☐ ORGASM
Pain / Pleasure / Ecstasy / Climax / Funky worm / Player's balling (players doin' their own thing) / Varee is love / Sleep talk / Walt's first trip / Laid it / What's going on / Singing in the morning / Food stamps y'all / I want to hear / Ain't that lovin' you
CDSEWD 062 / Jun '93 / Westbound

Ohlman, Christine

☐ HARD WAY, THE (Ohlman, Christine & Rebel Montez)
DELD 3011 / Dec '95 / Deluge

OHM

☐ GROUNDED TO THE INNER CURRENT
WSCD 011 / Feb '97 / Word Sound Recordings

Ohman, Kjell

☐ HAMMOND CONNECTION, THE (Ohman, Kjell & Arne Domnerus)
OPUS3CD 19402 / Nov '95 / Opus 3

Oho

☐ ECCE OHO
LW 3053 / 22 May '98 / Little Wing

Ohrlin, Glenn

☐ COWBOY'S LIFE, A
Desert sands / Platonia the pride of the plains / Shorty's saloon / Cowboy again for a day / Cancion mixteca / Fair lady of the plains / Night herding song / Cowboy's life / Texas cowboy / Ace int e hole / Barnacle bill / Spanish cavalier / Button willow tree / My bonny black bess / Long side the Santa Fe trail / Countain de las flores
ROUCD 0420 / Feb '98 / Rounder

Oi Melz

☐ KEINE ZEIT
KOCD 044 / 15 Dec '97 / Knock Out

☐ OI STRESS
KOCD 060 / 15 Dec '97 / Knock Out

Oi Polloi

☐ TOTAL ANARCHOI
REM 017 / Apr '92 / Released Emotions
STEPCD 073 / 24 Nov '97 / Step 1

Oiccinoi, Piero

☐ CAMILLE 2000
ET 905CD / 23 Mar '98 / Easy Tempo

Oige

☐ BANG ON
CDLDL 1241 / Jun '96 / Lochshore

☐ LIVE
LDLCD 1225 / Jan '95 / Lochshore

Oisin

☐ BEALOIDEAS
OSS 38CD / Jul '95 / Ossian

☐ CELTIC DREAM
OSS 85CD / Aug '94 / Ossian

☐ JEANNIE C, THE
EUCD 1215 / Sep '93 / ARC

☐ OISIN
OSS 37CD / Jul '95 / Ossian

☐ OVER THE MOOR TO MAGGIE
OSS 39CD / Jul '95 / Ossian

☐ WINDS OF CHANGE
EUCD 1069 / '91 / ARC

O'Jays

☐ CLASSIC PHILADELPHIA DAYS, THE
MCCD 330 / 16 Mar '98 / Music Club

☐ LOVE TRAIN (The Best Of The O'Jays)
Love train / Back stabbers / 992 Arguments / Survival / For the love of money / Put your hands together / Time to get down / Sunshine / Living for the weekend / I love music
4805052 / May '95 / Epic

☐ MY FAVOURITE PERSON/WHEN WILL I SEE YOU AGAIN
I just want to satisfy / Your body's here with me (but your mind's on the other side / My favourite person / One on one / I like to see us get down / Your true heart (and shining star) / Out in the real world / Don't walk away mad / I can't stand the pain / When will I see you again / House of fire / Letter to my friends / Put our heads together / Ain't nothin' wrong with good lovin' / Nice and easy
WESM 565 / Feb '98 / Westside

☐ RESPECT
Have you had your love today / Can't let you go / Closer to you / One wonderful girl / Heartbreaker / No can do / Don't let me down / That's how love is / Respect: O'Jays & *The Jaz* / Somebody else will / Out of my mind / Friend of a friend / Don't you know true love / Decisions
DC 886132 / 2 Feb '98 / Disky

☐ VERY BEST OF THE O JAYS, THE
Backstabbers / Love train / Darlin' darlin' baby / Used to be my baby / Brandy / Now that we found love / Put our heads together / Message in our music / Sing a happy song / Extraordinary girl / Give the people what they want / For the love of money / 992 arguments / Time to get down / Livin' for the weekend / Looky looky / One night affair / Deeper (in love with you) / Don't call me brother / Love train
4897502 / 20 Apr '98 / Epic

Ojorojo

☐ OJOROJO
EBM 008 / Jun '97 / East Bay Menace

Ok Nok...Kongo & 3 Jokers

☐ PLAYS THOMAS AGERGAARD AND JOHN TCHICAI
Oth street / Nu nu praecis nu / Diving / Dancing on one leg / Duo for en hund / Thrift shopping / Sorry about that / You / Play dead / Sommeran 68 / Ask yourself / Kaffepause / Bless your heart / Ok Nok goes Congo
STCD 4220 / Jun '98 / Storyville

Okafor, Ben

☐ GENERATION
She said / Shadows / Love train / Sanctify my soul / Call me / Living in a suitcase / Generation / Go see / Be my brother / Susan / Sweet lady / Hear this voice
PCDN 137 / Aug '92 / Plankton

O'Keefe, Danny

☐ BREEZY STORIES
7567814272 / Jan '96 / Atlantic

O'Keeffe, Maire

☐ HOUSE PARTY
CEFCD 165 / Oct '94 / Gael Linn

O'Keeffe, Padraig

☐ KERRY FIDDLES (O'Keeffe, Padraig & Denis Murphy/Julia Clifford)
TSCD 309 / May '94 / Topic

☐ SLIABH LUACHRA FIDDLE MASTER
RTECD 174 / Dec '93 / RTE/Europe 1

Okeh Wranglers

☐ BENEATH THE WESTERN SKIES
FCD 3038 / Apr '96 / Fury

Okin, Earl

☐ MANGO & OTHER DELIGHTS
RGFCD 014 / Oct '93 / Road Goes On Forever

Okolokolo

☐ LA LEGENDE DES INDIENS
992291 / Feb '97 / Wotre Music

Okoshi, Tiger

☐ ECHOES OF A NOTE
Hello Dolly / Basin Street blues / I get ideas / St. James infirmary / Rockin' chair / St. Louis blues / Sleepo time down south / Sunny side of the street / When the saints go marching in / What a wonderful world
JVC 20222 / Nov '97 / JVC

☐ FACE TO FACE
Face to face / Summertime / When the moon goes deep / Sentimental journey / Bubble dance / Fisherman's song / One note samba / Man with 20 faces / Don't tell me now / Who can I turn to / Eyes / Over the rainbow
JD 3318 / Sep '89 / JVC

☐ TWO SIDES TO EVERY STORY
Green dolphin street / What it was / Wiz or wizout / Monday blues / Yuki no furu machi wo / Yesterdays / Finders, keepers / My old Kentucky home / In your bones / Two sides to every story
JVC 20392 / Nov '97 / JVC

Okossun, Sonny

☐ AFRICAN SOLDIERS
FILERCD 414 / Jul '91 / Profile

☐ ULTIMATE COLLECTION, THE
AVCCD 003 / Jan '97 / AVC/Ivory

Okoudjava, Boulat

☐ LE SOLDAT EN PAPIER
LDX 274743 / Jan '94 / La Chant Du Monde

Okuta Percussion

☐ OKUTA PERCUSSION
SM 15042 / Aug '92 / Wergo

☐ OSIKA
EUCD 1343 / Apr '96 / ARC

Ol' Dirty Bastard

☐ RETURN TO THE 36 CHAMBERS
Intro / Shimmy shimmy ya / Baby c'mon / Brooklyn zoo / Hippa to da hoppa / Rawhide / Damage / Don't u know / Stomp / Goin' down / Drunk game / Snakes / Booklyn zoo / Proteck ya neck / Cuttin' headz / Dirty dancin' / Harlem world
7559616592 / Mar '95 / Warner Bros.

Ol' Skool

☐ OL' SKOOL
UD 53104 / 17 Nov '97 / Universal

Olatunji, Baba

☐ DROP THE BEAT
Beat of my drum / Loyin loyin / Ife l'oju e'aiye / Akiwowo (a capella) / Akiwowo / Se eni a fe l'amo - kere kere
RCD 10107 / Nov '91 / Rykodisc

☐ LOVE DRUM TALK
WO 160 / 5 Jan '98 / Chesky

Olbrisch, Martin

☐ FM 099.5
WER 2054 / Jan '98 / Wergo

Old & In The Way

☐ BREAKDOWN
ACD 28 / 2 Feb '98 / Acoustic Disc

☐ OLD AND IN THE WAY
Pig in the pen / Old and in the way / Hobo song / Wild horses / White dove / Midnight moonlight / Knockin' on your door / Panama red / Kissimmee kid / Land of the Navajo
SHCD 3746 / Feb '85 / Sugar Hill
GDCD 4014 / May '89 / Grateful Dead

Old & New Dreams

☐ PLAYING
Happy house / Mopti / New dream / Rush hour / Broken shadows / Playing
8291232 / Jun '86 / ECM

Old 97's

☐ WRECK YOUR LIFE
BS 009 / 19 Jan '98 / Bloodshot

Old Blind Dogs

☐ CLOSE TO THE BONE
LDLCD 1209 / Oct '93 / Lochshore

☐ FIVE
Glen Kabul/Trip to Pakistan/The fourth floor / Battle of Harlaw / Lord MacDonald's march to Harlaw/The Mither Tap/The cauldron / Parcel o' rogues / Walking nightmare/The shopgirl/Croix rousse / Janine's reel/ In and out the harbour/The hawk / Lowlands of Holland / Johnny o' Bradislee / Leaving Lochboisdale / Summerside/Mouy'ton Mayo/ Andros 2/Andros 3
CDLDL 1264 / 6 Oct '97 / Lochshore

☐ LEGACY
CDLDL 1233 / Oct '95 / Lochshore

☐ NEW TRICKS
LOC 1068CD / Jul '94 / Lochshore

☐ TALL TAILS
CDLDL 1220 / Oct '94 / Klub

Old Hat Band

☐ OLD HAT DANCE BAND
VT/OH 2CD / Jun '93 / Veteran Tapes

Old Man & The Sea

☐ OLD MAN & THE SEA, THE
SHANTY 1001 / 16 Mar '98 / Shanty

Old Man Stone

☐ SPORK
REVXD 211 / Aug '97 / Revolver

Old Man's Child

☐ BORN OF THE FLICKERING
CM 77147CD / Dec '96 / Century Media

☐ ILL NATURED SPIRITUAL INVASION
CM 77219CD / 22 Jun '98 / Century Media

☐ IN THE SHADES OF LIFE
SHAGRATH 005CD / Oct '96 / Hot

☐ PAGAN PROSPERITY
CM 77183CD / 1 Sep '97 / Century Media

Old Pike

☐ OLD PIKE
FLT 109 / 6 Oct '97 / Flat Earth

Old Rope String Band

☐ ROPERAMA DING DONG
ORSB 1CD / Aug '96 / Old Rope

Old School Players

☐ OLD SCHOOL BASS
73524413162 / 19 May '98 / DM

Old Swan Band

☐ STILL SWANNING AFTER ALL THESE YEARS
FRCD 31 / Jul '95 / Free Reed

Oldarra

☐ BASQUE SONGS
0630193452 / 20 Oct '97 / Erato

Oldfield, Mike

☐ AMAROK
Continuous music
CDV 2640 / Jun '90 / Virgin

☐ COMPLETE MIKE OLDFIELD, THE (2CD Set)
Arrival / In dulci jubilo / Portsmouth / Jungle gardenia / Guilty / Blue Peter / Waldberg (the peak) / Etude / Wonderful land / Moonlight shadow / Family man / Mistake / Five miles out / Crime of passion / To France / Shadow on the wall / Excerpt from Tubular bells / Sheba / Mirage / Platinum / Mount Teide / Excerpt from Ommadawn / Excerpt from Hergest Ridge / Excerpt from Incantations / Excerpt from The killing fields
CDMOC 1 / Oct '85 / Virgin

☐ CRISES
Crises / Moonlight shadow / In high places / Foreign affair / Taurus three / Shadow on the wall
CDVIP 118 / Mar '94 / Virgin VIP

☐ DISCOVERY
To France / Poison arrows / Crystal gazing / Tricks of the light / Discovery / Talk about your life / Saved by a bell / Lake
CDV 2308 / Apr '92 / Virgin

☐ EARTH MOVING
Holy / Far country / Runaway son / Earth moving / Nothing but / Hostage / Innocent / See the light / Blue night / Bridge to paradise
CDVIP 169 / Apr '97 / Virgin VIP

☐ ELEMENTS (The Best Of Mike Oldfield)
Tubular bells / Family man / Moonlight shadow / Heaven's open / Five miles out / To France / Foreign affair / In Dulci jubilo / Shadow on the wall / Islands / Etude / Sentinel / Ommadawn (excerpt) / Incantations / Amarok / Portsmouth
VTCD 18 / Aug '93 / Virgin

☐ ELEMENTS 1973-1991 (4CD Set)
Tubular bells (part one) / Tubular bells (part two) / Hergest ridge / In dulci jubilo / Portsmouth / Vivaldi concerto in C / Ommadawn (part one) / On horseback / William Tell overture / Argiers / First excursion / Sailor's hornpipe / Incantations / I'm guilty / Path / Blue Peter / Woodhenge / Punkadiddle (live) / Polka (live) / Platinum 3 and 4 / Arrival / Taurus 1 / QE2 / Wonderful land / Sheba / Five miles out / Taurus II / Family man / Mount Teidi / Peak / Crises / Moonlight shadow / Foreign affair / Shadow on the wall / Taurus III / Crime of passion / Jungle gardenia / To France / Afghan / Tricks of the light (instrumental) / Etude / Evacuation / Legend / Islands / Wind chimes / Flying start / Magic touch / Earth moving / Far country / Holy / Amarok / Heaven's open
CDBOX 2 / Oct '93 / Virgin

☐ EXPOSED (2CD Set)
Incantations / Tubular bells / Guilty
CDVD 2511 / Jul '86 / Virgin

☐ FIVE MILES OUT
Taurus II / Family man / Orabidoo / Mount Teidi / Five miles out
CDVIP 114 / Jun '94 / Virgin

☐ HEAVEN'S OPEN
Make make / No dream / Mr. Shame / Gimme back / Heaven's open / Music from the balcony
CDVIP 153 / Oct '96 / Virgin VIP

☐ HERGEST RIDGE
Hergest ridge
CDV 2013 / Apr '86 / Virgin

☐ INCANTATIONS
Incantations / Guilty
CDVDT 101 / Apr '92 / Virgin

☐ ISLANDS
Wind chimes (part 1) / Wind chimes / Islands / Flying start / Northpoint / Magic touch / Time has come / When the night's on fire
CDV 2466 / Apr '92 / Virgin

☐ OMMADAWN
Ommadawn (parts 1 and 2)
CDVIP 185 / Apr '97 / Virgin VIP

☐ ORCHESTRAL TUBULAR BELLS
Orchestral tubular bells (part 1) / Orchestral tubular bells (part 1) / Tubular bells (parts 1 and 2) / Orchestral tubular bells (part 2) / Orchestral tubular bells (part 2)
CDVIP 101 / Nov '93 / Virgin VIP

☐ ORCHESTRAL TUBULAR BELLS/ OMMADAWN/HERGEST RIDGE (Compact Collection Vol.1/3CD Set)
Orchestral tubular bells (part 1) / Continuous track / Orchestral tubular bells (part 2) / Continuous track / Hergest ridge / Hergest ridge / Ommadawn / Ommadawn
TPAK 15 / Oct '90 / Virgin

☐ QE2
QE2 / Taurus / Sheba / Conflict / Arrival / Wonderful land / Mirage / Celt / Molly / QE2 Finale
CDV 2181 / Oct '83 / Virgin

☐ QE2/PLATINUM/FIVE MILES OUT (Compact Collection Vol.2/3CD Set)
Platinum (part 1) / Airborn / Platinum (part 2) platinum / Platinum (part 3) charleston / Platinum (part 4) north star-platinum finale / Woodhenge / Sally / Punkadiddle / I got rhythm / Taurus 2 / Family man / Orabidoo / Mount teide / Five miles out / Taurus 1 / Sheba / Conflict / Arrival / Celt / Molly / Wonderful land / Mirage / Q.e.2 - q.e.2 finale
TPAK 16 / Oct '90 / Virgin

☐ SONGS OF THE DISTANT EARTH
4509985812 / Nov '94 / WEA

☐ TUBULAR BELLS VOL.1
Tubular Bells (Part 1) / Tubular Bells (Part 2)
CDV 2001 / '83 / Virgin

☐ TUBULAR BELLS VOL.1 (Remastered)
Tubular bells
CDVX 2001 / 25 May '98 / Virgin

☐ TUBULAR BELLS VOL.2
Sentinel / Dark star / Clear light / Blue saloon / Sunjammer / Red dawn / Bell / Weightless / Great plain / Sunset door / Tattoo / Altered state / Maya gold / Moonshine
4509906182 / Aug '92 / WEA

☐ TUBULAR BELLS VOL.3
Bag of secrets / Watchful eye / Jewel in the crown / Mighty fall / Serpent dream / Inner child / Man in the rain / Top of the morning / Moonwatch / More secrets / Far above the clouds
3984243492 / 31 Aug '98 / WEA

☐ TUBULAR BELLS/HERGEST RIDGE/ OMMADAWN (Remixes/3CD Set)
Tubular bells / Hergest ridge / Ommadawn / Phaeacian games / Star's end / Rio Grande / First excursion / Algiers / Portsmouth / In dulci jubilo / Speak (tho you only say farewell)
CDBOX 1 / Dec '89 / Virgin

☐ VOYAGER
Song of the sun / Women of Ireland / She moves through the fair / Wild goose flaps its wings / Mont St. Michel / Flowers of the forest / Dark island / Voyager / Celtic rain / Hero
0630158962 / Aug '96 / WEA

☐ XXV (The Best Of Mike Oldfield)
Tubular bells / Hergest ridge / Ommadawn / Incantation / Moonlight shadow / Portsmouth / Killing fields / Sentinel (tubular bells II) / Bell / Let there be light / Only time will tell / Voyager / Women of Ireland
3984212182 / 17 Nov '97 / WEA

Oldfield, Sally

☐ CELEBRATION
Mandela / Morning of my life / Woman of the night / Celebration / Blue water / My damsel heart / Love is everywhere
CLACD 103 / Apr '86 / Castle

☐ EASY
Sun is in my eyes / You set my gypsy blood free / Answering you / Boulevard song / Easy / Sons of the free / Hide and seek / First born of the earth / Man of storm
CLACD 102 / Apr '86 / Castle

☐ MIRRORS
Mirrors / Mandala / Water bearer / Boulevard song / You set my gypsy blood free / Sun in my eyes / Easy / Morning of my life / Love is everywhere / Love of a lifetime / Broken Mona Lisa / Path with a heart / Let it all go / She talk's like a lady / Man child / Never knew love could get so strong
5507262 / Jan '95 / Spectrum

☐ MORNING OF MY LIFE (2CD Set)
Mirrors / Night of the hunters moon / You set my gypsy blood free / Sun in my eyes / Easy / Boulevard song / I sing for you / Mandala / Morning of my life / Blue water / Celebration / Song of the lamp / Playing in the flame / Broken Mona Lisa / Man I love / Path with a heart / Water bearer / Weaver / Fire and honey / First born of the earth / Woman of the night / Love of a lifetime / River of my childhood / It's a long time a million light years away from home / Strange day in Berlin / Meet me in Verona / Never knew love could be so strong / Nenya / Song of the healer
SMDCD 198 / May '97 / Snapper

☐ PLAYING IN THE FLAME
Playing in the flame / Love of a lifetime / River of my childhood / Let it all go / Song of the lamp / Rare lightning / Manchild / It's a long time / Song of the being
CLACD 215 / Feb '91 / Castle

☐ STRANGE DAY IN BERLIN
Path with a heart / Million light years away from home / She talks like a lady / Meet me in Verona / Strange day in Berlin / Never knew love could get so strong / This could be a lover / There's a miracle going on
CLACD 216 / Feb '91 / Castle

☐ SUN IN MY EYES, THE
Mirrors / Morning of my life / Mandala / River of my childhood / Celebration / Sun in my eyes / Woman of the night / Water bearer / Boulevard song / Song of the lamp / You set my gypsy blood free / Path with a heart / Weaver / Man child / Playing in the flame / Strange day in Berlin
21042 / Sep '97 / Laserlight

☐ WATER BEARER
Water bearer / Songs of the quendi / Weaver / Mirrors / Night of the hunter's moon / Child of Allah / Song of the bow / Fire and honey / Song of the healer
CLACD 101 / Apr '90 / Castle

Oldfield, Terry

☐ EARTH SPIRIT
CD 413 / 6 Jul '98 / New World

☐ ILLUMINATION
CD 227 / 6 Jul '98 / New World

☐ OUT OF DEPTHS
CD 252 / 6 Jul '98 / New World

☐ SPIRAL WAVES
VP 117CD / Mar '93 / Voiceprint

☐ SPIRIT OF AFRICA
CD 242 / 6 Jul '98 / New World

☐ SPIRIT OF INDIA
CD 426 / 6 Jul '98 / New World

☐ SPIRIT OF THE RAINFOREST
CD 195 / 6 Jul '98 / New World

☐ SPIRIT TIBET
CD 257 / 6 Jul '98 / New World

Oldham, Will

☐ JOYA
O let it be / Antagonism / New gypsy / Under what was oppression / Gator / Open your heart / Be still and know God / Apocolypse no / I am still what I meant to be / Bolden boke boy / Idea and deed
WIGCD 039 / 3 Nov '97 / Domino

☐ WESTERN MUSIC
AFF 002 / 1 Dec '97 / Acuarela

Oldland, Misty

☐ SUPERNATURAL
I wrote you a song / Fair affair (Je T'Aime) / Got me a feeling / Imprison me / Why do I trust you / Caroline / Kissing the planet / One world / You are the one / Like I need / I often wonder / Groove eternity
47595882 / Apr '94 / Columbia

O'Leary, Christy

☐ NORTHERN BRIDGE
Trip over the mountain / Norwegian wedding march / Banks of Sullane / O'Keef's/I'd rather be married than left alone/Bill the weav / Young Reilly the fisherman / Peigin Leitir Mor / Rocking the cradle/ Chesnut tree / Moorlough Mary / Summer waltz / Bellman's polka / Jimmy mo mhile stor / Groves of Donaghmore
OBMCD 09 / Jan '97 / Old Bridge

O'Leary, Diarmuid

☐ CLASSIC IRISH BALLADS (O'Leary, Diarmuid & The Bards)
Isle of Innisfree / Come back Paddy Reilly / Spancil hill / Green fields of France / Follow me up to carlow / Fields of Athenry / Ferryman / Curragh of Kildare / Dublin in the rare old times / Down by the Sally gardens / Nancy spain / Band played waltzing Matilda / Cliffs of Dooneen / Whiskey in the jar / Bunch of thyme
TARACD 3018 / Nov '94 / Tara

O'Leary, Johnny

☐ DANCE MUSIC FROM THE CORK-KERRY BORDER
CR 01CD / Aug '96 / CR

☐ TROOPER, THE
CEFCD 132 / Jan '94 / Gael Linn

O'Lionaird, Iarla

☐ SEVEN STEPS TO MERCY, THE
CDRW 67 / 22 Sep '97 / Realworld

O'List, Davy

☐ FLIGHT OF THE EAGLE
Girls in my cars / Outside broadcast / Fax / Gone to the beach / Sealed with a kiss / I wish I had you on my side / You and I / Nuke / Walking talking / Flight of the eagle / Pale pale girl of the neat white uniform
JETCD 1013 / 19 Jan '98 / Jet

Oliva, Sandro

☐ WHO THE FUCK IS SANDRO OLIVA
EFA 034092 / Nov '94 / Muffin

Olive

☐ EXTRA VIRGIN (2CD Set)
Miracle / This time / Safer hands / Killing / You're not alone / Falling / Outlaw / Blood red tears / Curious / You are nothing / Muted / I don't think so / You're not alone
743214886872 / May '97 / RCA
74321481142 / 1 Nov '97 / RCA

Oliveira, Joao Pedro

☐ ELECTRONIC AND COMPUTER COMPOSITIONS
NUM 01 / Jun '97 / Numerica

Oliveira, Valdeci

☐ MACARENA (Latin Summer Hits) (Oliveira, Valdeca Y Banda Tropical)
Kizomba / Macarena / Sambolera mayi son / Brasil penta Brasil / Latin medley / Malaguena / Latin medley II / Tempo / Conga - Oye micanto / Latin medley III
12861 / Aug '96 / Laserlight

Oliver

☐ STANDING STONE
WHCD 001 / Mar '97 / Wooden Hill

Oliver, Bob

☐ BOB OLIVER & HIS HOT SEVEN (Oliver, Bob Hot Seven)
SOSCD 1312 / Nov '96 / Stomp Off

Oliver, Frankie

☐ LOOKING FOR THE TWIST
She lied to me / Give her what she wants / Love what you do for me / Who's gonna do it / Look how long / Live as one / Love and satisfaction / Melt into you / Show me / What is life / Looking for the twist / Down by the riverside
IJCD 3010 / 15 Sep '97 / Island Jamaica

Oliver, Joe 'King'

☐ CLASSIC YEARS, THE
New Orleans shout / Stingaree blues / West end blues / Edna / Rhythm club stomp / Showboat shuffle / Shake it and break it / Mule face blues / Don't you think I love you / Black snake blues / Every tub / Farewell blues / Tin roof blues / Willie the weeper
CDSGP 0194 / 27 Apr '98 / Prestige

☐ CLASSICS 1923
CLASSICS 650 / Nov '92 / Classics

☐ CLASSICS 1923-1926
CLASSICS 639 / Nov '92 / Classics

☐ CLASSICS 1926-1928 (Oliver, Joe 'King' & His Dixie Syncopators)
CLASSICS 618 / Nov '92 / Classics

☐ CLASSICS 1928-1930 (Oliver, Joe 'King' Orchestra)
CLASSICS 607 / Oct '92 / Classics

☐ CLASSICS 1930-1931
CLASSICS 594 / Sep '91 / Classics

☐ COMPLETE VOCALION & BRUNSWICK RECORDINGS (2CD Set)
Too bad / Snag it / Georgia man / Deep henderson / Jackass blues / Home town blues / Sorrow valley blues / Sugarfoot stomp / Wa wa wa / Tack Annie / Someday sweetheart / Dead man blues / New wang-wang blues / Dr. Jazz / Showboat shuffle / Every tub / Willie the weeper / Black snake blues / Farewell blues / Sobbin' blues / Tin roof blues / West End blues / Sweet Emmalina / Lazy mama / Got everything / Four or five times / Speakeasy blues / Aunt Hagar's blues / I'm watching the clock / Slow and steady / Papa de da da / Who's blue / Stop crying / Sugar blues / I'm crazy 'bout my baby / Loveless love / One more time / When I take my sugar to tea
CDAFS 10252 / Oct '92 / Affinity

☐ DIPPERMOUTH BLUES (His 25 Greatest Hits)
Chimes Blues: *Oliver, Joe 'King' & His Creole Jazz Band* / Canal street blues: *Oliver, Joe 'King' & His Creole Jazz Band* / Dippermouth blues: *Oliver, Joe 'King' & His Creole Jazz Band* / Snake rag: *Oliver, Joe 'King' & His Creole Jazz Band* / Chattanooga stomp: *Oliver, Joe 'King' & His Creole Jazz Band* / Riverside blues: *Oliver, Joe 'King' & His Creole Jazz Band* / Snag it: *Oliver, Joe 'King' & His Creole Jazz Band* / Deep Henderson: *Oliver, Joe 'King' & His Dixie Syncopators* / Wa wa wa: *Oliver, Joe 'King' & His Dixie Syncopators* / Someday sweetheart: *Oliver, Joe 'King' & His Dixie Syncopators* / Showboat shuffle: *Oliver, Joe 'King' & His Dixie Syncopators* / Willie the weeper: *Oliver, Joe 'King' & His Dixie Syncopators* / Black snake blues: *Oliver, Joe 'King' & His Dixie Syncopators* / Farewell blues: *Oliver, Joe 'King' & His Dixie Syncopators* / Sobbin' blues: *Oliver, Joe 'King' & His Dixie Syncopators* / Tin roof blues: *Oliver, Joe 'King' & His Dixie Syncopators* / West End blues: *Oliver, Joe 'King' & His Dixie Syncopators* / Speakeasy blues: *Oliver, Joe 'King' & His Dixie Syncopators* / Aunt hagar's blues: *Oliver, Joe 'King' & His Dixie Syncopators* / I'm watchin the clock: *Oliver, Joe 'King' & His Dixie Syncopators* / New Orleans shout: *Oliver, Joe 'King' Orchestra* / Everybody does it in Hawaii: *Oliver, Joe 'King' Orchestra* / Rhythm club stomp: *Oliver, Joe 'King' Orchestra* / Struggle buggy: *Oliver, Joe 'King' Orchestra* / Shake it and break it: *Oliver, Joe 'King' Orchestra*
CDAJA 5218 / Dec '96 / Living Era

☐ KING OF NEW ORLEANS, THE
West end blues / I'm watching the clock / I want you just for myself / New orleans shout / Snag it / Sugar foot stomp / Wa wa wa / Showboat shuffle / Speakeast blues / Aunt hagar's blues / You're just my type / Chimes blues / Canal street blues / Snake rag / Dippermouth blues / Chattanooga stomp / Camp meeting blues / Riverside blues
CD 14547 / Jan '94 / Jazz Portraits

☐ KING OLIVER & HIS ORCHESTRA 1929-30
West End blues / I've got that thing / Call of the freaks / Trumpet's prayer / Freakish light blues / Can I tell you / My good man Sam / What you want me to do / Sweet like this / Too late / I'm lonesome, sweetheart / I want you just myself / I can't stop loving you / Everybody does it in Hawaii / Frankie and Johnny / New Orleans shout / St. James Infirmary / I must have it / Rhythm club stomp / You're just my type / Edna / Boogie woogie / Mule face blues / Struggle buggy / Don't you think I love you / Olga / Shake it and break it / Stingaree blues / What's the use of living without you / You were only passing time with me / Nelson stomp / Stealing
ND 89770 / May '94 / Jazz Tribune

☐ KING OLIVER 1927-1931
TPZ 1009 / Oct '94 / Topaz Jazz

☐ KING OLIVER'S CREOLE JAZZBAND 1923-1924 (2CD Set) (Oliver, Joe 'King' & His Creole Jazz Band)
Just gone / Canal Street blues / Mandy Lee blues / I'm going away to wear you off my mind / Chimes blues / Weather bird rag / Dippermouth blues / Froggie moore / Snake rag / Sweet lovin' man / High society rag / Sobbin' blues / Where did you stay last night / Jazzin' baby blues / Alligator hop / Zulu's ball / Working man blues / Krooked blues / Chattanooga stomp / London cafe blues / Camp meeting blues / New Orleans stomp / Buddy's habits / Tears / I ain't gonna tell nobody / Room rent blues / Riverside blues / Sweet baby doll / Mabel's dream / Southern stomp / Kiss me sweet / Construction song / King Porter stomp / Tom cat
RTR 79007 / Nov '96 / Retrieval

☐ QUINTESSENCE, THE (1923-1928/2CD Set)
Just gone / Canal street blues / Mandy Lee blues / Weather bird rag / Dippermouth blues / Froggie Moore / Snake rag / Sweet lovin' man / High society rag / Sobbin' blues / Dipper mouth blues / Jazzin' babies blues / Alligator hop / Buddy's habit / I ain't gonna tell nobody / Riverside blues / Working man blues / Mabel's dream / Chattanooga stomp / London cafe blues / Camp meeting blues / Tom cat blues / Too bad / Snag it / Deep Henderson / Jackass blues / Sugar foot stomp / Wa wa wa / Showboat shuffle / Tin roof blues / You are such a cruel papa to me / My dif'rent kind of man / Tell me woman blues / Frisco train blues / In the bottle blues / What ya want me to do
FA 220 / Oct '96 / Fremeaux

☐ SHAKE IT AND BREAK IT
JHR 73536 / May '93 / Jazz Hour

Oliver, Sean

☐ SOLITAIRE
Can I flow / These are the days / You and me / Need to be alone / Rhythm / Magic / Can I flow / Solitaire / Words / Dear Mary / Sweetest goodbye / Driftin' / Funny love
IDBOOMCD 002 / 23 Mar '98 / Boom Tang

Oliver, Sy

☐ YES INDEED
BB 8722 / Sep '96 / Black & Blue

Oliveros, Pauline

☐ ELECTRONIC WORKS
PD 04 / Nov '97 / Paradigm

Olivia Tremor Control

☐ DUSK AT CUBIST CASTLE (2CD Set)
Opera house / Frosted ambassador / Jumping fences / Define a transparent dream / No growing / Holiday surprise / Courtyard / Memories of Jacqueline 1906 / Tropical bells / Can you come down with us / Marking time / Green typewriters / Spring succeeds / Theme for a very delicious grand piano / I can smell the leaves / Dusk at cubist castle / Gravity car / NYC 25
BRRC 10082 / Jun '97 / Blue Rose

☐ EXPLANATION VOL.2 (Instrumental Themes And Sequences)
FLY 017X / 24 Nov '97 / Flydaddy

☐ OLIVIA TREMOR CONTROL VS BLACK SWAN NETWORK
FLY 030 / 15 Jun '98 / Flydaddy

Ollie & The Nightingales

☐ OLLIE & THE NIGHTINGALES
You'll never do wrong / Don't make the good suffer / Don't do what I did / I've got a feeling / You're leaving me / Broke in love / ABCD / Mellow way you treat your man / Girl you make my heart sing / I've never found a girl / Showered with love
CDSXE 068 / Nov '92 / Stax

Olney, David

☐ DEEPER ME
CDPH 1117 / Feb '95 / Philo

☐ EYE OF THE STORM
CDPH 1199 / Sep '96 / Philo

☐ LIVE IN HOLLAND
SCR 35 / Dec '94 / Strictly Country

☐ REAL LIES
CDPH 1204 / Aug '97 / Philo

☐ TOP TO BOTTOM
APCD 080 / '92 / Appaloosa

Olneyville Sound System

☐ BECAUSE WERE ALL IN THIS TOGETHER
LOAD 015CD / Jun '97 / Load

Olodum

☐ EGITO MADAGASCAR
404325CD / Apr '97 / Continental

☐ LIBERDADE
Balanco da mare / Tambores de cores / Anjo meu / Todo amor / Anhangobau / Oke ode ile / Cinderela / I miss her / Them da Algeria / Samba do reconcavo / Tiro seco / Amado para sempre / Toque digital / Amagni
0630197812 / 15 Jun '98 / East West Brazil

Olomide, Koffi

☐ N'DJOLI/BA LA JOIE 1978-1979 (Olomide, Koffi/Ba La Joie)
NG 028 / Jan '97 / Ngoyarto

☐ TCHA TCHO
Tcha tcho du sorcier / Elle et moi / VIP / Mannequin / Henriquet / Mal aime / Experience / La ruta
STCD 1031 / Jul '90 / Stern's

Olsen, Kristina

☐ HURRY ON HOME
CDPH 1175 / Aug '95 / Philo

☐ LIVE FROM AROUND THE WORLD
Walking blues / Love Kristina / Folding bicycle / Hurry on home / Roomates / Kind of mood I'm in / Jane / Cry you a waterfall / Gila national forest / Better than TV / TV Free America / Come on in my kitchen / Alaska / Maria / Prop / Power of loving you / Gay friends / Your little brother sure can dance / Guitar camp / Something to despise / Live man in the dead of night / Proposal / In my arms / Dangerous / If I could tell you
CDPH 1195 / Mar '97 / Philo

☐ LOVE, KRISTINA
PH 1157CD / Oct '93 / Philo

Olson, Carla

☐ WAVE OF THE HAND (The Best Of Carla Olson)
WMCD 1046 / Mar '96 / Watermelon

Olsson, Bjorn

☐ INSTRUMENTAL MUSIK
DOL 054CD / 23 Feb '98 / Dolores

Olympic Death Squad

☐ BLUE
This is riot gear / Maple leaf / Show your age / Newfoundland / Sometimes I can breathe / Ski lump / Wakefield Street / Shortsleeve / Anti-kidnapping song / Yeah, uh-huh
TB 2002 / May '96 / Teenbeat

Olympics

☐ DOIN' THE HULLY GULLY
Big boy Pete / Little Pedro / Stay away from Joe / Big Chief, Little Puss / Stay where you are / What'd I say / Private eye / Baby it's hot / Dooley / Baby hully gully / Dodge City / I'll never fall in love again / Working hard
CDCHD 324 / Jul '91 / Ace

O'Malley, Tony

☐ NAKED FLAME, THE
Good times / Love of mine / I can understand it / My Buddy / For the children / Tell me why / Mr. Operator / Still crazy after all these years / Naked flame / Moody's mood / I'm in trouble
JHCD 040 / May '95 / Ronnie Scott's Jazz House

☐ SUNSHINE EVERY DAY
Sunshine
MMCD 001 / Jul '97 / Millenium

Omar

☐ FOR PLEASURE
My baby says / I'm still standing / Saturday / Keep steppin' / Magical mystery interlude / Outside / Little boy / Need you bad / Can't get nowhere / Confection / Magic mystical way / Making sense of it / Pleasure
74321208532 / 1 Sep '97 / RCA

☐ MUSIC
Music / You've got to move / Get to know you better / Tomorrow / Tasty morsel / Winner / Your loss, my gain / Don't sell yourself short / Who chooses the seasons / Last request / Walk in the park / In the midst of it
5124012 / Nov '92 / Talkin' Loud

☐ THERE'S NOTHING LIKE THIS
There's nothing like this / Don't mean a thing / You and me / Positive / I'm in love / Meaning of life / Stop messing around / Serious style / I don't mind the waiting / Fine (acapella)
5100212 / Jul '91 / Talkin' Loud

☐ THIS IS NOT A LOVE SONG
This is not a love song / This is not a love song / Wherever / Fallin' music for the pipe / Never too late / Golden brown / Lullaby / Waiting game / Spring step / World of you / Say nothin'
74321496262 / Aug '97 / RCA

Omar & The Howlers

☐ BLUES BAG
PRLD 70281 / Aug '91 / Provogue

☐ COURTS OF LULU
Rose tattoo / Do it for daddy / False faces / Pushin' fire / Booger boy / Jumpin' the gun / I've tried / Firewalker / Special love / Scared to speak / I'm wild about you / Moon bit fool / South congress blues
PRD 70452 / Mar '93 / Provogue

☐ I TOLD YOU SO
Border girl / Give me a chance / Shake for me / Magic man / Rocket to nowhere / I told you so / Ice cold woman / I'm wish to you baby / East side blues
DFG 8417 CD / Oct '93 / Dixie Frog

☐ LIVE AT THE PARADISO
PRD 70352 / Apr '92 / Provogue

☐ LIVE AT THE PARADISO
BB 9529CD / May '93 / Bullseye Blues

☐ MONKEY LAND
Monkey land / Big town shakedown / Night shadows / She's a woman / Dirty people / Next big thing / Tonight I think of you / Fire in the jungle / Modern man / Loud mouth woman / Ding dong clock
ANTCD 0011 / Jan '93 / Antones

☐ SOUTHERN STYLE
Ton of blues / I want you / Snake rhythm rock / Bessie Mae / Full moon on Main Street / Pot of gold / You keep watchin' me / Run for the levee / Burn it off the ground / Judgement day / Angel blues / I think it's time to go
PRD 70952 / Sep '96 / Provogue

OMC

☐ HOW BIZARRE
5334352 / Oct '96 / Polydor

OMD

☐ ARCHITECTURE AND MORALITY
New Stone Age / She's leaving / Souvenir / Sealand / Joan of Arc / Architecture and morality / Georgia / Beginning and the end
CDIDX 12 / Jan '95 / Virgin

☐ CRUSH
So in love / Secret / Bloc bloc bloc / Women 111 / Crush / Eighty eight seconds in Greensboro' / Native daughters of the Golden West / La femme accident / Hold you / Lights are going out
CDVIP 155 / Oct '96 / Virgin VIP

☐ DAZZLE SHIPS
Radio Prague / Genetic engineering / ABC auto indistry / Telegraph / This is Helena / International / Romance of the telescope / Silent running / Radio waves / Time zones / Of all the things we've made / Dazzle ships
CDVIP 170 / Apr '97 / Virgin VIP

☐ JUNK CULTURE
Junk culture / Tesla girls / Locomotion / Apollo / Never turn away / Love and violence / Hard day / All wrapped up / White trash / Talking loud and clear
CDVIP 215 / 3 Aug '98 / Virgin VIP

☐ LIBERATOR
Stand above me / Everyday / King of stone / Dollar girl / Dream of me / Sunday morning / Agnus dei / Love and hate you / Heaven is / Best years of our lives / Christine / Only tears
CDVIP 217 / 3 Aug '98 / Virgin VIP

☐ ORCHESTRAL MANOEUVRES IN THE DARK
Bunker soldiers / Almost / Mysterreality / Electricity / Messerschmit twins / Messages / Julia's song / Red frame/White light / Dancing / Pretending to see the future
DIDCD 2 / '87 / Virgin

☐ ORGANISATION
Enola Gay / Second thought / VCL X1 / Motion and heart / Statues / Misunderstanding / More I see you / Promise / Stanlow
DIDCD 6 / Jul '87 / Virgin

☐ PACIFIC AGE
Stay (The black rose and the universal wheel) / (Forever) live and die / Pacific age / Dead girls / Shame / Southern / Flame of hope / Goddess of love / We love you / Watch us fall
CDV 2398 / Jun '93 / Virgin

☐ SUGAR TAX
Sailing on the seven seas / Pandora's box / Then you turn away / Speed of light / Was it something I said / Big town / Call my name / Apollo XI / Walking on air / Walk tall / Neon lights / All that matters
CDV 2648 / Apr '91 / Virgin

☐ UNIVERSAL
Universal / Walking on the Milky Way / Very close to far away / Boy from the chemist is here to see you / Too late / New head / Moon and the sun / Gospel of St. Jude / Black Sea / That was then / If you're still in love with me / Victory waltz
CDV 2807 / Sep '96 / Virgin

Omega

☐ TRANSCENDENT
HICD 08554002 / Apr '96 / SPV

Omen

☐ BATTLE CRY
398414215CD / Nov '96 / Metal Blade

☐ CURSE
398414216CD / Nov '96 / Metal Blade

☐ ESCAPE TO NOWHERE
It's not easy / Radar love / Escape to nowhere / Cry for the morning / Thorn in your flesh / Poisoned / Nomads / King of the hill / No way out
RR 95442 / Nov '88 / Roadrunner

☐ REOPENING THE GATES
MASSCD 124 / Jun '97 / Massacre

☐ TEETH
398414206CD / Nov '96 / Metal Blade

Ominus

☐ 3RD ALBUM
KRLP 003CD / Jun '97 / Koyote

Omit

☐ QUAD (3CD Set)
HERMES 024/025/026 / 24 Nov '97 / Corpus Hermeticum

Omlo Vent

☐ MILD LANDING
CHILLUM 000 / Jan '96 / Chill Um

Omni Trio

☐ DEEPEST CUT
ASHADOW 1CD / Feb '95 / Moving Shadow

☐ HAUNTED SCIENCE
ASHADOW 6CD / Aug '96 / Moving Shadow

☐ SKELETON KEYS
Skeleton keys / Silver / Fire island / Ocean driver / Sanctuary / Atomic state / Red rain / Twin town karaoke / Trippin' VIP / Twin town karaoke
ASHADOW 10CD / Aug '97 / Moving Shadow

Omnia Opera

☐ OMNIA OPERA
Space bastard / Disbelief / Awakening / Floating settee / Each day / Brighter the sun / Bright sun / Freeze out
DELECCD 011 / May '93 / Delerium

Omnibus Wind Ensemble

☐ MUSIC BY FRANK ZAPPA
CD 19403 / Jun '96 / Opus 3

Omnicron

☐ GENERATION AND MOTION OF A PULSE, THE
IAE 003CD / May '95 / Instinct Ambient Europe

Omnivore

☐ FEEDING FRENZY
DUKE 045CD / 15 Jun '98 / Hydrogen Dukebox

☐ ONE GIANT LEAP
ACTIVE 005D / Sep '94 / Interactive

☐ ONE SMALL STEP
Omnivorous / On the tip of my tongue / Munchies / Ethereal music / 9/10ths submerged / At elegant memorial
ACTIVE 002CD / Feb '94 / Interactive

Omoumi, Hossein

☐ NEY (Persian Classical Music)
ALCD 181 / Sep '96 / Al Sur

☐ PERSIAN CLASSICAL MUSIC
NI 5359 / Sep '94 / Nimbus

OMU

☐ COOL BEAUTY
99 1601 / Jul '96 / Ninetynine

☐ OMU
99 2139 / Jul '96 / Ninetynine

O'Murchu, Marcas

☐ O BHEAL GO BHEAL
CICD 126 / Dec '97 / Clo Iar-Chonnachta

On The Corner

☐ MEETS THE WURZBURG PHILHARMONIC (On The Corner & Benny Bailey/Warzburg Philharmonic)
Emily / There'll never be another you / Peruvian nights / You and the night and the music / You won't forget me / Quarters and dimes / Man I love/It ain't necessarily so / Speak low / Medley / Will you still be mine
MR 874807 / Feb '98 / Mons

On Thorns I Lay

☐ ORAMA
HOLY 029CD / 3 Nov '97 / Holy

☐ SOUNDS OF BEAUTIFUL EXPERIENCE
HOLY 012CD / Jun '95 / Holy

Ondekoza

☐ DEVILS ON DRUMS
68917 / Apr '97 / Tropical

☐ KAGURA
68939 / Apr '97 / Tropical

☐ LEGEND
68965 / Apr '97 / Tropical

One Dimensional Man

☐ ONE DIMENSIONAL MAN
WDR 25CD / 15 Jun '98 / Wide

One Hit Wonder

☐ OUTFALL
Stay away / Powertrip / Floorlord / Go back to bed / 20 min / Corporate rock rules / Keep it together / Billy'd to the hilt / Saddle up / Useless / Kill (all the violent people) / Splitsville / All wrecked at z-man's / Bowl of cherries / Gorby doll / Head lights
158102 / Mar '97 / Nitro

One Inch Punch

☐ TAO OF THE ONE INCH PUNCH
Just enough / Gemini / Latitudes / Represent / Bu / Take it in stride / Metaphysics / Wallflower / Orson Welles' martians / If
CDHUT 39 / Sep '96 / Hut

One King Down

☐ BLOODLUST REVENGE
EVR 31 / Sep '97 / Equal Vision

One Riot One Ranger

☐ FACES MADE FOR RADIO
HYMN 11 / 18 Sep '97 / Fundamental

One Style MDV

☐ RIGHT TO SAY
CRAICD 034 / Oct '93 / Crai

One Way System

☐ ALL SYSTEMS GO
Ain't no answers / Give us a future / Jerusalem / Me and you / No return / Waste away / One way system / Gutterboy / Breakin' in / Forgotten generation / Victim / Slaughtered / Your ready now / Stab the judge / Riot torn city / Me and you / Just another hero / Jackie was a junkie / Jerusalem / 1980's / Spokesman / All you kids
AHOYCD 014 / 11 May '98 / Captain Oi

☐ BEST OF ONE WAY SYSTEM
Stab the judge / Give us a future / Just another hero / Jerusalem / Jackie was a junkie / Ain't no answers / No return / One way system / Gutter boy / Forgotten generation / Cum on feel the noize / Breakin' in / This is the age / Into the fires / Corrupted world / One day soon / Reason why / Children of the night / Shine again
CDPUNK 50 / Mar '95 / Anagram

☐ GUTTERBOX (2CD Set)
GET 21CD / 17 Nov '97 / Get Back

☐ RETURN TO BREIZH
OWS 4CD / Jun '97 / Visionary/ Jettisoundz

☐ WRITING ON THE WALL
Corrupted world / This is the age / One day soon / Nightmare / Neurotix / Reason why / Into the fires / Days are numbered / On the line / Life on the outside / Children of the night / Down / Shine again / Out of mind / Stab the judge / Me and you / Jackie was a junkie / Jerasalem / Give us a future / Magic roundabout
AHOYCD 021 / 2 Feb '98 / Captain Oi

O'Neal, Alexander

☐ LOVE MAKES NO SENSE
In the middle / If you let it / Aphrodisia / Love makes no sense / Home is where the heart is / Change of heart / Lady / All that matters to me / Since I've been loving you / What a wonderful world
549502 / Feb '93 / A&M

☐ LOVERS AGAIN
Do you right / Let's get together / Lovers again / Can you stand the rain / Baby come to me / No one but you / Body talkin' / More than my heart / Sleepin' / Carry on / Cry / Our love
1901115122 / 19 May '98 / Ichiban

O'Neal, Johnny

☐ ON THE MONTREAL SCENE
Let me off uptown / Homeboy blues / While the blood is running warm / Come Sunday / Over joyed / Just loving you / Happy days are here again / Why try to change me now / Easy walker
JUST 852 / May '96 / Justin Time

☐ SOULFUL SWINGING (O'Neal, Johnny & Dave Young)
You're looking at me / One by one / Too late now / Night mist blues / Close your eyes / Ain't misbehavin' / Masquerade is over / What's bop
JAM 91282 / Jun '97 / Just A Memory

O'Neal, Shaq

☐ RETURN, THE
CHIP 154 / Jan '95 / Jive

☐ SHAQ DIESEL
CHIP 146 / Jan '94 / Jive

☐ YOU CAN'T STOP THE REIGN
Shaquille (interlude) / Still can't stop the reign / DIVA radio (interlude) / It was all a dream / No love lost / Strait playin' / Best to worst / Legal money / Edge of night / SHE (interlude) / Just be good to me / More to life / Big dog stomp / Game of death / Outro (interlude) / Player / Don't want to be alone
IND 90087 / Nov '96 / Interscope

O'Neill, Sean

☐ 50 IRISH SINGALONG FAVOURITES (O'Neill, Sean Band)
ECD 3136 / Jan '95 / K-Tel

☐ IRISH PARTY SONGS (O'Neill, Sean Band)
At McCarthy's party / O'Hara from Tara / Blarney stone / Up the kingdom / Rakes of mallow / My beauty of Limerick / Kitty of Coleraine / Sweet Rosie O'Grady / O'Brien has no place to go / Galway races / Paddy works on the railway / Let Mr. Maguire sit down / Oul' lammas fair / Moonlight in Mayo / My Donegal shore / Any Tipperary Town / Bonny boy / When you were sweet sixteen / Mush mush tooral / Quare bungle rye / Cushy butterfield / Shamus O'Brien / Star of the county down / My Irish Molly O / Are you there Moriarty / Mick McGilligan's ball / Rose of Castlerae / Pretty little girl from Omagh / Where the grass grows the greenest / Ferry man / Gentle Mother / Old rustic bridge / One day at a time / Phil the fluter's ball / Harvest home / Little beggarman / Paddy McGinty's goat / Town of Ballybay / Slievenamon / Come back Paddy Reilly / Mountains of mourne / Doonaree / Cliffs of Dooneen / Banks of my own lovely Lee / Nightingale / Moonshine / My Bonnie lies over the ocean / Sing Irishman sing / Mick McGilligan's daughter / Old woman from Wexford / All for me grog / Famous Shamus / Dingle regatta
ECD 3342 / May '97 / K-Tel

☐ IRISH PUB SONGS (O'Neill, Sean Band)
If you're Irish/Bold O'Donoghue/I'll tell me Ma / Courtin' in the kitchen / Wild Rover/Molly Malone/I belong to Glasgow / Loch Lomond/When Irish eyes are smiling / Irish rover/Brennan on the moor/Wild colonial boy/Muirsheen / Rose of Aranmore/Where the Counties meet / Where my Eileen is waiting / Danny boy/Galway Bay/Rose of Tralee / Goodbye Johnny dear/Old Bog Road/Farewell to Galway / Whiskey in the jar/Waxies' dargle / Dicey Reilly/ Whiskey you're the Devil / Holy ground/It's a long way to Tipperary / Hello Patsy Fagan/Come down the mountain Katie Daley / When I was single/Love is teasing/Never wed an old man / Boys of Killybegs/ Tim Finnegan's wake / Old maid in a garret/Goodbye Mick / Dublin O'Shea/Moonshiner/Juice of Barley/ Rosin the bow / Maggie/Silver threads among the gold / Fiddler's green/Black Velvet band / Boul' Thady Quill/Boys from the County Armagh / Garden where the praties grow/Dan O'Hara / Home, boys, home/Tongs by the fire
KCD 435 / Jan '97 / Celtic Collections

O'Neill, Steven

☐ TAKE ME TO THE ISLAND
Take me to the island / Walk right back / Mothers love's a blessing / Tom Dooley / Medley / Green fields of Ireland / When I grow too old to dream / Forever and ever amen / Don't close your eyes / Wild colonial boy / Fields of Athenry / Spanish lady / Medley / Love is all around / You are my sunshine / If tomorrow never comes
TSCD 101 / Sep '97 / Irish

Ongala, Remmy

☐ KERSHAW SESSIONS
ROOTCD 004 / Mar '95 / Strange Fruit

☐ REMMY ONGALA & ORCHESTRE SUPER MATIMLIA (Ongala, Remmy & Orchestra)
Dodoma / One world / I want to go home / Inchi yetu (our country) / What can I say? (niseme nini) / No money, no life / Living together (tupendane) / Mrema / Kidogo kidogo (little by little)
CDRW 22 / Mar '92 / Realworld

☐ SONGS FOR THE POOR MAN (Ongala, Remmy & Orchestra)
Nasikitka / Karola / Kependa roho / Sauti ya mnyonge / Usingizi / Pamella / Muziki asili yake wapi / Mariam wangu / Kifo / Muziki asili yake wapi (version)
CDRW 6 / '90 / Realworld

Ongley, Mark

☐ SONG FOR ROS
HVRCD 0040 / Sep '93 / Hunter Valley

Only Attitude Counts

☐ 100%
LF 292CD / 25 May '98 / Lost & Found

Only Living Witness

☐ INNOCENTS
CM 77017CD / Feb '96 / Century Media

☐ PRONE MORTAL FORM
CM 770722 / Jun '94 / Century Media

Only Ones

☐ BABY'S GOT A GUN
Happy pilgrim / Why don't you kill yourself / Me and my shadow / Deadly nightshade / Strange mouth / Big sleep / Oh Lucinda / Re-union / Trouble in the world / Castle built on sand / Fools / My way out of here
4836622 / Mar '96 / Columbia

☐ EVEN SERPENTS SHINE
From here to eternity / Flaming torch / You've got to pay / No solution / In betweens / Out there in the night / Curtains for you / Programme / Someone who cares / Miles from nowhere / Instrumental
4785032 / Feb '95 / Columbia

☐ IMMORTAL STORY, THE
Lovers of today / Peter and the pets / Whole of the law / Another girl another planet / Special view (aka telescopic love) / Beast / It's the truth / No peace for the wicked / Immortal story / From here to eternity / In betweens / No solution / Curtains for you / Someone who cares / Miles from nowhere / Your chosen life / Baby's got a gun / Why don't you kill yourself / Oh Lucinda (love becomes a habit) / Big sleep
4712672 / Feb '92 / Columbia

☐ ONLY ONES LIVE, THE
Trouble in the world / Beast / Lovers of today / Why don't you kill yourself / As my wife says / Big sleep / City of fun / Programme / Happy pilgrim / Strange mouth / No peace for the wicked / Miles from nowhere / Another girl another planet / Me and my shadow
MAUCD 603 / Jul '89 / Mau Mau

☐ ONLY ONES, THE
Whole of the law / Another girl another planet / Breaking down / City of fun / Beast / Creature of doom / It's the truth / Language problem / No place for the wicked / Immortal story
4773792 / Aug '94 / Columbia

☐ REMAINS
Prisoner / Watch you drown / Flowers die / Devon song / My rejection / Baby's got a gun / Hope valley blues / Counterfeit woman / River of no return / I only wanna be your friend / Oh no / Don't hold your breath / Silent night / Don't feel too good
CDMGRAM 67 / Sep '96 / Anagram

Ono, Seigen

☐ NEKONOTOPIA NEKONOMANIA
Apple in the freezer / Enishie / Nekontopia nekonomania / My first wish / It's Denise / Person in the photography / 1989 / I think of you / Planador / Caramba / Berliner Nachte part 1 / Berliner Nachte part 2 / Berliner Nachte part 3 / Berliner Nachte part 4
MTM 29 / Apr '96 / Made To Measure

Ono, Yoko

☐ APPROXIMATELY INFINITE UNIVERSE (2CD Set)
RCD 10417/18 / Aug '97 / Rykodisc

☐ FEELING THE SPACE
RCD 10419 / Aug '97 / Rykodisc

☐ FLY (2CD Set)
RCD 10415/16 / Aug '97 / Rykodisc

☐ IT'S ALRIGHT
My man (mon homme) / Never say goodbye / Speck of dust / Loneliness / Tomorrow may never come / It's alright / I see rainbows / Dream love / Let the tears dry / Wake up
RCD 10422 / 18 Aug '97 / Rykodisc

☐ ONOBOX (6CD Set)
No bed for beatle John / Mind holes / Oh wind / Why / Why not / Greenfield morning I pushed an empty baby carriage all over / Touch me / Paper shoes / Mind train / Open your box / Toilet piece / Don't worry / Telephone pole / Midsummer New York / Path / Don't count the waves / Head play / Is winter here to stay / Yang yang / Death of Samantha / What did I do / Infinite universe / What a bastard the world is / Catman / I want my love to rest tonight / Shiranakatta / Peter the dealer / I felt like smashing my face in a clear glass window / Winter song / Kite song / Now or never / What a mess / I have a woman inside my soul / Move on fast / Looking over from my hotel window / Waiting for the sunrise / Growing pain / Yellow girl / Coffin car / Warrior woman / Woman of Salem / Run run run / If only / Thousand times yes / Straight talk / Angry young woman / Potbelly rocker / She hits back / Men men men / Woman power / It's been very hard / Mildred mildred / Let's turn the right turn / Walking on thin ice / Kiss kiss / Give me something / I'm moving on / Yes I'm your angel / Beautiful boys / Open your soul to me / Every man has a woman who loves him / Hard times are over / Don't be scared / Sleepless night / Sanity / Your hands / Let me count the ways / Forgive me my love / You're the one / There's no goodbye / Have you seen a horizon lately / I don't know why / Mindweaver / Even when your far away / Nobody sees me like you do / Silver horse / No no no / Toyboat / She gets down on her knees / Extensiion 33 / Never say goodbye / Spec of dust / My man / It's alright / Let the tears dry / Dream love / Hell in paradise / I love you Earth / In cape clear / Goodbye sadness / A story / Loneliness / Will you touch me / Dogtown / It happened / Tomorrow may never come / Winter friend / Heartburn stew / Yes I'm a witch / Yume o moto / Ooh / Namyohorengekyo / We're all water / Joseijoi banzai / Sisters o sisters
RCD 1022429 / 22 Sep '97 / Rykodisc

☐ RISING
Warzone / Wouldnit / Ask the dragon / New York woman / Talking to the universe / Turn the corner / I'm dying / Where do we go from here / Kurushi / Will I / Rising / Goodbye my love / Revelations
CDEST 2276 / Jan '96 / Capitol

☐ RISING MIXES
Talking to the Universe / Source / Ask the dragon / Where do we go from here / Rising / Franklin summer
CDP 8372680 / Jun '96 / Capitol

☐ SEASON OF GLASS
Goodbye sadness / Mindweaver / Even when you're far away / Nobody sees me like you do / Turn of the wheel / Dogtown / Silver horse / I don't know why / Extension 33 / No, no, no / Will you touch me / She gets down on her knees / Toy boat / Mother of the universe
RCD 10421 / 18 Aug '97 / Rykodisc

☐ STARPEACE
Hell in paradise / I love all of me / Children power / Rainbow revolution / King of the zoo / Remember raven / Cape clear / Sky people / You and I / It's gonna rain (living on tiptoe) / Starpeace / I love you, Earth
RCD 10423 / 18 Aug '97 / Rykodisc

☐ STORY, A
RCD 10420 / Aug '97 / Rykodisc

☐ WALKING ON THIN ICE
Walking on thin ice / Even when you're far away / Kiss kiss kiss / Nobody sees me like you do / Yangyang / No no no / Death of samantha / Mind weaver / You're the one / Spec of dust / Midsummer new york / Don't be scared / Sleepless nights / Kite song / She gets down on her knees / Give me something / Hell in paradise / Woman power / O'oh
RCD 20230 / Mar '97 / Rykodisc

Onset

☐ POOL OF LIFE REVISITED, THE
Rakin' em down / Taker (2nd take) / Cowboy and his wife / Precious love / Talkin' space travel blues / Too proud to start / Trees and plants / Glad rag (instrumental) / Mansion on the hill / Pool of life (instrumental) / For you / Two times forgotten man / Poor and lonely girl / Starlight tuneful 9 / Another man's crime / Let's go home
PROBE 040CD / 27 Jul '98 / Probe Plus

Onslaught

☐ POWER FROM HELL
Damnation / Onslaught (Power from hell) / Thermo neuclear devastation / Skullcrusher / Lord of evil / Death metal / Angels of death / Devil's legion / Street meets steel / Skullcrusher / Witch hunt / Mighty empress
PRAGE 001CD / Oct '96 / Powerage

Onyan

☐ CRAZY MAN
RAMCD 1021 / 24 Nov '97 / Ram

Onyas

☐ GET SHIT FACED WITH THE ONYAS
ANDA 196 / Jan '97 / Au-Go-Go

Onyx

☐ ALL WE GOT IZ US
Life or death / Last dayz / All we got iz us (Evil streets) / Purse snatchaz / Shout / I murder u / Betta off dead / Live niguz / Funkmotherfukaz / Most def / Act up / Getto mentalitee / Wrongs / Maintain / Walk in New York
5292652 / Oct '95 / Def Jam

☐ BACDAFUCUP
Bacdafucup / Bichasniguz / Throw ya gunz / Here 'n' now / Bust dat ass / Atak of de bal-hedz / Da mad face invasion / Blac vagina finda / Da bounca nigga / Nigga bridges / Onyx is here / Slam / Stik 'n' muve / Bichazbootleguz / Shifftee / Phat ('n' all dat) / De nex niguz / Getdafucout
5234472 / Jan '96 / Def Jam

☐ SHUT 'EM DOWN
5369882 / 1 Jun '98 / Def Jam

Oofotr

☐ OOFOTR
EKG 11CD / Aug '96 / Norske Gram

Oomph

☐ FOOLS NEVER FAIL
DY 152 / Jun '95 / Dynamica

☐ SPERM
Suck-taste-spit / Sex / War / Dickhead / Schisma / Feiert das kreuz / Love / Das ist freiheit / Kismet / Bresathtaker / Ich bin der weg / U-said (live)
DY 62 / Apr '94 / Dynamica

☐ WUNSCHKIND
DY 00212 / Nov '96 / Dynamica

Oomph

☐ BETWEEN TWO WORLDS
GV 135CD / May '94 / Global Village

Oosh

☐ VIEW, THE
Chat up / Missing lover / Spliff culture / Yard has no dandelion / Cloud / View / Charlie / No soul / I got this / Storm
4509962862 / Sep '94 / Magnet

OP8

☐ SLUSH (OP8 & Lisa Germano)
Slush
VVR 1000332 / Jun '97 / V2

Opal

☐ HAPPY NIGHTMARE BABY
SST 103CD / May '93 / SST

Opaz

☐ BACK FROM THE RAGGEDY EDGE (Opaz/Ray Hayden)
OPH 003CD / Aug '95 / Opaz

Opel, Jackie

☐ TOP SOUNDS FROM TOP DECK VOL.2 (A Love To Share) (Opel, Jackie/Ferdie Nelson)
Tears from my eyes: *Opel, Jackie* / Love to share: *Opel, Jackie* / Valley of green: *Opel, Jackie* / Sometimes I wonder: *Opel, Jackie* / Pictures of smoke: *Opel, Jackie* / Every word I say is true: *Opel, Jackie* / Take your time: *Opel, Jackie* / Turm to the almighty: *Opel, Jackie* / Valley of green: *Opel, Jackie* / Lonely and blue boy (yours): *Nelson, Ferdie* / Weeping and wailing: *Nelson, Ferdie* / War and strife: *Nelson, Ferdie* / Birds and bees: *Nelson, Ferdie* / Certainly: *Nelson, Ferdie*
WESM 510 / 22 Sep '97 / Westside

Open House

☐ SECOND STORY
GLCD 1144 / Oct '94 / Green Linnet

Operating Strategies

☐ DIFFICULTY OF BEING
EFA 11214 / Apr '93 / Danse Macabre

Operating Theatre

☐ RAPID EYE MOVEMENTS
UD 011CD / Oct '96 / United Dairies

Operation Ivy

☐ OPERATION IVY
LOOKOUT 10CD / Dec '96 / Lookout

☐ TAKE WARNING (A Tribute To Operation Ivy) (Various Artists)
GF 700012 / Sep '97 / Glue Factory

Operator

☐ ZERO DIVIDE
SOS 011CD / Nov '96 / North South

Opeth

☐ MORNINGRISE
CANDLE 015CD / Jul '96 / Candlelight

☐ MY ARMS YOUR HEARSE
CANDLE 025CD / 15 Jun '98 / Candlelight

☐ ORCHID
CANDLE 010CD / Sep '95 / Candlelight

Ophelias Dream

☐ ALL BEAUTY IS SAD
Rise / Mystere / Reflections / Piece for solo / Tears / Arabesque / Sophia's prayer / Saltarello / Sophia's reprise / Fragment / Dreams / Fairy dance / Fall
HYP 3919178CD / 13 Apr '98 / Hyperium

Ophthalamia

☐ JOURNEY INTO DARKNESS, A
AV 003 / May '94 / Avantgarde

☐ LONG JOURNEY, A
NR 026CD / 3 Aug '98 / Necropolis

Opium Den

☐ DIARY OF A DRUNKEN SUN
001AF2 / Jun '93 / Southern

Opium Taylor

☐ FADE MACHINE
CR 6CD / Oct '97 / Caulfield

Oppermann, Rudiger

☐ SAME SUN SAME MOON
SHAM 017CD / Feb '93 / Shamrock

Opposite Earth

☐ HEADSPACE
SPV 08528592 / May '98 / SPV

Oppressed

☐ BEST OF THE OPPRESSED, THE
DOJOCD 227 / Jan '96 / Dojo

☐ DEAD AND BURIED/FATAL BLOW
Victims / Work together / Urban soldiers / Ultra violence / Run from you / Riot / Leave me alone / Joe Hawkins / Government out / It ain't right / We're the oppressed / Angels with dirty faces / Bad man / ACAB / White flag / Fatal blow / Way of life / Last orders / Local constabulary
AHOYCD 402 / 2 Feb '98 / Captain Oi

☐ LIVE 1984
STEPCD 107 / 4 May '98 / Step 1

☐ OI OI MUSIC
AHOYCD 005 / 13 Apr '98 / Captain Oi

Oppressor

☐ AGONY
RRS 958CD / Jan '97 / Diehard

Opthalamia

☐ TO ELISHIA
NR 013CD / Jun '97 / Necropolis

Optic Eye

☐ LIGHT SIDE OF THE SUN
Sunburst (extended mix) / Brain of Morbius / Listening (Aural sculpture) / Chain reaction / Wobbling in space / Guitar man / Slaves of the crystal brain / On the other side / Far out race / Acid drops
CDTOT 17 / Oct '94 / Jumpin' & Pumpin'

Optic Nerve

☐ CHILDREN OF THE UNIVERSE
77021921 / Jun '97 / Omnisonus

☐ FOREVER AND A DAY
SCACD 104 / Jun '97 / Screaming Apple

Optica

☐ ALL THE COLOURS OF THE RAINBOW
KINXCD 2 / Apr '95 / Kinetix

☐ FUZZ
Plasma eruption / Evolute / Dueterum / Mercury / Spacetime / Magnatron phz / Circular cube / Fuzz / Spaced bong baby
KINXCD 6 / Apr '97 / Kinetix

Optical 8

☐ BUG
DSA 54048 / Dec '96 / CDSA

Optical Blue

☐ ONLY BECOME
GRCD 024 / 23 Mar '98 / Garageland

Optiganally Yours

☐ SPOTLIGHT ON
HED 065CD / Jun '97 / Headhunter

Optimum Wound Profile

☐ ASPHYXIA
WB 1120CD / May '95 / We Bite

Ora

☐ ORA
HBG 122/14 / Apr '94 / Background

Oracle

☐ POOL OF DREAMS
Dive deep / Jacob's pillow / Teardrop in the sun / Beyond the 9th wave / Where Michael Furey lay / Phantom queen / Selkie / Pool of dreams / Amairgen / To Eireann
090266877962 / Jul '98 / RCA Victor

☐ TREE
WM 2 / Jun '94 / Swim

Oraison, Jorge

☐ TANGOS Y MILONGAS (The Music Of Astor Piazzolla)
Cinco piezas para guitarra / La muerte del angel / Milonga del angel / Retrato de A. Gobbi / Contrabajeando / Milonga in ay menor / Otono porteno
KTC 1023 / 2 Mar '98 / Etcetera

Oral Groove

☐ COLLISIONVILLE
CR 810952 / Jul '97 / Cross

Orange 9mm

☐ DRIVER NOT INCLUDED
Glistening / Magnet / Toilet / Cutting draining / Sacrifice / Can't decide / Thickest glass / Guy a tone / High speed changer / Disclaimer / Suspect / Pissed
7567617462 / May '95 / Atlantic

☐ TRAGIC
Fire in the hole / Stick shift / Crowd control / Method / Dead in the water / Kiss it goodbye / Feel it / Failure / Take it away / Muted / Gun to your head / Tragic / Seven
7567829022 / Feb '97 / Atlantic

☐ ULTRAMAN VS. GODZILLA
NG 706CD / 13 Apr '98 / NG

Orange Cakemix

☐ ANOTHER ORANGE WORLD
DRL 0472 / 1 Sep '97 / Darla

☐ BLUE ISLAND SOUND
ER 1034 / Aug '97 / Elefant

☐ FLUFFY PILLOW
DRL 029 / Jan '97 / Fuzzy Box/Darla

☐ GRAPEFRUIT
BBPTC 24CD / Mar '97 / Black Bean & Placenta Tape Club

☐ LIKE WAVES IN SPACE
ER 307 / Sep '97 / Elefant

☐ LOVECLOUD AND SECRET TAPE
BBPTC 83 / Jul '97 / Black Bean & Placenta Tape Club

☐ SILVER LINING UNDER WATER
DRL 031 / Feb '97 / Darla

Orange Deluxe

☐ NECKING
GOODCD 4 / Jul '96 / Dead Dead Good

Orange Goblin

☐ FREQUENCIES FROM PLANET 10
Astral project / Magic carpet / Saruman's wish / Song of the purple fish / Aquatic fanatic / Lothlorian / Land of secret dreams / Orange goblin / Star shaped cloud
CDRISE 15 / 1 Dec '97 / Music For Nations

Orange Humble Band

☐ ASSORTED CREAMS
HAC 67 / 27 Apr '98 / Half A Cow

Orange Juice

☐ ORANGE JUICE, THE
Lean period / I guess I'm just a little too sensitive / Burning desire / Scaremonger / Artisans / What presence / Out for the count / Get while the gettings good / All that ever mattered / Salmon fishing in New York / Bury my head in my hands / Poor old soul
5399832 / 9 Mar '98 / Polydor

☐ ORANGE JUICE/YOU CAN'T HIDE YOUR LOVE FOREVER
Lean period / I guess I'm just a little bit too sensitive / Burning desire / Scaremonger / Artisans / What presence / Out for the count / Get while the gettings good / All that ever mattered / Salmon fishing in New York / Falling and laughing / Untitled melody / Wan light / Tender objects / Dying day / LOVE Love / Intuition told me / Upwards and onwards / Satellite city / Three cheers for our side / Consolation prize / Felicity / In a nutshell
8477272 / Jan '91 / Polydor

☐ RIP IT UP
Rip it up / Mud in your eye / Breakfast time / Flesh of my flesh / Hokoyo / Million pleading faces / Turn away / I can't help myself / Louise Louise / Tenterhook / Tongues begin to wag / Barbecue / Flesh of my flesh
5399812 / 9 Mar '98 / Polydor

☐ TEXAS FEVER
Bridge / Craziest feeling / Punch drunk / Day I went down to Texas / Place in my heart / Sad lament / Leaner period / Out for the count / Move yourself
5399822 / 9 Mar '98 / Polydor

☐ VERY BEST OF ORANGE JUICE, THE
Falling and laughing / Consolation prize / You old eccentric / LOVE love / Felicity / In a nutshell / Rip it up / I can't help myself / Flesh of my flesh / Tenterhooks / Bridge / Day I went down to Texas / Punch drunk / Place in my heart / Sad lament / Lean period / I guess I'm just a little too sensitive / Scaremonger / Artisans / Salmon fishing in New York / What presence / Out for the count
5136182 / Apr '92 / Polydor

☐ YOU CAN'T HIDE YOUR LOVE FOREVER
Falling and laughing / Untitled melody / Wan light / Tender object / Dying day / LOVE Love / Intuition told me / Upwards and onwards / Satellite city / Three cheers for our side / Consolation prize / Felicity / In a nutshell / You old eccentric / Intuition told me
5399802 / 9 Mar '98 / Polydor

Orange Peels

☐ SQUARE
All the world could pass me by / Something strange happens / Get it right / I don't mind the rain / Take me over / Everybody's gone / Spaghetti-o western / She is like a rose / On the way to somewhere / Slow train didn't you know / Man and superman / Tex / Love coming down
MF 23 / 22 Sep '97 / Minty Fresh

Orange Sector

☐ FAITH
CDZOT 18 / Aug '93 / Zoth Ommog

☐ KIDS IN AMERICA
CDZOT 126 / Nov '94 / Zoth Ommog

Orb

☐ ADVENTURES BEYOND THE ULTRAWORLD (2CD Set)
Little fluffy clouds / Earth (gala) / Supernova at the end of the universe / Back side of the moon / Spanish castles in space / Perpetual dawn / Into the fourth dimension / Outlands / Star 6 and 7 8 9 / Huge ever growing pulsating brain that rules from the centre
IMCD 234 / Sep '96 / Island

☐ AUNTIE AUBREY'S EXCURSIONS BEYOND THE CALL OF DUTY (2CD Set) (Various Artists)
Praying mantra: *Material* / Democracy: *Killing Joke* / Satellite serenade: *Suzuki, Keiichi* / Fast forward the future: *Zodiac Youth* / Higher than the sun: *Primal Scream* / Ambient state: *Ready Made* / So and slow it grows: *Wir* / Secret squirrel: *Shimizu, Yasuki* / You gotta say yes to another excess: *Yello* / Out of body: *Innersphere* / Happiest girl: *Depeche Mode* / Ship of fools: *Erasure* / O'locco: *Sun Electric* / Ploy: *Maurizio* / Men of wadodem: *Time Unlimited* / 2 Much: *Paradise X* / Home: *Pop Will Eat Itself* / What goes on: *Love Kittens*
DVNT 012CD / Jul '96 / Deviant

☐ LIVE 1993 (2CD Set)
Huge ever growing pulsating brain that rules from the centre / Plateau / OOBE / Little fluffy clouds / Star 6 and 7 8 9 / Towers of dub / Blue room / Valley / Perpetual dawn / Assassin / Outlands / Spanish castles in space
IMCD 245 / Mar '97 / Island

☐ OOBE ADVENTURE (CD/Book Set)
Alex vs. The KLF / Orb vs. Coldcut
SB 04 / 23 Feb '98 / Sonic Book

☐ ORBLIVION
Delta mkII / Ubiquity / Asylum / Bedouin / Molten love / Pi / SALT / Toxygene / Log of deadwood / Secrets / Passing of time / 72
CID 8055 / Feb '97 / Island

☐ ORBSTORY (Interview Disc)
ORBK 1 / Feb '97 / Sonic Book

☐ ORBUS TERRARUM
Valley / Plateau / Oxbow Lakes / Montagne D'Or / Orbus terrarum / Occidental / Slug dub
CID 8037
CIDX 8037 / 2 Feb '98 / Island

☐ UF.ORB
OOBE / UF Orb / Blue room / Towers of dub / Close encounters / Majestic / Sticky end
IMCD 219 / Mar '96 / Island

Orbison, Roy

☐ ALL TIME GREATEST HITS
Only the lonely / Leah / In dreams / Uptown / It's over / Crying / Dream baby / Blue angel / Working for the man / Candy man / Running scared / Falling / Claudette / Ooby dooby / I'm hurtin' / Mean woman blues / Lana / Blue bayou / Oh pretty woman
CD 67290 / Jan '89 / Monument

☐ BEST OF ROY ORBISON, THE
Oh pretty woman / Mean woman blues / Candy man / In dreams / Blue bayou / Pretty paper / Distant drums / I can't stop loving you / All I have to do is dream / It's over / Crying / Blue angel / Dream baby (how long must I dream) / Running scared / Only the lonely (know the way I feel)
4633502 / 27 Jul '98 / Columbia

☐ BLACK AND WHITE NIGHT (Orbison, Roy & Friends)
Oh pretty woman / Only the lonely / In dreams / Dream baby / Leah / Move on down the line / Crying / Mean woman blues / Running scared / Blue bayou / Candy man / Uptown / Ooby dooby / Comedians / (All I can do is) Dream of you / It's over
ROBW 78912 / Mar '98 / Orbison/ Demon

☐ COLLECTION, THE
Trying to get to you / Ooby dooby / Go go go / You're my baby / Domino / Sweet and easy to love / Devil doll / Cause of it all / Fools hall of fame / True love goodbye / Chicken hearted / I like love / Mean little mama / Problem child / This kind of love / It's too late / I never knew / You're gonna cry / One more time / Lovestruck / Clown / Claudette
CCSCD 147 / Feb '93 / Castle

☐ COLLECTION, THE
(I'd be) a legend in my time / Too soon to know / Lonesome number one / Time changed everything / Crawlin' back / Clown / Blues in my mind / Sweet dreams / Same street / Belinda / Give myself a party / A true love goodbye / I'm a southern man / Born to love me / Breakin' up is breakin' my heart / I give up / Can't wait / Under suspicion / I'm hurting / Ooby dooby / Claudette / Devil doll / Go go go / I like love / You're my baby
COL 027 / Mar '95 / Collection

☐ COMBO CONCERT
Only the lonely / Running scared / Crying / What'd I say / Dream baby / Mean woman blues / It's over / Oh pretty woman / Goodnight
HCC 1965D / 4 May '98 / Demon

☐ COMMUNICATION BREAKDOWN
RVCD 06 / 20 Jul '98 / Raven

☐ DEFINITIVE COLLECTION, THE
Oh pretty woman / Running scared / Falling / Love hurts / Mean woman blues / I can't stop loving you / Crowd / Blue bayou / Borne on the wind / Lana / Only the lonely / It's over / Crying / Pretty paper / All I have to do is dream / Dream baby (how long must I dream) / Blue angel / Working for the man / Candy man / In dreams
4805702 / 13 Jul '98 / Monument

☐ GOLDEN DAYS
Oh pretty woman / Running scared / Falling / Love hurts / Mean woman blues / I can't stop loving you / Crowd / Blue bayou / Borne on the wind / Lana / Only the lonely / It's over / Crying / Pretty paper / All I have to do is dream / Dream baby / Blue angel / Working for the man / Candy man / In dreams
4715552 / 27 Jul '98 / Monument
4715559 / 13 Jul '98 / Monument

☐ IN DREAMS (The Greatest Hits)
Only the lonely / Leah / In dreams / Uptown / It's over / Crying / Dream baby / Blue angel / Working for the man / Candy man / Running scared / Falling / I'm hurtin' / Claudette / Oh pretty woman / Mean woman blues / Ooby dooby / Lana / Blue bayou
ROGH 1000 / 1 Jun '98 / Orbison/ Demon

☐ IN DREAMS/ORBISONGS
In dreams / Lonely wine / Shahdaroba / No one will ever know / Sunset / House without windows / Dream / Blue bayou / (They call you) Gigolette / All I have to do is dream / Beautiful dreamer / My prayer / Oh pretty woman / Dance / (Say) you're my girl / Goodnight / Nightlife / Let the good times roll / (I get so) Sentimental / Yo te amo Maria / Wedding day / Sleepy hollow / Twenty two Days / Legend in my time
4749572 / Feb '94 / Monument

☐ KING OF HEARTS
You're the one / Heartbreak radio / We'll take the night / Crying / After the love has gone / Love in time / I drove all night / Wild hearts run out of time / Coming home / Careless heart
CDVUS 58 / Nov '92 / Virgin

☐ LEGEND IN HIS TIME
Lonesome number one / Oh such a stranger / Legend in my time / I'm a Southern man / Belinda / Under suspicion / No chain at all / Can't wait / I'm hurtin' / Same street / Blue blue day / Too soon to know / I don't really want you / Old love song / Born to love you / Big hearted me / What about me
CDMF 079 / '91 / Magnum Force

☐ LONELY & BLUE/CRYING
Only the lonely / Bye bye love / Cry / Blue avenue / I can't stop loving you / Come back to me my love / Blue angel / Raindrops / Legend in my time / I'm hurtin' / Twenty two days / I'll say it's my fault / Crying / Great pretender / Love hurts / She wears my ring / Wedding day / Summer song / Dance / Lana / Loneliness / Let's make a memory / Nite life / Running scared
4749562 / Feb '94 / Monument

☐ MAGIC OF ROY ORBISON, THE
322696 / Jul '97 / Koch Presents

☐ MASTERS, THE
Lonesome number one / Oh such a stranger / (I'd be a) legend in my time / (I'm a) southern man / Belinda / Under suspicion / No chain at all / Can't wait / I'm hurting / Same street / Blue blue day / Too soon to know / I don't really want you / Old love song / Born to love me / Big hearted me / What about me
EABCD 095 / 30 Mar '98 / Eagle

☐ MY BOOK OF DREAMS
I'm a southern man / Under suspicion / No chain at all / Belinda / Can't wait / I don't really want to / Lonesome number one / Oh such a stranger / Big hearted me / I'm hurting
RTD 3970023CD / 1 Dec '97 / Institute Of Art

☐ MYSTERY GIRL
You got it / Real world / Dream you / Love so beautiful / California blue / She's a mystery to me / Comedians / Windsurfer / Careless heart
CDV 2576 / Apr '92 / Virgin

☐ RCA SESSIONS, THE (Orbison, Roy & Sonny James)
Almost eighteen: *Orbison, Roy* / Bug: *Orbison, Roy* / I'll never tell: *Orbison, Roy* / Jolie: *Orbison, Roy* / Paper boy: *Orbison, Roy* / Sweet and innocent: *Orbison, Roy* / Seems to me: *Orbison, Roy* / Apache: *James, Sonny* / Magnetism: *James, Sonny* / Young love: *James, Sonny* / Lana: *James, Sonny* / Legend of the brown mountain light: *James, Sonny* / Listen to my heart: *James, Sonny* / Hey little ducky: *James, Sonny* / Innocent angel: *James, Sonny* / Broken wings: *James, Sonny* / Day's not over yet: *James, Sonny* / Dance her by me (one more time): *James, Sonny* / Time's running backwards for me: *James, Sonny*
BCD 15407 / Jul '87 / Bear Family

☐ ROCKER
Ooby dooby / Go go go / Trying to get to you / You're my baby / Rockhouse / Domino / Sweet and easy to love / Devil doll / Cause of it all / Fools hall of fame / True love goodbye / Chicken hearted / I like love / Mean little lover / Problem child / You tell me / I give up / One more time / Lovestruck / Clown / Claudette / This kind of love / It's too late / I never knew / You're gonna cry / I was a fool: *Orbison, Roy & Ken Cook* / Find my baby for me: *Orbison, Roy & Sonny Burgess* / Rockbilly gal: *Orbison, Roy & Hayden Thompson*
CPCD 8180 / Jun '96 / Charly

☐ ROCKHOUSE
Ooby dooby / I like love / Clown / Cause of it all / Domino / Chicken hearted / Go go go / This kind of love / You're my baby / Claudette / Rockhouse / It's too late / Mean little mama / Fools' hall of fame / You're gonna cry / True love goodbye / Devil doll / Sweet and easy to love / Problem child / Tryin' to get to you
305912 / Jan '97 / Hallmark

☐ ROY ORBISON
Ooby dooby / Claudette / This kind of love / It's too late / You're gonna cry / Mean little mama / Devil doll / Rock house / Sweet and easy to love / Trying to get to you / Go go go / Domino / Fool's hall of fame / Chicken hearted / You're my baby / Cause of it all
12330 / May '94 / Laserlight

☐ ROY ORBISON (3CD Set)
KBOX 344 / Oct '95 / Collection

☐ ROY ORBISON SONGBOOK (Various Artists)
In dreams: Jones, Tom / Dream baby: Shannon, Del / Oh pretty woman: Green, Al / It's over: Campbell, Glen / Crying: McLean, Don / Only the lonely: Wells, Kitty / Down the line: Hollies / Blue Bayou: Whitman, Slim / Claudette: Everly Brothers / Best friend: Cash, Johnny / You've got love: Holly, Buddy / Uptown: Gordon, Robert / Lookin' for love: Vee, Bobby / Leah: Higgins, Bertie / Crowd: Jennings, Waylon / Lana: Velvets / Careless heart: Tyler, Bonnie / Running scared: Shannon, Del / California blue: Humperdinck, Engelbert / Lovin' man: Francis, Connie
VSOPCD 215 / Apr '95 / Connoisseur Collection

☐ SUN YEARS, THE
Ooby dooby / Trying to get to you / Go go go / You're my baby / Rock house / Domino / Sweet and easy / Devil doll / Cause of it all / Fools' hall of fame / True love goodbye / Chicken hearted / It's too late / I never knew / You're gonna cry / You tell me / I give up / One more time / Lovestruck / Clown / Claudette / Jenny / Find my baby for me
BCD 15461 / Apr '89 / Bear Family

☐ VERY BEST OF ROY ORBISON, THE
Only the lonely / You got it / Oh pretty woman / In dreams / Crying: Orbison, Roy & KD Lang / Blue angel / Working for the man / Running scared / She's a mystery to me / Blue bayou / It's over / California blue / Claudette / Mean woman blues / Ooby dooby / Too soon to know / Falling / Dream baby / I drove all night / Pretty paper / Goodnight
CDV 2804 / Nov '96 / Virgin

Orbit

☐ LIBIDO SPEEDWAY
Yeah / Bicycle song / Wake up / Amp / Medicine / Rockets / Motorama / Nocturnal autodrive / Why you won't / Carnival / Chapel Hill / Paper bag / Gazer
5406522 / 2 Mar '98 / A&M

Orbit

☐ ORBIT
CD 1015 / Aug '98 / Music & Arts

Orbit, William

☐ BEST OF STRANGE CARGOS
Water from a vine leaf / Dark eyed kid / Gringatcho Demento / Fire and mercy / Via Calente / Time to get wize / Ruby Heart (transmogrified) / Atom dream / Harry Flowers / Love my way / Riding to Rio / Story of light / Silent signals / Painted rock / Water babies
EIRSCD 1079 / Jun '96 / IRS/EMI

☐ STRANGE CARGO VOL.1 (Hinterland)
Million town / She cries your name / Montok point / Hulaville / El ninjo / Name of the wave / Crimes of the future / Last dream of lucy mariner / Hinterland / Lost in blue / Say anything / Kiss of the bee
4509992952 / Dec '96 / N-Gram

☐ STRANGE CARGO VOL.3
Water from a vine leaf / Into the paradise / Time to get wize / Harry flowers / Touch of the night / Story of light / Gringatcho demento / Hazy shade of random / Best friend paranoia / Monkey king / Deus ex machina / Water babies
CDV 2707 / Mar '93 / Virgin

Orbital

☐ EVENT HORIZON (Film Soundtrack)
8289392 / 25 Aug '97 / Internal

☐ IN SIDES
Girl with the sun in her hair / Petrol / Box / Dwr budr / Adnans / Out there somewhere
8287632 / Apr '96 / Internal

☐ IN SIDES
Girl with the sun in her hair / Petrol / Box / Dwr budr / Adnans / Out there somewhere / Saint
TRCDR 10 / Apr '97 / Internal

☐ IN SIDES
123129CD / Apr '97 / Dutch East India

☐ ORBITAL
Moebius / Speed freak / Oolaa / Desert storm / Fahrenheit 303 / Steel cube idolatory / High rise / Chime / Midnight / Belfast / Untitled / Macro head
TRUCD 9 / Apr '97 / Internal

Orchestra

☐ NOT AS SOFTLY AS
MECCACD 1043 / Nov '94 / Music Mecca

Orchestra Baobab

☐ PIRATE'S CHOICE
Utru horas / Coumba / Ledi ndieme m'bodj / Werente serigne / Ray mbele / Soldadi / Utru horas (alternate take) / Coumba (alternate take)
WCD 014 / May '90 / World Circuit

Orchestra Jazz Siciliana

☐ PLAYS THE MUSIC OF CARLA BLEY
440 / Lone arranger / Dreams so real / Baby baby / Joyful noise / Egyptian / Blunt object
843 207 2 / Nov '90 / ECM

Orchestra Klezmer

☐ ORIENT EXPRESS MOVING SHNORERS
TE 010 / Feb '97 / EPM

Orchestra Marrabenta

☐ INDEPENDENCE
CD PIR 12 / Apr '89 / World Circuit

Orchestra Super Mazembe

☐ MALOBA D'AMOR
Kassongo / Shauri yako / Salima (parts 1 and 2) / Mwana nyiau (parts 1 and 2) / Nabinakate / Maloba d'amor / Samba (parts 1 and 2)
AFRIZZ 007 / May '90 / Disc Afrique

Orchestra Tango Cafe

☐ TANGO ARGENTINO
SSCD 001 / Jun '97 / Sounds Sensational

Orchestre Contrebasses

☐ BASS, BASS, BASS, BASS, BASS &
BASS
86232 / Oct '93 / Melodie

Orchestre De Tanger

☐ AL-ALA ANTHOLOGY VOL.7
W 260030 / Oct '96 / Inedit

Orchestre National

☐ A PLUS TARD (Orchestre National De Jazz)
LBLC 6554 / Nov '92 / Label Bleu

Orchestre National De Jazz

☐ IN TEMPO
5324382 / Jul '96 / Verve

☐ MERCI MERCI MERCI
5349452 / Aug '97 / Verve

☐ REMINISCING
5324372 / Jul '96 / Verve

Orchid Airburst

☐ SIXTY CYCLE STORIES
ORCH 1202 / Oct '95 / Guitar Tree

Orchidee

☐ TRADITIONAL CHINESE ZHENG AND QIN MUSIC
SM 16032 / Jan '93 / Wergo

Orchids

☐ STRIVING FOR THE LAZY PERFECTION
Obsession no.1 / Striving for the lazy perfection / Searching / Welcome to my curious heart / Avignon / Living Ken and Barbie / Beautiful liar / Kind of Eden / Prayers to St. Jude / Lovechild / Give a little honey / I've got to wake up / Perfect reprise
SARAH 617CD / Jan '94 / Sarah

Orchis

☐ 4000 WINTERS
Horsemen / Blood of bone / Blackwaterside / Hare / Jennet / Gallows man / Arcadia / Horn / He walks in winter / Megaera / Winter / Risen / From the iron wood
CYT 03CD / Jan '97 / Cryptanthus

Order From Chaos

☐ AN ENDING IN FIRE
OPCD 071 / 6 Jul '98 / Osmose

☐ DAWN BRINGER
SR 9507CD / Sep '95 / Shiadarshana

☐ STILLBIRTH MACHINE/CRUSHED INFAMY
OPCD 072 / 6 Jul '98 / Osmose

Order Odonata

☐ EXPERIMENTS THAT IDENTIFY CHANGE
BFLCD 18 / 1 Sep '98 / Butterfly

☐ TECHNICAL USE OF SOUND IN MAGICK
BFLCD 19 / 1 Sep '98 / Butterfly

Ordinaires

☐ ONE
Brenda / Brenda / Dance of the coco crispies / Slow boys / Surplus / Death squad / Imelda / Bacchanal / Death variation and waltz / Kashmir
BND 7CD / May '90 / One Little Indian

Ordo Equitum Solis

☐ HECATE
EFA 112822 / May '95 / Glasnost

☐ OES
EEE 015 / Nov '93 / Musica Maxima Magnetica

☐ PARASKENIA
EEE 18 / Aug '94 / Musica Maxima Magnetica

☐ SOLSTITII TEMPORIS SENSUS
EEE 07 / Nov '93 / Zoth Ommog

O'Reagan, Brendan

☐ WIND OF CHANGE, A
LUNCD 056 / Jun '89 / Mulligan

Orealis

☐ NIGHT VISIONS
GL 1152CD / Nov '95 / Green Linnet

☐ OREALIS
L'hiver sur richelieu-miss b's dreams / Spencer the rover / Trooper and the maid / Dream angus-elgol / Highland ways / Rob roy / Jannie walker / Plaisir de la table-eibhli gheal chuiun
GLCD 1106 / Nov '92 / Green Linnet

Orefiche, Armando

☐ ARMANDO OREFICHE & HIS HAVANA CUBAN BOYS
HQCD 59 / Dec '95 / Harlequin

☐ ARMANDO OREFICHE 1951-1961
Carnaval del Uruguay / Rumba azul / La culebra / Rumba colora / Anabacoa / Mambo no.8 / Priquitin pin pon / Bolero arabe / La conga se va / Siboney / Si me pudieras queer / Paris cheri / Granada / Ame maarouf / Comparsa de los congos / Green eyes (Aquellos ojos verdes) / Rumba blanca / Quiereme mucho / Me estoy enamorado de ti / Corazon para que / Chacha la negra / Primer beso / Vamos Jose / Karabali / Marta / Pavo real / Le negra quirina
HQCD 111 / Apr '98 / Harlequin

Oregon

☐ 45TH PARALLEL
VBR 20482 / Dec '90 / Vera Bra

☐ ALWAYS, NEVER AND FOREVER
Beppo / Balahto / Renewal / Oleander / Rapid transit / When the fire burns low / Aurora / Playground in nuclear winter / Guitarra picante / Apology nicaragua / Big fat orange / Always, never and forever
VBR 20732 / Sep '91 / Vera Bra

☐ CROSSING
Queen of Sydney / Pepe Linque / Alpenbridge / Travel by day / Kronach waltz / Glidj / Amaryllis / Looking glass / Crossing
8253232 / ' / ECM

☐ ECOTOPIA
Twice around the sun / Innocente / WBAI / Zephyr / Ecotopia / Leather cats / Redial / Song of the morrow
8331202 / Oct '87 / ECM

☐ ESSENTIAL OREGON, THE
Aurora / Grazing dreams / Cry of the peacock/coral / Tide pool / Naiads / Marguerite / Canyon song / Violin / Silence of a candle / Person to person / Dust devil / Ghost beads / Sail
VCD 109 / 27 Jul '98 / Vanguard

☐ NORTHWEST PASSAGE
Take heart / Don't knock on my door / Lost in the hours / Over your shoulder / Shadows / Joyful departure / Nightfall / Under a Dorian sky / Fortune cookie / Under the mountain / L'assassino che suona / Intro / Yet to be / Northwest passage
INT 31912 / 6 Oct '97 / Intuition

☐ OREGON
Rapids / Beacon / Toast / Beside a brook / Ariana / There was no Moon that night / Skyline / Impending bloom
8117112 / Oct '83 / ECM

☐ TROIKA
Charlotte's tangle / Gekko / Prelude / Mariella / Spanish stairs / Arctic turn/Land rover / Mexico for sure / Pale sun / I said OK / Tower / Minaret / Celeste
VBR 20782 / Feb '95 / Vera Bra

O'Reilly, Marie

☐ IRISH TREASURES AND ORIGINALS VOL.2
CIC 083CD / Nov '93 / Clo lar-Chonnachta

O'Reilly, Melanie

☐ SEA KINGDOM, THE
CMBCD 015 / May '96 / Cross Border Media

☐ TIR NA MARA
CBM 015CD / Jul '95 / Cross Border Media

Oreshko, Tony

☐ OFF THE CUFF (Oreshko, Tony & Ian Turner/Keith Chetwin)
RSCD 667 / Feb '98 / Raymer

Organik Mechanix

☐ DESTROY ALL RATIONAL JAZZ
ION 20062 / 6 Apr '98 / Ion

Organized Konfusion

☐ EQUINOX
Interior assain car / Don't want it / March 21 / 9x'x out of 10 / Questions / Soundamn / Move / Confrontations / Life and malice / Numbers / Shuga story / Interior car nite / Invetro / Chuck cheese / Interior Marisol's apt / Sin / Somehow someway / Epilogue / Medicine man
CDPTY 147 / 6 Oct '97 / Priority/Virgin

Orgy Of Pigs

☐ WHERE FEELINGS DIE
DOMCD 016 / Apr '95 / Dominator

O'Riada, Peadar

☐ AMIDST THESE HILLS
AHAON 053CD / Mar '98 / Bar None

☐ WINDS GENTLE WHISPER
AHAON 068CD / Mar '98 / Bar None

O'Riada, Sean

☐ MISE EIRE
CEFCD 080 / Jan '94 / Gael Linn

☐ O'RIADA
CEFCD 032 / Jan '94 / Gael Linn

☐ O'RIADA SA GAIETY
CEFCD 027 / Jan '94 / Gael Linn

☐ PLAYBOY OF THE WESTERN WORLD, THE
CEFCD 012 / Jan '91 / Gael Linn

Orichalcum

☐ ORICHALCUM AND THE DEVIANT (Orichalcum & The Deviant)
TIPCD 111 / Apr '97 / Tip

Orient Express

☐ ORIENT EXPRESS, THE
2796 / Jun '97 / Head

Oriental Brothers

☐ NWA ADA DI NMA
FLTRCD 527 / Apr '96 / Flame Tree

Orientation

☐ BOSPORUS BRIDGE
EFA 129732 / Jun '97 / Pantongue

Orientexpressen

☐ BALKANICA
Afrodites kullar / Uzni me sevdo / Trilliseste / Hora din voltine / Kucevacko kolo / Havanna club / Verbunk from Szatmar / Hora de la Goicea / Sokol mi leta visoko / Uskub / Kosmos / Regnet / Marice kolo repa/Maricas dans rovan / Bergets dans / Morgondans / Ciganski orijent / Starino stara planino / Savsat bari ve samasi / Joc din dracinti / Geamparalele / Novalukolo / Snosti si vidjach milia mamo / Shiovu/Supernova / Dennes vals
RESCD 510 / Jul '97 / Resource

☐ KARA TEN
PAN 143CD / Jan '94 / Pan

Original Danish Polcalypso Orchestra

☐ LIVE
CCRCD 97002 / May '97 / Copenhagen Calypso

Original Dixieland Jazz Band

☐ 75TH ANNIVERSARY, THE
Livery stable blues / Dixieland jazz band one-step / At the jazz band ball / Ostrich walk / Skeleton jangle / Tiger rag / Bluin' the blues / Fidgety feet / Sensation rag / Mourning blues / Clarinet marmalade / Lazy daddy / Margie Palesteena / Broadway rose / Sweet mama / Home again blues / Crazy blues / Jazz me blues / St. Louis blues / Royal garden blues / Dangerous blues / Bow wow blues
ND 90650 / May '92 / Bluebird

☐ COMPLETE ORIGINAL DIXIELAND JAZZ BAND, THE
Livery stable blues / Dixie jass band one-step / At the Jazz Band Ball / Ostrich / Skeleton jangle / Tiger rag / Bluin' the blues / Fidgety feet / Sensation rag / Mournin' blues / Clarinet marmalade / Lazy daddy / Margie / Palesteena / Broadway rose / Sweet Mama / Home again blues / Crazy blues / Jazz me blues / St. Louis blues / Royal Garden blues / Dangerous blues / Bow wow blues (My Mama treats me like a dog) / Skeeton jangle / Clarinet marmalade / Bluin' the blues / Tiger rag / Barn yard blues / Original Dixieland one-step / Bluin' the blues / Tiger rag / Ostrich walk / Original Dixieland one-step / Satanic blues / Toddlin' blues / Who loves you / Fidgety feet (War cloud)
ND 90026 / Jun '94 / Jazz Tribune

☐ DIXIELAND (Original Dixieland Stompers)
11012 / '86 / Laserlight

☐ FIRST JAZZ RECORDINGS 1917-1923
158492 / Nov '95 / Jazz Archives

☐ SENSATION
Livery stable blues / Sensation rag / Dixie jass band one-step / That teasin' rag / Tiger rag / Bluein' the blues / Fidgety feet / Clarinet marmalade / Lazy daddy / At the Jazz Band Ball / Look at 'em doing it now / Ostrich walk / Satanic blues / Lasses candy / Tell me / I've got a captain working for me now / Mammy o'mine / I've lost my heart in Dixieland / Margie / Singin' the blues
CDAJA 5023 / Oct '88 / Living Era

Original Gospel Harmonettes

☐ LOVE LIFTED ME
Is you all on the altar / I won't let go / Righteous on the march / Step by step / After a while / Camp meeting / Count your blessings / Healer / Thy will / He's so real to me / In my heart / Love lifted me / He died / Heaven is a beautiful place / You've been good to me / I must tell Jesus / Don't forget about me / Now I'm ready / Royal telephone / Hymn
CPCD 8115 / Jul '95 / Charly

Original Hi-Fi

☐ CHILI DUBS
ZD 12CD / Jun '97 / Zip Dog

Original Killing Floor

☐ ROCK THE BLUES
Woman you need love / Come home baby / Sunday morning / My mind can ride easy / Keep on walking / Lou's blues / Nobody by my side / Bedtime blues / Try to understand / Wet / Forget it / People change your mind
SEECD 355 / Sep '92 / See For Miles

Original Memphis Five

☐ ORIGINAL MEMPHIS FIVE & NAPOLEON'S EMPERORS/COTTON PICKERS (Original Memphis Five & Napoleon's Emperors/Cotton Pickers)
CBC 1049 / May '98 / Timeless

Original Mirrors

☐ HEARTBEAT (The Best Of The Original Mirrors)
Sharp words / Refelections / Boys, the boys / Flying / Chains of love / Could this be heaven / Boys cry / Night of the angels / Panic in the night / Feel like a train / Heart, twango and rawbeat / Dancing with the rebels / Teenbeat / When you're young / Things to come / Darling in London / Don't cry baby / Don't wear red / Swing together / Time has come
5325942 / Jun '96 / Mercury

Original Rockers

☐ ROCKERS TO ROCKERS
CDG 001 / Oct '93 / Different Drummer

Original Salt City Six

☐ PLAY THE CLASSICS
JCD 78 / Jul '93 / Jazzology

Original Salty Dogs Jazz Band

☐ 50TH ANNIVERSARY
BCD 44 / Dec '97 / GHB

☐ JOY JOY JOY
SOSCD 1233 / May '93 / Stomp Off

☐ ON THE RIGHT TRACK
BCD 62 / May '98 / GHB

☐ RAGTIME SPECIAL (2CD Set)
BAC 082 / Dec '97 / Bilarm

Original Sins

☐ SURBURBAN PRIMITIVE
BR 5005 / 1 Dec '97 / Blood Red Discs

Originals

☐ ANOTHER TIME, ANOTHER PLACE/ COME AWAY WITH ME
Fantasy interlude / Don't put me on / I've loved, I've lost, I've learned / Temporarily out of order / Ladies (we need you) / Take this love / It's alright / Jezebel / JEALOUS means I love you / While the cat's away / Come away with me / Stay with me / Blue moon / Thanks for your love (Happiness is you)
CDSEWD 084 / Jul '93 / Southbound

Originoo Gunn Clappaz

☐ DA STORM
Intro / Calm before da storm / No fear / Boom...boom...fucking prick / Gunn clapp / Emergency broadcast system / Hurricane starang / Danjer / Elements of da storm / Da storm / Wild cowboys in Bucktown / God don't like ugly / X-unknown / Elite fleet / Flappin'
CDPTY 140 / Nov '96 / Priority/Virgin

Orioles

☐ JUBILEE JIVE ROCKIN' WITH THE ORIOLES
I may be wrong / It ain't gonna be like that / I cross my fingers / Shrimp boats / Baby I love you so / Don't stop / I'm just a fool in love / Along about sundown / Yes indeed / There's no one but you / Hold me, squeeze me / Wanted / Don't cry baby / Happy go lucky local / Longing / Once upon a time / My baby's gonna get it / Good looking baby / So much / How blind can you be / Don't keep it to yourself / My loved one / Bring that money home / Waiting / CC rider / I miss you so / Baby please don't go / Barbara Lee
NEMCD 766 / Jun '96 / Sequel

☐ JUBILEE RECORDINGS, THE (6CD Set)
At night / Barbara Lee / It's too soon to know / Tell me so (Version 1) / I cover the waterfront / To be you / It seems so long ago / Lonely Christmas / Deacon Jones / Please give my heart a break / Tell me so (Version 2) / Dare to dream / Moonlight / Every dog-gone time / You're gone / Donkey serenade / It's a cold summer / Is my heart wasting time / I challenge your kiss / Kiss and a rose / So much / Forgive and forget / What are you doing New Year's Eve / Would you still be the one in my heart / Would you still be the one in my heart / You are my first love / If it's to be / I wonder when / Everything they said came true / I'd rather have you under the moon / We're supposed to be through / I need you so / Goodnight Irene / I cross my fingers / I cross my fingers / I can't seem to laugh anymore / Walking by the river / I miss you so / Lord's prayer / Oh holy night / I had to leave town / My prayer / I never knew / Pal of mine / Pal of mine / Happy go lucky local blues / Would I love you (Love you, love you) / Would I love you (Love you, love you) / When you're a long way from home / I'm just a fool in love / Barfly / Hold me squeeze me / Baby, please don't go / Don't tell her what happened to me / I may be wrong, but I think you're wonderful / Fool's world / You never cared for me / For all we know / Blame it on yourself / How blind can you be / When you're not around / Waiting / My loved one / Shrimp boats / Trust in me / Scandal / It's over because we're through / It ain't gonna be like that / Gettin' tired, tired, tired / Pretty, pretty rain / Why did you go / This I'll do my darling / Proud of you / No other love / Night has come / Don't stop / I promise you / My baby's gonna get it / Baby, I love you so / Once upon a time / I don't want to take a chance / Wanted / I'm beginning to think you care for me / Yes indeed / Don't keep it to yourself / I only have eyes for you / Once in a while / Good / Piccadilly / That's how I feel without you / Love birds / Don't cry baby / CC rider / Till then / Till then / Feeling Lo / Good looking baby / Along about sundown / You belong to me / Hold me, thrill me, kiss me / Teardrops on my pillow / Congratulations to someone / (Danger) Soft shoulders / Have you heard / Lonely wine / Bad little girl / Dem days (Are gone forever) / One more time / Crying in the chapel / Crying in the chapel / Don't you think I out to know / Maybe you'll be there / Drowning every hope I ever had / In the Mission of St. Augustine / (Please) Write and tell me why (Version 1) / (Please) Write and tell me why (Version 2) / Robe of Cavalry / There's no one but you / Don't go to strangers / Secret love / In the chapel in the moonlight / Thank the Lord, Thank the lord / Longing / If you believe / That's when the good Lord will smile / That's when the good Lord will smile / Runaround / Count your blessings / Fair exchange / I love you mostly / I need you baby / Moody over you / Please sing my blues tonight / Cigareetos / Sitting here / Bring the money home / Angel / Don't cry / Sure fire / Danger / Crying in the chapel / Tell me so / At night / Forgive and forget / Come on home / First of summer / Panama Joe / Night and day / Shimmy time / So long
BCD 15682 / Mar '93 / Bear Family

☐ SO MUCH FEELING
BMCD 3054 / Jul '97 / Blue Moon

Orion

☐ SOME THINK HE MIGHT BE KING ELVIS
That's alright Mama / Blue moon of Kentucky / Rockabilly rebel / See you later alligator / Suzie Q / I'm gonna be a wheel someday / Rockin' little angel / Crazy little thing called love / Long tall Sally / Memphis sun / Peggy Sue / Matchbox / There's no easy way / Baby please say yes / Born / If I can't have you / Ain't no good / Some you win, some you lose / Look me up (and lay it one me) / Old Mexico / Rainbow maker / Anybody out there / Midnight rendevous / Maybe tomorrow / She hates to be wrong / What now my love / Me and Bobby McGee
BCD 15548 / May '91 / Bear Family

Orion

☐ 1990
RSCD 218 / Feb '96 / Keltia Musique

☐ BLUE ROOM
KMRS 207CD / Feb '94 / Keltia Musique

Orionaa, Marilis

☐ CA-I
710728 / Dec '97 / La Voce

Orlando

☐ PASSIVE SOUL
Introduction / Furthest point away / Just for a second / Natures hated / On dry land / Contained / Afraid again / Happily unhappy / Don't sleep alone / Save yourself / Three letters / Here (so find me)
0630197182 / 29 Sep '97 / Blanco Y Negro

Orlando Consort

☐ EXTEMPORE (Orlando Consort & Perfect Houseplants)
Entering and leaving / Modus II / South wind / St. Martial / Quasi / Preceding / Bride / Viderunt omnes / Modus IV / Sanctus fontorum / Hearing is believing thank you / Offertorium / L'ange a la vierge / Modus III / Harmonium / Modus VI / Single tear / Hymnus
CKD 076 / 16 Mar '98 / Linn

Orlando, Johnny

☐ LET'S GIVE LOVE A TRY
ORCD 003 / Jan '96 / Orlando

Orlando, Tony

☐ KNOCK THREE TIMES (20 Greatest Hits)
Candida / Knock three times / I play and sing / Summer sand / What are you doing Sunday / Runaway / Happy together / Vaya con dios / You're a lady / Tie a yellow ribbon round the ole oak tree / Say, has anybody seen my sweet gypsy rose / Who's in the strawberry patch with Sally / Steppin' out (gonna boogie tonight) / Look in my eyes pretty woman / Love in your eyes / Up on the roof / Country / Look at / You say the sweetest things / Cupid / He don't love you (like I love you)
RMB 75085 / Jan '96 / Remember

☐ TIE A YELLOW RIBBON
Candida / Knock three times / Tie a yellow ribbon round the old oak tree / Who's in the strawberry patch with Sally / Look in my eyes pretty woman / Vaya con dios / Say has anybody seen my sweet gypsy Rose / Halfway to paradise / Bless you / You're all I need to get by / He don't love you (like I love you) / Cupid
308802 / 11 May '98 / Hallmark

Orleans, Joan

☐ AMAZING GRACE
321510 / Jul '97 / Koch International

Ornberg, Tomas

☐ THOMAS ORNBERG'S BLUE FIVE (Ornbergs, Tomas Blue Five)
OP 8003CD / Sep '91 / Opus 3

Ornicar Big Band

☐ JAZZ CARTOON
BBRC 8902 / Jun '92 / Big Blue

☐ L'INCROYABLE HUCK
BBRC 9106 / Nov '92 / Big Blue

☐ MAIS OU EST DONC ORNICAR
BBRC 9208 / Nov '92 / Big Blue

O'Rourke, Jim

☐ BAD TIMING
DC 120CD / 26 Aug '97 / Drag City

☐ HAPPY DAYS
REV 101 / 3 Nov '97 / Revenant

Orphan Newsboys

☐ LIVE AT LA
JCD 250 / Oct '93 / Jazzology

☐ ORPHAN NEWBOYS & MARTY GROSZ/PETER ECKLUND (Orphan Newsboys & Marty Grosz/Peter Ecklund)
JCD 280 / Sep '97 / Jazzology

Orphaned Land

☐ EL NORRA ALILA
HOLY 018CD / Sep '96 / Holy

☐ SAHARA
HOLY 007CD / Nov '94 / Holy

Orpheus

☐ BEST OF ORPHEUS, THE
Congress alley / Anatomy of I've never seen love like this / I've never seen love like this / Door knob / Can't find time to tell you / Can't find the time / Music machine / I'll stay with you / Never in my life / Dream / I'll fly / Just got back / Mine's yours / So far away in love / Borneo / She's not there / Love over there / Just a little bit / Walk away Renee / Roses / Magic air / Lovin' you / May I look at you / Brown arms in Houston / Me about you / I can make the sun rise / To touch our love again / By the size of my shoes / As they all fall / Joyful / Of enlightenment / I'll be there / Tomorrow man
CDWIK 2 / Aug '95 / Big Beat

Orpheus Boys Choir

☐ CHRISTMAS SONGS AND BALLADS
PDSCD 521 / 29 Sep '97 / Pulse

Orquesta Almendra

☐ MI ESCORPION 1946-1955
TCD 065 / Jul '96 / Tumbao Cuban Classics

Orquesta Aragon

☐ CHA CHA CHARANGA
TUMICD 071 / Apr '97 / Tumi

☐ LA CUBANISSIMA ORQUESTA ARAGON
CD 0015 / Mar '96 / Egrem

☐ LA INSUPERABLE
Caserita villarena / Guajira con tumbao / Charlas del momento / Para bailar lo mismo me da / Baila carola / Si sabes bailar mi son / Pare cochero / Muy junto al corazon / Que tenga sabor / Un real de hielo / Busca los lentes / Aprende muchacho
PSCCD 1001 / Feb '95 / Pure Sounds From Cuba

Orquesta Casino De La Playa

☐ ORQUESTA CASINO DE LA PLAYA
HQCD 51 / Aug '95 / Harlequin

Orquesta Cuerdas Latinas

☐ TANGOS INOLVIDABLES
A media luz / Sentimiento gaucho / El dia que me quieras / Quejas de bandoneon / Uno / Cuesta abajo / Yira yira / Mi noche triste / Volver / Cafetin de Buenos Aires / Vida mio / Confesion / Nostalgia / Jurame / Celos / El choclo
CD 12546 / May '97 / Music Of The World

Orquesta Hasta Domingo

☐ AMOR PURO
Amor puro y verdadero / Ay, mi amor / La necedad / Sediento de ti / Duende / Ya veras / Remedio no tengo / Ga met me mee / Spit spet / El compay
AL 73023 / Nov '96 / A

Orquesta Matecana

☐ QUE BUENO
RMD 812532 / 7 Apr '98 / RMM

☐ SENTIMENTAL Y SALVAJE
RMD 814952 / 7 Apr '98 / RMM

Orquesta Reve

☐ LA EXPLOSION DEL MOMENTO
Rundera (son) / La gente no se puede aguantar (changui son) / De mayo / Changui clave / Mas viejo que ayer, mas joven que manana / El palo de anon / Que te importa a ti / Espero que pase el tiempo / You no quiero que seas celosa / El ron pa despue / Que cuento es ese / Que lastima me da contigo mi amor
RWCD 4 / Jun '89 / Realworld

Orquesta Romeu

☐ BOCA LINDA
TCD 076 / Feb '97 / Tumbao

Orquesta Tipica Victor

☐ ORQUESTA TIPICA VICTOR 1926-1931
HQCD 90 / Jan '97 / Harlequin

☐ ORQUESTA TIPICA VICTOR 1926-1940
EBCD 85 / Jan '97 / El Bandoneon

Orquestra Was

☐ FOREVER'S A LONG, LONG TIME
5339152 / Mar '97 / Verve

Orr, David

☐ NEWFOUNDLAND
DOCD / May '98 / David Orr

Orta, Paulo

☐ GOOD NIGHT, BUENO NOCHE, BONNE NUIT
422493 / Nov '94 / New Rose

Ortega, Anthony

☐ ANTHONY ORTEGA ON EVIDENCE
EVCD 213 / Jan '94 / Evidence

Ortega, Fernando

☐ THIS BRIGHT HOUR
7017027612 / Oct '97 / Myrrh

Ortega, Ginesa

☐ SIENTO
HMI 987011 / May '97 / Harmonia Mundi

Orter, Hasan Cihat

☐ INSPIRATION - TURKEY (Anatolian Folk Music)
CDM 5658822 / Mar '96 / EMI Classics

Orti, Polo

☐ POLO
PSO 6966 / 1 Jun '98 / Karonte

Ortolan

☐ TRADITIONAL BRETON MUSIC
KMCD 71 / May '97 / Keltia Musique

Ortolani, Riz

☐ PORTRAIT OF A COMPOSER
74321492322 / 26 Jan '98 / Milan

Orton, Beth

☐ TRAILER PARK
She cries your name / Tangent / Don't need a reason / Live as you dream / Sugar boy / Touch me with your love / How far / Someone's daughter / I wish I never saw the sunshine / Galaxy of emptiness
HVNLP 17CD / Oct '96 / Heavenly

Ory, Kid

☐ CREOLE JAZZ BAND
Savoy blues / Good man is hard to find / Closer walk with thee / Shake that thing / Copenhagen / Royal garden blues / Mississippi mud / Roof blues / Indianaj
GTCD 12008 / Oct '93 / Good Time Jazz

☐ IN DENMARK 1959 (Ory, Kid & Red Allen)
Original dixieland one step / I wish I could shimmy like my sister Kate / Wolverine blues / St. James infirmary / Tin roof blues / Clarinet marmalade / Muskrat ramble / Do you know what it means to Miss New orleans / At the jazz band ball / Savoy blues / Indiana/Sheik of Araby / High society
STCD 6038 / Jun '98 / Storyville

☐ INTRODUCTION TO KID ORY 1922-1944, AN
4023 / Sep '95 / Best Of Jazz

☐ KID ORY 1944-1946
AMCD 19 / Jan '93 / American Music

☐ KID ORY AT THE CRYSTAL PIER 1947
AMCD 90 / Mar '97 / American Music

☐ KID ORY FAVOURITES
High society / Do what ory say / Down home rag / Careless love / Jazz me blues / Weary blues / Original dixieland one-step / Bourbon street parade / Panama / Oh, didn't he ramble / Beale street blues / Maryland, my maryland / 1919 rag / Eh la bas / Bugle call rag
FCD 60009 / May '95 / Fantasy

☐ KID ORY PLAYS THE BLUES
STCD 6035 / May '97 / Storyville

☐ KID ORY'S CREOLE JAZZ BAND (Ory, Kid Creole Jazz Band)
DOCD 1002 / Nov '96 / Document

☐ KID ORY'S CREOLE JAZZ BAND 1944-1945
Creole song / Get out of here / Blue for Jimmie Noone / South / Panama / Under the bamboo tree / Careless love / Do what Ory say / Maryland my Maryland / Down home rag / 1919 Rag / Oh didn't he ramble / Ory's creole trombone / Weary blues / Maple leaf rag / Original dixieland one-step
GTCD 12022 / Jul '94 / Good Time Jazz

☐ KID ORY'S CREOLE JAZZ BAND 1944-1946 (Ory, Kid Creole Jazz Band)
158872 / Apr '97 / Jazz Archives

☐ LEGENDARY KID, THE
Mahogany hall stomp / Sugar blues / At a georgia camp meeting / Snag it / There'll be some changes made / At the jazz band ball / Wang wang blues / By and by / Make me a pallet on the floor / Shine
GTCD 12016 / Oct '93 / Good Time Jazz

☐ THIS KID'S THE GREATEST (Ory, Kid Creole Jazz Band)
South Rampart Street Parade / Girls go crazy / How come you do me like you do / Four or five times / St. James infirmary / Bill Bailey, won't you please come home / Milneberg joys / Creole song / Bucket's got a hole in it / Creole love call / Ballin' the Jack / Aunt Hagar's blues
GTCD 12045 / Oct '93 / Good Time Jazz

O'Ryan

☐ INITIATE
No retreat no surrender / Still of the night / Whole lot of love / Believe / Emer May / Did it all for love / Something strong / Shape it up / What about love / Phoenix rises / Don't let it slip away / It must be love / Stop
PARAVP 006CD / 3 Aug '98 / Parachute Music

☐ SOMETHING STRONG
Stronger than love / Reaction / Don't let it slip away / Shaky ground / Something strong / Emer May / Blood upon a stone / Lying eyes / Deeper than the ocean
PARAVP 005CD / 10 Nov '97 / Parachute Music

Oryema, Geoffrey

☐ BEAT THE BORDER
River / Kel kweyo / Market day / Lapwony / Umoja / Gang deyo / Hard labour / Payira wind / Lajok / Nomad
CDRW 37 / Oct '93 / Realworld

☐ EXILE
Piny runa woko / Land of Anaka / Piri wango iya / Ye ye ye / Lacan woto kumu / Makambo / Jok omako nyako / Solitude / Lubanga / Exile
CDRW 14 / Sep '90 / Realworld

☐ NIGHT TO NIGHT
Sardinia memories / Medieval dream / At my window / Careless world / Miracle man / Naa dream / LPJ Christine / Dancing steps / To the Metro / Gari Moshi / Passage at dusk / Sardinia memories (early evening) / On this night / Bye Bye Lady Dame
CDRW 58 / Nov '96 / Realworld

Os Cempes

☐ OS CEMPES
DF 003CD / Aug '97 / Do Fol

Os Ingenuos

☐ CHOROS FROM BRAZIL
NI 5338 / Sep '94 / Nimbus

Os Mundi

☐ 43 MINUTEN
PMS 7070 / 26 Jan '98 / Repertoire

Osadebe, Chief Stephen Osita

☐ KEDU AMERICA
XENO 4044CD / Jun '96 / Xenophile

Osborne Brothers

☐ BLUEGRASS 1956-1968 (4CD Set)
Who done it / Ruby are you mad / My aching heart / Teardrops in my eyes / Wild mountain honey / Down in the willow garden / Ho, honey ho / Della Mae / She's no angel (is this) / My destiny once more / Two lonely hearts / Lost highway / Love pains / It hurts to know / If you don't, somebody else will / Give this message to your heart / You'll never know / I love you only / It's just the idea / Lonely, lonely me / Sweethearts again / Blame me / There's a woman behind every man / Fair and tender ladies / Each season changes you / Black sheep returned to the fold / First fall of snow / Old hickory / Old Joe Clark / Big Ben / Billy in the lowground / John Henry / Banjo boy chrimes / Walking cane / Red wing / Seeing Nellie home / Jesse James / Cumberland gap / Lost indian / Poor old cora / Five days of heaven / Ain't gonna rain no mo / Banjo boys / Send me the pillow that you dream on / Worried man blues / May you never be alone / New partner / How's the world treating you / Night train to Memphis / Mule skinner blues / White lightning / Bluegrass music's really gone to town / Lovey told me goodbye / Ballad of Jed Clampett / Memories never die / Mule train / Are you mad / Sourwood mountain / Sweet thing / Take this hammer / Don't even look at me / Cuckoo bird / Bluegrass express / Me and my old banjo / Pathway of teardrops / Gotta travel on / Salty dog blues / Kentucky / Bugle on the banjo (bugle call rag) / Cotton fields / Faded love / This heart of mine (can never say goodbye) / Charlie Cotton / I'll be alright tomorrow / Cut the cornbread / Hey hey bartender / Lonesome day / Big spike hammer / Memories / I know what it means to be lonesome / Up this hill and down / One tear / Making plans / Yesterday's gone / Footprints in the snow / Sure fire / Lonesome feeling / World of unwanted / Hard times / I'm leavin' / Kind of woman I got / One kiss away from loneliness / Let's say goodbye / Like we said hello / Someone before me / Walking the floor over you / Roll Muddy river / My favourite memory / Gal, you got a job to do / Rudy are you mad / Rocky top / When you wind down / Foggy mountain breakdown / Sisters (Billie Jean and Bonnie) / A-model / Lonesome road blues / Jessie James / Maiden's prayer / John Hardy / Little Willie / Hand me down my walking cane
BCD 15598 / Mar '95 / Bear Family

☐ BLUEGRASS 1968-1974 (4CD Set)
I'll never love another / I'll go steppin' too / Will you be lovin' another man / I'll never shed another tear / My little girl in Tenessee / Molly and Tenbrokks / Drivin' nails in my coffin / World of forgotten people / Cut the cornbread, mama / If I could count on you / I bowed on my knees and cried holy / Steal away and pray / Will you meet me over yonder / Where we'll never grow old / Medals for mother / Hide me O blest rock of ages / I pray my way out of trouble / How great thou art / What a friend we have in Jesus / Jesus sure changed me / Light at the river / That was yesterday / Working man / Banjo ringing Saturday night / Thanks for all the yesterdays / Midnight angel / Son of a sawmill man / No good sun of a gun / There'll be teardrops tonight / You win again / Blue moon of Kentucky / Where does the good times go / Put it off until tomorrow / Flyin' south / Will you visit me on Sundays / Nine pound hammer / When the grass grows over me / Tennessee hound dog / Somebody's back in town / Beneath still waters / Ruby are you mad / Siempre / Searching for yesterday / Listening to the rain / Georgia piney woods / Fightin' side of me / Let me be the first to know / Windy city / Kaw-Liga / My sweet love ain't around / You're running wild / My old Kentucky home / Tennesse stud / My heart would know / Muddy bottom / Colour me lonely / Take me home country roads / Tears are no strangers / Oh, the pain of loving you / Unfaithful one / Ballad of forty dollars / Tomorrow never comes / Sometimes you just can't win / Shelly's winter love / I wonder why you said goodbye / Tunnel of your mind / Eight more miles to Louisville / Love lifted me / Stand beside me, behind me / Miss you Mississippi / Teardrops will kiss the morning dew / Long lanky woman / Knoxville girl / Wash my face in the morning dew / Love's gonna live here / Today I started loving you again / Arkansas / Fireball mail / Midnight flyer / How long does it take (to be a stranger) / Blue heartache / Wabash cannonball / Try me one more time / Back to the country roads / Condition of Samuel Wilder's will / Tears / You're heavy on my mind / Checkin' her over / Lizzie Lou / Side saddle / High on a hill top / Sleep ridin' / Walk softly on the bridges / 7th of December / Fastest grass alive / Bluegrass melodies / We're holding on (to what we used to be) / Heartache looking for a home / MA special / I'm not that good at goodbye / Grandpa John / Little trouble / Born ramblin' man / Here today and gone tomorrow / El randa / In case you ever change your mind / Don't let the smokey mountains smoke get in / Summertime is past and gone / Highway headin' south
BCD 15748 / Nov '95 / Bear Family

☐ ONCE MORE VOL.1 & 2
SHCD 2203 / Jan '97 / Sugar Hill

Osborne, Jeffrey

☐ JEFFREY OSBORNE
New love / Eeny meeny / I really don't need no light / On the wings of love / Ready for your love / Who you talkin' to / You were made to love / Ain't nothin' missin' baby / Congratulations
CDMID 125 / Oct '92 / A&M

Osborne, Mary

☐ MEMORIAL, A
STCD 550 / '92 / Stash

Osborne, Mike

☐ CASE FOR THE BLUES, A
T.s. boogie / Lovesick / That's right / Mini-skirts and make up / Bottleneck blues / Spellbound / Home of the homeless / Crazy life / High heels / Foolin' with a fool / Nightmare blues / A woman never forgets
CCD 11037 / Jul '93 / Crosscut

☐ OUTBACK
FMRCD 07 / Oct '94 / Future

☐ SHAPES
FMRCD 10 / Mar '95 / Future

Osbourne, Joan

☐ EARLY RECORDINGS
Flyaway / Dreamin' about the day / His eyes are a blue million miles / Fingerprints / 4 camels / What you gonna do / Match burn twice / Billie listens / Wild world / Son of a preacher man / Get up Jack
5342352 / Nov '96 / Mercury

☐ RELISH
5266922 / Feb '96 / Mercury

Osbourne, Johnny

☐ BAD MAMA JAMA
RNCD 2059 / Jun '94 / Rhino

☐ DANCING TIME
LG 21099 / May '94 / Lagoon

☐ MR. BUDDY BYE
VPCD 1446 / Nov '95 / VP

☐ NIGHTFALL
DRSLSCD 2 / 20 Jul '98 / Diamond Range

☐ NIGHTFALL SHOWCASE
MRCD 1008 / Nov '97 / Majestic Reggae

☐ ROUGHER THAN THEM
VYDCD 08 / Sep '95 / Vine Yard

☐ SEXY THING
Groovin' / Yo yo / Sexy thing (version maxi) / What have got to do with it / Kill a sound tonight / Cool down / People get ready / Banana boat song (day-o) / Come a little bit closer / Back out / Groovy king of love / Sexy thing (instrumental)
LG 21092 / Apr '94 / Lagoon

☐ SINGS ROOTS AND CULTURE (2CD Set) (Osbourne, Johnny/Bobby Melody)
Bring the sensie come: *Osbourne, Johnny* / Rub a dub session: *Osbourne, Johnny* / Bad ma ma jamma: *Osbourne, Johnny* / Can't buy my love: *Osbourne, Johnny* / Never ending love: *Osbourne, Johnny* / Let him go: *Osbourne, Johnny* / Going your way: *Osbourne, Johnny* / Looking at you: *Osbourne, Johnny* / Little girl come home: *Osbourne, Johnny* / Roots man music: *Bobby Melody* / Ram the session: *Bobby Melody* / Low the sensie man: *Bobby Melody* / Get up and dance: *Bobby Melody* / Come home: *Bobby Melody* / Carol say she love me: *Bobby Melody* / Your mine: *Bobby Melody* / Rock it a ready: *Bobby Melody* / Too fussy fussy: *Bobby Melody*
MRCD 5 / Aug '97 / Midnight Rock

☐ TRUTHS AND RIGHTS
CDHB 3513 / Jul '92 / Heartbeat

Osbourne, Ozzy

☐ BARK AT THE MOON
Rock 'n' roll rebel / Bark at the moon / You're no different / Now you see it, now you don't / Forever / So tired / Waiting for darkness / Spiders
4816782 / Nov '95 / Epic

☐ BARK AT THE MOON/BLIZZARD OF OZ (2CD Set)
Rock 'n' roll rebel / Bark at the moon / You're no different / Now you see it (now you don't) / Forever / So tired / Waiting for darkness / Spiders / I don't know / Crazy train / Goodbye to romance / Dee / Suicide solution / Mr. Crowley / No bone movies / Revelation (Mother Earth) / Steal away (the night)
4652112 / Oct '95 / Epic

☐ BLIZZARD OF OZ
I don't know / Crazy train / Goodbye to romance / Dee / Suicide solution / Mr. Crowley / No bone movies / Revelation (mother earth) / Steal away (the night)
4816742 / Nov '95 / Epic

☐ DIARY OF A MADMAN
Over the mountain / Flying high again / You can't kill rock and roll / Believer / Little dolls / Tonight / SATO / Diary of a madman
4816772 / Nov '95 / Epic

☐ INTERVIEW, THE
SPEEK 007 / 16 Mar '98 / Talking Music

☐ LIVE AND LOUD (2CD Set)
Intro / Paranoid / I don't want to change the world / Desire / Mr. Crowley / I don't know / Road to nowhere / Flying high again / Guitar solo / Suicide solution / Goodbye to romance / Shot in the dark / No more tears / Miracle man / Drum solo / War pigs / Bark at the moon / Mama I'm coming home / Crazy train / Black Sabbath / Changes
4816762 / Nov '95 / Epic

☐ NO MORE TEARS
Mr. Tinkertrain / I don't want to change the world / Mama I'm coming home / Desire / No more tears / SIN / Hellraiser / Time after time / Zombie stomp / AVH / Road to nowhere
4816752 / 15 Jun '98 / Epic

☐ NO REST FOR THE WICKED
Miracle man / Devil's daughter (Holy war) / Crazy babies / Breakin' all the rules / Bloodbath in paradise / Fire in the sky / Tattooed dancer / Demon alcohol
4816812 / Nov '95 / Epic

☐ OZZIFIED (A Tribute To Ozzy Osbourne) (Various Artists)
TR 022CD / 22 Jun '98 / Tribute

☐ OZZMAN COMETH, THE
Black sabbath / War pigs / Goodbye to romance / Crazy train / Mr. Crowley / Over the mountain / Paranoid / Bark at the moon / Shot in the dark / Crazy babies / No more tears / Mama I'm coming home / I just want you / I don't want to change the world / Back on earth / Fairies wear boots / Beyond the wall of sleep
4872602 / 3 Nov '97 / Epic

☐ OZZMOSIS
Tomorrow / Dental / My little man / Mr. Jekyll doesn't hide / Old la / Tonight / Perry Mason / I just want you / Ghost behind my eyes / Thunder tonight / See you on the other side
4810222 / Oct '95 / Epic

☐ SPEAK OF THE DEVIL
Sympton of the universe / Snow blind / Black Sabbath / Fairies wear boots / War pigs / Wizard / Never say die / Sabbath bloody Sabbath / Iron man / Children of the grave / Paranoid
4816792 / Nov '95 / Epic

☐ TRIBUTE
I don't know / Crazy train / Believer / Mr. Crowley / Flying high again / Revelation (mother earth) / Steal away (the night) / Suicide solution / Iron man / Children of the grave / Paranoid / Goodbye to romance / No bone movies / Dee
4815162 / Nov '95 / Epic

☐ TRUST ME THE INTERVIEW
CBAK 4062 / Feb '94 / Baktabak

☐ ULTIMATE SIN
Ultimate sin / Secret loser / Never know why / Thank God for the bomb / Never / Lightning strikes / Killer of giants / Fool like you / Shot in the dark
4816802 / Nov '95 / Epic

Osby, Greg

☐ ART FORUM
Miss D'meena / Mood for thought / I didn't know about you / 2nd born to freedom / Dialectical interchange / Art forum / Don't explain / Half moon step / Perpetuity
CDP 8373192 / Aug '96 / Blue Note

☐ FURTHER ADO
Six of one / Transparency / Mentor's prose / Heard / 13th floor / Soldan / Of sound mind / Mental / Tenderly / Vixen's vance
CDP 8565432 / 13 Oct '97 / Blue Note

☐ GREG OSBY & SOUND THEATRE (Osby, Greg & Sound Theatre)
You big / Daigoro / Return to now / Shohachi bushi / Calculated risk / For real moments / Gyrhthmitoid / Knigrobade
8344112 / Mar '93 / jMT

☐ MINDGAMES
Dolemite / Mindgames / Thinking inside you / This is not a test / Excuse not / Mirror mirror / Silent attitude / Altered ego / All that matters / Chin lang
8344222 / Feb '89 / jMT

☐ SEASON OF RENEWAL
Sapphire / Enchantment / For the cause / Life's truth / Dialogue x / Season of renewal / Mischief makers / Word / Constant structure / Eye witness / Spirit hour
8434352 / Apr '90 / jMT

☐ ZERO
Sea of illusion / Interspacial affair / Minstrale / Two over one / OZthetica / Kekide / Savant cycles / Extreme behaviour / Deuce ana quota / Penetrating stare / Cencepticus in C
4937602 / 13 Jul '98 / Blue Note

Oscar, John

☐ JOHN OSCAR, EDDIE MILLER & GEORGE NOBLE (Oscar, John & Eddie Miller/George Noble)
DOCD 5191 / Oct '93 / Document

Oscar's Not Wild

☐ WINDOW IN TIME, A
ONW 1995 / May '95 / Oscar's Not Wild

O'Se, Sean

☐ IRISH HERITAGE
I know my love / Barleygrain / Down by the Tanyard side / Carrickfergus / Mister Mcgrath / Will ye go lassie / Killyburn braes / Streams of Bunclody / Little red fox / She lived beside the Anner / Bridin ban mo stor / Valley of Knockanure / Castle of Dromore / Shores of Americay
CHCD 2015 / Jun '98 / Outlet

Osha

☐ SIGN ON
08002 / 15 Jun '98 / AMP

O'Shamrock, Barney

☐ EVERGREEN ACCORDIAN
MACCD 318 / Aug '96 / Autograph

☐ FORTY SHADES OF GREEN
MACCD 204 / Aug '96 / Autograph

☐ IRISH ACCORDION, THE
Slievenamon / Old flames / Doonaree / Rose of Tralee / Rose of Mooncoin / Wild colonial boy / Irish American (medley) / How can you buy Killarney / Maggie / Fields of Athenry / Galway Bay / Molly Malone / Bunch of thyme / Danny boy / Hannigan's hooley / Banks of my own lovely Lee / When Irish eyes are smiling / Did your mother come from Ireland / Old bog road / Forty shades of green / Irish medley
PLATCD 11 / Jul '89 / Platinum

O'Shea, Steve

☐ IRISH PUB SONGS (47 Traditional Favourites)
Bould O'Donohue / Home boys home / Old woman from Wexford / Jug of punch / Brennan on the moor / Irish rover / Holy ground / Three lovely lassies / Charladies ball / Biddy Mulligan / Pride of Coombe / Harrigan / It's a long way to Tipperary / Dear ol'Donegal / Phil the fluter's ball / If you're Irish / Hannigan's hooley / Garden where the praties grow / Courtin' in the kitchen / Golden jubilee / It's a great day for the Irish / Stone outside Dan Murphy's door / Eileen O'Grady / Boys from County Armagh / Mick McGilligan's ball / Waxies dargle / Dicey Reilly / Down by the liffey side / My wild Irish rose / Nelly Kelly / Peggy O'Neill / Sweet Rosie O'Grady / Cockles and mussels / When Irish eyes are smiling / Danny Doogan's jubilee / Eileen Og / Star of CoDown / East-side west-side / Take me out to the ball game / Mary (a grand old name) / Who threw the overalls in Mrs Murphey's chowder / Boys from CoMayo / Lovely Leitrim / Homes of Donelgal / Where the three counties meet
305722 / May '97 / Hallmark

O'Shea, Tessie

☐ I'M READY, I'M WILLING
PASTCD 7078 / Sep '95 / Flapper

Osibisa

☐ AFRICAN FLIGHT
Time is right / Get up / Gumbe / Soldier boy / Jumbo / Abele / Kyrie Eleison / We gogo / Lost fisherman / Sakura
AIM 1057 / Jun '96 / Aim

☐ CELEBRATION (The Best Of Osibisa)
AIM 1036CD / Oct '93 / Aim

☐ CELEBRATION (2CD Set)
SMDCD 110 / 22 Sep '97 / Snapper

☐ HEADS
Kokoroko / Wango wango / So so mi la so / Sweet America / Ye tie wo / Che che Kule / Mentumi / Sweet sounds / Do you know
AIM 1047 / Apr '95 / Aim

☐ MONSORE
RMCCD 0203 / Aug '96 / Red Steel

☐ MOVEMENTS
Ko ko Rio ko / Pata pata / Lion's walk / Inkosi sikeleli Africa / Movements / Drums 2001 carnival / Jambo / Life / Happy feeling rhymes
INAK 8902CD / Jul '97 / In Akustik

☐ OJAH AWAKE
Coffee song / Warrior / Flying bird / Cherry field / Dance the body music / Ojah awake / Keep on trying / Hamattan / Sakabo
AIM 1056 / Jun '96 / Aim

☐ OSIBISA
Dawn / Music for Gong Gong / Ayiko Bia / Akwaaba / Oranges / Phallus C / Think about the people
AIM 1045 / Apr '95 / Aim

☐ SUNSHINE DAY (Their Greatest Hits)
Sunshine day / Do it / Right now / Time is right / Coffee song / Sakura / Gumbe / Get up / Dance the body music / Densu / Warrior / Kolomashie / Ojah awake / Sakabo / Soldier / Keep on trying
3036001122 / Jun '98 / Carlton

☐ SUPERFLY TNT
RMCCD 0196 / Aug '96 / Red Steel

☐ UNLEASHED IN INDIA
RMCCD 0200 / May '96 / Red Steel

☐ WELCOME HOME
AIM 1055 / Jun '96 / Aim

☐ WOYAYA
Beautiful seven / Y sharp / Spirits up above / Survival / Move on / Rabiatu / Woyaya
AIM 1046 / Sep '96 / Aim

Oskorri

☐ 25 - KANTU URTE
KD 453CD / May '97 / Elkar

☐ LANDALAN
KD 414CD / Nov '96 / Elkar

☐ PUB IBILTARIA VOL.1, THE (2CD Set)
KD 469/70 / Dec '97 / Elkar

Osland, Miles

☐ MY OL' KENTUCKY HOME (Osland, Miles Little Big Band)
SBCD 3015 / Jun '96 / Sea Breeze

Oslin, K.T.

☐ MY ROOTS ARE SHOWING
Silver tongue and goldplated lies / Sand mountain blues / Hold watcha got / Tear time / (I'll see you in) Cuba / My baby comes back / Pathway of teardrops / Miss the Mississippi and you / Heart needs a home / Down in the valley
7863669202 / Sep '96 / BNA

Osmium

☐ RISE UP
DMCD 1032 / Feb '92 / Demi-Monde

Osmonds

☐ VERY BEST OF THE OSMONDS
Crazy horses / Proud one / Make the world go away: *Osmond, Donny & Marie* / Love me for a reason / Young love: *Osmond, Donny* / When I fall in love: *Osmond, Donny* / Puppy love: *Osmond, Donny* / Down by the lazy river / Twelfth of never: *Osmond, Donny* / I'm leaving it (all) up to you: *Osmond, Donny & Marie* / Why: *Osmond, Donny* / One bad apple / Deep purple: *Osmond, Donny & Marie* / Too young: *Osmond, Donny* / Goin' home / Paper roses: *Osmond, Marie* / Morning side of the mountain: *Osmond, Donny & Marie* / Having a party / Let me in / I'm still gonna need you / I can't live a dream / Long haired lover from Liverpool: *Osmond, Jimmy* / Where did all the good times go: *Osmond, Donny* / Crazy horses
5270722 / Apr '96 / Polydor

Ossatura

☐ DENTRO
RERRERO 1 / Jun '98 / ReR/ Recommended

Ossian

☐ BEST OF OSSIAN, THE
St. Kilda wedding/Perrie werrie reel/Honourable Mrs. Moll's / 'S gann gunn d'irich mi chaoidh / Road to Drumleman / Sound of sleat/Aandowin' at the bow/Old reel / Will ye go to Flanders/Lord Lovat's lament / Duncan Johnstone/The duck/The curlew / Drunk at night, dry in the morning / I will set my ship in order / Rory Dall's sister's lament / Johnny Todd/Far from home / Jamie Raeburn/Broomielaw / Mrs. Stewart of Grantully/Be sud an'gille truagh/Harris danc
IRCD 023 / Mar '94 / Iona

☐ BORDERS
Troy's wedding / Biddy from sligo / Rory Dall's sisters / Lament / Chairlie, oh Chairlie / I will set my ship in order / John Macdonald's / Sandpit / Bide ye yet / 'Neath the gloamin / Star at e'en / New house in St Peter's / Ewe wi' the crookit horn / Willie Murray's
IRCD 007 / Aug '91 / Iona

☐ CARRYING STREAM, THE
Fisherrow/Noose and the ghillies / Black crags/ Barney's Balmoral/Mrs. Webster/Duke of Hamilton / Logan water/Pennan Den / Working man / Mo chaillin dileas donn / Port Lennox / Blustering home/ Flora MacDonald/David Glen's jig / Flower of France and England / Maighdeanan na Hairidh / Alick Cameron/Joe McGann's fiddle/Jenny's jig / Carrying stream
CDTRAX 127 / 1 Sep '97 / Greentrax

☐ DOVE ACROSS THE WATER
Duck / Duncan Johnstone / Curlew / Braw sailin' on the sea / Drunk at night, dry in the morning / Will ye go to Flanders / Take the beggin / Mile Marbhaisg / Dove across the water / Iona theme / March: The cunning workmen / Columbia / Iona theme (reprise)
IRCD 004 / Aug '91 / Iona

☐ LIGHT ON A DISTANT SHORE
Johnny Todd / Far from home / It was a' for our rightful king / Le chanson des livrees / Sun rises bright in France / Mrs. Stewart of Grantully / Be sud an' gille truagh / Calum Johnston's harris dance / Jamie Raeburn/Broomielaw / Light on a distant shore / Arrival / New York harbour / At work on the land / In the new world
IRCD 009 / Sep '91 / Iona

☐ OSSIAN
Corncrake / I hae a wife o'ma ain / Sitting in the stern of the boat / Ma rovin' eye / O mo dhuthaich (Oh my country) / Ossian's lament / Seventy second Highlanders' farewell to Aberdeen / Favourite dram / Ae fond kiss / Brose and butter / Monaghan jig / Jackson's bottle of brandy / Music of Spey / Let me in this ae night / Spoot O'Skerry / Willow Kishie / Simon's wart / Oidhche mhath leibh (goodnight to you)
SPRCD 1004 / Apr '97 / Springthyme

☐ SEAL SONG
Sound of sleat / Aandowin' at the bow / Old reel / To pad the road wi, me / Coilsfield house / Heilandmen cam doon the hill / Thornton jig / Aye waukin' o / Corn rigs / Lude's supper / Road to Drumleman / Fisherman's song for attracting seals / Lieutenant / Maguire walking / Floor / Mull of the mountains
IRCD 002 / Aug '91 / Iona

☐ ST. KILDA WEDDING
St Kilda wedding / Perrie werrie (reel) / Honourable Mr's Moll's reel / Give me a lass wi a lump o'land / Iomramh eadar il' a's uist / Dean cadalan samhach / Gala water David Manson / 'S gann gunn d'irich mi chaoidh / Farewell to whiskey / My love is the fair lad / Fourth bridge / Pretty peg / Braes o'strathblane / More grog coming / Tilley plump, DA / Foostra
IRCD 001 / Aug '91 / Iona

Ostanek, Walter

☐ GERMAN BEER DRINKING SONGS
HADCD 191 / Nov '95 / Javelin

Ostertag, Bob

☐ LIKE A MELODY
MVORL 1 / Jun '98 / ReR/ Recommended

☐ TWINS (Ostertag, Bob & Otomo Yoshihide)
CMDD 00030 / Jun '97 / Creative Man

Ostroushko, Peter

☐ HEART OF THE HEARTLAND
RHRCD 70 / Oct '95 / Red House

☐ PILGRIMS ON THE HEART ROAD
RHRCD 90 / Jun '97 / Red House

☐ SIUZ DUZ MUSIC
ROUC 0204 / Aug '95 / Rounder

O'Suilleabhain, Micheal

☐ BECOMING
Salve / Irish destiny-rising / Irish destiny-story / Irish destiny-anthem / Irish destiny-goodbye / Irish destiny-descent / Becoming / Letting go / So merrily dance / Irish destiny-hope / Around the house
CDVE 937 / 11 May '98 / Venture

☐ BETWEEN WORLDS
Oiche nollag/Christmas Eve / An tseangh liath/The old grey goose / An cailin deas cruite na mbo/The pretty milkmaid / Casadh na graige/The turning of the road / An mhaigdean cheansa/The gentle maiden / Fiach an mhada rua/The fox chase / Brian Boru / Idir eatarthu/Between worlds / Woodbrook / Ah, sweet dancer / Eleanor Plunkett / Heartwork / (Must be more) Crispy / River of sound / Lumen
CDVE 926 / Aug '95 / Venture

☐ MICHEAL O'SUILLEABHAIN
CEFCD 046 / Jan '92 / Gael Linn

O'Sullivan, Bernard

☐ CLARE CONCERTINAS (O'Sullivan, Bernard & Tommy McMahon)
Babes in the wood / Cooraclare polka / Clare dragoons / Sandy groves of Piedmont / Humours of Ennistymon / Old torn petticoat / Tommy People's favourite / Mount Fabus hunt / Ollie Conway's selection / Kilrush races / Clogher reel / Burren reel / Bonaparte's retreat / Bonaparte's march / Barron's jig / Jackson's jig / Miltown jig / Rodney's glory / Tommy McMahon's reel / Over the waves / Girl I left behind me / Maggie in the wood / Martin Taltry's jig / Thomas Friel's jig / Joe Cunnean's jig / Sean Ryan's hornpipe / Danganella hornpipe / Job of journeywork / Ash plant / Maid of Mount Cisco
GL 3092CD / Sep '94 / Green Linnet

O'Sullivan, Eoghan

☐ SMOKY CHIMNEY, THE (O'Sullivan, Eoghan & Gerry Harrington/Paul De Grae)
I'd rather be married than left/Glanntan frolics / Nora Chrionna/Rolling in the barrel/The torn jacket / Flowers of Limerick/Pearl O'Shaugnessy's barndances / Paddy Taylor's/The Donaghmore/ Denis Murphy's reel / Paddy Taylor's jigs / Seachain na Neantoga/Paisti Sceichin a'Rince/Aloe Vera reel / An clar bog deil / Cap and bell/Michael Relihan's/ Gorman's reel / Out of the mist/The furze in bloom/ The bells of Lismore / O'Sullivan's polka/ Callaghan's polka / Yellow wattle/Swallows in flight/ Micho Russell's jig / Temple Hill/The recent reel / Smoky chimney/The rose of Drishane / Charlie Mulvihill's/Humours of Lisheen/Tom Connor's jig
SPINCD 1001 / Sep '97 / Spin

O'Sullivan, Gilbert

☐ BY LARRY
PRKCD 25 / Mar '94 / Park

☐ EVERY SONG HAS ITS PLAY
Overture / Showbiz / Dear dream / I wish I could cry / Nothing to fear / Pretty Polly / Can't find my way home / Dishonourable profession / You don't own me/If I know you / Nobody wants to know / Young at heart (we'll always remain) / I've never been short of a smile / Showbiz (reprise) / If you commence before the start
PRKCD 30 / Jun '95 / Park

☐ GILBERT O'SULLIVAN SONG BOOK, THE (McCoy, Paul)
Alone again naturally / Get down / Matrimony / Clair / Nothing rhymed / We will / Ooh baby / At the very mention of your name / No matter how I try / Hang on to what you've got / Why oh why oh why / What's in a kiss / Ooh wakka do wakka day / Friend of mine / Permissive twit / Out of the question / Where peaceful waters flow / Can't get enough of you / I wish I could cry / Dear dream
SWBCD 214 / Apr '98 / Sound Waves

☐ I'M A WRITER NOT A FIGHTER
I'm a writer not a fighter / Friend of mine / They've only themselves to blame / Who knows, perhaps maybe / Where peaceful waters flow / Ooh baby / I have never loved you as much as I love you today / Not in a million years / If you love me like you love me / Get down
PRKCD 13 / May '94 / Park

☐ SINGER SOWING MACHINE
Heavens above / In bed by ten / Sex appeal / You better believe it / Please don't let my weakness show / I'll be the only one / Con-lab-lib / Doesn't it make you sick / Not so Great Britain / I don't care / I'm about / Break a leg / Say Ireland / End
PRKCD 41 / 1 Dec '97 / Park

☐ SOUNDS OF THE LOOP
Are you happy / Not that it bothers me / Sometimes / It's easy to see when you're blind / Having said that / Can't think straight / Best love I ever had / Divorce Irish style / Came and went / I'm not too young / I can give you / Can't think straight (Japanese version)
PRKCD 19 / Mar '93 / Park

O'Sullivan, Jerry

☐ GIFT, THE (Uilleann Pipes)
Mcgovern reel / Wendel wedding / Denis Murphy strathspey / Young Francis mooney / Mike in the wilderness / Wind chimes and nursery rhyhmes / Wayfaring stranger / Catherine mazurka / Clear blue sky / One rose / Sunderland lassies / Can you dance atobacco hill / Gavotte's bouree and gigue
SHANCD 78017 / 9 Mar '98 / Shanachie

☐ INVASION, THE
Chorus reel-ashmolean house / Robbie hannan's jigs / If ever you were mine / Larry redican's hornpipe-the green banner / Brendan begley's-donal debarra's-o'sullivan's (polkas) / Conspiracy-nuala's bonnet-the croton dam-the invasion / Colonel fraser / Sean coughlan's-gan ainm-sean coughlan's / Mary o'neill's fancy-gan ainm-gan ainm / Brendan begley's slides / O'carolan's farewell to music
GLCD 1074 / Feb '92 / Green Linnet

O'Sullivan, Maire

☐ FROM THERE TO HERE
CIC 076CD / Nov '93 / Clo Iar-Chonnachta

Oswald, John

☐ DISCOSPHERE
RERJOCD / Oct '96 / ReR/ Recommended

☐ PLEXURE
AVAN 016 / Sep '93 / Avant

Other

☐ OTHER, THE
DON 005CD / Apr '97 / Honest Don's

Other Dimensions In Music

☐ NOW
AUM 006 / 6 Jul '98 / Aum Fidelity

Other Half

☐ MR. PHARMACIST & THE LOST SINGLES
EVAB 13 / 1 Jun '98 / EVA

Other Side

☐ (DON'T LOOK BACK) BEHIND THE SHACK
Diggin' up the yard / Spying on the Devil / Cornbread / (Don't look back) behind the shack / Snake bite / Butcher / Payin' dues / Lion hunt
DSCD 001 / 23 Mar '98 / Desco

Other Two

☐ OTHER TWO AND YOU, THE
Tasty fish / Greatest thing / Selfish / Movin' on / Ninth configuration / Feel this love / Spirit level / Night voice / Innocence / Loved it (The other track)
5200282 / Nov '93 / Factory

Otherside

☐ BURN BABY BURN
JRVCD 101 / Oct '95 / Vous

Otis, Johnny

☐ GREATEST JOHNNY OTIS SHOW, THE (Various Artists)
Shake it Lucy baby: *Otis, Johnny* / Ma (he's making eyes at me): *Adams, Marie & The Three Tons Of Joy* / Willie and the hand jive: *Otis, Johnny* / Bye bye baby: *Adams, Marie* / Loop de loop: *Adams, Marie* / Can't you hear me calling: *Otis, Johnny* / Light still shines in my window: *Adams, Marie* / Hum ding a ling: *Otis, Johnny* / Well well well: *Williams, Mel* / Story untold: *Sterling, Jeannie & The Moonbeams* / All I want is your love: *Adams, Marie* / Good golly: *Otis, Johnny* / You just kissed me goodbye: *Williams, Mel* / Ring a ling: *Otis, Johnny* / Three girls named Molly doin' the hully gully: *Otis, Johnny* / Fool in love: *Adams, Marie* / Crazy country hop: *Otis, Johnny* / I'll do the same thin for you: *Lee, Marci & Johnny Otis* / What do you want to make those eyes at me for: *Adams, Marie* / Willie did the cha cha: *Otis, Johnny* / Mumblin' Mosie: *Otis, Johnny* / Let the sunshine in my life: *Otis, Johnny* / Castin' my spell: *Lee, Marci & Johnny Otis* / Telephone baby: *Lee, Marci & Johnny Otis*
CDCHD 673 / 26 Jan '98 / Ace

☐ JOHNNY OTIS SHOW/CREEPING WITH THE CATS (Otis, Johnny Show)
Midnight creeper (part 1) / Driftin' blues / Ali Baba's boogie / Let the sunshine in my life (once more) / Hey hey hey hey / Dog face (part 1) / Dog face (part 2) / Show me the way to go home / Sleepy shines butt shuffle / Organ grinder swing / Someday / Sadie / Butterball / Wa wa (part 1) / My eyes are full of tears / Turtle dove / Groove juice / Trouble on my mind / Number 69/ number 21 / Creeper returns / Stop, look and love me / Night is young (and you're so fine)
CDCHD 325 / Jul '91 / Ace

☐ LET'S LIVE IT UP
Let's rock (let's surf awhile) / Hand jive one more time / It must be love / I say I love you / She's alright / Baby I got news for you / California mash (the hash) / Darling / I'll be true / Let's live it up / That's the chance you've got to take / Hey hey song / Somebody call the station / Early in the morning blues / You better love me / Queen of the twist / Oh my soul / Wilted rose buds / I know my love is true / Cold cold heart / Bye bye baby (I'm leaving you) / Yes / In the evening
CDCHARLY 269 / Nov '92 / Charly

☐ NEW JOHNNY OTIS SHOW, THE
Drinkin' wine spo-dee-o-dee / Every beat of my heart / Jonella and Jack / What else can I do / Half steppin' woman / Why don't you do right / Big time scoop / I never felt this way before / Don't deceive me / So fine
ALCD 4726 / May '93 / Alligator

☐ ORIGINAL JOHNNY OTIS, THE
Harlem nocturne / My baby's business / Around the clock / Preston love's mansion / Boogie guitar / Little red hen / Hangover blues / New Orleans shuffle / If it's so baby / Rain in my eyes / I found out my troubles / I'm living OK / Ain't no use beggin' / You're fine but not my kind / Turkey hop part 1 / Turkey hop part 2 / Blues nocturne / Cry baby / Mistrustin' blues / Dreamin' blues / Cool and easy / Wedding boogie / Sunset to dawn / Honky tonk boogie / All nite long / Deceiving blues / Three magic words
SV 0266 / Oct '97 / Savoy Jazz

☐ OTISOLOGY
Hand jive '85 / Roll with me Henry / Let's go Johnny / I'm ready for love / I'm scared of you / Fonkitup / I can't help myself / I wanna come over / Nut pony
CDMF 095 / Jan '96 / Magnum Force

☐ SPIRIT OF THE BLACK TERRITORY BANDS, THE
ARHCD 384 / Apr '95 / Arhoolie

Otraslab

☐ OTRASLAB
AS 017CD / Mar '97 / Alley Sweeper

Ottawan

☐ GREATEST HITS
DC 869792 / Aug '96 / Disky

☐ VERY BEST OF OTTAWAN, THE
KWEST 5407 / Feb '93 / Kenwest

Ottopasuuna

☐ SUOKAASUA
TEXCD 002 / Nov '96 / Texicalli

☐ SWAMP GAS
AMF 202 / Mar '96 / Amigo

Otway, John

☐ ALL BALLS AND NO WILLY/WHERE DID I GO RIGHT
In dreams / Too much air not enough oxygen / Telex / Montreal / Baby, it's the real thing / Middle of winter / Nothing's gone / Halloween / House is burning / Mass communication / Turn off your dream / Make good music / It's a pain / Blue eyes of the belle / Best dream / What a woman / Frightened and scared / Waiting / Hurting her more / Highwayman
TMC 9605 / Apr '96 / Music Corporation

☐ COR, BABY THAT'S REALLY ME
Misty mountain / Gypsy / Murder man / Louisa on a horse / Really free / Geneve / Cheryl's going home / Beware of the flowers 'cause I'm sure they're going to get y / Baby's in the club / Best dream / Frightened and scared / DK 50/80 / Green grass of home / Turning point / Headbutts / Montreal / In dreams / Middle of winter / Jerusalem / Last of the mochicans / Racing cars (jet spotter of the track)
SBR 004CD / Oct '95 / Strike Back

☐ LIVE
In dreams / Misty mountain / Cor baby that's really free / Bluey green / Racing cars / Beware of the flowers / Josephine / Louisa on a horse / Baby it's real thing / Two little boys / Best dream / Frightened and scared / Cheryl's goin' home / House of the rising sun / Geneve
OTCD 4001 / Apr '95 / Amazing Feet

☐ OTWAY & BARRETT/DEEP AND MEANINGLESS (Otway, John & Wild Willy Barrett)
Misty mountain / Murder man / If I did / Racing cars / Louisa on a horse / Gypsy / Really free / Bluey green / Cheryl's goin' home / Trying times / Geneve / Place farm way / To anne / Beware of the flowers / Alamo / Oh my body is making me / Josephine / Schot / Riders in the sky / Running from the law / Riders in the sky / I wouldn't wish it on you / Can't complain
TMC 9302 / Jan '96 / Music Corporation

☐ TWO LITTLE BOYS
OTWAYS 1 / Sep '92 / Music Of Life

☐ UNDER THE COVERS & OVER THE TOP
I am the walrus / Woodstock / I will survive / Blockbuster / Theresa / Two little boys / Honey / Je t'aime chose savuage (i love you wild thing) / You ain't seen nothing yet / Billy don't be a hero / Space oddity
OTWAY 1CD / Oct '92 / Music Of Life

Otyg

☐ ALVEFARD
NPR 042CD / 15 Jun '98 / Napalm

Our Glassie Azoth

☐ EUTERPE SEQUENCE
CAM 011CD / 6 Jul '98 / Camera Obscura

Our Lady Peace

☐ CLUMSY
Superman's dead / Automatic flowers / Carnival / Big dumb rocket / 4AM / Shaking / Clumsy / Hello oskar / Let you down / Story of 100 aisles / Car crash
4874082 / 29 Sep '97 / Epic

Out Of Body Experience

☐ ILLEGAL STATE OF MIND, AN
VP 17 / Feb '94 / Spinefarm

Out Of Darkness

☐ CELEBRATION CLUB SESSION, THE
Walk on the water / Love to love / Worldpool / Cocaine / Valley (I'm gonna follow) / Child of the universe
PCDN 138 / Aug '93 / Plankton

Out Of My Hair

☐ DROP THE ROOF
In the groove again / Safe boy / Wide together / Drop the roof / I'd rather be / Why it doesn't snow / Mary / Gracie's social please me's / Thieves in the fanclub / That's all / Mr. Jones / Wendy / Judas flip
74321348372 / Jun '97 / RCA

Out Of Order

☐ OUT OF ORDER
VR 083CD / 17 Aug '98 / Victory

Out Of Worship

☐ OUT OF WORSHIP
SR 127 / 27 Apr '98 / Sub Rosa

Outback

☐ BAKA
Air play / Baka / An dro nevez / Other side / Hold on / On the streets / Buenaventura / Dingo go
HNCD 1357 / Apr '90 / Hannibal

☐ DANCE THE DEVIL AWAY
HNCD 1369 / Sep '91 / Hannibal

Outcast

☐ OUT OF TUNE
TPLP 74CD / Sep '96 / One Little Indian

Outcasts

☐ BLOOD AND THUNDER
ROSE 16CD / '84 / New Rose

☐ OUTCASTS PUNK SINGLES COLLECTION
You're a disease / Don't want to be no adult / Frustration / Just another teenage rebel / Love is for sops / Cops are comin' / Self conscious over you / Love you for ever / Cyborg / Magnum force / Gangland warfare / Programme love / Beating and screaming part 1 / Beating and screaming part 2 / Mania / Angel face / Gangland warfare (version 2) / Nowhere left to run / Running's over, time to pray / Ruby / Seven deadly sins / Swamp fever / 1969 / Psychotic shakedown / Blue murder
CDPUNK 62 / Sep '95 / Anagram

☐ SELF CONSCIOUS OVER YOU
Self conscious over you / Clinical love / One day / Love is for sops / You're a disease / Love you for never / Princess grew up a frog / Cyborg / School teacher / Spiteful Sue / Cops are comin' / Just another teenage rebel
DOJOCD 182 / Feb '94 / Dojo

Outer Circle

☐ OUTER CIRCLE
TNR 1101CD / 8 Jun '98 / Tooth & Nail

Outhere Brothers

☐ PARTY ALBUM
Don't stop (wiggle wiggle) / Interlude / Players get lonely / Interlude / Let's be-n-luv / Interlude / Whup it / Interlude (2) / If you wanna party / Interlude / Megamix (boom boom boom don't stop la la la hey he / La la la hey hey / On my mind / Boom boom boom / Boom boom boom
0630127812 / Dec '95 / Eternal

Outkast

☐ ATLIENS
U may die / Two dope boyz in a cadillac / Atliens / Wheelz of steel / Jazzybelle / Elevators / Ova da woods / Babylon / Wailin' / Mainstream / Decatur psalm / Millenium / ET / 13th floor/growin' old / Elevators
73008260322 / Sep '96 / Arista

☐ SOUTHERNPLAYALISTICADILLACH MUSIZ
Peaches (Intro) / Myintrotoletuknow / Ain't no thang / Welcome to Atlanta / Southernplayalisticadillacchmusiz / Call of the wild / Player's ball (Original) / Claimin' true / Club donkey ass / Funky ride / Git up, git out / Dat true / Crumblin' erb / Hootie hoo / DEEP Player's ball (Reprise) / Flim flam
73008260102 / Jul '94 / Arista

Outlaws

☐ DREAM OF THE WEST
Dream of the West / Outlaws / Husky team / Rodeo / Smoke signals / Ambush / Barbecue / Spring is near / Indian brave / Homeward bound / Western sunset / Tune for short cowboys
BGOCD 118 / Sep '91 / Beat Goes On

☐ RIDE AGAIN (Singles A's & B's)
Swingin' low / Spring is near / Ambush / Indian brave / Valley of the Sioux / Crazy drums / Last Stage West / Ku-Pow / Sioux serenade / Fort Knox / Return of the outlaws / Texan spiritual / That set the Wild West free / Hobo / Law and order / Do-da-day / Keep a knockin' / Shake with me
SEECD 303 / Oct '96 / See For Miles

Outlaws

☐ GREEN GRASS AND HIGH TIDES
There goes another love song / Knoxville girl / Song for you / Waterhole / Green grass and high tides / Breaker breaker / South Carolina / Freeborn man / Prisoner / Girl from Ohio / Stick around for rock 'n' roll / Hurry sundown / Gunsmoke / You are the show / Take it any way you want it / (Ghost) riders in the sky
07822189362 / 2 Feb '98 / RCA

Outlaws

☐ 14 GREAT COUNTRY SONGS
PT 618001 / Jun '96 / Part

Outlines

☐ BLIND ALLEY
L 8909302 / Jan '90 / Danceteria

Outrage

☐ SPIT
Mr. Rightman / Faith / To you / Smoke / How bad / Key / Never make the same / Live my life / Inner strength / Eagle
4509943082 / Feb '94 / WEA

Outrageous Cherry

☐ NOTHING'S GONNA CHEER YOU UP
3G 18 / Jun '97 / Third Gear

Outrider

☐ NO WAY OUT
Mourning rain / Turn away / Life's ballad / Love is killing me / Baby get back / I've been gifted by your love / My love will never die / There's no way out / Bigger than blue
CDSGP 001 / Aug '91 / Prestige

Outside

☐ ALMOST IN
Movin' on / 11.08am / Almost hot / Ruffneck radio / If you come with me / Almost out / Positivity / Kaleidoscopic summer / Travels / Almost there / Big city / 144 brooklyn palace mansions / Elena
DOR 18CD / Dec '93 / Dorado

☐ DISCOVERIES
First discovery / Sketchbook of a voyage / Moon after the fall / Parallel universe / Piano-scape / Finding ALH840001,65 / From here to infinity / Return
DOR 60CD / Jun '97 / Dorado

☐ ROUGH AND THE SMOOTH
DOR 43CD / Jul '95 / Dorado

☐ SUSPICIOUS
To fly as fast as thought / Black man and the Jew / Transmigration / Incient Itation / Don't know who I am / Resist / Overstanding / Revelation / Elements
DORO 69CD / 29 Jun '98 / Dorado

Outsiders

☐ RIPPED SHIRT
PLAN 004CD / Mar '94 / Planet

Outsiders

☐ CQ SESSIONS
CDP 1010DD / Jun '97 / Pseudonym

☐ OUTSIDERS, THE
CDP 1021DD / 22 Jun '98 / Pseudonym

Outskirts Of Infinity

☐ INCIDENT AT PILATUS
DSKCD 002 / Aug '94 / Dark Skies

☐ STONE CRAZY
CDINF 002 / May '90 / Infinity

Oval

☐ 94 DISKONT
EFA 006632 / May '95 / Mille Plateau

☐ DISKONT
THRILL 036CD / Dec '96 / Thrill Jockey

☐ OVAL AND CHRISTOPHE CHARLES DOK (Oval & Christophe Charles Dok)
THRILL 046CD / 26 Jan '98 / Thrill Jockey

☐ SYSTEMISCH
EFA 006592 / Nov '94 / Mille Plateau

Ovans, Tom

☐ DEAD SOUTH
Killing me / James Dean coming over the hill / 1945 / Here she comes / Folksinger / Rita, Memphis and the blues / Exile / Better off a lone / Real television / Pray for me / In the rain / Drowning man
FIENDCD 797 / Jun '97 / Demon

☐ NUCLEAR SKY
FIENDCD 783 / Jun '96 / Demon

☐ TALES FROM THE UNDERGROUND
Let it rain / Mr. Blue / Uncle Joe / Dance with me girl / Sailor / Angelou / Echoes of the fall / Lucky to be alive / Brakeman's blues / Real bono / Nine below zero / Waiting on you
SUR437CD / May '95 / Survival

Ovarian Trolley

☐ CIAO MEOW
CAR 26CD / 20 Oct '97 / Candy Ass

Overbo, Bjarne

☐ BJARNEKVAD
BK 22CD / Dec '97 / Buen

Overcast

☐ BEGGING FOR INDIFFERENCE
For indifference / Fate's design / Grifter / Forecast
EDISON 003 / 16 Feb '98 / Edison

☐ EXPECTATIONAL DILUTION
Grifter / Twodegreesbelow / Absolute threshold / As a whole / Allegiance to the flesh / Iconoclasm / Bleed into one / Diluting inertia / Faceless/Staredown / Follow
EDISON 005 / 16 Feb '98 / Edison

Overdose

☐ PROGRESS OF DECADENCE
CDFLAG 83 / Nov '94 / Under One Flag

☐ SCARS
CDMFN 213 / Nov '96 / Music For Nations

Overkill

☐ FUCK YOU AND THEN SOME
Fuck you / Rotten to the core / Hammerhead / Use your head / Electro violence / Fuck you / Hole in the sky / Evil never dies / Rotten to the core / Fatal if swallowed / Answer / Overkill
SPV 08518722 / May '97 / SPV

☐ I HEAR BLACK
Dreaming in Columbian / I hear black / World of hurt / Feed my head / Shades of grey / Spiritual void / Ghost dance / Weight of the world / Ignorance and innocence / Undying / Just like you
7567824762 / Apr '93 / Atlantic

☐ TRIUMPH OF WILL
SST 038CD / Oct '93 / SST

Overland

☐ YEAR ZERO
CRISIS 017CD / 3 Nov '97 / Crisis

Overlanders

☐ MICHELLE
REP 4095 / Aug '91 / Repertoire

Overli, Marit Haetta

☐ OHCAME
ICD 942 / Mar '96 / Idut

Overwhelming Colorfast

☐ MOONLIGHT AND CASTANETS
HED 052 / Oct '96 / Headhunter

Oviedo, Papi

☐ ENCUENTO ENTRE SONEROS
TUMICD 070 / Nov '97 / Tumi

Owada

☐ NOTHING
Hello / 1234 / Thirty thirty / New instrumental one / Short G / Feeling blue / Up and down / Short G / Not yours / Circle / 30 Seconds with the lights off / 1-1000 / Short G
PIANO 508 / 27 Oct '97 / Piano

Owen, Mark

☐ GREEN MAN
Green man / Clementine / Child / Are you with me / Naturally / Ask him to / Backpocket and me / Move on / Secondhand wonderland / My love / I am what I am / Is that what it's all about
74321435142 / Dec '96 / RCA

Owen Money

☐ MADE IN WALES
Made in Wales: Money, Owen / Keep on running: Money, Owen / Wide eyed and legless: Money, Owen / Thank you: Money, Owen / No matter what: Money, Owen / Please send me daffodils: Money, Owen / Kiss: Money, Owen / My special angel: Money, Owen / Home again: Money, Owen / Working man: Money, Owen / No matter how hard it gets: Money, Owen / Myfanwy: Money, Owen
CDWM 111 / Apr '97 / ACL

Owens, Buck

☐ BLUE LOVE
House down the block / You're for me / Down on the corner of love / Blue love / It don't show on me / Three dimension love / Why don't Mommy stay with Daddy and me / When I hold you / Country girl / I will love you always / Right after the dance / I'm gonna blow / Higher and higher and higher / Honeysuckle / Learnin' dirty tracks / Please don't take her love from me / That ain't right baby
CDSD 055 / 29 May '98 / Sundown

☐ BUCK OWENS SINGS HARLAN HOWARD
Foolin' around / Heartaches for a dime / Heartaches by the number / Let's agree to disagree / Keeper of the key / I don't believe I'll fall in love today / Pick me up on your way down / I'll catch you when you fall / Lyin' again / One you slip around with / Think it over / Keys in the mailbox / Foolin' around
CDSC 6101 / Dec '97 / Sundazed

☐ BUCK OWENS SINGS TOMMY COLLINS
If you ain't lovin' you ain't livin' / But I do / It tickles / I always get a souvenir / My last chance with you / Smooth sailin' / You gotta have a licence / High on a hill top / There'll be no other / Whatcha gonna do / No love have I / Down down down
CDSC 6102 / Dec '97 / Sundazed

☐ BUCK OWENS STORY VOL.1 1956-1964
Down on the corner of love / It don't show on me / House down the block / Right after the dance / I know what it means / Second fiddle / Under your spell again / Above and beyond / Excuse me (I think I've got a heartache) / Foolin' around / Under the influence of love / Mental cruelty / Loose talk / Nobody's fool but yours / Save the last dance for me / Kickin' our hearts around / You're for me / Act naturally / Love's gonna live here / My heart skips a beat / Close up the honky tonks / Hello trouble
PRS 23017 / Feb '95 / Personality

☐ BUCK OWENS STORY VOL.2 1964-1968
PRS 23018 / Feb '95 / Personality

☐ BUCK OWENS STORY VOL.3 1969-1989
PRS 23019 / May '95 / Personality

☐ IN JAPAN
Adios, farewell, goodbye, good luck, so long / I was born to be in love with you / Open up your heart / Second fiddle / Fiddle polka / Fishin' on the Mississippi / Way that I love you / Tokyo polka / Don't wipe the tears that you cry for him / Drum so low / Roll out the red carpet / We were made for each other / Closing remarks
CDSC 6103 / Dec '97 / Sundazed

☐ IT TAKES PEOPLE LIKE YOU TO MAKE PEOPLE LIKE ME
It takes people like you (to make people like me) / Way that I love you / We were made for each other / That's how I measure my love for you / If I knew / I'm gonna live it up / Where do the good times go / You left her lonely too long / Let the world keep on a turnin' / I've got it bad for you / Long, long ago / Heartbreak Mountain / It takes people like you (to make people like me) / Where do the good times go
CDSC 6105 / 17 Nov '97 / Sundazed

☐ LIVE AT CARNEGIE HALL 1966 (Owens, Buck & The Buckaroos)
Act naturally / Together again / Love's gonna live here / Medley / Medley / Waitin' in your welfare line / Buckaroo / Streets of Laredo / I've got a tiger by the tail / Fun 'n' games / Twist and shout / Medley
CMFCD 012 / Jan '93 / Country Music Foundation

☐ YOUR TENDER LOVING CARE
Your tender loving care / Song and dance / Only you (can break my heart) / What a liar I am / Someone with no one to love / Rocks in my head / Sam's place / If I had you back again / House of memories / Only you and you alone / Don't ever tell me goodbye / You made a monkey out of me / Your tender loving care / Sam's place
CDSC 6104 / Dec '97 / Sundazed

Owens, Calvin

☐ THAT'S YOUR BOOTY
CTC 203 / Mar '96 / Coast To Coast

☐ TRUE BLUE
True blue / Hot burning fever / Don't you want a man like me / Texas stomp / Sitting here / Sweet meat / Cherry red / Woke up screaming / Lick or split / Deviation / Don't you want a woman like me / Dreams come true
IMP 707 / Sep '95 / Top Cat

Owens, Jack

☐ IT MUST HAVE BEEN THE DEVIL (Owens, Jack & Bud Spires)
TCD 5016 / Mar '95 / Testament

Owens, Jay

☐ BLUES SOUL OF JAY OWENS
Come to my house / Steppin' stone / Bottom line / Chasing my dreams / Lake city, fla / Wishing well / Back row / Why do you treat me this way / Can't do the same thing again / Crosstown love / Missing you blues / My kind of woman / We're human
4509965962 / Jan '95 / WEA

Owens, Tex

☐ CATTLE CALL
Cattle call / Pride of the prairie / Dude ranch party (part 1) / Dude ranch party (part 2) / Rockin' alone in an old rocking chair / Two sweethearts / By the rushing waterfall / Give me the plains at night / Let me ride the range / Porcupine serenade / Lost indian call / Grandpa and the lovebug / Daddy's old rocking chair / I'll be happy / Lonesome for you / Red roses bring memories of you / Yesterday's roses / Lonely for you, oh so long / Cowboy call / While I'm nearly home / Don't hide your tears darling / Cattle call (theme song)
BCD 15777 / Nov '94 / Bear Family

Oxbow

☐ FUCK FEST
EFA 0440222 / 8 Jun '98 / Crippled Dick Hot Wax

☐ LET ME BE A WOMAN
EFA 127201 / Apr '95 / Crippled Dick Hot Wax

Oxford Circle

☐ LIVE AT THE AVALON
Mystic eyes / Since you've been away / You're a better man than I / Soul on fire / I got my mojo workin' / Baby please don't go / Foolish woman / Troubles / We gotta get out of this place / Today / Silent woman / Little girl / Hoochie coochie man / I'm a man / Foolish woman / Mind destruction / Raven / Troubles
CDWIKD 178 / 24 Nov '97 / Big Beat

Oxford Pro Musica Singers

☐ AMONG THE LEAVES SO GREEN
Among the leaves so green / Bushes and briars / Black sheep / Bobby Shaftoe / Dashing away / Early one morning / Greensleeves / Londonderry air / My sweetheart's like Venus / O waly, waly / She's like the swallow / Sourwood mountain / Afton water / Brigg fair / Ca' the yowes / Faithful Johnny / I love my love / Strawberry fair / Swansea Town / Keel row / Oak and the ash / Sailor and young Nancy / Three ravens / Turtle dove / Yarmouth fair
PROUCD 137 / Apr '95 / Proudsound

☐ IN THE MOOD
Ain't misbehavin' / Autumn leaves / Begin the beguine / Blue moon / Continental / Deep purple / I got rhythm / Laura / Let's do it / Over the rainbow / She was beautiful / Smoke gets in your eyes / Summertime / 'S wonderful / Tea for two / Night and day / In the mood
PROUCD 141 / May '96 / Proudsound

Oxford, Vernon

☐ KEEPER OF THE FLAME (5CD Set)
Watermelon time in Georgia / Roll big wheels roll / Woman let me sing you a song / Move to town in the fall / Nashville women / Goin' home / Let's take a cold shower / Field of flowers / Hide / Stone by stone / Behind every good man there's a woman / Forgetfulness for sale / Baby sister / Goin' home / Honky tonk girls / Babies, stop your crying / Blues come in / Treat yourself right / Little sister throw your red shoes away / Old folk's home / That's the way I talk / Touch of God's hands / Come back and see us / This woman is mine / Mansion on the hill / Wedding bells / Don't let a little thing like that / You win again / Touch of God's hands / Come back and see us / Nashville women / What will I live on tomorrow / Wine, women and songs / I'd rather see you wave goodbye / This is where I came in / What color is wind / Hazard County Saturday night / Rise of Seymour Simmons / How high does the cotton grow mama / I've got to get Peter off your mind / We came awfully close to sin / Love and Pearl and me / She's always there / I wish you would leave me alone / We sure danced us some goodn's / Woman you've got a hold of me / Soft and warm / Surprise birthday party / Shadows of my mind / Country singer / Anymore / God keeps the wild flowers blooming / Giving the pill / Beautiful junk / Mowing the lawn / Wait a little longer please Jesus / Clean your own tables / Your waiting me is gone / Don't be late / Leave me alone with the blues / One more night to spare / Only the shadows know / Redneck / Good old fashioned Saturday night honky / Midnight memories / Red hot women (and ice cold beer) / Backslider's wine / Redneck roots / Songs that losers choose / Images / Brother jukebox / Kaw-Liga / Your cheatin' heart / Hey good lookin' / When God comes and gathers his jewels / Baby we're really in love / Wedding bells / Cold cold heart / I saw the light / Settin' the woods on fire / I can't help it / You win again / Jambalaya / I'm so lonesome I could cry / Mansion on the hill / Funeral / Nobody's child / Who were Ann and Louis Adams / There's a better place / Joanna / Mommy do you think I'll get to heaven / State of depression / Woman / Maggie the baby is crying / If I had my wife to love over / I'll forgive you for the last time / If there was no country music / Cattle call / I love to sing / Walkin' my blues away / If kisses could talk / Gonna ease my worried mind / No one else is listening / Turn the record over / I think living is sweet / Blanket of stars / Great Stoneface / Rainy day / Somebody to love me / Let your light shine / Bringing Mary home / Bad moon risin' / Letters have no arms / Mother's not dead, she's only sleeping / Honky tonk troubles / Daughter of the vine / They'll never take her love from me / Angel band / Have you loved your woman today / Lonesome rainin' city / Veil of white lace / Sweeter than the flowers / Busiest memory in town / Wings of a dove / This world holds nothin' since you're gone / Family bible / Always true / Where the soul of man never dies / Lord, I've tried everything but you / Better way of life / Uncloudy day / His and hers / House of gold / Baby sister / Sad situation / Dust on the bible / Early morning rain / Last letter / You're the reason / Are they gonna make us outlaws again / Long black veil / I feel chained
BCD 15774 / Oct '95 / Bear Family

Oxley, Pete

☐ EAST COAST JOYS
Prelude / Feel free to fast forward / Sun at night / Being there / Hazelwaltz / Alchemie / Step inside love / Jutta and Ina's delightful discourse / Hercule, j'avance / Without a map / East coast joys
33JAZZ 034 / Apr '97 / 33 Jazz

Oxley, Tony

☐ ENCHANTED MESSENGER, THE (Oxley, Tony Celebration Orchestra)
1212842 / Dec '96 / Soul Note

Oxymoron

☐ PACK IS BACK, THE
KOCD 085 / Jun '97 / Knock Out

O'Yaba

☐ GAME IS NOT OVER, THE
Tomorrow nation / Fly away / Tsalane / Son be careful / Jahman / Satisfy me / Hallelujah / Rootsman story / Thube / Game is not over
SHCD 45005 / Apr '93 / Greensleeves

☐ ONE FOUNDATION
Mr. musician / Lean on me / Running away / Holala / How good is it / Armageddon / Too much traffic / Merry go round / Tell me mama / Always / One foundation
FLTRCD 523 / Feb '94 / Flame Tree

Oyewole, Abiodun

☐ 25 YEARS
When the revolution comes / 25 Years / Brothers working / Son's rising / Festival / Dread brother / Brown sugar / Sample this
RCD 10335 / Feb '96 / Black Arc

Oyster Band

☐ DEEP DARK OCEAN
Sail on by / Little brother / Only when you call / Native son / Not like Jordan / North star / Milford haven / Tory / Be my luck / No reason to cry / Drunkard's waltz
COOKCD 128 / Aug '97 / Cooking Vinyl

☐ DESERTERS
COOKCD 041 / Mar '92 / Cooking Vinyl

☐ HOLY BANDITS
When I'm up I can't get down / Road to Santiago / I look for you / Gone west / We shall come home / Cry cry / Here's to you / Moving on / Ramblin' Irishman / Fire is burning / Blood wedding
COOKCD 058 / Feb '95 / Cooking Vinyl

☐ LITTLE ROCK TO LEIPZIG
Jail song two / Gonna do what I have to do / Galopede / I fought the law / New York girls / Oxford girl / Too late now / Red barn stomp / Coal not dole / Johnny Mickey Barry's
COOKCD 032 / Apr '90 / Cooking Vinyl

☐ PEARLS FROM THE OYSTERS (2CD Set)
SMDCD 148 / 1 Jun '98 / Snapper

☐ RIDE
Too late now / Polish plain / Heaven to Calcutta / Tincans / This year, next year / New York girls / Gamblers / Take me down / Cheekbone City / Love vigilantes / My dog / Sins of a family
COOKCD 020 / Feb '95 / Cooking Vinyl

☐ SHOUTING END OF LIFE, THE
We'll be there / Blood red roses / Jam tomorrow / By northern lights / Shouting end of life / Long dark street / Our lady of the battle / Everywhere I go / Put out the lights / Voices / Don't slit your wrists / World turned upside down
COOKCD 091 / Jul '97 / Cooking Vinyl

☐ STEP OUTSIDE
Hal-an-Tow / Flatlands / Another quiet night in England / Milly Bond / Bully in the alley / Day that the ship goes down / Gaol song / Old dance / Bold Riley / Ashes to ashes
BAKECD 001 / May '90 / Cooking Vinyl
COOKCD 001 / Jun '97 / Cooking Vinyl

☐ TRAWLER
Hal-an-tow / Another quiet night in England / We could leave right now / Blood wedding / Oxford girl / Granite years / Ramblin' Irishman / Love vigilantes / Polish plain / 20th April / Lost and found / One green hill / Coal not dole / Bells of rhymney
COOKCD 078 / Oct '94 / Cooking Vinyl

☐ WIDE BLUE YONDER
Generals are born again / Pigsty Billy / Oxford girl / Following in father's footsteps / Lost and found / Coal creek mine / Rose of England / Careless life / Early days of a better nation / Lakes of Coolfin / Between the wars / Hal-an-tow / Flatlands / Another quiet night in England
COOKCD 006 / Aug '87 / Cooking Vinyl

Oz

☐ ROLL THE DICE
BMCD 11 / '92 / Black Mark

Ozark Mountain Daredevils

☐ ARCHIVE ALIVE
ACH 80007 / Jul '97 / Archive

☐ MODERN HISTORY
Everywhere she goes / Love is calling / I'm still dreaming / Turn it up / True love / Lonely knight / Over again / Heating up / River / Heart of the country / Wild the days
CDRR 303 / Jan '90 / Request

Ozkan, Talip

☐ ART OF THE TANBUR, THE
C 560042 / May '94 / Ocora

Ozone, Makoto

☐ NATURE BOYS
5312702 / Jun '96 / Verve

☐ STARLIGHT
Starlight / Riverside expressway / Night spark / 03 / I love to be face to face (Malta) / Sky / Spring stream / Chega de saudade / Moonstone / Tenderly
JD 3323 / Nov '90 / JVC

Ozric Tentacles

☐ CURIOUS CORN
SNACD 502 / 20 Oct '97 / Snapper

☐ EROLAND
DMCD 1024 / Feb '92 / Demi-Monde

☐ JURASSIC SHIFT
Sun hair / Stretchy / Feng shui / Jurassic shift / Pteranodon / Train oasis / Vita voom
SMMCD 547 / 23 Feb '98 / Snapper

☐ PUNGENT EFFULGENT
SMMCD 545 / 30 Mar '98 / Snapper

☐ STRANGEITUDE
White rhino tea / Sploosh / Saucers / Strangeitude / Bizzare bazaar / Space between your ears / Live trobbe
SMMCD 546 / 30 Mar '98 / Snapper

P

P

☐ P
I save cigarette butts / Zing splash / Michael Stipe / Oklahoma / Dancing queen / John Glenn / Mr. Officer / White man sings the blues / Die Anne / Scrapings from ring / Deal
CDPCS 7379 / Feb '96 / Capitol

P-Hux

☐ DELUXE
95022 / Jul '97 / Black Olive

P53

☐ P53
RERP53 / Jun '98 / ReR/Recommended

Paban Das Baul

☐ INNER KNOWLEDGE
Paramey param / Nodi bhora / Premer iskuley / Gour milena / Dhire dhire / Gharer karigar / Sahajey pagol / Khejur gachey hari / Mojar karkhana
WSCD 011 / Oct '97 / Womad Select

Pablo All Stars

☐ MONTREUX 1977
Cote D'Azur / Pennies from heaven / Camba de orfue / God bless the child / Sweethearts on parade
OJCCD 380 / Apr '93 / Original Jazz Classics

Pablo, Augustus

☐ AUGUSTUS PABLO PRESENTS ROCKERS INTERNATIONAL VOL.1 (Various Artists)
El Rockers: *Jah Iny* / El rockers: *Pablo, Augustus* / El Rockers: *Pablo, Augustus* / El rockers: *Rockers All Stars* / Three men in a truck back: *Williams, Delroy* / Free Jah Jah children: *Jah Bull* / Cool melody: *Pablo, Augustus* / Rastaman: *Earl 16* / Peaceful man dub: *Rockers All Stars* / Protect them: *Reid, Norris* / Give a little bit: *Te Track* / Destiny: *Pablo, Augustus* / People of the world: *Sisters Jam*
GRELCD 145 / Nov '92 / Greensleeves

☐ AUGUSTUS PABLO PRESENTS ROCKERS INTERNATIONAL VOL.2 (Various Artists)
Away with your fussing and fighting: *Delgado, Junior* / Selassi i veranda: *Jah Levi* / Zion a fe lion: *Jah Levi* / King David's melody: *Pablo, Augustus* / Cassava piece: *Pablo, Augustus* / 555 Crown Street: *Pablo, Augustus* / Solomon dub: *Pablo All Stars* / Rutland close: *Pablo All Stars* / False rasta: *Miller, Jacob* / Each one teach one: *Miller, Jacob* / Black force: *Reid, Norris* / Straight a yard: *Rockers All Stars* / Zimbian style: *Rockers All Stars* / Changing world version: *Rockers All Stars* / Changing world: *Earl 16*
GRELCD 168 / Nov '92 / Greensleeves

☐ AUTHENTIC GOLDEN MELODIES
CDRP 002 / Oct '92 / Rockers International

☐ BLOWING WITH THE WIND
Blowing with the wind / Twinkling star / Ancient harmonies / Creation blues / Zion UFO / Eastern code / Twenty one years later / First world call / This song / Drums to the king
GRELCD 149 / Sep '90 / Greensleeves

☐ DUBBING IN AFRICA
CRCD 68 / Jun '97 / Charm

☐ EAST MAN DUB
Only Jah Jah dub / Eastman dub / Look within dub / Isn't it time / It up to Jah dub / Big yard connection / African step / Original scientist / Corner stone
GRELCD 109 / '88 / Greensleeves

☐ HEALER DUB
CDRP 015 / Oct '96 / Rockers Productions

☐ HEARTICAL CHART
CDRP 004 / May '93 / Rockers Productions

☐ ITAL DUB
Big rip off / Roadblock / Curly dub / Well red / Gun trade / Shake up / Hillside airstrip / Barbwire disaster / Mr. Big / Ell's move / House raid / Shake down
TRCD 805 / Jun '95 / A&A Productions

☐ KING DAVID'S MELODY
King David's melody / Zion high / Mr. Bassie / West Abyssinia / Israel in harmony / Rockers mood / Sufferer's trod / Revelation time / Selfish youth / Corner stone dub / Kent Road
GRELCD 170 / Apr '92 / Greensleeves

☐ ONE STEP DUB
In the red dub / Hanging dub / Riot dub / One step dub / Zion way dub / Sunshine dub / Dubbing King James / Rastaman dub / Good looking dub / Night patrol dub
GRELCD 157 / Apr '96 / Greensleeves

☐ ORIGINAL ROCKERS VOL.1
Rockers dub / Up Warrikka Hill / Cassava piece / Tubby's dub song / Jah dread / Brace a boy / Thunder clap / Park Lane special / New style / AP special
GRELCD 8 / Aug '97 / Greensleeves

☐ PABLO & FRIENDS
RASCD 3220 / Nov '92 / Ras

☐ PRESENTS AUTHENTIC GOLDEN MELODIES
CDRP 003 / Nov '92 / Rockers Productions

☐ PRESENTS CULTURAL SHOWCASE
CDRP 001 / Nov '92 / Rockers Productions

☐ PRESENTS KING TUBBY
RNCD 2082 / Dec '94 / Rhino

☐ PRESENTS ROOTS DJ'S FROM THE 1970'S AND 1980'S
Take it easy / Dub / El rocker / Rocking dub / False rumour / Real rock / Zion a fe lion / Bob shuffle lion dub / Guide I Jah / Lion of Judah dub / Let Jah be praised / Braces a boy
ABB 131CD / Jun '97 / Big Cat

☐ REBEL ROCK RADIO
CDHB 34 / Aug '88 / Heartbeat

☐ RED SEA, THE
AQSCD 001 / 17 Aug '98 / Black Solidarity

☐ RISING SUN
Dub wiser / Hopi land / Rising sun / Fire red / Jah wind / Pipers of Zion / Day before the riot / African frontline / Melchesedec (the high priest) / Signs and wonders
SHCD 44009 / Jun '91 / Shanachie

☐ ROCKERS MEET KING TUBBY IN A FIRE HOUSE
SHANCD 43001 / Apr '88 / Shanachie

☐ THIS IS AUGUSTUS PABLO (Rebel Rock Reggae)
Dub organizer / Please sunrise / Point blank / Arabian roak / Pretty baby / Pablo in dub / Skateland rock / Dread eye / Too late / Assignment no.1 / Jah rock / Lover's mood
HBCD 34 / '88 / Heartbeat
ARM 2001 / 19 Jan '98 / Above Rock

☐ THRILLER
Pablo nah jester / Fat girl Jean / Marcus Garvey / Rocky road / Skibo road / Thriller / Pablo in red / Everything I own / Last of the jestering / Striker / Always dub / Cultural dub / Rough dub / Gamblin' dub / Sleng teng in dub
PRCD 605 / Sep '96 / President

☐ THRILLER VOL.2
SFCD 007 / 5 May '98 / Sprint

Pablo's Eye

☐ ALL SHE WANTS GROWS BLUE
She would stand alone / Episodic nature of life part 1 / New weather / Delay horizon / Roadsigns doorways / Adjuster / Sermon on the radio / Episodic nature of life part 2 / That night together with her / Bridge / City orange / Driving one night in the rain / Next morning / She told him the news
WM 11 / 29 Jun '98 / Swim

Pachakuti

☐ DISTANT VOICES
TEMCD 010 / 23 Mar '98 / Third Eye

Pacheco, Johnny

☐ PACHECO'S PARTY
Dile / Los compadres seguiran / La esencia del guaguanco / Latin gravy / Noche buena (Christmas eve) / Son del Callejon / Tengo uncarinito / Samrose como el guarapo / Tu barriga / El polverete / Amor en el arena / Danza del cocoye / Como cambian los tiempos / Anoranzas / Asi son bonco
CDHOT 512 / Sep '94 / Charly

Pacheco, Tom

☐ BARE BONES AND BARBED WIRE (2CD Set)
Jessica Brown / Streets of blue rain / Yellow ribbons / You will not be forgotten / Cell block one / Mining country / Hippie on a highway / Down on the promenade / Long gone / Strange gods / Your family and your friends / You again / Turnpikes truckstops / Ophelia / Just a little bullet / Robert and Ramona / Minnesota blue / Soul / Swan with a broken wing / Reverend Jake / Other side / Jesus in a leather jacket / Who was Sam McGuire / Big storm comin' / Yellow hair / Made in America / Van Gogh / Grand Canyon / Donna Marie / Last blue whale in the ocean
RGFTPDCD 040 / Jan '98 / Road Goes On Forever

☐ BLUE FIELDS
FJ 2007 / Aug '96 / Fjording

☐ EAGLE IN THE RAIN
TPCD 1 / 22 Jun '98 / Round Tower

☐ SUNFLOWERS AND SCARECROWS
Hippy on the highway / All they got is love / Strange gods / I was meant to pass through your life / If only someone said / Midnite waters of the rio grande / Swan with a broken wing / Merchant of death / Van gogh / Lost soul in the middle of nowhere / Sweet lucille / Drifting like a flower down the river / Rock 'n' roll roulette / If that's the way you want it / Is that you
RTMCD 30 / 20 Apr '98 / Round Tower

☐ TALES FROM THE RED LAKE
RTMCD 42 / Feb '93 / Round Tower

Pacher, Yves

☐ MUSIQUE BUISSONNIERE
Y 225210CD / Oct '93 / Silex

Pachinko

☐ BEHIND THE GREEN PACHINKO
VIRUS 190CD / Dec '96 / Alternative Tentacles

Pacific Jam Quartet

☐ PUT SOME JUICE ON IT
CUTUPCD 014 / 19 Jan '98 / Jump Cut

Pacou

☐ NO COMPUTER INVOLVED
EFA 292992 / 10 Aug '98 / Tresor

☐ SYMBOLIC WARFARE
EFA 292692 / Jul '97 / Tresor

Paczynski, Georges

☐ 8 YEARS OLD (Paczynski/Levinson/Jenny-Clark)
BBRC 9209 / Jan '93 / Big Blue

Padilla, Jose

☐ SOUVENIR
Orientation / I like clowns / Who do you love / Blues for Ibiza / Bosa Rosa / Colega / Alive / Train to Nottingham / Now for us / After the dance / Close to you / La Mar
5586442 / 13 Jul '98 / Manifesto

Padilla, Pedro

☐ VUELVA EN ALAS DEL PLACER (Padilla, Pedro Y Su Conjunto)
Llevame al cielo / En mi suelo Borincano / Dolores / Donde tu iras / Ay Maria / El dia que yo muera / Juramento / Triste y olvidado / La arboleda / Volver volver / Si yo tuviera un millon / Atardecer jibaro
ROUCD 5003 / Jun '97 / Rounder

Padmanabhan, Raajeswari

☐ MUSIC OF THE VEENA VOL.2
VICG 50382 / Mar '96 / JVC World Library

Padre, Miguel

☐ BRAZIL PERCUSSIONS
KAR 978 / May '96 / Kardum

Paduart, Ivan

☐ WHITE NIGHTS
Ecoline / White nights / Steps in the snow / Fairy tale / Heartsong / Between us / Guignolet kirsch / Closed eyes
AL 73061 / Nov '96 / A

Pagans

☐ LIVE ROAD KILL 1978-1989
SWIRL 024 / 20 Apr '98 / Sonic Swirl

Page & Plant

☐ NO QUARTER (Page, Jimmy & Robert Plant)
Nobody's fault but mine / Thank you / No quarter / Friends / Yallah / City don't cry / Since I've been loving you / Battle of Evermore / Wonderful one / Wah wah / That's the way / Gallows pole / Four sticks / Kashmir
5263622 / Oct '94 / Fontana

☐ WALKING INTO CLARKSDALE (Page, Jimmy & Robert Plant)
Shining in the light / When the world was young / Upon a golden horse / Blue train / Please read the letter / Most high / Heart in your hand / Walking into Clarksdale / Burning up / When I was a child / House of love / Sons of freedom
5583242
5580252 / 20 Apr '98 / Mercury

Page 12

☐ REVENGE AND MORE
Revenge and more
EFA 125342 / Dec '95 / Celtic Circle

Page, Betty

☐ DANGER GIRL
Teledrama / Killer / Mood one / Sweet and sour / Agent who / Path of crime / Sidewalk blues / Driving drums / Dark room / Johnny's dive / Big strip / Tearaway brass / Bass designs / Riviera chase / Danger girl / Ton up / Three crimes / Crime action / Something cool / Depression / Fall out / Top secret
QDKCD 012 / Oct '96 / QDK Media

☐ JUNGLE GIRL
Rumbanita / Fly by night / Jungle jazz / Dance of the insects / X cert / Let's go / Bianca blanca / Bongos bass 'n' beat / Industrial samba / Lucky mambo / Mambonanza / Man from Malibu / Man from Malibu / Moon over Rio / Roses mambo / Breaking point / Crimes / Detective theme / Jane Bond theme / Softly Sally / Swinging city / Attente / Sweet dancer / Sun girl
QDKCD 017 / 26 Jan '98 / QDK Media

☐ TRIBUTE TO BETTY PAGE (Various Artists)
CLP 99642 / Jul '97 / Cleopatra

Page, Hot Lips

☐ AMERICANS IN SWEDEN
BCD 20002 / Jun '98 / Bear

☐ CLASSICS 1929-1949
CLASSICS 4048 / Nov '97 / Classics

☐ CLASSICS 1938-1940
CLASSICS 561 / Oct '91 / Classics

☐ CLASSICS 1940-1944
CLASSICS 809 / Apr '95 / Classics

☐ CLASSICS 1944-1946
CLASSICS 950 / Nov '97 / Classics

☐ DOCTOR JAZZ VOL.6
STCD 6046 / Jul '96 / Storyville

☐ HOT LIPS PAGE
CD 14558 / Jul '94 / Jazz Portraits

☐ HOT LIPS PAGE STORY, THE
158892 / Jun '97 / Jazz Archives

Page, Jimmy

☐ BEFORE THE BALOON WENT UP (2CD Set)
DRESS 607 / 25 May '98 / Dressed To Kill

☐ MASTERS, THE
EABCD 089 / 30 Mar '98 / Eagle

☐ NO INTRODUCTION NECESSARY (Page, Jimmy & Friends)
Lovin' up a storm / Everything I do is wrong / Think it over / Boll weevil song / Livin' lovin' wreck / One long kiss / Dixie fried / Down the line / Fabulous / Breathless / Rave on / Lonely weekends / Burn up
CDTB 007 / Apr '93 / Thunderbolt

☐ OUTRIDER
Wasting my time / Wanna make love / Writes of winter / Only one / Liquid mercury / Hummingbird / Emerald eyes / Prison blues / Blues anthem
GED 24188 / Nov '96 / Geffen

☐ SESSION MAN VOL.1
Don't you dig this kinda beat / Sweet little baby / Roll over beethoven / Somebody told my girl / My baby left me / Once in a while / Money honey-that's alright / I just can't go to sleep / Certain girl-leave my kitten alone / How do you feel / Zoom, widge and wag / She just satisfies-keep movin' / Night comes down / Little by little / Surprise, surprise / Little games / Most likely you'll go your way / Dazed and confused
AIPCD 1041 / Jun '97 / AIP

☐ SESSION MAN VOL.2
Bald headed woman / See you later alligator / I can tell / Castin' my spell / Feminine look / I'll go crazy / Talkin' 'bout you / Honey hush-i like it / This sporting life / Baby I go for you / I'll come running / Is it true / I took my baby home / World keeps going round / Masters of war / You said / Train kept a rollin' / Everybody knows / Nothin' shakin' / White summer
AIPCD 1053 / Jun '97 / AIP

Page, Larry

☐ KINKY MUSIC (Page, Larry Orchestra)
Tired of waiting / Come on now / Something better beginning / You really got me / Don't ever change / Got my feet on the ground / All day and all of the night / One fine day / I go to sleep / Just can't go to sleep / Revenge / I took my baby home / Everybody's gonna be happy
MONDE 17CD / Oct '93 / Cherry Red

☐ MUSIC FOR NIGHT PEOPLE (Page, Larry Orchestra)
MCCD 246 / Jun '96 / Music Club

☐ UP, UP AND AWAY (Page, Larry Orchestra)
I say a little prayer / Les bicyclettes de Belsize / Up, up and away / Music for night people / From Larry with love / Zabadak / Light my fire / Girl on a string / We can work it out / Erotic soul / House of the rising sun / Venus / Slinky thighs / Tired of waiting for you
SUMCD 4127 / Jun '97 / Summit

Page, Patti

☐ WOULD I LOVE YOU
Now that I'm in love / Would I love you / Send my baby back to me / This is my song / Breeze / My lonely world / (How much is that) doggie in the window / I let a song go out of my heart / Whole world is singing my song / What a dream / Don't get around much anymore / Cross over the bridge / Steam heat / It's a wonderful world / I cried
JASCD 315 / May '94 / Jasmine

Page, Stu

☐ CAN'T SING THE BLUES (Page, Stu Band)
MTNCD 001 / Sep '96 / Milltown

Pahinui, Cyril

☐ 6 & 12 STRING SLACK KEY GUITAR
DCT 38010CD / Mar '96 / Dancing Cat

Pahinui, Gabby

☐ GABBY PAHINUI HAWAIIAN BAND
Alhoa ka manini / Ku 'U pua lei mokihana / Pu' uanahulu / Moani ke'ala / Blue Hawaiian moonlight / Moonlight lady / E nihi ka hele / Hawaiian love / Wahini U'I / Oli komo -chant / Ipo lei manu
EDCD 241 / Sep '91 / Edsel

Paice, Ashton, Lord

☐ BBC RADIO 1 IN CONCERT
SFRSCD 030 / Jul '97 / Strange Fruit

Paich, Marty

☐ PICASSO OF BIG BAND JAZZ, THE
From now on / Walkin' on home / Black rose / Tommy's toon / New soft shoe / What's new / Easy listnin' / Martyni time / Nice and easy
CCD 79031 / Feb '97 / Candid

Paige, Elaine

☐ CHRISTMAS
Walking in the air / Peace on Earth / Father Christmas eyes / Ave Maria / Wishing on a star / Santa Claus is coming to town / Coventry carol / Coldest night of the year / Light of the stable / I believe in Father Christmas / Thirty two feet and eight little tails / Winter's tale
2292420402 / Jul '95 / WEA

☐ CINEMA
Windmills of your mind / Out here on my own / Prisoner / Sometimes / Do you know where you're going to / Up where we belong / Unchained melody / Bright eyes / Alfie / Missing / Way we were / Rose
2292405112 / Jul '95 / WEA

☐ ELAINE PAIGE
If you don't want my love for you / Far side of the bay / So sad (to watch good love go bad) / Secrets / I want to marry you / Second time / Falling down to earth / Hot as sun / Last one to leave / How the heart approaches what it yearns / Miss my love today
2292462042 / Jul '95 / WEA

☐ ENCORE
As if we never said goodbye / Perfect year / Memories / I know him so well / Another suitcase in another hall / I don't know how to love him / On my own / I dreamed a dream / Mon dieu / Hymne a l'amour / Non je ne regrette rien / With one look / Don't cry for me Argentina
0630104762 / Nov '95 / East West

☐ FROM A DISTANCE
I only have eyes for you / From a distance / Bangkok / True colours / He's out of my life / Bohemian rhapsody / If I love you / As time goes by / Mad about the boy / Smoke gets in your eyes / September song / Oxygen / Song of a summer night / Love can do that / Well almost / Heart don't change my mind / Only the very best / Grow young
74321535792 / 24 Nov '97 / Camden

☐ LOVE CAN DO THAT
Love can do that / Oxygen / Heart don't change my mind / Same train / You don't own me / I only have eyes for you / Well almost / True colours / If I loved you / He's out of my life / Only the very best / Grow young
74321228802 / Sep '94 / RCA

☐ PERFORMANCE
I have dreamed / Anything goes / Heart don't change my mind / Another suitcase in another hall / Rose / Love hurts / What'll I do/Who / I only have eyes for you / He's out of my life / I know him so well / Don't cry for me Argentina / Memory / Memory (reprise)
74321446802 / Feb '97 / Camden

☐ PIAF
La vie en rose / La goualante du pauvre jean / Hymne a l'amour / C'est a hambourg / Les trois cloches / Mon dieu / Les amants d'un jour / La belle histoire d'amour / Je sais comment / Non, je ne regrette rien / L'accordeoniste
4509946412 / Dec '96 / WEA

☐ ROMANCE AND THE STAGE
They say it's wonderful / I got lost in his arms / As time goes by / Feeling good / More than you know / With every breath I take / Mad about the boy / I gaze in your eyes / Kismet suite / Stranger in paradise / He's in love / This is my beloved / Long before I knew you / How long has this been going on / Smoke gets in your eyes / September song / Song of a summer night
74321136152 / Sep '94 / RCA

☐ STAGES
Memory / Be on your own / Another suitcase in another hall / Send in the clowns / Running back for more / Good morning starshine / Don't cry for me Argentina / I don't know how to love him / What I did for love / One night only / Losing my mind / Tomorrow
K 2402282 / Jul '95 / WEA

Pain

☐ PAIN
NB 223CD / Jun '97 / Nuclear Blast

Pain Jerk

☐ SNAKECHARMER'S BEAUTIFUL DAUGHTER (Pain Jerk & Dogliveroil)
BWCD 1 / May '97 / Bentley Welcomes Careful Drivers

Pain Teens

☐ BEAST OF DREAMS
TR 41CD / Nov '95 / Trance

☐ DESTROY THE LOVER
TR 17CD / Jun '93 / Trance

☐ STIMULATION FESTIVAL
TR 10CD / Jul '92 / Trance

Paine Brothers

☐ HONKY HELL
ROSECD 291 / Sep '92 / New Rose

Paingod

☐ PAINGOD
CM 77163CD / Apr '97 / Century Media

Painkiller

☐ EXECUTION GROUND (3CD Set)
TZA 7317 / 15 Dec '97 / Tzadik

☐ GUTS OF A VIRGIN/BURIED SECRETS
Scud attack / Deadly obstacle collage / Damage to the mask / Guts of a virgin / Handjob / Portent / Hostage / Lathe of god / Dr Phibes / Purgatory of fiery vulvas / Warhead / Devil's eye / Tortured souls / One eyed pessary / Trailmaker / Blackhole dub / Buried secrets / Ladder / Executioner / Black chamber / Skinned / Toll
MOSH 198 / 9 Feb '98 / Earache

Painted Van

☐ RETURN OF TYRONE TIBBS, THE
DIFCD 2 / 30 Mar '98 / Different Drummer

Paintin' By Numbers

☐ BREAKBEAT SESSIONS VOL.1
343722 / Mar '96 / Koch Dance Force

Paisley Abbey Choir

☐ SINGALONG CAROLS
Hark the herald angels sing / First Noel / Ding dong merrily on high / On high / Away in a manger / See in yonder manger low / Holly and the ivy / Child in a manger / Good King Wenceslas / I saw three ships / O little town of Bethlehem / Once in Royal David's City / Unto us a boy is born / Angels from the realms of glory / Deck the halls with boughs of holly / Silent night / O come all ye faithful (adeste fidelis)
RECD 500 / Dec '97 / REL

Paisley, Bob

☐ LIVE IN HOLLAND (Paisley, Bob & The Southern Grass)
My home's across the Blue Ridge mountains / Have you lost all the love / Think of what you've done / Old Hickory cane / Margie / Lonesome valley / This and that / Dark hollow / Behind these prison walls of love / Slippin' away / Train 45 / Old love affair / Darlin' Nellie across the sea / Old, old house / Don't say goodbye if you love me
SCR 25 / Nov '97 / Strictly Country

Pajama Slave Dancers

☐ FULL METAL UNDERPANTS
ROSE 271CD / Dec '91 / New Rose

Pajeaud, Willie

☐ WILLIE PAJEAUD AND HIS BAND/KID THOMAS' DIXIELAND BAND (1955/1957) (Pajeaud, Willie & His Band/Kid Thomas' Dixieland Band)
Bucket's got a hole in it: *Pajeaud, Willie & His New Orleans Band* / Eh la blues: *Pajeaud, Willie & His New Orleans Band* / Bill Bailey: *Pajeaud, Willie & His New Orleans Band* / That's a plenty: *Pajeaud, Willie & His New Orleans Band* / Frankie and Johnny: *Pajeaud, Willie & His New Orleans Band* / Just a lucky so and so: *Pajeaud, Willie & His New Orleans Band* / Honeysuckle rose: *Pajeaud, Willie & His New Orleans Band* / Been a good woman blues: *Pajeaud, Willie & His New Orleans Band* / Old mill stream: *Valentine, 'Kid' Thomas Dixieland Band* / Ice cream: *Valentine, 'Kid' Thomas Dixieland Band* / I don't see me in your eyes anymore: *Valentine, 'Kid' Thomas Dixieland Band* / Maryland my Maryland: *Valentine, 'Kid' Thomas Dixieland Band* / Bucket's got a hole in it: *Valentine, 'Kid' Thomas Dixieland Band* / Over the waves: *Valentine, 'Kid' Thomas Dixieland Band*
504CD 31 / Mar '98 / 504

Pakeni

☐ DETERGENT BUBBLE BATH
SPV 07612692 / Aug '97 / SPV

Pakkos, Gustaf

☐ PAKKOS AND HJORT (Pakkos, Gustaf & Ole Hjort)
GCD 28 / May '96 / Grappa

Pal, Asit

☐ RHYTHMICALLY YOURS
CDJP 1038 / Jan '94 / Jazz Point

Palace

☐ ARISE THEREFORE
WIGCD 24
WIGCD 24X / Apr '96 / Domino

☐ DAYS IN THE WAKE (Palace Brothers)
DC 50CD / Dec '97 / Drag City

☐ LOST BLUES AND OTHER SONGS (Palace Music)
Ohio river boat song / Riding / Valentine's day / Trudy dies / Come in / Little blue eyes / Horses / Stable will / Untitled / O how I enjoy the light / Marriage / West palm beach / Gulf shores / (End of) travelling / Lost blues
WIGCD 033 / Apr '97 / Domino

☐ PALACE BROTHERS (Palace Brothers)
WIGCD 014 / Sep '94 / Domino

☐ THERE IS NO ONE WHAT WILL TAKE CARE OF YOU (Palace Brothers)
Idle hands are the devils playthings / Long before / I tried to stay healthy for you / Cellar song / Pulpit / There is no-one what will take care of you / O lord are you in need / Merida / King me / I had a good mother and father / Riding / O paul
ABBCD 050 / Aug '95 / Big Cat

☐ VIVA LAST BLUES (Palace Brothers)
More brother rides / Viva ultra / Brute choir / Mountain low / It's I who have left them / Work hard, play hard / New partner / Cat's blues / We all will ride / Old Jerusalem
WIGCD 021 / Aug '95 / Domino

Palace Songs

☐ HOPE
WIGCD 18 / Nov '94 / Domino

Palacio, Andy

☐ KEIMOUN
Raga puriyan kalyan
INT 31712 / Jul '97 / Intuition

Paladins

☐ LET'S BUZZ
Follow your heart / Follow your heart / Let's buzz / I don't believe / Mercy / Untamed melody / What side of the door am I on / Kiddio / Thing / Lawdy lawdy miss mary / Sneakin' around / Playgirl / I've been down before
ALCD 4782 / May '93 / Alligator

☐ MILLION MILE CLUB
Follow your heart / Everytime I see her / Lets buzz / 15 Days / Keep lovin' me / Kiddeo / Years since yesterday / Big Mary's / What side o' the door / One step
GAD 6015CD / 6 Jul '98 / 4AD

☐ PALADINS
Hold on / Make it / Honky tonk all night / Let's go / Lucky man / Lover's rock / Daddy yar / Come on home / Bad case of love / Let 'er roll / Slow down
CDWIK 64 / Apr '88 / Big Beat

☐ TICKET HOME
SECT2 10003 / Jul '94 / Sector 2

☐ YEARS SINCE YESTERDAY
Years since yesterday / Good lovin' / Going down to big mary's / Happy home / She's fine / Your new love / You and I / Don't stay out all night / Mean man / Right track
ALCD 4762 / Apr '93 / Alligator

Palata Singers

☐ SWING LOW (The 20th Anniversary)
FA 415 / Nov '96 / Fremeaux

Palatino

☐ PALATINO
Dawn / Aleas / Calabrian nights / Variazione tre / Animal love / Interlude / Truncs e petulunta / Glenn's walk / 20 Small cigars / Lulu is back in town
LBLC 6585 / Jul '96 / Label Bleu

Pale Forest

☐ LAYER ONE
VOW 065CD / 3 Aug '98 / Voices Of Wonder

Pale Fountains

☐ FROM ACROSS THE KITCHEN TABLE
Shelter / Stole the love / Jean's not happening / Bicycle thieves / Limit / Twenty seven ways to get back home / Bruised arcade / These are the things / It's only hard / From across the kitchen table / Hey / September sting
CDV 2333 / Jul '89 / Virgin

☐ PACIFIC STREET
Reach / Something on my mind / Unless / Southbound excursion / Natural / Faithful pillow (part 1) / You'll start a war / Beyond Friday's field / Abergele next time / Crazier / Faithful pillow (part 2)
CDV 2274 / Nov '89 / Virgin

Pale Saints

☐ COMFORTS OF MADNESS
Way the world is / Sea of sound / Little hammer / Deep sleep for Steven / Fell from the sun / Time thief / You tear the world in two / True coming dream / Insubstantial / Language of flowers / Sight of you
GAD 002CD / 6 Jul '98 / 4AD

☐ IN RIBBONS
Throwing back the apple / Ordeal / Thread of light / Shell / There is no day / Hunted / Hair shoes / Baby maker / Liquid / Neverending night / Featherframe / Thousand stars burst open
GAD 2004CD / 6 Jul '98 / 4AD

☐ SLOW BUILDINGS
King Fade / Angel (will you be my) / One blue hill / Henry / Under your nose / Little gestures / Song of Solomon / Fine friend / Gesture of a fear / Always I / Suggestion
GAD 4014CD / 6 Jul '98 / 4AD

Palermo, Ed

☐ BIG BAND ZAPPA (Palermo, Ed Big Band)
Peaches en regalia / Toads of the short forest / Who are the brain police/Holiday in Berlin / Twenty small cigars / King Kong / Aybe Sea/Inca roads / Waka/Jawaka/Son of Orange County / Sofa / Little house I used to love in/Mother people / Heavy duty Judy/Grand Wazoo / Finale from Carnival of the animals / We are not alone / Wai, Fn
TCD 4005 / 3 Nov '97 / Astor Place

Paley's Watch

☐ NOVEMBER
PCDN 144 / Aug '94 / Plankton

Palinckx

☐ BORDER (Live In Zurich)
INTAKTCD 043 / May '97 / Intakt

Palladinos

☐ TRAVELLING DARK
In this place here / Northern flashes / I'll keep you in mind / Rocking the black road / Down at the station / I won't be going South (for a while) / Boom town / Saturday night / In my city heart / Moon on the motorway
5402442 / May '94 / A&M

Pallas

☐ KNIGHTMOVES TO WEDGE
Stranger / Throwing stones at the wind / Win or lose / Imagination / Ratracing / Sanctuary / Just a memory / Dance through the fire
CENCD 002 / Oct '93 / Centaur

☐ SENTINEL
Shock treatment / Cut and run / Arrive alive / Rise and fall (part one) / East west / March on Atlantis / Rise and fall (part two) / Heart attack / Atlantis / Ark of infinity
CENCD 001 / Oct '93 / Centaur

Pallas, Laura

☐ BEST OF LAURA PALLAS, THE (Ski-ing In The Snow)
Ski-ing in the snow / Face from the past / Emergency / Hands off / Revenge is sweet / I go weak at the knees / Determination / Twenty twenty vision / Money can't buy (the love I give)
HTCD 58 / 20 Apr '98 / Hot Productions

Palm, Anna

☐ ARRIVING AND CAUGHT UP
Lake / Limbs / She's alive / Mumma / Air for Sharon / Masquerade / In need / Bloom / I can
PALMCD 1 / Feb '97 / Voiceprint

Palm Court Theatre Orchestra

☐ DOWN PEACOCK ALLEY
Haunting rag / Say a little prayer for me / Love for sale / Poem / Coon band contest / Charleston / Down south / Down Peacock Alley / Jealousy / Tell her at twilight / Fire flies / Fashionette / Yankyana / Savoy one step medley / Policeman's holiday / Vintage galop / La petite tonkinoise
FBCD 2007 / 17 Jun '98 / Chandos

☐ GRAND PASSIONS OF ALBERT W. KETELBEY, THE
In the moonlight / In a Persian market / Bells across the meadows / Cockney suite / Wedgewood blue / Clock and the Dresden figures / In a lovers garden suite / In a Chinese temple garden / Sanctuary of the heart / Jungle drums
FBCD 2002 / 18 Mar '98 / Flyback

☐ MUSIC FOR TEA DANCING (20 Strict Tempo Favourites)
Tea for two: *Palm Court Orchestra* / Wunderbar: *Palm Court Orchestra* / It's a lovely day today: *Palm Court Orchestra* / El choclo: *Palm Court Orchestra* / Always true to my fashion: *Palm Court Orchestra* / Getting to know you: *Palm Court Orchestra* / Why do I love you: *Palm Court Orchestra* / Can't help lovin' dat man: *Palm Court Orchestra* / Hey there: *Palm Court Orchestra* / Surrey with the fringe on top: *Palm Court Orchestra* / You'll never walk alone: *Palm Court Orchestra* / Mon amour: *Palm Court Orchestra* / You can't get a man with a gun: *Palm Court Orchestra* / Anything you can do: *Palm Court Orchestra* / Best thing for you: *Palm Court Orchestra* / Minette: *Palm Court Orchestra* / Sheik of Araby: *Palm Court Orchestra* / Kansas City: *Palm Court Orchestra* / Breeze and I: *Palm Court Orchestra* / Dinah: *Palm Court Orchestra*
306912 / Jun '97 / Hallmark

☐ PICNIC PARTY, THE
There's a ring around the Moon / Black eyes / Grasshoppers dance / Silver bird / Fiddlesticks rag / I'm forever blowing bubbles / Petite tonkinoise / Whistle for me / In the shadows / Polly / Down in Zanzibar / Ragtime bass player / Two little sausages / In a Persian market
CHAN 8437 / Mar '87 / Chandos

☐ PICNIC PARTY, THE
Grasshoppers dance / There's a ring around the moon / Black eyes / Silver birds / Fiddlesticks rag / I'm forever blowing bubbles / He'd have to get under - get out and get under / Parade of the tin soldiers / Humpty Dumpty - novelty rag / Cinderella's wedding / Rag doll - novelty foxtrot / Teddy bear's picnic / Happy frog - humorous march / Pattering feet - intermezzo two step / Dainty miss - novelette foxtrot / Whistle for me / In the shadows / Polly / Down in Zanzibar / Ragtime bass player / Two little sausages / In a Persian market
FBCD 2003 / 19 Nov '97 / Flyback

☐ PUTTIN' ON THE RITZ
Puttin' on the ritz / It must be true / Toot toot tootsie / Sheikh of Araby / Let's get friendly / Honeymoon Lane / Happy feet / Oh what a night / Roll along covered wagon / Ain't misbehavin' / She's a Latin from Manhattan / Horatio Nicholls' Californian serenade / Loving you / Tiger rag
CHAN 8703 / 17 Jun '98 / Chandos

☐ SALON TO SWING
CHAN 8856 / 17 Jun '98 / Chandos

Palm Skin Productions

☐ REMILIXIR
Condition Red / Fair seven / How the West was won / Osaka / Trouble rides a fast horse / Flipper / Introduction to falling / New love games for your monkey / Meantime / Kitty's adventures in meat / Walking through water / Beethoven Street
CDHUT 37 / Oct '96 / Hut

Palma, Triston

☐ IN DISCO STYLE ENTERTAINMENT (Palma, Triston & Jah Thomas)
MRCD 1003 / Feb '97 / Majestic Reggae

☐ TRISTON PALMA MEETS MICHAEL PALMER (2CD Set) (Palma, Triston & Michael Palmer)
Joker smoker: *Palma, Triston* / Babylon: *Palma, Triston* / Sad news: *Palma, Triston* / Peace and love in the ghetto: *Palma, Triston* / Ghetto living: *Palma, Triston* / Please stop your lying: *Palma, Triston* / Sing along: *Palma, Triston* / First time girl: *Palma, Triston* / Lover man: *Palma, Triston* / Ghetto dance: *Palmer, Michael* / Jamaica land: *Palmer, Michael* / Robbery: *Palmer, Michael* / She afe get it: *Palmer, Michael* / Cool nugh: *Palmer, Michael* / I want to dance with you: *Palmer, Michael* / Come natural: *Palmer, Michael* / Wha dis a guan: *Palmer, Michael* / Happy merry Christmas: *Palmer, Michael*
MRCD 3 / Jun '97 / Midnight Rock

Palmer, Clive

☐ MOYSHE MCSTIFF & TARTAN LANCERS OF THE SACRED HEART (COB)
E 550 / 27 Apr '98 / Elegy

Palmer, Holly

☐ HOLLY PALMER
Five little birds / Safety belt / Oxblood 2x4s / Fourteen year old moment / Come lie with me / Lickerish man / Wide open spaces / Three of us / Sal the gardener / Different languages / Scandinavian ladies
9362462812 / Sep '96 / Warner Bros.

Palmer, John

☐ BEYOND THE BRIDGE
SCD 28023 / Mar '97 / Sargasso

Palmer, Michael

☐ JOINT FAVOURITES (Palmer, Michael & Half Pint)
Crazy girl: *Half Pint* / What's going down: *Half Pint* / Tell me this tell me that: *Half Pint* / Day I can't forget: *Half Pint* / Freedom fighters: *Half Pint* / You're safe: *Palmer, Michael* / Belly lick: *Palmer, Michael* / Read your Bible: *Palmer, Michael* / I don't know why: *Palmer, Michael* / Saw you at the dance: *Palmer, Michael*
GRELCD 89 / Mar '95 / Greensleeves

Palmer, Robert

☐ ADDICTIONS VOL.1
Bad case of lovin' you (Doctor Doctor) / Pride / Addicted to love / Sweet lies / Woke up laughing / Looking for clues / Some guys have all the luck / Some like it hot / What's it take / Every kinda people / Johnny and Mary / Simply irresistable / Style kills
CID 9944 / Oct '89 / Island

☐ ADDICTIONS VOL.1/VOL.2 (2CD Set)
Bad case of lovin' you / Pride / Addicted to love / Sweet lies / Woke up laughing / Looking for clues / Some guys have all the luck / Some like it hot / What's it take / Every kinda people / Johnny and Mary / Simply irresistible / Style kills / Remember to remember / Sneakin' Sally through the alley / Maybe it's you / You are in my system / I didn't mean to turn you on / Can we still be friends / Men smart, women smarter / Too good to be true / Every kinda people / She makes my day / Best of both worlds / Give me an inch / You're gonna get what's coming / I dream of wires / Silver gun
ISDCD 2 / Nov '95 / Island

☐ ADDICTIONS VOL.2
Remember to remember / Sneakin' Sally through the alley / Maybe it's you / You are in my system / I didn't mean to turn you on / Can we still be friends / Man smart, woman smarter / Too good to be true / Every kinda people / She makes my day / Best of both worlds / Give me an inch / You're gonna get what's coming / I dream of wires / Silver gun
IMCD 246 / Mar '97 / Island

☐ CLUES
Looking for clues / Sulky girl / Johnny and Mary / What do you care / I dream of wires / Woke up laughing / Not a second time / Found you now
IMCD 21 / Jun '89 / Island

☐ DON'T EXPLAIN
Your mother should have told you / Light years / You can't get enough of a good thing / Dreams to remember / You're amazing / Mess around / Happiness / History / I'll be your baby tonight / Housework / Mercy mercy me/I want you / Don't explain / Aeroplane / People will say we're in love / Not a word / Top 40 / You're so desirable / You're my thrill
CDGOLD 1054 / Oct '96 / EMI Gold

☐ DOUBLE FUN
Every kinda people / Best of both worlds / Where can it go / Night people / Love can run faster / You overwhelm me / You really got me / Your gonna get what's coming
IMCD 23 / Jun '89 / Island

☐ HEAVY NOVA
Simply irresistable / More than ever / Change his ways / Disturbing behaviour / Early in the morning / It could happen to you / She makes my day / Between us / Casting a spell / Tell me I'm not dreaming
CDEMD 1007 / Feb '94 / EMI

☐ PRESSURE DROP
Give me an inch / Work to make it work / Back in my arms / Riverboat / Pressure drop / Here with you tonight / Trouble / Fine time / Which of us is the fool
IMCD 24 / Aug '89 / Island

☐ PRIDE
Pride / Deadline / Want you more / Dance for me / You are in my system / It's not difficult / Say you will / You can have it (take my heart) / What you waiting for / Silver gun
IMCD 22 / Jun '89 / Island

☐ RIPTIDE
Riptide / Hyperactive / Addicted to love / Trick bag / Get it through your heart / I didn't mean to turn you on / Flesh wound / Discipline of love / Riptide (reprise)
IMCD 25 / Jun '89 / Island

☐ SECRETS
Bad case of lovin' you (Doctor Doctor) / Too good to be true / Can we still be friends / In walks love again / Mean ol' world / Love stop / Jealous / Under suspicion / Woman you're wonderful / What's it take / Remember to remember
IMCD 26 / Aug '89 / Island

☐ SNEAKIN' SALLY THROUGH THE ALLEY
Sailing shoes / Hey Julia / Sneakin' Sally through the alley / Get outside / How much fun / From a whisper to a scream / Through it all there's you
IMCD 20 / Aug '89 / Island

☐ SOME PEOPLE CAN DO WHAT THEY LIKE
One last look / Keep in touch / Man smart, woman smarter / Spanish moon / Have mercy / Gotta get a grip on you (part 2) / What can you bring me / Hard head / Off the bone / Some people can do what they like
IMCD 69 / Nov '89 / Island

☐ VERY BEST OF ROBERT PALMER, THE
Addicted to love / Bad case of loving you / Simple irresistable / Get it on / Some guys have all the luck / I didn't mean to turn you on / Looking for clues / U R in my system / Some like it hot / Respect yourself / I'll be your baby tonight / Johnny and Mary / She makes my day / Know by now / Every kinda people / Mercy mercy me/I want you
CDEMD 1088 / Oct '95 / EMI

Palmer, Tom

☐ LIVING WITH THE FLAWS
TP 2CD / Aug '96 / Tap

Palmieri, Charlie

☐ MONTUNO SESSION, THE
Tema de maria cerantes / Tumba palo / Descarga charanson / 6-8 Modal latin jazz / Talking about the Danzon / Paracachero / Que no muera / Son de mi vida / Oriente
MRBCD 004 / Oct '95 / Mr. Bongo

Palmieri, Eddie

☐ PACHANGA TO JAZZ
El molestoso / Muneca / Mi mujer spiritual / Pa los congos / Bomba de corazon / Pensando en ti / La verdad / Lisa / Conga yumbambo / Buscandote
CDHOT 519 / Apr '95 / Charly

☐ PALMAS
7559616492 / Dec '94 / Nonesuch

☐ SALSA MEETS JAZZ
Vamanos pa'l monte / Prohibition de salida / Que lindo llambu / Sabroso guaguanco / Diecisiete punto uno / Azucar / Justicia / Yo no soy guapo / Cara vez que te veo / El cuarto / Noble cruise
CDHOT 511 / Sep '94 / Charly

☐ SUENO
Variations on a given theme / Azucar / Just a little dream / Covarde / Humpty Dumpty / La liberatad
INT 30082 / Apr '90 / Intuition

☐ SUENO
Variations on a given theme / Azucar / Just a little dream / Covarde / Humpty dumpty / Verdict on Judge Street / La libertad/Comparsa
INT 30112 / Sep '96 / Intuition

Palser, Barry

☐ YOU CAN'T ESCAPE (Palser, Barry Savoy Jazzmen)
RRCD 1012 / May '98 / Rose

Palusha

☐ ISOLATION
Isolation / Isolation
EV 0035CD / May '97 / Universal Language

Pameijer, Pam

☐ PAM PAMEIJER & HIS NEW JAZZ WIZARDS
SOSCD 1281 / Mar '95 / Stomp Off

☐ PLAY JELLY ROLL MORTON (Pameijer, Pam New Jazz Wizzards)
SOSCD 1318 / Feb '98 / Stomp Off

Pan

☐ OLOLY
Hangin' out for june / Taxi to sunrise / Make your wishes known / Glasters / Hove-alulu / See what you want / Fizz / Shares and shares alike / Hot on my heels / Running home / Didgerifunk
ABBCD 049 / Jun '93 / Big Cat

Pan African Orchestra

☐ OPUS 1
Wia concerto no. 1 / Yaa yaa kole / Mmenson / Explorations - high life structures / Akan drumming / Sisala sebrew / Explorations - ewe 6/8 rhythms / Box dream / Adawura kasa
CDRW 48 / Apr '95 / Realworld

Pan American

☐ PAN AMERICAN
KRANK 025CD / 2 Feb '98 / Kranky

Pan Assembly

☐ ROMANCE
CD 01C / May '97 / Carotte

☐ SO HOT SO SWEET
CD 04C / May '97 / Carotte

Pan Head

☐ TRIBUTE TO PAN HEAD
CRCD 29 / Mar '94 / Charm

Pan Pipes of the Andes

☐ FLIGHT OF THE CONDOR
PDSCD 511 / Sep '97 / Pulse

Pan Ram

☐ RATS
SPV 08460072 / Apr '96 / SPV

Pan Thy Monium

☐ KHAOOHS
OPCD 14 / Oct '93 / Osmose

Panacea

☐ LOW PROFILE DARKNESS
Low profile darkness
CHROME 9CD / Mar '97 / Chrome

☐ TWISTED DESIGNZ
EFA 813746 / 14 Apr '98 / Position Chrome

Panache Culture

☐ TRAVEL IN A DREAM
RN 0038 / Oct '95 / Runn

Panama Jazz Band

☐ ORIGINAL DIXIELAND ONE STEP
BCD 275 / Oct '92 / GHB

Panama Jazz Kings

☐ GO DUTCH 1998
RSCD 678 / Jul '98 / Raymer

Panamar Reed

☐ REMOTE SOUL MODULATION
IBCD 9 / Jul '97 / Internal Bass

Panasonic

☐ KULMA
Teurastamo / Luotain / Vapina / Puhdistus / Jakso / Murto neste / Kylma massa / Hahmo / Aines / 25 / Saato / Kurnutus / Rutina / Moottori
BFFP 132CD / Jan '97 / Blast First

☐ VAKIO
BFFP 118CD / Sep '95 / Blast First

Panatella, Slim

☐ SLIM PANATELLA & THE MELLOW VIRGINIANS (Panatella, Slim & The Mellow Virginians)
Blues for Dixie / Looking after business / Heat of the moment / Lime rock / Sweet Lorraine / Cow cow boogie / Blue skies / Miles and miles of Texas / When you say you love me / Peach pickin' time / Texas hambone blues / Stay a little longer / Fool about a cigrette / Dill pickle rag
ACS 024CD / Oct '94 / Acoustics

Panayi, Andy

☐ BLOWN AWAY (Panayi, Andy Quartet)
As catch can / Beeee / Old reliable / Asilah / Sonar / Festive minor / Minor mishap / Nicoise / Cherry / Tressillia / How long has this been going on / Blown away / Love me or leave me
JHCD 057 / 23 Feb '98 / Ronnie Scott's Jazz House

Pandera

☐ PIECE OF PARADISE, A
MNF 05382 / 15 Jun '98 / Manifold

Pandit, Korla

☐ ODYSSEY
Kartikeya / Love song of the Nile / Harem bells / Kumar / Tale of the underwater worshippers / Misirlou / Kashmiri love song / Song of India / Espana / No me quiero tanto / Festival of the flowers / Orchids in the moonlight / Estrellita / Granada / La comparsita / It happened in Monterey / Las mananitas / Besame mucho / Maria bonita / Joyful tango
FCD 24746 / Jan '97 / Fantasy

Pandoras

☐ IT'S ABOUT TIME
VOXXCD 2021 / Jan '94 / Voxx

☐ PSYCHEDELIC SLUTS
60736 / 15 Dec '97 / Erekta

☐ SPACE AMAZON
AA 064 / 24 Nov '97 / Arf Arf

Panegyris

☐ GREEK FOLK FAVOURITES (Panegyris & Dora Stratou)
TCD 1042 / Mar '97 / Tradition

Pangaea

☐ WELCOME TO THE THEATRE...
SPV 08510022CD / 8 Jun '98 / Angular

Panic

☐ EPIDEMIC
CDZORRO 24 / Jul '91 / Metal Blade

☐ FACT
Die tryin' / Close my eyes and jump / Burn one / Nonchalance / Two things (XYZ) / Hit and dragged / Rotator / Gone bad / Hell no fuck yes / Think about it
CDZORRO 60 / May '93 / Metal Blade

Panic
☐ GREMLIN GENERATION
PADCFC 001 / 19 Jan '98 / Phoenix

Pankow
☐ PANKOW
BYM 004CD / Oct '96 / Blank Your Mind

Panoply Academy Glee Club
☐ RAH
SC 19CD / 29 Jun '98 / Secretly Canadian

Pansy Division
☐ DEFLOWERED
LOOKOUT 87CD / Oct '94 / Lookout

☐ MORE LOVIN' FROM OUR OVEN
LK 175CD / 26 Sep '97 / Lookout

☐ PILE UP
DAMGOOD 60CD / Mar '95 / Damaged Goods

☐ UNDRESSED
LOOKOUT 70CD / Oct '94 / Lookout

☐ WISH I'D TAKEN PICTURES
LOOKOUT 133CD / Feb '96 / Lookout

Panta Rhei
☐ HOPA
829312 / Nov '96 / BUDA

Pantera
☐ COWBOYS FROM HELL
Cowboys from hell / Primal concrete sledge / Psycho holiday / Cemetery gates / Shattered / Medicine man / Sleep / Heresy / Domination / Clash with reality / Message in blood / Art of shredding
7567913722 / Jul '90 / Atco

☐ FAR BEYOND DRIVEN
Strength beyond strength / Becoming / Five minutes alone / I'm broken / Good friends and a bottle of Pils / Hard lines, sunken cheeks / Slaughtered / Twenty five years / Shedding skin / Use my third arm / Throes of rejection / Planet caravan
7567923022 / Mar '94 / Atco

☐ GREAT SOUTHERN TRENDKILL
Drag the waters / War nerve / It can't destroy my body / 13 steps to nowhere / Sandblasted skin / Underground in America / Suicide note part 1 / Suicide note part 2
7559619082 / May '96 / Atco

☐ OFFICIAL LIVE: 101 PROOF
New level / Walk / Becoming / 5 minutes alone / Sandblasted skin / Suicide note part 2 / War nerve / This love / Dom/Hollow / Strength beyond strength / I'm broken / Cowboys from hell / Cemetery gates / Fuckin' hostile / Where you come from / I can't hide
7559620682 / Aug '97 / East West

☐ VULGAR DISPLAY OF POWER
Mouth for war / New level / Walk / Fucking hostile / This love / Rise / No good for no one / Live in a hole / Regular people / By demons be driven / Hollow
7567917582 / Feb '92 / Atco

Pantoja, Antonio
☐ SONGS OF THE ANDES
VICG 53392 / Mar '96 / JVC World Library

Pantookas
☐ SALAD
DB 026 / Dec '97 / Dogbunny

Pants
☐ PANTS, THE
HIPCD 006 / Feb '97 / Hipster

Pantunes Music
☐ IN SEARCH OF SURFACE NOISE
SP 026 / 1 Dec '97 / Sprawl

Papa Elegua
☐ REV'E Y SU CHARANGON
CD 0078 / Mar '96 / Egrem

Papa Joe's All-Stars
☐ HOT AND HAPPY
BCD 346 / Jul '96 / GHB

Papa Ladji
☐ LES BALLET AFRICAINS
LYRCD 7419 / Aug '93 / Lyrichord

Papa Levi
☐ BACK TO BASICS
Jah rastafari selassie I / Nuff black / One night stand / Jah mi fear / Back to basics / Can't impress / Pretty she pretty / Narcotic
ARICD 103 / Apr '94 / Ariwa Sounds

☐ CODE OF PRACTICE
ARICD 060 / Sep '90 / Ariwa Sounds

Papa San
☐ DJ RULE - 3 THE HARD WAY (Papa San/Tulloch T/Double Ugly)
RNCD 2029 / Oct '93 / Rhino

☐ GI MI DI LOVING
794512 / Dec '95 / Melodie

☐ HARD ROAD
Remedy / Nah fight no religion / Hard road to travel / Believe in love / Another life / Kill anything / Good, bad and ugly / Waan hold me down / Road jungle / Freedom
119892 / Jun '97 / Musidisc UK

☐ PRAY FI DEM
RASCD 3115 / Apr '93 / Ras

☐ SISTEM, THE
PWD 7415 / Jul '93 / Pow Wow

Papa Wemba
☐ CLAN LANG LANGA - ZEA
CDS 6921 / Jan '97 / Sonodisc

☐ EMOTION
Yolele / Mandola / Show me the way / Fa fa fa fa fa (Sad song) / Rail on / Shofele / Image / Sala keba (Be careful) / Awa y' okeyi (If you go away) / Epelo / Ah ouais (Oh yes)
CDRW 52 / Mar '95 / Realworld

☐ MOLOKAI
Epelo / Awa y'okeyi / M'fono yami / Shofele / If the children cry / Image / Bakwetu / Zero / Excuse me / Esclave / Sakana
CDRW 71 / 1 Jun '98 / Realworld

☐ PAPA WEMBA
M'fono yami / Bakwetu / Analengo / Mukaji wanyi / Bokulaka / Hambayi ede / Esclave
STCD 1026 / Mar '89 / Stern's

☐ VIVA LA MUSICA 1978-1979 (Papa Wemba & Koffi Olomide)
NG 027 / Jan '97 / Ngoyarto

Papadimitriou, Sakis
☐ PIANO ORACLES
CDLR 163 / Oct '94 / Leo

☐ PLUS AND MINUS (Papadimitriou, Sakis & Lefteris Agouidakis)
CDLR 246 / Aug '97 / Leo

Papaila, Dan
☐ FULL CIRCLE
AL 73093 / Feb '98 / A

☐ POSITIVELY
Lover man / Prisms / Things ain't what they used to be / When a man loves a woman / Rush hour / Positively / That's the way of the world
CDSJP 403 / Sep '93 / Timeless Jazz

Papalote
☐ CHISELLED IN STONE
LARRCD 283 / Jun '94 / Larrikin

Papa'o
☐ BACK FROM SPACE
14999 / 5 Jan '98 / Spalax

Papa's Culture
☐ PAPA'S CULTURE BUT...
Swim / It's me / Time fekill 1 / Muffin man / Toes / Sometimes / Top 40 / Put me down / Who is) Mack daddy love / Bronze / Time fekill 2 / Fire
7559614322 / Dec '93 / Elektra

Papas Fritas
☐ HELIOSELF
MF 22 / Apr '97 / Minty Fresh

Papasov, Ivo
☐ BALKANOLOY
Miladeshki dance / Hristianova kopanitsa / Istoria na edna / Ivo's ruchenitsa / Song for Baba Nedelya / Ergenski dance / Mominsko horo / Tziganska ballada / Veseli Zborni / Proleten dance / Kasapsko horo
HNCD 1363 / May '91 / Hannibal

☐ ORPHEUS ASCENDING (Papasov, Ivo & His Bulgarian Wedding Band)
HNCD 1347 / May '89 / Hannibal

Paper Bags
☐ MUSIC TO TRASH
SST 200CD / May '93 / SST

Paperboy
☐ CITY TO CITY
NP 54992 / Jun '97 / Next Plateau

Papete
☐ BERIMBAU E PERCUSSAO (Music & Rhythms Of Brasil)
Cavalacanga / Procissao dos mortos / Domingo no parque / Ponteio / O bonde / Promessa de pescador / Agua de coco / Se num samba / A ova / Berimba / E assim que eu sou / Ponto de caboclo / Iguape / Bomba meu boi / Cachimbo / Maraca
USCD 7 / May '97 / Universal Sound

Papetti, Fausto
☐ GOLDEN YEARS
74321455922 / Nov '97 / Ricordi

Paphiti, Savvas
☐ GREEK POPULAR SONGS (Paphiti, Savvas & George Gregoriou)
EUCD 1236 / Nov '93 / ARC

Pappajohn, Lori ·
☐ CELTIC HARP FOR CHRISTMAS
RECD 522 / Dec '97 / REL

☐ CELTIC HARP OF DREAMS
Minstrel's dream / First snows of winter / Scarborough fair / What could have been/Tattyoko / All Water is wide / Stag and the hound / In spring we shall dance / Sunlight on fresh fallen snow / Seikilos song / Mountain lake / Then shall I love thee
RECD 517 / Jun '98 / REL

Papy Tex
☐ WASIWA (Papy Tex & Empire Bakuba)
CDS 7006 / Jan '97 / Sonodisc

Paquette, David
☐ OUTRAGEOUS
SACD 105 / Apr '94 / Solo Art

Paquin, Anna
☐ MAGNIFICENT NOSE, THE
74321237022 / Jul '96 / RCA

Parachute Men
☐ EARTH, DOGS AND EGGSHELLS
Mad sadie can't levitate / Mr. gas / Never alone / Don't cry jully / Miles away / Elizabeth / Earth, dogs and eggshells / Every other thursday / Yeah / Sleepless, sleepless, sleepless / Dream of kings / Fear of falling
FIRE 33024 / Oct '91 / Fire

☐ INNOCENTS, THE
Sometimes in vain / Innocents / No wonder / Tell everyone / Are you glad you came (live) / Goodbye / Past not forgotten / Maybe if I'd said / Quiet day / If I could wear your jacket... / Burgess meredith (live) / That's too bad (live)
FIRE 33014 / Oct '91 / Fire

Parachute Regiment
☐ PARAS, THE (Massed Bands Of The Parachute Regiment)
Green light / Airborne warrior / Red beret / Arnhem / Paras / Bruneval raid / Longest day / Sailing / Mount longdon / Marche des parachutist / Belges / Screaming eagles / Red devils / Aslo ran / Pomp and circumstance march No.4 / Ride of the valkyries / Delta wing / Three para songs / Songs of World War Two / American patrol / Elvis Presley, his greatest hits / Out of the sky / Echoes of an era / Space medley
BNA 5039 / '91 / Bandleader

☐ RIDE OF THE VALKYRIES (Band Of The Parachute Regiment)
Ride of the valkyries / 3Dgs / Nibelungen march / Dutch tragedy / Bridge too far / Airborne advance / Festive fanfare and interlude / Stage centre / Oregon / Going home / Dave Brubeck - a portrait in time / Beauty and the beast / Armenian dances
BNA 5126 / Jul '96 / Bandleader

Paracumbe
☐ TAMBO
ASHECD 2005 / Aug '97 / Ashe

Paradis, Vanessa
☐ VANESSA PARADIS
Natural high / Waiting for the man / Silver and gold / Be my baby / Lonely rainbows / Sunday mornings / Your love has got a handle on my mind / Future song / Paradise / Just as long as you are there / Lenny Kravitz
5139542 / Sep '92 / Polydor

☐ VANESSA PARADIS LIVE
5216932 / Mar '94 / Polydor

Paradise Alley
☐ HEARTBREAKERS AND HOMEWRECKERS
Little Suzie / Cryin' / Tell me why / Mystery girl / Walk it / No time to cry / Same old story / Don't say nothing / Don't fake it / All fall down / Do you feel lucky / Just pretending
DR 008 / 16 Mar '98 / Delinquent

Paradise Jazz Band
☐ BLOWIN' THE BLUES AWAY
JCD 229 / Jan '94 / Jazzology

Paradise Lost
☐ GOTHIC
CDVILE 26 / Mar '95 / Peaceville

☐ ICON
Embers fire / Remembrance (erinnerung) / Forging sympathies / Joys of the emptiness / Dying freedom / Widow / Colossal rains / Weeping words / Poison / True belief / Shallow seasons / Christendom / Deus misereatur
CDMFN 152 / Sep '93 / Music For Nations

☐ ONE SECOND
One second / Another day / Sane / Say just words / Sufferer / Take me down / Lydia / This cold life / I despair / Mercy / Blood of another / Soul courageous / Disappear
CDMFNX 222 / Jul '97 / Music For Nations

☐ PARADISE LOST
Intro / Deadly inner sense / Paradise lost / Our saviour / Rotting misery / Frozen illusion / Breeding fear / Lost paradise
CDVILE 17 / Apr '95 / Peaceville

☐ REFLECTION
CDMFN 243 / 31 Aug '98 / Music For Nations

☐ SHADES OF GOD
Mortals watch the day / Crying for eternity / Embraced / Daylight torn / Pity the sadness / No forgiveness / Your hand in mine / Word made flesh / As I die
CDMFN 135 / Jun '92 / Music For Nations

Paradise Motel
☐ LEFT OVER LIFE TO KILL
Calling you / Dead skin / Men who loved her / Watch illuminium / Skip bins / Desperate plain / Bad light / German girl / Ashes / Stones
INFECT 047CD / 13 Apr '98 / Infectious

Paradogs
☐ HERE COMES JOEY
PRD 70312 / Nov '91 / Provogue

Paradox
☐ BROKEN BARRICADE
Diagram 776 / Beyond the dream / Broken barricade / Mr. Davis / Inner secrets / Fantasia / Infinite moment / Rain song
5216872 / Mar '94 / Verve

Paragons
☐ 25 YEARS OF THE PARAGONS
RNCD 2099 / Mar '95 / Rhino

☐ GOLDEN HITS
Tide is high / On the beach / Only a smile / Happy go lucky girl / Same song / My best girl / So much pain / When the lights are low / Wear you to the ball / Silver bird / Yellow bird / I want to go / Island in the sun / Land of sea and sun / I wanna be with you / Riding high
LG 21028 / Jun '93 / Lagoon

☐ HEAVEN & EARTH
CDSGP 075 / May '94 / Prestige

☐ MY BEST GIRL WEARS MY CROWN
Happy go lucky girl / I want to go back / When the lights are low / On the beach / Island in the sun / Riding on a high and windy day / Silver bird / Same song / Tide is high / I wanna be with you / Happy mercy mercy / Wear you to the ball / I'm a worried man / Yellow bird / Say you mean the world to me / Only a smile / Paragons medley
CDTRL 299 / Mar '94 / Trojan

☐ RIDING HIGH
RNCD 2085 / Dec '94 / Rhino

Parallel Or 90 Degrees
☐ AFTERLIFECYCLE
Afterlifecycle / Ithinkthereforenothing / Run in rings / Coming up roses / Afterlifecycle conclusion / Flower King of flies / Third person
CYCL 016 / 17 Nov '97 / Cyclops

Paralysed Age
☐ BLOODSUCKER
EFA 112702 / Dec '94 / Glasnost

Paramaecium
☐ WITHIN THE ANCIENT FOREST
PGD 6950CD / Sep '96 / Pleitegier

Paramount Jazzband Of Boston

☐ AIN'T CHA GLAD
SOSCD 1205 / Aug '90 / Stomp Off

☐ PARAMOUNT JAZZ BAND, THE
Dans la rue d'antibes / Jelly roll / Joint is jumpin' / What a difference a day makes / On a slow boat to China / Old fashioned love / Come back sweet Papa / More I see you / Until the real thing comes along / It's a sin to tell a lie / I would do 'most anything for your love / Nevertheless (I'm in love with you) / Some of these days
CDTTD 596 / Aug '95 / Timeless Jazz

Paramount Singers

☐ WORK & PRAY ON
ARHCD 382 / Apr '95 / Arhoolie

Paramounts

☐ WHITER SHADES OF R & B
Poison Ivy / I feel good all over / Little bitty pretty one / Certain girl / I'm the one who loves you / It won't be long / Bad blood / Do I / Blue ribbons / Cuttin' in / You never had it so good / Don't ya like my love / Draw me closer / Turn on your love light / You've got what I want / Freedom
EDCD 112 / Aug '91 / Edsel

Paramour, Norrie

☐ PLAY THE HITS OF CLIFF RICHARD/ SHADOWS IN LATIN (2CD Set)
Finders keepers / I love you / Spanish harlem / Living doll / Please don't tease / Summer holiday / Bachelor boy / Lucky lips / Young ones / Don't talk to him / I could easily fall (in love with you) / In the country / Dance on / Atlantis / Foot tapper / Nivram / FBI / Guitar tango / Peace pipe / Rise and fall of Flingel Bunt / Wonderful land / Shindig / Little Princess / Stars fell on Stockton / Apache / Frightened
4956202 / 10 Aug '98 / Studio 2

Paranoid Visions

☐ AFTER THE FACTION
AXSO 1CD / Aug '96 / AX-S

Paranoise

☐ START A NEW RACE
OZ 003CD / Jul '93 / Ozone

Paranonia

☐ PARANONIA
NZCD 021 / Sep '95 / Nova Zembla

Paranza Di Somma Vesuviana

☐ SCENNENNO D'A MUNTAGNA
NT 6719 / Jan '94 / Robi Droli

Parasites

☐ RAT ASS PIE
GKCD 041 / 22 Jun '98 / Go-Kart

Pardesi Music Machine

☐ SHAKE YOUR PANTS
CDST 015 / May '90 / Star

Parenti, Tony

☐ STRUT YO' STUFF (Tony Parenti & Bands 1925-1929)
That's plenty / Cabaret echoes / Dizzy Lizzie / French market blues / La vida medley / Be yourself / 12th street blues / Creole blues / Strut yo' stuff / Midnight Papa / I need some lovin' / Cabaret echoes / Up jumped the devil / Weary blues / New crazy blues #1/#2 / African echoes / In the dungeon / When you and I were pals / Gumbo / You made me like it baby / Old man rhythm
DGF 4 / May '95 / Frog

☐ TONY PARENTI & HIS NEW ORLENIANS
JCD 1 / Oct '92 / Jazzology

Parga, Mario

☐ MAGICIAN, THE
Heatwave / Electric blue / Guitarmageddon / Winds of limbo / Sweat it out / Intensities / Silent seduction / Magician / Midnight cafe / Raining again / Psychotic strings
PCOM 1116 / Sep '91 / President

Parham, Tiny

☐ CLASSICS 1926-1929
CLASSICS 661 / Nov '92 / Classics

☐ CLASSICS 1929-1940 (Parham, Tiny & His Musicians)
CLASSICS 691 / May '93 / Classics

☐ TINY PARHAM 1926-1928
DOCD 5341 / May '95 / Document

☐ TINY PARHAM 1928-1930 (2CD Set)
CBC 1022 / Feb '97 / Timeless/Chris Barber Collection

Pariah

☐ BLAZE OF OBSCURITY
Missionary of mercy / Puppet regime / Canary / Retaliate / Hypochondriac / Enemy within
857595 / Jun '89 / Steamhammer

☐ KINDRED, THE
857528 / '89 / Steamhammer

Paris

☐ GUERRILLA FUNK
Prelude / It's real / One time fo' ya mind / Guerrilla funk / Blacks and blues / Bring it to ya / Outta my life / What'cha see / Forty ounces and a fool / Back in the days / Guerrilla funk (Deep fo' real mix) / It's real (Mix) / Shots out
CDPTY 108 / Nov '94 / Priority/Virgin

Paris Africans

☐ AFRICAN BICYCLETTE
829422 / Jun '97 / BUDA

Paris All-Stars

☐ LIVE IN SWEDEN 1997
KAR 001 / Dec '97 / True Track

Paris Combo

☐ PARIS COMBO
BP 3411 / 23 Mar '98 / Boucherie Productions

Paris, Dominique

☐ CABRETTE
CP 022602 / Oct '97 / Cinq Planetes

Paris, Jackie

☐ JACKIE PARIS/CARLOS FRANZETTI/ MARC JOHNSON
ACD 158 / Jan '94 / Audiophile

☐ NOBODY ELSE BUT ME
ACD 245 / Mar '95 / Audiophile

Paris, Jeff

☐ LUCKY THIS TIME
NTHEN 006CD / Sep '95 / Now & Then

Paris, Mica

☐ BLACK ANGEL
Interlude / Stay / Is it good enough / Carefree / Let me inside / Black angel / Perfect / Hate to love / Waiting / I'll give you more / Love's gone / Don't say goodnight / Baby angel / Should've known better
4958132 / 10 Aug '98 / Cooltempo

☐ CONTRIBUTION
Contribution / South of the river / If I love u 2 nite / Just to be with you / Take me away / Truth and honesty / Deep Afrika / More love / You can make a wish / Just make me the one / I've been watching you / Who can we blame / One world
IMCD 184 / Mar '94 / Island

☐ SO GOOD
Where is the love: *Paris, Mica & Will Downing* / My one temptation / Like dreamers do / Breathe life into me / Nothing hits your heart like soul music / Sway / Don't give me up / I'd hate to love you / Great impersonation / So good
IMCD 209 / Apr '95 / Island

☐ WHISPER A PRAYER
I never felt like this before / I wanna hold on to you / You put a move on my heart / We were made for love / Whisper a prayer / Too far apart / I bless the day / Two in a million / Positivity / Can't seem to make up my mind / You got a special way / Love keeps coming back
IMCD 221 / Mar '96 / Island

Paris Washboard

☐ LOVE NEST
SOSCD 1308 / Sep '96 / Stomp Off

☐ PARIS WASHBOARD AND LOUIS MAEZETIER (Paris Washboard & Louis Maezetier)
SOSCD 1326 / Sep '97 / Stomp Off

☐ TRUCKIN'
SOSCD 1293 / Nov '95 / Stomp Off

Parisa, Fatemer V.

☐ CLASSICAL VOCAL ART OF PERSIA, THE (Parisa, Fatemer V. & Seyyed N. Razavi)
VICG 5269 / Jun '96 / JVC World Library

☐ PARISA AT THE ROYAL FESTIVAL HALL (Persian Classical Music)
PS 65155 / Oct '95 / PlayaSound

Parish Hall

☐ SKID ROW RUNNER
AACD 016 / 27 Apr '98 / Audio Archive

Parish, John

☐ DANCEHALL AT LOUSE POINT (Parish, John & Polly Jean Harvey)
Girl / Rope bridge crossing / City of no sun / That was my veil / Urn with dead flowers in a drained pool / Civil war correspondent / Taut / Un cercle autour du soleil / Heela / Is that all there is / Dance hall at Louse Point / Lost fun zone
CID 8051
CIDX 8051 / Sep '96 / Island

Park, Graeme

☐ EAU DE HOUSE VOL.1
FRSHCD 2 / Oct '96 / Fresh

Parker, Billy

☐ BILLY PARKER AND FRIENDS
Something old, something new: *Parker, Billy & Jack Greene* / Memory number one: *Parker, Billy & Webb Pierce* / Too many irons in the fire: *Parker, Billy & Cal Smith* / Who said love was fair: *Parker, Billy & Jimmy Payne* / I believe I'm entitled to you: *Parker, Billy & Bill Carlisle* / Milk cow blues / Tomorrow never comes: *Parker, Billy & Ernest Tubb* / When I need love bad / Honky tonk girls: *Parker, Billy & Cal Smith* / Love don't know a lady: *Parker, Billy & Darrell McCall* / Take me back to Tulsa / Last country song: *Parker, Billy & Darrell McCall* / It's not me / If I ever need a lady / I see an angel every day / I'll drink to that / Why do I keep calling you honey, honey / Can I have what's left / What's a nice girl like you / One more last time / Hello out there
BCD 15521 / Oct '90 / Bear Family

Parker, Bobby

☐ BENT OUT OF SHAPE
BT 1086CD / May '93 / Black Top

☐ SHINE ME UP
BT 1119CD / Aug '95 / Black Top

Parker, Charlie

☐ 'ROUND MIDNIGHT
Night in Tunisia / Dizzy atmosphere / Groovin' high / Ko ko / Gypsy / Little Willie leaps in/52nd Street theme / Carvin' the bird / Charlie's wig / Barbados / Bird feathers / Charlie's theme / Be bop / Hot house / Ornithology / How high the moon
SUMCD 4053 / Nov '96 / Summit

☐ 1949 CONCERT AND ALLSTARS 1950-51
Ornithology / Cheryl / Ko ko / Bird of paradise / Now's the time / Perdido / Move / Rifftide / Cool blues / 52nd street theme / Anthropology / 'round midnight / Night in tunisia
UCD 19009 / Jun '95 / Forlane

☐ AUDIO ARCHIVE
Chasin' the bird / Crazeology / Yardbird suite / My old flame / Be bop a lula / Rocker / Bird of paradise / Don't blame me / Moose the mooche / Marmaduke / Street beat / Parker's mood / Theme / Bluebird / Relaxin' at Camarillo / 'Round midnight / Constellation / Slow boat to China
CDAA 021 / Jun '92 / Tring

☐ AUTUMN IN NEW YORK
LEJAZZCD 3 / Mar '93 / Le Jazz

☐ BEST OF THE BIRD, THE
Ko ko / Cheryl / Rifftide / Big foot / Be bop / Barbados / Oop bop sh'bam / 52nd street theme / Gypsy / Carvin' the bird / Bongo bop / Charlie's wig / Bird feathers
17020 / May '94 / Laserlight

☐ BIRD (The Original Recordings Of Charlie Parker)
Now's the time / Laura / Mohawk / Kim / Blues for Alice / Laird baird / KC Blues / Lover man / Just friends / Bird / April in Paris / Lester leaps in
8371762 / Nov '88 / Verve

☐ BIRD AND DIZ (Remastered) (Parker, Charlie & Dizzy Gillespie)
5214362 / Oct '97 / Verve Master Edition

☐ BIRD AT BIRDLAND (4CD Set)
CDDIG 16 / Jun '95 / Charly

☐ BIRD AT ST. NICK'S
OJCCD 41 / Jun '95 / Original Jazz Classics

☐ BIRD IN CONCERT 1946-1952
Sweet georgia brown / Blues for norman / I can't get started / Lady be good / After you've gone / Jatp blues / I got rhythm / Opener / Lester leaps in / Embraceable you / Closer / What is this thing called love / April in paris / Repetition / Easy to love / Rocker / Jam blues / What is this thing called love / Funky blues
CDB 1215 / Jul '92 / Giants Of Jazz

☐ BIRD LIVES (Various Artists)
Yardbird suite: *Pepper, Art* / Confirmation: *Ammons, Gene* / Ornithology: *Evans, Bill* / Parker's mood (bless my soul): *Jefferson, Eddie* / Scrapple from the apple: *Mitchell, Blue* / Au privave: *Moody, James* / Repitition: *Montgomery, Wes* / Billie's bounce: *Griffin, Johnny* / Steeplechase: *Hawes, Hampton* / Now's the time: *Morgan, Frank* / Relaxin' at Camarillo: *Henderson, Joe*
MCD 91662 / Apr '94 / Milestone

☐ BIRD MEETS DIZ (Parker, Charlie & Dizzy Gillespie)
LEJAZZCD 21 / Feb '94 / Le Jazz

☐ BIRD OF PARADISE
Red cross / Groovin' high ('whispering') / Hot house / Congo blues / Street beat ('lady be good') / Ko-ko ('cherokee') / Billie's bounce / Ornithology ('how high the moon') / Yardbird suite ('what price love') / Moose the mooche ('i got rhythm') / Lover man / Be bop / Bird's nest / Stupendous ('s wonderful') / Cheers / Relaxin' at camarillo / Chasin' the bird ('i got rhythm') / Cheryl / Bird of paradise ('all the things you are') / My old flame
JHR 73531 / Sep '93 / Jazz Hour

☐ BIRD OF PARADISE BE-BOP GENIUS 1947
Chasin' the bird / Cheryl / Buzzy / Milestones / Half nelson / Dexterity / Dewey square / Hymn / Bird of paradise / Embraceable you / Bird feathers / Klact-oveeseds-tene / Scrapple from the apple / My old flame / Out of nowhere / Don't blame me / Drifting on a reed / Quasimado
CD 56029 / Nov '94 / Jazz Roots

☐ BIRD RETURNS, THE
Chasin' the bird / Thriving on a riff / Koko / Half nelson / Scrapple from the apple / Cheryl / Barbados
SV 0155 / Oct '97 / Savoy Jazz

☐ BIRD SYMBOLS
Moose the mooche / Yardbird suite / Ornithology / Night in Tunisia / Bird's nest / Cool blues / Bird of paradise / Embraceable you / My old flame / Scrapple from the apple / Out of nowhere / Don't blame me
RHCD 5 / Jul '91 / Rhapsody

☐ BIRD YOU NEVER HEARD, THE
STCD 582 / Jun '94 / Stash

☐ BIRD'S BEST
5274522 / Oct '95 / Verve

☐ BIRD'S EYES VOL.10
W 2002 / Sep '93 / Philology

☐ BIRD'S EYES VOL.11
W 6222 / Apr '94 / Philology

☐ BIRD'S EYES VOL.12
W 8422 / Apr '94 / Philology

☐ BIRD'S EYES VOL.13
W 8432 / May '94 / Philology

☐ BIRD'S EYES VOL.14
W 8442CD / Jul '94 / Philology

☐ BIRD'S EYES VOL.15
PHIL 8452 / Oct '94 / Philology

☐ BIRD'S EYES VOL.16
PHIL 8462 / Oct '94 / Philology

☐ BIRD'S EYES VOL.19
W 8492 / Apr '95 / Philology

☐ BIRD'S EYES VOL.20
W 8502 / Apr '95 / Philology

☐ BIRD'S EYES VOL.21
W 8512 / Feb '96 / Philology

☐ BIRD'S EYES VOL.22
W 8522 / Feb '96 / Philology

☐ BIRD'S EYES VOL.7
214 W572 / Aug '91 / Philology

☐ BIRD'S EYES VOL.8
CD 241 W802 / May '92 / Philology

☐ BIRD'S EYES VOL.9
W 1202 / Sep '93 / Philology

☐ BIRD'S THE WORD 1944-1952 (2CD Set)
JWD 102308 / Oct '94 / JWD

☐ BLUEBIRD
Klact-oveeseds-tene ('the chase') / Don't blame me / Quasimodo ('embraceable you') / Crazeology / Bluebird / Parker's mood / Constellation (i got rhythm - honeysuckle rose) (bridge) / Marmaduke ('honeysuckle rose') / Slow boat to china / Scrapple from the apple (honeysuckle rose - I got rhythm) (/ Move / 52nd street theme (take 1) / 52nd street theme (take 2) / Cool blues / Ornithology ('how high the moon') / Rocker / Sly mongoose / Star eyes / Lester leaps in / How high the moon
JHR 73532 / Sep '93 / Jazz Hour

☐ BOSTON 1952
UPCD 2742 / Apr '97 / Uptown

☐ CARNEGIE HALL CHRISTMAS 1949
JASSCD 16 / '88 / Jass

☐ CHARLIE PARKER (2CD Set)
R2CD 4016 / 13 Apr '98 / Deja Vu

☐ CHARLIE PARKER
Bird's nest / How high the moon / Ko Ko / Moose the Mooch / Lover man (oh where can you be) / Klact-Oveeseds-Tene / Quasimodo / Cool blues / Stupendous / Red cross / Donna Lee / Move / Street beat / Relaxin' in Carmarillo / Bird of paradise / Carvin' the bird / Confirmations / Congo blues
BN 031 / Feb '97 / Blue Nite

☐ CHARLIE PARKER & JAY MCSHANN 1940-1944 (Parker, Charlie & Jay McShann Orchestra)
STCD 542 / Feb '91 / Stash

☐ CHARLIE PARKER 1944-1946
158802 / Feb '97 / Jazz Archives

☐ **CHARLIE PARKER 1947-1950**
CD 14549 / Jul '94 / Jazz Portraits

☐ **CHARLIE PARKER COLLECTION**
Bird of paradise / Crazeology / Hot house / Stupendous / Klact-oveededs-teine / Groovin' high / Yardbird suite / My old flame / Cool blues / Bird's nest / Cheryl / Donna lee / Be bop a lula / Congo blues / Constellation / Don't blame me / Ko ko / Lover man (oh where can you be) / Marmaduke / Moose the mooch / Out of nowhere / Parker's mood / Quasimodo / Relaxin' in Carmarillo / Street beat
COL 028 / Jun '95 / Collection

☐ **CHARLIE PARKER GOLD (2CD Set)**
D2CD 4016 / Jun '95 / Deja Vu

☐ **CHARLIE PARKER MEMORIAL BAND, THE (Charlie Parker Memorial Band)**
Marmaduke / Out of nowhere / Don't blame me / Sweet Rosa / Little Willie leaps / Max the invincible roach / Star eyes / Laird baird / Bird of paradise / Visa
CDSJP 373 / Nov '93 / Timeless Jazz

☐ **CHARLIE PARKER MEMORIAL VOL.1**
Another hair do / Bluebird / Bird gets the worm / Barbados / Constellation / Parker's mood / Ah leu cha / Perhaps / Marmaduke / Steeplechase / Merry go round / Buzzy
SV 0101 / Oct '97 / Savoy Jazz
CY 78982 / Jun '98 / Savoy Jazz

☐ **CHARLIE PARKER MEMORIAL VOL.2**
Barbados / Constellation / Parker's mood / Perhaps / Marmaduke / Donna Lee / Chasin' the bird / Buzzy / Milestones / Half nelson / Slippin' at Bells / Billie's bounce / Thriving on a riff
SV 0103 / Oct '97 / Savoy Jazz

☐ **CHARLIE PARKER ON DIAL (The Complete Sessions) (4CD Set)**
Diggin' diz / Moose and mooche / Yardbird suite / Ornithology / Night in Tunisia / Max making wax / Lover man / Gypsy / Be bop / Home cooking / Lullaby in rhythm / Blues on the sofa / Kopely plaza blues / This is always / Dark shadows / Bird's nest / Cool blues / Relaxin' at Camarillo / Cheers / Carvin' the bird / Stupendous / Dexterity / Bongo bop / Dewey Square / Hymn / Bird of paradise / Embraceable you / Bird feathers / Klactoveesedstein / Scrapple from the apple / My old flame / Out of nowhere / Don't blame me / Drifting on a reed / Quasimado / Charlie's wig / Bongo beep / Crazeology / How deep is the ocean
SPJCD 1014 / May '93 / Spotlite

☐ **CHARLIE PARKER ON DIAL (Original Choice Takes) (2CD Set)**
Diggin' diz / Moose the mooche / Yardbird suite / Ornithology / Night in Tunisia / Max making wax / Loveman / Gypsy / Be bop / This is always / Dark shadows / Bird's nest / Hot blues / Cool blues / Relaxin' at Camarillo / Cheers / Carvin' the bird / Stupendous / Dexterity / Bongo bop / Dewey Square / Hymn / Bird of paradise / Embraceable you / Bird feathers / Klactoveesedstein / Scrappel from the apple / My old flame / Out of nowhere / Don't blame me / Drifting on a reed / Quasimado / Charlie's wig / Bongo beep / Carazeology / How deep is the ocean
SPJCD 1092 / May '95 / Spotlite

☐ **CHARLIE PARKER STORY VOL.1, THE**
STBCD 2602 / Aug '95 / Stash

☐ **CHARLIE PARKER STORY VOL.2, THE**
STBCD 2603 / Aug '95 / Stash

☐ **CHARLIE PARKER STORY, THE**
Billie's bounce / Warming up a riff / Now's the time / Thriving on a riff / Meandering / Koko
SV 0105 / Oct '97 / Savoy Jazz

☐ **CHARLIE PARKER WITH MILES DAVIS**
30017 / Sep '92 / Giants Of Jazz

☐ **CHASIN' THE BIRD**
How high the moon / Moose the mooch / Be bop a lula / Yardbird suite / Crazeology / Slow boat to China / Riff raff / Scrapple from the apple / Star eyes / Sly mongoose / 'Round midnight / Theme / Rocker / Don't blame me / Relaxin' at Camarillo / Constellation / Bluebird / Parker's mood / Marmaduke / Bird of paradise / My old flame / Chasin' the Bird
GRF 063 / '93 / Tring

☐ **CLASSICS 1945-1947**
CLASSICS 980 / 24 Feb '98 / Classics

☐ **COLE PORTER SONGBOOK, THE**
Easy to love / Begin the beguine / Night and day / What is this thing called love / In the still of the night / I get a kick out of you / Just one of those things / My heart belongs to daddy / I've got you under my skin / Love for sale / I love Paris
8232502 / Feb '91 / Verve

☐ **COMPLETE BIRD AT BIRDLAND 1950-1951, THE (4CD Set)**
Hot house / Out of nowhere / Visa / Anthropology / Wee / What's new / Little willie leaps / Yesterdays / 52nd street theme III / Dizzy atmosphere / Wahoo / I can't get started / Wee / 52nd street theme IV / Slow boat to china / Night in tunisia / 52nd street theme V / 52nd street theme inc / Wahoo / 'Round midnight / This time the dream's on me / Dizzy atmosphere / Night in Tunisia / 52nd street theme / Street beat / Out of nowhere inc / Little willie leaps / 52nd street theme / Ornithology / I'll remember April / 52nd street theme / Slow 52nd street theme / Embraceable you / Cool blues / 52nd street theme / Conception / Deception / Jumpin' with Symphony Sid / Anthropology / Embraceable you / Cheryl / Salt peanuts / Jumpin' with Symphony Sid / Easy to love / Rocker / Jumpin' with Symphony Sid / Just friends / Everything happens to me / East of the sun / Laura / Dancing in the dark / Jumpin' with Symphony Sid / Introduction / Blue 'n' boogie / Anthropology / Round midnight / Night in Tunisia / Jumpin' with Symphony Sid / What is this thing called love / Laura / Repetition / Interview / They can't take that away from me / Easy to love / Hot house / Embraceable you / How high the moon
FBB 901 / Nov '96 / Ember

☐ **COMPLETE BIRTH OF BEBOP 1940-1942**
STCD 535 / Oct '91 / Stash

☐ **CRAZEOLOGY**
BN 030 / Apr '98 / Blue Nite

☐ **EARLY BIRD (The Best Of The 1945 Studio Recordings)**
LEJAZZCD 55 / Aug '96 / Le Jazz

☐ **EARLY BIRD 1940-1945**
158572 / Jul '96 / Jazz Archives

☐ **EVENING AT HOME WITH THE BIRD, AN (Jazz Immortal Series Vol. 1)**
There's a small hotel / These foolish things / Fine and dandy / Hot house
SV 0154 / Oct '97 / Savoy Jazz

☐ **GENIUS OF CHARLIE PARKER, THE**
Bird gets the worm / Bluebird / Klaunstance / Barbados / Merry go round / Donna Lee / Chasin' the Bird / Koko / Perhaps / Warming up a riff / Slim's jam / Poppity pop / Dizzy boogie / Flat foot floogie
CY 78991 / Jun '98 / Savoy Jazz

☐ **GITANES - JAZZ 'ROUND MIDNIGHT**
Why do I love you / Tico tico / My little suede shoes / Un poquito de tu amor / Estrellita / I'm in the mood for love / Begin the beguine / Temptation / Easy to love / East of the sun and West of the moon / I didn't know what time it was / If I should lose you / Out of nowhere / I'll remember April / Autumn in New York / Laura / Ballade / Lover
5109112 / Oct '91 / Verve

☐ **HIGHEST FLYING BIRD (14 Of His Classic Recordings)**
Moose the mooche / Yardbird smile / Orthinology / Scrapple from the apple / Rocker / Sly mongoose / Star eyes / This time the dream's on me / Cool blues / My little suede shoes / Lester leaps in / Laura
PAR 2002 / May '90 / Parade

☐ **IMMORTAL CHARLIE PARKER, THE**
Little Willie leaps / Donna Lee / Chasin' the Bird / Cheryl / Milestones / Half Nelson / Slippin' at Bells / Tiny's tempo / Red cross / Now's the time / Buzzy / Marmaduke
SV 0102 / Oct '97 / Savoy Jazz
CY 78983 / Jun '98 / Savoy Jazz

☐ **IMMORTAL SESSIONS VOL.1 1945-1948 (5CD Set)**
Dream of you / Seventh Avenue / Groovin' high / All the things you are / Dizzy atmosphere / Salt peanuts / Shaw nuff / Lover man / Hot house / Hallelujah / Get happy / Slam slam blues / Congo blues / Moose the mouche / Yardbird suite / Ornithology / Night in Tunisia / Moose the mouche / Yardbird suite / Max making wax / Lover man / Gypsy / Be bop / This is always / Dark shadows / Dark shadows / Hot blues / Blow top blues / Cool blues / Cool blues / Relaxin' at Camarillo / Cheers / Carvin' the bird / Stupendous / Stupendous / Relaxin' at Camarillo / Cheers / Carvin' the bird / Dexterity / Bongo bop / Bongo bop / Dewey Square / Dewey Square / Bird of paradise / Embraceable you / Klactoveesedstein / Scrapple from the apple / My old flame / Out of nowhere / Don't blame me / Drifting on a reed / Quasimodo / Quasimodo / Charlie's wig / Bird feathers / Crazeology / Ko ko / Groovin' high / Big foot / Ornithology / Hot house / Salt peanuts / Out of nowhere / How high the moon / White Christmas
EC 33252 / Nov '96 / Saga Jazz

☐ **IMMORTAL SESSIONS VOL.2 1949-1953 (5CD Set)**
Slow boat to China / Cheryl / Scrapple from the apple / Be bop / Hot house / Oop bop sh'bam / Barbados / Salt peanuts / Groovin' high / Perdido / 'Round midnight / Move / Street beat / Ornithology / Cool blues / 52nd Street theme / Conversation / Blue 'n' boogie / Conversation / Anthropology / Conversation / Round Midnight / Conversation / Night in Tunisia / Jumpin' with symphony Sid / Repetition / April in Paris / What is this thing called love / April in Paris / Out of nowhere / East of the sun / Easy to love / Rocker / Sly mongoose / Moose the mouche / Star eyes / This time the dream's on me / Cool blues / My little suede shoes / Lester leaps in / Perdido / Salt peanuts / All the things you are / Hot house / Night in Tunisia
EC 33192 / Nov '96 / Saga Jazz

☐ **IN A SOULFUL MOOD**
Moose the mooche / Yardbird suite / Ornithology / Night in tunisia / Loverman / Gypsy / Bird's nest / Hot blues / Cool blues / Relaxin' at camarillo / Cheers / Carvin' the bird / Stupendous / Bongo bop / Dewey square / All the things you are / Bird of paradise / Embraceable you / Klact-oveeseds-tene / Scrapple from the apple / My old flame / Out of nowhere / Don't blame me / Quasimodo / Crazeology / How deep is the ocean
MCCD 205 / Jul '95 / Music Club

☐ **IN SWEDEN 1950**
STCD 4031 / Oct '87 / Storyville

☐ **JAM SESSION**
Jam blues / What is this thing called love / All the things you are / Dearly beloved / Nearness of you / I'll get by / Everything happens to me / Man I love / What's new / Soeone to watch over me / Isn't it romantic / Funky blues
8335642 / Mar '90 / Verve

☐ **JAZZ AND BLUES (36 Outstanding Jazz Tracks/2CD Set)**
Bird feathers / Perdido / Groovin' high / Hot house / Be bop a lula / Crazeology / Parker's mood / Ornithology / Out of nowhere / Scrapple from the apple / Billy's bounce / Bluebird / Cheryl / Constellation / Don't blame me / Marmaduke / Cheers / My old flame / Bird's nest / How high the moon / Ko ko / Moose the mooch / Lover man (oh where can you be) / Klact-oveeseds-tene / Quasimodo / Cool blues / Stupendous / Red cross / Donna Lee / Move / Street beat / Relaxin' at carmarillo / Bird of paradise / Carvin' the bird / Confirmations / Congo blues
BN 207 / Aug '98 / Blue Nite

☐ **JAZZ AT THE PHILHARMONIC**
Sweet georgia brown (part 1 and 2) / Blues for norman (part 1 and 2) / I can't get started (part 1 and 2) / Lady be good (parts 1 and 2) / After you've gone (part 1 and 2) / Jatp blues (part 1, 2, 3, and 4) / I got rhythm (part 1, 2 and 3)
CD 53107 / May '92 / Giants Of Jazz

☐ **JAZZ AT THE PHILHARMONIC 1949**
Opener / Lester leaps in / Embraceable you / Closer / Flying home / How high the moon / Perdido
5198032 / Feb '94 / Verve

☐ **JAZZ MASTERS**
Confirmation / Oscar for treadwell / Dancing in the dark / Segment / Star eyes / Mango mangue / Repetition / Bird / KC blues / Melancholy baby / Blues for Alice / I can't get started / Kim / Just friends / She rote / Lover man
5198272 / 5 May '98 / Verve

☐ **JAZZ MASTERS (Charlie Parker Plays Standards)**
Love for sale / If I should lose you / Almost like being in love / Why do I love you / I remember you / Easy to love / Old folks / I got rhythm / Laura / Estrellita / What is this thing called love / Embraceable you / I love Paris / How high the moon
5218542 / 5 May '98 / Verve

☐ **JAZZ PORTRAITS**
Dizzy atmosphere / Hot house / Billie's bounce / Koko / Moose the mooche / Yardbird suite / Ornithology / Night in Tunisia / Lover man / Gypsy / Be bop / Bird's nest / Cool blues / Relaxin' at Camarillo / Cheers / Carvin' the bird / Stupendous / Donna Lee
CD 14504 / May '94 / Jazz Portraits

☐ **LIVE AT ST. NICKS**
OJCCD 41 / Jun '95 / Original Jazz Classics

☐ **LIVE AT TRADE WINGS**
LEJAZZCD 48 / Nov '95 / Le Jazz

☐ **MASTERS OF JAZZ (2CD Set)**
R2CD 8008 / 13 Apr '98 / Deja Vu

☐ **MASTERS, THE (2CD Set)**
EDMCD 031 / 30 Mar '98 / Eagle

☐ **MASTERWORKS 1946-1947**
Bird of paradise / Embraceable you / Crazeology / Dewey Square / My old flame / Relaxin' at Camarillo / Hymn / Klactoveesedstein / Don't blame me / Scrapple from the apple / Quasimodo / Dexterity / Night in Tunisia / Ornithology / Lover man / Yardbird suite / Moose the mooche / Gypsy / Be bop / Bird's nest / Out of nowhere / Cheers
CD 53007 / Mar '92 / Giants Of Jazz

☐ **MONTREAL 1953**
UPCD 2736 / Apr '97 / Uptown

☐ **NEWLY DISCOVERED SIDES BY THE IMMORTAL CHARLIE PARKER**
52nd Street / Night in Tunisia / Slow boat to China / Groovin' high / Big foot / Hot house
SV 0156 / Oct '97 / Savoy Jazz

☐ **NOW'S THE TIME (Parker, Charlie Quartet)**
Song is you / Laird baird / Kim / Cosmic rays / Chi chi / I remember you / Now's the time / Confirmation
8256712 / May '87 / Verve

☐ **NOW'S THE TIME (Remastered) (Parker, Charlie Quartet)**
Now's the time / I remember you / Confirmation / Chi chi / Song is you / Laird baird / Kim / Cosmic rays / Star eyes / Blues / I'm in the mood for love / Bird / Celebrity / Ballade / Cardboard / Visa
5397572 / 16 Mar '98 / Verve Master Edition

☐ **PARKER'S MOOD 1947-1950**
Bongo beep / Crazeology / Blue bird / Constellation / Parker's mood / Marmaduke / Merry go round / Visa / Passport / Diverse / Just friends / Summertime / Star eyes / Blues / I'm in the mood for love / Bloomdido / Oscar for the treadwell / Mohawk
CD 56036 / Jul '95 / Jazz Roots

☐ **QUINTESSENCE, THE (2CD Set)**
FA 225 / Jan '98 / Fremeaux

☐ **ROCKLAND PALACE CONCERT 1952 VOL.1**
East of the sun / What is this thing called love / Stardust / Ornithology / Easy to love / Just friends / Dancing in the dark / Gold rush / Don't blame me / April in Paris / Repitition / Everything happens to me / Sly mongoose / Sly mongoose / Rocker / Laura / Lester leaps in
JZCL 6010 / Nov '96 / Jazz Classics

☐ **ROCKLAND PALACE CONCERT 1952, THE (Complete Concert/2CD Set)**
East of the sun / What is this thing called love / Stardust / Ornithology / Easy to love / Just friends / Dancing in the dark / Gold rush / Don't blame me / April in Paris / Repitition / Everything happens to me / Sly mongoose / Sly mongoose / Rocker / Laura / Lester leaps in / Out of nowhere / I didn't know what time it was / I'll remember April / Cool blues / East of the sun / Just friends / My little suede shoes / What is this thing called love / Repitition / This time's the dreams on me / Moose the moche / Star eyes / Rocker
JZCL 5014 / Nov '96 / Jazz Classics

☐ **SAVOY RECORDINGS VOL.1**
VGCD 650107 / Jan '93 / Vogue

☐ **SAVOY RECORDINGS VOL.2**
VGCD 650108 / Jan '93 / Vogue

☐ **STREET BEAT**
CDSGP 088 / May '94 / Prestige

☐ **SWEDISH SCHNAPPS (& The Great Quintet Sessions 1949-1951)**
Si si / Swedish schnapps / Back home blues / Lover man / Blues for Alice / Au private / She rote / KC blues / Star eyes / Segment diverse / Passport
8493932 / Mar '92 / Verve

☐ **TRIUMPH OF CHARLIE PARKER**
CDCH 380 / Jan '89 / Milan

☐ **UNHEARD CHARLIE PARKER: BIRDSEED VOL.1 1947-1950**
STB 2500 / Apr '95 / Stash

☐ **WITH STRINGS (The Master Takes)**
5239842 / Feb '95 / Verve
BMCD 3023 / Mar '96 / Blue Moon

☐ **YARDBIRD SUITE**
Dizzy atmosphere / Hot house / Billie's bounce / Ko ko / Moose the mooche / Yardbird suite / Ornithology / Night in tunisia / Lover man / Gypsy / Be bop / Bird's nest / Cool blues / Relaxin' at camarillo / Cheers / Carvin' the bird / Stupendous / Donna lee
CD 56011 / Aug '94 / Jazz Roots

☐ **YARDBIRD SUITE**
Confirmation / Scrapple from the apple / Out of nowhere / Hallelujah / Get happy / Moose the moochie / Bird of paradise / Night in Tunisia / Dizzy atmosphere / Groovin' high / Ko ko / Gypsy / Carvin' the bird / Bird feathers / Be bop / Yardbird suite
CDMT 030 / Jul '97 / Meteor

Parker, Elaine

☐ **'S WONDERFUL**
Some of my best friends / Touch of your lips / In a sentimental mood / 'S Wonderful / Stardust / I did it all for you / Little girl blue / Carioca / They can't take that away from me / We could be flying / They say it's wonderful / Ol' man river / There's a small hotel / Joy / My foolish heart / Like a lover / Love for sale
JHCD 027 / Jan '94 / Ronnie Scott's Jazz House

Parker, Evan

☐ **50TH BIRTHDAY CONCERT**
CDLR 212/3 / Jan '95 / Leo

☐ **AT THE VORTEX (Parker, Evan Trio)**
EM 4022 / Jun '98 / Emanem

☐ **CHICAGO SOLO**
OD 12017 / Jan '98 / Okka Disk

☐ **CONIC SECTIONS**
Conic section 1 / Conic section 2 / Conic section 3 / Conic section 4 / Conic section 5
AHUM 015 / Jul '93 / Ah-Um

☐ **CORNER TO CORNER (Parker, Evan & John Stevens)**
OGCD 005 / May '94 / Ogun

☐ **LIVE AT LES INSTANTS CHAVIRES (Parker, Evan & Noel Akchote/ Lawrence Casserley/Joel Ryan)**
CDLR 255 / 1 Jun '98 / Leo

☐ **LONDON AIR LIFT**
FMPCD 89 / Jan '98 / Full Moon

☐ **MONKEY PUZZLE (Parker, Evan & Ned Rothenberg)**
CDLR 247 / Aug '97 / Leo

☐ **NATIVES AND ALIENS (Parker, Evan & Paul Lytton/Barry Guy)**
CDLR 243 / May '97 / Leo

☐ **SAXOPHONE SOLOS**
CPE 20022 / Jun '95 / Chronoscope

☐ **SOMEWHERE BI-LINGUAL (Parker, Evan & Noel Akchote/Paul Rogers/ Mark Sanders)**
STA 970911 / Nov '97 / Siesta

☐ **TEMPRANILLO**
NCM 4 / 21 Aug '97 / Fresh Sound

☐ **TOWARD THE MARGINS**
4535142 / Jun '97 / ECM

☐ **TWO OCTOBERS (Parker, Evan & Paul Lytton)**
EM 4009 / Sep '96 / Emanem

Parker, Fess

☐ **COMBINED POSSIBILITIES**
TC 008 / 27 Oct '97 / Thrill City

☐ **GREAT AMERICAN HEROES**
Daniel Boone / Little Nathan / Jim Bowie / Abraham Lincoln (the tall American) / George Washington / Patrick Henry (the Patriot) / Ballad of Davy Crockett / Andrew Jackson (Old Hickory) / Ben Franklin / Lewis and Clark / Johnny Clem / Ole Kit Carson
BCD 16113 / Nov '96 / Bear Family

Parker, Graham

☐ **12 HAUNTED EPISODES**
GRACD 204 / Apr '95 / Grapevine

☐ **ACID BUBBLEGUM**
Turn it into hate / Sharpening axes / Get over it and move on / Bubblegum cancer / Impenetrable / She never let me down / Obsessed with Aretha / Beancounter / Girl at the end of the pier / Baggage / Milk train / Character assassination / They got it wrong as usual
ESSCD 583 / Jul '97 / Essential

☐ **ALONE IN AMERICA LIVE**
White honey / Black honey / Soul corruption / Gypsy blood / Back in time / Change is gonna come / Watch the moon come down / Protection / Back to schooldays / Durban poison / You can't be too strong / Don't let it break you down
DIAB 845 / 26 Jan '98 / Diablo

☐ **ALONE IN JAPAN LIVE**
That's what they all say / Platinum blonde / Mercury poisoning / Sweet sixteen / No woman, no cry / Lunatic fringe / Long stem rose / Discovering Japan / Don't ask me questions / Watch the moon come down (revisited) / Just like Hermann Hesse / Too many knots to untangle / Chopsticks / Short memories
DIAB 849 / 26 Jan '98 / Diablo

☐ **BBC LIVE IN CONCERT**
WINCD 083 / Jun '96 / Windsong

☐ **BURNING QUESTIONS**
Release me / Too many knots to untangle / Just like Joe Meek's blues / Love is a burning question / Platinum blonde / Long stem rose / Short memories / Here it comes again / Mr. Tender / Just like Hermann Hesse / Yesterdays's cloud / Oasis / Worthy of your love / Substitute
DIAB 848 / 26 Jan '98 / Diablo

☐ **CHRISTMAS CRACKER**
Christmas is for mugs / New Year's revolution / Soul Christmas / Christmas is for mugs / New Year's revolution / Soul Christmas
GPCD 3 / Nov '94 / Demon

☐ **HOWLING WIND/HEAT TREATMENT (2CD Set)**
White honey / Nothing's gonna pull us apart / Silly thing / Gypsy blood / Between you and me / Back to schooldays / Soul shoes / Lady doctor / You've got to be kidding / Howling wind / Not if it pleases me / Don't ask me questions / Heat treatment / That's what they all say / Turned up too late / Black honey / Hotel chambermaid / Pourin' it all out / Back door love / Something you're goin' thru / Help me shake it / Fools' gold
5286032 / Aug '95 / Vertigo

☐ **HUMAN SOUL**
Little Miss Understanding / My love's strong / Dancing for money / Call me your doctor / Big man on paper / Soultime / Everything goes / Sugar gives you energy / Daddy's a postman / Green monkeys / I was wrong / You got the word (right where you want it) / Slash and burn
DIAB 846 / 26 Jan '98 / Diablo

☐ **LIVE ALONE DISCOVERING JAPAN**
7650522382 / 24 Mar '98 / GAD

☐ **MONA LISA'S SISTER**
Don't let it break you down / Under the mask of happiness / Back in time / I'm just your man / OK Heironymous / Get started, start a fire / Girl isn't ready / Blue highway / Success / I don't know / Cupid
DIAB 844 / 26 Jan '98 / Diablo

☐ **MONA LISA'S SISTER/HUMAN SOUL/ ALONE IN USA/THE UP ESCALATOR (4CD Set)**
Don't let it break you down / Under the mask of happiness / Back in time / I'm just your man / OK Heironymous / Get started, start a fire / Girl isn't ready / Blue highway / Success / I don't know / Cupid / Little Miss Understanding / My love's strong / Dancing for money / Call me your doctor / Big man on paper / Soultime / Everything goes / Sugar gives you energy / Daddy's a postman / Green monkeys / I was wrong / You got the word (right where you want it) / Slash and burn / White honey / Black honey / Soul corruption / Gypsy blood / Back in time / Change is gonna come / Watch the moon come down / Protection / Back to school days / Durban poison / You can't be too strong / Don't let it break you down / No holding back / Devil's sidewalk / Stupefaction / Love without greed / Julie Julie / Endless night / Paralysed / Manouvres / Empty lives / Beating of another heart
GRAHAM 1 / 26 Jan '98 / Diablo

☐ **NO HOLDING BACK (3CD Set)**
No holding back / Stupefaction / Empty lives / Manoeuvres / Love without greed / Don't let it break you down / Under the mask of happiness / I'm just your man / OK Hieronymus / Get started, start a fire / Cupid / Little misunderstanding / My love's strong / Dancing for money / Big man on paper / Everything goes / Daddy's a postman / You got the world (right where you want it) / She wants so many things / Strong winds / Kid with the butterfly net / Wrapping paper / Brand new book / Weeping statues / When I was king / Sun is gonna shine again / Release me / Just like Joe Meek's blues / Love is a burning question / Long stem rose / Here it comes again / Yesterday's cloud / Substitute / White honey / Black honey / Gypsy blood / Durban poison / Three Martini lunch / Hotel chambermaid / That's what they all say / Platinum blonde / Mercury poisoning / No woman no cry / Discovering Japan / Watch the moon come down / Chopsticks / Short memories / Christmas is for mugs / New York revolution / Soul Christmas / Protection
FBOOK 15 / Feb '97 / Demon

☐ **NOT IF IT PLEASES ME (Parker, Graham & The Rumour)**
White honey / Back door love / Don't ask me questions / Soul shoes / Hotel chambermaid / Pouring it all out / Help me shake it / Heat treatment / Lady Doctor / Silly thing / Fools gold / Gypsy blood / Not if it pleases me / New York shuffle / Kansas City
HUX 003 / 30 Mar '98 / Hux

☐ **PARKERILLA**
8422632 / Jan '94 / Vertigo

☐ **STRUCK BY LIGHTNING**
She wants so many things / They murdered the clown / Strong winds / Kid with the butterfly net / And it shook me / Wrapping paper / That's where she ends up / Brand new book / Weeping statues / Guardian angels / Children and dogs / Over the border (to America) / When I was King / Ten girls ago / Sun is gonna shine again
DIAB 847 / 26 Jan '98 / Diablo

☐ **TEMPORARY BEAUTY**
Temporary beauty / Another grey area / No more excuses / Dark side of the bright lights / Can't waste a minute / Big fat zero / You hit the spot / It's all worth nothing alone / Crying for attention / Thankless task / Fear not / You can't take your love for granted / Glass jaw / Passive resistance / Sound like chains / Just like a man / Life gets better / Last couple on the dance floor / Miracle a minute / Habit worth forming
74321487282 / May '97 / Camden

☐ **UP ESCALATOR, THE**
No holding back / Devil's sidewalk / Stupefaction / Love without greed / Julie Julie / Endless night / Paralysed / Manoeuvres / Empty lives / Beating of another heart
RE 1980 / Jun '96 / Razor & Tie
DIAB 843 / 26 Jan '98 / Diablo

☐ **VERTIGO (2CD Set) (Parker, Graham & The Rumour)**
Between you and me / I'm gonna use it now / You've got to be kidding / Howlin' wind / Back to schooldays / White honey / That's what they all say / Back door love / Back to school days / Silly thing / Chain of fools / Don't ask me questions / You can't hurry love / Soul shoes / Kansas City / Heat treatment / Hotel chambermaid / Black honey / Fools' gold / Hold back the night / (let me get) sweet on you / New York shuffle / Watch the moon come down / Raid / Lady doctor / I'm gonna tear your playhouse down / Heat in Harlem / Gypsy blood / Discovering Japan / Local girls / Nobody hurts you / You can't be too strong / Passion is no ordinary word / Saturday nite is dead / Love gets you twisted / Protection / Waiting for the UFO's / Don't get excited / Mercury poisoning / I want you back
5341002 / Oct '96 / Mercury

Parker, Johnny

☐ **AT THE 100 CLUB (Parker, Johnny Reunion Band & Ken Colyer)**
JCCD 3029 / Oct '97 / Jazz Crusade

Parker, Junior

☐ **LITTLE JUNIOR PARKER**
CDC 9002 / Oct '90 / LRC

Parker, Kenny

☐ **RAISE THE DEAD**
Too hot for me / Your girl's gone bad / Take it easy on a fool / She's the one for me / Shake hands with the devil / Baby cakes bop / Cryin' for help / You're so sharp / Blues for Mr. Bo / Crazy 'bout my baby / Brunoise / Afterglow
JSPCD 2109 / Jun '98 / JSP

Parker, Kim

☐ **BEAUTIFUL FRIENDSHIP, A (Parker, Kim & Hakan Rydin)**
FLCCD 146 / May '97 / Four Leaf Clover

☐ **SOMETIMES I'M BLUE**
SN 1133 / '86 / Soul Note

Parker, Knocky

☐ **KNOCKY PARKER & GALVANISED WASHBOARD BAND**
BCD 1 / Jan '94 / GHB

Parker, Leon

☐ **ABOVE AND BELOW**
Body movement / Bemsha swing / You don't know what love is / All my life / Above and below / Celebration / Epistrophy / BBBB / Evy / It's only a paper moon / Body movement II
4781982 / 26 Jan '98 / Sony Jazz

☐ **AWAKENING**
All my life / Tokyo / It is what it is / Mother Earth / Cruz / Axe bahia / Enlightenment / Awakening / Peaceful dream
CK 68076 / 1 Jun '98 / Sony Jazz

☐ **BELIEF**
Ray of light / Village song / Africa / Close your eyes / Calling out / Belief / Horizon Azul / Wide open / First child / In a sentimental mood / Belief (reprise)
4851382 / Sep '96 / Sony Jazz

Parker, Lewis

☐ **MASQUERADES AND SILHOUETTES**
Song of the desert / Crusades / 101 pianos (I've put out the lights) / Eyes of dreams / Shadows of Autumn / Theme from the ancients / Fake charades / Thousand fragments
CDSADX 4
CDSAD 4 / 25 May '98 / Melankolic

Parker, Maceo

☐ **DOING THEIR OWN THING (Parker, Maceo & All The Kings Men)**
Maceo / Got to getcha / Southwick / Funky woman / Shake it baby / Better half / Don't waste this world away / (I remember) Mr. Banks / Thank you for letting me be myself again
CPCD 8041 / Jun '94 / Charly

☐ **FUNKOVERLOAD**
Maceo's groove / Uptown up / Sing a simple song / Elephant's foot / Let's get it on / Youth of the world / We're on the move / Inner city blues / Going in circles / Do you love me
ESC 036572 / 24 Aug '98 / Escapade

☐ **FUNKY MUSIC MACHINE (Parker, Maceo & All The Kings Men)**
Funky music machine / I want to sing / Dreams / Feeling alright / Something / Born to wander / TSU / For no one / Make it with you / Funky tale to tell
CDSEWM 087 / Nov '93 / Southbound

Parker, Paul

☐ **BEST OF PAUL PARKER, THE**
HTCD 108 / 20 Apr '98 / Hot Productions

Parker, Ray Jr.

☐ **BEST OF RAY PARKER JNR (Parker, Ray Jr. & Raydio)**
Ghostbusters: *Parker, Ray Jr.* / You can't change that: *Raydio* / Woman needs love (just like you do): *Raydio* / More than one way to love a woman: *Raydio* / Stay the night: *Parker, Ray Jr.* / Let me go: *Parker, Ray Jr.* / Betcha can't love me just once: *Raydio* / Jack and Jill: *Raydio* / Other woman: *Parker, Ray Jr.* / Two places at the same time: *Parker, Ray Jr.* / Loving you: *Parker, Ray Jr.* / Girls are more fun: *Parker, Ray Jr.* / Is this a love thing: *Raydio* / For those who like to groove: *Raydio*
260365 / Dec '89 / Ariola

Parker, Robert

☐ **BAREFOOTIN'**
Barefootin' / Let's go baby (where the action is) / Little bit of something / Sneakin' Sally through the alley / Better luck in the summertime / You see me / Give me the country side of life / Get right down / Get ta steppin' / Hiccup / Hot and cold / Skinny dippin' / I like what you do to me / Disco doctor
CPCD 8013 / Feb '94 / Charly

Parker, Rupert

☐ **CLASSICAL WORKS**
MSPCD 9601 / Sep '96 / Mabley St.

☐ **DOUBLE HARP (2CD Set)**
(everything I do) I do it for you / Sacrifice / Unchained melody / Always a woman / Three times a lady / She's not there / More than words / Wonder why / One day I'll fly away / Albatross / Eternal flame / Best of my love / Oxygene / Miss you nights / On mabley street / Cafe andreas / With the flow / Through the mist (for tatiana) / She loves me not / Playing around / Walking down the road / Consequences iv / A clear winter's night / Hazy lazy days / Minstrel and the music box / Jah route / On a calm sea / Hot and bothered
MSPCD 9301 / Sep '93 / Mabley St.

☐ **ELECTRIC HARP - ORIGINAL WORKS**
MSPCD 9504 / Sep '95 / Mabley St.

☐ **HARPBEAT**
Earth song / How deep is your love / Tears in heaven / Unchained melody / You are not alone / Ironoco flow / Yesterday / Think twice / Free as a bird / Search for the hero / Kiss from a rose / I want to know what love is / Love is all around / Smile / Circle of life / Have you ever really loved a woman / Amazing grace
HARPCD 1 / Apr '96 / Focus

☐ **SOLO**
I will always love you / Wind beneath my wings / Sorry seems to be the hardest word / Don't give up / Jameela / Killing me softly / She loves me (she loves me not) / Summertime again / I dreamed a dream / Images / Wrapped around your finger / Imagine / Rain / Sometimes when we touch / Nights in white satin / Chica surena
MSPCD 9401 / Feb '94 / Mabley St.

☐ **SONGS FROM THE HARP (2CD Set)**
Bridge over troubled water / Lady in red / Saving all my love / Daniel / Jealous guy / Careless whisper / Jameela / Moondance / Without you / Can't help falling in love with you / Stay with me 'til dawn / Music of the night / Throwing it all away / Wonderful tonight / Could it be magic / Up where we belong / He was beautiful / Since I don't have you / Long and winding road / Nobody does it better / Annie's song / Bright eyes / Weather with you / Vincent / Variation on a dream / Hello / I heard it through the grapevine / Power of love
MSPCD 9404 / Nov '94 / Mabley St.

☐ **SONGS FROM THE HARP VOL.2 (2CD Set)**
MSPCD 9701 / 22 Sep '97 / Mabley St.

Parker, Sonny

☐ **COMPLETE SONNY PARKER 1948-1953, THE**
BMCD 6003 / Jul '96 / Blue Moon

Parker, Teddy

☐ **NACHTEXPRESS NACH ST. TROPEZ**
Nachtexpress nach St. Tropez / Hey little Lucy / Hatt ich ein weisses sportcoupe / Ich sah dich vorubergeh'n / Und dafur hast du nur ein Lacheln / Unser geheimnis / Geh' vorbei / Oh wie ist dah schon: *Parker, Teddy & Heidi Fischer* / Baby ich hol dich von der schule ab / Keine zeit / Wunderschones fremdes Madchen / Valentina / Heute bring' ich dich nach haus / So mussen teenager sein: *Parker, Teddy & Heidi Fischer* / Dream girl / Angela / Oh ja, oh yes, oh yeah / Baby muss das sein / Ein schones madchen so wie du / Oh Renata / Bossa nova in Panama / Holiday twist / In Copacabana / Liebe kalter als eis / Memphis Tennessee / Das madchen mit dem taurigen blick / Leider leider / Sieben tage ohne Susi / Das siehst du nur bei mir / Alles wird gut: *Parker, Teddy & Leonie Bruckner* / Bist du einsam heut' nacht: *Parker, Teddy & Leonie Bruckner*
BCD 15965 / Dec '96 / Bear Family

Parker, Terrence

☐ **DETROIT AFTER DARK**
Taste of heaven / Romancing da drum / You can do it / Play-ah-hate-ah / Floormaster / Real love / Once I was lost / Welcome 2 Southfield / 7 waves of soul / Detroit after dark
K7R 015CD / 13 Oct '97 / Studio K7

☐ **TRAGEDIES OF A PLASTIC SOUL**
K7R 007CD / Oct '96 / Studio K7

Parker, William

☐ **IN ORDER TO SURVIVE**
1201592 / Jan '96 / Black Saint

☐ **SUNRISE IN THE TONE WORLD (Parker, William & the Little Huey Creative Orchestra)**
AUM 002CD / 13 Apr '98 / Aum Fidelity

Parkin, Eric

☐ **MARIGOLD (Piano Impressions Of Billy Mayer)**
Legends of King Arthur / Almond blossom / April's fool / Harp of the winds / Marigold / Railroad rhythm / Shallow waters / From a Spanish lattice / Song of the fir tree / Nimble fingered gentleman / Evening primrose / Ace of diamonds / Ace of hearts / Joker
CHAN 8560 / '89 / Chandos

Parkins, Andrea

☐ **CAST IRON FACT**
KFWCD 184 / Oct '96 / Knitting Factory

Parkins, Zeena

☐ **NIGHTMARE ALLEY**
HYDROGEN 1 / 30 Mar '98 / Table Of The Elements

☐ **URSA'A DOOR**
VICTOCD 018 / Nov '94 / Victo

Parkinson, Chris

☐ **OUT OF HIS TREE**
PAN 147CD / Apr '94 / Pan

Parkinson, Doug

☐ **I'LL BE AROUND (Parkinson, Doug Southern Star Band)**
D 19855 / Oct '97 / Festival

☐ **IN AND OUT OF FOCUS 1966-1975**
Sally go 'round the roses / Hey Gyp (dig the slowness) / And things unsaid / I had a dream / Advice / Dear Prudence / Without you / This must be the end / Hair / Baby blue eyes / Then I run / Today I feel no pain / Purple curtains / Pour out all you've got / Got to get a message to you / Do not go gentle / Caroline / Gotta get a groove / Love gun / Love is like a cloudy day / Everlasting love
RVCD 58 / Feb '97 / Raven

Parks, Steve

☐ **MOVIN' IN THE RIGHT DIRECTION (The Complete Solid Smoke Sessions)**
All in a day / Just ask me / Everything's gonna be OK / Don't stop now / Sadness in my samba / Under the boardwalk/(I've got) sand in my shoes / Movin' in the right direction / One who really loves me / Golden key/Tag / You make it easy for me / Look in your eyes / Shimmy and jive / Wrong decision / Stop drop everything / Wonderful / Should've been wishing (instead of dreaming) / I hope your dreams come true / You excite me / Island so far away
WESA 817 / May '98 / Westside

Parks, Van Dyke

☐ **CLANG OF THE YANKEE REAPER**
Clang of the Yankee reaper / City on the hill / Pass that stage / Another dream / You're a real sweetheart / Love is the answer / Iron man / Tribute to Spree / Soul Train / Cannon in D
7599261852 / Jan '96 / Warner Bros.

☐ **DISCOVER AMERICA**
Jack Palance / Introduction / Bing Crosby / Steelband music / Four Mills brothers / Be careful / John Jones / FDR in Trinidad / Sweet Trinidad / Occapella / Sailin' shoes / Riverboat / Ode to Tobago / Your own comes first / G man hoover / Stars and stripes forever
7599261452 / Jan '96 / Warner Bros.

☐ **IDIOSYNCRATIC PATH**
Donovan's colours / John Jones / Pass that stage / Ode to Tobago / Attic / Clang of the Yankee reaper / Four mills brothers / You're a real sweetheart / Sailin' shoes / Vine street / Palm desert / Tribute to spree / Iron man / Sweet Trinidad / Be careful / Bing Crosby / Steelband music / Your own comes first / Stars and stripes forever
DIAB 807 / Oct '95 / Diablo

☐ **JUMP**
Jump / Opportunity for two / Come along / I ain't going home / Many a mile to go / Taps / Invitation to sin / Home / After the ball / Look away / Hominy grove
7599238292 / Jan '96 / Warner Bros.

☐ SONG CYCLE
Vine Street / Palm desert / Widow's walk / Laurel Canyon Boulevard / All golden / Van Dyke Parks / Public domain / Donovan's colours / Attic / By the people / Potpourri
EDCD 207 / Jul '88 / Edsel

Parlan, Horace

☐ HI-FLY (Parlan, Horace Trio)
SCCD 31417 / 21 Aug '97 / Steeplechase

☐ JOE VAN ENKHUIZEN MEETS THE RHYTHM SECTION
CDSJP 249 / '88 / Timeless Jazz

☐ ON THE SPUR OF THE MOMENT
On the spur of the moment / Skoo chee / And that I am so in love / Al's tune / Ray C / Pyramid / On the spur of the moment / Pyramid
8217352 / 2 Feb '98 / Blue Note

☐ US THREE
Us three / I want to be loved / Come rain or shine / Wadin' / Lady is a tramp / Walkin' / Return engagement
CDP 8565812 / Jun '97 / Blue Note

Parliament

☐ CLONES OF DR. FUNKENSTEIN, THE
Prelude / Gamin' on ya / Dr. Funkenstein / Children of production / Gettin' to know you / Do that stuff / Everybody is on the one / I've been watching you / Funkin' for fun
8426202 / Feb '91 / Casablanca

☐ EARLY YEARS, THE
Red hot Mama / Come in out of the rain / Fantasy is reality / Breakdown / Loose booty / Unfinished instrumental / I call my baby pussycat / Put love in your life / Little old country boy / Moonshine heather (takin' care of business) / Oh Lord, why Lord/Prayer / My automobile / There is nothing before me but thang / Funky woman / Livin' the life / Silent boatman
DEEPM 023 / Jun '97 / Deep Beats

☐ GIVE UP THE FUNK (The Best Of Parliament)
5269952 / Sep '95 / Mercury

☐ TEAR THE ROOF OFF THE SUCKER 1974-1980 (2CD Set)
P. funk (wants to get funked up) / Up for the down stroke / Bop gun (endangered species) / Dr. funkenstein's supergroovalisticprosifunkstication medl / Mothership connection (starchild) / Dr. funkenstein / Testify / Mr. wiggles / Aqua boogie (a psychoalphadiscobetabioaquadoloop) / All your goodies are gone / Do that stuff / Party people / Prelude / Give up the funk (tear the roof off the sucker) / Chocolate city / Funkentelechy / Theme from the black hole / Big bang theory / Children of production (live) / Flash light / Ride on / Fantasy is reality / Rumpofsteelskin / Agony of defeet / Funkin' for fun
5144172 / Jun '93 / Phonogram

Parliaments

☐ TESTIFYIN'
I wanna testify / Time / Good ole music / I can feel the ice melting / Don't be sore at me / All your goodies are gone / Little man / Goose (that laid the golden egg) / What you been growing / Look at what I almost missed / New day begins / Let's make it easy / All your goodies are gone / Baby I owe you something / I'll wait / I'll wait / Heart trouble
GSCD 119 / 29 Sep '97 / Goldmine

Parmley, David

☐ I KNOW A GOOD THING
I know a good thing when I feel it / Grandpa's radio / Have you come to say goodbye / She keeps hanging on / Someone took my place with you / Morristown / Excuse me / Down home / Someone on her mind / Sometimes silence says it all / Live and let live / From cotton to satin
SHCD 3777 / Jan '89 / Sugar Hill

Parnell, Geoff

☐ BRITPOP YEARS, THE
Alright / Wonderwall / Disco 2000 / High and dry / Girl like you / Changingman / Morning comes / Country house / Spaceman / Whatever / Venus as a boy / Two princes
CDMFP 6226 / Aug '96 / Music For Pleasure

Parnell, Jack

☐ LIVE FROM RONNIE'S
Jamfs are coming / Autumn leaves / Whisper not / El Cahon / Airigin / Tenor madness / Alone together / Fried bananas / You don't know what love is / Whee
CDSIV 1142 / Jul '95 / Horatio Nelson

Parnell, Lee Roy

☐ EVERY NIGHT'S A SATURDAY NIGHT
Lucky me, lucky you / You can't get there from here / One foot in front of the other / All that matters anymore / Every night's a Saturday night / Tender touch / Better word for love / Honky tonk night time man / Baton rouge / Mama screw your wig on tight
7822188412 / Jul '97 / RCA

☐ LOVE WITHOUT MERCY
What kind of fool do you think I am / Back in my arms again / Rock / Ain't no short way home / Love without mercy / Road scholar / Night after night / Done deal / Tender moment / Rollercoaster
07822186842 / Jan '94 / Arista

☐ ON THE ROAD
07822187392 / Jun '94 / Arista

☐ WE ALL GET LUCKY SOMETIMES
Little bit of you / Knock yourself out / Heart's desire / When a woman loves a man / If the house is rockin' / We all get lucky sometimes / Saved by the grace of your love / Givin' water to a drowning man / I had to let it go / Squeeze me in / Catwalk
07822187902 / Aug '95 / Arista

Parnell, Phil

☐ DEAR JO
SLAMCD 227 / Jan '98 / Slam

Parov, Nikola

☐ KILIM
Anonym / Trance Danubius / Diva's smile / Mayo woman / Satyr's night / Tsami / Ritual / Passio
HNCD 1408 / Mar '97 / Hannibal

Parr, John

☐ UNDER PARR
CHP 61514 / 5 Jan '98 / Bud

Parra, Violeta

☐ PAROLES AND MUSIQUES
3020782 / Jun '97 / Last Call

Parris, Rebecca

☐ LIVE AT CHAN'S
1856310022 / 27 Apr '98 / Shira

☐ SPRING
Alone at night / It's you / Tell me on a Ferris wheel / You look so good / Save your love for me / He comes to me for comfort / You'll finally understand / Not like this / Spring
8443132 / Apr '94 / Limelight

Parrondo, Jose

☐ RECITAL DE CANTE FLAMENCO (Parrondo, Jose & Miguel Iven)
Malaguenas / Tientos y tangos / Solea / Tonas / Peteneras / Seguiriyas / Bulerias
93052 / Jul '95 / Emocion

Parry, Dylan & Neil

☐ GOREUON (20 Welsh Country Songs) (Parry, Dylan & Neil/Traed Wadin)
Hen wlad llyn: *Parry, Dylan & Neil* / Eiddo i arall: *Parry, Dylan & Neil* / Cydio'n dy law: *Parry, Dylan & Neil* / Waunfawr: *Parry, Dylan & Neil* / Ei gwen yn y gwin: *Parry, Dylan & Neil* / Yr hen rebel: *Parry, Dylan & Neil* / Heli'n fy ngwaed: *Parry, Dylan & Neil* / Dyri i mi: *Parry, Dylan & Neil* / O mor braf fydd bod yn ol: *Parry, Dylan & Neil* / Ffrind: *Parry, Dylan & Neil* / Lliwiau: *Parry, Dylan & Neil* / Nid yw'r hen bentre fel y bu: *Parry, Dylan & Neil* / Troi'r cloc yn ol: *Parry, Dylan & Neil* / Blodau gwyn: *Parry, Dylan & Neil* / Potel fach o win: *Traed Wadin* / Mynd fel bom: *Traed Wadin* / Pys: *Traed Wadin* / Galilea: *Traed Wadin* / Hitio'r botel: *Traed Wadin* / 'Fory heb ei gyffwrdd: *Traed Wadin*
SCD 2161 / May '97 / Sain

Parry, Harry

☐ GONE WITH THE WIND
Basin Street ball / Crazy rhythm / Sophisticated lady / Mr. Five by Five / If I had you / I can't dance / Don't you know I care (or don't you care to) / Who's sorry now / Someone's in the kitchen with Dinah / Stardust / I never knew / Boogie rides to Yorke / Onm the sunny side of the street / Don't be that way / Angry / Darktown strutters ball / Blues around my bed / Champagne / My favourite dream / Blue Lou / Bounce me brother with a solid four / Honeysuckle rose / Gone with the wind / Parry party
RAJCD 840 / Sep '97 / Empress

Parsons, Alan

☐ ALAN PARSONS ON AIR
Blue blue sky / Too close to the sun / Blown by the wind / Cloudbreak / I can't look down / Brother up in Heaven / Fall free / Apollo / So far away / One day to fly / Blue blue sky
TOTCD 6 / Mar '97 / Total

☐ AMMONIA AVENUE (Parsons, Alan Project)
Prime time / Let me go home / One good reason / Since the last goodbye / Don't answer me / Dancing on a high wire / You don't believe / Pipeline / Ammonia Avenue
258885 / '88 / Arista

☐ BEST OF ALAN PARSONS LIVE, THE
INDELCD 17 / 25 May '98 / Indelible

☐ BEST OF ALAN PARSONS PROJECT, THE (Parsons, Alan Project)
I wouldn't want to be like you / Eye in the sky / Games people play / Time / Pyramania / You wouldn't believe / Lucifer / Psychobabble / Damned if I do / Don't let it show / Can't take it with you / Old and wise
610052 / Aug '95 / Arista

☐ EVE (Parsons, Alan Project)
Lucifer / You lie down with the dogs / I'd rather be a man / You won't be there / Winding me up / Damned if I do / Don't hold back / Secret garden / If I could change your mind
258981 / '88 / Arista

☐ EYE IN THE SKY (Parsons, Alan Project)
Syrius / Eye in the sky / Children of the moon / Gemini / Silence and I / You're gonna get your fingers burned / Psychobabble / Mammagamma / Step by step / Old and wise
258718 / Aug '95 / Arista

☐ GREATEST HITS LIVE
TOTCD 7 / Jul '97 / Total

☐ I ROBOT (Parsons, Alan Project)
I wouldn't want to be like you / Some other time / Breakdown / Don't let it show / Voice / Nucleus / Day after day / Total eclipse / Genesis ch.1 vs.32 / I robot
259651 / Mar '89 / Arista

☐ PLAYS THE ALAN PARSONS PROJECT (Powell, Andrew)
Lucifer (Mamma Gamma) / Time / Games people play / Robot suite / Damned if I do / Pavane / What goes up / Eye in the sky / Old and wise
DC 876742 / May '97 / Disky

☐ PYRAMID (Parsons, Alan Project)
Voyager / What goes up... / Eagle will rise again / One more river / Can't take it with you / In the lap of the gods / Pyramania / Hyper gamma spaces / Shadow of a lonely man
258983 / Apr '88 / Arista

☐ TRY ANYTHING ONCE (Parsons, Alan Project)
Three of me / Turn it up / Wine from the water / Breakaway / Jigue / Mr. Time / Siren song / Back against the wall / Re-jigue / Oh life (there must be more) / I'm talking to you / Dreamscape
74321167302 / Sep '96 / Arista

☐ TURN OF A FRIENDLY CARD (Parsons, Alan Project)
Turn of a friendly card / Gold bug / Time / Games people play / I don't wanna go home / Nothing left to lose / May be a price to pay
258982 / May '88 / Arista

☐ VERY BEST OF ALAN PARSONS PROJECT LIVE, THE (Parsons, Alan Project)
Sirius / Eye in the sky / Psychobabble / Raven / Time / Luciferama / Old and wise / You're gonna get your fingers burned / Prime time / Limelight / Don't answer me / Standing on higher ground / When / Take the money and run / You're the voice
09026682292 / Jan '96 / RCA Victor

☐ VULTURE CULTURE (Parsons, Alan Project)
Let's talk about me / Separate lives / Days are numbers (The traveller) / Sooner or later / Vulture culture / Hawkeye / Somebody out there / Same old song and dance
258884 / '88 / Arista

Parsons, Gram

☐ COSMIC AMERICAN MUSIC (The Grech Tapes 1972)
Song for you / Kentucky blues / Streets of Baltimore / Folsom Prison blues / Lovesick blues / New soft shoe / How much I've lied / Still feeling blue / Ain't no Beatle, ain't no Rolling Stone / How can I forget you / Cry one more time / Song for you / Streets of Baltimore / That's all it took / Somebody's back in town / More and more / Teaching Emmy to sweep out the ashes / Daddy's fiddle / We'll sweep out the ashes in the morning / Cold cold heart / That's all it took / Song for you
CDSD 077 / Aug '96 / Sundown

☐ GP/GRIEVOUS ANGEL
Still feeling blue / We'll sweep out the ashes in the morning / Song for you / Streets of Baltimore / She / That's all it took / New soft shoe / Kiss the children / Cry one more time / How much I've lied / Big mouth blues / Return of the grievous angel / Hearts on fire / I can't dance / Brass buttons / Thousand dollar wedding / Cash on the barrelhead / Hickory wind / Love hurts / Ooh Las Vegas / In my hour of darkness
7599261082 / Jan '94 / WEA

☐ LIVE 1973 (Parsons, Gram & Fallen Angels)
We'll sweep out the ashes / Country baptizing / Drug store truck drivin' man / Big mouth blues / New soft shoe / Cry one more time / Streets of Baltimore / That's all it took / Love hurts / California cottonfields / Encore medley
8122727262 / Mar '97 / Rhino

☐ SAFE AT HOME (Parsons, Gram International Submarine Band)
Blue eyes / I must have been somebody else / You've known a satisfied mind / Folsom Prison blues / That's alright Mama / Millers cave / I still miss someone / Luxury liner / Strong boy / Do you know how it feels to be lonesome
CDSD 071 / Aug '97 / Sundown

☐ WARM EVENINGS, PALE MORNINGS AND BOTTLED BLUES 1963-1973
Zah's blues: *Shilohs* / Blue eyes: *International Submarine Band* / Strong boy: *International Submarine Band* / Truck driving man: *International Submarine Band* / Hot burrito: *Flying Burrito Brothers* / Christine's tune: *Flying Burrito Brothers* / Sin City: *Flying Burrito Brothers* / Dark end of the street: *Flying Burrito Brothers* / Wild horses: *Flying Burrito Brothers* / She: *Parsons, Gram & Emmylou Harris* / New soft shoe: *Parsons, Gram & Emmylou Harris* / We'll sweep out the ashes in the morning: *Parsons, Gram & Emmylou Harris* / Brass buttons: *Parsons, Gram & Emmylou Harris* / Return of the grievous angel: *Parsons, Gram & Emmylou Harris* / Drug store truck drivin' man: *Parsons, Gram & Emmylou Harris* / Brand new heartache: *Parsons, Gram & Emmylou Harris* / Love hurts: *Parsons, Gram & Emmylou Harris* / I'm your toy
RVCD 24 / Jun '92 / Raven

Parsons, Niamh

☐ LOOSELY CONNECTED
Katie Campbell's rambles / Streets of Forbes / Tinkerman's daughter / Little big time / Lover's ghost / Man of Arran / North Amerikay / We two people / One morning in May / Play a merry jig / Where are you (tonight I wonder) / Don't give your heart away
CDTRAX 052 / May '92 / Greentrax

☐ LOOSEN UP
Big bad wolf / Seeing things / Fancy waistcoat / Clohinne winds / Gently born/Micky Dans / Closer to you / Briar and the rose / I know my faith (is worth much more than me) / Heartbound express / Loosen up
GLCD 1167 / Jul '97 / Green Linnet

Partisans

☐ POLICE STORY
GET 15CD / May '97 / Get Back

☐ TIME WAS RIGHT, THE
I never needed you / Anger and fear / Money rolls in / Only 21 / Time was right / White flag / 17 years / Change / Arms race / Come clean / Over dose / Partisans / Blind ambition / Change / Come clean / I never needed you / Time was right
AHOYCD 070 / 3 Nov '97 / Captain Oi

Partisans Of Vilna

☐ SONGS OF WORLD WAR II, THE
S'iz geven a zumertog / Yisrolik / Unter dayne vayse shtern / Yid, du partizaner / Blayene platn / Itzik Vitnberg / Shtiler, shtiler / Zemlyanka / Tsu eyns, tsvey, dray / Das Meydel vun Vald / Shtil di nakht / Zog nit keynmol
FF 70450 / 15 Dec '97 / Flying Fish

Parton, Dolly

☐ ESSENTIAL DOLLY PARTON VOL.1, THE (I Will Always Love You)
Nine to five / Simple woman / Think about love / But you know I love you / Do I ever cross your mind / Real love / You're the only one / Sweet summer lovin' / Heartbreak Express / Tie our love (in a double knot) / Islands in the stream: *Rogers, Kenny & Dolly Parton* / Two doors down / God won't get you / Don't call it love / To Daddy / Starting over again / Tennessee homesick blues / Save the last dance for me / Old flames (can't hold a candle to you) / I will always love you
74321665332 / Feb '96 / RCA

☐ ESSENTIAL DOLLY PARTON VOL.2, THE
Muleskinner blues / Touch your woman / Bargain store / Coat of many colours / My Tennessee mountain home / Joshua / Just because I'm a woman / Jolene / I will always love you / Light of a clear blue morning / Here you come again / Love is like a butterfly / We used to / Me and little Andy / It's all wrong but it's all right / All I can do / Heartbreaker / I really got the feeling / Seeker / Wings of a dove
7863669332 / May '97 / RCA

☐ HEART SONGS
Heart song / I'm thinking tonight of my blue eyes / Mary of the wild moor / In the pines / My blue tears / Applejack / Coat of many colours / Smoky mountain memories / Night train to Memphis / What a friend we have in Jesus / Hold fast to the right / Walter Henry Hagan / Barbara Allen / Brave little soldier / To Daddy / True blue / Longer than always / Wayfaring stranger / My Tennessee mountain home / Heart song (reprise) / Cas Walker theme / Black draught theme / PMS blues
4772762 / 13 Jul '98 / Columbia

☐ JOLENE
Jolene / When someone wants to leave / River of happiness / Early morning breeze / Highlight of my life / I will always love you / Randy / Living on memories of you / Lonely comin' down / It must be you
WMCD 5638 / May '94 / Disky

☐ TREASURES
Peace train / Today I started loving you again / Just when I need you most / Something's burning / Before the next teardrop falls / After the goldrush / Walking on sunshine / Behind closed doors / Don't let me cross over / Satin sheets / For the good times
RTD 80326 / Oct '96 / Rising Tide

☐ TRIO (Parton, Dolly/Linda Ronstadt/ Emmylou Harris)
Pain of loving you / Making plans / To know him is to love him / Hobo's meditation / Wildflowers / Telling me lies / My dear companion / Those memories of you / I've had enough / Rose wood casket / Farther along
9254912 / Feb '95 / WEA

☐ ULTIMATE COLLECTION, THE (A Life In Music)
Jolene / Islands in the stream / Here you come again / I will always love you / Love is like a butterfly / Everything's beautiful: *Parton, Dolly & Willie Nelson* / Just because I'm a woman / Why's you come in here lookin' like that / Last thing on my mind: *Parton, Dolly & Porter Wagoner* / In the ghetto: *Parton, Dolly & Willie Nelson* / Bargain store / 9 to 5 / Joshua / Heartbreaker / Rockin' years: *Parton, Dolly & Ricky Van Shelton* / To daddy / Coat of many colours / Yellow roses / Applejack / Eagle when she flies / Put it off until tomorrow: *Parton, Dolly & Loretta Lynn/ Tammy Wynette* / Dumb blonde / My Tennessee mountain home / Just when I need you most: *Parton, Dolly & Alison Krauss* / I will always love you
743214436325 / 27 Oct '97 / RCA

Partridge, Andy

☐ THROUGH THE HILL (Partridge, Andy & Harold Budd)
Hand 19 / Through the hill / Great valley of gongs / Western island of apples / Anima mundi / Hand 20 / Place of odd glances / Well for the sweat of the moon / Tenochtitlan's numberless bridges / Ceramic avenue / Hand 21 / Missing pieces in the game of salt and onyx / Mantle of peacock bones / Bronze coins showing genitals / Bearded aphrodite / Hand 22
ASCD 021 / 30 Mar '98 / All Saints

Party Animals

☐ GOOD VIBRATIONS
DB 47862 / Oct '96 / Deep Blue

☐ PARTY AT WORLD ACCESS NL
DB 47812 / 1 Dec '97 / Deep Blue

Party Diktator

☐ WORLDWIDE
DEP 003CD / Nov '92 / Dead Eye

Party Poppers

☐ 40 SING-ALONG FAVOURITES
Down at the old Bull And Bush / Daisy bell / Two lovely black eyes / Joshua / Oh oh Antonio / I'm forever blowing bubbles / Hello hello, who's your lady friend / You must have been a beautiful baby / Daddy wouldn't buy me a bow-wow / Waiting at the church / It's a long way to Tipperary / Pack up your troubles in your old kit back / Goodbye Dolly Gray / Bless 'em all / Hold your hand out, naughty boy / I do like to be beside the seaside / Lilly of Laguna / Tip toe tho' the tulips with me / Honeysuckle and the bee / Roamin' in the gloamin' / On mother Kelly's doorstep / Roll out the barrel / Who were you with last night / Don't dilly dally on the way / When you're smiling / Ma, he's making eyes at me / Side by side / (In) a shanty in old Shanty Town / On a slow boat to China / Bye bye blackbird / I'm shy, Mary Ellen, I'm shy / Let me call you sweetheart / When I grow too old to dream / On moonlight bay / By the light of the silvery moon / If you were the only girl in the world / You were meant for me / Ain't she sweet / Nellie Dean / Show me the way to go home
CDMFP 6105 / Jan '94 / Music For Pleasure

☐ ALL TOGETHER NOW (20 Sing-Along Anthems)
Three lions / We are the champions / Simply the best / We all stand together/All you need is love/Give peace a chan / On Ilkely Moor / We shall not be moved / When the Saints go marching in / Glory glory hallelujah / I'm forever blowing bubbles / Three lions / In my Liverpool home / He's got the whole world in his hands / Swing low, sweet chariot / Scotland the Brave / End of the road / Men of Harlech / I love you love me love / You'll never walk alone / Rule Britannia / Land of hope and glory / 'Ere we go
CDMFP 6278 / Nov '96 / Music For Pleasure

☐ LET'S HAVE A PARTY
Let's have a party / Agadoo / Let's twist again / March of the Mods / Birdie song / Simon says / Lambeth walk / Boomps a daisy / Y viva Espana / Paloma blanca / La Bamba / I came, I saw, I conga'd / Scotland the brave / Hokey cokey dance / Knees up Mother Brown / Can can / Hi ho silver lining / Last waltz / Auld lang syne
CDMFP 5948 / Oct '92 / Music For Pleasure

☐ SINGALONG CHRISTMAS PARTY
Here we come a wassailing / I believe / Rockin' around the Christmas tree / Mary had a baby / Jingle bell rock / Baby it's cold outside / Go tell it to the mountain / Twelve days of Christmas / Hark the herald angels sing / O come all ye faithful / Once in royal David's city / See amid the winters snow / Angels from the realms of glory / Wonderful Christmas time / Ding dong merrily on high / On Christmas night all / First Noel / Away in a manger
CH 877592 / 30 May '97 / Disky

☐ SINGALONG CHRISTMAS PARTY VOL.1
White Christmas / I saw Mommy kissing Santa Claus / Let it snow, let it snow, let it snow / Frosty the snowman / Happy holiday / That's what I'd like for Christmas / When Santa got stuck up the chimney / It's the most wonderful time of the year / We three kings of Orient are / Jingle bells / Good King Wenceslas / Kings' horses / Santa Claus is coming to town / Rudolph the red nosed reindeer / Holiday season / Mary's boy child / When a child is born / Silent night / Deck the halls with boughs of holly / Stop the cavalry / Have yourself a merry little Christmas / Christmas song / Do you hear what I hear / Christmas dreaming / Little donkey / Winter wonderland / It's beginning to look like Christmas / I saw three ships / All I want for Christmas (is my two front teeth) / Silver bells / Sleigh ride / Joy to the world / I wish it could be Christmas every day / Merry Christmas everybody / We wish you a merry Christmas / Auld lang syne / Christmas alphabet / Fairy on the Christmas tree / Jolly old St. Nicholas / Mr. Santa / Mistletoe and wine / Little drummer boy / O little town of Bethlehem / It came upon a midnight clear / God rest ye merry gentlemen
CDMFP 5795 / Dec '94 / Music For Pleasure

☐ SINGALONG CHRISTMAS PARTY VOL.2
Good Christian men rejoice / Here we come a-wassailing / I believe in Father Christmas / Rockin' around the Christmas tree / Mary had a baby boy / Jingle bell rock / Baby it's cold outside / Go tell it on the mountain / Twelve days of Christmas / Hark the herald angels sing / O come all ye faithful (adeste fidelis) / One in royal David's city / See amid the winter's snow / Angels from the realms of Glory / Saviour's day / Wonderful Christmas time / Ding dong merrily on high / On Christmas night all Christians sing / O Christmas tree / First Noel / Away in a manger / Happy Christmas (war is over) / Do they know it's Christmas / Scarlet ribbons / Coventry carol / While shepherds watched their flocks by night / Rocking carol / Rise up shepherd and follow / Last Christmas / Merry Christmas everyone / Rockin' around the Christmas tree (reprise)
CDMFP 6180 / Oct '96 / Music For Pleasure

Parveen, Abida

☐ BEST OF ABIDA PARVEEN, THE
SHCD 64086 / May '97 / Shanachie

Pasadena Roof Orchestra

☐ BEST OF THE PASADENA ROOF ORCHESTRA, THE
TRTCD 199 / Jun '95 / TrueTrax

☐ BREAKAWAY
Breakaway / Jeepers creepers / Piccolo Pete / Very thought of you / Continental / Temptation rag / Sweet Georgia Brown / Ain't misbehavin' / Play that hot guitar / Rockin' chair / That's a plenty / Zing went the strings of my heart / Tom Thumb's drum / Love is good for anything that ails you / Stompin' at the Savoy / Just one more chance / Man from the South
CD PRO 3 / Oct '91 / Pasadena Roof Orchestra

☐ COLLECTION, THE
It don't mean a thing if it ain't got that swing / Bye bye blackbird / Black bottom / Charleston / Temptation rag / Blue skies / What is this thing called love / Lullaby of Broadway / Nobody's sweetheart / You're the cream in my coffee / Singin' in the rain / Top hat, white tie and tails / I won't dance / Three little words / Stormy weather / Don't be that way / I'll see you again / Pasadena / Georgia / Whispering / Paddlin' Madelin' home / Varsity drag / Here's to the next time / Cheek to cheek
CCSCD 189 / Jul '88 / Castle

☐ GREATEST HITS
CD 845006 / Jan '94 / Bluebird

☐ HOME IN PASADENA
PDSCD 527 / Aug '96 / Pulse

☐ PASADENA - THE 25TH ANNIVERSARY
You ought to see Sally on sunday / Lullaby of broadway / Ol' man river / By the fireside / Puttin' on the ritz / Kansas city kitty / Old man blues / Happy days are here again / Home in Pasadena / You're my everything / Me and Jane in a plane / I want to be happy / Maple leaf ray / Some of these days / As time goes by / St. Louis blues
CDPRO 4 / Mar '94 / Pasadena Roof Orchestra

☐ RHYTHM IS OUR BUSINESS
CDPRO 5 / Oct '96 / Pasadena Roof Orchestra

☐ SENTIMENTAL JOURNEY
In the mood / In the mood / I can dream can't I / Someone to watch over me / 'deed I do / Boogie woogie bugle boy / Sentimental journey / Lullaby of broadway / Beer barrel polka / Side by side / Rum and coca cola / Hold tight / Blue skies / Don't sit under the apple tree / Bei mir bist du schoen (part 1) / Alexander's ragtime band / Ev'ry time we say goodbye
MCCD 110 / Jun '93 / Music Club

☐ STEPPING OUT
Who walks in / My melancholy baby / How 'm doin / Creole love call / Sahara / Skirts / Pennies from Heaven / Latin from Manhattan / Business in 'F' / I can't get started (with you) / Louisiana / Golden wedding / I only have eyes for you / Minnie the moocher / Stepping out / Pasadena
CDPRO 2 / Jan '90 / Pasadena Roof Orchestra

☐ TAKE ME BACK (Pasadena Roof Orchestra & The Swing Sisters)
When the midnight choo choo / Leaves for Alabam / Old yazoo / Dinah / Heebie jeebies / Nightinggale sang in Berkeley Square / It don't mean a thing if it ain't got that swing / Everybody loves my baby / Mood indigo / Civilization / Can't help lovin' that man / Sentimental gentleman fron Georgia / I'm sorry for myself / When I take my sugar to tea / Shoo shoo baby
EMPRCD 627 / Jun '96 / Emporio

Pasadenas

☐ DEFINITIVE COLLECTION, THE
Tribute (right on) / Riding on a train / Enchanted lady / New love / Love thing / Reeling / Another lover / Love changes / Cry my tears (posthumously yours) / Base is slipping / I'm doing fine now / Make it with you / I believe in miracles / Moving in the right direction / Let's stay together / Everybody is singing love songs / Little love / He'll give you all
4875632 / 13 Jul '98 / Columbia

☐ TRIBUTE (The Best Of The Pasadenas)
Tribute (right on) / Riding on a train / I'm doing fine now / Living in the footsteps of another man / Enchanted lady / Love thing / Another lover / New love / Let's stay together / Reeling / I believe in miracles / Funny feeling / Make it with you / Moving in the right direction / I'm doing fine now / Riding on a train
4812852 / 26 Jan '98 / Columbia

Pascoal, Hermeto

☐ MUSICA LIVRE DE HERMETO PASCOAL, A (The Free Music Of Hermeto Pascoal)
Bebe / Carinhoso / Pin / Sereiarei / Asa branca / Gaio de roseira
8246212 / Apr '94 / Verve

Pass, Joe

☐ APPASSIONATO
Relaxin' at Camarillo / Grooveyard / Body and soul / Nica's dream / Tenderly / When it's sleepy time down South / Red door / Gee baby ain't I good to you / Li'l darlin' / That's Earl brother / Stuffy / You're driving me crazy
CD 2310946 / Apr '94 / Pablo

☐ AT AKRON UNIVERSITY
It's a wonderful world / Body and soul / Bridgework / Tarde / Time in / Duke Ellington medley / Joy spring / I'm glad there is you
CD 2308249 / May '94 / Pablo

☐ AT THE MONTREUX JAZZ FESTIVAL 1975
You are the sunshine of my life / Very thought of you / Nobs / Li'l darlin' / Blues for Nina / How long has this been going on / More than you know / Grete / Nuages / I'm glad there is you / Willow weep for me
OJCCD 9342 / Nov '97 / Original Jazz Classics

☐ BETTER DAYS
EFA 120682 / May '95 / Hotwire

☐ BLUES DUES (Live At Long Beach City College)
Wave / Blues in G / All the things you are / Round midnight / Here's that rainy day / Duke Ellington's Sophisticated Lady melange / Blues dues / Bluesette / Honeysuckle rose
OJCCD 964 / Jul '98 / Original Jazz Classics

☐ BLUES FOR FRED
Cheek to cheek / Night and day / Blues for Fred / Oh lady be good / Foggy day / Be myself / They can't take that away from me / Dancing in the dark / I concentrate on you / Way you look tonight
CD 2310931 / Apr '94 / Pablo

☐ CHECKMATE (Pass, Joe & Jimmy Rowles)
What's your story Morning Glory / So rare / As long as I live / Marquita / Stardust / We'll be together again / Can't we be friends / 'Deed I do / 'Tis Autumn / God bless the child
CD 2310865 / May '94 / Pablo

☐ CHOPS (Pass, Joe & Niels Pederson)
Have you met Miss Jones / Oleo / Lover man / Five pound blues / Come rain or come shine / Quiet nights / Tricrotism / Old folks / Yardbird suite / Your own sweet way
OJCCD 786 / Jun '94 / Original Jazz Classics

☐ DUETS (Pass, Joe & John Pisano)
Alone together / Baileywick / S'il vous plait / Lonely woman / Nina's birthday song / You were meant for me / Satie / Blues for the wee folk / For him H / Back to back
23109592 / Dec '96 / Pablo

☐ EXIMIOUS (Pass, Joe Trio)
Foxy chick and a cool cat / Robbin's nest / Lush life / Serenata / We'll be together again / You to me are everything / Love for sale / Everything I got belongs to you / Night and day / Speak low
CD 2310877 / Apr '87 / Pablo

☐ FINALLY (Live In Stockholm) (Pass, Joe & Red Mitchell)
Shadow of your smile / Have you met Miss Jones / I thought about you / Doxy / All the things you are / These foolish things / Blue moon / For Django / Finally / Pennies from Heaven / Softly as in a morning sunrise
5126032 / Apr '93 / EmArCy

☐ I REMEMBER CHARLIE PARKER
Just friends / Easy to love / Summertime / April in Paris / Everything happens to me / Laura / They can't take that away from me / I didn't know what time it was / If I should lose you / Out of nowhere (concept 1) / Out of nowhere (concept 2)
OJCCD 602 / Nov '95 / Original Jazz Classics

☐ IRA, GEORGE AND JOE (Joe Pass Loves Gershwin)
Bidin' my time / How long has this been going on / Soon / Oh lady be good / But not for me / Foggy day / It ain't necessarily so / Our love is here to stay / 'S wonderful / Nice work if you can get it / Embraceable you
OJCCD 828 / Jun '95 / Original Jazz Classics

☐ JOE PASS IN HAMBURG
On a clear day / Polka For Nina / Dots and moonbeams / Love for sale / Indian summer / Sweet bossa / Fragments of blues / I'll know / Summer night / Waltz for Django / More than you know / Star eyes / Lullabye of the leaves / Soft winds / Sister Sadie
ACT 91002 / Sep '97 / Act

☐ JOY SPRING
Joy spring / Some time ago / Night that has a thousand eyes / Relaxin' at Camarillo / There is no greater love
CDP 8352222 / Jan '96 / Pacific Jazz

☐ LIVE AT DONTE'S (Pass, Joe Trio)
What have they done to my song Ma / You stepped out of a dream / Time for love / Donte's inferno / You are the sunshine of my life / Secret love / Sweet Georgia Brown / Stompin' at the Savoy / Darn that dream / Milestones / Lullaby of the leaves / What are you doing the rest of your life / Blues for Pam
CD 2620114 / Apr '87 / Pablo

☐ LIVE AT LONG BEACH COLLEGE
Wave / Blues in G / All the things you are / 'Round midnight / Here's that rainy day / Duke Ellington's sophisticated lady melange / Blues dues / Bluesette / Honeysuckle rose
CD 2308239 / Apr '87 / Pablo

☐ MY SONG
CD 83326 / Aug '93 / Telarc

☐ ONE FOR MY BABY
Bluesology / One for my baby (and one more for the road) / JP blues / Poinciana / I don't stand a ghost of a chance with you / I remember you / Bay city blues / Song is you
CD 2310936 / May '94 / Pablo

☐ SUMMER NIGHTS
Summer nights / Anouman / Douce ambience / For Django / D-Joe / I got rhythm / E blue eyes / Belleville / In my solitude / Tears / In a sentimental mood / Them there eyes
CD 2310939 / Apr '94 / Pablo

☐ VIRTUOSO
Night and day / Stella by starlight / Here's that rainy day / My old flame / How high the moon / Cherokee / Sweet Lorraine / Have you met Miss Jones / 'Round midnight / All the things you are / Blues for Alican / Song is you
CD 2310708 / May '94 / Pablo

☐ VIRTUOSO LIVE
Stompin' at the Savoy / Just the way you are / Eric's smoozies blues / Beautiful love / Daquilo que eu sei / In the wee small hours of the morning / Love for sale / Mack the knife / So what's new / (Back home again in) Indiana
CD 2310948 / Jul '94 / Pablo

☐ WHITESTONE
Light in your eyes / Shuffle city / Estate / Daquilo que eu sei / Whitestone / Lovin' eyes / Amancer / I can't help it / Tarde / Fleeting moments
CD 2310912 / May '94 / Pablo

Passage

☐ SEEDY (The Best Of The Passage)
Xoyo / Carnal / Sharp tongue / Devils and angels / Horseplay / Man of war / Armour / Fear / Good and useful life / Drugface / Love is as / Angleland / Certain way to go / Time will tell / 2711 / Wave / Taboos
CDMRED 146 / 29 Sep '97 / Cherry Red

Passaggio

☐ PASSAGGIO (QUINTET CELEA COUTURIER)
L'Ibere / Lucculus / Arno / Ole rafafa / Gala / Norvegian flamenco / Hip / Warm canto / Hep / My foolish heart / Tabato / L'autre
LBLC 6567 / Nov '95 / Label Bleu

Passing Fancy

☐ PASSING FANCY, A
FLASH 011 / Sep '97 / Flashback

Passion Play

☐ TIME STANDS STILL
NTHEN 033CD / 16 Feb '98 / Now & Then

Passion Street

☐ MILLION MILES AWAY
SCLCD 1 / 8 Nov '97 / Scenario

Passions

☐ PASSION PLAYS
I'm in love with a German film star / Runaway / Swimmer / Someone special / Bachelor girls / Skin deep / African mine / Jump for joy / Letter / Love is essential / Your friend / Sanctuary
5298602 / Jul '96 / Polydor

Passos, Monica

☐ CASAMENTO
EPC 100 / Nov '93 / EMP

Passport

☐ PASSPORT CONTROL
VSOPCD 246 / 8 Dec '97 / Connoisseur Collection

Pastels

☐ ILLUMINATI
Hits hurt / Cycle / Thomson colour / Unfair kind of fame / Fragile gang / Viaduct / Remote climbs / Rough riders / On the way / Leaving this island / G12 nights / Attic plan / Mechanised
WIGCD 034 / 6 Oct '97 / Domino

☐ MOBILE SAFARI
WIGCD 017 / Feb '95 / Domino

☐ SUCK ON THE PASTELS
Baby honey / Baby honey / Something going on / Million tears / Surprise me / She always cries on sunday / Baby honey / I'm alright with you / Couldn't care less / What's it worth
CRECD 031 / Jul '88 / Creation

Pastor, Tony

☐ CONFESSIN' 1940-1949 (Pastor, Tony & His Orchestra)
RACD 7114 / May '96 / Aerospace

□ TONY PASTOR ORCHESTRA 1941-1945
CCD 31 / Aug '95 / Circle

□ TONY PASTOR ORCHESTRA 1945-1950
CCD 121 / Aug '95 / Circle

Pastorius, Jaco

□ GOLDEN ROADS
SSCD 8074 / Apr '97 / Sound Hills

□ GOOD STITCH FOR GOLDEN ROADS, A
SSCD 8078 / 17 Nov '97 / Sound Hills

□ HOLIDAY FOR PANS
SSCD 8001 / Feb '94 / Sound Hills

□ HONESTLY
CDJP 1032 / Nov '91 / Jazz Point

□ JACO PASTORIUS
Donna Lee / Come on come over / Continuum / Kuru/ Speak like a child / Portrait of Tracy / Opus pocus / Okonkole y trompa / (Used to be a) cha-cha / Forgotten love
CD 81453 / Jan '95 / Sony Jazz

□ JAZZ STREET (Pastorius, Jaco & Brian Melvin)
No clack / Miles modes / Wedding waltz / Drums of Yadzarah / Jazz Street / May day / Out of the night
CDSJP 258 / Jun '89 / Timeless Jazz

□ LIVE IN ITALY
CDJP 1031 / Nov '91 / Jazz Point

Patato

□ RITMO Y CANDELA
RWCD 9702 / Feb '97 / Night & Day

Patchwork

□ ODEON
EFA 028852 / 14 Apr '98 / Spirit Zone

Pate, Johnny

□ AT THE BLUE NOTE
PS 008CD / Sep '95 / P&S

Paterson, Rod

□ SONGS FROM THE BOTTOM DRAWER (Rod Paterson Sings Burns)
Mary Morrison / Ye banks and braes / Wert thou in the cauld blast / Waukrife Minnie / Gray Twins / Parcel of rogues in a nation / Gae bring tae me a pint o'wine / Guidwife coont the lawin'/The coggie's revenge / Red red rose / Gloomy December / Man's a man / Ochone for somebody / Auld lang syne
CDTRAX 117 / Nov '96 / Greentrax

Pathologist

□ GRINDING OPUS OF FORENSIC MEDICAL PROBLEMS
MAB 008 / May '95 / MAB

□ PUTREFACTIVE AND CADAVEROUS ODES ABOUT NECROTICISM
MABCD 002 / Jun '93 / Plastic Head

Pathos

□ HOVERFACE
BMCD 123 / 3 Nov '97 / Black Mark

Patinkin, Mandy

□ DRESS CASUAL
Doodle doodle doo (medley) / On the Atchison, Topeka and the Santa Fe / Bein' green / Triplets / I'm always chasing rainbows / Evening primrose / Pal Joey (suite) / Sorry grateful / Being alive / Ya got trouble (in River City) / Giants in the sky / Mr. Arthur's place / Yossel, yossel / Hollywood (medley)
CD 45998 / May '91 / Columbia

□ EXPERIMENT
As time goes by / I'm old fashioned / Somewhere that's green / Someone is waiting / Something's coming / Multitudes of amys / Jitterbug waltz / So many people / C.od thing going / Taxi / I dreamed a dream / I wish I knew / Road you didn't take / Where or when / Always / How are things in glocca morra / Bring him home / Experiment
7559793302 / Jul '95 / Nonesuch

□ MAMALOSHEN
7559794592 / 6 Apr '98 / Nonesuch

□ MANDY PATINKIN
Over the rainbow / Coffee in a cardboard cup / Pretty lady / Brother can you spare a dime / Love unrequited / No more / Me and my shadow / No one is alone / Sonny boy / Rock-a-bye your baby with a Dixie melody / Casey (medley) / And the band played on / Marie / Once upon a time / Anyone can whistle / Soliloquy / I'll be seeing you / There's a rainbow 'round my shoulder / Top hat, white tie and tails / Puttin' on the ritz / Alexander's ragtime band / Swanee / My mammy / Handful of keys / Pennies from Heaven
CD 44943 / Apr '89 / CBS

Patino, Deborah

□ NOCTURNAL
NAR 081CD / Mar '95 / New Alliance

Patitucci, John

□ ANOTHER WORLD
Ivory coast / Ivory coast / Another world / My summer vacation / Soho steel / I saw you / Hold that thought / Norwegian sun / Griot / Showtime / Peace prayer / Shanachie / Till then / Ivory coast / Ivory coast
GRP 97252 / Aug '93 / GRP

□ HEART OF THE BASS
Concerto for jazz bass and orchestra / Heart of the bass / Four hands / Mullagh / Bach prelude in G major / Miniatures for solo bass
SCD 90012 / Mar '97 / Stretch

□ ONE MORE ANGEL
Quasimodo / Arrival / On the Hudson / Sachi's eyes / San Michele / One more angel / Romance / Snowbound / Notre dame / Beloved
CCD 47532 / Jun '97 / Concord Jazz

Pato Banton

□ COLLECTIONS
Baby come back / Bubbling hot / Don't sniff coke / Tudo de bom / Wize up / One world (not three) / Roots, rock, reggae / Gwarn / Go Pato / Bad man and woman / Never give in / Save your soul / All drugs out / Pato's opinion
CDVX 2765 / May '95 / Virgin

□ MAD PROFESSOR RECAPTURES PATO BANTON (Pato Banton & Mad Professor)
Recaptured / Riot / Satan / Tek me time / Mr. singh / Worries / Live as one
ARICD 043 / Oct '94 / Ariwa Sounds

□ NEVER GIVE IN
Absolute perfection / My opinion / Don't Worry / Handsworth riot / Gwarn / Pato and Roger come again / Never give in / Don't sniff coke / Sattle Satan / King step / Hello Tosh
GRELCD 108 / Feb '95 / Greensleeves

Paton, Dave

□ FRAGMENTS
Bonnie blue bonnets / This honest land / Falling / For a' that / Ca' the yowes / Westlin' winds / Jock o' Hazeldean / Scots wha'hae / Holy fair / Loch Lomond
CDLDL 1257 / Sep '97 / Lochshore

Patra

□ QUEEN OF THE PACK
Hardcore side / Hardcore / Think (about it) / Queen of the pack / Poor people's song / Wok the money / Romantic call / Cool-running side / Worker man / Sexual feeling / Be protected / Whining skill / Knock knock / In the mood
4741842 / Oct '93 / Epic

Patriarca, Ildo

□ HOLLYWOOD PARIS
Nocturna / El choclo / La mano gauche / Desde el alma / Rubi / Danzarin / Volver / La pugnalada / Sur / Soledad / Kicho / Golondrinas / A mis ancestros / Cuando tu no estas / La trampera / Los mareados / Flores negras / Verano porteno / Ojos negros
FA 427 / Nov '97 / Fremeaux

□ VERANO PORTENO
KAR 996 / Apr '97 / IMP

Patric C

□ HORRIBLE PLANS OF FLEX BUSTERMAN, THE
Intro (flex busterman) / Title / Enter your name / Fight the guards / Find the office / Crack the safe / Drive to the shaker house / Watch out for Zad / Set your weapons / Sex with annemone / Injection for life / Gingoos burgerstation / CALM / Now you know / Mental hangover / Hero / You failed / Everything has changed on LSD / You made it (perfect)
DHRCD 005 / Mar '97 / Digital Hardcore

Patrick Street

□ ALL IN GOOD TIME
Walsh's polkas / Prince among men (Only a miner) / Frank Quinn's reel / Lintheads / Pride of the Springfield Road / Lawrence Common / Goodbye Monday blues / Light and airy/All in good time / Mouth of Tobique/Billy Wilson / Girls along the road / Thames hornpipe / Fairy Queen / Dennis Murphy's reel/Bag of spuds/MacFarley's reel / Carrowclare / Lynch's barndances
SPDCD 1049 / Apr '93 / Special Delivery

□ ALL IN GOOD TIME
GLCD 1125 / May '95 / Green Linnet

□ BEST OF PATRICK STREET, THE
REMCD 502 / Feb '98 / Reactive

□ CORNERBOYS
GLCD 1160 / Feb '96 / Green Linnet

□ IRISH TIMES
SPCD 1033 / Mar '90 / Special Delivery

□ IRISH TIMES
GLCD 1105 / May '95 / Green Linnet

□ MADE IN CORK
Bring back the child/Paidin O'Rafferty / Coalminer/ Heather breeze/Turf house (reels) / Her mantle so green / Midnight ramble/Bogman/Old stage / Maurice O'Keefe's/Maurice O'Keefes (2)/Sonny Reardon's (Slow / Rainbow 'mid the willows / Where lillies bloom/Village tavern/Four cross roads / Spanking Maggie from the ross / Winding stairs/Ride a mile / When Adam was in paradise / Raven through the bog/Forester / Up to your neck in sand/Coffey's reel/John Brennan from Slig
GLCD 1184 / Nov '97 / Green Linnet

□ NO.2 PATRICK STREET
John McKenna's jigs / Braes of Moneymore / Hard by Seifin/Woodcock Hill / Tom Joad / Benton's jig/ Benton's dream / William Taylor / Caherlistrane/ Gallowglass/Kanturk jigs / Facing the chair / Sweeney's reel
GLCD 1088 / Feb '90 / Green Linnet

□ PATRICK STREET
Patrick street-the carraroe jig / Walter sammon's grandmother-concertina reel-brendand mcmah / Holy ground-the shores of lough gowna / Contentment is wealth-have a drink with me / French canadian set 'la cardeuse' / Loftus jones / Dream-indiana / Martin rochford's reel-roll out the barrel-the earl's cha / Mrs. o'sullivan's jig-caliope house / Man with the cap
GLCD 1071 / Apr '88 / Green Linnet

□ PATRICK STREET/ALL IN GOOD TIME
5016272104921 / Apr '93 / Special Delivery

Patrick, David M.

□ GREAT EUROPEAN ORGANS (David Patrick Plays The Blackburn Cathedral Organ)
PRCD 371 / Jul '92 / Priory

Patrick, Johnny

□ HAMMOND ORGAN HITS
PLSCD 231 / Jul '97 / Pulse

Patriot

□ CADENCE FROM THE STREET
GMM 103 / Jun '97 / GMM

Patry, Stefan

□ BAM BAM BAM
BB 898 / Apr '97 / Black & Blue

Patterson, Bobby

□ I GET MY GROOVE FROM YOU
I get my groove from you / Make sure you can handle it / If you took a survey / Everything good to you (don't have to be good for you) / How do you spell love / Recipe for peace / She don't have to see you (to see through you) / Right on Jody / Quiet, do not disturb / I just love you because I wanted to / One ounce of prevention / Whole funky world is a ghetto / What goes around comes around / It takes two to do wrong / Take time to know the truth / I'm in the wrong / If love can't do it (it can't be done) / I got a suspicion / Right place, wrong time
CPCD 8123 / Oct '95 / Charly

□ SECOND COMING
ICH 45412 / Aug '97 / Ichiban

□ TAKING CARE OF BUSINESS
Till you give in / You just got to understand / What's your problem baby / If I didn't have you / Long ago / Soul is our music / Let them talk / Sock some lovin' at me / I'm Leroy, I'll take her / Broadway ain't funky no more / I met my match / Don't be so mean / Good ol' days / Busy busy bee / Sweet taste of love / TCB or TYA / What a wonderful night for love / My thing is your thing / Keeping it in the family / My baby's coming back to me / Guess who / Knockout power of love / Trial of Mary McGuire / If a man ever loved a woman / You taught me how to love / I'm in love with you / Married lady / If I didn't know better / Who wants to fall in love
CDKEND 098 / Apr '91 / Kent

Patterson, Don

□ LEGENDS OF ACID JAZZ, THE (Patterson, Don & Booker Ervin)
PRCD 24178 / Apr '97 / Prestige

Patterson, Jordan

□ GIVE ME A CHANCE
Funky thang / Those pretty eyes / Life of misery / No educated woman / Thing I do for you / Blues hotel / Give me a chance / Your love is killing me / Fast lane / Natural
JSPCD 263 / Nov '95 / JSP

Patterson, Kellee

□ BEST OF KELLEE PATTERSON, THE
Overture / Heaven / Feeling old feelings / How I love your smile / Maiden voyage / I'm gonna love you a little bit more baby / Mister Magic / Don't misunderstand / If it don't fit don't force it / Nice girl / Stop look and listen to your heart / Turn on the lights / You are so beautiful / See you later / Be happy
MP 001 / 5 May '98 / Majestic Peak/ Dusty Grooves

□ KELLEE
I'm gonna love you just a little more, baby / What you don't know / Mister magic / You are so beautiful / I love music / Stop, look and listen to your heart / Jolene / Time to space / Once not long ago
HUBCD 3 / Oct '95 / Hubbub

Patterson, Ottilie

□ OTTILIE PATTERSON & CHRIS BARBER JAZZBAND 1955-1958
LA 30CD / Oct '93 / Lake

Patterson, Rashsaan

□ RAHSAAN PATTERSON
MCD 11559 / 11 May '98 / MCA

Pattersonaires

□ WHY NOT TRY MY GOD
I need thee / I'll fly away / We have come a long way / Go down Moses / God's promise / Why not try my god / Let your conscience be your guide / I found the answer / I won't let go
HMG 6504 / Sep '97 / Hightone

Patti

□ PARIS TENU
3020362 / Jun '97 / Arcade

Patto

□ MONKEY'S BUM
AACD 008 / Oct '97 / Audio Archive

□ ROLL 'EM SMOKE 'EM
Flat footed woman / Singing the blues on reds / Mummy / Loud green song / Turn turtle / I got rhythm / Peter Abraham / Can 'n 'P' and the attos (sea biscuits parts 1 and 2)
EDCD 510 / Nov '96 / Edsel

□ SENSE OF THE ABSURD
Hold your fire / You, you point your finger / How's your Father / See you at the dance tonight / Give it all away / Air raid shelter / Tell me where you've been / Magic door / Beat the drum / Bad news / Man / Hold me back / Time to die / San Antone / Red glow / Government man / Money bag / Sittin' back easy / Hanging rope
5286962 / Oct '95 / Mercury

Patton, 'Big' John

□ ACCENT ON THE BLUES
Rakin' and scrapin' / Freedom jazz dance / Captain nasty / Village lee / Lite nit / Don't let me lose this dream / Village lee / Buddy boy / 2J / Sweet pea
CDP 8539242 / Jan '97 / Blue Note

□ ORGANISATION (The Best Of Big John Patton)
Along came John / Silver meter / Bermuda clay house / Hot sauce / Fat Judy / Amanda / Turnaround / Latona / Footprints / Jerry / Chitlins con carne / Freedom jazz dance / Ain't that peculiar / Barefootin' / Boogaloo boogie / Sissy strut / Dirty fingers / Man from Tanganyika / Memphis
CDP 8307282 / Sep '94 / Blue Note

□ THIS ONE'S FOR JA (Patton, 'Big' John Quintet)
DIW 919 / Jan '97 / DIW

Patton, Charlie

□ ALL TIME BLUES CLASSICS
8420302 / Oct '96 / Music Memoria

□ CHARLIE PATTON VOL.1 1929
DOCD 5009 / Feb '92 / Document

□ CHARLIE PATTON VOL.2 1929
DOCD 5010 / Feb '92 / Document

□ CHARLIE PATTON VOL.3 1929-1934
DOCD 5011 / Feb '92 / Document

□ FOUNDER OF DELTA BLUES
YAZCD 2010 / Apr '95 / Yazoo

□ REMAINING TITLES 1929-1934
WSECD 103 / Nov '90 / Wolf

Patton, Mike

□ FRANZO OLTRANZISTA
TZA 7022 / Feb '97 / Tzadik

Pattullo, Gordon

□ CEILIDH DANCE PARTY (Pattullo, Gordon Ceilidh Band)
GRCD 88 / May '98 / Grasmere

□ FAIR PLAY
LAPCD 128 / Dec '97 / Lapwing

□ GOLDEN SOUND OF SCOTTISH MUSIC FROM STARS PAST AND PRESENT
CDGR 149 / Jun '95 / Ross

□ SCOTTISH ACCORDION FAVOURITES
EMPRCD 807 / 18 May '98 / Emporio

□ SCOTTISH ACCORDION HITS
Sailor's hornpipe / College hornpipe / Lowe's hornpipe / Chester hornpipe / Trumpet hornpipe / Cuckoo waltz / Painter's choice / Para handy / Miss Suzanne Barbour / Jean's fancy / Boys of the Lough / Tony Reid of Balnakilly / Mist covered mountains of home / Alpine holiday / New ashludie rant / Elizabeth Adair / Princess Margaret's jig / Jimmy Stephen / Lochanside / Battle's o'er / Heather bells / Happy hours polka / Dashing white sergeant / Lord Saltoun

/ Catchin' rabbits / Inchmickery / Misty islands of the highlands / Crossing the minch / Banjo breakdown / Les triolets / Dark island / Pigeon pie / Moors of Perth / Shufflin' Samuel/Whistling Rufus / Memories of Willie snaith of Hexham / Dancing fingers
GRCD 57 / Jun '93 / Grasmere

☐ SCOTTISH CELEBRATION, A
CDGR 160 / Jun '97 / Ross

Patty, Sandi

☐ ARTIST OF MY SOUL
You love me / Breathe on me / Speechless / Birds still dance / Artist of my soul / I will sing the wondrous story / You alone / Always / You set me free / Come to me / Doxology
7019911609 / Nov '97 / Word

Pau Brasil

☐ BABEL
Ka ka / Fabula / Tres segredos / Olho d'agua / Babel / Uluri / Cordiheira / Tocaia / Festa na rua
ACT 50092 / Jun '97 / Act

Paul & Margie

☐ TWENTY BEST FOLK SONGS OF AMERICA
EUCD 1202 / Sep '93 / ARC

Paul

☐ PAUL
GRAVITYCD 2 / Sep '95 / Sugar

Paul, Billy

☐ BILLY PAUL
MCCD 335 / 20 Apr '98 / Music Club

☐ FIRST CLASS
KWEST 5405 / Mar '93 / Kenwest

☐ VERY BEST OF BILLY PAUL, THE
Let 'em in / Me and Mrs. Jones / Let's make a baby / Thanks for saving my life / Billy boy / Am I black enough for you / Mrs. Robinson / Without you / It's too late / Brown baby / Ebony woman / You're my woman / Let's stay together / Only the strong survive / Bring the family back
489512 / 20 Apr '98 / Epic

Paul, Billy

☐ TEXAS ROSE
Texas rose / Buckshot buck / Strange dream / Little girl / Still water runs the deepest / Rodeo Queen / Rollin' / Blue water / 501 / Bottom dollar / Real thing / Pretty girl / '57 Fairlane / Farm / Nothin' can stop me / My house is your honky tonk / Hillbilly hula gal
BCD 16155 / Apr '97 / Bear Family

Paul, Bollenback

☐ ORIGINAL VISIONS
CHR 70022 / Sep '95 / Challenge

Paul, Daniel

☐ RHYTHMS OF PARADISE
SP 7165CD / Aug '96 / Soundings

Paul, Eugene

☐ GO-2-D-LIMIT
BFMCD 10 / 8 Sep '97 / Bushranger

Paul, Frankie

☐ 20 MASSIVE HITS
SONCD 0008 / Oct '90 / Sonic Sounds

☐ A WE RULE
A we rule / Rub a dub market / Run off him mouth / Free Jah children / Rastafari winner: *Paul, Frankie & Prince Jazzbo* / Stick a sensi / Give me time / Touch me all over / Missing you / Agony / Call the brigade / Shine on / We a don
RAS 3235 / May '97 / Ras

☐ ASKING FOR LOVE
CRCD 70 / 15 Sep '97 / Charm

☐ BACK TO THE ROOTS
Down in the ghetto / Bigger than jumbo / Heathen / Steady skanking / We rule the border / Don man (we rule the island) / Jah Jah children / Mystery lady / I just wanna love you / Miss your love / I can't say goodbye / Endless dreams / One in a million / Merry Christmas
RNCD 2043 / Apr '94 / Rhino

☐ CAN'T GET YOU OUT OF MY MIND
RRTGCD 7780 / Jul '90 / Rohit

☐ DANCEHALL DUO (Paul, Frankie & Pinchers)
Pot of coffee / Meant to be / Grammy / Nothing no deh / Turn over / Mass out / Take some time / No worry yourself / Who say what / Christian lady / Tato / Tickle me / Don't pressure me / Raggamuffin / Hungry belly / Warning / She's a maniac / Give me what we want / Rock you / Lady love
RASCD 3237 / Aug '88 / Ras

☐ DISTINCTIVE KINDA SINGER, A
GR 007CD / Mar '96 / Graylan

☐ DON MAN
Ram dancehall / How I care for you / All out of my mind / Sexy thing (you got the body) / End of the road / You remind me / Row the boat / It feels so real / Recession / Here I go again / Let's stay together
HBCD 146 / Sep '93 / Greensleeves

☐ EVERY NIGGER IS A STAR
Things you say / I wanna sex you up / Every nigger is a star / Lonely baby / Hey girl / Dismal / Let's chill / Let me show you / I'll take you up girl / Next to you / Ram dancehall / Dry your eyes
GRELCD 165 / Sep '91 / Greensleeves

☐ FIRE DEH A MUS MUS TAIL
BDCD 001 / Nov '92 / Blacka Dread

☐ FOREVER
Why don't you love me / Best thing in life / I will never look for love again / On and on / All things bright and beautiful / I'll be there / Burning / Forever / One more chance / African lady
WRCD 016 / Nov '97 / World

☐ FOREVER
RNCD 2128 / Nov '97 / Rhino

☐ FP THE GREATEST
FADCD 025 / Sep '92 / Fashion

☐ FREEDOM
CRCD 46 / 18 May '98 / Charm

☐ HEARTICAL DON
Don't take it personal / Heartical Don / Let's be friends / Forever: *Paul, Frankie & Bobby Womack* / Last night / Hypocrite / I've got to fight / I want to rock / Nothing in the world / Idle jubee
SPCD 104 / Jun '91 / Super Power

☐ I'M READY
SAXCD 006 / Mar '97 / Saxon Studio

☐ I'VE GOT THE VIBES
DBTXCD 3 / Nov '95 / Digital B

☐ IF YOU WANT ME GIRL
Nasty / Oh baby / Baby don't leave me alone / Special love / Move if you're moving / If you want me girl / Written all over your face / Mr. Paul come back / Have mercy oh Jah / Lay your head / I can see your face / You are the sun
CDTRL 354 / Jun '95 / Trojan

☐ LOVE LINE
My love stand for you / Solid as a rock / Crackle theme bone / I wanna dance / New stylee dismissal / Love line / Medley song / Apple on stick / Dry your eyes / So long
GGCD 003 / Jan '89 / Glory Gold

☐ PASS THE TU-SHENG-PENG/TIDAL WAVE
Pass the tu-sheng-peng / War is in the dance / Jump no fence / Hot number / Hooligan / Only you / Don't worry yourself / Prophet / Them a talk about / If you / Dem a go feel it / Beat down the fence / Baby come home / Music is the staff of life / She's got style / Tidal wave / Your love is amazing / King champion / You too greedy / Hold me
GRELCD 502 / '88 / Greensleeves

☐ RAS PORTRAITS
Keep the faith / Songs of freedom / Don't pressure me / Rub-a-dub market / Dance hall nice / Tato / Children of Israel / A we rule / Give me what we want / Work hard / Gimme that potion / Stick of sensi
RAS 3316 / Jun '97 / Ras

☐ REGGAE MAX
JSRNCD 10 / Apr '97 / Jet Star

☐ REJOICE
UPTCD 22 / Mar '97 / Uptempo

☐ SARA
FMCD 005 / Jan '97 / Fatman

☐ SHOULD I
CDHB 113 / Feb '92 / Heartbeat

☐ SLOW DOWN
VPCD 1034 / Apr '89 / VP

☐ SO STRONG
BDCD 009 / 22 Jun '98 / Blacker Dread

☐ TALK ALL YOU WANT
VPCD 1363 / Aug '94 / VP

☐ TIMELESS
TYCD 003 / Oct '92 / Tan Yah

☐ TURBO CHARGE (Paul, Frankie & Pinchers)
I need you: *Paul, Frankie* / Kuff (don't mess with me): *Paul, Frankie* / Chat mi back: *Paul, Frankie* / Life is a gamble: *Pinchers* / Traveller: *Paul, Frankie* / I'm in love again: *Paul, Frankie* / Musical calamity: *Pinchers* / Memories of love: *Pinchers*
SUPCD 1 / Mar '89 / Super Supreme

☐ WARNING
Tato / Tickle me / Don't pressure me / Raggamuffin / Hungry belly / Warning / She's a maniac / Give me what we want / Rock you / Lady love
RASCD 3027 / Nov '87 / Ras

☐ YOU TURN ME ON
RFCD 004 / Nov '96 / Record Factory

Paul, Les

☐ BYE BYE BLUES/TIME TO DREAM (Paul, Les & Mary Ford)
C5HCD 672 / 13 Jul '98 / See For Miles

☐ TOUCH OF CLASS, A (Paul, Les & Mary Ford)
Hummingbird / How high the moon / Magic melody / Amurkiriki / Texas lady / Cico robles (five oaks) / Whispering / Mockin' bird hill / Nola / Lover / Tennessee / Bye bye blues / Twelfth street rag / Chicken reel / How deep is the ocean / World is waiting for the sunrise / I really don't want to know / I'm fool to care
TC 886302 / 2 Feb '98 / Disky

Paul, Leston

☐ HOT AND SEXY (Paul, Leston & The New York Connection)
JW 170CD / 8 Jun '98 / JW

Pauling, Linus

☐ KILLING YOU WITH ROCK (Pauling, Linus Quartet)
SGCD 17 / 15 Jun '98 / September Gurls

Paulson, Bruce

☐ MINNESOTA (Paulson, Bruce Quartet)
SBCD 3017 / Jun '96 / Sea Breeze

Paulsson, Anders

☐ SPIRITUALS (Paulsson, Anders & St. Jacob's Chamber Choir)
Ain't got no time to die / Didn't my Lord deliver Daniel / Plenty good room / Po' Mo'ner got a home at las' / My Lord what a mornin' / Honoro / Bright morning stars / Toccata in D / Lullaby and anthem for the homeless / Deep river / Before the marvel of this night / Amazing grace / Feet of Jesus
BISNLCD 5006 / Dec '97 / BIS Northern Lights

Pauly, Danielle

☐ ACCORD'TONIC
177882 / 24 Apr '98 / Musidisc

☐ FLEUR DU JURA
Reve gourmand / L'epatante / Ballade matinale / Delice Catalan / Rapide digitale / Carte postale / Ballade Vosgienne / Clin d'oeil / File Indienne / Piccolo rag / Fleur du Jura / Exotic samba / Souffle Andalou / Matin tonique / Eclats de rire / Melody bolero / Valse des lucioles
CDSDL 353 / Mar '94 / Saydisc

Paupers

☐ ELLIS ISLAND/MAGIC PEOPLE
3997 / 20 Apr '98 / Headlite

Pausini, Laura

☐ LAURA PAUSINI
La solitudine / Lui non sta con te / Ragazze che / Perche non torna piu / Il coraggio che non c'e / Lettera / Tutt'al piu / Non c'e / Strani amori / Gente
4509998852 / Jun '95 / East West

☐ LE CHOSE CHE VIVE
Le cose che vivi / Angeli nel blu / Due innamorati come noi / Mi dispiace / Il mondo che vorrei / La voce / Un giornio senza te / 16 5 74 / Che storia e' / Seamisai / Ascolta il tuo cuore / Incancellabile
0630155552 / Feb '97 / East West

Pavarotti, Luciano

☐ PAVAROTTI AND FRIENDS (For War Child) (Various Artists)
Holy mother: *Clapton, Eric & Luciano Pavarotti/East London Gospel Choir* / St. Teresa: *Osbourne, Joan* / I guess that's why they call it the blues: *John, Elton* / New York, New York: *Minnelli, Liza & Luciano Pavarotti* / My love (il volo): *Zucchero* / Run, baby, run: *Crow, Sheryl & Eric Clapton* / Certe notti: *Ligabue & Luciano Pavarotti* / Angel: *Secada, Jon* / Spirito: *Litfiba* / Third degree: *Clapton, Eric* / La ci darem la mano: *Crow, Sheryl & Luciano Pavarotti* / Le ragazze fanno grandi sogni: *Bennato, Edoardo & Solis Quartet* / Granada: *Secada, Jon & Luciano Pavarotti* / Mediterranean sundance: *De Lucia, Paco & Al Di Meola/John McLaughlin* / Gesu bambino: *Osbourne, Joan & Luciano Pavarotti/East London Gospel Choir* / Live like horses: *John, Elton & Luciano Pavarotti*
4529002 / Dec '96 / Decca

☐ TOGETHER FOR THE CHILDREN OF BOSNIA (Pavarotti, Luciano & Friends)
Per colpa di chi / Serenta rap/Mattinata / Can we go higher / Ordinary world / Clap clap / Miss Sarajevo / Cosi celeste / Linger / Come back to Sorrento / Penso positivo / Vesti la giubba / Heaven can wait / Ave Maria / One / Long black veil / Funiculi, funicula / Nessun dorma
4521002 / Mar '96 / Decca

Pave The Rocket

☐ TAKEN IN
DER 365CD / 6 Jul '98 / Deep Elm

Pavement

☐ BRIGHTEN THE CORNERS
WIGCD 031 / Feb '97 / Domino

☐ BRIGHTEN THE CORNERS (3CD Set)
Stereo / Shady lane / J vs. S / Transport is arranged / Date with Ikea / Old to begin / Type slowly / Embassy row / Blue Hawaiian / We are underused / Passat dream / Starlings of the slipstream / Infinite spark / Stereo / Westie can't drum / Winner of / Shady lane / Cherry area / Slowly typed
WIG 031CDX / 9 Feb '98 / Domino

☐ CROOKED RAIN, CROOKED RAIN
Silence kit / Elevate me later / Stop breathing / Cut your hair / Newark wilder / Unfair / Gold sound z / 5-4 = unity / Range life / Heaven's a truck / Hit the plane down / Fillmore jive
ABB 56CD / Aug '95 / Big Cat

☐ SHADY LANE
PCCY 01134 / Dec '97 / Pony Canyon

☐ SLANTED AND ENCHANTED
Summer babe (winter version) / Trigger cut-wounded - kite at17 / No life singed her / In the mouth of a desert / Conduit for sale / Chesleys little wrists / Loretta's scars / Here / Two states / Perfume-v / Fame throwa / Jackals, false grails - the lonesome era / Our singer / Zurich is stained
ABB 34CD / Aug '95 / Big Cat
OLE 0382 / 16 Mar '98 / Matador

☐ WESTING (BY MUSKET AND SEXTANT)
You're killing me / Box elder / Maybe, maybe / She believes / Price yeah / Forklift / Spizzle trunk / Recorder grot / Internal k-dart / Poerfect depth / Recorder grot (rally) / Heckler spray / From now on / Angel carver blues-mellow jazz docent / Drive by fader / Debris slide / Home / Krell vid-user / Summer babe (winter version) / Mercy the laudromat / Baptiss blacktick / My first mine / My radio
ABB 40CD / Aug '95 / Big Cat

☐ WOWEE ZOWEE
We dance / Rattled by the rush / Black out / Brinks job / Grounded / Serpentine pal / Motion suggest itself / Lovermont / Extradition / Best friends arm / Grve architecture / At and T / Flux rad / Fight this generation / Kennel district / Spanos country rag / Half a canyon / Western homes
ABB 84CD / Apr '95 / Big Cat

Pavlovic, Milo

☐ SWINGING CHRISTMAS, A
ISCD 135 / May '98 / Intersound

Pavlov's Dog

☐ PAMPERED MENIAL
Julia / Late November / Song dance / Fast gun / Natchez trace / Subway Sue / Episode / Preludin / Of once and future kings
4690852 / Feb '95 / Columbia

☐ ST. LOUIS HOUNDS/THIRD
ANT 511 / 19 Jan '98 / Anthology

Pavone, Mario

☐ DANCER'S TALES
Dancer's tales / Bootleg / Lunch with Julius / Double diamond / Roma / Recovery / Alberta clipper / Foxwood shuffle
KFWCD 205 / 27 Jul '98 / Knitting Factory

☐ TOULON DAYS
804202 / Sep '92 / New World

Paw

☐ DEATH TO TRAITORS
5403912 / Aug '95 / A&M

☐ DRAGLINE
Gasoline / Sleeping bag / Jessie / Bridge / Couldn't know / Pansy / Lolita / Dragline / Veronica / One more bottle / Sugarcane / Hard pig
5400652 / Mar '94 / A&M

Pawar, Satya Dev

☐ SATYA DEV PAWAR (Music Of North India)
C 560092 / Jun '97 / Ocora

Pawnbrokers

☐ SUN SESSION, THE
MCG 20020 / 1 Dec '97 / Vampirella

Pax

☐ MAY GOD...
HBG 123/4 / Apr '94 / Background

Paxarino, Javier

☐ TEMURA - THE MYSTERY OF SILENCE
Conductus mundi / Cortesanos / Preludio y danza / Canto del viento / Suspiro del moro / Reuda de juglar / Tierra baja / Reyes y reinas / Temura / Mater aurea
892172 / Oct '94 / Act

Paxton, Tom

☐ AND LOVING YOU
Last hobo / Nothing but time / Home to me / Love changes the world / Missing you / You are love / And lovin' you / Every time / Bad old days / Panhandle wind / When we were good / All coming together
FF 70414 / Jul '95 / Flying Fish
NC 003CD / Dec '97 / New Country

☐ BEST OF TOM PAXTON, THE
Ramblin' boy / Can't help but wonder / When you shook your hair down / Katy / Outward bound / Marvellous toy / Wasn't that a party / Peace will come / Leavin' London / Bottle of wine / Jennifer's rabbit / My lady / Goin' to the zoo / Whose garden / Jimmy Newman / Last thing on my mind
308152 / 13 Oct '97 / Hallmark

☐ EVEN A GREY DAY
Even a grey day / I give you the morning / Love of loving you / When Annie took me home / Dance in the shadows / Annie's going to sing her song / Corrymeela / Outward bound / Wish I had a troubador / Hold on to me babe / Last thing on my mind
FF 70280 / Jul '95 / Flying Fish

☐ GOIN' TO THE ZOO
ROUCD 8046 / Sep '97 / Rounder

☐ HEROES
Presbyterian boy / Day in the country / Anita O J / Winter song / Death of Stephen Biko / Hand me down my jogging shoes / Phil / Lucy the junk dealer's daughter / Not tonight Marie / There goes the mountain
VMD 79411 / 27 Jul '98 / Vanguard

☐ I'VE GOT A YO YO
Bananas / E, I, Addie, Addie, O / I've got a yo yo / Magic whistle / Oops / Come and play catch with me / Crow's toes / Baseball kids / Suzy is a rocker / Fish are orderly / Ride my bike / I've got the measles / Don't be rude to a rhinoceros / Dinosaurs at play / Wooly booger / Subway song / Thought stayed free / Balloon-alloon-alloon / Crow that wanted to sing
ROUCD 8049 / Sep '97 / Rounder

☐ IT AIN'T EASY
FF 70574 / Jul '95 / Flying Fish

☐ LIVE FOR THE RECORD
Packwood / I don't want a bunny-wunny / Let's go to Michael Jackson's house / Michael and Lisa Marie / They call me Joey / Lament for a lost election / Tonya Harding / What did you learn in school today / Rambling boy / Last thing on my mind / Little girl / Names of the trees / Long way from your mountain / Dance in the kitchen / Modern maturity / I can't help but wonder where I'm bound / My favourite spring / Spin and turn / Bobbitt / On the road from Srebrenica / No time to say goodbye / Honour of your company / You are love
SHCD 1053 / Mar '98 / Sugar Hill

☐ NEW SONGS FROM THE BRIAR PATCH
Did you hear John Hurt / Pandora's box / Bring back the chair / Birds on the table / Talking Watergate / There goes the mountain / Cotton eyed Joe / You can eat dog food / You're so beautiful / Mr. Blue/White bones of Allende / Born on the fourth of July
VMD 79395 / Jan '96 / Vanguard

☐ ONE MILLION LAWYERS AND OTHER DISASTERS
FF 70356 / Jul '95 / Flying Fish

☐ POLITICS - LIVE
FF 70486 / Jul '95 / Flying Fish

☐ UP AND UP
Has Annie been in tonight / That's the way it seems to me / My favourite spring / Home to me / Feed the children / Bad old days / Hush old man / Life / Outlaw / Let the sunshine
78067417962 / 27 Apr '98 / Drive Archive

☐ VERY BEST OF TOM PAXTON, THE
FF 70519 / Jul '95 / Flying Fish

☐ WEARING THE TIME
SHCD 1045 / Sep '96 / Sugar Hill

Paycheck, Johnny

☐ GREATEST HITS
Take this job and shove it / Slide off your satin sheets / Somebody loves me / Motel time again / In memory of memory / Mr. Love maker / A11 / She's all I got / For a minute there / Only hell my mama ever raised / Loving you beats all I ever seen / Song and dance man / Keep on lovin' me / Jukebox Charlie / Something about you I love / Someone to give my love to / Green green grass of home / Don't monkey with another monkey's monkey / Heaven's almost as big as Texas / Close all the honky tonks / Almost persuaded / Release me / All the time / Crazy arms / Heartaches by the number / Apartment no. 9
GRF 070 / Feb '93 / Tring

☐ MR. HAG TOLD MY STORY
Turnin' off a memory / I've got a yearning / Carolyn / I'll leave the bottle on the bar / All night lady / I can't hold myself in line / Yesterdays's news just hit home today / You don't have very far to go / No more you and me / Someone told my story
379022 / 3 Aug '98 / Koch

☐ SHE'S ALL I GOT
She's all I got / You touched my life / She's everything to me / My elusive dreams / He will break your heart / You once lived here / Only love can save us now / Let's walk hand in hand / Livin' in a house full of love / Man that's satisfied
7901 / 2 Feb '98 / Koch

☐ SURVIVOR
Buried treasures / He left it all / IQ blues / I can't quit drinkin' / Everything is changing / Ol pay ain't checked out yet / Palimony / You're every step I take / I never got over you / I'm a survivor
VD 102 / Sep '90 / Dixie Frog

Payne, Cecil

☐ CASBAH
STCD 572 / Mar '94 / Stash

☐ CERUPA
Opening / Bolambo / I should care / Cerupa / Be wee / Cuba / Bosco / Brookfield andante
DE 478 / Mar '97 / Delmark

☐ SCOTCH AND MILK
Scotch and milk / Wilhelmenia / I'm goin' in / If I should lose you / Que pasaning / Cit sac / Lady Nia / Et vous too Cecil
DE 494 / Jul '97 / Delmark

Payne, Freda

☐ BAND OF GOLD/CONTACT
Band of gold / I left some dreams back home / Deeper and deeper / Rock me in the cradle / Unhooked generation / Love on borrowed time / Through the memory of my mind / This girl is a woman now / World don't owe you a thing / Now is the time to say goodbye / Happy heart / Easiest way to fall / I'm not getting any better / Suddenly it's yesterday / Bring the boys home / You brought the joy / You've got to love somebody (let it be me) / Instrumental prelude / Road we didn't take / Odds and ends / Cherish what is dear to you (while it's near to you) / I shall not be moved / Mama's gone
NEMCD 969 / 1 Jun '98 / Sequel

☐ BEST OF FREDA PAYNE, THE
CCSCD 811 / Mar '97 / Renaissance Collector Series

Payne, Jackie

☐ DAY IN THE LIFE (OF A BLUESMAN)
Main squeeze / You wrote the book / Take the keys / Day in the life (of a bluesman) / Talk to me baby / 25 miles from nowhere / I'm still cool / Hit the ground runnin' / Fallin' rain / Stand back baby / Come to me baby / Goin' out ridin' / Both of you
JSPCD 296 / Dec '97 / JSP

Payne, Jimmy

☐ NEW YORK FUNK VOL.2
GCD 79504 / Sep '95 / Gramavision

Payton, Nicholas

☐ FROM THIS MOMENT
In the beginning / You stepped out of a dream / Fair weather / Maria's melody / It could happen to you / Little re-re / From this moment on / Rhonda's smile / Sleepwalker / Blues for my brother / Taking a chance on love / To the essential one
5270732 / May '95 / Verve

☐ GUMBO NOUVEAU
5311992 / May '96 / Verve

☐ PAYTON'S PLACE
Zigaboogaloo / Three trumpeteers / Back to the source / Touch of silver / Concentric circles / L'il Duke's strut / Time travelling / With a song in my heart / Paraphernalia / Brownie a la mode / People make the world go round / Last goodbye
5573272 / 29 Jun '98 / Verve

Payvar, Faramarz

☐ PERSIAN HERITAGE, A (Classical Music Of Iran) (Payvar, Faramarz Ensemble & Khatereh Parvaneh)
7559720602 / Jan '95 / Nonesuch

Paz

☐ BEST OF PAZ, THE
AC-DC-3 / Time stood still / Laying eggs / Yours is the light / Crotales / Iron works / Bell tree / Buddha
SPJCD 554 / Oct '95 / Spotlite

☐ DANCING IN THE PARK
FORT 2 / Mar '96 / Turret

☐ LOVE IN PEACE
CHECD 00102 / Jan '92 / Master Mix

☐ MESSAGE, THE
Xenon / Message / Party / Citron presse / Slide time / Nylon stockings
CDCHE 6 / Aug '89 / Master Mix

☐ PEACE IS LOVE
Kandeen love song / Look inside / Amour em Paz / Dream sequence / Singing bowl / I can't remember / Bags
CDCHE 102 / Dec '91 / Master Mix

☐ SAMBA SAMBA
FORT 3CD / 16 Sep '97 / Turret

Paz, Eduardo

☐ NOMADEO
21086 / May '96 / Lyricon

Paz, Suarez

☐ MILONGA DEL ANGEL (Paz, Suarez Quinteto)
Calambre / Revirado / Caliente / Balada para mi muerte / Oblivion / Milonga del angel / Muerte del angel / Resurreccion del angel / Primavera portena / Decarissimo / La comorra
74321491362 / Jul '97 / Milan

Pazuzu

☐ AND ALL WAS SILENT
HNF 004CD / Oct '95 / Head Not Found

Peabody, Dave

☐ DOWN IN CAROLINA
APCD 127 / Sep '96 / Appaloosa

Peace Bureau

☐ PEACE BUREAU
EBCD 37 / Jan '95 / Eightball

Peace, Love & Pitbulls

☐ PEACE LOVE AND PITBULLS
(I'm the) Radio king kong / Dog church / Be my TV / Reverberation nation / Elektrik '93 / What's wrong / Nutopia / Futurehead / This is trash / Psycho / Hitch hike to Mars
BIAS 238CD / Apr '93 / Play It Again Sam

☐ RED SONIC UNDERWEAR
Itch / Das neue konzept / Warzaw / 2000 Ways of gettin' drunk / GOD (on vacation) / Animals / His head is spinnin' off / Good morning / War in my livin' room / Discussing the artist in pain / Pig machine / Skinny and white / Other life form / Complete guide (imitating a bulldozer) / Endless masturbation
BIAS 291CD / Oct '94 / Play It Again Sam

Peace Of Mind

☐ JOURNEY TO THE FORE
Things we do / Spirit of the juju / Strollin' / On the sly / Free fall / Times gone by / Peace of mind / Por que sera
IBCD 6 / Feb '97 / Internal Bass

Peach

☐ AUDIOPEACH
On my own / From this moment on / Made in vain / Perfect world / Sorrow town / Deep down together / Tell me / Give me tomorrow / Higher ground / Hush
CDSTUMM 153 / 29 Jun '98 / Mute

Peachey, Roland

☐ RHYTHM OF THE ISLANDS (Peachey, Roland & His Royal Hawaiians)
World is waiting for sunrise / Sing me a song of the Islands / Who's sorry now / South sea lullabies / Indian love call / Cherokee / Queja tamper / Tango of roses / Julian / Siboney / Brazil / Chez moi / My gal Sal / Serenade of the Islands / Goodbye Hawaii / Alohe Oe / Wabash blues / Blue Tahitian moon / Sweet Leilani / South Sea Island / Hawaiian paradise / J'Attendrai (au revoir) / Rhythm of the Islands / One rose / I'll see you again / One kiss / Honolulu / Hawaiian war chant / Sophisticated hula / Moonlight and roses
RAJCD 872 / 3 Aug '98 / Empress

Peacock, Annette

☐ PERFECT RELEASE, THE
Love's out to lunch / Solar systems / American sport / Loss of consciousness / Rubber hunger / Succubus / Survival
SEECD 460 / Oct '96 / See For Miles

☐ X-DREAMS
My mama never taught me how to cook / Real and defined androgens / Dear Bela / This feeling within' / Too much in the skies / Don't be cruel / Questions
SEECD 451 / Aug '96 / See For Miles

Peacock, Gary

☐ DECEMBER POEMS
Snow dance / Winterlude / Northern tale / December greenwings / Flower crystals / Celebrations
5310292 / Feb '96 / ECM

☐ GUAMBA
Guamba / Requiem / Celina / Thyme time / Lila / Introending / Gardenia
8330392 / Oct '87 / ECM

☐ ORACLE (Peacock, Gary & Ralph Towner)
Gaya / Flutter step / Empty carrousel / Inside inside / St. Helens / Oracle / Burly hello / Palermo ballad
5213502 / Feb '94 / ECM

☐ SHIFT IN THE WIND
So green / Fractions / Last first / Shift in the wind centers / Caverns beneath the zoth / Valentine
8201592 / Aug '86 / ECM

☐ TALES OF ANOTHER
Vignette / Tone field / Major / Trilogy / Trilogy (II) / Trilogy (III)
8274182 / Feb '86 / ECM

☐ VOICE FROM THE PAST - PARADIGM
Voice from the past / Legends / Moor / Allegory / Paradigm / Ode from tomten
5177682 / Feb '94 / ECM

Pearce, Alison

☐ MY LAGAN LOVE (AND OTHER SONGS OF IRELAND) (Pearce, Alison & Susan Drake)
Castle of Dromore / She moved through the fair / Next market day / Gartan mothers lullaby / I have a bonnet trimmed with blue / Little boats / I will walk with my love / Star of County Down
CDH 88023 / May '89 / Helios

☐ SONGS OF THE HEBRIDES (Pearce, Alison & Susan Drake)
Isle of my heart / Leaping galley / Spinning song / Sea longing / Crone's reel / Caristiona / Ullapool sailor's song / Eriskay lullaby / Reiving ships / O heartling of my heart / Birlinn of the white shoulders / Islay reapers' song / Ailein Duinn / Ship at sea / Loch Broom love song / Kirsteen / Sea wandering / Uncanny mannikin of the cattlefold / Death farewell
CDH 88024 / Feb '89 / Helios

Pearce, Bob

☐ KEEP ON KEEPIN' ON
TRCD 9913 / Apr '93 / Tramp

Pearce, Dick

☐ BIG HIT
FMRCD 17 / Aug '95 / Future

Pearce, Ian

☐ IAN PEARCE/PAUL FURNISS/S. GRANT
TLACD 03 / Mar '95 / Tasmanian Jazz Composers

☐ RETROSPECTION (Pearce, Ian Big Band)
Quince / Intermission riff / Here's that rainy day / Broadway medley / Mean to me / Satin doll / Love for sale / Moanin' / Meet Basie / All of me / There'll be some changes made / Mood Indigo / In Mulligan's shoes / Violets for your furs / Spiraling prism / Cherokee / Song for stan
TRIP 011 / 6 Jul '98 / Trip

Pearce, Monty

☐ COUNTRY STYLE MIX
Blanket on the ground/'57 chevrolet / Seven lonely days/Anytime/Quicksilver / There goes my everything/Are you lonesome tonight / Hasta luego/ Marcheta / I love you because/Just out of reach / Stand by your man / I'm a fool to care/I can't stop loving you / Distant drums/Nobody's darlin' but mine / Help me make it through the night/Make the world go away / South of the border (Down Mexico way)/ Mexicali rose / Angelo / Tango dorado / San Antonio rose / Brush those tears from your eyes / Anna Marie/ Oh How I miss you tonight / If the world stopped loving/Love me tender / Room full of roses/Someday (You'll want me to want you) / My grandfather's clock / Sioux City Sue/You are my sunshine / Pistol packin' mama/The yellow rose of Texas / Blue bayou / Rosanna
SAV 176CD / Jul '92 / Savoy

☐ EASY DANCING
SAV 186CD / May '93 / Savoy

☐ EASY DANCING VOL.5
SAV 237CD / Dec '95 / Savoy

☐ KING OF THE ROAD
Heartaches by the number / Shades of gold / Crystal chandeliers / Welcome to my world / King of the road / One has my name (the other has my heart) / Hello Mary Lou / Oh Lonesome me / I love you so much it hurts / After all these years / From a Jack to a King / Candy kisses / Take these chains from my heart
SAV 182CD / Feb '93 / Savoy

Pearl Jam

☐ INTERVIEW SESSIONS
CHAT 4 / 23 Feb '98 / Chatback

☐ NO CODE
Sometimes / Hail hail / Who you are / In my tree / Smile / Off he goes / Habit / Red mosquito / Lukin / Present tense / Mankind / I'm open / Around the bend
4844482 / Aug '96 / Epic

☐ TELLTALES (Interview Disc)
TELL 10 / Jun '97 / Network

☐ TEN
Once / Even flow / Alive / Why go / Black / Jeremy / Oceans / Porch / Garden / Deep / Release / Master/ Slave
4688842 / Feb '92 / Epic

☐ VITALOGY
Last exit / Spin the black circle / Not for you / Tremor Christ / Nothingman / Whipping / Pry, To / Corduroy / Bugs / Satan's bed / Better man / Ave davanita / Immortality / Stupid mop
4778612 / Nov '94 / Epic

☐ VS
Go / Animal / Daughter / Glorified G / Dissident / WMA / Blood / Rear view mirror / Rats / Elderly woman behind the counter in a small town / Leash / Indifference
4745492 / Oct '93 / Epic

☐ YIELD
Brain of J / Faithful / No way / Given to fly / Wish list / Pilate / Do the evolution / Untitled song / MFC / Low light / In hiding / Push me pull me / All those yesterdays
4893652 / 2 Feb '98 / Epic

Pearlfishers

☐ STRANGE UNDERWORLD OF THE TALL POPPIES, THE
MA 25 / Apr '97 / Marina

Pearls Before Swine

☐ BALAKLAVA
ESP 10752 / 16 Feb '98 / ESP

☐ ONE NATION UNDERGROUND
ESP 10542 / 16 Feb '98 / ESP

☐ SUNFOREST
Comin' back / Prayers of action / Forbidden city / Love and sex / Harding Street / Blind river / Someplace to belong / Sunforest / Sunshine and Charles
EDCD 548 / 2 Mar '98 / Edsel

Pearly Gates

☐ BEST OF PEARLY GATES, THE (Action)
HTCD 76 / 20 Apr '98 / Hot Productions

Pearson, Duke

☐ BAG'S GROOVE
I'm an old cowhand (take 5) / Say you're mine (take 4) / Le carrousel (take 3) / Exodus (take 1) / Bag's groove (take 1) / Jeannine (take 1) / I'm an old cowhand (take 3) / Say you're mine (take 3) / Le carrousel (take 2)
BLC 760149 / Jul '91 / Black Lion

Pearson, John

☐ BUSY BOOTIN' (Pearson, John & Roger Hubbard)
Busy bootin' / As I went down the railroad track / Write me a few lines / Wort Worth and Dallas blues / Barrelhouse woman / Streamline train / Jesus on the mainline / Jitterbug swing / East St. Louis fare thee well / Cigarette blues / Don't take everybody to be your friend / Stealin' / Walkin' blues
TX 1007CD / Jan '94 / Taxim

☐ GRASSHOPPERS IN MY PILLOW
LDR 92 / Apr '97 / Last Days

Pearson, Johnny

☐ SLEEPY SHORES
Sleepy shores / Nadia's theme / Heather / Concerto d'aranjuez / Feelings / Annie's song / All creatures great and small / Vincent / Just the way you are / Misty sunset / You don't bring me flowers / What's another year / Theme from the deerhunter / First time ever I saw your face / Killing me softly with his song / Winner takes it all / If
BR 1322 / Dec '95 / BR Music

☐ SLEEPY SHORES (The Best Of Johnny Pearson)
Sleepy shores / All creatures great and small / One day in your life / Misty sunset / Chi mai / Sing / If / What's another year / Sorry seems to be the hardest word / For your eyes only / Concerto de Aranjuez / Love story / People / Also sprach zarathustra / You needed me / I honestly love you / Winner takes it all / Don't cry for me Argentina
MCCD 304 / Jun '97 / Music Club

Pearson, Ralph

☐ ROMANTIC FLUTE
From a distance / Feel like making love / Baby come back to me / Close to you / Ben / Kiss from a rose / Don't want to lose you / Julia says / End of the road / Rainy days and Mondays / Smooth operator / I've had the time of my life / Woman in love / Saving all my love for you / That's what friends are for / Annie's song / Hello again / Make it with you
QED 220 / Nov '96 / Tring

Peatbog Faeries

☐ MELLOWOSITY
Lexy MacAskill / Eiggman / Manili beetle / Macedonian woman's rant / Angus Mackinnon / Leaving the road / Weary we've been/Dancing feet / Maids of mount Cisco / Mellowosity
CDTRAX 124 / Dec '96 / Greentrax

Peavy, Michael

☐ GOIN' FOR THE THROAT
MEP 1002 / Jun '98 / Michael Peavy Music

Pebbles

☐ FIRST ALBUM
SFTRI 498CD / 29 Sep '97 / Sympathy For The Record Industry

Pecadiloes

☐ CAUGHT ON VENUS
Congregation smiles / Blood orange / USSO / Cry / Wanting song / 10 feet tall / Deep reversal / Coming undone / Kirsten's beach / My mirrored window / Circles / Peace and quiet
FINE 003CD / 27 Apr '98 / Fine Art

Peddlers

☐ PART ONE
Time after time / Girl talk / Who can I turn to / Stormy weather / Smile / Empty club blues / You're the reason I'm living / It ain't no big thing / Sneaking up on you / Pentathlon / What now my love / Lover / Comin' home baby / On a clear day you can see forever / Basin Street blues / Nobody likes me / I'm a boy in love
4728352 / Jun '97 / Sony Jazz

Pedersen, Herb

☐ LONESOME FEELING
Last thing on my mind / Childish love / Fields have turned brown / Homecoming / Easy ride / Lonesome feeling / Willow garden / It's worth believing / Even the worst of us / Your love is like a flower
SHCD 3738 / Jul '95 / Sugar Hill

Pedersen, Leonardo

☐ I WANT A ROOF (Pedersen, Leonardo Jazzkapel)
MECCACD 1047 / Nov '94 / Music Mecca

Pedersen, Niels-Henning Orsted

☐ BASSIC TRIO, THE (2CD Set) (Pedersen, Niels-Henning Orsted Trio)
SCCD 37037 / Jan '98 / Steeplechase

☐ ETERNAL TRAVELLER, THE
Moto perpetu / En elefant kom marcherende / Jeg gik mig ud en Sommerday / Det haver sa nyeligen regnet / Hist hvor vejen slar en bugt / Jeg ved en Laerkerede / Sig manen langsomt haever / Dawn / Eternal traveller / Skul gammel venskab rejn forgo / Moto perpetu
CD 2310910 / Jul '98 / Pablo

☐ FRIENDS FOREVER (Pedersen, Niels-Henning Orsted Trio)
Hushaby / Kenny / Someday my prince will come / Elvira Madigan / Lullaby of the leaves / Shadow of your smile / Sometime ago / Days of wine and roses / Future child - friends forever
MCD 9269 / Jun '97 / Milestone

☐ THIS IS ALL I ASK
O tysta ensamhet / I skovens dybe stille ro / Traces of the past / Just in time / Summer song / Song is you / THis is all I ask / As is / Taking a chance / Fantasy in D minor
5396952 / 26 May '98 / Verve

☐ THOSE WHO WERE
5332322 / Nov '96 / Verve

Pedi, Don

☐ HOG WENT THROUGH THE FENCE YOKE AND ALL, THE (Mountain Dulcimer)
Old Aunt Jenny with her night cap on / Dandy lusk/ Puncheon floor / Five miles from town / Little Betty Ann / Hog went through the fence yoke and all / Pretty little widow / Mike in the wilderness / Little Daisy / Huldy in the sinkhole / Shortnin' bread/Jeff Sturgeon / Little Liza Jane / Old tobacco hills / Old time Sally Goodin
OMC 0011 / 20 Apr '98 / One Man Clapping

Pedicin, Michael Jr.

☐ BECAUSE OF LOVE
Something you said / Extraordinary love / Some other time / Just a little taste of your love: *Pedicin, Michael Jr. & Carla Benson* / Round town / Dr. B / Joy of life / Because we love: *Pedicin, Michael Jr. & Carla Benson* / 12th Street licks / Can't leave yet
CDPJA 1 / May '97 / Passion

Pedicin, Mike

☐ JIVE MEDICIN (Pedicin, Mike Quintet)
Mambo rock / I want to hug you, kiss you, squeeze you / Rock-a-bye / I'm hip / Large, large house / Jackpot / Fe-fi-fo-fum / Hot barcarolle / You gotta go / When the cats come marching in / Banjo rock / Large, large house / Rock-a-bye / Hotter than a pistol / Teenage fairy tale / Beat / Save us, Preacher Davis / Close all the doors / Td's boogie / Hucklebuck / Calypso rock / Hi'yo Silver / Tiger rag / Ain't that a shame / Crazy ball / I want you to be my baby / Night train / Sweet Georgia Brown / Rock-a-bye / Hotter than a pistol (live)
BCD 15738 / Oct '93 / Bear Family

Pee Bee

☐ JUMPIN' THE TRACKS (Pee Bee & The Night Train)
RKCD 9712 / Dec '97 / Rockhouse

Pee Dee Jazzband

☐ JUBILEE CONCERT, THE (2CD Set) (Pee Dee Jazzband & Monty Sunshine)
MECCACD 2103 / May '97 / Music Mecca

☐ JUBILEE TOUR 1996
MECCACD 1094 / May '97 / Music Mecca

Peebles, Ann

☐ FILL THIS WORLD WITH LOVE
CDBB 9564 / Jun '96 / Bullseye Blues

☐ FLIPSIDE
I can't let you go / Solid foundation / I'll get along / I still love you / Heartaches, heartaches / 99 lbs / Trouble, heartaches and sadness / I've been there before / One way street / Love vibration / Put yourself in my place / You got to feed the fire / I'm leavin' you / I don't lend my man / It was jealousy / When I'm in your arms / Good day for lovin / Being here with you / Let your love shine / I'd rather leave while I'm in love
HIUKCD 144 / Aug '93 / Hi

☐ GREATEST HITS
Ninety nine pounds / Walk away / Give me some credit / Heartaches, heartaches / Somebody's on your case / I still love you / Part time love / Generation gap between us / Slipped, tripped and fell in love / Trouble heartaches and sadness / I feel like breaking up somebody's home / I pity the fool / Do I need you / One way street / I can't stand the rain / Beware / Love vibration / Dr. Love Power / It was jealousy / Being here with you / I'm gonna tear your playhouse down / When in your arms / Good day for lovin' / Come to Mama / Old man with young ideas / If this is heaven
HIUKCD 100 / Apr '88 / Hi

☐ HI MASTERS, THE
I can't stand the rain / Beware / Love vibration / Doctor love power / Love played a game / It was jealousy / What you laid on me / Being here with you / I'm gonna tear your playhouse down / When I'm in your arms / Good day for loving / Come to mama / Old man with young ideas / I needed somebody / If this is heaven
HEX 38 / 4 Aug '98 / Hi

☐ ST. LOUIS WOMAN/MEMPHIS SOUL (3CD Set)
Beware / Crazy about you baby / I'll get along / Heartaches / Rescue me / 99lbs / Dr. Love Power / What you laid on me / Let your lovelight shine / Part time love / Love played a game / Old man with young ideas / Chain of fools / I didn't take your man / My man, he's a lovin' man / Somebody's on your case / It's your thing / Slipped, tripped and fell in love / It must be love / Respect / How strong is a woman / I don't lend my man / I pity the fool / You've got the papers / Breaking up somebody's home / Bip bam thank you Mam / I can't stand the rain / Being here with you / Come to Mama / Games / Handwriting on the wall / Do I need you / Livin' in lovin' out / You've got to feed the fire / I'm gonna tear your playhouse down / Make me yours / If this is Heaven / If we can't trust each other / Fill this world with love / Stand by your woman / Boy I gotta have you / You're more than I can stand / Mon belle amour / I still love you / Steal away / I needed somebody / You keep me hanging on / Walk away / Until you came into my life / Heartaches heartaches / You can't hold a man / Troubles, heartaches and sadness / It was jealousy / Put yourself in my place / I've been there before / Won't you try me / One way street / Love vibration / Lovin' you without love / I'm leaving you / I'm so thankful / I'd rather leave while I'm in love / You're gonna make me cry
HIBOOK 13 / Feb '97 / Hi

Peechees

☐ GAMES PEOPLE PLAY
KRS 285CD / Sep '97 / Kill Rock Stars

Peep

☐ JOY OF BEING, THE
KFWCD 204 / 25 Aug '97 / Knitting Factory

Peeping Tom

☐ EYES HAVE IT, THE
Room in the loft / Meeting of the waters / First of May / French polka / Be minor baby / Steamboat quickstep / Mote and beam / Beamish Mary / Tower green / Salty dog pokas / Annie's hornpipe / Liquor hornpipe / Highland hunt 1 / Highland hunt 2 / Duke of Grafton / Treat / Oscar Wood's jig / Serpent dance / Knockabower No.2 / Cobbler / Paddy and dandy / Wellington's advance / Connaught man's rambles / Lullaby waltzes / Prowed C / Mystery jig / Breach of Killiecrankie / Britches full of stitches / Showman's fancy / Alexander's favourite / Gaspe reel / Malarky / Redcar reel / Johnny comes marching home / Swallow's nest / Istanbull / Gighouse shuffle
FSCD 26 / Aug '94 / Folksound

☐ LOOKING GOOD
Hamilton Lament / Dumb post/Skylark / Healer/ Whimsey Park/Big-hearted man / Pipe on the hob / Hag at the churn / Silver spire / Eagle's whistle/Ailbe Grace's/McGillycuddy's / Jame's Riddell's jig/ Stanley steamer / Con cushion's hornpipe / King Tut's hornpipe / Woman in a black dress / Captain Sincerity jig / Old Clarence / Love for ever / Captain O'Kane / Lord Inchiquin/Baptist Johnstone / Road to Lisdoonvarna/Queen's School Lass/Drummond Castle
FSCD 40 / Jun '97 / Folksound

☐ SIGHT FOR SORE EYES, A
Camels are coming / Lizzie Lichine / Abbeyfield / Woolaton park / Charlie Stewart / Victors return / Routier 66 / Whirlpool / Les filles de St. Nicolas / MacMahon's march / Night on the gin / Bedbreaker / Rag on reels / Jolly Geordies / Ranting Ross / Catchgate crapshooter / Buttonhole / Rig-a-jig / Mother's ruin / Chateau / Enrico / Tuxedo junction / Boanupstekker / Jackanory jig / Scottish de lea / Miss Sayers Allemande
FSCD 21 / Aug '92 / Folksound

Peers, Donald

☐ BY A BABBLING BROOK
You fascinating you / You're in love / Homecoming waltz / By candlelight / No more / This is worth fighting for / Love nest / Moonlight cocktail / Hey little hen / Nevada / St. Mary's in the twilight / Russian rose / Tangerine / Just a little cottage / By the river of the roses / Forever and a day / Marie Elena / Johnny and Mary / Don't sweetheart me / London pride / Sing everybody sing / In a shady nook, by a babbling brook
SWNCD 008 / Oct '97 / Sound Waves

☐ IN A SHADY NOOK
In a shady nook / Don't sweetheart me / You're in love / It's love love love / By the river of roses / You fascinating you / London pride / I met her on a Monday / Isabel loves a soldier / I'm all right / Johnny and Mary / Lights out till reveille / Forever and a day / Just a little cottage / Russian rose / St. Mary's in the twilight / Tangerine / Moonlight cocktail / Three little sisters / Hey little hen / Nevada / Sing everybody sing / Marie Elena
RAJCD 846 / May '98 / Empress

☐ VERY BEST OF DONALD PEERS, THE
Everybody's talkin' (echoes) / In a shady nook, by a babbling brook / My blue heaven / Hold me close to you (silver waltz) / Stop the sun / My shy violet / I don't want to walk without you / Stranger on the shore / Sugar sugar / Love is the two of us / Happy face / I guess I'll get the papers and go home / Please don't go / Turn the world around the other way / I'm a dreamer (aren't we all) / I've lost my love / Come take my hand / Round and round / Games that lovers play / I understand (just how you feel) / I love you, you love me / I don't know / Somewhere my love / Give me one more chance
SOW 907 / May '93 / Sound Waves

Pegazus

☐ WINGS OF DESTINY
Wings of steel / Cry out / Braveheart / Mother Earth / Enchanted world / Life on Mars / Werewolf / Witches hex / Destiny
NB 3232 / 6 Jul '98 / Nuclear Blast

Pegboy

☐ EARWIG
QS 28CD / Nov '94 / Quarter Stick

☐ STRONG REACTION
QS 007CD / '94 / Quarter Stick

Pege, Aladar

☐ SOLO BASS, JAZZ AND CLASSIC
RST 91532 / Feb '91 / RST

Pegg, Dave

☐ BIRTHDAY PARTY (Pegg, Dave & Friends)
50th Birthday talking blues / You can never tell / Hi heel sneakers / Going to brownsville / You know how I feel / Johnny B Goode / New walking blues / Melody of words / Jug of punch / Paddy lay back / Weather the storm / Me with you / Shape I'm in / Weight / Like a rollin' stone
WRCD 027 / 26 Jan '98 / Woodworm

☐ COCKTAIL COWBOY GOES IT ALONE, THE
Cocktail cowboy / Jack Frost and the hooded crow / Barnes Morris / All the dance numbers / Swirling pit / Pipe Major Jock Laidlaws fancy / Journeymen / Carolans draught / Level pegging / Song for Sandy / Lord Mayo
FP 007CD / 26 May '98 / Folkprint

Peggio

☐ ALTERAZIONE DELLA STRUTTURA
WD 012CD / Jun '92 / Plastic Head

Pegram, George

☐ GEORGE PEGRAM
ROUCD 0001 / Feb '95 / Rounder

Peguri, Charles

☐ COMPOSITIONS 1907-30
FA 021CD / Nov '95 / Fremeaux

Peking Opera Troupe

☐ MONKEY KING, THE
VICG 50162 / Mar '96 / JVC World Library

Pekka Pohjola

☐ KATKAVAARAN LOHIKAARME
450996415 / Dec '94 / F-Music

☐ KEESOJEN LEHTO
LRCD 219 / Dec '94 / Love

Pelding

☐ SKUNK, THE
JFRCD 010 / 26 Jan '98 / Jazz Fudge

Pelican Daughters

☐ BLISS
SR 9456 / Jul '94 / Silent

Peligro

☐ PELIGRO
Coffee shop / King of the road / Love hate war / Hellations from hell / Spazztic nerve / Cat burglar / Cornfed knuckle head / Black bean chili thing / I spy / Hellnation / Beloved infidels / No TV show / Dirty / No way / Cat swing / Mystery
VIRUS 165CD / May '95 / Alternative Tentacles

Pell, Axel Rudi

☐ BALLADS, THE
SPV 08476642 / Jul '93 / Steamhammer

☐ BLACK MOON PYRAMID
SPV 08518282 / May '96 / SPV

☐ LIVE IN GERMANY
SPV 08576972 / May '95 / SPV

☐ MAGIC
Swamp Castle overture / Nightmare / Playing with fire / Magic / Turned to stone / Clown is dead / Prisoners of the sea / Light in the sky / Eyes of the lost
CD 08518362 / Jun '97 / Steamhammer

☐ OCEANS OF TIME
SPV 08518142 / 1 Sep '98 / SPV

Pell, Dave

☐ PLAYS AGAIN (Pell, Dave Octet)
FSRCD 5009 / Nov '96 / Fresh Sound

Pell Mell

☐ BUMPER CROP
SST 158CD / May '93 / SST

☐ STAR CITY
Sky lobby / Salvo / Orange roughy / Interloper / Smokehouse / On approach / Upstairs / In polka dots / Everything must go / Lowlight / Headset / Field of poppies / Gelatin / Coral
OLE 2882 / 19 Jan '98 / Matador

Pelland, Paul

☐ PAUL PELLAND & BOB PILSBURY (Pelland, Paul & Bob Pilsbury)
SOSCD 1212 / Oct '92 / Stomp Off

Pellegrino, Antonio

☐ CELESTIAL CHRISTMAS VOL.2
CDCEL 13038 / Oct '91 / Celestial Harmonies

Pellen, Jaques

☐ CELTIC PROCESSION
Y225028 / Jun '93 / Silex

☐ PELLEN & DEL FRA/GRITZ/WHEELER
DSC 250152 / Apr '94 / Diffusion Breizh

☐ SORSEREZ
GWP 011 / May '96 / Gwerz

Pelt

☐ BROWN CYCLOPAEDIA
VHF 25 / Dec '96 / VHF

☐ MAX MEADOWS
VHF 28 / Mar '97 / VHF

☐ TECHEOD
VHF 36 / 30 Mar '98 / VHF

Pelvis

☐ WHO ARE YOU TODAY
Hang my hat / Supergrass / Streetlight / Mistakes / 15 seconds of fame / What makes you dance / All too much / Attitude / Driver to the stars / Cold / Late night TV / Night and day
SETCD 044 / 29 Jun '98 / Setanta

Pelzl, Stefan

☐ TALES OF SISYPHOS (Pelzl, Stefan 'Ju Ju' & Idris Muhammad)
RST 91580 / Mar '95 / RST

Pemarwan, Gender Wayang

☐ MUSIC FOR THE BALINESE SHADOW PLAY
Gending petegak "Sekar Gendontan" / Gending pemungkah / Gending angkat - Angkatan / Gending mesem / Gending ankat-angkatan, Batel / Gending delem, Batle / Gending rebong / Gending langiang
CMPCD 3014 / Oct '94 / CMP

Pembroke, Jim

☐ CORPORAL CAULIFLOWERS MENTAL FUNCTION
LRCD 214 / Dec '97 / Love

☐ PIGWORM
Do the pigworm / Just my situation / Sweet Marie / Time to make a stand / No new games to play / Another telephone call / Resigned to surrender / Sweet revelation / That's the way it goes / No more terra firma
LRCD 103 / May '97 / Love

Pena, Miles

☐ MILES PENA
Un sueno prohibido / Es mi culpa / Corazon partido / Dame tu perdon / Un sentimental / Aire no viciado en mi existir / Habale / Cuenta conmigo
66058066 / Jul '95 / RMM

☐ MIS IDEAS
RMD 822662 / 7 Apr '98 / RMM

Pena, Paco

☐ ART OF PACO PENA
NI 7011 / Sep '94 / Nimbus

☐ AZAHARA
NI 5116 / Sep '94 / Nimbus

☐ ENCUENTROS (Pena, Paco & Eduardo Falu)
NI 5196 / Sep '94 / Nimbus

☐ FABULOUS FLAMENCO (Nice 'N' Easy Series)
Rondena / Sevillanas / Palmas y guitarra / Tientos la bahia / Clara fuente / Zorongo / Mantilla y peina / Milonga / Por la lagunilla / Rumbeando la milonga / Algerias de cordoba / De levante bulerias cortas / Zambra mora / Patio cordobes / Cantes por bulerias / Punta y tacon / Tristeza gitana
8206922 / Mar '92 / Eclipse

☐ FLAMENCO PURO
Llanto gitano / La piedra escrita / Giralda del Sevilla / De badajoz a Madrid / Agua viento nieve y frio / Ay mi romera / El bordon y la prima / Feria de Sevilla / Fiesta de traina y jerez
4439022 / Oct '96 / Decca

☐ MISA FLAMENCA
NI 5288 / Sep '94 / Nimbus

Penance

☐ PARALLEL CORNERS
CM 77077CD / Oct '94 / Century Media

☐ ROAD LESS TRAVELLED, THE
RISE 007CD / Jul '92 / Rise Above

Pencil

☐ SKANTRON
GROW 0192 / Jun '94 / Grass

Pencil Tin

☐ GENTLE HAND TO GUIDE YOU ALONG, A
BUS 10102 / Mar '97 / Bus Stop

Pendarvis, Tracy

☐ THOUSAND GUITARS, A
It don't pay / One of these days / Give me lovin' / All you gotta do / Thousand guitars / Is it too late / Please be mine / Hypnotized / Southbound line / Is it me / Uh huh oh yeah / Belle of the swannee / Eternally / Girl in my home town / Beat it / Thousand guitars / Bop a cha-cha baby / It's too late / Belle of the swannee / Southbound line / I need somebody / Philadelphia filly / First love / I feel a teardrop / School days / So tenderly / Get it / Crazy baby / Weird feeling / Hard luck / My girl Josephine / Drift in dreams / Just call on me
BB 55054 / Aug '97 / Buffalo Bop

Pendergrass, Teddy

☐ BEST OF TEDDY PENDERGRASS, THE
MCCD 334 / 16 Mar '98 / Music Club

☐ JOY
Joy / 2 a.m. / Good to you / I'm ready / Love is the power / This is the last time / Through the falling rain / Can we be lovers
7559607752 / Oct '94 / Elektra

☐ STAR COLLECTION
STCD 1004 / Jun '93 / Disky

☐ TOUCH OF CLASS, A
Can't we try / Love TKO / Let me love you / Come and go with me / Only you / Close the door / I don't love you anymore / Whole town's laughing at me / I can't live without your love / Nine times out of ten / You can't hide from yourself / Be sure / More I get the more I want / Life is a song worth singing / When somebody loves you back / Turn off the lights / You're my latest, greatest inspiration
TC 878022 / 2 Feb '98 / Disky

☐ YOU AND I
EAGCD 004 / Aug '97 / Eagle

Pendlebury Dream Team

☐ PENDLEBURY DREAM TEAM
PD 1008 / Feb '98 / Pendlebury

Pendragon

☐ 9.15 LIVE
Victims of life / Circus / Leviathan / Red shoes / Alaska / Black Knight / Please / Fly high fall far / Higher circles
PEND 3CD / '91 / Pendragon/Toff

☐ AS GOOD AS GOLD
NOB 4CD / Nov '96 / Pendragon/Toff

☐ FALLEN DREAMS AND ANGELS
Third World in the UK / Dune / Sister Bluebird / Fallen dreams and angels
MOB 2CD / Mar '95 / Pendragon/Toff

☐ JEWEL
Higher circles / Pleasure of hope / Leviathan / At home with the earth / Snowfall / Circus / Oh Divineo / Black night / Fly high fall far / Victims of life
PEND 2CD / '91 / Pendragon/Toff

☐ KOWTOW
I walk the rope / Solid heart / AM / Time for a change / Total recall / Haunting / Kowtow
PEND 1CD / Nov '88 / Pendragon/Toff

☐ LIVE IN KRAKOW 1996
MOB 5CD / 17 Nov '97 / Pendragon/Toff

☐ MASQUERADE OVERTURE
Masquerade overture / As good as gold / Paintbox / Pursuit of excellence / Guardian of my soul / Shadow / Masters of illusion
PEND 7CD
PEND 7CDL / Mar '96 / Pendragon/Toff

☐ REST OF PENDRAGON, THE
Saved by you / Lady luck / Chase the jewel / Elephants never grow old / Red shoes / Searching / Contact / Fly high fall far / Victims of life / Dark summer's day / Excalibur / Fly high fall far
PEND 4CD / Jun '91 / Pendragon/Toff

☐ UTRECHT - THE FINAL FRONTIER
NOB 3CD / Oct '96 / Pendragon/Toff

☐ VERY VERY BOOTLEG, THE (Live In Lille)
Excalibur / Totall recall / Queen of hearts / We'll go hunting deer / Solid heart
MOB 1CD / Feb '94 / Pendragon/Toff

☐ WINDOW OF LIFE
Walls babylon / Ghosts / Breaking the spell / Last man on earth / Nostradamus (stargazing) / Am I really losing you
PEND 6CD / Oct '93 / Pendragon/Toff

☐ WORLD, THE
Back in the spotlight / Voyager / Shane / Prayer / Queen of hearts / And we'll go hunting deer
PEND 5CD / Oct '91 / Pendragon/Toff

Pendulum Floors

☐ KICKING GOOD TIME WITH THE PENDULUM FLOORS
VVK 10 / Feb '97 / Villa Villakula

Pene, Omar

☐ DIRECT FROM DAKAR (Pene, Omar & Super Diamono)
Aral sa doom / Mouride / Rer / Soweto / Niane / Coumba / Xaliss / Gainde / Xamlene / Yaye boye / Banna / Diaraf / Douweye
WSCD 102 / Jul '97 / Womad Select

Penetration

☐ DON'T DICTATE (The Best Of Penetration)
Come into the open / Lifeline / Firing squad / Never / Life's a gamble / VIP / Danger signs / Stone heroes / Don't dictate / Free money / Shout above the noise / She is the slave / Party's over / Future daze
CDOVD 450 / Feb '95 / Virgin

☐ MOVING TARGETS
Future daze / Life's a gamble / Lovers of outrage / Vision / Silent community / Stone heroes / Movement / Too many friends / Reunion / Nostalgia / Freemoney
CDV 2109 / '89 / Virgin

☐ PENETRATION
Duty free technology / Firing squad / Race against time / In the future / Free money/Never / VIP / Don't dictate / Silent community / She is the slave / Danger signs / Last saving grace / Movement / Stone heroes / Vision / Future daze / Come into the open / Lovers of outrage / Too many friends / Killed in the rush
PILOT 001 / Sep '93 / Burning Airlines

Penetrators

☐ KINGS OF HIGH SPEED WEEK
S 3001 / Sep '97 / Southern Surf Syndicate

Penguin Cafe Orchestra

☐ BROADCASTING FROM HOME
Music for a found harmonium / Prelude and yodel / More milk / Sheep dip / White mischief / In the back of a taxi / Music by numbers / Another one from the colonies / Air / Heartwind / Isle of view (music for helicopter pilots) / Now nothing
EEGCD 38 / Apr '92 / EG

☐ CONCERT PROGRAMME
ZOPFD 002 / Jul '95 / Zopf

☐ MUSIC FROM THE PENGUIN CAFE
Chartered flight / Hugebaby / Penguin Cafe single / Sound of someone you love / Zopf
EEGCD 27 / Apr '92 / EG

☐ PENGUIN CAFE ORCHESTRA
Air a danser / Number 1-4 / Salty bean fumble / Yodel 1 / Telephone and rubber band / Cutting branches for a temporary shelter / Pythagoras' trousers / Yodel 2 / Paul's dance / Ecstasy of dancing fleas / Walk don't run / Flux / Simon's dream / Harmonic necklace / Steady state
EEGCD 11 / Apr '92 / EG

☐ PRELUDES, AIRS AND YODELS (A Penguin Cafe Primer)
AMBT 15 / Aug '96 / Virgin

☐ SIGNS OF LIFE
Bean fields / Southern jukebox music / Horns of the bull / Oscar tango / Snake and the lotus / Rosasolis / Sketch / Perpetuum mobile / Swing the cat / Wildlife / Dirt
EEGCD 50 / '87 / EG

☐ UNION CAFE
ZOPFD 001 / Jun '96 / Zopf

☐ WHEN IN ROME - LIVE
Air a danser / Yodel 1 / From the colonies / Southern jukebox music / Numbers 1-4 / Bean fields / Paul's dance / Oscar tango / Music for a found harmonium / Isle of view (music for helicopter pilots) / Prelude and yodel / Giles Farnaby's dream / Air / Dirt / Cutting branches for a temporary shelter / Telephone and rubber band
EEGCD 56 / Sep '88 / EG

Penguins

☐ EARTH ANGEL
Earth angel / Hey Senorita / Kiss a fool goodbye / Ookey ook / Love will make your mind go wild / Baby let's make some love / Lover or fool / Do not pretend / If you're mine / Be my lovin' baby / Cold heart / Sweet love / Let me make up your mind / Butterball / Money talks / Heart of a fool / Want me / That's how much I need you / I ain't gonna cry no more / No there ain't no news today / You're an angel
CDCH 249 / Nov '90 / Ace

Peniston, Ce Ce

☐ BEST OF CE CE PENISTON, THE
5408802 / 2 Mar '98 / A&M

☐ FINALLY
We got a love thang / Finally / Inside that I cried / Lifeline / It should have been you / Keep on walkin' / Crazy love / I see love / You win, I win, we lose / Virtue
3971822 / Apr '95 / A&M

☐ FINALLY
We got a love thang / Finally / Inside I cried / Lifeline / It should have been you / Keep on walkin' / Crazy love / I see love / You win I win we lose / Virtue / Finally
5408082 / 22 Sep '97 / A&M

☐ THOUGHT 'YA KNEW
Searchin' / I'm in the mood / Hit by love / Whatever it is / Forever in my heart / I'm not over you / Anyway you wanna go / Give what I'm givin' / Through those doors / Let my love surround you / Keep givin' me your love / If you love me, I will love you / Maybe it's the way
5401382 / Jan '94 / A&M

Penitent

☐ AS LIFE FADES AWAY
DPR 003CD / 15 Jun '98 / Napalm

Penn, Clarence

☐ PENN'S LANDING (Penn, Clarence Quartet)
CP time / Re-Evaluation / April's fool / Penn's landing / One for Tony / Quick fix / Barbara Anastasia
CRISS 1134CD / Sep '97 / Criss Cross

Penn, Dan

☐ DO RIGHT MAN
Dark end of the street / Do right woman do right man / Cry like a man / Zero willpower / Memphis women and chicken / Where there's a will (there's a way) / I'm your puppet / He'll take care of you / You left the water running / It tears me up
9362455192 / Oct '94 / Warner Bros.

☐ NOBODY'S FOOL
REP 4622 / 13 Jul '98 / Repertoire

Penn, Dawn

☐ COME AGAIN
CDTRL 370 / Jul '96 / Trojan

☐ NO NO NO
I want a love I can see / I'm sorry / You don't love me (no no no) / Night and day / My love takes over / First cut is the deepest / I'll do it again / Hurt / Samfi boy / Keep in touch / My man / Blue yes blue
7567923652 / Jun '94 / Warner Bros.

Pennington, Barbara

☐ BEST OF BARBARA PENNINGTON, THE (24 Hours A Day)
24 hours a day / Spend a little time with me / Midnight ride / I can't erase the thoughts of you / Running in another direction / All American boy / Way down deep in my soul / Fan the flame / On a crowded street / Out of the darkest night / Vertigo / Don't stop the world / There are brighter days / I've been a bad girl / You are the music within me / All time loser
HTCD 28 / 20 Apr '98 / Hot Productions

Pennou Skoulm

☐ PENNOU SKOULM
CD 854 / Jan '95 / Diffusion Breizh

Pennywise

☐ UNKNOWN ROAD
E 864292 / Aug '93 / Epitaph

☐ WILD CARD (A Word From The Wise)
TS 003CD / May '95 / Semaphore

Pensyl, Kim

☐ QUIET CAFE
78161998232 / 7 Apr '98 / FRH

☐ UNDER THE INFLUENCE
Minute by minute / Home at last / Short walk from home / Morning isle / That's the way of the world / Love light in flight / Mornin' / Little Willy C / Casting shadows / Buckles
SH 5019 / Mar '98 / Shanachie

☐ WHEN YOU WERE MINE
SH 5010 / Dec '94 / Shanachie

Pentagram

☐ ANATOLIA
CM 77218CD / 18 May '98 / Century Media

☐ BE FOREWARNED
Live free and burn / Too late / Ask no more / World will love again / Vampyre love / Life blood / Wolf's blood / Frustration / Bride of evil / Nightmare gown / Petrified / Timeless heart / Be forewarned
CDVILE 42 / Mar '95 / Peaceville

☐ DAY OF RECKONING
Day of reckoning / Broken vows / Madman / When the screams come / Burning saviour / Evil seed / Wartime
CDVILE 40 / Aug '93 / Peaceville

☐ RELENTLESS
Death row / All your sins / Sign of the wolf / Ghoul / Relentless / Run my course / Sinister / Deist / You're lost, I'm free / Dying world / Twenty buck spin
CDVILE 38 / Apr '93 / Peaceville

☐ RELENTLESS/DAY OF RECKONING
CDVILE 40 / May '95 / Peaceville

☐ TRAIL BLAZER
SULH 70178 / Jan '95 / Nuclear Blast

Pentangle

☐ ANNIVERSARY
HYCD 200122 / Sep '93 / Hypertension

☐ BASKET OF LIGHT
Light flight / Once I had a sweetheart / Springtime promises / Lyke wyke dirge / Train song / Hunting song / Sally go round the roses / Cuckoo / House carpenter
ESMCD 406 / Jun '96 / Essential

☐ CRUEL SISTER
Maid that's deep in love / When I was in my prime / Lord Franklin / Cruel sister / Jack Orion
ESMCD 458 / Jan '97 / Essential

☐ EARLY CLASSICS
Let no man steal your thyme / Mirage / Train song / In time / Trees they do grow high / Lyke wake dirge / Woman like you / Once I had a sweetheart / Springtime promises / Hunting song / Pentangling / Bruton town / No more my Lord / House carpenter
SHANCD 79178 / Mar '98 / Shanachie

☐ IN YOUR MIND
295942 / Oct '94 / Ariola

☐ LIGHT FLIGHT (2CD Set)
SMDCD 154 / Jul '97 / Snapper

☐ MAID THAT'S DEEP IN LOVE, A
SH 79066 / Jul '90 / Shanachie

☐ ON AIR
Cuckoo song / Hunting song / Light flight / People on the highway / No love is sorrow / Cherry tree carol / Jump baby jump / Lady of Carlisle / Train song / Hunting song / Light flight / In time / House carpenter / I've got a feeling
SFRSCD 046 / 8 Dec '97 / Strange Fruit

☐ ONE MORE ROAD
INDELCD 6 / 27 Mar '98 / Indelible

☐ PENTANGLE, THE
Let no man steal your thyme / Bells / Hear my call / Pentangling / Mirage / Way behind the sun / Bruton Town / Waltz / Travelling song
HILLCD 7 / Nov '96 / Wooded Hill

☐ SO EARLY IN THE SPRING
So early in the Spring / Blacksmith / Reynardine / Eminstra / Lucky black cat / Bramble briar / Lassie gathering nuts / Gaia / Baron of Brackley
PRKCD 35 / Jun '96 / Park
SPINCD 139 / Dec '97 / Spindrift

☐ SWEET CHILD
Market song / No more my lord / Turn your money green / Haitian fight song / Woman like you / Goodbye Pork Pie Hat / Three dances (Brentzel Gay/ La Rotta/The Earle of Salisbury) / Watch the stars / So early in the Spring / No exit / Time has come / Bruton Town / Sweet child / I loved a lass / Three part thing / Sovay / In time / In your mind / I've got a feeling / Trees they do grow high / Moon dog / Hole in the coal
ESMCD 354 / Jan '96 / Essential

Pentatonik

☐ PENTATONIK (2CD Set)
Movements / About that / La verite / Solution / Create / Sleeper / Part 4 live / Detox / Real / Green / Passion / Prophesy / Pantatonik melody
DVNT 001CD / Sep '95 / Deviant

Penthouse

☐ GUTTER EROTICA
Voyeur's blues / Gus' neck / La grotte d'amour / Road rash / Beauty in the beast / Deviant soiree / Harmonic surf spastic / Widow's chagrin / Mare Ingram's lament / Gin waltz / White coal / Lap dog shuffle / Face down
WDOM 34CD / 20 Apr '98 / World Domination

☐ RECKS
CRH 00009 / 24 Nov '97 / Carcrashh

Pentti Rasankangas

☐ ANKKAPAALLIKKO
OMCD 52 / Dec '93 / Olarin Musiiki Oy

Penuela, Antonita

☐ LA ESPABILA
9154 / Oct '96 / Divusca

People Like Us

☐ NO...REALLY
CD 378142 / Jul '97 / Koch Jazz

☐ PEOPLE LIKE US/ABRAXAS (People Like Us/Abraxas)
GBCD 001 / Oct '96 / GB

People Without Shoes

☐ THOUGHTS OF AN OPTIMIST
RGE 1022 / Nov '94 / Enemy

People's Temple Choir

☐ HE'S ABLE
GM 04CD / Jan '97 / Grey Matter

Peoples, Tommy

☐ HIGH PART OF THE ROAD (Peoples, Tommy & Paul Brady)
SHANCD 34007 / Jan '95 / Shanachie

☐ IRON MAN, THE
SHCD 79044 / May '95 / Shanachie

☐ TRANQUIL IRISH MUSIC PLAYED ON THE FIDDLE
TRADCD 008 / Mar '91 / GTD

Peoplespeak

☐ PEOPLESPEAK
Agitate the gravel / Rain / Wanawaki / Say it, do it / Others / Sometime / Burma / January
PS 1001 / Sep '92 / PS

Pep Rally

☐ DEADLINE
35520072 / Oct '96 / Onefoot

Pepgirlz

☐ DOWN 'N' DIRTY
ALIVECD 27 / Feb '97 / Alive

Pepl, Harry

☐ CRACKED MIRRORS (Pepl, Harry & Herbert Joos/Jon Christensen)
Wolkenbilder 1 / Reflections in a cracked mirror / Schikaneder delight / Die alte mar und das mann / More far out than east / Wolkenbilder 2 / Tintenfisch inki / Purple light
8334722 / Jul '88 / ECM

Peplowski, Ken

☐ CONCORD DUO SERIES...
Blue room / Why / Changes / Chasin' the Bird / Deep purple / You're my everything / S'posin' / Two not one / If I should lose you / In the dark / Just one of those things
CCD 4556 / Jun '93 / Concord Jazz

☐ DOUBLE EXPOSURE
(I would do) anything for you / There's no you / Lava / Blame it on my youth / Segment / High and flighty / Don't you know I care (or don't you care to) / Jubilee / Careless love / Imagination
CCD 4344 / Jul '88 / Concord Jazz

☐ GOOD REED
Luck be a lady / Dream theme / Homage concerto for clarinet and jazz orchestra / Deep / I've never been in love before / Purple gazelle / Royal garden blues
CCD 47672 / Jul '97 / Concord Jazz

☐ GRENADILLA
1343148092 / 14 Jul '98 / Concord Jazz

☐ ILLUMINATIONS
June night / Trubbel / Panama / Between the Devil and the deep blue sea / How long has this been going on / Jim Dawg / Smada / Alone together / Did I remember / Nancy with the laughing face / Best things in life are free / If we never meet again
CCD 4449 / Mar '91 / Concord Jazz

☐ IT'S A LONESOME OLD TOWN
More than ever / They can't take that away from me / It's a lonesome old town / These foolish things / Supposin' / Bonicrates de muletas / It never entered my mind / In my life / Last night when we were young / Eternal triangle / Zingaro / Crimehouse
CCD 4673 / Nov '95 / Concord Jazz

☐ LIVE AT AMBASSADOR AUDITORIUM
Kirk's works / Nuts / I don't stand a ghost of a chance with you / Best things in life are free / At long last love / Menina flor / I brung you finjans for your zarf / Why try to change me now / Exactly like you
CCD 4610 / Sep '94 / Concord Jazz

☐ MR. GENTLE AND MR. COOL (Peplowski, Ken Quintet)
Mr. Gentle and Mr. Cool / Please be kind / You do something to me / Body and soul / Makin' whoopee / Stray horn / Follow your heart / On a misty night / Syeeda's song flute / There'll be some changes made / Count your blessings instead of sheep / When day is done
CCD 4419 / Jul '90 / Concord Jazz

☐ NATURAL TOUCH (Peplowski, Ken Quintet)
I'll close my eyes / One I love (belongs to someone else) / Guess I'll hang my tears out to dry / Evidence / Evening / You never know / You must believe in spring / Flunk blues / Circles of threes / My buddy / How deep is the ocean / Say it isn't so / I thought about you
CCD 4517 / Aug '92 / Concord Jazz

☐ OTHER PORTRAIT, THE
Milestones/Anthropology / Dance preludes / Single petal of a rose / Concerto for clarinet and orchestra / Cadenza / Lonely woman / Duet
CCD 42043 / Nov '96 / Concord Concerto

☐ SONNY SIDE (Peplowski, Ken Quintet)
Ring dem bells / Bright moments / Don't take your love from me / When I take my sugar to tea / Ugly beauty / Sonny side / Everything I love / Who wants to know / Half nelson / Alone at last / Hallelujah
CCD 4376 / May '89 / Concord Jazz

☐ STEPPIN' WITH PEPS
Steppin' / Courtship / Among my souvenirs / Lotus blossom / No problems / Johnny come lately / Blue mood / Antigua / Lady's in love with you / Pretend / Huggles / Turn around
CCD 4569 / Sep '93 / Concord Jazz

☐ THREE CLARINETS (Peplowski, Ken & Antti Sarpila/Allan Vache)
NHCD 027 / Jul '96 / Nagel Heyer

Pepper, Art

☐ AMONG FRIENDS
What is this thing called love / 'Round midnight / What's new / I'll remember April / Among friends: Pepper, Art Quartet / I'm getting sentimental over you: Pepper, Art Quartet / Blue bossa: Pepper, Art Quartet / Besame mucho: Pepper, Art Quartet
STCD 4167 / Feb '90 / Storyville

☐ ART 'N' ZOOT (Pepper, Art & Zoot Sims)
CD 23109572 / Apr '96 / Pablo

☐ ART OF THE BALLAD, THE
Winter moon / Body and soul / Maybe next year / Blues in the night / Round midnight / Imagination / Over the rainbow
PRCD 110102 / Sep '98 / Prestige

☐ ART PEPPER MEETS THE RHYTHM SECTION
You'd be so nice to come home to / Red pepper blues / Imagination / Waltz me blues / Straight life / Jazz me blues / Tin tin deo / Star eyes / Birk's works
OJCCD 338 / Sep '93 / Original Jazz Classics
OJC20 3382 / Sep '98 / Original Jazz Classics

☐ ART PEPPER SAMPLER
You'd be so nice to come home to / Groovin' high / I love you / Too close for comfort / All the things you are / Softly as in a morning sunrise
OJCX 004 / Jan '98 / Original Blues Classics

☐ ARTHUR'S BLUES
Donna Lee / Road waltz / For Freddie / But beautiful / Arthur's blues
OJCCD 680 / May '93 / Original Jazz Classics

☐ COMPLETE GALAXY RECORDINGS 1978-1982, THE (16CD Set)
Miss who / Mambo koyama / Lover come back to me / Patricia / These foolish things / Chris's blues / Over the rainbow / Yardbrd suite / Ilove you / Pepper pot / These foolish things / Straight no chaser / Yesterdays / Night in Tunisia / Night in Tunisia / Diane / My friend John / Duo blues / Blues for Blanche / Landscape / Stardust / Donna Lee / Donna Lee / Blues for Blanche / So in love / Lover man / Body and soul / You go to my head / Tin tin deo / Stardust / Anthropology / In a mellow tone / Desafinado / My friend John / My friend John / True blues / Avalon / Trip / Landscape / Sometime / Mambo de la pinta / Red car / Over the rainbow / Mambo koyama / Straight life / Besame mucho / True blues / Avalon / Shadow of your smile / Landscape / Sometime / Mambo de la pinta / Over the rainbow / Mambo koyama / Straight life / Besame mucho / But beautiful / When you're smiling / Surf ride / Nature boy / Straight life #32 / September song / Make a list / Long ago and far away / Nature boy / Our song / Here's that rainy day / That's love / Winter moon / When the sun comes out / Blues in the night / Prisoner / Ol' man river / Here's that rainy day / Winter moon / When the song comes out / Our song / Prisoner of love / Mr. Big falls his JG hand / Close to you alone / There will never be another you / There will never be another you / Melolev / Goodbye again / Brazil / There will never be another you / Melolev / Goodbye again / Donna Lee / What's new / Landscape / Valse triste / Thank you blues / Road waltz / For Freddie / But beautiful / Mambo koyama / Landscape / Roadgame / Mambo koyama / Everything happens to me / Wee Allen's alley / Road waltz / Samba mom mom / When you're smiling / But beautiful / Roadgame / For Freddie / Arthur's blues / Over the rainbow / Tete a tete / Darn that dream / Body and soul / Way you look tonight / 'Round midnight / Night in Tunisia / Samba mom mom / Last thing blues / Over the rainbow / Body and soul / Goin' home / Samba mom mom / Mellow tone / Don't let the sun catch you cryin' / Isn't she lovely / Billie's bounce / Lover man / Sweetest sounds / You go to my head / Stardust / Don't let the sun catch you cryin' / Darn that dream / Don't let the sun catch you cryin'
GCD 1016 / Nov '96 / Galaxy

☐ COMPLETE VILLAGE VANGUARD SESSIONS, THE (Live 28-30th July 1977) (9CD Set)
Blues for heard / Scrapple from the apple / But beautiful / My friend John / Cherokee / Blues for Heard / Over the rainbow / Trip / Blues for Les / Night in Tunisia / No limit / Valse triste / My friend John / You go to my head / Cherokee / Blues for Heard / Blues for Heard / Anthropology / These foolish things / For Freddie / Blues for Heard / Las cuevas de Mario / Stella by starlight / Goodbye / Vanguard max / Blues for Heard / Vanguard max / Las cuevas de Mario / Goodbye / For Freddie / Blues for Heard / My friend John / More for Les / Cherokee / Blues for Heard / For Freddie / More for Les / Caravan / Labyrinth / My friend John
9CCD 44172 / Nov '96 / Contemporary

☐ FRIDAY NIGHT AT THE VILLAGE VANGUARD
Las cuevas de mario / But beautiful / Caravan / Labyrinth / Night in tunisia
OJCCD 695 / Nov '95 / Original Jazz Classics

☐ GETTIN' TOGETHER (Pepper, Art & Conte Candoli)
Whims of chambers / Bijou the poodle / Why are we afraid / Softly, as in a morning sunrise / Rhythm-a-ning / Diane / Gettin' together / Gettin' together (alternate) / Way you look tonight
OJCCD 169 / May '93 / Original Jazz Classics

☐ IN COPENHAGEN 1981 (2CD Set) (Pepper, Art & Duke Jordan)
Blues Montmartre / What is this thing called love / Over the rainbow / Caravan / Rhythm-a-ning / You go to my head / Basame mucho / Cherokee / Radio blues / Good bait / All the things you are
2GCD 82012 / Dec '96 / Galaxy

☐ INTENSITY
I can't believe that you're in love with me / I love you / Come rain or come shine / Long ago and far away / Gone with the wind / I wished on the moon / Too close for comfort
OJCCD 387 / Feb '92 / Original Jazz Classics

☐ JAZZ PROFILE
Art Pepper / Sam and the Lady / Over the rainbow / Pepper returns / You go to my head / Maba de la pinta / Minor yours / What is this thing called love / Cool bunny / Long ago and far away / Bunny / Alfie / On the road
CDP 8332442 / 6 Oct '97 / Blue Note

☐ LAURIE'S CHOICE
Allen's alley / Patricia / Straight life / Kobe blues
17012 / Aug '93 / Laserlight

☐ LIVE AT DONTE'S 1968 (2CD Set) (Pepper, Art Quintet)
FSCD 1039 / Nov '95 / Fresh Sound

☐ LIVING LEGEND
Orphelia / Here's that rainy day / What Laurie likes / Mr. Yohe / Lost life / Samba mom-mom
OJCCD 408 / Apr '93 / Original Jazz Classics

☐ MEMORIAL COLLECTION VOL.1
STCD 4128 / Feb '90 / Storyville

☐ MEMORIAL COLLECTION VOL.2
STCD 4129 / Feb '90 / Storyville

☐ MEMORIAL COLLECTION VOL.3
STCD 4130 / Feb '90 / Storyville

☐ MEMORIAL COLLECTION VOL.4
STCD 4146 / Feb '90 / Storyville

☐ MODERN JAZZ CLASSICS (Pepper, Art + Eleven)
Move / Groovin' high / Opus de funk / 'Round midnight / Four brothers / Shaw nuff / Bernie's tune / Walkin' shoes / Anthropology / Airegin / Walkin' / Donna Lee
OJCCD 341 / Jun '94 / Original Jazz Classics

☐ NO LIMIT
Rita sam / Ballad of the sad young men / My laurie / Mambo de la pinta / No limit
OJCCD 411 / Nov '95 / Original Jazz Classics

☐ ROADGAME
Roadgame / Road waltz / When you're smiling / Everything happens to me
OJCCD 774 / Sep '93 / Original Jazz Classics

☐ SAN FRANCISCO SAMBA
Blue bossa / Art meets Mr. Beautiful / Here's that rainy day / Samba mom-mom
CCD 14086 / Oct '97 / Contemporary

☐ SATURDAY NIGHT AT THE VILLAGE VANGUARD
OJCCD 696 / Nov '95 / Original Jazz Classics

☐ STRAIGHT LIFE
Surf ride / Nature boy / Straight life / September song / Make a list (make a wish) / Long ago and far away
OJCCD 475 / Jun '96 / Original Jazz Classics

☐ SURF RIDE
Tickle toe / Chili pepper / Susie the poodle / Brown gold / Holiday flight / Surf ride / Straight life / Cinnamon / Thyme time / Way you look tonight / Nutmeg / Art's oregano
CY 78819 / Jun '98 / Savoy Jazz

☐ THURSDAY NIGHT AT THE VILLAGE VANGUARD
Valse triste / Goodbye / Blues for les / My friend john / Blues for heard
OJCCD 694 / Nov '95 / Original Jazz Classics

☐ TRIP, THE
Trip / Song for Richard / Sweet love of mine / Junior cat / Summer knows / Red car
OJCCD 410 / Mar '93 / Original Jazz Classics

☐ TWO ALTOS (Pepper, Art & Sonny Redd)
Deep purple / Watkins production / Everything happens to me / Redd's head / These foolish things / What's new
SV 0161 / Oct '97 / Savoy Jazz

☐ WINTER MOON
Our song / Here's that rainy day / That's love / Winter moon / When the sun comes out / Blues in the night / Prisoner (love theme from 'Eyes of Laura Mars')
OJCCD 677 / Nov '95 / Original Jazz Classics

Pepsi & Shirlie

☐ HEARTACHE
Goodbye stranger / Can't give me love / What's going on inside your head / All right now / Lover's revolution / High time / Heartache / It's a shame / Surrender / Feels like the first time / Crime of passion / Someday
5500092 / May '93 / Spectrum

Percy X

☐ SPYX
SOMACD 4 / Feb '96 / Soma

Pere Ubu

☐ DATAPANIK IN THE YEAR ZERO (5CD Set)
30 seconds over Tokyo / Heart of darkness / Final solution / Cloud 149 / Untitled / My dark ages / Heaven / Nonalignment pact / Modern dance / Laughing / Street waves / Chinese radiation / Life stinks / Real world / Over my head / Sentimental journey / Humor me / Book is on the table / Navvy / On the surface / Dub housing / Caligaris mirror / Thriller / I will wait / Drinking wine spodyody / Ubu dance party / Blow daddy o / Codex / Fabulous sequel / 49 guitars and one girl / Small dark cloud / Small was fast / All the dogs are barking / One less worry / Make hay / Goodbye / Voice of the sand / Kingdom come / Rhapsody in pink / Arabia / Young Miles in the basement / Misery goats / Loop / Rounder / Birdies / Lost in art / Horses / Crush this horn / Long walk home / Petrified / Stormy weather / West side story / Thoughts that go by steam / Big Ed's used farms / Day such as this / Vulgar boatman / My hat / Horns are a dilemma / Real world / Laughing / Streetwaves / Humor me / Over my head / Sentimental journey / Life stinks / My dark ages / Modern dance / Codex / Ubu dance party / Big Ed's used farms / Real world / Birdies / Incredible truth / It's in imagination / Never again / Sunset in the Antipodes / Fix my horn / Baking bread / Atom mind / Autumn leaves / Dear Richard / You're gonna watch me / Amphetamine / She smiled wild / Jaguar ride / Steve Canyon blues / Home life / 30 seconds over Tokyo / Heart of darkness / Pushin too hard
COOKCD 098 / Aug '96 / Cooking Vinyl

☐ FOLLY OF YOUTH
Folly of youth / Ball 'n' chain / Down by the river II / Memphis
FRYCD 043 / Oct '95 / Cooking Vinyl

☐ MODERN DANCE, THE
Nonalignment pact / Modern dance / Laughing / Street waves / Chinese radiation / Life stinks / Real world / Over my head / Sentimental journey / Humour me
COOKCD 141 / 8 Jun '98 / Cooking Vinyl

☐ MODERN DANCE, THE/TERMINAL TOWER (2CD Set)
Non-alignment pact / Modern dance / Laughing / Street waves / Chinese radiation / Life stinks / Real world / Over my head / Sentimental journey / Humor me / Heart of darkness / 30 seconds over Tokyo / Final solution / Cloud 149 / Untitled / My dark ages / Heaven / Humor me (live) / Book is on the table / Not happy / Lonesome Cowboy Dave
MPG 74178 / Nov '95 / Movieplay Gold

☐ PENNSYLVANIA
Wooley bully / Highwaterville / Sad / Urban lifestyle / Silent spring / Mr. Wheeler / Muddy waters / Slow / Drive / Indian giver / Monday morning / Perfume / Fly's eye / Dukes Sahara ambitions / Wheelhouse
COOKCD 139 / 2 Mar '98 / Cooking Vinyl

☐ RAY GUN SUITCASE
Folly of youth / Electricity / Beach boys / Turquoise fins / Vaccum in my head / Memphis / Three things / Horse / Don't worry / Ray gun suitcase / Surfer girl / Red sky / Montana / My friend is a stooge of the media priests / Down by the river
COOKCD089 / Jul '95 / Cooking Vinyl

☐ TERMINAL TOWER
Heart of darkness / 30 seconds over Tokyo / Final solution / Cloud 49 / Untitled / My dark ages / Heaven / Humour me / Book is on the table / Not happy / Lonesome cowboy dance
COOKCD 142 / 8 Jun '98 / Cooking Vinyl

Peregoyo Y Su Combo Vacana

☐ TROPICALISMO (A Colombian Salsa Recording)
Rio De Juaji / La palma de chontaduro / Asi es mi tierra / Mi buenaventura / Descarga vacana / La pluma / Ola de agua / Chenchudino / Martha Cecilia / El canalete / Sabor de vacana / Descarga vacana / Che pachanga
WCD 015 / Dec '89 / World Circuit

Perelman, Ivo

☐ CAMA DE TERRA (Perelman, Ivo & Matthew Shipp/William Parker)
HMS 2372 / Dec '96 / Homestead

☐ EN ADIR (Traditional Jewish Songs)
CD 996 / Sep '97 / Music & Arts

☐ GEOMETRY (Perelman, Ivo Duo)
CDLR 248 / Aug '97 / Leo

☐ SEEDS VISION AND COUNTERPOINT (Perelman, Ivo Trio)
CDLR 252 / 1 Jun '98 / Leo

☐ STRINGS (Perelman, Ivo Duo)
CDLR 249 / Aug '97 / Leo

Perera, Roberto

☐ HARP AND SOUL
Romantica / Place in the sun / Don't say goodbye / Hotel California / Maybe this time / Breathe again / Love dance / Malambo / Harp beat / Siesta
INAK 3036 / Jul '97 / In Akustik

☐ SEDUCTION
INAK 30302CD / Nov '97 / In Akustik

Peress, Cindy

☐ WORLD IS WATCHING, THE
SHAM 1013CD / May '93 / Shamrock

Perez, Carlos Jose

☐ NOSTALGIAS 1936-1954
EBCD 77 / Jul '96 / El Bandoneon

Perez, Danilo

☐ CENTRAL AVENUE
IMP 12812 / 24 Aug '98 / Impulse Jazz

☐ JOURNEY, THE
Capture / Morning / Forest / Taking chains / Voyage / Arrival / Awakening / New vision / Panama 2000 / Reminisce / Flight to freedom / Anticipation / Flight / African wave / Libre spirits
01241631662 / Jul '94 / Novus

☐ PANAMONK
Monk's mood / Panamonk / Bright Mississippi / Think of one / Mercedes' mood / Hot bean strut / Reflections / September in Rio / Everything happens to me / 'Round midnight / Evidence and four in one / Monk's mood 2
IMP 11902 / Jun '96 / Impulse Jazz

Perez, Pocho

☐ EL NEGRITO
TUMICD 034 / '92 / Tumi

Perfect Disaster

☐ HEAVEN SCENT
Rise / Rise / Wires / Takin' over / Where will you go with me / Little sister (if ever days) / Shadows / Sooner or later / It's gonna come to you / Lee / Mood elevators (original version) / Bluebell (live) / B52 (live)
FIRE 33027 / Oct '90 / Fire

☐ UP
FIRE 33018 / Oct '91 / Fire

Perfect Houseplants

☐ SNAP CLATTER
Strictly for dancing / Curiosity threatens / Rag / Emerald / Gentle life / New day / Damp dog / Tango for stalling / Hush / Salome / EE
AKD 063 / Apr '97 / Linn

PErFect ThYroID

☐ MUSICAL BARNACLES
SHCD 5724 / May '97 / Shanachie

Perfidious Words

☐ HYDROGEN SKIES
TRI 005CD / 6 Jul '98 / Trinity

Perfume

☐ ONE
I'm alive / Lover / Watch me bleed / You and I / As I go blind / Carving your name / Your life is now / One / Haven't seen you / I'm no saint / Changes / Fallen / Things that I love / Wild honey
STARC 104 / Mar '97 / Big Star

☐ YESTERDAY RISING
Yesterday follows you / Rising star / Morpheus / Yoga / Lost in you / Climber / LIPS / Perfume / Anointed / Aylestone Lane
AROMALP 001CD / 23 Feb '98 / Aromasound

Perfume Tree

☐ FEELER
WDM 100742 / 25 May '98 / World Domination

Peril

☐ MULTIVERSE
SFCD 015 / Jun '97 / Sound Factory

Peris, Phillip

☐ DIDGERIDOO
Gone walkabout / Rainbow heartbeat / Bunyip calling / Down by the billabong / Under the shade of a coolabah tree
CP 10296 / May '97 / Cinq Planetes

Perkins, Bill

☐ FRONT LINE, THE (Perkins, Bill & Pepper Adams)
STCD 4166 / Feb '90 / Storyville

☐ I WISHED ON THE MOON
I wished on the moon / Remember / Beautiful love / Besame mucho / Opals / No more / Last port of call / Rockin' chair / Summer knows / Caravan
CCD 79524 / Feb '97 / Candid

☐ ON STAGE (Perkins, Bill Octet)
Song of the islands / One hundred years from today / Zing zang / Let me see / For dancers only / Just a child / As they revelled / When you're smiling / Let me see
4931632 / 18 May '98 / Pacific Jazz

☐ PERK PLAYS PREZ
FSR 5010CD / Apr '97 / Fresh Sound

☐ QUIETLY THERE (Perkins, Bill & Victor Felder)
Quietly there / Emily / Groover wailin' / Time for love / Sure as you're born / Just a child / Keester parade / Shining sea / Something different / Shadow of your smile
OJCCD 1766 / Jun '96 / Original Jazz Classics

☐ TENORS HEAD ON (Perkins, Bill & Richie Kamuca)
Cotton tail / I want a little girl / Blues for two / Indian summer / Don't be that way / Oh look at me now / Spain / Pick a dilly / Solid De Sylvia / Just friends / All of me / Limehouse blues / Sweet and lovely
CDP 7971952 / Feb '97 / Blue Note

☐ WARM MOODS (Perkins, Bill & Frank Strazzeri)
FSRCD 191 / Dec '92 / Fresh Sound

Perkins, Carl

☐ BEST OF AND THE REST OF, THE
(We're gonna) Rock around the clock / That's alright mama / Kaw-liga / Tutti frutti / Yes it's me and I'm in love again / Blue suede shoes / Be bop a lula / Maybellene / Whole lotta shakin' goin' on / Hang up my rock 'n' roll shoes / Shake, rattle and roll
CDAR 1025 / Mar '91 / Action Replay

☐ BEST OF CARL PERKINS, THE
MATCD 324 / Feb '95 / Castle

☐ BEST OF CARL PERKINS, THE
PLSCD 125 / Jul '96 / Pulse

☐ BLUE SUEDE SHOES
CDSGP 0164 / Aug '95 / Prestige

☐ BLUE SUEDE SHOES
MACCD 225 / Aug '96 / Autograph

☐ BLUE SUEDE SHOES
Blue suede shoes / Honky tonk gal / Movie Magg / Boppin' the blues / Honey don't / Let the jukebox keep on playing / Put your cat clothes on / Roll over Beethoven / Matchbox / Dixie fried / Pink pedal pushers / That's right / Turn around / All Mama's children / Everybody's trying to be my baby / I'm sorry I'm not sorry
SUMCD 4016 / Nov '96 / Summit

☐ BLUE SUEDE SHOES (His Original Greatest Hits)
Matchbox / Pink pedal pushers / Blue suede shoes / Turn around / Boppin' the blues / That's right / Let the jukebox keep on playing / All mama's children / Honky tonk girl / Dixie fried / Everybody's trying to be my baby / I'm sorry, I'm not sorry / Put your cat cloths on / Roll over Beethoven / Sure to fall / Honey don't / Movie magg / Your true love / Gone, gone, gone / Glad all over
305692 / Oct '96 / Hallmark

☐ BLUE SUEDE SHOES (The Best Of Carl Perkins)
Blue suede shoes / Pink pedal pushers / Restless / Me without you / Cotton top / High on love / Daddy sang bass / That's all right / Good rockin' tonight / I got a woman / Hey good lookin' / Matchbox / Mean woman blues / Boppin' the blues / Honey don't / Your true love / Champaign Illinois / Brown eyed handsome man / Shake rattle and roll / Pointed toe shoes / I'm gonna set my foot down / CC rider / True love is greater than friendship / Folsom prison blues
4914512 / 10 Aug '98 / Columbia

☐ BOPPIN' BLUE SUEDE SHOES
Movie magg / Let the jukebox keep on playing / Sure to fall / Honey don't / Blue suede shoes / Boppin' the blues / Dixie fried / Put your cat clothes on / Right string baby, but the wrong yo-yo / Everybody's tryin' to be my baby / That don't move me / Caldonia / Sweethearts or strangers / I'm so sorry, I'm not sorry / Matchbox / Roll over Beethoven / That's right / Forever yours / Your true love / YOU / Pink pedal pushers / I care / Lend me your comb / Look at that moon / Glad all over
CPCD 8102 / Jun '95 / Charly

☐ CLASSIC CARL PERKINS (5CD Set)
Honky tonk babe / Movie Magg / Honky tonk gal / Runaround / Turn around / Let the jukebox keep on playing / What you doin' when you're cryin' / You can't make love to somebody / Gone gone gone / Dixie bop / Perkin's wiggle / Blue suede shoes (take 1) / Blue suede shoes (take 2) / Blue suede shoes (take 3) / Honey don't / Tennessee / Sure to fall / All Mama's children / Everybody's tryin' to be my baby / Boppin' the blues / Put your cat clothes on / Only you / Right string baby, but the wrong yo-yo / All mama's children (false start) / Dixie fried / Dixie fried (false start) / I'm sorry I'm not sorry / That don't move me / Lonely street / Drink up and go home / Pink pedal pushers / Way you're living is breaking my heart / Take back my love / Somebody tell me / Instrumental / Red wing / Down by the riverside / Her love rubbed off / Caldonia / You can do no wrong / Sweethearts or strangers / Be honest with me / Your true love / Matchbox / Your true love (original tempo) / Keeper of the key / Roll over Beethoven / Try my heart out / That's right / Forever yours / YOU / I care / Lend me your comb / Look at the moon / Glad all over / Tutti frutti / Whole lotta shakin' goin' on / That's alright / Where the Rio de Rosa flows / Shake, rattle and roll / Long tall Sally / I got a woman / Hey good lookin' / Sittin' on top of the world / Good rockin' tonight / Jive after five / Rockin' record hop / Just tonight I'd call / Ready Teddy / Jenny Jenny / You were there / Because you're mine / Pop, let me have the car / Levi jacket and a longtall shirt / When the moon comes over the mountain / Sister twister / Ham bone / This life I live / Please say you'll be mine / Honey 'cause I love you / I don't see me in your eyes anymore / Highway of love / Pointed toe shoes / One-way ticket to lonliness / Drifter / Too much for a man to understand / LOVEVILLE / Big bad blues / Say when / Lonely heart / Love I'll never win / Let my baby be / Monkey shine / Mama of my song / One of these days / I wouldn't have you / Help me find my baby / After sundown / For a little while / Just for you / When the right time comes along / Fool I used to be / Forget me (next time around) / Hollywood city / I've just got back from there / Unhappy girls / Someday, somewhere someone waits for me / Anyway the wind blows
BCD 15494 / Feb '90 / Bear Family

☐ COUNTRY BOY'S DREAM (The Dollie Masters)
Country boy's dream / If I could come back / Star of the show / Poor boy blues / Detroit city / Dream on little dreamer / Stateside / Sweet misery / Unmitigated gall / Shine shine shine / Without you / You can take the boy out of the... / Almost love / Old fashioned singalong / Old number one / My old hometown / Back to Tennessee / It's you / I'll go wrong again / Dear Abby / Lake country, cotton country / All you need to know / Quite like you / Just as long / Just as long / Baby I'm hung on you / Tom and Mary Jane / Mama and Daddy / Valda
BCD 15593 / Apr '92 / Bear Family

☐ DEFINITIVE COLLECTION, THE (2CD Set)
CPCD 83382 / 30 Mar '98 / Charly

☐ FAMILY FRIENDS AND LEGENDS
Pink cadillac / Birth of rock and roll / Book faded brown / Don't stop the music / Wild texas wind / Half the time / Make it right / Godfather of rock and roll / Of love / Don't let go
CDMF 084 / 27 Apr '98 / Magnum Force

☐ FIRST KING OF ROCK 'N' ROLL, THE
Blue suede shoes / Honey don't / I'm walkin' / Matchbox / Suzie Q / Memphis / Maybellene / Slippin' and slidin' / Be bop a lula / Roll over Beethoven / Hound dog / Whole lotta shakin' goin' on / Lucille / Jailhouse rock / All shook up / That's alright mama / Bird dog / Rock Island line
ECD 3107 / Jan '95 / K-Tel

☐ HOUND DOG
MU 5062 / Oct '92 / Musketeer

☐ MAN AND THE LEGEND, THE
Blue suede shoes / Honey don't / I'm walkin' / Matchbox / Suzie Q / Memphis / Maybellene / Slippin' and slidin' / Be bop a lula / Roll over Beethoven / Hound dog / Whole lotta shakin' goin' on / Lucille / Jailhouse rock / All shook up / That's alright mama / Bird dog / Rock Island line / Singin' the blues / Got my mojo working
CDMF 039 / May '95 / Magnum Force

☐ MASTERS, THE
EABCD 060 / 24 Nov '97 / Eagle

☐ MEMORIAL ALBUM, THE
UAE 34132 / 27 Apr '98 / Memorial Album

☐ RARE TRACKS
MCG 200014 / Jun '97 / Vampirella

☐ SUN SESSIONS, THE
Blue suede shoes / Movie magg / Sure to fall / Gone, gone, gone / Honey don't / Turn around / Tennessee / All mama's children / Everybody's trying to be my baby / Matchbox / Your true love / Boppin' the blues / Honky tonk gal / Dixie fried / Let the jukebox keep on playing / Roll over beethoven / I'm sorry I'm not sorry / Pink pedal pushers / That's right / Lend me your comb / Glad all over / Put your cat clothes on
MCCD 191 / Nov '94 / Music Club

☐ TURN AROUND (Rare Demo Tracks 1963-1964)
3012822 / 25 Aug '97 / Culture Press

☐ UNISSUED CARL PERKINS, THE
CPCD 8301 / May '97 / Charly

☐ UP COUNTRY VOL.2
From a jack to a king / Tear in my beer / Top of the world / I love you because / Send me the pillow / There's a heartache following me / Rose marie / Happy anniversary / Call the preacher / Just walk on by (wait on the corner) / Little ol' dime / Livin' doll / Some days are diamonds / Gypsy woman / Some broken hearts never mend / Grandma's feather bed / King of the road / Travelling light / Sweet caroline / Diana / Singing the blues / Rock'n'roll waltz
SOV 021CD / Sep '93 / Sovereign

☐ UP THROUGH THE YEARS 1954-1957
Honky tonk gal / Movie magg / Turn around / Gone gone gone / Let the jukebox keep on playing / You can't make love to somebody / Blue suede shoes / Honey don't / Tennessee / Boppin' the blues / All Mama's children / Everybody's tryin' to be my baby / Dixie fried / I'm sorry I'm not sorry / You can do no wrong / Matchbox / Your true love / Put your cat clothes on / Only you / Pink pedal pushers / That's right / Lend me your comb / Glad all over / Right string baby, but the wrong yo-yo
BCD 15246 / Nov '86 / Bear Family

Perkins, Carl

☐ INTRODUCING CARL PERKINS
Way cross town / You don't know what love is / Lady is a tramp / Marble head / Woody 'n' you / West Side aka Mia / Just friends / It could happen to you / Why do I care / Lilacs in the rain / Carl's blues
CDBOP 008 / Jul '96 / Boplicity

Perkins, Roy

☐ RAM RECORDS STORY VOL.3 (Perkins, Roy 'Boogie Boy')
Drop top / That's what the mailman had to say / Hey lawdy Mama / Just another lie / Tell me you love me (And give me the reason why) / Am I the one / Ba da / Please be true / Cooking catfish / Tired of hanging around: *Page, Bobby & The Riff Raffs* / Drop top (Alt) / Ginning: *Patin, Scatman & The Ram Rods* / Girl next door: *Page, Bobby & The Riff Raffs* / I love my baby: *Page, Bobby & The Riff Raffs* / Red beans and rice: *Patin, Scatman & The Ram Rods* / Hey lawdy Mama (Take 1) / It's all over / These blues are here to stay / Anything your heart desires: *Simoneaux, Harry & The Riff Raffs* / Hippt ti yo: *Page, Bobby & The Riff Raffs* / This time: *Page, Bobby & The Riff Raffs* / Like twist: *Page, Bobby & The Riff Raffs* / Loneliness: *Page, Bobby & The Riff Raffs* / True love / Sweet Lily
CDCHD 619 / Mar '96 / Ace

Perkins, Willie

☐ AFTER HOURS (Perkins, Willie 'Pinetop')
CD 73088 / Mar '90 / Blind Pig

☐ BLUES LEGEND (Perkins, Willie 'Pinetop')
CDSGP 0292 / Sep '96 / Prestige

☐ BOOGIE WOOGIE KING (Perkins, Willie 'Pinetop')
ECD 260112 / Jan '92 / Evidence

☐ BORN IN THE DELTA (Perkins, Willie 'Pinetop')
Everyday I have the blues / For you my love / Love on yonder wall / Blues after hours / Murmur low / How long how long blues / Baby what do you want me to do / Blues oh blues
CD 83418 / 8 Sep '97 / Telarc Blues

☐ DOWN IN MISSISSIPPI (Perkins, Willie 'Pinetop')
HMG 1004 / Feb '98 / Hightone

☐ LIVE TOP (Perkins, Willie 'Pinetop')
DELD 3010 / Dec '95 / Deluge

☐ ON TOP (Perkins, Willie 'Pinetop')
DELCD 3002 / Jan '96 / Deluge

☐ PINETOP'S BOOGIE WOOGIE (Perkins, Willie 'Pinetop')
ANTCD 0020 / Nov '93 / Antones

☐ SWEET BLACK ANGEL (Perkins, Willie 'Pinetop')
Lend me your love / What's the matter with the mill / Five long years / Down the road I'll go / View from the top / Look on yonder wall / Who's ol' muddy shoes / I'd rather quit her than hit her / Rain / Pinetop's special / How long blues / Sweet black angel
5371872 / 20 Apr '98 / Verve

Perko, Jukka

☐ GARDEN OF TIME (Perko, Jukka & Severi Pyysalo)
ODE 4012 / Feb '94 / Ondine

Perlinpinpin Folc

☐ MUSIC FROM GASCONY
B 6834CD / Aug '96 / Auvidis/Ethnic

☐ MUSICA GASCONHA-ALS CURIOS
176192 / 1 Jun '98 / Musidisc

Perlman, Itzhak

☐ KLEZMER VOL.1 (In The Fiddler's House) (Various Artists)
CDC 5555552 / Mar '96 / EMI Classics

☐ KLEZMER VOL.2 (Live At The Fiddler's House) (Various Artists)
Doina: *Brave Old World* / A hora mit branfin: *Brave Old World* / Bukovina 212: *Brave Old World* / Lekho neraneo: *Brave Old World* / Healthy baby girl hora: *Klezmatics* / Golem dance: *Klezmatics* / Honga encore: *Klezmatics* / Nign: *Klezmatics* / Bulgars/The kiss: *Klezmatics* / Meron nigun/In the sukke: *Statman, Andy Klezmer Orchestra* / Sholem aleichem: *Statman, Andy Klezmer Orchestra* / Khaiterma: *Statman, Andy Klezmer Orchestra* / Andy's ride: *Statman, Andy Klezmer Orchestra* / A heymischer bulgar/Wedding dance: *Klezmer Conservatory Band* / Kale bazetsn/Khusidl: *Klezmer Conservatory Band* / Fun tashlikh: *Klezmer Conservatory Band* / A yingele fun poyln/Di mame is gegangen: *Klezmer Conservatory Band* / Processional / Klezmer suite / Ale brider
CDC 5562092 / Feb '97 / EMI Classics

Perlman, Ken

☐ DEVIL IN THE KITCHEN
MAR 6502CD / Aug '96 / Marimac

Pernice Brothers

☐ OVERCOME BY HAPPINESS
Crest fallen / Overcome by happiness / Sick of you / Clear spot / Dimmest star / Monkey suit / Chicken wire / Wait to stop / All I know / Shoes and clothes / Wherin obscurely / Ferris wheel
RCD 10447 / 25 May '98 / Rykodisc

Pernick, Karen

☐ APARTMENT 12
SH 8021 / Nov '96 / Shanachie

Peron, Carlos

☐ IMPERSONATOR VOL.2
BIASCD 116 / Aug '89 / Play It Again Sam

Perplexa

☐ PERPLEXA
SS 007 / May '97 / Small Stone

☐ THIS GLORIOUS FORWARD
SS 010 / 8 Jun '98 / Small Stone

Perrey, Jean Jacques

☐ AMAZING NEW ELECTRONIC POP SOUNDS
VMD 79286 / Oct '96 / Vanguard

☐ ESSENTIAL PERREY & KINGSLEY
VCD 71 / Oct '96 / Vanguard

☐ EVA (EXTRA VEHICULAR ACTIVITY)
EVA / Soul city / Porcupine rock / Mister james bond / Cat in the night / One note samba (Spanish flea) / Moog indigo / EVA / EVA / Mas que nada / Unidentified flying object / Winchester cathedral / Swans splashdown / Flight of the bumble bee / Fallout / Cosmic ballad
CDBGPM 109 / Aug '97 / Beat Goes Public

☐ MOOG INDIGO
Soul city / EVA / Rose and the cross / Cat in the night / Flight of the bumble bee / Moog indigo / Gossipo perpetuo / Country rock polka / Elephant never forgets / 18th century puppet / Hello Dolly / Passport to the future
CDBGPM 103 / Apr '96 / Beat Goes Public

Perri, Joel

☐ EL CONDOR DEL INDIO
EUCD 1067 / '89 / ARC

☐ EL CONDOR PASA (Magic Of The Indian Flute)
EUCD 1173 / '91 / ARC

☐ EL CONDOR PASA
EUCD 1055 / '89 / ARC

☐ MANDOLINE
EUCD 1047 / '89 / ARC

☐ MASTER OF THE INDIAN FLUTES
EUCD 1329 / Nov '95 / ARC

☐ SOUFFLE DE VENTE
EUCD 1029 / '89 / ARC

☐ TARANTELLA DEL DIAVOLO
EUCD 1077 / '89 / ARC

Perroches, Yann F.

☐ AN DROUG HIRNEZ
KMCD 79 / 21 Aug '97 / Keltia Musique

Perry, Al

☐ RETRONUEVO (Perry, Al & Dan Stuart)
NORM 169CD / Dec '94 / Normal

Perry, Bill

☐ LOVE SCARS
Love scars / Lost in the blues / Fade to blue / Down / Darkness of your love / Boogie blues / Settle down, Fred / Smokey Joe / I'm leaving you / In my lonely room / 80 West / Fade to blue (reprise)
VPBCD 31 / Jan '96 / Pointblank

Perry, Frank

☐ BELOVODYE - LAND OF THE WHITE WATERS
IS 03CD / Apr '94 / Isis

Perry, James

☐ PEACE LIKE A RIVER (Perry, James & Co.)
WCL 110242 / Jul '97 / White Cloud

Perry, Joel

☐ PERRY AIRS (Instrumental)
ZAZOU 1512 / Mar '98 / Zazou

Perry, John G.

☐ UNCLE SEABIRD
VP 169CD / Feb '95 / Voiceprint

Perry, Lazar

☐ TANGODELIC
IMP 945 / Nov '96 / IMP

Perry, Lee 'Scratch'

☐ AFRICA'S BLOOD (Various Artists)
Do your thing: *Barker, Dave* / Dreamland: *Upsetters* / Long sentence: *Upsetters* / Not guilty: *Upsetters* / Cool and easy: *Upsetters* / Well dread: *Addis Ababa Children* / My girl: *Upsetters* / Sawdust: *Upsetters* / Place called Africa: *Prince, Winston* / Isn't it wrong: *Hurricanes* / Go slow/Bad luck/Move me/Surplus: *Upsetters*
CDTBL 166 / Sep '96 / Trojan

☐ ARKOLOGY (3CD Set)
Dub revolution (part 1): *Perry, Lee 'Scratch' & The Upsetters* / One step forward: *Max Romeo* / One step dub: *Upsetters* / Vampire: *Irons, Devon* / Vamp a dub: *Upsetters* / Sufferer's time: *Heptones* / Sufferer's dub: *Upsetters* / Sufferer's heights: *Junior Dread* / Don't blame on I: *Congos* / Much smarter: *Meditations* / Much smarter dub: *Upsetters* / Life is not easy: *Meditations* / Life is not easy dub: *Upsetters* / Tedious: *Junior Murvin* / War in a Babylon: *Max Romeo* / Revelation dub: *Upsetters* / Mr. President: *Heptones & Jah Lion* / Chase the devil: *Max Romeo* / Dreadlocks in moolight / Dread at the mantrols: *Mikey Dread* / In these times: *Walker, Errol* / In these times dub: *Upsetters* / Norman: *Max Romeo & The Upsetters* / Police and thieves: *Junior Murvin* / Magic touch: *DaCosta, Glen* / Soldier and police war: *Jah Lion* / Grumblin' dub: *Upsetters* / Bad weed: *Junior Murvin* / John public: *Walker, Errol* / John public (version): *Walker, Errol & Enos Barnes* / Roots train: *Junior Murvin & Dillinger* / No peace: *Meditations* / No peace dub: *Meditations* / Rasta train: *Green, Raphael & Dr.Alimantado* / Party time (part 2): *Upsetters* / Vibrate on: *Pablo, Augustus & The Upsetters* / Vibrators: *Upsetters* / Bird in hand: *Upsetters* / Congoman: *Congos* / Dyon anasawa: *Upsetters & Full Experience* / Rastaman shuffle: *Upsetters* / Why must I (version): *Heptones & Lee Perry* / Make up your mind: *Heptones* / Closer together: *Upsetter Revue & Junior Murvin* / Groovy situation: *Rowe, Keith* / Groovy dub: *Rowe, Keith* / To be a lover (have some mercy): *Faith, George* / Soul fire / Curly locks / Feast of the Passover: *Congos* / Roast fish and cornbread / Corn fish dub
CRNCD 6 / Jul '97 / Island Jamaica

☐ AT THE BLACKHEART STUDIO (Perry, Lee 'Scratch' & The Scientist)
RN 7005 / Sep '96 / Rhino

☐ BATTLE AXE (Various Artists)
Battle axe: *Upsetters* / Place called Africa: *Byles, Junior* / Cheerio: *Upsetters* / Picture on my wall: *Ras Darkins* / Cool operator: *Wilson, Delroy* / Knock three times: *Upsetters* / Pop a pop: *Andy Capp* / Earthquake: *Upsetters* / Don't cross the nation: *Mark & Luke* / Dark moon: *Upsetters* / Rough and smooth: *Upsetters* / Groove me: *Upsetters* / Easy snapping: *Upsetters* / I'm yours: *Wilson, Delroy*
CDTBL 167 / Sep '96 / Trojan

☐ BEST OF LEE 'SCRATCH' PERRY, THE
UPCD 002 / Jul '97 / Upsetter

☐ BLACK ARK EXPERRYMENTS (Perry, Lee 'Scratch' & Mad Professor)
Thank you / Super ape in good shape / Jungle safari / From heaven above / Heads of government / Open door / Black ark experryments / Poop song / Come back
ARICD 114 / Jun '95 / Ariwa Sounds

☐ BUILD THE ARK (2CD Set) (Perry, Lee 'Scratch' & The Upsetters)
My little Sandra: *Graham, Leo* / Dubbing Sandra: *Upsetters* / Long long time: *Heywood, Winston* / White belly rat: *Upsetter* / Freedom street: *Donaldson, Eric* / Land of love: *Sons Of Light* / Crossover: *Murvin, Junior* / Travelling: *Keese, Debra & The Black Five* / Green Bay incident: *Lord Sassafrass* / Thanks and praise: *Ainsworth, Junior* / Feelings: *Isaacs, Sharon* / A wah dat: *Junior Dread* / White belly rat: *Perry, Lee 'Scratch'* / Peace and love: *Shaumark & Robinson* / Think so: *Meditations* / At the feast: *Congos* / Ethiopian land: *Lewis, Peter & Paul* / Brother Noah: *Shadows* / Mr. Money Man: *Hensworth, Danny* / Feelings version: *Upsetters* / Dub dat: *Upsetter* / Judas de white belly rat: *Upsetters* / Freedom dub: *Upsetters* / Peace a dub: *Upsetters* / Land of dub: *Upsetters* / Dub so: *Upsetters* / Nyambie dub: *Upsetters* / Landmark dub: *Upsetters* / Green Bay version: *Upsetters* / Noah dub: *Upsetters* / Dub money: *Upsetters*
CDPRY 003 / Mar '94 / Trojan

☐ DOUBLE SEVEN (Upsetters)
Kentucky skank / Double six: *U-Roy* / Just enough to keep me hanging on: *Isaacs, David* / In the laah / Jungle lion / We are neighbours: *Isaacs, David* / Soul man / Stick together: *U-Roy* / High fashion: *I-Roy* / Long sentence / Hail stones / Iron side / Cold weather / Waap you waa
CDTRL 70 / Jul '96 / Trojan

☐ DRY ACID (Various Artists)
Beware of the vampire: *Laing, Denzil* / Barbara: *Bennett, Val* / Prison sentence: *Upsetters* / Not me: *Ethiopians* / Cut down: *Ethiopians* / Uncle Desmond: *Mellotones* / Down in the park: *Inspirations* / Love oh love: *Inspirations* / Can't get no peace: *Morris, Eric Monty* / For a few dollars more: *Upsetters* / Strange whisperings: *West Indians* / Taste of killing: *Upsetters* / Hard to handle: *Dawkins, Carl* / My mob: *Upsetters* / Freedom train: *Wilson, Ernest* / Dark end of the street: *Kelly, Pat* / Since you are gone: *Kelly, Pat* / Return of the ugly: *Upsetters* / Till I can't: *Isaacs, David* / Rightful ruler: *Tosh, Peter & U-Roy* / I caught you: *Upsetters* / Never get away: *Donaldson, Eric* / Broken heart: *Brown, Busty* / Dry acid: *Upsetters* / Selassie: *Reggae Boys* / Facts of life: *Mellotones*
CDTRL 398 / Jun '98 / Trojan

☐ DUB AROUND THE WORLD
SFCD 5 / Nov '95 / Sprint

☐ DUB CONFRONTATION VOL.2 (Perry, Lee 'Scratch' & King Tubby)
LG 21107 / Apr '95 / Lagoon

☐ DUB FIRE
ARICD 134 / 14 Apr '98 / Ariwa Sounds

☐ DUB IN FIRE
ARICD 135 / 3 Aug '98 / Ariwa Sounds

☐ DUB TAKE THE VOODOO OUT OF REGGAE (Perry, Lee 'Scratch' & Mad Professor)
ARICD 131 / Sep '96 / Ariwa Sounds

☐ DUB THE OLD FASHIONED WAY (Perry, Lee 'Scratch' & Prince Jammy)
RN 7052 / 22 Jun '98 / Rhino

☐ EASTWOOD RIDES AGAIN (Upsetters)
Eastwood rides again / Hit me / Knock on wood / Popcorn / Catch this / You are adorable / Capsol / Power pack / Dollar in the teeth / Baby baby / Django / Red hot / Salt and pepper / Tight spot
CDTBL 125 / Sep '96 / Trojan

☐ EXCALIBURMAN
SLCD 6 / Sep '93 / Seven Leaves

☐ EXPERRYMENTS AT THE GRASS ROOTS OF DUB (Perry, Lee 'Scratch' & Mad Professor)
Jungle roots dub / Dubbing with the super ape / Alien in out a space / Sky high dub / Nucleus dub / Dub it wide open / Dub wise experryments / Pooping dub song / Black Ark come again
ARICD 115 / Oct '95 / Ariwa Sounds

☐ FROM THE HEART OF THE CONGO
RN 0029CD / Apr '94 / Runn

☐ FROM THE SECRET LABORATORY
Secret laboratory / Inspector gadget / (I got the) Groove / Vibrate on / African hitchiker / You thought I was dead / Too much money / Push, push / African headcharge in the Hackney Empire / Party time / Seven devils dead
RRCD 55 / 25 Aug '97 / Reggae Refreshers

☐ GIVE ME POWER (Perry, Lee 'Scratch' & Friends)
Sick and tired: *Grant, Neville* / Rasta no pickpocket: *Byles, Junior* / Don't cross the nation: *Little Roy* / Give me power: *Stingers* / News flash: *Graham, Leo & The Upsetters* / Justice to the people: *Perry, Lee 'Scratch' & The Upsetters* / Babylon burning / Ring of fire: *Upsetters* / Dig the grave: *Upsetters* / Thanks we get: *Upsetters* / Public enemy no.1: *Max Romeo* / Mid East rock: *Dillinger & The Upsetters* / Forward up: *Stingers* / Hot tip: *Prince Django* / To be a lover: *Duffus, Shenley* / Give me power: *King Wah* / Flashing echo: *Graham, Leo & The Upsetters*
CDTRL 254 / Sep '96 / Trojan

☐ GLORY DUB
RB 3015 / Oct '95 / Reggae Best

☐ GOOD, THE BAD AND THE UPSETTERS, THE (Perry, Lee 'Scratch' & The Upsetters)
Capo / Phil the fluter / Guns of navarone / What do you say / Straight to the head / Red or red / Mellow mood / Family man / Oney (happy clap) / Mama look (monkey man) / Snow white / Good, the bad and the upsetters
LG 21083 / Aug '93 / Lagoon

☐ GUITAR BOOGIE DUB
Guitat boogie dub / Guitar shuffle dub / Raving guitar dub / Misty guitar dub / Roots of guitar dub / Guitar rockers dub / Guitar melody dub / Guitar picking dub / Guitar rhythm dub / Guitar end dub
RNCD 2057 / May '94 / Rhino

☐ HEART OF THE ARK
Rastafari / Rastafari dub / 4 and 20 dread locks / Nuh fe run down / Ellaine / I've never had it so good / What's the use / Don't be afraid / Forward with love / Reggae music / Brotherly dub
SLCD 1 / Jul '94 / Seven Leaves

☐ HEAVY MANNERS (Perry, Lee 'Scratch' & The Upsetters)
RB 3001 / May '94 / Reggae Best

☐ HOLD OF DEATH
Zoic / Man zion / Black street / Ruf ruf step / Venus / Hold of death / Dayler gate / Victoria fight / Zebra / Rough already / Strange thing / Don't go / Stay away
RNCD 2007 / May '93 / Rhino

☐ IN DUB AROUND (Upsetters)
SFCD 005 / Jan '96 / Sprint

☐ INTRODUCING LEE PERRY
CB 6007 / May '96 / Blue Silver

☐ KING OF DUB, THE
HS 3CD / Jun '97 / Hit Squad

☐ KUNG FU MEETS THE DRAGON (Perry, Lee 'Scratch' & The Upsetters)
LG 21112 / Aug '95 / Lagoon
JLCD 5000 / Jul '97 / Justice League

☐ LEE PERRY ARCHIVE
Upsetter / You crummy / Rub and squeeze / Stay dread / Justice to the people / City too hot / Cow thief skank / Soul thief / Doctor Dick / Kentucky skank / Shocks of Mighty / People funny boy / Bionic rats / What a good woodman / Bathroom skank / Kill them all / What a botheration
RMCD 226 / Mar '98 / Rialto

☐ LORD GOD MUZIK
ZSCDII0 / Sep '91 / Heartbeat

☐ MEET AT KING TUBBY'S (Perry, Lee 'Scratch' & The Upsetters)
RNCD 2027 / Dec '93 / Rhino

☐ MEET SCIENTIST AT BLACK ART STUDIO (Perry, Lee 'Scratch' & The Upsetters)
GRCD 008 / Jun '96 / Graylan

☐ MEETS BULLWACKIE IN SATANS DUB
RE 178CD / Nov '94 / ROIR

☐ MEETS MAFIA & FLUXY IN JAMAICA (Perry, Lee 'Scratch' & The Upsetters)
A ruffa dub: *Perry, Lee 'Scratch'* / A badder dub: *Perry, Lee 'Scratch'* / A revengeful dub: *Perry, Lee 'Scratch'* / A wickeder dub: *Perry, Lee 'Scratch'* / A evilous dub: *Perry, Lee 'Scratch'* / A cut throat dub: *Perry, Lee 'Scratch'* / A upsetting dub: *Perry, Lee 'Scratch'* / A aggrovating dub: *Perry, Lee 'Scratch'* / A dangerous dub: *Perry, Lee 'Scratch'* / A murderous dub: *Perry, Lee 'Scratch'* / A brutal dub: *Perry, Lee 'Scratch'* / A serious dub: *Perry, Lee 'Scratch'*
LG 21025 / Jul '93 / Lagoon

☐ MEETS THE MAD PROFESSOR IN DUB VOL.1 & 2 (Perry, Lee 'Scratch' & Mad Professor)
ANGCD 8/9 / Jan '91 / Angella

☐ MEETS THE MAD PROFESSOR VOL.1
Two mad man in dub / World peace / Blood of the dragoon / Space dub / Power dub / Noah's ark / Recornation / Other side of midnight / Mark of the beast
LG 21068 / Feb '93 / Lagoon

☐ MEETS THE MAD PROFESSOR VOL.2
Torch of freedom / Public enemy / East of the river nile / Rough and smooth / Flaming torch / Hotter than hot / Navarone guns / Tuturing / Bone of witch / Music forever
LG 21069 / Feb '93 / Lagoon

☐ MILLIONAIRE LIQUIDATOR (Perry, Lee 'Scratch' & The Upsetters)
Introducing myself / Drum song / Grooving / All things are possible / Show me that river / I'm a madman / Joker / Happy birthday / Sexy lady / Time marches on
CDTRL 227 / Mar '94 / Trojan

☐ MUSICAL BONES (Upsetters)
JLCD 5002 / 13 Oct '97 / Justice League

☐ MYSTIC WARRIOR
AROCD 054 / Aug '90 / Ariwa Sounds

☐ ON THE WIRE
CDTRL 348 / Apr '95 / Trojan

☐ OPEN THE GATES (2CD Set) (Perry, Lee 'Scratch' & Friends)
CDPRY 2 / Mar '94 / Trojan

☐ ORIGINAL SUPER APE, THE (Perry, Lee 'Scratch' & The Upsetters)
CRCD 67 / Jun '97 / Charm

☐ OUT OF MANY - THE UPSETTER (Various Artists)
Introducing myself: *Perry, Lee 'Scratch' & The Upsetters* / Small axe: *Marley, Bob & The Wailers* / Place called Africa: *Prince, Winston* / Don't rock my boat: *Marley, Bob & The Wailers* / Feeling is right: *Cadogan, Susan* / Be thankful: *Clarke, Bunny* / Kuchy skank: *Upsetters* / Garden of life: *Sibbles, Leroy* / Kentucky skank: *Perry, Lee 'Scratch' & The Upsetters* / Reaction: *Marley, Bob & The Wailers* / Public jestering: *Judge Winchester* / Long way: *Byles, Junior* / Mr. Brown: *Marley, Bob & The Wailers* / Stick together: *U-Roy* / Freak out skank: *Upsetters* / Justice to the people: *Perry, Lee 'Scratch' & The Upsetters* / Travelling Debra: *Keese, Debra & The Black Five*
CDTRL 297 / Sep '96 / Trojan

☐ PEOPLE FUNNY BOY (The Early Upsetter) (Various Artists)
Honey love: *Walters, Burt* / Evol yenoh: *Walters, Burt* / Popeye on the shore: *Bennett, Val* / Nonesuch busted me bet: *Mellotones* / Handy cap: *Upsetters* / People funny boy: *Perry, Lee 'Scratch'* / Blowing in the wind: *Walters, Burt* / Spanish Harlem: *Bennett, Val* / Uncle Charlie: *Mellotones* / Tighten up: *Inspirations* / Place in the sun: *Isaacs, David*
CDTRL 339 / Sep '96 / Trojan

☐ PRESENTS BLACK ARK ALMIGHTY DUB
BCD 403 / Dec '94 / Black Ark

☐ PRODUCED AND DIRECTED BY THE UPSETTER (Various Artists)
I man free: *King Burnett* / Free man: *Upsetter* / Zion: *Flames* / Zion: *Upsetter* / Bike no license: *Clarke, Easton* / Unlicensed dub: *Upsetter* / Crying over you: *Heptones* / Crying dub: *Upsetter* / Financial crisis: *Silvertones* / Financial dub: *Upsetter* / False teaching: *Murvin, Junior* / Teaching dub: *Upsetter* / Backbiting: *Heywood, Winston & The Hombres* / Chastising dub: *Upsetter* / Houses of Parliament: *Meditations* / Dub of Parliament: *Upsetter* / Guide line: *Faith, George* / Dub line: *Upsetter* / Philistines on the land: *Murvin, Junior* / Bingo kid: *Upsetter*
PSCD 19 / 1 Jun '98 / Pressure Sounds

☐ REGGAE EMPEROR
RNCD 2137 / Apr '96 / Rhino

☐ REGGAE GREATS (Various Artists)
Party time: *Heptones* / Police and thieves: *Murvin, Junior* / Groovy situation: *Rowe, Keith* / Soul fire: *Perry, Lee 'Scratch'* / War in a Babylon: *Max Romeo* / Wisdom: *Jah Lion* / To be a lover: *Faith, George* / Roast fish and cornbread: *Perry, Lee 'Scratch'* / Croaking lizard: *Prince Jazzbo* / Dreadlocks in moonlight: *Perry, Lee 'Scratch'*
RRCD 10 / 25 Aug '97 / Reggae Refreshers
5544602 / 1 Jun '98 / Spectrum

☐ REMINAH DUB (Perry, Lee 'Scratch' & The Upsetters)
OMCD 11 / Mar '96 / Original Music

☐ RETURN OF DJANGO (Upsetters)
Return of Django / Touch of fire / Cold sweat / Drugs and poison / Soulful I / Night doctor / One punch / Eight for eight / Live injection / Man for MI5 / Ten to twelve / Medical operation
CDTRL 19 / Sep '96 / Trojan

☐ RETURN OF WAX (Perry, Lee 'Scratch' & The Upsetters)
JLCD 5003 / 27 Apr '98 / Justice League

☐ REVOLUTION DUB
Dub revolution / Womans dub / Kojak / Doctor on the go / Bush weed / Dreadlock talking / Own man / Dub the rhythm / Raindrops
RNCD 2120 / Sep '95 / Rhino

☐ SATAN'S DUB
Satan dub / Come home dub / Ooh la la dub / Upful dub fashion / President dub / Dub skeem / Strange dub / Bog walk skanking / Underecover dub / Stop stop dub / Moving in dub / Dub master
RUSCD 8241 / 25 May '98 / ROIR

☐ SCRATCH THE UPSETTERS AGAIN (Perry, Lee 'Scratch' & The Upsetters)
Bad tooth / Dentist / Out of space / One punch / Will you still love me tomorrow / Take one / Soul walk / I want to thank you / Mule train / Touch of fire / She is gone again / Result / Eastwood rides again / Hit me / Knock on wood / Popcorn / Catch this / You are adorable / Capsol / Power pack / Dollar in my teeth / Baby baby / Django / Red hot / Salt and pepper / Tight spot
CDTRL 352 / Sep '96 / Trojan

☐ SENSI DUB VOL.2 (Perry, Lee 'Scratch' & King Tubby)
OMCD 15 / Jul '93 / Original Music

☐ SENSI DUB VOL.2 & 3 (Perry, Lee 'Scratch' & King Tubby)
OMCD 015/16 / Sep '90 / Original Music

☐ SERIOUS DUB
CD 6107 / 29 Sep '97 / Music

☐ SOME OF THE BEST (Perry, Lee 'Scratch' & The Upsetters)
People funny boy: *Perry, Lee 'Scratch'* / Da da: *Upsetters* / Shocks of mighty: *Barker, Dave & The Upsetters* / Set me free: *Barker, Dave & The Upsetters* / Live injection: *Upsetters* / Freedom train: *Upsetters* / Finger mash: *Perry, Lee 'Scratch' & The Silvertones* / Duppy conqueror: *Marley, Bob & The Wailers* / Upsetting station: *Barker, Dave & The Upsetters* / Thanks we get: *Byles, Junior & Omar Perry* / Fu man version: *Thompson, Linval* / Kiss me neck: *Upsetters* / Keep on skanking: *Upsetters*
HBCD 37 / Jul '88 / Heartbeat

☐ SOUNDS FROM THE HOTLINE
Bionic rat / Ashes and dust / Righteous oily / In this iwa / Babylon a fall / Rainbow throne / Standing on the hill / News flash / When you walk / Sweet guava jelly / So you come, so you go / Free up the prisoners / Track 13
CDHB 76 / Aug '96 / Heartbeat

☐ SUPER APE (Perry, Lee 'Scratch' & The Upsetters)
Zion's blood / Croaking lizard / Black vest / Underground / Curly dub / Dread lion / Three in one / Patience / Dub along / Super ape in good shape
RRCD 13 / 25 Aug '97 / Reggae Refreshers

☐ SUPER APE IN THE JUNGLE
ARICD 112 / Jul '95 / Ariwa Sounds

☐ TECHNOMAJIKAL (Perry, Lee 'Scratch' & Dieter Meier)
RUSCD 8232 / Jul '97 / ROIR

☐ TIME BOOM
ONUCD 43 / Mar '94 / On-U Sound

☐ UPSETTER COLLECTION, THE (Upsetters)
Cold sweat / Return of Django / Check him out: *Bleechers* / Django shoots first / Kill them all: *Perry, Lee 'Scratch' & The Upsetters* / Vampire / Drugs and poison / Sipreano / Black IPA / Bucky skank: *Perry, Lee 'Scratch'* / Words of my mouth: *Gatherers* / Tipper special / Cow thief skank: *Perry, Lee 'Scratch' & Charlie Ace* / French connection / Better days: *Carlton & His Shoes* / Freak out skank
CDTRL 195 / Sep '96 / Trojan

☐ UPSETTER IN DUB
Noah sugar pan / Ketch a dub / Version train / Rootically dub / Son of the Black Ark / Lorna Skank / If the cap fits / Dub a come / Tedious dub / Rejoice in skank / Babylon thief dub / Foundation solid / Bagman / Better reach / Dub in time / Fun and games / Sipple dub / Bionic rat dub
CDHB 77 / May '97 / Heartbeat

☐ UPSETTER PRESENTING DUB
RN 7010 / Sep '96 / Rhino

☐ UPSETTER, THE (Upsetters)
Tide wave / Heat proof / To love somebody: *Brown, Buster* / Night doctor / Soulful one / Big noise / Man from MI5 / Dread luck / Kiddy-o: *Muskyteers* / Wolfman / Crying about you / Thunderball
CDTTL 13 / Sep '96 / Trojan

☐ UPSETTERS A GO GO (Upsetters)
CDHB 136 / Nov '95 / Heartbeat

☐ UPSETTERS AND THE STUDENT (Upsetters)
RN 7008 / Sep '96 / Rhino

☐ UPSETTING THE NATION 1969-1970 (Upsetters & Friends)
Eight for eight: *Upsetters* / Outer space: *Upsetters* / To love somebody: *Brown, Buster* / Soulful I: *Upsetters* / Man from MI5: *Upsetters* / I'll be waiting: *Termites* / Ten to twelve: *Upsetters* / Kiddy O: *Muskyteers* / Medical operation: *Upsetters* / Night Doctor: *Upsetters* / Self control: *Upsetters* / Crying about you: *Brown, Buster* / Thunderball: *Upsetters* / One punch: *Upsetters* / Vampire: *Upsetters* / Build my whole world around you: *Barker, Dave* / Prisoner of love: *Barker, Dave* / I was wrong: *Barker, Dave*
CDTRL 330 / Sep '96 / Trojan

☐ VERSION LIKE RAIN (Upsetters & Friends)
I want a wine: *Graham, Leo* / Double wine: *Upsetters* / Hot and cold: *Pablo, Augustus & The Upsetters* / Fever: *Cadogan, Susan* / Beat down Babylon: *Byles, Junior* / Outformer: *Upsetters* / Beat down babylon: *Upsetters* / Iron wolf: *Upsetters* / Stick together: *U-Roy* / This world: *Milton, Henry* / Influenza: *Upsetters* / Informer man: *Byles, Junior & Jah-T* / Babylon burning: *Maxie* / Freedom fighter: *Bunny & Ricky* / Bet you don't know: *Duffus, Shenley*
CDTRL 278 / Sep '96 / Trojan

☐ VOODOOISM (Various Artists)
Psalms 20: *Booms, James* / Proverbs of dub: *Upsetter* / Better future: *Walker, Errol* / Future dub: *Upsetter* / River: *Zap Pow* / Freedom: *Earl 16* / Africa: *Hombres* / Foundation dub: *Upsetter* / Voodooism: *Graham, Leo* / Dubism: *Upsetter* / African style: *Black Notes* / Wolf out deh: *Lloyd & Devon* / Shepherd Rod: *Upsetter*
PSCD 009 / Aug '97 / Pressure Sounds

☐ WHO PUT THE VOODOO PON REGGAE
ARICD 130 / Sep '96 / Ariwa Sounds

☐ WORDS OF MY MOUTH (The Producer Series) (Various Artists)
Words of my mouth: *Gatherers* / Words of my mouth: *Upsetters* / Kuchy skank: *Upsetters* / Rejoice in Jah Jah children: *Upsetters* / Rejoicing skank: *Silvertones* / Bushweed corntrash: *Bunny & Ricky* / Callying butt: *Upsetters* / Da ba day: *Upsetters* / Kiss me neck: *Upsetters* / Curly locks: *Byles, Junior* / Dreader locks: *Lee & Junior* / Many a call: *Unforgettables* / Too bad bull: *Bunny & Ricky* / Too bad cow: *Upsetters* / Fist of fury: *Perry, Lee 'Scratch'* / Herb vendor: *Horsemouth* / Cane river rock: *Upsetters* / Stay dead: *Perry, Lee 'Scratch'* / Kentucky skank: *Perry, Lee 'Scratch'* / Bathroom skank: *Perry, Lee 'Scratch'* / Spiritual whip: *Jah Lloyd*
CDTRL 374 / Oct '96 / Trojan

Perry, Linda

☐ IN FLIGHT
In my dreams / Freeway / Uninvited / Success / Life in a bottle / Fill me up / Knock me out / Too deep / Taken / Fruitloop / Daydream / Machine man / In flight
IND 90061 / Sep '96 / Interscope

Perry, Rich

☐ BEAUTIFUL LOVE
SCCD 31360 / May '95 / Steeplechase

☐ LEFT ALONE
SCCD 31421 / Nov '97 / Steeplechase

☐ WHAT IS THIS (Perry, Rich Quartet)
SCCD 31374 / Feb '96 / Steeplechase

Perry, Steve

☐ STREET TALK
Oh Sherrie / I believe / Go away / Foolish heart / It's only love / She's mine / You should be happy / Running alone / Captured by the moment / Strung out
4866602 / Nov '96 / Columbia

Persian Risk

☐ RISE UP
HV 1007 / Sep '97 / High Vaultage

Persiani, Andre

☐ STARLIGHT SOUVENIRS
FM 9 / Nov '97 / Night & Day

Person, Eric

☐ ARRIVAL
1212372 / Apr '93 / Soul Note

☐ MORE TALES TO TELL
1213072 / Jan '98 / Soul Note

☐ PROPHECY
1212872 / May '94 / Soul Note

Person, Houston

☐ GOODNESS
Hey driver / Goodness / Brother h. / Hard times / Jamilah / Close your eyes
OJCCD 332 / Dec '95 / Original Jazz Classics

☐ LEGENDS OF ACID JAZZ, THE
PRCD 24179 / Apr '97 / Prestige

☐ OPENING ROUND, THE
Sweet sucker / Let's stay together / Can't help lovin' that man / What's going on / When a man loves a woman / Blue spring / Song for a rainbow / Shenandoah
SAVCD 2005 / Jan '98 / Savant

☐ PERSONALITY
Kittitian carnival / Funky sunday afternoon / Pain / Shotgun / Touch of the bad stuff / He'll fight my battles / All in love is fair / Mayola / Until it's time for you to go / You are the sunshine of my life / Don't go to strangers / Easy walker
CDBGPD 070 / Mar '93 / Beat Goes Public

☐ SOMETHING IN COMMON (Person, Houston & Ron Carter)
Blue seven / I thought about you / Mack the knife / Joy Spring / Good morning heartache / Anthropology / Once in a while / Blues for two
MCD 5376 / Apr '91 / Muse

☐ TALK OF THE TOWN
MCD 5331 / Sep '92 / Muse

Persson, Bent

☐ LOUIS ARMSTRONG'S 50 HOT CORNET CHORUSES VOL.1 & 2
CKS 3411 / Jun '96 / Kenneth

☐ LOUIS ARMSTRONG'S 50 HOT CORNET CHORUSES VOL.3 & 4
Copenhagen / Someday sweetheart / Sidewalk blues / Jackass blues / Easy rider / Chant / Sugarfoot stomp / Grandpa's spells / Dixieland blues / Chicago breakdown / 29th and dearborn / Chattanooga stomp / Mr. Jelly Lord / Darktown shuffle / Panama blues / Dallas stomp / Stomp your stuff / Tampeekoe
CKS 3413 / Apr '94 / Kenneth

☐ SWINGING STRAIGHT (Persson, Bent Sextet)
SITCD 9218 / Jun '96 / Sittel

Persuaders

☐ THIN LINE BETWEEN LOVE AND HATE
Thin line between love and hate / Let's go down together / Blood brothers / You musta put something in your love / Thanks for loving me / Love gonna pack up / If this is what you call love / Mr. Sunshine / Thigh spy / Can't go no further and do no better
7567804142 / Jan '96 / Atlantic

Persuasions

☐ COMIN' AT YA
Return to sender / Don't let him take you love / Besame mucho / One mint julep / Let them talk / Mortal man / I'll be forever loving you / Just because / Drip drop / Crying in the chapel / Love me like a rock
FF 70093 / Nov '96 / Flying Fish

☐ NO FRILLS
You can have her / Under the boardwalk / Sand in my shoes / I was wrong / I woke up in love this morning / I wonder do you love the Lord like I do / Still ain't got no band / Victim / Treasure of love / Sweet was the wine / What are you doing New Year's Eve / Slip slidin' away
ROUCD 3083 / Aug '88 / Rounder

☐ RIGHT AROUND THE CORNER
BBCD 9556 / Oct '94 / Bullseye Blues

☐ SINCERELY
CDBB 9576 / Aug '96 / Bullseye Blues

☐ YOU'RE ALL I WANT FOR CHRISTMAS
You're all I want for Christmas / Jingle bell rock / Rudolph the red-nosed reindeer / Jesus song / This time of year / Do you hear what I hear / Silent night / What are you doing New Year's Eve / Christmas song / White Christmas / Hey Santa Claus / Merry Christmas baby / Christmas means love / Joy to the world
CDBB 9594 / Sep '97 / Bullseye Blues

Peruna Jazzmen

☐ ...AND THERE
MECCACD 2022 / Oct '97 / Music Mecca

☐ HERE...
MECCACD 2021 / Oct '97 / Music Mecca

☐ PERUNA JAZZMEN VOL.1 & 2
SOSCD 1003 / Dec '94 / Stomp Off

Perverted

☐ POETIC TERRORISM IN AN ERA OF GRIEF
GAP 028 / Jun '95 / Gap Recordings

Peshay

☐ PROMISED LAND/FUTURE HISTORY (Mixed By Peshay/2CD Set) (Various Artists)
MSS 0018 / 4 Nov '97 / Mutant Sound System

Pessary

☐ INWARD COLLAPSE
DPROMCD 2 / Oct '96 / Dirter Promotions

☐ LAID TO REST
DPROMCD 7 / Oct '96 / Dirter Promotions

Pest 5000

☐ INTERABANG
DUH 025 / 3 Nov '97 / Derivative

Pet Lamb

☐ TENDERNESS
BLUNT 0017 / 27 Jul '98 / Blunt

Pet Shop Boys

☐ ALTERNATIVE
In the night / Man could get arrested / That's my impression / Was that what is was / Paninaro / Jack the lad / You know where you went wrong / New life / I want a dog / Do I have to / I get excited (you get excited to) / Don Juan / Sound of the atom splitting / One of the crowd / You funny uncle / It must be obvious / We all feel better in the dark / Bet she's not your girlfriend / Losing my mind / Music for boys / Miserabilsm / Hey headmaster / What keeps mankind alive / Shameless / Too many people / Violence / Decadence / If love were all / Euroboy / Some speculation
CDPCSDS 166
CDPSCD 166 / Aug '95 / Parlophone

☐ BILINGUAL
Discoteca / Single / Metamorphosis / Electricity / Se a vida e (that's the way life is) / It always comes as a surprise / Red letter day / Up against it / Survivors / Before / To step aside / Saturday night forever
CDPCSD 170 / Sep '96 / Parlophone

☐ BILINGUAL (Limited Edition 2CD Set)
Discoteca / Single / Metamorphosis / Electricity / Se a vida e (that's the way life is) / It always comes as a surprise / Red letter day / Up against it / Survivors / Before / To step aside / Saturday night forever / Somewhere / Red letter day / To step aside / Before / Boy who couldn't keep his clothes on / Se a vida e (that's the way life is) / Discoteca
CDPCSDX 170 / Jul '97 / Parlophone

☐ DISCO VOL.2
Absolutely fabulous / I wouldn't normally do this kind of thing / Go West / Liberation / So hard / Can you forgive her / Yesterday, when I was mad / We all feel better in the dark
CDPCSD 159 / Sep '94 / Parlophone

☐ HITS OF THE PET SHOP BOYS, THE (PS Orchestra/Synthesizers)
Being boring / What have I done to deserve this / How can you expect to be taken seriously / So hard / It's a sin / Rent / Heart / I want a dog / Opportunities (let's make lots of money) / Love comes quickly / Suburbia / I'm not scared / Jealousy / Always on my mind / West end girls
QED 052 / Nov '96 / Tring

☐ INTROSPECTIVE
Left to my own devices / I want a dog / Domino dancing / I'm not scared / Always on my mind / It's alright / In my house
CDPCS 7325 / Feb '94 / Parlophone

☐ PET SHOP BOYS: INTERVIEW COMPACT DISC
CBAK 4021 / Nov '89 / Baktabak

☐ PLEASE
Two divide by zero / West End girls / Opportunities (Lets make lots of money) / Love comes quickly / Suburbia / Tonight is forever / Violence / I want a lover / Later tonight / Why don't we live together
CDP 7462712 / Jun '86 / Parlophone

☐ PLEASE/ACTUALLY/BEHAVIOUR (The Originals/3CD Set)
Two divided by zero / West end girls / Opportunities (lets make lots of money) / Love comes quickly / Suburbia / Tonight is forever / Violence / I want a lover / Later tonight / Why don't we live together / One more chance / Shopping / Rent / Hit music / What have I done to deserve this / It couldn't happen here / It's a sin / I want to wake up / Heart / King's Cross / Being boring / This must be the place I waited years to leave / To face the truth / How can you expect to be taken seriously / Only the wind / My October symphony / So hard / Nervously / End of the world / Jealousy
CDOMB 023 / 27 Jul '98 / Parlophone

☐ VERY
Can you forgive her / I wouldn't normally do this kind of thing / Liberation / Different point of view / Dreaming of the Queen / Yesterday, when I was mad / Theatre / One and one make five / To speak is a sin / Young offender / One in a million / Go west
CDPCSD 143 / Sep '93 / Parlophone

Petards

☐ ANTHOLOGY (Ein Kapitel Deutscher Rockgeschichte/6CD Set)
Baby run run run / Pretty Miss / Right time / She didn't / Sun came out at seven / Firetree / Summerwind / If you want to go away / Drive / I won't come back / Deeper blue / My little heart / Love is all around / Baby / Roses for Cathy / Confusion all day / Flittermouse / Never more / Out in the rain / Girl where are you going now / Fountain / Tonight / Mockingbird crying / Some sunny Sunday morning / Bridal ballad / Pretty Liza / On the road with my bag / Shoot me up to the moon / Lazy moon / Golden glass / Tiger rider / Rainbows and butterflies / Misty island / Tartarex / Everybody knows Matilda / Take me shake me / Blue fire light / Special sunset for a lady / Pictures / Dream / Mekka / Keep on / My world / Sunshine rainshine / Ruins of Tookamoon / Stone by now / Rover of the roam / Don't you feel like me / Good good Donna / Rainy day / Fowling / Cowboy / Willie's gun / Windy nevermore / Long way back home / Big boom / Too many heavens / Flame missing light / On the road drinking wine / Baby man / Spectrum / Hell my friend / Free / Hand of fortune / Rejoice your mind / Just like a lady / I take it easy / Bluebird yellowbird / Angela / Rose / Million rainbow / Song for my child / Highway child / My own city / Firefly / Gentle breeze / 1 to 7 (sing it with your baby child) / You are the song / Green river / Commotion / Proud Mary / I put a spell on you / Keep on chooglin' / Bad moon rising / Good golly Miss Molly / Suzie Q / Lodi / Born on a bayou / Fortunate son / Down on the corner / (And you all) talk about heaven / Alright tonight you'll be a woman / One more chance to be blue (burning rainbows) / Green eyed paradise / Speed freak / (Today is my) birthday / Alone / Dust of my way / Someday I'll cry / Come to me come to you / You better move right on / Goky and me / Who will sell his dreams / Roses / Papa's got a brand new bag / Friday on my mind / I'm a believer / Drive / She didn't / Right time / Ruby Tuesday / Matthew and son / Painter man / Stone free / Interview
BCD 16180 / Oct '97 / Bear Family

Peter & Gordon

☐ EP COLLECTION, THE
Leave my woman alone / Hurtin' is loving / Long time gone / Lady Godiva / I got to pieces / Woman / Flower lady / Night in rusty armour / Sunday for tea / Start trying someone else / Love me baby / Lucille / If I were you / Pretty Mary / World without love / Tell me how / You don't have to tell me / Tears don't stop / Soft as the dawn / Leave me alone / Roving rambler / I don't want to see you again / Devant toi je suis sans voix / True love ways / Ne me plains pas (don't feel sorry for me) / Le temps va le temps court (time is going, time is running) / L'unconnue (the unknown)
SEECD 426 / May '95 / See For Miles

☐ I GO TO PIECES/TRUE LOVE WAYS
COLCD 2715 / 3 Mar '98 / Collectables

☐ IN TOUCH WITH (Mono/Stereo)
Freight train / Land of Oden / Mess of blues / Two little love birds / Barbara Allen / I still love you / I don't want to see you again / My babe / Willow garden / Love me baby / I don't care what they say / My little girl's gone / Ain't that lovin' you baby / Leave me in the rain
DORIG 112 / 6 Oct '97 / EMI

☐ TRUE LOVE WAYS
True love ways / If I were you / I don't want to see you again / I go to pieces / Don't pity me / Knight in rusty armour / Sunday for tea / Jokers / To show I love you / Love me baby / Flower lady / I can remember
WB 885592 / 2 Feb '98 / Disky

☐ WOMAN/LADY GODIVA
COLCD 2716 / 3 Mar '98 / Collectables

☐ WORLD WITHOUT LOVE, A/I DON'T WANT TO SEE YOU AGAIN
COLCD 2717 / 3 Mar '98 / Collectables

Peter & The Test Tube Babies

☐ ALIEN PUBDUCTION
WB 1176CD / 19 Jan '98 / We Bite

☐ CRINGE
SPV 08430012 / Mar '96 / SPV

☐ JOURNEY TO THE CENTRE OF JOHNNY CLARKE'S HEAD
WB 3124CD / May '95 / We Bite

☐ LOUD BLARING PUNK ROCK CD, THE
Oral Annie / We're too drunk / Pick yer nose (And eat it) / Vicars / Snakebite / I lust for the disgusting things in life / Tupperware party / Breast cancer / TQBBJ's / Student wankers / Big mouth / Child molester / Porno queen / Being sick / Excuses / Beat up the mods / Get 'em in (and get 'em off) / Rock 'n' roll is shit
WB 3125CD / May '95 / We Bite

☐ MATING SOUNDS OF THE SOUTH AMERICAN FROG, THE
September part 1 / Guest list / One night stand / Let's burn / Jinx / Blown out again / Wimpeez / Easter bank holiday '83 / No invitation / Pissed punks (go for it) / Never made it / September part 2
WB 3123CD / May '95 / We Bite

☐ PISSED AND PROUD
Moped lads / Banned from the pubs / Elvis is dead / Up yer bum / Smash and grab / Run like hell / Shit stirrer / Intensive care / Keep Britain untidy / Transvestite / Maniac / Disco / I'm the leader of the gang (I am)
CDPUNK 3 / Apr '95 / Anagram

☐ PUNK SINGLES COLLECTION, THE
Banned from the pubs / Moped lads / Peacehaven wild kids / Run like hell / Up yer bum / Zombie creeping flesh / No invitation / Smash and grab / Jinx / Trapper ain't got a bird / Wimpeez / Never made it / Blown out again / Rotting in the fart sack / Ten deadly sins / Spirit of Keith Moon / Boozanza / Alchohol / Key to the city / Vicar's wank too
CDPUNK 64 / Oct '95 / Anagram

☐ SOBERPHOBIA
Keys to the city / Louise / Spirit of keith moon / Allergic to life / All about love / He's on the whiskey / Boozanza / Every time I see her / Ghost in my bedsit / Every second counts
WB 3128CD / May '95 / We Bite

☐ SUPERMODELS
WB 1139CD / Nov '95 / We Bite

☐ TEN DEADLY SINS
WB 3127CD / May '95 / We Bite

☐ TOTALLY TEST TUBED
Banned from the pubs / Moped lads / Peacehaven wild kids / Maniac / Transvestite / Elvis is dead / I lust for the disgusting things / TQGGBJ / Run like hell / Up yer bum / Vicar's wank too / Jinx / Trapper ain't got a bird / Blown out again / Never made it / Pissed punks (Go for it) / Spirit of Keith Moon / Zombie creeping flesh / Keys to the city / Louise wouldn't like it / Every second counts / All about love / September part 2
WB 3126CD / May '95 / We Bite

Peter, John

☐ JOHN PETER & RED HOT SEVEN (Featuring Wally Fawkes) (Peter, John & Red Hot Seven)
JCD 176 / Oct '91 / Jazzology

Peter, Paul & Mary

☐ C'MON FOLKS
TC 022 / Mar '94 / That's Country

☐ PETER, PAUL & MARY
Early in the morning / If I had a hammer (the hammer song) / Lemon tree / Cruel war / Sorrow / Bamboo / This train / Where have all the flowers gone / Autumn to may / If I had my way / It's raining / Five hundred miles
7599271572 / Jan '96 / WEA

Peters & Lee

☐ PETERS AND LEE
PCOM 1098 / Jun '89 / President

☐ WELCOME HOME
Welcome home / I'm confessin' / Let it be me / Love will keep us together / Air that I breathe / Suspicious minds / You make me feel brand new / Don't stay away too long / Endless love / Always on my mind / Rainbow / Hello / Hey Mr. Music man / Through all the years
308344 / 13 Jul '98 / Hallmark

☐ WORLD OF PETERS & LEE, THE
Welcome home / By your side / Vincent / Don't stay away too long / So sad (to watch a good love go bad) / Crying game / Hey Mr. Music Man / Wonderful baby / Last happy song / Rainbow / When somebody thinks you're wonderful / If I fell / Only you / Come to me / Song from Moulin Rouge (where your heart is) / You belong to me / Don't blame me / Guess you'll never know
5515392 / May '96 / Spectrum

Peters, Brian

☐ BEAST IN THE BOX, THE
Mr. James Knowles of Friezland/The Snake Pass hornpipe / Mayday/Miss Twentyman's delight/ Down with the French / New railroad / Spiral staircase/The squall/Royal Burlesque hornpipe / JOhannespolka / Adieu sweet lovely Nancy / Nantwich Fair/The white petticoat/The recruiting officer / Charming fair/What you will / Hojby schottische/Mats Edens schottische / October song / Double the Cape/Rusty gully / Studentenmarch / Jack's alive/Old Fluz/Duke William hornpipe / Working on a pushboat / Crystal wedding/The heart aches for home / Four seasons/Silly season
PUGCD 003 / Jun '98 / Pugwash

☐ CLEAR THE ROAD (Peters, Brian & Gordon Tyrrall)
HARCD 031 / Jun '96 / Harbour Town

☐ SEEDS OF TIME, THE
Manchester jig - welcome home / History lesson / Living in the past that never was / Cropper lads / Killy Fisher / My lad's ower bonny for the coal trade / Coffee and tea / Lowlands of Holland / Box in the attic / Northern Nanny / Low flier / Servant of the company / Sir William Stanier's favourite / Lovely Joan / Oyster girl / Lad with the trousers on / Mad Moll / False foudrage / Old holle hornpipe / Padlocks / Ruins by the shore / Dark island / Arran boat
HARCD 021 / May '92 / Harbour Town

☐ SHARPER THAN THE THORN
PUGCD 002 / Nov '96 / Pugwash

☐ SQUEEZING OUT SPARKS
PUG 001CD / Apr '94 / Pugwash

Peters, Gretchen

☐ BURIED TREASURES
CURCD 51 / 9 Mar '98 / Curb

☐ SECRET OF LIFE, THE
CURCD 31 / Dec '97 / Curb

Peters, Hal

☐ FIREBALL MAIL
GRCD 6038 / Feb '97 / Goofin'

Peters, Mike

☐ AER (Welsh Language Version Of 'Breathe') (Peters, Mike & The Poets)
CRAICD 047 / Dec '94 / Crai

☐ BREATHE (Peters, Mike & The Poets)
Poetic justice / All I wanted / If I can't have you / Breathe / Love is a revolution / Who's gonna make the peace / Spiritual / What the world can't give me / Levis and bibles / Beautiful thing / Into the 21st century / This is war / Message / Back into the system / It just don't get any better than this / Train a comin' / New chapter (reprise)
CRAI 042CD / Oct '94 / Crai

☐ FEEL FREE
Shine on (13th dream) / Message / Feel free / All is forgiven / My calling / Regeneration / RIP / What is it for / Psychological combat zone / Love we made / Breathe / Broken silence
TRACD 233 / Aug '96 / Transatlantic

☐ RISE
EAGCD 019 / 23 Feb '98 / Eagle

Petersen, Erik

☐ PROPELLER
SKR 37CD / Aug '97 / Startklart

Peterson, Dickie

☐ CHILD OF THE DARKNESS
CTCD 077 / 2 Feb '98 / Captain Trip

Peterson, Edward

☐ UPWARD SPIRAL
Probably / Upward spiral / Elliott Ness / Objects in the mirror are closer than they appear / Poem for tortured spirits / Onus B / Dan's idea / For Dan / I didn't know what time it was
DE 445 / Mar '97 / Delmark

Peterson, James

☐ TOO MANY KNOTS
Fish ain't bitin' / Flip floppin' my love / Call before you come home / Long handled spoon / Slob on the knob / Too many knots / Jacksonville / Every goodbye ain't gone / More than one way to skin a cat / Blind can't lead the blind / Killer rock
ICH 1130CD / Oct '93 / Ichiban

Peterson, Lucky

☐ I'M READY
I'm ready / It ain't right / You shook me / Junkyard / Who's been talkin' / I lost my faith last night / Tribute to the King / On the sea of love / Nothing but smoke / Spankin' Leroy / Don't cloud up on me / Precious Lord / Take my hand
5175132 / Mar '94 / EmArCy

☐ LUCKY STRIKES
Over my head / Can't get no loving on the telephone / Lucky strikes / Bad feeling / Earlene / Pounding of my heart / She spread her wings / Dead cat on the line / Heart attack
ALCD 4770 / May '93 / Alligator

☐ RIDIN'
Ridin' / Don't answer the door / Farther up the road / Kinda easy like / Baby, what you want me to do / Green onions / Little red rooster / You don't have to go
ECD 260332 / Sep '93 / Evidence
IS 9192 / Mar '96 / Isabel

☐ TRIPLE PLAY
Let the chips fall where they may / Your lies / Six o'clock blues / Repo man / I found a love / Jammin' in the jungle / Locked out of love / I'm free / Don't cloud up on me / Funky Ray
ALCD 4789 / May '93 / Alligator

Peterson, Master Joe

☐ MASTER JOE PETERSEN (The Phenomenal Boy Singer)
Smilin' through / My ain folk / No souvenirs / Rainbow valley / It's a sin to tell a lie / Sweetheart let's grow old together / Old rugged cross / Memories of childhood days / When they sound the last All Clear / You don't have to tell me / Two little tears / Badge from your coat / Perfect day / Little grey home in the West / My heart's in Old Killarney / Broken hearted clown / Choir boy / Goodnight my love
LCOM 5233 / May '94 / Lismor

Peterson, Oscar

☐ A LA SALLE PLEYEL (2CD Set) (Peterson, Oscar & Joe Pass)
I gotta right to sing the blues / Mirage / Tenderly / (Back home again in) Indiana / It never entered my mind / Ellingtonia / Take the 'A' train / In a sentimental mood / Satin doll / Lady of the lavender mist / Things ain't what they used to be / Sweet Georgia Brown / Darn that dream / Summer knows/ What are you doing the rest of your life / Everything I love / It's all right with me / Stella by starlight / Just you, just me / If / Honeysuckle rose / Blues for Bise / Pleyel Bis
26257052 / Nov '97 / Pablo

☐ AT THE MONTREUX JAZZ FESTIVAL 1975 (Peterson, Oscar Big Six)
Au privave / Here's that rainy day / Poor butterfly / Reunion blues
OJCCD 9312 / Nov '97 / Original Jazz Classics

☐ BURSTING OUT WITH THE ALL STAR BIG BAND/SWINGING BRASS
5296992 / Mar '96 / Verve

☐ COMPLETE PABLO CD COLLECTION, THE (10CD Set)
PACD 0012 / Nov '96 / Pablo

☐ DIGITAL AT MONTREUX
Old folks / Soft winds / (Back home again in) Indiana / That's all / Younger than Springtime / Caravan / Rockin' in rhythm / C jam blues / Solitude / Satin doll / Caravan (reprise) / On the trail
CD 2308224 / May '94 / Pablo

☐ ENCORE AT THE BLUE NOTE (Peterson, Oscar Trio)
Falling in love with love / Here's that rainy day / Goodbye old girl-he has gone (medley) / Gentle waltz / Billie's bounce / More I see you / I wished on the moon / Cool walk
CD 83356 / Oct '93 / Telarc

☐ **EXCLUSIVELY FOR MY FRIENDS (4CD Set)**
At long last love / Easy walker / Tin tin deo / I've got a crush on you / Foggy day / Like someone in love / On a clear day / I'm in the mood for love / Girl talk / Robbins' nest / I concentrate on you/Moon river / Waltzing is hip/Satin doll / Love is here to stay / Sandy's blues / Alice in wonderland / Noreen's nocturne / In a mellotone / Nica's dream / On Green Dolphin Street / Summertime / Sometime's I'm happy / Who can I turn to / Emily / Quiet nights / Sax no end / When lights are low / Someone to watch over me / Perdido / Body and soul / Who can I turn to / Bye bye blackbird / I should care / Lulu's back in town / Little girl blues / Take the 'A' train
5138302 / Apr '92 / MPS Jazz

☐ **FIRST RECORDINGS, THE**
I got rhythm / Louise / My blue heaven / Sheik of Araby / Flying home / C jam blues / If I could be with you / Humoresque / Blue moon / In a little Spanish town / Time on my hands / China boy / Runnin' wild / Sweet Lorraine / Honeydripper / East of the sun
IGOCD 2070 / Sep '97 / Indigo

☐ **GERSHWIN SONGBOOK, THE**
Man I love / Fascinating rhythm / It ain't necessarily so / Somebody loves me / Strike up the band / I've got a crush on you / I was doing all right / 'S wonderful / Oh lady be good / I got rhythm / Foggy day / Love walked in
5296982 / Apr '96 / Verve

☐ **GOOD LIFE, THE**
Wheatland / Wave / For count / Good life / On a clear day
OJCCD 627 / Feb '92 / Original Jazz Classics

☐ **HALLELUJAH TIME**
MCD 0502 / Nov '93 / Moon

☐ **HISTORY OF AN ARTIST**
RB blues / I wished on the moon / You can depend on me / This is where it's at / Okie blues / I want to be happy / Texas blues / Main stem / Don't get around much anymore / Swamp fire / In a sentimental mood / Greasy blues / Sweetie blues / Gay's blues / Good life / Richard's round / Lady of the lavender mist
CD 2310895 / Oct '92 / Pablo

☐ **JAM AT MONTREUX '77**
Ali and frazier / If I were a bell / Things ain't what they used to be / Just in time / Bye bye blues
OJCCD 378 / Feb '92 / Original Jazz Classics

☐ **JAZZ MASTERS**
Night train / Woody 'n' you / Willow weep for me / Younger than Springtime / West Coast blues / Love for sale / Noreen's nocturne / OP / Blues etude / Gal in Calico / D and E blues / Bossa beguine / Evrev / Honey dripper / Someday my Prince will come
5163202 / 5 May '98 / Verve

☐ **JAZZ MASTERS (Oscar Peterson Plays Broadway)**
5168932 / 5 May '98 / Verve

☐ **JAZZ PORTRAIT OF FRANK SINATRA, A (Peterson, Oscar Trio)**
You make me feel so young / Come dance with me / Learnin' the blues / Witchcraft / Tender trap / Saturday night is the loneliest night of the week / Just in time / It happened in Monterey / I get a kick out of you / All of me / Birth of the blues / How about you
8257692 / Mar '93 / Verve

☐ **JAZZ SOUL OF OSCAR PETERSON, THE/AFFINITY (Peterson, Oscar Trio)**
5331002 / Dec '96 / Verve

☐ **LAST CALL AT THE BLUE NOTE (Peterson, Oscar Trio)**
Jim / Yours is my heart alone / It never entered my mind-body and soul (medley) / Wheatland / March past / Blues etude
CD 83314 / Sep '92 / Telarc

☐ **LIKE SOMEONE IN LOVE (Peterson, Oscar Trio)**
Reunion blues / Lamp is low / Some day my prince will come / Con alma / Tangerine / Like someone in love / Satin doll / All right / Waltz for debby / Noreen's nocturne
JHR 73570 / Nov '93 / Jazz Hour

☐ **LIVE (Peterson, Oscar Trio)**
CD 2310940 / Apr '94 / Pablo

☐ **LIVE AT CBC STUDIOS 1960 (Peterson, Oscar Trio)**
My heart stood still / Blue for big Scotia / Autumn leaves / Sweet Georgia Brown / How about you / I got plenty of nothin' / Cookin' at the continetal / I didn't know what time it was / Let there be love / Dancing on the ceiling
JAS 95072 / 23 Mar '98 / Just A Memory

☐ **LIVE AT THE NORTH SEA JAZZ FESTIVAL, 1980**
Caravan / Straight no chaser / Like someone in love / There is no you / You stepped out of a dream / City lights / I'm old fashioned / Time for love / Bluesology / Goodbye / There is no greater love
CD 2620115 / Apr '94 / Pablo

☐ **LIVE IN 1953 (Peterson, Oscar Quartet & Buddy De Franco)**
EBCD 21112 / Feb '94 / Flyright

☐ **LLUBJANA 1964**
Satin doll / Fly me to the moon / Reunion blues / Wheatland / Lamp is low / Nightingale / Con alma / Band call
CD 53203 / May '95 / Giants Of Jazz

☐ **LLUBJANA 1964 VOL.2**
Like someone in love / Softly as in a morning sunrise / Tangerine / Waltz for debby / I remember clifford / Blues of the prairies / Hymn to freedom / Someday my prince will come / Yours is my heart alone
CD 53204 / May '95 / Giants Of Jazz

☐ **MORE I SEE YOU, THE**
In a mellow tone / Gee baby ain't I good to you / Squatty Roo / More I see you / When my dreamboat comes home / Ron's blues / For all we know / On the trail / Blues for LSA
CD 83370 / Jul '95 / Telarc

☐ **MOTIONS & EMOTIONS**
Sally's tomato / Sunny / By the time I get to Phoenix / Wanderin' / This guy's in love with you / Wave / Dreamsville / Yesterday / Eleanor Rigby / Ode to Billy Joe
8212892 / Jul '90 / MPS Jazz

☐ **NIGERIAN MARKETPLACE (Peterson, Oscar Trio)**
Nigerian marketplace / Au privave / Nancy with the laughing face / Misty / Waltz for Debby / Cake walk / You look good to me
CD 2308231 / Jun '93 / Pablo

☐ **NIGHT TRAIN (Remastered) (Peterson, Oscar Trio)**
5214402 / Oct '97 / Verve Master Edition

☐ **OSCAR AND BENNY (Peterson, Oscar & Benny Green)**
For all we know / When lights are low / Yours is my heart alone / Here's that rainy day / More I see you / Limehouse blues / Easy does it / Someday my prince will come / Scrapple from the apple / Jitterbug waltz / Barbara's blues
CD 83406 / 1 Jun '98 / Telarc Jazz

☐ **OSCAR IN PARIS (Live At The Salle Pleyel/2CD Set)**
Falling in love with love / Nighttime tranquille / Smudge / Love ballade / Sushi / Kelly's blues / She has gone / You look good to me / Peace / Sweet Georgia Brown / Here's that rainy day/We will love again
CD 83414 / 12 Jan '98 / Telarc

☐ **OSCAR PETERSON & STEPHANE GRAPPELLI (Peterson, Oscar & Stephane Grappelli Quartet)**
Them there eyes / Blues for musidisc / Makin' whoopee / Thou swell / Walkin' my baby back home / Autumn leaves / Looking at you / Folks who live on the hill / I won't dance / Time after time / My one and only love / My heart stood still / Flamingo / If I had you / Let's fall in love
403292 / Mar '96 / Accord

☐ **OSCAR PETERSON 1951**
JAS 9501 / Dec '95 / Just A Memory

☐ **OSCAR PETERSON AND HARRY EDISON (Peterson, Oscar & Harry Edison)**
Easy living / Days of wine and roses / Gee baby ain't I good to you / Basie / Mean to me / Signify / Willow weep for me / Man I love / You go to my head
OJCCD 738 / May '93 / Original Jazz Classics

☐ **OSCAR PETERSON AND ROY ELDRIDGE (Peterson, Oscar & Roy Eldridge)**
Little Jazz / She's funny that way / Way you look tonight / Sunday / Bad hat blues / Between the Devil and the deep blue sea / Blues for Chu
OJCCD 727 / Nov '95 / Original Jazz Classics

☐ **OSCAR PETERSON CHRISTMAS, AN**
Winter wonderland / Santa Claus is coming to town / Let it snow, let it snow, let it snow / Silent night / Jingle bells / White Christmas / Have yourself a merry little Christmas / Christmas waltz / I'll be home for Christmas / Away in a manger / O Christmas tree / O little town of Bethlehem / God rest ye merry gentlemen / What child is this
CD 83372 / Nov '95 / Telarc

☐ **OSCAR PETERSON IN CONCERT**
Bag's groove / I've got the world on a string / Daahoud / Gai / Sweet Georgia Brown / Tenderly / C jam blues / Pompton turnpike / Seven come eleven / Love for sale / Lollobrigida / Swingin' 'til the girls come home / Nuages / Avalon / Come to the Mardi Gras / Baby, baby, all the time / Easy does it / Sunday / Falling in love with love / Noreen's nocturne / Gypsy in my soul / Flamingo / Love you madly / 52nd Street
RTE 10022 / Apr '95 / RTE/Europe 1

☐ **OSCAR PETERSON IN CONCERT**
710443CD / Apr '95 / RTE/Europe 1

☐ **OSCAR PETERSON IN RUSSIA (2CD Set)**
I got it bad and that ain't good / I concentrate on you / Place St. Henri / Hogtown blues / On Green Dolphin Street / You stepped out of a dream / Wave / On the trail / Take the 'A' train / Summertime / Just friends / Do you know what it means to miss New Orleans / I loves you Porgy / Georgia on my mind / Li'l darlin' / Watch what happens / Hallelujah trail / Someone to watch over me
2CD 2625711 / Dec '96 / Pablo

☐ **OSCAR PETERSON MEETS ROY HARGROVE & RALPH MOORE (Peterson, Oscar & Roy Hargrove/ Ralph Moore)**
Tin tin deo / Rob Roy / Blues for Stephane / My foolish heart / Cool walk / Ecstasy / Just friends / Truffles / She has gone North York
CD 83399 / Nov '96 / Telarc Jazz

☐ **OSCAR PETERSON PLAYS COUNT BASIE**
Lester leaps in / Easy does it / 9.20 special / Jumpin' at the woodside / Blues for Basie / Broadway / Blue and sentimental / Topsy / One o'clock jump / Jump at five
5198112 / Apr '93 / Verve

☐ **OSCAR PETERSON PLAYS MY FAIR LADY & FIORELLO (Peterson, Oscar Trio)**
I've grown accustomed to her face / Get me to the church on time / Show me / I could have danced all night / On the street where you live / Wouldn't it be lovely / Rain in Spain / When did I fall in love / Little tin box / Home again / Til tomorrow / Politics and poker / Gentleman Jimmy / Unfair / On the side of the angels / Where do I go from here
5216772 / Mar '94 / Verve

☐ **OSCAR PETERSON PLAYS PORGY & BESS**
I got plenty o' nuttin' / I wants to stay here / Summertime / Oh dey's so fresh and fine / Oh lawd I'm on my way / It ain't necessarily so / There's a boat that's leavin' soon for New York / Oh Bess, oh where's my Bess / Here come de honey man / Bess you is my woman now
5198072 / Apr '93 / Verve

☐ **OSCAR PETERSON PLAYS THE COLE PORTER SONGBOOK (Peterson, Oscar Trio)**
In the still of the night / It's alright with me / Love for sale / Just one of those things / I've got you under my skin / Everytime we say goodbye / Night and day / Easy to love / Why can't you behave / I love Paris / I concentrate on you / It's de-lovely
8219872 / Jul '97 / Verve

☐ **OSCAR PETERSON TRIO + ONE CLARK TERRY (Peterson, Oscar Trio & Clark Terry)**
Brotherhood of man / Jim / Blues for Smedley / Roundalay / Mumbles / Mack the knife / They didn't believe me / Squeaky's blues / I want a little girl / Incoherent blues
8188402 / Jun '85 / EmArCy

☐ **OSCAR PETERSON TRIO AT STRATFORD SHAKESPEAREAN FESTIVAL, THE (Peterson, Oscar Trio)**
Falling in love with love / How about you / Flamingo / Swinging on a star / Noreen Nocturne / Gypsy in my soul / Nuages / How high the moon / Love you madly / 52nd Street / Daisy's dream
5137522 / Jul '93 / Verve

☐ **OSCAR PETERSON TRIO AT THE CONCERTGEBOUW (Peterson, Oscar Trio)**
Lady is a tramp / We'll be together again / Bluesology / Budo / I've got the world on a string / Daahoud / When lights are low / Evrev / Should I / Big fat Mama / Indiana / Joy spring / Elevation
5216492 / Mar '94 / Verve

☐ **OSCAR PETERSON, HARRY EDISON & EDDIE 'CLEANHEAD' VINSON (Peterson, Oscar & Harry Edison/Eddie 'Cleanhead' Vinson)**
Stuffy / This one's for jaws / Everything happens to me / Broadway / Slooo drag / What's new / Satin doll
CD 2310927 / Apr '94 / Pablo

☐ **PETERSON**
OJCCD 383 / Feb '92 / Original Jazz Classics

☐ **PIANO MOODS (The Very Best Of Oscar Peterson - 2CD Set)**
Bess you is my woman now / Laura / I've grown accustomed to her face / Night train / It ain't necessarily so / Just in time / Surrey with the fringe on top / Days of wine and roses / If I should lose you / Django / Here's that rainy day / Girl talk / Yesterday / This guy's in love with you / In the still of the night / Every time we say goodbye / Summertime / Tender trap / I loves you Porgy / When I fall in love / Waltz for Debby / I love Paris / It's impossible / Windmills of your mind / It never entered my mind / People / Watch what happens / Fly me to the moon / Baubles bangles and beads / Come rain or come shine / Georgia on my mind / Someone to watch over me / Who can I turn to / I concentrate on you / Moon river
5574632 / 26 May '98 / Verve

☐ **REUNION BLUES/GREAT CONNECTION (Swinging Co-operations)**
Satisfaction / Dream of you / Someday my prince will come / Reunion blues / Time for love / When I fall in love / Red top / Younger than Springtime / Where do we go from here / Smile / Soft winds / Just squeeze me / On the trail / Wheatland
5390852 / 10 Nov '97 / MPS Jazz

☐ **SATCH AND JOSH VOL.1 (Peterson, Oscar & Count Basie)**
Bun's blues / These foolish things / RB / Exactly like you / Jumpin' at the woodside / Louis B / Lester leaps in / Big stockings / S and J blues / Burning
OJCCD 959 / Jul '98 / Original Jazz Classics

☐ **SATCH AND JOSH VOL.2 (Peterson, Oscar & Count Basie)**
Roots / Red wagon / Home run / Sweethearts on parade / Li'l darlin' / Time is right / Cherry / Lester leaps in / She's funny that way / Lady Fizz
OJCCD 960 / Jul '98 / Original Jazz Classics

☐ **SATURDAY NIGHT AT BLUE NOTE (Peterson, Oscar Trio)**
Kelly's blues / Night time / Love ballade (medley) / If only you knew / You look good to me / Old folks / Reunion blues / Song to elitha
CD 83306 / Sep '91 / Telarc

☐ **SIDE BY SIDE (Peterson, Oscar & Itzhak Perlman)**
Dark eyes / Stormy weather / Georgia on my mind / Blue skies / Misty / Mack the knife / Night time / I loves you Porgy / On the trail / Yours is my heart alone / Makin' whoopee / Why think about tomorrow
CD 83341 / Oct '94 / Telarc

☐ **SILVER COLLECTION, THE**
My foolish heart / 'Round midnight / Someday my Prince will come / Come Sunday / Nightingale / My ship / Sleepin' bee / Portrait of Jennie / Goodbye / Con Alma / Maidens of Cadiz / My heart stood still / Woody 'n' you
8234472 / Feb '92 / Verve

☐ **SONG IS YOU, THE (2CD Set)**
5315582 / Aug '96 / Verve

☐ **TIME AFTER TIME**
Cool walk / Love ballade / Soft winds / Who can I turn to / Without a song / Time after time
CD 2310947 / May '94 / Pablo

☐ **TIMEKEEPERS (Peterson, Oscar & Count Basie)**
I'm confessin' that I love you / Soft winds / Rent party / (Back home again in) Indiana / Hey Raymond / After you've gone / That's the one
OJCCD 790 / Sep '93 / Original Jazz Classics

☐ **TRIBUTE TO MY FRIENDS, A**
Blueberry Hill / Sometimes I'm happy / Stuffy / Birk's works / Cotton tail / Lover man / Tisket-a-tasket / Rockin' chair / Now's the time
CD 2310902 / May '94 / Pablo

☐ **TRIBUTE TO OSCAR PETERSON, A (Live At The Town Hall) (Peterson, Oscar & Friends)**
Anything goes / Reunion blues / If you only knew / Bag's groove / Mumbles / Can't face the music / Here's to life / In a mellow tone / My foolish heart / Way you look tonight / Duke of Dubuque / Route 66 / Mack the knife
CD 83401 / Jun '97 / Telarc Jazz

☐ **TRIO, THE**
Blues etude / Chicago blues / Easy listening blues / Come Sunday / Secret love
CD 2310701 / May '94 / Pablo

☐ **TRIO, THE (Live From Chicago) (Peterson, Oscar Trio)**
I've never been in love before / In the wee small hours of the morning / Chicago / Night we called it a day / Sometimes I'm happy / Whisper not / Billy boy
8230082 / Feb '94 / Verve

☐ **TRIO, THE (Live From Chicago/ Remastered) (Peterson, Oscar Trio)**
5390632 / Oct '97 / Verve Master Edition

☐ **TRUMPET SUMMIT MEETS THE OSCAR PETERSON BIG FOUR (Peterson, Oscar Big Four)**
Daahoud / Chicken wings / Just friends / Champ
OJCCD 603 / Mar '92 / Original Jazz Classics

☐ **ULTIMATE OSCAR PETERSON, THE**
5397862 / 16 Mar '98 / Verve

☐ **VERY TALL (Peterson, Oscar Trio & Milt Jackson)**
On Green Dolphin Street / Work song / Heartstrings / John Brown's body / Wonderful guy / Reunion blues
8278212 / Sep '93 / Verve

☐ **VIENNA CONCERT 1968**
W 342CD / Apr '94 / Philology

☐ **WALKING THE LINE/ANOTHER DAY**
I love you / Rock of ages / Once upon a summertime / Teach me tonight / Windmills of your mind / I didn't know what time it was / All of you / Blues for Martha / Greensleeves / I'm old fashioned / All the things you are / Too close for comfort / JAMF's are coming / It never entered my mind / Carolina shout
5335492 / Nov '96 / MPS Jazz

☐ **WE GET REQUESTS (Remastered) (Peterson, Oscar Trio)**
5214422 / Oct '97 / Verve Master Edition

☐ **WEST SIDE STORY (Remastered) (Peterson, Oscar Trio)**
Something's coming / Somewhere / Jet song / Tonight / Maria / I feel pretty / Reprise
5397532 / 16 Mar '98 / Verve Master Edition

☐ **WITH RESPECT TO NAT**
When my sugar walks down the street / It's only a paper moon / Walkin' my baby back home / Sweet Lorraine / Unforgettable / Little girl / Gee baby ain't I good to you / Orange colored sky / Straighten up and fly right / Calypso blues / What can I say after I say I'm sorry / Easy listening blues
5574862 / 3 Aug '98 / Verve

Peterson, Ralph

☐ **FO'TET PLAYS MONK, THE (Peterson, Ralph Fo'tet)**
Jackie-ing / Skippy / Epistrophy / Played twice / Light blue / Criss cross / Four in one / Monkin' around / Spherically speaking / Well you needn't / Brilliant corners
ECD 22174 / Feb '97 / Evidence

☐ **RECLAMATION PROJECT, THE**
Further fo / Song of serenity / Long journey home / Insanity / Bottom / Turn it over / Just for today / Acceptance / For all my tomorrows / Keep it simple
ECD 22113 / Jun '95 / Evidence

Peterson, Ricky
☐ SMILE BLUE
GOJ 60042 / 8 Jun '98 / Go Jazz

☐ TEAR CAN TELL, A
GOJ 60162 / 8 Jun '98 / Go Jazz

Petra
☐ GOD FIXATION
If I had to die for someone / God fixation / Set for life / Falling up / Invitation / Shadow of a doubt / Hello again / St. Augustine's pears / Matter of time / Magnet of the world / Over the horizon
7019967604 / Apr '98 / Word

Petri, Michala
☐ MOONCHILD'S DREAM
09026625432 / Jul '95 / RCA

Petrie, Robin
☐ CONTINENTAL DRIFT (Petrie, Robin & Danny Carnahan)
FF 70442 / '88 / Flying Fish

Petrucciani, Michel
☐ AU THEATRE DES CHAMPS-ELYEES
Medley of my favourite songs / Night sun in Blois / Radio dial / I mean you/Round about midnight / Even mice dance / Caravan / Love letter / Besame mucho
FDM 365702 / Mar '95 / Dreyfus

☐ BOTH WORLDS
35 seconds of music and more / Brasilian like / Training / Colours / Petite Louise / Chloe meets Gershwin / Chimes / Guadelope / On top of the roof
FDM 365902 / 24 Nov '97 / Dreyfus

☐ CONFRENCE DE PRESSE VOL.2 (Petrucciani, Michel & Eddy Louiss)
Autumn leaves / Hub art / Caravan / Naissance / Rachid / Caraibes / Au p'tit jour / Summertime
FDM 365732 / Dec '95 / Dreyfus

☐ DARN THAT DREAM (Petrucciani, Michel Trio)
667722 / Apr '96 / Melodie

☐ LIVE
Nardis / Oleo / Le bricoleur de big sur / To erlinda / Say it again and again / Three forgotten magic words / Trouble / Round about midnight
CCD 43006 / '88 / Concord Jazz

☐ LIVE
Black magic / Miles Davis licks / Contradictions / Bite / Rachid / Looking up / Thank you note / Estate
CDP 7805892 / Oct '94 / Blue Note

☐ MARVELLOUS
Manhattan / Charlie Brown / Even mice dance / Why / Hidden joy / Shooting stars / You are my waltz / Dumb breaks / 92's Last / Besame mucho
FDM 365642 / Mar '94 / Dreyfus

Petters, John
☐ BLAME IT ON... (Petters, John & His Bechet Centenary Band)
RRCD 1009 / Jul '98 / Rose

☐ BOOGIE WOOGIE AND ALL THAT JAZZ VOL.1 (Petters, John & His Rhythm)
RRCD 003 / May '98 / Rose

☐ BOOGIE WOOGIE AND ALL THAT JAZZ VOL.2 (Petters, John & His Rhythm)
RRCD 006 / May '98 / Rose

☐ GERSHWIN CENTENARY ALBUM, THE (Petters, John Broadway Melodists)
RRCD 1013 / May '98 / Rose

☐ JOHN PETTERS & HIS RHYTHM WITH NEVILLE DICKIE (Petters, John & Neville Dickie)
RRCD 1002 / May '96 / Rose

☐ JOHN PETTERS NEW ORLEANS ALL STARS & KEN COLYER (Petters, John New Orleans All Stars & Ken Colyer)
RRCD 1011 / May '98 / Rose

☐ SPIRITUAL (Petters, John New Orleans Allstars/Creole Jazzband)
RRCD 1007 / Jun '96 / Rose

Pettersen, I.
☐ DEATNOGATTE (Pettersen, I. & T. Aslaken)
ICD 971 / Aug '97 / Idut

Pettersson, Andreas
☐ JOYRIDER
SITCD 9219 / Jun '96 / Sittel

☐ LIVE IN FINLAND
DRCD 238 / Jan '87 / Dragon

Petteway, Al
☐ WATERS & THE WILD, THE
MMCD 205 / Dec '94 / Maggie's Music

☐ WHISPERING STONES
MMCD 206 / Dec '94 / Maggie's Music

Pettiford, Oscar
☐ BASS HITS
Esquire blues / Man I love / Crazy rhythm / Disorder at the border / Pluckin' that thing / Honeysuckle rose / Blue skies / Kat's fur / Dee dee's dance / Something for you / Good bait / Salt peanuts / Be bop / Mop mop / Wrap your troubles in dreams / Frankie and Johnny (10 / Frankie and Johnny / Suddenly it jumped / Swamp fire / Don't drive this jive away
TPZ 1071 / 23 Feb '98 / Topaz Jazz

☐ MONTMARTRE BLUES
BLC 760124 / Feb '89 / Black Lion

☐ OSCAR PETTIFORD
BET 6017 / Jan '95 / Bethlehem

☐ VIENNA BLUES – THE COMPLETE SESSION
Cohn's limit / Gentle art of love / All the things you are / Stalag 414 / Vienna blues / Oscar's blues / Stardust / There will never be another you / Blues in the closet
BLCD 760104 / Jun '88 / Black Lion

Pettis, Jack
☐ HIS PETS, BAND AND ORCHESTRA (2CD Set)
KCM 0056 / Apr '97 / Kings Cross Music

Pettis, Pierce
☐ MAKING LIGHT OF IT
742362 / 16 Mar '98 / Charly

Petty, Norman
☐ 15 CLASSIC MEMORIES VOL.1
Mood indigo / Jambalaya / If you see me crying / Pretty's little polka / I'll string along with you / Oh you pretty woman / Hey good lookin' / Gimme a little kiss, will ya, huh / Jax boogie / It's been a long, long time / Little black samba / Half as much / Echo polka / Dream is a wish your heart makes / My blue heaven
CDCHM 443 / Jul '94 / Ace

☐ ORIGINAL NORMAN PETTY TRIO/ ENSEMBLE VOL.2 (15 More Classic Memories)
On the Alamo / Dirty Dum / Three little kisses / It's no sin / Bring your heart / Tennessee waltz / Walkin' to Missouri / Find me a golden street / China nights / Undecided / Mr. Tap-Toe / Candy and cake / As time goes by / Caravan / Kiss me goodnight
CDCHM 624 / Jul '96 / Ace

Petty, Tom
☐ DAMN THE TORPEDOES
Refugee / Here comes the girl / Even the losers / Century city / Don't do me like that / What are you doin' in my life / Louisiana rain
MCLD 19014 / Apr '92 / MCA

☐ FULL MOON FEVER
Free fallin' / I won't back down / Love is a long road / Face in the crowd / Runnin' down a dream / Feel a whole lot better / Yer so bad / Depending on you / Apartment song / Alright for now / Mind with a heart of it's own / Zombie zoo
MCD 06034 / 8 Sep '97 / MCA

☐ GREATEST HITS (Petty, Tom & The Heartbreakers)
American girl / Breakdown / Anything that's rock 'n' roll / Listen to her heart / I need to know / Refugee / Don't do me like that / Even the losers / Here comes my girl / Waiting / You got lucky / Don't come around here no more / I won't back down / Runnin' down a dream / Free fallin' / Learning to fly / Into the great wide open / Mary Jane's last dance / Something in the air
MCD 10964 / Oct '93 / MCA

☐ HARD PROMISES
Waiting / Woman in love / Nightwatchman / Something big / Kings Road / Letting you go / Thing about you / Insider / Criminal kind / You can still change your mind
MCLD 19077 / Nov '91 / MCA

☐ INTO THE GREAT WIDE OPEN
Learning to fly / King's highway / Into the great wide open / Two gunslingers / Dark of the sun / All or nothing / All the wrong reasons / Too good to be true / Out of the cold / You and I will meet again / Makin' some noise
MCD 10317 / 8 Sep '97 / MCA

☐ LET ME UP (I'VE HAD ENOUGH) (Petty, Tom & The Heartbreakers)
Jammin' me / Runaway train / Damage you've done / It'll all work out / My life / Think about me / All mixed up / Self made man / Ain't love strange / How many more days / Your world / Let me up (I've had enough)
MCLD 19141 / Nov '92 / MCA

☐ LONG AFTER DARK
One story town / You got lucky / Deliver me / Change of heart / Finding out / We stand a chance / Straight into darkness / Same old you / Between two worlds / Wasted life
MCLD 19078 / Jun '92 / MCA

☐ PACK UP THE PLANTATION
So you want to be a rock 'n' roll star / Needles and pins / Waiting / Breakdown / American girl / It ain't nothin' to me / Insider / Rockin' around (with you) / Refugee / I need to know / Southern accents / Rebels / Don't bring me down / You got lucky / Shout / Stories we could tell
MCLD 19142 / Nov '91 / MCA

☐ PLAYBACK (6CD Set)
Big jangle / Breakdown / American girl / Hometown blues / Anything that's rock 'n' roll / I need to know / Listen to her heart / When the time comes / Too much ain't enough / No second thoughts / Baby's a rock 'n' roller / Refugee / Here comes my girl / Even the losers / Shadow of a doubt / Don't do me like that / Waiting / Woman in love / Something big / Thing about you / Insider / You can still change your mind / Spoiled and mistreated / You got lucky / Change of heart / Straight into darkness / Same old you / Rebels / Don't come around here no more / Southern accents / Make it better (forget about me) / Best of everything / So you want to be a rock 'n' roll star / Don't bring me down / Jammin' me / It'll all work out / Mikes life, Mikes world / Think about me / Self made man / Good booty / Free fallin' / I won't back down / Love is a long road / Runnin' down a dream / Yer so bad / Alright for now / Learning to fly / Into the great wide open / All or nothin' / Out in the cold / Built to last / Mary Jane's last dance / Christmas all over again / Outer sides / Casa dega / Heartbreaker's beach party / Trailer / Cracking up / Psychotic reactions / I'm tired Joey boy / Lonely weekends / Gator on the lawn / Make that connection / Down the line / Peace in LA / It's raining again / Somethin' else / I don't know what to say to you / Kings highway / Through the cracks / On the street / Depot street / Cry to me / I can't fight it / Since you said you loved me / Louisiana rain / Keeping me alive / Turning point / Stop draggin' my heart around / Apartment song / Big boss man / Image of me / Moon pie / Damage you've done / Nobody's children / Got my mind made up / Ways to be wicked / Can't get her out / Waiting for tonight / Travellin' / Baby, let's play house / Wooden heart / God's gift to man / You get me high / Come on down to my house / You come through / Up in Missisipi tonight
MCAD 611375 / Nov '95 / MCA

☐ SHE'S THE ONE (Original Soundtrack)
Walls (circus) / Airport / Angel dream (no 2) / Hope on board / Asshole / Hope you never / Angel dream (no 4) / California / Climb that hill / Change that locks / Grew up fast / Supernatural radio / Zero from outer space / Walls (no 3) / Hung up and overdue
9362462852 / Aug '96 / Warner Bros.

☐ SOUTHERN ACCENTS
Rebels / It ain't nothin' to me / Don't come around here no more / Southern accents / Make it better / Spike / Dogs on the run / Mary's new car / Best of everything
MCLD 19079 / Nov '90 / MCA

☐ TOM PETTY & THE HEARTBREAKERS (Petty, Tom & The Heartbreakers)
Rockin' around (with you) / American girl / Luna / Mystery man / Fooled again (I don't like it) / Stranger in the night / Anything that's rock 'n' roll / Forever / Wild one / Home town blues / Breakdown
MCLD 19012 / Apr '92 / MCA

☐ WILDFLOWERS
You don't know how it feels / Wildflowers / You wreck me / Only a broken heart / Don't fade on me / Cabin down below / Hard on me / Wake up time / Crawling back to you / Higher place / To find a friend / Honey bee / It's good to be king / Time to move on / House in the woods
9362457592 / Oct '94 / WEA

☐ YOU'RE GONNA GET IT (Petty, Tom & The Heartbreakers)
When the time comes / You're gonna get it / Hurt / Magnolia / Too much ain't enough / I need to know / Listen to her heart / No second thoughts / Restless / Baby's a rock'n'roller
MCLD 19013 / Apr '92 / MCA

Peyroux, Madeline
☐ DREAMLAND
Walkin' after midnight / Hey sweet man / I'm gonna sit right down / (Getting some) Fun out of life / La vie en rose / Always a use / Prayer / Muddy water / Was I / Lovesick blues / Reckless blues / Dreamland
7567829462 / May '97 / Warner Bros.

PEZ
☐ WAITING
Into nothing / Downtown / Play this round / Slave fire / Nice present / Down forever / Makeshift / Shame / Up to you / Glass globe / 5 A.M. / Love = death / Waiting / Plaid rock
R 3582 / Oct '94 / Rough Trade

Pezz
☐ ONE LAST LOOK
BYO 046CD / 6 Oct '97 / Better Youth Organisation

PFM
☐ 10 ANNI LIVE (4CD Set)
02172 / Oct '97 / RTI

☐ ULISSE
RTI 11462 / May '97 / RTI

PFR
☐ LATE GREAT PFR
1631 / Oct '97 / Vireo

PGR
☐ CHEMICAL BRIDE, THE
SR 9218 / Jul '94 / Silent

☐ GRAVE (PGR/Merzbow/Asmus Tietchens)
SR 9114 / Jul '94 / Silent

Phafner
☐ OVERDRIVE
AK 009 / 20 Jul '98 / Akarma

Phair, Liz
☐ EXILE IN GUYVILLE
Six foot one / Help me Mary / Glory / Dance of the seven veils / Never said / Soap star Joe / Explain it to me / Canary / Mesmerizing / Fuck and run / Girls, girls, girls / Divorce song / Shatter / Flatter / Flower / Johnny sunshine / Gunshy / Stratford-on-Guy / Strange loop
OLE 0512 / Aug '93 / Matador

☐ JUVENILIA
Jealousy / Turning Japanese / Animal girl / California / South Dakota / Batmobile / Dead shark / Easy
OLE 1292 / Jul '95 / Matador

☐ WHIPSMART
Chopsticks / Supernova / Support system / X-ray man / Shane / Nashville / Go west / Cinco de mayo / Dogs of LA / Whipsmart / Jealousy / Crater lake / Alice springs / May Queen
7567924292 / Sep '94 / Warner Bros.

Phallus Dei
☐ ADORATIONS
DV 60007CD / 24 Nov '97 / Dark Vinyl

☐ CYBERFLESH
PA 002CD / Sep '93 / Paragoric

☐ LUXURIA
PA 008CD / May '95 / Paragoric

☐ ORPHEUS AND EURYDICE
PA 017CD / Jan '96 / Resurrection

☐ PONTIFEX MAXIMUS
DV 005CD / 24 Nov '97 / Dark Vinyl

☐ PORNOCRATES
PA 006CD / Mar '95 / Paragoric

Phantom
☐ LOST ALBUM, THE
FLASH 49 / 1 Jun '98 / Flash

Phantom 309
☐ SINISTER ALPHABET, A
TUPCD 003 / Jul '89 / Tupelo

Phantom Blue
☐ BUILT TO PERFORM
Nothing good / Time to run / Bad reputation / My misery / Little man / Better off dead / Anti love crunch / Loved ya to pieces / So easy / Lied to me / Little evil / You're free
RR 90272 / Mar '96 / Roadrunner

☐ PHANTOM BLUE
Going mad / Last shot / Why call it love / Frantic zone / Slow it down / Walking away / Fought it out / Never too late / Out of control
RR 94692 / Jun '89 / Roadrunner

Phantom City
☐ SHIVA RECOIL
Black data 1 / Black data 2
AMBT 21 / Apr '97 / Virgin

Phantom Payn Act
☐ BAD VIBES, ANYONE
GRCD 329 / Sep '94 / Glitterhouse

☐ TROUBLE WITH GHOSTS
GRCD 221 / Sep '94 / Glitterhouse

Phantom Rats
☐ KISS ME NOW
1+2CD 115 / 1 Jun '98 / 1+2

Phantom Rockers
☐ BORN TO BE WILD
TBCD 2002 / Mar '93 / Tombstone

Phantom Surfers
☐ EXCITING SOUNDS OF MODEL ROAD RACING
LK 183LPCD / Aug '97 / Lookout

☐ GREAT SURF CRASH OF '97, THE
LOOKOUT 155CD / Sep '96 / Lookout

Phantom's Opera
☐ FOLLOWING DREAMS
Play my guitar / I'm so tired / Heartache / I've had my share of loving you / Life is so natural / Following dreams / You're REM again / My love is it you / Have you ever been alone / In the middle of the night / Land of the damned / Love's got a problem with me
ESM 031 / 26 May '98 / Escape

☐ SO LONG TO BROADWAY
ESM 013 / 2 Mar '98 / Escape

Pharaohs

☐ LIVE TO ROCK
Pink cadillac / Wild cat blues / Midnight road / Go cool cat / Blues / Waitin' in school / South express / My baby left me / Memory songs / I'll cry instead / My dear / Rebel / Lonesome cowboy
JRCD 15 / Sep '97 / Jappin' & Rockin'

Pharaohs

☐ AWAKENING
LHCD 025 / Jul '96 / Luv n' Haight

☐ IN THE BASEMENT (Unreleased)
LHCD 026 / Nov '96 / Luv n' Haight

Pharcyde

☐ BIZARRE RIDE II THE PHARCYDE
4 better or 4 worse (interlude) / Oh shit / It's jigaboo time / 4 better or 4 worse / I'm that type of nigga / If I were President / Soul flower / On the DL / Pack the pipe (interlude) / Officer / Ya mama / Passing me by / Otha fish / Quinton's on the way / Pack the pipe / Return of the B-Boy
8287492 / Aug '96 / Go Beat

☐ LABCABINCALIFORNIA
Bullshit / Pharcyde / Groupie therapy / Runnin' / She said / Splattitorium / Somethin' that means somethin' / All live / Moment in time / It's all good / Hey you / Drop / Hustle / Little D / Devil music / End / Emerald butterfly / Just don't matter
8287332 / Apr '96 / Go Beat

Pharoan, Harry

☐ PAS A PAS
FA 428 / Nov '97 / Fremeaux

Phase 5

☐ MENTALE VERWANDLUNG
EFA 120562 / Apr '94 / Rap Nation

Phase 6

☐ SUPERSTEREO
PL 005CD / 17 Jul '98 / Plastic

Phauss

☐ GOD T PHAUSS
SR 9459 / Aug '94 / Silent

☐ PHAUSS, KARKOWSKI & BILTING (Phauss, Karkowski & Bilting)
SR 9217 / Jul '94 / Silent

Phelps, Joel R.

☐ JOEL R. PHELPS VOL.3
PAC 07 / 8 Jun '98 / Pacifico

Phelps, Kelly Joe

☐ LEAD ME ON
BCD 00152 / Sep '96 / Burnside

☐ ROLL AWAY THE STONE
Roll away the stone / Sail the Jordan / When the roll is called up yonder / Hosanna / Without the light / Footprints / Go there / See that my grave is kept clean / Cypress grove / That's alright / Doxology
RCD 10393 / 8 Sep '97 / Rykodisc

Phemales

☐ LOVE DON'T LIVE HERE ANYMORE
RATTI 01 / May '97 / Ratti

Phenobaridols

☐ FISH LOUNGE
SFTRI 348CD / Oct '95 / Sympathy For The Record Industry

Phenomena

☐ DREAM RUNNER (Phenomena II)
Stop / Surrender / Did it all for love / Hearts on fire / Jukebox / Double 6, 55, 44... / Move - you lose / Emotion mama / It must be love
PARAVP 002CD / 16 Mar '98 / Parachute Music

☐ INNER VISION (Phenomena III)
If you want to rock / How much do you love me / What about love / Shape it up / Whole lot of love / Rock house / Secret of love / Rock of soul / Banzi / Into the fire / Something strong
CDPAR 002 / Nov '92 / Parachute Music
PARAVP 003CD / 3 Nov '97 / Parachute Music

☐ PHENOMENA
Kiss of fire / Still the night / Dance with the devil / Phoenix rising / Believe / Who's watching you / Hell on wings / Twilight / Assassins of the night / Running with the park / Phenomena
PARAVP 004CD / 3 Nov '97 / Parachute Music

☐ PROJECT X
Phenomena / Double 6 55 44 / Whole lot of love / Still the night / What about love / Slave / Did it all for love / Phoenix rising / How much do you / Dance with the devil / Stop / Assasins of the night / Banzi / Who's watching you / It must be love / Believe / Stealing heaven
PARAVP 001CD / 3 Nov '97 / Parachute Music

Phew

☐ HIMITSU NO KNIFE
CMDD 00010 / Jun '97 / Creative Man

☐ PHEW
DSA 54016 / Jun '97 / God Mountain

☐ VIEW
DSA 54021 / Jun '97 / God Mountain

PHI

☐ SOUND IS SOUND
NZ 008CD / Jan '95 / Nova Zembla

Philadelphia Bluntz

☐ BLUNTED AT BIRTH
Blunt chronicles / Hostility / Mosquito / I like that / Shaky shaky / Slidehead / Transformer / Jugs / Dum dum dum
ZEN 005CD / Jul '95 / Indochina

☐ PHILADELPHIA BLUNTZ
Godzilla / Bluntz theme / Game over / Blue / Sister sister / Stir fry / Funk in the future / Bogus Eddy / Hullabaloo / Intro
8234292 / 2 Mar '98 / Autonomy

Philadelphia International All Stars

☐ LET'S CLEAN UP THE GHETTO
Trade winds / Let's clean up the ghetto / Ooh child / Now is the time to do it / Year of decision / Big gangster / New day / New world comin' / Old people / Save the children / Everybody's here
12218 / May '94 / Laserlight

Philharmonic Chamber Choir

☐ ALL IN THE APRIL EVENING
All in the April evening / Isle of Mull / Steal away / Dashing white sergeant / Were you there / Banks o'Doon / Peat fire / Smooring prayer / Loch Lomond / King Arthur / Belmont / Iona boat song / Herdmaiden's song / Bluebird / Faery song from "The Immortal Hour" / An eriskay love lilt
CDH 88008 / May '88 / Helios

Philharmonic Pop Orchestra

☐ CLASSIC LOVE SONGS
TRTCD 178 / Feb '96 / TrueTrax

☐ DOUBLE IMAGES
ISCD 111 / Jun '95 / Intersound

☐ PHILHARMONIC POP ORCHESTRA
ISCD 118 / '91 / Intersound

☐ POP CLASSICS
DCD 5303 / Dec '93 / Disky

☐ POP TO THE PAST
ISCD 106 / Jun '95 / Intersound

Philip & Lloyd

☐ BLUES BUSTERS, THE
RNCD 2122 / Nov '95 / Rhino

Philip, Michael

☐ AT THE RIVERSIDE (Philip, Michael Ceilidh Band)
SP 1035CD / May '93 / Springthyme

Philippe, Louis

☐ APPOINTMENT WITH VENUS
La pluie fait des claquettes / Man down the stairs / When I'm an astronaut / We live on an island / Orchard / Heaven is above me / Rescue the Titanic / Touch of evil / Ballad of Sophie Sololl / Angelica my love / I will / Exporado tales / Apertivo / Fires rise and die
ACME 5CD / 6 Oct '97 / El

☐ CLARET
You Mary you / Domenica / What if a day / Monsieur Leduc / Man down the stairs / Red shoes ballet suite / Anna / Anna s'en va / With you and without you / Aperitivo / La pluie fait des claquettes / Telephone box / I collect stamps / Guess I'm dumb / Ruben's room / All stands still / Do you know what her name was Peg / Night talk / Fires and rise and die / Yuri Gagarin
MONDE 4CD / May '92 / Richmond

☐ SUNSHINE
BAH 23 / 8 Sep '97 / Humbug

Philips, Flip

☐ SPANISH EYES
Spanish eyes / Nature boy / Fat Tessie's ass / Nancy / Makin' whoopee / Everything happens to me / Love story / Jeannie / This is all I ask
CHCD 71013 / Mar '97 / Candid

Philips, Glen

☐ ELEVATOR
Micro / Sex messiah / Inca silver metallic / Ario / John Marshall / Vista cruiser / DNA I ran / Rememory / Tower of babel / Rain tonight / Death ship
SST 136CD / May '93 / SST

Philips, Steve

☐ JUST PICKIN' (Philips, Steve & Mark Knopfler)
TROV 2 / Oct '96 / Buried Treasure

Philius

☐ TETRA
EFA 501152 / 1 Dec '97 / Sahko

Phillips, Anthony

☐ 1984
Prelude 84 / 1984 / Anthem 1984
CDOVD 321 / '89 / Virgin

☐ ANTHOLOGY
Women were watching / Prelude '84 / Anthem from Tarka / Lucy will / Tregenna afternoons / Unheard cry / Catch at the tables / Lights on the hill / Now what / Um and aargh / Slow dance / Tears on a rainy day / God if I saw her now / Nightmare / Last goodbyes / Collections / Sleepfall: The geese fly west
BP 201CD / Oct '95 / Blueprint

☐ ARCHIVE COLLECTION VOL.1
BP 279CD / 20 Apr '98 / Blueprint

☐ FINGER PAINTING
BP 209CD / Oct '95 / Blueprint

☐ GEESE AND THE GHOST, THE
Wind-tales / Which way the wind blows / Henry; portraits from tudor times / Fanfare / Lutes' chorus / Misty battlements / Henry goes to war / Death of a knight / Triumphant return / God if I see her now / Chinese mushroom cloud / Geese and the ghost (part 1) / Geese and the ghost (part 2) / Collections / Sleepfall the geese fly west / Master of time (demo)
CDOVD 315 / Nov '90 / Virgin

☐ GYPSY SUITE (Phillips, Anthony & Harry Williamson)
Gypsy suite / Tarka
BP 189CD / 15 Sep '97 / Blueprint

☐ INVISIBLE MEN
Sally / Golden bodies / Going for broke / It's not easy / Traces / Guru / My time has come / Love in a hot air balloon / I want your heart / Falling for love / Women were watching
BP 211CD / Mar '96 / Blueprint

☐ LIVE RADIO SESSIONS (Phillips, Anthony & Guillermo Cazenave)
Lights on the hill / Circle / Silver song / Return of Agent Mulder / Peggy in the skies / She'll be waiting / Sortilege / Lucy: An illusion / Busco a boscan / Collections
DM 31502 / 1 Jun '98 / Blueprint

☐ LIVING ROOM CONCERT
BP 218CD / May '96 / Blueprint

☐ MEADOWS OF ENGLEWOOD, THE (Phillips, Anthony & Guillermo Cazenave)
Peggy in the sky without diamonds / Meadows of Englewood / Lucy: an illusion / Agent Mulder never resolves a single case / Sortilege / She'll be waiting / Circle / Picaesca / Ocho pomelos con pimienta...prestame un mango pibe
CD 30 / Aug '97 / Astral

☐ MISSING LINKS VOL.1
Force majeure / Mountain voices / Lord of the smoking mirror / Sea horses / Dungeons / Between the rings / Evening ascent / Streamer / After the rain / Rottweiler / Sad fish / A song / Fountain pool / C.q. / Boulevard of fallen leaves / And a prayer / Tierra del fuego / Paradise found
PRO 012 / Jul '92 / Progress

☐ MISSING LINKS VOL.2 (The Sky Road)
Exile / Lifeboat suite / Bitter suite / Across the river Styx / Flock of souls / Along the towpath / Sky road / Tears on a rainy day / Tiwai: Island of the apes / Wild voices, quiet water / Suite / Serenita / Timepiece / Field of eternity / Beggar and the thief
BWKD 212 / May '94 / Brainworks

☐ MISSING LINKS VOL.3
Amazonas / Peruvian plains / Manatee garden / Turtle race / India wedding / Underwater forest / Fiesta del charangos / Slow hand sloth / River chase / Sacred kingdom / African dream / Bedouin train / Sandstorm / Kalahari march / Songoku / Schuan journey / Slow boat to china / Back in the land of the dragons / Shadow puppet / Sea jewel / End theme for five / Minnow dance / Sunken galleons / Haunting the dark seas / Time and tide / Okevanga / Under desert stars / Lost in a desert night / Blue lagoons
BP 272CD / 3 Nov '97 / Blueprint

☐ PRIVATE PARTS AND PIECES VOL.1
Beauty and the beast / Field of eternity / Tibetan yak-music / Lullaby - old father time / Harmonium in the dust / Tregenna afternoons / Stranger / Reaper / Autumnal / Flamingo shuffle / Seven long years / Silver song (demo)
BP 202CD / Oct '95 / Blueprint

☐ PRIVATE PARTS AND PIECES VOL.2 (Back To The Pavilion)
Lindsay / K2 / End of the season (postlude) / Heavens / Spring meeting / Romany's aria / China man / Nocturne / Magic garden / Von runkel's yorker music / Will o' the wisp / Tremulous / I saw you today / Back to the pavilion / An illusion
BP 203CD / Oct '95 / Blueprint

☐ PRIVATE PARTS AND PIECES VOL.3 (Antiques)
Whirlpools, cobblestones, catacombs (suite in d minor) / Danse nude / Esperansa / Elegy / Otto's face / Sand dunes / Old wive's tales / Motherforest
BP 204CD / Mar '96 / Blueprint

☐ PRIVATE PARTS AND PIECES VOL.4 (A Catch At The Tables)
Earth man / Dawn over the lake / Bouncer / Eduardo / Heart of darkness / Sea and the armadillo / Sistine / Erotic strings / A catch at the tables
BP 205CD / Apr '96 / Blueprint

☐ PRIVATE PARTS AND PIECES VOL.5 (Twelve)
January / February / March / April / May / June / July / August / September / October / November / December
BP 206CD / Apr '96 / Blueprint

☐ PRIVATE PARTS AND PIECES VOL.6 (Ivory Moon)
Sunrise over Sienna / Basking shark - sea dog's air / Safe havens / Tara's theme / Winter's thaw / Old house / Moonfall / Rapids / Let us now make love
BP 207CD / Apr '96 / Blueprint

☐ PRIVATE PARTS AND PIECES VOL.7
Beachrunner / End of the affair / Golden pathway / Behind the waterfall / Carnival / Through the black hole / Pluto garden / Sospirando / Elevenses / Goodbye serenade / Bubble squeak / Vanishing streets / Slow waves, soft stars
BP 208CD / May '96 / Blueprint

☐ PRIVATE PARTS AND PIECES VOL.8
Aubade / Infra dig / Santuary / La dolorosa / New England suite / New England suite (II) / New England suite (III) / Last goodbyes / Sunrise and sea monsters / Iona / Cathedral woods / If I could tell you / Jaunty roads / Spirals / Pieces of eight (I) Pressgang / Pieces of eight (II) Sargasso / Pieces of eight (III) Sea-shanty / In the maze / Unheard cry / Now they're all gone
BP 212CD / May '96 / Blueprint

☐ PRIVATE PARTS AND PIECES VOL.9
BP 229CD / Nov '96 / Blueprint

☐ SAIL THE WORLD (Music From The Whitbread Race 1994)
Opening theme / Fast work / Dark seas / Cool sailing / Wildlife choir / I wish this would never end / Salsa / Roaring forties / Lonely whales / Icebergs / Majestic whales / In the Southern ocean / Freemantle doctor / Long way from home / Wildlife flotilla / Big combers / Cool sailing II / Cape horn / Amongst mythical birds / Salsa II / Into the tropics / In the doldrums / Heading for home and victory
RES 102CD / Apr '97 / Resurgence

☐ SIDES
Um and aargh / I want your love / Lucy will / Side door / Holy deadlock / Souvenir / Sisters of remindum / Bleak house / Magdalen / Nightmare / Magdalen (instrumental)
BP 210CD / Apr '96 / Blueprint

☐ SLOW DANCE
BP 213CD / Mar '96 / Blueprint

☐ WISE AFTER THE EVENT
We're all as we lie / Birdsong and reprise / Moonshooter / Wise after the event / Pulling faces / Regrets / Greenhouse / Paper chase / Now what (are they doing to my little friends) / Squirrel
CDOVD 322 / '89 / Virgin

Phillips, Barre

☐ AQUARIAN RAIN
Bridging / Flow / Ripples edge / Inbetween I and E / Ebb / Promenade de Memoire / Eddies / Early tide / Water shed / Aquarian rain
5115132 / Mar '92 / ECM

☐ CAMOUFLAGE
VICTOCD 08 / Nov '94 / Victo

☐ JOURNAL VIOLONE VOL.2
Part 1 / Part 2 / Part 3 / Part 4 / Part 5 / Part 6
8473282 / Mar '94 / ECM

☐ THREE DAY MOON
A-i-a / Ms. P. / La folle / BRD / Ingul-Buz / SC and W
8473262 / Jun '92 / ECM

Phillips, Brewer

☐ HOME BREW
You don't have to go / For you my love / You're so cold / Hen house boogie / Lunchbucket blues / Don't you want to go home with me / Blue shadows / My baby don't love me no more / Laundromat blues / Looking for a woman / Cross examination / Homebrew / Right now / Tore down / Let the good times roll / Do what you will or may
DE 686 / Jun '97 / Delmark

Phillips, Eddie

☐ RIFFMASTER OF THE WESTERN WORLD
PL 102152 / Oct '90 / Promised Land

Phillips, Esther

☐ CONFESSIN' THE BLUES
I'm gettin' 'long alright / I wonder / Confessin' the blues / Romance in the dark / Cc rider / Cherry red / In the evenin' / I love paris / It could happen to you / Bye bye blackbird / Blow top blues / Jelly jelly blues / Long john blues
RSACD 807 / Oct '94 / Sequel

☐ LIVE AT THE RISING SUN
RS 0007CD / Jul '95 / Rising Sun

☐ WAY TO SAY GOODBYE, A
It's all in the game / Mama said / Going in circles / Nowhere to run / We are through / Fa fa fa fa fa (sad song) / Mr. Bojangles / Shake this off / Way to say goodbye
MCD 5302 / Feb '87 / Muse

Phillips, Flip

☐ AT THE HELM
CRD 327 / Mar '96 / Chiaroscuro

☐ FLIP PHILLIPS AND SCOTT HAMILTON (Phillips, Flip & Scott Hamilton)
A sound investment / Comes love / Blues for the midgets / With someone new / Maria elena / Great scott / A smooth one / Claw
CCD 4334 / Dec '87 / Concord Jazz

☐ FLIP PHILLIPS AT THE HELM 1993
CRD 127 / Feb '95 / Chiaroscuro

☐ FLIP WAILS - THE BEST OF THE VERVE YEARS
Zharg blues / Milano / Lover come back to me / Don't take your love from me / Blue room / Flippin' the blues / Dream a little / Dream of me / Funky blues / Cheek to cheek / Salute to Pres / Singin' in the rain / If I had you / Blues for the midgets / I didn't know what time it was / Three little words / Singin' the blues / Lady's in love / You'll never be the same / Music for a stripteaser / Topsy
5216452 / Jun '94 / Verve

☐ LIVE AT THE 1986 FLOATING JAZZ FESTIVAL
CRD 314 / Mar '96 / Chiaroscuro

☐ TRY A LITTLE TENDERNESS
CRD 321 / Mar '96 / Chiaroscuro

Phillips, John

☐ JOHN THE WOLF KING OF LA
April anne / Topanga canyon / Malibu people / Someone's sleeping / Drum / Captain / Let it bleed, genevieve / Down on the beach / Mississippi / Holland tunnel
EDCD 372 / Nov '92 / Edsel

Phillips, Simon

☐ PROTOCOL
Street wise / Protocol / V8 / Red rocks / Slofunk / Wall Street
CDGRUB 10 / Dec '88 / Food For Thought

Phillips, Simon

☐ ANOTHER LIFETIME
LIP 89542 / 19 Jan '98 / Lipstick

Phillips, Sonny

☐ LEGENDS OF ACID JAZZ, THE
Sure 'nuff sure 'nuff / Be yourself / Oleo / Mobile to Chicago / Other blues / Black on black / Check it out / Blues in Maude's flat / Proud Mary / Doll house
PRCD 24186 / 29 Jun '98 / Prestige

☐ SURE NUFF/ BLACK MAGIC
Sure nuff sure nuff / Be yourself / Oleo / Mobile to Chicago / Other blues / Make it plain / Wakin' up / Over the rainbow / Bean pie / I'm an old cowhand (from the Rio Grande) / Brotherhood
CDBGPD 063 / Jun '93 / Beat Goes Public

Phillips, Steve

☐ BEEN A LONG TIME GONE (Phillips, Steve & The Famous Five)
CL 001CD / Jul '95 / Clarion

☐ STEEL RAIL BLUES
UACD 102 / Jan '97 / Unamerican Activities

Phillips, Stu

☐ JOURNEY THROUGH THE PROVINCES, A
Village blacksmith / Champlain and St. Lawrence line / En roulant ma boule / Donkey riding / Legend of Perce rock / Horse trader / Canadee-i-o / Phantom priest / Dollard les ormeaux / Madelaine De Vecheres / Winter camp / Priest who slept one hundred years / Riverboat captain / Okanagan valley / Simon gun-a-noot / Mountain boy / Bill miner / Carthering O'Hare Schubert / When the iceworms nest again / Legend of the fernie fire / Grand hotel / Bill Barker's party / Alexander Mackensie / Moon over the rockies / Fraser's valley / Star child / Almighty voice / Albert Johnson / Chief's lament / Ernest Cashel / White stallion legend / Nigger John / Bull train / Banff cave / Fireworks
BCD 15721 / Aug '93 / Bear Family

Phillips, Todd

☐ TIMEFRAME
742302 / 30 Mar '98 / Compass

Phillips, Utah

☐ GOOD THOUGH
Cannonball blues / Queen of the rails / Going away / Frisco road / Starlight on the rails / Calling trains / Daddy what's a train / Moose turd pie / Old buddy goodnight / Phoebe Snow / Nickel plate road no.759 / Wabash cannonball/Tolono
CDPH 1004 / Feb '97 / Philo

☐ LOAFER'S GLORY (Phillips, Utah & Mark Ross)
RHR 103CD / Aug '97 / Red House

☐ PAST DIDN'T GO ANYWHERE, THE (Phillips, Utah & Ani Di Franco)
Bridges / Nevada city, California / Korea / Anarchy / Candidacy / Bum on the road / Enormously wealthy / Mess with people / Natural resources / Heroes / Half a ghost town / Holding on
RBR 009CD / Nov '96 / Righteous Babe
COOKCD 124 / Apr '97 / Cooking Vinyl

☐ TELLING TAKES ME HOME, THE
Telling takes me home / Goodnight-loving trail / John D. Lee / Dog canyon / Johnny Thurman / Pig hollow / Jesse's corrido / Enola gay / Rock me to sleep / Larimer street / Stupid's song (I have led a good life) / Scott's creek bluff / Weepy doesn't know / Yuba city / I remember loving you / Dancers / Room for the poor / Eddy's song / All used up / She'll never be mine
CDPH 1210 / Nov '97 / Philo

☐ WE HAVE FED YOU ALL A THOUSAND YEARS
Boss / We have fed you all a thousand years / Sheep and goats / Timberbeast's lament / Dump the bosses off your back / Lumberjack's prayer / Mr. Block / Preacher and the slave / Popular wobbly / Casey Jones - the union scab / Where the fraser river flows / Bread and roses / Joe Hill / Union burying ground / Two bums / Hallelujah / I'm a bum / Solidarity forever / There's power in a union
PHCD 1076 / May '93 / Philo

Phillips, Washington

☐ I AM BORN TO PREACH THE GOSPEL
CD 2003 / Sep '92 / Yazoo

Philly Groove Orchestra

☐ SOUNDS OF PHILLY
HADCD 186 / Nov '95 / Javelin

Philosopher's Stone

☐ PREPARATION
KRK 19CD / 22 Aug '97 / Kranky

☐ PREPERATION
KRANK 019CD / Jul '97 / Kranky

Phippen, Peter

☐ BOOK OF DREAMS
CR 7031CD / Nov '96 / Canyon

Phish

☐ BILLY BREATHES
7559619712 / Feb '97 / Elektra

☐ HOIST
7559616282 / Jun '97 / Elektra

☐ LAWN BOY
7559612752 / Jun '97 / Elektra

☐ LIVE ONE, A (2CD Set)
7559617772 / Jun '97 / Elektra

☐ PICTURE OF NECTAR, A
Llama / Eliza / Cavern / Poor heart / Stash / Manteca / Guelah papyrus / Magilla / Landlady / Glide / Tweezer / Mango song / Chalk dust torture / Faht / Catapult / Tweezer reprise
7559612742 / Jun '97 / Elektra

☐ SLIP STITCH AND PASS
Cities / Wolfman's brother / Jesus just left Chicago / Weigh / Mike's song / Lawn boy / Weekapaug groove / Hello my baby / Taste
7559621212 / 27 Oct '97 / Elektra

☐ STASH
Stash / Scent of a mule / Maze / Bouncing around the room / Gumbo / Sample in a jar / Split open and melt / Fast enough for you / Down with disease / You enjoy myself / If I could
7559619332 / Jul '96 / Elektra

Phlebotomized

☐ IMMENSE INTENSE SUSPENSE
CYBERCD 12 / Jan '95 / Cyber

☐ SKYCONTACT
CYBERCD 20 / Apr '97 / Cyber

Phluide

☐ BIFIDUS ACIDOPHILUS
NRCD 1065 / May '96 / Nation

Phobia

☐ MEANS OF EXISTENCE
SAH 47CD / 27 Jul '98 / Slap A Ham

☐ RETURN TO DESOLATION
RR 60932 / Oct '94 / Relapse

Phoenix Jig

☐ ST
SOHO 15CD / Aug '94 / Suburbs Of Hell

Phoenix Sax Quartet

☐ RETURN OF BULGY GOGO
Two cod pieces / Dance variations / In memoriam Scott Fitzgerald / Pantomine / In memoriam Django Reinhardt / Patterns / Flying birds / Fugue in G minor / Saxe blue / What then is love / Mock Joplin / Three musical mishaps / Quincey's rag / Return of the pink panther
URCD 106 / Apr '92 / Upbeat

Phoids

☐ PHOIDS, THE
Killer / One thing / I never worry / Iowa / Ride it home / True / Rosemarie / So long / Vertigo / I can't win / Broken gun / All night girl / Spark on the horizon
0591202 / 3 Aug '98 / Silvertone

Phono Comb

☐ FRESH GASOLINE
QS 43CD / Oct '96 / Quarter Stick

Photek

☐ MODUS OPERANDI
Hidden camera / Smoke rings / Aleph 1 / 124 / Axiom / Trans 7 / Modus operandi / KJZ / Fifth column / Minotaur
CDQED 1 / 15 Sep '97 / Science

☐ RISK VS. REWARD
6202 / Sep '97 / Astralwerks

Photon Band

☐ ALL YOUNG IN THE SOUL
DRL 059CD / 1 Jun '98 / Darla

Phunk Junkees

☐ INJECTED
I love it loud / Chuck / B-boy hard / Me 'n yer girl / Flippin' my wig / Devil woman / Snapped / White boy day / Roach clip / Liquid aggression / Smooth tip / People
6544925562 / Sep '95 / WEA

Phuture 303

☐ ALPHA AND OMEGA
A 1009CD / 15 Jun '98 / A1

Phychodrama

☐ ILLUSION, THE
MASSCD 079 / Nov '95 / Massacre

Phylr

☐ CONTRA LA PUERTA
INV 093CD / 27 Oct '97 / Invisible

Physics

☐ PHYSICS VOL.1
FJ 006 / 9 Feb '98 / Flapping Jet

Piaf, Edith

☐ ANTHOLOGIE
EN 523 / Feb '96 / Fremeaux

☐ CHANSONS DE FILMS 1936-1961
175112 / Nov '97 / Musidisc

☐ CHANSOPHONE 1936-1942
701272 / Jun '93 / Chansophone

☐ DIAMOND COLLECTION, THE
3004522 / Feb '97 / Arcade

☐ EARLY YEARS VOL.1 1936, THE
Hobo girls / Cezigue waltz / Stranger / My aperitif / Stay / Owls / Le fille et le chien / J'uis mordue / Pretty Julie / Even so / Take me for a spin / Go and dance / My lover in the colonial army / Sun was shining / He's not very sophisticated / Two musicians / Smuggler / Songs of the clothes / Little shop
DRGCD 5561 / Aug '96 / DRG

☐ EARLY YEARS VOL.2 1937, THE
DRGCD 5563 / Oct '96 / DRG

☐ EARLY YEARS VOL.3 1938-1945, THE
DRGCD 5565 / Nov '96 / DRG

☐ EARLY YEARS VOL.4 1947-1948, THE
Amour du mois de mal / Une chanson a trois / Si tu partais / Monsieur x / Les cloches sonnent / Le geste / Les vieux bateaux / Sophie / Cousu de fil blanc / Monsieur ernest a reussi
DRGCD 5569 / Feb '97 / DRG

☐ EDITH PIAF 1937-1947 (2CD Set)
FA 076 / 24 Apr '98 / Fremeaux

☐ EDITH PIAF IN CONCERT
3456001 / Oct '95 / RTE/Europe 1

☐ EDITH PIAF TRIBUTE (Various Artists)
La vie en rose: *Summer, Donna* / Hymn to love: *Hart, Corey* / Jezebel: *Wilson, Ann* / When I see her: *Scheff, Jason* / Effect you have on me: *Benatar, Pat* / Lovers of one day: *Newton, Juice* / Carousel for two: *Lins, Ivan* / No regret: *Harris, Emmylou* / Three bells: *Russell, Leon* / My legionnaire: *Oslin, K.T.* / Black denim and motorcycle boots: *Spedding, Chris* / In memory
DSHCD 7014 / May '94 / D-Sharp

☐ EMBRASSE MOI
Histoire de Coeur / J'ai Qui a L'Regarder / Un Monsieur Me Suit Dans La Rue / Coup de Grisou / Jimmy c'est Lui / Le Java de Cezigue / C'est toi le plus fort / Embrasse moi / On danse sur ma chanson / Entre Saint-Ouen et Clignancourt / Il Riait / Les Marins ca fait des voyages / Dans un Bouge du Vieux Port / C'est un Monsieur tres distingue / C'est Toujours le Meme Histoire / Le disque use / De L'Autre Cote De La Rue / 'Y a Pas D'Printemps / Quand Meme / 'Chand D'Habits
MDF 102603 / Nov '96 / Mudisque

☐ ETOILES DE LA CHANSON VOL.1 1935-1942
878162 / Jun '93 / Music Memoria

☐ ETOILES DE LA CHANSON VOL.2
8414762 / Sep '96 / Music Memoria

☐ GOLD COLLECTION, THE (2CD Set)
R2CD 4036 / 13 Apr '98 / Deja Vu

☐ HER GREATEST RECORDINGS 1935-1942
Mon legionnaire / Un coin tout bleu / Mon coeur est au coin d'une rue / Le grand voyage du pauvre negre / Ballade de Mr. Browning / D'etait une histoire d'amour / On danse sur ma chanson / De l'autre cote de la rue / C'est toi le plus fort / Fais-moi valser / Paris - Mediterranee / Mon apero / Le fanion de la legion / Mon amant de la coloniale / Entre se ouen et clignancourt / L'etranger / C'etait un jour de fete / Les momes de la cloche / Elle frequentait la rue pigalle / C'est lui que mon coeur a choisi / L'accordeoniste
CDAJA 5165 / Apr '95 / Living Era

☐ HYMN TO LOVE (Greatest Hits In English)
Hymn to love / One little man / La vie en rose / Chante moi / Simply a waltz / My God / Don't cry / Autumn leaves / I shouldn't care / Three bells / 'Cause I love you / My lost melody / Heaven have mercy / No regrets / Lovers for a day / Heureuse
PRMCD 4 / May '96 / Premier/EMI

☐ L'ACCORDEONISTE
AC 75101 / 27 Apr '98 / Arkadia

☐ L'IMMORTELLE
La vie en rose / Les trois cloches / Hymne a l'amour / Mon dieu / Jezebel / Le noel de la rue / Padam padam / La chanson de Catherine / Bravo pour le clown / Johnny tu n'es pas un ange / Heureuse / La goualante du pauvre Jean / Enfin le printemps / L'accordeoniste / Le chant d'amour / C'est a Hambourg / Les amants d'un jour / La foule / Mon manege a moi / Milord / La ville inconnue / A quoi ca sert l'amour / Le diable de la Bastille / Non, je ne regrette rien
CDEMC 3674 / Sep '96 / EMI

☐ LA BELLE HISTOIRE D'AMOUR
Non, je ne regrette rien / Quoi ca sert l'amour / La vie en rose / Les amants d'un jour / La foule / Heureuse / Mon dieu / Milord / Mon manege a moi / Les mots d'amour / C'est a Hambourg / Comme moi / Le droit d'aimer / Les feuilles mortes / Bravo pour le clown / AU bal de la chance / Je t'ai dans la peau / Monsieur et madam / Padam..padam / Soeur Anne / Johnny tu n'es pas un ange / Hymne a l'amour / La fete continue / Dany / Il pleut / Les flons flons du bal (live) / La goualante du pauvre Jean / L'accordeoniste / Un refrain courait dans le rue / Bal dans ma rue / La rue aux chansons / Le noel de la rue / Notre dame de Paris / Sous le ciel de Paris / Serenade du pave / Marie trottoir / Les orges de barbarie / Kiosque a journaux / La ville inconnue / Boulevard du crime / Le bruit des ville / Les gens
SA 872742 / Sep '96 / Disky

☐ LA MOME EARLY RECORDINGS 1936-44
PASTCD 7068 / Apr '95 / Flapper

☐ LA MOME PIAF
105012 / Mar '90 / Musidisc

☐ LA MOME PIAF
DBG 53059 / 3 Mar '98 / Double Gold

☐ LA MOME PIAF VOL.1
Les momes de la cloche / L'etranger / Reste / La fille et le chien / La julie jolie / Moi valser / Mon amant de la coloniale / Il n'est pas distingue / La java de cezique / Mon apero / Les hiboux / Je suis mordue / Fais / Va danser / Y avaid du soleil / Les deux menetriers
104 552 / Mar '90 / Musidisc

☐ LA MOME PIAF VOL.2
Mon legionnaire / Chants d'habits / Entre saint - queen et clingnancourt / Browning / Un jeune homme chantait / Le fanion de la legion / Tout fout le camp le chacal / Madeleine qu'avait du coeur / Le contrebandier / La petite boutique / Correcq et reguyer / Paris mediterranee / C'est toi le plus fort / Ding din dong / Le chacal
104 562 / Mar '90 / Musidisc

☐ LA MOME PIAF VOL.3
104 572 / Mar '90 / Musidisc

☐ LA RUE PIGALLE
Ne m'ecris pas / Le Petit Monsieur Triste / Elle frequentait la Rue Pigalle / Correqu' et Reguyer / Le Contrebandier / Browning / Ding din don / Le Chacal / Le Grand Voyage du Pauvre Negre / Je n'en connais pas la Fin / Les Deux Copains / L'Accordeoniste / J'ai Danse avec l'Amour / Ou sont-ils Mes Petits Copains / C'es la Moindre des Choses / C'etait un Jour de Fete / Simple comme Bonjour / Un Coin Tout Blue / Le Vagabond / C'etait une Histoire d'Amour
MDF 102606 / Nov '96 / Mudisque

☐ LA VIE EN ROSE 1940-1946
PASTCD 7820 / Sep '97 / Flapper

☐ LEGENDARY EDITH PIAF, THE
Heureuse / Non, Je ne regrette rien / La goualante du pauvre Jean / Padam padam / L'accordeoniste / La vie en rose / Les amants d'un jour / A quoi ca sert l'amour / Mon manege a moi / La foule / Les mots d'amour / Comme moi / Le droit d'aimer / Les feuilles mortes / Les flons flons du bal / Enfin le printemps / Mon dieu / C'est a Hambourg / Milord / Hymne a l'amour
CDMFP 6071 / Jun '89 / Music For Pleasure

☐ LITTLE SPARROW OF FRANCE
L'accoreoniste / Y'a pas d'printemps / Tu es partout / Le disque use / De L'autre cote de la rue / Le vagabond / C'etait une historie d'amour / C'etait un jour de fete / J'ai danse avec l'amour / Jen'en connais pas le fin / Le petit monsieur triste / Elle frequentait la rue Pigalle / C'est lui que mon coeur a choisi / Le grand voyage du pouvre negre / Mon legonnaire / Paris Mediterrannee / Les mames de la cloche
995762 / Apr '97 / EPM

☐ MON LEGIONNAIRE
Fas-Moi Vaiser / La Julie Jolie / Mon Amant de la Coloniale / Les deux Menetriers / Les Momes de la Cloche / L'Etranger / Mon Apero / Les Hiboux / Reste / J'suis Mordue / Va Danser / Le Fille et Le Chien / 'Y avit du Soleil / Il n'est pas Distingue / Mon Legionnaire / Un Jeune Homme Chantait / Paris-Mediterranee / C'est Lui que mon Coeur a Choisi / Le Fanion de la Legion / Le Mauvais Matelot
MDF 102605 / Nov '96 / Mudisque

☐ MON LEGIONNAIRE
AC 75106 / 27 Apr '98 / Arkadia

☐ MON LEGIONNAIRE
331642 / 24 Apr '98 / Musidisc

☐ RARE PIAF 1950-1962, THE
Hymn to love / Three bells / La vie en rose / Simply a waltz / Autumn leaves / One little man / Heaven have mercy / My lost melody / I shouldn't care / Don't cry / Cause I love you / No regrets / Toi tu l'entends pas / Fallait-Il
DRGCD 5570 / 26 May '98 / DRG

☐ SUCCES ET RARETES 1936-1945
701602 / Nov '96 / Chansophone

Piano Magic

☐ POPULAR MECHANICS
IRE 2102 / 20 Oct '97 / I

Piano Red

☐ ATLANTA BOUNCE
ARHCD 379 / Apr '95 / Arhoolie

☐ BLUES BLUES BLUES
BLCD 760181 / Apr '93 / Black Lion

☐ DOCTOR IS IN, THE (4CD Set)
Jumpin' the boogie / Rockin' with Red / Let's have a time tonight / Red's boogie / Right string baby, but the wrong yo-yo / My gal Jo / Baby, what's wrong / Well, well baby / Just right bounce / Diggin' the boogie / Layin' the boogie / Bouncin' with Red / It makes no difference now / Hey good lookin' / Count the days I'm gone / My boogie / Sales tax boogie / Voo doopee doo / Daybreak / She walks right in / I'm gonna tell everybody / I'm gonna rock some more / She's dynamite / Everybody's boogie / Your mouth's got a hole in it / Right and ready / Taxi, taxi 6963 / Decatur Street boogie / Sober / She knocks me out / Going away baby / Chitlin' hop / Decatur Street blues / I ain't fattenin' frogs for snakes / Big rock Joe from Kokomo / Play it no mind / Jump man jump / Do she love me / Peach tree parade / Red's blues / Six o'clock bounce / Jumpin' with daddy / Gordy's rock / Real good thing / Goodbye/Please tell me baby / You were mine for a while / Sweetest little something / Since I fell for you / Woo-ee / Rock baby / Teach me to forget / Wild fire / Please don't talk about me when I'm gone / South / Coo cha / Dixie roll / Boston scored / One glimpse of heaven / Blues blues / Work with it / Eighter from Decatur / Please come back home / Comin' on / Ain't nobody's fool / Don't get around much anymore / Umph-umph-umph / Got you on my mind / It's time to boogie / That's my desire / Teen-age bounce / Pay it no mind / Get up mare / 1-2-3 / My baby / Rock 'n' roll boogie / Nighttime / So worried / Blues, blues / Boogie re-bop / This old world / I feel good / Talk to me / Believe in me / Guitar walk / I've been rockin' / So shook up / Dr. Feelgood / Mr. Moonlight / Swabble / I'll be home one day / Sea breeze / I ain't gonna be a lowdown log no more / Don't let me catch you wrong / What's up doc / I'll give anything / Love is amazing / Bald headed Lena / It's a sin to tell a lie / Same old things keep happening / My gal Joe / Blang dong / I don't mind / Doctor's boogie / Let the house rock on / Doctor of love / It's sin to tell a lie / Good guys / Goodbye (I can't forget) / Don't tell me no dirty / Where did you go
BCD 15685 / Nov '93 / Bear Family

☐ PIANO 'C' RED
422399 / Feb '97 / Last Call

Pianorama

☐ CHRISTMAS CRACKER, A
Jingle bells medley / Sleigh ride / Home for the holidays / It's beginning to look like Christmas / Snowy white snow and jingle bells / Hark the herald angels sing / Silent night / Winter wonderland / I saw Mommy kissing Santa Claus / Mistletoe and holly medley / Christmas song / Does Santa Claus sleep with his whiskers / Once upon a wintertime/Mary's boy child / White Christmas / God rest ye merry gentlemen
DLCD 112 / Nov '95 / Dulcima

☐ LET YOURSELF GO
Let's face the music and dance / Is it true what they say about dixie / You brought a new kind of love / Swinging down the lane
DLCD 111 / Sep '91 / Dulcima

☐ SENSATIONAL SIXTIES, THE
Second time around / Softly as I leave you / Yesterday / Days of wine and roses
DLCD 108 / Sep '90 / Dulcima

☐ SHOW TIME IN DANCE TIME
Put me on a happy face/Me and my girl / Lambeth walk / On the street where you live/Dancing on the ceiling/If I rul / Mr. Snow/If I loved you/When the children are asleep / There's a small hotel / I'm gonna wash that man right outa my hair / I whistle a happy tune/Shall we dance/I want to be happy / Glamorous night/Waltz of my heart / Someday I'll find you/I'll see you again / Anything you can do / Surrey with the fringe on top / There's no business like shoe business / Best of times/June is bustin' out all over / We kiss in a shadow/I have dreamed / Bewitched, bothered and bewildered / Wonderful guy/ Wunderbar / They say it's wonderful/I won't send roses/Younger than spri / Edelweiss/This nearly was mine / Why do I love you/People will say we're in love/Doi' what co
DLCD 114 / May '94 / Dulcima

☐ WARTIME FAVOURITES
We're gonna hang out the washing on the Siegfried line / Run rabbit run / Hey little hen / Let the people sing / I've got sixpence / Roll out the barrel / Praise the lord and pass the ammunition / Mairzy doats and dozy doats / In the quartermaster's stores / I left my heart at the stage door canteen / If I had my way / I don't want to set the world on fire / You are my sunshine / Sgt Major's serenade / Don't sit under the apple tree / Dearly beloved / I'll be seeing you / Something to remember you by / Sailor with the navy blue eyes / Coming in on a wing and a prayer / I'm gonna get lit up (when the lights go on in London) / Fleet's in / That lovely weekend / Room 504 / Nightingale sang in Berkeley Square / It's foolish but it's fun / Elmer's tune / Lili Marlene / Yours / Jingle jangle / Deep in the heart of Texas / Oh Johnny oh / Wishing (will make it so) / Tangerine / Long ago and far away / Our love affair / It's a lovely day tomorrow / Wish me good luck as you wave goodbye / Kiss me goodnight, Sergeant Major / Nursie nursie / Ma, I miss your apple pie / You'll never know / Beneath the lights of home / Silver wings in the moonlight / Moonlight becomes you / When the lights go on again / All over the place / Down forget-me-not lane / White cliffs of Dover / We'll meet again
DLCD 106 / Apr '95 / Dulcima

Pianosauras

☐ GROOVY NEIGHBOURHOOD
Thriftshoppin' / Ready to rock / Sun will follow / Speakeasy song / Cherry street / Memphis / Going downtown / Love is a two way street / Center of the universe / Let it grow / A little love (never hurt) / Bubble gum music / Barbie / (a funny thing happened on the way to the) toystore / Eleanor day / Dimples / Letter
ROUCD 9010 / '88 / Rounder

Piazza, Rod

☐ BLUES IN THE DARK (Piazza, Rod & The Mighty Flyers)
BT 1062CD / '92 / Black Top

☐ CALIFORNIA BLUES
Chicken shack boogie / Bad bad boy / No more pretty presents / California blues / One mint julep / Worried life blues / Deep fried / Can't get that stuff no more / 4811 Wadsworth (aka blues for George) / It's too late brother / Low down dog
CDBTEL 7001 / Mar '97 / Black Top

☐ HARPBURN
BT 1087CD / Apr '93 / Black Top

☐ LIVE AT BB KING'S, MEMPHIS (Piazza, Rod & The Mighty Flyers)
BIGMO 1026 / Jul '94 / Big Mo

☐ TOUGH AND TENDER (Piazza, Rod & The Mighty Flyers)
Power of the blues / Quicksand / Tough and tender / Sea of fools / She can't say no / Teaser / Blues and trouble / Under the big top / Scary boogie / Hang ten boogie / Searchin' for a fortune
CDTC 1165 / Jul '97 / Tonecool

Piazzolla, Astor

☐ 5 TANGO SENSATIONS (Piazzolla, Astor & Kronos Quartet)
7599792542 / Jan '95 / Nonesuch

☐ 57 MINUTOS CON LA REALIDAD
Images / Milonga paras tres / Buenos Aires Huha Cero / Pasajes obscuras dos estellas / Tres minutus con la realidad / Mumuki / Sexteto / Adios nunino / Prelude to the cynical night (part 2)
INT 30792 / May '96 / Intuition

☐ ADIOS NONINO
Adios nonino / Otono porteno / Michelangelo '70 / Contramilonga a la funerala / Fuga y misterio / Coral / Fugata / Tocata rea / Tangata del alba / Allegro tangabile / Soledad / Final
CD 12508 / Nov '92 / Music Of The World

☐ ADIOS NONINO
BMT 504 / Nov '97 / Blue Moon

☐ ASTOR PIAZZOLLA
74321342672 / Jul '96 / Milan

☐ ASTOR PIAZZOLLA - A FLUTE AND PIANO TRIBUTE (De La Vega & Franzetti)
74321333282 / Jun '96 / Milan

☐ BALADA PARA UN LOCO AMELITA
Preludio para el ano 3001 / Balada para mi muerte / Balada para un loco / Vamos nina / Las ciudades / Los paraguas de buenos aires / La primera palabra / No quiero otro / Pequena cancion para matilde / Violetas populares / El gordo triste / Ojos de resaca / La muralla de china / Los pajaros perdidos / Se potessi ancora / Las islas / Chiquilin de bachin
CD 3508 / Nov '95 / Cameo

☐ BANDONEON SINFONICO
74321342682 / Jul '96 / Milan

☐ CONCERTO FOR BANDONEON & ORCHESTRA
7559791742 / Jan '95 / Nonesuch

☐ CONCIERTO DE NACAR
74321511392 / Feb '98 / Milan

☐ EL NUEVO TANGO DE BUENOS AIRES
74321342702 / Feb '97 / Milan Sur

☐ EL TANGO (Astor Quartet)
Revirado / Preludio para el ano 3001 / El tango poem / Decarissimo / Che tango che / Michelangelo 70 / Pachouli / My happiness / Instead of a tango / Los mareados / Milonga per tre
7559794622 / 13 Apr '98 / Nonesuch

☐ G-STRING QUARTET PLAYS ASTOR PIAZZOLLA (G-String Quartet)
Michelangelo '70 / Milonga for three / Butcher's death / Marejadilla / Tango apasionado / La camorra II / Milonga del angel / Fugo 9 / Verano del '79 / Coral
CD 364232 / Aug '96 / Koch Schwann

☐ LA CAMORRA
La Camorra 1 / La Camorra 2 / La Camorra 3 / Soledad / Fugata / Sur: Los Suenos / Sur: Regresso al amor
AMCL 1021CD / Jan '94 / American Clave

☐ LATE MASTERPIECES (Tango-Zero Hour/Rough Dancer/La Camorra 3CD Set)
Tanguedia III / Milonga del angel / Concierto para quinteto / Milonga loca / Michelangelo '70 / Contrabajissimo / Mumuki / Prologue tango apasionado / Milonga for three / Street tango / Milonga picaresque / Knife fight / Leonara's song / Butcher's death / Leijia's game / Milonga for three (reprise) / Bailongo / Leonora's love theme / Finale (tango apasionada) / Prelude to the cyclical night part 2 / Soledad / Camorra / Camorra II / Camorra III / Fugata / Sur - los Suenos / Sur - regresso al amor
AMCL 10222 / Feb '97 / American Clave

☐ LIBERTANGO
Libertango / Meditango / Undertango / Adios nonino / Violentango / Novi tango / Amelitango / Tristango
CD 62037 / Nov '93 / Saludos Amigos

☐ LIBERTANGO
68904 / May '97 / Tropical

☐ LIBERTANGO
74321511382 / 8 Nov '97 / Milan

☐ LIVE AT THE BBC 1989
Tanguedia III / Milonga del angel / Sex-tet / Michelangelo / Mumuki / Tango zero hour / Adios nonino / Tres minutos con la realidad
INT 32262 / 23 Feb '98 / Intuition

☐ LOS TANGUEROS (The Tangos Of Astor Piazzolla) (Ax, Emanuel & Pablo Ziegler)
Michelangelo / Milonga del angel / Tangata / Revirado / Verano portano / Soledad / Libertango / La muerta del angel / Decarissimo / Fuga y misterio / Adios nonino / Buenos Aires hors o
SK 62728 / Jan '97 / Sony Classical

☐ LUMIERE
Solitude / Mort / Lumiere / L'evasion / Bandoneon / Zita / Whisky / Escolaso
68942 / May '97 / Tropical

☐ LUNA (Piazzolla, Astor & The New Tango Sextet)
Hora cero / Tanguedia 3 / Milonga del angel / Camorra 3 / Preludio y fuga / Sex-tet / Luna
CDEMC 3723 / Oct '95 / Hemisphere

☐ MARRON Y AZUL
BMT 501 / 5 Jan '98 / Blue Moon

☐ MILONGA DEL ANGEL
Biyuya / Revirado / Caliente / Lunfardo / Decarisimo / Milonga del angel / La muerte del angel / Resurreccion del angel / Astor piazzolla-presentacion / Tristeza de un doble a / Escualo
CD 62036 / Oct '93 / Saludos Amigos

☐ MUERTE DEL ANGEL
74321511402 / Feb '98 / Milan

☐ PARIS 1955
3017742 / Feb '97 / Arcade

☐ PERSEUCTA AND BIYUYA
68943 / May '97 / Tropical

☐ PIAZZOLLA AND BORGES (Piazzolla, Astor & Jorge Luis Borges)
El Tango / Jacinto Chiclana / Alquien le Dice al Tango / El Titere Milonga / A Don Nicanor Paredes / Oda Intima a Buenos Aires / El Hombre de la Esquina Rosada
74321459712 / Apr '97 / Milan

☐ PIAZZOLLISSIMO 1974-1983
JAM 9103/52 / Mar '92 / Just A Memory

☐ ROUGH DANCER AND THE CYCLICAL NIGHT
AMCL 1019CD / Jan '94 / American Clave

☐ SPIRIT OF BUENOS AIRES, THE
MAN 4891 / Dec '96 / Mandala

☐ SPIRIT OF BUENOS AIRES, THE
MAN 4903 / Sep '97 / Mandala

☐ TANGAMENTE
JAM 9107/92 / Sep '93 / Just A Memory

☐ TANGO CATOLICO
ARNR 0894 / Jul '97 / Amiata

☐ TANGO PIAZZOLLA
MCCD 165 / Jul '94 / Music Club

☐ TANGO: ZERO HOUR
Tanguedia III / Milonga del angel / Concierto para quinteto / Milonga loca / Michelangelo '70 / Countrabajissimo / Mumuki
AMCL 1013CD / Jan '94 / American Clave

☐ TANGOS FOR FLUTE AND GUITAR (Gallois, Patrick & Goran Sollscher)
Histoire du tango for flute and guitar / 4 estaciones portens for guitar / 6 tango etudes for flute / Tango no.2
4491852 / May '97 / Deutsche Grammophon

☐ TANGUEDIA
Tanguedia / Sunny / Salvador allende / Combate en la fabrica / La maison de monique / Bidonville / Il pleut sur santiago / Jorge adios / Oblivion / Pulsacion n. 1 / Pulsacion n. 2 / Pulsacion n. 4 / Pulsacion n. 5
CD 62010 / Oct '93 / Saludos Amigos

☐ TRES MINUTOS CON LA REALIDAD
74321513392 / Feb '98 / Milan

☐ TRIDEZAS DE UN DOBLE A (Piazzolla, Astor Quinteto)
MES 159702 / Dec '92 / Messidor

☐ VIENNA CONCERT, THE
159222 / Sep '97 / Messidor

Piazzolla, Daniel

☐ DANIEL PIAZZOLLA Y SU OCTETO (Piazzolla, Daniel Y Su Octeto)
Violentango / El Diego / Romance del diablo / Mi viejo Piazzolla / Verano porteno / Tanti anni prima / Libertango / Los amantes / Lalla / Adios nonino
74321383422 / Aug '96 / Milan

Pic & Bill

☐ TAKING UP THE SLACK
BAN 4109CD / Sep '91 / Haven

Picasso Trigger

☐ T'AIN'T
Lo-fi Tennesse mountain angel / 455 / Infinite belching boy / Red headed retard / Kiss me where it counts / Anti'd
A 077D / Jan '95 / Alias

Piccadilly Dance Orchestra

☐ HAPPY DAYS ARE HERE AGAIN
MCCD 240 / Mar '96 / Music Club

Piccadilly Players

☐ HOT DANCE OF THE ROARING 20S
DCP 202D / Jul '98 / Diamond Cut

Pickens, Jo Ann

☐ PRAISE HIM LIVE (Pickens, Jo Ann & M. Boungou)
FA 416 / Feb '97 / Fremeaux

Pickett, Dan

☐ DAN PICKETT/SLIM TARHEEL 1949 (Pickett, Dan & Slim Tarheel)
Baby how long: *Pickett, Dan* / You got to do better: *Pickett, Dan* / Ride to funeral: *Pickett, Dan* / Decoration day: *Pickett, Dan* / Drivin' that thing: *Pickett, Dan* / That's grieving me: *Pickett, Dan* / Chicago blues: *Pickett, Dan* / Somebody changed the lock: *Tarheel Slim* / You're a little too slow: *Tarheel Slim* / Get on the road to glory: *Tarheel Slim*
FLYCD 25 / Oct '90 / Flyright

Pickett, Lenny

☐ **LENNY PICKETT & THE BORNEO HORNS (Pickett, Lenny & The Borneo Horns)**
Dance music for Borneo Horns (1-5) / Solo for saxaphone / Septer / Dance suite / Landscape
HNCD 1321 / May '89 / Hannibal

Pickett, Phil

☐ **BONES OF ALL MEN (Pickett, Phil & Richard Thompson)**
Short measure of my Lady Wynfylde's Rownde / Chi passa per sta strada / Fusi pavana plana / La canella / Son Quel duca de milano / La torza / Le forze D'Hercole / Lo ballo dell intorcia / My lady Carey's Dompe / Tutte venite armati / Passo e mezo / Pavana in passo e mezzo / La cara cossa del berdolini / El promo de lo pomaro / El marchexe de saluzzo / Eine guter neuer dantz / Tedesca dita la proficia / Der mohren auftzugkh / Branle hobozen
HINCD 1416 / 6 Apr '98 / Hannibal

Pickett, Wilson

☐ **BEST OF WILSON PICKETT, THE**
In the midnight hour / 634 5789 / I found a love / Mustang Sally / Ninety nine and a half (won't do) / Everybody needs somebody to love / Don't fight it / I'm a midnight mover / Funky Broadway / Soul dance number three / I'm in love / Land of a 1000 dances
7567812832 / Sep '94 / Atlantic

☐ **GREATEST HITS**
Hey jude / Don't knock my love / Don't let the green grass fool you / I'm in love / In the midnight hour / It's too late / Man and a half / I found a true love / You keep me hangin' on / She's looking good / Mama told me not to come / I'm a midnight mover / Get me back on time engine number 9 / Sugar sugar / Soul dance number three / Funky broadway / Ninety nine a half (wont do) / Don't fight it / If you need me / I found a love / 634 5789 / Everybody needs somebody to love / Land of 1 000 dances / Mustang sally
7567817372 / Mar '93 / Atlantic

☐ **HEY JUDE**
Save me / Hey Jude / Back in your arms / Toe hold / Night owl / My own style of loving / Man and a half / Sit down and talk this over / Search your heart / Born to be wild / People make the world
7567803752 / Jan '96 / Atlantic

☐ **I'M IN LOVE**
Jealous love / Stagger Lee / That kind of love / I'm in love / Hello sunshine / Don't cry no more / We've got to have love / Bring it on home / She is looking good / I've come a long way
8122722182 / Jan '96 / Atlantic

☐ **IF YOU NEED ME**
Baby don't weep no more for me / Down to my last heartbreak / I can't stop / Baby call on me / If you need me / Peace breaker / RB Special / I'm gonna love you / I'll never be the same / Give your lovin' right now
CWNCD 2018 / Jul '96 / Javelin

☐ **IF YOU NEED ME**
Baby don't weep no more / Down to my last heartbreak / I can't stop / Baby call on me / If you need me / Peace breaker / RB special / I'm gonna leave you / Give your lovin' right now
CDSGP 0392 / 13 Jul '98 / Prestige

☐ **IN PHILADELPHIA**
International playboy / International playboy / Engine number 9 / Don't let the green grass fool you / Ain't no doubt about it / Days go by / Come right here / Bumble bee (sting me) / Don't let the green grass fool you / (part ii) get me back on time engine number 9 / (part i) get me back on time engine number 9 / Help the needy / Run joey run
8122722192 / Jan '96 / Atlantic

☐ **IN THE MIDNIGHT HOUR**
In the midnight hour / Terdrops will fall / Take a little love / For better or worse / I found a love / That's a man's way / I'm gonna cry / Don't fight it / Take this love I've got / Come home baby / I'm not tired / Let's kiss and make up
8122712752 / Jul '94 / Atlantic

☐ **MAN AND A HALF, A (The Best Of Wilson Pickett/2CD Set)**
I found a love / Let me be your boy / If you need me / It's too late / I'm gonna cry / Come home baby / In the midnight hour / Don't fight it / I'm not tired / That's a man's way / 634 5789 / Ninety nine and a half (won't do) / Land of 1000 dances / Mustang Sally / Three time loser / Everybody needs somebody to love / Soul dance number three / You can't stand alone / Funky broadway / Fire and water / Call my name, I'll be there / Don't let the green grass fool you / Get me back on time / Cole, Cooke and Redding / She said yes / You keep me hangin' on / Hey Joe / Toe hold / Mini skirt Minnie / Hey Jude / Man and a half / She's looking good / I found a true love / I'm a midnight mover / I've come a long way / Jealous love / Stagger / I'm in love
8122702872 / Jul '93 / Atlantic

☐ **TAKE YOUR PLEASURE WHERE YOU FIND IT (The Best Of The RCA Years)**
Take your pleasure where you find it / Mr. Magic man / Soft soul boogie woogie / Mighty mouth / What good is a lie / I was too nice / Take a closer look at the woman you're with / Join me and let's be free / You're the one / I keep walking straight ahead / If you need me / Higher conciousness / Smokin' in the United Nations / Love is beautiful / Take a look / Sin was to blame / Take the pollution out your throat / Is your love life better / Baby man / I can't let my true love slip away
74321588142 / 15 Jun '98 / Camden

☐ **VERY BEST OF WILSON PICKETT, THE**
In the midnight hour / 634 5789 / Land of 1000 dances / Mustang Sally / Funky broadway / I'm in love / She's looking good / Hey Jude / Sugar sugar / Engine No.9 / Don't let the green grass fool you / Don't knock my love / Fire and water / I'm a midnight mover / I found a love / Everybody needs somebody to love
8122712122 / Jun '93 / Atlantic

Picketts

☐ **EUPHONIUM**
Good good wife / Action speaks louder than words / Just passin' through / Baba O'Riley / Night fell / House made from cards / Should I stay or should I go / Seven / Overworked overloaded underpaid / I can't close my eyes / Same town, same planet (different world)
ROUCD 9056 / Oct '96 / Rounder

☐ **WICKED PICKETTS, THE**
ROUCD 9046 / Aug '95 / Rounder

Pickford, Andy

☐ **DYSTOPIA**
Cephalostral / Dreifarbig bomber / Angstrom / Girl from planet X / Overlander / May / Furnace / Last sundown / Chase / Belvedere / Sundance / Sayonara
CENCD 014 / May '97 / Centaur

☐ **MAELSTROM**
Voyager / Cathedral / Blue world / Tetsuo / Synbiosis / Raumfahre / Oblivion / Hell's gate
CENCD 010 / Apr '95 / Centaur

☐ **REPLICANT**
Relicant / Blonde is a suitcase / Questions / No one can hear you / Adios amigos / Wasted / Zweifarbig bomber / Cloudwatching / Sayonara
CENCD 004 / Oct '93 / Centaur

☐ **TERRAFORMER**
Terraformer / Mesmereyes / Summers past / Akira / Djangotron / Out of the darkness / Get dyson / Darklands (don't be afraid) / Asgard / Twilight in Valhalla / Furnace / Still waters (run deep)
CENCD 008 / Jun '94 / Centaur

☐ **XENOMORPH**
SER 010 / Jun '96 / Something Else

Picture House

☐ **SHINE BOX**
Heavenly day / Somebody somewhere / Do I believe you / Fear of flying / Don't believe me / World and his dog / Fan club / 15th Time / Moments like these / Worldwide TV / I know better now / Empty nest
336112 / Nov '96 / Koch International

Pictures Of Tom

☐ **RIDICULOUS POSITIONS**
BAH 19 / Aug '94 / Humbug

Picturesque

☐ **SHINE IN EYES**
KILL 13 / 16 Mar '98 / Trustkill

Pidgeon, Rebecca

☐ **FOUR MARYS**
JD 165 / 24 Apr '98 / Chesky

☐ **NY GIRL'S CLUB**
CHECD 141 / Mar '96 / Chesky

Pie Finger

☐ **DALI SURPRISE, A**
CRELPCD 122 / Apr '92 / Creation

Pieces Of A Dream

☐ **BEST OF PIECES OF A DREAM, THE**
Intro / Club jazz / Keep it smooth / Baby it's your turn now / Cool side / My love / For you / Mt Airy Groove / Rising to the top / Fo-fi-fo / Warm weather / 'Round midnight / Shadow of your smile / Si Lala
CDP 8358002 / Apr '96 / Blue Note

☐ **PIECES**
Pieces / And a bag of chips / 1257 / D'vora / Sittin' up in my room / Voices of wisdom / Anyway you want it / Knikk's amile / Very first time / Epiphany / Cut to the chase / Signed sealed delivered
CDP 8540522 / 6 Oct '97 / Blue Note

Pied Pipers

☐ **GOOD DEAL MACNEAL 1944-1946**
Gotta be this or that / I'll buy that dream / Come rain or come shine / Easy street / There's good blues tonight / Linger in my arms / Aren't you glad you're you / It's only a paper moon / Route 66 / Sentimental journey / Just a-sittin' and a-rockin' / Doin' what comes natur'lly
HEPCD 33 / Aug '96 / Hep

Pied Pipers

☐ **SCOTTISH & IRISH MUSIC**
EUCD 1009 / Sep '93 / ARC

Pieranunzi, Enrico

☐ **ISIS (Pieranunzi, Enrico Quartet & Quintet)**
1210212 / Jan '94 / Soul Note

☐ **NO MAN'S LAND (Pieranunzi, Enrico Trio)**
1212212 / Oct '90 / Soul Note

Pierce, Billie

☐ **BILLIE & DEE DEE PIERCE WITH KID THOMAS VALENTINE 1960 (Pierce, Billie & Dee Dee/Kid Thomas Valentine)**
Tiger rag / Graveyard blues / Chiri-biri-bin / Who's sorry now / Careless love / Billie's boogie / Hot nuts / Eh la bas / Bill Bailey / You can depend on me / Little girl / Tin roof blues / Of all the wrongs / Down on the farm / Hindustan
504CD 36 / Mar '98 / 504

☐ **NEW ORLEANS-THE LIVING LEGENDS (Pierce, Billie & Joseph 'De De')**
St. louis blues / Goodbye daddy blues / Careless love / Brickhouse blues / Algiers hoodoo blues / Slow tonk blues / Gulf coast blues / Nobody knows you when you're down and out / Love song of the nile
OBCCD 534 / Nov '92 / Original Blues Classics

☐ **ONE FOR CHUCK**
SSC 1053D / Nov '91 / Sunnyside

Pierce, Dave

☐ **DAVE PIERCE'S DANCE ANTHEMS (2CD Set) (Various Artists)**
Sincere: Cole, MJ / Gunman: *187 Lockdown* / Horny: *Mousse T* / Free: *Ultra Nate* / Renegade master: *Wildchild* / Feel it: *Tamperer & Maya* / It's like that: *Run DMC & Jason Nevins* / Testify: *Stingily, Byron* / Insomnia: *Faithless* / Treat infamy: *Rest Assured* / Deeper love: *Ruff Driverz* / Sound of wickedness: *Tzant* / Gypsy boy gypsy girl: *Sharada House Gang* / London town: *JDS* / Something goin' on: *Terry, Todd* / Get up stand up: *Phunky Phantom* / Can you feel it: *CLS* / Meet her at the love parade: *Da Hool* / I can't help myself: *Lucid* / Let me show you: *Camisra* / You used to salsa: *Richie Rich* / Tears: *Tomiie, Satoshi* / Shine on: *Degrees Of Motion* / Papua New Guinea: *Future Sound Of London* / Higher state of consciousness: *Wink, Josh* / Lock up: *Zero B* / Disco's revenge: *Gusto* / London thing: *Garcia, Scott & MC Styles* / Yeke yeke: *Kante, Mory* / I'm alive: *Stretch n' Vern & Maddog* / Voulez vous: *Philly Beat & Sophia* / Let me be your fantasy: *Baby D* / Here I go: *DOP* / Ripped in two minutes: *A vs. B* / Move on up: *Trickster* / Encore une fois: *Sash* / Shine: *Space Brothers* / Seven days and one week: *BBE* / Voyager 1.56: *Mr. Spring* / Beat goes on: *All Seeing I*
5559602 / 18 May '98 / PolyGram TV

Pierce, Dede

☐ **DEDE & BILLIE PIERCE VOL.1 (Pierce, Dede & Billie)**
AMCD 79 / Nov '96 / American Music

☐ **DEDE & BILLIE PIERCE VOL.2 (Pierce, Dede & Billie)**
AMCD 80 / Nov '96 / American Music

☐ **DEDE PIERCE STOMPERS VOL.1**
AMCD 81 / Feb '95 / American Music

☐ **DEDE PIERCE STOMPERS VOL.2**
AMCD 82 / Feb '95 / American Music

Pierce, Hubbell

☐ **HUBBELL PIERCE & WILLIAM ROY SING AND PLAY COLE PORTER (Pierce, Hubbell & William Roy)**
ACD 110 / Nov '96 / Audiophile

Pierce, Jeffrey Lee

☐ **RAMBLIN' JEFFREY LEE & CYPRESS GROVE**
527901220 / Jun '93 / Solid

Pierce, Joshua

☐ **PORTRAIT OF BROADWAY, A (Pierce, Joshua & Dorothy Jonas)**
CDPC 5003 / Aug '90 / Prestige

Pierce, Nat

☐ **5400 NORTH (Pierce, Nat Quintet)**
5400 north / Pee Wee's blues / Loverman if I had you / Detour ahead / Love begins / Sweet Lorraine / Sweet and lovely / Blue Lou / There will never be another you / Foggy day (in London town) / Sign off
HEPCD 2004 / Sep '96 / Hep

☐ **BALLAD OF JAZZ STREET, THE**
Pretty little girl / Melancholy baby / Black Jack / Soulville / Sister Sade / Ballad of Jazz Street
HEPCD 2009 / Apr '97 / Hep

☐ **BOSTON BUST OUT, THE**
What can I say (after I'm sorry) / You were meant for me / King Edward the flatted fifth / That's the kinda girl / What's new / Paradise / Pat / Sheba
HEPCD 13 / Nov '95 / Hep

Pierce, Webb

☐ **HONKY TONK SONG**
There stands the glass / Slowly / Sparkling brown eyes / In the jailhouse now / Why baby why / Honky tonk song / Missing you / Don't do it darlin' / I ain't never / Is it wrong (for loving you) / Cow town / Fool, fool, fool / New love affair / Don't be the one / I know it was you / Just imagination / I love you dear / Call me your sweetheart / I found a true love / I'm only wishin' / Too late to worry now / I'll get by somehow
CTS 55423 / Jun '94 / Country Stars

☐ **KING OF THE HONKY-TONK**
CMFCD 019 / Sep '94 / Country Music Foundation

☐ **WONDERING BOY 1951-1958, THE (4CD Set)**
Drifting Texas sand / If crying would make you care / California blues / You scared the love right out of me / New silver bells / Wondering / You know I'm still in love with you / I'm gonna see my baby / That heart belongs to me / I just can't be true / So used to loving you / I haven't got the heart / I'll always take care of you / Backstreet affair / I'm only wishin' / Slowly / Last waltz / Bow thy head / Country church / I'll go on alone / That's me without you / Broken engagement / We'll find a way / It's been so long / Don't throw your life away / Too late to worry now / There stands the glass / There's a better home / Mother call my name in prayer / I'm walking the dog / You just can't be true / Slowly / Broken engagement / Slowly / Even tho' / Sparkling brown eyes / Bugle call from Heaven / Thank you dear Lord / Kneel at the cross / Leaning on the everlasting arms / You're not mine anymore / I'm gonna fall out of love with you / Your good for nothing heart / Just imagination / I love you dear / More and more / I found someone that's true / Waltz you saved for me / One day later / In the jailhouse now / Sneakin' all around / I don't care / Just how long / Why baby why / Yes I know why / I found a true love / Because I love you / Little Rosa / Let forgiveness in / Any old time / You make love to everyone / Teenage boogie / I'm really glad you hurt me / Teenage boogie / Oh so many years / One week later / When I'm with you / Can I find it in your heart / Crying over you / I'm tired / It's my way / Someday / Honky tonk song / I care no more / Bye bye love / Missing you / Let forgiveness in / Who wouldn't love you / New panhandle rag / I know it was you / Don't do it darlin' / Holiday for love / How long / New raunchy / I'll get by somehow / English sweetheart / Down Panama way / Foreign love / You'll come back / New love affair / Falling back to me / Sittin' alone / I'm letting you go / Tupelo County jail / Waiting a lifetime / True love never dies / I think of you / I won't be cryin' anymore / I owe it to my heart / Violet and a rose / After the boy gets the girl / You make me live again / Crazy arms / Pick me up on your way down / Life to go / My shoes keep walking back to you
BCD 15522 / Sep '90 / Bear Family

Pierre, Cameron

☐ **ABOUT TIME (IT HAPPENED)**
Friday night / Rejoicing / Didi's groove / Linstead market / God's gift / If only / Time / Kayas la / Never be lonely
OKCD 01 / Oct '96 / Okou

☐ **FRIDAY NIGHT**
Friday night / Didi's groove / Kayas la / If only / God's gift / Rejoicing / Linstead market / Never be lonely / Time
CCD 79743 / Jan '98 / Candid

Pierre, Marie

☐ **LOVE AFFAIR**
Choose me / Can't go through / I believe / Somebody else's man / Nothing gained (for loving you) / Humanity / Rowing / My best friend / Walk away / Over reacting
CDTRL 177 / Nov '95 / Trojan

Pierrepoint

☐ **FINAL SCAN**
EFA 125532 / 13 Oct '97 / Celtic Circle

☐ **IDOLIZED**
EFA 125462 / 13 Oct '97 / Celtic Circle

Pierron, Gerard

☐ **GASTON COUTE**
LDX 274947 / Nov '92 / La Chant Du Monde

Pierrot Lunaire

☐ **PIERROT LUNAIRE**
MPR 007 / Oct '97 / MP

Pierrot Premier

☐ **ORANGE CLOUDS**
HE 007 / Dec '96 / Home Entertainment

Pietasters

☐ **WILLIS**
Crazy monkey / Woman / Out all night / Ocean / Fat sack / Stoned feeling / Higher / Time won't let me / Crime / New breed / Moment
04052 / 20 Oct '97 / Epitaph

Pietro, Dave

☐ **FORGOTTEN DREAMS**
Forgotten dreams / Winter of discontent / Pheonix rising / Lighthouse / Mutability / If I should lose you / Vortex / Karuna
AL 73049 / Nov '96 / A

☐ **WIND DANCE**
Juba / I should have known / This is new / Ashes / Fortitude / Halcyon / Joyance / Waxing moon / Wind dance
AL 73114 / Jun '98 / A

Pifarley, Dominique

☐ **POROS (Pifarely, Dominique & Francois Couturier)**
Trois images / Poros / Labyrintus / La nit ravie / Retours / Warm canto / Vertigo / Images 4 2 3 / Gala
5397242 / 2 Mar '98 / ECM

Pig

☐ POKE IN THE EYE, A
EFA 2228CD / Feb '89 / Yellow

☐ PRAISE THE LARD
CLP 9980 / Apr '97 / Cleopatra

☐ WRECKED
TVT 72502 / 22 Sep '97 / TVT

Pigbag

☐ BEST OF PIGBAG, THE
Papa's got a brand new pigbag / Weak at the knees / Hit the O deck / Getting up / Brazil nuts / Jump the line / Another orangutango / Sunny day / Big bean / Can't see for looking / Six of one / Big bag / Listen listen little man
KAZCD 3 / Nov '87 / Kaz

Pigeonhed

☐ FULL SENTENCE, THE
It's like the man said / Full sentence / Marry me / Keep on keepin' on / Battle flag / Glory bound / P-Street / Phunpurephun / Who's to blame / 31st of July / More than just a girl / Fire's comin' down / For those gone on / Honor
SPCD 373 / Apr '97 / Sub Pop
9878702242 / Aug '97 / Warner Bros.

☐ PIGEONHED
SP 224B / 13 Oct '97 / Sub Pop

☐ PIGEONHED'S FLASHBULB EMERGENCY (Cavalcade Of Remixes)
Full sentence / Phunpurephun / Glory bound / Battle flag / Marry me / It's like the man said / Keep on keepin' on
9878704082 / 27 Apr '98 / Warner Bros.

Pigface

☐ BELOW THE BELT
INV 099CD / 29 Jun '98 / Invisible

☐ FEELS LIKE HEAVEN SOUNDS LIKE SHIT
INV 034CD / Nov '95 / Invisible

☐ GUB
Tapeworm / Bushmaster / Cylinder head world / Point blank / Suck / Symphony for taps / Greenhouse / Little sisters / Tailor made / War ich nicht immer ein guter junge / Blood and sand / Weightless
INV 009CD / Mar '96 / Invisible

☐ NEW HIGH IN LOW, A
INV 063CD / 1 Sep '97 / Invisible

☐ TRUTH WILL OUT
INV 026CD / Mar '96 / Invisible

☐ WASHING MACHINE MOUTH
INV 021CD / Mar '96 / Invisible

☐ WELCOME TO MEXICO
Love serenade (i hate you) / Blood and sand / Peaking too early (william) / Little sisters / Twice removed / Beneath my feet / Point blank / Stowaway / Suck / Weightless / T.f.w.o. / Lash-herb-taxi / Tapeworm / Breakfast conspiracy
INV 011CD / Mar '96 / Invisible

☐ WELCOME TO MEXICO...ASSHOLE
CDDVN 3 / Nov '91 / Devotion

Piggott, Mavis

☐ YOU CAN BE LOW
FLY 015CD / Jul '96 / Flydaddy/Blue Rose

Pigs In Space

☐ PIGS IN SPACE
21062 / 27 Jul '98 / Phonokol

Piirpauke

☐ METAMORPHOSIS LIVE 1977-1995
ZEN 2045CD / Apr '96 / Rockadillo

Pike, Dave

☐ BOPHEAD
Esteem cleaning / Bophead / Time for love / Dr. Jackle / Nita / Little Melonae / Ghost of a chance / Israel / Dig / Touch the moon / Grand street / Prelude to a kiss
URCD 033 / 24 Aug '98 / Ubiquity

☐ DAVE PIKE AND CHARLES MCPHERSON (Pike, Dave & Charles McPherson)
Scrapple from the apple / Off minor / Piano trio medley / Embraceable you / Up jumped Spring / Big foot
CDSJP 302 / Jun '89 / Timeless Jazz

☐ MASTERPIECES
5318482 / Dec '96 / MPS Jazz

☐ PIKE'S GROOVE (Pike, Dave & Cedar Walton Trio)
CRISS 1021CD / Oct '92 / Criss Cross

☐ TIMES OUT OF MIND
Dance of the Grebes / Wee / Times out of mind / Djalama / Morning in the park / I love my cigar
MCD 5446 / May '92 / Muse

Piket, Roberta

☐ UNBROKEN LINE (Piket, Roberta Quintet)
Brookland / Always / End of a love affair / Long long wait / Daily affirmation / Threnody / You'll never walk alone / Second guess / Unbroken line
CRISS 1140CD / Dec '97 / Criss Cross

Pilc, Jean Michel

☐ BIG ONE
EPC 890 / Jan '94 / European Music Production

Piledriver

☐ METAL INQUISITION/STAY UGLY
FMP 016CD / 6 Jul '98 / Full Moon

☐ MOUTHFUL OF VENUS' SODA, A
HEAD 4 / Feb '97 / Machinehead

Pilgrim Jubilee Singers

☐ BEST OF THE PILGRIM JUBILEE SINGERS, THE
NASH 4510 / Feb '96 / Nashboro

Pilgrim Travellers

☐ BEST OF THE PILGRIM TRAVELLERS VOL.1 & 2, THE
I was there when the spirit came / Blessed be the name / Standing on the highway / Jesus hits like the atom bomb / I've got a mother gone home / Jesus I'm thankful / Straight street / Mother bowed / Old rugged cross / Something within me / Soldier's plea / Satisfied with Jesus / My old home / Jesus met the woman at the well / What a blessing in Jesus I've found / I want my crown / God shall wipe all tears away / Weary traveller / I'll tell it wherever I go / He will remember me / Lord help me carry on / Now Lord (yes, my Lord) / Lord hold my hand
CDCHD 342 / May '91 / Ace

☐ BETTER THAN THAT
I could do better than that / Please watch over me / Long ago (wooden church) / I never knew joy before / Leaning on the everlasting arms / I'm going through / How about you / I'll be there (in that number) / All the way (I'm willing to run) / Your mother is your friend / Gonna walk right out / Move up to heaven / What a friend we have in Jesus / Hard road to travel / Look down that lonesome road / Go ahead / In my heart / I love Jesus / He's my friend / Life you save may be your own (the safety song) / Troubles in my home will have to end / Every prayer will find it's answer / Close to thee / Troubled in mind / Bless us today / Hold on / After while
CDCHD 564 / Mar '94 / Ace

☐ WALKING RHYTHM
What are they doing (my lord) / Stretch out / My prayer / Good news / Dig a little deeper / Everybody's gonna have a wonderful time up there / Nothing can change me (since I found the lord) / Jesus / Thank you jesus / What a friend we have in Jesus / It's a blessing / Not a one / He's pleading in glory / Jesus gave me water / Jesus he's the one / King jesus will roll all burdens away / My eternal-home / Pass me not, o gentle saviour / Footprints of Jesus / When i join the jubilee / Call him by his name / Welcome home / My road's so rough and rocky / I love the lord / Deliver me from evil / Jesus is the first line of defence / Peace of mind / Angels tell mother / WDIA plug
CDCHD 463 / Mar '93 / Ace

Pilgrim, Billy

☐ BILLY PILGRIM
Get me out of here / Insomniac / Try / Here we go again / Halfway home / Hula hoop / Hurricane season / Lost and found in tinseltown / Too many people / Mama says
7567825152 / May '94 / Warner Bros.

Pilgrimage

☐ 9 SONGS OF ECSTASY
Campus stella/Field of stars / Through the seas of life / Pilgrimage / Land of ecstasy / Rain or shine / Ceremony / Dark skies / Iberia / Path to the invisible
5362012 / 10 Nov '97 / Point Music

Pilgrims

☐ TERROR OF THE DEADLY MANTRA
Death house party / Phantom archer / Katjuschka / Don't fall asleep / Celery man / Humdrum and humbug / Go nuts / House of Gallows Hill / Ghost town / El Dorado / Big fat mama / Wild man / Creed of the pilgrims / Runic rhyme
RUMCD 010 / Feb '92 / Rumble

Pilkington, John

☐ FROM MY POINT OF VIEW
SPINCD 140 / Dec '97 / Spindrift

Pilkington, Mark

☐ MARK PILKINGTON
SCOTT 2CD / 8 Sep '97 / Mary Anne Scott

Pills

☐ ELECTROCAINE
5366502 / 9 Feb '98 / Mercury

Pilot

☐ FROM THE ALBUM OF THE SAME NAME
Just a smile / Magic / Lucky for some / Girl next door / Lovely lady smile / Sooner or later / Don't speak loudly / Over the moon / Never give up / High into the sky / Auntie iris / Sky blue
C5CD 567 / Jun '91 / See For Miles

☐ MAGIC
Sooner or later / January / Girl next door / Auntie Iris / Just a smile / You're my no.1 / Call me round / High into the sky / Magic / Passion piece / Penny in my pocket / Canada / Never give up / Over the moon / Don't speak loudly / Lovely lady smiles / Trembling
DC 865792 / Mar '97 / Disky

☐ MORIN HEIGHTS
Hold on / Canada / First after me / Steps / Mover / Penny in my pocket / Lies and lies / Running water / Trembling / Maniac / Too many hopes
C5CD 569 / Jun '91 / See For Miles

☐ SECOND FLIGHT
You're my number one / Love is / Call me round / 55 degrees north 3 degrees west / To you alone / Do me good / Heard it all before / Bad to me / You're devotion / January / Passion piece / Dear artist
C5CD 568 / Jun '91 / See For Miles

Pilot Ships

☐ PILOT SHIPS
ATAG 005CD / 15 Sep '97 / At A Glance

☐ THERE SHOULD BE AN ENTRY HERE
ATAG 004CD / Sep '97 / At A Glance

Pilotcan

☐ SOCIALLY INEPT DISCO
EVOL 2CD / May '97 / Evol

Pilsner

☐ AUTO SUGGESTION
GH 1075CD / 20 Jul '98 / Get Hip

Piltdown Men

☐ PILTDOWN MEN RIDE AGAIN, THE (Various Artists)
McDonald's cave: *Piltdown Men* / Brontosaurus stomp: *Piltdown Men* / Piltdown rides again: *Piltdown Men* / Bubbles in the tar: *Piltdown Men* / Great imposter: *Piltdown Men* / Goodnight Mrs. Flinstone: *Piltdown Men* / Gargantua: *Piltdown Men* / Fossil rock: *Piltdown Men* / Gargantua: *Piltdown Men* / Agricultural twist: *Piltdown Men* / Pretty girl is like a memory: *Piltdown Men* / Big lizzard: *Piltdown Men* / Flint stomp: *Piltdown Men* / Night surfin': *Piltdown Men* / Tequila bossa nova: *Piltdown Men* / Sentimental journey: *Fields, Ernie Orchestra* / Birmingham jail: *Fields, Ernie Orchestra* / Adam's rib: *Fields, Ernie Orchestra* / Green green: *Fields, Ernie Orchestra* / Leap frog: *Fields, Ernie Orchestra* / St. Louis blues: *Fields, Ernie Orchestra* / Lilies of the field: *Fields, Ernie Orchestra* / Swanee river: *Fields, Ernie Orchestra* / I'll cry instead: *Fields, Ernie Orchestra* / In the mood: *Fields, Ernie Orchestra* / Chloe: *Fields, Ernie Orchestra* / Swingin' drums: *May, Billy & His Orchestra* / Drum village: *Palmer, Earl* / Drum village: *Palmer, Earl*
CDCHD 681 / 27 Apr '98 / Ace

Pimlico

☐ HOUSEBOUND
Elephant hide / Revolve / Basement / Wings of fame / When I'm wrong / Who am I / Mongrels / I watch you / Poetry street / No answers here / You can't have me / Days of acceptance / TSOH
ASKCD 66 / Aug '98 / Vinyl Japan

Pimp Daddy Nash

☐ PRIVATE LEFTFIELD DOWNTEMPO FUZZ
78535100652 / 19 May '98 / World Domination

Pin Group

☐ RETROSPECTIVE, A
SB 68 / Mar '97 / Siltbreeze

Pinchers

☐ BANDELERO
Si mi ya / On the attack / Bandelero / Bigger gun / My heart is booked / Pretending / Let's make a deal / Dreams and illusions / Don't change on me / Brotherly love
JAMCD 8 / Sep '91 / Jammy's

☐ HOTTER
Play mate / Head back no careless / Hotter Mr. Pinchers / When (jive) / Border line / Be my friend / Nuff man / Have to die / Send another one come / Killer / Harder they come
VYDCD 014 / Jul '96 / Vine Yard

Pincock, Dougie

☐ SOMETHING BLEW
Gem so small / Piper's piper / Eric Bigstones' leaky boat / Douglas Adams' fancy / Fastest gasman / Video kid / Miss Cara Spencer / Return to Kashmagiro / Balnain household / Tanks for the memory / Macrmmon's sweetheart / Rest / Unrest / Twins / January girl / Handyman's legacy / Rogart refusal / Songs for Chris
CDTRAX 080 / Nov '94 / Greentrax

Pinder, Michael

☐ AMONG THE STARS
Power of love (can survive) / You can't take love away / Best things in life / Hurry on home / When you're sleeping / Fantasy flight / Among the stars / Upside down / Waters beneath the bridge / World today
OSR 0432 / Jul '97 / One Step

☐ PROMISE, THE
Free as a dove / You'll make it through / I only want to love you / Someone to believe in / Carry on / Message / Seed / Promise
OSR 0433 / Aug '97 / One Step

Pine, Courtney

☐ ANOTHER STORY
I've known rivers / Don't xplain / Tryin' times / 37th chamber / In sense song / Tryin' times / I've known rivers / Tryin' times / Don't xplain / Don't xplain / In sense song / I've known rivers
5369282 / 9 Mar '98 / Talkin' Loud

☐ DESTINY'S SONG & THE IMAGE OF PURSUANCE
Beyond the thought of my last reckoning / In pursuance / Vision / Guardian of the flame / 'Round midnight / Sacrifice / Prismic omnipotence / Alone / Raggamuffin's tale / Mark of the time
IMCD 114 / May '91 / Island

☐ JOURNEY TO THE URGE WITHIN
Mis-interpret / I believe / Peace / Delores St. S.F / As we would say / Children of the ghetto / When, where, how and why / CGC / Seen / Sunday song
IMCD 112 / May '91 / Island

☐ MODERN DAY JAZZ STORIES
Prelude - The water of life / 37th chamber / Don't Xplain / Dah blessing / In the garden of Eden / Creation stepper / After the damaja / Absolution / Each one (must) teach one / Unknown warrior (Song for my forefathers) / I've known rivers / Outro - guiding light / Prince of peace
5290282 / Jan '96 / Talkin' Loud

☐ TO THE EYES OF CREATION
Healing song / Zaire (Interlude) / Country dance / Psalm / Eastern standard time / X-calibur (Interlude) / Meditation of contemplation / Life goes round / Ark of Mark (Interlude) / Children hold on / Cleopatra's needle / Redemption song / Holy grail
IMCD 210 / Mar '95 / Island

☐ UNDERGROUND
Intro/inhale / Modern day jazz / Tryin' times / Oneness of mind / Invisible (higher vibe) / Book of (the dead) / Children of the sun / In-sense song / Silver surfer / Underground / Outro/Exhale / Save the children
5377452 / 15 Sep '97 / Talkin' Loud

☐ VISION'S TALE, THE
Introduction / In a mellow tone / Just you, just me / Raggamuffin's stance / There is no greater love / Skylark / I'm an old cowhand (from the Rio Grande) / God bless the child / And then (a warrior's tale) / Our descendants' descendants / CP's theme
IMCD 192 / Mar '94 / Island

☐ WITHIN THE REALMS OF OUR DREAMS
Sepia love song / Una muy bonita / Donna Lee / Up behind the beat / Time to go home / Delfeayo's dilemma / Raggamuffin and his lance / Slave's tale
IMCD 193 / Jul '94 / Island

Pineal Ventana

☐ BREATHE AS YOU MIGHT
ALT 31172 / Oct '97 / Ichiban

Pinetop 7

☐ NO BREATH IN THE BELLOWS
ALP 309 / 18 May '98 / Truckstop

☐ PINETOP 7
TRUCK 05CD / 13 Apr '98 / Atavistic

Pingxin, Xu

☐ ART OF THE CHINESE DULCIMER, THE
EUCD 1293 / Nov '95 / ARC

Pinhead Circus

☐ DETAILED INSTRUCTIONS FOR THE SELF INVOLVED
BYO 044CD / 4 Aug '97 / Better Youth Organisation

Pinhead Gunpowder

☐ GOODBYE ELLSTON AVENUE
LOOKOUT 168CD / Feb '97 / Lookout

☐ JUMP SALTY
LOOKOUT 105 / '94 / Lookout

Pink, Celinda

☐ UNCHAINED
I don't need no lover boy / You ain't leaving me without you / Hound dog / Pack your lies and go / I've changed since I've been unchained / Love her right off your mind / Taking my freedom / Found me a backdoor man / You better quit it / Sneakin' up your backdoor / Love you till the cows come home / Me and Bobby McGee / I've earned the right to sing the blues
SORCD 0085 / Aug '95 / D-Sharp

Pink Cream 69

☐ FOOD FOR THOUGHT
HGCD 0885 / 15 Jun '98 / High Gain

☐ LIVE
HGCD 5007 / 15 Jun '98 / High Gain

Pink Fairies

☐ GOLDEN YEARS 1969-1971, THE
CLP 01882 / 16 Mar '98 / Cleopatra

☐ KINGS OF OBLIVION
City kids / I wish I was a girl / When's the fun begin / Chromium plating / Raceway / Chambermaid / Street urchin
RWY 001CD / 13 Apr '98 / Blueprint

☐ LIVE AT THE ROUNDHOUSE
City kids / Waiting for the man / Lucille / Uncle Harry's last freakout / Going down
CDWIK 965 / Jul '91 / Big Beat

☐ MANDIES AND MESCALINE ROUND AT UNCLE HARRY'S
PILOT 031 / 11 May '98 / Burning Airlines

☐ MR. RAINBOW (Twink)
TWKCD 1 / Jul '90 / Twink

☐ NO PICTURE
TWKCD 8 / 5 Jan '98 / Twink

☐ ODDS AND BEGINNINGS (Twink)
TWKCD 3 / 19 Jan '98 / Twink

☐ OUT OF THE BLUES AND INTO THE PINK
HTDCD 46 / Jan '96 / HTD

☐ THINK PINK (Twink)
TWKCD 7 / 24 Nov '97 / Twink

Pink Floyd

☐ ANIMALS
Pigs on the wing 1 / Dogs / Pigs (three different ones) / Sheep / Pigs on the wing 2
CDEMD 1060 / Aug '94 / EMI

☐ ATOM HEART MOTHER
Atom heart mother / If / Summer '68 / Fat old sun / Alan's psychedelic breakfast
CDEMD 1072 / Oct '94 / EMI

☐ COLLECTION OF GREAT DANCE SONGS, A
One of these days / Money / Another brick in the wall pt 2 / Wish you were here / Shine on you crazy diamond / Sheep
CDP 790 732 2 / Nov '88 / EMI

☐ DARK SIDE OF THE MOON
Speak to me / Breathe / On the run / Time / Great gig in the sky / Money / Us and them / Any colour you like / Brain damage / Eclipse
CDEMD 1064 / Aug '94 / EMI

☐ DIVISION BELL, THE
Cluster one / What do you want from me / Poles apart / Marooned / Great day for freedom / Wearing the inside out / Take it back / Coming back to life / Keep talking / Lost for words / High hopes
CDEMD 1055 / Apr '94 / EMI

☐ FINAL CUT, THE
Post war dream / Your possible pasts / One of the few / Hero's return / Gunner's dream / Paranoid eyes / Get your filthy hands off my desert / Fletcher memorial home / Southampton dock / Final cut / Not now John / Two suns in the sunset / Hero's return (part 2)
CDEMD 1070 / Oct '94 / EMI

☐ FULL OF SECRETS (Interviews)
3D 014 / Dec '96 / Network

☐ INTERVIEW DISC
SAM 7005 / Nov '96 / Sound & Media

☐ LONDON 1966-1967
Interstellar overdrive / Nick's boogie
SFMDP 3 / 8 Jun '98 / See For Miles

☐ MEDDLE
One of these days / Pillow of winds / Fearless / San Tropez / Seamus / Echoes
CDEMD 1061 / Aug '94 / EMI

☐ MOON REVISITED, THE (Tribute To Dark Side Of The Moon) (Various Artists)
Speak to me: *Cairo* / Breathe: *Cairo* / On the run: *La Vague, Rob* / Time: *Shadow Gallery* / Great gig in the sky: *Dark Side Of The Moon* / Money: *Magellan* / Us and them: *Enchant* / Any colour you like: *World Trade* / Brain Damage: *Berry, Robert* / Eclipse
RR 89162 / Oct '95 / Roadrunner

☐ MORE
Cirrus minor / Nile song / Crying song / Up the Khyber / Green is the colour / Cymbaline / Party sequence / Main theme / Ibiza bar / More blues / Quicksilver / Spanish piece / Dramatic theme
CDEMD 1084 / Feb '96 / EMI

☐ OBSCURED BY CLOUDS
Obscured by clouds / When you're in / Burning bridges / Gold it's in the... / Wot's... uh the deal / Mudmen / Childhood's end / Free four / Stay / Absolutely curtains
CDEMD 1083 / Feb '96 / EMI

☐ ORCHESTRAL WORKS, THE (The Music Of Pink Floyd) (Royal Philharmonic Orchestra/David Palmer)
07863579602 / Nov '95 / RCA Victor

☐ PINK FLOYD: INTERVIEW PICTURE DISC
CBAK 4013 / Apr '88 / Baktabak

☐ PIPER AT THE GATES OF DAWN, THE
Astronomy domine / Lucifer Sam / Matilda mother / Flaming / Pow R Toc H / Take up thy stethoscope and walk / Interstellar overdrive / Gnome / Chapter 24 / Scarecrow / Bike
CDEMD 1073 / Oct '94 / EMI

☐ PLAYS THE HITS OF PINK FLOYD (Royal Philharmonic Orchestra)
Shine on you crazy diamond / Money / Us and them / Hey you / Another brick in the wall pt 2 / Wish you were here / Time / Great gig in the sky / In the flesh
EDL 28382 / Dec '94 / Edel

☐ PULSE (2CD Set)
Shine on you crazy diamond / Astronomy domine / What do you want from me / Learning to fly / Keep talking / Coming back to life / Hey you / Great day for freedom / Sorrow / High hopes / Another brick in the wall pt 2 / One of these days / Speak to me / Breathe / On the run / Time / Great gig in the sky / Money / Us and them / Any colour you like / Brain damage / Eclipse / Wish you were here / Comfortably numb / Run like hell
CDEMD 1078 / Jun '95 / EMI

☐ RELICS
Arnold Layne / Interstellar overdrive / See Emily play / Remember a day / Paintbox / Julia dream / Careful with that axe, Eugene / Cirrus minor / Nile song / Biding my time / Bike
CDEMD 1082 / Feb '96 / EMI

☐ ROCK AND POP REVIVAL PLAYS PINK FLOYD (Rock & Pop Revival)
RPR 9402 / Mar '95 / Scratch

☐ SAUCERFUL OF PINK, A (A Tribute To Pink Floyd) (Various Artists)
Set the controls for the heart of the sun: *Psychic TV* / Another brick in the wall: *Controlled Bleeding* / One of these days: *Spahn Ranch* / Wot's... uh the deal: *Sky Cries Mary* / Interstellar overdrive: *Spiral Realms* / Learning to fly: *Leaether Strip* / To Roger Waters, wherever you are: *Geesin, Ron* / Jugband blues: *Eden* / On the run: *Din* / Hey you: *Alien Sex Fiend* / Careful with that axe Eugene / Lucifer Sam: *Electric Hellfire Club* / Pigs on the wing 1: *Helios Creed* / Let there be more light: *Pressurehead* / Young lust: *Penal Colony* / Saucerful of secrets: *Exp* / Point me at the sky: *Melting Euphoria* / Nile song: *Far Flung*
CDBRED 120 / 15 Sep '97 / Anagram

☐ SAUCERFUL OF SECRETS, A
Let there be more light / Remember a day / Set the controls for the heart of the sun / Corporal Clegg / Saucerful of secrets / See saw / Jugband blues
CDEMD 1063 / Aug '94 / EMI

☐ THERE IS NO DARK SIDE (Interview Discs/2CD Set)
CONV 005 / Feb '97 / Network

☐ UMMAGUMMA (2CD Set)
Astronomy domine / Careful with that axe, Eugene / Set the controls for the heart of the sun / Saucerful of secrets / Sysyphus / Grantchester meadows / Several species of small furry animals gathered together... / Narrow way / Grand Vizier's garden party
CDEMD 1074 / Oct '94 / EMI

☐ US AND THEM (The Symphonic Music Of Pink Floyd) (Various Artists)
Time: *London Philharmonic Orchestra* / Brain damage: *London Philharmonic Orchestra* / Another brick in the wall (part 2): *London Philharmonic Orchestra* / Comfortably numb: *London Philharmonic Orchestra* / Breathe: *London Philharmonic Orchestra* / Money: *London Philharmonic Orchestra* / Great gig in the sky: *London Philharmonic Orchestra* / Nobody home: *London Philharmonic Orchestra* / Us and them: *London Philharmonic Orchestra* / Ambient time: *London Philharmonic Orchestra*
4466232 / Nov '95 / Point Music

☐ WALL, THE (2CD Set)
In the flesh / Thin ice / Another brick in the wall (part 1) / Happiest days of our lives / Another brick in the wall (part 2) / Mother / Goodbye blue sky / Empty spaces / Young lust / One of my turns / Don't leave me now / Another brick in the wall (part 3) / Goodbye cruel world / Hey you / Is there anybody out there / Nobody home / Vera / Bring the boys back home / Comfortably numb / Show must go on / In the flesh / Run like hell / Waiting for the worms / Trial / Outside the wall
CDEMD 1071 / Oct '94 / EMI

☐ WISH YOU WERE HERE
Shine on you crazy diamond / Welcome to the machine / Have a cigar / Wish you were here
CDEMD 1062 / Aug '94 / EMI

☐ WISHING (Interview Discs/2CD Set)
CONV 008 / Mar '97 / Network

Pink Kross

☐ CHOPPER CHIX FROM VP HELL
SKETCH 005CD / 27 Jul '98 / Teen C

Pink Lincolns

☐ PURE SWANK
DSR 53 / May '97 / Dr. Strange

Pink Turns Blue

☐ MUZAK
RTD 19519452 / Jul '95 / Our Choice

☐ PERFECT SEX
RTD 19519032 / Apr '94 / Our Choice

Pinky & Perky

☐ TOP POP PARTY
Moving on up / Mysterious girl / You're gorgeous / Ooh aah (just a little bit) / Macarena / Freedom / That's the way I like it / Walking on sunshine / Blockbuster / Leader of the gang / Bridget the midget / Octopus's garden / You to me are everything / Kissing in the back row of the movies / Baby love / That's living alright
CDMFP 6369 / May '97 / Music For Pleasure

Pinnacle

☐ CYBORG ASSASSIN
KSCD 9409 / Jun '97 / Kissing Spell

Pinski Zoo

☐ DE-ICER
Bubble fun / Dust bowl / Fridge / Ben Hur / White out / Bouncing mirror / Nathan's song / Nightjar / De-icer / Slab
SLAMCD 206 / Oct '96 / Slam

Pinter, Judith

☐ AT LAST THE WIND
CD 158 / Nov '92 / Narada

Pinza, Enzio

☐ GREAT VOICES OF THE CENTURY
CDMOIR 404 / Apr '95 / Memoir

Piolot, Maxime

☐ BRETON QUAND MEME
RSCD 212 / Apr '95 / Keltia Musique

Pioneers

☐ 20 ORIGINAL FAMOUS HITS
TPCD 001 / Apr '92 / Pioneer

☐ KICK DE BUCKET
RNCD 2064 / Jun '94 / Rhino

☐ LONG SHOT KICK DE BUCKET (The Best Of The Pioneers)
Shake it up / Give me a little loving / Long shot kick de bucket / Jackpot / Pan ya machete / No dope me pony / Run come walla / Catch the beat / Things got to change / Reggae beat / Easy come easy go / Long shot kick de bucket / Black bud / Poor remeses / Samfie man / Simmer down quashie / Battle of the giants / Money day / Cherri cherri / Twice round the daffodils / Starvation / Story book children / I need your sweet inspiration / Let your yeah be yeah / Give and take / Time hard
CDTRL 347 / Mar '97 / Trojan

Pip Proud

☐ ONE OF THOSE DAYS
EJ 21CD / 24 Aug '98 / Emperor Jones

Pipe

☐ SLOWBOY
MRG 123CD / Jul '97 / Merge

Piquet

☐ FAULTY CARESS, THE
CDPSST 2 / May '96 / Mute

Piranhas

☐ PIRANHAS, THE
Boyfriend / Love game / Green don't suit me / Fiddling while Babylon burns / Coffee / Something / Tension / Pleasure / Solo sex for two / Getting beaten up / Saxaphone / Final straw / Jilly / Coloured music / Yap yap yap / Happy families / Tension / Virginity / I don't want my body
CDMGRAM 115 / 15 Sep '97 / Anagram

Pirates

☐ DON'T MUNCHEN IT-LIVE IN EUROPE
Please don't touch / Lindy lou / Sweet love on my mind / I'm in love again / I can tell / Drinkin' wine (spo-dee-o-dee) / Four to the bar / You don't own me / Honey hush / Peter gunn / Gibson martin, fender / Don't munchen it / Going back home / Voodoo / Johnny b goode's good / That's the way you are / Shakin' all over / Talkin' 'bout you / Milk cow blues / Tear it up / Lonesome train / All in it together / Johnny b. goode
RPM 110 / Jul '93 / RPM

☐ FROM CALYPSO TO COLLAPSO
Jezebel / Good drink / Bad woman / Armageddon / Burning rubber / Turn up the heat / Lost and found / Slow down / Don't munchen it / Down to the bone / Friends for life
CDTB 156 / Nov '94 / Thunderbolt

☐ HOME AND AWAY (Live In The 1990's)
I can tell / Lindy Lou / Don't munchen it / Do the dog / Friends for life/Shakin' all over / All in together / Jezebel / Good drink, bad woman / Talkin' 'bout you / Lost and found
SJPCD 003 / Jan '97 / Angel Air

☐ LIVE IN JAPAN
All by myself / Ain't got no money / I can tell / Lonesome train (on a lonesome track) / Money honey / Don't munchen it / Can't believe you wanna leave / Goin' back home / Please don't touch / Honey hush / Peggy Sue / Burnin' rubber / Shakin' all over / All in it together
CDTB 143 / Apr '93 / Thunderbolt

☐ MASTERS, THE (2CD Set)
EDMCD 033 / 30 Mar '98 / Eagle

☐ OUT OF THEIR SKULLS (2CD Set)
Drinkin' wine spo-dee-o-dee / Don't Munchen it / Do the dog / That's the way you are / You don't own me / All in it together / Dr. Feelgood / Johnny B. Goode's good / Saturday night shoot out / Long journey home / Voodoo / Four to the bar / Diggin' my potatoes / Shake hands with the devil / You can't sit down / Hey Mary / Golden oldies / Alarmer / Lady (put the light on me) / Happy birthday rock 'n' roll / Going back home / Lemonade / 1.30 2.30 3.35 / Hard ride / Please don't touch / I can tell / Peter Gunn / Sweet love on my mind / Lonesome train / Gibson Martin Fender / Don't Munchen it / Honey hush / Tear it up / I'm in love again / You don't own me / Four to the bar / Shakin' all over / Milk cow blues / All in it together / Johnny B. Goode / Talkin' bout you / Witch queen of New Orleans / All by myself / Peter Gunn / Just another party / Something very strange / Cap in hand / Lights out / I'm into something good / All by myself
WESCD 201 / 22 Sep '97 / Westside

☐ SAILING THROUGH FRANCE
422265 / May '94 / New Rose

☐ WE'VE BEEN THINKING
Please don't touch / Good drink bad woman / Goin' back home / Better get better / Don't fool around with love / I am a man / Burnin' rubber / Armageddon / Rock bottom / Gibson martin fender / Blue suede shoes / Suenska Flicka
BMAC 0317S / 20 Apr '98 / BMA

Pirchner, Werner

☐ EU
Sonate vom rauhen leben / Streichquartett fur blaserquintett / Good news from the Ziller family / Kammer-symphonie 'Soiree Tyrolienne' / Do you know Emperor Joe / Two war and peace choirs / Kleine mes um 'c' fur den lieben gott / Solo sonata for bass-vibes
8294632 / '86 / ECM

Pirin Folk Ensemble

☐ BULGARIAN VOICES
EUCD 1340 / Apr '96 / ARC

Pirnales

☐ AQUAS
KICD 27 / Jun '93 / Digelius

☐ BEST BEFORE
OMCD 60 / Dec '94 / Olarin Musiiki Oy

Piron, A.J.

☐ DECEMBER ISSUE (Piron, A.J. New Orleans Orchestra)
AZCD 13 / Nov '93 / Azure

Pirttijarvi, Ulla

☐ RUOSSA EANAN
BACH 006CD / Mar '98 / Atrium

Pissing Razors

☐ PISSING RAZORS
Dodging bullets / Tortured / Where we come from / Permanent / Life of a lunatic / World of deceit / Disaster / Desperado / Sounds of doom / Season to die / Silent hatred / For what it's worth / Broken trust
N 02902 / 19 Jan '98 / Noise

Pist

☐ IDEAS ARE BULLETPROOF
ELM 005CD / 2 Mar '98 / Elevator

Pist.On

☐ NUMBER ONE
Parole / Turbulent / Grey flap / Shoplifters of the world unite / I am no one / Eight sides / Afraid of life / Electra complex / Down and out / Mix me with blood / My feet / Exit wound
CDMFN 211 / Nov '96 / Music For Nations

Pita

☐ SEVEN TONS FOR FREE
MEGO 009CD / Nov '96 / Mego

Pitbull

☐ CASUALTY
LF 049CD / Aug '93 / Lost & Found

☐ NEW ALL TIME LOW
LF 128CD / May '95 / Lost & Found

☐ PITBULL
LF 093CD / May '94 / Lost & Found

Pitbull Daycare

☐ SIX SIX SEX
0045702MIACD / 6 Jul '98 / High Gain

Pitch Shifter

☐ DESENSITIZED
Lesson one / Diable / Ephemerol / Triad / To die is to gain / (A higher form of) killing / Lesson two / Cathode / N/A / Gatherer of data / NCM / Routine
MOSH 075CD / 1 Sep '97 / Earache

☐ INDUSTRIAL
Landfill / Brutal cancroid / Gravid rage / New flesh / Catharsis / Skin grip / Inflamator / Eye
CDVILE 56 / Mar '95 / Peaceville

☐ INFOTAINMENT
Self replicating PSI / Introductory disclaimer / Underachiever / (We're behaving like) Insects / Virus / Product placement / (Harmless) Interlude / Bloodsweatsaliva / Hangar 84 / Whiteout / Phoenixology / Pitch sampler vol.1 / Pitch sampler vol.2
MOSH 137CD / May '96 / Earache

☐ SUBMIT
Gritter / Deconstruction / New flesh p.s.i. / Bastardiser / Dry riser inlet / Tendrill
MOSH 066CD / 1 Sep '97 / Earache

☐ WWW.PITCHSHIFTER.COM
GED 25163 / 2 Mar '98 / Geffen

Pitchblende

☐ AU JUS
Nine volt / Your own arturo / Ambient noise / Karoshi / Cupcake Jones / Tourniquet / X's for I's / Human lie / Detector / Showroom / Practice song / Short term / Talking / Psychic power control
OLE 1022 / Feb '95 / Matador

☐ GYGAX
Squeezing from the mole / New decadence / Burning man / Pertraining to the champ / Kevorkian / Mercator projection / Crumbs of affection / Sideling hill / Romanesque buttox
OLE 1902 / Feb '96 / Matador

Pitchford, Lonnie

☐ ALL AROUND MAN
Elvira / All around man / If I had posession over judgement day / Real rock music/Crawling King Snake / My babe / 55 blues / Bring it on home / This is the blues / Ghetto / CC rider / My sunny / Water in my gas tank / Louisiana blues / Lonesome blues / Sweet home Chicago / Don't you do that no more / If I had possession over judgement day / All around man / Drinkin' antiseptic
R 2629 / Feb '97 / Rooster

Pitney, Gene

☐ 20 GREATEST HITS
I wanna love my life away / Town without Pity / Man who shot Liberty Valance / Only love can break a heart / Twenty four hours from Tulsa / That girl belongs to yesterday / It hurts to be in love / I'm gonna be strong / I must be seeing things / Looking through the eyes of love / Princess in rags / Backstage (I'm lonely) / Nobody needs your love more than I do / Just one smile / Something's gotten hold of my heart / Somewhere in the country / Yours until tomorrow / Maria Elena / 24 Sycamore / Hello Mary Lou
PLATCD 3904 / Dec '88 / Platinum

☐ 24 HOURS FROM TULSA
Twenty four hours from Tulsa / Something's gotten hold of my heart / (I wanna) Love my life away / Town without pity / That girl belongs to yesterday / I'm gonna be strong / I must be seeing things / Looking through the eyes of love / Princess in rags / Backstage / It hurts to be in love / 24 Sycamore / Maria Elena / Yours until tomorrow / Somewhere in the country / Cold light of day / Just one smile / Nobody needs your love
MUCD 9021 / Apr '95 / Musketeer

☐ AT HIS BEST
PLSCD 190 / Apr '97 / Pulse

☐ BEST OF GENE PITNEY, THE
VVC 1001 / 21 Nov '97 / Avid

☐ BLUE GENE/MEETS THE FAIR YOUNG LADIES OF FOLKLAND
Twenty four hours from Tulsa / Autumn leaves / Half the laughter, twice the tears / I'll be seeing you / Lonely night dreams (of faraway arms) / Answer me, my love / Blue Gene / Yesterday's hero / Maybe you'll be there / Keep tellin' yourself / I can't runaway / House without windows / Take it like a man / Those eyes of Liza Jane / Laurie / Brandy is my true love's name / My suli-ram / Little Nell / Melissa and me / Oh Annie oh / Lyda Sue, Wh'dya do / Carrie / Hey pretty little black eyed Suzie / Song of Lorena / Darlin' Corey, ain't ya comin' down town / Ballad of Laura Mae / That girl belongs to yesterday
NEMCD 890 / Nov '96 / Sequel

☐ DEFINITIVE COLLECTION, THE (2CD Set)
(I wanna) love my life away / I laughed so hard I cried / Louisiana Mama / Town without pity / Every breath I take / (The man who shot) Liberty Valance / Only love can break a heart / If I didn't have a dime (to play the jukebox) / Half heaven, half heartache / Tower tall / Mecca / Teardrop by teardrop / True love never runs smooth / Donna means heartache / 24 hours from Tulsa / That girl belongs to yesterday / Yesterday's hero / Nobody needs your love more than I do / It hurts to be in love / Hawaii / I'm gonna be strong / Aladdin's lamp / I must be seeing things / Last chance to turn around / Looking through the eyes of love / Princess in rags / Baby ain't that fine / Everybody knows but you and me / It's not that I don't love you / Gene are you there / Backstage / (In the) cold light of day / Boss's daughter / Just one smile / Nessuni mi puo guidicare / Something's gotten hold of my heart / She's a heartbreaker / Conquistador / Somewhere in the country / Billy you're my friend / Maria Elena / Street called hope / Shady lady / 24 sycamores / Yours until tomorrow / Baby I need your lovin' / Hello Mary Lou / Angelica / Little Betty falling star / Half the laughter, twice the tears / If I were / June is as cold as December / Cry your eyes out / Not responsible / You've lost that lovin' feelin' / Pretty Annabelle / She lets her hair down (early in the morning) / Marianne
CPCD 81962 / Oct '96 / Charly

☐ EP COLLECTION, THE
Backstage / Looking thru the eyes of love / Princess in rags / Every breath I take / Mecca / It hurts to be in love / Boss's daughter / There's no living without your loving / (in the) cold light of day / True love never runs smooth / That girl belongs to yesterday / Twenty four hours from tulsa / Town without pity / If I didn't have a dime / I'm gonna find myself a girl / I'm gonna be strong / Tell the moon to go to sleep / Rising tide of love / Last chance to turn around / Ituoi anni piu belll / Lei mi aspetta / Jjjjjjjjjjjing things / Man who shot liberty valance / House without windows / Amici miei / Equando vedrai la ragazza (when you see my girl)
SEECD 313 / Apr '91 / See For Miles

☐ GENE PITNEY SINGS BACHARACH, DAVID AND OTHERS /PITNEY TODAY
NEMCD 896 / Jun '97 / Sequel

☐ GOLD COLLECTION, THE
Something's gotten hold of my heart / I'm gonna be strong / Looking through the eyes of love / That girl belongs to yesterday / 24 Sycamore / It hurts to be in love / Princess in rags / Backstage (I'm lonely) / (I wanna) love my life away / Maria Elena / Town without pity / I must be seeing things / Just one smile / Shady lady / 24 hours from Tulsa
SUMCD 4014 / Nov '96 / Summit

☐ GREATEST HITS
CDGFR 052 / Jun '92 / Tring

☐ GREATEST HITS
Man who shot Liberty Valance / It hurts to be in love / I'm gonna be strong / Mecca / Town without pity / 24 Hours from Tulsa / Backstage (I'm lonely) / Looking through the eyes of love / (I wanna) love my life away / Every breath I take / Something's gotten hold of my heart / True love never runs smooth / I must be seeing things / Princess in rags / Only love can break a heart / Half heaven, half heartache / Last chance to turn around / She's a heartbreaker / Just one smile / If I didn't have a dime (to play the jukebox) / Yesterday's hero
QED 087 / Nov '96 / Tring

☐ GREATEST HITS OF GENE PITNEY
MACCD 124 / Aug '96 / Autograph

☐ GREATEST SHITS
Something's gotten hold of my heart: *Pitney, Gene & Marc Almond* / 24 hours from Tulsa / That girl belongs to yesterday / I'm gonna be strong / I must be seeing things / Looking thru the eyes of love / Princess in rags / Backstage / Nobody needs your love / Just one smile / Town without pity / Something's gotten hold of my heart / In my life / Only one woman / First cut is the deepest / We've got tonight / Let the heartaches begin / There is no distance / Fool (if you think it's over) / All by myself
EAMCD 036 / 30 Mar '98 / Eagle

☐ HITS & MISSES
Man who shot Liberty Valance / Twenty four hours from Tulsa / Town without pity / Hello Mary Lou / Today's teardrops / Surefire bet / Donna means heartbreak / If I didn't have a dime / (I wanna) Love my life away / Every breath I take / Mecca / True love never runs smoothly / Teardrop by teardrop / Dream for sale / Half heaven, half heartache / Only love can break a heart / Bleibe bei mir (Town without pity) / I'll find you / Cradle of my arms / Please come back, baby / I'm going back to my love / Classical rock 'n' roll / Snuggle up baby / Strolling (through the park) / Faithful our love / Make believe lover (demo)
BCD 15724 / Feb '95 / Bear Family

☐ I'M GONNA BE STRONG/LOOKING THROUGH THE EYES OF LOVE
I'm gonna be strong / Walk / I love you more today / Who needs it / Follow the sun / Lips are redder on you / It hurts to be in love / Last two people on Earth / That girl belongs to yesterday / E se domani / Hawaii / I'm gonna find myself a girl / I must be seeing things / Marianne / Save your love / Down in the subway / If Mary's there / Don't take candy from a stranger / One day / She's still there / Just one smile / I lost tomorrow (yesterday) / Looking thru' the eyes of love / There's no living without your loving / I'll never get to love you / Last chance to turn around / Rising tide of love
NEMCD 891 / Nov '96 / Sequel

☐ LOOKING THROUGH THE EYES OF LOVE
PDSCD 526 / Aug '96 / Pulse

☐ MANY SIDES OF GENE PITNEY/ONLY LOVE CAN BREAK A HEART
NEMCD 888 / Jun '97 / Sequel

☐ SINGS THE GREAT SONGS OF OUR TIME/NOBODY NEEDS YOUR LOVE
Tonight / Misty / Unchained melody / Rags to riches / Anywhere I wander / As long as she needs me / Maria / Close to my heart / More / On the street where you live / All the way / Time and the river / Looking thru' the eyes of love / Blue colour / Angelica / River street / Eyes talk / No matter what you do / California / Backstage / Conquistador / Turn around / Dream world / Pretty flamingo / Nobody needs your love / Princess in rags / Amore mio / In love again
NEMCD 893 / Nov '96 / Sequel

☐ TWENTY FOUR HOURS FROM TULSA
Twenty four hours from Tulsa / Nobody needs your love / 24 sycamore / Princess in rags / Half heaven, half heartache / Shady lady / I must be seeing things / Looking through the eyes of love / It hurts to be in love / Somewhere in the country / Something's gotten hold of my heart / Man who shot liberty valance / Maria Elena / Backstage (I'm lonely) / I'm gonna be strong / Last chance to turn around / Just one smile / Yours until tomorrow / Only love can break a heart / Town without pity
TRTCD 157 / 18 May '98 / TrueTrax

☐ VERY BEST OF GENE PITNEY, THE
Twenty four hours from Tulsa / Something's gotten hold of my heart / Cold light of day / Yours until tomorrow / Backstage (I'm lonely) / Somewhere in the country / Town without pity / Looking through the eyes of love / Girl belongs to yesterday / I'm gonna be strong / Princess in rags / Nobody needs your love / Shady lady / I must be seeing things / Maria Elena / Street called hope / Just one smile / (I wanna) Love my life away / It hurts to be in love / Man who shot liberty valance
MCCD 155 / May '94 / Music Club

☐ VERY BEST OF GENE PITNEY, THE
24 hours from Tulsa / Town without pity / I'm gonna be strong / Something's gotten hold of my heart / Looking through the eyes of love / Man who shot Liberty Valance / Mecca / It hurts to be in love / Backstage / I wanna love my life away / Every breath I take / If I didn't have a dime / Yesterday's hero / Just one smile / Last chance to turn around / She's a heartbreaker / Half heaven, half heartache / Only love can break a heart / I must be seeing things / Princess in rags / True love never runs smooth
GFS 049 / May '97 / Going For A Song

☐ VERY BEST OF GENE PITNEY, THE
24 hours from Tulsa / Backstage (I'm lonely) / Every breath I take / True love never runs smooth / Only love can break a heart / If I didn't have a dime / Half Heaven half heartache / Looking through the eyes of love / Mecca / It hurts to be in love / That girl belongs to yesterday / Princess in rags / Man who shot Libery Valence / I must be seeing things
WB 885532 / 2 Feb '98 / Disky

☐ YOUNG AND WARM AND WONDERFUL/JUST ONE SMILE
NEMCD 895 / Jun '97 / Sequel

Pitre, Austin

☐ OPELOUSAS WALTZ
ARHCD 452 / Feb '97 / Arhoolie

Pittman, Barbara

☐ GETTING BETTER ALL THE TIME
I need a man / No matter who's to blame / Sentimental fool / Voice of a fool / Two young fools in love / I'm getting better all the time / Take my sympathy / Cold cold heart / Everlasting love / Eleventh commandment / Handsome man / Just one day / Love is a stranger / Lonely hours / Sentimental fool / Cold cold heart / Everlasting love / No matter who's to blame / I'm getting better all the time / Take my sympathy / Two young fools in love / I'm getting better all the time / I'm getting better all the time / Sentimental fool / I forgot to remember to forget / I'm getting better all the time
CPCD 8319 / Oct '97 / Charly

Pixies

☐ BOSSANOVA
Cecilia Ann / Velouria / Is she weird / All over the world / Down to the well / Blown away / Stormy weather / Rock music / Allison / Ana / Dig for fire / Happening / Hang wire / Havalina
GAD 010CD / 2 Feb '98 / 4AD

☐ DEATH TO THE PIXIES
Cecilia Ann / Planet of sound / Tame / Here comes your man / Debaser / Wave of mutilation / Dig for fire / Caribou / Holiday song / Nimrod's son / U Mass / Bone machine / Gigantic / Where is my mind / Velouria / Gouge away / Monkey gone to heaven / Debaser / Rock music / Broken face / Isla De Encanta / Hangwire / Dead / Into the white / Monkey gone to heaven / Gouge away / Here comes your man / Allison / Hey / Gigantic / Crackity Jones / Something against you / Tame / Wave of mutilation / Where is my mind / Ed is dead / Vamos / Tony's theme
DAD 7011CD
DADD 7011CD / 6 Oct '97 / 4AD

☐ DOOLITTLE
Debaser / Wave of mutilation / Dead / Mr. Grieves / La la I love you / There goes my gun / Silver / Tame / Here comes your man / Monkey gone to heaven / Crackity Jones / Number 13 baby / Hey / Gouge away
GAD 905CD / 2 Feb '98 / 4AD

☐ PIXIES AT THE BBC
Wild honey pie / There goes my gun / Dead / Subbaculture / Manta ray / Is she weird / Ana / Down to the well / Wave of mutilation / Letter to Memphis / Levitate / Caribou / Monkey gone to heaven / Hey / In heaven
GAD 8013CD / 6 Jul '98 / 4AD

☐ SURFER ROSA
Bone machine / Something against you / Gigantic / Where is my mind / Tony's theme / Vamos / Brick is red / Break my body / Broken face / River Euphrates / Cactus / Oh my golly / I'm amazed / Caribou / Vamos / Isla de Incanta / Ed is dead / Holiday song / Nimrod's song / I've been tired / Levitate me
GAD 803CD / 2 Feb '98 / 4AD

☐ TROMPE LE MONDE
Trompe le monde / Planet of sound / Alec Eiffel / Sad punk / Head on / U-mass / Palace of the Brine / Letter to Memphis / Bird dream of the Olympus Mons / Space (I believe in) / Subbacultcha / Distance equals rate times time / Lovely day / Motorway to Roswell / Navajo know
GAD 1014CD / 2 Feb '98 / 4AD

Pixinguinha

☐ ALFREDO DA ROCHA VIANNA FILHO
CDS 001 / 19 May '98 / Kuarup

Pizzaman

☐ PIZZAMANIA
RODE 05CD / Oct '96 / Cowboy

Pizzarelli, Bucky

☐ BUCKY PLAYS BIX
DAPCD 238 / Apr '89 / Audiophile

☐ MEMORIAL, A
STCD 551 / '92 / Stash

☐ NEW YORK SWING (Live At The 1996 Floating Jazz Festival) (Pizzarelli, Bucky & John Eunch/Jay Leonhart)
Till Tom special / All too soon / Benny's bugle / Somebody's heart belongs to me / What is this thing called love / Ill wind / Stars in my eyes / If I had you / Wholly cats / Song is you / Dot's cheesecake / Have you met Miss Jones / Always
CRD 355 / Feb '98 / Chiaroscuro

☐ SOLO FLIGHT 1981/86
STCD 573 / Feb '94 / Stash

☐ SOLOS AND DUETS (2CD Set) (Pizzarelli, Bucky & John)
You must believe in spring / Fols who live on the hill / Bad and the beautiful / Last night when we were young / Medley / Smoke gets in your eyes / One morning in May / Medley/Autumn leaves/Autumn in New York / Flashes / Spring can really hang you up the most / Concerto for guitar / Guess I'll have to change my plan / Out of this world / End of a love affair / Ill wind / Bewitched / 'Round midnight / Solo flight / Blah blah blah / Candlelights / All this and heaven too / Medley/My wonderful one/My best girl / Love for sale / Pretty women / Nuages / Sutton mutton / Close enough for love / Undecided / All through the night / This nearly was mine / Come rain or come shine / Nikki / Stems / In a mellow tone / Soon / Why did I chose you / Romanza and in the dark / Come rain or shine / (There is) no greater love / In a mist / Four brothers / Lush life / Sleeping bee / Blame it on my youth / Goodbye
JZCL 5007 / Nov '96 / Jazz Classics

Pizzarelli, John

☐ DEAR MR. COLE
Style is coming back in style / What can I say after I say I'm sorry / Little girl / You must be blind / Sweet Georgia Brown / It's only a paper moon / September song / On the sunny side of the street / Nature boy / This way out / Too marvellous for words / Route 66 / Sweet Lorraine / Straighten up and fly right / LOVE / Unforgettable / Portrait of Jenny / Honeysuckle rose
01241631822 / Apr '95 / Novus

☐ HIT THAT JIVE, JACK
STB 2508 / Sep '95 / Stash

☐ I LIKE JERSEY BEST
STB 2501 / Apr '95 / Stash

☐ NEW STANDARDS
Fools fall in love / Oh how my heart beats for you (Swing) / Beautiful moons ago / I'm your guy / Come on-a-my house / Beautiful Maria of my soul / I only want some / I'm alright now / Just a skosh / Why do people fall in love / Hearts like mine are broken every day / Better run before it's spring / Give me your heart / Look at us / Oh how my heart beats for you
01241631722 / Jul '94 / Novus

☐ ONE NIGHT WITH YOU
JD 153 / May '97 / Chesky

Pizzicato 5

☐ 5 X 5
Pizzicatomania / Twiggy, Twiggy / Baby love child / Me Japanese boy / This years girl # 2
OLE 0962 / Aug '94 / Matador

☐ HAPPY END OF THE WORLD
World is spinning at 45 rpm / Trailer music / It's a beautiful day / Love's prelude / Love's theme / My baby portable player sound / Mon amour Tokyo / Collision and improvisation / Porno 3003 / Arigato we love you / Ma vie l'ete de vie / Happy ending / Earth goes around
OLE 1982 / 15 Sep '97 / Matador

☐ HAPPY END OF YOU
Love's theme / Trailer music / Earth goes round / Porno 3003 / Porno 3003 / Happy ending / It's a beautiful day / Love's theme / My baby portable player sound / Trailer music / Contact / Collision and improvisation / World is spinning at 45rpm
OLE 2822 / 1 Jun '98 / Matador

☐ MADE IN USA
I / Sweet soul revue / Magic carpet ride / Readymade FM / Baby love child / Twiggy/Twiggy Vs. James Bond / This year's girl / I wanna be like you / Go go dancer / Catchy / Peace music
OLE 0992 / Aug '94 / Matador

☐ SOUND OF MUSIC BY PIZZICATO 5, THE
We love pizzicato five / Rock 'n' roll / Night is still young / Happy sad / Groovy is my name / Sophisticated catchy / Strawberry sleighride / If I were a groupie / Sweet Thursday / CJD / Fortune cookie / Airplane / Number five / Young / Night is still / Good / Peace music / CDJ
OLE 1662 / Jun '96 / Matador

PJ & Duncan

☐ PSYCHE
TCD 2746 / Nov '94 / Telstar

☐ TOP KATZ
TCD 2793 / Nov '95 / Telstar

PJ Harvey

☐ 4 TRACK DEMOS
Rid of me / Legs / Reeling / Snake / Hook / Fifty foot Queenie / Driving / Ecstasy / Hardly wait / Rub 'til it bleeds / Easy / M Bike / Yuri-G / Goodnight
IMCD 170 / Oct '93 / Island

☐ DRY
Oh my lover / O Stella / Dress / Victory / Happy and bleeding / Sheela na gig / Hair / Joe / Plants and rags / Fountain / Water
PURECD 010 / Mar '92 / Too Pure

☐ RID OF ME
Rid of me / Missed / Legs / Rub 'til it bleeds / Hook / Man size sextet / Highway 61 revisited / Fifty foot queenie / Yuri-G / Man size / Dry / Me Jane / Snake / Ecstasy
CID 8002 / Apr '93 / Island

☐ TO BRING YOU MY LOVE
To bring you my love / Meet ze monsta / Working for the man / C'mon Billy / Teclo / Long snake moan / Down by the water / I think I'm a mother / Send his love to me / Dancer
CID 8035 / Feb '95 / Island

☐ TO BRING YOU MY LOVE/THE B-SIDES ALBUM
To bring you my love / Meet ze monsta / Working for the man / C'mon Billy / Teclo / Long snake moan / Down by the water / I think I'm a mother / Send his love to me / Dancer / Reeling / Daddy / Lying in the sun / Somebody's down, somebody's name / Darling be there / Maniac / One time too many / Harder / Goodnight
CIDZ 8035 / Nov '95 / Island

☐ TRIBUTE TO POLLY HARVEY, A (Little Fish) (Various Artists)
DOP 56 / 6 Jul '98 / Dressed To Kill

Pla, Roberto

☐ RIGHT ON TIME (Pla, Roberto Latin Jazz Ensemble)
TUMICD 051 / Feb '96 / Tumi

Placebo

☐ ENGLAND'S TRANCE
Poppy dance / Comrade / Velvet claws / Gita / Blot / Fabian policy / Punishing Pierrot / Paying homage / Pseudo silhouette
SEECD 488 / 11 May '98 / See For Miles

☐ SHELLS
Big apple / Samurai team / Jezebel steel / Visionary / In Shisha / Horizons / Base / Blue babies
SEECD 489 / 11 May '98 / See For Miles

Placebo

☐ PLACEBO
Come home / Teenage angst / Bionic / 36 degrees / Hang on to your IQ / Nancy boy / I know / Bruise pristine / Lady of the flowers / Swallow
CDFLOOR 002 / Jan '97 / Elevator

Placebo Effect

☐ GALLERIES OF PAIN
EFA 11204 / Apr '93 / Danse Macabre

☐ MANIPULATED MIND CONTROL
EFA 053242 / Oct '94 / Ausfahrt

☐ PAST...PRESENT 1989-1995
EFACD 6330 / Jul '96 / Ausfahrt

Placid Angles

☐ CRY, THE
Scarlet season / Ocean / Fate / Casting shadows (on warm Sundays) / Now and always / Lavinia / Everything under the sun / Her elements / December tragedy (revisited)
PF 069CD / Jul '97 / Peacefrog

Plaid

☐ NOT FOR THREES
Abla eedio / Kortisan / Headspin / Myopia / Lat / Extort / Prague radio / Fer / Lady burst / Rakimou / Ol / Seph / Lilith / Forever / Getting / Milh
WARPCD 054 / 27 Oct '97 / Warp

Plainsong

☐ AND WHAT'S THAT
TX 2002CD / Dec '93 / Taxim

☐ ON AIR
Anyday women / Seeds and stems / Tigers will survive / Spanish guitar / That's all it could amount to / Time between / Raider / Call the tune / I'll fly away / Amelia Earhart's last flight / Truck driving man / Yo yo man / I'm so lonesome I could cry / Miss the Mississippi / Louise / Wreck of the old '97 / Carolina moon / Old kent road
SFRSCD 047 / 8 Dec '97 / Strange Fruit

☐ SISTER FLUTE
Pilgrims / Spirits / I love this town / People's Park / Reality / Can't explain / 53 miles from Spanish town / Roll away the stone / Freedom of the highway / Mount Shannon / Baby's calling me home / Falling stars / Loser's lounge
LICD 901327 / Dec '96 / Line

Planet Rockers

☐ 26 CLASSIC TRACKS
SPINCD 003 / Jun '97 / Spinout

☐ COMING IN PERSON
NOHITCD 005 / Jan '94 / No Hit

☐ INVASION OF THE PLANET ROCKERS
NOHITCD 007 / Jan '94 / No Hit

Planetary Assault Systems

☐ ARCHIVES
In from the night / Twilight / Trek / Flightdrop / Manipulator / Gated / Booster / Elec-tric / Starway ritual
PF 039CD / Feb '96 / Peacefrog

☐ ELECTRIC FUNK MACHINE
Searchin' / Menace / Exploration of the ravish / Return / Dream / Battle / Signal / Shaken / Parting
PF 063CD / Mar '97 / Peacefrog

Plant, Robert

☐ FATE OF NATIONS
Calling to you / Down to the sea / Come into my life / I believe / Twenty nine palms / Memory song (Hello, hello) / If I were a carpenter / Colours of a shade / Promised land / Greatest gift / Great spirit / Network news
5148672 / May '93 / Fontana

☐ MANIC NIRVANA
Hurting kind (I've got my eyes on you) / SSS and Q / Nirvana / Your ma said you cried in your sleep last night / Liars dance / Big love / I cried / Tie dye on the highway / Anniversary / Watching you
7567913362 / Aug '96 / Atlantic

☐ PICTURES AT ELEVEN
Burning down one side / Moonlight in Samosa / Pledge pin / Slow dancer / Worse than Detroit / Fat lip / Like I've never been gone / Mystery title
SK 259418 / '86 / Swansong

Plantastik

☐ WAK'D
KICKCD 72 / 2 Mar '98 / Kickin'

Planxty

☐ AFTER THE BREAK
Good ship kangaroo / East at glendart-brian o'lynn-pay at the reckoning (double / You rambling boys of pleasure / Blackberry blossom-lucky in love-the dairy maid (reels) / Rambling siuler / Lady on the island-the gatehouse maid-the virginia-call / Pursuit of farmer michael hayes / Lord mcdonald-the chattering magpie / Bonny light horseman / Smeceno horo
TARACD 3001 / Oct '89 / Tara

☐ COLD BLOW AND THE RAINY NIGHT
Johnny Cope / Reels / Cold blow and the rainy night / P stands for Paddy, I suppose / Polkas / Bansea's green glade / Nominsko horo / Little drummer / Lakes of Ponchartrain / Jigs / Green fields of Canada
SH 79011CD / '90 / Shanachie

☐ PLANXTY
Raggle taggle gypsy - Tabhair dom do lamh / Arthur Mcbride / Plaxty Irwin / Sweet thames flow softly / Junior Crehan's favourite - Corney is coming / West coast of Clare / Jolly Beggar - Reel / Only our rivers / Si bheag si mhor (follow me up to Carlow) / Merrily kissed the quaker / Blacksmith
SH 79009 / Mar '98 / Shanachie

☐ PLANXTY COLLECTION, THE
Jolly beggar / Merrily kissed the quaker / Lakes of Pontchartrain / Blacksmith / Hare in the corn / Frost is all over / Gander in the pratie hole / Cliffs of Dooneen / Cunla / Pat Reilly / Bean Phaidin / Raggle taggle gyspy/Tabhair dom do lamh / Denis Murphy's polka / The 42 pound cheque / John Ryan's polka / As I roved out
SH 79012 / Mar '98 / Shanachie

☐ WELL BELOW THE VALLEY, THE
SH 79010CD / '88 / Shanachie

☐ WOMAN I LOVED SO WELL, THE
True love knows no season / Out on the ocean/ Tiocfaidh tu abhaile liom / Roger O'Hehir / Tailor's twist / Kellswater / Johnny of Brady's lea / Woman I never forgot/Pullet/Ladies pantalettes / Little musgrave
TARACD 3005 / Jan '92 / Tara

Plasmatics

☐ NEW HOPE FOR THE WRETCHED
Tight black pants / Monkey suit / Living dead / Test tube babies / Won't you / Concrete shoes / Squirm (live) / Want you baby / Dream lover / Sometimes / Corruption / Butcher baby
STIFFCD 16 / Jan '94 / Disky

Plass, Wesley

☐ I'LL BE THERE
ISCD 120 / '91 / Intersound

☐ KEEP GOING
ISCD 162 / Sep '96 / Intersound

Plastic Cloud

☐ PLASTIC CLOUD, THE
LE 1002 / 15 Jun '98 / Laser's Edge

Plastic Noise Experience

☐ RAUSCHEN
KK 170 / 10 Nov '97 / KK

Plasticland

☐ DAPPER SNAPPINGS
EFA 156602 / Feb '95 / Repulsion

Plastico

☐ PLASTICO
97522ULT / May '96 / Edel

Plastikman

☐ CONSUMED
Contain / Consume / Passage (in) / Cor ten / Convulse / Ekko / Converge / Locomotion / In side / Consume / Passage (out)
NOMU 065CD / 18 May '98 / Nova Mute

☐ MUSIK
CDNOMU 37 / Nov '94 / Nova Mute

☐ SHEET ONE
NOMU 22CD / Oct '93 / Nova Mute

Plateau

☐ MUSIC FOR GRASS BARS
CLP 9966 / Jun '97 / Cleopatra

Platinum Dance Orchestra

☐ STRICT TEMPO (64 Great Dance Melodies)
Quickstep medley / Slow fox-trot medley / Samba medley / Barn dance medley / Tango medley / Palma waltz medley / Gypsy tap medley / Old time waltz medley / Rumba medley / Pride of Erin / Cha cha medley
PLATCD 03 / Dec '88 / Platinum

Platters

☐ 19 HITS
KCD 5002 / Apr '97 / King

☐ 20 CLASSIC TRACKS
MACCD 232 / Aug '96 / Autograph

☐ ALL THE HITS AND MORE (2CD Set)
Only you (and you alone) / Great pretender / (you've got) the magic touch / My prayer / Heaven on earth / You'll never never know / One in a million / I'm sorry / Twilight time / Smoke gets in your eyes / Harbor lights / Red sails in the sunset / I love you 1000 times / Don't hear, speak, see no evil / Devri / Alone in the night / I'll be home / What name shall I give you my love / Washed ashore (on a lonely island in the sea) / If I had a love / Wonder of you / I get the sweetest feeling / Delilah / Unchained melody / With this ring / Sweet sweet lovin' / Sonata / How beautiful our love is / Love must go on / I can't get used to sharing you / Why do you wanna make me blue / Going back to detroit / Run while it's dark / Get a hold of yourself / Shing-a-ling-a-loo / Doesn't it ring a bell / Baby baby / Think before you walk away / So many tears / Hard to get a thing called love / Why / Fear of losing you / Pledging my love / If I had you / Crying in the chapel / I love you, yes I do / All my love belongs to you / More I see you
DBG 53041 / Apr '95 / Double Gold

☐ AUDIO ARCHIVE
Great pretender / Smoke gets in your eyes / Magic touch / Only you / Twilight time / Wonder of you / I get the sweetest feeling / I'm sorry / I love you 1000 times / Red sails in the sunset / Sweet sweet lovin' / Delilah / Harbour lights / My prayer / Washed ashore / Heaven on earth / I love you yes I do / All my love belongs to you / More I see you / Sayonara
CDAA 007 / Jan '92 / Tring

☐ BEST OF THE PLATTERS, THE
Smoke gets in your eyes / Great pretender / My dream / Twilight time / You'll never never know / (You've got) The magic touch / One in a million / Enchanted / I'm sorry / Only you / Harbour lights / Red sails in the sunset / I wish / Sleepy lagoon / Ebb tide / Heaven on Earth / Remember when / My prayer
5517312 / Nov '95 / Spectrum

☐ BEST OF THE PLATTERS, THE
Only you (and you alone) / Smoke gets in your eyes / Great pretender / Twilight time / Harbour lights / I'm sorry / If I had you / How beautiful our love is / With this ring / I love you a thousand times / Red sails in the sunset / Washed ashore (on a lonely island in the sea) / Sweet sweet lovin' / Doesn't it ring a bell / Devri / Unchained melody / One in a million / Pledging my love / You've got the magic touch / My prayer
CD 6118 / Apr '98 / Music

☐ FOUR PLATTERS AND ONE LOVELY DISH (9CD Set)
Bark, battle and ball / I wanna / Why should I / Only you (and you alone) / Great pretender / I'm just a dancing partner / Winner takes all / Magic touch / My prayer / Someone to watch over me / I'm sorry / At your beck and call / Heaven on earth / Bewitched, bothered and bewildered / On my word of honor / Glory of love / Have mercy / Remember when / You'll never, never know / One in a million / I give you my word / It isn't right / You've changed / He's mine / I'll get by / I don't know why / Heart of stone / I'd climb the highest mountain / Temptation / In the still of the night / September in the rain / Wagon wheels / You can depend on me / Take me in your arms / You're making a mistake / My dream / Lie low / Darktown strutters ball / Mean to me / You are too beautiful / No power on earth / I'm gonna sit right down and write myself a letter / Time and tide / Love you funny thing / In the middle of nowhere / When you return / Let's start all over again / Oh promise me / Don't forget / Only because / Sweet sixteen / Mystery of you / Indif'rent / Sixteen tons / Goodnight sweetheart, it's time to go / My serenade / Try a little tenderness / My old flame / Sleepy time gal / Don't blame me / Wish me love / Helpless / I wish / No matter what you are / Twilight time / Twilight time / That old feeling / I'll take you home again Kathleen / It's raining outside / For the first time / Whispering wind / But not like you / Out of my mind / Don't let go / You don't say / Are you sincere / If I didn't care / Smoke gets in your eyes / Thanks for the memory / I can't get started (with you) / Somebody loves me / My blue heaven / Love in bloom / Prisoner of love / Until the real thing comes along / I'll never smile again / Tisket-a-tasket / Hula hop / Wish it were me / Enchanted / Where / Love of a lifetime / Sound and the fury / To each his own / Harbor lights / By the sleepy lagoon / By the river Sainte Marie / Rainbow on the river / Sad river / Ebb tide / Reflections in the water / My secret / What does it matter / Whispering grass / I'll be with you in apple blossom time / Lullaby of the leaves / Jeannine / Tumbling tumbleweeds / Trees / Orchids in the moonlight / Little white gardenia / Honeysuckle rose / Life is just a bowl of cherries / When you wore a tulip / Roses of picardy / Movin' in / One love / Immortal love / Love, your magic spell is everywhere / Love is just around the corner / Love me or leave me / It's love love love / Let's fall in love / Advertise it / Who wouldn't love you / (I'm afraid) the masquerade is over / Nearness of you / You'll never know / It's magic / I love you truly / Love is / Love is the sweetest thing / Love is a many splendoured thing / Don't let me fall in love / True lover / Rear view mirror / I miss you so / I just got rid of a heartache / Reaching for a star / All the things you are / Song for the lonely / Say a prayer / How will I know / Keep me in love / If only you knew / Summertime / Embraceable you / People will say we're in love / Poor butterfly / Stormy weather / Every little movement / More than you know / September song / That old black magic / My heart belongs to daddy / Sometimes I'm happy / But not for me / Heartbreak / Memories / Moon over Miami / On the top of my mind / In a little Spanish town / Shine on harvest moon / OH how I miss you tonight / I'll see you in my dreams / Moonlight memories / Moonlight and roses / My reverie / Full moon and empty arms / Once in a while / Sentimental journey / It might as well be spring / But beautiful / I only have eyes for you / Pennies from heaven / Singin' in the rain / Blues in the night / As time goes by / My romance / Moonlight and shadows / Sweet Leilani / Stay as sweet as you are / Here comes heaven again / Viva jujuy / Cuando calienta el sol / Maria Elena / Solamente tu / Siboney / Amor / Aquellos ojos verdes / Aquarela do Brazil / Tu dolce voz / La hora del crepusculo / Besame mucho / Malaguena salerosa / Strangers / Winter wonderland / White Christmas / Silent night / Santa Claus is coming to town / I'll be home for Christmas / For Auld Lang Syne / Rudolph the red nosed reindeer / All I want for Christmas (is my two front teeth) / Come home for Christmas / Jingle bell rock / Jingle bells jingle / Blue Christmas / Christmas time / Sincerely / PS I love you / Hut sut song / Banana boat song (Day O) / Mississippi mud / False hearted lover / Michael, row the boat ashore / Crying in the chapel / Java jive / Three coins in the fountain / Way down yonder in New Orleans / Three bells / Song from Moulin Rouge / Little things mean a lot / (We're gonna) Rock around the clock / Don't be cruel / Tammy / Volare / Mack the knife / Summer place / Exodus song / Twist / Love me tender / Anniversary song / Gypsy / When I fall in love / Big forget / Soothe me / Easy street / It could happen to you / Blues serenade / These foolish things / Somewhere along the way / Lover / House of the rising sun / Hard hearted Hannah
BCD 15741 / Jan '94 / Bear Family

☐ GOLDEN HITS COLLECTION
Great pretender / I love you because / Unchained melody / My prayer / With this ring / Red sails in the sunset / Twilight time / I love you 1000 times / Why / Alone in the night / Heaven on earth / Harbour lights / (you've got) the magic touch / Doesn't it ring a bell / Only you (and you alone) / Sweet sweet lovin' / If I had a love / I'm sorry / My way / Smoke gets in your eyes
PWK 071 / Sep '88 / Carlton

☐ GOLDEN HITS, THE
Only you / Twilight time / Smoke gets in your eyes / You'll never know / Sixteen tons / My prayer / Great pretender / You've got the magic touch / September song / Ebb tide / Harbour lights / Red sails in the sunset / On a slow boat to China / Sleepy lagoon / Lazy river / Moonlight on the Colorado / Crying in the chapel / Summertime
8264472 / '86 / Mercury

☐ GREAT PRETENDER, THE
Only you / Great pretender / Pledging my love / Twilight time / Harbour lights / Smoke gets in your eyes / With this ring / Sweet inspiration / Magic touch / Love you a thousand times / I believe / Put your hand in my hand / Red sails in the sunset / Shake it up mambo / Headin' home / My prayer
SUMCD 4013 / Nov '96 / Summit

☐ GREATEST HITS
GRF 215 / Mar '93 / Tring

☐ GREATEST HITS
Great pretender / Only you / My prayer / Twilight time / Smoke gets in your eyes / I'm sorry / With this ring / Harbour lights / He's mine / Magic touch / Lone in a million / Red sails in the sunset
CDSGP 014 / Oct '92 / Prestige

☐ GREATEST HITS
MACCD 126 / Aug '96 / Autograph

☐ MUSICOR YEARS, THE
With this ring / I love you 1000 times / I can't get used to sharing you / Don't hear, speak, see no evil / Washed ashore / Doesn't it ring a bell / Devri / Why do you wanna make me blue / Think before you walk / So many tears / Alone in the night / How beautiful our love is / Hard to get thing called love / Sweet sweet lovin' / Going back to Detroit / Run while it's dark / Fear of losing you / Not my girl / Get a hold of yourself / Shing-a-ling-a-loo / Baby baby / Love must go on / I'll be home / If I had a love / What name shall I give you my love / Magic touch / Sonata / Why
CDKEND 116 / Jul '94 / Kent

☐ ONLY YOU
Only you / Only you / Remember when / Great pretender / Twilight time / My prayer / (you've got) the magic touch / Heaven on earth / One in a million / I love you 1000 times / Harbor lights
15077 / Aug '92 / Laserlight

☐ PLATTERS
Great pretender / I love you 1000 times / One in a million / With this ring / Pledging my love / Devri / Harbour lights / Sweet sweet lovin' / Unchained melody / Only because / Twilight time / Doesn't it ring a bell / My prayer / Smoke gets in your eyes / Only you / I'm sorry / You'll never know / Magic touch / Red sails in the sunset / If I had you / Washed ashore
LECD 040 / May '94 / Dynamite

☐ PLATTERS (CD/CD Rom Set)
WWCDR 005 / Apr '97 / Weton-Wesgram

☐ PLATTERS (The Hits Collection)
Smoke gets in your eyes / Great pretender / My prayer / Only you / Twilight time / Harbour lights / Remember when / I'm sorry / I love you 1000 times / (You've got) the magic touch / With this ring / He's mine / I'll be home / Red sails in the sunset / Sweet sweet lovin' / Washed ashore
101552 / May '97 / A-Play Collection

☐ PLATTERS COLLECTION
Great pretender / Smoke gets in your eyes / (You've got) the magic touch / Only you / Twilight time / Wonder of you / I get the sweetest feeling / I'm sorry / I love you 1,000 times / Red sails in the sunset / Harbour lights / My prayer / Washed ashore (on a lonely island in the sea) / Heaven on earth / I love you yes I do / All my love belongs to you / More I see you
QED 012 / Nov '96 / Tring

☐ PLATTERS, THE
Great pretender / I love you 1000 times / One in a million / With this ring / Pledging my love / Devri / Harbour lights / Sweet, sweet lovin' / Unchained melody / Only because / Twilight time / Doesn't it ring a bell / My prayer / Smoke gets in your eyes / Only you (and you alone) / I'm sorry / You'll never know / (You've got) the magic touch / Red sails in the sunset / If I had you / Washed ashore (on a lonely island in the sea)
399525 / Jun '97 / Koch Presents

☐ REMEMBER WHEN
AIM 1026CD / Oct '93 / Aim

☐ SIXTIES PLATTERS (2CD Set)
Only you (and you alone) / Great pretender / (You've got) The magic touch / My prayer / Heaven on Earth / I'm sorry / Twilight time / Smoke gets in your eyes / Harbour lights / I love you a thousand times / If I'll be home / With this ring / Washed ashore (on a lonely island in the sea) / Sweet, sweet lovin' / If I had you / Lovely / I love you because / Baby, baby / Sonata / If I had a love / Going back to Detroit / Get a hold of yourself / Shing-a-ling-a-loo / Love must go on / I can't get used to sharing you / Why do you wanna make me feel blue / Run while it's dark / Devri / On the top of my mind / We ain't what we was / Doesn't it ring a bell / Fear of losing you / Not my girl / Don't hear, speak, see no evil / What name shall I give you / My love / Why / Think before you walk away / Hard to get a thing called love / How beautiful our love is / So many tears / Alone in the night (without you)
CPCD 82512 / Jan '97 / Charly

☐ SMOKE GETS IN YOUR EYES
MU 5071 / Oct '92 / Musketeer

☐ SMOKE GETS IN YOUR EYES (20 Greatest Hits)
Great pretender / Only you / My prayer / Twilight time / Smoke gets in your eyes / I'm sorry / With this ring / Harbour lights / He's mine / Magic touch / One in a million / Red sails in the sunset / Platters mix / Heading home / Sweet inspiration / Riding in the mainline / Cheer up brother / Put your hand / God saw the blood / How great thou art
PLATCD 144 / Mar '96 / Platinum

Platzgumer, Hans

☐ DER SEPERATOR
EFA 294626 / 29 Sep '97 / Disko B

Plaxico, Lonnie

☐ SHORT TAKES
MCD 5477 / Mar '93 / Muse

☐ WITH ALL YOUR HEART
With all your heart / When you went away / Ray / Basement jammin' / Sixteenth Movement / Avonelle / Southside soul / As I gaze / Since we parted
MCD 5525 / Jul '95 / Muse

Play Dead

☐ FIRST FLOWER
CLEO 7519CD / Jan '94 / Cleopatra

Playa

☐ CHEERS 2 YOU
Everybody wanna love somebody / I gotta know / Cheers 2 U / Push / Buggin' over you / I'll be 2 c u / Don't stop the music / One man woman / Together / I-65 / Top of the world / Miss Parker / All the way
5363862 / 23 Mar '98 / Mercury

Playboys

☐ EASY ROCKIN'
Shake your hips / Little Miss Pancake / Baby treat me right / Ritchie's rumba / Rakin' 'n' scrapin' / 24 hour girl / She sure can rock me / Revenge / Easy rockin' / Dizzy Miss Lizzy / Don't start cryin' now / Caldonia / Get on the right track / Rock-a-bye baby blues
JRCD 26 / Sep '97 / Jappin' & Rockin'

☐ INVITATION TO DEATH
FCD 3008 / Mar '97 / Fury

Players

☐ CHRISTMAS
EXPALCD 6 / Nov '91 / Expression

☐ CHRISTMAS
Holly and the ivy / In dulci jubilo-i saw three ships / Good king wenceslas / O little town of bethlehem / Angels, from the realms of glory / In the bleak midwinter / As with gladness / We three kings / Holly bears the berry / Coventry carol / Away in a manger / Joy to the world / Ding dong merrily on high / On christmas night (Sussex carol) / Jingle bells / Here we come a-wassailing / Past three o'clock / Rising of the sun / It came upon the midnight clear / God rest ye merry gentlemen / Hark the herald angels sing / Silent night / O come all ye faithful / Boar's head carol / Deck the hall with boughs of holly / We wish you a merry christmas
EXVP 8CD / Dec '96 / Expression

Players Association

☐ BORN TO DANCE
VMD 79398 / Oct '96 / Vanguard

☐ PLAYERS ASSOCIATION/TURN THE MUSIC UP
I like it / Moon in Pisces / Let's groove / Love hangover / For the love of you / Hustlin' / Turn the music up / Closer I get to you / Everybody dance (clap your hands) / I wish / More than a little bit / Ride the groove
CDSEWD 117 / 26 Jan '98 / Southbound

Playground

☐ RESILIENCE
Hide / Inbreds / Two / A total lack of sympathy / Propriety / Victoriapolis / Insignificance / Deveneration / Hateball / Calling the animals / Santa dog / Perfect love / Form and function / Sure
DPROMCD 5 / Nov '91 / Dirter Promotions

Playgroup

☐ EPIC SOUND BATTLES VOL.1 & 2
Bombs scare / Epic sound battles / Crunch / Slither / Burn up / Deep and mintyful / Silent mover / Epic one drop / Shock absorbers / No speed limit / Boggs might fly / Ballroom control / Going overdrawn / Going for a song / Haphazard / Squeek squawk / Shoot out / Lost in LA
CDBRED 28 / 22 Sep '97 / Cherry Red

Playle, Jerry

☐ BEYOND SILENCE
Another time / Riders on the storm / Toys / Nice pair / Senorina latina / World suite / Praying for rain / Mirage / Managua tormenta / Aries rising / Beyond silence
33JAZZ 022 / Apr '95 / 33 Jazz

Pleasers

☐ THAMESBEAT
LMCD 052 / Jan '97 / Lost Moment

Pleasure

☐ BEST OF PLEASURE, THE
Bouncy lady / Straight ahead / Sassafras girl / Let me be the one / Two for one / Tune in / Foxy lady / Ghettos of the mind / Joyous / Glide / Strong love / Ladies night out / Pleasure for your pleasure / No matter what / Selim
CDBGPD 036 / Jun '92 / Beat Goes Public

Pleasure Barons

☐ LIVE IN LAS VEGAS
HCD 8044 / Jul '94 / Hightone

Pleasure Fuckers

☐ FOR YOUR PLEASURE
GRITA 35127CD / Jun '96 / Grita

Plecid

☐ PLECID
ANJ 001CD / Apr '97 / Misanthropy

Pleiadians

☐ IFO
BFLCD 24 / 1 Sep '98 / Butterfly

Plethyn

☐ BLAS Y PRIDD/GOLAU TAN GWMWL
Y gwlliaid / Ffarwel i blwy Llangywer / Ifan Pant y Fedwen / Can y cathreiniwr / Y morwr / Y sgythan / Helyntion caru / Lluen / Merch o blwy Penderyn / Cystal gen i swlt / Marwnad yr ehedydd / Pentre Llanfihangel / Hwlio'r heli / Twll bach y clo / Golau tan gwmwl / Y deryn du a'i blufyn sidan / Lodes lan / Gwaed ar eu dwylo / Un peth rwy'n ei garu / Y cryman bach / Pelydrau / Adar man y mynydd / Ye ferch yn ffair Llanidloes / Gwenno Penygelli / Deio bach / Tan yn Llyn
SAIN 6045CD / Aug '94 / Sain

☐ DRWS AGORED
Cwm y coed / Myn Mair / Breuddwyd Glyndwr / Rho wen yn dy gwsg / La Rochelle / Philomela / Hon yw fy Olwen i / Y ceidwad / Ffarwel i Aberystweth / Wylaf dros Iwerddon / Y deryn pur / Cysga di fy mhlentyn tlws / Tafarn fach glyd ar y cei
SAIN 4033CD / Aug '94 / Sain

☐ SEIDIR DDOE
Lawr y lon / Cainc yr aradwr (the ploughman's tune) / Yma mae fy mywyd / Ambell I gan / I ysgafnhau y gwaith / Daw ein dydd (steal away) / Seidir ddoe / Johnnie keenan / Mae gen I freuddwyd / Hyddgen / Yr ochr draw / O'r pridd I'r pridd / Didlan
SCD 2083 / Dec '94 / Sain

Plews, Steve

☐ ANYWHERE (Plews, Steve Ensemble)
Anywhere / Thick withins / St. Magnus / 3675 Alta Brea / St. Magnus / Your territory / St. Magnus / Isthmus / Submantle / Tumuli / Cart low
ASSCD 15 / Jun '97 / ASC

☐ LIVE 1995 - MADE IN MANCHESTER
Idsong / God's mates / Riley's death / Sleepwalker / An idle person in love / Too much apple pie
ASCCD 6 / Jan '96 / ASC

☐ SECRET SPACES
Idsong / Humorists / Secret spaces / Fanfare for a pit pony / Free fantasia / Ivov / 188 / Pavanne for JW
ASCCD 3 / Sep '95 / ASC

Plexi

☐ CHEER UP
Hold tight / Hold tight / Save me / Here's a heart / Matthew and son / Do wha diddy diddy / Touch me, touch me / Last night in soho / Legend of xanadu / Hideaway / Bend it / Zabadak / It's so hard to love you / Okay
SPCD 360 / Oct '96 / Sub Pop

Pliers

☐ I WANNA BE YOUR MAN
RNCD 2066 / Aug '94 / Rhino

☐ LOVE IS BURNING
RN 7032 / 15 Dec '97 / Rhino

Plimley, Paul

☐ DENSITY OF LOVESTRUCK DEMONS (Plimley, Paul & Lisle Ellis/Donald Robinson)
CD 906 / Feb '96 / Music & Arts

Plimsouls

☐ KOOL TRASH
Playing with Jack / Feeling strange / Down / Falling awake / Pile up / 12 o'clock midnight / Kool trash / Lost / Dangerous book / Not of this world
121252 / 9 Feb '98 / Musidisc

☐ ONE NIGHT IN AMERICA
Hush hush / How long will it take / I want what you got / In this town / Help yourself / I'll get lucky / Now / Million miles away / Time won't let me / One more heartache / Dizzy Miss Lizzy / Come on now
422266 / May '94 / New Rose

Plotkin, James

☐ AURORA (Plotkin, James & Kazuyuki Null)
RKS 1113 / Feb '97 / Rawkus

Plug

☐ DRUM 'N' BASS FOR PAPA
ANGEL 1CD / Jul '96 / Blue Angel/ Rising High

☐ VISIBLE CRATER FUNK (Plug 1)
ANGEL 6CD / May '96 / Blue Angel

Plummer, Tonya

☐ I'M READY
JBR 001 / Oct '94 / Johnny Boy

Plunk

☐ SWELL
GAP 026 / Jun '95 / Gap Recordings

Pluramon

☐ PICK UP CANYON
EFA 006762 / Jul '96 / Mille Plateau

☐ RENDER BENDITS
EFA 080512 / 26 May '98 / Mille Plateau

Plush

☐ MORE YOU BECOMES YOU
Virginia / More you becomes you / (I didn't know) I was asleep / Party / Party / Soaring and Boring / (See it in the) Early morning / Instrumental / Save the people / Sailor
WIGCD 050 / 7 Sep '98 / Domino

Pluto

☐ DEMOLITION PLATES
ORCCD 5 / 1 Dec '97 / Octopus

☐ PLUTO...PLUS
I really want it / Crossfire / And my old rocking horse / Down and out / She's innocent / Road to glory / Stealing my thunder / Beauty Queen / Mr. Westwood / Something that you loved / Rag a bone Joe / Bare lady
SEECD 265 / Oct '89 / See For Miles

Pluto

☐ RISING
ITPAL 002CD / Jul '95 / ITP

PM Dawn

☐ BLISS ALBUM, THE
Intro / Reality used to be a friend of mine ... When midnight sighs / So on and so on / Plastic / Ways of the wind / To love me more / About nothing (for the love of destiny) / Norwegian wood (this bird has flown) / Beyond infinite affections / Looking through patient eyes / Filthy rich (I don't want to be) / More than likely / Nocturnal is in the house / When it's raining cats and dogs / I'd die without you
GEE 1001532 / 10 Aug '98 / Gee Street

☐ JESUS WEPT
GEE 1001542 / 10 Aug '98 / Gee Street

☐ OF THE HEART OF THE SOUL OF THE CROSS
Intro / Reality used to be a friend of mine / Paper doll / To serenade a rainbow / Comatose / Watchers point of view / Even after I die / Ode to a forgetful mind / Twisted mellow / Paper doll / In the presence of mirrors / Set adrift on memory bliss / Shake / If I wuz U
GEE 1001522 / 10 Aug '98 / Gee Street

Pnu Riff

☐ BETWEEN THE DOWNS
Comfy club / U think u know me / 3rd ear / Cosmic dancer / Bahagavather / Tauro / Goalie to God / Bumpy slide / Sweat on wood / Cushioned soul / Heavenly trump / Zip me up
HOLCD 30 / 20 Oct '97 / Holistic

Po

☐ DUCKS AND DRAKES
RUTCD 001 / Oct '93 / Rutland

☐ HORSE BLANKET WEATHER
RUTCD 6 / 22 Jun '98 / Rutland

☐ NOT MARKED ON THE ORDNANCE MAP
RUTCD 004 / Feb '96 / Rutland

☐ PAST PERFECT TENSE
ER 1046 / 19 Jan '98 / Elefant

Poachers Pocket

☐ FAIR GAME
WGSCD 267 / Feb '96 / Wild Goose

Pocket Fishermen

☐ FUTURE GODS OF ROCK
SECT2 10016 / Aug '95 / Sector 2

Poco

☐ BLUE AND GREY
MCAD 22068 / Apr '94 / One Way

☐ COWBOYS AND ENGLISHMEN
MCAD 22067 / Apr '94 / One Way

☐ CRAZY EYES
Blue water / Fool's gold / Here we go again / Brass buttons / Right along / Crazy eyes / Magnolia / Let's dance tonight
EK 66968 / Jul '95 / Epic

☐ ESSENTIAL COLLECTION, THE
HMNCD 008 / Jun '97 / Half Moon

☐ FORGOTTEN TRAIL (2CD Set)
Pickin' up the pieces / Grand junction / Consequently so long / First love / Calico lady / My kind of love / Hard luck / Last call (cold enchilada) / Honky tonk downstairs / Hurry up / You better think twice / Anyway bye bye / I guess you made it / C'mon / Hear that music / Kind woman / Just for me and you / Bad weather / Lullaby in September / You are the one / From the inside / Good feelin' to know / I can see everything / And settlin' down / Blue water / Fool's gold / Nothin's still the same / Skunk Creek / Here we go again / Crazy eyes / Get in the wind / Believe me / Rocky Mountain breakdown / Faith in the families / Western Waterloo / Whatever happened to your smile / Sagebrush serenade
4874832 / Jun '97 / Epic

☐ FROM THE INSIDE/GOOD FEELIN' TO KNOW
From the inside / Bad weather / What am I gonna do / You are the one / Railroad days / Do you feel it to / Ol' forgiver / What if I should say I love you / Just for me and you / And settlin' down / Ride the country / I can see everything / Go and say goodbye / Keeper of the fire / Early times / Good feelin' to know / Restrain / Sweet lovin'
BGOCD 359 / Jun '97 / Beat Goes On

☐ PICKIN' UP THE PIECES
Foreward / What a day / Nobody's fool / Calico lady / First love / Make me a smile / Short changed / Pickin' up the pieces / Grand junction / Oh yeah / Just in case it happens / Yes indeed / Tomorrow / Consequently so long / Do you feel it
EK 66227 / Jul '95 / Epic

☐ ROSE OF CIMARRON
Stealaway / Just like me / Rose of Cimarron / Company's coming / Slow poke / Too many nights too long / When you come around / Starin' at the sky / All alone together / Tulsa turnaround
MCAD 22076 / Apr '94 / One Way

☐ SEVEN
Drivin' wheel / Rocky mountain breakdown / Just call my name / Skatin' / Faith in the families / Krikkit's song / Angel / You've got your reasons
EK 66985 / Jul '95 / Epic

☐ VERY BEST OF POCO, THE
You better think twice / Just for me and you / Bad weather / Fools gold / Good feelin' to know / Another time around / Faith in the families / Just in case it happens/Yes indeed / Grand junction / Consequently so long / Railroad days / Sweet lovin' / Rocky mountain breakdown / Here we go again / C'mon / Right along / Man like me / Settlin' down / Skatin' / Pickin' up the pieces
BGOCD 370 / 30 Mar '98 / Beat Goes On

Podewell, Polly

☐ POLLY PODEWELL
ACD 276 / Aug '95 / Audiophile

Poets

☐ IN YOUR TOWER
STRIKE 901 / Jun '97 / Strike

Pogatschar, Helga

☐ MARS REQUIEM
EFA 155892 / Dec '95 / Gymnastic

Pogues

☐ BEST OF THE POGUES, THE
Fairytale of New York / Sally Maclennane / Dirty old town / Irish rover / Pair of brown eyes / Streams of whiskey / Rainy night in Soho / Fiesta / Rain street / Misty morning Albert Bridge / White City / Thousands are sailing / Broad majestic Shannon / Body of an American
9031754052 / Oct '91 / WEA

☐ HELL'S DITCH
Sunny side of the street / Sayonara / Ghost of a smile / Hell's ditch / Lorca's novena / Summer in Siam / Rain street / Rainbow man / Wake of the Medusa / House of the Gods / Five green Queens and Jean / Maidrin rua / Six to go
9031725542 / Mar '94 / WEA

☐ IF I SHOULD FALL FROM GRACE WITH GOD
If I should fall from grace with God / Turkish song of the damned / Bottle of smoke / Fairytale of New York / Metropolis / Thousands are sailing / South Australia' / Fiesta / Recruiting sergeant / Rocky road to Dublin / Galway races (medley) / Streets of sorrow/Birmingham six / Lullaby of London / Battle march / Sit down by the fire / Broad majestic Shannon / Worms
K 2444932 / Mar '94 / WEA

☐ PEACE AND LOVE
Gridlock / Young Ned of the hill / Cotton fields / Down all days / Lorelei / Boat train / Night train to Lorca / White City / Misty morning Albert Bridge / Blue heaven / USA / Gartloney rats / Tombstone / London you're a lady
K 2460862 / Mar '94 / WEA

☐ POGUE MAHONE
How come / Living in a world without her / When the ship comes in / Anniversary / Amadie / Love you till the end / Bright lights / Oretown / Pont Mirabeau / Tosspint / 4 o'clock in the morning / Where that love's been gone / Sun and the moon
0630112102 / Dec '96 / WEA

☐ RED ROSES FOR ME
Transmetropolitan / Battle of Brisbane / Auld triangle / Waxie's dargle / Sea shanty / Dark streets of London / Streams of whiskey / Poor Paddy / Dingle regatta / Greenland whale fisheries / Down in the ground where the dead men go / Kitty
K 2444942 / Mar '94 / WEA

☐ REST OF THE BEST, THE
If I should fall from grace with God / Sick bed of Cuchulainn / Old main drag / Boys from the county hell / Young Ned of the hill / Dark streets of London / Repeal of the licensing laws / Yeah yeah yeah yeah yeah / London girl / Honky tonk women / Summer in siam / Turkish song of the damned / Sunny side of the street / Hell's ditch
9031773412 / Mar '94 / WEA

☐ RUM, SODOMY AND THE LASH
Sick bed of Cuchulainn / Old main drag / Wild cats of Kilkenny / Man you don't meet every day / Pair of brown eyes / Sally Maclennane / Dirty old town / Jesse James / Navigator / Billy's bones / Gentleman soldier / And the band played waltzing Matilda / Pistol for Paddy Garcia
K 2444952 / Mar '94 / WEA

☐ WAITING FOR HERB
Tuesday morning / Smell of petroleum / Haunting / Once upon a time / Sittin' on top of the world / Drunken boat / Big city / Girl from the Wadi Hammamat / Modern world / Pachinko / My baby's gone / Small hours
4509934632 / Sep '93 / WEA

Pohjola, Pekka

☐ HEAVY JAZZ
PELPCD 7 / Feb '96 / Pohjola

☐ PEWIT
Rita / Melkein / Pewit / Suuri kallion ritari / Suuri kallion ritari / Toy rock / Toy rock / Ordinary music
PELPCD 8 / Dec '97 / Pohjola

Poindexter, Pony

☐ PLAYS 'THE BIG ONES'/GUMBO
Midnight in Moscow / Moon river / Twistin' USA / Poinciana / Love me tender / Green eyes / Fly me to the moon / San Antonio rose / Front o' town / Happy strut / Creole girl / 4-11-44 / Back o' town / Muddy dust / French market / Gumbo fillet
CDBGPD 077 / Sep '93 / Beat Goes Public

Poindexter, Steve

☐ MAN AT WORK
ACVCD 104 / Dec '95 / ACV

Pointer Sisters

☐ COLLECTION, THE
Yes we can-can / Fairytale / Fire / Happiness / He's so shy / Slow hand / I'm so excited / American music / Should I do it / If you wanna get back / Your lady / I need you / Jump / Automatic / Neutron dance / Baby come and get it / Dare me / Twist my arm / Goldmine
74321139572 / Jul '93 / RCA

☐ DARE ME
Automatic / Neutron dance / I'm so excited / Slowhand / Jump (for my love) / Heartbeat / Someday we'll be together / Dare me / Should I do it / I need you / I feel for you / American music / Baby come and get it / Heart to heart / Goldmine / See how the love goes / Everybody is a star / Fire
74321487332 / May '97 / Camden

☐ JUMP (Best Of The Pointer Sisters)
Jump / Someday we'll be together / Automatic / He's so shy / Should I do it / Slow hand / Heart to heart / Telegraph your love / I'm so excited / Goldmine / Back in my arms / I need you / Neutron dance / Dare me / See how the love goes / Overnight success: *Pointer, Anita* / I'm ready for love: *Pointer, June* / Fire
74321289862 / Aug '95 / RCA

Pointer, Noel

☐ NEVER LOSE YOUR HEART
SHCD 5007 / Dec '93 / Shanachie

Poison

☐ GREATEST HITS 1986-1996
Nothin' but a good time / Talk dirty to me / Unskinny bop / Every rose has its thorn / Fallen angel / I won't forget you / Stand / Ride the wind / Look what the cat dragged in / I want action / Life goes on / (Flesh and blood) sacrifice / Cry tough / Your mama don't dance / So tell me why / Something to believe in / Sexual thing / Lay your body down
CTMCD 312 / Feb '97 / Capitol

☐ LOOK WHAT THE CAT DRAGGED IN
Cry tough / I want action / I won't forget you / Play dirty / Look what the cat dragged in / Talk dirty to me / Want some, need some / Blame it on you / No. 1 bad boy / Let me go to the show
CDGOLD 1027 / May '96 / EMI Gold

☐ OPEN UP AND SAY AHH
Love on the rocks / Nothin' but a good time / Back to the rocking horse / Good love / Tearin' down the walls / Look but you can't touch / Fallen angel / Every rose has its thorn / Your mama don't dance / Bad to be good
CDEST 2059 / Feb '94 / Capitol

Poison 13

☐ WINE IS RED POISON IS BLUE
SP 273B / Nov '94 / Sub Pop

Poison Chang

☐ FROM JA TO UK - MC CLASH VOL.3 (Poison Chang & Top Cat)
FADCD 027 / Jul '93 / Fashion

☐ RUMBLE IN THE JUNGLE VOL.2 (Poison Chang & Cutty Ranks)
JFCD 02 / Aug '95 / Fashion

Poison Girls

☐ POISONOUS (2CD Set)
SMDCD 137 / 1 Jun '98 / Snapper

☐ STATEMENT (The Complete Recordings 1977-1989/2CD Set)
Revenge / Cat's eye / Piano lessons / Closed shop / I wanted the moon / Old tarts song / Crisis / Ideologically unsound / Bremen song / Political love / Jump Mama jump / Under the doctor / Reality attack / Persons unkown / State control / Bully boys / Tension / SS Snoopers / Promenade immortelle / Another hero / Hole in the wall / Underbitch / Alienation / Pretty Polly / Good time / Other / Daughters and sons / Tender love / Dirty work / Statement / Don't go home tonight / Fuckin' Mother / Where's the pleasure / Lovers are they worth it / Done it all before / Whiskey voice / Menage abbatoir / Take the toys / Soft touch / Toys / Velvet launderette / Rio disco stink / Cry no more / Mandy is having a baby / Fear is freedom / Happy now / Cinnamon garden / Offending article / Perfect crime / Tell the children / Cream dream / Real woman / Hot for love / Riot in my mind / Feeling the pinch / Desperate days / Voodoo pappadollar / Too close for comfort / Rockface / No more lies / Too proud / Price of grain / Stonehenge / Jenny / Girls over there / Let it go / Cupid / Mirror and glass / Abort the system / All the waystate banjo
COOKCD 087 / Aug '97 / Cooking Vinyl

☐ THEIR FINEST MOMENTS
REMCD 503 / Feb '98 / Reactive

Poison Idea

☐ BIGGER THAN GOD (Poison Idea Tribute) (Various Artists)
TRO 10CD / 10 Nov '97 / Tribute

☐ FEEL THE DARKNESS
64632 / Jan '97 / Epitaph

☐ PAJAMA PARTY
Kick out the jams / Vietnamese baby / We got the beat / Motorhead / Endless sleep / Laudy Miss Clawdy / Jailhouse rock / Flamethrower love / New rose / Doctor doctor / Up front / Harder they come / Green onions
SOLO 34CD / Aug '92 / Vinyl Solution

☐ PIG'S LAST STAND
SP 343 / Apr '96 / Sub Pop

☐ WAR ALL THE TIME
Temple / Romantic self destruction / Push the button / Ritual chicken / Nothing is final / Motorhead / Hot time / Steel rule / Typical / Murderer / Marked for life
SOL 40CD / Sep '94 / Vinyl Solution

Poisoned Electrick Head

☐ BIG EYE AM
ABT 098CD / Apr '94 / Abstract

☐ HANGED MAN
BP 236CD / Nov '96 / Blueprint

☐ POISONED ELECTRICK HEAD
Immortal / Unborn / What ya gonna be son / Garden of Eden / Creature feature / Twentieth Century man/ President's reply / Mortal
BP 237CD / 15 Sep '97 / Blueprint

Pojat, Pinnin

☐ PINNIN POJAT & ERKKI RANKAVIITA (Pojat, Pinnin & Erkki Rankaviita)
KICD 44 / Nov '96 / Kansanmusiikki Instituutti

Poke

☐ SASSY
SD 008 / 22 Jun '98 / Stereo Deluxe

Pokerface

☐ LIFE'S A GAMBLE
ESM 008 / 2 Mar '98 / Escape

Pokkela, Martti

☐ OLD AND NEW KANTELE
EUCD 1040 / '89 / ARC

Pokrovsky, Dmitri

☐ LES NOCES
7559793352 / Jan '95 / Nonesuch

Poland, Chris

☐ RETURN TO METALOPOLIS
RR 93482 / Sep '90 / Roadrunner

Polar

☐ LIVING INCINERATOR
Come in and take it all / Summer / Final hour / Fact isn't fiction / Just like you said / Golden gate / Two can live cheaper than one / In the same world / Last years me / Words / Broken home / City life
CDC 002 / May '97 / Christel Deesk

Polar Bear

☐ POLAR BEAR
DH 021 / Jun '97 / Dry Hump

Polaris

☐ POLARIS
IR 002 / 3 Mar '98 / Igloo

Polcer, Ed

☐ COAST TO COAST SWINGIN' JAZZ (Polcer, Ed & His All Stars)
JCD 198 / '91 / Jazzology

☐ SALUTE TO EDDIE CONDON (Polcer, Ed Allstars)
CD 004 / May '96 / Nagel Heyer

Pole

☐ SKY CONQUERORS ARE FALLING FROM THE SKY
WB 1180CD / 19 Jan '98 / We Bite

Pole

☐ CD1/LP1
Module / Fragen / Kirschenessen / Lachen / Berlin / Tanzen / Fremd / Paula / Fliegen
KIFF 012CD / 27 Jul '98 / Kiff SM

Polecat, Tim

☐ VIRTUAL ROCKABILLY
Thunder and lightnin' / Tornado / Jigsawman / Lady Medusa / Rockin' bones / Catman returns / Panic / Boys are back in town / Head on / Guardian angel / Shiver shiver / Rock until you drop / Pit / Jungle of the bass
NERCD 078 / Aug '94 / Nervous

Polecats

☐ CULT HEROES
Rockabilly guy / High-rise rockabilly / Chicken shack / Rock it up baby / Red hot rock / Marie celeste / My baby said / Left, right and centre / Bite the dust / My baby said
NERCD 001 / Oct '91 / Nervous

☐ LIVE AND ROCKIN'
Pink and black / Blue jean bop / Rock Billy Boogie / Hip hip baby / We say yeah / Runnin back / Miss Bobby Sox
DOJOCD 172 / Jun '94 / Dojo

☐ NINE
Get on the right track / Let's go crazy / Cat o' nine tails / Baby why did you have to go / Train kept a-rollin' / Spaghetti bollock naked / Sasquatch / Boppin' high school baby / Lay your head on my shoulder / Little red book / Headless horseman / Let's bop
JRCD 2 / Sep '97 / Jappin' & Rockin'

☐ WON'T DIE
Cotton pickin' rocker / I'm ready / Lady Medusa / Biro / Pink and black / Bang bang / Hip hip baby / Sunglasses after dark / Crackerjack / Magical curtain / Miss Bobbysox / She's the one to blame / Please give me something / Rockabilly guy / John I'm only dancing / Marie Celeste / Jeepster
JRCD 10 / Sep '97 / Jappin' & Rockin'

Poleo, Orlando

☐ EL BUEN CAMINO
El buen camino / Recordando / Merengue de hoy para OP / Teresa / A tiempo / Chachaworo / Tumbador / Renacimiento / Selva / Canto a chango
4891752 / 1 Jun '98 / Sony Jazz

Poletti, Jean-Paul

☐ CORSICAN POLYPHONY (Poletti, Jean-Paul & Sartene Male Voice Choir)
B 6841 / Oct '96 / Auvidis/Ethnic

Police

☐ GHOST IN THE MACHINE
Spirits in the material world / Every little thing she does is magic / Invisible sun / Hungry for you / Demolition man / Too much information / Rehumanise yourself / One world / Omega man / Secret journey / Darkness
CDMID 162 / Oct '92 / A&M

☐ MESSAGE IN A BOX (4CD Set)
Nothing achieving / Fallout / Dead end job / Next to you / So lonely / Roxanne / Hole in my life / Peanuts / Can't stand losing you / Truth hits everybody / Born in the 50s / Be my girl Sally / Masoko tanga / Landlord / Message in a bottle / Regatta de blanc / It's alright for you / Bring on the night / Deathwish / Walking on the moon / On any other day / Bed's too big without you / Contact / Does everyone stare / No time this time / Visions of the night / Friends / Don't stand so close to me / Driven to tears / When the world is running down / Canary in a coalmine / Voices inside my head / Bombs away / De do do do de da da da / Behind my camel / Man in a suitcase / Shadows in the rain / Other way of stopping / Sermon / Shamelle / Spirits in the material world / Every little thing she does is magic / Invisible sun / Hungry for you / Demolition man / Too much information / Rehumanise yourself / One world / Omega man / Secret journey / Darkness / Flexible strategies / Low life / How stupid Mr. Bates / Kind of loving / Synchronicity / Walking in your footsteps / O my God / Mother / Miss Gradenko / Synchronicity II / Every breath you take / King of pain / Wrapped around your finger / Tea in the Sahara / Murder by numbers / Someone to talk to / Don't stand so close to me '86 / Once upon a daydream / I burn for you
5401502 / Nov '93 / A&M

☐ OUTLANDOS D'AMOUR
Next to you / So lonely / Hole in my life / Roxanne / Peanuts / Can't stand losing you / Truth hits everybody / Born in the 50s / Be my girl Sally / Masoko Tango
CDMID 126 / Aug '91 / A&M

☐ POLICE LIVE, THE (2CD Set)
Next to you / So lonely / Truth hits everybody / Walking on the moon / Hole in my life / Fall out / Bring on the night / Message in a bottle / Bed's too big without you / Peanuts / Roxanne / Can't stand losing you / Landlord / Born in the 50's / Be my girl Sally / Synchronicity I / Synchronicity II / Walking in your footsteps / Message in a bottle / O my God / De do do do de da da da / Wrapped around your finger / Tea in the Sahara / Spirits in the material world / King of pain / Don't stand so close to me / Every breath you take / Roxanne / Can't stand losing you
5402222 / May '95 / A&M

☐ REGATTA DE BLANC
Message in a bottle / Regatta de blanc / It's alright for you / Bring on the night / Deathwish / Walking on the moon / On any other day / Bed's too big without you / Contact / Does everyone stare / No time this time
CDMID 127 / Oct '92 / A&M

☐ REGATTA MONDATTA (Various Artists)
Every little thing she does is magic: *Chaka Demus & Pliers* / Roxanne: *Aswad* / Spirits in the material world: *Pato Banton & Sting* / Jamaican in New York: *Shinehead* / Every breath you take: *Wright, Betty* / One world (not three): *Marley, Ziggy & Sting* /

Message in a bottle: *Priest, Maxi* / Can't stand losing you: *Steel Pulse* / Darkness: *Los Pericos* / Walking on the moon: *Sly & Robbie* / Bed's too big without you: *Hilton, Sheila* / Wrapped around your finger: *Jazz Jamaica*
VTCD 147 / Aug '97 / Virgin

☐ ROYAL PHILHARMONIC ORCHESTRA PERFORM CLASSIC POLICE (Royal Philharmonic Orchestra)
Overture / De do do do de da da da / Released / Every little thing she does is magic / Roxanne / Truth hits everybody / Arrested / Message in a bottle / Invisible sun / Walking on the moon / Finale
QED 036 / Nov '96 / Tring

☐ RPO PLAYS THE POLICE (Royal Philharmonic Orchestra)
Overture / Regatta de blanc / Spirits in the material world / Be my girl / Sally / De do do do de da da da / Released / Every little thing she does is magic / Roxanne / Trruth hits everybody / Arrested / Message in a bottle / Invisible sun / Walking on the moon / Don't stand so close to me / Finale
EMPRCD 588 / Oct '95 / Emporio

☐ SYNCHRONICITY
Synchronicity / Walking in your footsteps / Oh my God / Mother / Miss Gradenko / Synchronicity II / Every breath you take / King of pain / Wrapped around your finger / Tea in the Sahara
CDMID 186 / Mar '93 / A&M

☐ ZENYATTA MONDATTA
Don't stand so close to me / Driven to tears / When the world is running down / Canary in a coalmine / Voices inside my head / Bombs away / De do do do De da da da / Behind my camel / Man in a suitcase / Shadows in the rain / Other way of stopping
CDMID 128 / Oct '92 / A&M

Polish Nightingales

☐ MOST BEAUTIFUL CHRISTMAS CAROLS, THE
DCD 5231 / Nov '92 / Disky

Polite Force

☐ CANTERBURY KNIGHTS
Birdworld / Childsplay / Mr. Sax speaks / Solitude / Food of the Gods/Gruel for the slobs / Arabadnaz / Extension / They shoot Indians (in Brazil) / Hey diddle diddle / For pleasure / Ritual/Dance no.2 / Man from Mars
VP 187CD / Feb '97 / Voiceprint

Political Asylum

☐ ROCK YOU SUCKER
SKIP 59CD / Aug '97 / Broken

Polka Dogs

☐ ENTERTAINERS, THE
CDPAN 137 / Apr '93 / Pan

Polkemmet Grorud Pipe Band

☐ PIPE BANDS OF DISTINCTION
Kiss the children / Kiss the children / Snake hips / Mercury sweep / An albanach / Strathspey king / Catherine / Crossfire / Solll / Old hag you've killed me / Irish traditional reel / Granny mcleod / Happyland / Moving cloud / Hawk / She moved thro' the fair / Jill's jig / Humours of cork / Gold ring / Jim mcbay's welcome / John mcmillan of barra / Old toastie / Dick' gossip / Cup of tea / Barmaid / Mcpherson of inveran / Let there be drums / Beverly's wedding / Aspen bank / Pat's strathspey / Mick's reel / Silver spear / Albatross / Gillian's jig / Friars britches / Snug in the blanket / Battle's o'er / Harvest poem / My love she's but a lassie yet / High level hornpipe / Sailor's hornpipe
CD MON 808 / Jul '90 / Monarch

Pollack, Ben

☐ BEN POLLACK & HIS PICK-A-RIB BOYS
JCD 224 / Oct '93 / Jazzology

Pollard, Lisa

☐ I SEE YOUR FACE BEFORE ME
Stuffy / Nightingale sang in Berkley Square / Stalking / I let a song go our of my heart / Things we did last summer / Namely you / Old folks / All blues / Sometimes I'm happy / I see your face before me
CCD 4681 / Feb '96 / Concord Jazz

Pollard, Robert

☐ NOT IN MY AIRFORCE
Maggie turns to flies / Quicksilver / Girl named Captain / Get under it / Release the sunbird / John strange school / Parakeet troopers / One clear minute / Chance to buy an island / I've owned you for centuries / Ash gray proclamation / Flat beauty / King of Arthur Avenue / Roofer's union fight song / Psychic pilot clocks out / Prom is coming
OLE 2152 / Sep '96 / Matador

☐ WAVED OUT
Make use / Vibrations in the woods / Just say the word / Subspace biographies / Caught waves again / Waved out / Whiskey ships / Wrinkled ghost / Artificial light / People are leaving / Steeple of knives / Rumbling joker / Showbiz opera walrus / Pick seeds from my skull / Second step next language
OLE 3162 / 20 Jul '98 / Matador

Pollen

☐ BLUETTE
GROW 252 / Sep '94 / Grass

☐ COLOURS AND MAKE BELIEVE
DANCD 028 / Feb '90 / Danceteria

Pollier & Manchon

☐ REEDS AND HAMMERS
870CD / May '97 / Escalibur

Pollo Del Mar

☐ OCEAN IS NOT FOR COWARDS
POPCD 2162 / Oct '97 / Pop

Polonsky, Jonny

☐ HI MY NAME IS JONNY
Love lovely love / Truly ugly and dead too / In my mind / Evil scurvy love / Gone away / Downlow / Half mind / It's good to sleep / I didn't know what to dream at night / Uh-oh
74321300962 / May '96 / American

Polvo

☐ CELEBRATE THE NEW DARK AGE
TG 133CD / May '94 / Touch & Go

☐ EXPLODED DRAWING
TG 162CD / May '96 / Touch & Go

☐ SHAPES
TG 179CD / 22 Sep '97 / Touch & Go

☐ THIS ECLIPSE
TG 156CD / Nov '95 / Touch & Go

☐ TODAYS ACTIVE LIFESTYLES
TG 114CD / Apr '93 / Touch & Go

Poly Breath Percussion Band

☐ PB2 LIVE
PSFD 92 / Sep '97 / PSF

Polygon

☐ REFUGE
EFA 112852 / Jan '96 / Glasnost

Polygon Window

☐ SURFING ON SINE WAVES
Polygon window / Audax powder / Quoth / If it really is me / Supremacy il / Ut1 - dot / (0.07) / Quixote / Quino - phec
WARPCD 7 / Apr '96 / Warp

Polyphemus

☐ STONEHOUSE
BBQCD 171 / Sep '95 / Beggars Banquet

Polyphonic Size

☐ OVERNIGHT DAY, THE
ROSE 150CD / Aug '88 / New Rose

Polyploid

☐ TOUCH PROOF
INTRUCD 001 / Mar '97 / Intruder

Polyyanka Russian Gypsy Ensemble

☐ PLAY BALALAIKA PLAY
MCD 71371 / Jun '93 / Monitor

Pomeroy, Herb

☐ WALKING ON AIR (Pomeroy, Herb & Donna Byrne)
ARCD 19176 / Sep '97 / Arbors Jazz

Pomus, Doc

☐ 'TIL THE NIGHT IS GONE (A Doc Pomus Tribute) (Various Artists)
This magic moment / Sweets for my sweet / Lonely avenue / I'm on a roll / There must be a better world somewhere / Blinded by love / Mess of blues / Viva las vegas / Turn me loose / Young blood / Save the last dance for me / I count the tears / Still in love / Boogie woogie country girl
8122718782 / Apr '95 / Warner Bros.

Pond

☐ POND
SPCD 66/233 / Feb '93 / Sub Pop

☐ PRACTICE OF JOY BEFORE DEATH, THE
SPCD 143357 / Feb '95 / Sub Pop

Ponder, Jimmy

☐ JAMES STREET
JP / They can't take that away from me / September song / God bless the child / James street / Love theme from Spartacus / My one and only love / End of a beautiful friendship / In a sentimental mood / Mr.Magic / NYC
HCD 7017 / Jan '98 / Highnote

☐ JUMP
MCD 5347 / Sep '92 / Muse

☐ MEAN STREETS
MCD 5324 / Sep '92 / Muse

Pondi, Kerlenn

☐ FEST A GREN
CD 446 / Mar '98 / Arfolk

Ponomarev, Valery

☐ LIVE AT SWEET BASIL
RSRCD 131 / Oct '94 / Reservoir

☐ MEANS OF IDENTIFICATION
RSRCD 101 / Dec '94 / Reservoir

☐ PROFILE
RSRCD 119 / Nov '94 / Reservoir

☐ STAR IS FOR YOU, A
RSRCD 150 / Jan '98 / Reservoir

☐ TRIP TO MOSCOW
RSRCD 107 / Oct '89 / Reservoir

Ponsford, Jan

☐ VOCAL CHORDS
View / When the birds start to sing / Univerasal love / Turn your whole world / Are we there yet / Your eyes / Clip-clop song / Prejudice groove / Prejudice
ASCCD 5 / Oct '95 / ASC

Ponta Box

☐ PONTA BOX
Nothing from nothing/Well, you needn't / Fairy tale / Pin tuck / Fill in / Nabi's napping / Fifteen / Hero inn / Nefertiti/Pinocchio / Concrete / Pooh song
JVC 2002 / Nov '97 / JVC

Pontarddulais Male Voice Choir

☐ SING SONGS OF ENGLAND, SCOTLAND, IRELAND & WALES
Down among the dead men / Tom bowling / Linden lea / Golden slumbers / Annie Laurie / Flow gently sweet afton / Ye banks and braes / Will ye no come back again / Oft in the still of the night / Londonderry air / She moved through the fair / Cockles and mussels / March of the men of Harlech / All through the night / Davis of the white rock / Watching the wheat
WMCD 2002 / Oct '96 / ACL

☐ SOFTLY AS I LEAVE YOU
Softly as I leave you / Ride the chariot / Doilch I'r 'or / Finnish forest / Windmills of your mind / Thanks be to God / Evening's pastorale / Bryn myrddin / Christus redemptor (hyfrydol) / My Lord, what a morning / Memory / Lord's prayer / Bywyd y bugail / Mil harddach wyt na'r rhosyn gwyn / Comrades in arms
GRCD 8 / May '94 / Grasmere

☐ WELSH MALE VOICES SING GERSHWIN
Swanee / I got rhythm / Foggy day / Someone to watch over me / They can't take that away from me / I got plenty o' nuttin' / Nice work if you can get it / Embraceable you / How long has this been going on / 'S wonderful / Love is here to stay / But not for me / Somebody loves me / Oh lady be good / Summertime
3036000882 / Jul '97 / Carlton

Pontier, Francini

☐ TANGO (Pontier, Francini Orquesta)
VICG 53422 / Mar '96 / JVC World Library

Ponty, Jean-Luc

☐ ANTHOLOGY (2CD Set)
Question with no answer / Bowing-bowing / Echoes of the future / Aurora part 2 / Waking dream / REnaissance / New country / Enigmatic part 2 / Enigmatic ocean part 3 / Mirage / Egocentric molecules / Cosmic messanger / Ethereal mood / I only feel good with you / No strings attached / Stay with me / Taste for passion / Once a blue planet / Forms of life / Rhythms of hope / Mystical adventures (suite) part 4 / Mystical adventures (suite) part 5 / Jig / Final truth part 1 / Computer incantations for world peace / Individual choice / Nostalgia / Eulogy to Oscar Romeo / Infinite pursuit / In the kingdon of peace / Carcas / Forever together
8122721552 / Mar '96 / Atlantic

☐ GIFT OF TIME, THE
Prologue / New resolutions / Faith in you / No more doubts / Between sea and sky / Metamorphosis / Introspective / Perceptions / Gift of time
CK 40983 / Aug '97 / Sony Jazz

☐ LIVE AT CHENE PARK
Intro / Infinite pursuit / Tender memories / Between seal and sky / Caracas / Faith in you / After the storm / Gift of time / Eulogy for Oscar Romero / Amazon forest / Story teller / Elephant's in love / Journey's end
7567829642 / Apr '97 / Atlantic

☐ LIVE AT DONTE'S
Hypomode de sol / People / California / Eight-one / Foosh / Sara's theme / Pamukkale / Cantaloupe island
CDP 8356352 / Jan '96 / Pacific Jazz

☐ NO ABSOLUTE TIME
No absolute time / Savannah / Lost illusions / Dance of the spirits / Forever together / Caracas / African spirits / Speak out / Blue mambo / Child in you
592213 / May '94 / FNAC

☐ TCHOKOLA
4685222 / Jan '95 / Sony Jazz

Pony

☐ EL DORADO
HMS 2352 / Mar '97 / Homestead

Poobah

☐ WIZARD OF PSYCH
AE 2003 / 16 Mar '98 / Alibi

Pooh Sticks

☐ FORMULA ONE GENERATION
SFTRI 58 / Oct '96 / Sympathy For The Record Industry

☐ GREAT WHITE WONDER, THE
CHEREE 18CD / May '91 / Cheree

Pook, Jocelyn

☐ DELUGE
Requiem aeternam / Indigo dream / Oppenheimer / Thousand year dream / Forever without end / Blow the wind, pie jesu / Migrations / Goya's nightmare / Backwards priests / Forever without end / La blanche traversee / Flood
CDVE 933 / Feb '97 / Venture

Pooka

☐ POOKA
City sick / Bluebell / Car / Graham Robert Wood / Breeze / Nothing in particular / Dream / Boomerang / Demon / Rollin' stone / Between my knees / Sleepwalking
4509935152 / Sep '93 / WEA

☐ SPINNING
Mean girl / Higher / God sir / Shine / Lubrication / Rubber arms / Sweet butterfly / She is a rainbow / Insect / Spinning / This river / Ocean
TRDCD 1003 / 22 Sep '97 / Trade 2

Pool, Hamilton

☐ RETURN TO ZERO
WMCD 1031 / Apr '95 / Watermelon

Poole

☐ LATE ENGAGEMENT, THE
SPART 55CD / Jun '97 / Spin Art

Pooley, Ian

☐ MERIDIAN
VVR 1001952 / 29 Jun '98 / V2

☐ TIMES, THE
FIM 019CD / Apr '96 / Force Inc.

Poor Righteous Teachers

☐ BLACK BUSINESS
144 K / Da rill shit / Nobody move / Ni fresh / Here we go again / Selah / Black business / Get off the crack / None can test / Ghetto we love / Rich mon time / Lick shots
FILECD 443 / Aug '93 / Profile

☐ NEW WORLD ORDER
FILECD 471 / Oct '96 / Profile

Poorboys

☐ POORBOYS
APCD 057 / '92 / Appaloosa

Poors Of Reign

☐ WRECKED
FUCTCD 1 / Sep '91 / Fat Terry

Poozies

☐ CHANTOOZIES
We built fires / Mountaineer's sect / Les femmes chaussees / Willie's old trousers / Honesty / Foggy mountain top / Crazy raven / Waking up in wonderful wark / Dheanainn sugradh / Love on a farmboy's wages / Another train
HYCD 200132 / Mar '95 / Hypertension

Pop Du Monde Orchestra

☐ ESSENTIAL PAN FLUTES
(Everything I do) I do it for you / I will always love you / Cuts both ways / CAreless whisper / End of the road / I'll be there / Another day in paradise / First time / Promise me / I can't stop loving you / Tears in heaven / When a man loves a woman / When you tell me that you love me / Right here waiting / Lady in red / Unchained melody / Sacrifice / Why
DCA 865472 / Sep '96 / Disky

☐ GREAT INSTRUMENTAL LOVE SONGS
Under the bridge / Praying for a time / Soul provider / All woman / Show me heaven / I'm easy / Hold on / Another sad lovesong / Without you / Fields of gold / Your love is king / (Everything I do) I do it for you / I will always love you / Most beautiful girl in the world / Love is all around / Dreams / Eternal flame / Nothing compares 2 u
DC 872012 / Sep '96 / Disky

Pop Group

☐ WE ARE ALL PROSTITUTES
We are all prostitutes / Blind faith / Justice / Amnesty report / Feed the hungry / Where there's a will / Forces of oppression / Spanish inquisition / No spectators / Amnesty report
SCANCD 31 / 1 Jun '98 / Radarscope

☐ Y
Thief of fire / Snowgirl / Blood money / Savage sea / We are time / Words disobey me / Don't call me pain / Boys from Brazil / Don't sell your dreams
SCANCD 14 / May '96 / Radarscope

Pop Tarts

☐ WOMAN IS THE FUHRER OF THE WORLD
Halio franzi / Baby you can drive your car / Ok volgas / Kindheit jugend sex / Film d'amour / Pop starts / So'n scheiss / Europa-center / I turn my radio on / Buro
BUNG 037CD / 29 Jun '98 / Bungalow

Pop Will Eat Itself

☐ BBC RADIO 1 SESSIONS 1986-1987, THE
Black Country chainstore massacre / Demolition girl / Oh grebo I think I love you / Sweet sweet pie / Love missile / Ugly / Ha ha empty head / Picnic in the sky / Illusion of love / There is no love between us anymore / Evelyn
SFRSCD 005 / Apr '97 / Strange Fruit

☐ BOX FRENZY
Grebo guru / Beaver patrol / Let's get ugly / UBLUD / Inside you / Evelyn / There is no love between us anymore / She's surreal / Intergalactic love mission / Love missile F1-11 / Hit the hi tech groove / Razor blade kisses
CHAPCD 18 / 1 Sep '97 / Chapter 22

☐ CURE FOR SANITY
Incredible PWEI vs the moral majority / Dance of the mad bastards / Eighty eight seconds and still counting / X, Y and Zee / City Zen Radio 1990/2000 FM / Dr. Nightmare's medication time / Touched by the hand of Cicciolina / 1000 times no / Psychosexual / Axe of men / Another man's rhubarb / Medicine man speaked with forked tongue / Nightmare at 20,000 feet / Very metal noise pollution / 92 degrees F (the 3rd degree) / Lived in splendour, died in chaos / Beat that refused to die
74321157912 / Nov '93 / RCA

☐ DOS DEDOS MIS AMIGOS
Ich bin ein auslander / Kick to kill / Familus horribilus / Underbelly / Fatman / Home / Menofearthereaper / Everything's cool / RSVP / Babylon
INFECT 10CD / 29 Sep '97 / Infectious

☐ NOW FOR A FEAST
Black Country chainstore massacre / Monogamy / Oh Grebo I think I love you / Titanic clown / B-6-B-6 / Breakdown / Sweet sweet pie / Like an angel / I'm sniffin' with you hoo / Sick little girl / Mesmerized / There's a psychopath in my soup / Candydiosis / Devil inside / Orgone accumulator
CHAPCD 33 / 1 Sep '97 / Chapter 22

☐ SIXTEEN DIFFERENT FLAVOURS OF HELL
Urban futuristic / Get the girl, kill the baddies / Wise up sucker / Inject me / Axe of men / Can U dig it / Always been a coward baby / Karmadrome / Dance of the mad bastards / Another man's rhubarb / X, Y and Zee / 92 F / Touched by the hand of Cicciolina / Bullet proof / Def con one / Wake up, time to die / Pweization / Eat me, drink me, love me, kill me / Preaching to the perverted
74321153172 / Oct '93 / RCA

☐ THIS IS THE DAY, THIS IS THE HOUR
PWEI is a four letter word / Preaching to the perverted / Wise up sucker / Sixteen different flavours of hell / Inject me / Can U dig it / Fuses have been lit / Poison to the mind / Def con one / Radio PWEI / Shortwave transmission on up to the minuteman / Satellite ecstatica / Now now James we're busy / Wake up, time to die / Wise up sucker (remix)
74321157922 / Nov '93 / RCA

☐ TWO FINGERS MY FRIENDS (Remix Album)
Ich bin ein auslander / Kick to kill / Familus horribilus / Underbelly / Fatman / Cape connection / Home / Menofearthereaper / Everything's cool / RSVP / Babylon
INFECT 10CDR / 29 Sep '97 / Infectious

☐ WISE UP SUCKERS
England's finest / Eat me, drink me, love me, kill me / X, Y, and Zee / 92 degrees F / Wise up sucker / Can u dig it / Def con one / Pweization / Karmadrome / Get the girl, kill the baddies / Now now James, we're busy / Preaching to the perverted / Cicciolina / Wake up, time to die / Harry Dean Stanton / Inject me / Dance of the mad / Very metal noise pollution
74321393392 / Jan '97 / Camden

Popa Chubby

☐ 1,000,000 BROKEN GUITARS
Nobody knows you when you're down and out / What's your point / Dance the night away / Real thing / Laya what ya tryin' to do / Long way home / Protected / It all turns to gold / What's your problem / Naughty little people / Nobody loves me like I love myself
DFGCD 8466 / 5 Jan '98 / Dixie Frog

☐ FIRST CUTS, THE
DFGCD 8454 / 5 Jan '98 / Dixie Frog

☐ HIT THE HARD ONE LIVE
DFGCD 8459 / 5 Jan '98 / Dixie Frog

Pope, Mal

☐ COPPER KINGDOM
Copper kingdom / Fire and ice / Listen to me / Waiting for the heartaches / Soon you will be a man / You don't own me / Soul survivor / Life's a bitch / (You were a) friend of mine / Please don't go / Cover me
CDWM 112 / Oct '96 / ACL

Pope, Odean

☐ EPITOME (Pope, Odean Saxophone Choir)
1212792 / Nov '94 / Soul Note

Pope, Sister Lucy

☐ BEST OF SISTER LUCY POPE & THE PEARLY GATES, THE (Pope, Sister Lucy & The Pearly Gates)
NASH 4511 / Feb '96 / Nashboro

Popek, Krzysztof

☐ LETTERS AND LEAVES
PB 00139 / Apr '97 / Power Bros.

Popeluc

☐ BLUE DOOR
MATS 013CD / Aug '96 / Steel Carpet

Popguns

☐ A PLUS DE CENT
Harley Davidson / Star / Get out / Stay alive / So amazing / Crushed / What are you waiting for / Day break / Can I kick it / Crazy / Gesture
POP 001CD / 30 Mar '98 / Tall Pop

☐ A PLUS DE CENT
ZYX 204252 / Dec '96 / ZYX

☐ ANOTHER YEAR ANOTHER ADDRESS
CDMRED 135 / Oct '96 / Cherry Red

☐ LOVE JUNKY
I'll take you down / Get out / Star / Second time around / Someone to dream of / Under starlight / Miserable boy / How to face it / Here in heaven / Over your head / So cold
STONE 016CD / 30 Mar '98 / 3rd Stone

Popinjays

☐ BANG UP TO DATE WITH THE POPINJAYS
TPLP 28CD / Apr '90 / One Little Indian

☐ TALES FROM THE URBAN PRAIRIE
Queen of the parking lot / Feelin' / When I believed in you / Moonheart / Slowly I reach / Hurricane / Kentish Town / Buffalo / Down / Drive the train
TPLP 48CD / May '94 / One Little Indian

Popol Vuh

☐ CITY RAGA
239752 / Oct '95 / Milan

☐ HOSIANNA MANTRA
CD 20291432 / 16 Feb '98 / OHR

☐ IN DEN GARTEN PHARAOS
14875 / Oct '96 / Spalax

☐ SHEPHERD'S SYMPHONY
Shepherds of the future / Short visit to the great sorcerer / Wild vine / Shepherd's dream / Eternal love / Dance of the menads / Yes
MYSCD 114 / Aug '97 / Mystic

☐ SING FOR SONG DRIVES AWAY THE WOLVES
139142 / May '93 / Milan

Popp, Andre

☐ DELERIUM IN HI-FI (Popp, Andre & His Orchestra)
Perles de Cristal / Java / La Paloma / Beer barrel polka / La java du Diable / Jalousie / La polka du roi / Java des bombes atomiques / Adios muchachos / La polka du colonel / La java Martienne / La cumparsita
BASTA 3090312 / Sep '97 / Basta

☐ LA MUSIQUE QUI FAIT POPP (Metropole Orchestra)
Cine surprise / Polka des pequenors / Danse de l'ours / Skating mouse / Ballade des petits perons / Valse des abonnes absents / Hey Gaucho / Le pendule / Amandine / Circus parade / Ballet des taxiphones / Avalon / Du vent dans les voiles / Tunisia waltz / Sexy sax / Bop polka / Pas de geant / Java des bombes atomiques / French dondon / Chant du mystere / Hallelujah
BASTA 3090572 / Sep '97 / Basta

Poppies

☐ HONEYBEE
She is revolution / That's what we'll do / Love trippin' / Hello Saturday / Without freedom / All tomorrow's parties / Friends for life / La de da (a trilogy) / Wonderdrug / Soulflower / Mother groove / Love amplifier / Everyone's song
4509930682 / Jul '93 / East West

Popsicle

☐ ABSTINENCE
Make up / Mayfly / Sunkissed / Could be / Step inside my mind / Soul lacquer drug / Join my stream / 9 / Diving bell / Spaniel / Prussian blue / Histrionics
4509956792 / Feb '95 / WEA

Porcupine Tree

☐ COMA DIVINE
Bornlivedieintro / Signify / Waiting phase one / Waiting phase two / Sky moves sideways / Dislocated day / Sleep of no dreaming / Moonloop / Radioactive toy / Not beautiful anymore
DELECCD 067 / 20 Oct '97 / Delerium

☐ ON THE SUNDAY OF LIFE
Music for the head / Jupiter Island / Third eye surfer / On the Sunday of life / Nostalgia factory / Space transmission / Message from a self destructing turnip / Radioactive toy / Nine cats / Hymn / Footprints / Linton Samuel Dawson / And the swallows dance above the sun / Queen quotes Crowley / No luck with rabbits / Begonia seduction scene / This long silence / It will rain for a million years
DELECCD 008 / 3 Nov '97 / Delerium

☐ SKY MOVES SIDEWAYS, THE
Sky moves sideways (phase 1) / Dislocated day / Moon touches your shoulder / Prepare yourself / Moonloop / Sky moves sideways (phase 2)
DELECCD 028 / 3 Nov '97 / Delerium

☐ STAIRCASE INFINITIES
Cloud zero / Jokes on you / Navigator / Rainy taxi / Yellow hedgerow / Dreamscape
BP 217CD / Oct '95 / Blueprint

☐ UP THE DOWNSTAIR
What you are listening to... / Synesthesia / Monuments burn into moments / Always never / Up the downstair / Not beautiful anymore / Siren / Small fish / Burning sky / Fadeaway
DELECCD 020 / 3 Nov '97 / Delerium

☐ YELLOW HEDGEROW DREAMSCAPE
Mute / Landscare / Prayer / Daughter in excess / Delightful suicide / Split image / No reason to live, no reason to die / Wastecoat / Towel / Execution of the will of The Marquis De Sade / Track eleven / Radioactive toy / Am empty box / Cross/Yellow hedgerow dreamscape / Music for the head
MG 4291325 / Aug '94 / Metrognome

Pork

☐ SLOP
EJO 7CD / Oct '96 / Emperor Jones

Pork Pie

☐ OPERANOIA
Arthur Rainbow / Hippie / Merci Afrique / Candy lip / Get down / Ballade / Lazy day / Operanoia / Zulu stomp / Quiet American
INT 31582 / Feb '97 / Intuition

Porn Kings

☐ CLUBLAND
GLOBECD 7 / 15 Jun '98 / All Around The World

Porno For Pyros

☐ GOOD GOD'S URGE
Porpoise head / Good god's urge / Dogs rule the night / Bali eyes / Freeway / Wishing well / Thick of it all / 100 way / Kimberly austin / Tahitian moon
9362460522 / May '96 / Warner Bros.

☐ PORNO FOR PYROS
Sadness / Porno for pyros / Meija / Cursed female / Cursed male / Pets / Bad shit / Packin' 25 / Black girlfriend / Blood rag / Orgasm
9362452282 / Apr '93 / Warner Bros.

Porridge Men

☐ PLANET PORRIDGE
Gulravage / Wax reels / Mission 1 / Dr. Strange / Twilight storm / Mhairi bhan og / 93rd at Modder River / Jones / Coronach / Planet porridge / Mission 2
RECD 519 / Dec '97 / REL

Port Friendly

☐ WELCOME TO PORT FRIENDLY
RAIN 016CD / Aug '97 / Cloudland

Portabales, Guillermo

☐ AL VAIVEN DE MI CARRETA
TCD 084 / Apr '97 / Tumbao Cuban Classics

☐ EL CARRETERO
El carretero / Cumbiamba / Junto a un canaveral / Nostalgia guarjira / Tristeza guajira / Yo te canto puerto rico / Lamento cubano / Guateque campesino / Oye mi son / Al vaiven de mi carreta / Voy a santiago a mo / Flor de amor / Cuando sali de cuba / El arroyo que murmura / El amor de mi boohio / Romance guajiro
WCD 043 / Apr '96 / World Circuit

Portal, Michel

☐ CINEMAS
Histoire de vent / Max mon amour / Yeelen / Droit de response / Docteur petiot / Champ d'honneur / Yvan Ivanovitch
LBLC 6574 / Jun '96 / Label Bleu

Portastatic

☐ NATURE OF SAP, THE
MRG 120CD / Mar '97 / Merge

Porteous, Wyckham

☐ LOOKING FOR GROUND
BBEA 6 / Feb '96 / Bohemia Beat

Porter, Art

☐ FOR ART'S SAKE (Memorial Album)
Lake shore drive / Flight time / Mr. Porter / Little rock / Passion sunrise / Pocket city / Texas hump / Straight to the point / Lay your hands on me / Christmas song
5570602 / 20 Apr '98 / Verve

☐ POCKET CITY
Pocket city / Inside myself / Unending / Passion sunrise / Texas hump / Close to you / Little people / KGB / Broken promises / Meltdown / LA
5118772 / Feb '92 / Verve Forecast

☐ STRAIGHT TO THE POINT
Straight to the point / Someone like you / Autumn in Europe / Free spirit / We should stay in love / Day without you / Skirt chaser / Second time around / It's been awhile / It's your move / Unconditional love
5179972 / Feb '93 / Verve Forecast

Porter, Cole

☐ BEGIN THE BEGUINE (Various Artists)
MACCD 244 / Aug '96 / Autograph

☐ COLE PORTER
DVX 08082 / May '95 / Deja Vu

☐ COLE PORTER COLLECTION, A (Various Artists)
JASSCD 632 / Feb '92 / Jass

☐ COLE PORTER SONGBOOK (20 Instrumental Greats)
Another opening another show / Begin the beguine / C'est magnifique / From this moment on / I love Paris / It's all right with me / It's de-lovely / My heart belongs to daddy / Night and day / So in love / True love / What is this thing called love / Wunderbar / Allez-vous en / Why can't you behave / Can can / Where is the life that late I led / If I loved you truly / Were thine that special face / Well did you evah
GRF 109 / '93 / Tring

☐ COLE PORTER SONGBOOK, THE (2CD Set) (Various Artists)
I've got you under my skin: *Sinatra, Frank* / I get a kick out of you: *Merman, Ethel* / Anything goes: *Bennett, Tony* / You'd be so nice to come home to: *Crosby, Bing* / My heart belongs to daddy: *Fitzgerald, Ella* / Let's do it (let's fall in love): *Holiday, Billie* / You do something to me: *Sinatra, Frank* / True love: *Cole, Nat 'King'* / Just one of those things: *Sinatra, Frank* / You do something to me: *Dietrich, Marlene* / Miss Otis regrets: *Mills Brothers* / Love of my life: *Garland, Judy* / Rosalie: *Eddy, Nelson* / At long last love: *Sinatra, Frank* / How could we be wrong: *Bowlly, Al & Lew Stone Band* / I'm a gigolo: *Porter, Cole* / They all fall in love: *Hylton, Jack & His Orchestra* / Love for sale: *Holman, Libby* / All through the night: *Brown, Sam & Ambrose Orchestra* / Don't fence me in: *Laine, Frankie* / You'd be so easy to love: *Damone, Vic* / I love you: *Crosby, Bing* / Night and day: *Holiday, Billie* / Begin the beguine: *Sinatra, Frank* / At long last love: *Horne, Lena* / You're the top: *Merman, Ethel* / Thank you so much Miss Lowsborough Goodby: *Porter, Cole* / Blow Gabriel blow: *Gonella, Nat Orchestra* / Most gentlemen don't like love: *Hylton, Jack & His Orchestra* / Banjo (that man Joe play): *Hylton, Jack & His Orchestra* / Who knows: *Browne, Sam & Billy Tennant Orchestra* / Goodbye little dream goodbye: *Hylton, Jack & His Orchestra* / In the still of the night: *Silvester, Victor & His Ballroom Orchestra* / I've got my eyes on you: *Geraldo & His Orchestra* / Swingin' the jinx away: *Gonella, Nat & His Georgians* / It's bad for me: *Noble, Ray & Al Bowlly* / It's d'lovely: *Gibbons, Carroll & Savoy Hotel Orpheans* / I'm in love again: *Hylton, Jack & His Orchestra* / Experiment: *Noble, Ray & His Orchestra/Al Bowlly* / Hey good lookin': *Geraldo & His Orchestra*
PC 622 / 1 Jun '98 / Platinum Collection

☐ FIFTY MILLION FRENCHMEN
804172 / Aug '92 / New World

☐ FOREVER - COLE PORTER (Various Artists)
Anything goes: *Bennett, Tony & Count Basie Orchestra* / Begin the beguine: *Shaw, Artie* / I love you Samantha: *Crosby, Bing* / I've got you under my skin: *Bassey, Shirley* / It's alright with me: *Shore, Dinah* / Just one of those things: *Riddle, Nelson & Orchestra* / Do I love you: *Lee, Peggy & George*

Shearing / Love for sale: *London, Julie* / Miss Otis regrets: *Wilson, Nancy* / Night and day: *Getz, Stan* / True love: *Martin, Dean* / All of you: *Darin, Bobby* / I love Paris: *Starr, Kay* / High society calypso: *Armstrong, Louis* / I am in love: *Lee, Peggy* / I get a kick out of you: *Cole, Nat 'King'* / Ev'ry time we say goodbye: *Vaughan, Sarah* / My heart belongs to Daddy: *London, Julie* / Let's do it (let's fall in love): *Riddle, Nelson & Orchestra* / Now you has jazz: *Crosby, Bing & Louis Armstrong*
CDMFP 6263 / Nov '96 / Music For Pleasure

☐ WHO KNOWS
AMSC 571 / Jun '96 / Avid

Porter Ricks

☐ BIOKINETICS
EFA 503012 / Dec '96 / Chain Reaction

☐ PORTER RICKS
EFA 006922 / 8 Dec '97 / Mille Plateau

Porter, Willy

☐ DOG EARED DREAM
Angry words / Rita / Jesus on the grille / Boab tree / Watercolour / Cool water / Be here now / Flying / Glow / Cold wind / Out of the blue
01005821342 / Feb '96 / Private Music

Portion Control

☐ MAN WHO DID BACKWARDS SOMERSAULTS
TEQM 94003 / Jun '97 / TEQ

Portishead

☐ DUMMY
Mysterons / Sour times / Strangers / It could be sweet / Wandering star / Numb / Roads / Pedestal / Biscuit / Glory box
8285222 / Aug '94 / Go Discs

☐ GLORY TALK (Interview Disc)
RVCD 258 / 4 May '98 / Quantum Rockview

☐ PORTISHEAD
Cowboys / All mine / Undenied / Half day closing / Over / Humming / Mourning air / Seven months / Only you / Elysium / Western eyes
5391892
5394352 / 29 Sep '97 / Go Beat

Portnoy, Jerry

☐ HOME RUN HITTER (Portnoy, Jerry & The Streamliners)
IGOCD 2026 / Jul '95 / Indigo

☐ POISON KISSES (Portnoy, Jerry & The Streamliners)
MBCD 1202 / Sep '94 / Modern Blues

Portrait

☐ ALL THAT MATTERS
Here's a kiss / I can call you / All that matters / All natural girl / Friday night / Hold me close / Lovin' u is ah-ight / How deep is your love / Me oh my / Lay you down / Heartstrings / Much too much
CDEST 2251 / Apr '95 / Capitol

Portuondo, Omara

☐ DESAFIOS (Portuondo, Omara & Chucho Valdes)
Que te pedi / Indestructible / Si te contara / Cenzias / Lo que me queda por vivir / Danza naniga / Salvame / Mi mejor cancion / La montana / Como un milagro / No peudo ser filiz / Nieblas del Riachuelo / En nosotros
INT 32372 / 24 Aug '98 / Intuition

☐ OMARA PORTUONDO AND MARTIN ROJAS (Portuondo, Omara & Martin Rojas)
Siempre es 26 / Cuento para un nino / El desierto y la lluvia / A salvador allende en su combate por la vida / Chile presente / Lagrimas negras / Pena / Hasta siempre / Gracias a la vida / Te doy buna cancion / El manicero / Siboney / La era esta pariendo un corazon / Ayer el sol / Veinte anos / Los caminos
LRCD 130 / Dec '97 / Love

☐ PALABRAS
Ausencia / Palabras / Juguete / Descame suerte / Si me comprendieras / Drume negrita / Y tal vez / Tardes grises / La vida es un sueno / Si me pudieras querer / Mi ayer / Abre tus ojos
INT 31862 / Aug '97 / Intuition

Poser, Florian

☐ REUNION (Poser, Florian & Klaus Ignatzek)
BEST 1084CD / Apr '96 / Acoustic Music

Posey, Sandy

☐ 18 ORIGINAL COUNTRY CLASSICS
Born a woman / Single girl / What a woman in love won't do / I take it back / Are you ever coming home / Sunglasses / Twelfth of never / Here comes my baby back again / Just out of reach / It's all in the game / Don't touch me / I've been loving you too long / Will you love me tomorrow / Deep in Kentucky / It's not easy / Satin pillows / Arms full of sin / Hey mister
5525552 / Sep '96 / Spectrum

Posies

☐ DEAR 23
My big mouth / Apology / You avoid parties / Help yourself / Everyone moves away / Golden blunders / Any other way / Suddenly Mary / Mrs. Green / Flood of sunshine
GED 24305 / Nov '96 / Geffen

☐ FROSTING ON THE BEATER
Dream all day / Solar sister / Flavor of the month / Love letter boxes / Definite door / Burn and shine / Earlier than expected / Twenty questions / When mute tongues can speak / Lights out / She lied by living / Coming right along
GFLD 19298 / 2 Feb '98 / Geffen

☐ SUCCESS
PLCD 3232 / 20 Apr '98 / Pop Llama

Position Alpha

☐ GREAT SOUND OF SOUND, THE
DRCD 307 / Feb '98 / Dragon

☐ GREETINGS FROM THE RATS
DRCD 199 / Jan '88 / Dragon

☐ TITBITS
DRCD 252 / Oct '94 / Dragon

Positive Dub

☐ TRIBULATION VOL.3
WSPCD 007 / Aug '95 / WSP

Positive Life

☐ SYNAESTHETIC
RBADCD 10 / Oct '94 / Beyond

Possum Dixon

☐ POSSUM DIXON
Nerves / In buildings / Watch the girl destroy me / She drives / We're all happy / Invisible / Pharmaceutical itch / Executive slacks / Regina / John struck lucky / Elevators
IND 92291 / 8 Sep '97 / Interscope

☐ STAR MAPS
IND 92625 / 8 Sep '97 / Interscope

Post, Dietmar

☐ BIER KELLER SINGALONG (Post, Dietmar & The German Sound)
In Munchen steht ein Hofbrauhaus / Im himmel gibets kein bier / Die dorfmusik / Annaliese / Ich macht gern dein herzkopfen hor'n / Horch was kommt von draussen rein / Muss' I denn / Im bohmerwald / Walderslust\ / Ich hab' mein herz in heidelberg verlorlen / Ein heller und ein batzen / Tiroler holzhacker buam / Der olte Peter / Bergvagabunden / Als wir jungst in Regensburg waren / Lustig ist das zigeunerleben / Bruderlein trink / Du kannst nicht treu sein / Du liegst mirb in herzen / Mein vater war ein wandersmann
308482 / 20 Apr '98 / Hallmark

Poster Children

☐ DAISYCHAIN REACTION
Dee / Cancer / If you see kay / L-o-v-e / Freedom rock / Space gun / Water / Want it / Carver's / Ahain reaction / Frustration / Where we live
CRECD 131 / Jul '92 / Creation

☐ JUNIOR CITIZEN
Get a life / Drug I need / Wide awake / New boyfriend / One of us / Downwind / Mustaine / King for a day / Revolution year zero / Junior citizen / He's my star
9362457372 / Mar '95 / Warner Bros.

Potato Five

☐ FIVE ALIVE
Shuttle disaster / Spit 'n' polish / Call me master / Live up / Jail me / Stop that train / Harvest in the east / Hi-Jacked / Stopped by a cop / Do the jerk / Western special / Got to go
DOJOCD 181 / Jun '94 / Dojo

Potatomen

☐ ICELAND
LK 188CD / 1 Dec '97 / Lookout

Pothead

☐ DESSICATED SOUP
EFA 127592 / Jul '95 / Orangehaus

☐ RUMELY OIL PULL
EFA 11973 2 / Sep '94 / Orangehaus

Pothole

☐ DIRTY PICNIC
All the way / Cottonmouth / Zer loop / Thirst bracket / Janitor / Dirty picnic / Inseminoid / Tymone
INT 35042 / 17 Nov '97 / Intuition

Potlatch

☐ ALBUM BY POTLACH, AN
DOL 028CD / Mar '96 / Dolores

Potshot

☐ POTS AND SHOTS
AM 018CD / Oct '97 / Asian Man

Potter, Chris

☐ CONCENTRIC CIRCLES
El Morocco / Klee / Blues in concentric circles / Dusk / Lonely moon / You and the night and the music / Mortal coils / In a sentimental mood / Aurora
CCD 4595 / May '94 / Concord Jazz

☐ CONCORD DUO SERIES VOL.10
Hibiscus / Boulevard of broken time / Istanbul / Sail away / Tala / September song / New left (and we have our own talk show host) / Epistrophy / Hey Reggie / Giant steps
CCD 4695 / May '96 / Concord Jazz

☐ MOVING IN
Nero's fiddle / Book of kells / Moving in / Kiss to build a dream on / Rhubarb / South for the winter / Forest / Pelog / Chorale / Old faithful
CCD 4723 / Sep '96 / Concord Jazz

☐ PURE
Salome's dance / Checking out / Resonance / Bad guys / Boogie stop shuffle / Second thoughts / That's what I said / Fool on the hill / Bonnie rose / Easy to love / Distant present / Every time we say goodbye
CCD 4637 / Apr '95 / Concord Jazz

☐ SUNDIATA
CRISS 1107 / Dec '95 / Criss Cross

☐ UNSPOKEN
Wistful / Seven eleven / Hieroglyph / Amsterdam blues / Et tu brute / Unspoken / No cigar / Time zone / New vision
CCD 47752 / Sep '97 / Concord Jazz

Potter, Gary

☐ FRIENDS (Potter, Gary Quartet)
Yesterdays / Sandu / Bernie's tune / Nearness of you / Crazeology / Autumn leaves / Scrapple from the apple / All the things you are / Steffani / Nica's dream / Nuages / Friends
HHR 0001 / Oct '96 / Hi-Hat

Potter, Nic

☐ BLUE ZONE, THE
VP 103CD / Dec '90 / Voiceprint

Pottoka

☐ LE MYSTERE DU PEUPLE BASQUE
992397 / Sep '96 / Wotre Music

Potts, Bill

☐ JAZZ SOUL OF PORGY & BESS, THE
Summertime / Woman is a sometime thing / My man's gone now / It takes a long pull to get here / I got plenty o' nuttin' / Bess you is my woman now / It ain't necessarily so / Prayer / Strawberry woman's call, honey man / Crab man / I love your Porgy / Clara Clara / There's a boat that's leavin' soon for New York / Oh Bess, oh where's my Bess / Oh lawd, i'm on my way
CDP 7951322 / Feb '97 / Blue Note

Potts, Tommy

☐ LIFFEY BANKS, THE
CC 13CD / Jun '95 / Claddagh

Pounder

☐ E6
INV 087CD / May '97 / Invisible

Pourcel, Franck

☐ AND NOW/DANCING IN THE SUN (2CD Set)
She / Singin' in the rain / Nabucco / My boy / Entertainer / Emmanuelle / Sugar baby love / Soleado / Tie a yellow ribbon round the ole oak tree / One man woman one woman man / Theme from Serpico / Fluty / When I fall in love / Le premier pas / Dancing in the sun / Sympathy / Make it easy on yourself / C'est le refrain de ma vie / Wand'rin' star / Lady D'Arbanville / Things of life / No colour time of the day / Yellow river / Concerto pour une voix / Baby sitter / Snowbird / Comme j'ai toujours envie d'aimer / Close to you
4956232 / 10 Aug '98 / Studio 2

Pousseur, Henri

☐ ACOUSMATRIX VOL.4
BVHAASTCD 9010 / Dec '89 / Bvhaast

POV Shorthand

☐ FRACTION OF FAITH
RRS 955CD / 24 Nov '97 / Diehard

Poverty Stinks

☐ ANOTHER WORLD
You're going away / Another World / Only One / You can't give enough / There Must Be / Hitch hiker / She / Take Me Home / Man Like Anyone Else / Don't Follow Me / Getting deeper / One Love / Waltz / Poverty Stinks
SNAP 004 / Nov '92 / Soap

Poverty's No Crime

☐ AUTUMN YEARS, THE
Ghost of a stone / Future in my hands / Rain of gods / Beat it when it hurts / Autumn years / Seconds / Lead me to the door / Enter nowhere / Heroes return
TT 00242 / Jul '96 / T&T

Powder

☐ BIFF BANG POWDER
DR 1015 / Jun '97 / Distortions

Powder Monkeys

☐ TIME WOUNDS ALL HEELS
ANDA 219CD / Jun '97 / Au-Go-Go

Powell, Baden

☐ BADEN POWELL
330352 / Mar '96 / Musidisc

☐ BADEN POWELL & FILHOS
KAR 982 / Sep '96 / IMP

☐ BADEN POWELL LIVE IN HAMBURG
BEST 1037CD / Nov '93 / Acoustic Music

☐ CANTO ON GUITAR
Samba em preludio / Tres themas de fe Afro-Brasileira / Marcha Escocesa / Tributo a um amigo / Qua quara qua qua / Cegos do Nordeste
8218662 / Apr '94 / MPS Jazz

☐ FRANKFURT OPERA CONCERT 1975 (Powell, Baden & Trio)
68958 / Apr '97 / Tropical

☐ LIVE AT MONTREUX 1995
FA 410 / Jul '96 / Fremeaux

☐ MELANCOLIE
139 213 / '86 / Accord

☐ TRISTEZA ON GUITAR/POEMA ON GUITAR/APASSIANADO (Three Originals/2CD Set)
Tristeza / Canto de Xango / 'Round midnight / Sarava / Canto de / Ossanha / Manha de carnaval / Invencao em 7/12 / Das rosas / Som do carnaval / O astronauta / Fetinha pro poeta / Dindi / Consolacao / Tristeza e solidao / Samba triste / Euridice / All the things you are / Reza / Casa velha / Alcantra / Waltzing / Lembrancas / Abstrato / As flores / Balantofe / Brisa do mar
5192162 / Apr '94 / MPS Jazz

☐ VIVO NO TEATRO SANTA ROSA
HE 30CD / Apr '97 / Rare Brazil

Powell, Bud

☐ 'ROUND ABOUT MIDNIGHT AT THE BLUE NIGHT
Shawnuff / Lover man / There will never be another you / Monk's mood / Night in Tunisia / 'Round midnight / Thelonious / 52nd Street
FDM 365002 / Oct '93 / Dreyfus

☐ AMAZING BUD POWELL VOL.1, THE
Un poco loco (first take) / Un poco loco (second take) / Dance of the infidels / 52nd Street / It could happen to you / Night in Tunisia / Wail / Ornithology / Bouncing with Bud / Parisian thoroughfare / Wail (alt. take) / Dance of the infidels (alt. take) / You go to my head / Ornithology (alt. master) / Un poco loco (alt. take 2) / Over the rainbow
CDP 7815032 / Mar '95 / Blue Note

☐ BEST OF BUD POWELL ON VERVE, THE
5233922 / Mar '94 / Verve

☐ BLUES FOR BOUFFEMONT
In the mood for a classic / Una noche con frances / Relaxin' at Camarillo / Moose the mooche / Blues for Bouffemont / Little Willie leaps / My old flame / Star eyes / There will never be another you
BLCD 760135 / Apr '90 / Black Lion

☐ BOUNCING WITH BUD (Powell, Bud Trio)
DD 406 / Nov '89 / Delmark

☐ BUD PLAYS BIRD
Big foot / Shaw 'nuff / Buzzy / Yardbird suite / Relaxin' at Camarillo / Confirmation / Billie's bounce / Ko Ko / Barbados / Dewey Square / Moose the Mooch / Ornithology / Scrapple from the apple / Salt peanuts / Big foot (short version)
CDP 8371372 / Apr '96 / Roulette

☐ COMPLETE BLUE NOTE & ROOST RECORDINGS, THE (4CD Set)
I'll remember April / (Back home again in) Indiana / Somebody loves me / I should care / Bud's bubble / Off minor / Nice work if you can get it / Everything happens to me / Bouncing with Bud (alt. take 1) / Bouncing with Bud (alt. take 2) / Bouncing with Bud / Wail (alt. take) / Wail / Dance of the infidels (alt. take) / Dance of the infidels / 52nd Street / You go to my head / Ornithology / Ornithology (alt. take) / Un poco loco (alt. take 1) / Un poco loco (alt. take 2) / Un poco loco / Over the rainbow / Night in Tunisia / Night in Tunisia (alt. take) / It could happen to you / It could happen to you (alt. take) / Parisian thoroughfare / Autumn in New York / Reets and I / Reets and I (alt. take) / Sure thing / Collard greens and black eyed peas (alt. take) / Collard greens and black eyed peas / Polka dots and moonbeams / I want to be happy / Audrey / Glass enclosure / Embraceable you / Burt covers Bud / My heart stood still / You'd be so nice to come home to / Bag's groove / My devotion / Stella by straight / Woody 'n' you / Blue pearl / Blue pearl (alt. take) / Keepin' in the groove / Some soul /

Frantic fancies / Bud on Bach / Idaho / Don't blame me / Moose the mooche / John's abbey (alt. take) / Sub City (alt. take) / Sub City / John's abbey / Buster rides again / Like someone in love / Dry soul / Marma lade / Monopoly / Time waits / Scene changes / Down with it / Comin' up (alt. take) / Comin' up / Duid deed / Cleopatra's dream / Gettin' there / Crossin' the channel / Danceland / Borderick
CDP 8300832 / Oct '94 / Blue Note

☐ COMPLETE ESSENTIAL JAZZ FESTIVAL CONCERT, THE
Shaw 'nuff / Blues in the closet / Willow weep for me / John's abbey / Salt peanuts / All the things you are / Just you, just me / Yesterdays / Stuffy
BLCD 760105 / Jul '88 / Black Lion

☐ COMPLETE VERVE RECORDINGS, THE
5216692 / Nov '94 / Verve

☐ EARLY BUDS
Floogie boo / I don't know / Gotta do some war work / My old flame / Sweet Lorraine / Honeysuckle rose / Blue garden blues / Long tall Dexter / Dexter digs in / I can make you love me / Ray's idea / Serenade to a square / Good kick / Seven up / Blues in be bop / Epistrophy / Oop bop sh'bam / Rue Chaptal / Boppin' a riff / Fat boy / Webb City
TPZ 1059 / Mar '97 / Topaz Jazz

☐ PIANOLOGY (Powell, Bud & Thelonious Monk)
MCD 0552 / Apr '94 / Moon

☐ PORTRAIT OF THELONIOUS
Off minor / There will never be another you / Ruby my dear / No name blues / Thelonious monk's mood / I ain't foolin' / Squatty
CK 65187 / 1 Sep '97 / Sony Jazz

☐ SALT PEANUTS
BLCD 760121 / Aug '89 / Black Lion

☐ STRICTLY CONFIDENTIAL
BLCD 760196 / Nov '94 / Koch

☐ TRIBUTE TO CANNONBALL
Just one of those things / Cherokee / I remember clifford / Good bait / Jeannie / All the things you are / Myth / Jackie / My little cat (alternate) / Cherokee
CK 65186 / 1 Sep '97 / Sony Jazz

☐ ULTIMATE BUD POWELL, THE
5397882 / 16 Mar '98 / Verve

Powell, Cozy

☐ VERY BEST OF COZY POWELL, THE
5377242 / Aug '97 / Polydor

Powell, Dirk

☐ IF I GO TEN THOUSAND MILES
ROUCD 0384 / May '96 / Rounder

Powell, Jesse

☐ JESSE POWELL
Looking for love / All I need / Spend the night / I like / You don't know / You / Gloria, it's you that I need / Ooh I like it / Let go / If you like what you see / All alone / I will be loving you / Is it over
LSJD 11287 / Mar '96 / MCA

Powell, Jimmy

☐ MANDOLIN MOMENTS
Lara's theme / Sealed with a kiss / Spanish eyes / Godfather / Milanese waltz / Skye boat song / Certain smile / Serenata / Autumn leaves / LA paloma / Song for the seashore / Forever and ever / O sole mio / Breeze and I
PLATCD 32 / Jul '92 / Platinum

☐ R & B SENSATION
Sugar man / House of the rising sun / Captain Man / Nine live wire / Witness to a war / Progressive talking blues / I'm a rocker / On the beach / I can go down / Sugar baby / Slow down / Gonna find a cave / Strangers on a train / Slow lovin' man / Back in the USSR / Out of time / Ivory / Real cool / Hipster / Hold on / Rosavelt and Iralee / Do you really have a heart
SEECD 337 / Feb '92 / See For Miles

Powell, Keith

☐ KEITH POWELL STORY, THE
Come and join the party / Answer is no / Tore up / You better let him go / I should know better / Too much monkey business / Walkin' and cryin' / New Orleans / People get ready / Paradise / Beyond the hill / Come home baby / Goodbye girl / It was easier to hurt her / When you move you lose: *Powell, Keith & Billie Davis* / Tastes sour don't it: *Powell, Keith & Billie Davis* / Victory / Some people only / Two little people: *Powell, Keith & Billie Davis* / You don't know like I know: *Powell, Keith & Billie Davis* / Swinging tight: *Powell, Keith & Billie Davis* / That's really some good: *Powell, Keith & Billie Davis* / Song of the moon / It keeps rainin'
NEMCD 717 / Nov '94 / Sequel

Powell, Marilyn

☐ SEEDS
Seeds / Hurt / No one's gonna be a fool forever / Time for peace / Tonight / Why didn't I think of that / Old lover / Once upon a time / Up in the world / Crazy / For you / Like no one else / Music / If you're looking for a heartache / Star
PCOM 1130 / Oct '93 / President

Powell, Mel

☐ RETURN OF MEL POWELL, THE
CRD 301 / Mar '96 / Chiaroscuro

Powell, Sylvia

☐ REVUE
Butterfly / Perfect day / Ordinary point of view / Human touch / Cool brother / Walk the walk / Soleil / Kaleidoscope / New love / Satisfied
74321510282 / 13 Oct '97 / De-Construction

Power, Brendan

☐ BLOW IN
HBCD 0008 / Apr '96 / Hummingbird

☐ JIG-JAZZ
PKCD 001 / Mar '96 / PK

☐ NEW IRISH HARMONICA
PM 002CD / Jan '96 / Punch Music

☐ RIVERDANCE DISTILLED (Brendan Power Plays The Music From Riverdance)
Countess Cathleen / Reel around the sun / Slip into Spring / American wake / Lift the wings / Riverdance / Caoineadh chu chulainn / Firedance/Andalucia / Riverdance/Women of Sidhe / Marta's dance/ Russian dervish
CDTRAX 135 / Jun '97 / Greentrax

☐ STATE OF THE HARP
TCJAY 335 / Jul '94 / Jayrem

Power, Duffy

☐ BLUES POWER
Hell hound / Mary open the door / Holiday / Little boy blue / Open the door / I need you / Midnight special / Gin house blues / Fox and geese / Exactly like you / Fixing a hole / Roll over Beethoven / I've been lonely baby / Lawdy Miss Clawdy / Lily / Little man you've had a busy day / City woman / Halfway / Louisiana blues / One night / Leaving blues
SEECD 356 / Sep '92 / See For Miles

☐ JUST STAY BLUE
Love's gonna go / There's no living without your loving / I'm so glad you're mine / Dollar Mamie / Little boy blue / Little girl / Mary open the door / Hound dog / Rags and old iron / Just stay blue / Lilly / Hell hound / Love is shelter / Lawdy Miss Clawdy / Love's prescription / Halfway / Corine / Songs about Jesus / Lover's prayer / Swansong / River
RETRO 802 / Jun '95 / RPM

Power Mad

☐ ABSOLUTE POWER
Slaughterhouse / Nice dreams / Test the steel (Powermad) / BNR / Brainstorms / Absolute power / Return from the fear / Plastic town / Failsafe / Final frontier
VSD 5808 / May '97 / Varese Sarabande

Power Of Expression

☐ POWER OF EXPRESSION, THE
LF 107CD / Oct '94 / Lost & Found

☐ X-TERRITORIAL
CM 77120CD / Feb '96 / Century Media

Power of Omens

☐ EYES OF THE ORACLE
ERO 2004 / Jul '98 / Elevate

Power Pack Orchestra

☐ YOUR 40 ALL-TIME DANCE HITS
In the mood / Opus one / Don't get around much anymore / I'm beginning to see the light / American patrol / Touch of your lips / Spanish harlem / My cherie amour / Shadow of your smile / Guitar boogie shuffle / Nut rocker / Goody goody / Deep in the heart of Texas / Hoots mon / Lara's theme / Moon river / Green leaves of summer / You made me love you / Limehouse blues / St. Louis Blues / Body and soul / Stranger on the shore / Moonlight serenade / Mood indigo / Tuxedo Junction / It happened in Monterey / String of pearls / Brazil / Sucu sucu / Caravan / Copacabana / Lipstick on your collar / Let there be drums / Never on a Sunday / Spanish flea / Hernando's hideaway / New fangled tangle / Get happy / Continental / Last waltz
CDMFP 6083 / Mar '90 / Music For Pleasure

Power Station

☐ POWER STATION
Some like it hot / Murderess / Lonely tonight / Communication / Get it on / Go to zero / Harvest for the world / Still in your heart
CDPRG 1011 / Aug '93 / Parlophone
CDP 7461272 / 6 Jul '98 / EMI Gold

Power Steppers

☐ BASS ENFORCEMENT
WWCD 15 / Nov '95 / Wibbly Wobbly

☐ BASS RE-ENFORCEMENT
WWCD 20 / Oct '96 / Universal Egg

Powerhouse

☐ NIGHTLIFE/LOVIN' MACHINE
PRD 70182 / Nov '90 / Provogue

Powerhouse

☐ FIVE PLUS FOUR
YP 020CD / Mar '97 / Yellow

Powers, Johnny

☐ NEW SPARK (FOR AN OLD FLAME), A
Rattled / Rock you around the world / Something about you / Rocker Billy / Bigger heartaches / Trouble / Please please do / It'll be me / Honky tonkin' Saturday night / You win again / Singin' the blues / Stuck on you / Love to burn / New spark (for an old flame) / Love business / Say it / Help me I'm in need
NEXCD 259 / Oct '93 / Sequel

Powertwang

☐ SURFIN' DEAD
MADCD 017 / Dec '96 / Mental Disorder

Powrie, Glenna

☐ ASHA
MCD 5392 / Sep '92 / Muse

Powrie, Ian

☐ LEGEND OF THE FIDDLE
Ainsworth march/Laird of thrums/Andy Renwick's ferret / Banks of the Locheil/Duncan Johnstone / Provost of Forgandenny/Jimmy's aye diggin'/Sands of Murness / Billy Thom's reel / Lady Elizabeth / Willie Atkinson/Leila's garden/Captain Keeler / Dark island / Memories of Bobby Macleod/Christina McNair Caskie / Margaret's waltz/Heather blossom special / Alex MacArthur of Biggar/Lady Charlotte Campbell/Peerie Will / Our Highland Queen / Cambridge hornpipe/Hoo dinnae ye play mair/ Moray players / Laird of Corrieburn / Briony / David John Powrie/Calum John Builder / Will Powrie, the Angus ploughman / Back to the hills/Catching rabbits / Lament for Will Starr/Auchterarder VIP / Rural jig/Margaret Cook's fancy/Ainster fisherman
CDLOC 1096 / Oct '96 / Lochshore

Poza

☐ ODESSA
PS 65181 / Apr '97 / PlayaSound

Pozo, Chano

☐ LEGENDARY SESSIONS (Pozo, Chano & Arsenio Rodriguez/Machito & Orchestra)
TCD 017 / Dec '92 / Fresh Sound

Pracatan, Margarita

☐ LIVE AT THE EDINBURGH PALLADIUM
Introduction / Hello / Crazy / Stand by me / Sentimental reasons / Cenisas / Take a chance on me / I wanna hold your hand / From me to you / Embraceable you / I will survive / There's no business like showbusiness / Hello (reprise)
74321371532 / 1 Sep '97 / RCA

Prado, Perez

☐ BESAME MUCHO
CD 62034 / Apr '94 / Saludos Amigos

☐ CILIEGI ROSA
CD 62004 / Apr '94 / Saludos Amigos

☐ CUBA BAILABLES DE SIEMPRE
9944132312 / 31 Mar '98 / Orfeon

☐ EL REY DEL MAMBO
BM 514 / Jan '97 / Blue Moon

☐ GO GO MAMBO (Prado, Perez & His Orchestra)
TCD 013 / Dec '92 / Fresh Sound

☐ KING OF MAMBO (Prado, Perez 'Prez')
Patricia / Ruletero / Mambo no.8 / Guaglione / Mambo no.5 / Paris / Cherry pink and apple blossom white / Caballo negro (mambo batri) / In a little Spanish town / My Roberta / Why wait / Mambo jambo / Rockambo baby / La rubia / San Remo / One night / Adios pampa mia
ND 90424 / May '95 / RCA

☐ LATINO
Jumbo jumbo / Ni hablar / Muchachita / La rubia / Martinica / Mama Y tata / Mambo del 65 / Latino / Jing a ling, jing a lang / Al compas del mambo / La nina popof / Paso bakan / Mi gallo / Ole mambo / Peanut vendor / Ritmo de chunga / Gateando / Oh Caballo
CD 62079 / Jan '96 / Saludos Amigos

☐ MAMBO JAMBO
CD 62001 / Apr '94 / Saludos Amigos

☐ MAMBO MANIA/HAVANA 3 AM
Cherry pink and apple blossom white / Ballin' the Jack / Tomcat mambo / April in Portugal / Mambo a la Kenton / High and mighty / Marilyn Monroe mambo / St. Louis blues mambo / Skokiaan / Mambo a la Billy May / Mambo de chattanooga / Mambo en sax / La comparsa / Desconfianza / La faraona / Besame mucho / Freeway mambo / Granada / Almendra / Bacoa / Peanut vendor / Baia / Historia de un amor / Mosaico cubano
BCD 15462 / Feb '90 / Bear Family

☐ MAMBOS (Prado, Perez & Benny More)
La mucura / Babarabatiri / Ana maria / Mamboletas / Anabacoa / Que te pasa jose / Tocineta / Maria cristina / Rabo y oreja / Mambo ete / Viejo canengo / Locas por el mambo / Deja que suba la marea / A romper el coco / Mangolele / Tu solo tu
CD 62051 / May '94 / Saludos Amigos

☐ MASTERS, THE
EABCD 042 / 24 Nov '97 / Eagle

☐ OUR MAN IN HAVANA
Guaglione / Cherry pink and apple blossom white / Patricia / Mambo no.5 / Ruletero / Peanut vendor / One night / Mambo jambo / In a little Spanish town / Paris / La faraona / Flight of the bumblebee / La borrachita / My Roberta / Adios mi chaparrita / Beautiful Margaret / Freeway mambo / Maria bonita / Historia de un amor / La rubia / Leyenda Mexicana / Rockambo baby / OK Joe Calypso / Adios pampa mia / Mama teach me to dance
74321588102 / 15 Jun '98 / Camden

☐ PREZ (Prado, Perez 'Prez')
Maria Bonita/Cu-cu-rru-cu-cu-Paloma / La borrachita (I'll never love again) / Machaca / Adios mi chaparrita (goodbye my little angel) / Marta / Lullaby of Birdland / Flight of the bumblebee / Leo's special / Come back to Sorrento / Fireworks / Estrellita del Sur / Beautiful Margaret / OK Joe Calypso / Leyenda Mexicana / Marna teach me to dance
74321260522 / Jun '97 / RCA

☐ VOODOO SUITE/EXOTIC SUITE OF THE AMERICAS
Voodoo suite: *Prado, Perez & Shorty Rogers* / St. James Infirmary / In the mood / I can't get started (with you) / Jumpin' at the woodside / Stompin' at the Savoy / Music makers / Exotic suite of the Americas / Midnight in Jamaica / Mama yo quiero / Son of a gun / Jacqueline and Caroline / El relicario / I could have danced all night
BCD 15463 / Feb '90 / Bear Family

Prague Castle Guard & Police Wind Orchestra

☐ VIVAT FUCIK
Florentinsky pochod / Marinarella / Bosanska zora (koracnica) / Zimni boure / Kanizsi / Svaty Hubert / Sempre avanti / Dvorni intendant / Zvuky fanfar / Stary brucoun / Vjezd gladiatoru
4101072431 / Jun '97 / Edit

Prairie Oyster

☐ BLUE PLATE SPECIAL
She won't be lonely long / Watcha gonna do / Water's deep / If my broken heart would ever mend / Tonight there's a blue moon / Long gone daddy / In the summertime (you don't want my love) / Unbelievable love / Sunday driver / There she goes / One way track / Into the blue
VEL 970012 / 27 Apr '98 / Velvel

Praise 17

☐ IN HIS PRESENCE
He is worthy / All the praise belongs to you / Like a deer / In your presence / Higher than the highest Heaven / Your love / He loves me / I will restore / Jesus your name/Emmanuel/Jesus your name / This God that we worship / God of wonder / Jesus you are my life / It's you more like / Here I am / Here am I send me
7016361845 / Nov '97 / Maranatha

Praise Space Electric

☐ 2 LEAVING DEMONS
Doc's groove / Sinnerman / Rhythm rhythm / Singing the same song / Diggin' at the dig in / Freedom / 300,000 million years / Waves of joy / Drain your wobbles away / Cybergenetic experiment X / Pebbles
DELECCD 015 / Apr '94 / Delerium

Prajini, Zece

☐ PEASANT BRASS BAND
926552 / Sep '96 / BUDA

Pram

☐ NORTH POLE RADIO STATION, THE
Omnichord / Cinnabar / El Topo / Bathysphere / Fallen snow / Clockwork lighthouse / Sleepy sweet / Cow ghosts / Doors of empty cupboards
WIGCD 049 / 16 Mar '98 / Domino

☐ SARGASSO SEA
Loose threads / Little scars / Earthling and protection / Cotton candy / Three wild Georges / Serpentine / Crystal tips / Crooked tiles / Eels / Sea swells and distant squalls
PURECD 046 / Sep '95 / Too Pure

☐ STARS ARE SO BIG, THE EARTH IS SO SMALL
PURECD 026 / Sep '93 / Too Pure

Prana

☐ GEOMANTIK
MPCD 5 / Jul '97 / Matsuri

Prasit Thawon Ensemble

☐ THAI CLASSICAL MUSIC
NI 5412CD / Oct '94 / Nimbus

Pratt, Andy

☐ RESOLUTION (Pratt, Andy Collection)
RE 21162 / Oct '96 / Razor & Tie

Praxis

☐ **TRANSMUTATION**
Blast/War machine dub / Interface/Stimulation loop / Crash victim/Black science navigator / Animal behaviour / Dead man walking / Seven laws of woo / Interworld and the new innocence / Giant robot/ Machines in the modern city / After shock (Chaos never died)
ADC 5 / May '97 / Douglas Music

☐ **TRANSMUTATION LIVE**
GR 101011 / Mar '97 / Gravity

Praying For The Rain

☐ **SANCTUARY**
TWIN 103 / Jul '97 / Twin Arrows

Praying Mantis

☐ **CRY FOR THE NEW WORLD, A**
CDFLAG 80 / Sep '93 / Under One Flag

☐ **PREDATOR IN DISGUISE**
Can't see the angels / She's hot / This time girl / Time slipping away / Listen what your heart says / Still want you / Horn / Battle royal / Only you / Borderline / Can't wait forever
CDFLAG 77 / Feb '93 / Under One Flag

Preacher Boy

☐ **CROW**
Whisper / Black crow / Ruby Lou / Richmond / Sophie and Frankie Machine / Needle got you man / Doctor what have you done / Hello lover / Faces in the West / Postcards and ashtrays / Coal black dirt sky / Lullaby / Mortuary band
WAHTCD 002 / Apr '98 / Wah' Tup

☐ **GUTTERS AND PEWS**
Down and out in this town / Catfish / Ugly / Cold mountain music / I won't be there / Something is wrong / Buckshot / Railroad / New Orleans / In the darkened night / Back then we only cared for hell / 2 o'clock
BPCD 5034 / Nov '96 / Blind Pig

☐ **PREACHER BOY & THE NATURAL BLUES**
BPCD 5017 / Feb '95 / Blind Pig

Preacher Jack

☐ **NON STOP BOOGIE**
SACD 097 / Nov '96 / Solo Art

☐ **RETURN OF THE BOOGIE MAN**
All by myself / Say you'll stay until tomorrow / Break up / Yancey's bugle call / Public is my family, music is my life / Go tell it on the mountain / Mystery train / Jessie's boogie woogie / I'll be your baby / Who will buy the wine / Lovin' up a storm / Teardrop on a rose / Rounder boogie / May you never be alone like me / Be careful of stones that you throw / Just a closer walk with thee
ROUCD 3145 / Feb '97 / Rounder

Preager, Lou

☐ **CRUISING DOWN THE RIVER**
Saturday night / Sophisticated lady / Dodging around / Bring on the drums / Remember me / Don't take your love / I'll always be with you / I'd rather be me / Too bad / I close my eyes / Let's keep it that way / Cruising down the river / Did you ever get that feeling / Trees in / Good good good / Ashby De La Zouch / Let bygones be bygones / By that dream / Who could love / I'll get you alone / Sweet dreams / No one but you / Wonder of you / Down in the valley / Pretending
CDEA 6000 / Aug '97 / Vocalion

☐ **DANCING AT THE HAMMERSMITH PALAIS (Preager, Lou & His Orchestra)**
Saturday night / I'd rather be me / I'm beginning to see the light / In a little while / Bring on the drums / No one else will do / Too bad / I've got a heart filled with love / Trolley song / Waiting in Sweetheart Valley / I'll always be with you / Sophisticated lady / If I told a lie / Let's keep it that way / Doggin' around / I'll close my eyes / Lonely footsteps / Last waltz of the evening / Coming home / Remember me / Morning train / Don't take your love from me / Choc'late soldier from the USA
RAJCD 866 / Apr '96 / Empress

Precious Metal

☐ **WHAT YOU SEE IS WHAT YOU GET**
RMED 0197CD / 8 Jun '98 / Renaissance

Prefab Sprout

☐ **ANDROMEDA HEIGHTS**
Electric guitars / Prisoner of the past / Mystery of love / Life's a miracle / Anne Marie / Whoever you are / Steal your thunder / Avenue of stars / Swans / Fifth horseman / Weightless / Andromeda Heights
KWCD 30 / May '97 / Kitchenware

☐ **FROM LANGLEY PARK TO MEMPHIS**
King of rock 'n' roll / Cars and girls / I remember that / Enchanted / Nightingales / Hey Manhattan / Knock on wood / Golden calf / Nancy let your hair down for me / Venus of the soup kitchen
4601242 / May '97 / Columbia

☐ **JORDAN - THE COMEBACK**
Looking for Atlantis / Wild horses / Machine gun Ibiza / We let the stars go / Carnival 2000 / Jordan: The comeback / Jesse James symphony / Jesse James bolero / Moon dog / All the world loves lovers / All boys believe anything / Ice maiden / Paris Smith / Wedding march / One of the broken / Michael / Mercy / Scarlet nights / Doo wop in Harlem
4671612 / May '97 / Columbia

☐ **LIFE OF SURPRISES, A**
King of rock 'n' roll / When love breaks down / Sound of crying / Faron Young / Carnival 2000 / Goodbye Lucille / Cruel / I remember that / Cars and girls / We let the stars go / Life of surprises / Appetite / If you don't love me / Wild horses / Hey Manhattan / All the world loves lovers
4718862 / 2 Feb '98 / Columbia

☐ **PROTEST SONGS**
World awake / Life of surprises / Horsechimes / Wicked things / Dublin / Tiffanys / Talkin' scarlet / Till the cows come home / Pearly gates
4651182 / Feb '97 / Columbia

☐ **STEVE MCQUEEN**
Faron Young / Bonny / Appetite / When love breaks down / Goodbye Lucille / Hallelujah / Moving the river / Horsin' around / Desire as / Blueberry pies / When the angels
4663362 / May '97 / Columbia
4663369 / 13 Jul '98 / Columbia

☐ **STEVE MCQUEEN/FROM LANGLEY PARK TO MEMPHIS**
Faron Young / Bonny / When love breaks down / Goodbye Lucille / No. 1 / Hallelujah / Appetite / Moving the river / Horsin' around / Desire as / Blueberry pies / When the angels / King of rock 'n' roll / Cars and girls / I remember that / Enchanted / Nightingales / Hey Manhattan / Knock on wood / Golden calf / Nancy (let your hair down for me) / Venus of the soup kitchen
4784822 / Mar '95 / Columbia

☐ **SWOON**
Don't sing / Cue fanfare / Green Isaac / Here on the eerie / Cruel / Couldn't bear to be special / I never play basketball now / Ghost town blues / Elegance / Technique
4609082 / May '97 / Columbia

Pregnant

☐ **UNUSUAL LOVER**
SF 018CD / May '97 / Swarf Finger

☐ **WEEP HIPPIES WEEP**
SF 023CD / 6 Apr '98 / Swarf Finger

Prego

☐ **AVARELA**
ROEMOE 007CD / Aug '97 / RoMoe

☐ **MOCHA EXPRESS**
Mocha Express / Norbert's/Turn of the wheel / Grandjean/Laurel / Doigts de Carmen/Trois / Ami / Chasse a la Becasse / Madame Nuds Tarantella / Georgian twist / Littel green hat / Bailiffs bouree/ Marijean/Jeanmari / Trois matelots/Chemin du village / Adeles / Mexican hatstand/Winter sunshine / Boeing 747/Berceuse
FSCD 24 / Jun '97 / Folksound

Prelude

☐ **AFTER THE GOLDRUSH**
PACD 7015 / Sep '93 / Disky

☐ **AFTER THE GOLDRUSH**
OW 34432 / Nov '97 / One Way

☐ **PRELUDE ARCHIVE**
Platinum blonde / City tonight / When two worlds collide / America / After the goldrush / Only the lonely / Now the time has come / Harvest / Daybreak / One broken heart / Labour of love / Freedom / Life goes on / Lost in those eyes / Hold on to your dreams
RMCD 216 / Nov '97 / Rialto

Prelude To Cycle 6

☐ **PRELUDE TO CYCLE 6 VOL.2**
JFR 007CD / Jun '97 / Jazz Fudge

Prema

☐ **DRIVAL**
EVR 027CD / Apr '97 / Equal Vision

Premature Ejaculation

☐ **ANESTHESIA**
DV 018CD / Sep '93 / Dark Vinyl

Premi

☐ **10 YEARS ON**
DMUT 1212 / Aug '93 / Multitone

Premier Accordian Band

☐ **GO COUNTRY**
PLATCD 3924 / May '94 / Platinum

☐ **GO HAWAIIAN**
Clap clap sound / Aloha oe / Highland hulu / Beyond the reef / Now is the hour
PLATCD 3925 / May '94 / Platinum

☐ **GO SCOTTISH**
PLATCD 3926 / May '94 / Platinum

Prendergast, Kevin

☐ **LET'S GO BACK TO MAYO**
Let's go back to Mayo / I'm thinking about a lady / Three pubs in Bohola / Galway and you / Where the river Shannon flows / To the lady we call mother / I'll sing about Roscommon / My old home in Mayo / Boys from Killybegs / Galtee mountain boy / Our house is a home / Village of Dromore / My own Leitrim home / My Connemara shore / Ireland must be heaven / Lovely old Fintown
CD 21213 / Nov '97 / Laserlight

Presencer, Alain

☐ **SINGING BOWLS OF TIBET**
Invocation / Bowl voices / Shepherd's song / Lullaby / Bon-po chant / Lamentation / Symphony of the bowls
CDSDL 326 / Mar '94 / Saydisc

Presencer, Gerard

☐ **PLATYPUS**
AKD 079 / 3 Aug '98 / Linn

Preservation Hall Jazz Band

☐ **BECAUSE OF YOU**
SK 60327 / Jul '98 / Sony Classical

Presidents Of The USA

☐ **II**
Ladies and gentlemen part 1 / Lunatic to love / Volcano / March 5 / Twig / Bug City / Bath of fire / Tiki God / LIP / Froggie / Toob amplifier / Supermodel / Puffy little shoes / Ladies and gentlemen part 2 / Basketball dream
4850922 / Nov '96 / Columbia

☐ **PRESIDENTS OF THE USA**
Kitty / Feather pluckin' / Lump / Stranger / Boll weevil / Peaches / Dune buggy / We are not going to make it / Kick out the jams / Body / Back porch / Candy / Naked and famous / Wake up / Twig in the wind
4810392 / Oct '95 / Columbia
4843342 / Jul '96 / Columbia

☐ **PURE FROSTING**
Love delicatessen / Video killed the radio star / Mobile home / Japan / Back porch / Man (opposable thumb) / Tiki God (Tiki Lounge God) / Teenage girl / Slip away / Tremolo blooz / Cleveland rocks / Lump
4897026 / 30 Mar '98 / Columbia

Presley

☐ **AFRICAN SWIM**
SHCD 6018 / Jul '95 / Sky High

Presley, Elvis

☐ **24 KARAT HITS**
1117 / Sep '97 / Dunhill

☐ **AFTERNOON IN THE GARDEN, AN**
Also sprach Zarathustra / That's alright / Proud Mary / Never been to Spain / You don't have to say you love me / Until it's time for you to go / You've lost that lovin' feelin' / Polk salad Annie / Love me / All shook up / Heartbreak hotel / (Let me be your) teddy bear / Don't be cruel / Love me tender / Blue suede shoes / Reconsider baby / Hound dog / I'll remember you / Suspicious minds / Introductions by Elvis / For the good times / American trilogy / Funny how time slips away / I can't stop loving you / Can't help falling in love
07863674572 / Mar '97 / RCA

☐ **ALL TIME GREATEST HITS, THE (2CD Set)**
Heartbreak hotel / Blue suede shoes / Hound dog / Love me tender / Too much / All shook up / Teddy bear / Paralysed / Party / Jailhouse rock / Don't / Wear my ring around your neck / Hard headed woman / King Creole / One night / Fool such as I / Big hunk o' love / Stuck on you / Girl of my best friend / It's now or never / Are you lonesome tonight / Wooden heart / Surrender / His latest flame / Can't help falling in love / Good luck charm / She's not you / Return to sender / Devil in disguise / Crying in the chapel / Love letters / If I can dream / In the ghetto / Suspicious minds / Don't cry Daddy / Wonder of you / I just can't help believin' / American trilogy / Burning love / Always on my mind / My boy / Suspicion / Moody blue / Way down / It's only love
PD 90100 / Apr '97 / RCA

☐ **ALOHA FROM HAWAII**
What now my love / Fever / Welcome to my world / Suspicious minds / CC rider / Burning love / Hound dog / I'll remember you / Long tall Sally / Whole lotta shakin' goin' on / American trilogy / Big hunk o' love / Can't help falling in love / Something / You gave me a mountain / Steamroller blues / My way / Love me / Johnny B Goode / It's over / Blue suede shoes / I'm so lonesome I could cry / I can't stop loving you
07863676092 / 27 Apr '98 / RCA

☐ **ALTERNATIVE ALOHA**
Also sprach Zarathustra / CC rider / Burning love / Something / You gave me a mountain / Steamroller blues / My way / It's over / Blue suede shoes / I'm so lonesome I could cry / What now my love / Fever / Welcome to my world / Suspicious minds / I'll remember you / American trilogy / Big hunk o' love / Can't help falling in love / Blue Hawaii / Hound dog / Hawaiian wedding song / Ku-u-i-po
PD 86985 / Aug '88 / RCA

☐ **ALWAYS ON MY MIND**
Always on my mind / I just can't help believin' / Suspicious minds / Can't help falling in love / Are you lonesome tonight / Girl of my best friend / It's now or never / Love me tender / Fever / Surrender / Love me / Loving you / And I love you so / She's not you / Fool such as I / Suspicion / Love letters / Help me make it through the night / You don't have to say you love me / Kentucky rain / Gentle on my mind / Let it be me / Spanish eyes / It's only love / Wonder of you / Bridge over troubled water
743214898420 / 8 Sep '97 / RCA

☐ **ALWAYS ON MY MIND**
74321489842 / May '97 / RCA

☐ **AMAZING GRACE (His Greatest Sacred Performances)**
I believe / Peace in the valley / Take my hand precious Lord / It is no secret / Milky white way / His hand in mine / I believe in the man in the sky / He knows just what I need / Mansion over the hilltop / In my father's house / Joshua fit de Battle of Jericho / Swing low, sweet chariot / I'm gonna walk dem golden stairs / If we never meet again / Known only to him / Working on the building / Crying in the chapel / Run on / How great thou art / Stand by me / Where no one stands alone / So high / Farther along / By and by / In the garden / Somebody bigger than you and I / Without him / If the Lord wasn't walking by my side / Where could I go but to the Lord / We call on him / You'll never walk alone / Only believe / Amazing grace / Miracle of the rosary / Lead me, guide me / He touched me / I've got confidence / Evening prayer / Seeing is believing / Thing called love / Put your hand in the hand / Reach out to Jesus / He is my everything / There is no God but God / I, John / Bosom of Abraham / Help me / If that isn't love / Why me Lord / You better run / Lead me / Nearer my God to thee
07863 664212 / Oct '94 / RCA

☐ **AT THE WORLD'S FAIR/FUN IN ACAPULCO**
Beyond the bend / Relax / Take me to the fair / They remind me too much of you / One broken heart for sale (Film version) / I'm falling in love tonight / Cotton candy land / World of our own / How would you like to be / Happy ending / One broken heart for sale / Fun in Acapulco / Vino, dinero y amor / Mexico / El toro / Marguerita / Bullfighter was a lady / No room to rhumba in a sports car / I think I'm gonna like it here / Bossa nova baby / You can't say no in Acapulco / Guadalajara
74321134312 / Mar '93 / RCA

☐ **BACK IN MEMPHIS**
Inherit the wind / This is the story / Stranger in my own hometown / Little bit of green / And the grass won't pay no mind / Do you know who I am / From a jack to a king / Fair's moving on / You'll think of me / Without love (there is nothing)
ND 90599 / Oct '91 / RCA

☐ **BIOGRAPHY SERIES**
10022 / 3 Nov '97 / Metro Independent

☐ **BLUE HAWAII (Original Soundtrack)**
Blue Hawaii / Almost always true / Aloha oe / No more / Can't help falling in love / Rock-a-hula baby / Moonlight swim / Ku-u-i-pu / Ito eats / Slicin' sand / Hawaiian sunset / Beach boy blues / Island of love / Hawaiian wedding song / Steppin' out of line / Can't help falling in love / Slicin' sand / No more / Rock-a-hula baby / Beach boy blues / Blue Hawaii
07863674592 / Apr '97 / RCA
07863669592 / 2 Feb '98 / RCA

☐ **BLUE SUEDE SHOES (The Ultimate Rock 'n' Roll Collection)**
Blue suede shoes / Jailhouse rock / Hound dog / All shook up / Too much / Heartbreak hotel / Good rockin' tonight / Party / Got a lot o' livin' to do / Rip it up / One sided love affair / Teddy bear / Mystery train / Don't be cruel / Baby I don't care / Paralysed / His latest flame / King Creole / My baby left me / Hard headed woman / I need your love tonight / That's all right / Treat me nice / Rock-a-hula-baby / Big hunk o' love / Little sister / Ain't that loving you baby / Wear my ring around your neck / Stuck on you / Return to sender / Memphis Tennessee / Burning love / Way down
74321556282 / 16 Feb '98 / RCA

☐ **CLASSIC ELVIS**
Blue suede shoes / Hound dog / All shook up / I got a woman / Lawdy Miss Clawdy / Wear my ring around your neck / Big hunk o' love / Mean woman blues / It's now or never / Fever / Return to sender / That's alright Mama / Treat me nice / My baby left me / Hard headed woman / Mystery train
74321476822 / Apr '97 / Camden

☐ **COLLECTION VOL.1, THE**
That's alright / Heartbreak hotel / I was the one / Blue suede shoes / My baby left me / Hound dog / Don't be cruel / Peace in the valley / One night / Loving you / I want you, I need you, I love you / Love me tender / Love me / All shook up / That's when your heartache begins
74321289882 / Oct '96 / RCA

☐ **COLLECTION VOL.2, THE**
Teddy bear / Party / Jailhouse rock / Don't / Wear my ring around your neck / I got stung / It's now or never / Stuck on you / Girl of my best friend / Mess of blues / Are you lonesome tonight / Big hunk o' love / Fool such as I / My wish came true
74321330172 / Oct '96 / RCA

☐ **COLLECTION VOL.3, THE**
Wooden heart / Surrender / Wild in the country / Can't help falling in love / Rock-a-hula baby / His latest flame / Follow that dream / Good luck charm / She's not you / Return to sender / Devil in disguise / Bossa nova baby / Such a night / Crying in the chapel / Love letters
74321400532 / Aug '96 / RCA

☐ **COMMAND PERFORMANCES (The Essential 1960's Masters Vol.2 - 2CD Set)**
GI blues / Wooden heart / Shoppin' around / Doin' the best I can / Flaming star / Wild in the country / Lonely man / Blue Hawaii / Rock-a-hula baby / Can't help falling in love / Beach boy blues / Hawaiian wedding song / Follow that dream / Angel / King of the whole wide world / I got lucky / Girls, girls, girls / Because of love / Return to sender / One broken heart for sale / I'm falling in love tonight / They remind me too much of you / Fun in Acapulco / Bossa Nova baby / Marguerita / Mexico / Kissin' cousins / One boy two little girls / Once is enough / Viva Las Vegas /

What'd I say / Roustabout / Poison Ivy League / Little Egypt / There's a brand new day on the horizon / Girl happy / Puppet on a string / Do the clam / Harem holiday / So close, yet so far / Frankie and Johnny / Please don't stop loving me / Paradise Hawaiian style / This is my heaven / Spinout / All that I am / I'll be back / Easy come, easy go / Double trouble / Long legged girl with the short dress on / Clambake / You don't know me / Stay away / Joe / Speedway / Your time hasn't come yet, baby / Let yourself go / Almost in love / Little less conversation / Edge of reality / Charrol / Clean up your own backyard
07863666012 / Jun '95 / RCA

☐ COMPLETE MILLION DOLLAR SESSION, THE (Presley, Elvis & Carl Perkins/Jerry Lee Lewis)
You belong to my heart / When god dips his love in my heart / Just a little talk with Jesus / Walk that lonesome valley / I shall not be moved / Peace in the valley / Down by the riverside / I'm in a crowd but oh so lonely / Futher along / Blessed jesus hold my hand / As we travel along on the Jericho road / I just can't make it by myself / Little cabin on the hill / Summertime has passed and gone / I hear a sweet voice calling me / Sweetheart you've done me wrong / Keeper of the key / Crazy arms / Don't forbid me / Brown eyed handsome man / Out of sight out of mind / Don't be cruel / There's no place like home / When the saints go marching in / Softly and tenderly / Is it so strange / That's when your heartaches begin / Rip it up / I'm gonna bid my blues goodbye / That's my desire / At the end of the road / Jerry's boogie / You're the only star in my blue heaven / Elvis farewell
CDCHR 123 / Sep '97 / Charly

☐ COMPLETE SUN SESSIONS, THE
That's alright mama / Blue moon of Kentucky / Good rockin' tonight / I don't care if the sun don't shine / Milkcow blues boogie / You're a heartbreaker / Baby let's play house / I'm left, you're right, she's gone / Mystery train / I forgot to remember to forget / I love you because / Blue moon / Tomorrow's night / I'll never let you go / Just because / Trying to get to you / Harbour lights / When it rains it really pours
PD 86414 / Jul '87 / RCA

☐ DATE WITH ELVIS, A
Blue moon of Kentucky / Young and beautiful / Baby I don't care / Milk cow blue boogie / Baby let's play house / Good rockin' tonight / Is it so strange / I forgot to remember to forget
ND 90360 / Sep '89 / RCA

☐ EASY COME, EASY GO/SPEEDWAY (Double Feature/Original Soundtracks)
Easy come, easy go / Love machine / Yoga is as yoga does / You gotta stop / Sing you children / I'll take love / She's a machine / Love machine (alternate take) / Sing you children (alternate take) / She's a machine (alternate take 13) / Suppose (alternate mater) / Speedway / There ain't nothing like a song / Your time hasn't come yet, baby / Who are you, who am I / He's your uncle, not your dad / Let yourself go / Five sleepy heads / Suppose / Your groovy self
07863665582 / Mar '95 / RCA

☐ ELVIS - A PORTRAIT (In Performance/ Interviews & Musical Tributes - 2CD Set)
Hound dog / Are you lonesone tonight: *Davis, John* / Interview / There's good rockin' tonight / Interview / I just can't help believing: *Davis, John* / Heartbreak hotel / In the ghetto: *Davis, John* / Interview / I got a woman / Jailhouse rock: *Davis, John* / Maybellene / Return to sender: *Davis, John* / Interview / I was the one / Until it's time for you to go: *Davis, John* / Blue suede shoes / Lawdy Miss Clawdy: *Davis, John* / Interview / Tweedle Dee / When my blue moon turns to gold: *Davis, John* / Interview / Money honey / That's alright Mama: *Davis, John* / Interview / Blue moon of Kentucky / Don't be cruel: *Davis, John* / Long tall Sally / His latest flame: *Davis, John* / Baby let's play house / Wooden heart: *Davis, John* / Love me tender: *Davis, John*
MUCD 9517 / May '96 / Musketeer

☐ ELVIS - THE ALBUM
SGCD 001 / Nov '94 / Dynamite

☐ ELVIS 1956
Heartbreak hotel / My baby left me / Blue suede shoes / Glad you're mine / Tutti frutti / One sided love affair / Love me / Any place is paradise / Paralyzed / Ready Teddy / Too much / Hound dog / Any way you want me / Don't be cruel / Lawdy Miss Clawdy / Shake, rattle and roll / I want you, I need you / Rip it up / Heartbreak hotel / I got a woman / I was the one / Money honey
07863668172
07863668562 / Jun '96 / RCA

☐ ELVIS ARON PRESLEY (4CD Set)
78636745527 / 20 Apr '98 / RCA

☐ ELVIS ELVIS ELVIS
That's alright mama / Blue moon of Kentucky / Heartbreak hotel / Long tall Sally / I was the one / Money, honey / I've got a woman / Blue suede shoes / Hound dog / Baby let's play house / Maybellene / Good rockin' tonight / Tweedle dee
MUCD 9017 / Apr '95 / Musketeer

☐ ELVIS FOR EVERYONE
Your cheatin' heart / Summer kisses, Winter tears / Finders keepers / In my way / Tomorrow night / Memphis Tennessee / For the millionth and the last time / Forget me never / Sound advise Santa Lucia / Met her today / When it rains it really pours
7863534502 / Apr '95 / RCA

☐ ELVIS GOSPEL 1957-1971
Peace in the valley / Take my hand / Precious Lord / I'm gonna walk dem golden stairs / I believe in the man in the sky / Joshua fit de Battle of Jericho / Swing low, sweet chariot / Stand by me / Run on / Where could I go but to the Lord / So high / We call on him / Who am I / Lead me, guide me / Known only to him
74321187532 / Feb '94 / RCA

☐ ELVIS IN CONCERT
Elvis fans comment / Opening riff / 2001 / CC rider / That's alright / Are you lonesome tonight / You gave me a mountain / Jailhouse rock / How great thou art / I really don't want to know / Elvis introduces his father / Hurt
74321146932 / Jul '93 / RCA

☐ ELVIS IN PERSON
Blue suede shoes / Johnny B Goode / All shook up / Are you lonesome tonight / Hound dog / I can't stop loving you / My babe / Mystery train tiger man / Words / In the ghetto / Suspicious minds / Can't help falling in love
ND 83892 / Oct '91 / RCA

☐ ELVIS IS BACK
Make me know it / Fever / Girl of my best friend / I will be home again / Dirty, dirty feeling / Thrill of your love / Soldier boy / Such a night / It feels so right / Girl next door / Like a baby / Reconsider baby
ND 89013 / Feb '89 / RCA

☐ ELVIS IS STILL ALIVE (Various Artists)
MCG 20008 / Jun '97 / Vampirella

☐ ELVIS LIVE AT MADISON SQUARE GARDEN
2001 / That's alright mama / Proud Mary / Never been to Spain / You don't have to say you love me / You've lost that lovin' feelin' / Polk salad Annie / Love me / All shook up / Heartbreak hotel / Impossible dream / Hound dog / Suspicious minds / For the good times / American trilogy / Funny how time slips away / I can't stop loving you / Can't help falling in love / Why me Lord / How great thou art / Blueberry Hill / Can't stop loving you / Help me / Let me be there / My baby left me / Lawdy Miss Clawdy / Closing vamp
ND 90663 / Apr '92 / RCA

☐ ELVIS NBC SPECIAL (TV Soundtrack)
Trouble / Guitar man / Lawdy Miss Clawdy / Baby, what you want me to do / Heartbreak hotel / Hound dog / All shook up / Can't help falling in love / Jailhouse rock / Love me tender / Where could I go but to the Lord / Up above my head / Saved / Blue Christmas / One night / Memories / Nothingville / Big boss man / Little Egypt / If I can dream
ND 83894 / Mar '91 / RCA

☐ ELVIS NOW
Help me make it through the night / Miracle of the rosary / Hey Jude / Put your hand in the hand / Until it's time for you to go / We can make the morning / Early morning rain / Sylvia / Fools rush in / I was born ten thousand years ago
74321148312 / Jul '93 / RCA

☐ ELVIS PRESLEY
Blue suede shoes / I love you because / Tutti frutti / I'll never let you go / Money honey / I'm counting on you / I got a woman / One-sided love affair / Just because / Trying to get to you / I'm gonna sit right down and cry over you / Blue moon
ND 89046 / Oct '88 / RCA

☐ ELVIS PRESLEY (Historic Live Recordings & Interviews/2CD Set)
Heartbreak hotel / Long tall Sally / I was the one / Money honey / I've got a woman / Blue suede shoes / Hound dog / Baby let's play house / Maybellene / That's alright Mama / Blue moon of Kentucky / There's good rockin' tonight / Tweedle dee
SAV 001 / Apr '96 / Tring

☐ ELVIS PRESLEY COLLECTION VOL.4
Guitar man / US male / If I can dream / In the ghetto / Suspicious minds / Don't cry daddy / Wonder of you / You don't have to say you love me / There goes my everything / Rags to riches / I just can't help believing / American trilogy / Burning love / Always on my mind / It's only love
74321422662 / Feb '97 / RCA

☐ ELVIS PRESLEY INTERVIEWS, THE (3CD Set)
55581 / Mar '97 / Laserlight

☐ ELVIS PRESLEY LIVE
Heartbreak hotel / Long tall Sally / I was the one / Money honey / I've got a woman / Blue suede shoes / Hound dog / Baby let's play house / Maybellene / That's alright Mama / Blue moon of Kentucky / There's good rockin' tonight
JHD 068 / Apr '93 / Tring

☐ ELVIS PRESLEY LIVE ON STAGE IN MEMPHIS
CC rider / I got a woman / Love me / Trying to get to you / Long tall Sally / Flip flop and fly / Jailhouse rock / Hound dog / Why me Lord / How great Thou art / Blueberry Hill / Help me / American trilogy / Let me be there / My baby left me / Lawdy Miss Clawdy / Can't help falling in love / Closing vamp
07863506062 / Feb '94 / RCA

☐ ELVIS PRESLEY SONGBOOK, THE (A Tribute To The King) (Various Artists)
Heartbreak hotel: *D'Arby, Terence Trent* / Jailhouse rock: *King, Albert* / Mess o'blues: *Status Quo* / That's alright mama: *Stewart, Rod* / Suspicious mind: *Fine Young Cannibals* / I'm left you're right she's gone: *Lewis, Jerry Lee* / Devil in disguise: *Flying Burrito Brothers* / TROUBLE: *Gillan* / Teddy bear: *Youngblood, Sydney* / All shook up: *Beck, Jeff* / Too much: *Richard, Cliff* / Don't: *McLean, Don* / In the ghetto: *Cave, Nick* / Mean woman blues: *Orbison, Roy* / Burning love: *Spector, Ronnie* / Polk salad Annie: *White, Tony Joe* / Don't be cruel: *Swan, Billy* / Crawfish: *Thunders, Johnny & Patti Palladin*
VSOPCD 223 / May '96 / Connoisseur Collection

☐ ELVIS SINGS THE WONDERFUL WORLD OF CHRISTMAS
O come all ye faithful (Adeste Fidelis) / First Noel / On a snowy Christmas night / Winter wonderland / Wonderful world of Christmas / It won't seem like Christmas (without you) / I'll be home on Christmas day / If I get home on Christmas day / Holly leaves and Christmas trees / Merry Christmas baby / Silver bells
ND 81936 / Nov '93 / RCA

☐ ELVIS TAPES, THE
CDRD 001 / Jul '91 / Ace

☐ ELVIS TODAY
T-R-O-U-B-L-E / And I love you so / Susan when she tried / Woman without love / Shake a hand / Pieces of my life / Fairytale / I can help / Bringing it back / Green green grass of home
ND 90660 / Apr '92 / RCA

☐ ELVIS' CHRISTMAS ALBUM
Santa Claus is back in town / White Christmas / Here comes Santa Claus / I'll be home for Christmas / Blue Christmas / Santa bring my baby back to me / O little town of Bethlehem / Silent night / Peace in the valley / I believe / Take my hand, precious Lord / It is no secret
ND 90300 / Nov '96 / RCA

☐ ELVIS' GOLDEN RECORDS VOL.1
Hound dog / Loving you / All shook up / Heartbreak hotel / Jailhouse rock / Love me / Too much / Don't be cruel / That's when your heartache begins / Teddy bear / Love me tender / Treat me nice / Anyway you want me (that's how I will be) / I want you, I need you, I love you
07863674622 / 2 Feb '98 / RCA

☐ ELVIS' GOLDEN RECORDS VOL.2 (50,000 Elvis Fans Can't Be Wrong)
I need your love tonight / Wear my ring around your neck / My wish came true / I got stung / Loving you / Teddy bear / One night / Hunk o' love / I beg of you / Fool such as I / Don't cha think it's time / Jailhouse rock / Treat me nice / Don't
07863674632 / 2 Feb '98 / RCA

☐ ELVIS' GOLDEN RECORDS VOL.3
It's now or never / Stuck on you / Fame and fortune / I gotta know / Surrender / I feel so bad / Are you lonesome tonight / His latest flame / Little sister / Good luck charm / Anything that's part of you / She's not you
07863674642 / 2 Feb '98 / RCA

☐ ELVIS' GOLDEN RECORDS VOL.4
Love letters / It hurts me / What I'd say / Please don't drag that string around / Indescribably blue / Devil in disguise / Lonely man / Mess of blues / Ask me / Ain't that lovin' you baby / Just tell her Jim said hello / Witchcraft
07863674652 / 2 Feb '98 / RCA

☐ ELVIS' GOLDEN RECORDS VOL.5
Suspicious minds / Kentucky rain / In the ghetto / Clean up your own backyard / If I can dream / Burning love / If you talk in your sleep / For the heart / Moody blue / Way down
07863674662 / 2 Feb '98 / RCA

☐ ESSENTIAL COLLECTION, THE
Heartbreak hotel / Blue suede shoes / Hound dog / Don't be cruel / Love me tender / All shook up / Teddy bear / Jailhouse rock / King Creole / Girl of my best friend / It's now or never / Are you lonesome tonight / Wooden heart / His latest flame / Can't help falling in love / Good luck charm / She's not you / Return to sender / Devil in disguise / Crying in the chapel / In the ghetto / Suspicious minds / Wonder of you / I just can't help believin' / American trilogy / Burning love / Always on my mind / Moody blue
74321228712 / Aug '94 / RCA

☐ ESSENTIAL ELVIS VOL.1
Teddy bear / Loving you / Mean woman blues / Got a lot of livin' to do / Lonesome cowboy / Jailhouse rock / Treat me nice / Young and beautiful / Don't leave me now / I want to be free / Baby I don't care / Love me tender / Let me / Poor boy / We're gonna move / Party / Hot dog
74321573472 / 11 May '98 / RCA

☐ ESSENTIAL ELVIS VOL.2 (Stereo 57)
I beg of you / Have I told you lately that I love you / Blueberry Hill / Peace in the valley / Is it so strange / It is no secret / Mean woman blues / That's when your heartache begins
PD 90250 / Jan '89 / RCA

☐ ESSENTIAL ELVIS VOL.3 (Hits Like Never Before)
King Creole / Fool such as I / Your cheatin' heart / Don't cha think it's time / Lover doll / Danny / Crawfish / Ain't that lovin' you baby / I need your love tonight / I got stung / As long as I have you / Wear my ring around your neck / Big hunk o' love / Steadfast, loyal and true / King Creole (instrumental)
PD 90486 / May '90 / RCA

☐ ESSENTIAL ELVIS VOL.4 (A Hundred Years From Now)
I didn't make it on playing guitar / I washed my hands in muddy water / Little cabin on the hill / Hundred years from now / I've lost you / Got my mojo working / Keep your hands off of it / You don't have to say you love me / It ain't no big thing (but it's growing) / Cindy, Cindy / Faded love / Fool / Rags to riches / Just pretend / If I were you / Faded love / Where did they go Lord / It's only love / Until it's time for you to go / Patch it up / Whole lotta shakin' goin' on / Bridge over troubled water / Lord's prayer
07863668662 / Jul '96 / RCA

☐ FIFTIES INTERVIEWS, THE
Truth about me / Jacksonville, Florida / WMPS, Memphis / Witchita Falls, Texas / LaCrosse, Wisconsin / Little Rock, Arkansas / KLAC-TV, Memphis / New Orleans / New Orleans / St. Petersburg, Florida
CDMF 074 / Feb '91 / Magnum Force

☐ FLAMING STAR/WILD IN THE COUNTRY/FOLLOW THAT DREAM (Double Feature/Original Soundtracks)
Flaming star / Summer kisses, winter tears / Britches / A cane and a high starched collar / Black star / Flaming star (end title version) / Wild in the country / I slipped, I stumbled, I fell / Lonely man / In my way / Forget me never / Lonely man (solo) / I slipped, I stumbled, I fell (Alternate master) / Follow that dream / Angel / What a wonderful life / I'm not the marrying kind / Whistling tune / Sound advice
07863665572 / Mar '95 / RCA

☐ FOR LP FANS ONLY
That's alright Mama / Lawdy Miss Clawdy / Mystery train / Playing for keeps / Poor boy / Money honey / I'm counting on you / My baby left me / I was the one / Shake, rattle and roll / I'm left, you're right, she's gone / You're a heartbreaker / Tryin' to get to you / Blue suede shoes
ND 90359 / Sep '89 / RCA

☐ FRANKIE AND JOHNNY/PARADISE, HAWAIIAN STYLE (Double Feature/ Original Soundtracks)
Frankie and Johnny / Come along / Petunia, the gardener's daughter / Chesay / What every woman lives for / Look out, Broadway / I've got beginner's luck / Down by the riverside/When the saints go marching in / Shout it out / Hard luck / Please don't stop loving me / Everybody come aboard / Paradise, Hawaiian style / Queenie Wahine's papaya / Scratch my back / Drums of the islands / Datin' / Dog's life / House of sand / Stop where you are / This is my heaven / Sand castles
07863663602 / Jun '94 / RCA

☐ FROM ELVIS IN MEMPHIS
Wearin' that loved on look / Only the strong survive / I'll hold you in my heart / Long black limousine / It keeps right on a-hurtin' / I'm movin' on / Power of my love / Gentle on my mind / After loving you / True love travels on a gravel road / Any day now / In the ghetto
ND 90548 / Mar '91 / RCA

☐ FROM ELVIS PRESLEY BOULEVARD, MEMPHIS, TENNESSEE
Hurt / Never again / Blue eyes cryin' in the rain / Danny boy / Last farewell / For the heart / Bitter they are / Solitaire / Love coming down / I'll never fall in love again
74321146912 / Jul '93 / RCA

☐ FROM NASHVILLE TO MEMPHIS (The Essential 1960's Masters Vol.1 - 5CD Set)
Make me know it / Soldier boy / Stuck on you / Fame and fortune / Mess of blues / It feels so right / Fever / Like a baby / It's now or never / Girl of my best friend / Dirty, dirty feeling / Thrill of your love / I gotta know / Such a night / Are you lonesome tonight / Girl next door went a'walking / I will be home again / Reconsider baby / Surrender / I'm coming home / Gently / In your arms / Give me the right / I feel so bad / It's a sin / I want you with me / There's always me / Starting today / Sentimental me / Judy / Put the blame on me / Kiss me quick / That's someone you never forget / I'm yours / His latest flame / Little sister / For the millionth and last time / Good luck charm / Anything that's part of you / I met her today / Night rider / Something blue / Gonna get back home somehow / (Such an) Easy question / Fountain of love / Just for old times sake / You'll be gone / I feel that I've known you forever / Just tell her Jim said hello / Suspicion / She's not you / Echoes of love / Please don't drag that string around / Devil in disguise / Never ending / What now, what next, where to / Witchcraft / Finders keepers / Love me tonight / (It's a) Long lonely highway / Western Union / Slowly but surely / Blue river / Memphis Tennessee / Ask me / It hurts me / Down the alley / Tomorrow is a long time / Love letters / Beyond the reef / Come what may / Fools fall in love / Indescribably you / I'll remember you / If every day was like Christmas / Suppose / Guitar man/What'd I say (Original unedited master) / Big boss man / Mine / Just call me lonesome / Hi-heel sneakers / You don't know me / Singing trees / Too much monkey business / US male / Long black limousine / This is the story / Wearin' that loved on look / You'll think of me / Little bit of green / Gentle on my mind / I'm movin' on / Don't cry daddy / Inherit the wind / Mama liked the roses / My little friend / In the ghetto / Rubberneckin' / From a Jack to a King / Hey Jude / Without love (there is nothing) / I'll hold you in my heart / I'll be there / Suspicious minds / True love travels on a gravel road / Stranger in my own hometown / And the grass won't pay no mind / Power of my love / After loving you / Do you know who I am / Kentucky rain / Only the strong survive / It keep right on hurtin' / Any day now / If I'm a fool (For loving you) / Rain is moving on / Who am I / This time/I can't stop loving you (Informal recording) / In the ghetto (alt. take) / Suspicious minds (Alternate take 6) / Kentucky rain (Alt Take) / Big boss man / Down the alley (Alternate take 1) / Memphis, Tennessee (Alternate take 1) / I'm yours (alt. take) / His latest flame (Alternate take 4) / That's someone you never forget (alternate take) / Surrender (Alternate take 1) / It's now or never (Original undubbed master) / Love me tender/ Witchcraft
74321154302 / Oct '93 / RCA

☐ GI BLUES (Original Soundtrack)
Tonight is so right for love / What's she really like / Frankfurt special / Wooden heart / GI blues / Pocketful of rainbows / Shopping around / Big boots / Didja ever / Blue suede shoes / Doin' the best I can / Big boots / Shoppin' around / Frankfurt special / Pocketful of rainbows / Didja ever / Big boots / What's she really like / Doin' the best I can
07863674602 / Apr '97 / RCA
07863669602 / 2 Feb '98 / RCA

☐ GOLDEN CELEBRATION (5CD Set)
Harbour lights / That's alright Mama / Blue moon of Kentucky / I don't care if the sun don't shine / I'm left, you're right, she's gone / I'll never let you go (little darling) / When it rains it really pours / Shake, rattle and roll / Flip flop and fly / I got a woman / Baby let's play house / Tutti frutti / Blue suede shoes / Heartbreak Hotel / I was the one / Hound dog / I want you, I need you / I love you / I want you, I need you, I love you (dialogue) / Long tall Sally / Introductions and presentations / Don't be cruel (to a heart's that's true) / Ready Teddy / Love me tender / Love me / Too much / When my blue moon turns to gold again / Peace in the valley / Danny boy / Soldier boy / Fool / Earth angel / He's only a prayer away / My heart cries for you / Dark moon / Write to me from Naples / Suppose / Tiger man / Lawdy Miss Clawdy / Baby, what you want me to do / Are you lonesome tonight / Blue Christmas / One night / Trying to forget you
07863674562 / 9 Feb '98 / RCA

☐ **GOOD ROCKIN' (Live In 1955)**
Interview with Bill Collie / There's good rockin' tonight / Baby let's play house / Blue moon of Kentucky / I got a woman / That's alright Mama / Interview with Elvis / Tweedlee Dee / Baby let's play house / Maybellene / That's alright Mama / Blue moon of Kentucky / There's good rockin' tonight / I got a woman
307622 / Jul '97 / Hallmark

☐ **GOOD ROCKIN' TONIGHT (Original Hayride Recordings January 1955)**
That's alright Mama / Blue moon of Kentucky / Heartbreak hotel / Long tall Sally / I was the one / Money honey / I got a woman / Blue suede shoes / Hound dog / Baby let's play house / Maybellene / Good rockin' tonight / Tweedle Dee Tweedle Dum / Interview
PLATCD 146 / Mar '96 / Platinum

☐ **GOOD TIMES**
Take good care of her / Loving arms / I got a feelin' in my body / If that isn't love / She wears my ring / I got a thing about you baby / My boy / Spanish eyes / Talk about the good times / Good time Charlie's got the blues
07863 504752 / Feb '94 / RCA

☐ **GREAT COUNTRY SONGS**
I forgot to remember to forget / Blue moon of Kentucky / When my blue moon turns to gold again / Old Shep / Your cheatin' heart / (Now and then there's) A fool such as I / Just call me lonesome / There goes my everything / Kentucky rain / From a Jack to a King / I'll hold you in my heart (till I can hold you in my arms) / I really don't want to know / It keeps right on a hurtin' / Green green grass of home / Fairytale / Gentle on my mind / Make the world go away / You asked me to / Funny how time slips away / Help me make it through the night / Susan when she tried / He'll have to go / Always on my mind / Guitar man
07863668802 / Oct '96 / RCA

☐ **GREAT PERFORMANCES**
My happiness / That's alright Mama / Shake, rattle and roll / Flip flop and fly / Heartbreak hotel / Blue suede shoes / Ready teddy / Don't be cruel / Got a lot of livin' to do / Jailhouse rock / Treat me nice / King Creole / Trouble / Fame and fortune / Return to sender / Always on my mind / American trilogy / If I can dream / Unchained melody / Memories
74321436022 / Feb '97 / RCA

☐ **HARUM SCARUM/GIRL HAPPY (Double Feature/Original Soundtracks)**
Harem holiday / My desert serenade / Go eat young man / Mirage / Kismet / Shake that tambourine / Hey little girl / Golden coins / So close, yet so far / Animal instinct / Wisdom of the ages / Girl happy / Spring fever / Fort Lauderdale chamber of commerce / Startin' tonight / Wolf call / Do not disturb / Cross my heart and hope to die / Meanest girl in town / Do the clam / Puppet on a string / I've got to find my baby
74321134332 / Mar '93 / RCA

☐ **HE TOUCHED ME**
He touched me / I've got confidence / Amazing grace / Seeing is believing / He is my everything / Bosom of Abraham / Evening prayer / Lead me, guide me / There is no God but God / Thing called love / I, John / Reach out to Jesus
ND 90661 / Apr '92 / RCA

☐ **HEARTBREAK HOTEL**
Heartbreak hotel / Long tall Sally / I was the one / Money honey / I got a woman (I got a sweety) / Blue suede shoes / Hound dog / Baby let's play house / Maybellene / That's all right / Blue moon of Kentucky / Therre's good rockin' tonight / I got a woman (I got a sweety) / Tweedle dee
RM 1521 / Jun '97 / BR Music

☐ **HIS HAND IN MINE**
His hand in mine / I'm gonna walk dem golden stairs / My father's house / Milky white way / Known only to him / I believe / Joshua fit de battle of Jericho / Jesus knows what I need / Swing low, sweet chariot / Mansion over the hilltop / If we never meet again / Working on the building
ND 83935 / Oct '88 / RCA

☐ **HOLLYWOOD ALBUM/NASHVILLE ALBUM/LIVE IN LAS VEGAS 1969 (Collector's Gold - 3CD Set)**
GI blues / Pocket full of rainbows / Big boots / Black star / Summer kisses, winter tears / I slipped, I stumbled, I fell / Lonely man / What a wonderful life / Whistling tune / Beyond the bend / One broken heart for sale / You're the boss / Roustabout / Girl happy / So close, yet so far / Stop, look and listen / Am I ready / How can you lose what you never had / Like a baby / There's always me / I want you with me / Gently / Give me the right / I met her today / Night rider / Just tell her Jim said hello / Ask me / Memphis Tennessee / Love me tonight / Witchcraft / Come what may / Love letters / Going home / Blue suede shoes / I got a woman / Heartbreak hotel / Love me tender / Baby, what you want me to do / Runaway / Surrender/Are you lonesome tonight / Rubber neckin' / Memories / Introduction by Elvis Presley / Jailhouse rock/Don't be cruel / Inherit the wind/This is the story / Mystery train / Tiger man / Funny how time slips away / Loving you/Reconsider baby / What I'd say
PD 90574 / Aug '91 / RCA

☐ **HOW GREAT THOU ART**
How great Thou art / In the garden / Somebody bigger than you and I / Farther along / Stand by me / Without him / So high / Where could I go but to the Lord / By and by / If the Lord wasn't walking by my side / Run on / Where no one stands alone / Crying in the chapel
ND 83758 / Apr '88 / RCA

☐ **I WISH YOU A MERRY CHRISTMAS**
O come all ye faithful (Adeste Fidelis) / First Noel / On a snowy Christmas night / Winter wonderland / Wonderful world of Christmas / It won't seem like Christmas (without you) / I'll be home on Christmas Day / If I get home on Christmas Day / Holly leaves and Christmas trees / Merry Christmas baby / Silver bells / Santa Claus is back in town / White Christmas / Here comes Santa Claus / I'll be home for Christmas / Blue Christmas / Santa bring my baby back to me / O little town of Bethlehem / Silent night / Peace in the valley / I believe / Take my hand, precious Lord / It is no secret
ND 89474 / '87 / RCA

☐ **I'M 10,000 YEARS OLD (Elvis Country)**
Snowbird / Tomorrow never comes / Little cabin home on the hill / Whole lotta shakin' goin' on / Funny how time slips away / I really don't want to know / There goes my everything / It's your baby / Fool / Faded love / I washed my hands in muddy water / Make the world go away / I was born ten thousand years ago
74321146922 / Jul '93 / RCA

☐ **IF EVERY DAY WAS LIKE CHRISTMAS**
If every day was like Christmas / Blue Christmas / Here comes Santa Claus / White Christmas / Santa bring my baby back to me / I'll be home for Christmas / O little town of Bethlehem / Santa Claus is back in town / It won't seem like Christmas (without you) / If I get home on Christmas day / Holly leaves and Christmas trees / Merry Christmas baby / Silver bells / I'll be home on Christmas day (alternate version) / On a snowy Christmas night / Winter wonderland / Wonderful world of Christmas / O come all ye faithful (Adeste Fidelis) / First Noel / It won't seem like Christmas (without you) (alt. take) / If I get home on Christmas day (unreleased alternate take) / I'll be home on Christmas day / Christmas message from Elvis / Silent night / Holly leaves and Christmas trees (unreleased alternate take)
07863665062
07863664822 / Nov '95 / RCA

☐ **INTERVIEWS, THE (Outstanding Rare Insights Into The King Of Rock 'n' Roll)**
PLATCD 145 / Mar '96 / Platinum

☐ **JAILHOUSE ROCK (Original Soundtrack)**
Jailhouse rock / Treat me nice / I want to be free / Don't leave me now / Young and beautiful / (You're so square) baby I don't care / Jailhouse rock / Treat me nice / I want to be free / Young and beautiful / Love me tender / Let me / Poor boy / We're gonna move / Don't leave me now / Treat me nice / Let me / We're gonna move / Poor boy / Love me tender
07863674532 / 2 Feb '98 / RCA

☐ **KING CREOLE (Original Soundtrack)**
King Creole / As long as I have you / Hard headed woman / Trouble / Dixieland rock / Don't ask me why / Lover doll / Crawfish / Young dreams / Steadfast, loyal and true / New Orleans / King Creole / As long as I have you / Danny / Lover doll / Steadfast, loyal and true / As long as I have you / King Creole
07863674542 / 2 Feb '98 / RCA

☐ **KING OF ROCK 'N' ROLL, THE (The Complete 1950's Masters - 5CD Set)**
My happiness / That's alright / I love you because / Harbour lights / Blue moon of Kentucky / Blue moon / Tomorrow night / I'll never let you go / I don't care if the sun don't shine / Just because / Good rockin' tonight / Milkcow blue boogie / You're a heartbreaker / Baby let's play house / I'm left, you're right, she's gone / Mystery train / I forgot to remember to forget / Trying to get to you / When it rains it really pours / I got a woman / Heartbreak hotel / Money honey / I'm counting on you / I was the one / Blue suede shoes / My baby left me / One sided love affair / So glad you're mine / I'm gonna sit right down and cry over you / Tutti frutti / Lawdy Miss Clawdy / Shake, rattle and roll / I want you, I need you, I love you / Hound dog / Don't be cruel / Any way you want me (that's how I will be) / We're gonna move / Love me tender / Poor boy / Let me / Playing for keeps / Love me / Paralyzed / How do you think I feel / How's the world treating you / When my blue moon turns to gold again / Long tall Sally / Old Shep / Too much / Anyplace is paradise / Ready Teddy / First in line / Rip it up / I believe / Tell me why / Got a lot o' livin' to do / All shook up / Mean woman blues / Peace in the valley / That's when your heartaches begin / Take my hand precious Lord / It's no secret what God can do / Blueberry Hill / Have I told you lately that I love you / Is it so strange / Party / Lonesome cowboy / Hot dog / One night of sin / (Let me be your) teddy bear / Don't leave me now / I beg of you / One night / True love / I need you so / Loving you / When it rains, it really pours / Jailhouse rock / Young and beautiful / I want to be free / (You're so square) baby I don't care / Don't leave me now / Blue Christmas / Here comes Santa Claus (right down Santa Claus Lane) / Silent night / O little town of Bethlehem / Santa bring my baby back / Santa Claus is back in town / I'll be home for Christmas / Treat me nice / My wish came true / Don't Danny / Hard headed woman / Trouble / New Orleans / Crawfish / Dixieland rock / Lover doll / Don't ask me why / As long as I have you / King Creole / Young dreams / Steadfast, loyal and true / Don'tcha think it's time / Your cheatin' heart / Wear my ring around your neck / I need your love tonight / Big hunk o' love / Ain't that loving you baby / Fool such as I / I got stung / Fool fool fool / Tweedle dee / Maybellene / Shake, rattle and roll / Heartbreak hotel / Long tall Sally / Blue suede shoes / Money honey / We're gonna move / Old Shep / I beg of you / Loving you / Young and beautiful / I want to be free / King Creole / As long as I have you / Ain't that loving you baby
PD 90689 / Jul '92 / RCA

☐ **KING OF ROCK 'N' ROLL, THE (2CD Set/Documentary & Music)**
OTR 1100051 / Jun '97 / Metro Independent

☐ **KISSIN' COUSINS/CLAMBAKE/STAY AWAY, JOE (Double Feature/Original Soundtracks)**
Kissin' cousins / Smoky mountain bay / There's gold in the mountains / One boy two little girls / Catchin' on fast / Tender feeling / Anyone (could fall in love with you) / Barefoot ballad / Once is enough / Kissin' cousins / Clambake / Who needs money / House that has everything / Confidence / Hey hey hey / You don't know me / Girl I never loved / How can you lose what you never had / Clambake (Reprise) / Stay away, Joe / Dominic / All I needed was the rain / Goin' home / Stay away
07863663622 / Jun '94 / RCA

☐ **LEGEND BEGINS, THE (Elvis Live)**
That's alright mama / Blue moon of Kentucky / Tweedle Dee / Good rockin' tonight / Baby let's play house / I got a woman / Maybellene / Hound dog / Blue suede shoes / Money honey / I was the one / Long tall Sally / Heartbreak hotel
PWKS 4262 / Mar '96 / Carlton

☐ **LIVE A LITTLE.../TROUBLE WITH GIRLS/CHANGE OF HEART/CHARRO (Double Feature/Original Soundtracks)**
Almost in love / Little less conversation / Wonderful world / Edge of reality / Little less conversation (album version) / Charro / Let's forget about the stars / Clean up your own backyard / Swing low, sweet chariot / Swing low, sweet chariot / Signs of the zodiac / Almost / Whiffenpoof song / Violet / Clean up your own backyard (undubbed version) / Almost (undubbed version) / Have a happy / Let's be friends / Change of habit / Let us pray / Rubberneckin'
07863665592 / Mar '95 / RCA

☐ **LOVE LETTERS FROM ELVIS**
Love letters / When I'm over you / If I were you / Get my mojo working / Heart of Rome / Only believe / This is our dance / Cindy Cindy / I'll never know / It ain't no big thing (but it's growing) / Life
ND 89011 / Jun '88 / RCA

☐ **LOVE ME TENDER**
295 052 / May '95 / RCA

☐ **LOVE SONGS OF ELVIS PRESLEY, THE (Gracelands Chorale & Symphonette)**
Can't help falling in love / Are you lonesome tonight / Wooden heart / Don't be cruel / Love me tender / Don't / One night / I need your love tonight / It's now or never / Wear my ring around your neck / Anyway you want me (That's how I will be) / Stuck on you / Loving arms / I want you I need you I love you / Love me
ECD 3401 / 23 Feb '98 / K-Tel

☐ **LOVING YOU (Original Soundtrack)**
Mean woman blues / Teddy bear / Got a lot of livin' to do / Lonesome cowboy / Hot dog / Party / Blueberry Hill / True love / Don't leave me now / Have I told you lately that I love you / One night of sin / Loving you / Tell me why / Is it so strange / When it rains it really pours / I beg of you / Loving you / Party / Got a lot of livin' to do
07863674522 / 2 Feb '98 / RCA

☐ **MEMPHIS RECORD, THE**
Stranger in my own hometown / Power of love / Only the strong survive / Any day now / Suspicious minds / Long black limousine / Wearin' that loved on look / I'll hold you in my heart / After loving you / Rubberneckin' / I'm movin' on / Gentle on my mind / True love travels on a gravel road / It keeps right on a-hurtin' / You'll think of me / Mama like the roses / Don't cry daddy / In the ghetto / Fair is movin' on / Inherit the wind / Kentucky rain / Without love (there is nothing) / Who am I
74321187542 / Feb '94 / RCA

☐ **MOODY BLUE**
Unchained melody / If you love me (let me know) / Little darlin' / He'll have to go / Let me be there / Way down / Pledging my love / Moody blue / She thinks I still care
ND 90252 / Apr '88 / RCA

☐ **ON STAGE (February 1970)**
See rider blues / Release me / Sweet Caroline / Runaway / Wonder of you / Polk salad Annie / Yesterday / Proud Mary / Walk a mile in my shoes / Let it be me
ND 90549 / Mar '91 / RCA

☐ **ONE AND ONLY, THE**
Heartbreak hotel / Long tall Sally / I was the one / Money honey / I got a woman / Blue suede shoes / Hound dog / Interviews (Arkansas 1965) / Baby let's play house / Maybellene / That's alright mama / Blue moon of Kentucky / Good rockin' tonight / I got a woman / Tweedle dee
HADCD 151 / May '94 / Javelin

☐ **PLATINUM - A LIFE IN MUSIC (4CD Set)**
I'll never stand in your way / That's alright / Blue moon / Good rockin' tonight / Mystery train / I got a woman / Heartbreak hotel / I'm counting on you / Shake, rattle and roll/Flip, flop and fly / Lawdy, Miss Clawdy / I want you, I need you, I love you / Hound dog / Don't be cruel / Rip it up / Love me tender / When the saints go marching in / All shook up / Peace in the valley / Blueberry hill / Teddy bear / Jailhouse rock / New Orleans / I need your love tonight / Big hunk o'love / Bad Nauheim medley / Stuck on you / Fame and fortune / It's now or never / It feels so right / Mess of blues / Are you lonesome tonight / Reconsider baby / Tonight is so right for love / His hand in mine / Milky white way / I'm comin' home / I feel so bad / Can't help falling in love / Something blue / Return to sender / Bossa nova baby / How great thou art / Guitar man / You'll never walk alone / Oh how I love Jesus / Tennessee waltz / Blowin' in the wind / I can't help it / I'm beginning to forget you / After loving you / I got a woman / Tiger man / When my blue moon turns to gold again / Trying to get to you / If I can dream / In the ghetto / Suspicious minds / Power of my love / Baby what you want me do / Words / Johnny B Goode / Release me / CC rider / Wonder of you / Sound of your cry / You don't have to say you love me / Funny how time slips away / I washed my hands in muddy water / I was the one / Cattle call / Baby, let's play house / Don't / Money honey / What I'd say / Bridge over troubled water / Miracle of the rosary / He touched me / Bosom of Abraham / I'll be home on Christmas day / For the good times / Burning love / Separate ways / Always on my mind / American trilogy / Take good care of her / I've got a thing about you baby / Are you sincere / It's midnight / Promised land / Steamroller blues / And I love you so / TROUBLE / Danny boy / Moody blue / Hurt / For the heart / Pledging my way / Way down / My way / Jaycess speech
07863674692 / Jul '97 / RCA

☐ **POT LUCK WITH ELVIS**
Kiss me quick / Just for old times sake / Gonna get back home somehow / (Such an) Easy question / Steppin' out of line / I'm yours / Something blue / Suspicion / I feel I've known you forever / Night rider / Fountain of love / That's someone you never forget
ND 89098 / Apr '88 / RCA

☐ **PROMISED LAND**
Promised land / There's a honky tonk angel (who will take me) / Help me / Mr. Songman / Love song of the year / It's midnight / Your love's been a long time coming / If you talk in your sleep / Thinking about you / You ask me to
ND 90598 / Oct '91 / RCA

☐ **RAISED ON ROCK**
Raised on rock / Are you sincere / Find out what's happening / I miss you / Girl of mine / For ol' times sake / If you don't come back / Just a little bit / Sweet Angeline / Three corn patches
07863 503882 / Feb '94 / RCA

☐ **RHYTHM 'N' COUNTRY**
7863676722 / 10 Aug '98 / RCA

☐ **SOMETHING FOR EVERYBODY**
There's always me / Give me the right / It's a sin / Sentimental me / Starting today I'm yours / Gently / I'm coming home / In your arms / Put the blame on me / Judy / I want you with me / I slipped, I stumbled, I fell
ND 84116 / Nov '90 / RCA

☐ **SONGS OF ELVIS PRESLEY, THE (2CD Set) (Various Artists)**
Always on my mind: *Nelson, Willie* / That's all right mama: *Nelson, Ricky* / Love me tender: *Robbins, Marty* / Crying in the chapel: *Wynette, Tammy* / Surrender: *Campbell, Stacy Dean* / Blue suede shoes: *Perkins, Carl* / My baby left me: *Loggins & Messina* / There goes my everything: *Price, Ray* / I forgot to remember to forget: *Cash, Johnny* / Hound dog: *Moore, Scotty* / I really don't want to know: *Smith, Carl* / I don't care if the sun don't shine: *James, Sonny* / Mystery train: *Luman, Bob* / Don't be cruel: *Miller, Jody* / Help me: *Gatlin, Larry* / Lawdy Miss Clawdy: *Gilley, Mickey* / Mean woman blues: *Orbison, Roy* / In the ghetto: *Davis, Mac*
487872 / 26 Jan '98 / Columbia

☐ **SOUNDS OF ELVIS, THE (Various Artists)**
MACCD 294 / Aug '96 / Autograph

☐ **SPINOUT/DOUBLE TROUBLE (Double Feature/Original Soundtracks)**
Stop, look and listen / Adam and evil / All that I am / Never say yes / Am I ready / Beach shack / Spinout / Smorgasbord / I'll be back / Double trouble / Baby, if you'll give me all your love / Could I fall in love / Long legged girl with the short dress on / City by night / Old MacDonald / I love only one girl / There's so much world to see / It won't be long
07863663612 / Jun '94 / RCA

☐ **SUN SESSIONS, THE**
That's alright mama / Blue moon of Kentucky / I don't care if the sun don't shine / Good rockin' tonight / Milk cow blue boogie / You're a heartbreaker / I'm left, you're right, she's gone / Baby let's play house / Mystery train / I forgot to remember to forget / I love you because / Trying to get to you / Blue moon / Just because / I'll never let you go
ND 89107 / '88 / RCA

☐ **SYMPHONIC ELVIS (Moore, Scotty & Memphis Symphony Orchestra/Ettore Stratta)**
4509945732 / Aug '96 / Teldec Classics

☐ **THAT'S THE WAY IT IS**
I just can't help believin' / Twenty days and twenty nights / How the web was woven / Patch it up / Mary in the morning / You don't have to say you love me / You've lost that lovin' feelin' / I've lost you / Just pretend / Stranger in the crowd / Next step is love / Bridge over troubled water
74321146902 / Jul '93 / RCA

☐ **TOUCH OF PLATINUM VOL.1, A (2CD Set)**
I'll never stand in your way / That's alright Mama / Blue moon of Kentucky / Good rockin' tonight / Mystery train / I got a woman / Heartbreak Hotel / I'm counting on you / Shake, rattle and roll/Flip, flop and fly / Lawdy Miss Clawdy / I want you, I need you, I love you / Hound dog / Don't be cruel / Rip it up / Love me tender / When the Saints go marching in / All shook up / Peace in the valley / Blueberry Hill / Teddy bear / Jailhouse rock / New Orleans / I need your love tonight / Big hunk o' love / Bad Neuheim medley / Stuck on you / Fame and fortune / It's now or never / It feels so right / Mess of blues / Are you lonesome tonight / Reconsider baby / Tonight is so right for love / His hand in mine / Milky white way / I'm comin' home / I feel so bad / Can't help falling in love / Something blue / Return to sender / Bossa nova baby / How great thou art / Guitar man / You'll never walk alone / Oh how I love Jesus / Tennessee waltz / Blowin' in the wind / I can't help it / I'm beginning to forget you / After loving you
7863675922 / 23 Feb '98 / RCA

☐ **TOUCH OF PLATINUM VOL.2, A (A Life In Music/2CD Set)**
I got a woman / Tiger man / When my blue moon turns to gold again / Trying to get to you / If I can dream / In the ghetto / Suspicious minds / Power of my love / Baby what you want me to do / Words / Johnny B Goode / Release me / See see rider / Wonder of you / Sound of your cry / You don't have to say you love me / Funny how time slips away / I washed my hands in muddy water / I was the one / Cattle call / Baby let's play house / Don't / Money honey / What'd I say / Bridge over troubled water / Miracle of the rosary / He touched me / Bosom of Abraham / I'll be home on Christmas day / For the good times / Burning love / Seperate ways / Always on my mind / American trilogy / Take good care of her / I've got a thing about you / Are you sincere / It's midnight / Promised land / Steamroller blues / And I love you so / TROUBLE / Danny boy / Moody blue / Hurt / For the heart / Pledging my love / Way down / My way / Jaycees speech
74321595982 / 27 Jul '98 / RCA

☐ **VIVA LAS VEGAS/ROUSTABOUT (Double Feature/Original Soundtracks)**
Viva Las Vegas / If you think I don't need you / If you need somebody to lean on / You're the boss / What I'd say / Do the Vega / C'mon everybody / Lady love me / Night life / Today, tomorrow and forever / Yellow rose of Texas/The eyes of Texas / Santa Lucia /

Roustabout / Little Egypt / Poison ivy league / Hard knocks / It's a wonderful world / Big love, big heartache / One track heart / It's carnival time / Carmy town / There's a brand new day on the horizon / Wheels on my heels
74321134322 / Mar '93 / RCA

☐ **WALK A MILE IN MY SHOES (The Essential 1970's Masters - 5CD Set)**
Wonder of you / I've lost you / Next step is love / You don't have to say you love me / Patch it up / I really don't want to know / There goes everything / Rags to riches / Where did they go / Life / I'm leavin' / Heart of Rome / It's only love / Sound of your cry / I just can't help believin' / How the web was woven / Until it's time for you to go / We can make the morning / American trilogy / First time ever I saw your face / Burning love / It's a matter of time / Separate ways / Always on my mind / Fool / Steamroller blues / Raised on rock / For ol' times sake / I've got a thing about you baby / Take good care of her / If you talk in your sleep / Promised land / It's midnight / Loving arms / T-R-O-U-B-L-E / Mr. Songman / Bringing it back / Pieces of my life / Green, green grass of home / Thinking about you / Hurt / For the heart / Moody blue / She thinks I still care / Way down / Pledging my love / Twenty days and twenty nights / I was born about ten thousand years ago / Fool / Hundred years from now / Little cabin on the hill / Cindy Cindy / Bridge over troubled water / Got my mojo working / Keep your hands off it / It's your baby, you rock it / Stranger in the crowd / Mary in the morning / It ain't no big thing (but it's growing) / Just pretend / Faded love / Tomorrow never comes / Make the world go away / Funny how time slips away / I wash my hands in muddy water / Snowbird / Whole lotta shakin' goin' on / Amazing Grace / (That's what you get) For lovin' me / Lady Madonna / Merry Christmas baby / I shall be released / Don't think it's alright / It's still here / I'll take you home Kathleen / I will be true / My way / For the good times / Just a little bit / It's different now / Are you sincere / I got a feelin' in my body / You asked me to / Good time Charlie's got the blues / Talk about the good times / Tiger man / She thinks I still care / Danny boy / Love coming down / He'll have to go / CC rider / Men with broken hearts / Walk a mile in my shoes / Polk salad Annie / Let it be me / Proud Mary / Something / You've lost that lovin' feelin' / Heartbreak hotel / I was the one / One night / Never been to Spain / You gave me a mountain / It's impossible / Big hunk o'love / It's over / Impossible dream / Reconsider baby / I'll remember you / I'm so lonesome I could cry / Suspicious minds / Unchained melody / Twelfth of never / Softly as I leave you / Alla' en el Rancho Grande / Froggie went a-courtin' / Stranger in my home town
74321303312 / Sep '95 / RCA

Press Gang

☐ **BURNING BOATS**
PUSS 0002CD / Apr '94 / Cat

☐ **FIRE**
EFA 611012 / Jan '96 / Twah

Pressure Drop

☐ **ILLUSIVE**
Intro/Writing on the wall / Got to be for real / Silently bad minded / Foetus / My friend / Let me be me / Uh oh / Darkness / Don't run away / Dusk / Sounds of time / Obsessed / Road / End of the road
HANDCD 3 / 6 Oct '97 / Hard Hands/ Higherground

Pressure Of Speech

☐ **ART OF THE STATE**
Reverberations / Paralaxx / Jah-ell / A-morphic / Elone / X-on / Thomp / Surveillance / Swarm / Creepy people / Xi-beats / Stand
POS 100CD / May '94 / North South

☐ **OUR COMMON PAST OUR COMMON FUTURE**
POS 200CD / Mar '96 / North South

☐ **PHASE 1**
CLP 0095 / 6 Oct '97 / Cleopatra

Pressurehed

☐ **EXPLAINING THE UNEXPLAINED**
CLP 9910 / Mar '97 / Cleopatra

Preston, Billy

☐ **ENCOURAGING WORDS**
Right now / Little girl / Use what you got / My sweet Lord / Let the music play / Same thing again / I've got a feeling / Sing one for the Lord / When you are mine / I don't want you to pretend / Encouraging words / All things must pass / You've been acting strange / As long as I got my baby / All that I've got (I'm gonna give to you)
CDP 7812792 / Mar '93 / Apple

Preston, Jimmy

☐ **JIMMY PRESTON 1948-1950**
Messin' with Preston / Chop Suey Louie / Hucklebuck Daddy / Rock the joint / Early morning blues
FLYCD 33 / Apr '91 / Flyright

Preston, Johnny

☐ **BEST OF JOHNNY PRESTON, THE**
Do what you did / Feel so fine / Running bear / Hearts of stone / Cradle of love / That's all I want / I want a rock 'n' roll guitar / Charming Billy / I'm startin' to go steady with the blues / Leave my kitten alone / Chief heartbreak / New baby for Christmas / Madre de dios / Chosen few / You'll never walk alone / Little boy blue / Broken hearts anonymous / Four letter word / Dream / Sitting here crying / City of tears / Kissin' tree
STCD 6 / Oct '96 / Stomper Time

☐ **CHARMING BILLY (The Stereo Recordings)**
Charming Billy / Feel so good / Leave my kitten alone / Angels gave you to me / That's all I want / Just little boy blue / Hearts of stone / Chosen few / Chief heartbreak / Twist / Up in the air / Four letter word / Do what you did / Over and over / Sitting here cryin' / (I want a) rock 'n' roll guitar / Dream / I feel good / Let them talk / Lucky in love / I played around with my love / New baby for Christmas / She once belonged to me / I'm startin' to get steady with the blues / Madre de Dios / Pretend / You'll never walk alone / What am I living for / Please believe me / My imagination / Earth angel / Token of love / Guardian angel / Danny boy
BCD 16234 / Mar '98 / Bear Family

☐ **RUNNING BEAR**
Charming Billy / Running bear / Cradle of love / Chief heartbreak / My heart knows / That's all I want / Just little boy blue / Leave my kitten alone / Sitting here crying / I want a rock and roll guitar / Hearts of stone / Do what you did / I played around with my love / Chosen few / Up in the air / Kissin' tree / Four letter word / Feel so fine / She once belonged to me / New baby for christmas / City of tears / I'm startin' to go steady with the blues / Dream / Madre de dios / You'll never walk alone / Danny Boy / Broken heart anonymous
BCD 15473 / '88 / Bear Family

Pretenders

☐ **GET CLOSE**
My baby / When I change my life / Light of the moon / Dance / Tradition of love / Don't get me wrong / I remember you / How much did you get for your soul / Chill factor / Hymn to her / Room full of mirrors
2409762 / Oct '86 / WEA

☐ **LAST OF THE INDEPENDENTS**
Hollywood perfume / Night in my veins / Money talk / 977 / Revolution / All my dreams / I'll stand by you / I'm a mother / Tequila / Every mother's son / Rebel rock me / Colours / Forever young
4509958222 / May '94 / WEA

☐ **LEARNING TO CRAWL**
Middle of the road / Back on the chain gang / Time the avenger / Show me / Watching the clothes / Thumbelina / My city was gone / Thin line between love and hate / I hurt you / 2000 miles
9239802 / Jan '84 / WEA

☐ **LIVE AT THE ISLE OF VIEW**
Kid / Private life / Brass in pocket / Phone call / Lovers of today / Back on the chain gang / I go to sleep / Isle of view / Revolution / Criminal / Sense of purpose / Hymn to her / Chill factor / I hurt you / 2000 miles
0630120592 / Oct '95 / WEA

☐ **PRETENDERS II**
Adultress / Bad boys get spanked / Message of love / I go to sleep / Birds of paradise / Talk of the town / Pack it up / Waste not, want not / Day after day / Jealous dogs / English rose / Louie Louie
256924 / Jul '93 / WEA

☐ **PRETENDERS, THE**
Precious / Phone call / Up to the neck / Tattooed love boys / Space invaders / Wait / Stop your sobbing / Kid / Private life / Lovers of today / Brass in pocket / Mystery achievement
256774 / '83 / WEA

☐ **SINGLES, THE**
Stop your sobbing / Kid / Brass in pocket / Talk of the town / I go to sleep / Day after day / Message of love / Back on the chain gang / Middle of the road / 2000 miles / Show me / Thin line between love and hate / Don't get me wrong / Hymn to her / My baby / I got you babe / What you gonna do about it
2422292 / Dec '87 / WEA

Pretty Maids

☐ **SCREAM**
MASSCD 0472 / Mar '95 / Massacre

☐ **SCREAMIN' LIVE**
MASSCD 081 / Nov '95 / Massacre

☐ **SPOOKED**
MASSDP 119 / May '97 / Massacre

Pretty Things

☐ **CHICAGO BLUES JAM - 1991 (Pretty Things & Yardbird Blues Band)**
You can't judge a book by the cover / Down in the bottom / Hush hush / Can't hold out / Spoonful / She fooled me / Time is on my side / Long tall shorty / Diddley daddy / Ain't got you / Caress me baby / Here's my picture / Chain of fools / Don't start cryin' now
FIENDCD 708 / Oct '91 / Demon

☐ **ELECTRIC BANANA**
REP 4088 / Aug '91 / Repertoire

☐ **EMOTIONS**
Death of a socialite / Children / Sun / There will never be another day / House of ten / Out in the night / One long glance / Growing in my mind / Photographer / Bright lights of the city / Tripping / My time / House in the country / Me needing you / Progress
SMMCD 550 / 27 Apr '98 / Snapper
08589812 / 16 Feb '98 / SPV

☐ **EP COLLECTION, THE**
Don't bring me down / Rosalyn / Big boss man / We'll be together / I can never say / Honey I need / Rainin' in my heart / Sittin' all alone / Midnight to six man / LSD / Come see me / Buzz the jerk / Progress / We'll play house / Get the picture / Gonna find a substitute / Get a buzz / London town / Can't stand the pain / Me needing you / Roadrunner / Big city / Mama keep your big mouth shut / Judgement day / Cry to me / House in the country
SEECD 476 / Jun '97 / See For Miles

☐ **FALLEN ANGELS (Fallen Angels)**
Fallen angels / California / Thirteenth floor suicide / Dance again / Shine on baby / My good Friday / Cold wind / I keep on / Dogs of war / Girl like you / When the Russians came back / Crazy days
SRH 801 / Feb '97 / Start

☐ **GET THE PICTURE**
You don't believe me / Buzz the jerk / Get the picture / Can't stand the pain / Raining in my heart / We'll play house / You'll never do it baby / I had a dream / I want your love / London town / Cry to me / Gonna find me a substitute
08589802 / Sep '97 / SPV
SMMCD 549 / 27 Apr '98 / Snapper

☐ **MIDNIGHT TO 6**
Don't bring me down / Children / Cry to me / Judgement day / We'll be together / Honey I need / Progress / Midnight to six man / Get the picture / Roadrunner / I can never say / Mama keep your big mouth shut / I want your love / Raining in my heart
5501862 / Mar '94 / Spectrum

☐ **MORE ELECTRIC BANANA**
REP 4089 / Aug '91 / Repertoire

☐ **NOT SO PRETTY (A Tribute To The Pretty Things) (Various Artists)**
CORD 007CD / 24 Nov '97 / Corduroy

☐ **ON AIR**
Don't bring me down / Hey mamma / Midnight to six man / Buzz the jerks / LSD / Big boss man / Defecting grey / Cold stone / Sickle clowns / She's a lover
BOJCD 3 / Mar '92 / Band Of Joy

☐ **OUT OF THE ISLAND**
Cry to me / Baby doll / She's fine she's mine / Get the picture / Havana bound / Can't stop / Loneliest person/LSD / Private sorrow / Moon is rising / Big city / Cause and effect / Well known blues / You don't believe me / Judgement day
INAK 8708 / Jul '97 / In Akustik

☐ **PARACHUTE**
Scene one / Good Mr. Square / She was tall, she was high / In the square / Letter / Rain / Miss Fay regrets / Cries from the midnight circus / Grass / Sickle clowns / She's a lover / What's the use / Parachute
085898832 / 10 Nov '97 / SPV

☐ **PRETTY THINGS**
SMMCD 548 / 27 Apr '98 / Snapper

☐ **PRETTY THINGS 1967-1971 - THE SINGLES A'S & B'S**
Defecting Grey / Mr. Evasion / Talkin' about the good times / Walking through my dreams / Private sorrow / Balloon burning / Good Mr. Square / Blue serge blues / October 26 / Cold stone / Summertime / Circus mind / Stone hearted mama
SEECD 103 / Jun '96 / See For Miles

☐ **PRETTY THINGS, THE**
Roadrunner / Judgement day / 13 Chester Street / Big city / Unknown blues / Mama keep your big mouth shut / Honey I need / Oh baby doll / She's fine, she's mine / Don't you lie to me / Moon is rising / Pretty thing
08589792 / Sep '97 / SPV

☐ **SAVAGE EYE**
08589862 / 22 Jun '98 / SPV

☐ **SF SORROW**
SF Sorrow is born / Bracelets of fingers / She says good morning / Private sorrow / Balloon burning / Death / Baron Saturday / Journey / I see you / Well of destiny / Trust / Old man going / Loneliest person
8589822 / Oct '97 / SPV

☐ **SILK TORPEDO**
08589852 / 22 Jun '98 / SPV

☐ **SINGLES A'S AND B'S**
Defecting grey / Mr. Evasion / Talkin' about the good times / Walking through my dreams / Private sorrow / Balloon burning / Good Mr. Square / Blue serge blues / October 26 / Cold stone / Summertime / Circus mind / Stone hearted Mama
05889882 / Oct '97 / SPV

☐ **UNREPENTANT (Bloody But Unbowed/ 2CD Set)**
Rosalyn / Don't bring me down / Get yourself home / Roadrunner / Judgement day / Honey, I need / You don't believe me / Buzz the jerk / Cry to me / Midnight to six man / LSD / Death of a socialite / Growing in my mind / Defecting grey / SF sorrow is born / Private sorrow / Balloon burning / Old man going / Loneliest person / Scene one / In the square / Letter / Rain / Grass / Parachute / October 26 (Revolution) / Summertime / Peter / Rip off train / Havana bound / Dream/Joey / Bridge of God / Is it only love / Singapore silk torpedo / Under the volcano / Sad eye / Remember that boy / It's been so long / I'm calling / Office love / She don't / No future / God give me the strength (to carry on)
SSDCD 002 / 9 Mar '98 / Snapper

☐ **WHITER SHADE OF DIRTY WATER, A (Pretty Things 'Mates)**
He's waitin' / Strychnine / Pushin' too hard / Kicks / Candy / Louie Louie / 96 tears / Let's talk about girls / Sometimes good guys don't wear white / I'm a man / Red River rock / Midnight to 6 man
CDKVL 9031 / May '94 / Kingdom

☐ **WINE, WOMEN & WHISKEY (Pretty Things & Yardbird Blues Band)**
Wine, women and whiskey / Sure look good to me / No questions / Amble / It's all over now / Bad boy / Spoonful / French champagne / My back scratcher / Can't hold out / Diddley daddy / I'm cryin' / Gettin' all wet
FIENDCD 748 / Jan '94 / Demon

Previn, Andre

☐ **4 TO GO/LIGHT FANTASTIC**
9043158922 / 7 Apr '98 / Collectables

☐ **ANDRE PREVIN & FRIENDS PLAY SHOWBOAT**
4476392 / May '95 / Deutsche Grammophon

☐ **JAZZ AT THE MUSIKVEREIN**
5377042 / Aug '97 / Verve

☐ **KING SIZE (Previn, Andre Jazz Trio)**
I'll remember april / Much too late / You'd be so nice to come home to / It could happen to you / Low and inside / I'm beginning to see the light
OJCCD 691 / Nov '95 / Original Jazz Classics

☐ **PLAY A CLASSIC AMERICAN SONGBOOK (Previn, Andre & Thomas Stevens)**
It might as well be spring / My funny valentine / Slowly/Laura / Bewitched, bothered and bewildered / I could write a book / It could happen to you/Here's that rainy day / You go to my head / Cabin in the sky/ Takin' a chance on love / I didn't know what time it was/Little girl blue / Easy living
DRGCD 5222 / Apr '94 / DRG

☐ **PREVIN AT SUNSET**
I got it bad and that ain't good / Body and soul / Sunset in blue / All the things you are / Something to live for / Good enough to keep / That old blue magic / Blue skies / I found a new baby / Variations on a theme / Mulholland Drive
BLCD 760189 / Jun '94 / Black Lion

☐ **SOME OF THE BEST**
Thinking of you / Laura / When I fall in love / Invitation / Skylark / Nothing to do with love / My shining hour / Quiet nights of quiet stars (Corcovado) / Boat ride / You're gonna hear from me / Moonlight becomes you
12647 / Aug '97 / Laserlight

☐ **WE GOT RHYTHM (A Gershwin Songbook) (Previn, Andre & David Finck)**
They all laughed / Someone to watch over me / Lady be good / Foggy day / Do it again/Soon / I got rhythm / Embraceable you / He loves she loves/Our love is here to stay / Fascinatin' rhythm / Isn't it a pity / Boy what love has done to me/I've got a crush on you / Love walked in / Man I love / 'S wonderful
4534932 / 20 Apr '98 / Deutsche Grammophon

Previn, Dory

☐ **LIVE AT CARNEGIE HALL**
BGOCD 374 / 17 Aug '98 / Beat Goes On

☐ **MARY C. BROWN & THE HOLLYWOOD SIGN/ON MY WAY TO...**
BGOCD 381 / 27 Apr '98 / Beat Goes On

☐ **MYTHICAL KINGS AND IGUANAS/ REFLECTIONS IN A MUD PUDDLE**
BGOCD 383 / 16 Jan '98 / Beat Goes On

Previte, Bobby

☐ **DOWNTOWN LULLABY (Previte/ Sharp/Horvitz/Zorn)**
484 Broome / 500 West 52nd / Eighth between B & C / 77 white / 228 West Broadway / Bleeker and Bowery / 1 Morton St (Downtown lullaby)
DOF 2 / Jun '98 / Depth Of Field

☐ **DULL BANG, GUSHING SOUND, HUMAN SHRIEK (Bought & Sold) (Previte, Bobby 'Weather Clear')**
378212 / Aug '96 / Koch Jazz

☐ **HUE & CRY (Previte, Bobby 'Weather Clear')**
Hubbub / Smack dab / More heaven and earth / 700 Camels / Valerie / Hue and cry / For John Laughlan and all that we stood for
ENJ 80642 / Nov '94 / Enja

☐ **TOO CLOSE TO THE POLE**
Too close to the pole / 3 minute heels / Countess' bedroom / Save the cups / Eleventh hour / Too close to the pole (reprise)
ENJ 93062 / Nov '96 / Enja

Previte, Franke

☐ **MAKIN' THE POINT (Previte, Franke & The Knockouts)**
ESM 030 / 6 Apr '98 / Escape

Prevost, Eddie

☐ **LOCUS OF CHANGE**
MRCD 32 / Jun '97 / Matchless

☐ **MOST MATERIAL (2CD Set) (Prevost, Eddie & Evan Parker)**
MRCD 33 / Oct '97 / Matchless

☐ **SUPER SESSION (Prevost, Eddie, Parker, Guy & Rowe)**
MR 17 / '90 / Matchless

☐ **TOUCH (Prevost, Eddie New Trio)**
MRCD 34 / Oct '97 / Matchless

Prewitt, Archer

☐ IN THE SUN
SAKI 015CD / 23 Mar '98 / Hi-Ball

Prezident Brown

☐ BIG BAD AND TALENTED
RN 0032 / Jun '95 / X-Rated

☐ PREZIDENT BROWN
RNCD 0043 / Apr '97 / Runn

Price, Alan

☐ 1960'S FRENCH EP COLLECTION, THE (Price, Alan Set)
525742 / Jul '97 / Magic

☐ ALAN PRICE ARCHIVE
Jarrow song / Please don't stop the carnival / House of the rising sun / I'm coming back / Hi-li-hi-lo / I just got love / Simon Smith and his amazing dancing bear / Mama divine / I put a spell on you / Don't try / Shame / House that Jack built / Love that I needed / Don't make me suffer / Frozen moments / Just for you / I have tried / Music in the city / Mr. Sunbeam
RMCD 209 / Nov '97 / Rialto

☐ ANTHOLOGY (2CD Set)
SMDCD 204 / Jul '97 / Snapper

☐ BEST OF ALAN PRICE, THE
Simon smith and the amazing dancing bear / Jarrow song / I put a spell on you / Angel eyes / Just for you / In times like these / Too many people / Tickle me / House that jack built / Don't stop the carnival / Barefootin' / Falling in love again / Shame / Cherie / Hi lili hi lo / Baby of mine / Slow down / If I could
MCCD 109 / Jun '93 / Music Club

☐ GIGSTER'S LIFE FOR ME, A (Price, Alan & Electric Blues Company)
Boom boom boom / Rockin' pneumonia and the boogie woogie flu / Rollin' like a pebble in the sand / I put a spell on you / Good times-bad woman / Some change / Enough is enough / Whatcha gonna do / A gigster's life for me / (I got) business with the blues / How you've changed / Old love / What am I living for / Say it isn't true
IGOCD 2048 / Nov '95 / Indigo

☐ GREATEST HITS IN CONCERT
CDRIA 2000 / Sep '96 / Rialto

☐ LIVE IN CONCERT
Arrival / O lucky man / Left over people / Away away / Under the sun / In times like these / Simon smith and the amazing dancing bear / Poor people / Sell sell sell / Justice / Look over your shoulder / Keep on rollin' / City lights / Hi lili hi lo / I put a spell on you / It takes me back / Between today and yesterday / Changes / Jarrow song / Don't stop the carnival / House that jack built / Shame
GRF 209 / Mar '93 / Tring

☐ O LUCKY MAN (Original Soundtrack)
O lucky man / Poor people / Pastoral / Arrival / Look over your shoulder / Justice / My home town / Changes
9362461372 / Oct '96 / Warner Bros.

☐ PRICE IS RIGHT, THE
Barefootin' / Angel eyes / Jump children / Don't try / Slow down / I just got love / Simon Smith and his amazing dancing bears / Mercy mercy / If I could / Shame / Fifty pence / Please / Mama divine / Don't do that again
303492 / Jul '97 / Hallmark

☐ PRICE OF FAME, THE (Price, Alan & Georgie Fame)
Yeh yeh: *Fame, Georgie & The Blue Flames* / Simon Smith and his amazing dancing bear / Get away / Hi-li hi-lo / Sitting in the park / Barefootin' / Let the sun shine in / Shame / Ride your pony / Jarrow song / Papa's got a brand new bag / I put a spell on you / In the meantime: *Fame, Georgie & The Blue Flames* / House that Jack built / Sunny / Falling in love again / My girl / Baby of mine / Let the good times roll / Don't stop the carnival
5509312 / Oct '95 / Spectrum

☐ PRICELESS
Don't stop the carnival / House that Jack built / People are talking / I put a spell on you / Slow down / Hi-lilli-hi-lo / Shame / Don't slam that door / Travellin' man / In times like these / Guess who / Nobody can / Papers / Cherie / If I could / Too much
EMPRCD 593 / Oct '95 / Emporio

Price, Billy

☐ SOULD COLLECTION, THE
GD 41297 / Jun '98 / Green Dolphin

Price, Darren

☐ UNDER THE FLIGHTPATH
Airspace / Lose no time / Things change / Blueprints / Counterpoint / Intermission / Long haul / Phizz / Over and out
NOMU 48CD / Jun '97 / Nova Mute

Price, Kate

☐ DEEP HEARTS CORE
AMLCD 500 / Mar '96 / Priceless

☐ TIME BETWEEN, THE
PPCD 402 / Mar '96 / Priceless

Price, Kelly

☐ SOUL OF A WOMAN
5245162 / 17 Aug '98 / Island Black Music

Price, Leontyne

☐ CHRISTMAS SONGS (Price, Leontyne & Vienna Philharmonic/Herbert Von Karajan)
Silent night / Hark the herald angels sing / We three Kings of Orient are / Angels we have heard on high / God rest ye merry gentlemen / It came upon the midnight clear / Von himmel hoch, da komm ich her / Sweet li'l Jesus / Ave Maria / O holy night / Ave Maria / O holy night / Ave Maria / Alleluja
4489982 / Nov '96 / Decca

Price, Lloyd

☐ GREATEST HITS
MCD 11184 / 8 Sep '97 / MCA

☐ HEAVY DREAMS
Chee-koo baby / Coo-ee baby / Oooh-oooh-oooh / Restless heart / Tell me pretty baby / They say / I'm too young / Ain't it a shame / Jimmie Lee / Baby, don't turn your back on me / Old echo song / Too late for tears / Carry me home / Little Bea / Night and day / Oh love / Woe ho ho / Breaking my heart (All over again) / Iyi yi gomen-a-sai / Country boy rock / Heavy dreams / Why / I'm goin' back
CDCHD 512 / Jan '94 / Ace

☐ LAWDY
Lawdy Miss Clawdy / Mailman blues / Chee koo baby / Oo-ee baby / So long / Operator / Laurelle / What's the matter now / If crying was murder / Walkin' the track / Where you at / Lord, lord, amen / Carry me home / Frog legs / I wish your picture was you / Let me come home baby / Tryin' to find someone to love / Night and day blues / All alone / What a fire / Rock 'n' roll dance / I'm glad, glad / Baby please come home / Forgive me Clawdy
CDCHD 360 / Nov '91 / Ace

☐ LAWDY MISS CLAWDY (The Best Of Lloyd Price)
Lawdy Miss Clawdy / Just because / Won'tcha come home / Personality / I'm gonna get married / Where were you on our wedding day / Stagger Lee / Come into my heart / For love / Lady luck / Just call me and I'll understand / Never let me go / Question / Misty / Have you ever had the blues / Send me some lovin' / It ain't easy / They get down
AIM 2012CD / 20 Oct '97 / Aim

Price, Maryann

☐ ETCHED IN SWING
WM 1014CD / May '94 / Watermelon

Price, Ray

☐ HONKY TONK YEARS 1950-1966, THE (10CD Set) (Price, Ray & The Cherokee Cowboys)
Jealous lies / Your wedding corsage / If you're ever lonely darling / I saw my castles fall today / You've got my troubles now / I get the short end every time / Hey la la / Answer to The Last Letter / Till death do us part / Beyond the last mile / Heart aching blues / Weary blues / I made a mistake and I'm sorry / We crossed our heart / Your heart is too crowded / I lost the only one I know / I've got to hurry hurry hurry / Talk to your heart / I know I'll never win your love again / Road of no return / You're under arrest (for stealing my heart) / Move on in and stay / I can't escape from you / Won't you please be mine / Don't let the stars get in your eyes / My old scrapbook / Price of loving you / That's what I get for loving you / Cold shoulder / You weren't ashamed to kiss me last night / Wrong side of town / Time / Start the music / Gone again / Way you've treated me / Wrong side of town / Who stole that train / Let your heart decide / You always get by / Leave her alone / Wall around your heart / Release me / I'll be there (if you ever want me) / Last letter / Much too young to die / I love you so much I let you go / I could love you more / What if he don't love you / If you don't somebody else will / I'm alone because I love you / Oh yes darling / One broken heart (don't mean a thing) / Sweet little Miss Blue Eyes / Way she got away / Let me talk to you / Call the Lord and he'll be there / Man called Peter / As strange as it seems (I still love you) / I can't go home like this / Don't you know me anymore / I don't want it on my conscience / Run boy / You never will be true / Don't tempt me / Slowly dying / Crazy arms / You done me wrong / Wild and wicked world / Crazy / Are you wasting my time / Fallin' fallin' fallin' / Wasted words / I've got a new heartache / Don't do this to me / Letters have no arms / I'll sail my ship alone / Mansion on the hill / I can't help it / Remember me (I'm the one who loves you) / I saw my castles fall today / Let me talk to you / Please don't leave me / Blues stay away from me / Pins and needles (in my heart) / I love you because / Many tears ago / I'll be there (when you get lonely) / It's all your fault / My shoes keep walking back to you / Faded love / Gone / Bye bye love / Four walls / Fallen star / Don't do this to me / Walls of tears / Curtain in the window / Talk to your conscience / There'll be no teardrops tonight / Driftwood on the river / Deep water / I'll keep on loving you / I love you so much it hurts / I told you so / Ice cold heart / I've gotta have my baby back / Please don't leave me / Talk to your heart / I'm tired / Wondering / Walkin' the floor / Invitation to the blues / I've got to know / Heartaches must be your name / City lights / Kissing your picture (is so cold) / That's what it's like to be lonesome / Punish me tomorrow / Heartaches by the number / Wild and wicked world / Beyond the last mile / Same old me / Under your spell again / Broken hearts will haunt your soul / One more time / Who'll be the first / City lights / Old rugged cross / In the garden / How big is God / Until then / Help through my unbelief / When I take my vacation in heaven / Faith / Rock of ages / Softly and tenderly / When the roll is called up yonder / Just as I am / Where he leads me (I will follow) / Now the day is over / I can't run away from myself / I wish I could fall in love today / Heart over mind / Twenty-fourth hour / Walkin' slow (and thinking 'bout her) / Soft rain / Here we are again / You're stranger than me / This cold war with you / Imagiantion's wonderful thing / Walkin' slow (and thinking about her) / Soft rain / San Antonio Rose / Maiden's prayer / My confession / Whose heart are you breaking now / Roly poly / Bubbles in my beer / Home in San Antone / You don't love me (but I'll always care) / You done care what happens to me / Time changes everything / Kinda love I can't forget / Hang your head in shame / Night life / Lonely street / Wild side of life / Sittin' and thinkin' / Girl in the night / There's no fool like a young fool / If she could see me now / Bright lights and blonde haired women / Are you sure / Let me talk to you / This cold war with you / I've just destroyed the world / Walkin' slow (and thinking 'bout her) / Pride / Big shoes / Walk me to the door / You took her off my hands / Be a good girl / Make the world go away / I'll find a way (to free myself of you) / Let me talk to you / I've still got room (for one more heartache) / That's all that matters / Burning memories / Each time / Way to free myself / How long is forever / This cold war with you / Take me as I am (or let me go) / All right (I'll sign the papers) / I fall to pieces / Please talk to my heart / Cold cold heart / Still / I don't know why (I keep loving you) / Same old memories / Here comes my baby back again / Together again / Thing called sadness / Soft rain / Release me / Devil's dream / Linda Lou / Crazy arms / Lil' Liza Jane / Rubber dolly / Burnt fingers / Twinkle, twinkle little star / Maiden's prayer / Your old loveletters / Spanish two step / Liberty bells / Sing a sad song / Other woman / Tearful earful / Last letter / Born to lose / Just call me lonesome / Don't you ever get tired of hurting me / Funny how time slips away / Rose coloured glasses / Unloved, unwanted / Eye for an eye / Too much love is spoiling you / After effects / I'm not crazy yet / Way to survive / Another bridge to burn / Legend in my time / Take these chains in my heart / Don't touch me / Go away / I'd fight the world / I want to hear it from you / It should be easier now / Don't you believe her / Healing hands of time / Too late / Each time / Touch my heart / There goes my everything / It's only love / I lie a lot / Enough to lie / Swinging doors / Am I that easy to forget / Same two lips / Just for the record / I'm still not over you / I let my mind wander / Danny Boy
BCD 15843 / Nov '95 / Bear Family

☐ NIGHT LIFE
379282 / Dec '96 / Koch International

☐ OTHER WOMAN, THE
379472 / 7 Apr '98 / Koch

☐ SAN ANTONIO ROSE (Sings A Tribute To Bob Wills)
379172 / Aug '96 / Koch International

Price, Sammy

☐ 1944 WORLD JAM SESSION (Price, Sammy & His Bluesicians)
PCD 7074 / Nov '96 / Progressive

☐ BARRELHOUSE & BLUES
Honey Grove Blues / Rosetta / St. James Infirmary / West End boogie / In the evening / Keepin' out of mischief now / Struttin' with Georgia
BLCD 760159 / Oct '92 / Black Lion

☐ CLASSICS 1929-1941
CLASSICS 696 / Jul '93 / Classics

☐ KINGS OF BOOGIE WOOGIE, THE (Price, Sammy Trio)
King Boogie parts 1 and 2 / Makin' whoopee / Keepin' out of mischief now / Bass and piano talking / Please don't talk about me when I'm gone / My blue heaven / Saint James infirmary / Boogie woogie French style / Baby, won't you please come home / Trouble in mind / Blues in my heart
STCD 5011 / Dec '94 / Storyville

Prichard, Peter

☐ HARMONIC PIANO
WCL 11001 / May '94 / White Cloud

Pride

☐ ...AND THE GLORY
WWRCD 029 / 6 Apr '98 / Walzwerk

Pride & Glory

☐ PRIDE AND GLORY
Losin' your mind / Horse called war / Shine on / Lovin' woman / Harvester of pain / Chosen one / Sweet Jesus / Troubled wine / Machine gun man / Cry me a river / Toe'n the line / Found a friend / Fadin' away / Hate your guts
GFLD 19342 / Oct '96 / Geffen

Pride, Charley

☐ AMY'S EYES
White houses / Moody woman / Amy's eyes / After me, after you / I made love to you in my mind / Whole lotta love on the line / Nickles and dimes and love / Look who's looking / I wrote the songs that broke her heart / You hold my world together / Right one / Plenty good lovin'
RZRCD 525 / Apr '93 / Ritz

☐ BEST OF CHARLEY PRIDE, THE
MATCD 330 / Feb '95 / Castle

☐ BEST OF CHARLEY PRIDE, THE
I'm so afraid of losing you / Kaw liga / It's gonna take a little bit longer / Oklahoma morning / Does my ring hurt your finger / Crystal chandeliers / Happiness of having you / Shutters and boards / Kiss an angel good morning / My eyes can only see as far as you / Mississippi cotton picking Delta Town / Let me live in the light of his love / Louisiana man / Help me make it through the night / Lovesick blues / There goes my everything / Me and Bobby McGee
SUMCD 4178 / 23 Feb '98 / Summit

☐ CLASSICS WITH PRIDE
Most beautiful girl in the world / Always on my mind / You've got to stand for something / After all these years / I don't know why I love you but I do / It tomorrow never comes / Ramblin' rose / You'll never walk alone / Please help me, I'm falling / Here in the real world / Walk on by / I love you because / Four in the morning / It's just a matter of time / Ramona / What's another year
RZCD 0064 / Feb '92 / Ritz

☐ CONCERT COLLECTION
Kaw-Liga / I'm so afraid of losing you again / Oklahoma morning / It's gonna take a little bit longer / Crystal chandeliers / Medley / Shutters and boards / Happiness of having you / My eyes can only see as far / Kiss an angel good morning / Let me live in the light of His love / Mississippi cotton picking delta town / Help me make it through the night / Louisiana man / Medley
PLATCD 165 / Mar '96 / Platinum

☐ CRYSTAL CHANDELIERS
MUCD 3009 / Oct '94 / Musketeer

☐ CRYSTAL CHANDELIERS
Crystal chandeliers / Kaw-liga / (I'm so) Afraid of losing you again / Oklahoma morning / It's gonna take a little bit longer / Does my ring hurt your finger / Too good to be true / I'd rather love you / All I have to offer you is me / Wonder could I live there anymore / Is anybody goin' to San Antone / I'm just me / Shutters and boards / Happiness of having you / My eyes can only see as far as you / Kiss an angel good morning / Let me live in the light of his love / Mississippi cotton pickin' Delta Town / Help me make it through the night / Louisiana man / There goes my everything / Lovesick blues / Me and Bobby McGee
CD 6016 / Apr '96 / Music

☐ CRYSTAL CHANDELIERS (The Best Of Charley Pride)
PLSCD 145 / Apr '97 / Pulse

☐ CRYSTAL CHANDELIERS
Mississippi cotton picking delta town / My eyes can only see as far as you / Oklahoma morning / Medley / Kiss an angel good morning / Happiness of having you / It's gonna take a little bit longer / Shutters and boards / Louisiana man / Crystal chandeliers / Medley / I'm afraid of losing you / Kaw-liga / Let me live in the light of his love / Help me make it through the night
308082 / 13 Oct '97 / Hallmark

☐ ESSENTIAL CHARLEY PRIDE, THE
Just between you and me / Does my ring hurt your finger / Please help me I'm falling / All I have to offer you (is me) / Kaw-Liga / Is anybody going to San Antone / I'd rather love you / Wonder could I live there anymore / I can't believe that you've stopped loving me / She's too good to be true / Kiss an angel good mornin' / It's gonna take a little bit longer / I'm just me / Shoulder to cry on / Amazing love / My eyes can only see as far as you / I'll be leaving alone / Someone loves you honey / Burgers and fries / You're my Jamaica
7863674282 / May '97 / RCA

☐ GREATEST HITS
Kaw-liga / I'm so afraid of losing you again / Oklahoma morning / It's going to take a little bit longer / Crystals chandeliers / Does my ring hurt your finger / Too good to be true / I'd rather love you / All I have to offer you is me / I wonder could I live there anymore / Is anybody going to San Antone / I'm just me / Shutters and boards / Happiness of having you / My eyes can only see as far as you / Kiss an angel good morning / Let me live in the light of his light / Mississippi cotton picking Delta town / Help me make it through the night / Louisanna man / There goes my everything / Lovesick blues / Me and Bobby McGee
MU 5070 / Oct '92 / Musketeer

☐ GREATEST HITS LIVE
ECD 3316 / 18 Aug '97 / K-Tel

☐ IN PERSON
Last thing on my mind / Just between you and me / I know one / Lovesick blues / Image of me / Kaw-liga / Shutters and boards / Six days on the road / Streets of Baltimore / Crystal chandeliers / Introduction by Po Bowell
KOCCD 7984 / Mar '98 / Koch

☐ JUST FOR THE LOVE OF IT
Just for the love of it / Walk on by / For today / Me and Bobby McGee / Lonestar lonely / I've been there / Lovesick blues / I'll be leaving alone / Sea of heartbreak / Burnin' down the tavern / In the midnight hour / Walls / Hello love / I don't think she's in love anymore / I came straight to you / Where do I put her memory / Burnin' down the tarvern
RZRCD 559 / Jun '96 / Ritz

☐ KISS AN ANGEL GOOD MORNING
WMCD 5699 / Oct '94 / Disky

☐ MASTERS, THE
EABCD 015 / 24 Nov '97 / Eagle

☐ SENSATIONAL CHARLEY PRIDE
Louisiana man / She's still got a hold on you / Let the chips fall / Come on home and sing the blues to Daddy / Never more than I / Let me live / Take care of the little things / Even after everything's she's done / (It's just a matter of) making up my mind / It's the little things / Billy Bayou / We had all the good things going
379852 / 1 Sep '98 / Koch

☐ THROUGH THE YEARS
I'm just me / On the southbound / Is anyone going to San Antone / Just between you and me / Crystal chandeliers / Kaw liga / I know one / Hello darlin' / Did you think to pray / World stood still / Me and Booby McGee / Through the years / I think I'll take a walk / Poor boy like me / Nobody home to go home to / I can't believe you stopped loving me / Does my ring hurt your finger / I'd rather love you / That's my angel / Kiss an angel good mornin'
74321511972 / 1 Sep '97 / Camden

☐ VERY BEST OF CHARLEY PRIDE, THE
I'd rather love you / Is anybody going to San Antone / I'm so afraid of losing you again / Kiss an angel good morning / Just between you and me / All I have to offer you is me / Wonder could I live there anymore / I can't believe that you've stopped loving me / I'm just me / Crystal chandeliers / Amazing love / Happiness of having you / Easy part's over / I know one / Does my ring hurt your finger / For the good times / Kaw-liga / My eyes can only see as far as you / She's just an old love turned memory / Someone loves you honey
74321272142 / May '95 / RCA

Pride, Dickie

☐ SHEIK OF SHAKE, THE
Don't make me love you / You're singin' our love song to somebody else / Fabulous cure / Betty Betty (go steady with me) / Primrose Lane / Anything goes / Isn't this a lovely day (to be caught in the rain) / You turned the tables on me / Loch Lomond / Falling in love / Give the simple life / Slippin' and slidin' / Bye bye blackbird / Midnight oil / No John / Frantic / It's only a paper moon / I could write a book / Too close for comfort / There's a small hotel / They can't take that away from me / Lulu's back in town
SEECD 344 / Mar '92 / See For Miles

Pride Of Murray Pipe Band

☐ BEST OF SCOTTISH PIPES AND DRUMS, THE
EUCD 1164 / Jun '91 / ARC

Pride, Steve

☐ HAINT
SPURCD 001 / Jun '97 / Spur

Pridebowl

☐ DRIPPINGS OF THE PAST
BTR 007CD / Apr '96 / Bad Taste

☐ SOFT SONG EP
BTR 008CD / Jul '96 / Bad Taste

Priest, Maxi

☐ BEST OF ME, THE
Wild world / In the Springtime / Should I / How can we ease the pain: *Priest, Maxi & Beres Hammond* / Let me know / Housecall: *Priest, Maxi & Shabba Ranks* / Just a little bit longer / Caution / Some guys have all the luck / I know love: *Priest, Maxi & Tiger* / Strollin' on / Best of me / Crazy love / Woman in you / Peace throughout the world: *Priest, Maxi & Jazzie B* / Close to you
DIXCD 111 / Oct '91 / 10

☐ BONAFIDE
Just a little bit longer / Close to you / Never did say goodbye / Best of me / Space in my heart / Human work of art / Temptress / Peace throughout the world / You / Sure fire love / Life / Prayer for the world
DIXCD 92 / Jun '90 / 10

☐ COLLECTION, A
Strollin' on / Some guys have all the luck / How can we ease the pain / Groovin' in the midnight / Love don't come easy / Just a little bit longer / One more chance / Pretty little girl / Should I (put my trust in you) / Human work of art / Sure fire love / Fatty fatty
CDVIP 138 / Sep '95 / Virgin VIP

☐ FE REAL
Can't turn away / Promises / Just wanna know / Groovin' in the midnight / Make my day / Ten to midnight / Careless whispers: *Priest, Maxi & Carla Marshall* / One more chance / Sublime / Amazed are we / Hard to get
CDVIP 156 / Oct '96 / Virgin VIP

☐ INTENTIONS
Love train / Woman in you / Crazy love / Jehovah / Cry me a river / Strollin' on / Pretty little girl / Let me know / Festival time / Must be a way
CDVIP 218 / 3 Aug '98 / Virgin VIP

☐ MAN WITH THE FUN
That girl / Man with the fun / Watching the world go by / Message in a bottle / Heartbreak lover / Love will cross over / All kinds of people / Happy days / Golden teardrops / Are you ready for me / Ain't it enough / Human cry / Frienenemy / Won't let it slip away
CDVUS 110 / Jul '96 / Virgin

☐ YOU'RE SAFE
Should I / Hey little girl / Dancing mood / Sensi / Caution / Stand up and fight / In the Springtime / Fatty fatty / You're safe / Throw me corn
CDVIP 172 / Apr '97 / Virgin VIP

Priestley, Brian

☐ SALUTES 15 JAZZ PIANO GREATS
CD 90995 / Dec '95 / FMR/Spirit Of Jazz

☐ YOU TAUGHT MY HEART TO SING
SOJCD 9 / Dec '95 / FMR/Spirit Of Jazz

Prima, Louis

☐ BUONA SERA
RMB 75076 / Oct '95 / Remember

☐ BUONA SERA
GO 3824 / 1 Dec '97 / Golden Options

☐ CALL OF THE WILDEST/WILDEST SHOW AT TAHOE
Medley / Medley / Medley / Medley / When you're smiling (the whole world smiles with you) / Shiek of Araby / Autumn leaves / I've got the world on a string / Blow red blow / Pump song / There'll be no next time / Pennies from heaven / Birth of the blues / Closest to the bone / Sentimental journey / When the saints go marching in
4949952 / 8 Jun '98 / EMI

☐ CAPITOL COLLECTORS SERIES: LOUIS PRIMA
Just a gigolo/I ain't got nobody / Oh Marie / Buona sera / Jump, jive and wail / Basin Street blues / When it's sleepy time down South / Lip / Whistle stop / Five months, two weeks, two days / Banana split for my baby / There'll be no next time / When you're smiling / The sheik of Araby / Baby, won't you please come home / I've got the world on a string / Pennies from Heaven / Angelina/Zooma zooma / Beep beep / Embraceable you/I got it bad and that ain't good / Sing sing sing / That old black magic / Music goes 'round and around / Hey boy, hey girl / Lazy river / I've got you under my skin / You're just in love / Twist all night / St. Louis blues
CDP 7940722 / Jul '96 / Premier/EMI

☐ CAPITOL RECORDINGS, THE (8CD Set)
Buona sera / Oh Marie / Just a gigolo / I ain't got nobody / Body and soul / Jump, jive and wail / Nothing's too good for my baby / (I'll be glad when you're dead) you rascal you / Basin Street blues / When it's sleepy time down South / Night train / Lip / Whistle stop / Five months, two weeks, two days / Banana split for my baby / Be mine (little baby) / When you're smiling / Sheikh of araby / Birth of the blues / Blow red blow / When the saints go marching in / Sentimental journey / There'll be no next time / Closer to the bone / I've got the world on a string / Much too young to lose my mind / Don't let a memory / Pennies from heaven / Baby, won't you please come home / Autumn leaves / Pump song / Boulevard of broken dreams / Natural guy / Beep beep / If you were the only girl in the world / Bourbon street blues / Sing sing sing / That old black magic / Judy / Felicia no capacia / That's my home / Moonglow / Gotta see baby tonight / Fee fie foo / Music goes 'round and around / Fever / Don't you take your love from me / Hey boy, hey girl / Lazy river / Hey boy, hey girl (reprise) / Nothing's too good for my baby / Oh Marie (alternate take) / I've got you under my skin / Don't take your love from me / You're just in love / Harlem nocturne / Glow worm / Just one of those things / All night long / Lover come back to me / Everybody knows / Ain't misbehavin' / Way down yonder in New Orleans / Three handed woman / St. Louis blues / Twist all night / John ping pong / Ooh look what you've done to me / Big Daddy / Sunday lover / Little girl blue / Scuba diver / I want you to be my baby / Shadrack / Next time / Lady of Spain / Hello lover, goodbye tears / Undecided / Come rain or come shine / Go back where you stayed last night / On the sunny side of the street / Exactly like you / Foggy day / How high the moon / Angelina / Zooma somma (medley) / Don't worry bout me / In the mood for love / Come back to sorrento / I gotta right to sing the blues / Robin Hood / Oh babe / Them there eyes / Honeysuckle rose / Tiger rag / Just because / Embraceable you / I got it bad and that ain't good / Should I / I can't believe that you're in love with me / White cliffs of Dover / Holiday / Greenback dollar bill / Love of my life (o sole mio) / Too marvellous for words / I wish you love / I would do most anything for you / Shy / Rock-a-doodle-doo / Young and in love / Someone to watch over me / Nearness of you / Indian love call / Just as much / Sometimes / You are my love / Whip-poor-will / I understand / If we never meet again / Mr. Wonderful / When day is done / All the things you are / When your lover has gone / You go to my head / Imagination / Fools rush in / As you desire me / You better go now / Good behaviour / You'll never know / Man I love / It's magic / What is this thing called love / Stormy weather / There'll never be another you / It's been a long, long time / You're driving me crazy / Stardust / What can I say after I say I'm sorry / Nitey nite / Hurt me / I keep forgetting / High school affair / Nothing in common / How are you fixed for love / S'posin' / Song is you / I'll get by / Never knew / I'll never smile again / Sweet and lovely / All the way / Lullaby of the leaves / East of the sun and west of the moon / I can't get started (with you) / Cocktails for two / Bim bam / Twinkle in your eye / Ten little women / Equator / Seven out / Kiss your hand madame / Love charm / Love nest / Put your mind at ease / It's better than nothing at all / Hold out for love / Good gracious baby / Handle with care / Dig that crazy chick / Hey there / I love Paris / On the street where you live / Song from Moulin Rouge / Three coins in the fountain / Too young / Rock-a-bye your baby with a Dixie melody / Love is a many splendoured thing / Around the world / La vie en rose / Bugs / Tennessee waltz / French poodle / Chantilly lace / Up jumped a rabbit / Just say I love her / Easy rockin' / Honey love / Street scene / Perdido / Kansas City / Love of my life (o sole mio 2nd version) / Ol' man river / Smilin' Billy / Skinny Minnie / Better twist now baby / Twistin' the blues / Continental twist / Tag that twistin' dolly / Come and do the twist / O ma-ma twist / I feel good all over / Later, baby, later / Ol man river
BCD 15776 / Sep '94 / Bear Family

☐ GREATEST HITS
Lady in red / Music goes 'round and around / I'm an old cowhand (from the Rio Grande) / I'll be seeing you / I'll walk alone / My dreams are getting better all the time / Josephine please no lean on my bell / Hey ba ba re bop / Brooklyn boogie / Civilisation / Thousand island song / My cucuzza
JASCD 327 / Oct '94 / Jasmine

☐ LOUIS & KEELY (Prima, Louis & Keely Smith)
Night and day / All I do is dream of you / Make love to me / I don't know why / Tea for two / And the angels sing / I'm confessin' that I love you / Why do I love you / You're my everything / Cheek to cheek / I've grown accustomed to her face / Bei mir bist du schon
JASCD 326 / Jan '95 / Jasmine

☐ ON STAGE (Prima, Louis & Keely Smith)
JASCD 331 / Nov '95 / Jasmine

☐ ORIGINAL, THE
Buona sera / Oh Marie / Pennies from heaven / Angelina/Zooma zooma / Just a gigolo/I ain't got nobody / That old black magic / I've got you under my skin / Body and soul / It's magic / I'm in the mood for love / Night train / Banana split for my baby / Baby won't you please come home / Should I/I can't believe you're in love with me / Embraceable you/I got it bad and that ain't good / Basin Street blues/ When it's sleepy time down South / Music goes 'round and 'round
TO 864682 / 2 Feb '98 / Disky

☐ PRETTY MUSIC PRIMA STYLE VOL.1 & 2
Unforgettable / Ruby / Chicago / My Luanne / All through the day / Dearly beloved / There's a small hotel / My old flame / Sunday kind of love / It could happen to you / Young at heart / I'm old fashioned / Wonderland by night / Twilight time / By the light of the silvery moon / Moonlight in Vermont / I want some lovin' / I could have danced all night / Polka dots and moonbeams / You and the night and the music / Lovely way to spend an evening / Goodnight my love
JASCD 339 / Feb '98 / Jasmine

☐ REMEMBER (Prima, Louis & His Orchestra)
Robin Hood / St. Louis blues / I'll walk alone / Angeline / Some Sunday morning / I don't wanna be loved / You gotta see baby tonight / White cliffs of Dover / Just a gigolo / I ain't got nobody
DAWE 12 / Nov '93 / Magic

☐ RETURN OF THE WILD WEST (Prima, Louis & Keely Smith)
South of the border (Down Mexico way) / Come back to Sorrento / South Rampart Street Parade / I love you / For you / After you've gone / Grasshopper / Lonesome for you / Absent minded lover / I have but one heart / Ol' man mose / Chinatown, my Chinatown
JASCD 330 / Oct '94 / Jasmine

☐ RHYTHM MAN
It's the rhythm in me / Jamaica shout / Chinatown my Chinatown / Long about midnight / Worry blues / That's where the South begins / I still want you / Bright eyes / Sugar is sweet and so are you / Lady in red / Sing it way down low / Stardust / Chasing shadows / (Looks like) I'm breaking the ice / House rent party day / Le'ts have a jubilee / Basin street blues / In a little gypsy tearoom / Let's swing it / Put on an old pair of shoes / I'm living in a great big way / Swing me with rhythm
308662 / 20 Apr '98 / Hallmark

☐ TOGETHER (Prima, Louis & Keely Smith)
Together / Paradise / Teach me tonight / Nyow nyoy nyow (the pussycat song) / They can't take that away from me / I can't give you anything but love / When my baby smiles at me / Let's get away from it all / Mashuga / Let's call the whole thing off / Mutual admiration society / Begin the beguine
JASCD 325 / Feb '94 / Jasmine

☐ VERY BEST OF LOUIS PRIMA, THE
That's where the South begins / Stardust / Let's have a jubilee / (Looks like I'm) breaking the ice / It's the rhythm in me / Put on an old pair of shoes / Bright eyes / Swing me with rhythm / Chinatown, my Chinatown / Chasing shadows / Sugar is sweeter and so are you / In a little gypsy tea room / I'm living in a great big way / House rent party day / Jamaica shout / Let's swing it
SUMCD 4114 / May '97 / Summit

Prima Materia

☐ ALBERT AYLER'S BELLS (Prima Materia & Rashied Ali)
KFWCD 190 / Mar '97 / Knitting Factory

☐ MEDITATIONS (Prima Materia & Rashied Ali)
KFWCD 180 / Oct '96 / Knitting Factory

☐ MUSIC OF JOHN COLTRANE
KFWCD 158 / Feb '95 / Knitting Factory

Primal Fear

☐ PRIMAL FEAR
Primal fear / Chainbreaker / Silver and gold / Promised land / Formula one / Dollars / Nine lives / Tears of rage / Speedking / Battalions of hate / Running in the dust / Thunderdome
NB 302CD / 23 Mar '98 / Nuclear Blast

Primal Instinct

☐ HEART OF THE RAINFOREST
9632757022 / 24 Mar '98 / ETO

Primal Scream

☐ ECHO DEK
CRECD 224 / 27 Oct '97 / Creation

☐ GIVE OUT, BUT DON'T GIVE UP
Jailbird / Rocks / (I'm gonna) Cry myself blind / Funky jam / Big jet plane / Free / Call on me / Struttin' / Sad and blue / Give out but don't give up / I'll be there
CRECD 146 / Mar '94 / Creation

☐ PRIMAL SCREAM
Ivy Ivy Ivy / You're just dead skin to me / She power / You're just too dark to care / I'm losing more than I'll ever have / Gimme gimme teenage head / Kill the King / Lone Star girl
CRECD 054 / Sep '89 / Creation

☐ SCREAMADELICA
Movin' on up / Slip inside this house / Don't fight it, feel it / Higher than the sun / Come together / Damaged / Loaded / Shine like stars / Inner flight / I'm coming down
CRELPCD 076 / Sep '91 / Creation

☐ SONIC FLOWER GROOVE
Gentle Tuesday / Treasure trip / May the sun shine bright for you / Sonic sister love / Silent spring / Imperial / Love you / Leaves / Aftermath / We go down slowly rising
2292421822 / Jun '91 / WEA

☐ VANISHING POINT
Burning wheel / Kowalski / Stuka / Star / Get Duffy / Motorhead / Out of the void / Trainspotting / Medication / If they move, kill 'em / Long life
CRECD 178 / Jul '97 / Creation

Prime Movers

☐ ARC
Immortal / Interloper / Sheep / Crystalline / Revelation / Obsession / Rollercoaster / Sublime / Aural sea / Misled / Prelude: Dawn of love / Mandrake root / Breed 'n' burn
CND 005CD / Mar '93 / Cyanide

Prime Time

☐ UNKNOWN, THE
RS 0072882CD / 16 Mar '98 / Rising Sun

Prime Time Victim Show

☐ PRIME TIME VICTIM SHOW
35540052 / Jun '97 / Dig It All

Primer, John

☐ KEEP ON LOVIN' THE BLUES
Keep on lovin' the blues / Axe to grind / My pencil won't write no more / One minute / Oh yeah / When I reach out for your love / Close to you / You can't stop doing what you're doin' / Like a ship / I've been travellin' / Pay the price / Meet me at the crossroads
0630183832 / May '97 / Code Blue

Primettes

☐ LOOKING BACK (Primettes/Eddie Floyd)
Tears of sorrow: *Primettes* / Pretty baby: *Primettes* / Return of Stagger Lee: *Primettes* / Searching for my baby: *Primettes* / Baby won't you change your mind: *Primettes* / I'll get along: *Primettes* / All I need is you: *Primettes* / Bye bye baby: *Floyd, Eddie* / Never get enough of your love: *Floyd, Eddie* / I am her yo yo man: *Floyd, Eddie* / Lonely: *Floyd, Eddie* / Please don't leave me dear: *Floyd, Eddie* / I'll never find another girl like you: *Floyd, Eddie* / When you're in love: *Floyd, Eddie* / Whip: *Floyd, Eddie*
EMBCD 3398 / 30 Mar '98 / Ember

Primevals

☐ LIVE A LITTLE
St. Jack / Justify / Cotton head / Fertile mind / Prairie chain / Heya / Sister
ROSE 123CD / Sep '87 / New Rose

Primich, Gary

☐ COMPANY MAN
Company man / Turn your damper down / My home / Briar patch / What's it gonna be / Ain't you trouble / Big Daddy's coming home / Dry country blues / Hook, line and sinker / Varmint / Cold hand in mine / Jailbird
CDBT 1136 / Mar '97 / Black Top

☐ MR. FREEZE
Bad poker hand / I'm the one / Route 90 / Mr. Freeze / Go on fool / Dummy on your knee / Dallas Texas / Slap you silly / Jenny Brown / You came a long way from St. Louis / Red top / Easy ridin' mama / Let me go home whiskey
FF 70649 / Oct '96 / Flying Fish

☐ TRAVELLIN' MOOD
House rockin' party / Intro / Ding dong Daddy / Shake the boogie / Beer drinkin' woman / Triple trouble / Wild cat tamer / Caravan / Travellin' mood / She was a dreamer / School of hard knocks / Put the hammer down / Poodle bites / Knock me a kiss
FF 70635 / May '97 / Flying Fish

Primitive Instinct

☐ FLOATING TANGIBILITY
Heaven / 11-11 / Circles / Keep on running / Friend / Hypnotic / Slaves / One way man / Shame / Triludan
CYCL 003 / Jul '97 / Cyclops

Primitives

☐ BBC SESSIONS, THE
Stop killing me / Crash / Space head / Where the wind blows / Across my shoulder / Buzz buzz buzz / As tears go by / Dream walk baby / Ocean blue / Everything's shining bright / She don't need you / Things get in your way / Keep me in mind / Way behind me
PILOT 038 / 3 Aug '98 / Burning Airlines

☐ BEST OF THE PRIMITIVES, THE
Crash / Spacehead / Shadow / Thru the flowers / Nothing left / Out of reach / Summer rain / Sick of it / All the way down / Secrets / Can't bring me down / Way behind me / Noose / I almost touched you / You are the way / Lead me astray / Slip away / Give this world to you / Empathise / Earth thing / All the way down (beat version)
74321393432 / Jun '96 / Camden

☐ BOMBSHELL
Crash / Stop killing me / Sick of it / Way behind me / Thru the flowers / Lead me astray / Secrets / Out of reach / You are the way / Empathise / Earth thing / All the way down / Don't want anything to change / Way behind me (Acoustic) / Stop killing me (Acoustic) / As tears go by / Secrets (Demo) / Crash (Demo)
74321226352 / Sep '94 / RCA

Primo, Angelo

☐ CITY SCAPE
City scape / Inside my heart / Sunrise Brazilian / Midnight tango / Rain dance / Last time I saw your smile / Windswept / Conversations / When I needed you / Since you went away / When love is gone / For your love / Makeeba
AKA 1994 / 24 Nov '97 / AKA

Primordia

☐ GLEAMING EYE, THE
WSCD 003 / Oct '96 / World Serpent

Primordial

☐ JOURNEY'S END, A
AMAZON 015CD / 22 Jun '98 / Misanthropy

Primordial Undermind

☐ YET MORE WONDERS OF THE...
SGCD 7 / Sep '97 / September Gurls

Primrose, Christine

☐ AITE MO GHAOIL (PLACE OF MY HEART)
Ceann loch an duin / Curstaidh brus (christine brus) / Duanag a' chiobair (the shepherd's song) / Carlobhagh (carloway) / Strath ban (srathbane) / Coille an fhasaich (the woods of fhasach) / Greas ort dhachaidh a dh'eilean a'fhraoich (hurry on home / 'si morag 'si morag (it was morag) / ''nuair a chi thu caileag bhoidheach (whenever you see a pr / Calum sgaire / Nan caedaicheadh an tide dhomh (if the world would permit m / Nan tigheadh tu idir (if only you would come to me) / Comunn uibhist's bharraidh (the uist and barra association / ''n teid thu leam mo highean donn (will you come to me my b / A fhleasgaigh oig bi furachail (young men be cautious)
COMD 1006 / Feb '94 / Temple

☐ STU NAM CHUMHNE
COMD 2024 / Apr '95 / Temple

Primus

☐ BROWN ALBUM, THE
IND 90126 / Jul '97 / Interscope

☐ FRIZZLE FRY
To defy the laws of tradition / Too many puppies / Frizzle fry / You can't kill Michael Malloy / Pudding time / Spaghetti western / To defy / Ground hog's day / Mr. Know it all / John the fisherman / Toys go winding down / Sathington Willoby / Harold of the rocks
CAROLCD 1619 / Jun '97 / Caroline

☐ PORK SODA
Pork chop's little ditty / My name is mud / Welcome to this world / Bob / DMV / Ol' diamond back sturgeon / Nature boy / Wounded knee / Pork soda / Pressman / Mr. Krinkle / Air is getting slippery / Hamburger train / Hail santa
IND 92257 / Jul '96 / Interscope

☐ RHINOPLASTY
IND 90214 / 22 Jun '98 / Interscope

☐ SAILING THE SEAS OF CHEESE
Seas of cheese / Here come the bastards / Sgt. Baker / American life / Jerry was a race car driver / Eleven / Is it luck / Grandad's little ditty / Tommy the cat / Sathington waltz / Those damned blue-collar tweekers / Fish on (fisherman chronicles, chapter II) / Los bastardos
IND 91659 / Sep '97 / Interscope

☐ SUCK ON THIS
John the fisherman / Ground hog's day / Heckler / Pressman / Jellikit / Tommy the cat / Pudding time / Harold of the rocks / Frizzle fry
CAROLCD 1620 / Jun '97 / Caroline

☐ TALES FROM THE PUNCH BOWL
Professor nutbutter's house of treats / Mrs. Blaileen / Wynona's big brown beaver / Southbound pachyderm / Space farm / Year of the parrot / Hellbound 17 and 1/2 / Glass sandwich / Del davis tree farm / De anza jig / On the tweek again / Over the electric grapevine / Captain shiner
IND 92553 / Aug '96 / Interscope
IND 92665 / Jul '96 / Interscope

Prina, Stephen

☐ PUSH COMES TO LOVE
DC 147CD / 4 May '98 / Frontier

Prince

☐ 1999
1999 / Little red corvette / Delirious / Let's pretend we're married / DMSR / Automatic / Something in the water (does not compute) / Free / Lady cab driver / All the critics love U in New York / International lover
9237202 / Nov '84 / WEA

☐ AROUND THE WORLD IN A DAY
Around the world in a day / Paisley Park / Condition of the heart / Raspberry beret / Tambourine / America / Pop life / Ladder / Temptation
9252862 / May '85 / Paisley Park

☐ BATMAN (Original Soundtrack)
Future / Electric chair / Arms of Orion / Partyman / Vicki waiting / Trust / Lemon crush / Scandalous / Batdance
9259362 / Feb '95 / WEA

☐ BIOGRAPHY SERIES
10020 / 3 Nov '97 / Metro Independent

☐ CHAOS AND DISORDER
Chaos and disorder / I like it there / Dinner with Dolores / Same December / Right the wrong / Zannalee / I rock therefore I am / Into the light / I will / Dig u better dead / Had u
9362463172 / Jul '96 / WEA

☐ COME
Come / Space / Pheromone / Loose / Papa / Race / Dark / Solo / Letitgo / Orgasm
9362457002 / Dec '96 / WEA

☐ CONTROVERSY
Private joy / Ronnie talk to Russia / Let's work / Annie Christian / Jack U off / Sexuality / Controversy / Do me baby
256950 / '84 / WEA

☐ CRYSTAL BALL (4CD Set)
Crystal ball / Dream factory / Acknowledge me / Ripopgodazippa / Lovesign / Hide the bone / 2morrow / So dark / Movie star / Tell me how / Wanna be done / Interactive / Da bang / Calhoun Square / What's my name / Crucial / Honest man / Sexual suicide / Cloreen Bacon / Skin / Good love / Strays of the world / Days of wild / Last heart / Poom poom / She gave her angels / 18 and over / Ride / Get loose / P.control / Make your Mama / Happy / Goodbye / Truth / Don't play me / Circle of amour / 3rd eye / Dianne / Man in a uniform / Animal kingdom / Other side of the pillow / Fascination / One of your tears / Comeback / Welcome 2 the dawn
BCT 9871CD / 16 Mar '98 / BC

☐ DIAMONDS AND PEARLS (Prince & The New Power Generation)
Thunder / Daddy pop / Diamonds and pearls / Cream / Strollin' / Willing and able / Gett off / Walk don't walk / Jughead / Money don't matter 2 night / Push / Insatiable / Live 4 love
7599253792 / Feb '95 / Paisley Park

☐ DIRTY MIND
Dirty mind / When you were mine / Do it all night / Gotta broken heart again / Uptown / Head / Sister / Party up
256862 / Jan '86 / WEA

☐ EMANCIPATION (3CD Set)
Jam of the year / Right back here in my arms / Somebody's somebody / Get yo groove on / Courtin' time / Betcha by golly wow / We gets up / White mansion / Darned if I do / I can't make U love me / Mr. Happy / In this bed I scream / Sex in the summer / One kiss at a time / Soul sanctuary / Emale / Curious child / Dreamin' about U / Joint 2 joint / Holy River / Let's have a baby / Saviour / Plan / Friend lover sister mother wife / Slave / New world / Human body / Face down / La la la means I love you / Style / Sleep around / DA DA DA / My computer / One of us / Love we make / Emancipation
CDEMD 1102 / Nov '96 / New Power Generation

☐ EXODUS (New Power Generation)
NPG 61032 / Mar '95 / New Power Generation

☐ FOR YOU
For you / In love / Soft and wet / Crazy you / Just as long as we're together / Baby / My love is forever / So blue / I'm yours
256989 / Oct '87 / WEA

☐ GIRL 6 (Original Soundtrack)
How come u don't call me anymore / Hot thing / Adore / Cross / Girl 6 / Don't take 2 strangers / Nasty girl / Screams of passion / Count the days / She spoke 2 me / Pink cashmere / Girls and boys / Erotic city
9362462392 / Mar '96 / WEA

☐ GOLD EXPERIENCE, THE
Pussy control / Endorphinmachine / Shhh / We march / Most beautiful girl in the world / Dolphin / Now / 319 / Shy / Billy Jack Bitch / I hate U / Gold
9362459992 / Oct '95 / WEA

☐ GRAFFITI BRIDGE
Can't stop this feeling I got / Question of U / Round and round: *Campbell, Tevin* / Joy in repetition / Tick tick bang / Thieves in the temple / Melody cool / Graffiti bridge / Release it: *Time* / Elephants and flowers / We can funk / Love machine / Shake: *Time* / Latest fashion / Still would stand all time / New power generation
7599274932 / Aug '90 / WEA

☐ HITS AND B-SIDES, THE (3CD Set)
When doves cry / Pop life / Soft and wet / I feel for you / Why you wanna treat me so bad / When you were mine / Uptown / Let's go crazy / 1999 / I could never take the place of your man / Nothing compares 2 U / Adore / Pink cashmere / Alphabet Street / Sign o' the times / Thieves in the temple / Diamonds and pearls / 7 / Controversy / Dirty mind / I wanna be your lover / Head / Do me baby / Delirious / Little red corvette / I would die 4 U / Raspberry beret / If I was your girlfriend / Kiss / Peach / U got the look / Sexy MF / Gett off / Cream / Pope / Purple rain / Hello / 200 Balloons / Escape / Gotta stop (messin' about) / Horny toad / Feel U up / Girl / I love U in me / Erotic city / Shockadelica / Irresistible bitch / Scarlet pussy / La la la he he hee / She's always in my hair / Seventeen days / How come U don't call me anymore / Another lonely Christmas / God / 4 The tears in your eyes / Power fantastic
9362454402 / Sep '93 / Paisley Park

☐ HITS VOL.1, THE
When doves cry / Pop life / Soft and wet / I feel for you / Why you wanna treat me so bad / When you were mine / Uptown / Let's go crazy / 1999 / I could never take the place of your man / Nothing compares 2 U / Adore / Pink cashmere / Alphabet Street / Sign o' the times / Thieves in the temple / Diamonds and pearls / 7
9362454312 / Sep '93 / Paisley Park

☐ HITS VOL.2, THE
Controversy / Dirty mind / I wanna be your lover / Head / Do me baby / Delirious / Little red corvette / I would die 4 U / Raspberry beret / If I was your girlfriend / Kiss / Peach / U got the look / Sexy MF / Gett off / Cream / Pope / Purple rain
9362454352 / Sep '93 / Paisley Park

☐ INTERVIEW DISC
SAM 7009 / Nov '96 / Sound & Media

☐ LOVESEXY
I no / Alphabet Street / Glam slam / Anna Stesia / Dance on / Lovesexy / When 2 R in love / I wish U heaven / Positivity
9257202 / May '88 / Paisley Park

☐ METROPOLITAN ORCHESTRA PLAYS PRINCE, THE (Metropolitan Orchestra)
EMPRCD 705 / Mar '97 / Emporio

☐ NEW POWER SOUL (New Power Generation)
New power soul / Mad sex / Until u're in my arms again / When U love somebody / Shoo-bed-ooh / Push it up / Freaks on this side / Come on / One / (I like) funky music
74321605982 / 29 Jun '98 / New Power Generation/RCA

☐ PARADE (Original Soundtrack - Under The Cherry Moon) (Prince & The Revolution)
Christopher Tracy's parade / New position / I wonder U / Under the cherry moon / Girls and boys / Life can be so nice / Venus de Milo / Mountains / Do U lie / Kiss / Anotherloverholenyohead / Sometimes it snows in April
9253952 / Apr '86 / WEA

☐ PRINCE
I wanna be your lover / Why you wanna treat me so bad / Sexy dancer / When we're dancing close and slow / With you / Bambi / Still waiting / I feel for you / It's gonna be lonely
256772 / '86 / WEA

☐ PRINCE SONGBOOK, THE (A Tribute To Prince) (Various Artists)
Let's pretend we're married: *Turner, Tina* / When you were mine: *Lauper, Cyndi* / Love thy will be done: *Martika* / On the way up: *Fiorillo, Elisa* / Nothing compares 2 u: *Mary J* / Baby go go: *Hendryx, Nona* / 17 days: *Living Color* / Manic Monday: *Bangles* / Sex of it: *Kid Creole* / Do me baby: *Morgan, Meli'sa* / Sugar walls: *Easton, Sheena* / I hear your voice: *Labelle, Patti*
VSOPCD 248 / 26 Jan '98 / Connoisseur Collection

☐ PRINCE: INTERVIEW COMPACT DISC
CBAK 4018 / Nov '89 / Baktabak

☐ PURPLE RAIN (Original Soundtrack) (Prince & The Revolution)
Let's go crazy / Take me with U / Beautiful ones / Computer blue / Darling Nikki / When doves cry / I would die 4 U / Baby I'm a star / Purple rain
9251102 / Feb '95 / WEA

☐ PURPLE REIGN (The Synth Plays Prince) (Various Artists)
Take me with you / I wish u heaven / Arms of Orion / Raspberry beret / Kiss / Nothing compares 2 u / Girls and boys / 1999 / Little red Corvette / Paisley park / I feel 4 u / Thieves in the temple / Trust / Sign o' the times / Purple rain
308832 / 11 May '98 / Hallmark

☐ SIGN O' THE TIMES (Original Soundtrack - 2CD Set)
Play in the sunshine / Housequake / Ballad of Dorothy Parker / It / Starfish and coffee / Slow love / Hot thing / Forever in my life / U got the look / If I was your girlfriend / Strange relationship / I could never take the place of your man / Cross / It's gonna be a beautiful night / Adore / Sign o' the times
9255772 / Apr '87 / Paisley Park

☐ SYMBOL
My name is Prince / Sexy MF / Love 2 the 9s / Morning papers / Max / Segue / Blue light / I wanna melt with U / Sweet baby / Continental / Damn U / Arrogance / Flow / 7 / And God created woman / Three chains o' gold / Sacrifice of Victor
9362450372 / Oct '92 / Paisley Park

☐ SYMBOLIC BEGINNING (2CD Set) (94 East)
Just another sucker / If you feel like dancin' / Lovin' cup / Games / Dance to the music of the world / One man jam / If you see me / Games / I'll always love you / Better than you think / If we don't / You can be my teacher / Love love love / Dance to the music of the world / If you see me / Games / Better than you think
CPCD 81042 / Oct '97 / Charly

Prince Alla

☐ ONLY LOVE CAN CONQUER (Prince Alla 1976-1979)
BAFCD 14 / Mar '97 / Blood & Fire

Prince Buster

☐ FABULOUS GREATEST HITS
Earthquake / Texas hold-up / Freezing up Orange Street / Free love / Julie / Take it easy / Judge dread / Too hot / Ghost dance / Ten commandments / Al Capone / Barrister pardon
MSCD 1 / 23 Mar '98 / Prince Buster

☐ JUDGE DREAD
BBCD 809 / 23 Mar '98 / Blue Beat

☐ JUDGE DREAD ROCK STEADY/SHE WAS A ROUGH RIDER
Judge dread / Shearing you / Nothing takes the place of you / Ghost dance / Rock with feeling / Sweet appeal / Dark street / Judge dread dance / Show it now / Raise your hands / Change is gonna come / Rough rider / Dreams to remember / Scorcher / Hypocrites / Walk with love / Taxation / Bye bye baby / Tenderness / Wine or grind / Can't keep on running / Closer together / Going to the river
LOMACD 21 / Feb '94 / Loma

☐ ORIGINAL GOLDEN OLDIES VOL.1
Black head / Chineman / They got to come / Time longer than rope / Tommy will tell / Madness / Wash wash / Enjoy yourself / Danny dame and lorraine / Over and over / Creation
PBCD 9 / 23 Mar '98 / Prince Buster

☐ ORIGINAL GOLDEN OLDIES VOL.2
Oh carolina / Humpty dumpty / Millie girl / They got to come / Helena gency ten / African blood / Chubby / Shake a leg / Money can't buy life / War paint / Black head / Chineman
PBCD 10 / 23 Mar '98 / Prince Buster

☐ PROPHET, THE
LG 21100 / Sep '94 / Lagoon

Prince Charles

☐ DEAD IN THE PROJECTS, DEAD IN AMERICA (Prince Charles & The City Beat Band)
RE 096CD / Jun '97 / ROIR

☐ GREATEST HITZ (Prince Charles & The City Beat Band)
RE 115CD / Jun '97 / ROIR

Prince Charming Presents

☐ PSYCHOTROPICAL HEATWAVE
WSCD 013 / Dec '96 / Word Sound Recordings

Prince Far-I

☐ BLACKMAN LAND
Message from the king / Dream / Reggae music moving / Black man land / Marble stone / Wish I have a wing / Armageddon / Commandment of drugs / Badda card / Moses Moses / Some with roof / Foggy road / Put it out / King of kings / Ghetto living / River of Jordan
CDFL 9005 / Sep '90 / Frontline

☐ CRY TUFF DUB ENCOUNTER VOL.1
Message / Visitor / Right Way / Long Life / Encounter / Ghardaia Dub / Mansion of the almighty / Mozabites / Prince Of Peace / Abderrahmane
PSCD 13 / Apr '97 / Pressure Sounds

☐ CRY TUFF DUB ENCOUNTER VOL.3 (Prince Far-I & The Arabs)
PSCD 007 / Jan '96 / Pressure Sounds

☐ DUB TO AFRICA (Prince Far-I & The Arabs)
PSCD 002 / Apr '95 / Pressure Sounds

☐ DUBWISE
Throw away your gun / Love divine dub / If you want to do ya dub / Jah do that dub / No more war / Suru lere dub / Anambra dub / Kaduna dub / Oyo dub / Borno dub / Bendel dub / Ondo dub / Ogun dub
CDFL 9019 / Jun '91 / Frontline

☐ HEALTH AND STRENGTH
Frontline speech / Brother Joe / House of Jah / Health warning / Weatherman Tam / When the kning comes on earth / Eazy squeeze / Solomon's wisdom / Will to win / Clean hands pure heart / Leave Babylon
PSCD 18 / 23 Mar '98 / Pressure Sounds

☐ MEGABIT 25 1922 DUB
TWCD 1066 / 22 Sep '97 / Tamoki Wambesi

☐ MUSICAL REVUE (Prince Far-I & Suns Of Arqa)
RE 161CD / Jun '97 / ROIR

☐ SPEAR OF THE NATION (Umkhonto We Sizwe)
Survival / Ask ask / African queen / Stop the war / Jerry doghead / Special request
TWCD 1013 / Jul '93 / Tamoki Wambesi

☐ VOICE OF THUNDER
Ten commandments / Tribute to Bob Marley / Hold the fort / Everytime I hear the word / Head of the Buccaneer / Shall not dwell in wickedness / Give I strength / Kingdom of God / Coming from the rock / Skinhead
CDTRLS 204 / May '90 / Trojan

Prince Hammer

☐ RESPECT I MAN
TWCD 1026 / Oct '95 / Tamoki Wambesi

Prince Ital Joe

☐ LIFE ON THE STREETS (Prince Ital Joe & Marky Mark)
Life in the streets (intro) / United / Rastaman vibration / Happy people / To be important / In love / Babylon / Love of a mother / Into the light / In the 90's / Prankster / Life in the streets
4509963182 / Mar '95 / East West

Prince Jammy

☐ DANCEHALL KILLERS VOL.1
792062 / Nov '92 / Greensleeves

☐ HIS MAJESTY'S DUB (Prince Jammy & King Tubby)
SJCD 003 / Apr '93 / Sky Juice

☐ KAMIKAZI DUB
Throne of blood / Brothers of the blade / Shoalin temple / Kamikaze / Oragami black belt / Fist of fury / Opium den / Swords of vengeance / Downtown Shangai rock / Waterfront gang war
CDTRL 174 / Feb '97 / Trojan

☐ OSBOURNE IN DUB (Prince Jammy Presents Johnny Osbourne In Dub) (Prince Jammy/Johnny Osbourne)
Loving tonight / Reggae stylee / Dance dub / Jah is with you / Chopping dub / Pumping dub / Double trouble / See no evil / Pure is the soul / Rise up
CPCD 8307 / Aug '97 / Charly

☐ SLENG TENG EXTRAVAGANZA
792042 / Nov '92 / Greensleeves

☐ UHURU IN DUB (Prince Jammy Presents Black Uhuru In Dub) (Prince Jammy/Sly & Robbie)
Eden dub / Mystic mix / His imperial majesty / Weeping willow / Bad girls dub / Tonight is the night / Firehouse special / African culture / Crisis dub / Sound man style
CPCD 8281 / May '97 / Charly

Prince Jazzbo

☐ HEAD TO HEAD CLASH (Prince Jazzbo & I-Roy)
RASCD 3039 / May '89 / Ras

☐ STRAIGHT TO PRINCE JAZZBO'S HEAD (Various Artists)
CC 2718 / Apr '95 / Crocodisc

Prince Lincoln

☐ 21ST CENTURY (Prince Lincoln & Royal Rasses)
15STHCDA 01 / Apr '97 / 1-5 South

Prince Paul

☐ PSYCHOANALYSIS
WSCD 010 / Feb '97 / Word Sound Recordings

Princes Of Time

☐ PRINCES OF TIME
MAS 004 / Mar '96 / Mas I Mas

Princess Sharifa

☐ HERITAGE
ARICD 093 / Jan '94 / Ariwa Sounds

☐ TIME WILL TELL
NGCD 555 / 24 Nov '97 / Twinkle

Principal Edwards Magic Theatre

☐ SOUNDTRACK & ASMOTO RUNNING BAND
Enigmatic insomniac machine / Sacrifice / Death of Don Quixote / Third sonnet to sundry notes of music / To a broken guitar / Pinky / McAlpine's dream / McAlpine verses the asmoto / Asmoto running band / Asmoto celebration / Further asmoto celebration / Total glycerol esther / Freef (R') all / Autumn lady dancing / Kettering song / Weirdsong of breaking through at last
SEECD 412 / Oct '94 / See For Miles

Principato, Tom

☐ BLUE LICKS AND VOODOO THINGS
VDCD 111 / Jun '96 / Voodoo

☐ REALLY BLUE
Every minute, every hour / Sweet little woman / One for Danny / Stranger's eyes / Walkin' blues / Really blue / Standing at the crossroads again / In orbit / Kansas City blues / Baby please / In another dream / Here in my heart
VDCD 115 / May '97 / Voodoo

Principle

☐ DAMNED, THE (Principle & Silent Eclipse)
HAUS 2 / Jan '94 / Tribehaus Recordings

Principle, Peter

☐ REVAUX AU BONGO
MTM 2 / Nov '88 / Made To Measure

☐ SEDIMENTAL JOURNEY
MTM 4 / May '93 / Made To Measure

☐ TONE POEMS
MTM 18 / Nov '88 / Made To Measure

Prine, John

☐ GREAT DAYS (The John Prine Anthology/2CD Set)
Illegal smile / Spanish pipedream / Hello in there / Sam Stone / Paradise / Donald and Lydia / Late John Garfield blues / Yes I guess they should name a drink after me / Great compromise / Sweet revenge / Please don't bury me / Christmas in prison / Dear Abby / Blue umbrella / Common sense / Come back to us Barbara Lewis Hare Krishna Beauregard / Saddle in the rain / He was in heaven before he died / Fish anad whistle / That's the way that the world goes round / Bruised orange (chain of sorrow) / Sabu visits the twin cities alone / Automobile / Killing the blues / Down by the side of the road / Living in the future / It's happening to you / Storm windows / One red rose / Souvenirs / Aimless love / Oldest baby in the world / People putting people down / Unwed Fathers / Angel from montgomery / Linda goes to Mars / Bad boy / Speed of the sound of loneliness / It's a big old goofy world / Sins of Memphisto / All the best
8122714002 / Feb '94 / Atlantic

☐ LIVE ON TOUR
Picture show / Quit hollerin' at me / You got gold / Unwed fathers / Space monkey / Late John Garfield blues / Storm windows / Jesus the missing years / Humidity built the snowman / Illegal smile / Daddy's little pumpkin / Lake Marie / If I could / Stick a needle in my eye / You mean so much to me
OBR 015 / May '97 / Oh Boy

☐ LOST DOGS AND MIXED BLESSINGS
New train / Ain't hurtin' nobody / All the way with you / We are the lonely / Lake Marie / Humidity built the snowman / Day is done / Quit hollerin' at me / Big fat love / Same thing happend to me / This love is real / Leave the lights on / He forgot that it was Sunday / I love you so much it hurts
RCD 10333 / Mar '97 / Rykodisc

☐ PRIME PRINE
7567815042 / Feb '95 / WEA

Prinknash Abbey Monks

☐ CHRISTMAS CHANT (Prinknash Abbey Monks & Stanbrook Abbey Nuns)
Laetundebus / Christus factus est / Christe Redemptor / Dominus dixit / Isiah ch9, vv1-6 / Verbum Caro / Alma Redemptoris Mater / Dominus dixit / Kyrie eleison / Gloria in excelsis / Omnes de Saba / Alleluia / Laetentur / Sanctus (and Benedictus) / Agnus Dei / In splendoribus / Angelus ad Virginem / Ecce Nomen / Quem Vidistis / Angelus ad pastores / Hodie Christus natus est / Puer natus
CDSDL 369 / Oct '88 / Saydisc

Prins, Patrick

☐ MOVIN' MELODIES (2CD Set)
5406782 / Mar '97 / A&M

Printed At Bismark's Death

☐ TEN MOVEMENTS
EFA 112252 / Jan '94 / Danse Macabre

Prior, Andy

☐ ALRIGHT, OK YOU WIN
Alright, OK you win / Nevertheless (I'm in love with you) / I've got you under my skin / I'm a fool to want you / Beware the man with love in his eyes / Love changes everything / Our summer of love / You make me feel so young / All the things you are / Lover / In this world with you / Almost like being in love / Yeh yeh / Dream is a wish
CDG 10 / Nov '94 / DG

☐ AT LAST
At last / If I should lose you / Laura / Recipe for love / Very thought of you / Tangerine / Time for love / Why bother with love / Nearness of you / Sweet Georgia Brown / Moonlight in Vermont / West Side Stroy
CDG 6 / May '96 / DG

☐ MAGIC OF SINATRA, THE (A Tribute To Frank Sinatra & The Big Bands)
I've got the world on a string / Fly me to the moon: *Prior, Andy Orchestra* / Too close for comfort / Shadow of your smile / In the wee small hours of the morning: *Canale, Donna* / They can't take that away from me / In the mood: *Prior, Andy Orchestra* / All the way / Goody goody / I'll never smile again: *Prior, Andy Orchestra* / That old black magic / All or nothing at all / Strangers in the night: *Prior, Andy Orchestra* / Come rain or come shine / Brazil: *Canale, Donna* / Nice 'n' easy / Luck be a lady: *Prior, Andy Orchestra* / I wish you love / New York New York
PFLCD 1 / 8 Nov '97 / Perfectly Frank

☐ SHOT IN THE DARK, A (Prior, Andy & His Night Owls)
River stay 'way from my door / Hot toddy / Nightingale sang in Berkeley Square / Naked gun / I wish I were in love again / South Rampart Street Parade / That old black magic / Too little time / Peter Gunn / Puttin' on the ritz / Dragnet / Where or when / Warm breeze / Mack the knife / Victor and Hugo / Serenade in blue / Pennsylvania 6-5000 / Learning the blues
CDG 7 / '93 / DG

Prior, Maddy

☐ CAROLS AND CAPERS (Prior, Maddy & The Carnival Band)
Boar's head / Away in a manger / My dancing day / Monsieur Charpentier's Christmas stomp / See amid the winter's snow / Boy was born / Poor little Jesus / Turkey in the straw/Whiskey before breakfast / Wassail / Joy to the world / Cradle song / Shepherds rejoice / Old Joe Clark
PRK CD9 / Nov '95 / Park

☐ CHANGING WINDS
To have and to hold / Pity the poor / Night porter / Bloomers / Acappella Stella / Canals / Sovereign prince / Ali Baba / Mountain / In fighting / Another drink
BGOCD 213 / Dec '93 / Beat Goes On

☐ FLESH AND BLOOD
Sheath and knife / Rolling english road / Honest work / Finlandia / Hind horn / Bitty withy / Who am I / Cruel Mother / Boy on a horse / Jade / Brother Lawrence / Laugh and the kiss / Point / Heart of stone
PRKCD 38 / Apr '97 / Park

☐ FYRE AND SWORD (Prior, Maddy & Janet Russell)
Border spirit/Lock the door Lariston / Jackie Latin / Kinmont Willie / Dowie dens of Yarrow / Death of Parcy Reed / Dacre's gone to the war / Twa Corbies / Foray / Sleep my babe / Hughie the Graeme / Lord Maxwell's last goodnight / Battle of Otterburn / Lament of the border widow / Raiders / Peace on the border
FECD 131 / Apr '98 / Fellside

☐ HANG UP SORROW AND CARE
Prodigal's resolution / Playford tunes / World is turned upside down / Jovial begger / Leathern bottel / Iantha / An thou were my Ain Thing / Oh that I had but a fine man / Now O now I needs must part / Man is for the woman made / Northern catch/Little Barley Corne / Granny's delight/My Lady Foster's delight / Round of three country dances in one / Youth's the season made for joys / In the days of my youth / Never weatherbeaten saile / Old Simon the king
PRKCD 31 / Oct '95 / Park

☐ HAPPY FAMILIES (Prior, Maddy & Rick Kemp)
Happy families / Happy families / Rose / Mother and child / Here comes midnight / Bewcastle / Who's sorry now / Fire on the line / Goodbye / Alex / Low flying / Happy familes (reprise) / Bewcastle (instrumental)
PRKCD 4 / Aug '91 / Park

☐ MEMENTO (The Best Of Maddy Prior)
After the death / Long shadows / Grey funnel line / Baggy pants / Rose / Commit the crime / Newcastle / Mater dolorosa / Woman in the wings / Face to face / Doffin' mistress / Mother and child / Accappella Stella / Sovereign Prince / Deep in the darkest night / Alex / Paternoster / Hallelujah
PRKCD 028 / May '96 / Park

☐ SING LUSTILY AND WITH GOOD COURAGE (Prior, Maddy & The Carnival Band)
Who would true valour see / As pants the hart / How firm a foundation / Light of the world / O worship the king / O for a thousand tongues / Lo he comes
CDSDL 383 / Mar '94 / Saydisc

☐ TAPESTRY OF CAROLS, A (Prior, Maddy & The Carnival Band)
Sans Day carol / In dulci jubilo / God rest ye merry Gentlemen / It came upon a midnight clear / Holly and the ivy / Coventry carol / Ding dong merrily on high / Angel Gabriel / Angels from the realms of glory / Infant Holy / Virgin most pure / Unto us a boy is born / Rejoice and be merry / Joseph dearest / Personent Hodie / On Christmas night
CDSDL 366 / Mar '94 / Saydisc

☐ WOMAN IN THE WINGS
Woman in the wings / Cold flame / Mother and child / Gutter geese / Rollercoaster / Deep water / Long shadows / I told you so / Rosettes / Cats' eyes / Baggy pants
BGOCD 215 / Mar '94 / Beat Goes On

☐ YEAR
Snowdrops/Birth / Swimming song / Marigold/ Harvest home / Red and green / Long shadows / Somewhere along the road / What had you for supper / Saucy sailor / Fabled hare / Deep in the darkest night / Boys of bedlam / Twa corbies
PRKCD 20 / Oct '93 / Park

☐ YEAR/HAPPY FAMILIES (2CD Set)
PRKCD 33 / Dec '95 / Park

Prior, Snooky

☐ IN THIS MESS UP TO MY CHEST
ANT 0028CD / Sep '94 / Antones

Prism

☐ BEST OF PRISM, THE
RME 0113CD / 19 Jan '98 / Renaissance

☐ FROM THE VAULTS
RME 0145CD / Oct '97 / Renaissance

☐ LIVE 1975-1977
SP 97002 / Aug '97 / Shroom

Prison

☐ DISCIPLINE
LF 163CD / Jul '95 / Lost & Found

Prisonaires

☐ JUST WALKIN' IN THE RAIN
Just walking in the rain / Baby please / Dreaming of you / That chick's too young to fry / Softly and tenderly / My god is real / Prisoner's prayer / No more tears / I know / If I were king / I wish / Don't say tomorrow / What'll you do next / Two strangers / What about Frank Clemen / Friends call me a fool / Lucille / I want you / Surleen / All alone and lonely / Rockin' horse
BCD 15523 / Aug '91 / Bear Family

☐ JUST WALKIN' IN THE RAIN
CPCD 8120 / Aug '95 / Charly

Prisoners

☐ WISERMISERDEMELZA, THE
Go go / Hurricane / Somewhere / Think of me / Love me lies / Tonight / Here come the misunderstood / Dream is gone / For now and forever / Unbeliever / Far away
CDWIKD 937 / May '90 / Big Beat

Prisonshake

☐ FAILED TO MENACE
Last time I looked / Either way evil eye / Brilliant idea / Ever and ever / Some chick you fucked / Stumble / Asiento / Cigarette day / (Not without) Grace / Nothing has to hurt / Humor
OLE 0852 / Jul '94 / Matador

Pritchard, Bill

☐ DEATH OF BILL POSTERS
TMCD 004 / Aug '88 / Third Mind

Pritchard, Peter

☐ STUDIES FOR NEW ZEALAND HARMONIC PIANO VOL.2
WCL 11017 / Feb '96 / White Cloud

Privat, Jo

☐ MA BOITE A FRISSONS
MDCD 321 / Nov '96 / Media 7

☐ MANOUCHE PARTIE
NTCD 308 / Nov '96 / Nocturne

Private Class

☐ BEST OF PRIVATE CLASS, THE
HTCD 115 / 20 Apr '98 / Hot Productions

Pro Arte Guitar Trio

☐ AMERICA
WHL 2099 / Apr '96 / White Line

Pro-Pain

☐ BEST OF PRO-PAIN, THE
HGCD 0002 / 2 Mar '98 / High Gain

☐ CONTENTS UNDER PRESSURE
86622CIR
86632CIR / Jun '96 / Edel

☐ FOUL TASTE OF FREEDOM
Foul taste in freedom / Death on the dance floor / Murder 101 / Pound for pound / Every good boy does fine / Death goes on / Stench of piss / Picture this / Iraqnophobia / Johnny black / Lesson learned / God only knows
RR 90682 / Aug '96 / Roadrunner

☐ PRO-PAIN
HGCD 0001 / 2 Mar '98 / High Gain

☐ TRUTH HURTS
Make war (not love) / Bad blood / Truth hurts / Put the lights out / Denial / Let sleeping dogs lie / One man army / Down in the dumps / Beast is back / Switchblade knife / Death on the dancefloor / Pound for pound / Foul taste of freedom
RR 89852 / Sep '96 / Roadrunner

Pro-Tech

☐ ORBITING CATHEDRALS
EFA 084832 / 26 Aug '97 / Basic Channel

Problem Child

☐ IT'S NOT MY FAULT
LR 102 / 23 Feb '98 / Legend

Proby, P.J.

☐ CALIFORNIA LICENSE (Jett Powers)
Bop ting a ling / Blue moon/Cherry pie/Silhouettes / Linda tu / Stranded in the jungle / Tomorrow night / Stagger Lee / Caledonia / Mia amore / Hound dog / Forever my darling / Daddy's home / Rockin' pneumonia and the boogie woogie flu
SEECD 390 / Jan '97 / See For Miles

☐ EP COLLECTION, THE
Hold me / Tips of my fingers / Together / Sweet and tender romance / Somewhere / That means a lot / Lonely teardrop / She cried / Maria / My prayer / Wicked woman / Rockin' pneumonia / It's no good for me / I can't make it alone / Good things are coming my way / Nicky Hoeki / If I ruled the world / Christmas song / Silent night / White Christmas / Try to forget her / Linda Lu / Answer me / Stagger Lee / I love, therefore I am / Whatever will be will be (Que sera sera)
SEECD 440 / Jun '96 / See For Miles

☐ HEROES
American trilogy / I'm on fire / Hot California nights / Pools of thought / Love will tear us apart / Tainted love / In the air tonight / Old Fenian gun / Sign of the times / Heroes
CDPS 004 / 26 Jun '98 / Pulsar

☐ PHENOMENON/BELIEVE IT OR NOT
Just holding on / Mama told me not to come / Work with me Annie / Ling ting tong / Honey hush / Straight up / Butterfly high / She's looking good / You can't come home again / Pretty girls everywhere / Good rockin' tonite / Sanctification / When love has passed you by / I'm coming home / Give me time / Mary in the morning / It's your day today / I shall be released / Cry baby / Why baby why / I've got my eyes on you / I apologise baby / Judy in the junkyard
C5HCD 608 / Mar '98 / See For Miles

☐ THREE WEEK HERO
Three week hero / Day that Lorraine came down / Little friend / Empty bottles / Reflections (of your face) / Won't be long / Sugar Mama / I have a dream / It's too good to last / New directions / Today I killed a man / Medley
BGOCD 87 / Oct '90 / Beat Goes On

☐ VERY BEST OF P.J. PROBY, THE
Somewhere / Apologize / Let the water run down / No other love / Some enchanted evening / That means a lot / What ever will be (que sera sera) / Maria / Hold me / Together / Don't worry baby / You've come back / Zing went the strings of my heart / To make a big man cry / I can't make it alone / You can't come home again (if you leave now) / Question / It's your day today / Day that Lorraine came down / Pneumonia and boogie woogie flu
4961792 / 3 Aug '98 / Music For Pleasure

Process

☐ WORLD OF FIRE
CR 014CD / Jul '96 / Conversion

Proclaimers

☐ HIT THE HIGHWAY
Let's get married / More I believe / What makes you cry / Follow the money / These arms of mine / Shout shout / Light / Hit the highway / Long long time ago / I want to be a christian / Your childhood / Don't turn out like your mother
CDCHR 6066 / Feb '94 / Chrysalis

☐ SUNSHINE ON LEITH
I'm gonna be (500 miles) / Cap in hand / Then I met you / My old friend the blues / Sean / Sunshine on leith / Come on nature / I'm on my way / What do you do / It's Saturday night / Teardrops / Oh Jean
CD25CR 18 / Mar '94 / Chrysalis

☐ THIS IS THE STORY
Throw the 'r' away / Over and done with / Misty blue / Part that really matters / (I'm gonna) burn your playhouse down / Letter from America / Sky takes the soul / It broke my heart / First attack / Make my heart fly / Beautiful truth / Joyful Kilmarnock blues
CCD 1602 / Mar '93 / Chrysalis

Procol Harum

☐ 30TH ANNIVERSARY ANTHOLOGY (3CD Set)
Conquistador / She wandered through the garden fence / Something following me / Mabel / Cerdes (outside the gates of) / Christmas camel / Kaleidoscope / Salad days (are here again) / Good Captain Clack / Repent walpurgis / Quite rightly so / Shine on brightly / Skip softly (my moonbeams) / Wish me well / Rambling on / Magdalene (my regal zonophone) / In held twas I / Milk of human kindness / Too much between us / Devil came from Kansas / Boredem / Juicy John Pink / Wreck of the hesperus / All this and more / Crucification lane / Pilgrim's progress / Whiskey train / Dead man's dream / Still there'll be more / Nothing that I didn't know / About to die / Barnyard story / Piggy pig pig / Whaling stories / Your own chance / Whiter shade of pale / Lime street blues / Homburg / Good Captain Clack / Quite righty so / In the wee small hours of sixpence / Salty dog / Long gone geek / Monsieur Armand / Seem to have the blues (mostly all the time) / Whiter shade of pale / Whiter shade of pale / Homburg / Homburg / Comquistador / She wandered through the garden fence / Magdalene (my regal zonophone)
WESX 301 / 13 Oct '97 / Westside

☐ BEST OF PROCUL HARUM, THE
A whiter shade of pale / Quite rightly so / Conquistador / All this and more / Wreck of the hesperus / Too much between us / She wandered through the garden fence / Salad days (are here again) / Homburg / A salty dog / Kaleidoscope / Milk of human kindness / Good captain clack / Devil came from kansas / Boredom / Crucifiction lane
BRCD 106 / Jan '95 / BR Music

☐ BEST OF PROCUL HARUM, THE
REP 4680 / Feb '98 / Repertoire

☐ EXOTIC BIRDS AND FRUIT
Nothing but the truth / Beyond the pale / As strong as Samson / Idol / Thin end of the wedge / Monsieur Armand / Fresh fruit / Butterfly boys / New lamps for old
ESMCD 291 / Oct '95 / Essential

☐ GRAND HOTEL
Grand hotel / Roberts box / Fires (which burn brightly) / For liquorice John / Bring home the bacon / Souvenir of London / TV Caesar / Rum tale / Toujours l'amour
ESMCD 290 / Oct '95 / Essential

☐ HALCYON DAZE (The Best Of Procul Harum)
Whiter shade of pale / Cerdes (outside the gates of) / Kaleidoscope / Piggy pig pig / Too much between us / Quite rightly so / Shine on brightly / Salty dog / Long gone geek / Homburg / Magdalene (my regal zonophone) / Conquistador / Salad days (are here again) / Beyond the pale / Pandora's box
MCCD 315 / 6 Oct '97 / Music Club

☐ HOMBURG AND OTHER HATS (The Best Of Procul Harum)
ESSCD 295 / Oct '95 / Essential

☐ HOME
Whisky train / Dead man's dream / Still there'll be more / Nothing that I didn't know / About to die / Barnyard story / Piggy pig pig / Whaling stories / Your own choice
REP 4669 / Sep '97 / Repertoire

☐ LONG GOODBYE, THE (The Symphonic Procul Harum) (Various Artists)
Conquistador: *London Symphony Orchestra* / Homburg: *London Symphony Orchestra* / Grand hotel: *London Symphony Orchestra* / Pandora's box: *London Symphony Orchestra* / Repent walpurgis: *London Symphony Orchestra* / Strangers in space: *London Symphony Orchestra* / Simple sister: *London Philharmonic Orchestra* / (You can't) Turn back the page: *London Philharmonic Orchestra* / Butterfly boys: *London Philharmonic Orchestra* / Salty dog: *London Symphony Orchestra* / Whiter shade of pale: *London Symphony Orchestra* / Long goodbye: *Sinfonia Of London*
09026680292 / Feb '96 / RCA Victor

☐ PROCOL HARUM...PLUS
Conquistador / She wandered through the garden fence / Something following me / Mabel / Cerdes (outside the gates of) / Christmas camel / Kaleidoscope / Salad days (are here again) / Good Captain Clack / Repent Walpurgis / Whiter shade of pale / Homburg / Salad days (are here again) / Mabel / Cerdes (outside the gates of) / Something following me / Magdalene (my regal zonophone) / Quite rightly so / Shine on brightly
WESM 527 / May '98 / Westside

☐ PROCUL HARUM
Whiter shade of pale / Salty dog / Shine on brightly / Wreck of the Hesperus / Long gone geek / Whaling stories / Homburg / Conquistador / Whisky train / Good Captain Clack / Barnyard story / Kaleidoscope
CUCD 05 / Oct '94 / Disky

☐ PROCUL'S NINTH
Taking the time / Pandora's box / Fools gold / Uniquiet zone / Final thrust / I keep forgetting / Without a doubt / Piper's tune / Typewriter torment
ESMCD 292 / Oct '95 / Essential

☐ SALTY DOG, A
Salty dog / Milk of human kindness / Too much between us / Devil came from Kansas / Boredom / Juicy John Pink / Wreck of the Hesperus / All this and more / Crucifiction Lane / Pilgrims progress / Long gone geek
REP 4668 / Sep '97 / Repertoire

☐ SHINE ON BRIGHTLY
Quite rightly so / Shine on brightly / Skip softly my moonbeams / Wish me well / Rambling on / Magdalena / In held 'twas in I / Glimpses of Nirvana / 'Twas tea time at the circus / In the Autumn of my madness / Look to your soul / Grand finale / Whisky train / Dead man's dreams / Still there'll be more / Nothing that I didn't know / About to die / Barnyard story / Piggy pig pig / Whaling stories / Your own choice
REP 4667 / Sep '97 / Repertoire

☐ SOMETHING MAGIC
Something magic / Skating on thin ice / Wizard man / Mark of the claw / Strangers in space / Worm and the tree (1 to 3)
ESMCD 293 / Oct '95 / Essential

☐ WHITER SHADE OF PALE, A
RR 4666 / Jun '97 / Repertoire

Proctor, Chris

☐ ONLY NOW
Adrenaline / Tap room / Dialogues / Rambler/Kitty's wedding/Langstom's pony / Slickrock lament / Hotspot / Only now / October's window / Anymore
CDFF 665 / Mar '97 / Flying Fish

☐ STEEL STRING STORIES
FF 554CD / '92 / Flying Fish

☐ TRAVELOGUE
Mountaineer creek / War games / Ossana's gift / Valedictory / Henry's shuffle / Emerald winds / Rambling irishman-southwinds / Middle fork / Tammy-oh, what a beautiful morning / Seven-oh-four / Ruby tuesday
FF 70633CD / Apr '94 / Flying Fish

Prodigy

☐ EXPERIENCE
XLCD 110 / Nov '92 / XL

☐ FAT OF THE LAND
Smack my bitch up / Breathe / Diesel power / Funky shit / Serial thriller / Mindfields / Narayа / Firestarter / Climbatize / Fuel my fire
XLCD 121 / Jul '97 / XL

☐ MUSIC FOR THE JILTED GENERATION
Intro / Break and enter / Their law / Full throttle / Voodoo people / Speedway / Heat / Poison / No good / One love / 3 kilos / Skylined / Claustrophobic sting
XLCD 114 / Jul '94 / XL

☐ MUSIC FOR THE VOODOO PEOPLE (CD/Book Set)
What evil lurks / We gonna rock / Android / Everybody in the place
SB 011 / 2 Mar '98 / Sonic Book

Producer

☐ HELTER SKELTER (The Techno Annual Mixed By Producer/Clarkee - 2CD Set) (Various Artists)
CDHSR 098 / 18 May '98 / Helter Skelter

Product Of Society

☐ SCHIZOPHRENAGENIC
M 7020CD / Jul '96 / Mascot

Prof. B. Wolfff

☐ PROF. B. WOLFFF
SB 045 / 13 Jul '98 / Second Battle

Profane Grace

☐ SERENITY OF THE ENDLESS GRAVES
MORI 004CD / 22 Jun '98 / Dark Vinyl

Professionals

☐ PROFESSIONALS
Little boys in blue / Mad house / Just another dream / Kamikaze / 1-2-3 / Crescendo / Mods skins punks / Join the professionals / Has anybody got an alibi / All the way with you / Kick down the doors
CDOVD 459 / Jun '97 / Virgin

Professor Frisky

☐ ROUGHER
RN 0041 / Apr '95 / X-Rated

Professor Longhair

☐ BIG CHIEF
Big chief / Hey little girl / How long has that train been gone / I'm movin' on / Mess around / Medley / Tipitina / Little blues / Her mind is gone / Stagger Lee / Got my mojo working / Rum and coca cola / Mardi gras in New Orleans / Doin' it
CPCD 8231 / Nov '96 / Charly

☐ BIG EASY, THE
Big chief / Tipitina / Gone so long / How long has that train been gone / Messin' around / She ain't got no hair / Going to the mardi gras / Big chief / Her mind is gone / Baldhead
CDBM 094 / 28 Nov '97 / Blue Moon

☐ COMPLETE LONDON CONCERT, THE
Mess around / Hey now baby / Whole lotta lovin' / Go to the Mardi Gras / Bald head / Tipitna / Big chief / Every day I have the blues / Hey little girl / Rockin' pneumonia and the boogie woogie flu
JSPCD 202 / Jul '87 / JSP

☐ CRAWFISH FIESTA
ALCD 4718 / May '93 / Alligator

☐ GO TO THE MARDI GRAS
WCD 120609 / Jun '97 / Wolf

☐ HOUSEPARTY NEW ORLEANS STYLE (The Lost Sessions 1971-1972)
No buts and maybes / Gone so long / She walked right in / Thank you pretty baby / 501 boogie / Tipitina / Gonna leave this town / Cabbagehead / Hey little girl / Big chief / Cherry pie / Junco partner / Everyday I have the blues / G jam / Dr. Professor Longhair
ROUCD 2057 / Jun '95 / Rounder

☐ LAST MARDI GRAS
7567814062 / Jun '95 / Atlantic

☐ LIVE IN GERMANY
Stompin' with Fess / Mess around / Big chief / Everyday I have the blues / How long has that train been gone / Bald head (she ain't got no hair) / Whole lotta lovin' / Tipitina / Go to the Mardi Gras / Hey little girl / Got my mojo working
422379 / Feb '97 / Last Call

☐ LIVE ON THE QUEEN MARY
Tell me pretty baby / Mess around / Everyday I have the blues / Tipitina / I'm movin' on / Mardi Gras in New Orleans / Cry to me / Gone so long / Stagger Lee
S21 56844 / Apr '94 / One Way

☐ LONDON CONCERT, THE
Mess around / Hey now baby / Whole lot of loving / Go to the Mardi Gras / Baldhead / Tipitina / Big chief / Everyday I have the blues / Hey little girl / Lovely lady / Medley / Rockin' pneumonia / Rockin' with Fess / Pl boogie
JSPCD 805 / May '98 / JSP

☐ NEW ORLEANS PIANO
In the night / Tipitina / Ball the wall / Who's been fooling you / Hey wow baby / Mardi gras in new orleans / She walks right in / Hey little girl / Willie mae / Walk your blues away / Professor longhair blues / Boogie woogie / Longhair's blue rhumba
RSACD 808 / Oct '94 / Sequel

☐ ROCK 'N' ROLL GUMBO
Junco partner / Meet me tomorrow night / Doin' it / How long has that train been gone / Tipitina / Rockin' pnuemonia and the boogie woogie flu / Jambalaya / Mean ol' world / Stagger Lee / Mess around / Hey now baby / (They call me) Professor Longhair
5197462 / Apr '93 / Verve

☐ ROCK 'N' ROLL GUMBO
DD 3006CD / Feb '96 / Dancing Cat

Professor Shehab

☐ ATAXIA (Professor Shehab & Robert Musso)
BKA 0008 / 8 Jun '98 / Baraka Foundation

☐ EBN E SYNC (Professor Shehab & Loop)
WSCD 016 / Feb '97 / Word Sound Recordings

Professor's Blues Revue

☐ PROFESSOR STRUT (Professor's Blues Revue & Karen Carroll)
Come on down to the blues bar / I wanna be with you / Professor Strut / You're leaving me / Everything is you / They call it Stormy Monday / Jealous kind of woman / This little light of mine
DD 650 / Mar '97 / Delmark

Profit, Clarence

☐ SOLO AND TRIO SIDES
Don't leave me / There'll be some changes made / I got rhythm / Down home / Tropical nights / Tea for two / Body and soul / Blues / I didn't know what time it was / Dark eyes / Times Square blues / Hot and bothered / Azure / Kazoo moan: *Washboard Serenaders* / Washboards get together: *Washboard Serenaders* / In the middle of a kiss: *Georgia Washboard Stompers* / Every little moment: *Georgia Washboard Stompers*
CDMOIR 504 / Aug '93 / Memoir

Profondo Rosso

☐ NEXT STOP NEUROSIS
NEATD 1059 / 8 Sep '97 / Neat

☐ TO LIVE AND DIE IN THE UK
NEATD 1057 / Apr '97 / Neat

Profound Effect

☐ LASHING OUT
LF 156CD / Aug '95 / Lost & Found

Progenitor

☐ WISE WITHOUT EYES
Liberators having started / Nightbombing / Sway / Implosion / Meditator / Destroy Zeppelin l48 / Let tyrants tremble / She's gonna wind up on you / Tomorrow can wait
SBZCD 025 / 15 Sep '97 / Some Bizarre

Project 23

☐ 23
DOR 54CD / Oct '96 / Dorado

Project G-7

☐ TRIBUTE TO WES MONTGOMERY VOL.1, A
Impressions / Remembering Wes / Groove yard / Canadian sunset / Fried pies / Road song / Some rain or come shine / Serena / Yesterdays
ECD 22049 / Jul '93 / Evidence

☐ TRIBUTE TO WES MONTGOMERY VOL.2, A
More blues for Wes / Bock to bock / For heaven's sake / Montgomery blue / Finger pickin' / Never again / Polka dots and moonbeams / Samba Wes / West coast blues - three quarters of the house
ECD 22051 / Jul '93 / Evidence

Project Grape Escape

☐ VINE WAY TO ESCAPE, A
TX 2025 / 24 Nov '97 / Taxin

Project II

☐ TRANCA
BFLCD 4 / 1 Sep '98 / Butterfly

Project Kate

☐ WAY BIRDS FLY
EVR 028CD / May '97 / Equal Vision

Project Lo

☐ BLACK CANVAS
EFA 060142 / 26 Aug '97 / EFA

Project Pitchfork

☐ CHAKRA: RED
Human crossing / 2069 AD / Malicious delight / Alien crossing / Time / God wrote / Rush / December sadness / Temptation / Tower of lust / Celeste / I'll find my way home
SPV 8525942 / Mar '97 / SPV

☐ EARLY YEARS 1989-1993, THE
CD 99943182 / Sep '96 / SPV

☐ LAM BRAS
HYCD 21030 / Nov '92 / Hypertension

☐ RENASCENCE
SPV 05522063 / Oct '94 / SPV

☐ SOULS ISLAND
HYCD 210519 / Jul '93 / Hypertension

Project Pollen

☐ PROJECT POLLEN
EFA 123362 / 27 Oct '97 / Sideburn

Project X

☐ BLUEPRINT FOR XCESS
ESM 006 / 2 Mar '98 / Escape

☐ STRAIGHT EDGE REVENGE
LF 072 / Feb '94 / Lost & Found

Prolapse

☐ ITALIAN FLAG
Slash / Deanshanger / Cacophony no.A / Killing the bland / I hate the clicking man / Autocade / Tunguska / Flat velocity curve / Return of shoes / Day at death seaside / Bruxelles / Visa for violet and van / Three wooden heads
SCANCD 25 / 6 Oct '97 / Radarscope

☐ POINTLESS WALKS TO DISMAL PLACES
Serpico / Headless in a beat motel / Surreal Madrid / Doorstop rhythmic bloc / Burgundy spine / Black death ambulance / Chill blown / Hungarian suicide song / Tina this is Matthew stone
CDBRED 116 / 17 Nov '97 / Cherry Red

Promise

☐ PROMISE, THE
NTHEN 014CD / Sep '95 / Now & Then

Promise Ring

☐ HORSE LATITUDES
JT 1031 / Feb '97 / Jade Tree

☐ NOTHING FEELS GOOD
JT 1035CD / Oct '97 / Jade Tree

Prong

☐ FORCE FED/THIRD FROM SUN EP
185422 / Apr '97 / Southern

☐ PRIMITIVE ORIGINS
Disbelief / Watching / Cling to life / Denial / Dreams like that / In my view / Climate control / Persecution
185412 / Apr '97 / Southern

Propaganda

☐ 1,2,3,4
Vicious circle / Heaven give me words / Your wildlife / Only one word / How much love / Vicious / Ministry of fear / Wound in my heart / La carne, la morte e il diavolo
CDV 2625 / Apr '92 / Virgin

Propaghandi

☐ HOW TO CLEAN EVERYTHING
FAT 506CD / Aug '93 / Fatwreck Chords

☐ LESS TALK, MORE ROCK
FAT 666CD / May '96 / Fatwreck Chords

☐ PROPAGHANDI/I-SPY (Split CD) (Propaghandi/I-Spy)
FAT 666CD / Jul '95 / Fatwreck Chords

Propellerheads

☐ DECKSANDRUMSANDROCK ANDROLL
Take California / Echo and bounce / Velvet pants / Better / Oh yeah / History repeating: *Propellerheads & Shirley Bassey* / Bang on / Number of microphones / On her Majesty's secret service / Bigger / Cominagetcha / Spybreak
WALLCD 015 / 26 Jan '98 / Wall Of Sound

Propellor

☐ ORO
SCR 28 / 2 Mar '98 / Scratch

Prophanity

☐ STRONGER THAN STEEL
BLACK 010CD / 25 May '98 / Blackend

Prophet, Chuck

☐ BALINESE DANCER
Baton rouge / 110 degrees in the shade / Savannah / Balinese dancer / Starcrossed misbegotten love / One last dance / Who am I foolin / Heart breaks / Angel / Somewhere down the road
WOLCD 1031 / Feb '93 / China

☐ BROTHER ALDO
Look both ways / Rage and storm / Say it ain't so / Scarecrow / Queen bee / Brother aldo / Step right this way / Face to the wall / Tune of an evening / I'll be alright
FIRE 33022 / Oct '91 / Fire

☐ FEAST OF HEARTS
WOLCD 1061 / May '95 / China

☐ HOMEMADE BLOOD
Credit / You been gone / Inside track / Ooh wee / New Year's day / 22 Fillmore / Homemade blood / Whole lot more / Textbook case / K Mart family portrait / 'Til you came along / Parting song
COOKCD 114 / Mar '97 / Cooking Vinyl

Prophet, Michael

☐ BULL TALK
GRELCD 178 / Nov '92 / Greensleeves

☐ GUNMAN
GRELCD 509 / Apr '91 / Greensleeves

☐ LOVE IS AN EARTHLY THING
Rich man, poor man / Instructions / Never fall in love / Baby baby / Reggae music all right / Love is an earthly thing / It's a girl / Pretty face / Fussing and fighting
CPCD 8136 / Oct '95 / Charly

☐ SERIOUS REASONING
Fight to the top / Hear I prayer / Turn me loose / Gates of Zion / Praise you jah jah / Love and unity / Warn them / Conscious man / Give thanks / Serious reasoning
RRCD 48 / Jul '94 / Reggae Refreshers

Prophets Of Da City

☐ UNIVERSAL SOULJAZ
NATCD 54 / Jun '95 / Nation

Propositions

☐ AFRICANO
LHCD 002 / Jul '96 / Luv n' Haight

Prosser, Alan

☐ HALL PLACE
Sheepscar beck / Melancholy way / Harry Edward / Leaves of life / Two crows / Cromwell I / Something has got to change / Cromwell II / He feels no pain / Elham valley / Cold winter's night / By Lagan streams / Think of you / Money and love / Raise me up / Empire building
RD 001 / Feb '97 / Rafting Dog

Protector

☐ HERITAGE, THE
CC 020462CD / Jan '94 / Major

☐ LOST IN ETERNITY
CC 030057CD / Aug '95 / Major

Protheroe, Brian

☐ BRIAN'S BIG BOX (4CD Set)
Clog dancer / Money love / Moon over Malibu / Mickey Dollar dreams / Goodbye surprise / Pinball / Kinotata / Changing my tune / Monkey / Lady Belladonna / Fly now / Also in the limelight / Wrong Kinotata / Enjoy it / Good brand band / Scobo Queen / Cherry pie / Oh weeping will / Gertrude's garden hospital / Running through the city / I spy lady / Chase chase chase / Soft song / Pick-up / I/You / Every Roman knows / Evil eye / Under the greenwood tree / Dancing on black ice / Battling Annie / Never join the fire brigade / Hotel / Lucille / Face and I / Cold harbour / Dirty in love / Very very English / Practising attitudes / My lady's lament / Easy way to your heart / Tut tut girls / You can't keep a good girl down / Bored
BASTA 3090482 / Sep '97 / Basta

☐ I/YOU
I/You / Every Roman knows / Evil eye / Under the greenwood tree / Dancing on black ice / Battling Annie / Never join the fire / Brigade / Hotel / Lucille / Face and I
BASTA 3090452 / Sep '97 / Basta

☐ PICK UP
Enjoy it / Good brand band / Scobo Queen / Cherry pie / Oh weeping will / Gertrude's garden hospital / Running through the city / I spy lady / Chase chase chase / Soft song / Pick up
BASTA 3090462 / Sep '97 / Basta

☐ PINBALL
Clog dancer / Money love / Moon over Malibu / Mickey Dollar dreams / Goodbye surprise / Pinball / Kinotata / Changing my tune / Monkey / Lady Belladonna / Fly now / Also in the limelight / Wrong Kinotata
BASTA 3090472 / Sep '97 / Basta

Prototype 909

☐ JOINED AT THE HEAD
CAI 20032 / 29 Sep '97 / Caipirinha

Proud Ones

☐ OVER HERE OVER THERE
OHOT 002 / 9 Feb '98 / Reynolds

Proust, Jean-Michel

☐ HARLEM NOCTURNE
BB 899 / Apr '97 / Black & Blue

Proyecto Uno

☐ REMIXES, THE
61193410552 / 5 May '98 / Hola

Prud'Homme, Emile

☐ INOUBLIABLES DE L'ACCORDEON
882422 / Aug '93 / Music Memoria

Prunella Scales

☐ DRESSING UP THE IDIOT
800082 / Aug '97 / Mutiny

Pryor, Snooky

☐ COUNTRY BLUES
Miss Mattie Mae / Stop teasing me / Mr. Charlie's mule / Mighty long time / Can I be your friend / Break it on down / Dirty news / Wrapped in sin / Time waits on no one / Call the doctor
NEBCD 926 / Jul '97 / Sequel

☐ TOO COOL TO MOVE
Keyhole in your door / Can I be your friend / Bottle it up and go / Hold me in your arms / Don't you want to know / Cheatin' and lyin' / Walkin' with Snooky / Fire, Fire / Coal black mare / Lovin' you is killin' me / Boogie twist / My baby been gone / Please be careful
ANTCD 0017 / Nov '91 / Antones

Prysock, Arthur

☐ MORNING NOON AND NIGHT
Take care of yourself / Show me how to mambo / Morning noon and night / Woke up this morning / Blue velvet / You are too beautiful / April showers / What's new / They all say I'm the biggest fool / September in the rain / Gone again / Autumn in New York / Jet / In the still of the night / Cottage for sale / Autumn leaves
55574842 / 3 Aug '98 / Verve

Psarantonis

☐ DE PROFUNDIS
ML 4844 / 11 May '98 / Musurgia Graeca

☐ MY THOUGHTS ARE LIKE WINE OLD
ML 4775 / 11 May '98 / Musurgia Graeca

Psyched Up Janis

☐ SWELL
Vanity / I died in my teens / Shudder / Modest us / Subsonic why / Swirl like you / Chandelier / Dead green summer / Reddening star / New 5 / They / Fragments
5320312 / Apr '96 / This Way Up

Psychedelic Furs

☐ ALL OF THIS AND NOTHING
President gas / All that money wants / Imitation of Christ / Sister Europe / Love my way / Highwire days / Dumb waiters / Pretty in pink / Ghost in you / Heaven / Heartbreak beat / All of this and nothing
4611102 / Apr '91 / CBS

☐ BBC SESSIONS, THE
SFRSCD 003 / Feb '97 / Strange Fruit

☐ MIRROR MOVES
Ghost in you / Here come cowboys / Heaven / Heartbeat / My time / Like a stranger / Alice's house / Only a game / Highwire days
4503562 / May '94 / Columbia

☐ SHOULD GOD FORGET (A Retrospective/2CD Set)
India / Sister europe / Pulse / Mack the knife / Blacks / We love you / Imitation of christ / Soap commercial / Pretty in pink / Mr. Jones / Into you like a train / I wanna sleep with you / Merry go round / President gas / Love my way / Sleep comes down / I don't want to be your shadow / Alice's house / Ghost in you / Here comes cowboys / Heaven / Highwire days / Heartbeat / All of the law / Heartbreak beat / All the money wants / Entertain me / Should god forget / Torch / Get a room / Until she comes / All about you / There's a world outside
4873892 / 20 Oct '97 / Columbia

☐ TALK, TALK, TALK
Dumb waiters / Pretty in pink / I wanna sleep with you / No tears / Mr. Jones / Into you like a train / It goes on / So run down / All of this and nothing / She is mine
4836632 / Mar '96 / Columbia

Psychedelic Warriors

☐ WHITE ZONE
Frenzzy / Am I fooling / Pipe dreams / Heart attack / Time and space / White zone / Bay of Bengal / Moonbeam / Pulsating pussy / Love in space
EBSSCD 113 / Nov '96 / Emergency Broadcast System

Psychic Deli

☐ PSYCHEDELIC ELECTRONICA
PDCD 07 / 2 Mar '98 / Phantasm

Psychic TV

☐ AL OR AL
DCD 9054 / Jan '97 / Dossier

☐ ALLEGORY AND SELF
TOPY 038CD / Aug '91 / Temple

☐ AT STOCKHOLM (Genesis P. Orridge & The White Stains)
ETW 001 / Sep '97 / Etherworld

☐ BEAUTY FROM THEE BEAST
Roman P / Good vibrations / Hex sex / Godstar / Je t'aime / United 94 / Ev ov destruction / SMILE / IC Water / Horror house / Back to reality
VICD 006 / Sep '95 / Visionary/ Jettisoundz

☐ BEYOND THEE INFINITE BEAT
Money for E / SMILE / Bliss / Horror house / IC water / Stick insect
TOPY 049CD / Jul '90 / Temple
VICD 004 / Oct '94 / Visionary/ Jettisoundz

☐ CATHEDRAL ENGINE
EFA 084672 / Mar '95 / Dossier

☐ ELECTRIC NEWSPAPER VOL.1
DCD 9059 / Jan '97 / Dossier

☐ ELECTRIC NEWSPAPER VOL.2
DCD 9070 / Jan '97 / Dossier

☐ FORCE THE HAND OF CHANGE
Just drifting / Terminus / Stolen kisses / Caresse / Guiltless / No go go / Ov power / Message from the temple
CLEO 95952 / Jan '97 / Cleopatra

☐ FORCE THE HAND OF CHANGE (CD/Rom)
Just drifting / Terminus / Stolen kisses / Caresse / Guiltless / No go go / Ov power / Message from the temple / Terminus / Message from the temple
SBZ 026CD / 10 Nov '97 / Some Bizarre

☐ HOLLOW COST, A
VICD 003 / 29 Sep '97 / Visionary/ Jettisoundz

☐ KONDOLE
SR 9332 / Jan '94 / Silent

☐ KONDOLE/COPYCAT
TOPYCD 46 / Jul '89 / Temple

☐ LIVE AT THEE BERLIN WALL VOL.1
TOPYCD 052 CD / Sep '90 / Temple

☐ LIVE AT THEE BERLIN WALL VOL.2
TOPYCD 053 CD / Sep '90 / Temple

☐ LIVE IN BREGENZ
TOPY 020CD / Jan '91 / Temple

☐ MEIN GOETTINGEN
DCD 9046 / Jan '97 / Dossier

☐ MOUTH OF THE NIGHT
Dawn / Ordeal of innocence / Wedding / Rebis / Separation and undressing / Discopravity / Immune zone / Climax
VAULT 23 / Oct '96 / NMC

☐ PEAK HOUR
TOPY 068CD / Apr '95 / Temple

☐ RARE AND ALIVE
TIBCD 10 / Aug '93 / NMC

☐ SIRENS
Stargods / Skreemer / Reunited / Sirens
VICD 005 / Mar '95 / Cherry Red

☐ THEE TRANSMUTION OV MERCURY
EFA 084542 / Mar '94 / Dossier

☐ TOWARDS THEE INFINITE BEAT
Infinite beat / Bliss / Drone zone / SMILE / ICWater / Black rainbow / Short sharp taste ov mistress mix / Horror house / Jigsaw / Alien be-in / Stick insect / Money for E
VICD 002 / Sep '94 / Visionary/ Jettisoundz

☐ ULTRADRUG
Scoring / Tempted / Swallow / Bloodstream / B on E / Constant high / Back to reality / Eagle has landed / SUCK or know / Tempter / Still B on E / Gone paranoid / Loose nuts
VICD 001 / 29 Sep '97 / Visionary/ Jettisoundz

Psychik Warriors Ov Gaia

☐ KRAAK (Remixes)
Kraak
KK 131CD / Feb '96 / KK

☐ OBSIDIAN
Obsidian / Challenge / Patience
KK 090CD / Dec '92 / KK

☐ OV BIOSPHERES AND SACRED GROOVES (A Document Ov New Edge Folk Classics)
Obsidian / Challenge / Key / Linkage / Tides (they turn)
KK 065CD / '91 / KK
KK 65CDD / Apr '94 / KK

☐ RECORD OF BREAKS, A
KK 118CD / Oct '95 / KK

Psycho Bunnies

☐ VAMPIRE MISTRESS
And it hurts / Outsiders / Vampire mistress / Searchin' / I don't want you / Jolene / Fallen angels / Rock against romance / Not with you / He's 17 / Hey big Daddy / Blood and roses
RAGECD 110 / Feb '93 / Rage

Psycho Realm

☐ PSYCHO REALM
Pshyco city blocks / Big payback / Premonitions / Temporary insanity / Confessions of a drug addict / Who are you / Love letters / Love from the sick side / R U Experienced / Psyclones / Lost cities / La conecta / La conecta / Goin' in circles
4878382 / 10 Nov '97 / Columbia

Psychograss

☐ LIKE MINDS (American Vernacular Instrumentals In The Bluegrass Spirit)
Tree king creek / Third stone from the sun / Creaking tree / Hot nickels / Jeremy reel / Forgiven/Stuart Symington's summer song / Tennessee twister / Big monk / Garlic and sapphires / Fuzzy navel / Big gravel / Mind's meat / Ride the wild brains
SHCD 3851 / Mar '98 / Sugar Hill

Psychomuzak

☐ EXTASIE, THE
Exstasie / Diamond zombie / Far in / Concentrate (over concentration) / Concentration
DELECCD 018 / Feb '95 / Delerium

☐ SEND
DELECCD 054 / Jun '97 / Delerium

Psychosis

☐ SQUIRM
MASSCD 018 / Nov '93 / Massacre

Psychotic Waltz

☐ BLEEDING
CDVEST 74 / Jul '96 / Bulletproof

☐ INTO THE EVERFLOW
CDMVEST 80 / Feb '97 / Music For Nations

☐ MOSQUITO
CDVEST 27 / Sep '94 / Bulletproof

☐ SOCIAL GRACE, A
CDMVEST 79 / Feb '97 / Music For Nations

Psychotic Youth

☐ BAMBOOZLE
SPV 08056922 / May '95 / SPV

Psychotica

☐ PSYCHOTICA
Ice planet hell / Worship / Starfucker love / Little Prince / Stop / Call / Freedom of choice / 180 / Sleep / Flesh and bone / Blue fear / What is God / La chocha / Barcelona / Future cybernation / New man / Awakening
74321384832 / Sep '96 / American

Psychrist

☐ ABYSMAL FIEND
WHCD 004 / Apr '95 / Modern Invasion

Psyclone Rangers

☐ BEATIN' ON THE BAT POLE
WDO 0362 / Jul '96 / World Domination

☐ DEVIL MAY CARE
WDOM 015CD / Mar '95 / World Domination

☐ FEEL NICE
I wanna be Jack Kennedy / Spinnin' my head / Christie indecision / I feel nice / Hate noise / Stephen / Heaven / Riot girl / Bigger than a gun / Devil's down there / Perfect engine / You're not Edie Sedgwick
WDOM 005CD / May '94 / World Domination

Psyko Disko

☐ PSYKO DISKO
AFRCD 5 / May '97 / Flying Rhino

Ptacek, Rainer

☐ WORRIED SPIRITS
Powder keg / Limit to it / Opening aunt dora's box in 68 / New world / Long long way to the top of the world / Losing ground / Life is fine / Worried spirits / Tasted better going down (valerie) / Waves of sorrow / Stone's throw away / River of real time / Poor backslider / Funny how time slips away / Ain't givin it up (the new cooking blues)
FIENDCD 723 / Oct '93 / Demon

PTS

☐ CAMPAIGN
Whistle / Firing line / Shadows / Green / Blood / Red fields / Walk with me / Campaign / Sweet dreams / Blue / Again / Restless / Last campaign
PTSCD 03 / Jul '97 / P&C PTS

Public Announcement

☐ ALL WORK NO PLAY
5408822 / 20 Apr '98 / AM:PM

Public Domain

☐ RADIO NIGHTS
Radio nights / No shame / If I were you / Saving grace / Immortal way / Clues / China rain / Child in my heart / Shadow of Eden / Silence of your heart / Confetti / Marching on / Crimes of passion
199656 / 15 Jun '98 / Made To Measure

Public Enemy

☐ APOCALYPSE '91 (The Enemy Strikes Black)
Lost at birth / Rebirth / Can't truss it / I don't wanna be called yo niga / How to kill a radio consultant / By the time I get to Arizona / Move / One million bottlebags / More news at 11 / Shut 'em down / Letter to the New York Post / Get the fuck outta Dodge / Bring the noise / Nightrain
5234792 / Jul '95 / Def Jam

☐ FEAR OF A BLACK PLANET
Contract on the world love jam / Brothers gonna work it out / 911 is a joke / Incident at 666 FM / Welcome to the terrordome / Meet the G that killed me / Pollywanacraka / Anti-nigger machine / Burn Hollywood burn / Power to the people / Who stole the soul / Fear of a black planet / Revolutionary generation / Can't do nuttin' for ya man / Reggie Jax / Leave this off your fuckin' charts / B side wins again / War at 33 1/3 / Final count of the collision between us and them / Fight the power
5234462 / Jul '95 / Def Jam

☐ GREATEST MISSES
Tie goes to the runner / Hit da road Jack / Gett off my back / Gotta do what I gotta do / Air hoodlum / Hazy shade of criminal / Megablast / Louder than a bomb / You're gonna get yours / How to kill a radio consultant / Who stole the soul / Party for your right to fight / Shut 'em down
5234872 / Jul '95 / Def Jam

☐ HE GOT GAME
5581302 / 27 Apr '98 / Def Jam

☐ IT TAKES A NATION OF MILLIONS TO HOLD US BACK
Countdown to Armageddon / Bring the noise / Don't believe the hype / Cold lampin' wit' Flavor / Terminator X to the edge of panic / Mind terrorist / Louder than a bomb / Caught, can we get a witness / Show 'em whatcha got / She watch Channel Zero / Night of the living baseheads / Black steel in the hour of chaos / Security of the first world / Rebel without a pause / Prophets of rage / Party for your right to fight
5273582 / Jul '95 / Def Jam

☐ MUSE SICK-N-HOUR MESS AGE
Whole lotta love goin' on in the middle of hell / Theater part intro / Give it up / What side you on / Bedlam 13:13 / Stop in the name / What kind of power we got / So what'cha gonna do now / White heaven/Black hell / Race against time / They used to call it dope / Ain'tnuttinbuttersong / Live and undrugged / Thin line between law and rape / I ain't madd at all / Death of a carjacka / I stand accused / Godd complexx / Hitler day / Harry Allen's interactive super highway phone call to Chuck / Livin' in a zoo
5233622 / Aug '94 / Def Jam

☐ YO, BUM RUSH THE SHOW
You're gonna get yours / Sophisticated bitch / Miuzi weighs a ton / Time bomb / Too much posse / Rightstarter (message to a black man) / Public enemy no.1 / MPE / Yo, bum rush the show / Raise the roof / Megablast / Terminator X speaks with his hands
5274412 / Jul '95 / Def Jam

Public Image Ltd.

☐ ALBUM
FFF / Rise / Fishing / Round / Bags / Home / Ease
CDV 2366 / Feb '86 / Virgin

☐ FLOWERS OF ROMANCE
Four enclosed walls / Track 8 / Phenagen / Flowers of romance / Under the house / Hymies him / Banging the door / Go back / Francis massacre
CDV 2189 / Apr '90 / Virgin

☐ GREATEST HITS... SO FAR, THE
Public image / Death disco / Memories / Careering / Flowers of romance / This is not a love song / Rise / Home / Seattle / Body / Rules and regulations / Disappointed / Warrior / Don't ask me
CDV 2644 / Oct '90 / Virgin

☐ LIVE IN TOKYO
Annalisa / Religion / Low life / Flowers of romance / Death Disco / Solitaire / This is not a love song / Bad life / Banging the door / Under the house
VGDCD 3508 / Apr '92 / Virgin

☐ METAL BOX
Albatross / Memories / Swan lake / Poptones / Careering / No birds / Graveyard / Suit / Bad baby / Socialist / Chant / Radio 4
MTLCD 1 / Sep '96 / Virgin

☐ PARIS AU PRINTEMPS (PARIS IN SPRING)
Theme / Chant / Careering / Bad baby / Attack / Poptones / Lowlife
CDV 2183 / Apr '90 / Virgin

☐ PUBLIC IMAGE
Theme / Religion 1 / Religion 2 / Annalisa / Fodderstompf / Low life / Public image / Attack
CDV 2114 / Jun '88 / Virgin

☐ SECOND EDITION
Albatross / Memories / Swan lake / Pop tones / Careering / Socialist / Graveyard / Suit / Bad baby / No birds do sing / Chant / Radio 4
CDVD 2512 / Apr '92 / Virgin

☐ THAT WHAT IS NOT
Acid drops / Luck's up / Cruel / God / Covered / Love hope / Unfairground / Think tank / Emperor / Good things
CDV 2681 / Feb '92 / Virgin

☐ THIS IS WHAT YOU WANT... THIS IS WHAT YOU GET
Bad life / This is not a love song / Solitaire / Tie me to the length of that / Pardon / Where are you / 1981 / Order of death
CDV 2309 / Apr '90 / Virgin

Pucho

☐ BEST OF PUCHO, THE (Pucho & His Latin Soul Brothers)
Cantaloupe island / Vietnam mambo / Soul yamie / Something black / Shuckin' and jivin' / Got myself a good man / Maiden voyage / Strange thing mambo / Groover / Psychedelic pucho / Let love find you / Yambo / Swamp people / Dateline / Cloud 9 / Swing thing / Big stick
CDBGPD 069 / Feb '93 / Beat Goes Public

☐ GROOVIN' HIGH (Pucho & His Latin Soul Brothers)
CBD 27103 / 22 Jun '98 / Cannonball

☐ HEAT/JUNGLE FIRE (Pucho & His Latin Soul Brothers)
Heat / Georgia on my mind / Presence of your heart / Psychedelic Pucho / I can't stop loving you / Wanderin' rose / Let love find you / Candied yam / Payin' dues / Friendship train / Got myself a good man / Spokerman / Cloud 9 / Jamilah
CDBGPD 047 / Nov '92 / Beat Goes Public

☐ LEGENDS OF ACID JAZZ, THE (Pucho & His Latin Soul Brothers)
PRCD 24175 / Apr '97 / Prestige

☐ MUCHO PUCHO (Pucho & His Latin Soul Brothers)
Latin Soul Brothers / Mission Impossible / Kool and The Gang I / Heat / Blues march / DJ Russ Dewbury mambo / Pain / Got my mojo workin' / Floridian nights / Kool and The Gang II
CDSJP 443 / 23 Feb '98 / Timeless

☐ RIP A DIP (Pucho & His Latin Soul Brothers)
Sex machine / Trouble man / Caravan / Slippin' into darkness / Zebula / Pucho's Descarga II / Greasy greens / Milestones / Mambo with me / Hot barbecue / Rip a dip / Good news blues / Guaguanco / Ritmo Nueva York
CDBGPD 102 / Feb '96 / Beat Goes Public

Pud

☐ I'M THE SHARK
RECESS 40 / Sep '97 / Recess

Pudding Maker

☐ BOWIE, 72 AND OTHER STUFF
ORE 7 / Jan '97 / Wabana

Puente, Tito

☐ BARBARABATIRI
Babarabatirl / Ran kan kan / Oye como va / Gua cha rum / El plato roto / Llora timbero / A gozar timbero / Cuando te vea / Mi chiquita quiere bembe (cha cha cha bembe) / Saca tu mujer / Son montuno / Magia negra / Vete pa la luna / Llora corazon / Cuero pelao / De mi para tl
CD 62053 / May '94 / Saludos Amigos

☐ BLUE GARDENIA NEW YORK 1958 (Puente, Tito & Woody Herman)
Latin flight / New cha cha cha / Mambo herd / Tito meets woody / Cha cha chick / Blue gardenia / Prelude a la cha cha cha / It's coolin' time / Black orchids / Original no. 2 / Sinbad the sailor / Mambo bambo / Fire island
17031 / May '94 / Laserlight

☐ EL REY (Puente, Tito & His Latin Ensemble)
Oye como va / Autumn leaves / Ran kan kan / Rainfall / Giant steps / Linda Chicana / Medley: Stella by starlight / Delirio / Equinoxe / El rey del timbal
CCD 4250 / Jan '87 / Concord Jazz

☐ EL REY DE LA SALSA
BM 522 / Jan '97 / Blue Moon

☐ GOZA MI TIMBAL
Airegin / Cha cha cha / Pent-up house / Picadillo a lo Puente / All blues / Ode to Cachao / Straight no chaser / Lambada timbales
CCD 4399 / Jan '90 / Concord Picante

☐ IN SESSION
Teach me tonight / Flight to Jordan / In a heart beat / Un poco mas / Thunderbird / Miami girl / Obsession / Tigimo + 2 / Tritone / Mood's mood for love
66058037 / Jul '94 / RMM

☐ MAMBO DIABLO (Puente, Tito & His Latin Ensemble)
Mambo diablo / Take five / Lush life / Pick yourself up / Lullaby of Birdland / No pienses asi / China / Eastern joy dance
CCD 4283 / Sep '86 / Concord Picante

☐ MAMBO GOZON
Carioca / New cha cha / Timbalito / El agitador / Latin flight / Tito meets woody / Mambo buda / Cha cha cha de los pollos (cha cha for chicks) / Que sera (what is it) / Pa los rumberos (for dancers) / Cuban fantasy / El cayuco / 3-d mambo / Hong kong mambo / Mambo gozon / Varsity drag / Agua limpia todo / Llego mijan
CD 62008 / Oct '93 / Saludos Amigos

☐ MAMBO OF THE TIMES
Things to come / Jitterbug waltz / Mambo king / Passion flower / Baqueteo / Japan mambo / Mambo of the times / If you could see me now / Best is yet to come / El Titan
CCD 4499 / Mar '92 / Concord Jazz

☐ MASTER TIMBALERO (Puente, Tito & His Latin Ensemble)
Old arrival / Enchantment / Sakura / Azu ki ki / Espresso por favor / Nostalgia in Times Square / Chow mein / Creme de menthe / Sun goddess / Vaya puente / Master Timbalero / Bloomdido
CCD 4594 / May '94 / Concord Picante

☐ NIGHT BEAT
378472 / 7 Apr '98 / Koch Jazz

☐ NIGHT BEAT/MUCHO PUENTE
Live a little (let's face it) / Late late scene / Midnight lament (minor moods) / Night hawk (minor moods) / Night hawk (coconut and rice) / Malibu beat / Mambo beat / Night ritual / Floozie / Poor butterfly / Lullaby of the leaves / Duerme (time was) / Noche de ronda (be mine tonight) / Ecstasy / Tea for two / Son de la loma / Tito's guajira / Almendra / La ola marina / Un poquito de tu amor / What a difference a day makes / Night beat (mono) / Emerald beach / Carioca (mono)
BCD 15686 / May '93 / Bear Family

☐ ON BROADWAY (Puente, Tito & His Latin Ensemble)
TP's special / Sophisticated lady / Bluesette / Soul song / On Broadway / Maria Cervantes / Jo je ti / First light
CCD 4193 / Sep '88 / Concord Picante

☐ OYE COMO VA (The Dance Collection)
Mambo king / Mambo gallego / Chang / Mambo diablo / Ode to cacnao / Maria Cervantes / Machito forever / Picadillo a lo puente / Tito's colada / Delirio / Oye como va / Ran kan kan / El rey del timbal
CCD 47802 / 6 Oct '97 / Concord Picante

☐ PARE COCHERO
CCD 508 / Nov '95 / Caney

☐ ROYAL'T
Donna Lee / Tokyo blues / Virgo / Moanin' / Stompin' at the Savoy / Enquentro / Mambo gallego / Second wind / Royal't / Slam bam
CCD 4553 / Jun '93 / Concord Picante

☐ SALSA MEETS JAZZ
CCD 4354 / Sep '88 / Concord Jazz

☐ SENSATION
Fiesta a la king / Guajira for cal / 'Round midnight / Que sensacion / Jordu / Cantigo en la distancia / Morning / Spain
CCD 4301 / Apr '87 / Concord Picante

☐ SPECIAL DELIVERY
Be bop / Misterioso / Point East memories / Stablemates / On Green Dolphin Street / Autumn in Rome / Venus de Milo / Tito's colada / Barbara / Where you at / Flying home
CCD 4732 / Nov '96 / Concord Picante

☐ TITO MEETS MACHITO - THE MAMBO KINGS (Puente, Tito & Machito)
Mamboscope: *Machito & His Afro-Cubans* / Relax and mambo: *Machito & His Afro-Cubans* / Te he venido a buscar: *Machito & His Afro-Cubans/Graciela* / Sentimental mambo: *Machito & His Afro-Cubans* / Que bonito es Puerto Rico: *Machito & His Afro-Cubans/Graciela* / Feeding the chickens: *Machito & His Afro-Cubans* / Consternacion: *Machito & His Afro-Cubans* / Adivinanza: *Machito & His Afro-Cubans/Graciela* / El jamaiquino: *Machito & His Afro-Cubans* / Me miraste ye te mire: *Machito & His Afro-Cubans/Graciela* / Arollando: *Puente, Tito & Vicentico Valdes* / Pito Joe: *Puente, Tito* / Friquilandia: *Puente, Tito* / El yoyo: *Puente, Tito & Graciela* / Por tu amor: *Puente, Tito* / Caravan: *Puente, Tito* / Donkey serenade: *Puente, Tito* / Ricci Ricci: *Puente, Tito* / Undecided: *Puente, Tito* / Plaza stomp: *Puente, Tito*
CDHOT 612 / Dec '96 / Charly

☐ TOP PERCUSSION/DANCE MANIA
Elequana / Bragada / Obatala yeza / Alaumba chemache / Oguere madeo / Obraricosu / Four by two, part 1 / Conga alegre / Ti mon bo / Mon-ti / Hot timbales / El cayuco / Complication / Mambo gozon / Saca tu mujer / Liego mijan / Agua limpia todo / Cuando te vea / Mi chiquita quiere bembe / 3-D mambo / Varsity drag / Hong Kong mambo / Estoy siempre junto a ti
BCD 15687 / May '93 / Bear Family

☐ UN POCO LOCO (Puente, Tito & His Latin Ensemble)
Un poco loco / Swingin' shepherd blues / Alma con alma / El timbalon / Chang / Machito forever / Prelude to a kiss / Killer Joe / Triton
CCD 4329 / Oct '87 / Concord Picante

☐ YAMBEQUE
Yambeque / Guataca / Suave asi / Esperame / Delisse / Estoy siempre junto a ti / Plaza stomp / El yoyo / Oye lo que tiene el mambo / Ricci Ricci / Friquilandia / Arrollando / Cuban mambo / Guaguanco en tropicana / Preparen candela / Mambo en blues
CD 62081 / Jan '96 / Saludos Amigos

Puff Daddy

☐ NO WAY OUT
Victory: *Puff Daddy & The Family* / Been around the world: *Puff Daddy & The Family* / What you gonna do: *Puff Daddy & The Family* / Don't stop what you're doing: *Puff Daddy & The Family* / If I should die tonight: *Puff Daddy & The Family* / Do you know young G's: *Puff Daddy & The Family* / I love you baby: *Puff Daddy & The Family* / It's all about: *Puff Daddy & The Family* / I got the power: *Puff Daddy & The Family* / Friend: *Puff Daddy & The Family* / I'll be missing you: *Puff Daddy & The Family* / Can't nobody hold me down: *Puff Daddy & The Family*
8612730122 / Jul '97 / Puff Daddy

Puffball

☐ SIX PACK TO GO
BHR 058CD / Jun '97 / Burning Heart

Pugliese, Osvaldo

☐ EL DIA DE TU AUSENCIA
EBCD 96 / 24 Apr '98 / El Bandoneon

☐ LA YUMBA
BMT 010 / Jul '97 / Blue Moon

Pui-Yeun, Lui

☐ MUSIC OF THE PIPA
7559720852 / Jan '95 / Nonesuch

Puig, Cheo Belen

☐ ME HAN DICHO 1937-1940
TCD 078 / Jan '97 / Tumbao Cuban
Classics

Puissance

☐ LET US LEAD
CMI 42 / Jun '96 / Cold Meat Industry

Pukwana, Dudu

☐ COSMICS CHAPTER 90
Mra khali / Hamba (go away) / Big apple / Cosmics /
Blues for Nick / Zwelistsha
AHUM 005 / Aug '90 / Ah-Um

Pulindo, Roberto

☐ ROBERTO PULINDO Y LOS CLASICOS
Cuanto te debo / De garza a la palmita / Estoy
sufriendo por ti / Sonia / Mi pequenito / Schottische /
Mejor me voy / Una rosa para mi chica / Senorita
cantinera / Los pollos
EDCD 7040 / Jul '97 / Easydisc

Pulkas

☐ GREED
Loaded / Rubber room / Drown / Hippy fascist /
Betrayal / Control / This is it / Rebirth / Flesh / Eh /
Close to the enemy
MOSH 190CD / 27 Apr '98 / Earache

Pullen, Don

☐ CAPRICORN RISING
Break out / Break out / Joycie girl / Fall out
1200042 / Oct '90 / Black Saint

☐ LIFE LINE (Pullen, Don Quartet)
Great escape, or run John Henry run / Seriously
speaking / Soft seas / Nature's children / Protection /
Newcomer; seven years later
CDSJP 154 / Jan '92 / Timeless Jazz

☐ NEW BEGINNINGS
Jana's delight / Once upon a time / Warriors / New
beginnings / At the Cante Centrale / Reap the
whirlwind / Silence-death
CDP 7917852 / 1 Jun '98 / Blue Note

☐ RESOLUTION (Pullen, Don & H. Bluiett)
Happy spirit / Flux / A bad m.f. / Head drake / Before
yesterday / Spring's joy / Mahalia...no other one
1200142 / Oct '90 / Black Saint

☐ SIXTH SENSE, THE (Pullen, Don
Quintet)
BSR 0088 / '86 / Black Saint

Pullen, Stacey

☐ DJ KICKS (Various Artists)
K7 049CD / Oct '96 / Studio K7

Pulley

☐ 60 CYCLE HUM
Hold on / SOCD / Bad disease / Mandingo / If / What /
Where are you know / Simplify / Locked away /
Havasu / Seperated / Padded cell / Outside opinion /
Nodding off at the wheel
65212 / 10 Oct '97 / Epitaph

☐ ESTEEM DRIVEN ENGINE
64702 / Oct '96 / Epitaph

Pullman

☐ TURNSTYLES AND JUNKPILES
THRILL 055CD / 17 Aug '98 / Thrill
Jockey

Pulp

☐ DIFFERENT CLASS
Mis-shapes / Pencil skirt / Common people / I-spy /
Disco 2000 / Live bed show / Something changed /
Sorted for E's and wizz / FEELINGCALLEDLOVE /
Underwear / Monday morning / Bar Italia
CID 8041 / Oct '95 / Island

☐ FREAKS
Fairground / I want you / Being followed home /
Master of the universe / Life must be so wonderful /
There's no emotion / Anorexic beauty / Neverending
story / Don't you know / They suffocate at night
FIRECD 5 / Apr '93 / Fire

☐ GOES TO THE DISCO
Death II / Death goes to the disco / Countdown / My
legendary girlfriend / Is this house / This house is
condemned / Countdown / Love is blind / Mark of the
devil / Master of the universe
VSOPCD 256 / 13 Jul '98 / Connoisseur
Collection

☐ HIS 'N' HERS
Joyriders / Lipgloss / Acrylic afternoons / Have you
seen her lately / She's a lady / Happy endings / Do
you remember the first time / Pink glove / Someone
like the moon / David's last summer
CID 8025 / Apr '94 / Island

☐ INTRO - THE GIFT RECORDINGS
Space / OU (12" Mix) / Babies / Styloroc (Nites of
suburbia) / Razzamatazz / Sheffield: Sex city / Inside
Susan: A story in 3 songs
IMCD 159 / Oct '93 / Island

☐ THIS IS HARDCORE
Fear / Dishes / Party hard / Help the aged / This is
hardcore / TV movie / Little soul / I'm a man /
Seductive Barry / Sylvia / Glory days / Day after the
revolution
CID 8066 / 30 Mar '98 / Island

Pulse Legion

☐ EVOLVE
COPCD 034 / 22 Sep '97 / Cop
International

Pulsinger, Patrick

☐ PORNO
EFA 122752 / May '95 / Disko B

Puma, Joe

☐ SHINING HOUR
RSRCD 102 / Aug '97 / Reservoir

Punaruu, Tamarii

☐ KAINA MUSIC TRADITION
S 65812 / Feb '93 / Manuiti

Pungent Stench

☐ BEEN CAUGHT BUTTERING
Shrunken and mummified bitch / Happy re-birthday /
Games of humilation / S.m.a.s.h. / Brainpan blues /
And only hunger remains / Sputter supper / Sick
bizarre defaced creation / Splatterday night fever
NB 052CD / Jan '92 / Nuclear Blast

☐ CLUB MONDO BIZARRE
NB 079CD / Mar '94 / Nuclear Blast

☐ DIRTY RHYMES AND PYSCOTRONIC
NB 078CD / Jun '93 / Nuclear Blast

☐ FOR GOD YOUR SOUL
842973 / Aug '90 / Nuclear Blast

☐ PRAISE THE NAMES OF THE MUSICAL
ASSASSINS (The Best Of Pungent
Stench)
Pulsating protoplasma / Dead body love /
Miscarriage / In the vault / Rip you without care /
Festered offals / Pungent stench / Extreme
deformity / Nauseous secretion / Molecular
disembowelment / Ballard of mangled homeboy /
Daddy cruel / Tony / Madcatmachopsychoromantik
/ Extreme deformity / Festered offals / Pulsating
protoplasma / Pungent stench / Embalmed in
sulphuric acid
NB 293CD / 1 Dec '97 / Nuclear Blast

Punishable Act

☐ INFECT
N 02462 / Sep '94 / Noise

☐ PUNISHABLE ACT
PA / Running man / Scum / With what right / I don't
need no / Two faces / Full of hate / Have a gun will
shoot / More than a word / Why / Sign of a dead fellow
/ Hardcore preacher
N 02672 / Jun '96 / Noise

Punishers

☐ BEAT ME
RUMCD 015 / Aug '92 / Rumble

Punishment of Luxury

☐ LAUGHING ACADEMY
Puppet life / Funk me / Message / All white jack /
Obsession / Radar bug/Metropolis / British baboon /
Babalon / Excess bleeding heart / Laughing
academy / Secrets / Brain bomb / Engine of excess /
Jellyfish
DOJOCD 147 / Sep '93 / Dojo

☐ REVOLUTION BY NUMBERS
OVER 66CD / Aug '97 / Overground

Pura Fe & Ulali

☐ CAUTION TO THE WIND
SHCD 5013 / May '95 / Shanachie

Purdie, Bernard

☐ MASTER DRUMMERS VOL.1
URCD 002 / Jul '96 / Ubiquity

☐ MASTER DRUMMERS VOL.2
URCD 010 / Jul '96 / Ubiquity

☐ PURDIE GOOD/SHAFT
Cold sweat / Montego bay / Purdie good / Wasteland
/ Everybody's talkin' / You turn me on / Shaft / Way
back home / Attica / Them changes / Summer
madness / Butterfingers
CDBGPD 050 / Mar '93 / Beat Goes
Public

☐ SOUL TO JAZZ (Purdie, Bernard & WDR
Big Band)
Moanin' / Superstition / Iko Iko / Senor blues / When
a man loves a woman / Freedom jazz dance /
Sidewinder / Brother where are you / Wade in the
water / Work song / Land of 1000 dances / Gimme
some lovin' / Moanin'
92422 / Oct '96 / Act

☐ SOUL TO JAZZ VOL.2
Motherless child / New Orlean's strutt / La Place
Street / Nobody knows / Jubilation / Joshua / Mr.
Magic / Theme from 'Shaft' / Amen
ACT 92532 / Sep '97 / Act

Pure

☐ FEVERISH
3549801812 / 14 Apr '98 / Mammoth

Pure Gold

☐ YOU LIGHT UP MY LIFE
GBCD 001 / Nov '95 / Pure Gold

Pure Joy

☐ GETZ THE WORM
TGU 001 / 24 Nov '97 / Great Utopia

Pure Morning

☐ 2 INCH HELIUM BUDDHA
SCANCD 21 / Jun '96 / Radarscope

Pure Prairie League

☐ ANTHOLOGY
Tears / Take it before you go / You're between me /
Woman / Harmony song / It's all on me / Jazzman /
Angel no.9 / Leave my heart alone / Early morning
riser / Falling in and out of love / Amie / Boulder skies
/ Angel / Call me tell me / Two lane highway / Runner /
Just can't believe it / I can only think of you / Goin'
home
74321588082 / 15 Jun '98 / Camden

☐ MASTERS, THE
EABCD 031 / 24 Nov '97 / Eagle

☐ PURE PRAIRIE LEAGUE/IF THE SHOE
FITS
RMED 0208CD / 15 Dec '97 /
Renaissance

Pure Silk

☐ JOURNEY (THE MISSION IS
POSSIBLE), THE
SGCD 021 / 23 Feb '98 / Sir George

Puressence

☐ ONLY FOREVER
CID 8064 / 17 Aug '98 / Island

☐ PURESSENCE
Near distance / I suppose / Mr. Brown /
Understanding / Fire / Traffic jam in Memory Lane /
Casting lazy shadows / You're only trying to twist my
arm / Every house on every street / India
CID 8046 / Apr '96 / Island

Purged

☐ FORM OF RELEASE
398414138CD / 26 Aug '97 / Metal Blade

Puricelli, Marc

☐ MELTING POINT
Plunge / Prelude / So far away / Melting point /
Notturno / Island chain / Zambito / St. Louise / So
sweet is you / Brave moon / UC / Nothing changes
too
5220582 / Mar '94 / Limelight

Purify, James

☐ KEEP PUSHIN' (Purify, James & Bobby)
I'm your puppet / Help yourself to all of my lovin' /
Shake a tail feather / Keep pushin' me / You left the
water running / I take what I want / 16 tons / Soothe
me / I don't want to have to wait / Do unto me /
Everybody needs somebody / Last piece of love /
Something so good / I can remember / Hello there /
Something wrong / Let love come between us /
Goodness gracious / Untie me / We're finally gonna
make it / Wish you didn't have to go / So many
reasons / Knock on wood / Don't blame me / Hitch
hike / Got everything
74321535782 / 24 Nov '97 / Camden

Purim, Flora

☐ BUTTERFLY DREAMS
OJCCD 315 / Feb '92 / Original Jazz
Classics

☐ MILESTONE MEMORIES
Moon Dreams / Vera Cruz / Windows / Cravo E
Canela / What can I say / Casa Forte / Samba Michel /
Open your eyes you can fly / Overture
CDBGP 1008 / Mar '93 / Beat Goes
Public

☐ STORIES TO TELL
OJCCD 619 / Feb '92 / Original Jazz
Classics

Purna Das Baul

☐ BAULS OF BENGAL
CRAW 11 / Jan '96 / Crammed World

Purnell, Alton

☐ ALTON PURNELL & JOHN DEFFERARY
QUARTET/QUINTET, THE (Purnell,
Alton & John Defferary Quartet/
Quintet)
BCD 366 / May '98 / GHB

☐ ALTON PURNELL/KEITH SMITH'S
CLIMAX JAZZ BAND (Purnell, Alton &
Keith Smith)
BCD 264 / Aug '95 / GHB

Purple Helmets

☐ RIDE AGAIN
Brand new Cadillac / I'm crying / Rosalyn / She's not
there / First I look at the purse / Get yourself home /
Oh pretty woman / Homework / Don't you like what I
do / Money / Under the sun / Baby let me take you
home / She la la / Baby / Everything's alright
422283 / Jan '95 / New Rose

Purple Ivy Shadows

☐ NO LESS THE TREES THAN THE
STARS
Pawtucket / Feeble / Rebuilding the ancestral statue
/ Blue mtn. / Roadwise blood / Sustance / She
wouldn't have it / Stairs / Dancefloor's shiny under
junky / No health / Space is needed
SRRCD 029 / 13 Oct '97 / Slow River

Purple Outside

☐ MYSTERY LANE
NAR 052CD / Sep '90 / New Alliance

Purple Penguin

☐ DE-TUNED
Tombstone / Only you / Mountain / Tribhuwan / No
action / New Harlem / Mute noise / Razor / Passion /
So high / Pressure / Memphis / End theme
COTCD 004 / Feb '97 / Cup Of Tea

☐ QUESTION
Intro opening question / B-drum / Melody / Return /
Descendant / Non-deadly / Raw deal / Apollo /
Indoctrination / Western interlude / Diamond / Dust /
Closing question
COTCD 019 / 25 May '98 / Cup Of Tea

Purrone, Tony

☐ IN THE HEATH ZONE (Purrone, Tony
Quartet)
SCCD 31410 / Apr '97 / Steeplechase

☐ SIX STRING DELIGHT
SCCD 31438 / 1 Jun '98 / Steeplechase

Pursey, Jimmy

☐ REVENGE IS NOT THE PASSWORD
3012832 / Jul '97 / Arcade

Pursuit of Happiness

☐ WONDERFUL WORLD OF...
51010 / May '97 / Iron

Purvis, Geoff

☐ BORDER FIDDLER, THE (Purvis, Geoff
& The Border Country Dance Band)
Ian's fancy / Jean's reel / Richard Brannan's
favourite / Kings favourite / Portree jig / Colley's /
Colonel Rodney / Sheehan's reel / Tom Billy's /
Doonside up / Nab hornpipe / Rialto / Professor
Blackie / Rambling pitchfork / Swallow's reel /
Cherish the ladies / Humours of Glendart / Captain
Cameron's / Scotlandwell / Tricia's tune / Beeswing
/ Tykeside / Cuckoo waltz / Sally gardens /
O'Rourke's / Silver spear / Down in the broom /
Yellow haired laddie / Master MacDermot's / Dillon
Brown / Ron McDonald's / Joan C MacKenzie / Cork
Hill
FECD 3 / Aug '97 / Fellside

Purvis, Richard

☐ MUSIC FOR CHRISTMAS
TCD 1057 / 13 Oct '97 / Tradition

PUS

☐ DEATH FROM THE SKIES
BFRCD 005 / 24 Nov '97 / Bomb Factory

Puschnig, Wolfgang

☐ PIECES OF A DREAM
Long way from home / Second Heaven / In another
world / Far horizon / Long gone / I wish to be there /
Fourth man / Fremd bin ich eingezogen / Little suite /
Balsam project / Long remembered / It's quiet
around the lake
8373222 / Oct '94 / Amadeo

Push

☐ CAN'T FIGHT IT
PRCD 001 / Jul '96 / Push

Push

☐ DROWNING
Drowning / Divided / Purity / Betrayed / Killing me /
Die for you / Suicide ride / Worthless / Choked /
Alone
SCCD 2 / 1 Nov '97 / Street Culture

Push Pull

☐ PUSH PULL
SONG 1001 / Jun '97 / Active

Pushmipulyu

☐ TWO HANDS
WM 1 / Jun '97 / Wolly Mammoth

Pussy

☐ PUSSY
HBG 123/5 / Apr '94 / Background

Pussy Crush

☐ TORMENTING THE EMOTIONALLY
FRAIL
Mindless / Postcard / She ain't the one / Kill you / Do
it / Beat your heart out / Witch bitch / Ghost of am
empty bottle / Irrespectable / Fun, fun, fun / Loop /
Come back to me / Grunk / Mainline / That girl / Roof
surfing
LADIDA 039CD / Nov '94 / La-Di-Da

Pussy Galore

☐ CORPSE LOVE
HUT 013CD / Feb '92 / Hut
CAR 1706 / Sep '97 / Caroline

☐ DIAL M FOR MOTHERFUCKER
Understanding me / SM57 / Kicked out / Solo sex /
Undertaker / DWDA / Dick Johnson / 1hr later / Eat
me / Wax head / Wait a minute / Evil eye / ADWD vol.2
/ Hang on
PGCD 002 / 23 Mar '98 / Mute

☐ LIVE
ITR 050CD / 16 Feb '98 / In The Red

☐ RIGHT NOW
Pig sweat / White noise / Uptight / Bitch rock loser /
Wretch / Rope legend / Fuck you man / White people
/ New breed / Alright / Knock up / NYC 1999 / Punch
out / Pussy stomp / Trash can oil drum / Fix it / Really
stuck / Rancid / Hellspawn
PGCD 001 / 23 Mar '98 / Mute

☐ SUGARSHIT SHARP
Yu gung / Penetration of the centrefold / Handshake
/ ADWD / Sweetest little hi-fi / Brick / Renegade
PGEPCD 001 / 23 Mar '98 / Mute

Pussycat

☐ STAR PORTRAITS
Mississippi / Teenage queenie / It's the same old
song / Georgie / Wet day in september / Doin' la
bamba / I'll be your woman / If you ever come to
amsterdam / Mexicali lane / Help me living on / Bad
boy / You don't know
16028 / '93 / Laserlight

Pussycat Trash

☐ NON STOP HIP ACTION
SLAMPT 25CD / Mar '95 / Slampt
Underground

Pustit Musis

☐ PUSTIT MUSIS
Up on the roof / Saturday night at the movies / Save
the last dance for me / There goes my baby / This
magic moment / Dance with me / On broadway /
Sweets for my sweet / Please stay / Under the
boardwalk
R 0007 / Jun '97 / Rachot

Putrefy Factor 7

☐ TOTAL MIND COLLAPSE
EFA 125232 / Aug '95 / Celtic Circle

Putrid Offal

☐ EXULCERATION
CDAB 002 / Feb '94 / Adipocre

PVC

☐ PVC AFFAIR
DIVINE 006CD / Nov '95 / Taste

PX Pain

☐ MARROW
HGCD 003 / 1 Jun '98 / High Gain

Pyewackett

☐ MAN IN THE MOON DRINKS CLARET,
THE
MWCD 4007 / Jan '95 / Music & Words

Pygmy Archers Chorus

☐ POLYPHONY OF THE DEEP RAIN
FOREST (Music Of The Ituri Pygmies)
VICG 50152 / Mar '96 / JVC World
Library

Pygmy Children

☐ LOW LIFE DREAM
SPVCD 085123272 / 1 Jun '98 / SPV

Pyle, Pip

☐ 7 YEAR ITCH
7 Sisters / Chinese whispers / Strawberry fields
forever / 7 year itch / I'm really okay / Once around
the shelves / Long on / Shipwrecked / L'etat des
chooses / Foetal fanfare fandango
VP 198CD / 17 Aug '98 / Voiceprint

Pylon

☐ CHAIN
SKYCD 2020 / Sep '94 / Sky

Pylon King

☐ CITIZEN Z COUNTDOWN TO THE
CONTINUUM
FIRECD 050 / Jul '95 / Fire

Pyogenesis

☐ LOVE NATION SUGARHEAD
NB 205CD / Nov '96 / Nuclear Blast

☐ SWEET X RATED NOTHINGS/WAVES
OF EROTICA
NB 240CD / Apr '97 / Nuclear Blast

☐ SWEET X-RATED NOTHINGS
NB 1132 / Oct '94 / Nuclear Blast

☐ TWINALEBLEBLOOD
NB 136CD / Nov '95 / Nuclear Blast

Pyramid

☐ OUT OF CONTROL
Star / Wasted time / Good time gals / Ambition / Out
of control / Wiseman / Is this life / Call of the Gods /
Hells bells
PYRA 01 / Jul '96 / Scorpion

☐ PYRAMID
PSCD 0004 / 5 Jan '98 / Psi-Fi

Pyrolator

☐ WUNDERLAND
EFA 037632 / Feb '94 / Atatak

Q

Q65

☐ AFGHANISTAN
CDP 1002DD / Jun '97 / Pseudonym

☐ REVIVAL
CDP 1048DD / Nov '97 / Pseudonym

Q-Moog

☐ ARC OF BLUENESS (2CD Set)
Intro / Gazing upon a siren's dream / All my love / Share the fantasy / Across the sea of time / Mirabella / Angela / L-tex / Mesmerize / Egyptian night flight / Swingin' / Forbidden state / Leaving / Goodnight Detroit
SSR 191 / 1 Sep '97 / Crammed Discs

Q-Squad

☐ PSYCHED
N 02562 / Jul '95 / Noise

Q-Tex

☐ INTO THE LIGHT
Do you want me / Natural high / Heart of Asia / Lies / Deliverance / Water of life / Power of love / Symphonic / Believe / Promised me / Let the love / Pressure / Tonight / Dreams / Into the light
THIRD 11CD / Jul '97 / 23rd Precinct

Q-Tips

☐ LIVE AT LAST (Q-Tips & Paul Young)
You are the life inside of me / Sweet talk / Hi fidelity / Broken man / Empty bed / Get 'em up joe / Tracks of my tears / Man can't lose / You're gonna love me / Link / S.y.s.l.j.f.m. (the letter song) / Raise your hand / Soul man / Said I wasn't gonna tell nobody / Respect / Having a party / Sweet soul music / How sweet is it / Land of 1000 dances / Sweet talk '91 remix
RPM 102 / Oct '92 / RPM

Qaballah

☐ DUB IN FUSION
BKA 0002 / 6 Oct '97 / Baraka Foundation

Qasimov, Alim

☐ ART OF THE MUGHAM, THE (Azerbaidjan)
C 560112 / Dec '97 / Ocora

☐ MUGHAM OF AZERBAIDJAN, THE
C 560013 / Sep '93 / Ocora

QFX

☐ ALIEN CHILD
EPICD 9 / 1 Dec '97 / Epidemic

☐ FREEDOM
EPICD 3 / Apr '95 / Epidemic

☐ VOYAGE
EPICD 10 / 2 Feb '98 / Epidemic

Qkumba Zoo

☐ WAKE UP AND DREAM
07822189312 / Feb '97 / RCA

Qntal

☐ QNTAL 3
EFA 155912 / Dec '95 / Gymnastic

Quadrajets

☐ PAY THE DEUCE
ES 1242CD / 13 Feb '98 / Estrus

Quakes

☐ LIVE IN TOKYO
NERCD 084 / Feb '96 / Nervous

☐ NEW GENERATION
New generation / How brave are you / Stranded in the streets / Anonymous / Suburbia / Dateless night / Wonderin' / Behind the wheel / It's gone / Your castle / Gothic girl / Now I wanna / Lover's curse
NERCD 073 / Sep '93 / Nervous

☐ VOICE OF AMERICA
NERDCD 058 / Aug '90 / Nervous

Quall, Henry

☐ BLUES FROM ELMO TEXAS
DBS 8901 / 19 Mar '98 / Dallas Blues Society

Quarry, Marcia

☐ UPON MY FAITH
HPCD 1 / 18 May '98 / Hearts

Quartango

☐ COMPADRES
Androgyne / Barracuda / Bordel 1900 / Cafe 1930 / Por una Cabeza / Tierra querida / El portenito / Milonga del Angel / Nightclub / Concert 1990 / Adagio, tango and fuga / Nueve de Julio / Tohu Bohu
JUST 1122 / 23 Feb '98 / Justin Time

Quarterman, Sir Joe

☐ FREE SOUL
CPCD 8079 / Mar '95 / Charly

Quarteto Em Cy

☐ AMIGOS EM CY
CD 3681 / 12 May '98 / CID

☐ SING VINICIUS DE MORAES
KAR 984 / Oct '96 / IMP

Quartette

☐ QUARTETTE
RTMCD 79 / Nov '96 / Round Tower

Quartette Indigo

☐ AFRIKA AFRIKA
Conversation / So what / Love song / Hound dog / Afrika Afrika / Theme for the Eulipions / Night in Tunisia / This little of shine / Fizz water / Song for my Father / Rush hour / Akia's blues
SAVCD 2003 / Jan '98 / Savant

☐ QUARTETTE INDIGO
Ragtime dance / Naima / Andromeda / Footprints / Efua / Staurday night on Beale Street / Come Sunday / Ladies blues / Ruby my dear / Lift every voice and sing
LCD 15362 / Sep '94 / Landmark

Quartette Slavei

☐ BULGARIAN POLYPHONY VOL.4
VICG 53442 / Mar '96 / JVC World Library

Quartetto Cetra

☐ GOLDEN YEARS
74321455782 / Nov '97 / Ricordi

Quartz

☐ RESURRECTION
NM 012CD / Oct '97 / Neat Metal

Quatermass

☐ QUATERMASS
REP 4044 / Aug '91 / Repertoire

Quatre

☐ EARTHCAKE
LBLC 6539 / Jan '92 / Label Bleu

Quatro, Suzi

☐ DAYTONA DEMON
Daytona demon / Hit the road Jack / All shook up / Keep a knockin' / Shakin' all over / Sticks and stones / Love hurts / Wake up little Susie / Fever / Rolling stone / Rock 'n' roll hoochie choo / Glycerine Queen
WB 885862 / 2 Feb '98 / Disky

☐ GOLD COLLECTION, THE
Can the can / 48 crash / Devil Gate Drive / Daytona demon / All shook up / Keep a knockin' / I may be too young / I bit off a bit more than I could chew / Wake up little Susie / Heartbreak hotel / Love hurts / Don't break my heart / I've never been in love / Mama's boy / Race is on / If you can't give me love
CDGOLD 1004 / Mar '96 / EMI Gold

☐ IF YOU KNEW SUZI
Don't change my luck / Tired of waiting / Suicide / Evie / Race is on / If you can't give me love / Wiser than you
16159 / Apr '96 / Laserlight

☐ ROCK HARD
Rock Hard / Glad all over / Love is ready / State of mind / Woman cry / Lipstick / Hard headed / Ego in the night / Lonely is the hardest / Lay me down / Wish upon me
CSAPCD 102 / Jun '90 / Connoisseur Collection

☐ UNRELEASED EMOTION
VSOPCD 260 / 24 Aug '98 / Connoisseur Collection

VERY BEST OF SUZI QUATRO, THE

☐ VERY BEST OF SUZI QUATRO, THE
Devil gate drive / Four letter words / Stumblin' / She's in love with you / Wild one / Race is on / Can the can / Mama's boy / I may be too young / Tear me apart / 48 crash / Your mama won't like me / Rock hard / If you can't give me love
10182 / Oct '97 / Go On Deluxe

☐ WILD ONE, THE (Classic Quatro)
RE 21022 / 29 Jun '98 / Razor & Tie

Quattlebaum, Doug

☐ IF YOU'VE EVER BEEN MISTREATED
TCD 6003 / Sep '97 / Testament

Quatuor Vocal Russe De Nice

☐ RUSSIAN LITURGI SONGS
926972 / 24 Feb '98 / BUDA

Quaye, Finley

☐ MAVERICK A STRIKE
Ultra stimulation / It's great when we're together / Sunday shining / Even after all / Ride on and turn the people on / Way of the explosive / Your love gets sweeter / Supreme I preme / Sweet and loving man / Red rolled and seen / Failing / I need a lover / Maverick a strike
4887582 / 22 Sep '97 / Epic
4887586 / 27 Jul '98 / Epic

Quays, Ronan

☐ EBBING WINGS OF WISDOM
DNDC 008CD / Oct '96 / De Nova Da Capo

Quazar

☐ FLIGHT RECORDER
EFA 620802 / 27 Oct '97 / Superstition

☐ ZODIAC TRAX
Sunflower / Wanderlight / Khedan / Moonflower / Time / Gemini / Arrow / Rhythm dog / Zodiac trax / USA / Deeper and higher / 110
STAR 006CD / Jun '95 / Seven Stars

Qubism

☐ QUBISM
EMIT 2294 / Sep '94 / Time Recordings

Quebec, Ike

☐ BALLADS
Nacy with the laughing face / Born to be blue / Man love / Lover man / Willow weep for me / If I could be one hour with you / Everything happens to me / Imagination / There is no greater love
CDP 8566902 / Jul '97 / Blue Note

☐ BLUE AND SENTIMENTAL
Blue and sentimental / Minor impulse / Don't take your love from me / Blues for Charlie / Like / Count every star / That old black magic / It's all right with me
CDP 7840982 / Mar '95 / Blue Note

☐ CLASSICS 1944-1946
CLASSICS 957 / Nov '97 / Classics

☐ IT MIGHT AS WELL BE SPRING
It might as well be spring / Light reprieve / Easy don't hurt / Lover man / Ol' man river / Willow weep for me
8217362 / 2 Feb '98 / Blue Note

Quebec Pure Laine

☐ MUSIQUE TRADITIONELLE
PEML 0012CD / Apr '96 / Peml

Queen

☐ BIOGRAPHY SERIES
10021 / 3 Nov '97 / Metro Independent

☐ BRIAN MAY TALKS
BMTALK 1 / Nov '96 / UFO

☐ DRAGON ATTACK (A Tribute To Queen) (Various Artists)
Another one bites the dust / Tie your Mother down / Sheer heart attack / We are the champions / We will rock you / I want it all / Kep yourself alive / Get down, make love / One vision / Save me / It's late / I'm in love with my car
REVXD 209 / Dec '96 / Revolver
DERCD 091 / Nov '96 / Derock

☐ FLASH GORDON (Original Soundtrack)
Flash's theme / In the space capsule (the love theme) / Ming's theme (in the court of ming the merciless) / Ring (hypnotic seduction of dale) / Football fight / In the death cell (love theme reprise) / Execution of flash / Kiss (aura resurrects flash) / Arboria (planet of the tree men) / Escape from the swamp / Flash to the rescue / Vultan's theme (attack of the hawk men) / Marriage of dale and ming (and flash approaching) / Battle theme / Wedding march / Crash and dive on mingo city / Flash's theme reprise (victory celebrations) / Hero
CDPCSD 137 / Apr '94 / EMI

☐ FREDDIE MERCURY TALKS
FMTALK 1 / Nov '96 / UFO

☐ GAME, THE
Play the game / Dragon attack / Another one bites the dust / Need your loving tonight / Crazy little thing called love / Rock it (prime jive) / Don't try suicide / Sweet sister / Coming soon / Save me
CDPCSD 134 / Feb '94 / Parlophone

☐ GHOST OF A SMILE (Smile)
Earth / Step on me / Doin' alright / April lady / Blag / Polar bear / Man from Manhattan / Man from Manhattan (back again)
CDP 1049 / 22 Jun '98 / Pseudonym

☐ GREATEST HITS VOL.1
Bohemian rhapsody / Another one bites the dust / Killer queen / Fat bottomed girls / Bicycle race / You're my best friend / Don't stop me now / Save me / Crazy little thing called love / Now I'm here / Good old fashioned lover boy / Play the game / Flash / Seven seas of Rhye / We will rock you / We are the champions / Somebody to love
CDPCSD 141 / Jun '94 / Parlophone

☐ GREATEST HITS VOL.1 & 2
Bohemian rhapsody / Another one bites the dust / Killer queen / Fat bottomed girls / Bicycle race / You're my best friend / Don't stop me now / Save me / Crazy little thing called love / Somebody to love / Now I'm here / Good old fashioned lover boy / Play the game / Flash / Seven seas of Rhye / We will rock you / We are the champions / Kind of magic / Under pressure: Queen & David Bowie / Radio gaga / I want it all / I want to break free / Innuendo / It's a hard life / Breakthru' / Who wants to live forever / Headlong / Miracle / I'm going slightly mad / Invisible man / Hammer to fall / Friends will be friends / Show must go on / One vision
CDPCSD 161 / Oct '94 / Parlophone

☐ HOT SPACE
Staying power / Dancer / Back chat / Body language / Action this day / Put out the fire / Life is real (song for Lennon) / Calling all girls / Las palabras de amor (the words of love) / Cool cat / Under pressure: Queen & David Bowie
CDPCSD 135 / Feb '94 / Parlophone

☐ IN NUCE (Queen/Larry Lurex/Smile)
MS 1001 / Sep '97 / Milestone

☐ INNUENDO
Innuendo / I'm going slightly mad (edit) / I'm going slightly mad / Headlong / I can't live with you / Ride the wild wind / All God's people / These are the days of our lives / Delilah / Don't try so hard (edit) / Don't try so hard / Hitman (edit) / Hitman / Bijou (edit) / Bijou / Show must go on
CDPCSD 115 / Feb '91 / Parlophone

☐ INTERVIEW COLLECTION, THE
CBAK 4957 / Feb '94 / Baktabak

☐ INTERVIEW DISC
SAM 7002 / Nov '96 / Sound & Media

☐ JAZZ
Mustapha / Fat bottomed girls / Jealousy / Bicycle race / If you can't beat them / Let me entertain you / Dead on time / In only seven days / Dreamers ball / Fun it / Leaving home ain't easy / Don't stop me now / More of that jazz
CDPCSD 139 / Feb '94 / Parlophone

☐ JOHN DEACON TALKS
JDTALK 1 / Nov '96 / UFO

☐ KIND OF MAGIC, A
Princes of the universe / Kind of magic / One year of love / Pain is so close to pleasure / Friends will be friends / Who wants to live forever / Gimme the prize / Don't lose your head / One vision / Friends will be friends / Forever
CDP 7462672 / Jun '88 / EMI

☐ LIVE AT WEMBLEY '86 (2CD Set)
One vision / Tie your mother down / In the lap of the Gods / Seven seas of Rhye / Tear it up / Kind of magic / Under pressure / Another one bites the dust / Who wants to live forever / I want to break free / Impromptu / Brighton rock school / Now I'm here / Love of my life / Is this the world we created / Baby I love you / Hello Mary Lou / Tutti frutti / Gimme some loving / We will rock you / Friends will be friends / We are the champions / God save the Queen
CDPCSP 7251 / Jun '92 / Parlophone

☐ LIVE KILLERS (2CD Set)
We will rock you / Let me entertain you / Death on two legs / Killer queen / Bicycle race / I'm in love with my car / Get down, make love / You're my best friend / Now I'm here / Dreamers ball / Love of my life / 39 / Keep yourself alive / You're my best friend / Spread your wings / Brighton Rock / Bohemian rhapsody / Tie your mother down / Sheer heart attack / We are the champions / God save the Queen
CDPCSD 138 / Apr '94 / Parlophone

☐ MADE IN HEAVEN
It's a beautiful day / Made in Heaven / Let me live / Mother love / My life has been saved / I was born to love you / Heaven for everyone / Too much love will kill you / You don't fool me / Winter's tale
CDPCSD 167 / Nov '95 / Parlophone

☐ MIRACLE, THE
Party / Khashoggi's ship / Miracle / I want it all / Invisible man / Breakthru' / Rain must fall / Scandal / My baby does me / Was it all worth it / Hang on in there / Chinese torture
CDPCSD 107 / May '89 / Parlophone

☐ PASSING OPEN WINDOWS (A Symphonic Tribute To Queen) (Palmer, David & Royal Philharmonic Orchestra)
Bicycle race / Somebody to love / Killer Queen / Who wants to live forever / Death on two legs / Now I'm here / Innuendo / Love of my life / We are the champions / Keep passing open windows
SK 62851 / Apr '97 / Sony Classical

☐ PHOTO SESSION (2CD Set)
QU 2 / Nov '92 / UFO

☐ QUEEN
Keep yourself alive / Doing alright / Great King Rat / My fairy King / Liar / Night comes down / Modern times rock 'n' roll / Son and daughter / Jesus / Seven seas of Rhye
CDPCSD 139 / Apr '94 / Parlophone

☐ QUEEN EN ESPANOL (Queen Tribute In Spanish) (Various Artists)
162059 / Oct '97 / Hollywood

☐ QUEEN II
Procession / Father to son / White Queen (as it began) / Some day one day / Loser in the end / Ogre battle / Fairy feller's master-stroke / Nevermore / March of the black Queen / Funny how love is / Seven seas of Rhye
CDPCSD 140 / Apr '94 / Parlophone

☐ QUEEN ROCKS
No one but you / We will rock you / Tie your mother down / Seven seas of rhye / I can't live with you / Hammer to fall / Stone cold crazy / Fat bottomed girls / Keep yourself alive / Tear it up / One vision / Killer queen / Sheer heart attack / I'm in love with my car / Put out the fire / Headlong / It's late / I want it all
8230912 / 3 Nov '97 / Parlophone

☐ QUEEN'S RHAPSODY (Royal Philharmonic Orchestra)
EDLCD 2560 / Oct '94 / Silva Screen

☐ QUEEN: INTERVIEW COMPACT DISC
CBAK 4022 / Nov '89 / Baktabak

☐ ROGER TAYLOR TALKS
RTTALK 1 / Nov '96 / UFO

☐ ROYAL PHILHARMONIC ORCHESTRA PLAY QUEEN (Royal Philharmonic Orchestra)
Flash / Play the game / We are the champions / Don't stop me now / Love of my life / Killer queen / You're my best friend / Teo torriate / Under pressure / Crazy little thing called love / Bohemian rhapsody
CDMFP 5945 / Oct '92 / Music For Pleasure

☐ RPO PLAYS THE MUSIC OF QUEEN, THE (Royal Philharmonic Orchestra)
Barcelona / Flash / I want it all / Kind of magic / Great pretender / Bohemian rhapsody / Innuendo / Save me / Killer queen / I want to break free / Radio ga ga / We are the champions
EMPRCD 675 / Apr '97 / Emporio

☐ SHEER HEART ATTACK
Brighton rock / Tenement funster / Flick of the wrist / Lily of the valley / Now I'm here / In the lap of the gods / Stone cold crazy / Bring back that Leroy Brown / She makes me (stormtrooper in stilettos) / In the lap of the gods...revisited / Killer queen / Dear friends / Misfire
CDPCSD 129 / Jul '93 / Parlophone

☐ ULTIMATE QUEEN (20CD Box Set - From Queen To Made In Heaven)
QUEENBOX 20 / Nov '95 / Parlophone

☐ WORKS, THE
Radio ga ga / Tear it up / It's a hard life / Man on the prowl / Machines (or Back to humans) / I want to break free / Keep passing the open windows / Hammer to fall / Is this the world we created
CDPCSD 136 / Feb '94 / Parlophone

Queen Elizabeth

☐ QUEEN ELIZABETH
ESPCD 002 / Nov '94 / Echo

Queen Ida

☐ COOKIN' WITH QUEEN IDA
Zydeco / Gator man / C'est moi / Love is the answer / La bas two step / 1-10 express / Dancing on the bayou / Ranger's waltz / Hard headed woman / Lady be mine
GNPD 2197 / Sep '95 / GNP Crescendo

☐ MARDI GRAS
Comment ca va / Oh, what can you do / Home on the bayou / Since you been gone / Louisiana / Where are you now / Mardi Gras / Object of my affection / Cajun cookin' / Mr. Fine / Papa on the fiddle / Molina / New kid on the bayou / I can see clearly now
GNPD 2227 / Sep '95 / GNP Crescendo

Queen Latifah

☐ ORDER IN THE COURT
Bananas (who you gonna call) / Court is in session / No yes skit / No yes / Turn you on / Black on black love / Parlay / Paper / What you gonna do / It's alright / Phone call skit / Brownsville / I don't know / Life / Let her live
5309062 / 22 Jun '98 / Motown

Queen Majeeda

☐ CONSCIOUS
HBCD 90 / Jun '93 / Heartbeat

Queen Pen

☐ MY MELODY
INTD 90151 / 15 Dec '97 / Interscope

Queen Samantha

☐ BEST OF QUEEN SAMANTHA, THE (The Letter)
Letter / Give me action / What's in your mind / Get back (boogie dance) / Take a chance / So far away / Sweet San Francisco / Mama Rue (c'est moi) / Summer dream / Funky celebration / Don't stop I feel good / By myself / Singing hallelujah
HTCD 42 / 20 Apr '98 / Hot Productions

Queen Sylvia

☐ MIDNIGHT BABY
I'm hurtin' / Life and troubles / New York bound / Baby, What do I do / Midnight baby / Party / Can't get along / Why wonder / You treat me so mean / I love you
ECD 260572 / Sep '94 / Evidence

Queen Victoria School

☐ TUNES OF SCOTLAND
CDITV 611 / May '96 / Scotdisc

Queen's College Choir

☐ ORGAN OF QUEEN'S COLLEGE, OXFORD, THE (Queen's College Choir, Oxford)
CDCA 925 / '91 / Alpha

Queen's Division

☐ ARRIVAL (Minden Band Of The Queen's Division)
Fanfare / Princess of Wales' Royal Regiment / Royal Regiment of Fusiliers / Royal Anglian Regiment / Pride on parade / Queen's Division / Bells / Red Square Review / Bridges over the River Cam / Prelude to comedy / Solemn occasion / Musical snuff box / Grasshoppers dance / Rondon grottesco / Gypsy trumpeter / Reverie / Big band swing / Tin Pan Alley / Symphonic Gershwin / Spirit of pageantry
BNA 5124 / Jul '96 / Bandleader

Queen's Royal Scots Pipers

☐ QUEEN'S ROYAL SCOTS PIPERS, THE
EUCD 1312 / Jul '95 / ARC

Queensryche

☐ HEAR IN THE NOW
Sign of the times / Cuckoo's nest / Get a life / Voice inside / Some people fly / Saved / You / Miles away / Reach / All I want / Hit the black / Anytime/Anywhere / Spool
CDEMC 3764 / Mar '97 / EMI

Queers

☐ BEAT OFF
LOOKOUT 81CD / Jun '97 / Lookout

☐ DON'T BACK DOWN
LOOKOUT 140CD / Aug '96 / Lookout

☐ GROW UP
LOOKOUT 9CD / Jul '95 / Lookout

☐ LOVE SONGS
LOOKOUT 66CD / Jul '95 / Lookout

☐ MOVE BACK HOME
LOOKOUT 114CD / Jun '97 / Lookout

Quemener, Jean-Francois

☐ KAN HA DISKAN - CHANTS A DANSER
Konskried Sant Nikolas / D'an traon gant / Konskried Logivi / Mag c'han me d'an arme / Ne oeran ket petra / Konskried Saint-Trefin / Silvestric / Ar c'hentan gwezh / Ar c'hallez vihan / An desertour / 'Barzh un enez / Mari-Louise
CD 445 / Mar '98 / Arfolk

Quench

☐ SEQUENCHAL
INFECT 20CD / Nov '94 / Infectious

Quest

☐ LIVE AT THE MONTMARTRE
STCD 4121 / Feb '90 / Storyville

☐ NATURAL SELECTION
As always / Natural selection / Nocturnal / Amethyst suite / Fahamivu / Michiyo / Moody time / Nighty-nite
ECD 220822 / Feb '94 / Evidence

☐ QUEST
STCD 4158 / Feb '90 / Storyville

Quest

☐ CHANGE
NTHEN 031CD / Oct '96 / Now & Then

Question Mark

☐ 96 TEARS (Question Mark & The Mysterians)
RE 137CD / Nov '94 / ROIR

☐ 96 TEARS (Question Mark & The Mysterians)
ANT 3011 / Sep '97 / Anthology

☐ ACTION (Question Mark & The Mysterians)
MOVE 3001 / 20 Apr '98 / Move

☐ DO YOU FEEL IT BABY (Question Mark & The Mysterians)
CED 262 / 8 Jun '98 / Norton

☐ ORIGINAL RECORDINGS (Question Mark & The Mysterians)
QMATM 01 / 22 May '98 / Campark

☐ QUESTION MARK AND THE MYSTERIANS (Question Mark & The Mysterians)
COLCD 2004 / 24 Nov '97 / Collectables

Quicksand

☐ HOME IS WHERE I BELONG
SRMC 1030 / 5 Jan '98 / Siwan

Quicksilver Messenger Service

☐ ANTHOLOGY
Pride of man / Dino's song / Fool / Bears / Mona / Edward, the mad shirt grinder / Three or four feet from home / Fresh air / Just for love / Spindrifter / Local color / What about me / Don't cry my lady love / Hope / Fire brothers / I found love
BGOCD 270 / Mar '95 / Beat Goes On

☐ COMIN' THRU
Doin' time in the USA / Chicken / Changes / California state correctional facility blues / Forty days / Mojo / Don't lose it
BGOCD 88 / Jul '91 / Beat Goes On

☐ HAPPY TRAILS
Who do you love (part one) / When you love / Where you love / How do you love / Which do you love / Who do you love (part two) / Mona / Maiden of the cancer moon / Calvary / Happy trails
BGOCD 151 / Sep '92 / Beat Goes On

☐ JUST FOR YOU
Wolf run (part 1) / Just for love (part 1) / Cobra / Hat / Freeway flyer / Gone again / Fresh air / Just for love (part 2) / Wolf run (part 2)
BGOCD 141 / Jun '92 / Beat Goes On

☐ LIVE AT FIELD STONE (Duncan, Gary Quicksilver Messenger Service)
CTCD 071 / Dec '97 / Captain Trip

☐ MAIDEN OF THE CANCER MOON (2CD Set)
UR 006 / 13 Jul '98 / UR

☐ QUICKSILVER
Hope / I found love / Song for frisco / Play my guitar / Rebel / Fire brothers / Out of my mind / Don't cry my lady love / Truth
BGOCD 217 / Jan '94 / Beat Goes On

☐ QUICKSILVER MESSENGER SERVICE
Pride of man / Light your windows / Dino's song / Gold and silver / It's been too long / Fool
EDCD 200 / May '92 / Edsel

☐ SHADY GROVE
Shady grove / Flute song / Three or four feet from home / Too far / Holy moly / Joseph's coat / Flashing lonesome / Words can't say / Edward, the mad shirt grinder
EDCD 208 / Sep '90 / Edsel

☐ SHAPE SHIFTER (2CD Set) (Duncan, Gary Quicksilver Messenger Service)
P 007 / Sep '97 / Bymander

☐ SOLID SILVER
Gypsy lights / Heebie jeebies / Cowboy on the run / I heard you singing / Worryin' shoes / Letter / They don't know / Flames / Witches' moon / Bittersweet moon
EDCD 376 / Aug '93 / Edsel

☐ ULTIMATE JOURNEY
Who do you love / Pride of man / Codine / Dino's song / Gold and silver / Joseph's coat / Shady grove / Fresh air / Too far / Stand by me / What about me / Mona
SEECD 61 / Apr '93 / See For Miles

☐ WHAT ABOUT ME
What about me / Local color / Baby baby / Won't kill me / Long haired lady / Subway / Spindrifter / Good old rock and roll / All in my mind / Call on me
BGOCD 58 / Oct '90 / Beat Goes On

Quickspace

☐ PRECIOUS FALLING
Death and Annie / Take away / Mouse / Seven like that / Quickspace happy song #2 / Hadid / Melo / Minors / Cola lola / Obvious / Walk me home / Mountain waltz / Goodbye precious mountain
CHOOSY 013CD / 31 Aug '98 / Kitty Kitty Corporation

☐ QUICKSPACE
Swisher / Song for someone / Quasi-brau / Mouse tail / Winona / Docile I / Docile II
CHOOSY 006CD / Nov '96 / Kitty Kitty Corporation

☐ SUPO-SPOT
Happy song no.1 / Unique slippy / Extra plus / Found a way / Do it my own way / Whiff and spoof song / Exemplary swishy / Friend / Where have all the good times gone / Song for NME
CHOOSY 008CD / Jun '97 / Kitty Kitty Corporation

Quiet Boys

☐ BOSH
Righteous / Take four / Deeper / Blue 4 royal T / Inner sense / Prayer mat / Boshin' around / Conguero wronguero / Ghetto life / Never change / Love will find a way / Astral space
JAZIDCD 121 / Apr '95 / Acid Jazz

☐ CAN'T HOLD THE VIBE
Inside your mind / Let it go / Give it all u got / Make me say it again girl / Roaring fast / Long way from me / Sim ting / Att etude / Modal / Can't hold the vibe / Mellow blow
JAZIDCD 045 / Mar '92 / Acid Jazz

Quiet City

☐ QUIET CITY
CD 59002 / Aug '96 / Salt

Quiet Elegance

☐ YOU GOT MY MIND MESSED UP
After you / Mama said / Do you love me / Something you got / I'm afraid of losing you / You brought the sun back into my life / I need love / Tired of being alone / Will you be my man (in the morning) / You got my mind messed up / Your love is strange / Roots of love / Love will make you feel better / Have you been making out OK / Set the record straight / How's your love life baby
HIUKCD 109 / Dec '89 / Hi

Quiet Riot

☐ RANDY RHOADS YEARS, THE
Trouble / Laughing gas / Afterglow of your love / Killer girls / Picking up the pieces / Last call for rock 'n' roll / Breaking up is a heartache / Force of habit / It's not so funny / Look in any window
8122714452 / Feb '94 / Atlantic

Quietman

☐ SHHH (2CD Set)
PLAT 40CD / 20 Apr '98 / Platipus

Quigg, Stephen

☐ VOICE OF MY ISLAND
Steal away / Gallant Murray / Voice of my island / Almost every circumstance / Strong women rule us with their tears / Freewheeling now / Work o' the weavers / Come by the hills / Whatever you say say nothing / Annie McKelvie / Willie's gane tae Melville Castle / Last leviathan
CDTRAX 066 / Jul '93 / Greentrax

Quigley

☐ 1969 TILL GOD KNOWS WHEN
SOLVE 009 / 1 Jun '98 / Acetone

Quimantu

☐ MAR ADENTO
WGSCD 286 / Mar '98 / Wild Goose

Quin, Douglas

☐ ANTARTICA WILD SANCTUARY
9006231132 / 5 May '98 / Miramar

Quine, Robert

☐ BASIC (Quine, Robert & Fred Maher)
Pick up / Bluffer / Fala / Stray / Summer storm / Sixty five / Dark place / Despair / Village / Bandage bait
CDOVD 470 / Jul '96 / Virgin

Quinichette, Paul

☐ KID FROM DENVER, THE
Come rain or come shine / Come rain or come shine / Start here / Pennies from heaven / Happy feeling / Honeysuckle rose / Big deal / Kid from denver
BCD 136 / Aug '95 / Biograph

☐ ON THE SUNNY SIDE
Blue dots / Circles / On the sunny side of the street / Cool-lypso
OJCCD 762 / Feb '97 / Original Jazz Classics

Quink Vocal Ensemble

☐ INVISIBLE CITIES
Missa brevis / Priere / En begheeft myniet / Egidius waer besta bleven / Het visschertje / Trionfo di bacco e d'arianna / Madrigal / Psaume 121 / Due canti / Als ghys van de doodt sult zijn verbeten / Les mortels
CD 80384 / Apr '96 / Telarc

Quinn

☐ QUINN
Crown of life / Sacred revelation / In a perfect world / Prophecy / These four walls / In reverie / Autonomous / All alone / Lotus / Lavender moonlight / Red sky / Bardo thodol
SR 4001 / Jun '95 / PLR

Quinn, Bill

☐ TRIBUTE TO JIM REEVES, A
Whispering hope / Scarlet ribbons / Mexicali rose / Am I losing you / Just out of reach / Adios amigo / If only I had you / It hurts so much / Is it really over / You're free to go / This world is not my home / Four walls / I love you because / No one to cry to / (Not until) the next time / Anna Marie / Distant drums / He'll have to go / You're the only good thing / I won't forget you / Oh, how I miss you tonight
305132 / Jun '97 / Hallmark

Quinn, Brendan

☐ MELODIES AND MEDLEYS
My lady from Glenfarne / Lovely leitrim / My lovely rose of Clare / My heart skips a beat / Turn out the lights and love me tonight / Some broken hearts never mend / I recall a gypsy woman / Dublin in the rare old times / Any tipperary town / Among the Wicklow hills / He'll have to go / I won't forget you / I love you because
RZRCD 515 / Apr '92 / Ritz

☐ MYSTERY, THE
CBMCD 019 / Jul '96 / Cross Border Media

Quinn, Eimaer

☐ WINTER FIRE AND SNOW
PEACH 001 / Mar '97 / Peach

Quinn, Frank

☐ IF YOU ARE IRISH
If you are Irish / Rafferty's reel / Paddy McGinty's goat / Rakes of drummlish / Molly in the woods / Tan yard side / West port chorus / Shan van vough / Paddy Doyle / Leg of the duck / Eddie Dunn's favourite reel / Going to the fair / Donovan's reel / Goodbye Mike goodbye Pat / Old tea kettle / Green grow the rushes oh / Four courts / Far away in Australia / Peeler and the goat / New found reel / One night I came home to my Kitty / Jersey lightning / Emerald medley / Bunch of rushes / Irish farewell
ARHCD 7033 / May '97 / Arhoolie

Quinn, Freddy

☐ FREDDY QUINN 1956-1965
Sie hiess Mary Ann / Heimweh / Bel sante / Cigarettes and whisky / Junge komme bald wieder / So geht das jede nacht / Don't forbid me / At the hop / Stood up / Lonesome star / Heimatlos / Ein armer mulero / Ich bin bald wieder hier / Die gitarre und das meer / Unter fremden sternen / Guitar playing Joe / La guitarra Brasiliana / Der boss ist nicht hier / Ein schiff voll whiskey / You, you, you / Blue mirage / I'll hold you in my heart / By the way / Spanish eyes
BCD 15403 / Jul '87 / Bear Family

Quint

☐ TIME WOUNDS ALL HEALS
EGYPT 1 / 13 Apr '98 / Egypt

Quintana, Alfonsin

☐ VAMOS PA' LA RUMBA 1951-1953
TCD 082 / Jul '96 / Tumbao Cuban Classics

Quintana, Miguel

☐ DON GONZALO PRESENTA
CD 0798 / 5 Jan '98 / Fresh Sound

Quintessence

☐ SELF/INDWELLER
Cosmic surfer / Wonders of the universe / Hari om / Vishnu narain / Hallelujah / Celestrial procession / Self / Freedom / Water Goddess / Jesus is my life / Butterfly / It's all the same / Indweller / Portable realm / Holy roller / On the other side of the wall / Dedication / Bliss trip / Mother of the universe
DOCD 1982 / May '95 / Drop Out

Quinteto Da Paraiba

☐ MUSICA ARMORIAL (String Quartets From NE Brazil)
NI 5483 / Aug '96 / Nimbus

Quintetto Vocale Italiano

☐ FREEDOM JAZZ DANCE
1212472 / Nov '92 / Soul Note

Quintetto X

☐ NOVO ESQUEMA DA BOSSA
RTCD 402 / Jul '96 / Right Tempo

Quinto, Pancho

☐ EN EL SOLAR LA CUEVA DEL HUMO
RWCD 9704 / 5 Jan '98 / Fresh Sound

Quintron

☐ SATAN IS DEAD
BLB 052 / 29 Dec '97 / Bulb

Quipildor, Zamba

☐ PUESTA DE SOL
BMF 004 / Jul '97 / Blue Moon

Quireboys

☐ BIT OF WHAT YOU FANCY, A/BITTER SWEET AND TWISTED (Remastered/ 2CD Set)
7 o'clock man / Man on the loose / Whippin' boy / Sex party / Sweet Mary Ann / I don't love you anymore / Hey you / Misled / Long time comin' / Roses and rings / There she goes again / Take me home tonight / Heartbreaker / How do you feel / Mayfair / Misled / 7 o'clock / Long time comin' / Pretty girls / I don't love you anymore / Stop right there / Please me / Tramps and thieves / White trash blues / Can't park here / King of New York / Don't bite the hand that feeds you / Last time / Debbie / Brother Louie / Ode to you (baby just walk) / Hates to please / My Saint Jude / Take no revenge / Wild wild wild / Ain't love blind / Tramps and thieves / Don't bite the hand that feeds / Ode to you (baby just walk) / Sweet little girl
CTMCD 200 / Feb '97 / EMI

☐ FROM TOOTING TO BARKING
7 O'Clock / Hey you / Man on the loose / Mayfair / Where've you been to / Whipping boy / Devil of a man / Hates to please / I don't love you again / Roses and rings
ESMCD 400 / Jul '96 / Essential

☐ MINI CD
SURCD 014 / Sep '91 / Survival

Quirk

☐ MACHINA ELECTRICA AND FORNAX CHEMICA
MP 12CD / 12 Jan '98 / Matsuri

Quoite

☐ LOUNGE
DOSS 1201CD / Sep '96 / Possible

Quorthon

☐ QUORTHON
BMCD 6669 / May '94 / Black Mark

R

R Kelly

☐ 12 PLAY
Your body's callin' / Bump 'n' grind / Homie lover friend / It seems like your ready / Freak dat body / I like the crotch on you / Summer bunnies / For you / Back to the mood of things / Sadie / Sex me (parts 1 and 2) / 12 play
CHIP 144 / Mar '97 / Jive

☐ BORN INTO THE 90'S (R Kelly & Public Announcement)
She's loving me / She's got that vibe / Definition of a hotti / I know what you need / Keep it street / Born into the 90's / Slow dance / Dedicated / Honey love / Hangin' out / Hey love (can I have a word with you)
CHIP 123 / Mar '97 / Jive

☐ R. KELLY
CHIP 166 / Dec '95 / Jive

Rabbit's Hat

☐ OPTIC MANSION
DMCD 1034 / Oct '96 / Demi-Monde

Rabin, Oscar

☐ TWO IN LOVE
No souvenirs / I understand / Moonlight avenue / I'd know you anywhere / I ain't got nobody / Deep in the heart of Texas / Sometimes / You again / Tica-ti, tica-ta / Angeline / At the woodchopper's ball / Bluebirds in the moonlight / I fall in love with you every day / My wubba dolly / Starlight serenade / Predigree on pomander walk / Daddy / Down Argentina way / My sisters and I / Two in love / Sweet madness / Who's taking you home tonight
RAJCD 871 / 29 Jun '98 / Empress

Rabin, Trevor

☐ WOLF
Open ended / Heard you cry / Wolf / Do ya want me / Stop turn / Lost in love / Looking for a lady / Pain / Take me to a party / She's easy / Long Island sound
OW 33660 / Sep '97 / One Way

Rabson, Ann

☐ MUSIC MAKIN' MAMA
ALCD 4848 / Mar '97 / Alligator

RAC

☐ DIVERSIONS
Electro fish / High wire / Hula loops / Raindancer / Mindfield / Wavelength / Neo rio / Choobes / Detour
WARPCD 22 / Apr '94 / Warp

Raca Negra

☐ RACA NEGRA
1918192 / Jul '97 / EPM

Race, Hugo

☐ CHEMICAL WEDDING (Race, Hugo & The True Spirit)
GLOBCD 1 / 13 Apr '98 / Global Warming

☐ EARLS WORLD (Race, Hugo & The True Spirit)
NORMAL 125CD / May '94 / Normal

☐ RUE MORGUE BLUES (Race, Hugo & The True Spirit)
NORMAL 118CD / May '94 / Normal

☐ SECOND REVELATOR (Race, Hugo & The True Spirit)
NORMAL 135CD / May '94 / Normal

☐ SPIRITUAL THIRST (Race, Hugo & The True Spirit)
NORMAL 155CD / May '94 / Normal

☐ VALLEY OF LIGHT
PANNCD 10 / Mar '96 / Pandemonium

Racer Ten

☐ MELODIES AND MEMORIES
SEMAPHORE 35862 / Nov '96 / Onefoot

Racey

☐ SOME GIRLS
Some girls / Such a night / Cry baby cry / Not too young to get married / Shame / Let me take you home tonight / Rock it / Kitty / Little darlin' / There's a party goin' on / She's a winner / We are Racey
WB 885562 / 2 Feb '98 / Disky

☐ VERY BEST OF RACEY, THE
Some girls / Such a night to have a party / Lay your love on me / Boy oh boy / Everybody let's rock / Runaround Sue / Cry cry time / Way wow / Still comes out the same / Mad about the girl / Kitty / I mean it this time
10162 / Oct '97 / Go On Deluxe

Rachell, Yank

☐ CHICAGO STYLE
DD 649 / Nov '93 / Delmark

☐ MANDOLIN BLUES (Rachell, Yank & His Tenessee Jug Busters)
Texas Tony / Girl of my dreams / Do the boogie mama / Starvation in my kitchen / I'm gonna get up in the morning / Lonesome blues / Shout baby shout / Rocky mountain blues / Do the boogie mama / Stop knocking on my door / Doorbell blues / Move your hand / Get your morning exercise / When my baby comes back home / Up and down the line / Bye bye baby
DE 606 / Jul '98 / Delmark

Rachels

☐ HANDWRITING
QS 30CD / May '95 / Quarter Stick

☐ MUSIC FOR EGON SCHIELE
Q 35CD / Feb '96 / Quarter Stick

Racial Abuse

☐ CLIMB
LF 264CD / Dec '96 / Lost & Found

Racy, Ali Jhad

☐ MYSTICAL LEGACIES
LYRCD 7437 / Nov '97 / Lyrichord

RAD

☐ HIGHER PLANE
7BR 00562CD / 19 Jan '98 / Seven Bridges

Radakka

☐ MALICE OF TRANQUILITY
CM 77111CD / Jan '96 / Century Media

Radcliff, Bobby

☐ LIVE AT THE RYNBORN
Improvisations on Honky Tonk / Please have mercy / Tramp / Early in the morning / Introject / Been around the world / Kool And The Gang / Honeydripper / Ten years ago / Twist
CDBT 1141 / May '97 / Black Top

☐ THERE'S A COLD GRAVE IN YOUR WAY
BT 1110CD / Nov '94 / Black Top

Radha Krishna Temple

☐ RADHA KRISHNA TEMPLE
Govinda / Sri Guruvastak / Bhaja Bhakata/Arotrika / Hare Krsna mantra / Sri Isopanisad / Bhaja Hure Mana / Govinda Jai Jai / Prayer to the spiritual masters
CDP 7812552 / Mar '93 / Apple

Radial Blend

☐ ABANDON TIME
SOHO 19CD / Jan '95 / Suburbs Of Hell

☐ ENOUGH ROADS
SOH 021CD / Jul '95 / Suburbs Of Hell

Radiators

☐ ALIVE-ALIVE-O (Live In London 1978/ Rare Studio Tracks)
Contact / Sunday world / Roxy girl / Electric shares / Press gang / Prison bars / Million dollar hero / Television screen / Walking home alone again / Psychotic reaction / Blitzin' at the Ritz / Enemies / Teenager in love / Hucklebuck / Teenage head / Shake some action / 1970 (I feel alright) / Private world / Strangers in fiction / Take my heart and run / Buying gold in heaven / Gold diggers of 1981 (Hits for the blitz) / Ballad of the faithful departed
CDWIKD 164 / Jun '96 / Chiswick

☐ COCKLES AND MUSSELS (The Best Of The Radiators)
Television screen / Love detective / Sunday world / Prison bars / Party line / Roxy girl / Enemies / Try and stop me / Million dollar hero / Let's talk about the weather / Johnny Jukebox / Confidential / They're looting in the town / Who are the strangers / Kitty Ricketts / Ballad of the faithful departed / Walking home alone again / Dead the beast, dead the poison / Stranger than fiction / Dancing years / Under Cleary's clock / Plura Belle
CDWIKS 156 / Oct '95 / Chiswick

Radical Dance Faction

☐ BORDERLINE CASES
Surplus people / Borderline / Four chuck chant / Riverwise / Screpoint for a sickman / Chinese poem / Rogue trooper (live mix) / Back in the same place / Hot on the wire / Firepower
EZ 001CD / Jul '94 / Earthzone

☐ RAGGAMUFFIN STATEMENT
CD4DS 4A / May '95 / Inna State

Radical Retard

☐ ONCE I WOKE UP
C 6201CD / Mar '94 / R

Radio Big Band

☐ SPECIAL EDITION
Chicago / Auf wiedersehen sweetheart / I remember Clifford / Body and soul / For you, for me, for evermore / Broadway / Easy living / Oh I do like to be beside the seaside / Imagination / Big band treasure chest
RBB 002 / Feb '95 / Radio Big Band

Radio Birdman

☐ LIVING EYES (Remastered)
REDCD 53 / 12 Jan '98 / Red Eye

☐ RADIOS APPEAR (Remastered)
REDCD 49 / 12 Jan '98 / Red Eye

☐ RITUALISM (CD/Book Set)
CSREC 001 / Jun '97 / Citadel

Radio Flyer

☐ IN THEIR STRANGE WHITE...
PYV 012CD / Sep '97 / Polyvinyl

Radio Four

☐ THERE'S GONNA BE JOY
Earnest prayer / If you miss me from praying / How much I owe / Building a home / I need the spirit / Road's rocky / There's gonna be joy / That's all I need / Road's rough and rocky / How about you / When he calls / Whisper to Jesus / I received my blessings / One more river / What's he done for me / Walk around my bedside / Jesus never left me alone / What kind of man Jesus is / In my father's house / Believe every word he says / On my journey now / One day / Heaven is my goal / Jesus is my friend
CDCHD 448 / Jun '93 / Ace

Radio Kings

☐ MONEY ROAD
I can't win / Virginia / Shelf / Leave a light on / Thrity days / Money in her pocket / My day of reckoning / Song of love / Disturb me baby / I can't let go / Money road
CDBB 9601 / Feb '98 / Bullseye Blues

Radio Massacre International

☐ FROZEN NORTH (2CD Set)
Wrecks / What's the point of going to Crete / Small frozen north / Rosemary's baby / Drown / Frozen north 1 / Frozen north 2
CENCD 012 / Nov '95 / Centaur

☐ ORGAN HARVEST
CENCD 022 / 22 Jun '98 / Centaur

☐ REPUBLIC
Raw cane approach / Republic / Send off
CENCD 018 / Apr '97 / Centaur

Radio Rama

☐ BEST OF RADIO RAMA, THE
ZYX 204552 / 1 Jun '98 / ZYX

Radio Silence

☐ RADIO SILENCE
ESM 018 / 2 Mar '98 / Escape

Radio Stars

☐ SOMEWHERE (THERE'S A PLACE FOR US)
Radio stars / Dirty pictures / Beast of barnsley / Nervous wreck / My mother said / Is it really necessary / Arthur is dead boring (let's rot) / Johnny mekon / Good personality / Dear prudence / Nothing happened today / Eric / Macaroni and mice / God (pam old) sex in chains blues (part 1) / From a rabbit / Sail away / It's all over / I'm talking about you / Accountancy blues / Baffin island / Ghost of desperate dan / This is your next life / Sitting in the rain / Rock 'n' roll for the time being / No russians in russia / Real me / Somewhere there's a place for us / Goodnight
CDWIKD 107 / May '92 / Chiswick

Radio Sweethearts

☐ NEW MEMORIES
Lonely footsteps / Every other song / Beer and whiskey / Is anybody going to San Antone / House of gold / I saw the light / New memories / Headin' on down the highway / Red Cadillac and a black moustache / Don't make me wait / We've fallen out of love again / Out in the darkness
SR 10032 / Jul '97 / St. Roch

Radio Tarifa

☐ RUMBA ANGELINA
Rumba angelina / Oye china / Lamma bada / Manana / La canal / El baile de la bola / Soledad / La mosca / Tangos del arguijero / Nu alrest / La pastora / Ronda de sanabria / Bulerias turcas / Nina
WCD 042 / May '96 / World Circuit

☐ TEMPORAL
La tarara / Las cuevnas / Canion sefardi / Baile de almut / Tangos de la condicion / Conductus / Temporal / El mandil de Carolina / Vestido de flores
WCD 048 / Oct '97 / World Circuit

Radiohead

☐ AIRBAG
Airbag / Pearly / Meeting in the aisle / Reminder / Polythylene / Melatonin / Palo alto
8587012 / 13 Apr '98 / Parlophone

☐ BENDS, THE
Planet Telex / Bends / High and dry / Fake plastic trees / Bones / Nice dream / Just / My iron lung / Bullet proof... I wish I was / Black star / Sulk / Street spirit (fade out)
CDPCS 7372 / Mar '95 / Parlophone

☐ INTERVIEW DISC
SAM 7029 / Mar '97 / Sound & Media

☐ INTERVIEW SESSIONS
CHAT 12 / 3 Nov '97 / Chatback

☐ INTERVIEW, THE
SPEEK 004 / 16 Mar '98 / Talking Music

☐ ITCH
TOCP 8285 / 26 Jan '98 / Toshiba

☐ OK COMPUTER
Airbag / Paranoid android / Subterranean homesick alien / Exit music (for a film) / Let down / Karma police / Fitter, happier / Electioneering / Climbing up the walls / No surprises / Lucky / Tourist
CDNODATA 02 / May '97 / Parlophone

☐ PABLO HONEY
You / Creep / How do you / Stop whispering / Thinking about you / Anyone can play guitar / Ripcord / Vegetable / Prove yourself / I can't / Lurgee / Blow out
CDPCS 7360 / Mar '93 / Parlophone

Radish

☐ RESTRAINING BOLT
Little pink stars / Simple sincerity / Failing and leaving / Dear Aunt Arctica / Sugar free / Today's bargain / You in me / Still in wait / Promise / Apparition of purity / My guitar / Bedtime
5346442 / 15 Sep '97 / Mercury

Radium Cats

☐ OTHER WORLDS
Martian hop / Six foot down / Freak / Mygirl islike uranium / Idol with the golden head / Great shakin' fever / Return of the mystery train / Well I knocked (bim bam) / Strange, baby strange / Eraserhead / Let it rot / Zuvembi stroll / Pink hearse / Surfin' DOA
NERCD 068 / May '92 / Nervous

Radu, Dinu

☐ ROMANTIC PAN PIPES (Radu, Dinu & GSO)
I have a dream / Strawberry fields forever / Dark side of the moon / Scarborough fair / Sailing / Unchained melody / Amazing grace / If you leave me now / Something / Feelings / Here comes the sun / Sara / Yesterday / MacArthur park / Bird of paradise / House of the rising sun / Don't cry for me Argentina / Banks of the Ohio / Autumn dream / Let it be
CD 6002 / Nov '95 / It's Music

Rae Brothers New Orleans Jazz Band

☐ AT THE OUTGATE INN
PKCD 097 / Apr '98 / PEK

Rae, Dashiell

☐ SONG WITHOUT WORDS
NAGE 4CD / Feb '86 / Art Of Landscape

Rae, Ian & Morven

☐ BURNS BANKS AND BRAES (A Collection Of Robert Burns' Love Songs)
Robin Adair / O my love is like a red rose / Logan braes / Ye banks and braes / Thou hast left me ever / Jamie / John Anderson my Jo / The meeting in the highlands / Ca' the yowes / Till Jamie comes hame / Ae fond kiss
RAECD 1 / Feb '98 / Rae

Rae, Jesse

☐ COMPRESSION
EB 007 / 18 Sep '97 / Echo Beach

Raeburn, Boyd

☐ BOYD MEETS STRAVINSKY
Night in Tunisia / March of the Boyd / Summertime / You got me crying again / Boyd's nest / Blue prelude / Temptation / Dalvatore Sally / Boyd meets Stravinsky / I only have eyes for you / Over the rainbow / Body and soul / Blues echoes
SV 0185 / Oct '97 / Savoy Jazz

☐ BOYD RAEBURN 1944
CCD 22 / Mar '95 / Circle

☐ BOYD RAEBURN 1944-1945 (Raeburn, Boyd Orchestra)
CCD 113 / Mar '95 / Circle

☐ JEWELLS
Tonsilectomy / Forgetful / Rip Van Winkle / Yerxa / Temptation / Dalvatore Sally / Boyd meets Stravinsky / I only have eyes for you / Over the rainbow / Body and soul / Blue echoes / Little Boyd blue / Hep Boyd's / Man with a horn / Prelude to the dawn / Duck waddle / Love tales / Soft and warm / Lady is a tramp / How high the moon / Trouble is a man / St. Louis blues / It never entered my mind / Wait till you see her / It can't be wrong / When love comes
SV 0273 / Oct '97 / Savoy Jazz

☐ JUBILEE PERFORMANCES 1946 (Raeburn, Boyd & His Orchestra)
Tonsillectomy / Rip Van Winkle / Caravan / How deep is the ocean / Boyd meets Stravinsky / Dalvatore Sally / Night in Tunisia / Hep boyds
HEPCD 1 / Oct '95 / Hep

☐ TRANSCRIPTION PERFORMANCES 1946
Boyd's nest / Blue prelude / High tide / Picnic in the wintertime / Are you livin' old man / Tush / Concerto for Duke / Where you at / Out of this world / Boyd meets Stravinsky / Personality / Dalvatore Sally / Blue echoes / I only have eyes for you / Two spoos in an igloo / Temptation / I can't believe that you're in love with me / I don't know why / More than you know / Amnesia / Cartaphilius / Night in Tunisia / I cover the waterfront / Foolish little boy
HEPCD 42 / Nov '93 / Hep

Raekwon The Chef

☐ ONLY BUILT 4 CUBAN LINX
Striving for perfection / Knuckleheadz / Knowledge God / Criminology / Incarcerated scarfaces / Rainy dayz / Guillotine / Can it be all so simple / Shark niggaz / Ice water / Glaciers of ice / Verbal intercourse / Wisdom body / Spot rusherz / Ice cream / Wu gambinos / Heaven G hell / North star
07863666632 / Jul '95 / RCA

Rafferty, Gerry

☐ BAKER STREET
Baker Street / City to city / Get it right next time / Night owl / Sleepwalking / Right down the line / Waiting for the day / Days gone down (still got the light in your eyes) / Take the money and run / Change of heart / Don't close the door / Wastin' away / Royal mile / Bring it all home / On the way / Why won't you talk to me
4949412 / 1 Jun '98 / EMI Gold

☐ CAN I HAVE MY MONEY BACK
New street blues / Didn't I / Mr. Universe / Mary Skeffington / Long way round / Can I have my money back / Sign on the dotted line / Make you break you / To each and everyone / One drink down / Don't count me out / Half a chance / Where I belong
HILLCD 3 / Sep '96 / Wooded Hill

☐ CITY TO CITY
Ark / Baker Street / Right down the line / City to city / Sealin' time / Mattie's rag / Whatever's written in your heart / Home and dry / Island / Waiting for the day
CDFA 3119 / Jul '89 / Fame

☐ EARLY YEARS, THE
TRTCD 196 / 18 May '98 / TrueTrax

☐ NIGHT OWL
Days gone down / Night owl / Way that you do it / Why won't you talk to me / Get it right next time / Take the money and run / Family tree / Already gone / Tourist / It's gonna be a long night
CDFA 3147 / Jul '89 / Fame

☐ ONE MORE DREAM
5292792 / Oct '95 / PolyGram TV

☐ OVER MY HEAD
5235992 / Jul '95 / A&M

☐ SLEEPWALKING
Standing at the gates / Good intentions / Change of heart / On the way / Sleepwalking / Cat and mouse / Right moment / As wise as a serpent
7466082 / 1 Jun '98 / EMI

☐ SNAKES AND LADDERS
Royal mile / I was a boy scout / Welcome to Hollywood / Wastin' away / Look at the moon / Bring it all home / Garden of England / Johnny's song / Didn't I / Syncopatin' Sandy / Cafe le cabotin / Don't close the door
7466092 / 1 Jun '98 / EMI

☐ TRANSATLANTIC YEARS, THE
Look over the hill and far away / Patrick / Rick rack / Her father didn't like me anyway / Please sing a song for us / Blood and glory / Coconut tree / Steam boat row / Shoeshine boy / All the best people do it / Song for simon / Keep it to yourself / Can I have my money back / New street blues / Didn't I / Don't count me out / Make you, break you / To each and everyone / Mary skeffington / Half a chance / Where I belong
CCSCD 428 / Mar '95 / Castle

Rafferty, Mike & Mark

☐ DANGEROUS REEL, THE
AVL 95151CD / Nov '96 / Rapparee

Rag Pickers Of Tokyo

☐ RAG PICKERS OF TOKYO IN NEW ORLEANS
BCD 349 / Jun '96 / GHB

Rage

☐ END OF ALL DAYS
GUN 101CD / Oct '96 / Gun

☐ IN VAIN
GUN 166CD1
GUN 166CD2
GUN 166CD3 / 6 Jul '98 / Gun

☐ MISSING LINK
N 02172 / Aug '93 / Noise

☐ TEN YEARS IN RAGE
N 02912 / Sep '94 / Noise

☐ XIII (Rage & Lingua Mortis Orchestra)
GUN 156CD / 13 Apr '98 / Gun

Rage Against The Machine

☐ EVIL EMPIRE
People of the sun / Bulls on parade / Vietnow / Revolver / Snakecharmer / Tire me / Rollin' down Rodeo / Wind below / Without a face / Roll right / Year of tha boomerang
4810262 / Apr '96 / Epic

☐ RAGE AGAINST THE MACHINE
Bombtrack / Killing in the name / Take the power back / Settle for nothing / Bullet in the head / Know your enemy / Wake up / Fistful of steel / Township rebelion / Freedom
4722242 / Mar '93 / Epic

Ragermann

☐ DELICIOUS FRUIT
Delicious fruit / Gayonnah / Legend / Agaravinthia / Agion oros / Mother's aha / Grenadine / Daskallah / In the bush / Elevato / Hinne ma tov
INAK 9045CD / Jul '97 / In Akustik

Ragga Jam

☐ HOT RAGGA, COOL REGGAE
Shine / Compliments on your kiss / Dedicated to the one I love / You don't love me / Sweets for my sweet / Twist and shout / Family affair / Baby I love your way / Red red wine / I can see clearly now / Sign / On a ragga tip / She don't let nobody / Dub be good to me
QED 045 / Nov '96 / Tring

☐ RAGGA
Oh Carolina / Iron lion Zion / Sweat (a la la la la long) / Flex / All that she wants / Rock with you / Mr. Loverman / (I can't help) Falling in love with you / Bad boys / Deep / Girl, I've been hurt / Slow and sexy / Informer / Wheel of fortune
QED 129 / Nov '96 / Tring

Ragga Twins

☐ FREEDOM TRAIN
SUADCD 006 / Feb '93 / Shut Up & Dance

☐ REGGAE OWES ME MONEY
Intro / Homeless problem / Illegal gunshot / Love talk / Hooligan 69 / Spliffhead remix / Killing / Wipe the needle / Ragga trip / 18" speaker / Juggling
SUADCD 002 / Mar '91 / Shut Up & Dance

Raging Honkies

☐ BONER
Why you lie / Nothing / Floating bees / Closer to God / Roodis / Mary Lou / Underwear / Beautiful sandwich / She brings her everything / Alien / Boner
TRH 0022 / 23 Mar '98 / Smashed Hit

Raging Slab

☐ DYNAMITE MONSTER BOOGIE CONCERT
Anywhere but here / Weatherman / Pearly / So help me / What have you done / Take a hold / Laughin' and cryin' / Don't worry about the bomb / Lynne / Lord have mercy / National dust / Ain't ugly non
74321287592 / Jun '95 / American

☐ SING MONKEY SING
Shoulda known / Encounter / Never comin' down / Nobodies / Lay down / Gracious / C'mon and on / She like to / Better than what I did / Wrong / Gravity / Checkered demon / Skulls ending
74321359902 / Oct '96 / American

Ragnarok

☐ ARISING REALM
HNF 028CD / Jun '97 / Voices Of Wonder

☐ NATTFERD
HNF 012CD / Feb '96 / Head Not Found

☐ TO MEND THE OAKEN HEART
Haeled under heofenum / Rekindling an old flame / ...And the Earth shall be Holy / Arose by another name / Passion to a golden dawn / Where once ravens... / Fortuna imperatix mundi / Heartfire and forge / To mend the oaken heart
NM 018CD / Apr '97 / Neat Metal

Ragnarok

☐ RAGNAROK
SRS 3613CD / Jul '95 / Silence

Ragsdale, David

☐ DAVID AND GOLIATH
RME 0193CD / Nov '97 / Renaissance

Ragtime Millionaires

☐ LIFE IS GOOD SOMETIMES
Life is good sometimes / Jesus on the mainline / Two bridges / No fool like an old fool / Mr. Jelly Roll Baker / Spanish strings / My old clock / Strenuous life / Whatever you can get / Brother can you spare a dime / Andru's easy rdier / Hard hearted Hannah / Come back baby / Blues for Betty / Marbella blues / One way girl / When the dust settles
FECD 109 / Nov '96 / Fellside

☐ MAKING A MILLION
National seven / B flattened by the blues / Dark road blues / Snowy morning blues / Stone cold sober / Buckets of rain / Making a million / Rivers of beer / Corine Corina / Diddy wah diddy / Everywhere I go / Hi-heel sneakers / Warm summer rain / Old man's bike / Things we do / Highway robbery / Over the river / Ragtime millionaire / Where does all the money go
FE 095CD / Jan '94 / Fellside

Rah Band

☐ BEST OF THE RAH BAND, THE
MCCD 217 / Oct '95 / Music Club

Raheem

☐ TIGHT 4 LIFE
60504810012 / 7 Apr '98 / BREK

Rahman, A.R.

☐ VAN DE MATARAM
Maa tujhesalaam / Revival / Gurus of peace / Masoom / Tauba tauba / Only you / Missing / Thai mannai vanakkam / Musafir
4891242 / 20 Oct '97 / Columbia

Railroad Jerk

☐ ONE TRACK MIND
Gun problem / Bang the drum / Pollerkoaster / Riverboat / What did you expect / Home = hang / Forty minutes / Ballad of Railroad Jerk / Big white lady / Help yourself / Zero blues / Some girls waved / You better go now
OLE 1272 / Mar '95 / Matador

☐ THIRD RAIL
Clean shirt / Objectify me / You forgot / Natalie / You bet / Well / Dusty knuckle / Middle child / This is not to say I still miss you / Another nite at the bar / (I can't get no) Sleep / Sweet librarian
OLE 1992 / Oct '96 / Matador

Railway Children

☐ LISTEN ON (The Best Of The Railway Children)
Every beat of the heart / Everybody / Give it away / Music stop / What she wants / Something so good / Hours go by / After the rain / You're young / Collide / Somewhere south / Listen on / Over and over / Gentle sound / Monica's light / So right / In the meantime
CDOVD 451 / Feb '95 / Virgin

Railway Raver

☐ DROP ACID NOT BOMBS
Mine storm / Me Lacoste / Manton's run (on the run) / 202 to Ravetown / Elizabethan pornograph smugglers / To be a man like Ingersol / Land of confusion / Eyes of Garfield (part II) / Keith's trumpets / Nesmit's way / Acid for the '90's
CAT 066CD / 15 Jun '98 / Rephlex

Rain

☐ SEDIMENT
MET 001CD / Jan '97 / Metonymic

☐ SYCAMORE
METONYMIC 004CD / 30 Mar '98 / Metonymic

Rain, Billy

☐ SALAD DAYS
Circle jesus / Wild about you / On top of the world / Grown up / Roses / Christ wasn't here / Discover me / Feel / Sugarcake / Alfred hitchcock / Chocolate sky
4509961892 / Oct '94 / Oval 2

Rainbow

☐ DIFFICULT TO CURE
I surrender / Spotlight kid / No release / Magic / Vielleicht das nachster zeit / Can't happen here / Freedom fighter / Midtown tunnel vision / Difficult to cure
8000182 / Aug '84 / Polydor

☐ DOWN TO EARTH
All night long / Eyes of the world / No time to lose / Making love / Since you've been gone / Love's no friend / Danger zone / Lost in Hollywood
8237052 / Dec '86 / Polydor

☐ LIVE IN GERMANY 1976 (2CD Set)
Kill the king / Mistreated / Sixteenth century greensleeves / Catch the rainbow / Man on the silver mountain / Stargazer / Still I'm sad / Do you close your eyes
DPVSOPCD 155 / Oct '90 / Connoisseur Collection

☐ LONG LIVE ROCK 'N' ROLL
Long live rock 'n' roll / Lady of the lake / LA connection / Gates of Babylon / Sensitive to light / Kill the King / Shed / Rainbow eyes
8250902 / Jan '93 / Polydor

☐ ON STAGE
Kill the king / Man on the silver mountain / Blues / Starstruck / Catch the Rainbow / Mistreated / Sixteenth century Greensleeves / Still I'm sad
8236562 / Nov '86 / Polydor

☐ RAINBOW FAMILY ALBUM, THE (Various Artists)
VSOPCD 195 / Apr '94 / Connoisseur Collection

☐ RAINBOW RISING
Tarot woman / Run with the wolf / Starstruck / Do you close your eyes / Stargazer / Light in the black
8236552 / Nov '86 / Polydor

☐ RITCHIE BLACKMORE'S RAINBOW
Man on the silver mountain / Self portrait / Black sheep of the family / Catch the rainbow / Snake charmer / Temple of the king / If you don't like rock'n'roll / Sixteenth century greensleeves / Still I'm sad
8250892 / Jan '93 / Polydor

☐ STRAIGHT BETWEEN THE EYES
Death Alley driver / Stone cold / Bring on the night / Tite squeeze / Tearin' out my heart / Power / Miss Mistreated / Rock fever / Eyes on fire
5217092 / Apr '94 / Polydor

☐ STRANGER IN US ALL
Wolf to the moon / Cold hearted woman / Hunting humans (insatiable) / Stand and fight / Ariel / Too late for tears / Black masquerade / Silence / Hall of the mountain king / Still I'm sad
74321303372 / 11 May '98 / Arista

☐ VERY BEST OF RAINBOW, THE
5376872 / Aug '97 / Polydor

Rainbow Ffolly

☐ SALLIES FFORTH
She's alright / I'm so happy / Montgolfier / Drive my car / Goodbye / Hey you / Sun sing / Sun and sand / Labour exchange / They'm / No / Sighing game / Come on go / Go girl
SEECD 493 / 22 Jun '98 / See For Miles

Rainbow, Tucker

☐ PUSH ME TO WAR
ARICD 094 / Dec '94 / Ariwa Sounds

Rainbows

☐ AFTER THE STORM
5003 / 22 May '98 / LSD

Raincoats

☐ KITCHEN TAPES, THE
RUSCD 8238 / 23 Mar '98 / ROIR

☐ LOOKING IN THE SHADOWS
R 4032 / Jun '96 / Rough Trade

☐ MOVING
No-one's little girl / Ooh ooh la la la / Dance of hopping mad / Balloon / Mouth of a story / I saw a hill / Overheard / Rainstorm / Body / Animal rhapsody
R 3062 / Feb '94 / Rough Trade

☐ ODY SHAPE
Shouting out loud / Family treat / Only loved at night / Dancing in my head / Ody shape / And then it's OK / Baby song / Red shoes / Go away
R 3042 / Jan '94 / Rough Trade

☐ RAINCOATS, THE
Fairytale in the supermarket / No side to fall in / Adventures close to home / Off duty trip / Lola / Void / Life on the line / You're a million / In love / No looking
R 3022 / Sep '93 / Rough Trade

Raindrops

☐ COMPLETE RAINDROPS, THE
What a guy / Hanky panky / I won't cry / It's so wonderful / Da doo ron ron / When the boy's happy (the girl's happy too) / Kind of boy you can't forget / Isn't that love / Every little beat / Even though you can't dance / That boy's messin' up my mind / Not too young to get married / That boy John / Book of love / Let's go together / You got what I like / One more tear / Another boy like mine / Don't let go / Do wah diddy diddy / More than a man / Talk about me / Can't hide the hurtin'
NEMCD 713 / Nov '94 / Sequel

Rainer & Das Combo

☐ BAREFOOT ROCK
Mellow down easy / Unseen enemy / Life is fine / Barefoot rock / Sleepwalk / Around and around / That's how things get done / Broken promises / I am a sinner / If I had posession over judgement day / Where's that at / Last fair deal / How I wanted you / I wish you would
FIEND 756 / Oct '94 / Demon
GRCD 346 / Aug '97 / Glitterhouse

☐ NOCTURNES
GRCD 363 / Apr '97 / Glitterhouse

☐ TEXAS TAPES, THE
Power of delight / One man crusade / It's a matter of taste / Merciful God / (Making the) trains (run on time) / What's wrong romeo / Powder keg / Mush mind blues / Drive drive drive / Another man / That's how things get done / I am a sinner
FIENDCD 734 / Jun '93 / Demon

Rainey, Gertrude 'Ma'

☐ MA RAINEY
Jealous hearted blues / CC rider / Jelly bean blues / Countin' the blues / Slave to the blues / Chain gang blues / Bessemer bound blues / Wringin' and twistin' blues / Mountain Jack blues / Trust no man / Morning hour blues / Ma Rainey's black bottom / New boweavil blues / Black cat - Hoot owl blues / Hear me / Talking to you / Prove it on me blues / Victim of the blues / Sleep talking blues / Blame it on the blues / Daddy - Goodbye blues / Sweet rough man / Black eye blues / Leavin' this morning / Runaway blues
MCD 47021 / Jan '93 / Milestone

☐ MA RAINEY VOL.1 1923-1924
DOCD 5581 / 28 Oct '97 / Document

☐ MA RAINEY VOL.2 1924-1925
DOCD 5582 / 28 Oct '97 / Document

☐ MA RAINEY VOL.3 1925-1926
DOCD 5583 / 28 Oct '97 / Document

☐ MA RAINEY VOL.4 1926-1927
DOCD 5584 / 28 Oct '97 / Document

☐ MA RAINEY'S BLACK BOTTOM
Ma rainey's black bottom / Don't fish in my sea / Booze and blues / Farewell Daddy blues / Oh papa blues / Blues oh blues / Shave 'em dry / Lucky rock blues / Screetch owl blues / Georgia cake walk / Sleep talking blues / Yonder come the blues
YAZCD 1071 / Apr '91 / Yazoo

☐ PARAMOUNT SESSIONS VOL.1
HCD 12001 / Oct '92 / Black Swan

☐ PARAMOUNT SESSIONS VOL.5
HCD 12005 / May '95 / Black Swan

☐ RABBIT FOOT MINSTRELS
CD 53281 / May '98 / Giants Of Jazz

Rainfall Years

☐ 33RD MARCH
WSCD 007 / Oct '96 / World Serpent

Rainwater, Marvin

☐ CLASSIC MARVIN RAINWATER (4CD Set)
I gotta go get my baby / Daddy's glad you came home / Albino pink-eyed stallion / Sticks and stones / Tea bag Romeo / Tennessee houn' dog yodel / Dem low down blues / Where do we go from here / Hot and cold / Mr. Blues / Get off the stool / What am I supposed to do / I feel like leaving town (sometimes) / Why did you have to go and leave me / Gonna find me a bluebird / Because I'm a dreamer / So you think you've got troubles / Look for me (I'll be waiting for you) / Wayward angel / My brand of blues / My love is real / Lucky star / Majesty of love / You my darling you / Whole lotta woman (undubbed version) / Whole lotta woman / That's the way I feel / Baby don't go / Two fools in love / Because I'm a dreamer / Down in the cellar / Crazy love / Moanin' the blues / Gamblin' man / I dig you baby / Dance me daddy / Nothin' needs nothin' (like I need you) / Need for love (there's always) / No good runaround / Late for love (don't be) / Last time / Can I count on your love / Let me live again / Lonely island / Born to be lonesome / Love me baby (like there's no tomorrow) / That's when I'll stop loving you / Song of new love / Half breed / Valley of the moon / Young girls / Pale faced Indian (lament of the Cherokee) / Hard luck blues / She's gone / Yesterday's kisses / You're not happy / I can't forget / Boo hoo / Tough top cat / Honky tonk in your heart (There's a) / Hey good lookin' / Do it now / It wasn't enough / That little house / Part time lover / That aching heart / Love's prison / Bad girl / I saw your new love today / My old home town / Branded / Sing the girls a song / Indian burial / Black sheep / Troubles my little boy had / Sorrow brings a good man down / I want your heart / Talk to me / Run for your life boy / Old gang's gone / Cold woman / Oklahoma hills / Wedding rings / I love my country / Burning bridges / Black Jack McClain / Heart's hall of fame / Hit and run lover / Korea's mountain northland / Tainted gold / Don't tell my boy (in prison living a lie) / Don't try to change your little woman / Do you want to know / Engineer's song (the boy and the engineer) / Freight train blues / Key / Let's go on a picnic / Moment's of love / So long / Teardrops / Wanderer in me / What you got, you don't want / Would your mother be proud of you / You can't keep a secret
BCD 15600 / Nov '93 / Bear Family

☐ ROCKIN' ROLLIN' RAINWATER
Hot and cold / Mr. Blues / Get off the stool / There's a honky tonk in your heart / My brand of blues / Whole lotta woman / That's the way I feel / Baby don't go / Down in the cellar / Crazy love / Moanin' the blues / Gamblin' man / I dig you baby / Dance me Daddy / (There's always) A need for love / Don't be Late for love / Last time / Love me baby (like there's no tomorrow) / Valley of the moon / Young girls / Hard luck blues / I can't forget / Boo hoo / Tough top cat / Oklahoma Hills / Henryetta, Oklahoma
BCD 15182 / Jun '94 / Bear Family

☐ WHOLE LOTTA WOMAN
I dig you baby / Whole lotta woman / Baby don't go / Moanin' the blues / Crazy love / Mr. Blues / Hot and cold / Get off the stool / Down in the cellar / That's the way I feel / Dance me Daddy / Love me baby (like there's no tomorrow) / (There's always) A need for love / (Don't be late) For love / Last time / Young girls / Boo hoo / Tough top cat / (There's a honky tonk) In your heart / I can't forget / Gamblin' man / My brand of blues / Valley of the Moon / Hard luck blues / Oklahoma Hills / Henryetta, Oklahoma / Oklahoma
BCD 15812 / Jul '94 / Bear Family

Raise The Roof

☐ KEEPERS OF THE GROOVE
9920062 / Sep '97 / Via Jazz

Raised Fist

☐ STRONGER THAN EVER
BHR 046CD / Mar '97 / Burning Heart

☐ YOUR NOT LIKE ME
BHR 017CD / Feb '95 / Burning Heart

Raism

☐ AESTHETIC TERRORISM
KRONH 007CD / 15 Jun '98 / Kronh

☐ VERY BEST OF PAIN
KRONH 04CD / Jul '96 / Osmose

Raison D'Etre

☐ IN SADNESS SILENCE AND SOLITUDE
Reflecting in shadows / In absence of light / Well of sadness / Deep enshrouded / Falling twilight / Passing inner shield
CMI 57 / 2 Feb '98 / Cold Meat Industry

Raissa

☐ MEANTIME
Worm / Green as sea / Meantime / Murky / We are nowhere / Space where you were / Storm / Silver wind / Meantime (part two) / Forgive me / Time I can touch / Your summertime / Piccadilly / Meantime (part three)
5310372 / Oct '96 / Polydor

Raitt, Bonnie

☐ COLLECTION, THE
Finest lovin' man / Women be wise / Love me like a man / I feel the same / Angel from Montgomery / My first night alone without you / Louise / Runaway / Wild for you baby / True love is hard to find / Give it up or let me go / Under the falling sky / Love has no pride / Guilty / What is success / Sugar mama / About to make me leave home / Glow / Willya wontcha / No way to treat a lady
7599262422 / Dec '96 / WEA

☐ FUNDAMENTAL
Fundamental things / Cure for love / Round and round / Spit of love / Lover's will / Blue for no reason / Meet me halfway / I'm on your side / Fearless love / I need love / One belief away
8563972 / 30 Mar '98 / Capitol

☐ GIVE IT UP
Give it up or let me go / Nothing seems to matter / I know / If you gotta make a fool of somebody / Love me like a man / Stayed too long at the fair / Under the falling sky / You got to know how / You told me baby / Love has no pride
7599272642 / Feb '93 / WEA

☐ LONGING IN THEIR HEARTS
Love sneakin' up on you / Longing in their hearts / You / Cool clear water / Circle dance / I sho do / Dimming of the day / Feeling of falling / Steal your heart away / Storm warning / Hell to pay / Shadow of doubt
CDEST 2227 / Apr '94 / Capitol

☐ LUCK OF THE DRAW
Something to talk about / Good man, good woman / I can't make you love me / Tangled and dark / Come to me / No business / One part be my lover / Not the only one / Papa come quick (Jody and Chico) / Slow ride / Luck of the draw / All at once
CDEST 2145 / Jun '91 / Capitol

☐ NICK OF TIME
Nick of time / Thing called love / Love letters / Cry on my shoulder / Real man / Nobody's girl / Have a heart / Too soon to tell / I will not be denied / I ain't gonna let you break my heart again / Road's my middle name
CDEST 2095 / Apr '89 / Capitol

☐ ROAD TESTED
Thing called love / Something to talk about / Never make your move too soon / Shake a little / Matters of the heart / Love me like a man / Kokomo medley / My opening farewell / Dimming of the day / Longing in their hearts / Love sneakin' up on you / Burning down the house / I can't make you love me / I believe I'm in love with you / Rock steady / Angel from Montgomery
CDEST 2274 / Nov '95 / Capitol

Raiz De Pedra

☐ DIARIO DE BORDO
Q quem tai / Sao sepe / Linha azul / Amigos de longe / As historias de domingos / Munique / Levando a vida / Tempos de minuano / O Navio
8888222 / Apr '96 / Tiptoe

Raja-Nee

☐ HOT AND READY
Quick / Turn it up / Taunted / Walking away with it / Who's been givin' it up / Sex in a jeep / Hot and ready / Give it to me / Take your time / Dance hall druglord / I wanna get next to you / Bitchism
5490142 / Feb '95 / Perspective

Rakasha Mancham

☐ PHYIDAR
EEE 013CD / Sep '93 / Musica Maxima Magnetica

Rakha, Ustad Alla

☐ TABLA DUET (Rakha, Usted Alla & Zakir Hussain)
MR 1001 / Apr '95 / Moment

Rakim

☐ 18TH LETTER, THE (2CD Set)
UD2 53111 / 3 Nov '97 / Universal

Rakotozafy

☐ MADAGASIKARA VOL.4 (Valihala Malazi - Historical Recordings From The 1960's)
Salama 'nareo tompoko o / Ramanjareo / O zaza ny fandeha diasa / Botofetsy / Tonga teto lala / Hitako o / Mandrosoa lahy mahaeva / Isa, roa, telo / Rey lahy, rey lahy / Varavarankely / Sega vaovao valiha malaza / Mandihiza raha manan' eratra / Iadiavan janako aho rafozako / Ny fitiavana raho vao miaraka / Miasa tsara raha manambady / Tangalamena / Lekatseka / Samy faly / Fisaorana
CDORBD 028 / Jul '95 / Globestyle

Raksha Mancham

☐ CHOS KHOR
EEE 17 / Aug '94 / Musica Maxima Magnetica

Ralasic, Domagoy

☐ BAG IS PACKED (Ralasic, Domagoy & Benny Bailey)
Blues for Lady / For all we know / Lester leaps in / Body and soul / Peruvian nights / I should care / You'd be so nice to come home too / Manumission / Packed bag / What's waiting for me here / Loverman
CDSJP 441 / 23 Feb '98 / Timeless

Ram Jam World

☐ ROUGH AND READY
Planet earth / Cool summer time / Television / Searchin' / Throbbing gristle / Aphrodisiac / Five / Searchin' / Friday night saturday night / Body and rock / Love song / Corazon
3984205572 / 10 Nov '97 / WEA

Ramani, Dr. N.

☐ MUSIC IN THE RAGAS...
NI 5257 / Sep '94 / Nimbus

Ramases

☐ SPACE HYMNS
REP 4108 / Aug '91 / Repertoire

Ramazzotti, Eros

☐ DOVE C'E MUSICA
Dove c'e musica / Stella Gemella / Piu bella cosa / L'aurora / Lettera al futuro / Lo amero / Questo immenso show / Quasi amore / Yo sin tin / Lei pero / L'uragano meri / Buona vita
74321354412 / Aug '96 / Arista

☐ EROS
74321525452 / 20 Apr '98 / RCA

☐ EROS IN CONCERT (2CD Set)
Terra promesa / Nuovi eroi / Un cuore le ali / Emozione dopo emozione / Complemtamente enamorados / Fuegodal nulla / Adesso tu / Seguimi / Se bastasse un canzoe / Ce una strada in ceilo / Toma la luna / Amore contro / Taxi story / Dolce Barbara / Andare...in ogni senso / Fastastico amor / La luca bouna delle stelle / Occhi di speranza / Amarta es total / Musicale / Liberta liberta / Ciao pa canzoni lontane / Une historia imortante / Cantico / Ancora vita
354312 / 1 Sep '97 / RCA

☐ MUSICA E
259174 / Aug '95 / Arista

☐ TUTTE STORIE
Cose della vita / A mezza via / Un altra te / Memorie / In compagnia / Un grosso no / Favola / Non c'e piu fantasia / Nostalsong / Niente di male / Esodi / L'ulti ma rivoluzione / Silver e missie
74321143292 / Jan '94 / Arista

Ramey, Troy

☐ BEST OF TROY RAMEY & THE SOUL SEARCHERS, THE (Ramey, Troy & The Soul Searchers)
NASH 4505 / Feb '96 / Nashboro

Ramirez, Humberto

☐ ASPECTS
Aspects / Chapter 27 / Rumbero siempre / At peace / El ministro / Amanda / Golden view / Camino azul / Touch of beauty
66058039 / Jul '94 / RMM

☐ JAZZ PROJECT, THE
RMD 80774 / 24 Mar '98 / RMM

☐ PORTRAIT OF A STRANGER
El principe / Sanjuanero / Cuando estoy contigo (madrigal) / Catalina / Sonando con puerto rico / Un tipo con suerte / Ball players / My funny valentine / To the king / Portrait of a stranger / Cristina / Atmospheres
66058091 / Feb '96 / Tropi

Ramirez, Karen

☐ DISTANT DREAMS
Troubled girl / More than words / Stormy day / Lies / If we try / New reality / Looking for love / Maker shaker / Wings / People make the world go around / Looking for love
5369462 / 20 Jul '98 / Manifesto

Ramirez, Louie

☐ OTRA NOCHE CALIENTE (Ramirez, Louie & Ray De La Paz)
Otra noche caliente / El / Suddenly / Definitivamente / Soy feliz / Yo soy la rumba / Medley: Noche caliente hits
66058008 / Sep '93 / RMM

Ramirez, Manuel

☐ AL MAESTRO LAVOE
TUMI 076 / 10 Aug '98 / Tumi

Ramleh

☐ ADIEU ALL YOU JUDGES (Ramleh/ Skullflower)
BF 78 / Oct '96 / Broken Flag

☐ BE CAREFUL WHAT YOU WISH FOR
SFTRI 397CD / Jan '96 / Sympathy For The Record Industry

☐ WORKS VOL.3 (2CD Set)
DPROMCD 40 / Oct '96 / Dirter Promotions

Ramlosa Kvallar

☐ NIGHTS WITHOUT FRAMES
Sega / Magnus Ladulaten / Bogdan dansar / Castaneda / Vallaten / Den maskulina mystiken / Ide och lardomshistoria / Areskutan / Sista Mars / Esten / Ramlosa blues / Grekisk sorgmarsch
RESCD 507 / Jul '97 / Resource

Rammstein

☐ SCHNSUCHT
5373042 / 17 Nov '97 / London

Ramones

☐ ALL THE STUFF (AND MORE) VOL.1 (2CD Set)
Blitzkrieg bop / Beat on the brat / Judy is a punk / Now I wanna sniff some glue / Don't go down the basement / Loudmouth / Havana affair / 53rd and 3rd / I don't wanna walk around with you / I wanna be sedated / Glad to see you go / I remember you / Sheena is a punk rocker / Pinhead / Swallow my pride / California sun / I wanna be your boyfriend / You're gonna kill that girl / Babysitter / Listen to my heart / Let's dance / Today your love, tomorrow the world / I can't be / Gimme gimme shock treatment / Oh oh I love her so / Suzy is a headbanger / Now I wanna be a good boy / What's your game / Commando / Chainsaw / You should never have opened that door / California sun (live)
7599262202 / Aug '90 / Sire

☐ BLITZKRIEG OVER YOU (A Tribute To The Ramones) (Various Artists)
SPV 08487912 / 1 Sep '98 / SPV

☐ BRAIN DRAIN
I believe in miracles / Punishment fits the crime / Pet Semetary / Merry Christmas / Learn to listen / Zero zero UFO / All screwed up / Can't get you outta my mind / Ignorance is bliss
CCD 1725 / 6 Jul '98 / EMI Gold

☐ END OF THE CENTURY
Do you remember rock 'n' roll radio / I'm affected / Danny says / Chinese rocks / Return of Jackie and Judy / Let's go baby / Baby I love you / I can't make it on time / This ain't Havanna
E599274292 / Mar '94 / Sire

☐ IT'S ALIVE
Rockaway beach / Teenage labotomy / Blitzkrieg bop / I wanna be well / Glad to see you go / Gimme gimme shock treatment / You're gonna kill that girl / I don't care / Sheena is a punk rocker / Havana affair / Commando / Here today, gone tomorrow / Surfin' bird / Cretin hop / Listen to my heart / California sun / I don't wanna walk around with you / Pinhead / Suzy is a headbanger / Let's dance / Oh oh I lover her so / Now I wanna sniff some glue / We're a happy family
9362460452 / Jan '96 / Sire

☐ LEATHER FROM NEW YORK (CD/Book Set)
Carbona not glue / Blitzkreig bop / Chop suey / Wonderful widow of 18 springs
SB 08 / 23 Feb '98 / Sonic Book

☐ RAMONES MANIA (2CD Set)
I wanna be sedated / Teenage lobotomy / Do you remember rock 'n' roll radio / Gimme gimme shock treatment / Beat on the brat / Sheena is a punk rocker / I wanna live / Pinhead / Blitzkrieg bop / Cretin hop / Rockaway beach / Commando / I wanna be your boyfriend / Mama's boy / Bop 'till you drop / We're a happy family / Bonzo goes to Bitburg / Outsider / Psychotherapy / Wart hog / Animal boy / Needles and pins / Howling at the moon (sha la la) / Somebody put something in my drink / We want the airwaves / Chinese rocks / I just want to have something to do / KKK took my baby away / Indian giver / Rock 'n' roll high school
9257092 / Jun '88 / Sire

☐ WE'RE OUTTA HERE (The Ramones' Last Show)
EAGCD 010 / 22 Nov '97 / Eagle

☐ ZONKED (Ramone, Dee Dee)
OPM 2118CD / 13 Oct '97 / Other People's Music

Ramos, Kid

☐ TWO HANDS, ONE HEART
BM 9031 / Jul '95 / Black Magic

Rampage

☐ SCOUTS HONOR...BY WAY OF BLOOD
Intro / Flipmode is da squad / Da night B4 my shit / Talk of the town / Get da money and dip / Set up / Wild for da night / Flipmode enemy no.1 / Take it to the streets / Conquer da world / Hall of fame / Niggaz is bad / We getz down / Rampage outro
7559620222 / 4 Aug '97 / Elektra

Rampling, Danny

☐ IN THE MIX (2CD Set) (Various Artists)
DRCD 1 / Nov '95 / Metropole

☐ LOVE GROOVE DANCE PARTY VOL.1 & 2, THE (2CD Set) (Various Artists)
LGCD 1
LGCDSP 1 / May '96 / Metropole

☐ LOVE GROOVE DANCE PARTY VOL.3 & 4 (2CD Set) (Various Artists)
LGCDSP 2
LGCD 2 / Nov '96 / Metropole

☐ LOVE GROOVE DANCE PARTY VOL.5 & 6 (3CD Set) (Various Artists)
Release yo self: *Transatlantic Soul* / Pull me up: *Ground 96* / Spend the night: *Lewis, Danny J.* / Cure: *Simpson, Paul* / Touch me: *Romatt* / Testify: *Williams, Jay* / Take me over: *House of Glass* / I like it: *House of Glass* / Do me all over: *Icy Hot* / Goosebumps: *Nylx* / Discotheque: *U2* / Back to paradise: *Stingily, Byron* / You're not alone: *Olive* / House of the rising sun: *TBB* / Blue fear: *TBB* / Sydney: *Roughage* / El diablo: *Fuego* / Nightmare: *Brainbug* / Prospect: *DJ Misjah* / Ultra free state: *Crashforce* / Soul mantra: *Chris Liberator* / Free Tibet: *Astral Projection* / Lunar sunrise: *Terra Ferma* / Flash: *BBE*
LGCD 3 / May '97 / Metropole

Rampolokeng, Lesego

☐ END BEGINNINGS (Rampolokeng, Lesego & Kalahari Surfers)
RERLRSCD 1 / Jul '93 / ReR/ Recommended

Ramsey, Bill

☐ CALIFORNIA AND MORE...
Caldonia / Outskirt of town / Goin' to Chicago / Frankie and Johnny / St. James infirmary / Caldonia / Big fat Mama / When the saints go marchin' in / In the late late show / More I see you / Where or when / Worksong / Sunny / I'm gonna sit right down and write myself... / I'm beginning to see the light / Sophisticated lady/Satin doll / Misty / Route 66 / Honeysuckle rose / Ornithology/How high the moon / Girl from Ipanema / There will never be another you / Kansas City / Shadow of your smile
BCD 16151 / Oct '97 / Bear Family

☐ SOUVENIRS
Wumba tumba schokoladeneisverkaufer / Casa bambu / Erwar vom Konstantinopolitanischen / Gesangverein / Cecilia / Mach keinen heck meck / Go man go / Souvenirs / Hier konn matrosen vor anker gehn / Telefon aus Paris / Gina, Gina / Jeden tag 'ne andre party / Die welt ist rund / Pigalle (die gross mausefalle) / Care oriental / Das madchen mit dem aufregenden gang / Zuckerpuppe (aus der Bauchtanz truppe) / Mach ein foto davon / Weit weg von hier: *Ramsey, Bill & Chris Howland* / Missouri cowboy: *Ramsey, Bill & Peter Alexander* / Yes, fanny, ich tu das: *Ramsey, Bill & Margret Furer* / So ein stroll in tirol: *Ramsey, Bill & Margret Furer* / Nichts gegen die weiber: *Ramsey, Bill & Bibi Johns* / Got a call from Paris / Rockin' mountain / Gina Gina / Pigalle / Telefon fra Paris
BCD 15672 / Jun '92 / Bear Family

☐ WHEN I SEE YOU (Ramsey, Bill & Toots Thielemans)
BLR 84 022 / May '91 / L&R

Ramsey, Bo

☐ BO RAMSEY & THE BACKSLIDERS (Ramsey, Bo & The Backsliders)
DFGCD 8443 / Jun '96 / Dixie Frog

☐ IN THE WEEDS
In the weeds / Desert flower / Precious / Everything is comin' down / Big Bill / Sidetrack lounge / King of clubs / Trapped again / Ain't it hard / Forget you / Living in a cornfield
DFGCD 8461 / May '97 / Dixie Frog

Ramshackle

☐ CHIN ON THE CURB
0098602WHE / Jul '97 / Edel

☐ DEPTHOLOGY
BLRCD 30 / Nov '95 / Big Life

Ramzy, Hossam

☐ BALADI PLUS
EUCD 1083 / '91 / ARC

☐ BEST OF ABDUL HALIM HAFIZ, THE (Ramzy, Hossam & His Egyptian Ensemble)
EUCD 1195 / Apr '92 / ARC

☐ BEST OF OM KOLTHOUM, THE (Ramzy, Hossam & His Egyptian Ensemble)
EUCD 1194 / Apr '92 / ARC

☐ EGYPTIAN RAI (Ramzy, Hossam & Ensemble)
EUCD 1132 / '91 / ARC

☐ EL SULTAAN
EUCD 1122 / '91 / ARC

☐ ESHTA
EUCD 1121 / '91 / ARC

☐ GAMAAL RAWHANY
EUCD 1368 / Nov '96 / ARC

☐ INTRODUCTION TO EGYPTIAN DANCE RHYTHMS, AN
EUCD 1081 / '91 / ARC

☐ KOUHAIL
EUCD 1120 / '91 / ARC

☐ LATIN AMERICAN HITS FOR BELLYDANCE
EUCD 1259 / Mar '94 / ARC

☐ RHYTHMS OF THE NILE
EUCD 1104 / '91 / ARC

☐ RO HE (Classical Egyptian Bellydance)
EUCD 1082 / '91 / ARC

☐ SAMYA (The Best Of Farid Al Atrash)
EUCD 1232 / Nov '93 / ARC

☐ SOURCE OF FIRE
EUCD 1305 / Jul '95 / ARC

☐ ZEINA (The Best Of Mohammed Abdul Wahab)
EUCD 1231 / Nov '93 / ARC

Ranaldo, Lee

☐ CLOUDS (Ranaldo, Lee & William Hooker)
VICTOCD 054 / Feb '98 / Victo

☐ FROM HERE TO INFINITY
SST 113CD / May '93 / SST

Ranch Girls

☐ HILLBILLY HARMONY
GRCD 6071 / Dec '96 / Goofin'

Ranch Hands

☐ SWITCHED ON COUNTRY
Hello I love you / Sundown / Woman, beautiful woman / Ruby don't take your love to town / Gentle on my mind / Jolene / Let your love flow / Rhinestone cowboy / Oh lonesome me / Half the way / If I said you had a beautiful body / Detroit city / Down the Mississippi / Mississippi / Some days are diamonds / Slow hand / I don't wanna play house / If your cheatin' heart / Listen to the radio / You never gave up on me / Always on my mind / Love me tender / Honey / Sweetest things / Only love / Annie's song / Me and Bobby McGee / Help me make it through the night / When you were sweet sixteen / Love hurts / You needed me / Blue eyes crying in the rain / I will always love you / Wolverton Mountain / Coward of the county / Some broken hearts never mend / Take me home country roads / All I ever need is you / Heaven is my woman's love / You asked me to / Before the next teardrop falls / Banks of the Ohio / If you love me let me know / You're my best friend / I recall a gypsy woman / Shelter of your eyes / Silver threads and golden needles / Honey come back / Most beautiful girl in the world / Have I told you lately / I walk the line / Take me back
QED 121 / Nov '96 / Tring

Ranch House Favourites

☐ BACK TO TEXAS
RH 001 / May '98 / Ranch House

Ranch Romance

☐ BLUE BLAZES
Heartaches / What's wrong with you / Blue blazes / Indeed I do / Arizona moon / Racin' / Burnin' bridges / Buckaroo / Lost heart / Cuttin' a rug / Trouble / Baby doll / Lucky one
SHCD 3794 / Mar '98 / Sugar Hill

☐ FLIP CITY
SHCD 3813 / Jan '94 / Sugar Hill

☐ WESTERN DREAM
When the bloom is on the sage / Lovesick blues / Baby's on the town / St. Louis blues / Cowboys and indians / St. James Avenue / Gotta lot of rhythm in my soul / Ain't no ash will burn / Why don't you love me (Like you used to) / Birmingham fling / Last one to know / Western dream
SHCD 3799 / Mar '92 / Sugar Hill

Rancho Diablo

☐ CHICKEN WORLD
THIRTEENCD 1 / Feb '95 / Thirteenth Hour

Rancho Relaxo Allstars

☐ LIVE AT LUV PARADE
EFA 294712 / 1 Sep '98 / Disko B

☐ RANCHO RELAXO ALLSTARS VOL.1
EFA 122812 / Sep '96 / Disko B

Rancid

☐ LIFE WON'T WAIT (2CD Set)
Intro / Bloodclot / Black lung / Life won't wait / New dress / Warsaw / Hooligan / Crane fist / Leicester square / Backslide / Who would've thought / Cash culture and violence / Wolf / 1998 / Lady liberty / Wrongful suspicion / Turntable / Something in the world today / Corazon de oro / Coppers
64972 / 15 Jun '98 / Epitaph

Rancid Hell Spawn

☐ AXE HERO
STUNCH 6 / Sep '93 / Wrench

Randall

☐ HELTER SKELTER (Drum 'n' Bass Annual Mixed By Randall/DJ Hype - 2CD Set) (Various Artists)
CDHSR 097 / 18 May '98 / Helter Skelter

Randall, Jon

☐ WHAT YOU DON'T KNOW
This heart / If blue tears were silver / I came straight to you / If I hadn't reached for the stars / To pieces / Tennessee blues / What if you don't know / Only game in town / They're gonna miss when I'm gone / Just like you
74321272972 / Mar '95 / RCA

Randall, Ray

☐ POLLY SWALLOW
ROADCD 002 / May '98 / Roadant

Randles, Philip

☐ HEAR MY SONG
CDTS 040 / Nov '93 / Maestro

☐ ORGAN DANCE BONANZA
CDTS 052 / Dec '95 / Maestro

☐ PARTY DANCE BONANZA
CDTS 055 / Dec '95 / Maestro

Randolph, Boots

☐ YAKETY SAX
Percolator / Yakety sax (mono) / Hey Elvis / Difficult / I'm getting the message baby / Little big horn / Big daddy / Blue guitar / Greenback dollar / Sweet talk / Red light / La golondrina / Temptation / Battle of New Orleans / Sleepwalk / After you've gone / Little big horn / Sleep / So rare / Teach me tonight / Happy whistler / Estrellita / Big daddy / Bongo band / Yakety sax (stereo) / Hey Elvis
BCD 15459 / Apr '89 / Bear Family

Random Damage

☐ RANDOM DAMAGE
M 7014CD / Oct '95 / Mascot

Random Killing

☐ RANDOM KILLING
BMCD 078 / Nov '95 / Black Mark

☐ THOUGHTS OF AGGRESSION
BMCD 074 / Jun '95 / Black Mark

Randy

☐ NO CARROTS FOR THE REHABILITATED
DOLCD 011 / Feb '95 / Dolores

☐ REST IS SILENCE, THE
DOL 037CD / Oct '96 / Dolores

☐ THERE'S NO WAY
DOL 016CD / Aug '95 / Dolores

☐ THERE'S NO WAY WE'RE GONNA FIT IN
DOLCD 016 / Feb '95 / Dolores

Raney, Doug

☐ BACK IN NEW YORK
SCCD 31409 / Jul '97 / Steeplechase

☐ GUITAR, GUITAR, GUITAR
SCCD 31212 / Jul '88 / Steeplechase

☐ MEETING THE TENORS (Raney, Doug Sextet)
CRISS 1006CD / Feb '94 / Criss Cross

Raney, Jimmy

☐ BUT BEAUTIFUL (Raney, Jimmy Trio)
CRISS 1065CD / Oct '92 / Criss Cross

☐ GUITAR MOMENTS (2CD Set) (Raney, Jimmy & Doug Quartet)
SCCD 37031 / Jan '98 / Steeplechase

☐ MASTER, THE (Raney, Jimmy Quartet)
CRISS 1009CD / Nov '90 / Criss Cross

☐ SOLO
60170400082 / 14 Apr '98 / PREV

☐ STOLEN MOMENTS (Raney, Jimmy & Doug Quartet)
SCCD 31118 / Jul '88 / Steeplechase

☐ VISITS PARIS
74321429252 / Apr '97 / RCA

☐ WISTARIA (Raney, Jimmy Trio)
CRISS 1019CD / Nov '91 / Criss Cross

Raney, Sue

☐ WHEN YOUR LOVER HAS GONE/ SONGS FOR A RAINY DAY
When your lover has gone / I stayed too long at the fair / If I could be with you one hour tonight / My ideal / It looks like apple blossom / It's easy to remember / Moon song / Heart and soul / If you were there / My silent love / I remember you / I'll see you in my dreams / I get the blues when it rains / Impossible / Blossom fell / Wrap your trouble in dreams / Whipporr song / Rain on Rain / Rain on the roof / Blue tears / Exactly like you
CTMCD 121 / 15 Sep '97 / EMI

Rangecroft, John

☐ BLYTHE HILL (Rangecroft, John & Marcio Mattos/Stew Butterfield)
SLAMCD 228 / Jan '98 / Slam

Rangell, Nelson

☐ IN EVERY MOMENT
One world spirit / NY/LA / Someday / Golden / Boomtown / Wild river / Map of the stars / All this time / Tell me what you're thinking / Dancing with Ivy
GRP 96622 / 25 May '98 / GRP

☐ TO BEGIN AGAIN
1390072 / May '89 / Gaia

☐ TURNING NIGHT INTO DAY
Starting now / Turning night into day / Journey / All for you / For the rest of my life / Romantique / Godzilla / From spark to flame / April snow / All hearts, one heart / Today's top story / La repuesta (The answer)
GRP 98642 / Apr '97 / GRP

Ranglin, Alvin

☐ HOLY GROUND
CDHB 62 / Sep '90 / Heartbeat

Ranglin, Ernest

☐ BELOW THE BASSLINE
Congo man / Surfin' / King Tubby meets the rockers / Satta a masagana / 54-56 (was my number) / Ball of fire / Black disciples / Bourbon street skank / None shall escape the judgment / Nana's chalk pipe / Below the bass line
IJCD 4002 / May '96 / Island Jamaica Jazz

☐ IN SEARCH OF THE LOST RIDDIM
PALMCD 2001 / 29 Jun '98 / Palm Pictures

☐ MEMORIES OF BARBER MACK
Papa's bag juice / Fade away / For Juni / Undecided / Memories of Baber Mack / Stop that train / Blue mountains / Lovebird / Dancehall fever / Five thirty
IJCD 4004 / May '97 / Island Jamaica Jazz

☐ PLAY THE TIME AWAY
GM 001 / May '96 / Runn

☐ SOUL D'ERN
JHAS 611 / Aug '97 / Ronnie Scott's Jazz House

☐ SOUNDS & POWER
SOCD 50152 / Oct '96 / Studio One

Rankin Family

☐ ENDLESS SEASONS
As I roved out / River / Natives / Oganaich an or-fhuilt Bhulde/Am braighe / Forty days and nights / Eyes of Margaret / You feel the same way too / Endless seasons / Padstow / Blue eyed Suzie / Your boat's lost at sea
GRACD 217 / Jul '96 / Grapevine

☐ FARE THEE WELL LOVE
Orangedale whistle / An t each ruadh / Fair and tender ladies / Fiddle medley / Lime hill / Keep the country bonnie lassie / Jack daniel's reel / Little donald in the pig pen / Fisherhair's son / Tell my ma / You left a flower / Fare thee well love / Gillis mountain / Gaelic medley / Tripper's jig
GRMCD 002 / Jul '96 / Grapevine

☐ NORTH COUNTRY
Fare thee well love / North Country / Oich u agus h-iuraibh eile (love song) / Borders and time / Mull river shuffle / Golden rod jig / Lisa Brown / Ho ro my nut brown maiden / Tramp miner / Rise again / Boat song / Christy Campbell medley / Betty Lou's reel / Turn that boat around
GRMCD 216 / Jul '96 / Grapevine

☐ RANKIN FAMILY, THE
Mo run geal dileas (my faithful fair one) / Lonely island / Loving arms / Mairi's wedding michael rankin's reel / Roving gypsy boy / Chi mi na morgheanna (mist covered mountains) / Lament of the irish immigrant
GRMCD 001 / Jul '96 / Grapevine

Rankin File

☐ FOR THE RECORD
Call on me / Sense of kind / Words and wisdom / Canadian trilogy / Leaving home / Whispy / Leaving is the story of my life / Carefully / Lost it on the road / Met her on the shap / Drank his son to death / Circle turns again / Mrs. Mann and me / Mr. Sax
CDTRAX 057 / Dec '92 / Greentrax

Rankin, Iain

☐ OUT OF THE BLUE
Teardrop on the ocean / Thirty storeys high / We're still here / Out of nowhere / Go to hell but turn right / Daddy was a miner / McGingle's violin / Make love to me / One step forward and two steps back / Next time you talk to heaven / Wild horses / Let's do it all over again
CDTRAX 069 / Dec '93 / Greentrax

Rankin, Rita

☐ LANTERN BURN (Rankin, Rita & Mary)
Tiree love song / Hi horo na horo eile / Western highway / Chi mi 'n geamhradh / Eilidh / Medley / Fair love of my heart / Long for the sea / Medley / Greenwood side / Brown haired maiden of the smooth tresses / Darkest winter / Fear a' bhata / Sarah / Lantern burn
IRCD 053 / May '97 / Iona

Ranking Joe

☐ FAST FORWARD TO AFRICA
ARICD 107 / May '96 / Ariwa Sounds

Rannenberg, Christian

☐ LONG WAY FROM HOME
(Rannenberg, Christian & Pink Piano Allstars)
BEST 1006CD / Nov '93 / Acoustic Music

Rant

☐ MIXING IT
CMCD 074 / Jul '94 / Celtic Music

Raped

☐ COMPLETE RAPED PUNK COLLECTION, THE
Moving target / Raped / Escalator hater / Normal / BIC / ECT / Foreplay playground / Cheap night out / Babysitting / Shit / Cheap night out / Foreplay playground / LONDON / Raped / Slits / Cheap trash / Normal / Moving target / Knock on wood
CDPUNK 35 / 9 Mar '98 / Anagram

Rapeman

☐ TWO NUNS AND A PACK MULE
Steak and black onions / Monobrow / Up beat / Cotition ignition mission / Kim gordon's panties / Hated chinee / Radar love lizard / Marmoset / Just got paid / Trouser minnow / Budd / Superpussy / Log brass / Dutch courage
BFFP 33CD / Nov '88 / Blast First

Rapiers

☐ BACK TO THE POINT
FCD 3034 / Aug '94 / Fury

Rapone, Al

☐ PLAYS TRIBUTE TO CLIFTON CHENIER
Accordian man / Zydeco man / Oh Momon / Comin' home / Et Title file / Rock me baby / Tu le ton son ton / Zydeco ils sont pas sale / Sa m'appel fou / Chere catin / You used to call me / Key to the highway / Hey Negress / Rosa Lee / It's my soul
ATM 1133 / May '97 / Atomic Theory

Rapoon

☐ FIRES OF THE BORDERLANDS, THE
Hollow flight / Groundswell / Cires Divam / Snake of the Earth / Omaneska / Deserted shadows / Looking...not finding / Circling globes / Talking to a stick / Still so still / Softer light
RR 69782 / 23 Mar '98 / Relapse

Rara Machine

☐ VOUDOU NOU
Viktwa san glol / Voudou nou / Prese / Bade / Lagel / Pan'n se pan / Ginen yo / Nou groove (reggae rap by papa jube) / Se love
SHCD 64054 / Oct '94 / Shanachie

Rare

☐ PEOPLEFREAK
Life can / Something wild / Killer / Trains to nowhere / Same as always / Skanker / Sonny listen / Sweeter / Johnny boy / Soda / Seems like
KOLD 101CD / 13 Apr '98 / Arctic

Rare Air

☐ HARD TO BEAT
Hard times / Taxi suite / Inside out / Small as life / Marvin's march / Waiting room / Dee dee diddley bop / Onward blindly onward / Beam me up
GLCD 1073 / Feb '93 / Green Linnet

☐ PRIMEVAL
Fourth world reel / Jungle / Volunteer slavery / New swing reel / O'grady's little italy / Chicago shopping mall / Behind the garage / Hipbone / Highland life / Dreaming of the other side
GLCD 1104 / Feb '91 / Green Linnet

☐ SPACE PIPER
Treebranch / Mammoth no arms / Astral jig / Snake macmurray / La marche de tintin to india / C'est fou, c'est toi, c'est tout / Madhouse / Death of a space piper
GLCD 1115 / '92 / Green Linnet

Rare Bird

☐ SYMPATHY
Sympathy / You went away / Nature's fruit / Bird on a wing / What you want to know / Beautiful scarlet / Hammerhead / I'm thinking / As your mind flies by
CDOVD 280 / Apr '90 / Charisma

Rare Earth

☐ DIFFERENT WORLD
She's trouble / Livin' in a different world / Reach out / I got the feeling / Can't stop love / Lady madonna / Slippin' away / Livin' it up / How sweet it is (to be loved by you) / Hey pretty baby / Tobacco road
341002 / Feb '93 / Koch

Ras Iley

☐ KING OF THE STAGE
WCD 395 / Feb '94 / JW

Ras Ivi

☐ ARK OF COVENANT (Ras Ivi & The Family Of Rastafari)
SZCD 003 / Apr '95 / Surr Zema Musik

Ras Iyah

☐ RASTA SOUL JAH (Ras Iyah & The Shant-Ites)
FRCD 001 / 20 Apr '98 / Falasha

Ras Michael

☐ FREEDOM SOUND (Ras Michael & The Sons Of Negus)
Watch and prey / Written down there / Holy mount zion / I shall not remove / Roll river jordan, roll / Tenaestalin
RNCD 2015 / Sep '93 / Rhino

☐ KIBIR AM LAK (Ras Michael & The Sons Of Negus)
CC 2712 / Jul '94 / Crocodisc

☐ KNOW NOW (Ras Michael & The Sons Of Negus)
SHANCD 64019 / May '90 / Shanachie

☐ LOVE THY NEIGHBOUR (Ras Michael & The Sons Of Negus)
LLCD 001 / Mar '93 / Live & Learn

☐ NEW NAME (Ras Michael & The Sons Of Negus)
RB 3007 / May '94 / Reggae Best

☐ NYAHBINGHI (Ras Michael & The Sons Of Negus)
Keep cool babylon / Rise jah jah children (the lion sleeps) / Pretty little face / Carnal mind / Run come (throw away your stoney heart) / Come down (points and price) / Jah got the whole world in his hands / Roll river jordan / Cast them in the fire / Nyah man say / Rastaman chant / We're marching unto victory
CC 2710 / Apr '94 / Crocodisc

☐ RAS MICHAEL-ZION TRAIN (Ras Michael & Zion Train)
SST 168CD / May '93 / SST

☐ RASTAFARI (Ras Michael & The Sons Of Negus)
None a jah jah children no cry / Glory dawn / Give love / It is no secret / Sufferation / Mr. brown / Birds in the treetop / Truth and right / In zion
GRELCD 153 / Feb '91 / Greensleeves

☐ RASTAFARI DUB (Ras Michael & The Sons Of Negus)
RE 162CD / Nov '94 / ROIR

Ras Midas

☐ STAND UP WISE UP
14806 / Jun '97 / Spalax

Ras Rang

☐ EVOLUTION OF THUMRI VOL.1
NRCD 0081 / Sep '97 / Navras

☐ EVOLUTION OF THUMRI VOL.2
NRCD 0082 / Sep '97 / Navras

Rasco

☐ TIME WAITS FOR NO MAN
STH 20142 / 6 Jul '98 / Stone's Throw

Rascoe, Moses

☐ BLUES LIVE
FF 454CD / May '93 / Flying Fish

Rasha

☐ SUNDANIYAT
Aquis mahasnik biman / Azara al hay / Nari / Salib fuadi / Leali / Diya wo alan / Hadada / Al sheikh seiyaro / Sahib al me'irag / Aquis mahasnik Blman
INT 32142 / 27 Oct '97 / Intuition

Rashid, Xalid

☐ MUSIC FROM KURDISTAN, THE
926682 / Jun '97 / BUDA

Raskinen, Minna

☐ REVELATIONS
OMCD 64 / Nov '95 / Olarin Musiiki Oy

Rasle, Jean-Pierre

☐ CORNERMUSIQUE
CMCD 058 / Mar '94 / Celtic Music

Rasmus

☐ MASS HYSTERIA
BLSCD 4 / 8 Jun '98 / Bolshi

Rasmussen, Valdemar

☐ DEN SIGNEDE DAG
MECCACD 1017 / Nov '94 / Music Mecca

☐ ET YNDIGT LAND
MECCACD 1029 / Nov '94 / Music Mecca

☐ KOERLIGHED AF GOLD QUINTET
MECCACD 1078 / May '97 / Music Mecca

☐ ROCKIN' IN RHYTHM
MECCACD 2037 / Jan '98 / Music Mecca

☐ SONDERJYSK KAFFEBORD
MECCACD 1016 / Nov '94 / Music Mecca

☐ VELKOMMEN IGEN
MECCACD 1004 / Nov '94 / Music Mecca

Raspall, Elisabet

☐ TRIANGLES (Raspall, Elisabet Quintet)
FSNT 018 / Jan '98 / Fresh Sound New Talent

Raspberries

☐ POWER POP VOL.1
RPM 162 / Jun '96 / RPM

☐ POWER POP VOL.2
RPM 163 / Jun '96 / RPM

☐ RASPBERRIES PRESERVED (Various Artists)
PR 6317 / Oct '96 / Ginger

Rasputin & The Monks

☐ SUM OF MY SOUL/NO.1 (Rasputin & The Monks/Foul Dogs)
FLASH 48 / 16 Mar '98 / Flash

Rationals

☐ RATIONALS, THE
Barefootin' / Temptation 'bout to get me / Guitar army / Something's got a hold on me / Deep red / Sunset / Glowin' / Handbags and gladrags / Ha ha / Turn on / Look what you've done / Feelin' lost / Little girls cry / Leavin' here / Respect / I need you / Sing / Gloria / Out in the street / Poor dog
FLASH 46 / 1 Jun '98 / Flash

Ratpack

☐ OLD SKOOL MASTERS, THE (Mixed By Ratpack & Nicky Blackmarket/2CD Set) (Various Artists)
2 bad mice: 2 Bad Mice / Searchin' for my rizla: Ratpack / Devine rhythms: DJ Rap / DJ's unite: DJ Seduction / Uptempo: Tronikhouse / Closer to all your dreams: Rhythm Quest / Gonna feeling: Terrorize / Bouncer: Kicks Like A Mule / Don't go: Awesome 3 / Feels good: Manix / Tribal base: Rebel MC / Far out: Sonz Of A Loop Da Loop Era / I feel the heat: Urban Hype / Sound of the underground: Krome & Time / Captain of the ship: Ratpack / Sweet harmony: Liquid / Terrorist: Renegade / Yeah man: Dreem Teem / Renegade snare: Omni Trio / Drumz: Nasty Habits / Feeling so real: Moby / Roll the beats: DJ Hype / Champion sound: Q-Project / Geese toon: Nicky Blackmarket / Lighter: Sound Of The Future / R-type: Jo / Helicopter: Deep Blue / Spiritual aura: Origin Unknown / Kan ya feel it: Skool Of Hard Knocks / Original nuttah: UK Apachi & Shy FX
CDRAID 539 / 1 Jun '98 / Rumour

Rattle 'N' Reel

☐ OUTRAGEOUS
RNR 001CD / Oct '94 / RNR

Rattlers

☐ SCARE ME TO DEATH
Scare me to death / Little red / Mine all mine / Cat crept in / Blue zoot / Hey baby / Always yours / You're my baby / Rattlin' boogie / Knife edge baby
NERCD 047 / Sep '93 / Nervous

Rattlers

☐ PLEASURES IN MISADVENTURE
Born to grow old / Pedlar of York / Ten years from now / Long way down / Pawn in a blind man's game / Frog 'n' swan / Walter Doorplack / Traveller's dance / You really don't care / Roll away the blues / Justice and the law / Liar / Lock in / Two for the road
PMRCD 10 / '96 / Pagan Media

Rattlers

☐ RATTLED
BA 1119CD / Sep '97 / Bacchus Archives

Rattlesnake Kiss

☐ RATTLESNAKE KISS
Railroad / Sad Suzie / Angel / Alright by me / Nothing this good (could be real) / Wake up / Taste it / Don't make it right / All to me (that I was to you) / Kiss this
SOV 106CD / '92 / Sovereign

Rattray, Mark

☐ MUSICAL MAGIC (Rattray, Mark & Maggie Moon)
PLSCD 238 / Jul '97 / Pulse

Ratzer, Karl

☐ SATURN RETURNING
Just what you need / Finger snappin' good / Farmer's charm / Saturn returning / Main squeeze / Silent rain / Holy Mother song / Lobied
ENJ 93152 / May '97 / Enja

Raux, Richard

☐ UNDER THE MAGNOLIAS (Raux, Richard Quartet)
CDLLL 27 / Aug '93 / La Lichere

Rava, Enrico

☐ ANIMALS (Rava, Enrico 4uartet)
Animals / Bellflower / Bella / Spider blues / Clown / Moon revisited / Infant / High castle
INAK 8801CD / Jul '97 / In Akustik

☐ DNA 1996 (Rava, Enrico & Mario Rusca)
CD 53302 / May '98 / Giants Of Jazz

☐ PILGRIM AND THE STAIRS, THE
Pilgrim and the stars / Parks / Bella / Pesce naufrago / Surprise hotel / By the sea / Blancasnow
8473222 / Jul '95 / ECM

☐ PLOT, THE
Tribe / On the red side of the street / Amici / Dr. Ra and Mr. Va / Foto di famiglia / Plot
5232822 / Jul '95 / ECM

☐ QUARTET
Lavari casalinghi / Fearless five / Tramps / 'Round midnight / Blackmail
5232832 / Jul '95 / ECM

☐ VOLVER (Rava, Enrico & Dino Saluzzi Quintet)
Bout de souffle / Minguito / Luna-volver / Tiempos de ausencias / Ballantine for valentine visions
8313952 / Feb '88 / ECM

695

Ravana

☐ COMMON DAZE
Good grief / Urban child / When they cry / Words in a rhyme / Wounded / Reasons to live / Who'll run your mind / Passing / Wherever you are
PNCD 001 / Jul '97 / Prognetik

Ravao, Tao

☐ TANY MANGA (Ravao, Tao & V. Bucher)
AL 008 / 21 Aug '97 / Night & Day

Raven

☐ ALL FOR ONE
Take control / Mind over metal / Sledgehammer rock / All for one / Run silent, run deep / Hung drawn and quartered / Break the chain / Take it away / Seek and destroy / Athletic rock
NEATCD 1011 / '85 / Neat

☐ EVERYTHING LOUDER
Blind eye / No pain, no gain / Sweet Jane / Holy grail / Hungry / Insane / Everything louder / Between the wheels / Losing my mind / Get your fingers out / Wilderness of broken glass / Fingers do the walking / Bonus
08512162 / May '97 / SPV

☐ GLOW
SPV 08412092 / Jun '95 / SPV

☐ LIFE'S A BITCH
Savage and the hungry / Pick your window / Life's a bitch / Never forgive / Iron league / On the wings of an eagle / Overload / You're a liar / Fuel to the fire / Only the strong survive / Juggernaut / Playing with the razor / Finger on the trigger
111432 / 24 Aug '98 / Mayhem

☐ PACK IS BACK, THE
Pack is back / Gimme some lovin' / Screamin' down the house / Young blood / Hyperactive / Rock dogs / Don't let it die / Get into your car / All I want / Nightmare ride
111502 / 24 Aug '98 / Mayhem

☐ STAY HARD
Stay hard / When the going gets tough / On and on / Get it right / Restless child / Power and the glory / Pray for the sun / Hard ride / Extract the action / Bottom line
111372 / 24 Aug '98 / Mayhem

Raven, Jon

☐ FRAGILE LIFE
BROCD 137 / Aug '96 / Broadside

Raven, Marsha

☐ BEST OF MARSHA RAVEN, THE (Catch Me)
HTCD 75 / 20 Apr '98 / Hot Productions

Raven, Michael

☐ FLOWERS OF PICARDY (Raven, Michael & Joan Mills)
Flowers of Picardy / Sicilian waltz / Epitaph on an Army of Mercenaries / La Russe waltz / Paris polka / Dancing lady / Green fields of England / Robin Hood's dance / Maid of Provence / Stafford County fair / Trecynon polka / Over the wall / New tenpenny bit / My last farewell to Stirling / Carrickfergus / Bentley canal / With measured sound/Adson's Sarabande / Cluster of nuts / Mallorca / Oh, fair enough / Cypress curtain / Mrs. Anne Harecourt's galliard / Robin Hood and the tanner / Rhododendron/The singer/The old soldier / Backwoodsman / March to Kandahar / Unknown grave
MR 73 / Jun '97 / Michael Raven

☐ HALLIARD AND JON RAVEN, THE/THE JOLLY MACHINE (Raven, Michael & Nic Jones)
Calico printer's clerk / Unquiet grave / Ladies don't go a-thievin' / Midsummer fair / To the weavers gin ye / Long Lankin / Going for a soldier Jenny / Workhouse boy / Row bullies row / Lancashire lads / Thousand miles away / Love and murder / Last farewell / Jolly Joe / Rambling sailor / Chartists anthem / Nailmakers' lament / Charlie's song / Redditch needlemakers' lament / Landlord don't you cry / Freedom and reform / Potter's chant / Waiting for wages / Wednesbury town / Jolly machine / Collier's rant / John Whitehouse / Tommy Note / Dudley canal song
MR 77 / Jun '97 / Michael Raven

☐ MY OLD FRIEND (Raven, Michael & Joan Mills)
My old friend / Errol Flynn / Abbot's Bromley horn dance / Song for Diana / Because I liked you better / Sheba's daughter / Che Guevara / Is my dear lord asleep / Squire Mytton's gallop / English lanes / John Collins / Rebel leader's lament / Grey valley / Maid from the Northlands / Queen of the night / My bonny lads away / Loveliest of trees / Spanish Morris
MR 80 / Jul '98 / Michael Raven

☐ RECITAL (Raven, Michael & Joan Mills)
Lass from the low country / Queen's marsh / Ruth Ellis / Fortune my foe / Brink of the white rock / Blackbird wilt thou go / Green bushes / Lark's elegy / Dancing Delilah / Cafe Cantrell / Hampton lullaby / Black is the colour / Brisk young widow / Come live with me / Minuet de la Cour / Charlie's song / Zambra mora / Hednesford town / Chattering magpie / Moorlough shore / Pennsylvanian song/Captain Heapy / Biker's song / Dove / Illic jacet / Alman / Raglan Road
MR 70 / Jun '97 / Michael Raven

☐ RETROSPECTIVE
Dark eyes/Farruca / Three Renaissance dances / Soleares / Guido's rag / Melancholy Pavan / Willow rag / Lichfield Bower processional / Vals by Aguado / Rhumba Cubana / Lady Mary/Argent / Going with David to Towyn / Three Iberian dances / Over the stone/Rakes of Mallow/Tanguillio / Prelude/Warrior's welcome home / Comical fellow / Bushes and briars / Two butcher's sirtos / Suite in E / Helston furry dance / Midnights of November / Jigg ashling / Ladies go dancing at Whitsun / Beatrice Hill's reel/Morpeth Rant / Dowland's Alman / Please to see the King / Off to California / Poor murdered woman/Clee Hill reel
MR 75 / Jun '97 / Michael Raven

☐ REYNARDINE TAPES, THE (Raven, Michael & Joan Mills)
Brewer's lady / December day dance / Queen of the night / Star of Belle Isle / Greek Street / Old Dublin fireman / Lichfield Greenhill Bower Processional / Three hearty young poachers / Tulla reel/The castle / Stafford pageant song / White copper alley / Trent waters/Marion's rambles / Johnny Gallagher / Eternal father / Lord Thomas / Lakes of Pontchartrain / Poor law Bill / Hungarian hat / Crafty maid's policy / Maid on the shore/Black Mountain/ Gaunt man / Sally Gardens / Tarantos
CDMR 72 / Jun '97 / Michael Raven

☐ SHROPSHIRE LAD, A (Raven, Michael & Joan Mills)
On Wenlock Edge the wood's in trouble / Megan's daughter / Bredon Hill / Rhoslan reel / Half moon / White rose of summer / New mistress / Galaru/The blackbird / Along the fields / Is my team ploughing / Bard's dream / Ludlow recruit / Megan who lost her garter / Come pipe a tune / Lady mine/Gogerddan / Midnights of November / Long live Mary / Rising of the lark/Weep not for me / True lover / Beside the seashore/Good ale / Goldcup flowers / Where are you going / Deserter / Clover / Loitering with a vacant eye / Lady Owen's delight / Farewell to barn and stack and tree / My lady is more fair / Wenlock edge / Snowdon / When I was one and twenty / Farewell to Llangyfelach / Shrewsbury jail
MR 69 / Jun '97 / Michael Raven

☐ SONGS AND DANCES OF HEREFORDSHIRE (Raven, Michael & Joan Mills)
Lowlands of Holland / Jack Gore's galliard / Dives and Lazarus / Mr. Baskerville's volt / Foolish boy / Hunting the squirrel / Banks of sweet primroses / Ledbury timber-teams / Orange in bloom / Rich old lady / Holywell / Trees they do grow high / John Locke's polka / My mother bid me / Barbara Ellen / Milkmaid's song / Restless road / Speed the plough / Sheffield Park / Jack of the green / Thundermanshire / Moon shines bright / Blacksmith / Leaves of life / London town / Sheepskins / Rose in June / Blue-eyed stranger / Oh who is that / Cider Annie / Piers ploughman / Herefordshire lasses / Ledbury parson
MR 76 / Jun '97 / Michael Raven

☐ SONGS AND SOLOS (Raven, Michael & Joan Mills)
For Alan Green / Flowers in her hair / Nottingham swing/Bushes and briars / Octopus dancing / Winifred's dream/Winifred's jig / Lament for Owain Glyndwr / Slender boy/Waterloo dance / Irish girl / Bunch of rushes / Land of lost content / Vyrnwy waters / Mirror of my mind / Prelude in G/Mishca's restaurant / Pretty ploughboy / Lament for Peter Bellamy/Fred Jordan's galliard / Waiting for wages / Mainstone hornpipe/Byrne's hornpipe / Song of the fox / Gisburn lament/John of Paris/Bird on the wing / Midnight city / Lion cafe/Seth Brown's polkas / Lazy Jane / Kirton Grove/Dr. Fauster's tumblers / Schoon lief / Newcastle/A trip to Scarborough / Widow woman's daughter
MR 68 / Jun '97 / Michael Raven

☐ TAMING THE DRAGON'S STRINGS
Prelude / Dark lane/Now all is still/Raven's nest / Soulton Hall suite / Foxy's flying/Almost slain/Dead of Rajistan / Angelsey suite / You must come to Kilpeck / Stained glass/Food for dogs / Sarah Collins / Road to Lisdoonvarna/Road to Towyn / West / Linhope suite / Pell Well Hall/Wild bird weeping/ Little dog sleeping / Midsummer Hill / Polly Gale's Tarantella / I can remember/Cidery wine/Dark-haired daughters / Singing bird/The bard's love / Lovliest of trees / Captain's apprentice/Tobago bound / Dark invader (a dog called Bruno) / Dead elm / Teapot time / My lady's suite / But he would/Before I come again/Summer's end / My last farewell
CDMR 71 / Jun '97 / Michael Raven

☐ WELSH GUITAR
Grey cuckoo / Sailor's grave/You carefree young lads / Honied kiss/Glwysen / Sweet Richard / Rhaeadr Falls / Rising of the sun / Harp / Rheged/ Lady Treffael's conceit / Miller's song/Over the stone / Honied lip / Men of Wrexham's hornpipe / Glanbargoed / Farewell Marian / Machynlleth / Judgement/Old year passing / Spanish minuet/ Maids of Montgomery / Tretower Waltz / John Francis / Llanberis Pass / Flowers of the thorn / Maltraeth / Watching the wheat/Gwenllian / Captain Morgan's march/Lady Sker / Gwenllian's repose / Come what may/Glandyfi / Fanny blooming fair / Weep not for me / Ap Siencyn/Abergynolwen / Blackbird / Llangoffen / My love is a Venus / Springtime is returning / Welsh rabbit/Llyn Gwernan / Missing boat / Cornthresher hornpipe / Clover of Merioneth / Once a farmer
MR 74 / Jun '97 / Michael Raven

Ravengers

☐ GOOD TIME GIRLS AND NAUGHTY BOYS
DRCD 016 / 3 Aug '98 / Detour

Ravens

☐ GREATEST VOCAL GROUP OF THEM ALL
For you / Write me a letter / Until the real thing comes along / September song / Always / I'm afraid of you / Fool that I am / Together / It's too soon to know / White Christmas / Silent night / Deep purple / There's nothing like a woman in love / Careless love / If you didn't mean it / Someday / Lilacs in the rain / I've been a fool / I'm gonna paper my walls with your love letters / Sylvia / Tea for two / Without a song / It's the talk of the town / No more kisses for baby / Moonglow / Who's sorry now / I've got the world on a string
SV 0270 / Oct '97 / Savoy Jazz

☐ OL' MAN RIVER
Ol' man river / Summertime / Once in a while / I don't know why I love you like I do / House I live in / Get wise baby / Send for me if you need me / County every star / Be I bumblebee or not / Leave my gal alone / Rooster / I don't have to ride no more / Time is marching on / Marie / Rickey's blues
SV 0260 / Oct '97 / Savoy Jazz

☐ RARITIES
Until the real thing comes along / Once in a while / Phantom stage coach / Please believe me / I'm gonna take to the road / Comin' back home / Bless you / Cadillac song / I'm afraid of you / Tea for two / Get wise baby / House I live in / Ricky's blues / Sylvia
SV 0261 / Oct '97 / Savoy Jazz

Ravi

☐ KORA SO FAR
Ngama / Unity / Morning rain / Cala violina / Child's eyes / Hari bol / Journeying home / Orissa / River / Woods / Riding / Sea / Sacred dance / On the way
TERRCD 0013 / Jun '98 / Terra Nova

Raw Deal

☐ LOVE'S OKAY
ARMCD 001 / Mar '97 / Raw Deal

Raw Material

☐ RAW MATERIAL
HBG 123/2 / Apr '94 / Background

Raw Power

☐ FIGHT
GOD 014CD / Jul '95 / Godhead

☐ LIVE FROM THE GUTTER
GOD 023CD / Jan '97 / Godhead

Raw Sylk

☐ FYNE SYLK
07863675512 / 26 May '98 / RCA

Raw To The Core

☐ IN THE MOOD VOL.2
ITM 001CD / Oct '95 / KGR

Rawfrucht

☐ RAWFRUCHT
SR 113 / Mar '97 / Sub Rosa

Rawhead, Jason

☐ BACKFIRE
KKUK 005CD / '90 / KK

☐ COLLISION HYPE
KK 061CD / Jul '91 / KK

☐ JASON RAWHEAD
KK 024CD / '89 / KK

Rawicz & Landauer

☐ THEIR GREAT PIANO HITS
Parade of the tin soldiers / Waltz memories of vienna / Spinning wheel / Orpheus in the underworld-overture / Nola / Chopin selection / In a persian market / Liszt in rhythm / Viennese fantasy / Slavonic dance no. op. 46 / Rhapsody in blue / November (in the troika) / Schubert time (medley) / Spanish dances nos. 5, 2, 1 and 3 / Chopinezza / Invitation to the waltz / Slavonic dance no. 8 op. 46 / Austria-hungary (selection)
PASTCD 7040 / May '94 / Flapper

Rawls, Johnny

☐ CAN'T SLEEP AT NIGHT (Rawls, Johnny & L.C. Luckett)
R 2630 / Feb '97 / Rooster

☐ HERE WE GO
Here we go / Old flame / I would be nothing / Don't worry about it / Working my way back to you / Sweet woman / What a night / I got a problem / Gonna put you down / Candy man / I feel so good
JSPCD 271 / Oct '96 / JSP

☐ LOUISIANA WOMAN
I don't want no woman tyin' me down / Louisiana woman / It's all in the game / Watcha gonna do / Can't nobody / You got me going through changes / It's a shame / Blues (good as gold) / I got soul / Lover man / How much longer
JSPCD 286 / Sep '97 / JSP

Rawls, Lou

☐ BALLADS
At last / I wonder where our love has gone / If I were a magician / I'm still in love with you / Sweet slumber / Good morning blues / This bitter Earth / Save your love for me / One more time / Chains of love / Oh what a night / Good night love
CDP 8566892 / Jul '97 / Blue Note

☐ BEST OF LOU RAWLS
You'll never find another love like mine / See you when I get there / From now on / Groovy people / Sit down and talk to me / Trade winds / Let me be good to you / Bark bite (fight all night) / Dollar green / I wish it were yesterday / I wish you belonged to me / One life to live / Love is a hurtin' thing / Dead end street / Tobacco road
MCCD 348 / 15 Jun '98 / MCI Music

☐ BROTHERMAN (Lou Rawls Sings The Hits)
For what it's worth / Feeling alright / Mama told me not to come / Give me your love / On Broadway / Girl from Ipanema / Down here on the ground / You made me feel so very happy / Season of the witch / Dead end street / When love goes wrong / I can't make it alone / Letter / Love is a hurting thing / Your good thing (is about to end) / You're good for me / One for my baby one for the road / Soul serenade / (How do I say) I don't love you anymore
4939952 / 11 May '98 / Blue Note

☐ LOVE IS A HURTIN' THING
Red top / Just squeeze me (don't tease me) / You're the one / Dead end street / Love is a hurtin' thing / Bring it on home / Another Saturday night / Righteous woman (monologue) / I wanna little girl / Tobacco road / How long, how long blues / Your good thing is about to end / I wonder / Whole lotta woman
CTMCD 329 / Jul '97 / EMI

☐ SHADES OF BLUE/FAMILY REUNION
Did you ever love a woman / Cottage for sale / Be anything (but be mine) / You've lost that lovin' feelin' / I go crazy / Hoochie coochie man / Baby what you want me to do / Family reunion / I wish you belonged to me / Two happy hearts / Jealous lover / Today's the day / It's a tough job (but somebody's got to do it) / When love walked in the door (hurt walked out the other) / Who loves you baby / Fine with me / Unchained melody
WESM 526 / 15 Jun '98 / Westside

☐ SPOTLIGHT ON LOU RAWLS (Great Gentlemen Of Song)
Nobody but me / Street of dreams / God bless the child / Rockin' chair / St. James Infirmary / I wonder where our love has gone / Blues for the weepers / Stormy weather / Willow weep for me / Don't explain / Georgia on my mind / Ain't nobody's business if I do / When it's sleepy time down South / Just squeeze me / How long blues / Summertime / If it's the last thing I do / One for my baby (and one more for the road)
CZ 570 / Mar '96 / Premier/EMI

☐ STAR COLLECTION
STCD 1002 / Jun '93 / Disky

☐ TOUCH OF CLASS, A
You'll never find another love like mine / This song will last forever / Time will take care of everything / Show business / Tomorrow / Sit down and talk to me / You can bring me all your heartaches / Tabacco road / Love is a hurtin' thing / See you when I git there / Your good thing (is about to end) / Dead end street / Lady love / Fine brown frame
TC 868752 / 2 Feb '98 / Disky

☐ YOU'LL NEVER FIND
WMCD 5700 / Oct '94 / Disky

Rawside

☐ POLICE TERROR
WB 1133CD / Nov '95 / We Bite

Ray & Glover

☐ PICTURE HAS FADED
Tell me Mama / Jimmy Bell / Can't see your face / Downtown blues / Sittin' on top of the world / Long haired donkey / Ice blue / Going away blues / Afraid to trust 'em / Mellow chick swing / Saturday blues / New Buddy Brown / If it looks like jelly / As the years go passing by
TK 92CD036 / Aug '94 / T/K

Ray, Anthony

☐ REVELATION
ARC 1000 / Aug '96 / Active

Ray, Danny

☐ BEST OF DANNY RAY, THE
BJCD 07 / Nov '96 / Blackjack

Ray J

☐ EVERYTHING YOU WANT
Feel the funk intro / Let it go / Everything you want / Good thangs / Promise / Changes / Thank you / Let it go / Can't run can't hide / Rock with me / Love you from my heart / High on you / Because of you / Feel the funk outro
7559620172 / Jun '97 / East West

Ray, James

☐ DIOS ESTA DE NUESTRO LADO (Ray, James Gangwar)
Rev rev lowrider / Heart surgery / 35,000 times / Badlands / Hardwar / Cadillac coming / Bad gin / Santa Susana / Coo ca choo
MRAY 341 CD / Apr '92 / Merciful Release

☐ NEW KIND OF ASSASSIN, A (Ray, James Gangwar)
Mexico sundown blues / Texas / Mountain voices (remix) / Dust boat / Edie Sedgwick / Mexico sundown blues (edit)
MRAY 089 CD / Aug '92 / Merciful Release

☐ THIRD GENERATION (Ray, James Gangwar)
Cobalt blue / Sinner / Fuelled up / Take it / Third generation / Blue lover / Strange / Luxury / Ridge
SURG 001CD / Jun '93 / Surgury

Ray, Jimmy

☐ JIMMY RAY
4890682 / 10 Nov '97 / Sony Soho2

Ray, Johnnie

☐ AT THE PALLADIUM
Please don't talk about me / Glad / Rag doll / Hundred years from now / Somebody stole my gal / With these hands / Walkin' my baby back home / As time goes by / Such a night
BCD 15666 / Jun '92 / Bear Family

☐ BEST OF JOHNNIE RAY, THE
Just walkin' in the rain / Hey there / Cry / Such a night / Little white cloud that cried / Faith can move mountains / Let's walk that-a-way / Paths of paradise / (Here I am) Broken hearted / Who's sorry now / Somebody stole my gal / Herando's hideaway / All of me / You don't owe me a thing / Build your love / Ain't misbehavin' / I'll never fall in love again / Please Mr. Sun / Yes tonight Josephine / If you believe / Look homeward angel / Song of the dreamer / As time goes by / Walkin' my baby back home
4840402 / May '96 / Epic

☐ BEST OF JOHNNIE RAY/FRANKIE LAINE (Ray, Johnnie & Frankie Laine)
Walkin' my baby back home / Somebody stole my girl / Cry / Just walking in the rain / Here am i, broken hearted / Little white cloud that cried / Please mr. sun / You don't owe me a thing / What's the use / Hernando's hideaway / Moonlight gambler / Jealousy / High noon (do not forsake me) / Love is a golden ring / Rose rose I love you / I believe / That lucky old sun / Cry of the wild goose / Jezebel / Mule train
BTBCD 001 / Jun '93 / Sound Waves

☐ CRY
Yes tonight Josephine / Just walking in the rain / I've got so many million years / Johnnie's comin' home / Look homeward angel / Up above my head / Good evening friends / Up until now / How long blues / You don't owe me a thing / No wedding today / Build your love / Streets of memories / Miss me, just a little / Texas tambourine / Pink sweater angel / Soliloquy of a fool / Endlessly / Plant a little seed / I'll make you mine / Papa loves mambo / Ooo aah oh / Flip flop and fly / Alexander's ragtime band / Little white cloud that cried / Cry / Ma sez, Pa sez / Full time job / Such a night / Hernando's hideaway
BCD 15450 / May '90 / Bear Family

☐ GREAT JOHNNIE RAY, THE
PLSCD 278 / 1 Jun '98 / Pulse

Ray, Kenny 'Blue'

☐ BLESS MY AXE
TKCD 1062 / Jun '98 / Tone King

☐ GIT IT
TKCD 1060 / 5 Feb '98 / Tone King

☐ IN ALL OF MY LIFE
I can't take it / No time to waste / In all of my life / Listen to me baby / '56 Eldorado / Can't do this to me / Bayou boogie / You got me nervous / Blues for the iceman / Bluesman for life / For Jannie Ray / Bailin' on the gator / What's on your mind / Throw me the whiskey
JSPCD 289 / May '97 / JSP

☐ PULL THE STRINGS
TKCD 1059 / 5 Feb '98 / Tone King

☐ STRAT DADDY
BR 103 / 5 Feb '98 / Blue Ray

☐ WAY DOWN IN MEMPHIS
TKCD 1061 / 5 Feb '98 / Tone King

Ray, Lucy

☐ WHEN I GROW UP
When I grow up / Devil / Written in the stars / Calm / Life is a mess / I hate to lose / Where will I find my love / Mean to me / Love her / All those days / We will never parted
CYCLECD 004 / Feb '97 / Cycle

Ray, Michael

☐ MICHAEL RAY & THE COSMIC KREWE (Ray, Michael & The Cosmic Krewe)
Rhythm and muse / Discipline / Carefree / Champions / Charlie B's / 3-22-93 / Pathology / Beans and rice / Island in space / Echoes of boat people
ECD 220842 / May '94 / Evidence

Ray, Sugar

☐ KNOCKOUT (Ray, Sugar & The Bluetones)
VRCD 037 / Sep '94 / Varrick

Ray, Will

☐ INVISIBLE BIRDS
DFGCD 8449 / Jun '96 / Dixie Frog
RTMCD 84 / Feb '97 / Round Tower

Raye, Sol

☐ MONA LISA
FECD 17 / Jun '97 / First Edition

Rayfield, Split Lip

☐ SPLIT LIP RAYFIELD
BS 035CD / 20 Jul '98 / Bloodshot

Raymen

☐ REBEL YEARS 1985-1987, THE
SPV 07645762 / Mar '96 / SPV

Raymond, Clem

☐ LOST CLARINET OF CLEM RAYMOND (Raymond, Clem & Dick Oxtot/Golden Age Jazz Band)
Boogaloosa strut / Pontchartrain blues / Wolverine blues / I can't give you anything but love / Tell me your dreams / When you wore a tulip / Clem's blues / Just a little while to stay here / Reep du dah / Piedmont blues / B-flat blues / Shine / Haunted blues / Boogaloosa strut
DE 208 / Mar '97 / Delmark

Raymonde, Simon

☐ BLAME SOMEONE ELSE
It's a family thing / Love undone / Seventh day / In my place / Supernatural / If I knew myself / It's raining today / Muscle and want / Worship me / Fault of mine / Days / Tired twilight
BELLACD 001 / Sep '97 / Bella Union

Razed In Black

☐ OVERFLOW
CLP 9956 / Mar '97 / Cleopatra

Razor

☐ DECIBELS
HYPSD 1058CD / 19 Jan '98 / Hypnotic

☐ SHOTGUN JUSTICE
FPD 3094 / Mar '95 / Fringe

☐ VIOLENT RESTITUTION
857 571 / '89 / Steamhammer

Razor Baby

☐ TOO HOT TO HANDLE
Danger / Rock this place / Downtown / Outta hand sister / Move me / Too hot to handle / Got me running / Low down and dirty
HMAXD 102 / Aug '89 / Heavy Metal

Razor Skyline

☐ JOURNAL OF TRAUMA
COPCD 025 / Nov '96 / Cop International

Razorbacks

☐ FULL HOUSE
EARCD 90301 / Apr '98 / Eagle

☐ GO TO TOWN
OPM 2101CD / Mar '97 / Other People's Music

☐ I'M ON FIRE
FCD 3026 / Aug '93 / Fury

Razorcuts

☐ WORLD KEEPS TURNING, THE
Goodnight england / Mile high towers / Change / I won't let you down / Waterfall / Flowers for abigail / Across the meadow / Come my way / Snowbound / Steps to the sea / World keeps turning / Story teller / Try a little tenderness (live) / A contract with god / Sky high / Everyday eyes / Jade / Silhouette / Brighter now / I'll still be there / Last picture show
CRECD 045 / Feb '89 / Creation

Razzia

☐ LABYRINTH
IRC 032 / Mar '97 / Impact

RBT Big Band

☐ CLASSICS OF SWING (RBT Big Band/ RIAS Big Band)
Strike up the band / Apple honey / Limehouse blues / Begin the beguine / American patrol / Glenn Miller medley / Mr. Anthony's boogie / And the angels sing / Dob's boogie / Jumpin' at the woodside / Fatman boogie
BCD 16217 / Aug '97 / Bear Family

Re-Animator

☐ CONDEMNED TO ETERNITY
Don't eat the yellow snow / St. Alphonzo's pancake breakfast / Cosmik debris / Apostrophe / Stink foot / I'm the slime / 50/50 / Dinah-Moe Humm / Nanook rubs it / Father O'Blivion / Excentrifugal forz / Uncle Remus / Camarillo brillo / Dirty love / Zomby woof / Montana
CDFLAG 37 / Oct '89 / Under One Flag

☐ LAUGHING
Rude awakening / Laughing / Kipper 'n' / Research / Another fine mess / Too drunk to f / Monkey see, monkey dance / Don't patronise me / Instrumental / Pass the buck / Time and tide / Big black cloud
CDFLAG 53 / Feb '91 / Under One Flag

☐ THAT WAS THEN, THIS IS NOW
Take me away / 2 CV / Cold sweat / Hope / Last laugh / Kick back / Listen up / Sunshine times / That was then..This is now / DUAF
CDFLAG 67 / Oct '92 / Under One Flag

Re/Act

☐ REASON
HYP 0850470CD / 13 Apr '98 / Hypnobeat

Rea, Chris

☐ AUBERGE
Auberge / Gone fishing / You're not a number / Heaven / Set me free / Red shoes / Sing a song of love to me / Every second counts / Looking for the summer / And you my love / Mention of your name
9031756932 / Feb '91 / Magnet

☐ BLUE CAFE
Square peg round hole / Miss your kiss / Shadows of the big man / Where do we go from here / Since I found you / Thinking of you / As long as I have your love / Anyone quite like you / Sweet summer day / Stick by you / I'm still holding on / Blue cafe
3984216882 / 19 Jan '98 / East West

☐ ESPRESSO LOGIC
Espresso logic / Red / Soup of the day / Johnny needs a fast car / Between the devil and the deep blue sea / Julia / Summer love / New way / Stop / She closed her eyes
4509943112 / Oct '93 / Magnet

☐ GOD'S GREAT BANANA SKIN
Nothing to fear / Miles is a cigarette / God's great banana skin / Nineties blues / Too much pride / Boom boom / I ain't the fool / There she goes / I'm ready / Black dog / Soft top, hard shoulder
4509909952 / Nov '92 / Magnet

☐ LA PASSIONE (Original Soundtrack)
La Passione / Dov'e il signore / Le mans / Dov'e il signore part two / Disco la passione / You must follow / Shirley do you own a Ferrari / Girl in a sports car / When the grey skies turn to blue / Horses / Olive oil / Only to fly
0630166952 / May '97 / East West

☐ NEW LIGHT THROUGH OLD WINDOWS (The Best Of Chris Rea)
Let's dance / Working on it / Ace of hearts / Josephine / Candles / On the beach / Fool (if you think it's over) / I can hear your heartbeat / Shamrock diaries / Stainsby girls / Windy town / Driving home for Christmas / Steel river
2438412 / Oct '88 / Magnet

☐ ROAD TO HELL
Road to hell / Road to hell / You must be evil / Texas / Looking for a rainbow / Your warm and tender love / Daytona / That's what they always say / I just wanna be with you / Tell me there's a heaven
2462852 / Feb '95 / Magnet

☐ VERY BEST OF CHRIS REA, THE
Road to hell / Josephine / Let's dance / Fool if you think it's over / Auberge / Julia / Stainsby girls / If you were me / On the beach / Looking for the summer / Giverney / Go your own way / God's great banana skin / Wintersong / Gone fishing / Tell me there's a heaven
4509980402 / Oct '94 / Magnet

React 2 Rhythm

☐ WHATEVER YOU DREAM
Intoxication / Shine / Peace / All or nothing / Whatever you dream / Nu-yorker magic / Strangest dream / I know you like it
GRCD 002 / Mar '92 / Guerilla

Reactor Outside

☐ REACTOR OUTSIDE VOL.1
BR 001CD / Mar '97 / Blue Room Released

Read, Jaime

☐ END OF THE BEGINNING, THE
After the rains / Timewave / On the surface of the 9th moon / Collective consciousness / Harry runs out / Outwardly inward / Itty bitty pieces / Still LIFE / LHAS / Swans and elephants / Tribute to a gallop / Da breaks
FMDCD 001 / 1 Sep '97 / Fragmented

Reader, Eddi

☐ ANGELS AND ELECTRICITY
Kiteflyers hill / Prayer wheel / Postcard / Wings on my heels / On a whim / Hummingbird / Barcelona window / Bell book and candle / California / Follow my tears / Psychic reader / Please don't ask me to dance / Clear
63984228162 / 11 May '98 / Blanco Y Negro

☐ CANDYFLOSS AND MEDICINE
Candyfloss / Semi-precious / I loved a lad / Lazy heart / Darkhouse / Butterfly jar / Rebel angel / Glasgow star / Town without pity / Medicine
0630151202 / Jul '96 / Blanco Y Negro

☐ HUSH
Right place / Patience of angels / Dear John / Scarecrow / East of us / Joke (I'm laughing) / Exception / Red face big sky / Howling in ojai / When I watch you sleeping / Wonderful lie / Siren
4509961772 / Dec '96 / Warner Bros.

☐ MIRMAMA
What you do with what you've got / Honeychild / All or nothing / Hello in there / Dolphins / Blacksmith / That's fair / Cinderellas downfall / Pay no mind / Swimming song / My old friend the blues
74321158652 / Sep '94 / RCA

Reading, Bertice

☐ TED EASTON'S JAZZBAND & QUARTET
ACD 80 / Apr '93 / Audiophile

Reagan Youth

☐ LIVE AND RARE
NRA 72CD / 15 Dec '97 / New Red Archives

Reagon, Bernice Johnson

☐ RIVER OF LIFE
Come and go with me to that land / We are climbing Jacob's ladder / Guide my feet, while I run this race / Hallelu / Land on the shore / Running / Easy street / River of life / Since I laid my burden down / Buses are a coming freedom song / There is more love somewhere / I am a lady
FF 70411 / Sep '96 / Flying Fish

Reagon, Toshi

☐ KINDNESS
SFWCD 40095 / Jun '97 / Smithsonian Folkways

Real Abba Gold

☐ JANUS
Dancing Queen / This time / Summer night city / Chiquitita / Dancing to the music / Winner takes it all / Super trouper / If u wanna / Name of the game / Take a chance on me / Gimme gimme gimme / Lay all your love / Does your Mother know / 70's child / Thank you for the music / Waterloo / Strawberry girl
CDSGP 0382 / May '98 / Prestige

Real Cool Killers

☐ ILLUSIONS
Just for fun / Knife / Daddy's footsteps / Judgement day / Myrtle Gordon / Bitter end / Much more than a hero / Illusion / Stupid lines / Open the night
SUR 453CD / Jun '94 / Survival

Real Kids

☐ GROWN UP WRONG
CED 231 / Jun '97 / Norton

Real Life

☐ HEARTLAND
INT 847 710 / '88 / Interchord

☐ LITTLE PIECE OF HEAVEN, A
CANDRCD 80101 / Nov '94 / Candor

Real Live

☐ TURNAROUND, THE
Pop the trunk / Ain't no love / Iceberg Slick / They got me / Gimmicks / Larry-O meets Iceberg Slick / Turnaround / All I ask of you (comin' through) / Real live shit / Trilogy of error / Money shows / Crime is money / Day you die
7567926682 / Oct '96 / Atlantic

Real McCoy

☐ ANOTHER NIGHT
Another night / Come and get your love / If you should ever be lonely / Runaway / Sleeping with an angel / Ooh boy / Love and devotion / Automatic lover / Operator / I want you / Megablast
74321280972 / 1 Sep '97 / Arista

Real People

☐ LIVERPOOL - THE CALM BEFORE THE STORM (Real People & Rain)
Window pane: *Real People* / Truth: *Real People* / Everyday's the same: *Real People* / She: *Real People* / Believer: *Real People* / Seen the light: *Real People* / Some things must change: *Real People* / What u want: *Real People* / I don't belong: *Real People* / Run and hide: *Real People* / Car outside: *Real People* / Too much too young: *Real People* / All I want: *Rain* / Lemonstone desired: *Rain* / Here they are: *Rain* / Taste of rain: *Rain* / Inside out: *Rain* / Slippin' and slidin': *Rain*
4836602 / Feb '96 / Columbia

☐ REAL PEOPLE, THE
Window pane / I can't wait / For you / Truth / Everyday's the same / Wonderful / Open up your mind (let me in) / She / In your hands / Looking at you / Words / Another day
4680842 / Mar '97 / Columbia

☐ WHAT'S ON THE OUTSIDE
MGGRCD 19 / Nov '96 / Granite

Real Thing

☐ FEEL THE FORCE (2CD Set)
SMDCD 175 / Jul '97 / Snapper

☐ LET'S GO DISCO
You to me are everything / Why oh why (oh why) / You'll never know what you're missing / Raining through my sunshine / Love's such a wonderful thing / Can't get by without you / Whenever you want my love / Let's go disco / Boogie down (get funky now) / (We've gotta take it to the) Second stage / Won't you step into our world / Love takes tears / Children of the ghetto / What'cha say what'cha do / Keep an eye / Can you feel the force
21043 / Sep '97 / Laserlight

☐ REAL THING
Real Thing / Can you feel the force / Get back on the right track / Move on up / Whenever you want my love / Rainin' through my sunshine / You'll never know what you're missing / Can't get by without you / Can't get by without you / I love music / (Livin' on the) frontline / Baby don't go / Children of the ghetto / You to me are everything / You to me are everything / Can you feel the force
JHD 119 / Apr '93 / Tring

☐ VERY BEST OF THE REAL THING, THE
You to me are everything / Can't get by without you / Whenever you want my love / Love's such a wonderful thing / You'll never know what you're missing / One girl in my life / Plastic man / Rainin' through my sunshine / She's a groovy freak / Let's go disco / I want you back / Can you feel the force / Boogie down (get funky now) / (He's just a) Money maker / Young and foolish / I believe in you / Can you feel the force / Can't get by without you
SELCD 511 / Mar '98 / Castle Select

☐ YOU TO ME ARE EVERYTHING
You to me are everything / What'cha say, what'cha do / Can't get by without you / Love's such a wonderful thing / I want you back / Can you feel the force / Lady I love you all the time / Whenever you want my love / Love is a playground / Lightning strikes again / Boogie down / She's a groovy freak / You can't force the funk / He's just a moneymaker / You'll never know what you're missing / Dance with me / Watch out Carolina / Rainin' through my sunshine / Children of the ghetto
5507402 / Sep '94 / Spectrum

Reality

☐ REGGAE BEAT
Stand up and be counted / Donna / Set me free / Peaceful man / Rasta man / Singer man / Tell me what's going on in your mind / Revolution / All my life / Make a move / OK / Gonna live my life / Steppin' out
QED 137 / Nov '96 / Tring

☐ REGGAE, REGGAE, REGGAE
Stand up and be counted / Donna / Set me free / Peaceful man / Rasta man / Singer man / Tell me what's goin' on in your mind / Revolution / All my life / Make a move / OK / Gonna live my life / Steppin' out
SOV 008CD / '92 / Sovereign

Realizm

☐ DARK SIDE CHRONICLE
MRCCD 1004 / 17 Nov '97 / Marston

Rebekah

☐ REMEMBER TO BREATHE
Hey genius / Sin so well / Remember to breathe / Love song / I wish I could believe me / Pining / Keep it a secret / Be your own / Love trap / Cardboard boxes / To be special / Little black girl
7559621152 / 20 Apr '98 / Elektra

Rebello, Jason

☐ KEEPING TIME
Swings and roundabouts / Coral beads / Close your eyes / Silver surfer / Wind in the willows / Wind in the willows (piano) / Eraserhead (old piano) / Eraserhead (new piano) / Keeping time / Spider / Silver surfer (no sax) / Permanent love (full) / Permanent (edited) / Little man / Tic toc / Future / Untitled / Solo piece 1 / Solo piece 2
74321129042 / Feb '93 / Novus

☐ LAST DANCE (Rebello, Jason & Roy Rose)
Wind in the willows / Every little thing / Life is her friend / Play piano play / Last dance / Soul eyes / I am what you see / Tears / What is this thing called love / Foggy day / Adrian's wall / God bless the child
ATJR 001 / May '95 / All That

☐ MAKE IT REAL
When words fail / Summertime / Compared to what / Wake up / It's alright / Message / Wait and see / Beautiful day / It's at times like these / Heartless monster / Dolphin dance / When words fail (Reprise)
74321224082 / 1 Sep '97 / Novus

Rebello, Simone

☐ FASCINATING RHYTHM
Fascinating rhythm / Xylophonia / Rhythm song / Spinning song / Blues for gilbert / Tico tico / Rhapsodic fantasie / Helter skelter / Mexican dance for marimba no. 1 / Mexican dance for marimba no. 2 / Happy hammers / Our love is here to stay / Valse brillante / Zimba zamba
DOYCD 024 / Aug '93 / Doyen

☐ SECRET PLACE, A
Secret place / Leyenda / Saturday's child / Ensemble / Jupiter's dance / Marimba spiritual
DOYCD 040 / Jun '95 / Doyen

Rebelo, Nuno

☐ SABADO 2 - MINIMAL SHOW
GGG 001 / Jun '97 / Ananana

Rebirth Brass Band

☐ REBIRTH KICKIN' IT LIVE
ROUCD 2106 / Dec '94 / Rounder

☐ ROLLIN'
ROUCD 2132 / Oct '94 / Rounder

☐ WE COME TO PARTY
SH 6018 / Jun '97 / Shanachie

Rebirth Jazz Band

☐ HERE TO STAY
Mardi Gras medley / Chameleon / Lord, Lord, Lord you sure been good to me / Blue Monk / It ain't my fault / Shake your booty / Sweet Georgia Brown / Law / Let's tear it up / Here to stay
ARHCD 9002 / Sep '97 / Arhoolie

Rebo, Max

☐ LIVING MAXISM
GBMR 27 / Apr '97 / GBM

Rebroff, Ivan

☐ KALINKA MALINKA
WMCD 5692 / May '94 / Disky

☐ VERY BEST OF IVAN REBROFF VOL.1, THE
Evening chimes / Song of the Volga boatmen / Hava nagila / Im tiefen keller / Two white doves / Perestroika / Grosser alter don / Dark eyes / Schto nam gorje / Poj zyganka / Somewhere my love / Ol' man river / Kalinka malinka / La calunnia / Ach natascha / On the way from Petersburgh to Nowgorod / Cossack patrol
MDMCD 001 / Jun '93 / Moidart

☐ VERY BEST OF IVAN REBROFF VOL.2, THE
Mutterchen Russland / Hej Andrushka / If I were a rich man / My yiddishe momme / Lonely chimes / Barcarolle / Sah ein Knabein / Rosen steh'n / Elizabethan serenade / Moscow nights / Ach varmaeland / Mit der troike in die grosse Stadt / Ech dorogi / Ave Maria - plaisir d'amour / Cossacks must ride / Ode to joy
MDMCD 002 / Jun '94 / Moidart

Receiver

☐ CHICKEN MILK
Intro / Mood master / Mysterious / I'm afraid / Santa Maria / What da fuk / Phobia / Freeze over / O'Driscoll's curse / Hundred years
COTCD 013 / 27 Apr '98 / Cup Of Tea

Recoil

☐ BLOODLINE
CDSTUMM 94 / Apr '92 / Mute

☐ UNSOUND METHODS
Incubus / Drifting / Luscious apparatus / Stalker / Red River cargo / Control freak / Missing piece / Last breath / Shunt
CDSTUMM 159 / 27 Oct '97 / Mute

Records

☐ SMASHES, CRASHES AND NEAR MISSES
Starry eyes / Girl in golden disc / Teenarama / Up all night / I don't remember your name / Girls that don't exist / Hearts will be broken / All messed up and ready to go / Hearts in her eyes / Girl / Spent a week with you last night / Held up high / Rumour sets the woods alight / Same mistakes / Selfish love / Not so much the time / Affection rejected / Paint her face / Imitation jewellery / Rock 'n' roll love letter
CDOVD 456 / Feb '95 / Virgin

Recyclers

☐ VISIT
BDV 9716 / Mar '97 / Babel

Red 5

☐ FORCES
Intro / Lift me up / Deeper love / For this world / Red 5 jumps / Access / Fiesta fiesta / I love you...stop / Whales / Da beat goes / Gimme luv / Outro
DST 085702452 / Sep '97 / Dance Street

Red Alert

☐ BLOOD, SWEAT AND BEERS
KONCD 006 / Mar '97 / Knock Out

☐ BREAKING ALL THE RULES
DOXOCD 240 / May '96 / Dojo

☐ REBELS IN SOCIETY
GET 19CD / Oct '97 / Get Back

☐ WE'VE GOT THE POWER
We've got the power / They came in force / Crisis / You've got nothing / SPG / Art of brutality / Industrial slide
AHOYCD 12 / Jan '94 / Captain Oi

Red Army Choir

☐ RED ARMY CHOIR VOL.4
242073 / Feb '97 / Planett

☐ RED ARMY CHOIR, THE
LDX 274768 / Jan '94 / La Chant Du Monde

Red Aunts

☐ GHETTO BLASTER
I'm crying / Poison steak / Things you see things you don't / Midnight in the jungle / Exene / Fade in/fade out / Alright / Who / Skeleton hand / Wrecked / I'm bored with you / Cookin' cleanin' and cryin'
65282 / 6 Apr '98 / Epitaph

☐ NO.1 CHICKEN
E 86446 / Mar '95 / Epitaph

☐ SALTBOX
64732 / Aug '96 / Epitaph

Red Chair Fade Away

☐ CURIOUSER AND CURIOUSER
ENG 1013CD / Dec '97 / English Garden

☐ MESMERIZED
ENG 1012 / Apr '94 / English Garden

Red Clay Ramblers

☐ FAR NORTH (Original Soundtrack)
SHCD 8502 / Jan '97 / Sugar Hill

☐ LIE OF THE MIND, A (Original Soundtrack)
Run Sister run / South of the border (Down Mexico way)/In the pines / Honey babe / I love you a thousand ways / Home is where the heart is / Seeing it now / Blue Jay/The gal I left behind / Light years away / Cumberland mountain deer chase / Red rocking chair / Montana underscoring / Killing floor / I can't live without 'em blues / Folding the flag/Hard times
SHCD 8501 / Mar '89 / Sugar Hill

☐ RAMBLER
Cotton eyed Joe / Cajun Billy / Black smoke train / Saro Jane / Annie Oakley / Queen of Skye / Ninety and Nine / Mile long medley / Darlin' say/Pony cart / Hiawatha's lullaby / What does the deep sea say / Ryan's/Jordan reel / Barbeque / One rose/Hot buttered rum / Olkas
SHCD 3798 / Jan '92 / Sugar Hill

Red Crayola

☐ 3 SONGS ON A TRIP TO THE UNITED STATES
DC 105CD / Jun '97 / Drag City

☐ BLACK SNAKES
DC 104CD / Jun '97 / Drag City

☐ COCONUT HOTEL (Red Krayola)
DC 62 / Dec '96 / Drag City

☐ GOD BLESS THE RED KRAYOLA AND ALL WHO SAIL IN IT (Red Krayola)
Say hello to Jamie Jones / Music / Shirt / Listen to this / Save the house / Victory garden / Coconut hotel / Sheriff Jack / Free piece / Ravi Shankar / Parachutist / Dairy maids lament / Big / Leejol / Sherlock Holmes / Dirth of tilth / Tina's gone to have a baby / Jewels of the Madonna / Green of my pants / Night song
14898 / Nov '96 / Spalax

☐ HAZEL (Red Krayola)
DCD 98 / Jan '97 / Drag City

☐ KANGAROO (Red Krayola)
DC 80 / Dec '96 / Drag City

☐ LIVE IN THE 1960'S (2CD Set)
DC 92 / 27 Jul '98 / Dexter's Cigar

☐ PARABLE OF ARABLE LAND, THE
Free form freakout / Hurricane fighter plane / Transparent radiation / War sucks / Pink stainless tail / Parable of arable land / Former reflections enduring doubt
14887 / Nov '96 / Spalax

☐ PARABLE OF ARABLE LAND, THE/ GOD BLESS THE RED CRAYOLA
Free form freak out / Hurricane fighter plane / Transparent radiation / War sucks / Pink stainless tail / Parable of arable land / Former reflections enduring doubt / Say hello to Jamie Jones / Music / Shirt / Listen to this / Save the house / Victory garden / Coconut hotel / Sheriff Jack / Free piece / Ravi Shankar / Parachutist / Place for piano and electric bass guitar / Dairymaid's lament / Big / Leejol / Sherlock Holmes / Dirth of tilth / Tina's gone to have a baby / Jewels of the madonna / Green of my pants / Night song
CDCRH 112 / Jan '97 / Charly

☐ RED KRAYOLA (Red Krayola)
DC 52 / Dec '96 / Drag City

Red, Danny

☐ RIDDIMWIZE
Can't live it up / Be grateful / Mystic lady / Don't cry soundboy / Rollin' stone / Rise up / Riddimwize / Teaser / Cool bad boy / Tell me why / Riddimwize / Can't live it dub / Rise up dub / Be dubful
4777742 / Sep '94 / Columbia

Red Dawn

☐ NEVER SAY SURRENDER
NTHEN 010CD / Sep '95 / Now & Then

Red Devils

☐ KING KING
5144922 / Jan '94 / Phonogram

Red Dirt

☐ RED DIRT
AACD 006 / 27 Apr '98 / Audio Archive

Red Dragon

☐ BUN THEM
VPCD 1350 / Mar '94 / VP

Red Fox

☐ AS A MATTER OF FOX
Born again black man / Dry head shakira Pt 1 / Good body runs in ya family / No condom, no fun / Girl's vineyard (all fruits ripe) / I'm gonna take you home / Ghetto gospel / Pressure dem / Golden axe / Dry head shakira Pt 2 / Dem a murderer / Hey Mr. Rude bwoy / Dance hall scenario / Ya can't test me again
7559615312 / Sep '93 / Warner Bros.

☐ FACE THE FOX
VPCD 2047 / May '96 / VP

Red Guitars

☐ SEVEN TYPES OF AMBIQUITY
Paris france / Fact / Dive / Marimba jive / Sting in the tale / Slow to fade / Steeltown / Heartbeat go / Within four walls / Crocodile tears / Remote control / Shaken not stirred / Astronomy / Seven types of ambiguity / Jamaican homecoming / Be with me / Clean up / Age of swing / Train's on time / Good technology
RPM 109 / Jul '93 / RPM

Red Harvest

☐ HYBREED
D 00049CD / 10 Nov '97 / Displeased

☐ MASTER NATION
VOW 046CD / Jul '95 / Voices Of Wonder

☐ NOMANSLAND
Cure / Righteous majority / Acid / No next generation / Machines way / (Live and pay) The holy way / Crackman / Face the fact / Wrong arm of the law
BMCD 019 / Apr '92 / Black Mark

Red Heads

☐ COMPLETE 1925-1927
159042 / 24 Feb '98 / Jazz Archives

Red Hot 'n' Blue

☐ HAVIN' A BALL
FCD 3033 / '94 / Fury

☐ WAIT 'N' SEE
BBCD 005 / 12 May '98 / Bebe's

Red Hot Chili Peppers

☐ BLOOD SUGAR SEX MAGIK
Power of equality / If you have to ask / Breaking the girl / Funky monks / Suck my kiss / I could have lied / Mellowship slinky in B major / Righteous and the wicked / Give it away / Blood sugar sex magik / Under the bridge / Naked in the rain / Apache rose peacock / Greeting song / My lovely man / Sir psycho sexy / They're red hot
7599266812 / Oct '91 / Warner Bros.

☐ FREAKY STYLEY
Jungle man / Hollywood (Africa) / American ghost dance / If you want me to stay / Nevermind / Freaky styley / Blackeyed blonde / Brothers cup / Battle ship / Lovin' and touchin' / Catholic school girls rule / Sex rap / Thirty dirty birds / Yertle the turtle
CDFA 3309 / Nov '94 / Fame

☐ INTERVIEW DISC
SAM 7028 / Mar '97 / Sound & Media

☐ INTERVIEW, THE
SPEEK 008 / 16 Mar '98 / Talking Music

☐ ONE HOT MINUTE
Warped / Aeroplane / Deep kick / My friends / Coffee shop / Pea / One big mob / Walkabout / Tear jerker / One hot minute / Transcending
9362457332 / Sep '95 / Warner Bros.

☐ OUT IN LA
Higher ground / Hollywood (Africa) / If you want me to stay / Behind the sun / Castles made of sand / Special secret song inside / FU / Get up and jump / Out in LA / Green heaven / Police helicopter / Nevermind / Sex rap / Blues for meister / You always sing the same / Stranded / Flea fly / What it is / Deck the halls with boughs of holly
CDMTL 1082 / Sep '97 / EMI

☐ RED HOT CHILI PEPPERS
True men don't kill coyotes / Baby appeal / Buckle down / Get up and jump / Why don't you love me / Green heaven / Mommy, where's daddy / Out in LA / Police helicopter / You always sing / Grand pappy du plenty
CDFA 3297 / May '93 / Fame

☐ RED HOT CHILI PEPPERS/FREAKY STYLEY/UPLIFT MOFO PARTY PLAN (The Originals/3CD Set)
True men don't kill coyotes / Baby appeal / Buckle down / Get up and jump / Why don't you love me / Green heaven / Mommy where's daddy / Out in LA / Police helicopter / You always sing the same / Grand Pappy du plenty / Jungleman / Hollywood (Africa) / American ghost dance / If you want me to stay / Never mind / Freaky styley / Blackeyed blonde / Brother's cup / Battleship / Lovin' and touchin' / Catholic schoolgirls rule / Sex rap / 30 dirty birds / Yertle the turtle / Fight like a brave / Funky crime / Me

and my friends / Backwoods / Skinny sweaty man / Behind the sun / Subterranean homesick blues / Special secret song inside / No chump love sucker / Walkin' on down the road / Love trilogy / Organic anti-beatbox band
CDOMB 004 / 27 Jul '98 / EMI

Red Hot Peppers

□ MY LITTLE BIMBO
AZCD 15 / Dec '97 / Azure

Red House Painters

□ DOWN COLORFUL HILL
Twenty four / Medicine bottle / Down colorful hill / Japanese to English / Lord kill the pain / Michael
GAD 2014CD / 6 Jul '98 / 4AD

□ OCEAN BEACH
Cabezon / Summer dress / San Geronimo / Shadows / Over my head / Long distance runaround / Red carpet / Brockwell park / Moments / Drop
GAD 5005CD / 6 Jul '98 / 4AD

□ RED HOUSE PAINTERS
Grace Cathedral Park / Down through / Katy song / Mistress / Things mean a lot / Fun house / Take me out / Rollercoaster / New Jersey / Dragonflies / Mistress (piano version) / Mother / Strawberry Hill / Brown eyes
GAD 3008CD / 6 Jul '98 / 4AD

□ RED HOUSE PAINTERS
Evil / Bubble / I am a rock / Helicopter / New Jersey / Uncle Joe / Blindfold / Star spangled banner
GAD 3016CD / 6 Jul '98 / 4AD

□ SONGS FOR A BLUE GUITAR
Have you forgotten / Song for a blue guitar / Make like paper / Priest alley song / Trailways / Feel the rain fall / Long distance runaround / All mixed up / Revelation big sur / Silly love songs / Another song for a blue guitar
CID 8050 / Jul '96 / Island

Red Jasper

□ ACTION REPLAY
HTDDWCD 9 / Nov '92 / HTD

□ STING IN THE TALE
Faceless people / Guy Fawkes / TV screen / Second coming / Old Jack / Company director / Secret society / Magpie / I can hew
HTD CD 3 / Dec '90 / HTD

Red Letter Day

□ LETHAL
Choose noise / Alison / Insomnia / Lethal / Parallel suburbia / Diva / Clandestine / Worldstoomuch / Four / Insider / Drama queen / Thousand names for god
HTT 0322 / 20 Jul '98 / Holier Than Thou

Red London

□ DAYS LIKE THESE
KOCD 064 / 15 Dec '97 / Knock Out

□ LAST ORDERS PLEASE
KONCD 013 / Mar '97 / Knock Out

Red Lorry Yellow Lorry

□ BEST OF RED LORRY YELLOW LORRY, THE
CLEO 9404 / Jun '94 / Cleopatra

□ NOTHING WRONG
Nothing wrong / Do you understand / Calling / Big stick / Hands off me / She said / Sayonara / World around / Hard-away / Only dreaming / Never know / Pushing on / Time is tight
SITU 20CD / May '88 / Situation 2

□ SINGLES 1982-1987, THE
Beating my head / I'm still waiting / Take it all away / Happy / He's red / See the fire / Monkey's on juice / Push / Silence / Hollow eyes / Feel a piece / Chance / Generation / Spinning around / Hold yourself down / Regenerate / Walking on your hands / Which side / Jipp (instrumental mix) / Cut down / Burning fever / Pushed me / Crawling mantra / Hangman / All the same / Shout at the sky
CDMRED 109 / Feb '94 / Cherry Red

□ SMASHED HITS
Beating my head / He's red / Monkeys on juice / Spinning round / Cut down / Take it all / Hollow eyes / Generation / Hold yourself down / Chance
DOJOCD 210 / May '95 / Dojo

□ TALK ABOUT THE WEATHER/PAINT YOUR WAGON
CDMRED 115 / Jun '94 / Cherry Red

Red Monkey

□ MAKE THE MOMENT
TMU 028CD / 30 Mar '98 / Troubleman Unlimited

Red Moon Joe

□ ARMS OF SORROW
RRACD 013 / Oct '91 / Haven

Red Onion Jazzband

□ CREOLE RHAPSODY
BCD 309 / Jul '93 / GHB

Red Plastic Bag

□ ONE MORE (Red Plastic Bag & Mac Fingall)
WCD 499 / Oct '96 / JW

Red Rat

□ OH NO IT'S RED RAT
Shelly-Ann / Nuh live nuh weh: *Red Rat & Crissy D* / Big man little yute: *Red Rat & Goofy* / Girls dem highway: *Red Rat & Chico* / Tight up skirt / If a gaal wan try / Cruise: *Red Rat & Goofy* / Bomb attack / Rumours / Dwayne / Wrigley's / Love them bad: *Red Rat & Buju Banton* / Good boy / Italee / Charlene
GRELCD 246 / 17 Nov '97 / Greensleeves

Red Red Meat

□ RED RED MEAT
RRM 001 / Feb '95 / Sub Pop

□ THERE'S A STAR ABOVE THE MANGER TONIGHT
SPCD 387 / Feb '97 / Sub Pop

Red River

□ TEXAS ADVICE
Ride ride ride / Comin' to you live / Eight chrome and wings / Come on over / Dry country blues / Ain't workin' no more / Broke again / Lucky tonight / Cheap thrills / Texas advice / At the roadhouse tonite / I'll drink your booze / Talkin' to me / Something's gotta give / Goin' down / Mercury / Fools paradise / City doesn't weep
ROSE 210CD / Aug '90 / New Rose

Red Rodney

□ BIRD LIVES
MCD 5371 / Sep '92 / Muse

□ FIERY
Star eyes / You better go now / Stella by starlight / Red arrow / Box 2000 / Ubas
SV 0148 / Oct '97 / Savoy Jazz

□ RED GIANT
SCCD 31233 / '88 / Steeplechase

□ SOCIETY RED (Red Rodney & The Danish Jazz Army)
MECCACD 1003 / Oct '89 / Music Mecca

Red Rooster

□ ON THE MOVE
STINGCD 042 / 15 Jun '98 / Blue Sting

□ STRAIGHT FROM THE HEART
MAPCD 93005 / Aug '94 / Music & Words

Red Sekta

□ ANODIZE
EFA 125102 / May '95 / Celtic Circle

Red Shift

□ ETHER
Midnight clear / Bombers in the desert / Static / Ether
CLPCD 0013 / 22 Jun '98 / CDS

Red Shoe Diaries

□ RED SHOE DIARIES
WWRCD 6001 / Jun '95 / Wienerworld

Red Snapper

□ MAKING BONES
Sleepless / Crease / Image of you / Bogeyman / Tunnel / Like a moving truck / Spitalfields / Seeing red / Suckerpunch / 4 dead monks
WARPCD 056 / 13 Jul '98 / Warp

□ PRINCE BLIMEY
WARPCD 45 / Sep '96 / Warp

□ REELED AND SKINNED
WARPCD 33 / Jun '95 / Warp

Red Stripe Ebony Steel Band

□ BEST OF STEELDRUMS
EUCD 1110 / '91 / ARC

□ PRESENTS: POPULAR BEATLES SONGS
EUCD 1152 / '91 / ARC

Red Sun

□ THEN COMES THE WHITE TIGER (Red Sun & SamulNori)
5217342 / Oct '94 / ECM

Red Tail Chasing Hawks

□ BROTHER HAWK
CR 7029CD / Nov '96 / Canyon

Red Thunder

□ MAKOCE WAKAN
379162 / Dec '95 / Koch International

Red Velvet Trio

□ MILLION TEARS
TBCD 2007 / Mar '93 / Tombstone

Redbone, Leon

□ CHRISTMAS ISLAND
White Christmas / Winter wonderland / Frosty the snowman / Blue Christmas / There's no place like home for the holidays / Toyland / Christmas Island / That old Christmas moon / I'll be home for Christmas / Let it snow, let it snow, let it snow / Christmas ball blues
AS 8890CD / Jan '94 / August

□ NO REGRETS
SHCD 3761 / Jan '97 / Sugar Hill

□ RED TO BLUE
SHCD 3840 / Aug '95 / Sugar Hill

□ SUGAR
Ghost of the Saint Louis blues / Roll along Kentucky moon / Right or wrong / Laughing blues / Breeze / Whistling colonel / Sugar / Pretty baby / When I take my sugar to tea / What you want me to do / Messin' around / So relax / 14th Street blues
260555 / Mar '90 / Private Music

□ WHISTLING IN THE WIND
Dancin' on Daddy's shoes / When I kissed that girl goodbye / Bouquet of roses / Truckin' 101 / Sittin' by the fire / Crazy over Dixie / Little grass shack / Love letters in the sand / You're gonna lose your gal / If I could be with you one hour tonight / Crazy about my baby / I ain't got nobody
01005821172 / Apr '94 / Private Music

Redbones

□ CANDLE GARDENS
BIG 12 / 11 Nov '97 / Candle Gardens

Redcell

□ ESOTERIK/BLUE BINARY (Redcell/ Cmetric)
B12CD 2 / Jan '96 / B12

Redd, Freddie

□ CONNECTION, THE
Who killed Cock Robin / Music forever / Wigglin' / OD / Jim Dunn's dilemma / Time to smile / Sister salvation
CDBOP 019 / Jan '97 / Boplicity

□ SHADES OF REDD
Thespian / Blue blues blues / Shadows / Melanie Swift / Just a ballad for my baby / Ole / Melanie Swift / Ole
8217382 / 2 Feb '98 / Blue Note

Redd Kross

□ PHASESHIFTER
Jimmy's fantasy / Lady in the front row / Monolith / Crazy world / Dumb angel / Huge wonder / Visionary / Pay for love / Ms. lady evans / Only a girl / Saragon / After school special
5181672 / Jan '94 / Phonogram

□ SHOW WORLD
Pretty please me / Stoned / You lied again / Girl god / Mess around / One chord progression / Teen competition / Follow the leader / Vanity mirror / My secret life / Ugly town / Get out of myself / Kiss the goat
5242752 / Feb '97 / This Way Up

Redd, Sharon

□ SHARON REDD/REDD HOT
You got my love / Can you handle it / It's a lie / Try my love on for size / Leaving you is easier said than done / Love is gonna get ya / You stayed on my mind / Never give you up / You're the one / Send your love / Beat the street / In the name of love / Takin' a chance on love / We're friends again
DEEPM 009 / Jan '97 / Deep Beats

Redding, Noel

□ MISSING ALBUM, THE (Redding, Noel Band)
MSCD 005 / Feb '95 / Mouse

Redding, Otis

□ DOCK OF THE BAY (The Definitive Collection)
Shake / Mr. Pitiful / Respect / Love man / Satisfaction / I can't turn you loose / Hard to handle / Fa fa fa fa fa (sad song) / My girl / I've been loving you too long / Try a little tenderness / My lover's prayer / That's how strong my love is / Pain in my heart / Change is gonna come / (Sittin' on the) dock of the bay / Cigarettes and coffee / These arms of mine / Tramp
9548317092 / Nov '92 / Atlantic

□ I'VE BEEN LOVIN' YOU TOO LONG
TS 022 / Mar '94 / That's Soul

□ IMMORTAL OTIS REDDING, THE
I've got dreams to remember / You made a man out of me / Nobody's fault but mine / Thousand miles away / Happy song / Think about it / Waste of time / Champagne and wine / Fool for you / Amen
7567802702 / Mar '95 / Atlantic

□ IT'S NOT JUST SENTIMENTAL
Trick or treat / Loving by the pound 1 / There goes my baby / Remember me / Send me some lovin' / She's alright / Cupid / Boston monkey / Don't be afraid of love / Little ol' me / Loving by the pound 2 / You got good lovin' / Gone again / I'm coming home / (Sittin' on the) dock of the bay / Respect / Open the door / I've got dreams to remember / Come to me / Try a little tenderness / Stay in school
CDSXD 041 / Jan '92 / Stax

□ KING AND QUEEN (Redding, Otis & Carla Thomas)
Knock on wood / Let me be good to you / Tramp / Tell it like it is / When something is wrong with my baby / Lovey dovey / New year's resolution / It takes two / Are you lonely for me baby / Bring it on home to me / Ooh Carla ooh Otis
7567822562 / Nov '92 / Atlantic

□ LIVE AT THE WHISKEY-A-GO-GO VOL.1
I can't turn you loose / Pain in my heart / Just one more day / Mr. Pitiful / Satisfaction / I'm depending on you / Any ole way / These arms of mine / Papa's got a brand new bag / Respect
8122703802 / Oct '94 / Atlantic

□ LIVE AT THE WHISKEY-A-GO-GO VOL.2 (Good To Me)
Introduction / I'm depending on you / Your one and only man / Good to me / Chained and bound / Ol' man trouble / Pain in my heart / These arms of mine / I can't turn you loose / I've been loving you too long / Security / Hard day's night
CDSX 089 / Apr '93 / Stax

□ LOVE MAN
I'm a changed man / (Your love has lifted me) Higher and higher / That's a good idea / I'll let nothing separate us / Direct me / Love man / Groovin' time / Your feeling is mine / Got to get myself together / Free me / Lover's question / Look at that girl
8122702942 / Nov '92 / Atlantic

□ LOVE SONGS
These arms of mine / That's what my heart needs / Pain in my heart / That's how strong my love is / For your precious love / Nothing can change this love / I've been loving you too long / My girl / Just one more day / My lover's prayer / Try a little tenderness / Lovey dovey / I love you more than words can say / Lover's question / Love man / (Your love has lifted me) higher and higher
8122729552 / 4 May '98 / Rhino

□ OTIS (The Definitive Otis Redding/4CD Set)
Fa-fa-fa-fa-fa (sad song) / Knock on wood / Respect / Ole man trouble / I've been loving you too long / My girl / (i can't get no) satisfaction / I love you more than words can say / Open the door / Let me come on home / Just one more day / Tell the truth / Good to me / White christmas / I can't turn you loose / Pain in my heart / Tramp / I'm coming home / Mr pitiful / Love man / That's how strong my love is / Try a little tenderness / These arms of mine / Cigarettes and coffee / Chain gang / My lover's prayer / Lovey dovey / Come to me / Your one and only man / Ol' man trouble / Chained and bound / Slippin' and slidin' / Amen / Happy song (dum-dum-de-de-de-dum-dum) / Shout bamalama / Gettin' hip / She's all right / Hey hey baby / I can't turn you loose / I'm a changed man / Little time / Johnny's heartbreak / Hucklebuck / Sweet lorene / Any ole way / I'm depending on you / Don't leave me this way / That's what my heart needs / Don't be afraid of love / Match game / Free me / Merry Christmas baby / Direct me / You left the water running / New year's resolution / I'm sick y'all / It's growing / Mary's little lamb / I've got dreams to remember / Papa's got a brand new bag / Hard day's night / Day tripper / Security / For your precious love / Cupid / Hard to handle / Try a little tenderness / Respect / Security / Chained and bound / Fa-fa-fa-fa-fa (sad song) / I'm depending on you / (i can't get no) satisfaction / Mr pitiful / Just one more day / These arms of mine / Day tripper / Good to me / Your one and only man / I've been loving you too long / Pain in my heart / Shake / Pounds and hundreds (lbs + 100s) / Look at the girl / Gone again / Announcement / Trick or treat / Little ol' me / Glory of love / (sittin' on) the dock of the bay / You don't miss your water / Shake / Down in the valley / Change is gonna come
8122714392 / Oct '93 / Atlantic

□ OTIS BLUE
Ole man trouble / Respect / Change is gonna come / Down in the valley / I've been loving you too long / Shake / My girl / Wonderful world / Rock me baby / Satisfaction / You don't miss your water
7567803182 / Nov '92 / Atlantic

□ OTIS REDDING DICTIONARY OF SOUL
Fa fa fa fa fa (sad song) / I'm sick y'all / Tennessee waltz / My sweet Lorene / Try a little tenderness / Day tripper / My lover's prayer / She put the hurt on me / Ton of joy / You're still my baby / Hawg for you / Love have mercy
7567917072 / Nov '92 / Atlantic

□ OTIS REDDING STORY, THE (3CD Set)
These arms of mine / That's what my heart needs / Mary's little lamb / Pain in my heart / Something is worrying me / Security / Come to me / I've been loving you too long / Change is gonna come / Shake / Rock me baby / Respect / You don't miss your water / Satisfaction / Chain gang / My lover's prayer / It's growing / Fa fa fa fa fa (sad song) / I'm sick y'all / Sweet Lorene / Try a little tenderness / Day tripper / Stay in school / You left the water running / Happy song / Hard to handle / Amen / I've got dreams to remember / Champagne and wine / Direct me / Your one and only man / Chained and bound / That's how strong my love is / Mr. Pitiful / Keep your arms around me / For your precious love / Woman, a lover, a friend / Home in your heart / Ole man trouble / Down in the valley / I can't turn you loose / Just one more day / Papa's got a brand new bag / Good to me / Cigarettes and coffee / Ton of joy / Hawg for you /

Tramp / Knock on wood / Lovey dovey / New year's resolution / Ooh Carla ooh Otis / Merry Christmas baby / White Christmas / Love man / Free me / Look at that girl / Match game / Tell the truth / (Sittin' on the) dock of the bay
7567817622 / Mar '93 / Atlantic

☐ PAIN IN MY HEART
Pain in my heart / Dog / Stand by me / Hey hey baby / You send me / I need your lovin' / These arms of mine / Louie Louie / Something is worrying me / Security / That's what my heart needs / Lucille
7567802532 / Jun '93 / Atlantic

☐ SOUL ALBUM, THE
Just one more day / It's growing / Cigarettes and coffee / Chain gang / Nobody knows you (when you're down and out) / Good to me / Scratch my back / Treat her right / Everybody makes a mistake / Any ole way / 634 5789
7567917052 / Nov '92 / Atlantic

☐ SOUL BALLADS
That's how strong my love is / Chained and bound / Woman, a lover, a friend / Your one and only man / Nothing can change this love / It's too late for your precious love / I want to thank you / Come to me / Home in your heart / Keep your arms around me / Mr. Pitiful
7567917062 / Nov '92 / Atlantic

☐ TELL THE TRUTH
Demonstration / Tell the truth / Out of sight / Give away none of my love / Wholesale love / I got the will / Johnny's heartbreak / Snatch a little piece / Slippin' and slidin' / Match game / Little time / Swingin' on a string
8122702952 / Nov '92 / Atlantic

☐ TRIBUTE TO OTIS REDDING, A (Various Artists)
I can't turn you loose / (Sittin' on the) dock of the bay / These arms of mine / Respect / I've been loving you too long / Good to me / Let me come on home / Tribute to a king
JD 3320 / Jun '90 / JVC

Reddog

☐ AFTER THE RAIN
TX 1008CD / Jan '94 / Taxim

Reddy, Helen

☐ ANGIE BABY
Angie baby / You make me feel so young / Let's go up / I am woman / That's all / Ain't no way to treat a lady / Lost in the shuffle / Looks like love / Here in my arms / You and me against the world
307712 / Aug '97 / Hallmark

☐ BASIC ORIGINAL HITS
BA 860932 / Mar '96 / Disky

☐ FEEL SO YOUNG (The Helen Reddy Collection)
Angie baby / You make me feel so young / Let's go up / I am woman / That's all / Ain't no way to treat a lady / Lost in the shuffle / Looks like love / Here in my arms / You and me against the world
CDSGP 0124 / Apr '95 / Prestige

☐ LOVE SONGS
CDGOLD 1073 / Apr '97 / EMI Gold

Redell, Teddy

☐ ROCKIN' TEDDY REDELL
CLCD 4406 / Oct '96 / Collector/White Label

Redemption '87

☐ REDEMPTION '87
NA 031CD / Jul '96 / New Age

Rediske, Johannes

☐ RE-DISC BOUNCE (Rediske, Johannes Quintet)
Re-disc bounce / As long as I live / Tom cat mambo / Caravan / When the quail comes back to San Quentin / Once in awhile / Laura / Little white lies / Struttin' with some barbecue / Love for sale / I'm yours / So wird's nie wieder sein / Chrysanthemen blues / Opus in Barock / Stephanie / How deep is the ocean / Lover / Reisefieber / Herbst serenade / Jockey bounce / Hot toddy / Interview/Lullaby of Birdland
BCD 16119 / Oct '97 / Bear Family

Redman

☐ DARE IZ A DARKSIDE
5238462 / Dec '94 / RAL

☐ MUDDY WATERS
Intro / Iz he 4 real / Rock da spot / Welcome (Interlude) / Case closed / Pick it up / Smoke Buddah / Whateva man / On fire / What do ya feel / Skit / Creepin' / It's like that (My big brother) / Da bump / Sheshall / What U lookin' 4 / Rollin' / Soopaman luva 3
5334702 / Dec '96 / Mercury

☐ WHUT THEE ALBUM
Psycho ward / Time 4 sum aksion / Da funk / News break / So ruff / Rated R / Watch yo nuggets / Psycho dub / Jam 4 U / Blow your mind / Hardcore / Funky uncles / Redman meets Reggie Noble / Tonight's da night / Blow your mind (remix) / I'm a bad / Sessed one night / How to roll a blunt / Sooper lover interview / Day of sooperman lover / Encore
5235182 / Jul '97 / Def Jam

Redman, Dewey

☐ AFRICAN VENUS
African Venus / Venus and Mars / Mr. Sandman / Echo prayer / Satin doll / Take the 'A' train / Turnaround
ECD 220932 / Jul '94 / Evidence

☐ LIVING ON THE EDGE (Redman, Dewey Quartet)
1201232 / Oct '90 / Black Saint

Redman, Don

☐ CHANT OF THE WEED
Milenberg joys / Cherry / Some sweet day / Shim-me-sha-wabble / Save it pretty / Gee baby ain't I good to you / I'd love it / Way I feel today / Miss Hannah / Peggy / Talk to me / Rocky road / Chant of the weed / Shakin' the African / How'm I doin' (hey, hey) / Hot and anxious / I got rhythm / Underneath the Harlem moon / Nagasaki / How ya feelin' / Sophisticated lady / That blue eyed baby from Memphis / I got ya / Down home rag
TPZ 1043 / Apr '96 / Topaz Jazz

☐ CLASSICS 1931-1933
CLASSICS 543 / Dec '90 / Classics

☐ CLASSICS 1933-1936
CLASSICS 553 / Dec '90 / Classics

☐ CLASSICS 1936-1939 (Redman, Don & His Orchestra)
Moonrise on the lowlands / I gotcha / Who wants to sing my love song / Too bad / We don't know from nuthin' / Bugle call rag / Stormy weather / Exactly like you / Man on the flying trapeze / On the sunny side of the street / Swingin' with the fat man / Sweet Sue, just you
CLASSICS 574 / Oct '91 / Classics

☐ DOIN' WHAT I PLEASE
Beau Koo Jack / Bugle call rag / Cherry / Chant of the weed / Doin' what I please / Gee baby ain't I good to you / Got the jitters / Henderson stomp / Hot and anxious / Hot mustard / How'm I doin' / I got rhythm / Miss Hannah / Nagasaki / Paducah / Rocky Road / Save it pretty Mama / Shakin' the African / Sophisticated lady / Sugarfoot stomp / Sweet Leilani / Sweet Sue, just you / Swingin' with the fat man / That's how I feel today / Whiteman stomp
CDAJA 5110 / Sep '93 / Living Era

☐ FOR EUROPEANS ONLY
SCCD 36020 / Apr '97 / Steeplechase

☐ STAR DREAMS (Redman, Don All Stars)
78067412112 / 7 Apr '98 / Drive Archive

Redman, Joshua

☐ MOOD SWING
Sweet sorrow / Headin' home / Obsession / Past in the present / Faith / Alone in the morning / Mischief / Oneness of two (in three) / Dialogue / Rejoice / Chill
9362456432 / Sep '94 / Warner Bros.

☐ SPIRIT OF THE MOMENT, THE (Live At The Village Vanguard)
Just in time / Dialogue / My one and only love / Remember / Jig-a-jug / Second snow (part i) / Count me out / Lyric / Slapstick / Mt zion / Neverend / Wait no longer / Herbs and roots / St thomas / Second snow (part ii)
9362459232 / Aug '95 / Warner Bros.

Rednex

☐ SEX AND VIOLINS
Cotton eyed Joe / Hittin' the hay / Riding alone / Wish you were here / Mary Lou / Old pop in an oak / Nowhere in Idaho / Sad but true story of Ray Mingus / Fat Sally Lee / Shooter / McKenzie brothers / Rolling home / Wild and free
KGBD 502 / Mar '97 / Internal Affairs

Redolfi, Michel

☐ DETOURS
MM 303 / Oct '96 / Sargasso

Redouane, Aicha

☐ EGYPTE
C 560020 / Jan '94 / Ocora

Redpath, Jean

☐ FINE SONG FOR SINGING, A
I will make you brooches / Up the Noran water / Captive song of Mary Stuart / Wild geese / Capernaum / Now the die is cast / South wind / Song of wandering aengus / Rohallion / Tryst / John O'Dreams / Broom o'the Cowdenknowes / Annie Laurie / Broken brook
CDPH 1110 / '88 / Philo

☐ FIRST FLIGHT
Barbarry allan / She moved through the fair / Lassie wi' the yellow coatie / Rantin' laddie / Johnnie lad / Nicky tams / Wee cooper o'fife / Johnnie cope / Ploughboy, o / Kirk swaree / Tae the weavers / Crookit bawbee / Wae's me for prince charlie / Dainty davy / Gin I were a baron's heir / Gypsie laddie / Inverey / Caller o'u / Day we went tae rothesay, o / O wert thou in the cauld blast / Quiet land of erin / Clerk saunders
ROUCD 11556 / Jul '90 / Rounder

☐ JEAN REDPATH
CDPH 2015 / '90 / Philo

☐ LEAVING THE LAND
Leaving the land / Miss Admiral Gordon's Strathspey / Scarborough settler's lament / Un Canadien errant / Last minstrel show / Snow goose / Next time round / Sonny's dream / Maggie / Halloween / Leaving Lerwick harbour / Now I'm easy / Wild lass
CDTRAX 029 / Nov '90 / Greentrax

☐ LOWLANDS
PH 1066CD / Aug '94 / Philo

☐ MUSIC AND SONGS OF THE SCOTTISH FIDDLE
Cradle song / Gow's lamentation for Abercarny / Lowlands of Holland / Through the wood laddie / Gow's lament for the death of his brother / Willie Duncan / Mrs. Dundas of Arniston / Birks o' Aberfeldy / I'm a doun for lack o' Johnnie / Caledonia's wail for Niel Gow / Heiress / Wee bird cam' to our ha' door / Highland Harry / Flower o' the Quern / Gow's lament for the death of his second wife
LCOM 7009 / Feb '97 / Lismor

☐ SONGS OF ROBERT BURNS VOL.1 & 2, THE
Cauld kail in Aberdeen / To the Weavers gin ye go / Wantonness / My Tocher's the jewel / Charlie he's my darling / Lady Mary Ann / Amang the trees / Country lassie / De'il's awa' wi' tha exciseman / Johnnie Blunt / Winter it is past / Red, red rose / Logan water / Corn rigs / Had I the wyte / Nine inch will please a lady / Beware o' Bonie Ann / Cooper o' Cuddy / Sweetest May / Parcel o' rogues in a nation / Auld lang syne / Hey how Johnnie lad / Mary Morrison / Dusty miller / It was a' for our rightfu' King / Sae flaxen were her ringlets
CDTRAX 114 / Mar '96 / Greentrax

☐ SONGS OF ROBERT BURNS VOL.3 & 4, THE
Lass o' Ecclefechan / Banks o' Doon / Slave's lament / O fare ye weel my auld wife / Belles of Mauchline / Duncan Davison / Ploughman / Phillis the fair / Deuk's dang o'er my Daddie / Will ye go to the Indies / My Mary / Song, composed in August / Reel o' Stumpie / Green grow the rashes / O can yea labour lea / Wha is that at my bower door / Address to the woodlark / Long winter night / There grows a bonny brier bush / Taylor fell thro' the bed / Here's his health in water / Behold my love / Rattlin' roarin' Willie / Tam Glen / Thou hast left me ever / Jamie / I'll ay ca' in by yon town
CDTRAX 115 / Mar '96 / Greentrax

☐ SONGS OF ROBERT BURNS VOL.5 & 6, THE
Lea rig / My collier laddie / O this is no my ain lassie / My Nanie / Fragment / Posie / Mill, Mill O / O, were I on Parnassus Hill / German Lairdie / Battle of Sherramoor / Lament of Mary Queen of Scots / You're welcome, Willie Stewart / Killiecrankie / Galloway Tam / Strathallan's lament / Fornicator / Here's to thy health / Last may a braw wooer / Gloomy December / Jamie, come try me / White cockade / Cardin O't / Sandy and Jockie / Hey ca' thro'
CDTRAX 116 / Mar '96 / Greentrax

☐ SONGS OF ROBERT BURNS VOL.7, THE
Mauchline lady / O merry hae I been / Gallant weaver / Young highland rover / Cauld is the e'enin blast / My father was a farmer / My love / She's but a lassie yet / Ode to Spring / O' guid ale comes / Bonnie lass o'Albanie / O, for ane-and-twenty, Tam / Where are the joys
CDTRAX 039 / Nov '90 / Greentrax

☐ SONGS OF THE SEAS
PHCD 1054 / Aug '94 / Philo

Redskins

☐ LIVE
Lean on me / Red's strike the blues / Hold on / Unionise / Kick over the statues / 99 1/2 (Won't do) / Take no heroes / Let's make it work / Keep on keeping on / It can be done / Turning loose / Plateful of hatefull / Bring it down / Don't talk to me about the weather / Power is yours
DOJOCD 188 / Jun '94 / Dojo

☐ NEITHER WASHINGTON NOR MOSCOW
Power is yours / Kick over the statues / Go get organized / Let's make it work / It can be done / Keep on keeping on / Bring it down (this insane thing) / Hold on (don't run away) / Turnin' loose (these furious flames) / Take no heroes / Lean on me
8288642 / Jan '97 / London

Redway, Mike

☐ MOONLIGHT AND LOVE SONGS
Moonlight and love songs / Slow trapeze / Loving you / Sitting in the sun with you / It takes only a moment / Love is / Together / I'll sleep a little easier tonight / Our anniversary of love / Do you love me / Too many heartaches / Could it be love
RKD 14 / Dec '94 / Redrock

☐ THOSE BEAUTIFUL BALLAD YEARS
Lark in the clear air / Rose of Killarney / Passing by / On the banks of the Wabash / I love the moon / Barbara Allen / I dream of Jeannie with the light brown hair / Just awearyin' for you / I'll be your sweetheart / When you and I were young Maggie / Mighty like a rose
RKD 7 / Dec '94 / Redrock

Redwood

☐ COLOURBLIND
ALMCD 43 / 24 Nov '97 / Almo Sounds

Reece, Alex

☐ SO FAR
Feel the sunshine / Jazz master / Intro / Acid lab / Pulp friction / Candles / Ibiza / Intro / Out of time / U R
BRCD 621 / Aug '96 / 4th & Broadway

Reece, Dizzy

☐ ASIA MINOR
Shadow of khan / Story of love / Yamask / Spritus parkus / Summertime / Ackmet
OJCCD 1806 / Jul '94 / Original Jazz Classics

Reed, A.C.

☐ I GOT MONEY (Reed, A.C. & M. Vaughn)
Boogie all night / Boogie all night / My buddy buddy friend / This little voice / Big boss man / Mojo hand / Everything I do got to be funky / I got money / Computer took my job / Mojo on me
BLE 597272 / Oct '94 / Black & Blue

☐ I'M IN THE WRONG BUSINESS
I'm in the wrong business / I can't go on this way / Fast food Annie / This little voice / My buddy buddy friends / She's fine / These blues is killing me / Miami strut / Things I want you to do / Don't drive drunk / Hard times / Going to New York / Moving out of the ghetto
ALCD 4757 / May '93 / Alligator

Reed,'Blind'Alfred

☐ COMPLETE RECORDED WORKS 1927-1929, THE
DOCD 8022 / 24 Mar '98 / Document

Reed, Dalton

☐ LOUISIANA SOUL MAN
Read me my rights / Blues of the month club / Keep on loving me / Last to understand / Heavy love / Full moon / Keep the spirit / I'm only guilty of loving you / Party on the farm / Chained and bound
CDBB 9517 / Sep '92 / Bullseye Blues

☐ WILLING AND ABLE
BB 9547 / Apr '94 / Bullseye Blues

Reed, Dan

☐ LIVE AT LAST (Halfway Around the World/2CD Set) (Reed, Dan Network)
Cruise together / Under my skin / Heat / Blame it on the moon / Mix it up / Rainbow child / World has a heart too / Slam / Burnin' love / Tiger in a dress / Halfway around the world / Let it go / Stronger than steel/All my lovin' / Love don't work that way / Baby don't fade / Ritual / Forgot to make her mine / Chill out / I'm so sorry / Come back baby / Salt of joy / Tamin' the wild nights / Takin' it to the streets/ Stardate 1990 / Make it easy / Get to you / Colour this hour / Lover / You can leave your hat on / Baby now I / Seven Sisters Road / Long way to go / Woman
737885308326 / 10 Nov '97 / Video Media

Reed, Eric

☐ IT'S ALL RIGHT TO SWING
Wade in the water / In a lonely place / You don't know what it is to love / Boo Boo strikes again / Undecided / Blues for Akmad / Third degree / He cares / Pineus coneus / Come Sunday
5302552 / Feb '94 / MoJazz

☐ MUSICALE
Black, as in buhaina / Longhair's rumba / Cosa Nostra (our thing) / Frog's legs / Scandal I / Pete and repete / Love Devine / Baby sis / Scandal II / Shug / Upper wess side / Scandal III / No sadness, no pain / Blues to come
IMP 11962 / Oct '96 / Impulse Jazz

☐ PURE IMAGINATION
Overture / Maria / Hello young lovers / Pure imagination / 42nd Street / Send in the clowns / My man's gone now / Nice work if you can get it / You'll never walk alone / I got rhythm / Final / Don't cry for me Argentina
IMP 12442 / 9 Mar '98 / Impulse Jazz

☐ SOLDIER'S HYMN
Soldier's hymn / Greatest thing in all my life / Soft winds / Things hoped for / Coup de cone / Walk with me / Bee's knees / Miss Inferno / I didn't know what time it was / Sweet Lorraine / Mood indigo / Soldier's hymn
CCD 79511 / Feb '97 / Candid

☐ SWING AND I, THE
Swing and I / Gemini suite / Felix the cat / Ahmad's blues / Ka-boose / Frenzia / Spoonful of sugar / Listen here / Uncle lucius interlude / Old flame / Healing hand / Evergreen / Big dogs / Let us go into the house of the lord / Acknowledgement (part 1 from 'a love supreme') / Praise
5304682 / May '95 / MoJazz

Reed, Francine

☐ CAN'T MAKE IT ON MY OWN
D 2248862 / Oct '96 / Ichiban

Reed, Hugh

☐ TAKE A WALK ON THE CLYDE SIDE (Reed, Hugh & The Velvet Underpants)
ECLCD 9615 / Feb '96 / Eclectic

Reed, Jerry

☐ ESSENTIAL JERRY REED, THE
Guitar man / Alabama jubilee / Amos Moses / Thing called love / When you're hot, you're hot / Smell the flowers / Koko Joe / You think all the ramblin' out of me / Uptown poker club / Claw / Lord, Mr. Ford / Good woman's love / Eastbound and down / Let's sing our song / Crude oil blues / I love you, what can I say / Bird / Texas bound and flyin' / She got the goldmine (I got the shaft) / Another puff
74321665922 / Feb '96 / RCA

☐ GUITAR MAN
Guitar man / Folsom Prison blues / Devil went down to Georgia / Down on the corner / Thing called love / US male / Honkin' / Wabash cannonball / Tupelo Mississippi flash / 500 miles away from home / Struttin' / Amos Moses / Sweet memories / Sixteen tons / When you're hot you're hot / Blue moon of Kentucky / Don't it make you wanna go home / Promises / Bad bad Leroy Brown / Patches / Mule skinner blues / Ruby, don't take your love to town
74321415002 / Oct '96 / Camden

Reed, Jimmy

☐ ALL NIGHT BOOGIE
Oh John / Honest I do / Go on to school / Boogie in the night / I'm nervous / Caress me baby / My baby's so sweet / Little rain / I was so young / Shame shame shame
CWNCD 2029 / Jul '96 / Javelin

☐ BIG BOSS MAN
308422 / Apr '98 / Hallmark

☐ BIG BOSS MAN/DOWN IN VIRGINIA
Sugar sugar woman / Don't light my fire / Slow walking Mama / Jump and shout / Down in Virginia / Check yourself / I show an arrow to the sky / Ghetto woman blues / Big boss lady / I need you so / Judge should know / Give up and let me go / I'm leavin' / Shame shame shame / Run here to me baby / Life is funny / Two in one blues / My baby told me / Five years of good lovin' / When two people are in love / I've got to keep on rollin' / When I woke up this morning
SEECD 469 / Jan '97 / See For Miles

☐ BRIGHT LIGHTS, BIG CITY (Charly Blues Masterworks Vol.17)
You don't have to go / I don't go for that / Ain't that lovin' you baby / Can't stand to see you go / I love you baby / You've got me dizzy / Honey / Where you going / Little rain / Sun is shining / Honest I do / Down in Virginia / I'm gonna get my baby / Baby, what you want me to do / Found love / Hush hush / Big boss man / Bright lights big city / Aw shucks hush your mouth / Good lover / Shame shame shame
CDBM 17 / Apr '92 / Charly

☐ CARESS ME BABY
Honest I do / Found love / Ain't that lovin' you baby / Little rain / Hush hush / Boogie in the dark / Cold and lonesome / Close together / Caress me baby / I'm nervous / Oh, John / Shame shame shame / You're something else / I ain't got you / Going fishing
CDSGP 086 / Oct '93 / Prestige

☐ GUITAR, HARMONICA AND FEELING
High and lonesome / Jimmie's boogie / You don't have to go / Boogie in the dark / You upset my mind / She don't want me no more / I don't go for that / Ain't that lovin' you baby / You got for that / You got me dizzy / Honest I do / Sun is shining / End and odds / My bitter seed / Going to New York / Take out some insurance / Baby, what you want me to do / Hush hush / Found love / You gonna need my help / Found joy / Kind of lonesome / Blue Carnagie / Big boss man / Sugar sugar / Jimmy's rock / Bright lights big city / I'm going upside your head
CD 52012 / '92 / Blues Encore

☐ JIMMY REED - THE VEE JAY RECORDS (6CD Set)
High and lonesome / Jimmie's boogie / I found my baby / Roll and rhumba / You don't have to go / Boogie in the dark / Shoot my baby / Rockin' with Reed / You upset my mind / I'm gonna ruin you / Pretty thing / I ain't got you / She don't want me no more / Come on baby / I don't go for that / Baby, don't say that no more / Ain't that lovin' you baby / Can't stand to see you go / When you left me / I love you baby / My first plea / You got me dizzy / Honey don't let me go / Untitled instrumental / It's you baby / Honey, where you going / Do the thing / Little rain / Signals of love / Sun is shining / Baby, what's on your mind / Honest I do / State street boogie / Odds and ends / My baby (Down in Virginia) / You're something else / String to your heart / Go on to school / You got me crying / Moon is rising / Down in Virginia / I'm gonna get my baby / I wanna be loved / Caress me baby / I know it's a sin / You'n that sack / Going to New york / I told you baby / Take out some insurance / I'm nervous / You know I love you / Baby, what you want me to do / Goin' by the river / Goin' by the river / Where can you be / Hush hush / I was so wrong / Blue blue water / Please don't / Found love / You gonna need my help / Hold me close / Come love / Big boss man / Meet me / I got the blues / Sugar sugar / Got me chasing you / Down the road / Want to be with you baby / Jimmy's rock / Tell the world I do / You're my baby / Ain't gonna cry no more / Close together / You know you're looking good / Laughing at the blues / I'm a love you / Kind of lonesome / Found joy / Tell me you love me / Bright lights / Baby what's wrong / Aw shucks / Hush your mouth / I'm Mr. Luck / Blue Carnegie / Take it slow / Good lover / Down in Mississippi / Too much / I'll change my style / Let's get together / In the morning / You can't hide / Back home at noon / Lookin' for you baby / Kansas city baby / Oh John / Shame shame shame / Cold and lonesome / There'll be a day / Ain't no big deal / Mary Mary / Upside the wall / Baby's so sweet / I'm gonna help you / Up tight / Mixed up / I'm trying to please you / Five long years / CC rider / Outskirts of town / Trouble in mind / Comebacks / How long blues / Roll 'em Pete / Cherry red / Wee wee baby / St. Louis blues / Worried life blues / Blues for 12 strings / New Chicago blues / Wear something green / Help yourself / Heading for a fall / Going fishing / Left handed woman / I wanna be loved (Crazy love) / Fifteen years / New leaf / When you're doing alright / I'm going upside your head / Devil's shoestring 2 / You've got me waiting / I'm the man down there / When girls do it / Don't think I'm through
CDREDBOX 9 / Feb '94 / Charly

☐ LIVE AT LIBERTY HALL, HOUSTON 1972 (Reed, Jimmy & Johnny Winter)
Big boss man / Stop light / Down the road I go / Bright lights, big city
422349 / Feb '97 / Last Call

☐ MASTERS, THE
EABCD 045 / 24 Nov '97 / Eagle

☐ MASTERS, THE (2CD Set)
EDMCD 008 / 24 Nov '97 / Eagle

☐ NEW JIMMY REED ALBUM, THE/ SOULIN'
Big boss man / I wanna know / Got nowhere / Two ways to skin a cat / Heartaches and trouble / Tell me what you want me to do / Honey I'll make two / You don't have to go / Don't play me cheap / Two sides to every story / I'm just trying to cop a plea / Two heads are better than one / Buy me a hound dog / Feel like I want to ramble / I wake up at daybreak / Peepin' and hidin' / Don't press your luck woman / I'm not going to let you down / I'm knocking on your door / Crazy about Oklahoma / Cousin Peaches / Ain't no time for fussin' / Dedication to Sonny
SEECD 468 / Jan '97 / See For Miles

☐ TAKE OUT SOME INSURANCE
I found my baby / Boogie in the dark / I'm gonna ruin you / She don't want me no more / Do the thing / Odds and ends / My bitter seed / Moon is rising / I wanna be loved / Take out some insurance / Come love / Tell me you love me / Baby what's wrong / Too much / I'll change my style / Let's get together / Mary mary / When you're doing alright / I'm going upside your head / I'm the man down there
CDRB 13 / Jul '93 / Charly

☐ VERY BEST OF JIMMY REED, THE (& Roots Of The Blues vol.5 Compilation/ 3CD Set)
I found my baby / You don't have to go / I'm gonna ruin you / She don't want me no more / I don't go for that / Ain't that lovin' you baby / Can't stand to see you go / Love you baby / You got me dizzy / Honey, where you going / Do the thing / Little rain / Sun is shining / Odds and ends / Honest I do / My bitter seed / Moon is rising / Down in Virginia / I'm gonna get my baby / I wanna be loved / Take out some insurance / What do you want me to do / Hush-hush / Found love / Come love / Big boss man / Close together / Tell me you love me / Bright lights / Big city / Baby / What's wrong / Aw shucks / Hush your mouth / Good lover / Too much / I'll change my style / Let's get together / Shame shame shame / When you're doing alright / I'm going upside your head / I'm the man down there / St Louis Blues: *Smith, Bessie* / Matchbox: *Jefferson, Blind Lemon* / Big road blues: *Johnson, Tommy* / Got the blues can't be satisfied: *Hurt, 'Mississippi' John* / Going up the country: *Barbecue Bob* / Spoonful blues: *Patton, Charlie* / Dupree blues: *Walker, Willie* / Sugar Mama blues: *Tampa Red* / Honky tonk train blue: *Lewis, Meade 'Lux'* / Lead pencil blues: *Temple, Johnny* / Sweet home Chicago: *Johnson, Robert* / Just a dream: *Broonzy, 'Big' Bill* / Harmonica stomp: *Terry, Sonny* / Good morning blues: *Leadbelly* / Country jail blues: *Big Maceo* / Country blues: *Waters, Muddy*
VBCD 305 / Jul '95 / Charly

☐ VERY BEST OF JIMMY REED, THE (2CD Set)
I found my baby / You don't have to go / I'm gonna ruin you / She don't want me no more / I don't go for that / Ain't that lovin' you baby / Can't stand to see you go / I love you baby / You got me dizzy / Honey, where you going / Do the thing / Little rain / Sun is shining / Odds and ends / Honest I do / My bitter seed / Moon is rising / Down in Virginia / I'm gonna get my baby / I wanna be loved / I told you baby / Take out some insurance / Baby, what you want me to do / Hush hush / Found love / Come love / Big boss man / Close together / Tell me you love me / Bright lights, big city / Baby, what's wrong / Aw shucks / Hush your mouth / Good lover / Too much / I'll change my style / Let's get together / Shame shame shame / When you're doing alright / I'm going upside your head / I'm the man down there
CPCD 82522 / Oct '96 / Charly

Reed, Kay

☐ WE ARE ONE
GBW 006 / Jan '93 / GBW

Reed, Lou

☐ BELLS, THE
Stupid man / Disco mystic / I want to boogie with you / With you / Looking for you / City lights / All through the night / Families / Bells
262918 / Aug '92 / Arista

☐ BERLIN
Berlin / Lady Day / Men of good fortune / Caroline says / How do you think it feels / Oh Jim / Caroline says II / Kids / Bed / Sad song
7863674892 / 11 May '98 / RCA

☐ BETWEEN THOUGHT AND EXPRESSION (Lou Reed Anthology Box Set/3CD Set)
I can't stand it / Lisa says / Ocean / Walk on the wild side / Satellite of love / Vicious / Caroline says / How do you think it feels / Oh Jim / Caroline says / Kids / Sad song / Sweet Jane / Kill your sons / Coney Island baby / Nowhere at all / Kicks / Downtown dirt / Rock 'n' roll heart / Vicious circle / Temporary thing / Real good time together / Leave me alone / Heroin / Here comes the bride / Street hassle / Metal machine music / Bells / America / Think it over / Teach the gifted children / Gun / Blue mask / My house / Waves of fear / Little sister / Legendary hearts / Last shot / New sensations / My friend George / Doin' the things that we want to / Original wrapper / Video violence / Tell it to your heart / Voices of freedom
PD 90621 / Mar '92 / RCA

☐ BLUE MASK
My house / Women / Underneath the bottle / Gun / Blue mask / Average guy / Heroine / Waves of fear / Day John Kennedy died / Heavenly arms
ND 84780 / 2 Feb '98 / RCA

☐ CONEY ISLAND BABY
Crazy feeling / Charley's girl / She's my best friend / Kicks / Gift / Oooh baby / Ain't nobody's business if I do / Coney Island baby
ND 83807 / Dec '86 / RCA

☐ DIFFERENT TIMES (Lou Reed In The 70's)
I can't stand it / Love makes you feel / Lisa says / Walk on the wild side / Perfect day / Satellite of love / Vicious / Berlin / Caroline says / Sad song / Caroline says / Sweet Jane / Kill yor sons / Sally can't dance / Gift / She's my best friend / Coney Island baby
07863668642 / Aug '96 / RCA

☐ GROWING UP IN PUBLIC
How do you speak to an angel / My old man / Keep away / Standing on ceremony / So alone / Our love is here to stay / Power of positive drinking / Smiles / Think it over / Teach the gifted children
262917 / Aug '92 / Arista

☐ LEGENDARY HEARTS
Legendary hearts / Don't talk to me about work / Make up / Martial law / Last shot / Turn out the light / Pow wow / Betrayed / Bottoming out / Home of the brave / Rooftop garden
ND 89843 / Apr '91 / RCA

☐ LOU REED & VELVET UNDERGROUND (Reed, Lou/Velvet Underground)
Sunday morning: *Reed, Lou* / I'm waiting for the man: *Reed, Lou* / Venus in furs: *Reed, Lou* / Candy says: *Velvet Underground* / Pale blue eyes: *Velvet Underground* / Beginning to see the light: *Velvet Underground* / Satellite of love: *Reed, Lou* / Nowhere at all: *Reed, Lou* / Vicious: *Reed, Lou* / Perfect day: *Reed, Lou* / Walk on the wild side: *Reed, Lou* / How do you think it feels: *Reed, Lou* / Sweet Jane: *Reed, Lou* / White light/white heat: *Reed, Lou* / Sally can't dance: *Reed, Lou* / Wild child: *Reed, Lou* / I love you: *Reed, Lou* / Berlin: *Reed, Lou* / Coney Island baby: *Reed, Lou* / I love you, Suzanne: *Reed, Lou*
RADCD 21 / Oct '95 / Global TV

☐ LOU REED LIVE IN CONCERT
Sweet Jane / I'm waiting for the man / Martial law / Satellite of love / Kill your sons / Betrayed / Sally can't dance / Wages of fear / Average guy / White light, white heat / Some kinda love / Sister Ray / Walk on the wild side / Heroin / Rock 'n' roll
74321431572 / Oct '96 / Camden

☐ MAGIC AND LOSS
Dorita / What's good / Power and glory / Magician / Sword of damocles / Goodby mass / Cremation / Dreamin' / No change / Warrior king / Harry's circumcision / Gassed and stoked / Power and glory part II / Magic and loss
7599266622 / Jan '92 / Sire

☐ MASTERS, THE
EABCD 012 / 24 Nov '97 / Eagle

☐ NEW YORK
Romeo and Juliet / Halloween parade / Dirty boulevard / Endless cycle / There is no time / Last great American whale / Beginning of a great mystery / Busload of faith / Sick of you / Hold on / Good evening Mr. Waldheim / Christmas in February / Strawman / Dime store mystery
7599258292 / Feb '95 / Sire

☐ PERFECT DAY
Rock and roll heart / Perfect day / Coney Island baby / Men of good fortune / How do you speak to an angel / Downtown dirt / Real good time together / Vicious circle / Gift / Think it over / My friend George / Legendary hearts / Last shot / Leave me alone / Temporary thing / Gun / Sad song / Growing up in public
74321523752 / 29 Sep '97 / Camden

☐ PERFECT NIGHT
I'll be your mirror / Perfect day / Kids / Vicious / Busload of faith / Kicks / Talking book / Into the divine / Coney Island baby / New sensations / Why do you talk / Riptide / Original wrapper / Sex with your parents / Dirty Blvd.
9362469172 / 27 Apr '98 / Reprise

☐ ROCK 'N' ROLL HEART
I believe in love / Banging on my drum / Follow the leader / You wear it so well / Ladies pay / Rock 'n' roll heart / Temporary thing
262271 / Feb '93 / Arista

☐ SALLY CAN'T DANCE
Ride Sally ride / Animal language / Baby face / NY stars / Kill your sons / Billy / Sally can't dance / Ennui
ND 90308 / Feb '89 / RCA

☐ SET THE TWILIGHT REELING
Egg cream / Nyc man / Trade in / Sex with your parents (motherfucker) part ii / Proposition / Hooky wooky / Set the twilight reeling / Riptide / Adventurer / Hang on to your emotions / Finish line
9362461592 / Feb '96 / Sire

☐ SONGS FOR DRELLA (Reed, Lou & John Cale)
Smalltown / Open house / Style it takes / Work / Trouble with classicists / Starlight / Faces and names / Images / Slip away / It wasn't me / I believe / Nobody but you / Dream / Forever changed / Hello it's me
7599261402 / Apr '90 / WEA

☐ STREET HASSLE
Gimme some good times / Dirt / Street hassle / I wanna be black / Real good time together / Shooting star
262270 / Feb '93 / Arista

☐ STREET HASSLE/THE BELLS (2CD Set)
74321292092 / Jan '95 / RCA

☐ TRANSFORMER
Vicious / Andy's chest / Perfect day / Hangin' around / Walk on the wild side / Make up / Satellite of love / Wagon wheel / New York telephone conversation / I'm so free / Goodnight ladies
ND 83806 / Aug '95 / RCA

☐ TRANSFORMER/BERLIN (2CD Set)
74321292102 / Jan '95 / RCA

☐ WALK ON THE WILD SIDE (The Best Of Lou Reed)
Satellite of love / Wild child / I love you / How do you think it feels / New York telephone conversation / Walk on the wild side / Sweet Jane / White light, white heat / Sally can't dance / Nowhere at all / Coney Island baby / Vicious
ND 83753 / Oct '91 / RCA

Reed, Lucy

☐ BASIC REEDING
ACD 273 / Apr '93 / Audiophile

Reed, Preston

☐ ROAD LESS TRAVELLED, THE
FF 70423 / Oct '89 / Flying Fish

Reedstorm Saxophone Quartet

☐ JAZZ STANDARDS
BEST 1075CD / Nov '95 / Acoustic Music

Reedy, Winston

☐ GOLD
RNCD 2049 / Mar '94 / Rhino

Reef

☐ GLOW
Place your hands / I would have left you / Summer's in bloom / Lately stomping / Consideration / Don't you like it / Come back brighter / Higher vibration / I'm not scared / Robot riff / You're old / Lullaby
4869402 / Jan '97 / Sony Soho2

☐ INTERVIEW, THE
SPEEK 009 / 16 Mar '98 / Talking Music

☐ REPLENISH
Feed me / Naked / Good feeling / Repulsive / Mellow / Together / Replenish / Choose to live / Comfort / Loose / End
4806982 / Jun '95 / Sony Soho2

Reefa

☐ LOVE LIFE LIVE LOVE
STRSCD 4 / Oct '94 / Stress

Reel Union

☐ BROKEN HEARTED I'LL WANDER
LUNCD 033 / Nov '86 / Mulligan

Reeltime

☐ REELTIME
GL 1154CD / Jul '95 / Green Linnet

Reese, Della

☐ BEST THING FOR YOU, THE
What is there to say: *Reese, Della & Dick Stabile Orchestra* / You came a long way from St. Louis: *Reese, Della & Dick Stabile Orchestra* / If I ever should leave you: *Reese, Della & Dick Stabile Orchestra* / Be my love: *Reese, Della & Dick Stabile Orchestra* / Lamp is low/After the lights go down: *Reese, Della & Dick Stabile Orchestra* / Fly me to the moon: *Reese, Della & Dick Stabile Orchestra* / I could have danced all night: *Reese, Della & Dick Stabile Orchestra* / Swing low, sweet chariot: *Reese, Della & Dick Stabile Orchestra* / Best thing for you: *Reese, Della & John Cotter Orchestra* / Don't you know: *Reese, Della & John Cotter Orchestra* / Keep smiling at trouble: *Reese, Della & John Cotter Orchestra* / Don't cry Joe: *Reese, Della & John Cotter Orchestra* / I'm always chasing rainbows: *Reese, Della & John Cotter Orchestra* / Bill Bailey, won't you please come home: *Reese, Della & John Cotter Orchestra* / Put on a happy face/I want to be happy: *Reese, Della & John Cotter Orchestra* / But not for me: *Reese, Della & John Cotter Orchestra* / See what the boys in the backroom will have: *Reese, Della & John Cotter Orchestra* / Anything goes: *Reese, Della & John Cotter Orchestra* / My man: *Reese, Della & John Cotter Orchestra* / Nobody's sweetheart: *Reese, Della & John Cotter Orchestra*
JASCD 332 / May '97 / Jasmine

☐ COLLECTION, THE
VSD 5907 / 21 Apr '98 / Varese Sarabande

☐ DATE WITH DELLA REESE, A/THE STORY OF THE BLUES (Original Jubilee Recordings)
Story of the blues / Good morning blues / Empty bed blues / Squeeze me / You've been a good old wagon / Sent for you yesterday / St. James infirmary / Lover man / Things ain't what they used to be / Stormy weather / There's always the blues / Sometimes I'm happy / Happiness is a thing called Joe / Almost like being in love / Someone to watch over me / Birth of the blues / Pennies from heaven / Getting to know you / If I forget you / All of me / Nearness of you / Just one of those things
WESM 514 / 13 Oct '97 / Westside

☐ DELLA
Lady is a tramp / You're driving me crazy / If I could be with you one hour tonight / Three o'clock in the morning / Until the real thing comes along / Thou swell / You made me love you / I'm beginning to see the light / I'm always chasing rainbows / What's the reason (I'm not pleasin') / Softly my love / You're

nobody 'til somebody loves you / Baby won't you please come home / Moon love / Blue skies / Have you ever been lonely / Someday / I'll get by till the end of time / Please don't talk about me when I'm gone / Don't you know / Someday sweetheart
74321415012 / Oct '96 / Camden

☐ **JUBILEE YEARS, THE (The Singles 1954-1959)**
In the still of the night / Time after time / Fine sugar / Years from now / I've got my love to keep me warm / Headin' home / Daybreak serenade / My melancholy baby / One for my baby / In the meantime / More I see you / How can you not believe me / How about you / And that reminds me / I cried for you / By love possesed / I only want to love you / How can you lose (watcha' never had) / If not for you / I've got a feelin' you're foolin' / C'mon c'mon / Wishing (I wish) / You gotta love everybody / Sermonette / My dreams end at dawn / When I grow to old to dream: *Reese, Della & Kirk Stuart* / You're just in love: *Reese, Della & Kirk Stuart* / Time was: *Reese, Della & Kirk Stuart* / Once upon a dream: *Reese, Della & Kirk Stuart*
WESM 513 / 13 Oct '97 / Westside

☐ **LIVE 1963 GAURD SESSIONS (Reese, Della & Duke Wellington)**
EBCD 21102 / Feb '94 / Flyright

Reet Petite & Gone

☐ **USING THAT THING**
Somebody's been using that thing / That's no way to get along / Waiting for a runaway train / Bring it on home / Dixie fried / Go ahead buddy / Battle of New Orleans / Good time flat blues / Looking for the heart of Saturday night / Goodbye lonesome, hello baby doll / Steady rolling man / Little red hen / Moonshine madness / Reet petite and gone / It mek / Canned heat
TERRCD 004 / Feb '97 / Terra Nova

Reevers

☐ **FAREWELL TO THE HIGHLANDS**
SKERRIESCD 0001 / Feb '98 / Skerries Music

☐ **OVER THE SEA TO SKYE**
Maggie / Bonnie Strathyre / Nut brown maiden / My mountain home / Over the sea to Skye / Amazing Grace / Road and the miles to Dundee / 'Tis the last rose of summer / When you were sweet sixteen / Bonnie Mary of Argyle / Lewis bridal song / My love is like a red, red rose / Whistling gypsy / Will ye no' come back again / Lassie wi' the yellow coatie / Kelvin Grove / Loch Lomond / Auld lang syne
SKERRIESCD 0002 / Feb '98 / Skerries Music

Reeves, Conner

☐ **EARTHBOUND**
CDWILD 3 / Dec '97 / Wildstar

Reeves, Dianne

☐ **GRAND ENCOUNTER**
Old country / Cherokee / Besame mucho / Let me love you / Tenderly / After hours / Ha / Some other Spring / Side by side / I'm okay
CDP 8382682 / Nov '96 / Blue Note

☐ **QUIET AFTER THE STORM**
Hello haven't I seen you before / Comes love / Smile / Jive samba / Country preacher / Detour ahead / Vermonja / Sargaco mar / Nine / In a sentimental mood / When morning comes / Both sides now / Sing my heart
CDP 8295112 / Jun '95 / Blue Note

☐ **THAT DAY**
Will you love me tomorrow / Blue prelude / Close enough for love / Just a little lovin' / That day / Twelfth of never / Morning has broken / Dark truths / Exactly like you / Ain't nobody's business
8569732 / 3 Nov '97 / Blue Note

Reeves, Goebel

☐ **HOBO'S LULLABY**
Tramp's mother / I learned about women from her / Drifter (part 1) / Drifter (part 2) / When the clock struck seventeen / Blue undertaker's blues (part 1) / Blue undertaker's blues (part 2) / Fortunes galore / My mountain gal / Song of the sea / In the land of never was / Texas drifter's warning / Cowboy's lullaby / Hobo's lullaby / Drifter's buddy (drifter's prayer) / Cowboy's prayer / Happy days (I'll never leave old Dixieland) / Wayward son / Reckless Tex / Soldier's return / Miss Jackson, Tennessee / My mountain girl / Cold and hungry / Meet me at the crossroads, pal / Yodeling teacher / Kidnapped baby
BCD 15680 / Nov '94 / Bear Family

Reeves, Jim

☐ **18 VERY SPECIAL LOVE SONGS (Live From The Grand Ole Opry 1959)**
I'd like to be / I know me / Anna Marie / Have I told you lately that I love you / Your old love letters / Till the end of the world / Making believe / Four walls / According to my heart / Just call me lonesome / Blue boy / I missed me / Am I losing you / I love you more / If you were only mine / How's the world treating you / I'm beginning to forget you / If heartaches are the fashion
PLATCD 163 / Mar '96 / Platinum

☐ **ACCORDING TO MY HEART (At His Best)**
PLSCD 215 / Apr '97 / Pulse

☐ **BEST OF JIM REEVES, THE**
74321378412 / Jul '96 / RCA

☐ **BEST OF JIM REEVES, THE**
He'll have to go / Billy Bayou / According to my heart / Distant drums / Welcome to my world / I won't come in while he's there / Yonder comes a sucker / Four walls / Blue boy / I love you because / Anna Marie / Home / Am I losing you / Blue side of lonesome / Adios amigo / I won't forget you / I'm gonna change everything / I missed me / Partners / Losing your love / Waiting for a train / Is it really over
74321446842 / Feb '97 / Camden

☐ **DEAR HEARTS AND GENTLE PEOPLE**
Have I told you lately that I love you / Just call me lonesome / How's the world treating you / If heartaches are the fashion / Home / Dear hearts and gentle people / I'm beginning to forget you / Roly poly / Wind up doll / Sweet evening breeze / Your old love letters / Till the end of the world / Making believe / Oaklahoma hills / Highway to nowhere / If you were mine / Everywhere you go / I love you more / I've lived a lot in my time
CDSD 073 / 30 Jan '98 / Sundown

☐ **DISTANT DRUMS**
Distant drums / I won't forget you / Is it really over / I missed me / Snowflake / Letter to my heart / Losing your love / This is it / Not until the next time / Good morning self / Where does a broken heart go / Overnight / Gods were angry with me
WMCD 5635 / May '94 / Disky

☐ **ESSENTIAL JIM REEVES, THE**
Four walls / Blue boy / He'll have to go / Home / Am I losing you / Blizzard / I'm gettin' better / I know one / Adios amigos / I love you because / I'm gonna change everything / Welcome to my world / Is this me / I guess I'm crazy / This is it / Is it really over / Distant drums / I won't forget you / Blue side of lonesome / Suppertime
74321665892 / Feb '96 / RCA

☐ **GENTLEMAN JIM (4CD Set)**
I'm hurtin' inside / If you were mine / That's a sad affair / Yonder comes a sucker / Jimbo Jenkins / I've lived a lot in my time / Ichabod crane / My lips are sealed / Your old love letters / Waltzing on top of the world / Beyond a shadow of a doubt / Love me a little bit more / According to my heart / Each time you leave / Highway to nowhere / Breeze (blow my baby back to me) / Roly poly / Tweedle o'twill / Have I told you lately that I love you / Oklahoma hills / Pickin' a chicken / I've got just the thing for you / I'm the mother of a honky tonk girl: *Reeves, Jim & Carol Johnson* / Am I losing you / Don't tell me / I can't fly / Don't ask me why / Waiting for a train / Look behind you / Four walls / Honey, won't you please come home / Gods were angry with me / I know (and you know) / Young hearts / I heard my heart break last night / Image of me / Anna Marie / Sea breeze / Blue without my baby / I love you more / Theme of love (I love to say I love you) / Wishful thinking / Two shadows on your window / Everywhere you go (single version) / Teardrops in my heart / Yours / I don't see me in your eyes anymore / I get the blues when it rains / I care no more / Final affair / You belong to me / My happiness / Everywhere you go / Blues in my heart / Need me / That's my desire / He'll have to go / In a mansion stands my love / Billy Bayou / I'd like to be partners / I'm beginning to forget you / If heartaches are the fashion / Home after awhile / Overnight blue boy / Charmaine / Mona Lisa / Marie / Goodnight Irene / Linda / Maria Elena / My Mary Ramona / Margie / My Juanita / Sweet Sue, just you / Just you / Snowflake / But you love me daddy: *Reeves, Jim & Steve Moore* / But you love me daddy: *Reeves, Jim & Dorothy Dillard* / Throw another log on the fire / Making believe / Till the end of the world / How's the world treating you / Someday (you'll want me to want you) / Just call me lonesome / Fool such as I / May the good Lord bless and keep you / Dear hearts and gentle people / Satan can't hold me / Scarlet ribbons / How long has it been / Teach me how to pray / Evening prayer / Padre of old San Antone / Suppertime / It is no secret / God be with you / Beautiful life / In the garden / Precious memories / Whispering hope / Flowers / Sunset, the trees
BCD 15439 / Jun '89 / Bear Family

☐ **GENTLEMAN JIM (2CD Set)**
Mexican joe / Bimbo / Then I'll stop loving you / Penny candy / I'll follow you / Where does a broken heart go / Give me one more kiss / Shall we gather at the river (mother went a walkin') / Hillbilly waltz / Butterfly love / It's hard to love just one / Gypsy heart / Red eyed and rowdy / Beatin' on the ding dong / Wilder your heart beats the sweeter you love / Are you the one / El rancho del rio / Let me remember (things I can't forget) / How many / A woman's love / Tahiti / Padre of old san antone / My rambling heart / Echo bonita / Each beat of my heart / Let me love you just a little / I could cry / I'll always love you / You're the sweetest thing / Drinking tequila / Heart breaking baby / Wagon load of love / What were you doing (last night) / Whispering willow / Spanish violins / If you love me don't leave me / I'll tell the world I love you / I love you more / I'm beginning to forget you / Have I told you lately that I love you / Just call me lonesome / How's the world treating you / If heartaches are the fashion / Dear hearts and gentle people / Roly poly / Wind up doll / Sweet evening breeze / Your old love letters / 'til the end of the world / Making believe / Oklahoma hills / Highway to nowhere / If you were mine / Everywhere you go / I've lived a lot in my time / Interview
DBG 53031 / Apr '94 / Double Gold

☐ **GENTLEMAN JIM**
He'll have to go / Have I told you lately that I love you / I know one / Am I losing you / Your old love letters / Anna Marie / I'm beginning to forget you / I love you more / Waiting for a train / Mexican Joe / I missed me / According to my heart / Four walls / Bimbo / When God dips his love in my heart / Billy Bayou / Heartaches are the fashion / I'd like to be / Peace in the valley / Dear hearts and gentle people / I'm gettin' better / Yonder comes a sucker / Blue boy / Just call me lonesome / In a mansion stands my love
CD 6015 / Apr '96 / Music

☐ **HAVE I TOLD YOU LATELY**
If heartache's the fashion / Dear hearts and gentle people / 'til the end of the world / Etc. / Welcome to my world / Distant drums / Blizzard / I won't come in while he's there / I love you because / I won't forget you / He'll have to go / You're the only good thing (that's ever happened to me) / Adios amigo / There's a heartache following me / It hurts too much to see you go
MU 5046 / Oct '92 / Musketeer

☐ **HAVE I TOLD YOU LATELY THAT I LOVE YOU**
Am I losing you / He'll have to go / Have I told you lately that I love you / How's the world treating you / I love you more / Til the end of the world / I've lived a lot in my time / Oklahoma hills / I'm getting better / Bimbo / Anna Marie / Billy Bayou / Blue boy / Waiting for a train / When God dips his love in my heart / Just call me lonesome / If heartaches are in fashion / Your old love letters
300072 / Feb '98 / Hallmark

☐ **HE'LL HAVE TO GO**
He'll have to go / Bimbo / I'd like to be / Billy Bayou / In a mansion stands my love / I'm getting better / I know one / I missed me / Yonder comes a sucker / Waiting for a train / Am I losing you / According to my heart / Four walls / Mexican Joe / Anna Marie / Blue boy / Softly and tenderly / Peace in the valley
MUCD 9022 / Apr '95 / Musketeer

☐ **I LOVE YOU MORE (Live)**
If you were only mine / I love you more / Have I told you lately that I love you / Everywhere you go / Sweet evening breeze / Oklahoma hills where I was born / Evening prayer / Dear hearts and gentle people / I've lived a lot in my time / If heartaches are the fashion / Home / How's the world treating you / I'm beginning to forget you / Roly poly / Wind up / Your old love letters / Till the end of the world / Making believe / Just call me lonesome / Highway to nowhere / Beyond the shadow of a doubt
DATOM 3 / Apr '94 / Touch Of Magic

☐ **I LOVE YOU MORE**
CTS 55433 / Oct '95 / Country Stars

☐ **IMMORTAL JIM REEVES, THE (2CD Set)**
Four walls / Mexican Joe / Anna Marie / Blue boy / Softly and tenderly / He'll have to go / Bimbo / I'd like to be / Peace in the valley / Billy Bayou / In a mansion stands my love / I'm getting better / (Gimme that) Old tyme religion / I know one / I missed me / Yonder comes a sucker / Am I losing you / According to my heart / Beyond the shadow of a doubt / Evening prayer / Have I told you lately that I love you / Just call me lonesome / How's the world treating you / If heartaches are the fashion / Home / Dear hearts and gentle people / I'm beginning to forget you / Roly poly / Wind up / Sweet evening breeze / Your old love letters / Til the end of the world / Making believe / Oklahoma hills / Highway to nowhere / If you were mine / Everywhere you go / I love you more / I've lived a lot in my time / Waiting for a train
MUCD 9513 / May '96 / Musketeer

☐ **JIM REEVES**
Peace in the valley / Till the end of the world / Your old love letters / He'll have to go / According to my heart / Just call me lonesome / Four walls / If heartaches are the fashion / I'm beginning to forget you / How's the world treating you / Making believe / I love you more / I've lived a lot in my time / Dear hearts and gentle people / Blue boy / Am I losing you / Roly poly / In a mansion stands my love / I missed me / Have I told you lately that I love you
SUMCD 4028 / Nov '96 / Summit

☐ **JIM REEVES**
GFS 064 / Jul '97 / Going For A Song

☐ **JIM REEVES IN CONCERT**
Yonder comes a sucker / Blue boy / Just call me lonesome / In a mansion stands my love / He'll have to go / Have I told you lately that I love you / I know one / Am I losing you / Your old love letters / Anna Marie / I'm beginning to forget you / I love you more / Waiting for a train / Mexican Joe / I missed me / According to my heart / Four walls / Bimbo / When God dips his love in my heart / Billy Bayou / If heartaches are the fashion / Peace in the valley
TRTCD 128 / Dec '94 / TrueTrax

☐ **JIM REEVES LIVE AT THE OPRY**
SSLCD 208 / Jun '95 / Savanna

☐ **LIVE AT THE OPRY**
Yonder comes a sucker / Waiting for a train / Am I losing you / When God dips his love in my heart / According to my heart / Four walls / Mexican Joe / Anna Marie / Blue boy / Softly and tenderly Jesus is calling / He'll have to go / Bimbo / I'd like to be / Peace in the valley / Billy bayou / In a mansion stands my love / I'm getting better / Give me that old time religion / I know one / I missed me
CMFCD 008 / Oct '94 / Country Music Foundation

☐ **LIVE ON AIR**
Have I told you lately that I love you / Just call me lonesome / How's the world treating you / If heartaches are the fashion / Home / Dear hearts and gentle people / I'm beginning to forget you / Roly poly / Wind up / Sweet evening breeze (bring my baby back to me) / Your old love letters / 'Til the end of the world / Making believe / Oklahoma hills / Highway to nowhere / If you were mine / Everywhere you go / I love you more
QED 044 / Nov '96 / Tring

☐ **MASTERS, THE**
EABCD 022 / 24 Nov '97 / Eagle

☐ **MEXICAN JOE**
Mexican joe / Bimbo / Then I'll stop loving you / Penny candy / Drinking tequila / I'll follow you / Give me one more kiss / Hillbilly waltz / Butterfly love / It's hard to love just one / Gypsy heart / Red eyed and rowdy / Are you the one / Let me remember (things I can't forget) / How many / Padre of old san antone / My rambling heart / Echo bonita / Each beat of my heart / Let me love you just a little / Wagon load of love / You're the sweetest thing / Whispering willow / I'll always love you
CTS 55420 / Jun '94 / Country Stars

☐ **SPOTLIGHT ON JIM REEVES**
Have I told you lately that I love you / Just call me lonesome / How's the world treating you / If heartaches are the fashion / Home / Dear hearts and gentle people / I'm beginning to forget you / Roly poly / Wind up doll / Sweet evening breeze / Your old love letters / Till the end of the world / Making believe / Oklahoma hills / Highway to nowhere / If you were mine
HADCD 126 / Feb '94 / Javelin

☐ **TWELVE SONGS OF CHRISTMAS**
Jingle bells / Blue Christmas / Senor Santa Claus / Old Christmas card / Merry Christmas polka / White Christmas / Silver bells / C-H-R-I-S-T-M-A-S / O little town of Bethlehem / Mary's boy child / O come all ye faithful (Adeste Fidelis) / Silent night
ND 82758 / Oct '94 / RCA

☐ **ULTIMATE COLLECTION, THE (2CD Set)**
I love you because / Welcome to my world / Have you ever been lonely / Have I told you lately that I love you / He'll have to go / Make the world go away / Moon river / I won't forget you / When 2 worlds collide / Memories are made of this / You'll never know / Mona Lisa / Oh, how I miss you tonight / Mexican Joe / It hurts so much to see you go / There's a heartache following me / Am I losing you / Blue side of lonesome / Four walls / Adios amigo / Distant drums / I can't stop loving you / From a Jack to a King / Roses are red (my love) / Moonlight and roses / You're the only good thing / Am I that easy to forget / You're free to go / Not until the next time / Don't let me cross over / Anna Marie / Trying to forget / I won't come in while he's there / This world is not my home / Billy Bayou / Is it really over / White cliffs of Dover / Blue boy / Golden memories and silver tears / Danny Boy
74321410872 / Sep '96 / RCA Victor

☐ **WAITING FOR A TRAIN**
MACCD 142 / Aug '96 / Autograph

☐ **WELCOME TO MY WORLD (14CD Set)**
My heart's like a welcome mat / Teardrops of regret / Chicken hearted / I've never been so blue / What were you doing last night / Wagon load of love / I could cry / Mexican Joe / Butterfly love / Let me love you just a little / El rancho del rio / It's hard to love just one / Bimbo / Gypsy heart / Echo bonita / Then I'll stop loving you / Beatin' on a ding dong / My rambling heart / Padre of old San Antone / Mother went a-walkin / I love you (and Ginny Wright) / I'll follow you / Penny candy / Where does a broken heart go / Wilder your heart beats (False start) / Wilder your heart beats / Drinking tequila / Red eyed and rowdy / Tahiti / Give me one more kiss / Are you the one / How many / Hillbilly waltz / Let me remember (Things I can't forget) / Spanish violins / Woman's love / Whispering willow / If you love me don't leave me / Each beat of my heart / Let me love you just a little (Alternative) / Then I'll stop loving you (Alternative) / Hillbilly waltz (Alternative) / Mexican Joe (Alternative) / Marriage of Mexican Joe / You're the sweetest thing / I've forgotten you / Sand in my shoes / There's someone who loves you / Heartbreaking baby / Did you darling / Standby / I'll always love you / Never take no for an answer / Please leave my darling alone / You're slipping away from me / I'm hurtin' inside / If you were mine / That's a sad affair / Jimbo Jenkins / I've lived a lot in my time / Ichabod Crane / My lips are sealed / Your old love letters / Waltzing on top of the world / Beyond a shadow of a doubt / Love me a little bit more / According to my heart / Each time you leave / Highway to nowhere / Breeze (Blow my baby back to me) / Roly poly / Tweedle o'twill / Have I told you lately that I love you / Oklahoma hills / Pickin' a chicken / I've got just the thing for you / Mother of a honky tonk girl / Am I losing you / Don't tell me / I can't fly / Don't ask me why / Waiting for a train / Look behind you / Four walls / Honey, won't you please come home / Gods were angry with me / I know (And you know) / Please come home / Young hearts / Image of me / Two shadows on your window / Teardrops in my heart / Yours / I don't see me in your eyes anymore / I get the blues when it rains / I care no more / Final affair / You belong to me / My happiness / Everywhere you go (LP master) / Everywhere you go (Single master) / Blues in my heart / Need me / That's my desire / Anna Marie / Sea breeze / Blue without my baby / I love you more / Theme of love (I love to say I love you) / Wishful thinking / Charmaine / Mona Lisa / Marie / Goodnight Irene / Linda / Maria Elena / My Mary / Ramona / Margie / My Juanita / Sweet Sue, just you / Overnight / Blue boy / How long has it been / Teach me how to pray / Evening prayer / Suppertime / It is no secret / God be with you / Beautiful life / In the garden / Precious memories / Whispering hope / Flowers, the sunset, the trees / I'd like to be / Billy Bayou / Throw another log on the fire / Making believe / Till the end of the world / How's the world treating you / Someday (you'll want me to want you) / Just call me lonesome / Fool such as I / May the good lord bless and keep you / Dear hearts and gentle people / Satan can't hold me / Scarlet ribbons / If heartaches are the fashion / Home / Partners / I'm beginning to forget you / He'll have to go / In a mansion stands my love / After a while / Snowflake / But you love me Daddy / You'll never be mine again / Stand at your window / What would you do / Don't you want to be my girl (Poor little doll) / Dark moon / You're free to go / You're the only good thing (that's happened to me) / No one to cry to / OH how I miss you tonight / I'm getting better / Have I stayed away too long / Room full of roses / I was just walking out the door / We could / Take me in your arms and hold me / Almost / I missed me / I know one / Fool's paradise / Blizzard / Wreck of number nine / Letter edged in black / Tie that binds / Danny boy / Streets of Laredo / Rodger Young / Mighty everglades / It's nothing to me / That silver haired Daddy of mine / Wild rose / It hurts so much / Trouble in the amen corner / I'm waiting for ships that never come in / Farmer and the Lord / Gun / Spell of the Yukon / Shifting whispering sands / Seven days / Old tige / Annabel Lee / Why do I love you / Too many parties and too many pals / Men with broken hearts / Somewhere along the line / Missing angel / How can I write on paper (what I feel in my heart) / I never pass there anymore / Losing your love / Railroad bum / When two worlds collide / Fallen star / Most of the time / Blue side of lonesome / I won't forget you / Have you ever been lonely / There's always me / All dressed up and lonely / Welcome to my world / Be honest / I fall to pieces / Just walking in the rain / Blue skies / I'm a fool to care / It's no sin / Am I that easy to forget / Adios amigo / I'll fly away / Where do I go from here / This world is not my home / Oh gentle shepherd / Where we'll never grow old / I'd rathere have Jesus / Have thine own way / Night watch / Across the bridge / My cathedral / Take my hands precious Lord / We thank thee / I catch myself crying

/ (That's when I see the blues) In your pretty brown eyes / Where do I go to throw a picture away / Letter to my heart / Pride goes before a fall / Little ole you / I'm gonna change everything / Bolandse nooientjie / Ek verlang na jou / Die ou kalahari / Roses are red / Just out of reach / Memories are made of this / Stand in / After loving you / One that got away / I'd fight the world / When you are gone / Once upon a time / O little town of Bethlehem / Old Christmas card / Silent night / Mary's boy child / O come all ye faithful (Adeste fidelis) / White Christmas / Jingle bells / Merry Christmas polka / Blue Christmas / Senor Santa Claus / C-H-R-I-S-T-M-A-S / Daar doer in die bosveld / Ding dong / Draf maar aan ou ryperd / Die blonde matroos / JY is my liefling / Indie skadu van ou tafelberg / Sarie Marais / Geboorteplasie / Net 'n stille uurtjie / Nooientjie van die ou transvaal / Verre land / My blinde hart / Good morning self / Is this me / Teardrops on the rocks / Heartbreak in silhouette / Auf wiedersehen sweetheart / Golden memories and silver tears / Blue canadian rockies / White cliffs of Dover / Guilty / Hawaiian wedding song / True / Old Kalahari / I'm crying again / You are my love / Lonely music / There's a heartache following me / You kept me awake last night / Talking walls / Before I died / Little ole dime / Bottle take effect / World you left behind / I've enjoyed as much of this as I can stand / Don't let me cross over / From a Jack to a King / Silver bells / Born to be lucky / Kimberly Jim / Could I be falling in love / Search is ended / Strike it rich / I grew up / Diamonds in the sand / Stranger's just a friend / Roving gambler / Dolly with the dimpled knees / Nickel piece of candy / Love is no excuse / Look who's talking / Mexicali Rose / Carolina moon / Moon river / When I lost you / It's only a paper moon / Roses / There's a new moon over my shoulder / One dozen roses / Moonlight and roses / What's in it for me / Rosa Rio / Oh what it seemed to be / I guess I'm crazy / Angels dont' lie / Not until the next time / I won't come in while he's there / This is it / Make the world go away / There's that smile again / You'll never know / Is it really you / I can't stop loving you / In the misty moonlight / Missing you / Maureen / Distant drums / Storm / Trying to forget / I heard my heart break last night / Nobody's fool / Gypsy feet / Writing's on the wall / I love you because / It's nothing to me / Jim Reeves medley / When did you leave Heaven / Christmas alone / Ence upon a time / Jesus is calling / Wagon load of love / Wagon load of love / I'll tell the world I love you / Girl I left behind / Chittlin' blues / Dissatisfied / Penny for your thoughts / Near the cross / Humpty Dumpty heart / Naughty Angeline / Got you on my mind / Tjuana / Yonder comes a sucker / Mary Carter paint / Mary Carter paint / Mary Carter paint / Mary Carter paint / I'm glad you're better / Please forgive / Right words / You darling you / One little Rose / I'd rather not know / Ballad of 96 / Lonesome waltz / Your wedding / Read this letter / I let the world pass me by / Send me back my love / My hands are clean / Crying in my sleep / Deep dark water / Before you came along / Crying is my favourite mood / He will / Make me wonderful in her eyes / Beyond the clouds
BCD 15656 / Jul '94 / Bear Family

☐ YOUR OLD LOVE LETTERS
Have I told you lately that I love you / Just call me lonesome / How's the world treating you / If heartaches are the fashion / Home / Dear hearts and gentle people / I'm beginning to forget you / Roly poly / Wind up / Sweet evening breeze / Your old love letters / Till the end of the world / Making believe / Oklahoma blues / Highway to nowhere / If you were mine / Everywhere you go / I love you more / I've lived a lot in my time
GRF 199 / Jan '93 / Tring

Reeves, Martha

☐ DANCING IN THE STREET
Dancing in the street / Nowhere to run / In the midnight hour / It's the same old song / Come see about mee / I want you back / Jimmy mack / Heatwave / I say a little prayer / Gotta see Jane / Spooky / Get ready / I heard it through the grapevine
305442 / Oct '96 / Hallmark

☐ DANCING IN THE STREETS (Reeves, Martha & The Vandellas)
Dancing in the street / Nowhere to run / Heatwave / I'm ready for love / Third finger left hand / Jimmy Mack / Motoring / You've been in love too long / My baby loves me / I gotta let you go / Come and get these memories / Love like yours (Don't come knocking everyday) / Forget me not / Quicksand
5302302 / Jan '92 / Motown

☐ MARTHA REEVES
Wild night / You've got me for company / Facsimile / Ain't that peculiar / Dixie highway / Power of love / My man (you changed my tune) / Sweet misery / I've got to use my imagination / Storm in my soul / Many rivers to cross
SEECD 486 / Sep '97 / See For Miles

☐ MOTOWN EARLY CLASSICS (Reeves, Martha & The Vandellas)
Dancing in the street / Third finger, left hand / Jimmy Mack / I'll have to let him go / There he is (at my door) / Hitch hike / Moments (to remember) / Heatwave / Hello stranger / In my lonely room / Wait till my Bobby gets home / Jerk / Dance party / Motoring / Dancing slow / Wild one / Nowhere to run / Never leave your baby's side
5521172 / Jul '96 / Spectrum

☐ ULTIMATE COLLECTION (Reeves, Martha & The Vandellas)
5308582 / 10 Aug '98 / Motown

☐ WE MEET AGAIN/GOTTA KEEP MOVING
Free again / You're like sunshine / I feel like magic / One line from every love song / Love don't come no stranger / What are you doing the rest of your life / Dedicated to be your woman / Special to me / Skating in the streets / That's what I want / Really like your rap / Gotta keep moving / Then you came / If it wasn't for my baby
CDSEWD 083 / Jul '93 / Southbound

Reeves, Reuben

☐ COMPLETE VOCALIONS 1928-1933, THE
Dixie stomp / Drifting and dreaming / River blues / Parson blues / Papa skag stomp / Bugle call blues / Low down rhythm / Gotta feelin' for you / Blue sweets / Texas special blues / Black and blue / Moanin' low / Head low / Have you ever felt that way / Do I know what I'm doing / Shoo shoo boogie boo / Bigger and better than ever / Yellow five / Zuddan / MazeiScrews nuts and bolts
CBC 1039 / Sep '97 / Timeless Historical

☐ REUBEN REEVES & OMER SIMEON 1929-1933 (Reeves, Reuben 'River' & Omer Simeon)
JPCD 1516 / May '95 / Jazz Perspectives

Reeves, Vic

☐ I WILL CURE YOU
Theme tune / Dizzy / I remember punk rock / Black night / Meals on wheels / Oh mr songwriter / Born free / Sing hi the-new romantic / Empty kennel / Summer of '75 / Oh mr hairdresser / Abide with me
IMCD 242 / Mar '97 / Island

Reflection

☐ ERROMOMOUS WORLD
Night music in the sculptured air / Simple end to the beginning / Cold wind in the bright sun / Cold wind in a bright sun / Transparent / Errornormous bit / Flowers for the moon / Flowers for the moonlight / Journey around the unnamed border / Wall with paintings / Water/Blind/exhibition / Vertigo / Spiral bits / Many colours / Another sun / Beginning
CLR 432CD / Jul '97 / Clear

☐ MORERRORONUS WORLD, THE
Water/blind/exhibition / Lost tapes in Africa loops / Wall with paintings / Spiral bits / Transparent / Cube loop / Transparent / Another sun / Spiral bits
CLR 436CD / 10 Nov '97 / Clear

Refo:Mation

☐ PHARMAKOI/DISTANCE CRUNCHING HONCHOS
REFO 001 / Sep '97 / Phantom

Refrigerator

☐ ANCHORS OF BLOOD
COMM 040CD / Dec '96 / Communion

☐ REFRIGERATOR
SHR 101CD / 20 Oct '97 / Shrimper

Refugee

☐ REFUGEE
SRMC 6024 / Oct '97 / Siwan

Refused

☐ EVERLASTING
EVRCD 033 / Mar '97 / Equal Vision

☐ SHAPE OF PUNK TO COME, THE
BHR 071CD / 2 Mar '98 / Burning Heart

☐ SONGS TO FAN THE FLAMES...
BHR 061CD / 29 Sep '97 / Burning Heart

☐ THIS ALBUM CONTAINS OLD SONGS VOL.1
BHR 063CD / 29 Sep '97 / Burning Heart

☐ THIS ALBUM CONTAINS OLD SONGS VOL.2
BHR 064CD / 29 Sep '97 / Burning Heart

☐ THIS IS THE NEW DEAL
BHR 002CD / Oct '94 / Burning Heart

☐ THIS JUST MIGHT BE...
WB 3116CD / Jan '95 / We Bite
BHR 062CD / 29 Sep '97 / Burning Heart

Regan Youth

☐ REGAN YOUTH
NRA 13CD / Apr '92 / New Red Archives

Regenerator

☐ SOULSEEKER
SPV 08561542 / Dec '97 / SPV

Regenesis

☐ LIVE
Watchers of the skies / Carpet crawlers / I know what I like / Supper's ready / In the cage / Broadway melody of 1974 / Fly on a windshield / Lamb lies down on broadway
MYSCD 112 / Jul '97 / Mystic

Reggio, Felice

☐ I REMEMBER CHET
CD 214W1112 / Mar '92 / Philology

Regina, Elis

☐ BOSSA MAIOR
ELENCO 826621CD / Apr '97 / Rare Brazil

☐ FASCINACAO (The Best Of Elis Regina)
Menino das laranjas / Upa neguinho / Madalena / Lapinha / Corrida de jangada / Canto de Ossanha / Como nossos pais / O mestre sala dos mares / Vou deitar e rolar / O morro nao tem vez / Feio nao e bonito / Samba do carioca / Esse mundo a meu / Felicidade / Samba de negro / Vou andar por ai / Acender as velas / A voz de morro / O morro nao tem vez / Arrastao / Romaria / Mucuripe / Caso no campo / Fascinacao / Me dexias louca / Atras de porta / Cartomante / Dois pra la, drois pra ca / O rancho da goiabada
8368442 / Mar '94 / Verve

☐ MAY WIND
Vento de Maio / Sai dessa / Tiro ao alvaro / So deus quem sabe / O que foi feito devera / Nova estacao / Calcanhar de Aquiles / Outro cais / Rebento / O trem azul / O medo de amar...o medo de ser livre / Se eu quiser falar com deus / Aprendendo jogar
724382350323 / 19 Jan '98 / Hemisphere

Regina Regina

☐ REGINA REGINA
More than I wanted to know / Big bad broken heart / Asking for the moon / Far cry from him / Ticket out of Kansas / Border town road / I should be laughing / Right plan, wrong man / Before I know about you / She'll let that telephone ring
74321409712 / Apr '97 / Giant

Regis

☐ DELIVERED INTO HANDS OF INDIFFERENCE
DNCD 005 / 22 Jun '98 / Downwards

☐ GYMNASTICS
DNCD 002 / Jan '97 / Downwards

Regredior

☐ FORBIDDEN TEARS
SHR 010CD / Aug '95 / Shiver

Regulator Watts

☐ AESTHETICS OF NO-DRAG
DIS 1195CD / 22 Sep '97 / Dischord

☐ MERCURY
SD 10 / 24 Feb '98 / Slowdime/Dischord

Regulators

☐ CONSIDER IT DONE
STINGCD 040 / Jul '97 / Blue Sting

Regurgitator

☐ TU PLANG KON UAUK
3984203012 / 3 Nov '97 / Coalition

Rehberg & Bauer

☐ FABT
TO 32 / 12 Jan '98 / Touch

Rehmi, T.J.

☐ MIND FILTER
Mind filter / Raagmania / Fusionist / Who killed bhangra / Hit 'n' bliss / Elastic / Exploration 1995 / Prisoners of freedom / Skrutinizer / Destination / Is it legal / Return / Whisper the meaning / Second filter
NRCD 1070 / 25 May '98 / Nation

Rei, Panta

☐ DANCE CONTINUES, THE
DRCD 185 / Jan '88 / Dragon

Reich, Max

☐ FEW HOURS LEFT
MILL 058CD / 15 Jun '98 / Millenium

☐ SWEDISH WORKOUT
MILL 044CD / Mar '97 / Millenium

Reich, Steve

☐ CAVE, THE
7559791012 / Mar '96 / Nonesuch

☐ CITY LIFE (Reich, Steve Ensemble)
Proverb / Nagoya marimbas / City life
7559794302 / Oct '96 / Nonesuch

☐ DESERT MUSIC, THE
Desert music movements 1-5
9791012 / '86 / Nonesuch

☐ DESERT MUSIC/DIFFERENT TRAINS/ SIX MARIMBAS/TEHILLIM (4CD Set)
7559793762 / Jan '95 / Nonesuch

☐ DIFFERENT TRAINS (Reich, Steve & The Kronos Quartet)
Different trains / Electric counterpoint
9791762 / Jun '89 / Nonesuch

☐ DRUMMING
Part 1 / Part 2 / Part 3 / Part 4
9191702 / Mar '88 / Nonesuch

☐ EARLY WORKS
Come out 1966 / Piano phrase / Clapping music / It's gonna rain
7559791692 / Jan '95 / Nonesuch

☐ EIGHT LINES FOUR ORGANS
7559794812 / 9 Feb '98 / Nonesuch

☐ FOUR ORGANS - PHASE PATTERNS
642090MAN90 / Nov '94 / Mantra

☐ FOUR SECTIONS, THE (& The Music For Mallet Instruments Voices And Organ) (Reich, Steve & The London Symphony Orchestra)
7559792202 / Jan '98 / Nonesuch

☐ MUSIC FOR 18 MUSICIANS
Pulse
7559794482 / 20 Apr '98 / Nonesuch

☐ OCTET MUSIC FOR A LARGE ENSEMBLE
Music for a large ensemble / Violin phase / Octet
8272872 / '85 / ECM

☐ SIX MARIMBAS
Sextet / Six marimbas
9791382 / Jan '87 / Nonesuch

☐ TEHILLIM
Parts I and II / Parts III and IV
8274112 / '86 / ECM

☐ WORKS 1965-1995 (10CD Set)
7559794512 / Jun '97 / Erato

Reicha, Anton

☐ ANTON REICHA
999 0612 / Jul '92 / CPO

Reichel, Hans

☐ RETURN OF ONKEL BOSKOPP, THE (Reichel, Hans & Eroc)
REP 4688 / Oct '97 / Repertoire

Reichman, Joe

☐ JOE REICHMAN ORCHESTRA 1941-1942
CCD 84 / Sep '97 / Circle

Reid, Alan

☐ SUNLIT EYE, THE
Iolair na mara (The sea eagle) / Sleeping warrior / Whit can a lassie dae / Just a boy / Million dollar sweetie/Feiger's warning / Rantin' rovin' robin / Five bridges to cross / Medley / Love no more / Wilton street dawdle/Norman MacAskill of Lochinver / Mary Morison
COMD 2072 / Feb '98 / Temple

Reid, Duke

☐ BA BA BOOM (Various Artists)
Ba ba boom: *Jamaicans* / Only a smile: *Paragons* / Do it right: *Three Tops* / Carry go bring come: *Hinds, Justin & The Dominoes* / I'm in the mood for love: *Techniques* / Willow tree: *Ellis, Alton* / My best girl: *Paragons* / Sweet soul music: *Gladiators* / Breaking up: *Ellis, Alton* / Hopeful village: *Tennors* / Love up kiss up: *Termites* / Botheration: *Hinds, Justin & The Dominoes* / I'll be lonely: *Holt, John & Joya Landis* / Midnight confession: *Dillon, Phyllis* / Weather report: *Tennors* / Passion love: *Melodians*
CDTRL 265 / Nov '94 / Trojan

☐ DUKE REID'S BOOM SHAKA LAKA (Various Artists)
RNCD 2095 / Mar '95 / Rhino

☐ DUKE REID'S KINGS OF SKA (Various Artists)
RNCD 2098 / Mar '95 / Rhino

☐ DUKE REID'S ROCKING STEADY (Various Artists)
RNCD 2100 / Mar '95 / Rhino

☐ DUKE REID'S TREASURE ISLE (Various Artists)
CDHB 095/096 / Aug '92 / Heartbeat

☐ FROM BOOGIE TO NYAMBINGHI
LG 21082 / Jun '93 / Lagoon

☐ IT'S ROCKIN' TIME
CDTRL 279 / Mar '92 / Trojan

☐ JAMAICAN BEAT
LG 21038 / Jul '93 / Lagoon

☐ MIDNIGHT CONFESSION
Midnight confession / Midnight version / Let's build our dream / If you see jane / Darling please return / Don't touch me tomato / Tomato version / Give me your love / My desire / When the lights are low / Loving pauper / Those guys / Moonwalk / Remember that sunday / Working kind
LG 21084 / Aug '93 / Lagoon

☐ TRIBUTES TO SKATALITES
James bond / Yellow basket / River to the bank / Inez / Musical communion / Lucky seven / Latin goes ska / Don de lion / Independent anniversary ska / Eastern standard time / Garden of love / Don's memorial / Alipang / Teenage ska
LG 21015 / Jun '93 / Lagoon

☐ VERSION AFFAIR VOL.1
Peace and love / Peace and love / True true true / True true true / I see your face / I see your face / Buck and the preacher / Queen majesty / My voice is insured / Love is a treasure / Love is a treasure / Moonlight lover / Wake up jamaica / Moonlight groover / Judgement day / Judgement day / Picture on the wall / Picture on the wall
LG 21062 / Nov '92 / Lagoon

☐ VERSION AFFAIR VOL.2
Musical alphabet / Musical alphabet / Do it right / Do it right / Love is not a gamble / Love is not a gamble / You don't care / Great woogie / Don on bond street / Mother's tender care / Love I tender / Carry go bring home / For our desire / My girl / My girl / My girl / Wear you to the ball / Ball
LG 21066 / Mar '93 / Lagoon

Reid, Irene

☐ MILLION DOLLAR SECRET
What a difference a day makes / Here's to life / What I did for love / Big fat daddy / One eyed man / Didn't we / Million dollar secret / This bitter Earth
SAVCD 2007 / Jan '98 / Savant

Reid, Jim

☐ FREEWHEELING NOW (Reid, Jim & John Huband)
Hey Donald / Whar the dichty rins / Queer fowk / Cruachan Ben / O Gin I were a Baron's heir / Great storm is over / Music on his mind / Back in Scotland / Balaena / An t-eilean muileach / Lassie o' the morning / Moothie man / Oh dear me / Scattered / There's no indispensable man / Auld beech tree / Freewheeling now
SPRCD 1030 / Dec '93 / Springthyme

☐ I SAW THE WILD GEESE FLEE
Wild geese/Norland wind / Lassie wi the yellow coatie / Shearin's no for you / Stobbie parliament picnic / Upon the moss o' Burreldale / Up the Noran water / Bogie's Bonnie Belle / Flower of Northumberland / Foundry bar / Busk busk bonnie lassie / Spark among the heather / Rowan tree / Bogheid / Vinney den / Rohallion
SPRCD 1015 / Feb '97 / Springthyme

Reid, Jimmy

☐ FOREVER LOVED
1046770742 / 31 Mar '98 / Discovery

Reid, Junior

☐ BOOM SHACK A LACK
Cross over the border / Mother move / Big timer / Row your boat / There will be no darkness / Boom shak-a-lak / Drink out me royalty / Strange things / Sitting in the park / False rumours
GRELCD 78 / Sep '89 / Greensleeves

☐ DOUBLE TOP (Reid, Junior & Cornell Campbell)
TWCD 1033 / Jun '94 / Tamoki Wambesi

☐ JUNIOR REID & THE BLOODS (Reid, Junior & The Bloods)
RASCD 3154 / Jul '95 / Ras

☐ ONE BLOOD
One blood / Nuh so / Who done it / When it shows / Searching for better / Married life / Eleanor Rigby / Gruppie Diana / Sound / Dominant
JRCD 1 / Feb '90 / Big Life

☐ RAS PORTRAITS
All fruits ripe / Grammy / Rasta world dance / Anthem / Cry now / Listen to the voices / Dance na keep again / Gun court / Showers of blessing / Dread locks in the White House / Not a one man thing
RAS 3327 / Jun '97 / Ras

☐ TRUE WORLD ORDER
JRCD 1007 / 19 Jan '98 / JR

☐ VISA
Me have the view / Mr. Talkabout / Gun court / Him a touch it again / Friend enemy / Free that little tree / It's not a one man thing / Dreadlocks in the White House / No loafting / Cry now / Hospital, Cemetary or Jail / All fruits ripe / Youth man / Dance nah keep
GRELCD 194 / Sep '93 / Greensleeves

Reid, Loretto

☐ CELTIC METTLE (Reid, Loretto & Brian Taheny)
Plantxy Cowan / Youngest daughter / Fleur de Quebec / Brian's favourite / Rakish Paddy / Planxty Robinson / Celtic mettle / Turlough Carolan's tribute / Dill pickle rag / Canuck set / Wedding promise / Johnny's dream / That's lovely, that is / Nios mo na aisling / Banks / Mason's apron / Prayer for the children / Strum 301
IRCD 049 / May '97 / Iona

Reid, Lou

☐ UNTITLED
REB 1728CD / Apr '96 / Rebel

☐ WHEN IT RAINS
Ain't it funny / Cry cry darlin' / Hand of the higher power / You better hold onto your heart / Red, white and blue / Callin' your name / Mom's old picture book / One track man / Absence makes the heart grow fonder / First step to heaven / Nobody's loves like mine
SHCD 3788 / Jul '91 / Sugar Hill

Reid, Norris

☐ GIVE YAH THE PRAISES
CORP 013 / 8 Dec '97 / Rockers International

Reid, Sandra

☐ LA TRAVERSEE
LYRCD 7432 / Nov '97 / Lyrichord

Reid, Steve

☐ MYSTERIES (Reid, Steve Bamboo Forest)
Mysteries / Sunrise celebration / Prelude to Mr. Mystery / Mr. Mystery / Soul mates / Hideaway of love / Ancient profiles / Spirit path / Pyramid of the sun / Look to the sky / Atlantis / City of gold / Guardian of the falls
CD 83415 / Aug '97 / Telarc Jazz

☐ WATER SIGN
Warm Summer rain / Dolphin ride / Tell til tease / Treasures of the heart / Waterfall / Special thanks / Peruvian Princess / Aruba moon / Candle dance / Secret of the Himalayas / Water sign
CD 83396 / Sep '96 / Telarc Jazz

Reid, Terry

☐ BANG BANG YOU'RE
Bang bang (my baby shot me down) / Tinker taylor / Erica / Without expression / Sweater / Something's gotten hold of my heart / Season of the witch / Writing on the wall / Summertime blues / When I get home / Loving time
BGOCD 164 / Dec '92 / Beat Goes On

☐ ROGUE WAVES
Ain't no shadow / Baby I love you / Stop and think it over / Rogue wave / Walk away Renee / Believe in the magic / Then I kissed her / Bowangi / All I have to do is dream
BGOCD 140 / Apr '92 / Beat Goes On

☐ SEED OF MEMORY
Faith to arise / Seed of memory / Brave awakening / To be treated right / Ooh baby (makes me feels so young) / Way you walk / Frame / Fooling you
EDCD 425 / May '95 / Edsel

☐ TERRY REID
Superlungs my supergirl / Silver white light / July / Marking time / Stay with me baby / Highway 61 revisited/Friends / May fly / Speak now or forever hold your peace / Rich kids blues / Hand don't fit the glove / This time / Better by far / Fire's alive
BGOCD 168 / Dec '92 / Beat Goes On

Reiersrud, Knut

☐ HIMMELSKIP (Reiersrud, Knut & Iver Kleive)
FX 163 / Aug '96 / Kirkelig Kultuverksted

☐ TRAMP
FX 129CD / Apr '95 / Kirkelig Kultuverksted

Reign

☐ CONTROL OVER ANGER
False horizon / Last but one / End it all / I abstain / I think therefore I am / I die you die / System collapse / Reason for everything
CDBLEED 21 / 11 May '98 / Bleeding Hearts

Reign Ghost

☐ REIGN GHOST
LE 1004 / 16 Feb '98 / Laser's Edge

Reigndance

☐ PROBLEM FACTORY
Second time around / Temporarily an eternity / No room / Why divide / I'd tell you / Lazybones / You're wrong / Things will be different now / Luxury / Out of the question / Open arms / Better than I
RTD 15717602 / Jun '94 / World Service

Reijseger, Ernst

☐ COLLA PARTE
9100122 / Dec '97 / Winter & Winter

Reilly, Paddy

☐ 16 EMERALD CLASSICS VOL.1
DOCDX 9020 / Jun '96 / Dolphin

☐ 16 EMERALD CLASSICS VOL.2
DOCDX 9021 / Aug '96 / Dolphin

☐ 20 GOLDEN IRISH BALLADS
Fields of Athenry / Bunch of thyme / Spancil hill / Galway races / Lark in the morning / Peggy Gordon / Joe Hill / Four green fields / Come out ye black and tans / Cliffs of Dooneen / Hills of Kerry / Arthur McBride / Matt Hyland / Galtee Mountain boy / Bunclody / Crack was ninety in the Isle Of Man / Sweet Carnlough Bay / Jim Larkin / Nation once again
DOCDX 9006 / May '96 / Dolphin

☐ FIELDS OF ATHENRY
Town I loved so well / Farewell to Nova Scotia / Galtee mountain boy / Farewell to the Rhonda / John O'Dreams / Scorn not his simplicity / Crack was ninety in the Isle of Man / Dancing at Whitsun / Mulligan and me / Jim Larkin / Bunch of thyme
DOCDX 9002 / Jun '96 / Dolphin

☐ PADDY REILLY
Flight of the Earls / Black Velvet Band / Pat Murphy's meadow / Little grey home in the West / Star of County Down / Grace / Rose of Mooncoin / Emigrant's letter / Slievenamon / Wild rover / Fields of Athenry / Dublin minstrel / Heaven around Galway bay / Long before your time
KCD 480 / Jan '97 / Celtic Collections

☐ PADDY REILLY'S GREATEST HITS LIVE
CDIRISH 015 / Apr '97 / Outlet

Reilly, Robert

☐ TEMPTATION
Half a chance / Gone too long / Praying for rain / Long distance / North wind / Temptation / Towns like mine / Save me / After all these years / All I want
SCARTCD 3 / Jul '90 / Scarlett Recordings

Reilly, Tommy

☐ THANKS FOR THE MEMORY (Reilly, Tommy & James Moody)
CHAN 8645 / Oct '88 / Chandos

Reimer, Jan

☐ POINT OF NO RETURN, THE
BEST 1020CD / Nov '93 / Acoustic Music

Rein Sanction

☐ MARIPOSA
SP 43/208CD / Sep '92 / Sub Pop

Reinders, Ge

☐ AS'T D'R OP AAN KUMP
MWCD 1005 / Aug '94 / Music & Words

Reinhardt, Babik

☐ ALL LOVE
400012 / Aug '94 / Melodie

☐ LIVE
CDSW 8431 / Sep '91 / DRG

☐ LIVE
400032 / Aug '94 / Melodie

☐ VIBRATION
400452 / Sep '95 / Melodie

Reinhardt, Django

☐ ART OF DJANGO, THE/THE UNFORGETTABLE
Mystery Pacific / Little love, a little kiss / Running wild / Body and soul / Hot lips / Solitude / When day is gone / Tears / Rose room / Sheikh of Araby / Liebestraum no. 3 / Exactly like you / Miss Annabelle Lee / Ain't misbehavin' / Sweet Georgia Brown / Minor swing / Double scotch / Artillerie Lourde / St. James Infirmary / C Jam blues / Honeysuckle Rose / Dream of you / Begin the beguine / How high the moon / Nuages / I can't get started (with you) / I can't give you anything but love / Manoir de mes reves
BGOCD 198 / Jul '93 / Beat Goes On

☐ ATC BIG BAND LIVE 1945
JCD 628 / Mar '87 / Jass

☐ AUDIO ARCHIVE
Dinah / Oh lady be good / Tiger rag / I saw stars / Avalon / Smoke rings / I've found a new baby / Djangology / Crazy rhythm / Lily belle May June / Sweet Sue, just you / Confessin' / Continental / Sheikh of Araby / Blue drag / Swanee river / Ton doux sourire / Chasing shadows / I've had my moments / Some of these days
CDAA 024 / Oct '91 / Tring

☐ BEST OF DJANGO REINHARDT, THE
Limehouse blues / When day is done / St. Louis blues / Minor swing / My serenade / (I'll be glad when you're dead) you rascal you / Montimartre / I'll see you in my dreams / Naguine / Nuages / Blues Clair / Place de Brouckere / Manoir des mes reves / Django's tiger / Ol' man river / Diminishing / Oh lady be good / To each his own symphony
CDP 8371382 / Apr '96 / Blue Note

☐ BRUSSELS AND PARIS
Porto cabello / Duke and Dukie / Songs d'automne / Babik / Del Salle / Just one of those things / Double whiskey / Dream of you / Impromptu / Vamp / Keep cool / Fleche d'or / Troublant bolero / Nuits de Saint Germain des pres / Crazy rhythm / Anouman / DR Blues / Fine and Dandy / Le soir / Chez moi / I cover the waterfront / Deccaphonie
DRGCD 8473 / Jul '96 / DRG

☐ CLASSICS 1934-1935
CLASSICS 703 / Jul '93 / Classics

☐ CLASSICS 1935
CLASSICS 727 / Dec '93 / Classics

☐ CLASSICS 1935-1936
CLASSICS 739 / Feb '94 / Classics

☐ CLASSICS 1937 VOL.1
CLASSICS 748 / Aug '94 / Classics

☐ CLASSICS 1937 VOL.2
CLASSICS 762 / Jun '94 / Classics

☐ CLASSICS 1937-1939
CLASSICS 777 / Mar '95 / Classics

☐ CLASSICS 1938-1939
CLASSICS 793 / Jan '95 / Classics

☐ CLASSICS 1939-1940
CLASSICS 813 / May '95 / Classics

☐ CLASSICS 1940-1941
CLASSICS 852 / Feb '96 / Classics

☐ CLASSICS 1941-1942
CLASSICS 877 / Apr '96 / Classics

☐ CLASSICS 1942-1943
CLASSICS 905 / Nov '96 / Classics

☐ CLASSICS 1944-1946
CLASSICS 945 / 21 Aug '97 / Classics

☐ COMPLETE DJANGO REINHARDT VOL.2 1934-1935, THE (2CD Set)
FA 302 / Jul '96 / Fremeaux

☐ COMPLETE DJANGO REINHARDT VOL.3, THE (2CD Set)
FA 303 / Oct '96 / Fremeaux

☐ COMPLETE DJANGO REINHARDT VOL.4 1935-1936, THE (2CD Set)
FA 304 / Nov '96 / Fremeaux

☐ COMPLETE DJANGO REINHARDT VOL.5 1936-1937, THE (2CD Set)
FA 305 / Feb '97 / Fremeaux

☐ COMPLETE DJANGO REINHARDT VOL.6 1937, THE (2CD Set)
FA 306 / Jun '97 / Fremeaux

☐ COMPLETE DJANGO REINHARDT VOL.7 1937-1938, THE (2CD Set)
Serenade for a wealthy widow: *Warlop, Michel & Orchestra* / Taj mahal: *Warlop, Michel & Orchestra* / Organ grinder swing: *Warlop, Michel & Orchestra* / You rascal you / Solo de violon: *Warlop, Michel* / Christmas swing: *Warlop, Michel* / Stephen's blues: *Grappelli, Stephane* / Sugar: *Grappelli, Stephane* / Sweet Georgia Brown / Tea for two / Blues: *Brun, Phillippe & His Swing Band* / Easy goin: *Brun, Phillippe & His Swing Band* / College stomp: *Brun, Phillippe & His Swing Band* / Harlem swing: *Brun, Phillippe & His Swing Band* / It had to be you: *Brun, Phillippe* / Sweet sur: *Warlop, Michel* / 3 fragments: *Quintette Du Hot Club De France* / Les salade d'oncle France: *Quintette Du Hot Club De France* / Ric et pussy: *Quintette Du Hot Club De France* / Honeysuckle rose: *Quintette Du Hot Club De France* / Night and day: *Quintette Du Hot Club De France* / My sweet: *Quintette Du Hot Club De France* / Souvenirs: *Quintette Du Hot Club De France* / Daphne: *Quintette Du Hot Club De France* / Black and white: *Quintette Du Hot Club De France* / Stompin' at Decca: *Quintette Du Hot Club De France* / J'attendrai: *Grappelli, Stephane* / I fiif I had you: *Grappelli, Stephane* / Nocturne.: *Grappelli, Stephane* / Un soirerre en chantant: *Grappelli, Stephane* / Sifflez en travaillant: *Grappelli, Stephane* / I'm coming Virginia: *Carter, Benny & His Orchestra* / Farewell blues: *Carter, Benny & His Orchestra* / Blue light blues: *Carter, Benny & His Orchestra* / Bouncin' around: *Brun, Phillippe & His Swing Band* / Ridin' along the Moscowa: *Brun, Phillippe & His Swing Band* / Gotta date in Louisiana: *Brun, Phillippe & His Swing Band* / Gabriel swing: *Brun, Phillippe & His Swing Band* / Doin' the new low-down: *Brun, Phillippe & His Swing Band* / Djangology: *Brun, Phillippe & His Swing Band*
FA 307 / Nov '97 / Fremeaux

☐ COMPLETE DJANGO REINHARDT VOL.8 1938-1939, THE (2CD Set)
FA 308 / 24 Apr '98 / Fremeaux

☐ CRAZY RHYTHM
Crazy rhythm 1937 / Dinah / Tiger rag / Smoke rings / I've found a new baby / Djangology / After you've gone / Limehouse blues / Nagasaki / Georgia on my mind / Honeysuckle Rose / Out of nowhere / Sweet Georgia Brown / Bugle call rag / Between the devil and the deep blue sea / I got rhythm / Japanese sandman / St. Louis blues / Oh lady be good / Crazy rhythm 1935
CD 6048 / Oct '96 / Music

☐ DEFINITIVE DJANGO REINHARDT VOL.1 (First Original Hot Club Recordings 1934-1935)
I saw stars / I'm confessin' (that I love you) / Dinah / Tiger rag / Oh lady be good / I saw stars / Lily belle may june / Sweet sue, just you / I'm confessin' (that I love you) / Continental / Blue drag / Swanee river / Sunshine of your smile / Ultrafox / Avalon / Smoke rings / Clouds / Believe it, beloved / I've found a new baby / St. louis blues / Crazy rhythm / Sheik of araby / Chasing shadows / I've had my moments / Some of these days / Djangology
JSPCD 341 / Feb '93 / JSP

☐ **DEFINITIVE DJANGO REINHARDT VOL.2 (London Decca Recordings 1938-1939)**
Honeysuckle rose / Sweet Georgia Brown / Night and day / My sweet / Souvenirs / Daphne / Black and white / Stompin' at the Decca / Tornerai / If I had you / It had to be you / Nocturne / Flat foot floogie / Lambeth walk / Why shouldn't I / I've got my love to keep me warm / Please be kind / Louise / Improvisation no.2 / Undecided / HCQ strut / Don't worry 'bout me / Man I love
JSPCD 342 / Jan '94 / JSP

☐ **DEFINITIVE DJANGO REINHARDT VOL.3**
Billets doux / Swing from Paris / Them there eyes / Three little words / Appel direct / Hungaria / Jeepers creepers / Swing '39 / Japanese sandman / I wonder were my baby is tonight / Tea for two / My melancholy baby / Time on my hands / Twelfth year
JSPCD 343 / Apr '94 / JSP

☐ **DEFINITIVE DJANGO REINHARDT VOL.4**
JSPCD 344 / Oct '94 / JSP

☐ **DJANGO**
CDHD 234 / Feb '97 / Happy Days

☐ **DJANGO AND HIS AMERICAN FRIENDS VOL.1 & 2**
Avalon / Rosetta / Honeysuckle rose / Sweet Georgia Brown / I got rhythm / Japanese sandman / I ain't got nobody / Bill Coleman blues / I'm coming Virginia / Montmartre / I know that you know me / What a difference a day makes / Stardust / Crazy rhythm / Bugle call rag / Sweet Sue, just you / Eddie's blues / Baby, won't you please come home / Somebody loves me / Farewell blues / Low cotton / Solid old man / Object of my affection / Out of nowhere / Between the devil and the deep blue sea / Hangin' around Boulden / Big Boy Blues / I can't believe that you're in love with me / Blue light blues / Finesse
BGOCD 249 / Dec '94 / Beat Goes On

☐ **DJANGO REINHARDT**
Chicago / Shine / Bugle call rag / I got rhythm / Honeysuckle rose / Crazy rhythm / Exactly like you / Charleston / You're driving me crazy / Nuages / Rose room / Swing guitars / I know that you know / Nagasaki / Japanese sandman / Ain't misbehavin' / Minor swing / Georgia on my mind / Sweet Georgia Brown / Limehouse blues / After you've gone
399533 / Jun '97 / Koch Presents

☐ **DJANGO REINHARDT & HIS AMERICAN SWING BAND**
JASSCD 628 / Oct '92 / Jass

☐ **DJANGO REINHARDT 1935**
OJCCD 772 / Dec '93 / Original Jazz Classics

☐ **DJANGO REINHARDT 1935-1939**
CD 14555 / Jul '94 / Jazz Portraits

☐ **DJANGO REINHARDT 1935-1939**
Crazy rhythm / Honeysuckle rose / Out of nowhere / Sweet georgia brown / Between the devil and the deep blue sea / Bugle call rag / I got rhythm / Japanese sandman / Farewell blues / I know that you know / Finesse (night wind) / Blue light blues / I'm coming virginia / Sweet sue / Solid old man / Hangin' around boudon / Avalon / What a difference a day made
CD 56061 / Jul '95 / Jazz Roots

☐ **DJANGO REINHARDT 1938-1939**
JSP 343 / Jun '94 / JSP

☐ **DJANGO REINHARDT AND FRIENDS**
(I'll be glad when you're dead) you rascal you / Stephen's blues / Sugar / Sweet Georgia Brown / Tea for two / Younger generation / I'll see you in my dreams / Echoes of Spain / Naguine / What a difference a day makes / Tears / Limehouse blues / Daphne / At Jimmy's bar / Rosetta / Nuages / Pour vous (exactly like you) / Vendredi 13 / Petits mesonges (little white lies) / Stardust / Sweet Sue, just you / Swing de Paris
PASTCD 9792 / Jun '92 / Flapper

☐ **DJANGO REINHARDT ET SON QUINTETTE DU HOT CLUB DE FRANCE (Quintette Du Hot Club De France)**
403222 / Nov '93 / Musidisc

☐ **DJANGO REINHARDT PLAYS THE GREAT STANDARDS**
You're driving me crazy / Solitude / Ain't misbehavin' / Shine / Exactly like you / Body and soul / Nagasaki / When day is done / Running wild / Crazy rhythm / Honeysuckle rose / Out of nowhere / St. Louis blues / Georgia on my mind / Oh lady be good / After you've gone / Limehouse blues / Sweet Georgia Brown / Begin the beguine / I can't give you anything but love / Sweet Sue / All of me
RAJCD 808 / 9 Mar '98 / Empress

☐ **DJANGO REINHARDT/DJANGO IN ROME**
Charleston / Chicago / You're driving me crazy / In a sentimental mood / I've found a new baby / Alabamy bound / Lady be good / Minor swing / Viper's dream / Swingin' with Django / Paramount stomp / Bouncin' around / St. Louis blues / Swing guitar / Micro / Stormy weather / Blue skies / Man I love / Peanut vendor / It might as well be spring / Micro / Danse Norvegienne / Dinette / Reverie / Place De Brouckere / Black night / Boogie woogie
BGOCD 366 / 15 Jun '98 / Beat Goes On

☐ **DJANGO REINHARDT/STEPHANE GRAPPELLI (Reinhardt, Django & Stephane Grappelli)**
Oriental shuffle / Shine / Sweet chorus / In the still of the night / Exactly like you / I'se a muggin' / I can't give you anything but love / After you've gone / Limehouse blues / Nagasaki / Swing guitars / You're driving me crazy / Tears / Solitude / Hot lips / Mystery pacific / In a sentimental mood / Little love, a little kiss / Miss annabelle lee / Liebestraum no.3 / Ain't misbehavin' / Rose room
PASTCD 9738 / Sep '91 / Flapper

☐ **DJANGO WITH HIS AMERICAN FRIENDS (3CD Set)**
Avalon / Blue moon / Stardust / After you've gone / Georgia on my mind / Sweet Georgia brown / I got rhythm / Japanese sandman / Lady be good / I ain't got nobody / Big boy blues / Swing guitars / Somebody loves me / Fiddle blues / Farewell blues / Body and soul / Montmartre / Low cotton / Finesse / Solid old man / Djangoly
DRGCD 8493 / 24 Aug '98 / DRG

☐ **DJANGO'S MUSIC**
Tears / Limehouse blues / Daphne / At the Jimmy's bar / Festival swing '41 / Stockholm / Nympheas / Feerie / Seul ce soir / Bei dir war es immer so schoen / Nuages / Djangology / Eclats de culvres / Django rag / Dynamisme / Tons' D ebene / Chez moi a six heures / Bellville / Oubli / Zuiderzee blues / ABC / Galement / Melodie au crepescule / Blues d'autrefois / Place de brouckere
HEPCD 1041 / Oct '94 / Hep

☐ **DJANGOLOGY**
After you've gone / Limehouse blues / Nagasaki / Honeysuckle rose / Crazy rhythm / Out of nowhere / Chicago / Georgia on my mind / Shine / Sweet georgia brown / Bugle call rag / Between the devil and the deep blue sea / Exactly like you / Charleston / You're driving me crazy / Farewell blues / I got rhythm / I know that you know / Ain't misbehavin' / Rose room / Japanese sandman / Swing guitars / Minor swing / Nuages
CD 53002 / Mar '92 / Giants Of Jazz

☐ **DJANGOLOGY**
Dinah / Tiger rag / Oh lady be good / I saw stars / Lily Belle May June / Sweet Sue just you / Confessin' / Continental / Blue drag / Swanee river / Ton doux sourire / Ultrafox / Avalon / Smoke rings / Clouds / Believe it beloved / I've found a new baby / St. Louis blues / Crazy rhythm / Sheik of Araby / Chasing shadows / I've had my moment / Some of these days / Djangology
QED 071 / Nov '96 / Tring

☐ **DJANGOLOGY 49**
World is waiting for the sunrise / Hallelujah / I'll never be the same / Honeysuckle rose / All the things you are / Djangology / Daphne / Beyond the sea / Lover man / Marie / Minor swing / Ou est tu mon amour / Swing '42 / After you've gone / I got rhythm / I saw stars / Heavy artillery (artillerie lourde) / It's only a paper moon / Bricktop
ND 90448 / Apr '90 / Bluebird

☐ **GOLD COLLECTION, THE (2CD Set)**
R2CD 7002 / 13 Apr '98 / Deja Vu

☐ **HOT CLUB DE FRANCE**
BN 032 / Apr '98 / Blue Nite

☐ **I GOT RHYTHM**
I got rhythm / Crazy rhythm / My melancholy baby / Jeepers creepers / Sweet Georgia Brown / Honeysuckle rose / Liza / Nauges / Nuits de St. Germain des pres / Just one of those things / I cover the waterfront / I wonder where my baby is tonight
CDSGP 0106 / Jun '94 / Prestige

☐ **I GOT RHYTHM (Reinhardt, Django & Stephane Grappelli)**
Dinah / I'm confessin' that I love you / Swanee river / Sunshine of your smile / Believe it, beloved / Chasing shadows / I've had my moments / Some of these days / I got rhythm / Sheikh of araby / It don't mean a thing if it ain't got that swing / Viper's dream / Running wild / Ain't misbehavin' / Tears / Miss Annabelle Lee / Djangology / Daphne / Billets doux / Swing '39 / Tea for two / My melancholy baby / Younger generation / HCQ strut
PPCD 78110 / Feb '95 / Past Perfect

☐ **INDISPENSABLE DJANGO REINHARDT 1949-1950, THE**
Minor swing / Beyond the sea / World is waiting for the sunrise / Django's castle / Dream of you / Menilmontant / It's only a paper moon / I saw stars / Nuages / Swing guitars / All the things you are / Tisket-a-tasket / September song / Heavy artillery (Artillerie lourde) / Improvisation / Djangology / Daphne / I'll never be the same / Marie / Jersey bounce / I surrender dear / Hallelujah / Anniversary song / After you've gone / Swing '42 / Stormy weather / Brick top / Lover man / I got rhythm / Honeysuckle rose / St. Louis blues
ND 70929 / Mar '94 / RCA

☐ **INTRODUCTION TO DJANGO REINHARDT 1934-1942, AN**
4036 / Sep '96 / Best Of Jazz

☐ **JAZZ MASTERS**
5169312 / 5 May '98 / Verve

☐ **JAZZ PORTRAITS**
Limehouse blues / Nagasaki / After you've gone / You're driving me crazy / Ain't misbehavin' / Chicago / Georgia on my mind / Shine / Exactly like you / Charleston / Rose room / When day is done / Running wild (course movementee) / Swing guitars / Minor swing / Oriental shuffle / I can't give you anything but love / Sweet chorus
CD 14509 / May '94 / Jazz Portraits

☐ **LE QUINTETTE DU HOT CLUB DE FRANCE (Quintette Du Hot Club De France)**
Limehouse blues: *Reinhardt, Django* / Nagasaki: *Reinhardt, Django* / After you've gone: *Reinhardt, Django* / You're driving me crazy: *Reinhardt, Django* / Ain't misbehavin': *Reinhardt, Django* / Chicago: *Reinhardt, Django* / Georgia on my mind: *Reinhardt, Django* / Shine: *Reinhardt, Django* / Exactly like you: *Reinhardt, Django* / Charleston: *Reinhardt, Django* / Rose room: *Reinhardt, Django* / When day is done: *Reinhardt, Django* / Runnin' wild: *Reinhardt, Django* / Swing guitars: *Reinhardt, Django* / Minor swing: *Reinhardt, Django* / Oriental shuffle: *Reinhardt, Django* / I can't give you anything but love: *Reinhardt, Django* / Sweet chorus: *Reinhardt, Django*
CD 56020 / Aug '94 / Jazz Roots

☐ **LE QUINTETTE DU HOT CLUB DE FRANCE (Quintette Du Hot Club De France)**
CWNCD 2010 / Jun '95 / Javelin

☐ **LE QUINTETTE DU HOT CLUB DE FRANCE (2CD Set) (Reinhardt, Django & Stephane Grappelli/Quintette Du Hot Club)**
Dinah / Tiger rag / I saw stars / Ultrafox / Chasing shadows / It don't mean a thing / It was so beautiful / I'se a-muggin' / I can't give you anything but love / Nagasaki / Swing guitars / In the still of the night / Exactly like you / Charleston / You're driving me crazy / Tears / Solitude / Hot lips / Ain't misbehavin' / When day is done / Runnin' wild / Chicago / Liebestraum no.3 / Miss Anabelle Lee / Little love, a little kiss / Sheik of Araby / Swinging with Django / Paramount stomp / Honeysuckle rose / Night and day / My sweet / Souvenirs / Daphne / Stompin' at Decca / Billets doux / Them there eyes / Three little words / Appel indirect / Hungaria / My melancholy baby / Tea for two / Stockholm / Younger generation / Man I love / Rhythme futur / Swing 41 / Nuages / Coquette / Django's tiger / Embraceable you / Echoes of France (La Marseillaise)
CPCD 83122 / Nov '97 / Charly

☐ **LONDRES 1938, PARIS 1938 (Reinhardt, Django & Stephane Grappelli)**
879482 / Jun '93 / Music Memoria

☐ **MASTERS, THE**
EABCD 071 / 24 Nov '97 / Eagle

☐ **NUAGES (Reinhardt, Django & Coleman Hawkins)**
AJ 71431 / 27 Apr '98 / Arkadia

☐ **NUAGES 1934-1941 (Reinhardt, Django & Stephane Grappelli)**
Avalon / Blue drag / Confessin' / Continental / Dinah / Djangology / I saw stars / Improvisation / I've had my moments / Jive bomber / Low cotton / Nagasaki / Nocturne / Nuages / Oh Lady be good / Rose room / Smoke rings / Solid old man / Swanee river / Sweet chorus / Tiger rag / Ultrafox / When day is done
CDAJA 5138 / Feb '98 / Living Era

☐ **PARIS 1939, LONDRES 1939 (Reinhardt, Django & Stephane Grappelli)**
879492 / Jun '93 / Music Memoria

☐ **PECHE A LA MOUCHE (The Great Blue Star Sessions 1927-1953/2CD Set)**
Peche a la mouche / Minor blues / (I love you) for sentimental reasons / Danse Norvegienne / Blues for Barclay / Folie a amphion / Vette / Anniversary song / Swing 48 / September song / Brazil / I'll never smile again / New York City / Django's blues / Love's mood / I love you / Nuages / Moppin' the bride / Insensiblement / Mano blues / Primitif / Gypsy with a song / Night and day / Confessin' (that I love you) / Blues for Ike / September song / Night and day / Insensiblement / Manoir des mes reves / Nuages / Confessin' (that I love you)
8354182 / Mar '94 / Verve

☐ **PORTRAIT OF DJANGO REINHARDT, A (2CD Set)**
Dinah / Tiger rag / Lady be good / Blue drag / Djangology / Limehouse blues / Swing guitars / Sweet chorus / Tears / Rose room / Body and soul / Chicago / In a sentimental mood / Minor swing / Viper's dream / St. Louis blues / My serenade / Sweet Georgia Brown / Honeysuckle rose / Night and day / Tea for two / My sweet / Daphne / Improvisation / Nuages / Swing '39 / Stockholm / Naguine / Undecided / Man I love / Rhythme futur / Mabel / Sweet Sue / Les yeux noirs / Swing '41 / Fantaisie sur une danse Norvegienne / Dinette / Crepuscule / Swing '42 / Belleville / Douce ambiance / Manoir de mes reves / Blues clair / Embraceable you / Coquette / Swingtime in Springtime / On the sunny side of the street / Echoes of France
GALE 421 / 6 Oct '97 / Gallerie

☐ **PRESENTATION STOMP 1928-1934 (2CD Set)**
FA 301 / Apr '96 / Fremeaux

☐ **QUINTESSENCE, THE (1934-1943/2CD Set)**
FA 205 / Oct '96 / Fremeaux

☐ **QUINTESSENTIAL DJANGO REINHARDT & STEPHANE GRAPPELLI, THE (Le Quintette Du Hot Club De France/25 Classics 1934-1940) (Reinhardt, Django & Stephane Grappelli)**
Dinah / Oh lady be good / I saw stars / I'm confessin' that I love you / I've had my moments / Djangology / St. Louis blues / Limehouse blues / I got rhythm / I've found a new baby / After you've gone / Nagasaki / Swing guitars / Charleston / You're driving me crazy / Runnin' wild / Improvisation / Minor swing / Honeysuckle rose / Sweet Georgia Brown / Night and day / Daphne / Them there eyes / I'll see you in my dreams / Nuages
CDAJA 5267 / Apr '98 / Living Era

☐ **RARE DJANGO**
CDSW 8119 / Aug '91 / DRG

☐ **ROME SESSIONS VOL.1 1949-1950**
Waiting for the sunrise / Hallelujah / I'll never be the same / Honeysuckle rose / All the things you are / Daphne / La mer / Lover man / Marie / Anniversary song / Stormy weather / Russian songs medley / Jersey bounce / Sophisticated lady / Dream of you / At the Darktown strutter's ball / Royal Garden blues
8274472 / Jan '95 / Jazztime

☐ **SOUVENIRS (Jazz Recollections) (Reinhardt, Django & Stephane Grappelli)**
Honeysuckle Rose / Night and day / Sweet Georgia Brown / Souvenirs / My sweet / Liza / Stomping at Decca / Love's melody / Daphne / Lambeth walk / Nuages / HCQ Strut / Man I love / Improvisation no.2 / Undecided / Please be kind / Nocturne / I've got my love to keep me warm / Louise / Don't worry 'bout me
8205912 / Jun '88 / London

☐ **SWING DE PARIS (4CD Set)**
CDDIG 12 / Apr '95 / Charly

☐ **SWING FROM PARIS 1935-1939 (Reinhardt, Django & Stephane Grappelli)**
I got rhythm / St. Louis blues / Appel direct / Honeysuckle rose / Black and white / Limehouse blues / Moonglow / Billets doux / Daphne / China boy / Night and day / My sweet / It don't mean a thing if it ain't got that swing / Sweet Georgia Brown / Swing from Paris / I've found a new baby / Lambeth walk / Them there eyes / It was so beautiful / Three little words / HCQ strut / Swing '39
CDAJA 5070 / Feb '98 / Living Era

☐ **SWINGIN' WITH DJANGO (Reinhardt, Django & Stephane Grappelli)**
CDHD 206 / Feb '97 / Happy Days

☐ **UNFORGETTABLE DJANGO REINHARDT, THE**
China boy / Tornerai / My sweet / Souvenirs / Honeysuckle rose / Stompin' at Decca / I've found a new baby / Night and day / I've got my love to keep me warm / Improvisation / Limehouse blues / Them there eyes / Man I love / My melancholy baby / Hungaria / Appel direct / Three little words / Daphne / Tea for two / Billets doux / Ultrafox / I've had my moments
RHCD 6 / Dec '93 / Rhapsody

Reininger, Blaine

☐ **BRUSSELS/USA (The Best Of Blaine Reininger, Vol.1)**
Night air / Gigolo grasiento / Mystery and confusion / Ash and bone / Teenage theatre / Tombee de la nuit / Zeb znd Lulu / Software pancake house / To the green door / Cafe au lait / Come the spring / Ralf and Florian go Hawaiian / Right mind / Letter from home / Broken fingers / One-way man / El mensajero divino
TWI 9642 / May '96 / Les Disques Du Crepuscule

☐ **COLORADO SUITE (Reininger, Blaine & Mikel Rouse)**
MTM 3CD / Nov '88 / Made To Measure

Reischman, John

☐ **NORTH OF THE BORDER**
ROUCD 315 / Jan '94 / Rounder

Reisel, Jacqueline

☐ **SONGS IN YIDDISH & LADINO VOL.2**
YILADI 8803 / Sep '94 / Yiladi

Reiter, Jorg

☐ **CAN'T STOP IT**
ISCD 102 / '88 / Intersound

☐ **ON A DAY LIKE THIS**
ISCD 165 / Jul '96 / Intersound

Rejano, Jimenez

☐ **GRITAR POR MI ANDALUCIA**
9172 / Oct '96 / Divusca

Rejuvenate

☐ **MOMENT OF TRUTH**
LF 082CD / Sep '94 / Lost & Found

Rejuvination

☐ **INTRODUCTION**
SOMACD 2 / May '95 / Soma

Relativity

☐ **GATHERING PACE**
Blackwell court / Gathering pace / Rose catha na mumhan / Miss Tara Macadam / Ma theid tu unaonaigh / Siun ni dhuibhir / When she sleeps / Monday morning reel / Ceol Anna
GLCD 1076 / May '88 / Green Linnet

Reluctant Toby

☐ **ULTIMATE HOBBY**
NAR 126CD / 24 Nov '97 / New Alliance

REM

☐ AUTOMATIC FOR THE PEOPLE
Drive / Try not to breathe / Sidewinder sleeps tonite / Everybody hurts / New Orleans Instrumental No.1 / Sweetness follows / Monty got a raw deal / Ignoreland / Star me kitten / Man on the moon / Nightswimming / Find the river
9362450552 / Sep '92 / WEA

☐ BIOGRAPHY SERIES
10015 / 3 Nov '97 / Metro Independent

☐ BIRTH OF A MONSTER - INTERVIEW
VP 001 / Oct '94 / RPM

☐ DEAD LETTER OFFICE
Crazy / There she goes again / Burning down / Voice of Harold / Burning hell / White Tornado / Toys in the attic / Windout / Ages of you / Pale blue eyes / Rotary ten / Bandwagon / Femme fatale / Walter's theme / King of the road / Wolves, lower / Gardening at night / Carnival of sorts (boxcars) / 1,000,000 / Stumble
CDMID 195 / '94 / A&M

☐ DOCUMENT (Remastered)
Finest worksong / Welcome to the occupation / Exhuming McCarthy / Disturbance at the Heron House / Strange / It's the end of the world as we know it (and I feel fine) / One I love / Fireplace / Lightnin' Hopkins / King of birds / Ondfellows local 151 / Finest worksong / Last date / One I love / Time after time / Disturbance at the Heron House / Finest worksong
CTMCD 337 / 1 Sep '97 / EMI

☐ EPONYMOUS
Gardening at night / So Central rain / Driver 8 / Fall on me / Finest worksong / Talk about the passion / Can't get there from here / Romance / One I love / It's the end of the world as we know it (and I feel fine) / Radio free Europe / (Don't go back to) Rockville
4934572 / 20 Apr '98 / EMI

☐ FABLES OF THE RECONSTRUCTION (Remastered)
Feeling gravity's pull / Maps and legends / Driver 8 / Life and how to live it / Old man Kensey / Can't get there from here / Green grow the rushes / Kohoutek / Auctioneer (another engine) / Good advices / Wendell Gee / Crazy / Burning hell / Bandwagon / Driver 8 / Maps and legends
CTMCD 338 / 1 Sep '97 / EMI

☐ GREEN
Pop song '89 / Get up / You are the everything / Stand / World leader pretend / Wrong child / Orange crush / Turn you inside out / Hairshirt / I remember California / Untitled
9257952 / Nov '88 / WEA

☐ INTERVIEW DISC
SAM 7014 / Nov '96 / Sound & Media

☐ LIFE'S RICH PAGEANT (Remastered)
Begin the begin / Hyena / Just a touch / I believe / These days / Flowers of Guatemala / Cuyahoga / What if we give it away / Fall on me / Swan swan H / Tired of singing trouble / Rotary ten / Toys in the attic / Just a touch / Dream (All I have to do) / Swan swan H
CTMCD 339 / Sep '97 / EMI

☐ MONSTER
What's the frequency, Kenneth / Crush with eyeliner / King of comedy / I don't sleep, I dream / Star 69 / Strange currencies / Tongue / Bang and blame / I took your name / Let me in / Circus envy / You
9362457402 / Sep '94 / WEA

☐ MURMUR
Radio free Europe / Pilgrimage / Laughing / Talk about the Passion / Moral kiosk / Perfect circle / Catapult / Sitting still / 9-9 / Shaking through / We walk / West of the fields
CDMID 129 / Oct '92 / A&M

☐ NEW ADVENTURES IN HI FI
How the west was won and where it got us / Wake up bomb / New test leper / Undertow / E-bow the letter / Leave / Departure / Bittersweet me / Be mine / Binky the doormat / Zither / So fast, so numb / Low desert / Electrolite
9362463212
9362463202 / Sep '96 / Warner Bros.

☐ OUT OF TIME
Radio song / Losing my religion / Low / Near wild Heaven / Endgame / Shiny happy people / Belong / Half a world away / Texarkana / Country feedback / Me in honey
7599264962 / Mar '91 / WEA

☐ RECKONING
Harborcoat / Seven Chinese brothers / So central rain (I'm sorry) / Pretty persuasion / Time after time / Second guessing / Letter never sent / Camera / (Don't go back to) Rockville / Little America
CDMID 194 / Oct '94 / A&M

☐ SHINY CHATTY PEOPLE - INTERVIEW
CBAK 4041 / Jan '92 / Baktabak

☐ SURPRISE YOUR PIG (A Tribute To R.E.M.) (Various Artists)
SG 001 / Jul '92 / Plastic Head

Rembetika

☐ TALKING TO CHAROS
EUCD 1169 / '91 / ARC

Rembrandts

☐ LP
End of the beginning / Easy to forget / My own way / Don't hide your love / Drowning in your tears / This house is not a home / April 29 / Lovin' me insane / There goes Lucy / As long as I am breathing / Call me / Comin' home / What will it take / Other side of night / I'll be there for you
7559617522 / Sep '95 / Atlantic

☐ UNTITLED
Johnny have you seen her / Rollin' down the hill / Maybe tomorrow / One horse town / Chase the clouds away / Hang on clementine / I'll come callin' / In the back of your mind / Deepest end / Waiting to be opened / Hang on to forever / Sweet virginia
7567922002 / Jan '96 / Atlantic

Reminiscence Quartet

☐ PSYCODELICO
YP 009ACD / Jul '96 / Yellow

☐ RITMO BRASILIERO
YP 006CD / Jul '96 / Yellow

Reminiscent Drive

☐ MERCY STREET
Life is beautiful / Leg show / Nyc dharma / Serenade / King and the elphant / True love / Like twins / Back to Morocco / Mercy street / Codes of silence / There's always somebody to say you're wrong / Footprints / Two sides to every story / New Jerusalem / Dawn man / Relief
F 071CD / 27 Oct '97 / F-Communications

Remler, Emily

☐ EAST TO WEST
Daahoud / Sweet Georgie Fame / East to West / Snowfall / Hot house / Softly as in a morning sunrise
CCD 4356 / Sep '88 / Concord Jazz

☐ FIREFLY
Strollin' / Look to the sky / Perk's blues / Firefly / Movin' along / Taste of honey / Inception / In a sentimental mood
CCD 4162 / Sep '92 / Concord Jazz

☐ JUST FRIENDS VOL.2 (A Gathering In Tribute To Emily Remler) (Various Artists)
JR 005032 / Dec '92 / Justice

☐ RETROSPECTIVE VOL.1 (Standards)
Daahoud / How insensitive / Strollin' / Hot house / In your own sweet way / Joy Spring / Softly as in a morning sunrise / Afro blue / Del sasser / In a sentimental mood
CCD 4453 / Mar '91 / Concord Jazz

☐ RETROSPECTIVE VOL.2 (Compositions)
Macha spice / Nunca mais / Waltz for my grandfather / Catwalk / Blues for herb / Transitions / Firefly / East to West / Antonio / Mozambique
CCD 4463 / May '91 / Concord Jazz

☐ TAKE TWO (Remler, Emily Quartet)
Cannonball / In your own sweet way / For regulars only / Search for peace / Pocket west / Waltz for my grandfather / Afro blue / Eleuthra
CCD 4195 / Sep '92 / Concord Jazz

☐ THIS IS ME
JR 005012 / Sep '92 / Justice

Remora

☐ CLOCKWORK AMMONITE SHELLS, THE
REM 1 / 1 Dec '97 / Bentley Welcomes Careful Drivers

Remy, Tony

☐ METAMORFOLLOW-G
Spring high / Metamorfollow-G / Watching / Isabel 4 jojo / Just when I was falling / Syndicate / Never again / Miss U / Jah beans / Love me now / Close to music / Blue vibe: Vibe
ALTR 001 / 6 Oct '97 / Alltone

Rena Rama

☐ INSIDE - OUTSIDE
1182 / Oct '90 / Caprice

☐ JAZZ IN SWEDEN 1973
1049 / Mar '90 / Caprice

Renaissance

☐ ASHES ARE BURNING
Can you understand / Let it grow / On the frontier / Carpet of the sun / At the harbour / Ashes are burning
HTDCD 77 / 29 Sep '97 / HTD

☐ BLESSING IN DISGUISE (Haslam, Annie Renaissance)
Blessing in disguise / Pool of tears / Love lies, love dies / Can't turn the night off / In another life / Raindrops and leaves / Whisper from Marseilles / I light this candle / What he seeks / See this through your eyes / Sweetest kiss / Children (Of Medellin) / New life / After the oceans are gone
CDTB 151 / 29 May '98 / Thunderbolt

☐ CAMERA CAMERA
HTDCD 43 / Oct '95 / HTD

☐ DEATH OF ART
SHR 006CD / Aug '95 / Shiver

☐ ILLUSION
Love goes on / Golden thread / Love is all / Mr. Pine / Face of yesterday
REP 4513 / 16 Feb '98 / Repertoire

☐ INNOCENCE
Kings and Queens / Innocence / Island / Wanderer / Bullet / Sea / Island / Prayer for light / Walking away / Shining where the sun has been / All the falling angels
CRESTCD 033 / Feb '98 / Mooncrest

☐ KING BISCUIT PRESENTS...
Fanfare / Betrayal / Sultan / Love theme / Young prince and princess / Festival preparations / Fugue for sultan / Festival / Finale
KBFHCD 005 / 26 May '98 / King Biscuit

☐ NOVELLA
Can you hear me / Sisters / Midas man / Captive heart / Touching once (is so hard to keep)
7599265162 / Jan '96 / WEA

☐ OCEAN GYPSY
Ocean gypsy / Things I don't understand / Young prince and princess / Carpet of the sun / At the harbour / I think of you / Star of the show / Trip to the fair / Great highway
HTDCD 71 / Jun '97 / HTD

☐ OTHER WOMAN, THE
Northern lights / Love / Other woman / So blase / Love lies / Somewhere west of here / Lock in on love / Deja vu / Don't talk / Quicksilver
HTDCD 27 / Jan '95 / HTD

☐ PROLOGUE
Prologue / Kiev / Sounds of the sea / Spare some love / Bound for infinity / Rajah Khan
HTDCD 78 / 29 Sep '97 / HTD

☐ RENAISSANCE
Kings and queens / Innocence / Island / Wanderer / Bullet
REP 4512 / 16 Feb '98 / Repertoire

☐ SCHEHERAZADE AND OTHER STORIES
Tip to the fair / Vultures fly high / Ocean gypsy / Song of Scheherazade / Fanfare / Betrayal / Sultan / Love theme / Young prince and princess / Festival preparations / Fugue for the Sultan / Festival / Finale
HTDCD 59 / May '96 / HTD

☐ SONG FOR ALL SEASONS, A
Opening out / Day of the dreamer / Closer than yesterday / Kindness (at the end) / Back home once again / She is love / Northern lights / Song for all seasons
7599259592 / Jan '96 / WEA

☐ SONGS FROM RENAISSANCE DAYS (Haslam, Annie & Mike Dunford)
Africa / Dreamaker / Northern lights / No beginning no end / Only when I laugh / Body machine / Writers wronged / Island of Avalon / America / You
HTDCD 73 / Apr '97 / HTD

☐ SONGS FROM RENAISSANCE DAYS
REP 4672 / Nov '97 / Repertoire

☐ TIME LINE
Flight / Missing persons / Chagrin Boulevard / Richard IX / Entertainer / Electric avenue / Majik / Distant horizons / Orient express / Auto tech
HTDCD 42 / Oct '95 / HTD
REP 4655 / Jun '97 / Repertoire

☐ TURN OF THE CARDS
Running hard / I think of you / Things I don't understand / Black flame / Cold is being / Mother Russia
HTDCD 51 / Jan '96 / HTD

Renaldo & The Loaf

☐ ELBOW IS TABOO, THE
Street called straight / Boule / Hambo hodo / Dance for Sonambulist / Here's to the oblong boys / Bread song / Critical dance / Extracting the re-re
SBZ 036CD / 4 May '98 / Some Bizarre

Renault, Philippe

☐ BOSSA POUR SEPTEMBRE (Renault, Philippe Nonet)
BBRC 9105 / Dec '91 / Big Blue

Renbourn, John

☐ BEST OF JOHN RENBOURN, THE
PLSCD 147 / Feb '97 / Pulse

☐ BLACK BALLOON, THE
Moon shines bright / English dance / Bouree / Mist covered mountains of home / Orphan / Tarboulton / Pelican / Black balloon
PENT 001CD / Oct '93 / Pentangle

☐ COLLECTION, THE
CCSCD 429 / Mar '95 / Castle

☐ DEFINITIVE TRANSATLANTIC COLLECTION, THE
One for William / Waltz / After the dance / Lady Nothing's toye puffe / Trees they do grow high / Lady goes to church / Trotto Saltarello / Sweet potato / Shake shake Mamma / Hermit / Three pieces by O'Carolan / Lord Franklin / So clear / Moon shines bright / Pelican / Circle dance / New nothynge / Variations on Lady cary's Dompe
ESMCD 569 / 24 Nov '97 / Essential

☐ HERMIT, THE
Toye/Lord Willoughby's welcome home / Three pieces by O'Carolan / Princess and the puddings / Faro's rag / Hermit / Goat island / Old Mac Bladgitt / Pavanna (Anna bananna) / Bicycle tune / John's tune / Caroline's tune
SHCD 971425 / 23 Mar '98 / Shanachie

☐ JOHN BARLEYCORN (Renbourn, John Group)
Pavane 'belle, qui tiens ma vie'-tourdion / Maid on the shore / Death and the lady / Truth from above / Schafertanz-nachtanz / My johnny was a shoemaker / John barleycorn / Blackwater side / Gypsy dance / Jews dance / A bold young farmer / Sidi brahim / Talk about suffering
EDCD 472 / Feb '96 / Edsel

☐ JOHN RENBOURN/ANOTHER MONDAY
ESMCD 408 / Jun '96 / Essential

☐ LADY AND THE UNICORN, THE
Lady and the unicorn / Trotto / Saltrarello / Lamento di tristan / La rotta / Veri floris / Triple ballade / Bransie gay / Bransie de bourgogne / Alman / Melancholy galliard / Sarabande / My Johnny was a shoemaker / Westron wynde / Scarborough Fair
SHANCD 97022 / '92 / Shanachie

☐ LADY AND THE UNICORN, THE/THE HERMIT
Trotto / Saltarello / Lamento di Tristan / La rotta / Veri floris / Bransle gay / Bransle de Bourgogne / Alman / Melancholy Galliard / Sarabande / Lady and the unicorn / My Johnny was a shoemaker / Westeron Wynde / Scarborough fair / Hermit / Old Mac Bladgitt / Caroline's tune / Three pieces by O'Carolan / Princess and the puddings / Pavanna (Anna Bannana) / Toy for two lutes / Lord Willoughby's welcome home
ESMCD 436 / Oct '96 / Essential

☐ LIVE IN AMERICA (Renbourn, John Group)
Lindsay / English dance / Cruel mother / Breton dances / Trees they grow high / Farewell nancy / Van Diemen's land / High Germany / Sidi Brahim / Month of May is past/Night orgies / John Dory / So early in the spring / Fair flower / John Barleycorn is dead
FF 7013 / Sep '96 / Flying Fish

☐ LOST SESSIONS
Just like me / Sleepy john / Riverboat song / Green willow / Seven sleepers / To glastonbury / Floating stone / O death / Young man's song
EDCD 490 / Jul '96 / Edsel

☐ NINE MAIDENS, THE
New nothynge / Fish in the well / Pavan d'Aragon / Variations on my Lady Carey's dompe / Circle dance / Nine maidens
FF 70378 / Nov '96 / Flying Fish
EDCD 543 / 24 Nov '97 / Edsel

☐ SHIP OF FOOLS
FF 70466 / Nov '96 / Flying Fish

☐ SIR JOHN ALOT OF
Earle of Salisbury / Trees they do grow high / Lady goes to church / Morgana / Transfusion / Forty eight / My dear boy / White fishes / Sweet potato / Seven up
HILLCD 1 / Sep '96 / Wooded Hill

☐ SNAP A LITTLE OWL
GWCD 3 / Dec '97 / Guitar

☐ SO CLEAR (2CD Set)
Lucky thirteen / Sally go round the roses / Forty-eight / Tic-tocative / Lord Franklin / Lady Nothing's toye puffe / Hermit / Shake shake mama / Waltz / Faro Annie / White house blues / Can't keep from crying / My sweet potato / Kokokmo blues / So clear / Lady and the unicorn / Will the circle be unbroken / Bicycle tune / Judy / I know my babe / Lost lover blues / One for William / Jack Orion / Trees they do grow high / Goat island / Maid that's deep in love / Back on the road again / Bransle gay/Bransle de Bourgogne / Earle of Salisbury / Come on in my kitchen / Willy O'Winsbury / Old Mac Bladgitt / In time / Alman/Melancholy galliard / Blues run the game
SMDCD 152 / May '97 / Snapper

☐ TRAVELLER'S PRAYER
Bunyan's hymn (monks gate) / When the wind begins to sing / Wexford lullaby / I saw three ships/Newgate hornpipe / Planxty Llanthony/Loftus Jones / Faggotanz / At the break of the day / Travellers prayer / South wind/Feathered nest / Estampie
SHANCD 78018 / Jun '98 / Shanachie

Rendell, Don

☐ IF I SHOULD LOSE YOU (Rendell, Don & His Big Eight)
If I should lose you / Calas vinas / All too soon / I can dream, can't I / Out of my window / Under pressure blues / Blues house effect / Hard knott pass / Relaxing at Loweswater / Jumpin' at the lakeside
SPJCD 546 / May '93 / Spotlite

☐ WHAT AM I HERE FOR (Rendell, Don Five)
This time the dream's on me / For minor's only / What am I here for / Honest Injun / Lament / Goodbye pork pie hat / My romance / This I dig of you / Bluesroom / Antibes / Shades of blue / Parisian thoroughfare
SPJCD 551 / Sep '96 / Spotlite

Renegade Soundwave

☐ NEXT CHAPTER OF DUB, THE
CDSTUMM 90 / Apr '95 / Mute

☐ RENEGADE SOUNDWAVE 1987-1995 (2CD Set)
Kray Twins / Cocaine sex / Biting my nails / Lucky Luke / Space gladiator (satellite of dub) / Murder music / Pocket porn / Can't get used to losing you / Probably a robbery / Women respond to bass / Renegade Soundwave / Howyoudoin / Bubbaluba / Positive ID / Blast 'em out / Cocaine sex / Phantom / Ozone breakdown / Biting my nails / Thunder / Deadly / Transworld siren / Black eye boy / Renegade Soundwave / Last freedom fighter / Renegade priest / Positive mindscape / Blastik 1
CDSTUMM 152 / Jul '96 / Mute

☐ RENEGADE SOUNDWAVE IN DUB
Thunder / Bocterio / Deadly / Transition / Pocket porn due / Women respond to bass / Holgertron / Recognise and respond / Transworld siren / Black eye boy
CDSTUMM 85 / Oct '90 / Mute

☐ SOUNDCLASH
Blue eyed boy / Lucky luke / On tv / Probably a robbery / Traitor / Space gladiator / Murder music / Biting my nails / Pocket porn / Can't get used to losing you / Biting my nails (instrumental)
CDSTUMM 63 / Feb '90 / Mute

Renegades
☐ CADILLAC
23055 / Sep '97 / Oxford

Renegades Steel Orchestra
☐ BUMP AND WINE
795872 / Dec '95 / Melodie

Renold, Fritz
☐ STARLIGHT (Renold, Fritz & Bostonian Friends)
New kind... / Stella by starlight / Lydia meets benny / None of your business / My heart feels for you / Palliladoodap / Suite for maynard ferguson-Part I in memory of duke / Part II in memory of bird / Part III in memory of miles / Part IV in memory of trane
4880382 / 8 Sep '97 / Sony Jazz

Renson, Patrice
☐ SOFT COLOURS
175382 / 21 Aug '97 / Musidisc

Rent
☐ CAST ALBUM
Tune up / Voice mail / Tune up / Rent / You okay honey / Tune up / One song glory / Light my candle / Voice mail / Today 4 U / You'll see / Tango - Maureen / Life support / Out tonight / Another day / Will I / On the street / Santa Fe / I'll cover you / We're okay / Christmas bells / Over the moon / La vie boheme / I should tell you / La vie boheme B / Seasons of love / Happy New Year / Voice mail / Happy new year B / Take me or leave me / Seasons of love B / Without you / Voice mail / Contact / I'll cover you - reprise / Halloween / Goodbye love / What you own / Voice mail / Finale / Your eyes / Finale B / Seasons of love
DRD 50003 / Sep '96 / Dreamworks

Rent Party
☐ PIC NIC
422495 / Nov '94 / New Rose

Rent Party Revellers
☐ SHE WAS JUST A SAILOR'S SWEETHEART
SOSCD 1220 / Oct '92 / Stomp Off

Rentals
☐ RETURN OF THE RENTALS
Love I'm searching for / Waiting / Friends of p / Please let that be you / Brilliant boy / My summer girl / Departure / Sweetness and tenderness / These days / Naive / Move on
9362460932 / Jan '96 / Warner Bros.

Renzi, Mike
☐ PROVIDENCE JAM (A Beautiful Friendship)
STB 2506 / Sep '95 / Stash

REO Speedwagon
☐ BEST FOOT FORWARD
Roll with the changes / Take it on the run / Don't let him go / Live every moment / Keep on loving you / Back on the road again / Wherever you're goin' (it's alright) / Can't fight this feeling / Shakin' it loose / Time for me to fly / Keep pushin' / I wish you were there
4686032 / Oct '91 / Epic

☐ HI-INFIDELITY
Don't let him go / Keep on loving you / Follow my heart / In your letter / Take it on the run / Tough guys / Out of season / Shakin' it loose / Someone tonight / I wish you were there
CD 84700 / '88 / Epic

☐ HITS, THE
I don't want to lose you / Here with me / Roll with the changes / Keep on loving you / That ain't love / Take it on the run / Don't let him go / Can't fight this feeling / Keep pushin' / In my dreams / Time for me to fly / Ridin' the storm out
4655952 / 27 Jul '98 / Epic

Rep, Mike
☐ TREE STUMP NAMED DESIRE (Rep, Mike & The Quotas)
AW 037 / Dec '96 / Anyway

Repercussions
☐ EARTH AND HEAVEN
Promise me nothing / If there's a question / Gentle kind of love / Turn your card / Slice of heaven / It's a new day / Love like the sun / Keeping it all together / Test of time / Find your way
9362456442 / Feb '95 / Warner Bros.

Replacements
☐ ALL FOR NOTHING/NOTHING FOR ALL (2CD Set)
Left of the dial / Kiss me on the bus / Bastards of young / Here comes a regular / Skyway / Alex Chilton / Ledge / Can't hardly wait / I'll be you / Achin' to be / Talent show / Anywhere's better than here / Merry go round / Sadly beautiful / Nobody / Somebody take the wheel / Can't hardly wait / Birthday gal / Beer for breakfast / Till we're nude / Election day / Jungle rock / All he wants to do is fish / Date to church / Cruella DeVille / We know the night / Portland / Wake up / Satellite / Like a rolling pin / Another girl, another planet / Who knows
9362468072 / 24 Nov '97 / Reprise

☐ ALL SHOOK DOWN
Merry go round / Nobody / Sadly beautiful / When it began / Attitude / Torture / Last / One wink at a time / Bent out of shape / Someone take the wheel / All shook down / Happy town / My little problem
7599262982 / Feb '95 / Sire

☐ TIM
Hold my life / I'll buy / Kiss me on the bus / Dose of thunder / Waitress in the sky / Swingin' party / Bastards of young / Lay it down clown / Left of the dial / Little mascara / Here comes a regular
7599253302 / Jul '93 / Sire

Replicants
☐ REPLICANTS
Just what I needed / Silly love songs / Life's a gas / Cinnamon girl / How do you sleep / Destination unknown / No good trying / Are friends electric / Dirty work / Bewlay brothers / Ibiza bar
7244511172 / May '96 / Zoo Entertainment

☐ THIS IS OUR MESSAGE
GER 001CD / Nov '97 / 5RC

Repo, Teppo
☐ HERDSMAN'S MUSIC FROM INGRIA
KICD 7 / Dec '94 / Kansanmusiikki Instituutti

Reptilicus
☐ CRUSHER OF BONES
PRCD 001 / Oct '96 / Product

Republica
☐ REPUBLICA
Ready to go / Bloke / Bitch / Get off / Picture me / Drop dead gorgeous / Out of the darkness / Wrapp / Don't you ever / Holly / Ready to go
74321410522 / 11 May '98 / De-Construction

☐ REPUBLICA (2CD Set)
Ready to go / Bloke / Bitch / Get off / Picture me / Drop dead gorgeous / Out of the darkness / Wrapp / Don't you ever / Holly / Ready to go / Drop dead gorgeous / Bloke / Get off / Ready to go / Out of the darkness / Holly
74321536332 / 17 Nov '97 / De-Construction

Repulsa
☐ SEXPIG
SPV 084160522 / May '96 / SPV

REQ
☐ FREQUENCY JAMS
BRASSIC 7CD / 2 Mar '98 / Skint

☐ REQ ONE
BRASSIC 3CD / Feb '97 / Skint

Requiem In White
☐ OF THE WANT INFINITE
EFA 01557CD / Sep '96 / Apocalyptic Vision

Resa
☐ HAPPY NIGHTMARE
1213 / Oct '91 / Caprice

Reservoir
☐ PINK MACHINE
Go back / Let's fall in love again / Taking my shapes away / Weight of the world / 40 / Air coryell / Pink machine / Right there
ZERCD 2150 / 15 Sep '97 / Zero Hour

Reshma
☐ LEGEND, THE
DMUT 1280 / Mar '96 / Multitone

Residents
☐ 25TH ANNIVERSARY BOX SET (4CD Set)
Jambalaya / Don't be cruel / From the plains to Mexico / Double shot / Harry the head / Kaw-Liga / Jailhouse rock / It's a man's man's man's world / Satisfaction / World versus flying saucers / Flying / For Elsie / Let me be your teddy bear / Hit the road Jack / Have a bad day / Hunters / Gingerbread / Freak show / Cube E lite / God in three persons lite / God in three persons / Mole trilogy / Eskimo / Fingerprince / Third Reich 'n' roll / Not available / Meet the residents / Tryin' to beat it / Sad love song / Angry love song / Anganok / Teddy / I tried to cry / Struggle / Spaghetti sunday / Love me / Hallowed by thy ween / America
RESBOX 1 / May '97 / Cargo

☐ COMMERCIAL ALBUM
INDIGO 21302 / Dec '96 / Indigo

☐ DUCK STAB
TORSOCD 406 / Oct '87 / Torso

☐ DUCK STAB/BUSTER AND GLEN (2CD Set)
INDIGO 21272 / Dec '96 / Indigo

☐ ESKIMO
INDIGO 21362 / Dec '96 / Euro Ralph

☐ EYE SORE (A Stab At The Residents) (Various Artists)
INDIGO 21352 / Dec '96 / Euro Ralph

☐ FINGERPRINCE
TORSOCD 407 / Dec '87 / Torso

☐ FINGERPRINCE/BABY FINGERS (2CD Set)
INDIGO 21312 / Dec '96 / Indigo

☐ GEORGE AND JAMES
Rhapsody in blue / I got rhythm / Summertime / I'll go crazy / Try me / Think / I don't mind / Lost someone / Please please please / Night train
INDIGO 21222 / Dec '96 / Indigo

☐ GINGER BREAD MAN
INDIGO 21292 / Dec '96 / Indigo

☐ GOD IN THREE PERSONS
Hard and tenderly / Devotion / Thing about them / Their early years / Loss of a loved one / Touch / Service / Confused / Fine fat flies / Time / Silver sharp / Kiss of flesh / Pain and pleasure
TORSOCD 055 / '88 / Torso

☐ HAVE A BAD DAY
INDIGO 21332 / Dec '96 / Indigo

☐ LIVE IN HOLLAND
CD 018 / Jul '87 / Torso

☐ MEET THE RESIDENTS
CD 416 / Dec '88 / Torso
CD 2138 / 9 Mar '98 / Euro Ralph

☐ OUR FINEST FLOWERS
INDIGO 21212 / Dec '96 / Indigo

☐ OUR TIRED, OUR POOR, OUR HUDDLED MASSES (25th Anniversary/ 4CD Set)
Have a bad day concentrate / Hunters concentrate / Gingerbreadman concentrate / Six amber things / He also serves / Ship of fools / Freak show concentrate / Cube E concentrate / God in three persons concentrate / Mole trilogy concentrate / Easter women / Amber / Red rider / Floyd / Nameless soul / Love leaks out / Simple song / Moisture / Loneliness / When we were young / Eskimo concentrate / Constantinople / Blue rosebuds / Lizard lady / Fingerprince concentrate / Third reich 'n' roll concentrate / Not available concentrate / Meet the residents concentrate / Aircraft damage / Jambalaya / Don't be cruel / From the plains to Mexico / Double shot / Harry the head / Don't / Gingerbread man / Kawliga / Where is she / Jailhouse rock / This is a man's world / Jingle bells / Satisfaction / Loser weed / Earth vs. flying saucer / Beatles play the Residents and the Residents play the beatle / For Elsie / Teddy bear / Surrender / Hit the road Jack / Tryin to beat it / Sirensong / Ugly beauty / Anganok / Teddy / I tired to cry / Cry of a crow / Struggle / Spaghetti Sunday / Love me / Hallowed by thy ween / America
INDIGO 21372 / Jul '97 / Euro Ralph

☐ POOR KAW-LIGA'S PAIN
INDIGO 21242 / Dec '96 / Euro Ralph

☐ THIRD REICH AND ROLL
INDIGO 21232 / Dec '96 / Indigo

Resin Scraper
☐ HEARD MENTALITY
MAG 016 / Dec '96 / Mag Wheel

Resistance 77
☐ THROUGHBRED MEN
AHOYCD 031 / 10 Nov '97 / Captain Oi

Resistance D
☐ INEXHAUSTIBILITY
HHSP 005CD / Nov '94 / Harthouse

☐ ZTRING 2 OF LIFE
HHCD 004 / Mar '94 / Harthouse

Resolution
☐ SEATTLE BROTHERHOOD
LF 147CD / Jun '95 / Lost & Found

Resonance Vox
☐ RESONANCE VOX
Ame no suiyohbi / Barong / Partido forte / No money, no girl, no business (but we still have music) / Pona pela / Karula / Glory's stomp / On the beach / Iron claw / Merci brice / Flor
5218792 / May '95 / Verve

Resonator
☐ TELHARMONIUM
NOZACD 04 / 10 Aug '98 / Ninebar

Resort
☐ 1989
Right to remain silent / American faces / Horror show / Seven days and seven nights / King of the jungle / Waiting for a friend / Rock n roll / Rebels with a cause / Rubber Jenny / Freedom / Johnny Barden / Horror show / King of the jungle / Rag doll
AHOHCD 082 / 24 Nov '97 / Captain Oi

Respectable Groove
☐ TELL TALE DUCKS
Tell tale ducks / In no mood / Air / No calypso / Rocky road to Dublin / She moves through the fair / Think of the other things / Local aesthetic / Folia and friends / Lucky with the weather
FMRCD 29 / Jun '97 / Future

Rest In Pieces
☐ MY RAGE
LF 081CD / May '94 / Lost & Found

Restgerausch
☐ RESTGERAUSCH VOL.2
EFA 006902 / 29 Sep '97 / Mille Plateau

Resting Place Of The Mists
☐ NEW VALIHA AND MAROVANY MUSIC FROM MADAGASCAR
SH 64075 / Dec '96 / Shanachie

Restless
☐ BEAT MY DRUM
NUTACD 001 / Dec '88 / Madhouse

☐ DO YOU FEEL RESTLESS
NERCD 015 / '90 / Nervous

☐ EARLY YEARS 1981-83, THE
Rock the joint / High time / 20 flight rock / Modern romance / Sag, drag and fall / It's a scam / Why don't you just rock / Bottle on the beach / Here am I / Why didn't I stay at home / Slidin' on down the hill / Edge on you
NERCD 026 / '90 / Nervous

☐ FIGURE IT OUT
Road to paradise / Guitar man / Nowhere to go / Just an echo / Empty hands / Better than nothing / Still waiting / I go wild / Shopping around / Going back / His latest flame / Memoir blue
NERCD 072 / Jun '93 / Nervous

☐ GOT SOME GUTS
MCG 20021 / 1 Dec '97 / Vampirella

☐ LOST SESSIONS
They don't understand me anymore / Weekend girl / You'll never get the chance again / Bright light city / Ain't seen nobody like you / Golden hair / Storm is gone / Real mad man / Whiskey blues / Sympathy / Moonlight ride / Don't leave me
JRCD 19 / Sep '97 / Jappin' & Rockin'

☐ NO.7
NUTACD 6 / Oct '91 / Madhouse

☐ S'OK S'ALRIGHT (Harmony Brothers)
BSR 01 / Jul '97 / Blood Sucking

☐ THREE OF A KIND
All the time / Black magic / Centipede / It'd be a doggone lie / Breakup / Devil doll / I'm comin' home / Love crazy baby / Goose bumps / Honky tonk man / Morse code / Put me down
JRCD 14 / Sep '97 / Jappin' & Rockin'

☐ VERY BEST OF RESTLESS, THE
NERCD 087 / Sep '96 / Nervous

☐ WHY DON'T YOU JUST ROCK
It's a scam / Ice cold / Why don't you just rock / High time / Last chance baby / Tag man, tag / Long black shiny car / Face in my gin / Yellow cab to midnight / Morning comes slowly / Black cat / Travellin' / High time (version 2) / Later / That's all right
NERCD 004 / Jan '92 / Nervous

Restless Heart
☐ BEST OF RESTLESS HEART, THE
You can depend on me / Fast movin' train / Tender lie / Bluest eyes in Texas / Familiar pain / Wheels / That rock won't roll / Till I loved you / Why does it have to (wrong or right) / I'll still be loving you
PD 90608 / Feb '92 / RCA

☐ BIG IRON HORSES
Mending fences / We got the love / As far as I can tell / When she cries / Meet on the other side / Tell me what you dream / Blame it on love / Born in a high wind / Just in time / Big iron horses
74321138992 / Apr '93 / RCA

☐ MATTERS OF THE HEART
In this little town / Love train / Mind over matters of the heart / Baby needs new shoes / Hold you now / She's still in love / You're a stronger man than I am / Hometown boys / Sweet whiskey lies / I'd cross the line
07863663972 / Jun '94 / RCA

Resurrection

☐ I REFUSE
NA 019CD / Jul '96 / New Age

Retro Mastermixers

☐ SIXTIES MEGAMIX, VOL.2
Stars on 45 / No reply / I'll be back / Drive my car / Do you want to know a secret / We can work it out / I should have known better / Nowhere man / You're going to lose that girl / Ticket to ride / You're going to lose thst girl / Word / Elanor Rigby / Every little thing / And your bird can sing / Get back / Eight days a week / It won't be long / Day tripper / Wait / Stars on 45 / Good day sunshine / My sweet Lord / Here comes the sun / While my guitar gently weeps / Taxman / Hard days night / Things we said today / If I fell / You can't do that / Please please me / From me to you / I want to hold your hand / Stars on 45 / Dancing in the street / (I can't get no) Satisfaction / You really got me / All day and all of the night / Do wah diddy / Pretty flamingo / Black is black / Bend me shape me / High in the sky / Mr. Tambourine man / Proud Mary / Oh pretty woman / Letter / Baby let me take you home / How do you do it / I like it / Tossing and turning / Hippy hippy shake / Let's hang on / Sherry / Big girls don't cry / Walk like a man / Rag doll / Dawn (go away) / Yes I will / Stay / Just one look / Here I go again / I'm alive / There's a kind of hush / No milk today / Must to avoid / Hold tight / Legend of Xanadu / Sweets for my sweet / Sugar and spice / When you walk in the room / Needles and pins
301882 / Feb '98 / Hallmark

☐ VERY BEST 60'S MEGAMIX, THE
Let's dance / I get around / I saw her standing there / You really got me / Da doo ron ron / baby love / Lazy Sunday / Hi ho silver lining / Daydream believer / Young ones / Downtown / Young girl / Everlasting love / Get back / Something / Hey Jude / My Cherie amour / Walk on by / World without love / Wichita lineman / Fire / Jumping Jack flash / Substitute / Keep on running / I only wanna be with you / Locomotion / Pretty woman / Get off my cloud / I can see for miles / Pinball wizard / You've lost that lovin' feeling / Something in the air / Sun ain't gonna shine anymore / Concrete and clay / Do you know the way to San Jose / (There's) always something there to remind me / River deep mountain high / Clapping song / Boat that I row / Night has a thousand eyes
301232 / Jun '98 / Hallmark

☐ VERY BEST 70'S MEGAMIX, THE
Boogie nights / Funky town / Video killed the radio star / Voulez vous / SOS / Bang a boomerang / Money money money / Knowing me knowing you / Fernando / Winner takes it all / Papa was a rolling stone / Dance to the music / Sugar baby love / YMCA / Can you feel it / Ring my bell / Instant replay / Use it up and wear it out / Ma Baker / I was made for lovin' you / Don't stop 'til you get enough / Feel the need in me / Daddy cool / Hands up / Celebration / Le freak / We are family / Hot shot / Bad girls / Disco nights / Dance dance dance / Strut your funky stuff / Shine up / Lady bump / DISCO / Black is black / Boogie wonderland / Get up and boogie / Get off / Spacer / Love machine / Born to be alive / Givin' up givin' in / Another cha cha / Disco inferno / I was made for dancing / Xanadu / Jealousy / September
301272 / Jun '98 / Hallmark

☐ VERY BEST DISCO MEGAMIX, THE
Hands up / Celebration / One way ticket / Let's all chant / Le freak / We are family / Hot shot / Bad girls / Disco nights / Dance dance dance / Funkytown / Working my way back to you / Lady bump / DISCO / YMCA / Can you feel it / Ring my bell / Instant replay / Use it up and wear it out / Ma baker / I was made for loving you / Don't stop 'til you get enough / Feel the need in me / You make me feel (mighty real) / Got to give it up / Daddy cool / House of the rising sun / Feels like I'm in love / Born to be alive / Givin' up givin' in / Another cha cha / What a difference a day makes / Dance (disco heat) / Gimme some lovin' / Dance yourself dizzy / Cafe / Make love whenever you can / Macho man / In the bush / Can't stop the music / Daddy-o / Gotta go home / Black is black / Boogie wonderland / Get up and boogie / Get off / Spacer / Love machine / Shake your groove thing / It's a disco night / La Bamba / Contact / Haven't stopped dancing yet / Singing in the rain / I'm alive / Master blaster
301082 / Jun '98 / Hallmark

Retsin

☐ EGG FUSION
SMR 46CD / May '96 / Simple Machines

Return To Khafji

☐ RETURN TO KHAFJI
ABCD 004 / Jan '96 / Resurrection

Return To Sender

☐ FESTIVAL TOUR
NORMAL 175 / Dec '94 / Normal

Rev Brown

☐ BARE IN CHANGE
PRD 70742 / Mar '95 / Provogue

☐ PSYCHOMACHIA
There's a rumour going round / Nobody loves me / All I want / Happy face blues / Come 'ere babe / Big city ley bus / Voodoo chile (Slight return) / Sunset on time / Sad sad day / Dreamland / Hypnotised / Certified
PRD 70872 / Feb '96 / Provogue

Rev Hammer

☐ BISHOP OF BUFFALO
Lamb / Tranquility of solitude / Etain / Ellan vannin / Circular blues / (Worse and worse) like the son of a goat / Every step of the way / Drunkard's waltz / Blood whisky / Spanish lullaby / Shanty / Chase
COOKCD 063 / Feb '94 / Cooking Vinyl

☐ FREEBORN JOHN
COOKCD 111 / Mar '98 / Cooking Vinyl

☐ INDUSTRIAL SOUNDS AND MAGIC
Down by the river o / True blue / Punch drunk / Ole welsh soul / California bound / Raise that lion / Johnny reggae / Caledonia rain / Shuttin' the ole dirt down / Jimmy flannagan
COOKCD 046 / Jun '92 / Cooking Vinyl

Rev, Martin

☐ SEE ME RIDIN'
RUSCD 8220 / 16 Feb '98 / ROIR

Rev Rev

☐ EASTER ISLAND
FIREBUG 001 / 23 Mar '98 / Firebug

Revelation

☐ ADDICTED
Jack's in the box / Addiction / Jack the lad / Wicked woman / Witches and wizards / Freewheeling
CDR 108 / Jun '95 / Red Hot

Revelation

☐ NEVER COMES SILENCE
HELL 020CD / Dec '92 / Hellhound

☐ SALVATION'S ANSWER
Lost innocence / Salvations answer / Infinite nothingness / Paradox / Images of darkness / Long after midnight / Poets and paupers / Waiting for..the end
RISE 006CD / Mar '92 / Rise

☐ YET SO FAR
Soul barer / Eternal search / Little faith / Grasping the nettle / Morning sun / Fallen / Alone / Natural steps / Yet so far
H 00362 / Feb '95 / Hellhound

Revelators

☐ WE TOLD YOU NOT TO CROSS US
EFA 128842 / Apr '97 / Crypt

Revelers

☐ HARD TIMES SUNDAY SPIRITS
SPART 60CD / 23 Mar '98 / Spin Art

Revelino

☐ BROADCASTER
Radio speaks / Step on high / Down the streets / This song / All hope is fading / Rollercoaster / Close / Sixth sense / Statue of pride / Stay down / Dance again / Been and gone
120522 / Oct '96 / Musidisc

☐ REVELINO
Happiness is mine / My bones / Hello / Don't lead me down / Taking turns / Libertine / World going down / That's what Emily says / No forever girl / I feel so tired / She's got the face / Slave / Tonight
119242 / Mar '96 / Musidisc UK

Reverberation

☐ BLUE STEREO MUSIC
Cross your sky / Fancy swim / Blue ensemble / Let it blow on / When the ships come down / It's all over now / Roses celeste / Big ship / Autogyre / Been tumbling down / So glad to go / Doctor doctor / Nite time (slight return) / Oscillations astrales / Just a little bit scared / Turning back to blue
TAANG 140 / 15 Aug '97 / Taang
STONE 022CD / 30 Mar '98 / 3rd Stone

Revere, Paul

☐ ESSENTIAL RIDE 1963-1967, THE (The Best Of Paul Revere & The Raiders) (Revere, Paul & The Raiders)
Loule, Loule / Mojo workout / Over you / Crisco party / Walking the dog / Steppin' out / Just like me / Stepping stone / Kicks / Ballad of a useless man / Loule, go home / Take a look at yourself / Hungry / (You're a) Bad girl / Louise / Great airplane strike / In my community / Good thing / Why why why (is it so hard) / Ups and downs / Him or me, who's it gonna be
CD 48949 / Jul '95 / Columbia

☐ JUST LIKE US
SC 6127 / 1 Jun '98 / Sundazed

☐ LIKE LONG HAIR (Revere, Paul & The Raiders)
FLASH 40 / Jul '97 / Flash

☐ REVOLUTION (Revere, Paul & The Raiders)
Him or me / What's it gonna be / Reno / Upon your leaving / Mo'reen / Wanting you / Gone / Movin' on / I had a dream / Tighter / Make it with me / Ain't nobody who can make it like Leslie can / I hear a voice / Ups and downs / Try some of mine / Legend of Paul Revere
SC 6096 / Aug '97 / Sundazed

☐ SOMETHING HAPPENING (Revere, Paul & The Raiders)
Happening intro / Happens every day / Burn like a candle / Observation from flight 285 / Get out of my mind / Don't take it so hard / Communication / Love makes the world go round / Free / Good times / Happening '68 / Too much talk / It's happening
SC 6097 / Aug '97 / Sundazed

☐ SPIRIT OF '67, THE (Revere, Paul & The Raiders)
Good thing / All about her / In my community / Louise / Why why why / Oh to be a man / Hungry / Undecided man / Our candidate / 1001 Arabian nights / Great airplane strike / Bad girl / Hungry / Great airplane strike
SC 6095 / Aug '97 / Sundazed

Rev. Horton Heat

☐ FULL CUSTOM, THE
SPCD 248 / Apr '93 / Sub Pop

☐ SMOKE 'EM IF YOU GOT 'EM
Bullet / I'm mad / Bad reputation / It's a dark day / Big dwarf rodeo / Psychobilly freakout / Put it to me straight / Marijuana / Baby, you know who / Eat steak / D for Dangerous / Love whip
SPCD 25/177 / '90 / Sub Pop

☐ SPACE HEATER
INTD 90168 / 31 Aug '98 / Interscope

Revhead

☐ SHE
PEN 001 / Feb '97 / Music Of Life

Revolting Cocks

☐ BIG SEXY LAND
CDDVN 6 / Mar '92 / Devotion

☐ YOU GODDAMNED SON OF A BITCH
You goddamned son of a bitch / Cattle grind / We shall cleanse the world / 38 / In the neck / You often forget / T.v. mind / Union carbide / Attack ships on fire / No devotion
CDDVN 8 / Apr '92 / Devotion

Revolution 9

☐ YOU MIGHT AS WELL LIVE
You don't know what love is / Giving up the ghost / Now that your lover has gone / Winter song / You broke my heart / Damaged goods / Jessica / Jealousy / Amen to that / Song noir / Living with you / Patron Saint of lonliness / Shining guiding star
HABCD 1 / Jul '95 / Habana

Revolutionaries

☐ BLACK ASH DUB
Marijuana / Herb / Collie / Lambs bread / Rizla / LSD / Acapulco / Cocaine
CDTRL 186 / Jun '95 / Trojan

☐ JONKANOO DUB
JJCD 025 / 18 May '98 / Channel One

☐ MACCA POSTMAN DUB
JMC 200218 / Apr '95 / Jamaican Gold

☐ TOP RANKING DUB
DR 001CD / Sep '96 / Duke Reid

☐ WELL CHARGE
JJCD 034 / 6 Oct '97 / Channel One

Revolutionary Army Of The Infant Jesus

☐ GIFT OF TEARS
PROBECD 012 / Dec '93 / Probe Plus

☐ GIFT OF TEARS/MIRROR/LITURGIE
EFA 015512 / Oct '95 / Apocalyptic Vision

☐ PARADIS
EFA 015632 / Feb '96 / Apocalyptic Vision

Revolutionary Dub Warriors

☐ RE-ACTION DUB VOL.1 (Deliverence)
ONUCD 68 / Oct '94 / On-U Sound

Revolver

☐ COLD WATER FLAT
Cool blue / Shakesdown / Cradle snatch / I wear your chain / Nothing without you / Bottled out / Coming back / Cold water flat / Makes no difference all the same / Wave
CDHUT 8 / Apr '93 / Hut

Revolving Paint Dream

☐ MOTHER WATCH ME BURN
Dune buggy attack battalion / Dune buggy attack battalion / Fever mountain / (burn this house) down to the ground / Mother wash my tears away / Garbagebrain / Electra's crying loaded in the basement / Mandra mandra / Untitled love song / 300 (coda) / Mandro mandro (reprise) / Sun, sea, sand / Flowers in the sky / Stop the world / 7 seconds
CRECD 039 / May '94 / Creation

Revs

☐ REVS, THE
Just ask why / We're so modern / Stay with me / Julie got a raise / Selfish / Making time / Joyrider / Ten seconds of temptation
MASKCD 018 / Jan '93 / Vinyl Japan

Rex

☐ 3
185462 / 15 Sep '97 / Southern

☐ C
185322 / Oct '96 / Southern

☐ REX
185302 / Apr '95 / Southern

Rey, Alvino

☐ BY REQUEST
Blue rey / April in paris / Russian lullaby / Dardanella / Shiek of araby / Yesterdays / Blue lou / From the land of sky blue water / Bumble boogie / Two guitars / Stormy weather / Chinese lullaby / In an 18th century drawing room / Drowsy old riff / Rockin' chair / Nighty-night
HCD 249 / Jan '95 / Hindsight

Reyes, Jorge

☐ EK TUNKUL
7542977 / Feb '97 / Spalax

☐ NIERIKA
PS 9326 / Oct '93 / Silent

Reyes, Lucha

☐ CANCION MEXICANA
ALCD 019 / Jul '96 / Alma Latina

Reyes, Marcial

☐ PUERTO RICO IN WASHINGTON (Reyes, Marcial & Sus Pleneros De Bayamon)
SFWCD 40460 / Dec '96 / Smithsonian Folkways

Reykjavik Jazz Quartet

☐ REYKJAVIK JAZZ QUARTET
Changing weather / Alone together / So young / Flight 622 / Dark thoughts / Tongue in cheek / All the time / Hot house
JHCD 032 / Jul '94 / Ronnie Scott's Jazz House

Reynolds, Debbie

☐ DEBBIE/AM I THAT EASY TO FORGET
Love is a simple thing / S'posin' / You won't be satisfied / Moonglow / Hooray for love / Ev'ry time / You couldn't be cuter / Mean to me / Blue room / Here I am in love again / I like the likes of you / Time after time / Am I that easy to forget / Ask me to go steady / Summer romance / Aba daba honeymoon / I love you a thousand ways / Why not me / Just for a touch of your love / City lights / Too young to love / I can't love you anymore / Love is a thing
JASCD 604 / Oct '96 / Jasmine

Reynolds, Stan

☐ BIG BAND CHRISTMAS (Reynolds, Stan & Laurie Johnson)
PLSCD 266 / 29 Sep '97 / Pulse

Reynoso, Juan

☐ PLAYS SONES AND GUSTOS
CO 105 / Jan '94 / Corason

Rezillos

☐ ATTACK OF THE GIANT REVILLOS (Revillos)
Mind bending cuttie doll / Caveman raveman / Do the mutilation / Bitten by a lovebug / Hip city you were meant for me / Sputnik kids / She's fallen in love with a monster man / Man attack / Bongo man / Midnight / Man hunt / Tell him / Snatzomobile / Mad from birth to death / Graveyard groove / Your baby's gone / Santa claus is coming to town
RRCD 204 / Aug '95 / Receiver

☐ CAN'T STAND THE REZILLOS
Flying saucer attack / No / Someone's gonna get their head kicked in tonight / Top of the pops / 2000 AD / It gets me / Can't stand my baby / Glad all over / My baby does good sculptures / I like it / Gettin' me down / Cold wars / Bad guy reaction
7599269422 / Jan '96 / Sire

☐ FROM THE FREEZER (Revillos)
DAMGOOD 97CD / Sep '96 / Damaged Goods

☐ LIVE AND ON FIRE IN JAPAN (Revillos)
Secret of the shadow / Bongo brain / Rock-a-boom / She's fallen in love with a monster man / Where's the boy for me / Rev up / Bitten by a lovebug / Mad from birth to death / Bobby come back to me / Fiend / Scuba scuba / My baby does good / Sculptures / Do the mutilation / Somebody's gonna get their head kicked in tonight / Yeah yeah
ASKCD 046 / May '95 / Vinyl Japan

☐ MOTORBIKE BEAT (Revillos)
Motorbike / Where's the boy for me / Fiend / Rev up / Rock-a-boom / Bobby come back to me / Yeah yeah / On the beach / Bitten by a love bug / Cat call / Midnight / Z-X-7
MAUCD 643 / Jul '95 / Mau Mau

RF7
☐ ALL YOU CAN EAT
GTA 001CD / Aug '95 / Grand Theft Auto

RH Band
☐ THIRD ORDER PARASITISM
DFR 033 / 22 Sep '97 / Drunken Fish

Rhabstallion
☐ DAY TO DAY
Hard luck man / Chain reaction / Breadline / Day to day / I could not believe my eyes / Times ain't so bad / Runaway / Driving seat / Stranger stranger / Shock 'n' roll / Day go disco / Sioux child / You're to blame / Stranger stranger (Live)
ETHEL 001CD / 2 Feb '98 / Vinyl Tap

Rhapsody
☐ LEGENDARY TALES
SPV 08528562 / Dec '97 / SPV

Rhatigan
☐ LATE DEVELOPER
ORGAN 018CD / Jan '96 / Org

Rheinhallt H. Rowlands
☐ BUKOWSKI
ANKST 071CD / Jun '97 / Ankst

Rheostatics
☐ BLUE HYSTERIA
CARD 10392 / Dec '96 / Cargo

☐ INTRODUCING HAPPINESS '94
One more colour / Introducing happiness / Digital beach / Row / Earth monstrous hummingbirds / Onilley's strange dream / You are a treasure / Alomar / In this town / Cephallus worms uncle henry / Woods are full of cuckoos / Fish failin' / Me and stupid / Jesus was once a teenage fool / Take me in your hand / Full moon over russia / Claire / Fan letter to michael jackson
9362456702 / Aug '94 / Warner Bros.

Rhodes, Emitt
☐ DAISY FRESH
With my face on the floor / Somebody made for me / She's such a beauty / Long time no see / Lullaby / Fresh as a daisy / Live till you die / Promises I've made / You take the dark out of the night / You should be ashamed / Ever find yourself running / You must have / Birthday lady / Better side of life / Mirror / Really wanted you / Love will stone you / Golden child of God / Warm self sacrifice / Blue horizon / Shoot the moon / Only lovers decide / Tame the lion
EDCD 569 / 6 Jul '98 / Edsel

Rhodes, Kimmie
☐ JACKALOPES, MOONS AND ANGELS
3024442 / Nov '97 / Arcade

☐ WEST TEXAS HEAVEN
422505 / Feb '97 / New Rose

Rhodes, Sonny
☐ BLUES IS MY BEST FRIEND
KS 022 / Nov '94 / Flying Fish

☐ BORN TO BE BLUE
Born to be blue / End of my hope / Hide that wine / It's not funny anymore / All cried out / I'd rather be hot than cool / Five day rain / Can't get enough / Satan / She's my woman / Love don't get old / If I had the chance
KS 040 / May '98 / King Snake

☐ I DON'T WANT MY BLUES COLOURED BRIGHT
BM 9029 / May '94 / Black Magic

☐ IN EUROPE
APCD 023 / Mar '97 / Appaloosa

☐ JUST BLUES
I can't lose / Things I used to do / Please love me / House without love / Think / Cigarette blues / Strange things happening / It hurts me too / East Oakland stomp
ECD 26060 / Mar '95 / Evidence

Rhodes, Stephen
☐ MUSIC FOR HEALING
CD 260 / 6 Jul '98 / New World

☐ PERFUME
CD 236 / 6 Jul '98 / New World

Rhody, Alan
☐ DREAMER'S WORLD
TX 3005CD / Jan '94 / Taxim

Rhos Male Voice Choir
☐ WITH A VOICE OF SINGING
BNA 5083 / Aug '93 / Bandleader

Rhyne, Melvin
☐ BOSS ORGAN (Rhyne, Melvin Quartet)
CRISS 1080CD / May '94 / Criss Cross

☐ LEGEND, THE
CRISS 1059CD / May '92 / Criss Cross

☐ STICK TO THE KICK
J. Robin / Captain McDuff / Lady bird / Laura / Killer ray / Wail / It's love / Light life love / Stick to the kick
CRISS 1137CD / Dec '97 / Criss Cross

☐ TELL IT LIKE IT IS (Rhyne, Melvin & The Tenor Triangle)
1089CD / Mar '95 / Criss Cross

Rhythm & Noise
☐ CHASM'S ACCORD
ASP 0965CD / 22 Jun '98 / Asphodel

Rhythm & Sound
☐ SHOWCASE
GR 51CD / 29 Jun '98 / Burial Mix

Rhythm Cadillacs
☐ SHAKE THIS SHAK
ROCK CD 8808 / Oct '88 / Rockhouse

Rhythm Club Orchestra
☐ HOT 20'S STYLE
SOSCD 1327 / Feb '98 / Stomp Off

Rhythm Collision
☐ CLOBBER
DSR 039 / Nov '95 / Dr. Strange

☐ UNSAFE DRIVING IN 19 EASY STEPS
DSR 053CD / May '97 / Dr. Strange

Rhythm Devils
☐ APOCALYPSE NOW (Sessions)
Compound / Trenches / Street gang / Beast / Steps / Tar / Lance / Cave / Hall's bells / Kurtz / Napalm for breakfast
RCD 10109 / Sep '91 / Rykodisc

Rhythm Invention
☐ INVENTURES IN WONDERLAND
Tokyo / All jacked up / Inventures in wonderland / Zero ps / Chronoclasm / Methomania / Fresh momentum / Mad hi hatter / Pnutz / Ad infinitum / Fresh momentum (space dub) / Quattrocento / Exit
WARPCD 15 / Aug '93 / Warp

Rhythm Kings
☐ STRUTTIN' OUR STUFF
Green river / Walking on my own / Melody / Stuff (can't get enough) / Bad to be alone / I'm mad / Down in the bottom / Motorvatin' Mama / Jitterbug boogie / Going crazy overnight / Hole in my soul / Tobacco road
74321514412 / 6 Oct '97 / RCA Victor

Rhythm Orchids
☐ COMPLETE ROULETTE RECORDINGS (2CD Set)
Party doll / Don't make me cry / Hula love / Mary Lou / Maybellene / Cause I'm in love with you / Devil woman / Rock you little baby to sleep / Rockabilly walk / Rockhouse / (We're gonna) rock around the clock / Whenever I'm lonely / Swingin' Daddy / C'mon baby / Somebody touched me / Teasable, pleasable you / That's why I cry / Girl with the golden hair / All for you / I think I'm gonna kill myself / Just to be with you / Taste of the blues / I ain't takin' Sharon / Long lonely nights / Storm clouds / Something's got me going / You'll be glad / Eenie meenie minie moe / You made me love you / I'm stickin' with you / Everlovin' fingers / My baby's gone / Warm up to me baby / I trusted you / It's shameful / Cross over / Ever since that night / Aching hearts / Money honey / Raggedy Anne / Way back home / Last night / Stop wasting my time / Don't tell me your troubles / Can she kiss / I'm keeping you / Two step / By the light of the silvery moon / Stick with me / Whenever I'm lonely / My kind of woman / Blue moon / Always faithful / Wish I were tied to you / Walkin' on air / You're just wasting your time / (I need) your lovin' / Arms / Oh yeah, oh yeah, oh yeah / Mm mm / Just lookin'
NEDCD 278 / May '96 / Sequel

Rhythm Pigs
☐ BABY FALCON GETAWAY
WW 01 / Mar '96 / Werk Works

Rhythmaires
☐ 10TH ANNIVERSARY
RAUCD 006 / May '93 / Raucous

Rhythmakers
☐ RHYTHMAKERS 1932, THE
Bugle call rag / Oh Peter / Margie / Spider crawl / Who's sorry now / Take it slow and easy / Bald headed mama / (I would do) anything for you / Mean old bedbug blues / Yellow dog blues / Yes suh / Who stole the lock / Shine on your shoes / It's gonna be you / Somebody stole Gabriel's horn
158842 / Feb '97 / Jazz Archives

Rhythmic State Crew
☐ STATE CREW JAM (2CD Set)
Do your own thing / Funky MC / Power people / Get it together / Way it goes / Punks gonna pay / Now or never / Popped up / In the music / Keepin' on / Groove on / More those feet / State crew jam / Feels good / Time 2 get sweeter / Just when you want / No DS allowed / Get real / Can I get a yes / Bad MF / Creator / Rock with me / Soap on a rope / 3rd sound / 14th message / Critical mass
DCSR 013 / Apr '97 / Clubscene

Rialto
☐ RIALTO
Monday morning / Dream another dream / Broken Barbie doll / Summer's over / Untouchable / Hard candy / Quarantine / Lucky number / Love like amnesia
0630197452 / 6 Apr '98 / East West

☐ RIALTO
Monday morning 5:19 / Dream another dream / Broken Barbie doll / Summer's over / Untouchable / Hard candy / Quarantine / Lucky number / Love like Semtex / When we're together / Underdogs / Milk of amnesia
WOLCD 1086 / 13 Jul '98 / China

Rias Orchestra
☐ ORCHESTRAL COLOURS
ISCD 119 / '91 / Intersound

Ribeiro, Catherine
☐ CHANSONS DE LEGENDE
3027012 / 24 Feb '98 / Arcade

Ribeiro, Thomas
☐ JET SET SOIREE
My love ain't the kind / Contrast / Fool for you / Rocket ship / Rudy / Midnight rain / Shadows / Heartaches / Honey shampoo / Don't let me be / If it takes all night
BRCD 622 / Oct '96 / 4th & Broadway

Ribeiro, Zezo
☐ GANDAIO
Bom retiro / Caminhos de Azul / Gandaia / Agua de Pupila / Beriba / Ilha da Magia / Beatriz / A notre e pra quem sabe / Aguia de Aiia / So quero um xodo / Maluquinho / A falsa mare
INT 32482 / 27 Jul '98 / Intuition

Ribot, Marc
☐ DON'T BLAME ME
DIW 902 / Dec '95 / DIW

☐ PLAYS SOLO GUITAR WORKS OF FRANTZ CASSEUS
TWI 9792 / May '96 / Les Disques Du Crepuscule

☐ REQUIEM FOR WHAT'S-HIS-NAME
TWI 9692 / May '96 / Les Disques Du Crepuscule

☐ SHOE STRING SYMPHONETTES
TZA 7504 / Feb '97 / Tzadik

☐ SHREK
AVAN 033CD / Jul '94 / Avant

RIC
☐ DISTANCE
EFA 006552 / Sep '94 / Mille Plateau

Ricardos
☐ WILD SATURDAY NITE
RAUCD 026 / 10 Nov '97 / Raucous

Ricardos Jazzmen
☐ OLE MISS
MECCACD 1022 / Nov '94 / Music Mecca

Ricchizzi, Gianni
☐ RAGA YAMAN/RAGA BHUPALI
NI 5431 / Apr '95 / Nimbus

Ricci, George
☐ BIG HONK, A (Ricci, George & The Improverts/Lol Coxhill)
Big honk / Beyond the bell / Wave / Six fifty / Lost and found / Little mystery / Autumn leaves / Three songs for Dudu / I can't get started
SLAMCD 202 / Oct '96 / Slam

Rice
☐ FUCK YOU, THIS IS RICE
LOOKOUT 93CD / Nov '94 / Lookout

Rice, Boyd
☐ BOYD RICE PRESENTS LEGIONARI
H330 3CD / Oct '96 / Hierarchy

☐ EASY LISTENING FOR THE HARD OF HEARING (Rice, Boyd & Frank Tovey)
CDSTUMM 20 / May '96 / Mute

☐ HATESVILLE
H330 1CD / Oct '96 / Hierarchy

☐ MUSIC, MARTINIS...
BADVCCD 1969 / Oct '96 / New European

☐ RAGNAROK RUNE
WSB 13 / Oct '96 / World Serpent

Rice Brothers
☐ RICE BROTHERS VOL.1, THE
Grapes on the vine / This ole house / Original unlimited / Teardrops in my eyes / You're drifting away / Don't think twice, it's alright / Let it ride / Keep the light on Sadie / Soldier's joy / Whisper my name / Life is like a mountain railroad
ROUCD 0256 / '89 / Rounder

☐ RICE BROTHERS VOL.2, THE
ROUCD 0286 / Nov '94 / Rounder

Rice, Daryle
☐ FROM NOW ON
APCD 100 / Jun '94 / Appaloosa

Rice, Larry
☐ NOTIONS AND NOVELTIES
REB 1734CD / Dec '96 / Rebel

Rice, Ross
☐ UMPTEEN
10532 / Dec '97 / E-Squared

Rice, Tony
☐ ACOUSTICS
ROUCD 0317 / Jul '94 / Rounder

☐ BACKWATERS (Rice, Tony Unit)
Common ground / Just some bar in the french quarters / Backwaters / My favourite things / Child is born / On green dolphin street / Mississippi mambo
ROUCD 0167 / Aug '88 / Rounder

☐ CHURCH STREET BLUES
Church Street blues / Cattle in the cane / Streets of London / One more night / Gold rush / Any old time / Orphan Annie / House carpenter / Jerusalem Ridge / Last thing on my mind / Pride of man
SHCD 3732 / Jan '97 / Sugar Hill

☐ COLD ON THE SHOULDER
Cold on the shoulder / Wayfaring stranger / John Hardy / Fare thee well / Bitter green / Mule skinner blues / Song for life / Why don't you tell me so / If you only knew / Likes of me / I think it's going to rain today
ROUCD 0183 / Dec '86 / Rounder

☐ DEVLIN (Rice, Tony Unit)
Devlin / Is that so / Waltz for indira / Within specs / Untitled as of yet / Neon tetra / Night coach / Nardis / E b a / Mar west / Moses sole / Birdland breakdown / Whoa baby, every day I wake up with the blues / Vonetta / Makers mark
ROUCD 11531 / '88 / Rounder

☐ MANZANITA
Old train / Manzanita / Little sadie / Blackberry blossom / Nine pound hammer / Hold whatcha got / Blue railroad train / Ginseng sullivan / Midnight on the stormy deep / I hope you have learned / Stony point / Home from the forest
ROUCD 0092 / '88 / Rounder

☐ ME AND MY GUITAR
Me and my guitar / Four strong winds / Walls / Greenlight on the southern / Port tobacco / Early morning rain / Sixteen miles / Hard love / Tipper / Song for a winter's night / Sweetheart like you / Fine as fine can be
ROUCD 0201 / Aug '88 / Rounder

☐ NATIVE AMERICAN
Shadows / St. James hospital / Night flyer / Why me like a hundred miles / Changes / Brother to the wind / John Wilkes Booth / Summer wages
ROUCD 0248 / Aug '88 / Rounder

☐ PLAYS & SINGS BLUEGRASS
ROUCD 253 / Jan '94 / Rounder

☐ **RIVER SUITE FOR TWO GUITARS (Rice, Tony & John Carlini)**
SHCD 3837 / May '95 / Sugar Hill

☐ **TONY RICE**
Banks of the ohio / Rattlesnake / Mr. engineer / Plastic banana / Don't give your heart to a rambler / Farewell blues / Way downtown / Stoney creek / Hills of roane county / Eighth of january / Big mon / Temperance reel
ROUCD 0085 / '88 / Rounder

☐ **TONY RICE SINGS GORDON LIGHTFOOT**
ROUCD 0370 / Aug '96 / Rounder

Rice, Wyatt

☐ **NEW MARKET GAP**
ROUCD 272 / Dec '90 / Rounder

☐ **PICTURE IN A TEAR (Rice, Wyatt & Santa Cruz)**
Picture in a tear / Molly / Santa Cruz breakdown / Sweetest rose / He died a Rounder at 21 / Separate ways / Katy did / Someone's telling lies / It's goodbye and so long to you / Can't help but wonder where I'm bound / I just don't know what I'll do / In his love I'll abide
ROUCD 0372 / Oct '96 / Rounder

Rich, Buddy

☐ **BIG SWING FACE**
Norwegian wood / Big swing face / Monitor theme / Wack wack / Love for sale / Mexicali rose / Willowcrest / Beat goes on / Bugle call rag / Standing up in a hammock / Chicago / Lament for Lester / Machine / Silver threads among the blue / New blues / Od timey / Loose / Apples
CDP 8379892 / Jul '96 / Pacific Jazz

☐ **BUDDY AND SOUL**
Love and peace / St. Petersburg race / Soul lady / Street kiddie / Greensleeves / Soul kitchen / Hello I love you / Comin' home baby / Meaning of the blues / Ruth
BGOCD 23 / Jun '94 / Beat Goes On

☐ **BUDDY RICH AND HIS ORCHESTRA (Rich, Buddy & His Orchestra)**
15758 / Aug '92 / Laserlight

☐ **BUDDY RICH COLLECTION, THE (Rich, Buddy Big Band)**
Big swing face / Willowcrest / Alfie / Mexicali rose / Groovin' hard / Long day's journey / Preach and teach / Celebration / Basically blues / Critic's choice / Meaning of the blues / Winning the west / Group shot / Machine / I can't get started / Diabolus
BGOCD 377 / 15 Jun '98 / Beat Goes On

☐ **EASE ON DOWN THE ROAD (Rich, Buddy & His Big Band)**
Time check / Backwoods sideman / Nuttville / Playhouse / Senator Sam / Big Mac / Three day sucker / Ease on down the road / Tommy (medley) / Pieces of dreams / Lush life / Nik-nik / Layin' it down
CDC 8511 / Sep '93 / LRC
17095 / Mar '97 / Laserlight

☐ **EUROPE 77 (Rich, Buddy & His Orchestra)**
DAWE 60 / Nov '93 / Magic

☐ **HIS LEGENDARY 1947-1948 ORCHESTRA**
I've got news for you / Man could be a wonderful thing / Good bait / Blue skies / Just you, just me / I believe / What is this thing called love / Daily double / Nellie's nightmare / Little white lies / You go to my head / Queer Street / Fine and dandy / That's rich / I may be wrong, but I think you're wonderful / Robbin's nest / Four rich brothers / Carioca
HEPCD 12 / Aug '91 / Hep

☐ **LAST BLUES ALBUM VOL.1**
CDGR 192 / Dec '97 / Charly

☐ **LEGENDARY 1946-1948 ORCHESTRAS VOL.2, THE**
Let's blow / Poor little rich bud / Goof and I / What is this thing called love / On a slow boat to China / Robbin's nest / Over the rainbow / Flamingo / AAron's axe
HEPCD 56 / 16 Feb '98 / Hep

☐ **LIONEL HAMPTON PRESENTS BUDDY RICH (Rich, Buddy & Lionel Hampton)**
Moment's notice / Giant steps / Buddy's Cherokee / Take the 'A' train / I'll never be the same / Latin silk / Buddy's rock / My funny valentine
CDGATE 7011 / Jun '87 / Kingdom Jazz

☐ **MASTER OF DRUMS**
Moment's notice / Giant steps / Buddy's cherokee / Take the 'A' train / I'll never be the same / Latin silk
722 005 / May '93 / Scorpio

☐ **MERCY MERCY (Rich, Buddy & His Big Band)**
Mercy mercy mercy / Preach and teach / Channel 1 suite / Big Mama Cass / Goodbye yesterday / Acid truth / Alfie / Ode to Billie Joe / Chavala / Mr. Lucky / Chelsea Bridge / Get happy
CDP 8543312 / Mar '97 / Pacific Jazz

☐ **MERCY MERCY (Rich, Buddy & His Big Band)**
BGOCD 386 / 8 Dec '97 / Beat Goes On

☐ **RICH AND FAMOUS**
Red snapper / Time will tell / Ballad of the matador / Dancing man / Cotton tail / One and only love / Manhattan - the city / Manhattan - central park
CDMT 004 / Jul '95 / Meteor

☐ **SELECTIONS FROM WEST SIDE STORY (AND OTHER DELIGHTS) (Rich, Buddy & Maynard Ferguson)**
West Side Story / Kilimanjaro cookout / Prelude to a kiss / Waltz of the mushroom hunters / Pilatus / Foggy night / Maria / Got the spirit / At the sound of the trumpet
17092 / Jan '97 / Laserlight

☐ **SWINGIN NEW BIG BAND/KEEP THE CUSTOMERS SATISFIED**
Readymix / Basically blues / Critic's choice / My mans gone now / Up tight / Sister Sadie / More soul / West side story Medley: / Keep the customer satisfied / Long days journey / Midnight cowboy medley / Celebration / Groovin' hard / Juicer is wild / Winning the west
BGOCD 169 / Feb '93 / Beat Goes On

☐ **SWINGIN' NEW BIG BAND**
Readymix / Basically blues / Critic's choice / My man's gone now / Up tight (everything's alright) / Sister Sadie / More soul / West Side Story medley / What'd I say / Step right up / Apples / In a mellotone / Lament for Lester / Naptown blues / Hoe down
CDP 8352322 / Jan '96 / Pacific Jazz

☐ **TAKE IT AWAY (Rich, Buddy & His Big Band)**
Away we go / Machine / Rotten kid / New blues / Something for willie / Standing up in a hammock / Chicago / Luv / I can't get started / Group shot / Diabolus
BGOCD 210 / Oct '93 / Beat Goes On

Rich, Charlie

☐ **BEHIND CLOSED DOORS**
PLSCD 110 / Apr '96 / Pulse

☐ **BIG BOSS MAN**
379712 / May '98 / Koch Country

☐ **BOSS MAN**
340502 / Aug '95 / Koch

☐ **FABULOUS CHARLIE RICH, THE**
340492 / May '95 / Koch

☐ **GREATEST HITS**
Most beautiful girl / Very special love song / Since I fell for you / My elusive dreams / Every time you touch me (I get high) / Behind closed doors / Life has its little ups and downs / All over me / I love my friend / We love each other / Daddy don't you walk so fast / She / Sunday kind of woman / Rollin' with the flow / Almost persuaded / Spanish eyes
4721242 / 26 Jan '98 / Epic

☐ **LONELY WEEKENDS (The Sun Years 1958-1963 - 3CD Set)**
Whirlwind / Philadelphia Bay / Big man / Rebound / Everything I do is wrong / Lonely weekends / School days / Gonna be waitin' / Stay / On my knees / Who will the next fool be / Caught in the middle / It's too late / Just a little bit sweet / Midnite blues / Easy money / Sittin' and thinkin' / Finally found out / There's another place I can't go / I need your love / Red man / Juanita / Break up / That's how much I love you / Apple blossom time / CC rider / Come back / Sad news / Whirlwind / It's too late / School days / Rebound / Rebound / Time and again / Stop thief / Lonely hurt within / Big man / Stay / Goodbye Mary Ann / My heart cries for you / Unchained melody / Lonely weekends / Sail away / My baby done left me / That's rich / Everything I do is wrong / Too many tears / Rebound / I've lost my heart to you / What's my name / You made a hit / Stay / Now everybody knows / Jeannie with the light brown hair / Everyday / Popcorn Polly / Cloud nine / Gentle as a lamb / Wedding is over / I need your love / Lonely weekends / Little woman friend of mine / Little woman friend of mine / Ain't it a shame / Stop fakin' your love / It hurt me so / Juicehead baby / Loneliest days / Baby I need you / I said baby / Give in / There won't be anymore / Charlie's boogie / Every day / Yes Ma'am / Don't put no headstone on my grave / My baby done left me / Sail away / Graveyardville / Time's a-wasting / I love no one but you / Ways of a woman in love / Deep freeze / How blue can you be / Blue suede shoes / Sittin' and thinkin' / Untitled instrumental / Thanks a lot / Right behind you baby / Baby I need you / Oh lonely days / Life is a flower / Portrait of my love / I'm making plans / Donna Lee
BCD 16152 / Mar '98 / Bear Family

☐ **MASTERS, THE**
EABCD 023 / 24 Nov '97 / Eagle

☐ **MOST BEAUTIFUL GIRL IN THE WORLD**
Lonely weekends / Mohair sam / Life has its little ups and downs / Who will the next fool be / I take it on home / Behind closed doors / Most beautiful girl / There won't be anymore / My elusive dreams / My mountain dew / Rollin' with the flow / On my knees / Big boss man / Sittin' and thinkin' / You don't know me / Break up / Pass on by / Good time charlie's got the blues / CC rider / I feel like going home
CTS 55426 / Jun '94 / Country Stars

☐ **SET ME FREE**
340482 / May '95 / Koch

☐ **SINGS HANK WILLIAMS**
My heart would know / Take these chains from my heart / Half as much / You win again / I can't help it / Hey good lookin' / Your cheatin' heart / Cold cold heart / Nobody's lonesome for me / I'm so lonesome I could cry / Wedding bells / They'll never take her love from me / Love is after me / Pass on by / Hurry up freight train / Only me / When something is wrong with my baby / Don't tear me down / Can't get it right / I'll shed no tears / To fool a fool / Who will the next fool be / Big time operator / Renee / Motels, hotels
DIAB 810 / Oct '95 / Diablo

☐ **THAT'S RICH**
CPCD 8146 / Nov '95 / Charly

☐ **VERY BEST OF CHARLIE RICH, THE**
Most beautiful girl / Big boss man / Rollin' with the flow / Life has it's little ups and downs / Mohair Sam / Sittin' and thinkin' / My elusive dreams / Lonely weekends / You don't know me / Mountain dew / Behind closed doors / Take it on home / Break up / There won't be any more / On my knees / Pass on by / Good time Charlie's got the blues / Who will the next fool be
PLATCD 218 / Feb '97 / Platinum

Rich, Dave

☐ **AIN'T IT FINE**
Your pretty blue eyes / Ain't it fine / I'm glad / Didn't work out did it / I'm sorry goodbye / Darling I'm lonesome / Tuggin' on my heart strings / I love 'em all / I forgot / I think I'm gonna die / Lonely street / Our last night together / City lights / Rosie let's get cozy / Burn on love fire / Red sweater / I've learned / Red beads / School blues / Sunshine in my heart / Chicken house / That's what this whole world needs / Saved from sin / Brand new feeling / Where else would I want to be / Key to my heart / I've thought it over / Just like mine
BCD 15763 / Nov '94 / Bear Family

Rich Kids

☐ **GHOSTS OF PRINCES IN TOWERS**
Strange one / Hung on you / Ghosts of princes in towers / Cheap emotion / Marching men / Put you in the picture / Young girls / Bullet proof lover / Rich kids / Lovers and fools / Burning sounds
DOJOCD 151 / Sep '93 / Dojo

Rich Kids On LSD

☐ **RICHES TO RAGS**
E 864452 / Jan '95 / Epitaph

☐ **ROCK 'N' ROLL**
E 864262 / Jun '92 / Epitaph

Rich, Tony

☐ **BIRDSEYE**
3008260422 / 10 Aug '98 / Arista

☐ **WORDS (Rich, Tony Project)**
Hey blue / Nobody knows / Like a woman / Grass is green / Ghost / Leavin' / Billy goat / Under her spell / Little ones / Missin' you
73008260222 / May '96 / Arista

Rich, Tony

☐ **MAN OF CYRENE MOVEMENT VOL.1**
ANGCD 022 / 17 Nov '97 / Angella

Rich Young Ruler

☐ **RICH YOUNG RULER**
Feeling this way / You've got the right words / Wearing me out / Reach for me / Anyways / Alone again today / Run around / Even all your sorrows / She runs she hides / Take it anywhere / All your sorrows / Smile / In touch / If I could hold you
8441822662 / Apr '98 / Integrity

Richard, Cliff

☐ **21 TODAY**
Happy birthday to you / Forty days (to come back home) / Catch me / How wonderful to know / Tough enough / Fifty Years for every kiss / Night is so lonely / Poor boy / Y'arriva / Outsider / Tea for two / Without you / Mighty lonely man / My blue heaven / Shame on you
4954422 / 8 Jun '98 / EMI

☐ **32 MINUTES AND 17 SECONDS**
It'll be me / So I've been told / How long is forever / I'm walking the blues / Turn around / Blueberry hill / Let's make a memory / When my dreamboat comes home / I'm on my way / Spanish harlem / You don't know / Falling in love with you / Who are we to say / I wake up crying
4954432 / 8 Jun '98 / EMI

☐ **40 GOLDEN GREATS (2CD Set)**
Move it / Living doll / Travellin' light / Fall in love with you / Please don't tease / Nine times out of ten / Theme for a dream / Gee whiz it's you / When the girl in your arms (is the girl in your heart) / Girl like you / Young ones / Do you wanna dance / I'm lookin' out the window / It'll be me / Bachelor boy / Next time / Summer holiday / Lucky lips / It's all in the game / Don't talk to him / Constantly / On the beach / I could easily fall / Minute you're gone / Wind me up (let me go) / Visions / Blue turns to grey / In the country / Day I met Marie / All my love / Congratulations / Throw down a line / Goodbye Sam, hello Samantha / Sing a song of freedom / Power to all our friends / You keep me hangin' on / Miss you nights / Devil woman / I can't ask for anymore than you / My kinda life / Thief in the night
CDS 7924252 / Jun '89 / EMI

☐ **ALWAYS GUARANTEED**
One night / Once upon a time / Some people / Forever / Two hearts / Under your spell / This time now / My pretty one / Remember me / Always guaranteed
CDP 7467052 / '89 / EMI

☐ **CAROLS**
Saviour's day / Silent night / Little town / In the bleak mid-Winter / Sweet little Jesus boy / While shepherds watched their flocks by night / Mary / What you gonna name that pretty little baby / Joseph / God rest ye merry gentlemen / Unto us a child is born / Can it be true / O little town of Bethlehem
ALD 025 / Oct '95 / Alliance Music

☐ **CLIFF**
Apron strings / My babe / Down the line / I got a feeling / Jet black / Baby I don't care / Donna / Move it / Ready Teddy / Too much / Don't bug me baby / Driftin' / That'll be the day / Be bop a lula / Danny / Whole lotta shakin' goin' on
4954382 / 8 Jun '98 / EMI

☐ **CLIFF RICHARD AT THE MOVIES 1959-1974 (2CD Set)**
No turning back / Living doll / Mad about you / Love / Voices in the wilderness / Shrine on the second floor / Friday night / Got a funny feeling / Nothing is impossible / Young ones / Lessons in love / When the girl in your arms / We say yeah (it's wonderful to be young) / Outsider / Seven days to a holiday / Summer holiday / Let us take you for a ride / Stranger in town / Bachelor boy / Swingin' affair / Dancing shoes / Next time / Big news / Wonderful life / Girl in every port / Little imagination / On the beach / Do you remember / Look don't touch / In the stars / What've I gotta do / Matter of moments / Shooting star / Finders keepers / Time drags by / Washerwoman / La la la song / Oh senorita / This day / Paella / Two a penny / Twist and shout / I'll love you forever today / Questions / It's only money / Midnight blue / Game / Brumburger duet / Take me high / Anti-brotherhood of man / Winning
CDEMD 1096 / Jul '96 / EMI

☐ **CLIFF SINGS**
Blue suede shoes / Snake and the book worm / I gotta know / Here comes the summer / I'll string along with you / Embraceable you / As time goes by / Touch of your lips / Twenty flight rock / Pointed toe shoes / Mean woman blues / I'm walking / I don't know why / Little things mean a lot / Somewhere along the way / That's my desire
4954392 / 8 Jun '98 / EMI

☐ **INSTRUMENTAL MEMORIES (Various Artists)**
Young ones / Bachelor boy / Lucky lips / I could easily fall in love with you / It's all in the game / Move it / Miss you nights / From a distance / Devil woman / All I ask / Do you wanna dance / Travellin' light / Summer holiday / Living doll / Constantly / We don't talk anymore / Stronger than that / Some people / Please don't tease / Mistletoe and wine
309202 / 13 Jul '98 / Hallmark

☐ **LISTEN TO CLIFF**
What'd I say / Blue moon / True love will come to you / Lover / Unchained melody / Idle gossip / First lesson / Almost like being in love / Beat out that rhythm on a drum / Memories linger on / Temptation / I live for you / Sentimental journey / I want you to know / We kiss in a shadow / It's you / It'll be me / So I've been told / How long is forever / I'm walkin' the blues / Turn around / Blueberry Hill / Let's make a memory / When my dreamboat comes home / I'm on my way / Spanish Harlem / You don't know / Falling in love with love / Who are we to say / I wake up crying
4954412 / 8 Jun '98 / EMI

☐ **LOVE SONGS**
Miss you nights / Constantly / Up in the world / Carrie / Voice in the wilderness / Twelfth of never / I could easily fall / Day I met Marie / Can't take the hurt anymore / Little in love / Minute you're gone / Visions / When two worlds drift apart / Next time / It's all in the game / Don't talk to him / When the girl in your arms (is the girl in your heart) / Theme for a dream / Fall in love with you / We don't talk anymore
CDEMTV 27 / Mar '88 / EMI

☐ **ME AND MY SHADOWS**
I'm gonna get you / You and I / Cannot find a true love / Evergreen tree / She's gone / Left out again / You're just the one to do it / Lamp of love / Choppin' and changin' / We have it made / Tell me / Gee whizz / I love you / I'm willing to learn / I don't know / Working after school
4954402 / 8 Jun '98 / EMI

☐ **ON THE CONTINENT (5CD/Book Set)**
Bin verliebt / Die stimme der liebe / Schon wie ein traum / Vreneli / Rote lippen soll man kussen / Zuviel allein / Sag 'np' zu ihm / Das ist fei frage aller fragen / Nur mit dir / Es war keine so / Es war keine so wunderbar wie du / Es konnte schon morgen sein / Glaub' nur mir / Nur bei dir bin ich zu haus / Du bist mein erster gedanke / Was ist dabei / Das gluck ist rosarot / Was kann ich tunn / Ein girl wie du / Bilder von dir / Ein sonntag mit Marie / Es ist nicht gut allein zu sein / Mrs. Emily Jones / Ich kann treu sein / Sternengold / London ist nicht weit / Wonderful world / Marianne / Geh deinen weg nicht so allein / Twist im blut / Mr. Niemand / Die liebe ist immer heute / Fragen / Stell mich deinen eltern vor / Deine augen traumen Mary / Shoom llama boom boom / Story ohne happy end / Kein zug nch Gretna Green / Du du gefallst mir so / Lieben kann man einmal nur / Goodbye Sam das ist die liebe / Umbarella / Lass uns schnell vergessen / Das girl von nebenan / Du fragst mich immer wieder / Wenn du lachst du lachst / Ein spiel ohne grenzen / Concerto / Neben dir wird's keine geben / Zum heiraten bin ich dein typ / Der mann neben dir / Ich traume deine traume / Kleine taube / Gut dass es freunde gibt / Es gehoren zwei zum glucklichsein / Liebesleid / O mio signore / Come prima / Concerto d'autumno / Arrivederci roma / Legata ad un granello di sabbia / Nel blue dipinto di blu / Dicintello vuie / Casa senza finestre / Maria ninguem / Non l'ascoltare / Imagina un giorno / Oh no no / Congratulations / Chi lo sa / Non dimenticar chi ti arna / Chi lo sa / Boum / La mer / J'attendrai / C'est si bon / Quelle histoire / Releve mon defi / Je suis formidable / La ballade / L'amandier sauvage / Il faut chanter la vie / Je t'aime pour toujours / Perfidia / Frenesi / Tus besos / Amor amor amor / Solamente una vez / Quizas quizas quizas / Cancia de orfeo / Quien sera / Te quiero dijeste / Vaya con dios / Me lo dizo adela / Maria no mas / Que buena suerta / Todo el poder a los amigos
BCD 15903 / Nov '97 / Bear Family

☐ **PRIVATE COLLECTION (His Personal Best 1979-1988)**
Some people / Wired for sound / All I ask of you: *Richard, Cliff & Sarah Brightman* / Carrie / Remember me / True love ways / Dreamin' / Green light / She means nothing to me: *Richard, Cliff & Phil Everly* / Heart user / Little in love / Daddy's home / We don't talk anymore / Never say die (give a little bit

more) / Only way out / Suddenly: *Richard, Cliff & Olivia Newton-John* / Slow rivers: *Richard, Cliff & Elton John* / Please don't fall in love / Little town / My pretty one / Ocean deep / She's so beautiful / Two hearts / Mistletoe and wine
CDCRTV 30 / Nov '88 / EMI

☐ ROCK 'N' ROLL 1958-1963 (4CD Set)
Schoolboy crush / High class baby / My feet hit the ground / Don't bug me baby / King creole / TV hop / Rockin' robin / I'll try / High school confidential / Early in the morning / Somebody touched me / Livin' lovin' doll / Mean streak / Never mind / Steady with you / My babe / Move it / That'll be the day / Danny / Whole lotta shakin' goin' on / One night / Apron strings / Dynamite / I gotta know / Snake and the bookworm / Here comes summertime / Twenty flight rock / Blue suede shoes / Mean woman blues / Pointed toe shoes / I'm walkin' / Don't be mad at me / Willie and the hand jive / Nine times out of ten / Thinking of our love / Ever green tree / She's gone / Tell me / Where is my heart / Lamp of love / I'm gonna help you / I cannot find a true love / Working after school / You and I / I'm willing to learn / We have it made / Choppin' and changin' / It's you / I love you / In love / Catch me / Now's the time to fall in love / True love will come to you / First lesson in love / I want you to know / Blue moon / Tough enough / Mumblin' mosie / Fifty tears for every kiss / Unchained melody / What I'd say / Forty days / Without you / Shame on you / Spanish Harlem / Do you remember / I'm looking out of the window / You don't know / Take special care / Do ya wanna dance / Do ya wanna dance / Since I lost you / Dim dim the lights / Save my soul / I'm walkin' the blues / Summer holiday / Next time / Blueberry hill / A forever kind of love / Razzle dazzle / Reelin' and rockin' / It's all in the game / Lawdy Miss Clawdy / Breathless / Twenty flight rock / Jailhouse rock / Money honey / Heartbreak Hotel / Turn me loose / Who's gonna take it home / Lets stick together / What'd I say / Forty days / I got a funny feeling / Rosalie / Me and my shadows / Lessons in love / We say yeah / Hang up your rock and roll shoes / Dancing shoes / It'll be me
CDCLIFF 001 / 1 Dec '97 / EMI

☐ ROCK 'N' ROLL YEARS, THE
Lawdy Miss Clawdy / Move it / 20 flight rock / High class baby / My feet hit the ground / Livin' lovin' doll / Blue suede shoes / We say yeah / Mean streak / Nine times out of ten / That'll be the day / Choppin' and changin' / Do you wanna dance / Dancing shoes / Dynamite / What'd I say / Without you / Mean woman blues / Oh boy medley / Don't bug me baby / No turning back / Whole lotta shakin' goin' on / Living doll / I'm walking / Willie and the hand jive / Blueberry Hill / Please don't tease
CDEMD 1109 / Jul '97 / EMI

☐ SUMMER HOLIDAY (Richard, Cliff & The Shadows)
Seven days to a holiday / Summer holiday / Let us take you for a ride / Les girls / Foot tapper / Round and round / Stranger in town / Orlando's mime / Bachelor boy / Swingin' affair / Really waltzing / All at once / Dancing shoes / Yugoslav wedding / Next time / Big news
CDMFP 6021 / Apr '88 / Music For Pleasure

☐ WINNER, THE
Winner / Wild geese / Such is the mystery / Reunion of the heart / Discovering / There's more to life / Peace in our time / Under the gun / Yesterday, today, forever / Where you are / Be in my heart / Fighter / Thief in my heart / From a distance
ALD 020 / May '95 / Alliance Music

☐ YOUNG ONES, THE (Richard, Cliff & The Shadows)
Friday night / Got a funny feeling / Peace pipe / Nothing's impossible / Young ones / All for one / Lessons in love / No one for me but Nicky / What d'you know, we've got a show / Vaudeville routine / Mambo / Savage / We say yeah
CDMFP 6020 / Apr '88 / Music For Pleasure

Richard, Gary

☐ ONCE UPON FOREVER
M 38D / Aug '96 / World Disc

Richards, Ann

☐ I'M SHOOTING HIGH
I'm shooting high / Moanin' low / Nightingale / Blues in my heart / I've got to pass your house to get to my house / Deep night / Poor little rich girl / Should I / I'm in the market for you / Absence makes the heart grow fonder / Lullaby of Broadway / Will you still be mine
JASCD 310 / Jun '97 / Jasmine

☐ LIVE AT LOSERS/REMEMBER MILDRED BAILEY (Richards, Ann & Mavis Rivers)
VJ 018 / 24 Apr '98 / Vee Jay

Richards, Goff

☐ GOFF RICHARDS & THE BRITISH NUCLEAR FUEL BAND (Richards, Goff & BNFL Band)
QPRL 055D / Apr '93 / Polyphonic

Richards, Johnny

☐ LIVE IN HI-FI STEREO 1957-58 (Richards, Johnny Big Band)
JH 1010 / '91 / Jazz Hour

Richards, Keith

☐ LIVE AT THE HOLLYWOOD PALLADIUM '88 (Richards, Keith & The X-Pensive Winos)
Take it so hard / How I wish / I could have stood you up / Too rude / Make no mistake / Time is on my side / Big enough / Whip it up / Locked away / Struggle / Happy / Connection / Rockawhile
CDVUS 45 / Feb '92 / Virgin

☐ MAIN OFFENDER
999 / Wicked as it seems / Eileen / Words of wonder / Yap yap / Bodytalks / Hate it when you leave / Runnin' too deep / Will but you won't / Demon
CDVUS 59 / Oct '92 / Virgin

☐ TALK IS CHEAP
Big enough / Take it so hard / Struggle / I could have stood you up / Make no mistake / You don't move me / How I wish / Rockawhile / Whip it up / Locked away / It means a lot
CDV 2554 / '88 / Virgin

Richards, Red

☐ DREAMY
SKCD 23053 / Aug '94 / Sackville

☐ GROOVE MOVE (Richards, Red & George Kelly Sextet)
JP 1045 / May '95 / Jazz Point

☐ LULLABY IN RHYTHM
SKCD 23044 / Jun '93 / Sackville

☐ MY ROMANCE
CDJP 1042 / May '94 / Jazz Point

☐ SWING TIME
CDJP 1041 / May '94 / Jazz Point

Richards, Sue

☐ GREY EYED MORN
MMCD 201 / Dec '94 / Maggie's Music

☐ MORNING AIRE
MMCD 204 / Dec '94 / Maggie's Music

Richards, Terrie

☐ I CRIED FOR YOU (Richards, Terrie & Harry Allen/Howard Alden)
CHECD 00107 / Oct '93 / Master Mix

Richards, Tim

☐ OTHER SIDE (Richards, Tim Trio)
Other side / Body and soul / Coincidence calypso / Blues the most / Freedom jazz dance / Alice in Wonderland / String bean / Seven steps to heaven / Beautiful love / Milestones / Polkadots and moonbeams / Blues in three / Caravan / Georgia on my mind / Broccoli blues
33JAZZ 037 / 20 Apr '98 / 33 Jazz

Richards, Trevor

☐ TREVOR RICHARDS NEW ORLEANS TRIO
SOSCD 1222 / Oct '92 / Stomp Off

Richardson, Geoffrey

☐ VIOLA MON AMOUR
Rhapsodic uke / Blossomville / Borrowed kalimba / On the beech / Life drawing / Blossomville (reprise) / Viola mon amour / Diogenes and Alexander / Well tempered ukelele / Fifty four homes / Rhapsodic uke (reprise) / Diogenes and Alexander (reprise)
VP 132CD / Jun '93 / Voiceprint

Richardson, Jerome

☐ JAZZ STATION RUNAWAY
Jazz station runaway / Lady Rowena / Midnite strut / Warm valley / Con Man / Autumn lites / Freedom and salvation / Nouveau you know / Gumbo robo / In a sentimental mood / Groove merchant
TCB 97402 / 27 Oct '97 / TCB

Richardson, Jim

☐ REVISITED (Richardson, Jim 'Pogo')
Mellow D / Three in one / Hackensack / Beatrice / Improvisation no.2 / Tricotism / Oscar rides again / Pettiford / Two little pearls / Samba / Ease it / Margarine / Laverne Walk / Bossa nouveau
SPJCD 541 / Feb '97 / Spotlite

Richardson, John

☐ BELOVED
CD 430 / 6 Jul '98 / New World

☐ DRUMS OF A NATION
CD 441 / 6 Jul '98 / New World

Richardson, Neil

☐ BEAUTIFUL FRIENDSHIP, A (Richardson, Neil Singers)
369092 / 3 Aug '98 / Koch Jazz

Richardson, Wally

☐ SOUL GURU
Senior boogaloo / Elbow blues / Monday Monday / Surf side shuffle / Soul guru / Lonely rider / Khyber Pass boogaloo / Square heels, white stockings
BGPD 1113 / 24 Nov '97 / Beat Goes Public

Richey, Kim

☐ BITTER SWEET
5342552 / Mar '97 / Mercury

Richie, Lionel

☐ BACK TO FRONT
Do it to me / My destiny / Love oh love / All night long / Easy / Still / Endless love: *Richie, Lionel & Diana Ross* / Running with the night / Dancing on the ceiling / Sail on / Hello / Truly / Penny lover / Stuck on you / Say you, say me / Three times a lady
5300182 / 10 Aug '98 / Motown

☐ CAN'T SLOW DOWN
All night long / Stuck on you / Penny lover / Hello / Love will find a way / Running with the night / Only one / Can't slow down
5300232 / Jan '92 / Motown

☐ DANCING ON THE CEILING
Sela / Ballerina girl / Don't stop / Deep river woman / Love will conquer all / Tonight will be alright / Say you, say me / Night train (Smooth alligator) / Dancing on the ceiling / Love will find a way
5300242 / Jan '92 / Motown

☐ LIONEL RICHIE
Serves you right / Wandering stranger / Tell me / My love / Round and round / Truly / You are / You mean more to me / Just put some love in your heart
5300262 / Jan '92 / Motown

☐ LOUDER THAN WORDS
5322412 / Apr '96 / Mercury

☐ TIME
Zoomin' / I hear your voice / Touch / Forever / Everytime / Time / To the rhythm / Stay / Way I feel / Closest thing to heaven / Someday / Lady
5585182 / 29 Jun '98 / Mercury

☐ TRULY (The Love Songs)
5308432 / 19 Jan '98 / PolyGram TV

Richie Rich

☐ SEASONED VETERAN
Intro / Funk / It's on / Let's ride / 30 minutes / Real pimp / Guess who's back / Fresh out / Niggas done changed: *Richie Rich & 2Pac* / Pillow / Check 'em / Real shit / Questions / It's not about you / Do G's get to go to heaven / Touch myself: *Richie Rich & T-Boz*
5334712 / Nov '96 / Def Jam

Richie, Shane

☐ ALBUM, THE
Sorry seem to be a hardest world / How long / Just when I needed you most / Daydream believer / Little bit more / Love grows / If / How can I be sure / Angel's gate / She's gone / Bigger than the sky / Tired of being alone / I'm gonna make you love me / Now we don't talk / What a fool believes / Everybody wants to rule the world / Goodbye / Grease is the word
5394952 / 17 Nov '97 / PolyGram TV

Richies

☐ PET SUMMER
WB 1106CD / Dec '93 / We Bite

☐ WINTER WONDERLAND
WB 065CD / Jul '90 / We Bite

Richman, Jeff

☐ SAND DANCE
Sand dance / Ain't gonna wait / Ashes to ashes / Bamboo man / Remember earth / Never again someday / One hand, one heart / Kathmandu / 2025 / Bohemia / Smile from a stranger
ALCD 1014 / 24 Aug '98 / Alchemy

Richman, Jonathan

☐ BACK IN YOUR LIFE (Richman, Jonathan & Modern Lovers)
I'm a little airplane / Hey there little insect / Egyptian reggae / Ice cream man / I'm a little dinosaur / My little kookenhaken / South American folk song / New England / Morning of our lives
HILLCD 15 / Apr '97 / Wooded Hill

☐ COLLECTION, THE
CCSCD 397 / Apr '94 / Castle

☐ I, JONATHAN
Parties in the u.s.a. / Tandem jump / You can't talk to the dude / Velvet underground / I was dancing in the lesbian bar / Rooming house on venice beach / That summer feeling / Grunion run / A higher power / Twilight in boston
ROUCD 9036 / Jan '94 / Rounder

☐ JONATHAN RICHMAN
Malaguena de Jojo / Everyday clothes / Blue moon / I eat with gusto, damn you bet / Sleepwalk / Mistake today for me / Action packed / Fender Statocaster / Closer / Miracles will start to happen / Que reste t'il de nos amours / Cerco
ROUCD 9021 / Sep '94 / Special Delivery

☐ JONATHAN RICHMAN & BARRENCE WHITFIELD (Richman, Jonathan & Barrence Whitfield)
CDS 1 / '88 / Rounder

☐ JONATHAN RICHMAN & THE MODERN LOVERS (Richman, Jonathan & Modern Lovers)
Rockin' shopping centre / Back in the USA / Important in your life / New England / Lonely financial zone / Hi dear / Abominable snowman in the market / Hey there little insect / Here come the Martian Martians / Springtime / Amazing grace
CREV 008CD / Jan '93 / Rev-Ola

☐ JONATHAN, TE VAS A EMOCIONAR
ROUCD 9040 / Apr '94 / Rounder

☐ LIVE AT THE LONGBRANCH SALOON (Modern Lovers)
422439 / May '94 / New Rose
3038212 / 29 Jun '98 / Last Call

☐ MODERN LOVERS (Modern Lovers)
Roadrunner / Astral plane / Old world / Pablo picasso / I'm straight / She cracked / Hospital / Someone I care about / Girlfriend / Modern world / Dignified and old / Government centre
CREV 007CD / Nov '92 / Rev-Ola

☐ MODERN LOVERS LIVE (Modern Lovers)
Abdul and Cleopatra / She's gonna respect me / Lover please / Affection / Buzz buzz buzz / Back in your life / Party in the woods tonight / My love is a flower (just beginning to bloom) / I'm nature's mosquito / Emaline / Lydia / I hear you calling me
HILLCD 14 / Apr '97 / Wooded Hill

☐ PRECISE MODERN LOVERS ORDER (Modern Lovers)
ROUCD 9042 / Apr '95 / Rounder

☐ RADIO ON/STOP AND SHOP (2CD Set)
SMDCD 115 / Jul '97 / Snapper

☐ ROCK 'N' ROLL WITH THE MODERN LOVERS (Richman, Jonathan & Modern Lovers)
Sweeping wind / Ice cream man / Rockin' rockin' leprechauns / Summer morning / Afternoon / Fly into the mystery / South American folk song / Rollercoaster by the sea / Dodge Veg-O-matic / Egyptian reggae / Coomyah / Wheels on the bus / Angels watching over me
CREV 009CD / Feb '93 / Rev-Ola

☐ SURRENDER TO JONATHAN
Just look at me / When she kisses me / Egyptian reggae / Floatin' / My little girl's got a full time daddy now / Rock 'n' roll drummer straight from the hospy-tel / Satisfy / That little sleeper car / Surrender / I was dancing in the lesbian bar / To hide a little thought / French style / Not just a
9362462962 / Sep '96 / Vapour

☐ YOU MUST ASK THE HEART
ROUCD 9047 / May '95 / Rounder

Richmond, Kim

☐ PASSAGES
Passages / Old acquaintances / Passcaglia/My funny valentine / Melon bells / Street of dreams / Soft feelings / Chic-a-brac / Images and likeness / Indian summer / Nardis
SBCD 2043 / Jul '92 / Sea Breeze

Richthofen

☐ SEELENWALZER
GUN 132CD / Jun '97 / Gun

Richthofen & Brown Symphonic Suite

☐ FILM MUSIC OF HUGO FRIEDHOFER
8105 / May '97 / Facet

Ricketts, Glen

☐ I FOUND A LOVE
DKCD 7773 / Apr '96 / DK

Ricks, Glen

☐ FALL IN LOVE
VYDCD 015 / Jul '96 / Vine Yard

☐ OH CAROLINA
I'll forever keep on loving you / Rain from the skies / Oh carolina / Dancing mood / If loving you is wrong / Unchained melody / Cry me a river / Carry go bring come / Moving away / Nanny goat / Girl I'm out of my mind / It's time for loving
LG 21089 / Mar '96 / Lagoon

Ricks, Jerry

☐ DEEP IN THE WELL (Ricks, 'Philadelphia' Jerry)
R 2636 / Aug '97 / Rooster

Rico

☐ BLOW YOUR HORN (Rico & The Rudies)
CDTTL 12 / Aug '96 / Trojan

☐ BLOW YOUR HORN/BRIXTON CAT (Rico & The Rudies)
CDTRL 361 / Jan '96 / Trojan

☐ RICO'S MESSAGE - JAMAICAN JAZZ (Rodriguez, Rico All Stars)
444102 / Jun '97 / Rhino

☐ RISING IN THE EAST
JOVECD 3 / Sep '94 / Jove Music

☐ ROOTS TO THE BONE
Children of Sanchez / Midnight in Ethiopia / Free ganja / Take five / Far East / No politician / Firestick / Matches Lane / This day / Ramble / Lumumba / Africa / Man from Wareika / Over the mountain / Dial Africa
RRCD 54 / Apr '95 / Reggae Refreshers

☐ THAT MAN IS FORWARD
RRTCD 01 / 22 Jun '98 / Reggae Retro

☐ TRIBUTE TO DON DRUMMOND, A
TRRCD 01 / Jun '97 / Trybute

☐ YOU MUST BE CRAZY (Rico & The Rudies)
GROCD 002 / 10 Nov '97 / Grover

Ricochets

☐ MADE IN THE SHADE
Witchcraft / Migraine / Hey, girl / Yomping / I'm a loser / Crazy dream / King rocker / Black magic baby / Runnin' wild / Hit man / Worried 'bout you baby / Brand new Cadillac / Night ship / Everybody's rockin' / Don't blame me / Mama don't allow / Mad man / Worried 'bout you baby / Hit man
NERDCD 005 / May '97 / Nervous

Riddle, Leslie

☐ STEP BY STEP
Little school girl / Frisco blues / Broke and weary blues / Hilltop blues / Motherless children / Titanic / I'm out on the ocean a-sailing / I'm working on a building / I know what it means to be lonesome / Red river blues / One kind favor / If you see my saviour / Cannonball / Step by step
ROUCD 0299 / May '93 / Rounder

Riddle, Nelson

☐ JOY OF LIVING/LOVE IS A GAME OF POKER
Life is a bowl of cherries / You make me feel so young / Makin' whoopee / Bye bye blues / It's so peaceful in the country / Joy of living / It's a big wide wonderful world / June in January / Isn't this a lovely day / Floatin' like a feather / Thrill is gone / I love you / Time on my hands / I'll see you in my dreams / Lies / Dream / Blue moon / Linger awhile / All by myself / Sometimes I'm happy / Street of dreams
CTMCD 117 / Jun '97 / EMI

☐ TOUCH OF CLASS, A
Let's face the music and dance / Lisbon antigua / Port au prince / Route 66 / Younger than springtime / I'll get by / More I see you / You and the night and the music / For all we know / September in the rain / C'est magnifique / My baby just cares for me / I get along without you very well / Magic moments / I love you Paris
TC 886282 / 2 Feb '98 / Disky

Ride

☐ CARNIVAL OF LIGHT
CRECD 147 / Jun '94 / Creation

☐ GOING BLANK AGAIN
Leave them all behind / Twisterella / Not fazed / Chrome waves / Mouse trap / Time of her time / Cool your boots / Making jody smile / Time machine / Dx4
CRECD 124 / Jan '92 / Creation

☐ LIVE LIGHT
800022 / Jul '97 / Mutiny

☐ NOWHERE
Seagull / Kaleidoscope / In a different place / Polar bear / Dreams burn down / Decay / Paralysed / Vapour trail / Taste / Here and now / Nowhere
CRECD 074 / Oct '90 / Creation

☐ SMILE
Chelsea Girl / Drive Blind / All I can see / Close my eyes / Like A Daydream / Silver / Furthest Sense / Perfect time
CRECD 126 / May '94 / Creation

☐ TARANTULA
CRECD 180 / Mar '96 / Creation

Rideout, Bonnie

☐ KINDRED SPIRITS
MMCD 214 / Apr '96 / Maggie's Music

Riders In The Sky

☐ ALWAYS DRINK UPSTREAM FROM THE HERD
ROUCD 0360 / Jan '96 / Rounder

☐ BEST OF THE WEST
Cowboy jubilee / That's how the yodel was born / (ghost) riders in the sky / Don't fence me in / Ol' cowpoke / Wasteland / Blue bonnet lady / Blue montana skies / After you've gone / Here comes santa fe / Tumbling tumbleweeds / La cucaracha / Soon as the roundup's through / I ride an old paint / Riding alone / Hold that critter down / Ride with the wind / Cowboy song
ROUCD 11517 / '88 / Rounder

☐ BEST OF THE WEST RIDERS AGAIN
Three on the trail / Back in the saddle again / Cool water / Desperado trail / At the end of the rainbow trail / Down the trail to san antone / Blue shadows on the trail / Jingle jangle jingle / Pecos bill / Streets of laredo (the cowboy's lament) / West texas cowboy / Cowpoke / Old el paso / Sky ball paint / Compadres in the old sierro madre / Bound to hit the trail / Ojo caliente / Yodel blues / Pretty prairie princess / Chasin' the sun / When the bloom is on the sage / Singing a song to the sky / On the rhythm range / Red river valley / When payday rolls around
ROUCD 11524 / '88 / Rounder

☐ COWBOY SONGS
Jingle jangle jingle / Tumbling tumbleweeds / Don't fence me in / Cattle call / Ghost riders in the sky / Streets of Laredo / I ride an old paint / Red River Valley / Rawhide / Chasin' the sun / Back in the saddle again / Home on the range
EDCD 7005 / Oct '96 / Easydisc

☐ PUBLIC COWBOY NO.1 (The Music Of Gene Autry)
Back in the saddle again / Sioux City Sue / Mexicali rose / You are my sunshine / Have I told you lately that I love you / Can't shake the sands of Texas from my shoes / Silver haired Daddy of mine / Be honest with me / Blue Canadian Rockies / Lonely river / South of the border / Ridin' down the canyon
ROUCD 0410 / Nov '96 / Rounder

☐ SADDIE PAIS
Yippie-yi-yo and away we go / Old chisholm trail / Get along little doggies / Biscuit blues / Sweet betsy from pike / There's a great big candy roundup / I'm going to leave old texas now / Cowboy's abc / Clementine / "one, two, three" said the miner / Fiddle medley / Down the lullabye trail
ROUCD 8011 / '88 / Rounder

☐ YODEL THE COWBOY WAY
EDCD 7055 / 19 Jan '98 / Easydisc

Ridgley, Tommy

☐ NEW ORLEANS KING OF THE STROLL, THE
New Orleans king of the stroll / Double eyed whammy / Is it true / Should I ever love again / My ordinary girl / I've heard that story before / Heavenly / Girl from Kooka Monga / In the same old way / Three times / Only girl for me / I love you yes I do / Please hurry home
ROUCD 2079 / ' / Rounder

☐ SHE TURNS ME ON
For you my love / Sick and tired / Should I ever love again / Double eyed whammy / I want some money / Stacked deck / Bad luck / Jam up / Ooh lordy my baby / She turns me on / Stoop down / I've heard that story before
MBCD 1203 / Jun '93 / Modern Blues

☐ SINCE THE BLUES BEGAN
BT 1115CD / May '95 / Black Top

Ridley, Larry

☐ SUM OF THE PARTS
CDGR 230 / 30 Mar '98 / Charly

Ridout, Bonnie

☐ CELTIC CIRCLES
MMCD 209 / Dec '94 / Maggie's Music

☐ SOFT MAY MORN
MMCD 208 / Dec '94 / Maggie's Music

Riedel, Georg

☐ KIRBITZ
PHONTCD 9311 / Jul '96 / Phontastic

Ries, Tim

☐ UNIVERSAL SPIRITS (Ries, Tim Quintet)
Indeed / St Michael / Free three / Guardian angel / Some other time / Sonata / Jayne / When I'm through
CRISS 1144CD / 9 Mar '98 / Criss Cross

Riessler, Michael

☐ HELOISE
WER 80082 / Nov '93 / Wergo

☐ HONIG UND ASCHE
Debut / Honig und asche / Je ne parle pas / Ppiccola cosmogonia portatile / To nobly body / Zungen / Th... / En... / Rem... / Otang...
ENJ 93032 / 26 May '98 / Enja

☐ MOMENTUM MOBILE
Anekdoten / La rage / Ein itllige sprag / Luigi / Marathon / Ba binga / Marsch der ketzer / Ost - west / Old Orleans, New Orleans / Song mecanique
ENJ 90032 / Mar '95 / Enja

☐ TENTATIONS D'ABELARD
WER 8010 / Dec '95 / Wergo

Riff, Nick

☐ CLOAK OF IMMORTALITY
Cloak of immortality / Creature feature / Way out / Staring into space / Like a zen stray / Something indside / Temple of dreams / Ghost / Tribal elders / From beyond they speak / Go far go wide
DELECCD 017 / Apr '95 / Delerium

☐ FREAK ELEMENT
Strange disposition / Forbidden love / Other ones / Big fairy tale / Lose my mind / Fly away / Electic eye god / Vagabond unknown / Freak element
DELECCD 001 / Jun '92 / Delerium

Rig

☐ BELLY TO THE GROUND
Mark 1617 / Tania / Buried alive / Cattleaxe / Say that / Joe's alarm / Syphilis diller / Personal service announcement / Miracle / Cut voice / 9 iron
CRZ 035CD / Feb '94 / Cruz

Rigai, Amiram

☐ AMIRAM RIGAI PLAYS LOUIS MOREAU GOTTSCHALK
CDSF 40803 / Oct '93 / Smithsonian Folkways

Rigby, Amy

☐ DIARY OF A MOD HOUSEWIFE
379222 / Oct '96 / Koch International

Right Direction

☐ ALL OF A SUDDEN
LF 133CD / May '95 / Lost & Found

☐ ECHOES FROM THE PAST
LTR 03 / 15 Dec '97 / Lighttown

☐ TO RIGHT THE WRONG
CM 77216CD / 27 Apr '98 / Century Media

Right Said Fred

☐ UP
SNOGCD 1 / Mar '92 / Gut

Righteous Brothers

☐ GREATEST HITS
JHD 024 / Jun '92 / Tring

☐ INSPIRATIONS
Soul and inspiration / What now my love / Ebb tide / White cliffs of Dover / Go ahead and cry / Just once in my life / Stranded in the middle of no place / Great pretender / He will break your heart / Island in the sun / (I love you) for sentimental reasons / That lucky old sun / My darling Clementine / Georgia on my mind
5501972 / Mar '94 / Spectrum

☐ ORIGINAL ALBUMS
Rock 'n' roll heaven / Is it so wrong / Love is not a dirty word / Sing lady / Try again / And I thought you loved me / Never say I love you / Let me make the music / You turn me around / Young blood / Together again / Just another fool / Happy song / Dream on / Give it to the people / Substitute / Hold on to what you got / I just wanna be me / Lines / Nobody but you / All you get from love is a love song / Dr. rock 'n' roll / Father of the rock and roll / Hey girl / If that's the way you want it / High blood pressure
DCD 5285 / Dec '93 / Disky

☐ UNCHAINED MELODY
AVC 513 / Dec '92 / Avid

☐ YOU'VE LOST THAT LOVIN' FEELING
You've lost that lovin' feeling / He / Along came Jones / Harlem shuffle / Hold on I'm coming / I who have nothing / Save the last dance for me / Will you love me tomorrow / Bring it on home to me / I'm leaving it up to you / In the midnight hour / Come rain or come shine / Secret love / Somewhere / You'll never walk alone / Drown in my own tears / I believe / Let it be me
5512682 / Mar '96 / Spectrum

Rights Of The Accused

☐ KICK-HAPPY, THRILL-HUNGRY, RECKLESS AND WILLING
N 01672 / '91 / Noise

Rigsby, Don

☐ VISION, A
Wings of angels / Little spirit man / Rose among the thorns / I've just seen the rock of ages / Over in the gloryland / Angel of death / Higher than I / That home far way / On a high high mountain / God needed my mother / Drifting too far from the shore / It is Jesus / Vision of a golden crown
SHCD 3873 / 9 Mar '98 / Sugar Hill

Riisnaes, Knut

☐ CONFESSIN' THE BLUES (Riisnaes, Knut & Red Holloway)
GMCD 63 / Apr '98 / Gemini

☐ GEMINI TWINS
GMCD 175 / Oct '89 / Gemini

Rikoson All-Stars

☐ EVOLUCIONES DEL SON
CAT 1002 / 5 Jan '98 / Fresh Sound

Riley, Billy Lee

☐ CLASSIC RECORDINGS 1956-1960 (2CD Set)
Rock with me baby / Troublebound / Flyin' saucer rock 'n' roll / I want you baby / Red hot / Pearly Lee / Wouldn't you / Baby, please don't go / Rockin' on the moon / Is that all to the ball, Mr Hall / Itchy / Thunderbird / Down by the riverside / No name girl / Come back baby / Got the water boiling / Open the door Richard: *Riley, Billy & Ernie Barton* / Dark muddy bottom / Repossession blues / That's what I want to do / Too much woman for me / Flyin' saucer rock 'n' roll / I want you / She's my baby / Pearly Lee (unissued) / Red hot (unissued) / That's right / Searchin' / Chatter and college man / Your cash ain't nothin' but trash / Swanee river rock / Betty and Dupree / Let's talk about us / Got the water boiling (unissued) / Saturday night fish fry / Folsom Prison blues / Billy's blues / When a man gets the blues / Sweet William / Red hot (version) / Mud Island / My baby's got love
BCD 15444 / Jul '90 / Bear Family

☐ RED HOT
CPCD 8138 / Mar '96 / Charly

☐ ROCKIN' WITH BILLY (3CD Set)
Trouble bound / Rock with me baby / Flying saucers rock 'n' roll / I want you baby / She's my baby / Pearly lee / She's my baby / Pearly lee / Red hot / Wouldn't you know / Baby please don't go / Rock with me baby (dance with me honey) / That's right / Searchin' / College man / Your cash ain't nothin' but trash / Itchy / Thunderbird / Down by the riverside / No name girl / Swanee river rock / (come back baby) one more time / Got the water boiling / Betty and dupree / Let's talk about us / Saturday night fish fry / Folsom Prison blues / Billy's blues / Dark muddy bottom / When a man gets the blues / Sweet william / Open the door richard / Kay / Yulesville usa (rockin' stockings) / Rockin' old lang syne / Lookin' for my baby / Pilot town louisianna / Workin' on the river / Nitty gritty / Mississippi / Sun goin' down on frisco / Talahassie / Potter's field / Gallow's hill / My old home place / San francisco lady / Everybody's twistin' / I've been searching / What'd I say / White silver sands / Surfboard cha cha / Surf / Sink or swim / Wishy washy / Hucklebuck / Oops he slipped / Low tide / Let me tell you baby / Goin' to the river / Shimmy / Shimmy walk / Flying saucers rock 'n' roll / Red hot / No name girl / Swanee river rock / Down by the riverside / Open the door richard / Come back baby
CDSUNBOX 3 / Feb '93 / Charly

Riley, Howard

☐ BERNE CONCERT, THE (Riley, Howard & Keith Tippett)
FMRCD 08 / Mar '95 / Future

☐ CLASSICS (Riley, Howard & Art Themen Quartet)
Straight no chaser / Body and soul / All blues / 'Round midnight / Softly as in a morning sunrise
SLAMCD 222 / Feb '97 / Slam

☐ FEATHERS WITH JAKI (Riley, Howard & Jaki Byard)
'Round midnight / Straight no chaser / Swigger swagger / Feathers / Subway one / Sweet but short / Yesterdays / Subway two / Clochard
SLAMCD 215 / Oct '96 / Slam

☐ FLIGHT
FMRCD 26 / Dec '95 / Future

☐ INNER MINOR
Fast forward / Icon no more / Things / Wired / Dreaming / Inner minor / Home at last / Deflection / Glass / Au contraire / Starstruck / Walkway
ASCCD 16 / Aug '97 / ASC

☐ MAKING NOTES
SLAMCD 230 / Jun '98 / Slam

☐ WISHING ON THE MOON
FMRCD 14 / Aug '95 / Future

Riley, Jimmy

☐ 20 CLASSIC HITS
SONCD 0053 / Aug '93 / Sonic Sounds

☐ ATTENTION
PCD 0003 / Jul '96 / Blue Mountain

Riley, Paul

☐ WANDERER, THE
KMCD 44 / Feb '96 / KM

Riley, Philip

☐ PATTERN OF LANDS
WCL 110182 / Sep '96 / White Cloud

☐ VISIONS AND VOICES
WCL 110122 / May '95 / White Cloud

Riley, Steve

☐ 'TIT GALOP POUR MAMA (Riley, Steve & Mamou Playboys)
ROUCD 6048 / Dec '90 / Rounder

☐ BAYOU RULER (Riley, Steve & Mamou Playboys)
ROUCD 6083 / Jun '98 / Rounder

☐ LA TOUSSAINT (Riley, Steve & Mamou Playboys)
ROUCD 6068 / Jan '96 / Rounder

☐ LIVE (Riley, Steve & Mamou Playboys)
ROUCD 6058 / May '94 / Rounder

☐ TRACE OF TIME (Riley, Steve & Mamou Playboys)
Bayou noir / Mon vieux wagon / Old home waltz / Church point breakdown / Parlez-nous a boire / Lover's waltz / Sur le courtableau / La valse du regret / La Point-au-pic / Corner post / Zarico est pas sale
ROUCD 6053 / Jul '93 / Rounder

Riley, Terry

☐ KEYBOARD STUDIES
14542 / 2 Feb '98 / Spalax

☐ LAZY AFTERNOON AMONG THE CROCODILES (Riley, Terry & Stefano Scodanibbio)
AI 008 / Jun '97 / Pierrot Lun

☐ LISBON CONCERT
NA 087 / Oct '96 / New Albion

☐ PERSIAN SURGERY DERVISHES
NT 6715 / Jan '94 / Robi Droli

☐ POPPY NOGOOD AND THE PHANTOM BAND - ALL NIGHT FLIGHT
CORTI 04 / Jul '97 / Cortical

☐ RAINBOW IN CURVED AIR
A rainbow in curved air / Poppy nogood and the phantom band
4778492 / Oct '94 / Columbia

Rimes, Leann

☐ BLUE
CURCD 028 / Aug '96 / Curb

☐ EARLY YEARS
CURCD 038 / Feb '97 / Curb

☐ SITTING ON TOP OF THE WORLD
How do I live / Commitment / Looking through your eyes / Undeniable / Feels like home / Surrender / These arms of mine / Nothin' new under the moon / When am I gonna get over you / Rock me / More than anyone deserves / Insensitive / All the lovin' and the hurtin' / Sittin' on top of the world / Heart never forgets / Purple rain
CURCD 055
5560202 / 25 May '98 / London

☐ YOU LIGHT UP MY LIFE (Inspirational Songs)
You light up my life / Rose / Bridge over troubled water / I beleive / Ten thousand angels cried / Clinging to a saving hand / On the side of angels / I know who holds tomorrow / God bless America / How do I live / Amazing Grace / National Anthem
CURCD 046 / Sep '97 / Curb

Rimitti

☐ CHEIKHA
ABSOLCD 5 / Jan '97 / Absolute

☐ SIDI MANSOUR
ABSOLCD 2 / Apr '96 / Absolute

Rimmington, Sammy

☐ CHRISTMAS IN NEW ORLEANS
BCD 209 / Jan '94 / GHB

☐ GINGER PIG NEW ORLEANS JAZZ BAND
BCD 232 / Oct '92 / GHB

☐ ON TOUR (Rimmington, Sammy & His Band)
BCD 211 / Jun '95 / GHB

☐ ONE SWISS NIGHT
MECCACD 1021 / Jun '93 / Music Mecca

☐ SAMMY RIMMINGTON & HIS BAND (Rimmington, Sammy & His Band)
BCD 288 / Aug '94 / GHB

☐ SAMMY RIMMINGTON & KEN PYE'S CREOLE SERENADERS (Rimmington, Sammy & Ken Pye Creole Serenaders)
PKCD 071 / Mar '97 / PEK

Rimshots

☐ EVERYBODY BOP NOW
Ramblin' man / Hobo blues / Let's bop / Crazy fool / Early morning blues / You saved my heart / Oklahoma Hills / One more beer / Crazy 'bout my baby / Wide open road / Troubles / Cryin' early morning / My way or the highway / That's OK / Swamp gal / Honey babe / Yonder comes a sucker
JRCD 23 / Sep '97 / Jappin' & Rockin'

☐ SENTIMENTAL FOOLS
Honky tonk hardwood floor / Cattin' around / Sentimental fool / Won or lost / I had better times / Hock cat rock / Planet bop / Rust free / So tired of cryin' / I got a gal / I love the life I'm livin' / I fell in love / Don't come knocking at my door / Rock all night / Big river / Four minute warning / Shut up and drink your beer / Scratch on my record
JRCD 29 / Sep '97 / Jappin' & Rockin'

☐ TRIBUTE TO HANK WILLIAMS, A (Rimshots/Rusti Steel)
BBCD 004 / 12 May '98 / Bebe's

Rinaldi, Susana

☐ EL TANGO RESPLANDECIENTE
74321453302 / Feb '97 / Milan Sur

☐ MI VOX Y MI CIUDAD
BMT 502 / 5 Jan '98 / Blue Moon

Rincon Surfside Band

☐ SURFING SONGBOOK
VSD 5481 / Jan '95 / Varese Sarabande

Ringer, Jim

☐ BAND OF JESSE JAMES, THE (Best Of Jim Ringer)
CDPH 1202 / Aug '96 / Philo

☐ GOOD TO GET HOME
CIC 069CD / Nov '93 / Clo Iar-Chonnachta

Ringlets Trio

☐ ROCKS
RUMCD 003 / Aug '92 / Rumble

Ringo

☐ EYEWITNESS
LG 21102 / Apr '95 / Lagoon

Ringtailed Snorter

☐ LOOK BACK IN THE MIRROR
COPCD 040 / 13 Jul '98 / Cop International

☐ SEXUAL CHILD ABUSE
CDZOT 19 / Aug '93 / Zoth Ommog

Ringworm

☐ FLATLINE, THE
LF 135CD / Mar '95 / Lost & Found

Rinne Radio

☐ FINNISH AMBIENT TECHNO CHANT (Rinne Radio & Wimme)
Aromaa alt loni / Vedet / In nera / Amen / Blue drift / 5 am / Eeva's panka / Teo teo / Freepop birds / Texas / This / Ecstacy / Boaimmas / Aromaa
09026687522 / Aug '97 / Catalyst

☐ JOIK
Freepop birds / Helisma / Hot winters / Blue in purple / Aalloilla / Radio Soi - Freehop / This / Rohtasan / Vedet / Is / Villinraskas / Forest donk / Heaven
AAX 007 / May '97 / AAX

☐ ROK
ZEN 2047CD / Nov '96 / Rockadillo

☐ UNIK
Aatto / Saloma / Teo Teo / Aalloilla II / Aromaa / Eeva's Panka / Family man / D# / Fear of the unknown / Mp
AAX 005 / May '97 / AAX

Rinocerose

☐ RETROSPECTIVE
ED 022 / 20 Oct '97 / Elefant

Rinpoche, Chogyal

☐ CHOD: CUTTING THROUGH DUALISM
ARNR 0193 / Sep '97 / Amiata

Rio

☐ RIO
BLIPCD 102 / Mar '94 / Urban London

Riot

☐ BREATHREN OF TL, THE
RS 0072962CD / Jul '98 / Rising Sun

☐ FIRE DOWN BELOW
7559605762 / Jan '96 / Elektra

☐ FIRE DOWN UNDER
HV 1021 / Sep '97 / High Vaultage

☐ INISHMORE
398414150CD / 2 Mar '98 / Metal Blade

☐ LIVE
7559679692 / Jan '96 / Elektra

☐ NIGHTBREAKER
RS 00792972CD / Jun '98 / Rising Sun

☐ RESTLESS BREED
Restless breed / Hard lovin' man / CIA / When I was young / Loved by you / Loneshark / Over to you / Showdown / Dream away / Violent crimes
7559601342 / Jan '96 / Elektra

☐ RIOT LIVE
398414011CD / Jun '96 / Metal Blade

☐ ROCK CITY
Desperation / Warrior / Rock city / Overdrive / Angel / Tokyo rose / Heart of fire / Gypsy queen / This is what I get
398414009CD / Jun '96 / Metal Blade

Riot City

☐ RIOT CITY PUNK SINGLES COLLECTION
Fuck the tories / We are the Riot Squad / Civil destruction / Riots in the city / Why should we / Religion doesn't mean a thing / Lost cause / Suspicion / Unite and fight / Police power / Society's fodder / In the future / Friday night hero / There was no solution / Government schemes / No potential threat / Ten years time / Hate the law / Hidden in fear / Lost cause (demo) / Unite and fight (demo)
CDPUNK 41 / Jan '95 / Anagram

Riot Squad

☐ ANYTIME
I take it we're through / Bittersweet love / How is it done / Jump / It's never too late to forgive / Working man / Not a great talker / Anytime / Try to realise / Gonna make you mine / Gotta be the first time / Nevertheless / I wanna talk about my baby
REP 4192 / Aug '91 / Repertoire

Riot/Clone

☐ TO FIND A LITTLE BLUEBIRD
Wake up / Think for yourself / No more / Buy me / Air smiles / Nowhere to run / Student drones / Capitalism / Taste / Slave trade / You can make a difference / Instead of a title / C(R)AP / Falling on deaf ears again / Files / We only want a future / Tomorrow / To find a little bluebird / Anarchy / Running / Death to humanity / Why do you have to eat me / Society / Having fun / H-Block / Stereotypes / Sick games / Work / Bottled oi / Neu-vastation / Lucrative lies
BFRCD 001 / 5 Sep '97 / Bomb Factory

Riou

☐ EXHIBITION OF THE SAMPLES
KK 137CD / Sep '95 / KK

☐ POPS
KK 167CD / 1 Sep '97 / KK

Rip Masters

☐ DON'T TREAD ON ME
MSECD 18 / Jul '96 / Mouse

Riperton, Minnie

☐ BEST OF MINNIE RIPERTON, THE
Perfect angel / Lover and friend (Single version) / Memory lane / Woman of heart and mind / Loving you / Young waiting and able / Can you feel what I'm saying / Stick together / Wouldn't matter where you are / Stay in love / Inside my love / Here we go / Give me time (Single version) / You take my breath away / Adventures in paradise / Simple things / Light my fire
CDP 7805162 / Aug '93 / Capitol

☐ COME TO MY GARDEN
Les fleurs / Completeness / Come to my garden / Memory band / Rainy day in centerville / Close your eyes and remember / Oh by the way / Expecting / Only when I'm dreaming / Wherever we are
CDBM 080 / Aug '97 / Blue Moon
AIM 1060 / May '97 / Aim

☐ HER CHESS YEARS
MCD 09392 / 23 Feb '98 / Chess/MCA

Rippingtons

☐ KILIMANJARO
Morocco / Dream of the Sivens / Kilimanjaro / Love notes / Oceansong / Northern lights / Katrina's dance / Backstabbers / Los Cabos
GRP 95972 / 25 May '98 / GRP

Ripple

☐ BUT IT SURE IS FUNKY
I don't know what it is but it sure is funky / See the light in the window / You were right on time / Hell of a thing / This ain't no time to be giving up / Funky song / Be my friend / Willie pass the water / Get off / Hey lady / Sweet lady / Get ready for a biggie / I'll be right there trying / I can't see you loving nobody but me / Maybe it's you / Dance lady dance / Complain to the clouds but you can't change the weather / If the music can't do it (nobody can) / Break song / Cross collaterization / Ripplin'
CDSEWD 098 / Feb '97 / Southbound

☐ RIPPLE
You were right on time / Be my friend / I don't know what it is but it sure is funky / I'll be right there trying / Get off / See the light in the window / Funky song / Wilie pass the water / Dance lady dance / Ripplin'
CPCD 8093 / Apr '95 / Charly

Riptones

☐ EXTRA SAUCE
BS 022 / 19 Jan '98 / Bloodshot

Riqueni, Rafael

☐ MAESTROS
El bohio / Noches de cadix / Inspiration / Con salero y garbo / De chiclana a cai / Nostalgia flamenco / Recuerdo a sevilla / Sentir del sacromonte / Perfil flamenco / Mantilla e feria / Estrella amargura
EMO 93062 / Oct '95 / Act

Rishell, Paul

☐ BLUES ON A HOLIDAY
CDTC 1144 / May '94 / Tonecool

☐ I WANT YOU TO KNOW (Rishell, Paul & Annie Raines)
CDTC 1156 / Sep '96 / Tonecool

☐ SWEAR TO TELL THE TRUTH
CDTC 1148 / May '94 / Tonecool

Rising Sons

☐ RISING SONS, THE
Stateeboro blues / If the river was whiskey / By and by (poor me) / Candy man / Let the good times roll / 44 blues / 11th street overcrossing / Corine Corina / Tulsa county / Walkin' down the line / Girl with green eyes / Sunny's dream / Spanish lace blues / Devil's got my woman / Take a giant step / Flyin' so high / Dust my broom / Last fair deal gone down / Baby, what you want me to do / I got a little
4728652 / May '93 / Columbia

Rising Storm

☐ CALM BEFORE THE STORM
AA 034 / Jul '97 / Arf Arf

Risk

☐ DANCING (The Best Of Risk)
DOLECD 103 / Jan '95 / Dojo

☐ DIRTY SURFACES
0876234 / Aug '90 / Steamhammer

☐ HELL'S ANIMALS
Monkey business / Perfect kill / Dead or alive / Secret of our destiny / Sicilian showdown / Torture and pain / Mindshock / Megalomania / Russian nights / Epilogue
857593 / Jun '89 / Steamhammer

Risk, Laura

☐ JOURNEY BEGUN (Risk, Laura & Athena Tergis)
CUL 105CD / Oct '95 / Culburnie

Ritch, Kenny

☐ JUST A FEW TUNES
ATCD 050 / 2 Apr '98 / Attic

Ritchie Family

☐ BEST OF RITCHIE FAMILY, THE (Best Disco In Town)
Brazil / Dance with me / Best disco in town / Arabian nights medley / Life is music / Lady luck / African queens medley / Summer dance / American generation / Good in love / Put your feet to the beat / Gimme a break / All night all right / It's a man's world
HTCD 41 / 20 Apr '98 / Hot Productions

Ritchie, Jean

☐ CAROLS FOR ALL SEASONS
TCD 1058 / 13 Oct '97 / Tradition

☐ MOST DULCIMER, THE
GR 70714 / Dec '94 / Greenhays

☐ MOUNTAIN BORN (Ritchie, Jean & Sons)
Mountain born / Loving Hannah / Love somebody, yes I do / Cuckoo / You are my dearest dear / Barley-Bright / Abigail / Deep shady groves / When sorrows encompass me round / Come all you fair and tender / May day / My dear companion / Come let us sing / One more mile / Our meeting is over
GR 70725 / Oct '96 / Greenhays

☐ NONE BUT ONE/HIGH HILLS & MOUNTAINS
GR 70708 / Dec '94 / Greenhays

Rite Of Strings

☐ RITE OF STRINGS
Indigo / Renaissance / Song to John / Chillean pipe song / Topanga / Morocco / Change of life / LA cancion de sofia / Memory canyon
CDP 8341672 / Aug '95 / IRS/EMI

Ritenour, Lee

☐ ALIVE IN LA
Little bumpin' / Night rhythms / Boss city / San Juan sunset / Uptown / Waltz for Carmen / Wes bound / Pacific nights / Rio funk / Four on six
GRP 98822 / Jun '97 / GRP

☐ BEST OF LEE RITENOUR, THE
Sun song / Captain fingers / Caterpillar / Three days of the condor / Fly by night / Little bit of this and a little bit of that / Wild rice / Isn't she lovely
EK 36527 / Jul '95 / Sony Jazz

☐ FRIENDSHIP
Sea dance / Woody creek / Crystal morning / It's a natural thing / Samurai night fever / Life is the song we sing
JMI 20092 / Nov '93 / JVC

☐ GENTLE THOUGHTS
Captain caribe/Getaway / Chanson / Meiso / Captain fingers / Feel like makin' love / Gentle thoughts
JMI 20072 / Mar '94 / JVC

☐ LARRY & LEE (Ritenour, Lee & Larry Carlton)
Crosstown kids / Low steppin' / LA Underground / Closed door jam / After the rain / Remembering JP / Fun in the dark / Lota about nothin' / Take that / Up and adam / Reflections of a guitar player
GRP 98172 / Apr '95 / GRP

☐ RIO
Rainbow / San Juan sunset / Rio funk / It happens every day / Ipanema sol / Simplicidad / Little bit of this and a little bit of that
GRP 95242 / 25 May '98 / GRP

☐ STOLEN MOMENTS
Uptown / Stolen moments / 24th Street blues / Haunted heart / Waltz for Carmen / St. Bart's / Blue in green / Sometime ago
GRP 96152 / Apr '90 / GRP

☐ THIS IS LOVE
This is love / Mr. Papa / Can you feel it / Dream away / Alfie's theme / And you know what... / I love you / Baltimore / Oh yeah / Street runner / Dream walk / Pavane
5573912 / 29 Jun '98 / IE

Ritmo Oriental

☐ RITMO ORIENTAL IS CALLING YOU
Nena, asi no se vale / Yo traigo panatela / Que rico bailo yo / Martiza / La ritmo suena a areito / La ritmo te esta llamando / Maria baila el son / El que no sabe, sabe / Advertencia para todos / Si no hay posibilidad me voy
CDORB 034 / Jan '89 / Globestyle

Ritta, Canzoniere Della

☐ MALEVENTO
NT 6734CD / Apr '95 / Robi Droli

Ritter, Julie

☐ MEDICINE SHOW
NAR 122CD / Jul '95 / New Alliance

Ritter, Tex

☐ HIGH NOON
High noon / Boogie woogie cowboy / Pecos Bill / Dallas darling / Eyes of Texas / Night Herding song / Pony express / High noon / He's a cowboy auctioneer / Billy the kid / Texas rangers / Cattle call / Goodbye my little cherokee / There's a goldstar in her window / In case you change your mind / I was out of my mind / Dark days in Dallas
BCD 15634 / Feb '92 / Bear Family

Ritual Device

☐ HENGE
RED 92 / Jun '93 / Redemption

Rivas, Antonio

☐ LA PERLA DE ARSEGUEL
MWCD 3002 / Jun '92 / Music & Words

River Band

☐ MUKAREL
MECCACD 2002 / May '97 / Music Mecca

River City Brass Band

☐ CONCERT IN THE PARK
El capitan / Daisy bell / Sweet and low / Belle of chicago / Maple leaf rage / Whirlwind polka / Grand dutchess / Semper fidelis / Fireman's polka / On with the motley / William Tell overture / Love's old sweet song / Lassus trombone / Washington post / Lost chord / Believe me if / All those endearing / Young charms / Liberty bell / 12th Street rag / Stars and stripes forever
QMPR 604D / Mar '94 / Polyphonic

River City People

☐ SAY SOMETHING GOOD
What's wrong with dreaming / Walking on ice / Under the rainbow / Carry the blame / Say something good / Thirsty / When I was young / No doubt / I'm still waiting / Home and dry / Huskisson St. / Find a reason
CDFA 3295 / May '93 / Fame

Rivera, Hector

☐ AT THE PARTY WITH HECTOR RIVERA
At the party / Shingaling baby / My foolsih heart / Pra voz wilma / I got my eye on you / Got to make up your mind / Playing it cool / Crown my heart / Calypso number 10 / Do it to me / Asia minor / I want a chance for romance / Hueso E Pellenjo / Angue tu mamino querra (aka Lily)
CDBGPD 082 / Jan '94 / Beat Goes Public

Rivera, Wendell

☐ NO BOUNDARIES
WPR 411952 / 5 Jan '98 / Fresh Sound

Rivera, Willie

☐ EL DIA QE ME DEJES
El amor corre por mi cuenta / Puerto querido / Amiga mia / No podras escaparte / Dejate querer / Todo por quererte / El dia que me dejas / Ella quiere volver
66058068 / Dec '95 / RMM

Riverdales

☐ RIVERDALES, THE
LOOKOUT 120 / Sep '95 / Lookout

Rivero, Edmundo

☐ ARACA LA CANA
BMT 007 / 5 Jan '98 / Fresh Sound

Rivers, Blue

☐ BLUE BEAT IN MY SOUL (Rivers, Blue & The Maroons)
Guns of Navarone / Too much / Mercy mercy mercy / Phoenix city / Witchcraft man / Searching for you baby / I've been pushed around
SEECD 318 / May '91 / See For Miles

☐ FROM SKA TO REGGAE (Rivers, Blue & The Maroons)
Phoenix city / Phoenix city / Searching for you baby / Too much / I've got a good thing going / I found me somebody new / Sabu / Guns of navorone / Witchcraft man / Groovy ruby / Turn me and twist me / Mercy mercy percy / Tell me / Mabeleene
LG 21078 / May '93 / Lagoon

Rivers, James

☐ BEST OF NEW ORLEANS RHYTHM & BLUES VOL.3
MG 9009 / Feb '95 / Mardi Gras

Rivers, Johnny

☐ JOHNNY RIVERS IN ACTION/ CHANGES
Mountain of love / Promised land / I should have known better / I'm in love again / Rhythm of the rain / He don't love you like I love you / Cupid / Oh pretty woman / It's all over now / What am I doin' here with you / Moody river / Keep-a-knockin' / By the timer I get to Phoenix / Taste of honey / Days of wine and roses / California dreamin' / Do you want to dance / Cast your fate to the wind / Poor side of town / If I were a carpenter / Softly as I leave you / Shadow of your smile / Strangers in the night / Getting ready for tomorrow
BGOCD 355 / 15 Jun '98 / Beat Goes On

☐ LIVE AT THE WHISKEY-A-GO-GO/ HERE WE A-GO-GO AGAIN
Memphis / It won't happen with me / Oh lonesome me / Lawdy Miss Clawdy / Whisky A Go Go / Walking the dog / Brown eyed handsome man / You can have her / Multiplication / Medley: La Bamba/Twist and shout / Maybellene / Dang me / Hello Josephine / Hi-heel sneakers / Can't buy me love / I've got a woman / Baby, what you want me to do / Midnight special / Roll over Beethoven / Walk myself on home / Johnny B Goode / Whole lotta shakin' goin' on
BGOCD 241 / Feb '95 / Beat Goes On

☐ ORIGINAL, THE
Poor side of town / Memphis / Mountain of love / Secret agent man / Seventh son / Baby I need your loving / Tracks of my tears / Maybelline / Midnight special / Cupid / Where have all the flowers gone / Under your spell again / (I washed my hands in) muddy water / Summer rain / Help me Rhonda / Rockin' pneumonia - boogie woogie flu / Sea cruise / Swayin' to the music
TO 886252 / 2 Feb '98 / Disky

☐ REWIND/REALIZATION
Tracks of my tears / Carpet man / Tunesmith / Sidewalk song/27th street / It'll never happen again / Do what you gotta do / Baby I need your lovin' / For Emily whenever I may find her / Rosecrans Boulevard / Eleventh song / Sweet smiling children / Hey Joe / Look at your soul / Way we live / Summer rain / Whiter shade of pale / Brother where are you / Something strange / What's the difference / Going back to Big Sur / Positively 4th Street
BGOCD 401 / 3 Aug '98 / Beat Goes On

☐ ROCKS THE FOLK/MEANWHILE BACK AT THE WHISKY A GO GO
Tom Dooley / Long time man / Michael (row the boat ashore) / Blowin' in the wind / Green green / Where have all the flowers gone / If I had a hammer / Tall oak tree / Catch the wind / 500 miles / Mr. Tambourine man / Jailer bring me water / Seventh son / Greenback dollar / Stop in the name of love / Un-Square dance / Silver threads and golden needles / Land of 1000 dances / Parchment Farm / I'll cry instead / Break up / Work song / Stagger Lee / Suzie Q
BGOCD 299 / Oct '95 / Beat Goes On

Rivers, Sam

☐ PORTRAIT - LIVE
FMPCD 82 / May '97 / Full Moon

Riverside Ceilidh Band

☐ FIRST FOOTING
Gay Gordons / Gay Gordons (encore) / Strip the willow / Strip the willow (encore) / Dashing white sergeant / Dashing white sergeant (encore) / Song / Military two step / Pride of Erin waltz / Pride of Erin waltz (encore) / Eightsome reel / Highland schottische / Highland schottische (encore) / St. Bernard's waltz / St. Bernard's waltz (encore) / Canadian barn dance / Canadian barn dance encore
LISMOR 5241 / Jan '95 / Lismor

☐ HORSES FOR COURSES
LCOM 9035 / Apr '91 / Lismor

Riverside Gospel Congregation

☐ SOUL SALVATION (Best Loved Gospels)
302592 / 21 Aug '97 / Musidisc

Riverside Reunion Band

☐ MOSTLY MONK
Bemsha swing / West coast blues / 'Round midnight / Well you needn't / Gemini / Ruby my dear / In walked bud / Four on six / Work song
MCD 9216 / Aug '94 / Milestone

Riviere, Gaston

☐ FRANCE (Hurdy Gurdy)
926942 / 24 Feb '98 / BUDA

Riz Allstars

☐ REVEAL REPORT
EB 017 / 16 Feb '98 / Echo Beach

Rizzetta, Sam

☐ SEVEN VALLEYS - HAMMERED DULCIMER
FF 70489 / Jan '90 / Flying Fish

RLW

☐ PULLOVER
32-GERANIUM / Dec '96 / Table Of The Elements

RNC Wind Orchestra

☐ EDWARD GREGSON WIND MUSIC (RNC Wind Orchestra/Manchester Boys Choir)
Celebration / Metamorphoses / Missa brevis pacem / Sword and the crown / Festivo
DOYCD 043 / Sep '95 / Doyen

☐ GALLIMANFRY
Illyrian dances / SPQR / Suite Francaise / Mockbeggar variations / Deo gracias / Full fathom five / Galliman
DOYCD 042 / Sep '95 / Doyen

Roach, Archie

☐ CHARCOAL LANE/JAMU DREAMING (2CD Set)
D 30851 / Nov '96 / Mushroom

☐ LOOKING FOR BUTTERBOY
MUSH 15CD / 20 Oct '97 / Mushroom

Roach, Max

☐ DEEDS, NOT WORDS
OJCCD 304 / Feb '93 / Original Jazz Classics

☐ DRUMS UNLIMITED
Drum also waltzes / Nommo / Drums unlimited / St. Louis blues / For big Sid / In the red
7567813612 / Apr '95 / Atlantic

☐ EASY WINNERS (Roach, Max Double Quartet)
Bird says / Sis / Little booker / Easy winners
SNCD 1109 / '86 / Soul Note

☐ FREEDOM NOW SUITE
CCD 79002 / Feb '97 / Candid

☐ HISTORIC CONCERTS (2CD Set) (Roach, Max & Cecil Taylor)
121100/12 / Nov '93 / Soul Note

☐ IN THE LIGHT (Roach, Max Quartet)
In the light / Straight no chaser / Ruby my dear / Henry street blues / If you could see me now / Good bait / Tricotism
SNCD 1053 / '86 / Soul Note

☐ IT'S CHRISTMAS AGAIN
1211532 / May '95 / Soul Note

☐ IT'S TIME
It's time / Another valley / Sunday afternoon / Living room / Profit / Lonesome lover
IMP 11852 / Mar '96 / Impulse Jazz

☐ MAX
Crackle hut / Speculate / That ole devil called love / Audio blues / CM / Four X
GRP 18252 / 27 Jul '98 / Chess Mates

☐ MAX ROACH AND FRIENDS VOL.1
COD 018 / Mar '92 / Jazz View

☐ MAX ROACH AND FRIENDS VOL.2
COD 019 / Aug '92 / Jazz View

☐ MAX ROACH TRIO (Roach, Max Trio & The Legendary Hassan)
Three-four vs six-eight four-four ways / To inscribe / Pay not play not / Off my back jack / Hope so elmo / Almost like me / Din-ka street
7567822732 / Apr '95 / Atlantic

☐ MOP MOP
Kardouba / Stop motion / Night mountain / Cecillana / Mop mop / Jordu / Sophisticated lady / Who will buy / Love for sale / Long as you're living
LEJAZZCD 44 / Jun '95 / Le Jazz

☐ SCOTT FREE
Scott free (part 1) / Scott free (part II)
SNCD 1103 / '86 / Soul Note

☐ SPEAK, BROTHER, SPEAK
Speak brother speak (a variation)
OJCCD 646 / Nov '95 / Original Jazz Classics

☐ SURVIVORS
Survivors / Third eye / Billy the kid / Jasme / Drum also waltzes / Sassy Max (self portrait) / Smoke that thunders
SNCD 1093 / May '85 / Soul Note

☐ VARIATIONS ON THE SCENE
JHR 73589 / May '98 / Jazz Hour

Roach, Michael

☐ AIN'T GOT ME NO HOME
ST 001CD / 17 Oct '97 / Stella

☐ BLINDS OF LIFE, THE
STCD 003 / 17 Oct '97 / Stella

Roach, Nancy

☐ DOUBLE SCOTCH
CIC 066CD / Nov '93 / Clo Iar-Chonnachta

Roachford

☐ FEEL
Way I feel / How could I / Don't make me love you / Someday / Naked without you / Nothing free / Move on / Down / Testify / Time / Flow
4885262 / 13 Oct '97 / Columbia

☐ GET READY
Get ready / Survival / Funkee chile / Stone city / Wanna be loved / Bayou / Innocent eyes / Hand of fate / Takin' it easy / Higher / Vision of the future / Get ready (reprise)
4681362 / 11 May '98 / Columbia

☐ PERMANENT SHADE OF BLUE
Only to be with you / Johnny / Emergency / Lay your love on me / Ride the storm / This generation / I know you don't love me / Gus's blues (Intro) / Do we wanna live together / Cry for me / Guess I must be crazy / Higher love
4758422 / 2 Feb '98 / Columbia

☐ ROACHFORD
Give it up / Family man / Cuddly toy / Find me another love / No way / Kathleen / Beautiful morning / Lying again / Since / Nobody but you
4606302 / Apr '92 / Columbia

Road

☐ ROAD
I'm trying / Going down to the country / Mushroom man / Man dressed in red / Spaceship Earth / Friends / Road
GRC 016 / 16 Feb '98 / Growing Concern

Road Rage

☐ NOTHIN' TO DECLARE
BFRCD 004 / 24 Nov '97 / Bomb Factory

Road Runners

☐ JUMP CHILDREN
APCD 124 / Jun '96 / Appaloosa

Roadrunners

☐ CATCH US IF YOU CAN
SFAX 001 / Jan '97 / SFAX

Roadsaw

☐ NATIONWIDE
COTE 049 / 15 Jun '98 / Curve Of The Earth

Rob Base

☐ BREAK OF DAWN (Rob Base & DJ E-Z Rock)
60802CLU / Jul '95 / Edel

Rob Zombie

☐ HELLBILLY DELUXE
GED 25212 / 24 Aug '98 / Geffen

Robb, Terry

☐ ACOUSTIC BLUES TRIO
BCD 00192 / May '96 / Burnside

Robbins, Marty

☐ BEST OF MARTY ROBBINS, THE (2CD Set)
Story of my life / Unchained melody / El Paso / Hawaiian wedding song / Singin' the blues / Big iron / Love me tender / White sports coat (and a pink carnation) / Devil woman / Can't help falling in love / Ruby Ann / Riders in the sky / 18 yellow roses / Am I that easy to forget / Streets of Loredo / Summertime / I did what I did for Maria / By the time I get to Phoenix / La Paloma / You gave me a mountain
4851282 / Aug '96 / Columbia

☐ CONCERT COLLECTION
El Paso / Big iron on his hip / Jambalaya / Foggy mountain breakdown / Touch me with magic / Chime bells / Among my souvenirs / Jenny / Devil woman / Big boss man / That's alright Mama / Love me / Don't worry 'bout me / Ribbon of darkness / My woman my woman my wife / White sport coat and a pink carnation
PLATCD 162 / Mar '96 / Platinum

☐ COUNTRY 1951-1958 (5CD Set)
Tomorrow you'll be gone / I wish somebody else loves me / Love me or leave me alone / Cryin' 'cause I love you / I'll go on alone / Pretty words / You're breaking my heart / I can get along / I couldn't keep from crying / Just in time / Crazy little heart / After you leave / Lorelei / Castle in the sky / Your hearts turn to

break / Why keep wishing / Half way chance with you / Sing me something sentimental / At the end of a long lonely day / Blessed Jesus, Should I fall don't let me lay / Kneel and let the Lord take your load / Don't make me ashamed / It's a long, long ride / It looks like I'm just in your way / I'm happy 'cause you're hurtin' / My isle of golden dreams / Have thine own way / God understands / Aloha oe / What made you change your mind / Way of a hopeless love / Pain and misery / Juarez / I'm too big to cry / Call me up / It's a pity what money can do / Time goes by / This broken heart of mine / I'll love you 'til the day I die / Don't let me hang around / Pray for me mother of mine / Daddy loves you / That's alright Mama / Gossip / Maybellene / Pretty mama / Mean mama blues / Long gone lonesome blues / I can't quit (I've gone too far) / Singin' the blues / Tennessee toddy / Baby I need you / Long tall Sally / Mr. Teardrop / Respectfully Miss Brooks / You don't owe me a thing / I'll know your gone / How long will it be / Where d'ya go / Most of the time / Same two lips / Your heart of blue is showing through / Knee deep in the blues / Little rosewood casket / Letter edged in black / Twenty one years / Convict and the rose / Bus stop song / Dream the miner's child / Little box of pine in the 7:29 / Wreck of number nine / Sad lover / Little shirt my mother made for me / My mother was a lady / When it's lamplighting time in the valley / Wreck of the 12:56 / It's too late now / I never let you cross my mind / I'll step aside / Bouquet of roses / I'm so lonesome I could cry / Lovesick blues / Moanin' the blues / Rose of ol' Pawnee / I hang my head and cry / Have I told you lately that I love you / All the world is lonely now / You only want me when you're lonely / Crying steel guitar waltz / Beautiful Ohio / Now is the hour / Down where the tradewinds blow / Sweet leilani / Beyond the reef / Constancy / Don't sing aloha when I go / Song of the Islands / Moonland / Island echoes / Faded petal from a beautiful bouquet / When I turned and slowly walked away / Jody / House with everything but love / Nothing but sweet lies / Baby I need you / Kaw-liga / Paper / Face / Many tears ago / Address unknown / Waltz of the wind / Hands you're holding now / Wedding bells / Shackles and chains / Oh how I miss you / Footprints in the snow / It's driving me crazy

BCD 15570 / Aug '91 / Bear Family

☐ COUNTRY 1960-1966 (5CD Set)

Devil woman / It's your world / Lonely too long / Over high mountain / Fly, buterfly, fly / Because it's wrong / Like all other times / Little Robin / It kinda reminds me / Address unkown / Yesterday's roses / Each night at nine / People's valley / No one will ever know / I'm not ready yet / I feel another heartbeat coming on / Ribbin of darkness / Robing gambler / Foggy foggy river / Lolene / Just before the battle Mother / Beautiful dreamer / Long, long ago / Melba from Melbourne / Change that dial / Only a picture stops time / Southern Dixie flyer / Everybody's darling plus mine / She means nothing to me now / Making excuses / Rainbow / I've lived a lifetime in a day / You won't have her long / Things I don't know / Urgently needed / I'll have to make some changes / Nine tenth of the law / Sorting memories / Hello heartache / One window, four walls / Working my way through a heartache / Would you take me back again / Do me a favor / Sixteen weeks / Seconds to remember / Another lost weekend / Last night about this time / This song / Hello baby / Don't worry / Time and a place for everything / Sixtytwo's most promising fool / Too far gone / April fool's day / Rich man, rich man / I've got a woman's love / Never look back / I'm beginning to forget you / Progressive love / Hands your holding now / Ain't life a crying shame / Kinda halfway feel / Little rich girl / Will the circle be unbroken / Little spot in heaven / Evening prayer / With his hands on my shoulder / There's power in the blood / When the roll is called up yonder / Where should I go (but to the lord) / Almost persuaded / What God has done / You gotta climb / Great speckled bird / Who at my door is standing / Have thine own way, Lord / Cigarettes and coffe blues / No tears milady / Wine flowed freely / Shoe goes on the other foot tonight / Not so long ago / I hope you learn a lot / Begging to you / In the ashes of an old love affair / Love's a hurtin game / Worried / Time can't make me forget / Baby talk to me / Pieces of your heart / It kinda reminds me of me / My own native land / Private Wilson White / Ain't it right / You gave me a mountain / To be in love with her / Matilda / It finally happened / They'll never take her love from me

BCD 15655 / Nov '95 / Bear Family

☐ DRIFTER, THE

379342 / Jun '97 / Koch International

☐ ESSENTIAL MARTY ROBBINS, THE (2CD Set)

Tomorrow you'll be gone / I'll go on alone / Maybellene / Tennessee Toddy / I can't quit / Singin' the blues / Knee deep in the blues / Mister Teardrop / Story of my life / White sport coat (and a pink carnation) / She was only seventeen (He was one year more) / Just married / Ain't I the lucky one / Kaw-liga / Hanging tree / El Paso / Big iron / Song of the bandit / Cool water / Little sentimental / September in the rain / All the way / Unchained melody / Don't worry / Devil woman / Ruby Ann / Smokin' cigarettes and drinkin' coffee blues / I'm gonna be a cowboy / (Ghost) Riders in the sky / San Angelo / Man walks among us / Beautiful dreamer / Beyond the reef / Hawaiian wedding song / Yours (Quiereme mucho) / Tonight Carmen / Ribbon of darkness / Feleene / Hello heartache / Begging to you / I walk alone / You gave me a mountain / My woman, my woman, my wife / Among my souvenirs / Return to me / Some memories just won't die / El Paso city

4689092 / Jun '96 / Columbia

☐ GUNFIGHTER BALLADS AND TRAIL SONGS/MORE GUNFIGHTER BALLADS

Big iron / Cool water / Billy the kids / Hundred and sixty acres / They're hanging me tonight / Strawberry roan / El paso / In the valley / Master's calll / Running gun / Little green valley / Utah Carol / San Angelo / Prairie fire / Streets of Laredo / Song of the bandit / I've got no use for the woman / Five brothers / Little Joe the wrangler / Ride cowboy ride / This peaceful sod / She was young and she was pretty / My love

4840332 / Jun '96 / Columbia

☐ HAWAII'S CALLING ME

Lovely Hula hands / Sea and me / Night I came to shore / Echo island / Kuu ipo Lani (my sweetheart Lani) / Beyond the reef / Hawaiian wedding song / Drowsy waters / Hawaiian bells / My wonderful one / Blue sand / Hawaii's calling me / Ku lu a (love song of kalua) / Drowsy waters (Wailana) / Song of the Islands / Don't sing aloha when i go / Crying steel guitar waltz / My isle of golden dreams / Now is the hours (Maori Farewell song) / Sweet leilani / Down where the tradewinds blow / Aloha oe / Island echoes / Moonland / Constancy

BCD 15568 / May '91 / Bear Family

☐ MARTY AFTER MIDNIGHT

I'm in the mood for love / Misty / Looking back / September in the rain / Don't throw me away / Pennies from Heaven / Summertime / It had to be you / All the way / I'm having a ball / If I could cry / On the sunny side of the street

379332 / Jun '97 / Koch International

☐ MUSICAL JOURNEY TO THE CARIBBEAN AND MEXICO

Girl from Spanish Town / Kingston girl / Sweet bird of paradise / Jamaica farewell / Calypso girl / Back to Montego Bay / Girl from Spanish Town / Kingston girl / Woman gets her way / Mango song / Calypso vacation / Blue sea / Bahama Mama / Tahitian boy / Native girl / Girl from Spanish Town / Yours / You belong to my heart / La Borachita / La paloma / Quiereme mucho / Adios mariquita Llinda / Amor / Camellia

BCD 15571 / May '91 / Bear Family

☐ ROCK 'N' ROLL 'N' ROBBINS

That's all right / Long tall Sally / Long gone lonesome blues / Tennessee Toddy / Respectfully Miss Brooks / Mean Mama blues / Pretty Mama / Baby's gone / Teenager's Dad / Grown up tears / Mabelline / Ruby Ann

379322 / Jun '97 / Koch

☐ ROCKIN' ROLLIN' ROBBINS VOL.1

That's alright Mama / Maybellene / Pretty mama / Mean mama blues / Tenessee Toddy / Singin' the blues / I can't quit (I've gone too far) / Long tall sally / Mr. Teardrop / Respectfully Miss Brooks / You don't owe me a thing / Baby I need you / Pain and misery / Footprints in the snow / It's driving me crazy / It's a long, long ride / Call me up (and I'll come calling on you)

BCD 15566 / May '91 / Bear Family

☐ ROCKIN' ROLLIN' ROBBINS VOL.2

White sports coat and a pink carnation / Grown up tears / Please don't blame me / Teenage dream / Story of my life / Once a week date / Just married / Stairway of love / She was only seventeen / Sittin' in a tree house / Ain't I the lucky one / Last time I saw my heart / Hanging tree / Blues country style / Jeannie and Johnnie / Foolish decision

BCD 15567 / May '91 / Bear Family

☐ ROCKIN' ROLLIN' ROBBINS VOL.3

Ruby Ann (chart version) / Sometimes I'm tempted / No signs of loneliness here / While you're dancing / Teenager's Dad / Ruby Ann / Cap and gown (fast) / Last night about this time / I hope you learn a lot / Love can't wait / Cigarettes and coffee / Little rich girl / Hello baby (goodbye baby) / Baby's gone / Cap and gown (slow) / Whole lot easier / She was young and she was pretty / Cap and gown (New york recording) / Sweet cora / Ain't live a cryin' shame / Silence and tears / You've been so busy baby

BCD 15569 / Nov '93 / Bear Family

☐ UNDER WESTERN SKIES (4CD Set)

El Paso / Cool water / In the valley / Running gun / Big iron / Master's call / Little green valley / Hundred and sixty acres / Billy the kid / Strawberry roan / They're hanging me tonight / Utah Carol / Saddle tramp / She was young and she was pretty / Streets of Laredo / Little Joe / Wrangler / I've got no use for the woman / Billy Venero / This peaceful sod / Five brothers / San Angelo / Ballad of the alamo (thirteen days of glory) / Hanging tree / Jimmy Martinez / Ghost train / Song of the bandit / Wind / Prairie fire / My love / Ride cowboy ride / Red river valley / Bend in the river / When the work's all done this fall / Abilene rose / Dusty winds / Old red / Doggone cowboy / Small man / Red hill of Utah / Tall handsome stranger / Fastest gun around / Man walks among us / Johnny Fedavo / Cowboy in the continental suit / I'm gonna be a cowboy / Cry stampede / Oh, Virginia / Meet me tonight in Loredo / Take me to the prairie / Wind goes / Old pal / Real pal / Feleena / Never tie me down / Lonley old bunkhouse / Night time on the desert / Cottonwood tree / Mister shorty / When it's lamplighting time in the valley / Is there anything else I can say / Tonight Carmen / Waiting in Reno / Mission in Guadalajaro / Love's gone away / Bound for Old Mexico / Chaple bell chime / Don't go away Senor / In the valley of the Rio Grand / (Girl with) Gardenias in her hair / Spanish lullaby / That silver haired daddy of mine / Chant of the wanderer / (Ghost) Riders in the sky / South of the border (Down Mexico way) / Sundown (ballad of Bill Thaxton) / Queen of the big rodeo / Ava Maria Morales / Outlaws / El Paso city / I'm kin to the wind / Trail dreamin' / She's just a drifter / Way out there / Tumbling tumbleweeds / Pride and the badge / All around cowboy / Restless cattle / Dreamer / Lonely old bunkhouse / Shotgun rider

BCD 15646 / Nov '95 / Bear Family

Robbins, Richard

☐ VIA CRUCIS

4540552 / Jun '96 / Point Music

Robert & Johnny

☐ WE BELONG TOGETHER

We belong together / Broken hearted man / I don't stand a ghost of a chance with you / Baby come home / You're mine / Eternity with you / Dream girl / Oh my love / Million dollar bills / I got you / Give me the key to your heart / Wear this ring / Gosh oh gee / Don't do it / I believe in you / God knows / Bad Dan / Indian marriage / Your kisses / Baby baby / I hear my heartbeat / Togetherness / I'm truly truly yours / Please me please / Try me pretty baby / Baby girl of mine / Train to paradise

CDCHD 384 / Apr '93 / Ace

Robert, George

☐ LIVE AT THE CHORUS

Jeanine / Dolphin dance / Remembering Henri / Voyage / Village / Upper Manhattan Medical Group UMMG / Sandu

TCB 95102 / Sep '95 / TCB

☐ TRIBUTE (Robert, George Quintet)

JFCD 004 / Dec '94 / Jazz Focus

Robert, Jocelyn

☐ FOLIE/CULTURE

RERJORCD / Oct '96 / ReR/ Recommended

Robert, Yves

☐ TOUT COURT

ZZ 84103 / Jan '94 / Deux Z

Roberts, Al Jr.

☐ HELLO, IT'S REALLY ME (The Al Roberts Jr. Memorial Album)

Telephone rock / Les Paul / Spider in the bath / Too n-n-nervous to rock / You fell asleep on our wedding night / There oughta be a law / Electric chair rock 'n' roll / Too wrecked to rock / I'll be your hamburger king / Haunted house rock / Fatter by the hour / My gran 'pappy don' smoke no grass / Motorway food / 2% of 90% of 1% / Jailbait / Someone's torn out the very last page / Walkin' the cat / Another spot / She put the hurt on me / Don't give up your day job / Mother In Law / UFO rock and roll / Mama threw out my rock 'n' roll shoes / Little Lucy / He ate too many burgers / Rockabilly guitar man

NEMCD 928 / May '97 / Sequel

Roberts, David Thomas

☐ FOLK RAGTIME 1899-1914

SOSCD 1317 / Feb '98 / Stomp Off

Roberts, Dean

☐ MOTH PARK/SOUNDTRACKS TO UTOPIA

FORMA 001 / 23 Mar '98 / Formacentric Disk

Roberts, Hank

☐ BLACK PASTELS

Black pastels / Jamil / Mountain speaks / Rain village / Choqueno / This quietness / Granpappy's barn dance / Death dance / Scarecrow shakedown / Lucky's lament

8344162 / Feb '94 / jMT

Roberts, Howard

☐ REAL HOWARD ROBERTS, THE

Dolphin dance / Darn that dream / Lady wants to know / Gone with the wind / Serenata / Angel eyes / All blues

CCD 4053 / Apr '94 / Concord Jazz

Roberts, John

☐ NAULAKHA REDUX (Roberts, John & Tony Barrand)

GHM 104CD / Mar '98 / Golden Hind

Roberts, Kenny

☐ JUMPIN' AND YODELIN'

I never see Maggie alone / Broken teenage heart / Newsboy / I'm looking for the bully of the town / Arizona yodeler / Wedding bells / Boogie woogie yodel song / One way ticket / I believe I'm entitled to you / I miss my swiss / I'd like to kiss Susie again / Mighty pretty waltz / Yodel polka / Ding dong bells are ringing agian / When I'd yoo hoo in the valley / Choo choo ch' boogie / She taught me how to yodel / FOB Tennessee / Billy and Nanny goat / Same ol' tune / Hillbilly style / Cry baby blues / River of tears / I've got the blues / Choc'late ice cream cone / Honky tonk sweetheart / Hillbilly fever / Just a yodel for me / Dream little cowboy / I wouldn't hurt you for the world / I finally got Maggie alone

BCD 15908 / Feb '96 / Bear Family

Roberts, Marcus

☐ BLUES FOR THE NEW MILLENNIUM

Cross road blues / Jungle blues / Any time any place / That was then / Jade / When the morning comes / Heart of the blues / Whales from the orient / Servant of the people / Late rehersal / Express mail delivery / Early rehersal / I'll see you at one / It's Maria's dance

CK 68637 / 3 Nov '97 / Sony Jazz

☐ COLLECTED MARCUS ROBERTS, THE

Arrival / Truth is spoken here / Blue monk / Country by choice / Crepuscule with Nellie / Nebuchadnezzar / Jitterbug waltz / Preach Reverend preach / E. Dankworth / Embraceable you / Governor / Go tell it on the mountain

09026687202 / Jul '98 / RCA Victor

☐ GERSHWIN FOR LOVERS

Foggy day / Man I love / Our love is here to stay / Summertime / Someone to watch over me / It ain't necessarily so / Nice work if you cna get it / They can't take that away from me / How long has this been going on / But not for me

4777522 / Oct '94 / Columbia

☐ PORTRAITS IN BLUE (Roberts, Marcus & Orchestra Of St. Luke's/Robert Sadin)

Rhapsody in blue / I got rhythm / Yamekraw

SK 68488 / Aug '96 / Sony Classical

☐ TIME AND CIRCUMSTANCE

Soul mates / Exploration / Reflecting mirrors / Imperfect balance / Two rocks by the shore / Harvest time / Alone / Time and circumstance / Memories of one / Eternal dialogue / In retrospect / Optimism / When fire meets moonlight / Renewed vision

4844512 / 26 Jan '98 / Sony Jazz

Roberts, Paul

☐ CHRISTMAS ORGAN

PLSCD 265 / 29 Sep '97 / Pulse

☐ ORGAN MUSIC FROM AROUND THE WORLD

MACCD 363 / 26 Jan '98 / Autograph

Roberts, Paul Dudley

☐ FROM RAGS TO RICHES

They all laughed / Russian rag / Rosemary's waltz / One man went to mo-zart / Body and soul / Aba daba honeymoon / Memory / Little jazz bird / Entertainer / All I ask of you / Lesson one / Arrival of the queen of sheba / Feelings / Tiger rag ('hol'dat tigah') / Moon river / Lullaby of birdland / On the sunny side of the street / Believe that dreams come true / Gold diggers song / On broadway

DLD 1034 / May '93 / Dance & Listen

☐ I GOT RHYTHM

I got rhythm (quickstep) / 's wonderful (quickstep) / Eidelweiss (waltz) / Charmaine (waltz) / Pablo the dreamer (tango) / Isle of capri (tango) / Once in a while (foxtrot) / Smile to smile (foxtrot) / I told every little star (cha cha) / Old father thames (cha cha) / Arrivederci roma-perfidia (rumba) / Sealed with a kiss (rumba) / Happy days and lonely nights (jive) / Perdido (jive) / I don't want to walk without you (saunter) / Any dream will do (saunter) / There's a rainbow round my shoulder (swing) / I recall a gipsy woman (swing) / Softly as in a morning sunrise (tango) / Marta (tango)

DLD 1035 / Mar '93 / Dance & Listen

Roberts, Roy

☐ EVERY SHADE OF BLUE

KS 042CD / Jul '97 / King Snake

Roberts, Tom

☐ TOM ROBERTS

SACD 121 / Dec '97 / Solo Art

Robertson, Eck

☐ OLD TIME TEXAS FIDDLER

Brilliancy medley / Texas wagoner / Arkansas traveller / Great big taters / Sallie Gooden / There's a brownskin girl down the road somewhere / Ragtime Annie / Amarillo waltz / Done gone / Island unknown / Sally Johnson/Billy in the low ground / Turkey in the straw / Brown Kelly waltz / Run boy run

COUNTY 3515 / Jul '98 / County

Robertson, Jeannie

☐ JEANNIE ROBERTSON

Bonnie wee lassie who never said no / What a voice / My plaidie's awa' / Gypsy laddie / When I was no' but sweet sixteen / MacCrimmon's lament / Roy's wife of Aldivalloch / Lord Lovat

OSS 92CD / Aug '94 / Ossian

Robertson, Justin

☐ JOURNEYS BY DJ VOL.11 (2CD Set) (Various Artists)

JDJCD 11 / Jul '96 / JDJ

Robertson, Kim

☐ TREASURES OF THE CELTIC HARP

DMCD 114 / Feb '96 / Dara

☐ WOOD, FIRE AND GOLD

DM 119CD / Aug '96 / Dargason Music

Robertson, Lonnie

☐ LONNIE'S BREAKDOWN

Lonnie's breakdown / Ozark mountain waltz / Mountain reel / Old Parnell / Untitled reel in B flat / Old time breakdown in A / Lady on a steamboat / Fiddler's blues / Lonnie's hornpipe / Big sandy river / Jump fingers / Saddle old Kate / Rock all the babies to sleep / Speed the plough / Caney Mountain hornpipe / Hazy hills waltz / Taney County breakdown / Lantern in the ditch / Lonesome Polly Ann / Kaiser waltz / Old Joe / Johnny, bring the jug around the hill / Cincinnati hornpipe / Natural bridge blues / Untitled reel in D / Wink the other eye / Malindy / Unnamed B flat waltz / Rag in C / Rosebud reel / A and E rag / Bluebird waltz / Arkansas stomp / Katy Hill/Darky's dream/Brown leaf rag

ROUCD 0375 / Nov '96 / Rounder

Robertson, Robbie

☐ CONTACT FROM THE UNDERWORLD OF REDBOY

Sound is fading / Code of handsome lake / Making a noise / Unbound / Sacrifice / Stomp dance / Peyote healing / In the blood / Rattlebone / Lights / Take your partner by the hand

8542432 / 2 Mar '98 / Capitol

☐ NATIVE AMERICANS

Coyote dance / Mahk tchi (Heart of the people) / Ghost dance / Vanishing breed / It's a good day to die / Golden feather / Akua Tutu / Words of fire, deeds of blood / Cherokee morning song / Skinwalker / Ancestor song / Twisted hair

CDEST 2238 / Oct '94 / EMI

☐ ROBBIE ROBERTSON

Fallen angel / Showdown at big sky / Broken arrow / Sweet fire of love / American roulette / Somewhere down the crazy river / Hell's half acre / Sonny got caught in the moonlight / Testimony

GFLD 19294 / Oct '95 / Geffen

☐ STORYVILLE
Night parade / Hold back the dawn / Go back to your wood / Soap box preacher / Day of reckoning (burnin for you) / What about now / Shake this town / Breakin' the rules / Resurrection / Sign of the rainbow
GFLD 19295 / Oct '95 / Geffen

Robeson, Paul

☐ BIG FELLA
Lazybones / Scarecrow / Fat li'l feller with his Mammy's eyes / Wagon wheels / Deep river / My curly headed baby / Carry me back to green pastures / Old folks at home (Swanee river) / High water / My heart is where the mohawk flows tonight / So early in the morning / Carry me back to old Virginny / Goodnight ladies / Way down South in Dixie / Poor old Joe / Oh Susanna / My old Kentucky home / River stay 'way from my door / Hail the crown / Love song / Killing song / Black emperor / I don't know what's wrong / Lazin' / You didn't oughta do such things / Ecantadora Maria / David of the white rock / Thora / Love at my heart / Ebenezer / King Joe / Little black boy / Little piccaninny's gone to sleep / When it's sleepy time down South
CDHD 245 / Mar '98 / Happy Days

☐ GREAT VOICES OF THE CENTURY VOL.1, THE
Love song / Mighty like a rose / I'm goin' to tell God all o' my troubles: *Robeson, Paul & Lawrence Brown* / Song of freedom / St. Louis blues / Honey (dat's all) / Killing song / Oh no John: *Robeson, Paul & Lawrence Brown* / Carry me back to green pastures / Trees / Sylvia / At dawning / Songs my Mother taught me / Down lovers' lane / Cobbler's song / Swing low, sweet chariot / That's why darkies where born / Joshua fit de battle of Jericho: *Robeson, Paul & Lawrence Brown* / Black emperor / Ol' man river
CDMOIR 415 / Nov '94 / Memoir

☐ GREEN PASTURES
St. Louis blues / Rockin' chair / Mary had a baby, yes Lord / Love song / All God's chillun got wings / Banjo song / Bear the burden / When it's sleepy time down South / Killing song / High water / Lazybones / Carry me back to green pastures / Congo lullaby / Shortnin' bread / Snowball / Fat li'l feller with his mammy's eyes / Canoe song / River stay 'way from my door
CDAJA 5047 / Oct '88 / Living Era

☐ INIMITABLE PAUL ROBESON, THE
Carry me back to green pastures / Lonesome road / Hush-a-bye-lullaby / All through the night / Little man you've had a busy day / Wagon wheels / I ain't lazy, I'm just dreaming / Shenandoah / Song of the Volga boatmen / Roll away clouds / So shy / Dear old Southland / Blue prelude / Round the bend of the road / King Joe - Part one / King Joe - Part two / Rockin' chair / Solitude / Nothin' / Got something in my soul / St. Louis blues / Perfect day / Ma curly-headed baby / All God's chillun got wings / Lazybones
PAR 2065 / Jul '96 / Parade

☐ LONESOME ROAD, A
Ol' man river / My curly headed baby / Waterboy / I'm goin' to tell God all o' my troubles / Oh didn't it rain / There's no hiding place / Poor old Joe / Scandalise my name / Ezekiel saw de wheel / Sinner please doan' let this harves' pass / Just keepin' on / My Lindy Lou / Steal away / Mighty like a rose / Deep river / Hear the lambs a-cryin' / Git on board, li'l chilun / Old folks at home (Swanee river) / Witness / Oh rock me Julie / Li'l gal / I got a home in that rock / Lonesome road / Little Pal
CDAJA 5027 / Oct '88 / Living Era

☐ OL' MAN RIVER
Ol' man river / My old Kentucky home / Lazybones / My Lindy Lou / Poor old Joe / Old folks at home (Swanee river) / Just keepin' on / Little pal / Water boy / Joshua fit de battle of Jericho / Swing low, sweet chariot / Shenandoah / Wagon wheels / Got the South in my soul / St. Louis blues / Rockin' chair / River stay 'way from my door / Canoe song / Congo lullaby / Love song
RMB 75024 / Nov '93 / Remember

☐ OL' MAN RIVER
8418582 / Sep '96 / Music Memoria

☐ OL' MAN RIVER
Love song / St. Louis blues / All God's chillun got wings / Rockin' chair / Mary had a baby, yes Lord / Killing song / Lazybones / Carry me back to green pastures / High water / Snowball / When it's sleepy time down South / Fat li'l feller with his Mammy's eyes / Congo lullaby / Shortnin' bread / Canoe song / Banjo song / River stay 'way from my door / Ol' man river
CD 12519 / Feb '95 / Music Of The World

☐ OL' MAN RIVER
Ol' man river / Rockin' chair / Blind ploughman / Drink to me only with thine eyes / Cobbler's song / Mighty lak' a rose / St. Louis blues / Banjo song / It ain't necessarily so / Carry me back to the green pastures / Lazy bones / Dear old southland / Shenadoah / Sonny boy / River stay 'way from my door / That's why darkies were born / Mood indigo / Canoe song / Sleepy river / Sometimes I feel like a motherless child / Minstrel man
307912 / 15 Sep '97 / Hallmark

☐ OL' MAN RIVER
GO 3820 / 1 Dec '97 / Golden Options

☐ OL' MAN RIVER (His 25 Greatest)
Ol' man river / Steal away / Joshua fit de battle ob Jericho / Water boy / Swing low sweet chariot / Deep river / Lonesome road / Mighty lak' a rose / River stay 'way from my door / Rockin' chair / When it's sleepy time down south / Mah Lindy Lou / My curly headed baby / Carry me back to green pastures / Lazy bones / St. Louis blues / Congo lullaby / Canoe song / Shenandoah / It still suits me / Summertime / It ain't necessarily so / Just a-wearyin' for you / Song of the Volga boatmen / Little man you've had a busy day
CDAJA 5276 / May '98 / Living Era

☐ PAUL ROBESON
Lazybones / It ain't necessarily so / Sleepy river / My way / I don't know what's wrong / Song of the Volga boatmen / Canoe song / Roll up sailorman / That's why darkies were born / Swing low, Sweet chariot / Mammy's little kinky headed boy / Roll away clouds / Just a wearyin' for you / Deep river / Sea fever / Absent / Mighty like a rose / On ma journey / Just keepin' on / Woman is a sometime thing / You didn't oughta do such things / Lazin' / Ol' man river
PASTCD 7009 / May '93 / Flapper

☐ PAUL ROBESON
Ol' man river / Woman is a sometime thing / Summertime / Song of freedom / Black emperor / Fat li'l feller wid his mammy's eyes / Ma Lindy Lou / Love song / At dawning / Sleepy river / Lonely road / Mighty like a rose / Ma curley-headed baby / Canoe song / Honey / It ain't necessarily so / It takes a long pull to get there / All through the night / Cobbler's song / My way / No John no / St. Louis blues / Passing by / Eriskay love / Swing low sweet chariot
CDMFP 6352 / Jun '97 / Music For Pleasure

☐ PAUL ROBESON VOL.1
Sonny boy / It takes a long pull to get there / Summertime / Woman is a sometime thing / It ain't necessarily so / Congo lullaby / Canoe song / Mood indigo / Solitude / At dawning / All through the night / Lazybones / St. Louis blues / Old folks at home (Swanee River) / My old Kentucky home / My curly headed baby / Mighty like a rose / Waterboy / Deep river / Hammer song: *Robeson, Paul & Lawrence Brown* / Li'l David: *Robeson, Paul & Lawrence Brown* / Swing low, sweet chariot / Just a wearyin' for you / Ol' man river
GEMMCD 9356 / '89 / Pearl

☐ PAUL ROBESON VOL.2
Down in lovers' lane / Swing along / Bear the burden / All God's chillun got wings / Joshua fit de battle of Jericho / Old ark's a' movering / Ezekiel saw de wheel / Scandalise my name / Sinner please doan' let this harves' pass / Work all de summer / Didn't my Lord deliver Daniel / Dere's a man goin' roun' takin' names / Shenandoah / Little pal / Lonesome Road / Roll away clouds / Ho Ho / Climbing up / Song of freedom / Sleepy river / Trees / So John no / Song of the Volga boatmen / There is a green hill / Nearer, my God to thee / Fat li'l feller with his mammy's eyes / Mama's little baby love
GEMMCD 9382 / '90 / Pearl

☐ PEACE ARCH CONCERTS
FERCD 1442 / Mar '98 / Folk Era

☐ SONGS FOR FREE MEN
GEMMCD 9264 / Jan '97 / Pearl

Robi Rob's Clubworld

☐ ROBI ROB'S CLUBWORLD
Robi Rob's boriqua anthem / Shake that body / Love and happiness / Get funky / Make that money / Robi Rob's Clubworld / I live / Reach / Mi gente latina / Goodbye
4854802 / Oct '96 / Columbia

Robic, Ivo

☐ MIT SIE BZEHN FANGT DAS LEBEN ERST AN
Morgen / Mit siebzehn fangt das leben erst an / Rot ist der Wein / Muli song / Rhondaly / Ay ay ay Paloma / Endlich / Auf der sonnenseite der welt / So allein / In einer bar in buffalo / Liebeleer / Du bist niemand, wenn niemand dich lieb hat / Traume vom Gluck / Schau dich night um / Ich denk nuran's wiedersehn / Wenn ich in deine augen schau / Tiefes blaues meer / Glaub daran (das leben ist schon) / Jezebel / Lass dein little girl nie weinen / Geh zu ihm / Ein ganzes leben lang / Fremde in der nacht / Mond guter freund / Happy muleteer / So alone / Endless / On the sunny side of the world
BCD 15671 / Jun '92 / Bear Family

Robichaud Brothers

☐ SLIPPERY STICK, THE
Grand Lake reel/Silver wedding reel / Coal branch reel/Emile Arsenault's / Moccasin shuffle/Brae reel / Fred's tuna/Money musk / Bunkhouse jig / Cousin Bill/Fiddlin' Phil / Island ferry/Herring reel / Herring brook/The High level hornpipe / Father Legere's marches / Constitution breakdown/Dragger's reel / Atlantic polkas / Tullybardine/La Disputeuse / March from my mother / Dancing hornpipe / Slippery stick / Leprechaun jig / Miramichi fire / Bouctouche reel/ Saint Anne's reel / Watch City hornpipe / Traditional New Brunswick jig / Abegweit breakdown
ROUCD 7016 / Oct '96 / Rounder

Robicheaux, Coco

☐ LOUISIANA MEDICINE MAN
8451822 / Jan '98 / Sky Ranch

☐ SPIRITLAND
8413862 / Sep '96 / Sky Ranch

Robillard, Duke

☐ AFTER HOURS SWING SESSION
Trouble with me is you / Shivers / I can't believe that you're in love with me / Sweet Georgia Brown / Twist top / I'll never be the same / Tiny's tempo / Albi ain't here
NETCD 0033 / May '92 / Network

☐ DANGEROUS PLACE
Had to be your man / Going straight / Dangerous place / Don't get me shook up / Take my word for it / Can't remember to forget / Duke's advice / Nothing like you (where I come from) / I may be ugly (but I sure know how to cook) / All over but the paying / No time / Black negligee
VPBCD 41 / May '97 / Pointblank

☐ DUKE'S BLUES (Robillard, Duke Band)
Midnight cannon ball / Glamour girl / I still love you baby / Texas hop / Don't leave me baby / Tell me why / Something to remember you by / Love slipped in / Information blues / Don't treat me like that / Never let you go / Gee I wish / My heart is cryin' / Red's riff / Dyin' flu
VPBCD 29 / Jan '96 / Pointblank

☐ PLAYS BLUES (The Rounder Years)
Down by the delta / You got me / If this is love / Judgement day / High cost of loving / She made my mind / You're the one I adore / Don't come back / Anything it takes / Duke's mood / Just a human / Let me love you / Just kiss me / I think you know
CDBB 9598 / Nov '97 / Bullseye Blues

☐ PLAYS JAZZ (The Rounder Years)
Shivers / Sweet Georgia Brown / Jim jam / Albi ain't there / Zot / I'll never be the same / Shufflin' with some barbeque / Twist top / What's your story morning glory / Time's a wastin' / Cadillac slim / Exactly like you / Tiny's tempo / Glide on
CDBB 9597 / Nov '97 / Bullseye Blues

☐ ROCKIN' BLUES (Robillard, Duke & The Pleasure Kings)
If this is love / Too hot to handle / Rockin' blues / Tore up / Let me love you / Baby please come home / She's sweet / Duke's mood / One more time / Someone / She made my mind / Anything it takes / My plea / It's my own business / Give me all the love you got / Just kiss me / Give me your attention
ROUCD 11548 / '88 / Rounder

☐ SWING
Cadillac Slim / Jumpin' blues / Exactly like you / Glide on / Zot / I'll always be in love with you / Shuffin' with some barbeque / Durn tottin' / You'd better change your ways / Jim jam
ROUCD 3103 / Jun '96 / Rounder

☐ TEMPTATION
Rule the world / (You got my love) Sewed up / Live to give / Change is on / Life's funny / When my love comes down / This dream (still coming true) / Temptation / Never been satisfied / Born to love you / What's wrong
VPBCD 20 / Sep '94 / Virgin

☐ TURN IT AROUND (Robillard, Duke Band & Susan Forrest)
Down by the delta / Passionate kiss / Don't look at my girl like that / Just a human / Turn it around / Shoulda coulda woulda / High cost of loving / Sweets for my sweet / Tell me how / I think you know
ROUCD 3116 / Aug '96 / Rounder

☐ YOU GOT ME (Robillard, Duke & Guests)
ROUCD 3100 / '88 / Rounder

Robin, Roger

☐ REFLECTIONS
LOVCD 005 / Apr '95 / Love Injection

☐ UNDILUTED
LOVCD 004 / Nov '93 / Spider Ranks

Robin, Ruggero

☐ BIG ONE
CDSGP 0189 / Mar '96 / Prestige

☐ VICE VERSA
Dim screw / Nell'aria / Quasar / Devil blues / Rain forest / Notturno / Nicola / Latin Shorter blues / Waltz / Solarium / Musica viva Monk blues
CDSGP 0400 / May '98 / Prestige

Robin S

☐ FROM NOW ON
It must be love / Been so long / You know how to love me / Midnight / There is a need / Givin' u all that I've got / Shine on me / It's not enough / 24 hour love / All I do / We're in this together / It must be love / It must be love
7567927162 / Jun '97 / Big Beat/ Atlantic

☐ SHOW ME LOVE
Show me love / Luv 4 luv / I'm gonna love you right (tonight) / If we could just be friends / What I do best / My kind of man / I want to thank you / Once in a lifetime love / Back it up / Back and forth / Brighter day / Who's gonna raise the child
CHAMCD 1028 / Mar '97 / Champion

Robin, Thierry

☐ GITANS
Y 225035CD / Mar '94 / Silex

☐ KALI GADJI
Prelude / Panolero / Bleu indigo / Swing wassoulou / Lovari / Anita / Guitarra mia / L'ombre de Dieu / Salutations / Interlude / Le vent / Amande / Choucar zizou / Chaabi michto / Postlude
Y 225072 / Jul '98 / Silex

☐ LE REGARD NU
Y 225059 / May '96 / Silex

☐ PAYO MICHTO
Mehdi / Patchiv / Que tu amor / L'exil / Katchur khan / Payo michto / Cuivre / Variations sur indifference / Prelude a Marraine / Tona del lobo / Los tanguillos / La petite mer / Rumba do vesou
Y 225071 / Dec '97 / Auvidis Silex

Robine, Marc

☐ L'EXIL
984342 / 5 Jan '98 / EPM

☐ LES TEMPS DES CERISES
983462 / Jul '95 / EPM

Robinett, Henry

☐ LIFE X2 (Robinett, Henry Group)
Hayley's day / Life x2 / Chotto nihongo / We need more time / Another road / Just is / If and when / Not like before / Maradona / Tom and Mary got married
AL 73077 / Dec '97 / Nefertiti

☐ WHEN FORTRESSES FALL (Robinett, Henry Group)
When fortresses fall / Gift / Laura's eyes / Cloud bursting / Once a gaucho / Cedar / Forever be / Your look / Blue note / Behind Irish passions / Laws of returning
AL 73076 / Dec '97 / Nefertiti

Robinson, Carson

☐ HOME SWEET HOME ON THE PRAIRIE (25 Cowboy Classics)
Clementine / Annie Laurie / Camptown races / Ain't ya comin' out tonight / Happy-go-lucky / Goin' to have a big time tonight / Little green valley / Leave the purty girls alone / When your hair has turned to silver / Missouri valley / Strawberry roan / In the Cumberland mountains / Ev'rybody's goin' but me / Oh Susannah / Tree top serenade / I was born in old Wyoming / Smoky mountain Bill / Swanee kitchen door / Sweet Virginia / Darling Nellie Gray / There's a bridle hangin' on the wall / I'm leavin' on that blue river train / Ramblin' cowboy / I'm an old cow hand / Texas Dan / With a banjo on my knee / Home sweet home on the prairie
CDAJA 5187 / Jun '96 / Living Era

Robinson, Dana

☐ MIDNIGHT SALVAGE
ALC 131CD / Mar '98 / Alcazar

Robinson, David

☐ NEVER STOP LOVIN'
RYTCD 4188 / Jun '94 / Ichiban

Robinson, Elzadie

☐ ELZADIE ROBINSON VOL.1 1926-1928
DOCD 5248 / May '94 / Document

☐ ELZADIE ROBINSON VOL.2 1928-1929
DOCD 5249 / May '94 / Document

Robinson, Fenton

☐ I HEAR SOME BLUES DOWNSTAIRS
I hear some blues downstairs / Just a little bit / West side baby / I'm so tired / I wish for you / Tell me what's the reason / Going west / Killing floor / As the years go passing by
ALCD 4710 / May '93 / Alligator

☐ MELLOW FELLOW (Charly Blues Masterworks Vol.41)
Somebody loan me a dime / Sky is crying / Smokestack lightning / Little red rooster / Moanin' for my baby / Don't start me to talkin' / Stormy monday / Leave you in the arms (of your other man) / Let me come on home / Getaway / Sideman / Give you some air / I'm not through loving you / Mellow fellow / She's a wiggler / Little turch / I wanna ooh / Laughing and crying blues / I fell in love one time
CDBM 41 / Jun '93 / Charly

☐ NIGHTFLIGHT
ALCD 4736 / May '93 / Alligator

☐ SOMEBODY LOAN ME A DIME
ALCD 4705 / May '93 / Alligator

☐ SPECIAL ROAD
7-11 Blues / Love is just a gamble / Special road / Too many drivers / Baby, please don't go / Crying the blues / Find a way / RM blues / Slick and greasy / Blue Monday / Money problem / Nothing but a fool / Little torch
ECD 260252 / Feb '93 / Evidence

Robinson, Frank

☐ EAST COAST TEXAS BLUES (Robinson, Frank & 'Guitar' Curtis)
BMCD 9028 / Aug '96 / Black Magic

Robinson, Jeff

☐ ANY SHADE OF BLUE
73924470042 / 21 Apr '98 / Wildwest

Robinson, Jim

☐ CLASSIC NEW ORLEANS JAZZ VOL.2
BCD 128 / Oct '93 / Biograph

Robinson, Jimmie Lee

☐ LONELY TRAVELLER (Robinson, Jimmie Lee & The Ice Cream Men)
Lonely traveller / Easy baby / Can't be successful / Twist it baby / Leave my woman alone / I'll be your slave / Triflin' on you / All my life / 44 blues / Key to the highway / Times are getting harder / Lonely man / Robinson's rang tangle
DE 665 / Mar '97 / Delmark

Robinson, Keith

☐ PEACEFUL FLIGHT
D 2249312 / 1 Jun '98 / Ichiban

☐ PEACEFUL LIGHT (Robinson, Keith & Alex Bugnon)
7063024942 / 24 Mar '98 / Ichiban

Robinson, L.C.

☐ MOJO IN MY HAND (Robinson, L.C. 'Good Rockin')
Mojo in my hand / Up and downs / Pinetop's boogie woogie / Across the bay blues / LC's shuffle / Can't be a winner / I've got to go / Stop and jump / She got it from the start / Thing's so bad in California / New train time / I'm just a country boy / LC's theme / Jesus did I know / I don't know what I would do without the Lord / Something mighty sweet about the Lord / Ida red / LC's blues / Sweet Jesus
ARHCD 453 / Nov '96 / Arhoolie

Robinson, Perry

☐ FUNK DUMPLING (Robinson, Perry Quartet)
Moon over Moscow / Sprites delight / Wahayla / Farmer Alfalfa / Margareta / Funk dumpling / Home is where the hearth is
SV 0255 / Oct '97 / Savoy Jazz

Robinson, Reginald R.

☐ EUPHONIC SOUNDS
Joplin song fragment / Space coaster ride / Entertainer / Raggy rag / Pekin rag / Truly yours / Heliotrope bouquet / Babe it's too long off / Moon is shining in the skies / Euphonic sounds / Frog legs rag / Sweet envy / Daredevil's gallop / Ragtime bobolink / Adventures in wonderland / Incognito / Still water blues / Lift every voice and sing / Cottontail rag
DE 718 / Jul '98 / Delmark

☐ SOUNDS IN SILHOUETTE
Ragtime pauper / Masquerade ball / To Mimie / Lake St. / Dream Natasha / Conductor / Holly Hock march / Jack Johnson rag / Sounds in silhouette / Ventriloquist / Champ rags / Swampy Lee / Peacherine rag / Sedidus walk / Little Dave blues / Charles L Johnson medley / Honor'e Chester / Knuckle fingers / Lonely Mable
DE 670 / Mar '97 / Delmark

☐ STRONGMAN, THE
Maple leaf rag / Good times rag / Strong man / Troubador serenade / Spring rag / Portrait of Scott Joplin / Ebony Venus / Petunia rag / Ballerina figurine / Finesse / Boogie man creep / Just try and escape the devil / Show stopper / Hustler's two-step / Kid / Scamp / Poker face blues / Nile river ripples / Jester / Georgia Tom / Original slow drag / Honeymoon waltz
DD 662 / Mar '97 / Delmark

Robinson, Rev. Cleophus

☐ SOMEONE TO CARE
Get away Jordan / Before this time another year / Morning and evening / Someone to care / Let the church roll on / Near the cross / It won't hurt you to speak / Peace in the valley / When the sun goes down / Grace made a change / I know prayer changes things / Jesus met the woman at the well / Until I found the Lord / I'm going to leave you in the hands of the Lord / Going over yonder / Strange things happening / Consecrated / You've got to love everybody / No more than you can bear / I can't help it / We'll understand it better by and by / Farther along / Lord I'm in your care / When the saints go marching in / Sometimes I feel like a Motherless child / Waiting for Jesus
CDCHD 566 / Mar '94 / Ace

Robinson, Scott

☐ THINKING BIG
ARCD 19179 / Nov '97 / Arbors Jazz

Robinson, Smokey

☐ CHRISTMAS WITH THE MIRACLES (Merry Christmas From Motown) (Robinson, Smokey & The Miracles)
Santa Claus is coming to town / Let it snow, let it snow, let it snow / Winter wonderland / Christmas everyday / I'll be home for Christmas / Christmas song / White Christmas / Silver bells / Noel / O holy night
5504052 / Nov '96 / Spectrum

☐ GREATEST HITS (Robinson, Smokey & The Miracles)
Being with you / Tracks of my tears / I second that emotion / I'm the one you need / Mickey's monkey / Going to a go go / I don't blame you at all / If you can want / Just to see her / More love / Just my soul responding / Tears of a clown / Abraham, Martin and John / You've really got a hold on me / Shop around / What's so good about goodbye / Ooo baby baby / Love I saw in you was just a mirage / Quiet storm / One heartbeat / Baby, baby, don't cry / Cruisin'
5301212 / Mar '96 / Motown

☐ MOTOWN EARLY CLASSICS
Tracks of my tears / You've really got a hold on me / Shop around / You never miss a good thing / Way over there / Determination / Everybody's gotta pay some dues / If your mother only knew / What's so good about goodbye / Since you won my heart / Such is love, such is life / Monkey time / Wah-watusi / I gotta dance to keep from crying / From head to toe / Would I love you / Let me have some / Going to a Go-Go
5521252 / Jul '96 / Spectrum

☐ SMOKEY'S SONGBOOK (Various Artists)
Tears of a clown: *Monitors* / Tracks of my tears: *Contours* / Shop around: *Griffin, Billy* / My girl: *Stubbs, Joe* / More love: *5th Dimension* / Hunter gets captured by the game: *Marvelettes* / You beat me to the punch: *Wells, Mary* / You really got a hold on me: *Ward, Sammy* / Way you do the things you do: *Motor City Allstars* / Don't mess with the bill: *Marvelettes* / My guy: *Wells, Mary* / Since I lost my baby: *Crawford, Carolyn* / Going to a go go: *Monitors* / From head to toe: *Clark, Chris* / Whole lotta shakin' in my head: *Johnson, Marv* / Get ready: *Taylor, Bobby & The Vancouvers* / What's easy for two is so hard for one: *Wells, Mary* / Goodbye cruel love: *Griner, Linda* / My baby must be a magician: *Marvelettes* / My smile is just a frown: *Crawford, Carolyn*
3035990042 / Oct '95 / Motor City

☐ TRACKS OF MY TEARS, THE
Going to a go go / I'm the one you need / I second that emotion / If you can want / Tracks of my tears / Tears of a clown / I don't blame you at all / Shop around / You've really got a hold on me / Love I saw in you was just a mirage / Mickey's monkey / My girl has gone / Yesterlove / More love / Man in you / Ooo baby baby / Whole lot of shakin' in my heart / Choosey beggar / Point it out / We've come to far to end it now
5307942 / Apr '97 / Spectrum

☐ ULTIMATE COLLECTION (Robinson, Smokey & The Miracles)
5308572 / 10 Aug '98 / Motown

☐ ULTIMATE COLLECTION
5307752 / 10 Aug '98 / Motown

Robinson, Spike

☐ AT THE STABLES (Robinson, Spike & Gene Di Novi)
Indian love call / Quietly there / So do I / Only make believe / Maybe you'll be there / Laura / Theme from The Bad And The Beautiful / Stockholm LA / I can't get started / He loves she loves / I won't cry / All the things you are / Alan's song
HEPCD 2071 / Aug '97 / Hep

☐ IN TOWN WITH ELAINE DELMAR
Too close for comfort / You've changed / Just one of those things / In a sentimental mood / 'S Wonderful / Get out of town / Little girl blue / Everything I love / Young and foolish / Will you still be mine
HEPCD 2035 / Jun '93 / Hep

☐ PLAYS HARRY WARREN
This heart of mine / At last / Boulevard of broken dreams / There will never be another you / I had the craziest dream / Shadow waltz / Serenade in blue / This is always / More I see you / Chattanooga choo choo / Cheerful little earful / I only have eyes for you / Lulu's back in town / I wish I knew
HEPCD 2056 / Oct '94 / Hep

☐ SPIKE ROBINSON & GEORGE MASSO PLAY ARLEN (Robinson, Spike & George Masso)
Let's fall in love / Right as rain / I gotta right to sing the blues / Taking a chance on love / This time the dream is on me / Happiness is a thing called Joe / When the sun comes out / Last night when we were young / My shining hour / As long as I live / Come rain or come shine / Between the Devil and the deep blue sea
HEPCD 2053 / Oct '92 / Hep

☐ SPIKE ROBINSON'S TENOR MADNESS
Here we go again / T'ain't no use / Tickle toe / Pretty one / Take four / Travelin' light / You 'n' me / One good turn / Note / Tenor madness / Stockholm - LA / Just an old manuscript / Goof and I / Quick one
ESJCD 600 / Jun '97 / Essential Jazz

☐ STAIRCASE TO THE STARS
Gone with the wind / Beautiful love / Gypsy sweetheart / It's always you / It's a blue world / Summer thing / From here to eternity / Stairway to the stars / It should happen to you
HEPCD 2049 / Oct '91 / Hep

☐ THREE FOR THE ROAD (Robinson, Spike & Louis Stewart)
They didn't believe me / Dearly beloved / If you were mine / Yes sir that's my baby / Only a rose / My buddy / Song is you / For Heaven's sake / They say that falling in love is wonderful
HEPCD 2045 / Oct '90 / Hep

Robinson, Tad

☐ ONE TO INFINITY
Empty apartment blues / Coming home / At the end of the tunnel / Eight days, 1 week / Trouble in mind / Can't print it fast enough / One to infinity / Walking in the sunshine / Lonely man / Raining in New York / Little rascal / Give love a chance
DE 673 / Mar '97 / Delmark

Robinson, Tom

☐ BLOOD BROTHER (Robinson, Tom & Jakko)
We've never had it so good / Driving through the desert / Blood brother / What have I ever done to you / Baby rages on / Tomboy / Kiss and roll over / Hard cases / Can't stop / My own sweet way / Rigging it up, Duncannon / Happy in the homelands / Jonestown / War is over
CASVP 001CD / Jun '97 / Castaway Northwest

☐ GLAD TO BE GAY (Cabaret '79)
Pub hassle / Coldharbour Lane / Baby you're an angel / Glad to be gay / Stand together / Truce / Closing a door / 1967 (so long ago) / Even Steven / Sartorial eloquence / Mad about the boy / Easy Street / Good to be gay / Glad to be gay / Last rites / Gay switchboard jingle
CNWVP 004CD / Jul '97 / Castaway Northwest

☐ GOLD COLLECTION, THE
Don't take no for an answer / 2-4-6-8 Motorway / I shall be released / Long hot summer / Power in the darkness / Bully for you / Never going to fall in love (again) / Getting tighter / Our people / Martin / Right on sister / I'm all right Jack / All right all night / Law and order / Grey cortina / Glad to be gay
CDGOLD 1015 / Mar '96 / EMI Gold

☐ HAVING IT BOTH WAYS
Disrespect / One / Rum thunderbird / Cold cold ground / Fool to myself / Hot dog / Sorry / Raining in Connecticut / Congo blue / Castaway / Last word
COOKCD 097 / May '96 / Cooking Vinyl

☐ LAST TANGO/MIDNIGHT AT THE FRINGE
Stornoway / Atmospherics / Night tide / Nut rocker / Surabaya Johnny / Bonfire / Tango an der wand / Cabin boy / Back in the old country / Old friend / Never gonna fall in love again / Too good to be true / Glad to be gay / War baby / 2468 motorway
CNWVP 002CD / Aug '97 / Castaway Northwest

☐ LIVING IN A BOOM TIME
Intro / Living in a boom time / Blood brother / More lives than one / Yuppie scum / My own sweet way / Castle island / Rigging it up, duncannon / Brits come rolling back / War baby / Back in the ould country
COOKCD 052 / Feb '95 / Cooking Vinyl

☐ LOVE OVER RAGE
Roaring / Hard / Loved / Days / Driving green / Green / DDR / Fifty / Silence / Chance
COOKCD 066 / Jun '97 / Cooking Vinyl

☐ MODERN CLASSICS (2CD Set)
SMDCD 118 / 27 Apr '98 / Snapper

☐ NORTH BY NORTH WEST
Now Martins gone / Atmospherics / Can't keep away (Part II) / Looking for a bonfire / Merrily up on high / Those days / In the cold / Night tide / Duncannon / Love comes / Tango an der wand / Now Richards gone / Airtraum tango dob / Any favours / Out to lunch
CNWVP 003CD / Jun '97 / Castaway Northwest

☐ POWER IN THE DARKNESS (Robinson, Tom Band)
Up against the wall / Grey Cortina / Too good to be true / Ain't gonna take it / Long hot summer / Winter of '79 / Man you never saw / Better decide which side you're on / You gotta survive / Power in the darkness
COOKCD 076 / Oct '94 / Cooking Vinyl
RE 2018 / Aug '96 / Razor & Tie

☐ RISING FREE (The Best Of Tom Robinson)
2-4-6-8 Motorway / I shall be released / Don't take no for an answer / Glad to be gay / Martin / Right on sister / Alright Jack (live) / P against the wall / Grey cortina / Too good to be true / Long hot summer / Winter of '79 / Power in the darkness / Waiting for my man / Getting tighter / All right all night / Bully for you / Never gonna fall in love again
CDGOLD 1098 / Jun '97 / EMI Gold

☐ SECTOR 27 COMPLETE (Sector 27)
Can't keep away / Invitation: What have we got to lose / Not ready / Mary Lynne / Looking at you / Five 2 five / Totall recall / Where can we go tonight / Take it or leave it / Bitterly disappointed / Day after day / Dungannon / Stornoway / One fine day / Won't you tell me how I feel / Martin's gone / Christopher calling / Shutdown / Out in the cold again
5326422 / Jun '96 / Fontana

☐ STILL LOVING YOU
Feel so good, hurt so bad / Nothing like the real thing / Still loving you / Take me home again / You tattooed me / Drive all night / Living in a love town / Spain / This little romance / Wedding
CNWVP 006CD / 9 Feb '98 / Castaway Northwest

☐ TRB TWO (Robinson, Tom Band)
Alright all night / Why should I mind / Black angel / Let my people be / Blue murder / Bully for you / Crossing over the road / Sorry Mr. Harris / Law and order / Days of rage / Hold out
COOKCD 77 / Oct '94 / Cooking Vinyl
RE 2019 / Aug '96 / Razor & Tie

☐ WAR BABY
CNWVP 007CD / 20 Apr '98 / Castaway Northwest

Robson & Jerome

☐ HAPPY DAYS (The Best Of Robson & Jerome)
Oh happy day / Amazing grace / Crying in the rain / Unchained melody / (There'll be bluebirds over) The white cliffs of Dover / I believe / Upon the roof / What becomes of the broken hearted / Saturday night at the movies / You'll never walk alone / Moonlight serenade / Bring it on home to me / If I can dream / Crying in the rain / Skyliner
74321542602 / 17 Nov '97 / RCA

☐ ROBSON & JEROME
Unchained melody / Daydream believer / I believe / Sun ain't gonna shine anymore / Up on the roof / Amazing grace / Danny boy / (There'll be bluebirds over) The white cliffs of Dover / This boy / Little latin Lupe Lu / Love you forever / I'll come running back to you / If I can dream
74321323902 / Feb '97 / RCA

Robson, Mark

☐ CELTIC DREAMING, A
Celtic dream / Iona / Waylands Smithy / Jigs / Blood on the sand / Isle of glass / Sheebag sheemore / Water baby dreaming / Kangaroo moon dance
MS 240 / Nov '97 / MediaQuest

☐ IN SEARCH OF A SIMPLE LIFE
AGASCD 014 / 20 Oct '97 / Gliss

Roby, Charlie

☐ UTOPIA IS NOT HERE
MAL 0102CD / Aug '95 / Maladrin Music

Robyn

☐ ROBYN IS HERE
Bumpy ride / In my heart / You've got that somethin' / Do you know (what it takes) / Last time / Show me love / Just another girlfriend / Don't want you back / Do you really want me / How / Here we go / Robyn is here / I wish
74321509022 / 1 Jun '98 / Bush

ROC

☐ ROC
Desert wind / Excised / God willing / Hey you chick / Balloon / Real time / Plastic Jesus / I want you I need you I miss you / Gold bug / La heredia / 13 Summers / Hey Nicky / Sylvia's thighs / Ascension / Clouds
SETCD 022 / Jan '96 / Setanta

☐ VIRGIN
Dada / (Dis)count us in / Mountain / Cheryl / Corner off I-25 / Dead pool / Ever since yesterday / 25 reasons to leave me / KC / Cold chill just lately / Said what I said / Ocean and England
CDV 2829 / 8 Sep '97 / Virgin

Rocchi, Riccardo

☐ IT'S JUST A MELTING POT OF EMOTIONS
ACVD 011 / Nov '95 / ACV

Roccisano, Joe

☐ SHAPE I'M IN, THE (Roccisano, Joe & His Orchestra)
Borderland / New beginning / Mornings glory's story / Synthesis / Prism / Isabel / Shape I'm in / Piece of the pie / Don't stop now / Earth day / Blue Lou
LCD 15352 / Nov '93 / Landmark

Roche, Ives

☐ TAHITI COOL VOL.4
PS 65806 / Nov '91 / PlayaSound

Roche, Suzzy

☐ HOLY SMOKES
RHRCD 104 / Oct '97 / Red House

Roches

☐ CAN WE GO HOME NOW
Great gaels / Move / You (make my life come true) / Christlike / Home away from home / Can we go home now / When you're ready / I'm someone who loves you / So / My winter coat / Holidays
RCD 10299 / Mar '97 / Rykodisc

☐ ROCHES, THE
We / Hammond song / Mr. Sellack / Damned old dog / Troubles / Train / Married men / Runs in the family / Quitting time / Pretty and high
7599273902 / Jan '96 / WEA

Rock Bottom

☐ TONE
TRICKNOLOGY 1 / Apr '97 / Tricknology

Rock, Dickie

☐ BEST OF DICKIE ROCK AND THE MIAMI SHOWBAND, THE (Rock, Dickie & The Miami Showband)
PLSCD 291 / 1 Jun '98 / Pulse

Rock Goddess

☐ ROCK GODDESS/HELL HATH NO FURY
RMED 0218CD / 8 Jun '98 / Renaissance

☐ YOUNG & FREE
Young and free / Hello / So much love / Jerry / Streets of the city / Party never ends / Love has passed me by / Raiders / Love is a bitch / Boys will be boys / Sexy eyes / Rumour / Turn me loose / Hey lover
CDTB 155 / Jul '94 / Thunderbolt

Rock Island Line

☐ VERY BEST OF ROCK ISLAND LINE, THE
NERCD 094 / 13 Jul '98 / Nervous

Rock Melons

☐ STRONGER TOGETHER
TVD 93360 / Jan '95 / Mushroom

Rock, Pete

☐ MAIN INGREDIENT, THE (Rock, Pete & C.L. Smooth)
In the house / Carmel city / Physical / Sun won't come out / I got a love / Escapism / Main ingredient / World wide / All the places / Tell me / Take you there / Searching / Chick it out / In the flesh / It's on you / Get on the mic
7559616612 / Nov '94 / Elektra

☐ MECCA AND THE SOUL BROTHER (Rock, Pete & C.L. Smooth)
Return to the Mecca / For Pete's sake / Ghettos of the mind / Lots of lovin' / Act like you know / Straighten it out / Soul brother no 1 / Wig out / Anger in the nation / They reminisce over you (TROY) / On and on / It's like that / Can't front on me / Basement / If it ain't rough, it ain't right / Skinz
7559609482 / May '92 / Elektra

Rock Salt & Nails

☐ 4,6,2,1
FORCD 39 / Jul '96 / Fourth Recording Company

☐ MORE AND MORE
Don't know about you/Friday card school / Someday / Jack broke da prison door / Life / Lucy Bain / More prison door / Faroe rum / Oliver Jack / Willafjord / and more / Uneasy ride / Tilly plump set / Grandmother's eyes / Forced to return/Spootiskerry / Lucy Bain reprise
IRCD 030 / May '95 / Iona

☐ STAND YOUR GROUND
Flight / Landing light / PVS / Little bird / Wrong day / Well wynde suite / Sad and lonely day / Shadows on the wall / History / Dumpy's set
FORCD 50 / 6 Oct '97 / Fourth Recording Company

☐ WAVES
Man who ate mountains / Slockit light - Waiting for the Federals / Happy to be here / Jack broke da prison door / Faroe rum / Oliver Jack / Willafjord / Iron horse / Arkansas traveller / Welcome / Central house / Square da Mizzen / Doon hingin' tie / Waves / Hut on Staffin Island / Barmaid / Music for a found harmonium
IRCD 025 / Jan '94 / Iona

Rock Shop

☐ MR. LEE'S SWINGING AFFAIR PRESENTS
BA 115CD / Feb '97 / Bacchus Archives

Rockabeats

☐ BORN TO ROCK
PEPCD 122 / Jan '98 / Pollytone

Rockabillies

☐ WOODSTOCK VIA MEMPHIS
POCD 004 / Feb '96 / Popcorn

Rockabilly Mafia

☐ ANOTHER DRUNKEN NIGHT
RUMCD 002 / Aug '92 / Rumble

Rockats

☐ GOOD, THE BAD, THE ROCKIN', THE
DAGCD 6 / Feb '97 / Fury

☐ LAST CRUSADE
TBCD 2005 / Mar '93 / Tombstone

Rockell

☐ WHAT ARE YOU LOOKIN' AT
76869750092 / 27 Apr '98 / Robbins

Rocker, Lee

☐ ATOMIC BOOGIE HOUR (Rocker, Lee & Big Blue)
BT 1121CD / Sep '95 / Black Top

☐ LEE ROCKER'S BIG BAND
BT 1105CD / Sep '94 / Black Top

☐ NO CATS
Rumblin' bass / Miracle in Memphis / One way or another / Shaky town / Screaming hunger / Love me good / Little piece of your love / Memphis freeze / Mr. Newman / Into the viod / Movin' on / Hard rain / Naked bass
DFGCD 8465 / Jul '97 / Dixie Frog

Rockers Hi-Fi

☐ DJ KICKS (The Black Album) (Various Artists)
Rockers intro: *Farda P* / Theme from kung fu: *Danna, Jeff* / He builds the world: *Small Fish With Spine* / Feel: *Kid Loops* / Candles and versions: *Wraparound Sounds* / Up through the down pipe: *Grizzly* / Dub angel: *Snooze & DJ Cam* / Varispeed: *Electric J* / Callacop: *Deep Space Network* / Long life: *Prince Far-I & The Arabs* / Com-unique-ation: *Cee Mix* / RhyNever tell you: *thm & Sound/Tikiman* / Twisted system: *Terminal Head & Mr. Spee* / G13: *T-Power* / Saidisyabruklimmon: *Dr. Israel & Loop* / Bad head day: *Husik, Lida* / Dis ya opne: *More Rockers* / Rockers outro: *Farda P* / Black single: *Farda P*
K7 056CD / Jun '97 / Studio K7

☐ MISH MASH
8th shade / Theme from Mish Mash / Now I deliver / Uneasy skanking / Fling mi ting / Mish mash episode one / 90 degree fuzzwalk / Mish mash episode two / Going under / Paths of life / One with another / Mish mash episode three / Copycat
0630457952 / Aug '97 / WEA

Rocket From The Crypt

☐ RFTC
Eye on you / Break it up / I know / Panic scam / Made for you / Lipstick / You gotta move / You touch / Let's get busy / Dick on a dog / Back in the state / When in Rome (do the jerk) / Run kid run
ELM 50CDQ / 10 Aug '98 / Elemental
ELM 50CD / 6 Jul '98 / Elemental

☐ STATE OF THE ART IS ON FIRE, THE
SFTRI 320CD / Nov '96 / Sympathy For The Record Industry

Rockets

☐ ROCKETS, THE
Hole in my pocket / Won't you say you'll stay / Mr. Chips / It's a mistake / Let me go / Try my patience / I won't always be around / Pill's blues / Stretch your skin / Eraser
EDCD 520 / May '97 / Edsel

Rockin' Bandits

☐ WATCH OUT...WE'RE GONNA 'JUMP BACK'
Jump back boogie / Gonna rock with ya baby / Ain't gonna be your crazy cat / Long black train / Pretty little baby / I'm in love with you baby / Cruisin' blues / Oakie boogie / Angel girl / Lonely country girl / Two lane black top / My little baby / Folsom Prison blues / Rock-a-baby rock / Midnight shift / Rock 'n' roll Mama / I don't care / Everybody's tryin' to be my baby
FCD 3036 / Mar '95 / Fury

Rockin' Berries

☐ BOWL OF BERRIES
REP 4181 / Aug '91 / Repertoire

☐ HE IS IN TOWN
HADCD 205 / Jul '96 / Javelin

☐ IN TOWN
REP 4099 / Aug '91 / Repertoire

Rockin' Dopsie

☐ FEET DON'T FAIL ME NOW
AIMA 1 / Oct '95 / Rounder

Rockin' Ramrods

☐ BEST OF THE ROCKIN' RAMRODS
Jungle call / I wanna be your man / I'll be on my way / Don't fool with Fu Manchu / Tears melt the stones / Play it / Bright lit blue skies / Mr. Wind / Can't you see / Mary Mary / Flowers in my mind / Vacuum / Trees / Rainy days / Looking in my window / Who do you think you are / Of not being able to sleep / Dead thoughts of Alfred / I sure need you / When I wake up in the morning / Go with you / Changes / My vision has cleared / I don't want to, I will / Troubles
CDWIKD 151 / May '95 / Big Beat

Rockin' Rebels

☐ ROCKIN' REBELS
622442 / Apr '97 / Skydog

Rockin' Roosters

☐ BOP WITH THE ROOSTERS
PT 619005 / May '98 / Part

Rockin' Sidney

☐ LIVE WITH THE BLUES
JSPCD 213 / Mar '88 / JSP

☐ MY TOOT TOOT
My toot toot / My zydeco shoes / Joy to the south / Don't be a wallflower / Alligator waltz / Rock 'n' roll me baby / Joe Pete is in the bed / You ain't nothing but fine / If it's good for the gander / Twist to the zydeco / Dance and show off / Let me take you to zydeco / I got the blues for my baby / Louisiana creole man / If I could I would / No good woman / Send me some lovin' / Past bedtime / No good man / You don't have to go / It really is a hurtin' thing / Something's wrong / My little girl / Wasted days and wasted nights / Ya ya / Jalapena lena / Sweet lil' woman / Once is not enough / Cochon de lait
CDCH 160 / Jun '93 / Ace

Rockin' Vincent

☐ UNRELEASED
Grand hotel / Dixie boogie / Chantilly lace / End of the road / Music box swing / Ain't nobody's business if I do / Rockin' hearts / 42nd Street / Twenty flight rock / Puttin' on the ritz / Maxin's boogie / Some of these days / Let the good times roll / That's life
CDDS 9252 / Apr '94 / Down South

Rocking Dildos

☐ HORNY HIT PARADE
KRONH 011CD / 24 Nov '97 / Kronh

Rockingbirds

☐ WHATEVER HAPPENED TO THE ROCKINGBIRDS
Roll on forever / I like winter / Everybody lives with us / Band of dreams / We had it all / I woke up one morning / High part / Bitter tear / Before we got to the end / Hell / Let me down slow
COOKCD 084 / Aug '97 / Cooking Vinyl

Rockpile

☐ SECONDS OF PLEASURE
Teacher teacher / If sugar was as sweet as you / Heart / Now and always / Knife and fork / Play that fast thing / Wrong way / Pet you and hold you / Oh what a thrill you / When I write the book / Fool too long / You ain't nothing but fine
FIENDCD 28 / Oct '90 / Demon

Rocks

☐ COMBAT ZONE
KR 004CD / Aug '95 / Kangaroo

Rockwell, Bob

☐ AFTER HOURS
Confluence / You stepped out of a dream / Dominator / Love walked in / Relaxin' at Camarillo / Prisoner of love / Pentimento / So in love
GO 60292 / 24 Aug '98 / Go Jazz

☐ ON THE NATCH (Rockwell, Bob Quartet)
SCCD 31229 / Jul '88 / Steeplechase

☐ RECONSTRUCTION
SCCD 31270 / Nov '90 / Steeplechase

Rodan

☐ RUSTY
QS 24CD / Apr '94 / Quarter Stick

Roddy, Ted

☐ FULL CIRCLE
HCD 8065 / Oct '95 / Hightone

Roden, Jess

☐ JESS RODEN
Reason to change / I'm on your side / Feelin easy / Sad story / On broadway / Ferry cross / Trouble in the mind / What the hell
IMCD 143 / Aug '91 / Island

☐ PLAY IT DIRTY PLAY IT CLASS (Roden, Jess Band)
US dream / Stay in bed / Can't get next to you / Dirty bars / Me and crystal eye / Stone chaser / Ballad of big Sally / All night long
EDCD 567 / 4 May '98 / Demon

Rodger, Mart

☐ MANCHESTER DELIGHTED (Rodger, Mart & Manchester Jazz)
OWSCD 2604 / Oct '97 / Bowstone

Rodgers Melnick, Peter

☐ ARCTIC BLUE
Arctic blue / Tundra / Breakaway / Wolf / Take off / Dream / Dixie's revenge / Looking for trouble / Living and the dead / No man's land / Return to Devil's cauldron / Cut to the chase / Mitchell dies / Mine / Up in flames / Trappers and hunters / In the shadows / Viking Bob / Freeing the wolf
ND 63030 / Nov '94 / Narada

Rodgers, Clodagh

☐ MASTERS, THE
EABCD 076 / 24 Nov '97 / Eagle

☐ YOU ARE MY MUSIC (The Best Of Clodagh Rodgers)
Come back and shake me / Lady love bug / Carolina days / Let me be the one / I am a fantasy / Together / Goodnight midnight / It's different now / Nothing rhymed / I will / I'm gonna make you love me / Natural woman / One day / Betcha by golly wow / Everybody go home the party's over / Will you still love me tomorrow / What in the world / Together we will make it / Ease your pain / That's the way I've always heard it should be / Day by day / You are my music
74321415042 / Jan '97 / Camden

Rodgers, Jimmie

☐ AMERICA'S BLUE YODELER, 1930-1931
Blue yodel No. 8 / Jimmie's mean mama blues / I'm lonesome too / Mystery of number five / One rose / In the jailhouse now No.2 / For the sake of days gone by / Blue yodel No. 9 / TB Blues / Travellin' blues / Why there's a tear in my eye / Jimmie the kid / Wonderful city / Let me be your sidetrack
ROUCD 1060 / Sep '91 / Rounder

☐ AMERICAN LEGENDS
Rock all our babies to sleep / Peach pickin' time down in Georgia / Pistol packin' papa / Nobody knows but me / Mississippi river blues / Blue yodel no.9 (standin' on the corner) / Drunkard's child / Blue yodel no.10 / Blue yodel no.11 / Moonlight and skies / Mother, the queen of my heart / Those gambler's blues
12746 / May '97 / Laserlight

☐ DOWN THE OLD ROAD 1931-1932
Looking for a new mama / When the cactus is in bloom / Jimmie Rodgers visits the Carter Family / Carter Family and Jimmie Rodgers in Texas / Gambling dot blues / Southern cannonball / Roll along Kentucky moon / What's it my time ain't long / Hobo's meditation / Ninety nine years blues / Mississippi moon / Down the old road to home
ROUCD 1061 / Sep '91 / Rounder

☐ FATHER OF COUNTRY MUSIC, THE
You and my old guitar / My little lady / Prairie lullaby / When the cactus is in bloom / Pistol packin' Papa / Peach picking time in Georgia / I've only loved three women / Any old time / I'm lonesome too / Dear sunny South by the sea / Blue yodel no.10 / Sleep baby sleep / Never no mo' blues / Looking for a new Mama / No hard times / Gambling bar room blues / Frankie and Johnny / My old pal / Jimmie the kid / Blue yodel / Old pal of my heart / Sweet Mama hurry home / Roll along Kentucky moon
PASTCD 7814 / Apr '97 / Flapper

☐ FIRST SESSIONS, 1927-1928
Blue yodel / Soldier's sweetheart / Ben Dewberry's final run / Sleep, baby sleep / Mother was a lady / Dear old sunny south by the sea / Away out on the mountain / Treasures untold / Blue yodel no. 11 / Sailor's plea / In the jailhouse now / Memphis yodel / Brakeman's blues / Blue yodel no. 3
ROUCD 1056 / '90 / Rounder

☐ LAST SESSIONS, 1933
Blue yodel No. 12 / Dreaming with tears in my eyes / Cowhand's last ride / I'm free from the chain gang now / Yodeling my way back home / Jimmie Rodgers' last blue yodel / Yodeling ranger / Old pal of my heart / Years ago / Somewhere below the Mason Dixon line / Old love letters / Mississippi delta blues
ROUCD 1063 / Mar '92 / Rounder

☐ MEMORIES OF JIMMIE RODGERS (Various Artists)
When Jimmie Rodgers said goodbye: *Butcher, Dwight* / Life of Jimmie Rodgers/The death of Jimmie Rodgers: *Autry, Gene* / Good luck old pal (til we meet bye and bye): *Autry, Gene* / When Jimmie Rodgers said goodbye: *Autry, Gene* / Memories of Jimmie Rodgers: *O'Daniel, W. Lee* / Jimmie Rodgers' life: *Kincaid, Bradley* / Death of Jimmie Rodgers: *Kincaid, Bradley* / Mrs. Jimmie Rodgers' lament: *Kincaid, Bradley* / Little Jimmie's goodbye to Jimmie Rodgers: *Sizemore, Asher & Little Jimmie* / When Jimmie Rodgers said goodbye #2: *Houchins, Kenneth* / Good luck old pal (til we meet bye and bye): *Houchins, Kenneth* / Life of Jimmie Rodgers: *Kincaid, Bradley* / Death of Jimmie Rodgers: *Kincaid, Bradley* / Last thoughts of Jimmie Rodgers: *Tubb, Ernest* / Passing of Jimmie Rodgers: *Tubb, Ernest* / We miss him when the evening shadow falls: *Rodgers, Mrs. Jimmie* / My rainbow trail keeps winding on: *Rodgers, Mrs. Jimmie* / Women made a fool out of me: *Tubb, Ernest* / Nothing at all: *Wilburn Brothers* / Mr. Love: *Tubb, Ernest & Willburn Brothers* / Anniversary blue yodel: *Snow, Hank* / Waitin' for a train: *Reeves, Jim*
BCD 15938 / May '97 / Bear Family

☐ MY OLD PAL
Blue yodel no. 1 (T for Texas) / Away out on the mountain / Frankie and Johnny / Gamblin' bar room blues / When the cactus is in bloom / Sleep, baby, sleep / My old pal / Daddy and home / My Carolina sunshine girl / Why there's a tear in my eye / We miss him when the evening shadows fall / Never no no' blues / Blue yodel no. 3 / I'm sorry we met / Blue yodel no. 5 / Any old time / Lullaby yodel / Looking for a new mama
CDAJA 5058 / Mar '89 / Living Era

☐ NO HARD TIMES 1932
Blue yodel No. 10 / Whippin' that old TB / Rock all our babies to sleep / Home call / Mother, the queen of my heart / No hard times / Peach pickin' time in Georgia / Long tall mama blues / Gamblin' bar room blues / I've only loved three women / In the hills of Tennessee / Prairie lullaby / Miss the Mississippi and you / Sweet Mama hurry home
ROUCD 1062 / Feb '92 / Rounder

☐ ON THE WAY UP 1929
High powered Mama / Tuck away my lonesone blues / Frankie and Johnny / I'm sorry we met / Train whistle blues / Everybody does it in Hawaii / Jimmie's Texas blues / Home call / Blue yodel No. 6 / Yodeling cowboy / My rough and rowdy ways / Land of my boyhood dreams / Whisper your mother's name / I've ranged, I've roamed, I've travelled / Hobo Bill's last ride
ROUCD 1058 / '91 / Rounder

☐ ORIGINAL, THE
Honeycomb / Kisses sweeter than wine: *Rodgers, Jimmie* / Oh oh I'm falling in love again / Secretly / Are you really mine / Bimbombey / Make me a miracle / Ring a ling a lario / TLC / Waltzing Matilda / Child of clay / It's over / Wonderful you / Just a closer walk with thee / Wreck of the John B. / World I used to know
TO 886232 / 2 Feb '98 / Disky

☐ RIDING HIGH, 1929-1930
Anniversary blue yodel / That's why I'm blue / Mississippi river blues / She was happy till she met you / Blue yodel no. 11 / Drunkard's child / Nobody knows but me / Moonlight and the skies / Why did you give me your love / Pistol packin' papa / Why should I be lonely / Take me back again / Those gambler's blues / My blue eyed Jane
ROUCD 1059 / '91 / Rounder

☐ SINGING BRAKEMAN, THE (6CD Set)
Soldier's sweetheart / Sleep, baby, sleep / Ben Dewberry's final run / Mother was a lady / Blue yodel / Away out on the mountain / Dear old sunny south by the sea / Treasures untold / Brakeman's blues / Sailor's plea / In the jailhouse now / Blue yodel No. 2 / Memphis yodel / Blue yodel No. 3 / My old pal / Mississippi moon / My little old home down in New Orleans / You and my old guitar / Daddy and home / My little lady / I'm lonely and blue / Lullaby yodel / Never mo' blues / My Carolina sunshine girl / Blue yodel No. 4 / Waiting for a train / Desert blues / Any old time / Blue yodel No. 5 / High powered mama / I'm sorry we met / Everybody does it in Hawaii / Tuck away my lonesome blues / Train whistle blues / Jimmie's Texas blues / Frankie and Johnny / Homecall / Whisper your mother's name / Land of my boyhood dreams / Blue yodel No. 6 / Yodeling cowboy / My rough and rowdy ways / I've ranged, I've roamed, I've travelled / Hobo Bill's last ride / Mississippi river blues / Nobody knows but me / Anniversary blue yodel / She was happy till she met you / Blue yodel No. 11 / Drunkard's child / That's why I'm blue / Why did you give me your love / My blue eyed Jane / Why should I be lonely / Moonlight and skies / Pistol packin' papa / Take me back again / Those gambler's blues / I'm lonesome too / One rose / For the sake of days gone by / Jimmie's mean

mama blues / Mystery of number five / Blue yodel No. 8 / Blue yodel No. 9 / TB blues / Travellin' blues / Jimmie the kid / Why there's a tear in my eye / Wonderful city / Let me be your sidetrack / Jimmie Rodgers visits the Carter Family / Carter Family and Jimmie Rodgers in Texas / When the cactus is in bloom / Gambling polka dot blues / Looking for a new mama / What's it / My good gal's gone / Southern cannonball / Roll along Kentucky moon / Hobo's meditation / My time ain't long / Ninety nine year blues / Down the old road to home / Blue yodel No. 10 / Home call / Mother the queen of my heart / Rock all my babies to sleep / Whippin' that old TB / No hard times / Long tall mama blues / Peach pickin' time in Georgia / Gamblin' bar room blues / I've only loved three women / In the hills of Tennessee / Prairie lullaby / Miss the Mississippi and you / Sweet mama hurry home / Blue yodel No. 12 / Dreaming with tears in my eyes / Cowhand's last ride / I'm free from the chain gang now / Dream with tears in my eyes / Yodeling my way back home / Jimmie Rodgers' last blue yodel / Yodeling ranger / Old pal of my heart / Old love letters / Mississippi Delta blues / Somewhere below the Mason Dixon line / Years ago / Singing brakeman / Pullman porters / In the jailhouse now No.2 / Mule skinner blues / Mother, the queen of my heart / Never no mo' blues / Blue yodel No. 1
BCD 15540 / Mar '92 / Bear Family

☐ SONGS OF JIMMIE RODGERS, THE (A Tribute) (Various Artists)
Dreaming with tears in my eyes: *Bono* / Any old time: *Krauss, Alison & Union Station* / Waiting for a train: *Betts, Dickey Band* / Somewhere below the mason dixon line: *Carpenter, Mary-Chapin* / Miss the mississippi and you: *Ball, David* / My blue eyed jane: *Dylan, Bob* / Peach picking time down in georgia: *Nelson, Willie* / In the jailhouse now: *Earle, Steve & The V-Roys* / Blue yodel no.9: *Garcia, Jerry* / Hobo bill's last ride: *DeMent, Iris* / Gambling bar room blues: *Mellencamp, John* / Mule skinner blues: *Morrison, Van* / Why should I be lonely: *Neville, Aaron* / T is for Texas: *Yoakam, Dwight*
4851892 / 1 Sep '97 / Columbia

☐ TRAIN WHISTLE BLUES
Jimmie's mean mama blues / Southern Cannonball / Jimmie the kid / Travellin' blues / Mystery of number five / Memphis yodel / Blue yodel no. 4 (California blues) / Hobo Bill's last ride / Waiting for a train / Ben Dewberry's final run / My rough and rowdy ways / Blue yodel no. 7 (Anniversary blue yodel) / Brakeman's blues / Let me be your sidetrack / Hobo's meditation / Train whistle blues
CDAJA 5042 / Jun '86 / Living Era

☐ TRAIN WHISTLE BLUES (The Legendary Jimmie Rodgers)
379892 / 1 Jun '98 / Koch

☐ VERY BEST OF JIMMIE RODGERS, THE
Train whistle blues / Blue yodel / Brakeman's blues / Where there's a tear in my eye / Mississippi river blues / Jimmie Rodger's last yodel / Gambling bar room blues / Mystery of number five / Waiting for a train / Travelin' blues / My blue eyed Jane / Blue yodel / Pistol packin' papa / Miss the Mississippi and you / Somewhere down below the dixon line / Soldiers sweetheart / Hobo Bill's last ride / Peach picking time down in Georgia
74321535852 / 22 Nov '97 / Camden

☐ YODELLING RANGER, THE
Jimmie the kid / Roll along Kentucky moon / Looking for a new Mama / Round up time out West / Sleep, baby, sleep / Yodelling my way back home / Gamblin' bar room blues / In the hills of Tennessee / Old pal of my heart / My lovin' gal Lucille / Standin' on the corner / She was happy till she met you / Peach pickin' time in Georgia / I'm lonesome too / Jimmie Rodgers' last blue yodel / Yodelling ranger / Missisippi moon / Prairie lullaby / Down the old road to home / Jimmie Rodgers visits the Carter family / Carter family and Jimmie Rodgers
RAJCD 806 / Nov '97 / Empress

Rodgers, Jimmie

☐ SWEETER THAN WINE (The Very Best Of Jimmie Rodgers 1957-1962)
Honeycomb / Their hearts were full of spring / Kisses sweeter than wine / Long hot summer / Oh oh I'm falling in love again / Secretly / Make me a miracle / Are you really mine / Wizard / Bimbombey / Woman from Liberia / Because you're young / I'm gonna tell / Froggy went a-courting / Ring-a-ling lario / Wonderful you / Tucumari / TLC / Waltzing Matilda / Just a closer walk with thee / Wreck of the John B / Every time my heart sings / I'm going home / Little dog cried / Wanderin' eyes / English country garden
WESM 536 / 19 Jan '98 / Westside

Rodgers, Nile

☐ B MOVIE MATINEE
Groove master / Let's go out tonight / Stay out of the light / Same wavelength / Plan number 9 / State your mind / Face in the window / Doll squad
7599252902 / Jan '96 / Atlantic

Rodgers, Paul

☐ LIVE (The Loreley Tapes)
Little bit of love / Be my friend / Feel like making love / Louisiana blues / Muddy Waters blues / Rolling stone / I'm ready / Wishing well / Mister Big / Fire and water / Hunter / Can't get enough / Alright now
SPV 08544672 / Sep '97 / SPV

☐ MUDDY WATER BLUES
8284242 / Jun '93 / London

☐ NOW
Soul of love / Overloaded / Heart of fire / Saving grace / All I want is you / Chasing shadows / Love is all I need / Nights like this / Shadow of the sun / I lost it all / Holding back the storm
SPV 08544662 / Feb '97 / SPV

Roditi, Claudio

☐ DOUBLE STANDARDS
RSRCD 148 / Aug '97 / Reservoir

☐ JAZZ TURNS SAMBA
Moody's samba / Birks works / Speak low / Without a song / Come rain or come shine / Giant steps / Moanin' / Moment's notice / Donna Lee / Inside out
5216162 / Mar '94 / Groovin' High

☐ MILESTONES (Roditi, Claudio & Paquito D'Rivera)
Milestones / I'll remember April / But not for me / Pent-up house / Brussels in the rain / Mr. PC
CCD 79515 / Feb '97 / Candid

☐ TWO OF SWORDS
Two of swords / Rua dona margarida / Airegin / Portrait of art / Dom Joaquim braga / How I miss Rio / Secret love / Blues for HO / Pra him / Con alma / Thabo
CCD 790504 / Feb '97 / Candid

Rodney O

☐ EVERLASTING HITS (Rodney O & Joe Cooley)
79330894422 / 19 May '98 / Rect

Rodrigues, Amalia

☐ AMALIA RODRIGUES
DRGCD 5571 / Feb '97 / DRG

☐ BEST OF FADO, THE (2CD Set)
Triste sina / Ceu da minha rua / O namorico da rita / Conta errada / Fadista louco / As rosas do meu caminho / Fado marujo / Fado das tamanquinhas / Fado da adica / Raizes / Bailaricos / Fado alfachinha / Job / Anjo inutil / Quando os outros te batem, beijo-te eu / Fado final / Esquina do pecado / Chave da minha / Tentacao / Sem razao / Fria claridade / Campinos do ribatejo / Le porque tens cinco pedras / Ave Maria fadista / A minha cancao / Disse mal de ti / Fado amalia / Fado do ciume / Cansaco / Que deus me perdoe / Aquela rua / Fado lisboeta
DBG 53026 / Aug '96 / Double Gold

☐ COIMBRA
Coimbra / Uma casa portuguesa / Triste sina / Ceu da minha rua / Lisboa antiga / Barco negro / Fado dos fados / O namorico de rita / Fadista louco / As rosas do meu caminho / Fado da adica / Conta errada / Fado marujo / Quando os outros te batem, beijo-te eu / Fado das tamanquinhas / Raizes / Fado alfacinha / Fado final
CD 12502 / Nov '92 / Music Of The World

☐ FADO AMALIA (2CD Set)
ML 51101 / 27 Apr '98 / Musica Latina

☐ FIRST RECORDINGS, THE
995782 / Oct '96 / EPM

☐ LIVE AT THE OLYMPIA
MCD 71442 / Jun '93 / Monitor

☐ QUEEN OF THE FADO
Triste sina / Ceu da minha rua / O namorico da rita / Conta errada / Fadista louco / As rosas do meu caminho / Fado marujo / Fado das tamanquinhas / Fado da adica / Raizes / Bailaricos / Fado alfachinha / Job / Anjo inutil / Quando os outros te batem, beijo-te eu / Fado final
SOW 90107 / Sep '93 / Sounds Of The World

☐ UMA CASA PORTUGUESA (2CD Set)
ML 51102 / 27 Apr '98 / Musica Latina

☐ YESTERDAY AND TODAY (New York City 1990 & Rio De Janeiro 1945/2CD Set)
Variacoes / Maria Lisboa / Estranha forma de vida / Malhao de S.Simao / Amendoa amarga / Obsessao / Havemos de ir a viana / Meia noite e uma guitarra / Barco negro / Coimbra / Lisboa antiga / Grito / Marcha do centenario / Povo que lavas no rio / Fui ao mar buscar sardinhas / Com que voz / Prece / Fallaste corazon / Casa portuguesa / Canzone per te / Malhao / Troca de olhares / Tendinha / Fado do ciume / Maria da cruz / Perseguicao / Corria atras das cantigas / Los piconeros / So a noitinha / As penas / Sei finalmente / Sardinheiras / Ai mouraria / Carmencita / Ojos verdes / Passei por voce / Duas luzes
DBG 53060 / Jul '98 / Double Gold

Rodrigues, Jair

☐ JAIR DE TODAS AS BOSSAS
21742 / 12 May '98 / Som Livre

Rodriguez

☐ PROUD HEART
CSC 1002 / Oct '95 / Continental Song City

Rodriguez, Alfredo

☐ CUBA LINDA
Tumbao a peruchin / Cuba linda / Cuando vuelvo a tu lado / Canto de palo / Tumba, mi tumba (tumbao Francesa) / Mercedita ya me voy / Drume negrita / Para francia flores y para / Cuba tambien (Guaguanco)
HNCD 1399 / Nov '96 / Hannibal

Rodriguez, Bobby

☐ LATIN JAZZ CHRISTMAS, A
Feliz navidad / Have yourself a merry little Christmas / Es la navidad / Santa Claus is coming to town / Christmas song / Jingle bells / Deck the halls / White Christmas / Silent night / Oh Christmas tree / We three kings / Silver bells / It's time for Christmas
JVC 90272 / Oct '97 / JVC

Rodriguez, David

☐ LANDIN '92
BRAM 1992352 / Nov '93 / Brambus

☐ TRUE CROSS, THE
DJD 3202 / May '94 / Dejadisc

Rodriguez, Johnny

☐ YOU CAN SAY THAT AGAIN
HCD 8073 / Jul '96 / Hightone

Rodriguez, Johnny

☐ JOHNNY RODRIGUEZ 1936-1940
HQCD 76 / Jul '96 / Harlequin

Rodriguez, Tito

☐ MAMBO MONA (Rodriguez, Tito y Los Lobos del Mamboa)
TCD 014 / Dec '92 / Fresh Sound

☐ MUCHO CHA CHA
Cha cha cha Para Ti / This is mambo / Baranga / Asi Asi / Sabroso mambo / Todo es cha cha cha / Rico Rica cha / Agua con Azucar / Piel canela / Sun sun babae / Ya soy Feliz / La rumba no se Acabo / La renta / El Rinconcito / El Guaguanco del Caramelero / Los Cacos del amor
CD 62093 / Mar '97 / Saludos Amigos

Rodriques, Amalia

☐ OBSESSAO
Que fazes ai Lisboa / Romance / Nasci para ser ignorante / Alma minha / O ai o linda / Prece / Rondel do alentejo / Chora marinquinhas chora / Entrega / Sete anos de pastor / Flor do verde pinto / Obsessao
DRGCD 5572 / 26 May '98 / DRG

Rods

☐ RODS, THE
Power lover / Crank it up / Hungry for some love / Music man / Woman / Nothing going on in the city / Get ready to rock'n'roll / Ace in the hole / Rock hard / Roll with the night
HV 1015 / Sep '97 / High Vaultage

☐ WILD DOGS
HV 1016 / Sep '97 / High Vaultage

Roea, Jude

☐ MYSTIC IN THE MAKING
Ice age / Hippos / You occupy me / Mystic in the making / Don't give up / Tears (are only man made rivers) / Your background goes with you / Shoulder to shoulder / When I lost you / Chinese water / Fingerprints / Frigid as england
CDSGP 082 / Oct '94 / Prestige

Roedelius, Hans Joachim

☐ AFTER THE HEAT
SKYCD 3021 / 15 Jun '98 / Sky

☐ AQUARELLO
Mirador / Deep blue / Puente / Tranquilidad / More of it / Elena / La forza / Tiny bit / Isleta / Il camino / Remember / De quoi / South of Gregdale
ASCD 035 / 16 Mar '98 / All Saints

☐ DURCH DIE WUSTE
SKYCD 3051 / May '95 / Sky

☐ GESCHENK DES AUGENBLICKS
Gesckenk des Augenblicks / Adieu Quichotte / Troubadour / Kleine blume irgendwo / Ohn' unterlass / Gefundene zeit / Sehnsucht ich will dich lassen / Das sanfte / Tag fur tag / Zu fussen der berge am ufer des sees / Wurzeln des glucks
CDOVD 483 / Jun '97 / EG

☐ PINK, BLUE AND AMBER
CTCD 040 / Jul '97 / Captain Trip

Roelof, Annemarie

☐ MUSIC FROM THE LAND OF MILK AND HONEY
VICTOCD 048 / Nov '97 / Victo

Roessingh, Karel

☐ THINKING OF YOU
MCD 1762 / Aug '96 / Midsummer

Roger, Aldus

☐ CAJUN LEGEND, A
LLCD 1007 / Feb '94 / La Louisianne

Roger, Roger

☐ GRANDS TRAVAUX (Metropole Orchestra)
Grands travaux / Traffic boom / Danse lunaire / Teleski / Fete Foraine / Contorsions (the grip of fear) / Paris Pullmann / Polka mauve / Machinisme / Clowneries / La foret enchantee / Djanina / Nounous et Pioupious / Le moustique / Profondeurs (lunar landscape) / Eccentric walk / Scenic railway
EW 9521 / Sep '97 / Eigen Wijs

Rogers, Billy

☐ GUITAR ARTISTRY OF BILLY ROGERS, THE
Billy's bop / My funny valentine / Tell me a bedtime story / How insensitive / Egocentric ions / I've grown accustomed to her face / E.s.p. / Body and soul / Fee-fi-fo-fum / Good morning heartache
STCD 566 / May '93 / Stash

Rogers, Jimmy

☐ BILL'S BLUES (Rogers, Jimmy/Hubert Sumlin/Big Bill Hickey)
ATD 1112CD / Dec '94 / Atomic Theory

☐ BLUES 1927-1933, THE (2CD Set)
FA 254 / Oct '96 / Fremeaux

☐ BLUES FOLLOW ME ALL DAY LONG (The Complete Shelter Recordings Of Jimmy Rogers Vol.2)
Act like you love me / Broken hearted blues / Information please / Bad luck blues / Gold-tailed bird / Lonesome blues / Brown-skinned woman / That's alright Mama / You're sweet / Sloppy drunk / Live at Ma Bee's / House rocker / Pretty baby / You're the one / Blues (follow me all day long) / Slick chick / I lost a good woman / Dorcie Belle
CZ 566 / Feb '96 / Premier/EMI

☐ COMPLETE CHESS RECORDINGS, THE
MCD 09372 / Jul '97 / Chess/MCA

☐ FEELIN' GOOD
BPCD 5018 / Feb '95 / Blind Pig

☐ JIMMY ROGERS WITH RONNIE EARL & THE BROADCASTERS
Okie dokie stomp / Okie dokie stomp / Same old blues / Rock this house / Gold tailed bird / Why did you do it / Can't sleep for worrying / Walking by myself / Left me with a broken heart / Got my mojo working / You can read my letter buy you can't read my mind / Shake your moneymaker / You're sweet
CCD 11033 / Jan '94 / Crosscut

☐ LUDELLA
422294 / May '94 / New Rose

☐ SLOPPY DRUNK
Sloppy drunk / I can't sleep for worrying / Mistreated baby / Slick chick / Pretty baby / Left me with a broken heart / I lost the good woman / You're so sweet / Last time / Shelby county / Tricky woman / Sloppy drunk / Gold tailed bird / Walking by myself / That's alright / Ludella
ECD 260362 / Sep '93 / Evidence

☐ THAT'S ALL RIGHT
I'm in love / That's alright Mama / Ludella / Goin' away baby / Today today blues / World is in a tangle / Hard working man / Back door friend / Mistreated baby / Left me with a broken heart / Blues all day long (leave me alone) / Chicago bound / Sloppy drunk / You're the one / Walking by myself / If it ain't me / I can't believe / What have I done / Don't turn me down / Rock this house / You don't know
CD 52040 / Oct '96 / Blues Encore

Rogers, Kenny

☐ 20 GREAT LOVE SONGS
Lady / She believes in me / We've got tonight: *Rogers, Kenny & Sheena Easton* / Crazy / You decorated my life / Don't fall in love with a dreamer: *Rogers, Kenny & Kim Carnes* / Share your love with me / What are we doin' in love: *Rogers, Kenny & Dottie West* / Through the years / Love song / I don't need you / Love the world away / Every time two fools collide: *Rogers, Kenny & Dottie West* / Daytime friends / All I ever need is you: *Rogers, Kenny & Dottie West* / Til I can make it on my own: *Rogers, Kenny & Dottie West* / Desperado / You are so beautiful / Green green grass of home / So in love with you
LS 886072 / 2 Feb '98 / Disky

☐ BEST OF KENNY ROGERS, THE (Rogers, Kenny & The First Edition)
CTS 55402 / Jan '92 / Country Stars

☐ BEST OF KENNY ROGERS, THE
TRTCD 175 / Jul '96 / TrueTrax

☐ BEST OF KENNY ROGERS, THE
HMNCD 025 / 16 Mar '98 / Half Moon

☐ CHRISTMAS
Christmas everyday / Kentucky homemade Christmas / Carol of the bells / Kids / Sweet little Jesus boy / Christmas is my favourite time of year / White Christmas / My favourite things / O' holy night / When a child is born
CDMFP 6242 / Oct '96 / Music For Pleasure

☐ COLLECTION, THE
Ruby don't take your love to town / Reuben james / Shine on ruby mountain / Me and bobby mcgee / For the good times / Poem for a little lady / It's raining in my mind / Stranger in my place / Where does rosie go / Tell it all brother / Just dropped in (to see what condition my condition is in) / Tulsa turnaround / My washington woman / Something's burning / Elvira / Loser / Goodtime liberator / Always leaving, always gone / Girl get a hold of yourself / Way it used to be / She even woke me up to say goodbye / King of oak street / Shadow in the corner of your mind / Ticket to nowhere / Homemade lies
COL 031 / Oct '95 / Collection

☐ COUNTRY CLASSICS
Lady / Don't fall in love with a dreamer / Ruby (don't take your love to town) / She believes in me / Lucille / You decorated my life / Every time two fools collide / All I ever need is you / You needed me / Together again / You've lost that loving feeling / Why don't we

go somewhere and love / But you know I love you / Love lifted me / Love or something like it / Another somebody done somebody / My world begins and ends with you / Just the way you are / You and me / We love each other
CDMFP 6322 / Apr '97 / Music For Pleasure

☐ COUNTRY COLLECTION (Rogers, Kenny & The First Edition)
For the good times / She even woke me up to say goodbye / Me and Bobby McGee / King of Oak Street / Ticket to nowhere / Tell it all brother / Way it used to be / Just dropped in / Heed the call / Church without a name / But you know I love you / Poem for my little lady / Hurry up love / Run thru your mind / Sleep comes easy / Always leaving, always gone / I believe in music / Ruby, don't take your love to town
MUCD 9023 / Apr '95 / Musketeer

☐ DAYTIME FRIENDS (The Very Best Of Kenny Rogers)
Gambler / Daytime friends, nightime lovers / Lucille / Ruby, don't take your love to town / Don't fall in love with a dreamer / Coward of the county / You decorated my life / Reuben James / She believes in me / Long arm of the law / Till I make it on my own / Son of Hickory Holler's tramp / Sweet music man / Green green grass of home / We've got tonight / Something's burning / Desperado / Lady / Abraham, Martin and John / Everytime two fools collide
CDEMTV 79 / Sep '93 / EMI

☐ DUETS (Rogers, Kenny & Dottie West)
All I ever need is you / Till I can make it on my own / Just the way you are / You needed me / Let it be me / Together again / Midnight flyer / You've lost that lovin' feelin' / Let's take the long way around the world / Hey won't you play another somebody done somebody wrong song / Every time two fools collide / You and me / What's wrong with us today / Beautiful lies / That's the way it could have been / Why don't we go somewhere and love / Baby I'm a want you / Anyone who isn't me tonight / Loving gift / We love each other
CDMFP 6111 / Mar '94 / Music For Pleasure

☐ FOR THE GOOD TIMES
PLSCD 109 / Mar '96 / Pulse

☐ FOR THE GOOD TIMES (2CD Set)
24051 / Jun '96 / Delta Doubles

☐ FOR THE GOOD TIMES
For the good times / She even woke me up to say goodbye / Me and Bobby McGee / King of Oak Street / Ticket to nowhere / Tell it all brother / Way it used to be / Just dropped in (to see what condition my condition was in) / Heed the call / Church without a name / But you know I love you / Poem for my little daddy / Sleep comes easy / Always leaving always gone / I believe in music / Ruby don't take your love to town
CD 6117 / Apr '98 / Music

☐ GIFT, THE
7014711024 / 24 Nov '97 / Word

☐ HITS COLLECTION, THE (Rogers, Kenny & The First Edition)
Ruby don't take your love to town / Something's burning / What am I gonna do / If wishes were horses / Shine on Ruby Mountain / For the good times / Lay it down / Sunshine / Ticket to nowhere / Where does Rosie go / Tell it all brother / Always leaving, always gone / Loser / Tulsa turnaround / Me and Bobby McGee / All God's lonely children / Once again she's all alone
100352 / May '97 / A-Play Collection

☐ KENNY ROGERS STORY, THE (20 Golden Greats)
Lucille / Lady / Long arm of the law / You decorated my life / Sweet music man / Ruby, don't take your love to town / Love or something like it / Through the years / You are so beautiful / Don't fall in love with a dreamer / Gambler / Daytime friends / We've got tonight / Love lifted me / Coward of the county / Reuben James / Desperado / She believes in me / Something's burning / Blaze of glory
CDEMTV 39 / Dec '87 / Liberty

☐ LOVE COLLECTION, THE
She believes in me / You are so beautiful / I only have eyes for you / Evergreen / I can't help falling in love / You light up my life / When a man loves a woman / Always / You decorated my life / Through the years / Always and forever / My funny valentine / Somewhere my love / Love is a many splendoured thing
10132 / Oct '97 / Go On Deluxe

☐ LOVE SONGS
Have I told you lately that I love you / Evergreen / Lucille / I only have eyes for you / Crazy / Misty / She believes in me / When I fall in love / Always and forever / You decorated my life / Ruby, don't take your love to town / Unchained melody / I will always love you / Can't help falling in love / Love me tender / Endless love / I swear / Wind beneath my wings / Lady / We've got tonight
KENNYCD 1 / 17 Nov '97 / Virgin

☐ RUBEN JAMES
WMCD 5663 / May '94 / Disky

☐ RUBY (Rogers, Kenny & The First Edition)
Just dropped in (to see what condition my condition was in) / Me and Bobby McGee / Way it used to be / King of Oak street / Poem for my little lady / Always leaving always gone / But you know I love you / Tell it all brother / Sleep comes easy / I believe in music / Ruby don't take your love to town / Heed the call / For the good times / Church without a name / Run through your mind / She even woke me up to say goodbye / Hurry up love / Ticket to nowhere
301422 / Feb '98 / Hallmark

☐ RUBY DON'T TAKE YOUR LOVE TO TOWN
Ruby, don't take your love to town / Green green grass of home / Sweet music man / Love or something like it / You and me / King of Oak Street / Reuben James / Puttin' in overtime at home / Daytime friends / Let it be me / Buried treasure / Son of Hickory Holler's tramp / I wasn't man enough / Mother country music / Lay down beside me / Lucille
CDMFP 6001 / Sep '88 / Music For Pleasure

☐ RUBY DON'T TAKE YOUR LOVE TO TOWN
Ticket to nowhere / Conditions (Just dropped in) / She even woke me up to say goodbye / My Washington woman / Run thru your mind / Sleep comes easy / After all / For the good times / Something's burning / Hurry up love / Trying just as hard / Ruby, don't take your love to town / Heed the call / We all got to help each other / Poem for my little lady / Where does Rosie go / Sunshine / Reuben James / Loser / Church without a name / Green green grass of home / Sweet music man / Daytime friends
MU 5066 / Oct '92 / Musketeer

☐ RUBY DON'T TAKE YOUR LOVE TO TOWN
Ruby, don't take your love to town / Reuben James / Shine on Ruby mountain / Ticket to nowhere / Conditions (just dropped in) / She even woke me up to say goodbye / My Washington woman / Run thru your mind / Sleep comes easy / After all / For the good times / Something's burning / Hurry up love / Trying just as hard / Heed the call / We all got to help each other / Poem for my little lady / Where does Rosie go / Sunshine / Loser / Church without a name / Me and Bobby McGee / Always leaving, always gone / Calico silver / Way it used to be / Goodtime liberator
GRF 027 / Feb '93 / Tring

☐ RUBY DON'T TAKE YOUR LOVE TO TOWN
Ruby don't take your love to town / Tulsa turnaround / Elvira / Ruben james / Love woman / King of oak street / Shine on ruby mountain / Me and bobby mcgee / Where does rosie go / For the good times / Something's burning / Tell it all brother / I'm gonna sing you a sad song susie / Molly / We all got to help each other / Ticket to nowhere
15075 / Aug '91 / Laserlight

☐ RUBY DON'T TAKE YOUR LOVE TO TOWN (Rogers, Kenny & The First Edition)
Ruby don't take your love to town / Me and Bobby McGee / Poem for my little lady / For the good times / Good lady of Toronto / Where does Rosie go / What am I gonna do / All God's lonely childern / Lay it down / Tulsa turnaround / Tell it all brother / Love woman / I'm gonna sing you a sad song Suzie / King of Oak Street / Shine on Ruby Mountain / Heed the call / Molly / Camptown ladies / We all got to help eachother / After all
CDSGP 094 / Mar '94 / Prestige

☐ RUBY DON'T TAKE YOUR LOVE TO TOWN (Rogers, Kenny & The First Edition)
Ruby don't take your love to town / Reuben James / Shine on Ruby Mountain / Conditions (just dropped in) / She even woke me up to say goodbye / My Washington woman / For the good times / Something's burning / Heed the call / We all got to help each other / Poem for my little lady / Where does Rosie go / Sunshine / Me and Bobby McGee / Calico silver / Elvira
QED 010 / Nov '96 / Tring

☐ SPOTLIGHT ON KENNY ROGERS
Ruby, don't take your love to town / Me and Bobby McGee / Poem for my lady / For the good times / Good lady of Toronto / Where does Rosie go / What am I going to do / All God's lonely children / Lay it down / Tulsa turn around / Tell it all brother / Love woman / I'm going to sing a sad song Suzie / King of Oak Street / Shine on Ruby Mountain / Heed the call / Molly / Camptown ladies / We all got to help each other / After all
HADCD 104 / Feb '94 / Javelin

☐ VERY BEST OF KENNY ROGERS, THE
What I did for love / Ruby, don't take your love to town / Don't fall in love with a dreamer: *Rogers, Kenny & Kim Carnes* / Gambler / Daytime friends / Love is strange: *Rogers, Kenny & Dolly Parton* / She believes in me / Lucille / Lady / Coward of the county / You decorated my life / Love lifted me / Something's burning / Islands in the stream: *Rogers, Kenny & Dolly Parton*
7599264572 / Nov '90 / WEA

Rogers, Richard

☐ SOUL TALKING
Woop de woo / Something good inside / Soul talking / Keep giving me love / Give you my love / Underground / My own love / Waiting on a sign / Isn't it a shame / Everybody knows
XECD 9 / Oct '96 / Expansion

Rogers, Roy

☐ VERY BEST OF THE SINGING COWBOYS, THE (Rogers, Roy & Gene Autrey)
Be honest with me: *Autry, Gene* / There's a ranch in the rockies: *Rogers, Roy* / There's a bridle hanging on the wall: *Robinson, Carson & His Pioneers* / Blue yodel no.5: *Autry, Gene* / Colorado sunset: *Rogers, Roy* / Home on the range: *Robinson, Carson & His Pioneers* / No one to call me darling: *Autry, Gene* / No children allowed: *Rogers, Roy* / Old November moon: *Autry, Gene* / Candlelight in the window: *Robinson, Carson & His Pioneers* / Pistol packin' papa: *Autry, Gene* / I'm leavin' on that blue river train: *Autry, Gene* / WHisper your mother's name: *Autry, Gene* / I left her standing there: *Robinson, Carson & His Pioneers* / What's gonna happen to me: *Autry, Gene* / Tumbling tumbleweeds: *Savage, Jack & His Cowboys* / Sierra Sue: *Autry, Gene* / Ramblin' cowboy: *Robinson, Carson & His Pioneers* / Going back to Texas: *Savage, Jack & His Cowboys* / Rhythm of the hoofbeats: *Autry, Gene* / I was born in old Wyoming: *Robinson, Carson & His Pioneers* / I'll always be a rambler: *Autry, Gene*
SWNCD 020 / Nov '97 / Sound Waves

Rogers, Roy

☐ BLUES ON THE RANGE
CCD 11026 / '92 / Crosscut

☐ PLEASURE AND PAIN
VPBCD 47 / 1 Jun '98 / Pointblank

☐ RHYTHM & GROOVE
Vida's place / My heart's desire / Call on me / Built for comfort / Feel my care / For the love of a woman / Shakin' hands with the devil / Your mind is on vacation / Proud man / Blues for Brazil / Love me or leave me / Ever since I lost you / Wrong number / Remembering you
VPBCD 33 / Mar '96 / Pointblank

☐ SLIDE ZONE
Get back in line / Spent money / House of blue dreams / Lover's moon / Livin' on borrowed time / Ode to the Delta / Not fade away / Slide zone / Lookin' up at downside / Rough house / Still a long ways to go / Off the cuff
CDP 8294172 / Sep '94 / Liberty

☐ TRAVELLIN' TRACKS (Rogers, Roy & Norton Buffalo)
BPCD 5003 / Jan '93 / Blind Pig

Rogers, Sally

☐ CLOSING THE DISTANCE (Rogers, Sally & Claudia Schmidt)
FF 425CD / May '93 / Flying Fish

☐ WE'LL PASS THEM ON
RHRCD 71 / Aug '95 / Red House

☐ WHEN HOWIE MET SALLY (Rogers, Sally & Howie Bursen)
FF 538CD / '92 / Flying Fish

Rogers, Shorty

☐ AMERICA THE BEAUTIFUL (Rogers, Shorty & Bud Shank)
America the beautiful / Less is more / New dreams / Casa de luz / Lotus bud / Un poco loco / Good news / Here's that old martian again / Trult truly / Fun
CCD 79510 / Feb '97 / Candid

☐ BIG SHORTY ROGERS EXPRESS, THE
Blues express / Pink squirrel / Coop de graas / Infinity promenade / Short stop / Boar-jibu / Pay the piper / Home with sweets / Tales of an African lobster / Contours / Chiquito loco / Sweetheart of Sigmund Freud
74321185192 / Jul '94 / RCA

☐ EIGHT BROTHERS (Rogers, Shorty & Bud Shank/Lighthouse All Stars)
Back to the basie-ics / Yesterday, today and forever / Unfinished dream / Magic man / Eight horns / Stray horns / Like it is / Battle hymn of the Republic / Essence of tenderness / Double trouble / No additives, no preservatives
CCD 79521 / Feb '97 / Candid

Rogers, Stan

☐ BETWEEN THE BREAKS - LIVE
FOG 002CD / Jul '94 / Fogerty's Cove

☐ FOGERTY'S COVE
FOG 1001CD / Jul '94 / Fogerty's Cove

☐ FOR THE FAMILY
R 002CD / Jul '95 / Folk Tradition Canada

☐ FROM FRESH WATER
FOG 007CD / Jul '94 / Fogerty's Cove

☐ NORTHWEST PASSAGE
FOG 004CD / Jul '94 / Fogerty's Cove

☐ TURNAROUND
FOG 001CD / Jul '94 / Fogerty's Cove

Rogers, Sydney

☐ MIRACLE WORKER
ETH 2214CD / 8 Dec '97 / Ethnic Flight

Rogers, Tammy

☐ IN THE RED (Rogers, Tammy & Don Heffington)
In the red / At the nest / Flaco's farewell / St.Moritz / Tate's news / Rest in the arms of angels / Bagpipes / Whiplash / Get out while you can / John's tune / Psalms / Amazing grace
DR 00022 / Dec '97 / Dead Reckoning

☐ TAMMY ROGERS
DR 00052 / Dec '97 / Dead Reckoning

Rogers, Wayne

☐ INFRACTION
TW 1041CD / 24 Nov '97 / Twisted Village

Rogers, Weldon

☐ TRYING TO GET TO YOU
Sale of broken hearts / So long good luck goodbye / Trying to get to you / My only love / Please return my broken heart / I'm building a...on the moon / Dim lights thick smoke and loud loud music / For always / Yes forever / Everybody wants you / I still want you / I'm gonna be around / If I had one day to live / Lying lips and a cheating heart / You made me love you / Talk of the town / That was in the deal / Bright lights / This song is just for you / Back door of Heaven / Cimarron / As long as you are mine / Living with a heartache / Our rendezvous / I'm gonna love again / I lost the moon / I haven't seen myself in years / Mr. Mountain Lion / I've got the yearning / Would you still want me
BCD 16165 / Feb '98 / Bear Family

Rogerson, Diana

☐ BEASTINGS
UD 041CD / Oct '96 / United Dairies

Rogie, S.E.

☐ DEAD MEN DON'T SMOKE MARIJUANA
Kpindigbee / Time in my life / Nor weigh me lek dat / Jaimgba tutu / Koneh pelawoe / Jojo yalah jo / Nyalomei luange / African gospel / Nyalimagotee / Dieman noba smoke tafee
CDRW 46 / May '94 / Realworld

Rogoff, Jill

☐ ACROSS THE NARROW SEAS
ALC 129CD / May '97 / Alcazar

Roguish Armament

☐ ROGUISH ARMAMENT
SFT 01CD / Apr '98 / Striving For Togetherness

Rojitas

☐ REGALAME TU ENCANTO
74321401342 / Sep '96 / Milan

Roland From Poland

☐ BALTIC BEATS
EEKCD 002 / 8 Jun '98 / Mouse

Roland, Paul

☐ DANSE MACABRE
Witchfinder General / Madame Guillotine / Great Edwardian air raid / Hanging judge / Still falls the snow / Matilda mother / Gabrielle / Requiem / Buccaneers / In the opium den / Twilight of the rock
422296 / May '94 / New Rose

☐ DUEL
422297 / May '94 / New Rose

☐ GARGOYLES
GASCD 703 / Jul '97 / Gaslight

☐ HOUSE OF DARK SHADOWS
422299 / May '94 / New Rose

☐ STRYCHNINE
422431 / May '94 / New Rose

Rolie, Gregg

☐ GRINGO
100334 / Mar '97 / Point

Roll, Jim

☐ READY TO HANG
Old love / Mary Ann / Never gonna dry (these eyes) / Backseat / Fall / Ready to hang / This time / Train / My saviour / Double time / She said / Another lover / If I were a sailor
OMC 0010 / 20 Apr '98 / One Man Clapping

Rollerskate Skinny

☐ SHOULDER VOICES
PILLCD 3 / Sep '93 / Placebo

Rollinat, Maurice

☐ LA MORT LUI RICANE
983872 / Feb '97 / EPM

Rolling Stones

☐ 12 X 5
Around and around / Confessin' the blues / Empty heart / Time is on my side / Good times, bad times / It's all over now / 2120 South Michigan Avenue / Under the boardwalk / Congratulations / Grown up wrong / If you need me / Suzie Q
8444612 / Jun '95 / London

☐ AFTERMATH
Mother's little helper / Stupid girl / Lady Jane / Under my thumb / Don'tcha bother me / Goin' home / Flight 505 / High and dry / Out of time / It's not easy / I am waiting / Take it or leave it / Think / What to do
8444662 / Jun '95 / London

☐ **BEGGARS BANQUET**
Sympathy for the devil / No expectations / Dear Doctor / Parachute woman / Jigsaw puzzle blues / Street fighting man / Prodigal son / Stray cat blues / Factory girl / Salt of the Earth
8444712 / Jun '95 / London

☐ **BETWEEN THE BUTTONS**
Let's spend the night together / Yesterday's papers / Ruby Tuesday / Connection / She smiled sweetly / Cool calm and collected / All sold out / My obsession / Who's been sleeping here / Complicated / Miss Amanda Jones / Something happened to me yesterday
8444682 / Jun '95 / London

☐ **BIG HITS VOL.1 (High Tide And Green Grass)**
Have you seen your mother, baby, standing in the shadow / Paint it black / It's all over now / Last time / Heart of stone / Not fade away / Come on / Satisfaction / Get off my cloud / As tears go by / Nineteenth nervous breakdown / Lady Jane / Time is on my side / Little red rooster
8444652 / Jun '95 / London

☐ **BIG HITS VOL.2 (Through The Past Darkly)**
Paint it black / Ruby Tuesday / She's a rainbow / Jumpin' Jack Flash / Mother's little helper / Let's spend the night together / Honky tonk women / Dandelion / 2000 Light years from home / Have you seen your mother, baby, standing in the shadow / Street fighting man
8444722 / Jun '95 / London

☐ **BIOGRAPHY SERIES**
10024 / 3 Nov '97 / Metro Independent

☐ **BLACK AND BLUE**
Hot stuff / Hand of fate / Cherry oh baby / Memory motel / Hey Negrita / Fool to cry / Crazy mama / Melody (inspiration by Billy Preston)
CDV 2736 / Aug '94 / Virgin

☐ **BRIAN JONES INTERVIEW**
RSBJ 1 / Aug '96 / UFO

☐ **BRIDGES TO BABYLON**
Flip the switch / Anybody seen my baby / Low down / Already over me / Gunface / You don't have to mean it / Out of control / Saint of me / Might as well get juiced / Always suffering / Too tight / Thief in the night / How can I stop
CDV 2840
CDVX 2840 / 29 Sep '97 / Virgin

☐ **CHARLIE WATTS INTERVIEW**
RSCW 1 / Aug '96 / UFO

☐ **DECEMBER'S CHILDREN (AND EVERYBODY'S)**
She said yeah / Talkin' 'bout you / You better move on / Look what you've done / Singer not the song / Route 66 / Get off my cloud / I'm free / As tears go by / Gotta get away / Blue turns to grey / I'm movin' on
8444642 / Jun '95 / London

☐ **DIRTY WORK**
One hit (to the body) / Fight / Harlem shuffle / Hold back / Too rude / Winning ugly / Back to zero / Dirty work / Had it with you / Sleep tonight
CDV 2743 / Aug '94 / Virgin

☐ **EMOTIONAL RESCUE**
Summer romance / Send it to me / Let me go / Indian girl / Where the boys go / Down in the hole / Emotional rescue / She's so cold / All about you / Dance (part 1)
CDV 2737 / Aug '94 / Virgin

☐ **EXILE ON MAIN STREET**
Rocks off / Rip this joint / Casino boogie / Tumbling dice / Sweet Virginia / Torn and frayed / Sweet black angel / Loving cup / Shake your hips / Happy / Turd on the run / Ventilator blues / I just want to see his face / Let it loose / All down the line / Stop breaking down / Shine a light / Soul survivor
CDV 2731 / Aug '94 / Virgin

☐ **FLASHPOINT**
Continental drift / Start me up / Sad sad sad / Miss you / Ruby Tuesday / You can't always get what you want / Factory girl / Little red rooster / Paint it black / Sympathy for the devil / Brown sugar / Jumpin' Jack Flash / Satisfaction / Highwire / Sex drive / Rock and a hard place / Can't be seen
CDV 2855 / 27 Apr '98 / Virgin

☐ **FLOWERS**
Ruby Tuesday / Have you seen your mother, baby, standing in the shadow / Let's spend the night together / Lady Jane / Out of time / My girl / Backstreet girl / Please go home / Mother's little helper / Take it or leave it / Ride on baby / Sittin' on a fence
8444692 / Jun '95 / London

☐ **GET YER YA-YA'S OUT (Rolling Stones Live In Concert)**
Jumpin' Jack Flash / Carol / Stray cat blues / Love in vain / Midnight rambler / Sympathy for the devil / Live with me / Little Queenie / Honky tonk women / Street fighting man
8444742 / Jun '95 / London

☐ **GOATS HEAD SOUP**
Dancing with Mr. D / 100 years ago / Coming down again / Doo doo doo doo (Heartbreaker) / Angie / Silver train / Hide your love / Winter / Can you hear the music / Star star
CDV 2735 / Aug '94 / Virgin

☐ **GOT LIVE IF YOU WANT IT**
Under my thumb / Get off my cloud / Lady Jane / Not fade away / I've been loving you too long / Fortune teller / Last time / Nineteenth nervous breakdown / Time is on my side / I'm alright / Have you seen your mother, baby, standing in the shadow / Satisfaction
8444672 / Jun '95 / London

☐ **HOT ROCKS 1964-1971 (2CD Set)**
Satisfaction / Get off my cloud / Paint it black / Under my thumb / Ruby Tuesday / Let's spend the night together / Jumpin' Jack Flash / Sympathy for the devil / Honky tonk women / Gimme shelter / You can't always get what you want / Brown sugar / Time is on my side / Heart of stone / Play with fire / As tears go by / Mother's little helper / Nineteenth nervous breakdown / Street fighting man / Midnight rambler / Wild horses
8444752 / Jun '95 / London

☐ **INSTRUMENTAL MEMORIES (Various Artists)**
(I can't get no) satisfaction / Honky tonk woman / Fool to cry / Ruby Tuesday / Moonlight mile / Beast of burden / Wild horses / Stupid girl / You can't always get what you want / Tumblin' dice / Under my thumb / Angie / Let's spend the night together / Miss you / Brown sugar / Gimme shelter / It's only rock 'n' roll (but I like it)
309212 / 13 Jul '98 / Hallmark

☐ **INTERVIEW DISC**
TELL 05 / Dec '96 / Network

☐ **INTERVIEW DISC**
SAM 7011 / Nov '96 / Sound & Media

☐ **IT'S ONLY ROCK 'N' ROLL**
If you can't rock me / Ain't too proud to beg / It's only rock 'n' roll / Till the next goodbye / Luxury / Time waits for no one / Dance little sister / If you really want to / Short and curlies / Fingerprint file
CDV 2733 / Aug '94 / Virgin

☐ **JAGGER/RICHARD SONGBOOK (Various Artists)**
Last time: *Who* / Nineteenth nervous breakdown: *Flamin' Groovies* / Street fighting man: *Stewart, Rod* / Heart of stone: *Mekons* / Mother's little helper: *Coughlan, Mary* / Ruby Tuesday: *Melanie* / Out of time: *Farlowe, Chris* / Congratulations: *West Five* / Wild horses: *Flying Burrito Brothers* / Tell me: *Webb, Cassell* / Silver train: *Naked Prey* / Sympathy for the devil: *Ferry, Bryan* / Lady Jane: *Merrick, Tony* / Take it or leave it: *Searchers* / Sleepy city: *Mighty Avengers* / That girl belongs to yesterday: *Pitney, Gene* / As tears go by: *Faithfull, Marianne* / Honky tonk women: *Turner, Ike & Tina* / So much in love: *Inmates* / Will you be my lover tonight: *Bean, George* / Sitting on a fence: *Twice As Much* / Satisfaction: *Redding, Otis* / Connection: *Montrose* / Sister Morphine: *Faithfull, Marianne*
VSOPCD 159 / Apr '91 / Connoisseur Collection

☐ **JAMMING WITH EDWARD (Hopkins/Cooder/Jagger/Wyman/Watts)**
Boudoir stomp / It hurts me too / Edward's thrump up / Blow with Ry / Interlude a la el hopo / Loveliest night of the year / Highland fling
CDV 2779 / May '95 / Virgin

☐ **JUMP BACK (The Best Of The Rolling Stones 1971-1993)**
Harlem shuffle / Start me up / Brown sugar / It's only rock 'n' roll / Mixed emotions / Angie / Tumbling dice / Fool to cry / Rock and a hard place / Miss you / Hot stuff / Emotional rescue / Respectable / Beast of burden / Waiting on a friend / Wild horses / Bitch / Undercover of the night
CDV 2726 / Dec '93 / Virgin

☐ **KEITH RICHARDS INTERVIEW**
RSKR 1 / Aug '96 / UFO

☐ **LET IT BLEED**
Gimme shelter / Love in vain / Country honk / Live with me / Let it bleed / Midnight rambler / You got the silver / Monkey man / You can't always get what you want
8444732 / Jun '95 / London

☐ **LIFE AND TIMES (Documentary and Music)**
OTR 1100049 / Jun '97 / Metro Independent

☐ **LOVE YOU LIVE**
Fanfare for the common man / Honky tonk women / If you can't rock me / Get off my cloud / Happy / Hot stuff / Star star / Tumbling dice / Fingerprint file / You gotta move / You can't always get what you want
CDV 2857 / 27 Apr '98 / Virgin

☐ **MICK JAGGER INTERVIEW**
RSMJ 1 / Aug '96 / UFO

☐ **MORE HOT ROCKS (Big Hits And Fazed Cookies/2CD Set)**
Tell me / Not fade away / Last time / It's all over now / Good times, bad times / I'm free / Out of time / Lady Jane / Sittin' on a fence / Have you seen your mother, baby, standing in the shadow / Dandelion / We love you / She's a rainbow / 2000 light years from home / Child of the moon / No expectations / Let it bleed / What to do / Money / Come on / Fortune teller / Poison ivy / Bye bye Johnny / I can't be satisfied / Long long while
8444782 / Jun '95 / London

☐ **OUT OF OUR HEADS**
She said yeah / Mercy mercy / Hitch hike / That's how strong my love is / Good times / Gotta get away / Talkin bout you / Cry to me / Oh baby / Heart of stone / Under assistant West Coast promotion man / I'm free
8444632 / Jun '95 / London

☐ **PAINT IT BLUE (The Songs Of The Rolling Stones) (Various Artists)**
RUF 1020 / 24 Nov '97 / Ruf

☐ **ROCK 'N' ROLL CIRCUS (December 11th 1968) (Various Artists)**
Song for Jeffrey: *Jethro Tull* / Quick one while he's away: *Who* / Ain't that a lot of love: *Taj Mahal* / Something better: *Faithfull, Marianne* / Yer blues: *Dirty Mac* / Whole lotta Yoko: *Ono, Yoko & Ivry Gitlis/ Dirty Mac* / Jumping Jack flash: *Rolling Stones* / Parachute woman: *Rolling Stones* / No expectations: *Rolling Stones* / You can't always get what you want: *Rolling Stones* / Sympathy for the devil: *Rolling Stones* / Salt of the Earth: *Rolling Stones*
5267712 / Oct '96 / London

☐ **ROLLING STONES**
Route 66 / I just want to make love to you / Honest I do / I need you baby / Now I've got a witness / Little by little / I'm a king bee / Carol / Tell me (you're coming back) / Can I get a witness / You can make it if you try / Walking the dog
8444602 / Jun '95 / London

☐ **ROLLING STONES BOX SET**
RS 1 / Oct '92 / UFO

☐ **ROLLING STONES INTERVIEWS, THE (3CD Set)**
55582 / Mar '97 / Laserlight

☐ **ROLLING STONES NOW, THE**
Everybody needs somebody / Down home girl / You can't catch me / Heart of stone / What a shame / I need you baby / Down the road apiece / Off the hook / Pain in my heart / Oh baby (we got a good thing goin') / Little red rooster / Surprise surprise
8444622 / Jun '95 / London

☐ **ROYAL PHILHARMONIC ORCHESTRA PLAY THE ROLLING STONES (Royal Philharmonic Orchestra)**
DCD 5296 / Sep '93 / Disky

☐ **SHARED VISION VOL.2 (The Songs Of The Rolling Stones) (Various Artists)**
5358452 / Oct '96 / London

☐ **SINGLES COLLECTION, THE (The London Years/2CD Set)**
Come on / I want to be loved / I wanna be your man / Stoned / Not fade away / Little by little / It's all over now / Good times, bad times / Tell me / I just want to make love to you / Time is on my side / Congratulations / Little red rooster / Off the hook / Heart of stone / What a shame / Last time / Play with fire / Satisfaction / Under assistant West coast promotion man / Spider and the fly / Get off my cloud / I'm free / Singer not the song / As tears go by / Gotta get away / Nineteenth nervous breakdown / Sad day / Paint it black / Stupid girl / Long long while / Mother's little helper / Lady Jane / Have you seen your mother, baby, standing in the shadow / Who's driving your plane / Let's spend the night together / Ruby Tuesday / We love you / Dandelion / She's a rainbow / 2000 light years from home / In another land / Lantern / Jumpin' Jack Flash / Child of the moon / Street fighting man / No expectations / Surprise surprise / Honky tonk women / You can't always get what you want / Memo from Turner / Brown sugar / Wild horses / I don't know why / Try a little harder / Out of time / Jiving sister Fanny / Sympathy for the devil
8444812 / Jun '95 / London

☐ **SOME GIRLS**
Miss you / When the whip comes down / Just my imagination / Some girls / Lies / Faraway eyes / Respectable / Before they make me run / Beast of burden / Shattered
CDV 2734 / Aug '94 / Virgin

☐ **STEEL WHEELS**
Sad, sad, sad / Mixed emotions / Terrifying / Hold on to your hat / Hearts for sale / Blinded by love / Rock and a hard place / Can't be seen / Almost hear you sigh / Continental drift / Break the spell / Slippin' away
CDV 2742 / Aug '94 / Virgin

☐ **STICKY FINGERS**
Brown sugar / Sway / Wild horses / Can't you hear me knocking / You gotta move / Bitch / I got the blues / Sister Morphine / Dead flowers / Moonlight mile
CDV 2730 / Aug '94 / Virgin

☐ **STILL LIFE (American Concert 1981)**
Under my thumb / Let's spend the night together / Shattered / Twenty flight rock / Let me go / Time is on my side / Just my imagination / Start me up / Satisfaction / Take the 'A' train / Star spangled banner
CDV 2856 / 27 Apr '98 / Virgin

☐ **STRIPPED**
Street fighting man / Like a rolling stone / Not fade away / Shine a light / Spider and the fly / I'm free / Wild horses / Let it bleed / Dead flowers / Slipping away / Angie / Love in vain / Sweet Virginia / Little baby
CDV 2801 / Nov '95 / Virgin

☐ **SYMPHONIC MUSIC OF THE ROLLING STONES, THE (Featuring Mick Jagger/ Marianne Faithfull/Michael Hutchence) (London Symphony Orchestra/Peter Scholes)**
Street fighting man / Paint it black / Under my thumb / As tears go by / Sympathy for the devil / Dandelion / Ruby Tuesday / Angie / She's a rainbow / Gimme shelter / Jumpin' Jack Flash
09026625262 / Jun '94 / RCA Victor

☐ **SYMPHONIC ROLLING STONES (Hanover Radio Philharmonic Orchestra)**
Satisfaction / Last time / Paint it black / Emotional rescue / As tears go by / Out of time / Angie / 19th nervous breakdown / Lady Jane / Fool to cry
QED 227 / Nov '96 / Tring

☐ **TATTOO YOU**
Start me up / Hang fire / Slave / Little T and A / Black limousine / No use in crying / Neighbours / Worried about you / Tops / Heaven / Waiting on a friend
CDV 2732 / Aug '94 / Virgin

☐ **THEIR SATANIC MAJESTIES REQUEST**
Citadel / In another land / Sing this all together (see what happens) / She's a rainbow / Lantern / Gomper / 2000 light years from home / On with the show / 2000 man
8444702 / Jun '95 / London

☐ **UNDER COVER**
Too much blood / Pretty beat up / Too tough / All the way down / It must be hell / Undercover of the night / She was hot / Tie you up (The pain of love) / Wanna hold you / Feel on baby
CDV 2741 / Aug '94 / Virgin

☐ **VOODOO LOUNGE**
Love is strong / You got me rocking / Worst / Out of tears / I go wild / Brand new car / Sweethearts together / Suck on the jugular / Blinded by rainbows / Baby break it down / Thru and thru / Mean disposition / New faces / Moon is up / Sparks will fly
CDV 2750 / Jul '94 / Virgin

☐ **WHO ARE THE STONES (Interview Disc)**
CBAK 4008 / Apr '88 / Baktabak

Rollinghead

☐ **LONG BLACK FEELING**
GROW 0072 / Apr '94 / Grass

Rollini, Adrian

☐ **BOUNCIN' IN RHYTHM**
TPZ 1027 / Sep '95 / Topaz Jazz

Rollins, Henry

☐ **BIG UGLY MOUTH**
QS 9CD / Jul '92 / Quarter Stick

☐ **BLACK COFFEE BLUES**
213CD 021 / May '97 / 2.13.61

☐ **COME IN AND BURN**
Shame / Starve / All I want / End of something / On my way to the cage / Thursday afternoon / During a city / Neon / Spilling over the side / Inhale exhale / Saying goodbye again / Rejection / Disappearing act
DRD 50011 / Mar '97 / Dreamworks

☐ **DEEP THROAT BOX SET**
QS 13CD / Jul '92 / Quarter Stick

☐ **DO IT (Rollins Band)**
IRS 986978CD / 13 Apr '98 / Interchord

☐ **HARD VOLUME**
IRS 986979CD / 13 Apr '98 / Interchord

☐ **HOT ANIMAL MACHINE/DRIVE BY SHOOTING**
IRS 986976CD / 13 Apr '98 / Interchord

☐ **HUMAN BUTT**
QS 12CD / Jul '92 / Quarter Stick

☐ **LIFE TIME (Rollins Band)**
Burned beyond recognition / What am I doing here / 1000 times beyond / Lonely / Wreckage / Gun in mouth blues / You look at you / If you're alive / Turned out
IRS 986977CD / 13 Apr '98 / Interchord

☐ **LIVE AT MCCABES**
QS 11CD / Jul '92 / Quarter Stick

☐ **SWEAT BOX**
QS 10CD / Jul '92 / Quarter Stick

☐ **TURNED ON (Rollins Band)**
Lonely / Do it / What have I got / Tearing / Out there / You didn't need / Hard / Followed around / Mask / Down and away / Turned inside out / Deitmar song / Black and white / What do you do / Crazy lover
QS 02CD / Dec '90 / Quarter Stick

Rollins, Sonny

☐ **+3**
What a difference a day made / Biji / They say it's wonderful / Mona Lisa / Cabin in the sky / HS / I've never been in love
MCD 92502 / Apr '96 / Milestone

☐ **ALFIE**
Alfie's theme / He's younger than you are / Street runner with child / Transition theme for minor blues or little Malcolm loves his / On impulse / Alfie's theme differently
IMP 12242 / Apr '97 / Impulse Jazz

☐ **ALL THE THINGS YOU ARE**
Yesterdays / Summertime / Lover man / 'Round midnight / Afternoon in Paris / It could happen to you / All the things you are / Just friends / At McKies / Now's the time / My one and only love / Travellin' light
ND 82179 / Jul '90 / Bluebird

☐ **BEST OF SONNY ROLLINS, THE**
Decision / Poor butterfly / Why don't I / Misterioso / Tune up / How are things in Glocca Morra / Sonnymoon for two / Softly as in a morning sunrise / Striver's row
CDP 7932032 / Jan '96 / Blue Note

☐ **BRIDGE, THE**
Without a song / Where are you / John S / Bridge / God bless the child / You do something to me
09026685182 / Oct '96 / RCA Victor

☐ COMPLETE BLUE NOTE RECORDINGS, THE (5CD Set)
Decision / Bluesnote / How are things in Glocca Morra / Plain Jane / Sonnysphere / Why don't I / Wail march / Misterioso / Reflections / You stepped out of a dream / Poor butterfly / Tune up / Asiatic raes / Wonderful wonderful / Surrey with the fringe on top / Blues for Philly Joe / Namely you / Night in Tunisia / I've got you under my skin / Night in Tunisia / Softly as in a morning sunrise / Four / Woody 'n' you / Old devil moon / What is this thing called love / Softly as in a morning sunrise / Sonnymoon for two / I can't get started / I'll remember April / Get happy / Strivers row / All the things you are / Get happy
8213712 / 10 Nov '97 / Blue Note

☐ COMPLETE PRESTIGE RECORDINGS, THE (7CD Set)
Elysee / Opus V / Hilo / Fox hunt / Morpheus down / Blue room / Whispering / I know / Conception / Out of the blue / Denial / Bluing / Dig / My old flame / It's only a paper moon / Time on my hands / Mambo bounce / This love of mine / Shadrack / On a slow boat to China / With a song in my heart / Scoops / Newk's fadeaway / Compulsion / Serpent's tooth / 'Round midnight / In a sentimental mood / Stopper / Almost like being love / No Moe / Think of one / Let's call this / Friday the 13th / Soft shoe / Confab in tempo / I'll take romance / Airegin / Oleo / But not for me / Doxy / Movin' out / Swingin' for Bumsy / Silk 'n' satin / Solid / I want to be happy / Way you look tonight / More than you know / There's no business like show business / Paradox / Raincheck / There are such things / It's all right with me / In your own sweet way / No line / Vierd blues / I feel a song coming on / Pent-up house / Valse hot / Kiss and run / Count your blessings / My reverie / Most beautiful girl in the world / Paul's pal / When your lover has gone / Tenor madness / You don't know what love is / St. Thomas / Strode rode / Blue 7 / Moritat / I've grown accustomed to her face / Kids know / House I live in / Bird medley / B swift / My ideal / Sonny boy / Two different worlds / Ee-ah / B quick
7PCD 4407 / Nov '96 / Prestige

☐ COMPLETE RCA VICTOR RECORDINGS, THE (6CD Set)
Without a song / Where are you / John S / Bridge / God bless the child / You do something to me / Don't stop the carnival / If I ever would leave you / Jungoso / Bluesongo / Night has a thousand eyes / Brown skin girl / 52nd Street theme / Four / Oleo / Dearly beloved / Doxy / You are my lucky star / I could write a book / There will never be another you / Yesterdays / All the things you are / Summertime / Just friends / Lover man / At McKie's / Now's the time / Blue 'n' boogie / I remember Clifford / 52nd Street theme / St. Thomas / Round midnight / Afternoon in Paris / Four / I remember Clifford / St. Thomas / Django / Afternoon in Paris / Now's the time / Four / Autumn nocturne / Night and day / Love letters / My one and only love / Three little words / Travellin' light / I'll be seeing you / My ship / It could happen to you / Long ago and far away / Winter wonderland / When you wish upon a star / Travellin' light
09026686752 / 6 Oct '97 / RCA Victor

☐ CUTTING EDGE, THE
Cutting edge / To a wild rose / First moves / House is not a home / Swing low, sweet chariot
OJCCD 468 / Nov '95 / Original Jazz Classics

☐ DANCING IN THE DARK
Just Once / O T Y O G / Promise / I'll String Along With You / Allison
MCD 9155 / Oct '93 / Milestone

☐ DON'T ASK
Harlem boys / File / Disco Monk / My ideal / Don't ask / Tai-chi / And then my love I found you
OJCCD 915 / May '97 / Original Jazz Classics

☐ EAST BROADWAY RUN DOWN
East Broadway run down / Blessings in diguise / We kiss in a shadow
IMP 11612 / Sep '95 / GRP

☐ EASY LIVING
Isn't she lovely / Down the line / My one and only love / Arroz con pollo / Easy living / Hear what I'm saying
OJCCD 893 / Nov '96 / Original Jazz Classics

☐ ESSENTIAL, THE
Pannonica / La villa / Dearly beloved / Every time we say goodbye / Cutie / Last time I saw Paris / Happiness is a thing called Joe / Someday I'll find you / Freedom suite
FCD 60020 / Oct '93 / Fantasy

☐ EUROPEAN CONCERTS
BS 18007 / Jul '96 / Bandstand

☐ FALLING IN LOVE WITH JAZZ
For all we know / Tennesse waltz / Little girl blue / Falling in love with love / I should care / Sister / Amanda
MCD 9179 / Oct '93 / Milestone

☐ FREEDOM SUITE
OJCCD 67 / Oct '92 / Original Jazz Classics

☐ G-MAN
G-man / Kim / Don't stop the carnival / Tenor madness
MCD 9150 / Oct '93 / Milestone

☐ GLOBAL WARMING
Island lady / Echo side blue / Global warming / Mother Nature's blues / Change partners / Clear cut boogie
MCD 92802 / Jul '98 / Milestone

☐ HERE'S TO THE PEOPLE
Why was I born / I wish I knew / Here's to the people / Dr. Phil / Someone to watch over me / Young Roy / Lucky day / Long ago and far away
MCD 91942 / Mar '92 / Milestone

☐ HORN CULTURE
Pictures in the reflection of a golden horn / Sais / Notes for eddie / God bless the child / Love man / Good morning heartache
OJCCD 314 / Sep '93 / Original Jazz Classics

☐ IN DENMARK VOL.1
MCD 0372 / Aug '92 / Moon

☐ IN DENMARK VOL.2
MCD 0382 / Aug '92 / Moon

☐ JAZZ GREATS
St. Thomas / Round midnight / Four / Night and day / Just friends / My one and only love / Now's the time / Don't stop the carnival / You do something to me / Brown skin girl / There will never be another you
74321556882 / Feb '98 / RCA Victor

☐ LOVE AT FIRST SIGHT
Little lulu / Dream that we fell out of / Strode rode / Very thought of you / Caress / Double feature
OJCCD 753 / Apr '93 / Original Jazz Classics

☐ MOVING OUT
Movin' out / Swingin' for bumsy / Silk 'n' satin / Solid / More than you know
OJCCD 58 / Feb '92 / Original Jazz Classics

☐ NEWK'S TIME
Tune up / Asiatic races / Wonderful, wonderful / Surrey with the fringe on top / Blues for Philly Joe / Namely you
CDP 7840012 / Mar '95 / Blue Note

☐ NEXT ALBUM
Playin' in the yard / Poinciana / Everywhere calypso / Keep hold of yourself / Skylark
OJCCD 312 / Apr '92 / Original Jazz Classics

☐ OLD FLAMES
Darn that dream / Where or when / My old flame / Time slimes / I see you face before me / Delia / Prelude to a kiss
MCD 9215 / Jan '94 / Milestone

☐ OLEO
Oleo / It could happen to you / I've told every little star / Will you still be mine / I remember you / There'll never be another you / Woody 'n' you / But not for me
JHR 73552 / Jan '93 / Jazz Hour

☐ PLUS FOUR
OJCCD 243 / Feb '92 / Original Jazz Classics

☐ QUARTETS, FEATURING JIM HALL
God bless the child / John S / You do something to me / Where are you / Without a song / Bridge / If ever I would leave you / Night has a thousand eyes
ND 85643 / Apr '88 / Bluebird

☐ ROLLINS MEETS CHERRY VOL.1
MCD 0532 / May '94 / Moon

☐ ROLLINS MEETS CHERRY VOL.2
MCD 0542 / Apr '94 / Moon

☐ ROLLINS PLAYS FOR BIRD (Rollins, Sonny Quintet)
OJCCD 214 / Mar '93 / Original Jazz Classics

☐ ROLLINS ROUND MIDNIGHT
Yesterdays / Summertime / Without song / 'Round midnight / You do something to me / Lover man / There will never be another you / Where are you / God bless the child / Just friends / My one and only love / All the things you are
74321393442 / Jun '96 / Camden

☐ SAXOPHONE COLOSSUS
Strode rode / Blue 7 / Moritat / St. Thomas / You don't know what love is
OJCCD 291 / Feb '92 / Original Jazz Classics
OJC20 2912 / Sep '98 / Original Jazz Classics

☐ SILVER CITY (A Celebration Of 25 Years On Milestone/2CD Set)
Autumn nocturne / Duke of iron / Cabin in the sky / Harlem boys / Where or when / To a wild rose / Tennessee waltz / G-man / McGhee / Someone to watch over me / I'm old fashioned / Just once / Lucky day / Darn that day / Darn that dream / Silver city / Skylark / Tell me you love me / Biji
MCD 25012 / Jan '97 / Milestone

☐ SONNY BOY
Ee-ah / B. quick / B. swift / House I live in / Sonny boy
OJCCD 348 / May '93 / Original Jazz Classics

☐ SONNY ROLLINS & CO 1964
Django / Afternoon in Paris / Now's the time / Four / Blue 'n' boogie / Night and day / Three little words / My ship / Love letters / Long ago and far away / Winter wonderland / When you wish upon a star / Autumn nocturne
07863665302 / Apr '95 / Bluebird

☐ SONNY ROLLINS 1951-1958 (2CD Set)
I know / Time on my hands / Stopper / In a sentimental mood / Friday the 13th / Soft shoe / Airegin / Doxy / Swingin' for bumsy / Solid / Way you look tonight / Paradox / Valse hot / Tenor madness / My reverie / Most beautiful girl in the world / St. thomas / Strode rode / Blue seven / Moritat / I've grown accustomed to her face / House I live in / Sonny boy / How are things in glocca morra / Misterioso / Reflections / Come, gone / Solitude / Funky hotel blues / Freedom suite / Oleo
CDB 1213 / Jul '92 / Giants Of Jazz

☐ SONNY ROLLINS AND THE CONTEMPORARY LEADERS PLUS
I've told every little star / Rock-a-bye your baby with a dixie melody / How high the moon / You / I've found a new baby / I've found a new baby (alternate take) / Alone together / In the chapel in the moonlight / Song is you / Song is you (alternate take)
OJCCD 340 / Apr '86 / Original Jazz Classics

☐ SONNY ROLLINS ON IMPULSE
On Green Dolphin Street / Everything happens to me / Hold 'em Joe / Blue room / Three little words
IMP 12232 / Apr '97 / Impulse Jazz

☐ SONNY ROLLINS SAMPLER
Toot toot Tootsie / Come, gone / How high the moon / Cutting edge / Every time we say goodbye / Poinciana
OJCX 005 / Jan '98 / Original Jazz Classics

☐ SONNY ROLLINS WITH THE MODERN JAZZ QUARTET (Rollins, Sonny & Modern Jazz Quartet)
Stopper / Almost like being in love / No Moe / In a sentimental mood / Scoops / With a song in my heart / Newk's fadeaway / Time on my hands / This love of mine / Shadrack / On a slow boat to China / Mambo bounce / I know
OJCCD 11 / Sep '93 / Original Jazz Classics

☐ SONNY ROLLINS/VOL.2/NEWK'S TIME (3CD Set)
Decision / Bluesnote / Plain Jane / Sonnysphere / How are things in Giocca Morra / Why don't I / Wail march / Misterioso / Reflections / You stepped out of a dream / Poor butterfly / Tune up / Asiatic raes / Wonderful wonderful / Surrey with the fringe on top / Blues for Philly Joe / Namely you
CDOMB 008 / Oct '95 / Blue Note

☐ SOUND OF SONNY, THE
Last time I saw Paris / Toot toot tootsie / Dearly beloved / Cutie / Mangoes / Just in time / What is there to say / Every time we say goodbye / It could happen to you
OJCCD 29 / Feb '92 / Original Jazz Classics

☐ STOCKHOLM 1959
DRCD 229 / Jan '88 / Dragon

☐ TENOR MADNESS
OJCCD 124 / Feb '92 / Original Jazz Classics

☐ TENOR MADNESS
Tenor madness / When your lover has gone / Paul's pal / My reverie / Most beautiful girl in the world
OJC20 1242 / Sep '98 / Original Jazz Classics

☐ THIS LOVE OF MINE
CDSGP 043 / Mar '93 / Prestige

☐ TOUR DE FORCE
OJCCD 95 / Sep '93 / Original Jazz Classics

☐ WORK TIME
OJCCD 7 / Mar '93 / Original Jazz Classics

Rolls Royce Brass Band

☐ BEST OF BRASS, THE
Fanfare and flourishes / With one look / Twelfth street rag / We've only just begun / Oklahoma / Share my yoke / Ticket to ride / Love changes everything / Pop looks Bach / Trumpets wild / Swing low, sweet chariot / Solitaire / Pie Jesu / Magic flute / Star lake / Coronation march
QED 176 / Nov '96 / Tring

☐ PLAYS THE BEST OF BRASS
Men of Harlech / Coronation march / Pastime with good company / Fanfare and flourishes / With one look / Twelfth Street rag / We've only just begun / Oklahoma / Share my yoke / Ticket to ride / Love changes everything / Pop looks Bach / Trumpets wild / Swing low, sweet chariot / Solitaire / Pie Jesu / Magic flute
WMCD 2003 / Oct '96 / ACL

Romane

☐ OMBRE (Gypsy Manouche A La Django)
IMP 943 / Sep '96 / IMP

☐ QUINTET
JSL 023 / Jan '95 / JSL

☐ SAMOIS-SUR-SEINE
3001809 / 24 Apr '98 / IMP

☐ SWING FOR NININE
BPE 127 / Nov '92 / Kardum

☐ SWING IN NASHVILLE
IMP 949 / Jun '97 / IMP

Romano, Aldo

☐ CANZONI
T'ho voluto bene / Romana non fare la stupida stasera / Munastario a Santa Chiara / Sapore di sale / Torna a surriente / O sole mio / Anima e core / Reginella / Come prima / Senza fina
ENJACD 91022 / Jun '97 / Enja

☐ CARNET DE ROUTES
Standing ovation / Vol / Daoulaged / Boroko dance / Annonbon / Les petits lits blancs / Flash memoire / Korokoro / Entrave
LBLC 6569 / Nov '95 / Label Bleu

☐ NON DIMENTICAR
5182642 / May '94 / Polydor

Romanowski, Jeff

☐ DREAMS
55086CD / Jul '97 / Strictly Rhythm

Romantic Gorilla

☐ ROMANTIC GORILLA
POLLUTE 42 / 12 Jan '98 / Sound Pollution

Romantics

☐ MADE IN DETROIT
You and your folks, me and my folks / Love it up / I wanna know / Runaway / Leave her alone
CDSEWT 705 / Mar '93 / Westbound

Rome

☐ ROME
I belong to you (every time I see your face) / Do you like this / Crazy love / Just once, once more, three times / I gotta be down / Do me right / That's the way I feel about cha / Real love / Feelin' kinda good / Let me come home / Never find another love like mine / Real joy / Heaven
078636744124 / May '97 / RCA

Romeo's Daughter

☐ DELECTABLE
CDMFN 153 / Oct '93 / Music For Nations

Romer, Hanne

☐ AKIJAVA (Romer, Hanne & Marietta Wandall Duo)
MECCACD 1012 / Nov '94 / Music Mecca

Romero, Chan

☐ FIFTIES FLASH BACK
RKCD 9501 / Mar '96 / Rockhouse

Romero, Pepe

☐ FLAMENCO
Fiesta en Jerez / Fandangos por Verdiales / Garrotin / Tanguillos / Peteneras / Jota / Carabana Gitana / Farruca y rumba / Zorongo / Lamento Andaluz / Spanish dance: *Romero, Angel* / Recuerdos de la Alhambra / Vidalita: *Romero, Celedonio*
4343612 / Apr '96 / Philips

Romero, Rafael

☐ MARIO BOIS COLLECTION VOL.18
LDX 2741027 / Dec '96 / Le Chant Du Monde

Romeros

☐ ROYAL FAMILY OF THE SPANISH GUITAR, THE (Traditional Spanish Folk & Guitar Music)
4343852 / May '97 / Mercury Living Presence

Romeu, Antonio

☐ EL MAGO DE LAS TECLAS 1937-1940 (Romeu, Antonio Orquesta)
TCD 067 / Jul '96 / Tumbao Cuban Classics

☐ ORIENTE Y OCCIDENTE (Romeu, Antonio Orquesta)
TCD 072 / Jul '96 / Tumbao Cuban Classics

Romiosini

☐ PICTURES OF CRETE
EUCD 1049 / '89 / ARC

☐ SONGS AND DANCES FROM GREECE
EUCD 1163 / '91 / ARC

Ron-E Was Another 1

☐ SEXOCET
REVXD 182 / Mar '93 / FM

Rondat, Patrick

☐ AMPHIBIA
LMP 9804003CD / Apr '98 / Limb

Rondo Veneziano

☐ CONCERTO PER MOZART
261362 / Sep '96 / Private Music

☐ CONCERTO PER VIVALDI
Autumno / Inverno / Estro armonico / Il piacere / La cetra / Primavera / Cimento dell'armonico / Estate / La stravaganza
262489 / Jun '97 / RCA

☐ POESIA DI VENEZIA
259826 / Aug '95 / Private Music

☐ VENEZIA 2000
Sinfonia per un addio / Serenissima / Notte amalfitana / Rondo Veneziano / Aria di festa / Arlecchino / San Marco / Canal grande / Arabesco / Scaramucce / Giochi d'acqua / Colombina
610299 / 1 Sep '97 / Arista

☐ VISIONI DI VENEZIA
260213 / Aug '95 / Private Music

Ronettes

☐ BEST OF THE RONETTES, THE
Be my baby / Why don't they let us fall in love: *I Wonder* / Baby I love you: *I Wonder* / Best part of breaking up: *I Wonder* / So young / When I saw you / Do I love you / You baby / How does it feel / Born to be together / Is this what I get for loving you / Paradise / Here I sit / I wish I never saw the sunshine / Everything under the sun / You came, you saw, you conquered
CDP 7803162 / Oct '92 / EMI

Roney, Antoine

☐ TRAVELER, THE
Traveller / Cry of.... / Chief rahab / Mayan owl / Tempus fugit / On Green Dolphin street / Estate / Weaver of dreams / Bean and the boys
MCD 5469 / Jul '94 / Muse

☐ WHIRLING
MCD 5546 / Feb '96 / Muse

Roney, Wallace

☐ INTUITION
MCD 5346 / Sep '92 / Muse

☐ SETH AIR
Melchizedek / Breath of Seth Air / Black people suffering / 28 rue pigalle / Lost / People / Gone / Wives and lovers
MCD 5441 / Sep '92 / Muse

☐ STANDARD BEARER, THE
MCD 5372 / Sep '92 / Muse

☐ VERSES
MCD 5335 / Sep '92 / Muse

Roni Size

☐ MUSIC BOX (Various Artists)
FCYCD 01 / 10 Nov '97 / Full Cycle

☐ NEW FORMS (2CD Set) (Reprazent)
Railings / Brown paper bag / New forms / Let's get it on / Digital / Matter of fact / Mad cat / Heroes / Share the fall / Watching windows / Beatbox / Morse code / Destination / Intro / Hi potent / Trust me / Change my life / Share the fall / Down / Jazz / Ballet dance
5349332 / Jun '97 / Talkin' Loud
5349342 / 8 Sep '97 / Talkin' Loud

Ronnie & Clyde

☐ IN GLORIOUS BLACK AND BLUE
Natural one / Theme from a lazy life / Bad memory / Macro-scopic / Twice removed / Last hand / Nine million miles / Natural two / From a great height / 33rd caller
WM 15 / 23 Feb '98 / Swim

Ronny & The Daytonas

☐ GTO (The Best Of Ronny & The Daytonas)
GTO / Bucket T / Hot rod city / Hey little girl / Little rail job / Antique '32 Studebaker Dictator coupe / Little scrambler / No wheels / Beach boy / Tiger-a-go-go / Sandy / I'll think of summer / If I had my way / When stars shine bright / Nanci / Then the rains came / Somebody to love me / Goodbye baby / Teenage years / California bound
SC 11046 / Aug '97 / Sundazed

Ronson, Mick

☐ BBC LIVE IN CONCERT (Hunter Ronson Group)
Once bitten twice shy / How much more can I take / Beg a little love / Following in your footsteps / Just another night / Sweet dreamer / (Give me back my) wings / Standin' in my light / Bastard / Loner / You're never to old to hit the big time / All the way from Memphis / Irene Wilde
SFRSCD 057 / 30 Mar '98 / Strange Fruit

☐ MAIN MAN (2CD Set)
SMDCD 119 / 20 Apr '98 / Snapper

☐ MICK RONSON MEMORIAL ALBUM, THE (2CD Set)
CIT 2CD / 10 Jan '98 / Fabric Of Life

☐ ONLY AFTER DARK (2CD Set)
Love me tender / Growing up and I'm fine / Only after dark / Music is lethal / I'm the one / Pleasure man / Hey Ma get Papa / Slaughter on 10th Avenue / Leave my heart alone / Love me tender (live) / Slaughter on 10th Avenue (Live) / Billy Porter / Angel number nine / This is for you / White light, white heat / Play don't worry / Hazy days / Girl can't help it / Empty bed (lo me no andrei) / Woman / Seven days (B'side) / Stone love / I'd rather be me
GY 003SP / May '95 / NMC

☐ PLAY DON'T WORRY
Billy Porter / Angel No. 9 / This is for you / White light, white heat / Play don't worry / Hazy days / Girl can't help it / Empty bed (lo me ne andrei) / Woman / Seven days / Stone love (soul love) / I'd rather be me / Life on Mars / Pain in the city / Dogs (French girl) / 28 days jam / Woman
SMMCD 504 / 29 Sep '97 / Snapper

☐ RISE AND FALL OF BERNIE GRIPPLESTONE AND THE RAT FROM HULL, (Rats)
Spoonful / I've got my eyes on you baby / I've got to see my baby / New Orleans / Rise and fall of Bernie Gripplestone / Stop and get a hold of myself / Mick's boogie / Morning dew / Early in Spring / Telephone blues / It ain't easy / I feel free
SJPCD 022 / Jun '98 / Angel Air

☐ SLAUGHTER ON TENTH AVENUE
Love me tender / Growing up and I'm fine / Only after dark / Music is lethal / I'm the one / Pleasure man/ Hey Ma get Papa / Slaughter on Tenth Avenue / Leave my heart alone / Love me tender / Slaughter on Tenth Avenue
SMMCD 503 / 29 Sep '97 / Snapper

Ronstadt, Linda

☐ CRY LIKE A RAINSTORM, HOWL LIKE THE WIND
Still within the sound of my voice / Cry like a rainstorm / All my life: *Ronstadt, Linda & Aaron Neville* / Don't know much: *Ronstadt, Linda & Aaron Neville* / Adios / Trouble again / I keep it hid / So right, so wrong / Shattered / When something is wrong with my baby / Goodbye my friend
9608722 / Oct '89 / Elektra

☐ EVERGREEN (Stone Poneys)
7801292 / 1 Jun '98 / Capitol

☐ FOR SENTIMENTAL REASONS
When you wish upon a star / Bewitched, bothered and bewildered / You go to my head / But not for me / My funny valentine / I get along without you very well / Am I blue / (I love you) for sentimental reasons / Straighten up and fly right / Little girl blue / 'Round midnight
9604742 / Sep '86 / Elektra

☐ GREATEST HITS
You're no good / Silver threads and golden needles / Desperado / Love is a rose / That'll be the day / Long long time / Different drum / When will I be loved / Love has no pride / Heatwave / It doesn't matter anymore / Tracks of my tears
253055 / Jul '94 / WEA

☐ GREATEST HITS VOL.1
You're no good / Silver threads and golden needles / Desperado / Love is a rose / That'll be the day / Long long time / Different drum / When will I be loved / Love has no pride / Heatwave / It doesn't matter anymore / Tracks of my tears
253055 / '84 / Asylum

☐ GREATEST HITS VOL.2
It's so easy / I can't let go / Hurt so bad / Blue bayou / How do I make you / Back in the USA / Ooh baby baby / Poor, poor pitiful me / Tumbling dice / Just one look / Someone to lay down beside me
252255 / Jul '94 / Elektra

☐ HAND SOWN HOME GROWN (Ronstadt, Linda & Stone Poneys)
7801252 / 1 Jun '98 / Capitol

☐ HASTEN DOWN THE WIND
Lose again / Tattler / If he's ever near / That'll be the day / Lo siento me vida / Hasten down the wind / Rivers of Babylon / Give one heart / Try me again / Crazy / Down so low / Someone to lay down beside me
K 9606102 / Sep '89 / Elektra

☐ HEART LIKE A WHEEL
7460732 / 1 Jun '98 / Capitol

☐ LINDA RONSTADT
Rock me on the water / Crazy arms / I won't be hangin' around / I still miss someone / In my reply / I fall to pieces / Ramblin' round / Birds / Faithful / Rescue me
7801272 / 1 Jun '98 / Capitol

☐ ROUND MIDNIGHT
What's new / I've got a crush on you / Guess I'll hang my tears out to dry / Crazy he calls me / Someone to watch over me / I don't stand a ghost of a chance with you / What'll I do / Lover man / Goodbye / When I fall in love / Skylark / It never entered my mind / Mean to me / When your lover has gone / I'm a fool to want you / You took advantage of me / Sophisticated lady / Can't we be friends / My old flame / Falling in love again / Lush life / When you wish upon a star / Bewitched, bothered and bewildered / You go to my head / But not for me / My funny valentine / I get along without you very well / Am I blue / (I love you) for sentimental reasons / Straighten up and fly right / Little girl blue / 'Round midnight
9604892 / Jul '94 / Elektra

☐ SILK PURSE
7801262 / 1 Jun '98 / Capitol

☐ STONE PONEYS AND FRIENDS VOL.3 (Ronstadt, Linda & Stone Poneys)
7801302 / 1 Jun '98 / Capitol

☐ WHAT'S NEW
Skylark / Mean to me / My old flame / What's new / Lush life / Love man / Goodbye / (I love you) for sentimental reasons / Crazy he calls me / When I fall in love
9602602 / Sep '83 / Elektra

☐ WINTER LIGHT
Heartbeats accelerating / Do what you gotta do / Anyone who had a heart / Don't talk (put your head on my shoulder) / Oh no, not my baby / It's too soon to know / I just don't know what to do with myself / River for him / Adonde voy / You can't treat the wrong man right / Winter light
7559615452 / Dec '93 / Elektra

Roof

☐ UNTRACEABLE CIGAR, THE
RN 4 / Jun '96 / Konkurrent

Rooks

☐ CHIMES
NL 0036 / Jul '97 / Not Lame

☐ DOUBLE DOSE OF POP, A (Rooks/20 Cent Crush)
NL 0033 / Jul '97 / Not Lame

☐ ENCORE ECHO
NLA 003 / 29 Jun '98 / Not Lame

☐ WISHING WELL
NL 048 / 29 Jun '98 / Not Lame

Room

☐ HALL OF MIRRORS
CD 700 / Sep '92 / Music & Arts

Room

☐ PRE-FLIGHT
SRMC 0043 / 5 Jan '98 / Siwan

Roomates

☐ CAN'T LIVE ON MEMORIES
PEPCD 124 / 27 Feb '98 / Pollytone

Roomful Of Blues

☐ DANCE ALL NIGHT
BBCD 9955 / Jul '94 / Bullseye Blues

☐ DRESSED UP TO GET MESSED UP
Money talks / What happened to the sugar / Let's ride / Yes indeed / Albi's boogie / Last time / Oh oh / Dressed up to get messed up / He knows the rules / Whiplash
CDVR 018 / '88 / Varrick

☐ FIRST ALBUM, THE
CDVR 035 / '88 / Varrick

☐ HOT LITTLE MAMA
Hot little mama / Big question / New Orleans shuffle / Sufferin' mind / Caravan / Loan me a helping hand / Long distance operator / Something to remember you by / Two bones and a pick / Little fine healthy thing / Sugar coated love / Jeep's blues
CDCHM 39 / Jul '91 / Ace

☐ LIVE AT LUPO'S HEARTBREAK HOTEL
Gator's groove/Welcome to Lupo's / Coconut milk / Three hours past midnight / Three hundred pounds / House of joy / Pink champagne / Please don't leave / That's my life / Please don't leave me / Zydeco boogaloo
CDVR 024 / Nov '96 / Varrick

☐ ROOMFUL OF BLUES
32003CD / May '96 / Thirty Two

☐ ROOMFUL OF CHRISTMAS
Christmas celebration / I told Santa Claus / Christmas song / White Christmas / Have yourself a merry little Christmas / Good morning blues / Let it snow / Run Rudolph run / I want you with me Christmas / I want to spend Christmas with you
CDBB 9591 / Sep '97 / Bullseye Blues

☐ TURN IT ON, TURN IT UP
CDBB 66001 / Jun '96 / Bullseye Blues

☐ UNDER ONE ROOF
She'll be so fine / Running out of time / We b 3 / Standing here at the crossroads / Smack dab in the middle / Let me live / Still livin' in prison / Switchin' in the kitchen / From you / Q's blues / Easy baby / Farmer John / Baby, baby, baby / Rogue elephant
CDBB 9569 / Feb '97 / Bullseye Blues

Rooney, Jim

☐ BRAND NEW TENNESSEE WALTZ
Brand new Tennessee waltz / Be my friend tonight / Amanda / Heaven become a woman / We must believe in magic / Fish and whistle / Dreaming my dreams / Six white horses / Satisfied mind
APCD 067 / Jul '94 / Appaloosa

Roos, Randy

☐ PRIMALVISION
Ancestor / Black elk / Raven's light / Craftman's prelude / Chameleon's dance / Craftsman / Between states / Desert vision / Badlands / View from the summit / Ancestor's reprise
ND 62015 / Oct '95 / Narada

Rootjoose

☐ RHUBARB
RAGECD 6 / 6 Oct '97 / Rage

Rootless

☐ ROTTEN WOOD FOR SMOKING BEES
WALLCD 8 / May '95 / Wall Of Sound

Roots

☐ DO YOU WANT MORE
Intro / There's something goin' on / Proceed / Distortion to static / Mellow my man / I remain calm / Datskat / Lazy afternoon / Vs Rahzel / Do you want more / What goes on part 7 / Essaywhuman / Swept away / You ain't fly / Silent treatment / Lesson part 1 / Unlocking
GED 24708 / 8 Sep '97 / Geffen

☐ FROM THE GROUND UP
It's comin' / Distortion to static / Mellow my man / Dat scat / Worldwide / Do you want more
5189412 / Jun '94 / Talkin' Loud

☐ ILLADELPH HALF LIFE
Intro / Respond/react / Section / Panic / It just don't stop / Episodes / Push up ya lighter / What they do / Vs. scratch / Concerto of the desperado / Clones / Universe at war / No alibi / Dave vs. us / No great pretender / Hypnotic / Ital (the universal side) / One shine / Adventures in wonderland / Outro
GED 24972 / Nov '96 / Geffen

☐ ORGANIX
Root is comin' / Pass the popcorn / Anti-circle / Writers block / Good music (prelude) / Good music / Grits / Leonard I-V / I'm out deah
RRCD 001 / Jun '97 / Remedy

Roots All Stars

☐ GATHERING OF THE SPIRITS, THE
Big turtle river: *Mystic Revelations Of Rastafari* / Blackman king: *Culture* / Jesus is a condition: *Big Youth* / Sitting in babylon: *Hinds, Justin* / Blackman pride: *Mighty Diamonds* / Someday we'll all be free: *Mowatt, Judy* / What about the land: *Mutabaruka* / Woman of the ghetto: *Griffiths, Marcia* / Murder: *Moses, Pablo* / Iron lion Zion: *Ranglin, Ernest* / Your love: *Ellis, Hortense* / Mystic groove: *Mystic Revelations Of Rastafari*
SHANCD 45040 / Jun '98 / Shanachie

Roots Control

☐ DREAD WESTERN
WSCD 008 / Feb '97 / Word Sound Recordings

Roots Radics

☐ FREELANCE
Earsay / Rainbow / I'm not a king / Too much fuss / Party time / Everywhere Natty go / Dance with me / Midnight / Mash it up / Reggae on Broadway
CDKVL 9021 / Jan '87 / Kingdom

☐ LIVE AT CHANNEL ONE
LAP 100CD / Jul '95 / Live & Learn

☐ RADICALLY RADICS
Radically radics / Dancehall massive / Nengeh nengeh / For you / Love thicker than blood / Give thanks and praise / Singing in the dancehall / Bingy Bunny medley / No bun it down / Watcha gonna do / Water more than flour (be my Queen) / Skettle / Siddling deh / Teach dem / Dancehall massive / Reggae for kids
RASCD 3234 / Nov '96 / Ras

☐ SCIENTIST AND JAMMY STRIKE BACK
Storming the death star / Mission impossible / Alien aborts / Buck Rogers in the Black Hole / Death of Mr. Spock / Princess takes her revenge / Crushing of the Stormtroopers / Flash Gordon meets Luke Skywalker / Son of Darth Vader / C3PO + R2D2 = The force
CDTRL 210 / Oct '97 / Trojan

Roots Syndicate

☐ ROOTS OF DUB VOL.1 - GARVEY
DTCD 19 / Nov '93 / Disctex

☐ ROOTS OF DUB VOL.3 - MANDELA
DTCD 20 / May '94 / Discotex

Rootsman

☐ 52 DAYS TO TIMBUKTU
TEMCD 008 / 16 Feb '98 / Third Eye

☐ CITY OF DJINN (Rootsman & Muslimgauze)
TEMCD 009 / Aug '97 / Third Eye

☐ IN DUB WE TRUST
TEMCD 002 / Jul '95 / Third Eye

☐ INTERNATIONAL LANGUAGE OF DUB
TEMCD 004 / Jan '96 / Third Eye

☐ INTO THE LIGHT
TEMCD 05 / Sep '96 / Third Eye

☐ OUT OF THE DARKNESS (Rootsman Remixed)
TEMCD 006 / May '97 / Third Eye

☐ PRESENTS THIRD EYE DIMENSIONS
EB 011 / May '97 / Echo Beach

☐ UNION OF SOULS (Rootsman & Celtara)
TEMCD 013 / 13 Jul '98 / Third Eye

Rooyen, Jerry Van

☐ AT 250 MILES PER HOUR
EFA 043792 / Dec '96 / Crippled Dick Hot Wax

Roparz, Gwenola

☐ BARADOZ
BUR 877CD / Mar '98 / Escalibur

☐ BRETON MUSIC FOR THE CELTIC HARP
CD 130 / Jan '95 / Diffusion Breizh

Rope

☐ ROPE HOTEL
Logging back the day / Fellini / Brother black / Bubble machine / Soupzen / Deconjazz / Desert dream dub
GEIST 002CD / 9 Mar '98 / Geist

Ropers

☐ WORLD IS FIRE, THE
TURN 33CD / Jun '97 / Turntable Friend

Rorive, Jean-Pierre

☐ ORGAN AND SAXOPHONE CONTEMPLATION (Rorive, Jean-Pierre & Andre Lamproye)
74321452962 / May '97 / Jade

Ros, Edmundo

☐ CELEBRATION
Cuban love song / South America take it away / Come closer to me / Amapola / Wedding samba / What a difference a day makes / Guantanamera / Brazil / I, yi, yi, yi, yi / Alma llanera / Papa says / I've grown accustomed to her face / Girl from Ipanema / Mala Guena / Forbidden games / Peanut vendor / Laughing samba / How near is love / Colonel Bogey / Coffee song
8440522 / Jan '91 / Eclipse

☐ CHIQUITA BANANA 1946-1947
Without you / It was never like this / Take it away / Coconut song / Cavaquinho / Come closer to me / Coax me a little bit / Tampico / Her bathing suit never got wet / Chiquita banana / Stone cold dead in the market / I've got the sun in the morning / Man is brother to a mule / Rio / Quien no nora no mama / El truco de pernambuco / Coffee song / Another night like this / Maracas / Rainy night in Rio / El toreador / Managua Nicaragua / South America take it away
HQCD 105 / Jan '98 / Harlequin

☐ COME WITH ME MY HONEY
Tico Tico / With me my honey / Linda Muier / Le Seguire (I'm so in love) / Brazil Moreno / Rum and Limonada / Jesusita en Chihuahua / Negra Consentida / Three caballeros / Los Hijos de Buda / Toku / Marie Elena / No te importe saber / La conga del amor / Nightingale / Soltero es mejor / Divina mujer / When I love I love / Conga boom / Te quiero dijis / Tropical magic
RAJCD 867 / Jul '97 / Empress

☐ EDMUNDO ROS & HIS RUMBA BAND VOL.3
HQCD 73 / Jul '96 / Harlequin

☐ EDMUNDO ROS 1939-1941
HQCD 15 / '92 / Harlequin

☐ EDMUNDO ROSS & HIS RUMBA BAND (Ros, Edmundo & his Rumba Band)
Tico tico / Alma llanera / Nightingale / La conga del amor / Taboo / Blen blen blen / Aquellos ojos verdes / Chica chica boom chic / Te quiero dijiste / Maria Elena / Mama yo quiero / Quiereme mucho / Conga boom / They met in Rio / Tropical magic / Mama yo busco un querer / Soltero es mejor / Samba lele
CD 62126 / Nov '97 / Saludos Amigos

☐ MUCH MUCH TOO MUCH
That's the way love goes / Goombay / Hot potatoe mambo / Much much too much / Sweet and gentle / Freddy / Sunshine and ole / Si senor / Brasil moreno / Tico tico / Le seguire / Three caballeros / Jesusita en chihuahua / No can do / Coax me / Little bit / El torador / Take it away / Her bathing suit never got wet / Stone cold dead in the market / Los hijos de buda / Te quiero dijiste / Taboo / Fufunando / Tropical magic / Samba lele / Nightingale / Buenas noches
CDEA 6006 / Feb '98 / Vocalion

☐ THAT LATIN SOUND (Ros, Edmundo & His Orchestra)
Peanut vendor / Frenesi / Brazil / Tico tico / Maria Elena / Perfidia / Taboo / Miami beach rhumba / Mambo no.5 / Lady of Spain / Cielito Lindo / Felicidade / Delicado / Rumba rhapsody / Wedding samba / Carioca / La Paloma / Quireme mucho
PLSCD 245 / 27 Oct '97 / Pulse

☐ TROPICAL MAGIC
HQCD 50 / Mar '95 / Harlequin

Ros, Lazaro

☐ OLORUN
GLCD 4022 / Nov '94 / Green Linnet

☐ SONGS FOR ELEGUA (Ros, Lazaro & Olorun)
ASHECD 2001 / Nov '96 / Ashe

Rosa Lee State

☐ DUSTED CHOCOLATE ALMOND CROISSANT
PLANKCD 29 / May '97 / Plankton

Rosa Mota

☐ BIONIC
From her to maternity / Shelf life / Victoria Falls / This grudge / Frostbitten / Pigeon / Space junk / Scenic layby / La chienne est dans l'arbre / Sometimes narcoleptic / Angel
13THCD 3 / Feb '97 / Thirteenth Hour

☐ DRAG FOR A DRAG
Baby flowers / Are we having fun yet / Cold / Riverblind / Fed / Roma
PILLMCD 2 / Jun '93 / Placebo

☐ WISHFUL SINKING
13THCD 2 / Jan '95 / Thirteenth Hour

Rosales, Gerardo

☐ VENEZUELA SONORA
La mano en el mono / De Venezuela para el mundo / Tumba y bongo / Chivo Venezolano / Chivo Cubano / Brujeria / Tremenda negra / Culo'e puya pa'l mundo / Quinta anauco / Popurri del tio Simon
AL 73053 / Nov '96 / A

Rosana

☐ LUNAS ROTAS
MCD 76015 / Apr '97 / MCA

Rose, Adonis

☐ SONG FOR DONISE (Rose, Adonis Quintet)
Dia's blues / Estrella del mar / Seventy ninth street / Song for Donise / Reflections / My foolish heart / ESP / Love walked in
CRISS 1146 / Jun '98 / Criss Cross

Rose, Alan

☐ PAST AND PRESENT
FRCD 033 / Oct '94 / Foam

Rose Among Thorns

☐ BUTTERFLY DREAMS
Plaids deep stained in red / Don't cry for me / Hero / Don't turn around / Journeys from afar / I'm going to get there / Run run run / Stepping stones / Butterfly dreams / My homelands calling me
HTDCD 31 / 9 Mar '98 / HTD

☐ HIGHLITES
HTDCD 63 / Jun '96 / HTD

☐ ROSE AMONG THORNS
Prologue / Journey / Keep me warm / Dancing drum / Lady of Hay / Heart and Soul / So much to tell / Losers 'n' Dreamers / Lunar love / Hold on / Sail away / Take me home
HTDCD 6 / May '91 / HTD
RME 0131CD / May '97 / Renaissance

☐ THIS TIME IT'S REAL
HTDCD 8 / Jul '92 / HTD
RME 0132CD / May '97 / Renaissance

Rose Chronicles

☐ HAPPILY EVER AFTER
067003010825 / Feb '97 / Nettwerk

Rose, David

☐ STRIPPER & OTHER FAVOURITES, THE (Rose, David & His Orchestra)
Stripper / Embraceable you / I get a kick out of you / Amazing grace / Someone to watch over me / American in paris / (ghost) riders in the sky / Night and day / Love is a many splendored thing / I've got you under my skin / Almost like being in love / Very thought of you / Theme from "carnival" / This guy's in love with you / Our love is here to stay / Holiday for strings / When I fall in love / Feelings / First time ever I saw your face / If you could read my mind
EMPRCD 501 / Apr '94 / Emporio

Rose Garden

☐ NOVENNA
Viola / Hands of God / Man who loves the sea / Lillium / Before my heart burns out quite / I believed in you / Rosa / True love
HYP 3910184CD / 13 Apr '98 / Hyperium

Rose, Jon

☐ BRAIN WEATHER
RERBJRCD 2 / Oct '96 / ReR/ Recommended

☐ FENCE, THE
RERJR 5 / Jun '98 / ReR/Recommended

☐ PERKS
RERJR 3 / Jun '98 / ReR/Recommended

☐ VIOLIN MUSIC FOR RESTAURANTS
RERBJRCD / Apr '90 / ReR/ Recommended

Rose Marie

☐ DANNY BOY
When your old wedding ring was new / Make the world go away / Among my souvenirs / This is my Mother's day / Old rugged cross / When I leave the world behind / Pal of my cradle days / Sunshine of your smile / My mother's eyes / Answer to everything / Strollin' / Underneath the arches / Let the rest of the world go by / After all these years / Ave Maria / You'll never know / My blue heaven / Danny boy / We'll meet again / Wheel of fortune / When I grow too old to dream / Little one / Now is the hour / I apologise / Anniversary waltz
PLSCD 167 / Feb '97 / Pulse

☐ HEARTBREAKERS
It's a heartache / Sometimes when we touch / Crazy / Without you / Let the heartaches begin / Cry me a river / Heartbreaker / Heartaches / Crying / There's nothing in my life / You don't know me / I will always love you / She's got you / True love ways
CDDPR 121 / May '94 / Premier/MFP

☐ SONGS FROM THE HEART
MACCD 168 / Aug '96 / Autograph

☐ WHEN I LEAVE THE WORLD BEHIND
When I leave the world behind / Danny boy / Take it to the limit / It must be him / It comes from the heart / Too darn bad / It ain't easy bein' easy / Rock 'n' roll waltz / You can never stop me loving you / Looking for love / Right to sing it blue / It's a sin to tell a lie / You'll never walk alone / No regrets
MCCD 064 / '92 / Music Club

☐ WHEN YOUR OLD WEDDING RING WAS NEW
When your old wedding ring was new / Make the world go away / This is my mother's day / Old rugged cross / When I leave the world behind / Wheel of fortune / When I grow too old to dream / We'll meet again / Legend in my time / Just for old times sake / Pal of my cradle days / Sunshine of youe smile / My mother's eyes / Answer to everything / Let the rest of the world go by / After all these years / Ave Maria / My blue heaven / Danny Boy / Now is the hour
TRTCD 152 / Oct '94 / TrueTrax

Rose, Michael

☐ BE YOURSELF
CDHB 187 / Feb '96 / Heartbeat

☐ BE YOURSELF DUB (Dubwize: Big Sound Frontline)
CDHB 192 / Jun '96 / Heartbeat

☐ DANCE WICKED
Happiness / Dance wicked / Lion in the jungle: *Rose, Michael & Maxi Priest* / Run dem a run / Dreadlocks / Reality / Landlord / See and blind / I don't want to say goodbye / Mind made up / Never get me down / Life in the ghetto / Mind made up / Mind made up
CDHB 214 / Jun '97 / Heartbeat

☐ DUB WICKED (Michael Rose Meets Mafia & Fluxy At The Grass Roots Of Dub)
Dub well happy / Wicked dub / Lion jungle dub / Gold mine / Dreadlocks in dub / Reality dub / Straight to landlord's head / Blinding version / Goodbye / Mind this yah dub / Dub up / Ghetto life
CDHB 215 / Jun '97 / Heartbeat

☐ MICHAEL ROSE
CDHB 144 / Apr '95 / Heartbeat

☐ NUH CARBON
GRELCD 227 / Jul '96 / Greensleeves

☐ RISING STAR
RFCD 003 / Oct '95 / Record Factory

☐ RUDE BOYS/SHORT TEMPER
CRCDM 4 / Aug '96 / Heartbeat

☐ SELASSIE SHOWCASE
032033 / 26 Jan '98 / Fashion

☐ VOICE OF THE GHETTO
VPCD 1431 / Aug '95 / VP

Rose, Ndiaye Doudou

☐ DJABOTE
Ligue you ndeye / Cheikh anta diop / Rose rhythm / Sidati aidara / Baye kene ndiaye / Chants du burgam / Khine sine / Khine saloume / Walo / Tabala ganar / Diame / Ndiouk
CDRW 43 / Feb '94 / Realworld

Rose Of Avalanche

☐ ALWAYS THERE
FIRE 33007 / Oct '91 / Fire

Rose Royce

☐ GREATEST HITS LIVE
Carwash / I wanna get next to you / Wishing on a star / Love don't live here anymore / Do your dance / Is it love you're after / I love the feeling / Magic touch / Band in production
100282 / May '97 / A-Play Collection

☐ LIVE
Is it love you're after / I'm in love / Wishing on a star / Magic touch / Do your dance / I wanna get next to you / Love don't live here anymore / Car wash
305662 / Oct '96 / Hallmark

☐ LOVE DON'T LIVE HERE ANYMORE (The Greatest Hits Live)
Carwash / Wishing on a star / Is it love you're after / I wanna get next to you / Do your dance / I love the feeling / Love don't live here anymore / Magic touch
AIM 1061CD / Sep '97 / Aim

☐ ROSE ROYCE
Is it love you're after / I love the feeling / Wishing on a star / Magic touch / Band introduction / Do your dance / I wanna get next to you / Love don't live here anymore / Car wash
JHD 103 / Aug '93 / Tring

☐ VERY BEST OF ROSE ROYCE LIVE, THE
Is it love you're after / I'm in love (and I love the feeling) / Wishing on a star / Magic touch / Do your dance / I wanna get next to you / Love don't live here anymore / Car wash
SUMCD 4079 / Nov '96 / Summit

Rose, Sammy

☐ FOOL'S GOLD
You're gonna miss me / One in the red dress / Destination heartbreak / Rose's lament / My heart can't take the beating / Jealous bone / Cold heart stare / Till I'm over you / Backside view / Sugar please / Fool's gold
BCD 15876 / Mar '95 / Bear Family

Rose Tattoo

☐ ASSAULT AND BATTERY
Out of this place / All the lessons / Let it go / Assault and battery / Magnum maid / Rock 'n' roll is king / Manzil madness / Chinese Dunkirk / Sidewalk Sally / Suicide city
REP 4011 / Aug '91 / Repertoire

☐ BEST OF ROSE TATTOO, THE
Rock 'n' roll outlaw / Remedy / Nice boys / One of the boys / Bad boy for love / Butcher and fast Eddy / Manzil madness / All the lessons / Assault and battery / Rock 'n' roll is king / Branded / Scarred for life / It's gonna work itself out / We can't be beaten / Southern stars / I wish / Death or glory / Saturday's rage / Freedom's flame
DOJOCD 126 / Jun '95 / Dojo

☐ NEVER TOO LOUD (2CD Set)
REP 4601 / Dec '97 / Repertoire

☐ ROCK 'N' ROLL OUTLAWS
Rock 'n' roll outlaw / Nice boys / Butcher and fast Eddy / One of the boys / Remedy / Bad boy for love / TV / Stuck on you / Tramp / Astra wally
REP 4010 / Aug '91 / Repertoire

☐ ROSE TATTOO
REP 4103 / Aug '91 / Repertoire

☐ SCARRED FOR LIFE
Scarred for life / We can't be beaten / Juice on the loose / Who's got the cash / Branded Texas / It's gonna work itself out / Sydney girls / Dead set / Revenge
REP 4049 / Aug '91 / Repertoire

☐ SOUTHERN STARS
Southern stars / Let us live / Freedom's flame / I wish / Saturday's rage / Death or glory / Pirate song / You've been told / No secrets / Radio said rock 'n' roll is dead
REP 4050 / Aug '91 / Repertoire

Rose, Tim

☐ GAMBLER, THE
I just want to make love to you / He was born to be a lady / Dance on ma belle / It'll be alright on the night / Runaway / Moving targets / Gambler / Blow me back Santa Ana / So much to lose / Is there something 'bout the way I hold my gun / Bowery Avenue / Laurie
PCOM 1117 / Nov '91 / President

☐ HAUNTED
SKIRT 51 / 26 May '98 / Best Dressed

☐ HIDE YOUR LOVE AWAY (The Collection 1970-1974)
It takes a little longer / Ode to an old ball / Boogie boogie / If I were a carpenter / Boogie boogie / I know these two people / Georgia by moonlight / Dim light a burnin' / Sympathy / You can't stop yourself / Sad song / Cryin' shame / (You've got to) hide your love away / Jamie Sue / Cotton growin' man / You can't keep me / I gotta get a message to you / Darling you were all that I had / Where did you go to my lovely / Goin' down in hollywood
MMR 700 / Jul '98 / Flying Thorn

☐ TIM ROSE/THROUGH ROSE COLOURED GLASSES
BGOCD 378 / 24 Nov '97 / Beat Goes On

Rose, Wally

☐ RAGS, BLUES, JOYS
SACD 109 / Jul '93 / Solo Art

Rosebud

☐ THUNDERMUG HONEYPOT
VC 135 / 20 Apr '98 / Vinyl Communication

Rosehips

☐ ROSEHIPS, THE
SHHHCD 971 / 15 Jun '98 / Secret

Rosenberg Trio

☐ CARAVAN
Viajeiro / Melodie au crepuscle / Pent-up house / La promenade / Embraceable you / Tears / Zebra / Chez moi / Stephaneske / Caravan / I surrender dear / Donna Lee / Night and day / Manoir de mes reves / Batida diferente / Manha de carnaval
5230302 / Aug '94 / Verve

☐ COLLECTION, THE
5371522 / Oct '97 / Verve

☐ GYPSY SWING
It don't mean a thing if it ain't got that swing / Django / Tequila / Miro tata Mimer (For my dad Mimer) / Do you know where you're going to / Cherokee / Bluesette / Guitar boogie / Rosemary's baby / Silk and steel / Cavatina / Hungaria / Children of Sanchez / Yours is my heart alone / Begin the beguine / Latscheben / How insensitive
5278062 / Mar '96 / Verve

☐ ROSENBERG TRIO LIVE AT THE NORTH SEA JAZZ FESTIVAL 1992
For Sephora / Minor swing / Les yeux noirs / Chega de saudade / Be bop / Bossa dorada / Pent-up house / Sweet Georgia Brown / Nuages / Honeysuckle rose / Wasso's waltz / Armando's rumba / Blue bossa / Swing de Paris / Les feuilles mortes / Spain / Sweet Georgia Brown
5194462 / Feb '92 / Verve

Rosenberg, Susan

☐ UPPA MARMORNS HOGA BERG
GCD 31 / May '97 / Giga

Rosengren, Bernt

☐ BIG BAND
1214 / Jul '89 / Caprice

☐ BOMBASTIC 1959-1960 (Rosengren, Bernt & Lasse Werner)
DRCD 287 / Feb '98 / Dragon

☐ PORGY AND BESS (Rosengren, Bernt & Carrl Frederik Orrje Trio)
LICD 3167 / Jan '97 / Liphone

☐ UG, THE
DRCD 211 / Jan '88 / Dragon

Rosenstein, Kimmel

☐ RAMBLIN' AWAY
COPP 0149CD / Dec '96 / Copper Creek

Rosenthal, Ted

☐ LIVE AT MAYBECK RECITAL HALL VOL.38
It's all right with me / Long ago and far away / Lennie's pennies / Better you than me / You're a joy / Jesu joy of man's desiring / Drop me a line / 117th Street / Gone with the wind / Hallucinations / You've got to be modernistic
CCD 4648 / Jun '95 / Concord Jazz

☐ ROSENTHOLOGY
Love walked in / Snowscape / Slippin' and slidin' / Will you still be mine / Wow / Strike up the band / Primrose path / All the things you are / Scene is clean / Gig / Someone to watch over me / Over the bars
CCD 4702 / Jun '96 / Concord Jazz

Roses, Renee

☐ AS WE ARE NOW
Black holes / Land of five rivers / Abstraction blues / Mizmahta / Non-fiction / Bulldog's chicken run / As we are now / Absinthe / Pee wee
8568102 / 5 Jan '98 / Blue Note

Rosetta Stone

☐ ADRENALINE
CLEO 12752 / Feb '95 / Cleopatra

☐ CHEMIVAL EMISSIONS
CLP 315 / 17 Aug '98 / Cleopatra

☐ EYE FOR THE MAIN CHANCE
MIN 01CD / Aug '94 / Minority/One

☐ FOUNDATION STONES
CLEO 9323CD / Jan '94 / Cleopatra

☐ ON THE SIDE OF ANGELS
MIN 02CD / Aug '94 / Minority/One

☐ TYRANNY OF INACTION
MIN 03CD / Jan '95 / Minority/One

Rosicrucian

☐ NO CAUSE FOR CELEBRATION
BMCD 57 / Aug '94 / Black Mark

☐ SILENCE
Column of grey / Way of all flesh / Within the silence / Esoteric traditions / Autocratic faith / Nothing but something remains / Aren't you bored enough / Back in the habit / Defy the oppression / Do you know who you're crucifying
BMCD 025 / Oct '92 / Black Mark

Rosolino, Frank

☐ FRANK TALKS (Rosolino, Frank Quartet)
Blue Daniel / How about you / Straight no chaser / There is no greater love / Waltz for Diane
STCD 8284 / Jul '98 / Storyville

Ross, Andy

☐ BEST OF THE DANSAN YEARS VOL.1, THE (Ross, Andy Orchestra & Victor Silvester Orchestra)
Cornet carillon (waltz) / Chi mai (waltz) / Nothing can last forever (waltz) / Diane (waltz) / Rose in the bud (waltz) / Luna rossa (tango) / Blue moon (slow foxtrot) / Blue star (slow foxtrot) / Love walked in (slow foxtrot) / Love is here to stay (slow foxtrot) / New york, new york (slow foxtrot) / Can't buy me love (quickstep) / Cheek to cheek (quickstep) / Hello dolly (quickstep) / Easy to love (quickstep) / You do something to me (quickstep) / Emperor waltz (viennese waltz) / Ll'l darlin' (cha cha cha) / Killing me softly (rumba) / Amparita roca (pasodoble)
DACD 001 / Jul '92 / Dansan

☐ COME DANCING
You make me feel so young / Nice and easy does it / Day in, day out / Night and day / Jean / If this were the last song / Blue tango / Golden tango / Light Cavalry / September song / Feed the birds / Nice work if you can get it / Fascinatin' rhythm / Mr. Melody / Copacabana / Save the best for last / Speak softly love / Amparita Roca / Fat man boogie / Bill / Over the rainbow / Innuendo / Bohemian rhapsody / Radio Ga Ga / We are the champions
4756422 / Jun '94 / Columbia

☐ COME DANCING (Ross, Andy & His Orchestra)
Let's face the music and dance / People will say we're in love / Flight of the foo birds / That old feeling / What now my love / Jesse / Weekend in New England / Guitar tango / Delilah / Hey daddy / On Broadway / September / Brazil / Copacabana / All in love is fair / History of love / El adorno / Leroy Brown / It had to be you / As if we never said goodbye
CDMFP 6183 / Oct '95 / Music For Pleasure

☐ DANCE PARTY FAVOURITES (Ross, Andy & His Orchestra)
Disco medley / Salsa medley / Skip to me Lu/She'll be coming round the mountain / Killing me softly / Hill St. blues / Praterleben / You'd be so nice to come home to / Dancing in the dark / One love / Amazing Grace / Our love is here to stay / Manhattan / Typhoon / Feelings / Way we were / El Pico / Ain't misbehavin' / Something stupid / Love me tonight / Michael row the boat ashore
DACD 017 / Nov '96 / Dansan

Ross, Annie

☐ MUSIC IS FOREVER
Coffee time / It had to be you / Going to Chicago blues / Twisted / I hadn't anyone till you / Marajuana / Jackie / That old feeling / It never entered my head / One meat ball / Farmer's market / Where do you start / Music is forever
DRGCD 91446 / Mar '96 / DRG

☐ SINGS A HANDFUL OF SONGS
FSCD 61 / Oct '90 / Fresh Sound

☐ SKYLARK
Gypsy in my soul / I love Paris / I didn't know about you / Lady's in love with you / 'Tain't what you do / Don't let the sun catch you crying / Between the devil and the deep blue sea / Don't worry 'bout me / I've told every little star / Manhattan / Please don't talk about me when I'm gone / Skylark
DRGCD 8470 / Oct '96 / DRG

Ross, Billy

☐ BILLY ROSS & JOHN MARTIN (Ross, Billy & John Martin)
Hut on Staffin Island/Lone bush / Smith's a gallant fireman / Battle of Sheriffmuir / Dheanainn sugradh / Lass from Erin's Isle / Dr. MacInnes' fancy/Lexy MacAskill / Avondale / Scandinavian polkas / Bold navvy man / Braes of Lochel / Jenny Dang the weaver/Malcolm the tailor / Auld meal mill
SPRCD 1029 / Feb '94 / Springthyme

Ross, Diana

☐ ALL THE GREAT LOVE SONGS
I'm still waiting / My man (mon homme) / All of my life / Love me / After you / All night lover / Sparkle / It's my turn / Cryin' in my heart out for you / Endless love
5300562 / Mar '96 / Motown

☐ ANTHOLOGY VOL.1 & 2
Reach out and touch / Ain't no mountain high enough / Remember me / Reach out, I'll be there / Surrender / I'm still waiting / Good morning heartache / Touch me in the morning / You're a special part of me: *Ross, Diana & Marvin Gaye* / Last time I saw him / My mistake (was to love you): *Ross, Diana & Marvin Gaye* / Sleepin' / Sorry doesn't always make it right / Do you know where you're going to / I thought it took a little time (but today I fell in love) / One love in my lifetime / Baby, I love your way / Young mothers / Brown baby/Save the children / Love hangover / Gettin' ready for love / Your love is so good for me / You got it / Top of the world / Lovin', livin' and givin' / What you gave me / Boss / It's my house / Upside down / I'm coming out / It's my turn / One more chance / Cryin' my heart out for you / My old piano / My man (mon homme) / Endless love: *Ross, Diana & Lionel Richie* / Imagine / Too shy to say
5301992 / Jan '93 / Motown

☐ DIANA EXTENDED (The Remixes)
Boss / Love hangover / Upside down / Someday we'll be together / I'm coming out / Chain reaction / You're gonna love it
CDGOLD 1020 / Apr '96 / EMI Gold

☐ EATEN ALIVE
Eaten alive / Oh teacher / Experience / Chain reaction / More and more / I'm watching you / Love on the line / I love being in love with you / Crime of passion / Don't give up on each other / Eaten alive (extended)
CDEMD 1051 / Nov '93 / EMI

☐ FORCE BEHIND THE POWER
Change of heart / When you tell me that you love me / Battlefield / Blame it on the sun / You're gonna love it / Heavy weather / Force behind the power / Heart don't change my mind / Waiting in the wings / You and I / One shining moment / If we hold on together / No matter what you do
CDEMD 1023 / Feb '97 / EMI

☐ INSTRUMENTAL MEMORIES (Various Artists)
Baby love / Endless love / One love in my life / Why do fools fall in love / Floy joy / Last time I saw him / Ain't no mountain high enough / You can't hurry love / Touch me in the morning / Automatically sunshine / Stop in the name of love / It's my turn / Chain reaction / River deep mountain high / Reach out and touch / What becomes of the broken hearted / Let my heart do the walking / Crumbs from the table
307272 / 20 Apr '98 / Hallmark

☐ MERRY CHRISTMAS
5504032 / Nov '94 / Spectrum

☐ MOTOWN EARLY CLASSICS (Ross, Diana & The Supremes)
Stop in the name of love / You bring back memories / Come on boy / Time changes things / Run, run, run / Whisper you love me boy / Where did our love go / Ask any girl / Honey boy / Any girl in love (knows what I'm going through) / Come see about me / Mother dear / Baby love / (I'm so glad) Heartaches don't last always / You've really got a hold on me / Baby doll / Who could ever doubt my love / I'm in love again
5521202 / Jul '96 / Spectrum

☐ MOTOWN'S GREATEST HITS
Ain't no mountain high enough / Touch me in the morning / I'm still waiting / I'm gonna make you love me / Upside down / My old piano / You keep me hangin' on / Happening / Reflections / Baby love / You can't hurry love / Where did our love go / Stop in the name of love / All of my life
5300132 / Feb '92 / Motown

☐ ONE WOMAN (The Ultimate Collection)
Where did our love go: *Supremes* / Baby love: *Supremes* / You can't hurry love: *Supremes* / Reflections: *Ross, Diana & The Supremes* / Reach out and touch / Ain't no mountain high enough / Touch me in the morning / Love hangover / I'm still waiting / Upside down / Do you know where you're going to / Endless love: *Ross, Diana & Lionel Richie* / Why do fools fall in love / Chain reaction / When you tell me that you love me / One shining moment / If we hold on together / Best years of my life / Your love / Let's make every moment count
CDONE 1 / Oct '93 / EMI

☐ SILK ELECTRIC
Muscles / So close / Still in love / Fool for your love / Turn me over / Who / Love's lies / In your arms / Anywhere you run to / I am me
CDEMD 1050 / Nov '93 / EMI

☐ STOLEN MOMENTS - THE LADY SINGS JAZZ & BLUES LIVE
Fine and mellow / Them there eyes / Don't explain / What a little moonlight can do / Mean to me / Lover man / Gimme a pigfoot and a bottle of beer / Little girl blue / There's a small hotel / I cried for you / God bless the child / Our love is here to stay / You've changed / Strange fruit / Good morning heartache / Ain't nobody's business if I do / My man (mon homme) / Fine and mellow (Reprise) / Where did we go wrong
CDEMD 1044 / Apr '93 / EMI

☐ STOP IN THE NAME OF LOVE
Baby love / Heatwave / Heartaches don't last always / Mother dear / Always in my heart / Get ready / Everything is good about you / Shake me, wake me (when it's over) / Who could ever doubt my love / Honey boy / Ask any girl / I'm in love again / Any girl in love (knows what I'm going through) / Stop in the name of love
5500712 / May '93 / Spectrum

☐ TAKE ME HIGHER
If you're not gonna love me right / I never loved a man before / Swing it / Keep it right there / Don't stop / Gone / I thought that we were still in love / Voice of the heart / Only love can conquer all / I will survive
CDEMD 1085 / Sep '97 / EMI

☐ TOUCH (Supremes)
This is the story / Nathan Jones / Here comes the sunrise / Love it came to me this time / Johnny Raven / Have I lost you / Time and love / Touch / Happy (is a bumpy road) / It's so hard for me to say goodbye
5302112 / Jan '93 / Motown

☐ TOUCH ME IN THE MORNING
Touch me in the morning / All of my life / We need you / Leave a little room / I won't last a day without you / Little girl blue / My baby / Imagine / Brown baby / Save the children
5301652 / Mar '96 / Motown

☐ ULTIMATE COLLECTION
5308272 / 10 Aug '98 / Motown

☐ VERY SPECIAL SEASON, A
Winter wonderland / White Christmas / Wonderful Christmas time / What the world needs now / Happy Christmas (war is over) / Let it snow, let it snow, let it snow / Amazing grace / His eye is on the sparrow / Silent night / Overjoyed / O holy night / Someday at Christmas / Ave Maria / Christmas song
CDEMD 1075 / Nov '97 / EMI

☐ VOICES OF LOVE
Touch me in the morning / You're all I need to get by / Your love / So close / It's my turn / You are everything / When you tell me that you love me / Forever young / I am me / One shining moment / If we hold on together / Only love can conquer all / I'm still waiting / Missing you / Gone / In the ones you love / You are not alone / I hear (the voice of love)
CDEMD 1100 / Nov '96 / EMI

☐ WHERE DID OUR LOVE GO (Supremes)
Where did our love go / Stoned love / I still believe / Baby love / You're my driving wheel / Nathan Jones / Stop, I don't need no sympathy / You can't hurry love / If I lose again / I hear a symphony / He's my man / Colours of love / Come see about me / I'm gonna let my heart do the walking / Stop in the name of love
ANT 001 / Nov '96 / Tring

☐ WHY DO FOOLS FALL IN LOVE
Why do fools fall in love / Sweet surrender / Mirror mirror / Endless love / It's never too late / Think I'm in love / Sweet nothin's / Two can make it / Work that body
CDGOLD 1044 / Jul '96 / EMI Gold

☐ YOU KEEP ME HANGING ON (Ross, Diana & The Supremes)
Where did our love go / Baby love / Stop in the name of love / You can't hurry love / Reflections / Love child / Some day we'll be together / You keep me hangin' on / Happening / I hear a symphony / Why must we fall in love / No matter what sign you are / Honey bee / Whisper you love me boy / Forever came today / Young folks / Ask any girl / You send me / Some things you never get used to / Keep an eye
5307922 / Apr '97 / Spectrum

Ross, Dr. Isiah

☐ BOOGIE DISEASE
ARHCD 371 / Apr '95 / Arhoolie

☐ CALL THE DOCTOR
TCD 5009 / Oct '94 / Testament

☐ I WANT ALL MY FRIENDS TO KNOW
My little woman / Cat squirrel / I want all my friends to know / Boogie for the doctor / Hobo blues / Little school girl / That's alright mama
JSPCD 243 / Apr '91 / JSP

☐ ONE MAN BAND
Dr. Ross's rock / My little woman / Mama's blues / Thirty two twenty / Chicago breakdown / Good morning little school girl / Hobo blues / Fox chase / Going down slow / Boogie woogie
CDTAK 7087 / 27 Jul '98 / Takoma

Ross, Jerry

☐ JERRY ROSS SYMPOSIUM, THE
Ma belle amie / Everything is beautiful / When love slips away / For the love of him / Let me love you one more time / Little green bag / But for love / Montego love theme / If you do believe in love / Venus / How can I be sure/Day by day / Take it out on me / I saw the light/Life and breath / Superwoman / If we only have love/Oh girl / It happened on a Sunday morning / Too late to turn back now/I wanna be where you are / Brandy (you're a fine girl) / It's the same old love / Too young / Duck you sucker
NEMCD 722 / May '95 / Sequel

Ross, Malcolm

☐ HAPPY BOX
MA 33 / 26 Jan '98 / Marina

☐ LOW SHOT
MA 14 / Sep '95 / Marina

Ross, Richard

☐ COMING FROM KANSAS CITY
Body and Fenderman / I wanna get funky / Comeback / God bless the child / I wanna make love to you / Jelly jelly / Just a dream / I'd rather drink muddy water / Since I fell for you / Gee baby ain't I good to you / Trick bag
AL 73072 / Jul '97 / A

Ross, Ricky

☐ NEW RECORDINGS
INTER 001 / 6 Oct '97 / Internationale

☐ WHAT YOU ARE
Good enening Philadelphia / Icarus / Cold easter / What you are / Radio on / When sinners fall / Jack singer / Lovers / Wake up and dream / Rosie Gordon lies so still / Promise you rain / Love isn't hard it's strong
4839988 / Jun '96 / Epic

Ross, Steve

☐ CLOSE TO COLE PORTER
Close / Ev'rything I love / I've got a shooting box in Scotland / I'm throwing a ball tonight / Me and Marie / Begin the beguine / When the summer moon comes 'long / Get a kick out of you anything goes / Down in the depths / Picture of me without you / Night and day / What's this thing called love / Ev'ry time we say goodbye / They couldn't compare to you / Can-can / You don't know paree / I concentrate on you / Take me back to Manhattan / I happen to like New York / I've got you under my skin
SCATCD 1 / Jun '96 / Sophisticat

Ross, T.T.

☐ SAY YOU WANNA BE LOVED
RN 7033 / 10 Nov '97 / Rhino

Rossbach, John

☐ NEVER WAS PLUGGED
ALZCD 126 / Feb '96 / Alcazar

Rosselson, Leon

☐ GUESS WHAT THEY'RE SELLING AT THE HAPPINESS COUNTER
Hugga mugga chugga lugga humbugga boom chit / Story line / Barney's epic homer / Boys will be boys / My daughter, my son / Do you remember / Abiezer coppe / On her silver jubilee / Ugly ones / Susie / Invisible married breakfast blues / Years grow tall / Invisible man / Pills / Across the hills / Battle hymn of the new socialist party / World's police / Voices / Voice that lives inside you
CFCD 003 / Feb '88 / Fuse

☐ INTRUDERS
CFCD 005 / Nov '95 / Fuse

☐ PERSPECTIVES
Ant and the grasshopper / Perspectives / They're going to build a motorway / Plan / Man who puffs the big cigar / Garden of stone / History lesson / Ballad of a spycatcher / Song of the moderate man / Consider the majority / Saint / No cause for alarm / Experts / In the park / Last chance / Rules of the game / Somebody's stolen the end of my dream / Topside down party
CFCD 006 / Feb '97 / Fuse

☐ ROSSELSONGS
Tim McGuire / Penny for the guy / Palaces of gold / We sell everything / Stand up for Judas / Sing a song to please us / She was crazy, he was mad / Not quite but nearly / Let your hair hang down / Don't get married, girls / I didn't mean it / No-one is responsible / Still is the memory green in my mind / Whoever invented the fishfinger / Who reaps the profits, who pays the price / It wasn't me, I didn't do it / Bringing the news from nowhere / World turned upside down
CFCD 001 / '88 / Fuse

☐ WO SIND DIE ELEFANTEN
Neighbours' cat / Poet, the wife and the monkey / Wo sind die elefanten / Juggler / Whatever happened to Nannerl / Song of the old communist / Where's the enemy / William / General Lockjaw briefs the british media / Out of the fires and smoke of history
CFCD 002 / Feb '89 / Fuse

Rossendale Male Voice

☐ VALLEY OF SONG, THE (Rossendale Male Voice Choir)
Ma belle marguerite / Donkey serenade / I gave my love a cherry / Phil the fluter's ball / Down in the valley / What shall we do with the drunken sailor / Hippopotamus song / Muss I denn / There is nothin' like a dame / I will give my love an apple / Ghost's high noon / Yesterday / Mad dogs and Englishmen / Cease thy affections / Lighthouse keeper and the mermaid / Blow the wind southerly / Old superb
CHAN 6602 / Jun '94 / Chandos

Rosser, Neil

☐ GWYNFYD (Rosser, Neil A'i Bartneriaid)
CRAICD 043 / Dec '94 / Crai

Rossi, Francis

☐ KING OF THE DOGHOUSE
King of the doghouse / I don't know / Darling / Give myself to love / Isaac Ryan / Happy town / Wherever you go / Blue water / Fighter / Someone show me
CDV 2809 / Sep '96 / Virgin

Rossi, Tino

☐ EN CROISIERE AVEC LUI
Le chaland qui passe / Je voudrais un joli bateau / Amapola / Le bateau des Iles / Adieu Hawai / Le pousse-pousse / Tarantelle / Santa Lucia / O sole mio / Ecoutez les mandolines / Reginella / La chanson du voilier / Mon ile d'amour / Loin des guitares / Tant qu'ily aura des etoiles / Le joyeux bandit / Giovinella / Ma Ritournelle / Soirs D'Espagne / De Nice a Monte Carlo
UCD 19111 / Apr '96 / Forlane

☐ ETOILES DE LA CHANSON
8422092 / Nov '96 / Music Memoria

☐ HISTOIRES D'AMOUR
Voulez-vous, madame / Rien qu'un chant d'amour / Pres du feu qui chante / Au bal de l'amour / Le chant du gardian / Toi que mon coeur appelle / Maria / Un soir, une nuit / Ce matin meme / J'ai deux mots dans mon coeur / Paquita / Donne moi ton sourire / Serenade sans espoir / J'attendrai / Tu etais la plus belle / Tristesse / Serenade pres de Mexico / Dites-lui de ma part / Soir de pluie / Ce soir
UCD 19110 / Nov '95 / Forlane

☐ J'ATTENDRAI
Tango de Marilou / Ou voulez vous aller / Aubade: Vainement, ma bien aimee / Reviens / Marinella / Serenade / Si tu le voulais / Bella Ragazzina / Romance de Maitre Pathelin / Catari, Catari (Core 'ngrato) / Amapola / Roses de Picardie / Le Paradis du reve / C'est a Capri / Chant d'amour de Tahiti / Pour t'avoir au clair de lune / Sernade Portugaise / Tant qu'il y aura des etoiles / Si vous l'aviez compris / Reginella / O Corse, ile d'amour / Vieni, vieni / J'attendrai
CDMOIR 520 / Mar '97 / Memoir

☐ L'INCOMPARABLE
Serenade de tosellI / Romance de nadir / Romance de maitre pathelin / Ou voulez-vous aller / La berceuse de jocelyn / Si tu le voulais / Aubade du roi d'ys / La reve de des grieux / Le paradis du reve / Ideale / Roses de picardie / Pour t'avoir au clair de lune / Serenade portugalse / Catari, catarl / Si vous l'avez compris / Reviens
UCD 19053 / Jun '95 / Forlane

☐ PARIS VOICI PARIS
O corse ile d'amour / Catari / Vieni vieni / Ecris moi / O sole mio / Berceuse de Jocelyn / Tant qu'il y aura des etoiles / C'est a capri / Un jour je te dirai / O ciuciarella / Minuit chretiens / Chanson pour Nina / L'amour est une etolie / Paris voice Paris / Mia piccolina / Chanson pour ma brune / J'attendrai / Noel en mer / Tango de marilou / Pescadore / Credo / Guitare d'amour / Tchi tchi / Marinella
CDAJA 5168 / Dec '95 / Living Era

☐ TINO ROSSI ANTHOLOGY
EN 524 / Sep '96 / Encyclopaedia

Rosso, Nini

☐ GOLDEN YEARS
74321455882 / Nov '97 / Ricordi

Rossy

☐ ONE EYE ON THE FUTURE, ONE EYE ON THE PAST
Zana drazana / Ny any aminay / Tanalahy / Anamalao / Misy goika / Faraniaina / Molia / Mangina zaza / Marary vady / Bory hely / Tiako / Raha tanora / Mandry ve / Ramasy / Sira sira / Oaylah / 'ndeha hody
SHCD 64046 / May '93 / Shanachie

Rostock Vampires

☐ TRANSYLVANIAN DISEASE
NB 014CD / Oct '89 / Nuclear Blast

Rosvett

☐ FATAL
BIRD 045CD / Oct '94 / Birdnest

Roswall, Niklas

☐ NIKLAS ROSWALL
AW 15CD / Aug '97 / Tongang

Roswells

☐ ROSWELLS, THE
TDR 90940 / 16 Mar '98 / TDR

Roswoman, Michele

☐ OCCASION TO RISE (Roswoman, Michele Trio)
Lazy bird / Sweet eye of hurricane Sally / Occasion to rise / Prelude to a kiss / Weird nightmare / First trip / We are / Nite flite / Eee-yaa / West Africa
ECD 22042 / Mar '93 / Evidence

Rota, Nino

☐ HARMONIA ENSEMBLE
JSL 015 / Aug '93 / JSL

Rotary Connection

☐ SONGS
Respect / Weight / Sunshine of your love / Got my mojo working / Burning of the midnight lamp / Tales of brave Ulysses / This town / We're going wrong / Salt of the Earth
CDARC 520 / Mar '95 / Charly

Roth, Arlen

☐ GUITAR
Change is gonna come / Dreams of mexico / Fool like me / Landslide / Farther along / Laughing at the blues / Kids on the block / Not her usual man / Poor side of town / Restless age / North sea / On a cold, dark night / August nights
ROUCD 11538 / '88 / Rounder

☐ TOOLIN' AROUND
Tequila: *Roth, Arlen & Danny Gatton* / Let it slide: *Roth, Arlen & Jerry Douglas/Sam Bush* / Goin' back: *Roth, Arlen & Bill Lloyd* / Whiter shade of pale / Rollin' home: *Roth, Arlen & Albert Lee* / Black water: *Roth, Arlen & Duane Eddy* / I can't stop loving you / Housefire: *Roth, Arlen & Duke Robillard* / When a man loves a woman / Six days on the road: *Roth, Arlen & Brian Setzer* / No woman, no cry / '56 Buick Roadmasters from space
BPM 300CD / May '97 / Blue Plate

Roth, David

☐ DIGGING THROUGH THE CLOSET
FE 1414 / Dec '94 / Folk Era

☐ RISISNG IN LOVE
FE 1410 / Dec '94 / Folk Era

Roth, David Lee

☐ BEST OF DAVID LEE ROTH, THE
Don't piss me off / Yankee rose / A lil' ain't enough / Just like paradise / Big train / Big trouble / It's showtime / Hot dog and a shake / Skyscraper / Shyboy / She's my machine / Stand up / Tobacco road / Easy street / California girls / Lust a gigolo/I ain't got nobody / Sensible shoes / Goin' crazy / Ladies nite in Buffalo / Land's edge
8122729412 / 3 Nov '97 / Warner Bros.

☐ CRAZY FROM THE HEAT
Easy Street / Just a gigolo / I ain't got nobody / California girls / Coconut grove
7599252222 / Jul '92 / WEA

☐ EAT 'EM AND SMILE
Yankee rose / Shy boy / I'm easy / Ladies nite in Buffalo / Goin' crazy / Tobacco Road / Elephant gun / Big trouble / Bump and grind / That's life
9254702 / Aug '86 / WEA

☐ SKYSCRAPER
Hot dog and a shake / Stand up / Hina / Perfect timing / Two fools a minute / Knucklebones / Just like paradise / Bottom line / Skyscraper / Damn good / California girls / Just a gigolo
9258242 / Jan '89 / WEA

Roth, Uli John

☐ ELECTRIC SUN - RETROSPECTIVE VOL.1 (Earthquake)
992215 / 13 Apr '98 / Event

☐ ELECTRIC SUN - RETROSPECTIVE VOL.2 (Firewind)
922216 / 13 Apr '98 / Event

☐ ULI JOHN ROTH (3CD Set)
DTKBOX 71 / 1 Jun '98 / Dressed To Kill

Rothberg, Patti

☐ BETWEEN THE 1 AND THE 9
Flicker / Inside / This one's mine / Treat me like dirt / Looking for a girl / Forgive me / Up against the wall / Perfect stranger / Out of my mind / Change your ways / Remembering tonight / It's alright
CDCHR 6114 / Sep '96 / Chrysalis

Rothemburg, Dave

☐ UNAMUNO
FY 7006CD / Dec '97 / Robi Droli

Rothenberg, Ned

☐ POWER LINES
804762 / Jan '96 / New World

Rothenberg/Boone/Velez

☐ ON THE CLIFFS OF THE HEART
NT 6744 / Aug '96 / New Tone

Rother, Michael

☐ CHRONICLES VOL.1
CLP 184 / 20 Apr '98 / Purple Pyramid

Rotterdam Conservatory Charanga Orchestra

☐ CUBA - THE CHARANGA
Badas de Oro / Reina Isabel / Lindas Cubanos / El barbero de Sevilla / La flauta magica / Angoa / El niche / La mora / El que mas goza / Fefita / Masacre / La enganadora
NI 5528 / Oct '97 / Nimbus

Rotterdam Conservatory Orquesta Tipica

☐ CUBA - CONTRADANZAS & DANZONES
Las Alturas de Simpson / Los Ojos de Pepa / Ya esta el cafe, o me voy a la Aplandora / La Tedezco / Cadete constitucional / El Panuelo de Pepa / Almendra / Ayes del Alma / San Pascual Bailon / Yo no bailo mas Catalina / El Dedo de Landaluce / Three Rigadones from Le Grande Duchesse / El Sungambelo / El Bombin de Barreto / Pero por que / Milicianos en New York / Two danzas
NI 5502 / Nov '96 / Nimbus

Rotterdam Terror Corps

☐ FROM DUSK TILL DAWN
MR 009 / 10 Jun '98 / Megarave

Rotting Christ

☐ THY MIGHTY CONTRACT
CM 77196CD / 10 Nov '97 / Century Media

☐ TRIARCHY OF THE LOST LOVERS
CM 77128CD / May '96 / Nuclear Blast

Rotundo, Francisco

☐ EL VIEJO VALS
BMT 004 / Feb '97 / Blue Moon

Rough Cut

☐ COME OUT
Almighty / Gun shot / Physically fit / Phoo jah / Ghetto livin' / Cool one / 100% pure love / Almighty space mix / Come out / Ghetto livin' / Bubble and wine / Cool one / Baby girl
ZD 11CD / Mar '97 / Zip Dog

Rough 'n' Tumble

☐ ROUGH 'N' ROLL
PT 614001 / Jun '96 / Part

Rough Red

☐ BETTER RED THAN DEAD
Flying Dutchman's Inn / Sailor's life / Stand and deliver / Lady on the wire / Backstage desperado / Innocent victim / Long train running / Sea song / Man on the land / Cause we were lovers / Way to liberty / I don't like these tears / Night train
SW 98003 / 27 Jul '98 / Streetwise

Rough Silk

☐ CIRCLE OF PAIN
MASSCD 115 / Jan '97 / Massacre

☐ MEPHISTO
MASSCD 144 / 24 Nov '97 / Massacre

Rough Trade

☐ ROUGHEST TRADE
Crimes of passion / All touch / Lie back and let me do everything / Weapons / Birds of a feather / Grade B movie / Baptism of fire / High school confidential / Shaking the foundations / Territorial / America bad and beautiful
WKFMXD 43 / '86 / FM

Roulettes

☐ STAKES AND CHIPS
Bad time / What you gonna do / Settle down / Taste of honey / Find out the truth / I'll remember tonight / You don't love me / Stubborn kind of fellow / I hope he breaks your heart / I can't think of anyone else / Shake / Soon you'll be leaving me / Mebody / This little girl / Can you go / Tell tale tit / Long cigarette / Junk / Jackpot / Yesterday, today and tomorrow / Tracks of my tears / I can't stop
BGOCD 130 / Apr '92 / Beat Goes On

Roupe

☐ ENTELCHY
CDRE 02 / Feb '97 / Resource

☐ STROM
INMCD 002 / Mar '95 / GPR

Rouse, Charlie

☐ BRAZIL
ADC 11 / 23 Mar '98 / Douglas Music

☐ CINNAMON FLOWER
RCD 10053 / '91 / Rykodisc

☐ EPISTROPHY
Nutty / Blue monk / Epistrophy / Ruby my dear / 'Round midnight
LCD 15212 / Jun '89 / Landmark

☐ LES JAZZ MODES
BCD 134/135 / Aug '95 / Biograph

☐ MOMENT'S NOTICE (Rouse, Charlie Quartet)
Clucker / Let me / Joobobie / Well you needn't / Royal love / Child is born / Little sherri / Royal love / Clucker
STCD 8268 / Oct '97 / Storyville

Rouse, Josh

☐ DRESSED UP LIKE NEBRASKA
Suburban sweetheart / Dressed up like Nebraska / Invisible / Late night conversation / Flair / White trash period of my life / Simple thing / Woman lost in serious problems / Lavina / Reminiscent
SRRCD 036 / 27 Apr '98 / Slow River

Rouse, Mikel

☐ DENNIS CLEVELAND
NW 80506 / Dec '96 / New World

☐ WALK IN THE WOODS (Rouse, Mikel & Broken Consort)
MTM 6CD / Sep '88 / Made To Measure

Roussos, Demis

☐ ADAGIO
Morning has broken / Tous les je vous aime / Oxygen / Too many dreams / Les mots qui font peur / Adagio / Italian song / Take me home / Spleen / Sergueii
QED 222 / Nov '96 / Tring

☐ ADAGIO
Morning has broken / Tous les je vous aime / Oxygen / Too many dreams / Les mots qui font peu / Adagio / Italian song / Take me home / Spleen / Sergueii
100122 / May '97 / A-Play Collection

☐ CHRISTMAS ALBUM
Kyrieeleis / O come all ye faithful (adeste fidelis) / When a child is born / Il est ne le divin enfant / Hark the herald angels sing / Little drummer boy / Es ist ein' rose entsprungen / Ave maria / Silent night / What child is this / Mary's boy child / Gloria in excelsis deo / Petit papa noel / Minuit chretien / First Noel / Amazing grace / Jerusalem of gold / Glory glory hallelujah
3036001192 / 15 Sep '97 / Carlton

☐ DIAMOND COLLECTION, THE
602144 / Feb '97 / Arcade

☐ FAVOURITE RARITIES
RA 95012 / Sep '94 / BR Music

☐ GOODBYE MY LOVE (2CD Set)
Rain and tears / End of the world / I want to live / Marie jolie / It's five o'clock / Spring summer winter and fall / Break / We shall dance / My reason / Forever and ever / Goodbye my love goodbye / My friend the wind / Lovely lady of Arcadia / Island of love / Summerwine: *Roussos, Demis & Nancy Boyd* / Summer in her eyes / Tropicana bay: *Roussos, Demis & Nancy Boyd* / In my dreams / Bridge over troubled water / Let it be me / Nature boy / Because / Anytime at all / I miss you / Sung da de di / Where is your love today / Fly away with me / Friends of a lifetime / Think it over / One that I loved / Smiling eyes / Rain and tears
BS 81052 / Nov '97 / BR Music

☐ GREEK, THE
Le grec / Spleen / Beauty of your eyes / Apres la fin du monde / Prier / Tout ce que je cherche est en toi / Comme le vent d'hier / Futureless forever / Quand je t'aime / Moon and I / Time / Dance of love / My song of love / On ecrit sur les murs (graffiti) / Amico sincero / Qui plus que mol / Petite fille / Wanna die the way I love you / Young love
BR 1292 / May '94 / BR Music

☐ LES INOUBLIABLES DE...
472303 / Feb '97 / Flarenasch

☐ LOST IN LOVE
Happy to be an island in the sun / Forever and ever / Can't say how much I love you / When forever has gone / Goodbye my love goodbye / My reason / Lost in love / I just don't know what to do with myself / Lost in a dream / Velvet mornings / Midnight is the time I need you / Gypsy lady / Senora (I need you) / Cancion de boda (The wedding song)
5500692 / May '93 / Spectrum

☐ MORNING HAS BROKEN
Morning has broken / Oxygen / Adagio / Les mots qui font peur / Italian song / Take me home / Tous lee 'je vous aime' / Spleen (Baudelaire) / Too many dreams / Sergueii
305582 / Oct '96 / Hallmark

Route 66

☐ ROUTE 66
I'm moving out / You know I need you / It's not over / Black and white / I know it's not true / I'm not a punk / Keep on trying / Boys with mascara / You need affection / It's hard (a Trogg story) / It ain't nice / It's not over / I can tell / How do you feel right now / Did you / I like what I am / Give or fake / I just can't wait much longer / Cement garden / Give or fake / Always makin' time
SPJCD 005 / 22 Apr '98 / Angel Air

Routine

☐ ROUTINE
99 2147 / Jul '96 / Ninetynine

Rova

☐ JOHN COLTRANE'S ASCENSION
1201802 / Mar '97 / Black Saint

☐ WORKS VOL.1, THE
1201762 / Sep '95 / Black Saint

☐ WORKS VOL.2, THE
1201862 / Aug '97 / Black Saint

Rova Saxophone Quartet

☐ CHANTING THE LIGHT OF FORESIGHT
NA 064 / May '94 / New Albion

☐ CROWD, THE (Rova)
ARTCD 6098 / Apr '92 / Hat Art

☐ FROM THE BUREAU OF BOTH
1201352 / Apr '93 / Black Saint

☐ SAXOPHONE DIPLOMACY (Rova)
ARTCD 6068 / Nov '91 / Hat Art

☐ THIS TIME WE ARE BOTH
NA 041 / Aug '91 / New Albion

Row, Porter

☐ FREE 'N' EASY
FRCD 032 / Oct '94 / Foam

Rowallan Consort

☐ NOTES OF JOY
COMD 2058 / Feb '95 / Temple

Rowan, Peter

☐ ALL ON A RISING DAY
Midnight highway / Last train / Howlin' at the moon / Mr. Time clock / Behind these prison walls of love / Deal with the devil / Undying love / Wheel of fortune / All on a rising day / Freedom walkabout / Prayer of a homeless wanderer / John O'Dreams
SHCD 3791 / Oct '94 / Sugar Hill

☐ AWAKE ME IN THE NEW WORLD
Shaman's vision / Dreams of the sea / Pulcinella sails away / Caribbean woman / Dance with no shoes / Sugarcane / For Gods, for Kings and for gold / Awake me in the new world / All my relations / Remember that I love you / Maria de las Rosas / African banjo / Sailing home dance of Pulcinella
SHCD 3807 / May '93 / Sugar Hill

☐ BLUEGRASS BOY
Night time / Wild geese cry again / Jealous heart and a worried mind / Will work for food / Stable boy blues / Green willow / Let the harvest go to seed / Ruby ridge / Pretty little blanco river waltz / Weep not for the dead / Pure white sail / Bluegrass boy
SHCD 3859 / Mar '98 / Sugar Hill

☐ DUST BOWL CHILDREN
Dust bowl children / Before the streets were paved / Electric blanket / Little mother / Barefoot country road / Seeds my daddy sowed / Tumbleweed / Dream of a home / Rainmaker
SHCD 3781 / Jul '90 / Sugar Hill

☐ FIRST WHIPPOORWILL, THE
I'm on my way back to the old home / I'm just a used to be / I believed in you darling / Sweetheart you done me wrong / When the golden leaves begin to fall / I was left on the street / Goodbye old pal / When you are lonely / First whipperwill / Sitting alone in the moonlight / Boat of love / It's mighty dark to travel
SHCD 3749 / Jul '93 / Sugar Hill

☐ MEDICINE TRAIL
Riding high in Texas / My foolish pride / River of stone / Revelation / Lying on the line / Medicine trail / Blues come bother me / Dreaming I love you / Maui momma / Prairie lullabye
FF 70205 / Sep '96 / Flying Fish

☐ NEW MOON RISING (Rowan, Peter & The Nashville Bluegrass Band)
That high lonesome sound / Trail of tears / Memories of you / Moth to a flame / I'm gonna love you / One way / New moon rising / Jesus made the wine / Cabin of love / Meadow green
SHCD 3762 / Nov '94 / Sugar Hill

☐ PETER ROWAN AND RED HOT PICKERS (Rowan, Peter & The Red Hot Pickers)
Hobo song / Old old house / Willow garden / Jimmie Brown the newsboy / Wild Billy Jones / Hiroshima mon amour / Come ye tender hearted / Oh Susanna / Rosalie McFall / Good woman's love
SHCD 3733 / Dec '95 / Sugar Hill

☐ TREE ON A HILL (Rowan Brothers)
SHCD 2823 / Jun '94 / Sugar Hill

☐ WALLS OF TIME
Roving gambler / Lone pilgrim / Raglan Road / Going up the mountain / Casey's last ride / Moonshiner / Thirsty in the rain / Walls of time / Plains of waterloo / Hiroshima mon amour / Old old house / Willow garden
SHCD 3722 / Oct '96 / Sugar Hill

☐ WILD STALLIONS
APCD 016 / Apr '94 / Appaloosa

Rowe, Carlyle

☐ DARLING
DTCD 27 / Nov '96 / Discotex

Rowe, Keith

☐ DIMENSION OF PERFECTLY ORDINARY, A
MR 19 / '90 / Matchless

Rowland, Dennis

☐ GET HERE
Circle dance / Detour head / I don't care who knows (baby I'm yours) / Comeback / Autumn in New York / Get here / Don't you know I care / Things have got to change / I've grown accustomed to her face / Waiting for love / I think it's going to rain roday
CCD 4693 / May '96 / Concord Jazz

☐ NOW DIG THIS
All blues / My ship / I could write a book / Easy living / Someday my prince will come / 'Round midnight / You don't know love is / Pfrancing (no blues) / Meaning of the blues/Lament
CCD 47512 / Aug '97 / Concord Jazz

Rowland, Mike

☐ MYSTIC ANGEL
CD 285 / 6 Jul '98 / New World

Rowles, Jimmy

☐ PEACOCKS (Rowles, Jimmy & Michael Hashim)
STB 2511 / Sep '95 / Stash

☐ REMEMBER WHEN
Oh lady be good / Peacocks / Things are looking up / Outsity / Come Sunday / Let's fall in love / Remember when / Just like a butterfly / Grooveyard
CDCHE 11 / Oct '91 / Master Mix

☐ SUBTLE LEGEND VOL.1
Devastating cherub / Limehouse blues / Now that you're gone / Some other spring / Jitterbug waltz / Tell it like it is / Do you know why the stars come out at night / Looking at you / Sweet Lorraine / Devil's island / Humoresque / Isfahan / Ballad of Thelonius Monk
STCD 8287 / Jun '98 / Storyville

Rowsome, Leo

☐ CLASSICS OF IRISH PIPING VOL.1
Boil the breakfast early/Heather breeze / Savoureen deelish/Clare's dragoons / Blackbird / St. Patrick's day / Boolavogue/Old Bog road / Boys of Wexford/ Kelly the boy from Killane / Rights of man/Wexford/ Dunphy's hornpipe / Broom/Star of Munster/ Milliner's daughter / Collier's reel/The maid of Tramore / Independent hornpipe/The star hornpipe / Frieze breeches / Tomorrow morning/Cloone hornpipe / Cook in the kitchen/Rakes of kildare / Sweep's hornpipe/The friendly visit / Jockey to the fair / My darling asleep/Tongues of fire / Higgin's hornpipe/The queen of May / Fairie's revels/I won't be a nun / Shandon bells/Haste, to the wedding / Rocky road to Dublin
TSCD 471 / Sep '93 / Topic

Rox Diamond

☐ ROX DIAMOND
Heart of mine / Nothin' I won't do / Familiar strangers / Never too late / Forever yours / Get the lead out (of my heart) / You're not the only one / Lovin' you / One way street / Face to face / You'll get what's coming
CDATV 25 / Jul '92 / Active

Roxette

☐ CRASH, BOOM, BANG
Harleys and Indians (riders in the sky) / Crash boom bang / Fireworks / Run to you / Sleeping in my car / Vulnerable / First girl on the moon / Place your love / I love the sound of crashing guitars / What's she like / Do you wanna go the whole way / Lies / I'm sorry / Love is all (shine your light on me) / Go to sleep
CDEMD 1056 / Apr '94 / EMI

☐ DON'T BORE US, GET TO THE CHORUS
June afternoon / You don't understand me / Look / Dressed for success / Listen to your heart / Dangerous / It must have been love / Joyride / Fading like a flower / Big L / Spending my time / How do you do / Almost unreal / Sleeping in my car / Crash boom bang / Vulnerable / She doesn't live here anymore / I don't want to get hurt
CDEMTV 98 / Oct '95 / EMI

☐ JOYRIDE
Joyride / Hotblooded / Fading like a flower (every time you leave) / Knockin' on every door / Spending my time / I remember you / Watercolours in the rain / Big L / Soul deep / (Do you get) excited / Church of your heart / Small talk / Physical fascination / Things will never be the same / Perfect day
CDEMD 1019 / Mar '91 / EMI

☐ LOOK SHARP
Look / Dressed for success / Sleeping single / Paint / Dance away / Cry / Chances / Dangerous / Half a woman, half a shadow / View from a hill / I could never give you up / Shadow of a doubt / Listen to your heart
CDEMC 3557 / Apr '89 / EMI

☐ PEARLS OF PASSION
Soul deep / Secrets thats she keeps / Goodbye to you / Call your name / Surrender / Voices / Neverending love / Call of the wild / Joy of a toy / From one heart to another / Like lovers do / So far away / Pearls of passion / It must have been love / Turn to me / Neverending love / Secrets that she keeps / I call your name / Neverending love / I call your name
8361962 / 27 Oct '97 / EMI

Roxxi

☐ DRIVE IT TO YA HARD
RH 1491 / May '91 / FM

Roxy Music

☐ AVALON
More than this / Space between / India / While my heart is still beating / Main thing / Take a chance with me / Avalon / To turn you on / True to life / Tara
EGCD 50 / Apr '92 / EG

☐ AVALON/FLESH AND BLOOD/ MANIFESTO (3CD Set)
TPAK 34 / Oct '94 / Virgin

☐ CONCERT CLASSICS
Manifesto / Angel eyes / Trash / Out of the blue / Song for Europe / Still falls the rain / Ain't that so / Stronger than the years / Ladytron / In every dream home a heartache / Love is the drug / Do the strand / Re make/re model
CRANCH 2 / 15 Jun '98 / Ranch Life

☐ COUNTRY LIFE
Thrill of it all / Three and nine / All I want is you / Out of the blue / If it takes all night / Bittersweet / Triptych / Casanova / Really good time / Prairie rose
EGCD 16 / Jan '87 / EG

☐ FLESH AND BLOOD
In the midnight hour / Oh yeah / Same old scene / Flesh and blood / My only love / Over you / Eight miles high / Rain rain rain / Running wild / No strange delight
EGCD 46 / Sep '91 / EG

☐ FOR YOUR PLEASURE
Do the Strand / Beauty Queen / Strictly confidential / Editions of you / In every dream home a heartache / Bogus man / Grey lagoons / For your pleasure
EGCD 8 / Sep '91 / EG

☐ HEART STILL BEATING (LIVE)
India / Can't let go / While my heart is still beating / Out of the blue / Dance away / Impossible guitar / Song for Europe / Love is the drug / Like a hurricane / My only love / Both ends burning / Avalon / Editions of you / Jealous guy
EGCD 77 / Oct '90 / EG

☐ MANIFESTO
Ain't that so / Cry cry cry / Dance away / Manifesto / My little girl / Spin me round / Still falls the rain / Trash / Stronger through the years
EGCD 38 / Sep '91 / EG

☐ ROXY MUSIC
Bitters end / Bob medley / Chance meeting / If there is something / Ladytron / Re-make/Re-model / 2HB / Would you believe / Sea breezes
EGCD 6 / Sep '91 / EG

☐ STRANDED
Street life / Just like you / Amazon / Psalm / Serenade / Song for Europe / Mother of pearl / Sunset
EGCD 10 / Sep '91 / EG

☐ THRILL OF IT ALL, THE (Roxy Music 1972-1982/4CD Set)
Re-make/Re-model / Ladytron / If there is something / 2HB / Chance meeting / Sea breezes / Do the Strand / Beauty Queen / Strictly confidential / Editions of you / In every dream home a heartache / Bogus man / For your pleasure / Street life / Just like you / Amazona / Song for Europe / Mother of pearl / Sunset / Thrill of it all / Three and nine / All I want is you / Out of the blue / Bitter sweet / Casanova / Really good time / Prairie Rose / Love is the drug / Sentimental fool / Could it happen to me / Both ends burning / Just another high / Manifesto / Trash / Angel eyes / Stronger through the years / Ain't that so / Dance away / Oh yeah / Same old scene / Flesh and blood / My only love / Over you / No strange delight / More than this / Avalon / While my heart is still beating / Take a chance with me / To turn you on / Tara / Virginia Plain / Numberer / Pyjamarama / Pride and the pain / Manifesto (remake) / Hula kula / Trash 2 / Your application's failed / Lover / Sultanesque / Dance away (remix) / South Downs / Always unknowing / Main thing / India / Jealous guy
CDBOX 5 / Nov '95 / Virgin

☐ VIVA ROXY MUSIC
Out of the blue / Pyjamarama / Bogus man / Chance meeting / If there is something / In every dream home a heartache / Do the Strand / Can't let go / My only love / Like a hurricane / Jealous guy
EGCD 25 / Sep '91 / EG

Roy C

☐ SHOTGUN WEDDING
Shotgun wedding / I'm gonna make it / I want to be where you are / She's gone (she took the TV and telephone) / Medley / To make you feel like a woman / Leaving on the morning train / I'm not going to eat a thing / I'm still in love with you / Love me til tomorrow / Second time around / I want to marry you / That's when I'll take you home / Rock me all night / Since I met you baby / Pick up the pieces / Love crazy / Somebody's right / Peepin' through the window / I keep holding on
NEMCD 764 / Jul '97 / Sequel

Roy, Freddie

☐ TO LOVE SOMEBODY
FJ 3301CD / 8 Jun '98 / FJ

Roy, Harry

☐ DANCE BAND YEARS, THE (2CD Set) (Roy, Harry & His Band)
Wednesday night hop / Hut-Sut song / Sweet little sweetheart / And the angels sing / There goes that song again / Corn silk / Big noise from Winnetka / Shake down the stars / Chica chica boom chic / Lilacs in the rain / Oh you crazy moon / Begin the beguine / It's funny to everyone but me / Struttin' with some barbecue / Gaucho serenade / Rosita / Drummer boy / There's a little Irish Colleen / On Broadway / They can't black out the moon / Why doesn't somebody tell me these things / Back to back / Keep an eye on your heart / Tumbling tumbleweeds / Comin' thro' the rye / Tzigane swing / Lady likes to love / Tavern in the town / No name rag / Two lovely people / Waitin' for the train to come in / Man and his drum / What will I tell my heart / Booglie wooglie piggy / My last year's gal / I can't give you anything but love / That lovely weekend / It's always you / Kindergarten conga / Stepping out at midnight / Basin Street call / Mama, that moon is here again / Lady who didn't believe in love / Kiss me hello / Home again blues / Dark town strutters ball / Chattanooga choo choo / Here you are / There are such things / Bugle call rag
PDSCD 551 / 13 Oct '97 / Pulse

☐ GREETINGS FROM YOU
Tangerine / Hold your hats on / Oh the pity of it all / Humpty Dumpty heart / When I love I love / Was it love / Sentimental interlude / You bring the boogie woogie out in me / Greetings from you / Zoot suit / Do you care / When daddy comes home / Darling Daisy / Elmer's tune / Madelaine / Chattanooga choo choo / Tica ti tica ta / It's funny to everyone but me / In the middle of a dance / Blues in the night / Green eyes / Shrine of St. Cecilia
RAJCD 803 / May '97 / Empress

☐ HARRY ROY
Tiger rag / Canadian capers / Who walks in when I walk out / If I can't have Anna in Cuba / When I told the village belle / Campesina / Ever so quiet / Every time I look at you / Bugle call rag / Mr. Magician / My dog love's your dog / Nasty man / Harry Roy's new stage show / Valentina / Becky, play your violin / World is so small / Coconut oil (mama don't want)
PASTCD 9741 / Sep '91 / Flapper

☐ HARRY ROY AND HIS ORCHESTRA (Roy, Harry & His Orchestra)
Bugle call rag / Alexander's ragtime band / 12th Street rag / Somebody stole my gal / Roy rag / Keep young and beautiful / Emaline / My last year's gal / Waiting for tomorrow and you / Tiger rag / Chinatown, my Chinatown / I've got my love to keep me warm / You've got me crying again / Snowball / Sing another line / When it's darkness on the night / I was in the mood / Let's swing it / Me, myself and I / Back to back / You're a sweetheart / Here comes the sandman / This year's kisses / Bom di bom / Nobody's sweetheart / She had to go and lose it at the Astor
CDMFP 6361 / Jun '97 / Music For Pleasure

□ KING OF HOT-CHA, THE (Roy, Harry & His Orchestra)
Bugle call rag / Chinatown my Chinatown / Cuban Pete / La Cucaracha / Goody goodbye / Goosey goosey / Heigh-ho / Hot time in town / I want the waiter with the water / King Porter stomp / Let's have a jubilee / Lullaby of Broadway / Maple leaf rag / My girl's a rhythm fan / No name rag / Red pepper / Roy rag / Sarawaki / That's a plenty / That's the way I like to hear you talk / What a difference a day made / Where did Robinson Crusoe go / You made me care
CDAJA 5225 / Aug '97 / Living Era

□ SHOOT THAT TIGER
Medley / Goody goody / Diddle dum dee / Man from Harlem / Chinatown my Chinatown / Limehouse blues / Casa loma stomp / Fox medley / Is it true what they say about Dixie / Cuban Pete / Nobody's sweetheart / Bugle call rag / Tiger rag / Canadian capers / Gershwin medley / Let's call the wole thing off / They can't take that away from me / Rita the rumba / Boo hoo / Sing baby sing / Bye bye baby / Where did Robinson Crusoe go with Friday on a Saturday night / Harry Roy stage show medley / Alone / Intro / Sarawacki / St. Louis blues / Piano madness / Somebody stole my gal
CDEA 6001 / Aug '97 / Vocalion

□ THAT OLD FEELING
Stay as sweet as you are / My old flame Johnston / I'm on a see-saw / Cuban Pete / Is it true what they say about Dixie / And the angels sing / Three little fishes / Boo hoo / That old feeling / A-tisket a-tasket / Comin' thro the rye / Bei mir bist du schon / She's tall she's tan she's terrific / Night is filled with music / Yam / Tavern in the town / There's a little Irish coleen on Broadway / Nice work if you can get it / Mama that moon is here again / You can't stop me from dreaming / Highland swing / Goodnight children everywhere
SWNCD 013 / Sep '97 / Sound Waves

Roy, Larry

□ QUARTER TO THREE (Roy, Larry & Marilyn Lerner)
JTR 84372 / Oct '92 / Justin Time

Roy, Stephane

□ KALEIDOS
IMED 96 / Jun '97 / Diffunzioni Musicali

Roy, William

□ WHEN I SING ALONE
ACD 213 / Nov '96 / Audiophile

Royal Air Force

□ 70 YEARS (Royal Air Force Central Band)
Brave defenders / Royal Air Force march past / Spitfire prelude and fugue / Lawrence of Arabia / Four caballeros / TV sports themes / Oor Wullie / Fanfare on the RAF call / March and dance of the comedians / Little light music / Viva musica / Introduction and march from the Battle Of Britain / Those magnificent men in their flying machines / Concert march- Cockleshell heroes / Elegy / March: Uxbridge
BNA 5009 / Jun '87 / Bandleader

□ AD ASTRA (Band Of The RAF)
BNA 5142 / 13 Apr '98 / Bandleader

□ BIG BAND SPECTACULAR (Royal Air Force Squadronaires Band)
There's something in the air / Lover / Splanky / John Brown's other body / Stardust / Doin' Basie's thing / Autumn leaves / Sweet Georgia Brown / Glenn Miller Medley / In the mood / Little brown jug / String of pearls / Moonlight serenade / St. Louis blues march / Song of India / All the things you are / Captiva sound / That warm feeling / South Rampart Street Parade / Switch in time / Pennsylvania 6-5000 / Scott's place / Basie straight ahead / Bedtime for drums / Sounds familiar
BNA 5007 / Jun '87 / Bandleader

□ BRANDENBURG GATE (Band Of The RAF Germany)
Under the double eagle / Hoch und deutschmeister / Old comrades / Berliner luft / Celebration march / Colonel Bogey / Buck private / Bridge too far / Marche des parachutistes belges / BB and CF / Black adder / Entrance of the court / Auf der alm / Plaisir d'amour / Swiss miss / Suite Francaise / Brandenburg gate / Night flight to Madrid / Armenian dances
BNA 5046 / '91 / Bandleader

□ CELEBRATION (Staff Band Of WRAC)
ATS March / Preludium and fugue / Nimrod / Last past and reveille / Jubilant prelude / Crown imperial / Colonel Bogey / Twin eagle strut / Songs of World War Two / Auld lang syne / Furchtlos und treu / Clarinet carousel / Cornet carillon / Where no man has gone before / You needed me / Lassus trombone / Sabre dance / Tyrolean tuba / Living in the UK / Stage centre / WRAC March
BNA 5036 / '91 / Bandleader

□ CHRISTMAS CELEBRATION (Central Band Of The Royal Air Force/St. Clemant Danes Choir)
O come all ye faithful (adeste fidelis) / Whence is this goodly fragrance / Away in a manger / Twelve days of Christmas / Christians awake / Sussex mummers carol / It came upon a midnight clear / Christmas bells / In the bleak mid-Winter / Mary had a baby, yes Lord / Three Christmas carols / Sussex carol / Carol fantasy / O little one sweet / Carol of the drum / We three Kings / Hark, the herald angels sing
QMPR 603D / Oct '97 / Polyphonic

□ FESTIVAL OF MUSIC 1987, A (Massed Bands Of The Royal Air Force)
Fanfare and National Anthem / Jaguar / Marvin Hamlish showcase / Trumpet concerto-3rd movement (Hadyn) / Those magnificent men in their flying machines / Eleanor Rigby / Overture: Prince Igor / Marching with Sousa / Pines of the Appian Way
QPRM 112D / Oct '97 / Polyphonic

□ FESTIVAL OF MUSIC 1988, A (Massed Bands Of The Royal Air Force)
Flying Dutchman / Trumpet blus and cantabile / Nimrod / Slaughter on 10th Avenue / Procession of the nobles / Prelude on three / Welsh hymn tunes / Year of the dragon
QPRM 113D / Oct '97 / Polyphonic

□ FESTIVAL OF MUSIC 1989, A (Massed Bands Of The Royal Air Force)
Air crew on parade / Rhapsody in blue / Air of freedom / Phantom of the opera / Battle of Britain / Hampton Court / English dances / In the mood / Nightingale sang in Berkeley Square / After you've gone / To the few
QPRM 114D / Oct '97 / Polyphonic

□ FESTIVAL OF MUSIC 1991, A (Massed Bands Of The Royal Air Force)
Fanfare of the Royal Air Force call / Yorkshire overture / Buffoonery / Four Scottish dances / Sword and the crown / Fanfare and processional / Queen Alexandra / Stars and stripes for ever / Blues skies / Foggy day / Welsh rhapsody / Stardust / Film music of Miklos Rozsa / Evening hymn / Last poet and sunset
QPRM 117D / Oct '97 / Polyphonic

□ FESTIVAL OF MUSIC 1992, A (Massed Bands Of The Royal Air Force)
QPRM 119D / Oct '97 / Polyphonic

□ FESTIVAL OF MUSIC 1994, A (Massed Bands Of The Royal Air Force)
Fanfare for the common man / March of friendship / Time piece / African symphony / Weber / Second concerto for clarinet / Travelogue / Big country / European excursion / Sahra omania / 1812 Overture
QPRM 122D / Oct '97 / Polyphonic

□ FESTIVAL OF MUSIC 1995, A (A Victory Salute) (Massed Bands Of The Royal Air Force)
633 Squadron / Dawn flight / Great escape / O mio babbino caro / Foggy day / My funny valentine / Armenian dance / Love changes everything / Global variations / Riverdance / Anthem / 76 trombones / Think of me / Malaguena / Songs of World War II / Dambusters march / Nimrod / Evening hymn and sunset / Royal Air Force march past
QPRM 123D / Oct '97 / Polyphonic

□ FESTIVAL OF MUSIC 1996, A (Massed Bands Of The Royal Air Force)
Spitfire prelude and fugue / Those magnificent men in their flying machines / Tribute to Al Bowlly / Mr. Jums / Jewel song from Faust / 633 squadron / Birdland / Tico tico / All I ask of you / In the mood / Tis the last rose of summer / Kings go forth / Dambusters march / Royal Air Force march past
QPRM 125D / Oct '97 / Polyphonic

□ GRAND PARADE (Royal Air Force Central Band)
Tiger squadron / Mad major / March of the bowmen / Pathfinder's march / Touchdown / March: The love of three oranges / Flight of the tees / Grand parade / Oak and the ash / Black Hole / March: Things to come / Spirals / Adagio / Detectives - Hill Street Blues / Kojak / Cagney and Lacey / Dempsey and makepeace
BNA 5028 / '88 / Bandleader

□ GREAT BRITISH MUSIC FOR WIND BAND VOL.1 (Western Band Of The RAF)
James Cook / Circumnavigator / Countdown / Theatre of music / Swiss festival overture / Christmas suite / All afoot / Music for a festival
QPRM 115D / Oct '97 / Polyphonic

□ HEROES OF THE AIR (Royal Air Force Central Band)
Battle of Britain suite (Walton) / Spitfire prelude and fugue / Conquest of the air / Battle of Britain suite (Josephs) / Coastal command
CDPR 500 / Jul '92 / Premier/MFP

□ MARCHES OF THE ROYAL AIR FORCE (Royal Air Force Central Band)
Royal Air Force March past / Jolly airman / Aircrew on parade / High flight / Skywatch / Flying review / With pomp and pride / Strike command march past / Tornado / Aces high / Royal air force college march / Songs of the early airmen / Acorn / Call to adventure / Royal Air Force Association march / Newcomers / Militant miss / Skywriter / Keepers of the peace / Radio / Jaguar / Holyrood / Per ardua ad astra / Grand march 'RAF'
BNA 5037 / Apr '95 / Bandleader

□ MARCHING THROUGH THE 20TH CENTURY (Band Of The Royal Air Force College Cranwell)
It's a long long way to tipperary / Pack up your troubles / Dunedin / Colonel bogey / Calling all workers (music while you work) / St. louis blues march / Arromanches / Pomp and circumstance march no. 1 (elgar) / Stars and stripes forever / Crown imperial (walton) / Holyrood / Skywards / Cranwell / Lincolnshire poacher / Raf college march / R.a.f. march past / Knightsbridge / 633 squadron / Dam busters march (coates) / Pathfinders / Things to come
BNA 5103 / Mar '94 / Bandleader

□ MASSED BANDS OF THE RAF
Fantasy of RAF call / Knights of the air / Spitfire prelude / Bugler's holiday / Skyliner / Cheek to cheek / Conquest of the air / Flute concerto / Coastal command / Call of the trumpet / Dam busters march / Cavalry of the clouds / Colditz march / Clarinet candy / Battle for freedom / Salute to Britsh songs (medley) / Pathfinder's march / Reach for the sky / RAF march past
QPRM 121D / Oct '97 / Polyphonic

□ MIGHTY VOICE, THE (Central Band of The Royal Air Force)
Sinfonietta no.2 / Old English suite / Pantomime / Delta dances / River song / Ragtime / New Orleans / Negro spiritual / Mountain song / Mighty voice
QPRM 124D / Oct '97 / Polyphonic

□ RAF HQ BOMBER COMMAND SEXTET 1943-1944 (RAF HQ Bomber Command Sextet)
Clarinet marmalade / Rug cutter's swing / Washboard blues / Woo woo / At sundown / Squatty roo / Buddy's blues / Muskrat ramble / Christopher Columbus / Sweet Georgia Brown / 295 jump / Heartbreak blues / Jamboree jive / Low down empty railway station blues / King Porter stomp / Big noise from Winnetka / Ain't cha got music / Stevedore stomp / Ain't misbehavin' / One o'clock jump / It's the talk of the town / How am I to know / I wish I were twins / Soft winds
CYCD 74508 / Feb '97 / Celebrity

□ REACH FOR THE SKY (Bands Of The Royal Air Force)
MU 5007 / Oct '92 / Musketeer

□ SWING SQUADRON (Royal Air Force Squadronaires Band)
There's something in the air / Opus 1 / Satin doll / Sheikh of Araby / Body and soul / Volando / String of pearls / When the squads go marching in / I've got my love to keep me warm / Beyond the bar / In the mood / Wind machine / Swing squadron / Here's that rainy day / Best blue / Bones away / Li'l darlin' / Flying home
BNA 5043 / '91 / Bandleader

□ SWORD AND THE CROWN, THE (Central Band of The Royal Air Force)
A pittsburgh overture / A pittsburgh overture / Ballad for band / On stanton moor (a derbyshire suite) / Cat and the fiddle (a derbyshire suite) / Lord musgrave's dining room / Well dressing (a derbyshire suite) / Celebration
QPRM 120D / Oct '97 / Polyphonic

□ TRIBUTE TO THE FEW (Massed Bands Of The Royal Air Force)
QPRM 116D / Oct '97 / Polyphonic

Royal Artillery

□ CALL FOR THE GUNS (Royal Artillery Band)
Call for the guns / Overture- The force of destiny / Nocturne / Blaze away / Lucy Long / Washington post / Festive overture / Gymnopedie No.1 / March: la pere la victoire / March: Rapier / Selections from Barnum / Regimental quick march / Regimental slow march
BNA 5054 / Apr '91 / Bandleader

□ MARCHES FOR EUROPE (Royal Artillery Band)
BNA 5080 / Apr '93 / Bandleader

Royal, Billy Joe

□ BILLY JOE ROYAL
7567823272 / Jan '96 / Atlantic

□ DOWN IN THE BOONDOCKS
MMCD 5741 / Jun '92 / Mammoth

□ SPOTLIGHT ON BILLY JOE ROYAL
Down in the boondocks / Cherry Hill park / I knew you when / Up on the roof / On Broadway / Save the last dance for me / Stand by me / Hush / To love somebody / Tulsa / Campfire girls / I gotta be somebody / Raindrops keep falling on my head / Please come to Boston
HADCD 101 / Feb '94 / Javelin

Royal Choral Society

□ CAROL COLLECTION
Once in Royal David's City / In dulci jubilo / I saw three ships / Fist nowell / Holly and the ivy / O little town of Bethlehem / God rest ye merry gentlemen / Silent night / While shepherds watched their flocks by night / Good King Wenceslas / Bethlehem down / Coventry carol / O come all ye faithful (adeste fidelis) / Hark the herald angels sing
3036700022 / Oct '95 / Carlton

□ CHRISTMAS CAROLS
Welcome Yule / In dulci jubilo / Ding dong merrily on high / Zither carol / Hark the herald angels sing / Jesu word of God / Little David play on yo' harp / First Nowell / Hawaiian lullaby / Cowboy carol / Korean lullaby / All God's chillun / While shepherds watched / To a baby / Bethlehem / Adoramus te / Sing ye birds / Silent night, holy night / Cherry tree carol / Praise ye the Lord / Christmas day / Winter carol / Dark the night / O come all ye faithful (adeste fidelis) / Christmas is coming the geese are getting fat / Shepherds farewell
CDEA 5503 / Nov '97 / Dutton Laboratories

Royal Corps/Signals

□ SIGNALLER, THE (Band Of The Royal Corps Of Signals)
Regimental quick march / Begone dull care / Signaller / Swift and sure / Regimental slow march / HRH Princess Royal / On Richmond Hill bah'at / Donkey serenade / Lassus trombone / Vimy ridge / Master / Jubilee overture / Largo al factotum / Blandford suite / Nessun dorma / Rondo for horns / Carnival of Venice / Concerto for drum set / Farandole / History of the Royal Corps of Signals
BNA 5114 / Aug '95 / Bandleader

Royal Corps/Transport

□ CONCERT BANDSTAND (Band Of The Royal Corps Of Transport)
Wait for the wagon (regimental march) / Marche americaine / Ship to shore (march) / Bombasto (march) / Spanish march / 88th regiment (march) / Allegretto / Trumpet voluntary / Free and easy / Gypsy baron (overture) / Romance / Bourree / Au fond du temple saint (duet from 'the pearl fishers') (/ Music box dancer / El rancho grande / Sing, sing, sing / Carillon / Glad chatter (xylophone duet) / Napoleon galop / Trumpet by candlelight / Marinarella (overture)
BNA 5071 / Aug '92 / Bandleader

□ MUSIC FROM THE GREAT HORSE SHOWS (Staff Band Of The Royal Corps Of Transport)
Fanfare / Tribute to next milton / Trotting medley / Television horse show themes / Music for heavy horses / Interval music / Another show / Cantering medley / Hunters, the judging music / Hunting medley / Quadrille time / Tribute to the horse / Finale
BNA 5035 / '91 / Bandleader

Royal Crescent Mob

□ GOOD LUCKY KILLER
EMY 1432 / Sep '97 / Enemy

Royal Doulton Band

□ HYMNS FOR BAND
Praise my soul the king of heaven / Onward christian soldiers / King of love my shepherd is / Day thou gavest Lord is ended / All things bright and beautiful / Lord's my shepherd / Amazing grace / Immortal, invisible, God only wise / Holy city / Now the day is over / He who would valiant be / All people that on earth do dwell / Old rugged cross / Now thank we all our God / Ave Maria / O praise ye the lord / Let us with a gladsome mind / Abide with me / Jerusalem / How sweet the name of Jesus sounds
BNA 5008 / Jul '87 / Bandleader

□ HYMNS FOR BAND VOL.2
Holy holy holy / Glorious things of thee are spoken / Therr is a green hill far away / Dear Lord and Father of mankind / I will sing the wondrous story / Thine is the glory / Pie Jesu / All the toil and sorrow done / Fill thou my life / Guide me o thou great Jehovah / Fight the good fight / Morning has broken / Jesus Christ is risen today / Be thou my guardian and my guide / Rejoice the Lord is King / Stand up, stand up for Jesus / Jesu joy of man's desiring / We plough the fields and scatter / Nearer my God to thee / I vow to thee my country
BNA 5034 / '91 / Bandleader

□ MARCHING FORWARD
Voice of the guns / B.b. and c.f. / Under the double eagle march (j.f. wagner) / Stars and stripes forever / Sons of the brave / Concorde march / Beautiful gardens march (schoenfeld march) / Entry of the gladiators / Punchinello / Marche militaire / Royal doulton march / El abanico / Wellington march / Minton march / Victor's return / Death or glory / Florentiner march
BNA 5049 / Feb '91 / Bandleader

Royal Dragoon Guards

□ FAME AND RENOWN
BNA 5111 / Oct '94 / Bandleader

Royal Electrical/ Mechanical Engineers Corps Band

□ OPERATIC FESTIVAL, AN
Niblungen march / Le roi d'ys overture / Vissi d'arte / Easter hymn / Flower duet / Carmen suite / Marriage of Figaro overture / Deep inside the sacred temple / Impressario overture / Slaves chorus / Una voce poco fa / Coronation scene
BNA 5129 / Dec '96 / Bandleader

Royal Engineers

□ LISTEN TO THE BAND (Band Of The Royal Engineers)
BNA 5141 / 13 Apr '98 / Bandleader

□ MUSIC FOR AN AMERICAN OCCASION
BNA 5125 / Jul '96 / Bandleader

Royal Family

□ STRAIGHT FROM THE UNDERGROUND
Coronation / Never made me a man / Tame 1 unleashed / My policy / Freddy's back / Night train / Boingsville / Straight from the underground / E.I. theme
SPOCK 2CD / Oct '90 / Music Of Life

Royal Flush

□ GHETTO MILLIONAIRE
TVT 66102 / 6 Oct '97 / TVT/Blunt

Royal Folkloric Troupe Of Tahiti

☐ COCO'S TAMAEVA
S 65808 / Mar '92 / Manuiti

☐ COCO'S TEMAEVA VOL.2
S 65815 / Feb '94 / Manuiti

Royal Highland Fusiliers

☐ AFORE YE GO
Fanfare / March / Song for Suzanne / March: Birkenhead / Pipe dreams / March: Be ye also ready / Scottish serenade / Victory salute / Oft in the stilly night / Pipe set / Bays of Harris / Sunset salute / Seventy Ninth Farewell to Gibraltar / My own land / Tenth HLI crossing the Rhine / Misty morn / March: Assaye / Seventy Fourth Officers' mess call / Company marches (pipes) / Regimental marches (pipes) / Regimental slow march / Regimental quick march / March medley
BNA 5102 / Jan '94 / Bandleader

Royal Highland Regiment

☐ PROUD HERITAGE
Reveille / Company marches / Headquarter company marches / Working day calls / Daily parade calls / Battalion parade tunes / Crimean long reveille / Retreat marches / Officer's mess blues night / Officer's mess guest night / March off parade / Lights out
LCOM 5221 / Sep '93 / Lismor

Royal Hunt

☐ CLOWN IN THE MIRROR
RRCD 90092 / Feb '97 / Rondel

☐ PARADOX
50610422 / 29 Sep '97 / Semaphore

Royal Hussars

☐ SABRE AND SPURS (Royal Hussars Regiment Band)
Fanfare - Arrival / Princess of Wales march / Sabre and spurs / With sword and lance / Cavalry walk / Parade / March of the 18th Hussars / Golden spurs / Cavalry of the Steppes / Step lightly / New Colonial / Old Panama / Ca ira / Light of foot / Waveney namur / British eights / Rogue's march / Lincolnshire poacher / Regimental quick and slow marches
BNA 5033 / Aug '89 / Bandleader

Royal Liverpool Philharmonic Orchestra

☐ LIVERPOOL POPS
You'll never walk alone / Educating Rita / Lancashire overture (medley) / Imagine / Hard day's night / Scaffold tribute (medley) / TV medley / Liverpool day (medley) / All together now (medley)
3036801072 / Jun '98 / Carlton

Royal Logistic Corps

☐ ON PARADE (Band Of the Royal Logistic Corps)
On parade / Wait for the wagon / Village blacksmith / Pioneer corps / Sugar and spice / First post / Sostenare / Oregon / Concerto for cornet / Flugelhorn and trumpet / Concerto for band / You'd be so nice to come home to / Concerto for clarinet / Power and glory / Forest of Arden
BNA 5117 / Aug '95 / Bandleader

Royal Marines

☐ ASHOKAN FAREWELL, THE
Ashokan farewell / Rhapsody for trombone / Traumerei / Rhapsody for euphonium / Clarinet concerto in C / Gabriel's oboe / Trumpet concerto / Xylophonist's apprentice / Swan / Bach flute sonata no.4 in C / Evening breeze
CLCD 10595 / Nov '95 / Clovelly

☐ BEATING RETREAT AND TATTOO
Fanfare / Salute to heroes / Soldiers to the sea / March and air / Silver bugles / Army of the Nile / Marines' walk / Sea solider / Montafortabeek / Top malo / Dunkirk veterans / Famous songs of the British Isles / Evening hymn and sunset / Britannic salute / God save the Queen / Heart of Oak / Fanfara alla danza / Admiral's regiment / Westering home / Per mare / Per terram / Wee Mac / Maranatha / Claymore / Semper / Supremus / Sussex by the sea / Commando patrol / At the close of the day / Lost post / Nimrod / Marines' hymn / Life on the ocean wave
GRCD 45 / '91 / Grasmere

☐ BEST OF THE ROYAL MARINES, THE
MMCD 424 / Jun '92 / Music Masters

☐ BEST OF THE ROYAL MARINES, THE
Strike up the band / Radetsky march / Sailing / March: Things to come / March of youth / Anything goes / Thunderbirds / Gibraltar march / My way / Symphonic marches of John Williams / Hearts of oak/A life on the ocean wave/Prelude and sunset / SSAFA march / Jerusalem / Navy day / Unchained melody / Holyrood / Cockleshell heroes / Here's a health unto her Majesty / Big country / On the quarterdeck
PWKS 4202 / May '94 / Carlton

☐ BIG BAND SOUND, THE (Royal Marines Dance Band)
Stars and stripes forever / Makin' whoopee / Li'l darlin' / Samba de los gatos / Pink Panther / Frankie and Johnny / Route 66 / Drink tolly only / Yankee doodle dandy / Moonlight serenade / American patrol / Hot toddy / Georgia / Take the 'A' train / Stardust / Rabble rouser / Swing low / Cruisin' for a bluesin'
CLCD 10796 / Jun '96 / Clovelly

☐ BY LAND AND SEA
National emblem / Preobrakensky march / Top malo / Concert march- Cockleshell heroes / Captain general / President elect / By land and sea / Anchors aweigh / Post horn gallop / Picconautical / In party mood / Falcon crest / Overture- Monte Carlo or bust / Barwick Green / Elizabeth Tudor
BNA 5030 / '88 / Bandleader

☐ COMPLETE MARCHES OF KENNETH ALFORD
Thin red line / Holyrood / Vedette / Colonel bogey / Great little army / On the quarterdeck / Middy / Voice of the guns / Vanished army / Mad major / Cavalry of the clouds / Dunedin / Old panama / H.m. jollies / Standard of st. george / By land and sea / Army of the nile / Eagle squadron / Lilliburlero / A life on the ocean wave / Vesper hymn
CLCD 102 / Jan '94 / Clovelly

☐ GLOBE AND LAUREL
On parade / Globe and laurel / Officer of the day / Cavalry of the Steppes / Uncle Sammy / Dad's army march / Belphegor / Advance guard / My regiment / Brass buttons / Gladiator's farewell / Punjab / Contemptibles / Voice of the guns / Robinson's grand entree / Dunedin / Vimy ridge / On the square
BNA 5023 / Aug '89 / Bandleader

☐ KALEIDOSCOPE (Royal Marines Commando Forces Band)
March: Royal buglers / Jubilee overture / Londonderry air / Shepherd's hey / Valdres / March / Irish washerwoman / West Side story selection / Can't buy me love / Passion eyes / Time after time / All through the night / Kaleidoscope / Black is black / Lady in red / Blue rondo a la Turk / Whiter shade of pale
BNA 5064 / May '92 / Bandleader

☐ LIFE ON THE OCEAN WAVE
Life on the ocean wave / Salute the sovereign / Portsmouth / Evening hymn - the day / Thou gavest Lord is ended/Sunset / By land and sea / Bugle fanfare / Drum display / Victory / On the quarterdeck / Greensleeves / Men of action / Cockleshell heroes / Hands across the sea / Warship / Anchors aweigh / Officers of the day / Picconautical / Troika / Post horn gallop / Salute to James Last / Nobilmente
MCCD 073 / Jun '92 / Music Club

☐ MARCHES OF THE SEA
Lifeboatmen / Lifeboatmen / Dunkirk veterans / Trafalgar / In the eye of the storm / Warship / Navy blue / Middy / H.m. jollies / Padstow lifeboat / Mansfield matelot / Leviathan / Raleighing cry / Nelson touch / Up periscope / Plymouth sound march / Soldiers of the sea
CLCD 101 / Jan '94 / Clovelly

☐ MUSIC THAT STIRS THE NATION
MU 5008 / Oct '92 / Musketeer

☐ OLD COMRADES - NEW COMRADES
Old comrades / In the Bristol fashion / Lichfield / Cairo Road / Ventis secundis / Sea shanties / Parade of brass / Blue devils / New comrades / HM jollies / Broadlands / Little swiss piece / HMY Britannia / Nation / Up periscope / Glorious victory
GRACC 1 / May '94 / Grasmere

☐ ON THE QUARTERDECK
A life on the ocean wave / A life on the ocean wave / Royal bugler / Trafalgar / H.m. ship jollies / Heart of oak / Splice the mainbrace / By land and sea / Warship / Under the white ensign / Soldier an' sailor too / Preobranjensky march / Uncle sammy / Portsmouth / General mitchell (march) / Advance guard / Sea soldier
3036100022 / '95 / Carlton

☐ PLAY THE CLASSICS (Bands Of HM Royal Marines)
Fanfare for the common man / Radetsky / Festive overture op 96 / Great gate of Kiev / Lohengrin prelude / Aranjuez mon amour / Allegro deciso / Montagus and capulets / Finlandia / Procession of the nobles / Marche militaire / Love of three oranges / Light cavalry
308962 / 11 May '98 / Hallmark

☐ PORTSMOUTH
Heart of oak / Portsmouth / Warship / Splice the mainbrace / Nelson touch / Trafalgar / Viscount Nelson / Hands across the sea / Under the white ensign / Sea songs / Victory / Salute to the sovreign / Bugle fanfare / Drum display / Evening hymn / Sunset / Fantasia on British sea songs / Land of hope and glory
BNA 5020 / Jun '93 / Bandleader

☐ ROYAL MARINES FOREVER (The Greatest Tunes From Their Greatest Bands/2CD Set)
Rule Brittania / March of youth / Aranuez mon amour / Birdland / Allegro deciso / Swing low, sweet chariot / Nautical suite / Splice the mainbrace / Sea Harriers / Huntsman / True and fair / Pineapple Poll / Drum display / Royal review / Nibelungen march / Drum and bugle display / Greensleeves / On parade / Skye boat song / Fugue and swing / SSAFA march / Battle of Trafalgar / Heart of oak / Life on the ocean wave / Prelude and sunset
330462 / Mar '97 / Hallmark

☐ SPECTACULAR SOUNDS OF, THE (Royal Marines/Argyll & Sutherland Highlanders)
Fanfare royal occasion / Life on the ocean wave / Highland laddie / Famous songs of the British Isles medley / Fine old English gentleman / To be a farmer's boy / Here's a health unto His Majesty / British Grenadiers / Minstral boy / Annie Laurie / Men of Harlech / Pipe selection / Gordon boy (lang) / Barren rocks of Aden / Brown haired maiden / Marie's wedding / Major ACS Boswell / Captain D P Thomson / Lieutenant Colonel H L Clark / Sea shanties medley / What shall we do with the drunken sailor / Portsmouth / Rovin' / Hornpipe / Highland fling / Dornoch links / Marquis of Huntly / Man's a man for a' that / Arrival / Black bear / Fanfare no.1 / Royal salute / Drumbeatings / Time off / Argyll broadswords / Glendaurel highlanders / O'er the bows to Ballindalloch / Miss Ada Crawford / Because he was a bonny lad / Piper o'Drummond / Sleepy Maggie / All the blue bonnets are over the mountain / Soldiers return / Chariots of fire / Crown imperial / Day thou gavest Lord is ended / Sunset / Rule Britannia / Auld lang syne / Scotland the brave / Campbells are coming
CDMFP 6315 / Feb '97 / Music For Pleasure

Royal Military School Of Music

☐ KNELLER HALL (Kneller Hall RMS Band)
Blow away the morning dew / Pinapple poll suite No.1 / Great little army / First suite in Eb for military band / Three humouresques / Tocatta mariale / HRH The Duke Of Cambridge / Sir Godfrey Kneller / Original suite / Serenade / Celebration
BNA 5109 / Aug '94 / Bandleader

☐ SULLIVAN SALUTE (Kneller Hall RMS Band)
Procession March / Overture Iolanthe / Three little maids from school / Incidental music to Henry VIII / March / King Henry's song / Graceful dance / Danish march / Overture the yeomen of the guard / Absent Minded Beggar / Lost Chord / Battle of St.Gertrude / March of the Peers / Overture / Di Ballo
BNA 5067 / Aug '92 / Bandleader

Royal Northern College Of Music Brass Band

☐ VISTAS (The Music Of Martin Ellerby)
New World dances / Requiescant Aberfan / Euphonium concerto / Concerto for brass / Vistas
QPRL 085D / Oct '97 / Polyphonic

Royal Philharmonic Orchestra

☐ CHRISTMAS ALBUM
Shepherd's pipe carol / Walking in the air / Nativity carol / Stable carol / Candlelight carol / De virgin Mary had a baby boy / Donkey carol / Holly and the ivy / Away in a manger / God rest ye merry gentlemen / First Noel / O come all ye faithful (adeste fidelis) / Once in royal David's city / Unto us is born a son / O little town of Bethlehem / Good king Wenceslas / Hark the herald angels sing
120022 / Oct '97 / Jingle

☐ CHRISTMAS ALBUM, THE
Shepherd's pipe carol / Walking in the air / Nativity carol / Stable carol / Candlelight carol / Virgin Mary had a baby boy / Donkey carol / Holly and the ivy / Away in a manger / God rest ye merry gentlemen / First Noel / O come all ye faithful (adeste fidelis) / Once in royal David's city / Unto us is born a son / O little town of Bethlehem / Good King Wenceslas / Hark the herald angels sing
TRP 083 / Nov '96 / Tring

☐ CLASSICS FOR THE MILLIONS (Royal Philharmonic Orchestra/Louis Clark)
SYCD 6320 / May '94 / Disky

☐ CLASSICS OF LOVE
Three times a lady / If you leave me now / Up where we belong / You don't bring me flowers / Imagine / Weekend in New England / Miss you nights / One day I'll fly away / Memory / With you I'm born again / One day in your life / Sun ain't gonna shine anymore
CDMFP 5792 / Apr '90 / Music For Pleasure

☐ DIANA, PRINCESS OF WALES (Musical Reflections)
SELCD 500 / 24 Nov '97 / Castle

☐ DREAMS
Unchained melody / Groovy kind of love / (Everything I do) I do it for you / Show me heaven / Take my breath away / My girl / Twin Peaks (Falling) / Second time (Bilitis) / Wind beneath my wings / It must have been love / Love changes everything / Music of the night / Any dream will do / Memory / Cavatina / Chariots of fire / Up where we belong / Hopelessly devoted to you / I've had the time of my life / Arthur's theme
MOCD 3003 / Feb '95 / More Music

☐ HOOKED ON CLASSICS - THE ULTIMATE COLLECTION
Symphony of the seas / Hooked on Mendelssohn / Hooked on classics / Dance of the furies / Hooked on romance / Hooked on Rodgers and Hammerstein / Night at the opera / Also sprach Zarathustra / Hooked on Bach / Journey through the classics / Scotland the brave / Tales of the Vienna woods / Can't stop the classics / Hooked on romance (part 2) / Hooked on baroque
MCCD 003 / Feb '91 / Music Club

☐ LOVE SONGS
Time of my life / My girl / Stand by me / Show me heaven / Take a look at me now / Twin peaks / Hero / Arthur's theme / Look of love / Some enchanted evening / Secret love / Cavaleria rusticana / Hopelessly devoted to you / True love ways / Pachelbel canon / Someone to watch over me
11910 / Feb '96 / Music

☐ MEMORIES
Unchained melody / Groovy kind of love / (Everything I do) I do it for you / Up where we belong / Take my breath away / It must have been love / Lily was here / Chariots of fire / Speak softly love / Any dream will do / Love changes everything / Lara's theme / Second time / Send in the clowns / Memory / Cavatina
11984 / Feb '96 / Music

☐ RPO PLAYS ROCK CLASSICS
Simply the best / Time aftrer time / Eye of the tiger / Lost in France / Take my breath away / Another brick in the wall / Power of love / Good vibrations / I want to know what love is / House of the Rising Sun / Baker Street / Ruby Tuesday / Every breath you take / We don't need another hero / Wicked game / We are the champions
CD 6051 / Jan '97 / Music

☐ VERY BEST OF HOOKED ON CLASSICS, THE (4CD Set)
Hooked on classics (Part 1 and 2) / Hooked on romance / Hooked on classics (Part 3) / Hooked on Bach / Hooked on Tchaikovsky / Hooked on a song / Hooked on Mozart / Hooked on Mendelssohn / Hooked on a can can / Also sprach zarathrustra (Excerpt) / Journey through the classics / Hooked on Haydn / Hooked on Romance(Opus 3) / Viva Vivaldi / Dance on the furies / Scotland the brave / Journey through the classics (part 2) / Journey through America / Hooked on marching / Symphony of the seas / Hooked on Rodgers and Hammerstein / Can't stop the classics / Hooked on America / Hooked on romance (part 2) / Night at the opera / Tales of the Vienna waltz / Hooked on Baroque / If you knew Sousa / If you knew Sousa (and friends) / Hooked on Baroque (part 2): *New World Ensemble* / Hooked on Adagio: *New World Ensemble* / Hooked on Gigue: *New World Ensemble* / Hooked on a Fugue: *New World Ensemble* / Hooked on Handel: *New World Ensemble* / Hooked on Vivaldi: *New World Ensemble* / Hooked on Scarlatti: *New World Ensemble* / Hooked on Baroque part 2 (reprise): *New World Ensemble*
ECD 3355 / May '97 / K-Tel

☐ WAY WE WERE, THE (Royal Philharmonic Orchestra Plays Ballads)
Where do I begin / Way we were / Summertime / Moon river / Edelweiss / As time goes by / Music of the night / Over the rainbow / My girl / Against all odds / Somewhere / Theme from a summer place / Evergreen / Blue velvet / People / When I fall in love
CD 6119 / Apr '98 / Music

Royal Scots Dragoon Guards

☐ AMAZING GRACE
Amazing grace / Scotland the brave / Cornet carillon / Russian imperial anthem / Abide with me / Dark island / Ode 'An die Freude' (Song of joy) / Scottish soldier / Road to the isles / Drummer's call / Belmont (by cool Siloam's shady rill) / Bunessan / Banda / Little drummer boy / Standchen / Day is ended / Wooden heart / Going home
74321578182 / 11 May '98 / RCA

☐ AMAZING GRACE
Medley / Speed your journey (Song of the Hebrew slaves) / Moonliner rock march / Medley / Y viva Espana / Medley / Barock '75 / Medley / Brazil / Tribute to Duthart / Medley / Amazing grace / Una paloma blanca / 6/8 marches / Rock 'n' roll march / Largo / Theme in glory / Retreat airs / Rockout / 4/4 marches / Medley
TRTCD 134 / Dec '94 / TrueTrax

☐ AMAZING GRACE
74321292802 / Jul '95 / RCA

☐ AMAZING GRACE
PLSCD 185 / Apr '97 / Pulse

☐ IN THE FINEST TRADITION (Royal Scots Dragoon Guards Pipes & Drums)
Amazing grace / Three DG's / Send in the clowns / Symphonic marches of John Williams / Way old friends do / McPhedran's strathspey / Highland whiskey / Mermaid song / Troy's wedding / Mason's apron / Seventy Ninth farewell to Gibraltar / Highland cathedral / Scotland the brave / Black bear / Carillon / Going home / My home / Skye boat song / Irish air / Ballochmyle / Mrs. Lily Christie / Farewell to the creeks / Garb of old gaul / Moonstar
BNA 5017 / 15 Jun '98 / Bandleader

☐ ROYAL SCOTS DRAGOON GUARDS
Amazing grace / Gallowa' hills / Lili Marlene / Skye boat song / Black Watch polka / Battle of the Somme / Highland wedding / Mill in the Glen / Hills of home / Crossing the Rhine / Dovecote Park
MCCD 105 / May '93 / Music Club

☐ SCOTTISH SALUTE
Scottish selection / Scottish selection / Bright eyes / Moorhouse memories / Drummers call / March, strathspey and reel / Scottish selection / Shepherd's song / Yorkshire bells / Hazel's dream / 44 marches / Piper's dance
CDITV 455 / Jul '89 / Scotdisc

☐ SECOND TO NONE
LCOM 5248 / Aug '95 / Lismor

☐ TUNES OF GLORY
CDLOC 1069 / Sep '94 / Lochshore

☐ VERY BEST OF THE ROYAL SCOTS DRAGOON GUARDS, THE
Amazing grace / Little drummer boy / Scotland the brave / Highland laddie / Morning has broken / Ode to joy (ode 'an die freude) / Day is ended / Reveille / Scottish waltz / Hayken's serenade / Russian imperial anthem / Going home
74321339362 / Jan '96 / Camden

Royal Scottish Orchestra

☐ CHRISTMAS FANFARE, A
Jingle bells / Il est ne / Jesus ahatonia / We wish you a merry Christmas / Ding dong merrily on high / Past 3 o'clock / O come, all ye faithful / Once in Royal David's City / Torches / Christmas fantasy / Hark the herald angels sing / Good King Wenceslas / Great and mighty wonder / Christmas piece / Schneewalzer / Two Christmas fanfares / Caribbean Christmas / Christmas song
CDCA 923 / Nov '91 / Alpha

Royal Society Jazz Orchestra

☐ 20TH LIVE
CCD 170 / Sep '97 / Circle

☐ ROYAL SOCIETY JAZZ ORCHESTRA
SOSCD 1208 / Jan '93 / Stomp Off

Royal Tahitian Dance Co.

☐ ROYAL TAHITIAN DANCE CO.
MCD 71758 / Jun '93 / Monitor

Royal, Teddy

☐ ROYAL BLUE
SP 1003CD / Apr '97 / Morning Groove

Royal Trux

☐ ACCELERATOR
I'm ready / Yellow kid / Banana question / Another year / Juicy juicy juice / Liar / New bones / Follow the winner / Stevie
WIGCD 045 / 27 Apr '98 / Domino

☐ CATS AND DOGS
Teeth / Flag / Friends / Spectre / Skywood greenback mantra / Turn of the century / Up the sleeve / Hot and cold skulls / Tight pants / Let's get lost / Driving in that car
WIGCD 006 / Jul '93 / Domino

☐ ROYAL TRUX
Air / Move / Hallucination / Sometimes / Lightning boxer / Blood flowers / Sun on the run
WIGCD 005 / Jun '93 / Domino
DC 5 / Dec '96 / Drag City

☐ SINGLES LIVE UNRELEASED (2CD Set)
WIG 040CD / 10 Nov '97 / Domino

☐ SWEET SIXTEEN
Don't try too hard / Morphic resident / Pickup / Cold joint / Golden rules / You'll be staying in room 323 / Can't have it both ways / 10 days 12 nights / Microwave made / Sweet sixteen / I'm looking through you / Roswell seeds and stems / Pol Pot pie
CDHUT 43 / Apr '97 / Hut

☐ THANK YOU
Night to remember / Sewers of Mars / Ray O Vac / Map of the city / Granny grunt / Lights on the levee / Fear strikes out / (Have you met) Horror James / You're gonna lose / Shadow of the wasp
CDHUT 23 / Feb '95 / Hut

☐ TWIN INFINITIVES
Solid gold tooth / Ice cream / Jet pet / Rtx-usa / Kool down wheels / Chances are the comets in our future / Yin jum versus the vomit creature / Osiris / (edge of the) ape oven / Florida avenue theme / Lick my boots / Glitterbust / Funky son / Ratcreeps / New york avenue bridge
WIGCD 8 / Jan '94 / Domino

Royal Ulster Constabulary

☐ PIPE BANDS OF DISTINCTION
Barren rocks of aden / Barren rocks of aden / Come by the hills / Steal away / Cliffs of Dooneen / Robert's pipes / Reggie's foot / Prelude no 2 / Hornpipe prelude no 2 / Snug in a blanket / Gigue's prelude no 2 / Prelude no 2 reprise / Swingin' safari / Cock o' the north / Sweet maid of mull / Major john mclellan / Ship in a bottle / John mcdonald of glencoe / Lord alexander kennedy / Maggie cameron / John mckechnie / Nameless jig / A dram before you go / Green hills of tyrol / Battle's o'er / Lochanside / York reel / Maid behind the bar / Three strange men behind yonder mountain / Prelude no 1 / Sam bailie's gigue / Prelude no 1 reprise / Highland cathedral / Bind / Redford cottge / Angus mckinnon / Donald cameron / Arniston castle / Bessie mcintyre / Lady jean herman / Banjo breakdown / Lady jean herman / I love a lassie / We're no awa tae bide awa / Bluebells of scotland / Minstrel boy / She moves through the fair / Craigabodaich / Davidson's fancy / Spirits of old pultney / Skansen's reel / Andy renwick's ferret / Old mountain road / Rakish paddy
CDMON 814 / Jul '94 / Monarch

Royal Welsh Fusiliers

☐ TO THE BEAT OF A DRUM (Royal Welsh Fusiliers & Blaenavon Male Voice Choir)
Fanfare - the 300th / Men of Glamorgan / Lilliburlero / Grenadiers slow march / How stands the glass around / Quick march of the 23rd regiment / Marquis of Granby / Sospan fach / My Lord what a morning / Girl I left behind me / Lass of Richmond Hill / Calon lan / Soldiers of the Queen / Goodbye Dolly Gray / US Marine Corps hymn / Myfymwy / We'll keep a welcome / Vive la Canadienne / Keep the home fires burning / It's a long way to Tipperary / March of the Grenadiers / Royal Welch Fusiliers / Wish me luck as you wave me goodbye / Rachie / Cwm Rhondda / That astonishing infantry / British Grenadiers / Men of Harlech / Land of my fathers (Hen wlad fy nhadau) / God save the Queen
BNA 5026 / Aug '89 / Bandleader

Royal Yeomanry

☐ MUSIC OF ERIC COATES, THE
Dam buster's march / Three bears suite / Youth of Britain / Man from the sea / Calling all workers / By the sleepy lagoon / London again suite / Oxford street / Langham place / Mayfair / Music everywhere
302632 / Jun '97 / Hallmark

Roza, Lita

☐ SOMEWHERE, SOMEHOW, SOMEDAY
That's the beginning of the end / I've got my eyes on you / Oh dear what can the matter be / But beautiful / I'll never say Never Again again / End of a love affair / Not mine / As children do / There's nothing better than love / Allentown jail / Once in a while / Nel blu di pinto di blu / This is my town / Maybe you'll be there / Sorry, sorry, sorry / I could have danced all night / All alone / Other woman / Love can change the stars
C5CD552 / Jan '90 / See For Miles

Rozalla

☐ COMING HOME
ROZCD 1 / 27 Apr '98 / RM

☐ LOOK NO FURTHER
I love music / You never love the same way twice / This time I found love / Baby / Look no further / Do you believe / Work me / If love is a dream / All that I need / Love work / I can't wait / Losing my religion / I love music (Mix) / Baby (Mix) / You never love the same way twice (Mix)
4779829 / Mar '95 / Epic

RPB & Mac

☐ BAJAN INVASION
WCD 501 / Apr '97 / WIRL

RPM

☐ RUDESS/MORGENSTEIN PROJECT
Don't look down / Sloth / Drop the puck / Crossing over / Never again / Tailspin / Odd man out / Masada / Cartoon parade / Over the edge
DOMO 710202 / 20 Oct '97 / Domo

Rua

☐ AO-TEA-ROA
Music from the jungles of Caledonia / Raider / Jeltic music / Moon and St. Christopher / Caribbean celts / Allelujah / HAyfever / College boy / Band on the run / Eleanor Rigby / Waltzurka / Winter's rage / Arrival in Auckland / Highland cream
CDTRAX 103 / Nov '95 / Greentrax

☐ HOMELAND
Cave of the sun / Jock o'hazeldean / Homeland / Last battle / Diamontina drover / Millworker / Simple song / Dublin reel / Sean sa cheo / First time ever / Java jive / Jimmy ward's jig / Jungle johnny (the red haired rafter) / Maurice spence's / Molloy's / Sailing into walpole's marsh
CDTRAX 061 / Mar '93 / Greentrax

☐ LIVE IN THE CATHEDRAL
CDODE 1391 / Jul '94 / ODE

Rub Ultra

☐ LIQUID BOOTS AND BOILED SWEETS
Brown box nitro (dog's life) / Blasted freak / Health horror and the vitamin urge / Oily man eel / Your nasty hair / Generate / Whale boy / Free toy / Cat's gone underground / Suspend your belief / Castles / Voodoo accident
FLATCD 21 / Oct '95 / Hi-Rise

Rubalcaba, Gonzala

☐ BEST OF GONZALA RUBALCABA, THE
74321424352 / Jun '97 / Milan

☐ DIZ
Hot house / Woody 'n' you / I remember Clifford / Donna Lee / Bouncing with Bud / Smooch / Ah-leu-cha / Night in Tunisia / Con Alma
CDP 8304902 / Sep '95 / Blue Note

☐ GIRALDILLA
Rumbero / Proyecto latino / Giraldilla / Campo finda / Encuentros / Presidente / Comienzo
MES 158012 / Apr '93 / Messidor

☐ IMAGINE - LIVE IN AMERICA
Imagine / Contagio / First song / Woody 'n' you / Circuilo II / Perfidia / Mima
CDP 8304912 / Jan '96 / Blue Note

☐ LIVE IN HAVANA 1986
158302 / Sep '97 / Messidor

☐ LIVE IN HAVANA VOL.1 & 2
15960 / Aug '89 / Ronnie Scott's Jazz House

☐ MI GRAN PASION
15999 / Apr '89 / Messidor

Rubbersmell

☐ INDIAN FLESH - INDIAN DOME
CHILLUM 001 / Jan '96 / Chill Um

Rubella Ballet

☐ AT THE END OF THE RAINBOW
Money talks / False promise / Arctic flowers / Dreamer / Animal house / It'll never happen to me / Love potion / Rainbow love / 't' (emotional blackmail)
BND 2CD / Feb '90 / One Little Indian

☐ GREATEST TRIPS
Ballet dance / Something to give / Unemployed / Krak trak mk. 1 / 't' (emotional blackmail) / Belfast / Dream of honey / Newz at 10 / Slant + slide / Me / Krak trak mk. 2 / Blues / Exit / Money talks (dub) / Love life / Tangled web / T.v. screem / Death train / See saw / Twister / Mescalito / Cowboy hero
BND 3 CD / Feb '90 / One Little Indian

Ruben & The Jets

☐ FOR REAL
If I could only be your love again / Dedicated to the one I love / Show me the way to your heart / Sparkie / Wedding bells / Almost grown / Charlena / Mah man flash / Santa karl / Spider woman / All nite long
EDCD 406 / Nov '94 / Edsel

Rubettes

☐ BEST OF THE RUBETTES, THE
Sugar baby love / Tonight / Under one roof / Judy run run / I'm just dreaming / I can do it / Jukebox jive / Little darlin' / Julia / Foe dee oh dee / You're the reason why / Sha na na song
8438962 / Sep '90 / Polydor

☐ JUKE BOX JIVE
Sugar baby love / Baby I know / Under one roof / I'm just dreaming / Little darling / Don't do it baby / I can do it / Juke box jive / Julia / Tonight / Foe-dee-o-dee / Ooh la la / Sha na na song / You're the reason why
GRF 213 / Mar '93 / Tring

☐ VERY BEST OF THE RUBETTES, THE
Sugar baby love / Tonight / Jukebox jive / I can do it / Foe-dee-oh-dee / Little darling / You're the reason why / Under one roof / Baby I know / My Buddy Holly days / Put a back beat to that music / Julia / Sha-na-na-na song / Judy run run / Beggarman / I'm just dreaming / You could have told me / Dancing in the rain / Lola / Movin' / Kid runaway
5543312 / Oct '97 / Spectrum

Rubicon

☐ ROOM 101
BBQCD 170 / Apr '95 / Beggars Banquet

Rubin, Harold

☐ BLUE BAG
BLUEBAG / Sep '97 / Blue Bag

Rubin, Joel

☐ BEREGOVSKI'S KHASENE (Rubin, Joel Jewish Music Ensemble)
Tsu der khupe geyn / Volekhl / Baveynen di kale / Makonovetski's gas nign / Russian sher / Taksim / Sakhnovski's dobranotsh / Skotshne / Tish nigunim / Gershfeld's Bulgarish / Ahavo rabo / Zayt gezunt
SM 16142 / Jun '97 / Wergo

☐ CLASSIC YIDDISH CLARINET SOLOS OF THE 1920'S
SM 16152 / Jul '98 / Wergo

Rubin, Ruth

☐ YIDDISH SONGS OF THE HOLOCAUST: A LECTURE/RECITAL
GV 150CD / May '94 / Global Village

Rubin, Vanessa

☐ PASTICHE
In a sentimental mood / Simone / I'm just a lucky so and so / When love is new / Black Nile / I only have eyes for you / Mosaic / Estoy siempre junto a ti / Weekend / Certain love / Arise and shine
01241631522 / Apr '93 / Novus

Rubinoos

☐ RUBINOOS, THE (Remastered)
I think we're alone now / Leave my heart alone / Hard to get / Peek-a-boo / Rock 'n' roll is dead / Memories / Nothing a little love won't cure / Wouldn't it be nice / Make it easy / I never thought it would happen / Fallin' in love / I wanna be your boyfriend / Lightning love affair / Drivin' music / Jennifer / 1,2,3 forever
HILLCD 20 / Jul '97 / Wooded Hill

Ruby

☐ SALT PETER
CRECD 166RL
CRECD 166 / Apr '96 / Creation

Rucker, Vernis

☐ STRANGER IN THE SHEETS
Fishin' for a man / You've been good for me / He's cheating on you / There must be someone for me / Fever / There's a hurt where my heart used to be / Put love first / Then came you / Stormy Monday / Dead to right / Strangers in the sheets
CDCH 508 / Jan '94 / Ace

Ruckus

☐ ALLEY PUNK ROCK
LRR 023 / Oct '96 / Last Resort

Rud, Mike

☐ WHYTE AVENUE
JFCD 016 / May '97 / Jazz Focus

Rudd, Roswell

☐ FLEXIBLE FLYER
What are you doing the rest of your life / Maiden voyage / Suh blah buh sibi / Waltzing in the sagebrush / Moselle variations
CDBLC 760215 / Mar '96 / Black Lion

Rudder, David

☐ BELOVED
CR 028 / 27 Apr '98 / Lypsoland

☐ GILDED COLLECTION 1986-1989
CR 019CD / May '97 / Lypsoland

☐ GILDED COLLECTION 1990-1993
CR 024CD / May '97 / Lypsoland

☐ LYRICS MAN
CR 023CD / May '97 / Lypsoland

☐ TALES FROM A STRANGE LAND
CR 025CD / May '97 / Lypsoland

☐ WRAPPED IN PLAIN BROWN
CR 026CD / May '97 / Lypsoland

Rude Girls

☐ MIXED MESSAGES
FF 511CD / '92 / Flying Fish

Rudi

☐ BIG TIME (The Best Of Rudi)
Big time / Number one / Overcome by fumes / I spy / Genuine reply / Sometimes / Ripped in two / Who you / Time to be proud / Without you / Pressure's on / Yummy, yummy, yummy / Tigerland / When I was dead / Bewarewolf / Prince of pleasure / Love goes on / Crimson / 14 steps / Cops
CDPUNK 77 / Aug '96 / Anagram

Rudimentary Peni

☐ DEATH CHURCH
BOOB 004CD / Apr '94 / Outer Himalayen

☐ ECHOES OF ANGUISH
BOOBOO 6CD / 29 Jun '98 / Himalayan

☐ EPS OF RP
BOOB 003CD / Sep '94 / Outer Himalayen

☐ POPE ADRIAN 37TH PSYCHRISTIATRIC
BOOB 005CD / Sep '95 / Outer Himalayen

Rudiments

☐ BITCH BITCH BITCH
DILL 011 / Jun '97 / Dill

Rudolf Rocker

☐ EXOTIC SOUNDS OF RUDOLPH ROCKER
MKCD 09 / 23 Feb '98 / Mook

Rudolph, Adam

☐ GIFT OF THE GNAWA
FF 571CD / May '93 / Flying Fish

☐ MOVING PICTURES
FF 612CD / Feb '93 / Flying Fish

Ruf Der Heimat

☐ RUF DER HEIMAT
EFA 127652 / Aug '95 / Konnex

Ruff 2 Da Smoove

☐ RUFF 2 DA SMOOVE
CDBR 10 / Feb '95 / Body Rock

Ruffin, Jimmy

☐ GREATEST MOTOWN HITS
What becomes of the broken hearted / Baby I've got it / I've passed this way before / Gonna give her all the love I've got / World so wide, nowhere to hide / Don't you miss me a little bit baby / Everybody needs love / It's wonderful (to be loved by you) / Gonna keep on tryin' till I win your love / This guy's in love with you / Farewell is a lonely sound / Stand by me: *Ruffin, Jimmy & David* / As long as there is l-o-v-e love / Sad and lonesome feeling / I'll say forever my love / Don't let him take your love from me / Maria / Living in a world I created for myself / Let's say goodbye tomorrow / He ain't heavy, he's my brother: *Ruffin, Jimmy & David*
5300572 / Jan '93 / Motown

☐ MOTOWN EARLY CLASSICS
What becomes of the broken hearted / Since I've lost you / How can I say I'm sorry / Baby I've got it / Gonna give her all the love I've got / 96 tears / You've got what it takes / Farewell is a lonely sound / I'll say forever my love / Stand by me: *Ruffin, David & Jimmy* / Set 'em up (move in for the thrill): *Ruffin, David & Jimmy* / Living in a world I created for myself / Lonely lonely man am I / I want her love / I'll never let you get away / Honey come back / Your love was worth waiting for: *Ruffin, David & Jimmy* / Turn back the hands of time: *Ruffin, David & Jimmy*
5521232 / Jul '96 / Spectrum

Ruffins, Kermit

☐ BIG BUTTER & EGG MAN, THE
JR 11022 / Jun '94 / Justice

☐ WORLD ON A STRING
JR 001101 / Apr '93 / Justice

Ruffner, Mason

☐ EVOLUTION
I got a flame / King's highway / Angel love / Lament in 68 / Let the spirit go / Loaded down / You are the best / Evolution song / Ragman / Steel rain / Warriors bliss / Farewell
PRD 70632 / May '94 / Provogue

Ruffnexx Sound System

☐ RUFFNEXX
Get ready / Stick by me / Fire / Warning / Land of the free / Only one girl (+ elements of / Own kinda style / Hand pon da trigga / Burial / Luv bump / Give u the good / Knit one (+ elements of / Strong foundation / Eeny meeny / Big britches
9362456052 / Jul '95 / Warner Bros.

Rufus

☐ RUFUSIZED/MASTERJAM (2CD Set)
MCD 33006 / Aug '96 / MCA

Rufus Show

☐ UGLY FISH
Spill blood / Craving / Higher inside / I'm awake / Mosquito / Receive
COP 01 / 11 May '98 / Copro

Ruins

☐ REFUSAL FOSSIL
GR 45CD / 19 Jan '98 / Skingraft

☐ SYMPHONICA
TZA 7215 / 1 Jun '98 / Tzadik

Ruiz, Floreal

☐ MARIONETA
BMT 008 / Jul '97 / Blue Moon

Ruiz, Hilton

☐ HANDS ON PERCUSSION
Ornithology / Blues for cos / Mambo for vibes / 'Round midnight / Cotton tail / Jack's tune / Like Sonny / Maneguitos way / Salute to Eddie
66058061 / May '95 / RMM

☐ HEROES
'Round midnight / Sonny mood / Guataca / Little suede shoes / Lover man / For Maz / Maiden voyage / Con alma / Tune up / Praise
CD 83338 / May '94 / Telarc

☐ LIVE AT BIRDLAND (Ruiz, Hilton Sextet)
Something grand / New arrival / Blues for two tenors / Mr. Kenyatta / Lisa / Night in Tunisia / I'll call you later / On green dolphin street / Footprints
CCD 79532 / Feb '97 / Candid

Ruiz, Jim

☐ OH BROTHER WHERE ART THOU (Ruiz, Legendary Jim Group)
MF 11 / Jun '95 / Minty Fresh

Rum & Black

☐ WITHOUT ICE
Bogey man / Wicked / Whispers / Your funky emotion / In memory of / Tablet man / Insomnia / We were robbed of our...(religion, culture and god) / Nightmare man / Black revolutionaries / F the legal station / Yakuso / Beauty / This is the way (part 2) / Slaves
SUADCD 3 / Sep '91 / Shut Up & Dance

Rumbata

☐ ENCUENTROS
CHR 70032 / Nov '95 / Challenge

Rumbel, Nancy

☐ NOTES FROM THE TREE OF LIFE
Tree of life / Lullaby / Night tribe / Anansi / Passing fancy / Song of hope / Dona nobis pacem / Coyote dance / Delicate balance / Satie
ND 61050 / Dec '95 / Narada

Rumble

☐ RUMBLE
Safe / Dontress / Suspect / Take me / Look at the kid / All I know / Serious ting / Crack song / Black man wagon / Follow me / Booyaka booyaka
GEECD 12 / Nov '93 / Gee Street

Rumble Cats

☐ WILD BLUE YONDER
RKCD 9701 / Feb '97 / Rockhouse

Rumillajta

☐ CITY OF STONE
TUMICD 001 / '92 / Tumi

☐ HOJA DE COCA
TUMICD 002 / '92 / Tumi

☐ PACHAMAMA
TUMICD 003 / '92 / Tumi

☐ WIRACOCHA
RUM 1871CD / Jan '90 / Rumillajta

Rumour

☐ FROGS SPROUTS CLOGS AND KRAUTS
REP 4219 / Aug '91 / Repertoire

☐ RUMOUR
Frogs / Sprouts / Clogs / Krauts
STIFFCD 14 / Jan '94 / Disky

Rump

☐ HATING BRENDA
CARCD 24 / Apr '94 / Caroline

Rumsey, Howard

☐ LIGHTHOUSE ALL STARS VOL.3 (Rumsey, Howard Lighthouse All Stars)
Swing shift / Out of somewhere / Mexican passport / Big girl / Vivi Zapata / No.1 / Mambo los feliz / Song is you / Jazz invention / Snap the whip / Love letters / Witch doctor no.1
OJCCD 266 / Jan '97 / Original Jazz Classics

☐ LIGHTHOUSE ALL STARS VOL.6
Who's sleepy / Isn't it romantic / Mad at the world / East of the sun / Long ago and far away / Sad shack / If I should lose you / Prelude to a kiss / Dickie's dream
OJCCD 386 / Jun '95 / Original Jazz Classics

☐ MUSIC FOR LIGHTHOUSEKEEPING (Rumsey, Howard Lighthouse All Stars)
Love me or levey / Taxi war dance / Octavia / Mambo las vegas / Jubilation / I deal / Latin for lovers / Topsy
OJCCD 636 / Feb '92 / Original Jazz Classics

☐ OBOE/FLUTE
Aquarium / Warm winds / Night in tunisia / Albatross / Blue sands / Swing house / Still life / Bag's groove / Hermosa summer / Bit of basie / Waikikian / Happy town
OJCCD 154 / Jun '95 / Original Jazz Classics

Run DMC

☐ BACK FROM HELL
Sucker DJ's / What's it all about / Faces / Pause / Back from hell / Groove to the sound / Naughty / Not just another groove / Ave / Bob your head / Kick the frama lama lama / Word is born / Don't stop / P upon a tree / Livin' the city / Party time
FILECD 401 / Nov '90 / Profile

☐ GREATEST HITS 1983-1998
Sucker MC's / Walk this way: *Run DMC & Aerosmith* / Together forever / King of rock / Run's house / It's tricky / Pause / You be illin' / My Adidas / Here we go / Rock box / What's it all about / Hard times / Beats to the rhyme / Jam Master Jay / Peter Piper / It's like that / Christmas in Hollis / It's like that / It's tricky
FILECD 474 / 26 May '98 / Profile

☐ RAISING HELL
Peter Piper / It's tricky / My Adidas / Walk this way: *Run DMC & Aerosmith* / Is it live / Perfection / Hit it Run / Raising hell / You be illin' / Dumb girl / Son of Byford / Proud to be black
FILECD 217 / Jul '95 / Profile

☐ RUN DMC
Hard times / Rock box / Jam-master Jay / Hollis crew (Krush groove 2) / Sucker MC's (Krush-groove 1) / It's like that / Wake up / Thirty days / Jay's game
FILERCD 202 / Apr '91 / Profile

☐ RUN DMC TOGETHER FOREVER (Greatest Hits 1983 - 91)
FILERCD 419 / Sep '91 / Profile

Run On

☐ NO WAY
Something sweet / Lab rats / As good as new / Look / Bring her blues / 1/2 of 1/2 / Anything you say / Road / Days away / Out for a walk / Ropa vieja / Sinnerman
OLE 2292 / Feb '97 / Matador

☐ SIT DOWN
Owe you / Go there / Xmas trip / Double Gemini / Half of half
OLE 2832 / 17 Nov '97 / Matador

☐ START PACKING
Tried / Baap / Go there / A to Z / Miscalculation / In strength / Xmas trip / Doesn't anybody love the dark / Tell me / You said / Coffee together / Surprise
OLE 1532 / Mar '96 / Matador

Run Westy Run

☐ HARDLY, NOT EVEN
SST 192CD / May '93 / SST

☐ RUN WESTY RUN
SST 199CD / Feb '89 / SST

Runaways

☐ AND NOW...THE RUNAWAYS
Saturday night special / Eight days a week / Mama weer all crazee now / I'm a million / Right now / Take over / My buddy and me / Little lost girls / Black leather
CDMGRAM 63 / Mar '97 / Cherry Red

Runaways

☐ CLASSIC TALES
Intro / Levitation / Cowboys / Summer vacation / Finders creepers / Skit one / Punky wisdom / Piano toon / Kaleidoscope tunrtable styles / Futurism / Skit two / Past present future / Crime story / Runaway love / Anatomical design
UDRCD 003 / 13 Oct '97 / Ultimate Dilemma

Rundgren, Todd

☐ ANTHOLOGY (Utopia)
Freedom fighters / Wheel / Trapped / You make me crazy / Very last time / One world / Lysistrata / Overture mountain top and sunrise communion with / Play this game / Mated / Feet don't fail me now / I just want to touch you / Set me free / Crybaby / Love is the answer / Love in action
8122708922 / May '95 / WEA

☐ ANTHOLOGY
Open my eyes / We gotta get you a woman / Wailing wall / Be nice to me / Hello it's me / I saw the light / It wouldn't have made any difference / Couldn't I just tell you / Sometimes I don't know what to feel / Just one victory / Dream goes on forever / Last ride / Don't you ever learn / Real man / Black and white / Love of the common man / Cliches / All the children sing / Can we still be friends / You cried wolf / Time heals / Compassion / Hideaway / Bang the drum all day / Drive / Johnee jingo / Something to fall back on
8122714912 / Jul '93 / WEA

☐ BACK TO THE BARS
Real man / Love of the common man / Verb: To love / Love in action / Dream goes on forever / Sometimes I don't know what to think / Range war / Black and white / Last ride / Cliches / Don't you ever learn / Never never land / Black Maria / Zen archer / I'm so proud / Oh baby baby / La la means I love you / I saw the light / It wouldn't have made any difference / Eastern intrigues / Initiation / Couldn't I just tell you / Hello it's me
8122711092 / Feb '93 / WEA

☐ BALLAD OF TODD RUNDGREN
Long flowing robe / Ballad (Denny and Jean) / Bleeding / Wailing wall / Range war / Chain letter / Long time a long way to go / Boat on the Charles / Be nice to me / Hope I'm around / Parole / Remember me
8122708632 / Mar '93 / WEA

☐ EVER POPULAR TORTURED ARTIST EFFECT, THE
Hideway / Influenza / Don't hurt yourself / There goes your baybay / Tin soldier / Emporer of the highway / Bang the drum all day / Drive / Chant
8122708762 / Mar '93 / WEA

☐ FAITHFUL
Happenings ten years time ago / Good vibrations / Rain / Most likely you'll go your way and I'll go mine / If six was nine / Strawberry Fields forever / Black and white / Love of the common man / When I pray / Cliches / Verb: To love / Boogies (hamburger hell)
8122708682 / Mar '93 / WEA

☐ HEALING
Healer / Pulse / Flesh / Golden goose / Compassion / Shine / Healing
8122708742 / Mar '93 / WEA

☐ INITIATION, THE
Real man / Born to synthesize / Death of rock and roll / Eastern intrigues / Initiation / Fair warning / Treatise on cosmic fire / Fire of mind or solar fire / Fire of spirit or electric fire / Internal fire or fire by friction
8122708662 / Mar '93 / WEA

☐ PASSPORT COLLECTION, THE (Utopia)
Itch in my brain / Love with a thinker / Bring me my longbow / If I didn't try / Too much water / Maybe I could change / Crybaby / Welcome to my revolution / Winston Smith takes it on the jaw / I will wait / Fix your gaze / Play this game / Style / Stand for something / Secret society / Zen machine / Mated / Wildlife / Mimi gets mad / Mystified / More light / Man of action / Monument
8122722872 / Jul '96 / WEA

☐ RUNT
Broke down and busted / Believe in me / We got to get you a woman / Who's that man / Once burned / Devil's bite / I'm in the clique / There are no words / Let's swing / Last thing you said / Don't tie my hands / Birthday carol
8122708622 / Mar '93 / WEA

☐ SOMETHING ANYTHING
I saw the light / I wouldn't have made any difference / Wolfman Jack / Cold morning light / It takes two to tango / Sweeter memories / Intro / Breathless / Night the carousel burned down / Saving grace / Marlene / Song of the viking / I went to the mirror / Black Maria / One more day (no word) / Couldn't I just tell you / Torch song / Little red lights / Overture / Money: messin' with the kid / Dust in the wind / Piss Aaron / Hello it's me / Some folks is even whiter than me / You left me sore / Slut
8122711072 / Mar '93 / WEA

☐ TODD
How about a little fanfare / I think you know / Spark of life / Elpee's worth of toons / Dream goes on forever / Lord Chancellor's nightmare / Drunken blue rooster / Last number 1 lowest common denomination / Useless begging / Sidewalk cafe / Izzat love / Heavy metal kids / In and out of the chakras we go / Don't you ever learn / Sons of 1984
8122711082 / Mar '93 / WEA

☐ UP AGAINST IT
PCCY 01121 / 20 Apr '98 / Canyon

☐ WITH A TWIST
I saw the light / Influenza / Can we still be friends / Mated / It wouldn't have made any difference / Love is the answer / Fidelity / Never neverland / Hello it's me / I want you / Dream goes on forever
8598662 / 20 Oct '97 / EMI

☐ WIZARD, A TRUE STAR, A
International feel / Never never land / Tic tick tick it wears off / You / Need your head / Rock 'n' roll / Pussy / Dogfight giggle / You don't have to camp around / Flamingo / Zen archer / Just another onionhead / Da da dali / When the shit hits the fan / Sunset Boulevard / Le feel internacionale / Sometimes I don't know what to feel / Does anybody love you / I'm so proud / Ooo baby baby / La la means I love you / Cool jerk / Hungry for love / I don't want to tie you down / Is it my name / Just one victory
8122708642 / Mar '93 / WEA

Rundqvist, Gosta

☐ GOSTA RUNDQVIST & KRISTER ANDERSON (Rundqvist, Gosta & Krister Andersin)
SITCD 9212 / Aug '94 / Sittel

Runners

☐ PHONETIC
Secret world / Neon man / Journeying / Funk talk / C Sands / Phonetic / Hours / Stomp
CDEYE 0010 / Sep '95 / i2i

Running Wild

☐ BLACKHAND INN
NCD 007 / Jan '96 / Noise

☐ BLAZON STONE
NCD 005 / Jan '96 / Noise

☐ DEATH OR GLORY
Riding the storm / Renegade / Evilution / Running blood / Highland glory (the eternal flight) / Marooned / Bad to the bone / Tortuga bay / Death or glory / Battle of Waterloo / March on
NCD 004 / Jan '96 / Noise

☐ FIRST YEARS OF PIRACY, THE
N 01842 / Jan '92 / Noise

☐ MASQUERADE
N 02612
N 02619 / Oct '95 / Noise

☐ PILE OF SKULLS
NCD 006 / Jan '96 / Noise

☐ RIVALRY, THE
GUN 155CD / 23 Feb '98 / Gun

Runrig

☐ BEAT THE DRUM
Stepping down the glory road / Satellite flood / Harvest / Apple came down / Hearthammer / Pride of the summer / Loch Lommond / Solus na madainn / Flower of the west / Ravenscraig
4935832 / 16 Feb '98 / EMI Gold

☐ CUTTER AND THE CLAN, THE
Alba / Cutter / Hearts of olden glory / Pride of the summer / Worker for the wind / Rocket to the moon / Only rose / Protect and survive / Our earth was once green / Aubhal as airds
CCD 1669 / May '95 / Chrysalis

☐ GAELIC COLLECTION 1973-1988, THE (2CD Set)
RR 009 / Jun '98 / Ridge

☐ HEARTLAND
O cho mealt / This darkest winter / Lifeline / Air a' chuan / Dance called America / Everlasting gun / Skye / Cnoc na faille / Wire / An ataireachd ard / Ferry / Tuireadh lain ruaidh
RRCD 005 / Feb '86 / Ridge

☐ HIGHLAND CONNECTION, THE
Gainhna gaella / Mairi / What time / Fichead bliadhna / Na luing air seoladh / Loch lomond / Na h-uain a's t-earrach / Foghar nan eilean '78 / Twenty five pounder / Going home / Morning tide / Cearcal a chuain
RRCD 001 / Aug '89 / Ridge

☐ LONG DISTANCE (The Best Of Runrig)
(Stepping down the) glory road / Alba / Greatest flame / Rocket to the moon / Abhainn an t-sluaigh / Protect and survive / Rhythm of my heart / Hearthammer / An ubhal as airde / Wonderful / Mighty Atlantic/Mara theme / Flower of the west / Every river / Siol ghoraidh / Hearts of olden glory / Skye / Loch Lomond
CDCHR 6116 / Oct '96 / Chrysalis

☐ MARA
Day in a boat / Nothing but the sun / Mighty Atlantic/ Mara theme / Things that are / Road and the river / Meadhan oidche air on acairseid / Wedding / Dancing floor / Thairis air a ghleann / Lighthouse
CDCHR 6111 / Nov '95 / Chrysalis

☐ ONCE IN A LIFETIME
Dance called America / Protect and survive / Chiu mi'n geamradh / Rocket to the moon / Going home / Cnoc na feille / Nightfall on Marsco / S to mo leannan / Skye / Loch Lomond
CCD 1695 / Nov '88 / Chrysalis

☐ RECOVERY
'An toll dubh / Rubh nan cudeigean / 'Ic lain 'ic shaumais / Recovery / Instrumental / Nightfall on Marsco/'S tu mo leannan / Breaking the chains / Fuaim a bhlair / Tir an airm / Old boys / Dust
RRCD 002 / Aug '89 / Ridge

☐ SEARCHLIGHT
News from Heaven / Every river / City of lights / Eirinn / Tir a'mhurain / World appeal / Tear down these walls / Only the brave / Siol ghoraidh / That final mile / Smalltown / Precious years
CCD 1713 / Sep '89 / Chrysalis

☐ TRANSMITTING LIVE
Urlar / Ard / Edge of the world / Greatest flame / Harvest moon / Wire / Precious years / Every river / Flower of the West / Only the brave / Alba / Pog aon oidche earraich (on kiss one spring evening)
CDCHR 6090 / Nov '94 / Chrysalis

Runswick, Daryl

☐ HUMOURS OF DARYL RUNSWICK, THE
BML 014 / Feb '96 / British Music

☐ VOICE THEATRE OF DARYL RUNSWICK, THE (Runswick, Daryl/ Electric Phoenix)
BML 015 / Feb '96 / British Music

Runt O' The Litter

☐ KNOT THE METRONOME
Cricklewood set / Jock Stewart/The blackberry bush / Morrison's jig / Bowlegged tailor set / Coming down in the rain / Roving gambler off to California / Pipe on the hob / Nancy Spain / Summer sent you / Reconciliation set / Contradiction set / Twa Corbies/ New mown hay / Ae fond kiss/Banish misfortune
IRCD 038 / Aug '96 / Iona

Rupaul

☐ FOXY LADY
Happy / Party train / Little bit of love / Snapshot / Foxy lady / R u nasty / Falling / Dolores / Work that body / Celebrate / Snatched for the Gods / If you were a woman and I was a man
8122722562 / Mar '97 / Rhino

Rupkina, Yanka

☐ KALIMENKO DENKO
HNCD 1334 / May '89 / Hannibal

Rural Blues

☐ GOIN' UP THE COUNTRY/SATURDAY NIGHT FUNCTION
BGOCD 384 / 27 Apr '98 / Beat Goes On

Rurutu Choir

☐ POLYNESIAN ODYSSEY
SHCD 64065 / Sep '96 / Shanachie

Rusby, Kate

☐ HOURGLASS
PRCD 02 / Mar '97 / Pure

☐ KATE RUSBY & KATHRYN ROBERTS (Rusby, Kate & Kathryn Roberts)
Recruited collier / Ned on the hill / Lorry ride / Queen and the soldier / Courting is a pleasure / Constant lovers / Dark eyed sailor / Hunting the hare / Plains of Waterloo / Exile
PRCD 01 / May '95 / Pure

Rush

☐ 2112
Lessons / Passage to Bangkok / Something for nothing / Tears / Twilight zone / 2112 overture / Temples of Syrinx / Discover / Presentation / Oracle / Dream / Soliloquy / Grand finale
5346262 / Jul '97 / Mercury

☐ ALL THE WORLD'S A STAGE
Anthem / Bastille day / By-Tor and the snow dog / At the tobes of Hades / Across the Styx / Of the battle / Epilogue / Fly by night / In the mood / In the end / Lakeside park / Something for nothing / 2112 overture / Temples of syrinx / Presentation / Soliloquy / Grand finale / What you're doing / Working man / Finding my way
8225522 / Apr '87 / Mercury

☐ CARESS OF STEEL
Bastille day / Fountain of Lamneth / In the valley / Didacts and narpets / No one at the bridge / Panacea / Bacchus plateau / Fountain / I think I'm going bald / Lakeside park / Necromancer / Into the darkness / Under the shadow / Return of the Prince
8225432 / Apr '87 / Mercury

☐ CHRONICLES
Finding my way / Fly by night / Bastille day / 2112 overture / Temples of syrinx / Farewell to kings / Trees / Freewill / Tom Sawyer / Limelight / Subdivisions / Distant early warning / Big money / Force ten / Mystic rhythms / Working man / Anthem / Lakeside Park / What you're doing / Closer to the heart / La villa strangiato / Spirit of radio / Red Barchetta / Passage to Bangkok / New world man / Red sector A / Manhattan Project / Time stand still / Show don't tell
8389362 / Sep '90 / Vertigo

☐ COUNTERPARTS
Animate / Stick it out / Cut to the chase / Nobody's hero / Between sun and moon / Alien shore / Speed of love / Double agent / Leave that thing alone / Cold fire / Everyday glory
7567825282 / Oct '93 / WEA

☐ EXIT... STAGE LEFT
Spirit of radio / Red Barchetta / YYZ / Passage to Bangkok / Closer to the heart / Beneath, between and behind / Jacob's ladder / Broon's bane / Trees / Xanadu / Freewill / Tom Sawyer / La villa strangiato
8225512 / Apr '87 / Mercury

☐ FAREWELL TO KINGS, A
Farewell to Kings / Xanadu / Closer to the heart / Cinderella man / Madrigal / Cygni X-1
5346282 / Jul '97 / Mercury

☐ FLY BY NIGHT
Anthem / Beneath, between and behind / Best I can / By-Tor and the snow dog / At the tobes of Hades / Across the Styx / Of the battle / Epilogue / Fly by night / In the end / Making memories / Rivendell
5346242 / Jul '97 / Mercury

☐ GRACE UNDER PRESSURE
Distant early warning / After image / Red sector A / Enemy within / Body electric / Kid gloves / Red lenses / Between the wheels
5346342 / Jul '97 / Mercury

☐ HEMISPHERES
Apollo / Armageddon / Circumstances / Cygnus / Dionysius / Prelude / Sphere / Trees / La villa strangiato
5346292 / Jul '97 / Mercury

☐ HOLD YOUR FIRE
Force team / Time stand still / Open secrets / Prime mover / Lock and key / Tai Shan / High water
8324642 / '88 / Mercury

☐ MOVING PICTURES
Tom Sawyer / Red Barchetta / YYZ / Limelight / Camera / Witch hunt / (Part III of Fear) / Vital signs
5346312 / Jul '97 / Mercury

☐ PERMANENT WAVES
Spirit of radio / Freewill / Jacob's ladder / Entre nous / Different strings / Natural science
5346302 / Jul '97 / Mercury

☐ POWER WINDOWS
Big money / Grand design / Manhattan Project / Marathon / Territories / Middletown dreams / Emotion detector / Mystic rhythms
8260982 / Nov '85 / Mercury

☐ PRESTO
Show don't tell / Chain lightning / Pass / War paint / Scars / Presto / Super conductor / Anagram (for Mongo) / Red tide / Hand over fist / Available light
7820402 / Dec '89 / WEA

☐ ROLL THE BONES
Dreamline / Bravado / Roll the bones / Face up / Where's my thing / Big wheel / Heresy / I don't stand a ghost of a chance with you / Neurotica / You bet your life
7567822932 / Sep '91 / WEA

☐ RUSH
Before and after / Finding my way / Here again / In the mood / Need some love / Take a friend / What you're doing / Working man
8225412 / Apr '87 / Mercury

☐ RUSH RETROSPECTIVE 1974-1980
Spirit of the radio / Trees / Something for nothing / Freewill / Xanadu / Bastille day / By Tor and the snow dog / Anthem / Closer to the heart / 2112 Overture / Temples of syrinx / La Villa strangiato / Fly by night / Finding my way
5349092 / Aug '97 / Mercury

☐ RUSH RETROSPECTIVE 1981-1987
Big money / Red barchetta / Subdivisions / Time stand still / Mystic rhythms / Analog kid / Distant early warning / Body electric / Mission / Limelight / Red sector a / New world man / Tom Sawyer / Force ten
5439102 / Aug '97 / Mercury

☐ RUSH: INTERVIEW PICTURE DISC
CBAK 4055 / Apr '92 / Baktabak

☐ SHOW OF HANDS, A
Big money / Subdivisions / Marathon / Turn the page / Manhattan project / Mission / Distant early warning / Mystic rhythms / Witch hunt / Rhythm method / Force ten / Time stands still / Red sector A / Closer to the heart
8463462 / Jan '89 / Mercury

☐ SIGNALS
Subdivisions / Analog kid / Chemistry / Digital man / Weapon / New world man / Losing it / Countdown
5346332 / Jul '97 / Mercury

☐ TEST FOR ECHO
Test for echo / Color of right / Totem / Virtuality / Limbo / Carve away the stone / Resist / Dog years / Time and motion / Driven / Half the world
7567829252 / Aug '96 / WEA

☐ WORKING MAN (A Tribute To Rush) (Various Artists)
RR 88712 / Sep '96 / Roadrunner

Rush, Chris

☐ THERE'S NO BONES IN ICE CREAM
Living in New York / Insanity / Murder rate / Macho / PMS / War on drugs / Happiness and shame / Terror / Vegetarianism / Aliens / Reincarnation / Killer bees / Boogers
SC 6134 / 17 Nov '97 / Sundazed

Rush, Jennifer

☐ JENNIFER RUSH
Madonna's eyes / Twenty five lovers / Come give me your hand / Nobody move / Never gonna turn back again / Ring of ice / Into my dreams / I see a shadow (not a fantasy) / Surrender / Power of love
4609472 / 27 Jul '98 / Columbia

☐ POWER OF JENNIFER RUSH, THE
Destiny / Heart over mind / Ring of ice / Ave Maria (Survivors of a different kind) / Power of love / Higher ground / Flames of paradise: *Rush, Jennifer & Elton John* / Twenty five lovers / I come undone / Same heart: *Rush, Jennifer & Michael Bolton* / If you're ever gonna lose my love
4691632 / Feb '92 / Columbia

Rush, Otis

☐ AIN'T ENOUGH COMIN' IN
Don't burn down the bridge / That will never do / Somebody have mercy / Fool for you / Homework / My jug and I / She's a good 'un / It's my own fault / Ain't enough comin' in / If I had any sense, I'd go back home / Ain't that good news / As the years go passing by
5187692 / Apr '94 / This Way Up

☐ COLD DAY IN HELL
DD 638 / Jul '93 / Delmark

☐ DOUBLE TROUBLE (Charly Blues Masterworks Vol.24)
All your love / Three times a fool / She's a good 'un / It takes time / Double trouble / My love will never die / My baby is a good 'un / Checking on my baby / Jump sister Bessie / I can't quit you baby / If you were mine / Groaning the blues / Keep on loving me baby / Sit down baby / Love that woman / Violent love
CDBM 24 / Apr '92 / Charly

☐ DOUBLE TROUBLE - LIVE IN JAPAN 1986
Introduction/Tops / All your love / Please, please, please / Killing floor / Stand by me / Lonely man / Double trouble / Right place, wrong time / Got my mojo working / Gambler's blues
NEGCD 277 / Oct '95 / Sequel

☐ LIVE AND AWESOME
RBASE 30012 / May '97 / Red Base

☐ LIVE IN EUROPE
Cut you loose / All your love / You're breaking my heart / I wonder why / Feel so bad / Society woman/ Love is just a gamble / Crosscut saw / I can't quit you baby / I'm tore up / Looking back
ECD 260342 / Sep '93 / Evidence
IS 9212 / Mar '96 / Isabel

☐ LOST IN THE BLUES
Hold that train / You've been an angel / Little red rooster / Trouble, trouble / Please love me / You don't have to go / Got to be some changes made / You got me runnin' / I miss you so
ALCD 4797 / Aug '92 / Alligator

☐ SCREAMIN' & CRYIN'
ECD 260142 / Jan '92 / Evidence

☐ SO MANY ROADS
DE 643 / Dec '95 / Blind Pig

☐ TOPS
Right place, wrong time / Crosscut saw / Tops / Feels so bad / Gambler's blues / Keep on loving me baby / I wonder why
BP 3188CD / May '94 / Blind Pig

Rush, Tom

☐ BLUES, SONGS AND BALLADS
Duncan and Brady / I don't want your millions mister / San Francisco Bay blues / Mole's moan / Rye whiskey / Big fat woman / Nine pound hammer / Diamond Joe / Mobile Texas line / Joe Turner / Every day in the week / Alabamy bound / More pretty girls / I wish I could shimmy like my sister Kate / Original talking blues / Pallet on the floor / Drop down mama / Rag mama / Barb'ry Allen / Cocaine / Come back baby / Stagger Lee / Baby, please don't go
CDWIK 948 / Aug '90 / Big Beat

☐ TOM RUSH/WRONG END OF THE RAINBOW
Driving wheel / Rainy day man / Drop down Mama / Old man song / Lullaby / These days / Wild child / Colors of the sun / Livin' in the country / Child's song / Wrong end of the rainbow / Biloxi / Merrimac County / Riding on a railroad / Came to see me yesterday in the merry month of May / Starlight / Sweet baby James / Rotunda / Jazzman / Gnostic serenade
BGOCD 361 / Jul '97 / Beat Goes On

Rushen, Patrice

☐ HAVEN'T YOU HEARD (The Best Of Patrice Rushen)
Hang it up / When I found you / Haven't you heard / Settle for my love / Givin' it up is givin' up / Look up / Never gonna give you up / Forget me nots / Breakout / Remind me / Number one / Feels so real (won't let go) / Get off (you fascinate me)
0349723882 / 18 Aug '97 / Rhino

☐ STRAIGHT FROM THE HEART
Forget me nots / I was tired of being alone / All we need / Number one / Where there is love / Breakout / If only / Remind me / She will take you down to love
8122735082 / Jul '96 / Elektra

Rushing, Jimmy

☐ GEE BABY AIN'T I GOOD TO YOU (Rushing, Jimmy Allstars)
805302 / Feb '98 / New World

☐ JIMMY RUSHING WITH THE COUNT BASIE ORCHESTRA 1938-1945 (Rushing, Jimmy & Count Basie Orchestra)
Jimmy's blues / Take me back, baby / Harvard blues / Gee, baby ain't I good to you / One two three-o' Lairy / Rusty dusty blues / For the good of your country / Lost the blackout blues / Undecided blues / I'm gonna move to the outskirts of town / Goin' to Chicago blues / It's the same old South / I left my baby / I can't believe that you're in love with me / How long blues / You can depend on me / Baby, don't tell on me / Blues I like to hear / Do you wanna jump children / Evil blues
CD 53298 / Jul '97 / Giants Of Jazz

☐ MR. FIVE BY FIVE
TPZ 1019 / May '95 / Topaz Jazz

☐ RUSHING LULLABIES
I'm coming Virginia / Knock me a kiss / Harvard blues / Mister five by five / Travellin' light / June night / It's a sin to tell a lie / Rosalie / Jimmy's blues / Someday sweetheart / When you're smiling / Somebody stole my gal / You can't run around blues / Say you don't mean it / 'Deed I do / Pink champagne / Did you ever / I cried for you / Three long years / I can't believe that you're in love with me / Good rockin' tonight / One evening / Russian lullaby / Travel the road of love
CK 65118 / Jun '97 / Sony Jazz

☐ SWINGS THE BLUES
Sent for you yesterday and here you come today / Blue devil blues / Won't you be my baby / Boogie woogie / He ain't got rhythm / Listen my children and you shall hear / Good morning blues / Don't you miss your baby / Blues in the dark / Now will you be good / Do you wanna jump children / Evil blues / You can't run around / Undecided blues / Take me back, baby / Goin' to Chicago blues / I'm gonna move to the outskirts of town / Lazy lady blues / Jimmy's blues / Blues I like to hear
RPCD 637 / Apr '97 / Robert Parker Jazz

☐ WHO WAS IT SANG THAT SONG (Rushing, Jimmy Allstars)
Baby won't you please come home / 'C' Jam blues / I surrender dear / Deed I do / Almost home / Blue / Stormy Monday blues / Jelly jelly / Moten stomp / All of me
805102 / May '97 / New World

☐ YOU AND ME THAT USED TO BE, THE
You and me that used to be / Fine and mellow / When I grow too old to dream / I surrender dear / Linger awhile / Bei mir bist du schon / My last affair / All God's chillun got rhythm / More than you know / Home / Thanks a million
ND 86460 / Apr '89 / Bluebird

Ruskin-Spear, Roger

☐ ELECTRIC SHOCK PLUS
All by yourself in the moonlight / I'm a fly / Mattress man / Blue baboon / Liberty laughing song / Doctor Rock / Patrick Moore / Make yourself a happiness pie / Living doll / Trouser freak / Trouser press / Release me / Drop out / Still loving you
DJC 005 / 19 Feb '98 / Blueprint

☐ ELECTRIC SHOCKS
All by yourself in the moonlight / I'm a fly / Mattress man / Blue baboon / Liberty laughing song / Doctor rock / Patrick Moore / Make yourself a happiness pie / Living doll / Trouser freak / Trouser press / Release me / Drop out
DJC 005 / 26 Jan '98 / DJC

Russell & Hardin

☐ EARLY YEARS
EDCD 498 / Nov '96 / Edsel

Russell Family

☐ OF DOOLIN, COUNTY CLARE
Campbell's reel / Heather breeze/The Traveller / St. Kevin of Glendalough / Potlick/The Peeler's jacket / Five mile chase / Russell's hornpipe/Fisher's hornpipe / Poor little fisher boy / Walls of Liscarroll/ The battering ram / Garrett Barry's reel / Tommy glenny's reel / Connemara stockings/The Westmeath hunt / When Musheen went to Bunnan / Tatter Jack Walsh / De'il among the tailors / Roscrea cows / Fair haired boy/The black haired lass / Off to California / Give the girl her fourpence / Nora Daly
GLCD 3079 / May '93 / Green Linnet

☐ RUSSELL FAMILY OF DOOLIN, CO. CLARE, THE
Campbell's reel / Heather breeze/The traveller / St. Kevin of Glendalough / Potlick/The peeler's jacket / Five mile chase / Russell's hornpipe/Fisher's hornpipe / Poor little fisher boy / Walls of Liscarroll/ The battering ram / Garrett Barry's reel / Tommy Glenny's reel / Connemara stockings/The westmeath hunt / When Musheen went to Bunnan / Tatter Jack Walsh / De'il among the tailors / Roscrea cows / Fair haired boy/The black haired lass / Off to California / Give the girl her fourpence / Nora Daly
OSS 8CD / Jan '94 / Ossian

Russell, Anna

☐ ENCORE
SFK 60316 / Jul '98 / Sony Classical

Russell, Brenda

☐ GREATEST HITS
Piano in the dark / So good, so right / Gravity / Kiss me with the wind / Get here / Dinner with Gershwin / Stop running away / In the thick of it / If only for one night / Way back when / Justice in truth / Le restaurant
5525402 / Sep '96 / Spectrum

Russell, Calvin

☐ CRACK IN TIME, A
Crack in time / Big brother / Nothin' / Behind the eight ball / Automated / North Austin slim / One step ahead / Living at the end of a gun / I should have been home / My way / This is my life / Little stars / Moments / Wagon to stars
422303 / May '94 / New Rose

☐ DREAM OF THE DOG
422020 / Apr '95 / Last Call

☐ LE VOYAGEUR
422489 / Jan '95 / New Rose

☐ SOLDIER
422422 / May '94 / New Rose

☐ SOUNDS FROM THE FOURTH WORLD
422306 / Nov '94 / New Rose

☐ THIS IS MY LIFE
302592 / Jan '98 / Last Call

Russell, Devon

☐ MONEY SEX AND VIOLENCE
RNCD 0010 / Jan '91 / RN

Russell, George

☐ AT BEETHOVEN HALL (The Complete Recordings)
Freein' up / Lydia and her friends / Lydia in Bags' groove / Lydia's confirmation / Lydia 'round midnight / Takin' Lydia home / You are my sunshine / Oh jazz po' jazz / Volupte
5390842 / 26 May '98 / MPS Jazz

☐ ELECTRONIC SONATA FOR SOULS LOVED BY NATURE (1968)
Part 1 / Part 2
1210342 / Jan '94 / Soul Note

☐ EZZ-THETICS (Russell, George Sextet)
OJCCD 70 / Oct '92 / Original Jazz Classics

☐ IT'S ABOUT TIME (Russell, George Living Time Orchestra)
It's about time / Event
LBLC 6587 / Mar '97 / Label Bleu

☐ JAZZ IN THE SPACE AGE (Russell, George & His Orchestra)
Chromatic Universe I / Dimensions / Chromatic Universe II / Lydiot / Waltz from outer space / Chromatic Universe III
GRP 18262 / 27 Jul '98 / Chess Mates

☐ JAZZ WORKSHOP, THE
378502 / 7 Apr '98 / Koch Jazz

☐ LIVE IN AN AMERICAN TIME SPIRAL (Russell, George New York Band)
SNCD 1049 / '86 / Soul Note

☐ LONDON CONCERT VOL.1 (Russell, George Living Time Orchestra)
STCD 560 / May '93 / Stash

☐ LONDON CONCERT VOL.2 (Russell, George Living Time Orchestra)
STCD 561 / May '93 / Stash

☐ LONDON CONCERT, THE (Live At Ronnie Scott's) (Russell, George Living Time Orchestra)
LBLC 6527/8 / Nov '95 / Label Bleu

☐ NEW YORK BIG BAND
SNCD 1039 / '86 / Soul Note

☐ OTHELLO BALLET SUITE/ ELECTRONIC ORGAN SONATA 1
1210142 / Oct '90 / Soul Note

☐ OUTER VIEW
OJCCD 616 / Jun '95 / Original Jazz Classics

☐ VERTICAL FORM VI (Live In Sweden 1977)
Event
1210192 / Nov '90 / Soul Note

Russell, Hal

☐ FINISH SWISS TOUR, THE
Monica's having a baby / Aila/35 basic / Temporarily / Raining violets / For MC / Dance of the spider people / Ten letters of love / Hal the weenie / Linda's rock vamp / Mars theme
5112612 / Oct '91 / ECM

☐ HAL RUSSELL STORY
Intro and fanfare / Toy parade / Trumpet march / Riverside jump / Krupa / You're blase / Dark rapture / World class / Wood chips / My little grass shack / O and B / For M / Gloomy Sunday / Hair male / Bossa G / Mildred / Dope music / Two times two / Ayler song / Rehcabnettul / Steve's freedom principle / Lady in the lake / Oh well
5173642 / Jun '93 / ECM

Russell, Janet

☐ BRIGHT SHINING MORNING
HARCD 026 / Oct '93 / Harbour Town

☐ DANCIN' CHANTIN' (Russell, Janet & Christine Kydd)
Rattlin' roarin' Willie / Fisherman's wife / Logan water / Les filles des forges / Maire Nighean Alastair / Up and awa' wi' the laverock / Duncan Gray / Lady Mary Anne / Reel o' stumpie / Tail toddle / Terror time / Strathmartine Braes / Clerk Saunders / La Caille / Pride's awa' / Bluebell polka / Parting glass / Jock since ever
CDTRAX 077 / Sep '94 / Greentrax

☐ JANET RUSSELL AND CHRISTINE KYDD (Russell, Janet & Christine Kydd)
Buy broom besoms / Dainty Davie / Up wi' the Carls o'Dysart / De'il's awa' wi' tha exciseman / Deja mal Mariee / Bonnie at morn / Children of Africa / My Donald / Ode to big blue / Tae the weavers gin ye gang / Old and strong / Mountain song / Do you love an apple / Last carol / Stand up fight for your rights / Everyone 'neath a vine and fig tree
CDTRAX 011 / Aug '93 / Greentrax

Russell, John

☐ BIRTHDAYS (Russell, John & Roger Turner)
EM 4010 / Sep '96 / Emanem

Russell, Leon

☐ LEGEND IN MY TIME
ARKK 10022 / 6 Apr '98 / ARKK
ELDCD 004 / 4 May '98 / Eldorado

Russell, Luis

☐ CLASSICS 1926-1929
CLASSICS 588 / Aug '91 / Classics

☐ CLASSICS 1930-1934 (Russell, Luis & His Orchestra)
CLASSICS 606 / Oct '92 / Classics

☐ COLLECTION 1926-1934, THE
COCD 7 / May '93 / Collector's Classics

☐ LUIS RUSSELL & HIS ORCHESTRA (Russell, Luis & His Orchestra)
Savoy shout / Call of the freaks / Mahogany hall stomp / African jungle / Feelin' the spirit / Jersey lightning / Dalls blues / St Louis blues / Doctor blues / Saratoga shout / Song of the Swanee / Louisiana swing / On revival day / Muggin' lightly / Panama / High tension / Case on Dawn (ease on down) / At the Darktown strutter's ball / My blue heaven / Ghost of the freaks / Hokus pokus / Moods (primitive) / Ol' man river
TPZ 1039 / Feb '96 / Topaz Jazz

☐ SAVOY SHOUT
JSPCD 308 / Aug '89 / JSP

Russell, Micho

☐ IN OUR OWN DEAR LAND
GTDCD 134 / Dec '97 / GTD

☐ LIMESTONE ROCK, THE
GTDHCD 104 / Jul '93 / GTD

☐ MAN FROM CLARE, THE
TRADHCD 011 / Jul '93 / GTD

☐ TRADITIONAL IRISH MUSIC FROM COUNTY CLARE
CMCD 077 / Nov '97 / Celtic Music

Russell, Pee Wee

☐ INDIVIDUALISM OF PEE WEE RUSSELL, THE
Love is just around the corner / Squeeze me / Ballin' the Jack / I'd do most anything for you / California here I come / St. James infirmary / Baby, won't you please come home / Lady's in love with you / Struttin' with some barbecue / St. Louis blues / Sweet Lorraine / Sentimental journey / If I had you / Coquette / Lady is a tramp
SV 0271 / Oct '97 / Savoy Jazz

☐ JAZZ ORIGINAL
Love is just around the corner / Embraceable you / Serenade to a shylock / Serenade to a shylock / Sunday / I ain't gonna give nobody... / Georgia grind / Jig walk / Deuces wild / Last time I saw Chicago / About face / Don't leave me, Daddy / Rosetta / Squeeze me / Take me to the land of Jazz / Take me to the land of Jazz / Rose of Washington square / Rose of Washington square / Keepin' out of mischief now / DA blues / DA blues / Wailin' DA blues
CMD 14042 / Feb '97 / Commodore Jazz

☐ JAZZ REUNION (Russell, Pee Wee & Coleman Hawkins)
If I could be with you one hour tonight / Tin tin deo / Mariooch / All too soon / 28th and 8th / What am I here for
CCD 79020 / Feb '97 / Candid

☐ LAND OF JAZZ
TPZ 1018 / Apr '95 / Topaz Jazz

☐ PORTRAIT OF PEE WEE
FSCD 126 / Jan '91 / Fresh Sound

☐ WE'RE IN THE MONEY
BLCD 760909 / Jan '89 / Black Lion

Russell, Tom

☐ COWBOY REEL
El Liano / Bad half hour / Basque / Claude Dallas / Navajo rug / Indian cowboy / Gallo del cielo / Rayburn Crane / Sonora's death row / Zane grey / Roanie
MRCD 161 / '92 / Munich

☐ HEART ON A SLEEVE
One and one / Heart on a sleeve / Blinded by the light of love / Touch of grey / Wild hearts / St. Olav's gate / Gallo del cielo / Mandarin oranges / Cropduster / Canadian whiskey / Chinese silver / Bowl of red
BCD 15243 / Aug '86 / Bear Family

☐ HURRICANE SEASON (Russell, Tom Band)
Black pearl / Lord of the trains / Beyond the blues / Jack Johnson / Chocolate cigarette / Winnipeg / Evangeline hotel / Dollars worth of gasoline / Hurricane season / Haley's comet
RTMCD 49 / Jun '97 / Round Tower

☐ OUT OF CALIFORNIA
RTMS 9603CD / Sep '96 / Round Tower

☐ POOR MAN'S DREAM (Russell, Tom Band)
Blue wing / Heart of the working man / Veteran's day / Walkin' on the moon / Outbound plane / Bergenfield / Spanish burgundy / Gallo del cielo / La frontera / Navajo rug / Under the gun / White trash song
RTMCD 48 / Feb '96 / Round Tower
PHCD 1139 / Sep '96 / Philo

☐ ROAD TO BAYAMON (Russell, Tom Band)
Home before dark / US Steel / Downtown train / Love makes a fool of the wise / Definition of a fool / As the crow flies / Road to Bayamon / Alkali / Wise blood / Joshua tree / Mexcal / William Faulkner in Hollywood / Fire
PH 1116CD / '89 / Philo

☐ ROSE OF THE SAN JOAQUIN, THE
RTMCD 71 / Oct '95 / Round Tower

Russki Color

☐ RUSSKI COLOR (Traditional Folk Melodies From Russia)
LDX 274955 / Jan '93 / La Chant Du Monde

Russo, Marc

☐ WINDOW, THE
Southern tale / Shake / Intro / Window / Crooked numbers / Elizabeth / Whatever you want / Weekend / School / In the rain / Notes next to the notes
JVC 20352 / Jul '94 / JVC

Rust Farm

☐ RUST FARM
Until I know her name / Shadows on the hill / Two by two / Rust farm fire / Only witness / Belfast / Rose's bar and grill / Road to Cody / Six foot pine box / Downpour
DARINGCD 3032 / 16 Mar '98 / Daring

Rustavi Choir

☐ GEORGIAN VOICES
7559792242 / Jan '95 / Nonesuch

☐ HEROIC SONGS AND HYMNS FROM GEORGIA
Odoiya / Chona / Tskhenosnuri / Romelni kerubinta / Hasanbegura / Didou nana / Adila ali pasha / Naduri / Batonedo / Kvira / Chven mshvidoba / Maqruli / Gikharoden shen tsminado deopalo / Utush lashruli / Perkhuli / Charulo
SHANCD 65014 / 9 Mar '98 / Shanachie

Rusted Root

☐ WHEN I WOKE
Drum trip / Ecstasy / Send me on my way / Cruel sun / Cat turned blue / Beautiful people / Martyr / Rain / Food and creative love / Lost in a crowd / Laugh as the sun / Infinite tamboura / Back to the Earth
5227132 / Aug '95 / Mercury

Rustichelli, Paolo

☐ MYSTIC JAZZ
Femmes / Bold man / Capri / Merkel bokrug / Full moon / El topo / Bridge / Black plastic / Capri
5134152 / Apr '92 / PolyGram Jazz

Rustlers

☐ LINE DANCING FOR COWBOYS AND COWGIRLS
SPINCD 03 / 23 Feb '98 / Quantum Leap

Ruth Ruth

☐ LAUGHING GALLERY
74321302772 / Nov '95 / American

☐ LITTLE DEATH
64802 / Sep '96 / Epitaph

Rutherford, Charles

☐ COLLAGE (Rutherford, Charles Jazz Pacific Orchestra)
SB 2088 / Sep '97 / Sea Breeze

Rutherford, Mike

☐ SMALLCREEPS DAY
Between the tick and the tock / Working in line / After hours / Cats and rats in this neighbourhood / Smallcreep alone / Out into the daylight / At the end of the day / Moonshine / Time and time again / Romani / Every road / Overnight job
CASCD 1149 / Jun '89 / Charisma

Rutherford, Paul

☐ 1989 AND ALL THAT (Rutherford, Paul & George Haslam)
1939 / Orion / 1977 / 1984 / Come Sunday / 1986 / Sigma / London lights / 1989
SLAMCD 301 / Oct '90 / Slam

☐ GENTLE HARM OF THE BOURGEOISIE, THE
EM 4019 / Nov '97 / Emanem

☐ SEQUENCES 72 AND 73 (Rutherford, Paul & Iskra 1912)
EM 4018 / Nov '97 / Emanem

Ruthless Rap Assassins

☐ THINK - IT AIN'T ILLEGAL YET
What did you say your name was / Listen to the hit / Why me / Think / Hard and direct / I got no time / Radio / Down and dirty / No tale, no twist / Pick up the pace / (I try to) flow it out / Less mellow
CDEMC 3604 / Oct '91 / Murdertone

Rutles

☐ ARCHAEOLOGY
Major Happy's up and coming once upon a good time band / Rendezvous / Questionnaire / We've arrived (and to prove it we're here) / Lonely-phobia / Unfinished words / Hey Mister / Easy listening / Now she's left you / Knicker elastic King / I love you / Eine kleine middle klasse musik / Joe Public / Shangri-la / I don't know why / Back in '64
CDVUS 119
CDVUSX 119 / Oct '96 / Virgin

Ruts

☐ CRACK, THE
Babylon's burning / Dope for guns / SUS / Something that I said / You're just a... / It was cold / Savage circle / Jah war / Criminal mind / Backwater / Out of order / Human punk
CDV 2132 / Jul '90 / Virgin

☐ DEMOLITION DANCING
RRCD 182 / Apr '94 / Receiver

☐ RHYTHM COLLISION DUB VOL.1 (Ruts DC & Mad Professor)
RE 151CD / Nov '94 / ROIR

☐ RHYTHM COLLISION VOL.1 (Ruts DC & Mad Professor)
EB 002 / 1 Jun '98 / Echo Beach

☐ RULES
EFA 123032 / Jul '94 / Vince Lombard

☐ SOMETHING THAT I SAID (The Best Of The Ruts)
In a rut / H-eyes / Babylon's burning / Dope for guns / SUS / Something that I said / You're just a... / It was cold / Savage circle / Jah war / Criminal mind / Backbiter / Out of order / Human punk / Staring at the rude boys / Love in vain / West one (Shine on me)
CDOVD 454 / Feb '95 / Virgin

Ruzicka, Karel

☐ YOU'RE NEVER ALONE
CR 00122 / Nov '95 / Czech Radio

RX

☐ BEDSIDE TOXICOLOGY
INV 091CD / 29 Jun '98 / Invisible

Ryan, Barry

☐ BEST OF BARRY RYAN VOL.1, THE
5114712 / Oct '97 / Polyphon

☐ ELOISE
Love is love / Kitsch / Hunt / My mama / I'm sorry Susan / From my head to my toe / Can't let you go / Eloise / Colour of my love / We did it together / It is written / Caroline / Love always comes tomorrow / Goodbye
5503852 / Jan '95 / Spectrum

Ryan, Cathie

☐ CATHIE RYAN
SH 78008 / Mar '97 / Shanachie

Ryan, Marion

☐ AT HER BEST
Love me forever / Stairway of love / Hit the road to dreamland / Jeepers creepers / Mr. wonderful / I'm beginning to see the light / Cry me a river / That's happiness / There will never be another you / Oh-oh I'm falling in love again / I'll take romance / World goes round and round / My heart belongs to daddy / It might as well be spring / I need you / Make the man love me / Always and forever / High life / Why do fools fall in love / Wait for me / Hot diggity (dog ziggity boom) / Sailor boy, talk to me in english / Please don't say goodnight / Chantez chantez
C5MCD 614 / Jun '94 / See For Miles

Ryan, Mick

☐ WIDOW'S PROMISE, THE (Ryan, Mick & Pete Harris)
Widow's promise / Bonny light horseman / Old couple / Poor old horse / Man I killed / Channels / Hash House blues / Ramble away / Salisbury Plain / Love is life / Adieu adieu
TERRCD 011 / 27 Apr '98 / Terra Nova

Ryan, Sean

☐ BACK HOME TO THE CLIFFS OF MOHIR
St Andrew's / Swallow / Reavey's / Brook / Slabh bloom / Frost is all over / Charlie Mulvihille's / McCollum's / Kiss me Kate / Sean Ryan's / Eel in the sink / Larry Redican's / Providence / Trip to Nenagh / Anne Sheehy's / Stage / Pipe on the hob / Coleman's / Tommy Coen's reels 1 and 2 / Thornton's / Tommy McGuire's / Fahy's jigs 1 and 2 / Bashful bachelor / McIntyre's / Star of munster / Paddy Kelly's / Killavil / Father Quinn's / McGreevey's
PTICD 1012 / Mar '97 / Pure Traditional Irish

☐ MINSTREL'S FANCY
CEFCD 169 / Dec '95 / Gael Linn

☐ TAKE THE AIR
CEFCD 142 / Jan '94 / Gael Linn

Rybin Choir

☐ SERBIAN AND BULGARIAN
RELIGIOUS CHANTS
RUS 288087 / May '96 / Saison Russe

Ryce, Daryle

☐ I WALK WITH... (Ryce, Daryle & Loonis
McGlohon Trio/Quartet)
ACD 141 / Nov '96 / Audiophile

☐ UNLESS IT'S YOU
ACD 271 / Apr '93 / Audiophile

Rydell, Bobby

☐ BEST OF BOBBY RYDELL, THE
CDSGP 0156 / Jul '95 / Prestige

Ryder, Anna

☐ EYE TO EYE
RM 01CD / Oct '93 / Rowdy

Ryder, Mitch

☐ BREAKOUT (Ryder, Mitch & The Detroit
Wheels)
Walking the dog / I had it made / In the midnight hour
/ Ooh-poo-pah-doo / I like it like that / Little latin lupe
lu / Medley / Shakin' with Linda / Stubborn kind of
fellow / You get your kicks / I need help / Any day now
/ Breakout
CDSC 6008 / Jan '94 / Sundazed

☐ DETROIT BREAKOUT (An Ultimate
Anthology/2CD Set) (Ryder, Mitch &
The Detroit Wheels)
Jenny take a ride / Come see about me / Turn on your
lovelight / Just a little bit / I hope / Shake a tail feather
/ Please please please / I'll go crazy / I got you (I feel
good) / Sticks and stones / Bring it on home to me /
Baby Jane (mo mo Jane) / Walking the dog / I had it
made / In the midnight hour / Ooh poo pah doo / I like
it like that / Little latin lupe / Devil with the blue dress
on/Good golly Miss Molly / Shakin' with Linda /
Stubborn kind of fellow / You get your kicks / I need
help / Any day now / Break out / Baby I need your
loving/Theme for Mitch / Mitch Ryder radio promo /
Sock it to me baby / I can't hide it / Slow fizz / Walk on
by / Shakedown / Face in the crowd / I'd rather go to
jail / Wild child / Too many fish in the sea/Three little
fishes / Joy / You are my sunshine / Ruby baby /
Personality/Chantilly lace / Let it be me / I make a fool
of myself / Born to lose / If you go away / What now
my love / Whole lotta shakin' goin' on / Sally go round
the roses / Brown eyed handsome man / I need lovin'
you / That's it I quit I'm movin' on
WESD 202 / 10 Nov '97 / Westside

☐ DETROIT MEMPHIS EXPERIMENT,
THE
REP 4117 / Aug '91 / Repertoire

☐ SOCK IT TO ME (Ryder, Mitch & The
Detroit Wheels)
Sock it to me baby / I can't hide it / Takin' all I can get /
Slow fizz / Walk on by / I never had it better /
Shakedown / Face in the crowd / I'd rather go to jail /
Wild child / Medley / You are my sunshine / Ruby
baby and peaches on a cherry tree
CDSC 6009 / Jan '94 / Sundazed

☐ TAKE A RIDE (Ryder, Mitch & The
Detroit Wheels)
Shake a tail feather / Come see about me / Let your
love light shine / Just a little bit / I hope / Jenny take a
ride / Please please please / I'll go crazy / I got you /
Sticks and stones / Bring it on home to me / Baby
Jane (mo-mo Jane) / Joy
CDSC 6007 / Jan '94 / Sundazed

Rye Coalition

☐ HEE SAW DHUH KAET
GERN 029CD / 20 Oct '97 / Gern
Blandsten

Ryerson, Ali

☐ BRASIL - QUIET DEVOTION
First Rita / Todos os sentidos / Send in the clowns /
I'm not buying it / Double rainbow / Camila / Pensado
bern / Stellar by midnight / Estate / Incantations /
Praeludium II / Quiet devotion
CCD 47622 / Jun '97 / Concord Picante

☐ IN HER OWN SWEET WAY
Preface / To start again / Everything changed /
Parisagem cosmica / Martina / In your own sweet
way / Sail away / Blue in green / Sometime ago /
Chega de saudade / So remember me
CCD 4687 / Feb '96 / Concord Jazz

☐ PORTRAIT IN SILVER
Windows / Beatrice / Ausencia / Shadowlight /
Beautiful love / Zingaro / Very early / Jardin de la
paresse / Lament / Summer knows
CCD 4638 / Apr '95 / Concord Jazz

Ryg, Jorgen

☐ COLLECTION, THE (The Complete
Recordings Of Jorgen Ryg/2CD Set)
MECCACD 2104 / May '97 / Music
Mecca

Rygg, Leif

☐ LENGT
SF 1CD / Mar '96 / Spelarhaugen

Rykers

☐ BROTHER AGAINST BROTHER
LF 102CD / Oct '94 / Lost & Found

☐ FIRST BLOOD
LF 187CD / Oct '95 / Lost & Found

☐ LESSON IN LOYALTY, A
Test of faith / As the laughter dies / Lesson in loyalty /
Naturally / Still / Triggered / Cold/lost/sick / 25 /
Gutless / Sober / Shadowplay / Straight / Peak /
Finally / Emergency / Who laughs at last
0630189282 / Aug '97 / WEA

☐ PAYBACK TIME
LF 080CD / Jun '94 / Lost & Found

Ryman, John

☐ ARTIFICE AND ARCHITECTURE
MILL 006MCD / Nov '94 / Millenium

Rypdal, Terje

☐ AFRICA PEPPERBIRD (Rypdal, Terje &
Jan Garbarek)
Sharabee / Mahjong / Beast of Kommodo / Blow
away zone / MYB / Concentus / Africa pepperbird /
Blupp
8434752 / Oct '90 / ECM

☐ AFTER THE RAIN
Autumn breeze / Air / Now and then / Wind / After the
rain / Kjare maren / Little bell / Vintage year / Multer /
Like a child, like a song
5231592 / Jul '95 / ECM

☐ BLUE (Rypdal, Terje & Chasers)
Curse / Kompet Gar / I disremember quite well / Og
hva synes vi om det / Last nite / Blue / Tanga / Om
bare
8315162 / Jul '87 / ECM

☐ CHASER
Ambiguity / Once upon a time / Geysir / Closer look /
Orion / Chaser / Transition / Imagi
8272562 / Dec '85 / ECM

☐ DESCENDRE
Askjed / Circles / Innseiling / Men of mystery / Spell
8291182 / Jun '86 / ECM

☐ EOS (Rypdal, Terje & David Darling)
Eos / Bedtime story / Light years / Melody / Mirage /
Adagietto / Laser
8153332 / Sep '88 / ECM

☐ IF MOUNTAINS COULD SING
Return of per ulv / It's in the air / But on the other
hand / If mountains could sing / Private eye / Foran
peisen / Dancing without reindeers / One for the
roadrunner / Blue angel / Genie / Lonesome guitar
5239872 / Feb '95 / ECM

☐ ODYSSEY
8353552 / Sep '88 / ECM

☐ QED
Quod erat demonstradum opus 52 1st-5th
movements / Largo Opus 55
5133742 / Jan '92 / ECM

☐ RYPDAL/VITOUS/DEJOHNETTE
(Rypdal, Terje/Miroslav Vitous/Jack
Dejohnette)
Sunrise / Den forste sne / Will / Believer / Flight /
Seasons
8254702 / Aug '85 / ECM

☐ SART (Rypdal, Terje/Stenson/Jan
Garbarek)
Sart / Fountain of tears (parts 1 and 2) / Song of
space / Close enough for jazz / Irr / Lontano
8393052 / Nov '89 / ECM

☐ SINGLES COLLECTION, THE
There is a hot lady in my bedroom and I need a drink /
Sprott / Mystery man / Last hero / Strange behaviour
/ U.'n.i. / Coyote / Somehow, somewhere / Crooner
song
8377492 / Apr '89 / ECM

☐ SKYWARDS
Skywards / Into the wildness / It's not over until the
fat lady sings / Pleasure is mine I'm sure / Out of this
world / Shining / Remember to remember
5337682 / Mar '97 / ECM

☐ TERJE RYPDAL
Keep it like that tight / Rainbow / Electric fantasy /
Lontano II / Tough enough
5276452 / Jul '95 / ECM

☐ TO BE CONTINUED (Rypdal, Terje/
Miroslav Vitous/Jack Dejohnette)
Maya / Mountains in the clouds / Morninglake / To be
continued / This morning / Topplue, vooter and
skjerf / Uncomposed appendix
8473332 / Mar '92 / ECM

☐ UNDISONUS
837 755 2 / Mar '90 / New Note

☐ WAVES
Per ulv / Karusell / Stenskoven / Waves / Dain curse /
Charisma
8274192 / Feb '86 / ECM

☐ WHAT COMES AFTER
Bend it / Yearning / Icing / What comes after / Se
jours / Back of j
8393062 / Nov '89 / ECM

☐ WHENEVER I SEEM TO BE AWAY
Silver bird is heading for the sun / Hurt / Whenever I
seem to be far away
8431662 / Jun '92 / ECM

☐ WORKS
Waves / Den forste sne / Hung / Better off without
you / Innseiling / Rainbow / Topplue, vooter and
skjerf / Descendre
8254282 / Jun '88 / ECM

Rzewski, Frederick

☐ NIGHT CROSSING
CD 998 / Aug '97 / Music & Arts

☐ NORTH AMERICAN BALLADS &
SQUARES
ARTCD 6089 / Jan '92 / Hat Art

S

Saafi Bros.

☐ MYSTIC CIGARETTES
BR 032CD / 17 Nov '97 / Blue Room
Released

Saariaho, Kaija

☐ PRIVATE GARDENS
ODE 9062 / 2 Mar '98 / Ondine

Sababougnouma

☐ SABABOUGNOUMA (Balafons &
Africans Drums)
PS 65156 / Oct '95 / PlayaSound

Sabia

☐ LIVE IN CULVER CITY
FF 70494 / Jul '89 / Flying Fish

Sabicas

☐ SABICAS Y LOS CANTAORES
BMCD 523 / 24 Apr '98 / Blue Moon

Sabine

☐ SABINE
WJ 50 / 6 Apr '98 / Wurlitzer Jukebox

Sablon, Jean

☐ FRENCH SWINGING TROUBADOUR,
THE
995712 / Jul '96 / EPM

☐ JE TIRE MA REVERENCE
Ce petit Chemin / Depuis que je suis a Paris / Jesais
que vous etes Jolie / Miss Otis regrets / Melancolie /
Il ne faut pas Briser en Reve / Seul / La Chanson Des
Rues / Un seul couvert, please, James / Vous qui
passez sans me voir / Sur les Quais du Vieux Paris /
J'ai ta Main / Le Fiacre / J'Attendrai / Sur le Pont
D'Avignon / Mon village au Clair de Lune / Je tire ma
reverence / Ma Mie / Serenade Portugaise / Utrillo
MDF 102611 / Nov '96 / Mudisque

☐ JEAN SABLON 1933-1946
FA 062 / Apr '97 / Fremeaux

☐ JEAN SABLON IN PARIS
Syracuse / Mercia vous / Reviens / Qui vivra verra /
La chanson des rues / C'est le printemps / Ciel de
paris / Un seul couvert, please, James / Je tire ma
reverence / Reverie / Laura / La cabane en paris / Mom'
de mon coeur / Praline / La bouillabaisse / Ce n'est
que votre main, madame / Et mimi / J'ai peur de
l'automne / Utrillo / Sur les quais du vieux paris / J'ai
ta main / Sur le pont d'avignon / Le fiacre /
J'attendrai avec / Alone (seul)
CDXP 606 / Jan '89 / DRG

☐ PORTRAIT OF JEAN SABLON, A (2CD
Set)
Parce que je vous aime / Je suis sex appeal / Depuis
que je suis a Paris / Le jour ou je te vis / Vous ne savas
pas / Je suis que vous etes jolie / Miss Otis regrets /
Continental / Si jaime Suzy / Darling je vous aime
beaucoup / Rendez vous sous la pluie / Un seul
couvert please James / Plein rein / Ce petit chemin /
La derniere bergere / Begin beguine / Quand on est
au volant / Vous qui passez sans me voir / La
chansondes rues / Ces petites / Seul / Puisque vous
partez en voyage / Prenez garde au grand mechant
loup / J'attendrau / La cabane au village / Paris tu n'as
pas change / Le doux caboulot / Sereande sans
espoir / Mon village au clair de la lune / Il ne faut pas
briser un reve / Melancolie / Le fiacre / Sur les quai du
vieux Paris / Serenade Prtuggaise / Ma mie / Sur le
pont d'vignon / Pour vous j'ai vrai fait celtie chanson
/ J'ai te main / J'suis par millionaire / Allez lui dire que
l'aime / Cette chanson est pour vous madame /
Rhum et coca cola / Libellule / Quamnd l'amour
meurt / Laura 1946 / Reverie / Je tire ma reverence
GALE 419 / 6 Oct '97 / Gallerie

☐ SI TU MAINES
PASTCD 7058 / Apr '95 / Flapper

☐ SUCCES ET RARETES 1932-1939
701582 / Sep '96 / Chansophone

Sabot

☐ VICE VERSA/SOMEHOW I DON'T
THINK SO
SKIP 54 / Mar '97 / Broken

Sabot, Jean

☐ HARMONICA FIDDLE (Sabot, Jean &
Olivier Rozent)
HFCD 001 / Mar '96 / Diffusion Breizh

Saboteurs

☐ ESPIONAGE GARAGE
AP 202CD / 26 Jan '98 / American Pop

Sabrejets

☐ HELLBENT
Hellbent / Going down to Memphis / Born to boogie /
In and out of love / Wild cat / Bang zoom / Long gone
/ Rooftop boogie / Midnight train / Wiggle
RAUCD 023 / Apr '97 / Raucous

Sabres Of Paradise

☐ DEEP CUTS (Various Artists)
Ooh baby: Secret Knowledge / Roy revisited:
Waxworth Industries / Musical science: Musical
Science / Internal: Blue / Take the book: Waxworth
Industries / X: Corridor / Voga God: Jack Of Sworcfs /
Sugar Daddy: Secret Knowledge / Smokebelch II:
Sabres Of Paradise
SOP 001CD / Oct '93 / Sabres Of
Paradise

☐ HAUNTED DANCEHALL
Bubble and slide / Bubble and slide II / Duke of
Earlsfield / Flight path estate / Planet D / Wilmot /
Tow truck / Theme / Theme 4 / Return to Planet D /
Ballad of Nicky McGuire / Jacob Street 7am / Chapel
Street market 9am / Haunted dancehall
WARPCD 26 / Nov '94 / Warp

☐ SABRESONIC VOL.2
WARPCD 34 / Jul '95 / Warp

Sabri Brothers

☐ GREATEST HITS
SH 64090 / Jun '97 / Shanachie

☐ QAWWALI
7559720802 / 26 Jan '98 / Nonesuch

☐ YA MUSTAPHA
Khwaja ka diwana / Tajdar-e-haram / Ya mustapha /
La Ilaha Il-Allah
XENO 4041CD / Nov '96 / Xenophile

☐ YAH HABIB
Saqia aur pila / Ya sahib ul jamal / Allah hi allah tan
mein tar / Kal kamaliya wale
CDRW 12 / '89 / Realworld

Sabri, Sarwar

☐ MASTER DRUMMER OF INDIA
EUCD 1138 / '91 / ARC

Sabrina

☐ ALL OF ME
Like a yo-yo / All of me / Doctor's orders / Boys
(summertime love) / Funky girl / My Chico / Pirate of
love / Sexy girl / Guys and dolls / Sex
CD 6113 / Jan '98 / Music

☐ BOYS
Like a yo-yo / All of me / Doctor's orders / Boys
(summertime love) / Funky girl / My Chico / Pirate of
love / Sexy girl / Guys and dolls / Sex
QED 131 / Nov '96 / Tring

☐ BOYS
Like a yo yo / All of me / Doctor's orders / Funky girl /
My Chico / Pirate of love / Sexy girl / Guys and dolls /
Sex
100052 / May '97 / A-Play Collection

Sabu

☐ BETWEEN THE LIGHT
USG 10232 / 29 Jun '98 / USG

☐ HEARTBREAK
Angeline / Call of the wild / Shake, rattle and roll /
Just for the moment / Hot flash / Heartbreak / Tuff
stuff / Still alive / Breakin' out / New girl in town
HMAXD 36 / May '89 / Heavy Metal

Sacasas, Anselmo

☐ ANSELMO SACASAS ORCHESTRA
VOL.3 1942-1944
HQCD 77 / Jan '97 / Harlequin

☐ SOL TROPICAL 1945-1949
TCD 079 / Jul '96 / Tumbao Cuban
Classics

Saccharine Trust

☐ PAST LIVES
SST 149CD / May '93 / SST

Sachdev, G.S

☐ LIVE IN CONCERT AT HAYWARD CA
LYRCD 7422 / Dec '94 / Lyrichord

☐ SOLO BANSURI
LYRCD 7405 / '91 / Lyrichord

Sackville

☐ LOW EBB
CARTCD 2 / Dec '96 / Car Tunes

Sackville All Stars

☐ CHRISTMAS RECORD
Santa Claus is coming to town / We three kings / At
the Christmas ball / Winter wonderland / Go tell it on
the mountain / Good King Wenceslas / Santa Claus
came in the spring / Silent night / Let it snow, let it
snow, let it snow / Old time religion
SKCD 23038 / Jun '93 / Sackville

☐ SATURDAY NIGHT FUNCTION
John Hardy's wife / Trouble in mind / Jive at five /
Russian lullaby / Good Queen Bess / Arkansas blues
/ Saturday night function / Rosalie
SKCD 23028 / Jun '93 / Sackville

☐ TRIBUTE TO LOUIS ARMSTRONG, A
Song of the islands / (I'll be glad when you're dead)
you rascal you / Save it pretty Mama / On the sunny
side of the street / Willie the weeper / I gotta right to
sing the blues / Kiss to build a dream on / Big butter
and eggman / Pennies from heaven / Keepin' out of
mischief now / Sweethearts on parade
SKCD 23042 / Feb '89 / Sackville

Sacramento, Marcos

☐ MODERNIDADE DA TRADICAO, A
829202 / Mar '96 / BUDA

Sacramentum

☐ COMING OF CHAOS, THE
CM 77178CD / 13 Oct '97 / Century
Media

☐ FAR AWAY FROM THE SUN
CDAR 034 / Dec '96 / Fatwreck Chords

☐ FINIS MALORUM
CDAR 023 / Mar '95 / Adipocre

Sacred Denial

☐ SIFTING THROUGH THE WRECKAGE
Sifting through the wreckage / When I sleep /
Brothers inventions / Some curiosity / Conquer / No
way / Take a look around / Violent affection
082955 / '90 / Nuclear Blast

Sacred Hearts

☐ BROKEN DREAMS
TWISTBIG 3CD / Mar '94 / Twist

Sacred Mushroom

☐ SACRED MUSHROOM, THE
EVAB 30 / 1 Jun '98 / EVA

Sacred Reich

☐ AMERICAN WAY, THE
Love ..... hate / Crimes against humanity / I don't
know / State of emergency / American way / Way it is
/ Flavors
RR 93925 / Jun '91 / Roadrunner

☐ HEAL
398414106CD / Feb '96 / Metal Blade

☐ IGNORANCE
Death squad / Victim of demise / Layed to rest /
Ignorance / No believers / Violent solutions / Rest in
peace / Sacred Reich / Administrative decisions
398417008CD / Mar '96 / Metal Blade

☐ STILL IGNORANT LIVE
398414145CD / 24 Nov '97 / Metal Blade

☐ SURF NICARAGUA
Surf nicaragua / One nation / War pigs / Draining you
of life / Ignorance / Death squad
398417009CD / Mar '96 / Metal Blade

Sacred Spirit

☐ SACRED SPIRIT VOL.1 (Chants &
Dances Of The Native Americans)
How the West was lost / Winter ceremony /
Counterclockwise circle dance / Celebrate wild rice /
Cradlesong / Advice for the young / Wishes of
happiness and prosperity / Elevation / Intertribal
song to stop the rain / Heal the soul / Brandishing the
tomahawk
CDVX 2753 / Oct '95 / Virgin

☐ SACRED SPIRIT VOL.2 (Culture Clash)
Intro / Culture clash / Lay down / On the road /
Legends / No more cotton / Interlude (to be a slave) /
Sun won't talk no more / Black progress / Roots /
Babes in the juke house / Brownskins, Tennesse /
Interlude (to be a slave part 2) / Slow and easy /
Sonnet xviii
CDV 2827 / Apr '97 / Virgin

Sacred Steel

☐ REBORN IN STEEL
398414146CD / 2 Mar '98 / Metal Blade

Sacrilege

☐ LOST IN THE BEAUTY YOU SLAY
BS 009CD / Nov '96 / Burning Sun

☐ TURN BACK TRILOBITE
Father time (beneath the gaze) / Silent dark / Soul
search / Awaken (suryanamaskar) / Key to nirvana /
CDFLAG 29 / Jan '89 / Under One Flag

☐ WITHIN THE PROPHECY/BEHIND THE
REALMS OF MADNESS
Sight of the wise / Captive / Winds of vengeance /
Spirit cry / Flight of the nazgul / Fear within / Life line /
Shadow form Mordor / Deaths door / Violation of
something scared / Closing irony / Out of sight / Out
of mind
PRAGE 004CD / 16 Feb '98 / Powerage

Sad Cafe

☐ EVERYDAY HURTS (The Best Of Sad
Cafe)
Everyday hurts / Strange little girl / Hungry eyes /
Black rose / Sail on / I'm in love again / La di da / My
oh my / Nothing left Toulouse / I believe (love will
survive) / Angel / Let love speak for itself / Losing you
/ Dreaming / Take me to the future / Crazy osyter
74321500252 / Jun '97 / Camden

☐ MISPLACED IDEALS/FACADES (2CD
Set)
RMED 00196 / 20 Apr '98 / Renaissance

Sad Lovers & Giants

☐ E MAIL FROM ETERNITY
CDMGRAM 104 / Mar '96 / Cherry Red

Sad Rockets

☐ PLAYS
EFA 006272 / 2 Feb '98 / Source

Sad Whisperings

☐ SENSITIVE TO AUTUMN
FDN 2007CD / Dec '93 / Foundation
2000

Sadat X

☐ WILD COWBOYS
Lump lump / Wild cowboys / Sauce for birdheads /
Open bar / Hang 'em high / Do it again / Game's
sober / Smoking on the low / Pretty people /
Interview / Stages and lights / Move on / Funkiest /
Escape from New York / Hashout
7863669222 / Aug '96 / RCA

Saddar Bazaar

☐ CONFERENCE OF THE BIRDS, THE
Sukoon / Arc of ascent (part 1) / Kiff riff / Garden of
essence / Sukoon (reflection) / Shamsa (sunburst) /
Baraka / Arc of ascent (part 2) / Freedom rider /
Neelum blue
DELECCD 034 / Jul '97 / Delerium

Sade

☐ BEST OF SADE, THE
Your love is king / Hang on to your love / Smooth
operator / Jezebel / Sweetest taboo / Is it a crime /
Never as good as the first time / Love is stronger than
pride / Paradise / Nothing can come between us / No
ordinary love / Like a taboo / Kiss of life / Please send
me someone to love / Cherish the day / Pearls
4777932 / Oct '94 / Epic

☐ DIAMOND LIFE
Smooth operator / Your love is king / Hang on to your
love / When am I gonna make a living / Frankie's first
affair / Cherry pie / Sally / I will be your friend / Why
can't we live together
4811782 / 27 Jul '98 / Epic

☐ LOVE DELUXE
No ordinary love / Feel no pain / I couldn't love you
more / Like a tattoo / Kiss of life / Cherish the day /
Pearls / Bullet proof soul / Mermaid
4726262 / Oct '92 / Epic

☐ PROMISE
Is it a crime / Sweetest taboo / War of the hearts /
Jezebel / Mr. Wrong / Never as good as the first time /
Fear / Tar baby / Maureen / You're not the man /
Punch drunk
4655752 / Mar '90 / Epic

☐ STRONGER THAN PRIDE
Love is stronger than pride / Paradise / Nothing can
come between us / Haunt me / Turn my back on you /
Keep looking / Clean heart / Give it up / I never
thought I'd see the day / Siempre hay esperanza
4604972 / May '88 / Epic

735

Sadies

☐ PRECIOUS MOMENTS
Guns speak / Dying is easy / Glass of wine / Red cloth / Cheat / Cowhand / Pretty Polly / Clam chowder / Seventy six / Wagonwheel / Snow squadron / Same song / Wrap around / Tell her lies and feed her candy / Rubber bat / Clear a path / Rabid monkey / Barborosa / Lil cottontail
BS 034 / Jun '98 / Bloodshot

Sadist

☐ CRUST
D 00056CD / 10 Nov '97 / Displeased

Sadistik Exekution

☐ WE ARE DEATH FUCK YOU
CD 022 / Oct '94 / Osmose

Sadness

☐ DANTEFERNO
GOD 020CD / Mar '96 / Godhead

Sadolikar, Shruti

☐ RAGA MIYAN KI TODI/RAGA BIBHAS
NI 5346 / Sep '94 / Nimbus

Sadus

☐ CHRONICLES OF CHAOS
M 7025CD / 29 Sep '97 / Mascot

☐ ELEMENTS OF ANGER
Aggression / Crutch / Words of war / Safety in numbers / Mask / Fuel / Power of one / Stronger than one / Unreality / In the end
M 7026CD / 29 Sep '97 / Mascot

Saetas

☐ SONGS FROM ANDALUZA
B 6785 / Oct '94 / Auvidis/Ethnic

Saffire

☐ BROADCASTING
ALCD 4811 / May '93 / Alligator

☐ CLEANING HOUSE
ALCD 4840 / May '96 / Alligator

☐ HOT FLASH (Saffire The Uppity Blues Woman)
Two in the bush is better than one in the hand / Sloppy drunk / One good man / Dirty sheets / Tom cat blues / Learn to settle for less / You'll never get me out of your mind / (Mr Insurance man) take out that thing / Hopin' it'll be alright / Little bit of your loving goes a very long way / Shopping for love / Elevator man / Torch song / Torch song (part 2) / Why don't you do right / Prove me wrong / (No need) Pissin' on a skunk
ALCD 4796 / May '93 / Alligator

☐ LIVE AND UPPITY (Saffire The Uppity Blues Woman)
Introduction / Cold pizza and warm beer / You'll never get me out of your mind / One good man / Hold me close / Silver beaver / Mr. Insurance Man / Thing that you need / 1-800-799-7233 / You can have my husband / Hopin' it'll be alright / Bitch with a bad attitude / Dump that chump / Lonely nights / Middle aged blues boogie / Crazy / Some cold and rainy day
ALCD 4856 / Apr '98 / Alligator

☐ OLD, BORROWED AND BLUE (The Uppity Blue Woman)
ALCD 4826 / Dec '94 / Alligator

☐ UPPITY BLUES WOMAN, THE
Middle aged blues boogie / Take it on back / Annie's blues / Even yuppies get the blues / Drown in my own tears / Three time loser / Fess up when you mess up / Silent thunder in my heart / School teacher's blues / I almost lost my mind / Wild women don't have the blues
ALCD 4780 / May '93 / Alligator

Saft, James

☐ RAGGED JACK (Saft, James & Cuong Vu)
AVANT 68 / May '97 / Avant

Saga

☐ DEFINING MOMENTS (Greatest Hits)
VSD 1007 / 24 Mar '98 / Varese Sarabande

☐ DETOURS LIVE
SPV 08818002 / May '98 / SPV

☐ PHASE ONE 1978
SA 98051 / 3 Mar '98 / Midstream

☐ PLEASURE AND THE PAIN
BNA 0016 / Jun '97 / Bonaire

Sage, Carson

☐ FINAL KITCHEN BLOWOUT (Sage, Carson & The Black Riders)
EFA 11393D / Jul '93 / Musical Tragedies

Sage, Greg

☐ 14 SONGS FOR GREG SAGE & THE WIPERS (Various Artists)
TK 91CD010 / May '94 / T/K

☐ SACRIFICE (FOR LOVE)
LS 92372 / Nov '91 / Roadrunner

Sagittarius

☐ PRESENT TENSE
SC 11053 / 22 Jun '98 / Sundazed

☐ SANITY OF MADNESS
VOW 049CD / Jul '95 / Voices Of Wonder

Sagoo, Bally

☐ BOLLYWOOD FLASHBACK
Chura liya / Yeh sama hai pyar ka / O saathi re / Quarbani quarbani / Mehbooba mehbobba / Roop tera mastana / Jab hum jawan honge / Waada honge / Waada na tod / Choli ke peeche
4776972 / 8 Sep '97 / Columbia

☐ RISING FROM THE EAST
Tum bin jiya / Ban mein aati thi / Nach malanga / Dil cheez / Tere nain / Jitna humne aaja ve maahi / Teri akhiyan / Laila / Milna julna / Dil cheez (remix)
4850162 / Oct '96 / Columbia

Sahm, Doug

☐ BACK TO THE 'DILLO (Sahm, Doug & Augie Meyers/Assorted Friends)
Introduction / It's just the same ole story / Get on up / I pity the fool / Think about it baby / Carol / Susie Q / Crazy arms / George Jones song / Nuevo laredo / Purple haze / Outro song
EDCD 558 / 1 Jun '98 / Edsel

☐ BEST OF THE ATLANTIC SESSIONS, THE
Texas tornado / Nitty gritty / Is anybody going to san antone / Poison love / Wallflower / Dealer's blues / Ain' that loving you / San francisco fm blues / I get off / Juan mendoza / Box car hobo / Image of me / Tennessee blues / Blue horizon / Your friends / Song about myself / Hard way / Betty jo / Chicano
RSACD 813 / Oct '94 / Sequel

☐ GET A LIFE
Get a life / St Olav's gate / Goodbye San Francisco hello Amsterdam / Give back the key to my heart / Malmo mania / On bended knee / Louis Riel / Ballad of Davy Crockett / Sooner or later / Invitation to the blues
MUSA 505 / Jun '98 / Munich

Sahraoui, Cheb

☐ N'SEL FIK (Sahraoui, Cheb & Chaba Fadela)
N'sel fik / La verite / Hala la la / Rah galbi mrid / Ya eli nsitini / N'sel fik (Nouvelle version) / Ma andi zhar maak / Ana melit / Loukene ma nebghih / Mazal naachak
COOKCD 057 / Oct '93 / Cooking Vinyl

Saigon Kick

☐ MOMENTS FROM THE FRINGE
CRIDE 3 / 31 Aug '98 / Ranch Life

☐ WATER
One step closer / Space oddity / Water / Torture / Fields of rape / I love you / Sgt. Steve / My heart / On and on / Way / Sentimental girl / Close to you / Whne you were mine / Reprise
7567923002 / Jun '94 / Atlantic

Saih Pitu, Gamelan

☐ HEAVENLY ORCHESTRA OF BALI, THE
Gending lasem - saih selisir / Gending lasem - saih selisir / Gending tabuh gari - saih selisir / Gending unduk - saih baro
CMPCD 3008 / Jul '92 / CMP

Sailor

☐ GREATEST HITS
La cumbia / Traffic jam / Sailor / Girls of Amsterdam / Let's go to town / Josephine Baker / Girls girls girls / Jacaranda / Glass of champagne / Panama / Old Nickelodian sound / One drink too many / Give me la samba / Stiletto heels / Out of money / Quay hotel / Stay with me now / Keep off the streets at night / Private eye / Hat check girl / Starlight
4805732 / 13 Jul '98 / Columbia

Sain, Oliver

☐ PARTY HEARTY (The Best Of Oliver Sain)
Booty bumpin' (double bump) / Soul serenade / Strollin' / 20-75 / Mr. King and Mr. Jordan / St. Louis breakdown / Comin' down soul / On the hill / Baby scratch my back / London express / Country funk / Night time / Harlem nocturne / Bus stop / Prayer / Just a lonely man / Going back to Memphis / Feel like dancin' / Apricot splash / Hey butterfly
CDSEWD 110 / Aug '96 / Southbound

Saindon, Ed

☐ ON THE SUNNYSIDE
On the sunnyside of the street / Oh, lady be good / Love is here to stay / I can't give you anything but love / Ain't misbehavin' / Back home in Indiana / Memories of you / Moonglow / Rosetta / When you wish upon a star / Limehouse blues / I found a new baby / It could happen to you / You brought a new kind of love to me / Sweet Lorraine / Sweet Georgia Brown
AL 73068 / Mar '97 / Challenge

Sainkho

☐ OUT OF TUVA
CRAW 6 / Jan '96 / Crammed World

Saint & Campbell

☐ TIME ON THE MOVE
COPCD 2 / Feb '95 / Copasetic

Saint James Infirmary

☐ SAINT JAMES INFIRMARY
ALLIED 093CD / 19 Jan '98 / Allied

Saint Preux

☐ LA TERRA MONDO
WOLCD 1066 / Jan '96 / China

Saint Vitus

☐ DIE HEALING
H 00352 / Jan '95 / Hellhound

Saint-Paul, Lara

☐ MAMMA
PCOM 1141 / Nov '95 / President

Saintcatee

☐ MUSIC FOR
MASSCD 086 / Feb '96 / Massacre

Sainte-Marie, Buffy

☐ BEST OF BUFFY SAINTE-MARIE, THE (2CD Set)
Soulful shade of blue / Summer boy / Universal soldier / Better to find out for yourself / Cod'ine / He's a keeper of the fire / Take my hand for a while / Ground hog / Circle game / My country 'tis of thy people you're dying / Many a mile / Until it's time for you to go / Rolling log blues / God is alive, magic is afoot / Guess who I saw in Paris / Pineywood hills / Now that the buffalo's gone / Cripple Creek / I'm gonna be a country girl again / Vampire / Little wheel spin and spin / Winter boy / Los Pescadores / Sometimes when I get to thinkin'
VCD 3 / Jun '98 / Vanguard

☐ I'M GONNA BE A COUNTRY GIRL AGAIN
VMD 79280 / Oct '96 / Vanguard

☐ LITTLE WHEEL SPIN AND SPIN
Little wheel spin and spin / House carpenter / Waly waly / Rolling log blues / My country 'tis of thy people you're dying / Men of the fields / Timeless love / Sir Patrick Spens / Poor man's daughter / Lady Margaret / Sometimes I get to thinkin / Winter boy
VMD 79211 / 27 Apr '98 / Vanguard

☐ QUIET PLACES
VMD 79330 / Oct '96 / Vanguard

☐ SHE USED TO WANNA BE A BALLERINA
Rollin' mill man / Smack water jack / Sweet September morning / She used to wanna be a ballerina / Bells / Helpless / Moratorium / Surfer / Song of the French partisan / Soldier blue / Now you've been gone for a long time
VMD 79311 / Oct '95 / Vanguard

☐ UP WHERE WE BELONG
Darling don't cry / Up where we belong / Piney Wood Hills / Cripple Creek / God is alive / Until it's time for you to go / Universal soldier / Goodnight / Dance me around / He's an Indian cowboy in the rodeo / Now that the buffalo's gone / Soldier blue / Eagle man / changing woman / Bury my heart at Wounded Knee / Starwalker
CDEMC 3745 / Mar '96 / Premier/EMI

Saints

☐ (I'M) STRANDED
TX 51243CD / 17 Nov '97 / Triple XXX

☐ ETERNALLY YOURS
422309 / May '94 / New Rose
TX 51244CD / 3 Nov '97 / Triple XXX

☐ EVERYBODY KNOWS THE MONKEY
What do you want / Easy money / Working overtime / Fall of an empire / Mustard / Vaguely Jesus / What are you waiting for / Everything turns sour / Playboy of the western world / Come back and visit / S+M+M's / Glorious wonder
3037772 / 24 Apr '98 / Last Call
ARC 334 / 4 May '98 / Arcade

☐ HOWLING
Howling / Shadows / Something, somewhere, sometime / Something wicked / Only stone / Good Friday / Blown away / Last and laughing mile / You know I know / Only dreaming / Second coming / All for nothing
BLUCD 029 / Oct '96 / Blue Rose
TX 51245CD / 26 Jan '98 / Triple XXX

☐ KNOW YOUR PRODUCT (The Best Of The Saints)
I'm stranded / (This) perfect day / Lipstick on your collar / River deep mountain high / Demolition girl / One way street / Story of love / Kissin' cousins / No time / Wild about you / Messin' with the kid / Nights in Venice / Do the robot / Know your product / Run down / Lost and found / Memories are made of this / Private affair / Minor aversion / No, your product / Swing for the crime / All times through paradise
CDGO 2069 / Oct '96 / EMI Gold

☐ PREHISTORIC SOUNDS
422312 / May '94 / New Rose

Saints Of Eden

☐ OTHER SIDE, THE
ECHO 001CD / 3 Aug '98 / Metech

Saisse, Philippe

☐ NEXT VOYAGE
5374162 / Aug '97 / Verve Forecast

Sakamoto, Ryuichi

☐ 1996
Day a gorilla gives a banana / Rain / Bibo no aozora / Last Emperor / 1919 / Merry Christmas Mr. Lawrence / May in the backyard / Sheltering sky / Tribute to NJP / High heels / Aneoko no torso / Wuthering heights / Parolibre / Acceptance / Little Buddha / Before long / Bring them home
74321372422 / Jun '96 / Milan

☐ B-2 UNIT
SPALAX 14500 / Oct '96 / Spalax

☐ BEAUTY
You do me / Calling from Tokyo / Rose / Asadoya yunta / Futique / Amore / We love you / Diabaram / Pile of time / Romance / Chinsagu no hana
CDVUS 14 / Aug '91 / Virgin

☐ HEARTBEAT
Heartbeat / Rap the world / Triste / Lulu / High tide / Song lines / Nuages / Sayonara / Borom gal / Epilogue / Heartbeat (Tainai Kaiki) / Returning to the womb / Cloud
CDVUS 46 / Jun '92 / Virgin

☐ MUSICAL ENCYCLOPEDIA
Field work / Etude / Paradise lost / MAY in the backyard / Steppin' into Asia / Tibetan dance / Zen-gun / In a forest of feathers
DIXCD 34 / Jul '87 / 10

☐ SMOOCHY
74321440072 / Feb '97 / Milan

Salacious Crumb

☐ VARIATIONS FOR CATWALKS AND COSMOPOLITANS
ICO 312 / 30 Mar '98 / Infracom

Salad

☐ ICECREAM
UV / Written by a man / Yeah yeah / Broken bird / Wanna be free / Size more woman than her / Cardboy King / Namedrops / Foreign cow / Terrible day / Wolves over Washington / Sky's our terminal
CID 8056 / May '97 / Island

Salah, Sadaoui

☐ ANTHOLOGY OF ARAB MUSIC VOL.1
AAA 106 / Sep '95 / Club Du Disque Arabe

Salako

☐ RE-INVENTING PUNCTUATION
JPRCD 002 / 17 Aug '98 / Jeepster

Salamander

☐ RED AMPERSAND
CAM 008CD / 9 Feb '98 / Camera Obscura

Salaryman

☐ SALARYMAN
Rather / Inca picnic / Voids and superclusters / New centurions / Burning at the stake / I need a monkey / Hummous
EFA 049962 / Jul '97 / City Slang

Salas Humara, Walter

☐ LEAN
RTS 9 / Jul '94 / Normal

Salas, Patricia

☐ CHRISTMAS IN LATIN AMERICA
EUCD 1088 / '91 / ARC

Salas, Steve

☐ BACK FROM THE LIVING (Salas, Steve Colourcode)
USG 120072 / Apr '97 / USG

☐ ELECTRIC POW WOW
Q 2572 / Jul '97 / Aquarius

☐ LE BOOTLEG - LIVE IN PARIS (Salas, Steve Colourcode)
Do your own thang / Start again / Stand up / Detroit rock city / Too many mountains / Tell your story walking / Harder they come / Sex machine / Drain you / Fear
USG 10122 / 11 Aug '97 / USG

☐ VIVA LA NOISE
USG 10242 / 3 Aug '98 / USG

Salem

☐ KADDISH
MRO 15CD / Apr '95 / Morbid Sounds

Salem, Kevin

☐ GLIMMER
RR 88772 / Sep '96 / Roadrunner

☐ SOMA CITY
RR 89792 / Oct '95 / Roadrunner

Salgan, Horacio

☐ MANO BRAVA (Salgan, Horacio & Ubaldo De Lio)
74321453322 / Feb '97 / Milan Sur

☐ TANGO VOL.1
MAN 4830 / May '94 / Mandala

Salim, Abdel Gadir

☐ NUJUM AL-LAIL - STARS OF THE NIGHT
Gidraishinna / Al-lemoni / Nujum al-lail / Nitlaga nitlaga / Jeenaki / A'abir sikkah
CDORB 039 / May '89 / Globestyle

Salim, Abdu K.

☐ IN THE PATH OF THE LIGHT
591162 / Nov '97 / Musidisc

Salinas, Isaac

☐ TRIBUTO A AGUSTIN LARA (100 Anos De Su Musica)
9944132102 / 3 Mar '98 / Orfeon

Salisbury Cathedral Choir

☐ HOW LOVELY ARE THY DWELLINGS
CDE 84288 / Aug '94 / Meridian

Salma & Sabina

☐ EK BAAR MILO HUMSE
IMUT 1023 / Mar '96 / Multitone

Salmon, Kim

☐ ESSENCE (Salmon, Kim & The Surrealists)
REDCD 21 / May '94 / Normal

☐ HELL IS WHERE MY HEART LIVES
REDCD 34 / Jun '94 / Red Eye

☐ HEY BELIEVER
GRCD 349 / Nov '94 / Glitterhouse

☐ HIT ME WITH THE SURREAL FEEL (Salmon, Kim & The Surrealists)
ITR 33CD / Dec '96 / In The Red

☐ JUST BECAUSE YOU CAN'T SEE IT (Salmon, Kim & The Surrealists)
BLACKCD 9 / May '94 / Black Eye

☐ KIM SALMON & THE SURREALISTS (Salmon, Kim & The Surrealists)
GRCD 381 / 8 Sep '97 / Glitterhouse

☐ SIN FACTORY (Salmon, Kim & The Surrealists)
REDCD 33 / Mar '94 / Red Eye

☐ YA GOTTA LET ME DO MY OWN THING (Salmon, Kim & The Surrealists)
HAC 63 / 26 Aug '97 / Half A Cow

Salsa Blanca

☐ MANUELA
TUMICD 035 / '93 / Tumi

Salsa Celtica

☐ MONSTRUOS Y DEMONIUS ANGELS AND LOVERS
Salsa celtica / La reina rumbera / Guajira del sol / Osain / Paisa / No hay olvido, pablito / La batea / Koukou / Frente a frente / El cometa bop / Escorpion / Loco y loco / Kulu
ECLCD 9717 / Aug '97 / Eclectic

Salsoul Orchestra

☐ BEST OF THE SALSOUL ORCHESTRA, THE
Ooh I love it / Salsoul hustle / You're just the right size / Nice and naasty / Runaway / Standing and waiting for love / Ritzy mambo / Dance a little closer / Salsoul 3001 / How high / Tangerine / Take some time out / Seconds
CDGR 177 / Aug '97 / Charly

☐ NICE 'N' NAASTY
It's good for the soul / Nice 'n' naasty / It don't have to be funky (To be a groove) / Nightcrawler / Don't beat around the bush / Standing and waiting on love / Salsoul 3001 / We've only just begun/Feelings / Ritzy mambo / Jack and Jill
CPCD 8077 / Mar '95 / Charly

☐ SALSOUL ORCHESTRA, THE
Salsoul hustle / Get happy / Chicago bus stop (ooh, I love it) / You're just the right size / Tangerine / Tale of three cities / Salsoul rainbow / Love letters
CPCD 8059 / Nov '94 / Charly

☐ STREET SENSE
Zambesi / Burning spear / Somebody to love / Street sense / 212 North 12th / Sun after the rain
CPCD 8098 / Apr '95 / Charly

Salt

☐ AUSCULATE
Impro / Honour me / Beauty / God damn carneval / Obsession / Bluster / Lids / So / Witty / So I ached / Flutter / Sense / Undressed
CID 8045 / Mar '96 / Island

Salt n' Pepa

☐ BLACK'S MAGIC
Expression / Doper than dope / Negro wit' an ego / You showed me / Do you want me / Swift / I like to party / Black's magic / Start the party / Let's talk about sex / I don't know / Live and let die / Independent / Expression (Brixton bass mix)
8281642 / Nov '91 / FFRR

☐ BLITZ OF SALT 'N' PEPA HITS, A (Remix)
Push it / Expression / Independent / Shake your thang (It's your thing) / Twist and shout / Let's talk about sex / Tramp / Do you want me / My mic sounds nice / I'll take your man / I gotcha / You showed me
8282692 / Oct '91 / FFRR

☐ BRAND NEW
8289592 / 24 Nov '97 / FFRR

☐ GREATEST HITS
Push it / Expression / Independent / Shake your thang (it's your thing) / Twist and shout / Let's talk about sex / I like it like that / Tramp / Do you want me / My mic sounds nice / I'll take your man / I gotcha / I am down / You showed me
8282912 / Oct '91 / FFRR

☐ HOT COOL VICIOUS
Beauty and the beat / Tramp / I'll take your man / It's alright / Chick on the side / I desire / Showstopper / My mic sounds nice
8282962 / Nov '91 / FFRR

☐ SALT WITH A DEADLY PEPA, A
Intro jam / Salt with a deadly pepa / I like it like that / Solo power / Shake your thang (it's your thing) / I gotcha / Let the rhythm run / Everybody get up / Spinderella's not a fella / Solo power (Syncopated soul) / Twist and shout / Hyped on the mic / Push it
5500412 / May '93 / Spectrum

☐ VERY NECESSARY
Groove me / No one does it better / Somebody's gettin' on my nerves / Whatta man: *Salt n' Pepa & En Vogue* / None of your business / Step / Shoop / Heaven or hell / Big shot / Sexy noises turn me on / Somma time man / Break of dawn / PSA we talk / Shoop / Start me up
8283772 / 17 Aug '98 / FFRR

Salt Tank

☐ SCIENCE AND NATURE
Into the light of the shining path / Olympic 638 / Eugina (pacific diva) / Taj / Gaza strip / Isabella's dream / TT / Swell (Eden) / Final charge (D up) / Free lunch
TRUCD 11 / May '96 / Internal

☐ WAVE BREAKS
Diamond halo / Da blues / Wave intruder / Cjax / Ritual / Badlands / Angels landing / Afterhours
8289182 / 3 Mar '98 / FFRR

Salta

☐ SALTA
AMCD 736 / Aug '97 / Amigo

Salter, Sam

☐ IT'S ON TONIGHT
Your face / After 12, before 6 / It's on tonight / Give me my baby / There you are / I love you both / Show you that I care / Everytime a car drives by / Thinkin' and trippin' / It took a song / On my heart / Coulda been me
3008260402 / 29 Sep '97 / Arista

Salty Dogs Jazzband

☐ LONG, DEEP & WIDE
BCD 237 / Jan '93 / GHB

Saluzzi, Dino

☐ CITE DE LA MUSIQUE
Cite de la musique / Introduccion y Milonga del ausente / El Rio y el abuelo / Zurdo / Romance / Winter / How NY heart sings / Gorrion / Coral para mi pequeno y legano pueblo
5333162 / Mar '97 / ECM

☐ KULTRUM
Kultrum pampa / Gabriel kondor / Agua de paz / Pajaros Y ceibos / Ritmo arauca / El rio Y el abuelo / Pasos que quedan / Por el sol Y por la lluvia
8214072 / May '92 / ECM

☐ MOJOTORO (Saluzzi, Dino Group)
Mojotoro / Tango a mi padre / Mundos / Lustrin / Viernes santo / Milonga (la punalada) / El camino
5119522 / May '92 / ECM

☐ ONCE UPON A TIME - FAR AWAY IN THE SOUTH
Jose, Valeria and Matias / And the Father said... / Revelation / Silence / And he loved his brother, till the end / Far away in the south... / We are the children
8277682 / Apr '86 / ECM

☐ RIOS
Los them / Minguito / Fulano de tal / Sketch / He loved his brother 'til the end / Penta y uno / JAD / Lunch with pancho villa / My one and only love / Rios
VBR 21562 / Nov '95 / Intuition

☐ SOLO BANDONEON (Saluzzi, Dino & Andina)
8371862 / Feb '89 / ECM

Salvagnini, Massimo

☐ VERY FOOL
Very fool / Bleeding shreds / Dream dram drum / Sigmund was here / Alcoholic baby / Sharps / Star guys / My favourite disease / Meat bubbles / Stupid question / Heretic ostrich / Twelve for two / Algoritmo / Old news / 'Tis autumn
CDSGP 095 / Jul '95 / Prestige

Salvation

☐ HUNGER DAYS 1985-1989
TIMESLIPTSCD 01 / 2 Feb '98 / Vinyl Tap

Salvation Army

☐ O COME ALL YE FAITHFUL (Salvation Army Band/Choir)
74321435262 / Oct '96 / RCA

☐ ONWARD CHRISTIAN SOLDIERS (Salvation Army Band/Choir)
Onward christian soldiers / Fight the good fight / Love divine / What a friend we have in Jesus / O Worship the king / Rock of ages / He who would valiant be / When I survey the wonderous cross / How great thou art / Old rugged cross / Praise my soul / Lord's my shepherd / Abide with me / There is a green hill far away / Eternal Father strong to save / All things bright and beautiful / How sweet the name of Jesus sounds / Guide me, o thou great Jehovah / King of love / Goldcrest
306932 / May '97 / Hallmark

Salvatore, Sergio

☐ ALWAYS A BEGINNING
Always and beginning / Revolving door / What is this thing called love / Moon river / Darn that dream / Lullaby in time / Pink panther theme / Waltz / Isn't it romantic / After all / Note to Henry
CCD 4704 / Jun '96 / Concord Jazz

☐ POINT OF PRESENCE
Point of presence / Pocket change / Haunted hearts / So you said / To you / Norwegian wood / Sul tirino / Out of nowhere / Antonio J. / HHeadline / Prelude / Before her time
N2K 10018 / Oct '97 / N2K

Sam & Dave

☐ GREATEST HITS
MU 5034 / Feb '95 / Musketeer

☐ HOLD ON I'M COMING
Hold on I'm comin' / If you got the loving / I take what I want / Ease me / I got everything I need / Don't make it so hard on me / It's a wonder / Don't help me out / Just me / You got it made / You don't know like I know / Blame me (don't blame my heart)
7567802552 / Jul '91 / Atlantic

☐ I THANK YOU
I thank you / Everybody got to believe in somebody / These arms of mine / Wrap it up / If I didn't have a girl like you / You don't know what you mean to me / Don't turn your heater on / Talk to the man / Love is after me / Ain't that a lot of love / Don't waste that love / That lucky old sun
8122710122 / Mar '93 / Atlantic

☐ SAM & DAVE
It feels so nice / I got a thing going on / My love belongs to you / Listening for my name / No more pain / I found out / It was so nice while it lasted / You ain't no big thing baby / I need love / She's alright / Keep a walkin' / If she'll still have me / Garden of Earth / Azethoth / Queen Street gang / Clean innocent fun / Metempsychosis
EDCD 388 / Jun '94 / Edsel

☐ SOUL MAN (The Best Of Sam & Dave)
You don't know like I know / Hold on I'm comin' / Said I wasn't gonna tell nobody / You got me hummin' / When something is wrong with my baby / Soul man / I thank you / Soul sister, brown sugar / Don't pull your love out / Can't you find another way / You don't know what you mean to me
AIM 2003CD / May '97 / Aim

☐ SOUL MEN
Soul man / May I baby / Broke down piece of man / Let it be me / Hold it baby / I'm with you / Don't knock it / Just keep holding on / Good runs the bad way / Rich kind of poverty / I've seen what loneliness can do
8122702962 / Jul '93 / Atlantic

☐ SOUL MEN
Soul man / You don't know what you mean to me / Soothe me / When something is wrong with my baby / Can't you find another way / Hold on I'm coming / You don't know like I know / Don't pull your love / I thank you / You got me hummin' / I said I wasn't gonna tell anyone / Soul sister brown sugar
307692 / Aug '97 / Hallmark

☐ SWEAT AND SOUL (The Anthology 1965-1971)
Place nobody can find / Goodnight baby / I take what I want / You don't know like I know / Hold on I'm comin' / I got everything I need / Don't make it so hard on me / Blame me (Don't blame my heart) / You got me hummin' / When something is wrong with my baby / Small portion of your love / I don't need nobody (to tell me bout my baby) / That's the way it's gotta be / Said I wasn't gonna tell nobody / Soothe me / I can't stand up for falling down / Toe hold / Soul man / May I baby / Just keep holding on / Good runs the bad way / Rich kind of poverty / I've seen what loneliness can do / My reason for living / I thank you / Wrap it up / Broke down piece of man / Shop around / Stop / Starting over again / Jody Ryder got killed / Don't pull your love / Knock it out the park / Standing in the safety zone / Baby baby don't stop now / One part love, two part pain / I'm not an indian giver / Holdin' on / You left the water running / Born again / Soul sister brown sugar / Don't turn your heater on / Ain't that a lot of love / Can't you find another way of doing it / Everybody got to believe in somebody / You don't know what you mean to me / This is your world / Come on in / Hold it baby
8122712532 / Dec '93 / Atlantic

☐ SWEET SOUL MUSIC
Soul man / Hold on I'm comin' / Soul sister, brown sugar / Love the one you're with / Funky street / Mustang sally / Land of 1000 dances / How sweet it is (to be loved by you) / Respect / I thank you / Sweet soul music / I'll be doggone / Funky broadway / 634-5789 / Good lovin' / Satisfaction
ECD 3212 / Mar '95 / K-Tel

☐ TWO GREAT SOUL MEN
HADCD 208 / Jul '96 / Javelin

Sam & Valley

☐ MY FAVOURITE CLINIC
CAT 048CD / Jun '97 / Rephlex

Sam Black Church

☐ LET IN LIFE
TAANG 77CD / Dec '93 / Taang

☐ SAM BLACK CHURCH
TAANG 76CD / Jun '93 / Taang

Sam-ang Sam Ensemble

☐ ECHOES FROM THE PALACE
CDT 140CD / Apr '96 / Music Of The World

Samael

☐ BLOOD RITUAL
84 97374 / Dec '92 / Century Media

☐ CEREMONY OF OPPOSITES
CM 77064CD / Mar '94 / Century Media

☐ EXODUS
CM 77210CD / 11 May '98 / Century Media

☐ PASSAGE
CM 77127CD / Sep '96 / Century Media

☐ SAMAEL 1987-1992
CM 7708522 / Jan '95 / Century Media

Samain

☐ INDOMITUS
BLCR 7001CD / Dec '96 / Destruktive Kommndoh

Samaroo Jets

☐ QUINTESSENCE
Meditation / Tico tico / (Everything I do) I do it for you / Bee's melody / I'll be there / Alma llanera / Portrait of Trinidad / Coming in from the cold / O mere sona / Memory / Unforgettable / Two to go / Heal the world / One moment in time / Pan rising
DE 4024 / Jul '94 / Delos

Sambada

☐ TROPICALE
Rush hour / Street walk / South of the border / Sunburst / Livewire / Tropicale / City nights / Mardi gras / Kabanos / Storyteller
TAPR 104CD / 16 Oct '97 / Thin Air Music

Sambalanco Trio

☐ SAMBALANCO TRIO
1501 / Apr '97 / Rare Brazil

Sambeat, Perico

☐ DUAL FORCE
Body / Luso / Wonderful, wonderful / Lament / Dual force / Ask me now / Plot
JHCD 031 / Jun '94 / Ronnie Scott's Jazz House

☐ JINDUNGO (Sambeat, Perico & B. Barth)
FSNT 029 / Jan '98 / Fresh Sound New Talent

Sambora, Richie

☐ STRANGER IN THIS TOWN
Rest in peace / Church of desire / Stranger in this town / Ballad of youth / One light burning / Mr. Bluesman / Rosie / River of love / Father time / Answer
8488952 / Sep '91 / Phonogram

☐ UNDISCOVERED SOUL
5369722 / 2 Mar '98 / Mercury

Samer Band

☐ MUSIC OF THE ROMANIES
378182 / Sep '96 / Koch World

Samiam

☐ CLUMSY
As we're told / Time by the dime / Cradle / She's a part of me / No size that small / Simca / Routine / Tag along / Bad day / Capsized / Stepson
7567826422 / Aug '94 / Atlantic

☐ YOU ARE FREAKING ME OUT
BHR 059CD / Jun '97 / Burning Heart

Samiou, Domna

☐ JOURNEY THROUGHOUT GREECE, A
ML 0179 / 11 May '98 / Musurgia Graeca

Samite

☐ SILINA MUSANGO
XENO 4047CD / Jun '96 / Xenophile

Samla Mammas Manna

☐ MALTID
RESCD 505 / Oct '93 / Resource

Sammes, Mike

☐ IT HAD TO BE YOU
AVC 564 / May '96 / Avid

Sammy

☐ DEBUT ALBUM
FIRECD 40 / Jun '94 / Fire

☐ TALES OF GREAT NECK GLORY
FIRECD 58 / Jun '96 / Fire

Sammy Dread

☐ ROADBLOCK
JJCD 068 / 25 May '98 / Channel One

☐ STRONGER THAN BEFORE
RGCD 040 / Apr '97 / Rocky One

☐ WRAP UP A DRAW
SLCD 14 / Mar '96 / Seven Leaves

Sample, Joe

☐ COLLECTION, THE
Carmel / Woman you're driving me mad / Rainy day in Monterey / Sunrise / There are many stops alone the way / Rainbow seeker / Fly with the wings of love / Burning up the carnival / Night flight / Oasis
GRP 96582 / 25 May '98 / GRP

☐ OLD PLACES, OLD FACES
Free yourself / Clifton's gold / Hippies on a corner / First love / Angels on my mind / Miles of blue (blue miles) / Tones for ben / Old places old faces / Black and white (as simple as) / Souly creole
9362461822 / Feb '96 / East West

Sampou, Les

☐ FALL FROM GRACE
Holy land / Alibis / Things I should've said / Home again / Ride the line / Flesh and blood / Weather vane / I already know / String of pearls / Fall from grace / Bull's-eye / Two strong arms
CDFF 657 / Nov '96 / Flying Fish

Sampson, Dave

☐ SWEET DREAMS (The Complete Dave Sampson & The Hunters) (Sampson, Dave & The Hunters)
Sweet dreams / It's lonesome / If you need me / See you around / Why the chicken / 1999 / Goodbye twelve, hello teens / Talking in my sleep / Little girl of mine / Walking to heaven / Easy to dream / That's all / I've got a crush on you / Don't fool around / Why the chicken / Teenage dream / Wide wide world / Sandy Sandy moved away / My blue heaven / Sweet dreams
RPM 180 / Jul '97 / RPM

Sampson, Don Michael

☐ COPPER MOON
APCD 110 / Jan '96 / Appaloosa

Samson

☐ BBC SESSIONS, THE
HV 1006 / Sep '97 / High Vaultage

☐ BURNING EMOTION
Burning emotion / Tramp / Tell me / No turning back / Stranger / Don't turn away / Tomorrow / Silver screen / Too late / Don't close your eyes / Can't live without your love / Don't tell me it's over / Room 109 / Good to see you / Fight for your life
CDTB 169 / Apr '95 / Thunderbolt

☐ HEAD ON
Hard times / Take it like a man / Vice versa / Manwatcher / Too close to rock / Thunderburst / Hammerhead / Hunted / Take me to your leader / Walking out on you
REP 4037 / Aug '91 / Repertoire

☐ JOINT FORCES (Samson, Paul)
Burning emotion / No turning back / Russians / Tales of the fury / Reach out to love / Chosen few / Tramp / Power of love / Tell me
CDTB 148 / Oct '94 / Thunderbolt

☐ LIVE AT READING '81
Big brother / Take it like a man / Nice girl / Earth mother / Vice versa / Bright lights / Walking out on you / Hammerhead / Riding with the angels / Gravy train
REP 4040 / Aug '91 / Repertoire

☐ LIVE AT THE MARQUEE (Samson, Paul)
Burning emotion / Stranger / Vice versa / Fighting man / Matter of time / Afraid of the light / Tell me / Turn on the lights / Earth Mother / Tomorrow / Don't turn away
CDTB 157 / Nov '94 / Thunderbolt

☐ MASTERS, THE (2CD Set)
EDMCD 027 / 30 Mar '98 / Eagle

☐ NINETEEN NINETY-THREE
Hey you / Dream / Back to you / Word
CDTB 159 / Feb '96 / Thunderbolt

☐ REFUGE
Good to see you / Can't live without your love / Turn on the lights / Love this time / Room 109 / Sate of emergency / Don't tell me it's over / Look to the future / Someone to turn to / Too late / Samurai sunset / Silver screen
CDTB 163 / Sep '95 / Thunderbolt

☐ SAMSON
CMGCD 008 / Aug '93 / Communique

☐ SHOCK TACTICS
REP 4038 / Aug '91 / Repertoire

☐ SURVIVORS
It's not as easy as it seems / I wish I was the saddle of a school girl / Big brother / Tomorrow or yesterday / Koz / Six foot under / Wrong side of time / Mr. rock 'n' roll / Primrose shuffle / Telephone / Leavin' you
REP 4039 / Aug '91 / Repertoire

☐ THANK YOU AND GOODNIGHT
CDTB 160 / Mar '95 / Thunderbolt

Samsonov, Andrei

☐ VOID IN
Void / CoH / Post M / Whispers / White
CDPSST 3 / Feb '97 / Mute

Samuels, Dave

☐ TJADERIZED (A Cal Tjader Tribute)
Tjaderized / Bachi / Soul sauce / Delta sierra / Viva cepeda / Triste / Tres palabras / Resemblence / Yeah / Hand me down / Duo plus four
5570862 / 26 May '98 / Verve

Samuels, Elaine

☐ DANCE OF LIFE
RKR 015CD / Mar '98 / RKR

Samurai

☐ SAMURAI
LRCD 9612 / 9 Mar '98 / Landren

San Francisco Starlight Orchestra

☐ CHEERFUL LITTLE EARFUL
SOSCD 1296 / Sep '96 / Stomp Off

☐ DOIN' THE RACOON
SOSCD 1271 / Apr '94 / Stomp Off

San Miguel, Tomas

☐ CON TXALAPARTA
15641 / Jan '95 / Nuevos Medios

☐ LEZAO
Aleacion en danza / Una leyenda aurea / Akelarre / Kantico en flor de piedra / Devociones / El bertsolari / Latidos / Txalaparta mistica / El naciemiento de maritxu / Pleyades / Zalkdi dantza / Sintomas
ND 63034 / Apr '96 / Narada

San Pedro Slim

☐ ANOTHER NIGHT ON THE TOWN
TRCD 9930 / 1 Dec '97 / Tramp

Sanabria, Bobby

☐ NEW YORK CITY ACHE (Sanabria, Bobby & Ascension)
FF 630CD / Dec '93 / Flying Fish

Sanasol

☐ DEEP THOUGHTS
BIGBABE 1CD / 2 Feb '98 / Hey Babe

Sanborn, David

☐ BACKSTREET
I told U so / When you smile at me / Believer / Backstreet / Tear for crystal / Bums cathedral / Blue beach / Neither one of us
9239062 / Oct '87 / Warner Bros.

☐ BEST OF DAVID SANBORN, THE
Neither one of us (wants to be the first to say go / Carly's song / Lisa / Tear for crystal / As we speak / Chicago song / Slam / Dream / Lotus blossom / Leslie ann / Rain on christmas / Over and over / Let's just say goodbye / Anything you want / It's you / Hideaway
9362457682 / Nov '94 / Warner Bros.

☐ LOVE SONGS
I do it for your love / Lisa / When you smile at me / Imogene / Straight to the heart / Water is wide / Seduction / You are everything / It's you / One in a million / All I need is you / You don't know me
9362460022 / Nov '95 / Warner Bros.

☐ PEARLS
For all we know / Come rain or come shine / Try a little tenderness / Superstar / Willow weep for me / This masquerade / Nobody does it better / Smoke gets in your eyes / Pearls / Everything must change
7559617592 / Mar '95 / Warner Bros.

☐ TAKING OFF
Butterfat / Duck ankles / 'way 'cross georgia / Whisperer / Black light / It took a long time / Flight / Blue night / Funky banana
7599272952 / Oct '94 / Warner Bros.

☐ UPFRONT
Snakes / Benny / Crossfire / Full house / Soul serenade / Hey / Bang bang / Ramblin'
7559612722 / May '92 / Warner Bros.

☐ VOYEUR
Let's just say goodbye / It's you / Wake me when it's over / One in a million / Run for cover / All I need is you / Just for you
256900 / Dec '81 / Warner Bros.

Sanchez

☐ BOOM BOOM BYE BYE
GRELCD 186 / Jul '93 / Greensleeves

☐ BRING BACK THE LOVE
Bring back the love / Any day now / Where did I go wrong / True true / If you only knew / Impossible / Trust me too much / Wildflower / Strange / Good to be there / Bring back the love / If you only knew
WRCD 001 / Nov '97 / World

☐ BROWN EYE GIRL
VPCD 1392 / Aug '95 / VP

☐ CAN WE TALK
Can we talk / Searching / Take your time / Brown eye girl / Here I am / In the rain / Are you still in love with me / One of the poorest people / Love me forever / I want her / Only take a while / I can't stay mad at you
GRELCD 211 / Dec '94 / Greensleeves

☐ FOREVER
CRCD 44 / 18 May '98 / Charm

☐ GOLDEN VOICE OF REGGAE, THE
Melt away / Baby come home / Pretty darling / After you who could there be / Jealousy / You saw the best in me / Christmas time is here again / Alpha and Omega / Mr. Have it all / Broken hearted / My sound
WRCD 018 / Jun '97 / World

☐ I CAN'T WAIT
VYDCD 3 / Sep '95 / Vine Yard

☐ MISSING YOU
NWSCD 8 / Mar '94 / New Sound

☐ NUMBER ONE DUB
RE 173CD / Jun '97 / ROIR

☐ ONE IN A MILLION
VPCD 1483 / Jul '97 / VP

☐ REGGAE MAX
JSRNCD 1 / Mar '96 / Jet Star

☐ SANCHEZ & FRIENDS
RNCD 2036 / Jan '94 / Rhino

☐ SANCHEZ MEETS COCOA T (Sanchez & Cocoa T)
SONCD 0051 / Jul '93 / Sonic Sounds

☐ SANCHEZ VOL.1
PHCD 2008 / Aug '94 / Penthouse

☐ SANCHEZ VOL.2
PHCD 2011 / Aug '94 / Penthouse

☐ SWEETEST GIRL, THE
Let me love you down / Lonely / Old friends / My sound / Come on baby / April the sweetest girl / Greatest love of all
RRTGCD 7708 / May '89 / Rohit

Sanchez, Armando

☐ SON DE LA LOMA
CCD 9036 / 5 Jan '98 / Fresh Sound

Sanchez, Cuco

☐ SU VOS SU INSPIRACION Y SUS MEJORES INTERPRETES
9944132072 / 3 Mar '98 / Orfeon

Sanchez, David

☐ DEPARTURE, THE
Ebony / Woody 'n' you / Interlude 1 / You got it diz / Santander / I'll be around / Departure / Nina's mood / Cara De Payaso / Interlude 2 / CJ / Postlude
4765072 / Jul '94 / Columbia

☐ OBSESION
Los Aretes / Omorro nao tem vez / Lamento Borincano / Sonando con Puerto Rico / Obsesion / Essa mulher / Capullito de Alheli
CK 69116 / 18 May '98 / Sony Jazz

☐ SKETCHES OF DREAMS
Africa Y Las Americas / Bomba blues / Falling in love / Extensions / Tu y mi cancion / Mal social / Sketches of dreams / Easy to remember / Little Melanie
4803252 / May '95 / Sony Jazz

☐ STREET SCENES
Caras negras / Street scenes / Urban frequency / Dee like the breeze / Los cronopios / Four in one / Carmina / Soul of el barrio / Street scenes downtown / Elements
4851372 / Sep '96 / Sony Jazz

Sanchez, Joaquin

☐ FAVOURITE PANPIPE SPIRIT
Catchapaya / Sound of silence / Orinoco flo / Sapnish eyes / Morning has broken / Girl from Ipanema / Theme from The Mission / O sole mio / Moon over the Andes / Theme from the Thorn Birds / Guantanmera / Storms in Africa / Wave / Chi mai / El condor pasa / Light of experience / Scarborough fayre / That's amour / Spanish Harlem / Flight of the condor
4943522 / 27 Apr '98 / Music For Pleasure

Sanchez, Michael

☐ WINDOWS
Tholos / After the rain / Out of the window / Old tree / Procession / Unforgettable day / Humming birds / Only the children / Gold diggers / Moonbeam / Calumet / Yodle dance / Yellowstone
39840582 / 21 Aug '97 / Blue Flame

Sanchez, Poncho

☐ BAILA MI GENTE - SALSA
Yumbambe / El conguero / Cuidate compai / Mama guela / Baila mi gente / Son son charari / Dichoso / Con migo / Sonando / Co co my my / Soul sauce (guachi guara) / Ven morena
CCD 4710 / May '96 / Concord Jazz

☐ BIEN SABROSO
Ahora / Bien sabroso / Nancy / Keeper of the flame / Brisa / Sin timbal / Una mas / Half and half / I can
CCD 4239 / Jul '88 / Concord Picante

☐ CONGA BLUE (A Tribute To Mongo Santamaria)
Black stockings / Besame Mama / Mambo de Cuca / Conga blue / Dulce amor / Manila / Watermelon man / Happy now / Mon pa mon po / Para ti
CCD 4726 / Oct '96 / Concord Picante

☐ EL CONGUERO
Siempre me va bien / Mi negra / Shiny stockings / Si no hay amor / Yumbambo / Agua dulce / Night walk / Tin tin deo / Cuidado
CCD 4286 / Jul '88 / Concord Picante

☐ EL MEJOR
Just a few / Son son charari / Suenos / Lip smacker / Angel / Monk / El jamaiquino / Dichoso / Suave cha / Typhoon
CCD 4519 / Sep '92 / Concord Picante

☐ FREEDOM SOUND
Brown and blue / Transdance / Aleluia / Freedom sound / You don't know what love is / Prestame tu corazon / MJ's funk / (Baila el) suave cha / When we were one / Latin bit / SCratch
CCD 47782 / 6 Oct '97 / Concord Picante

☐ FUERTE - STRONG
Fuerte / Baila mi gente / It could happen to you / Lo llores, mi corazon / Ixtapa / Co co my my / Siempre te amare / Alafia / Daahoud
CCD 4340 / May '88 / Concord Picante

☐ **LA FAMILIA**
La familia / Cuidate compal / Mamba inn - on green dolphin street / Senegal / El conguero / Well you needn't / Campechana / Mambo pa 't' / Time for love / Let a woman be a woman / Let a man be a man
CCD 4369 / Feb '89 / Concord Jazz

☐ **NIGHT WITH PONCHO SANCHEZ, A**
Siempre me va bien / Bien sabroso / Alafia / Time for love / Sonando / Tito medley / La familia
CCD 4558 / Jul '93 / Concord Picante

☐ **PARA TODOS**
Five brothers / Cold duck time / Ugetsu / Angue tu / Cha cha / Happy blues / Lament / Ven morena / Rapture / Meeker's blues / Afro blue
CCD 4600 / Jun '94 / Concord Picante

☐ **SONANDO**
Night in Tunisia / Sonando / Summer knows / Con tres tambores bata / Almendra / Sueno / Cals pals / Peruchin / Este san
CCD 4201 / Nov '89 / Concord Picante

☐ **TRIBUTE TO CAL TJADER**
Soul sauce / Tripocville / I showed them / Somewhere in the night / Song for Cal / Morning / Tu crees que / Leyte / Song for Pat / Liz-Anne / Poinciana cha cha / Oran
CCD 4662 / Oct '95 / Concord Jazz

Sanchez, Roger

☐ **MIXMAG LIVE VOL.16 (Americana - Roger Sanchez/DJ Pierre) (Various Artists)**
MMLCD 016 / Jul '96 / Mixmag Live

☐ **MUZIK MASTERS (Mixed By Roger Sanchez/Dave Clarke/Fabio) (Various Artists)**
Southside: *Clarke, Dave* / Stand up: *Lovetribe* / Funk 4 people: *Black Phunk* / Love me now: *Secret Knowledge* / Compose: *DJ Linus* / We are one: *DJ Q* / Spacedance: *DJ Q* / Desire: *Nu Colours* / Release yo' self: *Transatlantic Soul* / Let's do it: *Republic* / Rhumba: *Sanchez, Roger* / L'ombelico del mundo: *Jovanotti* / I wanna dance all nite: *Bohannon, Hamilton* / Hypnodelic: *Kervorkian, Francois* / No big thang: *Johnson, Paul* / What a sensation: *Ken Lou* / Jazz it up: *Reel 2 Real* / First contact: *Outline* / Ital: *Regis* / Outrun: *Banglater, Thomas* / Badger bite: *Surgeon* / Mecano: *ODC & Carl Lekebusch* / Live appearance: *Acid Kid* / Back and forward: *Acid Kid* / L Trax: *Fitzpatrick, Lester* / Times square: *Blunted Boy Wonder* / Killer beez: *Smith, Kareem* / D-tech: *Santeone* / Runnin': *DJ Milton* / Running in October: *DJ Valium* / Something different: *Group X* / Bell winch: *Cheap Knob Gags* / Distant avenues: *Delgardo, Raoul* / Narcotic influence: *Empirion* / On da run: *DJ Deeon* / Drums in a grip: *De Wulf, Frank* / Spacefunk: *Digital* / Artificial barrier: *Source Direct* / Free la funk: *JMJ & Ritchie* / Flow: *Model 500* / Flotation: *Subject 13* / One and only: *PFM* / Carlito's way: *Carlito* / Heaven: *Carlito* / Airtight: *Funky Technicians*
74321398302 / Aug '96 / De-Construction

☐ **SECRET WEAPONS VOL.1**
Spirit lift you up / Boom / Fill me / D-Day / Free your body / There it iz / Never give up / Rejoice / I need you
ORCD 013 / Feb '94 / One

☐ **UNITED DJ'S OF AMERICA VOL.7/ NEW YORK (Various Artists)**
Flame: *Fine Young Cannibals* / Stalker: *Green Velvet* / Hindu lover: *D'Jaimin* / Mas groove: *Fisher, Cevin* / Studio 54: *Bones, Frankie* / C-lime woman: *TPM* / Release yo'self: *Translantic Soul* / Problem child: *DPD* / Revival: *Hilmes, Braxton & Mark Grant* / Love commandments: *Jackson, Gisele* / Stand tall: *Department Of Soul* / Get up: *Stingily, Byron* / Can I get a witness: *Nesby, Ann*
UNDJACD 7 / Apr '97 / Stress

Sancton, Tommy

☐ **LOUISIANA FAIRYTALE (Sancton, Tommy & The Crescent Serenaders)**
BCD 360 / Nov '96 / GHB

Sand

☐ **DYNAMIC CURVE**
Fellatio / This thinking feeling moment / Consent / Communion / Infinite / Absolution
CRECD 089 / May '94 / Creation

☐ **FIVE GRAINS**
Grain one / Grain two / Grain three / Grain four / Grain five
CRECD 127 / Nov '92 / Creation

☐ **ULTRASONIC SERAPHIM (2CD Set)**
UDORCD 2/3 / Oct '96 / United Durtro

Sandberg, Ulf

☐ **ULF SANDBERG QUARTET, THE (Sandberg, Ulf Quartet)**
Bolivia / Blue reflections / I mean you / Manhattan transfusion / Driftin' / Samba for someone / Like a child / Carlton in and out / Bolivia (alternative version) / Tildess
JAZIDCD 074 / Jun '93 / Acid Jazz

Sanders, John Lee

☐ **WORLD BLUE**
HYCD 295155 / Jul '95 / Hypertension

Sanders, Lisa

☐ **ISN'T LIFE FINE**
EAR 011 / Nov '96 / Earth Music

Sanders, Pharoah

☐ **AFRICA**
You've got to have freedom / Naima / Origin / Speak low / After the morning / Africa
CDSJP 253 / Feb '91 / Timeless Jazz

☐ **AFRICA/MOON CHILD/WELCOME TO LOVE (Pharoah Sanders On Timeless/ 3CD Set)**
You've got to have freedom / Naima / Origin / Speak low / After the morning / Africa / Heart to heart / Duo / Moon child / Moon rays / Night has a thousand eyes / All or nothing at all / Soon / Moniebah / You don't know what love is / Nearness of you / My one and only love / I want to talk about you / Soul eyes / Nancy / Polka dots and moonbeams / Sat it (over and over again) / Lament / Bird song
CDSJP 005 / Sep '96 / Timeless

☐ **BLACK UNITY**
IMP 12192 / Apr '97 / Impulse Jazz

☐ **CRESCENT WITH LOVE (Sanders, Pharoah Quartet)**
ECD 220099 / Oct '97 / Evidence

☐ **GREAT MOMENTS WITH PHAROAH SANDERS**
This is for you John / Origin / Naima / Africa / You don't know what love is / Night has a thousand eyes / Polka dots and moonbeams / Moniebah
WWJ 3005 / 27 Apr '98 / World Wide Jazz

☐ **HEART IS A MELODY**
Ole / On a misty night / Heart is a melody of time (Hiroko's song) / Goin' to Africa / Naima / Rise 'n' shine
ECD 220632 / Nov '93 / Evidence

☐ **IZIPHO SAM**
CDGR 226 / 16 Mar '98 / Charly

☐ **JEWELS OF THOUGHT**
Hum Allah hum Allah hum Allah / Sun in Aquarius
IMP 12472 / 23 Mar '98 / Impulse Jazz

☐ **JOURNEY TO THE ONE**
Greetings to Idris / Doktor Pitt / Kazuko (peace child) / After the rain / Soledad / You've got to have freedom / Yemenja / Easy to remember / Think about the one / Bedria
ECD 220162 / Jul '92 / Evidence

☐ **KARMA**
Creator has a master plan / Creator has a master plan / Colours
IMP 11532 / Nov '95 / Impulse Jazz

☐ **MESSAGE FROM HOME**
5295782 / Mar '96 / Verve

☐ **MOONCHILD**
Moon child / Moon rays / Night has a thousand eyes / All or nothing at all / Soon / Mananberg
CDSJP 326 / Aug '90 / Timeless Jazz

☐ **PHAROAH**
IN 1027CD / Jan '97 / India Navigation

☐ **PRAYER BEFORE DAWN, A**
Light at the edge of the world / Dedication to James W Clark / Softly for Shyla / After the rain / Greatest love of all / Midnight at Yoshi's / Living space / In your own sweet way / Christmas song
ECD 22047 / Mar '93 / Evidence

☐ **REJOICE**
Rejoice / Highlife / Nigerian juju hilife / Origin / When lights are low / Moment's notice / Central park west / Ntjilo ntjilo / Bird song / Farah
ECD 220202 / Jul '92 / Evidence

☐ **SAVE OUR CHILDREN**
Save our children / Midnight in Berkley Square / My jewels of love / Kazuko / Ancient song / Far-off sand
5572972 / 3 Aug '98 / Verve

☐ **SHUKURU**
ECD 220222 / Aug '92 / Evidence

☐ **THEMBI**
Astral travelling / Red black and green / Thembi / Love / Morning prayer / Bailophone
IMP 12532 / 23 Mar '98 / Impulse Jazz

☐ **WELCOME TO LOVE**
You don't know what love is / Nearness of you / My one and only love / I want to talk about you / Soul eyes / Nancy / Polka dots and moonbeams / Say it (over and over again) / Lament / Bird song
CDSJP 358 / May '91 / Timeless Jazz

Sanders, Ric

☐ **NEITHER TIME OR...**
Remembrance day / Gymnopedie for an angel / Three jigs for jamie / Selfish giant suite / Little owl / Black bryony / Domino / Blue roses 1-1v / Unbroken promise / Hopes and dreams
WRCD 017 / Feb '92 / Woodworm

☐ **WHENEVER**
NP 001CD / Aug '89 / Nico Polo

Sanderson, Tommy

☐ **KEEP ON DANCING (Sanderson, Tommy & His Orchestra)**
Speak softly love (waltz) / Paradise waltz / Sons and daughters (waltz) / For lovers only (tango) / I kiss your hand madame (tango) / Tango of the bells (tango) / Harlem nocturne (slow foxtrot) / Can I forget you (slow foxtrot) / I don't know why-thanks for the memory (slow foxtrot) / Keep on dancing (quick step) / Best things in life are free (quick step) / Uptown girl (cha cha) / Music to watch girls by (cha cha) / Toy balloons (cha cha) / Shogun sambia (samba) / Best years of our lives (samba) / Nightingale (rumba) / Close your eyes (rumba) / Games that lovers play (rumba) / Tangerine (rumba) / Jersey bounce (jive) / Perdido (jive)
CDTS 003 / Aug '93 / Maestro

Sandira

☐ **ISHMAL DU BACH**
INDO 002 / Jul '92 / Plastic Head

Sandke, Randy

☐ **AWAKENING**
Cloudy / Orphic mystery / Ellington-Strayhorn bouquet / Fungue state / Overture for the year 2000 / Rememberance / Unanswered question / Persistence / Awakening / Sea change
CCD 420492 / 16 Mar '98 / Concord Concerto

☐ **BUCK CLAYTON LEGACY**
CD 018 / May '96 / Nagel Heyer

☐ **BUCK CLAYTON REMEMBERED**
CD 006 / May '96 / Nagel Heyer

☐ **CALLING ALL CATS**
Calling all cats / Mr. Snow / I wished on the moon / Bad times at Bennington / Blues a' poppin' / Machaut / It's alright with me / In a metatone / Lida / I love you Samantha / What a beautiful yesterday / Blue room / Azalea
CCD 4717 / Aug '96 / Concord Jazz

☐ **CHASE, THE**
Lullaby of Broadway / Jordu / Ill wind / Booker / Chase / Folks who live on the hill / Primordial blooze / Oh miss Hannah / Hyde Park / So in love / Randy's Rolls Royce
CCD 4642 / May '95 / Concord Jazz

☐ **GET HAPPY**
Get happy / Tuscaloosa / Sicilienne / Humph / Sonata / Let me sing and I'm happy / You / Regret / Deception / Black beauty / Owl eyes / Boogie stop shuffle / Me and my shadow
CCD 4598 / Jun '94 / Concord Jazz

☐ **I HEAR MUSIC**
Wildfire / Thanks a million / Say it / Dream song / Muddy water / With a song in my heart / See you later / I gotta right to sing the blues / Domino / I hear music / I love Louis / Lullaby for Karen / BG postscript
CCD 4566 / Aug '93 / Concord Jazz

☐ **NEW YORKERS**
JCD 222 / Oct '93 / Jazzology

☐ **RANDY & JORDAN SANDKE & SANDKE BROTHERS**
Orange julius / Elegy for albert / Dragon dance / Bix's place / Beggars and swallowtails / Brownstones / Rosita's / Relaxin' at clifford's / Oyster marmalade / Black beauty / Nostalgia / Hog step / Cornet chop suey / Don't take your love from me / Forty-third and pluto
STCD 575 / Feb '94 / Stash

Sandler, Albert

☐ **ALBERT SANDLER AND HIS ORCHESTRA (Sandler, Albert & His Orchestra)**
Portrait of a toy soldier / Casino Tanze - Valse / Kisses in the dark / Faust - Selection / Rosa Mia - Tango serenade / Minuetto from Mozart's symphony (39) / Yvonne (waltz) / Allegro / Salut d'amour / From me to you / Folk tune and fiddle dance / By the sleepy lagoon / With you / Fairies' gavotte / Melody at dusk (Violin solo) / Souvenir d'Ukraine / Always in my heart / Boccherini's minuet in A / Japansy - Intermezzo / Biens Aimes - Waltz / King steps out
PASTCD 9732 / '90 / Flapper

Sandman

☐ **WITCHCRAFT**
MPCD 13 / 16 Mar '98 / Matsuri

Sandoval, Arturo

☐ **BEST OF ARTURO SANDOVAL, THE**
74321424382 / Jun '97 / Milan

☐ **HOT HOUSE**
Funky cha cha / Rhythm of our world / Hot house / Only you (no se tu) / Sandunga / Titio / Closely dancing / Mam-bop / New images / Cuban American medley / Brassman's holiday
N2K 10023 / 29 Jun '98 / N2K

☐ **JUST MUSIC**
El misterioso / Sambeando / Georgia on my mind / Libertao carnaval / Saving all my love / Al chicoy / My love
JHCD 008 / Jan '94 / Ronnie Scott's Jazz House

☐ **LATIN TRAIN, THE**
Be bop / La guarapachanga / Marte belona / Waheera / I can't get started (with you) / La PP / Royal poinciana / Latin train / Candela/Quimbombo / Drume negrita / Orula
GRP 98202 / May '95 / GRP

☐ **NO PROBLEM**
Nuestro blues / Los elefantes / Donna Lee / Rimsky / Campana / Fiesta mojo
JHCD 001 / Jan '94 / Ronnie Scott's Jazz House

☐ **STRAIGHT AHEAD (Sandoval, Arturo & Chucho Valdes)**
King Pete's heart / My funny valentine / Mambo influenciado / Claudia / Blues '88 / Blue monk
JHCD 007 / Feb '94 / Ronnie Scott's Jazz House

☐ **SWINGIN'**
Moontrane / Swingin' / Moment's notice / Streets of desire / Real Mcbop / Weirdfun / Dizzy's atmosphere / Reflection / Woody / It never gets old / Mack "The Knife"
GRP 98462 / Jun '96 / GRP

☐ **TUMBAITO**
MES 158742 / Apr '93 / Messidor

Sandoval, Bernado

☐ **AURORA**
173232 / Jan '97 / Musidisc

☐ **VIDA (2CD Set)**
170952 / Jan '97 / Musidisc

Sandoz

☐ **DARK CONTINENT**
TONE 4CD / Jun '96 / Touch

☐ **DIGITAL LIFEFORMS**
TO 21 / Oct '95 / Touch

☐ **EVERY MAN GOT DREAMING**
TO 28 / Oct '95 / Touch

☐ **GOD BLESS THE CONSPIRACY**
ALPHACD 2 / Jun '97 / Alphaphone

☐ **INTENSELY RADIOACTIVE**
TO 23 / Jun '94 / Touch

Sandoz Lab Technicians

☐ **LET ME LOSE MY MIND GRACEFULLY**
HERMES 027 / 23 Mar '98 / Corpus Hermeticum

Sandpipers

☐ **GUANTANAMERA**
Guantanamera / Carmen / La bamba / La mer (beyond the sea) / Louie, Louie / Things we said today / Enamorado / What makes you dream, pretty girls / Stasera gli angeli non volano (for the last time) / Angelica
5404152 / Sep '95 / A&M

Sandra

☐ **CLOSE TO SEVEN**
Don't be aggressive / Mirrored in your eyes / I need love / No taboo / When the rain doesn't come / Steady me / Shadows / Seal it forever / Love turns to pain / Your way to india
CDVIR 13 / Mar '92 / Virgin

☐ **PAINTINGS IN YELLOW**
Hiroshima / Life may be a big insanity / Johnny wanna live / Lovelight in your eyes / One more night / Skin I'm in / Paintings in yellow / Journey / Cold out here / I'm alive / Paintings / Come alive / End
CDV 2636 / Oct '90 / Virgin

Sands, Colum

☐ **ALL MY WINDING JOURNEYS**
SC 1035CD / Apr '96 / Spring

Sands Family

☐ **FOLK FROM THE MOURNES**
Rathfriland on the hill / Mourne Maggie / We'll never go home / Land / Maid of Ballydoo / I wish I was single / Praties are dug / Rambling irishman / Children's medley / Mourne rambler / Rocks of Gibralter
PTICD 3001 / Mar '97 / Pure Traditional Irish

☐ **SANDS FAMILY COLLECTION**
SC 1030CD / Jan '94 / Spring

Sands, Tommy

☐ **BEYOND THE SHADOWS**
County down / Shadow of o'casey / Dresden / We will rise again / Flower of fiddlers green / When the boys come rolling home / 1999 / Clown / No sleep tonight / Red wine / Home away from home / Make me want to stay
GLCD 3068 / Jun '93 / Green Linnet

☐ **HEART'S A WONDER, THE**
GLCD 1158 / Dec '95 / Green Linnet

☐ **SINGING OF THE TIMES**
GLCD 3044 / Oct '93 / Green Linnet

Sands, Tommy

☐ **WORRYIN' KIND, THE (The Capitol Recordings)**
Worryin' kind / Ring my phone / Blue ribbon baby / Man like wow / One day later / I ain't gettin' rid of you / Every little once in a while / I love you because / Ring-a-ding-ding / Rock light / Maybellene / Hearts of stone / Oop shoop / Hey Miss Fannie / Tweedle dee /

Such a night / Honey love / Little mama / Chicken and the hawk / Big date / Soda pop pop / Sing boy sing / Teen age crush / Wicked woman / Is it ever gonna happen / Goin' steady / Bigger than Texas / Hawaiian rock / Jimmy's song / Wrong side of love
BCD 15643 / Mar '92 / Bear Family

Sandunga

☐ VALIO LA PENA ESPERAR
TUMICD 042 / '93 / Tumi

Sandvik Small Band

☐ SANDVIK SMALL BAND
SITCD 9217 / Feb '95 / Sittel

Sanford, Don

☐ SAPPHIRE IN SEQUENCE VOL.2 (Sanford, Don & Tommy Sanderson)
CDTS 053 / Dec '95 / Maestro

Sangare, Oumou

☐ KO SIRA
Kayini wura / Sigi kurunl / Mani djindala / Saa magnl / Dugu kamelemba / Bi furu / Nawo nawo / Ko sira
WCD 036 / May '95 / World Circuit

☐ MOUSSOIOU
Djama kaissoumou / Diarabi / Woula bara diagna / Moussolou / Diya gneba / Ah ndiya
WCD 021 / May '95 / World Circuit

☐ WOROTAN
Kun fe ko / N'guatu / Baba / Worotan / Denw / N'diya ni / Tiebaw / Sabu / Fantan ni mone / Djorolen
WCD 045 / Jul '96 / World Circuit

Sangeet, Apna

☐ JAM TO THE BHANGRA VOL.1
DMUT 1242 / Apr '96 / Multitone

Sangiolo, Maria

☐ BLUE EARTH
123712432 / 17 Mar '98 / Signature

Sangkar Agung Ensemble

☐ JEGOG VOL.1
VICG 50262 / Feb '96 / JVC World Library

☐ JEGOG VOL.2
VICG 52182 / Feb '96 / JVC World Library

Sangsters

☐ BEGIN
Jesse / Feed the children / Heart like a wheel / Chorus song / Lea rig / White cockade / Sheath and knife / C-rap / Some kind of love / Will ye gang love / Steal away / Helen of Kirkconnel / Simple melody / Golden, golden / Silence and tears / Quiet comes in
CDTRAX 065 / Jul '93 / Greentrax

Sanguis Et Cinis

☐ SCHICKSAL
MOS 002CD / 6 Jul '98 / Trinity

☐ WIE DER UNBERUHRTE TRAUM EINER JUNGFRAU
TRI 008CD / 20 Jul '98 / Trinity

Sanity Assassins

☐ RESISTANCE IS USELESS
RRCD 011 / 13 Apr '98 / Retch

Sankey, Ira D.

☐ JUST AS I AM
Count your blessings / Have you been to Jesus / I will sing the wonderous story / It is well / Just as I am / My Jesus, I love thee / O Happy day / Rock of ages / Shall we gather at the river / Stand up for Jesus / Trust and obey / We're marching to Zion / What a friend we have in Jesus / When the roll is called up yonder
KMCD 987 / Apr '97 / Kingsway

Sanne

☐ LANGUAGE OF THE HEART
Haven't I been good to you / Language of the heart / Love done right / Last chance for love / Love don't bother me / What does it matter / Walking that fine line / Come to the water / Grip of love / When a woman pretends
CDV 2744 / Jul '94 / Virgin

Sannes, Eivin

☐ JUBILEE
GMCD 93 / Feb '98 / Gemini

☐ SANDU
GMCD 67 / Apr '98 / Gemini

Sansone, Jumpin' Johnny

☐ CRESCENT CITY MOON
Give me a dollar / Anything anytime / Your kind of love / Popeyes and a hubigs part 2 / Sweet baby / Crawfish walk / Destination unknown / Crescent city moon / Uncle Joe / Just say yes / Talkin' is over (the walkin' has begun) / Please please me
CDBB 9585 / Feb '97 / Bullseye Blues

Sansone, Maggie

☐ ANCIENT NOELS (Sansone, Maggie & Ensemble Galilei)
MMCD 108 / Dec '94 / Maggie's Music

☐ DANCE UPON THE SHORE
MMCD 109 / Dec '94 / Maggie's Music

☐ MIST AND STONE
MMCD 106 / Dec '94 / Maggie's Music

☐ MUSIC IN GREAT HALL (Sansone, Maggie & Ensemble Galilei)
MMCD 107 / Dec '94 / Maggie's Music

☐ TRADITIONS
MMCD 104 / Dec '94 / Maggie's Music

Santa Cruz

☐ WAY OUT
MCD 60031 / 17 Nov '97 / MCA

Santa Esmeralda

☐ BEST OF SANTA ESMERALDA, THE (You're My Everything)
Don't let me be misunderstood / House of the rising sun / Another cha cha / You're my everything / C'est magnifique / Green talisman / Street fighting man / Wages of sin / Sevilla nights / Gloria / Eternal light
HTCD 43 / 20 Apr '98 / Hot Productions

Santamaria, Mongo

☐ AFRO BLUE
Un dia de playa / Mayeya / Com mi rotmo / La tumba / El campesino / Manteca / Bonita / Para ti / Come candela / Afro blue
CCD 47812 / 6 Oct '97 / Concord Picante

☐ AFRO ROOTS
Afro blue / Che que re que che que / Rezo / Ayanye / Onyaye / Bata / Meta rumba / Chano pozo / Los Conquitos / Monte Adentro / Imaribayo / Mazacote / Yeye / Congobel / Macunsere / Timbales y bongo / Yambu / Bricamo / Longoito / Conga pa Gozar / Mi Guaguanco / Columbia
PCD 24018 / Oct '93 / Pablo

☐ AT THE VILLAGE GATE
OJCCD 490 / Feb '92 / Original Jazz Classics

☐ BRAZILIAN SUNSET
Bonita / Costa del oro / Summertime / Gumbo man / Brazilian sunset / When love begins / Being here with you / Soca mi nice / Dawn's light / Breaking it in / Watermelon man / Sofrito
CCD 79703 / Mar '96 / Candid

☐ JARRIBA
Quindimbia / Sabroso / Siempre en ti / Chombo chavada / A ti no mas / Mi novia / Antonio y Pedro / Quajira at the Blackhawk / Palo mayombe / Loco por ti / Come candela / Olga Pachanga / Mongo's theme / Entre amigos / Hilda melodia / Pay Joaquin / Lucy Cha / Manteco / Frederico / Eres tu / Esta melodia / Guaguanco flamenco
FCD 24738 / Aug '96 / Fantasy

☐ LIVE AT JAZZ ALLEY
Home / Bonita / Philadelphia / Para II / Manteca / Ponce / Come Candela / Iblano / Juan Jose / Afro blue
CCD 4427 / Aug '90 / Concord Picante

☐ MAMBOMONGO
Mambomongo / Happy as a fat rat in a cheese factory / Gabrielle / Jelly belly / That's good / New one / Amancecer / Good Doctor / Little T / Manteca
CDHOT 501 / Oct '93 / Charly

☐ MONGO EXPLODES/WATERMELON MAN
Skins / Fatback / Hammer head / Dot dot dot / Cornbread guajira / Dirty willie / Sweet potato pie / Bembe blue / Dulce amor / Tacos / Para ti / Watermelon man / Funny money / Cut that cane / Get the money / Boogie cha cha blues / Don't bother me no more / Love oh love / Yeh yeh / Peanut vendor / Bayou root / Suavito
CDBGPD 062 / Apr '93 / Beat Goes Public

☐ MONGO INTRODUCES LA LUPE (Santamaria, Mongo Orchestra)
Besito pa ti / Kiniqua / Canta bajo / Uncle Calypso / Montuneando / Que lindas son / Oye este guaguanco / Este mambo (this is my mambo) / Quiet stroll
MCD 9210 / Apr '94 / Milestone

☐ MONGO RETURNS
MCD 92452 / Feb '96 / Milestone

☐ MONGO'S MAGIC
Dr. Gasca / O mi shango / Lady Marmalade / Iberia / Naked / Funk up / Secret admirer / Song for you / Princess / What you don't know / Funk down / Leah
CDHOT 516 / Apr '95 / Charly

☐ OLE OLA
CCD 4387 / Aug '89 / Concord Picante

☐ OUR MAN IN HAVANA
Jamaicuba / Manila / He guapacha / Cha cha rock / Vengan pollos / Barandanga / Linda guajira / Vamos a gozar / Miss patti cha cha / Viva la felicidad / Il tele mina for chango (god of thunder) / Olla de for olla (wif of chango) / Yemaya olodo for olla (mother of chango) / Yeye-o for ochun (counterpart of venus) / Wolenche for chango (god of thunder) / Aqua limpia (guaguanco) / Ochun mene (columbia) / Mexico (guaguanco) / Manana son manana (columbia) / Complicaciones (guaguanco)
FCD 24729 / Oct '93 / Fantasy

☐ PORTRAITS OF CUBA
JD 145 / Jun '97 / Chesky

☐ RED HOT
Watermelon man / A mi no me enganan / Jai alai / Jamaican sunrise / Afro-Cuban fantasy / Sambita
ESMCD 585 / 29 Sep '97 / Essential

☐ SABROSO
Que maravilloso / En la felicidad / Pachanga pa ti / Tulibamba / Mambo de cuco / El bote / Pito pito / Guaguanco mania / Ja ja ja / Tula hula / Dimelo / La luna me voy / Para ti
OJCCD 281 / Sep '93 / Original Jazz Classics

☐ SKINS
Skins / Fatback / Hammer head / Dot dot dot / Dirty willie / Sweet tater pie / Bembe blue / Dulce amor / Tacos / Corn bread guajira / Tumbalele / Happy now / Country song / Congo blue / Carmela / Hombre / Chombolero / Not hardly / African song
MCD 47038 / Oct '93 / Milestone

☐ SOCA ME NICE
Con mi ritmo / Cookie / Cu-bop alert / Day tripper / Kathy's waltz / Quiet fire / Soca me nice / Tropical breeze
CCD 4362 / Nov '88 / Concord Jazz

☐ SOY YO
La manzana (the apple) / Sweet love / Soy yo (that's me) / Salazar / Mayeya / Oasis / Smooth operator / Un dia de playa (a day at the beach)
CCD 4327 / Oct '87 / Concord Picante

☐ WATERMELON MAN
Summertime / Gumbo man / Brazilian sunset / Where love begins / Being here with you / Soca mi nice / Dawn's light / Breaking it in / Watermelon man / Sofrito
EMPRCD 569 / May '95 / Emporio

Santana

☐ ABRAXAS
Singing winds / Crying beasts / Black magic woman / Gypsy queen / Oye como va / Incident at Neshabur / Se acabo / Mother's daughter / Samba pa ti / Hope you're feeling better / El nicoya
CD 32032 / Mar '91 / CBS

☐ ABRAXAS
Singing winds / Crying beasts / Black magic woman/ Gypsy Queen / Oye como va / Incident at Neshabur / Se a cabo / Mother's daughter / Samba pa ti / Hope you're feeling better / El Nicoya / Se a cabo / Toussaint l'overture / Black magic woman/Gypsy Queen
4895432 / 6 Apr '98 / Columbia

☐ ABRAXAS/AMIGOS/CARAVANSERAI (3CD Set)
Singing winds / Crying beasts / Black magic woman/ Gypsy queen / Oye como va / Incident at Neshabur / Se a cabo / Mother's daughter / Samba pa ti / Hope you're feeling better / El Nicoya / Dance sister dance / Tell me you are tired / Let it shine / Gitano / Take me with you / Europa (earth's cry, heaven's smile) / Let me / Eternal caravan of reincarnation / Waves within / Look up (to see what's coming down) / Just in time to see the sun / Song of the wind / All the love of the universe / Future primitive / Stone flower / La fuente del ritmo / Every step of the way
4853232 / 3 Nov '97 / Columbia

☐ ACAPULCO SUNRISE
Acapulco sunrise / Coconut grove / Hawaii / Hot tamales / El corazon manda / Studio jam No. 1 / Studio jam No. 2 / With a little help from my friends / Travellin' blues
CDTB 087 / '91 / Thunderbolt

☐ ACAPULCO SUNRISE
Acapulco sunrise / Coconut grove / Hot tamales / With a little help from my friends / Every day I have the blues / Jam in E / Travellin' blues / Jammin' home / Latin tropical / Let's get ourselves together
QED 117 / Nov '96 / Tring

☐ ACAPULCO SUNRISE
Jin-Go-La-Ba / Soul sacrifice / Acapulco sunrise / Coconut Grove / Hot Tamales / With a little help from my friends / Every day I have the blues / Jam in E / Let's get ourselves together
100182 / May '97 / A-Play Collection

☐ AS THE YEARS GO BY
Jin-go-lo-ba / El corazon manda / La puesta del sol / Persuasion / As the years go by / Soul sacrifice / Fried neckbones and home fries / Santana jam
QED 056 / Nov '96 / Tring

☐ AWAKENING (2CD Set)
CPCD 83312 / 16 Mar '98 / Charly

☐ BEST OF SANTANA, THE
She's not there / Black magic woman/Gypsy queen / Carnaval / Let the children play / Jugando / Vera Cruz / No one to depend on / Evil way / Oye como va / Jin-go-lo-ba / Soul sacrifice / Europa / Dealer / One chain (don't make no prison) / Samba pa ti / Dance, sister, dance / Hold on / Lightening in the sky / Aquamarine
4682672 / Jun '92 / Columbia

☐ BORBOLETTA
Spring manifestations / Cantos de los flores / Life is anew / Give and take / One with the sun / Aspirations / Practice what you preach / Mirage / Here and now / Flor de canela / Promise of a fisherman / Borboletta
4746852 / Feb '97 / Columbia

☐ CARAVANSERAI
Eternal caravan of reincarnation / Waves within / Look up (to see what's coming down) / Just in time to see the sun / Song of the wind / All the love of the universe / Future primitive / Stone flower / La fuente del ritmo / Every step of the way
CD 65299 / '88 / CBS

☐ COLLECTION, THE
Jingo / Soul sacrifice / Persuasion / Every day I have the blues / La puesta del sol / As the years go by / Latin tropical (Short version) / Jam in E / Jam in G minor / With a little help from my friends / Santana jam
COL 046 / Jul '96 / Collection

☐ DANCE OF THE RAINBOW SERPENT, THE (3CD Set)
Evil ways / Soul sacrifice / Black magic woman/ Gypsy queen / Oye como va / Samba pa ti / Everybody's everything / Song of the wind / Toussaint l'overture / In a silent way / Waves within / Flame sky / Naima: *Santana, Carlos & John McLaughlin* / I love you too much / Blues for Salvador / Aqua marine / Bella / River / I'll be waiting / Love is you / Europa / Move on / Somewhere in Heaven / Open invitation / All I ever wanted / Hannibal / Brightest star / Wings of grace / Se eni a fe l'amo-kere kere: *Santana & Olatunji* / Mudbone / Healer / Chill out (things gonna change): *Santana & John Lee Hooker* / Sweet black cherry pie: *Santana & Larry Graham* / Every now and then: *Santana & Vernon Reid* / This is this: *Santana & Weather Report*
4893232 / 6 Apr '98 / Legacy

☐ EARLY YEARS, THE
MU 5025 / Oct '92 / Musketeer

☐ EVOLUTION
Jingo / El corazon manda / La puesta del sol / Persuasion / As the years go by / Soul sacrifice / Fried neckbone and home fries / Latin tropical / Let's get ourselves together / Acapulco sunrise / Coconut grove / Hawaii / Hot tamales / Jam in E / Jammin' home / With a little help from my friends / Travellin' blues
CDTB 502 / Feb '94 / Thunderbolt

☐ FIRST ALBUM, THE
8414102 / May '96 / Sky Ranch

☐ GREATEST HITS
Evil ways / Jin-go-lo-ba / Hope you're feeling better / Samba pa ti / Persuasion / Black magic woman / Oye como va / Everything's coming up roses / Se acabo / Everybody's everything
CD 32386 / Jun '92 / Columbia

☐ ILLUMINATIONS (Santana, Carlos & Alice Coltrane)
Guru Sri Chinmoy Aphorism / Angel of air / Angel of water / Bliss: The eternal now / Angel of sunlight / Illuminations
4838102 / Mar '96 / Columbia

☐ LATIN TROPICAL
Soul sacrifice / Fried neckbones and home fries / Santana jam / Latin tropical / Let's get ourselves together
MM 007 / 29 Jun '98 / MagMid

☐ LIVE
Evil ways / Let's get ourselves together / Jin-Go-La-Ba / Rock me / Just ain't big enough / Funky piano / Way you do me
101182 / May '97 / A-Play Collection

☐ LIVE AT THE FILLMORE 1968 (2CD Set)
Jingo / Persuasion / Treat / Chunk a funk / Fried neckbones / Conquistadore rides again / Soul sacrifice / As the years go passing by / Freeway
4851062 / Mar '97 / Columbia

☐ LOTUS (2CD Set)
Meditation / Going home / A1 funk / Every step of the way / Black magic woman / Gypsy queen / Oye como va / Yours is the light / Batukada / Xibaba (she-ba-ba) / Stone flower / Waiting / Castillos de'arena / Se acabo / Samba pa ti / Savor / Toussaint l'overture / Incident at Neshabur / Lotus
4679432 / Jun '96 / Columbia

☐ MASTERS, THE (2CD Set)
EDMCD 025 / 24 Nov '97 / Eagle

☐ MILAGRO
Introduction / Milagro / Somewhere in Heaven / Saja / Your touch / Life is for living / Red prophet / Agua que va caer / Make somebody happy / Free all the people / Gypsy / We don't have to wait / Adois
5131972 / Nov '93 / Polydor

☐ MOONFLOWER (2CD Set)
Dawn-go within / Carnaval / Let the children play / Jugando / I'll be waiting / Zulu / She's not there / Bahia / Black magic woman / Gypsy queen / Dance, sister, dance / Europa / Flor d'luna / Soul sacrifice / El Morocco / Transcendance / Savor / Toussaint l'overture
4633702 / Jun '96 / Columbia

☐ ODYSSEY
CDTB 178 / Jul '96 / Thunderbolt

☐ ONENESS SILVER DREAMS GOLDEN REALITY
Chosen hour / Arise awake / Light versus darkness / Jim Jeannie / Transformation day / Victory / Silver dreams golden smiles / Cry of the wilderness / Guru's song / Oneness / Life is just a passing parade / Golden dawn / Free as the morning sun / I am free / Song for Devadip
4872382 / Mar '97 / Columbia

☐ PERSUASION
Jingo / El corazon manda / La puesta del sol / Persuasion / As the years go by
CDTB 071 / Jun '89 / Thunderbolt

☐ PERSUASION
Jingo / El corazon manda / La puesta del sol / Persuasion / As the years go by
MM 003 / 27 Apr '98 / MagMid

☐ SACRED FIRE (Live In South America)
Angels all around us / Vive la vida / Esperando / No one to depend on / Black magic woman/Gypsy queen / Oye como va / Samba pa ti / Guajira / Make somebody happy / Toussaint l'overture / Soul sacrifice/Don't try this at home / Europa / Jingo
5210822 / Nov '93 / Polydor

☐ SAMBA PA TI
Earth's cry heaven's smile / Moonflower / I love you much too much / Guru's song / Illuminations / Transformation day / Samba pa ti / Aquamarine / Tales of Kilimanjaro / Life is a lady / Holiday / Revelations / Lightnin'
4625632 / Oct '95 / Columbia

☐ SANTANA
Waiting / Evil ways / Shades of time / Savor / Jin-go-lo-ba / Persuasion / Treat / You just don't care / Soul sacrifice
CD 32003 / Feb '92 / Columbia
CK 64212 / Nov '94 / Mastersound

☐ SANTANA
Acapulco sunrise / Jam in E / Everyday I have the blues / Coconut grove / Hot tamales / Jam in G minor / With a little help from my friends
12568 / Apr '96 / Laserlight

☐ SANTANA (2CD Set)
Acapulco sunrise / Soul sacrifice / Fried neckbones and some home fries / El corazon manda / Jam in E / Everyday I have the blues / Hot tamales / Santana jam / Persuasion / Jin-go-lo-ba / Coconut grove / Let's get ourselves together / Latin tropical / Jam in G minor / La puesta de sol / As the years go by
24359 / May '97 / Laserlight

☐ SANTANA
Waiting / Evil ways / Shades of time / Savor / Jingo / Persuasion / Treat / You just don't care / Soul sacrifice / Savor / Soul sacrifice / Fried neckbones
4895422 / 6 Apr '98 / Columbia

☐ SANTANA BOX SET (3CD Set)
Jingo / El corazon manda / La puesta del sol / Persuasion / As the years go by / Soul sacrifice / Santana jam / Let's get ourselves together / Fried neckbones and some home fries / Latin tropical / Jam in E / Jam in G minor / With a little help from my friends / Travellin' blues / Everyday I have the blues / Jammin' home
KBOX 346 / Nov '95 / Collection

☐ SANTANA LIVE
Evil ways / We've got to get together / Rock me / Just ain't good enough / Funky piano / Way you do to me
GRF 279 / Apr '93 / Tring

☐ SANTANA/ABRAXAS (2CD Set)
Waiting / Evil ways / Shades of time / Savor / Jin-go-lo-ba / Persuasion / Treat / You just don't care / Soul sacrifice / Singing winds / Crying beasts / Black magic woman / Gypsy queen / Oye como va / Incident at Neshabur / Se acabo / Mother's daughter / Samba pa ti / Hope you're feeling better / El nicoya
4652212 / Jun '93 / Columbia

☐ SANTANA/WELCOME/3 (3CD Set)
Waiting / Evil ways / Shades of time / Savor / Jin-go-lo-ba / Persuasion / Treat / You just don't care / Soul sacrafice / Going home / Love demotion and surrender / Samba de sausalito / When I look in your eyes / Yours is the night / Mother Africa / Light or life / Flame-sky / Welcome / Marbles / Lava / Faith interlude / Them changes / Free from funkafide filth / Batuka / No one to depend on / Taboo / Toussant l'overture / Everybody's everything / Guajira / Jungle strut / Everything's coming our way / Para los rumberous
4886772 / 3 Nov '97 / Columbia

☐ SWING OF DELIGHT, THE (Santana, Carlos)
Swapan tari / Spartacus love theme / Phuler matan / Song for my brother / Jharna Kala / Gardenia in llave / Golden hours / Shere Khan / Tiger
4880022 / Aug '97 / Sony Jazz

☐ THIRD
Batuka / No one to depend on / Taboo / Toussaint l'overture / Everybody's everything / Guajira / Jungle strut / Everything's coming our way / Para los rumberos / Batuka / Jungle strut / Gumbo
4895542 / 6 Apr '98 / Columbia

☐ ULTIMATE COLLECTION, THE
Jin go la ba / Evil ways / Soul sacrifice / Black magic woman/Gypsy queen / Oye come va / Se a cabo / Sambo pa ti / Everybody's everything / No one to depend on / Guajira / Para los rumberos / La fuente del ritmo / Song of the wind / Love / Devotion and surrender / Mirage / Eouropa (earth's cry heaven's smile) / Dance sister dance (baila mi hermana) / Carnaval / Let the children play / Revelations / She's not there / I'll be waiting / Flor D'Luna (moonflower) / One chain don't make no prison / Well alright / Aqua marine / All I ever wanted / You know that I love you / Winning / Sensitive kind / I love you too much / Hold on / Nowhere to run / Say it again / How long / Veracruz / Gypsy woman / Havana moon / Blues for salvator
SONYTV 47CD / 3 Aug '98 / Sony TV

☐ VERY BEST OF SANTANA, THE
Europa (earths cry, heavens smile) / Black magic woman / Oye como va / Samba pa ti / Carnaval / She's not there / Soul sacrifice / Let the children play / Jugando / No one to depend on / Evil ways / Dance sister dance (baila mi hermana) / Jingo-lo-ba / Everybody's everything / Hold on / One chain (don't make no prison) / Lightning in the sky / Aqua marine / Chill out (things gonna change)
CDX 32386 / Apr '97 / Columbia

☐ VIVA SANTANA (Live/2CD Set)
Everybody's everything / Black magic woman/ Gypsy queen / Guajira / Jungle strut / Jingo / Ballin' / Bambara / Angel negro / Incident at Neshabur / Just let the music speak / Super boogie/Hong Kong blues / Song of the wind / Abi cama / Vilato / Paris finale / Brotherhood / Open invitation / Aquamarine / Dance, sister, dance / Europa / Peraza 1 / She's not there / Bambele / Evil ways / Daughter of the night / Peraza II / Black magic woman/Gypsy Queen (Live) / Oye como va / Persuasion / Soul sacrifice
4625002 / Jun '97 / Columbia

Santana
☐ SUCH IS LIFE
Mr. President / Black European / Beware / Make a joyful noise / Call on me / Call on me dub / Signs of the times / Wonderful world / You're my woman / My woman dub / Such is life
NGCD 540 / Feb '94 / Twinkle

Santana Brothers
☐ BROTHERS
Transmutation / Industrial / Thoughts / Luz amor y vida / En aranjuez con tu amor / Contigo (with you) / Blues latino / La danza / Brujo / Trip / Reflections / Morning in Marin
CID 8034 / Sep '94 / Island

Santana, Steve
☐ HEAVILY PROTECTED
NGCD 553 / 24 Nov '97 / Twinkle

Santaolalla, Gustavo
☐ RONROCO
Way up / Atacama / Jardin / Zenda / Iguazu / Del Pago / Gaucho / Coyita / De Ushuaia a La Quiaca / Lela / Pampa / La Vuelta
7559794612 / 26 Jan '98 / Nonesuch

Santasara
☐ KING OF THE GYPSIES
Ilusion de abril / Amor sincero / Comprenderas / Soledad / Quierro verte / Felicidade / Libre soy / Fue asinaci gitano / Nuevo amor / Josefa
3036400132 / Apr '96 / Carlton

Santers, Rick
☐ REVITALIZE
DSD 19604 / 5 Jan '98 / Dandelion

Santiago, Al
☐ TAMBO
RLCD 1001 / 29 Jun '98 / Ryko Latin

Santos, John
☐ HACIA EL AMOR (Santos, John & Coro Folklorico Kindembo)
Elegua-iroko / Merceditas / Chango / Tierra de mis suenos / Caridad / Guiro for oya / Toque for oya / Una carta abierta / Fiesta arara / Presidente Mandela / Siempre viviras / Dejame divertirme / Odudua / Hacia el amor
XENO 4034CD / Apr '96 / Xenophile

☐ MACHETAZO (10 Years On The Edge) (Santos, John & The Machete Ensemble)
XENO 4029 / Mar '95 / Xenophile
230320182 / 17 Mar '98 / Bembe

Santos, Sergio
☐ ABOIO
829472 / 21 Aug '97 / BUDA

Santos, Turibio
☐ VALAS AND CHORUS
CDCH 574 / Nov '91 / Milan

Santucci & Scopa
☐ ON THE UNDERGROUND
RTCL 807CD / Jul '96 / Right Tempo

Sanvoisen
☐ EXOTIC WAYS
N 02212 / Jan '95 / Noise

☐ SOUL SEASONS
Spirits / Mindwars / Behind my dreams / Difference / Soul seasons / Against the fears / Broken silence / Waiting for the rain / Somebody's stolen my name
N 02792 / Feb '97 / Noise

Saoco
☐ MACHO MUMBA
CDGR 262 / 3 Aug '98 / Charly

☐ SIEMPRE SERE GUAJIRO
CDGR 155 / May '97 / Charly

Sapho
☐ CHANTE OUM KALSOUM AND ATLAL
172142 / Nov '97 / Musidisc

☐ DIGITAL SHEIKHA
BARBARITY 008 / 17 Nov '97 / Barbarity

Sapphires
☐ BEST OF THE SAPPHIRES, THE
Where is Johnny now / Your true love / Who do you love / Oh so soon / I found out too late / I've got mine you better get yours / Where is your heart (Moulin Rouge) / Gotta be more than friends / Wild child / Come on and love me / Baby you've got me / Hearts are made to be broken / Let's break up for a while / Our love is everything / Thank you for loving me / Gotta have your love / Gee I'm sorry baby / Evil one / How could I say goodbye / Gonna be a big thing / You'll never stop me from loving you / Slow fizz
NEMCD 676 / Aug '94 / Sequel

Saprize
☐ NO
RTD 19519162 / Nov '94 / Our Choice

Saquito, Nico
☐ GOODBYE MR. CAT
Al vaiven de mi carreta / Me tenian amarrado con fe / Maria Cristina / Meneame la cuna, Ramon / A orillas del cauto / Estoy hecho tierra / Que lio company Andres / Adios company gato
WCD 035 / Feb '94 / World Circuit

Sara K
☐ HOBO
Me misin' you / If I don't see you later / Brick house / I really do / Written in stone / You'll never walk alone / Oh well / Hobo / Oughtta be happy by now / I couldn't change your mind / Sizzlin' / Moving big picture
JD 155 / May '97 / Chesky

Saraceno, Blues
☐ PLAID
Last train out / Remember when / Elvis talking (you think it's over but it's not) / Never look back / Full tank / Scratch / Jaywalkin' / Friday's walk / Deliverance / Little more cream please / Shakes / Girth / Before the storm / Lighter shade of plaid / Funk 49 / Cat's squirrel / Jitter blast / LA Vignette / Frazzin' / Exit 21 / Tommy gun
592228 / Nov '93 / Semetery

Sarasota Slim
☐ DEEP IN THE SOUTHERN TRENCHES (Live 1995)
AP 1302 / Nov '96 / Appaloosa

Sarbib, Saheb
☐ IT COULDN'T HAPPEN WITHOUT YOU
Conjunctions / It couldn't happen without you / Watchmacallit / You don't know what love is / East 11th Street / Sasa's groove / Crescent
SN 1210982 / Oct '94 / Soul Note

Sarcophagus
☐ FOR WE ARE CONSUMED
RRS 957CD / Jul '96 / Progress

Sardaby, Michel
☐ NIGHT CAP (Sardaby, Michel Trio)
SSCD 8004 / Nov '93 / Sound Hills

Sardonica
☐ GRINS AGAIN
MPL 008CD / Apr '97 / Mutant Punk

Sardou, Michel
☐ SALUT
710770 / Jan '98 / Trema

Sarge
☐ CHARCOAL
MUDCD 019 / Nov '96 / Mud

☐ GLASS INTACT
MUDCD 028 / 30 Mar '98 / Mud

Sargent, Gray
☐ SHADES OF GREY (Sargent, Gray Trio)
Let's get lost / Gray haze / Don't take your love from me / I know why / My foolish heart / AP in the PM / You don't know what love is / Nightingale sang / This time the dream's on me / My ideal / Long ago and far away / Love is a many splendoured thing
CCD 4571 / Sep '93 / Concord Jazz

Sargoth
☐ LADY EDEN IN ASHES
BDP 006CD / 20 Jul '98 / Invasion

Sarnath
☐ OVERSHINE
SHR 019CD / Jul '96 / Shiver

Sarpila, Antti
☐ HOT TIME IN UMEA (Tribute To Benny Goodman) (Sarpila, Antti/Ulf Johansson/Ronnie Gardiner)
Body and soul / After you've gone / So rare / Running wild / Man I love / Exactly like you / I want to be happy / These foolish things / It had to be you / China boy / Indian summer / Sweet Sue, just you / Stealin' apples / I've found a new baby / Memories of you
NCD 8833 / Aug '94 / Phontastic

☐ ORIGINAL ANTTI SARPILA
ASCD 1 / Oct '94 / Hep

☐ SWINGING ANTTI SARPILA
ASCD 4 / Oct '94 / Hep

☐ TWO CLARINETS (Sarpila, Antti & Allan Vache)
NHCD 026 / Jul '96 / Nagel Heyer

Sarstedt, Peter
☐ ENGLAND'S LANE
RTMCD 89 / 17 Nov '97 / Round Tower

☐ PETER SARSTEDT/AS THOUGH IT WERE A MOVIE
I am a cathedral / Sons of Cain are Abel / No more lollipops / Stay within myself / You are my life / Sayonara / Where do you go to my lovely / Blagged / My Daddy is a millionaire / Once upon an everyday / Mary Jane / Time was leading us home / Many coloured semi precious Easter eggs / Time, love, hope, life / Overture / As though it were a movie / Open a tin / Step into the candlelight / Take off your clothes / Letter to a friend / Overture / Boulevard / Sunshine is expensive / Artist / Friendship song / Juan / I'm a good boy / National anthem / Frozen orange juice / Aretusa loser
BGOCD 274 / May '95 / Beat Goes On

SAS Band
☐ SAS BAND, THE
BRGCD 25 / 22 Jun '98 / Bridge

Sash
☐ IT'S MY LIFE (2CD Set)
Mighty break / Final pizzi / Cheating twister / Stay: *Sash & La Trec* / Sweat: *Sash & La Trec* / Hoopster: *Sash & Nonex* / It's my life / Encore une fois / Ecuador: *Sash & Rodriguez* / It's my life / Encore une fois / Ecuador
SRCD 54242CD / Dec '97 / Byte Blue
MULTYCD 1 / 13 Oct '97 / Multiply

Sash, Leon
☐ I REMEMBER NEWPORT (Sash, Leon Trio)
Easy to remember / I remember Newport / Aren't you glad you're you / Pennies from Heaven / Polka dots and moonbeams / Misty / Our love is here to stay / There will never be another you / Lullaby of the leaves / I remember Newport / Aren't your glad you're you / Our love is here to stay
DD 416 / Jul '97 / Delmark

Sasha
☐ MIXMAG LIVE VOL.3 (Sasha/CJ Mackintosh) (Various Artists)
MMLCD 003 / Jul '96 / Mixmag Live

☐ QAT COLLECTION VOL.2, THE
74321223362 / Aug '94 / De-Construction

☐ SASHA REMIXES, THE (Various Artists)
Nasty rhythm: *Creative Thieves* / Alright: *Urban Soul* / Closer: *Mr. Fingers* / Feel the drop: *BM EX* / Peace and harmony: *Brothers In Rhythm* / Let you go: *Van-Rooy, Marina* / Always: *Urban Soul* / Talk to me: *Hysterix* / No more: *Unique 3* / Everything's gonna change: *Rusty* / Anambra part 2: *Ozo* / Sea of tranquility: *London Beat*
KOLDCD 002 / Jun '93 / Equator

Sasha
☐ ALL OR NOTHING
DMUT 1270 / Nov '93 / Multitone

☐ CULTURAL VIBES
DMUT 1294 / Mar '96 / Multitone

Satan
☐ COURT IN THE ACT
Into the fire / Trial by fire / Blades of steel / No turning back / Broken treaties / Break free / Hunt you down / Ritual / Dark side of innocence / Alone in the dock / Dynamo / Pull the trigger / Break free
NM 019CD / Apr '97 / Neat Metal

☐ SUSPENDED SENTENCE/INTO THE FUTURE
851 819 / '89 / Steamhammer

Satan & Adam
☐ LIVING ON THE RIVER
No more doggin' / Unlucky in love / Ode to Billy Joe / Sanctified blues / Little red rooster / Pick up the pieces of my life / Proud Mary / I'll get you / I got a woman / Whole lotta nothin' / Staggea lee
CDFF 666 / 16 Mar '98 / Flying Fish

Satanic Surfers
☐ 666 MOTOR INN
BHR 053CD / Feb '97 / Burning Heart

☐ HERO OF OUR TIME
BHR 027CD / Oct '95 / Burning Heart

☐ KEEP OUT
BHR 018CD / Feb '95 / Burning Heart

Satans Pilgrims
☐ SOUL PILGRIMS
ES 1226CD / Nov '95 / Estrus

Satan's Rats
☐ WHAT A BUNCH OF RODENTS
OVER 46CD / Feb '96 / Overground

Satchel
☐ FAMILY
Isn't that right / Without love / Not too late / Criminal justice / Breathe deep / Time "O" the year / For so long / Some more trouble / Tomorrow / Roll on / Breathe deep (instrumental outro)
4844282 / Sep '96 / Epic

Satchmo Legacy Band
☐ SALUTE TO POPS VOL.1
1211162 / Sep '89 / Soul Note

☐ SALUTE TO POPS VOL.2
1211662 / Jan '93 / Soul Note

Satelliters
☐ WYLDE KNIGHTS OF ACTION
ID 123347CD / Aug '97 / Dionysus

Satisfact
☐ SATISFACT
KLP 65CD / Mar '97 / K

Satriani, Joe
☐ CRYSTAL PLANET
Up in the sky / House full of bullets / Crystal planet / Love thing / Trundrumbalind / Lights of heaven / Raspberry jam delta-V / Ceremony / With Jupiter in mind / Secret prayer / Train of angels / Piece of liquid / Psycho monkey / Time / Zz's song
4894732 / 2 Mar '98 / Relativity

☐ DREAMING II
Crush of love / Ice nine / Memories / Hordes of locusts
4736042 / May '93 / Relativity

☐ EXTREMIST, THE
Friends / Extremist / War / Cryin' / Rubina's blue sky happiness / Summer song / Tears in the rain / Why / Motorcycle driver / New blues
4716722 / Aug '92 / Relativity

☐ FLYING IN A BLUE DREAM
Flying in a blue dream / Mystical potato head groove thing / Can't slow down / Headless / Strange / I believe / One big rush / Big bad moon / Feeling / Phone call / Day at the beach / Back to Shalla-bal / Ride / Forgotten / Bells of Lal / Into the light
4659952 / May '93 / Relativity

☐ G3 LIVE IN CONCERT (Satriani, Joe/ Eric Johnson/Steve Vai)
Going down: *Vai, Steve* / My guitar wants to kill: *Vai, Steve* / Red house: *Vai, Steve* / Cool no.9: *Satriani, Joe* / Flying in a blue dream: *Satriani, Joe* / Summer song: *Satriani, Joe* / Zap: *Johnson, Eric* / Manhattan: *Johnson, Eric* / Camel's night out: *Johnson, Eric* / Answers: *Vai, Steve* / For the love of God: *Vai, Steve* / Attitude song: *Vai, Steve*
4875392 / May '97 / Relativity

☐ JOE SATRIANI
Cool # 9 / Down, down, down / Luminous flesh giants / SMF / Look my way / Home / Moroccan sunset / Killer bee bop / Slow down blues / (You're) My world / Sittin' around
4811022 / Oct '95 / Relativity

☐ NOT OF THIS EARTH
Not of this Earth / Snake / Rubina / Memories / Brother John / Enigmatic / Driving at night / Hordes of locusts / New day / Headless horseman
4629722 / May '93 / Relativity

☐ NOT OF THIS EARTH/SURFING WITH THE.../FLYING IN A BLUE DREAM (3CD Set)
Not of this Earth / Snake / Rubina / Memories / Brother John / Enigmatic / Driving at night / Hordes of locusts / New day / Headless horseman / Surfing with the alien / Ice nine / Crushing day / Always with me, always with you / Satch boogie / Hill of the skulls / Circles / Lords of Karma / Midnight / Echo / Flying in a blue dream / Mystical potato head groove thing / Can't slow down / Headless / Strange / I believe / One big rush / Big bad moon / Feeling / Phone call / Day at the beach (New rays from the ancient sun) / Back to Shalla-bal / Ride / Forgotten / Forgotten / Bells of lal / Into the light
4775192 / Oct '94 / Relativity

☐ SURFING WITH THE ALIEN
Surfing with the alien / Ice 9 / Crushing day / Always with me, always with you / Satch boogie / Hill of the skull / Circles / Lords of Karma / Midnight / Echo
4629732 / May '93 / Relativity

☐ TIME MACHINE
Time machine / Mighty turtle head / All alone / Banana mango / Thinking of you / Crazy / Speed of light / Baroque / Dweller on the threshold / Banana mango / Dreaming / I am become death / Saying goodbye / Woodstock jam / Satch boogie / Summer song / Flying in a blue dream / Cryin' / Crush of love / Tears in the rain / Always with me, always with you / Big bad moon / Surfing with the alien / Rubina / Circles / Drum solo / Lords of karma / Echo
4745152 / Oct '93 / Relativity

Saturnine
☐ FLAGS FOR UNKNOWN TERRITORIES
DRT 031 / Nov '96 / Dirt

Saturn's Flea Collar
☐ MONOSYLLABIC
K 170CD / Aug '96 / Konkurrel

Satyricon
☐ DARK MEDIEVAL TIMES
FOG 001 / Sep '94 / Panorama

☐ NEMESIS DIVINA
FOG 012CD / Mar '96 / Moonfog

☐ SATYRICON/ENSLAVED (Satyricon/ Enslaved)
FOG 009CD / Feb '96 / Moonfog

☐ SHADOWTHRONE, THE
FOG 003 / Nov '94 / Moonfog

Saunders, Merl
☐ BLUES FROM THE RAINFOREST (Saunders, Merl & Jerry Garcia)
SMT 2133 / 16 Mar '98 / SMT

☐ FIESTA AMAZONICA
SMT 2183 / 16 Mar '98 / SMT

☐ FIRE UP PLUS
My problems got problems / Night they drove old dixie down / Save mother earth / Imagine / Welcome to the basement / Man-child / After midnight / Expressway (to your heart) / Soul roach / Benedict rides / System / Lonely avenue
FCD 7711 / Aug '97 / Fantasy

☐ IT'S IN THE AIR
SMT 2163 / 19 Jan '98 / SMT

☐ KEYSTONE ENCORES (Saunders, Merl & Jerry Garcia/John Kahn/Bill Vitt)
Hi-heel sneakers / It's too late (she's gone) / I second that emotion / One kind of favour / Money honey / How sweet it is
FCD 7703 / Sep '97 / Fantasy

☐ LIVE AT KEYSTONE VOL.1 (Saunders, Merl & Jerry Garcia/John Kahn/Bill Vitt)
Keepers / Positively 4th street / Harder they come / It takes a lot to laugh It takes a train to cry / Space / It's no use / Merl's tune
FCD 7701 / Sep '97 / Fantasy

☐ LIVE AT KEYSTONE VOL.2 (Saunders, Merl & Jerry Garcia/John Kahn/Bill Vitt)
That's all right mama / My funny valentine / Someday baby / Like a road leading home / Mystery train
FCD 7702 / Sep '97 / Fantasy

Saunders, Tom
☐ EXACTLY LIKE YOU (Saunders, Tom Wild Bill Davison Band)
CD 023 / Aug '97 / Nagel Heyer

Saunderson, Kevin
☐ FACES & PHASES (2CD Set)
SIXXCD 6 / Nov '96 / Six6

Saury, Maxim
☐ LIVE AT THE CAVEAU DE LA HUCHETTE (Saury, Maxim Jazz Music)
Way down yonder in New Orleans / Mister New Orleans blues / Limehouse blues / If you see comin' / Rencontre / Tishomingo blues / Tea for two / Black and blue / Mister Christopher / Basin Street blues / Saint Louis blues
17149 / Apr '98 / Laserlight

Sauter, Eddie
☐ THAT'S ALL (Sauter-Finegan Orchestra)
DAWE 80 / Mar '97 / Magic

Sauvage, Catherine
☐ CHANTE LEO FERRE
100662 / 1 Jun '98 / Musidisc

Savae
☐ NATIVE ANGELS
IAGO 204CD / Apr '96 / Iago

Savage
☐ BABYLON
NM 016CD / Oct '97 / Neat Metal

☐ HOLY WARS
NM 004CD / Oct '97 / Neat Metal

☐ HYPERACTIVE
We got the edge / Eye for an eye / Hard on your heels / Blind hunger / Gonna tear ya heart out / Running scared / Stevie's vengeance / Cardiac / All set to sing / Keep it on ice / She don't need you / We got the power
CDMETAL 10 / Apr '97 / Anagram

☐ LOOSE 'N' LETHAL
Let it loose / Cry wolf / Berlin / Dirty money / Ain't no fit place / On the rocks / China run / White hot / No cause to kill / Devil take you / Back on the road
NM 017CD / Apr '97 / Neat Metal

Savage
☐ AFRICAN ACHIEVEMENT
Africa / Rescue me / Curiosity / Give a little more / Oh Jah / Mr. President / Bad boy / Super power / I will be / Liberation / Love
AADSAVCD 001 / Apr '97 / Celestial

Savage, Alan
☐ SONGS FROM THE WILDERNESS
Gone to Australia / Wounded / Who needs another love song / Tradition / Northern rain / I'm not angry / Psycho Michael / Wilderness road / Nothing's going to get me down / Comatose no.101 / Not so great escape
NSKYCD 001 / 20 Apr '98 / Northern Sky

Savage, Bryan
☐ SOUL TEMPTATION
HOMCD 45623 / 21 Apr '98 / Higher Octave

Savage, Chantay
☐ I WILL SURVIVE (DOIN' IT MY WAY)
Alright / I will survive / All night, all day / Baby...drive me crazy / Pillow talk / I'm willing / Love, need, want / All my love / 90's in the red / Turned away / Brown sugar / Let's do it right / Body / Calling / Do you my way / I will survive
74321381622 / May '96 / RCA

Savage Garden
☐ SAVAGE GARDEN
To the moon and back / I want you / Truly madly deeply / Tears of pearls / Universe / Carry on dancing / Violet / Break me shake me / Thousand words / Mine / Santa Monica
4871612 / 2 Mar '98 / Columbia

Savage Resurrection
☐ SAVAGE RESURRECTION
Thing in 'E' / Every little song / Talking to you / Tahitian melody / Jammin' / Fox is sick / Someone's changing / Remlap's cave party / Appeal to the happy / Expectations
SEECD 497 / 10 Aug '98 / See For Miles

Savage Rose
☐ WILD CHILD
SRMC 0076 / 5 Jan '98 / Siwan

Savage Young Beatles
☐ CRY FOR A SHADOW
SYB 1CD / Jun '97 / Gecko

Savannah Jazzband
☐ I CAN'T ESCAPE FROM YOU
I can't escape / Kinklets / Sing on / I don't see me / All alone / Smiles / Gravier street / Shake it and break it / A miner's dream of homes / Lead me saviour / Buddy's habit / Curse of an achin heart / Trog's blues / At the cross / South rampart st. parade
LACD 29 / Jul '93 / Le Jazz

☐ IT'S ONLY A BEAUTIFUL PICTURE
Swannee river / Hilarity rag / Bouncing around / Nobody knows the trouble I've seen / Redwing / Gatemouth / Second line / Move the body over / Only a beautiful picture / Love songs of the nile / Creole belles / I double dare you / Chloe / (on the road to) home sweet home / I get the blues when it rains / Let me call you sweetheart
LACD 51 / Jun '95 / Lake

☐ OUT IN THE COLD
Running wild / Yellow dog blues / Save your sorrow / Mama's gone goodbye / African queen / When my dreamboat comes home / Wabash blues / Nobody's fault but mine / Willie the weeper / Savoy blues / Ole Miss rag / Out in the cold / Tipi tipi tin / Yes, yes in your eyes / Out of nowhere / Original Dixieland one step
LACD 82 / Jun '97 / Lake

☐ SAVANNAH JAZZ BAND
I can't escape / Kinklets / Sing on / I don't see me / All alone / Smiles / Gravier street / Shake it and break it / Miner's dream of homes / Lead me saviour / Buddy's habit / Curse of an aching heart / Trog's blues / At the cross / South Rampart Street Parade
LACD 99 / Jun '93 / Lake

Savatage
☐ DEAD WINTER DEAD
086202RAD
086252RAD / Oct '95 / Edel

☐ DUNGEONS ARE CALLING, THE
398414075CD / Mar '97 / Metal Blade

☐ EDGE OF THE THORNS
0089492CTR / 24 Nov '97 / Edel

☐ EDGE OF THORNS
Edge of thorns / He carves his stone / Lights out / Skraggy's tomb / Labyrinths / Follow me / Exit music / Degrees of sanity / Conversation piece / All that I bleed / Damien / Miles away / Sleep
7567824882 / Mar '93 / Atlantic

☐ FIGHT FOR THE ROCK
Fight for the rock / Out on the streets / Crying for love / Day after day / Edge of midnight / Hyde / Lady in disguise / She's only rock 'n' roll / Wishing well / Red light paradise
0089462CTR / 1 Dec '97 / Edel

☐ GHOST IN THE RUINS (Tribute To Chris Oliva)
SPV 08512142 / Apr '96 / SPV

☐ GUTTER BALLET
Of rage and war / Temptation revelation / Silk and steel / Hounds / Mentally yours / Gutter ballet / When the crowds are gone / She's in love / Unholy / Summer's rain
0089442CTR / 1 Dec '97 / Edel

☐ HALL OF THE MOUNTAIN KING
Twenty four hours ago / Beyond the doors of dark / Legion / Strange wings / Prelude to madness / Hall of the mountain king / Price you pay / White witch / Last down / Devastation
0089482CTR / 1 Dec '97 / Edel

☐ HANDFUL OF RAIN
CDVEST 32 / Aug '94 / Bulletproof
SPV 08518022 / 29 Jun '98 / SPV

☐ JAPAN LIVE '94
IRSCD 993015 / Apr '97 / Hengest
SPV 08518852 / Mar '98 / SPV

☐ POWER OF THE NIGHT
Power of the night / Unusual / Warriors / Necrophilia / Washed out / Hard for love / Fountain of youth / Skull session / Stuck on you / In the dream
0089472CTR / 1 Dec '97 / Edel

☐ SIRENS
Sirens / Holocaust / I believe / Rage / On the run / Twisted little sister / Living for the night / Scream murder / Out on the streets
398414076CD / Mar '97 / Metal Blade

☐ STREETS
Streets / Jesus saves / Tonight he grins again / Strange reality / Little too far / You're alive / Sammy and Tex / Can you hear me now / New York City don't mean nothing / Ghost in the ruins / Agony and ecstacy / Heal my soul / Somewhere in time / Believe
0089452CTR / 1 Dec '97 / Edel

☐ WAKE OF MAGELLAN, THE
Ocean / Welcome / Turns to me / Mornign sun / Another way / Blackjack guillotine / Paragons of innocence / Complaint in the system / Underture / Wake of Magellan / Anymore / Storm / Hourglass
0089832CTR / 3 Nov '97 / Edel

Saves The Day
☐ CAN'T SLOW DOWN
EVR 042CD / 20 Jul '98 / Equal Vision

Savia Andina
☐ SAVIA ANDINA
TUMICD 040 / '93 / Tumi

Saviour Machine
☐ 11
MASSCD 094 / Mar '96 / Massacre

☐ LEGEND VOL.2
MASSCD 156 / 4 May '98 / Massacre

Savitt, Jan
☐ FUTURISTIC SHUFFLE 1938-1941 (Savitt, Jan & His Orchestra)
RACD 7113 / May '96 / Aerospace

☐ LIVE IN HI-FI 1938 (Savitt, Jan & The Top Hatters)
JH 1024 / Feb '93 / Jazz Hour

Savolainen, Jarmo
☐ TRUE IMAGE
True image / 80/81 / Sco-lastic / Down the line / Scene from above / Long ago and far away / Inky-pinky / Scenario / Things are the way they are / Inseperable / We don't know
AL 73031 / Nov '96 / A

Savoy Bearcats
☐ NEW YORK VOL.3
DGF 12 / Mar '97 / Frog

Savoy Brown
☐ ARCHIVE ALIVE
ACH 80014 / 27 Apr '98 / Archive

☐ BRING IT HOME
CTC 0107 / Jul '95 / Coast To Coast

☐ LET IT RIDE
CD 0848882 / Mar '96 / SPV

☐ SAVAGE RETURN
8442432 / Jan '96 / Deram

Savoy Jazzmen

☐ 30TH ANNIVERSARY 1962-1992
322909 / Feb '93 / Koch

Savoy, Marc

☐ BENEATH A GREEN OAK TREE (Savoy, Marc & Dewey Balfa/D.L. Menard)
ARHCD 312 / Apr '95 / Arhoolie

☐ HOME MUSIC WITH SPIRITS (Savoy-Doucet Cajun Band)
ARHCD 389 / Apr '95 / Arhoolie

☐ LIVE AT THE DANCE (Savoy-Doucet Cajun Band)
ARHCD 418 / Apr '95 / Arhoolie

☐ NOW AND THEN (Savoy-Smith Cajun Band)
Evangeline Playboys special / Rainbow waltz / Wee pee special / Old carpenter's waltz/Contredanse de Mamou / Blues de Basile / Walker special / C'est un pecher de dire un menterie / Le moulin casse / Savoy family waltz / Choupique / One step de McGees/O ma Josephine / Separation waltz / Baisse bas / Lovesick waltz / Two step de prairie soileau
ARHCD 457 / Nov '96 / Arhoolie

☐ TWO-STEP D'AMEDE (Savoy-Doucet Cajun Band)
ARHCD 316 / Apr '95 / Arhoolie

Savoy Singers

☐ GILBERT AND SULLIVAN FAVOURITES
Dance a cachuka / I've got a little list / When the foreman bares his steel / We sail the ocean blue/I'm called little / Buttercup / Three little maids from school / When I was a lad / List and learn / Sun whose rays are all ablaze / I am the very model of a modern Major-General / Carefully on tiptoe stealing / One of us will be a queen / Tit willow / There is beauty in the bellow of the blast / Poor wand'ring one / Take a pair of sparkling eyes / Finale from HMS Pinafore
308692 / 20 Apr '98 / Hallmark

Savoy Sultans

☐ EVERYTHING SWINGS
Air mail special / Stolen sweets / Stomping at the Savoy / Sentimental journey / It don't mean a thing / In the mood / Just you, just me / Take the 'A' train / Funky Willie / Undecided
VN 1005 / Nov '96 / Viper's Nest

Savoy, Tanya

☐ BETTER SHADE OF GREEN
SOR 61111CD / Aug '97 / So Real

Saw Doctors

☐ ALL THE WAY FROM TUAM
Green and red of mayo / You got me on the run / Pied piper / My heart is livin' in the sixties still / Hay wrap / Wake up sleeping / Midnight express / Broke my heart / Exhilarating sadness / All the way from Tuam / FCA / Music I love / Yvonne / Never mind the strangers
SAWDOC 002CD / Oct '94 / Shamtown

☐ IF THIS IS ROCK AND ROLL I WANT MY OLD JOB BACK
I useta lover / Only one girl / Why do I always want you / It won't be tonight / Irish post / Sing a powerful song / Freedom fighters / That's what she said last night / Red cortina / Presentation boarder / Don't let me down / Twenty five / What a day / N17 / I hope you meet again
SAWDOC 001CD / Oct '94 / Shamtown

☐ SAME OUL TOWN
SAWDOC 004CD / Feb '96 / Shamtown

☐ SING A POWERFUL SONG
Green and red of Mayo / It won't be tonight / Wake up sleeping / Macnas parade / What a day / Hay wrap / N17 / Exhilarating sadness / Red cortina / Clare Island / To win just once / Share the darkness / I useta lover
SAWDOC 005CD / 10 Nov '97 / Shamtown

Sawai, Tadao

☐ KOTO MUSIC
PS 65180 / Apr '97 / PlayaSound

Sawhney, Nitin

☐ DISPLACING THE PRIEST
Oceans and rain / In the mind / Herccica latino / Saudades / Displacing the priest / Bengali song / Streets / Voices / Pieces of ten / Vidya
CASTE 2CD / Oct '96 / OutCaste

☐ MIGRATION
CASTE 1CD / Jan '96 / OutCaste

☐ SPIRIT DANCE
River pulse / Skylight / Taste / Pieces of ten / Wind and rain / Twilight daze / Chase the sun / Spirit dance
SDCD 7001 / Mar '94 / Spirit Dance

Sax & Ivory

☐ BEST OF SAX & IVORY, THE
PKCD 61194 / Sep '94 / K&K

Sax Appeal

☐ FLAT OUT
Dervish / Wasps / Smiffy / Trains / Semi conscious / Kites / Sand in my shoes / Chee o wa wa cha cha
JITCD 9503 / 13 Oct '97 / Jazzizit

☐ LET'S GO
Zoot suit / Wild river / Let's go / Makambo triangle / Longshore drift / One step further / Monkish / Rio / Stompin' on the saveloy / Midnight
JITCD 9401 / Jul '94 / Jazzizit

☐ OUTSIDE IN
Outside in / Meek / Greens / Two of a kind / Waco Jaco / Gotta getta dep / Dimanche matin / Sonic samba / Whisperer / Outside in
JITCD 9606 / Mar '97 / Jazzizit

Sax, Mostafa

☐ BEST OF EGYPTIAN BELLY DANCE MUSIC
EUCD 1131 / '91 / ARC

Saxomania

☐ SAXPAK
Portrait of a flirt / Sophisticated lady / Liza / Holberg prelude / I'll remember April / Twelfth Street rag / Candlelights / Holiday for strings / String of pearls / Saxophobia / Westminster waltz / I'm old fashioned / Four brothers / Promenade / Czardas / Perfidia / Marriage of Figaro overture / Lover man / Continental / Girl with the flaxen hair / Turkey in the straw / Shepherd's hey / Nola / Yankee doodle
CDWHL 216 / Feb '97 / White Line

Saxon

☐ COLLECTION OF METAL, A
747 (Strangers in the night) / Rock 'n' roll gypsy / And the bands played on / Back on the streets / Ride like the wind / Big teaser / I can't wait anymore / Broken heroes / Raise some hell / Denim and leather / Rock the nations / Motorcycle man / Everybody up / Rock city / Set me free / Play it loud
CDGOLD 1055 / Oct '96 / EMI Gold

☐ DENIM AND LEATHER
Princess of the night / Never surrender / Out of control / Rough and ready / Play it loud / And the bands played on / Midnight rider / Fire in the sky / Denim and leather
CDGOLD 1011 / Mar '96 / EMI Gold

☐ DOGS OF WAR
Dogs of war / Burning wheels / Big tivin rolling / Dold on / Great white buffalo / Demolition alley / Walking through Tokyo / Give it all away / Yesterday's gone
08576012 / Nov '96 / SPV

☐ DONNINGTON
Motorcycle man / Still fit to boogie / Freeway mad / Backs to the wall / Wheels of steel / Bap shoo ap / 747 / Stallions of the highway / Machine gun
IRSCD 993011 / Apr '97 / Intercord

☐ EAGLE HAS LANDED VOL.2, THE
CMC 186258 / 13 Jul '98 / CMC

☐ GREATEST HITS LIVE
Opening theme / Heavy metal thunder / Rock 'n' roll gypsy / And the bands played on / Twenty thousand feet / Ride like the wind / Motor cycle man / 747 (Strangers in the night) / See the light shining / Frozen rainbow / Princess of the night / Wheels of steel / Denim and leather / Crusader / Rockin' again / Back on the streets again
ESMCD 132 / May '95 / Essential

☐ LIVE AT THE MONSTERS OF ROCK
IRS 933011CD / Jan '96 / Intercord

☐ UNLEASH THE BEAST
SPV 08518762 / Sep '97 / SPV

☐ WHEELS OF STEEL/STRONG ARM OF THE LAW (Remastered/2CD Set)
Motorcycle man / Stand up and be counted / 747 (Strangers in the night) / Wheels of steel / Freeway mad / See the light shining / Street fighting man / Suzie hold on / Machine gun / Judgement day / Wheels of steel / See the light shining / Wheels of steel / 747 (Strangers in the night) / Stallions of the highway / Heavy metal thunder / To hell and back again / Strong arm of the law / Taking your chances / 20,000 feet / Hungry years / Sixth form girls / Dollars 1 PM / 20,000 feet / Hungry years / Strong arm of the law / Heavy metal thunder
CTMCD 201 / Feb '97 / EMI

Saxon, Al

☐ HOOKED ON THE '40'S (Saxon, Al '40s Band)
In the mood / Little white lies / Swinging on a star / Say something sweet to your sweetheart / Sentimental journey / I cried for you / I'll string along with you / Lullaby of broadway / 12th street rag / September in the rain / On the sunny side of the street / Dream / I've got my love to keep me warm / Lazy river / Paper doll / Sunday, Monday or always / That's my desire / There I've said it again / Blue moon / I've heard that song before / Baby face / April showers / Toot toot tootsie / Swanee skyliner / I can dream can't I
EMPRCD 515 / Jul '94 / Emporio

☐ HOOKED ON THE 40'S (Saxon, Al '40s Band)
In the mood / Little white lies / Swinging on a star / Say something sweet to your sweetheart / Sentimental journey / I cried for you / I'll string along with you / Lullaby of Broadway / Twelfth Street Rag / September in the rain / On the sunny side of the street / Dream / I've got my love to keep me warm / Lazy river / Paper doll / Sunday, Monday or always / That's my desire / There, I've said it again / Blue moon / I've heard that song before / Baby face / April showers / Toot toot Tootsie goodbye / Swanee / Skyliner / I can dream, can't I / On a slowboat to China / Baby it's cold outside / Ev'ry time we say goodbye / I'm always chasing rainbows / When you were sweet sixteen / I had the craziest dream / You'll never know / I'll be with you in apple blossom time / Don't sit under the apple tree / With my eyes wide open I'm dreaming / You made me love you / Lovely way to spend an evening / Don't get around much anymore / In a shanty in old Shanty Town
ECD 3080 / Jun '97 / K-Tel

Saxtet

☐ SAFER SAX
SERCD 8000 / Aug '93 / Serendipity

Say-So

☐ SAY-SO
ORCD 9709 / Oct '97 / Pamplin

Sayama, Masahiro

☐ PLAY ME A LITTLE MUSIC
JD 3305 / Jul '88 / JVC

Sayer, Cynthia

☐ CYNTHIA SAYER
JCD 270 / Dec '97 / Jazzology

Sayer, Leo

☐ 20 GREAT LOVE SONGS
When I need you / Orchard Road / Raining in my heart / Unchained melody / More than I can say / Oh girl / Let it be / How beautiful you are / I can't stop loving you / Dancing the night away / Giving it all away / Have you ever been in love / Heart (stop beating in time) / Don't wait until tomorrow / Til you come back to me / I will not stop fighting / Never had a dream come true / Sea of heartbreak / No holding back / Only dreaming
LS 870582 / 2 Feb '98 / Disky

☐ ANOTHER YEAR
D 20013 / 9 Mar '98 / Festival

☐ ENDLESS FLIGHT
Hold on to my love / You make me feel like dancing / Reflections / When I need you / No business like love business / I hear the laughter / Magdalena / How much love / I think we fell in love too fast / Endless flight
AHLCD 35 / May '96 / Hit
D 20017 / 9 Mar '98 / Festival

☐ HAVE YOU EVER BEEN IN LOVE
Until you come back to me / Sea of heartbreak / More than I can say / Darlin' / Don't wait until tomorrow / How beautiful you are / Orchard road / Aviation / Heart (Stop beating in time) / Your love still brings me to my knees / Have you ever been in love / Wounded heart / Love games / Never has a dream come true
AHLCD 37 / May '96 / Hit

☐ JUST A BOY
Telepathy / Train / Bells of St. Mary's / One man band / In my life / When I came home this morning / Long tall glasses / Another time / Solo / Giving it all away
AHLCD 36 / May '96 / Hit

☐ LEO SAYER
D 20010 / Jun '97 / Festival

☐ LIVING IN A FANTASY
Time ran out on you / Where did we go wrong / You win, I lose / More than I can say / Millionaire / Once in a while / Living in a fantasy / She's not coming back / Let me know / Only foolin'
D 20016 / 9 Mar '98 / Festival

☐ LOVE BALLADS
More than I can say / Orchard Road / When I need you / Till you come back to me / Bye bye now my sweet love / Darlin' / Don't wait until tomorrow / Have you ever been in love / Sea of heartbreak / Aviation / How beautiful you are / Heart (stop beating in time) / Your love still brings me to my knees / Love games / Wounded heart / Never had a dream come true
12899 / Feb '97 / Laserlight

☐ LOVE SONGS
MCCD 273 / Dec '96 / Music Club

☐ SILVERBIRD
Innocent bystanders / Goodnight old friend / Drop back / Silver bird / Show must go on / Dancer / Tomorrow / Don't say it's over / Slow motion / Oh wot a life / Why is everybody going home
AHLCD 34 / May '96 / Hit

☐ YOU MAKE ME FEEL LIKE DANCING
How much love / You make me feel like dancing / Thunder in my heart / Reflections / No business like love business / I hear the laughter / Magdalena / Moonlighting / Long tall glasses / Hold on to my love / Paris dies in the morning / Rumours / Wonder where the lions are / I think we fell in love too fast / Endless flight / Dancin' the night away
12970 / Nov '97 / Laserlight

Sayles, Charlie

☐ I GOT SOMETHING TO SAY
Mississippi saxophone / Man / Hip guy / Zydeco / I got something to say / Little walter's blues / Hey joe / I love my baby / I like what I like / Two timin' woman / Funky sound / Screecher / Well now / I got something to say / Hip guy / Well now / Mississippi saxophone / I love my baby / Little walter's blues
JSPCD 261 / Nov '95 / JSP

Sayles, Emmanuel

☐ EMMANUEL SAYLES & THE BARRY MARTIN BAND (Sayles, Emmanuel & Barry Martyn Band)
BCD 359 / Apr '97 / GHB

Sayles Silverleaf Ragtimers

☐ SAYLES SILVERLEAF RAGTIMERS
BCD 8 / Aug '95 / GHB

Sayyah, Emad

☐ MODERN BELLY DANCE MUSIC FROM LEBANON VOL.1
EUCD 1099 / '91 / ARC

☐ MODERN BELLY DANCE MUSIC FROM LEBANON VOL.2
EUCD 1226 / Sep '93 / ARC

☐ MODERN BELLY DANCE MUSIC FROM LEBANON VOL.4
EUCD 1332 / Mar '96 / ARC

Scabs

☐ SKINTIGHT
BIASCD 102 / '89 / Play It Again Sam

Scaffold

☐ VERY BEST OF SCAFFOLD, THE
Thank u very much / Lily the pink / Two days Monday / Three blind jellyfish / Goodbat nightman / Do you remember / 1-2-3 / Stop blowing those charity bubbles / Gin gan goolie / All the way up / Liverpool Lou / Do the Albert
WB 885572 / 2 Feb '98 / Disky

Scaggiari, Stefan

☐ STEFAN ITELY (Scaggiari Trio)
Just in time / I'm old fashioned / Icarus / All the way / Honeysuckle rose / Samba de bunda / Old folks / Where or when / Bittersweet / I've got the world on a string / Golden lady / Windswept high
CCD 4570 / Sep '93 / Concord Jazz

☐ STEFAN OUT
Love walked in / Felix / Love for sale / Make me a memory / Willow weep for me / Ill wind / Bolivia / When you're around / I am singing / If I could / Windows / For all we know
CCD 4659 / Aug '95 / Concord Jazz

Scaggs, Boz

☐ BOZ SCAGGS
I'm easy / I'll be long gone / Another day (another letter) / Now you're gone / Finding her / Look what I've got / Waiting for a train / Loan me a dime / Sweet release
7567815452 / May '93 / Atlantic

☐ COME ON HOME
It all went down the drain / Ask me 'bout nothin' (but the blues) / Don't cry no more / Found love / Come on home / Pictures of a broken heart / Love letters / I've got your love / Early in the morning / Your good thing (is about to end) / T-Bone shuffle / Sick and tired / After hours / Goodnight Louise
CDVUS 124 / Apr '97 / Virgin

☐ MY TIME (Boz Scaggs Anthology 1969-1997/2CD Set)
Runnin' blue / Dinah Flo / Slowly in the West / Full lock powerslide / Old time lovin' / Might have to cry / Hello my lover / Freedom for the station / He's a fool for you / We're gonna roll / My time
4873972 / 20 Oct '97 / Columbia

☐ SILK DEGREES
What can I say / Georgia / Jump street / What do you want the girl to do / Harbour lights / Lowdown / It's over / Love me tomorrow / Lido shuffle / We're all alone
4719682 / Feb '97 / Columbia

☐ SOME CHANGE
You got my letter / Some change / I'll be the one / Call me / Fly like a bird / Sierra / Lost it / Time / Illusion / Follow that man
CDVUS 73 / Jun '94 / Virgin

Scala, Primo

☐ PRIMO SCALA & HIS ACCORDION BAND (Scala, Primo Accordion Band)
PASTCD 7084 / Apr '98 / Flapper

Scales Brothers

☐ OUR HOUSE
Bamene bekon / All but one / Sambasara / Boneafield / Nsisim alouk / Province of China / Cascatas / Years later
ENJACD 91062 / Jun '97 / Enja

Scalpel

☐ ECLIPSE
NRCD 1 / 22 Jun '98 / Naive

Scalplock

☐ BROKEN HISTORY
XIONCDEP 01 / 15 Dec '97 / Insurrection

☐ TO HATE IS TO CURE
XIONCD 1 / 13 Jul '98 / Insurrection

Scan X

☐ CHROMA
Dust / Grey lights / Secrets / Voodoo / Earthquake / Wood / Blackmoon / Turmoil / Blue 072c / Requiem / Red dogs / Wasteland
F 040CD / Jun '96 / F-Communications

Scandinavian Jazz Quartet

☐ NIGHT IN BILBAO, A (Scandinavian Jazz Quartet & Lars Jansson)
MECCACD 2031 / Oct '97 / Music Mecca

Scanner

☐ DELIVERY
Spirit of speech / Digital anchor / Treble spin / Fingerbug / Heidi / Barcode / Radio sprite / Throne of hives / Affaire / Vie one / My lost love hunting your lost face
MOSH 174CDL
MOSH 174CD / May '97 / Earache

☐ HYPERTRACE
N 01113 / 1 Sep '98 / Noise

☐ MENTAL RESERVATION
MASSCD 058 / Oct '95 / Massacre

☐ TERMINAL EARTH
Law / Not alone / Wonder / Buy or die / Touch the light / Terminal earth / From the dust of ages / Challenge
N 01412 / 1 Sep '98 / Noise

Scanner

☐ GARDEN IS FULL OF METAL (Scanner & Derek Jarman)
SR 104 / 24 Nov '97 / Sub Rosa

☐ NEW YORK SOUNDSCAPE (Scanner & Shea/Nus)
QUANTUM 153 / Jan '97 / Sub Rosa

☐ PARIS SESSIONS (Scanner & Shea/Main)
QUANTUM 102 / Nov '96 / Sub Rosa

☐ SCANNER VOL.1
ASH 11 / Jan '95 / Ash International

☐ SULPHUR
SR 95 / Feb '96 / Sub Rosa

Scarab

☐ SECRETS OF THE PAST AND FUTURE
WSCD 019 / Jun '97 / Word Sound Recordings

Scarce

☐ DEADSEXY
Honey simple / Freakshadow / Days like this / Stella / Glamourising / Cigarettes / Girl through me / Karona krome / All sideways / Thrill me / Sense of quickness / Given / Obviously midnight
PDOXCD 001 / Jul '95 / Paradox

☐ RED
ABB 79 / Aug '95 / Big Cat

Scared Of Chaka

☐ HOW TO LOSE
MTR 366CD / 20 Apr '98 / Empty

☐ MASONIC YOUTH
MTR 334CD / Oct '96 / Empty

Scarface

☐ DIARY, THE
Intro / White sheet / No tears / Jesse James / G's / I seen a man die / One / Goin' down / One time / Hand of the dead body / Mind playin' tricks '94 / Diary / Outro
CDVUS 81 / Oct '94 / Virgin

☐ UNTOUCHABLE, THE
Intro / Untouchable / No warning / Southside / Sunshine: *Scarface & Lisa Crawford* / Money makes the world go round: *Scarface & Daz* / For real / Ya money or ya life / Mary Jane / Smile: *Scarface & 2Pac/Johnny P* / Smartz / Faith / Game over: *Scarface & Dr. Dre/Ice Cube/Too Short* / Outro: *Scarface & Dr. Dre/Ice Cube/Too Short*
CDVUS 125 / Mar '97 / Noo Trybe

Scarfo

☐ LUXURY PLANE CRASH
ELO / Jet samshed flat / Safecracker / Don't let go / Japanese cameras / Jazz cigarette / Cosmonaut no.7 / Pajo gear / Chomsky airport / Lifeline / Prison architect
BLUFF 045CD / Jul '97 / Deceptive

☐ SCARFO
Eyesore / Coin op / Skinny / Backwater / Car chase / Thow it all / Wailing words
BLUFF 017CD / Oct '95 / Deceptive

Scarlet

☐ CHEMISTRY
I can't save you from yourself / I feel a little sentimental / Bad girl / Chemistry / Understand me too / Fantasy / Take it like a woman / Man in me / You're not him / Do you think of me
0630146592 / Jul '96 / East West

☐ NAKED
I really like the idea / Virgin / Independent love song / I wanna be free (to be with him) / Love hangover / Sirens of silence / Naked / Moonstruck / Shine / Man in a cage
4509976432 / Dec '96 / WEA

Scarlet Blue

☐ CASTLES IN THE SAND
BLUE 1 / Nov '96 / Scarlet

Scarlett, Mose

☐ FUNDAMENTAL THINGS, THE
Moon is a silver dollar / Sweet Georgia Brown / Kiss to build a dream on / It's a sin to tell a lie / After you've gone / Nobody's sweetheart / As time goes by / Nine pound hammer / My walking stick / Sheik of Araby / How long blues / Big bad Bill / Miss Otis regrets / Marie / Hobo's lullaby
PD 013 / Jul '98 / Borealis

Scarp

☐ SCARP
BNQ 94CD / Jul '94 / Arax Pan Global

Scarr, Angie

☐ DANGER ZONE
SSAS 001 / Jan '98 / Sliding Scale

Scarymeanie Demons

☐ DRAGON'S BREATH
To the victor the spoils / Oddsocks and tennis shoes / Saga / Time to go / Under the clear blue / Merlin (free the stone) / Chain mail crusader / Dragon's breath / Want you for your love / Sleepy Sunday
CDRPM 0035 / 11 May '98 / RP Media

Scat Opera

☐ ABOUT TIME
Premonition / B.g.v. / About time / Family man / Tarred with the same brush / Filo / Pighead / Be mine / On your own / Flex / Overture
CDMFN 111 / Feb '91 / Music For Nations

☐ FOUR GONE CONFUSION
Reminsce in bitterness / Geee-forced / Points of madness / Think big / Inferiority complex i.c. / (i dig that) oral mastication / Sit down, shut up and listen / Babble on tongue / Men and there tiny minds / Ignoramus / Old fuddy duddy / Calculated
CDMFN 140 / Oct '92 / Music For Nations

Scatman John

☐ SCATMAN'S WORLD
Welcome to Scatland / Scatman's world / Only you / Quiet desperation / Scatman / Sing now / Popstar / Time (take your time) / Mambo jambo / Everything changes / Song of Scatland / Hi Louis / Scatman (remix)
74321298792 / Feb '97 / RCA

Scatterbrain

☐ MINDUS INTELLECTUALIS
Write that hit / Beer muscles / Everybody does it / Funny thing / How could I love you / Dead man blues / Down with the ship
CDVEST 33 / Sep '94 / Bulletproof

Scelsi, Giacinto

☐ BOT-BA (Scelsi, Giacinto & Marianne Schroeder)
ARTCD 6092 / Oct '92 / Hat Art

Scenic

☐ AQUATICA
WD 00382 / 20 Apr '98 / World Domination

☐ INCIDENT AT CIMA
IP 050CD / Nov '96 / Independant Press

Schankman Twins

☐ DUALITY
CWRCD 4816 / Mar '98 / City West

Schaphorst, Ken

☐ OVER THE RAINBOW (The Music Of Harold Arlen)
Out of this world / Man that got away / If I only had a brain / Lullaby / Ding dong, the witch is dead / Come rain or come shine / Accentuate the positive / Stormy weather / Get happy / Life's full of consequence / That old black magic / I've got the world on a string / Over the rainbow
AC 4204 / May '97 / Accurate

Schatz, Lesley

☐ BANJO PICKIN' GIRL
Winter it is past / Trouble in mind / Cruel sister / Barbara Allen / Little Joe the wrangler / Zebra Dun / Streets of Laredo / Jesse James / Tom Dula / Banjo pickin' girl / Early one morning / Arthur McBride / Jack O'Hazlegreen / Great Silkie / Silver dagger / Rowan tree / White coral bells / Flor del pino / Tumbalalaika / Will the circle be unbroken
BCD 15729 / May '93 / Bear Family

☐ BRAVE WOLFE
Red river valley / Gypsy Davey / Oh Susanna / Brave Wolfe / Banks of the Ohio / I never will marry / Greensleeves / Greenpeace / I ride an old paint / Shady grove / Rising sun blues / Train that carried my man from town / Shortnin' bread / Cripple creek / Mole in the ground / Old Joe Clarke / Nine pound hammer / Turkey in the straw / Sinner man / Careless love / Pretty little horses
BCD 15735 / May '93 / Bear Family

☐ COYOTE MOON/ RUN TO THE WIND
It's about time / Alberta blue / Freight train bound / Way she would sing / Printed word / Coyote moon / Boppin' at the gamble / Going home / Old tin pot / Les' wish / Alberta waltz / Molly and tenbrooks / To each his own / I'll be on the road again / Run to the wind / Chinese silver / Slow dance / Wind (stay away) / Only sound you'll hear / Empty hands
BCD 15513 / May '90 / Bear Family

☐ HELLO STRANGER
Hello stranger / Shenandoah / Wayfaring stranger / Apple blossom time / Beautiful river valley / Sweetest gift / Water is wide / Somewhere in Tennessee / Froggie went a-courtin' / Farewell to Nova Scotia / Home on the range / Down in the valley / Whiskey in the jar / Girl I left behind / Lily of the west / Did he mention my name / Spanish is a loving tongue / Cancion de cuna / La source / Brahms lullaby
BCD 15725 / May '93 / Bear Family

☐ WALLS, HEARTS AND HEROES
Walls and borders / Gotta go (Bremen Train) / Dry land / Lonely bird / Back to your arms / Girl gone wild / Old old doll / Take a stand (for the children) / I can hear ya callin' / Foothill's lullaby / My heart stands (at your door) / Gypsy blue / Wastin' the moon / Merlin and the cowboy / I can dance (like Arthur Murray) / New crescent moon / Once a dream / Way o' walkin' / Old Wooley / Christmas wish / In the cabin walls / Un Canadien errant
BCD 15674 / Jun '92 / Bear Family

Schatz, Mark

☐ BRAND NEW OLD TYME WAY
ROUCD 0342 / Jun '95 / Rounder

Schaube, Niko

☐ ON THE OTHER HAND
860112 / Feb '98 / Naxos Jazz

Schechter, Gregori

☐ DER REBE ELIMELECH (Schechter, Gregori Klezmer Festival Band)
EUCD 1324 / Nov '95 / ARC

Scheelar, Earl

☐ EARL SCHEELAR & HIS FUNKY NEW ORLEANS JAZZ BAND (Scheelar, Earl Funky New Orleans Jazz Band)
BCD 367 / Dec '97 / GHB

Scheer

☐ INFLICTION
Shea / Howling boy / Wish you were dead / In your hand / Demon / Babysize / Sad loved girl / Driven / Screaming / Goodbye
GAD 6006CD / 6 Jul '98 / 4AD

Schell, Daniel

☐ IF WINDOWS THEY HAVE (Schell, Daniel & Kara)
Un celte / Remi sace an lacis dore / Vienna Carmen / Moustiquaries / If windows they have / Bigna zomer en ik loop altjid / Listen to short wave: Je suis dans / Tapi la nuit / Buches/logs/holz
MTM 13 / Sep '88 / Made To Measure

Schema

☐ SOONER THAN YOU THINK
AWA 11 / 8 Dec '97 / Armed With Anger

Schenker, Michael

☐ ANTHOLOGY (Schenker, Michael Group)
Rock bottom: *UFO* / Let it roll: *UFO* / Shoot shoot: *UFO* / Natural thing: *UFO* / Too hot to handle: *UFO* / Love to love: *UFO* / Doctor doctor: *UFO* / Only you can rock me: *UFO* / Armed and ready / Attack of the mad axeman / Are you ready to rock / Assault attack / Rock my nights away / Dogs of war / Rock will never die
VSOPCD 185 / Apr '93 / Connoisseur Collection

☐ ASSAULT ATTACK (Schenker, Michael Group)
Assault attack / Rock you to the ground / Dancer / Samurai / Desert song / Broken promises / Searching for a reason / Ulcer
BGOCD 321 / Aug '96 / Beat Goes On

☐ BEST OF MICHAEL SCHENKER GROUP, THE (Schenker, Michael Group)
Armed and ready / Cry for the nations / Victim of illusion / Into the arena / Are you ready to rock / Attack of the mad axeman / On and on / Assault attack / Dancer / Searching for a reason / Desert song / Rock my nights away / Captain Nemo / Let sleeping dogs lie / Bijou pleasurette / Lost horizons
MCCD 160 / May '94 / Music Club

☐ BUILT TO DESTROY (Schenker, Michael Group)
Rock my nights away / I'm gonna make you mine / Dogs of war / Systems failing / Captain Nemo / Still love that little devil / Red sky / Time waits for no one / Walk the stage
BGOCD 344 / Jan '97 / Beat Goes On

☐ CHAMPIONS OF ROCK (Schenker/McAuley Group)
Save youself / Bad boys / Anytime / Get down to business / Shadow of the night / What we need / I am your radio / There has to be another way / This is my heart / Destiny / Take me back
CR 869932 / Mar '97 / Disky

☐ MICHAEL SCHENKER GROUP/MSG (Schenker, Michael Group)
BGOCD 316 / Jul '96 / Beat Goes On

☐ ONE NIGHT AT BUDOKAN (Schenker, Michael Group)
Armed and ready / Cry from the nations / Attack of the mad axeman / Axeman / But I want more / Victim of illusion / Into the arena / On and on / Never trust a stranger / Let sleeping dogs lie / Courvoisier concerto / Lost horizons / Doctor doctor / Are you ready to rock
BGOCD 312 / Jun '96 / Beat Goes On

☐ WRITTEN IN SAND (Schenker, Michael Group)
XRCN 1283 / 1 Dec '97 / Zero

Scherer, Peter

☐ CRONOLOGIA
TZ 7502 / Oct '96 / Tzadik

Schiano, Mario

☐ SOCIAL SECURITY
VICTOCD 043 / Mar '97 / Victo

Schicke/Fuhrs/Frohling

☐ COLLECTED WORKS (2CD Set)
LE 1017/18 / 15 Jun '98 / Laser's Edge

Schieder, Illo

☐ SIEBEN EINSAME TAGE
Sieben einsame tage / Junge manner sind zum Kussen da / Wie oft du mich kusst / Teddy mach Tanzmusik / Mambo baion / Wie kahnn man nur so lingen / Bingen bangel boy boogie / Fred dich auf Sontag / Immer wieder du / Heut' dir / Jonny hat recht / Mambo caballero / Diese nacht an fremden ufern / Dolly Dick / Geh nicht an mir vorbei / Raketen rock / Ich traumte heute irgendawann / Sag doch bitte du zu mir / Hejo / Allez hopp / Danny / Teenager Mamie / So verliebt war ich nie / Ein junges herz / Karussel d'amour / Glocken der liebe halt ihn / Er nannte mich madam / Ich bind rund und gesund
BCD 16135 / Oct '97 / Bear Family

Schifrin, Lalo

☐ BLACK WIDOW
Black widow / Flamingo / Quiet village / Moonglow and theme from picnic / Jaws / Baia / Turning point / Dragonfly / Frenesi / Tabu / Baia / Con alma
ZK 65128 / 8 Sep '97 / Sony Jazz

☐ DISSECTION AND RECONSTRUCTION OF MUSIC FROM THE PAST...
5377512 / 22 Sep '97 / Verve Elite

☐ MORE JAZZ MEETS THE SYMPHONY
Sketches of miles / Down here on the ground / Chano / Begin the beguine / Django / Old friends / Madrigal / Portrait of Louis Armstrong
4509955892 / Aug '94 / Warner Bros.

Schleprock

☐ HIDE AND SEEK
LRR 004 / Oct '96 / Last Resort

☐ LONG TIME AGO
CD 05 / Nov '97 / Cool Guy

Schlong

☐ FISH BOOTY
BL 5 / Dec '96 / Bun Length

Schloss, Cynthia

☐ THIS IS LOVE
CRCD 26 / Nov '93 / Charm

Schlott, Volker

☐ DAY BEFORE, THE (Schlott, Volker Quartett)
BEST 1026CD / Nov '93 / Acoustic Music

☐ WHY NOT (Schlott, Volker Quartett)
BEST 1083CD / Apr '96 / Acoustic Music

Schmid, Wolfgang

☐ PARADOX (Schmid, Wolfgang & Billy Cobham/Bill Bickford)
Fonkey donkey / Four more years / Quadrant / Myohmyohyeoye / Walking in five / Jam O'James / Late nite / Shoes in seven / Five in
8888242 / Nov '96 / Tiptoe

Schmidt, Claudia

☐ CLAUDIA SCHMIDT
FF 70066 / Mar '89 / Flying Fish

☐ IT LOOKS FINE FROM HERE
RHRCD 64 / Jul '95 / Red House

☐ MIDWESTERN HEART
FF 241CD / May '93 / Flying Fish

Schmidt, Irmin

☐ IMPOSSIBLE HOLIDAYS (Original Soundtrack)
Dreambite / Le weekend / Surprise / Shudder of love / Lullaby big / Time the dreamkiller / Gormenghast drift
IRMIN 2CD / Jan '95 / The Fine Line

☐ MUSK AT DUSK (Original Soundtrack)
IRMIN 1CD / Jan '95 / The Fine Line

☐ MUSK AT DUSK/IMPOSSIBLE HOLIDAYS (2CD Set)
SPOONCD 37/38 / 19 Jan '98 / Spoon

☐ SOUNDTRACKS 1978-1993 (3CD Set)
SPOONCD 32/33/34 / Oct '94 / Grey Area

Schmidt, Marie

☐ SOPHISTICATED LADIES TO YOU (Schmidt, Marie & Benita Haastrup/Helle Marstrand)
MECCACD 1091 / May '97 / Music Mecca

Schmitt, Timothy B.

☐ PLAYIN' IT COOL
Playin' it cool / Lonely girl / So much in love / Something's wrong / Voice / Wrong number / Take a good look around you / Tell me what you dream / Gimme some money
7559603592 / Jul '96 / WEA

Schneidenbach, Vera

☐ EINE FROHLICHE LANDPARTIE
BCD 16243 / May '98 / Bear Family

☐ MEINE WELT IST DIE MUSIK
BCD 16240 / May '98 / Bear Family

☐ SINGE JEDEN TAG EIN LIED
BCD 16241 / May '98 / Bear Family

☐ WAS KANN SCHONER SEIN
BCD 16242 / May '98 / Bear Family

Schneider TM

☐ MOIST
Moist / Moonboots / Masters / Raum im ort / Up-tight / Eiweiss / Starfuck / Kid / Camping
087022 / 18 May '98 / City Slang

Schneider, Larry

☐ ALI GIRL (Schneider, Larry Quartet)
SCCD 31429 / Jan '98 / Steeplechase

Schneider, Maria

☐ COMING ABOUT (Schneider, Maria Jazz Orchestra)
El viento / Love theme from Spartacus / Bombshelter beast / Night watchmen / Coming about / Giant steps / Waxwing
ENJ 90692 / Jul '96 / Enja

☐ EVANESCENCE (Schneider, Maria Jazz Orchestra)
Wyrgly / Evanescence / Gumba blue / Some circles / Green piece / Gush / My lament / Dance you monster to my soft song / Last season
ENJ 80482 / Apr '94 / Enja

Schneiderman, Rob

☐ DARK BLUE
RSRCD 132 / Oct '94 / Reservoir

☐ NEW OUTLOOK
RSRCD 106 / Oct '89 / Reservoir

☐ RADIO WAVES
RSRCD 120 / Nov '94 / Reservoir

☐ SMOOTH SAILING
RSRCD 114 / Nov '94 / Reservoir

☐ STANDARDS
RSRCD 126 / Nov '94 / Reservoir

Schnitzler, Conrad

☐ 00/44
EFA 069792 / 16 Feb '98 / Marginal Talent

Schnyder, Daniel

☐ TARANTULA
With the devil on the backseat / Water / Samiel / Angst / Cairo / Caio cadenza / Mister / Wedding song / No smoking / Short life / Memoires / Tarantula / Cool sweets / Dolphy's dance / Homunculus / El cigaro
ENJ 93022 / Nov '96 / Enja

Schoenberg, Loren

☐ JUST A-SETTIN' AND A-ROCKIN'
MM 5039 / Oct '94 / Music Masters

☐ TIME WAITS FOR NO ONE
MM 5032 / Aug '94 / Music Masters

Schoenfelt, Phil

☐ BLUE HIGHWAY
ISAM 1006 / 17 Aug '98 / Idiot Savant Music

Scholl, Bernd

☐ SECRET GARDEN
SKYCD 3052 / Sep '95 / Sky

Schon, Neil

☐ BEYOND THE THUNDER
Call of the wind / Cool breeze / Zanzibar / Caribbean blue / Someone's watching over me / Iguassa falls / Boulevard of dreams / Big moon / Bandalero / Espanique / Deep forest / Send me an angel
HOMCD 7073 / 10 Nov '97 / Higher Octave
VHOCD 8 / 25 May '98 / Virgin

☐ ELECTRIC WORLD
Emperor / Eye on the world / Breaking waves / Scram / Medicine man / Emerald forest / Mandolin sky / One and only / All our yesterdays / Living desert / Prayer for peace / Night spirit / NYC / Highway 1 / Electric world / Memphis voodoo / High mileage / Dragon / Midnight express / My past life / Gypsy dance
VHOCD 5 / 25 May '98 / Higher Octave

☐ UNTOLD PASSION/HERE TO STAY (No More Lies) (Schon, Neil & Jan Hammer)
RE 821762 / 1 Sep '98 / Razor & Tie

Schoolly D

☐ ADVENTURES OF SCHOOLLY D
RCD 20050 / May '92 / Rykodisc

Schopfer, Klaus-Peter

☐ JUST A SMILE AWAY
ISCD 175 / May '98 / Intersound

Schott, John

☐ IN THESE GREAT TIMES
TZA 7115 / Feb '97 / Tzadik

Schramm, Dave

☐ VI
RTS 6 / Jul '94 / Normal

Schrammel & Slide

☐ DEUX
BEST 9011CD / Nov '95 / Acoustic Music

Schramms

☐ DIZZY SPELL
CPR 006 / 27 Jul '98 / Checkered Past

☐ LITTLE APOCALYPSE
OKCD 33022 / 6 Jul '98 / Okra

☐ ROCK, PAPER, SCISSORS, DYNAMITE
OKCD 33017 / 6 Jul '98 / Okra

☐ WALK TO DELPHI
OKRACD 007 / Nov '94 / Okra

Schroeder, John

☐ SPACE AGE SOUL (Schroeder, John Orchestra & Sounds Orchestral)
Hungry for love / Soul coaxin' / Ain't that peculiar / Soul trek / Agent double-o soul / Sweet soul talk / Soul destroyer / Soul for sale / Get out of my life woman / Where did our love go / Working in a coalmine / You've lost that loving feelin' / Sunny / Rescue me / Papa's got a brand new pig bag / You can't hurry love / Summertime / Lovin' you girl / How sweet it is (to be loved by you) / When a man loves a woman / Black is black
NEMCD 769 / Jun '96 / Sequel

Schroer, Oliver

☐ JIGZUP
Victory of love / Toby's reel/The Job / Laughing in her sleep / Horseshoes and rainbows / Far away by the sea/Lady Diane Laundy/Seanaghan Kennedy's / Ansgar's jig/Kari's jig / Blow November wind/Sea of change / Devil and the little faces / Hub of the wheel / Jump up/Ghost dance / Roro / December 16th/ Shooting star / If geese could sing / Bright eyes
IRCD 039 / Mar '97 / Iona

Schubert, Matthias

☐ BLUE AND GREY SUITE
Nichol's dime / La maitre / Blue and grey suite / Wariatka
ENJ 90452 / Oct '95 / Enja

Schuetz, Michael

☐ JUST LIKE THAT
ISCD 163 / Sep '96 / Intersound

Schulkowsky, Robyn

☐ HASTENING WESTWARD (Schulkowsky, Robyn & Nils Petter Molvaer)
4493712 / Nov '95 / ECM

Schulz, Bob

☐ BOB SCHULZ AND HIS FRISCO JAZZ BAND (Schulz, Bob Frisco Jazz Band)
SOSCD 1315 / Sep '97 / Stomp Off

☐ TOGETHER AGAIN (Schulz, Bob & The Riverboat Ramblers)
BCD 279 / Jul '93 / GHB

☐ TRIBUTE TO TURK MURPHY (Schulz, Bob & His Frisco Band)
SOSCD 1288 / Nov '95 / Stomp Off

Schulze, Klaus

☐ ARE YOU SEQUENCED
186972 / Sep '97 / Eye Of The Storm

☐ AUDENTITY
Cellistica / Tango-saty / Amourage / Opheylissem / Spielglocken / Sebastian im traum
CDTB 505 / Mar '97 / Thunderbolt

☐ BABEL
Nebuchadnezzar's dream / Foundation / Tower raises / First clouds / Communication problems / Gap of alienation / Immuring insanity / Heaven under feet / Deserted stones / Facing abandoned tools / Vanishing memories / Sinking into oblivion / Far from earth
CDVE 5 / May '94 / Venture

☐ BEYOND RECALL
Grongo Nero / Trancess / Brave old sequence / Big fall / Airlight
CDVE 906 / Mar '93 / Venture

☐ BODY LOVE
Stardancer / Blanche / P.t.o.
CDTB 123 / Jan '90 / Thunderbolt

☐ DIG IT
CDTB 144 / Mar '94 / Thunderbolt

☐ DOME EVENT, THE
Dome event / Andante / Nachtmusik Schattenhaft / Allegro / Energisch In gemesenem schritt / Sehr behaglich / Unbeschwert / Ohne hast / Scherzo: Un poco loco / Event: Rhythmisch uppig, Dann vergrugt Bewegt / Presto / Ubermutig, Sturmisch bewegt Heftig / Un poco loco (Reprise) / Crescendo / Finale: Tuttu synthi / After eleven
CDVE 918 / Mar '93 / Venture

☐ DREAMS
Classical move / Five to four / Dreams / Klaustrophony
CDTB 039 / Aug '95 / Thunderbolt

☐ DRESDEN PERFORMANCE/DRESDEN IMAGINARY SCENES
Dresden I / Dresden II / Dresden V / Dresden II / Dresden IV
CDVED 903 / Nov '90 / Venture

☐ DRIVE INN (Schulze, Klaus & Rainer Bloss)
Drive Inn / Sightseeing / Truckin' / Highway / Racing / Road to clear / Drive out
CDTB 028 / May '86 / Thunderbolt

☐ DUNE
Dune / Shadows of ignorance
CDTB 145 / '86 / Thunderbolt

☐ EN=TRANCE (2CD Set)
En=trance / A-numerique / Fm. delight / Velvet system
CDTB 061 / '89 / Thunderbolt

☐ IRRLICHT
CDTB 133 / '86 / Thunderbolt

☐ MIDITERRANEAN PADS
Decent changes / Miditerranean pads / Percussion / Planante
CDTB 081 / Jan '90 / Thunderbolt

☐ MIRAGE
Aeronef / Eclipse / Exvasion / Lucidinterspace / Destinationvoid / Xylotones / Cromwaves / Willowdreams / Liquidmirrors / Springdance
CDTB 033 / Nov '86 / Thunderbolt

☐ MOONDAWN
Floating / Mindphaser
CDTB 093 / Feb '91 / Thunderbolt

☐ PICTURE MUSIC
Totem / Mental door
CDTB 098 / Jan '91 / Thunderbolt

☐ POLAND LIVE 83
CDTB 504 / Nov '94 / Thunderbolt

☐ ROYAL FESTIVAL HALL VOL.1
Yen / Out of limbo / Lull before the storm / Tempest / Paradoxe too / Pastorlae and departure / Yearning / Placid yen / Breath of life / Back to limbo / Silence and sequence / Perigee / Gentle wind / Fire-riser / Clear water
CDVE 916 / Nov '92 / Venture

☐ ROYAL FESTIVAL HALL VOL.2
Ancient ambience / Gothic ground / In days of yore / Pavane and galliard / Dusty spiderwebs and a shorn monk / Basse danse join medieval maracas / Primeval murmur / Pedal away (castle rock) / Anchorage / Variation on b.f.
CDVE 917 / Nov '92 / Venture

☐ TIMEWIND
Bayreuth return / Wahnfried 1883
CDCA 2006 / Jun '88 / Virgin

☐ TRANCEFER
Few minutes / Silent running
CDTB 146 / Jun '94 / Thunderbolt

☐ X
Friedrich nietzsche / Georg trakl / Frank herbert / Friedemann bach / Ludwig II / Von bayern / Heinrich von kleist
CDTB 501 / Mar '96 / Thunderbolt

Schulze, Manfred

☐ VIERTENS NUMMER 12 (Schulze, Manfred Blaserquintett)
FMPCD 87 / Jan '98 / Full Moon

Schurch, Dorothea

☐ INTERNI PENSIERI
INTAKTCD 046 / May '97 / Intakt

Schurr, Diane

☐ DEEDLES
Very thought of you / New York state of mind / Teach me tonight / I'm beginning to see the light / I'll close my eyes / Reverend Lee / I'm just foolin' / Rock me on the water / Can't stop a woman in love / Amazing Grace
GRP 95102 / 25 May '98 / GRP

☐ DIANE SCHUUR & THE COUNT BASIE ORCHESTRA (Schurr, Diane & Count Basie Orchestra)
Deedles' blues / Caught a touch of your love / Travelin' light / I just found out about love / Travelin' blues / I loves you, porgy / You can have it / Only you / Everyday / We'll be together again / Until I met you / Climbing higher mountain
GRP 95502 / Feb '92 / GRP

☐ DIANE SCHUUR COLLECTION
Love dance / Easy to love / By design / Very thought of you / Caught a touch of your love / How long has this been going on / Teach me tonight / Funny (but I still love you) / I'll close my eyes / Louisiana sunday afternoon / Come rain or come shine / Sure thing
GRP 95912 / Jun '89 / GRP

☐ HEART TO HEART (Schurr, Diane & B.B. King)
No one ever tells you / I can't stop loving you / You don't know me / If I had to be you / I'm putting all my eggs in one basket / Glory of love / Try a little tenderness / Spirit in the dark / Freedom / At last / They can't take that away from me
GRP 99722 / May '94 / GRP

Schussler Du

☐ SCHUSSLER DU
NV 47CD / Oct '96 / Nasty Vinyl

Schutz

☐ SEVEN WORDS
0630176762 / Jul '97 / Warner Bros.

Schutz, Michael

☐ DON'T LOOK BACK (Schutz, Michael & Marco Bronzini)
ISCD 115 / Oct '91 / Intersound

Schutze, Paul

☐ ABYSMAL EVENINGS
Red hand / Slow burning ghosts / Close heat of starlight / Font / Abysmal evenings / Lotus voltage / Delta haze / Night dissolved in the lakes of heaven
AMBT 19 / Sep '96 / Virgin

☐ ANNIHILATING ANGELS
TCCD 9714 / Sep '97 / Tone Casualties

☐ APART
Rivers of mercury / Skin of air and tears / Sleeping knife dance / Visions of a sand drinker / Coldest light / Eyeless and naked / Ghosts of animals / Taken (apart) / Consequence / Memory of water / Throat full of stars / Sleep
AMBT 6 / Feb '95 / Virgin

☐ DEUS EX MACHINA
TCCD 9712 / Sep '97 / Tone Casualties

☐ ISABELLE EBRAHARDT: THE OBLIVION SEEKER
TCCD 9720 / Sep '97 / Tone Casualties

☐ NEW MAPS OF HELL
ABB 104CD / Aug '96 / Big Cat

☐ NINE SONGS FROM THE GARDEN OF WELCOME LIES (Improvisations For Organ & Percussion)
TCCD 9722 / Sep '97 / Tone Casualties

☐ RAPTURE OF METALS
ABB 105CD / Aug '96 / Big Cat

☐ REGARD - MUSIC BY FILM
TCCD 9719 / Sep '97 / Tone Casualties

☐ SECOND SITE
AMBT 23 / 8 Sep '97 / Virgin

☐ SITE ANUBIS
ABB 106CD / Jun '96 / Big Cat

☐ SURGERY OF TOUCH
TCCD 9713 / Sep '97 / Tone Casualties

Schwartz, Jonathan

☐ ANYONE WOULD LOVE YOU
MCD 5325 / Sep '92 / Muse

Schwarz, Rudy

☐ SALMON DAVE
EFA 113882 / May '94 / Musical Tragedies

Schwehr, Cornelius

☐ POCO A POCO SUBITO
ARTCD 6191 / Jan '97 / Hat Art

Schweizer, Irene

☐ IRENE SCHWEIZER & ANDREW CYRILLE (Schweizer, Irene & Andrew Cyrille)
INTAKTCD 008 / May '97 / Intakt

☐ IRENE SCHWEIZER & GUNTER SOMMER (Schweizer, Irene & Gunter Sommer)
INTAKTCD 007 / May '97 / Intakt

☐ IRENE SCHWEIZER & HANS BENNINK (Schweizer, Irene & Hans Bennink)
INTAKTCD 010 / May '97 / Intakt

☐ IRENE SCHWEIZER & LOUIS MOHOLO (Schweizer, Irene & Louis Moholo)
INTAKTCD 006 / May '97 / Intakt

☐ LES DIABOLIQUES (Schweizer, Irene & Maggie Nicols/Joelle Leandre)
INTAKTCD 048 / Aug '97 / Intakt

☐ MANY AND ONE DIRECTION
INTAKTCD 044 / May '97 / Intakt

Schwitters, Kurt

☐ URSONATE
ARTCD 6109 / May '92 / Hat Art

Sciaky, Carla

☐ AWAKENING
GLCD 2115 / Feb '95 / Green Linnet

Scientist

☐ AT CHANNEL ONE STUDIO (Scientist & The Mad Professor)
RN 7021 / Jun '97 / Rhino

☐ DUB IN THE ROOTS TRADITION
BAFCD 12 / May '96 / Blood & Fire

☐ HEAVYWEIGHT DUB CHAMPION
Seconds away / Straight left / Upper cut / Kidney punch / Saved by the bell / Right across / Jab / 1-2 / Below the belt / Knock out
GRELCD 13 / Sep '92 / Greensleeves

☐ KING OF DUB
11 Guava Road dub / 13 Bread Lane dub / Burning Lane dub / 18 Drumalie Avenue / Gad man the prophet / Rise with version / Next door dub / Forgive them oh jah / Mass murder and corruption / King Tubby's hi-fi / Raw dub / Jack Ruby's hi power / Cultural vibes / Everlasting version / Knockout version / King Sturgav
CDKVL 9029 / Mar '87 / Kingdom

☐ REPATRIATION DUB
TWCD 1058 / Nov '95 / Tamoki Wambesi

☐ SCIENTIST ENCOUNTERS PAC-MAN
Under surveillance / Price's wrath / Space invaders re-group / World cup squad lick their wounds / Vampire initiative / Malicious intent / Dark secret of the box / SOS / Man trap / Look out - behind you
GRELCD 46 / Mar '94 / Greensleeves

☐ SCIENTIST MEETS THE SPACE INVADERS
Beam down / Red shift / Time warp / Cloning process / Pulsar / Laser attack / Dematerialise / Fission / Supernova explosion / Quasar
GRELCD 19 / May '97 / Greensleeves

☐ SCIENTIST RIDS THE WORLD OF THE EVIL CURSE OF THE VAMPIRES
Voodoo curse / Dance of the vampires / Blood on his lips / Cry of the werewolf / Mummy's shroud / Corpse rises / Night of the living dead / Your teeth in my neck / Ghost of Frankenstein / Plague of zombies
GRELCD 25 / May '90 / Greensleeves

☐ SCIENTIST UPSET THE UPSETTER, THE (Scientist & The Upsetter)
HS 1CD / Jun '97 / Hit Squad

☐ SCIENTIST WINS THE WORLD CUP
GRELCD 37 / 8 Jun '98 / Greensleeves

Scientists

☐ ABSOLUTE
REDCD 23 / May '94 / Red Eye

Scientists Of Sound

☐ 1.4-4 OR BUST
DLCD 2 / Oct '96 / Downlow

Scion Sashay Success

☐ VOICES IN THE SAND
RFCD 007 / 27 Apr '98 / Record Factory

Scissor Girls

☐ WE PEOPLE SPACE WITH PHANTOM
ALP 63CD / Feb '97 / Atavistic

Sclavis, Louis

☐ ACOUSTIC QUARTET
Sensible / Bafouee / Abrupto / Elke / Hop / Seconde / Beata / Rhinoceros
5213492 / Feb '94 / ECM

☐ CEUX QUI VEILLENT LA NUIT
Derniers regards / L'abstraite anglaise / L'aurore / Procession / L'ombre / Qumran / Ceux qui veillent la nuit / Manoir / Saro / Tenzin / Rapports certains
LBLC 6596 / Jul '96 / Label Bleu

☐ DANSES ET AUTRES SCENES
Desillusion intro / Desillusion java / Germania valse / La guerre / Germania marche / Bourree en Provence / Lien / Tarentelle flamande / L'eglise / Lits blanc / Lits blanc / VAlse de Bardamu / Valse de Bardamu / Valse bardamu / La poule noire / Le moindre regard / Marche de breugel / Avant veille / Ceux qui veillent la nuit / Danse de l'ecume / Souffle d'ecume / AValse de mer / Tango de mer / La moitie / L'autre moitie largo / L'autre valse / L'autre danse / Une tristesse infinie
LBLC 6616 / 23 Mar '98 / Label Bleu

☐ LES VIOLENCES DE RAMEAU (Sclavis Sextet, Louis)
Le diable et son train / De ce trait enchante / Enez punir son injustice / Charmes / La torture d'Alphise / Usage de faux / Reponses a gavotte / Charmes / Pour vous...ces quelques fleurs / Ismenor / Post-mesotonique
5331282 / Oct '96 / ECM

☐ ROUGE (Sclavis, Louis Quintet)
One / Nacht / Kali la nuit / Reflet / Reeves / Les bouteilles / Moment donne / Face nord / Rouge / Yes love
5119292 / Mar '92 / ECM

Scneiderman, Rob

☐ DANCING IN THE DARK
RSRCD 152 / Feb '98 / Reservoir

Scobey, Bob

☐ BOB SCOBEY & HIS FRISCO BAND VOL.1
JCD 275 / Mar '97 / Jazzology

☐ BOB SCOBEY'S FRISCO BAND
Down in jungletown / Sweet georgia brown / Memphis blues / Battle hymn of the republic / Beale street mama / Bill bailey won't you please come home / Careless love / Mobile / Beale street blues / Coney island washboard / Melancholy / Chicago / South / Sailin' down chesapeake bay / Big butter and egg man / Peoria / Do you know what it means to miss new orleans / Huggin' and a chalkin' / Long gone / Blues my naughty sweetie gives to me / Ace in the hole / Silver dollar / All the wrongs you've done to me
CD 53143 / Jan '94 / Giants Of Jazz

☐ DIRECT FROM SAN FRANCISCO
Ostrich walk / Indiana / Sobbin' blues / Curse of an aching heart / Michigan water blues / Sensation / Doctor jazz / Jazz me blues / Travelin' shoes / A closer walk with thee / Ja-da / San
GTCD 12023 / Oct '93 / Good Time Jazz

☐ GREAT BOB SCOBEY, THE
JCD 285 / Dec '97 / Jazzology

☐ SCOBEY & CLANCY (Scobey, Bob & Clancy Hayes)
When the midnight choo choo leaves for alabam / St. james infirmary / Home / At the devil's ball / St. louis blues / Angry / I ain't gonna give nobody none of my jelly-roll / Love me or leave me / I want to go back to michigan (down on the farm) / You can depend on me / Lights out blues
GTCD 12009 / Oct '93 / Good Time Jazz

Scofield, John

☐ A GO GO
A go go / Chank / Boozer / Southern Pacific / Jeep on 35 / Kubrick / Green tea / Hottentot / Chicken dog / Deadzy
5399792 / 6 Apr '98 / Verve

☐ I CAN SEE YOUR HOUSE FROM HERE (Scofield, John & Pat Metheny)
I can see your house from here / Red one / No matter what / Everybody's party / Message to my friend / No way Jose / Say the brothers name / SCO / Quite rising / One way to be / You speak my language
CDP 8277652 / Mar '94 / Blue Note

☐ LIQUID FIRE
GCD 79501 / May '95 / Gramavision

☐ LIVE
ENJACD 30132 / Nov '94 / Enja

☐ OUT LIKE A LIGHT
ENJA 40382 / Nov '94 / Enja

☐ PICK HITS LIVE
Picks and pans / Heaven will / Blue matter / Trim / Make me / Pick hits / Protocol / Thanks again / Georgia on my mind
GRV 88052 / Feb '91 / Gramavision

☐ ROUGH HOUSE
ENJA 30332 / Nov '94 / Enja

☐ SHINOLA
ENJA 40042 / 17 Nov '97 / Enja

☐ SLO SCO
GV 794302 / Dec '90 / Gramavision

☐ SOLAR (Scofield, John & John Abercrombie)
CSAPCD 122 / May '96 / Connoisseur Collection

☐ TURNAGE'S BLOOD ON THE FLOOR (Scofield, John & Peter Erskine/Martin Robertson)
4552922 / 20 Apr '98 / Decca

☐ WHO'S WHO
Looks like meringue / Cassidae / Beatles / Spoons / Who's who / How the west was won / Beckon call / New strings attached / How to marry a millionaire / Fat dancer
OW 34512 / Jun '97 / One Way

Scooter

☐ AGE OF LOVE
0064012CLU / 26 Jan '98 / Club Tools

☐ ROUGH TOUGH AND DANGEROUS (Singles 1994-1998/2CD Set)
Hyper hyper / Move your ass / Friends / Endless summer / Back in the UK / Let me be your valentine / Rebel yell / I'm raving / Break it up / Fire / Age of love / No fate / Fire / Rebel yell / Break it up / Age of love / Vallee de larmes / Rhapsody in e / Friends / Across the sky / Endless summer / Back in time / Unity without words / Euphoria / Let me be your valentine / I'm raving / Fire
0064502CLU / 10 Aug '98 / Club Tools

Scorn

☐ DELIVERANCE
Deliverance / Deliverance through dub / Delivered / To high heaven / Black sun rising / Exodus
MOSH 176CD / Feb '97 / Earache

☐ ELLIPSIS
Silver rain fell / Exodus / Dreamscape / Night ash black / Night tide / Falling / End / Automata / Light trap / Dreamscape 2
SCORNCD 001 / 1 Sep '97 / Earache

☐ GYRAL
Six hours one week / Time went slow / Far in out / Stairway / Forever turning / Black box / Hush / Trondheim - Gaule
SCORNCD 002 / 1 Sep '97 / Earache

☐ LOGGHI BAROGGHI
Look at that / Do the geek / Next days / Spongie / Out of / It's on / Logghi barogghi / Black box 2 / Nut / Mission / Pithering twat / Fumble / Weakener / Go
MOSH 158CD / 1 Sep '97 / Earache

☐ WHINE
KK 174CD / 27 Oct '97 / KK

☐ WHITE IRISES BLIND
White irises blind / Black ash dub / Drained / Host of scorpions / Lick forever dog / On ice / Heavy blood / Stairway
MOSH 175CD / Feb '97 / Earache

Scorpions

☐ BEST OF ROCKERS 'N' BALLADS, THE
Rock you like a hurricane / Can't explain / Rhythm of love / Big city nights / Lovedrive / Is there anybody there / Holiday / Still loving you / No one like you / Blackout / Another piece of meat / You give me all I need / Hey you / Zoo / China white
CDFA 3262 / Oct '91 / Fame

☐ DEADLY STING
Coming home / Rock you like a hurricane / No one like you / Lovedrive / Bad boys running wild / I'm leaving you / Passion rules the game / China white / Walking on the edge / Coast to coast / Loving you Sunday morning / Another piece of meat / Dynamite / Can't live without you / Edge of time
CDEMC 3698 / Feb '95 / EMI

☐ LIVE BITES
Tease me please me / Is there anybody there / Rhythm of love / In trance / No pain no gain / When the smoke is going down / Ave Maria no morro / Living for tomorrow / Concerto in V / Alien nation / Hit between the eyes / Crazy world / Wind of change / Heroes don't cry / White dove
5269032 / 15 Sep '97 / Mercury

☐ LOVE AT FIRST STING
Bad boys running wild / Rock you like a hurricane / I'm leaving you / Coming home / Same thrill / Big city nights / As soon as the good times roll / Crossfire / Still loving you
CDFA 3224 / Aug '89 / Fame

☐ LOVEDRIVE
Loving you Sunday morning / Another piece of meat / Always somewhere / Coast to coast / Can't get enough / Is there anybody there / Lovedrive / Holiday
CDFA 3080 / Nov '88 / Fame

☐ PURE INSTINCT
Wild child / Stone in my shoe / Where the river flows / Time will call your name / Are you the one / But the best for you / You and I
0630145242 / Apr '96 / East West

Scorpions

☐ ANTHOLOGY 1959-1965
WHCD 004 / Mar '97 / Wooden Hill

Scotland FC

☐ TARTAN ARMY (Scottish World Cup Anthems) (Scotland FC & Supporters)
Easy easy: *Scotland World Cup Squad 1974* / Purple heather: *Stewart, Rod & Scotland Euro '96 Squad* / Say it with pride: *Scotland World Cup Squad 1990* / Ole ole: *Stewart, Rod & Scotland Euro '96 Squad* / Scotland for me: *Cameron, Andy* / Que sera: *Cameron, Andy* / Big trip to Mexico: *Scotland World Cup Squad 1986* / We have a dream: *Scotland World Cup Squad 1982* / We're the Scottish supporters: *Mr. Abic* / We're on the ball: *Daly, Glen & The Fans Of Scotland* / Scotland Scotland: *Scotland World Cup Squad 1974* / Fergie's fusiliers: *Gunn, Ben* / Scotland evermore: *Tartan Lads* / Ally's tartan army: *Cameron, Andy* / Viva Scotland: *Gunn, Ben* / Scotland easy okay: *Cameron, Andy* / Wembley '77: *Gunn, Ben* / Cameron's capers: *Cameron, Andy* / Scotland's aim: *Sandy Scot* / Ballad of Kenny Daglish: *Big Bad Jock*
CDGAFFER 26 / 18 May '98 / Cherry Red

Scotrail Vale Of Atholl Pipe Band

☐ BOTH SIDES OF THE TRACKS
LAPCD 115 / Dec '88 / Lapwing

☐ NO RESERVATIONS
Zito the bubbleman / Marjorie Lowe / Gallowglass / Jig / House in St. Peter's / Monymusk / Mrs. Stewart of Grantully / Miss Monaghan's / Maggie's pancakes / Hawk / March, strathspey and reel / John MacDonald of Glencoe / Athol cummers / John Morrison of Assynt House / Isobel Blackley / Sweeney's Reel / Molly Rankine's / Hogties' reel / Kenny the Sparrowman / Boys of Ballmote / Double Rise / Brest St. Mark jig / Hag at the churn / Smeceno Horo / Moutains of Pomeroy / Thomas Maxwell of Briarsbush / Garba Chriochan / Snug in the blanket / Congress reel / John Keith Laing / Hills of Kowloon / LL Wade's Welcome to Inverness / Lyndhurst / Killoran Bay / St. Jean-des-Vignes / Summertime / Big parcel / Jim Blakeley / Mrs. Macleod of Raasay / Galician jigs
LAPCD 122 / '89 / Lapwing

Scots Guards Bands

☐ ON PARADE (Scots Guards Pipes & Drums Band)
Garb of old gaul (slow march) / Garb of old gaul (slow march) / 10th battalion h.l.i. crossing the rhine (march) / Lilliburlero (quick march) / Golden spurs (slow march) / Wee macgregor (patrol) / Hieland' laddie (regimental quick march) / Les huguenots (slow march) / Scotland the brave (quick march) / Hielan' laddie (regimental quick march) / Cock o' the north (patrol) / Kilworth hills (retreat march) / H. m. jollies (quick march) / Ecossaise (slow march) / On the quarter deck (quick march) / Gathering of the clans (patrol) / Birdcage walk (quick march)
CC 292 / Jun '93 / Music For Pleasure

Scott 4

☐ ELEKTRO AKOUSTIC UND VOLKSMECHANIK
East winter / Work / Afternoons / You set the scene / Broken stones / I've been tamed / Lucky strike / On off
STL 004CD / 20 Jul '98 / Satellite

☐ RECORDED IN STATE
Start up / Deutsche LP record / East winter / Aspirins / Your kingdom to dust / Plane / Cheese four tracks / Miss Goddess nr.2 / Zilch / Choke bore / Philly's song
STL 09CD / 9 Feb '98 / Satellite

Scott, Bobby

☐ FOR SENTIMENTAL REASONS
(I love you) for sentimental reasons / Night lights / Lovewise / More I see you / Gee baby ain't I good to you / I keep going back to Joe's / Mamselle / That's all / That Sunday that summer / Nature boy
MM 5025 / Oct '94 / Music Masters

☐ SLOWLY
MM 5053 / Aug '94 / Music Masters

Scott, Darrell

☐ ALOHA FROM NASHVILLE
Head South / Banjo clark / You'll never leave Harlan again / It's a great day to be alive / I wish / Ballad of Martha White / It's the whiskey that eases the pain / Spelling bee romance / Life is cheap / Heartbreak town / Title of the song
SHCD 3864 / Mar '98 / Sugar Hill

Scott, E.C.

☐ COME GET YOUR LOVE
BPCD 75019 / Jul '95 / Blind Pig

☐ HARD ACT TO FOLLOW
BPCD 5044 / Feb '98 / Blind Pig

Scott Grooves

☐ PIECES OF A DREAM
Expansions / Sax speaks / Mothership reconnection / New day / Scat groove / Bumpin' on the underground / Feels so good
SOMACD 010 / 25 May '98 / Soma

Scott, Hector

☐ BREATH O' JUNE (Scott, Hector & Neil McFarlane/Fiona Cameron)
When she cam ben, she bobbit / Leith Wynd / Ae fond kiss / Oh whistle and I'll come tae you, my lad / Berceuse / Saltarello / O wert thou in the cauld blast / John Anderson my Jo / Breath o' June / Echoes from Ayrshire / Sow's tail / Scottish fantasy - 3rd movement / Bonnie laddie, highland laddie / Red, red rose / Waverley / Ye banks and braes of Bonnie Doon / Should auld acquaintance be forgot / Air and dances
CDLOC 1102 / Sep '97 / Lochshore

Scott, Jack

☐ CLASSIC SCOTT (5CD Set)
Greaseball / Baby she's gone / You can bet your bottom dollar / Two timin' woman / I need your love / My true love / Leroy / With your love / Indiana waltz / No one will ever know / I can't help it / I'm dreaming of you / Midgie / Save my soul / Geraldine / Goodbye baby / Way I walk / I never felt like this / Bella / Go wild little Sadie / What am I living for / There'll come a time / Baby Marie / Baby baby / What in the world's come over you / Goo deal Lucille / Oh little one / So used to loving you / Cruel world / Window shopping / Burning bridges / Your cheatin' heart / I can't escape from you / Cold cold heart / I could never be ashamed of you / They'll never take her love from me / Crazy heart / You win again / Half as much / I'm sorry for you my friend / Take these chains from my heart / My heart would know / May you never be alone / It's my way of loving you / My King / I'm satisfied with you / Am I the one / It only happened yesterday / True love is blind / Fancy meeting you again / Cool water / Take my hand, precious Lord / When the Saints go marching in / Swing low, sweet chariot / Ezekiel saw de wheel / Joshua fit de battle of Jericho / Little David play your harp / Roll Jordan roll / Down by the riverside / Old time religion / Gospel train / I want to be ready / Just a closer walk with thee / He'll understand and say Well Done / Lonesome Mary / Patsy / Is there something on your mind / Found a woman / Little feeling called love / Now that I / True true love / One of these days / Strange desire / My dream come true / Steps one and two / Sad story / You only see what you wanna see / I can't hold your letters (in my arms) / Cry cry cry / Grizzly bear / Part where I cried / Green green valley / Strangers / Laugh and the world laughs with you / Meo myo / All I see is blue / Jingle bell slide / There's trouble brewin' / Thou shalt not steal / I knew you first / I prayed for an angel / Blue skies (movin' in on me) / What a wonderful night out / Wiggle on out / Tall tales / Flakey John / Seperation's now granted / I don't believe in tea leaves / Standing on the outside looking in / Looking for Linda / I hope, I think, I wish / Gone again / Let's learn to live and love again / Don't hush the laughter / This is where I came in / Road keeps winding / With your love (stereo) / Indiana waltz (stereo) / No one will ever know (stereo) / I can't help it (stereo) / I'm dreaming of you (stereo) / Midgie (stereo) / Save my soul (stereo) / Geraldine (stereo) / Goodbye baby (stereo) / Way I walk (stereo) / If only / When the Saints go marching in (take 19) / Go away from here (crying in my beer) / Before the bird flies / Insane / My special angel / I keep changing my mind / Hard luck Joe / Billy Jack / Mary marry me / Face to the wall / I still love you enough / As you take a walk through my mind / You make it hard not to love you / You're just not gettin' better / Apple blossom time / Blues stay away from me / Stones / Bo's going to jail / Country witch
BCD 15534 / Aug '92 / Bear Family

☐ JACK SCOTT/WHAT IN THE WORLD'S COME OVER YOU
Save my soul / With your love / Leroy / No one will ever know / Geraldine / I can't help it / Indiana waltz / Midgie / My true love / Way I walk / I'm dreaming of you / Goodbye baby / What in the world's come over you / Oh, little one / Am I the one / I'm satisfied with you / My King / It's my way of loving you / Burning bridges / Baby, baby / So used to loving you / Cruel world / Good deal Lucille / Window shopping
BGOCD 303 / Nov '95 / Beat Goes On

☐ SCOTT ON GROOVE
Flakey John / Jingle bell slide / There's trouble brewin' / Tall tales / Wiggle on out / I knew you first / Blue skies (moving in on me) / I prayed for an angel / Separation's now granted / Thou shalt not steal / Road keeps winding / Let's learn to live and love again / Don't hush the laughter / This is where I came in / Looking for Linda / I hope, I think, I wish / Standing on the outside looking in / Gone again / I don't believe in tea leaves / What a wonderful night out
BCD 15445 / '88 / Bear Family

☐ WAY I WALK, THE
Leroy / Midgie / Way I walk / Goodbye baby / Go wild Little Sadie / Geraldine / Save my soul / Baby she's gone / Two timin' woman / I never felt like this / My true love / I'm dreaming of you / With your love / I can't help it / No one will ever know / Indiana waltz / Baby Marie / Bella / There comes a time / I need your love / You can bet your bottom dollar / What am I living for / There's trouble brewin' / Lonesome Mary / Greaseball
RCCD 3002 / Aug '90 / Rollercoaster

Scott, Jimmy

☐ ALL OVER AGAIN
Sometimes I feel like a Motherless child / Evening in Paradise / If I ever lost you / (I'm afraid) the masquerade is over / Please forgive me / How else / If you are but a dream / Way you look tonight / Things that are love / Everybody's somebody's fool / Once / What good would it be / Imagination / How can I go on without you / Time on my hands / Very truly yours / Show goes on / Someone to watch over me / Street of dreams / Don't cry baby / Why don't you open your heart / Everybody needs somebody / Guilty / When did you leave Heaven
SV 0263 / Oct '97 / Savoy Jazz

☐ DREAM
Don't take you love from me / It shouldn't happen to a dream / I cried for you / So long / You never miss the water / It's the talk of the town / I'm through with love / Laughing on the outside / Dream
9362456292 / Jul '94 / Warner Bros.

☐ LIVE IN NEW ORLEANS (Scott, 'Little' Jimmy)
All of me / When your lover has gone / Everybody's somebody's fool / Lonliest house on the street / Anytime anyplace anywhere / Duelling tenors / Body and soul / Flying home
CDCHM 664 / Jul '97 / Ace

☐ LOST AND FOUND
I have dreamed / Stay with me / Folks who live on the hill / For once in my life / Dedicated to you / Day to day / Unchained melody / Sometimes I feel like a Motherless child / Exodus / I wish I knew
RSACD 804 / Dec '94 / Sequel

☐ VERY TRULY YOURS
Imagination / How can I go on / Time on my hands / When did you leave Heaven / Guilty / Everybody needs somebody / Why don't you open your heart / Don't cry baby / Street of dreams / Someone to watch over me / Show goes on / Very truly yours
SV 0239 / Oct '97 / Savoy Jazz

Scott, Mike

☐ BRING 'EM ALL IN
Bring 'em all in / Iona song / Edinburgh Castle / What do you want me to do / I know she's in the building / City full of ghosts (Dublin) / Wonderful disguise / Sensitive children / Learning to love him / She is so beautiful / Wonderful disguise (reprise) / Long way to the light / Building the city of light
CDCHR 6108 / Sep '95 / Chrysalis

☐ STILL BURNING
Questions / My dark side / Open / Love anyway / Rare precious and gone / Dark man of my dreams / Personal / Strawberry man / Sunrising / Everlasting arms
CDCHR 6122 / 29 Sep '97 / Chrysalis

Scott, Ossie

☐ AT THEIR BEST (Scott, Ossie & Tan Tan)
SPCD 05 / Nov '96 / Superpower

Scott, Ray

☐ YOU DRIVE ME CRAZY
CLCD 4412 / Jan '97 / Collector/White Label

Scott, Raymond

☐ POWERHOUSE VOL.1
STCD 543 / '92 / Stash

Scott, Ronnie

☐ JAZZMAN (CD/Book Set)
BKB 002 / Jun '95 / Elm Tree

☐ NEVER PAT A BURNING DOG (Scott, Ronnie Quintet)
Contemplation / I'm glad there is you / White caps / All the things you are / This love of mine / When love is new / Little sunflower
JHCD 012 / Jan '94 / Ronnie Scott's Jazz House

☐ NIGHT HAS A THOUSAND EYES, THE (Scott, Ronnie & Sonny Stitt)
Night has a thousand eyes / Sonny day for Ronnie / Bye bye blackbird
JHAS 614 / 24 Oct '97 / Ronnie Scott's Jazz House

☐ WHEN I WANT YOUR OPINION I'LL GIVE IT TO YOU
JHAS 610 / Mar '97 / Ronnie Scott's Jazz House

Scott, Shirley

☐ BLUES EVERYWHERE
Autumn leaves / Blues everywhere / Oasis / Embraceable you / Triste / 'Round midnight / Theme
CCD 79525 / Feb '97 / Candid

☐ OASIS
MCD 5388 / Sep '92 / Muse

☐ SKYLARK (Scott, Shirley Trio)
Skylark / I still want you/You are my heart's delight / All the things you are / Alone together / Peace / McGee and me / Party's over/Theme
CCD 79536 / Feb '97 / Candid

☐ WALKIN' THING, A
Carnival / DT blues / Walkin' thing / When a man loves a woman / What makes Harold sing / Shades of Bu / How am I to know / Remember
CCD 79719 / Jan '97 / Candid

Scott, Sonny

☐ COMPLETE RECORDINGS 1933
SOB 035252 / Dec '92 / Story Of The Blues

☐ SONNY SCOTT
DOCD 5450 / May '96 / Document

Scott, Stephen

☐ AMINAH'S DREAM
Aminah's dream / Behind the scenes / Young Confucius / Positive images / Pit and the pendulum / When God created woman / Lil bro'...life goes on / You are too beautiful / Moontrane / In the spur of the moment
5179962 / Jul '93 / Verve

☐ BEAUTIFUL THING, THE
5331862 / Feb '97 / Verve

Scott, Tom

☐ BLOW IT OUT
EK 46108 / Aug '97 / Sony Jazz

☐ BORN AGAIN
Children of the night / Back burner / Free hand / Close view / Silhouettes / Way back when / Song no.1 / Born again
GRP 96752 / 25 May '98 / GRP

☐ FLASHPOINT
Get a grip / Seat of your pants / Night drifter / Coast to coast / Flashpoint / Cool sensation / Down to the wire / Lost in love / Watercolors
GRP 95712 / Oct '88 / GRP

☐ NEW YORK CONNECTION
Dirty old man / Uptown and country / New York connection / Garden / Time and love / M8idtown rush / Looking out for number 7 / Appolonia (foxtrata) / You're gonna need me
EK 64961 / Aug '96 / Sony Jazz

☐ PRICELESS JAZZ
Desire / Morning rays / Sarah, Sara / Bhop / Hollywood Walk / Children of the night / Jungle wave / Too hot / Anytime, anyplace / Body and soul
GRP 98962 / 23 Mar '98 / GRP

☐ TOM CAT
Rock island pocket / Tom cat / Day way / Keep on doin' it / Love poem / Good morning Mr and Mrs America and all the ships / Backfence cattin' / Mondo / Refried
EK 64960 / Aug '96 / Sony Jazz

☐ TOM SCOTT AND THE LA EXPRESS
Bless my soul / Sneakin in the back / King Cobra / Dahomey dance / Nunya / Easy life / Spindrift / Strut your stuff / LA expression / Vertigo
EK 64959 / Aug '96 / Sony Jazz

Scott, Tommy

☐ COUNTRY CEILIDH PARTY
CDITV 633 / 8 Sep '97 / Scotdisc

☐ COUNTRY HOLIDAY
I never loved no one but you / Does my ring hurt your finger / I'd rather love you / All I have to offer you / Rose Marie / Distant drums / This world is not my home / Cry / Any time / Someday you'll want me to want you / Crying time / Together again / But when I dream / Lovesick blues / Rock of ages / Kiss an angel good morning / There goes my everything / Pretty woman / Blanket on the ground / Stop / If I had my life to live over / Let me be there
LCDITV 606 / Nov '95 / Scotdisc

☐ GOING HOME
Going home / Pride of bonnie scotland / Flower of scotland / Sands of time / Cailin mo ruinsa / Abide with me / Barren rocks of aden-wha saw the tattie howkers / Glencoe / Bonnie lass o' fyvie-mharies wedding / Skye boat song / China doll / Amazing grace / Scotland forever (instrumental version with pipes and string
CDITV 564 / Oct '92 / Scotdisc

☐ HAIL HAIL CALEDONIA
O'scotland / Hail hail caledonia / Save the last dance for me / Spanish eyes / Way to amarillo / Road to dundee / Far far away / Mormond braes / Lintin addy / Mormon braes reprise / Hiking song / Nut brown maiden / Ricky doo dum day / Grannie's heilan hame / My wee lauds a sojer / Oor wee school / Fish 'n' chip song / World is coming to an end / One day at a time / When you walk in the room / Beautiful sunday / Sweet caroline / Any dream will do / Gypsy woman / Yellow rose of texas / Dixie / Gypsy woman reprise / My love she's but a lassie yet / Kate dalrymple / Clean pea strae / Monster of loch ness / Goodnight irene / How great thou art / Scotland my home
CDITV 597 / Nov '94 / Scotdisc

☐ HOLIDAY IN IRELAND
CDITV 610 / Mar '96 / Scotdisc

☐ ORIGINAL HOPSCOTCH
PLATCD 3923 / May '94 / Platinum

☐ PIPES AND STRINGS OF SCOTLAND VOL.1
Pride of bonnie Scotland / Ode to joy / Abide with me / Scottish banner / 'Tis a gift (to be simple) / Bonnie Mary of Argyle / Send in the clowns / Jesu joy of man's desiring / Rose of Kelvingrove / Song of the wind / Scott's choice / Light of the morning / Little drummer boy / Carnival is over
CDITV 456 / Aug '89 / Scotdisc

☐ SCOTLAND FOREVER
From scotland with love / Scotland forever / Sailing-amazing grace / Rothesay bay-will ye go lassie go / Old rugged cross / My ain folk / Silver threads among the gold / Rowan tree / Bonnie wee jeannie mccoll-cock o' the north / Morag of dunvegan-mingulay boat song / Old scots mother mine / Johnny lad, the auld maid in a garret / Going home
CDITV 545 / Sep '91 / Scotdisc

☐ TOMMY SCOTT AND HIS PIPES AND DIXIE BANDS
CDITV 521 / Nov '90 / Scotdisc

☐ TOMMY SCOTT COLLECTION
Scotland forever / My ain folk / Going home / Old Scots mother mine / Glencoe / Rowan tree / Abide with me / Road to Dundee / Amazing grace / Flower of Scotland / Bonnie Mary of Argyle / Auld lang syne
CDITV 431 / Nov '87 / Scotdisc

☐ TOMMY SCOTT'S COUNTRY HOP
Rose garden / If I said you had a beautiful body / Corina corina / Achy breaky heart / Orange blossom special / My son calls another man daddy / Half as much / I can't help it / You win again / Wildwood flower / Arkansas traveller / Please help me I'm falling / My elusive dreams / Fiddle-me-bob / She taught me to yodel / Is anybody going to san antone / Haste ye back / Scots wha hae / Bonnie gallowa' / Jock's awa / Wayward wind / Devil woman / Ruby ann / You're the only good thing (that's happened to me) / I fall to pieces / Adios amigo / Orange blossom special / Skip to ma lou / Hand me down my walking cane / Cotton fields / Five little fingers / I really don't want to know / This song is just for you / I just wanna dance with you / I saw the light / Keep on the sunny side / What a friend we have in jesus / I saw the light (reprise) / Moonlight and roses / Mexicali rose / A room full of roses / Donald where's your troosers / Mcpherson's farewell / Killiecrankie o / Smith's reel / Candy kisses / Like strangers / Eyes of texas / William tell / Wreck of the old '97 / Puttin' on the style / Wabash cannonball / Bird of paradise
CDITV 569 / May '94 / Scotdisc

☐ TOMMY SCOTT'S HOPSCOTCH CEILIDH PARTY
CDITV 528 / Dec '90 / Scotdisc

☐ TOMMY SCOTT'S ROYALE HIGHLAND SHOWBAND (Scott, Tommy's Royale Highland Showband)
Red river rose / March march march all the way / Morag of Dunvegan / Mingulay boat song / Maggie may / Day is ended / PK's salute / Pigeon on the gate / Pipes O'Drummond / De'il among the tailors / Kilt is my delight / Pipers patrol / Mount Fuji / Water is wide / Flute salad / Dark island / May kway o'may kway / High road to Linton
CDITV 426 / Jun '87 / Scotdisc

☐ TOMMY SCOTT'S SCOTLAND
Annie Laurie / Dark Lochnagar / Great Glen / Skye boat song / Amazing grace / Flower of Scotland / Will ye no' come back again / Scotland forever / My love is like a red red rose / Flowers of the forest / Rowan tree / Green trees of Tyrol / My Ain folk / Auld lang syne
CD ITV 411 / Dec '86 / Scotdisc

☐ TOMMY SCOTT'S SCOTLAND
Sailing / Water is wide / Piper o' Dundee / It is no secret / Marching home / Twelfth of never / My Grannie's party/Govan Billiard Hall/Fitba' crazy / Dream Angus / Charmaine Marie Dianne / Wee Aberdonian/Kilty kilty Caulbaum / Doo fell off a dyke/ We were only playing leave o' / Blackboard of my heart / Stand beside me / Too young / Long black veil / Atholl Highlanders/A hundred pipers / Kenmure's up and awa' / Minute you're gone / Stop / Heartache following me/He'll have to go / Island of Tiree / Mull of Kintyre / From a jack to a king / Dumbarton's drums
CDITV 630 / 3 Nov '97 / Scotdisc

☐ TOMMY SCOTT'S STREET PARTY (Various Artists)
Scotland forever / Will ye come tae ma party / Goodnght Irene / Silver threads among the gold / Achy breaky heart / Auld lang syne / Bonnie wee Jeannie McColl / My ain folk / When your old wedding ring was new / Nobody's child
CDITV 617 / Oct '96 / Scotdisc

Scott, Tommy

☐ TOMMY SCOTT
CLCD 2854 / Jul '97 / Collector/White Label

Scott, Tony

☐ CLARINET ALBUM, THE (Scott, Tony Quartet)
W 1132 / Nov '93 / Philology

☐ DIALOGUE WITH MYSELF, LIKE A CHILD'S WHISPER
W 762 / Dec '95 / Philology

☐ MUSIC FOR YOGA MEDITATION AND OTHER JOYS
Prahna / Shiva / Samadhi / Hare krishna / Hatha / Kundalina / Sahasrarra / Treveni / Shanti
8353712 / Mar '94 / Verve

☐ MUSIC FOR ZEN MEDITATION (Remastered)
5214442 / Oct '97 / Verve Master Edition

☐ SUNG HEROES
Misery (to lady day) / Portrait of Anne Frank / Remembrance of Art Tatum / Requiem for 'Hot Lips' Page / Blues for an African friend / For Stefan Wolpe / Israel / Memory of my father / Lament to manolete
SSC 1015D / Sep '86 / Sunnyside

☐ TONY SCOTT IN AFRICA
Mayibue Afrika Uhuuru (Long live Afrika freedom) / Calling the Gods / Freedom day / Rain prayer / Aaee-aaoo / Witch doctor / Voodoo
CD 12536 / Jun '96 / Music Of The World

Scott-Adams, Peggy

☐ HELP YOURSELF
BILLCD 100 / Mar '97 / Secret Love

Scott-Heron, Gil

☐ FIRST MINUTE OF A NEW DAY (Scott-Heron, Gil & Brian Jackson/Midnight Band)
TVT 43502 / 17 Mar '98 / TVT

☐ FROM SOUTH AFRICA TO SOUTH CAROLINA
TVT 43402 / 17 Mar '98 / TVT

☐ MINISTER OF INFORMATION
Winter in america / Alien / Bottle / Is that jazz / Washington d.c. / Gun / B movie
CCSCD 403 / Apr '94 / Castle

☐ MOVING TARGET
Fast lane / Washington DC / No exit / Blue collar / Explanations / Ready or not / Black history of the world
254921 / Feb '97 / Arista

☐ REFLECTIONS
Storm music / Grandma's hands / Is that jazz / Morning thoughts / Inner city blues / Siege of New Orleans / Gun / B Movie
254094 / Feb '97 / Arista

☐ REVOLUTION WILL NOT BE TELEVISED, THE
Revolution will not be televised / Sex education - ghetto style / Get out of the ghetto blues / No knock / Lady Day and John Coltrane / Pieces of a man / Home is where the hatred is / Brother / Save the children / Whitey on the moon / Did you hear what they said / When you are who you are / I think I'll call it morning / Sign of the ages / Or down you fall / Needle's eye / Prisoner
ND 86994 / Apr '89 / Bluebird

☐ SMALL TALK AT 125TH AND LENOX (A New Black Poet)
Introduction / Revolution will not be televised / Omen / Brother / Comment / Small talk at 125th and Lenox / Subject was faggots / Evolution (and flashbacks) / Plastic pattern people / Whitey on the moon / Vulture / Enough / Everyday / Paint it black / Who'll pay reparations on my soul
07863666112 / Jun '97 / Flying Dutchman

☐ SPIRITS
Message to the messengers / Spirits / Give her a call / Lady's song / Spirits past / Other side (parts 1-3) / Work for peace / Don't give up
MUMCD 9415 / Aug '94 / Mother

☐ WINTER IN AMERICA (Scott-Heron, Gil & Brian Jackson)
Peace go with you brother / Rivers of my Fathers / Very precious time / Back home / Bottle / Song for Bobby Smith / Your Daddy loves you / H2Ogate blues / Peace go with you brother
CDGR 225 / 2 Feb '98 / Charly
TVT 43202 / 17 Mar '98 / TVT

Scottish Country Dance Band

☐ SCOTTISH CEILIDH MUSIC
Gay Gordons / Murdo McKenzie of Torridon/ Lyndhurst / Lochaber gathering/MacKenzie hay/ The Brolum / Agnes waltz / Kilberry castle/The rose among the heather/The old pipe reel / Hornpipes / Bobby Jacks compliments to Mary Prentice/ Kenneth MacDonald's / Canadian barn dance / McNeill of Ugadale/Lyndhurst / Scottish waltz / Marches / Saddle the pony/The rakes of Kildare/ Humours of Glendart / Seamos McNeil/Pipe Major Sam Scott / Black mask / Miss Elspeth Campbell/ Lady Lever park / Rakish highlandman/Major Makie / Murdo McKenzie of Plockton/Miss Stewart of Bombay / Sands of Kersal / Duke of Fife's welcome to Deeside/Dr. McHardy/Jean's reel / Ballochyle/ Echoes of Ob
RECD 495 / Jan '98 / REL

Scottish Division School Of Music Band

☐ MARCHING FOR SCOTLAND
BNA 5145 / 15 Jun '98 / Bandleader

Scottish Fiddle Orchestra

☐ CANADA 'O' CANADA
RECD 520 / Jul '98 / REL

☐ EDINBURGH THE FESTIVAL CITY
Ceud mile failte / Bonnie wells o' Wearie / Bugle call / Flowers of Edinburgh/Lass o' Patie's Mill / East Neuk o' Fife/Bottom of the punch bowl / Loch Lomond / Whistling Rufus / Flower of Scotland / Circassian circle / March of the cellos / Bluebells of Scotland / McFarlane o' the Sprots / Barnyards o' Delgaty/ Mormond braes/Bonnie lass o' Fyvie / Muckin' o' Geordie's byre / Scotland again / Maple sugar / Blackthorn stick/Jackson's jig/Rory O'More/ Roaring Jelly / Pet o' the Pipers / Nessun dorma
RECD 491 / Dec '97 / REL

☐ FIDDLER'S PARTY, THE
Bluebell polka / Military two step / Canadian barn dance / Strip the willow / Lomond waltz / Dashing white sergeant / Eva three step / Gay Gordons / Highland schottische / Britannia two step / St. Bernard's waltz / Boston two step / GGay Gordons / Highland schottische / Duke of Perth / Eightsome reel
RECD 485 / Dec '97 / REL

☐ LEGENDARY SCOTTISH FIDDLE ORCHESTRA, THE (Scottish Fiddle Orchestra & John Mason)
RECD 498 / Dec '97 / REL

☐ LET GLASGOW FLOURISH
Ceud mile failte / Flower of Portencross / White cockade/Captain Byng/Ballyoran polka/Megan's tune / Wild mountain thyme / Jewel in the Crown jigs / Braes of Ballochmyle / Andy MacKay's farewell to Tayside Police / Hills of Galloway/Moss of Cree/ Cairnsmore of Fleet / Auld lang syne / Dashing white sergeant/Rakes o' Mallow/The waves of Troy / Stronsay wedding/The siege of Eniss/Reel of Kildinguie / Dance of the Basses / Amigos para siempre / Scotland the Brave/The saints / Dark Lochnagar / Bridgeport reel/Gypsy hornpipe/Norm Burgess breakdown / Back up and push/Crazy creek / Swinging reels
RECD 492 / Jan '98 / REL

☐ NORTHERN LIGHTS
RECD 487 / Dec '97 / REL

☐ OVER THE WATER
Fiddlers to the fore / Music o' Spey / Hen's mairch ower the midden / Eamonn Gilmartin's eclipse / Phil the fluter's ball / Irish washerwoman / Miss Fanny Poer / Irish favourites / Listen to the mockingbird / Fiddler of Dooney / Give me your hand / Mary o' Argyll / Scots wha hae / Danny boy
RECD 489 / Jan '98 / REL

☐ PRINCE OF THE MISTS
Eriskay love lilt / Yellow haired laddie / Wae's me for Prince Charlie / Rise and follow Charlie / March of the cameron men / Pibroch of Donald dhu / Highland love my love was born / Charlie is my darlin' / Bells of the churches / Hey Johnnie Cope / Wi' a hundred pipers / Loch Lomond / Campbells are coming/ Highland laddie / Grenadier's march/Highland laddie / Culloden day / Flowers o' the forest / Welcome to Uist / Over the sea to Skye / Will you no come back again / Coronation march
RECD 484 / Dec '97 / REL

☐ SCOTTISH FIDDLE ORCHESTRA AT THE ROYAL ALBERT HALL, THE
Elizabeth's Royal Albert medley / Orkney two step / Scotland yet / Butterfly polka medley / Jigs from the Gow collection / Massacre of Glencoe / Old woolly jumper medley / Musical flea / Robert Wilson favourites medley / Irish fantasia medley / Western Isles medley / Crookit Bawbee / Eightsome reel medley / Auld lang syne / Elizabeth's Royal Albert
RECD 504 / Dec '97 / REL

☐ SCOTTISH FIDDLE ORCHESTRA PLAYS TORONTO
RECD 521 / Jan '98 / REL

Scottish Gas Caledonia Pipe Band

☐ OUT OF THE BLUE
2/4 marches / March / Strathspey and reel / Irish hornpipe rhythms / Pipe band medley / Irish set / Reels / Slow air / Hornpipes and reels / Jigs
CDTRAX 064 / Nov '93 / Greentrax

Scottish National Pipe & Drum Corps

☐ SCOTLAND THE BRAVE
CNCD 5958 / Jul '93 / Disky

Scottish Philharmonic Singers

☐ SCOTTISH PHILHARMONIC SINGERS
In praise of Islay / Rosebud by my early walk / Johnny Cope / Fairy lullaby / Scots wha hae / Island herdsmaid / Duncan Gray / Iona boat song / Ossianic processional / Flow gently sweet Afton / Charlie is my darling / Skye boat song / Fife fisher song / Ye banks and braes o' bonnie Doon / Ca' the Yowes / Loch Lomond / Island sheiling song / Eriskay love lilt / Flowers o' the forest / Donald Ewan's wedding
LCOM 9043 / Apr '91 / Lismor

Scottish Power Pipe Band

☐ TARTAN WEAVE
CDMON 836 / Aug '95 / Monarch

Scottish Regiments

☐ TUNES OF GLORY
MOICD 006 / Jun '94 / Moidart

Scotto, Renata

☐ GREAT VOICE
HR 4291/92 / Mar '91 / New Note

Scottsville Squirrel Barkers

☐ BLUEGRASS FAVOURITES
Shady grove / Home sweet home / Katy Klyne / Swamp root / Willow tree / Walking cane / Three finger breakdown / Cripple Creek / Crown Junction breakdown / Reuben
DIAB 855 / 1 Jun '98 / Diablo

Scotty

☐ UNBELIEVABLE SOUNDS
Draw you brakes / Children children / Penny for your song / Jam rock style / I worry / Musical chariot / Sing along / Rose marie / Sesame street / Lonely man / Riddle I this / Monkey drop / I count the skank / Clean race / Skank in bed / Unbelievable sounds
CDTRL 264 / 19 Jan '98 / Trojan

Scram C Baby

☐ TASTE
GAP 018 / Feb '94 / Gap Recordings

Scratch Bongowax

☐ LET ME BE
1+2CD 089 / 1 Jun '98 / 1+2

Scrawl

☐ BLOODSUCKER
SMR 17D / May '93 / Simple Machines

Scream

☐ FUMBLE/BANGING THE DRUM
DIS 82D / Jul '93 / Dischord

☐ STILL SCREAMING/THIS SIDE UP
DIS 81D / Jul '93 / Dischord

Scream

☐ LET IT SCREAM
HR 609942 / Oct '97 / Hollywood

Scream

☐ NO MORE CENSORSHIP
RASCD 4001 / Dec '88 / Ras

Screamin' Cheetah Wheelies

☐ SCREAMIN' CHEETAH WHEELIES
Shakin' the blues / Ride the tide / Something else / This is the time / Slow burn / Leave your pride (at the front door) / Jami / Sister mercy / Majestic / Moses brown / Let it flow
7567825072 / Mar '94 / WEA

Screaming Lord Sutch

☐ MURDER IN THE GRAVEYARD
Great balls of fire / I'm a hog for you baby / Bonie moronie / Jack the ripper / All black and hairy / Murder in the graveyard / Good golly miss molly / Tutti frutti / Run for your life
FCD 3023 / Mar '95 / Fury

☐ RAVING LOONEY PARTY FAVOURITES
I'm a hog for you baby / Monster rock / Penny Penny / Jenny Jenny / Keep a knockin' / Long tall Sally / Jack The Ripper / Rockabilly madman / Murder in the graveyard / All black and hairy / London rocker / Rock and shock / Scream and scream
303042 / Jul '97 / Hallmark

Screaming Trees

☐ ANTHOLOGY (2CD Set)
SST 260CD / May '93 / SST

☐ BUZZ FACTORY
Black sun morning / Flower web / End of the universe
SST 248CD / Mar '89 / SST

☐ CHANGE HAS COME
Change has come / Days / Flashes / Time speaks her golden tongue / I've seen you before
SP 48B / Dec '96 / Sub Pop

☐ DUST
Halo of ashes / Make my mind / Look at you / Dying days / Sworn and broken / All I know / Witness / Traveler / Dime western / Gospel plow
4839802 / Jul '96 / Epic

☐ EVEN IF AND ESPECIALLY WHEN
Transfiguration / Straight out to any place / World painted / Don't look down / Girl behind the mask / Flying / Cold rain / Other days and different planets / Pathway / You know where it's at / Back together / In the forest
SST 132CD / May '93 / SST

☐ INVISIBLE LANTERN
Ivy / Walk through to this side / Line and circles / Shadow song / Grey diamond desert / Smoke rings / Second I awake / Invisible lantern / Even if / Direction of the sun / Night comes creeping / She knows
SST 188CD / Sep '88 / SST

☐ OTHER WORLDS
SST 105CD / May '93 / SST

Screaming Tribesmen

☐ I'VE GOT A FEELING
RCD 1006 / May '93 / Rykodisc

Screams For Tina

☐ SCREAMS FOR TINA
CDSATE 11 / Nov '94 / Zoth Ommog

Screeching Weasel

☐ ANTHEM FOR A NEW TOMORROW
LOOKOUT 76CD / Jun '97 / Lookout

☐ ANTHEM FOR THE NEW NATIONS
LOOKOUT 76CD / Jan '97 / Lookout

☐ BARK LIKE A DOG
FAT 547CD / Dec '96 / Fatwreck Chords

☐ BOOGARA
LOOKOUT 62CD / Jan '97 / Lookout

☐ HOW TO MAKE ENEMIES
LOOKOUT 97CD / Jan '97 / Lookout

☐ KILL THE MUSICIANS
LOOKOUT 95CD / Jan '97 / Lookout

☐ MY BRAIN HURTS
LOOKOUT 50CD / Jun '97 / Lookout

☐ SCREECHING WEASEL
VML 072 / 5 Jan '98 / VML

☐ TELEVISION CITY DREAM
Count to three / Speed of mutation / Dummy up / Your morality / Dirty needles / Breaking point / Outside of you / We are generation X / Identity crisis / First day of winter / Plastic bag / I don't give a fuck / Only a test / Pervert at large / Burn it down
FAT 572CD / 17 Aug '98 / Fatwreck Chords

☐ WIGGLE
LOOKOUT 63CD / Jan '97 / Lookout

Screeper

☐ GOLDEN BOY EP
MOUTHY 5CD / Jun '97 / Mouthy Production

Screw

☐ BURNING IN WATER
Orifice / Burning in water, drowning in flame / Cold angel press / Charlemagne / Gemini / Indestructible / Feast / Once alive / Sympathy for the devil / Poisonous / Prey flesh
398417015CD / Jun '96 / Metal Blade

Screw Radio

☐ TALK RADIO VIOLENCE
SST 324CD / Jan '96 / SST

Screwdriver

☐ TEACH DEM
GS 70037 CD / Apr '92 / Greensleeves

Script

☐ 21 SYNTHESIZER SPACE HITS
CDCH 076 / Feb '91 / Milan

Scritti Politti

☐ CUPID AND PSYCHE '85
Word girl / Small talk / Absolute / Little knowledge / Don't work that hard / Perfect way / Lover to fall / Wood beez (pray like Aretha Franklin) / Hypnotize / Flesh and blood / Absolute (version) / Hypnotize (version) / Wood Beez (version)
CDV 2350 / Jun '85 / Virgin

☐ PROVISION
Boom there she was / Overnite / First boy in this town (Lovesick) / All that we are / Best thing ever / Oh Patti (don't feel sorry for loverboy) / Bam salute / Sugar and spice / Philosophy now / Oh Patti (don't feel sorry for loverboy) (extended) / Boom there she was (dub)
CDV 2515 / Aug '91 / Virgin

Scrivenor, Gove
☐ SHINE ON
742542 / 1 Sep '98 / Compass

☐ SOLID GOVE
Good time lady / Sugar babe / Pigeon river breakdown / Cocaine blues / If your man gets busted / Walkin' my blues away / Make my love come rollin' down / Minuet for the backroads / Black cat bone / Going to the country / Jesu joy of man's desiring / Rainbow willie / Reason to believe / Before believing / Everybody's dancin' / Two rivers in Montana / Close the door lightly / All I want to do is / I'll fly away
CDFF 672 / 16 Mar '98 / Flying Fish

Scroat Belly
☐ DADDY'S FARM
BS 017 / 19 Jan '98 / Bloodshot

Scruff
☐ ANGST 1974-1976
NHM 40210 / 13 Apr '98 / Northern Heights

☐ WANNA MEET THE SCRUFFS
NHM 40212 / 13 Apr '98 / Northern Heights

Scruffs
☐ MIDTOWN
NHM 40216 / 20 Jul '98 / Northern Heights

☐ TEENAGE GIRLS
NHM 40214 / 20 Jul '98 / Northern Heights

Scruggs, Earl
☐ ARTIST'S CHOICE (The Best Tracks 1970-1980) (Scruggs, Earl Revue)
You ain't goin' nowhere / T for Texas / Rambling 'round your city / Sally Gooding / Foggy mountain breakdown / Down in the flood / Salty dog blues / Travellin' prayer / My Tennessee mountain home / I shall be released / Swimming song / Bleeker street rag / Third rate romance / Instrumental in D minor / I still miss someone / Mansion on the hill / Nashville skyline rag / Black mountain blues / Lonesome Ruben
EDCD 552 / 6 Apr '98 / Edsel

Scuba
☐ UNDERWATER SYMPHONIES
CRECD 136 / Oct '95 / Creation

Scud Mountain Boys
☐ EARLY YEAR, THE (2CD Set)
SPCD 389 / 1 Sep '97 / Sub Pop

☐ MASSACHUSETTS
SPCD 342 / 8 Sep '97 / Sub Pop

Scully & Bunny
☐ LONG LONG TIME
SONCD 0092 / Jul '97 / Sonic Sounds

Scum Boys
☐ VAMP ATTACK
RUMCD 008 / Jun '91 / Rumble

Scum Of Toytown
☐ STRIKE
WOWCD 41 / Mar '95 / Words Of Warning

Scum Rats
☐ GO OUT
RUMCD 001 / Aug '92 / Rumble

☐ LET ME BE BAD
RUMCD 005 / Aug '92 / Rumble

☐ LIVE AT THE BIG RUMBLE
RUMCD 014 / Aug '92 / Rumble

SDL
☐ SPACE AGE FRONTIER
DBMLABCD 5 / Oct '95 / Labworks

SDR Big Band
☐ EASY LIFE
ISCD 160 / Sep '96 / Intersound

Sea & Cake
☐ BIZ
EFA 121152 / Oct '95 / Moll
TKCD 70951 / 20 Apr '98 / Thrill Jockey

☐ BRIEF HISTORICAL..., A
TKCB 70952 / 22 Jun '98 / Thrill Jockey

☐ NASSAU
EFA 121122 / May '95 / Moll

☐ SEA AND CAKE, THE
Jacking the ball / Polio / Bring my car I feel to smash it / Flat lay the waters / Choice blanket / Culabra cut / Bombay / Showboat angel / So long to the captain / Lost in autumn
R 3102 / Feb '94 / Rough Trade

Sea, David
☐ GROOVE MISSION
JVC 90101 / Mar '97 / JVC

Sea Horses
☐ LISTEN
Asking heaven and heart / Salute to the sun / Exaltations / Angles of incidence / Pray / Satori / Kissing flowers / For our emotions / Open veins / Insufferance / Confession
SH 777 / Apr '91 / Mandala

Sea Nymphs
☐ SEA NYMPHS, THE
ALPHCD 021 / May '95 / Alphabet Business Concern

Sea Tiger
☐ CYBERPORPOISE, THE
TMU 022CD / 20 Oct '97 / Troubleman Unlimited

Sea Train
☐ MARBLEHEAD MESSENGER, THE
Oh my love / Sally goodin / Creepin' midnight / I'm willin' / Song for job / Home to you / 13 questions / Marble head messenger / London song / Gramercy / State of georgia's mind / Mississippi moon / How sweet thy song / Losing all the years
S21 57661 / Apr '94 / One Way

Sea Urchins
☐ STARDUST
Cling film / Cling film / You're so much / Pristine christine / Sullen eyes / Everglades / Solace / Please rain fall / A morning odyssey / Wild grass pictures / Day into day
SARAH 609CD / Mar '95 / Sarah

Seabrook, Terry
☐ CAN'T STOP NOW (Seabrook, Terry Cubana Bop)
Cubana bop / This nearly was mine / Moanin' / Autumn leaves / Myles from home / Can't stop now / For us / Peruchin / Cantaloupe island / Flight / Que caliente / Soundwaves / Festival mambo / One by one
CBCD 1 / May '96 / TSM

Seaford College Chapel Choir
☐ FOR THE BEAUTY OF THE EARTH
GRCD 71 / Nov '95 / Grasmere

Seager, Bert
☐ RESONANCE (Seager, Bert Trio)
Doloroso / I remember you / Winter thaw / What'll I do / Trinkle tinkle / Waltzing Nidana / Memories of you / Solar / Someday / Snapshot
AC 5021 / Sep '97 / Accurate

Seahorses
☐ DO IT YOURSELF
I want to know / Blinded by the sun / Love is the law / Boy in the picture / Love me and leave me / Suicide Drive / Happiness is egg shaped / Round the universe / Hello / 1999
GED 25134 / May '97 / Geffen

☐ INTERVIEW SESSIONS
CHAT 10 / 18 May '98 / Chatback

Seal
☐ SEAL
Beginning / Deep water / Crazy / Killer / Whirlpool / Future love paradise / Wild / Show me / Violet
ZTT 9CD / May '91 / ZTT

☐ SEAL VOL.2
Bring it on / Prayer for the dying / Dreaming in metaphors / Don't cry / Fast changes / Kiss from a rose / People asking why / Newborn friend / If I could / I'm alive / Bring it on (reprise)
4509962562 / May '94 / ZTT

Seal, Joseph
☐ MIGHTY WURLITZER
MACCD 151 / Aug '96 / Autograph

☐ WURLITZER
TRTCD 184 / May '95 / TrueTrax

Seals, Dan
☐ IN A QUIET ROOM VOL.1
TDC 010 / Mar '96 / Tour Data Corporation

☐ IN A QUIET ROOM VOL.2
LOA (love on arrival) / God must be a cowboy at heart / Nights are forever without you / My baby's got good timing / Addicted / We are one / Still reelin' / Three time loser / My old yellow car / Wood
SERCD 103 / Apr '98 / Serengeti

Seals, Son
☐ BAD AXE
Don't pick me for your fool / Going home (where women got meat on their bones) / Just about to lose your clown / Friday again / Cold blood / Out of my way / I think you're foolin' me / I can count on my blues / Can't stand to see her cry / Person to person
ALCD 4738 / May '93 / Alligator

☐ CHICAGO FIRE
ALCD 4720 / May '93 / Alligator

☐ LIVE AND BURNING
ALCD 4712 / May '93 / Alligator

☐ LIVING IN THE DANGER ZONE
Frigidaire woman / I can't lose the blues / Woman in black / Tell it to another fool / Ain't that some shame / Arkansas woman / Danger zone / Last four nickels / My time now / Bad axe / My life
ALCD 4798 / May '93 / Alligator

☐ MIDNIGHT SON
ALCD 4708 / May '93 / Alligator

☐ NOTHING BUT THE TRUTH
ALCD 4822 / Sep '94 / Alligator

☐ SON SEALS BLUES BAND (Seals, Son Blues Band)
Mother In Law Blues / Sitting at my window / Look now baby / Your love is a cancer / All you love / Cotton pickin' blues / Hot sauce / How could she leave me / Going home tomorrow / Now that I'm down
ALCD 4703 / Feb '94 / Alligator

☐ SPONTANEOUS COMBUSTION (Son Seals Live)
Crying for my baby / Don't pick me for your fool / Mother blues / No no baby / Your love is like a cancer / I need my baby back / Sitting here thinking / Every goodbye ain't gone / Sun is shining / Landlord at my door / Trouble trouble / Don't lie to me
ALCD 4846 / Nov '96 / Alligator

Seam
☐ ARE YOU DRIVING ME CRAZY
EFA 049602 / Jul '95 / City Slang

☐ HEADSPARKS
EFA 0407626 / Apr '92 / City Slang

☐ PROBLEM WITH ME
EFA 0492326 / Sep '93 / City Slang

Sean Nua
☐ OPEN DOOR, THE
Happy to meet sorry to part / Cliffs of Moher / Eaves dropper / Curios cat / Open door / Innisheer / Foggy dew / Drops of brandy / Blacksmiths reel / Rapids / Jig of stops / O ro song of the sea / Tabby reel / Young Joe / Bob's parting glass / Rainmakers / Clara's vale / SSession / Breretons / Sean Seery's / Ta me mo shui / John Welsh's / Bill Sullivans
SHAN 79082CD / Mar '98 / Shanachie

Seance
☐ FORNEVER LAID TO REST
Who will not be dead / Reincarnage / Blessing of death / Sin / Haunted / Fornever laid to rest / Necronomicon / Wind of Gehenna / Inferna cabbala
BMCD 017 / Jun '92 / Black Mark

☐ SALTRUBBED EYES
BMCD 44 / Jan '94 / Black Mark

Sear Bliss
☐ HAUNTING, THE
TM 1205CD / 2 Mar '98 / Mascot

☐ PAGAN WINTER
TM 1202CD / Mar '97 / Mascot

Search & Destroy
☐ MUSIC FOR HAPP-E PARTIES
DB 47922 / Sep '96 / Deep Blue

Search Party
☐ MONTGOMERY CHAPEL
FLASH 63 / 1 Jun '98 / Flash

Searchers
☐ BEST OF THE SEARCHERS, THE
Needles and pins / Love potion no.9 / Sweets for my sweet / Listen to me / Hungry for love / Farmer John / Take it or leave it / Where have all the flowers gone / Someday we've gonna love again / Don't throw your love away / Some other guy / When you walk in the room / He's got no love / Ain't gonna kiss you / When I get home / WHat have they done to the rain / Have you ever loved somebody / Sugar and spice / Take me for what I'm worth / Goodbye my love
MCCD 291 / May '97 / Music Club

☐ BRITISH 60'S, THE (Searchers/Gerry & The Pacemakers)
Sweets for my sweet: *Searchers* / Take it or leave it: *Searchers* / Goodbye my love: *Searchers* / When you walk in the room: *Searchers* / Don't throw your love away: *Searchers* / Take me for what I'm worth: *Searchers* / Needles and pins: *Searchers* / Sugar and spice: *Searchers* / What have they done to the rain: *Searchers* / Someday we're gonna love again: *Searchers* / How do you do it: *Gerry & The Pacemakers* / Ferry across the Mersey: *Gerry & The Pacemakers* / You'll never walk alone: *Gerry & The Pacemakers* / It's still rock'n'roll to me: *Gerry & The Pacemakers* / Roll over Beethoven: *Gerry & The Pacemakers* / Unchained melody: *Gerry & The Pacemakers* / Imagine: *Gerry & The Pacemakers* / Running man: *Gerry & The Pacemakers* / I want you just the way you are: *Gerry & The Pacemakers* / Don't let the sun catch you crying: *Gerry & The Pacemakers*
PLATCD 206 / Feb '97 / Platinum

☐ EP COLLECTION, THE
When you walk in the room / Missing you / Oh my lover / This empty place / No one else could love me / What have they done to the rain / Goodbye my love / Till I met you / Can't help forgiving you / I don't want to go on without you / Till you say you'll be mine / Sweets for my sweet / Since you broke my heart / Too many miles / Take me for what I'm worth / Take it or leave it / Someday we're gonna love again / Bumble bee / System / Love potion no.9 / Money / Alright / Just like me / Everything you do / If I could find someone / It's all been a dream / Hungry for love / Sea of heartbreak / Ain't gonna kiss ya / Don't cha know
SEECD 275 / Jul '89 / See For Miles

☐ GERMAN, FRENCH AND RARE RECORDINGS
REP 4102 / Aug '91 / Repertoire

☐ GREATEST HITS COLLECTION
Sweets for my sweet / Sugar and spice / Needles and pins / Don't throw your love away / Someday we're gonna love again / When you walk in the room / What have they done to the rain / Goodbye my love / He's got no love / When I get home / Take me for what I'm worth / Take it or leave it / Have you ever loved somebody / Love potion no.9 / Bumble bee / Goodnight baby / Listen to me / I don't want to go on without you / Ain't gonna kiss ya / Since you broke my heart
SELCD 509 / Mar '98 / Castle Select

☐ MIKE PENDER'S SEARCHERS
GRF 185 / Jan '93 / Tring

☐ NEEDLES AND PINS
Needles and pins: Tyler, Bonnie / When you walk in the room / I don't want to go on without you / What have they done to the rain / Farmer John / Someday we're gonna love again / Goodbye my love / All my sorrows / Sugar and spice / Take me for what I'm worth / Love potion no.9 / Don't throw your love away / Stand by me / Be my baby / Magic potion / Sweets for my sweet
21020 / Jul '97 / Laserlight

☐ SEARCHERS, THE
Sweets for my sweet / Sugar and spice / Needles and pins / Saints and sinners / Missing you / Goodbye my love / Glad all over / Have you ever loved somebody / Love potion no.9 / Take it or leave it / When you walk in the room / What have they done to the rain / It's all been a dream / Someday we're gonna love again / Don't throw your love away / He's got no love / Take me for what I'm worth / Alright / Money / When I get home
CDMFP 5922 / Oct '91 / EMI

☐ SIRE SESSIONS, THE (Rockfield 1979-1980)
Hearts in her eyes / Switchboard Susan / Feeling fine / This kind of love affair / Lost in your eyes / It's too late / No dancing / Coming from the heart / Don't hang on / Love's gonna be strong / Back to the war / Love's melody / Silver / Infatuation / She made a fool of you / Almost Saturday night / You are the new day / Everything but a heartache / Radio romance / Murder in my heart / September gurls / Another night / Changing
RVCD 64 / 23 Mar '98 / Raven

☐ SWEETS FOR MY SWEET
Sweets for my sweet / He's got no love / Take me for what I'm worth / What have they done to the rain / Someday we're gonna love again / Take it or leave it / Needles and pins / Have you ever loved somebody / Don't throw your love away / When you walk in the room / Sugar and spice / Goodbye my love
5507412 / Sep '94 / Spectrum

Sears, Al
☐ SEAR-IOUSLY
125th Street, New York / Shake hands / Tan skid lad / Brown boy / Huffin' and puffin' / Sear-iously / Mag's alley / Fo yah / In the good old summertime / Ivory cliffs / Easy Ernie / Vo sa / Goin' uptown / Tweedle dee / Come and dance with me / Come a runnin' / Tom, Dick 'n' Henry / Tina's canteen / Right now, right now / Midnight wail / Love call / Rock 'n' roll ball / Here's the beat / Great googa mooga / Fo ya
BCD 15668 / Jun '92 / Bear Family

Season 2 Risk
☐ MEN ARE MONKEYS - ROBOTS WIN
THK 54 / 1 Jun '98 / Thick

Seaton, B.B.

☐ EVERYDAY PEOPLE
Now I know / Good to me / Just a little more time / Private lessons / Everyday people / Gimme little love / Tell me if you're ready / Still look sexy / Some day I'll be free / Photographs and souvenirs
RNCD 2012 / Jul '93 / Rhino

☐ GREATEST HITS
CDSBS 001 / Aug '96 / Soul Beat

Seaweed

☐ FOUR
SPCD 110/286 / Sep '93 / Sub Pop

☐ SEAWEED
Inside / Love gut / Carousel / Patch work / Just a smirk / Installing / Star girl / Deer trap
TUPCD 028 / Oct '91 / Tupelo

☐ SPANAWAY
EC2A 0034 / Nov '96 / Polydor

Sebadoh

☐ BAKESALE
WIGCD 011 / Jun '95 / Domino

☐ BUBBLE AND SCRAPE
Soul and fire / Two years two days / Telecosmic alchemy / Fantastic disaster / Happily divided / Sister / Cliche / Sacred attention / Elixir is zog / Emma get wild / Sixteen / Homemade / Forced love / No way out / Bouquet for a siren / Think (let tomorrow bee) / Flood
WIGCD 004 / Jun '95 / Domino

☐ HARMACY
WIGCD 026 / Aug '96 / Domino

☐ MAGNET'S COIL
CORX 016CD / Feb '97 / Cortex

☐ ROCKING THE FOREST
WIGCD 2 / Jun '95 / Domino

☐ SEBADOH III
HMS 1682 / 1 Jun '98 / Homestead

☐ SEBADOH VS. HELMET
Notsur dnuora selcric / Brand new love / Mean distance / Burned / New worship / Good things, proud man / P. moon / Cecilia chime in melee / Soulmate
WIGCD 003 / Jun '95 / Domino

☐ SMASH YR HEAD ON PUNK ROCK
SP 176 / 22 May '98 / Sub Pop

Sebastian, John B.

☐ I WANT MY ROOTS (Sebastian, John B. & The J-Band)
Mobile line / I want my roots / Goin' to Germany / Big road blues / Just don't stop till you're all worn out / Ain't nowhere to hobo anymore / Milk cow blues / Rain hey rain / Satesboro blues / New jug band waltz / Tappin' that thing / Yank Rachell boogie / Divin' duck / KC moan
MM 65137 / Oct '97 / Music Masters

Sebesky, Don

☐ I REMEMBER BILL (A Tribute To Bill Evans)
Waltz for Debby / I remember Bill / So what / Quiet now / All the things you are / Peace piece / Bill not Gil / Very early / TTTT (Twelve tone tune two) / Autumn leaves / Blue in green / I'm getting sentimental over you / Epilogue / Bill Evans interview
09026689292 / 1 Jun '98 / RCA Victor

Sebestyen, Marta

☐ APOCRYPHA
HNCD 1368 / Apr '97 / Hannibal

☐ BEST OF MARTA SEBESTYEN, THE
En csak azt csodalom / Termetes / Szol a kakacs mar / Repulj madar, repulj / Da je visnya / Hindi lullabye / Istenem istenem / Shores of Loch Brann/Hazafele / Szeress egyet, s legyen szep / Tavasz, tavasz / Gold, silver or love / Szerelem, szerelem
HNCD 1412 / Mar '97 / Hannibal

☐ KISMET
Devoika mome / Sino moi / Leaving Derry Quay / Eleni / Gold, silver or love / Hindu lullabye / Shores of loch brann / Hazafele / If I were a rose (ha en rozsa velnek) / Imam sluzhba (the conscript)
HNCD 1392 / Feb '96 / Hannibal

☐ MARTA SEBESTYEN AND MUZIKAS (Sebestyen, Marta & Muzikas)
Vetettem violat / Szeress egyet, s legyen szep / Harom arva / Fujnaka fellegek / Hajnali nota / Egy par tanc mezosegrol / Szeki m agyar a "misie" / Fuvom azenekem / Feher galamb szallt a hazra / Teremtes
HNCD 1330 / Apr '97 / Hannibal

Sebo, Ferenc

☐ HUNGARIAN FOLK MUSIC (Sebo, Ferenc Ensemble)
Love, love-where were you at night, titmouse / Jew's harp music / Dances of gyimes / Shepherds have become cheap-the brave mounted warrior / Dances of szek / Wheat must ripen / Let god give / Devil's harps-a mist-herd has arisen / Hymn in all times / Those roaming / I looked / For a birthday / Mysteries / Forever / Seventh one
ROUCD 5005 / Feb '93 / Rounder

☐ LA HONGRIE (Sebo, Ferenc Ensemble)
ARN 64415 / 5 Jan '98 / Arion

Secada, Jon

☐ HEART, SOUL & A VOICE
Whipped / Take me / If you go / Good feelings / Where do I go from you / Fat chance / Mental picture / Stay / La la la / Don't be silly / Eyes of a fool / Si te vas (If you go) / Tuyo (Take me)
SBKCD 29 / Feb '95 / SBK

☐ SECADA
Too late too soon / Heaven is you / Believe / Get me over you / It's enough / Ready for love / I live for you / Who will take care of me / After all is said and done / Forever is as long as it lasts / Too late too soon / Amandolo
SBKCD 32 / Jun '97 / SBK

Seck, Mansour

☐ N'DER FOUTA TOORA VOL.2
STCD 1073 / Mar '96 / Stern's

Seck, Thione

☐ DAALY
STCD 1070 / Jan '97 / Stern's

☐ DAKAR SOUND VOL.5
2002851 / Jan '97 / Dakar Sound

Secola, Keith

☐ CIRCLE
NORMAL 162CD / Mar '94 / Normal

Secombe, Harry

☐ COLLECTION, THE
On the street where you live / Where is love / Gigi / Speak softly to me / O Mimi Tu Piu Non Torni: *Secombe, Harry & Delme Bryn-Jones* / Au fond du Temple Saint: *Secombe, Harry & Delme Bryn-Jones* / Day by day / Send in the clowns / I've grown accustomed to her face / If ever I would leave you / Onward christian soldiers / It is no secret / Swing low, sweet chariot / Beautiful Isle of somewhere / All things bright and beautiful / How great thou art / Battle Hymn of the Republic / Desiderata / Whispering hope / Lord's my shepherd / Perfect day / God be in my head
3036000732 / Feb '97 / Carlton

☐ HIGHWAY FAVOURITES
Guide me thou great redeemer / Little understanding / O love that will not let me go / Jerusalem / Rock of ages / God be in my head / All things bright and beautiful / Who's the one / Onward Christian soldiers / Old rugged cross / 23rd Psalm / For the beauty of the earth / Cover me with love / There is a green hill / Prayer perfect / How great thou art / Song of joy / Abide with me
KMCD 832 / May '95 / Kingsway

☐ MY FAVOURITE CAROLS
Here we come a-wassailing / While shepherds watched their flocks by night / Good King Wenceslas / Silent night / First Noel / O come all ye faithful (Adeste Fidelis) / That's what I'd like for Christmas / Mary's boy child / Once in Royal David's City / Holly and the ivy / God rest ye merry gentlemen / White Christmas / Ave Maria / Nessun dorma
5509302 / Nov '96 / Spectrum

☐ SIR HARRY
On the street where you live / Where is love / Gigi / Speak softly love / O mimi tu piu non tornl / Day by day / Send in the clowns / I've grown accustomed to her face / If ever I would leave you / Au fond du temple saint (duet from 'the pearl fishers') (/ Onward christian soldiers / It is no secret / Swing low, sweet chariot / Beautiful isle of somewhere / All things bright and beautiful / How great thou art / Battle hymn of the republic / Desiderata / Whispering hope / Lord's my shepherd / Perfect day / God be in my head
PRCD 143 / May '93 / President

☐ THIS IS MY SONG
This is my song / Younger than springtime / When you wish upon a star / Story of a starry night / Father of girls / Falling in love with love / September song / Three coins in the fountain / Impossible dream / Come back to Sorrento / Catari, catari / Some enchanted evening / O sole mio / Nessun dorma
5501882 / Mar '94 / Spectrum

☐ VERY BEST OF HARRY SECOMBE, THE
If I ruled the world / Moulin rouge / Girls were made to love and kiss / Vienna, city of my dreams / Man without love / Lead kindly light / Falling in love with you / Santa Lucia / Summer song / Bless this house / This is my song / Grinzing / Love is a many splendoured thing / Funiculi funicula / I long to see the day / Il lamento de Federico / Stranger in paradise / Be my love / Here in my heart / Abide with me
5527192 / Jan '97 / Spectrum

Second Hand

☐ DEATH MAY BE YOUR SANTA CLAUS
Funeral / Hangin' on a eyelid / Lucifer and the egg / Somethin' you got / Cyclops / Sic transit gloria mundi / Revelations ch16 vs, 9-21 / Take to the skies / Death may be your santa claus / Baby you are another monster
SEECD 479 / Jul '97 / See For Miles

Second Life

☐ SECOND LIFE
SB 040 / Jun '97 / Second Battle

Second Sight

☐ SECOND SIGHT
Night fries / Red Hills of Kwanda / Dance to the music / Knight supreme / Rosetta rock / Blood and mercury / Marble moon beams / Table rasa / Dangerous dream / Sin city circumstance / If 6were 4
SH 5716 / Mar '98 / Shanachie

Second Voice

☐ DAWN (2CD Set)
EFA 129062 / May '96 / Kodex

Seconds Flat

☐ SECONDS FLAT
Good life / Me and my friend heartache / Slow dance across the moon / She likes / Murphy's law / Three o'clock / In your arms / Stella / Gone / Trapped between the lines / Fire and brimstone / Walk away / Saluda
GLCD 2126 / Oct '97 / Green Linnet

Seconds, Kevin

☐ STOUDAMIRE
EAR 021CD / 26 Aug '97 / Earth

Secrecy

☐ RAGING ROMANCE
N 01822 / '91 / Noise

Secret

☐ SECRET, THE
SECTCD 3 / 6 Jul '98 / Secret

Secret Affair

☐ GLORY BOYS BEHIND CLOSED DOORS
Glory boys / Shake and shout / Going to a go go / Time for action / New dance / Days of change / Don't look down / One way world / Let your heart dance / I'm not free (but I'm cheap)
74321276182 / Jul '95 / RCA

☐ LIVE AT THE BRIDGE
Days of change / Glory boys / Shake 'n' shout / Get ready / My world / Sorry wrong number / Going to a go go / Don't look down / Time for action / Let your heart dance / I'm not free but I'm cheap / When the show is over / Road runner / Dancing in the street / Soho strut / Land of hope / Soul foundation / Time for action (encore) / Let your heart dance (encore)
RRCD 250 / 27 Oct '97 / Receiver

☐ VERY BEST OF SECRET AFFAIR, THE (Time For Action)
Time for action / Glory boys / My world / Sound of confusion / Do you know / Soho strut / Big beat / Hide and seek / So cool / Do you know / One way world / Let your heart dance / Streetlife parade / Looking through my eyes / Days of change / Going to a go-go / Lost in the night (Mack The Knife) / Shake and shout / New dance / I'm not free (but I'm cheap)
74321487322 / May '97 / Camden

Secret Garden

☐ SONGS FROM A SECRET GARDEN
Nocturne / Song from a secret garden / Sigma / Papillon / Serenade to spring / Atlantia / Heartstrings / Adagio / Rap / Chaconne / Cantoluna / Ode to simplicity
5282302 / 26 May '98 / Philips

Secret Goldfish

☐ AQUA-PET
BENT 012CD / Jun '96 / Creeping Bent

Secret Knowledge

☐ SO HARD
Hard theme / Love me now / I dig your ass / Love beads / Sugar daddy / Dracula / Drac-drums / Escape to New York / Dirty low down dog / Dear Johnny / 2 much of nuthin' / Fire
74321342442 / Sep '96 / De-Construction

Secret Life

☐ SOLE PURPOSE
PULSE 18CD / Feb '95 / Pulse 8

Secret Square

☐ SECRET SQUARE
E6 003CD / Feb '97 / Elephant 6

Secret Stars

☐ GENEALOGIES
SHR 107CD / 30 Mar '98 / Shrimper

☐ SECRET STARS
SHR 80CD / Dec '96 / Shrimper

Secrets

☐ TEENAGE RAMPAGE
OPM 2113CD / 24 Nov '97 / Other People's Music

Section Brain

☐ HOSPITAL OF DEATH
MABCD 005 / Jan '94 / MAB

Sector

☐ INDUSTRIAL COSMETICS
AT 01CD / Jun '95 / Atmosphere

☐ ORANGE
AT 06CD / Jan '96 / Atmosphere

Sedaka, Neil

☐ BEST OF NEIL SEDAKA, THE
74321113142 / Aug '94 / RCA

☐ BEST OF THE REST OF NEIL SEDAKA, THE
CDC 500 / 20 Apr '98 / Rock & Pop

☐ BREAKING UP IS HARD TO DO
WMCD 5698 / Oct '94 / Disky

☐ GREATEST HITS
Sing me / Standing on the inside / Laughter in the rain / Oh, Carol / Stairway to heaven / Hey little devil / Happy birthday sweet sixteen / Calendar girl / New York city blues / Love will keep us together / Solitaire / Lonely night (angel face) / Sad eyes / Bad blood / Immigrant / Breaking up is hard to do
PLATCD 365 / '91 / Platinum

☐ GREATEST HITS
I go ape / Oh Carol / Stairway to heaven / Run Sampson run / You mean everything to me / Calendar girl / I must be dreaming / Little devil / Happy birthday sweet sixteen / Next door to an angel / Let's go steady again
ND 89171 / Apr '90 / RCA

☐ GREATEST HITS IN CONCERT
JHD 015 / Jun '92 / Tring

☐ GREATEST HITS LIVE
MU 5028 / Oct '92 / Musketeer

☐ GREATEST HITS LIVE
I'm a song, sing me / Standing on the inside / Laughter in the rain / Oh Carol / Medley / Calender girl / New York City blues / Love will keep us together / Solitaire / Lonely night (angel face) / Sad eyes / Bad blood / Immigrant / Breaking up is hard to do
QED 186 / Nov '96 / Tring

☐ HIS GREATEST HITS OF THE 60'S
Oh Carol / Little devil / I go ape / Happy birthday sweet sixteen / Breaking up is hard to do / Calendar girl / Stairway to heaven / Next door to an angel / King of clowns / You mean everything to me / One way ticket (to the blues) / Sweet little you
CDMFP 5819 / Oct '91 / Music For Pleasure

☐ HOLLYWOOD CONCERT
CD 3504 / Aug '94 / Cameo

☐ HUNGRY YEARS, THE
VAR 5948 / 13 Jul '98 / Varese Sarabande

☐ IMMACULATE NEIL SEDAKA, THE
Sing me / Standing on the inside / Laughter in the rain / Oh carol / Stairway to Heaven / Little devil / Happy birthday sweet sixteen / Calendar girl / New York City blues / Love will keep us together / Solitaire / Lonely night (Angel face) / Sad eyes / Bad blood / Immigrant / Breaking up is hard to do
PLATCD 151 / Mar '96 / Platinum

☐ IN PERSON
I am a song (sing me) / Standing on the inside / Laughter in the rain / Oh, Carol / Climb up (stairway to heaven) / Hey little devil / Happy birthday sweet sixteen / Calendar girl / New York City blues / Love will keep us together / Solitaire / Lonely night / Sad eyes / Bad book / Immigrant / Breaking up is hard to do
307102 / Jun '97 / Hallmark

☐ LAUGHTER AND TEARS
Standing on the outside / Love will keep us together / Solitaire / Other side of me / Little lovin' / Lonely nights / Brighton / I'm a song, sing me / Breaking up is hard to do / Laughter in the rain / Cardboard California / Bad blood / Queen of 1964 / Hungry years / Betty Grable / Beautiful you / That's when the music takes me / Our last song together
5500322 / May '93 / Spectrum

☐ LAUGHTER IN THE RAIN
MACCD 234 / Aug '96 / Autograph

☐ MASTERS, THE
EABCD 021 / 24 Nov '97 / Eagle

☐ NEIL SEDAKA
295054 / Jul '92 / Ariola Express

☐ NEIL SEDAKA
GFS 063 / Jul '97 / Going For A Song

☐ OH CAROL
WMCD 5650 / May '94 / Disky

☐ SEDAKA'S BACK
VAR 5902 / 13 Jul '98 / Varese Sarabande

☐ **SINGER & HIS SONGS, THE**
Oh Carol / Breaking up is hard to do / Rainy day bells / Little devil / Can't get you out of my mind / Happy birthday sweet sixteen / No getting over you / I go ape / Betty grable / Calendar girl / When a love affair is through / Next door to an angel / Clown time / Stairway to heaven / One way ticket (to the blues) / You turn me on / My son and I / Miracle song
MCCD 148 / Feb '94 / Music Club

☐ **SOLITAIRE**
Prelude / Solitaire / Silent movies / Rosemary blues / Little song / God bless Joanna / Cardboard California / Gone with the morning / I wish I had a carousel / Adventures of a boy child wonder / Is anybody going to miss you / Better days are coming / What have they done to the moon / One more mountain to climb / Home / I'm a song / Don't let it mess your mind / Beautiful you / That's when the music takes me
MUCD 9024 / Apr '95 / Musketeer

☐ **SPOTLIGHT ON NEIL SEDAKA**
Rosemary blue / One more mountain to climb / Silent movies / What have they done to the moon / Super bird / Cardboard California / God bless Joanna / Little song / Prelude / Gone with the morning / Ring-a-rock / While I dream
HADCD 118 / Feb '94 / Javelin

☐ **STEPPIN' OUT**
VAR 5952 / 13 Jul '98 / Varese Sarabande

☐ **SWEET SIXTEEN**
Happy birthday sweet sixteen / Standing on the inside / I'm a love song (sing me) / Laughter in the rain / Oh Carol / Stairway to heaven / Hey little devil / Calendar girl / New York City blues / Love will keep us together / Solitaire / Lonely night (angel face) / Sad eyes / Bad blood / Immigrant / Breaking up is hard to do
CD 6013 / Apr '96 / Music

☐ **TALES OF LOVE AND PASSION**
ARTFULCD 12 / 14 Sep '98 / Artful

☐ **VERY BEST OF NEIL SEDAKA, THE**
Calendar girl / Oh Carol / King of clowns / Next door to an angel / Let's go steady again / Breaking up is hard to do / Happy birthday sweet sixteen / Little devil / I go ape / Stairway to heaven / Diary / You mean everything to me
74321446812 / Feb '97 / Camden

Seddiki, Sidi

☐ **SHOUFI**
Shouffin qouna / Maliki / Liam / Haram aliq / Bent nass / Galbi / Zin / Melkoum / Qaoun allah / Lachir
CDORB 063 / Oct '90 / Globestyle

Sedrenn

☐ **ON OUR WAY**
KMCD 62 / Jul '96 / Keltia Musique

See Me Suffer

☐ **CHEESE**
EFA 127082 / Feb '96 / Old World

Seeds

☐ **BAD PART OF TOWN/LIVE ALBUM BEDTIME (Seeds/Sky Saxon)**
842110 / May '94 / EVA

☐ **EVIL HOODOO**
March of the flower children / Wind blows your hair / Tripmaker / Try to understand / Evil hoodoo / Chocolate river / Pushin' too hard / Falling off the edge / Mr. Farmer / Up in her room / Can't seem to make you mine / Pictures and designs / Flower lady and her assistant / Rollin' machine / Out of the question / Satisfy you
DOCD 1998 / Jul '91 / Drop Out

☐ **FADED PICTURE, A**
Thousand shadows / Where is the entrance way to play / Fallin' / Nobody spoil my fun / Daisy Mae / No escape / Lose your mind / Now a man / Just let go / I tell myself / Faded picture / Up in her room
DIAB 834 / 26 Jan '98 / Diablo

☐ **FLOWER PUNK (3CD Set)**
Can't seem to make you mine / No escape / Evil hoodoo / Girl I want you / Pushin' too hard / Try to understand / Nobody spoil my fun / It's a hard life / You can't be trusted / Excuse excuse / Fallin' in love / Mr. Farmer / Pictures and designs / Tripmaker / I tell myself / Faded picture / Rollin' machine / Just let go / Up in her room / March of the flower children / Travel with your mnd / Out of the question / Painted doll / Flower lady and her assistant / Now a man / Thousand shadows / Two fingers pointing on you / Where is the entrance way to play / Six dreams / Fallin' / Pretty girl / Moth and the flame / I'll help you / Cry wolf / Plain spoken / Gardener / One more time / Creepin' about 20 / Buzzin' around / Mr. Farmer / No escape / Satisfy you / Night time girl / Up in her room / Gypsy plays his drums / Can't seem to make you mine / Mumble bumble / Forest outside your door / 900 million people daily all making love / Pushin' too hard / Wind blows your hair / Other place / She's wrong / Fallin' off the edge / Chocolate river / Daisy Mae / Wind blows your hair / Satisfy you / Wildblood / Sad and alone / Lose your mind / Thousand shadows
FBOOK 16 / Feb '97 / Demon

☐ **IN SEARCH OF BRIGHTER COLORS (Saxon, Sky & Fire Wall)**
I hear the mountains crash / Lightning lightning / Put something sweet between your lips / Barbie doll look / Big screen / Baby baby / Come on pretty girl / Kick kick / Paisley rocker / Come a here right now
ROSE 155CD / Dec '88 / New Rose

☐ **SEEDS, THE**
GRR 3518 / 3 Mar '98 / Benso

Seedy Arkhestra

☐ **PUZZLE**
You can't so that / Shing a ling / Thousand tears / How will I know / Despite the tears / Puzzle / Burn / Baby would you take care of me / Flog your dead horse
TCD 4008 / 20 Apr '98 / Astor Place

Seefeel

☐ **CH-VOX**
CAT 038CD / Nov '96 / Rephlex

☐ **QUIQUE**
PURECD 028 / Oct '93 / Too Pure

☐ **SUCCOUR**
WARPCD 28 / Mar '95 / Warp

Seeger, Mike

☐ **3RD ANNUAL REUNION**
ROUCD 0313 / Jan '95 / Rounder

☐ **CLOSE TO HOME (Old Time Music From Mike Seeger's Collection 1952-1967) (Various Artists)**
SFWCD 40097 / Aug '97 / Smithsonian Folkways

☐ **FRESH OLD TIME MUSIC**
ROUCD 0262 / Aug '88 / Rounder

☐ **THIRD ANNUAL FAREWELL REUNION**
ROUCD 0313 / Nov '94 / Rounder

☐ **WAY DOWN IN NORTH CAROLINA (Seeger, Mike & Paul Brown)**
Wandering boy / I have no one to love me (but the sailor) / Down to Tampa / Rout / Trader boatman / Green icy mountain / Cacklin' hen / Make me a pallet / Goodbye, little Bonnie / What'll I do with the baby-o / Way down in North Carolina / Rabbit chase / New river train / Tee la lollee / Loving Emma / Little Maggie / Walking that pretty girl home / Cousin Sally Brown / Chilly winds / That girl I love / Let me fall
ROUCD 0383 / Jun '96 / Rounder

Seeger, Peggy

☐ **ALMOST COMMERCIALLY VIABLE**
New spring morning / Bread and wine / Let's pretend / Polonium / Primrose Hill / Sweet heroin / Garden of flowers / Guilty / Night song / Good war / Morning comes too soon / You don't know how lucky you are / Give 'em an inch / My joy of you / Holiday song / Once again / Getting it right
FECD 130 / Jun '98 / Fellside

☐ **AMERICAN FOLK SONGS FOR CHILDREN (2CD Set) (Seeger, Peggy & Mike)**
Yonder she comes / Down comes a lady / Who's that tapping at the window / Such a getting upstairs / Toodala / How old are you / Jimmy Rose he went to town / What shall we do when we all go out / Goodbye Julie / Goodbye old paint / Oh, oh, the sunshine / Sweet water rolling / Wind blow East / Rain, come wet me / It rained a mist / Rain or shine / One cold and frosty morning / By'm bye / Jim along Josie / There was a man and he was mad / Riding in the buggy, Miss Mary Jane / Billy Barlow / Juniper tree / Old Joe Clarke / Down by the Greenwood Sidey-O / Roll that brown jug down to town / As I walked out one holiday / She'll be coming round the mountain / Juba / Run, chillen run / All around the kitchen / I'm going to join the army / Scraping up sand in the bottom of the sea / Old Mister Rabbit / Old Molly Hare / Oh, John the rabbit / Little pig / Bought me a cat / Hop old squirrel / My horses ain't hungry / Did you go to the Barney / Have a little dog / Frog went a-courtin' / Little bird, little bird / Free little bird / Poor old crow / Ducks in the Millpond / Jim Crack Corn / Eency weency spider / Dog tick / Who built the ark: Noah, Noah / Mary wore her red dress / Pretty little girl with the red dress on / This lady she wears a dark green shawl / Walk along John / Do, do pity my case / Hanging out the linen clothes / Lula gal / Old Aunt Kate / What did you have for your supper / Baby dear / Johnny get your hair cut / I got a letter this morning / Rose, Rose and up she rises / What'll we do with the baby / Hush little baby / Pick a bale of cotton / This old hammer / Train is a-coming / Little black train / When the train comes along / John Henry / Every Monday morning / Going down to town / Sailing in the boat / Blow boys blow / Fire down below / Sally go round the sunshine / This old man / Skip to my Lou / When I was a young maid / Closet key / Built my lady a fine brick house / Where oh where is pretty little Susie / Jingle at the windows / Adam had seven sons / Here sits a monkey / Go to sleepy / Monday morning go to school / Hush 'n' bye / Turtle dove / Mary had a baby / Jesus born in Bethlea / Cherry tree carol
ROUCD 8001 / Feb '97 / Rounder

☐ **AMERICAN FOLK SONGS FOR CHRISTMAS (Seeger, Peggy & Mike)**
ROUCD 0268/69 / '90 / Rounder

☐ **CLASSIC PEGGY SEEGER**
Cumberland gap / Lady of Carlisle / Come all ye fair and tender maidens / Deer song / I never will marry / Devilish Mary / Fair maid by the shore / Three banjo tunes / Wife of Usher's well / Rambling gambler / Cruel war is raging / Trooper and the maid / When I was in my prime / So early, early in the Spring / Chickens they are crowing / Who's that knocking at my window / Lass of Roch Royal / Who's going to shoe your pretty foot / Englewood Mine / Just as the tide was flowing / Kicking mule / Heartless lady / Tittery Nan / Loving Reilly / If he'd be a buckaroo
FE 105CD / Mar '96 / Fellside

☐ **MIKE & PEGGY SEEGER (Seeger, Peggy & Mike)**
ROUCD 11543 / '88 / Rounder

☐ **ODD COLLECTION, AN**
ROUCD 4031 / May '96 / Rounder

☐ **SONGS OF LOVE AND POLITICS (The Folkways Years 1955-1992)**
Pretty saro / Lady what you do all day / Broomfield hill / Squire and the colic / Jellon graeme / Going to the west / Jane jane / When I was single / Wedding dress song / Freight train blues / Song of myself / First time ever I saw your face / My son / Song for calum / Little girl child / Gonna be an engineer / Song of choice / Talking wheelchair blues / Nobody knew she was there / Thoughts of time / Garden of flowers
SFWCD 40048 / Nov '94 / Smithsonian Folkways

Seeger, Pete

☐ **AMERICAN INDUSTRIAL BALLADS**
SF 40058CD / Aug '94 / Smithsonian Folkways

☐ **BIRDS BEASTS BUGS AND FISHES**
SFW 45039 / May '98 / Smithsonian Folkways

☐ **DARLING COREY & GOOFING OFF SUITE**
SFCD 40018 / Jun '93 / Smithsonian Folkways

☐ **FEEDING THE FLAME**
FF 541CD / '92 / Flying Fish

☐ **IF I HAD A HAMMER (Songs Of Hope & Struggle)**
SFW 40096 / 1 Jun '98 / Smithsonian Folkways

☐ **LINK IN THE CHAIN, A (2CD Set)**
Living in the country / My Oklahoma home blowed away / Get up and go / Oh I had a golden thread / Never wed an old man / Queen Anne front / Cryderville jail / Waist deep in the Big Muddy / This land is your land / Draft dodger rag / Pill / Where have all the flowers gone / My name is Lisa Kalvelage / Turn, turn, turn / Guantanamera / Last train to Numermberg / Keep your eyes on the prize / Oh freedom / We shall overcome / Coral Creek march / Pretty Boy Floyd / Hobo's lullaby / Aimee Semple McPherson / Cowboy's lament / Jesse James / Belle stars / Harry Sims / Mrs. McGrathe / Jay Gould's daughter / Nameless lick / What did you learn in school today / Henry my son / Put your finger in the air / Michael row the boat ashore / This old car / Be kind to your parents / Cumberland mountain bear chase / This land is your land
4851102 / Nov '96 / Columbia

☐ **LIVE AT NEWPORT 1963-1965**
Intro / Manyura manyah / Malaika / Oh Mary don't you weep / Foolish frog / Deep blue sea / Never wed an old man / Old Joe Clark/Never wed an old man / Holy ground / Darlin' Corey/Skip to my Lou/Going across the mountains / Midnight special / It takes a worried man / Coral creek march / Where have all the flowers gone / Down by the riverside
VCD 77008 / Oct '94 / Vanguard

☐ **TRADITIONAL CHRISTMAS CAROLS**
SFWCD 40024 / Oct '97 / Smithsonian Folkways

☐ **WHERE HAVE ALL THE FLOWERS GONE (The Songs Of Pete Seeger/2CD Set) (Various Artists)**
Where have all the flowers gone: *Sands, Tommy & Dolores Keane/Vedran Smailovic* / Kisses sweeter than wine: *Browne, Jackson & Bonnie Raitt* / Water is wide: *Gorka, John* / Of time and rivers flowing: *Havens, Richie* / My name is Lisa Kalvelage: *Di Franco, Ani* / Turn turn turn: *Cockburn, Bruce* / Festival of flowers: *Hinojosa, Tish* / Step by step: *Sweet Honey In The Rock* / Blessed be the nation: *Terkel, Studs* / My father's mansions: *Bragg, Billy & Eliza Carthy* / Sailing down my golden river: *Brown, Greg* / Goofing off suite: *Trischka, Tony* / Those three are on my mind: *Harris, Kim & Reggie* / How can I keep from singing: *Cordelia's Dad* / All mixed up: *Peter, Paul & Mary* / Empty pocket blues: *Gilbert, Ronnie & Robin Flower/Libby McLaren* / Get up and go: *Paxton, Tom* / Old Riley: *Stewart, John* / If I had a hammer: *Griffith, Nanci* / Wimoweh: *Weavers* / We shall overcome: *Springsteen, Bruce* / Bells of Rhymney: *McGuinn, Roger* / Oh had I a golden thread: *Collins, Judy* / False from true: *Davis, Guy* / Letter to Eve: *Indigo Girls* / Waist deep in the big muddy: *Gaughan, Dick* / All my children of the sun: *Robbins, Tim* / Living in the country: *Simpson, Martin* / One grain of sand: *Odetta* / Old Father Hudson sailing down dirty stream: *Neill, Casey* / Torn flag: *Trudell, John* / Doublin: *Kahn, Si* / To everyone in the world: *Fink, Cathy & Marcy Marxer* / Over the hills: *Makem, Tommy* / I come and stand at every door: *Hills, Anne* / My rainbow race: *Donovan* / Quiet early morning: *Near, Holly* / Oh sacred morning: *Terkel, Studs* / And still I am searching: *Seeger, Pete*
APRCD 1024 / 17 Mar '98 / Appleseed

Seeing Stars

☐ **SEEING STARS**
BLCD 12 / 23 Mar '98 / Borderline

Seekers

☐ **CARNIVAL OF HITS (Durham, Judith & The Seekers)**
Morningtown Ride / World of our own / Island of dreams / Red rubber ball / Colours of my life / Georgy girl / Land is your land / Carnival is over / When will the good apples fall / Someday one day / Kumbaya / 59th Street Bridge song / Walk with me / Leaving of Liverpool / I'll never find another you / Little light of mine / Times they are a-changin' / We shall not be moved / One world love / Keep a dream in your pocket
CDEMTV 83 / Apr '94 / EMI

☐ **COLLECTION, THE**
I'll never find another you / World of our own / Carnival is over / Someday one day / Walk with me / Morningtown ride / Georgy girl / When will the good apples fall / Emerald city / We shall not be moved / Island of dreams / Open up them pearly gates / Rumbaya / Blowin' in the wind / Wreck of the old '97 / Lemon tree / Whiskey in the jar / Five hundred miles / Gypsy rover / South Australia / Danny boy / Waltzing Matilda / Water is wide
DC 886942 / 2 Feb '98 / Disky

☐ **LIVE IN CONCERT (25 Year Reunion Celebration) (Durham, Judith & The Seekers)**
When the stars begin to fall / With my swag all on my shoulder / Plaisir d'amour / Morningtown ride / You're my spirit / Kumbaya / Gospel medley / Come the day / One world love / When will the good apples fall / Devoted to you / Colours of my life / Time and again / Red rubber ball / I am Australian / I'll never find another you / Georgy girl / World of our own / Carnival is over / Keep a dream in your pocket
CDDPR 130 / Mar '95 / Premier/MFP

☐ **VERY BEST OF THE SEEKERS, THE**
I'll never find another you / World of our own / Carnival is over / Someday one day / Walk with me / Mornigntown ride / Georgy girl / When will the good apples fall / Emerald city / We shall not be moved / Island of dreams / Open up them pearly gates / Kumbaya / Wreck of the old '97 / Lemon tree / Whiskey in the jar / Five hundred miles / Gyspy rover / South Australia / Danny boy / Waltzing Matilda / Water is wide
CDMFP 6378 / 13 Oct '97 / Music For Pleasure

☐ **WORLD OF OUR OWN, A**
World of our own / Don't think twice, it's all right / Leaving of Liverpool / Land is your land / Two summers / Times they are a-changin' / Just a closer walk with thee / Don't tell me my mind / Allentown jail / Four strong winds / You can tell the world / Whistling Rufus
DORIG 122 / 6 Oct '97 / EMI

Seekers Of The Truth

☐ **OUT OF IGNORANCE**
LF 243CD / Sep '96 / Lost & Found

Seelenluft

☐ **BELLATRAX**
CLEO 0052 / 2 Feb '98 / Hypnotic

Seelenwinter

☐ **IF SOUL TURNS INTO FLESH**
MASSCD 102 / Sep '96 / Massacre

☐ **SEELENWINTER**
MASSCD 048 / Mar '95 / Massacre

Seelos, Ambros

☐ **DANCE GALA '90 (Seelos, Ambros Orchestra)**
Lambada / Lambada / Disco / Tango / Quickstep / Samba / Jive / Foxtrot / Vienna waltz / Blues / Cha cha / Mambo / Slow waltz / Slow fox / Charleston
322287 / Dec '92 / Koch

☐ **DANCE GALA '91 (Seelos, Ambros Orchestra)**
Soca / Soca / Quickstep / Cha cha / Rumba / Slow waltz / Samba / Slow fox / Vienna waltz
322462 / Dec '92 / Koch

☐ **DANCE GALA '92 (Seelos, Ambros Orchestra)**
Vienna waltz / Vienna waltz / Tango / Charleston / Samba / Disco
322665 / Dec '92 / Koch

☐ **DANCE GALA '93 (Seelos, Ambros Orchestra)**
Blues / Blues / Foxtrot / Samba / Mambo / Rock twist
322863 / Dec '92 / Koch

☐ **DANCE GALA VOL.1 : FORMAL BALLROOM DANCING (Seelos, Ambros Orchestra)**
340052 / Apr '93 / Koch

☐ **LET'S GO DANCING (Seelos, Ambros Orchestra)**
Donde vas a Bailar / Spanish flamenco matadors / Hablando suave / Baby trumpets / Love is my life / Goofus / Festival de Corcovado / Drive in jive / Moonflight / Manzanillo / Irgendwann / We belong together / You and me / Girl / Quinto quinto / Pianowellen
323579 / May '96 / Koch International

☐ **TANZ GALA (3CD Set) (Seelos, Ambros Orchestra)**
Matrimonie / Angel eyes will shine forever / Tango soiree / Strauss-Bukett / Autumn leaves / Quickstep medley / Melodie of love / Alexander's ragtime band / Optimistico / El citterio / Don't cry for me Argentina / Mambo mambo / In the mood / Everybody dance lambada / Evening party / Music for dancers / Happy soca / Las chicas / No more bolero / Samba medley / On the highway / Lambada for everybody / Rising generation / Soca night / Dancing fever / True love / Pfingstrosen / Adios Papa mia / Flowers for the ladies / Love is a many splendored thing / That old black magic / South of the border / Ole Brasil / Mucho cha cha / Amores / Vamos amigos / Dance dance dance / Down in the valley / Violetta / Magic moments / Zing went the strings of my heart / Wiener fiaker / Wake up / Riverboat blues / Lady Charleston / Tintarella di luna / Believe it or not
395703 / Aug '97 / Koch Presents

☐ TYPICAL LATIN (Seelos, Ambros Orchestra)
Rhythm only (cha cha) / Manzanillo (cha cha) / Donde vas a bailar (cha cha) / Rhythm only (samba) / Quinto quinto (samba) / Festival de corovado (samba) / Rhythm only (rumba) / Love is my life (rumba) / We belong together (rumba) / Spanish guitars and castagnettes (pasa doble) / Spanish flamenco matadors (paso doble) / Rhythm only (jive) / Walking down the highway (jive) / Drive in jive (jive)
340092 / Aug '93 / Koch

Seely

☐ JULIE ONLY
Bitsa Jane / Meteor shower / Sealskin / Red flume / Crystal Clara / Shine / Lucky penny / Bubblebath / Past Sap Street and go on / Exploring the planets / Inside / Bugles / Wind and would / How to live like a King's kid
PURECD 061 / Nov '96 / Too Pure

☐ PARENTHA SEE
TE 2007 / Nov '96 / Third Eye

☐ SECONDS
Intro / Syballine / Soft City / Like white / Too fjord / Sandpiper / Hourglass / Love letters to rambler / San Salvador / Consumer pet / It's your day Karen / Adios / Outro
PURE 069CD / 29 Sep '97 / Too Pure

Seelyhoo

☐ FIRST CAUL, THE
Miss Sarah MacFadyen/Farewell to Rock o' Cleary / Mick's knitted triplets/Brumely brae/Jenny's chickens / Air sgiathan na h-oidhche / First leg/Last leg / Mhurchaidh bhig a chinn a chonnais/Dairmaid's reel / Sometimes it doesn't work/Lucky cap/Potato tree / Hoy's dark and lofty Isle / Superwasp/Along the coast of Norway/Neckbuster / Sean McGuire/ Bear Island/Drever's reel / Cuin a chi mi thusa luaidh / Stornsay weaver/Trip to California / Dh'iomain mam bo / Lost job/Old copperplate/Diesel accordion / Walk/Miss Lyall's / Fly to Rousay/Porto the rat/Dale's place
CDTRAX 102 / Jan '96 / Greentrax

☐ LEETERA
Spioradan briste (the broken spirits) / Grace brechin / Hoy high/Hoy low / Bidh clann ulaidh (the Ulster man)
CDTRAX 160 / 1 Aug '98 / Greentrax

Seers

☐ PSYCH OUT
Wildman / Rub me out / One summer / Welcome to deadtown / I'll be there / You keep me praying / Walk / Sun is in the sky / Fly away / Breathless / Freedom trip / (All late nite) tequila drinking blues / Magic potion / Lightning strikes
CDBRED 86 / Feb '90 / Cherry Red

Seersucker

☐ PUSHING ROPE
SKYCD 5010 / Sep '94 / Sky

Seffer, Debora

☐ SILKY
CDLLL 157 / Aug '93 / La Lichere

Seffer, Yochk'o

☐ RETROSPECTIVE (2CD Set)
FA 070 / Nov '97 / Fremeaux

Segal, Misha

☐ ZAMBOOKA
MM 65068 / Oct '94 / Music Masters

Segan

☐ TO MY LORD
FA 408 / Jul '96 / Fremeaux

Seger, Bob

☐ AGAINST THE WIND (Seger, Bob & The Silver Bullet Band)
Horizontal bop / You'll accompany me / Her strut / No man's land / Long man's land / Long twin silver line / Against the wind / Good for me / Betty Lou's gettin' out tonight / Fire lake / Shinin' brightly
CDP 7460602 / Feb '95 / Capitol

☐ FIRE INSIDE, THE (Seger, Bob & The Silver Bullet Band)
Take a chance / Real love / Sightseeing / Always in my heart / Fire inside / Real at the time / Which way / Mountain / Blind love / She can't do anything wrong
CDEST 2149 / Feb '95 / Capitol

☐ GREATEST HITS
Roll me away / Night moves / Turn the page / You'll accomp'ny me / Hollywood nights / Still the same / Mainstreet / Old time rock 'nd' roll / We've got tonight / Against the wind / Fire inside / Like a rock C'est la vie / In your time
CDEST 2241 / Feb '95 / Capitol

☐ IT'S A MYSTERY (Seger, Bob & The Silver Bullet Band)
Rite of passage / Lock and load / By the river / Manhattan / I wonder / It's a mystery / Revisionism Street / Golden boy / I can't save you Angelene / Sixteen shells from a 30-6 / West of the moon / Hands in the air
CDEST 2271 / Feb '96 / Capitol

☐ LIVE BULLET
Nutbush City Limits / Travellin' man / Beautiful loser / Jody girl / Looking back / Get out of Denver / Let it rock / I've been working / Turn the page / UMC / Bo Diddley / Ramblin' gamblin' man / Heavy music / Katmandu
CDP 7460852 / Feb '95 / Capitol

☐ NIGHT MOVES
Rock 'n' roll never forgets / Night moves / Fire down below / Sunburst / Sunspot baby / Mainstreet / Come to poppa / Ship of fools / Mary Lou
CDP 7460752 / Feb '95 / Capitol

☐ NINE TONIGHT
Nine tonight / Trying to live my life without you / You'll accompany me / Hollywood nights / Night moves / Rock 'n' roll never forgets / Let it rock / Old time rock 'n' roll / Mainstreet / Against the wind / Fire down below / Her strut / Feel like a number / Fire lake / Betty Lou's gettin' out tonight / We've got tonight
CDP 7460862 / Feb '95 / Capitol

☐ STRANGER IN TOWN
Hollywood nights / Still the same / Old time rock 'n' roll / Till it shines / Feel like a number / Ain't got no money / We've got tonight / Brave strangers / Famous final scene
CDP 7460742 / Feb '95 / Capitol

Segundo, Compay

☐ LO MEJOR DE LA VIDA
3984232672 / 20 Apr '98 / Coalition

☐ YO VENDO AQUI
0630194612 / Jul '97 / Warner Bros.

Seidel, Janet

☐ ART OF LOUNGE, THE
LB 9702 / Feb '98 / La Brava

☐ DOODLIN' (Seidel, Janet & Tom Baker)
LB 9504 / Jul '98 / La Brava

☐ LITTLE JAZZ BIRD
LB 0001 / Jun '98 / La Brava

☐ WINTER MOON
LB 0002 / Jul '98 / La Brava

Seis Del Solar

☐ ALTERNATE ROOTS
MES 158312 / Apr '95 / Messidor

☐ DECISION
Sentimento de cancion / Island walk / Una sola casa / Un nuevo dia / Decision / Sea dance / Mirage / Entregate / Heart dues / Newtown
MES 158212 / Apr '96 / Messidor

Seizure

☐ LIFE IN FREEFALL
Words like razors / Godhead / Silver spoon / Half the man / Progress / John Doe by choice / Social high / Politically correct / Gratitude / Caffeine and filters / Entrapment
COP 03 / 11 May '98 / Copro

Seka, Monique

☐ OKAMAN
503842 / Apr '95 / Declic

Selah Jubilee Singers

☐ SELAH JUBILEE SINGERS VOL.1 1939-1941
DOCD 5499 / Nov '96 / Document

☐ SELAH JUBILEE SINGERS VOL.2 1941-1944
DOCD 5500 / Nov '96 / Document

Seldin, Ronnie Nyogetsu

☐ ICHI ON BUTTSU
LYRCD 7436 / Nov '97 / Lyrichord

Seldom Scene

☐ 15TH ANNIVERSARY CELEBRATION LIVE
Sittin' on top of the world / Big train from Memphis / Lorena / Dark as a dungeon / Blue Ridge / Raised by the railroad line / Don't know my mind / Drifting too far from the shore / Those memories of you / Keep me from blowing away / Wheels / Carolyn at the broken wheel inn / If I needed you / Rose of old Kentucky / I couldn't find my walkin' shoes / Workin' on a building / Say you lied / High on a hilltop / Sweetest gift / Take me on your life boat
SHCD 2202 / Jul '88 / Sugar Hill

☐ ACT 4
SHCD 3709 / Nov '95 / Sugar Hill

☐ AFTER MIDNIGHT
Lay down Sally / Hearts overflowing / Old hometown / Stompin' at the Savoy / Border incident / After midnight / If I had left it up to you / Heartsville Pike / Stolen love / Let old Mother Nature have her way
SHCD 3721 / Dec '94 / Sugar Hill

☐ AT THE SCENE
Girl I know / Jamaica say you will / Open up the window, Noah / Winter wind / Heal it / Weary pilgrim / It turns inside out / Champion / Born of the wind / Peaceful dreams
SHCD 3736 / Mar '92 / Sugar Hill

☐ BLUEGRASS - THE WORLD'S GREATEST SHOW (Various Artists)
When somebody wants to leave: *Seldom Scene* / House of the rising sun: *Seldom Scene* / Hickory wind: *Seldom Scene* / Wild Kentucky road: *Seldom Scene* / Alabama jubilee: *Seldom Scene* / Old train: *Seldom Scene* / Through the bottom of the glass: *Seldom Scene* / Out among the stars: *Seldom Scene* / Two little boys: *Country Gentlemen* / Today has been a lonesome day: *Country Gentlemen* / Bringing Mary home: *Country Gentlemen* / I'll stay around: *Original New South* / I'm not broke, but I'm badly bent: *Original New South* / Fireball: *Original New South* / Why don't you tell me so: *Original New South* / Freeborn man: *Original New South* / Train 45: *Original New South* / Fox on the run: *Country Gentlemen* / Waiting for the boys to come home: *Country Gentlemen* / Ages and ages ago: *Country Gentlemen* / Saturday night at the Opry: *Country Gentlemen* / Feel like my time ain't long: *Country Gentlemen*
SHCD 2201 / Mar '89 / Sugar Hill

☐ CHANGE OF SCENERY, A
Breaking new ground / Casting a shadow in the road / Settin' me up / Alabama clay / I'll be a stranger there / West Texas wind / Satan's choir / In despair / What goes on / One way rider
SHCD 3763 / Sep '88 / Sugar Hill

☐ DREAM SCENE
Dry run creek / Going up on the mountain / Willie Roy / Tulsa chili bop / When I get my rewards / They're at rest together / Boatman / Love of the mountains / Little sparrow (fair and tender ladies) / Shape I'm in / Blue diamond / Bad moon rising
SHCD 3858 / Mar '98 / Sugar Hill

☐ LIKE WE USED TO BE
SHCD 3822 / Mar '94 / Sugar Hill

☐ SCENE 20 (20th Anniversary Concert/ 2CD Set)
Intro (Haven't I got the right to love you) / Gardens and memories / House of gold / Picture's of life's other side / Satan's jewelled crown / Will you ready to go home / Were you there / Weary pilgrim / Leavin' harlan / Take him in / Stompin' at the Savoy / Something in the wind / Muddy water / Open up the window / Breakin' new ground / Old train / Wait a minute / Blue ridge cabin home / Gypsy moon / In the pines / And on bass / Another lonesome day / Have mercy on my soul / House of the rising sun/Walk don't run / In the midnight hour
SHCD 2501 / Mar '98 / Sugar Hill

☐ SCENIC ROOTS
If you ever change your mind / Lost in your memory / Wrath of God / Before I met you / Red Georgia Clay / I've cried my last tear / Not in my arms / Highway of heartache / Long black veil / Last call to glory / Distant train / How mountain girls can love
SHCD 3785 / Jul '90 / Sugar Hill

Selected Works

☐ FUSED
DBYCD 1 / 23 Feb '98 / Downboy

Selecter

☐ GREATEST HITS
Three minute hero / Too much pressure / Celebrate the bullet / Bomb scare / Deep water / Time hard / They make me mad / Bristol and Miami / Missing words / James Bond / On my radio / Whisper / Carry go bring home / Murder / Washed up and left for dead / Last tango in dub
CDGOLD 1034 / May '96 / EMI Gold

☐ GREATEST HITS LIVE
Too much pressure / On my radio / Missing words / Murder / Three minute hero / Everyday (time hard) / Other side of love / Whisper / Street feeling / Selecter / Washed up and left for dead / Out on the streets again / Train to skaville / Trout / Whip them down / Ladders / Neurotica / California screaming / Orange street / My sweet collie
EMPRCD 663 / Oct '96 / Emporio

☐ HAIRSPRAY
TX 51214CD / Oct '95 / Triple X

☐ HAPPY ALBUM, THE
Reselecterization / Whip then down / Sweet and dandy / Neurotica / California / Screaming / I want justice / Trout / Mother knows best / Ladders
DIAB 841 / 24 Nov '97 / Diablo

☐ I WANT JUSTICE LIVE
RRCD 252 / 2 Feb '98 / Receiver

☐ LIVE AT ROSKILDE
Three minute hero / California screaming / I want justice / Missing words / Neurotica / Selecter / Train to skaville / Hairspray / Carry go bring / Murder / Madness / Orange street / My sweet collie
CDBM 114 / Nov '96 / Blue Moon

☐ LIVE INJECTION
Live injection / Whip them down / Three minute hero / California screaming / Everyday / I want justice / Missing words / Neurotica / Selector / James Bond / Train to Skaville / On my radio / Too much pressure / Murder / Orange street / My sweet collie / Madness
CDBM 108 / Jun '96 / Blue Moon

☐ LIVE INJECTION
SUMCD 4156 / Jan '98 / Summit

☐ PRIME CUTS VOL.1
Something's burning / Coming up / Dial my number / Woke up laughing / Touissants children / Whisper of the rain / Nameless / Use me up / I really didn't have the time / Clear water / No regrets / On my radio
CDBM 103 / Nov '94 / Blue Moon

☐ PRIME CUTS VOL.2
On my radio / Three minute hero / Whisper / Shoorah, shoorah / Celebrate the bullet / Missing words / Out on the streets / Tell me what the others do / Street feeling / Selecter / Best of both worlds / Too much pressure
CDBM 106 / Jun '96 / Blue Moon

☐ PUCKER
DOJOCD 218 / Sep '95 / Dojo

☐ RARE SELECTER VOL.1
Madness / Three minute hero (live) / Train to skaville (live) / On my radio '91 / James bond (live) / Madness / Selecter / To much pressure (live) / On my radio '91 / Orange street (live) / Sweet dreams (live) / Madness
DOJOCD 199 / Nov '94 / Dojo

☐ RARE SELECTER VOL.2
Deep water / Deep water / Washed up and left for dead (live) / Out on the streets (live) / Madness (live) / Rough rider (live) / Missing words (live) / Deep water / Touissants children / Tell me what the others do / Coming up
DOJOCD 201 / Mar '95 / Dojo

☐ RARE SELECTER VOL.3 (Versions)
DOJOCD 205 / May '95 / Dojo

☐ SELECTERIZED (The Best Of The Selecter 1991-1996)
On my radio / Whip them down / Hairspray / Three minute hero / Sugar town / Die happy / California screaming / Selecter / Madness / Ladders / Missing words / My perfect world / Too much pressure 96 / Whisper / Celebrate the bullet / On my radio 91
DOJOCD 270 / Oct '96 / Dojo

☐ TOO MUCH PRESSURE (2CD Set)
Madness / On my radio 1991 / Selecter / Deep water / Missing words / Three minute hero / Too much pressure / I can see clearly now / Best of both worlds / Shoorah shoorah / Coming up / Something's burning / Touissants children / Tell me what the others do / On my radio / Madness: *Selecter & Prince Buster* / Rough rider: *Selecter & Prince Buster* / James Bond / Train to Skaville / Orange street / Sweet dreams / Celebrate the bullet / Washed up and left for dead / Out on the streets / Carry go bring come / Murder / My collie not a dog / I want justice / Copasetic / Reggae beat
SMDCD 138 / May '97 / Snapper

☐ VERY BEST OF SELECTER, THE
TX 51238CD / 3 Nov '97 / Triple XXX

Self, Ronnie

☐ BOP A LENA
Bop a Lena / I ain't going nowhere / You're so right for me / Ain't I'm a dog / Too many lovers (unissued) / Date bait / Big blon' baby / Petrified / Flame of love / Big fool / Black night blues / Pretty bad blues / Three hearts later / Rocky Road blues / Do it now / Bless my broken heart / This must be the place / Big town / Some other world / Instant man / Oh me, oh my / Whistling words / Past, present and future / So high / I've been there / Moon burn (unissued) / Some things you can't change / Houdini / Go go cannibal (unissued) / Ugly stick (unissued)
BCD 15436 / Jul '90 / Bear Family

Self Transforming Machine Elves

☐ BITONE
NZCD 025 / Apr '95 / Nova Zembla

Selfhaters

☐ ABYSMAL RICHNESS OF THE INFINITE PROXIMITY OF THE SAME, THE
TZA 7123 / 1 Jun '98 / Tzadik

Sellers Engineering Band

☐ BRASS BAND CONCERT
Oklahoma / Love on the rocks / Black and white rag / Under the double eagle / Somewhere over the rainbow / Dem bones / Someone to watch over me / Hora stacato / Love changes everything / Raymonde overture / Teddy bears' picnic / Nightingale sang in Berkeley Square / Send in the clowns
305072 / Jun '97 / Hallmark

☐ LAND OF HOPE AND GLORY
DOYCD 065 / 28 Mar '98 / Doyen

☐ WE LOVE A PARADE
Entry of the Gladiators / Seventy six Trombones / Royal trophy / Dam busters march / Toeador's march / Arromanches / Marche militaire / Parade of the tin soldiers / Marche slave / Punchinello / I love a parade / Gladiator's farewell / Musical joke / Shield of Liberty / Radetzky march / Rhapsody on Scottish marches / Coronation march
CHAN 4527 / Aug '93 / Chandos

Selvaggio, Pete

☐ GALLERIA
378302 / Nov '96 / Koch Jazz

Sema 4

☐ IN MEMORY OF...
DRCD 015 / Feb '97 / Detour

Semara Ratih Gamelan

☐ GONG SEMARA DANA
Jagra parwata / Kindama / Catur angurit / Gora angurit / Gora merdawa / Lengker
VICG 54552 / Oct '96 / JVC

Semper, George
☐ MAKIN' WAVES
HUBCD 14 / Jan '97 / Hubbub

Sempiternal Death Reign
☐ SPOOKY GLOOM, THE
FDN 8099CD / Jan '92 / Plastic Head

Senders
☐ JUMPIN' UPTOWN
BLUELOONCD 031 / Dec '96 / Blue Loon

Sene, Yande Coude
☐ NIGHT SKY IN SINE SALOUM
SH 64085 / May '97 / Shanachie

Senensky, Bernie
☐ RHAPSODY
I hear a rhapsody / Come rain or come shine / Goodbye, Mr Evans / Winnibop / Together / Winnie's revenge / Yesterday's thoughts / Someday my prince will come
CDSJP 434 / Sep '96 / Timeless Jazz

Senfluk, Jerry
☐ SWING EXPRESS
Air conditioning breakdown / Si tu vois ma mere / I'll never say never again / Just a gigolo / Sweet Lorraine / Nuages / I love Paris / Mountains of Mourne / Mon homme / Minor swing / Pas de chat / Raindrops
CDRPM 0039 / 13 Jul '98 / RP Media

Senghor, Sonar
☐ LOST AFRICA (Senghor, Sonar Troupe)
TCD 1044 / Mar '97 / Tradition

Sensa Yuma
☐ EVERY DAY'S YOUR LAST DAY
RRCD 013 / 13 Apr '98 / Retch

Sensation
☐ BORN TO LOVE YOU
WRCD 36 / Nov '92 / Techniques

Sensational
☐ LOADED WITH POWER
WSCD 022 / 27 Oct '97 / Word Sound Recordings

Sensefield
☐ BUILDING
REG 8CD / Jun '96 / Regal
☐ BUILDING
REV 046CD / Jan '97 / Revelation
☐ KILLED FOR LESS
REG 9CD / Aug '96 / Regal
☐ SENSEFIELD
REV 033CD / Oct '94 / Revelation

Senseless Things
☐ EMPIRE OF THE SENSELESS
Homophobic asshole / Keepsake / Tempting Kate / Hold it down / Counting friends / Just one reason / Cruel moon / Primary instinct / Rise (Song for Dean and Gene) / Ice skating at the Milky Way / Say what you will / Runaways
4735252 / Mar '93 / Epic

Senser
☐ ASYLUM
Book of flies / Charming demons / Adrenaline / Strange asylum / Burn out / Desensitised / Lizard / Oyster / Weatherman
TOPPCD 064
TOPPCDX 064 / 20 Apr '98 / Ultimate
☐ STACKED UP
State of mind / Key / Switch / Age of panic / What's going on / One touch one bounce / Stubborn / Door game / Peanut head / Peace / Eject / No comply / Worth
TOPPCD 008 / Mar '94 / Ultimate

Sensorama
☐ WELCOME
LADOCD 2022 / Oct '95 / Ladomat

Sensurreal
☐ NEVER TO TELL A SOUL
BMU 005CD / Feb '95 / Beam Me Up
☐ OCCASIONAL SERIES
BMU 013CD / Jun '96 / Beam Me Up

Sentenced
☐ AMOK
CM 77076CD / Apr '95 / Century Media

☐ DOWN
CM 77146CD / Nov '96 / Century Media
☐ FROZEN
CM 77246CD / 3 Aug '98 / Century Media
☐ GREATEST KILLS
CM 77199CD / 10 Nov '97 / Century Media
☐ LOVE AND DEATH
CM 77101CD / Oct '95 / Century Media
☐ SHADOWS OF THE PAST
CM 7716CD / Jan '96 / Century Media

Senter, Boyd
☐ BOYD SENTER 1928-1930
'Tain't clean / Eniale blues / Just so-so / I wish I could shimmy / Mobile blues / Prickly heat / No more / Original Stackos'Lee blues / Original chinese blues / Somebody's wrong / Wabash blues / Goin' back to Tennessee / Rich man, poor man, beggar man, thief / I'm in the jailhouse now / Doin' you good / Shine / Sweetheart blues / Beale street blues / Copenhagen (Stomp) / No one / Waterloo / Give it to me right away / Smiles
CBC 1032 / Aug '98 / Timeless Jazz

Sentorian
☐ GENTLE PUSH TO PARADISE
JR 001CD / 10 Nov '97 / Displeased

Sentridoh
☐ COLLECTION OF PREVIOUSLY RELEASED SONGS, A (Barlow, Lou & His Sentridoh)
EFA 049402 / May '94 / City Slang
☐ ORIGINAL LOSING LOSERS
SHR 67CD / Dec '96 / Shrimper

Separation
☐ SEPARATION
DFR 19 / 15 Sep '97 / Desperate Flight

September 67
☐ LUCKY SHOE
Busy building / Setting the old house on fire / Fire engine red / Lucky shoe / What's wrong with Alice / Giant / Mercy is the red bird / Don't break / Hazel Motes / Poor boy / Cassandra on the dance floor / Little lantern face / Bring back the weight
CDVX 2828 / Mar '97 / Virgin

Septeto Habanero
☐ ORGULLO DE LOS SONEROS
262572 / 1 Jun '98 / Lusafrika

Septeto Hananero
☐ 75 YEARS LATER
CORA 126 / Nov '95 / Corason

Septeto Santiaguero
☐ SEPTETO SANTIAGUERO
Santiaguero soy / La bomba lacrimosa / Sazonando / Ya que estoy en mi Cubita / Alma de Coral / Esa Nina 'Que Cintura / Yo lo Aseguro / No pare los pies / Mientes / Silverio, facundo y la luna / Suena guajira / La hija de Pepe / Te Pico la Abeja / El Guao
INT 32082 / 17 Nov '97 / Intuition

Septic Death
☐ SOMEWHERE IN TIME
LF 283CD / 27 Oct '97 / Lost & Found

Septic Flesh
☐ FALLEN TEMPLE
HOLY 033CD / 13 Apr '98 / Holy
☐ MYSTIC PLACES OF DAWN
HOLY 005CD / May '94 / Holy
☐ OPHIDIAN WHEEL
HOLY 023CD / Mar '97 / Holy
☐ SEPTIC FLESH
HOLY 012CD / Jun '95 / Holy

Sepultura
☐ ARISE
RR 87632 / 24 Nov '97 / Roadrunner
☐ BENEATH THE REMAINS
Sarcastic existence / Slaves of pain / Lobotomy / Hungry / Primitive future / Beneath the remains / Inner self / Stronger than hate / Mass hypnosis
RR 87662 / 24 Nov '97 / Roadrunner
☐ BESTIAL DEVASTATION
SBD 001 / Mar '97 / Bestial Productions

☐ BLOOD ROOTED
Procreation (of the wicked) / Inhuman nature / Policia / War / Crucificados pelo sistema / Symptom of the universe / Mine / Lookaway / Dusted / Roots bloody roots / Drug me / Refuse resist / Slave new world / Propaganda / Beneath the remains/Escape to the void / Kaiowas / Clenched fist / Biotech is Godzilla
RR 88212 / Aug '97 / Roadrunner
☐ CHAOS AD
Refuse/Resist / Territory / Slave new world / Amen / Kaiowas / Propaganda / Biotech is Godzilla / Nomad / We are not as others / Manifest / Hunt / Clenched fist / Policia / Inhuman nature
RR 90002 / Dec '96 / Roadrunner
☐ CHAOS AD (US Edition)
RR 88592 / Oct '96 / Roadrunner
☐ MORBID VISIONS
Morbid visions / Mayhem / Troops of doom / War / Crucifixion / Show me the wrath / Funeral rites / Empire of the damned / Curse / Bestial devastation / Anti Christ / Necromancer / Warriors of death
RR 87652 / 24 Nov '97 / Roadrunner
☐ ROOTS
RR 89002 / Nov '96 / Roadrunner
☐ ROOTS OF SEPULTURA (2CD Set)
RR 89008 / Nov '96 / Roadrunner
☐ SCHIZOPHRENIA
Intro / From the past comes the storms / To the wall / Escape from the void / Inquisition / Screams behind the shadows / Septic schizo / Abyss / RIP / Troops of doom
RR 87642 / 24 Nov '97 / Roadrunner
☐ SEPULTURAL FEAST (A Tribute To Sepultura) (Various Artists)
Curse/Antichrist: Sacramentum / Necromancer: Deathwish / Warriors of death: Mystifier / Morbid visions: Swordmaster / Troops of doom: Dimension Zero / Crucifixion: Lord Belial / Beneath the remains: Defleshed / Inner self: Impious / Mass hypnosis: Children Of Bodom / Arise: Crown / Territory: Exhumation / Roots: Ton Of Bricks / Cut throat: Gardenian / Ratamahatta: Denial
BS 015CD / 15 Jun '98 / Black Sun

Sequence
☐ SISTERS OF RAP, THE (The Best Of The Sequence)
Monster jam with Spoonie Gee / Funk you up / And you know that / Simon says / We don't rap the rap / Funky sound (tear the roof off) / I don't need your love / Love changes / Unaddressed letter / Sequence party / Fi-ya up that funk / Funk that you mothers
DEEPM 002 / Nov '96 / Deep Beats

Sequential One
☐ ENERGY
085703752 / 29 Jun '98 / House Nation

Serban, Andrei
☐ ROMANIAN FOLK MUSIC (Serban, Andrei & His Orchestra)
SYN CD 150 / Apr '93 / Syncoop

Sereba, Kouame Gerard
☐ KILIMANDJARO
KGS 004CD / Dec '94 / Musikk Distribujson

Serenata Mexicana
☐ CANCIONES DE MEXICO
MRM 004 / Feb '94 / Modern Blues

Serenity
☐ BREATHING DEMONS
HOLY 020CD / Jan '97 / Holy
☐ THEN CAME SILENCE
HOLY 010CD / Feb '95 / Holy

Serenity
☐ 31 (Organic Technolo) (Serenity Dub)
INCCD 3306 / Mar '96 / Incoming
☐ 41 (Digital Roots)
INCCD 3307 / Mar '96 / Incoming

Sergeant Fury
☐ TURN THE PAGE
SPV 08412082 / Apr '95 / SPV

Sergeant, Will
☐ THEMES FROM GRIND
Theme / Favourite branches / Aquarius dub
HAPSCD 001 / 26 Jan '98 / 92 Happy Customers/Ochre

Sermon, Erick
☐ DOUBLE OR NOTHING
Intro / Bomdigi / Freak out / In the heat / Tell 'em / In the studio / Boy meets world / Welcome / Live in the backyard / Set it off / Focus / Move on / Smooth thought / Do your thing / Man above / Message / Open fire
5292862 / Nov '95 / RAL

☐ NO PRESSURE
Payback II / Stay real / Imma gitz mine / Hostile / Do it up / Safe sex / Hittin' switches / Erick Sermon / Hype / Li'l grazy / Ill shit / Swing it over here / All in the mind / Female species
52335132 / Jan '96 / Def Jam

Serpent
☐ IN THE GARDEN OF THE SERPENT
RAD 006CD / Apr '96 / Radiation

Serpent Power
☐ SERPENT POWER
VMD 79252 / Oct '96 / Vanguard

Serpico
☐ RUMBLE
EVRCD 030 / Mar '97 / Equal Vision

Serrapere, Jo
☐ MY BLUE HEAVEN
OMC 0009 / 20 Apr '98 / One Man Clapping

Serrie, John
☐ ENCHANTRESS
Dyt it / Seamless / Enchantress / As was / Precious / Free hand / Heartfelt / Dance one / Shortly / Image
CD 83392 / Nov '96 / Telarc Jazz

Serti, Doug
☐ JOY SPRING
Blues walk / Tears inside / Star eyes / Indiana / I cried for you / Joy spring / Eternal triangle
STCD 565 / May '93 / Stash

Servat, Giles
☐ A-RAOK MONT KUIT
KM 45 / Sep '94 / Keltia Musique

Servotron
☐ ENTERTAINMENT PROGRAM FOR HUMANS
LOUDEST 28 / 27 Apr '98 / One Louder
☐ NO ROOM FOR HUMANS
LOUDEST 19 / Jun '97 / One Louder
☐ SPARE PARTS
LOUDEST 22 / Jun '97 / One Louder

Seth, Pandit Raghunath
☐ RAGAS
Alaap and jor / Gat composition / Gat composition / Alaap / Gat composition / Gat composition / Alaap / Gat composition 95) / Gat composition / Dhun in Bhajan style
NRCD 0083 / Feb '98 / Navras

SETI
☐ GEOMETRY OF NIGHT
INCCD 3310 / Jul '96 / Incoming
☐ KNOWLEDGE
ASH 21CD / Jan '95 / Ash International
☐ PHAROS (2CD Set)
IAE 001 / Apr '95 / Instinct Ambient Europe

Setona
☐ AFRICAN CROSSROADS
39840942 / 21 Aug '97 / Blue Flame

Setters
☐ SETTERS, THE
WM 1020 / Jul '94 / Watermelon

Setzer, Brian
☐ ALL SHOOK UP
COLCD 0705 / 24 Nov '97 / Collectables
☐ BRIAN SETZER ORCHESTRA, THE (Setzer, Brian Orchestra)
Lady luck / Ball and chain / Sittin' on it all the time / Good rockin' Daddy / September skies / Brand new cadillac / There's a rainbow 'round my shoulder / Route 66 / Your true love / Nightingale sang in Berkeley Square / Straight up / Drink that bottle down
74321195772 / Apr '94 / Arista
☐ HIGH SCHOOL CONFIDENTIAL
COLCD 0702 / 24 Nov '97 / Collectables
☐ RIP IT UP
COLCD 0704 / 24 Nov '97 / Collectables
☐ ROCK THIS TOWN
COLCD 0701 / 24 Nov '97 / Collectables
☐ ROCKABILLY BOOGIE
COLCD 0707 / 24 Nov '97 / Collectables

☐ SHAKE, RATTLE AND ROLL
COLCD 0706 / 24 Nov '97 / Collectables

☐ STRAY CAT STRUT
COLCD 0703 / 24 Nov '97 / Collectables

Sevag, Oystein

☐ GLOBAL HOUSE
01934111482 / Sep '95 / Windham Hill

Seven Day Diary

☐ SKIN AND BLISTER
World becomes you / Air / Starfish / He can / Walkaway / Bleeding / Violence / Stay / Sleep / Today and everyday / Back to nature / Giant
9362458702 / May '95 / Warner Bros.

Seven Dials Band

☐ MUSIC OF DICKENS AND HIS TIME, THE
College hornpipe / Some folks who have grown old / Ratcatcher's daughter / Home, sweet home / Begone dull care / Ivy green / Young jolly waterman / Soldier's tear / Old towler / Fine old English gentleman / David Copperfield polkas / All's well / Country life / Shiverand Shakery (The man who couldn't get warm) / Mr. Wardle's carol / Christmas carol quadrilles / Believe me if all those endearing young charms / Workhouse boy / Child's hymn / Sir Roger de Coverley
BEJOCD 9 / Feb '97 / Beautiful Jo

Seven Grand Housing Authority

☐ NO WEAPONS FORMED AGAINST WE SHALL PROSPER
EFA 063402 / Aug '97 / Ausfahrt

Seven Mary Three

☐ ROCKCROWN
Lucky / Rockcrown / Needle can't burn / Honey of generation / Home stretch / People like new / Make up your mind / Gone away / Times like these / I could be wrong / Angry blue / Houdini's angels / This evening's great excuse / Player piano / Oven
7567830182 / Jun '97 / Warner Bros.

Seven Seconds

☐ MUSIC, THE MESSAGE, THE
Ghost / Such and such / Music / Message / Kinda future / My gravity / See you tomorrow / Get a different life / Talkbox / My list / First ya told us / Born without a mind / Punk rock teeth / Girl song / I can remember / Even better plan / Kids are united
481452 / Dec '95 / Epic

☐ OURSELVES
722762 / Feb '95 / Restless

☐ SOUL FORCE REVOLUTION
723442 / Feb '95 / Restless

Seven Sioux

☐ ANOTHER
XM 029CD / Apr '92 / X-Mist

Seven Storey Mountain

☐ LEPER ETHICS
AMC 16CD / 6 Apr '98 / Art Monk Construction

Sevenchurch

☐ BLEAK INSIGHT
Perceptions / Low / Surreal wheel / Crawl line / Sanctum / Autobituary
N 02222 / Sep '93 / Noise

Sevens

☐ SEVENS
AK 2CD / Apr '97 / Akashic

Seventh Avenue Stompers

☐ FIDGETY FEET
Fidgety feet / Basin Street blues / Muskrat ramble / How come you do me like you do / Struttin' with some barbecue / St. Louis blues / Yellow dog blues / Sunday / Ferry boat romp / Blues like they used to be
SV 0252 / Oct '97 / Savoy Jazz

Severed Heads

☐ CUISINE (WITH PISCATORIAL)
Pilot in hell / Seven of oceans / Finder / Estrogen / King of the sea / Host of quadrille / Life in the whale / Twister / Ugly twenties / Piggy smack / Golden height / I'm your antidote / Tingler (they shine within) / Goodbye / Her teeth the ally / Skippy roo kangaroo / Ottoman / Quest for oom pa pa / Wonder of all the world
NETCD 028 / Mar '92 / Nettwerk

Severin

☐ ACID TO ASHES
DIS 72VCD / Sep '92 / Dischord

Severinsen, Doc

☐ UNFORGETTABLY DOC
What is this thing called love / Love / Unforgettable / Lush Life / Georgia On My Mind / Speak Low / Music Of The Night / Bad and the beautiful / Someone to watch over me / Misty / Wind beneath my wings / Memory
CD 80304 / Sep '92 / Telarc

Seward, Alec

☐ LATE ONE SATURDAY EVENING
What has Annie got / Risin' sun shine on / Her ways are so sweet / CC rider / Goin' down slow / Rock me Darlin' / Late one Saturday evening / Blues all round my head / Feel so good / Blues all around my bed / Trouble in mind / Creepin' blues / Cousin John / I wish I'd listened
TBA 13007 / Aug '96 / Blues Alliance

Sex Gang Children

☐ ARCO VALLEY (Andi Sex Gang)
FREUDCD 24 / Jul '89 / Jungle

☐ BLIND
CLEO 51222 / Jun '94 / Cleopatra

☐ ECSTASY AND VENDETTA OVER NEW YORK
CLEO 3833 / Aug '94 / Cleopatra

☐ PLAY WITH CHILDREN
CLEO 6957 / May '94 / Cleopatra

☐ SHOUT AND SCREAM (2CD Set)
AOP 50 / Feb '97 / Dressed To Kill

☐ WELCOME TO MY WORLD
RRCD 253 / 2 Mar '98 / Receiver

Sex Pistols

☐ ALIVE
God save the Queen / Pretty vacant / Problems / EMI / Liar / New York / Anarchy in the UK / No feelings / Submission / I wanna be me / Seventeen / Satellite / Anarchy in the UK (live) / Did you no wrong (live) / I'm a lazy sod (live) / New York (live) / Stepping stone (live) / Liar (Live) / Pretty vacant (live) / Suburban kids (live) / Submission (live) / Substitute (live) / No feeling (live) / Problems (live) / Don't give me no lip, child (live) / No fun (live)
ESDCD 321 / Oct '95 / Essential

☐ BETTER LIVE THAN DEAD
DOJOCD 73 / Feb '94 / Dojo

☐ EARLY DAZE (The Studio Collection)
I wanna be me / No feelings / Anarchy in the UK / Satellite / Seventeen / Submission / Pretty vacant / God save the queen / Liar / EMI / New York / Problems
DOJOCD 119 / May '93 / Dojo

☐ FLOGGING A DEAD HORSE
Anarchy in the UK / I wanna be me / God save the Queen / Did you no wrong / Pretty vacant / Holidays in the sun / No fun / My way / Something else / Silly thing / C'mon everybody / Stepping stone / Great rock 'n' roll swindle / No one is innocent
CDV 2142 / Oct '86 / Virgin

☐ GREAT ROCK 'N' ROLL SWINDLE, THE (Highlights)
God save the Queen (Symphony) / Great rock 'n' roll swindle / You need hands: *McLaren, Malcolm* / Silly thing / Lonely boy / Something else / (We're gonna) Rock around the clock / C'mon everybody / Who killed Bambi / No one is innocent: *Biggs, Ronnie* / L'anarchie pour le UK / My way
CDVDX 2510 / Jan '92 / Virgin

☐ INTERVIEW DISC
SEX 1CD / May '96 / Total

☐ KISS THIS
Anarchy in the UK / God save the Queen / Pretty vacant / Holidays in the sun / I wanna be me / Did you no wrong / Satellite / Don't give me no lip child / Stepping stone / Bodies / No feelings / Liar / Problems / Seventeen / Submission / EMI / My way / Silly thing
CDV 2702 / Oct '92 / Virgin

☐ KISS THIS (Limited Edition With Live In Trondheim CD)
Anarchy in the UK / God save the Queen / Pretty vacant / Holidays in the sun / I wanna be me / Did you no wrong / Satellite / Don't give me no lip child / Stepping stone / Bodies / No feelings / Liar / Problems / Seventeen / Submission / EMI / My way / Silly thing / Anarchy in the UK (live) / I wanna be me (live) / Seventeen (live) / New York / EMI (live) / No fun / Problems (live) / God save the Queen (live)
CDVX 2702 / Oct '92 / Virgin

☐ LIVE AND LOUD
Seventeen / New York / EMI / Belsen was a gas / Bodies / Holidays in the sun / No feelings / Problems / Pretty vacant / Anarchy in the UK / I wanna be me / God save the queen / No fun
DOJOCD 71 / Nov '92 / Dojo

☐ LIVE AT CHELMSFORD PRISON
Lazy sod / New York / No lip / Stepping stone / Suburban kids / Submission / Liar / Anarchy in the UK / Did you no wrong / Substitute / No fun / Pretty vacant / Problems / I wanna be me
DOJOCD 66 / Mar '93 / Dojo

☐ LIVE AT WINTERLAND
God save the queen / I wanna be me / Seventeen / New York / EMI / Belsen was a gas / Bodies / Holidays in the sun / Liar / No feelings / Problems / Pretty vacant / Anarchy in the UK / No fun
WENCD 008 / Nov '96 / When

☐ MINI ALBUM, THE
DOJOCD 265 / Jun '96 / Dojo

☐ NEVER MIND THE BOLLOCKS, HERE'S THE SEX PISTOLS
Holidays in the sun / Bodies / No feelings / Liar / God save the Queen / Problems / Seventeen / Anarchy in the UK / Submission / Pretty vacant / New York / EMI
CDVX 2086 / Oct '86 / Virgin

☐ NEVER MIND THE BOLLOCKS/SPUNK
Holidays in the sun / Bodies / No feelings / Liar / God save the queen / Problems / Seventeen / Anarchy in the UK / Submission / Pretty vacant / New York / EMI / Feelings / Just me / Nookie / No future / Lots of fun / Who was it / New York (Looking for a kiss) / EMI / Satellite
SPUNK 1 / Jun '96 / Virgin

☐ NEVERMIND THE FILTHY LUCRE (Interviews & Excerpts From Winterland 1978)
SUCK 1 / 9 Mar '98 / Suck My Filthy

☐ NO FUTURE UK
Pretty vacant / Seventeen / Satellite / No feelings / I wanna be me / Submission / Anarchy in the u.k. / Anarchy in the u.k. / No fun / God save the queen / Problems / Pretty vacant / Liar / E.m.i. / New york
RRCD 117 / Jul '93 / Receiver

☐ PIRATES OF DESTINY
Lydon speaks / No feelings / Lazy sod / GLC councillor comments on punk / Problems / Medley / Australian TV ad / Pretty vacant / I wanna be me / McLaren talks / Schools are prisons / McLaren gabs / Lydon chats / Woodstock baby / Substitute / No lip / Stepping stone / Johnny B. Goode / Roadrunner / Watcha gonna do about it / Through my eyes / Lazy sod
DOJOCD 222 / Jan '96 / Dojo
ESMCD 609 / 26 Jan '98 / Essential

☐ RAW
Pretty vacant / Submission / EMI / Anarchy in the UK / Don't give me no lip child / Liar / Seventeen / Dolls / No feelings / No fun / Problems / I wanna be me / Substitute
EMPRCD 716 / Jun '97 / Emporio

☐ SEX PISTOLS (Fully Illustrated Book & Interview Disc)
SAM 7033 / Jun '97 / Sound & Media

☐ SEX PISTOLS ARCHIVE
Pretty vacant / Submission / Anarchy in the UK / Don't give me no lip child / Liar / God save the Queen / Seventeen (I'm a lazy sod) / Dolls (New York) / No feelings / Problems / I wanna be me / Substitute / No fun / Satellite / EMI / New York (looking for a kiss) / Pretty vacant / Anarchy in the UK
RMCD 218 / Nov '97 / Rialto

☐ WANTED (The Goodman Tapes)
Malcolm McLaren interview / Suburban kid / Here we go again / No lip / No fun / Pretty vacant / Revolution in the classroom / God save the Queen / Bill Grundy interview / Unlimited supply / Anarchy in the UK / Submission
DOJOCD 216 / Jun '95 / Dojo
ESMCD 608 / 26 Jan '98 / Essential

Sexepil

☐ SUGAR FOR THE SOUL
Point black / I come / Jerusalem / Buffalo thunder / Snowbird / Bittersweet / 2000 / I love you like no other / India song / Take us home again / Jaws of the underground / Those days are gone
0630107692 / Feb '96 / East West

Sexpod

☐ HOME
PILLMCD 6 / Jan '95 / Placebo

S'Express

☐ ULTIMATE
Theme from S'Express / Superfly guy / Hey music lover / L'age de gateau / Can you feel me / Blow me another lollypop / Come II (am/ok) / Pimps pushers and prostitutes / Nothing to lose / Find 'em fool 'em forget 'em / Mantra for a state of mind / Supersonic lover / Brazil
74321603402 / 27 Jul '98 / Camden

Sexsmith, Ron

☐ OTHER SONGS
Thinking out loud / Strawberry blonde / Average Joe / Thinly veiled disguise / Nothing good / Pretty little cemetry / It never fails / Clown in broad daylight / At different times / Child star / Honest mistake / So young / While you're waiting / April after all
IND 90123 / Jul '97 / Interscope

☐ RON SEXSMITH
Secret heart / There's a rhythm / Words we never use / Summer blowin' town / Lebanon, Tennesse / Speaking with the angel / In place of you / Heart with no companion / Several miles / From a few streets over / First chance I get / Wastin' time / Galbraith street
IND 92485 / May '96 / Interscope

Sexteto Habanero

☐ SEXTETO HABANERO 1926-1931
HQCD 53 / Aug '95 / Harlequin

☐ SEXTETO HABANERO 1926-1948
HQCD 82 / Nov '96 / Harlequin

Sexteto Occidente

☐ YO NO TUMBO CANA
TCD 087 / 24 Apr '98 / Tumbao

Sexton, Ann

☐ YOU'RE GONNA MISS ME
I had a fight with love (and I lost) / I'm his wife, you're just a friend / You got to use what you got / Color my world blue / I want to be loved / You've been doing me wrong for so long / Who's gonna love you / You can't win / Love love love / You're letting me down / You've been gone too long / Come back home / Keep on holding on / Loving you, loving me / You're gonna miss me / If I work my thing on you / You're losing me / Sugar Daddy / Be serious / Have a little mercy
CPCD 8012 / Feb '94 / Charly

Sexton Ming

☐ ROGUE MALE (Scxton Ming & Steady)
SWEE 007CD / Aug '97 / Sweet

Sexy Death Soda

☐ CALIFORNIAN STATE POLICE
BL 34 / 15 Jun '98 / Bongload

Seydina

☐ LIBAAS
AL 005 / 21 Aug '97 / Night & Day

Seymour, Daren

☐ AUROBINDO: INVOLUTION (Seymour, Daren & Mark Van Hoen)
ASH 24CD / Jan '95 / Ash International

Seyoum, Betsat

☐ URBAN AZMARIS OF ETHIOPIA (Seyoum, Betsat & Abbebe Fekade)
Enegenagnalen / Ambassel / Bati / Abeba abeba / Anteye / Tizita / Aysh ayshenna / Anteye / Endenesh gedawo / Yelewem abay / Enegenegnalen
122166 / Feb '96 / Long Distance

SF Seals

☐ NOWHERE
Back again / Don't underestimate me / 8's / Janine's dream / Still / Day 12 / Winter song / Baby blue / Demons on the corner / Missing
OLE 0892 / Jun '94 / Matador

☐ TRUTH WALKS IN SLEEPY SHADOWS
SF sorrow / Ladies of the sea / Ipecec / Locked out / Bold letters / Flashback caruso / Pulp / Soul of Patrick Lee / Kid's pirate ship / How did you know / Stellar lullabye
OLE 1622 / Sep '95 / Matador

SFP

☐ THIS TIME IT'S PERSONAL
This time it's personal / All I do / Days like this / My love is the shhh / Take it or leave it / Act like you want it / Feel so good / What in the world / Somebody's always talkin' / I got love / She's always in my hair / I don't get down like that / Playin' the field / Think of you / Outro
9362467532 / 9 Mar '98 / Warner Bros.

SFT

☐ SCHWARMA
CDSTUMM 151 / Sep '96 / Mute

SFX

☐ SFX ALBUM, THE (SFX & Alan Murphy)
NAIMCD 004 / Apr '97 / Naim Audio

Shabazz, Lakim

☐ PURE RIGHTEOUSNESS
SDCD 1 / Mar '89 / Jet Star

Shabba Ranks

☐ AS RAW AS EVER
Trailor load a girls / Where does slackness come from / Woman tangle / Gun pon me / Gone up / Ambi get scarce / Housecall: *Shabba Ranks & Maxi Priest* / Flesh axe / Mi di girls dem love / Fist a ris / Jame: *Shabba Ranks & KRS 1* / Park yu benz
4681022 / Apr '95 / Epic

☐ BEST BABY FATHER/JUST REALITY
VYDCD 06 / Sep '95 / Vine Yard

☐ CAAN DUNN (The Best Of Shabba Ranks)
VPCD 1450 / Dec '95 / VP

☐ FACE
SRCD 05 / 13 Jul '98 / Shang

☐ GOLDEN TOUCH
Golden touch / Mi nuh romp with it / Love up your woman / Build bridges instead / House husband / Private property / If a my youth / Digit it / Kill mi dead / Wicked in bed (part two)
GRELCD 141 / Apr '90 / Greensleeves

☐ KING OF DANCEHALL
080892 / Sep '94 / Melodie

☐ LOVE PUNANNY BAD
080862 / Apr '93 / Jammy's

☐ MR. MAXIMUM
GRELCD 172 / Jun '92 / Greensleeves

☐ RAPPING WITH THE LADIES
Telephone love deh pon mi mind / Just be good to me / Steady man / Mr. loverman / Hardcore loving / Action packed / Twice my age / Don't test me
GRELCD 150 / Aug '90 / Greensleeves

☐ VIP
Born as a Don / VIP / Best baby father / Woman mi run down / What a nite / No to coke / Shock out and have fun / Just reality / Whe you get it from / Gal yu good / Back and bellyrat / Roots and culture / Wicked inna bed / Rammer / Crab-louse a go round / Mandela free / Are you sure / Pay down pon it
SUMCD 4084 / Nov '96 / Summit

Shack

☐ WATERPISTOL
Sgt. Major / Neighbours / Stranger / Dragonfly / Mood of the morning / Walter's song / Time machine / Mr. Appointment / Undecided / Hazy / Hey Mama / London town
MAR 16 / 23 Feb '98 / Marina

Shades

☐ SHADES
Who are you / Eventually / Serenade / What would you do / Why / Love never dies / Tell me (I'll be around) / Last to know / Every time I think of you / I believe / How deep is your love / I believe / Time will reveal
5307362 / 15 Sep '97 / Motown

Shades Apart

☐ SEEING THINGS
REV 057CD / Mar '97 / Revelation

Shades Of Kenton Jazz Orchestra

☐ ROUND MIDNIGHT
Here's that rainy day / Chiapas / Painted rhythm / Artistry in boogie / Intermission riff / Hey there / Stella by starlight / Stairway to the stars / Reuben's blues / Over the rainbow / Swinghouse / Artistry in rhythm
HEPCD 2043 / Feb '89 / Hep

Shades Of Rhythm

☐ SHADES OF RHYTHM
Exactly / Sweet sensation / Homicide / Everybody / Lonely days, lonely nights / Sound of eden / Lies / Armageddon / Exorcist / Summer of '89
9031762762 / Jan '92 / ZTT

Shadow

☐ ETERNAL ENERGY
CR 005 / 15 Jun '98 / Crossroads

☐ SHADOW MEETS NANNY GOAT (Shadow & Nanny Goat)
VPCD 1236 / Jul '92 / VP

Shadow Project

☐ FROM THE HEART
TX 60003CD / 8 Jun '98 / Triple XXX

Shadow Ring

☐ HOLD ONTO ID
SB 75CD / 27 Oct '97 / Siltbreeze

☐ WAXWORK ECHOES
HERMES 019 / Nov '96 / Corpus Hermeticum

Shadowfax

☐ ESPERANTO
CDEB 2523 / May '93 / Earthbeat

Shadowland

☐ MAD AS A HATTER
USI (United states of insanity) / Mephisto bridge / Flatline / Seventh year / Father / Burning / Zuleika / Mad as a hatter / Salvation comes
VGCD 003 / May '96 / Verglas Music

☐ RING OF ROSES
Whistleblower / Jigsaw / Scared of the dark / Painting by numbers / Hall of mirrors / Kruhulick syndrome / Ring of roses / Dorian Gray / I, Judas
VGCD 006 / Jul '97 / Verglas Music

☐ THROUGH THE LOOKING GLASS
Matter of perspective / Hunger / Dreams of the ferryman / Half moon street / When the world turns to white / Waking hour / Through the looking glass / Mind games / So the music stops
VGCD 010 / 23 Feb '98 / Verglas Music

Shadowman

☐ FORCE MULTIPLIER
VC 119CD / 8 Sep '97 / Vinyl Communication

Shadows

☐ ANOTHER STRING OF HOT HITS AND MORE
Wonderful land / Atlantis / Black is black / Goodbye yellow brick road / River deep, mountain high / Rise and fall of Flingel Bunt / Midnight cowboy / Pinball wizard / See me, feel me / Apache / God only knows / Stardust / Walk don't run / Most beautiful girl / Good vibrations / Something / Superstar / Trains and boats and planes / Honky tonk women / FBI / Kon-Tiki
CDMFP 6002 / Oct '87 / Music For Pleasure

☐ APACHES PLAY THE HITS OF THE SHADOWS, THE (Apaches)
Apache / Kon Tiki / Man of mystery / Wonderful land / Atlantis / FBI / Dance on / Red river rock / Blue shadows / Guitar tango / War Lord / Maroc 7 / Mary Anne / Riders in the sky / Theme from The Deer Hunter (Cavatina) / Slaughter on tenth avenue / Don't cry for me Argentina / Sailing
QED 041 / Nov '96 / Tring

☐ AT ABBEY ROAD
Gonzales / Wonderful land / Witch doctor / What a lovely tune / Boys / Guitar tango / All day / Atlantis / It's been a blue day / Razzmatazz / Nothing folks / John's rocker / I wish I could shimmy like my good sister Arthur / Don't stop now / Benno san / Zero X / Thunderbirds / Scotch on the socks / Tennesee waltz / Slaughter on 10th Avenue / Chitty chitty bang bang / No no Nina / Don't cry for me Argentina / God only knows
CDABBEY 104 / 13 Oct '97 / EMI

☐ AT THEIR VERY BEST
Apache / Man of mystery / Shindig / Wonderful land / Rise and fall of flingel bunt / Deer hunter / Boys / Frightened city / Theme for young lovers / Dance on / Savage / FBI / Guitar tango / Genie with the light brown lamp / Atlantis / Foot tapper / Don't cry for me Argentina / Kon-Tiki / Geronimo / Stranger
8415202 / Apr '94 / Polydor

☐ BEST OF HANK MARVIN & THE SHADOWS, THE (Marvin, Hank & The Shadows)
Another day in paradise / Every breath you take / Jessica / Rise and fall of Flingel Bunt / Atlantis / I will always love you / Foot tapper / Cavatina / Heartbeat / (Everything I do) I do it for you / Riders in the sky / Dance on / Hot rox / Sylvia / Moonlight shadow / Apache / Mrs. Robinson / Walking in the air / Lady in red / Don't cry for me Argentina / Guitar tango / Wonderful land / Kon-Tiki / FBI
5238212 / Oct '94 / Polydor

☐ BEST OF THE SHADOWS, THE
FBI / Kon-Tiki / Guitar tango / Wonderful land / Atlantis / Savage / Frightened city / Lost city / Little bitty tear / Apache / Rise and fall of flingel bunt / Don't make my baby blue / Chattanooga choo choo / In the mood / Lonely bull / Dakota / Don't it make you feel good / Zambesi / Temptation
DC 878662 / Mar '97 / Disky

☐ DANCE ON
Apache / Apache / Atlantis / Gonzales / Breeze and I / Perfidia / Ranka chank / Stingray / Geronimo / Bongo blues / Theme for young lovers / Three galleons / South of the border / Don't cry for me argentina
16090 / Oct '95 / Laserlight

☐ EP COLLECTION VOL.1, THE
Perfidia / 36-24-36 / All day / My grandfather's clock / Lady Penelope / Zero X theme / Thunderbird / Finders keepers / Mustang / Shane / Giant / Shotgun / Las tres carabelas / Adios muchachos / Valencia / Granada / Tonight / Fandango / Little princess / Gonzales / Jet black / Driftin' (live)
SEECD 246 / '88 / See For Miles

☐ EP COLLECTION VOL.2, THE
Omoide no nagisa / Londonderry air / Boys / Foot tapper / Les girls / Shazam / Sleepwalk / Bongo blues / Flyder and the spy / Chinchilla / Gin iro no michi / Kimi to itsumademo / Boys / Round and round / Friends / Guitar boogie / FBI / Ranka chank / Autumn / Walkin'
SEECD 296 / Sep '90 / See For Miles

☐ EP COLLECTION VOL.3, THE
Quartermaster's stores / It's been a blue day / I wish I could shimmy like my sister Arthur / Sweet dreams / Driftin' / Don't be a fool with love / Be bop a lula / Late night set / 1861 / Spring is nearly here / Back home / Some are lonely / Alice in Sunderland / Blue star / Jet black / Feelin' fine / Saturday dance / Perfidia / Chu chi / Find me a golden street / Bongo blues / It's a man's man's man's world
SEECD 375 / Oct '93 / See For Miles

☐ EVENING IN NIVRAM, AN (The Music Of The Shadows) (Various Artists)
MS 0004CD / 13 Oct '97 / Musick

☐ FIRST 20 YEARS AT THE TOP (75 Classic Original Recordings 1959-1979)
Feelin' fine / Don't be a fool with love / Driftin' / Jet black / Saturday dance / Lonesome fella / Apache / Quartermaster's stores / Stranger / Man of mystery / FBI / Midnight / Frightened city / Back home / Kon-Tiki / 36-24-36 / Savage / Peace pipe / Wonderful land / Stars fell on Stockton / Guitar tango / What a lovely tune / Boys / Dance on / All day / Foot tapper / Breeze and I / Atlantis / I want you to want me / Shindig / It's been a blue day / Geronimo / Shazam / Theme for young lovers / This hammer / Rise and fall of Flingel bunt / It's a man's man's man's world / Rhythm and greens / Miracle / Genie with the light brown lamp / Little princess / Mary Anne / Chu chi / Stingray / Alice in Sunderland / Don't make my baby blue / My grandfather's clock / War lord / I wish I could shimmy like my sister Arthur / Arthur / I met a girl / Late night set / Place in the sun / Will you be there / Dreams I ddream / Scotch on the socks / Maroc 7 / Bombay duck / Tomorrow's cancelled / Somewhere / Running out of world / Dear old Mrs Bell / Trying to forget the one you love / Slaughter on 10th Avenue / Turn around and touch me / Jungle jam / Let me be the one / Run Billy run / It'll be me babe / Another night / Love deluxe / Don't cry for me Argentina / Cavatina / En aranjuez con tu amor / Heart of glass / Riders in the sky
CDSHAD 2 / May '95 / EMI

☐ FROM HANK, BRIAN, BRUCE AND JOHN
Snap, crackle and how's your dad / Thing of beauty / Letter / Wild roses / Holy cow / Last train to Clarksville / Day I met Marie / Evening glow / Naughty nippon lights / San Francisco / Tokaido line / Alentjo / Let me take you there / Mister, you're a better man than I
BGOCD 20 / Apr '90 / Beat Goes On

☐ GOOD VIBRATIONS (3CD Set)
Dance on / Atlantis / Bandit / Guitar tango / Superstar / 36-24-36 / Stardust / Foottapper / Kon-tiki / God only knows / Peace pipe / Trains and boats and planes / Apache / Honky tonk woman / Bo Diddley / FBI / Theme from Deer Hunter (cavatina) / Something / Man of mystery / Geronimo / Classical gas / Midnight / Parisienne walkways / Don't make my baby blue / What a lovely tune / Don't cry for me Argentina / Frightened city / South of the border / Most beautiful girl / Baker street / Rodrigo's guitar concerto de aranjuez / Bright eyes / Walk don't run / Good vibrations / Rise and fall of Flingel Blunt / Shindig / Wonderful land / Mary Anne / Shazam / Perfidia / Breeze and I / Midnight cowboy / Goodbye yellow brick road / Rumble / Savage / Black is black / Riders in the sky / Slaughter on 10th avenue
SA 872782 / Sep '96 / Disky

☐ HITS OF THE SHADOWS (Delta Guitars)
Apache / Man of mystery / FBI / Kon Tiki / Wonderful land / Quatermasters store / Guitar tango / Dnce on / Red river rock / Foot tapper / Atlantis / Shindig / Geronimo / Theme from young lovers / Blue shadows / Rise and fall of Flingel Bunt / Parisiene walkways / Riders in the sky
CD 6079 / Jun '97 / Music

☐ HITS RIGHT UP YOUR STREET
Telstar / Chi mai / We don't talk anymore / Imagine / Woman / Hats off to Wally / One day I'll fly away / Summer love / Misty / This ole house / Winner takes all / Sailing / Thing-me-jig / More than I can say / Cowboy cafe / Third man / Nut rocker
PWKS 4106 / Jul '96 / Carlton

☐ JIGSAW
Jigsaw / Prelude in E major / Cathy's clown / Friday on my mind / Chelsea boot / With a hmm hmm on my knee / Tennessee waltz / Stardust / Semi-detached suburban Mr. James / Winchester cathedral / Maria Elena / Green eyes
BGOCD 66 / '89 / Beat Goes On

☐ MOONLIGHT SHADOWS
Moonlight shadow / Walk of life / I just called to say I love you / Every breath you take / Nights in white satin / Hello / Power of love / Three times a lady / Against all odds / Hey Jude / Dancing in the dark / I know him so well / Memory / Imagine / Sailing / Whiter shade of pale
5524162 / Sep '96 / Spectrum

☐ ORIGINAL, THE
Wonderful land / Shindig / Atlantis / FBI / Savage / Guitar tango / 36-24-36 / Midnight / Rise and fall of Flingel Bunt / Shazam / Dakota / Slaughter on tenth avenue / Rumble / Walk don't run / Geronimo / Peace pipe / Perfidia / Riders in the sky
TO 860132 / 2 Feb '98 / Disky

☐ REFLECTION
Eye of the tiger / Crockett's theme / Right here waiting / Every little thing she does is magic / Sealed with a kiss / Uptown girl / Strawberry Fields forever / Riders in the sky / Flashdance / Something's gotten hold of my heart / Love changes everything / Nothing's gonna stop us now / Bilitis / You'll never walk alone / Always on my mind
8471202 / Oct '90 / Polydor

☐ ROCKIN' WITH CURLY LEADS
Pinball wizard / See me feel me / Years away / Humbucker / Deep roots / Jungle jam / Gracie / Good vibrations / Turn around and touch me / Wide mouthed frog / Rockin' with curly leads / Gutbucket / Jumpin' Jack input
BGOCD 84 / Oct '90 / Beat Goes On

☐ SHADOW MUSIC (Stereo/Mono)
I only want to be with you: *Hollies* / Fourth Street: *Hollies* / Magic doll: *Hollies* / Stay around: *Hollies* / Maid Marion's theme: *Hollies* / Benno-San: *Hollies* / Don't stop now: *Hollies* / In the past: *Hollies* / Fly me to the moon: *Hollies* / Now that you're gone: *Hollies* / One way to love: *Hollies* / Razzmatazz: *Hollies* / Sigh (un prospero): *Hollies* / March to Drina: *Hollies*
4951512 / 29 Jun '98 / EMI

☐ SHADOWS AND FRIENDS, THE
Let me be the one / Theme from the deerhunter / Peace pipe / Mary anne / Atlantis / Breeze and I / Perfidia / 1861 / Wonderful land / Faithful / Marmaduke / Lady of the morning / Music makes my day / You never can tell / Lonesome mole / Black eyes / Silvery rain / Please mr. please
BR 1372 / May '94 / BR Music

☐ SHADOWS ARE GO
SCP 9711 / 20 Apr '98 / Scamp

☐ SHADOWS IN THE NIGHT
Lady in red / Love changes everything / Power of love / Winner takes it all / Sealed with a kiss / All I ask of you / One moment in time / Careless whisper / I just called to say I love you / I want to know what love is / I guess that's why they call it the blues / Missing / Going home / Right here waiting / Chi Mai / Dancing in the dark
8437982 / Apr '93 / PolyGram TV

☐ SHADOWS PLAY ANDREW LLOYD WEBBER AND TIM RICE, THE
Whole new world / Phantom of the opera / Memory / Tell me on a Sunday / I know him so well / Starlight Express suite / I'd be surprisingly good for you / Don't cry for me Argentina / Can you feel the love tonight / Love changes everything / Oh what a circus / Music of the night / Take that look off your face / All I ask of you / Another suitcase in another hall / One night in Bangkok
5394792 / 10 Nov '97 / PolyGram TV

☐ SHADSTRAX
Mountain's of the moon / Summer of love '59 / Outdigo / Cowboy cafe / Hats off to Wally / Cat 'n' mouse / Elevenis / Turning point / Old romantics / Spot the ball / Fender bender / Change of address / Life in the jungle / Fourth man / Midnight creepin' / Shady lady / Thing-me-jig / Stack it / No dancing / Shoba / Shadoogie
SEECD 494 / 13 Jul '98 / See For Miles

☐ SIMPLY SHADOWS
I know you were waiting (for me) / We don't need another hero / Walking in the air / Careless whisper / Don't give up / I guess that's why they call it the blues / Heart will break tonight / Lady in red / Pulaski / Take my breath away / Eastenders / I want to know what love is / Skye boat song / Jealous guy / Chain reaction / Howard's Way
8336822 / Oct '87 / Polydor

☐ SOUND OF THE SHADOWS, THE
Brazil / Lost city / Little bitty tear / Blue sky / Blue sea / Bossa roo / Five hundredd miles / Cotton pickin' / Deep purple / Five hundred miles / Santa ama / Windjammer / Dean's theme / Breakthru / Let it be me / National provincial samba
DORIG 105 / Jul '97 / EMI

☐ STEP FROM THE SHADOWS (Marvin, Hank & Bruce Welch/John Farrar)
Marmaduke / Lady of the morning / Time to care / Lonesome mole / Black eyes / Brownie Kentucky / Skin deep / Faithful / You never can tell / Hard to live with / Music makes my day / Mistress fate and father time / Silvery rain / Wish you were here / Thousand conversations / Tiny Robin / Thank heavens I've got you / Please Mr. please
SEECD 78 / 8 Jun '98 / See For Miles

☐ STEPPIN' TO THE SHADOWS (16 Great Tracks As Only The Shadows Can Play Them)
You win again / I wanna dance with somebody (who loves me) / He ain't heavy, he's my brother / Candle in the wind / Farewell my lovely / Mountains of the moon / Nothings gonna change my love for you / Heaven is a place on earth / When the going gets tough / Alone / All I ask of you / Stack it / Shoba / You keep me hangin' on / Some people / One moment in time
8393572 / May '89 / Polydor

☐ STRING OF HITS
Riders in the sky / Parisienne walkways / Classical gas / Deer hunter / Bridge over troubled water / You're the one that I want / Heart of glass / Don't cry for me Argentina / Song for Duke / Bright eyes / Rodrigo's guitar concerto de aranjuez / Baker Street
CDMFP 5724 / Nov '91 / Music For Pleasure

☐ THEMES AND DREAMS
Crockett's theme / Up where we belong / Take my breath away / Deer hunter / Walking in the air / If you leave me now / One day I'll fly away / Africa / Every breath you take / Memory / Nights in white satin / Candle in the wind / You win again / Sailing / Just the way you are / Moonlight shadow
5113742 / Nov '91 / Polydor

☐ THOUSAND CONVERSATIONS, A (The Best Of Hank Marvin & Bruce Welch/ John Farrar) (Marvin, Hank & Bruce Welch/John Farrar)
You're burning bridges / Faithful / Marmaduke / Ronnie / Tiny Robin / All day all night / Silvery rain / Simplify your head / Music makes my day / Lonesome mole / Faraway falling / Skin deep / If I rewrote yesterdays / My home town / Help me onto your wagon / Wish you were here / Lady of the morning / Thousand conversations / Come back to nature / Thank Heaven I've got you / Love oh love / Small and lonely light / Please Mr please / Galadiel
CDMFP 6402 / 13 Oct '97 / Music For Pleasure

☐ VERY BEST OF THE SHADOWS, THE
Apache / Man of mystery / FBI / Frightened city / Kon-tiki / Savage / Wonderful land / Guitar tango / Dance on / Foot tapper / Atlantis / Shindig / Geronimo / Theme for young lover's / Rise and fall of fingle bunt / Genie with the light brown lamp / Mary Anne / Stingray / Don't make my baby blue / Warlord
CDMFP 6385 / 13 Oct '97 / Music For Pleasure

☐ VOCALS
Bandit / Saturday dance / Feelin' fine / Don't be a fool / Baby my heart / Lonesome fella / All my sorrows / Mary Anne / My way / Will you be there / Little bitty tear / Me oh my / That's the way it goes / Stay around / One way to love / Day I met Marie / Dreams I dream / Don't make my baby blue / This hammer / Be bop a lula
SEECD 475 / Feb '97 / See For Miles

Shadows

☐ DARK SIDE OF THE SHADOWS, THE
DOG 9109CD / Aug '95 / Wild Dog

☐ IT AIN'T EASY BEIN' SLEAZY
DOG 9105CD / Aug '95 / Wild Dog

☐ PALE INTERPRETATIONS
DOG 91122 / Oct '97 / Wild Dog

Shadows Of Knight

☐ BACK DOOR MEN
SC 6156 / 1 Jun '98 / Sundazed

☐ GLORIA
SC 6155 / 1 Jun '98 / Sundazed

Shadrack Chameleon

☐ SHADRACK CHAMELEON
GF 110 / 16 Mar '98 / Gear Fab

Shady

☐ WORLD
BBQCD 166 / Nov '94 / Beggars Banquet

Shady Grove Band

☐ CHAPEL HILLBILLY WAY
FF 70639 / Feb '95 / Flying Fish

☐ MULBERRY MOON
FF 544CD / '92 / Flying Fish

Shady Mix

☐ BOTTOMLANDS
Bottomlands / River Road / Down to the levee / Louisiana 1927 / Cash on the barrelhead / Chicken fence rag / Satisfied mind / Good love / Mississippi (rolls on forever) / Roseville Fair / Indian Creek / Mississippi lullaby
BCD 16280 / May '98 / Bear Family

Shafer, Robert

☐ HILLBILLY FEVER
Dixie fried / Beam me up Scotty Moore / Just another ambush / Drink you off my mind / Every kind of music / Hillbilly fever / Haze over coal river / Will your lawer talk to God / Cadillac man / I want a lavender cadillac / Bumble boogie / Return of the flatwoods monster
UPSTART 028 / Feb '97 / Upstart

Shafer, Ted

☐ ORIGINAL JELLY BLUES (Shafer, Ted Jelly Roll Jazz Band)
SOSCD 1278 / May '95 / Stomp Off

☐ SAN FRANCISCO (Shafer, Ted Jelly Roll Jazz Band)
MMRCCD 1 / '93 / Merry Makers

☐ TED SHAFER'S JELLY ROLL JAZZ BAND VOL.2 (Shafer, Ted Jelly Roll Jazz Band)
MMRCCD 14 / Feb '98 / Merry Makers

☐ TOE-TAPPING DIXIELAND (Shafer, Ted Jelly Roll Jazz Band)
MMRCCD 13 / Mar '97 / Merry Makers

Shaffer, Doreen

☐ SUGAR SUGAR
JFCD 4648 / Mar '95 / Joe Frazier

Shaftman

☐ SHAFTMAN
EFACD 11517 / 17 Nov '97 / Crypt

Shaggs

☐ SHAGGS, THE
CREV 019CD / Nov '94 / Rev-Ola

Shaggy

☐ BOOMBASTIC
In the summertime / Boombastic / Something different / Forgive them father / Heartbreak Suzie / Finger Smith / Why you treat me so bad / Woman a pressure / Train is coming / Island lover / Day oh / Jenny / How much more / Gal you a pepper
CDV 2782 / Oct '95 / Virgin

☐ IN DUB
DOCD 003 / Jun '96 / Graylan

☐ MIDNITE LOVER
My dream / Perfect song / Warm and tender love / Geenie / Sexy body girls / Piece of my heart / Think ah so it go / Midnite lover / Mission / Way back home / John Doe / Thank you Lord
CDV 2838 / Aug '97 / Virgin

☐ ORIGINAL DOBERMAN
Kibbles and bits / Bullet proof buddy / Chow / Alimony / Wildfire / PHAT / Glamity power / Get down to it / Man a yard / Soldering / Lately / Jump and rock / We never danced to the rub-a-dub sound
GRELCD 208 / Jul '97 / Greensleeves

☐ PURE PLEASURE
Soon be done / Give thanks and praise / Lust / Oh Carolina / Tek set / Bedroom bounty hunter / Nice and lovely / Love how them flex / All virgins / Ah-e-a-oh / It bun me / Big up / Bow wow wow / Follow me / Mampie / Oh Carolina (Raas bumba claat version)
GRELCD 184 / Jul '97 / Greensleeves

Shaheen, Simon

☐ SALTANAH (Shaheen, Simon & Vishnwa Mohan Bhatt)
Dawn / Ghazal / Saltanah / Mists / Dusk
WLAES 51CD / Feb '97 / Waterlily Acoustics

☐ TURATH
Bashraf farahfaza / Sama'i farahfaza / Taqasim on violin / Longa farahfaza / Taqasim on the beat / Sama'i nahawand / Tahmilah suznak / Sama'i nahawand / Bashraf kurd / Taqasim on nay / Sama'i kurd
CMPCD 3006 / Jul '92 / CMP

Shai

☐ IF I EVER FALL IN LOVE
Sexual interlude / Comforter / If I ever fall in love / Sexual / Together forever / If I ever fall in love (accapella) / Flava / Baby, I'm yours / Waiting for the day / Changes / Don't wanna play / Lord I've come
MCLD 19354 / Apr '97 / MCA

Shaikh, Adham

☐ DRIFT
AMB 60062 / Feb '97 / Instinct

☐ JOURNEY TO THE SUN
IAE 006CD / Jul '95 / Instinct Ambient Europe

Shaka Man

☐ DEJAZZMATCH
IR 01012 / 18 May '98 / Ion

Shaka Shamba

☐ NAMEBRAND
Tender loving / Certain thing can't done / Girls fat / Take me home country roads / Panty waist / Mine, mine, mine / Shape-eisha / More money / One love / Peep / Them a boast / Namebrand / Bait / Pickney / Chatty chatty / Idiot man
GRELCD 203 / Apr '94 / Greensleeves

Shaka, Tom

☐ HIT FROM THE HEART
Chicken man blues / I been to mardi gras / Deep night blues (instr.) / Rock'n'roll water / Please send me someone to love / Leavin' texas blues / Whatcha gonna do / Crosscut boogie (instr.) / Stone sober / Goin' away baby / Goin' back to germany / Wrist twister rag (instr.) / Blues shaker / Rock a while baby / Barrelhousin' (instr.)
CCD 11025 / '92 / Crosscut

☐ HOT 'N' SPICY
Matchbox blues / Crawlin' kingsnake / Ain't it a shame / You gotta move / God don't never change / No more dirty war blues / Vegetarian blues / Stop breaking down / Slide my way back home / Abilene texas blues / Sad letter blues / Let's boogie on
CCD 11036 / Jan '94 / Crosscut

☐ TIMELESS IN BLUES
CDST 03 / Nov '95 / Stumble

Shakatak

☐ CHRISTMAS ALBUM, THE
Happy Christmas to ya / Winter wonderland / White Christmas / O little town of Bethlehem / Silent night / Christmas time again / Christmas in Rio / Good King Wenceslas / Let it snow, let it snow, let it snow / Sing (Little one) / God rest ye merry gentlemen / Lonely on Christmas day / Jingle bells / Christmas song / Away in a manger / Auld lang syne
CDINZ 3 / Nov '96 / Debut

☐ COLLECTION, THE
Down on the street / Day by day / Invitations / Dark is the night / You'll never know / Don't blame it on love / Lady (To Billie Holiday) / Holding on / Streetwalkin' / Night birds / Easier said than done / Out of this world / Dr. Dr / Bitter sweet / Something special / Light of my life / Turn the music up / Mr. Manic and Sister cool
5520202 / 4 May '98 / Spectrum

☐ FULL CIRCLE
Brazillian love affair / Catwalk / Out of my sight / Sweet Sunday / You are / Walk in the night / Haze / Diamond in the night / Midnight temptation / Havana express / Tonight's the night / Blue azure
CDINZ 4 / Feb '95 / Inside Out

☐ JAZZ CONNECTIONS VOL.1
Deja vu'll see ya / L'aggio l'amour / Out of the blue / One for cara / Eyes of the sea / Dance like Fred Astaire/Jazz creepin'/bermuda rig / Blue note / Twilight time / Interlude
CDSHAK 1 / Sep '96 / Inside Out

☐ JAZZ CONNECTIONS VOL.2
Damokani suite / Golden wings / Quiet storm / Paradise/prelude / Nights over Tokyo / One day, one night, one love / Only yesterday / Cavalcante/Island girl / One more
CDSHAK 2 / Sep '96 / Inside Out

☐ JAZZ CONNECTIONS VOL.3
Heart to heart / China Bay / My utopia/Pastel shade/ Climbing high/Perfect smile / Madinina / Disorder at the border / Whispers in the night / Lazy / This boy is mine / Silk emotion
CDSHAK 3 / Sep '96 / Inside Out

☐ JAZZ CONNECTIONS VOL.4
Sunshiny day / High life / Open your eyes / Marie Louise / Sea dreamin' / No one knows/Why me / Runnin' away / Endurance / Nothing but a dream hideaway / Conquistador
CDSHAK 4 / Sep '96 / Inside Out

☐ JAZZ CONNECTIONS VOL.5
First love/Hungry / Just the way we are / Kagape / Dreamtime / Chi-chi-castanengo racing / With the wind / Story of my life / Catch me if you can / After midnight / Please don't go / Undercurrent
CDSHAK 5 / Sep '96 / Inside Out

☐ JAZZ CONNECTIONS VOL.6
Danceland / Runaway Bay / Coco kazu/One day soon / Midnight walkin' / Just the way it goes deadline / Run with the tide/Nocturne / Looking for rainbows / Two people (one love story) / When night falls
CDSHAK 6 / Sep '96 / Inside Out

☐ LET THE PIANO PLAY
CDINZ 5 / 29 Sep '97 / Debut

☐ LIVE AT RONNIE SCOTT'S
Invitations / Streetwalkin' / Beyond our reach / Day by day / Don't say that again / Blue note / Lumiere / Easier said than done / You are / Mr. Manic and Sister Cool / Chi chi castenago / Night birds / Let the piano play / Down on the street
IGOXCD 514 / 22 Apr '98 / Indigo

☐ ORCHESTRAL HITS OF SHAKATAK (Shakatak Orchestra & Nigel Wright)
Livin' in the UK / Stranger / Easier said than done / Rio nights / You never know / Invitations / Out of this world / Light of my life / Dark is the night / Night birds / Brazilian dawn
SUMCD 4134 / Sep '97 / Summit

☐ OUT OF THIS WORLD
Dark is the night / Don't say that again / Slip away / On nights like tonight / Out of this world / Let's get together / If you can see me now / Sanur
OW 30014 / Sep '94 / One Way

☐ STREET LEVEL
One day at a time / Street level / Sleepin' alone / Siberian breeze / Anyway you want it / Night ain't over yet / Watchin' the rain / Without you / Jump 'n' pump / Empty skies / Calm before the storm / Vibe tribe
CDINZ 1 / Mar '93 / Debut

☐ UNDER THE SUN
Soul destination / Don't walk away / Paradise island / Rest of your life / Crosstown / One for the boyz / Beyond the reach / Can't stop running / Sweat / It's over / Fly by night / Shine your light
CDINZ 2 / Nov '92 / Debut

Shakedown Club

☐ SHAKEDOWN CLUB, THE
BDV 9403CD / Jul '94 / Babel

Shaker

☐ KISS ME
TPLP 70CD / May '96 / One Little Indian

Shakers

☐ TRANSATLANTIC SHAKEDOWN
QOM 101 / Nov '97 / Keltia Musique

Shakespears Sister

☐ SACRED HEART
Heroine / Run silent / Run deep / Dirty mind / Sacred heart / Heaven in your arms / You're history / Break my heart / Red rocket / Electric moon / Primitive love / Could you be loved / Twist the knife / You made me come to this
8281312 / May '92 / London

Shakin' Apostles

☐ AUSTIN TEXAS
BLUCD 0036 / 20 Apr '98 / Blue Rose

Shakta

☐ SILICON TRIP
BFLCD 23 / 1 Sep '98 / Butterfly

Shakuhachi Surprise

☐ SPACE STREAKINGS OVER MOUNT SHASTA
GR 35CD / Oct '96 / Skingraft

Shalamar

☐ BIG FUN
Right time for us / Take me to the river / Right in the socket / Second time around / I owe you one / Let's find the time for love / Girl
NEBCD 791 / Jul '96 / Sequel

☐ FRIENDS
Night to remember / Don't try to change me / Help me / On top of the world / I don't wanna be the last to know / Friends / Playing to win / I just stopped by because I had to / There it is / I can make you feel good
NEBCD 789 / Jul '96 / Sequel

☐ LOOK, THE
Closer / Dead giveaway / You can count on me / Right here / No limits / Disappearing act / Over and over / You're the one for me / You won't miss love (Until it's gone) / Look
NEBCD 788 / Jul '96 / Sequel

☐ NIGHT TO REMEMBER, A
Night to remember / There it is / I can make you feel good / Over and over / My girl loves me / Amnesia / Leave it all up to love / Whenever you need me / Uptown festival / Second time around / Lovely lady / Work it out / Sweeter as the days go by / On top of the world / Don't try to change me / You won't miss love (until it's gone)
5507542 / Mar '95 / Spectrum

☐ NIGHT TO REMEMBER, A (Shalamar's Greatest Hits/2CD Set)
Shalamar disco gardens / Uptown festival / Ooh baby baby / Take that to the bank / Second time around / Right in the socket / I owe you one / Full of fire / Make that move / This is for the lover in you / Attention to my baby / Somewhere there's a love / Sweeter as the days go by / I can make you feel good / Night to remember / There it is / Friends / Dead giveaway / Disappearing act / Over and over / Dancing in the sheets / Deadline USA / Amnesia / My girl loves me / Circumstantial evidence / Games / Night to remember / Take that to the bank / There it is / Mix to remember
DEEPM 032 / 26 Jan '98 / Deep Beats

☐ THREE FOR LOVE
Full of fire / Attention to my baby / Somewhere there's a love / Some things never change / Make that move / This is for the lover in you / Work it out / Pop along kid
NEBCD 790 / Jul '96 / Sequel

☐ VERY BEST OF SHALAMAR, THE
Friends / Take that to the bank / Second time around / There it is / Make that move / I can make you feel good / I owe you one / Uptown festival / Dancing in the sheets / Disappearing act / Night to remember / Dead giveaway / Amnesia / Deadline USA / My girl loves me / Over and over / Circumstantial evidence / Sweeter as the days go by
CCSCD 803 / Sep '95 / Renaissance Collector Series

Shaljean, Bonnie

☐ FAREWELL TO LOUGH NEAGH
Roslin Castle / Captain O'Neill / Colonel O'Hara / Sir Festus Burke / Foweles in the frith / Edi beo thu hevene quene / Summer is icumen in / Clocks back reel / Kilburn jig / Diarmuid's well / Wild Irishman / Her mantle so green / Planxty Drew / Mary O'Neill / Maid of Derry
CDSDL 372 / Mar '94 / Saydisc

Sham 69

☐ A FILES, THE
EFACD 12359 / Jul '97 / Empty

☐ ADVENTURES OF THE HERSHAM BOYS, THE
Money / Fly dark angel / Joey's on the street again / Cold blue in the night / Mister, you're a better man than I / Lost on highway 46 / Voices / Questions and answers / What have we got / If the kids are united / Borstal breakout
DOJOCD 258 / Mar '96 / Dojo
ESMCD 515 / Jun '97 / Essential

☐ BEST OF SHAM 69, THE (2CD Set)
Borstal breakout / Family life / Tell us the truth / Angels with dirty faces / Cockney kids are innocent / If the kids are united / Hurry up Harry / That's life / Questions and answers / Hersham boys / You're a better man than I / Money / Joey's on the street / Tell the children / Unite and win / Poor cow / Game / What have we got / Red London / I don't wanna / Rip off / I'm a man / Ulster boy / It's never to late / Hey little rich boy / They don't understand / What about the lonely / George Davis is innocent
ESDCD 350 / Nov '95 / Essential

☐ BEST OF SHAM 69, THE
Borstal breakout / Family life / Tell us the truth / Angels with dirty faces / Cockney kids are innocent / If the kids are united / Hurry up Harry / That's life / Questions and answers / Hersham boys / You're a better man than I / Money / Joey's on the street / Tell the children / Unite and win / Poor cow / Game / What have we got
ESMCD 512 / Jun '97 / Essential

☐ BORSTAL BREAKOUT (2CD Set)
SMDCD 141 / 16 Feb '98 / Snapper

☐ FIRST, THE BEST AND THE LAST
Borstal breakout / Hey little rich boy / Angels with dirty faces / Cockney kids are innocent / If the kids are united / Sunday morning nightmare / Hurry up Harry / Questions and answers / Give the dog a bone / Hersham boys / Tell the children / Unite and win
5134292 / Apr '94 / Polydor

☐ GAME
Game / Lord of the flies / In and out / Human zoo / Give a dog a bone / Tell the children / Spray it on the wall / Simon / Poor cow / Dead or alive / Deja Vu / Run wild run free / Unite and win / Daytripper
DOJOCD 259 / Mar '96 / Dojo
ESMCD 516 / Jun '97 / Essential

☐ INFORMATION LIBRE
Break on through / Uptown / Planet trash / Information libertaire / Caroline's suitcase / Feel it / King Kong drinks cocacola / Saturdays and strangeways / Breeding dinosaurs / Wild and wonderful
DOJOCD 236 / Jan '96 / Dojo

☐ LIVE IN JAPAN
What have we got / Angels with dirty faces / Mr. you're a better man than I / Tell the children / Poor cow / How the west was won / Caroline's suitcase / Borstal breakout / Vision and the power / If the kids are united / Money / Hersham boys / Rip and tear
DOJOCD 105 / Feb '94 / Dojo

☐ MASTERS, THE (2CD Set)
EDMCD 030 / 30 Mar '98 / Eagle

☐ SHAM 69 LIVE
If the kids are united / Joey's on the street again / James Dean / Ulster boy / Rip off / They don't understand / Questions and answers / Day tripper / Who gives a damn / What have we got / That's life / Red London / Everybody's innocent / White riot / Borstal breakout / Tell us the truth
EMPRCD 582 / Oct '95 / Emporio

☐ SHAM'S LAST STAND
What have we got / I don't wanna / They don't understand / Angels with dirty faces / Tell us the truth / That's life / Rip off / Cockney kids are innocent / Voices / Borstal breakout / Pretty vacant / White riot / If the kids are united / Hurry up Harry / Hersham boys / Questions and answers
DOJOCD 95 / Apr '93 / Dojo

☐ SOAPY WATER AND MR. MARMALADE
AICD 001 / Mar '97 / A+I
3012792 / 25 May '98 / Rhino

☐ TELL US THE TRUTH
We got a fight / Rip off / Ulster / George Davis is innocent / They don't understand / Borstal breakout / Family life / Hey little rich boy / I'm a man I'm a boy / What about the lonely / Tell us the truth / It's never too late / Who's generation / What have we got
DOJOCD 256 / Mar '96 / Dojo
ESMCD 513 / Jun '97 / Essential

☐ THAT'S LIFE
Leave me alone / Who gives a damn / Everybody's right, everybody's wrong / That's life / Win or lose / Hurry up Harry / Evil way / Reggae pick up part 1 / Sunday morning nightmare / Reggae pick up part 2 / Angels with dirty faces / Is this me or is this you
DOJOCD 257 / Mar '96 / Dojo

☐ UNITED
If the kids are united / What have we got / Red lion / Voices / Angels with dirty faces / Questions and answers / That's life / Borstal breakout / Joey's on the street / They don't understand / Tell us the truth / Hersham boys
304462 / Jun '97 / Hallmark

☐ VERY BEST OF THE HERSHAM BOYS, THE
Angels with dirty faces / If the kids are united / Hurry up Harry / Questions and answers / Hersham boys / You're a better man than I / Tell the children / Who gives a damn / Lost on highway 46 / I'm a man I'm a boy / Tell us the truth / Borstal breakout / Fly dark angel / We gotta fight / They don't understand / Ulster / Joey's on the street / Win or lose
SELCD 504 / 30 Mar '98 / Castle Select

Shamaani Duo

☐ HUNKA LUNKA
SNAP 355CD / Nov '96 / Snap

Shamanic Tribes On Acid

☐ 303 TO INFINITY
Mandala moon / Starglider / Tantalus / Book of changes / Golden bell / Elastic psychedelic / Spiral 303 / Herbal meditation / Omega sunset / Acid punk
KINXCD 7 / Mar '97 / Kinetix

☐ ACID APOCALYPSE
Acid Medusa / Exploding psychedelic / Fulfil your destiny / Aliens love to talk / Mad hatters acid tea party / Omnifarious spliffcrous / Drugged to the eyeballs / Bass ritual / Et lover / Apache trance / No armageddon
KINXCD 11 / 17 Nov '97 / Kinetix

Shame Idols

☐ ROCKET CAT
310712 / Jul '97 / Frontier

Shamen

☐ AXIS MUTATIS
TPLP 52CDL
TPLP 52CD / Oct '95 / One Little Indian

☐ COLLECTION, THE (2CD Set)
Pro gen / Omega amigo / Move any mountain / Make it mine / Hypereal / LSI / Ebeneezer Goode / Boss drum / Phorever people / Re evolution / Comin' on strong / Possible worlds / Destination eschaton / Transamazonia / Heal (seperation) / MK2A / Indica / Hyperreal selector / Boss drum / Human NRG / Move any mountain / Lightspan soundwave / Hear me / Make it mine / Make it mine / Phorever people / Transamazonia / MK2A / Re evolution / Ebeneezer Goode / Ebeneezer Goode / Possible worlds / Destination eschaton / Comin' on / LSI / Heal / Cannabeo / Transmazonia / Heal / MK2A
TPLP 72CDR / Jan '97 / One Little Indian
TPLP 72CDE / 20 Apr '98 / One Little Indian

☐ DIFFERENT DRUM
Boss drum / l.s.i. (beat edit) / Ebeneezer goode (beat edit) / Coming on strong (beatmasters 7") / Phorever young (beatmasters heavenly edit) / Spacetime / Librae solidi denari / Fatman (shamen instrumental) / Scientas / Re-iteration / l.s.i. (maurice love sex instrumental) / Ebeneezer goode (i.o.c. ambient mix) / Deevolution (shamen instrumental) / Coming unstrung / Boss drum
TPLP 42CDR / Nov '93 / One Little Indian

☐ DROP
Something about you / Passing away / Young 'til yesterday / World theatre / Through with you / Where do you go / Do what you will / Happy days / Through my window / Velvet box / I don't like the way the world is / Other side / Four letter girl
MAUCD 613 / Nov '91 / Mau Mau

☐ EN-TACT
TPLP 22CD / Oct '90 / One Little Indian

☐ HEMPTON MANOR
Freya / Urpflanze / Cannabeo / Khat / Bememe / Indica / Rausch / Kava / El-fin / Monoriff
TPLP 62CD / Oct '96 / One Little Indian

☐ IN GORBACHEV WE TRUST
Synergy / Raspberry infundibulum / Adam strange / Transcendental / Raptyouare / Sweet young thing / War prayer / Jesus loves Amerika / Misinformation / In Gorbachev we trust
FIENDCD 666 / Jan '89 / Demon

☐ ON AIR (The BBC Sessions)
Human energy / Omega amigo / Progen / Hyperreal / Make it mine / Possible worlds / In the bag / Space time / Make it mine USA / Boss drum / Ebeneezer goode
SFRSCD 055 / 30 Mar '98 / Strange Fruit

Shampoo

☐ GIRL POWER
Girl power / News flash / I know what boys like / Bare knuckle girl / Zap pow / War paint / You love it / Boys are us / We play dumb / I'm gonna scream / Don't call me babe
FOODCD 16 / Sep '96 / Food

Shamrock Man

☐ 50 LOVELY IRISH SONGS (Everyone's Favourites)
PADDYCD 2 / Apr '98 / Commercial

Shamrock Singers

☐ WHEN IRISH EYES ARE SMILING
MACCD 202 / Aug '96 / Autograph

Shamrox

☐ TEAR AND A SMILE FROM THE EMERALD ISLE, A
Whiskey in the jar / Holy ground / Black velvet band / Danny boy / Mountains of Mourne / Rovin' I will go / I'll tell me Ma / Parting glass / Cliffs of Dooneen / Irish rover / Maries wedding / She moves through the fair / Star of County Down / Red is the rose / Water is wide / Leaving of Liverpool / Molly Malone / Carrickfergus / Whistling gypsy / Wild rover
P 1032 / Dec '97 / Pricepoint

Shand, Gordon

☐ RSCDS VOL.23 (Shand, Gordon Scottish Dance Band)
Auld alliance / Alltshellach / Glens of Angus / Dean bridge of Edinburgh / Miss Hadden's reel / Glasgow country dance / Reivers / Swilcan / Mrs. Hamilton of Wishaw / Rudha dubh / Starry eyed lassie / Let's meet again
RSCDSCD 011 / Jul '98 / Royal Scottish Country Dance Society

Shand, Jimmy

☐ 20 GOLDEN TRACKS
Shandon bells / Biddy the bowl wife / Frost is all over / Pet o' the pipers / George Harrison's reel / Come let us dance and sing / Davy Nick Nack / Soft lowland tongue / Annie Laurie / My Nannie's awa' / I lo'ed nae a lassie but ane / Stone court / Mrs. Jimmy Shand's fancy / Miss Maria Stewart / Black dance / Thurso wedding / Wandering drummer / Breadalbane reel / Aikey brae / Muckle Friday fair / St. Andrew's parade / Bobby Watson / Lord Lyndoch / Duke of Gordon / Laird o' Thrums / Lady Anne Hope / Muckin' o' Geordie's byre / Lady Nellie Wemyss / Braidleys house / Major Mackie / Queens bridge / Calton hill / Hopeful lover / Cailin mo Ruinsa / Leaving Barra / Morag of Dunvegan / Cock o' the North / Jeannie King / Brydie's polka / Standchen / Paddywhack / Dan the cobbler / Saddle the pony / Come o'er the stream Charlie / Rothesay Bay / Sound the Pibroch / My love is like a red red rose / O Gin I were a Baron's heir / Wonder hornpipe / Harvest home / Trumpet hornpipe / If you're Irish come into the parlour / With my shillelagh under my arm / Galloway House / Georgina Catherine MacDonald's fancy / Earl Gray
CDGR 154 / Feb '96 / Ross

☐ DANCING WITH THE SHANDS (Shand, Jimmy & Jimmy Shand Jr.)
Grand march/The star o' Robbie Burns / Kelvin Grove/Rothesay Bay/Horo my nut brown maiden / Scots wa' hae / John McDonald's march/Gay Gordons / Duke of Perth/Lass o' Patties Mill / Davy Knick Knack / Fiddle solo / La-Va / Eva three step / Swedish masquerade / Virginia reel/She'll be coming round the mountain / Let him go let him tarry/ Maggie/I'm a Yankee doodle dandy / Pride of Erin/ Peggy O'Neill / Mississippi dip/Beer barrel polka / Strip the willow/Muckin' o' Geordie's byre / Athernie Lodge Redpath/Kenmuires on and awa' / O' gin I were a baron's heir / Memories of Orkney / Bluebell polka / Military two step/Golden wedding two step / St. Bernard's waltz/My bonnie lies over the ocean / Won't you buy me pretty flowers / Oh dear what can the matter be
RECD 497 / Jan '98 / REL

☐ JIMMY SHAND PLAYS JIMMY SHAND
Lord and Lady Elgin of Broomhall / Maresland two-step / Lady Angela Alexander/Sir Kenneth J.W. Alexander / Threave castle polka / Ian Thompson's farewell to the Fife Police / Francis Wright's waltz / Memories of Willie Smith / Ian Powrie's welcome to Dunblane / Windy Edge Barndance / Lunan Bay/ Tom and Mary Lyon's waltz / It's grand among your ain folk / David Anderson Shand's 40th birthday / Heather mixture two-step / Alice Mearns/Ian and Bunty Redford's silver wedding march / Jimmy Shand's compliments to Harry Lawson/Dr. A.K. Tulloch / Whitley Chapel barndance / John McDonald's march / Miss Jean Thomson's 100th birthday/Miss Jeannie King / Bryce Laing's welcome to Auchtermuchty / Guardian's of the gulf / Margaret Innes/Robert Innes of Pitterweem
CD 6073 / Oct '97 / Music

☐ LAST TEN YEARS, THE (Shand, Jimmy & His Band)
Georgina Catherine MacDonald's fancy / Lord Randal's bride / Calton Hill reel / Lady Elgin of Broomhall / Lord Elgin of Broomhall / Green glens of Antrim / Come back to Erin / Bryce Laing's welcome to Auchtermuchty / John and Mary's Young's golden wedding anniversary / Threave Castle polka / Major Norman Orr Ewing / Crossing the new Forth Bridge / Seventy second Highlanders' farewell to Aberdeen / Jimmy Shand's 80th year / Now is the hour / At the end of a perfect day / MacKenzie highlanders / Glengarry quickstep / Teribus / Sweet maid of Glendaruel / Francis Wright's waltz / Suptd. Ian Thompson's farewell to the Fife police / Jimmy Shand's compliments to Willie Laird / Guardians of the Gulf / Royal Guard Regiment of HM Sultan Of Oman / Heather mixture twostep / Badge of Scotland / Fifty first Highland Division / Hills of Alva / MacNeils of Ugadale / John D Burgess / Hugh MacPherson / Piper's weird / Flower o' the Quern / Cradle song / Lochanside / Bill Dickman of Stonehouse / Woodlands polka / Scottish horse / Bugle horn / MacDonald's awa' tae the war / Gentle maiden / Believe me, if all those endearing young charms / Come back Paddy Reilly to Ballyjamesduff / James Duff / Rose of Tralee / Ian Powrie's welcome to Dunblane / Jimmy Shand's compliments to Ian Powrie / Whitley chapel barn dance / Miss Elder / John MacDonald of Glencoe / Maresland twostep
WGRCD 13 / Dec '89 / Ross

☐ LEGENDARY JIMMY SHAND MBE, THE
Newcastle reel medley / Grannie Heilan hame medley / Scotland the brave medley / Braes of Elchie medley / Agnes waltz / MacKenzie highlanders medley / Maggie and Jock / Cumberland reel medley / Strathspey medley / Royal Scots polka / Welcome home fisher lads / Ian and Bunty medley / Auld reekie / Lady Dorothea medley / L'entrainante / 6.20 two step / Brides of Erin medley / Pipe matches medley / Light and airy medley / Somebody stole my gal medley / Reel/Georgia medley
RECD 514 / Jun '97 / REL

☐ LEGENDARY JIMMY SHAND, THE
Linton ploughman / Marching with Jimmy Shand / Gaelic waltz selection / Gay Gordons / When you and I were young Maggie / Bluebell polka / Irish two step / Royal Scots polka / I'll take you home agin Kathleen / Highland schottische / Swilcan / Northern lights of Aberdeen / Black dance
CDSL 8284 / Feb '97 / EMI Gold

☐ SCOTTISH FANCY, A (Shand, Jimmy & His Band)
White heather jig / Grosvenor House strathspey / Campbells are coming / Balmoral strathspey / Miss Hadden's reel / Quiet and snug strathspey / Hooper's jig / Waltz country dance / Galloway House reel / Express / La tempete / Marie's wedding / Road to the isles / Waverley
GRCD 37 / Sep '89 / Grasmere

Shand, Jimmy Jr.

☐ BEST OF JIMMY SHAND JR., THE
Auchtermuchty Gala march / Lass from Glasgow Town / Badenoch polka / Gay Gordons medley / Shamrock waltzes medley / Reels medley / Ring family two step / Rabbie Burns marches / Trip to Bavaria medley / Singalong waltz medley / Jigs medley / Medley / Gay Gordons medley #2 / Welcome Christmas morning / Eva three step medley
EMPRCD 721 / Jun '97 / Emporio

Shane, Mark

☐ TREASURE ISLAND
JJZ 9603 / Nov '96 / Jukebox

☐ WITH THEE I SWING (Shane, Mark & Terry Blaine)
NHCD 040 / Jan '98 / Nagel Heyer

Shangaie

☐ CHANSON MARINEES
CD 857 / Aug '95 / Diffusion Breizh

Shangoya

☐ ALIVE AT 25
Donkey / Swing the ting / Paly on / Rhythm of the rump / Lively up yourself / Dollar wine / Breezin' / Cool runnings
MOUP 6025 / 16 Mar '98 / Mouthpiece

☐ COLLECTION, THE
MPD 6006 / Nov '94 / Flying Fish

Shangri-Las

☐ BEST OF THE SHANGRI-LAS, THE
Remember (walkin' in the sand) / Leader of the pack / What is love / Give him a great big kiss / Maybe / Out in the streets / Give us your blessings / Heaven only knows / Never again / What's a girl supposed to do / Dum dum ditty / Right now and not later / Train from Kansas City / I can never go home anymore / Long live our love / Sophisticated boom boom / He cried / Dressed in black / Past, present and future / Paradise / Love you more than yesterday / Sweet sound of Summer / I'll never learn / Take the time / Footsteps on the roof
5527642 / Feb '97 / Spectrum

☐ COLLECTION, THE
Leader of the pack / Leader of the pack / Remember (walking in the sand) / I can never go home anymore / Give him a great big kiss / Give us your blessings / Out in the streets / Maybe / Long live our love / So much in love / Sophisticated boom boom / Dum dum ditty / Bulldog / Dressed in black / I'm blue / Never again / Right now and not later / Shout / Boy / Train from kansas city / You cheated, you lied / Heaven only knows / Goodnight my love / He cried / What's a girl supposed to do
COL 043 / Mar '95 / Collection

☐ GOLD
GOLD 069 / Aug '96 / Gold

☐ HIT SINGLE COLLECTABLES
DISK 4512 / Apr '94 / Disky

☐ MYRMIDONES OF MELODRAMA
Remember (walkin' in the sand) / It's easier to cry / Leader of the pack / What is love / Give him a great big kiss / Maybe / Out in the streets / Boy / Give us your blessings / Heaven only knows / Right now and not later / Train from Kansas city / I can never go home anymore / Bulldog / Long live our love / Sophisticated boom boom / He cried / Dressed in black / Past, present and future / Love you more than yesterday / Paradise / Never again / I'm blue / What's a girl supposed to do / Dum dum ditty / You cheated, you lied / Give him a great big kiss (alt take) / Dating courtesy Pt 1 / Dating courtesy Pt 2 / Hate to say I told you so / Wishing well
RPM 136 / Apr '95 / RPM

Shank, Bud

☐ BLOWIN' COUNTRY (Shank, Bud & Bob Cooper)
Dinah / Mutual admiration society / Steve Allen theme / I've grown accustomed to her face / Blowin' country / Love nest / As long as there's music / Just in time / Two lost souls / Thanks for the memory / Romantic guy / Sweet Georgia brown / Gypsy in my soul / I want to be happy / What I'll do
4948462 / 20 Jul '98 / Pacific Jazz

☐ BUD SHANK AND BILL PERKINS (Shank, Bud & Bill Perkins)
Paradise / Fluted columns / I hear music / Royal garden blues / Sinner kissed an angel / It had to be you / Fluted columns / I hear music / Brother can you spare a dime / Blues in the night / Bojangles of Harlem / It's a new world / Angel eyes / Sonny speaks / Ain't got a dime to my name
4931592 / 18 May '98 / Pacific Jazz

☐ CRYSTAL COMMENTS (Shank, Bud & Bill Mays, Alan Boradbent)
Scrapple from the apple / How are things in glocca morra / I'll take romance / Solar / Body and soul / On green dolphin street
CCD 4126 / Feb '94 / Concord Jazz

☐ DOCTOR IS IN, THE
Doctor is in / Embraceable you / If I should lose you / JP'S afternoon / I can't get started / I'm old fashioned / Once I had a secret love / Sonatina for Melissa / Over the rainbow / Doctor is out
CCD 79520 / Feb '97 / Candid

☐ I TOLD YOU SO
I told you so / My funny valentine / Continental / Emily / Dance of the little ones / My old flame / Limehouse blues
CCD 79533 / Feb '97 / Candid

☐ LOST CATHEDRAL, THE
ITMP 970087 / Oct '95 / ITM

☐ NEW GOLD (Shank, Bud Sextet)
Port Townsend / Alternate rout / Let me tell you why / Straight no chaser / Perkolater / Grizzly / Finger therapy (for Sherman) / Linda / Killer Joe / Funcused blues / Little rootie tootie
CCD 79707 / Feb '97 / Candid

☐ PLAYS THE MUSIC OF BILL EVANS
FSR 5012CD / Nov '97 / Fresh Sound

☐ SUNSHINE EXPRESS
Sunshine express / Flim flam / Here's that rainy day / John c / C'est what / Horizon / No. 10 shuffle / Westward passage
CCD 6020 / Sep '91 / Concord Jazz

Shankar, Lakshminarayana

☐ MRCS
Adagio / March / All I care / Reasons / Back again / Al's hallucinations / Sally / White buffalo / Ocean waves
8416422 / Jun '91 / ECM

☐ NOBODY TOLD ME
Chittham irangaayo / Chodhanai thanthu / Nadru dri dhom - tillana
8396232 / Nov '89 / ECM

☐ PANCHA NADAI PALLAVI
Ragam tanam pallavi / Ragam: Sankarabharanam / Talam mahalakshmi tala / 9/12 beats / Pancha nadai pallavi
8416412 / Jun '90 / ECM

☐ SONG FOR EVERYONE
Paper nut / I know / Watching you / Conversation / Song for everyone / Let's go home / Rest in peace
8237952 / Apr '85 / ECM

☐ WHO'S TO KNOW
Ragam tanam pallavi / Ananda nadamaadum tillai sankara
8272692 / Dec '85 / ECM

Shankar, Ravi

☐ AT THE WOODSTOCK FESTIVAL
Raga puriya-Dhanashri / Gat in Sawarital / Tabla solo in Jhaptal / Raga manj-khama
BGOCD 117 / Jul '91 / Beat Goes On

☐ CHANTS OF INDIA
Vandanaa Trayee / Omkaaraaya Namaha / Vedic chanting / Asato Maa / Sahanaa Vavatu / Poornamadah / Gaayatri / Mahaa Mrityunjaya / Veenaa-Murali / Geetaa / Mangalam / Hari Om / Svfgara Mantra / Prabhugee / Sarve Shaam
CTMCD 340 / 1 Sep '97 / EMI Classics

☐ CONCERT FOR PEACE LIVE AT THE ROYAL ALBERT HALL (2CD Set)
MRCD 1013 / Oct '95 / Moment

☐ FESTIVAL FROM INDIA
BGOCD 301 / Nov '95 / Beat Goes On

☐ FROM INDIA
Raga palas kafl / Raga bilashkani todl / Bangla dhun
CD 12522 / Feb '95 / Music Of The World

☐ IMPROVISATIONS
Improvisation on the theme music from pather panchall / Fire night / Karnataki (raga kirvani) / Raga rageshri (part 1) (alap) (part 2) (jor) (part 3) (gat)
BGOCD 115 / Jul '91 / Beat Goes On

☐ IN CONCERT
BGOCD 302 / May '96 / Beat Goes On

☐ IN NEW YORK
Raga bairaga / Nata bhariravl / Raga marwa
BGOCD 144 / Jun '92 / Beat Goes On

☐ IN SAN FRANCISCO
Raga bhupal todi-tala ardha jaital / Tabla solo-shikar tal / Dhun (a morning raga in sindhi-bhairavi) tala dadra
BGOCD 197 / Dec '93 / Beat Goes On

☐ INDIA'S MASTER MUSICIAN
Kafi-holi (spring festival of colors) / Dhun (folk airs) / Mishra pilco, in thumbri style / Raga puriya dhamasbrl / Raga charu kishl
BGOCD 218 / Jan '94 / Beat Goes On

☐ INSIDE THE KREMLIN
Prarambh / Shanti mantra / Three ragas in D minor / Sandhya / Tarana / Bahu-rang
259620 / Feb '89 / Arista

☐ LIVE AT THE MONTEREY FESTIVAL
Raga Bhimpalasi / Tabla solo in Ektal / Dhun
BGOCD 147 / Jul '93 / Beat Goes On

☐ PANDIT RAVI SHANKAR
C558 674 / '88 / Ocora

☐ PORTRAIT OF A GENIUS
Tala rasa ranga / Dhun / Tabla-dhwanl / Song from the hills / Tala-tabla tarang / Gai kirwanl / Raga multan
BGOCD 99 / '91 / Beat Goes On

☐ RAGA JOGESHWARI
IN 5739 / 11 May '98 / Interra

☐ RAGAS (2CD Set)
Palas kafi / Bilashkani todi / Ramdas malhar / Malika
FCD 247142 / Mar '96 / Fantasy

☐ RAGAS AND TALAS
BGOCD 409 / 17 Aug '98 / Beat Goes On

☐ RAVI - IN CELEBRATION (4CD Set) (Shankar, Ravi/Various Artists)
Charukeshi / Bhatiyar / Adarini / Marwa / Dhun Kafi / V7 1/2 / Jait / Sandhya raga / Ghanashyam / Tilak shyam / Duet for sitar and violin / Sitar concertos 1 and 2 / Morning love / Indo Japan finale / Enchanted dawn / Vandana / Hey Nath / Pather Panchali / Supaney me aye / West eats meat / Oh bhagawan / Friar Park / Tana mana / I am missing you / Ta Na Tom / Fire night / Sanware Sanware / Dispute and violence / Shanti mantra
CDS 5555772 / Mar '96 / Angel

☐ RAVI - IN CELEBRATION (Highlights) (Shankar, Ravi/Various Artists)
Dhun Kafi: *Shankar, Ravi* / Supaney mein aye: *Shankar, Ravi* / 2nd Movement Sitar Concerto: *Shankar, Ravi* / 3rd Movement Sitar Concerto no.1: *Shankar, Ravi* / West eats meat: *Shankar, Ravi* / Tilak Shyam: Shankar, Ravi / I am missing you: *Shankar, Ravi*
CDC 5556172 / Sep '96 / Angel

☐ RAVI SHANKAR
C 570000CD / Jul '95 / Ocora

☐ RAVI SHANKAR & ALI AKBAR KHAN IN CONCERT 1972 (2CD Set) (Shankar, Ravi & Ali Akbar Khan)
Raga / Hem bihag / Manj Khamaj part 1 / Manj Khamaj part 2 / Sindhi Bhairavi
CDSAPDO 1002 / Feb '97 / Apple

☐ RAVI SHANKAR IN VENICE
ED 1031 / Mar '96 / Edelweiss

☐ SITAR CONCERTOS (2CD Set) (Shankar, Ravi & Yehudi Menuhin/ Andre Previn)
CZS 5726552 / 4 May '98 / EMI Classics

☐ SOUND OF THE SITAR
Raga Malkauns / Tala Sawari (Tabla Solo) / Pahari Dhun
BGOCD 171 / Apr '93 / Beat Goes On

☐ TANA MANA (Shankar, Ravi Project)
Chase / Tana mana / Village dance / Seven and 10 1/2 / Fir park / Romantic voyage / Memory of Uday / West eats meat / Reunion / Supplication
259962 / Nov '89 / Private Music

☐ TOWARDS THE RISING SUN (Shankar, Ravi & Friends)
Padhasapa / Kaharwa / Rokudan / Namah shivaya / Tribute to Nippon / Homage to Baba Allauddin
4495992 / Jun '96 / Deutsche Grammophon

☐ TRANSMIGRATION MACABRE
Madness / Anxiety / Submission / Transmigration / Reflection / Fantasy / Torment / Death / Retribution
C5CD 596 / Mar '97 / See For Miles

Shanks, Andy

☐ DIAMONDS IN THE NIGHT (Shanks, Andy & Jim Russell)
Balgonie barn/Thirty year man / Ash pirates / Rags and days / Streets and dances / Money, guns and the green green forest / St. Andrew in the window / Compass heart / Road here / Diamonds in the night / Midnight city buses / Mogadishu / Fiddler / Wake
CUL 112D / Jun '97 / Culburnie

Shanley, Eleanor

☐ DESERT HEART
GRACD 225 / 11 May '98 / Grapevine

☐ ELEANOR SHANLEY
GRACD 206 / Apr '95 / Grapevine

Shannon Castle Singers

☐ MEDIAEVAL BANQUET
DOLCD 1007 / Jul '96 / Dolphin

Shannon Singers

☐ 60 SHADES OF GREEN
CDIRISH 002 / Mar '96 / Outlet

☐ CHRISTMAS PARTY
CCSCD 801 / Jan '95 / Outlet

☐ GOLDEN COLLECTION OF IRISH SONGS
CDIRISH 008 / Oct '95 / Outlet

Shannon, Del

☐ ALL THE HITS AND MORE
Runaway / Hats off to Larry / Hey little girl / So long baby / Cry myself to sleep / Little town flirt / Two kinds of teardrops / Two silhouettes / Keep searchin' (we'll follow the sun) / Stranger in town / Broken promises / Swiss maid / From me to you / Handy man / Do you wanna dance / You never talked about me / Kelly / Give her lots of lovin' / Over you / Break up / Why don't you tell him / Jody / Sue's gotta be mine / Answer to everything
QED 098 / Nov '96 / Tring

☐ BEST OF DEL SHANNON, THE
Runaway / Hats off to Harry / So long baby / Dream baby / Hey little girl / Break up / Cry myself to sleep / You never talked about me / Swiss maid / Little town flirt / Hey baby / Two kinds of teardrops / Kelly / Mary Jane / From me to you / Stranger in town / Keep searchin' (we'll follow the sun) / Do you wanna dance / Handy man / Runaround Sue / That's the way love is / Sues gotta be mine / Two silhouettes / World without love
CD 6011 / Apr '96 / Music

☐ DEFINITIVE COLLECTION, THE (2CD Set)
Search / I'll always love you / Runaway / Snake / Jody / Hats off to Larry / Don't gild the lily lily / So long baby / Answer to everything / Hey little girl / I don't care anymore / Ginny in the mirror / I won't be there / Cry myself to sleep / I'm gonna move on / Swiss maid / You never talked about me / Little town flirt / Wamboo / Two kinds of teardrops / Kelly / From me to you / Two silhouettes / Sue's gotta be mine / Since she's been gone / My wild one / She cried / I wake up crying / That's the way love is / Time of day / Mary Jane / Stains on my letter / Handy man / Give her lots of lovin' / Do you wanna dance / This is all I have to give / Keep searchin' (we'll follow the sun) / Broken promises / Stranger in town / Rag doll / Over you / Break up / Why don't you tell him / Move it on over / She still remembers Tony / I can't believe my ears / I wish I wasn't me tonight / His latest flame / Running scared / Runaround sue / Dream baby / Go away little girl / Hey baby / Kaw-liga / Hey good looking / I go to pieces / She thinks I still care / I'll be lonely tomorrow / I can't fool around anymore / Pepsi ads
CPCD 83152 / Oct '97 / Charly

☐ DEL SHANNON 1961-1990 (A Complete Career Anthology/2CD Set)
Runaway / Hats off to Larry / So long baby / Hey little girl / Cry myself to sleep / You never talked about me / Jody / Swiss maid / Ginny in the mirror / Little town flirt / Two kinds of teardrops / From me to you / Two silhouettes / Sue's gotta be mine / That's the way love is / Handy man / Mary Jane / Keep searchin' (follow the sun) / Stranger in town / Break up / Why don't you tell him / Move it on over / I go to pieces / Under my thumb / Show me / Letter / Runaway '67 / Cut and come again / Friendly with you / Led along / Mind over matter / Thinkin' it over / Gemini / Sister Isabelle / Kelly / Distant ghost / Deadly game / Help me / Oh how happy / And the music plays on / Tell her no / Cry baby cry / Restless / Sea of love / Drop down and get me / To love someone / Cheap love / Broken down angel / Something to believe in / Hot love / Walk away / Calling out my name / Who left who / Runaway / Crying / Do you wanna dance / Pepsi spot
RVCD 51 / Feb '98 / Raven

☐ DROP DOWN AND GET ME
Sea of love / Life without you / Out of time / Sucker for your love / To love someone / Cheap love / Drop down and get me / Maybe tomorrow / Liar / Never stop tryin' / Midnight train
VAR 5927 / 15 Jun '98 / Varese Sarabande

☐ FURTHER ADVENTURES OF CHARLES WESTOVER, THE
Thinkin' it over / Be my friend / Silver birch / I think I love you / River cool / Colour flashing hair / Gemini / Runnin' on back / Conquer / Been so long / Magical music box / New Orleans / She / Runaway / What's the matter baby / Early in the morning / In my arms again
BGOCD 402 / 3 Aug '98 / Beat Goes On

☐ GOLD
GOLD 051 / Aug '96 / Gold

☐ GREATEST HITS
Runaway / Hats off to Larry / Little town flirt / Swiss maid / Hey little girl / Two kinds of teardrops / So long baby / She's gotta be mine / From me to you / Handyman / Do you want to dance / Big hurt / Keep searchin' (we'll follow the sun) / Stranger in town / Break up / Cry myself to sleep / Two silouettes / Don't gild the lily / Lily / Ginny in the mirror / I go to pieces
CPCD 8001 / Oct '93 / Charly

☐ GREATEST HITS
MU 5017 / Oct '92 / Musketeer

☐ LITTLE TOWN FLIRT/HANDY MAN
Two kinds of teardrops / Dream baby / Happiness / Two silhouettes / She thinks I still care / My wild one / Runaround Sue / From me to you / Kelly / Hey baby / Go away little girl / Little town flirt / Memphis / That's the way love is / Ruby baby / I'll be lonely tomorrow / I can't fool around anymore / Handy man / Crying / Mary Jane / World without love / Sorry (I ran all the way) / Give her lots of lovin' / Twist and shout
BGOCD 388 / 30 Mar '98 / Beat Goes On

☐ LIVE IN ENGLAND/AND THE MUSIC PLAYED ON
Hats off to Larry / Handyman / Swiss maid / Hey little girl / Little town flirt / Kelly / Crying / Two kinds of teardrops / Coopersville yodel / Answer to everything / Keep searchin' (we'll follow the sun) / What's the matter baby / So long baby / Runaway / It's my feeling / Mind over matter / Silently / Cut and come again / My love has gone / Led along / Life is nothing / Music plays on / Easy to say / Friendly with you / Raindrops / He cheated / Leaving you behind / Runaway '67
BGOCD 280 / Jun '95 / Beat Goes On

☐ RUNAWAY
Runaway / Hats off to larry / So long baby / Hey little girl / Cry myself to sleep / Swiss maid / Little town flirt / Two kinds of teardrops / Two silhouettes / She's got to be mind / Handy man / Keep searchin' / Stranger in town / Do you want to dance / Break up / Mary jane / Running scared / Runaround sue / Hey baby / His latest flame
RMB 75027 / Nov '93 / Remember

☐ RUNAWAY (The Ultimate Collection)
Runaway / Kelly / So long baby / Swiss maid / Hats off to Larry / Answer to everything / Cry myself to sleep / Two kinds of teardrops / Don't gild the lily, Lily / Jody / Keep searchin' (we'll follow the sun) / From me to you / Do you want to dance / Handy man / Little town flirt / You never talked about me / Two silhouettes / Hey little girl / I go to pieces / Sue's gotta be mine
3036000792 / Jul '97 / Carlton

☐ RUNAWAY WITH DEL SHANNON/ HATS OFF TO DEL SHANNON
Misery / Day dreams / His latest flame / Prom / Search / Runaway / I wake up crying / Wide wide world / I'll always love you / Lies / He doesn't care / Jody / Swiss maid / Cry myself to sleep / Ginny in the mirror / You never talked about me / Don't gild the lily, Lily / I won't be there / Hats off to Larry / Answer to everything / Hey little girl / I'm gonna move on / I don't care anymore / So long baby
BGOCD 367 / 26 Sep '97 / Beat Goes On

☐ SINGS HANK WILLIAMS/1661 SECONDS
BGOCD 404 / 17 Aug '98 / Beat Goes On

☐ THIS IS DEL SHANNON
Runaway / Hats off to Larry / Prom / (Marie's the name) his latest flame / So long baby / Answer to everything / Hey little girl / You never talked about me / Ginny in the mirror / I won't be there / Cry myself to sleep / Swiss maid / Little town flirt / Two kinds of teardrops / Kolly / From me to you / Two silhouettes / That's the way love is / Mary Jane / Handy man / Sorry (I ran all the way home) / Keep searchin' (we'll follow the sun) / Stranger in town / Break up / Move it on over / She still remembers Tony / Needles and pins / I go to pieces / I can't believe my ears / I wish I wasn't me tonight / Sue's gonna be mine / Do you wanna dance
MCCD 326 / Nov '97 / Music Club

☐ THIS IS MY BAG/TOTAL COMMITMENT
BGOCD 307 / Mar '96 / Beat Goes On

☐ VERY BEST OF DEL SHANNON, THE
Runaway / Stranger in town / Keep searchin' (we'll follow the sun) / Needles and pins / Rag doll / I wake up crying / Wide wide world / Lies / Do you wanna dance / I go to pieces / Over you / I'll always love you / Prom / Broken promises
WB 885512 / 2 Feb '98 / Disky

Shannon, Hugh

☐ SALOON SINGER (2CD Set)
ACD 171/172 / Jul '96 / Audiophile

☐ TRUE BLUE HUGH
ACD 140 / Apr '93 / Audiophile

Shannon, Mem

☐ MEM SHANNON'S 2ND BLUES ALBUM
Wrong people are in charge / Old men / Charity / Say that then (The parlez-vous francais song) / One thin dime / Mirror, mirror / My humble opinion / Down broke / Do you 'yuh' what I say / Mr. Blues / Blues is back
HNCD 1409 / Apr '97 / Hannibal

Shannon, Preston

☐ BREAK THE ICE (Shannon, Preston Band)
BB 9545CD / Aug '94 / Bullseye Blues

Shannon, Sharon

☐ EACH LITTLE THING
GRACD 226 / Mar '97 / Grapevine

☐ OUT THE GAP
ROCDG 14 / Jan '95 / Grapevine

☐ SHARON SHANNON
Glentown / Blackbird / Queen of the West / Retour des hirondelles/Tune for a found harmonium / Miss Thomson and Derry reel / Munster hop / Tickle her leg / Marguerita suite / Coridinio / Anto's cajun cousins / Cornphiopa corafinne and skidoo / Marbhna luimni / Phil Cunningham sets / Woodchoppers/Reel des Voygeurs
ROCDG 8 / Jan '95 / Grapevine

Shannon, Simon

☐ BLOODY JESUS
RMCD 006 / 9 Mar '98 / Ready Made

Shannon, Tom

☐ ROCKIN' REBELS
Tom Shannon show logo / Wild weekend / Rockin' crickets / Whole lotta shakin' goin' on / Another wild weekend / Rumble / Hully gully rock / Flibbity jibbitt / Honky tonk / Happy popcorn / Monday morning / Sweet little sixteen / Buffalo blues / Tequila / Wild rebel / Third man theme / Wild weekend cha cha / Ram-bunk-shush / Telstar / Donkey walk / Stripper / Coconuts / Loaded dice / Anyway you want me / Theme from the rebel / Wild weekend theme
CDCHD 426 / May '94 / Ace

Shantel

☐ HIGHER THAN THE FUNK
Tell me why it is oh so hard to be oh so lovely / Philosophy / Where the story ends life begins / Intro / Letter from the editor / Ding dong ding / I am exactly what you are looking for / Tosca session / I am not afraid / Really good photo / Unending / Fiercly independent / All I want / Little sound / Blessed
K7R 021CD / 18 May '98 / Studio K7

Shanti, Oliver

☐ TAI CHI
SKV 006CD / Jul '95 / Sattva Art

Shanty Crew

☐ SEA SHANTIES & SAILOR SONGS (Classics From The Great Days Of Sail 1840-1890)
Prologue: the leef fore brace / Old moke pickin' on the banjo / Can't ye hio / Where am I to go, M'Johnnies / One more day / Rolling coal / Randy dandy o / Ranzo ray / Yankee john, stormalong / Frankie's trade / Bring em down / Do let me 'lone susan / General Taylor / Gals o'Dublin town / Paddy Doyle's boots / Bully in the alley / Heave away boys heave away / Johnny Bowker / Common Sailors / Spanish ladies / I'm bound away / Shallow brown / Fire down below / John Kanaka / Cheer'ly man / Hi-o, come roll me over / East Indiaman / Paddy lay back / Epilogue: d'ye mind
BHCD 9601 / Dec '96 / Brewhouse

Shaolin Wooden Men

☐ SHAOLIN WOODEN MEN
NZ 013 / Jul '94 / Nova Zembla

Shapeshifter

☐ MYSTERY OF BEING
HY 85921054 / Apr '94 / Hyperium

Shapiro, Helen

☐ AT ABBEY ROAD 1961-1967
Don't treat me like a child / You don't know / Walkin back to happiness / Walkin back to happiness / Kiss n' run / I want to be happy / Let's talk about love / Tell me what he said / Little Miss Lonely / Teenager sings the blues / I can't say no to your kiss / Sometime yesterday / I don't care / Basin st blues / Every one but the right one / Keep away from other girls / Dozen other boys / Queen for tonight / Time and time again / Look who is it / Fever / Look over your shoulder / It's in his kiss / I wish I'd never loved you / Shop around / Keep your hands off my baby / You're my remedy / I'm going out the same way I came in
4934522 / 23 Feb '98 / EMI

☐ EP COLLECTION, THE
Little devil / I don't care / Don't treat me like a child / You don't know / Teenager in love / Lipstick on your collar / Beyond the sea / Little Miss Lonely / Day the rains came / Tell me what he said / Walkin' back to happiness / I apologise / Let's talk about love / When I'm with you / Because they're young / St. Louis blues / Goody goody / Birth of the blues / Keep away from other girls / After you've gone
SEECD 272 / Mar '98 / See For Miles

☐ **ESSENTIAL COLLECTION, THE**
Don't treat me like a child / You don't know / Walkin' back to happiness / Tell me what he said / Let's talk about love / Little Miss Lonely / Keep away from other girls / Queen for tonight / Woe is me / Look who it is / Fever / Look over your shoulder / Tomorrow is another day / Shop around / I wish I'd never loved you / When I'm with you / Marvellous lie / Kiss n' run / I apologise / Sometime yesterday / I don't care / Cry my heart out / Daddy couldn't get me one of those / Walking in my dreams / Ole father time / He knows how how to love me / I walked right in / You won't come home / I was only kidding / It's so funny I could cry
CDMFP 6400 / 13 Oct '97 / Music For Pleasure

☐ **HELEN IN NASHVILLE**
Not responsible / I cried myself to sleep last night / Young stranger / Here today and gone tomorrow / It's my party / No trespassing / I'm tickled pink / I walked right in / Sweeter than sweet / You'd think he didn't know me / When you hurt me / I cry / Woe is me
C5CD545 / '89 / See For Miles

☐ **HELEN SHAPIRO**
Don't treat me like a child / You don't know / Walkin' back to happiness / Tell me what he said / Let's talk about love / Little Miss Lonely / Keep away from other girls / Queen for tonight / Woe is me / Look who it is / Fever / Look over your shoulder / Tomorrow is another day / Shop around / I wish I'd never loved you / When I'm with you / Marvellous lie / Kiss 'n' run / I apologise / Sometime yesterday / I don't care / Cry my heart out / Daddy couldn't get me one of those / Walking in my dreams / Ole Father Time / He knows how to love me / I walked right in / You won't come home / I was only kidding / It's so funny I could cry
CC 259 / Oct '90 / Music For Pleasure

☐ **IMMER DIE BOYS**
Frag'mich nicht warum / Komm sei wieder gut / Den ton kenn'ich schon / Gestern nachmittag / Ich war der star heute nacht / Glaube mir, Jonny / Schlafen kann ich nie / Warum gerade ich / Immer die boys / Rote rosen und vergissmeinnicht / Sag dass es schonist / Ich such mir meinen brautigam alleine aus / Der weg zu de inem herzen / Das ist nicht die feine englische art / Walkin' back to happiness / Don't treat me like a child / Tout ce qu'il voudra / J'ai tant de remords / Parlons d'amour / Sans penser a rien
BCD 15509 / Jul '90 / Bear Family

☐ **QUALITY OF MERCER, THE/ STRAIGHTEN UP AND FLY RIGHT (The Best Of The 1980's/2CD Set)**
001A/B / Nov '97 / Katalyst

☐ **SENSATIONAL**
Teenager sings the blues / Blues in the night / Are you lonesome tonight / Tearaway Johnny / Without your love / Aren't you the lucky one / Every one but the right one / It's alright without me / Lookin' for my heart / Basin Street blues / You must be readin' my mind / Till I hear the truth from you / Sensational / Easy come, easy go / Remember me / End of the world / It might as well rain until September / Here in your arms / Only once / Just a line / Forget about the bad things / Wait a little longer / In my calendar / Empty house
RPM 151 / Jul '95 / RPM

☐ **SING SWING TOGETHER...AGAIN (Shapiro, Helen & Humphrey Lyttelton Band)**
Shiny stockings / Sentimental journey / Someone to watch over me / Red beans and rice / Maybe/Java live / All too soon / That old familiar trouble / Beale Street blues / Echoing the blues / Moving into Spring / I must tell Jesus / Body and soul / Medley / How long has this been going on / Caravan
CLGCD 034 / 13 Jul '98 / Calligraph

☐ **TOPS WITH ME**
Little devil / Will you love me tomorrow / Because they're young / Day the rains came / Are you lonesome tonight / Teenager in love / Lipstick on your collar / Beyond the sea / Sweet nothin's / You mean ev'rything to me / I love you / You got what it takes
DORIG 107 / 1 Sep '97 / EMI

Shapiro, Yaacov

☐ **BEST OF YIDDISH FOLK SONGS**
Kinder jorn / Vu bistu geven / Aroiskumen zolstu main meidl / Shabes shabes / Unter boimer / Abisl zin abisl reign / Rebe elimelech / Shlof shoin main jankele / Idish gesl / Kadish / Di zun is fargangen / Skeshenever shtikele / Hobn mir a meidl / Hop maine humentashn
EUCD 1216 / Sep '93 / ARC

☐ **YIDDISH TRADITIONAL SONGS**
EU 1337CD / Mar '96 / ARC

Sharakan Early Music Ensemble

☐ **MUSIC OF ARMENIA VOL.2, THE**
131162 / Aug '96 / Celestial Harmonies

Shareh, Oku

☐ **TURTLE DANCE SONGS OF SAN JUAN PEBLO**
803012 / Sep '92 / New World

Shark Taboo

☐ **BLACK ROCK SANDS**
PLASCD 021 / Nov '89 / Plastic Head

Sharkboy

☐ **MATINEE**
NUDECD 2 / Apr '94 / Nude

☐ **VALENTINE TAPES**
NUDECD 4 / Sep '95 / Nude

Sharkey

☐ **HARD LIFE**
Death by stereo / Hard life / Enuff / Product of society / Even angels fade away / Distant dreams / Awakening / Pain killer / You complete me / Forever flying / Funk D'hardcore
REACTCD 131 / 20 Jul '98 / React

Sharkey, Feargal

☐ **FEARGAL SHARKEY**
Good heart / You little thief / Ghost train / Ashes and diamond / Made to measure / Someone to somebody / Don't leave it to nature / Love and hate / Bitter man / It's all over now
CDVIP 166 / Oct '96 / Virgin VIP

Sharks

☐ **COLOUR MY FLESH**
Hanger 84 / Grave robber / Desire calls / Time bomb / Blue water, white death / Rat race / Man with the x-ray eyes / Jet boy / On the run / Too little, too late / Parasite / Sgt rock
CDMPSYCHO 14 / Jun '97 / Anagram

☐ **PHANTOM ROCKERS**
Moonstomp / Skeleton rock / It'a all over now / Crazy maybe / Take a razor to your head / Death row / Love bites / Short shark shock / Ruff stuff / Phantom rockers / Charlie / Slipped disc / I can't stop / Electrifyin'
NERCD 008 / Oct '91 / Nervous

☐ **RECREATIONAL KILLER**
Screw / Bye bye girl / Charlie (93 version) / Recreational killer / Dealer / Hooker / Surfcaster / Morphine daze / Publican gullican / Gettin' even with you / Something in my basement / Blockhouse / I'm hooked on you / Schizoid man / Charlie 2 / Scratchin' my way out
CDMPSYCHO 13 / Jun '97 / Anagram

Sharma, Pandit Shiv Kumar

☐ **60TH BIRTHDAY RELEASE**
Alap, Jor and Jhala / Gat in Jhaptal / Gat in Ektal
NRCD 0094 / 6 Jul '98 / Navras

☐ **GOLDEN HERITAGE (Sharma, Pandit Shiv Kumar & Rahul Sharma)**
Alaap jor jhala / Gat composition / Dhun in 6 beat / Gat composition
NRCD 0089 / Feb '98 / Navras

☐ **RAGA PURIYA**
NRCD 0060 / May '96 / Navras

Sharma, Shivkumar

☐ **CALL OF THE VALLEY**
Rag pahadi / Ghara dadra / Dhun mishra / Bageshwari / Rag piloo / Bhoop / Rag des
CDEMC 3707 / Apr '95 / EMI

☐ **RAG MADHUVANTI/RAG MISRA TILANG**
NI 5110 / Sep '94 / Nimbus

Sharon, Ralph

☐ **MAGIC OF COLE PORTER, THE (Sharon, Ralph Trio)**
You're the top / All through the night / Easy to love / Get out of town / You'd be so nice to come home to / I concentrate on you / I've got you under my skin / Down in the depths / So in love / Anything goes / Let's do it / From this moment on / What is this thing called love / Do I love you / Night and day / I love Paris / Love for sale / I love you / It's all right with me / All of you / I get a kick out of you / Why should I / Just one of those things / Long last love / Begin the beguine / Sorta Porter
CDSIV 1123 / Jul '95 / Horatio Nelson

☐ **MAGIC OF GEORGE GERSHWIN, THE (Sharon, Ralph Trio)**
Fascinating rhythm / They all laughed / Somebody loves me / 'S Wonderful / But not for me / Soon / I loves you Porgy / I got rhythm / They can't take that away from me / Someone to watch over me / Man I love / Our love is here to stay / There's a boat that's leavin' soon for New York / Rhapsody in blue / Foggy day / Embraceable you / Liza / How long has this been going on / Swanee / Love walked in / Oh lady be good
CDSIV 1116 / Jul '95 / Horatio Nelson

☐ **MAGIC OF IRVING BERLIN, THE (Sharon, Ralph Trio)**
Now it can be told / Easter parade / I got lost in her arms / There's no business like show business / White christmas / Let yourself go / I love a piano / They say it's wonderful / Be careful it's my heart / I got the sun in the morning / I used to be color blind / Shakin' the blues away / Say it isn't so / Let's face the music and dance / Pretty girl is like a melody / All of my life / Russian lullaby / Deserving irving
CDSIV 1134 / Jul '95 / Horatio Nelson

☐ **MAGIC OF JEROME KERN, THE (Sharon, Ralph Trio)**
Smoke gets in your eyes / Folks who live on the hill / Long ago and far away / Nobody else but me / Song is you / Who / In love in vain / Remind me / All the things you are / She didn't say yes / Last time I saw paris / Yesterdays / I won't dance / I'm old fashioned
CDSIV 1138 / Oct '96 / Horatio Nelson

☐ **MAGIC OF RODGERS & HART, THE (Sharon, Ralph Trio)**
I didn't know what time it was / Falling in love with love / Most beautiful girl in the world / Lover / Wait till you see her / Slaughter on 10th Avenue / You are too beautiful / I wish I were in love again / Bewitched, bothered and bewildered / Ten cents a dance / Have you met Miss Jones / It's easy to remember / Where or when / Mountain greenery / I could write a book / Mimi / On your toes / Thou swell / My romance / This can't be love / My funny valentine / Lady is a tramp / There's a small hotel / Little girl blue / Isn't it romantic / Blue room / It never entered my mind / Blues for Rodgers and Hart
CDSIV 1130 / Nov '96 / Horatio Nelson

☐ **PLAY THE HARRY WARREN SONGBOOK (Sharon, Ralph Trio)**
That's amore / You're getting to be a habit with me / September in the rain / This heart of mine / My heart tells me / You must have been a beautiful baby / Spring isn't everything / Serenade in blue / At last / More I see you / Shuffle off to Buffalo / You'll never know / Jeepers creepers / I only have eyes for you / Affair to remember / I've got a gal in Kalamazoo / Lullaby of Broadway / Harry's minor lament
DRGCD 5245 / 27 Oct '97 / DRG

☐ **PORTRAIT OF HAROLD**
My shining hour / Ill wind / Let's fall in love / This time the dream's on me / It's only a paper moon / Portrait of Harold / Come rain or come shine / It was written in the stars / Between the devil and the deep blue sea / Man that got away / I've got the world on a string / Out of this world / Sing my heart / Sleepin' bee / Hit the road to dreamland / Right as the rain / That old black magic
DRGCD 91447 / May '96 / DRG

☐ **SWINGS THE SAMMY CAHN SONGBOOK (Sharon, Ralph Trio & Gerry Mulligan)**
My king of town / Teach me tonight / Mario Lanza medley - Be my love / Guess I'll hang my tears out to dry / It's magic / It's you or no one / Call me irresponsible / Blues for Sammy / Things we did last summer / Autumn in Rome / I should care / All the way / Time after time / Tender trap
DRGCD 5232 / Feb '95 / DRG

Sharon Stoned

☐ **LICENSE TO CONFUSE**
OUT 1252 / Sep '97 / Brake Out

Sharp, Brian

☐ **AMOR AMOR**
Thunder and lightning polka / Amor, amor / Return to mijas / Tocatta and fugue / True love ways / Stars fall on alabama / All in the april evening / My fair lady (selection) / I'm putting all my eggs in one basket (foxtrot) / Amapola-an apple for the teacher (mayfair quickstep) / Bye bye baby-diamonds are a girls best friend (mayfair quick / Don't blame me-if I had you (saunter together) / Garden in the rain-by the fireside (saunter together) / No other lcve (square tango) / Touch of your lips (sereda tango) / Missing / Great little army / King and I (selection)
CDGRS 1247 / Feb '93 / Grosvenor

☐ **FREEWAY**
Freeway / Girl talk / La reine de saba / Girl from corsica / Look to the sky / My one and only love / What a diff'rence a day made / Body and soul / I'll never say goodbye / More-'til / Joanne / Love is the sweetest thing / Somewhere in time / Nighthawk / It's magic dream / Tribute to david whitfield / Cara mia / Answer me / When you lose the one you love / Book / I'll find you
CDGRS 1212 / Feb '93 / Grosvenor

☐ **ORCHESTRAL KEYBOARDS**
Freeway / West of sunset / Pizzicato polka / East Enders theme / Somewhere in time / MacArthur Park / Melody on the move / In the middle of a serenade / Coronation scot / Howard's Way / Body and soul / Garden party
OS 240 / 29 Jun '98 / Bandleader

Sharp, Dee Dee

☐ **WHAT COLOUR IS LOVE/DEE DEE**
I believe in love / Just as long as I know you're mine / Tryin' to get the feeling again / I wanna be your woman / Flashback / Nobody could take your place / What color is love / I'd really love to see you tonight / Hang your portrait / What color is love / Breaking and entering / Let's get this party started / I love you anyway / Easy money / Invitation / Evryday affair / If we're gonna stay together / See you later
WESM 515 / 16 Mar '98 / Westside

Sharp, Elliott

☐ **ABSTRACT REPRESSIONISM 1990-1999**
VICTOCD 019 / Nov '94 / Victo

☐ **ARC VOL.2 (The Seventies)**
ALP 92CD / Jun '97 / Atavistic

☐ **BLACKBURST (Sharp, Elliot & Zeena Parkins)**
VICTOCD 044 / Mar '97 / Victo

☐ **DATACIDE**
EMY 1162 / Sep '97 / Enemy

☐ **FIGURE GROUND**
TZA 7505 / Feb '97 / Tzadik

☐ **HAMMER, ANVIL, STIRRUP (Sharp, Elliott & The Soldier String Quartet)**
SST 232CD / Dec '89 / SST

☐ **IN THE LAND OF THE YAHOOS**
In the land of the yahoos / Free society / Fundementia / L-I-love / Sink or swim / Station break / Gulagogo / Ras-ten / Ornament and crime / Shopping maul / Ratnap
SST 128CD / Feb '88 / SST

☐ **INTERFERENCE (Sharp, Elliott & Carbon)**
ALP 50CD / Jun '97 / Atavistic

☐ **ISM/ARC (Sharp, Elliott & Carbon)**
ALP 61CD / Jun '97 / Atavistic

☐ **MONSTER CURVE**
Geometry / Iso / Helicopters / Inverse proportions / Cia pope / Last laugh / Vicious cycle / Singularity / Intervention / Squig / Turbulence / Dusts / Lacunar / Not-yet-time
SST 208CD / May '93 / SST

☐ **PSYCHO-ACOUSTIC (Sharp, Elliot & Zeena Parkins)**
VICTOCD 026 / Oct '94 / Victo

☐ **TECTONICS FIELD AND STREAM**
KFWCD 227 / 3 Aug '98 / Knitting Factory

☐ **TECTONICS VOL.1**
EFA 127622 / Jun '95 / Atonal

☐ **TECTONICS VOL.2 (Field & Stream)**
EFA 129382 / Apr '97 / Atonal

☐ **TOCSIN (Sharp, Elliott & Carbon)**
EMY 1342 / Sep '97 / Enemy

Sharp, John

☐ **BETTER THAN DREAMS**
RR 54CD / May '96 / Reference Recordings

Sharpe, Jack

☐ **CATALYST (A Tribute To Tubby Hayes) (Sharpe, Jack Big Band)**
Milestones / You know I care / Sharpe edge / Suddenly last Tuesday / Keith / Souriya / Allisamba
CDFRG 716 / Jun '89 / Frog

☐ **ROARIN' (Sharpe, Jack Big Band)**
I'm beginning to see the light / Old folks / Mayfly / Wait and see / 100 degrees proof / Skylark / All the things you are / K and J / J and B
JHCD 016 / Jan '94 / Ronnie Scott's Jazz House

Sharpe, Ray

☐ **LINDA LU**
Linda Lu / Monkey's uncle / Oh my baby's gone / That's the way I feel / Kewpie doll / Red sails in the sunset / Silly Dilly Millie / Bus song / TA blues / Long John / Gonna let it go this time / Bermuda / Give'n up / For you my love / Justine / On the street where you live / There'll come a day / Dallas / So sorry / Hey little girl / Thank you so much / New Linda Lu / TA blues / Long John / Kewpie doll / On the street where you live / Red sails in the sunset
BCD 15888 / Nov '95 / Bear Family

Sharpe, Rocky

☐ **FABULOUS ROCKY SHARPE & THE REPLAYS (Sharpe, Rocky & The Replays)**
Rama lama ding dong / Imagination / Love will make you fail in school / Martian hop / Shout shout (knock yourself out) / Heart / Never / Come on let's go / Looking for an echo / Teenager in love / Never be anyone else but you / Get a job
CDFAB 009 / Oct '91 / Ace

☐ **SO HARD TO LAUGH (Sharpe, Rocky & The Razors)**
I wonder why / Drip drop / Daddy cool / Devil or angel / One summer night / So hard to laugh so easy to cry / What's your name / Mathilda / Poison ivy / That's my desire / Pretty little angel eyes / As long as I'm moving / Whole lotta shakin' goin' on / Splish splash
CDWIKM 116 / Mar '93 / Chiswick

Sharpshooters

☐ **CHOKED UP**
SDW 0182 / Jan '97 / Shadow

Sharriff, Imam Omar

☐ **RAVEN, THE**
ARHCD 365 / Apr '95 / Arhoolie

Sharrock, Linda

☐ **LIKE A RIVER**
5230152 / Mar '95 / Amadeo

☐ **ON HOLIDAY**
God bless the child / Ain't nobody's business if I do / Them there eyes / Lady sings the blues / Lover man / You go to my head / Good morning heartache
8433812 / Feb '94 / Polydor

Sharrock, Sonny

☐ **GUITAR**
EMY 1022 / Sep '97 / Enemy

☐ HIGHLIFE (Sharrock, Sonny Band)
EMY 1192 / Sep '97 / Enemy

☐ INTO ANOTHER LIGHT
EMY 1562 / Sep '97 / Enemy

☐ LIVE IN NEW YORK
EMY 1082 / Sep '97 / Enemy

☐ SEIZE THE RAINBOW
EMY 1042 / Sep '97 / Enemy

Shaskeen

☐ COLLECTION OF JIGS AND REELS, A
Rambling pitchfork/Maids of Glenroe/Paddy McMahon's jig / Tommy Mulhair's jig/Castletown Connors/House in the glen / Kylebrack ramblers/ Graf spee shanagolden / Rick's rambler/Pleasure of hope / Jenny tie the bonnet/Lucy Campbell/Dunne hills / Blacksmith's anvil/Bucks of Oranmore/ Crosses of Annagh / Geese in the bog/Basket of turf/ Banna strand / Devaney's goat/Dogs among the bushes / Shaskeen/Lady Anne Montgomery/ Morrison's reel/Eileen Curran / St. Ruth's bush/Fox hunter's reel/Scotch Mary / Ash plant/Flanagan's boreen/Monsignor's blessing / Gilligan's apples/ Jackson's mistake / Galway reel/Crowley's no.2 / Bunch of thyme / Boys of Trillick/Flowers of spring / Jackie Colman's/O' Dwyer's/Martin Wynne's favourite / Pipe on the hob/Lark on the Strand/ Paddy McMahon's no.2 / Caqthy's fling/Carraroe jig/Anything for John Joe / Navvy on the line/Dublin reel/Day of the clipper
309132 / 13 Jul '98 / Hallmark

☐ IRISH TRADITIONAL MUSIC AND SONG
CDIRISH 010 / Oct '95 / Outlet

☐ SILVER JUBILEE COLLECTION
FA 3509CD / Jul '95 / GTD

☐ TRADITIONAL MUSIC FROM BELFAST
IRISHCD 10 / Jun '96 / Outlet

Shatner, William

☐ BEST OF WILLIAM SHATNER & LEONARD NIMOY, THE (Shatner, William & Leonard Nimoy)
MCLD 19328 / 1 Dec '97 / MCA

☐ TRANSFORMED MAN, THE
King Henry The Fifth / Elegy For The Brave / Theme From Cyrana / Mr. Tambourine Man / Hamlet / It Was A Very Good Year / Romeo And Juliet / How Insensitive / Spleen / Lucy In The Sky With Diamonds / Transformed man
CREV 004CD / Nov '92 / Rev-Ola

Shava Shava

☐ DIGGIN' THE ROOTS
DMUT 1248 / Jan '94 / Multitone

Shave The Monkey

☐ DRAGONFLY
APE 3002CD / Oct '94 / Pecheron

☐ MAD ARTHUR
APE 3003CD / Apr '96 / Pecheron

☐ UNSEELIE COURT
APE 3001CD / Oct '94 / Pecheron

Shaver

☐ TRAMP ON YOUR STREET
Heart of Texas / Oklahoma wind / Georgia on a fast train / Live forever / If I give my soul / Tramp on your street / KAND Corsicana, Texas / Good ol' USA / Hottest thing in town / When the fallen angels fly / Take a chance on romance / Old chunk of coal / I want some more/Tenntex tear down
DFGCD 8430 / Jun '96 / Dixie Frog

Shaver, Billy Joe

☐ I'M JUST AN OLD CHUNK OF COAL (But I'm Gonna Be A Diamond Soon)
379042 / Mar '98 / Koch

☐ OLD FIVE AND DIMERS LIKE ME
379382 / Feb '97 / Koch

☐ RESTLESS WIND
Texas uphear Tennessee / Good Lord knows / Ride me down easy / When I get my wings / Ain't no good in Mexico / Love you till the cows come home / Woman is the wonder of the world / When the word was thunderbird / America, you are my woman / Restless wind / Evergreen / Billy B Damned / We stayed too long at the fair / Honky tonk heroes / I'm going crazy in 3/4 time / Gypsy boy / Chicken on the ground / Everything, everywhere's / Slow rollin' low / Silver wings of time / Believer / You asked me to / Lately I've been leaning towards the blues / I couldn't be me without you / Music city USA
BCD 15775 / Jun '94 / Bear Family

Shaver, Eddy

☐ BAPTISM OF FIRE
Pleasure and pain / Velvet chains / Lighting a torch / Call me a doctor / Drown in love / Hair of the dog / Prayer in paradise / King of fools / If it don't kill you / Good news blues / Baptism of fire
DFGCD 8452 / Oct '96 / Dixie Frog

Shavers, Charlie

☐ BLUES SINGERS
Freight train blues / My Daddy rocks me / I am a woman / Low down dirty groundog / Jive is here / Downhearted blues
CBC 1025 / Sep '95 / Timeless Jazz

☐ CLASSICS 1944-1945
CLASSICS 944 / Jun '97 / Classics

☐ MOST INTIMATE, THE (The Finest Of Charlie Shavers - The Bethlehem Years)
BET 6019 / Jan '95 / Bethlehem

☐ YOUNG SHAVERS
Havin' a ball / Margie / Undecided / It feels good / Sweet Georgia Brown / Front and centre / Royal Garden blues / Jumping in the pump room / Blues petite / Georgia cabin / Texas moaner blues / Tweed me / Comin' back / St. Louis blues / Step on it / Riding on 52nd Street / My man / El salon de gutbucket / Bottle's empty / For lovers only / Black market stuff / Laguna leap / I'll never be the same / Swingin' on Central / Kicks
TPZ 1064 / Apr '97 / Topaz Jazz

Shaw, Adrian

☐ TEA FOR THE HYDRA
WO 27CD / Jun '96 / Woronzow

Shaw, Artie

☐ 22 ORIGINAL BIG BAND RECORDINGS (Shaw, Artie Orchestra)
What is this thing called love / My heart stood still / This can't be love / Lover come back to me / I can't give you anything but love / Lambeth walk / Together / I'm yours / Small fry / Softly as in a morning sunrise / Shine on harvest moon / Stardust / Out of nowhere / What's new / If I had you / I cover the waterfront / Just you, just me / Carioca / You're mine you / Sweet adeline / I can't believe that you're in love with me / I'm coming virginia
HCD 401 / Jun '95 / Hindsight

☐ ARTIE SHAW
Oh lady be good / Back bay shuffle / Comes love / Temptation / Begin the beguine / Traffic jam / Stardust / Deep purple / What is this thing called love / Summit ridge drive / Octaroon / Yam / You got me / Nightmare / Serenade to a savage / Moonglow
22705 / Nov '95 / Music

☐ ARTIE SHAW
15713 / Apr '94 / Laserlight

☐ ARTIE SHAW & HIS ORCHESTRA (Shaw, Artie Orchestra)
'S wonderful / Man and his dream / April in Paris / Summertime / I cover the waterfront / Blues / I could write a book / Don't take your love from me / Beyond the blue horizon / Maid with the flaccid air / Time on my hands / Deep purple / Prelude in C major
15757 / Aug '92 / Laserlight

☐ ARTIE SHAW & HIS ORCHESTRA VOL.1 1938 (Shaw, Artie Orchestra)
April in my heart / Night over Shanghai / Small fry / Just a kid named Joe / When I go a-dreamin' / Leapin' at the Lincoln / What is this thing called love / Lambeth walk / They say / Shine on harvest moon / Out of nowhere / Simple and sweet / Blue interlude / Apple blossom time / Deep in a dream
HCD 139 / Sep '96 / Hindsight

☐ ARTIE SHAW & HIS RHYTHM MAKERS 1938 (Shaw, Artie & Rhythm Makers)
Toy trumpet / Any old time / Powerhouse / Call of the freaks / Lost in the shuffle / If dreams come true / 'S wonderful / Meade Lux special / Sweet and low / Indian love call
TAX 37092 / Aug '94 / Tax

☐ ARTIE SHAW 1940-1941
Frenesi / Alice blue gown / Temptation / Sweet Sue / King for a day / Out of nowhere / Jungle drums / Frenesi / Along the Santa Fe trail / Looking for yesterday / Everything's jumpin' / Concerto for clarinet / Frenesi / Whispers in the night / There I go / Prelude in C sharp / DR Livingstone I presume / Nobody knows the trouble I've seen / Blues in the night / There'll be some changes made / Little gates special
HEPCD 19 / Jun '97 / Hep

☐ ARTIE SHAW IN HOLLYWOOD VOL.2 1940-1941 (Shaw, Artie Orchestra)
HEPCD 55 / 29 Sep '97 / Hep

☐ ARTIE SHAW ORCHESTRA VOL.2 (Shaw, Artie Orchestra)
Stardust / They say / My heart stood still / Begin the beguine / Dancing in the dark / Serenade to a savage / Day in, day out / I don't want to walk without you / Rockin' chair / Temptation / Carioca / Out of nowhere / Softly as in a morning sunrise / Blues in the night / Back bay shuffle / Jungle drums / All the things you are / Someone's rocking my dreamboat / I poured my heart into a song / Rose room / Smoke gets in your eyes / My blue heaven
PASTCD 7038 / Mar '94 / Flapper

☐ ARTISTRY OF THE ARTIE SHAW ORCHESTRA 1949, THE (Shaw, Artie Orchestra)
FSCD 2012 / Sep '96 / Fresh Sound

☐ ASTONISHING ARTIE SHAW, THE
Love and learn / Free wheeling / Rose room / Fee fi fo fum / Oh lady be good / I've a strange new rhythm in my heart / Just you, just me / I surrender Dear / Vilia / Let'er go / You can tell she comes from Dixie / It ain't right / Streamline / Cream puff / Non-stop flight / Sweet Adeline / Blues / I'll be with you in apple blossom time / Prosschai
PAR 2027 / Jul '94 / Parade

☐ BATTLE OF THE BANDS (Shaw, Artie & Benny Goodman)
Bugle call rag / Traffic jam / Don't be that way / Begin the beguine / If I could be with you (one hour tonight) / Any old time: *Shaw, Artie & Benny Goodman/Billie Holiday* / Goodnight my love: *Shaw, Artie & Benny Goodman/Ella Fitzgerald* / At sundown / Sing sing sing (with a swing) / Concerto for clarinet (parts 1 & 2) / One o' clock jump / Frenesi / And the angels sing / Little jazz / Farewell blues / Everything is jumpin'
09026631272 / 10 Aug '98 / RCA Victor

☐ BEGIN THE BEGUINE
Nightmare / Indian love call / Back bay shuffle / Any old time / Traffic jam / Comes love / What is this thing called love / Begin the beguine / Oh lady be good / Frenesi / Serenade to a savage / Deep purple / Special delivery stomp / Summit Ridge Drive / Temptation / Stardust / Blues (parts 1 and 2) / Moonglow / Moon ray / Carioca
ND 86274 / Apr '88 / Bluebird

☐ BEGIN THE BEGUINE
Any old time: *Shaw, Artie & Billie Holiday* / April in Paris / Back bay shuffle / Begin the beguine / Concerto for clarinet / Dancing in the dark / Deep purple / Donkey serenade / Frenesi / I surrender dear / Moonglow / Nightmare / Oh Lady be good / Rosalie / Special delivery stomp / St. James infirmary / Stardust / Summit Ridge Drive / Traffic jam / Yesterdays
CDAJA 5113 / Aug '93 / Living Era

☐ BIG BAND BASH (Shaw, Artie Orchestra)
CD 53093 / Mar '92 / Giants Of Jazz

☐ CHANT
Streamline / Sweet Lorraine / Love is good for anything that ails you / No more tears moonlight and shadows / Was it rain / All alone / All God's chillun got rhythm / It goes to your feet / Because I love you / Night and day / I surrender dear / Blue skies / Someday sweetheart / Afraid to dream / If you should ever leave / Sweet Adeline / How dry I am / Am I in love / Fe, fi, fo, fum / Please pardon us, we're in love / Chant / Blues
HEPCD 1046 / Jul '96 / Hep

☐ CLASSICS 1936
CLASSICS 855 / Feb '96 / Classics

☐ CLASSICS 1936-1937
CLASSICS 886 / Jul '96 / Classics

☐ CLASSICS 1937
CLASSICS 929 / Apr '97 / Classics

☐ CLASSICS 1938
CLASSICS 965 / Jan '98 / Classics

☐ CONCERTO FOR CLARINET (Shaw, Artie Orchestra)
One night stand / Traffic jam / Summit ridge drive / Prosschai / I surrender Dear / Marinella / Oh lady be good / You can tell she comes from Dixie / Darling not without you / Moonlight and shadows / Concerto for clarinet / You're a sweet little headache / Sometimes I feel like a Motherless child / Monsoon / Non stop flight / I have eyes / You're giving me a song and a dance / Special delivery stomp / Why begin again / Serenade to a savage / Free for all
RAJCD 830 / 6 Apr '98 / Empress

☐ CREAM OF ARTIE SHAW & HIS ORCHESTRA, THE
Stardust / They say / My heart stood still / Begin the beguine / Dancing in the dark / Serenade to a savage / Day in, day out / I don't want to walk without you / Rockin' chair / Temptation / Carioca / Out of nowhere / Softly as in a morning sunrise / Blues in the night / Back bay shuffle / Jungle drums / All the things you are / Someone's rocking my dreamboat / I poured my heart into a song / Rose room / Smoke gets in your eyes / My blue heaven
PASTCD 9779 / Nov '92 / Flapper

☐ GLOOMY SUNDAY (Shaw, Artie Orchestra)
Begin the beguine / Moonglow / Oh lady be good / Gloomy Sunday / Man I love / Temptation / Night/ Mare / Diga diga doo / Carioca / Donkey serenade / Frenesi / Serenade to a savage / Deep purple / I didn't know that time it was / Yesterdays / Rosalie / Indian love call / Jungle drums
CD 56003 / Aug '94 / Jazz Roots

☐ GREAT ARTIE SHAW & HIS ORCHESTRA, THE
CWNCD 2001 / Jun '95 / Javelin

☐ IN THE BEGINNING - 1936
Japanese sandman / Pretty girl is like a melody / I used to be above love / No regrets / South island magic / It ain't right / Sugar foot stomp / Thou swell / You've giving me a song and dance / Darling, not without you / One two button your shoe / Let's call a heart a heart / A skeleton in the closet / There's something in the air / Take another guess / There's frost on the moon / Love and learn / Moon face / Same old line / You can tell she comes from dixie / Sobbin' blues / Copenhagen / Cream puff / My blue heaven
HEPCD 1024 / Dec '87 / Hep

☐ IN THE BLUE ROOM/IN THE CAFE ROUGE
Nightmare / Together / My reverie / Sobbin' blues / Jeepers creepers / In the mood / Non-stop flight / Begin the beguine / Old stamping ground / Chant / Stardust / Carioca / At sundown / I'm sorry for myself / Maria, my own / Diga diga doo / Moonray / Everything is jumpin' / St. Louis blues / I've got my eye on you / My blue heaven / El Rancho Grande / Sweet Sue, just you / Man from Mars
74321185272 / Oct '94 / RCA Victor

☐ INDIAN LOVE CALL (Shaw, Artie Orchestra)
JHR 73535 / May '93 / Jazz Hour

☐ INTRODUCTION TO ARTIE SHAW 1937-1942, AN
4016 / Apr '95 / Best Of Jazz

☐ JAZZ GREATS
Begin the beguine / Stardust / I cover the waterfront / Comes love / Deep purple: *Forrest, Helen* / Moonglow / Any old time: *Holiday, Billie* / Frenesi / Lover come back to me / To a Broadway rose / Indian love call / Temptation / Oh lady be good / St. Louis blues
74321499712 / 6 Oct '97 / RCA Victor

☐ JAZZ PORTRAITS (Shaw, Artie Orchestra)
Begin the beguine / Moonglow / Oh lady be good / Gloomy Sunday / Man I love / Temptation / Nightmare / Diga diga doo / Carioca / Donkey serenade / Frenesi / Serenade to a savage / Deep purple / I didn't know what time it was / Yesterdays / Rosalie / Indian love call / Jungle drums
CD 14501 / May '93 / Jazz Portraits

☐ LIVE IN 1938-1939 VOL.1
PHONTCD 7609 / Apr '94 / Phontastic

☐ LIVE IN 1938-1939 VOL.2
PHONTCD 7613 / Apr '94 / Phontastic

☐ LIVE IN 1938-1939 VOL.3
PHONTCD 7628 / Apr '94 / Phontastic

☐ LIVE IN HI-FI
JH 1031 / Jul '93 / Jazz Hour

☐ LIVE PERFORMANCES 1938-1939 (Shaw, Artie Orchestra)
Nightmare (opening theme) / Rose room / Comes love (vocal helen forrest) / Carioca / You're mine you / Go fly a kite (vocal tony pastor) / Yesterdays / Don't worry 'bout me (vocal helen forrest) / My heart stood still / Traffic jam / Melancholy lullaby (vocal helen forrest) / In the mood / Sweet adeline (vocal tony pastor) / Lover come back to me / Two sleepy people / I'm coming virginia / One foot in the groove / Just a kid named joe (vocal tony pastor) / Blue interlude / Day in, day out (vocal helen forrest) / Leapin' at the lincoln / Artie speaks / Moonray (vocal helen forrest) / What is this thing called love / Small fry (vocal tony pastor) / Lambeth walk / Lillacs in the rain (vocal helen forrest) / Out of nowhere / Man from mars / Deep in a dream / Softly as in a morning sunrise / I used to be color blind (vocal tony pastor) / Just you, just me / Stardust / Night over shanghai (vocal helen forrest) / If I had you / Put that down in writing (vocal tony pastor) / Sweet sue / Between a kiss and a sigh (vocal helen forrest) / Together / St. louis blues / You're a lucky guy (vocal tony pastor) / Shine on harvest moon / I can't believe that you're in love with me / Oh you crazy moon (vocal tony pastor) / I'm yours / What's new / It had to be you / This can't be love (vocal helen forrest) / Everything's jumpin' / I can't give you anything but love (vocal tony pastor) / I cover the waterfront / Over the rainbow / Back bay shuffle / Summer souvenirs / Ya got me / Got the mis'ry / I didn't know what time it was / Yam / I haven't changed a thing (vocal helen forrest) / If what you say is true / Maria, my own / Last night / Hold your hats / Nightmare
HBCD 502 / Nov '93 / Hindsight

☐ MORE LAST RECORDINGS - THE FINAL SESSIONS (2CD Set)
MM 65101/2 / Oct '94 / Music Masters

☐ NON STOP FLIGHT
Blues (part 1) / Blues (part 2) / It's a long way to Tipperary / I've a strange new rhythm in my heart / If it's the last thing I do / Nightmare / Shoot the likker to me, John Boy / Free-wheeling / Let 'er go / Strange loneliness / Monsoon / I'm yours / Just you, just me / Free for all / Whistle while you work / One song / Goodnight, Angel / There's a new moon over the old mill / Non-stop flight / I'll be with you in apple blossom time
HEPCD 1048 / Sep '96 / Hep

☐ OLD GOLD MELODY & MADNESS SHOWS
JH 1050 / Jul '96 / Jazz Hour

☐ OLD GOLD SHOWS 1938-1939 (Shaw, Artie Orchestra)
JH 1009 / '91 / Jazz Hour

☐ RADIO YEARS VOL.1 1938, THE (Shaw, Artie Orchestra)
Nightmare / Sobbin' blues / I can't believe that you're in love with me / They say / It had to be you / My revenue / Sweet Adeline / Who blew out the flame / Copenhagen / Nightmare (closing theme) / Nightmare (theme) / Begin the beguine / You're a sweet little headache / Old stamping ground / What is this thing called love / Jungle drums / It had to be you / Thanks for everything / Copenhagen / Nightmare (closing theme)
JUCD 2018 / Nov '94 / Jazz Unlimited

☐ STARDUST (20 Swing Band Classics)
Stardust / Jungle drums / Day in day out / April in Paris / St. James Infirmary / Yesterday / Gloomy Sunday / Smoke gets in your eyes / Keepin' myself for you / Deep in a dream / Deep purple / It had to be you / My blue Heaven / Concerto for clarinet / Any old time / All the things you are / Donkey serenade / Dancing in the dark / I don't want to walk without you / Don't take your love from me
306672 / Jul '97 / Hallmark

☐ TRAFFIC JAM (Live Broadcasts 1938-1939)
Nightmare / Begin the beguine / Deep in a dream / Back bay shuffle / Non-stop flight / I have eyes / Carioca / Better-than-average-girl / Jungle dreams / I cried for you / Back bay shuffle / My heart belongs to daddy / I want my share of love / Diga diga doo / Diga diga doo / It's all yours / Rosalie / Zigeuner / Copenhagen / Pastel blue / Traffic jam / I'm in love with the honorable Mr. So-And-So / Chant / Prosschai / Nightmare (theme)
VN 1008 / Nov '96 / Viper's Nest

☐ WHAT IS THIS THING CALLED LOVE
Let's walk / Love of my life / How deep is the ocean / Glider / Hornet / They can't convince me / I got the sun in the morning / Along with me / You do something to me / In the still of the night / Begin the beguine / My heart belongs to Daddy / Night and day / What is this thing called love / I've got you under my skin / Get out of town / For you, for me, for evermore / Changing my tune / Love for sale / Guilty / And so to bed / Don't you believe it dear / It's the same old dream / I believe
PLCD 557 / Feb '97 / President

Shaw Brothers

☐ COLLECTION, THE
FE 2041 / Dec '94 / Folk Era

Shaw, Eddie

☐ CAN'T STOP NOW (Shaw, Eddie & The Wolf Gang)
Greedy man / Can't stop now / Casino blues / Howlin' for my darling / Stole my daughter / We're gonna make it / Rockin' with Eddie / Love me or leave me / Chicago man / Playing with the blues / Don't use me baby / Country boy / I gotta tell somebody
DE 698 / Jun '97 / Delmark

☐ IN THE LAND OF THE CROSSROADS
Delta bound / Tears are falling / Fannie Mae Jones / I got to go / She didn't tell me everything / My friend Rosco / Dunkin' donut woman / Take home pay / Wine head mole / Chicago man / Operator / Blues at the crossroads
R 2624 / Feb '97 / Rooster

☐ MOVIN' & GROOVIN' MAN
Highway bound / Blues dues / Blues for tomako / Dunkin' donut woman / Louisiana blues / Movin' and groovin' man / Sad and lonesome / Big leg woman / I've got to tell somebody / My baby and me
ECD 260282 / Feb '93 / Evidence

Shaw, Elidh

☐ HEEPIRUMBO
My dad Paddy / Just for Gordon / 70th year / Simon's waltz / Blowjob / Highland jigs / Scottie dance band heaven / Liz Carroll's / Inveran / Finisher
CDTRAX 131 / 1 Nov '97 / Greentrax

Shaw, Ian

☐ ECHO OF A SONG, THE
JHCD 048 / Oct '96 / Ronnie Scott's Jazz House

☐ GHOSTSONGS
Danny boy / Spinning wheel / When Sassy sings / Broken blue heart / Me, myself and I / Some other time/People will say we're in love / Lover man / Calling you / Sophisticated lady/I've got it bad and that ain't good / Somewhere / Goodbye Pork Pie Hat / Blame it on my youth
JHCD 025 / Jan '94 / Ronnie Scott's Jazz House

☐ TAKING IT TO HART
I wish I were in love again / Where or when / Have you met miss jones / I could write a book / My romance-any old place with you / Little girl blue / I didn't know what time it was / My funny valentine / Blue moon / This can't be love / It never entered my mind / This funny world / With a song in my heart
JHCD 036 / Mar '95 / Ronnie Scott's Jazz House

Shaw, Marlena

☐ DANGEROUS
Out of this world / Whisper not / Ooo-wee-baby you're the one for me / Blackberry winter / Close enough for love / Dangerous / Nearness of you / Dim the lights / You make me feel brand new / You're my everything / Beautiful friendship / Give me one more chance / Keep on trustin'
CCD 4707 / Jul '96 / Concord Crossover

☐ ELEMENTAL SOUL
Your mind is on vacation / Paint your pretty picture / How deep is the ocean / Where do you start / Once again we've begun to love / Handy man / Why oh why / Brothers / 'Round midnight / I'm alone again / My old flame / Our love is here to stay
CCD 47742 / Aug '97 / Concord Jazz

☐ FEEL THE SPIRIT (Shaw, Marlena & Joe Williams)
In the beginning / My Lord / Feel the spirit / Go down Moses / Wade in the water / Great camp meeting / Were you there / Walk with me / I couldn't hear nobody pray / In my heart / Little David / His eye is on the sparrow / Pass it on / Lord's prayer / Doxology
CD 83362 / Jun '95 / Telarc

Shaw, Pat

☐ LIES & ALIBIS (Shaw, Pat & Julie Matthews)
FATCAT 001CD / Jun '93 / Fat Cat

Shaw, Robert

☐ MA GRINDER, THE
ARHCD 377 / Apr '95 / Arhoolie

Shaw, Sandie

☐ ALWAYS SOMETHING THERE TO REMIND ME
Always something there to remind me / Monsieur Dupont / You've not changed / Heaven knows I'm missing him now / Stop / Today / Think it all over / Words / You've been seeing her again / Those were the days / Tonight in Tokyo / Maple village / What now my love / Right to cry
QED 133 / Nov '96 / Tring

☐ ALWAYS SOMETHING THERE TO REMIND ME
Always something there to remind me / Maple Village / Voice in the crowd / Show me / Maybe I'm amazed / Scarborough fair / You've been seeing her again / Turn on the sunshine / That's why / Today / Ne me quitte pas / Time after time / What now my love / Words
WB 878602 / Mar '97 / Disky

☐ CHOOSE LIFE
Dragon king's daughter / Mermaid / Let down your hair / East meets west / Bark back at dogs / Life is like a star / Moontalk / Sister sister / Wish I was
RETRO 801 / Jun '95 / RPM

☐ CLASSIC ARTISTS
JHD 048 / Jun '92 / Tring

☐ COLLECTION, THE
Puppet on a string / Long live love / (there's) always something there to remind me / Girl don't come / Message understood / Think it all over / Tomorrow / You've not changed / Words / Ne me quitte pas / Love me do / I get a kick out of you / Ev'ry time we say goodbye / Scarborough fair / Smile / You've been seeing her again / Maybe I'm amazed / (i can't get no) satisfaction / Homeward bound / Love me please love me / One note samba / Those were the days my friend / Stop / Right to cry / What now my love
COL 067 / Jan '95 / Collection

☐ COOL ABOUT YOU
I don't owe you anything / Jeane / Frederick / Are you ready to be heartbroken / Steven / Girl don't come / Nothing less than brilliant / Hello angel / Love of the century / I love peace / Girl called Johnny / Cool about you / Flesh and blood / Strange bedfellows / Comrade in arms / Nothing less than brilliant / Are you ready to be heartbroken / Anyone who had a heart
RPM 181 / 9 Feb '98 / RPM

☐ COVER TO COVER
Scarborough fair / Lay lady lay / Satisfaction / Rose garden / Jeane / I get a kick out of you / Reviewing the situation / Walking the dog / Maybe I'm amazed / What now my love / Ne me quitte pas / Love me do / Homeward bound / Sympathy for the devil / (Get your rocks on) Route 66 / Those were the days
EMPRCD 625 / Jun '96 / Emporio

☐ EP COLLECTION, THE
Tell the boys / Had a dream last night / Viva l'amore con te / Poutvu que ca dure / Run / Tomorrow / Hurting you / Message understood / How can I tell you / Talk about love / Gotta see my baby every day / Long live love / Stop feeling sorry for yourself / You can't blame him / I'll stop at nothing / Girl don't come / (there's) always something there to remind me / Don't you know / Nothing comes easy / Ya-ya-da-da / Stop before you start / Rien n'emechera l'amour / Quello che tu cerchi amica / Ask any woman / I'll cry myself to sleep / As long as you're happy baby
SEECD 305 / '90 / See For Miles

☐ GREATEST HITS
Puppet on a string / Message understood / Nothing comes easy / Had a dream last night / Long live love / Stop feeling sorry for yourself / Hide all emotion / Tomorrow / You won't forget me / (There's) Always something there to remind me / Tell the boys / I'd be better off without you / No moon / Girl don't come / Think sometimes about me / Love walk home / Don't you count on it / Don't you want me anymore
RM 1545 / Apr '97 / BR Music

☐ GREATEST HITS OF SANDIE SHAW
MACCD 171 / Aug '96 / Autograph

☐ LONG LIVE LOVE
(there's) always something there to remind me / Baby I need your loving / Girl don't come / I get a kick out of you / It's in his kiss / Long live love / Puppet on a string / Message understood / When I fall in love / Think sometimes about me / One day / How glad I am / Tell the boys / Stop feeling sorry for yourself
WMCD 5611 / May '94 / Disky

☐ LONG LIVE LOVE (All Her Hits)
DC 869812 / Aug '96 / Disky

☐ LOVE ME PLEASE LOVE ME
Love me please love me / One note samba / Smile / Yes my darling daughter / Ne me quitte pas / Every time we say goodbye / Way that I remember him / Hold 'im down / I get a kick out of you / Time after time / That's why / By myself / Tonight in Tokyo / You've been seeing her again / You've not changed / Don't make me cry / Today / London / Don't run away / Stop
RPM 124 / Mar '94 / RPM

☐ NOTHING LESS THAN BRILLIANT (The Best Of Sandie Shaw)
Always something there to remind me / Long live love / Girl don't come / Message understood / Nothing less than brilliant / Hand in glove / Are you ready to be heartbroken / Girl called Johnny / I'll stop at nothing / Heaven knows I'm missing him now / You've not changed / Monsieur Dupont / I don't owe you anything / Anyone who had a heart: Shaw, Sandie & BEF / Comrade in arms / Hello angel / Strange bedfellows / Words / Every time we say goodbye / Your time is gonna come / Frederick / Please help the cause against loneliness / Tomorrow / Nothing comes easy / Puppet on a string
CDVIP 183 / Apr '97 / Virgin VIP

☐ PUPPET ON A STRING
Puppet on a string / Message understood / Nothing comes easy / Everybody loves a lover / Lemon tree / Had a dream last night / Long live love / Stop feeling sorry for yourself / You won't forget me / Tell the boys / Girl don't come / Think sometimes about me / Long walk home / You don't love me know more / If you ever need me / (There's) Always something there to remind me
21038 / Sep '97 / Laserlight

☐ PUPPET ON A STRING
REP 4092 / Aug '91 / Repertoire

☐ REVIEWING THE SITUATION
Reviewing the situation / Lay lady lay / Mama roux / Sun in my eyes / Walkin' the dog / Love me do / Oh gosh / Your time is gonna come / Coconut groove / Sympathy for the devil / Think it all over / Send me a letter / Heaven knows I'm missing him now / So many things to do / By tomorrow / Maple village / Wight is wight / That's the way he's made / Rose garden / Maybe I'm amazed
RPM 101 / Jul '93 / RPM

☐ SANDIE SHAW SUPPLEMENT, THE
Route 66 / Homeward bound / Scarborough Fair / Right to cry / Same things / Our song of love / Satisfaction / Words / Remember me / Change of heart / Aranjuez mon amour / What now my love / Show me / One more lie / Together / Turn on the sunshine / Those were the days / Make it go / Monsieur Dupont / Voice in the crowd
RPM 112 / Oct '93 / RPM

☐ SANDIE/ME
Everybody loves a lover / Gotta see my baby everyday / Love letters / Stop feeling sorry for yourself / Always / Don't be that way / It's in his kiss (The shoop shoop song) / Downtown / You won't forget me / Lemon tree / Baby, I need your loving / Talk about love / You don't love me no more / I don't need that kind of lovin' / Down dismal ways / Oh no he don't / When I was a child / Do you mind / How glad I am / I know / Till the night begins to die / Too bad you don't want me / One day / When I fall in love
SEECD 436 / Oct '95 / See For Miles

Shaw, Thomas

☐ BORN IN TEXAS
TCD 5027 / Oct '95 / Testament

Shaw, Tommy

☐ SEVEN DEADLY ZENS
6076862542 / 30 Jun '98 / CMC
SPV 08518492 / 1 Sep '98 / SPV

Shaw, Woody

☐ LIVE/BEMSHA SWING (2CD Set)
Bemsha swing / Ginseng people / Well you needn't / Eric / United / Nutty / In a Capricornian way / Star eyes / Theloniously speaking
CDP 8290292 / Aug '97 / Blue Note

☐ TIME IS RIGHT, THE
1231682 / Apr '93 / Red

☐ TWO MORE PIECES OF THE PUZZLE
60412320692 / 19 May '98 / Thirty Two

Shazam

☐ SHAZAM
CPR 2248 / 2 Mar '98 / Copper

Shazar, Pal

☐ THERE'S A WILD THING IN THE HOUSE
Falling is a form of flying / Penny for your thoughts / San Francisco Bay / Three sheets to the wind / Small talk with the ticket man / If it's you that I got here / Ain't nobody's mistress but my own / Then I met Anna / Scared / Wade went wild / Sentimental breakdown
TRACD 113 / Apr '96 / Transatlantic

She

☐ PENANCE
Hallelujah / She / Marlene miles away / Stand by your bed / Blossom tear coloured blown / Kiss my arse / Betty Bucksuttle / Red, greens and blues / Pour no more / I'm going down / Baby blues / Panic attack
PROBE 042CD / Mar '96 / Probe Plus

Shea, David

☐ DOWN RIVER, UP STREAM (Shea, David & DJ Grazhoppa)
DSL 003D / Nov '96 / Downsall Plastics

☐ LIVE SESSIONS (Shea, David & Scanner/Robert Jampson)
QUANTUM 051 / Sep '96 / Sub Rosa

☐ MORT AUX VACHES
MAVI CD / 2 Mar '98 / Lowlands

☐ SATYRICON
SR 111 / Apr '97 / Sub Rosa

☐ SHOCK CORRIDOR
AVAN 013 / Nov '92 / Avant

☐ TOWER OF MIRRORS, THE
SR 94 / Mar '96 / Sub Rosa

Sheainn, Mairtin

☐ BLATH NA HOIGE
CICD 128 / Aug '97 / Clo Iar-Chonnachta

Shear, Jules

☐ BETWEEN US
10352 / 23 Feb '98 / HST

Shearing, George

☐ ALONE TOGETHER (Shearing, George & Marian McPartland)
O grande amor / To Bill Evans / All through the night / Born to be blue / They say it's Spring / Alone together / There'll be other times / Nobody else but me / Chasing shadows / Improvisation on a theme
CCD 4171 / Feb '91 / Concord Jazz

☐ BEST OF GEORGE SHEARING, THE
Midnight in the air / Have you met Miss Jones / Dancing on the ceiling / Cuban love song / Folks who live on the hill / Nothing ever changes my love for you / Friendly persuasion (thee I love) / Later / Cheek to cheek / Sand in my shoes / Kinda cute / September in the rain / East of the sun and West of the moon / Estampa Cubano / Ship without a sail / Laura / Bernie's tune / Canadian sunset
CDP 8335702 / Nov '95 / Capitol Jazz

☐ BLUES ALLEY JAZZ
One for the woofer / Autumn in New York / (I'm afraid) the masquerade is over / Soon it's gonna rain / High and inside / For every man there's a woman / This couldn't be the real thing / Up a lazy river
CCD 4110 / Nov '89 / Concord Jazz

☐ BREAKIN' OUT (Shearing, George Trio)
Just squeeze me (but don't tease me) / Day dream / Hallucinations / What'll I do / Break out the blues / Don't get around much anymore / Twelve tone blues / Prelude to a kiss / There is no greater love
CCD 4335 / Dec '87 / Concord Jazz

☐ BURNISHED BRASS/SATIN BRASS
Memories of you / Lulu's back in town / If you were mine / Burnished brass / These things you left me / Mine / Beautiful love / Cuckoo in the clock / Sometimes I feel like a motherless child / Cheek to cheek / Blame it on my youth / Basie's movement / Deep night / In the blue of evening / I could write a book / Sleepy Manhattan / If I had you / Just plain Bill / First floor please / Chelsea bridge / Ship without a sail / Stairway to the stars / You look like someone / Night flight
CTMCD 120 / Jun '97 / EMI

☐ COLLECTION, THE
Missouri scrambler / Overnight bop / How come you love me like you do / Stomp in F / Riff up them stairs / Boogie ride / Spookie woogie / Oh lady be good / You stepped out of a dream / Softly as a morning sunrise / Five flat flurry / Southern fried / Wednesday night hop / Pretty girl is like a melody / More than you know / Cymbal Simon / How could you / These foolish things / Blue boogie / Trunk call / Squeezin' the blues / Delayed action
RAJCD 881 / Nov '96 / Empress

☐ DEXTERITY
Dexterity / You must believe in Spring / Sakura / Long ago and far away / Can't we be friends / As long as I live / Please send me someone to love / Duke Ellington medley
CCD 4346 / Jul '88 / Concord Jazz

☐ ELEGANT EVENING, AN (Shearing, George & Mel Torme)
I'll be seeing you / Love and the moon / Oh you crazy moon / No moon at all / After the waltz is over / This time the dream is on me / Last night when we were young / You changed my life / I had the craziest dream / Darn that dream / Brigg fair / My foolish heart / You're driving me crazy
CCD 4294 / Jul '87 / Concord Jazz

☐ EVENING AT CHARLIE'S, AN (Shearing, George & Mel Torme)
Just one of those things / On Green Dolphin Street / Dream dancing / I'm hip / Then I'll be tired of you / Caught in the middle of my years / Welcome to the club / Nica's dream / Chase me Charlie / Love is just around the corner
CCD 4248 / Sep '84 / Concord Jazz

☐ EVENING WITH GEORGE SHEARING, AN (Shearing, George & Mel Torme)
All God's chillun got rhythm / Born to be blue / Give me the simple life / Good morning heartache / Manhattan hoedown / You'd be so nice to come home to / Nightingale sang in Berkeley Square / Love / It might as well be Spring / Lullaby of Birdland
CCD 4190 / Mar '87 / Concord Jazz

☐ FAVOURITE THINGS
My favourite things / Angel eyes / Ina calm / Not you again / Taking a chance on love / Let me / Summer song / Anna's song / Anyone can whistle / Moonray / I'm getting off here / PS I love you / It amazes me
CD 83398 / Mar '97 / Telarc Jazz

☐ GEORGE SHEARING IN DIXIELAND (Shearing, George & Dixie Six)
Clap your hands / Truckin' / New Orleans / Take five / Blue monk / Alice in Dixieland / Mighty like the blues / Destination moon / Soon / Lullaby of Birdland / Desafinado
CCD 4388 / Sep '89 / Concord Jazz

☐ GRAND PIANO
When a woman loves a man / It never entered my mind / Mack the knife / Nobody else but me / Imitations / Taking a chance on love / If I had you / How insensitive / Easy to love / While we're young
CCD 4281 / Sep '86 / Concord Jazz

☐ HOW BEAUTIFUL IS THE NIGHT (Shearing, George & The Robert Farnon Orchestra)
Dancing in the dark / Heather on the hill / Oh, lady be good / More than you know / Our waltz / How beautiful is night / Once upon a time / Days gone by / Put on a happy face / Haunted ballroom / Just imagine / Surrey with the fringe on top
CD 83325 / May '93 / Telarc

☐ I HEAR A RHAPSODY (Live At The Blue Note)
Bird feathers / Dreamsville / End Of A Love Affair / Zingaro / Duke / I hear a rhapsody / (I'm afraid) the masquerade is over / Horizon / Just a mood / Wail / Too Late Now
CD 83310 / Sep '92 / Telarc

☐ JAZZ MASTERS
5299002 / 5 May '98 / Verve

☐ JAZZ MOMENTS
Makin' whoopee / What is this thing called love / What's new / Like someone in love / Heart of winter / Blues in 94 / Symphony / When Sunny gets blue / Wonder why / Mood is mellow / Gone with the wind / It could happen to you
CDP 8320852 / Aug '95 / Capitol Jazz

☐ LATIN LACE/LATIN AFFAIR
Story of love / Serenata / Tu mi delirio / Cali mambo / Rondo / To the ends of the Earth / Moon was yellow / Wonder struck / Sand in my shoes / Mambo caribe / It's not for me to say / Mambo no.2 / All or nothing at all / Let's call the whole thing off / Afro IV / Magic / It's easy to remember / Estampa cubana / You stepped out of a dream / Mambo balahu / Dearly beloved / Juana Palangana / This is Africa / Anywhere
4949932 / 8 Jun '98 / EMI

☐ LIVE AT THE CAFE CARLYLE (Shearing, George & Don Thompson)
Pent-up house / Shadow of your smile / Teach me tonight / Cheryl / Blues for breakfast / PS I love you / I cover the waterfront / Tell me a bedtime story / Stratford stomp / Inside
CCD 4246 / '88 / Concord Jazz

☐ LONDON YEARS 1939-1943
How come you like me like you do / Stomp in F / Squeezing the blues / Southern fried / Missouri scrambler / Overnight hop / Delayed action / Beat me Daddy, eight to the bar / How could you / Pretty girl is like a melody / These foolish things / More than you know / Softly as in a morning sunrise / You stepped out of a dream / Spoodie woogie / Moon ray / Rosetta / I'll never let a day pass me by / Coquette / Out of nowhere / Can't we be friends / I don't stand a ghost of a chance with you / Guilty / I found a new boogie / Sweet Lorraine
HEPCD 1042 / Feb '95 / Hep

☐ MIDNIGHT ON CLOUD 69
Sorry wrong rumba / Cotton top / Be bop's fables / Midnight on cloud 69 / Little white lies / I'm yours / Moon over Miami / Cherokee / Life with feather / Four bars short / Time and tide / Night and day
CY 18065 / Jun '98 / Savoy Jazz

☐ MORE GRAND PIANO
My silent love / Change partners / My favourite things / You don't know what love is / Ramona / People / East of the sun and west of the moon / I can't get started (with you) / Dream / Wind in the willows
CCD 4318 / Jul '87 / Concord Jazz

☐ ON A CLEAR DAY (Shearing, George & Brian Torff)
Love for sale / On a clear day (You can see forever) / Brasil '79 / Don't explain / Happy days are here again / Have you met Miss Jones / Lullaby of Birdland
CCD 4132 / Dec '93 / Concord Jazz

☐ ONCE AGAIN THAT SHEARING SOUND
East of the sun and west of the moon / I like to recognise the tune / I'll never smile again / I hear music / Girl talk / Autumn serenade / Consternation / Stars in my eyes / Strollin / Very early / Conception / Peace / Lullaby of birdland
CD 83347 / Sep '94 / Telarc

☐ PAPER MOON (The Songs Of Nat 'King' Cole) (Shearing, George Trio)
Straighten up and fly right / I'm lost / Sweet Lorraine / Nature boy / Homeward bound / I'm thru with love / It's only a paper moon / Gee baby ain't I good to you / Lost April / Peaches / You've changed / I'd love to make love to you / Could ja / I can't see for lookin'
CD 83375 / May '96 / Telarc

☐ PERFECT MATCH, A (Shearing, George & Ernestine Anderson)
Trust in me / I'll take romance / Body and soul / Best thing for you / I remember clifford / On the sunny side of the street / Lullaby old birdland / Second time around / Falling in love with love / That's for me / I won't dance / Some other time / Touch of your lips / Things we did last summer
CCD 4357 / Oct '88 / Concord Jazz

☐ PIANO
It had to be you / Daisy / Thinking of you / Sweet and lovely / It's you or no one / Wendy / Am I blue / Miss Invisible / You're my everything / John O'Groats / Waltz for Claudia / For you / Children's waltz / Happiness is a thing called Joe
CCD 4400 / Jan '90 / Concord Jazz

☐ SATIN AFFAIR/CONCERTO FOR MY LOVE
Early autumn / You were never lovelier / Stardust / Baubles, bangles and beads / It's not you / Party's over / Midnight sun / Here's what I'm here for / I like to recognise the tune / My own / My romance / Bolero no.3 / Portrait of Jennie / I'm in the mood for love / Answer me my love / I wish you love / Love letters / I fall in love too easily / Love is the sweetest thing / Portrait of my love / PS I love you / Lady love be mine / In love in vain / Love child
BGOCD 269 / Apr '95 / Beat Goes On

☐ SWINGIN'S MUTUAL, THE (Shearing, George & Nancy Wilson)
Things we did last Summer / All night long / My gentleman friend / Born to be blue / I remember Clifford / On Green Dolphin Street / Let's live again / Whisper not / Nearness of you / Evansville / Don't call me / Inspiration / You are there / Wait till you see her / Blue Lou / Oh, look at me now / Lullaby of Birdland
CDP 7991902 / Mar '95 / Blue Note

☐ TWO FOR THE ROAD (Shearing, George & Carmen McRae)
I don't stand a ghost of a chance with you / Gentleman friend / Cloudy morning / If I should lose you / What is there to say / You're all I need / More than you know / Too late now / Ghost of yesterday / Two for the road
CCD 4128 / '89 / Concord Jazz

☐ WALKIN'
That's earl, brother / My one and only love / Pensativa / Walkin' / When she makes music / Celia / Subconscious Lee / Suddenly / Bag's groove / Every time we say goodbye / Loot to boot
CD 83333 / Apr '95 / Telarc

Shearing, Peter G.

☐ VIKING DREAM
CDSGP 9006 / Apr '95 / Prestige

Sheavy

☐ ELECTRIC SLEEP
Virtual machine / Velvet / Destiny rainbow / Electric sleep / Born in a daze / Automation / Oracle / Stardust / Savannah / Saving me
CDRISE 17 / 16 Mar '98 / Rise Above

Shed Seven

☐ CHANGE GIVER
Dirty soul / Speakeasy / Long time dead / Head and hands / Casino girl / Missing out / Dolphin / Stars in your eyes / Mark / Ocean pie / On an island with you
5236152 / Sep '96 / Polydor

☐ LET IT RIDE
Return / Let it ride / Heroes / Halfway home / Devil in your shoes / She left me on Friday / Hole / Drink your love / Stand up and be counted / Chasing rainbows / Goodbye
5573592 / 1 Jun '98 / Polydor

☐ MAXIMUM HIGH, A
Getting better / Magic streets / Where have you been tonight / Going for gold / On standby / Out by my side / Lies / This day was ours / Ladyman / Falling from the sky / Bully boy / Parallel lines
5310392 / Apr '96 / Polydor
5333772 / Sep '96 / Polydor

☐ MAXIMUM HIGH, A/THE B-SIDES (2CD Set)
Getting better / Magic streets / Where have you been tonight / Going for gold / On standby / Out by my side / Lies / This day was ours / Ladyman / Falling from the sky / Bully boy / Parallel lines / Long time dead / Around your house / Swing my wave / Out by my side / Immobilise / Killing time / This is my house / Barracuda / Mobile 10 / Stepping on hearts / Never again / Song seven / Making waves / Sleep easy / Only dreaming
5334162 / Sep '96 / Polydor

Shedad, Hal Al

☐ TEXTURE OF TOMORROW
TMU 030CD / 4 May '98 / Troubleman Unlimited

Sheehan, Stephen

☐ EYES OF THE WILDERNESS
ROSE 199 CD / Jun '90 / New Rose

Sheep On Drugs

☐ DOUBLE TROUBLE
INV 057CD / Jun '96 / Invisible

☐ GREATEST HITS
Uberman / Acid test / Fifteen minutes of fame / Track X / Suzie Q / Catch 22 / Mary Jane / Motorbike / TV USA / Chard / Cheep
CID 8006 / Mar '93 / Island

☐ NEVERMIND THE METHADONE
INV 067CD / 27 Oct '97 / Invisible

☐ ON DRUGS
Intro / Chasing dreams / English rose / Let the good times roll / Beefcake / Segway / A2H / Clucking / Slap happy / Slim Jim / Lolita / Slow suicide / Hi-fi low-life / Dirtbox blues
CID 8020 / Apr '94 / Island

☐ ONE FOR THE MONEY
INV 061CD / Feb '97 / Invisible

Sheer Taft

☐ ABSOLUTELY SHEER
CRELPCD 121 / Jun '92 / Creation

Sheer Terror

☐ LOVE SONGS FOR THE UNLOVED
Love song for the unloved / Tale of moran / Jimmy's high life / Not waving, drowning / Rock bottom on the kitchen floor / Skinhead girl / Drunk, divorced and downhill fast / Broken / Outro / College boy / For Rudy the Kraut / Walnut St / Be still my heart / Walls / Everything's life / Goodbye farewell
BLK 023ECD / Jan '97 / Blackout

Sheffield Wednesday FC

☐ WE ARE THE OWLS (A Tribute To Sheffield Wednesday Football Club) (Various Artists)
We are the owls: *Sheffield Wednesday FC* / We love you Sheffield Wednesday: *Sheffield Wednesday FC* / We love you Wednesday: *Carrack, Paul* / It's a praise for Sheffield Wednesday: *Big Ron's Barmy Army* / Singing the blues: *Curran, Terry* / Wednesday chart: *Curran, Terry* / If it's Wednesday it must be Wembley: *Curran, Terry* / Steel city: *Hillsbrough Crew* / Alive and well: *Carter, Lynn* / March for Wembley: *Carter, Lynn* / Derby daze: *Wednesday Blues* / Owls are on the way: *Wednesdaynites* / Oh yes: *Wednesday Kop Band*
CDGAFFER 22 / 17 Nov '97 / Cherry Red

Shehan, Steve

☐ ASAROUF
5347572 / 5 Jan '98 / Triloka

Sheik Chinna Moulana

☐ NADHASWARAM
SM 15072 / Nov '92 / Wergo

Sheik, Duncan

☐ DUNCAN SHEIK
She runs away / In the absence of sun / Barely breathing / Reasons for living / Serena / November / Out of order / Little hands / End of outside / Home / Days go by
7567828792 / Sep '96 / Atlantic

Sheila

☐ BEST OF SHEILA, THE
3033802 / 24 Feb '98 / Arcade

Sheldon, Jack

☐ HOLLYWOOD HEROES (Sheldon, Jack Quintet)
Joint is jumpin' / Pardon my southern accent / Poor butterfly / Lover / Rosetta / I thought about you / I want to be happy
CCD 4339 / May '88 / Concord Jazz

☐ ON MY OWN (Sheldon, Jack & Ross Tomkins)
Accentuate the positive / Love of mine / Blues in the night / How about you / Day drama / Opus one / Losing my mind / I can't get started (with you) / New York medley / Laughing on the outside / Avalon / Over the rainbow
CCD 4529 / Oct '92 / Concord Jazz

☐ PLAYING FOR CHANGE
UPCD 2743 / Nov '97 / Uptown

☐ QUARTET AND THE QUINTET (Sheldon, Jack Quartet & Quintet)
Contour / It's only a paper moon / Leroy's blues / Cheek to cheek / Streets of Madashi / Get out of town / Ah moore / Dozo (let's go) / Mad about the boy / Toot Sweet / Jack departs / What is there to say / Groovus mentus / Beach wise / Palermo walk / Blues / Irresistable you / Guatemala / I'm getting sentimental over you
4931602 / 18 May '98 / Pacific Jazz

Shellac

☐ AT ACTION PARK
TG 141CD / Nov '94 / Touch & Go

☐ TERRAFORM
TG 200CD / 11 May '98 / Touch & Go

Shelley, Michael

☐ HALF EMPTY
BD 9038 / Nov '97 / Big Deal

☐ TOO MANY MOVES
BIGDEAL 9056 / 20 Jul '98 / Big Deal

Shelley, Pete

☐ HOMOSAPIEN
RE 2126 / May '98 / Razor & Tie

☐ XL-1
GRACD 202 / Aug '94 / Grapevine

Shelleyan Orphan

☐ BUMROOT
R 2792 / Mar '92 / Rough Trade

Shelor, Sammy

☐ LEADING ROLL
Pretty little girl / Mountain girl / Ernest T. Grass / Lonesome scene of winter / North Carolina breakdown / Allen's dream / Walls / Janey belle / I'm onto you / Crossroad blues / Without a word / Darlin' child
SHCD 3865 / Mar '98 / Sugar Hill

Shelter

☐ ATTAINING THE SUPREME
EVR 007CD / Apr '97 / Equal Vision

☐ BEYOND PLANET EARTH
RR 88282 / 22 Sep '97 / Revelation

☐ MANTRA
RR 89382 / Oct '95 / Roadrunner

☐ PERFECTION
REV 016CD / Jan '96 / Revelation

☐ QUEST FOR CERTAINTY
REV 066CD / 2 Mar '98 / Revelation

Shelton, Anne

☐ EARLY YEARS OF ANNE SHELTON, THE
SWNCD 003 / Oct '95 / Sound Waves

☐ HERE'S ANNE SHELTON
There goes that song again / Nightingale sang in Berkeley Square / We mustn't say goodbye / Where or when / Last time I saw Paris / Fools rush in / Lili marlene / At last / Blues in the night / I'll never smile again / You'll never know / Coming in on a wing and a prayer / Only forever / Begin the beguine / Taking a chance on love / My yiddish momme / Kiss the boys goodbye / Swingin' on a star
306282 / Jan '97 / Hallmark

☐ LET THERE BE LOVE
While the music plays on / Daddy / Better not roll those blue blue eyes / Minnie from Trinidad / Russian rose / St. Louis blues / Yes my darling daughter / Until you fall in love / Little steeple pointing to a star / Let there be love / Amapola / Tomorrow's sunrise / Fools rush in / Always in my heart / How about you / How green was my valley / I don't want to walk without you / My devotion / Taxi driver's serenade / South wind / Only you / My yiddishe Momme
RAJCD 815 / Sep '97 / Empress

☐ NIGHTINGALE SANG, A
I'll be with you in apple blossom time / Last time I saw Paris / Daddy, blues in the night / Kiss the boys goodbye / Begin the beguine / You'd be so nice to come home to
PASTCD 7048 / Aug '94 / Flapper

☐ NOW HEAR THIS
Now hear this / Hurry home / Where can I go / Great pretender / Souvenir d'italie / Too young to go steady / Carnival is closed today / Volare / Sail along silv'ry moon / Where were you when I needed you / It's you / Harbour lights / Dancing with tears in my eyes / Nein nein fraulein / Daydreams / My one and only love / Forever / Tonights my night / Tread softly (you're treading on my heart) / How green was my valley / Village of St. Bernadette / I hear that song again / You're not living in vain / Lay down your arms
C5MCD 624 / Jul '95 / See For Miles

☐ SENTIMENTAL JOURNEY
Crazy / Tangerine / Sentimental journey / Nightingale sang in Berkeley Square / Don't fence me in / I'll walk alone / Run rabbit run / When the lights go on again / White cliffs of Dover / You'll never know / After all / Don't sit under the apple tree / I left my heart at the stage door canteen / Roll out the barrel / I'll get by / Boogie woogie bugle boy / I'll be seeing you / Chattanooga choo choo / Lili Marlene / Just look around
PLCD 537 / Nov '94 / President

☐ SOLDIER'S SWEETHEART MEMORIAL ALBUM, THE
I'll never smile again / I'll be seeing you / There goes that song again / Yes my darling daughter / Fools rush in / I don't want to walk without you / You'd be so nice to come home to / Coming in on a wing and a prayer / Last time I saw paris / I don't want to set the world on fire / Nightingale sang in Berkeley Square / Taking a chance on love / Only you / Daddy / My yiddishe momme / Until you fall in love / Ampola / St. Louis blues / Kiss the boys goodbye / Lili Marlene
PAR 2061 / Mar '95 / Parade

Shelton, Louie

☐ HOT AND SPICY
71577689292 / 21 Apr '98 / Sin-Drome

Shelton, Roscoe

☐ ROSCOE SHELTON SINGS
Are you sure / Think it over / Pleadin' for love / I was wrong, played with love / I've been faithful / Say you really care / It's my fault / Something's wrong / Baby look what your doin' to me / Miss you so / Is it too late babe / Let me believe in you / Crazy over you / We've been wrong / Baby it's true love / Fool wrapped up in love / Blue and miserably unhappy / I'm so ashamed but I didn't know / I'm tellin' you baby, that's all / Lonely heartaches / Why didn't you tell me (for so long) / Why do you worry me / There is nothing I can do / Save me want your lovin' sometime
EXCD 3007 / Dec '96 / Ace

☐ SHE'S THE ONE
APCD 114 / Oct '95 / Appaloosa

☐ TENNESSEE R 'N' B LIVE (The Excello Legends) (Shelton, Roscoe & Earl Gaines/Clifford Curry)
Is it too late babe / Three times seven / Provider / Somebody somewhere / Think it over / You can make it if you try / Baby kiss me again / Next time (excuse me) / She shops till she drops / Door is still open / Stagger Lee
APCD 140 / Dec '97 / Appaloosa

Shenasa, Mas'oud

☐ SANTOUR, THE
AAA 140 / Dec '96 / Club Du Disque Arabe

Shepard, Jean

☐ MELODY RANCH GIRL, THE (5CD Set)
Twice the lovin' (in half the time) / Crying steel guitar waltz / Keep it a secret / Nobody else can love you like I do / I'd rather die young / Dear John letter: *Shepard, Jean & Ferlin Husky* / My wedding ring / With all these memories / Forgive me John: *Shepard, Jean & Ferlin Husky* / Why did you wait / You'll come crawlin' / Mysteries of life / Let's kiss and try again: *Shepard, Jean & Ferlin Husky* / Glass that stands beside you / Two whoops and a holler / Don't fall in love with a married man / What'll you have: *Shepard, Jean & Ferlin Husky* / It tickles: *Shepard, Jean & Simon Crum* / Please don't divorce me / Did you tell her about me / Don't rush me / You sent her an orchid (you sent me a rose) / Take possession / Satisfied mind / Beautiful lies / I thought of you / You're calling me sweetheart again / He loved me once and he'll love me again / Girls in disgrace / This has been your life / Just give me love / Thank you just the same / Over and over / Tell me what I want to hear / Shadows on the wall / I'll thank you all my life / I learned it all from you / Hello old broken heart / Sad singin' and slow ridin' / It's hard to tell the married from the free / Did I turn down a better deal / Passing love affair / I married you for love / I'm thinking tonight of my blue eyes / Be honest with me / Under suspicion / I want you to go where no one knows me / Tomorrow I'll be gone / If you can walk away / Go on, go on / I lost you after all / It scares me half to death / You're just the kind of guy / Too late with the roses / Other woman / Act like a married man / I used to love you / Weak and the strong / You'd better go / Thief in the night / Memory / I love you because / You win again / You can't break the chains of love / Secret of life / Jealous heart / Sweet temptation / I'll take the blame / I'll never be free / I'll hold you in my heart / I hate myself / You're telling me sweet lies again / He's my baby / Just another girl / Jeopardy / Are you certain / Better love next time / Have heart, will love / Heartaches, teardrops and sorrow / I didn't mean to make you cry / Sweetheart don't come back / How do you tell it to a child / One you slip around with / Mysteries of life / Did I turn down a better deal / Root of all evil (is a man) / Where people go / Lonely little world / I don't apologise for loving you / Mockin' bird hill / Another / Blues stay away from me / If you haven't, you can't feel the way I do / Under your spell again / Waltz of the angels / One white rose / Big midnight special / You're the only good thing / Colour song / Got you on my mind / For the children's sake / Nobody but myself / No one knows / Would you be satisfied / If you were losing him to me / Second best / Two voices, two shadows, two faces / Go on with your dancing / I can't seem to say goodbye / So wrong, so fast / How long does it hurt (when a heart breaks) / I don't remember / Leave me alone / Biggest cry / I've got to talk to Mary / It's torture / Your conscience or your heart / I turned right around and went home / I've learned to live with you / Nobody like you / Lake Lonely / It's never too late / One less heartache / Tear dropped by / When your house is not a home / I can't cry him away / That's what lonesome is / Foggy river / When two world collide / Loose talk / I can't stop loving you / Big wheel / Born to lose / If you've got the money, I've got the time / Half a mind / Cigarettes and coffee blues / That's what it's like to be lonesome / Violet and a rose / Just call me lonesome / Two little boys / He plays the bongo (I play the banjo) / Second fiddle (to an old guitar) / Ain't nobody's business if I do: *Shepard, Jean & Cal Smith* / It was too late: *Shepard, Jean & Cal Smith* / Someone's gotta cry / Ain't you ashamed / Don't take advantage of me / Let me be the judge / More to love than this / Franklin County moonshine
BCD 15905 / Dec '96 / Bear Family

Shepard, Ollie

☐ COMPLETE RECORDED WORKS VOL.1 1937-1939
DOCD 5434 / May '96 / Document

☐ COMPLETE RECORDED WORKS VOL.2 1939-1941
DOCD 5435 / May '96 / Document

Shepherd, Cybill

☐ MAD ABOUT THE BOY
TWI 4702 / Mar '96 / Les Disques Du Crepuscule

Shepherd, Dave

☐ GOOD ENOUGH TO EAT
BLC 760514 / Nov '97 / Black Lion

☐ GOOD ENOUGH TO KEEP
BLCD 760514 / Nov '95 / Black Lion

☐ TRIBUTE TO BENNY GOODMAN, A (Shepherd, Dave Quintet)
Putting on the ritz / Audio rag / Man I love / Any questions / Running ragged / Poor butterfly / Second thoughts / Peter piper / Lady said it / Limehouse blues / I found a new baby / Mahzel / When the saints go marching in / Losing no time / Air mail special / Three's company
AVC 595 / Jun '97 / Avid

Shepherd, James

☐ RHYTHM AND BLUES (Shepherd, James Versatile Brass)
Arrival of the Queen of Sheba / Moonlight in Vermont / Long John's hornpipe / Lazybone blues / Three English dances / Rhythm and blues / Little white donkey / Fantasy and vibrations / Three miniatures
QPRL 035D / '88 / Polyphonic

☐ VERSATILE BRASS
DOYCD 031 / Nov '93 / Doyen

Shepherd, Kenny Wayne

☐ LEDBETTER HEIGHTS
Born with a broken heart / Deja voodoo / Aberdeen / Shame shame shame / One foot on the path / Everybody gets the blues / While we cry / I'm leaving you (commit a crime) / Riverside / What's goin' down / Ledbetter Heights
74321288292 / Apr '96 / Giant

☐ TROUBLE IS... (Shepherd, Kenny Wayne Band)
Slow ride / True lies / Blue on black / Everything is broken / I don't live today / (Long) gone / Somehow somewhere someway / I found love (when I found you) / King's highway / Nothing to do with love / Chase the rainbow / Trouble is
74321462702 / 15 Jun '98 / Giant

Shepherd, Meg

☐ TRANSMUTATIONS (Shepherd, Meg & Alcides Lanza)
ESP 9601CD / Jun '97 / Shelan

Shepp, Archie

☐ BLACK GYPSY
500792 / Sep '96 / Musidisc

☐ BLASE
My angel / There is a balm in Gilead / Sophisticated lady / Touareg / Blase
LEJAZZCD 26 / Aug '94 / Le Jazz

☐ FIFTH OF MAY (Shepp, Archie & Jasper Van't Hof)
CDLR 45004 / Jul '88 / L&R

☐ FIRE MUSIC
Ham bone / Malcolm Malcolm Semper Malcolm / Los Olvidados
MCAD 39121 / Jun '89 / Impulse Jazz

☐ FOUR FOR TRANE
Syeeda's song flute / Mr. Syms / Cousin Mary / Niema / Rufus
IMP 12182 / Apr '97 / Impulse Jazz

☐ FREEDOM (Shepp, Archie Quintet)
JMY 10072 / Aug '91 / JMY

☐ GOIN' HOME (Shepp, Archie & Horace Parlan)
SCCD 31079 / Jul '88 / Steeplechase

☐ I KNOW ABOUT THE LIFE
SKCD 23026 / Jun '93 / Sackville

☐ IN MEMORY OF ARCHIE SHEPP (Shepp, Archie & Chet Baker)
Dedication to bessie smith's blues / Dedication to bessie smith's blues / Confirmation / When lights are low / How deep is the ocean / Old devil moon / My ideal
CDLR 45006 / Jul '88 / L&R

☐ LIVE IN PARIS (Shepp, Archie & Eric Le Lann)
LOZ 10 / Apr '97 / Arcade

☐ LIVE IN SAN FRANCISCO
Keep your heart right / Lady sings the blues / In a sentimental mood / Sylvia / Wedding / Wherever June bugs go / Things ain't what they used to be / Three for a quarter one for a dime
IMP 12542 / 23 Mar '98 / Impulse Jazz

☐ LOVER MAN
Stars are in your eyes / Lover man / Brand new world / Breaking a new day / Yesterdays / My funny valentine / Lush life / Squeeze me in
CDSJP 287 / Jun '89 / Timeless Jazz

☐ MAMA ROSE
SCCD 31169 / Jul '88 / Steeplechase

☐ MAMA TOO TIGHT
Portait of Robert Thompson (as a young man) / Mama too tight / Theme for Ernie / Basheer
IMP 12482 / 23 Mar '98 / Impulse Jazz

☐ MONTREUX VOL.1
Lush life / U-jamaa / Crucificado / Miss Toni
FCD 741027 / Sep '88 / Freedom

☐ PARLAN DUO REUNION (Shepp, Archie & Horace Parlan)
Sophisticated lady / Cousin flo / A flower is a lovesome thing / Call me pannonica / When lights are low / Stardust
CDLR 45003 / Oct '88 / L&R

☐ RISING SUN
RS 0005 / Oct '94 / Just A Memory

☐ SEA OF FACES, A
Hipnosis / Song for Mozambique / I know 'bout life / Lookin' for someone to love
1200022 / Sep '95 / Black Saint

☐ SOMETHING TO LIVE FOR
Flower is a lovesome thing / My foolish heart / Strange fruit / You're blase / Something to live for / Georgia on my mind / Hello, young lovers / California blues
CDSJP 439 / Apr '97 / Timeless

☐ SOUL SONG
ENJA 40502 / 17 Nov '97 / Enja

☐ SPLASHES (Shepp, Archie Quartet)
Arrival / Reflexions / Groovin' high / Steam / Manhattan
CDLR 45005 / Jul '88 / L&R

☐ STEAM
ENJACD 20762 / 17 Nov '97 / Enja

☐ STREAM
Stream / Along came betty / Blues for donald duck / U-jamaa / Crucificado / Miss toml
JHR 73520 / Sep '93 / Jazz Hour

☐ THERE'S A TRUMPET IN MY SOUL
There's a trumpet in my soul suite (part 1) / Samba da rua / Zaid (part 1) / Down in Brazil / There's a trumpet in my soul suite (part 2) / Zaid (part 2) / It is the year of the rabbit / Zaid (part 3)
FCD 41016 / Dec '87 / Freedom

☐ TRUMPET IN MY SOUL
FCD 74106 / Oct '89 / Freedom

☐ YASMINA, A BLACK WOMAN
Yasmina, a black woman / Sonny's back / Body and soul
LEJAZZCD 51 / Oct '95 / Le Jazz

Sheppard, Andy

☐ ANDY SHEPPARD & INCLASSIFICABLE (Sheppard, Andy & Inclassificable)
Where we going / Slow boat / Hush hush / RCA / Ocean view / Is everything alright up there / Too close to the flame / Ships in the night / Sharp practice
LBLC 6583 / Jul '95 / Label Bleu

☐ IN-CO-MOTION
ASAP / Eargliding / Backstage passes / Movies / Upstate / Let's lounge / Pinky
IMCD 195 / Jul '94 / Island

☐ INTRODUCTIONS IN THE DARK
Romantic / Rebecca's / Optics / Conversations / Forbidden fruit
IMCD 116 / May '91 / Antilles/New Directions

☐ MOVING IMAGE (Sheppard, Andy & Steve Lodder)
5338752 / Nov '96 / Verve

☐ SOFT ON THE INSIDE
Soft on the inside / Rebecca's silk stockings / Carla, Carla, Carla / Adventures in the rave trade
IMCD 194 / Jul '94 / Island

Sher, Oscar

☐ CLASSICAL SPANISH GUITAR OF OSCAR SHER, THE
La fiesta / Que c'est triste / Love theme from 'romeo and juliet' / Aranjuez / Cancion del sur / El dia que me quieras / Gracias a la vida / Sur / Guajira / Esta tarde vi llover / Luz del amanecer / Que nadia sepami sufrir / Viva jujuy / La distancia tu / Adio nonino
QED 104 / Nov '96 / Tring

Sherburn, Chris

☐ FOOTHOLD (Sherburn, Chris & Denny Bartley)
Choice wife / Night visiting song / Monaghan twig / Miltown / I drew my ship / On the tear / Diggers / Floating crowbar / Freeborn man / Innocents abroad / Little beggarman / Rocking the baby / Sullivan's John / Miltown 2 (stand your ground)
SOMCD 003 / Nov '97 / Sound Out Music

☐ LAST NIGHT'S FUN (Sherburn, Chris & Denny Bartley)
SOM 002 / Oct '95 / Sound Out Music

Sheridan, John

☐ SOMETHING TELLS ME (Sheridan, John Allstar Band)
ARCD 19182 / Oct '97 / Arbors Jazz

Sheridan, Tony

☐ FIRST (Sheridan, Tony & The Beatles)
Ain't she sweet / Cry for a shadow / When the saints go marching in / Why / If you love me baby / What'd I say / Sweet Georgia Brown / Let's dance / Ruby baby / My Bonnie / Nobody's child / Ready Teddy / Ya ya / Kansas City
5500372 / May '93 / Spectrum

☐ LIVE AND DANGEROUS (Documentary/Live) (Sheridan, Tony & The Beat Brothers)
OTR 1100019 / Jun '97 / Metro Independent

☐ SHERIDAN IN CONTROL (Documentary/Live)
OTR 1100018 / Jun '97 / Metro Independent

Sheriff, Dave

☐ FLY AWAY (Sheriff, Dave Nashville Superpickers)
Fly away / Four wheel cowboy / Heart made of stone / More than one heart / Strong love / Unforgotten hero / Love like mine / Cowgirl swing / She (who must be obeyed) / Cajun strut
DS 008 / 1 Jun '98 / Stomp

Sherman, Bim

☐ ACROSS THE RED SEA
Golden locks / Revolution / Slummy ghetto / You are the one / Just like a king / Across the Red Sea / Golden morning star / Awake the slum / Party time / Sit and wonder
ONUCD 17 / 8 Jun '98 / On-U Sound

☐ CRAZY WORLD
CEND 1600 / Oct '96 / Century

☐ CRUCIAL CUTS VOL.1
CEND 400 / Sep '94 / Century

☐ IN A RUB A DUB STYLE
OMCD 013 / May '95 / Original Music

☐ IT MUST BE A DREAM
My woman / Just can't stand it / Can I be free from crying / Missing you / Lovers leap / Simple life / Solid as a rock / It must be a dream / Bewildered / Over the rainbow / Golden locks
MNTCD 1005 / Jun '97 / Mantra

☐ LION HEART DUB
CEND 1800 / Jan '97 / Century

☐ MIRACLE
MNTCD 1004 / Jun '96 / Mantra

☐ REALITY (Sherman, Bim & Dub Syndicate)
CEND 1700 / Nov '92 / Century

☐ TAKEN OFF
CEND 2001 / Nov '94 / Century

☐ WHAT HAPPENED
Heaven / Earth people / Guilty / What happened / Keep on trying / Cool down the pressure / Let the spirit move you / Don't crucify my love / So jah say / Truth / Seven times I rise and fall / Queen of hearts
MNTCD 1012 / 3 Aug '98 / Mantra

Sherman, Daryl

☐ CELEBRATING MILDRED BAILEY (Sherman, Daryl & John Cocuzzi)
ACD 295 / Nov '96 / Audiophile

Sherriff, Dave

☐ UK LINE DANCE TOP TEN
DS 009 / 20 Jul '98 / Stomp

Sherrys

☐ POP POP POP-PIE
Pop Pop Pop-Pie / Your hand in mine / Dancin' the Strand / Double order mashed potatoes / Dance / Slop time / Fly / At the hop / Let's stomp again / Bristol twistin' Danny / New cha cha cha / Last dance / Last dance / Oh la la limbo / Saturday night / I've got no one / Society / My guy / Monk, monk, monkey / That boy of mine
BCD 16105 / Nov '96 / Bear Family

Sherwood, Bobby

☐ BOBBY SHERWOOD ORCHESTRA VOL.1 1944-1946 (Sherwood, Bobby Orchestra)
CCD 28 / Nov '96 / Circle

☐ BOBBY SHERWOOD ORCHESTRA VOL.2 1944-1946 (Sherwood, Bobby Orchestra)
CCD 115 / Nov '96 / Circle

Sheshbesh

☐ SHESHBESH
Jonona / Nelson / Romance / Kramim / Longa yurgo / Amman Amman / Segoh / Wared / Kumran / Shortwave
8888302 / 24 Aug '98 / Tiptoe

Sheta, Yussef

☐ EGYPT
3026732 / 24 Feb '98 / Long Distance

Shew, Bobby

☐ TRUMPETS NO END (Shew, Bobby & Chuck Findley)
DCD 4003 / Mar '90 / Delos

Shicheng, Lin

☐ ART OF THE PIPA
C 560046 / Nov '93 / Ocora

Shide & Acorn

☐ LEGEND OF THE DREAMSTONES
KSCD 9310 / Jun '97 / Kissing Spell

☐ PRINCESS OF THE ISLAND
KSCD 9460 / Jun '97 / Kissing Spell

Shield

☐ VAMPIRESONGS
DFR 10 / Feb '97 / Desperate Flight

Shield, Roy

☐ MUSICAL TRANSITIONS FOR RADIO
EW 9627 / Sep '97 / Eigen Wijs

Shields, Chris

☐ HAUNT ME
Haunt me / Fool / Talking 'bout that feeling / Never the same again / Gently fade away / In another time / Your tender touch / Things you do to me / Thousand dreams / Secret love / But the neighbours ain't / Mother love
CRAZCD 195 / Sep '93 / Go Crazy

Shields, Lonnie

☐ BLUES IS ON FIRE
Every man needs a good woman / Man is under pressure / Going to the juke joint / Play me a song / Doin' time / Blues is on fire / Best friend stole my woman / All the way down / Daddy told me so / Let me be the one / Party down / Freedom
JSPCD 298 / Sep '97 / JSP

☐ TIRED OF WAITING
Woman is dangerous / Tears become my tears / If you want my loving (Come to me) / I got the blues / If you know Jesus / Full time loving / Coming of the lord / One more chance / Busy man / All I need is your love / Cheating on me / Full time lover
JSPCD 270 / Oct '96 / JSP

Shift

☐ SPACESUIT
EVR 025CD / May '97 / Equal Vision

Shihab, Sahib

☐ AND ALL THOSE CATS
Set up / Peter's waltz / Yah yah blues / End of a love affair / Om mani padame hum / Bohemia after dark / Campi's idea / Jay Jay / Waltz for Seth / Herr fixit / Stoned ghosts / Companionship / CT and CB / Dijdar / Talk some yak e dak
RW 102CD / 24 Apr '98 / Schema

☐ CONVERSATIONS
BLCD 760169 / Oct '93 / Black Lion

☐ JAZZ SAHIB
SMTWTFS blues / Jamilla / Moors / Blu-a-round / Le'sneak / Ballad to the East / Ba-dut-du-dat
SV 0141 / May '98 / Savoy Jazz

Shihad

☐ CHURN
Factory / Screwtop / Scacture / Stations / Clapper-loader / I only said / Derail / Bone orchard / Happy meal
N 02492 / Jul '94 / Noise

☐ KILLJOY
N 02542 / Apr '95 / Noise

☐ LA LA LAND
N 02693 / Nov '96 / Noise

☐ SHIHAD
N 02692 / Mar '97 / Noise

Shimita El Diego

☐ MYSTIC (Shimita El Diego & Zaitoum)
CD 64002 / Jan '97 / Sonodisc

Shindell, Richard

☐ BLUE DIVIDE
SH 8014 / Dec '94 / Shanachie

☐ REUNION HILL
SH 8027 / Aug '97 / Shanachie

Shine, Brendan

☐ ALWAYS A WELCOME
There's always a welcome / I'm your man from Strabane / Lovely Isle of Green / Gather up me bags / Loagh key / Irish Elvis Presley / Bury me not on the lone prairie / I'm a savage for bacon and cabbage / My Galway Queen / Time marches on / David's dream / Meet me in Tralee / Old faithful / Big green Mercury / Joe come on home
CDPLAY 1031 / Dec '92 / Play

☐ BEST OF BRENDAN SHINE, THE
3036300122 / May '97 / Carlton

☐ COLLECTION, THE
PLACD 101 / Oct '94 / Play

☐ FAR FAR AWAY
APLCD 1039 / Nov '96 / Avid

☐ I WANNA STAY WITH YOU
I wanna stay with you / Lay down beside me / When the lovin' is through / Hello Darlin' / One more chance / Saints and sinners / Drive me to drink / Walkin' on new grass / Squeeze box / Shoe the donkey / It dosen't matter anymore / Some broken hearts never mend / Dad / Goodbye / (There's) The door / If tomorrow never comes / Love bug / Rock 'n' roll kids / Not counting you / When two lovers meet
3036000082 / Nov '95 / Carlton

☐ I'LL SETTLE FOR OLD IRELAND (18 Country & Irish Favourites)
Are we making love / Dear hearts and gentle people / I will settle for old Ireland / When two lovers meet / Broken pledge / Jeannie Marie / Abbeyshrule / Soft sweet and warm / Woodlands of Loughlin / Time on my hands / By the devil / Down the wrong road again / Humours of Scariff / Ballinasloe fair / My Eileen is waiting for me / Ballinamona hat / Seasons of my heart / Faster horses
306052 / Jan '97 / Hallmark

☐ IF YOU EVER GO OVER TO IRELAND (2CD Set)
Forty miles from Poplar Bluff / Once a day / Bunch of violets blue / I'll do it all again / Coastline of Mayo / Lovin' you (so long now) / Say it again / Astoreen Bawn / Boy inside me / Mama tried / How much time / Bright city lights / Oul' Ballymoe / Spancil hill / Roving Galway boy / Sadie of my dreams / Low back car / What do I care / Woman to woman / Kikfenora jigs / Bonnish Jenny / Dear God / Girl who broke my heart / More than words can tell / Loving you / Hello Mr DJ / I like beer / Living with the shades pulled down / Geese in the bog / Make me dream / It's no secret / Goodnight Irene / King and queen of fools / Say it's not you / Yes I'm feeling better / If you ever go over to Ireland
330132 / Jul '96 / Hallmark

☐ WITH LOVE
Old Tralee / Thank god for kids / Good times / These are the sounds I love / Murphy's widow / Moon behind the hill / Old grey suit / Pipes of Donegal / My son / Diddling song / Only our rivers run free / Bunch of violets blue / Now I'm easy / Did you miss me
PLAYCD 1037 / Mar '96 / Play

Shinehead

☐ TRODDIN'
Troddin' thru / Buff bay / Accident / More than a feeling / Woman like you / Keep on singin' / Me and them / Sniper / Keep on / Good girls bad boys / Never been in love B4 / Reprimand / Boom bangin' / Best creation
7559616672 / Sep '94 / Warner Bros.

Shines, Johnny

☐ JOHNNY SHINES
HCD 8028 / Jul '94 / Hightone

☐ JOHNNY SHINES WITH BIG WALTER HORTON (Shines, Johnny & Big Walter Horton)
TCD 5015 / Mar '95 / Testament

☐ MASTERS OF MODERN BLUES SERIES
TCD 5002 / Aug '94 / Testament

☐ MR. COVER SHAKER
Devil's daughter / Look behind the door / Two steps to hell / Face in the courthouse / Blood ran like wine / May I apologize / Blood ran like wine / I'm getting old / Mother's place / Mr. cover shaker / Shotgun whupin' / Lost love letter blues / Stand by me
BCD 125 / Jan '93 / Biograph

☐ STANDING AT THE CROSSROADS
TCD 5022 / May '95 / Testament

☐ TRADITIONAL DELTA BLUES
Sitting on top of the world / Ramblin' blues / Tell me mama / Bumble bee blues / It ain't nobody's fault but mine / Arguing and boodling / Delta pine / Pony blues / Milk cow blues / Dynaflow blues / Glad rags / Pet rabbit / Little wolf / Jim string
BCD 121 / '92 / Biograph

Shiney Gnomes

☐ MC CREATRIX
RTD 19519172 / Feb '95 / Our Choice

Ship Of Fools

☐ CLOSE YOUR EYES (FORGET THE WORLD)
In the wake of / Where is here / Passage by night / L=SD2 / SOL93 / Starjumper / Western lands / Close your eyes (forget the world)
KTB 013CD / Jun '93 / Dreamtime

☐ OUT THERE SOMEWHERE
Elevator / Diesel spaceship / First light / Guidance is internal / Out there somewhere / From time / Eternal guidance
CDKTB 18 / Apr '95 / Dreamtime

Shipp, Matthew

☐ BEFORE THE WORLD
FMPCD 81 / Sep '97 / Full Moon

☐ BY THE LAW OF MUSIC (Shipp, Matthew Trio)
Signal / By the law of music / Implicit / Fair play / Grid / Whole movement / Game of control / Point to point / PX / Grid / Coo / XZU / Solitude
ARTCD 6200 / Jun '97 / Hat Art

☐ CIRCULAR TEMPLE (Shipp, Matthew Trio)
Circular temple
74321327582 / Mar '96 / Infinite Zero

☐ CRITICAL MASS
213CD 003 / Jun '96 / 2.13.61

☐ FLOW OF X (Shipp, Matthew Quartet)
Flow of x / Flow of silence / Flow of y / Flow of M / Flow of U / Instinctive codes
213CD 026 / Jun '97 / 2.13.61

☐ MULTIPLICATION TABLE, THE
HATOLOGY 516 / May '98 / Hatology

☐ PRISM (Shipp, Matthew Trio)
BKM 58CD / Nov '96 / Brinkman
KFW 998CD / Feb '97 / Knitting Factory/ Ectoplasm

☐ SYMBOL SYSTEMS
NMR 1 / 16 Feb '98 / No More

☐ THESIS (Shipp, Matthew & Joe Morris)
HATOLOGY 506 / Oct '97 / Hatology

☐ ZO (Shipp, Matthew Duo)
RR 1262 / Dec '94 / Rise

Shipping News

☐ SAVE EVERYTHING
QS 50CD / 22 Aug '97 / Quarter Stick

Shirehorses

☐ WORST ALBUM IN THE WORLD EVER...EVER
Now I know where we're going kid / Ta la / You're gormless / West country boy / Hapless boy lard / Feel like shite / Lardy boy / Girl like you / Single bloke / Sha la la la tum tee tum / Ugly bleeder / Ballad of Franny Lee / Joe's fucked off / Bill oddity / Frank Spencer blues explosion / Cum on skweeze me boilz / You're a bastard
3984208512 / 3 Nov '97 / East West

Shirelles

☐ BABY IT'S YOU
Baby it's you / Irresistible you / Thing I want to hear (pretty words) / Big John / Same old story / Voice of experience / Soldier boy / Thing of the past / Twenty one / Make the night a little longer / Twisting in the USA / Putty in your hands
CDSC 6012 / Jan '94 / Sundazed

☐ BEST OF THE SHIRELLES, THE
Dedicated to the one I love / Look a here baby / Tonight's the night / Will you still love me tomorrow / Boys / Mama said / Thing of the past / What a sweet thing that was / Big John / Putty in your hands / Baby it's you / Soldier boy / Welcome home baby / Mama here comes the bride / Stop the music / It's love that really counts / Everybody loves a lover / Foolish little girl / Abracadabra / Don't say goodnight and mean goodbye / What does a girl do / Don't let it happen to us / Girl is not a girl / Sha la la / His lips get in the way / Thank you baby / Doomsday / Maybe tonight / Shades of blue / Don't go home (My little darling) / Last minute miracle / Wait till I give the signal
CDCHD 356 / Apr '92 / Ace

☐ BEST OF THE SHIRELLES, THE
VVC 1002 / 15 Dec '97 / Avid

☐ DEFINITIVE COLLECTION, THE (2CD Set)
Dedicated to the one I love / Look-a-here baby / Teardrop and a lollipop / Doin' the ronde / Please be my boyfriend / I saw a tear / Tonight's the night / Dance is over / Will you love me tomorrow / Boys / Mama said / Blue holiday / Thing of the past / What a sweet thing that was / Big John / Twenty one / Baby it's you / Things I want to hear / Soldier boy / Love is a swingin' thing / Welcome home baby / Mama here comes the bride / Stop the music / It's love that really counts / Everybody loves a lover / I don't think so / Foolish little girl / Not for all the money in the world / Don't say goodnight and mean goodbye / I didn't mean to hurt you / Abra ka dabra / What does a girl do / Don't let it happen to us / Things go better with Coca Cola / It's a mad mad mad mad world / 31 flavours / Tonight you're gonna fall in love with me / 20th century rock 'n' roll / Sha la la / His lips get in the way / Thank you baby / Doomsday / Maybe tonight / Are you still my baby / Ssh I'm watching the movie / March / Everybody's goin' mad / My heart belongs to you / (Mama) my soldier boy is coming home / I met him on a Sunday / Till my baby comes home / Whatever will be will be (Que sera sera) / Shades of blue / When the boys talk about the girls / Teasin' me / Look away / Don't go home (my little darlin') / Nobody's baby after you / Bright shiny colours / Too much of a good thing / Last minute miracle / Wait until I give the signal / Hippie walk / Commercial
CPCD 81902 / Sep '96 / Charly

☐ FABULOUS SHIRELLES
Will you still love me tomorrow / Soldier boy / Dedicated to the one I love / Foolish little girl / Mama said / Baby it's you / Big John / Welcome home baby / Everybody loves a lover / Don't say goodnight and mean goodbye / Tonight's the night / What does a girl do
CDFAB 011 / Oct '91 / Ace

☐ GIVE A TWIST PARTY (Shirelles & King Curtis)
Mama here comes the bride / Take the last train home (instr.) / Welcome home baby / I've got a woman / I still want you / Take the last train home (vocal) / Love is a swingin' thing / Ooh-poo-pah-doo / New Orleans / Mr. Twister / Potato chips
CDSC 6013 / Jan '94 / Sundazed

☐ LOST & FOUND
Good good time / Long day, short night / You'll know when the right boy comes along / Rocky / Go tell her / Remember me / For my sake / Celebrate your victory / Hands off, he's mine / Crossroads in your heart / He's the only guy I'll ever love / One of the flower people / I'm feeling it too / If I had you / There goes my heart / Shh, I'm watching the movie
CDCHD 521 / May '94 / Ace

☐ MASTERS, THE
EABCD 068 / 6 Mar '98 / Eagle

☐ SHIRELLES, THE
GOLD 070 / Jul '96 / Gold

Shirley & Lee

☐ SWEETHEARTS OF THE BLUES 1952-1963, THE (4CD Set)
Sweethearts / I'm gone / Real thing / Korea / Baby / Shirley, come back to me / Shirley's back / Shirley's back / Why did I / So in love / So in love / Reason why / Time has come / I love you so / Proposal / Two happy people / Lee goofed / Every fool has his day / Down in my heart / Keep on / Confessin' / When the sun goes down / Tryin' to fool me / Rumours blue / Comin' over / Takes money / I didn't want you / You'd be thinking of me / I'll thrill you / Feel so good / Lee's dream / I'll do it / Tell me so / That's what I'll do / Little world / Let the good times roll / Do you mean to hurt me so / Everything / We will be forever happy / I feel good / That's what I wanna do / Now that's over / I want to dance / Marry me / Before I go / Don't you know / Rock all night / Rockin' with the clock / Flirt / Love no one but you / Live on the farm / Everybody's rockin' / Don't leave me here to cry / Come on and have your fun / All I want to do is cry / True love never dies / When day is done / So tired / SHirley come back to me / Like you used to do / Bewildered / Who are we fooling / Keep loving me / You move me / Let's live it up / I've been loved before / I'll never be free / After last night / I love the way you love / Your love makes the difference / I was lucky / Lover's mistake / Everybody needs somebody / Your day is coming / Two peas in a pod / Good for nothing baby / Well-a well-a / Our kids / They've got to understand / Call me a fool / Hard to believe / Behind the make up / Keep the magic working / Girl you're married now / It's been so long / Joker / Together we stand / My last letter / I'm old enough / You wouldn't / Little thing / Engagement / Don't stop now / Hey little boy / Golden rule / Honky tonk music / Dancing world / Thank you / Wouldn't be here / Brink of disaster / Paper doll / When I fall in love / Don't marry too soon / Honey bee / When a girl meets a boy / Never let me go / Surf Heaven / Surfer's hangout / Somebody put a juke box in the study hall
BCD 15960 / Apr '97 / Bear Family

Shirley, Roy

☐ BLACK LION NEGUS RASTAFARI
CDLINC 011 / Dec '95 / Lion Inc.

☐ CONTROL THEM VOL.1
GRCD 004 / Jul '96 / Sprint

☐ GET IN THE GROOVE (Shirley, Roy & Stranger Cole/Ken Parker)
RGCD 0038 / Apr '97 / Rocky One

Shirts

☐ TELL ME YOUR PLANS
Tell me your plans / Laugh and walk away / One last change / Out on the ropes / Running through the night / Triangulum / Too much trouble / Lonely android / Reduced to a whisper / Empty never after / Teenage crutch / 10th floor clown / Story goes / They say the sun shines / Poe
DC 886082 / 2 Feb '98 / Disky

Shiv

☐ FLAYED AND ASHAMED
Unsatisfaction / Crazy cooter / Fruit pie / Coworker / QRXT65723 / Plumber / Leave now / Punk / Swazi spoon position / Emk / Long distance dedication / Bank it / High-neckin
THI 570202 / Jan '97 / Thirsty Ear

Shiva

☐ FIREDANCE
How can I / En cachent / Wild machine / Borderline / Stranger lands / Angel of monz / Rendezvous with death / User / Call me in the morning / Shiva / Rock lives on / Sympathy
CDMETAL 8 / Jan '97 / Anagram

Shiva Burlesque

☐ BURLESQUE
NATEUK 15 / 18 Sep '97 / Fundamental

☐ MERCURY BLUES
DRCD 7 / 18 Sep '97 / Fundamental

Shiva's Headband

☐ TAKE ME TO THE MOUNTAINS
MD 055 / 30 Mar '98 / Mystic Diva

Shiver

☐ WALPURGIS
RF 601 / Jun '97 / Red Fox

Shivers

☐ BURIED LIFE, THE
GRCD 398 / May '97 / Glitterhouse

☐ SHIVERS, THE
GRCD 372 / Aug '95 / Glitterhouse

Shizuo

☐ SHIZUO VS. SHIZOR
Sweat / Punks / Braindead / New kick / Emptiness / Duty / Sexual high / Tight / Dr. LSD / Zen / Crack meets the hammer / Blondo / Making love / Chill
DHRCD 007 / Jun '97 / Digital Hardcore

Shizzoe, Hank

☐ LOW BUDGET
CCD 11046 / Nov '94 / Crosscut

☐ PLENTY OF TIME (Shizzoe, Hank & Loose Gravel)
Being there with you / Indian girl / Arrows through my heart / Train song / One fine day / She's back in town / Life of a thief / What can I forget / Silvertone guitar / 1-800-grand-prize / I love you but it leads to nothing / Between the lines / Same time same place
CCD 11060 / May '98 / Crosscut

Shlomit

☐ SONGS IN HEBREW
340862 / Jun '96 / Koch International

Sho Nuff

☐ FROM THE GUT TO THE BUTT
Funkasize you / Steppin' out / You chose me / Thinking of you / Get it together / Watch me do it / I live across the street / Come on / Mix match man / Total answer
CDSXE 092 / Aug '93 / Stax

Shoales, Ian

☐ I GOTTA GO
213CD 016 / May '97 / 2.13.61

Shock

☐ PINULTIMATE
FRCD 007 / 6 Jul '98 / Frontier

Shock Headed Peters

☐ FEAR ENGINE, THE
CP131 05CD / Oct '96 / Cyclops

☐ NOT BORN BEAUTIFUL
CP131 03CD / Oct '96 / Cyclops

☐ SEVERAL HEADED ENEMY
CP131 01CD / Oct '96 / Cyclops

☐ TENDERCIDE
CP131 07CD / Oct '96 / Cyclops

Shock Therapy

☐ DARK YEARS, THE
EFA 08440CD / Oct '92 / Dossier

☐ HATE IS A FOUR LETTER WORD
SPV 08419572 / May '95 / SPV

☐ HEAVEN AND EARTH
EFA 084552 / Mar '94 / Dossier
SPV 08419552 / Jun '95 / SPV

Shocked, Michelle

☐ ARKANSAS TRAVELER
33 rpm Soul / Come a long way / Secret to a long life / Contest coming (Cripple creek) / Over the waterfall / Shaking hands (Soldier's joy) / Jump Jim crow / Hold me back (Frankie and Johnny) / Strawberry jam / Prodigal daughter (Cotton eyes Joe) / Blackberry blossom / Weaving way / Arkansas traveller / Woody's rag
5121892 / Apr '92 / London

☐ MERCURY POISED
On the greener side / Anchorage / Come along way / Quality of mercy / Street corner ambassador / Too little too late / If love was a train / When love was a train / When I grow up / Prodigal daughter / Over the waterfall / Holy spirit / Stillborn
5329602 / Nov '96 / London

Shocking Blue

☐ 20 GREATEST HITS
REP 4125 / Aug '91 / Repertoire

☐ AT HOME
REP 4041 / Aug '91 / Repertoire

☐ BEST OF SHOCKING BLUE, THE
Lucy brown is back in town / Send me a postcard / Long lonesome road / Venus / Mighty joe / Never marry a railroad man / Hello darkness / Shocking you / Blossom lady / Out of sight, out of mind / Inkpot / Rock in the sea / Eve and the apple / Oh lord / Let me carry your bag / This america / Love buzz / Hot sand / Loving you / Too young
CSAPCD 114 / Jan '94 / Connoisseur Collection

☐ SCORPIO'S DANC
REP 4086 / Aug '91 / Repertoire

Shoenfelt, Phil

☐ GOD IS THE OTHER FACE OF THE DEVIL
Charlotte's room / Gambler / Alchemy / Hospital / Black rain / Only you / Martha's well / Killer inside / Well of souls / Pale light shining
BAH 11 / Oct '93 / Humbug

☐ LIVE IN PRAGUE
7102692 / May '96 / NMC

Shoes

☐ AS IS (2CD Set)
BV 105962 / Jan '97 / Black Vinyl

☐ BLACK VINYL SHOES
Boys don't lie / Do you wanna get lucky / She'll disappear / Tragedy / Writing a postcard / Not me / Someone finer / Capital gain / Fatal running start / Okay it really hurts / Fire for a while / If you'd stay / Nowhere so fast
CREV 016CD / Sep '93 / Rev-Ola
BV 100922 / Nov '96 / Black Vinyl

☐ BOOMERANG/SHOES ON ICE
BV 181902 / Nov '96 / Black Vinyl

☐ FRET BUZZ
BV 104952 / Nov '96 / Black Vinyl

☐ PRESENT TENSE/TONGUE TWISTER
BV 198882 / Nov '96 / Black Vinyl

☐ PROPELLER
BV 102942 / Nov '96 / Black Vinyl

☐ SHOES BEST
BV 197872 / Nov '96 / Black Vinyl

☐ SILHOUETTE
Get my message / Will you spin for me / When push comes to shove / Shining / It's only you / Twist and bend it / I wanna give it to you / Turn around / Running wild / Oh, Angeline / Bound to fade / Suspicion
BV 151912 / Nov '96 / Black Vinyl

☐ STOLEN WISHES
BV 101892 / Nov '96 / Black Vinyl

Shoggoth

☐ COMBINATION
ERO 1002 / Jul '98 / Elevate

Shoham, Jeremy

☐ JUST EAST OF JAZZ (Shoham, Jeremy & James Woodrow)
JEOJCD 1 / May '97 / Just East Of Jazz

Sholle, Jon

☐ CATFISH FOR SUPPER
Mississippi gal / Plum cake / Sweet kind of love / EBA / Bully samba / Catfish for supper / Bugle call rag / Triangle / Railroad blues / Oahu blues / You're there / I don't love nobody / Peach tree shuffle
ROUCD 3026 / Nov '96 / Rounder

☐ OUT OF THE FRYING PAN
Durham's bull / Jon's jump / Pike County breakdown / Golden slippers / Sweet Sue / Red wing / Farewell blues / Hunza guitar boogie / 8th of January / Woody's rag / Banks of the Ohio / Put on your old grey bonnet / D medley / Corrina
ROUCD 0398 / Jun '97 / Rounder

Shonen Knife

☐ BRAND NEW KNIFE (2CD Set)
MCD 80071 / 15 Sep '97 / MCA

☐ EXPLOSION
BD 9047 / Nov '97 / Big Deal

☐ HAPPY HOUR
UMD 80515 / 27 Jul '98 / Universal

☐ LET'S KNIFE
Riding the rocket / Bear up bison / Twist Barbie / Tortoise theme 2 / Antonio baka guy / Ah Singapore / Flying jelly attack / Black bass / Cycling is fun / Watchin' girl / I am a cat / Tortoise theme 1 / Devil house / Insect collector / Burning farm
RUST 001CD / Jan '93 / August

☐ ROCK ANIMALS
RUST 009CD / Jan '94 / August

☐ WE ARE VERY HAPPY YOU CAME
Lazybone / Public bath / Goose steppin' mama / I wanna eat choco bars / Suzy is a headbanger / Boys / Red kross
RUST 004CD / Apr '93 / August

Shontz, Bill

☐ TEDDY BEAR GREATEST HITS
8536542362 / 17 Mar '98 / Lightyear

Shooglenifty

☐ SHOOGLENIFTY LIVE AT SELWYN HALL
WS 008CD / Aug '96 / Womad Select

☐ VENUS IN TWEED
Pipe tunes / Horace / Point Road / Venus in tweeds / Waiting for Conrad / Two fifty to Vigo / Paranoia / Buying a blanket / Tammienorrie / Point Road (mix)
CDTRAX 076 / Aug '94 / Greentrax

☐ WHISKY KISS, A
Da eye wifey / She's in the attic / Song for Susie / Whisky kiss / Good drying / Hoptsoi / Price of a pig / Farewell to Nigg
CDTRAX 106 / Jun '96 / Greentrax

Shootyz Groove

☐ HIPNOSIS
Regardless / Manhole / Lilly Pad / POnce / Inter zone / Anchor / Fantasy no.5 / Triangle music / Groovyland / Nothing for you / Diamond mine / Other side / Reverse side / 8 million times
RR 88292 / Jun '97 / Roadrunner

☐ JAMMIN IN VICIOUS ENVIRONMENTS
ABT 101CD / May '95 / Abstract

Shop Assistants

☐ WILL ANYTHING HAPPEN
I don't wanna be friends with you / All day long / Before I wake / Caledonian Road / All that ever mattered / Fixed grin / Somewhere in China / Train from Kansas City / Home again / Seems to be / After dark / All of the time / What a way to die / Nature lover
OVER 62CD / Jun '97 / Overground

Shopping Trolley

☐ SHOPPING TROLLEY
Whistle song / Moose / Hyde park corner / Bring back the mary hopkin days / In the morning / Graham, return / Len smoothchurch / I'm a fool, hardy / Roundabout
HNCD 1349 / Jan '90 / Hannibal

Shore, Dinah

☐ BEST OF DINAH SHORE, THE
I've got my eyes on you / Just a-whistlin' and a-whittlin' / Shake down the stars / Yes my darling daughter / Down Argentina way / I hear a rhapsody / I do do you / Honeysuckle rose / If it's you / Daisy bell (on a bicycle made for two) / You and I / Is it taboo / Don't leave me daddy / Happy in love / Sometimes / Blues in the night / Three little sisters / Manhatten serenade
SUMCD 4177 / 11 May '98 / Summit

☐ BLUES IN THE NIGHT
As we walk into the sunset / Blues in the night / Body and soul / Boy in khaki, a girl in lace / Chloe / Down Argentina way / He's my guy / Honeysuckle rose / Manhattan serenade / Memphis blues / Mocking Bird lament / Mood indigo / Murder he says / My man / Skylark / Smoke gets in your eyes / Somebody loves me / Something to remember you by / Sophisticated lady / Stardust / Three little sisters / Yes my darling daughter / You and I / You'd be so nice to come home to
CDAJA 5136 / Jun '94 / Living Era

☐ DINAH SINGS PREVIN PLAYS/ SOMEBODY LOVES ME (2CD Set)
Man I love / April in Paris / That old feeling / I've got you under my skin / Then I'll be tired of you / Sleepy time girl / Melancholy baby / My funny valentine / It had to be you / I'll be seeing you / If I had you / It's easy to remember / East of the sun / I hadn't anyone till you / When I grow too old to dream / Something to remember you by / Remember / All alone / I only have eyes for you / My baby / Somebody loves me
4930672 / Jan '98 / Capitol

☐ DINAH'S SHOW TIME 1944-1947
You're a builder upper / Can't you read between the lines / Sometimes I'm happy / Linger in my arms a little longer / Rainy night in Rio / Laura / Just one of those things / Love me or leave me / Dreamer / Tallahassee / How high the moon / Night and day / Dixieland band: Button up your overcoat / I've got the world on a string / Way you look tonight / Smoke gets in your eyes / Shoo, shoo baby / Yesterdays / Man I love / Zing went the strings of my heart / I'll walk alone / Tess's torch song / Lover come back to me / Gotta be this or that
HEPCD 45 / Feb '95 / Hep

☐ DINAH, ALL THE WAY
St Louis blues / I got a man / Shake rattle and roll / Let the good times roll / Boogie blues / Blues in the night / Dinella blues / When day is done / Music maestro please / Smoke gets in your eyes / All the way / Baia / These foolish things / Mountain high valley low / Roll on Mississippi roll on / When I fall in love / Spring will be a little late this year / It never entered my mind / I can dream can't I / Ball ha'i / Tall hope / My man's gone now / Start the new year right
JASCD 342 / 6 Apr '98 / Jasmine

☐ EMI PRESENTS THE MAGIC OF DINAH SHORE
April in Paris / Blues in the night / One I love (belongs to somebody else) / Falling in love with love / Gypsy / I've got you under my skin / Love is here to stay / Man I love / My funny Valentine / Sentimental journey / Somebody loves me / My melancholy baby / It's all right with me / It had to be you / I'll walk alone / I only have eyes for you / Buttons and bows / Lover come back to me / Way down yonder in New Orleans / Song is ended
CDMFP 6372 / May '97 / Music For Pleasure

☐ LEGENDARY SONG STYLIST
MACCD 357 / 26 Jan '98 / Autograph

☐ LIKE SOMEONE IN LOVE
I thought about you / Last night / Imagination / Say it / Jim / You can't brush me off / My man / Is it taboo / All I need is you / I don't want to walk without you / Maybe / Something to remember you by / Now I know / Night is young and your so beautiful / I'll walk alone / My romance / Like someone in love / I can't tell why I love you but I do / Sleigh ride in July
ROYCD 201 / Jul '96 / Flare

☐ MAD ABOUT YOU, SAD WITHOUT YOU
Thrill of a new romance / I like to recognise the tune / Darn that dream / Smoke gets in your eyes / Outside of that I love you / How come you do me like you do / Somebody loves me / Mocking bird lament / I'm through with love / Somebody nobody loves / All alone / Not mine / Skylark / One dozen roses / I can't give you anything but love / Mad about him, sad without him / Dearly beloved / Boy in khaki, a girl in lace / Murder, he says / You'd be so nice to come home to
HQCD 43 / Jun '94 / Harlequin

☐ RHAPSODY (18 Classic Superb Performances)
I've got my eyes on you / Just a whistlin' and whistlin' / Shake down the stars / Yes my darling daughter / Down Argentina way / I hear a rhapsody / I do, do you / Honeysuckle rose / If it's you / Daisy bell (On a bicycle made for two) / You and I / Is it taboo / Don't leave me Daddy / Happy in love / Sometimes / Blues in the night / Three little sisters / Manhattan serenade
PLATCD 159 / Mar '96 / Platinum

☐ VERY BEST OF DINAH SHORE, THE
SWNCD 006 / Oct '95 / Sound Waves

☐ YOU'D BE SO NICE TO COME HOME TO
PASTCD 7821 / Jun '97 / Flapper

Short, Bobby

☐ CELEBRATING 30 YEARS AT THE CAFE CARLYLE (Short, Bobby Orchestra)
I like the likes of you / I've got my eyes on you / From this moment on / You've got that thing / Carioca / Guess who's in town / Moten swing / You're driving me crazy / How's your romance / At long last love / I can't get started / Hooray for love / Body and soul / Just one of those things / Romance in the dark / On the street of dreams / Picture me without you
CD 83428 / Mar '98 / Telarc Jazz

☐ LIVE AT THE CARLYLE
Do I hear you saying I love you / Tea for two / Night and day / Too marvellous for words / Our love is here to stay / Drop me off in Harlem / Body and soul / I can't give you anything but love / I can dream, can't I / I get a kick out of you / Satin doll / Nearness of you / Paradise / Easy to love / After you, who / Every time we say goodbye
CD 83311 / Mar '92 / Telarc

☐ SONGS OF NEW YORK (Live At The Cafe Carlyle)
New York New York / Penthouse serenade / She's a latin from Manhattan / Autumn in New York / East side of heaven / When love beckoned (in fifty-second street) / Way out west on West End Avenue / Black butterfly/Harlem butterfly medley / My personal property / Broadway / Sidewalks of New York / Take me back to Manhattan / Upper Madison Avenue blues
CD 83346 / Feb '96 / Telarc

Short List

☐ RIFF BURGLAR
CDTB 188 / 27 Mar '98 / Thunderbolt

Short n' Curlies

☐ BITTER 'N' TWISTED
KONCD 019 / Mar '97 / Knock Out

Short Wave Channel

☐ SHORT WAVE CHANNEL, THE
723248616429 / 5 Jan '98 / Wrenched

Shorter, Wayne

☐ ATLANTIS
Endangered species / Three Marias / Last silk hat / When you dream / Who goes there / Atlantis / Shere Khan / Criancas / On the eve of departure
4816172 / 26 Jan '98 / Sony Jazz

☐ HIGH LIFE
Children of the night / At the fair / Maya / On the Milky Way Express / Pandora awakened / Virgo rising / High life / Midnight in Carlotta's hair / Black swan (in memory of Susan Portlynn Romeo)
5292242 / Mar '96 / Verve

☐ INTRODUCING WAYNE SHORTER
VJ 007 / 24 Feb '98 / Vee Jay

☐ JAZZ PROFILE
Black Nile / Mahjong / Witch hunt / Fee fi fo fum / Chaos / Chief Crazy Horse / Schizophrenia / Super nova / Calm
CDP 8590722 / 6 Oct '97 / Blue Note

☐ JUJU
Juju / Deluge / House of Jade / Mahjong / Yes or no / Twelve more bars to go / Juju / House of Jade
CDP 8376442 / Jun '96 / Blue Note

☐ NATIVE DANCER
Ponta de Areia / Beauty and the beast / Tarde / Miracle of the fishes / Diana / Ana Maria / Lilia / Joanna's theme
4670952 / Jan '95 / Columbia

☐ NIGHT DREAMER
Night dreamer / Oriental folk song / Virgo / Virgo (alternate take) / Black Nile / Charcoal blues / Armageddon
7841732 / 1 Jun '98 / Blue Note

☐ SECOND GENESIS
Ruby and the pearl / Pay as you go / Second Genesis / Mr. Chairman / Tenderfoot / Albatross / Getting to know you / I didn't know what time it was
LEJAZZCD 9 / Mar '93 / Le Jazz

☐ SECOND GENESIS
VJ 016 / 24 Feb '98 / Vee Jay

☐ SPEAK NO EVIL
Fee fi fo fum / Dance cadaverous / Speak no evil / Infant eyes / Wild flower / Out to lunch / Straight up and down / Witch hunt
CDP 7465092 / Mar '95 / Blue Note

☐ THIS IS JAZZ
Endangered species / Lusitanos / Port of entry /
Three Marias / Eurydice / When it was now / Beauty
and the beast / Mahogany bird / Diana
CK 64973 / Oct '96 / Sony Jazz

☐ WAYNING MOMENTS
VJ 014 / 24 Feb '98 / Vee Jay

Shortino, Paul

☐ IT'S ABOUT TIME
HGCD 0890 / 15 Jun '98 / High Gain

Shorty

☐ FRESH BREATH
GR 14CD / Jun '94 / Skingraft

Shotgun

☐ SHOTGUN RIDES AGAIN
RAUCD 027 / 10 Nov '97 / Raucous

Shotgun Rationale

☐ ROLLERCOASTER
EFA 11894 CD / Jun '93 / Vince Lombard

Shotgun Symphony

☐ FORGET THE RAIN
Carousel of broken dream / Line / What if / Eyes of
anger / Playing with fools / Yesterday's gone / Two
songs / My escape / Waiting for the sun / XLV
410222 / Mar '97 / Sha-La

Shotmaker

☐ MOUSE EAR
TMU 013CD / Feb '97 / Troubleman
Unlimited

Shotts & Dykehead
Caledonia Pipe Band

☐ ANOTHER QUIET SUNDAY
COMD 2037 / Feb '94 / Temple

☐ BY THE WATERS EDGE
Hornpipe - The walrus / March, strathspey and reel /
Slow air "By the waters edge" / Jigs and slow air /
Slow air "Farewell to camraw" / Strathspey and reel /
Medley / Slow air "Piper alpha" / Dance jigs / 6/8
Marches / Retreat marches
LCOM 5229 / Aug '94 / Lismor

Shotwell

☐ CELERY BEEF AND IRON
SKIP 063CD / 22 Sep '97 / Broken

Shoukichi, Kina

☐ MUSIC POWER FROM OKINAWA
(Shoukichi, Kina & Champroose)
Haisai ojisan / Uwaki bushi / Red ojisan / Bancho
guwa / Agarizachi / Sukuchinamun /
Ichimushiguwanu yuntaku / Bashaguwa suncha /
Shimagawa song / Tokyo sanbika
CDORBD 072 / Oct '91 / Globestyle

Shoulders

☐ TRASHMAN'S SHOES
Charm / On Sunday / Trashman shoes / Beckoning
bells / Weatherman / I'll take what's left / Lula's bar
and pool / Unkle action / Whole way to the halfway
house / All the nights to come / Fare thee well
DJD 3208 / May '94 / Dejadisc

Shout

☐ IN YOUR FACE
Borderline / Give me an answer / Getting ready /
Getting on with life / Ain't givin up / When the love is
gone / Faith and love / In your face / Moonlight
sonata / Waiting on you
CDMFN 92 / May '89 / Music For
Nations

☐ SHOUT
ESM 014 / 2 Mar '98 / Escape

Show & AG

☐ GOODFELLAS
Never less than ill / You know now / Check it out / Add
on / Next level / Time for ... / Got the flava /
Neighborhood sickness / All out / Medicine / Got ya
back / Next level / You want it
8286412 / Oct '95 / FFRR

Show Of Hands

☐ BACKLOG 1987-1991
CDIS 08 / Mar '95 / Isis

☐ BEAT ABOUT THE BUSH
Beat about the bush / Class of Seventy Three /
Armadas / Nine hundred miles / Shadows in the dark
/ Galway farmer / White tribes / Day has come / Hook
of love / Cars / Blue cockade / Mr. May's/Gloucester
hornpipe / Oak
CDIS 05 / Mar '94 / Isis

☐ COLUMBUS (DIDN'T FIND AMERICA)
Columbus (Didn't find America) / Exile / Breakfast for
Altan / Scattering tears
CDIS 07 / Apr '94 / Isis

☐ DARK FIELDS
HMCD 03 / 3 Aug '98 / Hands On

☐ LIE OF THE LAND
Hunter / Unlock me / Well / Keeper / Captains /
Weary / Ratcliffe highway / Safe as houses / Man in
green / Preacher / M Ferguson / Exile
HMCD 02 / 3 Aug '98 / Hands On

☐ LIVE AT THE ROYAL ALBERT HALL
Columbus (didn't find America) / Day has come /
Preacher / Cuthroats, crooks and con men / Blue
cockade / Soldiers joy / Exile / Man in green / Dove /
Well / Hunter / Captains / Blind fiddler / Santiago /
Galway farmer / Time after time
HMCD 01 / 3 Aug '98 / Hands On

☐ SHOW OF HANDS 'LIVE'
Silver dagger / Blind fiddler / Don't it feel good / I still
wait / Exile / Yankee clipper / Man of war / Bonnie
Light Horseman / I'll put a stake through his heart /
Low down in the broome / Six o'clock waltz / Sit you
down / Wolf at the door / Caught in the rain / Santiago
/ It's all your fault
CDIS 06 / Mar '95 / Isis

Showaddywaddy

☐ 20 GREATEST HITS
JHD 017 / Jun '92 / Tring

☐ 25 STEPS TO THE TOP
REP 4171 / Aug '91 / Repertoire

☐ HITS COLLECTION BOX (3CD Set)
Hey rock 'n' roll / Under the moon of love / Rock 'n'
roll lady / You got personality / When / Weekend /
Dancing party / Go Johnny go / '68 Teenage queen /
Sea cruise / Who put the bomp in the bomp bomp
bomp / Come on let's go / I'll never get over you /
That's rock 'n' roll / Do wah diddy / C'mon everybody
/ Three steps to heaven / Trocadero / You got what it
takes / Multiplication / I wonder why / Heartbeat /
Bony moronie / Rave on / Johnny remember me /
Rock 'n' roll music / Footsteps / Take me in your
arms / Pretty little one / Twist and shout / It's only
make believe / Alley oop / Pretty little angel eyes /
Sweet music / Heavenly / Temptation / Say mama /
Sweet little rock 'n' roller / Why do lovers break each
others hearts / Night at daddy gees / Good times /
Blue moon / Remember then / Shake / Only love /
Lookin' back / If you know what I mean
10352 / Oct '97 / Go On Deluxe

☐ HITS COLLECTION VOL.1
Hey rock and roll / Under the moon of love / Rock 'n'
roll lady / You got personality / When / Weekend /
Dancing party / Go Johnny go / '68 Teenage queen /
Sea cruise / Who put the bomp in the bomp bomp
bomp / Come on let's go / I'll never get over you /
That's rock 'n' roll / Do wah diddy / C'mon everybody
10042 / Oct '97 / Go On Deluxe

☐ HITS COLLECTION VOL.2
Three steps to heaven / Trocadero / You got what it
takes / Multiplication / I wonder why / Heartbeat /
Bony moronie / Rave on / Johnny remember me /
Rock 'n' roll music / Footsteps / Take me in your
arms / Pretty little one / Twist and shout / It's only
make believe / Alley oops
10052 / Oct '97 / Go On Deluxe

☐ HITS COLLECTION VOL.3
Pretty little angel eyes / Little bit of soap / Sweet
music / Heavenly / Temptation / Say mama / Sweet
little rock 'n' roller / Why do lovers break each other's
hearts / Night at daddy gees / Good times / Blue
moon / Remember then / Shake / Only love / Lookin'
back / If you know what I mean
10062 / Oct '97 / Go On Deluxe

☐ MASTERS, THE
EABCD 075 / 24 Nov '97 / Eagle

☐ VERY BEST OF SHOWADDYWADDY,
THE
Hey rock 'n' roll / Rock 'n' roll lady / Sweet music /
Three steps to Heaven / Heartbeat / Under the moon
of love / When / You got what it takes / Dancin' party /
I wonder why / Little bit of soap / Pretty little angel
eyes / Remember then / Sweet little rock 'n' roller
DJD 3208 / May '94 / Dejadisc

☐ VERY BEST OF SHOWADDYWADDY,
THE (2CD Set)
CPCD 82872 / Sep '97 / Charly

☐ VERY BEST OF SHOWADDYWADDY,
THE
Under the moon of love / Hey rock 'n' roll / Three
steps to heaven / Heartbeat / When / You got what it
takes / Dancin' party / Little bit of soap / Pretty little
angel eyes / Sweet music / Sweet little rock 'n' roller/
I wonder why / Rock 'n' roll lady / You got personality
10072 / Oct '97 / Go On Deluxe

Showcase Showdown

☐ APPETITE OF KINGS
ELM 011CD / 2 Mar '98 / Elevator

Shozo

☐ SOUNDS OF BREATH
SYN 7 / Apr '97 / Knock On Wood

Shreeve, Mark

☐ ASSASSIN
Assassin / Angel of fire / Tyrant / System six
CENCD 005 / Jun '94 / Centaur

☐ CRASH HEAD
Crash head / Darkness comes / Edge of darkness /
Dead zone / Shrine / Angels of death / It / Night
church / Hellraiser
CENCD 007 / Sep '94 / Centaur

☐ LEGION
Legion / Storm column / Flags / Sybex factor /
Domain 7 / Con / Stand
CENCD 006 / Sep '94 / Centaur

☐ RED SHIFT
Red shift / Spin / Shine / Blue shift
CLPCD 002 / Apr '97 / Champagne Lake

Shri

☐ DRUM THE BASS
CASTE 4CD / May '97 / OutCaste

Shriekback

☐ SACRED CITY
Signs / Psycho drift / Bastard sons of enoch / (open
up your) filthy heart (to me) / Exquisite corpse / Below
/ Beatles peace crossing / Hymn to the local gods /
Every force evolves a form / 3 a.m.
SHRIEK 1CD / Feb '94 / World
Domination

Shrieve, Michael

☐ FASCINATION
CMPCD 67 / Jan '95 / CMP

☐ TWO DOORS (2CD Set)
CMPCD 74 / Jan '96 / CMP

Shrike

☐ NEURO FLOOD
Evidence / Slut / Malediction / Neuro flood / Eternal
war / Nearly killed / Rage / Plastic icon / Fragile
human games
HTT 03002 / 17 Mar '98 / Holier Than
Thou

Shrimp Boat

☐ CAVALE
Pumpkin lover / Duende suite / Line song / Blue
green song / What do you think of love / Swinging
shell / Creme brulee / I'll name it Sue / Free love
overdrive / Dollar bill / Apples / Smooth ass / Small
wonder / Oranges / Henny penny
R 3002 / Jul '93 / Rough Trade

Shrinathji, Jai Jai

☐ DEVOTIONAL SONGS
Shloka / Mangalaa / Shangaar / Gwaal / Raajbhog /
Uthaapan / Bhog / Aarti / Shayan / Dhoon
NRCD 0069 / Feb '98 / Navras

Shrivastav, Baluji

☐ CLASSICAL INDIAN RAGAS
EUCD 1101 / '91 / ARC

☐ CLASSICAL INDIAN SITAR AND
SURBAHAR RAGAS
EUCD 1139 / '91 / ARC

Shrubs

☐ VESSELS OF THE HEART
DOM 2CD / Nov '88 / Public Domain

Shu, Shomyo Shingon

☐ BUDDHIST RITUAL "LIVE"
LDX 274976 / May '94 / La Chant Du
Monde

Shu-De

☐ KONGUREY
SUMCD 4003 / Nov '96 / Summit

☐ VOICES FROM THE DISTANT STEPPE
Sygyt khoomei kargyraa / Aian dudal (Songs of
devotion and praise) / Beezhinden (Coming back
from Beijing) / Buura / Durgen chugaa (Tongue
twisters) / Throat singing and igil / Yraazhy kys (The
singing girl) / Shyngyr-shyngyr / Baian-dudai /
Khomus solo / Meen khemchim / Opei yry (A lullaby) /
Tyva-uruankhai / Chasphy-khem (The river chashby)
/ Kadarchynying / Kham
CDRW 41 / Jan '94 / Realworld

Shub Niggurath

☐ LES MORTS VONT VITE
8613 / 23 Feb '98 / Musea

Shudder To Think

☐ FUNERAL AT THE MOVIES
DIS 54CD / '94 / Dischord

☐ GET YOUR GOAT
Love catastrophe / Shake your halo down / White
page / Goat / Pebbles / Baby drop / Hair pillow / She
wears he-harem / Rain-covered cat / Funny
DIS 67CD / '94 / Dischord

☐ PONY EXPRESS RECORD
ABB 65CD / Aug '95 / Big Cat

Shuffle Demons

☐ BOP RAP
SP 1124CD / Oct '93 / Stony Plain

☐ STREETNIKS
SP 1128CD / Oct '93 / Stony Plain

☐ WHAT DO YOU WANT
SP 1152CD / Oct '93 / Stony Plain

Shufflin'Joe

☐ AFRICAN JAZZ PIONEERS
669882 / Nov '96 / Melodie

Shugg

☐ SHUGG VS. COCKPIT (2CD Set) (Shugg
& Cockpit)
BSR 202CD / Nov '96 / Bittersweet

Shull, Tad

☐ DEEP PASSION
CRISS 1047CD / May '91 / Criss Cross

Shut Up & Dance

☐ BLACK MEN UNITED
PULSE 22CD / Oct '95 / Pulse 8

☐ DEATH IS NOT THE END
Death is not the end / Raving I'm raving /
Autobiography of a crackhead / Cape fear / Here
comes a different type of rap track not the usual 4 ba
/ Green man / Java bass / So what you smoking /
Runaways / Blue colour climax / Pure white black life
/ Art of moving butts / Down the barrel of a gun / My c-
lab crashed and did this
SUADCD 005 / Jun '92 / Shut Up &
Dance

Shutdown

☐ AGAINST THE ODDS
VR 071CD / 30 Mar '98 / Victory

☐ EMITS A REAL BRONZE CHEER
CDHOLE 003 / Mar '95 / Golf

☐ SIGNS OF CHANGE
LF 224CD / 25 May '98 / Lost & Found

☐ TURNING THE TIDE
SFT 15CD / 13 Apr '98 / Striving For
Togetherness

Shy

☐ ONCE BITTEN TWICE SHY
NM 030 / 18 May '98 / Neat Metal

Shy FX

☐ FORMULA, THE (Various Artists)
EBONCD 001 / Sep '96 / Ebony

☐ JUST AN EXAMPLE
SOURCDLP 4 / Oct '95 / SOUR

Shyboy

☐ SHYBOY
ESM 026 / 2 Mar '98 / Escape

Shyheim

☐ LOST GENERATION, THE
Shit iz real / Dear God / Jiggy comin' / 5 elements /
Shaolin style / Real bad boys / What makes the world
go round / Can you feel it / Life as a shorty / Don't
front/Let's chill / Things happen / See what I see /
Shaolin mercy / Still there / Young godz
CDVUS 109 / Jun '96 / Virgin

Shyster

☐ FEBRUARY
MR 059 / 13 Jul '98 / Man's Ruin

Si (Cut) Dub

☐ BEHIND YOU
SOHSP 025 / Mar '97 / Sprawl

Siam

☐ LANGUAGE OF MENACE, THE
NTHEN 011CD / Sep '95 / Now & Then

☐ PRAYER
A2Z 85009CD / Jul '96 / A-Z

Sibbles, Leroy

☐ IT'S NOT OVER
VPCD 1452 / Dec '95 / VP

Sibeba

☐ HIJAS DEL SOL
Sibeba / People from here / Foreigners / Agreement
between two sisters / Fertility rite / Moon / Daughters
of the sun / Turn around / Aids / Traditional ways /
Ship of man / Crow of the rooster / In the lap / Birds
are sleeping / Tirso de molina
INT 31782 / Aug '96 / Intuition

Siberil, Soig

☐ DIGOR
GWP 005CD / Aug '93 / Gwerz

☐ ENTRE ARDOISE ET GRANIT
GWP 013CD / Sep '96 / Gwerz

Siberry, Jane

☐ BOUND BY THE BEAUTY
DSBD 31058 / 15 Dec '97 / Duke St.

☐ CHILD (2CD Set)
SHEEB 2 / 27 Oct '97 / Sheeba

☐ COLLECTION 1984-1989, A
DSRMD 31093 / 15 Dec '97 / Duke St.

☐ JANE SIBERRY
SRCD 0022 / Nov '97 / Street

☐ NO BORDERS
DSBD 31006 / 15 Dec '97 / Duke St.

☐ SPECKLESS SKY, THE
One more colour / Seven steps to the wall / Very large hat / Mien bitte / Vladimir - Vladimir / Mimi on the beach / Map of the world / Empty city / Taxi ride
DSBD 31019 / Nov '97 / Duke St.

☐ TEENAGER
SHEEB 1 / Feb '97 / Sheeba

☐ WALKING, THE
White tent the raft / Red high heels / Goodbye / Ingrid / Lena is a white table / Walkin' / Lobby / Bird in the gravel
DSBD 31040 / Nov '97 / Duke St.

Siburn, Innes

☐ STARDUST
Your star will shine / Free me / Like a rainbow / Have you ever loved a woman / Hard times / I didn't mean to do wrong / Quiet by your side / My little hurricane / That's alright / Fun missing you / Midnight train
PRD 71062 / 1 Dec '97 / Provogue

Sick Of It All

☐ LIVE IN A WORLD FULL OF HATE
LF 073CD / Dec '93 / Lost & Found

☐ SCRATCH THE SURFACE
No cure / Insurrection / Consume / Goatless / Maladjusted / Free spirit / Desperate fool / Force my hand / Cease fire / Farm team / Return to reality / Scratch the surface / Step down / Who sets the rules
7567924222 / Nov '94 / WEA

☐ SPREADING THE HARDCORE REALITY
LF 084MCD / May '94 / Lost & Found

Sick On The Bus

☐ SICK ON THE BUS
BUSCD 001 / Mar '96 / Bus Pop

Sick Things

☐ SOUNDS OF SILENCE, THE
ANDA 220CD / Sep '97 / Au-Go-Go

Sickler, Don

☐ MUSIC OF KENNY DORHAM (Sickler, Don/Jimmy Heath/Cedar Walton)
RSRCD 111 / Nov '94 / Reservoir

Sicko

☐ YOU ARE NOT THE BOSS OF ME
CRACKLE 003CD / 24 Nov '97 / Crackle

☐ YOU CAN FEEL THE LOVE
EFA 123582 / Mar '94 / Empty

Side By Side

☐ YOU'RE ONLY YOUNG ONCE
LF 040CD / Sep '95 / Lost & Found

Sidebottom, Frank

☐ FRANK SIDEBOTTOM'S ABC AND D
Born in Timperley / Anarchy in Timperly / Timperley sunset / Wild thing in Timperley / Next train to Timperley / Oh Timperley / Surfin' Timperley / Xmas is really fantastic / O come all ye faithful (adeste fidelis) / I wish it could be xmas everyday / Xmas medley / Twist 'n' shout / Benefit of Mr. Kyte / Flying / It was nearly 20 years ago today / Mull of Timperley / Guess who's been on match of the day / Robbins aren't bobbins / Puff 'n' blow / Estudiantes (striped shirts/black panties) / Radio ga ga / Save me / We will rock you / Frank Gordon / I am the champion / Everybody loves Queen / I should be so lucky / Love poem for Kylie / Bohemian rapsody / Bros medley / What for from my mum / Firm favourite ads / Elvis medley / Hit the north / Electricity / Hey you riot policeman / Blackpool fool / Indie medley / Mr. Custard / Zoo scrapbook / Hey you street artist / Monopoly song
CDMRED 143 / Apr '97 / Cherry Red

Sidekick Kato

☐ I THINK I'M IN LOVE
JFR 036 / Nov '97 / Johann's Face

Sideral

☐ MIL PARSECS
PODUKCD 023 / Jan '96 / Pod England

Sidestepper

☐ SOUTHERN STAR
DEPECD 003 / 16 Sep '97 / Deep South

Sidewinder

☐ COLONIZED
Vodun conspiracy / Scarification dub / Total destruction of mind and body / Return to BC / Homosapien meets the microbe / Ballistic loop / Zero gravity / Ten ton ghetto blaster / Big bang theory / Photic driver / Infrasonic version / Psycho-acoustic dub / Cryonic suspension / Silicon based predator / Forbidden zone / Destination DNA / Drummer as mechanism / Concrete jungle probe / Enter the beast / White viper sound system / Termite colony / Omega bug
EFA 006782 / Oct '96 / Mille Plateau
AMBT 17 / Sep '96 / Virgin

Sidi Bou Said

☐ BROOOCH
TOPPCD 005 / Jul '94 / Ultimate

☐ OBSESSIVE
Obsessive / Like you / Stoppe / Funny body / Zazie / Mionotaur / Harold and Maude / 20,000 Horses / Seams undone / Rat king / Bella / Bridge song
TOPPCD 053 / Apr '97 / Ultimate

Sidibe, Sali

☐ FROM TIBUKTU TO GAO
SHAN 65011CD / Oct '93 / Shanachie

Sidran, Ben

☐ COOL PARADISE
She steps into a dream / Searching for a girl like you / If someone has to wreck your life / Lip service / Language of the blues / Cool paradise / Desire of love / Bye bye blackbird / Walking with the blues / So long
GOJ 60012 / 8 Jun '98 / Go Jazz

☐ HEAT WAVE
Mitsubishi boy / Lover man / Lover man / Brown eyes / On the cool side / Old Hoagy / Heatwave / Take it easy greasy / Up a lazy river / That's what the note said / Lost in the stars
GOJ 60092 / 8 Jun '98 / Go Jazz

☐ LIVE AT THE CELEBRITY LOUNGE
Sentimental journey / Turn to the music / Chat / I wanna be a be bopper / House of blue lights / Look here / Avinu Malchenu / Gege's mouth drums / Gege's groove / Old folks / Blues for the celebrity lounge
GOJ 60252 / 29 Jun '98 / Go Jazz

☐ MR. P'S SHUFFLE
GOJ 60192 / 8 Jun '98 / Go Jazz

Siebel, Paul

☐ PAUL SIEBEL
CDPH 1161 / Nov '95 / Philo

Siebert, Budi

☐ PYRAMID CALL
Life power / Sunrise / Feather of thruth / Third eye / Sphinx / Flight of the falcon / Voice of the heart / Cosmic soul / Golden kobra / Sunset / Illuminated pyramid / Ankh of the earth / Life dream / Horus / Remember all
CD 256 / Jun '95 / Narada

☐ WILD EARTH
Wild earth / Dancing with the bear / Beauty within / Black rain - Grey snow / Winds from the south / Silent earth / Phoenix rises / Round my way / On your shores / Gentle earth
ND 63031 / Mar '95 / Narada

Siegal, Dan

☐ CLAIRVOYANCE
60863177772 / 14 Jul '98 / ULG

Siegal Schwall

☐ SIEGAL SCHWALL REUNION CONCERT, THE
You don't love me like that / Devil / Leaving / Hey, Billie Jean / I wanna love ya / I think it was the wine / I don't want you to be my girl / When I've been drinking / Hush hush
ALCD 4760 / May '93 / Alligator

Siegel, Corky

☐ CHAMBER BLUES
ALCD 4824 / Nov '94 / Alligator

Siegel, Janis

☐ SLOW HOT WIND
VSD 5552 / May '95 / Varese Sarabande

Sieger, Lucinda

☐ I BELIEVE
TIRCD 002 / Mar '96 / Totem

Siehenburgen

☐ GRIMJAUR
NPR 044CD / 8 Jun '98 / Napalm

Sielwolf

☐ V
KK 124CD / Apr '97 / KK

Sierra, Fredy

☐ VALLENATO (Sierra, Fredy & Eglio Vega)
TUMICD 041 / Jun '93 / Tumi

Sierra Maestra

☐ DUNDUNBANZA
Juana pena / Dundubanza / No me llores / Bururu barara / Change ta veni / Mi guajira son / Cangrejo fue a estudiar / Kila qique y chocolate / El gago / El reloj de pastora
WCD 041 / Oct '94 / World Circuit

☐ TIBIRI TABARA
Tibiri Tabara / Donde va chichi / Yo soy tiburon / Marieta / Son para ti / Felipe Blanco / En el Silecencio de la noch / El Guararey de Pastora / Con la Espuela / Anabacoa
WCD 051 / 3 Nov '97 / World Circuit

Sierra, Ruben

☐ IMAGEN VIVA
Cuando la recuerdo / Eres mia / Imagen viva / Voy a dejarte lina cancion / Lo mismo que ayer / Esta es tru cama / Demliestame / Mi fanatica mayor / Eso eres tu
66058056 / Feb '95 / RMM

Siffre, Labi

☐ IT MUST BE LOVE
Too late / Make my day / (just) a little more line / Maybe / There's nothing in the world like love / Thank your lucky star / Why did you go / Fool me a good night / It must be love / Crying loving laughing lying / Entertainment value
MCCD 141 / Nov '93 / Music Club

☐ MAN OF REASON
City of dreams / Most people sleep alone / Matter of love... / Lovers in arms / All fall down / Reason / When lights are on / Sensible betrayal in the city / Wash away your troubles in love / School days
WOLCD 1015 / May '91 / China

☐ REMEMBER MY SONG
MRBCD 011 / 2 Mar '98 / Mr. Bongo

Sigh

☐ GHASTLY FUNERAL THEATRE
Soushiki / Shingontachikawa / Doman seman / Imiuta / Shikigami / Higeki
NIHIL 17CD / Feb '97 / Cacophonous

☐ HAIL HORROR HAIL
Hail horror hail / 12 souls / Burial / Dead sing / Invitation to die / Pathetic / Curse of izanagi / Seed of eternity
NIHIL 24 / 8 Dec '97 / Cacophonous

☐ INFIDEL ART
Izuna / Zombie terror / Desolation / Last elegy / Suicidogenic / Beyond centuries
NIHIL 7CD / Jun '97 / Cacophonous

☐ SCORN DEFEAT
ANTIMOSH 007CD / Apr '94 / Deathlike Silence

Siglo XX

☐ FEAR AND DESIRE
Fear and desire / Everything is on fire / Lost in violence / Sorrow and pain / Thirty five poems / On the third day / My sister called silence / Pain came
CDBIAS 087 / '88 / Play It Again Sam

☐ FLOWERS FOR THE REBELS
Sister in the rain / Fear / No one is innocent / Afraid to tell / Sister suicide / Till the act is done / Shadows / Flesh and blood / Ride
CDBIAS 051 / '88 / Play It Again Sam

☐ UNDER A PURPLE SKY
CDBIAS 145 / Jan '90 / Play It Again Sam

Signs Of Trouble

☐ SIGNS OF TROUBLE
Shameless / Good love / Rainmaker / Till now / Take my hand / Signs of trouble / She's mine / Smiling / God knows / Harmony / Hour of need
SOT 1997 / Jun '97 / Signs Of Trouble

Signs Ov Chaos

☐ DEPARTURE
RR 87192 / 24 Aug '98 / Roadrunner

☐ FRANKENSCIENCE
Thee devil's tongue / Kode ov thee future / Honey / Believe / Phunky dogg / Body suction / Pheel tha pulse / Praise / Comin' t'get ya / Discipline through fear / Phunky punctuation / Science ov love / Rhythm ov love / P-Phaze
MOSH 162CD / Sep '96 / Earache

Sigue Sigue Sputnik

☐ DRESS FOR EXCESS
Albinoni vs. Star Wars / Boom boom satellite / Hey Jayne Mansfield superstar / Super crook blues / Rio rocks / Success / Dancerama / Orgasm / MAD (mutually assured destruction) / Is this the future
7487002 / 1 Jun '98 / Parlophone

☐ FIRST GENERATION VOL.1, THE
Rockit miss USA / Sex bomb boogie / 21st century boy / Teenage thunder / She's my man / Love missile F1-11 / Jayne Mansfield / Ultra violence / Krush groove girls / Rock-a-jet baby / Rebel rebel
FREUDCD 35 / Dec '90 / Jungle

☐ FIRST GENERATION VOL.2, THE
FREUDCD 55 / Jun '96 / Jungle

☐ FLAUNT IT
Love missile F1-11 / Sex bomb boogie / Atari baby / Rocket Miss USA / 21st Century boy / Massive retaliation / Teenage thunder / She's my man
7463422 / 1 Jun '98 / Parlophone

Siiger, Asger

☐ CHANGE OF SCENE (Siiger, Asger Trio)
MECCACD 2016 / Oct '97 / Music Mecca

Silberbart

☐ 4 TIMES SOUNDRAZING
941063 / 5 Jan '98 / Germanofon

Silberstein, Moshe

☐ SHALOM ISRAEL
CNCD 5953 / Jul '93 / Disky

Sileas

☐ BEATING HARPS
Pipers / Silver whistle / Oh wee white rose of Scotland / Solos / Puirt a buel / Shore of Gruinard / Ca' The Yowes / Dogs / Beating harps
GLCD 1089 / Oct '93 / Green Linnet

☐ DELIGHTED WITH HARPS
Brigs / Cadal chan fhaigh mi (I can get no sleep) / Reels / Eppie Morrie / Air and reel / Da day dawn / Little cascade / Tha mulad / 'S coltach mi ri craobh gun duilleag / John Anderson, my Jo / Judges dilemma / Inverness gathering
LAPCD 113 / Dec '88 / Lapwing

☐ HARPBREAKERS
LAPCD 127 / Dec '97 / Lapwing

☐ PLAY ON LIGHT
Buain a'choirce / May Colvin / Cumba easbuig earraghaidbeal / Laill leatbag / Cameron MacFayden/Dr. Cameron's casebook / Miss Kirsten Lindsay Morrison / Mo dhombnullan fhein / Planxty crockery / Domhnall dubh / Pi li li liu / Dr. Florence Campbell of Jammalamadugu / Duncan Johnstone / Castlebay scrap/Stuarts rant / Ain't no sunshine/ Flawless juggler / Miss Ann Cameron of Balvenie / Amy's rollerskates/Paddy's leather britches / Sior chaineadh
CDTRAX 118 / Oct '96 / Greentrax

Silencers

☐ BLOOD AND RAIN (The Singles 1986-1996)
SILENCD 1 / Sep '96 / JLP

☐ BLUES FOR BUDDHA
Answer me / Scottish rain / Real McCoy / Blues for Buddha / Walk with the night / Razor blades of love / Skin games / Wayfaring stranger / Sacred child / Sand and stars / My love is like a wave
PD 71859 / 2 Feb '98 / RCA

☐ DANCE TO THE HOLY MAN
Singing ginger / Robinson Crusoe in New York / Bullet proof heart / Art of self-deception / I want you / One inch of heaven / Hey Mr. Bank Manager / This is serious / John the revelator / Afraid to love / Rosanne / Electric storm / When the night comes down / Robinson rap / Just can't be bothered / Cameras and colliseums
PD 74924 / 1 Sep '97 / RCA

☐ LETTER FROM ST. PAUL, A
Painted moon / I can't cry / Bullets and blue eyes / God's gift / I see red / I ought to know / Letter from St. Paul / Blue desire / Possessed
PD 71336 / 1 Sep '97 / RCA

☐ SECONDS OF PLEASURE
I can feel it / Cellar of dreams / Small mercy / It's only love / Misunderstood / Life can be fatal / Unhappiest man / Walkmans and magnums / Street walker song / My prayer / Unconcious
74321141132 / 2 Feb '98 / RCA

☐ SILENCERS
NER 3011 / Jul '97 / Total Energy

☐ SO BE IT
INDELCD 9 / 27 Mar '98 / Indelible

Silent Death

☐ STONE COLD
MASSCD 044 / Jan '95 / Massacre

Silent Partners

☐ IF IT'S ALL RIGHT, IT'S ALL RIGHT
ANTCD 0010 / Jan '93 / Antones

Silent Phase

□ THEORY OF SILENT PHASE, THE
Waterdance / Body rock / Air puzzle / Meditive fusion / Earth (interlude) / Spirit of sankofa / Spirit journey / Fire (prelude) / Psychotic funk / Electric relaxation / Love comes and goes / Forbidden dance
TMT 001CD / Nov '95 / R&S

Silent Poets

□ FIRM ROOTS
992158CD / Nov '96 / Ninetynine

□ FIRM ROOTS (Remixes)
992162CD / 16 Sep '97 / Ninetynine

□ POTENTIAL MEETING
99 2123 / Jul '96 / Ninetynine

Silent Witness

□ SILENT WITNESS
ESM 015 / 2 Mar '98 / Escape

Silk

□ LOSE CONTROL
Interlude / Happy days / Don't keep me waiting / Girl U for me / Freak me / When I think about you / Baby it's you / Lose control / It had to be you / I gave to you
7559613942 / Mar '93 / Keia/Elektra

□ SILK
Hooked on you / Because of your love / It's so good / Don't rush / I can go deep / What kind of love is this / Don't go to bed mad / Don't cry for me / Now that I've lost you / How could you say you love me / Remember me
7559618492 / Nov '95 / Keia/Elektra

Silk Saw

□ COME FREELY, GO SAFELY
SR 107CD / May '96 / Sub Rosa

□ DYSTOPIA
SR 116 / Jul '97 / Sub Rosa

Silkworm

□ BLUEBLOOD
TG 191CD / 20 Jul '98 / Touch & Go

□ DEVELOPER
Give me some skin / Never met a man I didn't like / City glows / Developer / Devil is beating his wife / Ice station zebra / Waiting on a train / Song with one part / Goodnight Mr. Maugham / It's too bad
OLE 2202 / Apr '97 / Matador

□ EVEN A BLIND CHICKEN FINDS A KERNAL OF CORN NOW AND THEN (2CD Set)
Slipstream / Little sister / Scruffy / St.Patricks day / Homoactivity / Scrawl / Three beatings / Slow burn / Our secret / Chain / Inside outside / Shithead / Slipstream / Scruffy tumour / No revolution / Eye window / Pearl harbour / Motel blues / Violet / Around a light / In the bleak midwinter / Incanduce California / Insider / Hangman / Smoochy life
OLE 1592 / 9 Feb '98 / Matador

□ FIREWATER
Nerves / Drink / Wet firecracker / Slow hands / Cannibal, cannibal / Tarnished angel / Quicksand / Ticket tulane / Don't make plans this Friday / Caricature of a joke / Killing my ass / River / Miracle mile / Lure of beauty / Severence pay / Swings
OLE 1582 / Feb '96 / Matador

Sill, Gary

□ SATIE - THREE GYMNOPEDIES
INVCD 090 / Aug '96 / Invincible

Silly Sisters

□ NO MORE TO THE DANCE
Blood and gold / Cake and ale / Fine horseman / How shall I / Hedger and ditcher / Agincourt Carol / Barring of the door / What'll we do / Almost every circumstance / Old miner
TSCD 450 / Aug '88 / Topic

□ SILLY SISTERS
Burnin' o'Auchidoon / Lass of roch royal / Seven joys of Mary / My husband's got no courage in him / Singing the travels / Silver whistle / Grey funnel line / Geordie / Seven wonders / Four loom weaver / Game of cards / Dame Durden
BGOCD 214 / Jan '94 / Beat Goes On

Silly Wizard

□ EARLY YEARS, THE
LAPCD 130 / Dec '97 / Lapwing

□ GLINT OF SILVER, A
Roarin' ronald / Man who shot the windmill / A glint of silver / What'll be king but cherlie / Lover's heart / When summer ends / Chill eastern winds / Willie archer / Simon mackenzies welcome to his twin sisters / Blackbird of sweet avondale
GLCD 1070 / Mar '87 / Green Linnet

□ KISS THE TEARS AWAY
Queen of Argyl / Golden golden / Finlay M Macrae / Banks of the Lee / Sweet Dublin Bay / Mo nighean donn / Gradh mo chroidhe / Banks of the Bann / Greenfields of Glentown / Galtee reel / Bobby Casey's number two / Wing commander Donald MacKenzie's reel / Loch Tay boat song
SHANCD 79037 / Apr '88 / Shanachie

□ LIVE AT CENTER STAGE
GLV 1 / Mar '95 / Green Linnet

□ LIVE WIZZARDRY
Queen of argyll / Mrs. martha knowles-the pitnacree ferryman-the new bob / Parish of dunkeld-the curlew / Valley of strathmore / Miss shepherd-sweeny's buttermilk-mcglinchey's reels / Ramblin rover / Blackbird / Scarce o' tatties-lyndhurst / Banks of the lee / Donald mcgillavry / Golden golden / Broom of the cowdenknowes
GLCD 3036/37 / Oct '93 / Green Linnet

Silos

□ ASK THE DUST
NORMAL 166 / Jun '95 / Normal

□ DIABLO
NORMAL 163 / May '94 / Normal

□ HASTA LA VICTORIA
NORMAL 143 / May '94 / Normal

Silva, Alan

□ IN THE TRADITION (Silva, Alan & Johannes Bauer/Roger Turner)
IS 166 / Aug '97 / Basta/Insitu

□ MY COUNTRY (Silva, Alan & Celestrial Communication Orchestra)
CDLR 302 / Apr '89 / Leo

Silva, Chelo

□ LA REINA TEJANA DEL BOLERO
ARHCD 423 / Jan '96 / Arhoolie

Silva, Maynard

□ HOWL AT THE MOON (Silva, Maynard & The New Hawks)
WCD 12088 / Apr '97 / Wolf

Silva, Orlando

□ NO TEMPO DO RADIO (4CD Set)
RVCD 115/6/7/8 / 12 May '98 / Revivendo

Silvadier, Pierre-Michel

□ D'AMOUR FOU D'AMOUR
A 16 / Dec '95 / Seventh

Silver Apples

□ BEACON
WK 103 / 26 Jan '98 / Whirlybird

□ CONTACT
WR 102 / Sep '97 / Whirlybird

□ DECATEUR
WR 106CD / 23 Mar '98 / Whirlybird

□ ELECTRONIC EVOCATIONS (A Tribute To The Silver Apples) (Various Artists)
RAPTCD 002 / May '97 / Enraptured

□ SILVER APPLES
MCD 11680 / 8 Jun '98 / MCA

□ SILVER APPLES, THE
WR 101 / Sep '97 / Whirlybird

Silver Birch

□ SILVER BIRCH
DORIS 3 / Jan '96 / Vinyl Tap

Silver Bullit

□ SILVERBULLIT
EFA 054072 / 11 May '98 / Clear Spot

Silver Cat

□ RASTAMAN MELODY
JGMCD 003062 / 22 Dec '97 / Joe Gibbs

Silver Convention

□ BEST OF SILVER CONVENTION, THE (Get Up And Boogie)
Fly robin fly / Save me / I like it / Another girl / Get up and boogie / Play me like a yo-yo / San Francisco hustle / No no Joe / You've got what it takes / I'm not a slot machine / Everybody's talking ('bout love) / Telegram / Blame it on the music / Mission to Venus / Spend the night
HTCD 23 / Apr '98 / Hot Productions

□ GREATEST HITS
Get up and boogie / Save me / Everybody's talking 'bout love / Fly Robin fly / Tiger baby / No no Joe / Play me like a yo yo / Thank you Mr. DJ / Love in a sleeper / San Francisco hustle / Telegram / Get it up / I like it / Blame it on the music / You've got what it takes / Spend the night with me / Breakfast in bed
100462 / May '97 / A-Play Collection

□ GREATEST HITS, THE
Fly robin fly / Get up and Boogie / Save me / Telegram / Tiger baby / Everybody's talking 'bout love / Always another girl / Dancing in the aisle / No no Joe / Son of a gun / You've got what it takes / San Francisco hustle / Acuestate conmigo / Lady bump / Ooh what a night
MCCD 358 / 20 Jul '98 / Music Club

Silver, Horace

□ BEST OF HORACE SILVER VOL.1, THE (Blue Note Years)
Opus de funk / Doodlin' / Room 608 / Preacher / Senor blues / Cool eyes / Home cooking / Soulville / Cookin' at the continental / Peace / Sister Sadie / Blowin' the blues away
CDP 7911432 / Dec '95 / Blue Note

□ FURTHER EXPLORATIONS
Outlaw / Melancholy mood / Pyramid / Moon rays / Safari / Ill wind
CDP 8565832 / Jun '97 / Blue Note

□ HARDBOP GRANDPOP, THE
I want you / Hippest cat in Hollywood / Gratitude / Hawkin' / Diggin' on Dexter / We've got silver at six / Hardbop Grandpop / Lady from Johannesburg / Serenade to a teakettle
IMP 11922 / Jun '96 / Impulse Jazz

□ JAZZ MASTERS
Doodlin' / Senor blues / Song for my Father / Preacher / Sister Sadie / Cape verdean blues / Jody grind
4934662 / 16 Feb '98 / EMI Jazz

□ JAZZ PROFILE
Safari / Enchantment / Pyramid / Finger poppin' / Where you at / Song for my Father / Blue silver / Barbara / Activation
CDP 8332082 / 6 Oct '97 / Blue Note

□ PERSCRIPTION FOR THE BLUES, A
Perscription for the blues / Whenever Lester plays the blues / You gotta shake that wing / Yodel Lady blues / Brother John and Brother Gene / Free at last / Walk on / Sunrise in Malibu / Docotr Jazz
IMP 12382 / 22 Sep '97 / Impulse Jazz

□ SILVER'S BLUE
Silver's blue / To beat or not to beat / How long has this been going on / I'll know / Shoutin' out / Hank's tune / Night has a thousand eyes
4765212 / Dec '95 / Sony Jazz

□ SILVER'S SERENADE
Silver's serenade / Let's get to the nitty gritty / Sweet sweetie dee / Dragon lady / Nineteen bars
8212882 / 19 Jan '98 / Blue Note

□ SONG FOR MY FATHER (Cantiga Para Meu Pai) (Silver, Horace Quintet)
Song for my Father / Natives are restless tonight / Calcutta cutie / Que pasa / Kicker / Lonely woman / Sanctimonious Sam / Sighin' and cryin' / Silver threads among the soul
CDP 7841852 / Mar '95 / Blue Note

□ TOKYO BLUES
Too much Sake / Sayonara blues / Tokyo blues / Cherry blossom / Ah so
CDP 8533552 / Nov '96 / Blue Note

Silver Jews

□ NATURAL BRIDGE
WIGCD 028 / Oct '96 / Domino

□ STARLITE WALKER
WIGCD 15 / Oct '94 / Domino

Silver King Band

□ LIVE AT THE DIVE
DZCD 009 / Apr '97 / Danger Zone

Silver Leaf Jazz Band

□ STREETS & SCENES OF NEW ORLEANS
GTCD 15001 / May '95 / Good Time Jazz

Silver Leaf Quartette Of Norfolk

□ COMPLETE RECORDED WORKS
DOCD 5352 / Jun '95 / Document

Silver, Mike

□ DEDICATION
SR 0194CD / Apr '95 / Silversound

□ ROADWORKS (Live)
Too many lies / Angel in deep shadow / Pretoria / Heatwave / Somebody's angel / Old fashioned Saturday night / Where would you rather be tonight / Let it be so / Not that easy / NASA / Down South / Circle of stones / Nothing to do with me / Sailors all / Certain something / Time for leaving / Mine for ever more
SR 0190CD / Aug '90 / Silversound

Silver Sun

□ SILVER SUN
Test / Golden skin / Dumb / Julia / Far out / Last day / Service / Yellow light / Lava / 2 digits / This 'n' that / Wonderful / Bad haircut / Nobody / Animals feets
5372082 / May '97 / Polydor

Silverchair

□ FREAKSHOW
Slave / Freak / Abuse me / Lie to me / No association / Cemetry / Pop song for us rejects / Door / Learn to hate / Petrol and chlorine / Roses / Nobody came
4871032 / Feb '97 / Murmur

□ FROGSTOMP
Israel's son / Tomorrow / Faultline / Pure massacre / Shade / Blind / Leave me out / Suicidal dream / Madman / Undecided / Cicada / Findaway
4803402 / Sep '95 / Murmur

Silverfish

□ FAT AXL
WIJ 006CD / Jan '91 / Wiiija

□ ORGAN FAN
This bug / This bug / Suckin' gas / Petal / Fin' strange way to get attention / Big bad baby pig squeal / Elvis leg / Dechainee / Scrub me mama with that boogie beat / Rock on / Joos
CRECD 118 / May '92 / Creation

Silverhead

□ 16 AND SAVAGED
REP 4646 / Jun '97 / Repertoire

Silvers, Jim

□ MUSIC MAKIN' MAMA FROM MEMPHIS
Cannonball yodel / Paul's saloon / My, my, my / Each season changes you / Goodbye California (Hello Illinois) / You gotta let all the girls know you're a cowboy / I wanna see Las Vegas / Waltz across Texas / Model 2017 / Old faithfull / Music makin' mama from Memphis / Last to get the news / Julie / Cash on the barrelhead / For your own good / I ate the whole damn hog / Call me a cab / Blue night / Cryin' my heart out over you / Ain't it strange / Last to get the news / Music makin' mama from Memphis / Losin' you (might be the best thing yet) / Scrap of paper and a 20 cent pen / Ocean of dreams
BCD 15555 / Jan '92 / Bear Family

Silverstate

□ GONDWANA RAIN
CDSGP 0318 / Mar '97 / Prestige

Silvertones

□ SILVER BULLETS
I'll take you home / Early in the morning / Sugar sugar / Souvenir of Mexico / Rejoice Jah Jah children / Rejoicing skank / That's when it hurts / Soul sister / Rock me in your soul / Sweet and loving baby / He'll break your heart / Are you sure
CDTRL 69 / Nov '96 / Trojan

Silvester, Victor

□ BALLROOM DANCING WITH THE VICTOR SILVESTER ORCHESTRA (Silvester, Victor & His Ballroom Orchestra)
PLSCD 223 / Jul '97 / Pulse

□ BEST OF THE VICTOR SILVESTER ORCHESTRA, THE (Silvester, Victor Orchestra)
I once had a heart Margarita / Dear madam / Summer evening in Santa Cruz / Keep calling me a sweetheart / Apple for the teacher / Blue orchids / My heart belongs to daddy / I'll remember / Don't count your chickens / Fare thee well / When you wish upon a star / Where or when / House beautiful / So deep is the night / Love bells / I'm in love for the last time / Love everlasting / We'll meet again / That's life I guesss / Yours for a song / Don't say goodbye / Give a little whistle
CD 6133 / Jul '98 / Music

□ COME DANCE WITH ME - 20 BALLROOM FAVOURITES (Silvester, Victor & His Ballroom Orchestra)
I can dream, can't I / Come dance with me / C'est si bon / Always true to you in my fashion / Waltz of my heart / Autumn leaves / I wonder where my baby is tonight / C'est magnifique / Unforgettable / Tea for two / Whisper while you waltz / By candle light / Lady is a tramp / 'S Wonderful / Till there was you / Moonlight serenade / Charleston / Mr. Sandman / April in Paris / It happened in Monterey
CC 8233 / Jan '94 / Music For Pleasure

□ COME DANCING VOL.1
MU 3007 / Oct '92 / Musketeer

□ COME DANCING VOL.2
MU 3008 / Oct '92 / Musketeer

□ SLOW SLOW QUICK QUICK SLOW (Silvester, Victor & His Ballroom Orchestra)
It's de lovely / Keep calling me sweetheart / Dear love, my love / Sweetest song in the world / Hypnotised / That's life I guess / In the still of the night / Sleep tight / Slumming on Park Avenue/I've got my love to keep me warm / This years kisses / So rare / Where is our bluebird of Melody Lane / Chicago/I'm just wild about Harry/When you're smiling / I once had a heart / Margarita / Hear my song Violetta / Three o'clock in the morning/Ting-a-ling/till we meet again / Sweetheart waltz / Afraid to dream / Moonlight / Beautiful Ohio/Tonight you belong to me
RAJCD 890 / 2 Feb '98 / Empress

☐ STRICTLY BALLROOM (Silvester, Victor & His Ballroom Orchestra)
Too close for comfort / Lady's in love with you / Call me irresponsible / You're my everything / Amore baciami / I give my heart / Belle of the ball / Gotta be this or that / Old devil moon / My foolish heart / It can't be wrong / Foggy day / Boy next door / Around the world / At the jazz band ball / Cerveza / One / Al di la / Copacabana / La cumparsita / I'll go where your music takes me / You were never lovelier / One I love (Belongs to somebody else)
TRTCD 150 / Dec '94 / TrueTrax

☐ STRICTLY BALLROOM
MACCD 143 / Aug '96 / Autograph

☐ STRICTLY TEMPO DANCING (4CD Set)
PBXCD 411 / 20 Apr '98 / Pulse

☐ TRULY GREAT DANCE MELODIES (Silvester, Victor & His Ballroom Orchestra)
DCD 5365 / Apr '94 / Disky

☐ VICTOR SILVESTER
MCCD 339 / 20 Apr '98 / Music Club

Silvestri, Alan

☐ SHATTERED
262208 / Nov '91 / Milan

Simbi

☐ KREOL
IG 059 / Aug '96 / Imogena

☐ VODOU BEAT
XENO 4038 / Dec '95 / Xenophile

Simeon, Omer

☐ OMER SIMEON 1926-1929
157752 / Jul '93 / Hot 'n' Sweet

Simien, Terrance

☐ THERE'S ROOM FOR US ALL
BT 1096CD / Jan '94 / Black Top

☐ ZYDECO ON THE BAYOU
Zydeco on the bayou / Back in my baby's arms / Stop the train / Zydeco zambada / Don't cry no more / I'll do it all over again / Intro / Ta casse mon coeur / Love we shared / I'll say so long / Will the circle be unbroken / Moi su pas tracasser
FIENDCD 715 / Apr '92 / Demon

SIMM

☐ WELCOME
DOSSCD 002 / Mar '97 / Possible

Simmons, 'Little' Mack

☐ COME BACK TO ME BABY
WCD 120884 / Nov '96 / Wolf

☐ LITTLE MACK IS BACK
ELECTRO-FI 3355 / 5 Feb '98 / Electro-Fi

☐ SOMEWHERE ON DOWN THE LINE
EF 3356 / 19 Mar '98 / Electro-Fi

Simmons, Patrick

☐ ARCADE
Out on the streets / So wrong / Don't make me do it / Why you givin' up / Too long / Knocking at your door / If you want a little love / Have you seen her / Sue sad / Dream about me
7559602552 / Jan '97 / Elektra

Simms, Ginny

☐ GINNY SIMMS MEMORIAL ALBUM, THE
VN 150 / Nov '94 / Viper's Nest

Simon & Garfunkel

☐ BEST OF SIMON & GARFUNKEL, THE (RTE Concert Orchestra)
8990052 / Oct '95 / Naxos

☐ BOOKENDS
Bookends / Save the life of my child / America / Overs / Voice of old people / Old friends / Fakin' it / Punky's dilemma / Hazy shade of winter / At the zoo / Mrs. Robinson
CD 63101 / Dec '85 / CBS

☐ BRIDGE OVER TROUBLED WATER
Bridge over troubled water / El condor pasa / Cecilia / Keep the customer satisfied / So long, Frank Lloyd Wright / Boxer / Baby driver / Only living boy in New York / Why don't you write me / Bye bye love / Song for the asking
4804182 / Jul '95 / Mastersound
4624882 / 27 Jul '98 / Columbia

☐ BRIDGE OVER TROUBLED WATER/ SOUNDS OF SILENCE/THE GRADUATE (3CD Set)
Bridge over troubled water / El condor pasa / Cecilia / Keep the customer satisfied / So long, Frank Lloyd Wright / Boxer / Baby driver / Only living boy in New York / Why don't you write me / Bye bye love / Song for the asking / Sound of silence / Leaves that are green / Blessed / Kathy's song / Somewhere they can't find me / Anji / Homeward bound / Most peculiar man / April come she will / We've got a groovy thing goin' / I am a rock / Richard Cory / Sound of silence / Singleman party foxtrot / Mrs. Robinson / Sunporch cha-cha-cha / Scarborough fair/Canticle / On the strip / April come she will / Folks / Scarborough fair/Canticle / Great effect / Bright green pleasure machine / Whew / Mrs. Robinson / Sound of silence
4853242 / Oct '96 / Columbia

☐ DEFINITIVE SIMON AND GARFUNKEL, THE
Wednesday morning 3am / Sound of silence / Homeward bound / Kathy's song / I am a rock / For Emily, wherever I may find her / Scarborough Fair/ Canticle / 59th Street Bridge song / Seven o'clock news/Silent night / Hazy shade of winter / El condor pasa (If I could) / Mrs. Robinson / America / At the zoo / Old friends / Bookends theme / Cecilia / Boxer / Bridge over troubled water / Song for the asking
MOODCD 21 / 18 Aug '97 / Columbia

☐ GRADUATE, THE (Original Soundtrack)
Sound of silence / Singleman party foxtrot / Mrs. Robinson / Sunporch cha-cha-cha / Scarborough Fair/Canticle / On the strip / April come she will / Folks / Scarborough Fair/Canticle / Great effect / Big bright green pleasure machine / Whew
CD 32359 / Feb '94 / Columbia

☐ GREATEST HITS
Mrs. Robinson / For Emily, wherever I may find her / Boxer / 59th Street Bridge song / Sound of silence / I am a rock / Scarborough Fair / Canticle / Homeward bound / Bridge over troubled water / America / Kathy's song / If I could / Bookends / Cecilia
CD 69003 / Mar '87 / CBS

☐ INSTRUMENTAL MEMORIES (Various Artists)
Bridge over troubled water / Homeward bound / El Condor Pasa (If I could) / Sound of silence / 59th Street Bridge song (Feelin' groovy) / Scarborough Fair/Canticle / Kathy's song / Old friends/Bookends / Hazy shade of winter / Boxer / Mrs. Robinson / Only living boy in New York / Cecilia / America / I am a rock / Song for the asking
308202 / 13 Oct '97 / Hallmark

☐ OLD FRIENDS (3CD Set)
Bleeker street / Sounds of silence / Sun is burning / Wednesday morning 3am / He was my brother / Sparrow / Peggy O / Benedictus / Somewhere they can't find me / We've got a groovy thing goin' / Leaves that are green / Richard Cory / I am a rock / Sounds of silence / Homeward bound / Blues run the game / Kathy's song / April come she will / Flowers never bend in the rainfall / Patterns / Danging conversation / Scarborough fair/ Canticle / 59th Street bridge song / For Emily / Wherever I find her / 7 o'clock news / Hazy shade of winter / At the zoo / A poem on the underground wall / Red rubber ball / Blessed / Anji / A church is burning / Fakin' it / Save the life of my child / You don't know where your intrests lie / Funky's dilemma / America / Comfort and joy / Star carol / Mrs. Robinson / Old friends / Most peculiar man / Bye bye love / Boxer / Baby driver / Why don't you write me / Feuilles O / Keep the customer satisfied / So long Frank Lloyd Wright / Song for the asking / Cecilia / El condor pasa / Bridge over troubled water / Only living boy in New York / Hey schoolgirl / That silver haired daddy of mine / My little town
C3K 64780 / 3 Nov '97 / Legacy

☐ PARSLEY, SAGE, ROSEMARY AND THYME
Scarborough Fair / Patterns / Cloudy / Big bright green pleasure machine / 59th Street Bridge song / Dangling conversation / Flowers never bend with the rainfall / Simple desultory philippic / For Emily, wherever I may find her / Poem on the underground wall / Seven o'clock news / Silent night
CD 32031 / Apr '89 / CBS

☐ SIMON & GARFUNKEL COLLECTION, THE
I am a rock / Homeward bound / America / 59th Street Bridge song / Wednesday morning 3am / El condor pasa / At the zoo / Scarborough Fair / Boxer / Sound of silence / Mrs. Robinson / Keep the customer satisfied / Song for the asking / Hazy shade of Winter / Cecilia / Old friends / Bookends / Bridge over troubled water
CD 24005 / Apr '88 / CBS

☐ WEDNESDAY MORNING 3AM
You can tell the world / Last night I had the strangest dream / Bleecker Street / Sparrow / Benedictus / Sound of silence / He was my brother / Peggy O / Go tell it on the mountain / Sun is burning / Times they are a changin' / Wednesday morning 3 AM
4633752 / Feb '96 / Columbia

Simon & The Bar Sinisters

☐ LOOK AT ME I'M COOL
CD 023 / Aug '95 / Upstart

Simon, Carly

☐ BEST OF CARLY SIMON, THE
That's the way I've always heard / Right thing to do / Mockingbird / Legend in your own time / Haven't got time for the pain / You're so vain / No secrets / Night owl / Anticipation / Attitude dancing
9548304602 / May '91 / WEA

☐ CLOUDS IN MY COFFEE (3CD Set)
Let the river run / You belong to me / Nobody does it better / Coming around again / Jesse / Stuff that dreams are made of / You're so vain / Touched by the sun / Haven't got time for the pain / Better not tell her / Legend in your own time / Mockingbird / That's the way I've always heard it should be / All I want is you / Right thing to do / Like a river / Anticipation / Give me all night / Angel from Montgomery / Raining / I'm all it takes to make you happy / Easy on the eyes / Turn of the tide / Libby / Have you seen me lately / My new boyfriend / Voulez-vous danser / Night before Christmas / Halfway 'round the world / Life is eternal / We have no secrets / Why / Take me out to the ballgame / Back the way / Itsy bitsy spider / Play with me / My luv is like a red, red rose / It happens every day / Boys in the trees / Julie through the glass / Orpheus / Never been gone / Happy birthday / Devoted to you / Davy / Do the walls come down / Danny boy / Dink's blues / We're so close / Someone waits for you / Born to break my heart / Time after time / What shall we do with the child / I've got a crush on you / Something wonderful / You're the love of my life / I get along without you very well / By myself / I see your face before me
07822187982 / Mar '96 / Arista

☐ COMING AROUND AGAIN
Itsy bitsy spider / If it wasn't love / Coming around again / Give me all night / As time goes by / Do the walls come down / It should have been me / Stuff that dreams are made of / Two hot girls / You have to hurt / All I want is you / Hold what you've got
261038 / Nov '90 / Arista

☐ FILM NOIR
You won't forget me / Ev'rytime we say goodbye / Lili Marlene / Last night when we were young: *Simon, Carly & Jimmy Webb* / Spring will be a little late this year / Film noir / Laura / I'm a fool to want you / Fools coda / Two sleepy people: *Simon, Carly & John Travolta* / Don't smoke in bed / Somewhere in the night
7822189842 / 6 Oct '97 / Arista

☐ GREATEST HITS LIVE
You're so vain / Nobody does it better / Coming around again / It happens every day / Anticipation / Right thing to do / Do the walls come down / You belong to me / Two hot girls / All i want is you / Never been gone
259196 / Aug '95 / Arista

☐ LETTERS NEVER SENT
Intro / Letter never sent / Lost in your love / Like a river / Time works on all the wild young men / Touched by the sun / Davy / Halfway 'round the world / What about a holiday / Reason / Private / Catch it like a fever / Born to break my heart / I'd rather it was you
07822187522 / 2 Feb '98 / Arista

☐ MY ROMANCE
My romance / By myself / I see your face / When your lover is gone / In the wee small hours of the morning / My funny valentine / Something wonderful / Little girl blue / He was good to me / What has she got / Bewitched, bothered and bewildered / Danny boy / Time after time
262019 / Jan '92 / Arista

☐ NO SECRETS
Right thing to do / Carter family / You're so vain / His friends are more than fond of Robin / We have no secrets / Embrace me, you child / It was so easy / Waited so long / Night owl / When you close your eyes
7559606842 / Jul '93 / WEA

Simon Chase

☐ WITCH DOCTOR, THE
35700 / Nov '96 / Sphinx Ministry

Simon, Edward

☐ EDWARD SIMON
Colega / Alma llanera, part 1 / Alma llanera, part 2 / Caballo viejo / Slippin' and slidin' / Stop looking to find (it finds you) / Magic between us / Teen's romance
KOKO 1305 / Nov '95 / Kokopelli

Simon, Joe

☐ DROWNING IN THE SEA OF LOVE
Glad to be your lover / Something you can do today / I found my dad / Mirror don't lie / Ole night owl / You are everything / If / Let me be the one (the one who loves you) / Pool of bad luck
CDSEW 021 / Apr '90 / Southbound

☐ GREATEST HITS (The Spring Years 1970-1977)
Your time to cry / Help me make it through the night / You're the one for me / All my hard times / Georgia blue / Drowning in the sea of love / Pool of bad luck / Power of love / Trouble in my home / I found my Dad / Step by step / Cleopatra Jones / River / Carry me / Best time of my life / Get down get down (get on the floor) / Music in my bones / I need you, you need me / Come get to this / Easy to love / You didn't have to play no games / One step at a time / For your love love love
CDSEWD 102 / May '97 / Southbound

☐ MOOD, HEART AND SOUL/ TODAY
Neither one of us / I would still be there / Good time Charlie's got the blues / Covering the same old ground / Walking down lonely street / Best time of my life / What we gonna do now / I'm in the mood for you / Carry me / Come back home / Let's spend the night forever / I just want to keep love to you / Let the good times roll / Come get to this / What a wonderful world / I need you, you need me / I'll take care of you / Music for my lady
CDSEWD 971 / Apr '91 / Southbound

☐ MR. SHOUT
Say (that your love is true) / My adorable one / Doreetha: *Golden Tones* / When you're near / Let's do it over / You left me here to cry alone: *Golden Tones* / Ocean of tears: *Golden Tones* / It's a miracle / Land of love / Everybody needs somebody / (Just) Call my name / It's all over / Pledge of love / Troubles / I see your face / I keep remembering / Goodnight Irene / When you're near / No one else will do / Just like yesterday / Only a dream / Whoo pee / Bring it on home to me / When I'm gone
CDCHD 663 / Aug '97 / Ace

☐ MY ADORABLE ONE
CDRB 28 / Aug '95 / Charly

☐ SOUNDS OF SIMON
To lay down beside you / I can't see nobody / Most of all / No more me / Your time to cry / Help me make it through the night / My woman, my woman, my wife / I love you more / Georgia blue / All my hard times
CDSEWD 954 / Oct '90 / Southbound

☐ SOUNDS OF SIMON/SIMON COUNTRY
To lay down beside you / I can't see nobody / Most of all / No more me / Your time to cry / Help me make it through the night / My woman, my woman, my wife / I love you more than anything / Georgia blue / All my hard times / Do you know what it's like to be lonesome / You don't know me / To get to you / Before the next teardrop falls / Someone to give my love to / Good things / Kiss an angel good morning
CDSEW 954 / Oct '90 / Southbound

Simon, John

☐ LEGACY
It's you or no one / Ceora / Strollin' / Nomis / Aries
MCD 5566 / Aug '96 / Muse

Simon, Jona

☐ PIANO AFTER MIDNIGHT (Simon, Jona Trio)
CDSGP 0140 / Apr '95 / Prestige

Simon, Michel

☐ LA COMPILATION
Deux sous de violettes / Deux sous de violettes / Viens, viens, madeleine / Memere / Printemps sans amour / L'herbe tendre / La baya / Elle est epatante / Ah le joli jeu / Un petit negro ou amour noir et blanc / La calcographie / Si vous etiez un coquin / Dans sa baignoire / La femme est faite pour l'homme / Pourquoi m'as tu fait ca / La villette / Coeur de parisienne / Comme de bien entendu / Le vase de soissons / Jean de la lune entree de cloclo acte 1 / Jean de la lune c'est parce que je t'aime acte II
UCD 19087 / Jun '95 / Forlane

Simon, Paul

☐ ANTHOLOGY
Sound of silence / Cecilia / El condor pasa / Boxer / Mrs. Robinson / Bridge over troubled water / Me and julio down by the schoolyard / Peace like a river / Mother and child reunion / American tune / Loves me like a rock / Kodachrome / Gone at last / Still crazy after all these years / Something so right / Fifty Ways to leave your lover / Slip slidin' away / Late in the evening / Hearts and bones / Rene and Georgette Magritte with their dog after the war
9362454082 / Oct '93 / WEA

☐ CAPEMAN (Songs From The Broadway Musical)
Adios Hermanos / Born in Puerto Rico / Satin summer nights / Bernadette / Vampires / Quality / Can I forgive him / Sunday afternoon / Killer wants to go to college / Time is an ocean / Virgil / Killer wants to go to college / Trailways bus
9362468142 / 24 Nov '97 / WEA

☐ CONCERT THE PARK - AUGUST 15TH, 1991
Obvious child / Boy in the bubble / She moves on / Kodachrome / Born at the right time / Train in the distance / Me and Julio down by the schoolyard / I know what I know / Cool cool river / Bridge over troubled water / Proof / Coast / Graceland / You can call me Al / Still crazy after all these years / Loves me like a rock / Diamonds on the soles of her shoes / Hearts and bones / Late in the evening / America / Boxer / Cecelia / Sound of silence
7599267372 / Nov '91 / WEA

☐ GRACELAND
Boy in the bubble / Graceland / I know what I know / Gumboots / Diamonds on the soles of her shoes / You can call me Al / Under African skies / Homeless / Crazy love Vol 2 / All around the world or the myth of fingerprints
9254472 / Sep '86 / WEA

☐ HEARTS AND BONES
Think too much / Train in the distance / Cars are cars / Late great Johnny Ace / Allergies / Hearts and bones / When numbers get serious / Song about the moon / Rene and Georgette Magritte with their dog after the war
9239422 / '83 / WEA

☐ LIVE RHYMIN' - IN CONCERT
Me and Julio down by the schoolyard / Homeward bound / American tune / El condor pasa / Duncan / Boxer / Mother and child reunion / Sound of silence / Jesus is the answer / Bridge over troubled water / Loves me like a rock / America
9255902 / Dec '87 / WEA

☐ ONE TRICK PONY
Late in the evening / That's why God made the movies / One-trick pony / How the heart approaches what it yearns / Oh Marion / Ace in the hole / Nobody / Jonah / God bless the absentee / Long long day
256846 / Feb '94 / WEA

☐ PAUL SIMON
Mother and child reunion / Duncan / Everything put together falls apart / Run that body down / Armistice Day / Me and Julio down by the schoolyard / Peace like a river / Papa hobo / Hobo blues / Paranoia blues / Congratulations / Kodachrome / Tenderness / Take me to the Mardi Gras / Something so right / One man's ceiling is another man's floor / American tune / Was a sunny day / Learn how to fall / St. Judy's comet / Loves me like a rock
9255882 / Dec '87 / WEA

☐ PAUL SIMON SONGBOOK (Various Artists)
VSOPCD 173 / Jun '92 / Connoisseur Collection

☐ RHYTHM OF THE SAINTS
Obvious child / Boy in the bubble / She moves on / Kodachrome / Born at the right time / Train in the distance / Me and Julio down by the schoolyard / I know what I know / Cool cool river / Bridge over troubled water / Proof / Coast / Graceland / Further to fly
7599260982 / Oct '90 / WEA

☐ STILL CRAZY AFTER ALL THESE YEARS
Still crazy after all these years / My little town: Simon, Paul & Art Garfunkel / I do it for your love / Fifty ways to leave your lover / Night game / Gone at last: Simon, Paul & Phoebe Snow/Jessie Dixon Singers / Some folk's lives roll easy / Have a good time / You're kind / Silent eyes
9255912 / Dec '87 / WEA

☐ THERE GOES RHYMIN' SIMON
Kodachrome / Tenderness / Take me to the Mardi Gras / Something so right / One man's ceiling is another man's floor / American tune / Was a sunny day / Learn how to fall / St. Judy's comet / Loves me like a rock
9255892 / Dec '87 / WEA

Simon, Tito

☐ I CRIED A TEAR
I cried a tear / Every beat of my heart / I'd rather go blind / River of tears / That's where it's at / Tell it like it is / After loving you / Hold on to what you've got
FECD 10 / Apr '93 / First Edition

Simon, Vannessa

☐ DEFINITIVE SOURCE
KDCD 7 / Jun '97 / Congo

Simona, Tiziana

☐ GIGOLO (Simona, Tiziana & Kenny Wheeler)
ITM 0014CD / '89 / ITM

Simone

☐ EMI YEARS, THE
To begin with / Canoe canoe / Kings and queens of Maracatu / Enatao vale a pena / Drop of water / Itamaradiao / Piece of me / Face to face / I'm returning / Carnival waltz / Cicada / Passion and faith / Brunete queen / Thirst of the fish / Made to measure / What will be / People of Brasilian race / Speak heart
HEMIMDCD 108 / 6 Oct '97 / Hemisphere

Simone, Nina

☐ BALTIMORE
Baltimore / Everything must change / Family / My father / Music for lovers / Rich girl / That's all I want from you / Forget / Balm in Gilead / If you pray right
4769062 / Jan '95 / Sony Jazz

☐ BEST OF NINA SIMONE, THE
In the morning / I shall be released / Day and night / It be's that way sometimes / I want a little sugar in my bowl / My man's gone now / Why (the king of love is dead) / Compensation / I wish I knew (how it would feel to be free) / Go to hell / Do what you gotta do / Suzanne
ND 90376 / Sep '89 / RCA

☐ BEST OF NINA SIMONE, THE (2CD Set)
RADCD 84 / 26 Jan '98 / Global TV

☐ BLUES, THE
Do I move you / Day and night / In the dark / Real real / My man's gone now / Backlash blues / I want a little sugar in my bowl / Buck / Since I fell for you / House of the rising sun / Blues for Mama / Pusher / Turn me on / Nobody's fault but mine / Go to hell / I shall be released / Gin house blues
ND 83101 / Apr '91 / Novus

☐ BROADWAY, BLUES & BALLADS
Don't let me be misunderstood / Night song / Laziest girl in town / Something wonderful / Don't take all night / Nobody / I am blessed / Of this I'm sure / See line woman / Our love / How can I / Last rose of summer
5181902 / Feb '94 / Verve

☐ COLLECTION, THE
My way / House of the rising sun / Save me / Here comes the sun / I love you porgy / I wish I knew how it would feel to be free / Gin house blues / Seems I'm never tired lovin' you / My sweet Lord / Times they are a-changin' / I want a little sugar in my bowl / Mr Bojangles / I shall be released / Ain't got no / I got life / to love somebody / Angel of the morning
ND 90566 / Feb '97 / RCA

☐ DO NOTHIN' TILL YOU HEAR FROM ME
Just in time / House of the rising sun / It don't mean a thing if it ain't got that swing / I loves you Porgy / Gin house blues / Assingment song / Solitude / Sea lion woman / No opportunity necessary, no experience needed / Black is the colour of my true love's hair / Wild is the wind / Nobody / Don't let me be misunderstood / Do nothin' 'til you hear from me / I got it bad and that ain't good / Hey Buddy Bolden / My way
GRF 022 / '93 / Tring

☐ FEELING GOOD (The Very Best Of Nina Simone)
5226692 / Jul '94 / Verve
5227472 / 23 Feb '98 / Verve

☐ FOLKSY NINA/WITH STRINGS
CCLCD 62082 / 3 Aug '98 / Collectables

☐ FORBIDDEN FRUIT/AT NEWPORT
CCLCD 62072 / 3 Aug '98 / Collectables

☐ GOLD COLLECTION, THE (2CD Set)
R2CD 4022 / 13 Apr '98 / Deja Vu

☐ GREAT NINA SIMONE, THE
Love me or leave me / Mood indigo / I loves you Porgy / Little girl blue / Central Park blues / Don't smoke in bed / For all we know / He needs me / African mailman / Please don't let me be misunderstood / I ain't got no I got life / Ain't no use / After you've gone / Four women / Good bait / Plain gold ring / He's got the whole world in his hands / My baby just cares for me
MCCD 312 / 8 Sep '97 / Music Club

☐ IN CONCERT
RMB 75011 / Nov '93 / Remember

☐ JAZZ MASTERS
Black is the colour of my true love's hair / I put a spell on you / Love me or leave me / Little girl blue / My baby just cares for me / I loves you Porgy / Work song / Ne me quitte pas / Wild is the wind / See line woman / Strange fruit / Pirate Jenny / Four women / Mississippi goddam / Don't let me be misunderstood / I hold no grudge
5181982 / 5 May '98 / Verve

☐ JAZZ MASTERS (Nina Simone Sings Nina Simone)
Sugar in my bowl / Old Jim Crow / Go limp / Four women / Images / Come ye / Be my husband / Take me to the water / I'm going back home / If you pray right / Fodder on my wings / If you knew me/Let it be me / Last rose of Summer / Mississippi goddam
5298672 / 5 May '98 / Verve

☐ LADY BLUE (2CD Set)
My baby just cares for me / Don't smoke in bed / He's got the whole world in his hands / Mood indigo / He needs me / African mailman / Love me or leave me / I love you Porgy / Good bait / For all we know / Central Park blues / You'll never walk alone / Plain gold ring / Little girl blue / My baby just cares for me / House of the rising sun / Don't let me be misunderstood / Ain't got no/I got life / No opportunity necessary, no experience needed / Young, gifted and black / Ain't no use / After you've gone / Assignment song / Gin house blues / Do what you gotta do / Mississippi goddam / See line woman / Other woman / Four women / I just to know I'm alive
CPCD 82402 / Oct '96 / Charly

☐ LET IT BE ME (Live At Vine Street)
My baby just cares for me / Sugar in my bowl / Fodder on my wings / Be my husband / Just like a woman / Balm in Gilead / Stars / If you pray right (Heaven belongs to you) / If you knew / Let it be me / Baltimore / Four women / Mississippi Goddam
8314372 / May '87 / Verve

☐ LITTLE GIRL BLUE (Jazz As Played In An Exclusive Side Street Club)
Mood indigo / Don't smoke in bed / Love me or leave me / He needs me / My baby just cares for me / Little girl blue / Central park blues / I loves you Porgy / Good bait / Plain gold ring / You'll never walk alone
BET 6021 / Jan '95 / Bethlehem

☐ LIVE AND KICKIN'
FREUDCD 32 / Nov '89 / Jungle

☐ MASTERS, THE
EABCD 017 / 24 Nov '97 / Eagle

☐ MASTERS, THE (2CD Set)
EDMCD 022 / 24 Nov '97 / Eagle

☐ MOON OF ALABAMA (2CD Set)
Old jim crown / Pirate jenny / Don't smoke in bed / Go limp / Don't let me be misunderstood / Devil's workshop / See line woman / Gin house blues / Brown baby / I'm gonna say / Promises / Children go where I send you / Zungo / If he changed my name / God, god, god / If you knew / Mr. smith / Fodder on her wings / Be my husband / I loves you, porgy / Other woman / Mississippi goddam / Moon over alabama / For a while / See line woman / I sing just to know that I'm alive / My baby just cares for me
JD 1214 / Oct '96 / Jazz Door

☐ MY BABY JUST CARES FOR ME
My baby just cares for me / Don't smoke in bed / Mood indigo / He needs me / Love me or leave me / I loves you Porgy / You'll never walk alone / Good bait / Central Park blues / Plain gold ring / Little girl blue / My baby just cares for me (Ext.version) / My baby just cares for me (mix)
CPCD 8002 / Aug '96 / Charly

☐ MY BABY JUST CARES FOR ME
BN 033 / Apr '98 / Blue Nite

☐ NINA SIMONE
295055 / Feb '95 / Ariola

☐ NINA SIMONE
House of the rising sun / I loves you Porgy / Love me or leave me / You took my teeth / Do what you gotta do / Saratoga / Sea line woman / African mailman / After you've gone / Ain't no use / Don't smoke in bed / Four women / Fodder on her wings / Good bait / It's cold out here / Just in time / Central Park blues / You'll never walk alone / My baby just cares for me / Mood indigo / I don't mean a thing / Angel of the morning / Do nothin' till you hear from me / Gal from Joe's / I like the sunrise / Work song / You better know / I love you porgy / He needs me / Little girl blue / Spring is here / Since my love is gone / Black is the colour / Solitude
BN 034 / Feb '97 / Blue Nite

☐ NINA SIMONE & HER FRIENDS (An Intimate Variety Of Vocal Charm)
BET 6020 / Jan '95 / Bethlehem

☐ NINA SIMONE - THE 1960'S VOL.1 (Je Me Quitte Pas)
I loves you Porgy / Plain gold ring / Pirate Jenny / Old Jim Crow / Don't smoke in bed / Go limp / Mississippi Goddam / I put a spell on you / Tomorrow is my turn / Ne me quitte pas / Marriage is for old folks / July tree / Gimme some / Feeling good / One September day / Blues on purpose / Beautiful land / You've got to learn / Take care of business
8385432 / Apr '94 / Mercury

☐ NINA SIMONE IN CONCERT/I PUT A SPELL ON YOU
I loves you Porgy / Plain gold ring / Pirate Jenny / Old Jim Crow / Don't smoke in bed / Go limp / Mississippi Goddam / I put a spell on you / Tomorrow is my turn / Ne me quitte pas / Marriage is for old folks / July tree / Gimme some / Feeling good / One September day / Blues on purpose / Beautiful land / You've got to learn / Take care of business
8465432 / Feb '97 / Mercury

☐ RELEASED
Backlash blues / Blues for Mama / I shall be released / It be's that way sometimes / I want a little sugar in my bowl / My man's gone now / Why (the king of love is dead) / I wish I knew how it would feel to be free / Do what you gotta do / Do I move you / In the dark / Look of love / Since I fell for you / Mr. Bojangles / Just like a woman / Turn me on / Nobody's fault but mine / Ain't got no / I got life / I loves you Porgy / Gin House blues
74321431552 / Jan '97 / Camden

☐ RISING SUN COLLECTION
RSCD 004 / Apr '94 / Just A Memory

☐ SAGA OF THE GOOD LIFE AND HARD TIMES
Nobody's fault but mine / I get along without you very well / Come ye / In the morning / Ain't got no / I got life / Do I move you / Sunday in Savannah / Why (the king of love is dead) / Mississippi goddam / In love in vain / Man with a horn / I loves you Porgy / I'll look around / Music for lovers / Ain't got no...(Take 3) / Take my hand precious Lord
7863669972 / 1 Sep '97 / RCA

☐ SINGLE WOMAN
Single woman / Lonesome cities / If I should lose you / Folks who live on the hill / Love's been good to me / Papa, can you hear me / Il n'y a pas d'amour / Just say I love him / More I see you / Marry me
7559615032 / Aug '93 / Elektra

☐ SPOTLIGHT ON NINA SIMONE
Work song / Angel of the morning / Ain't got no...I got life / You can have him / Lovin' woman / Little Liza Jane / Here comes the sun / My way / Fine and mellow / Nina's blues / Porgy
HADCD 109 / Feb '94 / Javelin

☐ TOUCHING AND CARING
It's cold out there / Porgy / I sing just to know that I'm alive / For a while / Fodder on her wings / Touching and caring / Saratoga / You must have another lover
CDSGP 0278 / 2 Feb '98 / Prestige

☐ ULTIMATE DIVAS
5390502 / 10 Nov '97 / Verve

Simonelli, Victor

☐ UNDERGROUND HOUSE PARTY (Various Artists)
NBCD 95007 / 18 May '98 / Nite & Blue

Simons, Tito

☐ TAKE A LOOK
Without love / Only the lonely know / Lavenders blue / Oh Patricia / Boom biddi boom / Black pearls / Oh Leona / Count the hours / Take a look around / Lord's army / Cheating games / Reggae is a music from Jamaica
WSRCD 104 / Sep '96 / World Sound

Simonsson, Simon

☐ DRANGKAMMARLTAR (Simonsson, Simon & Olle Eriksson)
GCD 32 / May '97 / Giga

Simper, Nick

☐ SLIPSTREAMING/FUTURE TIMES
Candice Larene / Rocky road blues / Independent man (Hey Mama) / Slipstreaming / Schoolhouse party / Sister / Mississippi lady / Time will tell / Pull out and start again / Get down, lay down / She was my friend / Future times / Undercover man / Something's burning / Hard drink and easy women
RPM 125 / Jun '97 / RPM

Simple Minds

☐ CELEBRATION
Life in a day / Chelsea girl / Premonition / Factory / Calling your name / I travel / Changeling / Celebrate / Thirty frames a second / Kaleidoscope
CDV 2248 / Apr '90 / Virgin

☐ EMPIRES AND DANCE
I travel / Today I died again / This fear of Gods / Celebrate / Constantinople line / Twist, run, repulsion / Thirty frames a second / Kant-kino / Room / Capital city
CDV 2247 / Jun '88 / Virgin

☐ GLITTERING PRIZE 1981-1992
Waterfront / Don't you forget about me / Alive and kicking / Sanctify yourself / Love Song / Someone, somewhere in summertime / See the lights / Belfast child / American / All the things she said / Promised you a miracle / Ghostdancing / Speed your love to me / Glittering prize / Let there be love / Mandela Day
SMTVD 1 / Oct '92 / Virgin

☐ GOOD NEWS FROM THE NEXT WORLD
She's a river / Night music / Hypnotised / Great leap forward / Seven deadly sins / And the band played on / My life / Criminal world / This time
CDV 2760 / Jan '95 / Virgin

☐ LIFE IN A DAY
Someone / Life in a day / Sad affair / All for you / Pleasantly disturbed / No cure / Chelsea girl / Wasteland / Destiny / Murder story
VMCD 6 / Jul '87 / Virgin

☐ LIFE IN A DAY/REAL TO REAL CACOPHONY/EMPIRES AND DANCE (3CD Set)
Someone / Life in a day / Sad affair / All for you / Pleasantly disturbed / No cure / Chelsea girl / Wasteland / Destiny / Murder story / I travel / Today I died again / Celebrate / This fear of gods / Capital city / Constantinople / Line / Twist-run-repulsion / Thirty frames a second / Kant-kino / Room / Real to reel / Naked eye / Citizen (dance of youth) / Carnival (shelter in a suitcase) / Factory / Cacophony / Veldt / Premonition / Changeling / Film theme / Calling your name / Scar
TPAK 2 / Oct '90 / Virgin

☐ LIVE - IN THE CITY OF LIGHT (2CD Set)
Ghostdancing / Big sleep / Waterfront / Promised you a miracle / Someone, somewhere in summertime / Oh jungleland / Alive and kicking / Don't you forget about me / Once upon a time / Book of brilliant things / East at Easter / Sanctify yourself / Love song / Sun city / Dance to the music / New gold dream
CDSM 1 / May '87 / Virgin

☐ NEAPOLIS
Song for the tribes / War babies / Glitterball / Tears of a guy / Superman vs supersoul / Lighting / If I Had wings / Killing Andy Warhol / Androgny
4937122
4937120 / 16 Mar '98 / Chrysalis

☐ NEW GOLD DREAM (81-82-83-84)
Someone, somewhere in summertime / Colours fly and catherine wheel / Promised you a miracle / Big sleep / Somebody up there likes you / New gold dream / Glittering prize / Hunter and the hunted / King is white and in the crowd
CDV 2230 / Apr '92 / Virgin

☐ ONCE UPON A TIME
Once upon a time / All the things she said / Ghostdancing / Alive and kicking / Oh jungleland / I wish you were here / Sanctify yourself / Come a long way
CDV 2364 / Oct '85 / Virgin

☐ REAL LIFE
Real life / See the lights / Let there be love / Woman / Stand by love / Let the children speak / African skies / Ghost rider / Banging on the door / Travelling man / Rivers of ice / When two worlds collide
CDVIP 175 / Apr '97 / Virgin VIP

☐ REAL TO REAL CACOPHONY
Real to real / Naked eye / Citizen (dance of youth) / Veldt / Carnival (shelter in a suitcase) / Factory / Cacophony / Premonition / Changeling / Film theme / Calling your name / Scar
CDVIP 157 / Oct '96 / Virgin VIP

☐ SONS AND FASCINATION
In trance as mission / Sweat in bullet / Seventy cities as love brings the fall / Boys from Brazil / Love song / This earth that you walk upon / Sons and fascination / Seeing out the angel / Theme for great cities / American / Twentieth century promised land / Wonderful in young life / Careful in career / League of nations / Sound in seventy cities
CDV 2207 / Apr '86 / Virgin

☐ SPARKLE IN THE RAIN
Up on the catwalk / Book of brilliant things / Speed your love to me / Waterfront / East at Easter / Street hassle / White hot day / C moon / Kick inside of me / Shake off the ghosts / Cry like a baby
CDV 2300 / Mar '92 / Virgin

☐ STREET FIGHTING YEARS
Street fighting years / Wall of love / Take a step back / Let it all come down / Belfast child / Soul crying out / This is your land / Kick it in / Mandela day / Biko
MINDD 1 / May '89 / Virgin

Simpleton

☐ HEAVEN ME REACH
Young girl magician / Actions speak louder than words / Heaven me reach / Need a little magic / Mr. Gunhead / You plant the seed / Them talk about man / See it deh / Them fe hear / So you born
WRCD 005 / Nov '97 / World

☐ QUARTER TO 12
GRELCD 226 / Jun '96 / Greensleeves

Simply Red

☐ BLUE
Mellow my mind / Blue / Say you love me / To be free / Air that I breathe / Some day in my life / Air that I breathe / Night nurse / Broken man / Come get me angel / Ghetto girl / Love has said goodbye again / High fives
3984230972 / 18 May '98 / East West

☐ HOLDING BACK THE YEARS (The Greatest Hits 1985-1996)
Holding back the years / Money's too tight to mention / Right thing / It's only love / New flame / You've got it / If you don't know me by now / Stars / Something got me started / Thrill me / Your mirror / For your babies / So beautiful / Angel / Fairground
0630165522 / Oct '96 / East West

☐ LIFE
You make me believe / So many people / Lives and loves / Fairground / Never never love / So beautiful / Hillside Avenue / Remembering the first time / Out on the range / We're in this together
0630120692 / Oct '95 / East West

☐ MEN AND WOMEN
Right thing / Infidelity / Suffer / I won't feel bad / Every time we say goodbye / Let me have it all / Love fire / Move on out / Shine / Maybe someday
2420712 / Feb '95 / East West

☐ NEW FLAME, A
It's only love / New flame / You've got it / To be with you / More / Turn it up / Love lays its tune / She'll have to go / If you don't know me by now / Enough
2446892 / Feb '89 / East West

☐ PICTURE BOOK
Come to my aid / Sad old red / Look at you now / Heaven / Jericho / Money's too tight to mention / Holding back the years / Open up the red box / No direction / Picture book
9031769932 / Mar '92 / East West

☐ SIMPLY SAX (The Music Of Simply Red) (Kelles, Erwin & John Thirkel)
Sad old red / Holding back the years / Right thing / Everytime we say goodbye / It's only love / New flame / You've got it / To be with you / She'll have to go / If you don't know me by now / Something got me started / Stars / Thrill me / For your babies / Your mirror / Fairground / Remembering the first time / Never never love / We're in this together
ANT 013 / Nov '96 / Tring

☐ STARS
Something got me started / Stars / Thrill me / Your mirror / She's got it bad / For your babies / Model / How could I fall / Freedom / Wonderland
9031752842 / Oct '91 / East West

Simpson, Carole

☐ ALL ABOUT CAROLE
You make me feel so young / Listen little girl / You forgot your gloves / Sure thing / Gentleman friend / Your name is love / Everytime / Oh look at me now / Time / I'll be around / There will never be another you / Just because we're kids
JASCD 309 / Jul '95 / Jasmine

Simpson, Chris

☐ LISTEN TO THE MAN
CMCD 019 / Dec '97 / Celtic Music

Simpson, Graham

☐ MUSIC OF IRELAND, THE
GWCD 4 / Dec '97 / Guitar

Simpson, Martin

☐ 61 HIGHWAY
BEJ 012CD / Aug '96 / Beautiful Jo

☐ BAND OF ANGELS (Simpson, Martin & Jessica)
RHRCD 96 / Oct '96 / Red House

☐ CLOSER WALK WITH THEE, A
Weary blues / Old rugged cross / Salutation march / Spinning wheel / Savoy blues / Moose march / If I had my life to live over / East coast trot / Just a closer walk with thee / Marie / Chimes blues / Wreck of ol' 97 / Does Jesus care / Dinah / Saratoga swing
FLE 1007CD / Jul '94 / Fledg'ling

☐ COLLECTION, THE
First cut is the deepest / Roving gambler / This war may last you for years / Masters of war / Reuben's train / Handsome Mollly / Moonshine / Green linnet / Grinning in your face / Shawnee town / Moth / For Jessica, sad or high kicking / No depression in heaven / Stillness in company / Lakes of Ponchartrain / Doney girl / Essequibo river / Keel row
SHCD 79089 / Jun '94 / Shanachie

☐ COOL AND UNUSUAL
RHRCD 110 / Oct '97 / Red House

☐ KAMBARA MUSIC IN NATIVE TONGUES
Waltzing's for dreamers / Slow pageant / He'll have to go / El Jarabe loco / Dancer's gait / Running kind
WLACS 63CD / Jun '98 / Waterlily Acoustics

☐ LEAVES OF LIFE
Intro/Lord Gregory / Jock O'Hazeldean / Lucy Wan / Streets of Forbes / Bantry girl's lament / Leaves of life / Banks of the bann / Greenfields of America / Fairflower of Northumberland / Bonny George Campbell / McCrimmons lament / Rosie Anderson
SH 97008 / Mar '98 / Shanachie

☐ MARTIN SIMPSON LIVE
BEJOCD 011 / Apr '96 / Beautiful Jo

☐ MUSIC FOR THE MOTHERLESS CHILD (Simpson, Martin & Wu Man)
One more day / A minor blues / White snow in Spring / Dives and lazarus / Coo coo bird / Sometimes I feel like a Motherless child
WLACS 49CD / Feb '97 / Waterlily Acoustics

☐ NOBODY'S FAULT BUT MINE
DAMCD 013 / Dec '97 / Dambuster

☐ SMOKE AND MIRRORS
Poormouth / See that my grave is kept clean / Broke down engine / New kitchen blues / Hard love / I want my crown / Will this house be blessed / Delia / Lock, stock and barrel / Spoonful / Me and my chauffeur / Big road blues / Road kill / Gone fishing
RHYD 5011 / Oct '95 / Rhiannon

☐ SPECIAL AGENT
FLED 3005 / Nov '95 / Fledg'ling

☐ WHEN I WAS ON HORSEBACK
Pretty saro/Long steel rail / Garryowen / Bonny at morn / Bob's song / Flower / Vaughans jig / Granuaile / When I was on horseback / Keel row / Shallow brown / Palins of waterloo / Bonny bunch of roses / Young man / Shearing's not for you / Bogies bonny belle
SHANCD 97016 / Mar '98 / Shanachie

Simpson, Melanie

☐ OLD VERDI, THE
ATCD 048 / Dec '97 / Attic

Simpsons

☐ SIMPSONS SING THE BLUES, THE
School day / Born under a bad sign / Moanin' Lisa blues / Deep deep trouble / God bless the child / I love to see you smile / Springfield soul stew / Look at all those idiots / Sibling rivalry / Do the Bartman
GED 24308 / Nov '96 / Geffen

Sims, Frankie Lee

☐ LUCY MAE BLUES
Lucy Mae blues / Don't take it out on me / Married woman / Wine and gin bounce / Boogie 'cross the country / Jelly roll baker / I'm so glad / Long gone / Raggedy and dirty / Yeh, baby / No good woman / Walking boogie / Frankie's blues / Crying won't help you / I done talked and I done talked / Lucy Mae blues (Part 2) / Rumba my boogie / I'll get along somehow / Hawk shuffle / Frankie Lee's 2 O' Clock jump
CDCHD 423 / Sep '92 / Ace

Sims, Pete 'La Roca'

☐ SWINGTIME
Drum town / Body and soul / Susan's waltz / Tomorrow's expectation / Candyman / Nihon Bashi / Candu Amanda's song
CDP 8548762 / Aug '97 / Blue Note

☐ TURKISH WOMEN AT THE BATH
412320522 / 17 Mar '98 / Thirty Two

Sims, Zoot

☐ AT RONNIE SCOTTS '61 (Sims, Zoot Quartet)
FSRCD 134 / Dec '90 / Fresh Sound

☐ BLUES FOR TWO (Sims, Zoot & Joe Pass)
Blues for two / Dindi / Remember / Poor butterfly / Black and blue / Pennies from Heaven / I hadn't anyone till you / Take off
OJCCD 635 / Feb '92 / Original Jazz Classics

☐ BOHEMIA AFTER DARK
9.20 special / Man I love / 55th and state / Blue room / Gus's blues / That old feeling / Bohemia after dark / Woody 'n' you / I don't stand a ghost of a chance (with you) / September in the rain / Nearness of you / Skylark / Two sleepy people
JHR 73578 / May '94 / Jazz Hour

☐ DOWN HOME (Sims, Zoot Quartet)
Jive at five / Doggin' around / Ascap / Avalon / I cried for you / Bill Bailey, won't you please come home / Goodnight sweetheart / There'll be some changes made / I've heard that blues before
CDGR 122 / Mar '97 / Charly

☐ ELEGIAC (Sims, Zoot & Bucky Pizzarelli)
STCD 8238 / May '96 / Storyville

☐ FOR LADY DAY
Easy living / That ole devil called love / Some other Spring / I cover the waterfront / You go to my head / I cried for you / Body and soul / Travellin' light / You're my thrill / No more / My man (mon homme)
CD 2310942 / Jan '94 / Pablo

☐ GETTING SENTIMENTAL
I'm getting sentimental over you / Restless / Fred / Caravan / Dream dancing / Very thought of you / Love me
CHCD 71006 / Mar '97 / Candid

☐ HAPPY OVER HOAGY (Sims, Zoot & Al Cohn Septet)
JASSCD 5 / '88 / Jass

☐ IF I'M LUCKY (Sims, Zoot & Jimmy Rowles)
Where our love has gone / Legs / If I'm lucky / Shadow waltz / You're my everything / It's all right with me / Gypsy sweetheart / I hear a rhapsody
OJCCD 683 / Nov '95 / Original Jazz Classics

☐ IN A MELLOW TONE (2CD Set)
Groovin' high / Emily / All things you are / Take the 'A' train / Lester leaps in / Girl from Ipanema / That ole devil called love / Caravan / I got it bad and that ain't good / In a mellow tone / Over the rainbow / Softly as in a morning sunrise / Jitterbug waltz
JLR 103604 / May '96 / Live At EJ's

☐ IN COPENHAGEN
STCD 8244 / May '95 / Storyville

☐ LIVE IN PHILLY
60412320562 / 7 Apr '98 / Thirty Two

☐ ON THE KORNER
2310953 / Nov '95 / Pablo

☐ PASSION FLOWER (Zoot Sims Plays Duke Ellington)
It don't mean a thing if it ain't got that swing / In a mellow tone / I got it bad and that ain't good / I let a song go out of my heart / Black butterfly / Do nothin' 'til you hear from me / Your love has faded / Bojangles / Passion flower
OJCCD 9392 / Nov '97 / Original Jazz Classics

☐ QUARTET AND SEXTET
Night and day / Night and day / Night and day / Slingin' hash / Slingin' hash / Tenorly / Tenorly / Tenorly / Zoot and zoot / I understand / Don't worry about me / Crystal Toot's suite / Late Tiny Kahn / Call it anything / Zoot's suite / Once in a while / Great drums
74321511522 / 19 Jan '98 / Vogue

☐ QUIETLY THERE
911900402 / 31 Mar '98 / JVC

☐ RARE DAWN SESSIONS
BCD 131 / Oct '94 / Biograph

☐ SOMEBODY LOVES ME
Summerset / Honeysuckle rose / Summer thing / Somebody loves me / Gee baby ain't I good to you / Nirvana / (Back home again in) Indiana / Memories of you / Come rain or come shine / Up a lazy river / Send in the clowns / Airmail special / Ham hock blues / Ring dem bells
17085 / Mar '97 / Laserlight

☐ SOPRANO SAX
Someday sweetheart / Moonlight in Vermont / Wrap up your troubles in dreams (and dream your troubles awa / Blues for Louise / Willow weep for me / Wrap up / (I don't stand) A ghost of a chance with you / Baubles bangles and beads
OJCCD 9022 / May '98 / Original Jazz Classics

☐ SUDDENLY IT'S SPRING
Brahm's...I think / I can't get started (with you) / MacGuffie's blues / In the middle of a kiss / So long / Never let me go / Suddenly it's spring / Emaline
OJCCD 742 / May '93 / Original Jazz Classics

☐ SUMMER THING, A
Summer set / Honeysuckle rose / Summer thing / Somebody loves me / Gee baby, ain't I good to you / Nirvana / Back home again in Indiana / Memories of you / Come rain or come shine / Up a lazy river / Send in the clowns
15754 / Aug '92 / Laserlight

☐ TONITE'S MUSIC TODAY (Sims, Zoot & Bob Brookmeyer)
BLCD 760907 / Jun '88 / Black Lion

☐ ZOOT SIMS & THE GERSHWIN BROTHERS
Man I love / How long has this been going on / Oh lady be good / I've got a crush on you / I got rhythm / Embraceable you / 'S wonderful / Someone to watch over me / Isn't it a pity / Summertime
OJCCD 444 / Feb '93 / Original Jazz Classics

☐ ZOOT SIMS AND BOB BROOKMEYER (Sims, Zoot & Bob Brookmeyer)
King / Lullaby of the leaves / I can't get started (with you) / Snake eyes / Morning fun / Whooeeeeee / Someone to watch over me / My old flame / Boxcars
BLCD 760914 / '88 / Black Lion

☐ ZOOT SIMS IN PARIS
Captain jetter / Nuzzolese blues / Everything I love / Evening in paris / On the alamo / My old flame / Little jon special
CDSW 8417 / Jan '89 / DRG

☐ ZOOT SIMS VOL.1 1944-1950
BMCD 1038 / 21 Aug '97 / Blue Moon

☐ ZOOT SIMS VOL.2 1950-1951
BMCD 1039 / 21 Aug '97 / Blue Moon

Sin Alley

☐ DETROIT 442
DD 035CD / Jan '97 / Demolition Derby

Sinatra, Frank

☐ 'S WONDERFUL (Rarities From The Radio Years)
'S wonderful / Sometimes I'm happy / Between the devil and the deep blue sea / Long ago and far away / Some other time / Come out wherever you are / I'll walk alone / Everything I have is yours / Speak low / This is always / It's been a long long time / Thou swell / Out of nowhere / There goes that song again / Is you is or is you ain't my baby / You keep coming back like a song / It can't be wrong / Great day / And then you kissed me / My ideal / Again / April showers / Exactly like you / Three little words / What a difference a day made / With a song in my heart / I'm in the mood for love / You took advantage of me / Just you just me / Don't blame me
3037300052 / May '98 / Coolnote

☐ 16 MOST REQUESTED SONGS
All or nothing at all / You'll never know / Saturday night is the loneliest night of the week / Dream / Put your dreams away / Day by day / Nancy with the laughing face / Oh what it seemed to be / Soloqay (part 1 and 2) / Five minutes more / Things we did last summer / Coffe song (they've got a awful lot of coffee in Brazil) / Time after time / Mam'selle / Fools rush in / Birth of the blues
4805132 / May '95 / Columbia

☐ 20 CLASSIC TRACKS
Come fly with me / Around the world / French foreignlegion / Moonlight in Vermont / Autumn in New York / Let's get away from it all / April in Paris / Brazil / London by night / It's nice to go travelling / Come dance with me / Somwthing's gotta give / Just in time / Dancing in the dark / Too close for comfort / I could have danced all night / Saturday night is the loneliest night of the week / Cheek to cheek / Baubles bangles and beads / Day in day out
4939812 / 16 Mar '98 / EMI Gold

☐ 20 CLASSIC TRACKS: FRANK SINATRA
Come fly with me / Around the world / French Foreign Legion / Moonlight in Vermont / Autumn in New York / Let's get away from it all / April in Paris / London by night / It's nice to go travellin' / Come dance with me / Something's gotta give / Just in time / Dancing in the dark / Too close for comfort / I could have danced all night / Saturday night is the loneliest night of the week / Cheek to cheek / Baubles, bangles and beads / Day in, day out
CDMFP 50530 / Mar '92 / Music For Pleasure

☐ 20 GREAT LOVE SONGS
Lovely way to spend an evening / I only have eyes for you / When your lover has gone / There's no you / I fall in love too easily / All the things you are / I dream of you (more than you dream of me) / They say it's wonderful / I have but one heart / Girl that I marry / Five minutes more / Dream / If I loved you / Where or when / Song is you / How deep is the ocean / I should care / September song / I fall in love with you every day / Among my souvenirs
LS 886312 / 2 Feb '98 / Disky

☐ 40 FAMOUS SONGS FROM THE MUSICALS (2CD Set)
You'll never walk alone / Girl that I marry / Begin the beguine / September song / Oh, what a beautiful morning / People will say we're in love / Song is you / You're lonely and I'm lonely / It's a lovely day tomorrow / Without a song / I'll be seeing you / World is in my arms / Just one of those things / You do something to me / Ol' man river / You are love / They didn't believe me / Love me or leave me / There's no business like show business / 'S wonderful / Embraceable you / Kiss me again / Where or when / All the things you are / If I loved you / Someone to watch over me / These foolish things (remind me of you) / Why shouldn't I / Bess, oh where's my bess / They say it's wonderful / Soliloquy / Lost in the stars / Falling in love with love / You make me feel so young / I'll string along with you / I've got my love to keep me warm / On the sunny side of the street / Who told you I cared / I don't why (I just do)
DBG 53057 / Jul '97 / Double Gold

☐ 50 FAMOUS SONGS FROM THE MOVIES (2CD Set)
Too romantic / Say it / This is the beginning of the end / April played the fiddle / I haven't time to be a millionaire / Call of the canyon / I could make you care / Our love affair / I'd know you anywhere / Do you know why / Not so long ago / You lucky people, you / It's always you / Dolores / I'll never let a day pass by / Love me as I am / How about you / Poor you / I'll take Tallulah / Last call for love / Be careful, it's my heart / You'll never know / Night and day / You make me feel so young / I'm in the mood for love / Sunday, Monday or always / If you please / I couldn't sleep a wink last night / Lovely way to spend an evening / Music stopped / White Christmas / I begged her / What makes the sunset / I fall in love too easily / Stormy weather / Charm of you / Embraceable you / I should care / Friend of yours / Over the rainbow / House I live in (that's America to me) / You are too beautiful / I only have eyes for you / Paradise / All through the day / Two hearts are better than one / That old black magic / Somewhere in the night / Five minutes more / Somebody loves me
DBG 53056 / Jul '97 / Double Gold

☐ ALL ALONE
7599270222 / May '98 / Reprise

☐ ALL OF ME (50 Great Performances/ 2CD Set)
Blue skies / I don't stand a ghost of a chance / Music stopped / You make me feel so young / Just one of those things / You do something to me / Begin the beguine / Ol' man river / For you / Night and day / Nevertheless / Out of nowhere / You are love / I've got my love to keep me warm / On the sunny side of the street / Hundred years from today / I wonder who's kissing her now / I'm in the mood for love / Don't blame me / They didn't believe me / Tenderly / Love me or leave me / Somebody loves me / I'll string along with you / 'S wonderful / It might as well be spring / Day by day / Lily Belle / I'll be seeing you / Home on the range / All of me / Stars in your eyes / Ole buttermilk sky / I'll get by (as long as I have you) / Chickery chick / Sweet Lorraine / Gimme a little kiss, will ya huh / All the things you are / Put your dreams away (for another day) / It had to be you / San Fernando Valley / Long ago and far away / It could happen to you / Amor / I'll walk alone / With a song in my heart / Over the rainbow / Close to you / Saturday night (is the lonliest night of the week) / Nancy
DBG 53055 / Jul '97 / Double Gold

☐ ALL OF ME (2CD Set)
CPCD 83242 / 29 Jun '98 / Charly

☐ ALL OR NOTHING AT ALL (25 Early Hits 1939-1947)
All or nothing at all: *Sinatra, Frank & Harry James Orchestra* / I'll be seeing you: *Sinatra, Frank & Tommy Dorsey Orchestra* / Fools rush in where angels fear to tread: *Sinatra, Frank & Tommy Dorsey Orchestra* / I'll never smile again: *Sinatra, Frank & Pied Pipers/Tommy Dorsey Orchestra* / Our love affair: *Sinatra, Frank & Tommy Dorsey Orchestra* / Oh look at me now: *Sinatra, Frank & Connie Haines/ Tommy Dosey Orchestra* / It's always you: *Sinatra, Frank & Tommy Dorsey Orchestra* / Dolores: *Sinatra, Frank & Pied Pipers/Tommy Dorsey Orchestra* / This love of mine: *Sinatra, Frank & Tommy Dorsey Orchestra* / Blue skies: *Sinatra, Frank & Tommy Dorsey Orchestra* / Night and day: *Sinatra, Frank & Tommy Dorsey Orchestra* / In the evening: *Sinatra, Frank & Tommy Dorsey Orchestra* / There are such things: *Sinatra, Frank & Pied Pipers/Tommy Dorsey Orchestra* / It started all over again: *Sinatra, Frank & Pied Pipers/Tommy Dorsey Orchestra* / You'll never know: *Sinatra, Frank & Bobby Tucker Singers* / People will say we're in love: *Sinatra, Frank & Bobby*

Tucker Singers / I couldn't sleep a wink last night: *Sinatra, Frank & Bobby Tucker Singers* / Saturday night is the lonliest night of the week: *Sinatra, Frank & Axel Stordhal Orchestra* / Someone to watch over me: *Sinatra, Frank & Axel Stordhal Orchestra* / Nancy with the laughing face: *Sinatra, Frank & Axel Stordhal Orchestra* / Oh what it seemed to be: *Sinatra, Frank & Axel Stordhal Orchestra* / They say it's wonderful: *Sinatra, Frank & Axel Stordhal Orchestra* / Five minutes more: *Sinatra, Frank & Axel Stordhal Orchestra* / Mam'selle: *Sinatra, Frank & Axel Stordhal Orchestra* / White Christmas: *Sinatra, Frank & Axel Stordhal Orchestra*

CDAJA 5275 / May '98 / Living Era

☐ ALWAYS (Love Songs)

AMSC 628 / 16 Feb '98 / Avid

☐ AMONG MY SOUVENIRS

Five minutes more / Oh what it seemed to be / Begin the beguine / Full moon and empty arms / Someone to watch over me / You go to my head / These foolish things / I don't know why / Day by day / You are too beautiful / I only have eyes for you / I don't stand a ghost of a chance with you / Why shouldn't I / Try a little tenderness / All through the day / One love / How cute can you be / Bess, oh where's my Bess / They say it's wonderful / Somewhere in the night / Coffee song / Among my souvenirs / September song / Things we said last Summer

CDGR 109 / Jan '97 / Charly

☐ AT THE MOVIES

From here to eternity / Three coins in the fountain / Young at heart / She's funny that way / Just one of those things / Someone to watch over me / Not as a stranger / Tender trap / Our town / Impatient years / Love and marriage / Look to your heart / Johnny Concho theme (Wait for me) / All the way / Chicago / Monique / They came to Cordura / High hopes / All my tomorrows

CDP 7993742 / Apr '93 / Capitol

☐ AUDIO ARCHIVE

You make me feel so young / Night and day / 'S Wonderful / Somebody loves me / Begin the beguine / It all depends on you / Just one of those things / Ol' man river / Love me or leave me / They say it's wonderful / Nevertheless / Don't blame me / Out of nowhere / On the sunny side of the street / Blue skies / You are my love / Music stopped / I don't stand a ghost of a chance with you / They did not believe me / You do something to me

CDAA 005 / Jun '92 / Tring

☐ BEGIN THE BEGUINE

MU 5043 / Oct '92 / Musketeer

☐ BEST OF THE COLUMBIA YEARS, THE (4CD Set)

Don't look down / Like a rolling stone / When the world falls down / Trouble with me / Life's a prayer / You and me / Colour me / Take a long line / Midnight love / All the young dudes / I only have eyes for you / Kiss me again / (There'll be a) Hot time / Music stopped / I couldn't sleep a wink last night / Way you look tonight / I'll be around / You've got a hold on me / Lovely way to spend an evening / She's funny that way / Speak low / Close to you / My shining hour / Long ago (and far away) / Some other time / Come out come out wherever you are / Put your dreams away / And then you kissed me / All the things you are / All of me / Nancy / Mighty lak' a rose / Falling in love with you / Cradle song / I'll follow my secret heart / There's no you / Someone to watch over me / Let me love you tonight / Just close your eyes / If you are but a dream / Strange music / Dick Haymes, Dick Todd / None but the lonely heart / Ol' man river / Homesick / The night is young / Aren't you glad / You bought a new kind of love / I'll never smile again / Without a song / Was the last time I saw you (the last) / Don't forget tonight / Oh what it seemed to be / Over the rainbow / Bess oh where's my Bess / My romance / Song is you / I fall in love with you / They say it's wonderful / You are too beautiful / Come rain or shine / Stormy weather / People will say we're in love / Saturday night / White Christmas / I fall in love too easily / Embraceable you / My melancholy baby / Where or when / I should care / Dream

4910282 / 15 Jun '98 / Columbia

☐ BLUE NOTE PLAYS SINATRA (Various Artists)

Come rain or come shine: *Blakey, Art & The Jazz Messengers* / All or nothing at all: *Hubbard, Freddie* / Guess I'll hang my tears out to dry: *Gordon, Dexter* / Dancing in the dark: *Adderley, Cannonball* / I've got you under my skin: *Rollins, Sonny* / Witchcraft: *Three Sounds* / I love Paris: *Terrasson, Jacky* / It never entered my mind: *Davis, Miles* / Nancy: *Quebec, Ike* / This love of mine: *Green, Benny* / Angel eyes: *Lovano, Joe* / It was a very good year: *Three Sounds*

CDP 8352822 / Mar '96 / Blue Note

☐ CAPITOL YEARS, THE (3CD Set)

I've got the world on a string / Lean baby / I love you / South of the border (Down Mexico way) / From here to eternity / They can't take that away from me / I get a kick out of you / Young at heart / Three coins in the fountain / All of me / Taking a chance on love / Someone to watch over me / What is this thing called love / In the wee small hours of the morning / Learnin' the blues / Our town / Love and marriage / Tender trap / Weep they will / I thought about you / You make me feel so young / Memories of you / I've got you under my skin / Too marvellous for words / Don't like goodbyes / How little it matters, how little we know / Your sensational / Hey jealous lover / Close to you / Stars fell on Alabama / I got plenty o' nuttin' / I wish I were in love again / Lady is a tramp / Night and day / Lonesome road / If I had you / Where are you / I'm a fool to want you / Witchcraft / Something wonderful happens in summer / All the way / Chicago / Let's get away from it all / Autumn in New York / Come fly with me / Everybody loves somebody / It's the same old dream / Put your dreams away / Here goes / Angel eyes / Guess I'll hang my tears out to dry / Ebb tide / Only the lonely / One for my baby (and one more for the road) / To love and be loved (Single version) / I couldn't care less / Song is you / Just in time / Saturday night is the loneliest night of the week / Come dance with me / French Foreign Legion / One I love (Belongs to someone else) / Here's that rainy day / High hopes / When no one cares / I'll never smile again / I've got a crush on you / Embraceable you / Nice 'n' easy / I can't believe that you're in love with me / On the sunny side of the street / I've heard that song before / Almost like being in love / I'll be seeing you / I gotta right to sing the blues

CDS 7943172 / Nov '90 / Capitol

☐ CHAIRMAN OF THE BORED (A Tribute To Frank Sinatra) (Various Artists)

GROW 12122 / Oct '93 / Grass

☐ CHRISTMAS SONGS

White Christmas / Silent night / Adeste fideles (O come all ye faithful) / Jingle bells / Have yourself a merrly little Christmas / Christmas dreaming (A little early this year) / It came upon the midnight clear / O little town of Bethlehem / Santa Claus is coming to town / Let it snow, let it snow, let it snow / Medley / Ave Maria / Winter wonderland / Lord's prayer

4782562 / 3 Nov '97 / Columbia

☐ CLASSIC YEARS VOL.1, THE

CDSGP 091 / Nov '93 / Prestige

☐ CLASSIC YEARS VOL.2, THE

CDSGP 157 / Mar '95 / Prestige

☐ COLLECTION, THE

Begin the beguine / Day by day / Time after time / Night and day / Be careful it's my heart / Fools rush in / I'll be seeing you / Everything happens to me / A sinner kissed an angel / Blue skies / From the bottom of my heart / How about you / I think of you / Imagination / It's always you / Oh look at me now / Ol' man river / Our love affair / Somebody loves me / Stardust / Street of dreams / Lamplighter's serenade / Song is you / Whispering / This is the beginning of the end

COL 051 / Apr '95 / Collection

☐ COLLECTION, THE (3CD Set)

390202 / May '98 / Hallmark

☐ COLLECTION, THE (3CD Set)

All or nothing at all / Without a song / Fools rush in / I'll never smile again / East of the sun (and west of the moon) / Everything happens to me / I'll be seeing you / This love of mine / Imagination / Steets of dreams / One I love (belongs to somebody else) / Moments in the moonlight / It's a lovely day tomorrow / Daybreak / Dolores / Let's get away from it all / Violets for your furs / Lamplighter's serenade / Song is you / Day by day / Nancy (with the laughing face) / Begin the beguine / Full moon and empty arms / You are too beautiful / I have but one heart / You'll never walk alone / Stella by starlight / How cute can you be / My romance / There but for you go I / I should care / Coffee song / September song / Poinciana / Girl that I marry / That old black magic / Five minutes more / My shawl / Put your dreams away (for another day) / Night and day / Where or when / I fall in love with you everyday / My heart stood still / Amor / Speak low / Sweet Loraine / It could happen to you / Just one of those things / More than you know / It had to be you / What makes the sunset / Two hearts are better than one / It's magic / I'm in love / You brought a new kind of love / To me / My heart tells me it might as well be spring / Swinging on a star / How deep is the ocean / Nevertheless / Out of nowhere / You took advantage of me / If I could be with you (one hour tonight) / Come rain or come shine

390592 / 17 Aug '98 / Hallmark

☐ COME DANCE WITH ME

Come dance with me / Something's gotta give / Just in time / Dancing in the dark / Too close for comfort / I could have danced all night / Saturday night is the loneliest night of the week / Day in, day out / Cheek to cheek / Baubles, bangles and beads / Song is you / Last dance

CDP 7484682 / Nov '92 / Capitol

☐ COME FLY WITH ME

Come fly with me / Around the world / Isle of Capri / Moonlight in Vermont / Autumn in New York / On the road to Mandalay / Let's get away from it all / April in Paris / London by night / Brazil / Blue Hawaii / It's nice to go travellin'

CDP 7484692 / Nov '92 / Capitol

☐ COMPLETE CAPITOL SINGLES COLLECTION, THE (4CD Set)

Lean baby / I'm walking behind you / I've got the world on a string / My one and only love / Anytime anywhere / From here to Eternity / I love you / South of the border / Take a chance / Young at heart / Don't worry 'bout me / I could have told you / Rain (falling from the skies) / Three coins in the fountain / Gal that got away / Half as lovely (twice as true) / It worries me / When I stop loving you / White Christmas / Christmas waltz / Someone to watch over me / You, my love / Melody of love / I'm gonna live till I die / Why should I cry over you / Don't change your mind about you / Two hearts two kisses / From the bottom to the top / If I had three wishes / Learnin' the Blues / Not as a stranger / How could you do a thing like that to me / Same old Saturday night / Fairy tale / Love and marriage / Impatient years / (Love is the) tender trap / Weep they will / You'll get yours / Flowers mean forgiveness / (How little it matters) how little we know / Five hundred guys / Johnny Concho theme (wait for me) / You're sensational / Well did you evah / Mind if I make love to you / Who wants to be a millionaire / You forgot all the words (while I still remember the tune) / Hey jealous lover / Your love for me / Can I steal a little love / So long my love / Crazy love / Something wonderful happens in summer / You're cheatin' yourself (if you're cheatin' on me) / All the way / Chicago / Witchcraft / Tell her you love her / Christmas waltz / Mistletoe and holly / Nothing in common / How are you fixed for love / Same old song and dance / Minique / Mr. Success / Sleep warm / No one ever tells you / To love and be loved / Time after time / French Foreign Legion / All my tomorrows / High hopes / They came to Cordura / Talk to me / River, stay 'way from my door / It's over, it's over, it's over / This was my love / Nice 'n' easy / You'll alwways be the one I love / Ol' McDonald / My blue heaven / Sentimental baby / Sentimental journey / American beauty Rose / Moon was yellow / I've heard that song before / Five minutes more / I'll remember April / I love Paris / Hidden Persuassion / Ya better stop / Sea song / Look to your heart / I believe / Love looks so well on you

CDFRANK 53 / Oct '96 / Premier/EMI

☐ COMPLETE COLUMBIA RECORDINGS 1943-1952, THE (4CD Set)

Close to you / People will say we're in love / If you are but a dream / Saturday night (is the loneliest night in the week) / White Christmas / I fall in love too easily / Ol' man river / Stormy weather / Embraceable you / She's funny that way / My melancholy baby / Where or when / All the things you are / I should care / Dream / Put your dreams away / Over the rainbow / If I loved you / Someone to watch over me / You go to my head / These foolish things / House I live in / Nancy / Full moon and empty arms / Oh what it seemed to be / I don't stand a ghost of a chance with you / Why shouldn't I / Try a little tenderness / Begin the beguine / They say it's wonderful / That old black magic / How deep is the ocean (how blue is the sky) / Home on the range / Five minutes more / Things we did last summer / Among my souvenirs / September song / Blue skies / Guess I'll hang my tears out to dry / Lost in the stars / There's no business like show business / Time after time / Brooklyn bridge / Sweet Lorraine / Always / Mam'selle / Stella by starlight / My romance / If I had you / One for my baby (and one more for the road) / But beautiful / You're my girl / All of me / Night and day / S'posin' / Night we called it a day / Song is you / What'll I do / Music stopped / Fools rush in / I've got a crush on you / Body and soul / I'm glad there is you / Autumn in New York / Nature boy / Once in love with Amy / Some enchanted evening / Huckle-buck / Let's take an old fashioned walk / It all depends on you / Bye bye baby / Don't cry Joe (let her go, let her go, let her go) / That lucky old sun (just rolls around heaven all day) / Chattanoogie shoe shine boy / American beauty rose / Should I (reveal) / You do something to me / Lover / When you're smiling (the whole world smiles with you) / London by night / Meet me at the Copa / April in Paris / I guess I'll have to dream the rest / Nevertheless / Am I loved / Hello, young lovers / We kiss in a shadow / I'm s fool to want you / Love me / Deep night / I could write a book / I hear a rhapsody / My girl / Birth of the blues / Azure-te (Paris blues) / Why try to change me now

C4K 64681 / Nov '95 / Columbia

☐ COMPLETE REPRISE STUDIO RECORDINGS, THE (20CD Set)

Leaving on a jet plane / Something / Didn't we / Little green apples / Stormy weather / Bein' green / Love walked in (vocal only) / My way / Mack the knife / Drinking again / I concentrate on you / I've got you under my skin / All of you / At long last love / Ol' man river / Soliloquy from / An old-fashioned christmas / Little drummer boy / We wish you the merriest / Pennies from heaven / Please be kind / Looking at the world thru rose coloured glasses / Moon river / Days of wine and roses / In the wee small hours of the morning / Second time around / Second time around / Witchcraft / All the way / (how little it matters) how little we know / Man in the looking glass / How old am i / Wives and lovers / Good life / Hello dolly / Best is yet to come / More / I believe in you / Nancy / Triste / Someone to light up my life / Drinking water / This happy madness / Wave / I will drink the wine / Sunrise in the morning / My sweet lady / Lady day / You're nobody till somebody loves you / Blue lace / Some travelling music / Out beyond the window / Empty is / Love's been good to me / From promise to promise / Night / I've been to town / Beautiful strangers / Lonesome cities / Single man / Man alone / Man alone / Mrs robinson / If you go away / For once in my life / Watch what happens / All my tomorrows / Gentle on my mind / Pretty colours / Moody river / Cycles / Rain in my heart / By the time I get to Phoenix / Softly as I leave you / That's life / Forget domani / Somewhere in your heart / Something stupid / World we knew (over over) / Born free / Some enchanted evening / Some enchanted evening / This town / This is my song / You are there / How insensitive / If you never come to me / Girl from ipanema / Change partners / Dindi / Meditation / Once I loved (o amor em paz) / All or nothing at all / All or nothing at all / Call me / You're driving me crazy / Downtown / Most beautiful girl in the world / On a clear day (you can see forever) / Yes sir that's my baby / My baby just cares for me / Hello young lovers / Bewitched / After you've gone / Teach me tonight / Younger than springtime / Twin soliloquies (wonder how it feels) / We open in venice / When I'm not near the girl I love / Old devil moon / I've never been in love before / Guys and dolls / Bang bang (my baby shot me down) / That's what god looks like to me / Theme from new york new york / How do you keep the music playing / Love me tender / Song sung blue / Isn't she lovely / Zing went the strings of my heart / Have you met miss jones / It's a wonderful world / I never knew / Please don't talk about me when I'm gone / Don't cry joe-let her go let her go let her go / Falling in love with love / I've got my love to keep me warm / (you'd be so) easy to love / You and the night and the music / When I take my sugar to tea / Coffee song / Be careful it's my heart / Let's fall in love / Once upon a time / Street of dreams / Oldest established (permanent floating crap game i / Love and marriage / Baby just like you / Satisfy me one more time / Let's face the music and dance / Let's face the music and dance / I wanna be around / Wandering / Everybody ought to be in love / Stargazer / Star / Young at heart / Song of the sabia / Macarthur park / But not for me (vocal only) / My shining hour / More than you know / It had to be you / Have yourself a merry little christmas / Goodbye (she quietly says) / Don't be a do badder / Fugue for tinhorns / Sunny / If I had you / I love you / Empty tables / Empty tables / I sing the songs (i write the songs) / Only couple on the floor / I believe I'm gonna love you / Hurt doesn't go away / Bang bang (my baby shot me down) / Finale before the music ends / Only one to a customer / Girls I never kissed / World war none / Something / All the way home / Searching / Love makes us whatever we want to be / They all laughed / Barbara / Future (conclusion) song without words / Future (conclusion) I've been there / Future / Saddest thing of all / You're so right (for what's wrong in my life) / Linda / All or nothing at all (2) / Send in the clowns / Walk away / Let me try again / Game is over / Life's a trippy thing / Feelin' kinda sunday / I'm not afraid / Lady day / For a while / Michael and peter / Elizabeth / What a funny girl (you used to be) / What's now is now / Watertown / She says / In the shadow of the moon / Day in the life of a fool / Desafinado / Bonita / Don't ever go away (por causa de voce) / From both sides now / My way of life / Follow me / I like the sunrise / Yellow days / Don't sleep in the subway / This is my love / Quiet nights of quiet stars (corcovado) / Baubles bangles and beads / You're gonna hear from me / What now my love / Summer wind / Moon was yellow (and the night was young) / Moonlight mood / Moonlight becomes you / Reaching for the moon / Moon got in my eyes / Moon song / Moment to moment / Golden moments / I'll only miss her when I think of her / Ev'rybody has the right to be wrong (at least onc / When somebody loves you / Tell her (you love her each day) / When the wind was green / Any time at all / Pass me by / Available / Since marie has left paree / Then suddenly love / I heard the bells on christmas day / Mister booze / Style / I like to lead when I dance / I can't believe I'm losing you / You never had it so good / Let us break bread together / You're a lucky fellow mr smith / Early american / Talk to me baby / Love isn't just for the young / Some enchanted evening (2) / Oh what it seemed to be / You brought a new kind of love to me / Come blow your horn / Look of love / We'll gather lilacs in the spring / Now is the hour / Roses of picardy / Gypsy / London by night / I'll follow my secret heart / Pick yourself up / I'm beginning to see the light / Boys' night out / Nothing but the best / Everybody's twistin' / Come waltz with me / Are you lonesome tonight / Oh how I miss you tonight / Indiscreet / Together / When I lost you / Charmaine / Song is ended / Name it and it's yours / As you desire me / Moonlight on the ganges / In the blue of evening / Foggy day / Girl next door / Love is just around the corner / Nice work if you can get it / Christmas memories / Christmas waltz / I wouldn't trade christmas / Bells of christmas / Twelve days of christmas / Go tell it on the mountain / Stay with me / One note samba (samba de uma nota so) / Tangerine / Come back to me / I wish you love / Very thought of you / Gal that got away it never entered my mind / It's sunday / Here's to the band / Sweet lorraine / I love my wife / Just as though you were here / Forget to remember / Indian summer / All I need is the girl / Oh you crazy moon / I wished on the moon / Here's to the losers / California / America the beautiful / Me and my shadow / Don'cha go 'way mad / Don't take your love from me / Tina / Last dance / Emily / Emily / My foolish heart / They can't take that away from me / Don't be that way / Remember / Give her love / Winchester cathedral / Somewhere my love (lara's / Sand and sea / I will wait for you / Garden in the rain / (i left my heart) in san francisco / Hundred years from today / It's all right with me / Best of everything / Until the real thing comes along / L a is my lady / Dear heart / If I should lose you / What time does the next miracle leave / You and me (we wanted it all) / Just the way you are / For the good times / Summer me winter me / I had the craziest dream / Song is you / What'll I do / Close to you / To love a child / I loved her / South—to a warmer place / Monday morning quarterback / Long night / Thanks for the memory / Hey look no crying / Serenade in blue / Good thing going / Say hello / Anytime(ill be there) / Train / Goin' out of my head / Poor butterfly / Moon love (adapted from tchaikovsky's 5th symphony / Luck be a lady / All alone / Granada / In the still of the night / One I love (belongs to somebody else) / Polka dots and moonbeams / It's always you / Take me / Without a song / Daybreak / East of the sun (and west of the moon) / There are such things / Imagination / I'm getting sentimental over you / That's all / Prisoner of love / Misty (vocal version) / Night and day / Night and day / I hadn't anyone till you / It started all over again / Come fly with me / Ring-a-ding-ding / Moonlight serenade / Goody goody / Fine romance / Like a sad song / Dry your eyes / Best I ever had / Ain't she sweet / Come rain or come shine / Fly me to the moon / Sweet caroline / So in love / I'll never smile again (until I smile at you) / Stardust / Everything happens to me / Everything happens to me / Yesterday / I can't stop loving you / Hallelujah I love her so / Curse of an aching heart / House I live in / Summer knows / You turned my world around / Tie a yellow ribbon (round the ole oak tre) / You are the sunshine of my life / Bad bad leroy brown / I'm gonna make it all the way / Winners / There used to be a ball park / You will be my music / Dream away / Noah / Nobody wins / Whatever happened to christmas / My kind of town / I would be in love (anyway) / Nancy / It was a very good year / This is all I ask / Last night when we were young / It gets lonely early / Don't wait too long / September of my years / September song / I see it now / Love is a many splendoured thing / It might as well be spring / It might as well be spring / Swinging on a star / Secret love / In the cool cool cool of the evening / Three coins in the fountain / Way you look tonight / Pocketful of miracles / Call me irresponsible / Put your dreams away / This nearly was mine / You'll never walk alone / My heart stood still / I have dreamed / Lost in the stars / Love is the tender trap / I only have eyes for you / My kind of girl / I'm gonna sit right down and write myself a letter / I won't dance / Learnin' the blues / Strangers in the night / What are you doing the rest of your life / I get a kick out of you / Yesterdays / Impossible dream / I'll be seeing you / If / Nightingale sang in berkeley square / We'll meet again / Send in the clowns / Continental (aka the painless dentist song)

9362460132 / Jan '96 / Reprise

☐ CONCERT SINATRA, THE

I have dreamed / My heart stood still / Lost in the stars / Bewitched, bothered and bewildered / This nearly was mine / You'll never walk alone / Ol' man river / Soliloquy

7599270242 / May '98 / Reprise

☐ CYCLES

Rain in my heart / Both sides now / Little green apples / Pretty colours / Cycles / Wandering / By the time I get to Phoenix / Moody river / My way of life / Gentle on my mind

7599270482 / May '98 / Reprise

☐ DANCEHALL DAYS, THE

Fools rush in / Hear my song Violetta / Over the rainbow / How about you / Blue skies / Sunshine of your smile / These foolish things remind me of you / Embraceable you / In blue of the evening / Stardust / Without a song / I haven't time to be a millionaire / Whispering / Nancy / Do I worry / Night we called it a day / Oh look at me now / Polka dots and moonbeams / You'll never walk alone / I'll be seeing you

ECD 3293 / Feb '97 / K-Tel

☐ DANCEHALL YEARS

Fools rush in / Hear my song / Over the rainbow / How about you / Blue skies / Sunshine of your smile / These foolish things / Embraceable you / In the blue of the evening / Stardust / Without a song / I haven't time to be a millionaire / Whispering / Nancy / Do I worry / Night we called it a day / Oh look at me now / Polka dots and moonbeams / You'll never walk alone / I'll be seeing you

SUMCD 4186 / 23 Feb '98 / Summit

☐ DANCING IN THE DARK

Lady is a tramp / I get a kick out of you / I've got you under my skin / Moonlight in Vermont / When your lover has gone / Bewitched / Imagination / At long last love / My funny valentine / My blue heaven / Come fly with me / Dancing in the dark / All the way / You make me feel so young / On the sunny side of the street / Love me or leave me / For you / Where or when / Moon was yellow / Just one of those things / I've got my love to keep me warm / Road to Mandalay / You are love / They didn't believe me / I could have danced all night

CD 6039 / Sep '96 / Music

☐ **DAYS OF WINE AND ROSES (Moon River & Other Academy Award Winners)**
Days of wine and roses / Moon river / Way you look tonight / Three coins in the fountain / In the cool, cool, cool of the evening / Secret love / Swinging on a star / It might as well be Spring / Continental / Love is a many splendoured thing / All the way
7599270262 / May '98 / Reprise

☐ **DUETS**
Exactly like you: *Sinatra, Frank & Nat 'King' Cole* / Medley: *Sinatra, Frank & Bing Crosby* / Some enchanted evening: *Sinatra, Frank & Janet Blair* / Personality: *Sinatra, Frank & Van Johnson* / Tea for two: *Sinatra, Frank & Dinah Shore* / Stephen Foster medley: *Sinatra, Frank & Lawrence Tebbit* / This can't be love: *Sinatra, Frank & Margaret Whiting* / Make believe: *Sinatra, Frank & Jane Powell* / Figaro: *Sinatra, Frank & Carlos Ramirez* / Come out come out wherever you are: *Sinatra, Frank & Eileen Barton* / Parody medley: *Sinatra, Frank & Bing Crosby* / Lover come back to me: *Sinatra, Frank & Dorothy Kirstin* / Birth of the blues: *Sinatra, Frank & Louis Armstrong* / Somebody loves me: *Sinatra, Frank & Pied Pipers* / You'd be so nice to come home to: *Sinatra, Frank & June Hutton* / Yes indeed: *Sinatra, Frank & Sy Oliver* / Don't bring lulu: *Sinatra, Frank & Jack Carson* / There's no business like show business: *Sinatra, Frank & Doris Day/Hit Paraders* / No can do: *Sinatra, Frank & Lena Romany* / Together: *Sinatra, Frank & Eileen Barton/The Vims* / Among my souvenirs: *Sinatra, Frank & Bing Crosby*
CD 6098 / 29 Sep '97 / Music

☐ **DUETS AND RARITIES (2CD Set)**
R2CD 4057 / 9 Mar '98 / Deja Vu

☐ **DUETS VOL.1**
Lady is a tramp: *Sinatra, Frank & Luther Vandross* / What now my love: *Sinatra, Frank & Aretha Franklin* / I've got a crush on you: *Sinatra, Frank & Barbara Streisand* / Summer wind: *Sinatra, Frank & Julio Iglesias* / Come rain or come shine: *Sinatra, Frank & Gloria Estefan* / New York, New York: *Sinatra, Frank & Tony Bennett* / They can't take that away from me: *Sinatra, Frank & Natalie Cole* / You make me feel so young: *Sinatra, Frank & Charles Aznavour* / Guess I'll hang my tears out to dry: *Sinatra, Frank & Carly Simon* / In the wee small hours of the morning: *Sinatra, Frank & Carly Simon* / I've got the world on a string: *Sinatra, Frank & Liza Minnelli* / Witchcraft: *Sinatra, Frank & Anita Baker* / I've got you under my skin: *Sinatra, Frank & Bono* / All the way: *Sinatra, Frank & Kenny G* / One for my baby (and one more for the road): *Sinatra, Frank & Kenny G*
CDEST 2218 / Nov '93 / Capitol

☐ **DUETS VOL.2**
For once in my life: *Sinatra, Frank/Stevie Wonder/Gladys Knight* / Moonlight in Vermont: *Sinatra, Frank & Linda Ronstadt* / Foggy day: *Sinatra, Frank & Willie Nelson* / Come fly with me: *Sinatra, Frank & Luis Miguel* / Fly me to the moon: *Sinatra, Frank & Jobim* / Embraceable you: *Sinatra, Frank & Lena Horne* / House I live in: *Sinatra, Frank & Neil Diamond* / Luck be a lady: *Sinatra, Frank & Chrissie Hynde* / Bewitched, bothered and bewildered: *Sinatra, Frank & Pattie LaBelle* / Best it yet to come: *Sinatra, Frank & Jon Secada* / How do you keep the music playing: *Sinatra, Frank & Lorrie Morgan* / Funny Val: *Sinatra, Frank & Lorrie Morgan* / When or where: *Sinatra, Frank/Steve Lawrence/Edie Gorme* / My kind of town (Chicago is): *Sinatra, Frank & Frank Sinatra Jr.* / Mack the knife: *Sinatra, Frank & Jimmy Buffett* / Christmas song: *Sinatra, Frank & Nat 'King' Cole*
CDEST 2245 / Nov '94 / Capitol

☐ **EARLY YEARS, THE (2CD Set)**
AVC 552 / Jan '96 / Avid

☐ **EARLY YEARS, THE**
Night and day / Hair of gold, eyes of blue / That's my affair / I don't believe in rumours / I've had this feeling before / Trolley song / Surrey with the fringe on top / Candy / Lullaby of Broadway / Blue skies / Just one of those things / I've got my love to keep me warm / On the sunny side of the street / Out of nowhere / Somebody loves me / Love me or leave me
SUMCD 4082 / Nov '96 / Summit

☐ **EVERYTHING HAPPENS TO ME**
9362461162 / May '98 / Reprise

☐ **FIRST DEFINITIVE PERFORMANCES, THE (2CD Set)**
AMSC 566 / Jun '96 / Avid

☐ **FRANCIS A. & EDWARD K. (Sinatra, Frank & Duke Ellington)**
7599270452 / May '98 / Reprise

☐ **FRANCIS ALBERT SINATRA & ANTONIO CARLOS JOBIM (Sinatra, Frank & Antonio Carlos Jobim)**
Girl from Ipanema: *Sinatra, Frank* / Dindi: *Sinatra, Frank* / Change partners: *Sinatra, Frank* / Quiet night of quiet stars: *Sinatra, Frank* / Meditation: *Sinatra, Frank* / If you never come to me: *Sinatra, Frank* / How insensitive: *Sinatra, Frank* / Concentrate on you: *Sinatra, Frank* / Baubles, bangles and beads: *Sinatra, Frank* / Once I loved: *Sinatra, Frank*
7599270412 / May '98 / Reprise

☐ **FRANK AND BING'S CHRISTMAS (Sinatra, Frank & Bing Crosby)**
White Christmas: *Crosby, Bing* / Silver bells / Rudolph the red nose reindeer / O come all ye faithful (adeste fidelis): *Crosby, Bing* / Silent night holy night / Jingle bells / Santa Claus is coming to town / O little town of Bethlehem / Have yourself a merry little christmas / It came upon the midnight clear / Let it snow let it snow let it snow / Christmas song / White christmas: *Sinatra, Frank* / O come all ye faithful (adeste fidelis): *Sinatra, Frank* / Jingle bells / Hark the herald angels sing / I'll be home for Christmas / Christmas waltz / Christmas dreaming
GFS 997 / 20 Oct '97 / Going For A Song

☐ **FRANK SINATRA (2CD Set)**
R2CD 4011 / 13 Apr '98 / Deja Vu

☐ **FRANK SINATRA (3CD Set)**
Blue skies / Somebody loves me / Sweethearts on parade: *Sinatra, Frank & Louis Armstrong* / Be careful that's my heart / Fools rush in / I'll be seeing you / Imagination / It's always you / Everything happens to me / Begin the beguine / Sinner kissed an angel / I think of you / Ol' man river / Stardust / Whispering / Lamplighter's serenade / I've got my love to keep me warm / From the bottom of my heart / Night and day / Personality / Our love affair / On the sunny side of the street / Lover come back to me / There's no business like show business: *Sinatra, Frank & Doris Day* / How about you / Some enchanted evening / Take me / Tea for two: *Sinatra, Frank & Dinah Shore* / Oh look at me now / This is the beginning of the end / This love of mine / Song is you / One I love belongs to somebody else / You make me feel so young / Make believe / Street of dreams / Nancy with the laughing face / Come out come out wherever you are / Exactly like you: *Sinatra, Frank & Nat 'King' Cole* / Don't bring Lulu: *Sinatra, Frank & Jack Carson* / No can do: *Sinatra, Frank & Lena Romany* / Birth of the blues: *Sinatra, Frank & Louis Armstrong* / I saw you first: *Sinatra, Frank & Marcy McGuire* / This can't be love: *Sinatra, Frank & Margaret Whiting* / Yes indeed: *Sinatra, Frank & Sy Oliver* / Figaro: *Sinatra, Frank & Carlos Ramirez* / Together: *Sinatra, Frank & Eileen Barton* / Till we meet again: *Sinatra, Frank & Bing Crosby* / Meet me tonight in Dreamland: *Sinatra, Frank & Bing Crosby* / Thee's a long trail: *Sinatra, Frank & Bing Crosby* / (I don't stand) A ghost of a chance / I fall in love with you everyday / Laura / Love me or leave me / 'S wonderful / You do something to me
KBOX 364 / Nov '96 / Collection

☐ **FRANK SINATRA**
Blue skies / My melancholy baby / Day by day / Fools rush in / Song is you / I fall in love tooeasily / Begin the beguine / Everything happens to me / Night and day / Lamplighter's serenade / Somebody loves me / Time after time / That old feeling / Stardust
GOLD 141 / 18 May '98 / Gold

☐ **FRANK SINATRA AND FRIENDS**
300022 / May '98 / Hallmark

☐ **FRANK SINATRA COLLECTION, THE**
Night and day / Whispering / How about you / Our love affair / Begin the beguine / I've got my love to keep me warm / (I don't stand) A ghost of a chance / Blue skies / Out of nowhere / Somebody loves me / Love me or leave me / Tea for two / Stardust / You made me feel so young / On the sunny side of the street / Come fly with me / Just one of those things / I've got you under my skin / I get a kick out of you / Moonlight in Vermont / My funny valentine / I could have danced all night
PAR 2068 / Nov '96 / Parade

☐ **FRANK SINATRA COLLECTION, THE (A Tribute To A Legend - 4CD Set)**
On the sunny side of the street / Begin the beguine / Don't blame me / It all depends on you / Somebody loves me / 'S wonderful / Love me or leave me / Tenderly / Nevertheless (I'm in love with you) / They didn't believe me / I've got my love to keep me warm / It only happens when I dance with you / My happiness / I wonder who's kissing her now / Hundred years from today / I don't know why / Little white lies / Between the devil and the deep blue sea / Fools rush in / Hear my song, Violetta / Over the rainbow / How about you / Blue skies / Sunshine of your smile / These foolish things (remind me of you) / Embraceable you / In the blue of the evening / Stardust / Without a song / I haven't time to be a millionaire / Whispering / Nancy / Do I worry / Night we called it a day / Oh, look at me now / Polka dots and moonbeams / You'll never walk alone / I'll be seeing you / There are such things / Night and day / This love of mine / Time after time / Too romantic / How do you do without me / Love lies / I think of you / I'll never smile again / Be careful, it's my heart / Last call for love / It's a lovely day for love / Our love affair / I'd know you anywhere / Love me as I am / I'll never let a day pass by / Violets for your furs / You're breaking my heart all over again / Say it / I could make you care / This is the beginning of the end / You lucky people, you / Sweet Lorraine / Lamplighter's serenade / Free for all / Poor you / Dolores / Call of the canyon / Not so long ago / Light a candle in the chapel / Imagination / April played the fiddle / Song is you / Dig down deep / Fable of the rose / Who / We three / Daybreak / East of the sun (and west of the moon) / One I love belongs to someone else / Somewhere a voice is calling / Looking for yesterday
ECD 3330 / Mar '97 / K-Tel

☐ **FRANK SINATRA COLLECTOR'S EDITION**
DVX 08032 / Apr '95 / Deja Vu

☐ **FRANK SINATRA GOLD (2CD Set)**
D2CD 4011 / Jun '95 / Deja Vu

☐ **FRANK SINATRA SINGS FOR ONLY THE LONELY**
Only the lonely / Angel eyes / What's new / It's a lonesome old town / Willow weep for me / Goodbye / Blues in the night / Guess I'll hang my tears out to dry / Ebb tide / Spring is here / Gone with the wind / One for my baby (and one more for the road) / Sleep warm / Where or when
CDP 7484712 / Feb '88 / Capitol

☐ **FRANK SINATRA SINGS HIS GREATEST HITS**
All of me / I could write a book / I've got a crush on you / Night and day / Saturday night (is the loneliest night in the week) / Brooklyn Bridge / Nancy / House I live in / Birth of the blues / Body and soul / April in Paris / I'm glad there is you / Sweet Lorraine / Time after time / Laura / Song is you / I'm a fool to want you / Put your dreams away
4875062 / Jun '97 / Columbia

☐ **FRANK SINATRA SINGS RODGERS & HAMMERSTEIN**
Oh what a beautiful mornin' / People will say we're in love / Surrey with the fringe on top / If I loved you / You'll never walk alone / Soliloquy / It might as well be Spring / That's for me / A fellow needs a girl / So far / Younger than Springtime / Some enchanted evening / Bali ha i / Hello young lovers / We kiss in a shadow / I whistle a happy tune
4814262 / Aug '96 / Columbia

☐ **FRANK SINATRA SINGS THE GREATS VOL.1, THE**
Just one of those things / 'S Wonderful / On the sunny side of the street / Ol' man river / Somebody loves me / Music stopped
BSTCD 9102 / May '92 / Best Compact Discs

☐ **FRANK SINATRA SINGS THE GREATS VOL.2, THE**
Swinging on a star / Lover come back to me / Girl that I marry / Come fly with me / I get a kick out of you / I've got you under my skin / Moonlight in Vermont / April in Paris / She's funny that way / Lady is a tramp / You make me feel so young / All the way / I could have danced all night / Just one of those things / Willow weep for me / Dancing in the dark / At long last love / All of me
BSTCD 9112 / Apr '94 / Best Compact Discs

☐ **FRANK SINATRA SINGS THE SELECT COLE PORTER**
I've got you under my skin / I concentrate on you / What is this thing called love / You do something to me / At long last love / Anything goes / Night and day / Just one of those things / I get a kick out of you / You'd be so nice to come home to / I love Paris / From this moment on / C'est magnifique / It's all right with me / Mind if I make love to you / You're sensational
CDP 7966112 / Aug '91 / Capitol

☐ **FRANK SINATRA SINGS THE SELECT JOHNNY MERCER**
Too marvellous for words / Day in, day out / Laura / Jeepers creepers / Blues in the night / Something's gotta give / Fools rush in / PS I love you / When the world was young / That old black magic / Autumn leaves / I thought about you / Dream / One for my baby (and one more for the road)
CDP 7803262 / Apr '95 / Capitol

☐ **FRANK SINATRA SINGS THE SELECT RODGERS & HART**
Lover / Glad to be unhappy / I din't know what time it was / Where or when / It's easy to remember / There's a small hotel / Wait till you see her / Little girl blue / My funny valentine / It never entered my mind / Blue moon / I could write a book / Dancing on the ceiling / Lady is a tramp / Spring is here / I wish I was in love again / Bewitched, bothered and bewildered
CDP 7803232 / Apr '95 / Capitol

☐ **FRANK SINATRA SINGS THE SELECT SAMMY CAHN**
Come fly with me / Time after time / (Love is) the tender trap / Guess I'll hang my tears out to dry / Love and marriage / Saturday night (is the loneliest night in the week) / All the way / I've heard that song before / All my tomorrows / It's the same old dream / Come dance with me / Three coins in the fountain / Day by day / To love and be loved / High hopes / It's the last thing I do / Five minutes more / Last dance
PRMCD 14 / Oct '96 / Premier/EMI

☐ **FRANK SINATRA STORY, THE (40 Swing & Ballad Classics 1939-1953/ 2CD Set)**
From the bottom of my heart / On a little street in Singapore / East of the sun / I'll never smile again / It started all over again / You'll never know / I couldn't sleep a wink last night / If you are but a dream / Saturday night (is the loneliest night in the week) / There's no you / White Christmas / I dream of you (more than you dream I do) / I fall in love too easily / Ol' man river / Embraceable you / All or nothing at all / Just as though you were here / Close to you / Shine / Our love / When your lover has gone / She's funny that way / My melancholy baby / All the things you are / I should care / Dream / Over the rainbow / If I loved you / Jesus is a rock / My shawl / Someone to watch over me / You go to my head / These foolish things / I don't know why / Nancy / Long ago and far away / Guess I'll hang my tears out to dry / Yes indeed / Tenderly / This can't be love
7210227 / May '98 / Carlton

☐ **FRANK SINATRA, DEAN MARTIN & SAMMY DAVIS JR. VOL.1 (Sinatra, Frank & Dean Martin/Sammy Davis Jr.)**
JH 1033 / Oct '93 / Jazz Hour

☐ **FRANK SINATRA, DEAN MARTIN & SAMMY DAVIS JR. VOL.2 (Sinatra, Frank & Dean Martin/Sammy Davis Jr.)**
JH 1034 / Oct '93 / Jazz Hour

☐ **GOLD COLLECTION, THE**
D2CD 11 / Dec '92 / Deja Vu

☐ **GOLDEN DAYS OF RADIO**
Begin the beguine / Out of nowhere / It only happens when I dance with you / Love me or leave me / I'm in the mood for love / I've got my love to keep me warm / Little white lies / Don't blame me / Lady from 29 palms / It all depends on you / Hair of gold, eyes of blue / 's'wonderful / Nevertheless / Hundred years from today / I don't know why / I wonder who's kissing her now / Between the devil and the deep blue sea / They didn't believe me / My happiness / Tenderly / I'll string along with you / What can I say I'm sorry / On the sunny side of the street / Somebody loves me
PWKS 4225 / Jun '98 / Carlton

☐ **GOT THE WORLD ON A STRING**
I've got the world on a string / Them there eyes / If I could be with you one hour tonight / Under a blanket of blue / Just you just me / Let's fall in love / Hands across the table / You must have been a beautiful baby / Someone to watch over me / I'll string along with you / Thou swell / You took advantage of me / Where or when / This can't be love / Try a little tenderness / Platinum blues / I'm confessin' that I love you / Sometimes I'm happy / My funny valentine / That old black magic
CDSB 007 / 1 Jun '98 / Starburst

☐ **GREAT SONGS FROM GREAT BRITAIN**
9362452192 / May '98 / Reprise

☐ **GREAT STANDARDS**
Nancy / Someone to watch over me / You go to my head / Homesick that's all / September song / These foolish things / Things we did last summer / Kiss me again / Among my souvenirs / I dream of you / How deep is the ocean / That old black magic / Somewhere in the night / If you are but a dream / Charm of you / I fall in love with you ev'ry day / There but for you go I / Begin the beguine / I fall in love too easily / Girl that I marry / What makes the sunset / Paradise / Almost like being in love / You are too beautiful
RAJCD 894 / 9 Mar '98 / Empress

☐ **GREATEST HITS (The Early Years)**
If you are but a dream / Nancy / Girl that I marry / House I live in / Saturday night (is the loneliest night in the week) / Five minutes more / I have but one heart (O Marenariello) / Time after time / People will say we're in love
4625612 / Dec '95 / Columbia

☐ **GREATEST HITS 1940-1947 (2CD Set)**
CPCD 83212 / 30 Mar '98 / Charly

☐ **GREATEST HITS VOL.1**
7599272362 / May '98 / Reprise

☐ **GREATEST HITS VOL.2**
Shadow of your smile / Yesterday / Blue lace / For once in my life / Born free / My way / Little green apples / Both sides now / Mrs. Robinson / Call me irresponsible / Gentle on my mind / Love's been good to me
7599272372 / May '98 / Reprise

☐ **GUYS AND DOLLS (Reprise Musical Repertory Theatre)**
9362450142 / May '98 / Reprise

☐ **HELLO YOUNG LOVERS**
Netherless / What can I say after I say I'm sorry / Hello, young lovers / Love me or leave me / You toook advantage of me / Let's fall in love / Them there eyes / Somebody loves me / On the sunny side of the street / 'S Wonderful / Under a blanket of blue / I don't know why / Thou swell / I'm confessin' that I love you / Out of nowhere / Hundred years from today / Between the devil and the deep blue sea / What is this thing called love / Night and day / Just you, just me
MUCD 9025 / Apr '95 / Musketeer

☐ **HIS WAY (2CD Set)**
AOP 67 / 6 Jul '98 / Dressed To Kill

☐ **HIT PARADE SHOWS MAY 1949**
JH 1036 / Aug '94 / Jazz Hour

☐ **I REMEMBER TOMMY**
9362452672 / May '98 / Reprise

☐ **I'LL BE SEEING YOU (Sinatra, Frank & Tommy Dorsey)**
I'll be seeing you / Fools rush in / It's a lovely day today / Tomorrow / World is in my arms / We three (my echo, my shadow and me) / Dolores / Everything happens to me / Let's get away from it all / Blue skies / There are such things / Daybreak / You're part of my heart
07863664272 / Oct '94 / Bluebird

☐ **I'M IN THE MOOD FOR LOVE**
's wonderful / I've got my love to keep me warm / I'm in the mood for love / Begin the beguine / Somebody loves me / Tenderly / I don't know why / I'll string along with you / On the sunny side of the street / They didn't believe me / Lady from the 29 palms / Hair of gold eyes of blue / It only happens when I dance with you / Nevertheless I'm in love with you / Between the devil and the deep blue sea / My happiness
300142 / Jul '96 / Hallmark

☐ **IN CELEBRATION**
EXC 101 / Nov '95 / Exclusive

☐ **IN CELEBRATION**
Night and day / What makes the sunset / In the middle of May / Re-enactment of a scene from 'Anchors Aweigh' / I fall in love too easily / I begged her: *Sinatra, Frank & Gene Kelly* / Charm of you / Put your dreams away / Lulu's back in town / You brought a new kind of love to me: *Sinatra, Frank & Peggy Lee* / You keep coming back like a song / Body and soul / This is always / Over the rainbow / All of me / Tenderly / What is this thing called love / Dancing in the dark / If I could be with you one hour tonight / That old black magic
CD 6108 / Oct '97 / Music

☐ **IN THE WEE SMALL HOURS**
In the wee small hours of the morning / Glad to be unhappy / I get along without you very well / Deep in a dream / I see your face before me / Can't we be friends / When your lover has gone / What is this thing called love / I'll be around / Ill wind / It never entered my mind / I'll never be the same / This love of mine / Last night when we were young / Dancing on the ceiling
CDP 7968262 / Nov '92 / Capitol

☐ **INIMITABLE FRANK SINATRA, THE (18 Hit Songs)**
Come fly with me / Dancing in the dark / All the way / You make me feel so young / Love me or leave me / On the sunny side of the street / Blue skies / Begin the beguine / I didn't stand a ghost of a chance / Night and day / Somebody loves me / Just one of those things / You are my love / They didn't believe me / Out of nowhere / I've got my love to keep me warm / For you / Road to Mandalay
PLATCD 157 / Mar '96 / Platinum

☐ **INSTRUMENTAL MEMORIES (Various Artists)**
Lady is a tramp / You make me feel so young / Something stupid / One for my baby / That old black magic / All the way / Come fly with me / My way / Chicago / Strangers in the night / Witchcraft / Nancy / Tender trap / I've got you under my skin / I get a kick

out of you / New York, New York / Nutbush city limits: *Turner, Tina* / Steamy windows: *Turner, Tina* / Missing you: *Turner, Tina* / What's love got to do with it: *Turner, Tina* / Disco inferno: *Turner, Tina* / Golden eye: *Turner, Tina*
306942 / Jun '97 / Hallmark

☐ **IT MIGHT AS WELL BE SPRING (Sinatra, Frank & Count Basie)**
7599010122 / May '98 / Reprise

☐ **JAZZ AND BLUES (36 Outstanding Jazz Tracks/2CD Set)**
Blue skies / Somebody loves me / Sweethearts on parade / Be careful it's my heart / Fools rush in / I'll be seeing you / Imagination / It's always you / Everything happens to me / Begin the beguine / A sinner kissed an angel / I think of you / Ol' man river / Stardust / Whispering / Lamplighter's serenade / I've got my love to keep me warm / From the bottom of my heart / Night and day / Personality / Our love affair / On the sunny side of the street / Lover come back to me / There's no business like show business / How about you / Some enchanted evening / Take me / Tea for two / Oh look at me / This is the beginning of the end / This love of mine / Song is you / One I love belongs to somebody else / You make me feel so young / Make believe / Street of dreams
BN 212 / Aug '98 / Blue Nite

☐ **JAZZ GREATS (Sinatra, Frank & Tommy Dorsey)**
Night and day / Imagination / I'll never smile again / Blue skies / One I love / Fools rush in / Stardust / In the blue of the evening / Polka dots and moonbeams / Without a song / This love of mine / I think of you / Once in a while / How am I to know / Sky fell down
74321499632 / 6 Oct '97 / RCA Victor

☐ **KID FROM HOBOKEN, THE (4CD Set)**
CDDIG 6 / Feb '95 / Charly

☐ **LA IS MY LADY**
LA is my lady / Best of everything / How do you keep the music playing / Teach me tonight / It's all right with me / Mack the knife / Until the real thing comes along / Stormy weather / If I should lose you / Hundred years from today / After you've gone
7599251452 / May '98 / Reprise

☐ **LET'S BE FRANK (A Tribute To Frank Sinatra) (Various Artists)**
HIPD 40112 / 30 Jun '98 / Hippo

☐ **LIGHT UP TIME SHOWS 1949, THE**
EBCD 21162 / Feb '94 / Flyright

☐ **LIVE (Seattle 9/6/1957)**
JH 3001 / Jun '95 / Jazz Hour

☐ **LIVE DUETS 1943-1957**
VCD 1101 / Jun '94 / Voice

☐ **LIVE IN AUSTRALIA (Sinatra, Frank & Red Norvo)**
Perdido / Between the devil and the deep blue sea / I could have danced all night / Just one of those things / I get a kick out of you / At long last love / Willow weep for me / I've got you under my skin / Moonlight in Vermont / Lady is a tramp / Brief monologue from Frank / Angel eyes / Come fly with me / All the way / Dancing in the dark / One for my baby / All of me / On the road to Mandalay / Night and day
CDP 8375132 / Mar '97 / Blue Note

☐ **LIVE IN CONCERT**
You are the sunshine of my life / What now my love / My heart stood still / What's new / For once in my life / If / In the still of the night / Soliloquy / Maybe this time / Where or when / You will be my music / Strangers in the night / Angel eyes / New York, New York / My way
CDEST 2272 / Dec '95 / Premier/EMI

☐ **LOVE SONGS (Sinatra, Frank & Tommy Dorsey)**
I'll never smile again / Stardust / Dolores / Everything happens to me / This love of mine / I'll guess I'll have to dream the rest / Violets for your furs / There are such things / Daybreak / It started all over again / Only forever / Just as though you were here / Night we called it a day / Lamplighter's serenade / Song is you / Night and day
09026687012 / Mar '97 / RCA Victor

☐ **LOVELY WAY TO SPEND AN EVENING, A**
Lovely way to spend an evening / You'll never know / People say we're in love / Oh what a beautiful morning / I couldn't sleep a wink last night / I fall in love too easily / Stormy weather / When your lover has gone / She's funny that way / You'll never walk alone / Someone to watch over me / You go to my head / These foolish things / Day by day / Nancy with the laughing face / You are too beautiful / Full moon and empty arms / Try a little tenderness / Girl that I marry / Things we did last summer / Among my souvenirs / Stormy weather / Song
CDAJA 5249 / Nov '97 / Living Era

☐ **MAIN EVENT, THE (Frank Sinatra Live)**
Overture / It was a very good year / All the way / My kind of town (Chicago is) / Lady is a tramp / I get a kick out of you / Let me try again / Autumn in New York / I've got you under my skin / Bad, Bad Leroy Brown / Angel eyes / You are the sunshine of my life / House I live in / My way
7599272192 / May '98 / Reprise

☐ **MAN ALONE, A**
Man alone / Night / I've been to town / From promise to promise / Single man / Beautiful strangers / Lonesome cities / Love's been good to me / Empty is / Out beyond the window / Some travelling music
7599270502 / May '98 / Reprise

☐ **MAN AND HIS MUSIC, A (2CD Set)**
7599270322 / May '98 / Reprise

☐ **MASTERS OF JAZZ (2CD Set)**
R2CD 8009 / 13 Apr '98 / Deja Vu

☐ **MASTERS, THE**
EABCD 048 / 24 Nov '97 / Eagle

☐ **MASTERS, THE**
EABCD 096 / 30 Mar '98 / Eagle

☐ **MEMORIAL ALBUM, THE**
UAE 34062 / 29 Jun '98 / Members Edition

☐ **MOONLIGHT SINATRA**
7599270362 / May '98 / Reprise

☐ **MUSIC FROM HIS MOVIES**
GO 3805 / 1 Dec '97 / Golden Options

☐ **MY KIND OF BROADWAY**
7599270312 / May '98 / Reprise

☐ **MY WAY**
Watch what happens / Hallelujah, I love her so / Yesterday all my tomorrows / My Way / For once in my life / If you go away / Mrs. Robinson / Didn't we / Day in the life of a fool
7599270492 / May '98 / Reprise

☐ **MY WAY (The Best Of Frank Sinatra)**
My way / Strangers in the night / New York New York / I get a kick out of you / Somethin' stupid / Moon river / What now my love / Summer wind / For once in my life / Love and marriage / They can't take that away from me / My kind of town / Fly me to the moon / I've got you under my skin / Best is yet to come / It was a very good year / Come fly with me / That's life / Girl from Ipanema / Lady is a tramp / Bad bad Leroy Brown / Mack The Knife / Love's been good to me / LA is my lady
9362467102 / May '98 / Reprise

☐ **MY WAY (The Best Of Frank Sinatra/2CD Set)**
My way / Strangers in the night / New York New York / I get a kick out of you / Somethin' stupid / Moon river / What now my love / Summer wind / For once in my life / Love and marriage / They can't take that away from me / My kind of town / Fly me to the moon / I've got you under my skin / Best is yet to come / It was a very good year / Come fly with me / That's life / Girl from Ipanema / Lady is a tramp / Bad bad Leroy Brown / Mack The Knife / Love's been good to me / LA is my lady / Let's face the music and dance / Come rain or come shine / Night and day / Very thought of you / Pennies from Heaven / Bewitched / America the beautiful / All the way / In the wee small hours of the morning / Way you look tonight / Three coins in the fountain / Softly as I leave you / All or nothing at all / Yesterday / Moonlight serenade / Somewhere my love / Mrs. Robinson / Something / You are the sunshine of my life / Send in the clowns / It had to be you / Best of you
9362467122 / May '98 / Reprise

☐ **NEW YORK NEW YORK (His Greatest Hits)**
I get a kick out of you / Something stupid / Moon river / What now my love / Summer wind / Mrs. Robinson / My way / Strangers in the night / For once in my life / Yesterday / That's life / Girl from Ipanema / Lady is a tramp / Bad, Bad Leroy Brown / Ol' man river
9362467442 / 8 Dec '97 / Reprise

☐ **NIGHT AND DAY**
Blue skies / I don't stand a ghost of a chance (with you) / Music stopped / You make me feel so young / Just one of those things / You do something to me / Begin the beguine / Ol' man river / For you / Night and day / Nevertheless / Out of nowhere / You are love / I've got my love to keep me warm / On the sunny side of the street / One hundred years from today / I wonder who's kissing her now / I'm in the mood for love / Don't blame me / They didn't believe me (foxtrot) / Tenderly / Love me or leave me / Somebody loves me / I'll string along with you / 's wonderful
RMB 75020 / Nov '93 / Remember

☐ **NIGHT AND DAY (20 Classics)**
CWNCD 2017 / Jul '96 / Javelin

☐ **NIGHT AND DAY**
LOK 01CD / Jan '94 / Night & Day

☐ **OH LOOK AT ME NOW (20 Classic Tracks)**
Oh look at me now / Night we called it a day / East of the sun (and west of the moon) / Sunshine of your smile / Without a song / Violets for your furs / I'll be seeing you / How about you / You lucky people you / Nancy / One I love belongs to somebody else / This love of mine / Polka dots and moonbeams / Blue skies / Fools rush in / I'll never smile again / Light a candle in the chapel / Imagination / In the blue of the evening / I think of you
302772 / Feb '98 / Hallmark

☐ **OL' BLUE EYES**
Come fly with me / I get a kick out of you / All the way / You make me feel so young / Love me or leave me / On the sunny side of the street / Stardust / Begin the beguine / Lady is a tramp / Night and day / Somebody loves me / Just one of those things / You are love / They didn't believe me / Moonlight in Vermont / I've got my love to keep me warm / My funny valentine / I've got you under my skin
SUMCD 4163 / 26 Jan '98 / Summit

☐ **OL' BLUE EYES IS BACK**
You will be my music / Winners theme / Nobody wins / Send in the clowns / Dream away / Let me try again / There used to be a ball park / Noah / You're so right (for what's wrong in my life)
7599021552 / May '98 / Reprise

☐ **OLD GOLD SHOWS 1946**
JH 1040 / Feb '95 / Jazz Hour

☐ **OLD GOLD SHOWS VOL.1, THE (2CD Set)**
Introduction / Stars in your eyes / Talk / There's no you / Old Gold commercial / Gotta be this or that: *Pied Pipers* / If I loved you / Talk with music / Embraceable you: *Sinatra, Frank & The Crosby Kids* / Old Gold commercial #2 / Closing / On the atchison, Topeka and the Snata Fe / I'll buy that dream: *Pied Pipers* / Skit: *Pied Pipers* / Old commercial: *Pied Pipers* / My melancholy baby / You was right: *Lee, Peggy* / Surrey with fringe on top: *Pied Pipers* / I fall in love too easily / Old gold commercial / Talk / House I live in / You'll never know / As time goes by / Are you glad you're you / It might as welll be you / In the middle of May / Button up your overcoat / Day by day / Lily Belle / Ol' man river / There's no you / Paris aye, aye / It's been a long long time / It's only a paper moon / All the things you are / Skit with music / Two hearts are better than one / Let it snow let it snow let it snow
OTA 101976 / Jun '97 / BR Music

☐ **OLD GOLD SHOWS VOL.2, THE (2CD Set)**
That's for me / Kiss goodnight: *Sinatra, Frank & Patty Andrews* / Old gold commercial: *Sinatra, Frank & Patty Andrews* / We'll be together again: *Sinatra, Frank & Patty Andrews* / How deep is the ocean: *Sinatra, Frank & Patty Andrews* / Begin the beguin: *Andrews Sisters* / At the paramount: *Andrews Sisters* / Old gold commercial: *Andrews Sisters* / Tampico: *Pied Pipers* / Without a song: *Pied Pipers* / I'll never smile again: *Sinatra, Frank & Tommy Dorsey/Pied Pipers* / I begged her / I fall in love with you every day / Great day / Good king Wenceslas/ Wassail song / Embraceable you: *Pied Pipers* / Symphony / Father time / Lullaby / Let's start the new year right: *Sinatra, Frank & Bob Mitchell Boys Choir* / You'll never walk alone / America the beautiful / But I did: *Maxwell, Marilyn* / Stranger in town: *Pied Pipers* / Till the end of time: *Pied Pipers* / Felicia no capricia: *Prima, Louis* / Some Sunday morning: *Prima, Louis* / House I live in / You keep coming back like a song / This is always
OTA 101977 / Jun '97 / On The Air

☐ **OLD GOLD SHOWS VOL.3, THE (2CD Set)**
Chickery chick / Dearest darling / I can't love you more than I do: *Pied Pipers* / It's been a long, long time: *Sinatra, Frank & Pied Pipers* / Waiting for the train to come: *Lee, Peggy* / You bought a new kind of love to me: *Sinatra, Frank & Peggy Lee* / Over the rainbow / Some Sunday morning / What a deal: *Pied Pipers* / Shamrock song / (Get your kicks on) Route 66: *Cole, Nat 'King' Trio* / Exactly like you: *Sinatra, Frank & Nat 'King' Cole* / House I live in / Just one of those things / My ideal / One more dream / I only have eyes for you: *Sinatra, Frank & Benny Goodman Sextet* / Waitin' for the train to come: *Pied Pipers* / It might as well be Spring / Runnin' wild: *Goodman, Benny Sextet* / Home on the range / Sweet Lorraine / All through the day / Should I: *Pied Pipers* / Day by day / My heart tells me / That old black magic
OTA 101979 / Nov '97 / On The Air

☐ **ON THE AIR 1935-1955**
RTD 3970029CD / 1 Dec '97 / Institute Of Art

☐ **ONE AND ONLY, THE (3CD Set)**
All or nothing at all / On a little street in Singapore / Melancholy mood / Imagination / I'll never smile again / East of the sun (and west of the moon) / Stardust / Oh look at me now / Dolores / Everything happens to me / This love of mine / How about you / Just as though you were here / Street of dreams / Be careful It's my heart / In the blue of the evening / There are such things / Daybreak / It started all over again / Fools rush in (where angels fear to tread) / Oh what it seemed to be / You'll never know / I couldn't sleep a wink last night / White christmas / Saturday night is the loneliest night of the week / I dream of you (more than I dream I do) / I fall in love too easily / Nancy (with the laughing face) / Dream / I should care / If I loved you / You'll never walk alone / Time after time / Day by day / They say it's wonderful / Five minutes more / Things we did last summer / Stella by starlight / Mam'selle / Put your dreams away / Song is you / I fall in love with you everyday / I only have eyes for you / You keep coming back like a song / Over the rainbow / Long ago (and far away) / Amor / Oh what a beautiful mornin' / Guess I'll hang my tears out to dry / Some other time / It's been a long long time / My ideal / Just one of those things / The house I live in (that's America to me) / This is always / Taking a chance on love / You took advantage of me / Nevertheless (I'm in love with you) / Hello young lovers / What is this thing called love / Don't blame me / Just you just me
PBXCD 318 / 3 Aug '98 / Pulse

☐ **OUR LOVE AFFAIR (20 Swinging Standards)**
304232 / May '98 / Hallmark

☐ **PLATINUM COLLECTION, THE (2CD Set)**
You make me feel so strong / On the sunny side of the street / For you / They didn't believe me / Just one of those things / (Ididn't stand) a ghost of a chance / Out of nowhere / Love me or leave me / I think of you / Lamplighter's serenade / Street of dreams / This is the beginning of the end / Be careful it's my heart / Sinner kissed an angel / How about you / Our love affair / Laura / Tenderly / Nevertheless / You are love / Ol' nman river / Music stopped / You d / You do something to me / They say it's wonderful / Under a blanket of blue / How deep is the ocean / What can I say after I say I'm sorry / Hello young lovers / You took advantage of me / Let's fall in love / Them there eyes / S'wonderful / I don't know why / I'm confessin' / One hundred years from today / Between the devil and the deep blue sea / What is this thing called love / Night and day / Just you just me
PC 601 / 10 Nov '97 / Platinum Collection

☐ **PLATINUM COLLECTION, THE (2CD Set)**
Somebody loves me / On the sunny side of the street / Begin the beguine / I've got my love to keep me warm / Blue skies / (I didn't stand) A ghost of a chance / Out of nowhere / Love me or leave me / I think of you / Lamplighter's serenade / Street of dreams / This is the beginning of the end / Be careful it's my heart / Sinner kissed an angel / How about you / Our love affair / Whispering / Tenderly / Nevertheless / Tea for two / Ol' man river / This love of mine / Stardust / They say it's wonderful / How deep is the ocean / What can I say after I say I'm sorry / Hello young lovers / You took advantage of me / Let's fall in love / Them there eyes / S'wonderful / Under a blanket of blue / I don't know why / Thou swell / I'm confessin' / One hundred years from today / Between the devil and the deep blue sea / What is this thing called love / Night and day
PC 627 / 3 Aug '98 / Start

☐ **POINT OF NO RETURN, THE**
When the world was young / I'll remember April / September song / Million dreams ago / I'll see you again / There will never be another you / Somewhere along the way / It's a blue world / These foolish things / As time goes by / I'll be seeing you / Memories of you
CDP 7483342 / Nov '92 / Capitol

☐ **PORTRAIT OF FRANK SINATRA, A**
GALE 411 / May '97 / Gallerie

☐ **PORTRAIT OF SINATRA, A (2CD Set)**
All or nothing at all / If you are but a dream / Night and day / Sweet Lorraine / Guess I'll hang my tears out to dry / Nancy / House I live in / Blue skies / There's no you / When your lover has gone / Stormy weather / Nearness of you / These foolish things / Saturday night (is the loneliest night in the week) / Where or when / Someone to watch over me / Put your dreams away / All of me / There's no business like show business / Falling in love with love / You go to my head / Everybody loves somebody / I believe / Why was I born / I've got a crush on you / Body and soul / That old feeling / Almost like being in love / September song / It never entered my mind / I only have eyes for you / Song is you / Don't cry Joe / It all depends on you / Continental / I'm a fool to want you
4874972 / Jul '97 / Columbia

☐ **RADIO YEARS 1939-1955, THE (6CD Set)**
All or nothing / After all / I've got my eyes on you / Polka dots and moonbeams / Deep night / Whispering / Sky fell down / On the isle of May / It's a blue world / Fable of the rose / Marie / I'll get by / Lover is blue / Careless / I'll never smile again / Our love affair / East of the sun and west of the moon / One I love / Shadow on the sand / That's how it goes / I get a kick out of you / Let's get lost / Embraceable you / Night and day / Close to you / I couldn't sleep a wink last night / Falling in love with you / Music stopped / My ideal / Speak low / People will say we're in love / Long ago and far away / Sweet Lorraine / Swinging on a star / These foolish things / Very thought of you / All the things you are / My melancholy baby / Homesick / That's all / Till the end of time / What makes the sunset / I fall in love too easily / I begged her / Don't forget tonight tomorrow / That's for me / I found a new baby / I'm always chasing rainbows / Aren't you glad you're you / It might as well be spring / Lily belle / If I loved you / Slowly / Great day / I only have eyes for you / Oh what it seemed to be / Full moon and empty arms / Exactly like you / Summertime/It ain't neccessarily so / Bess, oh where's my bess / I fall in love with you every day / It's a good day / My sugar is so refined / Ole buttermilk sky / Lullaby of broadway / I won't dance
CDMT 901 / Aug '95 / Meteor

☐ **REMEMBERS THE MOVIES**
Three little words / Where or when / That old black magic / If I had my way / My ideal / Till the end of time / Make believe / I only have eyes for you / Somebody loves me / Empty saddles / That's for me / It's been a long long time / White Christmas / You'll never know / As time goes by / Easy to love/I've got you under my skin / On the Atchinson topeka and santa fe / People will say we're in love / Don't fence me in / With a song in my heart / Hot time in the town of Berlin / I'll remember April / There goes that song again
CD 60016 / Sep '97 / Great Movie Themes

☐ **REPRISE COLLECTION, THE (4CD Set)**
Something / Send in the clowns / I get a kick out of you / Nightingale sang in berkeley square / Drinking again / My way / What are you doing the rest of your life / Please be kind / Soliloquy from / Pennies from heaven / Summer wind / All or nothing at all / It was a very good year / This is all I ask / September song / Best is yet to come / Way you look tonight / Second time around / Moonlight serenade / Come rain or come shine / Fly me to the moon / Lady is a tramp / There used to be a ball park / My kind of town / Nancy / Wave / You're nobody till somebody loves you / Shadow of your smile / Man alone / That's life / Something stupid / How insensitive / Dindi / Once I loved (o amor em paz) / Zing went the strings of my heart / (you'd be so) easy to love / Coffee song / Let's fall in love / Street of dreams / Love and marriage / You make me feel so young / My shining hour / Oh you crazy moon / I wished on the moon / Here's to the losers / California / America the beautiful / Me and my shadow / Don'cha go 'way mad / Don't take your love from me / Gal that got away it never entered my mind / It's sunday / Here's to the band / Sweet lorraine / I love my wife / Just as though you were here / Forget to remember / Indian summer / All I need is the girl / Tina / Last dance / Emily / Garden in the rain / Song is you / What'll I do / Long night / Theme from new york new york / More than you know / Empty tables / I only miss her when I think of her / Luck be a lady / All alone / Without a song / Night and day / It started all over again / I have dreamed / Strangers in the night / Love walked in (vocal only) / Mack the knife / I concentrate on you / I've got you under my skin
7599263402 / May '98 / Reprise

☐ **REPRISE YEARS, THE**
All the way / Come rain or come shine / I get a kick out of you / Night and day / All or nothing at all / I've got you under my skin / Didn't we / Strangers in the night / It was a very good year / Call me irresponsible / One for my baby (and one more for the road) / My kind of town (Chicago is) / September of my years / Luck be a lady / Something stupid / New York, New York / My way
7599265222 / Dec '93 / Reprise

☐ **RING A DING DING**
7599270172 / May '98 / Reprise

☐ **ROMANTIC FRANK SINATRA, THE (2CD Set)**
From the bottom of my heart / Melancholy mood / My buddy / Here comes the night / All or nothing at all / Ciribiribin / Night we called it a day / Lamplighter's serenade / Song is you / Night and day / You'll never know / Close to you / Sunday, Monday or always / People will say we're in love / Oh what a beautiful

morning / I couldn't sleep a wink last night / Lovely way to spend an evening / If you are but a dream / There's no you / I dream of you / What makes the sunset / I fall in love to easily / Saturday night (is the loneliest night in the week) / Charm of you / Ol' man River / Stormy weather / When your lover has gone / Embraceable you / Kiss me again / She's funny that way / Mighty lak' a rose / Cradle song / Friend of yours / Dream / Homesick, that's all / I should care / If I loved you / You'll never walk alone / Stars in your eyes / My shawl / House I live in / America the beautiful / Nancy / Put your dreams away
CPCD 82582 / Jan '97 / Charly

☐ **RRSO PLAYS FRANK SINATRA, THE (RRSO)**
EMPRCD 803 / 18 May '98 / Emporio

☐ **SALUTE TO SINATRA, A (Various Artists)**
I'll never smile again: *Aldrich, Ronnie & His Piano/The Festival Orchestra* / Night and day: *Chacksfield, Frank & His Orchestra* / All or nothing at all: *James, Harry Orchestra* / Lovely way to spend an evening: *Mantovani & His Orchestra* / Dream: *Mantovani & His Orchestra* / Stella by starlight: *Aldrich, Ronnie & His Orchestra* / Some enchanted evening: *Mantovani & His Orchestra* / Learnin' the blues: *Heath, Ted & His Music* / Three coins in the fountain: *Chacksfield, Frank & His Orchestra* / Love and marriage: *Mantovani & His Orchestra* / Tender trap: *Heath, Ted & His Music* / All the way: *Chacksfield, Frank & His Orchestra* / Lady is a tramp: *Chacksfield, Frank & His Orchestra* / Just one of those things: *Chacksfield, Frank & His Orchestra* / It's nice to go trav'ling: *Franks, Gordon & His Orchestra* / Me and my shadow: *Howard, Johnny & His Orchestra* / Strangers in the night: *Mantovani & His Orchestra* / Somethin' stupid: *Aldrich, Ronnie & His Piano/The Festival Orchestra* / My way: *Mantovani & His Orchestra* / Send in the clowns: *Mantovani & His Orchestra*
5545682 / 3 Aug '98 / Spectrum

☐ **SCREEN SINATRA**
From here to eternity / Three coins in the fountain / Young at heart / Just one of those things / Someone to watch over me / Not as a stranger / Tender trap / Wait for me (Johnny Concho theme) / All the way / Chicago / Monique-Song from Kings Go Forth / They came to Cordura / To love and be loved / High hopes / All my tomorrows / It's all right with me / C'est magnifique / Dream
CDMFP 6052 / Mar '89 / Music For Pleasure

☐ **SENTIMENTAL GENTLEMAN 1940-1942 (2CD Set)**
I'll be seeing you / Polka dots and moonbeams / Fools rush in / Imagination / East of the sun (and west of the moon) / I'll never smile again / Whispering / One I love (belongs to somebody else) / Love lies / Our love affair / We three (my echo, my shadow and me) / Do you know why / Marie / 14. star dust / How am I to know / Oh look at me now / You might have belonged to another / It's always you / You lucky people / Without a song / Everything happens to me / Let's get away from it all / This love of mine / Free for all / I guess I'll have to dream the rest / Blue skies / Sinner kissed an angel / Violets for your furs / How about you / Snootie little cutie / Street of dreams / In the blue of evening / There are such things / It started all over again / Who / Song is you
FA 974 / Apr '97 / Fremeaux

☐ **SEPTEMBER OF MY YEARS**
September of my years / How old am I / Don't wait too long / It gets lonely early / This is all I ask / Last night when we were young / Man in the looking glass / It was a very good year / When the wind was green / Hello, young lovers / I see it now / Once upon a time / September song
7599010142 / May '98 / Reprise

☐ **SHE SHOT ME DOWN**
Good thing going / Hey look, no crying / Thanks for the memory / Long night / Bang bang / Monday morning quarterback / South to a warmer place / I loved her / Gal that got away / It never entered my mind
7599272512 / May '98 / Reprise

☐ **SINATRA (Music From The CBS Mini-Series - 2CD Set)**
Where the blue of the night meets the gold of the day: *Crosby, Bing* / Temptation: *Crosby, Bing* / All or nothing at all / Shake down the stars / Without a song / Street of dreams / I'll be seeing you / I'll never smile again / Sing sing sing: *Goodman, Benny* / Where or when / Stormy weather / Our love affair / I fall in love too easily / Hucklebuck / Fairy tale / Lover man: *Holiday, Billie* / You go to my head / I'm a fool to want you / It was a very good year / Autumn in New York / It all depends on you / They can't take that away from me / Come fly with me / High hopes / One for my baby (and one more for the road) / You make me feel so young / That's life / All the way / New York, New York / My way
9362450912 / May '98 / Reprise

☐ **SINATRA 'N' DURANTE (Sinatra, Frank & Jimmy Durante)**
MACCD 364 / 26 Jan '98 / Autograph

☐ **SINATRA 80TH ALL THE BEST (2CD Set)**
Lean baby / I'm walking behind you / I've got the world on a string / From here to eternity / South of the border (Down Mexico way) / Young at heart / Three coins in the fountain / Come fly with me / Someone to watch over me / Melody of love / Night and day / Learnin' the blues / Same old Saturday night / Love and marriage / Impatient years / (Love is) the tender trap / (How little it matters) How little we know / Johnny Concho theme (wait for me) / Lady is a tramp / Well did you evah / Hey jealous lover / I've got you under my skin / All the way / Chicago / Witchcraft / How are ya fixed for love / No one ever tells you / Time after time / In the wee small hours of the morning / You make me feel so young / I get a kick out of you / All my tomorrows / High hopes / What is this thing called love / Moon was yellow (and the night was young) / I love Paris / Blues in the night / Guess I'll hang my tears out to dry / Nice 'n' easy / Thye Christmas song
CDESTD 2 / Dec '95 / Premier/EMI

☐ **SINATRA AND COMPANY**
7599270532 / May '98 / Reprise

☐ **SINATRA AND SEXTET LIVE IN PARIS**
9362454872 / May '98 / Reprise

☐ **SINATRA AND STRINGS**
7599270202 / May '98 / Reprise

☐ **SINATRA AND SWINGIN' BRASS**
7599270212 / May '98 / Reprise

☐ **SINATRA AT THE SANDS (Sinatra, Frank & Count Basie)**
Come fly with me / I've got a crush on you (vocal only) / I've got you under my skin / Shadow of your smile / Street of dreams / One for my baby (and one more for the road) / Fly me to the moon / One o'clock jump / You make me feel so young / All of me / September of my years / Get me to the church on time / It was a very good year / Don't worry 'bout me / Makin' whoopee / Where or when / Angel eyes / My kind of town (Chicago is)
7599010192 / May '98 / Reprise

☐ **SINATRA CHRISTMAS ALBUM, THE**
Jingle bells / Christmas song / Mistletoe and holly / I'll be home for Christmas / Have yourself a merry little Christmas / Christmas waltz / First Noel / Hark the herald angels sing / O little town of Bethlehem / O come all ye faithful (Adeste fidelis) / It came upon a midnight clear / Silent night / White Christmas / Christmas waltz (alternate)
CDMFP 5797 / Nov '97 / Music For Pleasure
9362457432 / May '98 / Reprise

☐ **SINATRA SINGS THE SONGS OF VAN HEUSEN AND CAHN**
7599267232 / May '98 / Reprise

☐ **SINATRA SWINGS (3CD Set)**
Lady is a tramp / I get a kick out of you / I've got you under my skin / Moonlight in Vermont / When your lover has gone / Bewitched / Imagination / At long last love / My funny Valentine / My blue heaven / Come fly with me / Dancing in the dark / All the way / You make me feel so young / On the sunny side of the street / Love me or leave me / For you / Where or when / Moon was yellow / Just one of those things / I've got my love to keep me warm / Road to Mandalay / You are love / They didn't believe me / I could have danced all night / Exactly like you: *Sinatra, Frank & Nat 'King' Cole* / Till we meet again/Meet me tonight in dreamland: *Sinatra, Frank & Bing Crosby* / There's a long, long trail a-winding: *Sinatra, Frank & Bing Crosby* / Some enchanted evening / Personality / Tea for two: *Sinatra, Frank & Dinah Shore* / De Camptown races/Beautiful dreamer / This can't be love: *Sinatra, Frank & Margaret Whiting* / Make believe / Figaro: *Sinatra, Frank & Carlos Ramirez* / Come out, come out wherever you are / It could happen to you/I heard you cried last night: *Sinatra, Frank & Bing Crosby* / I'll get by/I don't believe it, but say it again: *Sinatra, Frank & Bing Crosby* / Out of nowhere/Going my way/Sunday, Monday or always: *Sinatra, Frank & Bing Crosby* / Lover, come back to me / Birth of the blues: *Sinatra, Frank & Louis Armstrong* / Somebody loves me / You'd be so nice to come home to / Yes indeed / Don't bring Lulu / There's no business like show business: *Sinatra, Frank & Doris Day* / No can do / Together / Among my souvenirs/September song/As time goes by: *Sinatra, Frank & Bing Crosby* / Night and day: *Sinatra, Frank & Bing Crosby* / What makes the sunset / In the middle of May / Anchors aweigh: *Sinatra, Frank & Gene Kelly* / I begged her: *Sinatra, Frank & Gene Kelly* / I fall in love too easily / Charm of you / Put your dreams away / Lulu's back in town / You brought a new kind of love to me: *Sinatra, Frank & Peggy Lee* / You keep coming back like a song / Body and soul / This is always / Over the rainbow / All of me / Tenderly / What is this thing called love / Dancing in the dark / If I could be with you one hour tonight / That old black magic
55174 / Oct '97 / Music

☐ **SINATRA'S SINATRA (A Collection Of Frank's Favourites)**
I've got you under my skin / In the wee small hours of the morning / Second time around / Nancy / Witchcraft / Young at heart / All the way / How little it matters, how little we know / Pocketful of miracles / Oh what it seemed to be / Call me irresponsible / Put your dreams away
7599270252 / May '98 / Reprise

☐ **SINATRA-BASIE (An Historical Musical First) (Sinatra, Frank & Count Basie)**
7599270232 / May '98 / Reprise

☐ **SOFTLY AS I LEAVE YOU**
7599270282 / May '98 / Reprise

☐ **SOME NICE THINGS I'VE MISSED**
You turned my world around / Sweet Caroline / Summer knows / Tie a yellow ribbon / Satisfy me one more time / If / What are you doing the rest of your life / Bad, Bad Leroy Brown / You are the sunshine of my life
7599272152 / May '98 / Reprise

☐ **SONG IS YOU, THE (3CD Set) (Sinatra, Frank & Tommy Dorsey)**
Sky fell down / Too romantic / Shake down the stars / Moments in the moonlight / I'll be seeing you / Say it / Polka dots and moonbeams / Fable of the rose / This is the beginning of the end / Hear my song Violetta / Fools rush in / Devil may care / April played the fiddle / I haven't time to be a millionaire / Imagination / Yours is my heart alone / You're lonely and I'm lonely / East of the sun and west of the moon / Head on my pillow / It's a lovely day tomorrow / I'll never smile again / All this and heaven too / Where do you keep your heart / Whispering / Trade winds / One I love (belongs to somebody else) / Call of the canyon / Love lies / I could make you care / World is in my arms / Our love affair / Looking for yesterday / Tell me at midnight / We three (my echo, my shadow and me) / When you awake / Anything / Shadows on the sand / You're breaking my heart all over again / I'd know you anywhere / Do you know why / Long ago / Stardust / Oh look at me now / You might have belonged to another / You lucky people you / It's always you / I tried / Dolores / Without a song / Do I worry / Everything happens to me / Let's get away from it all / I'll never let a day pass me by / Love me as I am / This love of mine / I guess I'll have to dream the rest / You and I / Neiani / Free for all / Blue skies / Two in love / Pale moon / I think of you / How do you do without me / Sinner kissed an angel / Violets for your furs / Sunshine of your smile / How about you / Snootie little cutie / Poor you / I'll take Tallulah / Last call for love / Somewhere a voice is calling / Just as though you were here / Street of dreams / Take me / Be careful it's my heart / In the blue of evening / Dig down deep / There are such things / Daybreak / It started all over again / Light a candle in the chapel / Too romantic / Shake down the stars / Hear my song Violetta / You're lonely and I'm lonely / Our love affair / Violets for your fur / Night we called it a day / Lamplighter's serenade / Song is you / Night and day / I'm getting sentimental over you / Who / I hear a rhapsody / I'll never smile again / Half way down the street / Some of your sweetness (got into my heart) / Once in a while / Little love / It came to me / Only forever / Marie / Yearning / How am I to know / You're part of my heart / Announcements / You're stepping on my toes / You got the best of me / That's how it goes / When daylight dawns / When sleepy stars begin to fall / Goodbye lover, goodbye / One red rose / Things I love / In the blue of evening / Just as though you were here / Frank Sinatra's farewell to the Tommy Dorsey Orchestra / Song is you
07863663532 / Jan '97 / Bluebird

☐ **SONGBOOK (2CD Set)**
You make me feel so young / All the way / On the sunny side of the street / On the road to Mandalay / Dancing in the dark / For you / Come fly with me / They don't believe me / Just one of those things / I've got you under my skin / I get a kick out of you / My funny valentine / Bewitched / Lady is a tramp / At long last love / Moonlight in Vermont / My blue heaven / When your lover has gone / Imagination / I could have danced all night / Begin the beguine / I've got my love to keep me warm / (I didn't stand a) Ghost of a chance / Blue skies / Out of nowhere / Somebody loves me / Love me or leave me / Tea for two / This love of mine / Stardust / Night and day / I think of you / Lamplighter's serenade / Street of dreams / Whispering / This is the beginning of the end / Be careful, it's my heart / Sinner kissed an angel / How about you / Our love affair
MUCD 9509 / May '96 / Musketeer

☐ **SONGS FOR YOUNG LOVERS & SWING EASY**
My funny valentine / Girl next door / Foggy day / Like someone in love / I get a kick out of you / Little girl blue / They can't take that away from me / Violets for your furs / Just one of those things / I'm gonna sit right down and write myself a letter / Sunday / Wrap your troubles in dreams / Taking a chance on love / Jeepers creepers / Get happy / All of me
CDP 7484702 / Nov '92 / Capitol

☐ **SPOTLIGHT ON FRANK SINATRA**
I wonder who's kissing her now / I'll string along with you / Devil and the deep blue sea / Speak low / Mimi / At long last love / Lover is blue / Day by day / Five more minutes / After I say I'm sorry / Serenade of the bells / Long ago and far away / I wish I didn't love you so / You're the top / It's all up to you / Some other time
HADCD 131 / Feb '94 / Javelin

☐ **STARS SALUTE SINATRA, THE (Various Artists)**
Night and day: *Astaire, Fred* / How about you: *Garland, Judy* / Sunday, Monday or always: *Crosby, Bing* / Fools rush in: *Miller, Glenn* / One for my baby (and one more for the road): *Horne, Lena* / They can't take that away from me: *Dorsey, Jimmy* / I get a kick out of you: *Merman, Ethel* / Sweet Lorraine: *Tatum, Art* / Yesterdays: *Holiday, Billie* / Jeepers creepers: *Armstrong, Louis* / Imagination: *Fitzgerald, Ella* / I'll follow my secret heart: *Coward, Sir Noel* / Lady is a tramp: *Dorsey, Tommy* / All or nothing: *Haymes, Dick* / Glad to be unhappy: *Wiley, Lee* / I'll never smile again: *Shelton, Anne* / I didn't know what time was: *Shaw, Artie* / Where are you: *Bailey, Mildred* / Embraceable you: *Hackett, Bobby* / Blues in the night: *Shore, Dinah* / River stay 'way from my door: *Waters, Ethel* / When your love has gone: *Austin, Gene* / Always: *Durbin, Deanna* / Mood indigo: *Ellington, Duke*
CECD 4 / 31 Jul '98 / Collector's Edition

☐ **STRANGERS IN THE NIGHT**
Strangers in the night / Summer wind / All or nothing at all / Call me / You're driving me crazy / On a clear day (You can see forever) / My baby just cares for me / Downtown / Yes sir that's my baby / Most beautiful girl in the world
7599010172 / May '98 / Reprise

☐ **SUNDAY MORNING OR ALWAYS**
CPCD 8157 / Nov '95 / Charly

☐ **SWING & DANCE WITH FRANK SINATRA**
Saturday night (is the loneliest night in the week) / All of me / I've got a crush on you / Huckle buck / It all depends on you / Bye bye baby / All of me / Should I / You do something to me / Lover / When you're smiling / It's only a paper moon / My blue heaven / Continental / Meet me at the Copa / Nevertheless / There's something missing / Farewell / Farewell to love
4851882 / Aug '96 / Columbia

☐ **SWING ALONG WITH ME**
7599270182 / May '98 / Reprise

☐ **SWING EASY**
Jeepers creepers / Taking a chance on love / Wrap your troubles in dreams (and dream your troubles away) / Lean baby / I love you / I'm gonna sit right down and write myself a letter / Get happy / All of me / How could you do a thing like that to me / Why should I cry over you / Sunday / Just one of those things
CDMFP 5973 / Oct '92 / Music For Pleasure

☐ **THAT'S LIFE**
7599270392 / May '98 / Reprise

☐ **THERE ARE SUCH THINGS (Sinatra, Frank & Tommy Dorsey)**
Blue skies / Call of the canyon / Daybreak / East of the sun and west of the moon / Everything happens to me / Fools rush in / Hear my song Violetta / How about you / I'll never smile again / Imagination / Let's get away from it all / One I love (belongs to somebody else) / Polka dots and moonbeams / Sinner kissed an angel / Somewhere a voice is calling / Stardust / There are such things / This love of mine / Too romantic / Violets for your furs / Whispering / Without a song / Yours is my heart alone
CDAJA 5106 / Apr '93 / Living Era

☐ **THERE'LL BE SOME CHANGES MADE**
VCD 1102 / Jun '94 / Voice

☐ **THIS IS FRANK SINATRA 1953-1957 (2CD Set)**
I've got the world on a string / Three coins in the fountain / Love and marriage / From here to eternity / South of the border (Down Mexico way) / Rain / Gal that got away / Young at heart / Learnin' the blues / My one and only love / Tender trap / Don't worry 'bout me / Look to your heart / Anytime anywhere / Not as a stranger / Our town / You, my love / Same old Saturday night / Fairy tale / Impatient years / I could have told you / When I stop loving you / If I had three wishes / I'm gonna live till I die / Hey jealous lover / Everybody loves somebody / Something wonderful happens in summer / Half as lovely / You're cheating' yourself (if you're cheatin' on me) / You'll always be the one I love / You forgot all the words / How little it matters, how little we know / Time after time / Crazy love / Johnny Concho theme (wait for me) / If you are but a dream / So long, my love / It's the same old dream / I believe / Put your dreams away
CDDL 1275 / Nov '94 / EMI

☐ **THIS LOVE OF MINE**
From the bottom of my heart / Melancholy mood / My buddy / It's funny to everyone but me / On a little street in Singapore / East of the Sun and West of the moon / Our love affair / This love of mine / Blue skies / How about you / There are such things / Night we called it a day / Lamplighter's serenade / Song is you / Night and day / Close to you / You'll never know / Sunday Monday or always / I begged her / If you are but a dream / People will say we're in love / Oh what a beautiful morning
CDMOIR 511 / Sep '95 / Memoir

☐ **THIS ONE'S FOR TOMMY**
VCD 1103 / May '95 / Viper's Nest

☐ **TIME AFTER TIME**
Time after time / Our love / All or nothing at all / On a little Street in Singapore / East of the sun and West of the moon / I'll never smile again / Everything happens to me / This love of mine / There are such things / Just as though you were there / People will say we're in love / Lovely way to spend an evening / I couldn't sleep a wink last night / Night and day / White Christmas / You'll never know / Long ago (and far away) / Guess I'll hang my tears out to dry / Saturday night / I'll walk alone / Exactly like you / I fall in love too easily / Body and soul / You'll be so nice to come home to / Our love is here to stay / I can't believe that you're in love with me / Day by day
CECD 001 / 27 Apr '98 / Collector's Edition

☐ **TOUCH OF CLASS, A**
As time goes by / You'll never know / How deep is the ocean / I only have eyes for you / People will say we're in love / Embraceable you / September song / Blue skies / They say it's wonderful / Begin the beguine / Fools rush in / Let's get away from it all / You'll never walk alone / There will never be another you / Things we did last summer / In the blue of the evening / Day by day / Too romantic
TC 877042 / 2 Feb '98 / Disky

☐ **TRIBUTE TO THE GUV'NOR, A**
Saturday night is the loneliest night / You'll never know / Oh what a beautiful morning / Stormy weather / People will say we're in love / At long last love / Sunday morning or always / Day by day / Close to you / Night and day / Lovely way to spend an evening / White Christmas / I dream of you (more than you dream of me) / Cradle song / What makes a sunset / Ol' man river / If you please / Embraceable you / Kiss me again / I fall in love too easily
ALPCD 101 / Mar '97 / Alpha Entertainments

☐ **TRILOGY (Past Present & Future/2CD Set)**
7599274772 / May '98 / Reprise

☐ **TRIPLE GOLD (3CD Set)**
Come fly with me / All or nothing at all / Love me as I am / Night and day / Melancholy mood / Let's get away from it all / Sky fell down / Not so long ago / We three / Shake down the stars / On a little street in Singapore / Fable of the rose / Blue skies / Light a candle in the chapel / There are such things / Looking for yesterday / Snooty little cutie / Shadows on the sand / Poor you / All the way / Lady is a tramp / I'll never let a day pass / In the blue of the evening / You make me feel so young / Ciribiribin / All this and heaven too / Do I worry / Without a song / Two in love / Pale moon / I havn't time to be a millionaire / It's funny to everyone but me / I get a kick out of you / Where do you keep your heart / Moments in the moonlight / Call of the canyon / Trade winds / Last call for love / Here comes the night / Road to Mandalay / I've got you under my skin / Oh what a beautiful morning / Dancing in the dark / Night they called it a day / Everything happens to me / Say it / Oh look at me now / Sunshine of your smile / Who told you I cared / Just as though you were me / Moonlight in Vermont / How do you do without me / Tell me at midnight / Do you know why / Violets for your furs / April played the fiddle / You're breaking my heart all over again / You're lonely and I'm lonely / I guess I'll have to dream the rest / I could have danced all night
TG 331 / 8 Sep '97 / Start

☐ **TRIPLE GOLD (3CD Set)**
Begin the beguine / All or nothing at all / Love me as I am / Night and day / Melancholy mood / Let's get away from it all / Sky fell down / Not so long ago / We three / Shake down the stars / On a little street in Singapore / Fable of the rose / Blue skies / Light a candle in the chapel / There are such things /

Looking for yesterday / Snooty little cutie / Shadows on the sand / Poor you / (I didn't stand) A ghost of a chance / Out of nowhere / I'll never let a day pass / In the blue of the evening / Somebody loves me / Ciribiribin / All this and heaven too / Do I worry / Without a song / Two in love / Pale moon / I haven't time to be a millionaire / It's funny to everyone but me / Love me or leave me / Where do you keep your heart / Moments in the moonlight / Call of the canyon / Trade winds / Last call for love / Here comes the night / Tea for two / This love of mine / Oh what a beautiful morning / Stardust / Night they called it a day / Everything happens to me / Say it / Oh look at me now / Sunshine of your smile / Who told you I cared / Just as though you were here / I think of you / How do you do without me / Tell ma at midnight / Do you know why / Violets for your furs / April played the fiddle / You're breaking my heart all over again / I guess I'll have to dream the rest / Be careful it's my heart
TG 335 / 6 Jul '98 / Start

☐ UNHEARD FRANK SINATRA VOL.1 & 2, THE (2CD Set)
Your hit parade theme and opening announcements / I've heard that song before / As time goes by / As time goes by / Let's get lost / If you please / Pistol packin' mama / I'll be seeing you / I love you / Your hit parade end theme show closer excerpt / Everything I have is yours / I can't get out of this mood / Miss Annabelle Lee / Too much in love / Amor / As long as there is music / Dancing in the dark / It could happen to you / Come out wherever you are / It had to be you / If loveliness were music / More and More / More than you know / Easter parade / Candy / This is always / You keep coming back like a song / End theme put your dreams away / They say it's wonderful / Opening theme and D-Day announcement / They'll be a hot time in the town of Berlin / Song is you / Where or when / America the beautiful / Nancy with the laughing face / I've got a woman crazy for me / It could happen to you / I'll be seeing you / Begin the beguine / Speak low / Opening and announcements / It's only a paper moon / I fall in love too easily / Charm of you / Oh Bess where's my Bess / It might as well be Spring / House that I live in that's America to me / Coffee song (they've got an awful lot of coffee in Brazil) / Lost in the stars / Closing theme put your dreams away / I saw you first / Lovely way to spend an evening / I couldn't sleep a wink last night
VOICE 1100 / Aug '97 / Voice

☐ V DISCS - THE COLUMBIA YEARS 1943-1952, THE (2CD Set)
I only have eyes for you / Kiss me again / (There's gonna be a) Hot time in the town of Berlin / Music stopped / I couldn't sleep a wink last night / Way you look tonight / I'll be around / You've got a hold on me / Lovely way to spend an evening / She's funny that way / Speak low / Close to you / My shining hour / Long ago and far away / Some other time / Come out come out wherever you are / Put your dreams away / And then you kissed me / All the things you are / All of me / Nancy with the laughing face / Mighty like a rose / Falling in love with love / Cradle song / I'll follow my secret heart / There's no you / Someone to watch over me / Let me love you tonight / Just close your eyes / If you are but a dream / Strange music / Dick Haymes, Dick Todd and Como / None but the lonely heart / Ol' man river / Homesick, that's all / Night is young and you're so beautiful / Aren't you glad you're you / You brought a new kind of love to me / I'll never smile again / Without a song / Was the last time I saw you (the last time) / Don't forget tonight tomorrow / Oh - What it seemed to be / Over the rainbow / Where is my Bess / My romance / Song is you / Fall in love with you ev'ry day / They say it's wonderful / You are too beautiful / Come rain or come shine / Stormy weather
C2K 66135 / Oct '94 / Legacy

☐ V-DISCS, THE (The Columbia Years/ 2CD Set)
Don't look down / Like a rolling stone / When the world falls down / Trouble with me / Life's a prayer / You and me / Colour me / Take a long line / Midnight love / All the young dudes / I only have eyes for you / Kiss me again / (There'll be a) Hot time / Music stopped / I couldn't sleep a wink last night / Way you look tonight / I'll be around / You've got a hold on me / A lovely way to spend an evening / She's funny that way / Speak low / Close to you / My shining hour / Long ago (and far away) / Some other time / Come out come out wherever you are / Put your dreams away / And then you kissed me / All the things you are / AAll of me / Nancy / Mighty lak' a rose / Falling in love with love / Cradle song / I'll follow my secret heart / There's no you / Someone to watch over me / Let me love you tonight / Just close your eyes / If you are but a dream / Strange music / Cradle song / Dick Haymes Dick Todd / None but the lonely heart / Ol' man river / Homesick that's all / Night is young / Aren't you glad / You brought a new kind of love
4910272 / 13 Jul '98 / Columbia

☐ VERY BEST OF THE RADIO DAYS, THE
Love me or leave me / Out of nowhere / Nevertheless (I'm in love with you) / I've got my love to keep me warm / This is always / Begin the beguine / My happiness / Between the devil and the deep blue sea / I'm in the mood for love / Hundred years from today / Little white lies / I don't know why / What can I say after I'm sorry / S'wonderful / Lady from 29 palms / Tenderly / Guess I'll hang my tears out to dry / Some other time / Just as though you were here / I couldn't sleep a wink last night / Don't blame me / Somebody loves me / Hair of gold eyes of blue / I'll string along with you / Thou swell / Saturday night is the lonliest night of the week / I wonder who's kissing her now / On the sunny side of the street
SELCD 516 / 30 Mar '98 / Castle Select

☐ WATERTOWN
9362456892 / May '98 / Reprise

☐ WORLD WE KNEW, THE
7599270432 / May '98 / Reprise

☐ YOU MAKE ME FEEL SO YOUNG
You make me feel so young / 'S wonderful / Love me or leave me / On the sunny side of the street / Blue skies / They say it's wonderful / Begin the beguine / Ol' man river / Don't blame me / It all depends on you / I fall in love with you / Music stopped / I don't stand a ghost of a chance with you / You do something to me / Night and day / Somebody loves me / Just one of those things / Nevertheless / You are love / They did not believe me / Out of nowhere / I've got my love to keep me warm / For you
GRF 136 / '93 / Tring

☐ YOUNG BLUE EYES
CDGR 107 / Jan '96 / Charly

☐ YOUNG SINATRA
Oh what a beautiful morning / If you please / Saturday night is the loneliest night of the week / Sunshine of your smile / East of the sun and west of the moon / Delores / I guess I'll have to dream the rest / Blue skies / I'll never smile again / Whispering / Take me / Be careful it's my heart / Without a song / This love of mine / Lamplighter's serenade / Night and day / If you are but a dream / Kiss me again / There's no you / I dream of you / I begged her / I fall in love too easily / Embraceable you / When your love has gone
CDHD 263 / Feb '97 / Happy Days

Sinatra, Nancy

☐ BOOTS
As tears go by / Day tripper / I move around / It ain't me babe / These boots are made for walking / In my room / Lies / So long babe / Flowers on the wall / If he'd love me / Run for your life / City never sleeps at night / Leave my dog alone / In our time / These boots are made for walkin' (mono)
NANCD 104 / Nov '96 / Nancy

☐ GREATEST HITS (Featuring Frank Sinatra & Lee Hazlewood)
Storybook children / These boots are made for walking / Sugar town / Something stupid / How does that grab you, darlin' / Summer wine / Sundown sundown / I've been down so long / Sand / Oh lonesome me / Ladybird / Jackson / You've lost that lovin' feelin' / Some velvet morning / Did you ever / Elusive dreams / Greenwich village folksong man / So long, babe
PLATCD 3903 / Oct '88 / Platinum

☐ GREATEST HITS
These boots are made for walking / Summertime / Things / Did you ever / Friday's child / You only live twice / Highway song / Elusive dreams / Storybook children / Sugar town / Something stupid / Jackson / Sand / Sundown sundown / Some velvet morning / I've been down so long / Tony rome / How does that grab you darlin' / Lady bird / So long babe
PA 7112 / Apr '94 / Paradiso

☐ GREATEST HITS
NANCD 102 / Jul '96 / Nancy

☐ HITS OF NANCY & LEE (Sinatra, Nancy & Lee Hazelwood)
NANCD 101 / Jul '96 / Nancy

☐ HOW DOES THAT GRAB YOU
NANCD 105 / Feb '97 / Nancy

☐ NANCY IN LONDON
On Broadway / End / Step aside / I can't grow peaches on a cherry tree / Summer wine / Wishin' and hopin' / This little bird / Shades / More I see you / Hutchinson Jail / Friday's child / 100 years / You only live twice / Tony Rome / Life's a trippy thing
NANCD 103 / Nov '96 / Nancy

☐ ONE MORE TIME
NANCD 107 / 19 Jan '98 / Nancy

☐ SUGAR
NANCD 106 / Feb '97 / Nancy

Sinclair, Bob

☐ PARADISE
Voix intro / Get into the music / Disco 2000 selector / Gym tonic / Ghetto / NY city music / Auto stepousse / Ultimate / Sacre francais / Vision of paradise / Underground people
YP 043CD / 30 Jun '98 / Yellow

Sinclair, Dave

☐ MOON OVER MAN
Wanderlust / Tropic island / Mallorcan dance / Make yourself at home / Harry / Moon over man / Where have I gone / Ice cream / Make a brand new start / Moving on / Lost in the woods / Reminiscermemoring / Honky dorry / Piano player / Back for tea / Here to stay
BP 119CD / Aug '96 / Blueprint

☐ MOON OVER MOON
Wanderlust / Tropical island / Mallorcan dance / Make yourself at home / Harry / Where have I gone / Make a brand new start / Moving on / Lost in the woods / Reminiscermemoring / Honky dorry / Piano player / Back for tea / Here to stay
VP 119CD / May '93 / Voiceprint

Sinclair, Richard

☐ CARAVAN OF DREAMS
Going for a song / Cruising / Only the brave / Plan it Earth / Heather / Keep on coming / Emily / Felafel shuffle / Five go wilde
HTDCD 7 / Sep '96 / HTD

☐ EVENING OF MAGIC, AN
HIDCD 17 / Jan '94 / HTD

Sinclair, Rod

☐ BREAKS AND BONDS
CMCD 071 / Dec '97 / Celtic Music

Sinclar

☐ LA BONNE ATTITUDE
84413522 / 13 Jul '98 / Source

Sincola

☐ CRASH LANDING IN TEEN HEAVEN
Rundown / Not 100% pure / Happy MF / One hit wonder / Nerd God / Legendary nowhere / Letterbomb / Star '79 / In the bone garden / Start/Stop / Canal / Red Danube
CAROL 003CD / Sep '96 / Caroline

☐ SINCOLA
RR 1232 / Feb '94 / Rise

Sindelfingen

☐ ODGIPIG
HBG 122/10 / Apr '94 / Background

Sindy Kills Me

☐ SINDY KILLS ME
Clearblue / Snakeskin jacket
PANNCD 14 / Jul '96 / Pandemonium

Sine

☐ VITAL SINES
Eaglesfield skyline / Stand up and be counted / Valentine / Good day for goodbyes / Anne-elise / Nirvana / Black sea rover / Go away / Better man
MIN 07CD / 15 Sep '97 / Minority/One

Sinfield, Pete

☐ STILLUSION
Can you forgive a fool / Night people / Will it be you / Hanging fire / House of hopes and dreams / Wholefood boogie / Piper / Under the sky / Envelopes of yesterday / Song of the sea goat / Still
BP 152CD / Aug '96 / Blueprint

Sinfonye

☐ RED IRIS
GCD 920701 / Dec '97 / Glossa

Singabangqobi

☐ GREATER IS HE
FIFCD 1001 / Oct '92 / Friends In Fellowship

Singer, Hal

☐ RENT PARTY
Cornbread / Teddy's dream / One for Willie / Neck bones / Rent party / Singer song / Rice and red beans / Swing shift / Hot rod / Rock 'n' roll / Indian love call / Frog hop / Hometown / Down for Dean / Easy living / Hound's tooth / Mr. Movin's groovin' / Crossroads
SV 0258 / May '98 / Savoy Jazz

Singers & Players

☐ GOLDEN GREATS VOL.1
ONUCD 4 / Sep '89 / On-U Sound

☐ GOLDEN GREATS VOL.2
ONUCD 26 / Jul '95 / On-U Sound

☐ LEAPS AND BOUNDS
Moses / Make a joyful noise / Alla la-dreadlocks soldier / Autobiography (dread operator) / Breaking down the pressure / Dog park / Vegetable matter / Striving
CDBRED 58 / Sep '91 / Cherry Red

☐ REVENGE OF THE UNDERDOG
ONUCD 11 / 15 Dec '97 / On-U Sound

☐ WAR OF WORDS
ONUCD 5 / 2 Mar '98 / On-U Sound

Singers Unlimited

☐ MAGIC VOICES (7CD Set)
5391302 / 8 Dec '97 / MPS Jazz

Singh, Talvin

☐ ANOKHA (Talvin Singh Presents Soundz Of The Asian Underground) (Various Artists)
Jaan: *Singh, Talvin* / Flight IC 408: *State Of Bengal* / Kizmet: *Lelonek* / Shang high: *Future Soundz Of India* / Chitagong chill: *State Of Bengal* / Mumbai theme tune: *Rahman, A.R.* / Distant sun: *Singh, Talvin* / Heavy intro: *Amar* / Equation: *Equal I* / Spiritual masterkey: *Osmani Soundz* / Accepting tranquility: *Milky Bar Kid* / K-ascendant: *Biswas, Kingsuk*
CIDM 1120 / Feb '97 / Omni

☐ OK
CIDX 8075 / 7 Sep '98 / Omni

Singing Francine

☐ HARASSMENT
GSCD 2414 / 8 Jun '98 / Strakers

Singing Kettle

☐ GREATEST HITS VOL.1
KOP 27CD / Aug '95 / Kettle

Singing Melody

☐ SINGING MELODY
If I'm crazy / Send come call me / You bring me joy / Love thing I'm going down / Love thing / I'm going down / Give it all up / In the mood / Rock bottom / Nothing wrong / Brighter day / Turn the lights down / Cross dem border
119902 / Jun '97 / Musidisc UK

Singing Sweet

☐ DON'T SAY NO
CFCD 2 / Apr '93 / Colin Fat

Single Cell Orchestra

☐ DEAD VENT 7
EFA 003182 / Jul '95 / Reflective

☐ KNOCKOUT DROPS
EFA 709622 / Sep '96 / Asphodel

☐ SINGLE CELL ORCHESTRA
ASP 0962CD / 22 Jun '98 / Asphodel

Single Gun Theory

☐ EXORCISE THIS WASTELAND
NTCD 039 / '88 / Nettwerk

☐ FLOW RIVER OF MY SOUL
W 230088 / May '95 / Edel

☐ LIKE STARS IN MY HAND
NETCD 020 / Nov '91 / Nettwerk

Singleton, T-Bone

☐ WALKIN' THE FLOOR
Sunset blues / Walkin' the floor / Reconcile / Don't ever go / Boogie train / Light in a dark place / Gonna make me cry / Let me be your man / Tryna get along / Power up
JSPCD 267 / May '96 / JSP

Sinikka

☐ HAR DU LYTTET TIL ELVENE OM NATTA
GR 4017CD / Mar '96 / Grappa

Sinister

☐ DIABOLICAL SUMMONING
NB 278CD / 13 Oct '97 / Nuclear Blast

☐ HATE
NB 131CD / Jul '95 / Nuclear Blast

Sinkadus

☐ AURUM NOSTRUM
Snalblast / Manuel / Agren / Attestupan
CYCL 048 / Mar '97 / Cyclops

☐ LIVE AT PROGFEST 1997 (2CD Set)
Manuel / Agren / Jag anglamarks bane / Snalblast / Attestupan
CYCL 061 / 20 Apr '98 / Cyclops

Sinner

☐ BOTTOM LINE
342612 / Oct '95 / No Bull

☐ DANGEROUS CHARM
N 01013 / Nov '87 / Noise

☐ IN THE LINE OF FIRE
343472 / May '96 / Koch International

☐ JUDGEMENT DAY
332312 / Sep '97 / No Bull

☐ JUDGEMENT NIGHT
HGCD 0616 / 15 Jun '98 / High Gain

☐ NATURE OF EVIL, THE
Devil's river / Question of honour / Justice from hell / Nature of evil / Some truth / Darksoul / Faith and conviction / Rising / Walk on the darkside / Trust no one / Sun goes down
NB 3242 / 27 Jul '98 / Nuclear Blast

☐ NO MORE ALIBIS
343462 / Mar '96 / No Bull

☐ RESPECT
342702 / Dec '95 / No Bull

Sinners

☐ TURN IT UP
MNWCD 213 / Jan '92 / MNW

Sinoath

☐ RESEARCH
POLYPH 003CD / Jul '96 / Polyphemus

☐ STILL IN GREY DYING
1 STSINONCD / May '95 / SPV

Sinsisters

☐ MEMORIES OF A HAPPY HELL
OPM 2120CD / 15 Jan '98 / Other People's Music

Sintesis

☐ EN BUSCA UNA NUEVA FLOR
CDSD 03 / 9 Feb '98 / Sol & Dene

Sinti

☐ SINTI
Going to the USA / Que pasa / Dark eyes (Ojos negros) / Flintstones / Hi Pat / Isn't she lovely / For Wesley / Blues for Ike / Patchiena / My emotion / Chez moi / On my mind / For Hans / Fricha / Limehouse blues / Caravan / Dina
4837452 / 26 Jan '98 / Sony Jazz

Siouxsie & The Banshees

☐ HYENA
Take me back / Running town / Pointing bone / Blow the house down / Dazzle / We hunger / Belladonna / Swimming horses / Bring me the head of the preacher man
8215102 / Mar '95 / Wonderland

☐ JOIN HANDS
Poppy day / Regal zone / Placebo effect / Icon / Premature burial / Playground twist / Mother / On mein papa / Lord's prayer
8390042 / Mar '95 / Wonderland

☐ JU JU
Spellbound / Into the light / Arabian knights / Halloween / Monitor night shift / Sin in my heart / Head cut / Voodoo dolly
8390052 / Mar '95 / Wonderland

☐ KALEIDOSCOPE
Happy house / Tenant / Trophy / Hybrid / Clockface / Lunar camel / Christine / Desert kisses / Red light / Paradise place / Skin
8390062 / Mar '95 / Wonderland

☐ KISS IN THE DREAMHOUSE, A
Cascade / Green fingers / Obsession / She's a carnival / Circle / Melt / Painted bird / Cacoon / Slowdive
8390072 / Mar '95 / Wonderland

☐ NOCTURNE
Intro (The rite of spring) / Israel / Dear Prudence / Paradise place / Melt / Cascade / Pulled to bits / Nightshift / Sin in my heart / Slowdive / Painted bird / Happy house / Switch / Spellbound / Helter skelter / Eve white, Eve black / Voodoo dolly
8390092 / Mar '95 / Wonderland

☐ PEEP SHOW
Peek-a-boo / Killing jar / Scarecrow / Carousel / Burn-up / Ornaments of gold / Turn to stone / Rawhead and bloody bones / Last beat of my heart / Rhapsody
8372402 / Mar '95 / Wonderland

☐ RAPTURE, THE
O Baby / Tearing apart / Stargazers / Fall from grace / Not forgotten / Sick child / Lonely one / Falling down / Forever / Rapture / Double life / Love out me
5237252 / 15 Sep '97 / Wonderland

☐ SCREAM, THE
Pure / Jigsaw feeling / Overground / Carcass / Helter skelter / Mirage / Metal postcard / Nicotine stain / Surburban relapse / Switch
8390082 / Mar '95 / Wonderland

☐ STRAWBERRY GIRL (A Tribute To Siouxsie & The Banshees) (Various Artists)
DOP 52 / 1 Jun '98 / Doppelganger

☐ SUPERSTITION
Kiss them for me / Fear (Of the unknown) / Cry / Drifter / Little sister / Shadowtime / Silly thing / Got to get up / Silver waterfalls / Softly / Ghost in you
8477312 / Mar '95 / Wonderland

☐ THROUGH THE LOOKING GLASS
Hall of mirrors / Trust in me / This wheel's on fire / Strange fruit / This town ain't big enough for the both of us / You're lost little girl / Passenger / Gun / Little Johnny Jewel
8314742 / Mar '95 / Wonderland

☐ TINDERBOX
Candy man / Sweetest chill / This unrest / Cities in dust / Cannons / Party's fall / 92 / Land's end / Quarterdrawing of the dog / Execution / Lullaby / Umbrella / Cities in dust (Extended version)
8291452 / Mar '95 / Wonderland

☐ TWICE UPON A TIME
5171602 / Mar '95 / Wonderland

Sipahi, Nesrin

☐ SHARKI LOVE SONGS FROM ISTANBUL (Sipahi, Nesrin & The Kudsi Erguner Ensemble)
Kimseler gelmez senin feryadi ates barina / Gulzare nazar kildim virane misal almus / Nedir bu halin ey meh cemalim / Semti dildare bu demler guzerin varmi sab / Ey bad-i saba yar ile vuslat ne zamandir / Ben seni sevdim sevsli kaynayip costum / Sana ey canimin cani efendim kirildim, kustum, incindim / Iftirakindir sebep nale vu feryadima / Af eyle sucum ey gul-i ter basima kakma / Dun gece ye's ile kendimden gectim / Saydeyledi bu gonlumu bir gozleri ahu / Etti a guzel ahde vefa mujdeler olsun / Bir ruzgardir gelir gecer sanmistim
CMPCD 3009 / Jul '92 / CMP

Siperkov

☐ GIPSY MUSIC
SYNCD 163 / Jun '94 / Syncoop

Sipiagin, Alexander

☐ IMAGES
Tarde / Freaker / Little dancer / Song 1 / Novgorod bells / Midwestern night dream
TCB 98602 / 23 Mar '98 / TCB

Sir Bald Diddley

☐ NITROGEN PEROXIDE
WIGCD 013 / Apr '97 / Alopecia

☐ PIE GO-MANIA (Diddley, Sir Bald & His Wig-Outs)
PIECD 001 / Feb '96 / Alopecia

☐ WHAT'S IN YOUR FRIDGE
WIGLP 003 / May '95 / Alopecia

Sir Doug & The Texans Tornados

☐ TEXAS ROCK FOR COUNTRY ROLLERS
I love the way you love: *Sir Doug & The Texans* / Cowboy Peyton place / Give back the key to my heart / Wolverton mountain / Floataway / I'm missing you / Gene Thomas medley: sometimes / Cryin' inside / Country groove / You can't hide a redneck (under that hippy hair)
EDCD 535 / 1 Sep '97 / Edsel

Sir Douglas Quintet

☐ COLLECTION, THE
She's about a mover / Mendocinodynamite / I'll go crazy / Baby tell me / Next time you see me / Turn on your lovelight / Ain't that loving you / Slow down / Crazy arms / If you ever need me / I can't believe you wanna leave / Just a moment / More 'n' more / Mr. pitiful / Night train / Papa ain't salty / Crazy daisy / Please please please / Sapphire / Things I used to do / Whirlaway / Why why why
COL 060 / Mar '95 / Collection

☐ LIVE LOVE
Introduction / Dynamite woman / One way crash course love affair / My girl / Drivin' wheel / Starry eyes / Emotional goner / Henrietta / Glad for your sake / Knock on wood
EDCD 557 / 1 Jun '98 / Edsel

☐ TEXAS FEVER (The Best Of Sir Douglas Quintet)
AIM 2018CD / 24 Nov '97 / Aim

Sir Galtfrid's Trombones

☐ DON'T BE AFRAID
LICD 3169 / Jan '97 / Liphone

Sir Lancelot

☐ LEGENDARY SIR LANCELOT, THE
LYRCD 7406 / '91 / Lyrichord

☐ TRINIDAD IS CHANGING (1940's/ 1950's)
Century of the common man / Trinidad is changing / Donkey City / Neighbour neighbour leave me door / Night in Central Park / Ugly woman / Scandal in the family / Young girls today / Oken karange / Sweet like a honey bee / Pan American way / Gimme crab and callaloo / Mary Ann / Take me take me (to San Pedro) / Matilda Matilda / West Indian families
FLYCD 942 / May '95 / Flyright

Sir Mix-A-Lot

☐ CHIEF BOOT KNOCKA
Sleepin' with my fonk / Take my stash / Double my stash / Don't call me Da Da / Just da pimpin' in me / Let it beaounce / Brown shuga / Put 'em on the glass / Nast dog / I checks my bank / Ride / What's real / Chief boot knocka / Monsta' mack
74321243422 / Aug '95 / American

☐ MACK DADDY
One time's got no case / Mack Daddy / Baby got back / Swap meet lovie / Seattle ain't bullshit / Lock jaw / Boss is back / Testarossa / Rapper's reputation / Spring on the cat / Jack back / I'm your new God / No holds barred
74321248472 / Jun '95 / American

☐ RETURN OF THE BUMPASAURUS
You can have her / Da bomb / Buckin' my horse / Mob style / Top ten list / Man u luv ta hate / Bark like you want it / Bumpasaurus cometh / Bumpasaurus / Denial / Aunt Thomasina / Jump on it / Aintsta / Sag / Message to a drag artist / Lead yo horse / Plaything / Funk fo da bvld / Slide
74321372442 / Sep '96 / American

☐ SEMINAR
Seminar / Beepers / National anthem / My hooptie / Goretex / (peek-a-boo) Game / I got game / I'll roll you up / Something about my benzo / My bad side
74321248462 / Jun '95 / American

☐ SWASS
Buttermilk biscuits (keep on square dancin') / Posse on Broadway / Gold / Swass / Rippin' / Attack on the stars / Mail dropper / Hip hop solider / Iron man / Bremelo / Square dance rap / Romantic interlude / F the b's
74321248452 / Jun '95 / American

Sircle Of Silence

☐ SUICIDE CANDYMAN
342142 / Dec '95 / No Bull

Siren

☐ SIREN
REP 4202 / Aug '91 / Repertoire

☐ STRANGE LOCOMOTION (Siren & Kevin Coyne)
REP 4083 / Aug '91 / Repertoire

☐ STRANGE LOCOMOTION/SIREN
Ze-ze-ze-ze / Get right church / Wake up my children / Wasting my time / Sixteen women / First time I saw your face / Gardener man / And I wonder / Asylum / Bertha Lee / I wonder where / Relaxing with Bonnie Lou / Some dark day / Hot potato / Soon / Gigolo / I'm all aching / Strange locomotion / Shake my hand / Lonesome ride / Fat moaning minnie / Squeeze me
SEECD 413 / Oct '94 / See For Miles

Siren Circus

☐ POEMS ON A GHOST OF A SUBJECT
SCD 28024 / Jun '97 / Sargasso

Sirkel

☐ SIRKEL (Sirkel & Ric Sanders)
BAJ 171549CD / May '97 / Baj

Sirota, Ted

☐ REBEL ROOTS (Sirota, Ted Rebel Souls)
NAIMCD 014 / Mar '97 / Naim Audio

Sirrah

☐ ACME
Acme / Passover 1944 / On the verge / AU tomb / Iridium / Pillbox impression / Panacea / Bitter seas / In the final moment
CDMFN 025 / Sep '96 / Music For Nations

☐ WILL TOMORROW COME
To bring order / For the sake of nothing / Patron / Lash / Will tomorrow come / High treason / Sepsis / Rhea / Madcap / Floor's embrace
CDMFN 225 / Aug '97 / Music For Nations

Sirtos Ensemble

☐ FOLK MUSIC OF GREECE
HMP 3903060 / Oct '94 / HM Plus/ Quintana

Sissoko, Mama

☐ AMOURS JARABI
829402 / Jun '97 / BUDA

Sista

☐ 4 ALL THE SISTAS AROUND THE WORLD
Hip hop / Hit u up / Sweat you down / Find my love / 125th Street / Secret admirer / I don't mind / Feel of your lips / Good thang / I wanna be wit u / Brand new
7559616532 / Aug '94 / East West

Sister 7

☐ THIS THE TRIP
This the trip / Bottle rocket / Know what you mean / Nobody's home / Flesh and bones / Perfect / Say good-bye / Tumblin down / Under the sun / Shelter / Some things are free
078221883528 / Jul '97 / RCA

Sister Aaron

☐ PURIFICATION
E 113992 / Dec '93 / Musical Tragedies

Sister Audrey

☐ POPULATE
African is ziow / (if) I love you / Nobody's fool / Put a little love away / No work / Children of the ghetto / Populate / Daylight and darkness / English girl / Love was all I had / No work dub
ARICD 070 / Nov '91 / Ariwa Sounds

Sister C.B.

☐ SPIRIT OF THE ZITHER, THE (Sister C.B. Of Carmel De Lucon)
74321340062 / May '96 / Milan

Sister Carol

☐ BLACK CINDERELLA
CDHB 193 / Apr '97 / Heartbeat

☐ CALL MI SISTER CAROL
HBCD 93 / Nov '94 / Heartbeat

☐ LYRICALLY POTENT
CDHB 213 / Jun '96 / Heartbeat

☐ POTENT DUB
SH 45035 / Oct '97 / Shanachie

Sister Double Happiness

☐ HORSEY WATER
SPCD 137337 / Nov '94 / Sub Pop

☐ SISTER DOUBLE HAPPINESS
SST 162CD / May '93 / SST

Sister Grant

☐ DOWN AT CROSS (Sister Grant & The Gospelettes)
KGC 107 / Apr '94 / Kangaroo

☐ HARBOUR IN JESUS (Sister Grant & The Gospelairs)
KGC 104 / Apr '94 / Kangaroo

Sister Hazel

☐ SOMEWHERE MORE FAMILIAR
UND 53030 / 20 Apr '98 / Universal

Sister Machine Gun

☐ METROPOLIS
TVT 72442 / Jul '97 / TVT

Sister Morphine

☐ SISTER MORPHINE
789010792 / Mar '97 / Emerald City

Sister Psychic

☐ SURRENDER, YOU FREAK
Surrender you freak / Part of love / Velvet dog / I can't breathe / Happiness / Kim the waitress / Little bird / Death by fascination / Sleepwalking / Clapper (wish I was blind) / Blue river / Eddie Mars / On the floor
727442 / Mar '94 / Restless

Sister Rebekah

☐ AFRICAN HEARTBEAT
NGCD 554 / 24 Nov '97 / Twinkle

Sister Sledge

☐ ALL AMERICAN GIRLS
All American girls / He's just a runaway / If you really want me / Next time you'll know / Happy feeling / Ooh you caught my heart / Make a move / Don't you let me lose it / Music makes me feel good / I don't want to say goodbye
8122719142 / May '95 / Rhino

☐ AND NOW...SISTER SLEDGE...AGAIN
FMDXD 190 / Mar '93 / FM

☐ LIVE
Everybody dacne / Frankie / Lost in music / Thinking of you / We are family / True love / He's the greatest dancer / Love of the Lord / Brother, brother stop
EMPRCD 712 / Apr '97 / Emporio

☐ LOVE SOMEBODY TODAY
Got to love somebody / You fooled around / I'm a good girl / Easy street / Reach your peak / Pretty baby / How to love / Let's go on a vacation
8122719132 / May '95 / Rhino

☐ SISTER SLEDGE LIVE
Everybody dance / Thinking of you / He's the greatest dancer / True love / Frankie / Brother brother stop / Love of the Lord / We are family / Medley
SUMCD 4077 / Nov '96 / Summit

☐ VERY BEST OF SISTER SLEDGE, THE
We are family / He's the greatest dancer / All American girls / Pretty baby / Got to love somebody / Frankie / Lost in music / Thinking of you / Mama never told me / Reach your peak / Lost in music (mix)
9548318132 / Feb '93 / WEA

☐ WE ARE FAMILY
He's the greatest dancer / Lost in music / Somebody loves me / Thinking of you / We are family / Easier to love / You're a friend to me / One more time
8122715872 / Jun '95 / Rhino

Sisters Of Glory

☐ GOOD NEWS IN HARD TIMES
Walk around heaven all day / Oh happy day / Rough side of the mountain / Precious lord / Will the circle be unbroken / His eye is on the sparrow / How I got over / Yes / Move on up a little higher / No charge / He's right on time / Precious memories / I won't be back no more / He's got the whole world in his hands / Surely god is able / I love the lord
9362459902 / Aug '95 / Warner Bros.

Sisters Of Mercy

☐ FIRST, LAST AND ALWAYS
Black planet / Walk away / No time to cry / Rock and a hard place / Marian (version) / First and last and always / Possession / Nine while nine / Amphetamine logic / Some kind of stranger
9031773792 / Jun '92 / Merciful Release

☐ FIRST, LAST FOREVER
CLEO 6642CD / Jan '94 / Cleopatra

☐ GIFT (Sisterhood)
Jihad / Colours / Giving ground / Finland red, Egypt white / Rain from heaven
11316842 / Jun '94 / Merciful Release

☐ SISTERS OF MERCY: INTERVIEW PICTURE DISC
CBAK 4010 / Apr '88 / Baktabak

☐ SLIGHT CASE OF OVERBOMBING, A (Greatest Hits Vol.1)
Under the gun / Temple of love / Vision thing / Detonation Boulevard / Dr. Jeep / More / Lucretia my reflection / Dominion/Mother Russia / This Corrosion / No time to cry / Walk away / Body and soul
4509935792 / Aug '93 / Merciful Release

☐ SOME GIRLS WANDER BY MISTAKE
Alive / Floorshow / Phantom / 1969 / Kiss the carpet / Lights / Valentine / Fix / Burn / Kiss the carpet (reprise) / Temple of love / Heartland / Gimme shelter / Damage done / Watch / Home of the hit-men / Body electric / Adrenochrome / Anaconda
9031764762 / Apr '91 / Merciful Release

☐ THOUGHTS AND PRAYERS
3D 004 / Dec '96 / Network

Sisters Unlimited

☐ NO BED OF ROSES
Voices / More than a paycheck / Collier's lassie / Love-lar-l / A stor mo chrol / Dance to your daddy-cockle gatherers-tail toddle / My rebellious adolescent / Chipko / Mother I feel you under my feet-sun wind and water / Women o' dundee / Keep your nose out of mama's business / Dancing on the gravel / Mrs. joan lias / Childbirth shanty (no bed of roses) / Sleep well / Your cheating heart
FE 104CD / Jun '95 / Fellside

☐ NO LIMITS
No going back / Promises / Breastfeeding baby in the park / Tomorrow / Mouth music / My better years / Working girl blues / Dance / Old and strong / My true love once / When I was single / On children / No man's momma / Forgive and forget / We were there
HARCD 013 / Nov '91 / Harbour Town

Sistine Choir

☐ CHRIST IS BORN
TCD 1059 / 13 Oct '97 / Tradition

Sit n' Spin

☐ PAPPY'S CORN SQUEEZIN'
MRCD 116 / Mar '97 / Munster

Sitter

☐ PASTELLO
379372 / Sep '97 / Koch

Sivann, Sylvie

☐ TRADITIONAL JEWISH MUSIC
PS 65178 / Mar '97 / PlayaSound

Sivertsen, Kenneth

☐ REMEMBERING NORTH
Nimis (near but far) / Cock ones head / Remembering / Going home / Division / Sideblink / From Paris to Mosterhamn / Procession / Tony's rain / Journey / Rain
NYC 60072 / Aug '94 / NYC

Sivuca

☐ NORTE FORTE
68959 / Apr '97 / Tropical

Siwa, Tala Mena

☐ SAE ENA
MWCD 5001 / Aug '96 / Music & Words

Six & Violence

☐ LETTUCE PREY
ANDCD 9 / Feb '97 / A New Day

☐ XMAS PIGS
SFTSAVCD / 26 May '98 / Striving For Togetherness

Six And A Half

☐ NEW YORK PARIS NICE
Road 66 / Berimbau / Quand ca balance / Lush life / La javanaise / Looking up / Que reste t il de nos amours / Bluesette / Take the 'A' train / La valse des lilas / St Thomas / Je me suis fait tout petit
FDM 365842 / May '97 / Dreyfus

Six By Seven

☐ THINGS WE MAKE, THE
Beautiful shape / European me / Candlelight / For you / Spy song / Something wild / Brilliantly cute / Oh dear / 88-92-96 / Comedown
MNTCD 1011 / 25 May '98 / Mantra

Six Feet Under

☐ ALIVE AND DEAD
398414118CD / Oct '96 / Metal Blade

☐ HAUNTED
398414093CD / Oct '95 / Metal Blade

☐ WARPATH
398414128CD / 26 Aug '97 / Metal Blade

Six Finger Satellite

☐ PARANORMALIZED
SPCD 366 / Dec '96 / Sub Pop

☐ PIGEON IS THE MOST POPULAR BIRD, THE
Untitled / Home for the holy day / Untitled / Laughing Larry / Untitled / Funny like a clown / Untitled / Deadpan / Untitled / Hi lo jerk / Untitled / (Love) via satellite / Untitled / Save the last dance for Larry / Untitled / Zeroes and ones / Untitled / Neuro-harmonic conspiracy / Untitled (10) / Takes one to know one / Symphony in A
SPCD 268 / Aug '93 / Sub Pop

☐ SEVERE EXPOSURE
SP 299B / Dec '96 / Sub Pop

Six Fingered People

☐ TEMPTATIONS
BR 034CD / 23 Mar '98 / Blue Room

Six Going On Seven

☐ SELF MADE MESS
SOME 02CD / 11 May '98 / Some

Six String Drag

☐ SIX STRING DRAG
HYMN 4 / 24 Nov '97 / Fundamental

Six Winds

☐ ANGER DANCE
BVHAASTCD 9305 / Feb '86 / Bvhaast

Six Yard Box

☐ IMAGINATION IS GREATER THAN KNOWLEDGE
Sweet leaf / What's the point / K4R Part III / Cat is wiser / Pictures of matchstick men (12" mix) / Clutter up buttering / Spellbound / K4R Part IV / Pictures of matchstick men (Reggae mix)
MOSH 087CD / Apr '93 / Earache

Sixpence None The Richer

☐ SIXPENCE NONE THE RICHER
We have forgotten / Anything / Waiting room / Kiss me / Easy to ignore / Puedo escribir / I can't catch you / I won't stay long / Love / Moving on
7017032616 / Nov '97 / Myrrh

Sixteen Deluxe

☐ BACKFEED MAGNETBABE
TR 37CD / May '95 / Trance

Sixteen Souls

☐ STRANGE GIRL
ALOCD 001 / 1 Jun '98 / Alola

Sixths

☐ WASP'S NESTS
FACD 206 / Jul '95 / Factory Too

Sizzla

☐ BLACK WOMAN AND CHILD
Black woman and child / Hard ground / More guidance / Make it secure / Oh what a joy / Love is divine / One away / Guide us over / Give them the ride / Babylon a use dem brain: *Sizzla & Capleton* / Princess Black: *Sizzla & Edi Fitzroy* / No time to gaze / Too much to bear / Mi Lord: *Sizzla & Determine* / Give them the ride
GRELCD 243 / 6 Oct '97 / Greensleeves

☐ REGGAE MAX
JSRNCD 19 / 1 Jun '98 / Jet Star

Sjosten, Lars

☐ IN CONFIDENCE
DRCD 197 / Sep '88 / Dragon

☐ SELECT NOTES
CAPRICE 1216 / May '89 / Caprice

Skaboosh

☐ FREETOWN
Movin' up an' movin' on / Fanfare / Bareback ridin / Freedom / Time / Startin from scratch / Spain / Ain't got any money / I want to grow old with you by my side
BP 128CD / Aug '96 / Blueprint

Skagarak

☐ BIG TIME
It's never too late / Ain't you got a mother / Somebody like me / I want you / Hold you love you give you / Edge of illusion / Hold on just one more time / Wonder if you really know / Big time / It's never too late
10192 / Oct '97 / Go On Deluxe

Skaggs, Ricky

☐ FAMILY AND FRIENDS
Lost and I'll never find the way / Two different worlds / River of memory / Talk about sufferin' / Think of what you've done / Toy heart / Hallelujah I'm ready / Say / Won't you be mine / Won't it be wonderful there / River of Jordan
ROUCD 0151 / Aug '88 / Rounder
CDSD 015 / Sep '94 / Sundown

☐ SKAGGS & RICE (Skaggs, Ricky & Tony Rice)
Bury me beneath the willow / Mansions for me / There's more pretty girls than one / Memories of mother and dad / Where the soul of man never dies / Talk about sufferin' / Will the roses bloom / Tennessee blues / Old crossroads / Have you someone (in heaven waiting)
SHCD 3711 / Jan '97 / Sugar Hill

☐ SWEET TEMPTATION
I'll take the blame / Cabin home on the hill / Baby I'm in love with you / I'll stay around / Could you love me one more time / Sweet temptation / Put it off until tomorrow / Baby girl / Forgive me / I know what it means to be lonesome
SHCD 3706 / Aug '96 / Sugar Hill

☐ THAT'S IT
Red apple rag / At the Darktown strutter's ball / Florida blues / Bubble gum song / Whitesburg / Meeting house branch / Sweet Georgia Town / Hook and line / Southern moon / Twenty one fiddle salute / That's it / Evergreen shore
CDSD 040 / Dec '86 / Sundown

Skandalous Allstars

☐ HIT ME
SH 5720 / Mar '97 / Shanachie

☐ PUNK STEADY
1969 / Sailin' on / I wanna be sedated / Anarchy in the UK / Because the night / Living dead / Orgasm addict / Rock the casbah / Take the skinheads bowling / One way or another / Because the dub
SHANCD 5728 / 9 Mar '98 / Shanachie

Skanga

☐ SKANGA
Truly madly deeply / America calling / Crazy angel / Freetown / Dreamers paradise / Monkey wedding / Housemaster / She fills my eyes / Mr. Margaret / Rude to be rude
5409612 / 10 Aug '98 / A&M

Skankin' Pickle

☐ GREEN ALBUM
DSR 042 / Jun '97 / Dr. Strange

☐ SKAFUNKRASTAPUNK
Road zombie / It's not too late / Doing something naughty / Hulk Hogan / Racist world / Burnt head / Asian man / Ska / Fight / How funk / Fakin' Jamaican / 24 second song / You shouldn't judge a man by the hair on his butt / Peter Piper and Mary
DILL 012CD / Jun '97 / Dill

☐ SKANKIN' PICKLE FEVER
Hussein skank / Pseudo punk / Silly willy / Ice Cube, Korea wants a word with you / Toothless and grey / Pass you by / Dub / Song 3 / Whatever happened / Anxiety attack / Skinless friend / Larry Smith / I missed the bus / Roland Alphonso's dub / Hand twister / David Duke is running for president / Hit my brain
DILL 014CD / Jun '97 / Dill

Skaos

☐ BACK TO LIVE
EFA 946252 / Dec '95 / Pork Pie

☐ BEWARE/CATCH THIS BEAT
Going insane / After midnight / Destination skaville / JB's / These boys / Munsters / I love to dance / Invicible seven / Jesse James / Prison / Frankenstein's party / Do the ska / Oh Sally / Straight to your heart / Brainkiller / Jungle beat / Everything (Girl) but you / Better beware / Bonehead (I just can't stand it) / Super hero / Living in Bavaria
LOMACD 29 / Feb '94 / Dojo

Skarn

☐ DRIFT
SKARN 0197CD / Dec '97 / Skarn

Skatalites

☐ BALL OF FIRE
James Bond theme / Latin goes ska / Confucius / Occupation / Rock fort rock / Eastern standard time / Ball of fire / Swing easy / Ringo / Freedom sound
IJCD 4005 / Aug '97 / Island Jamaica

☐ FOUNDATION SKA (2CD Set)
Christine Keeler / Fidel Castro / Simmer down / Alley pang / Exodus / King Solomon / Eastern standard time / World's fair / Two for one / I should've known better / Hot cargo / Black Sunday / Ska la Parisienne / Don D Lion / Dick Tracy / Hanging tree / Scandal ska / Occupation / Old rocking chair / Third man ska / Ringo's theme ska / Ringo's theme / Nimrod / Woman a come / Cleopatra / Beardsman ska / Addis Ababa / Silver dollar / View / Dr. Kildare / Killer diller / Naked city
CDHB 185/6 / Sep '97 / Heartbeat

☐ HI BOP SKA
SH 45019 / Dec '94 / Shanachie

☐ HOG IN A COCOA (Skatalites & Friends)
John james / Yea yea yea baby / Higher the monkey climbs / Rukumbine / Next door neighbour / What a man doeth / Over the river / Run joe / Hog in a cocoa / Samson / Housewife's choice / When I call your name / Woman come / Penny reel
LG 21016 / May '93 / Lagoon

☐ LIBERATION SKA
Liberation ska (the one for you) / Count ossie wareika hill hero / Amus (sitting and waiting) / Peeping tom / Muma muma / Biwaki sykoko / Hallelujah / Raggae blues (down presser man) / Rasta stand firm / Out a sink in a sink
RNCD 2056 / May '94 / Rhino

☐ SKA AUTHENTIC VOL.1
SOCD 9006 / Mar '96 / Studio One

☐ SKAMANIA (2CD Set)
DOXOCD 266 / Jul '96 / Dojo

☐ SKATALITES AND DON DRUMMOND, THE
RN 7046 / 13 Apr '98 / Rhino

☐ SKATALITES AND FRIENDS AT RANDY'S
VPCD 1497 / 20 Apr '98 / VP

☐ SKATALITES, THE
444112 / Jun '97 / Jet Set

☐ STRETCHING OUT (2CD Set)
RUSCD 8237 / 16 Feb '98 / ROIR

☐ TOP SOUNDS FROM TOP DECK VOL.3 (Ska-Boo-Da-Da)
Ska boo da ba / Confucius / Chinatown / Reburial / Smiling / Ska-ra-van / Ringo rides / Surftide seven / Lawless street / Marcus Junior / Ghost town / China clipper / Ska-ra-van / Lawless Street
WESM 518 / 19 Jan '98 / Westside

☐ TRIBUTE TO THE SKATALITES, A (Freedom Sounds)
SH 5727 / Nov '97 / Shanachie

Skeaping, Lucie

☐ RAISINS AND ALMONDS (Skeaping, Lucie & The Burning Bush)
Yoi m'enamori d'un aire (I fell in love with the charms) / Tum Balalaika (Play balalaika) / Chassidic melody No. 24 / Tsen kopikes (Ten kopeks) / Adio querida (Good bye my love) / Puncha, puncha (The perfumed rose) / Sha, Shtil (Shh, Quiet) / Una matica de ruda (a little bunch of rue) / Chassidic melody No. 13 / Di alte kashe (The eternal question) / Avrix mi galanica (Open, my sweet) / Gey ikh mir shpatsirn (As I went walking) / Una hija tiene el rey (The King has a daughter) / Di mezinke oysgegebn (My youngest daughter's married) / Mi padre era de Francia / Oyfn pripetchik (On the hearth) / Chassidic melody No. 10, La rose enflorece (The rose blooms) / Rozhinkes mit mandlen / Zog nit keynmol (Never say)
CDSDL 395 / Mar '94 / Saydisc

Skeduz

☐ RAG AR PLINN
KMCD 72 / Jun '97 / Keltia Musique

Skee Lo

☐ I WISH
Superman / I wish / Never crossed my mind / Top of the stairs / Come back to me / Waitin' for you / Holdin' on / You ain't down / Crenshaw / This is how it sounds / Burger song / I wish (Street mix)
5297892 / Dec '95 / Wild Card

Skeletal Earth

☐ DE-EVOLUTION
DAR 0172 / Mar '95 / Desperate Attempt

☐ EULOGY FOR A DYING FOETUS
FDNCD 8215 / Jan '92 / Plastic Head

Skeletal Family

☐ BURNING OIL/FUTILE COMBAT
LOMACD 40 / May '95 / Loma

☐ SINGLES PLUS
Trees / Just a friend / Night / Waiting here / She cries alone / Wind blows / Eternal / Waiting here (version) / Night (version) / So sure / Batman / Lies / Promised land / Stand by me / Puppet / Waltz / Guilt
CDMGRAM 75 / Mar '94 / Cherry Red

Skeleton

☐ SKELETON
BW 091 / 27 Apr '98 / B&W

Skeleton Crew

☐ BLUE MANIA
Satisfaction guaranteed / Glory hunter / Watch your step / Can't buy love with money / Mother earth / Blues got me / Trail of tears / Chinese eyes / Mississippi burning / See me later / Walking in my sleep
109042 / Mar '92 / Musidisc

Skeletons

☐ NOTHING TO LOSE
Nothin' to lose / Charming Billie / It's OK to be lonely / I'm goin' home/Mad old lady / Pay to play / Tubb's theme / World you grace / I ain't lyin' / Whiffle ball song / Downhearted / Cool summer / Educated fool / Country boys don't cry / Get what you need
HCD 8080 / Jun '97 / Hightone

Skellern, Peter

☐ CHEEK TO CHEEK
Cheek to cheek / Continental / Puttin' on the Ritz / Top hat, white tie and tails / Stormy weather / All or nothing at all / Bye bye / Love is the sweetest thing / Two sleepy people / Deep purple / Raining in my heart / Where do we go from here / They all laughed / Way you look tonight
74321152192 / Sep '93 / Ariola Express

☐ MASTERS, THE
EABCD 018 / 24 Nov '97 / Eagle

☐ SENTIMENTALLY YOURS
Too much I'm in love / Raining in my heart / They can't take that away from me / Still magic / Love is the sweetest thing / Isn't this a lovely day / Where do we go from here / Continental / When somebody thinks you're wonderful / Skylark / Deep purple / Over her / Way you look tonight / Two sleepy people / You and I / Cheek to cheek / While I'm away / Sweet words / Put out the flame / Night and day
74321393332 / Jan '97 / Camden

☐ STARDUST MEMORIES
Lazybones / Georgia on my mind / Skylark / Java jive / Stardust / Whispering grass / If I didn't care / My resistance is low / Memphis in june / I don't want to set the world on fire / Puttin' and takin' / Every night about this time / Rockin' chair / Someone's rockin' my dreamboat
4509981322 / Dec '96 / Warner Bros.

☐ WORLD OF PETER SKELLERN, THE
Hold on to love / You're a lady / Tattooed lady / Too much, I'm in love / Society ladies / My lonely room / Our Jackie's getting married / Vicarious vestments / Skin and bone / Make it easy for me / Uncle Sam / No more Sunday papers / Sad affair / Piano rag / Up for the shoot / Big time Indian chief / Honey chil' / Sleepy guitar
5512722 / May '96 / Spectrum

Skelton, John

☐ ONE AT A TIME
PAN 146CD / Oct '93 / Pan

Sketch

☐ COSMOSIS
33JAZZ 003CD / Jun '93 / 33 Jazz

Skew Siskin

☐ ELECTRIC CHAIR MUSIC
GUN 110CD / Nov '96 / Gun

Skid Row

☐ 40 SEASONS (The Best Of Skid Row)
Youth gone wild / 18 and life / Piece of me / I remember you / Threat / Psycho love / Monkey business / Quicksand Jesus / Slave to the grind / Into another / Frozen / My enemy / Breakin' down / Beat yourself blind / Forever / Fire in the hole
7567831032 / 6 Jul '98 / Atlantic

☐ B SIDE OURSELVES
Psychotherapy / C'mon and love me / Delivering the goods / What you're doing / Little wing
7567824312 / Oct '92 / Atlantic

☐ SKID ROW
Big guns / Sweet little sister / Can't stand the heartache / Piece of me / Eighteen and life / Rattlesnake shake / Youth gone wild / Here I am / Makin' a mess / I remember you / Midnight tornado
7819362 / Feb '95 / Atlantic

☐ SLAVE TO THE GRIND
Monkey business / Slave to the grind / Threat / Quicksand Jesus / Psycho love / Get the fuck out / Livin' on a chain gang / Creepshow / In a darkened room / Riot act / Mudkicker / Wasted time
7567822422 / Jun '91 / Atlantic

☐ SUBHUMAN RACE
My enemy / Subhuman race / Remains to be seen / Ironwill / Breakin' down / Medicine jar / Face against my soul / Into another / Frozen / Firesign / Bonehead / Beat yourself blind / Eileen
7567827302 / Dec '96 / Atlantic

Skid Row

☐ SKID ROW (Gary Moore, Brush Shiels and Noel Bridgeman)
Benedict's cherry wine / Saturday morning man / Crystal ball / Mr. Deluxe / Girl called Winter / Morning Star Avenue / Silver bird
CLACD 343 / Jun '94 / Castle

Skids

☐ DUNFERMLINE
Into the valley / Charles / Saints are coming / Scared to dance / Sweet suburbia / Of one skin / Night and day / Animation / Working for the Yankee dollar / Charade / Masquerade / Circus games / Out of town / Goodbye civilian / Woman in Winter / Hurry on boys / Iona / Fields
CDVM 9022 / Jul '93 / Virgin

☐ SCARED TO DANCE
Into the valley / Scared to dance / Of one skin / Dossier (of fallibility) / Melancholy soldiers / Hope and glory / Saints are coming / Six times / Calling the tune / Integral plot / Scale / Charles
CDV 2116 / Jun '90 / Virgin

☐ SWEET SUBURBIA (The Best Of The Skids)
Into the valley / Charles / Saints are coming / Scared to dance / Sweet suburbia / Of one skin / Night and day / Animation / Working for the Yankee dollar / Charade / Masquerade / Circus games / Out of town / Goodbye civilian / Woman in winter / Hurry on boys / Iona / Fields
CDOVD 457 / Feb '95 / Virgin

Skiff-A-Billy

☐ SKIFF-A-BILLY
SKCD 001 / Jul '98 / Skiff-A-Billy

Skillet Lickers

☐ SKILLET LICKERS
CUY 3509CD / Apr '96 / County

Skillz

☐ PROMISE
50570 / Jun '97 / Raging Bull

Skimmer

☐ COMPITOENAIL
CRACKLE 002 / 2 Mar '98 / Crackle

Skin

☐ EXPERIENCE ELECTRIC
Experience electric / Only one / Blow my mind / Shine like diamonds / Pleasure / Love like suicide / Tripping / Soul / Falling / Winners and losers / Bittersweet / Aphrodites child
SRECD 705 / 1 Sep '97 / Reef

Skin Alley

☐ SKIN ALLEY
AACD 017 / 27 Apr '98 / Audio Archive

☐ TO PAGHAM AND BEYOND
AACD 022 / Jun '97 / Audio Archive

Skin, Flesh & Bones

☐ DUB IN BLOOD VOL.1
SSCD 001 / Oct '96 / Sunshot

☐ DUB IN BLOOD VOL.2
SSCD 002 / Oct '96 / Sunshot

Skin Of Tears

☐ SHIT HAPPENS
LF 198CD / Jan '96 / Lost & Found

Skin The Peeler

☐ FRIENDS AND LOVERS
STP 101CD / Mar '94 / Skindependent

☐ WORLD DANCE
CDSTP 100 / Dec '91 / Skindependent

Skinlab

☐ BOUND, GAGGED AND BLINDFOLDED
CM 77174 / Apr '97 / Century Media

Skinner, Billy

☐ KOSEN RUFU
AC 3333 / Nov '93 / Accurate

Skinny

☐ WEEKEND
CHEKCD 501 / 20 Apr '98 / Cheeky

Skinny Puppy

☐ BACK AND FORTH SERIES TWO
Intro / Sleeping beast / K-9 / Monster radio man / Quiet solitude / Pit / Sore in a masterpiece/Dead of winter / I'lnovis on a stick / To a baser nature / AM/ Meat flavour / My voice sounds like shit / Smothered hop / Explode the PA / Assimilate / Edge of insanity
W230078 / Jan '93 / Nettwerk

☐ BRAP (2CD Set)
08922402 / Apr '96 / Westcom

☐ CLEANSE, FOLD AND MANIPULATE
First aid / Addiction / Shadow cast / Draining faces / Mourn / Second touch / Tear or beat / Trauma hounds / Anger / Epilogue
NETCD 019 / Nov '90 / Nettwerk

☐ MIND: THE PERPETUAL INTERCOURSE
One time one place / God's gift / Three blind mice / Love / Stairs and flowers / Antagonism / 200 years / Dig it / Burnt with water
NTCD 037 / '88 / Nettwerk

☐ PROCESS, THE
Jahya / Death / Candle / Hardest head / Cult process / Curcible / Blue serge / Morter / Amnesia / Cellar heart
74321310972 / Feb '96 / American

☐ RABIES
NETCD 023 / Jul '90 / Nettwerk

☐ REMISSION AND BITES
BIAS 048 / Jan '87 / Play It Again Sam

☐ TESTURE
CD315439 / '89 / Nettwerk

☐ VIVISECT VI
Dogshit / VS gas attack / Harsh stone white / Human disease (SKUMM) / Who's laughing now / Testure / State aid / Hospital waste / Fritter (Stella's home)
NETCD 021 / Nov '90 / Nettwerk

☐ WORLOCK (Twelve Inch Anthology)
W230041 / '89 / Nettwerk

Skip Bifferty

☐ SKIP BIFFERTY
ESSEX 1003CD / 5 Jan '98 / Essex

Skip Rats

☐ LET YOUR HAIR DOWN
RAUCD 032 / Dec '97 / Raucous

Skippies

☐ WORLD UP
NR 422455 / Jan '94 / New Rose

Skirt

☐ CHOKING ON SUGAR
SH 5715 / Nov '96 / Shanachie

Skitzo

☐ SKITZO MANIA
Skitzo mania / Dr. Death / Shipwreck Island / Witching hour / Lonesome train (on a lonesome track) / Possessed / I'm going Skitzo / Caledonia / Poltergeist / Your cheatin' heart / Under pressure / House of the rising sun
NERCD 028 / May '87 / Nervous

☐ TERMINAL DAMAGE
Empty room / Frustrated / Game / Sore point / Honey don't / Victim / Psycho ward / Terminal damage / Double talkin' baby / No return / Green door / Condemned to death / Transfusion / Living on the edge
NERCD 039 / Sep '88 / Nervous

☐ VERTIGO
NERCD 090 / Jun '97 / Nervous

Skjelbred, Ray

☐ CHICAGO SESSIONS (Skjelbred, Ray Quartet)
SACD 98 / Jul '93 / Solo Art

Skjerveheim, Lars

☐ HEIMLENGT
BK 13 / Mar '96 / Buen

Skolvan

☐ SWING & TEARS
KM 46 / Oct '94 / Keltia Musique

Skooby

☐ HITCH A RIDE WITH SKOOBY
ASSCD 004 / Jul '96 / Funky Ass

☐ JUST COOKIN'
ASSCD 001 / Jul '96 / Funky Ass

Skooshny

☐ EVEN MY EYES
MZR 3 / Feb '97 / Minus Zero

☐ SKOOSHNY
MZR 1CD / Jul '97 / Minus Zero

Skorr

☐ POPULAR UKRAINIAN DANCES (Skorr & Ukrainian Ensemble)
MCD 71446 / Jun '93 / Monitor

Skoubie Dubh Orchestra

☐ SPIKE'S 23 COLLECTION
LDL 1210CD / Jul '94 / Lochshore

Skrapp Metal

☐ SENSITIVE
PAR 2008CD / Nov '92 / PAR

Skrew

☐ ANGEL SEED XXII
398414142CD / 13 Oct '97 / Metal Blade

☐ SHADOW OF DOUBT
398417025CD / Apr '96 / Metal Blade

Skull Control

☐ RADIO DANGER
ILCD 1013 / 9 Mar '98 / Iloki

Skull Snaps

☐ SKULL SNAPS
My hang up is you / Having you around / Didn't I do it to you / All of a sudden / It's a new day / I'm your pimp / I turn my back on love / Trespassing / I'm falling out of love
CPCD 8094 / Apr '95 / Charly

Skullflower

☐ IIIRD GATEKEEPER
HD 001 / Nov '92 / Headdirt

☐ TRANSFORMER
SFTRI 325CD / Jan '96 / Psychedelic Noise

Skunk Anansie

☐ PARANOID AND SUNBURNT
TPLP 55CD / Oct '95 / One Little Indian

☐ STOOSH
Yes it's fucking political / All I want / She's my heroine / Infidelity (only you) / Hedonism (just because you feel good) / Twisted (everyday hurts) / We love your apathy / Brazen (weep) / Pickin' on me / Milk is my sugar / Glorious pop song
TPLP 85CD / Oct '96 / One Little Indian

Skunkhour

☐ SKUNKHOUR
Pullatickin / Cow and a pig / Horse / Booty full / Back to basics / Sheep of Sam / Free man / Do you like it / State / Erichina
JAZIDCD 113 / Jul '95 / Acid Jazz

Sky

☐ BEST OF SKY, THE
Toccata / Westway / Sanara / Gymnopedie No.1 / Moonroof
MCCD 172 / Sep '94 / Music Club

☐ SKY (Sky 1/Sky 2/Sky 3) (3CD Set)
MCBX 001 / Sep '95 / Music Club

☐ SKY VOL.1
Westway / Carrillon / Danza / Gymnopedie No.1 / Cannonball / Where opposites meet
MCCD 077 / Jun '92 / Music Club

☐ SKY VOL.1
MER 008 / Mar '93 / Tring

☐ SKY VOL.2
Hotta / Dance of the little fairies / Sahara / Fifo / Vivaloi / Tuba smarties / Ballet-volta / Gavotte and variations / Andante / Tristan's magic garden / El cielo / Scipio (part 1 and 2) / Toccata
MCCD 078 / Jun '92 / Music Club

☐ SKY VOL.2
MER 009 / Mar '93 / Tring

☐ SKY VOL.3
Grace / Chiropodie no.1 / Westwind / Sarabande / Connecting rooms / Moonroof / Sister Rose / Hello / Dance of the big fairies / Matheeco / Keep me safe and keep me warm / Shelter me from darkness
MCCD 079 / Jun '92 / Music Club

Sky Cries Mary

☐ FRESH FRUITS FOR THE LIBERATION
WDM 100762 / 29 Jun '98 / World Domination

☐ RETURN TO THE INNER EXPERIENCE
Walla walla / Moving like water / Gone / 2000 Light years from home / When the fear stops / Lay down your head / Rain / Ocean which humanity is / Broken down / Rosaleen / Bus to gate / Joey's aria / We will fall
WDOM 006CD / May '94 / World Domination

☐ THIS TIMELESS TURNING
WDOM 011CD / Oct '94 / World Domination

Sky High

☐ AFRICAN VENGANCE (Sky High & The Mau Mau)
CD 1004 / Sep '94 / Sky High

☐ LION JUNGLE (Sky High & The Mau Mau)
SHCD 2001 / Jan '95 / Ras

☐ MARCUS GARVEY CHANT (Sky High & The Mau Mau)
RASCD 3107 / Nov '92 / Ras

☐ SKYHIGH IN DUBLAND VOL.1 (Sky High & The Mau Mau)
SH 2003 / Jun '96 / Skyhigh

Sky, Patrick

☐ SONGS THAT MADE USA FAMOUS
GCD 4101 / Jan '98 / Genes

Skyclad

☐ ANSWER MACHINE
MASSCD 128
MASSDC 128 / 15 Sep '97 / Massacre

☐ BURNT OFFERING FOR THE BONE IDOL, A
War and disorder / Broken promised land / Spinning Jenny / Salt on earth (another man's poison) / Karmageddon (the suffering silence) / Ring stone round / Men of straw / R'vannith / Declaration of indifference / Alone in death's shadow
N 01862 / Mar '92 / Noise

☐ BURNT OFFERING, A
N 01862 / Nov '96 / Noise

☐ IRRATIONAL ANTHEMS
MASSCD 084 / Jan '96 / Massacre

☐ JONAH'S ARK
Thinking allowed / Cry of the land / Schadenfreude / A near life experience / Wickedest man in the world / Earth mother, the sun and the furious host / Ilk of human blindness / Tunnel visionaires / A word to the wise / Bewilderbeast / It wasn't meant to end this way
N 02092 / Nov '96 / Noise

☐ OLD ROPE
N 02752 / Nov '96 / Noise

☐ PRINCE OF THE POVERTY LINE
N 02392 / Nov '96 / Noise

☐ QUI AVANT GARDE A CHANCE
MASSCD 104 / Nov '96 / Massacre

☐ SILENT WHALES OF LUNAR SEA
N 02282 / Nov '96 / Noise

☐ TRACKS FROM THE WILDERNESS
N 01943 / Nov '96 / Noise

Skylab

☐ SKYLAB NO.1
River of bass / Seashell / Depart / Next / Ghost dance / Shhh / Indigo / Ah ee hu / Electric blue / Six nine / Tokyo 1 / Tokyo elevator
LATCD 21 / Dec '95 / L'Attitude

Skylark

☐ ALL OF IT
Fair Jane/Townsend's jig/Captain White's jig / Pretty Susan / Tryst / Heel and toe / Siuil arun / Contradiction set / All of it / Ball and pin / In contempt / Teelin polkas / Braes of Balquhidder / Dewdrops on the corn/Pat McKenna's jig/Cook in the kitchen / For a new baby
GLCD 3046 / Aug '92 / Green Linnet

☐ LIGHT AND SHADE
Mad French / Brown girl / Sunflower / Neil Mulligan's jig / Upon St. Nicholas boat / Cruel wars / O'Donnel's fancy/Get up old woman and shake yourself / Star above the garter / Little pack of tailors / Frank Quinn's and Peter McArdle's highlands / Factory girl / Up in smoke / Young and foolish / Munster bacon/ The hawk/Paddy Kierce's jig / Boys of Mullaghbawn / Gypsy
CC 57CD / Feb '92 / Claddagh

☐ RAINING BICYCLES
CC 62CD / Aug '96 / Claddagh

Skylarks

☐ BEST OF THE SKYLARKS, THE
NASH 4005 / Feb '96 / Nashboro

Skyliners

☐ SINCE I DON'T HAVE YOU
Since I don't have you / This I swear / I'll be seeing you / Lonely way to be / If I loved you / Warm / When I fall in love / Tired of me / Pennies from Heaven / It happened today / Zing went the strings of my heart / One night, one night / Tomorrow / Lorraine from Spain / I can dream, can't I
CDCH 78 / May '91 / Ace

Skypark

☐ AM I PRETTY
Here come the bugs / Cycle me through / Am I pretty / Shelter / My mirror / Wizard of Id / Emily's love song / Face of an angel / See through me / Christ will save you / Nondescript / Starbux girl
7019951600 / Jun '98 / Word

Skyray

☐ TRANQUILLISER
OCH 006LCD / 18 May '98 / Ochre

Skyscraper

☐ SHOOTERS
DSCD 003 / 6 Apr '98 / Dynosupreme

☐ SUPERSTATE
DSCD 001 / Nov '95 / Dynosupreme

Skyy

☐ BEST OF SKYY, THE
CDGR 157 / Aug '97 / Charly

Slab

☐ FREEKY SPEED
DUKE 020CD
DUKE 020CDL / Apr '96 / Hydrogen Dukebox

Slack, Freddie

☐ FREDDIE SLACK ORCHESTRA, THE (Slack, Freddie & His Orchestra)
JH 1051 / Feb '98 / Jazz Hour

Slackers

☐ REDLIGHT
Cooking for Tommy / Watch this / Married girl / I still love you / Soldier / Fried chicken / You must be good / Redlight / Tin tin deo / Alone / Rude and wreckless / Come back baby
04032 / 3 Nov '97 / Epitaph

Slade

☐ AMAZING KAMIKAZE SYNDROME, THE
My oh my / Run runaway / C'est la vie / Slam the hammer down / Cocky rock boys / In the doghouse / Ready to explode / Razzle dazzle man / Cheap 'n' nasty love / High and dry
CLACD 419 / Nov '96 / Castle

☐ COLLECTION, THE
Run run away / Everyday / We'll bring the house down / Ruby red / (And now the waltz) c'est la vie / Do you believe in miracles / Still the same / My oh my / All join hands / Wheels ain't comin' down / 7 year bitch / Myzterious mizster Jones / Lock up your daughters / Me and the boys / Gudbye t' jane / Mama weer all crazee now / Love is like a rock
CCSCD 444 / Nov '96 / Castle

☐ CRACKERS
Let's dance / Santa Claus is coming to town / Hi ho silver lining / We'll bring the house down / Cum on feel the noize / All join hands / Okey cokey / Merry Christmas everybody / Do you believe in miracles / Let's have a party / Get down and get with it / My oh my / Run runaway / Here's to (the New Year) / Do they know it's Christmas / Auld lang syne / You'll never walk alone / Mama weer all crazee now
CCSCD 401 / Nov '93 / Castle

☐ FEEL THE NOIZE (The Very Best Of Slade)
Get down and get with it / Coz I love you / Look wot you dun / Take me bak 'ome / Mama weer all crazee now / Gudbuy t'Jane / Cum on feel the noize / Skweeze me, pleeze me / My friend Stan / Everyday / Bangin' man / Far far away / How does it feel / In for a penny / We'll bring the house down / Lock up your daughters / My oh my / Run run away / All join hands / Radio wall of sound / Merry xmas everybody
5371052 / Jan '97 / Polydor

☐ GENESIS OF SLADE, THE (Rare Recordings From 1964-1966) (Various Artists)
TMC 9606 / Mar '97 / Music Corporation

☐ KEEP ON ROCKIN'
I hear ya callin' / Hot luv / Do you want me / Black and white world / Miracle / Cum on let's party / Johnny played the guitar / Howlin' wind / Red hot / Dirty foot lane / Merry xmas now
30092 / Oct '97 / Go On Deluxe

☐ NOBODY'S FOOL
8491832 / May '91 / Polydor

☐ OLD, NEW, BORROWED AND BLUE
8491812 / May '91 / Polydor

☐ PLAY IT LOUD
Raven / See us here / Dapple rose / Could I / One way hotel / Shape of things to come / Know who you are / I remember / Pouk hill / Angelina / Dirty joker / Sweet box
8491782 / May '91 / Polydor

☐ SLADE ALIVE VOL.1
Hear me calling / In like a shot from my gun / Darling be home soon / Know who you are / Keep on rocking / Get down with it / Born to be wild
8411142 / Apr '91 / Polydor

☐ SLADE ALIVE VOL.2
Get on up / Take me bak 'ome / My baby left me / Be / Mama weer all crazee now / Burning in the heat of love / Everyday / Gudbuy t'Jane / On eyed Jacks with moustaches / C'mon feel the noize
8491792 / May '93 / Polydor

☐ SLADE IN FLAME
How does it feel / Them kinda monkeys can't swing / So far, so good / Summer song / OK yesterday was yesterday / Far far away / This girl / Lay it down / Heaven knows / Standing on the corner
8491822 / May '91 / Polydor

☐ SLADE ON STAGE
Rock and roll / When I'm dancin' I ain't fightin' / Everyday / Lock up your daughters / We'll bring the house down / Night to remember / Gudbye to Jane / Mama weer all crazee now
CLACD 420 / Nov '96 / Castle

☐ SLADEST
Cum on feel the noize / Look wot you dun / Gudbuy t' Jane / One way hotel / Skweeze me pleeze me / Pouk Hill / Shape of things to come / Take me back 'ome / Coz I luv you / Wild winds are blowing / Know who you are / Get down and get with it / Look at last nite / Mama weer all crazee now
8371032 / May '93 / Polydor

☐ SLAYED
How d'you ride / Whole world's goin' crazee / Look at last nite / I won't let it 'appen agen / Move over / Gudbuy t' Jane / Gudbuy gudbuy / Mama weer all crazee now / I don't mind / Let the good times roll
8491802 / May '91 / Polydor

☐ TILL DEAF DO US PART
Rock 'n' roll preacher / Lock up your daughters / Till deaf do us part / Ruby red / She brings out the devil in me / Night to remember / M'hat m'coat / It's your body not your mind / Let the rock roll out of control / That was no lady that was my wife / Knuckle sandwich Nancy / Till deaf resurrected
CLACD 415 / Nov '96 / Castle

☐ WE'LL BRING THE HOUSE DOWN
We'll bring the house down / Night starvation / Wheels ain't coming down / Hold on to your hats / My baby's got it / When I'm dancin' I ain't fightin' / Dizzy mama / Nuts, bolts and screw / Lemme love into ya / I'm a rocker
CLACD 418 / Nov '96 / Castle

☐ WHATEVER HAPPENED TO SLADE
8491842 / May '93 / Polydor

☐ YOU BOYZ MAKE BIG NOIZE
Love is like a rock / That's what friends are for / Still the same / Fools go grazy / She's heavy / We won't give in / Won't you rock with me / Ooh la la in LA / Me and the boys / Sing shout (knock yourself out) / Roaring silence / It's hard having fun nowadays / You boyz make big noize / Boyz
CLACD 417 / Nov '96 / Castle

Slagle, Steve

☐ ALTO BLUE (Slagle, Steve Quartet)
SCCD 31416 / 21 Aug '97 / Steeplechase

☐ REINCARNATION
SCCD 31367 / Apr '96 / Steeplechase

☐ SPREAD THE WORD
SCCD 31354 / May '95 / Steeplechase

SLAM

☐ HEADSTATES
SOMACD 5 / May '96 / Soma

Slammer

☐ NIGHTMARE SCENARIO
What's your pleasure / Greed / In the name of god / Just another massacre / Architect of pain / Every breath / I know who I am / Corruption / Think for yourself / L'ultima
HMRXD 170 / Apr '91 / Heavy Metal

Slant 6

☐ INZOMBIA
DIS 94CD / May '95 / Dischord

☐ SODA POP RIP OFF
DIS 91CD / Mar '94 / Dischord

Slap n' The Cats

☐ HOTRODS AND HAIRCUTS
S2CD 195 / May '98 / PMI

Slapback

☐ IF IT AIN'T BROKE DON'T FUNK WITH IT
50535 / 15 Sep '97 / Raging Bull

Slapdash

☐ ACTUAL REALITY
NB 197CD / Nov '96 / Nuclear Blast

Slapp Happy

☐ CA VA
VVR 1001662 / 27 Apr '98 / Banana

☐ CASABLANCA MOON/DESPERATE STRAIGHTS
Casablanca moon / Me and Paravati / Half way there / Michelangelo / Dawn / Mr. Rainbow / Secret / Little something / Drum / Haiku / Slow moon's rose / Some questions about hats / Owl / Worm is at work / Bad alchemy / Europa / Desperate straights / Riding tigers / Apes in capes / Strayed / Giants / Extracts from the Messiah / In the sickbay / Caucasian lullaby
CDOVD 441 / Oct '93 / Virgin

Slapshot

☐ 16 VALVE HATE
LF 195CD / Aug '95 / Lost & Found

☐ BLAST FURNACE
WB 2098CD / Jun '93 / We Bite

☐ LIVE AT THE SO36
WB 2111CD / May '94 / We Bite

☐ OLDTYME HARDCORE
CMCD 77129 / Jun '96 / Century Media

☐ STEP ON IT/BACK ON THE MAP
Step on it / Chameleon / No time left / You've lost it / Show the way / Same mistake / No friend of mine / I've had enough / Could it be / No guts no glory / Rise and fall / Hang up your boots / Enforcer / Chant / In your face / Might makes right / Gilligan / Back on the map / Addiction / Where theres smoke / It's happening today / Chip on my shoulder / Moment of truth / Killing frost
TAANG 28CD / Nov '92 / Taang

☐ SUDDEN DEATH
TAANG 40CD / Nov '92 / Taang

☐ UNCONSCIOUSNESS
WB 21142 / Oct '94 / We Bite

Slapstick

☐ LOOKIT
AM 003 / Feb '97 / Asian Man

☐ SLAPSTICK
AM 009 / Jun '97 / Asian Man

Slash's Snake Pit

☐ IT'S FIVE O'CLOCK SOMEWHERE
Neither can I / Dime store rock / Beggers and hangers on / Good to be alive / What do you want to be / Monkey chow / Back and forth again / I hate everybody (but you) / Be the ball / Doin' fine / Take it away / Jizz da pit lower / Some city ward
GED 24730 / Feb '95 / Geffen

Slater, Holly

☐ MOOD WAS THERE, THE
JHCD 053 / 27 Oct '97 / Ronnie Scott's Jazz House

Slater, Luke

☐ FOUR CORNERED ROOM
Time melts / Reality of space / Surface bound / Lost / Needs of the many / 7th plain / Astra naut-e / Trite / Seeing sense / Real life ceremony / Grace
GPRCD 3 / Feb '94 / GPR

☐ FREAK FUNK
Purely / Score one / Origin / Score two / Are you there / Score three / Engine one / Freak funk / Zebediah / Bless bless / Filter / Time dancer / Score four / Love / Black cloud / Walking the line / High wire
NOMU 057CD / 20 Oct '97 / Nova Mute

☐ LUKE SLATER 1992-1994
PF 068CD / Aug '97 / Peacefrog

☐ MY YELLOW WISE RUG
GPRCD 8 / Sep '94 / GPR

☐ X-FRONT VOL.2
PF 11CD / Oct '93 / Peacefrog

Slatkin, Leonard

☐ ANDERSON - THE TYPEWRITER
Belle of the ball / First day of spring / Sleigh ride / Plink, plank, plunk / Blue tango / Forgotten dreams / Buglers' holiday / Pennywhistle song / Clarinet candy / A trumpeter's lullaby / Fiddle faddle / Jazz pizzicato / Jazz / Syncopated clock
09026680482 / Aug '95 / RCA

Slaton, Wendi

☐ TURN AROUND AND LOOK
JR 006012 / Nov '92 / Justice

Slaughter

☐ ETERNAL LIVE
86249 / 22 May '98 / CMC
SPV 08518162 / 1 Sep '98 / SPV

☐ FEAR NO EVIL
SPV 08576002 / May '95 / SPV

Slaughter Joe

☐ PIED PIPER OF FEEDBACK
I'll follow you down / She's so out of touch / Surely some of slaughters blues / Fall apart / Napalm girl / Positively something wild / Tangerine / I know you rider (i know my rider) / Lonesome death of thurston moore / If I die before I wake
CRECD 084 / May '94 / Creation

Slaughter, Alvin

☐ YES
Jesus you are welcome / God is good / Move in this place / Mercy refused / Alleluia praise Jehovah / Servant's prayer / I need thee every hour / He's already provided / Worthy worthy / I say yes/Yes midnight cry / Jesus is mine
11182 / Oct '97 / Hosanna

Slaughter, John

☐ ALL THAT STUFF AIN'T REAL
Red tail light / Get some rest / Louisiana 1927 / I've got the proof / Something you got / Ready to fall / Lost and found / On my way to heaven / St James' infirmary / I can't swim / Don't fool yourself / Shame on you
CDSJP 430 / Oct '95 / Timeless Jazz

☐ NEW COAT OF PAINT, A (Slaughter Blues Band)
Riding with the king / Walking on sunset / I believe to my soul / Paint my mailbox blue / Watch your step / Cold cold feeling / Woke up this morning / Help me / Don't go the strangers / New coat of paint
CDSJP 313 / Jun '92 / Timeless Jazz

Slave

☐ FUNK STRIKES BACK, THE
ICH 1144CD / Feb '94 / Ichiban

☐ MASTERS OF THE FUNGK
D 2248622 / Jan '96 / Ichiban

☐ REBIRTH
Are you ready / Way you dance / My everything / Everybody's talkin' / Thrill me / Victim of circumstance / I love you / Andy's ways / Behind closed doors / How is this love
ICH 1055CD / Oct '93 / Ichiban

☐ STELLAR FUNK (The Best Of Slave)
Slide / Party song / Stellar funk / Are you ready for love / Way out / Feel so real / Dancin' in the key of life / Weak at the knees / Nobody can be you / Wait for me / Snap shot / Just a touch of love / Stolen jam
8122715922 / Mar '94 / Atlantic

Slave Master

☐ UNDER THE 6
Godless / Heal / Damnation / Come out / Day of requital / Final call / Walk the water / Down / Each one teach one / Freedom
RCD 10302 / Jun '94 / Black Arc

Slave One

☐ REPULSOR
FDN 2015CD / Jun '97 / Mascot

Slaves

☐ TALKING REGGAE
669122 / Nov '92 / Greensleeves

Slawterhaus

☐ LIVE
VICTOCD 013 / Nov '94 / Victo

Slayan, Piter

☐ MASTERS OF MINANGKABAU, THE (Music From Sumatra) (Slayan, Piter & M. Halim)
CDMANU 1531 / Jul '97 / ODE

Slayer

☐ DECADE OF AGGRESSION
Hell awaits / Anti-christ / War ensemble / South of Heaven / Raining blood / Altar of sacrifice / Jesus saves / Captor of sin / Born of fire / Post mortem / Spirit in black / Dead skin mask / Seasons in the abyss / Mandatory suicide / Angel of death / Hallowed point / Blood red / Die by the sword / Expendable youth / Chemical warfare / Black magic
74321248512 / Dec '94 / American

☐ DIABOLUS IN MUSICA
Bitter peace / Death's head / Stain of mind / Overt enemy / Perversions of pain / Love to hate / Desire / In the name of God / Screaming from the sky / Wicked / Point / Scrum
4913022
4913029 / 8 Jun '98 / Columbia

☐ HELL AWAITS
Hell awaits / At dawn they sleep / Praise of death / Captor of sin / Hardening of the arteries / Kill again / Haunting the chapel / Necrophiliac / Crypts of eternity
398414031CD / Feb '96 / Metal Blade

☐ LIVE UNDEAD/HAUNTING THE CHAPEL
398414011CD / Feb '96 / Metal Blade

☐ REIGN IN BLOOD
Angel of death / Piece by piece / Necrophobic / Altar of sacrifice / Jesus saves / Criminally insane / Reborn / Epidemic / Post mortem / Raining blood
74321248482 / Dec '94 / American

☐ SATANIC SLAUGHTER VOL.1 (A Tribute To Slayer) (Various Artists)
BS 003CD / Nov '95 / Black Sun

☐ SATANIC SLAUGHTER VOL.2 (A Tribute To Slayer) (Various Artists)
BS 006CD / Nov '96 / Black Sun

☐ SEASONS IN THE ABYSS
War ensemble / Blood red / Spirit in black / Expendable youth / Dead skin mask / Hallowed point / Skeletons of society / Temptation / Born of fire / Seasons in the abyss
74321248502 / Dec '94 / American

☐ SHOW NO MERCY
Evil has no boundaries / Die by the sword / Metal storm / Black magic / Final command / Show no mercy / Anti-christ / Fight till death / Aggressive perfector / Tormentor / Crionics / Face the Slayer
398414032CD / Feb '96 / Metal Blade

☐ SOUTH OF HEAVEN
South of heaven / Silent scream / Live undead / Behind the crooked cross / Mandatory suicide / Ghosts of war / Read between the lies / Cleanse the soul / Dissident aggressor / Spill the blood
74321248492 / Dec '94 / American

☐ UNDISPUTED ATTITUDE
Disintegration / Leeches / Abolish government / Can't stand you / Drunk drivers against mad mothers / Guilty of being white / I hate you / Filler / I don't want to hear it / Spiritual law / Mr. Freeze / Violent pacification / Memories of tomorrow / Richard hung himself / I wanna be your dog / Gemini
74321357592 / May '96 / American

Slazenger, Jake

☐ DAS IST EIN GROOVY BEAT JA
WARPCD 42 / Jul '96 / Warp

☐ MAKESARACKET
CLR 410CD / Jun '95 / Clear

Sleater-Kinney

☐ CALL THE DOCTOR
CHSW 13CD / Dec '96 / Chainsaw

☐ CALL THE DOCTOR
Call the doctor / Hibcap / Little mouth / Anonymous / Stay where you are / Good things / I wanna be your Joey / Ramone / Taking me home / Taste test / My stuff / I'm not waiting / Heart attack
OLE 2682 / 1 Jun '98 / Matador

☐ DIG ME OUT
Dig me out / One more hour / Turn it on / Drama you've been craving / Heart factory / Words and guitar / It's enough / Little babies / Not what you want / Buy her candy / Things you say / Dance song '97 / Jenny
OLE 2692 / 6 Oct '97 / Matador
KRS 279CD / 23 Mar '98 / Kill Rock Stars

☐ SLEATER-KINNEY
Don't think you wanna / Day I went away / Real man / Her again / How to play dead / Be yer mama / Sold out / Slow song / Lora's song / Last song
OLE 2672 / 1 Jun '98 / Matador

Sledge, Percy

☐ 20 GREATEST HITS
When a man loves a woman / (sittin' on) the dock of the bay / Try a little tenderness
MU 5016 / Oct '92 / Musketeer

☐ BLUE NIGHT
You got away with love / Love come knockin' / Why did you stop / I wish it would rain / Blue night / These ain't raindrops / Your love will save the world / First you cry / Going home tomorrow / Grand blvd / I've got dreams to remember
VPBCD 21 / Nov '94 / Pointblank

☐ GREATEST HITS
When a man loves a woman / It tears me up / Sudden stop / Walkin' in the sun / Cover me / Warm and tender love / My special prayer / Good love / Just out of reach / Out of left field / Thief in the night / You're pouring water on a drowning man / My adorable one / When a man loves a woman (2nd version)
CDSGP 044 / Apr '93 / Prestige

☐ IT TEARS ME UP (The Best Of Percy Sledge)
When a man loves a woman / I'm hanging up my heart for you / Put a little lovin' on me / Love me like you mean it / It tears me up / Warm and tender love / Love me tender / Dark end of the street / Take time to know her / Try a little tenderness / Bless your sweet little soul / True love travels on a gravel road / Sudden stop / Stop the world tonight / It's all wrong but it's all right / Drown in my own tears / Out of left field / Kind woman / Cover me / That's the way I want to live my life / Push Mr. Pride aside / It can't be stopped / Rainbow road
8122702852 / Mar '93 / Atlantic

☐ LITTLE TENDERNESS, A
When a man loves a woman / Cover me / Take time to know her / Try a little tenderness / I've been loving you too long / It tears me up / My special prayer / Bring it on home / If loving you is wrong / You send me / Walkin' in the sun / Behind closed doors / Love among people / Warm and tender love / I'll be your everything
SUMCD 4009 / Nov '96 / Summit

☐ PERCY SLEDGE & OTIS REDDING (Sledge, Percy/Otis Redding)
UAE 30092 / Jan '98 / Members Edition

☐ PERCY SLEDGE COLLECTION
When a man loves a woman / My special prayer / Take time to know her / Try a little tenderness / (sittin' on) the dock of the bay / Out of left field / It tears me up / Just out of reach / Cover me / Tell it like it is / I'll be your everything / Sudden stop / Behind closed doors / Blue water / Hard to be friends / I believe in you / If this is the last time / Love away people / Warm and tender love / My adorable one / Good love / Thief in the night / Walkin' in the sun / You're pouring water on a drowning man / Make it good and make it last
COL 048 / Jun '95 / Collection

☐ SPOTLIGHT ON PERCY SLEDGE
Warm and tender love / Cover me / You're pouring water on a drowning man / My special prayer / Take time to know her / My adorable one / Sudden stop / Good love / Walking in the sun / It tears me up / Make it good and make it last / Out of left field / Behind closed doors / Just out of reach / Thief in the night / When a man loves a woman
HADCD 125 / Feb '94 / Javelin

☐ WANTED AGAIN
Keep the fire burning / Kiss an angel good morning / If you've got the money honey / Today I started loving you again / Wabash cannonball / Wanted again / Hey good lookin' / He'll have to go / She thinks I still care / For the good times
DIAB 859 / 1 Jun '98 / Diablo

☐ WHEN A MAN LOVES A WOMAN
When a man loves a woman / Warm and tender love / Bring it on home to me / Behind closed doors / Try a little tenderness / Tell it like it is / My special prayer / (Sittin' on the) dock of the bay / (If loving you is wrong) I don't want to be right / Take time to know her / It tears me up / I've been loving you too long / Cover me / You send me
ECD 3087 / Jan '95 / K-Tel

☐ WHEN A MAN LOVES A WOMAN (The Best Of Percy Sledge)
When a man loves a woman / Warm and tender love / It tears me up / Take time to know her / Just out of reach / My special prayer / Out of left field / Baby help me / Sudden stop / Cover me / Adorable one / Dark end of the street
AIM 2002CD / May '97 / Aim

☐ WHEN A MAN LOVES A WOMAN
When a man loves a woman / Warm and tender love / Just out of reach / Cover me / It tears me up / My special prayer / Take time to know her / You're all around me / Out of left field / Dark end of the street / Sudden stop / Adorable one
100582 / May '97 / A-Play Collection

☐ WHEN A MAN LOVES A WOMAN
322698 / Jul '97 / Koch Presents

Sleep

☐ JERUSALEM
DS 01 / 1 Jun '98 / Dopesmoker

☐ SLEEP VOL.1
TUPCD 034 / Feb '92 / Tupelo

☐ SLEEPS HOLY MOUNTAIN
Dragonaut / Druid / Evil gypsy / Some grass / Aquarian / Holy mountain / Inside the sun / From beyond / Nain's baptism
MOSH 079CD / 1 Sep '97 / Earache

Sleep Chamber

☐ SECRETS OV 23
EEE 014CD / Sep '93 / Musica Maxima Magnetica

☐ SIRKUS
D 1024CD / 3 Nov '97 / Daft

☐ SOME GODZ DIE YOUNG
45932E / Jun '97 / Funfundvierz

Sleeper

☐ IT GIRL, THE
Lie detector / Sale of the century / What do I do now / Good luck Mr. Gorsky / Feeling peaky / Shrinkwrapped / Dress like your Mother / Statuesque / Glue ears / Nice guy Eddie / Stop your crying / Factor 41 / Click off gone
74321364772 / 2 Feb '98 / Indolent

☐ PLEASED TO MEET YOU
Please please please / She's a good girl / Rollercoaster / Miss you / You got me / Breathe / Superclean / Firecracker / Because of you / Romeo me / Nothing is changing / Motorway man / Traffic accident
SLEEPCD 016 / Nov '97 / Indolent

☐ PREPARING FOR TOMORROW'S BREAKDOWN
EXC 0122 / Jun '94 / Excursion

☐ SMART
Inbetweener / Swallow / Delicious / Hunch / Amuse / Behead / Lady love your countryside / Vegas / Poor flying man / Alice in vain / Twisted / Pyrotechnician
SLEEPCD 007 / 1 Sep '97 / Indolent

Sleeping Dogs Wake

☐ HOLD ME UNDER THE STARS
39101133 / Jan '97 / Hyperium

☐ SPIDERBILLY'S SNAKEDANCE
39101263 / Jan '97 / Hyperium

☐ THRENODY
39101202 / Jan '97 / Hyperium

☐ UNDER THE STARS
39101262 / Jan '97 / Hyperium

☐ UNDERSTANDING
39101192 / Jan '97 / Hyperium

☐ WALK ON
39100793 / Jan '97 / Hyperium

Sleepy People

☐ TYPHOID AND SWANS
EDGY 105 / 2 Mar '98 / Edgy

Sleepyhead

☐ LATE NIGHT THINKING
SFR 202 / Oct '97 / Sealed Fate

Sleight Of Hand

☐ SECEDE
HMRXD 196 / Nov '95 / Heavy Metal

Slick Pelt

☐ HELL FROM THE HILLS
SP 001 / Aug '96 / Slick Pelt

Slick Rick

☐ BEHIND BARS
5238472 / Feb '95 / Def Jam

☐ GREAT ADVENTURES OF SLICK RICK, THE
Treat her like a prostitute / Ruler's back / Children's story / Moment I feared / Let's get crazy / Indian girl / Teenage love / Mona Lisa / Kit (what's the scoop) / Hey young world / Teacher teacher / Lick the balls
5273592 / Jan '96 / Def Jam

☐ RULER'S BACK, THE
5234802 / Jan '96 / Def Jam

Slick Shoes

☐ BURN OUT
TNR 1105CD / 3 Aug '98 / Tooth & Nail

Slickee Boys

☐ FASHIONABLE LATE
ROSE 147CD / May '88 / New Rose

☐ LIVE AT LAST
Gotta tell my why / Dream lovers / Missing part / Sleepless nights / Disconnected / Droppin' off to sleep / Brain that refused to die / Death lane / Life of the party / Pictures of matchstick men / When I go to the beach / Jailbait Janet / This party sucks / Here to stay
ROSE 169CD / Aug '89 / New Rose

Slide

☐ UNSTABLE
TRAN 617CD / 29 Jun '98 / Transient

Slide 5

☐ RHODE TRIP
URCD 015 / Jul '96 / Ubiquity

Slight Slappers

☐ SLIGHT SLAPPERS/SHORT HATE TEMPER (Slight Slappers/Short Hate Temper)
POLLUTE 43CD / 9 Feb '98 / Sound Pollution

Slightly Bewildered String Band

☐ SLIGHTLY BEWILDERED
SC 1095CD / Aug '96 / Starc

Slim

☐ SLIM
What it is / Abducted / Water / Triple threads / Your chair / My dangerous life / Idyll
EMIT 0097 / Apr '97 / Emit

Slim Moon

☐ WON'T YOU DANCE WITH THIS MAN
KRS 268CD / 22 Sep '97 / Kill Rock Stars

Slimani, Abdel Ali

☐ MRAYA
Laziza / Habibti / Zeyna / Mraya / Yasmin / Alger / Hadi / Ana guellile / Ana guellile (dub)
CDRW 55 / Jan '96 / Realworld

Slingbacks

☐ ALL POP, NO STAR
No way down / Wasted / Hey Douglas / Trashy broken heart / Sometimes I hate you / All pop, no star / Autumn teen sound / Boy who wanted a heroine / Insufferable / Better think hard / Whorehouse priest / Junkstruck / Stupid boyfriend
CDV 2816 / Oct '96 / Virgin

Slinger, Cees

☐ LIVE AT THE NORTH SEA JAZZ FESTIVAL
MCD 198244 / Oct '92 / Limetree

Slint

☐ SPIDERLAND
TG 64CD / 14 Sep '98 / Touch & Go

Slipmatt

☐ DREAMSCAPE VOL.1 - EXTRA SENSORY PERCEPTION (Mixed By Slipmatt/DJ Sy & Randall - 3CD Set) (Various Artists)
DSRCD 001 / 5 Jan '98 / Dreamscape

☐ HARDCORE HEAVEN VOL.1 (Mixed By Slipmatt/Dougal/Seduction/Sy - 2CD Set) (Various Artists)
HMLCD 101 / Mar '97 / Heaven

☐ HELTER SKELTER (The Annual Mixed By DJ Slipmatt/DJ Dougal - 2CD Set) (Various Artists)
CDHSR 096 / 18 May '98 / Helter Skelter

☐ MIXMAG LIVE VOL.18 (Hardcore Happiness - Stu Allen/Slipmatt) (Various Artists)
MMLCD 018 / Jul '96 / Mixmag Live

☐ SLIPMATT TAKES CONTROL (Various Artists)
KICKCD 29 / Nov '95 / Kickin'

Slippers

☐ CHANCE TO DANCE, A
GRCD 6049 / Nov '96 / Goofin'

Slipstream

☐ BE GROOVY OR LEAVE
CHECD 69 / 8 Dec '97 / Che

☐ SIDE EFFECTS
CHE 37CD / Nov '95 / Che

Slits

☐ CUT
Instant hit / So tough / Spend spend spend / Shoplifting / FM / Ping pong affair / Newtown / Love and romance / Typical girls / Adventures close to home
IMCD 90 / Feb '90 / Island

☐ IN THE BEGINNING (An Anthology)
Vindictive / Boring life / Slime / New town / Love and romance / Shoplifting / Number one enemy / Number one enemy / In the beginning / New town / Man next door / I heard it through the grapevine / Typical girls / Fade away / In the beginning
FREUDCD 057 / Aug '97 / Jungle

☐ PEEL SESSIONS, THE
Love and romance / Vindictive / New town / Shoplifting / So tough / Instant hit / FM / Difficult fun / In the beginning / Earthbeat
SFRSCD 052 / 23 Feb '98 / Strange Fruit

Sloan

☐ ONE CHORD TO ANOTHER
MURSD 023 / Apr '97 / Murder

Sloane, Carol

☐ AS TIME GOES BY
Caravan / My foolish heart / I thought about you / As time goes by / Where or when / I only have eyes for you / Misty / There'll be some changes made / Angel eyes / My one and only love / Sunday
PRCDSP 206 / 27 Apr '98 / Prestige

☐ HEART'S DESIRE
Secret love / Memories of you / Heart's desire / September in the rain / Devil may care / You must believe in Spring / Them there eyes / Never never land / My ship / He loves and she loves / Fairy tales / Robbin's nest / You'll see / For Susannah Kyle
CCD 4503 / May '92 / Concord Jazz

☐ OUT OF THE BLUE
Prelude to a kiss / More I see / Aren't you glad you're you / Deep purple / Little girl blue / Life is just a bowl of cherries / Who cares / My silent love / My ship / Will you still be mine / Night and day
378102 / May '96 / Koch Jazz

☐ SONGS CARMEN SANG
I'm gonna lock my heart (and throw away the key) / What can I say after I say I'm sorry / If the moon turns green / Sunday / Suppertime / Just you, just me / It's like reaching for the moon / What a little moonlight can do / Cloudy morning / Autumn nocturne / That old black magic / Folks who live on the hill / I'm an errand girl for rhythm
CCD 4663 / Sep '95 / Concord Jazz

☐ SONGS ELLA AND LOUIS SANG, THE (Sloane, Carol & Clark Terry)
I won't dance / Tenderly / Don't be that way / Can't we be friends / Gee baby, ain't I good to you / Autumn in New York / Let's do it / Stars fell on Alabama / Moonlight in Vermont / Blueberry Hill / Stompin' at the Savoy / When it's sleepy time down South
CCD 47872 / 10 Oct '97 / Concord Jazz

☐ SONGS SINATRA SANG, THE
I've got you under my skin / In the still of the night / One for my baby / At long last love / I'll be around / Fly me to the moon / In the wee small hours of the morning / You make me feel so young / Night we called it a day / You go to my head / I fall in love too easily / Best is yet to come / Young at heart
CCD 4725 / Sep '96 / Concord Jazz

☐ SWEET & SLOW
Sometime ago / One morning in May / I'm way ahead of the game / I'm getting sentimental over you / Until I met you / Sweet and slow / You're getting to be a habit / Woman's intuition / Baubles, bangles and beads / Older man / One hour / I got it bad and that ain't good
CCD 4564 / Aug '93 / Concord Jazz

☐ WHEN I LOOK IN YOUR EYES
Simple life / Isn't this a lovely day (to be caught in the rain) / Midnight sun / Take your shoes off, baby / I didn't know about you / Soon / Old devil moon / Let's face the music and dance / Something cool / Tulip or turnip / I was telling him about you / When I look in your eyes / Will you still be mine
CCD 4619 / Nov '94 / Concord Jazz

Slobberbone

☐ BARREL CHESTED
Barrel chested / Lame / Engine Joe / Front porch / I'll be damned / Billy prichard / Little drunk fists / Get gone again / Your excuse / Haze of drink / One rung
DRCD 7019 / 9 Mar '98 / Doolittle

☐ CROW POT PIE
DRCD 5109 / 16 Feb '98 / Doolittle

Sloe Gin Joes

☐ SLOE GIN JOES
Hot link / Fryin' pan / I can't go home like this / Gettin' a dog / Let's drive / Chicken stew / Club soda / She's my baby doll
EC 1003 / Apr '97 / Ever Cool

Slok

☐ THEY CALL IT JUNGLE
Exalted / Brasilian jazz / Urban station / They call it jungle / Armonic head / Arka / Wandau / Do you remember / Dance hall / One to go / London / Escape / Mystical thought
4888442 / 15 Sep '97 / Irma

Sloman, John

☐ DISAPPEARANCES CAN BE DECEPTIVE
Foolin' myself / Breathless / Jealous / In too deep / Save us / Now you say goodbye / Perfect strangers / She talks about you / Parting you / Hooked on a dream
WKFMXD 114 / Aug '88 / FM

Sloppy Seconds

☐ KNOCK YOUR BLOCK OFF
TAANG 71CD / Jun '93 / Taang

☐ LIVE - NO TIME FOR TUNING
SPV 08456982 / Dec '96 / SPV
TX 51231CD / Oct '96 / Triple X

☐ MORE TROUBLE THAN THEY'RE WORTH
158182 / 3 Aug '98 / Nitro

☐ SLOPPY SECONDS
TAANG 059CD / Jun '92 / Taang

☐ WHERE THE EAGLES DARE
MA 113231CD / Nov '92 / Musical Tragedies

Slotek

☐ 7
EFA 012172 / Apr '97 / Word Sound Recordings

Slovak Radio Symphony Orchestra

☐ NATIONAL ANTHEMS OF THE WORLD VOL.1 (Acadia To Burundi)
8223386 / Apr '98 / Marco Polo

☐ NATIONAL ANTHEMS OF THE WORLD VOL.2 (Cambodia To France)
8223387 / Apr '98 / Marco Polo

☐ NATIONAL ANTHEMS OF THE WORLD VOL.3 (Gabon To Kyrgyzstan)
8223388 / Apr '98 / Marco Polo

☐ NATIONAL ANTHEMS OF THE WORLD VOL.4 (Laos To Oman)
8223835 / Apr '98 / Marco Polo

☐ NATIONAL ANTHEMS OF THE WORLD VOL.5 (Pakistan To Syria)
8223836 / Apr '98 / Marco Polo

☐ NATIONAL ANTHEMS OF THE WORLD VOL.6 (Taiwan To Zimbabwe)
8223852 / Apr '98 / Marco Polo

Slovenly

☐ HIGHWAY TO HANNOS
SST 287CD / May '93 / SST

☐ RIPOSTE
Way untruths are / Old / new / On the surface / Prejudice / Emma / Enormous critics / Myer's dark / Not mobile / As if it always happens / Little resolve
SST 089CD / May '93 / SST

☐ WE SHOOT FOR THE MOON
Running for public office / Self pity song / Don't cry no tears / Talking machines / What's it called / You cease to amaze me / We shoot for the moon / A year with ne head / Spy surf / No unlawful sex / She was bananas / A warm night / Hellectro / Things fall apart
SST 209CD / Mar '89 / SST

Slow Gherkin

☐ DOUBLE HAPPINESS
AM 012CD / Aug '97 / Asian Man

Slow Loris

☐ 10 COMMANDMENTS, THE
185392 / Oct '96 / Southern

Slowburn

☐ BLISSED OUT BEATS
CDRAID 529 / Mar '96 / Rumour

Slowdive

☐ JUST FOR A DAY
Spanish air / Celia's dream / Catch the breeze / Ballad of sister sue / Erik's song / Waves / Brighter / Sadman / Primal
CRECD 094 / Aug '91 / Creation

☐ PYGMALION
Rutti / Crazy for you / Miranda / Trellisaze / Cello / Just heaven / Visions of la / Blue skied an' clear / All of us
CRECD 168 / Feb '95 / Creation

☐ SOUVLAKI
Alison / Machine gun / 40 days / Sing / Here she comes / Souvlaki space station / When the sun hits / Altogether / Melon yellow / Dagger
CRECD 139 / May '93 / Creation

Slowly

☐ MING
CHILLXCD 003 / Apr '95 / Chillout

Slowpoke

☐ MADCHEN
GROW 222 / Oct '94 / Grass

Sludge Nation

☐ BLOW YOUR SPEAKERS
LEFT 47CD / Nov '96 / Rhythm King

Sludgeworth

☐ SLUDGEWORTH
LOOKOUT 131CD / Nov '95 / Lookout

Slugbait

☐ MEDIUM TO HEAVY FLOW
DPROMCD 26 / Jul '95 / Dirter Promotions

Slum Turkeys

☐ COMMUNICATE
COX 029CD / Apr '92 / Meantime

Slusser, David

☐ DELIGHT AT THE END OF THE TUNNEL
TZA 7024 / Jul '97 / Tzadik

Slut

☐ SENSATION
SISSY 006CD / 20 Oct '97 / Sticksister

Slutt

☐ MODEL YOUTH
Angel / Breaking all the rules / Twisted / Women of the night / Revolution / Atomic envelope / TKO / Thrill me / Shooting for love / Through the fire / Too far to run / Model youth / Blue suede shoes
NEATCD 1043 / '88 / Neat

Sly & Robbie

☐ BLAZING HORNS IN DUB
RNCD 2097 / Mar '95 / Rhino

☐ BONANZA STORY (Taxi Gang & Friends)
VPCD 2064 / 24 Nov '97 / VP

☐ CARIB SOUL (Various Artists)
RASCD 3089 / Apr '92 / Ras

☐ CRUCIAL REGGAE (Driven By Sly & Robbie) (Various Artists)
Music is my desire: *Moses, Pablo* / New age music: *Inner Circle* / Just like that: *Toots & The Maytals* / Saturday evening: *Third World* / Reggae fever: *Steel Pulse* / One love jamdown / Rainbow culture: *Aswad* / Jogging: *McGregor, Freddie* / Happiness: *Uhuru* / Some guys have all the luck: *Tucker, Junior*
RRCD 37 / Jul '92 / Reggae Refreshers

☐ DUB ROCKERS DELIGHT
Leaving dub / Dub glory / Righteous dub / Dub to my woman / Night of dub / Dub softly / Doctor in dub / Bound in dub / Dub in government / Jah in dub
CDBM 055 / '91 / Blue Moon

☐ FRIENDS
Friday / Night nurse: *Sly & Robbie/Simply Red* / Seems to me I'm losing: *Sly & Robbie/Ali Campbell* / Only a smile: *Sly & Robbie/Maxi Priest* / You'd be so nice to come to: *Sly & Robbie/Liba* / Penny lover: *Sly & Robbie/Ambilique* / Mission impossible / Candy girl: *Sly & Robbie/Danny Madden* / Ghetto girl: *Sly & Robbie/Simply Red* / All this love: *Sly & Robbie/One Plus One* / Shoulder to cry on: *Sly & Robbie/Liba* / Satisfaction: *Sly & Robbie/Ambilique* / Night nurse (Jah Wobble mix): *Sly & Robbie/Simply Red* / Friday (street mix) / Candy girl (street mix): *Sly & Robbie/Danny Madden*
3984206002 / 29 Sep '97 / East West

☐ I CAME I SAW I CONQUERED
JJCD 29 / 17 Aug '98 / Channel One

☐ LA TRENGGAE (Sly & Robbie/Taxi Gang)
VPCD 2069 / 22 Dec '97 / VP

☐ MAMBO TAXI
Mission Impossible theme / Good the bad and the ugly / Fire in de oven / La bamba / Live it up / Village caller / Sunny Sunday / Mambo taxi / Alfred Hitchcock / Theme from the Apartment / Rasta reggae / Far out
DSR 19841 / Jun '97 / Taxi

☐ MAMBO TAXI (Taxi Gang)
Mission impossible: *Sly & Robbie/Neville Hinds* / Good, the bad and the ugly: *Sly & Robbie/Neville Hinds* / Fire in de oven: *Sly & Robbie* / La bamba: *Sly & Robbie/Ambelique & Chevelle* / Live it up: *Sly & Robbie/Ansil Collins* / Village caller: *Sly & Robbie/Robbie Lyn* / Sunny Sunday: *Sly & Robbie/Dean Fraser* / Mambo taxi: *Sly & Robbie/Nambo Robinson* / Alfred Hitchcock: *Sly & Robbie/Neville Hinds* / Apartment: *Sly & Robbie/Franklyn Bubbler Waul* / Rasta reggae: *Sly & Robbie/Nambo Robinson* / Far out: *Sly & Robbie/Robbie Lyn*
5244102 / 25 Aug '97 / Island Jamaica

☐ MONEY DUB
RNCD 2063 / Jun '94 / Rhino

☐ OVERDRIVE IN OVERDUB
SONCD 0055 / Jan '94 / Sonic Sounds

☐ POWERMATIC DANCEHALL VOL.1 (Various Artists)
RASCD 3111 / Mar '93 / Ras

☐ REGGAE GREATS (A Dub Experience)
Destination unknown / Assault on Station 5 / Joyride / Demolition city / Computer malfunction / Jailbreak / Skull and crossbones / Back to base
RRCD 29 / Sep '91 / Reggae Refreshers

☐ REMEMBER PRECIOUS TIMES
RASCD 3109 / Mar '93 / Ras

☐ SENSI DUB VOL.1 & 7 (Sly & The Revolutionaries/Jah Power Band)
OMCD 030 / Sep '95 / Original Music

☐ SLY & ROBBIE PRESENT JACKIE MITTOO (Sly & Robbie/Jackie Mittoo)
RNCD 2108 / Jun '95 / Rhino

☐ SLY & ROBBIE'S RAGGA PON TOP (Various Artists)
Move with the crowd: *Baby Wayne* / Little crook: *Papa San* / Hold me: *Joseph Stepper* / Ole horse: *Red Dragon* / Thief: *Captain Berkley* / Boom boom bye: *Redrose & Round Head* / Rum shaker: *Nardo Ranks* / Love lullaby: *General Degree* / Give her the credit: *Papa San* / Mony fi spend: *Captain Berkley* / Makosa: *Papa San*
111932 / Feb '94 / Musidisc

☐ SLY AND ROBBIE HITS 1987-1990
SONCD 0010 / Jan '91 / Sonic Sounds

☐ SLY, WICKED AND SLICK (Dunbar, Sly)
Rasta fiesta / Sesame Street / Lover's bop / Senegal market / Mr. Music / Queen of the minstrels / Dirty Harry / Oriental taxis
CDFL 9018 / Jun '91 / Virgin

☐ TAXI CHRISTMAS, A (Taxi Gang)
RASCD 3102 / Dec '92 / Ras

☐ TAXI FARE
Triplet / Devil pickney / Rock music iil / Pure and true / Vla music / Fort augustus / Sitting and watching / Baltimore / Taxi connection / Bang bang / Red hot / Those tricks / Unmetered taxi
HBCD 39 / Jul '87 / Heartbeat

Small Faces

☐ AUTUMN STONE, THE (Remastered)
Here comes the nice / Autumn stone / Collibosher / All or nothing / Red balloon / Lazy Sunday / Call it something nice / I can't make it / Afterglow of your love / Sha la la la lee / Universal / If I were a carpenter / Every little bit hurts / My mind's eye / Tin soldier / Just passing / Itchycoo park / Hey girl / Wide-eyed girl on the wall / Whatcha gonna do about it / Wham bam thank you mam / Donkey rides penny a glass / All or nothing / Tin soldier / Rollin' over
ESMCD 478 / May '97 / Essential

☐ BEST OF THE SMALL FACES, THE
Sha la la la lee / My mind's eye / Universal / Watcha gonna do about it / Hey girl / I can't make it / All or nothing / Here comes the nice / Afterglow of your love / Tin soldier / Autumn stone / Rollin' over / Lazy Sunday / Every little bit hurts / I feel much better / Itchycoo park
SUMCD 4001 / Nov '96 / Summit

☐ DECCA ANTHOLOGY 1965-1967
Whatch'a gonna do about it / What's a matter baby / I've got mine / It's too late / Sha-la-la-la-lee / Grow your own / Hey girl / Almost grown / Shake / Come on children / You'd better believe it / One night stand / Sorry she's mine / Own up time / You need loving / Don't stop what you're doing / E too D / All or nothing / Understanding / My minds eye / I can't dance with you / Just passing / Patterns / Runaway / Yesterday, today and tomorrow / That man / My way of giving / (Tell me) Have you ever seen me / Take this hurt off me / Baby don't you do it / Plum Nellie / You've really got a hold on me / Give her my regards / Imaginary love / It's not what you do
8445832 / Mar '96 / London

☐ DEFINITIVE ANTHOLOGY, THE (2CD Set)
REP 4429 / Nov '97 / Repertoire

☐ GREATEST HITS
REP 4597 / Dec '97 / Repertoire

☐ HIT SINGLE COLLECTABLES
DISK 4504 / Apr '94 / Disky

☐ IMMEDIATE YEARS, THE (4CD Set)
You really got me / Money money / What'cha gonna do about it / Sha la la la lee / Hey girl / My mind's eye / My mind's eye / All or nothing / Yesterday, today and tomorrow / I can't make it / Just passing / Here comes the nice / Itchycoo Park / I'm only dreaming / Tin soldier / I feel much better / Lazy Sunday / Rollin' over / Universal / Donkey rides, a penny, a glass / Afterglow of your love / Wham, bam, thank you Mam / I can't make it / Just passing / Here comes the nice / Itchycoo Park / I'm only dreaming / Tin soldier / I feel much better / Universal / Donkey rides, a penny, a glass / Wham, bam, thank you Mam / (Tell me) Have you ever seen me / Something I want to tell you / Feeling lonely / Happy boys happy / Things are going to get better / My way of giving / Green circles / Become like you / Get yourself together / All our yesterdays / Talk to you / Show me the way / Up the wooden hills to Bedfordshire / Eddie's dreaming / Ogden's nut gone flake / Afterglow of your love / Long agos and world's apart / Rene / Song of a baker / Lazy Sunday / Happiness Stan / Rollin' over / Hungry intruder / Journey / Happydaystoytown / Rollin' over (live) / If I were a carpenter / Every little bit hurts (live) / All or nothing (live) / Tin soldier (live) / Call it something nice / Autumn stone / Every little bit hurts / Collibosher / Red balloon / Don't burst my bubble / (Tell me) Have you ever seen me / Green circles / Picaninny / Pig trotters / War of the worlds / Wide-eyed girl on the wall / Tin soldier (instrumental) / Green circles / Wham, bam, thank you Mam / Collibosher / Hungry intruder / Red balloon / Autumn stone / Wide-eyed girl on the wall
CDIMMBOX 1 / Oct '95 / Immediate

☐ ITCHYCOO PARK
CD 12208 / Aug '93 / Laserlight

☐ MASTERS, THE (2CD Set)
EDMCD 023 / 24 Nov '97 / Eagle

☐ OGDEN'S NUT GONE FLAKE
Ogden's nut gone flake / Afterglow of your love / Long agos and worlds apart / Rene / Son of a baker / Lazy Sunday / Happiness Stan / Rollin' over / Hungry intruder / Journey / Mad John / Happy days toy town / Tin soldier
ESMCD 477 / May '97 / Essential

☐ QUITE NATURALLY RARE
Rollin' over / Son of a baker / I feel much better / Talk to you / Tin soldier / Autumn stone / Become like you / I can't make it / Donkey rides, a penny a glass / Rene / I'm only dreaming / Hungry intruder / Red balloon / Just passing
DOJOCD 60 / Oct '92 / Dojo

☐ SMALL FACES
(Tell me) Have you ever seen me / Something I want to tell you / Feeling lonely / Happy boys happy / Things are going to get better / My way of giving / Green circles / Become like you / Get yourself together / All our yesterdays / Talk to you / Show me the way / Up the wooden hills to Bedfordshire / Eddie's dreaming
CDIMM 004 / Feb '94 / Charly

☐ SMALL FACES (Remastered)
Tell me have you seen her / Something I want to tell you / Feeling lonely / Happy boys happy / Things are going better / My way of giving / Green circles / Become like you / Get yourself together / All our yesterdays / Talk to you / Show me the way / Up the modern hill to bed / Eddie's dreaming / Itchycoo park / I'm only dreaming / I feel much better / Tin soldier / Here comes the nice
ESMCD 476 / May '97 / Essential

☐ VERY BEST OF THE SMALL FACES, THE (2CD Set)
What'cha gonna do about it / Sha la la la lee / Hey girl / All or nothing / My mind's eye / I can't make it / Here come the Nice / Talk to you / Itchycoo park / I'm only dreaming / Tin soldier / I feel much better / Universal / Donkey rides, a penny, a glass / Wham, bam, thank you mam / (Tell me) have you ever seen me / Things are going to get better / My way of giving / Get yourself together / All our Sundays / Ogden's nut gone flake / Afterglow (of your love) / Long agos and worlds apart / Rene / Song of a baker / Lazy Sunday / Happiness Sam / Rollin' over / Hungry intruder / Journey / Mad John / Happydaystoytown / Picaninny / Green circles / Call it something nice / Autumn stone / Red balloon / If I were a carpenter / Every little bit hurts / Don't burst my bubble
CPCD 82602 / Nov '96 / Charly

Small Factory

☐ FOR IF YOU CANNOT FLY
QUIGD 6 / Feb '95 / Quigley

Small Fish With Spine

☐ ULTIMATE SUSHI
Fung koo / Opium den / Foul play / Concubine / High fibre / In your own bubble / Siolim
OXIDECD 001 / 2 Feb '98 / OMW

Small, Fred

☐ EVERYTHING POSSIBLE
FF 70625CD / Dec '93 / Flying Fish

☐ I WILL STAND FAST
FF 704941 / Oct '89 / Flying Fish

☐ JAGUAR
FF 570CD / May '93 / Flying Fish

☐ NO LIMIT
ROUCD 4018 / Jan '94 / Rounder

Small, Judy

☐ BEST OF THE 80'S
CMMCD 007 / Jun '94 / Larrikin

☐ SECOND WIND
CMM 008CD / Jul '94 / Larrikin

☐ WORD OF MOUTH (The Best Of Judy Small)
Alison and me / How many times / Mothers, daughters, wives / Manly ferry song / Walls and windows / Much too much trouble / Golden arches / Speaking hands, hearing eyes / One voice in the crowd / Song for Jacqueline / Alice Martin / Mary Parker's lament / Family maiden aunt / You don't speak for me / Women of our time / Futures exchange
CDTRAX 050 / Mar '92 / Greentrax

Small, Michael

☐ MOBSTERS
VSD 5334 / Aug '91 / Varese Sarabande

Smaller

☐ BADLY BADLY
BETCD 003 / Apr '97 / Better

Smallwood, Richard

☐ FOLLOW THE STAR
430972 / Oct '97 / Benson

Smart, Leroy

☐ BEST OF LEROY SMART, THE
JJCD 033 / 29 Sep '97 / Channel One

☐ EVERY TIME
RASCD 3139 / Jun '94 / Ras

☐ IMPRESSIONS OF BURNING SOUNDS
CDBS 564 / Mar '97 / Burning Sounds

☐ LEROY SMART & FRIENDS
LG 21113 / Aug '95 / Lagoon

☐ LET EVERYONE SURVIVE
JMC 200207 / May '89 / Jamaican Gold

☐ PRIVATE MESSAGE
DGVCD 2024 / Sep '93 / Dynamite & Grapevine

☐ REGGAE IS JAH MUSIC
Reggae is Jah music / More than a million / This world / Love that I have / She love it in the morning / Love Jah / Best friend of mine / Criticising / Love me tonight / Reggae is Jah music / Let every man survive / Collie give me wisdom / You are mine / Black and white / You never need me / Sugar my coffee / Jah is at hand / I still pray / If you want my love / Live up right
CDGR 189 / Nov '97 / Charly

☐ TALK'BOUT FRIEND
VYDCD 09 / Sep '95 / Vine Yard

Smart Went Crazy

☐ CON ART
DIS 112CD / 17 Nov '97 / Dischord

☐ NOW WE'RE EVEN
DISS 96CD / Jan '96 / Dischord

Smartbomb

☐ SMARTBOMB
CMD 046 / 1 Jun '98 / Creative Man

Smarties

☐ OPERATION THUNDERBUNNY
859 314 / Jun '89 / Steamhammer

SMASH

☐ SELF ABUSED
Revisited no. 5 / Barrabas / Oh ovary / Altruism / Reflections of you (Remember me) / Self abused / Scream silent / Another love / Another shark in the deep end of my swimming pool / Real surreal / Dear Lou / Bang bang bang (Granta 25) / Time / ALLYC / Trainspotter
FLATCD 6 / Sep '94 / Hi-Rise

Smash Mouth

☐ FUSH YU MANG
IND 90142 / 3 Nov '97 / Interscope

Smashed Gladys

☐ SMASHED GLADYS
HMUSA 49 / Nov '85 / Heavy Metal

Smashers

☐ LOUD, CONFIDENT AND WRONG
APCD 076 / Jun '92 / Appaloosa

Smashing Pumpkins

☐ ADORE
Pug / Tear / Blank page / Tale of Dusty and Pistol Pete / Daphne descends / Shame / Ava adore / Behold the nightmare / Once upon time / For Martha / Appels and oranjes / Annie-dog / Perfect / 17 / To Sheila / Crestfallen
CDHUTX 51
CDHUT 51 / 1 Jun '98 / Hut

☐ GISH
I am one / Siva / Rhinoceros / Bury me / Crush / Snail / Fristessa / Window paine / Daydream / Suffer
HUTCDX 2 / May '94 / Hut

☐ GREAT PUMPKIN THAT NEVER ARRIVED, THE (Interview Disc)
DIST 004 / Mar '96 / Disturbed

☐ INTERVIEW DISC
SAM 7019 / Nov '96 / Sound & Media

☐ INTERVIEW SESSIONS
CHAT 1 / 8 Dec '97 / Chatback

☐ MELLON COLLIE AND THE INFINITE SADNESS (2CD Set)
Mellon Collie and the infinite sadness / Tonight tonight / Jellybelly / Zero / Here is no why / Bullet with butterfly wings / To forgive / Fuck you (an ode to no one) / Love / Cupid De Locke / Galapogos / Muzzle / Porcelina of the vast oceans / Take me down / Where boys fear to tread / Bodies / Thirty three / In the arms of sleep / 1979 / Tales of a scorched earth / Thru the eyes of Ruby / Stumbleine / XYU / We only come out at night / Beautiful / Lily (my one and only) / By starlight / Farewell and goodnight
CDHUTD 30 / Nov '95 / Hut

☐ PISCES ISCARIOT
Soothe / Frail and bedazzled / Plume / Whir / Blew away / Pissant / Hello Kitty Kat / Obscured / Landslide / Starla / Blue / Girl named Sandoz / La Dolly Vita / Spaced
CDHUT 41 / Oct '96 / Hut

☐ SIAMESE DREAM
Cherub rock / Quiet / Today / Hummer / Rocket / Disarm / Soma / Geek USA / Mayonaise / Spaceboy / Silverfuck / Sweet sweet / Luna
CDHUT 11 / Jun '93 / Hut

Smear, Pat

☐ SO YOU FELL IN LOVE WITH A MUSICIAN
SST 294CD / May '93 / SST

Smeck, Roy

☐ ON WITH THE DANCE (Smeck, Roy & His Hawaiian Serenaders)
On with the dance / Heaven can wait / Ti-pi-tin / Alone / In a shanty in old shanty town / My mom / When the poppies bloom again / Cheek to cheek / I'll miss you in the evening / You took the words right out of my heart / Take me by my boots and saddle / You're a sweetheart / Love me forever / But where are you / Remember me / Isn't this a lovely day / Sweet as a song / Chasing shadows / Wishing / Serenade in the night / Dream sweetheart / While we danced at the mardigras
RAJCD 891 / 6 Oct '97 / Empress

Smell Of Incense

☐ ALL MIMSY WERE THE BOROGROVES
COSC 018 / 20 Apr '98 / Colours

☐ THROUGH THE GATES OF THE DEEP
SGCD 15 / 20 Apr '98 / September Gurls

Smersh

☐ EMMANUELLE GOES TO BANGKOK
Touch of Venus / Great Ceasar's ghost / Burn / Titanic fantastic / Blonde devil / You remind me of summer / Armoured man / Under your hoop / Brown out / Riding with the Pharoahs / Discotes
KK 47CD / Apr '90 / KK

☐ GREATEST STORY EVER DISTORTED, THE
Licorice rope / Jack your metal / Japanese princess / Bootie heaven / Spook house
KK 19CD / Mar '89 / KK

Smietana, Jarek

☐ FLOWERS IN MIND
338502 / Sep '96 / Koch Jazz

☐ JAREK SMIETANA QUARTET
338262 / Nov '96 / Koch Jazz

Smiles

☐ CURE FOR THE COMMON
Not so lonely / Say something / Lara / To you / Please / End of the world / It doesn't have to be you / Again and again / Landslide / Just too much
5408192 / Mar '98 / A&M

Smith & Mighty

☐ BASS IS MATERNAL
ZCDKR 2 / Nov '95 / More Rockers

☐ DJ KICKS (Various Artists)
Amid the ether: *Blue & Red* / Rwanda: *Smith & Mighty/Andy Scholes* / Jah pure and clear: *Peter D* / Walk on: *Smith & Mighty* / Same: *Smith & Mighty/Tammy Paine* / Quite frankly: *DJ Lynx* / Mr. A and R man: *Wilks* / Irrational: *Receiver* / Anymore: *Smith & Mighty/Jackie Jackson* / Night fall: *More Rockers* / First time: *On* / Sole sentient: *Ratman* / Higher dub: *Smith & Mighty* / Never felt this way: *More Rockers* / Sound boy: *More Rockers* / Show love: *More Rockers* / Rainbows: *Virginia* / New world: *Virginia* / Off the edge: *Klash, Jaz* / Bass speaker: *Flynn & Flora* / 1 2 3 Break: *More Rockers* / Tripitaka: *Wraparound Sounds* / Vibrations: *Gang Related* / DJ Kicks/I don't know: *Smith & Mighty/Alice Perera*
K7 065CD / 9 Mar '98 / Studio K7

Smith, Al

☐ HEAR MY BLUES
Night time is the right time / Pledging my love / I've got a girl / I'll be alright / Come on pretty baby / Tears in my eyes / Never let me go / I've got the right kind of lovin'
OBCCD 514 / Apr '94 / Original Blues Classics

☐ MIDNIGHT SPECIAL
Five long years / You're a sweetheart / Baby don't worry 'bout me / Ride on midnight special / Bells / Goin' to Alabama / I'll never let you go / I can't make it by myself
OBCCD 583 / Oct '96 / Original Blues Classics

Smith, Barkin' Bill

☐ BLUEBIRD BLUES (Smith, Barkin' Bill & Dave Specter/Ronnie Earl)
Things I'd do for you / Tell me what's the reason / Bluebird blues / Wind chill / Get me while I'm free / Buzz me / Lie to me / Railroad station blues / Our course is run / Take a little walk with me
DD 652 / Mar '97 / Delmark

☐ GOTCHA
Sufferin' mind / As long as I have you / Down the line / Someday after awhile / Too fine for cryin' / You're too much / Blue guitar / Get your kicks / I love to love you / One kiss / I got what I wanted / Hot tomato / No rollin' blues / What makes these things happen to me
DE 672 / Mar '97 / Delmark

Smith, Bessie

☐ AMERICAN LEGENDS
T'aint nobody's business / Baby, won't you please come home / St. Louis blues / Reckless blues / Sobbin' hearted blues / Cold in hand blues / You've been a good old wagon / I ain't got nobody / Sing, sing prison blues / Follow the deal on down / Nobody can bake a sweet jelly roll like mine / I'm wild about that thing
12737 / May '97 / Laserlight

☐ AUDIO ARCHIVE
I'm down in the dumps / Take me for a buggy ride / Do your duty / He's got me goin' / Kitchen man / You've got to give me some / I used to be your sweet mama / Devil's gonna git you / Thinking blues / Send me to the 'lectric chair / Trombone cholly / Cake walkin' babies from home / Yellow dog blues / Soft pedal blues / Dixie flyer blues / Nashville woman blues / Careless love blues / JC Holmes blues / I ain't gonna play no second fiddle
CDAA 032 / Jan '91 / Tring

☐ BESSIE SMITH
DVBC 9092 / May '95 / Deja Vu

☐ BESSIE SMITH 1925-1933
Yellow dog blues / Nashville woman's blues / I ain't gonna play no second fiddle / I want every bit of it / Money blues / One and two blues / Muddy water (a mississippi moan) / Lock and key / Good man is hard to find / Dyin' by the hour / Foolish man blues / I used to be your sweet mama / Standin' in the rain blues / I'm wild about that thing / Nobody knows you when you're down and out / Blue spirit blues / Do your duty / Gimme a pigfoot (and a bottle of beer) / I'm down in the dumps
CD 53090 / Mar '92 / Giants Of Jazz

☐ BLUE SPIRIT BLUES
I'm down in the dumps / Blue spirit blues / Kitchen man / Foolish man blues / Thinking blues / Devil's gonna git you / Send me to the 'lectric chair / I'm wild about that thing / You've got to give me some / Standing in the rain blues / He's got me goin' / Do your duty / Dyin' by the hour / Lock and key / Gimme a pigfoot / Take me for a buggy ride / I used to be your sweet mama / Trombone cholly / Alexander's ragtime band / Good man is hard to find
GRF 102 / '93 / Tring

☐ CLASSICS 1923
CLASSICS 761 / Jun '94 / Classics

☐ CLASSICS 1923-1924
CLASSICS 787 / Nov '94 / Classics

☐ CLASSICS 1924-1925
CLASSICS 812 / May '95 / Classics

☐ CLASSICS 1925-1927
CLASSICS 843 / Nov '95 / Classics

☐ CLASSICS 1927-1928
CLASSICS 870 / Apr '96 / Classics

☐ CLASSICS 1928-1929
CLASSICS 897 / Oct '96 / Classics

☐ COMPLETE RECORDINGS VOL.5, THE (2CD Set)
Need a little sugar in my bowl / Safety Mama / Do your duty / Gimme a pigfoot / Take me for a buggy ride / I'm down in the dumps / Yellow dog blues / Nashville woman's blues / Careless love blues / Muddy water (a mississippi moan) / Bessie and the ladies / Life on the road / Life on the road II / Life on the road III
4835852 / Feb '96 / Columbia

☐ DO YOUR DUTY
IGOCD 2008 / Nov '94 / Indigo

☐ DOWN HEARTED BLUES
GO 3811 / 1 Dec '97 / Golden Options

☐ EMPRESS OF THE BLUES
Gimme a pigfoot and a bottle of beer / Downhearted blues / Yellow dog blues / Careless love / Good man is hard to find / St. Louis blues / Do your duty / Cold in hand blues / Send me to the 'lectric chair / Empty bed blues / Nobody's blues but mine / Alexander's ragtime band / Them's graveyard words / New Orleans hopscotch blues / One and two blues / Take me for a buggy ride / Squeeze me / Nobody knows you (When you're down and out)
CBCD 001 / 27 Apr '98 / Collector's Blues

☐ EMPRESS OF THE BLUES, THE (Charly Blues Masterworks Vol.31)
Downhearted blues / Gulf coast blues / Aggravatin' papa / Baby won't you please come home / Tain't nobody's business if I do / Whoa tillie, take your time / My sweetie went away / Any woman's blues / Weeping willow blues / St. louis blues / Reckless blues / Careless love blues / I ain't gonna play no second fiddle / I ain't got nobody / Empty bed blues (parts 1 and 2) / Nobody knows you when you're down and out / Do your duty / Gimme a pigfoot (and a bottle of beer)
CDBM 31 / Jan '93 / Charly

☐ EMPTY BED BLUES (Her 23 Greatest)
Downhearted blues / Keep on rainin' / St. Louis blues / Cold in hand blues / Cake walkin' babies / Yellow dog blues / At the Christmas ball / Jazzbo Brown from Memphis Town / Gin house blues / Baby doll / Lost your head blues / Backwater blues / Trombone cholly / Send me to the 'lectric chair / Dyin' by the hour / Empty bed blues / Put it right here / I'm wild about that thing / Kitchen man / Nobody knows you when you're down and out / New Orleans hop scoop blues / Do your duty / Gimme a pig foot and a bottle of beer
CDAJA 5213 / Sep '96 / Living Era

☐ ESSENTIAL BESSIE SMITH, THE (2CD Set)
4873989 / 26 Jan '98 / Sony Jazz

☐ GREATEST BLUES SINGER IN THE WORLD, THE
Downhearted blues / Gulf coast blues / Nobody in town can bake a sweet jelly roll like mine / Jailhouse blues / Graveyard dream blues / Cemetery blues / Frosty morning blues / Haunted house blues / Easy come, easy go blues / Follow the deal on down / Sinful blues / Lady luck blues / Reckless blues / Cold in hand blues / Mean old bedbug blues / Yellow dog blues / Sweet mistreater / Empty bed blues / Blue spirit blues / Black mountain blues / In the house blues / Nashville woman's blues
CD 52009 / '92 / Blues Encore

☐ INTRODUCTION TO BESSIE SMITH 1923-1933, AN
4030 / Mar '96 / Best Of Jazz

☐ MAMA'S GOT THE BLUES
TPZ 1002 / Jul '94 / Topaz Jazz

☐ MASTERS, THE
Gimme a pigfoot (and a bottle of beer) / Down hearted blues / Yellow dog blues / Careless love blues / Good man is hard to find / St. Louis blues / Do your duty / Cold in hand blues / Send me to the 'lectric chair / Empty bed blues / Nobody's blues but mine / Alexander's ragtime band / Them's graveyard words / New Orleans hop scop blues / One and two blues / Take me for a bunny ride / Squeeze me / Nobody knows you when your down and out
EABCD 099 / 30 Mar '98 / Eagle

☐ QUINTESSENCE, THE (2CD Set)
Down hearted blues / Gulf coast blues / Aggravatin' papa / Beale Street mama / Graveyard dream blues / Cemetry blues / Any woman's blues / Boweavil blues / Weeping willow blues / Reckless blues / Sobbin' hearted blues / Cake walkin' babies from home / Yellow dog blues / Soft pedal blues / Nashville woman's blues / Careless love blues / I ain't gonna play second fiddle / At the Christmas ball / Squeeze me / Money blues / Baby doll / Young woman blues / Back water blues / After you've gone / Alexander's ragtime band / Muddy water / There'll be a hot time in the old town tonight / Trombone cholly / Foolish man blues / Empty bed blues / St. Louis blues / Wasted life blues / On revival day / Shipwreck blues / Need a little sugar in my bowl / Take me for a buggy ride
FA 223 / Nov '97 / Fremeaux

☐ RECKLESS BLUES
Reckless blues / Sweet mistreater / Yellow dog blues / Blue spirit blues / Cold in hand blues / Follow the deal on down / Nashville woman's blues / Graveyard dream blues / Black mountain blues / Cemetery blues / Empty bed blues / Jail house blues / Haunted house blues / Downhearted blues / Mean old bedbug blues / Gulf coast blues / Easy come, easy go blues / Lady luck blues
CD 14546 / Jan '94 / Jazz Portraits

☐ ST. LOUIS BESSIE & ALICE MOORE VOL.1 1927-1929
DOCD 5290 / Dec '94 / Document

☐ ST. LOUIS BESSIE & ALICE MOORE VOL.2 1934-1941
DOCD 5291 / Dec '94 / Document

Smith, Bob

☐ VISIT
CD 1518 / Jul '97 / Virgo

Smith, Bobby

☐ THAT'S FOR SURE (Smith, Bobby & The Erskine Hawkins Alumni)
Bess's boogie / Desert night / Mopsticks / Blue keys / Wee Gee blues / Lazy Suzy / That's for sure / Sweet and lovely / Flip a coin / Poodgy / Skippin' and hoppin' / After hours / Disco / Smoothie / Better get right / Dash hound / Cinder bottom / Tippin' in / Swan / Station break / Helicopter / Buffalo nickel
DE 484 / Jun '97 / Delmark

☐ WOOF
ZAZOU 1312 / Mar '98 / Zazou

Smith, Brian

☐ MOONLIGHT SAX
NELCD 104 / Aug '93 / Timbuktu

☐ UNFORGETTABLE SAX
NELCD 105 / Aug '93 / Timbuktu

Smith, Bryan

☐ BEST OF BRYAN SMITH VOL.1, THE (Smith, Bryan & His Piano)
On mother kelly's doorstep-on the sunny side of the street / She wears my ring (rumba) / You belong to my heart (rumba) / Those lazy hazy crazy days of summer (quickstep) / Cinqo de mayo (quickstep) / Here in my heart (foxtrot) / Why do I love you (foxtrot) / Wedding (waltz) / Beautiful ohio (waltz) / Mambo jambo (samba) / Laughing samba (samba) / Tijuana party (cha cha) / Pinacolada (cha cha) / Tom hark (jive) / When I'm sixty-four (jive) / Do something (quickstep) / Whistling rufus (quick step) / Just one more chance (foxtrot) / Lovely way to spend an evening (foxtrot) / Time after time (tango) / Addio amore (tango)
CDTS 002 / Aug '93 / Maestro

☐ BLUE ISLANDS (Smith, Bryan & New Hawaiians)
Jealous heart / Oh lonesome me / Don't stay away too long / Arrivederci Roma / Who's sorry now / My foolish heart / I talk to the trees / Pagan love song / Coming home
DACD 016 / Aug '96 / Dansan

☐ BRYAN'S CHRISTMAS BOX
CDTS 017 / Dec '95 / Maestro

☐ DANSAN SEQUENCE COLLECTION VOL.2, THE (Smith, Bryan & His Dixielanders)
Muskrat ramble (quickstep) / At a georgia camp meeting (quickstep) / Dinah-my melancholy baby (quickstep) / Back home in tennessee-lily of laguna (balmoral blues) / We'll all go riding on a rainbow-yankee doodle boy (quicks / Daisy bell-she's a lassie from lancashire (old time waltz) / On a slow boat to china-april showers strollin' (foxtrot) / I wanna be like you (quickstep) / Birthday cakewalk (quickstep) / Pal must be a pal forever-life's desire (waltz) / I'll always love you-wyoming lullaby (waltz) / Chattanooga choo choo (jive) / Tom hark (jive) / Roll out the barrel (quickstep)
DNSN 902 / Oct '93 / Dansan

☐ FOR ME AND MY GAL
Robin's return / Keep your seats please / Chinese laundry blues / When I'm cleaning windows (The window cleaner) / How wonderful to know / I'm confessin' / If I could only make you care / Vilia / Wedding / Waltz of my heart / Fold your wings / Turkey in the straw / Waiting for the Robert E Lee / Alabama jubilee / For me and my gal / Whispering / Heart of my heart / Leaning on a lamp post / Echo of a serenade / Return to me / Addio / Harbour lights / Black and white rag / Temptation rag / Johnson rag / LOVE / Dream / I left my heart in San Francisco / Lovely way to spend an evening / Just one more chance / Forgotten dreams / Singing piano / Drigo's serenade / Anytime's kissing time / Perhaps, perhaps, perhaps / My blue heaven / Oh lady be good / Side by side / On the sunny side of the street / Enjoy yourself / Little brown jug / Diamonds are a girls best friend
DACD 014 / Jun '96 / Dansan

☐ MARCHING AND WALTZING
Off we go / Fire on the horizon / Tesoro mio / Good old vienna / Gypsy blood / Thrills / Here goes / Gaily through the world / Freitags waltz / Montags waltz / Light horse march / Here, there and everywhere / Wiener lipizzaner (the lipiaaner of vienna)
DLCD 113 / May '94 / Dulcima

☐ MUSIC MUSIC MUSIC
Music music music / Stumbling / Crazy Otto rag / Careless hands / Song of my life / Cuban love song / El cumbanchero / Back in your own back yard / All of me / Play a simple melody / Put your arms around me honey / Ivory rag / Don't bring Lulu / Spanish eyes / Beautiful lover
DACD 015 / Aug '96 / Dansan

☐ WHISTLING RUFUS
Whistling Rufus / Carolina / Abie my boy / Wheezy Anna / You're adorable / What more can I say / If I had my way / Hold me / Underneath the arches / Amazing grace / All through the night / Plaisir d'amour / El cumbanchero / Let him go let him Tarry / Tavern in the town / She'll be coming round the mountain / Tom Dooley / Blue ribbon gal / Clementine / My bonnie lies over the mountain / Bill Bailey / I'm in love with two sweethearts / Girl in the Alice blue gown / Let us be sweethearts over again / Miss you / Greatest mistake of my life / All by yourself in the moonlight / Heartbreaker / Sweet Sue just you / Red River valley / Down at the old bull and bush / Ash grove / Two lovely black eyes / One of those songs / Just loving you / Careless hands / I love you beacause / Years may come years may go / Matchstalk men and mathstalk cats and dogs / Melodie d'amour / Song of my life
DACD 013 / Jun '96 / Dansan

Smith, Byther

☐ ADDRESSING THE NATION WITH THE BLUES
Hello Mrs. Brown / I was coming home / Looking for a woman / Play the blues on the moon / What have I done / You should be proud of your daughter / What is this / Addressing the nation with the blues / Movin' on / I wish my mother was here / Put your arms around me
JSPCD 2105 / Jun '98 / JSP

☐ ALL NIGHT LONG
DE 708 / Jan '98 / Delmark

☐ I'M A MAD MAN
BB 9527CD / May '93 / Bullseye Blues

☐ MISSISSIPPI KID
Judge of honor / Don't hurt me no more / President's daughter / Living in pain / Ashamed of myself / I don't know where you go / Blues on the moon / Your daughter don't want me no more / Give me my white robe / Runnin' to New Orleans / Cora, you made a man out of me / Monticello lonely / Mississippi kid
DE 691 / Feb '97 / Delmark

Smith, Carl

☐ SATISFACTION GUARANTEED (5CD Set)
Guilty conscience / I just droppped in to say goodbye / My lonely heart's runnin' wild / Washing my dreams in tears / I overlooked an orchid / This side of heaven / I won't be at home / Mr. Moon / If teardrops were pennies / There's nothing as sweet as my baby / Let's live a little / Me and my broken heart / Don't just stand there / Please come back home / There'll never be another Mary / My lonely heart's runnin' wild / Let old Mother Nature have her way / Little girl in my home town / I just dropped in to say goodbye / Are you teasing me / That's the kind of love I'm looking for / Nail-scarred hand / We shall meet some day / How about you / Blood that stained the old rugged cross / Gethsemane / Softly and tenderly / Amazing Grace / I'll be list'ning / Our honeymoon / Sing her a love song / Lovin' is livin' / I want to take my baby home with me / Trademark / This orchid means goodbye / Just wait 'til I get you alone / Do I like it / Darlin' am I the one / Hey Joe / If you tried as hard to love me / Love oh crazy love / Time's a-wastin' / No second chance / Satisfaction guaranteed / House that love built / Who'll buy my heartaches / Oh no / What am I going to do with you / Doggone it baby, I'm in love / If I could hold back the dawn / Back up Buddy / Look what thought's done to me / I just dropped in to say goodbye / Lovin' is livin' / Go boy go / More than anything else in the world / If you saw her through my eyes / No I don't believe I will / Loose talk / Time changes everything / Baby I'm ready / Kisses don't lie / Wait a little longer please / Works of the Lord / Answers / My dream of the old rugged cross / I just don't care anymore / Oh stop / Baby I'm ready / There's a bottle where she used to be / Wicked lies / Old lonesome times / I've changed / There she goes / No second chance / Come back to me / Don't tease me / If you do dear / I just dropped in to say goodbye / I feel like cryin' / You're free to go / Outlaw / Snowdeer / Doorstep to heaven / You are the one / If you want it, I've got it / Before I met you / Mr. Moon / San Antonio Rose / Live and let live / You are my sunshine / Steel guitar rag / This world is not my home / Standing on promises / Old Camp meeting days / When the roll is called up yonder / You can't hurt me anymore / That's the way I like you best / I won't be mad I'll be glad / That's what you think / Pass me not / Glory land way / Anywhere is home / When they ring them golden bells / No trespassing / Try to take it like a man / Mr. Lost / Happy Street / Amazing Grace / Why, why / Emotions / You're so easy to love / You're name is beautiful / Dry your darling's eyes / Best years of your life / Slowly / More and more / I overlooked an orchid / Let's live a little / Mr. Moon / Night train to Memphis / Honky tonk man / Hang your head in shame / I love you a thousand ways / Sweet little Miss Blue Eyes / If teardrops were pennies / We're not going steady anymore / Guess I've been around too long / Goodnight Mister Sun / Walking the slow walk / Love was born / It's all my heartache / Lonely girl / I'll kiss the past goodbye / Be good to her / Ten thousand drums / Tall, tall gentleman / I'll walk with you / Tomorrow night / Make the waterwheel roll / Past / I betcha my heart I love you / It's a lovely lovely world
BCD 15849 / May '96 / Bear Family

Smith, Carmelita

☐ PEACE AND LOVE
IMCD 01 / Jan '97 / CIS

Smith, Carrie

☐ FINE AND MELLOW
ACD 164 / May '95 / Audiophile

Smith, Charlene

☐ FEEL THE GOOD TIMES
Feel the good times / Count on me / Sometimes / I learned my lesson / Too much for me / Let it slide / I got what you need / World goes round / No more lies / What'cha do
WOLCD 1069 / Jul '95 / China

☐ LIFE IS HIGH
Treat me right / Everything is you / Pillow talk / I was / Feel the rhythm / Mood keeps on rising / You are everything / Whenever you want / Life is high / Do you like it / Taste of Chardonnay
ZEN 014CD / 11 May '98 / Indochina

Smith, Cheikh M.

☐ TOUBABOU
WCOA 203CD / May '93 / World Circuit

☐ TOUBABOU BALAFOLA
OA 203 / Feb '94 / PAM

Smith, Christina

☐ LIKE DUCKS (Smith, Christina & Jean Hewson)
BCD 108 / Jul '98 / Borealis

Smith, Clara

☐ CLARA SMITH VOL.1 1923-1924
DOCD 5364 / Jul '95 / Document

☐ CLARA SMITH VOL.2 1924
DOCD 5365 / Jul '95 / Document

☐ CLARA SMITH VOL.3 1925
DOCD 5366 / Jul '95 / Document

☐ CLARA SMITH VOL.4 1926-1927
DOCD 5367 / Jul '95 / Document

☐ CLARA SMITH VOL.5 1927-1929
DOCD 5368 / Jul '95 / Document

☐ CLARA SMITH VOL.6 1930-1932
DOCD 5369 / Jul '95 / Document

Smith, Connie

☐ ESSENTIAL CONNIE SMITH, THE
Once a day / Nobody but a fool (would love you) / I can't remember / Cry cry cry / Then and only then / If I talk to him / Ain't had no lovin' / Hurtin's all over / I never once stopped loving you / You and your sweet love / Cincinatti Ohio / I'll come running / Burning a hole in my mind / Run away little tears / Ribbon of darkness / Just one time / Just for what I am / Love is the look you're looking for / If it ain't love (let's leave it alone) / How great Thou art
07863668242 / Aug '96 / RCA Nashville

Smith, Craig

☐ CRAIG SMITH
Sandy river belle / Two long years / St. Louis blues / Charade / Curly headed woman / Humoresque / Memory of your smile / Girl I left behind me / Annie Laurie / Rose of Alabama / Clinch Mountain backstep / My old Kentucky home / Moscow nights
ROUCD 0357 / May '97 / Rounder

Smith, Curt

☐ MAYFIELD
SOUND 0001 / 13 Apr '98 / Zerodisc

Smith, Darden

☐ DEEP FANTASTIC BLUE
First day of the sun / Broken branches / Running kind / Skin / Silver and gold / Drowning man / Different train / Chariots / Stop talking / Hunger
FIENDCD 930 / Jun '97 / Demon

☐ NATIVE SOIL
Bus stop bench / Red sky / Little Maggie / Veteran's day / Sticks and stones / Keep an open mind / Wild West show / Painter's song / Two dollar novels / God's will / Clatter and roll
WM 1009 / Jun '93 / Watermelon

Smith, David

☐ COMING
ARCD 01 / 27 Apr '98 / Angella

Smith, Debi

☐ MORE THAN ONE
Virginia/Shenandoah / Mother's hands / Hang the moon / Life outside this town / Snowbound / Everyone's got a story / Old river / Sleep / Intertwined / First choice / More than once / Out to forget / He doesn't work on love / Italy and France
SHANCD 8032 / Jun '98 / Shanachie

Smith, Derek

☐ DARK EYES (Smith, Derek Trio)
PRSCDSP 204 / May '94 / Prestige

☐ DEREK SMITH PLAYS THE MUSIC OF JEROME KERN
Ol' man river / Fine romance / Folks who live on the hill / I'm old fashioned / Long ago and far away / Way you look tonight / I won't dance
PCD 7055 / Jun '93 / Progressive

☐ PLAYS PASSIONATE PIANO
Liebestraum / Mattinata / Melody in f / Variations on a theme by paganinl / Etude / Waves of the danube / I love you truly / Moonlight sonata (beethoven) / Because / Lullaby / Traumerei / Ave maria
MICH 4526 / Sep '92 / Hindsight

☐ TRIO 1994, THE (Smith, Derek & Milt Hinton/Bobby Rosengarden)
CRD 322 / Mar '96 / Chiaroscuro

Smith, Elliot

☐ EITHER/OR
KRS 269CD / 11 May '98 / Kill Rock Stars

☐ EITHER/OR
Speed trials / Alameda / Ballad of big nothing / Between the bars / Pictures of me / No name no.5 / Rose parade / Punch and Judy / Angeles / Cupids trick / 2:45 am / Say yes
WIGCD 051 / 1 Jun '98 / Domino

☐ ELLIOT SMITH
Needle in the hay / Christian brothers / Clementine / Southern belle / Single file / Coming up roses / Satallite / Alphebet town / St Ides heaven / Good to go / White lady loves you more / Biggest lie
REWIGCD 001 / 3 Aug '98 / Domino
KRS 246CD / 16 Mar '98 / Kill Rock Stars

☐ ROMAN CANDLE
Roman candle / Condor Avenue / No name I / No name II / No name III / Drive all over town / No name IV / Last call / Kiwi mad-dog 20/20
REWIGCD 002 / 3 Aug '98 / Domino

☐ ROMAN CANDLES
CSR 132 / 2 Mar '98 / Cavity Search

☐ XO
DRD 50048 / 24 Aug '98 / Dreamworks

Smith, Ernie

☐ AFTER 30 YEARS LIFE
ESCD 1 / 24 Nov '97 / Ernie Smith

☐ I'LL SING FOR JESUS
PKCD 0121398 / 23 Mar '98 / K&K

Smith, Eugene

☐ GROOVIN' AT THE EMBERS
PS 015CD / Jan '98 / P&S

Smith, Floyd

☐ RELAXIN' WITH FLOYD
BB 8752 / Jan '97 / Black & Blue

Smith, Gary

☐ 7 IMPROVISATIONS (Smith, Gary & John Stevens)
SOUL 9 / Jun '96 / Soul Static Sound

☐ STEREO
Chelsea / Brutal / Chelsea / Primitive No.2 / Chelsea / Trio / Glissandi/polyrhythms / Primitive No.3 / Musical interlude / HF / MMM / Primitive No.1 / MM / Slab / Chelsea
CPE 20032 / Jun '97 / Chronoscope

Smith, Geoff

☐ 15 WILD DECEMBERS
SK 66605 / Jan '97 / Sony Classical

☐ BLACKFLOWERS
SK 62686 / Jun '97 / Sony Classical

Smith, Gregg

☐ I WANNA ROCK YA
ULT 45342 / Aug '97 / Ichiban

☐ PARTY WARRIOR
Lowdown / Hlues in my blood / Money talks / Party warrior / Stick and stay / Stuck on you / Young men don't get the blues / You are / Crying in the chapel / Looking for a lady / Bank and benefits / First one
CDSGP 013 / Mar '92 / Prestige

Smith, Hal

☐ CALIFORNIA HERE I COME
JCD 182 / Feb '91 / Jazzology

☐ HAL SMITH & HIS CREOLE SUNSHINE JAZZ BAND
BCD 350 / Jun '96 / GHB

☐ MILNEBURG JOYS
BCD 277 / Oct '92 / GHB

☐ MUSIC FROM THE MAUVE DECADES (Smith, Hal & Keith Ingram/Bobby Gordon)
SKCD 22033 / Aug '94 / Sackville

☐ STEALIN' APPLES (Smith, Hal California Swing Cats)
JCD 279 / Dec '97 / Jazzology

☐ SWING BROTHER SWING (Smith, Hal California Swing Cats)
JCD 255 / Jul '96 / Jazzology

Smith, Howie

☐ SECOND DOOR ON THE LEFT (Smith, Howie Group)
SBCD 3019 / Jun '96 / Sea Breeze

Smith, Huey

☐ HAVING A GOOD TIME (The Very Best Of Huey 'Piano' Smith Vol.1) (Smith, Huey 'Piano' & The Clowns)
Rockin' pneumonia and the boogie woogie flu / Rockin' pneumonia and the boogie woogie flu / Little Liza Jane / Everybody's whalin' / Free single and disengaged / Just a lonely clown / Don't you just know it / High blood pressure / We like birdland / Havin' a good time / Don't you know yockomo / Well I'll be John Brown / Would you believe it (I have a cold) / Genevieve / Tu-bar-cu-lucas and the sinus blues / Dearest darling / Beatnik blues / For cryin' out loud / She got low down / Mean mean man / Pop-eye / Scald-dog / Little chickee wha wha / I think you're jiving me
WESM 516 / 13 Oct '97 / Westside

Smith, Hurricane

☐ BEST OF HURRICANE SMITH, THE
Don't let it die / Writer sings the song / Oh babe what would you say / Who was it / My Mother was her name / Beautiful day beautiful night / Back in the country / Getting to know you / Many happy returns / Wonderful Lily / Auntie Vi's / Take Suki home
WB 885882 / 2 Feb '98 / Disky

Smith, Ivy

☐ IVY SMITH & COW COW DAVENPORT 1927-1930 (Smith, Ivy & Cow Cow Davenport)
BDCD 6039 / May '93 / Blues Document

Smith, Jabbo

☐ ACE OF RHYTHM, THE
What can a poor fellow do / Black and tan fantasy / Willow tree / 'Sippi / Thou swell / Got butter on it / Ready hockum / Jazz battle / Little Willie blues / Sleepy time blues / Sweet and low blues / Take me to the river / Ace of rhythms / Let's get together / Sau sha stomp / Michigander blues / Decatur street tutti / Till times get better / Croonin' the blues / Boston skuffle / Tanguay blues / Moanful blues / Band box stomp / Rub me some more / Rhythm in Spain
TPZ 1072 / 4 May '98 / Topaz Jazz

☐ CLASSICS 1929-1938
CLASSICS 669 / Oct '92 / Classics

☐ COMPLETE 1928-1938 SESSIONS, THE (2CD Set)
158112 / Dec '93 / Jazz Archives

☐ JABBO SMITH 1929-1938
Got butter on it / Ready hokum / Jazz battle / Little Willie blues / Sleepy time blues / Take your time / Sweet 'n' low blues / Take me to the river / Ace of rhythms / Let's get together / Sua sha stomp / Michigander blues / Decatur Street tutti / Till times get better / Lina blues / Weird and blue / Croonin' the blues / I got the stinger / Boston skuffle / Tanguay blues / Band box stomp / Moanful blues
RTR 79013 / Nov '96 / Retrieval

Smith, Jack

☐ ROCKABILLY PLANET
FF 70510 / Jul '89 / Flying Fish

Smith, Jeffrey

☐ LITTLE SWEETER, A
Eleanor Rigby / Lush life / Misty / Love for sale / Sentimental touch / Bal de Vienne / Polka dots and moonbeams / Moanin' / Dindi / Fairweather / Come Sunday
5377902 / 8 Dec '97 / Verve

Smith, Jimmy

☐ ALL THE WAY LIVE (Smith, Jimmy & Eddie Harris)
You'll see / Autumn leaves / Child is born / 8 Counts for Rita / Old folks / Sermon
MCD 9251 / Jun '96 / Milestone

☐ ANGEL EYES
5276322 / Nov '96 / Verve

☐ BACK AT THE CHICKEN SHACK
Back at the Chicken Shack / When I grow too old to dream / Minor chant / Messy Bessy / On the sunny side of the street
CDP 7464022 / Mar '95 / Blue Note

☐ BASHIN'
5390612 / Oct '97 / Verve Master Edition

☐ CAT, THE (The Incredible Jimmy Smith)
Joy House / Basin Street blues / Cat / Carpetbaggers / St. Louis blues / Chicago serenade / Delon's blues / Blues in the night / Love cage theme
8100462 / Apr '89 / Verve

☐ CAT, THE (The Incredible Jimmy Smith/ Remastered)
Joy House / Cat / Basin Street blues / Carpetbaggers / Chicago serenade / St. Louis blues / Delon's blues / Blues in the night
5397562 / 16 Mar '98 / Verve Master Edition

☐ CHRISTMAS COOKIN'
God rest ye merry gentlemen / Jingle bells / We three Kings / Christmas song / White Christmas / Santa Claus is coming to town / Silent night / Baby it's cold outside / Greensleeves
5137112 / Apr '92 / Verve

☐ CRAZY BABY
When Johnny comes marching home / Makin' whoopee / Night in Tunisia / Sonnymoon for two / Mack the knife / What's new / Alfredo
CDP 7840302 / 1 Jun '98 / Blue Note

☐ DYNAMIC DUO, THE (Remastered) (Smith, Jimmy & Wes Montgomery)
5214452 / Oct '97 / Verve Master Edition

☐ FOURMOST
Midnight special / Main stem / Summertime / Things ain't what they used to be / Soulful brothers / My funny valentine / Quiet nights of quiet stars
MCD 9184 / Oct '93 / Milestone

☐ FURTHER ADVENTURES OF JIMMY & WES (Smith, Jimmy & Wes Montgomery)
King of the road / Maybe September / OGD (road song) / Call me / Milestones / Mellow mood / 'Round midnight
5198022 / Feb '94 / Verve

☐ HOME COOKIN'
CC rider / Sugar Hill / I got a woman / Messin' around / Gracie / Come on baby / Motorin' along / Since I fell for you / Apostrophe / Motorin' along / Since I fell for you
CDP 8533602 / Nov '96 / Blue Note

☐ IN CONCERT WITH EUROPE 1 (28/5/65 - 2CD Set) (Smith, Jimmy Trio)
RTE 15082 / Aug '97 / RTE/Europe 1

☐ JAZZ MASTERS
Organ grinder's swing / Preacher / Side mouthin' / I'll close my eyes / Blues and the abstract truth / OGD (road song) / Hobo flats / Bashin' / Meditation / Walk on the wild side / Johnny come lately / Maybe September / G'wan train
5218552 / 5 May '98 / Verve

☐ JAZZ PROFILE
You get cha' / Get happy / Summertime / Blues after all / Hackensack / Sista rebecca / Minor chant / Cherry
CDP 8332062 / 6 Oct '97 / Blue Note

☐ NEW SOUND A NEW STAR, A (2CD Set)
Way you look tonight / You get'cha / Midnight sun / Lady be good / High and the mighty / But not for me / Preacher / Tenderly / Joy / Champ / Bayou / Deep purple / Moonlight in Vermont / Ready 'n' able / Turquoise / Bubbis / Gone with the wind / Jamey / My funny Valentine / Slightly Monkish / I can't give you anything but love / Judo mambo / Willow weep for me / Lover come back to me / Well you needn't / Fiddlin' the minors / Autumn leaves / I cover the waterfront
CDP 8571912 / Aug '97 / Blue Note

☐ PRIME TIME
Here comes c.t. / Farther on up the road / C jam blues / Simple soul song / Honky tonk / No doubt about it / I got mine / Matter of fact
MCD 9176 / Oct '93 / Milestone

☐ STANDARDS
Little girl blue / Bye bye blackbird / I'm just a lucky so and so / Ruby / September song / I didn't know what time it was / Memories of you / But beautiful / Mood indigo / While we're young / It might as well be spring / Last dance
8212822 / 2 Feb '98 / Blue Note

☐ SUM SERIOUS BLUES
Sum serious blues / Around the corner / Hurry change if you're comin' / Sermon / You've changed / Moof's blues / Open for business / I'd rather drink Muddy Water
MCD 9207 / Apr '94 / Milestone

☐ TALKIN' VERVE (The Roots Of Acid Jazz)
5315632 / Aug '96 / Verve

Smith, Jimmy

☐ OBSCURE BLUES SHOUTERS (Smith, Jimmy/Max Bailey)
BMCD 6010 / Nov '97 / Blue Moon

Smith, Johnny

☐ JOHNNY SMITH
5377522 / 22 Sep '97 / Verve Elite

☐ LEGENDS (Smith, Johnny & George Van Eps)
I'm old fashioned / Macho's lullaby / 'Round midnight / Wally's waltz / Black black black / Golden earrings / Romance de los pinos / Nortena / Maid with the flaxen hair / Waltz / Old castle / Sevilla / Cheek to cheek / Foggy day / Tangerine / Sunny / Why was I born / I didn't know what time it was / Tea for two / Man I love / For you / I hadn't anyone till you / I could write a book
CCD 4616 / Oct '94 / Concord Jazz

Smith, Johnny

☐ GEARS (Smith, Johnny 'Hammond')
Tell me what to do / Los conquistadores chocolates / Lost on 23rd Street / Fantasy / Shifting gears / Can't we smile
OJCCD 914 / May '97 / Original Jazz Classics

☐ GEARS/FOREVER TAURUS (Smith, Johnny 'Hammond')
Tell me what to do / Los conquistadores chocolates / Lost on 23rd Street / Fantasy / Shifting gears / Can't we smile / Old devil moon / Countdown / Walk in sunshine / Ghetto samba / Cosmic voyage / My ship / Forever Taurus
CDBPGD 037 / Oct '92 / Beat Goes Public

☐ LEGENDS OF ACID JAZZ, THE (Smith, Johnny 'Hammond')
PRCD 24177 / Apr '97 / Prestige

☐ THAT GOOD FEELING/TALK THAT TALK (Smith, Johnny 'Hammond')
That good feeling / Bye bye blackbird / Autumn leaves / I'll remember April / Billie's bounce / My funny valentine / Puddin' / Talk that talk / Affair to remember / End of a love affair / Minors allowed / Riptide / Misty / Benny's diggin' / Portrait of Jennie
CDBGPD 061 / Jun '93 / Beat Goes Public

Smith, Kate

☐ EMERGENCE OF A LEGEND 1930-1939
TT 401 / May '98 / Take Two

Smith, Keely

☐ BE MY LOVE
Be my love / You're nobody 'til somebody loves you / You made me love you / Smoke gets in your eyes / How deep is the ocean / Don't let the stars get in your eyes / I'd climb the highest mountain / Pretend / I'm gonna sit right down and write myself a letter / Fascination / My reverie / It's all in the game
JASCD 321 / Feb '94 / Jasmine

☐ BECAUSE YOU'RE MINE
Because you're mine / Canadian sunset / No other love / Memories are made of this / My special angel / Please Mr.Sun / Only you / Because / Tell me why / Moments to remember / Prisoner of love / Loveliest night of the year
JASCD 333 / Dec '96 / Jasmine

☐ CHEROKEELY SWINGS
To each his own / Where is your heart (Moulin Rouge) / My heart cries for you / Yellow bird / That lucky old sun / Too young / True love / Secret love / Rags to riches / Young at heart / Stranger in paradise / My devotion
JASCD 323 / Jan '95 / Jasmine

☐ DEARLY BELOVED
JASCD 328 / Nov '95 / Jasmine

☐ KEELY CHRISTMAS
White Christmas / Christmas island / O little town of Bethlehem / Jingle bells / Here comes Santa Claus / O holy night / Silent night / Christmas song / Hark the herald angels sing / I'll be home for Christmas / Rudolph the red nosed reindeer / O come all ye faithful (Adeste fidelis) / Blue Christmas
JASCD 329 / Oct '94 / Jasmine

☐ SPOTLIGHT ON KEELY SMITH
It's magic / You go to my head / Stardust / I can't get started (with you) / When your lover had gone / Sweet and lovely / Stormy weather / Fools rush in / Song is you / Mr. Wonderful / It's been a long, long time / I'll never smile again / Someone to watch over me / I'll get by / Don't take your love from me / Lullaby of the leaves / There will never be another you / Imagination / On the sunny side of the street / I wish you love
CDP 7803272 / Apr '95 / Capitol

☐ SWING YOU LOVERS
Swing you lovers / I love to you / Misty / I love you / If I could be with you one hour tonight / Hello, young lovers / All or nothing at all / All night long / Talk to me / Everybody loves a lover / They say it's wonderful / At long last love
JASCD 322 / Jul '94 / Jasmine

☐ TWIST WITH KEELY SMITH/DOIN' THE TWIST WITH LOUIS PRIMA (Smith, Keely/Louis Prima)
Twist: *Smith, Keely* / I know: *Smith, Keely* / Peppermint twist: *Smith, Keely* / Ya ya twist: *Smith, Keely* / Sticks and stones: *Smith, Keely* / Twistin' the night away: *Smith, Keely* / Let's twist again: *Smith, Keely* / What I'd say: *Smith, Keely* / Twistin' cowboy Joe: *Smith, Keely* / Mother goose twist: *Smith, Keely* / Shout: *Smith, Keely* / When the saints go twistin' in: *Smith, Keely* / Twist: *Prima, Louis* / Continental twist: *Prima, Louis* / Tag that twistin' dolly: *Prima, Louis* / Marie: *Prima, Louis* / Alright, okay, you win: *Prima, Louis* / Doin' the twist: *Prima, Louis* / Let's twist again: *Prima, Louis* / Night train: *Prima, Louis* / Route 66: *Prima, Louis* / Glow worm: *Prima, Louis* / Honeydripper: *Prima, Louis* / Side by side: *Prima, Louis*
JASCD 334 / Dec '96 / Jasmine

☐ WHAT KIND OF FOOL AM I
What kind of fool am I / Fly me to the moon / More I see you / But not for me / What's new / Don't blame me / If I should lose you / Then I'll be tired of you / But beautiful / Love me tender / Nature boy / I love you so much it hurts
JASCD 324 / Jun '94 / Jasmine

Smith, Keith

☐ KEITH SMITH & HIS CLIMAX BLUES BAND (Smith, Keith & His Climax Blues Band)
BCD 27 / Aug '94 / GHB

☐ PORTRAIT OF KEITH SMITH VOL.1, A (Mr. Hefty Jazz)
Thriller rag / Mrs. Noone's blues / Get out of here and go on home / Sorry to leave this city / I can't escape from you (you can't escape from me) / ODJB one step / Franklin Street blues / Weary blues / Ting-a-ling / Blues and booze / Georgia on my mind / Milenberg joys / Blues for Mr. Hefty / Sister Kate / Everybody loves somebody sometime / Royal garden blues / Goin' home now
LACD 67 / Sep '96 / Lake

☐ PORTRAIT OF KEITH SMITH VOL.3, A (The Swing Is Here Again) (Smith, Keith Hefty Jazz All Stars)
Chicken ain't nothin' but a bird / Patrol wagon blues / Just sittin' and a rockin' / Perdido Street blues / Sweet Marijuana Brown / Caldonia / Let's fly away / I love you / Medi two / You're a lucky guy / After you've gone / Red rides again / Gee baby ain't I good to you / Struttin' with some barbecue / 'S wonderful / Dippermouth blues
LACD 80 / May '97 / Lake

Smith, Kendra

☐ FIVE WAYS TO DISAPPEAR
Aurelia / Bohemian zebulon / Temporarily Lucy / In your head / Space unadorned / Maggots / Drunken boat / Dirigible / Valley of the morning sun / Judge not / Get there / Saturn / Bold marauder
GAD 5006CD / 6 Jul '98 / 4AD

Smith, Kenny

☐ STUDEBAKER
Studebaker / Me and my farmall / Lay me to rest / Bill Cheatham / Lay this broken heart to rest / Snow shoes / Preachin' by the roadside / Red-eyed benny hen / New Sunday school / Amanda's reel / One horse wagon / St. Anne's reel
SHCD 3869 / Mar '98 / Sugar Hill

Smith, Laura

☐ LAURA SMITH VOL.1 (1924-1927)
DOCD 5429 / Jul '96 / Document

Smith, Leo

☐ DIVINE LOVE
5291262 / Jul '96 / ECM

☐ KULTURE JAZZ
Don't you remember / Kulture of jazz / Song of humanity / Fire-sticks, crysanthemums and moonlight / Seven rings of light in the Holy Trinity / Louis Armstrong counterpointing / Albert Ayler in a spiritual light / Kemet Omega reigns (for Billie Holiday) / Love supreme (for John Coltrane) / Mississippi delta sunrise (for Bobbie) / Mother: Sarah Brown-Smith-Wallace / Healer's voyage on the sacred river / Uprising
5190742 / Jun '93 / ECM

Smith, Linda

☐ PREFERENCE
SPY 7CD / Jun '97 / Harriet

Smith, Little George

☐ HARMONICA ACE
Rockin' / Telephone blues / Blues in the dark / Blues stay away / Have myself a ball / I found my baby / Oopin' doopin' doopin' / California blues / Hey Mr. Porter / Early one Monday morning (take 1) / Love life / Cross-eyed Suzie Lee / You don't love me / Early one Monday morning (take 2)
CDCHD 337 / Jun '91 / Ace

Smith, Lonnie Liston

☐ COSMIC FUNK (Smith, Lonnie Liston & Cosmic Echoes)
Cosmic funk / Footprints / Beautiful woman / Sais (Egypt) / Peaceful ones / Naima
7863505912 / Jun '97 / Flying Dutchman

☐ EXPANSIONS
Expansions / Dessert nights / Summer days / Voodoo woman / Peace / Shadows / My love
ND 80934 / Mar '94 / RCA

☐ FLAVOURS
500802 / Sep '96 / Musidisc

☐ MOVE YOUR HAND
Charlie Brown / Layin' in the cut / Move your hand / Sunshine superman / Dancin' / In an easy groove
CDP 8312492 / Mar '96 / Blue Note

☐ TRANSFORMATION
Chance for peace (give peace a chance) / Nubian nights / Caribbean sunrise / Space princess / Quiet moments / Angels of the night / Transformation / Expansions / Moon beams / Queen of hearts / Beautiful girl / Chance for peace
ME 007022 / 25 May '98 / Soulciety

☐ VERY BEST OF LONNIE LISTON SMITH, THE
Space princess / Get down everybody (it's time for world peace) / Desert nights / Voodoo woman / Chance for peace / Visions of a new world / Song for the children / Fruit music / Quiet moments / Quiet dawn / Sunbeams / Expansions / Prelude (live) / Expansions (live)
74321137612 / Jul '93 / RCA

Smith, Louis

☐ THERE GOES MY HEART (Smith, Louis Quintet)
SCCD 31415 / 21 Aug '97 / Steeplechase

Smith, Mamie

☐ MAMIE SMITH VOL.1 1920-1921
DOCD 5357 / Jun '95 / Document

☐ MAMIE SMITH VOL.2 (Get Hot)
DOCD 5358 / Jun '95 / Document

☐ MAMIE SMITH VOL.3 1922-1923
DOCD 5359 / Jun '95 / Document

☐ MAMIE SMITH VOL.4 (First Lady Of The Blues)
DOCD 5360 / Jun '95 / Document

Smith, Marc

☐ PAST, PRESENT AND FUTURE
Procastinator / Taking over me / Kickstart / Oh no / Boom and pow / Pump up the noise / Nexus / Journey / Relax your mind / Do that to me / Echoplex
CSR 014 / Jun '97 / Clubscene

Smith, Margot

☐ TASTE
IMM 002CD / 9 Mar '98 / Immersion

Smith, Marvin

☐ KEEPER OF THE DRUMS
Just have fun / Miss Ann / Love will find a way / Song of joy / Creeper / Now I know / Thinking of you / Simple samba song
CCD 4325 / Sep '87 / Concord Jazz

☐ ROAD LESS TRAVELLED, THE (Smith, Marvin 'Smitty')
Neighbourhood / Wish you were here with me part 1 / Gothic 17 / Road less travelled / I'll love you always / Salsa blue / Concerto in BG / Wish you were here with me part 2
CCD 4379 / Jul '89 / Concord Jazz

Smith, Mel

☐ STORY OF FATHER CHRISTMAS, THE
4694752 / 3 Nov '97 / Columbia

Smith, Melvin

☐ AT HIS BEST (2CD Set)
Up on the hill / School boy blues / Reliefin' blues / They ain't gonna tell it right / Rampaging Mama / Homesick blues / Come back my darlin' / Real true gal / Everybody's got the blues / I remember / California baby / Looped / Baby I'll be there / I'm out of my mind / Woman trainer / Business man's blues / Sarah Kelly / Six times six / Call me darling, call me swetheart, dear / What's to become of me / Hot ziggety zag / Letter to my baby / I don't have to hunt no more / Every pound / Miss Brown / I feel like goin' home / It went down easy / Why do these things have to be / Things you oughta know / No baby / You can't stay here / Crazy baby
BCD 15703 / Nov '94 / Bear Family

Smith, Michael

☐ TIME
FF 70613 / Nov '94 / Flying Fish

Smith, Michael W.

☐ CHRISTMAS (Smith, Michael W./ Hollywood Presby./American Boys Choir)
Sing, choirs of angels: *Smith, Michael W.* / Lux venit (The Light comes) / Arise, shine, for your light has come / Anthem for Christmas / First snowfall / Christ the Messiah / No eye had seen: *Smith, Michael W. & Amy Grant/Hollywood Presby. Choir* / All is well / Memoirs / Gloria / Silent night
RRACD 0052 / Dec '89 / Reunion

☐ GO WEST YOUNG MAN
RRACD 0063 / Jan '91 / Reunion

☐ LIVE THE LIFE
Missing person / Love me good / Live the life / Never been unloved / I believe in you now / Don't give up / Let me show you the way / I know your name / Matter of time / In my arms again / Song for Rich / Hello goodbye
CD 10007Y / May '98 / Reunion

Smith, Mike

☐ ON A COOL NIGHT (Smith, Mike Quintet & Ron Friedman)
Don't scare me none / Speak no evil / Jeanie / Stars fell on Alabama / Autumn leaves / Stu's blues / On a cool night / Big P
DD 448 / Mar '97 / Delmark

☐ SINATRA SONGBOOK, THE
DE 480 / Aug '95 / Delmark

☐ TRAVELER (Smith, Mike Quintet)
Traveller / Rosebud / Child's paradise / Chromatose / Nepotism / Monte Carlo / Witch hunt / If you never come to me / Angel eyes / Full tilt
DE 462 / Mar '97 / Delmark

☐ TRAVELLER, THE (Smith, Mike Quintet)
Traveler / Rosebud / A child's paradise / Chromatose / Nepotism / Monte carlo / Witch hunt / If you never come to me / Angel eyes / Full tilt
DDCD 462 / Nov '93 / Delmark

☐ UNIT 7 (A Tribute to Cannonball Adderley)
Unit 7 / Hi fly / La luz de la luna / Work song / Jeanine / Pisces / Dat dere / Little taste
DD 444 / Mar '97 / Delmark

Smith, Orville

☐ WALKING ON A TIGHTROPE
RIZ 00042 / Oct '96 / Riz

Smith, Patti

☐ BAREFOOT (A Tribute To Patti Smith) (Various Artists)
DOP 50 / 1 Jun '98 / Doppelganger

☐ DREAM OF LIFE
People have the power / Going under / Up there, down there / Paths that cross / Dream of life / Where duty calls / Looking for you (I was) / Jackson song / As the night goes by / Wild leaves
07822188282 / 1 Sep '97 / Arista

☐ EASTER
Till victory / Space monkey / Because the night / Ghost dance / Babelogue / Rock 'n' roll nigger / Privilege / We three / Twenty fifth floor / Easter / Break it up / High on rebellion / Godspeed
07822188262 / 1 Sep '97 / Arista

☐ GONE AGAIN
Gone again / Beneath the Southern cross / About a boy / My madrigal / Summer cannibals / Dead to the world / Wing ravens / Wicked messenger / Fireflies / Farewell reel
07822187472
07822384742 / Jul '96 / Arista

☐ HORSES
Gloria / Redondo beach / Birdland / Free money / Kimberly / Break it up / Land / Horses / Land of a thousand dances / La mer / Elegie / My generation
07822188272 / 1 Sep '97 / Arista

☐ PEACE AND NOISE
Waiting underground / Whirl away / 1949 / Spell / Don't say nothing / Dead city / Blue poles / Death singing / Memento mori / Last call
7822189862 / 6 Oct '97 / Arista

☐ RADIO ETHIOPIA
Ask the angels / Ain't it strange / Poppies / Pissing in the river / Pumping (my heart) / Distant fingers / Radio Ethiopia / Abyssinia
07822188252 / 1 Sep '97 / Arista

☐ WAVE
Frederick / Dancing barefoot / Citizen ship / Hymn revenge / Seven ways of going / Broken flag / Wave / So you want to be a rock 'n' roll star
07822188292 / 1 Sep '97 / Arista

Smith, Paul

☐ BY THE FIRESIDE
Cupid took me for a ride / Way you look tonight / By the fireside / Wandering / Out of nowhere / 'S Wonderful / Over the rainbow / Great lie / Jumper / Lauri Lou / Pick yourself up / I only have eyes for you
SV 0225 / May '98 / Savoy Jazz

☐ SOFTLY BABY (Smith, Paul Quartet)
Softly / Taking a chance on love / Easy to love / Long live Phineas / I didn't know what time it was / I'll remember April / Invitation / I got rhythm / Man I love / Blues a la PT
JASCD 311 / Jun '97 / Jasmine

Smith, 'Pigmeat' Pete

☐ JAZZ WOODBINE (New Originals In Fingerpicking/Bottleneck Blues Tradition)
PIGME 008 / Apr '97 / Pigme

Smith, Ray

☐ SHAKE AROUND
CPCD 8117 / Aug '95 / Charly

Smith, Roger

☐ MY COLORS
Miss Wiggle (so what) / Hopscotch / Can you stand the rain / Only we know / Fallin' behind / Just bacause / Hermosa / I'm ready / Elly Mae / Illusionary dreamer / Serenade you / R Y B W and others / Put your faith in me
JVC 20632 / Dec '96 / JVC

☐ UNEXPECTED TURNS
EM 4014 / Dec '96 / Emanem

Smith, Slim

☐ 20 RARE GROOVES
Baby I need your loving / Love make me do foolish things / Let it be me / Please stay / Jenny come lately / It's real / People rock steady / Trying to find a home / Thank you lord / Don't go / Put yourself in my place / Love me tender / Wonderful day / People are talking / Moving on / Give me the right / Vow / Say you want to be loved / What would I give / Gypsy woman
RNCD 2050 / Mar '94 / Rhino

☐ 20 SUPER HITS
SONCD 0004 / Jan '91 / Sonic Sounds

☐ FOREVER (Smith, Slim & The Uniques)
Ain't too proud to beg / Everybody needs love / Slip away / Let me go girl / People get ready, do rock steady / Love and devotion / Watch this sound / Out of love / A-yuh / Just a miracle / That's the way love is / Run come / Precious love / Standing in / Freedom song / Sitting in the park / Send me some loving / Everybody needs love / Gypsy woman / Never let me go / Speak no evil / My conversation / Beatitude / I am lost / Girls like dirt / One fine day / Please stay / Version of love / Forever / My girl
RN 7013 / Apr '97 / Rhino

☐ RAIN FROM THE SKIES
Love power / It's alright / Don't tell your mama / Love and affection / Sunny side of the sea / Money love / Travel on / Stand up and fight / Sitting in the park / Turning point / Time has come / Take me back / Will you still love me / Burning fire / This feeling / Rain from the skies / Just a dream / Send me some lovin' / Blinded by love / Where do I turn / My conversation
CDTRL 303 / Mar '94 / Trojan

Smith, Steve

☐ VITALIVE
One flight up / Looks bad, feels good / Jave and nail / (what lies) beyond / I should care / Mac attack / Johnny cat / Perfect date / Island holiday / Europa (earth's cry heaven's smile)
VBR 20512 / Dec '90 / Vera Bra

Smith, Steven R.

☐ AUTUMN IS THE END
DRL 075 / 3 Aug '98 / Darla

Smith, Stuff

☐ CLASSICS 1936-1939
CLASSICS 706 / Jul '93 / Classics

☐ LIVE AT MONTMARTRE
STCD 4142 / Feb '90 / Storyville

☐ MAD GENIUS OF VIOLIN VOL.1 1936-1944, THE
158912 / Jun '97 / Jazz Archives

☐ ONYX CLUB SPREE
I hope Gabriel likes my music / I'm putting all my eggs in one basket / I don't want to make history (I just want to make love) / 'Taint no use / After you've gone / You're a viper / Robins and roses / It ain't right / Old Joe's hittin' the jug / Serenade for a wealthy widow / Twilight in Turkey / Where is the sun / Upstairs / Onyx club spree / My thoughts / My blue Heaven / It's up to you / I've got you under my skin / Crescendo in drums / Joshua / Is is / Time and again
TPZ 1061 / Feb '97 / Topaz Jazz

☐ STUFF SMITH TRIO WORLD JAM SESSIONS RECORDING 1943
PCD 7053 / Jun '96 / Progressive

Smith, Tab

☐ ACE HIGH
Cottage for sale / Sunny side of the street / Tis Autumn / Teddy's brannin' / Strange / These foolish things / Ace high / Auf wiedersehn / Cuban boogie / My mother's eyes / I've had the blues all day / You belong to me / Red hot and blue / Bit of blues / Pennies from heaven / Seven up / I live true to you / Cherry / My baby / Closin' time
DD 455 / Mar '97 / Delmark

☐ BECAUSE OF YOU
DD 429 / Dec '89 / Delmark

☐ JUMPTIME 1951-1952
Because of you / Slow motion / Dee Jay special / Sin / Under a blanket of blue / How can you say we're thru / Wig song / Hands across the table / One man dip / Down beat / Brown baby / Knotty-headed women / Boogie joogie / Can't we take a chance / All my life / Jump time / This love of mine / Ain't got nobody / Love is a wonderful thing / Nursery rhyme jump
DD 447 / Mar '97 / Delmark

☐ TOP 'N' BOTTOM
DE 499 / Jan '98 / Delmark

Smith, Tim

☐ EXTRA SPECIAL OCEANLAND WORLD
ALPHCD 020 / Jun '96 / Alphabet Business Concern

Smith, Tommy

☐ AZURE
Gold of the azure / Escape ladder / Siesta / Smile of flamboyant wings / Vowel song / Constellation - the morning star / Calculation / Dancer / Dialogue of the insects / Blue
AKD 059 / May '97 / Linn

☐ MISTY MORNING AND NO TIME
Intrusion / Estuary / Incident / Memorial / Root of it / You went away / Dipper / Rag and bone / Sounds of the day / Country dance / Misty morning and no time / Day break / Two friends / Trapped
AKD 040 / May '95 / Linn

☐ REMINISCENCE (Smith, Tommy & Forward Motion)
AKD 024 / Feb '94 / Linn

☐ SOUND OF LOVE, THE (The Ballads Of Duke Ellington & Billy Strayhorn)
Flower is a lovesome thing / Chelsea Bridge / Isfahan / In a sentimental mood / Duke Ellington's sound of love / Sophisticated lady / Passion flower / Star-crossed lovers / Solitude / Prelude to a kiss / Cottontail / Johnny comes lately
AKD 084 / 9 Feb '98 / Linn

Smith, Tony

☐ BIG CAT
Renegade / Arabella / Botswana / Don't lose it / Dark bark / Cruisin' / Big cat / South wind / Angie
JITCD 9502 / Sep '95 / Jazzizit

☐ RUNNER
Talkback / Runner / Suspicious / Michelle's song / Horse / Sleepwalking / Phase phase / Githie manitou / Whirlpool
JITCD 9708 / Jul '97 / Jazzizit

Smith, Trixie

☐ TRIXIE SMITH VOL.1 1922-1924
DOCD 5332 / May '95 / Document

☐ TRIXIE SMITH VOL.2 1925-1939
DOCD 5333 / May '95 / Document

Smith, TV

☐ IMMORTAL RICH
Immortal rich / Living world / Walk the plank / We want the road / High society / Head on clear / Day we caught the big fish / Thin green line / Let 'em go / In there / Earth 2
BAH 21 / Jan '95 / Humbug

☐ RIP
Leisuretime / My string will snap / New ways are best / Free world / Silicon valley holiday / Luxury in exile / Buried by the machine / Ghosts / Ready for the axe to drop / Newshound / Beauty treatment / Lord's prayer
BAH 5 / Mar '93 / Humbug

Smith, Warren

☐ CALL OF THE WILD
Cave in / I don't believe I'll fall in love today / After the boy gets the girl / Whole lot of nothin' / Odds and ends / Call of the wild (unissued) / Old lonesome feeling / Call of the wild / Book of broken hearts / I fall to pieces / Foolin' around / Take good care of her / Pick me up on your way down / Just call me lonesome / Heartbreak Hotel / I still miss someone /

Kissing my pillow / I can't stop loving you / Why baby why: *Smith, Warren & Shirley Collie* / Why I'm walkin': *Smith, Warren & Shirley Collie* / Five minutes of the latest blues / Put me back together again / Bad news gets around / Hundred and sixty pounds of hurt / That's why I sing in a honky tonk / Big city ways / Blue smoke / Judge and jury / Future x / She likes attention
BCD 15495 / Apr '90 / Bear Family

☐ CLASSIC SUN RECORDINGS
Rock 'n' roll Ruby / I'd rather be safe than sorry / Black Jack David / Ubangi stomp / Darkest cloud / So long I'm gone / Who took my baby / I couldn't take the chance / Miss Froggie / Red Cadillac and a black moustache / Stop the world (and let me off) / I fell in love / Got love if you want it / Old lonesome feeling (incomplete) / Tell me who / Tonight will be the last night / Dear John / Hank Snow medley / Do I love you / Uranium rock / Goodbye Mr. Love / Sweet sweet girl / I like your kind of love / My hanging day
BCD 15514 / Apr '92 / Bear Family

☐ ROCKABILLY LEGEND
CPCD 8119 / Aug '95 / Charly

Smith, Wayne

☐ SLENG TENG (Smith, Wayne & Prince Jammy's Computerised Dub)
Under me sleng teng / In thing / Love don't love me / My Lord my God / Icky all over / E 20 / Like a dragon / Hard to believe / Leave her for you / Walk like granny
GRELCD 513 / May '92 / Greensleeves

☐ WICKED IN A DANCE HALL
RRTGCD 7785 / Jul '90 / Rohit

Smith, Whispering

☐ WHISPERING SMITH
PASTCD 7074 / Oct '95 / Flapper

Smith, Will

☐ BIG WILLIE STYLE
Y'all know / Gettin' jiggy with it / Candy / Chasing forever / Keith B real / Don't say nothin' / Miami / Yes yes y'all / I loved you / Keith B real / It's all good / Just the two of us / Keith B real / Big willie style / Men in black / Just cruisin'
4886622 / 10 Nov '97 / Columbia

Smith, Willie

☐ CLASSICS 1925-1937 (Smith, Willie 'The Lion')
CLASSICS 662 / Nov '92 / Classics

☐ CLASSICS 1937-1938 (Smith, Willie 'The Lion')
CLASSICS 677 / Mar '93 / Classics

☐ CLASSICS 1938-1940 (Smith, Willie 'The Lion')
CLASSICS 692 / May '93 / Classics

☐ LION AND THE LAMB, THE (Smith, Willie 'The Lion' & His Cubs)
What can I do with a foolish little thing like you do / Harlem joys / Lost / Mutiny in the parlour / Swampland is calling / More than that / I can see you all over the place / Achin' hearted blues / Morning air / Echoes of Spring / Concentrating / Fading star / Passionette / Rippling waters / Breakaway / Between the devil and the deep blue sea / Tea for two / I'll follow you / Finger buster / Lion and the lamb / I'm coming Virginia / Limehouse blues / Strange fruit / You're the limit / 12th Street rag / Bugle call rag
TPZ 1057 / Nov '96 / Topaz Jazz

☐ LION ROARS AGAIN (Smith, Willie 'The Lion')
CBC 1012 / Jun '93 / Bellaphon

☐ LION ROARS, THE (His Greatest 1934-1944) (Smith, Willie 'The Lion')
Ida sweet as apple cider: *Alabama Jug Band* / Somebody stole my gal: *Alabama Jug Band* / Apologies: *Mezzrow, Mezz & His Orchestra* / Sendin' the vipers: *Mezzrow, Mezz & His Orchestra* / Mutiny in the parlour: *Mezzrow, Mezz & His Swing Band* / Panic is on: *Mezzrow, Mezz & His Swing Band* / What can I do with a foolish little girl like you: *Smith, Willie 'The Lion' & His Cubs* / Harlem joys: *Smith, Willie 'The Lion' & His Cubs* / Echoes of spring: *Smith, Willie 'The Lion' & His Cubs* / Swing brother swing: *Smith, Willie 'The Lion' & His Cubs* / Swampland is calling me: *Smith, Willie 'The Lion' & His Cubs* / Old stamping ground: *Smith, Willie 'The Lion' & His Cubs* / Let's mop it: *Smith, Willie 'The Lion' & His Cubs* / Muskrat ramble: *Smith, Willie 'The Lion' & His Cubs* / Morning air / Fading star / Finger buster / Rippling waters / Lion and the lamb / I'm coming Virginia: *Bechet, Sidney & His New Orleans Feetwarmers* / Limehouse blues: *Bechet, Sidney & His New Orleans Feetwarmers* / Strange fruit: *Bechet, Sidney* / Black and blue: *Kaminsky, Max Jazz Band* / Jazz me blues: *Kaminsky, Max Jazz Band*
CDAJA 5272 / May '98 / Living Era

☐ LIVE 1945 (Smith, Willie & Harry James All Stars)
Introduction / Sweet Georgia brown / These foolish things (remind me of you) / Honeysuckle rose / Body and soul / Introduction / Sweet Georgia brown / It's the talk of the town / Tea for two
VN 1011 / Aug '97 / Viper's Nest

☐ PORK AND BEANS (Smith, Willie 'The Lion')
Pork and beans / Moonlight cocktail / Spanish Venus / Junk man rag / Squeeze me / Love will find a way / I'm just wild about Harry / Memories of you / Alexander's ragtime band / All of me / Ain't misbehavin' / Man I love / Summertime / Ain't she sweet
BLCD 760144 / Jan '85 / Black Lion

Smither, Chris

☐ ANOTHER WAY TO FIND YOU
High heel sneakers/Big boss man / Another way to find you / Down in the flood / Lonely time / Lonesome Georgia Brown / Catfish / Every mother's son / I got mine / Don't it drag on / Love you like a man / I feel the same / Friend of the devil / Shake sugaree / Tulane / Have you seen my baby / Song for Susan / Homunculus
FF 70568 / Nov '96 / Flying Fish

☐ HAPPIER BLUE
Happier blue / Memphis in the meantime / Devil's real / No more cane on the Brazos / Mail order mystics / No reward / Already gone / Killing the blues / Rock 'n' roll doctor / Magnolia / Honeysuckle dog / Take it all / Time to spend
FIENDCD 739 / Mar '94 / Demon

☐ I'M A STRANGER TOO/DON'T DRAG IT ON
COLCD 5838 / May '97 / Collectables

☐ IT AIN'T EASY
GCD 1031 / Jan '98 / Genes

☐ SMALL REVELATIONS
HCD 8077 / Feb '97 / Hightone

☐ UP ON THE LOWDOWN
HCD 8060 / Apr '95 / Hightone

Smithereens

☐ 1234
(You is) a guarantee / For love / Promiscious / Trouble in mind / Speed of life / Time ticks tragedy / Just enuf / He's a sucker
BASTA 3090542 / Oct '97 / Basta

Smiths

☐ ASK ME, ASK ME, ASK ME (Interview)
3D 008 / Jan '97 / Network

☐ BEST OF THE SMITHS VOL.2, THE
Boy with the thorn in his side / Headmaster ritual / Heaven knows I'm miserable now / Ask / Oscillate wildly / Nowhere fast / Still ill / That joke isn't funny anymore / Shakespeare's sister / Girl afraid / Reel around the fountain / Last night I dreamt somebody loved me / There is a light that never goes out
4509904062 / Nov '92 / WEA

☐ EXTRAORDINARY ORDINARINESS (CD/Book Set)
SB 007 / 23 Feb '98 / Sonic Book

☐ HATFUL OF HOLLOW
William, it was really nothing / What difference does it make / These things take time / This charming man / How soon is now / Handsome devil / Hand in glove / Still ill / Heaven knows I'm miserable now / This night has opened my eyes / You've got everything now / Accept yourself / Girl afraid / Back to the old house / Reel around the fountain / Please, please, please let me get what I want
4509918932 / Feb '95 / WEA

☐ INTERVIEW, THE
SPEEK 014 / 16 Mar '98 / Talking Music

☐ LOUDER THAN BOMBS
Is it really so strange / Sheila take a bow / Shoplifters of the world unite / Sweet and tender hooligan / Half a person / London / Panic / Girl afraid / Shakespeare's sister / William, it was really nothing / You just haven't earned it yet baby / Heaven knows I'm miserable now / Ask / Golden lights / There is a light that never goes out
4509938332 / Feb '95 / WEA

☐ MEAT IS MURDER
Headmaster ritual / Barbarism begins at home / Rusholme ruffians / I want the one I can't have / What she said / Nowhere fast / That joke isn't funny anymore / Well I wonder / Meat is murder
4509918952 / Feb '95 / WEA

☐ QUEEN IS DEAD, THE
Queen is dead / Frankly, Mr. Shankly / I know it's over / Never had no one ever / Cemetry gates / Bigmouth strikes again / Boy with the thorn in his side / Vicar in a tu tu / There is a light that never goes out / Some girls are bigger than others
4509918962 / Feb '95 / WEA

☐ RANK
Queen is dead / Panic / Vicar in a tutu / Ask / Rusholme ruffians / What she said / Cemetry gates / London / Draize Train / Boy with the thorn in his side / Is it really so strange / I know it's over / Still ill / Bigmouth strikes again
4509919002 / Feb '95 / WEA

☐ SMITHS IS DEAD, THE (Various Artists)
Queen is dead: *Boo Radleys* / Frankly Mr. Shankly: *High Llamas* / I know it's over: *Trash Can Sinatras* / Never had no one ever: *Bragg, Billy* / Cemetry gates: *Frank & Walters* / Bigmouth strikes again: *Placebo* / Boy with the thorn in his side: *Bis* / Vicar in a tutu: *Therapy* / There is a light that never goes out: *Divine Comedy* / Some girls are bigger than others: *Supergrass*
4867452 / Nov '96 / Epic

☐ SMITHS SINGLES
Hand in glove / Heaven knows I'm miserable now / What difference does it make / This charming man / What difference does it make / This charming man / Shoplifters of the world unite / Heaven knows I'm miserable now / William it was really nothing / Girlfriend in a coma / Hand in glove / How soon is now / Shakespeare's sister / How soon is now / William it was really nothing / That joke isn't funny anymore / Bigmouth strikes again / I started something I couldn't finish / Boy with a thorn in his side / There is a light that never goes out / Last night I dreamt that somebody loved me / Panic / Ask / Shakespeare's sister / That joke isn't funny anymore / Shoplifters of the world unite / Sheila take a bow / Bigmouth strikes again / Ask / Girlfriend in a coma / I started something I couldn't finish / Boy with the thorn in his side / Panic / Last night I dreamt somebody loved me / There is a light that never goes out / Sheila take a bow
4509990902 / Feb '95 / WEA

☐ SMITHS, THE
Reel around the fountain / You've got everything now / Miserable lie / Pretty girls make graves / Hand that rocks the cradle / This charming man / Still ill / Hand in glove / What difference does it make / I don't owe you anything / Suffer little children
4509918922 / Feb '95 / WEA

☐ SMITHS: INTERVIEW COMPACT DISC
CBAK 4025 / Nov '89 / Baktabak

☐ STRANGEWAYS HERE WE COME
Rush and a push and the land is ours / I started something I couldn't finish / Death of a disco dancer / Girlfriend in a coma / Stop me if you think you've heard this one before / Last night I dreamt somebody loved me / Unhappy birthday / Paint a vulgar picture / Death at one's elbow / I won't share you
4509918992 / Feb '95 / WEA

☐ WORLD WON'T LISTEN, THE
Panic / Ask / London / Big mouth strikes again / Shakespeare's sister / There is a light that never goes out / Shoplifters of the world unite / Boy with the thorn in his side / Asleep / Unloveable / Half a person / Stretch out and wait / That joke isn't funny anymore / You haven't earned it yet baby / Rubber ring / Oscillate wildly / Money changes everything
4509918982 / Feb '95 / WEA

Smog

☐ DOCTOR CAME AT DAWN
WIGCD 027 / Sep '96 / Domino

☐ JULIUS CAESAR
Strawberry rash / Your wedding / Thirty seven push-ups / Stalled on the tracks / One less star / Golden / When you talk / I am Star Wars / Connections / When the power goes out / Chosen one / What kind of angel / Stick in the mud
OLE 0972 / Jul '94 / Matador

☐ RED APPLE FALLS
Morning papers / Blood red bird / Red apples / I was a stranger / To be of use / Red apple falls / Ex-con / Inspirational / Finer days
WIGCD 035 / May '97 / Domino

☐ SEWN TO THE SKY
DC 74CD / Dec '96 / Drag City

☐ WILD LOVE
EFAD 49522 / Mar '95 / Skunk

Smoke City

☐ FLYING AWAY
Underwater love / Devil mood / With you / Numbers / Mr. Gorgeous (and Miss Curvaceous) / Aguas de Marco (Joga Bosa) / Dark walk / Jamie Pan / Julietta / Flying away
CHIP 194 / 17 Nov '97 / Jive

Smoke No Bones

☐ SMOKE NO BONES
ONER 006 / Apr '97 / One Drop

Smokehouse

☐ EDGE OF THE SWAMP
KSCD 044 / 15 Jun '98 / King Snake

☐ SWAMP JIVE
ICH 9017CD / Oct '93 / Ichiban

Smokie

☐ ALICE (WHO THE X IS ALICE)
Who the fuck is Alice / Lay back in the arms of someone / If you think you know how to love me / Needles and pins / Don't play your rock 'n' roll to me / Oh Carol / I'll meet you at midnight / It's your life / Boulevard of broken dreams / I feel love / For a few dollars more / Take good care of my baby / This side of paradise / Something's been making me blue / Wild angels / Naked love / It's my heart / Living next door to Alice / Can't cry hard enough
WAGCD 247 / 3 Aug '98 / North Of Watford

☐ BEST OF SMOKIE, THE
Living next door to Alice / Needles and pins / Oh Carol / Lay back in the arms of someone / Something's been making me blue / Couldn't live / Talking her 'round / Train song / Loser / Miss you / Run to you / Here lies a man / Now you think you know / No-one could ever love you more / Goin' tomorrow / Will you love me / You took me by surprise / Stranger with you
74321476832 / Apr '97 / Camden

☐ COLLECTION VOL.1, THE
Living next door to Alice / Mexican girl / Wild wild angels / Something's been making me blue / If you think you know how to love me / For a few dollars more / Don't play your rock 'n' roll to me / Needles and pins / It's your life / Baby it's you / Changing all the times / Lay back in the arms of someone / Oh Carol / I'll meet you at midnight
262538 / Jun '92 / Arista

☐ HITS COLLECTION BOX (3CD Set)
Needles and pins / Lay back in the arms of someone / Living next door to Alice / Naked love / Don't play that game with me / For a few dollars more / Wild wild angels / Boulevard of broken dreams / Hot girls and summer nights / Tambourine man / My heart is true / Can't cry hard enough / You're so different tonight / Think about the night / Heartbreak angel / Working for the weekend / Oh Carol / Listen to the radio / Don't play your rock 'n' roll / Never turn your back on your friends / Rock away your teardrops / Take good care of my body / Chasing shadows / Surfin' / Something's making me blue / In the middle of a lonely dream / Lyin' in the arms of the one you love / Bang bang / Cry in the night / Fistful of dollars / Rain came down / Love take me away / If you think you know how to love me / It's your life / I'll meet you at midnight / Hold on tight / I feel love / Falling apart / Derry girl / Young hearts / Norwegian girl / Can't this be love / Like an eagle / Love sometimes takes time / Sometimes you cry / Love is out of the question / I'd die for you / Alice
10332 / Oct '97 / Go On Deluxe

☐ HITS COLLECTION VOL.1
Needles and pins / Lay back in the arms of someone / Living next door to Alice / Naked love / Don't play that game with me / For a few dollars more / Wild wild angels / Boulevard of broken dreams / Hot girls and summer nights / Tambourine man / My heart is true / Can't cry hard enough / Your so different tonight / Think about the night / Heartbreak angel / Working for the weekend
10002 / Oct '97 / Go On Deluxe

☐ HITS COLLECTION VOL.2
Oh carol / Listen to your radio / Don't play your rock 'n' roll to me / Never turn your back on your friends / Rock away your teardrops / Take good care of my baby / Chasing shadows / Surfin' / Something's been making me blue / In the middle of the lonely / Lyin' in the arms of the one you love / Bang bang / Cry in the night / Fistful of dollars / Rain came down / Love take me away
10012 / Oct '97 / Go On Deluxe

☐ HITS COLLECTION VOL.3
If you think you know how to love / It's your life / I'll meet you at midnight / Hold on tight / I feel love / Falling apart / Derry girl / Young hearts / Norwegian girl / Can't this be love / Like an eagle / Love sometimes takes time / Sometimes you cry / Love is out of the question / I'd die for you / Alice
10022 / Oct '97 / Go On Deluxe

☐ ROCK AWAY YOUR TEARDROPS
My heart is true / Cry in the night / Hold on for the night / Never fight again / Rock away your teardrops / Second choice / Hold on tight / Only love hurts / Looking daggers / Hot girls and summer nights / If you think you know how to love me
100542 / May '97 / A-Play Collection

☐ SMOKIE
GFS 060 / Jul '97 / Going For A Song

☐ SMOKIE GREATEST HITS LIVE
I'll meet you at midnight / Lay back in the arms of someone / Medley / Something's making me blue / Wild angels / If you think you know how to love me / Don't play myour rock 'n' roll to me / Rock away your teardrops / Cry in the night / Oh Carol / Needles and pins / Living next door to Alice / Whiskey in the jar
PLATCD 3916 / Apr '93 / Platinum

☐ VERY BEST OF SMOKIE, THE
Mexican girl / Baby it's you / Living next door to Alice / Something's been making me blue / It's your life / If you think you know how to love me / Oh Carol / Take good care of my baby / Needles and pins / Lay back in the arms of someone / Don't play your rock 'n' roll to me / What can I do / I'll meet you at midnight / For a few dollars more / Who the fuck is Alice
10032 / Oct '97 / Go On Deluxe

Smokin' Beats

☐ READY TO FLY (2CD Set)
SMBLPCD 001 / 18 Aug '97 / Smokin' Beats

Smoking Popes

☐ BORN TO QUIT
Midnight moon / Rubella / Gotta know right now / Mrs. You and Me / Just broke up / My lucky day / Need you around / Can't help the teardrop / Adena / On the shoulder
CDEST 2277 / Mar '96 / Capitol

☐ DESTINATION FAILURE
Star struck one / No more smiles / I know you love me / You spoke to me / Paul / Can't find it / Capital Christine / Before I'm gone / Megan / Let's hear it for love / Pure imagination / I was right / They lied / End of your time / Pretty pathetic / Follow the sound
8382172 / 2 Mar '98 / Capitol

Smoking The Century Away

☐ SMOKING THE CENTURY AWAY
SR 201 / 6 Apr '98 / Smogless

Smooth

☐ REALITY
5490332 / 30 Mar '98 / Perspective

☐ SMOOTH
Mind blowin' / It's Summertime / Way back when / Blowin' up my pager / PYT / Swing it to the left side / Good stuff / Love groove / Jeeps and Benzos / Ghetto style / Undercover lover / Let it go
CHIP 162 / Aug '95 / Jive

Smoothe Da Hustler

☐ ONCE UPON A TIME IN AMERICA
FILECD 467 / Apr '96 / Profile

Smoothies

☐ PICKLE
185292 / Sep '95 / Southern

Smooths
☐ VERY OWN VEGAS
SD1 024 / 17 Nov '97 / Side One

Smothers, Smokey
☐ BOSSMAN
BM 9022 / Jun '93 / Black Magic

☐ SECOND TIME AROUND
Bluesman / Second time around / Soft winds / Crack head woman / I get evil / Clouds in my heart / Got to be some changes made / In the zone / Somebody / Let me in / My baby's gone / I better go now
CCD 11051 / Feb '97 / Crosscut

Smudge
☐ HOT SMOKE AND SASSAFRAS
WIGCD 019 / Feb '95 / Domino

☐ MANILOW
WIGCD 7 / Feb '94 / Domino

☐ MO POONTANG
HAC 62 / 23 Mar '98 / Half A Cow

☐ TEA, TOAST & TURMOIL
Spoilt brat / Straight face down / Outside / Make all our dreams come true / Pulp / Plug it up / Divan / Alison / Don't want to be Grant McLennan / Stranglehold / Dabble / Leroy de Foix / Tea, toast and turmoil / Foccacia / Steak and chips / Babaganouj
SALD 207 / Oct '93 / Shake

Smugglers
☐ SELLING THE SIZZLE
LOOKOUT 136CD / Mar '96 / Lookout

Smulyan, Gary
☐ LURE OF BEAUTY, THE (Smulyan, Gary Quintet)
CRISS 1049CD / Nov '91 / Criss Cross

☐ SAXOPHONE MOSAIC (Smulyan, Gary Nonet)
1092CD / Jan '95 / Criss Cross

☐ WITH STRINGS
Bad and the beautiful / Lush life / Thanks for you / It happens quietly / Don't follow the crowd / We've got a sure thing / Beware my heart / Moment of truth / Yesterday's gardenias / Two for the seesaw
CRISS 1129CD / Jul '97 / Criss Cross

Smurfs
☐ GO POP AGAIN
True blue / So natural / Shout / Roller / Smurfin' alive / Shy smurf's in the ring / Hush hush / Dancing Queen / Smurf walk / Line dance smurf / 31524 / Yodelling smurfs / Papa smurfs / Grandpa we love you
CDEMTV 155 / 25 Aug '97 / EMI

☐ GREATEST HITS
Smurfy girl / Papa smurfs party / We like to smurf it / Slam dunk da smurf / Smurfs are back / Keep on smurfing / Smurfhillbilly Joe / I've got a little puppy / Don't stop smurfing / True blue / Ooh aah just a little bit / Smurfing party / Roller blade smurf / Hush hush / Smurf macarena / Line dance smurf / Smurfs are coming home / Papa smurf
4941972
4941952 / 6 Apr '98 / EMI

☐ SMURF'S CHRISTMAS PARTY, THE
Christmas with the Smurfs / Rockin' round the Christmas tree / Rudolph the red-nosed reindeer / Winter wonderland / Frosty the snowman / I wish it could be Christmas every day / I saw Smurfette kissing Santa Claus / Merry Christmas everybody / All I want for Christmas is my two front teeth / Wonderful Christmastime / Let it snow / Christmas with the Smurfs / Silent night / Mistletoe and wine / Smurfland Christmas song (Mary's boy child) / White Christmas / Last Christmas / Little boy (Smurf that Santa Claus forgot) / On this Smurfary day / Smurfs in the snow / Lonely this Christmas / Smurfland Christmas song / Your Christmas wish / We wish you a merry Christmas
CDEMTV 140 / Nov '97 / EMI

☐ SMURFS GO POP, THE
Smurfs are back / Mr. Smurftastic / I've got a little puppy / Noisy Smurf / Find the Smurf / Smurfland / Our Smurfing party / Don't stop Smurfing / Smurfhillbilly Joe / We're the Smurfs / Smurfland Olympics / Smurfing ways / Mr. Blobby and the Smurfs / Football forever / Smurfing world
CDEMTV 121 / Jul '96 / EMI

☐ SMURFS HITS 1997 VOL.1
Wannabe a smurf star / Smurfs get upside your head / Smurf it up / Smurfs are coming home / Keep on smurfing / Smurf drummer / Get yourself smurfing / Small talk / Laughter smurf / Ooh aah smurf a little bit / Smurfing down the highway / Smurfbilly rock / Smurf Macarena / Only way / Your first school
CDEMTV 150 / Feb '97 / EMI TV

Smut
☐ BLOOD, SMUT AND TEARS
Cave / Alone / Spirit / Symphony / No sacrifice / Women / Baby Jack / Emotional suicide / Take back the night / Object of intentions / Autumn storm / Goodness, no grief
892402 / Apr '94 / Spanish Fly

Smyth, Gilli
☐ EVERY WITCHES WAY
Simple / Bold and brazen / Show is over / We who were raging / Beltaine / Four horsemen / Medicine woman / Animal / Magic / Lammas / I am witch / Lady wise / Simples
VP 139CD / Jun '93 / Voiceprint

Snafu
☐ SNAFU/SITUATION NORMAL (2CD Set)
Long gone / Said he the judge / Monday morning / Drowning in the sea of love / Country nest / Funky friend / Goodbye USA / That's the song / Dixie Queen / Sad Sunday / No more / No bitter taste / Brown eyed beauty and the blue assed fly / Lock and key / Big dog lusty / Playboy blues / Jessie Lee / Ragtime roll
SJPCD 030 / 20 Jul '98 / Angel Air

Snagapuss
☐ WHAP DEM MERLENE
SVCD 4 / Feb '94 / Shocking Vibes

Snagga
☐ LINE UP ALL THE GIRKS DEM
HCD 7007 / Aug '94 / Hightone

Snail, Azalia
☐ BLUE DANUBE
NORMAL 197CD / Jan '96 / Normal

Snake Corps
☐ SPICE
Science kills / Nothing / This is seagull / Come the glorious day / House of man / Calling you / Strangers / Man in the mirror / More than the ocean / Yesterday with you / In flux / Colder than the kiss / Party's over / Sky in your eyes / Dreamland
CDMGRAM 97 / Oct '95 / Anagram

Snake Finger
☐ NIGHT OF DESIRABLE OBJECTS
AIM 1011CD / Oct '93 / Aim

Snakepit Rebels
☐ SNAKEPIT REBELS
FLCCD 114 / Jun '91 / Tring

Snap
☐ SNAP ATTACK (The Best Of Snap)
Power / Ooops up / Cult of Snap / Mary had a little boy / Colour of love / Rhythm is a dancer / Exterminate / Do you see the light / Welcome to tomorrow / First last eternity / World in my hand / Rame
74321384864 / Aug '96 / Arista

☐ WELCOME TO TOMORROW
Green grass grows (earth follows) / It's a miracle (people need to love one another) / Rame / Dream on the moon / Welcome to tomorrow (are you ready) / World in my hands (we are one) / First last eternity (till the end) / Waves / Where are the boys, where are the girls / It's not over
74321223842 / Oct '94 / Arista

☐ WORLD POWER
Power / Cult of snap / I'm gonna get you (to whom it may concern) / Mary had a little boy / Ooops up / Believe the hype / Witness the strength / Blase blase
260682 / Aug '95 / Arista

Snap Her
☐ QUEEN BITCH OF ROCK 'N' ROLL
NRA 67CD / 15 Dec '97 / New Red Archives

Snapcase
☐ LOOKINGLASSELF
VR 013CD / Sep '96 / Victory

☐ PROGRESSION THROUGH UNLEARNING
VR 51CD / Apr '97 / Victory

Snatch
☐ CORNBREAD & ALISON MEOWLY
FM 03 / Nov '96 / Fundamental

Snatch It Back
☐ DYNAMITE
Little miss pleasure / Kind of loving I need / I'm not your fool / Ballad of edward johnson / Dynamite / Bad reputation / Feel so good / Good morning mr. jones / I like you / Maxime / Jump sister bessie / Talk to your daughter / One kiss / Tore up
TRCD 9904 / Nov '93 / Tramp

☐ EVIL
TRCD 9907 / Nov '93 / Tramp

Sneak's Noyse
☐ CHRISTMAS NOW IS DRAWING NEAR
Good people all this Christmastide / Sweet was the song the virgin sang / Down in yon forest / Holly and the ivy / Joseph was an old man / Angelus ad Virginem / Hail Mary full of grace / Tomorrow shall be my dancing day / Furry day carol / Deck the halls with boughs of holly / God bless you merry gentlemen
CDSDL 371 / Oct '86 / Saydisc

Sneetches
☐ LIGHTS OUT WITH THE SNEETCHES
I need someone / In my car / Lonelei / Fifty four hours / I don't expect her for you / Home again / No one knows / Only for a moment
CRECD 077 / Apr '91 / Creation

☐ OBSCUREYEARS
CREV 031CD / Nov '94 / Rev-Ola

☐ SOMETIMES THAT'S ALL WE HAVE
Unusual sounds / Don't turn back / In a perfect place / Empty sea / Sometimes that's all we have / Run in the sun / Mrs. markle / Nowhere at all / Take my hand / Another shitty day / You're gonna need her / It's looking like me
CRECD 043 / May '94 / Creation

☐ STARFUCKER
BUS 10062 / May '95 / Bus Stop

Snell, Adrian
☐ ALPHA AND OMEGA
MYRCD 1210 / '86 / Myrrh

☐ MY HEART SHALL JOURNEY... (The Best Of Adrian Snell)
WMD 001 / Oct '97 / Word

Snell, Howard
☐ FOUR SEASONS, THE (Snell, Howard Brass)
Water music / Brandenburg concerto no.3 / Four seasons
QPRZ 007D / Oct '97 / Polyphonic

☐ JEUX D'ENFANTS (Snell, Howard Brass)
To deum / Jeux d'enfants / Londonderry air / Exhibition can can / Bridal song / Xylophonia / Beethoven's beano / Stardust / Anyone can whistle / Debussy suite / Shepherdess of the Alps / Canzonetta / Waltz / Capriol suite
QPRZ 010D / Oct '97 / Polyphonic

☐ PREMIERE (Snell, Howard Brass)
Les soirees musicales / Symphony no. 4 in G / Syrinx / Divertimento / Irving Berlin suite / Mother Goose suite
QPRZ 005D / Oct '97 / Polyphonic

Snenska Hotkvinetten
☐ SVENSKA HOTKVINETTEN
DRCD 223 / Jan '88 / Dragon

Snetberger, Ferenc
☐ BUDAPEST CONCERT, THE
Budapest mood / Springtime in winter / Song to the east / Brazil / Dolphin / Little bossa / Variation / Tangoa free / Bossa for Egberto / Manha de carnaval / Budapest encore
8888232 / Jul '96 / Tiptoe

☐ OBSESSION
Wanton spirit / E-Bossa / Szivarvany / FS Five / Gypsy / Hanging out / Obsession / I remember / Song to the East / Pava
8888342 / 29 Jun '98 / Tiptoe

☐ SIGNATURE
Toni's carnival II / Passages / Obsession / Tangoa free / Poems for my people / Surprise / Variation
ENJ 90172 / May '95 / Enja

SNFU
☐ ...AND NO ONE ELSE WANTED TO PLAY
BYO 009CD / Oct '96 / Better Youth Organisation

☐ BETTER THAN A STICK IN THE EYE
CAR 001CD / Oct '96 / Cargo

☐ FYULABA
64722 / Sep '96 / Epitaph

☐ IF YOU SWEAR, YOU'LL CATCH NO FISH
BY 017CD / Oct '96 / Better Youth Organisation

☐ LAST OF THE BIG TIME SUSPENDERS, THE
CAR 011CD / Oct '96 / Cargo

☐ ONE VOTED MOST LIKELY TO SUCCEED, THE
E 864412 / Mar '95 / Epitaph

☐ SOMETHING GREEN AND LEAFY THIS WAY COMES
E 86430CD / Dec '93 / Epitaph

Snidero, Jim
☐ SAN JUAN (Snidero, Jim Sextet)
1232652 / Feb '97 / Red

☐ WHILE YOU'RE HERE (Snidero, Jim Quartet)
1232412 / Mar '92 / Red

Sniff 'n' The Tears
☐ BEST OF SNIFF 'N' THE TEARS, A
Driver's seat / What can daddy do / Thrill of it all / Looking for you / One love / Driving beat / Night life / Snow White / Roll 'em blues / Poison pen mail / Hungry eyes / Steal my heart / Ride blue divide
CDWIK 102 / Aug '91 / Chiswick

☐ FICKLE HEART
Driver's seat / New lines on love / Carve your name on my door / This side of the blue horizon / Sing / Rock 'n' roll music / Fight for love / Thrill of it all / Slide away / Last dance / Looking for you
CDWIKM 9 / Aug '91 / Chiswick

☐ GAMES UP, THE
Game's up / Moment of weakness / What can daddy do / Night life / If I knew then / One love / Five and zero / Poison pen mail / Rodeo drive
CDWIKM 92 / Aug '90 / Chiswick

☐ LOVE/ACTION
Driving beat / Put your money where your mouth is / Snow White / For what they promise / Without love / Steal my heart / That final love / Don't frighten me / Love action / Shame
CDWIKM 96 / Feb '91 / Chiswick

☐ NO DAMAGE DONE
PRD 70482 / Jan '92 / Provogue

☐ RIDE BLUE DIVIDE
Hand of fate / Hungry eyes / Roll the weight away / Like wildfire / Trouble is my business / You may find your heart / Gold / Ride blue divide / Company man
CDWIKM 97 / Apr '91 / Chiswick

Snoop Doggy Dogg
☐ DOGGY STYLE
Bathtub / G funk intro / Gin and juice / Tha shiznit / Lodi Dodi / Murder was the case / Serial killa / Who am I (What's my name) / For all my niggaz and bitches / Ain't no fun / Doggy dogg world / Gz and hustlas / Pump pump
IND 92279 / Feb '97 / Interscope

☐ THA DOGGFATHER
Intro / Doggfather / Ride 4 me / Up jump tha boogie / Freestyle conversation / When I grow up / Snoop bounce / Gold rush / (Tear 'em off) me and my doggz / You thought / Vapors / Groupie / 2001 / Six minutes / (DJ) Wake up / Snoop's upside ya head / Blueberry / Traffic jam / Doggyland / Downtown assassins / Outro
IND 90038 / Feb '97 / Interscope

Snooze
☐ MAN IN THE SHADOW
Snooze theme / So close and yet so far / Your consciousness goes bip / Before sunrise / Tribute to Horace / Killer with a gun / Pretty good privacy / I wanna be with you / Middle class lady / Down for mine / Anais plot / Man in the shadow / Chase
SSR 172CD / Mar '97 / SSR

Snoozer
☐ SNOOZER
LIDO 3CD / 8 Sep '97 / Lidocaine

Snout
☐ NEW POP DIALOGUE
ANDA 207CD / 22 Sep '97 / Au-Go-Go

Snow
☐ MURDER LOVE
Si wi dem nuh know we / Murder love / Bad men / Rivertown / Babylon / Yesterday / Anything for you / Things to say / Let's get it on (+ elements from / Sexy girl / If you like the sound / Dream / Time
7567617372 / Mar '95 / East West

Snow, Hank
☐ ESSENTIAL HANK SNOW, THE
Rhumba boogie / I'm moving on / Golden rocket / Unwanted sign upon your heart / Music makin' Mama from Memphis / Goldrush is over / I don't hurt anymore / Fool such as I / Gal who invented kissin' / I went to your wedding / Would you mind / Lady's man / Yellow roses / Miller's cave / Beggar to a king / I've been everywhere / Ninety miles an hour (down a dead end street) / Let me go lover / Wishing well (down in the well) / Hello love
7863669312 / May '97 / RCA

☐ MASTERS, THE
EABCD 035 / 24 Nov '97 / Eagle

☐ SINGING RANGER VOL.1 (The Complete Early 50's Hank Snow/4CD Set)
I'm movin' on / With this ring / Rumba boogie / Paving the highway with tears / Golden rocket / Your locket has broken my heart / Unwanted sign upon my heart / (I wish upon) my little golden horseshoe / Confused with the blues / You pass me by / Love entered the iron door / I cried but my tears were too late / One more ride / Hobo Bill's last ride / Wreck of ol' 97 / Ben Dewberry's final run / Mystery of number five / Engineer's child / Law of love / Nobody's child / I wonder where you are tonight / Star spangled waltz / Blind boy's dog / Marriage vow / Only rose / Anniversary of my broken heart / Music makin'

mama from Memphis / Highest bidder / Gold rush is over / Love's game of let's pretend / Bluebird Island: *Snow, Hank & Anita Carter* / Down the trail of aching hearts: *Snow, Hank & Anita Carter* / Lady's man / Fool such as I / Why do you punish me / Chattin' with a chick in Chattanooga / Greatest sin / Married by the Bible, divorced by the law / There wasn't an organ at our wedding / Zeb Turner's gal / Golden river / Moanin' / I knew that we'd meet again / Yodeling cowboy / On that old Hawaiian shore with you / On that old Hawaiian shore with you / I'm movin' on to glory / Jesus wept / Pray / These things shall pass / He'll understand and say well done / I just telephone upstairs / I'm in love with Jesus / Gal who invented kissin' / Spanish fireball / Honeymoon on a rocketship / Between fire and water / Boogie woogie flying cloud / I can't control my heart / For now and always / Message from the tradewinds / I traded love / Next voice you hear / When Mexican Joe met Jole Blon / I went to your wedding / Jimmie the kid / My blue eyed Jane / When Jimmie Rodgers said goodbye: *Snow, Hank & Jimmie Rodgers* / Southern Cannonball / Anniversary blue yodel / Why did you give me your love / Mississippi river blues / In daddy's footsteps / Gloryland march / Christmas roses / Reindeer boogie / Frosty the snowman / Silent night / My mother / Just keep a movin' / My sweet Conchita / Panamama / Unfaithful / Wabash blues / It's you, only you that I love: *Snow, Hank & Betty Cody* / Would you mind / In an old Dutch garden / Owl and I / I don't hurt anymore / Stolen moments / Hilo march / Act 1, act 2, act 3 / Yellow roses / No longer a prisoner / Sweet Marie / My Arabian baby / Bill is falling due / Blossoms in the springtime / I'm glad I'm on the inside (looking out) / When it's reveille time in Heaven / My religion's not old fashioned / Invisible hands / Little children / Alphabet / God's little candles / God's little candles

BCD 15426 / Nov '88 / Bear Family

☐ SINGING RANGER VOL.2 (4CD Set)

Love's call from the mountain (unissued) / I've forgotten you / That crazy mambo thing / Let me go, lover / Old spinning wheel: *Snow, Hank & Chet Atkins* / At the Darktown strutter's ball: *Snow, Hank & Chet Atkins* / Silver bell: *Snow, Hank & Chet Atkins* / Under the double eagle: *Snow, Hank & Chet Atkins* / It's you, only you that I love: *Snow, Hank & Anita Carter* / Keep your promise, Willie Thomas: *Snow, Hank & Anita Carter* / Crying, waiting, hoping / Someone mentioned your name / I'm glad to see you once again / Mainliner (the hawk of the West) / Cuba rhumba / Scale to measure love / Blue sea blues / Twelfth Street rag / Rainbow boogie / Vaya con dios / Madison madness / Can't have you blues / Dog bone (unissued) / Born to be happy / Golden rocket / Hobo Bill's last ride / Stolen moments / Pray / Nothing but sweet lies (unissued) / Conscience I'm guilty / Hula rock / Two won't care / Party of the second part (unissued) / These hands / Reminiscin': *Snow, Hank & Chet Atkins* / New Spanish two-step: *Snow, Hank & Chet Atkins* / In an 18th century drawing room / La cucaracha / Born to lose (unissued) / I'm movin' in / Sunshine serenade / El rancho grande / Grandfather's clock / Lover's farewell / Carnival of Venice / Old Doc Brown / That pioneer mother of mine / Blind boy's prayer / Lazybones / What do I know today / Trouble, trouble, trouble / First nighters / How to play the guitar / Little britches / What is father / Horse's prayer / Wedding bells / Loose talk / I almost lost my mind / Sing me a song of the islands / Memories are made of this / These tears are not for you / Singin' the blues / My life with you / Poison love / Among my souvenirs / Born to lose / It's been so long darling / La paloma / Oh wonderful world / Chant of the wanderer / I really don't want to know / Squid jiggin' ground / New blue velvet band / Calypso sweetheart / I'm hurtin' all over (unissued) / My memory (unissued) / Party of the second part marriage and divorce / Unfaithful (unissued) / Tangled mind / My arms are a house / Love's call from the mountain / On a Tennessee Saturday night (unissued) / Big wheels / Woman captured me / I heard my heart break last night / I wish I was the moon / My lucky friend / Whispering rain / I'm hurtin' all over / I'm here to get my baby out of jail / Don't make me go to bed and I'll be good / Convict and the rose / There's a little box of pine on the 729 / Put my little shoes away / Letter edged in black / Old Shep / Prisoner's prayer / Drunkard's child / Little Buddy / Nobody's child / Blue Danube / Waltz, Kitty waltz (unissued) / Brahms lullaby / Sleepy Rio Grande / Brahms lullaby

BCD 15476 / Jul '90 / Bear Family

☐ SINGING RANGER VOL.3 (12CD Set)

Casey Jones was his name / Southbound / Streamlined cannonball / (I heard that) Lonesome whistle / Waiting for a train / Wreck of the number nine / Pan American / Big wheels / Ghost trains / Chattanooga choo choo / Last ride / Crazy engineer / One more ride / Wreck of ol' 97 / Crazy little train of love / Any old time / Blue yodel no. 10 / Travellin' blues / Never no' mo' blues / Gambling polka dot blues / You and my old guitar / Roll along Kentucky moon / Moonlight and skies / One rose (that's left in my heart) / Tuck away my lonesome blues / Down the old road to home / I'm sorry we met / Chasin' a rainbow / Doggone that train / Father time and mother love / I heard my heart break last night / Walkin' and talkin' / Rockin' rollin' ocean / Miller's cave / Dreamer's island / Change of the tide / I'm movin' on / Golden rocket / My mother / I don't hurt anymore / Conscience I'm guilty / I'm asking for a friend / Bluebird Island / Fool such as I / Marriage vow / With this ring I thee wed / My Nova Scotia home / Tramp's story / Lifetime blues / Maple leaves / Casey's washerwoman boogie / Hawaiian sunset / Man who robbed the bank of Santa Fe / Man behind the gun / Restless one / Call of the wild / Laredo / Way out there / Patanio, the pride of the plains / Queen of Draw Poker Town / On the rhythm range / Chant of the wanderer / Wayward wind / Following the sun all day / Texas plains / Teardrops in my heart / Tumbling tumbleweeds / Heartbreak trail / Cool water / Riding home / At the rainbow's end / It's a little more like Heaven / I went to your wedding / Just a faded petal from a beautiful bouquet / Blue roses / Human / Breakfast with the blues / Down the trail of aching hearts / Let me go, lover / Tangled mind / Next voice you hear / Stolen moments / Gal who invented kissin' / Gold rush is over / Ninety miles an hour (down a dead end street) / My memories of you / Wishing well / I stepped over the line / Ninety days / Wedding picture / I've cried a mile / Listen / Friend / When today is a long time ago / Black diamond / Ancient history / You're losing your baby / You're the reason / Poor little Jimmie / Beggar to a king / Countdown / Down at the pawnshop / I know you / You take the future (and I'll take the past) / Dog bone / If I try hard enough / Poison love / Legend in my time / Bury me deep / Fraulein / Mansion on the hill / Send me the pillow that you dream on / On a petal from a faded rose / Return to me / Heart belongs to me / I'll go on alone / I care no more / I love you because / Address unknown / Rumba boogie / Music makin' Mama from Memphis / These hands / Letter from Vietnam to mother / Born for you / Late and great love of my heart / Promised to John: *Snow, Hank & Anita Carter* / If today were yesterday: *Snow, Hank & Anita Carter* / For sale: *Snow, Hank & Anita Carter* / Rose of old Monterey: *Snow, Hank & Anita Carter* / My adobe hacienda: *Snow, Hank & Anita Carter* / I never will marry: *Snow, Hank & Anita Carter* / Mockin' Bird Hill: *Snow, Hank & Anita Carter* / No letter today: *Snow, Hank & Anita Carter* / I dreamed of an old love affair: *Snow, Hank & Anita Carter* / If it's wrong to love you: *Snow, Hank & Anita Carter* / When my blue moon turns to gold again: *Snow, Hank & Anita Carter* / Let's pretend: *Snow, Hank & Anita Carter* / Pair of broken hearts: *Snow, Hank & Anita Carter* / I've been everywhere / Jamaica farewell / Blue Canadian Rockies / Geisha girl / When it's Springtime in Alaska / Galway Boy / My Filipino rose / Lili Marlene / Melba from Melbourne / Atlantic coastal line / Isle of Sicily / Gypsy and me / I ain't been anywhere / Sonny boy / Indian love call / Unchained melody / Beautiful dreamer / My Isle of golden dreams / Brahms lullaby / Blue tango / Dark moon / Vaya con dios / In an old Dutch garden / By an old Dutch mill / I can't stop loving you / Convict and the rose / Limbo rock / Hold me tight / Tammy / Everybody does it in Hawaii / I saw the light / Green leaves of Summer / Difficult / Wheels / Tiptoeing / Waltz you saved for me / Lay my head beneath the rose / Whispering hope / Wabash blues / Sentimental journey / Am I losing you / I get the blues when it rains / Sweet Marie / Birth of the blues / White Christmas / Little stranger (in a manger) / Christmas roses / Silent night / C-H-R-I-S-T-M-A-S / Blue Christmas / Reindeer boogie / Frosty the snowman / Christmas wants / Rudolph the red nosed reindeer / God is my Santa Claus / Long eared Christmas donkey / Face on the ballroom floor / Dangerous Dan McGrew / Cremation of Sam McGee / Spell of the Yukon / Ballad of blasphemous Bill / Ballad of one eyed Mike / Ballad of hard luck Henry / My friends / He'll understand and say well done / I saw a man / Rich man am I / Jesus wept / I'm movin' on to glory / Gloryland march / Farther along / Invisible hands / Last mile of the way / Sweet hour of prayer / These things shall pass / His hands / What then / Lord's way of sayin' goodnight / Dear Lord / Remember me / I see Jesus / My religion's not old fashioned / I'm glad I'm on the inside (looking out) / Runt / How big is God / Shop worn / Man who is wise / This train / I'll go marching into glory / I'd rather be on the inside looking out / Lord it's me again / Lord I do believe / Learnin' a new way of life / Wildflower / Little Joe / Put your arms around me / Color song / Your little band of gold / Prisoner's dream / Answer to Little Blossom / There's a star spangled banner waving / Old Rover / Mother I thank you for the bible you gave / Prisoner's song / Walking the last mile / Rockin' alone in an old rocking chair / Lonesome / She wears my ring / White silver sands / Trouble in mind / Mary Ann regrets / Six days on the road / Bummin' around / From a Jack to a King / Handcuffed to love / What more can I say / I wish my heart could talk / Hula love / Cry my guitar, cry on / Beyond the reef / To you my sweetheart, aloha when I go / Hawaiian cowboy / My little grass shack in Kealakekua, Hawaii / On the beach in Waikiki / Tradewinds / Pearly shells / On that old Hawaiian shore with you / Now is the hour / Tears in the tradewinds / King's serenade / Whispering tradewinds / Spanish fireball / Cross the Brazos at Waco / El Paso / Caribbean / Senorita Rosalita / Cuba rhumba / Nuevo laredo / Blue rose of the Rio / Maria Elena / Adios amigo / Among my souvenirs / Miami snow / Springtime in the Rockies / Blossoms in the Springtime / At the first fall of snow / Snowbird / Seasons / Roses in the snow / Flying South / January / You're as welcome as the flowers in May / Peach pickin' time in Georgia / All nite cafe / Tip of my fingers / He dropped the world in my hands / Blue blue day / It kinda reminds me of me / All the time / Blue side of lonesome / There goes my everything / Once more you're mine again / Million and one / Green green grass of home / Wound time can't erase / I just wanted to know how the wind was blowin' / Who will answer / Cure for the blues / That's when the hurtin' sets in / Rome wasn't built in a day / Name of the game was love

BCD 15502 / Jun '92 / Bear Family

☐ SINGING RANGER VOL.4 (9CD Set)

If I ever get back to Georgia / Gentle on my mind / Honey / Sweet dreams / Break my mind / Where has all the love gone / Green green green / Oh lonesome me / Like a bird / I really don't want to know / (As love goes) so goes my heart / Vanishing breed / It's a hard wind that blows / Brand on my heart / Francesca / When today is a long time ago / Come the morning / I wish it was mine / Cure for the blues / Crying time / There's the chair / Snowbird / I thew away the rose / Me and Bobby McGee / Just bidin' my time / I'm moving / Silver rails / Go with my heart / Wabash cannonball / Engineer's child / Casey Jones was his name / Fire ball mail / Folsom Prison blues / Lonely train / That same old dotted line / I'm movin' in / Train my woman's on / Durquesne, Pennyslvania / Canadian pacific / Crack in the box car door / North to Chicago / City of New Orleans / Texas silver zephyr / Get on my love train / My blue river rose / Blue velvet band / Wanderin' on / Old doc brown / Stolen moments / When that someone you love doesn't love you / My mother / Nobody's child / Little buddy / Hobo's meditation / My rough and rowdy ways / Frankie and Johnny / She was happy till she met you / Away out on the mountain / Cowhand's last ride / Everybody does it in Hawaii / I've ranged, I've roamed, I've travelled / Ninety nine year blues / Mother, the queen of my heart / Whisper your mother's name / Home call / My blue eyed Jane / Waiting for a train / Pistol packin' Papa / TB Blues / My little old home down in New Orleans / Why did you give me your love / In the jailhouse now / Gambling polka dot blues / One rose (that's left in my heart) / Hobo Bill's last ride / Nobody knows but me / Hello love / One minute past eternity / No one will ever know / For the good times / Sunday morning coming down / Everytime I love her / Seashores of old Mexico / Gypsy feet / Ribbon of darkness / My way / Bob / Friend / Governor's hand / Rolling thunder in my mind / I'm not at all sorry for you / My dreams tell it like it was / It's over, over nothing / Till the end of time / Four in the morning / I've got ot give it all to you / Daisy a day / Today I started loving you again / I have you and that's enough for me / I washed my hands in muddy water / It just happened that way / Last thing on my mind / Big silver screen at the Strand / Six string Tennessee flat top box / Somewhere my love / Why me Lord / Born to be with you / I keep dreaming of you all the time / Birth of the blues / Hijack / Come live with me / That's you and me / Paper roses / Why do you punish me / Mama tried / Prisoner's song / All I can hold to / You're easy to love / Just want you to know / Right or wrong / Colorado country morning / Top of the morning / She even woke me up to say goodbye / So good to be back with you / Follow me / Merry go round of love / Almost lost my mind / You're wondering why / Ninety miles an hour (down a dead end street) / Breakfst with the blues / Trying to get my baby off my mind / Trouble in mind / I'm gonna bid my blues goodbye / Love is so elusive / I've done at least one thing / Don't rock the boat / If you could just remember / That heart belongs to me / I'm still moving on / Inside out / Somewhere, someone is waiting for you / I put her on (and wore away her time) / Who's been here since I've been gone / Night I when he dropped the world in my hands / Night I stole Sammy Morgan's gin / I wonder where you are tonight / I takes to long / Nevertheless / Forever and one day / Just one of a kind / My happiness / Mysterious lady from St.Martinique / Ramblin' rose / Good gal is good to find / Hula love / Things / Pain didn't show / Stop me from loving you / My first night alone / It was love / All I want to do is touch you / There is something about you / What we had is over / Stay a while / Hasn't it been good together / After the love has gone / Check / Forbidden lovers / Love takes two / It's too far gone / It's over, over nothing / First hurt / Golden rocket / I've been everywhere / I almost lost my mind / Caribbean / I'm movin' on / Send me the pillow that you dream on / I don't hurt anymore / Fools such as I / It makes no difference now / Spanish eyes / Sweetheart of sigma / Over the rainbow (instr) / Tradewinds over Mamala Bay (instr) / Indian love call / You belong to me / Wabash blues (instr) / King's serenade / Make the world go away (instr) / Oh wonderful world (instr) / My isle of golden dreams (instr) / Tuck away my lonesome blues (instr) / Tammy (instr) / Beautiful Ohio (instr) / Song of India / Sunrise serenade (Inst) / Misty dawn (instr) / Vaya con dios / I remember you love in my prayers / I'm movin' on (live) / Send me the pillow you dream on / In the misty moonlight / Orange blossom special / Tammy / Black diamond / Whispering tradewinds (snow in Hawaii) / Hawaiian sunset

BCD 15787 / Apr '94 / Bear Family

☐ THESAURUS TRANSCRIPTIONS, THE (5CD Set)

Weary river / Bury me deep / Let's pretend / Address unknown / Golden river / Blue yodel no. 12 / I'm here to get my baby out of jail / Brand on my heart / With this ring I thee wed / I wonder where you are tonight / Fire on the mountain / Draggin' / Steel guitar rag / Wabash blues / I'm movin' on / Handcuffed to love / Convict and the rose / Anniversary blue yodel / Frankie and Johnny / Closed for repairs / End of the world / I wonder if you feel the way I do / Pins and needles / Where romance calls / Streamlined cannonball / Trouble in mind / Last letter / Headin' down the wrong highway / Lonely / Blue eyes cryin' in the rain / These tears are not for you / Jealous heart / Hawaiian cowboy / I'm thinking tonight of my blue eyes / Whispering hope / It is no secret / Molly darling / I'll remember you love in my prayers / Blue dreams / Blow yo' whistle freight train / Lonely river / I'll never let you go little darling / Texas plains / Born to lose / Too many tears / Travellin' blues / Faded rose, a broken heart / Yodeling ranger / Roll along Kentucky moon / Zeb Turner's gal / Sun has gone down on our love / I walk alone / Old Shep / Mississippi river blues / Linda Lou / My good gal's gone / Breeze / This cold war with you / I love you Nellie / Beautiful dreamer / 12th Street rag / Bye bye blues / Hilo march / Orange blossom special / Beaumont ride / Just when I needed you / Ninety nine years blues / My blue eyed Jane / Yodeling cowboy / Cannonball / It's been so long darling / Lover's farewell / You nearly lose your mind / Kentucky waltz / There's a pony standing in his stall / Among my souvenirs / Little old home down in New Orleans / Go on alone / Cowhand's last ride / I almost lost my mind / Patanio, the pride of the plains / That heart belongs to me / Peach pickin' time in Georgia / Alabama jubilee / Farewell blues / In an old dutch garden / Sally Goodin / Arkansas traveller / Petal from a faded rose / It's a sin / Wedding bells / At mail call today / Those blue eyes don't sparkle anymore / Have I stayed away too long / San Antonio rose / Each minute seems a million years / Blue steel blues / Then I turned and walked slowly away / Blue rose of the Rio / My wubba dolly / Tuck away my lonesome blues / Land of my childhood dreams / Wreck of ol' 97 / My life with you / One rose (that's left in my heart) / I'm coming home / Song of the saddle / Easter parade / Peter Cottontail / My rough and rowdy ways / Sing me a song of the Islands / Little Joe / White Christmas / Blue Christmas / Making believe / Any old time / Never no mo' blues / When my blue moon turns to gold again / Katy Hill / Put your arms around me / I was sorta wonderin' / Over the waves / Do right daddy blues / As long as I live / Loose talk / Waltz you saved for me / Memories are made of this / I really don't want to know / Wayward wind / Chant of the wanderer / Put on your old grey bonnet / When you and I were young Maggie / Sentimental journey / Birth of the blues

BCD 15488 / Feb '91 / Bear Family

☐ YODELLING RANGER, THE 1936-1947 (5CD Set)

Prisoned cowboy / Lonesome blue yodel / Blue for old Hawaii / We met down in the hills of old Wyoming / My San Antonio Mama / My little swiss maiden / Was there ever a pal like you / Blue velvet band / Someday you'll care / I'll ride back to lonesome valley / Bluer than blue / Yodelling back to you / There's a picture on Pinto's bridle / Texas cowboy / On the Mississippi shore / Under Hawaiian skies / She's a rose from the Garden of Prayer / Wanderin' on / Broken wedding ring / You didn't have to tell me / His message home / Answer to The Blue Velvet Band / I'll tell the world I love you / Polka dot blues / Alphabet song / Galveston rose / Broken dreams / Let's pretend / Days are long, I'm weary / I traded my saddle for a rifle / When that someone you love doesn't love you / Rainbow's end / We'll never say goodbye, Just say so long / I'm sending you red roses / Goodnight litle buckaroos / When my blue moon turns to gold again / Dream tide / Seal our parting with a kiss / You'll regret those words my darling / You promised to love me to the end of the world / Just across the bridge of gold / There's a pony that's lonely tonight / Old moon of Kentucky / Rose of the Rio / Lonely and heartsick / Your last kiss has broken my heart / When it's over I'll be coming back to you / Mother is praying / Soldier's last letter / Riding along, singing a song / Don't hang around me anymore / Only a rose from my mother's grave / Too many tears / Your little band of gold / Sunny side of the mountain / You broke the chain that held our hearts / My blue river rose / You played love on the strings of my heart / How she could yodel / Headin' home / Dry those tears little girl and don't cry / In memory of you dear old pal / Can't have you blues / Just waiting for you / Just waiting for you / My kalua sweetheart / I'll not forget my mother's prayer / Darling I'll always love you / Blue ranger / Just a faded petal from a beautiful bouquet / My sweet Texas Bluebonnet Queen / I'm gonna bid my blues goodbye / Down where the dark waters flow / Answer to Galveston Rose / Brand on my heart / No golden tomorrow / On that old Hawaiian shore with you / You've broken my heart / Linda Lou / My mother / Drunkard's son / Within this broken heart of mine / My Filipino rose / Night I stole Sammy Morgan's gin / My two timin' woman / Wasted love / Broken hearted / You sad kiss goodbye / Somewhere along life's highway / Out on the open range / Little buddy / Journey my baby back home / I knew that we'd meet again / Within this broken heart of mine (Alt) / My two timin' woman (Alt) / Wasted love (Alt) / Life story, Part 1 / Life story, Part 2 / Marriage and divorce / I don't hurt anymore

BCD 15587 / Mar '93 / Bear Family

Snowboy

☐ BEST OF SNOWBOY, THE (Snowboy & The Latin Section)

Night in Tunisia / Wild spirit / Mr. PC / Beyond the snowstorm / Mambito / Where's the one / Snow snow quick quick snow / In the wee small hours of the morning / Flintstones / 42nd and Broadway / Anarchy in the UK / Something's coming

JAZIDCD 102 / Nov '94 / Acid Jazz

☐ DESCARGA MAMBITA (Snowboy & The Latin Section)

Bella bella / Mambito / In the wee small hours of the morning / Mambo in two parts / Where's the one / Snow-snow-quick-quick-snow / Descarga mozambique

JAZIDCD 040 / Sep '91 / Acid Jazz

☐ PIT BULL LATIN JAZZ (Snowboy & The Latin Section)

JAZIDCD 126 / Oct '95 / Acid Jazz

☐ SOMETHING'S COMING

September rains / Salute to elegua / Flintstones / Dreamstate / Greeting from Southend / 42nd and Broadway / Interlude in son / Dilo como yo / Anarchy in the UK / Something's coming / Chant to aggayu / Somewhere

JAZIDCD 092 / Jan '94 / Acid Jazz

Snowmen

☐ CHRISTMAS AND NEW YEAR

PLSCD 264 / 29 Sep '97 / Pulse

Snowmen

☐ SOUNDPROOF

NORMAL 172CD / Feb '95 / Normal

Snub

☐ 360 DEGREE CONVICTION

360 degree conviction / Mondo Cain / Deadbeat / Three on a meathook / Black out

COP 04 / 11 May '98 / Copro

Snuff

☐ CAUGHT IN SESSION

Win some / From both sides / I think we're alone now / Another girl / Now you don't remember me / No one home / Inst. jingle no.1 / Funny faces / Inst. jingle no.2 / Vikings on the tundra / B / Batten down the hedges / Short jingle

MASKCD 073 / 15 Sep '97 / Vinyl Japan

☐ DEMMAMUSSABEBONK

Martin / Defeat / Dick trois / Nick Northern / Look mum there's vikings on the Tundra again / Batten down the hatches / Gone to the dogs / Sunny places / Horse and cart / Squirrels / Cricklewood / B / Punchline / Who

BLUFF 023CD / Jan '96 / Deceptive

☐ KILBURN NATIONAL 27.11.90

Somehow / Porro / Hairy womble / City crusty is attacked by soap / Damage is done / I see / What kind of love / Hazy shade of winter / Day of the PX's / Do nothing / Too late / Win some lose some

ASKCD 048 / Jan '97 / Vinyl Japan

☐ POTATOES AND MELONS AT WHOLESALE PRICES (Direct To You The Public)

Come and gone / Ye olde folke twatte / Time dub / Magic moments / Russian fields / Rivers of Babylon / Theme from Whatever happened to the likely lads / Pink purple

BLUFF 042CD / Jun '97 / Deceptive

☐ REACH

KLP 12CD / Jun '97 / K

☐ TWEET TWEET MY LOVELY

No reason / Ticket / Timebomb / Iyehf taidu leikh / Nick Motown / Brickwall / Arsehole / Bob / All you need / Etc / Thief / Verdidnit / Bit cosy / Take me home

BLUFF 056CD / 4 May '98 / Deceptive

Snuka

☐ SNUKA BLOODY SNUKA

PME 0022 / 4 Nov '97 / Paradigm

So Much Hate

☐ LIES

XM 040 / Dec '93 / X-Mist

Soares, Fernando Machado

☐ FADO FROM COIMBRA

C 559 041 / Feb '89 / Ocora

SOB

☐ WHAT'S THE TRUTH
RISE 4 CD / Dec '90 / Rise

Sober

☐ FIRST STEP
BIRD 049 / Jun '97 / Birdnest

☐ YEAH YEAH YEAH
BIRD 98CD / Feb '97 / Birdnest

Sobin A'r Smaeliaid

☐ A RHAW
Treni in partenza / Paradwys ff wl / Lledar du / Llongau caernarfon (the ships of caernarfon) / Lawr y lon / Sibrwd dy gelwydd / Y ferch danddaearol / Rocio / Quarry (man's) arms / Carmen gloria / O bell
SCD 2017 / Feb '95 / Sain

Sobule, Jill

☐ HAPPY TOWN
829912 / 23 Feb '98 / Lava

Social Disorder

☐ GOIN' THE DISTANCE
LF 153CD / Jul '95 / Lost & Found

Social Distortion

☐ LIVE AT THE ROXY
TB 70930CD / 20 Jul '98 / Time Bomb

☐ MAINLINER
0930435022 / Sep '96 / RCA
435022 / Apr '97 / Time Bomb

☐ MOMMY'S LITTLE MONSTER
0930435002 / Sep '96 / RCA
435002 / Apr '97 / Time Bomb

☐ PRISON BOUND
0930435012 / Sep '96 / RCA
435012 / Apr '97 / Time Bomb

☐ WHITE LIGHT, WHITE HEAT, WHITE TRASH
Dear lover / Don't drag me down / Intitled / I was wrong / Through these eyes / Down on the world again / When the angels sing / Gotta know the rules / Crown of thorns / Pleasure seeker / Down here / Under my thumb
4843742 / Sep '96 / Epic

Social Justice

☐ UNITY IS STRENGTH
LF 136CD / May '95 / Lost & Found

Society Burning

☐ TACTIQ
CDREC 036 / 11 Aug '97 / Reconstriction

Society Of Soul

☐ BRAINCHILD
Geneses / EMBRACE / Changes / It only gets better / Interlude / Brainchild / Ghetto fuh life / Right tonight / Judas / Pushin' / Migratention / Sonja Marie / Wind / Blac mermaid / Peaches n' erb / No hard feelings
73008260232 / Jun '96 / Arista

Society Syncopators

☐ REVOLUTIONARY BLUES
NEW 2022 / Jul '96 / Australian Jazz

Socrates

☐ BREAKING THROUGH
809122 / Nov '97 / Minos

☐ WAITING FOR SOMETHING
4807482 / Nov '97 / Minos

Soderberg, Nono

☐ HOT WIRES
GRCD 6076 / 2 Feb '98 / Goofin'

Sodom

☐ AGENT ORANGE
Agent orange / Tired and red / Incest / Remember the fallen / Magic dragon / Exhibition bout / Ausgebombt / Baptism of fire
SPV 847597 / Feb '97 / SPV

☐ BETTER OFF DEAD
Eye for an eye / Saw is the law / Capture the flag / Never healing wound / Resurrection / Shellfire defense / Turn your head around / Bloodtrials / Better off dead / Stalinorgel
8476261 / Nov '90 / Steamhammer

☐ GET WHAT YOU DESERVE
SPV 08476762
SPV 08476542 / Feb '97 / SPV

☐ IN THE SIGN OF EVIL
Outbreak of evil / Blasphemer / Burst command 'til war / Sepulchral voice / Witching metal
SPV 0857533 / Feb '97 / SPV

☐ MAROONED - LIVE
SPV 08476852 / Feb '97 / SPV

☐ MASQUERADE IN BLOOD
SPV 08576962 / Feb '97 / SPV

☐ MORTAL WAY OF LIVE
SPV 857576 / Feb '97 / SPV

☐ OBSESSED BY CRUELTY
857 533 / '88 / Steamhammer

☐ PERSECUTION MANIA
SPV 857509 / Feb '97 / Steamhammer

☐ TEN BLACK YEARS (The Best Of Sodom)(2CD Set)
Tired and red / Saw is the law / Agent orange / Wachturm/Erwachtet / Sodomy and lust / Remember the fallen / Nuclear winter / Outbreak of evil / Resurrection / Bombenhagel / Masquerade in blood / Bullet in the head / Stalinhagel / Shellshock / Angel dust / Hunting season / Abuse / 1000 days of Sodom / Gomorrah / Unwanted youth / Tarred and feathered / Iron fist / Jabba The Hut / Silence is consent / Incest / Shellfire defense / Gone to glory / Fratricide / Verrecke / One step over the line / My atonement / Sodomized / Aber bitte mit sahne / Die stumme ursel / Mantelmann
SPV 08618342 / Feb '97 / SPV

☐ THIS WAY OF LIFE
847576 / '90 / Steamhammer

☐ TIL DEATH DO US PART
GUN 119CD / Feb '97 / Gun

Sodre, Raimundo

☐ REAL
68972 / Apr '97 / Tropical

Sod's Opera

☐ COME ON LADS
I haven't seen old Hitler / D-Day dodgers / Ode to a Gezira lovely / Tins / Ballad of Wadi Maktilla / Dying soldier / Service police song / Kiss me goodnight, Sergeant Major / Thanks for the memory / Come on chaps / Firth of Forth / Down the mine / Sailor's wife / Longmoor / I don't want to join the army / Bloody Orkney / We are the boys / Africa star / Sinking of the Graf Spee / My bomber lies over the ocean / When this bloody war is over / Gay Caballero / Onward 15th Army group / Highland division's farewell to Sicily / Bless 'em all
BEJOCD 7 / Jun '95 / Beautiful Jo

Soegaard Ensemble

☐ CHRONOX
LEOLABCD 040 / Feb '98 / Leo Lab

Sofa Head

☐ PRE MARITAL PREDICAMENT
COXCD 001 / Jan '91 / Meantime

Sofa Surfers

☐ TRANSIT
MCD 70053 / 9 Feb '98 / MCA

Sofia Singers

☐ TRADITION SINGS ON
925992CD / Aug '94 / BUDA

Soft Boys

☐ CAN OF BEES
RCD 20231 / Nov '92 / Rykodisc

☐ INVISIBLE HITS
RCD 20233 / Nov '92 / Rykodisc

☐ SOFT BOYS 1976-1981, THE (2CD Set)
Wey wey hep uh hole / It's not just the size of a walnut / Ugly Nora / Yodelling hoover / Hear my Brane / Face of death / Wading through a ventilator / Give it to The Soft Boys / I want to be an angelpoise lamp / Fatman's son / Where are the prawns / Psychedelic love / Heartbreak hotel / Caroline says / We like bananas / Pigworker / Do the chisel / Return of the sacred crab / That's when your heartache begins / Book of love / Sandra's having her brain out / Leppo and the jooves / Rat's prayer / Have a heart, Betty (I'm not fireproof) / Mystery train / He's a reptile / Rock 'n' roll toilet / Insanely jealous / Underwater moonlight / I wanna destroy you / Queen of eyes / Kingdom of love / Positive vibrations / Gigolo aunt / Train around the bend / Only the stones remain
RCD 10234/35 / Aug '93 / Rykodisc

☐ UNDERWATER MOONLIGHT
I wanna destroy you / Kingdom of love / Positive vibrations / I got the hob / Insanely jealous / Tonight / You'll have to go sideways / I'm an old pervert / Queen of eyes / Underwater moonlight
RCD 20232 / Nov '92 / Rykodisc

Soft Cell

☐ ART OF FALLING APART, THE
Forever the same / Where the heart is / Numbers / Heat / Kitchen sink drama / Baby doll / Loving you hating me / Art of falling apart / Hendrix medley / Martin / Barriers / It's a mug's game
5582662 / 22 Jun '98 / Some Bizarre/ Mercury

☐ MEMORABILIA - THE SINGLES (Soft Cell & Marc Almond)
Memorabilia / Tainted love / Bedsitter / Say hello, wave goodbye / What / Torch / Soul inside / Where the heart is / I feel love / Tears run rings / Lover spurned / Something's gotten hold of my heart
8485122 / Apr '91 / Some Bizarre/ Mercury

☐ NON STOP ECSTATIC DANCING
Memorabilia / Where did our love go / What / Man could get lost / Chips on my shoulder / Sex dwarf / Tainted love/Where did our love go / Memorabilia / What / So / Torch / Insecure me
5582652 / 22 Jun '98 / Some Bizarre/ Mercury

☐ NON STOP EROTIC CABARET (Remastered)
Frustration / Tainted love / Seedy films / Youth / Sex dwarf / Entertain me / Chips on my shoulder / Bedsitter / Secret life / Say hello, wave goodbye / Where did our love go / Memorabilia / Facility girls / Fun city / Torch / Insecure me / What / So
5325952 / Jun '96 / Some Bizarre

☐ SAY HELLO TO SOFT CELL
Bedsitter / Say hello wave goodbye / Man could get lost / Facility girls / Sex dwarf / Torch / It's a mug's game / Born to lose / Heat / Art of falling apart / You only live twice / Where was your heart (when you needed it most) / Mr. Self Destruct / Disease and desire / Numbers / Frustration
5520862 / Mar '96 / Spectrum

☐ THIS LAST NIGHT IN...SODOM
Mr. Self destruct / Slave to this / Meet murder my angel / Best way to kill / L'esqualita / Down in the subway / Surrender to a stranger / Soul inside / Where was your heart (when you needed it most) / Disease and desire / Born to lose / You only live twice / 007 theme / Her imagination
5582672 / 1 Jun '98 / Some Bizarre/ Mercury

Soft Machine

☐ ALIVE AND WELL RECORDED IN PARIS
White kite / Eos / Odds bullets and blades, pt I / Odds bullets and blades, pt II / Song of the sunbird / Puffin' / Huffin / Number three / Nodder / Surrounding silence / Soft space
SEECD 290 / Jan '90 / See For Miles

☐ BUNDLES
Hazard profile / Gone sailing / Bundles / Land of the bag snake / Man who waved at trains / Peff / Four gongs two drums / Floating world
SEECD 283 / '89 / See For Miles

☐ HARVEST YEARS, THE (The Best Of Soft Machine)
Hazard profile / Gone sailing / Bundles / Land of the bag snake / Man who waved at trains / Peff / Four gongs, two drums / Songs of Aeolus / Kayoo / Aubade / Second bundle / Camden tandem / One over the eight / Number three / Nodder / Soft space
C5MCD 623 / Apr '97 / See For Miles

☐ JET PROPELLED PHOTOGRAPHS
That's how much I need you now / Save yourself / I should've known / Jet propelled photograph / When I don't want you / Memories / You don't remember / She's gone / I'd rather be with you
CDGR 188 / Oct '97 / Charly

☐ LIVE 1970
Out-bloody-rageous / Facelift / Pig / Orange skin food / Door opens and closes / 10-30 returns to the bedroom / Moon in June
BP 290CD / 22 Jun '98 / Blueprint

☐ LIVE AT THE PARADISO
Hulloder / Dada was here / Thank you Pierrot Lunaire / Have you ever bean green / Pataphysical introduction part 2 / As long as he lies perfectly still / Fire engine passing with bells clanging / Hibou, anemone and bear / Fire engine passing with bells clanging (reprise) / Pig / Orange skin food / Door opens and closes / 10.30 returns to the bedroom
BP 193CD / Oct '96 / Blueprint

☐ LIVE AT THE PROMS
Out-rageous / Facelift / Esther's nosejob / Pig / Orange skin food / Door opens and closes / Pigling bland / 10.30 returns to the bedroom
CDRECK 5 / Aug '88 / Reckless

☐ LONDON 1967 (Soft Machine/Mark Leeman/Davey Graham)
14557 / Jun '97 / Spalax

☐ RUBBER RIFF
Crunch / Pavan / Jombles / Little floating music / Hi power / Little Miss B / Splot / Rubber riff / Sam's short shuffle / Melina / City steps / Gentle turn / Porky / Travelogue
BP 190CD / 10 Nov '97 / Blueprint

☐ SOFT MACHINE VOL.1 & 2 (2CD Set)
Hope for happiness / Joy of a toy / Hope for happiness (reprise) / Why am I so short / So boot if at all / Certain kind / Save yourself / Priscilla / Lullaby letter / We did it again / Plus belle qu'une poubelle / Why are we sleeping / Box 25/4 / Pataphysical introduction Part 1 / Concise British alphabet Part 1 / Hibou, anenome and bear / Concise British alphabet Part 2 / Hulloder / Dada was here / Thank you Pierrot Lunaire / Have you ever bean green / Pataphysical introduction Part 2 / Out of tunes / As long as he lies perfectly still / Dedicated to you but you weren't listening / Fire engine passing with bells clanging / Pig / Orange skin food / Door opens and closes / 10.30 returns to the bedroom
CDWIKD 920 / Sep '89 / Big Beat

☐ SOFTS
Aubade / Tale of taliesin / Ban ban caliban / Song of Aeolus / Out of season / Second bundle / Kayoo / Camden tandem / Nexus / One over the eight / Etika
SEECD 285 / Jan '90 / See For Miles

☐ THIRD
Facelift / Slightly all the time / Moon in June / Out bloody rageous
4714072 / Jul '96 / Columbia

☐ VIRTUALLY (Live In Bremen 1971)
RUNE 100 / 1 Jun '98 / Cuneiform

Softballetforms

☐ REMIX FOR ORDINARY PEOPLE
SSR 160CD / Feb '96 / SSR

Softies

☐ IT'S LOVE
KLP 43CD / Oct '95 / K

☐ WINTER PAGEANT
KLP 61CD / Jan '97 / K

Soilent Green

☐ STRING OF LIES
RR 69852 / 13 Apr '98 / Relapse

Soilwork

☐ STEEL BATH SUICIDE
POSH 0012CD / 6 Jul '98 / Listenable

Soki Vangu

☐ SOKI VANGU/BELLA BELLA VOL.3 1975-1980 (Soki Vangu & Bella Bella)
NG 031 / Jan '97 / Ngoyarto

Sol Brothers

☐ ESSENTIAL MIXES
DCIS 001 / 20 Apr '98 / Dance Club International

Sol Invictus

☐ BLACK EUROPE (Sol Invictus Live)
WSCDL 002 / Oct '96 / World Serpent

☐ BLADE, THE
Blade / In Heaven / Time flies / House above the world / Laws and crowns / Once upon a time / See how we fall / Gealdor / From the wreckage / Nothing here / Remember and forget
TURSA 014CD / Apr '97 / Tursa

☐ CUPID AND DEATH
TURSA 011CD / Oct '96 / Tursa

☐ DEATH OF THE WEST
TURSA 008CD / Oct '96 / Tursa

☐ IN THE RAIN
TURSA 010CD / Oct '96 / Tursa

☐ KILLING TIDE
TURSA 003CD / Oct '96 / Tursa

☐ KING AND QUEEN
TURSA 006CD / Oct '96 / Tursa

☐ LE CROIX
TURSA 007CD / Oct '96 / Tursa

☐ LET US PRAY (Sol Invictus Live)
TURSA 005CD / Oct '96 / Tursa

☐ LEX TALIONIS
TURSA 001CD / Oct '96 / Tursa

☐ SOL VERITAS LUX
SVL 002CD / Sep '90 / Tursa

☐ TREES IN WINTER
TURSA 002CD / Oct '96 / Tursa

Sol Y Canto

☐ SANCOCHO
ROUCD 6055 / Dec '94 / Rounder

☐ SENDERO DEL SOL
Tamboe y guitarra / Que bonita luna / Pregonero / Gracias a la vida / Ijexa (Filhos de Gandhi) / Zamba del grillo / En esta tarde gris / Sal a caminar / Bulerias del charco / En mi viejo San Juan / Alejandro's ghost
ROUCD 6063 / Sep '96 / Rounder

Sola, Payita

☐ SONG OF ARGENTINA - THE PERCUSSIONISTS OF GUINEA
825012 / Apr '91 / BUDA

Solal, Martial

☐ A PIACERE - TRIPTYQUE (Solal, Martial & Francois Mechali)
590067 / Sep '96 / Musidisc

☐ IMPROVISE POUR FRANCE MUSIQUE (2CD Set)
Just you, just me / Don't blame me / L'ami remy est effare / Ballade / Cheek to cheek / 'Round midnight / Ah non / Woodin' you / Cuivre a la mer / Tout va tres bien madame la marquise / Somebody loves me / Night in Tunisia / Hommage a tex a very / Tea for two / Lover man / Cumparsita / Darn that dream / Take the 'A' train / I can't get started (with you) / Corcovado
JMS 186382 / Dec '95 / JMS

☐ JUST FRIENDS
Just friends / Coming yesterday / Willow weep for me / You stepped out of a dream / Hommage a Frederic Chopin / Sapristi / Summertime / Sacrebleu / I'm getting sentimental over you
FDM 365922 / 17 Nov '97 / Dreyfus

Solar Plexus
☐ IMAGES OF THE 5TH DIMENSION
CLP 208 / 16 Mar '98 / Hypnotic

Solar Quest
☐ PARANOID ALIENS
Kaptain Xoas / Stowaway / Too close encounters / Crossing the void / Mutant replicants don't work / Somewhere out there / Space pirates / Impulse power struggle / Ritual of the stars / Plan that worked (almost) / Air loss / Of course of course / Paranoid aliens
PRIMACD 6 / 20 Jul '98 / Prima Vera

Solar Race
☐ HOMESPUN
OREZCD 546 / May '97 / Silvertone

☐ PEEL SESSIONS, THE
ORECD 542 / Oct '96 / Silvertone

Solar, Ria
☐ IN DER MITTE VON SAMOA
Lollipop / In der mitte von Samoa / Irgendetwas musste heute noch passieren / Bitte bitte bleib doch bei mir: Solar, Ria & Bobby Franco / Du / Oooo Peter / Click clock / Happiness / Deine blauen augen / Hotta chocolata / Ich weiss was die fehlt / Fur mich ist heute Sonntag / Serenade brasiliana / Schon ist die liebe: Solar, Ria & Bert Varell / Nie / Wovon traumen junge madchen / Pepita aus Mallorca / Wai ki ki / Nimm mich mit zu den himmelblauen bergen / O Mirabelle: Solar, Ria & Bobby Franco / Er hiess Maurice: Solar, Ria & Bobby Franco / Liebe kusse und sehnsucht / Ich glaub an dich / Ich bleibe immer bei dir
BCD 16184 / Nov '97 / Bear Family

Solarus
☐ EMPTY NATURE
Messaianic slur / In heaven for eternity / Whipspawn / Subjugation / Malignant soul punisher / Whipspawn
RR 69652 / 1 Sep '97 / Relapse

Solas
☐ SOLAS
SH 78002 / Jun '96 / Shanachie

☐ SUNNY SPELLS AND SCATTERED SHOWERS
SHCD 78010 / Jun '97 / Shanachie

Solberg, James
☐ ONE OF THESE DAYS (Solberg, James Band)
Too damn much lovin' / One of these days / One false move / Still called the blues / Cheaper to keep her / There must be a better world somewhere / Can it be / Ringin' in my head / Litehouse keeper / Nobody to blame / Do you call that a buddy / Love made a fool out of me / Ain't no way / Everyday
ATM 1120 / Aug '94 / Atomic Theory
DFGCD 8453 / Sep '96 / Dixie Frog

Soledad Bravo
☐ CANTOS REVOLUCIONAROS DE AMERICA
3026132 / 5 Jan '98 / Last Call

Soley
☐ SPECIAL SOUKOUSS
PS 66404 / Apr '97 / PlayaSound

Solid Doctor
☐ BEATS MEAN HIGHS
PORK 030 / May '96 / Pork

Solid Harmonie
☐ I'LL BE THERE FOR YOU
8946662 / 2 Feb '98 / Virgin

☐ SOLID HARMONIE
I'll be there for you / I want you to want me / To love once again / Come and get it / Walk away / You got the flava / He's playing hard to get / Forever I do / I wanna love you / Fantasy / I gotta get my groove on / When we kiss (missing you)
0517972 / 20 Apr '98 / Jive

Solid Senders
☐ EVERYTHING'S GONNA BE ALRIGHT
TR 9920CD / Aug '94 / Tramp

Solidor, Suzi
☐ SUZI SOLIDOR 1933-1939
121 / Nov '92 / Chansophone

Soling, Johnny
☐ JOHNNY SOLING
GRD 27 / May '96 / Grappa

Solis, Sebastian
☐ EL GAUCHO, EL INKA
EUCD 1033 / '89 / ARC

☐ FESTIVAL LATINO (Solis, Sebastian, Patricia Salas & Pablo Carcamo)
EUCD 1074 / '91 / ARC

☐ FROM CUBA TO TIERRA DEL FUEGO
EUCD 1066 / '89 / ARC

Solitaire
☐ RITUAL GROUND
SR 9341 / Jan '94 / Silent

Solitaires
☐ WALKING ALONG WITH
Walking along / Wedding / How long / I really love you so (honey babe) / Please remember my heart / Blue valentine / Later for you baby / Honeymoon / Angels sang / Girl is gone / I don't stand a ghost of a chance with you / Chances I've taken / Give me one more chance / Please kiss this letter / You've sinned / What did she say / Wonder why / South of the border (Down Mexico way) / Fine little girl / Nothing like a little girl / At night / When will the lights shine for me / Light a candle in the chapel / My dear / Come back my love / Stranger in paradise / Time is here
CDCHD 383 / Oct '92 / Ace

Solitude Aeturnus
☐ ADAGIO
MASSCD 161 / 3 Aug '98 / Massacre

☐ DOWNFALL
IRSCD 993022 / Jan '97 / Hengest

Solo
☐ SOLO
What a wonderful world / Back 2 da street / Blowin' my mind / Cupid / Heaven / Xxtra / It's such a shame / He's not good enough / Another Saturday night / Everybody loves to cha cha / Where do u want me to put it / Keep it right here / I'm sorry / Under the boardwalk / In bed / (Last night I made love) Like never before / Prince Street / Holdin' on / Change is gonna come / Solo strut
5490172 / Dec '95 / Perspective

Solo, Napoleon
☐ SHOT
BBSCD 006 / Oct '89 / Blue Beat

Solo, Ralph
☐ CAR ACCIDENTS, GUITAR ACCIDENTS
BBPTC 6 / Oct '96 / Black Bean & Placenta Tape Club

Soloff, Lew
☐ LITTLE WING
66055015 / Jul '92 / Sweet Basil

Soloman Grundy
☐ SOLOMAN GRUNDY
NAR 049CD / Sep '90 / New Alliance

Soloman, Luke
☐ IN MOTION
DI 0792 / 8 Jun '98 / Distance

Solstice
☐ LAMENTATIONS
CANDLE 007CD / Aug '94 / Candlelight

Solstice
☐ CIRCLES
ANDCD 13 / Feb '97 / A New Day

☐ HALCYON
GOD 026CD / Jun '97 / Godhead

☐ PRAY
SPV 08476902 / May '95 / SPV

Solution AD
☐ HAPPILY EVER AFTER
Atypical day / Fearless / Haunt / Salty sweet / It's not funny / Ask me again / Human bean / Silent / Hope / Called johnny / Comfortable / Something I'd like to forget
7567927082 / Oct '96 / Atlantic

Solve, Gilda
☐ MY SIMPLE SONG
BB 646 / Apr '97 / Black & Blue

Some Velvet Sidewalk
☐ LOWDOWN
KLP 77CD / 17 Nov '97 / K

Someck, Ronny
☐ REVENGE OF THE STUTTERING CHILD, THE (Someck, Ronny & Elliott Sharp)
TZA 7117 / 6 Oct '97 / Tzadik

Somerville, Jimmy
☐ DARE TO LOVE
Heartbeat / Hurt so good / Cry / Love thing / By your side / Dare to love / Someday we'll be together / Alright / Too much of a good thing / Dream gone wrong / Come lately / Safe in these arms / Because of him
8285402 / 15 Sep '97 / London

☐ SINGLES COLLECTION, THE
Smalltown boy / Don't leave me this way / It ain't necessarily so / Comment te dire adieu / Never can say goodbye / Why / You are my world / For a friend / I feel love / There's more to love / So cold the night / To love somebody / Run from love / Tomorrow / Disenchanted / Read my lips / You make me feel (Mighty real)
8282682 / Aug '91 / London

Somethin' For The People
☐ SOMETHIN' FOR THE PEOPLE
Damned if I do / With you / Make it happen / You don't have to be alone / There I go / Still the man / And it don't stop / Hood thang / You know what would be a trip / On my mind / She's the kinda girl / Waiting / Can you feel me / Don't wanna break your heart / You want this party started / Take it easy
9362460602 / Jul '96 / Warner Bros.

Something Else
☐ PLAYING WITH TUNES
BF 20 / Sep '97 / Bruce's Fingers

Something Happens
☐ BEDLAM A GO-GO
Inviral love / Diane on the cross / Daisyhead / It's strange, believe me / Are you going to suffer it / Hit the parade / Beautiful country / Crystal ballroom / Select / Speak, shut up / Uncut / Behind your teeth / Fellow feeling
CDV 2695 / Jul '92 / Virgin

☐ BEEN THERE, SEEN THAT, DONE THAT
Beach / Incoming / Take this with you / Forget Georgia / Way I feel / Both men crying / Don't care / Give it away / Tall girls club / Shoulder high / Here comes the only one again / Be my love / Promised / Seven days 'til 4 am / Free and easy
CDV 2561 / Oct '88 / Virgin

☐ STUCK TOGETHER WITH GOD'S GLUE
What now / Hello hello hello hello hello (petrol) / Parachute / Esmerelda / I had a feeling / Kill the roses / Brand new God / Room 29 / Patience business / Devil in Miss Jones / Good time coming / Feel good / Skyrockets
CDV 2628 / May '90 / Virgin

Something Pretty Beautiful
☐ SOMETHING PRETTY BEAUTIFUL
CRECD 075 / May '94 / Creation

Somewhere In Europe
☐ GESTURES
BADVCCD 45 / Oct '96 / New European

☐ IRON TREES ARE IN FULL BLOOM, THE
TSCD 1 / Oct '96 / These Silences

☐ SAVAGE DREAMS
TSCD 2 / Oct '96 / These Silences

Sommerfolk
☐ BEHAKLICHKEIT
BEST 1009CD / Nov '93 / Acoustic Music

Somnambulist
☐ SOMNAMBULIST
LE 1027 / 15 Jun '98 / Laser's Edge

Son 14
☐ CUBANIA (Son 14 & Tiburon)
TUMICD 065 / Feb '97 / Tumi

Son De La Loma
☐ BLINDMAN'S GIFT/REGAL DEL CIEGO
RLCD 1002 / 29 Jun '98 / Ryko Latin

Son Of Noise
☐ ACCESS DENIED - BULLSHIT AND POLITICS VOL.1
COM 102152 / Sep '98 / Tribehaus Recordings

Son Volt
☐ STRAIGHTAWAYS
Caryatid easy / Back into your world / Picking up the signal / Left a slide / Creosote / Cemetery savior / Last minute shakedown / Been set back / No more parades / Way down Watson
9362465182 / Aug '97 / Reprise

Sonar Nation
☐ CYLINDERS IN BLUE
ABT100CD / May '95 / Abstract

Sonartribe
☐ SIGNALS
DUK 004 / 9 Feb '98 / Digital UK

Sonerien Du
☐ REDER NOZ
EOG 005CD / Nov '96 / EOG

☐ TREDAN
CD 829 / Apr '95 / Diffusion Breizh

Song Of The Native Land Ensemble
☐ INSTRUMENTAL TEXTURES
Four generations / Lullaby of the South / Love song / River Lam and reminiscence / Market in spring / Festivities in the homeland mountains and rivers / Flowing water, golden sapeque, spring wind, dragon and tiger / Season for picking fruit / Morning on the terraced fields / Song of the black haired horse / Sakura
VICG 54542 / Oct '96 / JVC

Songrien Du
☐ TRADITION VIBRANTE
KMCD 004 / Jul '90 / Keltia Musique

Songs: Ohia
☐ SONGS: OHIA
SC 03 / May '97 / Secretly Canadian

Sonia
☐ ALMOST CHOCOLATE
CDPH 1207 / 19 Jan '98 / Philo

Sonic Boom
☐ WHAT CAME BEFORE AFTER
SFTRI 493 / 26 Jan '98 / Sympathy For The Record Industry

Sonic Experience
☐ DEF TILL DAWN
STUCD 2 / Nov '93 / Strictly Underground

Sonic Violence
☐ TRANSFIXION
Asphyxia / Mind field / Factory / Torment / J.f.r.o. / Drill / Malice / Catalepsy
KTB 004CD / May '92 / Dreamtime

Sonic Voyager
☐ ENDLESS MISSION
APR 006CD / 6 Oct '97 / April

Sonic Youth
☐ 1000 LEAVES
GED 25203 / 11 May '98 / Geffen

☐ ANAGRAMA
Anagrama / Improvisation ajout'e / Tremens / Mieux: de corrosion
SYR 1CD / Jun '97 / Sonic Youth

☐ BAD MOON RISING
Intro / Brave men run in my family / Socoety is a hole / I love her all the time / Ghost bitch / I'm insane / Justice is might / Death valley '69
BFFP 1 CD / Nov '86 / Blast First

☐ CONFUSION IS SEX/KILL YOUR IDOLS
BFFP 113CD / Mar '95 / Blast First

☐ DAYDREAM NATION
Teen age riot / Silver rocket / Sprawl / 'cross the breeze / Eric's trip / Total trash / Hey tonl / Providence / Candle / Rain king / Kissability / Wonder-hyperstation-eliminator jr. (trilogy)
BFFP 34CD / Oct '88 / Blast First

☐ DIRTY
100% / Swimsuit issue / Theresa's sound world / Drunken butterfly / Shoot / Wish fulfillment / Sugar kane / Orange rolls, angel's spit / Youth against facism / Nic fit / On the strip / Chapel hill / Stalker / JC / Purr creme brulee
GFLD 19296 / Oct '95 / Geffen

☐ EVOL
Green light / Star power / Secret girl / Tom violence / Death to our friends / Shadow of a doubt / Marilyn moore / In the kingdom of 19 pound / Madonna, sean and me bubblegum
BFFP 4CD / Nov '86 / Blast First

☐ EXPERIMENTAL JET SET, TRASH AND NO STAR
Winner's blues / Bull in the heather / Starfield road / Skink / Screaming skull / Self-obssessed and sexxee / Bone / Androgynous mind / Quest for the cup / Waist / Doctor's orders / Tokyo eye / In the mind of the bourgeois reader / Sweet shine
GFLD 19329 / Sep '96 / Geffen

☐ GOO
Dirty boots / Tunic (song for Karen) / Mary Christ / Kool thing / Mote / My friend Goo / Disappearer / Mildred Pierce / Cinderella's big score / Scooter and Jinx / Titanium expose
GFLD 19297 / Oct '95 / Geffen

☐ HOLD THAT TIGER
Intro / Schizophrenia / Torn valence / White cross / Kotton krown / Stereo sanctity / Brother James / Pipeline kill / Catholic block / Tuff gnarl / Death valley 69 / Beauty lies in the eye / Expressway to your skull / Pacific coast highway / LoudmouthLoudmouth / Don't wanna walk around with you / Today yr love / Beat on the brat
GOO 2CD / 17 Aug '98 / Goofin'

☐ SCREAMING FIELDS OF SONIC LOVE
BFFP 119CD / Apr '95 / Blast First

☐ SILVER SESSION FOR JASON KNUTH
SKR 1 / 13 Jul '98 / SKR

☐ SISTER
Schizophrenia / (i got a) catholic block / Beauty lies in the eye / Stereo sanctity / Pipeline-kill time / Tuff gnarl / Pacific coast highway / Hot wire my heart / Cotton crown / White cross / Master-dik
BFFP 20CD / Jun '87 / Blast First

☐ SONIC DEATH (Early Sonic Youth - Live 1981-1983)
BFFP 32CD / '89 / Blast First

☐ WASHING MACHINE
Becuz / Junkie's promise / Saucer-like / Washing machine / Unwind / Little trouble girl / No Queen blues / Panty lies / Skip tracer / Diamond sea
GED 24825 / 8 Sep '97 / Geffen

☐ WHITEY ALBUM, THE (Ciccone Youth)
Needle gun / G force / Platform 11 / Me and Jill / Hi everybody / Children of Satan / Moby Dick / Into the groovy / March of the Ciccone robots / Macbeth / Burning up / Two cool rock chicks listening to Neu / Addicted to love / Making the nature scene / Tuff titty rap
BFFP 28CD / Mar '88 / Blast First

Sonics

☐ FIRE AND ICE/THE LOST TAPES
JRCD 7009 / Oct '96 / Jerden

☐ HERE ARE THE SONICS/BOOM
422331 / May '94 / New Rose

☐ MAINTAINING MY COOL
JRCD 7001 / Oct '96 / Jerden

☐ PSYCHO-SONIC
Witch / Do you love me / Roll over beethoven / Boss hoss / Dirty robber / Have love will travel / Psycho / Money (that's what I want) / Walking the dog / Night time is the right time / Strychnine / Good golly Miss Molly / Hustler / Psycho (Live) / Cinderella / Don't be afraid of the dark / Skinny Minnie / Let the good times roll / Don't you just know it / Jenny Jenny / He's waiting / Louie Louie / Since I fell for you / Hitch hike / It's alright / Shot down / Keep on knockin' / Witch (Live) / Witch
CDWIKD 115 / Feb '93 / Big Beat

☐ SINDERELLA
BCD 4011 / Jan '97 / Bomp

Sonic's Rendezvous Band

☐ SWEET NOTHING
MA 9878 / 8 Jun '98 / Mack Aborn

Sonnier, Jo El

☐ CAJUN LIFE
Cajun life / Tes yeux bleu / Allons a Lafayette / Bayou teche / Les flames d'enfer / Lacassine special / Chere Alice / Louisiana blues / Les grande bois / Perrodin two step
ROUCD 3049 / Aug '88 / Rounder

☐ CAJUN PRIDE
Lake Arthur special / Juste une affair / Pine Grove blues / Lawtell two step / La valse de grand mamou / French blues / Mamou two step / Midnight waltz / Step it fast / Jolie fille / Armede Ardoin / Johnnie fais bien
ROUCD 6069 / May '97 / Rounder

☐ CAJUN ROOTS
ROUCD 6059 / Jul '94 / Rounder

☐ CAJUN YOUNG BLOOD (Sonnier, Jo El & Sidney Brown/Robert Bertrand)
Jump little frog / Rolling pin / I'm leaving you / Durald waltz / Bean / I'd like to forget / Monkey on my back / Little petite / One I love / Johnny B Goode / Cafe sho / My blue letter / Fee fee poncho / Hurricane Audry / Auntie's peanuts / There's no goodbyes / Didn't come home / Tasso gumbo / Valse de Rose Marie / (Ship of) broken heart / My 50 cents / Legend oflry LeJeune / Monkey played fiddle / We passed your door / I'd like to forget / Aye yeah / Last waltz / Big wheel rolling
CDCHD 598 / Jul '96 / Ace

Sonny & Cher

☐ BEAT GOES ON, THE
What now my love / But you're mine / It's the little things / Beautiful story / Just you / Laugh at me / Baby don't go / Little man / Beat goes on / My best friend's girl is out of sight / Love don't come / Leave me be / Have I stayed too long / Revolution kind / Why don't they let us fall in love / Living for you / Sing c'est la vie / Hello / Good combination / I got you babe / I got you babe
7567917962 / Mar '93 / Atlantic

☐ GREATEST HITS
MCD 11745 / 25 May '98 / MCA

☐ IN CASE YOU'RE IN LOVE
Beat goes on / Groovy kind of love / You baby / Monday / Love don't come / Podunk / Little man / We'll sing in the sunshine / Misty roses / Stand by me / Living for you / Cheryl's goin' home / Beautiful story / Good combination / Plastic man
SC 6141 / Jul '98 / Sundazed

☐ LOOK AT US
I got you babe / Unchained melody / Then he kissed me / Sing c'est la vie it's gonna rain / 500 miles / Just you / Letter / Let it be me / You don't love me / You've really got a hold on me / Why don't they let us fall in love / It's the little things / Don't talk to strangers
SC 6139 / Jul '98 / Sundazed

☐ WONDROUS WORLD OF SONNY & CHER, THE
Summertime / Tell him / I'm leaving it all up to you / But you're mine / Bring it on home to me / Set me free / What now my love / I look for you / Laugh at me / Turn around / So fine / Revolution kind / Have I stayed too long / Crying time
SC 6140 / Jul '98 / Sundazed

Sonny Sixkiller

☐ I'M IN THE BAND
COG 007 / 13 Apr '98 / Vital Cog

Sonora Pine

☐ SONORA PINE VOL.2, THE
QS 47CD / Aug '97 / Quarter Stick

☐ SONORA PINE, THE
QS 39CD / May '96 / Quarter Stick

Sons Do Muino

☐ NA CHAO DE SOUTO
AB 003CD / Aug '97 / Do Fol

Sons Of Blues

☐ LIVE 1982
Never make your move to soon / Did you ever love a woman / Eyesight to the blind / Sweet little angel / My kind of woman / Reconsider baby / Detroit, Michigan / Goin' on main street
ECD 260492 / Sep '94 / Evidence

Sons Of Champlin

☐ LOOSEN UP NATURALLY
1982-A / Thing to do / Misery isn't free / Rooftop / Everywhere / Don't fight it, do it / Get high / Black and blue rainbow / Hello sunlight / Things are gettin' better / Freedom
SEECD 441 / Jun '96 / See For Miles

Sons Of Geronimo

☐ TWIST
REVXD207 / Aug '97 / Revolver

Sons Of Hercules

☐ SONS OF HERCULES
Piece of mine / Crawlin' back / IOU Nothing / Damaged goods / Lost in space / Guttersnipe / Black and blue / Shakin' street / Angel on fire / Carving knife
119432 / Jun '96 / Musidisc UK

Sons Of Selina

☐ NOUR D'OUI
Climb / Life is but / Existing services / Gamato manopano / Of the first water / Once every so often / Four plus twenty / Growing bold / Anxiety / It's a boy / On a promise / Dreamshadow
DELECCD 025 / Aug '94 / Delerium

Sons Of Soul

☐ SONS OF SOUL
50536 / Jun '97 / Raging Bull

Sons Of The Desert

☐ GREEDY
Chop-a-nose day / All gone / Lambs' tidgerrs / Don't praise her / Greedy as I get / OKB / Bruno / Bear baiting / Tear-apart change bag / Beat the trees / Arrogant and ungrateful / Cornered (in a barn) / Holiday home / (I'm) Blind / Sperm jacket
LBLC 2527 / Nov '96 / Indigo

Sons Of The Pioneers

☐ WAGON WEST (4CD Set)
Forgive and forget / Cool water / Timber trail / Stars and stripes on Iwo Jima / You're getting tired of me / Gold star mother with silvery hair / You'll be sorry when I'm gone / I wear your memory in my heart / Cowboy camp meetin' / Tumbling tumbleweeds / Out California way / Grievin' my heart out for you / No one to cry to / Everlasting hills of Oklahoma / Chant of the wanderer / Blue prairie / Trees / Letter marked unclaimed / Baby doll / Penny for your thoughts / Have I told you lately that I love you / Let's pretend / Cigarettes, whiskey and wild, wild women / Teardrops in my heart / My best to you / Will there be sagebrush in Heaven / You don't know what lonesome is / You never miss the water / Lead me gently home father / Too high, too wide, too low / Out in pioneertown / Hundred and sixty acres / Seawalker / Read the bible every day / Last round-up / Two eyes, two lips but no heart / Cowboy country / Bar-none ranch (in the sky) / Where are you / Calico apron and a gingham gown / Happy birthday polka / Let me share your name / Wind / Whiffenpoof song / Old rugged cross / Power in the blood / Touch of God's hand / Rounded up in glory / Santa Fe, New Mexico / Down where the Rio flows / My feet takes me away / Red River valley / Serenade to a coyote / Missouri is a devil of a woman / No rodeo dough / Sentimental, worried and blue / Little grey home in the West / I still do / Riders in the sky / Room full of roses / No one here but you / Lie low little doggies (the cowboy's prayer) / Let's go west again / Love at the country fair / Wedding dolls / Outlaws / Roses / Eagle's heart / Land beyond the sun / I told them all about you / Wagons west / Rollin' dust / Song of the wagonmaster / Chuckawalla swing / Old man atom / What this country needs / Baby, I ain't gonna cry no more / Little white cross / America forever / Daddy's little cowboy / Moonlight and roses / Bring your roses to her now / San Antonio rose / Mexican rose / Lonesome / Wonderous word / Resurrectus / Waltz of roses / Lord's prayer / Heartbreak hill / Holeo / Diesel smoke / Almost / Empty saddles / There's a goldmine in the sky / Old pioneer / Home on the range / If you would only be mine / Sierra Nevada / River of no return / Lilies grows high / Lonely little
BCD 15640 / Aug '93 / Bear Family

Sons Of The San Joaquin

☐ GOSPEL TRAILS
SHCD 6022 / Jun '97 / Shanachie

Sons Of The Subway

☐ RUFF RUGGED AND REAL
BETCD 004 / Aug '97 / Infonet

Sophia

☐ FIXED WATER
FLOWCD 004 / Nov '96 / Flower Shop

☐ INFINITE CIRCLE
FLOWCD 008 / 7 Sep '98 / Flower Shop

Sopor Aeternus

☐ ICH TOTE
EFA 01552 / Dec '95 / Apocalyptic Vision

☐ TODESWUNSCH
EFA 015592 / Dec '95 / Apocalyptic Vision

Sorabji/Marek/Buso

☐ CATHEDRALS IN SOUND
AIRCD 9043 / Aug '92 / New Note

Soraya

☐ ON NIGHTS LIKE THIS
5290002 / Jun '97 / London

☐ WALL OF SMILES
5585592 / 13 Jul '98 / London

Sorbye, Lief

☐ SPRINGDANCE
EUCD 1056 / '89 / ARC

Sorgen/Rust/Stevens Trio

☐ NOVELLA
CDLR 253 / 1 Jun '98 / Leo

Sorotan Belle

☐ SOROTAN BELLE
KDCD 349 / May '97 / Elkar

Sorrels, Rosalie

☐ ALWAYS A LADY
Mehitabel's theme / Baby rocking medley / Song for david / Hey little girl / Apple of my eye / Caterpillar and the butterfly / Did I knock / Red wine at noon / When I was in my prime / Song for my birthday / Moth
GLCD 2110 / May '93 / Green Linnet

☐ BE CAREFUL THERE'S A BABY IN THE HOUSE
Be careful there's a baby in the house / Baby rocking medley / You're always welcome at our house / Mehitabel and her kittens / God bless the child / Don't play 'em unless you've got 'em / Aces, straights and flushes / Lost children street / Right to life / Rim of the world / 1972-new hampshire (fear and loathing on the campaign trail / L.a. nights / Two years later / Jesse's corrido / Sing like the rain (last song for david) / I cannot sleep for thinking of the children
GLCD 2100 / '92 / Green Linnet

☐ BORDERLINE HEART
GLCD 2119 / Sep '95 / Green Linnet

☐ LONG MEMORY, THE (Sorrels, Rosalie & Utah Phillips)
RHRCD 83 / May '96 / Red House

☐ MISCELLANEOUS RECORD VOL.1
GLCD 1042 / Nov '88 / Green Linnet

☐ THEN CAME THE CHILDREN
Then came the children / Bride 1945 / Girls in our town / Rosie jane / Mother's day song / Delia rose / What was the colour / Song for daughters-mama / Rosalie, you can't go home again
GLCD 2099 / '92 / Green Linnet

☐ TRAVELIN' LADY RIDES
Traveling lady / I like it / We were kinda crazy then / Trucker's cafe / Going away / I remember loving you / With talkin' wolverine 14 / Feather ben / Bad girl's lament / Post card from india
GLCD 2109 / May '93 / Green Linnet

☐ WHAT DOES IT MEAN TO LOVE
GL 2113 / Feb '94 / Green Linnet

Sorrow

☐ TAKE A HEART
REP 4093 / Aug '91 / Repertoire

Sorrow

☐ UNDER THE YEW POSSESSED
PIX 001CD / Oct '96 / Piskidisc

Sort Of Quartet

☐ PLANET MAMON
SST 315CD / Jul '95 / SST

Sortie

☐ SORTIE
JUST 472 / Oct '92 / Justin Time

Sortileges

☐ PIANO AND LUTE (The Music Of Cherif Kheddam)
AAA 129 / Sep '97 / Club Du Disque Arabe

Sorts

☐ MORE THERE
SLOWDIME 13CD / 6 Apr '98 / Slowdime

Sosa, Mercedes

☐ SINO
68961 / May '97 / Tropical

Soskin, Mark

☐ FIVE LANDS
Lookout Street / Listening room / One once / 17 / Close at hand / Now then / Fuchsia / Five lands / House of cards / Bye gone for Roberto
TCB 98402 / 27 Jul '98 / TCB

Soto, Cristobal

☐ TRADITION OF MANDOLIN IN VENEZUELA
927152 / 24 Apr '98 / BUDA

Soto, Vicente

☐ SORDERA
20102CD / Aug '97 / Sonifolk

Soukous Express

☐ SOUKOUS EXPRESS VOL.2 (Ambience Night)
CDP 5238 / Jan '97 / Piros/Sonodisc

SOUL

☐ WHAT IS IT/CAN YOU FEEL IT
Down in the ghetto / Get ready / Burning spear / Express yourself / Soul / Message from a black man / Memphis underground / Can you feel it / Tell it like it is / Do what ever you want to do / Peace of mind / My cherie amour / Love, peace and power / To mend a broken heart / Sleeping beauty
CDBGPD 107 / Jul '96 / Beat Goes Public

Soul Asylum

☐ CANDY FROM A STRANGER
Creatures of habit / I will still be laughing / Close / See you later / No time for waiting / Blood into wine / Lies of hate / Draggin' out the lake / Blackout / Game / Cradle chain
4872652 / 18 May '98 / Columbia

☐ GRAVE DANCERS UNION
Somebody to shove / Black gold / Runaway train / Keep it up / Homesick / Get on out / New world / April fool / Without a trace / Growing into you / 99% / Sun maid
4722532 / Oct '92 / Columbia

☐ HANG TIME
Down on up to me / Little too clean / Sometime to return / Cartoon / Beggars and choosers / Endless farewell / Standing in the doorway / Marionette / Ode / Jack of all trades / Twiddly dee / Heavy rotation
CDMID 189 / Nov '93 / A&M

☐ LET YOUR DIM LIGHT SHINE
Misery / To my own devices / Shut down / Hope up / Primises broken / Bittersweet / String of pearls / Crawl / Caged rat / Eyes of a child / Just like anyone / Tell me when / Nothing to write home about / I did my best
4803202 / 2 Feb '98 / Columbia

Soul Bossa

☐ COME INTO SOUL BOSSA
DISHY 23CD / Jun '97 / Dishy Recordings

Soul Bossa Trio

☐ ABSTRACT TRUTH
BOM 05CD / Jul '96 / Bomba

☐ DANCING IN THE STREET
BOM 02CD / Jul '96 / Bomba

☐ SOUL BOSSA TRIO
CBCD 003 / Jul '96 / Cubop

☐ TASTE OF SOUL BOSSA
BOM 01CD / Jul '96 / Bomba

☐ WILD JUMBO
BOM 07CD / Nov '96 / Bomba

Soul Brothers

☐ SOUL OF SOWETO
Umlohla / Siyayi dudula / Indlada / Umlenze / Kuyeza nakuwe / Bazobuya / Uzongihumbula / Ngixolele / Inhlonipho / Umnandi / Uthando lwenu / Hamba ntombi
MOU 40332 / Oct '95 / Mountain

Soul Cages

☐ MOMENTS
MASSCD 085 / Feb '96 / Massacre

☐ SOUL CAGES
MASSCD 032 / Jun '94 / Massacre

Soul Children

☐ FRICTION/ BEST OF TWO WORLDS
I'll be the other woman / What's happening baby / Can't let you go / It's out of my hands / Just one moment / We're gettin' too close / Love makes it right / Bring it here / Thanks for a precious nothing / Put your world in my world (best of two worlds) / Give me one good reason / Got to get away from it all / Hang ups of holding on / Wrap it up tonight / Let's make a sweet thing sweeter / Finish me off / Don't break away
CDSXD 056 / Jun '93 / Stax

☐ SINGLES, THE/OPEN DOOR POLICY
Don't take my kindness for weakness / It ain't always what you do (it's who you let see you do it) / Hold on I'm comin' / Make it good / Ridin' on love's merry go-round / Love is a hurtin' thing / Poem on the school house door / Come back kind of love / Signed, sealed, delivered (I'm yours) / I don't know what this world is coming to / Hearsay / Stir up the boogie, Part II / Who you used to be / Strangers / Summer in the shade / Can't give up a good thing / Butt la rose / Hard living with a man / Believing
CDSXD 101 / Jan '94 / Stax

Soul Coughing

☐ IRRESISTIBLE BLISS
Super bon bon / Soft serve / White girl / Soundtrack to Mary / Lazybones / 4 out of 5 / Paint / Disseminated / Collapse / Sleepless / Idiot kings / How many cans
8287592 / Apr '97 / Slash

☐ RUBY VROOM
Is Chicago is not Chicago / Sugar free jazz / Casiotone nation / Blue eyed devil / Bus to Beelzebub / True dreams of Wichita / Screenwriter's blues / Moon Sammy / Supra genius / City of motors / Uh zoom zip / Down to this / Mr. Bitterness / Janine
8285552 / 17 Aug '98 / Slash

Soul, David

☐ BEST OF DAVID SOUL, THE
Don't give up on us / Tattler / Silver lady / I wish I was / It sure brings out the love in your eyes / Seem to miss so much (coalminer's song) / Let's have a quiet night in / Going in with my eyes open / One more mountain to climb / Topanga / 1927 Kansas city / Landlord / Nobody but a fool or a preacher / Bird on the wire
MCCD 152 / Feb '94 / Music Club

Soul Defenders

☐ SOUL DEFENDERS AT STUDIO ONE
CDHB 066 / Jun '91 / Heartbeat

Soul Family Sensation

☐ BURGER HABIT
TPLP 45CD / Sep '93 / One Little Indian

☐ NEW WAVE
Perfect life / Messed up and blue / Sheffield song / Day you went away / Japanese technology / 747 tonight / I don't even know if I should call you baby / Whoever said / Other stuff / All across the network / 747 tonight (lenny deetrego dub) / Beat author / All across the network
TPLP 35CD / Sep '91 / One Little Indian

Soul For Real

☐ CANDY RAIN
Candy rain / Every little thing I do / All in my mind / If you want it / I wanna be your friend / Ain't no sunshine / Spend the night / I don't know / I fonly you knew / Thinking of you / Piano interlude
MCD 11125 / Mar '95 / MCA

Soul Generation

☐ BATTLE OF THE BANDS (Soul Generation/The Joneses)
That's the way it's gotta be (body and soul): *Soul Generation* / Ray of hope: *Soul Generation* / Super fine: *Soul Generation* / Praying for a miracle: *Soul Generation* / Million dollars: *Soul Generation* / In your way: *Soul Generation* / Wait so long: *Soul Generation* / Key to your heart: *Soul Generation* / Sweet thing: *Soul Generation* / I wonder what she's doing: *Soul Generation* / Baby (there is nothing you can do): *Joneses* / Pretty, pretty: *Joneses* / Pull my string: *Joneses* / Hold up: *Joneses* / I can't see what you see in me: *Joneses* / Mary Mary: *Joneses* / Lovin' you: *Joneses* / She loves you: *Joneses* / Sweet water boy: *Joneses* / Win your love: *Joneses*
NEMCD 930 / Jul '97 / Sequel

Soul II Soul

☐ SOUL II SOUL VOL.1 - CLUB CLASSICS
Keep on movin' / Back to life / Feel free / Live rap / Dance / Jazzie's groove / Fairplay / Happiness / Holdin' on Bambelea / African dance / Acapella
DIXCD 82 / Mar '89 / 10

☐ SOUL II SOUL VOL.2 - 1990 A NEW DECADE
Get a life / Jazzie B / Daddae Harvey / Love comes through / People / Missing you / Courtney blows / 1990 a new decade / Dreams a dream / Time (untitled) / In the heat of the night / Our time has now come / Nomsa caluza / Sonti mndebele
DIXCD 90 / Apr '92 / 10

☐ SOUL II SOUL VOL.3 - JUST RIGHT
Joy / Take me higher / Storm / Direction / Just right / Move me no mountain / Intelligence / Future / Mood / Everywhere
DIXCD 100 / Apr '92 / 10

☐ SOUL II SOUL VOL.4 - THE CLASSIC SINGLES 1988-1993
Back to life / Keep on movin' / Get a life / Dreams a dream / Missing you / Just right / Move me no mountain / People / Fairplay / Jazzie's groove / Wish / Joy / Keep on movin' (mixes) / Back to life (mixes)
CDV 2724 / Oct '93 / Virgin

☐ SOUL II SOUL VOL.5 - BELIEVE
Love enuff / Ride on / How long / Feeling / Universal love / Be a man / Zion / Don't you dream / Game dunn / Sunday / Pride / I care / B groove / Believe
CDV 2739 / Jul '95 / Virgin

☐ SOUL II SOUL VOL.6 - TIME TO CHANGE
Camdino soul / Pleasure dome / Thank you / Dare to differ / Get away / Love ain't around / Represent / Time for change / I feel love / Limit is the sky
CID 8060 / 1 Sep '97 / Island

Soul Jah

☐ URBANOLOGY
HLCD 3 / 3 Nov '97 / Hard Leaders

Soul, Jimmy

☐ IF YOU WANT TO BE HAPPY (The Very Best Of Jimmy Soul)
If you want to be happy / I can't hold out any longer / Some kinda nut / Twistin' Matilda (and the channel) / Take me to Los Angeles / Call me / When I get my car / Everybody's gone ape / Guess things happen that way / She's alright / Church street in the summertime / Church street in summertime / I want to know if you love me / You're nothin' / I hate you baby / My little room / You can't have your cake / I know why dreamers cry / Hands off / I love you so / Treat 'em rough / I need your love / Tell me why / Don't release me / When Matilda comes / Go 'way Christina
CDCHD 593 / Jan '96 / Ace

Soul Junk

☐ 1953
HMS 2362 / Nov '96 / Homestead

Soul Oddity

☐ TONE CAPSULE
Mezzo modular / Welcome back to earth / Little alien / People party / Freq shift / Clipped / Soul communication / DJ Tokyo / Cruxx / Fugue
ASW 6173 / Jun '96 / Astralwerks

Soul Society

☐ SMILING FACES (Soul Society & Roy Ayers)
Funky nassau / Spaced out / Everybody loves the sunshine / Pusher / Money mad / Smiling faces / Thank you / Big John is my name / Feed me your love / Pleasure for your pleasure
ME 00662 / 2 Mar '98 / Soulciety

Soul Station

☐ CUT'N THE GROOVE
YRB 004 / Jun '97 / Yardbird Suite

Soul Stirrers

☐ HEAVEN IS MY HOME
Christ is all / He's my rock (wait on Jesus) / In a few more days / Golden bells / Sinner run to Jesus / Heaven is my home (take 1) / Heaven is my home (Take 2) / Till then / Out on a hill / Swing low, sweet chariot / Loved ones are waiting / Love of God / When the gates swing open / Lord laid his hands on me / That's all I need to know / My life belongs to him / There's not a friend like Jesus / Heaven is my home
CDCHD 478 / Jul '93 / Ace

☐ JESUS GAVE ME WATER
Jesus gave me water / Christ is all / Come let us go back to god / I'm on the firing line / How far am I from canaan / Jesus done just what he said / He's my rock (wait on jesus) / Joy joy to my soul / I'm gonna build on that shore / Until Jesus calls me home / Jesus will lead me to that promised land / It wont' be long / Let me go home / Someday somewhere / Jesus paid the debt / End of my journey / He's my friend / I have a friend above all others / I gave up everything to follow him / Come and go to that land / Any day now / Jesus I'll never forget / All right now / Pray / Come to go to that land / I'm so happy in the service of the lord
CDCHD 464 / Mar '93 / Ace

☐ LAST MILE OF THE WAY, THE
Last mile of the way / Mean old way / That's heaven to me / Were you there (false starts) / Were you there / Lord remember me / Pilgrim of sorrow / He's my guide / He's my guide (incomplete) / Last mile of the way (incomplete) / All right now / He'll make a way / Jesus I'll never forget / Come and go to that land / Just as I am / He'll welcome me / He's my friend / Jesus paid the debt / Jesus will lead me to that promised land / Jesus will lead me to that promised land / It won't be very long / How far am I from Canaan (incomplete) / How far am I from Canaan / Let me go home
CDCHD 563 / Mar '94 / Ace

☐ THIS IS MY PRAYER
BMCD 3050 / 5 Jan '98 / Blue Moon

Soul Syndicate

☐ MOODIE DUB VOL.1 (Soul Syndicate & Black Slate)
MMLP 952 / Mar '94 / Moodie

☐ MOODIE IN DUB VOL.3
MMCD 1032 / Sep '94 / Moodie

Soul Train

☐ JAZZ IN SWEDEN 1986
1335 / Feb '90 / Caprice

Soulburn

☐ FEEDING ON ANGELS
CM 77217CD / 6 Jul '98 / Century Media

Souled American

☐ FROZEN
CPR 008 / 27 Jul '98 / Checkered Past

☐ NOTES CAMPFIRE
EFA 121192 / Feb '97 / Moll

Soulfly

☐ SOULFLY
Eye for an eye / No hope no fear / Bleed / Tribe / Bumba / First commandment / Bumbklaatt / Soulfly / Umbabaraumba / Fire / Song remains insane / No.4 / Prejudice / Karmageddon / Congasera / Ain't no feeble bastard / Possibilities of life's destruction
RR 87482
RR 84489 / 20 Apr '98 / Roadrunner

Soulfood

☐ BREATHE (2CD Set)
Creation / Breathe / Chameleon / Wisdom / Wayob / Vision / Great mystery / Invocation / Liquid / Deeper / Deconstruction / Sage / Mystic / Altered states
RCD 10394 / 16 Mar '98 / Rykodisc

Soulquake System

☐ FIRM STATEMENT
BMCD 126 / 11 May '98 / Black Mark

Souls At Zero

☐ TASTE FOR THE PEVERSE, A
086272CTR / Oct '95 / Edel

Soulside

☐ SOON COME HAPPY
DISCHORD 51 / Feb '91 / Dischord

Soumah, Momo Wandel

☐ GUINEE MATCHOWE
926532 / Jul '96 / BUDA

Sound

☐ THUNDER UP
CDBIAS 053 / Apr '87 / Play It Again Sam

Sound Factory

☐ DANCE HITS FOR KIDS
Wannabe / Quit playing games / Freedom / Mysterious girl / Sexy eyes / Soldier soldier / Macarena / Where do you go / Who do you think you are / Be my lover / Ooh aah just a little bit / Ready or not / Little boy / 2 Become 1
KI 881312 / Jul '97 / Disky

Sound Information

☐ COLLECTION, THE
EBSC 005 / Jan '97 / Echo Beach

Sound Patrol

☐ SWEETENED NO LEMON
ORG 012CD / 23 Feb '98 / Organico

Soundgarden

☐ A SIDES, THE
5408332 / 3 Nov '97 / A&M

☐ BADMOTORFINGER
Rusty cage / Outshined / Slaves and bulldozers / Jesus christ pose / Face pollution / Somewhere / Searching with my good eye closed / Room a thousand years wide / Mind riot / Drawing flies / Holy water / New damage
3953742 / Oct '91 / A&M

☐ DOWN ON THE UPSIDE
Applebite / Never the machine forever / Tighter and tighter / No attention / Switch opens / Overfloater / Unkind / Boot camp / Rhinosaur / Zero chance / Dusty / Ty Cobb / Blow up the outside world / Burden in my hand / Never named
5405262 / May '96 / A&M

☐ LOUDER THAN LOVE
Ugly truth / Hands all over / Gun / Power trip / Get on the snake / Full on Kevin's Mom / Loud love / I wake / Now wrong no right / Uncovered / Big dumb sex
CDA 5252 / Sep '89 / A&M

☐ SCREAMING LIFE
SPCD 12 / Dec '96 / Sub Pop

☐ SCREAMING LIFE/FOPP
Hunted down / Entering / Tears to forget / Nothing to say / Little Joe / Hand of God / Kingdom of come / Swallow my pride / Fopp / Fopp (dub)
SPCD 12A/B / Feb '94 / Sub Pop

☐ SUPERUNKNOWN
Let me drown / My wave / Fell on black days / Mailman / Superunknown / Head down / Black hole sun / Spoonman / Limo wreck / Day I tried to live / Kickstand / Fresh tendrils / 4th of July / Half / Like suicide / She likes surprises
5402152 / Mar '94 / A&M

☐ ULTRAMEGA OK
Flower / All your lies / 665 / Beyond the wheel / 667 / Mood for trouble / Circle of power / He didn't / Smokestack lightnin' / Nazi driver / Head injury / Incessant mace / One minute of silence
SST 201CD / Nov '88 / SST

Sounds From The Ground

☐ KIN
WWCD 14 / Nov '95 / Wibbly Wobbly

Sounds Incorporated

☐ SOUNDS INCORPORATED
Spartans / Detroit / Rinky dink / My little red book / Hall of the mountain king / One mint julep / Last night / Crane / Emily / Mogambo / Bullets / Spanish Harlem / Little bird / If we lived on top of a mountain / Old and the new / Grab this thing / Boil over / I'm comin' through / Fingertips / I'm in love again
SEECD 371 / Feb '97 / See For Miles

Sounds Of Blackness

☐ AFRICA TO AMERICA: THE JOURNEY OF THE DRUM
Hold on (Part 1) / I'm going all the way / Ah been 'buked (Part 1) / I believe / Hold on (Part 2) / Everything's gonna be alright / Sun up to sundown / Lord will make a way / He took away all my pain / Place in my heart / Harder they are, the bigger they fall / Drum (Africa to America) / Royal Kingdoms/ Rise/My Native Land / Very special love / Strange fruit / Black butterfly / You've taken by blues and gone / Livin' the blues / Ah been 'buked (Part 2) / I'm going all the way (Brixton flavour)
5490092 / Apr '94 / Perspective

☐ EVOLUTION OF GOSPEL
Chains / Optimistic / Ah been workin' / Pressure / Testify / Gonna be free one day / Stand / Pressure / Your wish is my command / Hallelujah Lord / We give you thanks / He holds the future / What shall I call him / Better watch your behaviour / Please take my hand / I'll fly away / Harambee
3953612 / Oct '91 / Perspective

☐ TIME FOR HEALING
Africana / Spirit / We are gonna make it through / Hold on (change is coming) / Love will never change / Love train / God cares / Hold on (don't let go) / Crisis / We are gonna make it through / You can make it if you try / Blackness blues / Spiritual medley / So far away / Familiar waters / Time for healing / We are gonna make it through / Kwanzaa-umoja-uhuru
5490292 / May '97 / Perspective

Sounds Of Christmas Orchestra

☐ SWINGING CHRISTMAS, A
Jingle bells / Sleigh ride / Merry Christmas darling / It's the most wonderful time of the year / Johnny bring the pine tree in / Carol of the bells / I heard the bells on Christmas day / Caroling, caroling / Deck the halls / O Tannenbaum / We wish you a merry Christmas / O come, O come Emmanuel / What child is this / Gentle Mary laid her child / Angels from the realms of Glory / Christmas is / Silver bells / Mistletoe and holly / Christmas is the warmest time of year / Toyland / Sleep well little children / We need a little Christmas / It's beginning to look a lot like Christmas / Christmas waltz / Joy to the world / God rest ye merry gentlemen / Angels we have heard on high / Silent night / Christmas song (chestnuts roasting on an open fire) / I'll be home for Christmas / White Christmas / Do you hear what I hear / It came upon a midnight clear / O little town of Bethlehem / First Noel / Hark the herald angels sing / Winter wonderland / Let it snow, let it snow, let it snow / Have yourself a merry little Christmas
CDVIP 141 / Nov '96 / Virgin VIP

Sounds Of The Future

☐ FEAR OF THE FUTURE EP
FORM 28 / Sep '93 / Formation

Sounds Orchestral

☐ BEST OF SOUNDS ORCHESTRAL, THE
PLSCD 225 / Jul '97 / Pulse

☐ CAST YOUR FATE TO THE WIND
Something's coming / Cast your fate to the wind / Scarlatti potion no.9 / While we danced at the mardi gras / When love has gone / To wendy with love / Sounds anonymous / Carnival / Downtown / Scarlatti potion no.5 / Love letters / Like the lonely
NEMCD 617 / Nov '91 / Sequel

☐ EASY PROJECT VOL.5, THE (Sounds Rare)
Have faith in your love / Sounds like Jacques / Go home girl / Do nothin' 'til you hear from me / Porcelain / Ain't that peculiar / Boy and a girl / Fifth Avenue walkdown / Our love story / From Nashville with love / Image / Gloria Gloria / Blue tango / Blue bolero / West of Carnaby / Hopping dance / Black is black / I couldn't live without your love / Mas que nada / Baubles bangles and beads
NEMCD 992 / Aug '97 / Sequel

☐ SOUNDS ORCHESTRAL MEETS JAMES BOND
Thunderball / Solitaire / Goldfinger / Mr. Kiss Kiss Bang Bang / Blues for pussy / Mr. Oddjob / Moonshot / James Bond theme / Spectre / From Russia With Love / Kissy Suzuki / 007 theme
NEBCD 908 / Sep '96 / Sequel

Soundsmith

☐ AQUANAUT
WJ 29CD / 9 Feb '98 / Wurlitzer Jukebox

Soundtech Steel Orchestra

☐ BANKS
CCD 0022 / Apr '96 / CRS

Soundtrack Of Our Lives

☐ EXTENDED REVELATION
4227862 / 22 May '98 / Telegram

☐ WELCOME TO INFANT FREEBASE
0630188712 / 10 Nov '97 / Coalition

☐ WELCOME TO THE INFANT FREEBASE
166522 / 22 May '98 / Telegram

Soup Dragons

☐ HOTWIRED
BLRCD 15 / May '92 / Big Life

☐ HYDROPHONIC
One way street / Don't get down (Get down) / Do you care / May the force be with you / Contact high / All messed up / Time is now / Freeway / Rest in peace / JF junkie / Automatic speed queen / Out of here / Motherfunker / Painkilla / Cruel lust / Black and blues / Hypersonic re-entry
5227812 / Sep '94 / Mercury

☐ LOVEGOD
SOUPCD 2R / Jul '90 / Big Life

Source

☐ ORGANISED NOISE
Vagator / Eclipse / Neuromancer / Real thing / Squeeze / Analysis / Release it / Beyond time
RS 93005CD / May '93 / R&S

Source Direct

☐ CONTROLLED DEVELOPMENTS
ASW 6225 / 17 Nov '97 / Astralwerks

Source Experience

☐ DIFFERENT JOURNEYS
Unkown territory / Gate 41 / Point zero / Pressure drop / Diatonic shift / Intruder / X-ray / Night shift / Voices of the spirit
RS 94056CD / Nov '94 / R&S

Souskay

☐ SOUSKAY
CD 69812 / '91 / Melodie

South African National Symphony Orchestra

☐ CLASSIC UNCHAINED MELODIES
CDSGP 1098 / Sep '95 / Prestige

South, Eddie

☐ CLASSICS 1923-1937
CLASSICS 707 / Jul '93 / Classics

☐ CLASSICS 1937-1941
CLASSICS 737 / Feb '94 / Classics

☐ EDDIE SOUTH IN PARIS 1929 & 1937
Doin' the raccoon / Two guitars / Eddie's blues / Sweet Georgia Brown / Oh lady be good / Dinah / Daphne / Somebody loves me / I can't believe that you're in love with me / Swing interpretation of the first movement of the concerto / Fiddle blues / Improvisations on the first movement of the concerto
DRGCD 8405 / Sep '93 / DRG

South 'Frisco Jazz Band

☐ BIG BEAR STOMP
SOSCD 1307 / Jul '96 / Stomp Off

☐ BROKEN PROMISES
SOSCD 1180 / Aug '90 / Stomp Off

☐ GOT EVERYTHING, DON'T WANT ANYTHING
SOSCD 1240 / Nov '92 / Stomp Off

☐ SAGE HEN STRUT
SOSCD 1143 / Apr '94 / Stomp Off

☐ SOUTH 'FRISCO JAZZ BAND VOL.1
MMRCCD 4 / Feb '94 / Merry Makers

☐ SOUTH 'FRISCO JAZZ BAND VOL.1
SOSCD 1027 / Dec '94 / Stomp Off

☐ SOUTH 'FRISCO JAZZ BAND VOL.2
MMRCCD 7 / Feb '94 / Merry Makers

☐ THESE CATS ARE DIGGIN' US
SOSCD 1035 / Mar '95 / Stomp Off

South, Svenn

☐ SOUTH CONNECTION
LAB 001 / Sep '96 / Lab

Southampton FC

☐ SUPER SAINTS (14 Southampton Classics) (Various Artists)
Saints for the cup: *Frisco* / Legend of a saint: *Valley Slags* / It ain't easy: *Keegan, Kevin* / When the saints go marching in: *Soccer Rockers* / Red stripes: *Chorley, Richard* / Woolston ferry: *Chorley, Richard* / Micky Channon: *Monty* / Saints of Southampton: *SO15* / Bring the saints back to St.Marys: *Valley Slags* / Make me an island: *Ball, Alan* / Shearer was a saint: *Dingo* / When the saints go marching in / Number 7: *Shearer's Ghost*
CDGAFFER 27 / 24 Aug '98 / Cherry Red

Souther, Richard

☐ ILLUMINATION
SK 62853 / Jun '97 / Sony Classical

Southern Culture On The Skids

☐ DITCH DIGGIN'
SH 21142 / Nov '96 / Safe House

☐ FOR LOVERS ONLY
SH 21082 / Nov '96 / Safe House

☐ GIRL FIGHT
SFTRI 266CD / Dec '96 / Sympathy For The Record Industry

Southern Exposure

☐ SMALL TOWN
Little company / Walls of time / Wheel hoss / Gypsy breeze / African breeze / I'm just a used to be / Green light / Moonshine whiskey / Wild Bill Jones / Bonaparte's retreat / Small town
GRP 002 / Sep '93 / Get Real Productions

Southern Pacific

☐ COUNTY LINE
7599258952 / Jan '96 / WEA

☐ ZUMA
Midnight highway / Honey I dare you / New shade of blue / Dream on / Invisible man / Wheels on the line / Just hang on / All is lost / Bail out / Trail of tears
7599256092 / Jan '96 / WEA

Southern Sons

☐ DEEP SOUTH GOSPEL
ALCD 2802 / Oct '93 / Alligator

☐ SOUTHERN SONS 1941-1944/ RICKMONDS HARMONISING QUARTET 1943 (Southern Sons/ Rickmonds Harmonising Quartet)
DOCD 5492 / Nov '96 / Document

Southern, Jeri

☐ DREAM'S ON JERI, THE
I've got five dollars / You better go now / Mad about the boys / Everything but you / It must be true / Occaisional man / Come by Sunday / I remember you / When I fall in love / Gipsy in my soul / We're not children anymore / It's d'lovely / Life does the girl a favour / September in the rain / I thought of you last night / This time the dream's on me / I hadn't anyone till you / Something I dreamed last night / He was too good for me / Just in time / Married I can always get
JASCD 340 / Feb '98 / Jasmine

☐ MEETS COLE PORTER/AT THE CRESCENDO
Don't look at me that way / Get out of town / Looking at you / It's all right with me / Let's fly away / Why shouldn't I / You're the top / After you / Which / I concentrate on you / It's bad for me / Weren't we fools / I thought of you last night / I get a kick out of you / Dancing on the ceiling / Blame it on my youth / Remind me / You better go now / I'm just a woman / Something I dreamed last night / Nice work if you can get it / When I fall in love
CTMCD 112 / Mar '97 / EMI

☐ SOUTHERN BREEZE
FSRCD 104 / Jan '93 / Fresh Sound

☐ SOUTHERN STYLE, THE/PRELUDE TO A KISS
I'll take romance / Let's fall in love / One day I wrote his name upon the sand / I'll wear the green willow / It's delovely / My letters / Too marvellous for words / Gypsy in my soul / Debonair / I don't where to turn / I hadn't anyone till you / Scarlet ribbons / Prelude to a kiss / Cross my heart / I don't want to walk without you / Please be kind / Trust in me / Try a little tenderness / You're mine you / Speak low / Hold me / Close to you / Close as pages in a book / Touch of your lips
MCLD 19380 / 22 Jun '98 / MCA

☐ YOU BETTER GO NOW/WHEN YOUR HEART'S ON FIRE
You better go now / Give me time / Something I dreamed last night / Man that got away / When I fall love / Just got to have him around / Dancing on the ceiling / Speak softly to me / What good am I without you / I thought of you last night / That ole devil called love again / Remind me / Smoke gets in your eyes / Can I forget you / Little girl blue / I remember you / He was good to me / You're driving me crazy / You make me feel so young / Someone to watch over me / Autumn in New York / My ship / No more / Let me love you
JASCD 602 / Aug '96 / Jasmine

Southern, Sheila

☐ WITH LOVE (Southern, Sheila & Royal Philharmonic Orchestra)
What are you doing the rest of your life / My funny valentine / My coloring book / How beautiful is night / Nearness of you / Losing my mind / Country girl / My one and only love / Memory / Touch me in the morning / She's out of my life
CDSIV 1107 / Nov '96 / Horatio Nelson

Southlanders

☐ WE
We / Sorry / Could it be / Hey girl / Each and every day / Hi pops / Make it tonight / Didn;t want to leave you / Don't you ever change / Come back to me / It must be love / I am a mole and I live in a hole
CDRPM 0037 / 4 May '98 / RP Media

Southside Johnny

☐ BEST OF SOUTHSIDE JOHNNY & THE ASBURY JUKES, THE (Southside Johnny & The Asbury Jukes)
I don't want to go home / Fever / This time it's for real / Love on the wrong side of town / Without love / Having a party / Got to get you off my mind / Snatchin' it back / Sweeter than honey / You mean so much to me / Little by little / Got to be a better way home / This time baby's gone for good / Hearts of stone / Take it inside / Talk to me / Next to you / Trapped again
4735882 / '89 / Sony Music

☐ SPITTIN' FIRE (2CD Set)
It's been a long time / Talk to me / Fever / Blue radio / Trapped again / We'll make the world stand still / Love on the wrong side of town / Day in and day out / Wild horses / Little Calcutta / Fade away / It's all over now / Hoochie coochie man / I played the fool / Lovey dovey / Coming back / All night long / I don't want to go home
120272 / Feb '97 / Musidisc UK

Souvenir, William

☐ NA'F MI WANG
MWCD 3012 / Aug '96 / Music & Words

☐ TIN TELE, A
MWCD 3010 / Jul '95 / Music & Words

Soviet Army Chorus

☐ POPULAR SELECTIONS (Soviet Army Chorus & Band)
MCD 71500 / Jun '93 / Monitor

Soviet France

☐ ELSTRE
CHARRMCD 5 / Jul '90 / Charrm

☐ IN.VERSION
CHARRMCD 24 / Oct '96 / Charrm

☐ MOHNOMISCHE
CHARRMCD 4 / '84 / Charrm

Sovine, Red

☐ GREATEST HITS
DCD 7828 / 6 Mar '98 / Avid

Sovory

☐ SOVORY
5277512 / Oct '96 / Polydor

SOW

☐ JE M'AIME
39100932 / Jan '97 / Hyperium

Soweto String Quartet

☐ RENAISSANCE
Imbube / Writing on the wall / Songs my Mother taught me / Weeping / Eureka / Thula sizwe khay'elisha / Pata pata / Mangwane/Ee'motswala / Sikelela / Sophiatown / My lover / Blue mountain / Imbube
74321462712 / 6 Oct '97 / RCA Victor

☐ ZEBRA CROSSING
Mbayi mbayi / Zebra crossing / Zulu lullaby / Kwela / Paul Simon 'Graceland' collection / Bossa baroque / Shut up and listen / St. Agnes and the burning train / Kadeni kwazulu / Nytilo nytilo / Where were you taking me to / Nkosi sikelel' iAfrica / Mbayi mbayi
74321268652 / May '96 / RCA Victor

Soyer, Nigel

☐ I AM HERE
JVC 006 / 9 Feb '98 / Jo Go

SPA

☐ SPA
Made in heaven / It looks like rain / Fellow ship of man / I've had you all / Nice nice nice / Reprise / Just a ride / Chemical chance / DNA / Wing / Hog heaven / Well / Christians who kill
NSKYCD 004 / 22 Sep '97 / Northern Sky

Space

☐ VERY BEST OF SPACE, THE
Magic fly / Carry on, turn me on / Air force / Save your love for me / Space media / Deeper zone / Baby's paradise / Let me know the wonder / Blue tears / Secret dreams
QED 143 / Nov '96 / Tring

Space

☐ SPIDERS
Neighbourhood / Mister psycho / Female of the species / Money / Me and you vs the world / Lovechild of the queen / No-one understands / Voodoo roller / Drop dead / Dark clouds / Major pager / Kill me / Charlie M / Growler
GUTCD 1 / Sep '96 / Gut

☐ TIN PLANET
Begin again / Avenging angels / Tom Jones / One o' clock / Be there / Man / Liddle biddy help from Elvis / Unluckiest man in the world / Piggies / Bad days / There's no you / Disco dolly / Silence / Fran in Japan
GUTTIN 005
GUTCD 005 / 9 Mar '98 / Gut

Space Cadets

☐ ASTROBILLY ROCKIN'
Astrobilly rockin' / In space / Crash landed / Lost on Earth / Lady M / Dreaming a dream / Space hopper / Awakadeeawakadoo / We're gonna rock rock rock / Where can my baby be / Did he jump or was he pushed / Troubled man / Say yes to me / We just wanna be loved / I'm a space cadet / Big moon / We are the Space Cadets / Rockin' with the Space Cadets / Time to rock / Rocket ship / Rockin' on thin ice / Let's get crazy / Cadet walk
JRCD 20 / Sep '97 / Jappin' & Rockin'

Space Cossacks

☐ INTERSTELLAR STOMP
MUSICK 005CD / 16 Mar '98 / Musick

Space Cowboys

☐ LOCKED 'N' LOADED
RTD 19512672 / Nov '92 / Our Choice

Space Explosion

☐ SPACE EXPLOSION
CTCD 067 / Dec '97 / Captain Trip
CLP 01752 / 23 Mar '98 / Purple Pyramid

Space Farm

☐ GOING HOME TO ETERNITY
LW 4036 / 2 Mar '98 / Little Wing

Space Monkeys

☐ DADDY OF THEM ALL
Acid house killed rock and roll / Blowing down the stylus / Sugar cane / Inside my soul / Ready for the rampage / Dear Dhinus / Smile America / Let i t shine / We are the supercool / Sweetest dream / March of the scarecrows
FACD 225 / 5 May '98 / Factory Too

Space Negros

☐ DIG ARCHAEOLOGY 1975-1986
AA 040 / 15 Dec '97 / Arf Arf

☐ DIG ARCHAEOLOGY 1980-1990
AA 035 / 15 Dec '97 / Arf Arf

☐ DIG ARCHAEOLOGY 1981-1983
AA 055 / 15 Dec '97 / Arf Arf

☐ DO GENERIC ETHNIC MUZAK
AA 038 / 15 Dec '97 / Arf Arf

Space Streakings

☐ 7-TOKU
GR 18CD / Nov '94 / Skingraft

Space Tribe

☐ ULTRAVIOLET CATASTROPHE (2CD Set)
SZ 031 / 24 Nov '97 / Spiritzone

Spacebox

☐ KICK UP
CTCD 025 / Jul '97 / Captain Trip

Spaceheads

☐ ROUND THE OUTSIDE (Live)
DBC 208CD / Mar '97 / Darkblue

Spacehog

☐ CHINESE ALBUM, THE
One of these days / Goodbye violet race / Lucy's shoes / Mungo city / Sky;ark / Sand in your eyes / Captain Freemans / 2nd avenue / Almond kisses / Carry on / Anonymous / Beautiful girl
9362468512 / 9 Mar '98 / Elektra

☐ RESIDENT ALIEN
Zeroes / To be a millionaire, was it likely / Spacehog / Starside / In the meantime / Candyman / Never coming down / Shipwrecked / Last dictator / Only a few / Never coming down / Cruel to be kind / Space is the place
7559618342 / Feb '97 / Elektra

Spacemaid

☐ SUPERCOOL
Baby come on / Supercool / Girl who sold the world / Beautiful boys beautiful girls / Boy racer / I see comets / Just a song / Do you remember rock 'n' roll radio / Fake fur $50 vamp / Bigger than life / Pink hotel
STARC 108 / 22 Sep '97 / Big Star

Spacemen 3

☐ DREAM WEAPON
ORBIT 001CD / Oct '95 / Space Age

☐ FOR ALL THE FUCKED UP CHILDREN OF THE WORLD
SFTRI 1368CD / 5 Jan '98 / Sympathy For The Record Industry

☐ LIVE IN EUROPE
ORBIT 002CD / Oct '95 / Space Age

☐ LOSING TOUCH
MR 011CD / Apr '92 / Munster

☐ PEFORMANCE
REF 33011 / Oct '91 / Fire

☐ PERFECT PRESCRIPTIONS
Take me to the other side / Walking with Jesus / Ode to street hassle / Ecstasy symphony / Transparent radiation / Feel so good / Things'll never be the same / Come down easy / Call the doctor
REF 33006 / Oct '91 / Fire

☐ PLAYING WITH FIRE
Honey / Come down softly to my soul / How does it feel / I believe it / Revolution / Let me down gently / So hot (wash away all of my tears) / Suicide / Lord can you hear me / Suicide (live) / Repeater (how does it feel) (live)
FIRE 33016 / Oct '91 / Fire

☐ RECURRING
Big City / Just to see you smile / I love you / Set me free/I've got the key / Set me free / Why couldn't I see / Just to see you smile / When tomorrow hits / Feel so sad / Hypnotised / Sometimes / Feeling just fine (head full of shit) / Billy Whizz/Blue 1 / Drive/Feel so sad / Feeling just fine (alternative mix)
FIRE 33023 / Oct '91 / Fire

☐ SOUND OF CONFUSION
Losing touch with my mind / Hey man / Rollercoaster / Mary anne / Little doll / 2.35 / O.d. catastrophe
RED 33005 / Oct '91 / Fire

☐ SPACEMEN ARE GO
BCD 4044 / Jan '97 / Bomp

☐ TAKING DRUGS TO MAKE MUSIC
BCD 4047 / Jan '97 / Bomp

☐ TRIBUTE TO SPACEMAN 3, A (Various Artists)
ROCKETGIRL 2 / 15 Jun '98 / Rocket Girl

Spaceship Eyes

☐ TRUTH IN THE EYES OF A SPACESHIP
CLEO 2482 / 12 May '98 / Cleopatra

Spaceshits

☐ WINTER DANCE PARTY
SFTRI 488CD / Jul '97 / Sympathy For The Record Industry

Spacetime Continuum

☐ REMIT RECAPS
ASW 61002 / Nov '96 / Astralwerks

Spaceways

☐ TRAD
Time changes space / At home with the snake / City / Charlie X / Pink panza / Rice / Requiem for Ra / Kurosawa meets slow Charlie / Crimes / Riding on the tip / Man who fell to Easton / Death of a silent planet / Pinhead plutonium / Better / Tyner
COTCD 002 / Sep '96 / Cup Of Tea

Spacewurm

☐ ARMY OF GOD
VC 111CD / Jun '97 / Vinyl Communication

☐ SEARCHING FOR THE...
VC 130CD / 2 Mar '98 / Vinyl Communication

Spacious Mind

☐ COSMIC MINDS AT PLAY
GRCD 006 / 23 Mar '98 / Garageland

☐ ORGANIC MIND SOLUTION
GRCD 011 / 23 Mar '98 / Garageland

☐ SAILING THE SEAGOAT
GRCD 018 / 23 Mar '98 / Garageland

Spady, Clarence

☐ NATURE OF THE BEAST
Baby baby baby / Answer to the man / Change my way of livin' / Nature of the beast / Bad axe / Built for comfort / Picture of love / Hi-heeled sneakers / Good fool is hard to find / Blues walk / Gospel blues
ECD 260802 / Sep '96 / Evidence

Spaelimenninir

☐ FLOD OG FJORA
SHD 18 / 2 Apr '98 / Tutl

Spahn Ranch

☐ ARCHITECTURE
CLP 9977 / Apr '97 / Cleopatra

☐ BLACKMAIL STARTERS KIT
CLEO 94772 / Jun '94 / Cleopatra

☐ BREATH & TAXES
CDZOT 116 / Aug '94 / Zoth Ommog

☐ RETRO FIT
CLEO 1952 / 14 Apr '98 / Cleopatra

Spallanzani & Boda Quintet

☐ GONE FOR A WALK
MECCACD 2029 / Oct '97 / Music Mecca

Spand, Charlie

☐ CHARLIE SPAND 1929-1931
DOCD 5108 / Nov '92 / Document

Spandau Ballet

☐ BEST OF SPANDAU BALLET, THE
To cut a long story short / Freeze / Musclebound / Chant no.1 (I don't need this pressure on) / Paint me down / She loved like diamond / Instinction / Lifeline / True / Gold / Only when you leave / I'll fly for you / Highly strung / Round and round / Fight for ourselves / Through the barricades / How many lies / Raw / Be free with your love
CCD 1894 / Sep '91 / Chrysalis

☐ BEST OF SPANDAU BALLET, THE (18 Original Hits/3CD Set)
Only when you leave / Age of blows / Foundation / Coffee club / Nature of the beast / Glow / Musclebound / Pleasure / Heaven is a secret / Code of love / Pharaoh / Always in the back of my mind / Highly strung / Revenge for love / Mandolin / Missionary / Innocence and science / With the pride / To cut a long story short
LAD 873262 / Nov '96 / Disky

☐ COLLECTION, THE
CDGOLD 1081 / Apr '97 / EMI Gold

☐ HEART LIKE A SKY
Be free with your love / Crashed into love / Big feeling / Matter of time / Motivator / Raw / Empty spaces / Windy town / Handful of dust
4844722 / Jul '97 / Columbia

☐ JOURNEYS TO GLORY
To cut a long story short / Reformation / Mandolin / Muscle bound / Ages of blows / Freeze / Confused / Toys
CDGOLD 1046 / Jul '96 / EMI Gold
DC 875512 / May '97 / Disky

☐ PARADE
Only when you leave / Highly strung / I'll fly for you / Nature of the beast / Revenge for love / Always in the back of my mind / With the pride / Round and round
CDGOLD 1010 / Mar '96 / EMI Gold

☐ SINGLES COLLECTION, THE
Gold / Lifeline / Round and round / Only when you leave / Instinction / Highly strung / True / Communication / I'll fly for you / To cut a long story short / Chant no.1 (I don't need this pressure on) / She loved like diamond / Paint me down / Freeze / Musclebound
CCD 1498 / Apr '86 / Chrysalis

☐ THROUGH THE BARRICADES
Barricades - introduction / Cross the line / Man in chains / How many lies / Virgin / Fight for ourselves / Swept / Snakes and lovers / Through the barricades / With pride
4502592 / Feb '94 / CBS

☐ TWELVE INCH MIXES
Gold / Lifeline / Round and round / Only when you leave / Instinction / Highly restrung / True / Communication / I'll fly for you / To cut a long story short / Chant no.1 (I don't need this pressure on) / She loved like diamond / Paint me down / Freeze / Musclebound
CCD 1574 / Feb '94 / Chrysalis

Spaniels

☐ GOODNITE SWEETHEART
CDGR 173 / Jul '97 / Charly

Spanier, Herbie

☐ ANTHOLOGY 1962-1993
JUST 552 / Feb '94 / Justin Time

Spanier, Muggsy

☐ CLASSIC YEARS, THE
Relaxin' at the Tauro / At the jazz band ball / Royal garden balls / Eccentric / Someday sweetheart / (I want a) big butter and egg man / Riverboat shuffle / Lonesome road / Dinah / Dippermouth blues / Egyptian-Ella / That da-da strain / Dallas blues / I'm crazy about love / Livery stable blues / Bluin' the blues / I wish I could shimmy like my sister Kate / At sundown
CDSGP 0171 / 4 May '98 / Prestige

☐ CLASSICS 1939-1942
CLASSICS 709 / Jul '93 / Classics

☐ CLASSICS 1939-1944
CD 14570 / May '95 / Jazz Portraits

☐ CLASSICS 1944
CLASSICS 907 / Nov '96 / Classics

☐ CLASSICS 1944-1946
CLASSICS 967 / Jan '98 / Classics

☐ COMPLETE V-DISC SESSIONS, THE (Spanier, Muggsy & Bud Freeman)
That's a plenty / Squeeze me / Jazz me blues / Pee Wee speaks / Pat's blues / Tin roof blues / Cherry / China boy / Royal garden blues / You took advantage of me / Love is just around the corner / Coquette / For musicians only / Latest thing in hot jazz
JUCD 2049 / Dec '97 / Jazz Unlimited

☐ MANHATTAN MASTERS 1945
STCD 6051 / Jun '98 / Storyville

☐ MUGGSHOT
At Sundown / Baby, won't you please come home / Bluin' the blues / Bullfrog blues / Chicago / China boy / Dallas blues / Darktown strutters ball / Down to Steamboat Tennessee / Four or five times / Friars Point Shuffle / Hesitating blues / I wish I could shimmy like my sister Kate / I've found a new baby / Mobile blues / Nobody's sweetheart / Relaxin' at the Touro / Royal Garden blues / Sugar / That's a plenty / There'll be some changes made / Why can't it be poor little me / (I'll be glad when you're dead) you rascal you / You're bound to look like a monkey
CDAJA 5102 / Mar '93 / Living Era

☐ MUGGSY SPANIER 1939 (The Ragtime Band Sessions)
Big butter and egg man / Someday sweetheart / Eccentric (That eccentric rag) / That da da strain / At the jazz band ball / I wish I could shimmy like my sister Kate / Dippermouth blues / Livery stable blues / Riverboat shuffle / Relaxin' at the Touro / At sundown / Bluin' the blues / Lonesome road / What did I do to be so black and blue / Mandy, make up your mind
07863665502 / Jun '95 / Bluebird

☐ MUGGSY SPANIER 1939-1944
Big butter and egg man / Someday sweetheart / Eccentric (that eccentric rag) / That da da strain / At the jazz band ball / I wish I could shimmy like my sister Kate / Dippermouth blues / Livery stable blues / Riverboat shuffle / Relaxin' at the Touro / At sundown / Bluin' the blues / Lonesome road / Dinah / (What did I do to be so) black and blue / Mandy make up your mind / Oh lady be good / Memphis blues / Whistlin' the blues / Sweet Lorraine / Four or five times / That's a plenty / Sweet Sue just you
CD 53222 / Jan '98 / Giants Of Jazz

☐ MUGGSY SPANIER ALL STARS (Spanier, Muggsy All Stars)
STCD 6033 / May '97 / Storyville

Spanish Fly

☐ ANYTHING YOU WANT
When we get married / Girl don't take your love / Daddy's home / Anything you want / Believe in me / Young love / Let's get together / Daddy's home (spanish version) / Treasure of my heart / Baby / Crimson and clover / Loneliest nights / All I need / Light a candle
9362459262 / Jun '95 / Warner Bros.

☐ FLY BY NIGHT (Original Ballet Soundtrack & Insert Tongue Here)
Movement no.1/Opening / Movement no.2/Snake lady / Transition no.1 / Movement no.3/Sisters / Transition no.2 / Movement no.4/Pas De Deux / Movement no.5/End of the night / Some other sisters / Joshua prayer / Tongue insert/Tongue sandwich / Love song 110
AC 5024 / May '97 / Accurate

☐ RAGS TO BRITCHES
KFWCD 114 / Feb '95 / Knitting Factory

Spanish Gipsy

☐ CON AMOR
EUCD 1190 / Apr '92 / ARC

Spann, Otis

☐ BIGGEST THING SINCE COLOSSUS (Spann, Otis & Fleetwood Mac)
My love depends on you / Walkin' / It was a big thing / Temperature is rising (1002 F) / Dig you / No more doggin' / Ain't nobody's business if I do / She needs some loving / I need some air / Someday baby
4759722 / Feb '95 / Blue Horizon

☐ BLUES IS WHERE IT'S AT, THE
Popcorn man / Brand new house / Chicago blues / Steel mill blues / Down on Sarah street / Ain't nobody's business if I do / Nobody knows Chicago like I do / My home is on the Delta / Spann blues
BGOCD 221 / Mar '94 / Beat Goes On

☐ BLUES NEVER DIE
Blues never die / I got a feeling / One more mile to go / Feeling good / After while / Dust my broom / Straighten up baby / Come on / Must have been the Devil / Lightning / I'm ready
OBCCD 530 / Nov '92 / Original Blues Classics

☐ BOTTOM OF THE BLUES, THE
Heart loaded with trouble / Diving duck / Shimmy baby / Looks like twins / I'm a fool / My man / Down to earth / Nobody knows / Dr. blues
BGOCD 92 / Nov '90 / Beat Goes On

☐ CHICAGO BLUES
TCD 5005 / Oct '94 / Testament

☐ CRYIN' TIME
Home to Mississippi / Blues is a botheration / You said you'd be on time / Crying time / Blind man / Someday / Twisted snake / Green flowers / New boogaloo / Mule kicking in my stall
VMD 6514 / Feb '96 / Vanguard

☐ GOOD MORNING MR. BLUES
APR 3016CD / Dec '96 / Analogue Revival

☐ LIVE THE LIFE (Spann, Otis & Muddy Waters)
TCD 6001 / Sep '97 / Testament

☐ OTIS SPANN IS THE BLUES
Hard way / Take a little walk with me / Otis in the dark / Little boy blue / Country boy / Beat-up team / My daily wish / Great Northern stomp / I got rambling on my mind / Worried life blues
CCD 79001 / Feb '97 / Candid

☐ WALKING THE BLUES
It must have been the devil / Otis blues / Going down slow / Half ain't been told / Monkey face woman / This is the blues / Evil ways / Come day go day / Walking the blues / Bad condition / My home is on the delta
CCD 79025 / Feb '97 / Candid

Spanoudakis, Stamatis

☐ STONE YEARS
ML 3411 / 11 May '98 / Musurgia Graeca

Spare Snare

☐ ANIMALS AND ME
CHUTECD 010 / 24 Aug '98 / Chute

☐ DISCO DANCING EP
100GM 08 / Oct '97 / 100 Guitar Mania

☐ LIVE AT HOME
Thorns (version 1) / Shine on now / Wired for sound / Super slinky / As a matter of fact / Skateboard punk rocker / Bugs / My better half / Call the birds / Thorns (version 2)
CHUTECD 005 / 13 Apr '98 / Chute

☐ WESTFIELD LANE
ORE 8 / Feb '97 / Wabana

Sparke, Philip

☐ BRITANNIA
DOYCD 049 / 11 May '98 / Doyen

Sparkle

☐ SPARKLE
Good life / Time to move on / Lean on me / I'm gone / Turn away / What about / Be careful / Nothing can compare / Quiet place / Lovin' you / Straight up / Vegas / No greater / Play on / Plenty good lovin'
0521462 / 20 Jul '98 / Jive

Sparklehorse

☐ GOOD MORNING SPIDER
Pig / Painbirds / Saint Mary / Good morning spider / Sick of goodbyes / Box of stars / Sunshine / Chaos of the galaxy/Happy man / Hey Joe / Come on in / Maria's little elbows / Cruel sun / All night home / Ghost of his smile / Hundreds of sparrows / Box of stars / Junebug
4960142 / 20 Jul '98 / Parlophone

☐ VIVADIXIESUBMARINE TRANSMISSIONPLOT
Homecoming queen / Weird sisters / 850 double pumper holley / Rainmaker / Spirit ditch / Tears on fresh fruit / Saturday / Cow / Little bastard choo choo / Hammering the cramps / Most beautiful widow in town / Heart of darkness / Ballad of a cold lost marble / Someday I will treat you good / Sad and beautiful world / Gasoline horseys
CDEST 2280 / May '96 / Capitol

Sparkler

☐ WICKER PARK
Hey long hair / I'll keep you warm / Discover / What are you waiting for / For you / Don't despair / Hey 17 / Motorcycle / You know who you are / Magic Lantern / Another star / Grand arrival
74321441152 / May '97 / Revolution

Sparkman, Steve

☐ SMITH RIDGE (A Tribute To The Stanley Style)
COP 142CD / Apr '96 / Copper Creek

Sparkmarker

☐ 500 WATT BURNER
CRISIS 012 / Mar '97 / Crisis

Sparks

☐ BIG BEAT
Big boy / I want to be like everybody else / Nothing to do / I bought Mississippi river / Fill-er up / Everybody's stupid / Thrown her away (and get a new one) / Confusion / Screwed up / White woman / I like girls / Tearing the place apart / Gone with the wind
IMCD 201 / Jul '94 / Island

☐ GRATUITOUS SAX AND SENSELESS VIOLINS
Gratuitous sax / When do I get to sing 'My Way' / (When I kiss you) I hear Charlie Parker playing / Frankly Scarlett I don't give a damn / I thought I told you to wait in the car / Hear no evil, see no evil, speak no evil / Now that I own the BBC / Tsui Hark / Ghost of Liberace / Let's go surfing / Senseless violins
74321232672 / Jun '97 / Arista

☐ HALF NELSON
8122713002 / Jul '93 / Atlantic

☐ IN THE SWING
This town ain't big enough for the both of us / Hasta manana Monsieur / Amateur hour / Lost and found / Never turn your back on mother earth / I like girls / I want to hold your hand / Get in the swing / Looks, looks, looks / England / Big boy / Something for the girl with everything / Marry me / Gone with the wind
5500652 / May '93 / Spectrum

☐ INDISCREET
Hospitality on parade / Happy hunting ground / Without using hands / Get in the swing / Under the table with her / How are you getting home / Pineapple / Tits / This ain't 1918 / Lady is lingering / In the future / Looks, looks, looks / Miss the start, miss the end / Profile / I want to hold your hand / England
IMCD 200 / Jul '94 / Island

☐ KIMONO MY HOUSE
This town ain't big enough for the both of us / Amateur hour / Falling in love with myself again / Here in heaven / Thank God it's not Christmas / Hasta manana Monsieur / Talent is an asset / Complaints / In my family / Equator / Barbecutie / Lost and found
IMCD 198 / Jul '94 / Island

☐ MAEL INTUITION (It's a Mael Mael Mael World/The Best Of The Sparks 1974-76)
This town ain't big enough for the both of us / Hasta manana monsieur / Tearing the place apart / At home, at work, at play / Never turn your back on Mother Earth / Get in the swing / Amateur hour / Looks, looks, looks / Thanks but no thanks / Gone with the wind / Something for the girl with everything / Thank God it's not Christmas
IMCD 88 / Feb '90 / Island

☐ PLAGIARISM
RR 87912 / 27 Oct '97 / Roadrunner

☐ PROPAGANDA
Propaganda / At home, at work, at play / Reinforcements / BC / Thanks but no thanks / Don't leave me alone with her / Never turn your back on Mother Earth / Something for the girl with everything / Achoo / Who don't like kids / Bon voyage / Alabamy right / Marry me
IMCD 199 / Jul '94 / Island

☐ SO IMPORTANT
So important / Walk down memory lane / Madonna / Love-o-rama / Toughest girl in town / You got a hold of my heart / Let's make love / Just got back from heaven / Lot's of reasons / Stop me if you've heard this one before
12571 / Oct '95 / Laserlight

☐ SPARKS
REP 4052 / Aug '91 / Repertoire

☐ WOOFER IN TWEETERS CLOTHING, A
REP 4051 / Aug '91 / Repertoire

Sparks Brothers

☐ SPARKS BROTHERS 1932-1935
DOCD 5315 / Dec '94 / Document

Sparks, J.J.

☐ ONE IN A MILLION
JJCD 001 / Mar '98 / Altara

Sparks, Melvin

☐ LEGENDS OF ACID JAZZ, THE
Thank you (Falettin' me be mice elf again) / I didn't know what time it was / Charlie Brown / Stinker / Spill the wine / Who's gonna take the weight / Spark plug / Conjunction Mars / Alone together / Dig dis
PRCD 24171 / Oct '96 / Prestige

☐ SPARKS/AKILAH
Thank you / I didn't know what time it was / Charlie Brown / Stinker / Spill the wine / Love the life you live / On the up / All wrapped up / Akilah / Blues for JB / Image of love
CDBGPD 064 / Jan '93 / Beat Goes Public

☐ TEXAS TWISTER
Whip whop / Gathering together / Judy's groove / Texas twister / Ain't no woman (Like the one I got) / I want to talk about you / Star in the crescent / I've got to have you / Mocking bird / Looking for a love / Get ya some / Get down with the get down / Bump and stomp / In the morning / If you want my love
CDBGPD 092 / Aug '95 / Beat Goes Public

Sparks, Tim

☐ NUTCRACKER SUITE
BEST 1028CD / Nov '93 / Acoustic Music

Sparrow

☐ CARNIVAL JAMBACK SOCA BALLADS
BLS 1019CD / Aug '95 / BLS

☐ SOCA LOVER
BLSCD 1020 / Apr '97 / BLS

Sparrow

☐ HATCHING OUT...PLUS
I'm coming back / Well I can tell you / Don't ask me / Nightmare / Many things are clear / Rollercoaster / Dream song / Rainsung song / Break my heart again / Round and round / Hiawatha / Hello goodbye
SEECD 434 / Jan '97 / See For Miles

Sparrow Dragon

☐ AGAIN
Dragon dance / Let me try again / Sad sweet dreamer / Obeah wedding / And I love her so / Hustle / My way / No kind of man at all / If / Again
RNCD 2011 / Jun '93 / Rhino

Sparrow, Johnny

☐ DANCIN' TIME VOL.3
SAV 240CD / Dec '95 / Savoy

Spasm

☐ SPASM
INV 048CD / Jan '96 / Invisible

Spaulding, James

☐ BRILLIANT CORNERS
MCD 5369 / Sep '92 / Muse

☐ GOTSTABE A BETTER WAY
MCD 5413 / Sep '92 / Muse

☐ SMILE OF THE SNAKE, THE
Third avenue / Serenity / Smile of the snake / Lenora / Tonight only / Premonition / Yes it is / Panchito / Love is not a dream / Havana days
HCD 7006 / Jan '98 / Highnote

Spazz

☐ BIBLE STUDIES (Spazz/Subversion)
DEP 004CD / 24 Nov '97 / Deported

☐ SWEATIN' TO THE OLDIES
SAH 36 / Jun '97 / Slap A Ham

Spdfgh

☐ LEAVE ME LIKE THIS
DRT 030 / Nov '96 / Dirt

Speak

☐ KNEE DEEP IN GUILT
REV 064CD / 16 Feb '98 / Revelation

Speake, Martin

☐ AMAZING GRACE
Iris / Quasimodo / I'll follow my secret heart / It's you / Subconscious Lee / Amazing grace / How about you / How my heart sings / Little girl I'll miss you / Topsy / Toxicology
SPJCD 558 / Jun '97 / Spotlite

☐ TRUST
Golden rooster / Heron / Magic show / In our time / Accidental flamboyant / Notebook / We three / Fever pitch / Bouncy / Lullaby
33JAZZ 035 / Feb '98 / 33 Jazz

Speaker Bite Me

☐ INNER SPEED
FLOWCD 007 / 20 Oct '97 / Flower Shop

Spear Of Destiny

☐ BBC LIVE IN CONCERT
Land of shame / Strangers in our town / Pumpkin man / Embassy song / Never take me alive / Outlands / Was that you / Miami Vice / Rocket ship / Once in her lifetime / All you young men / Mickey / Liberator
WINDCD 055 / Mar '94 / Windsong

☐ LIVE AT THE LYCEUM 22.12.85
Rainmaker / Rocket ship / Attica / Come back / Up all night / Mickey / Young men / World service / Playground of the rich / Grapes of wrath / I can see / Liberator / Prisoner of love / Incinerator / These days are gone / Do you believe in the westworld
MAUCD 638 / Jun '93 / Mau Mau

☐ PSALM 1 (Elephant Daze/Live At The Forum - 2CD Set)
Pray for me / Land of shame / Europa / Betrayed / Elephant daze / Shape of things to come / Spirit tribe / At her majesty's request / Children of the damned / Revolver / Dream time / Price you pay / Embassy song / Tinsel town / View from a tree / So in love with you / Strangers in our town / Soldier soldier / Rocket ship / Pumpkin man / Young men / Radio radio / Liberator
SOD 002DCD / 9 Mar '98 / Eastworld

☐ PSALM 2 (Outlands - The Demos/Live At The National - 2CD Set)
Strangers in our town / Whole worlds waiting / Was that you / Jack Straw / Land of shame / Miami vice / Never take me alive / Traveller / Land of shame / Embassy song / Strangers in our town / Pumpkin man / Embassy song / Never take me alive / Outlands / Was that you / Miami vice / Rocket ship / Once in her lifetime / All you young men / Mickey / Liberator
SOD 003DCD / 30 Mar '98 / Eastworld

☐ PSALM 3 (Manor Mobile In Session/ Barrowlands Live 1985 - 2CD Set)
SOD 004DCD / 22 Jun '98 / Eastworld

☐ RELIGION
SOD 001CD / 3 Nov '97 / Eastworld

☐ SOD'S LAW
Goldmine / Into the rising sun / Black country girl / Bull comes down / Slow me down / Taking care of business / In the city / Babylon talking / Crystalize / Killing ground / Captain America / Chemical head / Paradise / Burn out
SMMCD 512 / 29 Sep '97 / Snapper

☐ TIME OF OUR LIVES (The Best Of Spear Of Destiny)
Never take me alive / Outlands / Traveller / Strangers in our town / Miami Vice / Time of our lives / Man that never was / So in love with you / March or die / I remember / Radio radio / Life goes on / If the guns / Was that you
CDOVD 449 / Feb '95 / Virgin

Spearhead

☐ CHOCOLATE SUPA HIGHWAY
Africa on line / Chocolate supa highway / Keep me lifted / Food for tha masses / U can't sing R song / Payroll (stay strong) / Madness in tha hood (Free ride) / Rebel music (3 O'clock roadblock) / Why oh why / Comin' to gitcha / Life sentence / Ganja babe
CDEST 2293 / Mar '97 / Capitol

☐ HOME
People in the middle / Love is da shit / Piece o' peace / Positive / Of course you can / Hole in the bucket / Home / Dream team / Runfayalifel crime to be broke in America / 100,000 miles / Red beans and rice / Caught without an umbrella
CDEST 2236 / Sep '94 / Capitol

Spearman's Double Trio

☐ SMOKEHOUSE
1201572 / Oct '94 / Black Saint

Spears, Billie Jo

☐ BEST OF BILLIE JO SPEARS, THE (New Recordings Of Her Greatest Hits...And More)
'57 Chevrolet / I will survive / Misty blue / Blanket on the ground / I don't want to talk about it / I'm not easy / Couldn't love have picked a better place to die / I'm gonna love lovin' you / What I've got in mind / Wisdom of a fool / Come back when you can stay forever / Blue Orleans / Something for your memory to do / I've never loved anyone more / Sing me an old fashioned song
ECD 3400 / 14 Apr '98 / K-Tel

☐ BLANKET ON THE GROUND
Blanket on the ground / I'm so lonesome I could cry / You never can tell / Sweet dreams / Look what they've done to my song / If it ain't love / You're my man / Ease the want in me / Dallas / It makes no difference now / Sunshine / He's on the run again / Fever / One more chance / Cheatin' kind / I'll take a melody / My own kind / I'll never be free / Danny / I fall to pieces
CD 6121 / Apr '98 / Music

☐ COUNTRY CLASSICS
Blanket on the ground / What I've got in mind / Today I started loving you again / Don't ever let go of me / All I want is you / I've never loved anyone more / Say it again / I fall to pieces / True love / Love ain't the question / Every time I sing a love song / I've got to go / Since I fell for you / Come on home / What a love I have in you / There's more to a tear than meets the eye / What the world needs now is love / Love ain't gonna wait for us / I love you because / Put a little love in your heart
CDMFP 6320 / Apr '97 / Music For Pleasure

☐ GREATEST HITS
WMCD 5680 / Nov '93 / Disky

☐ LOVE SONGS
Blanket on the ground / What I've got in mind / Today I started loving you again / Don't ever let go of me / All I want is you / I've never loved anyone before / Say it again / I fall to pieces / True love / Love ain't the question (love ain't the answer) / Every time I sing a love song / I've got to go / Since I fell for you / Come on home / What a love I have in you / There's more to a tear than meets the eye / What the world needs now is love / Love ain't gonna wait for us / I love you because / Put a little love in your heart
CDMFP 6112 / Mar '94 / Music For Pleasure

☐ MISTY BLUE
Midnight love / Silver wings and golden rings / What I've got in mind / Misty blue / Stay away from the apple tree / Lonely heart club / Mr. walker it's all over / Never did like whiskey / Marty gray / Wishing won't make it so
15476 / Nov '92 / Laserlight

☐ OUTLAW WOMAN
Why must all goods times be memories / It's not easy / Outlaw woman / Come back (when you can stay forever) / Couldn't love have picked a better place to die / I'm gonna love lovin' you / Wisdom of a fool / Blue orleans / I don't want to talk about it / Something for your memory to do
3036300092 / May '96 / Carlton

☐ QUEEN OF COUNTRY MUSIC, THE
Cry / Country roads / Make the world go away / Slow hand / I believe / Love letters in the sand / You light up my life / Heartaches by the number / Always on my mind / Raindrops keep falling on my head / Misty / Paper roses / If you love me (let me know) / Amazing grace
CDMFP 6272 / Sep '96 / Music For Pleasure

☐ SINGS THE COUNTRY GREATS
'57 Chevrolet / Loving him was easier / Hey won't you play another somebody done somebody wrong song / Till something better comes along / Sing me an old fashioned song / Every time I sing a love song / See the funny little clown / That's what friends are for / Blanket on the ground / Ode to Billy Joe / Misty blue / I don't wanna play house / Hurt / Stand by your man / He's got more love in his little finger / Take me to your world
CDMFP 5784 / May '91 / Music For Pleasure

☐ UNMISTAKABLY
Every time I close my eyes / One smokey rose / Mutual aquaintance / I got this train to ride / If wishes were wings / We need to walk / Keep me from dreamin' / Star / We're over / It won't be long
ETCD 194 / Sep '92 / Etude

Special A

☐ SPECIAL A ENCOUNTERS MIXMAN
BLKMCD 008 / Dec '94 / Blakamix

Special Beat

☐ TEARS OF A CLOWN (Live)
RRCD 248 / 23 Mar '98 / Receiver

Special Duties

☐ '77 IN '97
'77 in '97 / Shadow / Judge and jury / No place for reason / Crass war / London town / Punk rocker '97 / Top 40 / Adios amigos / Mutt / Who the hell is buying that crap / It's a saturday / I am the curse / SPG / Violent society / I think of you / Stiff little dub / Doing yourself no good
AHOYCD 075 / 3 Nov '97 / Captain Oi

☐ 77 IN 82
Too much talking / Government policies / Britain in '81 / Colchester council / Rise and fight / Violent youth / First time / Distorted youth / Depression / It ain't our fault / There'll be no tomorrow / Violent society / CND / They don't care about me / Delayed reaction / Rondelet control / Violent society / It ain't our fault / Colchester council / Police state / We gotta fight / It just ain't me / Special duties / bullshit crass / Your doing yourself no good / Violent society / Colchester council
AHOYCD 035 / 6 Jul '98 / Captain Oi

☐ DISTORTED TRUTH
GET 20CD / 11 Nov '97 / Get Back

Special Ed

☐ LEGAL
FILERCD 297 / Sep '90 / Profile

Special EFX

☐ BODY LANGUAGE
Body heat / Seduction / Sunset / Night rhythm / Till we meet again / Spy vs spy / When love cries / Papa jinda / Mikes D / Free
JVC 20512 / Nov '95 / JVC

☐ CATWALK
Nitty gritty / Mercy mercy me / Passions / Dancing cobra / Siana / George can't dance / So happy, so sad / Hip hop bop / Forever this love / Concrete jungle
JVC 20382 / Oct '94 / JVC

☐ HERE TO STAY
Nine lives of the cat / Heavenly delight (Your face) / Here to stay / Since you've been away / Lights out / Unfinished business / Lucky seven / New passage / Who's smiling now / Real deal / Brave new world
JVC 90152 / Apr '97 / JVC

☐ PLAY
New beginnings / Sunsplash / Going home / Rites of passage / Euro cowboy / Nivia / Love your smile / Romantic fool / That's happiness / On the run
JVC 20172 / Nov '97 / JVC

☐ SPECIAL DELIVERY
Safari / Sambuca nights / Much too soon / Forever hold your peace / Foggy streets of London / Slug / Waiting / Katalin
FCD 0004 / Nov '95 / Limetree

Special Project

☐ KID LOOPS VS. COOL BREEZE
FILT 012CD / Nov '96 / Filter

Specials

☐ CONCRETE JUNGLE (2CD Set) (Specials & Friends)
RRDCD 008 / 2 Mar '98 / Receiver

☐ LIVE AT THE MOONLIGHT CLUB
It's up to you / Do the dog / Monkey man / Blank expressions / Nite klub / Concrete jungle / Too hot / Too much too young / Little bitch / Longshot kick de bucket
CCD 5011 / 15 Sep '97 / EMI Gold

☐ SPECIALS SINGLES, THE (The Best Of The Specials)
Gangsters / Message to you Rudy / Nite club / Too much too young / Guns of Navarone / Rat race / Rude boys outa jail / Stereotype / Internation jet set / Do nothing / Ghost town / Why / Friday night / Saturday morning / Racist friend / Free Nelson Mandela / What I like most about you is your girlfriend
CCD 5010 / Aug '91 / Chrysalis

☐ SPECIALS, THE
Message to you Rudy / Do the dog / It's up to you / Nite klub / Doesn't make it alright / Concrete jungle / Too hot / Monkey man / (Dawning of a) New era / Blank expression / Stupid marriage / Too much too young / Little bitch / You're wondering now
CCD 5001 / Nov '92 / Chrysalis

☐ TODAY'S SPECIALS
Take five / Pressure drop / Hypocrite / Goodbye girl / Little bit / Time has come / Somebody got murdered / 007 / Simmer down / Maga dog / Bad boys
KUFFCD 2 / Mar '96 / Kuff

☐ TOO MUCH TOO YOUNG
Too much too young / Enjoy yourself (it's later than you think) / Man at C and A / Rude boys outa jail / I can't stand it / Do the dog / Blank expression / (Dawning of a) New era / Monkey man / Hey little rich girl / Pearl's cafe / Little bitch / Rat race / Message to you Rudy / Do nothing / You're wondering now
CDGOLD 1022 / May '96 / EMI Gold

Specimen

☐ AZOIC
FREUDCD 054 / Jun '97 / Jungle

Speckled Red

☐ DIRTY DOZENS, THE
Dirty dozens / Right string but the wrong yo yo / If you've ever been down / Wilkins street stomp / Cow cow blues / Just blues / Red's boogie woogie / Going down slow / Highway 61 blues / After dinner blues / Cryin' in my sleep / Early in the morning / Love is like a faucet / Speckled Red speaks / Delmar blues / Feel so good / Dirtier dozens / Dirtiest dozens
DE 601 / Nov '96 / Delmark

☐ SPECKLED RED 1929-1938
DOCD 5205 / Oct '93 / Document

Speckmann

☐ SPECKMANN
NB 056CD / Feb '92 / Nuclear Blast

Specter, Dave

☐ BLUEPLICITY (Specter, Dave & The Bluebirds)
DD 664 / May '94 / Delmark

☐ BLUES SPOKEN HERE (Specter, Dave & Lynn Lenny)
Blues spoken here / Why my baby (keeps on botherin' me) / Senor blues / Boss funk / I stepped in quicksand / Just a dream / City boy blues / Kiddio / Blues on my mind / Listen here / Moanin' / Roll 'em Pete
DE 721 / Jul '98 / Delmark

☐ LEFT TURN ON BLUE
Get back home / Stop hold it / Killer Jack / Till the end of time / Party girl / Juice head baby / Left turn on blue / Unleavened soul / Hopeless / What's the matter / Tremble / Roll baby roll / When will the blues leave
DE 693 / Feb '97 / Delmark

☐ LIVE IN EUROPE (Specter, Dave & The Bluebirds)
CCD 11047 / Nov '95 / Crosscut

Spector, Phil

☐ BABY I LOVE YOU (The Delta Wall Of Sound Pays Tribute To Phil Spector) (Delta Wall Of Sound)
Da doo ron ron / Be my baby / River deep mountain high / Then he kissed me / Unchained melody / Baby I love you / Fine fine boy / Under the moon of love / Little boy / He's a rebel / You've lost that loving feeling / I wonder / Chapel of love / Pretty little angel eyes / Save the last dance for me / To know him is to love him / Why do lovers break eachothers hearts / Spanish Harlem / Best part of breakin' up / Girls can tell
CD 6127 / Jul '98 / Music

☐ CHRISTMAS GIFT FOR YOU FROM PHIL SPECTOR, A (Various Artists)
White Christmas: *Love, Darlene* / Frosty the snowman: *Ronettes* / Bells of St. Mary's: *Soxx, Bob B. & The Blue Jeans* / Santa Claus is coming to town: *Crystals* / Sleigh ride: *Ronettes* / Marshmallow world: *Love, Darlene* / I saw Mommy kissing Santa Claus: *Ronettes* / Rudolph the red nosed reindeer: *Crystals* / Winter wonderland: *Love, Darlene* / Parade of the wooden soldiers: *Crystals* / Christmas (baby please come home): *Love, Darlene* / Here comes Santa Claus: *Soxx, Bob B. & The Blue Jeans* / Silent night: *Spector, Phil & Artists*
PSCD 1005 / Dec '95 / EMI

Spector, Ronnie

☐ DANGEROUS
RVCD 48 / Dec '95 / Raven

Spectre

☐ ILLNESS, THE
WSCD 006 / Feb '96 / Word Sound Recordings

☐ MISSING TWO WEEKS, THE
Covert dub / Spectre overseas / Missing two weeks / Throw down spears / Spectre in the dance / Mad Frank lends a hand / Blow / Vibration version / Tribute to scratch / Errors / Prez / End games
74321296552 / Feb '96 / Natural Response

☐ SECOND COMING, THE
EFA 012242 / 9 Feb '98 / Word Sound Recordings

Spectrum

☐ FEELS LIKE I'M SLIPPING AWAY
ORBIT 010CD / 27 Apr '98 / Space Age

☐ FOREVER ALIEN
ORBIT 008CD / 27 Apr '98 / Space Age

Spectrum

☐ GHOSTS
RVCD 18 / 8 Jun '98 / Raven

Specula

☐ ERUPT
Desolation nightmare / She walks in sunshine / Hello pain / Forever loving you / Can't we all / Stand by / Rock stepper / Inertia / Steal your love / Dual
SCT 0422 / Aug '95 / Scat

Spedding, Chris

☐ CAFE DAYS
422340 / Nov '94 / New Rose

☐ ENEMY WITHIN
OPM 2103CD / Mar '97 / Other People's Music

☐ GUITAR GRAFITTI
Video life / Radio times / Time warp / Midnight boys / Bored, bored / Walkin' / Breakout / Frontal lobotomy / Hey Miss Betty / More lobotomy
422342FC054 / Nov '94 / Fan Club

☐ GUITAR JAMBOREE
422343FC / Nov '94 / Fan Club

☐ I'M NOT LIKE EVERYBODY ELSE
I'm not like everybody else / Box number / I got a feeling / Crying game / Depravity / Musical press / Contract / Counterfeit / Shot of rhythm and blues / Mama coco
422345FC055 / Nov '94 / Fan Club

☐ JUST PLUG HIM IN
422346FC081 / Nov '94 / Fan Club

☐ MEAN AND MOODY
For what we are about to hear / Backwood progression / Only lick I know / Listen while I sing my song / Saw you yesterday / Hill / Don't leave me / White lady / She's my friend / London town / Dark end of the street / Please Mrs. Henery / Never carry mor than you can eat / Words don't come / Backwood theme
SEECD 372 / Jan '97 / See For Miles

Speed

☐ ONE
BSM 1015 / 6 Apr '98 / Bluestone
SPV 08511152 / 29 Jun '98 / SPV

Speed, Charlie

☐ HEARTLAND
Echoes / Sugar free (ready to rock) / Please don't go / Fooling me / Ten years old / Sleep and me / Looking for my baby / Blue / Heartful of soul / To be a man / Sun go down
SUGCD 00001 / Feb '98 / Sugar Free

☐ SILVER STRINGS
Silver strings / Walk away / Should I wait / In the city / Winds of change / Blue / Cry freedom / Rock 'n' roll blues / Throwing stones / Working fields / It's understood
SUGCD 00002 / Feb '98 / Sugar Free

Speed Queens

☐ SPEED QUEENS
SFTRI 454CD / Feb '97 / Sympathy For The Record Industry

Speed The Plough

☐ MARINA
Just a little / Written each day / Said and done / Once in a while / Late birds / Saint restored / High wire / Love song / Bayswater lane / Hard friend to keep / Hourglass / In the atmosphere / Marina
ESD 81102 / Jul '96 / East Side Digital

Speedball Baby

☐ CINEMA
K 182CD / 30 Mar '98 / Konkurrent

☐ I'M GONNA STOMP MR. HARRY LEE
SFTRI 531CD / 20 Apr '98 / Sympathy For The Record Industry

Speedfreak

☐ DESTRUCTION BY SPEED
EFA 007502 / Sep '94 / Shockwave

☐ FOR YOU
EFA 008762 / Feb '96 / Shockwave

Speedy J

☐ G SPOT
WARPCD 27 / Mar '95 / Warp

☐ G SPOT & LIVE (2CD Set)
378462 / Nov '96 / Frantic

☐ GINGER
WARPCD 14 / Jun '93 / Warp

☐ PUBLIC ENERGY NO.1
Tuning in / Patterns / Melanor / In-formation / Pure energy / Haywire / Hayfever / Telsa / Drainpipe / Canola / As the bubble expands
NOMU 54CD / Apr '97 / Nova Mute

Speegle, David

☐ DIM LIGHTS AND CANDLES
CDSGP 017 / Jan '93 / Prestige

Spektakel

☐ SPEKTAKEL
LE 1026 / 15 Jun '98 / Laser's Edge

Spell

☐ SEASONS IN THE SUN
CDSTUMM 126 / Oct '93 / Mute

Spellbound

☐ SPACE ROCKIN'
PT 603002 / Jun '96 / Part

Spelling Misteaks

☐ WE STILL HATE
IFPIL 282 / 23 Mar '98 / Windsorcastle

Spelmansforbund, Blekinge

☐ SONGS AND DANCES FROM SWEDEN
EUCD 1108 / '91 / ARC

Spence, Bill

☐ HAMMERED DULCIMER RETURNS, THE
FHR 041CD / Nov '95 / Front Hall

☐ HAMMERED DULCIMER, THE
FHR 302CD / Nov '95 / Front Hall

Spence, Joseph

☐ BAHAMIAN GUITARIST
ARHCD 349 / Apr '95 / Arhoolie

☐ OUT ON THE ROLLING SEA (A Tribute To Joseph Spence) (Various Artists)
HPR 2004CD / Jul '94 / Hokey Pokey

Spencer, Elvin

☐ PICKING UP THE PIECES
GWX 42222 / Aug '96 / Ichiban

Spencer, Joel

☐ BRIGHTER SIDE, THE (Spencer, Joel & Kelly Sill)
Fear of flying / Rosebud / Greater fool / Additional dialogue / Naomi / Brighter side / Ironic line / Charlie's tonic
TJA 10026 / Feb '96 / Jazz Alliance

Spencer, John B.

☐ BACK PAGES VOL.1 (The Lout's LP)
RTMCD 34 / Nov '90 / Round Tower

☐ BACK PAGES VOL.2 (Blue Smarties)
RTMCD 35 / Nov '93 / Round Tower

☐ BACK PAGES VOL.3 (Out With A Bang)
RTMCD 36 / Jan '94 / Round Tower

☐ BACK PAGES VOL.4 (Judas & The Obscure)
RTMCD 37 / Nov '93 / Round Tower

☐ LEFT HAND OF LOVE, THE
RTMCD 82 / May '97 / Round Tower

☐ PARLOUR GAMES
Parlour games / Billy / Slow beers / Sweet Lucinda / Poor little rich boy / Drive-in movies / Behold the king is dead / Dead man's shoes / Alone together / Left hand of love / Count ten / London I knew / Going down South / Quiet nights
RTMCD 23 / Feb '91 / Round Tower

☐ SUNDAY BEST
RTMCD 39 / May '92 / Round Tower

Spencer, Jon

☐ CRYPT STYLE (Spencer, Jon Blues Explosion)
EFA 115022 / Jan '94 / Crypt

☐ EXTRA WIDTH (Spencer, Jon Blues Explosion)
Afro / History of lies / Back slider / Soul letter / Soul typecast / Pant leg / Hey mom / Big road / Train / Inside the world of the Blues Explosion / World of sex
OLE 0522 / Aug '93 / Matador

☐ JON SPENCER BLUES EXPLOSION (Spencer, Jon Blues Explosion)
Write a song / IEV / Exploder / Rachel / Chicken walk / White tail / 78 Style / Changed / What to do / Waterman / Biological / Intro A / Vacuum of loneliness / Feeling of love / Shoot it / Support a man / Comeback / History of sex / Eliza Jane / Eye to eye
CAROLCD 1719 / Jun '97 / Caroline

☐ JON SPENCER BLUES EXPLOSION, THE
HUTCD 003 / Apr '92 / Hut

☐ MO' WIDTH (Spencer, Jon Blues Explosion)
ANDA 166CD / Feb '97 / Au-Go-Go

☐ NOW I GOT WORRY (Spencer, Jon Blues Explosion)
Skunk / Identity / Wail / Fuck shit up / 2 kindsa love / Love all of me / Chicken dog / Rocketship / Dynamite lover / Hot shot / Can't stop / Firefly child / Eyeballin' / RL got soul / Get over here / Sticky
CDSTUMM 132 / May '97 / Mute

☐ ORANGE (Spencer, Jon Blues Explosion)
Bell bottoms / Ditch / Dang / Very rare / Sweat / Cowboy / Orange / Brenda / Dissect / Blues X man / Full grown / Flavor / Greyhound
OLE 1052 / Sep '94 / Matador

Spencer, Leon

☐ LEGENDS OF ACID JAZZ, THE
Slide / Someday my Prince will come / Message from The Meters / First gravy / 5-10-15-20 / Sneak preview / Louisiana Slim / Mercy mercy me / (They long to be) close to you / Our love will never die / Trouble with love
PRCD 24185 / 29 Jun '98 / Prestige

Spencer, Sarah

☐ LAISSEZ LES BONS TEMPS ROULER (Spencer, Sarah Rue Conti Jazz Band)
Mardi Gras in New Orleans / My life will be sweeter / Somebody else is taking my place / In the garden / Whoopin' blues / Mama Inez / What a friend we have in Jesus / Junco partner / Bogalousa strut / Lead me saviour / Sweet fields
LACD 22 / Jan '93 / Lake

Spendel, Christoph

☐ CITY KIDS
If you were here / City kids / Just like a smile / Phat city / French girls / Modern jazz / Wild and wonderful / Night magic / Blue light / Ocean avenue / Moon over Florida / Eastside song
TCB 01052 / Jun '96 / TCB

☐ READY FOR TAKE OFF
Salsito / Carly / Ready for take off / Monday in July / Rain / Queen's plaza / Downtown / Tapsi strikes again
CDLR 45010 / Dec '88 / L&R

☐ SPENDEL
White cars / New York PM / Mr. Cameo / Midnight / Columbus circle / Byton funk / Banana republic / Eilat / Otto's magic bus / Hugo update / Suite 11F / Piano graffity / Manhattan candlelight
CDLR 45014 / Jan '90 / L&R

Spermbirds

☐ EATING GLASS
XM032CD / Apr '92 / X-Mist

☐ RICH MAN'S HIGH
IRS 5977055 / Feb '94 / Community

☐ THANKS
DEP 02CD / Jun '93 / Dead Eye

Spero, Patricia

☐ MEDIEVAL HARP
CD 433 / 6 Jul '98 / New World

Sperrmull

☐ SPERRMULL
SB 055 / 13 Jul '98 / Second Battle

Sphere

☐ PUMPKIN'S DELIGHT
1232072 / Apr '93 / Red

Spice & Co

☐ CAMOUFLAGE
CRSCD 007 / Apr '96 / CRS

☐ FIRST DECADE, THE
CRSCD 011 / Apr '96 / CRS

☐ IN DE CONGALINE
CRSCD 009 / Apr '96 / CRS

☐ TOUR OF DUTY HITS VOL.1
CCD 0043 / 1 Dec '97 / CRS

☐ TOUR OF DUTY HITS VOL.2
CCD 0044 / 1 Dec '97 / CRS

☐ WORLD DANCE, THE
CRSCD 003 / Apr '96 / CRS

Spice

☐ VARIO BEL AIR
SPV 08511182CD / Nov '96 / SPV

Spice Girls

☐ BIOGRAPHY SERIES
10027 / 3 Nov '97 / Metro Independent

☐ INTERVIEW
61585836112 / 19 May '98 / Baktabak

☐ SING-A-LONG WITH SPICE GIRLS (Various Artists)
Wannabe / Say you'll be there / 2 become 1 / Love thing / Last time lover / Mama / Who do you think you are / Something kinda funny / Naked / If u can't dance
35161 / Apr '98 / Karaoke

☐ SINGALONGA SPICE
SUMCD 4150 / 27 Oct '97 / Summit

☐ SPICE
Wannabe / Say you'll be there / 2 become 1 / Love thing / Last time lover / Mama / Who do you think you are / Something kinda funny / Naked / If U can't dance
CDV 2812 / Oct '96 / Virgin

☐ SPICE GIRLS KARAOKE (Various Artists)
AVCS 614 / 15 Dec '97 / Avid

☐ SPICEWORLD
Spice up your life / Stop / Too much / Saturday night divas / Never give up on the good times / Move over / Do it / Denying / Viva forever / Lady is a vamp
CDV 2850 / 3 Nov '97 / Virgin

Spider

☐ SPIDER/BETWEEN THE LINES
RMED 0183CD / 15 Dec '97 / Renaissance

Spider Babies

☐ ADVENTURES IN SEX AND VIOLENCE
GI 0132 / Mar '97 / GI Productions

Spiderfoot

☐ SPIDERFOOT
SPID 1 / May '97 / Immigrant

Spiders

☐ COMPLETE IMPERIAL RECORDINGS, THE (2CD Set)
I didn't want to do it / You're the one for a thrill / Mellow Mama / Lost and bewildered / Tears begin to flow / Why do I love you / Love's all I'm puttin' down / I'll stop crying / Mmm mmm baby (hey baby) / Walking around in circles / I'm searchin' / Real thing / She keeps me wondering / Three times seven equals twenty one / That's enough / Sukey Sukey Sukey / Bells in my heart / Am I the one / Don't knock / True (you don't love me) / Witchcraft / You played the part / Is it true / How I feel / That's the way to win my heart / Goodbye / I'll be free / Don't pity me / Dear Mary / A1 in my heart / Without love / Someday bye and bye / That's my desire / Better be on my way / Honey bee / I'm glad for your sake / Poor boy / Bells are ringing / I miss you times / You're the one / Tennessee Slim
BCD 15673 / Jun '92 / Bear Family

Spiders

☐ BACK
PECD 471 / Jun '97 / Cirula Elect

Spier, Bernd

☐ OHNE EIN BESTIMMTES ZIEL
Memphis Tennessee / Ohn ein bestimmtes Ziel / Hey Mr. Postman / Heut' bei mir-Und dann / Ein dufte party / Das kannst dur mir nicht verlieren / Was ich an dir am meis ten liebe / Das war mein schonster Tanz / Sag nicht goodbye / Chone Madchen muss man lieben / Keiner weiss, dass wir uns lieben / Ich bin nicht schuld daran / Du bist schoner als die ander'n / Einmal geht der Vorhang zu / Du bizt fur mich geboren / Der neue tag beginnt / Wenn erst der abend kommt / Danke schon / Julia / Mir geht es wunderbar: Spier, Bernd & Uwe / Komm zu mir: Spier, Bernd & Uwe / Two strangers / I only came to dance with you / Million and one times / Rose Marie / Pretty Belinda / Klopf dreimal / Lass dein little girl nie weinen
BCD 15591 / Mar '92 / Bear Family

Spike & Tyla's Hotknive

☐ FLAGRANTLY YOURS
CDBLEED 18 / Jul '96 / Bleeding Hearts

Spiky Joys

☐ JUST ANOTHER PUNK (Spiky Joys/ Attached)
KOCD 065 / 15 Dec '97 / Knock Out

Spillane, Davy

☐ ATLANTIC BRIDGE
Atlantic Bridge / Davie's reels / Daire's dream / Tribute to Johnny Doran / O'Neill's statement / Sliverish / By the river of gems / Pigeon on the gate / In my life / Lansdowne blues
COOKCD 009 / Aug '88 / Cooking Vinyl

☐ OUT OF THE AIR
Atlantic bridge / Daire's dream / Mystic seacliffs / Litton Lane / River of gems / Storm / Road to Ballyalla / One for Phil
COOKCD 016 / Jun '97 / Cooking Vinyl

☐ PEACE WITHIN, THE (Spillane, Davy & The BMC Band)
Burrenstone sunrise / One of these days / Pick a bale o'cotton / Interlude / Emigrant / Peace within / (Gotta) let it go / Kissin' in your sleep / You don't love me / Istanbul blues / Oh well / Adam and Eve / Nobody's hero
RRCD 21983 / 5 May '98 / Right Recordings

☐ PIPEDREAMS
Shifting sands / Undertow / Shorelines / Call across the canyon / Midnight walker / Mistral / Rainmaker / Stepping in silence / Morning wings / Corcomroe
TARACD 3026 / Oct '94 / Tara

☐ PIPER'S ROCK, THE (Spillane, Davy & Robert Hannan)
LUNCD 023 / Dec '97 / Mulligan

☐ PLACE AMONG THE STONES, A
Darklight / Promised rain / Place among the stones / Western whisper / Starry night / Elgeebar / Callow Lake / Forever frozen / Always travelling / Near the horizon
4769302 / Oct '95 / Columbia

☐ SHADOW HUNTER, THE
Lucy's tune / Indiana drones / Carron streams / Watching the clock / Walker of the snow / Hidden ground / White crow / Moyasta junction / Journeys of a dreamer / One day in June / Equinox / Host of the air
COOKCD 030 / Apr '90 / Cooking Vinyl

Spillane, John

☐ WELLS OF THE WORLD
HBCD 0011 / 24 Nov '97 / Hummingbird

Spin Doctors

☐ HOMEBELLY GROOVE
What time is it / Off my line / Freeway of the plains / Lady Kerosene / Yo baby / Little Miss can't be wrong / Shinbone Alley / Refrigerator car / Sweet widow / Stepped on a crack / Yo mama's a pajama / Rosetta stone
4728962 / Dec '93 / Epic

☐ POCKET FULL OF KRYPTONITE
Jimmy Olsen's blues / What time is it / Little miss can't be wrong / Forty or fifty / Refrigerator car / More than she knows / Two princes / Off my line / How could you want him (When you know you could have me) / Shinbone Alley / Hard to exist
4682509 / 8 Sep '97 / Epic

Spina

☐ LE MEILLEUR DES MONDES
Calcutta / Lipstick on the gun / Ghost cie / Death match / One / Le gritche / Asphalt / Le sang / Big foot / Neuronal destruction / North
120962 / 11 Aug '97 / Wowoka

Spina Bifida

☐ ZIYADHA
CDAR 010 / Feb '94 / Adipocre

Spinal Tap

☐ THIS IS SPINAL TAP
Hell hole / Tonight I'm gonna rock you / Heavy duty / Rock 'n' roll creation / America / Cups and cakes / Big bottom / Sex farm / Stonehenge / Gimme some money / Flower people
8178462 / Aug '90 / Polydor

Spinanes

☐ ARCHES AND AISLES
SPCD 417 / 3 Aug '98 / Sub Pop

☐ MANOS
SPCD 114292 / Nov '93 / Sub Pop

☐ NOEL, JONAH AND ME
SPCD 328 / May '94 / Sub Pop

☐ STRAND
SPCD 345 / Feb '96 / Sub Pop

Spine

☐ TRANSITION
Ride my own spine / NAC / Irreversible / Sickness to insanity / Salt the sores / But now that I'm gone / We are theirs / Leave neveragaining
SST 302CD / Mar '94 / SST

Spinners

☐ MAGGIE MAY
PLSCD 174 / Apr '97 / Pulse

☐ ONE AND ONLY, THE
Lord of the dance / All day singing / Blaydon races / Last thing on my mind / Amazing grace / We shall not be moved / Guantanamera / Jamaica farewell / To be a farmer's boy / Foggy dew / Greensleeves / Lovely Joan / North country maid / Liverpool hornpipes / Collier's rant / Dane the flora / Banks of the Ohio / Shepherd lad / Waters o' Tyne / Lamorna / Bucket of the mountain dew / When I first came to this land / So long (it's been good to know yuh)
CC 8239 / Nov '94 / EMI

Spiny Anteaters

☐ ALL IS WELL
KRANK 004CD / Mar '97 / Kranky

☐ CURRENT
KRANK 011 / Mar '97 / Kranky

☐ LAST SUPPER
BING 014 / 23 Mar '98 / Ba Da Bing

Spiral Jetty

☐ BAND OF GOLD
Don't walk away / Tourists send postcards / Breathe / Queen bitch / Tongue-black pie / Drunken lies / Coat of hair / La / Cherry's lament / Social age
OUT 1102 / Sep '97 / Brake Out

Spiral Realms

☐ CRYSTAL JUNGLES OF EOS
CLEO 96102 / 1 May '98 / Cleopatra

☐ SOLAR WIND
CLEO 9764 / 13 Jul '98 / Cleopatra

☐ TRIP TO G9
CLEO 95002 / 1 May '98 / Cleopatra

Spiral Tribe

☐ SOUND OF TEKNIVAL, THE (Various Artists)
3014772 / Nov '96 / Techno Import

Spirea X

☐ FIREBLADE SKIES
Smile / Nothing happened yesterday / Rollercoaster / Chlorine dream / Fire and light / Spirea 9 / Speed reaction / Confusion in my soul / Signed d.c. / Sisters and brothers / Sunset dawn
GAD 1017CD / 6 Jul '98 / 4AD

Spires Of Oxford

☐ SPIRES OF OXFORD
LOUD 013CD / Jul '97 / Colourful Clouds

Spirit

☐ CALIFORNIA BLUES
CREW 22004 / Sep '97 / Werc Crew

☐ CLEAR (Remastered)
Dark eyed woman / Apple orchard / So little time to fly / Ground hog / Policeman's ball / Ice / Give a life, take a life / I'm truckin' / Clear / Caught / New dope in town / 1984 / Sweet Stella baby / Fuller brush man / Coral
4844162 / Nov '96 / Columbia

☐ FAMILY THAT PLAYS TOGETHER, THE
I got a line on you / It shall be / Poor Richard / Silky Sam / Drunkard / Darlin' if / All the same / Jewish / Dream within a dream / She smiled / Aren't you glad
4773552 / Aug '94 / Epic

☐ FAMILY THAT PLAYS TOGETHER, THE (Remastered)
I got a line on you / It shall be / Poor Richard / Silky Sam / Drunkard / Darlin' if / It's all the same / Jewish / Dream within a dream / She smiles / Aren't you glad / Fog / So little to say / Mellow fellow / Now or anywhere / Space chile
4851742 / Nov '96 / Columbia

☐ LIVE AT LA PALOMA
CREW 22003 / Jul '97 / Werc Crew

☐ MADE IN GERMANY
RD 172200 / 16 Feb '98 / Roof

☐ MERCURY YEARS, THE (2CD Set)
5346022 / Jun '97 / Mercury

☐ SPIRIT
Fresh garbage / Uncle Jack / Mechanical world / Taurus / Girl in your eyes / Straight arrow / Topanga windows / Gramophone man / Water woman / Great canyon fire in general / Elijah
4809652 / Aug '95 / Epic

☐ SPIRIT (Remastered)
Fresh garbage / Uncle Jack / Mechanical world / Taurus / Girl in your eye / Straight arrow / Topanga windows / Gramophone man / Water woman / Great canyon fire in general / Elijah / Veruska / Free spirit / If I had a woman / Elijah (alternate take)
4851752 / Nov '96 / Columbia

☐ TIME CIRCLE (2CD Set)
Fresh garbage / Uncle Jack / Mechanical world / Taurus / Girl in your eye / Straight arrow / Topanga windows / Gramophone man / Great canyon fire in general / I got a line on you / It shall be / Poor Richard / Silky Sam / Sherozode / All the same / Dream within a dream / Aren't you glad / Eventide / Green gorilla / Rehearsal theme / Fog / Now or anywhere / Dark eyed woman / So little time to fly / Ground hog / Ice / I'm truckin' / New dope in town / 1984 / Sweet Stella baby / Nothin' to hide / Nature's way / Animal zoo / Love has found a way / Why can't I be free / Mr. Skin / When I touch you / Street worm / Morning will come / Turn to the right
4712682 / Jun '96 / Legacy

☐ TWELVE DREAMS OF DR. SARDONICUS
Nothin' to hide / Nature's way / Animal zoo / Love has found a way / Why can't I be free / Mr. Skin / Space child / When I touch you / Street worm / Life has just begun / Morning will come / Soldier / We've got a lot to learn / Potatoland / Open up your heart / Morning light / Potatoland (prelude) / Potatoland (introduction) / Turn to the right / Donut house / Fish fry road / Information / My friend
4766032 / Apr '94 / Epic

☐ TWELVE DREAMS OF DR. SARDONICUS (Remastered)
Prelude - Nothin' to hide / Nature's way / Animal zoo / Love has found a way / Why can't I be free / Mr. Skin / Space child / When I touch you / Street worm / Life has just begun / Morning will come / Soldier / Rougher road / Animal zoo (mono single version) / Morning will come (alternate mono mix) / Red light roll on
4851732 / Nov '96 / Columbia

Spirit Feel

☐ SPIRIT FEEL
TPLP 77CD / Mar '95 / One Little Indian

Spirit Level

☐ KINDRED SPIRITS
URCD 009 / Jul '96 / Ubiquity

NEW YEAR
FMRCD 03 / Jan '89 / Future

ON THE LEVEL
Over the moon / Spiral staircase / Seventh heaven / Tollbridge / Merhaba mustafa / Y ya la quiero / Sometime never / You and I / Looking on the bright side / La dolce vita
33JAZZ 021 / Apr '95 / 33 Jazz

Spirit Of Memphis Quartet
TRAVELLING ON
HMG 6507 / Feb '98 / Hightone

Spirit Of Science
SPIRIT OF SCIENCE (2CD Set)
Untitled tracks / Sunishta
NSKYCD 002 / 20 Apr '98 / Northern Sky

Spirit Of The Day
LABOUR DAY
Darkhouse / Profiteers / Run boy / Expensive/ Cinema of pain / Take it from the source / Political / Hounds that wait outside your door / Drinking man / Gottingen street
SP 1123CD / Oct '93 / Stony Plain

Spirit Of The West
OLD MATERIAL 1984-1986
SP 1141CD / Oct '93 / Stony Plain

WEIGHTS AND MEASURES
0630197162 / 20 Apr '98 / East West

Spirit Of Youth
COLOURS THAT BLEED
ED 026CD / 13 Jul '98 / Good Life

Spirit Traveller
PLAYING HITS FROM MOTOR CITY
Signed, sealed, delivered (I'm yours) / Since I lost my baby / Ain't that peculiar / Ain't nothing like the real thing / You keep me hangin' on / OOO baby baby / Tracks of my tears / Ain't no mountain high enough / I love you / It's growing / You've really got a hold on me
JVC 20292 / Feb '94 / JVC

Spirits Of Rhythm
SPIRITS OF RHYTHM 1932-1934
Underneath the Harlem moon / How deep is the ocean / Nobody's sweetheart / I got rhythm / I've got the world on a string / Rhythm / I'll be ready when the great day comes / My old man / Way down yonder in New Orleans / From Monday on / As long as I live / Junk man / Dr. Watson and Mr. Holmes / That's what I hate about love / Shoutin' in that amen corner / It's a long way to Tipperary / I woke up with a teardrop in my eye / Exactly like you / I'm walking this town / We've got the blues
RTR 79004 / Nov '96 / Retrieval

Spiritual Beggars
ANOTHER WAY TO SHINE
CDMFN 198 / Mar '96 / Music For Nations

MANTRA 111
Homage to the betrayed / Lack of prozac / Cosmic romance / Monster astronauts / Euphoria / Broken morning / Superbossanova / Bad karma / Send me a smile / Inside charmer / Sad queen boogie / Mushroom tea
CDMFM 231 / 9 Feb '98 / Music For Nations

SPIRITUAL BEGGARS
WAR 002CD / Apr '96 / Wrong Again

Spiritualized
LADIES AND GENTLEMEN WE ARE FLOATING IN SPACE (12xCD Single Set)
Ladies and gentlemen we are floating in space / Come together / I think I'm in love / All of my thoughts / Stay with me / Electricity / Home of the brave / Individual / Broken heart / No God only religion / Cool waves / Cop shoot cop
DEDCD 034S / Jul '97 / Dedicated

Spiro
POLE STAR
UNCCD 4 / 19 Jan '98 / Uncle

Spiro & Wix
MOTION
Tara's theme / Cloudscapes / Glory season / Days of honour / Race of champions / Save the robot / Slow motion / Airborne / Summits at zero / LBW / Deceptive bends
PRMCD 8 / Aug '96 / Premier/EMI

Spiro, Mark
NOW IS THEN
WESTCD 5 / Mar '97 / West Coast

Spiro, Michael
BATA KETU (Spiro, Michael & Mark Lamson)
Prelude / Elegua/Exu / Osain/Osanyin / Chango/ Xango / Iroko / Ochosi/Oxossi / Ochun/Oxum
INT 32172 / Jun '97 / Intuition

Spirogyra
BELLS BOOTS AND SHAMBLES
REP 4137 / 1 Jun '98 / Repertoire

OLD BOOT WINE
REP 4173 / Aug '91 / Repertoire

ST. RADIGUNS
Future won't be long / Island / Magical Mary / Captain's log / At home in the world / Cogwheels, crutches and cyanide / Time will tell / We were a happy crew / Love is a funny thing / Duke of Beaufoot
REP 4070 / 1 Jun '98 / Repertoire

Spitfire
FEVERISH
DANCD 097 / Mar '95 / Danceteria

Spitfire Band
SPITFIRE BAND SWINGS FROM STAGE TO SCREEN
ACD 2500 / '88 / Attic

Spitnik Devils
FOR BUTTSUCKERS AND OTHER FUCKERS
PCD 037 / Nov '96 / Progress

Spivak, Charlie
CHARLIE SPIVAK
CCD 017 / Oct '93 / Circle

CHARLIE SPIVAK ORCHESTRA 1940-1941, THE (Spivak, Charlie & His Orchestra)
CCD 16 / May '98 / Circle

UNCOLLECTED 1943-1946, THE (Spivak, Charlie & His Orchestra)
Stardreams / Mean to me / Serenade in blue / I used to love you / Cuddle up a little closer / Blue Lou / Laura / More than you know / Stardust / Accentuate the positive / Solitude / Travellin' light / Blue champagne / Let's go home / It's the same old dream / Saturday night
HCD 105 / Oct '95 / Hindsight

Spivey, Victoria
VICTORIA SPIVEY VOL.1 1926-1927
DOCD 5316 / Mar '95 / Document

VICTORIA SPIVEY VOL.2 1927-1929
DOCD 5317 / Mar '95 / Document

VICTORIA SPIVEY VOL.3 1929-1936
DOCD 5318 / Mar '95 / Document

VICTORIA SPIVEY VOL.4 1936-1937
DOCD 5319 / Mar '95 / Document

WOMAN BLUES (Spivey, Victoria & Lonnie Johnson)
OBCCD 566 / Jul '95 / Original Blues Classics

Spizz
SPIZZ NOT DEAD SHOCK 1978-1988
CDMRED 130 / May '96 / Cherry Red

UNHINGED (Spizz Energi)
DAMGOOD 36 / Mar '94 / Damaged Goods

SPK
DIGITALIS AMBIGUA, GOLD AND POISON
NTCD 035 / Feb '88 / Nettwerk

INFORMATION OVERLOAD UNIT
SPKCD 1 / Sep '92 / Grey Area

LEICHENSCHREI (Sozialistisches Patienten Kollektiv)
Genetik transmission / Post mortem / Desolation / Napalm/Terminal patient / Cry from the sanatorium / Baby blue eyes / Israel / Internal bleeding / Chamber musik / Despair / Agony of the plasma / Day of pigs / Wars of Islam / Maladia Europa
SPKCD 2 / Aug '92 / Grey Area

ZAMI LEHMANNI
SPKCD 3 / Sep '92 / Grey Area

Splack Pack
BIG BOOTY HITS
5429189162 / 5 May '98 / Pandisc

Splash 4
KICKS IN STYLE
ES 1235CD / Feb '97 / Estrus

Splashband
RIDDIM A TON
CCD 0028 / Apr '96 / CRS

Splatcats
RIGHT ON
PRD 70092 / May '90 / Provogue

Splatter
FROM HELL TO ETERNITY
SECT2 10010 / Oct '96 / Sector 2

Spleen
LITTLE SCRATCHES
SF 025 / 15 Jun '98 / Swarf Finger

SOUNDTRACK TO SPLEEN
SF 006CD / Jan '97 / Swarf Finger

Splendora
IN THE GRASS
379122 / Dec '95 / Koch International

Splinter Test
SULPHUR - LOW SEED REPLICATION
Debris ov murder / Sulphur - low seed replication / Burned out but building
NERO 23 / Apr '97 / Twilight Command

Splintered
JUDAS CRADLE
DPROMCD 17 / Dec '93 / Dirter Promotions

RLW
BRCD 961005 / Nov '96 / Black Rose

Split Enz
ANNIVERSARY
D 98010 / Apr '95 / Mushroom

BEST OF SPLIT ENZ, THE
Titus / Late last night / Matinee idyll 129 / Amy (darling) / Lovey dovey / Time for a change / Crossroads / Another great divide / Bold as brass / My mistake / I see red / I got you / One step ahead / History never repeats / Six months in a leaky boat / Message to my girl
CDCHR 6059 / Jan '94 / Chrysalis

GOLD COLLECTION, THE
Late last night / Amnother great divide / My mistake / Stranger than fiction / Walking down the road / Crosswords / History never repeats / MAtinee idyll / Lovey dovey / Time for a change / Charley / Bold as brass / I see red / I got you
8210872 / 6 Oct '97 / EMI Gold

STRANGER THAN FICTION
Late last night / Another great divide / My mistake / Stranger than fiction / Walking down a road / History never repeats / Crosswords / MAtinee idyll / Lovey dovey / Time for a change / Charley / Bold as brass / I see red / I got you
DC 882882 / 2 Feb '98 / Disky

Split Second
VENGEANCE COD
HYCD 210526 / Feb '94 / Hypertension

Split Up
FATES GOT A DRIVER
DOG 031CD / Aug '95 / Doghouse

Splitsville
ULTRASOUND
BD 9037 / Jul '97 / Big Deal

Splodgenessabounds
IN SEARCH OF THE SEVEN GOLDEN GUSSETS (Splodge)
Pooh oo's trumped / In search of the seven / Old 'ya cherries / Tough shit Wilson / My baked bean / Crabs / Over dramatic songs (in very low voices) / Freefall from paradise / Graffiti / Renfrew / Very unfunny comedian / What's thru this doorrrrr / Pathetique / Pilchard freak / Mouth and trousers / We luv you / Give it some bollox / No no yeah / Les Splodge singers / 'Ole in the wall / Slooshshalongamix / Cigarette / Seven golden gussets / Dellar / Lager top / Sandra / My grandma
AHOYCD 089 / 8 Jun '98 / Captain Oi

LIVE
RRCD 237 / 23 Mar '98 / Receiver

Spo-Dee-O-Dee
GOTTA HAVE IT
OTHCD 003 / 1 Dec '97 / On The Hill

Spock's Beard
BEWARE OF DARKNESS
Beware of darkness / Thoughts / Doorway / Chataugua / Walking on the wind / Waste away / Time has come
GEPCD 1018 / Mar '97 / Giant Electric Pea

KINDNESS OF STRANGERS
Good don't last / Radiant is / In the mouth of madness / Cakewalk on easy street / June / Strange world / Harm's way / Flow / True believer / Constant flow of sound / Into the source
GEPCD 1022 / 26 Jan '98 / Giant Electric Pea

LIGHT
GEPCD 1017 / Oct '96 / Giant Electric Pea

Spondo
SPONDO
670012 / 24 Feb '98 / Melodie

Sponge
ROTTING PINATA
Pennywheels / Rotting pinata / Giants / Neenah Menasaha / Miles / Plowed / Drownin' / Molly / Fields / Rainin'
4769822 / Sep '96 / Columbia

Spongetones
BEAT AND TORN
BV 129932 / Nov '96 / Black Vinyl

OH YEAH
BV 120642 / Nov '96 / Black Vinyl

TEXTURAL DRONE THING
BV 122462 / Nov '96 / Black Vinyl

Spontaani Vire
SPONTAANI VIRE
J 15CD / Nov '96 / JCD

Spontane, Ricky
SPONTANE TIME
JPS 003CD / 27 Apr '98 / Old Eagle

Spontaneous Combustion
SPONTANEOUS COMBUSTION/ TRIAD
Speed of light / Listen to the wind / Leaving / 200 lives / Down with the moon / Reminder / Spaceship / Brainstorm / Child life / Love and laughter / Pan / Rainy day / Monolith
SEECD 472 / Feb '97 / See For Miles

Spontaneous Music Ensemble
KARYOBIN
CPE 20012 / Jan '94 / Chronoscope

QUINTESSENCE VOL.1
EM 4015 / Jul '97 / Emanem

QUINTESSENCE VOL.2
EM 4016 / Jul '97 / Emanem

SUMMER '67
EM 4005 / Dec '95 / Emanem

WITHDRAWAL 1966-1967
EM 4020 / Nov '97 / Emanem

Spontaneous Music Orchestra
FOR YOU TO SHARE
EM 4023 / Jul '98 / Emanem

Spookey Ruben
WENDY MCDONALD/LIVE IN JAPAN
TVT 54132 / Mar '97 / TVT

Spooky
FOUND SOUND
Central heating / Miscellaneous / Onglon / Bamboo / Aphonia / Tungsten / Lowest common denominator / Relapse / Hypo-allergenic / Fingerbobs / Plan B / Concusseon / Interim / Consume / Silver / Seneschal
GENRCD 1 / Jul '96 / Generic

GARGANTUAN
Don't panic / Schmoo / Aqualung / Little bullet part 1 / Little bullet part 2 / Land of Oz / Something's got to give / Orange coloured liquid / Schmoodub / Let go
GENRCD 2 / Oct '96 / Generic

Spooky Tooth

☐ BEST OF SPOOKY TOOTH, THE
Tobacco Road / Better by you, better than me / It's all about a roundabout / Waitin' for the wind / Last puff / Evil woman / That was only yesterday / I am the walrus / Self seeking man / All sewn up / Times have changed / As long as the world keeps turning / Weight
IMCD 74 / '89 / Island

☐ CEREMONY (Spooky Tooth & Pierre Henry)
Have mercy / Jubilation / Confession / Prayer / Offering / Hosanna
MANTRA 017 / Sep '97 / Mantra
EDCD 565 / 1 Jun '98 / Edsel

☐ LAST PUFF
I am the walrus / Wrong time / Something to say / Nobody there at all / Down river / Son of your father / Last puff
EDCD 468 / Feb '96 / Edsel

Spoon

☐ HOLDING FLOWERS
HYMN 3 / 24 Nov '97 / Fundamental

☐ SOFT EFFECTS
Mountain to sound / Waiting for the kid to come out / I could see the dude / Get out the state / Loss leaders / Don't but the realistic / Government darling
OLE 2362 / Feb '97 / Matador

☐ TELEPHONO
Don't buy the realistic / Not turning off / All the negatives have been destroyed / Cvantez / Nefarious / Claws tracking / Dismember / Idiot driver / Towner / Wanted to be your friend / Theme to Wendel / Stivers / Primary / Government darling / Plastic Mylar
OLE 2012 / May '96 / Matador

Spooned Hybrio

☐ SPOONED HYBRIO
Heaven's knot / Naturally occuring anchors / Tiny planes / Stolen clothes / Lynched / 1936 / Geting not to know / Somehow some other life / A pocketful of dust / Ecnalumba / Boys in zinc
GU 5CD / Oct '93 / Guernica

Spore

☐ FEAR GOD
TAANG 75CD / Dec '93 / Taang

☐ GIANT
TANNG 81 / Aug '94 / Taang

☐ SPORE
TAANG 74CD / Jun '93 / Taang

Sports Guitar

☐ HAPPY ALREADY
Romeo goes / Youth / Happy already / Chasing bugs / Look shit / Mistake / Fish / Neighbourhood / Come home / Wine / So healthy
OLE 2852 / 11 May '98 / Matador

☐ MARRIED 3 KIDS
Very weird / Never waste / Help / Chords / So shy / Reliable / Hero / Dinner / Life's a plain / Doesn't matter / Get you out / Robocop / Wanna walk / Croonin'
OLE 2432 / Aug '97 / Matador

Sposito, John

☐ VOYAGER IV
CDSGP 9017 / Jun '95 / Prestige

☐ VOYAGER V
CDSGP 9027 / Jun '95 / Prestige

☐ VOYAGER VI
CDSGP 9028 / Jun '95 / Prestige

Spot

☐ SPOT
BLACKRILLS 6 / 15 Dec '97 / Black Rills

Spragga Benz

☐ TWO BADD DJ'S (Spragga Benz & Beenie Man)
VPMHCD 3105 / May '97 / VP

Sprague, Carl T.

☐ CLASSIC COWBOY SONGS
Home on the range / It is no secret / Following the cowtrail / Girl I loved in sunny Tennessee / When the work's all done this fall / Kissing / Club meeting / Bad companions / Rounded up in glory / Red river valley / Roll on little dogies / Last great roundup / Last fierce charge / Gambler / Boston burglar / Orphan girl / Utah Carol / Just break the news to mother / Chicken / Cowman's prayer / Sarah Jane / My Carrie Lee / Zebra Dun / Mormon cowboy / Cowboy's meditation / Kicking mule
BCD 15456 / Dec '88 / Bear Family

Spriguns

☐ JACK WITH A FEATHER (Spriguns Of Tolgus)
HBG 122/9 / Apr '94 / Background

Spring

☐ SPRING
REP 4472 / Dec '97 / Repertoire

Spring

☐ SPRING AND FRIENDS
Chuck it up / Puerto habana / Gunshot / Pinky poo / Skool bus / Suburbs / Be my star / Hotel / Blisters and bruises
BUNG 0162 / 16 Mar '98 / Bungalow

☐ TOKYO DRIFTER
ER 1011 / 27 Apr '98 / Elefant

Spring Heel Jack

☐ 68 MILLION SHADES
Take one / Midwest / 60 Seconds / Pan / Plates / Bar / Eesti / Roger Tessier / Island / Suspensions / Take two / Take three
TRDCD 1000 / Jul '96 / Trade 2

☐ BUSY CURIOUS THIRSTY
Bells / Casino / Bank of America / Galapagos 3 / Halle bop / Happy baby / Sirens / Bells / Fresh kills landfill / Wrong guide
TRCD 1004 / 15 Sep '97 / Trade 2

☐ THERE ARE STRINGS
Only you / Masquerade / Flying again / Oceola / Where do you fit in / Derek / There are strings / Colonades / Lee Perry part 1 / Day of the dead
R 3533 / Aug '95 / Rough Trade

Springer, Mark

☐ EYE
EXIT 1 / 11 May '98 / Exit

Springfield, Dusty

☐ AM I THE SAME GIRL
Son of a preacher man / Stay awhile / All I see is you / I close my eyes and count to ten / Take another little piece of my heart / This girl's in love with you / Second time around / Don't let me lose this dream / Sunny / They long to be close to you / Welcome home / Just one smile / Windmills of your mind / Breakfast in bed / Haunted / Give me time / Am I the same girl / Spooky
5520932 / Mar '96 / Spectrum

☐ BLUE FOR YOU
I just don't know what to do with myself / Your hurtin' kinda love / Will you still love me tomorrow / Every day I have to cry / Some of your lovin' / No easy way down / If you go away / Goin' back / Morning please don't come / How can I be sure / What do you do when love dies / I can't make it alone / My colouring book / Yesterday when I was young
5500052 / May '93 / Spectrum

☐ DUSTY (The Silver Collection)
I only want to be with you / Stay awhile / I just don't know what to do with myself / Wishin' and hopin' / Losing you / Give me time / Twenty four hours from Tulsa / If you go away / Just one smile / Son of a preacher man / All I see is you / You don't have to say you love me / I close my eyes and count to ten / Some of your lovin' / In the middle of nowhere / Little by little / How can I be sure / Look of love / My colouring book / Brand new me / I'll try anything / Goin' back / Anyone who had a heart / Am I the same girl
8341282 / Jan '88 / Philips

☐ DUSTY (The Legend Of Dusty Springfield/4CD Set)
How can I be sure / Stay awhile / I just don't know what to do with myself / Son of a preacher man / All cried out / I will come to you / Some of your lovin' / Give me time / I'm coming home again / What's it gonna be / Losing you / Nothing has been proved / Yesterday when I was young / Your hurtin' kinda love / I only want to be with you / All I see / I'll try anything / I close my eyes and count to ten / Brand new me / Your love still brings me to my knees / Magic garden / What good is I love you / You don't have to say you love me / Baby don't you know / Wishin' and hopin' / Corrupt ones / Tanto so che moi me passa / How can I learn to say goodbye / Summer is over / Where am I going / Something in your eyes / I only wanna laugh / Sweet lover no more / Meditation / Come for a dream / Once upon a time / Will you still love me tomorrow / Goodbye / Lose again / I want to be a free girl / Don't say it baby / Heartbeat / He's got something / What do you do when love dies / Time after time / Softcore / When the midnight train leaves for Alabam / La bamba / Love like yours / Go ahead on / What have I done to deserve this / In the middle of nowhere / Another night / Little by little / That's the kind of love I've got for you / In private / I just wanna be there / Mama's little girl / I can't give back the love I feel for you / Oh no not my baby / Donnez moi / Reputation / Mockingbird / Am I the same girl / When the lovelight starts shining / Take me for a little while / Bring him back / Every ounce of strength / Blind sheep / Goin' back / I think it's going to rain today / Tupelo honey / Chained to a memory / Who can I turn to / If you go away / What are you doing the rest of your life / Love me by name / No easy way down / Never love again / I just fall in love again / That's how heartaches are made / I don't want to hear it anymore / I wish I'd never loved you / Just a little lovin' / Who will take my place / I'd rather leave while I'm in love / Sandra / I've been wrong before / If it hadn't been for you / I had a talk with my man / Second time around / Close to you / Look of love
5222542 / Aug '94 / Philips

☐ DUSTY IN MEMPHIS (Remastered)
Just a little lovin' / So much love / Son of a preacher man / I don't want to hear it anymore / Don't forget about me / Breakfast in bed / Just one smile / Windmills of your mind / In the land of make believe / No easy way down / I can't make it alone / Willie and Laura Mae Jones / That old sweet roll (hi de ho) / What do you do when love dies
5286872 / Sep '95 / Mercury

☐ EVERYTHING'S COMING UP DUSTY
Won't be long / Oh no not my baby / Long after tonight is all over / La bamba / Who can I turn to / Doodlin' / If it don't work out / That's how my heartaches are made / It was easier to hurt him / I've been wrong before / I can't hear you / I had a talk with my man / Packin' up
BGOCD 74 / Sep '89 / Beat Goes On

☐ EVERYTHING'S COMING UP DUSTY (Remastered)
5368522 / 9 Mar '98 / Mercury

☐ GIRL CALLED DUSTY, A (Remastered)
Mama said / You don't own me / Do re mi / When the lovelight starts shining through his eyes / My colouring book / Mockingbird / Twenty four hours from Tulsa / Nothing / Anyone who had a heart / Will you love me tomorrow / Wishin' and hopin' / Don't you know / I only want to be with you / He's got something / Every day I have to cry / Can I get a witness / All cried out / I wish I'd never loved you / Once upon a time / Summer is over
5345202 / Feb '97 / Mercury

☐ GOIN' BACK (The Best Of Dusty Springfield 1962-1994)
Wishin' and hopin' / Little by little / All cried out / Losing you / Son of a preacher man / All I see is you / In the middle of nowhere / What have I done to deserve this / Goin' back / Island of dreams / I'll try anything / Reputation / Stay awhile / In private / Time and time again / I just don't know what to do with myself / I only want to be with you / Windmills of your mind / Silver threads and golden needles / Look of love / I won't be there / Some of your lovin' / Look of love / I close my eyes and count to ten / Nothing has been proved / You don't have to say you love me
8487892 / May '94 / Philips

☐ HITS COLLECTION
Look of love / How can I be sure / Stay a while / I just don't know what to do with myself / Son of a preacher man / All cried out / I will come to you / Some of your lovin' / Give me time / I'm coming home again / Windmills of your mind / Losing you / I can't make it alone / Yesterday when I was young / Your hurtin' kinda love / I only want to be with you / All I see is you / I'll try everything / I'll close my eyes and count to ten / You don't have to say you love me / What good is love for you
5375492 / Oct '97 / Spectrum

☐ REPUTATION
Reputation / Send it to me / Arrested by you / Time waits for no one / I was born this way / In private / Daydreaming / Nothing has been proved / I want to stay here / Occupy your mind
CDFA 3320 / Apr '95 / Fame

☐ REPUTATION AND RARITIES
Reputation / Send it to me / Arrested by you / Time waits for no one / Born this way / In private / Daydreaming / Nothing has been proved / I want to stay here / Occupy your mind / Any other fool / When love turns blue / Getting it right
CDGOLD 1077 / 15 Sep '97 / EMI Gold

☐ REPUTATION AND RARITIES
Reputation / Send it to me / Arrested by you / Time waits for no one / Born this way / In private / Daydreaming / Nothing has been proved / I want to stay here / Occupy your mind / Any other fool / When love turns blue / Getting it right / In private
DC 886122 / 2 Feb '98 / Disky

☐ SOMETHING SPECIAL (2CD Set)
Something special / Reste encore un instant / Je ne peux pas t'en vouloir / I'll love you for a while / Needle in a haystack / Tu che ne sai / Di fronte a l'amore / I will always want you / I'm gonna leave you / Small town girl / I've got a good thing / Don't forget about me / No stranger am I / Don't speak of love / Earthbound gypsy / Wasn't born to follow / Song for you / Haunted / I am your child / You set my dreams to music / Give me the night / Baby blue / Your love still brings me to my knees / It goes like it goes / Just one smile / Something in your eyes / I'd rather leave while I'm in love / Let me love you before you go / Tupelo honey / I just fall in love again / What are you doing the rest of your life / Who will take my place / Who can I turn to / Joe / Who could be lovin' you other than me / I've been wrong before / I can't make it alone / Close to you / My colouring book / If you go away / Sandra / No easy way down / Breakfast in bed / Long after tonight is all over / This girl's in love with you / I think it's gonna rain today / Love me by name / Look of love
5288182 / Apr '96 / Mercury

☐ SONGBOOKS, THE
5528632 / 16 Feb '98 / Mercury

☐ VERY FINE LOVE, A
Roll away / Very fine love / Wherever would I be / Go easy on me / You are the storm / I can't help the way I don't feel / All I have to offer you is love / Lovin' proof / Old habits die hard / Where is A
4785082 / 27 Jul '98 / Columbia

☐ WHERE AM I GOING (Remastered)
5369622 / 9 Mar '98 / Mercury

Springfield, Rick

☐ BEST OF RICK SPRINGFIELD, THE
74321431602 / Oct '96 / Camden

Springfields

☐ OVER THE HILLS AND FAR AWAY (2CD Set)
Dear John / I done what they told me / Breakwaway / Good news / Wimoweh mambo / Black hills of Dakota / Row row row / Green leaves of summer / Silver dollar / Allentown jail / Lonesome traveller / Dear hearts and gentle people / They took John away / Eso es el amor / Two brothers / Tzena tzena tzena / Bambino / Goodnight Irene / Frar away places / Silver threads and golden needles / Aunt Rhody / Swahili papa / Gotta travel on / Island of dreams / Johnson boys / Settle down / There's a big wheel / Greenback dollar / Midnight special / Wabash cannonball / Alone with you / Cottonfields / Foggy mountain top / Little by little / Maggie / Darling Allalee / Mountain boy / My baby's gone / Waf woof / Say I won't be there / Little boat / Come on home / Pit-a-pat / If I was down and out / Marcabamba / No sad songs for me / Where have all the flowers gone
5349302 / Jun '97 / Philips

Springsteen, Bruce

☐ BORN IN THE USA
Cover me / Born in the USA / Darlington County / Working on the highway / Downbound train / I'm on fire / No surrender / Bobby Jean / I'm goin' down / Glory days / Dancing in the dark / My hometown
CD 86304 / Aug '84 / CBS

☐ BORN TO RUN
10th Avenue freeze out / Thunder road / Born to run / Back streets / She's the one / Meeting across the river / Jungleland / Night
CD 69170 / '83 / CBS
4804162 / Jul '95 / Mastersound

☐ BRUCE SPRINGSTEEN SONGBOOK (Various Artists)
VSOPCD 224 / May '96 / Connoisseur Collection

☐ DARKNESS ON THE EDGE OF TOWN
Badlands / Adam raised a Cain / Something in the night / Candy's room / Racing in the street / Promised land / Factory / Streets of fire / Prove it all night / Darkness on the edge of town
CD 86061 / Jul '84 / CBS

☐ DARKNESS ON THE EDGE OF TOWN/ NEBRASKA (2CD Set)
Badlands / Adam raised a Cain / Something in the night / Candy's room / Racing in the street / Promised land / Factory / Streets of fire / Prove it all night / Darkness on the edge of town / Atlantic city / Mansion on the hill / Johnny 99 / Highway patrolman / State trooper / Used cars / Nebraska / Open all night / My father's house / Reason to believe
4716072 / Jul '94 / Columbia

☐ DARKNESS ON THE EDGE.../ GREETINGS FROM ASBURY.../THE WILD... (3CD Set)
Badlands / Adam raise a cain / Something in the night / Candy's room / Racing in the street / Promised land / Factory / Streets of fire / Prove it all night / Darkness on the edge of town / E Street shuffle / Sandy / Kitty's back / Wild Billy's circus story / Incident on 57th Street / Rosalita (come out tonight) / New York City serenade / Blinded by the light / Growin' up / Mary Queen of Arkansas / Does this bus stop at 82nd Street / Lost in the flood / Angel / For you / Spirit in the night / It's hard to be a saint in the city
4853252 / 3 Nov '97 / Columbia

☐ GHOST OF TOM JOAD, THE
Ghost of Tom Joad / Straight time / Highway 29 / Youngstown / Sinola cowboys / Line / Balbo Park / Dry lightning / New timer / Across the border / Galveston Bay / Best was never enough
4816502 / Nov '95 / Columbia

☐ GREATEST HITS
Born to run / Thunder road / Badlands / River / Hungry heart / Atlantic City / Dancing in the dark / Born in the USA / My hometown / Glory days / Brilliant disguise / Human touch / Better days / Streets of Philadelphia / Secret garden / Murder incorporated / Blood brothers / This hard land
4785552 / Feb '95 / Columbia

☐ HUMAN TOUCH
Human touch / Soul driver / Fifty seven channels (and nothin' on) / Cross my heart / Gloria's eyes / With every wish / Real world / All or nothing at all / Man's job / I wish I were blind / Long goodbye / Real man / Pony boy
4714232 / Mar '92 / Columbia

☐ LIVE 1975-1985 (3CD Set) (Springsteen, Bruce & The E Street Band)
Thunder road / Adam raised a Cain / Spirit in the night / 4th of July, Asbury Park (Sandy) / Paradise by the 'c' / Fire / Growing up / It's hard to be a saint in the city / Backstreets / Rosalita / Raise your hand / Hungry heart / Two hearts / Cadillac ranch / You can look (but you'd better not touch) / Independence day / Badlands / Because the night / Candy's room / Darkness on the edge of town / Racing in the street / This land is your land / Nebraska / Johnny 99 / Reason to believe / Born in the USA / Seeds / River / War / Darlington County / Working on the highway / Promised land / Cover me / I'm on fire / Bobby Jean / My home town / Born to run / No surrender / 10th Avenue freeze out / Jersey girl
4502272 / Nov '86 / CBS

☐ LUCKY TOWN
Better days / Lucky town / Local hero / If I should fall behind / Leap of faith / Big muddy / Living proof / Book of dreams / Souls of the departed / My beautiful reward
4714242 / Mar '92 / Columbia

☐ NEBRASKA
Nebraska / Atlantic city / Mansion on the hill / Johnny 99 / Highway patrolman / State trooper / Used cars / Open all night / My father's house / Reason to believe
4633602 / Feb '89 / CBS

☐ PLUGGED - MTV IN CONCERT
Red headed woman / Better days / Atlantic city / Darkness on the edge of town / Man's job / Human touch / Lucky town / I wish I were blind / Thunder road / Light of day / If I should fall behind / Living proof / My beautiful reward
4738604 / 8 Sep '97 / Columbia

☐ RIVER, THE (2CD Set)
Ties that bind / Sherry darling / Jackson Cage / Two hearts / Independence day / Hungry Heart / Out in the street / Crush on you / You can look (but you'd better not touch) / I wanna marry you / River / Point blank / Cadillac Ranch / I'm a rocker / Fade away / Stolen car / Ramrod / Price you pay / Wreck on the highway / Drive all night
4773762 / Sep '94 / Columbia

☐ TUNNEL OF LOVE
Ain't got you / Tougher than the rest / All that heaven will allow / Spare parts / Cautious man / Walk like a man / Tunnel of love / Two faces / Brilliant disguise / One step up / When you're alone / Valentine's day
4602702 / Oct '87 / CBS

☐ WILD, THE INNOCENT AND THE E STREET SHUFFLE, THE
E Street shuffle / 4th of July, Asbury Park (Sandy) / Kitty's back / Wild Billy's circus / Incident on 57th Street / Rosalita / New York City serenade
CD 32363 / Apr '89 / CBS

Sprinkler

☐ WATER SIGN
CID 8072 / 14 Sep '98 / Island

Sprinkler

☐ MORE BOY, LESS FRIEND
SP 211CD / Nov '92 / Sub Pop

Sprocket Wheel

☐ SINGLES
SKIP 68 / 20 Apr '98 / Broken

Sproton Layer

☐ WITH MAGNETIC FIELDS DISRUPTED
NAR 055CD / May '93 / New Alliance

Sproule, Daithi

☐ HEART MADE OF GLASS, A
Lonely Waterloo / Turkish revery / Gabham molta bride / Patty's tune / Bold Belfast shoemaker / Banks of Claudy / September / Gleanntain ghlas ghaoth dobhair / House carpenter / Beaver brig / Bonny bunch of roses / Cailin na gruaige doinne/Little star
GLCD 1123 / May '93 / Green Linnet

Sprouse, Blaine

☐ INDIAN SPRINGS (Sprouse, Blaine & Kenny Baker)
Oh demi slippers / Molly darlin' / Owensboro / Avalon / September waltz / Three days in Dublin / Coker creek / K and W waltz / Cotton town breakdown / Indian springs
ROUCD 0259 / '89 / Rounder

Sprout, Tobin

☐ CARNIVAL BOY
Natural alarm / Cooler jocks / E's navy blue / Bone yard / Carnival boy / Martin's mounted head / Gas daddy gas / To my beloved Martha / White flyer / I didn't know / Gallant men / It's like soul man / Hermit stew / Last man well known to kingpin
OLE 2162 / Sep '96 / Matador

☐ MOONFLOWER PLASTIC (Welcome To My Wig Wam)
Get out of my throat / Moonflower plastic (You're here) / Paper cut / Beast of souls / Little odd / Angels hang their socks / On the moon / All used up / Since I... / Back chorus / Curious things / Exit planes / Little bit of dread / Hit junky dives / Water on the boaters back
OLE 2442 / 25 Aug '97 / Matador

☐ TOBIN SPROUT
LUNA 08 / 2 Mar '98 / Luna

Spudmonsters

☐ MOMENT OF TRUTH
MASSCD 109 / Nov '96 / Massacre

☐ STOP THE MADNESS
MASSCD 017 / Jun '95 / Massacre

Spurgin, Steve

☐ DISTANT FACES
167013 / 24 Nov '97 / Hollywood

Spybey

☐ SPYBEY/THERIAULT (Spybey/ Theriault)
SCRATCH 26 / 26 Aug '97 / Scratch

Spyra

☐ PHONEHEAD
PS 0666CD / Mar '97 / Fax

Spyro Gyra

☐ 20/20
Unwritten letter / Ruled by Venus / 20/20 / Three sisters / Sweet baby James / Deep end / Together / Dark-eyed lady / South American Sojourn / Rockaway to sunset / Return of the pygmy
GRP 98682 / May '97 / GRP

☐ HEART OF THE NIGHT
Heart of the night / De la luz / Westwood moon / Midnight / Playtime / Surrender / Valentino's / Believe / As we sleep / When evening falls / J squared / Best thing
GRP 98492 / Apr '96 / GRP

☐ LOVE & OTHER OBSESSIONS
Lost and found / Ariana / Serengeti / Fine time to explain / Third street / Group therapy / Horizon's edge / Let's say goodbye / On liberty road (for South Africa) / Rockin' a heart place / Baby dreams / Open season
GRP 98112 / Mar '95 / GRP

☐ MORNING DANCE
Morning dance / Jubilee / Rasul / Song for Lorraine / Starburst / It doesn't matter / Little Linda / End of Romanticism / Heliopolis
74321202612 / May '94 / MCA

☐ ROAD SCHOLARS
Heart of the night / Breakfast at Igor's / Morning dance / Shaker song / Shanghai gumbo / Innocent soul / South American sojourn / Ariana / De la luz / Daddy's got a new girl now / Best friends
GRP 99132 / 30 Mar '98 / GRP

Spys

☐ SPYS/BEHIND ENEMY LINES
RME 0115CD / Dec '97 / Renaissance

Squadronaires

☐ THERE'S SOMETHING IN THE AIR
There's something in the air / South Rampart Street Parade / C jam blues / Pompton turnpike / Ringle dingle / Anchors aweigh / Commando patrol / Boston bounce / Rimg dem bells / Cow cow boogie / High society / Mistakes / Mission on Moscow / That's a plenty
HEPCD 44 / Dec '90 / Hep

☐ THERE'S SOMETHING IN THE AIR
Chattanooga choo choo / Beat me Daddy, eight to the bar / Blues in the night / Pennyslyania polka / Me and Melinda / Be careful it's my heart / Jersey bounce / Tropical magic / Jealous / Lover's lullaby / String of pearls / Cow cow boogie / Commando patrol / Drummin' man / Darktown strutters ball / Boogie woogie bugle boy / My mother would love you / (Back home again in) Indiana / Lament to love / All of me / There's something in the air
RAJCD 816 / 6 Apr '98 / Empress

☐ THERE'S SOMETHING IN THE AIR
All of me / Anchors aweigh / Blue Lou / Bounce me brother with a solid four / Chattanooga choo choo / Cherokee / Darktown strutters ball / Daybreak / Dolores / Drummin' man / Goodnight sweet neighbour / How sweet you are / (Back home again in) Indiana / Jazz me blues / Jersey bounce / Ringle dingle / Sinner kissed an angel / Some sunny day / South Rampart Street Parade / String of pearls / That day it rained / That's a-plenty / There's something in the air / Way down yonder in New Orleans / You're my baby
CDAJA 5128 / Mar '94 / Living Era

☐ WARTIME MEMORIES
There's something in the air tonight / Skyliner / We're gonna hang out the washing on the Siegfried Line / Nightingale sang in Berkeley Square / White cliffs of Dover / Foggy day / South Rampart Street Parade / Lili Marlene / I'll be seeing you / We'll meet again / Little brown jug / You'll never know / I'm gonna get lit up (when the lights go on in London) / News bulletins from throughout the war
CDMFP 6123 / May '94 / Music For Pleasure

Square 1

☐ SWEETNESS
SO 97001 / 29 Sep '97 / Square 1

Square Window

☐ 10 SONGS FOR GIRLS AND BOYS
ELM 8002CD / 13 Jul '98 / E-Melt

Squarepusher

☐ BURNING TREE
WARPCD 053 / 10 Nov '97 / Warp

☐ FEED ME WEIRD THINGS
CAT 037CD / Jun '96 / Rephlex

☐ HARD NORMAL DADDY
Coopers world / Beep street / Rustic raver / Airdog D9 / Chin hippy / Papalon / Ex boogie / Fat controller / Vic acid / Male pill part 13 / Rat/P's and Q's / Rebus
WARPCD 50 / Apr '97 / Warp

Squatweiler

☐ NEW MOTHERSTAMPER
SPART 56 / Jun '97 / Spin Art

Squeeze

☐ ARGY BARGY
Pulling mussels / Another nail in my heart / Separate beds / Misadventure / I think I'm go-go / Farfisa beat / Here comes that feeling / Vicky verky / If I didn't love you / Wrong side of the moon / There at the top
5408032 / 2 Feb '98 / A&M

☐ COOL FOR CATS
Slap and tickle / Revue / Touching me touching you / It's not cricket / It's so dirty / Hop, skip and jump / Up the junction / Hard to find / Slightly drunk / Goodbye girl / Cool for cats / Up the junction (live)
5408042 / 2 Feb '98 / A&M

☐ COSI FAN TUTTI FRUTTI
Big beng / By your side / I won't ever go drinking again / Hits of the year / Heartbreaking world / No place like home / Last time forever / I learnt how to pray / King George Street
5408022 / 2 Feb '98 / A&M

☐ EAST SIDE STORY
In quintessence / Someone else's heart / Tempted / Piccadilly / There's no tomorrow / Woman's world / Is that Love / F-hole / Labelled with love / Someone else's bell / Mumbo Jumbo / Vanity fair / Messed around
5408052 / 2 Feb '98 / A&M

☐ EXCESS MODERATION (2CD Set)
Take me I'm yours / Model / Revue / Christmas Day / Blood and guts / Going crazy / Knack / If I didn't love you / Separate beds / I think I'm go go / What the butler saw / Piccadilly / Trust / Tempted / Woman's world / Squabs on forty fab / Elephant ride / Tongue like a knife / His house her home / When the hangover strikes / Apple tree / Within these walls without you / On my mind tonight / Hope fell down / No place like home / What have they done / Tough love / Striking matches / Peyton Place / Dr. Jazz / Melody Motel / Slaughtered, gutted and heartbroken / Maidstone / House of love / Truth / Letting go / It's over / Loving you tonight / Cold shoulder / Some fantastic place
5406512 / Nov '96 / A&M

☐ GREATEST HITS
Take me I'm yours / Goodbye girl / Cool for cats / Up the junction / Slap and tickle / Another nail in my heart / Pulling mussels / Tempted / Labelled with love / Black coffee in bed / Annie get your gun / Last time forever / Hourglass / Trust me to open my mouth / Footprints / If it's love / Is that love / King George street / No place like home / Love circles
3971812 / May '92 / A&M

☐ RIDICULOUS
Electric trains / Heaven knows / Grouch of the day / Walk away / This summer / Got to me / Long face / I want you / Daphne / Lost for words / Great escape / Temptation for love / Sound asleep / Fingertips
5404402 / 15 Sep '97 / A&M

☐ ROUND AND A BOUT, A
Footprints / Pulling mussels / Black coffee in bed / She doesn't have to shave / Is that love / Dr. Jazz / Up the junction / Slaughtered / Gutted and heartbroken / Is it too late / Cool for cats / Take me I'm yours / If it's love / Hourglass / Labelled with love / Annie get your gun / Boogie woogie country girl / Tempted
EIRSCD 1084 / Jun '96 / IRS/EMI

☐ SIX OF ONE (6CD Set)
Big beng / By your side / King George Street / I learnt to pray / Last time forever / No place like home / Heartbreaking world / Hits of the year / Break my heart / I won't ever go drinking again / Love's a four letter word / Fortnight saga / Pulling mussels / ANother nail in my heart / Misadventure / I think I'm go go / Farfisa beat / Here comes that feeling / Vivky verky / If I didn't love you / Wrong side of the moon / There at the top / Funny how it goes / Go / Slap and tickle / Revue / Touching me touching you / It's not cricket / It's so dirty / Knack / Hop skip and jump / Up the junction / Hard to find / Slighty drunk / Goodbye girl / Cool for cats / I must go / Ain't it sad / In quintessence / Someone else's heart / Tempted / Picaddilly / There's no tomorrow / Heaven / Woman's world / Is that love / F-Hole / Labelled with love / Someone else's bell / Mumbo jumbo / Vanity fair / Messed around / Axe has now fallen / Looking for a love / Sex master / Bang bang / Strong in reason / Wild sewerage tickles brasil / Out of control / Take me I'm yours / Call / Model / Remember what / First thing wrong / Hestitation / Get smart / Deep cuts / Heartbreak / Out of touch / I can't hold on / Points of view / Stronger than the stranger on the shore / Onto the dnce floor / When the hangover strikes / Black coffee in bed / I've returned / Tongue like a knife / His house her home / Very first dance / Elephant ride / I can't get up anymore / When love goes to sleep
5408012 / 20 Oct '97 / A&M

☐ SOME FANTASTIC PLACE
Everything in the world / Some fantastic place / Third rail / Loving you tonight / It's over / Cold shoulder / Talk to him / Jolly comes home / Images of loving / True colours (the storm) / Pinocchio
5401402 / Oct '93 / A&M

☐ SQUEEZE
Sex master / Bang bang / Strong in reason / Wild sewerage tickles Brazil / Out of control / Take me I'm yours / Call / Model / Remember what / First thing wrong / Hesitation / Get smart
5408062 / 2 Feb '98 / A&M

☐ SWEETS FROM A STRANGER
Out of touch / I can't hold on / Point of view / Stranger than the stranger on the shore / Onto the dance floor / When the hangover strikes / Black coffee in bed / I've returned / Tongue like a knife / His house, her home / Very first dance / Elephant ride
5408072 / 2 Feb '98 / A&M

Squiban, Didier

☐ BREST 1996 - PENN-AR-BRED
L'OZ 08CD / Aug '96 / L'Oz

☐ MOLENE
L'OZ 17CD / Mar '98 / L'Oz

Squidboy

☐ ILLITERATTI
ALLIED 96CD / 22 May '98 / Allied

☐ KIDS TALK TO KILLERS
ALLIED 74CD / Sep '96 / Allied

Squip

☐ WENN UBERHAUDT
9604CD / May '97 / Verlag DS

Squire

☐ BIG SMASHES
TANGCD 4 / Aug '92 / Tangerine

☐ GET READY TO GO
TANGCD 7 / Aug '94 / Tangerine

Squire, Chris

☐ FISH OUT OF WATER
Hold out your hand / You by my side / Silently falling / Lucky seven / Safe (canon song)
7567815002 / Jan '96 / Atlantic

Squires, Dorothy

☐ BEST OF DOROTHY SQUIRES, THE
SOW 713 / Nov '94 / Sound Waves

☐ BEST OF DOROTHY SQUIRES, THE
When you lose the one you love / It's the talk of the town / I still believe / This is my Mother's day / Don't search for love / Things go wrong / Gypsy / I saw that look in your eyes / Without you / Precious love / Danger ahead, beware / Dear to me / If you love me / Is there any room in your heart / Come home to my arms / I'll close my eyes / Tree in the meadow / What is the reason / Someone to love / I'm walking behind you / Banana boat song / It's a pity to say goodnight / In all the world
PLSCD 241 / 27 Oct '97 / Pulse

☐ DANGER AHEAD
Danger ahead / Laughing on the outside / It's a pity to say goodnight / My first love my last love for always / For sentimental reasons / Memories of you / Three beautiful words of love / Let the rest of the world go by / Gipsy / I'll close my eyes / Dreams of yesterday / Coming home / I'm in the mood for love / I'm gonna hold you in my arms / Curly top / Yippe-olly-ay-ho / I'd like to get you alone / Old apple tree will bloom again / When China boy meets China girl / Under the willow tree / Goodnight until tomorrow
PLCD 569 / 6 Jul '98 / President

☐ LIVE AT THE LONDON PALLADIUM (3CD Set)
My way / Back in your own backyard/Everything is beautiful / Do I worry / Swanee, Swanee river/Ol' man river/Lazy river / For once in my life / Autograph book / Why did I choose you / If you love me (Hymne a l'amour) / Man that got away / My way / 'S wonderful/ They say it's wonderful/Wonderful one / Don't take your love from me / It's the talk of the town / It can't be done / Gibraltar anthem / Safe in my arms again / Didn't we / Say it with flowers / Mother's day/The gypsy/A tree in the meadow / I'm walking behind you / I can live again / I've gotta be me / My way / My way / Happy heart / There goes my heart / Shaking the blues away / Where do I begin / Bewitched / Till / Autograph book / What a wonderful world / As long as he needs me / On Mother Kelly's doorstep / Mother's day / Everything's coming up roses / My way / Life goes on / For once in my life / If he walked into my life / Where have all the flowers gone / When the world is ready / Glory hallelujah (Battle hymn of the Republic) / Pack up your troubles in your old kit bag / Goodbye Dolly Gray / It's a long way to Tipperary / Mama / When there's love in your heart / I've gotta be me / My way
STE 7071 / Mar '97 / Sterndale

☐ SAY IT WITH FLOWERS
Say it with flowers / And so to sleep again / Roses of Picady / Gypsy / Someone other than me / Do I worry / Secret that's never been told / Legend of the well / On the sunny side of the street / Song of the valley / Mother's day / Look around / Snowflakes / To be worthy of you / Bewitched / Old soft shoe / Two strangers meet / Our song
CDMFP 6216 / Apr '96 / Music For Pleasure

☐ WITH ALL MY HEART
Gypsy / It's a pity to say goodnight / When you lose the one you love / I'll close my eyes / Changing partners / Danger ahead beware / Don't search for love / White wings / With all my heart / When I grow too old to dream / Yes I'll be here / Torremolinos / Tree in the meadow / I still believe / In all the world / Come home to my arms / Safe in my arms / Sorrento and you / Mother's day / Coming home / I'm walking behind you / Someone to love / Blue blue blue / Reflections on the water
C5CD 604 / Jul '98 / See For Miles

Squires, Rosemary

☐ ELLA FITZGERALD SONGBOOK (Squires, Rosemary & Maxine Daniels & Babrbara Jay)
Tisket-a-tasket / It don't mean a thing if it ain't got that swing / But not for me / They all laughed / This cant' be love / Someone to watch over me / Soon / Every time we say goodbye / Foggy day / That old black magic / Miss Otis regrets / Love for sale / Take a chance on love / Cheek to cheek / Frim fram sauce / Ten cents a dance / Manhattan / Thou swell / Looking for a boy / Fine romance / How about you / Anything goes / They can't take that away from me / I concentrate on you / Dream dancing / You do something to me / Airmail special / Mack the knife
SPJCD 556 / Oct '94 / Spotlite

Squirrel Bait

☐ SKAG HEAVEN
DEX 11 / Feb '97 / Drag City

☐ SQUIRREL BAIT
DEX 10 / Feb '97 / Drag City

Squirrel Nut Zippers

☐ HOT
5570382 / 16 Mar '98 / Polydor

Squirtgun

☐ ANOTHER SUNNY AFTERNOON
LOOKOUT 167CD / Feb '97 / Lookout

☐ SHENADIGANS
LOOKOUT 118CD / Oct '95 / Lookout

SRC

☐ SRC/MILESTONES
Black sheep / Daystar / Exile / Marionette / Onesimpletask / Paragon council / Refugeve / Interval / No secret destination / Show me / Eye of the storm / I remember your face / In the hall of the mountain King / Bolero / Checkmate / Our little secret / Turn into love / Up all night / Angel song
C5HCD 667 / 29 Jun '98 / See For Miles

Srinivas, U.

☐ DAWN RAGA
WS 003CD / Aug '96 / Womad Select

☐ DREAM (Srinivas, U. & Michael Brook)
Dance / Think / Run / Dream
CDRW 47 / May '95 / Realworld

☐ MODERN MANDOLIN MAESTRO
Ghananayakam / Ninnvvina / Arulseya / Ragam madhyamavati / Thanam / Palinchu kamakshi / Saravana bhava / Malai pozudinile / Folk note
CDORBD 068 / Mar '91 / Globestyle

☐ RAMA SREERAMA
Gajavadhana / Maryaadakadaya / Saranambhava karuna / Rama sreerama (ragam, thanam, pallavi) and ragamalika / Ganamurthy / Kaliyugavaradana
CDRW 39 / Jul '94 / Realworld

SSD

☐ POWER
TAANG 050CD / Jun '92 / Taang

SSV

☐ GO FIGURE
Nice / Knife paper stone and guns / Two in the nose / Bad vultee / Gone / Drugsar / High school / Feel no pain / Go figure / Shut the fuck up
3984212602 / 10 Nov '97 / WEA

St. Christopher

☐ DIG DEEP BROTHER 1984-1990
Forevermore starts here / To the mountain / Charmelle / Who's next on Cupid's hit list / Climb on forever / If I could capture / My fond farewell / Even the sky seems blue / Rivers run dry / Awe / I wish I hadn't seen her / Remember me to her / Tell the world / Our secret / Crystal clear / Rollercoaster / Where in the world / Josephine why / All of a tremble / On the death of my son / Sinking ships / For one so weak / My fortune / How can you tell / Wanda
ASKCD 026 / Jun '93 / Vinyl Japan

☐ LIONESS
Loneliness is a friend of mine / Tangled up in blue / Jewels in your hair / Utopian / Hell / She looks like you / With her in mind / Where you are, everything is / As good as married / Flirtation / Loneliness is a friend of mine (reprise)
ASKCD 053 / Oct '96 / Vinyl Japan

☐ LOVE YOU TO PIECES
Away / Ladder / Crush / Baptise me baby / Wildest dreams / Everything now / Magic spell / Liberty / For the world to see / Dive / Stars belong to me / Pieces
ASKCD 027 / Feb '94 / Vinyl Japan

☐ MAN I COULD SCREAM
ASK 006CD / '92 / Vinyl Japan

St. Clair, Carl

☐ STRAIGHT FROM THE HEART
CRCD 53 / 13 Jul '98 / Charm

St. Clair, Isla

☐ INHERITANCE
Flowers of the forest / Ye Jacobites by name / Smile in your sleep / Farewell tae tarwathie / Fear a'bhata / MacCrimmon's lament / Fifty first highland division's farewell to Sicily / Come ye o'er frae france / Hush ye noo / Norland wind / Freedom come-all-ye / Hills of Ardmorn
MOICD 008 / May '93 / Moidart

☐ SCENES OF SCOTLAND
Lest we forget / Queen Edinbro' / Couthy Cullen / Ballachuilish / Call tae arms / Lament for the commandos/Dunkirk / Lullin' the littlin' / Toast to Stornaway / Lifeboat / Spinning wheel / Glen Isla/ Green ruby waltz / Glencoe / Bonnie boats o'Buckie / Poet and lover
CDTRAX 119 / Oct '96 / Greentrax

☐ TATTIES AND HERRIN' - THE LAND
Tatties and herrin' / Plooman laddies / Wi' my rovin' eye / Arlin's fine braes / Up the Noran Water / Bogie's bonnie belle / Kirk o' Birnieboozle / Drumdelgie / Chairlie o' Chairlie / Band o' shearers / Johnny Sangster / Guise o' tough / Barnyards of Delgaty / Nicky Tams / Dying ploughboy / Twa recruitin' sergeants / Emigrant's farewell to Donside / Hilly's man / Tatties and herrin'
CDTRAX 145 / 1 Oct '97 / Greentrax

☐ TATTIES AND HERRIN' - THE SEA
Tatties and herrin' / Song of the fish gutters / Skippin Barfit / Lullin the littlin / Children's nonsense songs / Bonnie fisher lassie / Fisherman's lassie / Shoals of herring / Greenland whale / Farewell tae Tarwathie / Mermaid / Bonnie boats o' Buckie / Herrin's heid / Johnny my man / Will your anchor hold / Lifeboat / Song of the fisherman's wife / Couthy Cullen / Tatties and herrin'
CDTRAX 146 / 1 Oct '97 / Greentrax

St. Claire, Bette

☐ AT BASIN STREET EAST
FSRCD 56 / Jan '98 / Fresh Sound

St. Clement Danes Choir

☐ MOST BEAUTIFUL CHRISTMAS SONGS, THE
DCD 5133 / Nov '92 / Disky

☐ TRADITIONAL ENGLISH CHRISTMAS CAROLS
CNCD 5934 / Nov '92 / Disky

St. Domingo De Silos Monks Choir

☐ LIGHT OF SILOS, THE (The Soul Of Chant/Ave Maria/2CD Set)
Soul of chant / Soul of chant / Fons bonitatis de angelis / Cum jubilo / Orbis factor / Ave maria
74321402892 / Oct '96 / Milan

St. Eloi Juniors

☐ PREMYE FWA
CDS 7327 / Jan '97 / Sonodisc

St. Etienne

☐ CASINO CLASSICS (The Remix Album) (2CD Set)
Like a motorway / Join our club / Pale movie / Speedwell / Only love can break your heart / Who do you think you are / Avenue / Hug my soul / Like a motorway (David Holmes remix) / Angel / Filthy / People get real / Nothing can stop us / Sometimes in winter / Sea / Burnt out car / He's on the phone / Cool kids of death / Angel (Broadcast mix)
HVNLP 16CDL
HVNLP 16CD / Oct '96 / Heavenly

☐ FOXBASE ALPHA
This is Radio Etienne / Only love can break your heart / Wilson / Can't sleep / Girl VII / Spring / She's the one / Stoned to say the least / Nothing can stop us / Etienne gonna die / London belongs to me / Like the swallow / Dilworth's theme
HVNCD 1 / Sep '91 / Heavenly

☐ GOOD HUMOUR
CRECD 225
CRECD 225L / 4 May '98 / Creation

☐ SO TOUGH
Mario's cafe / Railway Jam / Date with spelman / Calico / Avenue / You're in a bad way / Memo to pricey / Hobart paving / Leafhound / Clock milk / Conichita matrinez / No rainbows for me / Here come clown feet / Junk the morgue / Chicken soup
HVNLP 6CD / Jan '93 / Heavenly

☐ TIGER BAY
Urban clearway / Former lover / Hug my soul / Like a motorway / On the shore / Marble lions / Pale movie / Cool kids of death / Western wind / Tankerville / Boy scouts of America
HVNLP 8CD / Feb '94 / Heavenly

☐ TOO YOUNG TO DIE (The Singles Collection 1991-1995)
HVNLP 10CD / Nov '95 / Heavenly

☐ YOU NEED A MESS OF HELP TO STAND ALONE
Who do you think you are / Archway people / California snow story / Kiss and make up / Duke duvet / Filthy / Join our club / Paper / People get real / Some place else / Speedwell
HVNLP 7CD / Nov '93 / Heavenly

St. Field, John

☐ CONTROL
LV 012CD / 16 Mar '98 / Lost Vinyl

St. Germain

☐ BOULEVARD
Deep in it / Thank U Mum (4 everything you did) / Street scene / Easy to remember / Sentimental mood / What's new / Dub experience II / Forget it
F 002CD / Aug '96 / F-Communications

St. James Infirmary

☐ ST. JAMES INFIRMARY
ALLIED 93CD / 12 Jan '98 / Allied

St. John's College Cambridge Choir

☐ CAROLS FOR CHRISTMAS
Ding dong merrily on high / O little town of Bethlehem / Born on Earth / Twelve days of Christmas / Up good Christen folk / Silent night / Good King Wenceslas / While shepherds watched their flocks by night / God rest ye merry gentlemen / Holly and the ivy / Away in a manger / Shepherd's pipe carol / First Noel / I saw three ships / Suo gan / Hark the herald angels sing
4501112 / Nov '96 / Belart

☐ CHRISTMAS CAROLS
God rest ye merry gentlemen / Ding dong merrily on high / O little town of Bethlehem / Unto us a boy is born / Good King Wenceslas / Holly and the ivy / I sing of a maiden / Two Welsh carols / Silent night / Hark the herald angels sing / Jesus Christ the apple tree / In the bleak midwinter / O come all ye faithful (Adeste Fidelis) / Shepherd's pipe carol / On Christmas night / Away in a manger / There is no rose / Balulalow
CHAN 8485 / '86 / Chandos

St. John, Bridget

☐ ASK ME NO QUESTIONS
REP 4203 / Aug '91 / Repertoire

☐ ASK ME NO QUESTIONS/SONGS FOR THE GENTLEMEN
To B without a hitch / Autumn lullaby / Curl your toes / Like never before / Curious crystals of unusual purity / Barefeet and hot pavements / I like to be with you in the sun / Lizard-long-tongue-boy / Hello again (of course) / Many happy returns / Broken faith / Ask me no questions / Day a way / City crazy / Back to stay / Seagull Sunday / If you's been there / Song for the Laird of Connaught Hall (part 2) / Making losing better / Lady and the gentle man / Downderry daze / Pebble and the man / It seems very strange
SEECD 408 / Sep '94 / See For Miles

☐ JUMBLEQUEEN
Sparrowpit / Song for the waterden widow / I don't know if I can take it / Some kind of beautiful / Last goodnight / Curious and woolly / Want to be with you / Jumblequeen / Sweet painted lady / Long long time
BGOCD 260 / Feb '95 / Beat Goes On

☐ TAKE THE FIFTH
RGFCD 026 / Oct '95 / Road Goes On Forever

☐ THANK YOU FOR
Nice / Thank you for / Lazarus / Good baby goodbye / Love minus zero, no limit / Silver coin / Happy day / Fly high / To leave your cover / Every day / Song as long as it wants to go on
SEECD 428 / Jul '95 / See For Miles

St. John, Kate

☐ INDESCRIBABLE NIGHT
There is sweet music here that softer falls / Paris skies / Now the night comes stealing in / Fireflies / Le premier bonheur du jour / Green park blues / Wherefore art thou / Variety lights / On the bridge / Indescribable night / Shadows of doubt / Chat voyeur / Mr. Goodbyes
ASCD 025 / Jun '95 / All Saints

☐ SECOND SIGHT
Don't they know you've gone / Where the wind blows / Songs and silhouettes / Flicker of gold / My lonely love / Notti senza amore / J'attendrai / Fireworks / Foolish dance / Dark heavens / Colonel Sinnot's song of love
ASCD 034 / Sep '97 / All Saints

St. Johnny

☐ HIGH AS A KITE
Go to sleep / Highway / Stupid / High as a kite / Velocity / Matador / My father's father / Ashes and slashes
R 2966 / Feb '93 / Rough Trade

St. Just

☐ LA CASA DEL LAGO
SRMC 6017 / 5 Jan '98 / Siwan

St. Louis Jimmy

☐ GOIN' DOWN SLOW
Poor boy / Nothin' but the blues / Mother's day blues / Some sweet day / My heart is loaded with trouble / I'm St. Louis bound / Goin' down slow / Sweet as she can be / Monkey faced woman
OBCCD 584 / Oct '96 / Original Blues Classics

St. Louis Ragtimers

☐ ST. LOUIS RAGTIMERS
SOSCD 1267 / Oct '93 / Stomp Off

☐ ST. LOUIS RAGTIMERS VOL.1, THE
BCD 361 / Dec '97 / GHB

☐ ST. LOUIS RAGTIMERS VOL.2, THE
BCD 362 / Jun '96 / GHB

St. Mark, Keverenn Brest

☐ TU PE DU
KBSM 001CD / Mar '96 / KBSM

St. Michael Singers

☐ YE SERVANTS OF GOD (St. Michael Singers, Coventry/Paul Leddington Wright)
Christ the Lord is risen today / Christ whose glory / Jesu lover of my soul / Jesus the name high over all / O for a heart to praise / Ye servants of God / Thou God of truth
KMCD 891 / May '96 / Kingsway

St. Paul's Cathedral Choir

☐ CAROLS FROM ST. PAUL'S CATHEDERAL (St. Paul's Cathedral Choir/Life Guards)
O come all ye faithful (Adeste Fidelis) / Away in a manger / First Noel / Ding dong merrily on high / Holly and the ivy / O little town of Bethlehem / Joy to the world / In dulci jubilo / Once in Royal David's City / Sussex carol / See amid the winter's snow / In the bleak midwinter / Mary's lullaby / Silent night / Hark the herald angels sing
CDPR 124 / Nov '94 / Premier/MFP

☐ CHRISTMAS CAROLS AT ST.PAUL'S CATHEDRAL
Once in royal David's city / See amid the winter's snow / Away in a manger / Unto us a star is born / Christians awake / Coventry carol / I saw three ships / It came upon a midnight clear / We three kings of orient are / While shepards watched / Holly and the ivy / Hark the herald angels sing
GFS 998 / 20 Oct '97 / Going For A Song

St. Peters, Crispian

☐ FOLLOW ME
REP 4199 / Aug '91 / Repertoire

St. Philip's Boys Choir

☐ ANGEL VOICES VOL.1
Song of joy / Song of joy / For the beauty of the earth / I have a dream / O for the wings of a dove / San damiano / Be still for the presence of the lord / Always there (howard's way theme) / Glory to thee my god this night / One voice / How can I keep from singing / Praise to the lord the almighty / Panis angelicus (franck) / Adoramus te / Morning has broken / Sailing / Sing for ever / Orinoco flow / Be still my soul / Silent night
MCCDX 001 / 6 Oct '97 / Music Club

☐ ANGEL VOICES VOL.2
MCCD 259 / 6 Oct '97 / Music Club

☐ ANGEL VOICES VOL.3
Saviour's day / Walking in the air / In dulci jubilo / White Christmas / O come all ye faithful (adeste fidelis) / Away in a manger / God rest ye merry gentlemen / In the bleak mid Winter / Misteltoe and wine / O little town of Bethlehem / Once in royal David's City / Christmas song / First Noel / Silent night / While shepherds watched their flocks by night / Mary's boy child / Gaudette / When a child is born / Do you hear what I hear
MCCDX 019 / 6 Oct '97 / Music Club

St. Tropez

☐ BEST OF ST. TROPEZ, THE (Fill My Life With Love)
HTCD 79 / 20 Apr '98 / Hot Productions

St. Vitus

☐ BORN TOO LATE
Born too late / Clear windowpane / Dying inside / H.a.a.g. / Lost feeling / War starter / Thirsty and miserable / Look behind you / End of the end
SST 082CD / Oct '87 / SST

☐ HEAVIER THAN THOU
SST 266CD / May '93 / SST

☐ MOURNFUL CRIES
Creeps / Dragon time / Shooting gallery / Bitter truth / Troll / Looking glass
SST 161CD / Sep '88 / SST

☐ V
Living backwards / When emotion dies / Ice monkey / Angry man / I bleed black / Patra / Jack Frost / Mind food
H 00052 / Apr '90 / Hellhound

Stabi, Bjorn

☐ ORSLATAR
GCD 35 / Dec '97 / Giga

Stack

☐ ABOVE ALL
GF 111 / 23 Mar '98 / Gear Fab

Stackhouse, Houston

☐ CRYIN' WON'T HELP YOU
Kind hearted woman / Bricks in my pillow / Bye bye blues / My babe / Sweet black angel / Pony blues / Cry on, cry on / Sweet home chicago / Cryin' won't help you / I got something / Maggie campbell blues / I'm getting tired / Big road blues
EDCD 383 / Oct '94 / Edsel

Stackridge

☐ BBC RADIO 1 IN CONCERT
God speed the plough / Lummy days / Tea time / Anyone for tennis / Amazing Agnes / She taught me how to yodel / 32 west mall / Syracuse the elephant / Volunteer / Whose that up there with Bill Stokes / No-one's more important than the earthworm / Dora the female explora
SFRSCD 032 / Jul '97 / Windsong

☐ BBC RADIO 1 SESSIONS, THE
SFRSCD 040 / 27 Oct '97 / Strange Fruit

☐ FRIENDLINESS
SIVCD 0010 / Aug '96 / Red Steel

☐ FRIENDLINESS...PLUS
EDCD 487 / Aug '96 / Edsel

☐ MAN IN THE BOWLER HAT
Fundamentally yours / Pinafore days / Last plimsoll / To the sun and the moon / Road to Venezuela / Galloping gaucho / Humiliation / Dangerous beacon / Indifferent hedgehog / God speed / Do the stanley / C'est la vie / Let there be lids
EDCD 488 / Jul '96 / Edsel

☐ STACKRIDGE
Grande piano / Percy the penguin / Three legged table / Dora the female explorer / Essence of porphyry / Marigold conjunction / 32 West Mall / Marzo plod / Slark
SIVCD 0009 / Nov '96 / Red Steel
EDCD 518 / Mar '97 / Edsel

Stackwaddy

☐ BUGGER OFF
Rosalyn / Willie the pimp / Hoochie coochie man / It's all over now / Several yards / You really got me / I'm a lover not a fighter / Meat pies 'ave come but band's not here yet / It ain't easy / Long tall shorty / Repossession boogie / Girl from Ipanema
REP 4082 / Aug '91 / Repertoire

☐ STACKWADDY/BUGGER OFF
Roadrunner / Bring it to Jerome / Mothballs / Sure nuff 'N' yes I do / Love story / Suzie Q / Country line special / Rollin' stone / Mystic eyes / Kentucky / Rosalyn / Willie the pimp / Hoochie coochie man / It's all over now / Several yards / You really got me / I'm a lover not a fighter / Meat pies 'ave come but band's not here yet / It ain't easy / Long tall shorty / Repossession boogie
SEECD 407 / Sep '94 / See For Miles

Stacy Cats

☐ ROCKJIVE
RKCD 9312 / May '93 / Rockhouse

Stacy, Jess

☐ CLASSICS 1935-1939
CLASSICS 795 / Mar '95 / Classics

☐ EC-STACY
TPZ 1050 / Aug '96 / Topaz Jazz

☐ JESS STACY (20 Great Piano Performances 1935-1945)
Barrelhouse / Rhythm rhythm (I got rhythm) / Take me to the land of jazz / Rose of Washington Square / I got rhythm / Blue room / Carnegie jump / Darktown strutters ball / Mad house / Roll 'em / Big John special / Opus 3/4 / Vultee special / Ec-Stacy / Spain / Down to steamboat Tennessee / Daybreak serenade / It's only a paper moon / In a mist / Candlelights / In the dark / I ain't got nobody / Blue fives / Ridin' easy / Sing sing sing
CDAJA 5172 / May '95 / Living Era

☐ STACY STILL SWINGS
CRD 133 / Mar '96 / Chiaroscuro

Stadacona Band

☐ ON THE QUARTERDECK
On the quarter deck / Parade of the tall ships / Helen Creighton folk songs / Vedette / Overture to an unwritten comedy / Concertino for flute / Seven seas overture / Les arrivals / Gladiator's farewell / You needed me / Shadows in the moonlight / I just fall in love again / Processions of the nobles / Nova scotia farewell / Barrett's privateers / HM Jollies / Heart of oak
BNA 5113 / Jun '95 / Bandleader

Staff, Freddy

☐ ROMANCE AND SWING (Staff, Freddy Big Band)
Love story / Baker Street / Here's that rainy day / Can't smile without you / Way we were / Stardust / She / My silent love / Cherry / Strictly instrumental / It's been a long long time / Harry's best / I don't want to walk without you / I'll walk alone
ASA 2 / 19 Apr '98 / ASA

Stafford, Jo

☐ AUTUMN IN NEW YORK/STARRING...
Autumn in New York / Smoke gets in you eyes / Haunted heart / If I loved you / In the still of the night / Some enchanted evening / Just one of those things / Almost like being in love / Make believe / Throught the years / Best things in life / Serenade of the bells / No othe love / Red river valley / Ivy / Fools rush in / Sunday kind of love / Gentlemen is a dope / Symphony / Tumbling weeds / You keep coming back like a song / Day by day
CTMCD 124 / 15 Sep '97 / EMI

☐ COMING BACK LIKE A SONG (25 Hits 1941-1947)
Yes indeed / Manhattan serenade / It could happen to you / Long ago and far away / I love you / Trolley song / Out of this world / Candy / There's no you / That's for me / Symphony / Day by day / Baby won't you please come home / I'll be with you in apple blossom time / You keep coming back like a song / Things we did last summer / Promise / Sonata / Ivy / Temptation / I'm so right tonight / Feudin' and fightin' / Serenade of the bells / Black is the colour / White Christmas
CDAJA 5268 / Apr '98 / Living Era

☐ FOR YOU
CDMOIR 513 / Nov '95 / Memoir

☐ JO STAFFORD STORY, THE
Old acquaintance / I remember you / Too marvellous for words / How sweet you are / It could happen to you / Trolley song / Boy next door / I love you / Long ago and far away / I didn't know about you / Walkin' my baby back home / There's no you / That's for me / Symphony / On the sunny side of the street / Candy / Over the rainbow / I'll be with you in apple blossom time / Let's take the long way home / Sometimes I'm happy / Fools rush in / Ridin' on the gravy train / This is always / Things we did last summer
JASMCD 2544 / Apr '97 / Jasmine

☐ ONE AND ONLY, THE
I promise you / Friend of yours / Why can't you behave / This is the moment / Roses of Picardy / Smiling through / Last mile home / Red River Valley / If I ever love again / Happy times / On the out-going tide / If I loved you / Goodnight Irene / Autumn leaves / Some time / La vie en rose / Our very own / I hate men / Congratulations / Old rugged cross
CDSL 8276 / Nov '95 / Music For Pleasure

☐ SOLDIERS' SWEETHEARTS (3CD Set) (Stafford, Jo/Vera Lynn/Anne Shelton)
You belong to me: *Stafford, Jo* / Allentown jail: *Stafford, Jo* / Come rain or come shine: *Stafford, Jo* / On London Bridge: *Stafford, Jo* / As I love you: *Stafford, Jo* / Make love to me: *Stafford, Jo* / Shrimp boats: *Stafford, Jo* / Tennessee waltz: *Stafford, Jo* / I'll be seeing you: *Stafford, Jo* / Whispering hope: *Stafford, Jo* / Teach me tonight: *Stafford, Jo* / Jambalaya: *Stafford, Jo* / Thank you for calling, goodbye: *Stafford, Jo* / Ay round the corner: *Stafford, Jo* / If: *Stafford, Jo* / Keep it secret: *Stafford, Jo* / Stardust: *Stafford, Jo* / Hawaiian war chant: *Stafford, Jo* / If you've got the money, I've got the time: *Stafford, Jo* / Embraceable you: *Stafford, Jo* / Every night when the sun goes in: *Stafford, Jo* / I should care: *Stafford, Jo* / It is no secret: *Stafford, Jo* / St. Louis blues: *Stafford, Jo* / We'll meet again: *Lynn, Vera* / Wishing (will make it so): *Lynn, Vera* / Mexicali Rose: *Lynn, Vera* / I paid for the lie that I told you: *Lynn, Vera* / I shall be waiting: *Lynn, Vera* / Little Sir Echo: *Lynn, Vera* / Little boy that Santa Claus forgot: *Lynn, Vera* / Goodnight children everywhere: *Lynn, Vera* / My own: *Lynn, Vera* / Who's taking you home tonight: *Lynn, Vera* / Bells of St. Mary's: *Lynn, Vera* / Harbour lights: *Lynn, Vera* / It's a sin to tell a lie: *Lynn, Vera* / Lonely sweetheart: *Lynn, Vera* / Memory of a rose: *Lynn, Vera* / It's a lovely day tomorrow: *Lynn, Vera* / I'll pray for you: *Lynn, Vera* / Nightingale sang in Berkeley Square: *Lynn, Vera* / Medley: *Lynn, Vera* / Wish me luck as you wave me goodbye: *Lynn, Vera* / I'll never smile again: *Shelton, Anne* / There goes that song again: *Shelton, Anne* / Yes my darling daughter: *Shelton, Anne* / Fools rush in: *Shelton, Anne* / I don't want to walk without you: *Shelton, Anne* / You'd be so nice to come home to: *Shelton, Anne* / Coming in on a wing and a prayer: *Shelton, Anne* / Last time I saw Paris: *Shelton, Anne* / I don't want to set the world on fire: *Shelton, Anne* / Nightingale sang in Berkeley Square: *Shelton, Anne* / Taking a chance on love: *Shelton, Anne* / Only you: *Shelton, Anne* / Daddy: *Shelton, Anne* / My Yiddishe Momme: *Shelton, Anne* / Until you fall in love: *Shelton, Anne* / Amapola: *Shelton, Anne* / Kiss the boys goodbye: *Shelton, Anne* / Lili Marlene: *Shelton, Anne* / I'll be seeing you: *Shelton, Anne*
PAK 905 / May '95 / Parade

☐ SPOTLIGHT ON JO STAFFORD (Great Ladies Of Song)
It was just one of those things / I didn't know about you / Walking my baby back home / Too marvellous for words / In the still of the night / Autumn leaves / Sugar / Haunted heart / Best things in life are free / Boy next door / Sometimes I'm happy / Fools rush in / On the sunny side of the street / I remember you / Always true to you in my fashion / La vie en rose / Over the rainbow / I'll be with you in apple blossom time
CZ 565 / Mar '96 / Premier/EMI

☐ TOO MARVELLOUS FOR WORDS
You and your love / What is this thing called love / Walkin' my baby back home / Pistol packin' Mama / Boy in khaki, a girl in lace / How sweet you are / I love you / Symphony / Too marvellous for words / This is always / I'll be with you in apple blossom time / Things we did last summer / Lullaby of Broadway / Georgia / Out of this world / Blue moon / Cindy / I didn't know about you / Long ago and far away / There's no you / You keep coming back like a song / Day by day / I've never forgotten
CDMOIR 522 / Apr '95 / Memoir

☐ VERY BEST OF JO STAFFORD, THE
You belong to me / Allentown jail / Come rain or come shine / On London Bridge / As I love you / Make love to me / Shrimp boats / Tennessee waltz / I'll be seeing you / Whispering hope / Teach me tonight / Jambalaya / Thank you for calling goodbye / Ay-round the corner / If / Keep a secret / Keep a secret / Stardust / Hawaiian war chant / St. Louis blues / It is no secret / I should care / Every night when the sun goes in / Embraceable you / If you've got the money, I've got the time / Hawaiina war chant
PAR 2064 / May '96 / Parade

Stafford, Terell

☐ CENTRIPETAL FORCE
Addio / I'll wait / Skylark / Old devil moon / Child is born / Mia / For the broken hearted / My romance / Daahoud / Somebody bigger than you and I
CCD 79718 / Jul '97 / Candid

☐ TIME TO LET GO
Time to let go / Was it meant to be / Polka dots and moonbeams / Qui qui / On the trail / Why / Soon / Send in the clowns / Just a closer walk with thee
CACD 79702 / Feb '97 / Candid

Stage Bottles

☐ BIG KICK
MBRCD 016 / 20 Jul '98 / Knock Out

Stagg, Richard

☐ JAPANESE BAMBOO FLUTE, THE
EUCD 1103 / '91 / ARC

Stahl, Jeanie

☐ MYSTERIES
DARINGCD 3017 / Nov '95 / Daring

Stahlhammer

☐ KILLERINSTINKT
HGCD 0651 / 15 Jun '98 / High Gain

☐ WIENER BLUT
HGCD 0959 / 15 Jun '98 / High Gain

Staines, Bill

☐ FIRST MILLION MILES VOL.2, THE
Rodeo rose / Only a song / January snow / Sunny road / Redbird's wing / Shores of Prudhoe Bay / Bird in the wind / Border blues / Sunshine islands / First lullabye / Sweet sunny South / Heart alone / Northland / Gambler's game / Stone face / Coyote / Last Margarita's at Monterey / Lovers and losers / Spirit song
ROUCD 11580 / Jun '98 / Rounder

☐ GOING TO THE WEST
RHRCD 56 / Oct '95 / Red House

☐ LOOKING FOR THE WIND
RHRCD 79 / Dec '95 / Red House

☐ ONE MORE RIVER
RHRCD 111 / May '98 / Red House

Stains

☐ SONGS FOR SWINGING LOVERS
DOXOCD 260 / Jul '96 / Dojo

Stainsby, Trevor

☐ RHYTHM OF RETURN, THE
HWYLCD 3 / May '89 / Hwyl

Stakka Bo

☐ GREAT BLONDINO, THE
5316582 / Apr '96 / Polydor

Stalag 13

☐ IN CONTROL
LF 058 / Aug '93 / Lost & Found

Stalker

☐ UNBALANCED
SDC 01 / 1 Sep '97 / Sankeys Doap

Stallings, Mary

☐ FINE AND MELLOW
CCD 1001 / Jul '98 / Clarity

☐ I WAITED FOR YOU (Stallings, Mary & Gene Harris)
When or where / Love dance / I waited for you / Blues in my heart / Dedicated to you / It's crazy / Serenade in blue / But not for me / I wanna be loved / Only trust your heart / Ain't nobody's business if I do
CCD 4620 / Nov '94 / Concord Jazz

☐ SPECTRUM
Black coffeee / Daydream / I just dropped by to say hello / If I had you / Just as though you were here / No love, no nothin' / Robbin's nest / Say it isn't so / Soft winds / Solitude / Some other time / Tears in heaven / Things are looking up
CCD 4689 / Apr '96 / Concord Jazz

Stallions

☐ HEY BABY IT'S THE STALLIONS
168122 / 4 May '98 / Junk

Stallone, Frank

☐ CLOSE YOUR EYES
I can't believe / Close your eyes / I got a ring to sing the blues / Saturday night / Exactly like you / By the river St. Marie / Gee baby ain't I good to you / I didn't know what time it was / Baby won't you please come here / Long ago and far away
30373 00022 / Mar '96 / Carlton

Stamford Bridge

☐ COME UP AND SEE US SOMETIME/ THE FIRST DAY OF YOUR LIFE
Little boy blue / Roly poly / Johnny Rebel / Happiness and rainy days / Come up and see me sometime / Face in the crowd / Falling in and out of love / Chelsea / Molly Perkins / Wonder lady / Yours sincerely / Vicar's daughter / What do I care / Rise Sally rise / Mother of nature / Goodbye today, hello tomorrow / Let's go to San Francisco / Who knows what I need / Move out of town / First day of your life / Letter from America / Chaquita Maria / Tumbleweed town / Arizona lost and gone / Four letter word / Ossie / World of fantasy
SEECD 478 / Jun '97 / See For Miles

Stamm, Marvin

☐ BOP BOY
MM 65065 / Oct '94 / Music Masters

☐ MYSTERY MAN
MM 65085 / Oct '94 / Music Masters

Stampin' Ground

☐ DEMONS RUN AMOK
WB 1169CD / Jun '97 / We Bite

☐ STAMPIN' GROUND
WB 1148MCD / Sep '96 / We Bite

Stanciu, Simon

☐ MUSIQUE TZIGANE EN ROUMAINE
ARN 64236 / Aug '93 / Arion

Stand Up

☐ WORDS IN MOTION
CI 0052 / Mar '93 / CI

Standells

☐ DIRTY WATER
Medication / Little Sally Tease / There is a storm comin' / Nineteenth nervous breakdown / Dirty water / Pride and devotion / Sometimes good guys don't wear white / Hey Joe / Why did you hurt me / Rari / Why pick on me / Paint it black / Mi hai fatto innamorare / Black hearted woman / Girl and the moon / Mr. Nobody / My little red book / Mainline / Have you ever spent the night in jail
CDSC 6019 / Apr '94 / Sundazed

☐ DIRTY WATER/THE HOT ONES
EVA 842121B5 / Nov '94 / EVA

☐ HOT ONES, THE
Last train to Clarksville / Wild thing / Sunshine superman / Sunny afternoon / Li'l Red Riding Hood / Eleanor Rigby / Black is black / Summer in the city / You were the one / School girl / Ten o'clock scholar / When I was a cowboy / Don't ask me what to do / Misty lane / Standell's love them
CDSC 6021 / Apr '94 / Sundazed

☐ HOT ONES, THE/TRY IT
Last train to Clarksville / Wild thing / Sunshine superman / Sunny afternoon / Li'l Red Riding Hood / Eleanor rigby / Black is black / Summer in the city / Nineteenth nervous breakdown / Dirty water / Can't help but love you / Ninety nine and a half (won't do) / Trip to paradise / St. James infirmary / Try it / Barracuda / Did you ever have that feeling / All fall down / Poor shell of a man / Riot on sunset strip
CDWIKD 112 / Mar '93 / Big Beat

☐ IS THIS THE WAY YOU GET YOUR HIGH
Dirty water / Rari / Sometimes good guys don't wear white / Medication / There is a storm comin' / Nineteenth nervous breakdown / Why did you hurt me / Why pick on me / Paint it black / Black hearted woman / Mainline / Mr. Nobody / Wild thing / Riot on Sunset Strip / Try it / Barracuda / Poor shell of a man / Can't help but love you / Ninety nine and a half (won't do) / Animal girl / Soul drippin' / Enimal girl
CDWIKD 114 / Jun '93 / Big Beat

☐ STANDELLS RARITIES (& Riot On Sunset Strip)
Riot on sunset strip / Sunset Sally: *Mugwumps* / Sunset theme: *Sidewalk Sounds* / Old country: *Travis, Debra* / Don't need your lovin': *Chocolate Watch Band* / Children of the night: *Mom's Boys* / Make the music pretty: *Sidewalk Sounds* / Get away from here / Like my baby: *Drew* / Sitting there standing: *Chocolate Watch Band* / Love me / Batman / Our candidate / Boy who is lost / It's all in your mind / School girl / I hate to leave you / Looking at tomorrow / Don't say nothing at all / Try it (Alternate vocal) / Rari (Extended version)
CDWIKD 113 / Jun '93 / Big Beat

☐ TRY IT
Can't help but love you / Ninety nine and a half (won't do) / Trip to paradise / St. James infirmary / Try it / Did it ever have the feeling / All fall down / Poor shell of a man / Riot on sunset strip / Get away from here / Animal girl / Soul drippin' / Can you dig it
CDSC 6022 / Apr '94 / Sundazed

☐ WHY PICK ON ME
Why pick on me / Paint it black / Mi hai fatto innamorare / I hate to leave / Black hearted woman / Sometimes good guys don't wear white / Girl and the moon / Looking at tomorrow / Mr. Nobody / My little red book / Mainline / Have you ever spent the night in jail / Our candidate / Don't say nothing at all / Boy who is lost
SC 6020 / Oct '97 / Sundazed

Stanford Prison Experiment

☐ GATO HUNCH
You're the Vulgarian / Repeat removal / (Very) Put out / Cansado / Flap / So far, so good / El nuevo / Accomplice / Harcord idiot / Swoon / Worst case scenario
WDOM 020CD / Aug '95 / World Domination

☐ STANFORD PRISON EXPERIMENT
Disbelief / Take it / Written apology / Super monkey / Get on / Course / What's an epidemic / Mr. teacher dad / It's expected I'm gone / Frozen / Sheepst / Rob hates
WDOM 009CD / Jun '94 / World Domination

Stanko, Tomasz

☐ BALLADYNA
First song / Tale / Num / Duet / Balladyna / Last song / Nenaliina
51928922 / Nov '93 / ECM

☐ LEOSIA
Morning heavy song / Die weisheit von le comte lautreamont / Farewell to Maria / Brace / Trinity / Forlorn walk / Hungry howl / No bass trio / Euforila / Leosia
5316932 / Apr '97 / ECM

☐ LITANIA (Music Of Krzystof Komeda)
Svantatic / Sleep safe and warm / Nightime daytime requiem / Ballada / Litania / Sleep safe and warm / Repetition / Ballad for Bernt / Witch
5375512 / Sep '97 / ECM

☐ MATKA JOANNA
Monastery in the dark / Green sky / Malador's war song / Tales for a girl, 12 / Matka joanna from the angels / Cain's brand / Nun's wood / Celina / Two preludes for tales / Klostergeist
5239862 / Oct '95 / ECM

☐ TWET
PBR 33860 / Aug '95 / Power Bros.

Stanley & The Turbines

☐ AFRICA
LG 21117 / Aug '96 / Lagoon

☐ BIG BAMBOO
Big bamboo / Young gal / Calypso on the island / Balm yard / Dream of me / Carnival / Memories / Oh Beverly / Where have all the young girls gone
JMC 200203 / Feb '93 / Jamaican Gold

Stanley Brothers

☐ CLINCH MOUNTAIN BLUEGRASS
Introduction / Orange blossom special / How mountain girls can love / Model T / Man of constant sorrow / Gathering flowers for the Master's bouquet / Choo choo coming / All aboard for Baltimore / White dove / Hard times / Jordan / Rank stranger / Little birdie / Shout little Luly / Clinch Mountain backstep / Hard times / Little Maggie / How mountain girls can love / Man of constant sorrow / Little glass of wine / Big tildy / Orange blossom special
VCD 77018 / Jan '96 / Vanguard

☐ EARLIEST RECORDINGS (Complete Rich-R-Tone 78s 1947-1952)
REV 203 / 3 Nov '97 / Revenant

☐ SHADOWS OF THE PAST
COPCD 101 / May '96 / Copper Creek

☐ SONGS OF THE STANLEY BROTHERS (Various Artists)
Long journey home: *Jim & Jesse* / Say, won't you be mine: *Skaggs, Ricky* / Man of constant sorrow: *Furtado, Tony & Tim O'Brien* / Girl behind the bar: *Dry Branch Fire Squad* / If I lose: *Grisman, David* / Harbor of love: *Johnson Mountain Boys* / Clinch Mountain backstep: *Munde, Alan* / Vision of Mother: *Val, Joe & New England Bluegrass Boys* / Dream of a miner's child: *Boyens, Phyllis & Hazel Dickens* / White dove: *Jim & Jesse/Ricky Scaggs* / You'd better get right: *Williams, Vern* / Rank strangers to me: *Hot Rize*
EDCD 7022 / Feb '97 / Easydisc

☐ STANLEY BROTHERS & THE CLINCH MOUNTAIN BOYS (2CD Set) (Stanley Brothers & The Clinch Mountain Boys)
Won't you be mine / This weary heart you stole away / I'm lonesome without you / Our last goodbye / Poison lies / Dickson County breakdown / I long to see the old folks / Voice from on high / Memories of mother / Could you love me (one more time) / Nobody's love is like mine / I just got wise / Blue moon of Kentucky / Close by / Calling from heaven / Harbor love / Hard times / Baby girl / Say you'll take me back / I worship you / You're still on my mind / I hear my saviour calling / Just a little talk with Jesus / So blue / You'd better get right / Tragic love / Lonesome and blue / Orange blossom special / Clinch mountain blues / Big Tilda / Will he wait a little longer / Angel Band / Cry from the cross / Who will call you sweetheart / I'm lost, I'll never find the way / Let me walk, Lord, by your side / Lonesome night / Flood / Fling ding / I'll never grow tired of you / Loving you too well / Daybreak in Dixie / If that's the way you feel / Life of sorrow / I'd rather be forgotten / No school bus in heaven / Meet me tonight / Ain't nobody's business if I do
BCD 15681 / Oct '93 / Bear Family

☐ STANLEY BROTHERS & THE CLINCH MOUNTAIN BOYS 1949-1952 (Stanley Brothers & The Clinch Mountain Boys)
Vision of mother / White dove / Gathering flowers for the master's bouquet / Angels are singing / It's never too late / Have you someone (in Heaven waiting) / Little glass of wine / Let me be your friend / We'll be sweethearts in Heaven / I love no one but you / Too late to cry / Old home / Drunkard's hell / Fields have turned brown / Hey hey hey / Lonesome river / I'm a man of constant sorrow / Pretty Polly / Life of sorrow / Sweetest love / Wandering boy / Let's part the best of friends
BCD 15564 / Nov '93 / Bear Family

☐ STANLEY SERIES VOL.3
COPCD 5511 / Feb '96 / Copper Creek

Stanley, Michael

☐ MISERY LOVES COMPANY (More Of The Best 1975-1983) (Stanley, Michael Band)
RE 2125 / Feb '97 / Razor & Tie

Stanley, Ralph

☐ CLINCH MOUNTAIN COUNTRY (2CD Set)
How mountain girls can love / Shouting on the hills of glory / Pretty Polly / Window up above / I just got wise / If that's the way you feel / Nobody's love is like mine / Memories of Mother / Lonesome river / Old love letters / She's more to be pitied / When I wake up to sleep no more / Another night / Gold watch and chain / Thy burdens are greater than mine / I'll take the blame / How can we thank him for what he has done / I've just seen the rock of ages / Pig in a pen / I only exist / Lonesome night / Pretty little Miss in the garden / Darkest hour is just before dawn / Stone walls and steel bars / Beautiful star of Bethlehem / Let me love you one more time / White dove / Will you ever miss me at all / Lonesome banjo man / Are you afraid to die / Way down deep / If I lose / I'm going that way / Gathering flowers for the master's bouquet / My deceitful heart / Bright morning star
REB 5001 / Jun '98 / Rebel

☐ LIVE IN JAPAN (Stanley, Ralph & The Clinch Mountain Boys)
How mountain girls can love / Leather britches / Sitting on top of the world / Love me darling just tonight / Clinch mountain backstep / Uncle pen / Memories of mother / Little maggie / Listen to the mockingbird / Ridin' that midnight train / Baby girl / Sourwood mountain / I saw the light / Orange blossom special / Blue moon of Kentucky / Long journey home / Pretty polly / Daybreak in Toronto / All the good times are past and gone / How far to little rock / Mountain dew / Rank strangers / Walkin' in my sleep / I'm a man of constant morrow / I hear a choo choo coming / Old country church / Hard times / White dove / Old time pickin'
REBCD 2002 / 9 Mar '98 / Rebel

☐ MASTERS OF THE BANJO (Stanley, Ralph & Tony Ellis/Seleshe Damassae)
ARHCD 421 / Apr '95 / Arhoolie

☐ MY ALL AND ALL
Jesus on the mainline / He's my all and all / I hope to meet you in the morning / This old troublesome world / Loving grace of God / Uncloudy day / I'm not ashamed / We are drinking from the fountain / Take me home / While eternal ages roll / Two coats / I firmly promise you
REBCD 1740 / Jul '97 / Rebel

☐ RALPH STANLEY - SATURDAY NIGHT AND SUNDAY MORNING (2CD Set)
FRC 9001 / Oct '93 / Freeland Recording Company

☐ SHORT LIFE OF TROUBLE
REB 1735CD / Dec '96 / Rebel

☐ SONGS MY MOTHER TAUGHT ME
75044206552 / 19 May '98 / FRC

Stansfield, Lisa

☐ AFFECTION
This is the right time / Mighty love / Sincerity / Love in me / All around the world / What did I do to you / Live together / You can't deny it / Poison / When are you coming back / Affection / Wake up baby / Way you want it
260379 / Aug '95 / Arista

☐ LISA STANSFIELD
Never gonna fall / Real thing / I'm leavin' / Suzanne / Never, never gonna give you up / Don't cry for me / Line / Very thought of you / You know how to love me / I cried my last tear last night / Honest / Somewhere in time / Got me missing you / Footsteps / Real thing / People hold on
74321458512 / Mar '97 / Arista

☐ REAL LOVE
Change / Real love / Set your loving free / I will be waiting / All woman / Soul deep / Make love to ya / Time to make you mine / Symptoms of loneliness and heartache / It's got to be real / First joy / Tenderly / Little more love
262300 / Jul '96 / Arista

☐ SO NATURAL
So natural / I give you everything / Marvellous and mine / Little bit of heaven / Goodbye / Sweet memories / She's always there / Turn me on / Never set me free / Wish I could always be this way / In all the right places
74321172312 / 1 Sep '97 / Arista

Stanshall, Vivian

☐ TEDDY BOYS DON'T KNIT
King Kripple / Slave valse / Gums / Biwilderbeeste / Calypso to calapso / Tube / Ginger geezer / Cracks are showing / Flung a dummy / Possibly an arm chair / Fresh faced boys / Terry keeps his clips on / Bass Macaw and broken bottles / Nose hymn / Everyday I have the blues / Smoke signals at night / Nouveau riffe
CASCD 1153 / Jun '91 / Charisma

Stanton, Ian

☐ ROLLIN' THUNDER
SRCD 003 / Nov '96 / Stream

Staple Singers

☐ BEALTITUDE: RESPECT YOURSELF
This world / Respect yourself / Name the missing word / I'll take you there / This old town / We the people / Are you sure / Who do you think you are / I'm just another soldier / Who
CDSXE 001 / May '91 / Stax

☐ GREAT DAY
Gloryland / Everybody will be happy / Here me call, here / Nobody knows the trouble I've seen / I'm willin' / Great day / Do you know him / New-born soul / Dying man's plea / New home / Wish I had answered / Better home / Old time religion / Swing low, sweet chariot / Motherless children / Gamblin' man / I know I've been changed / Jesus is all / You got shoes / What are they doing (in heaven today) / Will the Lord rememeber me / My dying bed / Let Jesus lead you / Praying time / I can't help from cryin' sometime / Masters of war
CDCH 391 / May '92 / Ace

☐ RESPECT YOURSELF (The Best Of The Staple Singers)
Heavy makes you happy / Long walk to DC / This world / Respect yourself / I see it / We'll get over / Take you there / Oh la de da / Are you sure / If you're ready (come go with me) / Touch a hand, make a friend / City in the sky / People come out of your shell / You've got to earn it / Love is plentiful / Got to be some changes made / Be what you are / This old town / Slow train / My main man
CDSX 006 / Oct '87 / Stax

☐ SOUL FOLK IN ACTION/WE'LL GET OVER
We've got to get ourselves together / (Sittin' on the) dock of the bay / Top of the mountain / Slow train / Weight / Long walk to DC / Got to be some changes made / Ghetto / People, my people / I see it / This year / We'll get over / Give a damn / Everyday people / End of our road / Tend to your own business / Solon bushi / Challenge / God bless the children / Games people play / Wednesday in your garden / Gardener / When will be paid (For the work we did)
CDSXD 109 / Jul '94 / Stax

☐ STAPLE SWINGERS
This is a perfect world / What's your thing / You've got to earn it / You're gonna make me cry / Little boy / How do you move a mountain / Almost / I'm a lover / Love is plentiful / Heavy makes you happy / I like the things about you / Give a hand take a hand
CDSXE 035 / Feb '91 / Stax

☐ UNCLOUDY DAY
Uncloudy day / Let me ride / Help me Jesus / I'm coming home / God's wonderful love / Low is the way / Ain't that good news / This may be the last time / I had a dream / Going away / I know I got religion / Will the circle be unbroken / Stand by me / Come up in glory / Pray on / Somebody save me / Each day / So soon / Too close / Let's go home
CPCD 8087 / Apr '95 / Charly

Staples, Mavis

☐ DON'T CHANGE ME NOW
Ready for the heartbreak / Sweet things you do / Chokin' kind / House is not a home / Security / Good to me / You send me / I'm tired / Why can't it be like it used to be / You're the fool / You're all I need / I have learned to do without you / How many times / Endlessly / Since I fell for you / Since you became a part of my life / Don't change me now / You're driving me (to the arms of a stranger) / Pick up the pieces / Chains of love / What happened to the real me / It makes me wanna cry
CDSX 014 / Aug '88 / Stax

☐ SPIRITUALS AND GOSPELS (Staples, Mavis & Lucky Peterson)
5335622 / Nov '96 / Verve

☐ VOICE, THE
0060542 / May '95 / Edel

Staples, Pops

☐ FATHER FATHER
Father Father / Why am I treated so bad / Too big for your britches / Jesus is going to make up (My dying bed) / Downward road / People get ready / Hope in a hopeless world / You got to serve somebody / Waiting for my child / Simple man / Glory glory
VPBCD 19 / May '94 / Pointblank

☐ PEACE IN THE NEIGHBORHOOD
World in motion / Love is a precious thing / America / Down in mississippl / This may be the last time / (peace to) the neighborhood / Miss cocaine / Pray on my child / I shall not be moved
VPBCD 8 / Mar '92 / Pointblank

Star Accordion Band

☐ SCOTTISH FAVOURITES VOL.2
These are my mountains / Song of the Clyde / Dancing in Kyle / Sottish soldier / Donald, where's yer troosers / Crooked bawbee / There was a lad
CDSLP 606 / May '97 / Lochshore

Star Blanket Jr.

☐ GET UP AND DANCE
CR 6268CD / Nov '96 / Canyon

Star Pimp

☐ SERAPHIM 280Z
Slave girl / Size zero / Yoko Phono / Snowball / Little tattoo / Pee test / Greatest hits of love / Human dolphin / Palmolive / Vegan pussy / Gold / Titty / Vocal fader
TUP 0502 / Jan '94 / Tupelo

Starbean

☐ REFUTING THE EXTRATERRESTRIAL HYPOTHESIS
DUH 026 / 3 Nov '97 / Derivative

Starbelly

☐ STARBELLY
NLL 003 / 29 Jun '98 / Not Lame

Starclub

☐ IHOJIN
INDIGO 35012 / Oct '96 / Pop Biz

Stardust, Alvin

☐ HITS GO ON
STIFFCD 18 / Nov '93 / Disky

☐ I'M A MOODY GUY (Fenton, Shane & The Fentones)
I'm a moody guy / Five foot two / Eyes of blue / Why little girl / It's all over now / It's gonna take magic / Cindy's birthday / Too young for sad memories / Fallen leaves on the ground / You're telling me / Walk away / Don't do that / I'll know / Fool's paradise / You need love / Somebody else not me / I ain't got nobody / Hey Miss Ruby / Hey Lulu / I do, do you / Breeze and I
SEECD 369 / Feb '97 / See For Miles

☐ VERY BEST OF ALVIN STARDUST, THE
My coo ca choo / Pretend / Jealous mind / You you you / Red dress / I feel like Buddy Holly / Good love can never die / Rock 'n' roll united / Shakin' all over / Don't trust that guy / Gotta do it all again / Just to hear your voice / Suddenly / So near to Christmas
10172 / Oct '97 / Go On Deluxe

Starfish Pool

☐ AMPLIFIED TONES
NZ 034 / May '95 / Nova Zembla

☐ CHILL OUT N CONFUSED
NZ 016 / Oct '94 / Nova Zembla

Starfish TX

☐ FRUSTRATED
TR 55CD / Mar '97 / Trance Syndicate

☐ STELLAR SONIC SOLUTIONS
TR 40CD / Oct '95 / Trance

Stargazers

☐ BACK IN ORBIT
Crazy but true / Loretta / It's only a paper moon / Baby, baby, baby / Got that beat / Walking beat / Sweet Georgia Brown / Dig that rock'n'roll / Stargazer's blues / Crazy man crazy / Every cloud has a silver lining / Feeling happy
CDCH 312 / Mar '91 / Ace

☐ FROFFEE COFFEE
Froffee coffee / Fools fall in love / Swingin' on a star / Oh baby doll / County line / Milkcrate mania / What's the matter with music now / Just a gigolo / Willow weep / Where would we be tonight / Mack the knife / Song about a train / Sugar and spice
JRCD 27 / Sep '97 / Jappin' & Rockin'

☐ ROCK THAT BOOGIE
Rock that boogie / Big bad wolf / Hi ho silver / Teenage party / Better believe it / I got a baby / Move over baby / Caravan / La rock 'n' roll / Rockin' rollin' home / Tonight's the night / Little jump, a little swing / Rock lomond / Caldonia / Fat man / Gleam in your eyes / Time goes by / Flying high / Swinging aye / Rebound / Bounce me brother
JRCD 7 / Sep '97 / Jappin' & Rockin'

☐ SPEAKING CLOCK SAYS...ROCK, THE
Lights out / Rockin' Robin / In a little Spanish town / See you later alligator / Pete's beat / Stop beatin' around the mulberry bush / Cat / Just go wild over rock 'n' roll / Lady killer / Florida twist / Shake, rattle and roll / Eat your heart out Annie
JRCD 4 / Sep '97 / Jappin' & Rockin'

Starkey Banton

☐ POWERS YOUTH (Starkey Banton & Dub Organiser)
FABCD 002 / 22 Sep '97 / Dub Organiser

Starkweather

☐ CROSSBEARER
TOODAMNHY 32 / May '94 / Too Damn Hype

☐ INTO THE WIRE
Shroud / Shards / Unto me / Murder in technicolour / Into the wire / Slither
EDISON 001 / 16 Feb '98 / Edison

Starlet

☐ FROM THE ONE YOU LEFT BEHIND
PARCD 027 / 18 Aug '97 / Parasol

Starlight Conspiracy

☐ SOUNDS LIKE A SILVER HOLLER
CTA 009 / May '97 / Catapult

Starlight Orchestra

☐ MUSIC FROM A FRENCH CAFE
Aubade d'oiseaux / Ca gaze / Reine de musette / Automne / La valse des as / Le denicheur / Sous les ponts de Paris / Retour des hirondelles / Bourrasque / Jongleur / Brise Napolitaine / Les triolets / Romance de la nuit / Vendredi treize / Reve d'accordeoniste / Les papillons de la nuit / Perles de cristal / A la bonheur / Bel oiseau / Princesse accordeon / Une partie de petanque / Mazurka fantaisie
QED 079 / Nov '96 / Tring

☐ SUMMER LOVING
Sealed with a kiss / Under the influence of love / Let your love flow / Daytime friends / Physical / Happening / Albatross / It never rains in southern California / Hard rock cafe / Isn't she lovely / Hopelessly devoted to you / You light up my life / Song sung blue / Blue bayou / Green onions / Rhapsody in white / Stranger on the shore / Hustle / Wipeout / Summer of '42
QED 099 / Nov '96 / Tring

Starlights

☐ SOLDERING
HBCD 102 / Jan '94 / Heartbeat

Starling, John

☐ LONG TIME GONE
Long time gone / Turned you to stone / Half a man / Jordan / White line / Hobo on a freight train to heaven / Last thing I needed / Brother juke box / Carolyn at the Broken Wheel Inn / He rode all the way to Texas / Drifting too far from the shore / Dark hollow / (I heard that) Lonesome whistle / Roads and other reasons / Sin City
SHCD 3714 / '88 / Sugar Hill

☐ WAITIN' ON A SOUTHERN TRAIN
New Delhi freight train / We know better / Carolina star / Other side of life / Waitin' on a southern train / Heart trouble / Homestead in my heart / Hey bottle of whisky / Those memories of you / Slow movin' freight train
SHCD 3724 / Aug '95 / Sugar Hill

Starlings

☐ TOO MANY DOGS
As long as you feel worse / Party / Other people's children / D-d-d-dum / Too many dogs / Loch aangeles monster / We can save you / Tears before bedtime / Mr wishy washy / Pushed and pulled
4509951952 / Apr '94 / Anxious

☐ VALID
Now take that / That's it you're in trouble / Unhealthy / Start again / Bad Dad / Right school / Shoot up hill / Sick puppy / Jack
4509902852 / Aug '92 / Anxious

Starmarket

☐ CALENDER
DOL 038CD / Jul '96 / Dolores

☐ STARMARKET
DOL 022CD / Jun '95 / Dolores

Starpimp

☐ DOCUDRAMA
KRS 265CD / Nov '96 / Kill Rock Stars

Starr, Andy

☐ DIG THEM SQUEAKY SHOES
She's a going Jessie / One more time / Rockin' rollin' stone / Deacon Jones / No room for your kind / Round and round / I wanna go south / Give me a woman / Dig them squeaky shoes / Dirty bird song / Do it right / Rockin' reelin' country style / Tell me why / For the want of your love / Love is a simple thing / Me and the fool / Lover man / Knee shakin' / Evil Eve / Little bitty feeling / Lost in a dream / Pledge of love / Do it right now / I'm seeing things (I shouldn't see) / Somali Dolly / I waited for you to remember
BCD 15890 / Jun '95 / Bear Family

Starr, Edwin

☐ 20 GREATEST MOTOWN HITS
Stop her on sight (SOS) / Twenty five miles / Headline news / Agent double o soul / Backstreet / I want my baby back / Funky music sho nuff turns me on / Soul master / You've got my soul on fire / Who's right, who's wrong / War / Stop the war now / Way over there / Take me clear from here / Cloud 9 / There you go / Gonna keep on tryin' till I win your love / Time / My weakness is you / Harlem
5300642 / Jan '93 / Motown

☐ MOTOWN EARLY CLASSICS
Stop her on sight (SOS) / Agent Double-O Soul / Headline news / My weakness is you / If my heart could tell the story / Way over there / You beat me to the punch / Oh how happy / Love is my destination / Time is passin' by / Mighty good lovin' / I am the man for you baby / I'm glad you belong to me / I am your man / Backyard lovin' man / Twenty-five miles / She should have been home / We'll find a way
5521212 / Jul '96 / Spectrum

☐ STOP HER ON SIGHT (SOS)
Stop her on sight (SOS) / Headline news / Time is passin' by / I am the man for you baby / Love is my destination / We'll find a way / Oh how happy / You beat me to the punch / Twenty-five miles / Backyard lovin' man / Running back and forth / Mighty good lovin' / All around the world / I'm glad you belong to me / She should have been home / I am your man
5512862 / Aug '95 / Spectrum

☐ TIMELESS ENERGY
Smooth / Did I jump (or fall in love) / Dream big / On the boulevard of broken hearts / Bedtime story / Can't stop (thinking about you) / Give you back the loving / Just another fool in love / (Get up) Whirlpool of love / Rumours / Patch up / Wait for me / Old flame / Summer madness / Show you love / Long night / If it could only be
3036450012 / Mar '96 / Carlton

Starr, Frankie

☐ ELEVATOR BOOGIE
Elevator boogie / That's the way the big ball bounces / Sky writin' airplane / I don't care what you used to be / I love you too much to leave you / I'm paying the price / Cross my heart (I'm not double crossing you) / There's a vacancy / Your kind wasn't meant for me / My heart can't stand another tear / I want someone to love / You broke your heart breaking mine / Your Daddy's looped again: *Starr, Frankie & Dot Allen* / My woman ain't pretty / Elevator baby / That crazy dream / Between you, me and the gatepost / Great fireball / Little Joe Weatherly / Tear stained bible / John 3-16 / Our love is at an end: *Starr, Frankie & Marty Robbins* / For a lifetime: *Starr, Frankie & Marty Robbins* / I've lost my love and you: *Starr, Frankie & Marty Robbins* / I want someone to love: *Starr, Frankie & Marty Robbins*
BCD 15990 / Nov '96 / Bear Family

Starr, Kay

☐ EMI PRESENTS THE MAGIC OF KAY STARR
Comes a-long a-love / Side by side / Changing partners / Am I a toy or a treasure / Crazy / Going to Chicago blues / Half a photograph / I love Paris / I'm the lonesomest gal in town / If you love me, really love me / It had to be you / Lazy river / Lovesick blues / More than you know / Nevertheless I'm in love with you / On a slowboat to China / PS I love you / Rock 'n' roll waltz / Singing the blues / Wheel of fortune / You're just in love / When a woman loves a man / I'll always be in love with you / Fool fool fool / Allez vous en (go away)
CDMFP 6292 / May '97 / Music For Pleasure

☐ I CRY BY NIGHT/LOSERS WEEPERS
I'm alone because I love you / I cry by night / Baby, won't you please come home / More than you know / Lover man (oh where can you be) / My kinda love / It had to be you / Whispering grass / Nevertheless / What do you see in her / PS I love you / I'm still in love with you / You always hurt the one you love / I should care / I'm a fool to care / Don't take your love from me / When I lost you / Only forever / Gonna get a guy / Please don't talk about me when I'm gone / I miss you so / Faded summer love / When a man loves a woman / Into each life some rain must fall
CTMCD 113 / Mar '97 / EMI

☐ I'VE GOT TO SING 1944-1948
He's funny that way / All of me / Honeysuckle rose / Them there eyes / Love me or leave me / Nobody knows the trouble I've seen / What a difference a day makes / Who's foolin who / Ain't misbehavin' / Cabin in the sky
HEPCD 50 / Apr '98 / Hep

☐ KAY STARR
Wheel of fortune / I'll always be in love with you / If you love me (really love me) / Comes a-long-a-love / Two brothers / Lovesick blues / Side by side / You've got to see Mama ev'ry night / If I could be with you one hour tonight / Mississippi / Bonaparte's retreat / You broke your promise / Half a photograph / Come on a my house / I wanna love you / Three letters / I wish I had a wishbone / Tell me how long the trains been gone / Mama goes where Papa goes / Tonight you belong to me / Changing partners / Dancing on my tears / Waiting at the end of the road / I forgot to forget / Rock 'n' roll waltz
CC 8238 / Nov '94 / EMI

☐ KAY STARR 1947
Them there eyes / Nevertheless / It's a good day / Maybe you'll be there / Pretty baby / Please love me / Stars fell on alabama / Best things in life are free / It happens every spring / I only have eyes for you / Leave me a memory or two / For the first time / So tired / I've got my love to keep me warm
HCD 214 / Jun '94 / Hindsight

☐ MOONBEAMS AND STEAMY DREAMS
STCD 534 / Oct '91 / Stash

☐ MOVIN'
On a slow boat to China / I cover the waterfront / Around the world / Sentimental journey / Night train / Riders in the sky / Goin' to Chicago blues / (Back home again in) Indiana / Song of the wanderer / Swingin' down the lane / Lazy river / Movin'
JASCD 307 / Mar '95 / Jasmine

☐ RISING STARR, A (2CD Set)
Love with a capital you / Baby me / Sharecroppin' blues / If I could I could be with you (one hour tonight) / Come out come out wherever you are / What a diff'rence a day made / Into each life some rain must fall / You always hurt the one you love / Stormy weather / Flyin' too high / My future just passed / What can I say after I say sorry / Betcha I getcha / Nobody knows the trouble I've seen / Ain't misbehavin' / Honeysuckle rose / What a diff'rence a day made / Dixieland band / There's a lull in my life / Should I / Honey / I ain't gonna cry / Don't meddle with my mood / Love me or leave me / Sweet Lorraine / He's funny that way / Baby won't you please come home / Honeysuckle rose / I'm confessin' that I love you / All of me / Who's fooling who / I cried for you / You're just about right for me / Frying pan / Sunday / After you've gone / St. Louis blues / Stardust / Where or when / I've got my love to keep me warm / Woman always understands / It's whatcha do with whatcha got / Pretty baby / So tiered / Please love me / Them there eyes / Lonesomest gal in town / You've got to see mama ev'ry night
JASCD 337/8 / 8 Nov '97 / Jasmine

☐ SINGS STANDARDS
Pretty baby / Them there eyes / I ain't gonna cry / It happens every spring / If I could be with you / So tired / Mama goes where papa goes / Honeysuckle rose / Best things in life are free / You've got to see mama every night / I've got my love to keep me warm / Should I / Stars fell on Alabama / Don't meddle in my mind / Honey / I only have eyes for you / Ain't misbehavin' / Nevertheless / It's a good day
307792 / Aug '97 / Hallmark

☐ WHAT A DIFFERENCE A DAY MADE
Dixieland band / There's a lull in my life / Ain't misbehavin' / What a difference a day made / What can I say dear after I say I'm sorry / Nobody knows the trouble I've seen / What goes up must come down / Honeysuckle rose / My future just passed / Betcha I getcha / You're always there / Don't do something to someone else / Blame my absentminded heart / It's a great feeling
HCD 229 / Mar '96 / Hindsight

Starr, Ringo

☐ BEAUCOUPS OF BLUES
Beaucoups of blues / Love don't last long / Fastest growing heartache in the west / Coochy coochy / Silent homecoming / Waiting / Loser's lounge / I wouldn't have it any other way / Wine, women and and loud happy songs / Without her / Woman of the night / I'd be talking all the time / Fifteen dollar draw
CDPAS 10002 / May '95 / Apple

☐ LIVE FROM MONTREUX (Starr, Ringo & His All-Starr Band)
Really serious introduction / I'm the greatest / Don't go where the road don't go / Yellow submarine / Desperado / I can't tell you why / Girls talk / Weight of the world / Bang the drum all day / Walking nerve / Black Maria / In the city / American woman / Boys / With a little help from my friends
RCD 20264 / Oct '93 / Rykodisc

☐ SENTIMENTAL JOURNEY
Sentimental journey / Night and day / Whispering grass / Bye bye blackbird / I'm a fool to care / Stardust / Blue turning grey over you / Love is a many splendoured thing / Dream / You always hurt the one you love / Have I told you lately that I love you / Let the rest of the world go by
CDPCS 7101 / May '95 / Apple

☐ VERTICAL MAN
5585982 / 3 Aug '98 / Mercury

Stars Of Faith

☐ FAMOUS SPIRITUALS, NEGRO SPIRITUALS
BB 3222 / Sep '95 / Black & Blue

☐ LIVE AT MONTREUX
BLE 591862 / Apr '92 / Black & Blue

Stars Of The Lid

☐ BALLASTED ORCHESTRA
KRANK 015CD / Jan '97 / Kranky

☐ GRAVITATIONAL PULL VS. THE DESIRE FOR AN AQUATIC LIFE
KRANK 20 / 6 Oct '97 / Kranky

☐ PER ASPERA AD ASTRA
KRANK 028CD / 24 Aug '98 / Kranky

Starseeds

☐ PARALLEL LIFE
Parallel life / Behind the sun / Timequakes / Sonne, mond und sterne / Heavensairportcoffeeshoprestaurant / Subspace radio signals / Earth moon and stars / Regina from the future / Elsewhere
MILL 30CD / 24 Aug '98 / Millenium

Starsound

☐ BEST OF STARS ON 45, THE
MCCD 192 / Nov '94 / Music Club

Starsound Orchestra

☐ I'M IN THE MOOD FOR ROMANCE
LPCD 1023 / Apr '94 / Disky

Starspeed Transmission

☐ METAMORPHIC ILLUMINATION
NZ 012CD / Aug '94 / Nova Zembla

Stasis

☐ ALBUM
OPCD 1 / Apr '97 / Op-Art

☐ INSPIRATION
Natural people / Sound files nos 68 / Inside / Exosphere / Sound files nos 13 / They shit chips don't they / Pork chop hill / Sound files nos 94 / World out of time / Inspiration / Sound files nos 7 / Welcome to the new age disco
PF 028CD / Aug '95 / Peacefrog

State Of Grace

☐ EVERYONE ELSE'S UNIVERSE
Conspiracy / Perfect and wild / See-saw / Hello (fall out the lions) / Rose II / Name of the game
STONE 028CD / 16 Mar '98 / 3rd Stone

☐ JAMBOREEBOP
Whetherette / Smile / And love will fall / Flourescent sea / Hello / Mystery / Bitter sun / Different world / Rose / New fear / Truth / Jamboreebop
STONE 014CD / 30 Mar '98 / 3rd Stone

☐ PACIFIC MOTION
Sooner or later / Miss you IV / Camden / Love pain and passion II / Bitter sun II / Ruby sky / Head / PS High / Miss you (Arizona mix)
STONE 008CD / 30 Mar '98 / 3rd Stone

State Of The Heart

☐ CHRISTMAS MOODS
White Christmas / Spaceman came travelling / I believe in Father Christmas / Mistletoe and wine / Last Christmas / Wonderful Christmastime / Rockin' around the Christmas tree / Merry Christmas everybody / I wish it could be Christmas everyday / Another rock'n'roll Christmas / Frosty the snowman / Rudolph the red nosed reindeer / I saw Mommy kissing Santa Claus / Winter wonderland / Fairytale of New York / Santa Claus is coming to town / Please come home for Christmas / Lonely this Christmas / Happy Xmas (war is over) / Christmas song / Blue Christmas / Do they know it's Christmas / Let it snow, let it snow, let it snow / When a child is born / Stay another day / First Noel
VTCD 105 / Nov '96 / Virgin

☐ PURE SAX
Love me for a reason / Careless whisper / Save the best for last / Can you feel the love tonight / Most beautiful girl in the world / Holding back the years / You are not alone / I wonder why / Crazy for you / After the love has gone / How am I supposed to live without you / True / Lily was here / End of the road / Goodnight girl / I want to know what love is / I believe / My funny valentine
CDVIP 182 / Apr '97 / Virgin VIP

☐ SAX AT THE MOVIES
Unchained melody / Love is all around / Show me heaven / Because you loved me / How deep is your love / Kiss from a rose / Can you feel the love tonight / Somewhere out there / (Everything I do) I do it for you / Glory of love / Arthur's theme (Best that you can get) / (I've had) The time of my life / Up where we belong / When a man loves a woman / My funny valentine / Take my breath away / It must have been love / Gangsta's paradise (Pasttime paradise)
CDVIP 181 / Apr '97 / Virgin VIP

☐ SAX COLLECTION, THE (2CD Set)
Love me for a reason / Careless whisper / Save the best for last / Girl from Ipanema / Most beautiful girl in the world / Holding back the years / You are not alone / I wonder why / Crazy for you / After the love has gone / How am I supposed to live without you / True / Lily was here / End of the road / Goodnight girl / I want to know what love is / I believe / Baker Street / Unchained melody / Love is all around / Show me heaven / Because you loved me / How deep is your love / Kiss from a rose / Can you feel the love tonight / Somewhere out there / (Everything I do) I do it for you / Glory of love / Arthur's theme (best that you can get) / (I've had) the time of my life / Up where we belong / When a man loves a woman / My funny valentine / I will always love you / Take my breath away / It must have been love / Waiting for a star to fall / Gangsta's paradise (pastime paradise)
VTDCD 122 / Mar '97 / Virgin

State Street Ramblers

☐ STATE STREET RAMBLERS
CJR 1003 / May '96 / Gannet

☐ STATE STREET RAMBLERS VOL.1 1927-1931
JPCD 1512 / Dec '94 / Jazz Perspectives

☐ STATE STREET RAMBLERS VOL.2 1931-1936
JPCD 1513 / Dec '94 / Jazz Perspectives

Statetrooper

☐ STATETROOPER
Shape of things to come / Set fire to the night / Dreams of the faithful / Stand me up / Veni vidi vici / Last stop to heaven / She got the look / Too late / Armed and ready
WKFMXD 91 / May '87 / FM

Static Icon

☐ SIN MACHINE
MA 672 / Apr '96 / Machinery

☐ SLAVE
It's a lifestyle / Taste the pain / Desire / Whip it / Unite / Krakow / Why do we believe / Overcome
MA 682 / Mar '97 / Machinery

Static Seekers

☐ BODY AUTOMATIC
AXS 007CD / Sep '90 / Axis

Statics

☐ PUNK ROCK 'N' ROLL
RIPOFF 026CD / Sep '97 / Rip Off

Statik Sound System

☐ TEMPESTA
Free to choose what / So close / Essential times / Dr. Wheeler / Valentine / Dreams of mine / Sonar / Jack / Amazed by you / In our own dub / Jack laid bare
COTCD 003 / Oct '96 / Cup Of Tea

☐ TEMPESTA (The Reworkings)
Living in essential times / Sonar / Essential times / Dreams of mine / Amazed by you / Jack / Dr. Wheeler / Valentine / Amazed by you / Free to choose / Outside now
COTCD 009 / Jul '97 / Cup Of Tea

Statis

☐ FROM THE OLD TO THE NEW
From the old / Utopia planetia / Moon bong / Behind the smile / Beatings skins / Ale house blues / Samba de fat bloke / Moody old teacher / Gun
PF 046CD / Jun '96 / Peacefrog

Statman, Andy

☐ ANDY'S RAMBLE
ROUCD 0244 / Dec '94 / Rounder

☐ BETWEEN HEAVEN AND EARTH (Statman, Andy Quartet)
SH 64079 / Feb '97 / Shanachie

☐ **SONGS OF OUR FATHERS (Traditional Jewish Melodies) (Statman, Andy & David Grisman)**
ACS 014CD / Apr '97 / Acoustics

Staton, Candi

☐ **BEST OF CANDI STATON, THE**
Six nights and a day / Run to me / Here I am again / Honest I do love you / As long as he takes care of home / Dreamer of a dream / He's making love to you / Halfway to heaven / I ain't got nowhere to go / When you wake up tomorrow / Take my hand precious lord / Victim / One more chance on love / Young hearts run free
9362457302 / Nov '95 / Warner Bros.

☐ **GLORIFY**
Sing a song / He is Lord / To glorify your name / It's not easy / Have you tried God / First face / I want to see / God's got it / He's coming back
CDBM 075 / '91 / Blue Moon

☐ **GOSPEL ALBUM, THE**
Hallelujah / Stand up (and be a witness) / He's always been there / It's not easy / I'm depending on you / First face I want to see / Have you tried god / Let not your heart be troubled / He is lord / You don't know the god you serve / Blood rushes
3036450022 / May '97 / Carlton

☐ **STAND UP AND BE A WITNESS**
Stand up / I'm depending on you / You don't know / He's always there / Advance / God's got an answer / Until you make it through / Glory of Jesus / Hallel
CDBM 077 / Apr '90 / Blue Moon

☐ **STANDING ON THE PROMISES**
Blood rushes / No not one / There is the power in the word / Glory to his name / Living on the edge of time / Let not your heart be troubled / Oh I want to see him / When he reached down his hand for me / Finally, finally
CDBM 096 / Oct '93 / Blue Moon

Statton, Alison

☐ **SHADY TREES, THE (Statton, Alison & Spike)**
Where to start / Unspoken word / Rain / Blind faith / Pontymister / Time out / Stages / Corridors of blue / Dream monsters / Seed remains / Platfrom tickets / Sidings / Crucial timing / Point of view
ASKCD 068 / 1 Sep '97 / Vinyl Japan

☐ **TIDAL BLUES (Statton, Alison & Spike)**
Greater notion / In this world / Empty hearth / Open eyes / Take heart / Lemming time / Mr. Morgan / Hidden combat / Seaport town / Find and seek / Tidal blues / Alternations
ASKCD 037 / Oct '94 / Vinyl Japan

Status Quo

☐ **AIN'T COMPLAINING**
8346042 / Feb '91 / Vertigo

☐ **BACK TO THE BEGINNING (2CD Set)**
CDLIK 81 / Sep '91 / Decal

☐ **BEST OF STATUS QUO, THE**
TRTCD 198 / Jul '96 / TrueTrax

☐ **DOG OF TWO HEAD (Remastered)**
Umleitung / Nanana / Something's going on in my head / Mean girl / Gurdundula / Railroad / Someone's learning / Tune to the music / Good thinking / Time to fly / Nanana (alternative version) / Mean girl (alternative version)
ESMCD 626 / 3 Aug '98 / Essential

☐ **DON'T STOP**
Fun fun fun: *Status Quo & The Beach Boys* / When you walk in the room / I can hear the grass grow / You never can tell (it was a teenage wedding) / Get back / Safety dance / Raining in my heart / Don't stop / Sorrow / Proud Mary / Lucille / Johnny and Mary / Get out of Denver / Future's so bright (I gotta wear shades) / All around my hat: *Status Quo & Maddy Prior*
5310352 / Feb '96 / PolyGram TV

☐ **FEW BARS MORE, A**
Whatever you want / What you are proposing / Softer ride / Price of love / Drifting away / She don't fool me / Who gets the love / Let's work together / Bring it on home / Backwater / I saw the light / Don't stop me now / Come rock with me / Rockin' all over the world
5500022 / May '93 / Spectrum

☐ **GREATEST HITS (2CD Set)**
Pictures of matchstick men / Ice in the sun / Down the dustpipe / In my chair / Paper plane / Mean girl / Caroline / Break the rules / Down down / Roll over lay down / Rain / Mystery song / Wild side of life / Rockin' all over the world / Again again / Whatever you want / Living on an island / What you're proposing / Lies
5535072 / 13 Oct '97 / PolyGram TV

☐ **HELLO**
And it's better now / Blue eyed lady / Caroline / Claudie / Forty five hundred times / Reason for living / Roll over lay down / Softer ride
8481722 / Feb '91 / Vertigo

☐ **ICE IN THE SUN**
SSLCD 204 / Jun '95 / Savanna

☐ **ICE IN THE SUN**
PLSCD 206 / Apr '97 / Pulse

☐ **INTROSPECTIVE**
Mean girl / Ice in the sun / Pictures of matchstick men / Interview part one / Down the dustpipe / Little Miss Nothing / Is it really me / Interview part two
CINT 5003 / Nov '90 / Baktabak

☐ **IT'S ONLY ROCK & ROLL**
Wanderer / Don't waste my time / Something 'bout you baby I like / Blue eyed lady / Accident prone / Where am I / Little dreamer / Ain't complaining / Hard ride / Mess of blues / You don't own me / Your smiling face / Name of the game / Enough is enough
5501902 / Sep '94 / Spectrum

☐ **LIVE (2CD Set)**
Backwater / Big fat mama / Bye bye Johnny / Caroline / Don't waste my time / Forty five hundred times / In my chair / Is there a better way / Junior's wailing / Just take me / Little Lady / Most of the time / Rain / Roadhouse blues / Roll over lay down
5103342 / Aug '98 / Vertigo

☐ **LIVE AT THE NEC**
Caroline / Roll over lay down / Backwater / Little lady / Don't you drive my car / Whatever you want / Hold you back / Rockin' all over the world / Over the edge / Don't waste my time
8189472 / Feb '91 / Vertigo

☐ **MA KELLY'S GREASY SPOON**
Spinning wheel blues / Daughter / Everything / Shy fly / Junior's wailing / Lakky lady / Need your love / Lazy poker blues / Is it really me / Gotta go home / April, Spring, Summer and Wednesdays
ESMCD 621 / 6 Jul '98 / Essential

☐ **NEVER TOO LATE/BACK TO BACK**
Never too late / Something bout you baby I like / Take me away / Falling in falling out / Carol / Long ago / Mountain lady / Don't stop me now / Enough is enough / Riverside / Mess of blues / Ol rag blues / Can't be done / Too close to the ground / No contract / Win or lose / Marguerita time / Your kind of love / Stay the night / Going down town tonight
8480882 / Feb '91 / Vertigo

☐ **ON THE LEVEL**
Broken man / Bye bye Johnny / Down down / I saw the light / Most of the time / Night ride / Over and one / What to do / Where am I
8481742 / Feb '91 / Vertigo

☐ **OTHER SIDE OF STATUS QUO, THE**
Magic / Power of rock / Don't give it up / Rotten to the bone / You lost the love / Heartburn / Perfect remedy / A B Blues / Keep me guessing / Joanne / Doing it all for you / Lonely / That's alright / I wonder why / Gerundula / Long legged girl with the short dress on / Forty five hundred times / Junior's wailing
VSOPCD 213 / Feb '95 / Connoisseur Collection

☐ **PICTURES OF MATCHSTICK MEN**
Down the dustpipe / Mean girl / Gerundula / Price of love / Make me stay a little bit longer / Josie / Hurdy gurdy man / Something going on in my heart / Green tambourine / Pictures of matchstick men / Ice in the sun / Black veils of melancholy / Laticia / I who have nothing / Tune to the music / Spicks and specks / Umleitung / Nanana
5507272 / Mar '95 / Spectrum

☐ **PICTURESQUE MATCHSTICKABLE MESSAGES FROM THE STATUS QUO**
Black veils of melancholy / When my mind is not alive / Ice in the sun / Elizabeth dreams / Gentleman Joe's sidewalk cafe / Paradise flat / Technicolour dreams / Spicks and specks / Sheila / Sunny cellophane skies / Green tambourine / Pictures of matchstick men
ESMCD 620 / 6 Jul '98 / Essential

☐ **PILEDRIVER**
All the reasons / Big fat mama / Don't waste my time / O baby / Paper plane / Roadhouse blues / Unspoken words / Year
REP 4119 / Aug '91 / Repertoire

☐ **QUO/BLUE FOR YOU**
Backwater / Just take me / Break the rules / Drifting away / Don't think it matters / Fine fine fine / Lonely man / Slow train / Is there a better way / Mad about the boy / Ring of a change / Blue for you / Rain / Rollin' home / That's a fact / Ease your mind / Mystery song
8480892 / 15 Sep '97 / Vertigo

☐ **ROCKIN' ALL OVER THE WORLD**
Baby boy / Can't give you more / Dirty water / For you / Hard time / Hold you back / Let's ride / Rockin' all over the world / Too far gone / Who am I / You don't own me / Rockers rollin'
8481732 / Feb '91 / Vertigo

☐ **SINGLES COLLECTION 1968-1972, THE (2CD Set)**
Pictures of matchstick men / Gentleman Joe's sidewalk cafe / Black veils of melancholy / To be free / Ice in the sun / When my mind is not live / Technicolour dreams / Paradise flats / Make me stay a little bit longer / Auntie Nellie / Are you growing tired of my love / So ends another life / Price of love / Little Miss Nothing / Down the dustpipe / Face without a soul / In my chair / Gerdundula / Tune to the music / Good thinking (Batman) / Mean girl / Everything / Gerdundula / Lakky lady / Railroad / I (who have nothing) / Neighbour neighbour / Hurdy gurdy man / Laticia / (We ain't got) nothing yet / I want it / Almost but not quite there / Wait a minute / Walking with my angel / When he passed by / Spics and specks / Neighbour neighbour / Pictures of matchstick men / Price of love / Josie / Tune to the music / Time to fly / Nanana / Ricky/Laughing machine / So is it really me / Gerdundula / Tune to the music / Something going on in my head
CCSCD 821 / 1 Jun '98 / Castle

☐ **SPARE PARTS (Remastered)**
Face without a soul / You're just what I was looking for today / Are you growing tired of my love / Antique Angelica / So ends another life / Poor old man / Mr mind detector / Clown / Velvet curtains / Little Miss nothing / When I wake / Nothing at all / Price of love / Josie / Do you live in fire / Hey little woman / Are you growing tired of my love (original mono version)
ESMCD 625 / 3 Aug '98 / Essential

☐ **STATUS QUO**
Pictures of matchstick men / Price of love / Mr. Mind detector / Are you growing tired of my love / Lakky lady / Umleitung / Ice in the sun / Gentleman Joe's sidewalk cafe / Spicks and specks / Clown / Josie / Shelia / Green tambourine / In my chair / Lazy poker blues / Little miss nothing
21037 / Nov '97 / Laserlight

☐ **THIRSTY WORK**
Goin' nowhere / I didn't mean it / Confidence / Point of no return / Sail away / Like it or not / Soft in the head / Queenie / Lover of the human race / Sherri don't fail me now / Rude awakening time / Back on my feet / Restless / Ciao ciao / Tango / Sorry
5236072 / Aug '94 / Vertigo

☐ **TWELVE GOLD BARS VOL.1**
Rockin' all over the world / Down down / Caroline / Paper plane / Break the rules / Again and again / Mystery song / Roll over lay down / Rain / Wild side of life / Whatever you want / Living on an island
8000622 / Nov '84 / Vertigo

☐ **WHATEVER YOU WANT/JUST SUPPOSIN'**
Whatever you want / Shady lady / Who asked you / Your smiling face / Living on an island / Come rock with me / Rockin' on / Runaway / Breaking away
8480872 / Feb '91 / Vertigo

Stauber, Beverly

☐ **NAIL MY FEET TO THE KITCHEN FLOOR**
NERCD 064 / '91 / Nervous

Stead, Joe

☐ **EXTRAVAGANT SCHEMES**
APL 002CD / Nov '96 / APL

Steady Ernest

☐ **OUT OF LINE**
Off and running / Juma (Way too long) / Time will tell / Utter east / Take it easy / Hold em' back / New world / Please go away / Singular I / Mercy / Out of line / Roll on / That's allright
DOJOCD 197 / Jun '94 / Dojo

Steakknife

☐ **GODPILL**
EFA 120112 / Nov '95 / X-Mist

☐ **SONGS MEN HAVE DIED FOR**
50584 / 13 Oct '97 / Semaphore

Stealer's Wheel

☐ **BEST OF STEALER'S WHEEL, THE**
Stuck in the middle with you / Nothing's gonna change my mind / Star / This morning / Steamboat row / Next to me / Right or wrong / Go as you please / Benediction / Waltz / Blind faith / Late again / Wheelin' / Jose
CSAPCD 106 / Jun '90 / Connoisseur Collection

☐ **STEALERS WHEEL/FERGUSLIE PARK**
Late again / Stuck in the middle with you / Another meaning / I get by / Outside looking in / Johnny's song / Next to me / Jose / Gets so lonely / You put something better inside me / Good businessman / Star / Wheelin' / Waltz (you know it makes sense) / What more could you want / Over my head / Blind faith / Nothing's gonna change my mind / Steamboat row / Back on my feet again / Who cares / Everybody will turn out fine
5409272 / Jul '98 / A&M

Stealth

☐ **ZERO TO MACH 7**
TOTO 82 / 11 May '98 / 2112

Steam Jenny

☐ **WELCOME BACK**
CDLOC 1082 / Oct '94 / Lochshore

Steamboat Band

☐ **RUMOURS & RIDERS**
Got no tears / Died without sleeping / Everybody needs the morning rain / Fall from grace / Hit the bottle again / Take your hands off the wheel / Just like me / Running to Waycross / Goodbye Mary Jane / Take a little time (Off my hands) / Restless lullaby / She's coming my way / Let it pass me by
5274732 / Apr '95 / Polydor

Steamboat Willie

☐ **MAMA'S GONE GOODBYE**
JCD 276 / May '98 / Jazzology

Steamhammer

☐ **MOUNTAINS**
REP 4066 / Aug '91 / Repertoire

☐ **SPEECH**
REP 4139 / Aug '91 / Repertoire

Steaming Jungle

☐ **RUPUNI SAFARI**
ARICD 111 / Sep '95 / Ariwa Sounds

Steampacket

☐ **ROCK GENERATION**
14555 / Jun '97 / Spalax

☐ **STEAMPACKET**
REP 4090 / Aug '91 / Repertoire

Stecher, Jody

☐ **HEART SONGS (Stecher, Jody & Kate Brislin)**
Orphan train / Walkin' through your town in the snow / Hood river roll on / Scofield mine disaster / Miner's lullaby / Rock salt and nails / Green rolling hills of West Virginia / Ragged old man / Jury set him free / Faded rose / John D. Lee / Golden mansion / I remember loving you
ROUCD 0424 / Jul '97 / Rounder

☐ **STAY AWHILE (Stecher, Jody & Kate Brislin)**
ROUCD 0334 / Apr '95 / Rounder

Steckar, Marc

☐ **PACKWORK (Steckar, Marc Tubapack)**
BBRC 9310 / Jan '94 / Big Blue

Steeky

☐ **THINK YOU'RE FUNNY I'LL CUT A HOLE IN YOUR HEAD AND PISS IN**
REJ 1000012 / 15 Dec '97 / Rejected

Steel

☐ **AUTO CYNICISM**
EFA 080521 / 1 Jun '98 / Mille Plateau

☐ **STEEL**
EFA 006662 / Oct '95 / Mille Plateau

Steel Band Des Caraibes

☐ **STEEL MUSIC FROM THE CARIBBEAN**
824552 / Nov '90 / BUDA

Steel, Eric

☐ **BACK FOR MORE**
911 / Something for nothing / Low down / Crazy lady / Stray cat blues / Back for more / Meant to be / Material law / Insert gently
KILCD 1003 / Oct '93 / Killerwatt

Steel Fury

☐ **LESSER OF TWO EVILS**
859 803 / '89 / Steamhammer

Steel Pole Bath Tub

☐ **LURCH**
Christina / Hey you / Paranoid / I am Sam I am / Bee sting / Swerve / Heaven on dirt / Lime away / River / Time to die / Welcome aboard it's love / Hey Bo Diddley / Thru the windshield of love / Tear it apart
TUPCD 16 / Jul '90 / Tupelo

☐ **MIRACLE OF SOUND IN MOTION, THE**
Pseudoephendrine hydrochloride / Train to Miami / Exhale / Thumbnail / Down all the days / Carbon / Bozeman / Borstal / 594 / Waxl
TUP 472 / Apr '93 / Tupelo

☐ **SOME COCKTAIL SUGGESTIONS**
Ray / Living end / Slip / Hit it / Speaker phone / Wasp jar
TUP 0512 / Jan '94 / Tupelo

Steel Prophet

☐ **GODDESS PRINCIPLE, THE**
MASSE 001 / Aug '95 / Massacre

Steel Pulse

☐ **HANDSWORTH REVOLUTION**
Handsworth revolution / Bad man / Soldiers / Sound check / Prodigal / Ku klux klan / Prediction / Macka splaff
RRCD 24 / Nov '90 / Reggae Refreshers

☐ **RAGE AND FURY**
Emotional prisoner / Role model / I spy / Brown eyed girl / Real terrorist / Black and proud / Ku klux klan / House of love / Blame on me / Black enough / Peace party / Spiritualize it / KKK in the jungle
WMDCD 4
927672 / 29 Sep '97 / Mase

☐ **RASTAFARI CENTENNIAL**
State of emergency / Blues dance raid / Taxi driver / Makka medley / Ku klux klan / Ravers / Soldiers / Steppin' out / Chant a psalm / Rally round
MCD 10631 / 8 Sep '97 / MCA

☐ **RASTANTHOLOGY (The Best Of Steel Pulse)**
WMDCD 3 / Oct '96 / Wise Man Doctrine

☐ **REGGAE GREATS**
Sound system / Babylon makes the rules / Don't give in / Soldier / Prodigal son / Ku klux klan / Macka splaff / Drug squad / Reggae fever / Handsworth revolution
5528862 / Jul '97 / Spectrum

□ **SOUND SYSTEM (The Island Anthology/2CD Set)**
Handsworth revolution / Bad man / Soldiers / Sound check / Prodigal son / Ku klux klan / Prediction / Macka splaff / Bun dem / Nyah love / Unseen guest / Sound system / Jah pickney / Tribute to the martyrs / Babylon makes the rules / Uncle George / Biko's kindred lament / Blasphemy / Macka plaff / Drug squad / Harassment / Reggae fever / Shining / Heart of stone / Rumours / Caught you dancing / Burning flame / Higher than high / Nyahbinghi voyage / Don't give in
5243232 / Jul '97 / Island Jamaica

□ **TRIBUTE TO THE MARTYRS**
Unseen guest / Sound system / Jah Pickney / Biko's kindred lament / Tribute to the martyrs / Babylon makes the rules / Uncle George / Blasphemy
RRCD 17 / Sep '90 / Reggae Refreshers

Steele, Davy

□ **CHASING SHADOWS**
Kishmul's galley / Brand new day / Loch Tay boat song / Jimmy Waddell/Lochanside / Long hellos, short goodbyes / Tam glen/Dancing in Dinan / Tibby Dunbar/The brothers reconciliation / Calton weaver / Leave her Johnny, leave her / Chasing shadows / Scotland yet
HYCD 297171 / May '97 / Hypertension

□ **SUMMERTIME**
CMCD 046 / Apr '94 / Celtic Music

Steele, Jan

□ **VOICES AND INSTRUMENTS (Steele, Jan & John Cage)**
All day / Distant saxophones / Rhapsody spaniel / Experiences no.1 / Experiences no.2 / Wonderful widow of eighteen springs / Forever and sunsmell / In a landscape
CDOVD 481 / Jul '97 / EG

Steele, Jay

□ **NATURAL GUITAR VOL.2, THE**
2687 / Aug '96 / NorthSound

Steele, Jevetta

□ **HERE IT IS**
Say a little prayer for you / Baby are you / And how / You're gonna love me / Here it is / Calling you / In this man's world / Good foot / Skip 2 my u my darling / Where do we go from here / Love will follow
108772 / Mar '92 / Musidisc UK

Steele, Tommy

□ **EP COLLECTION, THE**
Rock with the caveman / Wedding bells / Doomsday rock / Singin' the blues / Take me back baby / Handful of songs / Rebel rock / Will it be you / Happy guitar / Knee deep in the blues / Put a ring on her finger / Young love / Come on let's go / Elevator rock / Only man on the island / Time to kill / Little white bull / Number twenty two across the way / You gotta go / Singin' time / Cannibal pot / Build up / Water, water
SEECD 347 / Oct '96 / See For Miles

□ **ROCK 'N' ROLL YEARS, THE (Steele, Tommy & The Steelemen)**
Rock with the caveman / C'mon let's go / Butterfly / Give give give / Elevator rock / Rebel rock / You gotta go / Build up / Put a ring on her finger / You were mine / Swallow tail coat / Singin' the blues / Doomsday rock / Knee deep in the blues / Two eyes / Take me back baby / Writing on the wall / Hey you / Teenage party / Plant a kiss / Rock around the town / Drunken guitar / Tallahassee lassie
SEECD 203 / Oct '96 / See For Miles

□ **SINGING IN THE RAIN AND OTHER GREAT STANDARDS**
Singing in the rain / Rambling rose / Tip toe through the tulips / When the red red robin / (I'd like to get you) on a slow boat to China / You made me love you / On mother kelly's doorstep / I'll be with you in apple blossom time / In a shanty in old shanty town / Underneath the arches / Carolina in the morning / My mammy / April showers / Is it true what they say about Dixie / Baby face / I wonder who's kissing her now / Hey good lookin' / On the sunny side of the street / Zip-a-dee-doo-dah / When you're smiling / Bells are ringing for me and my girl / Me and my girl / My lucky star / You must have been a beautiful baby / Oh you beautiful doll / Boiled beef and carrots / Any old iron / Knocked 'em out in the old kent road / My old man's a dustman / My old man said follow the van / I've got a lovely bunch of coconuts / Consider yourself / I'm getting married in the morning / I'm Henery the eighth, I am / Knees up Mother Brown / Roll out the barrel
300742 / Jul '96 / Hallmark

□ **WORLD OF TOMMY STEELE, THE**
Singin' the blues / Little white bull / Handful of songs / Shiralee / Half a sixpence / Rock with the caveman / Water water / Come on let's go / Sweet Georgia Brown / Where's the birdie / Nairobi / What a mouth / If the rain's got to fall / Where have all the flowers gone / Only man on the island / Knee deep in the blues / Butterfingers / Number 22 across the way / She's too far above me / Happy guitar
5520162 / May '96 / Spectrum

Steeler

□ **STRIKE BACK**
851 861 / '88 / Steamhammer

□ **UNDERCOVER**
857 512 / '89 / Steamhammer

Steeles

□ **HEAVEN HELP US ALL**
Heart in my hand / Tide keeps lifting me / Never get over you / Well done / I don't wanna be without U / Heaven help us all / It'll be alright / Oh what a gift / Those were the days / Big God
7559612902 / Aug '93 / Nonesuch

Steeleye Span

□ **ALL AROUND MY HAT**
Black jack David / Hard times of old England / Cadwith anthem / All around my hat / Gamble gold (Robin Hood) / Wife of Usher's well / Sum wavves (Tunes) / Dance with me / Bachelors hall
CDGOLD 1009 / Mar '96 / EMI Gold

□ **BACK IN LINE**
Edward / Lanercost / Lady diamond / Isabel / A cannon by telemann / Blackleg miner / Peace on the border / Scarecrow / Take my heart / White man / Somewhere in london / Spotted cow / One misty moisty morning
PRKCD 8 / Aug '91 / Park

□ **BELOW THE SALT**
Spotted cow / Rosebuds in June / Jigs / Sheepcrook and black dog / Royal forester / King Henry / Gaudete / John Barleycorn / Saucy sailor
BGOCD 324 / Sep '96 / Beat Goes On

□ **BEST OF AND THE REST OF STEELEYE SPAN, THE**
Blacksmith / Prince charlie stuart / Marrowbones / Reels / Western wynde / Dark eyed sailor / All things are quite silent / Rave on / Lonely on the water / Wee weaver / Brisk young butcher / Boys of bedlam / Blacksmith / My johnny was a shoemaker
CDAR 1012 / Oct '94 / Action Replay

□ **BEST OF STEELEYE SPAN LIVE IN CONCERT, THE**
PRK 27CD / Oct '94 / Park

□ **BEST OF STEELEYE SPAN, THE**
Gaudete / All around my hat / Thomas the rhymer / Alison Gross / Little Sir Hugh / Cam ye o'er frae France / Long lankin / Gone to America / Let her go down / Black jack David / Bach goes to Limerick
CCD 1467 / '88 / Chrysalis

□ **COLLECTION IN CONCERT, THE**
Blacksmith / Weaver / Spotted cow / One misty moisty morning / King Henry / Fox / Two butchers / Jack Hall / Canon / Shaking of the sheets / All around my hat / Tunes / Gaudete
PRKCD 27 / Nov '94 / Park

□ **COMMONERS CROWN**
Little Sir Hugh / Bach goes to Limerick / Long lankin / Dogs and ferrets / Galtee farmer / Demon lover / Elf call / Weary cutters / New York girls
BGOCD 315 / Jul '96 / Beat Goes On

□ **EARLY YEARS, THE**
Blacksmith / Marrowbones / Western wynde / All things are quite silent / Lovely on the water / Boys of Bedlam / My Johnny was a shoemaker / Cold haily windy night / Horn of the hunter / Jigs / Prince Charlie Stuart / Reels / Dark eyed sailor / Rave on / Brisk young butcher / Wee weaver / When I was on horseback / Ploughboy and the Cockney / One night as I lay on my bed
VSOPCD 132 / Apr '89 / Connoisseur Collection

□ **KING, THE (The Best Of The Early Years)**
Calling song / Fisherman's wife / Copshawholme fair / All things are quite silent / My Johnny was a shoemaker / Fly up my cock / Two corbies / One night as I lay on my bed / Cold haily, windy night / Prince Charlie Stewart / Lark in the morning / King / Rave on / Ploughboy and the cockney / Gower wassail / Paddy Clancy's jig / Willie clancy's fancy / Skewball
CRESTCD 022 / Nov '96 / Mooncrest

□ **LIVE AT LAST**
Athol highlanders / Walter Bulwer's polka / Saucy sailor / Black freighter / Maid and the palmer / Hunting the wren / Montrose / Bonnets so blue / False knight on the road
BGOCD 342 / Mar '97 / Beat Goes On

□ **NOW WE ARE SIX**
Seven hundred elves / Edwin / Drink down the moon / Now we are six / Thomas the rhymer / Mooncoin jig / Long-a-growing / Two magicians / Twinkle twinkle little star / To know him is to love him
SHANDCD 79060 / Jul '98 / Shanachie

□ **ORIGINAL MASTERS**
Sir James the rose / Black jack David / All around my hat / Wife of Usher's well / Fighting for strangers / Thomas the rhymer / Seven hundred elves / Long lankin / Elf call / Cam ye o'er frae France / Bonnie moorhen / Alison Gross / Mooncoin jig / Drink down the moon / Stewball / Lovely on the water / Jigs / Brides favourite / Tansey's fancy / One misty moisty morning / Saucy sailor / Gaudete
BGOCD 322 / Mar '97 / Beat Goes On

□ **PARCEL OF ROGUES, A**
One misty moisty morning / Alison Gross / Bold poachers / Ups and down / Robbery with violins / Wee wee man / Weaver and the factory maid / Rogues in a nation / Can ye o'er frae France / Hares on the mountain
BGOCD 323 / Oct '96 / Beat Goes On

□ **ROCKET COTTAGE**
London / Bosnian hornpipes / Ofreo / Nathan's reel / Twelve witches / Brown girl / Fighting for strangers / Silgo maid / Sir James the Rose / Drunkard
BGOCD 318 / Jul '96 / Beat Goes On

□ **SAILS OF SILVER**
Sails of silver / My love / Barnet Fair / Senior service / Gone to America / Where are they now / Let her go down / Longbone / Marigold/Harvest home / Tell me why / Lark in the morning / Thomas / Johnny was a shoe maker
PRKCD 40 / Jul '97 / Park

□ **SAILS OF SILVER**
Sails of silver / My love / Barnet Fair / Senior service / Gone to America / Where are they now / Let her go down / Longbone / Marigold/Harvest home / Tell me why
BGOCD 371 / 15 Jun '98 / Beat Goes On

□ **SPANNING THE YEARS (2CD Set)**
Blacksmith / My Johnny was a shoe maker / King / Lovely on the water / Marrowbones / Rave on / Gaudette / John Barleycorn / Alison Gross / Robbery with violins / Rogues in a nation / Cam ye o'er frae France / Thomas the rhymer / To know him is to love him / New York girls / Long lankin / Black jack David / Hard times of Old England / All around my hat / London / Fighting for strangers / Black freighter / Victory / False knight on the road / Rag doll / Let her go down / Sails of silver / Gone to America / My love / Lady diamond / Blackleg miner / One misty moisty morning / Fox / Following me / Tam lin
CDCHR 6093 / Apr '95 / Chrysalis

□ **STACK OF STEELEYE SPAN, A (Their Finest Folk Recordings 1973-1975)**
Blacckleg miner / Dark-eyed sailor / Hills of Greenmore / Lowlands of Holland / Blacksmith / Bryan O'Lynn/Hag with the monkey / Boys of bedlam / False knight on the road / Female drummer / Lovely on the water / Four nights drunk / When I was on horseback / Marrowbones / Captain Coulston / Dowd's favourite/10 pound float/Morning dew / Wee weaver
EMPRCD 668 / Oct '96 / Emporio

□ **STORM FORCE TEN**
Awake awake / Sweep chimney sweep / Wife of the soldier / Victory / Black freighter / Some rival / Treadmill song / Seventeen come Sunday
BGOCD 337 / Dec '96 / Beat Goes On

□ **TEMPTED AND TRIED**
Padstow / Fox / Two butchers / Following me / Seagull / Cruel mother / Jack Hall / Searching for lambs / Shaking of the sheets / First house in Connaught / Sailor's bonnet / Betsy Bell and Mary Gray
SHANCD 64020 / Jul '98 / Shanachie

□ **TIME**
Prickly bush / Old maid in the Garrett / Harvest of the moon / Underneath her apron / Cutty Wren / Go from my window / Elf knight / Water is wide / You will burn / Corbies / Song will remain
PRKCD 34 / Mar '96 / Park

□ **TONIGHT'S THE NIGHT LIVE**
Tonight's the night / Ca the ewes / Gentleman soldier / Tam lim / Padstow / Fighting for strangers / White man / Weaver / Ten long years / Dawn of the day / Cam ye / All around my hat
SHANCD 79080 / Jul '98 / Shanachie

Steelhouse Blues

□ **METALLIC BLUE**
199647 / 23 Mar '98 / Made To Measure

Steely & Cleevie

□ **PLAY STUDIO ONE VINTAGE**
CDHB 116 / May '92 / Heartbeat

□ **STEELY & CLEEVIE PRESENTS HARDCORE**
SCCD 2 / Oct '93 / Steely & Cleevie

Steely Dan

□ **AJA**
Black cow / Aja / Deacon blues / Peg / Home at last / I got the news / Josie
MCLD 19145 / Nov '90 / MCA

□ **ALIVE IN AMERICA**
Babylon sister / Green earrings / Bodhisattva / Reelin' in the years / Josie / Book of liars / Peg / Third world man / Kid Charlemagne / Sign in stranger / Aja
74321286912 / 1 Sep '97 / Giant

□ **ANDROID WAREHOUSE (2CD Set)**
AOP 65 / 25 May '98 / Dressed To Kill

□ **ART CRIMES**
Any old dude will tell you / Little with sugar / Android warehouse / Any world (that I'm welcome to) / Brain tap shuffle / Brooklyn / Caves of altamira / Charlie freak / Come back baby / Don't let me in / Mock turtle's song / Old regime / Parker's band / Roaring of the lamb / Soul ram / Sum mountain / Barrytown
RTD 3970019CD / 1 Dec '97 / Institute Of Art

□ **ASIA**
DMCA 102 / Jan '85 / MCA

□ **BEST OF STEELY DAN, THE (Remastered)**
Reelin' in the years / Rikki don't lose that number / Peg / FM (no static at all) / Hey nineteen / Deacon blues / Black Friday / Bodhisattva / Do it again / Haitian divorce / My old school / Midnite cruiser / Babylon sisters / Kid Charlemagne / Dirty work / Josie
MCD 10967 / Nov '93 / MCA

□ **CAN'T BUY A THRILL**
Do it again / Dirty work / Kings / Midnite cruiser / Only a fool / Reelin' in the years / Fire in the hole / Brooklyn (owes the charmer and me) / Change of the guard / Turn that heartbeat over again
MCLD 19017 / Apr '92 / MCA

□ **CATALYST (2CD Set) (Becker, Walter & Donald Fagen)**
Sun mountain / Barrytown / Take it out on me / Caves of Altamira / Charlie Freak / You go where I go / Any world (that I'm welcome to) / Little with sugar / Android warehouse / More to come / Parker's band / Oh wow it's you again / Stone piano / Yellow peril / Roaring of the lamb / This seat's been taken / Ida Lee / Undecided / Horse in town / Let George do it / Old regime / Brain tap shuffle / Mock turtle's song / Soul ram / Brooklyn / Don't let me in / Sun Mountain / Come back baby / I can
CDTB 503 / 24 Oct '97 / Thunderbolt

□ **CITIZEN 1972-1980 (The Best Of Steely Dan/4CD Set)**
Do it again / Dirty work / Kings / Midnite cruiser / Only a fool would say that / Reelin' in the years / Fire in the hole / Brooklyn (owes the charmer under me) / Change of the guard / Turn that heartbeat over again / Bodhisattva / Razor boy / Boston rag / Your gold teeth / Showbiz kid / My old school / King of the world / Pearl of the quarter / Rikki don't lose that number / Night by night / Any major dude will tell you / Barrytown / East St. Louis toodle-oo / Parker's band / Through with buzz / Pretzel logic / With a gun / Charlie Freak / Monkey in your soul / Bodhisattva (live) / Black Friday / Bad sneakers / Rose darling / Daddy don't live in that New York City no more / Dr. Wu / Everyone's gone to the movies / Chain lightning / Your gold teeth II / Any world (that I'm welcome to) / Throw back the little one / Kid Charlemagne / Caves of Altmira / Don't take me alive / Sign in stranger / Fez / Green earrings / Haitian divorce / Everything you did / Royal scam / Here at the western world / Black cow / Aja / Peg / Deacon blues / Home at last / I got the news / When Josie comes home / FM / Babylon sisters / Hey nineteen / Glamour profession / Gaucho / Time out of mind / My rival / Third world man / Everyone's gone to the movies (demo)
MCAD 410981 / Jan '94 / MCA

□ **COUNTDOWN TO ECSTASY**
Bodhisattva / Razor boy / Boston rag / Your gold teeth / Showbiz kid / My old school / Pearl of the quarter / King of the world
MCLD 19018 / Apr '92 / MCA

□ **GAUCHO**
Babylon sisters / Hey nineteen / Glamour profession / Gaucho / Time out of mind / My rival / Third world man
MCLD 19146 / Oct '92 / MCA

□ **KATHY LIED**
Black Friday / Bad sneakers / Rose darling / Daddy don't live in that New York City no more / Dr. Wu / Everyone's gone to the movies / Your gold teeth II / Chain lightning / Any world (that I'm welcome to) / Throw back the little ones
MCLD 19082 / Nov '92 / MCA

□ **MASTERS, THE (Becker, Walter & Donald Fagen)**
Android warehouse / Horse in town / More to come / Parker's band / Ida Lee / Stone piano / Any world / Take it out on me / This seat's been taken / Barrytown / Brain tap shuffle / Come back baby / Don't let me in / Old regime / Brooklyn (owes the charmer under me) / Mock turtle song / Soul ram / I can't function / Yellow peril / Let George do it
EABCD 086 / 30 Mar '98 / Eagle

□ **OLD REGIME**
Brain tap shuffle / Come back baby / Don't let me in / Old regime / Brooklyn / Mock turtle song / Soul rain / I can't function / Yellow peril / Let George do it
CDTB 040 / May '87 / Thunderbolt

□ **PRETZEL LOGIC**
Rikki don't lose that number / Night by night / Any major dude will tell you / Barrytown / East St. Louis toodle-oo / Parker's band / Thru with buzz / Pretzel logic / With a gun / Charlie freak / Monkey in your soul
MCLD 19081 / Nov '91 / MCA

□ **REELIN' IN THE YEARS (The Very Best Of Steely Dan/2CD Set)**
Do it again / Reelin' in the years / My old school / Bodhisattva / Showbiz kid / Rikki don't lose that number / Pretzel logic / Black Friday / Bad sneakers / Dr. Wu / Haitian divorce / Kid Charlemagne / Fez / Peg / Josie / Deacon blues / Hey nineteen / Babylon sisters
MCLDD 19147 / Dec '92 / MCA

□ **ROYAL SCAM, THE**
Kid Charlemagne / Sign in stranger / Fez / Caves of Altmira / Don't take me alive / Green earring / Haitian divorce / Everything you did / Royal scam
MCLD 19083 / Nov '92 / MCA

□ **SPOTLIGHT ON STEELY DAN**
Braintap shuffle / Come back baby / Don't let me in / Stone piano / Brooklyn / Mock turtle song / Soul ram / I can't function / Yellow peril / Let George do it / Parker's band / Any world (that I'm welcome to) / Barrytown / Ida Lee
HADCD 103 / Feb '94 / Javelin

□ **STONE PIANO**
Android warehouse / Horse in town / More to come / Parker's band / Ida Lee / Stone piano / Any world (that I'm welcome to) / Take it out on me / This seat's been taken / Barrytown
CDTB 054 / Apr '88 / Thunderbolt

□ **SUN MOUNTAIN**
Berry town / Android warehouse / More to come / Sun mountain / Ida Lee / Any world (that I'm welcome to) / Stone piano / Caves of Altmira / Horse in town / Roaring of the lamb / Parker's band / Oh wow it's you / You go where I go / This seat's been taken / Little with sugar / Take it out on me
CDTB 139 / Nov '92 / Thunderbolt

Steeplechase

□ **STEEPLECHASE**
HV 1010 / Sep '97 / High Vaultage

Stefanet, Anatol

☐ ART OF THE BRATSCH, THE
927082 / 24 Apr '98 / BUDA

Steffen, Bruno

☐ CITY OF GLASS (Steffen/Althaus Quartet)
BRAM 1990132 / Nov '93 / Brambus

☐ IN BETWEEN (Steffen, Bruno & Heiner Althaus)
BRAM 1992372 / Nov '93 / Brambus

Steffen, Peter

☐ ALS ICH EIN KLEINER JUNGE WAR
Als ich ein kleiner junge war / Huh-a-ho / Zwei sommer lang / Wenn morgen dann die sonne / Es war an der riviera / Tag fur tag / Sag, warum willst du von mir gehen / Schau in meine augen / Auf meinen jungen kann ich / Eine himmelblaue kutsche / Der puppenspieler / Pepinos freund pasquale / Wie im September / Es liegt mir am herzen / Die kleine stadt will schlafen geh'n / Est musst du mal zur schule geh'n / Dir, dir nur allein / Tabu / Twist / Ich bin dein, du bist mein / Sag' Papa / Hilo-Hulalei / Sie war ein kind der heide / Bein auseinandergeh'n / Hor mal mein junge / Drei zartliche kusse / Wer im November nicht liben kann / Goodbye, auf wiedersehn
BCD 15996 / Jul '96 / Bear Family

Steffens, Dirk

☐ 7TH STEP
SB 030 / Jun '97 / Second Battle

Stegall, Keith

☐ PASSAGES
5284372 / Feb '96 / Mercury

Steig, Jeremy

☐ ELEGANT HUMP
500812 / Sep '96 / Musidisc

Stein

☐ KONIGZUCKER
RTD 19516982 / Mar '95 / Our Choice

Stein, Hal

☐ CLASSIC SESSIONS (Stein, Hal & Warren Fitzgerald)
PCD 7050 / Jun '93 / Progressive

Stein, Ira

☐ SPUR OF THE MOMENT
Way back when / Fiddletown / Footsteps / Tributaries / Continuum II / La source / Spur of the moment / Winter wind / Pinnacles / Horseshoe hill / Dominique
ND 63029 / Jul '94 / Narada

Steinbecks

☐ AT HOME OR ABROAD
US 13CD / Dec '97 / Shine

☐ STEINBECKS, THE
SHINEUS 23 / 16 Mar '98 / Summershine

Steinman, Jim

☐ BAD FOR GOOD
Bad for good / Lost boys and golden girls / Love and death and an American guitar / Stark raving love / Out of the frying pan (and into the fire) / Surf's up / Dance in my pants / Left in the dark
4720422 / Oct '92 / Epic

☐ ORIGINAL SIN (Pandora's Box)
Invocation / Original sin (the natives are restless tonight) / Twentieth century fox / Safe sex (when it comes 2 loving U) / Good girls go to heaven (bad girls go everywhere) / Requiem metal / I've been dreaming up a storm lately / It's all coming back to me now / Opening of the box / Want ad / My little red book / It just won't quit / Pray lewd / Future ain't what it used to be
CDVIP 171 / Apr '97 / Virgin VIP

Stekpanna

☐ STANDIN' TALL
Stekpanna / Hunnie / My funny Valentine / Daydreaming / Davina dragon / Vykortsvy / Smoke on the water / Going Dutch / Ain't it cool / Alfredo and the mayor / Blues i moll / Gateway
GBHCD 01 / Sep '97 / Flat Five

Stelin, Tena

☐ SACRED SONGS
Paranoid circle / Paranoid dub / Sacred songs / Sacred dub / Urban ghetto youth / Urban dub / Miva dalla amlak / Amlak dub / New world / New dub / Freedom fighter / Freedom dub / Armageddon / Armageddon dub / Content to stay / Content dub
WRCD 008 / Nov '97 / World

☐ SUN AND MOON (Stelin, Tena & Centry)
Sun and moon / Version / Jah vibes / Version / Jah can help us / Version / Clean up the world / Version / Babylon won't succeed / Version / Smash nazi-ism / Version / Great is jah / Version / Guitar solo dub
DUBVCD 010 / Dec '94 / Dub Vintage

☐ TAKE A LOOK AT THE WORLD
DUBVCD 011 / Dec '94 / Dub Vintage

Stella Maris

☐ WHY HAS OUR MILK GOT EYES
YACD 008 / 27 Apr '98 / Yassaba

Steltch

☐ RHYTHM OF BUST
SON 003 2 / Mar '93 / Sonic Noise

Stems

☐ WEED OUT (Live At The Old Melbourne 1986)
HOWR 8 / Jun '97 / House Of Wax

Stendal Blast

☐ WAS VERDORRT
EFA 155842 / May '95 / Gymnastic

Stenson, Bobo

☐ REFLECTIONS (Stenson, Bobo Trio)
Enlightener / My man's gone now / Not / Dorrmattan / Q / Reflections in D / 12 Tones old / Mindiatyr
5231602 / Feb '96 / ECM

☐ SOUNDS AROUND THE HOUSE, THE
1206 / Jan '89 / Caprice

☐ VERY EARLY (Stenson, Bobo Trio)
DRCD 304 / Feb '98 / Dragon

☐ WAR ORPHANS (Stenson, Bobo Trio)
Oleo de mujer con sombrero / Natt / My little green / of January / War orphans / Sediment / Bengali blue / Melancholia
5397232 / 2 Feb '98 / ECM

Stensson, Ewan

☐ PRESENT DIRECTIONS
DRCD 218 / Aug '87 / Dragon

Step Forward

☐ IT DID MAKE A DIFFERENCE
DFR 14 / Jan '97 / Desperate Flight

Stephanie

☐ BEST OF STEPHANIE, THE
3020222 / Jun '97 / Arcade

Stephen C

☐ NATURAL PIANO VOL.2, THE
2898 / Aug '96 / NorthSound

Stephens, Anne

☐ TEDDY BEARS PICNIC
PASTCD 7067 / Jun '95 / Flapper

Stephens, Richie

☐ MIRACLES
VPCD 1457 / Apr '96 / VP
CRCD 48 / Jan '96 / Charm

☐ SPECIAL WORK OF ART
PHCD 2062 / Mar '97 / Penthouse

☐ WINNER
GRECD 248 / 27 Apr '98 / Greensleeves

Stephens, Tanya

☐ RUFF RIDER
VPCD 1521 / 20 Apr '98 / VP

☐ TOO HYPE
VPCD 1507 / 24 Nov '97 / VP

Stephenson, Martin

☐ BEYOND THE LEAP
Losing all part of the team / Testing time / Great star of fraternity / Wholly humble heart / Carry me friend / Crying / Song of love and desertion / Great spirit / Out of communion / Waves / Hollow days / Indian summer
FIENDCD 938 / 3 Nov '97 / Demon

☐ SWEET MISDEMEANOUR (The Best Of Martin Stephenson & The Daintees)
FIEND 770CD / Nov '95 / Demon

☐ THERE COMES A TIME (Stephenson, Martin & The Daintees)
8283982 / Jul '93 / Kitchenware

☐ YOGI IN MY HOUSE
Solomon / In fire / Taker on the globe / Think only of the child / New wave / Spirit child / Bridge of nae hope / Fair company / Gone the gipsey davey / What's the word / Early one morning / Smokin' with the motherman / Relentless
FIENDCD 762 / Feb '95 / Demon

Steppenwolf

☐ AT YOUR BIRTHDAY PARTY/ STEPPENWOLF
Don't cry / Chicken wolf / Lovely meter / Round and down / It's never too late / Sleeping dreaming / Jupiter child / She'll be better / Cat killer / Rock me / God fearing man / Mango juice / Happy birthday / Ball crusher / Forty days and forty nights / Fat Jack / Renegade / Foggy mental breakdown / Snow blind friend / Who needs ya / Earschplittenloudenboomer / Hippo stomp
BGOCD 336 / Dec '96 / Beat Goes On

☐ BORN TO BE WILD
Born to be wild / Magic carpet ride / Rock me / It's never too late / Move over / Monster / Hey lawdy mama / Screaming night hog / Who needs ya / Snowblind friend / Ride with me / For ladies only / Pusher / Sookie sookie / Jupiter's child / Tenderness
MPG 74016 / May '93 / Movieplay Gold

☐ FEED THE FIRE
CMC 8239092 / 13 Jul '98 / CMC

☐ FIVE FINGERS DISCOUNT (Kay, John & Steppenwolf)
Five fingers discount / You / All I want is what you got / None of the above / Balance / Down to Earth / Hot night in a cold town / Hold your head up / For rock 'n' roll / Every man for himself
100452 / May '97 / A-Play Collection

☐ LIVE
BGOCD 412 / 17 Aug '98 / Beat Goes On

☐ MONSTER
Draft resister / Power play / Move over / Fag / What would you do (if I did that to you) / From here to there eventually
BGOCD 126 / Sep '91 / Beat Goes On

☐ PARADOX
CMC 8239082 / 13 Jul '98 / CMC

☐ RISE AND SHINE
Let's do it all / Do or die / Wall / Keep rockin' / Sign on the line / Time out / Rise and shine / Daily blues / Rock 'n' roll war / We like it, we love it
CMC 8239102 / 13 Jul '98 / CMC

Steppes

☐ ALIVE ALIVE OH
VOXXCD 2065 / Feb '92 / Voxx

☐ HARPS AND HAMMERS
Land of hope / Scare you off / Let me love you / Panic attack / Keep it clean / Hey girl / Safe and sound / Key to my heart / You may say / Pretty debris
VOXXCD 2064 / Feb '91 / Voxx

Steps Ahead

☐ LIVE IN TOKYO 1986
Beirut / Oops / Self portrait / Sumo / Cajun / Safari / In a sentimental mood / Trains
NYC 60062 / May '94 / NYC

☐ NYC
Well in that case / Lust for life / Red neon, go or give / Charanga / Get it / NYC / Stick jam / Absolutely maybe / Festival paradiso
INT 30072 / Apr '90 / Intuition

☐ VIBE
Buzz / From light to light / Penn station / Vibe / Green dolphin street / Miles away / Staircase / Renezvous / Crunch / Waxing and wanning / Miles away reprise (the gentle giant)
NYC 60122 / Feb '95 / NYC

☐ YIN YANG
Praise / Sidewalk maneuvers / Taxi / Gory details / Nite owl / Waltz / Agitate the gravel / Floaty thing / Okapi / Steppish / Sara's touch
NYC 60012 / Jul '92 / NYC

Stereo Maximus

☐ QUILOMBO
ABB 028CD / Oct '91 / Big Cat

Stereo MC's

☐ 33-45-78
On 33 / Use it / Gee street / Neighbourhood / Toe to toe / What is soul / Use it (part 2) / Outta touch / Sunday 19th March / This ain't a love song / Ancient concept / On the mike / Back to the future
IMCD 127 / Apr '91 / Island

☐ CONNECTED
Connected / Ground level / Everything / Sketch / Fade away / All night long / Step it up / Playing with fire / Pressure / Chicken shake / Creation / End
BRCD 589 / Oct '92 / 4th & Broadway

☐ SUPERNATURAL
I'm a believer / Scene of the crime / Declaration / Elevate my mind / What's gonna do / Two horse town / Ain't got nobody / Goin' back to the wild / Lost in music / Life on the line / Set the loose / What's the word / Early one morning / Smokin' with the motherman / Relentless
IMCD 185 / Mar '94 / Island

Stereolab

☐ DOTS AND LOOPS
Brakhage / Miss Modula / Flower called nowhere / Diagonals / Prisoner of Mars / Rainbo conversation / Refractions in the plastic pulse / Parsee / Tickertape of the unconscious / Contronatura
DUHFCD 017 / 22 Sep '97 / Duophonic UHF Discs

☐ EMPEROR TOMATO KETCHUP
Metronomic underground / Cybele's revenge / Percolator / Les yper-sound / Spark plug / OLV 26 / Noise of carpet / Tomorrow is already here / Emperor tomato ketchup / Monstre sacre / Motoroller scalatron / Slow fast hazel / Anonymous collective
DUHFCD 11 / Mar '96 / Duophonic UHF Discs

☐ FIRES (Stereolab & Ui)
St. Elmo's fire / Less time / Impulse rah
DS45CD 19 / 23 Feb '98 / Duophonic 45's

☐ GROOP PLAYED SPACE AGE BACHELOR PAD MUSIC, THE
Avant garde (MOR) / Groop played chord X / Space age bachelor pad music / Ronco symphony / We're not adult orientated / UMF-MFP / We're not adult orientated
PURECD 019 / Mar '93 / Too Pure

☐ MARS AUDIAC QUINTET
DUHFCD 05 / Aug '94 / Duophonic UHF Discs

☐ PENG
PURECD 011 / May '92 / Too Pure

☐ REFRIED ECTOPLASM
DUHFCD 09 / Sep '95 / Duophonic UHF Discs

☐ SWITCHED ON
Super electric / Doubt / Au grand jour / Way will be opening / Brittle / Contact / High expectation / Light that will cease to fail / Changer
SLUMBERLAND 22 / 15 Dec '97 / Slumberland

☐ TRANSIENT RANDOM NOISE BURSTS
DUHFCD 02 / Sep '93 / Duophonic UHF Discs

Stereophonic Space Sound Unlimited

☐ PLAYS LOST TV THEMES
DD 0126CD / Apr '97 / Dr. Dream

Stereophonics

☐ WORD GETS AROUND
VVR 1000432
VVR 1000438 / Aug '97 / Banana

Stereotaxic Device

☐ STEREOTAXIC DEVICE
KK 046CD / Jan '91 / KK

Stergiou, Kyriakos

☐ SUN AND THE MOON, THE (2CD Set)
ML 01945 / 11 May '98 / Musurgia Graeca

Steril

☐ VENUS TRAP
08543292 / Feb '97 / Westcom

Sterling

☐ MONSTERLINGO
Is this the time / Intravenous / Three hand man / Out of the sunlight / Shiver / Crawl Mary / Dream queen / 5x bigger / Addlestone rock / Headless / Good sun / Him
MNTCD 1006 / Apr '97 / Mantra

Sterling Jubilee Singers

☐ JESUS HITS LIKE THE ATOM BOMB
Jesus hits like the atom bomb / Devotional / Peace in the valley / God shall wipe all tears away / Little wooden church on the hill / Lord's prayer / Will he welcome me there / Job / I never heard a man / My Jesus knows / Every time I try to do my best / Operator / Testimony / Benediction
805132 / Jun '97 / New World

Sterling, Peter

☐ GYPSY ROAD
M 44D / Aug '96 / World Disc

Stern, Leni

☐ SECRETS
ENJA 50932 / Mar '97 / Enja

☐ WORDS
LIP 890282 / May '95 / Lipstick

Stern, Mike

☐ BETWEEN THE LINES
7567828352 / 29 Jun '98 / Elektra

☐ GIVE AND TAKE
7567830362 / 29 Jun '98 / Elektra

☐ UPSIDE DOWNSIDE
7567816562 / 29 Jun '98 / Elektra

Stern, Peggy

☐ PLEIADES (Stern, Peggy Trio)
W 822 / Apr '94 / Philology

Sternklang

☐ FREESTYLESPACEPHUNK
BSCD 014 / Jul '97 / BeatService

Steroid

☐ JISM HARVESTER
Low slung autopsy / Spit jesu / Real time evolution / True force / Protocolic countdown / Brains for higher / Ram the user
CLAYCD 115 / Apr '93 / Clay

Stetson Stompers

☐ 100% LINE DANCE MUSIC
Hillybilly rock, hilibilly roll / Honkytonk crowd / Cannibals / Any man of mine / Pick up the fiddle / All you ever do is bring me down / Dancin' cowboys / Perez prez / Baby come back / County auction / Whose bed has your boots been under / End of the line / Little bitty / Orange blossom special
RBCD 544 / Apr '97 / Sharpe

☐ COUNTRY LINE DANCING MUSIC
Chattahoochee / Not counting you / Streets of Bakersfield / Achey breaky heart / Sweet dream baby / Sheriff is a huntin' me a man / These boots are made for walking / Just call me lonesome / New way to light up an old flame / Mama knows the highway / Summertime blues / Guitars and cadillacs
RBCD 531 / May '96 / Sharpe

Steven, Karen

☐ DANCE ON THE FIDDLE
KLSCD 1 / Dec '97 / Karen Steven

Stevens, Beth & April

☐ SISTERS
Wishful thinking / Sisters / Who's crying for you now / Tired old heart / What about me / My old friend the blues / In my time of dying / Jeanie and Tommy / Blue / Tomorrow is forever / Bed of roses / When we're gone long gone
ROUCD 0396 / Oct '96 / Rounder

Stevens, Cat

☐ BUDDAH AND THE CHOCOLATE BOX
Music / Oh very young / Sun/C79 / Ghost town / Jesus / Ready to love / King of trees / Bad penny / Home in the sky
IMCD 70 / Nov '89 / Island

☐ CATCH BULL AT FOUR
Sitting / Boy with a moon and star on his head / Angelsea / Silent sunlight / Can't keep it in / 18th Avenue (Kansas City nightmare) / Freezing steel / O'Caritas / Sweet scarlet / Ruins
IMCD 34 / Jul '89 / Island

☐ EARLY TAPES
I love my dog / First cut is the deepest / Bad night / I'm so sleepy / Blackness of the night / School is out / Northern wind / View from the top / Come on and dance / Where are you / Granny / Moonstone / Ceylon city / Kitty
5501082 / Oct '93 / Spectrum

☐ FOREIGNER
Foreigner suite / Hurt / How many times / Later / Hundred I dream
IMCD 72 / Nov '89 / Island

☐ I HAVE NO CANNONS THAT ROAR (Various Artists)
Mother father sister brother / When adhans are called / Blossom brown / Where are Makkah and Madinah / Spring of Tasnim / Hey homeland / Allah is enough for me / Last flight / I have no cannons that roar / Little ones / I am a son of yours
J 70003CD / 13 Apr '98 / Jamal

☐ LIFE OF THE LAST PROPHET, THE (Early Life/Prophethood/Migration/ Conquest Of Makkah) (Islam, Yusuf)
Tala'a al-badru' alayna / La iiaha illa allah / Muhammad al mustafa
MOL 7001CD3 / 6 Jul '98 / Mountain Of Light

☐ MONA BONE JAKON
Lady D'Arbanville / Maybe you're / Pop star / I think I see the light / Trouble / Mona bone jakon / I wish I wish / Katmandu / Fill my eyes / Timer / Time / Lillywhite
IMCD 35 / '89 / Island

☐ TEA FOR THE TILLERMAN
Where do the children play / Hard headed woman / Wild world / Sad Lisa / Miles from nowhere / But I might die tonight / Longer boats / Into white / On the road to find out / Father and son / Tea for the tillerman
IMCD 36 / '89 / Island

☐ TEASER AND THE FIRECAT
Wind / Ruby love / If I laugh / Changes IV / How can I tell you / Tuesday's dead / Morning has broken / Bitter blue / Moon shadow / Peace train
IMCD 104 / Mar '90 / Island

☐ VERY BEST OF CAT STEVENS, THE
Where do the children play / Wild world / Tuesday's dead / Lady D'Arbanville / First cut is the deepest / Oh very young / Ruby love / Morning has broken / Moonshadow / Matthew and son / Father and son / Can't keep it in / Hard headed woman / Old school yard / I love my dog / Another Saturday night / Sad Lisa / Peace train
8401482 / Jun '95 / Island

Stevens, Kenni

☐ YOU
Who's been lovin' you / Hurt this way / Never gonna give you up / 24-7-365 / You don't know / I bleed for you / You / Didn't mean to hurt you / Work me up / Anne
CDDB 502 / May '88 / Debut

Stevens, Meic

☐ ER COF AM BLANT Y CWM
Er cof am blant y cwm / Yr eglwys ar y cei / Tafarn Elfed / Sabots Bernie / Morwen y medd / Yfory y plant / Angau opera ffug y clon / Mae gen i gariad / Bwda Bernie / Brenein y bop / Iraq
CRAICD 036 / Mar '94 / Crai

☐ MLHANGEL
CRAICD 059 / Jan '98 / Crai

☐ WARE'N NOETH
SCD 4088 / May '97 / Sain

☐ Y BALEDL
Dim ond cysgodion / Y peintiwr coch / Sandoz yn loudon square / Erwan / Ysbryd solfa / Gwenllian / Mor o gariad / Noson oer nadolig / Capel branwen / Tywyllwch / Breuddwydion / Bobby sands / Cwm llwm / Dic penderyn / Rhyddid ffug / Y meirw byw / Ar y mynydd / Hiraeth bregus / Bethan mewn cwsg
SCD 2001 / Feb '95 / Sain

Stevens, Mike

☐ JOY
Long road / Rainbow warrior / Searchin' / Catalina dawn / Skyride / Tell me / Joy / Harbour island breeze / Jean Pierre / Healing heart
DOMECD 5 / Oct '95 / Dome

Stevens, Peter

☐ TAKEN BY THE LIGHT (Stevens, Peter Band)
35638 / Nov '96 / Sphinx Ministry

Stevens, Ray

☐ BEST OF RAY STEVENS, THE
Everything is beautiful / Mr. Businessman / Unwind / Yakety yak / Bridget the Midget / Gitarzan / Along came Jones / Turn your radio on / Mama and a papa / Moonlight special / Streak / Time for us / She belongs to me / Young love / Raindrops keep falling on my head / Indian love call / Something / Leaving on a jet plane / Bye bye love / Misty
MOCD 3011 / Feb '95 / More Music

☐ BIGGEST AND THE BEST, THE
Everything is beautiful / Gitarzan / All my trials / Mr. Businessman / Streak / Have a little talk with myself / Unwind / Along came Jones / Losin' streak / Bridget the midget / Turn your radio on / Ahab the Arab / Sunset strip / Misty / Sunday mornin' comin' down / Moonlight special / Young love / Mama and a Papa / America communicate with me / Indian love call
3036000872 / Jul '97 / Carlton

☐ HIT SINGLE COLLECTABLES
DISK 4510 / Apr '94 / Disky

Stevens, Shakin'

☐ BEST OF SHAKIN' STEVENS, THE
This ole house / You drive me crazy / It's late / Green door / Teardrops / Oh Julie / Love worth waiting for / I'll be satisfied / Marie Marie / It's raining / Give me your heart tonight / Shirley / Cry just a little bit / Rockin' good way (to mess around and fall in love) / Letter to you / Why do you treat me this way
4662652 / 27 Jul '98 / Epic

☐ GREATEST HITS
This ole house / You drive me crazy / Letter to you / It's raining / Green door / Hot dog / Teardrops / Breaking up my heart / Oh Julie / Marie Marie / Love worth waiting for / It's late / Give me your heart tonight / Shirley / Blue Christmas / Cry just a little bit / Rockin' good way / I'll be satisfied
4669932 / Sep '93 / Epic

☐ HITS OF SHAKIN' STEVENS VOL.1, THE
Hot dog / Lipstick powder and paint / Turning away / Because I love you / Little boogie woogie (in the back of my mind) / Come see about me / What do you want to make those eyes at me for / Feel the need in me / How many tears can you hide / True love / Love attack / I might / Radio / Que sera sera / Josephine / Merry christmas everyone
4910262 / 3 Aug '98 / Epic

☐ SHAKIN' STEVENS
You mostest girl / Sexy ways / Honey hush / Evil hearted / Jungle rock / My baby died / Reet petite / Monkey's uncle / Silver wings / Memphis earthquake / Rock around with ollie vee / Story of the rockers / Frantic / Baby blue / Ready teddy / Tear it up / Justine / Oakie boogie / Wine, wine, wine / Blue swinging mama
GRF 234 / Aug '93 / Tring

☐ UNIQUE ROCK'N'ROLL CHRISTMAS, THE
Rockin' little Christmas / White Christmas / Sure won't seem like Christmas / I'll be home this Christmas / Merry Christmas everyone / Silent night / It's gonna be a lonely Christmas / Best Christmas of them all / Merry Christmas pretty baby / Christmas wish / Blue Christmas / So long Christmas
4692602 / Nov '91 / Epic

Stevens, T.M.

☐ BOOM OUT OF CONTROL
USG 35829422 / Apr '97 / USG

Stevens, Tanya

☐ BIG THINGS A GWAN
RNCD 0034 / May '97 / Runn

Stevens, Vic

☐ NO CURB AHEAD (Stevens, Vic Mistaken Identities)
EFA 060132 / 26 Aug '97 / Lolo

Stevenson, Savourna

☐ CALMAN THE DOVE (Stevenson, Savourna & Davy Spillane)
Calman the wolf / White swan / An Buachaille / Calman the dove / Where there's women there's trouble / I mo Cridh / Mesmerising Nessy / Bell ringer / Sith as a' ghaillionn
COOKCD 137 / 26 Jan '98 / Cooking Vinyl

☐ CUTTING THE CHORD
Aeolian / Basse Breton rhapsody / Cutting the chord / Harplands / Blues in 10
ECLCD 9308 / Jan '96 / Eclectic

☐ TUSITALA, TELLER OF TALES
ECLCD 9412 / Jan '96 / Eclectic

☐ TWEED JOURNEY
Source / Fording the tweed / Waulk from the tweed / Lost bells / Trows and Cowdieknowes / Percussion solo / Forest flowers / Tweed journey
ECLCD 9001 / Jan '96 / Eclectic

Stevie B

☐ HIT COLLECTION (2CD Set)
ZYX 204462 / Nov '97 / ZYX

☐ SUMMER NIGHTS
ZYX 204562 / 26 May '98 / ZYX

Stewart Family

☐ STEWARTS O'BLAIR (Stewart, Belle & Family)
Come a' you jolly Ploomen / Lakes of Shillin / Bonnie hoose o'Airlie / Moving on song / Nobleman / Jock Stewart / Inverness-shire / Banks of the Lee / Betsy belle / Dawning of the day / My dog and gun / Berryfields o'Blair / I'm no coming oot the noo / Mickey's warning / Hatton woods / Parting song / Canntaireachd
OSS 96CD / Aug '94 / Ossian

Stewart, Al

☐ 24 CARAT
Running man / Midnight rocks / Constantinople / Merlin's time / Mondo sinistro / Murmansk run/Ellis Island / Rocks in the ocean / Paint by numbers / Optical illusion / Here in Angola / Indian summer / Pandora / Delia's gone / Princess Olivia
CDP 78004242 / 29 Sep '97 / EMI

☐ BEST OF AL STEWART, THE (Centenary Collection)
On the border / Song on the radio / Year of the cat / Time passages / Midnight rocks / Merlin's time / Broadway hotel / One stage before / Indian summer / Lori, don't go right now / Electric Los Angeles sunset / Running man / Paint by numbers / Mondo sinistro / Night train to Munich / Almost Lucy / Life between the wars
CTMCD 310 / Feb '97 / EMI

☐ FAMOUS LAST WORDS
INDELCD 3 / 27 Apr '98 / Indelible

☐ LAST DAYS OF THE CENTURY
Last days of the century / Real and unreal / King of Portugal / Where are they now / License to steal / Josephine Baker / Antarctica / Ghostly horses of the plain / Red toupee / Bad reputation / Fields of France
CDEMS 1626 / 29 Sep '97 / EMI

☐ LIVE AT THE ROXY LA 1981
Running man / Time passages / Merlin's time / If it doesn't come naturally / Roads to Moscow / Nostradamus / World goes to Riyadh / Nostradamus / Soho / On the border / Valentina way / Clarence frogman henry / Year of the cat
CDEMS 1625 / 29 Sep '97 / EMI

☐ ON THE BORDER
On the border / Year of the cat / 3 mules / Flying sorcery / Merlin's time / Clifton in the rain / Betty Boop's birthday / Man for all seasons / Song on the radio / Pandora / Running man / Night train to Munich / If it doesn't come naturally / Leave it / Life between the wars / Fields of France / You should have listened to Al
4949422 / 1 Jun '98 / EMI Gold

☐ ORANGE
You don't even know me / Amsterdam / Songs out of the clay / News from Spain / I don't believe you / Once an orange, always an orange / I'm falling / Night of the 4th of May
4844412 / Jul '96 / Columbia

☐ RHYMES IN ROOMS
Flying sorcery / Soho (needless to say) / Time passages / Josephine Baker / On the border / Nostradamus / Fields of France / Clifton in the rain / Small fruit song / Broadway hotel / Leave it / Year of the cat
CDFA 3315 / Feb '95 / Fame

☐ TIME PASSAGES
Valentina way / Life in dark water / Man for all seasons / Almost Lucy / Time passages / Palace of Versailles / Timeless skies / End of the day / Song on the radio
CDFA 3312 / Dec '94 / Fame

☐ TIME PASSAGES/YEAR OF THE CAT/ RUSSIANS AND AMERICANS (The Originals/3CD Set)
Valentina way / Life in dark water / Man for all seasons / Almost Lucy / Time passages / Palace of Versailles / Timeless skies / End of the day / Song on the radio / Lord Grenville / On the border / Midas shadow / Sand in your shoes / If it doesn't come naturally, leave it / Flying sorcery / Broadway hotel / One stage before / Year of the cat / Lori don't go right now / Gypsy and the rose / Accident on 3rd Street / Strange girl / Russians and Americans / Cafe society / 1-2-3 / Candidate
CDOMB 020 / 27 Jul '98 / EMI

☐ TO WHOM IT MAY CONCERN (Al Stewart 1966 - 1970)
Elf / Turn into earth / Bedsitter images / Swiss Cottage manoeuvres / Carmichaels / Scandinavian girl / Pretty golden hair / Denise at sixteen / Samuel, oh how you've changed / Cleave to me / Long way down from Stephanie / Ivich / Belecka doodle day / Lover man / Clifton in the rain / In Brooklyn / Old Compton Street blues / Ballad of Mary Foster / Life and life only / You should have listened to Al / Love chronicles / My enemies have sweet voices / Small fruit song / Gethsemane, again / Burbling / Electric Los Angeles sunset / Manuscript / Black Hill / Anna / Room of roots / Zero she flies
CDEM 1511 / Nov '93 / EMI

☐ YEAR OF THE CAT
Lord Grenville / On the border / Midas shadow / Sand in your shoes / If it doesn't come naturally, leave it / Flying sorcery / Broadway hotel / One stage before / Year of the cat
CDFA 3253 / Apr '91 / Fame

Stewart, Amii

☐ BEST OF AMII STEWART, THE (2CD Set)
SMDCD 166 / Jul '97 / Snapper

☐ BEST OF AMII STEWART, THE
HTCD 106 / 20 Apr '98 / Hot Productions

Stewart, Andy

☐ ANDY STEWART COLLECTION, THE (20 Scottish Favourites)
Scottish soldier / Dr. Finlay / Cambeltown Loch / Battle's o'er / Highlandman's Umbrella / I'm off to Bonnie Scotland / Road to the Isles / Scotland yet / Farewell 51st farewell / Muckin' O' Geordie's byre / Donald, where's yer troosers / Girl from Glasgow town / Ho ro my nut brown maiden / Tunes of glory / Wild rover / Road and the miles to Dundee / Courtin' in the kitchen / Lassie come and dance with me / I love to wear a kilt / Going doon the water
CDMFP 5700 / Mar '93 / Music For Pleasure

☐ ANDY STEWART'S SCOTLAND
Come in, come in / Donald where's your troosers / A scottish soldier / Mcallister (comedy verse) / Lochside / Campbeltown loch / Andy where's your kilt / Muckin o' geordie's byre / Kissin' in the dark / Road and the miles to dundee / Rumour (comedy verse) / Bonnie lass o' fyvie / Tunes of glory / Maggie / Nicky tams / Barnyards o' delgaty / Take me back / Tobermory (comedy verse) / De ye ken lang syne / Nice to be a grandad
CDITV 563 / May '93 / Scotdisc

☐ FOREVER IN SONG
Donald, where's yer troosers / Highlandman's umbrella / Lock Marie island / Lovely Stornoway / Dancing in kyle / Song of the Clyde / In praise of Islay / Rothesay bay / Joy of my heart / Loch Lomond / Stop your ticklin' jock / Roamin' in the gloamin' / Wee Deoch an' Doris / Keep right on to the end of the road / Away up in Clachan / Gordon for me / Jock McKay / My ain hoose / Westering home / Wild mountain thyme / Horee - horo / Wild rover / Waggle o' the kilt / It's nice to get up in the morning / Tobermoray / Safest o' the family / I' foo the noo / Wedding of Sandy McNab / Will ye no' come back again / Skye boat song / Come ower the stream, Charlie / Rise and follow Charlie / Take me back / Barren rocks of Aden / Farewell 51st farewell / Jock Cameron / Bee baw babbity / Queen Mary / Height starvation song / Do re mi / Ye canny shove yer granny aff a bus / Andy where's yer kilt / Hiking song / Ho ro my nut brown maiden / Uist tramping song / Marching through the heather / I belong to Glasgow / Sailign up the Clyde / We've got a baby in the house / Ninety four this morning / Johnny Lad / Bonnie wee Jeannie McColl / Soor milk cairt / Wee toon clerk / Dashing white sergeant / Tartan ball / Lassie come and dance with me / Country dance / There was a lad / Polly Stewart / De'il's awa' wi' tha exciseman / Man's a man for a' that / Tartan / Campbells are coming / Johnny cope / Piper O'Dundee / Old Scottish waltz / Bonnie wells o'wearie / Back in bonnie Scotland / Bonnie Scotland / Haste ye back / Scotland the brave / We're no awa' tae bide awa' / Mairi's wedding / Thistle of Scotland / Muckin' O' Geordie's byre / Lass O'Fyvie / Nickie tams / Barnyards o'delgaty / Auld lang syne
PLATCD 3921 / Nov '93 / Platinum

☐ VERY BEST OF ANDY STEWART, THE
Andy where's your kilt / I belong to Glasgow / Sailing up the Clyde / We've got a baby in the hoose / Ninety-four this morning / Mull of Kintyre / Bee baw babbity / Queen Mary / Height starvation song / Ye canny shove yer granny aff a bus / My ain house / Westering home / Wild mountain thyme / Horee-horo / Wild rover / Scotland the brave / We're no awa'tae bide awa / Mairie's wedding / Thistle of Scotland / Rumour / Stop yer ticklin' Jock / Roamin' in the gloaming / Wee deoch'n'Doris / Keep right on to the end of the road / Will ye no come back again / Skye boat song / Come over the stream Charlie / Rise and follow Charlie / Green grow the rushes / My love she's but a lassie yet / Bonnie Jean / Donald where's your troosers / Highlandman's umbrella / Loch Marie islands / Lovely Stornaway / Dancing in Kyle / Song of Clyde / In praise of Isla / Rothesay bay / Joy of my heart / Granny's heilan name / Johnny lad / Bonnie wee Jeannie McColl / Soor milk cairt / Wee toon clerk / Northern lights of Aberdeen / Rothesay bay / I belong to Glasgow / There was a lad / Polly Stewart /

De'il's awa' wi' tha exciseman / Man's a man / When you and I were young Maggie / We're no awa 'tae bide awa' / Old Scottish waltz / Bonnie well o'wearie / Back to bonnie Scotland / Bonnie Scotland / Hast ye back / Auld lang syne
MCVD 30008 / Nov '96 / Emerald Gem

Stewart, Andy M.

☐ AT IT AGAIN (Stewart, Andy M. & Manus Lunny)
At it again / My heart it belongs to she / Haughs of cromdale / Exile of erin-air I mo sheasamh ar an tra (as I stand o / Tae the weaver's gin ye go / If I never spend a morning without you / Monday morning / Beid og ni mhailley-bridget o'malley / Mary mheaigl's (reel) / Frank mors (hornpipe) / Trip to lerwick (jig)
GLCD 1107 / Feb '92 / Green Linnet

☐ BY THE HUSH
Haud your tongue dear sally / Ramblin rover / By the hush / Orphan's wedding / Patrick sheehan / Parish of dunkeld-the curlew / They wounded old ireland / I'd cross the wild atlantic
GLCD 3030 / Oct '93 / Green Linnet

☐ DONEGAL RAIN
Ramblin' Irishman / Matt Hyland / Gallant Murray (gathering of Athole)/White rose / Queen amangst the heather / Tibbie Fowler o' the glen / Reckless affection / Irish stranger / Mary and the hielan' sodger / Banks of sweet Dundee / When you took your love / Donegal rain
GLCD 1183 / Nov '97 / Green Linnet

☐ DUBLIN LADY (Stewart, Andy M. & Manus Lunny)
Take her in your arms / Where are you / Dublin Lady / Freedom is like gold / Bogie's bonnie belle / Dinny the piper / Heart of the home / Humours of whiskey / Tak' it man tak' it
GLCD 1083 / Feb '92 / Green Linnet

☐ FIRE IN THE GLEN (Stewart, Andy M./ Phil Cunningham/Manus Lunny)
SHAN 79062 CD / Oct '89 / Shanachie

☐ MAN IN THE MOON
GLCD 1140 / Apr '94 / Green Linnet

☐ SONGS OF ROBERT BURNS, THE
GLCD 3059 / '92 / Green Linnet

Stewart, Bob

☐ WELCOME TO THE CLUB (Stewart, Bob & Hank Jones)
Day in, day out / I'll never be the same / Body and soul / September in the rain / Don't misunderstood / Fools rush in / Then I'll be tired of you / Just friends / Did I remember / When Sunny gets blue / What a little moonlight can do / Love look away / Every time we say goodbye / Very thought of you
CDLR 45017 / Aug '90 / L&R

Stewart, Dave

☐ AS FAR AS DREAMS CAN GO (Stewart, Dave & Barbara Gaskin)
Locomotion / Lenina Crowe / I'm losing you / Roads girdle the globe / Do I still figure in your life / When the guards are asleep / Make me promises / Do we see the light of day / As far as dreams can go
BRCD 9008940 / '88 / Broken

☐ BIG IDEA, THE (Stewart, Dave & Barbara Gaskin)
Levi Stubbs' tears / My scene / Grey skies / Subterranean homesick blues / Heatwave / Crying game / Deep underground / Shadowland / Mr. Theremin / New Jerusalem
BRCD 9009330 / '90 / Broken

☐ BROKEN RECORDS - THE SINGLES (Stewart, Dave & Barbara Gaskin)
I'm in a different world / Leipzig / It's my party / Johnny Rocco / Siamese cat song / Busy doing nothing / Rich for a day / Waiting in the wings / Emperor's new guitar / Hamburger song / Henry and James / World spins so slow
BRCD 9008900 / '87 / Broken

☐ SELECTED TRACKS (Stewart, Dave & Barbara Gaskin)
STIFFCD 24 / Jan '94 / Disky

☐ SPIN (Stewart, Dave & Barbara Gaskin)
Walking the dog / Cloths of heaven / Eight miles high / Ameila / Trash planet / Golden rain / Your lucky star / Cast your fate to the wind / Louie Louie / Sixties never die / Star blind
BRCD 9011400 / Aug '92 / Broken

☐ UP FROM THE DARK (Stewart, Dave & Barbara Gaskin)
I'm in a different world / Leipzig / It's my party / Lenina Crowe / Do I still figure in your life / Busy doing nothing / I'm losing you / Roads girdle the globe / When the guards are asleep / World spins so slow / Siamese cat song / Do we see the light of day / Henry and James / As far as dreams can go
BRCD 10011 / '86 / Broken

Stewart, David A.

☐ GREETINGS FROM THE GUTTER
Heart of stone / Greeting from the gutter / Crazy sister / Chelsea lovers / Jealousy / St. Valentine's day / Kinky sweetheart / Damien save me / Tragedy street / You talk a lot / Oh no, not you again
4509975462 / Dec '96 / East West

Stewart, Davie

☐ DAVIE STEWART
MacPherson's rant / Jolly beggar / 74th Highlanders farewell to Edinburgh / I'm often drunk and I'm seldom sober / Set of jigs / Overgate / Merchant's son / Daft piper / Boolavogue / Harvest home / Dowie dens o' Yarrow
CDTRAX 9052 / 1 Jul '98 / Greentrax

Stewart, Gary

☐ GARY'S GREATEST
HCD 8030 / Jun '94 / Hightone

☐ I'M A TEXAN
HCD 8050 / Jul '94 / Hightone

☐ OUT OF HAND
Drinkin' thing / Honky tonkin' / I see the want to in your eyes / This old heart won't let go / Draggin' shackles / She's actin' single (I'm drinkin' doubles) / Back sliders' wine / Sweet country red / Out of hand / Williamson County
HCD 8026 / Sep '94 / Hightone

Stewart, Grant

☐ DOWNTOWN SOUNDS (Stewart, Grant Quintet)
CRISS 1085CD / May '94 / Criss Cross

☐ MORE URBAN TONES (Stewart, Grant Quartet)
Nica's tempo / I should care / You go to my head / Rabbitron / All through the night / You sweet and fancy lady / Manhattan Bridge / Pie eye blues
CRISS 1124CD / 20 Oct '97 / Criss Cross

Stewart, John

☐ AIRDREAM BELIEVER
SHCD 8015 / Aug '95 / Shanachie

☐ BANDERA
FERCD 1436 / Mar '98 / Folk Era

☐ CALIFORNIA BLOODLINES...PLUS
California bloodlines / Razor back woman / She believes in me / Omaha rainbow / Pirates of Stone County Road / Shackles and chains / Heart full of woman and a bellyful of Tenness / Willard / Big Joe / Mother country / Lonesome picker / You can't look back / Missouri birds / July you're a woman / Never goin' back / Friend of Jesus / Marshall wind
SEECD 87 / Apr '98 / See For Miles

☐ CALIFORNIA BLOODLINES/WILLARD MINUS TWO
California bloodlines / Razor back woman / She believes in me / Omaha rainbow / Pirates of Stone County Road / Shackles and chains / Mother Country / Some lonesome picker / You can't look back / Missouri birds / July you're a woman / Never goin' back / Big Joe / Julie / Judy angel rain / Belly full of Tennessee / Friend of Jesus / Clack clack / Hero from the war / Back in Pomona / Willard / Golden rollin' belly / All American girl / Oldest living son / Earth rider
BCD 15468 / Jul '89 / Bear Family

☐ CANNONS IN THE RAIN/WINGLESS ANGELS
Durango / Chilly winds / Easy money / Anna on a memory / All time woman / Road away / Armstrong / Spirit / Wind dies down / Cannons in the rain / Lady and the outlaw / Hung on your heart / Rose water / Wingless / Angels / Some kind of love / Survivors / Summer child / Josie / Rise stone blind / Mazatlan / Let the big horse run
BCD 15519 / Oct '90 / Bear Family

☐ CHILLY WINDS
FE 1401CD / Dec '94 / Folk Era

☐ COMPLETE PHOENIX CONCERTS, THE
Wheatfield lady / Kansas rain / You can't look back / Pirates of Stone County Road / Runaway fool of love / Roll away the stone / July you're a woman / Last campaign trilogy / Oldest living son / Little road and a stone to roll / Kansas / Cody / California bloodlines / Mother country / Cops / Never goin' back / Freeway pleasure / Let the big horse run
BCD 15518 / Feb '91 / Bear Family

☐ LIVE AT THE TURF INN SCOTLAND
FE 1428 / Aug '96 / Folk Era

☐ PUNCH THE BIG GUY
SHCD 08009 / Mar '94 / Shanachie

☐ ROUGH SKETCHES
FE 1437CD / May '97 / Folk Era

Stewart, Louis

☐ OVERDRIVE
All the things you are / Oh lady be good / Polka dots and moonbeams / Oleo / Yesterdays / Stompin' at the savoy / Body and soul / Walkin' / My shining hour
HEPCD 2057 / Aug '94 / Hep

Stewart, Margaret

☐ FHUAIR MI POG (Stewart, Margaret & Allan MacDonald)
Fhuair mi pog a laimh an righ / Bha caileag as t-earrach / Cille pheadair / Dol dhan taigh bhuan leat / O Mhairi's tu mo Mhairi / I ho ro's na hug oro eile / He na milibhig / Slainte bhon t-seann duthaich / Ochoin a righ gur tinn an galair an gradh / Cro chinn t-saile / Cumha mhic an-toisich / Ruidhlichean pioba / Uamh an oir/Cumha an t-seana chlaidheimh / S'olc an obair do theachdairean cadal / Port na hpucai / I got a kiss of the king's hand / There was a girl / Kilphedir / Going to the eternal dwelling with you / Mary you are my Mary
CDTRAX 132 / 2 Feb '98 / Greentrax

Stewart, Mark

☐ CONTROL DATA
CDSTUMM 93 / Mar '96 / Mute

☐ MARK STEWART
Survival / Survivalist / Anger / Hell is empty / Stranger / Forbidden colour / Forbidden / Fatal / Attraction
CDSTUMM 43 / Oct '87 / Mute

☐ METATRON
Hysteria / Shame / Collision / Faith healer / These things happen / My possession / Possession dub / Mammon
CDSTUMM 62 / Apr '90 / Mute

Stewart, Michael

☐ BLUE PATCHES (Stewart, Michael 'Patches')
HIBD 8016 / 6 May '97 / Hip Bop

Stewart, Michael 'Patches'

☐ PENETRATION
HIBD 8018 / 1 Sep '98 / Hip Bop

Stewart, Priscilla

☐ PRISCILLA STEWART 1924-1928
DOCD 5476 / Sep '96 / Document

Stewart, Rex

☐ CLASSICS 1934-1946
CLASSICS 931 / Apr '97 / Classics

☐ INTRODUCTION TO REX STEWART 1920-1941, AN
4005 / Dec '93 / Best Of Jazz

☐ REX STEWART STORY 1926-1945, THE
158622 / Oct '96 / Jazz Archives

☐ REXATIOUS (His Greatest Recordings 1926-1941)
Jackass blues / Old black Joe's blues / Rocky road / Do you believe in love at first sight / Stingaree / Baby ain't you satisfied / Rexatious / Lazy man's shuffle / Back room romp / Tea and trumpets / Monmartre / Low cotton / Finesse / I know that you know / Solid old man / Bugle call rag / Diga diga doo / Mobile bay / Subtle Slough / Showboat shuffle / Kissin' my baby goodnight / Trumpet in spades / Morning glory / Boy meets horn
CDAJA 5200 / May '96 / Living Era

Stewart, Robert

☐ JUDGEMENT
1232682 / Aug '97 / Red

Stewart, Rod

☐ ACOUSTIC MOODS OF ROD STEWART (Various Artists)
Maggie May / This old heart of mine / I don't want to talk about it / Angel / You wear it well / Have I told you lately / Downtown train / Tonight's the night / Oh no not my baby / Mandolin wind / Tom Traubert's blues / Reason to believe / You're in my heart / Killing of Georgie / First cut is the deepest / I was only joking / Cindy incidentally / Sailing
308792 / 11 May '98 / Hallmark

☐ ATLANTIC CROSSING
Three times a loser / Alright for an hour / All in the name of rock 'n' roll / Drift away / Stone cold sober / I don't want to talk about it / It's not the spotlight / This old heart of mine / Still love you / Sailing
256151 / Feb '87 / WEA

☐ BEST OF ROD STEWART, THE
Maggie May / You wear it well / Baby Jane / Do ya think I'm sexy / I was only joking / This old heart of mine / Sailing / I don't want to talk about it / You're in my heart / Young Turks / What am I gonna do (I'm so in love with you) / First cut is the deepest / Killing of Georgie / Tonight's the night / Every beat of my heart / Downtown train
9260342 / '89 / WEA

☐ BLONDES HAVE MORE FUN
Do ya think I'm sexy / Dirty weekend / Ain't love a bitch / Best days of my life / Is that the thanks I get / Attractive female wanted / Blondes have more fun / Last summer / Standing in the shadows of love / Scarred and scared
7599273762 / Jan '91 / WEA

☐ BODY WISHES
Dancin' alone / Baby Jane / Move me / Body wishes / Sweet surrender / What am I gonna do / Ghetto blaster / Ready now / Strangers / Again / Satisfied
9238772 / Jul '84 / WEA

☐ CAMOUFLAGE
Infatuation / All right now / Some guys have all the luck / Can we still be friends / Bad for you / Heart is on the line / Camouflage / Trouble
9250952 / Jul '84 / WEA

☐ EARLY YEARS, THE
I just got some / Bright lights big city / Ain't that lovin' you baby / Mapper's blues / Why does it go on / Shake / Keep your hands off her / Don't you tell nobody / Just like I treat you / Day will come / Little Miss Understood / Come home baby
ECD 3109 / Jan '95 / K-Tel

☐ EVERY BEAT OF MY HEART
Who's gonna take me home / Another heartache / Night like this / Red hot in black / Here to eternity / Love touch / In my own crazy way / Every beat of my heart / Ten days of rain / In my life / Trouble
9254462 / Jul '86 / WEA

☐ EVERY PICTURE TELLS A STORY
Every picture tells a story / Seems like a long time / That's alright / Amazing grace / Tomorrow is such a long time / Maggie May / Mandolin wind / I'm losing you / Reason to believe
5580602 / 3 Aug '98 / Mercury

☐ FOOTLOOSE AND FANCY FREE
Hot legs / You're insane / You're in my heart / Born loose / You keep me hangin' on / (If loving you is wrong) I don't want to be right / You gotta nerve / I was only joking
9273232 / Jun '89 / WEA

☐ GASOLINE ALLEY
Gasoline alley / It's all over now / Only a hobo / My way of giving / Country comfort / Cut across shorty / Lady Day / Jo's lament / I don't want to discuss it
5580592 / 3 Aug '98 / Mercury

☐ HANDBAGS AND GLADRAGS (The Mercury Recordings 1970-1974/2CD Set)
Every picture tells a story / Interludings / You wear it well / You put something better inside / Only a hobo / Reason to believe / It's all over now / Cut across shorty / Los Paraguayos / Mandolin wind / Crying laughing loving lying / Street fighting man / Man of constant sorrow / I know I'm losing you / Lay Day / So tired / Oh no not my baby / What made Milwaukee famous (has made a loser out of me) / Maggie May / Gasoline alley / Dixie toot / Everytime we say goodbye / Twistin' the night away / True blue / Lochinvar farewell / Italian girls / Mama you've been on my mind / Country comfort / Sweet little rock 'n' roller / I wouldn't change a thing / I'd rather go blind / Angel / Missed you / Dirty old town
5288232 / Oct '95 / Mercury

☐ IF WE FALL IN LOVE TONIGHT
I don't want to talk about it / Tom traubert's blues / Tonight's the night / You're in my heart / My heart can't tell you no / Broken arrow / Forever young 1996 / All for love / Sometimes when we touch / When I need you / For the first time / If we fall in love tonight / This / Have I told you lately / Downtown train / First cut is the deepest
9362464672 / Nov '96 / WEA

☐ LEAD VOCALIST
I ain't superstitious: Beck, Jeff Group / Handbags and gladrags / Cindy incidentally: Faces / Stay with me: Faces / True Blue / Sweet lady Mary: Faces / Hot legs / Stand back / Ruby Tuesday / Shotgun wedding / First I look at the purse / Tom Traubert's blues
9362452582 / Feb '93 / WEA

☐ MAGGIE MAY
Maggie May / Oh no not my baby / Twistin' the night away / Mandolin wind / Jodie / I'd rather go blind / Cindy's lament / Seems like a long time / Country comfort / (I know) I'm losing you / I wouldn't ever change a thing / Blind prayer / Hard road / I've grown accustomed to her face
5511102 / Jul '95 / Spectrum

☐ NEVER A DULL MOMENT
True blue / Los Paraguayos / Mama you been on my mind / Italian girls / Angel / Interludings / You wear it well / I'd rather go blind / Twistin' the night away
5580612 / 3 Aug '98 / Mercury

☐ NIGHT ON THE TOWN, A
Ball trap / Pretty flamingo / Big bayou / Wild side of life / Trade winds / Tonight's the night / First cut is the deepest / Fool for you / Killing of Georgie
7599273392 / Jun '93 / WEA

☐ OLD RAINCOAT WON'T LET YOU DOWN, AN
Street fighting man / Man of constant sorrow / Blind prayer / Handbags and gladrags / Old raincoat won't ever let you down / I wouldn't ever change a thing / Cindy's lament / Dirty old town
5580582 / 3 Aug '98 / Mercury

☐ OUT OF ORDER
Lost in you / Wild horse / Lethal dose of love / Forever young / My heart can't tell you no / Dynamite / Nobody knows you (when you're down and out) / Crazy about her / Try a little tenderness / When I was your man
9256842 / Jul '92 / WEA

☐ ROD STEWART
GFS 061 / Jul '97 / Going For A Song

☐ SING IT AGAIN ROD
Reason to believe / You wear it well / Mandolin wind / Country comforts / Maggie May / Handbags and gladrags / Street fighting man / Twistin' the night away / Los Paraguayos / (I know) I'm losing you / Pinball wizard / Gasoline alley
5580622 / 3 Aug '98 / Mercury

☐ SMILER
Sweet little rock 'n' roller / Lochnagar / Farewell / Sailor / Bring it on home to me / Let me be your car / (You make me feel like) a natural man / Dixie toot / Hard road / I've grown accustomed to her face / Girl from the North Country / Mine for me
5580632 / 3 Aug '98 / Mercury

☐ SPANNER IN THE WORKS
Windy town / Downtown lights / Leave Virginia alone / Sweetheart / This / Lady Luck / You're the star / Muddy, Sam and Otis / Hang on St. Christopher / Delicious / Soothe me / Purple heather
9362458672 / May '95 / WEA

☐ STORYTELLER (Complete Anthology 1964-1990/4CD Set)
Good morning little school girl / Can I get a witness / Shake / So much to say / Little Miss understood / I've been drinking / I ain't superstitious / Shapes of things / In a broken dream / Street fighting man / Handbags and gladrags / Gasoline alley / Cut across

shorty / Country comforts / It's all over now / Sweet lady Mary / Had me a real good time / Maggie May / Mandolin wind / I'm losing you / Reason to believe / Every picture tells a story / Stay with me / True blue / Angel / You wear it well / I'd rather go blind / Twistin' the night away / What made Milwaukee famous (has made a loser out of me) / Oh no not my baby / Pinball wizard / Sweet little rock 'n' roller / Let me be your car / You can make me dance / Sing or anything / Sailing / I don't want to talk about it / Stone cold sober / To love somebody / Tonight's the night / First cut is the deepest / Killing of Georgie / Get back / Hot legs / I was only joking / You're in my heart / Do ya think I'm sexy / Passion / Oh God / I wish I was home tonight / Tonight I'm yours (don't hurt me) / Young turks / Baby Jane / What am I gonna do (I'm so in love with you) / People get ready / Some guys have all the luck / Infatuation / Love touch / Every beat of my heart / Lost in you / My heart can't tell you no / Dynamite / Crazy about her / Forever young / This old heart of mine / Downtown train
9259872 / Nov '89 / WEA

☐ TONIGHT I'M YOURS
Tonight I'm yours / How long / Tora tora tora / Tear it up / Only a boy / Just like a woman / Jealous / Sonny / Young Turks / Never give up on a dream
7599236022 / Jun '93 / WEA

☐ TRIBUTE TO ROD STEWART, A (Various Artists)
62592800982 / 7 Apr '98 / DERO

☐ UNPLUGGED...AND SEATED
Hot legs / Tonight's the night / Handbags and gladrags / Cut across Shorty / Every picture tells a story / Maggie May / Reason to believe / People get ready / Have I told you lately that I love you / Tom Traubert's blues / First cut is the deepest / Mandolin wind / Highgate shuffle / Stay with me / Having a party
9362452892 / May '93 / WEA

☐ UP ALL NIGHT
9362458672 / Apr '95 / WEA

☐ VAGABOND HEART
Rhythm of my heart / Rebel heart / Broken arrow / It takes two / When a man's in love / You are everything / Motown song / Go out dancing / No holding back / Have I told you lately that I love you / Moment of glory / Downtown train / If only
7599265982 / Mar '91 / WEA

☐ VERY BEST OF ROD STEWART, THE
5588732 / 24 Aug '98 / Mercury

☐ WHEN WE WERE THE NEW BOYS
Cigarettes and alcohol / Ooh la la / Rocks / Superstar / Secret heart / Hotel chambermaid / Shelly my love / When we were the new boys / Weak / What do you want me to do
9362467922 / 1 Jun '98 / WEA

Stewart, Sandy

☐ SONGS OF JEROME KERN (Stewart, Sandy & Dick Hyman)
ACD 205 / Jun '95 / Audiophile

Stewart, Slam

☐ CLASSICS 1945-1946
CLASSICS 939 / Jun '97 / Classics

☐ SHUT YO' MOUTH
DE 1024 / Mar '91 / Delos

☐ SLAM BAM
BB 8612 / Feb '96 / Black & Blue

☐ SLAM STEWART MEMORIAL ALBUM (Stewart, Slam & Bucky Pizzarelli)
STB 2507 / Sep '95 / Stash

☐ SLAMBOREE
BB 888 / Nov '97 / Black & Blue

☐ TWO BIG NICE (Stewart, Slam & Major Holley)
Slam mule / What is this thing called love / Three blind mice / Ah nice o pays des merveilles / Ethel's oldest boy / Mama don't allow no bass playing in here / Excuse me ludwig / Blue skies / Salty mama cassoulet / Lush life / Lamb stew for slam
BLE 591242 / Apr '91 / Black & Blue

Stewart, Wendy

☐ ABOUT TIME VOL.1
Hip hip bouree / Pheasant feathers; Bonawe highlanders / Stirling castle / Rachel Rose / Harp song of the Dane women / Miss Gordon of Gight / St. Bride's coracle;The streams of Abernethy / Puinneagan Cail; William Joseph Guppy / King's house; Wild west waltz
CDTRAX 059 / Jan '93 / Greentrax

☐ ABOUT TIME VOL.2
MacLeod of Mull / Kitchen papaer / January man / Rachel Rae / Fish feis / Probabobably / Maggie's pancakes / Break yer bass drone / Fotheringay / Pavane / Barbara Grigor / Little cascade / Dances with friends / Dusty Miller / Love and whiskey / Bobbing Joan / An caiorac / Carolan's welcome / Drummond castle
CDTRAX 126 / Mar '97 / Greentrax

Stex

☐ SPIRITUAL DANCE
Chapter 22 / Take this feeling / If I were you / Not coming back / Moses / Still feel the rain / Inside out / Free this innocent soul / Pray / Never gonna see me
SBZCD 004 / Sep '92 / Some Bizarre

Stickman

☐ AFTERHOURS (2CD Set)
STICK 047CD / 26 Sep '97 / Stickman

☐ MUSICA
K7 041CD / Oct '96 / Studio K7

Stiff Kittens

☐ EAT THE PEANUT
PSYC 4 / Aug '94 / Psychic

Stiff Little Fingers

☐ ALTERNATIVE CHARTBUSTERS
Suspect device / Alternative Ulster / Gotta getaway / At the edge / Nobody's heroes / Tin soldier / Just fade away / Silver lining / Johnny was / Last time / Mr. Fire Coalman / Two guitars clash
AOK 103 / Jan '92 / Plastic Head

☐ FLAGS AND EMBLEMS
(It's a) long way to paradise / Stand up and shout / Each dollar a bullet / Cosh / Beirut moon / Game of life / Human shield / Johnny 7 / Die and burn / No surrender
DOJOCD 243 / Jul '95 / Dojo

☐ FLY THE FLAGS
Long way to paradise / Roots, radicals, rockers and reggae / Nobody's hero / No surrender / Gotta getaway / Just fade away / Cosh / Johnny 7 / Barbed wire love / Stand up and shout / Johnny was / Wasted life / Beirut moon / Fly the flag / Suspect device / Doesn't make it alright / Each dollar a bullet / Alternative Ulster
DOJOCD 75 / Nov '92 / Dojo

☐ GET A LIFE
Get a life / Can't believe in you / Road to kingdom come / Walk away / No laughing matter / Harp / Forensic evidence / Baby blue (What have they been telling you) / I want you / Night the wall came down / Cold / When the stars fall from the sky / What if I want more
ESMCD 488 / Apr '97 / Essential

☐ GO FOR IT
Just fade away / Go for it / Only one / Hit and misses / Kicking up a racket / Safe as houses / Gate 49 / Silver lining / Piccadilly Circus / Back to front
DOJOCD 148 / Sep '93 / Dojo

☐ GREATEST HITS LIVE
Alternative Ulster / Roots, radicals, rockers and reggae / Silver lining / Wait and see / Gotta getaway / Just fade away / Wasted life / Nobody's heroes / At the edge / Listen / Barbed wire love / Fly the flag / Tin soldiers / No sleep til belfast / Suspect device / Alternative Ulster
DOJOCD 110 / May '93 / Dojo

☐ HANX
Nobody's hero / Gotta getaway / Wait and see / Barbed wire love / Fly the flag / Alternative Ulster / Johnny was / At the edge / Wasted life / Tin soldiers / Suspect device
CDFA 3215 / Feb '89 / Fame

☐ NOW THEN
Falling down / Won't be told / Love of the common people / Price of admission / Touch and go / Bits of kids / Welcome to the whole week / Big city nights / Talkback / Is that what you fought the war for
CDGOLD 1090 / Apr '97 / EMI Gold

☐ STIFF LITTLE FINGERS
SFRCD 1 / Nov '89 / Strange Fruit

☐ TINDERBOX
SLF 100CD / Jun '97 / Spitfire

Stiffs

☐ NIX NOT NOTHING
Chelsea / Sad song / 250624 / Space nothing / Fairy tales / Generation crap / Engineering / Blow away baby / Work / Quick Wotson / Mary Pickford / Die mother die / Fear in the night
74321279692 / Jul '95 / American

Stigers, Curtis

☐ TIME WAS
This time / Keep me from the cold / Every time you cry / Anything you want / There's more to making love (than layin' down) / Time was / Ghost of you and me / It never comes / Cry / Somebody in love / Big one / New York is rockin' / There will always be a place
74321282792 / 1 Sep '97 / Arista

Stigma A Go Go

☐ IT'S ALL TRUE
GROW 0312 / Feb '95 / Grass

Stigmata

☐ HYMNS FOR AN UNKNOWN GOD
TDH 017 / Feb '97 / Too Damn Hype

☐ SOLUM MENTE INFIRMIS
Greedmachine / Solum mente infirmis / Bleedin' within / Ground zero / Sacred man / Just a nautic tale / In your eyes / Last victory / Fool
NO 2982 / 26 Jan '98 / Noise

Still Patient

☐ NIGHTMARE ARRIVAL
AIW 076CD / 13 Oct '97 / Resurrection

☐ SALAMAND/CATACLYSM (2CD Set)
HYP 3910191CD / 18 May '98 / Hyperium

Stille Volk

☐ HANTAOMA
HOLY 024CD / Apr '97 / Holy

Stillpoint

☐ MAPS WITH EDGES
RBADCD 16 / Jul '96 / Beyond

Stills, Chris

☐ 100 YEAR THING
100 year thing / Lucifer and Jane / Voyeur / Last stop / Razorblades / If I were a mountain / Rattlesnakes / Desert sands / God won't make you a man / Trouble / Countryside / Tears of envy / Doors to the world
7567830222 / 6 Apr '98 / Atlantic

Stills, Stephen

☐ LONG MAY YOU RUN (Stills, Stephen & Neil Young)
Long may you run / Make love to you / Midnight on the bay / Black coral / Ocean girl / Let it shine / 12/8 blues / Fontaine bleau / Guardian angel
7599272302 / Jun '93 / Reprise

☐ MANASSAS (Stills, Stephen Manassas)
Song of love / Crazies / Cuban bluegrass / Jet set / Anyway / Both of us (bound to lose) / Fallen eagle / Jesus gave love away for free / Colorado / So begins the task / Hide it so deep / Don't look at my shadow / It doesn't matter / Johnny's garden / Bound to fall / How far / Move around / Love gangster / What to do / Right now / Treasure (take one) / Blues man
7567828082 / Nov '95 / Atlantic

☐ STEPHEN STILLS
Love the one you're with / Do for the others / Church (part of someone) / Old times, good times / Go back home / Sit yourself down / To a flame / Black Queen / Cherokee / We are not helpless
7567828092 / Nov '95 / Atlantic

Stillsuit

☐ AT THE SPEED OF LIGHT
TVT 71002 / Mar '97 / TVT

Stilluppsteypa

☐ ONE SIDE MONA LISA/THE FRONT SIDE ONLY
F 8 / Jan '97 / Fire Inc.

☐ STILLUPPSTEYPA/IRR.APP.(EXT.) (Stilluppsteypa/Irr.App.(Ext.))
F 13 / Sep '97 / Fire Inc.

Stiltskin

☐ MIND'S EYE, THE
WWD 1 / Oct '94 / White Water

Sting

☐ BRING ON THE NIGHT (2CD Set)
Bring on the night / Consider me gone / Low life / We work the black seam / Driven to tears / Dream of the blue turtles / Demolition man / One world / Love is the seventh wave / Moon over Bourbon Street / I burn for you / Another day / Children's crusade / I've been down so long / Tea in the Sahara
3967052 / Aug '98 / A&M

☐ DREAM OF THE BLUE TURTLES, THE
If you love somebody set them free / Love is the seventh wave / We work the black seam / Russians / Children's crusade / Shadows in the rain / Consider me gone / Dream of the blue turtles / Moon over Bourbon Street / Fortress around your heart
DREMD 1 / Jun '85 / A&M

☐ FIELDS OF GOLD (The Best Of Sting 1984-1994)
When we dance / If you love somebody set them free / Fields of gold / They dance alone / If I ever lose my faith in you / We'll be together / Nothing 'bout me / Fragile / Englishman in New York / All this time / Seven days / Mad about you / Russians / Love is the seventh wave / It's probably me: *Sting & Eric Clapton* / Demolition man / This cowboy song
5403072 / Nov '94 / A&M

☐ MERCURY FALLING
Hounds of winter / I hung my head / Let your soul be your pilot / I was brought to my senses / You still touch me / I'm so happy I cant' stop crying / All four seasons / Twenty five to midnight / La belle dame sans regrets / Valparaiso / Lithium sunset
5404862 / Mar '96 / A&M

☐ MUSIC OF STING, THE (London Symphony Orchestra)
Russians / Moon over Bourbon Street / Synchronicity II / Fortress around your heart / King of pain / Invisible sun / Every breath you take / Why should I cry for you / Wrapped around your finger / They dance alone
EIRSCD 1081 / Jun '96 / IRS/EMI

☐ NOTHING LIKE THE SUN
Lazarus heart / Be still my beating heart / Englishman in New York / History will teach us nothing / They dance alone / Fragile / We'll be together / Straight to my heart / Rock steady / Sister Moon / Little wing / Secret marriage
CDA 6402 / Oct '87 / A&M

☐ SOUL CAGES, THE
Island of souls / All this time / Mad about you / Jeremiah blues (Part 1) / Why should I cry for you / Saint Agnes and the burning train / Wild wild sea / Soul cages / When the angels fall
3964052 / Jan '91 / A&M

☐ STING (Interview)
3D 012 / Dec '96 / Network

☐ STRANGE FRUIT (Sting & Gil Evans)
ITM 1499 / 15 Dec '97 / ITM

☐ TEN SUMMONER'S TALES
Prologue (If I ever lose my faith in you) / Love is stronger than justice (The magnificent seven) / Fields of gold / Heavy cloud no rain / She's too good for me / Seven days / St. Augustine in hell / It's probably me / Everybody laughed but you / Shape of my heart / Something the boy said / Epilogue (Nothing 'bout me)
5400752 / Mar '93 / A&M

☐ VERY BEST OF STING AND THE POLICE, THE (Police/Sting)
Message in a bottle: *Police* / Can't stand losing you: *Police* / Englishman in New York: *Sting* / Every breath you take: *Police* / Seven days: *Sting* / Walking on the moon: *Police* / Fields of gold: *Sting* / Fragile: *Sting* / Every little thing she does is magic: *Police* / De do do do de da da da: *Police* / If you love somebody set them free: *Sting* / Let your soul be your pilot: *Sting* / Russians: *Sting* / If I ever lose my faith in you: *Sting* / When we dance: *Sting* / Don't stand so close to me: *Police* / Roxanne: *Police* / Roxanne: *Sting & The Police*
5404282 / 10 Nov '97 / A&M

Sting & The Radio AC

☐ NUCLEAR WASTE
Nuclear waste / Digital love / Spiral diatribe / No-ozone blue / Nuclear megawaste
BP 181CD / Sep '96 / Blueprint

Stinga, Paul

☐ CHARMS OF THE ROMANIAN MUSIC (Stinga, Paul & His Orchestra)
Sirba de la seaca / Batrineasca / Taraneasca de la burau Jeni / Suite de Moldavie I / Suite de Moldavie II / Purtata de la bistrica / Suite de muntenie / Hora din rasomiresti / Joc din bihor / Suite de banat / Suite de Transilvanie
PV 787021 / May '87 / Disques Pierre Verany

Stingily, Byron

☐ PURIST, THE
Flying high / Back to paradise / Beautiful night / You make me feel / Get up / Sing a song / Found a love / Keep love going / Run to me / Feeling good feeling happy / Temptation / It's over / Don't fall in love / Testify / Flying high
5580082 / 9 Feb '98 / Manifesto

Stink

☐ SPLITTING NOTHING UP
ALLIED 88 / Nov '97 / Allied

Stinkerbell

☐ HISSEY FIT
LRR 016 / Oct '96 / Last Resort

Stinnerborg, Magnus

☐ HARV
AM 737CD / Dec '97 / Amigo

Stitt, Sonny

☐ AUTUMN IN NEW YORK
Stardust / Cherokee / Autumn in New York / Gypsy / Lover man / Matterhorns / Hello / Nightwork
BLCD 760130 / Apr '90 / Black Lion

☐ BACK IN MY OWN HOME TOWN
(I'm afraid) the masquerade is over / Duty free / I can't get started (with you) / My little suede shoes / Simon's blues / Streamline Stanley / There will never be another you
BLE 597542 / Dec '90 / Black & Blue

☐ BACK TO MY OWN HOME TOWN
BB 8772 / Feb '97 / Black & Blue

☐ BATTLE OF THE SAXES (Stitt, Sonny & Richie Cole)
AIM 1010CD / Oct '93 / Aim

☐ CONSTELLATION
Constellation / I don't stand a ghost of a chance with you / Webb City / By accident / Ray's idea / Casbah / It's magic / Topsy
MCD 5323 / Sep '92 / Muse

☐ GOOD LIFE, THE (Stitt, Sonny & The Hank Jones Trio)
Deuces wild / Autumn leaves / Angel eyes / Bye bye blackbird / Polka dots and moonbeams / My funny valentine / As time goes by / Ain't misbehavin' / Good life / Body and soul
ECD 220882 / Jun '94 / Evidence

☐ HOW HIGH THE MOON
Koko / Easy living / It's hipper than that / How high the moon / Lover man / Fools rush in (where angels fear to tread) / Lonesome Road / I want to go home / Katea / Flame and frost / Night has a thousand eyes / Our day will come / My main man
GRP 18172 / 8 Jun '98 / Chess Jazz

☐ JAZZ MASTERS
5276512 / 5 May '98 / Verve

☐ JUST FRIENDS (Stitt, Sonny & Red Holloway)
Way you look tonight / Forecast / You don't know what love is / Getting sentimental over you / Lester leaps in / Just friends / All God's chillun got rhythm
LEJAZZCD 40 / May '95 / Le Jazz

☐ JUST FRIENDS
Waltz for Diane / Streamlined Stanley / Yes Jesus loves me / Lester leaps in / Just friends / Way you look tonight
CDSGP 0187 / 27 Apr '98 / Prestige

☐ LAST STITT SESSIONS VOL.1 & 2
MCD 6003 / Sep '92 / Muse

☐ LEGENDS OF ACID JAZZ, THE
Turn it on / Bar-b-que man / Miss Riverside / Cry me a river / There are such things / Goin' to DC / Aires / Black vibrations / Calling card / Where is love / Them funky changes
PRCD 24169 / Oct '96 / Prestige

☐ MADE FOR EACH OTHER
Samba de orfeo / Funny / Glory of love / Very thought of you / Blues for JJ / Funny / Night has a thousand eyes / Honey / Night has a thousand eyes
DD 426 / Jul '97 / Delmark

☐ ONLY THE BLUES
5377532 / 22 Sep '97 / Verve Elite

☐ PRESTIGE FIRST SESSIONS
Avalon / Later / Ain't misbehavin' / Mean to me / Stairway to the stars / Touch of the blues / Count every star / Nice work if you can get it / There will never be another you / Blazin' / To think you've chosen me / After you've gone / Our very own / S'wonderful / Nevertheless / Jeepers creepers / Imagination / Cherokee / Thrill of your kiss / If the moon turns green / Down with it / For the fatman / Splinter / Confessin'
PCD 24115 / Dec '95 / Prestige

☐ SALT AND PEPPER (Stitt, Sonny & Paul Gonsalves)
Salt and pepper / S'posin' / Theme from the Lord Of The Flies / Perdido / Star dust / Surfin' / Lester leaps in / Estrellita / Please don't talk about me / Touchy / Never..sh / My mother's eyes / I'm getting sentimental over you
IMP 12102 / Mar '97 / Impulse Jazz

☐ SONNY STITT SITS IN WITH THE OSCAR PETERSON TRIO (Stitt, Sonny & Oscar Peterson Trio)
I can't give you anything but love / Au private / Gypsy / I'll remember April / Scrapple from the apple / Moten swing / Blues for Pres, Sweets and Ben and all the other funky ones / I didn't know what time it was / I remember you / I know that you know
8493962 / Mar '91 / Verve

☐ SONNY'S BLUES (Archive Series - Live At Ronnie Scott's)
Ernest's blues / Home sweet home / Mother / My Mother's eyes / Sonny's theme song / Blues with Dick and Harry / It could happen to you / Oh Lady be good
JHAS 603 / Jun '95 / Ronnie Scott's Jazz House

☐ SOUL CLASSICS
Soulshack / When sunny gets blue / Night crawler / Goin' down slow / Right now / When it's sleepy time down south / Walk on by / Lover man / Goin' to d.c.
OJCCD 6003 / Jul '94 / Original Jazz Classics

☐ STITT, EDISON & DAVIS (Stitt, Sonny & Harry 'Sweets' Edison/Eddie 'Lockjaw' Davis)
DM 15017 / Jul '96 / DMA Jazz

☐ THERE IS NO GREATER LOVE (Stitt, Sonny, Harry 'Sweets' Edison & Eddie 'Lockjaw' Davis)
Oh lady be good / What's new / There is no greater love / Chef / I can't get started / Four / Old folks / Lax / Yesterdays / Lester leaps in
JHR 73557 / Jan '93 / Jazz Hour

Stivell, Alan

☐ A LANGONNET
FDM 36203 / Oct '94 / Dreyfus

☐ AGAIN
FDM 361982 / Oct '93 / Dreyfus

☐ BRIAN BORU
Brian Boru / Let the plinn / Mna na heireann / Ye banks and braes o' bonnie Doon / Mairi's wedding / Ceasefire / De ha bla / Sword dance / Parlamant lament / Lands of my fathers
FDM 362082 / Jul '95 / Dreyfus

☐ CELTIC SYMPHONY (Tir Na Nog)
Journey to inner spaces / Nostalgia for the past and future / Song and profound lake that I interrogate / Dissolution in the great all / Regaining consciousness / Vibratory communion with the universe / In quest of the Isle / Landing on the isle of the pure world / First steps on the Isle / Discovery of the radiant city / March towards the city / Universal festival / Sudden return to the relative and interrogative world
ROUCD 11523 / '88 / Rounder

☐ CHEMINS DE TERRE
FDM 36202 / Oct '94 / Dreyfus

☐ HARPE CELTIQUE
FDM 36200 / Oct '94 / Dreyfus

☐ HARPES DU NOUVEL AGE
Tremen'ra pep tra (part 1) / Pedenn ewid breizh / Tremen'ra pep tra (part 2) / Spered santel / Dor I / Cumh chlaibhers / Lament for the children / Mcdonuill of the isles / Dor il / Rory dall's love tune / Kervalan / Luskellerezh / Dihun'ta / Dans fanch mitt / Suite ecossaise / Dor iil
FDM 36206 / Oct '94 / Dreyfus

☐ I DOUAR
United Earth / La memoire de l'humain / Hope / Ensemble (understand) / Crimes / United Earth / Scots are right / Ever / Kenavo Glenmor / Una's love / Aet on (into the universe's breath) / United Earth
FDM 362092 / 29 Jun '98 / Dreyfus

☐ JOURNEE A LA MAISON
DRYF 8343164 2 / Jan '93 / Dreyfus

☐ LEGEND
CMCD 022 / Dec '97 / Celtic Music

☐ LEGENDE
FDM 36205 / Oct '94 / Dreyfus

☐ REFLETS
FDM 36201 / Oct '94 / Dreyfus

☐ TERRE DES VIVANTS
FDM 36204 / Oct '94 / Dreyfus

☐ TRO AR BED
Ar C'Hoant dimezin / Rouantelezh Vreizh / Dugelezh Vreizh / Stok Ouzh an Enez / Liegemen of the trembling slopes / We shall survive / Cailin og deas / O'Carolan's farewell/The musical priest / An nighean dubh / Fest hypnoz
FDM 36187 / Aug '97 / Dreyfus

☐ ZOOM (2CD Set)
Eliz iza / Suite des Montagnes / Marig ar Pollanton / Ys / Atrde cuan / Maro ma mestrez / Suzy McGuire / Kimiad / Jenovefa / Stok ouzh an enez / Negro song / Rory Dall's love tune / La dame du lac / An advod / Mna na heireann / Suite Irlandaise / Suite Sudarmoricaine / Tri martolod / Rouantelezh vreizh / Beg ar van / Raog mont d'ar skol / An alarch / Deliverance / Ne bado ket atao / An nighean dubh / Ar bale / Spred hollvedel / Da ewan / REturn / Brian Boru / Pop plinn / Ian Morrison Reel / Lands of my fathers
FDM 361892 / Jun '97 / Dreyfus

Stoa

☐ URTHONA
HY 39100592 / Jul '93 / Hyperium

Stocai

☐ CHAMPAGNE BRAND
Poolside polka / Cafe Charbons jig/The Queen of hearts / Scottish a Virmoux/Biscuit shuffle / Boodell lope/Lambert waddle / Dampolska / Hornet / Sail away ladies/Horseshoes and rainbows / Boddington/TJ's / Tender trap / Sty at night / Iron legs/Champagne brawl
HARCD 033 / Apr '98 / Harbour Town

Stoch, Karol

☐ POLISH MOUNTAIN FIDDLE MUSIC VOL.1 (Fire In The Mountains) (Stoch, Karol Band)
YAZ 7012 / Aug '97 / Yazoo

Stockhausen, Karlheinz

☐ KONTAKTE
E 87 / Jun '97 / Ecstatic Peace

Stockhausen, Markus

☐ COSI LONTANO...QUASI DENTRO (So Far Almost Inside)
8371112 / Feb '89 / ECM

☐ SOL MESTIZO
Creation / Takirari / Emanacion / Reconciliation / Yemaye / La conquista / In your mind / Adentro / Davindad / Zampona / Canto indio / Refelxion / Loncanao / Queca / Desolacion / Asfalto
92222 / Feb '96 / Act

☐ TAGTRAUM (Stockhausen, Markus & Simon)
Glocken / Kuche / Passacaglia / Himmel auf / Ungewitter / Gamelan / Weltraum / Ping pong / Klangduo / Feuerwerk / Yeah / Zwei Bruder / Gran finale / Tagtraum / Miles mute / Wustenwind / Esprit / Bumerang
UBM 1139 / Dec '92 / New Note

Stockholm Jazz Orchestra

☐ JIGSAW
DRCD 213 / Jan '88 / Dragon

☐ SOUNDBITES (Stockholm Jazz Orchestra & James McNeely)
DRCD 311 / May '97 / Dragon

Stockton's Wing

☐ CROOKED ROSE, THE
Master's daughter / Some fools cry / Aaron's key / When you smiled / Angel / Humours of Clonmult / Black Hill / Prince's feather / Chasing down a rainbow / Catalina / Lonesome road / Stars in the morning East
TARACD 3028 / May '92 / Tara

☐ LETTING GO
Letting go / Maids of Castlebar / Jig mayhem / Another day / All the time / Eastwood / Rossclogher jigs / I'll believe again / Anyone out there / Sliabh Lucan polkas / Hold you forever
TARA 3036 / Nov '95 / Tara

☐ STOCKTON'S WING
Master's daughter/Blessings/Denis O'Brien's reel / Some fools cry / Aaron's key/Rose in the heather/ O'Dea's jig / When you smiled / Angel / Humours of Clonmult/Lough Gowna/The congress / Black Hill / Prince's feather/Corner House / Chasing down a rainbow / Catalina / Lonesome Road / Stars in the morning East
KCD 475 / Jan '97 / Celtic Collections

Stoddart, Pipe Major

☐ GREATEST PIPERS VOL.3
LS 5151CD / Apr '95 / Lismor

☐ PIPERS OF DISTINCTION
Jean allan / Jean allan / Laird of drumblair / Stirling castle / Thick lies the mist on yonder hill / Duke of gordon's birthday / Clean peas strae / Malcolm the traitor / De'il in the kitchen / Inverinate house / Abercairney highlanders / Lochaber gathering / 74th's farewell to edinburgh / Maggie cameron / Blair drummond / Sheepwife / Miss proud
CDMON 806 / Jul '90 / Monarch

☐ WORLD'S GREATEST PIPERS VOL.3, THE
LCOM 5151 / Sep '95 / Lismor

Stojiljkovic, Jova

☐ BLOW 'BESIR' BLOW
Sampionski cocek / Safetov cocek / Vranjsko / Izrael orijent / Cifteteli / Jovino kolo / Durak i srecko / Djokino cocek / Beogradska cocek / Ekstra cocek / Romski cocek
CDORBD 038 / Feb '96 / Globestyle

Stoker

☐ SYNCOPATE
Straight no chaser / Killer Joe / Mood indigo / Side winder / Good morning heartache / Walk tall / St. Thomas / Sister Mamie / Jeannine / All blues / Ronnie's Bonnie / Blue in green
ACD 6 / May '97 / Douglas Music

Stokes, Frank

☐ CREATOR OF THE MEMPHIS BLUES
Memphis rounders blues / Unnamed blues / Nehi mamma blues / Tain't nobody's business if I do (part 2) / Mr. crump don't like it / Mistreatin' blues / It won't be long now / Chicken you can roost behind the moon / You shall / Sweet to mama / Stomp that thing / Wasn't that doggin' me / Beale town bound / It's a good thing
YAZCD 1056 / Jun '91 / Yazoo

☐ FRANK STOKES DREAM (Memphis blues anthology)
YAZCD 1008 / Mar '92 / Yazoo

☐ VICTOR RECORDINGS 1928-1929, THE
DOCD 5013 / Feb '92 / Document

Stoll, Steve

☐ BLUNTED BOY WONDER, THE
Drop zone / Out of context / Model T / Reciproheat / Top heat / Falling / Mosquito / Slipstream / GTI / Magnetic / One to nothing / Colour blind
NOMU 064CD / 23 Mar '98 / Nova Mute

☐ DAMN ANALOG TECHNOLOGY
SM 80332 / Feb '97 / Profile

☐ DOCUMENT
A1 013CD / 6 Jul '98 / A1

Stoller, Rhet

☐ EMBER LANE
Travelling song / Perpetual Summer / Sea breeze / Concerto for a rainbow / Lucky five / Ember lane / Tree top woman / Sandy's rave up / Ocean serenade / Down the line
SEECD 348 / 3 Nov '97 / See For Miles

Stomp That Pussy

☐ HATE IS THE MOVE
LF 057 / Jan '94 / Lost & Found

Stompin' Shoes

☐ CATS RULE
PT 624001 / Oct '97 / Part

Stone

☐ EMOTIONAL PLAYGROUND
Small tales / Home base / Last chance / Above the grey sky / Mad Hatter's den / Dead end / Adrift / Haven / Years after / Time dive / Missionary of charity / Emotional playground
8410562 / Feb '92 / Black Mark

Stone, Billy

☐ WEST TEXAS SKY
Brand new shade of red / Into every life (A little love must fall) / When two people meet / Just like a diamond / West Texas sky / Was you / Pictures never lie / You just don't know what you've got / Holmes county home / Miz Leah / Family reunion / My heart jumped over the moon / All love needs / Love love love / That empty chair / Last Dallas cowboy / Walter petty / What in the world (Is this coming to) / This old / Grandma's old gas stove / Master electrician / Ain't no telling what a fool will do / What are we trying to prove / Sight for sore ears / Little brother
BCD 15736 / May '93 / Bear Family

Stone Breath

☐ SONGS OF MOONLIGHT RAIN
CAM 001CD / Mar '97 / Camera Obscura

Stone By Stone

☐ I PASS FOR HUMAN
SST 247CD / Jul '89 / SST

Stone, Carl

☐ MOM'S
NA 049 / Nov '92 / New Albion

Stone, Cliffie

☐ TRANSCRIPTIONS 1945-1949
Draggin' the bow / Beautiful brown eyes / Mine all mine / Mule skinner blues / Little cabin home on the hill / Blue steel blues / Stuck up blues / Mandolin boogie / Bill Cheatham / Red's boogie / Freight train blues / After you've gone / Flop eared mule / Sugar hill / Cactus set-up / Daughter of Jolie Blon / Steel guitar rag / Free little bird / Honky tonkin' / Oh lady be good / Sally Goodin / Little rock getaway
RFDCD 08 / Oct '91 / Country Routes

Stone, Gordon

☐ TOUCH AND GO
ALZCD 124 / Feb '96 / Alcazar

Stone, Jesse

☐ JESSE STONE ALIAS CHARLES CALHOUN
Ace in the hole / Mister jelly fingers / Hey, sister Lucy (what makes your lips so) / Donkey and the elephant / Keep your big mouth shut / Sneaky Pete / I came home unexpectedly / Who's zat / Bling a ling a ling / Don't let it get away / Get it while you can / Who killed 'er / Cole slaw (sirghum switch) / Do it now / Easy walkin' / Oh that'll be joyful / Runaway / Smack dab in the middle / (I don't know) Why the car won't go / Come and dance with me / Hey tiger / Night life / Barrelhouse / Rocket / My pigeon's gone / Jamboree / Stash / Tall and short / Crawfish / Tadpole wiggle
BCD 15695 / Feb '96 / Bear Family

Stone, Lew

☐ BEST OF LEW STONE/LEGENDARY MONSEIGNEUR BAND 1932-1934, THE
Radio announcement / Oh Susannah / Goodbye blues / Lying in the hay / Blue jazz / A brivelle der Mama / My woman / Junkman blues / Look what I've got / You'll always be the same sweetheart to me / I can't write the words / Brighter than the sun / Milenberg joys / Oh Mr. Moon / Eadie was a lady / Nagasaki / Weep no more my baby / White jazz / Canadian capers / World is so small / Call of the freaks / Tiger rag / I hate myself / Garden of weed / Rain rain go away
509812 / Jul '98 / Claves

☐ CREAM OF LEW STONE & HIS BAND, THE (Stone, Lew & His Band)
Undecided / Ups and downs / Coffee in the morning / Moon remembered, but you forgot / Shades of Hades / Flat foot floogie / Apple blossom time / Why waste your tears / Nine pins in the sky / Dark clouds / Serenade for a wealthy widow / There's something wrong with the weather / Frog on the water-lily / Get happy / I get along without you very well / I want the waiter / Lonely / Beale Street blues / Louisiana hayride / My wubba Dolly / Music maestro please / St. Louis blues
PASTCD 7041 / Mar '94 / Flapper

Stone Love

☐ GO GO WINE
STONECD 1 / Mar '97 / Stone Love

☐ IT'S A STONE LOVE THING (Various Artists)
VPCD 2066 / 26 Jan '98 / VP

☐ STONE LOVE - CHAMPION SOUND (Various Artists)
SGCD 17 / Nov '94 / Sir George

☐ STONE LOVE ON THE ROAD VOL.1 (Various Artists)
SGCD 13 / Mar '93 / Sir George

☐ STONE LOVE ON THE ROAD VOL.3 (Various Artists)
SGCD 18 / Nov '94 / Sir George

☐ STONE LOVE PRESENTS GO GO WINE (Various Artists)
OPCD 2048 / Oct '96 / Stone Love

☐ STONE LOVE VOL.3 (Various Artists)
VPCD 1448 / Nov '95 / VP

Stone Roses

☐ COMPLETE STONE ROSES, THE
So young / Tell me / Sally Cinnamon / All across the sands / Here it comes / Elephant stone / Full fathom five / Hardest thing in the world / Made of stone / Going down / She bangs the drum / Mersey paradise / Standing here / I wanna be adored / Waterfall / I am the resurrection / Where angels play / Fool's gold / What the world is waiting for / Something burning / One love
ORECD 535 / Jul '96 / Silvertone

☐ GARAGE FLOWER
GARAGECD 1 / Nov '96 / Silvertone

☐ INTERVIEW, THE
SPEEK 012 / 16 Mar '98 / Talking Music

☐ SECOND COMING
Breaking into heaven / Driving South / Ten storey love song / Daybreak / Your star will shine / Straight to the man / Begging you / Tightrope / Good times / Tears / How do you sleep / Love spreads
GED 24503 / 8 Sep '97 / Geffen

☐ STONE ROSES
I wanna be adored / Waterfall / She bangs the drum / Don't stop / Bye bye badman / Elizabeth my dear / (Song for my) Sugar spun sister / Made of stone / Shoot you down / This is the one / I am the resurrection
ORECD 502 / Mar '97 / Silvertone

☐ TURNS INTO STONE
Elephant stone / Hardest thing in the world / Going down / Mersey paradise / Standing here / Where angels play / Simone / Fool's gold / What the world is waiting for / One love / Something's burning
ORECD 521 / Mar '97 / Silvertone

☐ WHAT A TRIP
CBAK 4045 / Jan '91 / Baktabak

Stone, Sly

☐ BEST OF SLY AND THE FAMILY STONE, THE (Sly & The Family Stone)
Dance to the music / I want to take you higher / Thank you (falettinme be mice elf agin) / I get high on you / Stand / M'lady / Skin I'm in / Everyday people / Sing a simple song / Hot fun in the summertime / Don't call me nigger whitey / Brave and strong / Life / Everybody is a star / If you want me to stay / (You caught me) smilin' / Whatever will be will be (Que sera sera) / Running away / Family affair
4717582 / 1 Jun '98 / Epic

☐ EVERY DOG HAS ITS DAY (Sly & The Family Stone)
CDSGP 0125 / Dec '94 / Prestige

☐ FRESH (Sly & The Family Stone)
In time / If you want me to stay / Let me have it all / Frisky / Thankful 'n' thoughtful / Skin I'm in / I don't know / Keep on dancing / Whatever will be will be (Que sera sera) / If it were left up to me / Babies makin' blues
4851702 / Sep '96 / Epic

☐ IN THE STILL OF THE NIGHT (Sly & The Family Stone)
In the still of the night / Searchin' / Don't say I didn't warn you / Ain't that lovin' you baby / Swim / Every dog has his day / Suki suki / Seventh son / I can't turn you loose / Take my advice / Watermelon man / I ain't got nobody / I you were blue / Rock dirge / High love / Life of fortune and fame
CDTB 129 / Sep '91 / Thunderbolt

☐ MASTERS, THE (Sly & The Family Stone)
EABCD 100 / 30 Mar '98 / Eagle

☐ PRECIOUS STONE (In The Studio With Sly Stone 1963-1965) (Various Artists)
Swim: *Sly & Rose* / Scat swim: *Stone, Sly* / I taught him: *Scott, Gloria* / Don't say I didn't warn you: *Scott, Gloria* / Help me with my broken heart: *Stone, Sly* / Out of sight: *Stone, Sly* / Nerve of you: *O'Connor, Emile* / Every dog has his day: *O'Connor, Emile* / On Broadway: *Stone, Sly* / Searchin': *Stone, Sly* / Lord, Lord: *Stone, Sly* / Seventh son: *Stone, Sly* / Jerk: *Sly & Sal* / That little old heartbreaker: *Freeman, Bobby* / I'll never fall in love again: *Freeman, Bobby* / Ain't that lovin' you baby: *Preston, Billy* / Buttermilk: *Stone, Sly* / Fake it: *George & Teddy* / Laugh: *George & Teddy* / Little Latin lupe lu: *Preston, Billy* / Dance all night: *Sly & Freddie* / Temptation walk: *Stone, Sly* / Underdog: *Stone, Sly* / Radio spot: *Stone, Sly* / Can't you tell I love her: *Preston, Billy* / Life of fortune and fame: *Preston, Billy* / Take my advice: *Preston, Billy* / As I get older: *Preston, Billy*
CDCHD 539 / Aug '94 / Ace

☐ SPOTLIGHT ON SLY & FAMILY STONE (Sly & The Family Stone)
Honest / Ain't that lovin' you baby / Watermelon man / Hi love / Life of fortune and fame / Don't say I didn't warn you / Take my advice / In the still of the night / If you were blue / Searchin' / Every dog has his day / I ain't got nobody / Seventh son / I can't turn you loose / Swim / Nerves
HADCD 119 / Feb '94 / Javelin

☐ THERE'S A RIOT GOIN' ON (Sly & The Family Stone)
Luv 'n' Haight / Just like a baby / Poet / Family affair / Africa talks to you - 'The Asphalt Jungle' / There's a riot goin' on / Brave and strong / (You caught me) smilin' / Time / Spaced cowboy / Running away / Thank you for talking to me Africa
4670632 / Apr '94 / Epic

☐ WHOLE NEW THING, A (Sly & The Family Stone)
Underdog / If this room could talk / Run run run / Turn me loose / Let me hear it from you / Advice / I cannot make it / Trip to your heart / I hate to love her / Bad risk / That kind of person / Dog
EK 66424 / Jul '95 / Epic

Stone Soup

☐ STONE SOUP
MTMCD 199620 / Apr '97 / Made To Measure

Stone Temple Pilots

☐ CORE
Dead and bloated / Sex type thing / Wicked garden / No memory / Sin / Naked Sunday / Creep / Piece of pie / Plush / Wet my bed / Crackerman / Where the river goes
7567824182 / Nov '92 / Atlantic

☐ PURPLE
Meat plow / Vasoline / Lounge fly / Interstate love song / Still remains / Pretty penny / Silvergun superman / Big empty / Unglued / Army ants / Kitchenware and candy bars
7567826072 / Jun '94 / Atlantic

☐ TINY MUSIC...SONGS FROM THE VATICAN GIFT SHOP
Press play / Big bang baby / And so I know / Art school girl / Trippin' on a hole in a paper heart / Seven caged tigers / Daisy / Ride the cliche / Adhesive / Lady picture show / Tumble in the rough / Pop's love suicide
7567828712 / Mar '96 / Atlantic

Stone The Crows

☐ BBC LIVE IN CONCERT
Keep on rollin' / Don't think twice it's alright / Big Jim Salter / Mr. Wizard / Goin' down / On the highway / Palace of the king / Penicillin blues / Sunset cowboy / Niagra / Good time girl / Acapella
SFRSCD 049 / 23 Feb '98 / Strange Fruit

☐ BBC SESSIONS VOL.1 1969-1970, THE
Raining in your heart / Friend / Mad dogs / Love 74 / Things are getting better
SFRSCD 054 / 30 Mar '98 / Strange Fruit

☐ BBC SESSIONS VOL.2 1970-1971, THE
Faces / Let it down / Big Jim Salter / Keep on rolling / Going down / On the highway / Mr. Wizard / Good time girl / Penicilin blues
SFRSCD 068 / 27 Jul '98 / Strange Fruit

☐ CONTINUOUS PERFORMANCE
On the highway / One more chance / Penicillin blues / King Tut / Good time girl / Niagara / Sunset cowboy
REP 4627 / 26 Jan '98 / Repertoire

☐ ODE TO JOHN LAW
REP 4624 / 26 Jan '98 / Repertoire

☐ TEENAGE LICKS
REP 4625 / 26 Jan '98 / Repertoire

Stoneback, Rob

☐ CAUGHT IN THE WEB (Stoneback, Rob Big Band)
SB 2085 / Sep '97 / Sea Breeze

Stonecoat

☐ CHEROKEE MYTH
9632757012 / 24 Mar '98 / ETO

Stoned

☐ ED'S DINER
ASR 12 / Jun '97 / Ampersand

☐ MUSIC FOR THE MORONS
ASR 6 / Oct '96 / Ampersand

Stoneham, Harry

☐ HIGH WIDE AND HAMMOND/ HAMMOND HITS THE HIGHWAY (2CD Set)
Carioca/Coffee song/Brazil / You are the sunshine of my life/Golden lady/My cherie amour / Oh babe what would you say/you won't find another fool like / Spanish flea/Bean bag/Brasilia / Can't take my eyes off of you/Happy heart / Lilly la lune/What do I/Ra ta ta / Tie a yellow ribbon round the ole oak tree / Vado via/ Fire and rain/Twenty four hours from Tulsa/(There's) I couldn't live without your love / Afrkaan beat/ Wimoweh/Swingin' safari/Prepare ye the way of t / Delicado/Manana (is soon enough for me)/South American way / I love you because/Welcome to my world/Big spender/Pink pant / Acapulco 1922/ Tijuana taxi/So what's new / For all we know/On days like these/Those were the days/Casat / Limon limonero/Dancing in the sun / I will wait for you/ Watch what happens / Aquarius/Freedom come freedom go / Tabu/Quiet village / Mogul theme/I spy/ Avengers theme
4956182 / 10 Aug '98 / Studio 2

☐ LIVE AT ABBEY ROAD (Stoneham, Harry Trio)
Oh lady be good / My foolish heart / Jersey bounce / East of the sun and west of the moon / I should care / Harlem nocturne / Strike up the band / Out of nowhere / Georgia on my mind / How high the moon / (Back home again in) Indiana / Moonlight in vermont / Now is the time
GRCD 55 / Oct '92 / Grasmere

Stoneking, Fred

☐ SADDLE OLD SPIKE (Fiddle Music From Missouri)
Birdie in a snowbank / Horse and buggy-o / Sugar Betty Ann / Evelyn's waltz / Honey Creek special / Burt County breakdown / Buzzard in a pea patch / Who's going to talk to Dinah / Blackberry waltz / Old Indiana / Old gray goose / Muddy weather / McCowan's waltz / Needle in a haystack / Cherry blossoms / Saddle old Spike / Green's waltz / Dance around Molly / Humansville / Blackberry one-step / Walk along, John / Willott's hornpipe / No little home to go to / Rye whiskey / Goodbye Liza Jane / Frisky Jim
ROUCD 0381 / Nov '96 / Rounder

Stoneman, Ernest V.

☐ HILLBILLY MUSIC (Stoneman, Ernest V. & His Dixie Mountaineers)
DCP 400D / Jul '98 / Diamond Cut

Stony Sleep

☐ MUSIC FOR CHAMELEONS
ABB 138CD / Jul '97 / Big Cat

Stool Pigeons

☐ GERRY ACROSS THE MERSEY
SFTRI 502CD / Oct '97 / Sympathy For The Record Industry

Stop

☐ NEVER
FOR 0010 / Feb '96 / Backs

Storm & Stress

☐ STORMANDSTRESS
TG 173CD / Jul '97 / Touch & Go

Storm

☐ STORM, THE
You keep me waiting / I've got a lot to learn about love / In the raw / You're gonna miss me / Call me / Show me the way / I want you back / Still loving you / Touch and go / Gimme love / Take me away / Can't live without love
7567917412 / May '96 / Atlantic

Storm

☐ NORDAVIND
FOG 004CD / May '95 / Moonfog

Stormclouds

☐ NIGHTMARES IN THE SKY
CLOUD 2CD / Jun '97 / Rainfall

☐ NOT OF THIS EARTH
ER 1040 / 20 Oct '97 / Elefant

Storming Heaven

☐ LIFE IN PARADISE
199610 / Oct '96 / Made To Measure

Stormwitch

☐ SHOGUN
SPV 8476842 / Oct '94 / SPV

Stormy Monday Band

☐ LIVE AT 55
BLUE 10102 / Nov '91 / Blues Beacon

Storvan

☐ AN DEIZIOU KAER
KMCD 65 / Sep '96 / Keltia Musique

Story Board

☐ STORY BOARD
PMC 1113 / Jan '93 / Pan Music

Storyteller

☐ STORYTELLER
Floor of the park / Man in the moon passage song / Alice Brown / Lake / Ginger bread man / Over the hills / Story / First week in January / Has been / Morning glow / Ballad of old Three-Laps / Song for Buster / Love's a blind / Night games / Bosworth field / Laugh that came too soon / Beautiful affair / Wolf in the water / Fall in all directions
HILLCD 22 / Nov '97 / Wooded Hill

Storyville

☐ DOG YEARS
Enough / Understone / Don't make me suffer / Who's left standing / Two people / Born without you / Talk to me / Keep a handle on it / There's a light / Fairplay / Ain't no fun / Lucky
7567831112 / 22 Jun '98 / Atlantic

Storyville New Orleans Jazz Band

☐ MEMORIES FROM OLAND
MECCACD 2008 / May '97 / Music Mecca

Stott Orchestra

☐ CHRISTMAS BY THE FIRESIDE
PLSCD 261 / 29 Sep '97 / Pulse

Stotzem, Jacques

☐ CLEAR NIGHT
BEST 1030CD / Nov '93 / Acoustic Music

☐ STRAIGHT ON
BEST 1013CD / Nov '93 / Acoustic Music

Stover, Don

☐ THINGS IN LIFE
ROUCD 0014 / Feb '95 / Rounder

Stradlin, Izzy

☐ 117
GED 25202 / 16 Mar '98 / Geffen

☐ IZZY STRADLIN AND THE JU JU HOUNDS
Somebody knockin' / Pressure drop / Time gone by / Shuffle it all / Bucket o'trouble / Train tracks / How will it go / Cuttin' the rug / Take a look at the guy / Come on now inside
GED 24490 / Jun '97 / Geffen

Stradling, Rod

☐ RHYTHMS OF THE WORLD
FMSD 5021 / Oct '91 / Rogue

Strafe Feur Rebellion

☐ LUFTHUNGER (Ten Catastrophes In The History Of The World & Music)
TO 19 / Mar '91 / Touch

Straight Beat

☐ FLUIDOSCOPE
MI 2005 / 16 Jul '97 / Milano 2000

Straight Faced

☐ BROKEN
F 022CD / Apr '97 / Fearless

☐ CONDITIONED
Conditioned / Pedestal / Against / Revolve / How would I know / Course for destruction / Rumour mill / Dr. Heckle / Let down / Waste of time / Let's do this / Greed motivates / Brought this on / Regret / You wouldn't understand
65382 / 27 Jul '98 / Epitaph

☐ GUILTY
F 024CD / Apr '97 / Fearless

Straight Jackets

☐ KING BEE
MCG 20007 / May '98 / Vampirella

Straijer, Horacio

☐ STRAIJER-HURTADO (Straijer, Horacio & Horacio Hurtado)
Desde abajo / Leguero / So what / Someday my prince will come / TM / Pueblo sin nimbre / Vuelta de rocha / Little Hay Road / Un salto al vacio / Paseante / Orilla del cielo
SLAMCD 503 / Oct '96 / Slam

Strain

☐ HERE AND NOW
NA 032CD / Jul '96 / New Age

Strait, George

☐ BLUE CLEAR SKY
Blue clear sky / Carried away / Rockin' with arms of your memory / She knows when you're on my mind / I ain't never seen no on like you / I can still make Cheyenne / King of the mountain / Do the right thing / I'd just as soon go / Need I say more / Check yes or no
MCD 11428 / Apr '96 / MCA

☐ CARRY YOUR LOVE WITH ME
Round about way / Carrying your love with me / One night at a time / She'll leave you with a smile / Won't you come home (and talk to a stranger) / Today my world slipped away / I've got a funny feeling / Nerve / That's me (every chance I get) / Real good place to start
MCD 11584 / Apr '97 / MCA

☐ EASY COME EASY GO
Stay out of my arms / Just look at me / Easy come, easy go / I'd like to have that one back / Lovebug / I wasn't fooling around / Without me around / Man in love with you / That's where my baby feels at home / We must be loving right
MCAD 10907 / Mar '94 / MCA

☐ HOLDING MY OWN
You're right I'm wrong / Holding my own / Gone as a girl can get / So much like my dad / Trains make me lonesome / All of me (loves all of you) / Wonderland of love / Faults and all / It's all right with me / Here we go again
MCAD 10532 / Jun '92 / MCA

☐ LEAD ON
You can't make a heart love somebody / Adalida / I met a friend of yours today / Nobody has to get hurt / Down Louisiana way / Lead on / What am I waiting for / Big one / I'll always be loving you / No one but you
MCAD 11092 / Jan '95 / MCA

☐ ONE STEP AT A TIME
UMD 80486 / 20 Apr '98 / Universal

☐ STRAIT OUT OF THE BOX (4CD Set)
I just can't let you go on dying like this / (That don't change) way I feel about you / I don't want to talk it over anymore / Unwound / Blame it on Mexico / Her goodbye hit me in the heart / If you're thinking you want a stranger (there's one coming h / Any old love won't do / Fool hearted memory / Marina Del Rey / I can't see Texas from here / Heartbroke / What would your memory do / Amarillo by morning / I thought I heard you calling my name / Fire I can't put out / You look so good in love / 80 Proof bottle of tear stopper / Right or wrong / Let's fall of pieces together / Does Fort Worth / Ever cross your mind / Cowboy rides away / Fireman / Chair / You're something special to me / Haven't you heard / In too deep / Lefty's gone / Nobody in his right mind would've left her / It ain't cool to be crazy about you / Ocean front property / Rhythm of the road / Six pack to go / All me Ex's live in Texas / Am I blue / Famous last words of a fool / Baby blue / If you ain't lovin' (you ain't livin) / Baby's gotten good at goodbye / Bigger man than me / Hollywood squares / What's going on in my world / Ace in the hole / Love without end, amen / Drinking champagne / I've come expect it from you / You know me better than that / Chill of an early fall / Lovesick blues / Milk cow blues / Gone as a girl can get / So much like my Dad / Trains make me lonesome / Wonderland of love / I cross my heart / Heartland / When did you stop loving me / Overnight male / King of broken hearts / Where the sidewalk ends / Easy come, easy go / I'd like to have that one back / Lovebug / Man in love with you / Just look at me / Stay out of my arms / Big balls in Cowtown / Big one / Fly me to the moon / Check yes or no / I know she still loves me
MCAD 411263 / Nov '95 / MCA

☐ VERY BEST OF GEORGE STRAIT 1981-1987, THE
Unwound / If you're thinking you want a stranger (there's one coming h / Fool hearted memory / Marina del rey / Amarillo by morning / Fire I can't put out / You look so good in love / Right or wrong / Let's fall to pieces together / Does Fort Worth ever cross your mind / Cowboy rides away / Fireman / Chair / You're something special to me / Nobody in his right mind would have left her / It ain't cool to be crazy about you / Ocean front property / All my ex's live in Texas / Am I blue
MCLD 19867 / 23 Mar '98 / MCA

Strakers Rebles Orchestra

☐ NUF HEAT
GSCD 2412 / 2 Feb '98 / Strakers

Strandberg, Paul

☐ FUTURISTIC RHYTHM
SITCD 9210 / Aug '94 / Sittel

☐ PAUL STRANDBERG AND HIS GANG WITH KIKI DESPLANT (Strandberg, Paul Gang & Kiki Desplant)
SOSCD 1329 / Sep '97 / Stomp Off

Strange Brew

☐ EARTH OUT
CDROB 40 / Feb '96 / Rob's Records

Strange Creek Singers

☐ STRANGE CREEK SINGERS
When I can read my titles clear / In the pines / Sunny side of life / Poor old dirt farmer / Sally Ann / I truly understand that you love another man / Old black choo choo / Today has been a lonesome day / No never no / New river train / Get acquainted waltz / Will the circle be unbroken / Black lung / Difficult run part 2
ARHCD 9003 / Sep '97 / Arhoolie

Strange Parcels

☐ DISCONNECTION
ONUCD 57 / Jul '94 / On-U Sound

Strange, Billy

☐ STRANGE COUNTRY
TCD 1032 / Nov '96 / Tradition

Strangebrew

☐ PASSPORTS
Skylife / Fathoms / Communique 1 / Hot water music / Eartha quake / Report 2 / In forensic / Broken notes despatch 3 / Morning to bed / Single science / Are you who / Glue finger / Le bombardier
JOYCD 17 / 17 Aug '98 / Pleasure

Strangelove

☐ LOVE AND OTHER DEMONS
Casualties / Spiders and flies / Living with the human machines / She's everywhere / Sway / Beautiful alone / Elin's photograph / 20th century cold / 1432 / Sea of black
FOODCD 15 / Jun '96 / Food

☐ STRANGELOVE
Superstar / Freak / Someday soon / Wellington Road / Whatever happened to the runaway brothers / Another night in / Greatest show on Earth / Little Queenie / She's on fire / Mona Lisa / Jennifer's song
FOODCD 24 / 6 Oct '97 / Food

☐ TIME FOR THE REST OF YOUR LIFE
Sixer / Time for the rest of your life / Quiet day / Sand / I will burn / Low life / World outside / Return of the real me / All because of you / Fire (show me light) / Hopeful / Kite / Is there a place
FOODCD 11 / Sep '97 / Food

Strangeloves

☐ I WANT CANDY
ZK 47075 / 16 Mar '98 / Legacy

Stranger

☐ ROLLING THUNDER
ORCCD 2 / Jul '96 / Octopus

Strangers On A Train

☐ KEY PART 1/THE PROPHECY
Arrival / Sacrifice / New world / Silent companion / Crossing the wasteland / Perchance to dream / Lightshow / Occam's tears / Losing a hold on life / From the outside in / Healing the rift / Key
VGCD 011 / 26 Jan '98 / Verglas Music

☐ KEY PART 2/THE LABRYNTH
Darkworld / Hijrah / Labrynth / Vision clears / Endzone
VGCD 013 / 15 Jun '98 / Verglas Music

Strangeways

☐ AND THE HORSE
HDRCD 04004 / 13 Apr '98 / Hangdog

☐ ANY DAY NOW
HDRCD 05005 / 13 Apr '98 / Hangdog

☐ NATIVE SONS
HDRCD 02002 / 13 Apr '98 / Hangdog

☐ STRANGEWAYS
HDRCD 01001 / 13 Apr '98 / Hangdog

☐ WALK IN THE FIRE
HDRCD 03003 / 13 Apr '98 / Hangdog

Stranglers

☐ ACCESS ALL AREAS
Genetix / Grip / Golden boy / Straighten out / 5 minutes / Paradise row / Money / Nice and sleazy / Princess of the streets / European female / Still life / Goodbye Toulouse / Sinister / Let me introduce you to the family / All day and all of the night / Duchess / Nuclear device / English towns / No more heroes
SOF 001CD / 13 Apr '98 / Blueprint

☐ ALL TWELVE INCHES
Midnight Summer dream / Skin deep / No mercy / Let me down easy / Nice in Nice / Always the sun / Big in America / Shakin' like a leaf / All day and all of the night / Was it you / 96 tears / Sweet smell of success
4714162 / Sep '96 / Epic

☐ AURAL SCULPTURE
Ice queen / Skin deep / Let me down easy / No mercy / North winds / Uptown / Punch and Judy / Spain / Laughing / Souls / Mad hatter
4746762 / Feb '97 / Epic

☐ COLLECTION 1977-1982, THE
(Get a) grip (on yourself) / Peaches / Hangin' around / No more heroes / Duchess / Walk on by / Waltzinblack / Something better change / Nice 'n' sleazy / Bear cage / Who wants the world / Golden brown / Strange little girl / La folie
CDFA 3230 / Aug '89 / Fame

☐ COLLECTION, THE
CDGOLD 1071 / Apr '97 / EMI Gold

☐ COLLECTION, THE
Golden brown / No more heroes / Pin up / Sometimes / Mean to me / London lady / Cruel garden / Tank / Goodbye toulouse / Straighten out / Waltzin' black / Who wants the world / It only takes two to tango / Hanging around
DC 881872 / 2 Feb '98 / Disky

☐ DEATH & NIGHT & BLOOD
RRCD 187 / May '94 / Receiver

☐ EARLY YEARS 1974-1976 (Rare, Live & Unreleased)
(Get a) Grip (on yourself) / Bitching / Go Buddy go / (Get a) grip (on yourself) (live) / Sometimes / Bitching (live) / Peasant in the big shitty / Hanging around / Peaches
CLACD 401 / Jun '94 / Castle

☐ FELINE
Midnight summer dream / It's a small world / Ships that pass in the night / European female / Let's tango in Paris / Paradise / All roads lead to Rome / Blue sister / Never say goodbye
4844692 / Jul '97 / Epic

☐ FRIDAY 13TH
EAGCD 006 / 22 Sep '97 / Eagle

☐ GREATEST HITS 1977-1990
Peaches / Something better change / No more heroes / Walk on by / Duchess / Golden brown / Strange little girl / European female / Skin deep / Nice in Nice / Always the sun / Big in America / All day and all of the night / 96 tears / No mercy
4675412 / Nov '90 / Epic

☐ HIT MEN, THE (The Complete Singles 1977-1990)
Grip '89 (get a) grip (on yourself) / London lady / Peaches / Go buddy go / Hanging around / Choosey Susie / Something better change / Straighten out / No more heroes / English towns / 5 minutes / Nice 'n' sleazy / Toiler on the sea / Mean to me / Walk on by / Duchess / Nuclear device (wizard of aus) / Don't bring Harry / Raven / Bear cage / Who wants the world / Waltzinblack / Thrown away / Just like nothing on earth / Let me introduce you to the family / Golden brown / La folie / Tramp / Strange little girl / European female / Midnight summer dream / Paradise / Skin deep / No mercy / Let me down easy / Nice in nice / Always the sun / Big in America / Shakin like a leaf / Was it you / All day and all of the night / 96 tears / Sweet smell of success
CDEMC 3759 / Jan '97 / EMI

☐ LA FOLIE
Non-stop / Everybody loves you when you're dead / Tramp / Let me introduce you to the family / Ain't nothin' to it / Love to hate / Pin up / Two to tango / Golden brown / How to find true love and happiness in the present day / La folie / Cruel garden
CDFA 3083 / 1 Jun '98 / EMI Gold

☐ LIVE (X-CERT)
(Get a) grip (on yourself) / Dagenham Dave / Burning up time / Dead ringer / Hangin' around / Feel like a wog / Straight out / Do you wanna / Five minutes / Go buddy go / Peasant in the big shitty / In the shadows / Big shitty
CDFA 3313 / 1 Jun '98 / EMI Gold

☐ LIVE AT THE HOPE & ANCHOR (The Requests Show - Nov 22 1977)
Tits / Choosey Susie / Goodbye Toulouse / Bitching / School Mam / Peasant in the big shitty / In the shadows / Walk on by / Princess of the streets / Go buddy go / No more heroes / Straighten out / Peaches / Hangin' around / Dagenham Dave / Sometimes / Bring on the nubiles / London lady
CDFA 3316 / Feb '95 / Fame

☐ MASTERS, THE
Summer in the city / Valley of the birds / Golden boy / Face / Daddy's riding the range / Paradise row / In heaven she walks / Still life / Money / Lies and deception / Joy de viva / Skin deep / Golden brown / No more heroes
EABCD 111 / 30 Mar '98 / Eagle

☐ MENINBLACK
Waltzinblack / Just like nothing on Earth / Second coming / Waiting for the meninblack / Turn the centuries turn / Two sunspots / Four horsemen / Thrown away / Manna machine / Hallo to our men / Top secret
CDFA 3208 / Sep '88 / Fame

☐ NO MORE HEROES
I feel like a wog / Bitching / Dead ringer / Dagenham Dave / Bring on the nubiles / Something better change / No more heroes / Peasant in the big shitty / Burning up time / English towns / School Mam / In the shadows / Straighten out / Five minutes / Rok it to the moon
PRDFCD 6 / Jul '96 / Premier/EMI

☐ NO MORE HEROES (A Tribute To The Stranglers) (Various Artists)
ELM 020CD / 27 Apr '98 / Elevator

☐ RADIO ONE
ESSCD 283 / Nov '95 / Essential

☐ RATTUS NORVEGICUS (Stranglers IV)
Sometimes / Goodbye Toulouse / London lady / Princess of the streets / Hangin' around / Peaches / (Get a) Grip (on yourself) / Ugly / Down in the sewer: Falling / Down in the sewer: Trying to get out again / Rat's rally / Choosy Susie / Go Buddy go / Peasant in the big shitty
PRDFCD 5 / Jul '96 / Premier/EMI

☐ RAVEN, THE
Longships / Raven / Dead loss Angeles / Ice / Baroque bordello / Nuclear device / Shah shah a go go / Don't bring Harry / Duchess / Meninback / Genetix / Bear cage
7466152 / 1 Jun '98 / EMI

☐ STRANGLERS ARCHIVE (Live In London)
Something better change / No mercy / London lady / Uptown / Midnight summer dream / Golden brown / Nice 'n' sleazy / Let me down easy / She was quite close to me / Dead ringer / Strange little girl / Burning up time / Punch and Judy / Straighten out / European female / Peaches
RMCD 220 / Nov '97 / Rialto

☐ WRITTEN IN RED
Valley of the birds / In heaven she walks / In a while / Silver into blue / Blue sky / Here / Joy de viva / Miss you / Daddy's riding the range / Summer in the city / Wonderful land
EAMCD 001 / 30 Mar '98 / Eagle

Strangulated Beatoff

☐ STRANGULATED BEATOFF
GR 49CD / 8 Jun '98 / Skingraft

Strapping Fieldhands

☐ GOBS ON THE MIDWAY
SB 53 / Feb '97 / Siltbreeze

Strapping Young Lad

☐ HEAVY AS A REALLY HEAVY THING
CM 770922 / May '95 / Century Media

☐ NO SLEEP 'TIL BEDTIME
CM 77227CD / 22 Jun '98 / Century Media

Strasser, Hugo

☐ 60'S, THE (Strasser, Hugo & His Dance Orchestra)
La bamba / La bamba / Viends danser la bostella / Girl from ipanema / Limbo rock / My boy lollipop / Letkiss / Memphis, tennessee / Hully gully firehouse / Zorba's dance / C'mon and swim / I get around / Wooly bully / Yesterday man
16055 / May '94 / Laserlight

☐ DANCES IN STRICT RHYTHM (2CD Set)
Popocatepetl twist / Yesterday man / Woolly bully / My boy lollipop / Letkiss / Memphis Tennessee / Hully gully firehouse / La bamba / C'mon and swim / Girl from Ipanema / Limbo rock / Viens danser la bostella / I get around / Knock knock who's there / El condor pasa / Save your kisses for me / Rivers of Babylon / Love story / Pariser tango / Raindrops keep falling on my head / Waterloo / Is this the way to Amarillo / Viva Espana / Yes sir, I can boogie / Paloma blanca / New York, New York / Ein bisschen frieden / Atlantis is calling / La isla bonita / Nikita / I just called to say I love you / Hey mambo / Copacabana / Midnight lady / Reet petite / Theater
24339 / Dec '96 / Laserlight

☐ HUGO STRASSER'S DANCE PARTY (Strasser, Hugo & His Dance Orchestra)
Crazy rhythm / Congratulations / Love story / I could have danced all night / Fascination / Ramona / Maria from Bahia / Samba cielito / Reet petite / Red roses for a blue lady / Moonlight and roses / Undecided / Frenesi / La cumparsita / Kiss of fire / Spanish gypsy dance / Y viva Espana / Wunderbar
GRCD 38 / Nov '89 / Grasmere

☐ LATIN RHYTHMS
Chante (samba) / Chante (samba) / Tara's theme (rumba) / String of pearls (jive) / Y viva espana (pasa doble) / Brasil (samba) / Happy farmer (cha cha cha) / Begin the beguine (rumba) / Swing hugo swing (jive) / Lambada / Love story (rumba) / Cha cha piccolino (cha cha cha) / Ay, ay, ay, maria (samba) / Gitano (paso doble) / Chattanooga shoe shine boy (jive) / Dye me canto (salsa-mambo)
16119 / Jun '95 / Laserlight

Stratford Mercenaries

☐ NO SIGHING STRAINS OF VIOLINS
185582 / 13 Jul '98 / Southern

Strathclyde Police Pipers

☐ CHAMPION OF CHAMPIONS (Champions of The World)
Marches / Jigs / Strathspey and reel / Polkas / Hornpipes / Slow air
LCDM 9028 / Aug '90 / Lismor

☐ SIX IN A ROW 1981-1986
March, strathspey and reel / Marches / Slow air - Jigs and hornpipe / 9/8 marches / 2/4 marches / Solo pipe selection / Drum salute / Slow air, hornpipe and jigs / March, strathspey and reel / Slow air, hornpipe and jigs / March, strathspey and reel
LCOM 5165 / Aug '96 / Lismor

☐ STRATHCLYDE POLICE PIPERS, THE
Major manson at clachantrushal-clan maccoll (24 marches) / Major manson at clachantrushal-clan maccoll (24 marches)
LCOM 5201 / Jul '91 / Lismor

Stratovarius

☐ EPISODE
TT 0222 / May '96 / T&T

☐ FOURTH DIMENSION
Against the wind / Distant skies / Galaxies / Winter / Startovarious / Lord of the wasteland / 030366 / Nightfall / We hold the key / Twilight symphony / Call of the wilderness
TT 0142 / Feb '95 / T&T

☐ TWILIGHT TIME
TT 0022 / '94 / T&T

☐ VISIONS
Kiss of Judas / Black diamond / Forever free / Before the Winter / Legions / Abyss of your eyes / Holy light / Paradise / Coming home / Visions (Southern cross)
TT 0312 / May '97 / T&T

☐ VISIONS OF EUROPE (Live/2CD Set)
Forever free / Kiss of Judas / \Father time / Distant skies / Season of change / Speed of light / Twilight symphony / Holy solos / Visions / Will the sun rise / Forever / Black diamond / Against the wind / Paradise / Legions
TT 00382 / 9 Mar '98 / T&T

Straume, Bjorgulv

☐ FRA AETT TIL AETT
BS 96CD / Nov '96 / BS

Straus, Ste

☐ STE REAL
Je suis prete / Met play - G mix / Yo boom / Trop dur pour un seul homme / Track cheul / Nee gangstaa / Met play - East coast mix
122053 / Nov '94 / Plug It

Stravaig

☐ MOVIN' ON
Birkin tree / (Back home again in) Indiana / Song of the fishgutters / Terror time / Pressers / Dumfries hiring fair / Dundee weaver / Bonnie wee lassie's answer / My aim countrie / Miller tae ma trade / Davey fae / Bonnie lass come ower the buru / Another clearing time / Di nanina
CDTRAX 074 / Jul '94 / Greentrax

Straw Dogs

☐ COMPLETE DISCOGRAPHY, THE
LF 199CD / Jan '96 / Lost & Found

☐ UNDER THE HAMMER
LF 030CD / Apr '92 / Lost & Found

Straw, Syd

☐ WAR AND PEACE
5324572 / Oct '96 / Mercury

Strawberry Alarm Clock

☐ STRAWBERRIES MEAN LOVE
Incense and peppermints / Rainy day mushroom pillow / Sit with the guru / Tomorrow / Black butter - present / Love me again / Pretty song from psych out / World's on fire / Birds in my tree / Birdman of Alkatrash / Small package / They saw the fat one coming / Strawberries mean love
CDWIKD 56 / Jan '92 / Big Beat

Strawberry Story

☐ CLAMMING FOR IT
Gone like summer / Pushbutton head / I still want you / Ashlands Road / Close my eyes / Kissamatic lovebubble / Chicken biscuit / Buttercups and daisys / Made of stone / Caroline / Twenty six / Shame about Alice / Behind this smile / Freight train / Midsummer's daydream / Tell me now
ASKCD 025 / Jun '93 / Vinyl Japan

Strawbs

☐ BURSTING AT THE SEAMS
Flying / Lady fuschia / Stormy down / River / Down by the sea / Part of the union / Tears and pavan / Winter and the Summer / Lay down / Thank you / Will you go / Backside / Lay down
5409362 / 6 Jul '98 / A&M

☐ CHOICE SELECTION OF STRAWBS
Lay down / Lemon pie / Lady fuschia / Autumn / Glimpse of heaven / Hangman and the papist / New world / Round and round / I only want my love to grow in you / Benedictus / Hero and heroine / Song of a sad little girl / Tears and pavan / To be free / Part of the union / Down by the sea
CDMID 173 / Oct '92 / A&M

☐ DEEP CUTS/BURNING FOR YOU (2CD Set)
I only want my love to grow on you / Turn me around / Hard hard winter / My friend peter / Soldier's tale / Simple visions / Charmer / (Wasting my time) thinking of you / Beside the Rio Grande / So close and yet so far away / Burning for me / Cut like a diamond / I feel your loving coming on / Barcarole (for the death of Venice) / Alexander the great / Keep on trying / Back in the old routine / Heartbreaker / Carry me home / Goodbye (is not an easy word to say)
RGFCD 027 / Aug '96 / Road Goes On Forever

☐ FROM THE WITCHWOOD
Glimpse of heaven / Witchwood / Thirty days / Flight / Hangman and the Papist / Sheep / Cannondale / Shepherd's song / In amongst the roses / I'll carry on beside you / I'll keep the devil outside
5409392 / 6 Jul '98 / A&M

☐ GHOSTS (Remastered)
Ghosts / Lemon pie / Starshine/Angel wine / Where do you go (when you need a hole to crawl in) / Life auction / Don't try to change me / Remembering / You and I (when we were young) / Grace darling / Changes arrange us
5409372 / 3 Aug '98 / A&M

☐ GRAVE NEW WORLD
Benedictus / Hey little man... Thursday's child / Queen of dreams / Heavy disguise / New world / Hey little man... Wednesday's child / Flower and the young man / Tomorrow / On growing older / Ah me ah my / Is it today Lord / Journey's end / Here it comes / I'm going home
SRMC 0075 / Oct '97 / Siwan
5409342 / 6 Jul '98 / A&M

☐ GREATEST HITS LIVE
RGFCD 015 / Jul '95 / Road Goes On Forever

☐ HALCYON DAYS (The Very Best Of The Strawbs/2CD Set)
Ghosts / On growing older / Man who called himself Jesus / Stormy down / I turned my face into the wind / Queen of dreams / Witchwood / Keep the devil outside / Hangman and the Papist / Benedictus / Golden salamander / Tokyo Rosie / Hero and heroine / Pick up the pieces / Lay down / Ciggy Barlust / Out in the cold / Round and round / Oh how she changed / Battle / Grace Darling / Blue angel / Here it comes / Shepherd's song / We'll meet again sometime / Martin Luther King's dream / Burn baby burn / Shine on silver sun / Why and wherefore / Floating in the wind / Absent friend / Part of the union / Will ye go / River / Down by the sea / Tell me what you see in me
5406622 / Feb '97 / A&M

☐ HEARTBREAK HILL
RGFWC 024 / Apr '95 / Road Goes On Forever

☐ HERO AND HEROINE (Remastered)
Autumn / Sad young man / Just love / Shine on silver sun / Hero and heroine / Midnight / Out in the cold / Round and round / Lay a little light on me / Hero's theme / Still small voice / Lay a little light on me
5409352 / 3 Aug '98 / A&M

☐ JUST A COLLECTION OF ANTIQUES AND CURIOS (Remastered)
Martin Luther King's dream / Antique suite / Temperament of mind / Fingertips / Song of a sad little girl / Where is the dream of your youth / Vision of the Lady Of The Lake / We'll meet again sometime / Forever
5409382 / 3 Aug '98 / A&M

☐ RINGING DOWN THE YEARS/DON'T SAY GOODBYE (2CD Set)
Might as well be on Mars / King / Forever ocean blue / Grace darling / Afraid to let you go / Tell me what you see in me / Ringing down the years / Stone cold is the woman's heart / Taking a chance / Boy and his dog / Let it rain / We can make it together / Tina dei fada / Big brother / Something for nothing / Evergreen / That's when the crying starts / Beat the retreat
RGFCD 039 / 20 Apr '98 / Road Goes On Forever

☐ STRAWBS IN CONCERT, THE
WIN 069 / Apr '95 / Windsong

☐ UNCANNED PRESERVES (2CD Set)
RGFCD 003 / '92 / Road Goes On Forever

Strawhead

☐ TIFFIN
DRCD 902 / '90 / Dragon

☐ VICTORIAN BALLADS
DRGNCD 941 / Mar '94 / Dragon

Strawman

☐ LOTTERY, THE
ALLIED 53 / May '95 / Allied

Stray

☐ ALIVE AND GIGGIN'
Leave it down to us / Fire and glass / After the storm / Take a life / Jericho / I believe it / Mr. Wind / Buying time / Running wild / All in your mind
MYSCD 108 / Jul '97 / Mystic

☐ DEFINITIVE COLLECTION, THE (2CD Set)
Suicide / Jericho / Son of the father / Our song / After the storm / Leave it out / I believe it / Pretty things / Gambler / Somebody called you / Right from the start / For the people / End / Houdini / Take it easy / Give a little bit / Mr. Wind / One night in Texas / Take a life / All in your mind / Taken all the good things / Around the world in eighty days / Time machine / Only what you make it / Yesterday's promises / Move on / In reverse/Some day
CCSCD 833 / 24 Aug '98 / Castle

☐ HEARTS OF FIRE
REP 4112 / Aug '91 / Repertoire

☐ LIVE AT THE MARQUEE
MYSCD 104 / Jun '96 / Mystic

☐ LOST AND FOUND (2CD Set)
SMDCD 125 / Jul '97 / Snapper

☐ NEW DAWN
Dawn rising / New dawn / No future / Dangerous games / Maybe you want me / Trouble / Man in my head / White knuckle fever / Futher to fall / Rock steady / Jimijam / I want more / In the name of God
MYSCD 119 / 26 Jan '98 / Mystic

☐ STAND UP AND BE COUNTED
REP 4136 / Aug '91 / Repertoire

Stray Cats

☐ BEST OF THE STRAY CATS, THE
Stray cat strut / Rock this town / Rebels rule / Built for speed / Little Miss Prissy / Too hip gotta go / My one desire / I won't stand in your way / C'mon everybody / Fishnet stockings / Runaway boys / (She's) Sexy and 17 / Baby blue eyes / Jeanie, Jeanie, Jeanie / You don't believe me / Ubangi stomp / Double talkin' baby / Storm the Embassy / Rumble in Brighton / Gonna ball
74321446822 / Jan '97 / Camden

☐ CHOO CHOO HOT FISH
Elvis on velvet / Cry baby / Please don't touch / Sleepwalk / Lust 'n' love / Cross of love / Beautiful blues / Can't go back to memphis / Jade idol / My heart is a liar / Mystery train
ESMCD 424 / Aug '96 / Essential

☐ MASTERS, THE
EABCD 014 / 24 Nov '97 / Eagle

☐ ORIGINAL COOL
Somethin' else / Oh boy / Twenty-flight rock / I fought the law / Lonesome tears / Your true love / Be bop a lula / Blue jean cop / Can't help falling in love / Flying saucer rock 'n' roll / Chet ditty (hidden charms) / Trying to get to you / Let it rock / Stood up / Train kept a rollin'
ESMCD 395 / Jul '96 / Essential

☐ RUNAWAY BOYS (2CD Set)
Elvis on velvet / Cry baby / Please don't touch / Sleepwalk / Lust and love / Beautiful blues / Cross of love / My heart is a liar / Mystery train / Somethin' else / Twenty flight rock / I fought the law / Lonesome tears / Your true love / Bluejean bop / Can't help falling in love / Flying saucers rock 'n' roll / Stood up / Blast off / Runaway boys / Stray cat strutt / Rock this town / Sexy and seventeen / Built for speed / Look at the cadillac / Race is on / Bring it back again / Something's wrong with my radio / Double talking baby / Let's go faster / Too hip gotta go / Rumble in Brighton / Gene and Eddie / Elvis on velvet / Cry baby / Gina
SMDCD 182 / May '97 / Snapper

☐ STRAY CATS ARCHIVE
Stray Cat strut / Runaway boys / Rockabilly rules OK / Built for speed / Tonight's the night / Summertime blues / Elvis on velvet / Foggy mountain breakdown / Tear it up / Bring it back again / Something's wrong with my radio / Stray Cat blues / Gene and Eddie / Fishnet stockings / Race is on / Cry baby / Gina / Too hip gotta go / I fought the law / Something else
RMCD 211 / Nov '97 / Rialto

Strayhorn, Billy

☐ BILLY STRAYHORN PROJECT, THE
Grievin' / Smada / After all / Intimacy of the blues / Juniflip / Johnny come lately / Something to live for / Sunset and the mocking bird (the queen's suite) / My little brown book / Lotus blossom / I'm checking out, goodbye
STCD 533 / Feb '91 / Stash

Strazzeri, Frank

☐ I REMEMBER YOU (Strazzeri, Frank Trio)
FSCD 123 / Jan '91 / Fresh Sound

☐ NOBODY ELSE BUT ME
FSR 5020CD / 24 Feb '98 / Fresh Sound

Stream

☐ NOTHING IS SACRED
Chasin' the dragon / Snake eyed moon / Rock bottom / Camouflage / Fade to black / Bed of fire / Blood for gold / Far from the maddening crowd / Other side / Still believe
FRCD 005 / 18 May '98 / Frontier

☐ TAKE IT OR LEAVE IT
342792 / Dec '95 / No Bull

Streem

☐ FLOODMARK
Slide / Melter / Re-fuel / Coming down / Heat haze / Lunar scan / Indigo / Nothing new / Moonraker / Static / Floodmark theme
RR 87312 / 13 Apr '98 / Roadrunner

Street Buzz

☐ STREET BUZZ VOL.1
Such a good feelin' / Rescue me / You gotta get it out / Fun funky and frivilous / Tarantula / Can't break the flow / Gambi / Time you realise / Tell me / Summer blues / Passion / Love and happiness / Path
STRP 001CD / 13 Oct '97 / Strapped

Street Corner Symphony

☐ PULSATING DISCO MOODS FOR LOVING AND DANCING
SCRCD 001 / 30 Mar '98 / Street Corner

Street Jazz Unit

☐ SEEIN' THE LIGHT
SCCD 304CD / 16 Oct '97 / Schema

Street Talk

☐ COLLABORATION
USG 10162 / 20 Apr '98 / USG

Street Troopers

☐ TAKE THE BATTLE TO THE STREETS
KOCD 049 / Apr '97 / Knock Out

Streets

☐ KING BISCUIT PRESENTS...
88034 / Nov '97 / King Biscuit

Streetwalkers

☐ RED CARD
REP 4147 / Aug '91 / Repertoire

Strehli, Angela

☐ BLONDE & BLUE
ROUCD 3127 / Jan '94 / Rounder

Streisand, Barbra

☐ BACK TO BROADWAY
Some enchanted evening / Everybody says don't / Music of the night / Speak low / As if we never said goodbye / Children will listen / I have a love / I've never been in love before / Luck be a lady / With one look / Man I love / Move on
4738802 / Jun '93 / Columbia

☐ BARBRA STREISAND ALBUM, THE
Cry me a river / My honey's loving arms / I'll tell the man in the street / Taste of honey / Who's afraid of the big bad wolf / Soon it's gonna rain / Happy days are here again / Keepin' out of mischief now / Much more / Come to the supermarket / Sleepin' bee
4749042 / Jan '94 / Columbia

☐ BARBRA STREISAND LIVE (2CD Set)
Overture / As if we never said goodbye / Opening remarks / I'm still here/Everybody says don't/Don't rain on my parade / Can't help lovin' dat man / I'll know / People / Lover man / Therapist dialogue 1 / Will he like me / Therapist dialogue 2 / He touched me / Evergreen / Therapist dialogue 3 / Man that got away / On a clear day (you can see forever) / Entr'acte / Way we were / You don't bring me flowers / Lazy afternoon / Disney medley / Not while I'm around / Ordinary miracles / Yentl medley / Happy days are here again / My man for all we know / Somewhere
4775992 / Oct '94 / Columbia

☐ CHRISTMAS ALBUM
Christmas song / Jingle bells / Have yourself a merry little Christmas / White Christmas / My favourite things / Best of gifts / Silent night / Gounod's Ave Maria / O little town of Bethlehem / I wonder as I wander / Lord's prayer
4605362 / 3 Nov '97 / Columbia

☐ GREATEST HITS VOL.1
We're not makin' love anymore / Woman in love / All I ask of you / Comin' in and out of your life / What kind of fool / Main event/Fight / Someone that I used to love / By the way / Guilty / Memory / Way he makes me feel / Somewhere
4658452 / Nov '89 / CBS

☐ GREATEST HITS VOL.2
Evergreen / Prisoner / My heart belongs to me / Songbird / You don't bring me flowers: *Streisand, Barbra & Neil Diamond* / Way we were / Sweet inspiration / Where you lead / All in love is fair / Superman / Stoney end
CD 86079 / '86 / CBS

☐ GUILTY
Guilty / Woman in love / Run wild / Promises / Love inside / What kind of fool / Life story / Never give up / Make it like a memory
CD 86122 / '83 / CBS

☐ HIGHER GROUND
I believe / You'll never walk alone / Higher ground / At the same time / Tell him / On holy ground / If I could / Circle / Water is wide / Leading with your heart / Lessons to be learned / Everything must change / Avinu malkeinu
4885322 / 10 Nov '97 / Columbia

☐ HIGHLIGHTS FROM JUST FOR THE RECORD
You'll never know / Sleepin' bee / Miss Marmelstein / I hate music / Nobody's heart (belongs to me) / Cry me a river / Judy Garland medley / Get happy / Happy days are here again / People / Second hand rose / My name is Barbra / Act II medley / Best things are life are free / You wanna bet / Come rain or come shine / Don Rickles (monologue) / Sweetest sounds / You're the top / What are you doing the rest of your life / Crying time / Medley / Quiet thing / There won't be trumpets / Evergreen / Between yesterday and tomorrow / You don't bring me flowers: *Streisand, Barbra & Neil Diamond* / Papa, can you hear me / I know him so well / Warm all over
4716402 / Jul '92 / Columbia

☐ LIVE CONCERT AT THE FORUM
Sing / Make your own kind of music / Starting here, starting now / Don't rain on my parade / Monologue / On a clear day (You can see forever) / Sweet inspiration / Where you lead / Didn't we / My man (mon homme) / Stoney end / Happy days are here again / People
4879432 / Jul '97 / Columbia

☐ LOVE SONGS
Memory / You don't bring me flowers / My heart belongs to me / Wet / New York state of mind / Man I love / No more tears / Comin' in and out of your life / Evergreen / I don't break easily / Kiss me in the rain / Lost inside of you / Way we were / Love inside
CD 10031 / Sep '84 / CBS

☐ ONE VOICE
Somewhere / Evergreen / Something's coming / People / Over the rainbow / Guilty / Papa, can you hear me / Way we were / It's a new world / Happy days are here again / America the beautiful
4508912 / May '87 / CBS

☐ PEOPLE
Absent minded me / When in Rome / Fine and dandy / Suppertime / Will he like me / How does the wine taste / I'm all smiles / Autumn / My lord and master / Love is a bore / Don't like goodbyes
4604982 / Oct '95 / Columbia

☐ STAR IS BORN, A
Watch closely now / Queen Bee / Everything / Lost inside of you / Hellacious acres / Love theme / Woman in the moon / I believe in love / Crippled crow / With one more look at you
4749052 / Jan '94 / Columbia

Strength Through Joy

☐ FORCE OF TRUTH AND LIES, THE
NERO 6CD / Oct '96 / Twilight Command

☐ SALUTE TO LIGHT (2CD Set)
NERO 11CD / Oct '96 / Twilight Command

Stressball

☐ STRESSBALL
IRS 981201CD / 6 Oct '97 / Pavement

Stretch

☐ LIFEBLOOD
REP 4087 / Aug '91 / Repertoire

Stretch

☐ YOU CAN'T BEAT YOUR BRAIN FOR ENTER...
REP 4200 / Aug '91 / Repertoire

Stribling, Simon

☐ SIMON STRIBLING
JCD 257 / Jul '96 / Jazzology

Stricklin, Al

☐ BROTHER AL STRICKLIN NOW
Al's rag / South / San Antonio rose / Old piano roll blues / Maiden's prayer / Dark eyes / Anytime / Mexicali rose / Live bait / Faded love / Up the lazy river / Take me back to Tulsa
EDCD 559 / 1 Jun '98 / Edsel

Strictly Ballroom

☐ HIDE HERE FOREVER
WAX 0001 / Aug '97 / Waxploitation

Strictly Inc.

☐ STRICTLY INC.
Don't turn your back on me / Walls of sound / Only seventeen / Serpent said / Never let me know / Charity balls / Something to live for / Piece of you / Island in the darkness / Strictly incognito
CDV 2790 / Sep '95 / Virgin

Strife

☐ IN THIS DEFIANCE
VR 054 / Apr '97 / Victory

☐ ONE TRUTH
VR 16CD / Apr '95 / Victory

Strike

☐ I SAW THE FUTURE
Intro / I have peace / I saw the future / Morning after / Inspiration / Come with me / U sure do / Wrapped inside the rhythm / My love is real / Shut it / My love is for real / No compromise / Live for today
FRSHCD 3 / Jun '97 / Fresh

Strike Boys

☐ SELECTED FUNKS
Strike girls and strike boys / Jet set / Rhyme / Nada por las senoritas / New school of strike / Shadows / Don't you worry / Take it / Our melody / World of dreams / Times out
WALLCD 018 / 31 Aug '98 / Wall Of Sound

String A Longs

☐ WHEELS
Wheels / Brass buttons / Should I / Scottie / Nearly sunrise / Sunday / My blue heaven / Mathilda / Skippin' / Mira bird / Happy melody / Panic button / Walk don't run / Summertime / Perfidia / Bulldog / Spinnin' my wheels / Red river twist / Take a minute / You don't have to go / Torquay / Harbour lights / Tell the world / Are you lonesome tonight / My babe / Heartaches / Replica
CDCHD 390 / Jan '93 / Ace

String Beings

☐ LATE FOR THE DANCE
STRINGCD 1 / Feb '98 / Laurie Fisher

String Driven Thing

☐ MACHINE THAT CRIED, THE (The Band's Official Version)
Heartfeeder / To see you / Night club / Sold down the river / Two timin' rama / Travelling / People on the street / House / Machine that cried / River of sleep / If only the good / It's a game / Part of the city
OZITCD 0021 / May '97 / Ozit

☐ MACHINE THAT CRIED, THE
REP 4207 / Aug '91 / Repertoire

☐ STUDIO 1972-1973/LONDON 1995
OZITCD 0022 / 6 Apr '98 / Ozit

☐ SUICIDE (Live In Berlin)
Let me down / Nightclub / Two timin' rama / Suicide / To see you / Dreams into dust / My real hero / Circus / Park circus / You miss me / Road goes on
OZITCD 0018 / May '97 / Ozit

String Quartet

☐ WARM EVENINGS
CCD 4050 / Nov '89 / Concord Jazz

String Trio Of New York

☐ AREA CODE 212
1200482 / Dec '96 / Black Saint

☐ ASCENDANT
STCD 532 / Oct '91 / Stash

☐ BLUES
1201482 / Sep '95 / Black Saint

☐ OCTAGON
120131 / Apr '94 / Black Saint

☐ REBIRTH OF A FEELING
1200682 / May '94 / Black Saint

STRING TRIO OF NEW YORK & ANTHONY DAVIS (String Trio Of New York & Anthony Davis)
CD 994 / Sep '97 / Music & Arts

Stringfellow, Ken

☐ THIS SOUNDS LIKE GOODBYE
MRCD 123 / 10 Nov '97 / Munster
AHA 1004CD / 16 Feb '98 / Hidden Agenda

Stringle, Julian

☐ PATHFINDER
Pathfinder / Fortune green / Wendy blue / Catwalk / In sentimental mood / Samba for Liza / Paris / Softly as in a morning sunrise / Billie's bounce / Joker / Kia
MSPCD 9501 / Apr '95 / Mabley St.

Strings Of Paris

☐ BALLROOM DANCE FESTIVAL
American patrol (quickstep) / Vienne, mon amour (waltz) / Ole guapa (tango) / New york, new york (slow foxtrot) / Black bottom (charleston) / Habe mitleid (beguine) / Coffee song (samba) / Ob-la-di ob-la-da (cha cha cha) / O sole mio (rumba) / Paso doble del toreador (paso doble) / Rock around the clock (jive) / Beethoven 5th (disco disco) / I get a kick out of you (quickstep) / Three quarter (waltz) / Noche de estrella (tango) / Let there be love (slow foxtrot) / Compudance (electric boogie) / Michelle (blues) / Mais que nada (samba) / My prayer (rumba) / Over the rainbow (cha cha cha) / In the mood (jive) / Spanish gypsy dance (paso doble) / Boogie boy (disco)
BMC 87117 / Jun '95 / Beautiful Music Collection

☐ PANFLUTE MEMORIES
Lonely shepherd / Lonely shepherd / El condor pasa / Feelings / Love story / Rose / Douce melodie / My way / Yesterday / Amazing grace / Rondo russo / Concerto d'aranjuez / Hirtenlied / Romance d'amour / Czardas rumania / Barcarolle
BMC 87125 / Jun '95 / Beautiful Music Collection

Striplin, Sylvia

☐ GIVE ME YOUR LOVE
CDGR 235 / 27 May '98 / Charly

Stripling Brothers

☐ STRIPLING BROTHERS VOL.1 1928-1934
DOCD 8007 / Apr '97 / Document

☐ STRIPLING BROTHERS VOL.2 1934-1936
DOCD 8008 / Apr '97 / Document

Stritch, Elaine

☐ STRITCH
Are you having any fun / You're getting to be a habit with me / That's the beginning of the end / Angels sing / Let it snow, let it snow, let it snow / That's my boy / I don't want to walk without you / Too many rings around Rosie / Object of my affection / Easy street / If / There's a lull in my life / You took advantage of me
DRGCD 91434 / Aug '95 / DRG

Strobe

☐ CIRCLE NEVER ENDS
BBA 11 / Mar '94 / Big Cat

Strobinell

☐ BREIZH HUD
KMCD 66 / Jul '96 / Keltia Musique

Strohm, John P.

☐ CALEDONIA (Strohm, John P. & The Hello Strangers)
Slip away / Tangelo / Jennifer and Jean / Someone besides me / Geronimo's Cadillac / Fool / Backseat driver / Kill the lights / Freightliner / Powderkeg / Love theme / Thelma / See you around
FLT 126 / Dec '96 / Flat Earth
FIENDCD 932 / Aug '97 / Demon

Strong Deformity

☐ POWER OF PAIN
COM 002CD / 28 Jul '97 / Core & More

Strong, Jon

☐ FOLLOW ME
Follow me / In your dreams / Joined at the hip / Call my number / Same world / Killing fields of love / Bad news on the mountain / Diamond shine / Judas kiss / Gun metal grey
AKD 023 / Oct '93 / Linn

Strongheart

☐ RITUAL
HNRCD 005 / May '97 / Hengest

Strontium 90

☐ POLICE ACADEMY
Visions of the night / New world blues / 3 o'clock shot / Lady of delight / Electron romance / Every little thing she does is magic / Towers tumble / Electron romance / Lady of delight
CDV 2846 / 1 Sep '97 / Virgin

Stroscio, Cesar

☐ RIO DE LA PLATA
829052CD / Jul '95 / BUDA

☐ RUISENORES DE NUEVO (Stroscio, Cesar & Juan Gelman)
829562 / 24 Apr '98 / BUDA

Strother, Percy

☐ IT'S MY TIME
Get out of my house / I tried so hard to fake love / I'm doing fine without you baby / She gives me good loving all the time / Don't let your so called friends come between you and me / Joy to my life / He don't realise the woman he's got / It's my time baby / Tonight is my night baby / Ain't nobody take your place / I can't take you back this time / I don't cheat on my woman
JSPCD 295 / Nov '97 / JSP

Strozier, Frank

☐ CLOUDY AND COOL
VJ 013 / 24 Apr '98 / Vee Jay

☐ FANTASTIC FRANK STROZIER, THE
VJ 012 / 24 Apr '98 / Vee Jay

☐ WHAT'S GOIN' ON
SCCD 31420 / Nov '97 / Steeplechase

Strung Out

☐ ANOTHER DAY IN PARADISE
FAT 517CD / Jan '97 / Fatwreck Chords

☐ SUBURBANTEENAGE WASTELANDBLUES
FAT 537CD / Jun '97 / Fatwreck Chords

☐ TWISTED BY DESIGN
FAT 570CD / 11 May '98 / Fatwreck Chords

Strunz, Jorge

☐ FRONTERA (Strunz, Jorge & Adeshir Farah)
Quetzal / Zona liberada / Reng / Cassiopeia / Rio nuevo / Abrazo / Amritsar / Dervish
MCD 9123 / Nov '95 / Milestone

☐ GUITARS (Strunz, Jorge & Adeshir Farah)
Curandero / Curandero / Suenos / Zambalera / Tropico / Talisman / Feathered serpent / Mirage
MCD 9136 / Jun '95 / Milestone

Stryker, Dave

☐ BIG ROOM
SCCD 31426 / Jan '98 / Steeplechase

Strymdingars

☐ STRYMGYNTA
CRAICD 053 / Jan '98 / Crai

Stuart, Dan

☐ CAN O' WORMS
NORMAL 189 / May '95 / Normal

☐ RESTRONUEVO (Stuart, Dan & Al Perry)
NORMAL 169CD / Aug '94 / Normal

Stuart, Marty

☐ BUSY BEE CAFE
One more ride / Blue railroad train / I don't love nobody / Watson's blues / Busy bee cafe / Down the road / Boogie for Clarence / Get in line brother / Soldier's joy / Long train gone
SHCD 3726 / Jan '97 / Sugar Hill

☐ MARTY STUART
If it ain't got you / Whiskey ain't working / Hillbilly rock / Now that's country / Burn me down / Likes of me tempted / This one's gonna hurt you / Little things / Weight / Western girls / Don't be cruel
MCD 11237 / Mar '95 / MCA

Stubbert, Brenda

☐ IN JIG TIME
CDTRAX 139 / Aug '97 / Greentrax

Stubblefield, Clyde

☐ ORIGINAL FUNKY DRUMMER
MOLCD 44 / 6 Apr '98 / Music Of Life

Stubblefield, John

☐ MORNING SONG
Blues for the moment / King of harts / So what / Morning song / Blue moon / Night in Lisbon / Shaw of Newark / In a sentimental mood / Slick stud and sweet thang / Here and there / Here's one
ENJ 80362 / Feb '94 / Enja

Stubborn All Stars

☐ OPEN SEASON
AP 6009CD / 17 Aug '98 / Another Planet

Stubbs, Ray

☐ SPOONFUL OF BOOGIE, A
DTACD 4 / Dec '97 / Delta

Stube, Rolf

☐ ROLF STUBE AND THE JAZZ POLICE
LB 9712 / Jul '98 / La Brava

Stubseid, Gunnar

☐ STUBSEID AND MOLLER (Stubseid, Gunnar & Ale Moller)
HCD 7123 / May '97 / Helio

Stuck Mojo

☐ PIGWALK
CM 77133CD / Sep '96 / Century Media

☐ RISING
Crooked figurehead / Trick / Assassination of a popstar / Rising / Southern pride / Throw the switch / Hang 'em high (losers theme) / Tears / Pipebomb / Surburban ranger
CM 77188CD / 30 Mar '98 / Century Media

☐ SNAPPIN' NECKS
CM 77088CD / Aug '95 / Century Media

☐ VIOLATED
CM 77122CD / May '96 / Century Media

Studebaker John

☐ OUTSIDE LOOKIN' IN (Studebaker John & The Hawks)
BPCD 75022 / Jul '95 / Blind Pig

☐ TIME WILL TELL (Studebaker John & The Hawks)
Rolling and tumbling around / Here no more / On this highway / Fear / Road / Running into the rain / She plays hard / Playing with fire / Forever / Nasty Mother / Running scared / Time will tell
BPCD 5042 / 6 Oct '97 / Blind Pig

☐ TREMOLUXE (Studebaker John & The Hawks)
BPCD 5031 / Apr '96 / Blind Pig

Studer, Freddy

☐ SEVEN SONGS
Sans titre / Ein blindenhund und ein / Bellydance on a chessboard / Hajime / Soly sombra / I don't hear anything / SFK
VBR 20562 / Jun '91 / Vera Bra

Stun Leer

☐ ONCE
Love is a liar / Go don't go / If you want love / Eye to eye / Foolin' / No words can say / Come to me / All the kings horses / Hungry eyes / Deliver
199648 / 16 Mar '98 / Made To Measure

Stuntz's Blue Leg Expedition

☐ TRAVELLING BY SPORE
SGCD 13 / Sep '97 / September Gurls

Stupids

☐ PERUVIAN VACATION & VIOLENT NUN
CLAYCD 116 / Apr '94 / Clay

☐ RETARD PICNIC
CLAYCD 117 / Apr '94 / Clay

Sturr, Jimmy

☐ I LOVE TO POLKA
ROUCD 6067 / Jun '95 / Rounder

☐ LIVING ON POLKA TIME
ROUCD 6082 / Aug '97 / Rounder

☐ POLKA ALL NIGHT LONG
All night long / Swirl / Tavern in the town / Edelweiss / Alice / Krakow Bridge / Cajun fiddle / Big Ball's in Cowtown / Dizzy fingers / Green valley / My Sophie / Can't afford to be a star / Alice
ROUCD 6077 / Nov '95 / Rounder

☐ POLKA YOUR TROUBLES AWAY
ROUCD 6057 / Oct '94 / Rounder

Stutzpunkt Wien 12

☐ UFO BEOBACHTUNGEN
UNLESS 1 / 9 Feb '98 / Touch

Stuve, Bill

☐ BIG NOISE
Just got lucky / Big noise / Centipede crawl / Must have been the devil / Sherry twist / Big money blues / She walked right in-honey hush / Cuttin' in / Was it something I said / Black diamond / I got to find my baby / Feel so good
TRCD 9906 / Nov '93 / Tramp

Stuyvesant Stompers

☐ LIVE IN NEW YORK 1951-1952
STCD 6057 / Oct '97 / Storyville

Style Council

☐ ESSENTIAL COLLECTION, THE
Speak like a child / Headstart for happiness / Long hot Summer / Paris match / It just came to pieces in my hands / My ever changing moods / Whole point of no return / Ghosts of Dachau / You're the best thing / Big boss groove / Man of great promise / Homebreakers / Down in the Seine / Stones throw away / With everything to lose / Boy who cried wolf / Cost of loving / Changing of the guard / Why I went missing / It's a very deep sea
5294832 / Feb '96 / Polydor

☐ HERE'S SOME THAT GOT AWAY
Love pains / Party chambers / Whole point of no return / Ghosts of dachau / Sweet loving ways / Casual affair / Woman's song / Mick's up / Waiting on a connection / Night after night / Piccadilly trail / When you call me / My very good friend / April's fool / In love for the first time / Big boss groove / Mick's company / Bloodsports / Who will buy / I ain't goin' under / I am leaving / Stone's throw away
5193722 / Jun '93 / Polydor

☐ HOME AND ABROAD (LIVE)
My ever changing moods / Lodgers / Head start for happiness / When you call me / Whole point of no return / With everything to lose / Homebreaker / Shout to the top / Walls come tumbling down / Internationalists
8291432 / Aug '86 / Polydor

☐ IN CONCERT
Meeting over yonder / Up for grabs / Long hot summer / One nation under a groove / Le depart / Spring Summer Autumn / Hanging on to a memory / It just came to pieces in my hand / Here's one that got away / My ever changing moods / Man of great promise / Boy who cried wolf / Stones throw away / Speak like a child / Micks up / You're the best thing / Move on up / Down in the Seine / It's a very deep sea / Heavens up
5331432 / 9 Feb '98 / Polydor

☐ INTRODUCING THE STYLE COUNCIL
Long hot summer / Head start for happiness / Speak like a child / Long hot summer (Club mix) / Paris match / Mick's up / Money go round (Club mix)
8152772 / Aug '90 / Polydor

☐ OUR FAVOURITE SHOP
Homebreaker / All gone away / Come to Milton Keynes / Internationalists / Stones throw away / Stand up comics instructions / Boy who cried wolf / Man of great promise / Down in the Seine / Lodgers / Luck / With everything to lose / Our favourite shop / Walls come tumbling down / Shout to the top
8257002 / Aug '90 / Polydor

☐ SINGULAR ADVENTURES OF THE STYLE COUNCIL, THE (Greatest Hits Vol.1)
You're the best thing / Have you ever had it blue / Money go round / My ever changing moods / Long hot summer / Lodgers / Walls come tumbling down / Shout to the top / Wanted / It didn't matter / Speak like a child / Solid bond in your heart / Life at a top peoples health farm / Promised land / How she threw it all away / Waiting / Have you ever had it blue (12" mix) / Long hot summer (12" mix)
8378962 / Mar '89 / Polydor

Styler, Glyn

☐ LIVE AT THE MERMAID LOUNGE
TRUCK 03D / Apr '97 / Truckstop

Stylistics

☐ BEST OF THE STYLISTICS, THE
Can't give you anything (but my love) / Let's put it all together / I'm stone in love with you / You make me feel brand new / Sing baby sing / Na na is the saddest word / Sixteen bars / Star on a TV show / Funky weekend / Break up to make up / Can't help falling in love / Peek-a-boo / 7000 Dollars and you / You'll never go to heaven (if you break my heart)
8429362 / May '90 / Mercury

☐ BEST OF THE STYLISTICS, THE
Can't give you anything (but my love) / You make me feel brand new / Let's put it all together / I'm stone in love with you / Funky weekend / You'll never get to heaven (if you break my heart) / Peek-a-boo / Stop, look, listen (to your heart) / Betcha by golly wow / Sing baby sing / Star on a TV show / Na na is the saddest word / 7000 Dollars and you / Break up to make up / Love at first sight / Only for the children / You're a big girl now / You are everything
5511142 / Mar '96 / Spectrum

Styrenes

☐ WE CARE SO YOU DON'T...
SCAT 63CD / 20 Apr '98 / Scat

Styx

☐ BEST OF TIMES, THE (The Best Of Styx)
Best of times / Babe / Boat on the river / Mr. Roboto / Show me the way / Renegade / Borrowed time / Blue collar man (long nights) / AD 1928 / Rockin' the paradise / Sing for the day / Too much time on my hands / Don't let it end / Lady '95 / Little Suzie / It takes love
5404652 / Jul '97 / A&M

☐ BOAT ON THE RIVER
3969592 / Mar '95 / A&M

☐ PARADISE THEATRE
AD 1928 / Rockin' in paradise / Too much time on my hands / Nothing ever goes as planned / Best of times / Lonely people / She cares / Snowblind / Halfpenny, two penny / AD 1958 / State street Sadie
CDMID 154 / Oct '92 / A&M

☐ RETURN TO PARADISE (2CD Set)
SPV 08529182 / 3 Aug '98 / SPV

Su, Nat

☐ J-WAY, THE (Su, Nat Quartet)
FSNT 038 / 1 Jun '98 / Fresh Sound New Talent

Sub Dub

☐ DANCEHALL MALFUNCTION
ASP 0972CD / 22 Jun '98 / Asphodel

Sub Zero

☐ HAPPINESS WITHOUT LOVE
TDH 0016 / Dec '96 / Too Damn Hype

☐ HAPPINESS WITHOUT PEACE
CMCD 77157 / Mar '97 / Century Media

Subarachnoid Space

☐ ALMOST INVISIBLE
RR 69592 / Aug '97 / Relapse

☐ EITHER OR
UC 041 / Jun '97 / Unit Circle

Subcircus

☐ SUBCIRCUS
I want you like an accident / U love U / 20th century bitch / Shelly's on the telephone / Storm fly baby / 86'D / Gravity girl and analogue / Las zoot suit / Article 11 (early departure) / So strange
ECHCD 013 / Sep '96 / Echo

Subdudes

☐ ANNUNCIATION
(You'll be) satisfied / Why can't I forget about you / Angel to be / I know / Late at night / Miss Love / Poverty / Message man / Save me / Fountains flow / Cold nights / Sugar pie / It's so hard
72902103232 / Jun '94 / High Street

☐ PRIMITIVE STREAK
All the time in the world / Carved in stone / Break down these walls / Why do you hurt me so / Faraway girl / Love somebody / Lonely soldier / Too soon to tell / Do me a favour / She / Don't let 'em / Sarita / Love o' love
72902103442 / Jun '96 / High Street

Subhumans

☐ 29-29 SPLIT VISION
FISH 16CD / 6 Jul '98 / Bluurg

☐ DAY THE COUNTRY DIED
XLP 1CD / 6 Jul '98 / Bluurg

☐ EPLP
FISH 14CD / 6 Jul '98 / Bluurg

☐ FROM THE CRADLE TO THE GRAVE
FISH 8CD / 6 Jul '98 / Bluurg

☐ PISSED OFF, WITH GOOD REASON
417242 / Dec '96 / Frantic

☐ TIMEFLIES/RATS
FISH 25CD / 6 Jul '98 / Bluurg

☐ WORLDS APART
FISH 12CD / 6 Jul '98 / Bluurg

Subject 13

☐ BLACK STEELE PROJECT, THE
Dinner time jazz / Just 4 you / Good guys bad guys / Atmosphere / True skillz / High noon / Slice of soul / So much feel / Eastern promise / Mystical flyte
SEL 20CD / 8 Sep '97 / Selector

Sublette, Ned

☐ MONSTERS FROM THE DEEP (Sublette, Ned & Lawrence Weiner)
TRECD 117 / 22 Sep '97 / Triple Earth

☐ SHIPS AT SEA SAILORS AND SHOES (Sublette, Ned & Lawrence Weiner)
TRECD 112 / Jul '98 / Triple Earth

Sublime

☐ ROBBIN' THE HOOD
GASD 11475 / 12 Jan '98 / Gasoline Alley

☐ SUBLIME
GASD 11413 / 12 Jan '98 / Gasoline Alley

Submarine

☐ KISS ME TILL YOUR EARS BURN OFF
FAN 1022 / Mar '94 / Fantastick

☐ SUBMARINE
I can't be satisfied / Electric bathing / Jnr. elvis / Empty / Lips and fingers / Never be alright again / Fading / Jodie foster / Alright sunshine song
TOPPCD 007 / Mar '94 / Ultimate

Submissives

☐ ANVIL WILL WEAR OUT MANY A HAMMER, AN
DON 006CD / Jun '97 / Honest Don's

Subotnick, Morton

☐ AND THE BUTTERFLIES BEGIN TO SING
805142 / Aug '97 / New World

Subramaniam, Dr. L.

☐ ELECTRIC MODES VOL.1 & 2
WLAES 4CD / Nov '95 / Waterlily Acoustics

☐ KALYANI
WLAES 19CD / Nov '95 / Waterlily Acoustics

☐ PACIFIC RENDEZVOUS
CDMANU 1508 / Mar '96 / Manu

☐ RAGA HEMEVATI
NI 5227 / Sep '94 / Nimbus

☐ SARASVATI
WLAES 24CD / Nov '95 / Waterlily Acoustics

☐ THREE RAGAS FOR SOLO VIOLIN
NI 5323 / Sep '94 / Nimbus

Subramanium, Karaikudi

☐ MASTERS OF RAGA
SM 16082 / Sep '95 / Wergo

Subsonics

☐ FOLLOW ME DOWN
GH 1064 / 20 Jul '98 / Get Hip

Substance

☐ SESSION ELEMENTS
EFA 503052 / 20 Apr '98 / Chain Reaction

Subsurfing

☐ FROZEN ANTS
Number readers / Face with corn / Frozen ants / Sleepless snake / Angel fish / She swims above the horizon / HSJ
AMB 5941CD / Apr '95 / Apollo

Subtle Plague

☐ IMPLOSION
NORM 159CD / Mar '94 / Normal

☐ INDEPENDENT STUDY
TR 30060062 / 27 Apr '98 / Trocadero

☐ SECRET LIVES
TR 20102 / 18 May '98 / Trocadero

Subtropic

☐ HOMEBREW
REFCD 6 / Dec '95 / Subtropic

Suburban Studs

☐ COMPLETE STUDS COLLECTION
Suburban stud / Dissatisfied / Rumble / Resistor / I hate school / My generation / Traffic jam / Revenge / Questions / Necro / Razor blades / Two victims / Young power / Panda control / Bondage / Throbbing lust / No faith / Snipper / Hit and run / I hate school (live) / Sinkin down / Hudini charms / Savier of love / White light / All that jazz / Supernatural / Questions (sax version) / No faith (sax version)
CDPUNK 21 / Oct '93 / Anagram

Subversives

☐ PROTEST AND DANCE
STEPCD 102 / 4 May '98 / Step 1

Subvert

☐ SUBVERT
SFLS 282 / Dec '94 / Selfless

Subway Sect

☐ WE OPPOSE ALL ROCK 'N' ROLL
Nobody's scared / Don't split it / Parallel lines / Chain smoking / Rock 'n' roll even / Ambition / Double negative / Head held high / Stool pigeon / Watching the devil / Spring is grey / Stop that girl / Exit no return / Staying out of view / Parallel lines
OVER 53CD / Dec '96 / Overground

Success-n-Effect

☐ BACK-N-EFFECT
Angel dust / Blueprint / Robo's housin' / Seven Gs I'll flow / Slick the slick / Real deal (Holyfield) / Mack of the year / Jump 2 it (house from the South) / Slow flow / So many faces / Nuthin' but success / 360
ICH 1108CD / Oct '93 / Ichiban

Suck Pretty

☐ 3 HEADS
KFWCD 181 / Oct '96 / Knitting Factory

Sudden, Nikki

☐ 7 LIVES LATER
GRCD 403 / May '97 / Glitterhouse

☐ BACK TO THE COAST
Back to the coast / Death is hanging over me / In your life / Jangle town / Feather beds / Flower bed romance / Last bandit / Great pharoah / Crossroads / Broken tooth
CRECD 083 / May '94 / Creation

☐ DEAD MEN TELL NO TALES
When I cross the line / Before I leave you / Dog latin / Wooden leg / Dog rose / How many lies / Cup full of change / Kiss at dawn
CRECD 016 / Feb '91 / Creation

☐ DEAD MEN TELL NO TALES/TEXAS (Sudden, Nikki & The Jacobites)
CRECD 018 / Feb '91 / Creation

☐ GROOVE CREATION (Sudden, Nikki & The French Revolution)
See my rider / Murder valley / French revolution blues / Breaking lines / Groove / Sea dog blues / Great pharaoh / Poor relation / Wild cathedral / Beethoven's ring / Back to the coast / Too bad for you / Village green
CRECD 041 / Apr '89 / Creation

☐ JEWEL THIEF
UFO 004CD / Oct '91 / UFO

☐ KISS YOU KIDNAPPED CHARABANC (Sudden, Nikki & Roland S. Howard)
Wedding hotel / Rebel grave / Sob story / Snowplough / Quick thing / Feather beds / French revolution blues / Crossroads / Don't explain / Hello wolf (little baby) / Better blood / Debutante blues / Girl without a name / Wedding hotel (The Moose)
CRECD 022 / Nov '90 / Creation

☐ SEVEN LIVES LATER
ISAM 1004 / 13 Oct '97 / Idiot Savant Music

Suddenly Tammy

☐ TAMMY
Stacey's trip / Plant me / Way up / Babee / Can't decide / Lamp / Instrumental / Ryan / Fearless / Mt rushmore / How me / Disease / No respect girl / Pretty back
9362455242 / May '94 / Warner Bros.

☐ WE GET THERE WHEN WE DO
Stacey's trip / Plant me / Way up / Pretty back / Bebee / No respect girl / Can't decide / Disease / Lamp / How me / Instrumental / Fearless / Ryan / Mount Rushmore
9362458312 / Mar '95 / Warner Bros.

Sudhalter, Dick

☐ AFTER AWHILE
Dream a little dream of me / People will say we're in love / Tea for two / Blue room / My heart stood still / Love nest / Rose of Washington Square / After awhile
CHR 70014 / May '96 / Challenge

☐ DICK SUDHALTER & THE ANGLO-AMERICAN ALLIANCE (Sudhalter, Dick Anglo-American Alliance)
JCD 274 / Dec '97 / Jazzology

☐ FRIENDS WITH PLEASURE
ACD 159 / Mar '95 / Audiophile

Suede

☐ COMING UP
Trash / Filmstar / Lazy / By the sea / She / Beautiful ones / Starcrazy / Picnic by the motorway / Chemistry between us / Saturday night
NUDE 6CD / Sep '96 / Nude

☐ DOG MAN STAR
Introducing the band / We are the pigs / Heroine / Wild ones / Daddy's speeding / Power / New generation / This Hollywood life / Two of us / Black or blue / Asphalt world / Still life
NUDE 3CD / Oct '94 / Nude

☐ INTERVIEW DISC
SAM 7031 / Mar '97 / Sound & Media

☐ SCI FI LULLABIES (2CD Set)
NUDE 9CD / 6 Oct '97 / Nude

☐ SUEDE
So young / Animal nitrate / She's not dead / Moving / Pantomine horse / Drowners / Sleeping pills / Breakdown / Metal Mickey / Animal lover / Next life
NUDE 1CD / Mar '93 / Nude

Suesse, Diana

☐ KEYBOARD WIZARDS OF THE GERSHWIN ERA VOL.2
GEMMCD 9202 / Dec '95 / Pearl

Suffer

☐ GLOBAL WARMING
NPR 002CD / Mar '94 / Napalm

Suffocation

☐ DESPISE THE SUN
VULT 0002 / 16 Mar '98 / Vulture

☐ HUMAN WASTE
Infesting the crypt / Synthetically flevived / Mass obliteration / Catalonia / Jesus wept / Human waste
RR 60152 / 26 Jan '98 / Relapse

Sufi

☐ LIFE'S RISING
Bluesunslide / Lover / Into the blue / Chrysalids / Desert flower / From slow syrup silence rise time tilted glances / Lostaday / Still pool reflects a clear moon / Beloved / Soon
AMBT 9 / Jun '95 / Virgin

☐ LOVERS AND TRIPPERS
AGENT 4CD / Jun '97 / Secret Agent

Sufit, Alisha

☐ ALISHA THROUGH THE LOOKING GLASS
SUFIT 010 / Oct '96 / Magic Carpet

☐ LOVE AND THE MAIDEN
MC 1002CD / Oct '96 / Magic Carpet

Sugar

☐ BEASTER
Come around / Tilted / Judas cradle / JC auto / Feeling better / Walking away
CRECD 153 / Apr '93 / Creation

☐ COPPER BLUE
Act we act / Good idea / Changes / Helpless / Hoover dam / Slim / If I can't change your mind / Fortune teller / Slick / Man on the moon
CRECD 129 / Jul '92 / Creation

☐ FILE UNDER EASY LISTENING
Gift / Company book / Your favorite thing / What you want it to be / Gee Angel / Panama city motel / Can't help you anymore / Granny cool / Believe what you're saying / Explode and make up
CRECD 172 / Sep '94 / Creation

Sugar Blue

☐ BLUE BLAZES
RRCD 901301 / Dec '94 / Ruf

☐ FROM PARIS TO CHICAGO
157562 / Feb '93 / Blues Collection

☐ IN YOUR EYES
TRIP 7711 / Oct '95 / Ruf

Sugar Creek

☐ PLEASE TELL A FRIEND
LSDDU 5004 / 8 Jun '98 / LSD

Sugar Experiment Station

☐ ULTRAMONOTONE
SCAN 008CD / 2 Mar '98 / Scandinavia

Sugar Loaf Express

☐ SUGAR LOAF EXPRESS (Sugar Loaf Express & Lee Ritenour)
Sugar loaf express / Morning glory / That's the way of the world / Slippin' in the back door / Tomorrow / Lady soul
JMI 20082 / Nov '93 / JVC

Sugar Plant

☐ AFTER HOURS
Guide / No.4 / Licorice / Here rain comes / Behind the door / Drifting / I hate morning / Microwaves / Synapse / Freezy / Blanc / Brazil
WD 00462 / Mar '97 / World Domination

Sugar Ray

☐ FLOORED
RPM / Breathe / Anyone / Fly / Speed home California / High anxiety / Tap, twist, snap / American pig / Stand and deliver / Cash / Invisible / Right direction / Fly
7567830062 / Aug '97 / Lava/Atlantic

☐ LEMONADE AND BROWNIES
Snug harbor / Iron mic / Rhyme stealer / Hold your eyes / Big black woman / Dance party USA / Danzig needs a hug / 10 seconds down / Streaker / Scuzzboots / Caboose / Drive by / Mean machine / Greatest
7567827432 / Aug '95 / Atlantic

Sugar Ray

☐ SWEET AND SINGIN'
Jack She's on the ball / You better move on / Need my baby / Tomorrow night / Lost mind / It's a low down dirty shame / Love life and money / You better change your way of loving / Money marbles and chalk / My sweet love ain't around / No good woman
CDBB 9607 / Jun '98 / Bullseye Blues

Sugar Ray's Flying Fortress

☐ BIM BAM BABY
All night long / Mr. Blues is coming to town / Jukebox / We'll be together again / Frim fram sauce / Bei min bist du schon / Take the 'A' train / Oh Marie / Bim bam baby / Don't go, don't go / Dark eyes / You got me reelin' and rockin'
CDCHD 627 / Apr '96 / Ace

Sugar Shack

☐ 5 WEEKS AHEAD OF MY TIME
ES 1238CD / 8 Sep '97 / Estrus

☐ SHOTGUN FOR TWO
ANDA 183CD / Feb '97 / Au-Go-Go

Sugarbuzz

☐ THREE MILE THICK
PARCD 022 / 16 Feb '98 / Parasol

Sugarcubes

☐ GREAT CROSSOVER POTENTIAL, THE
Birthday / Cold sweat / Mama / Motor crash / Deus / Regina / Pump / Planet / Water / Hit / Vitamin / Walkabout / Gold / Chihuahua
TPLP 333CD / 13 Jul '98 / One Little Indian

☐ HERE TODAY TOMORROW NEXT WEEK
Tidal wave / Regina / Speed is the key / Dream TV / Nail / Pump / Eat the mango / Fear / Dear plastic / Shoot him / Water / Day called zero / Planet
TPLP 15CD / 11 May '98 / One Little Indian

☐ IT'S IT
Birthday / Birthday / Birthday / Leash called love / Blue eyed pop / Blue eyed pop / Motorcrash / Motorcrash / Planet / Planet / Gold / Gold / Water / Water / Regina / Regina / Mama / Mama / Pump / Pump / Hit / Hit / Birthday / Birthday / Coldsweat / Coldsweat
TPLP 40CD / 11 May '98 / One Little Indian

☐ LIFE'S TOO GOOD
Traitor / Motorcrash / Birthday / Delicious demon / Mama / Cold sweat / Blue eyed pop / Deus / Sick for toys / Fucking in rhythm and sorrow
TPLP 5CD / 11 May '98 / One Little Indian

☐ STICK AROUND FOR JOY
Gold / Hit / Leash called love / Lucky night / Happy nurse / I'm hungry / Walkabout / Hetero scum / Vitamin / Chihuahua
TPLP 30CD / 11 May '98 / One Little Indian

Sugargliders

☐ WE'RE ALL TRYING TO GET THERE
Letter from a lifeboat / Strong / Seventeen / Aloha street / Ahprahran / Theme from Boxville / Unkind / Trumpet play / Will we ever learn / Reinventing penicillin / 90 days of moths and rust / Top 40 sculpture
SARAH 619CD / Feb '94 / Sarah

Sugarhill Gang

☐ BEST OF THE SUGARHILL GANG, THE
Rapper's delight / Apache / Showdown with the furious five / Passion play / Hot hot summer day / Lover in you / Rapper's reprise / Eighth Wonder / Word is out / Kick it live from 9 to 5 / Livin' in the fast lane
NEMCD 747 / Aug '95 / Sequel

Sugarman Three

☐ SUGAR'S BOOGALOO
Sugar's boogaloo / Papa's got a brand new bag / Sock monkey / Sunshine superman / Skunk walk / Suzy Q / Sweet tooth / Red wine / Hot sauce / Hankerin'
DSCD 002 / 25 May '98 / Desco

Sugarplastic

☐ RADIO JEJUNE
SUGARFIX 001 / Dec '96 / Nail Imports

Sugarsmack

☐ TOP LOADER
CDDVN 24 / Oct '93 / Devotion

Sugarsnatch

☐ MAD COWS AND ENGLISHMEN
STEPCD 098 / Sep '97 / Step 1

Sugartown

☐ SLOW FLOWS THE RIVER
MA 31 / 1 Sep '97 / Marina

☐ SWIMMING IN THE HORSEPOOL
MA 9 / Mar '95 / Marina

Suggs

☐ LONE RANGER, THE
I'm only sleeping / Camden Town / Alcohol / 4 am / Tune / Cecilia / Haunted / Off on holiday / Green eyes / Fortune fish / She's gone
0630124782 / Dec '95 / WEA

☐ THREE PYRAMIDS CLUB, THE
3984238152 / 31 Aug '98 / WEA

Sugimoto, Taku

☐ OPPOSITE
HATN 802 / May '98 / Hat Noir

Suhler, Jim

☐ RADIO MOJO (Suhler, Jim & Monkey Beat)
LUCKY 9203CD / May '93 / Lucky Seven

☐ SHAKE (Suhler, Jim & Monkey Beat)
LUCKY 9207 / Feb '95 / Lucky Seven

Suicidal Flowers

☐ BURN MOTHER BURN
Burn Mother burn / Fatwah / Rhythm of the bell / Bite the hand / Abuse your mind / Gieger acid nightmare / Angel falling / Coyote / Ease II / Surfin' on heroin / That's rock 'n' roll
DELECCD 043 / May '96 / Delerium

Suicidal Tendencies

☐ FNG
Suicide's an alternative - you'll be sorry / Join the army / Trip at the brain / Suicidal failure / I shot the devil / Suicidal maniac / Institutionalised / I feel your pain and I survive / How will I laugh tomorrow / Possessed / If I don't wake up / Two wrongs don't make a right (but they make me feel a lot / I saw your mommy... / Human guinea pig / Sublimal / Surf and slam / Possessed to skate / I vary more / Feeling's back / Little each day / Suicyco mania / Pledge your allegiance
CDVM 9003 / Jun '92 / Virgin

☐ HOW WILL I LAUGH TOMORROW WHEN I CAN'T EVEN SMILE TODAY
Trip at the brain / Hearing voices / Pledge your allegiance / How will I laugh tomorrow / Miracle / Surf and slam / If I don't wake up / Sorry / One too many times / Feeling's back / Suicyco mania
CDV 2551 / Sep '88 / Virgin

☐ JOIN THE ARMY
Suicidal maniac / Join the army / You got, I want / Little each day / Prisoner / War inside my head / I feel your pain and I survive / Human guinea pig / Possessed to skate / No name, no words / Cyco / Two wrongs don't make a right (but they make me feel better) / Looking in your eyes
CDV 2424 / Jun '87 / Virgin

☐ SUICIDAL TENDENCIES
Suicide's an alternative / You'll be sorry / Two sided politics / I shot the devil / Subliminal / Won't fall over today / Institutionalized / Possessed / I saw your Mommy / Fascist pig / I want more / Suicidal failure
01042 / Apr '97 / Epitaph

Suicide

☐ GHOST RIDERS
Rocket USA / Dream baby dream / Rock 'n' roll (is killing my life) / Sweet white lady / Ghost rider / Harlem
RUSCD 8239 / 30 Mar '98 / ROIR

☐ SUICIDE
Ghost rider / Rocket USA / Cheree / Johnny / Girl / Frankie teardrop / Che
RS 7001 / 8 Sep '97 / Red Star

☐ SUICIDE (2CD Set)
Ghost rider / Rocket USA / Cheree / Johnny / Girl / Frankie Teardrop / Che / Cheree / I remember / Keep your dreams / Mr. Ray / Las Vegas man / 96 tears / Keep your dreams / I remember / Harlem / 23 minutes over / Dominick
BFFP 133CDL / 9 Mar '98 / Blast First

☐ WHY BE BLUE
OUT 1082 / Sep '97 / Brake Out

☐ ZERO HOUR
RS 7005 / 15 Sep '97 / Red Star

Suicide Machines

☐ BATTLE HYMNS
Someone / Hating hate / Give / Hope / Black and white world / Numbers / High society / Pins and needles / Confused / DDT / Punck / Step one / In the end / Face another day / What you say / Speak no evil / Empty room / Independence parade / Sympathy / Strike / Sides / Jah
1620602 / 18 May '98 / Hollywood

☐ DESTRUCTION BY DEFINITION
1620482 / 13 Oct '97 / Polydor

Suicide Twins

☐ SILVER MISSILES & NIGHTINGALES
Dance / Heaven made you / Declaration / Mainline service / What a price to pay / Silver missiles and nightingales / Coming down slow / Best is yet to come / Sweet pretending / Countryfied inner city blues
ESMCD 276 / Apr '95 / Essential

Sukay

☐ HUAYRASAN - MUSIC OF THE ANDES
Huayrasan / Khuyaylla / Mandolinita / Anoranzas / Tu eres mentirosa / San bartolomito / Yayakarwi / Mi promesas / Tarkas, choquellas, toyos / Carrito pasajerito / San juan
FF 70501 / Jul '89 / Flying Fish

☐ INSTRUMENTAL, THE (Music Of The Andes)
FF 70108 / Nov '94 / Flying Fish

Sukia

☐ CONTACTO ESPACIAL CON EL TERCER SEXO
Dream machine / Feel'n free / Vaseline and sand / Play colt / Gary super macho / Mr. Robot / We have the technology / Touching me touching you / Sukia / Amok / Dirty afro / Dream machine / Dream machine / Dream machine / Dream machine
MW 073CD / May '97 / Mo Wax

☐ CONTACTO ESPACIAL CON EL TERCER SEXO
NB 0001 / Mar '97 / Nickelbag

Sukpatch

☐ HAULIN' GRASS AND SMOKIN' ASS
SLABCO 36CD / Mar '97 / Slabco

☐ HONKY TONK OPERATION
SLABCO 38CD / 30 Sep '97 / Slabco

Sukuma, Stewart

☐ AFRIKITI
68990 / 24 Apr '98 / Tropical

Sulam

☐ KLEZMER MUSIC FROM TEL AVIV
SM 15062 / Jul '92 / Wergo

Sullen

☐ SULLEN
EXPCD 007 / Jul '96 / EXP

Sullivan, 'Big' Jim

☐ BIG JIM'S BACK/TIGER
Rubber hip gnome / Home / Arabella swampchild / Laid back rock and roll song / Cascade / Takin' it easy / Louisiana lovelips / Ballad of Billy Tyler / Country boy picker / Lay me / Ordinary girl / Lay back stay back / Prayer / I'm not crying / Long time / Suzy slicker / Tyger, tyger
GEMCD 021 / 2 Feb '98 / Diamond

☐ TEST OF TIME
EFA 132862 / Jul '94 / Ozone

Sullivan, Charles

☐ KAMAU
Carefree / Dreams die young in the eyes of the native son / Patrice / Last embrace / Looking for love
AJ 0121 / Jun '96 / Arabesque

Sullivan, Christine

☐ IT'S ABOUT TIME
LRJ 257 / Oct '93 / Larrikin

Sullivan, Ira

☐ BLUE STROLL
Wilbur's tune / My old flame / Blue stroll / 63rd Street theme / Bluzinbee / Wilbur's tune
DE 402 / Jul '97 / Delmark

☐ NICKY'S TUNE (Sullivan, Ira Quintet)
Secret love / When Sunny gets blue / Nicky's tune / Wilbur's tune / My secret love / Wilbur's tune / Mock and roll blues / Nicky's tune
DD 422 / Mar '97 / Delmark

Sullivan, Jerry

☐ JOYFUL NOISE, A (Sullivan, Jerry & Tammy)
Get up John / He called me baby / I'm working on a building / Soldiers of the cross / Gates of Zion / Think about that promise / When Jesus passed by / Brand new church / Gospel plow / What a wonderful saviour he is
CMFCD 016 / Jan '93 / Country Music Foundation

Sullivan, Joe

☐ CLASSICS 1933-1941
CLASSICS 821 / Jul '95 / Classics

☐ PIANO ARTISTRY OF JOE SULLIVAN, THE
Squeeze me / I got it bad / It's the talk of the town / My silent town / Memories of you / Deep purple / Moon is low / Reflections / 24 hours at Booth's / Bass romps away / Night and day / High dudgeon / Brushin' off the boogie / Heavy laden / What's your name / An armful of you / Solid eclipse / Breezin' / Can't we get together / Never heard of such stuff / There'll come a time when you need me / If you can't be good be careful
JUCD 2051 / 9 Mar '98 / Jazz Unlimited

Sullivan, K.T.

☐ CRAZY WORLD
DRGCD 91413 / Jun '93 / DRG

☐ SING MY HEART
Sing my heart / This time the dream's on me / Hit the road to dreamland / Let's take a walk around the block / Little drops of rain / Right as the rain / Ill wind I gotta right to sing the blues / Fun to be fooled / Sleepin' bee / Two ladies in de shade of de banana tree / Out of this world / My shining hour / I wonder what became of me / If I only had a brain / Don't like goodbyes / Silent spring / It's a new world
DRGCD 91437 / Dec '95 / DRG

Sullivan, Maxine

☐ CLASSICS 1937-1938
CLASSICS 963 / Nov '97 / Classics

☐ CLASSICS 1938-1941
CLASSICS 991 / 24 Apr '98 / Classics

☐ CLOSE AS PAGES IN A BOOK (Sullivan, Maxine & Bob Wilber)
As long as I live / Gone with the wind / Rockin' rhythm / Darn that dream / Every time / Harlem butterfly / Loch Lomond / Too many tears / Jeepers creepers / Restless / You're driving me crazy / Close as pages in a book
ACD 203 / May '95 / Audiophile

☐ EASY TO LOVE
PASTCD 7099 / Jun '96 / Flapper

☐ GREAT SONGS OF THE COTTON CLUB, THE
Happy as the day is long / You gave me everything but love / As long as I live / Raisin' the rent / 'Neath the pale Cuban moon / Ill wind / Between the Devil and the deep blue sea / I love a parade / Harlem holiday / Get yourself a new broom / Stormy weather / In the silence of the night / That's what I hate about love / Primitive prima donna / I've got the world on a string
CD 270 / Jul '87 / Milan

☐ IT'S WONDERFUL
Loch Lomond / I'm coming Virginia / Annie Laurie / Blue skies / Easy to love / Folks who live on the hill / Darling Nellie Grey / Nice work if you can get it / 'S Wonderful / Dark eyes / Brown bird singing / You went to my head / Moments like this / Please be kind / It was a lover and his lass / Spring is here / Down the Old Ox Road / St. Louis blues / L'amour toujours l'amour / Might and day / Kinda lonesome / It ain't necessarily so / Say it with a kiss
CDAFS 1031 / Feb '92 / Affinity

☐ LOCH LOMOND (Sullivan, Maxine & John Kirby)
CCD 47 / Aug '94 / Circle

☐ LOCH LOMOND (Her 24 Greatest Hits 1937-1942)
Loch Lomond / I'm comin' Virginia / Annie Laurie / Blue skies / Easy to love / Folks who live on the hill / Darling Nelly Gray / Nice work if you can get it / Moments like this / It was a lover and his lass / Dark eyes / St. Louis blues / Night and day / Kinda lonesome / It ain't necessarily so / Say it with a kiss / I dream of Jeannie with the light brown hair / I'm happy about the whole thing / Corn pickin' / Just like a gypsy / Kentucky babe / When your lover has gone / My ideal / Ma curly headed baby
CDAJA 5253 / Sep '98 / Living Era

☐ MAXINE SULLIVAN & IKE ISAACS QUARTET (Sullivan, Maxine & Ike Isaacs Quartet)
ACD 154 / Jul '96 / Audiophile

☐ MAXINE SULLIVAN & SCOTT HAMILTON (Sullivan, Maxine & Scott Hamilton)
Sweet georgia brown / As long as I live / I got a right to sing the blues / Something to remember you by / Wrap your troubles in dreams (and dream your troubles away) / Georgia on my mind / You were meant for me / Hundred years from today / Just one of those things / I'm crazy 'bout my baby and my baby's crazy 'bout me / I hadn't anyone till you / Cheatin' on me / You're driving me crazy / Loch lomond
CCD 4351 / Jul '88 / Concord Jazz

☐ MAXINE SULLIVAN 1944-1948
LEGENDCD 6004 / Dec '92 / Fresh Sound

☐ MAXINE SULLIVAN AT VINE STREET
I'm crazy 'bout my baby / Accentuate the positive / Say it with a kiss / Jeepers creepers / Old music master / Bob White / Personality
CDSW 8436 / Nov '92 / DRG

☐ MAXINE SULLIVAN CELEBRATES THE MUSIC OF HARRY WARREN
DAPCD 229 / Jan '93 / Audiophile

☐ QUEEN VOL.1, THE (Like Someone In Love)
CKS 3402 / Aug '97 / Kenneth

☐ QUEEN VOL.5, THE
What a difference a day makes / Until the real thing comes along / You were meant for me / I'm in the mood for love / You're driving me crazy / Thanks for the memory / Fine and dandy / Song is you / I don't stand a ghost of a chance with you / Should I / Very thought of you / There'll be some changes made / I hadn't anyone till you / After I say I'm sorry / Something to remember you by
CKS 3406 / Jun '94 / Kenneth

☐ SAY IT WITH A KISS
Stop you're breaking my heart / Loch Lomond / I'm coming Virginia / Annie Laurie / Blue skies / Easy to love / Folks who live on the hill / Nice work if you can get it / 'S wonderful / Moments like this / Please be kind / It was a lover and his lass / Dark eyes / Spring is here / Night and day / Kinda lonesome / Say it with a kiss / If I had a ribbon now / Molly Malone / Heart you stole from me / Every time we say goodbye / This heart of mine / Mad about the boy / I must have that man / I can't get started
JASMCD 2543 / Apr '97 / Jasmine

☐ SPRING IS NOT EVERYTHING
APCD 229 / '89 / Audiophile

☐ UPTOWN (Sullivan, Maxine & Scott Hamilton Quintet)
You were meant for me / I thought about you / Goody goody / Something to remember you by / Wrap your troubles in dreams (and dream your troubles away) / You're a lucky guy / Georgia on my mind / By myself / I got the right to sing the blues / Just one of those things
CCD 4288 / '85 / Concord Jazz

Sullivan, Tony

☐ CELTIC CREDENTIALS
HM 601CD / Aug '96 / Halshaw Music

Sultans

☐ CASUAL SEX IN THE CINEPLEX (Sultans Of Ping FC)
Back in a tracksuit / Indeed you are / Veronica / Two pints of rasa / Stupid kid / You talk too much / Give him a ball (and a yard of grass) / Karaoke queen / Let's go shopping / Kick me with your leather boots / Clitus Clarke
4724952 / Feb '93 / Epic

☐ GOOD YEAR FOR TROUBLE
ATHY 05CD / Aug '96 / Rhythm King

Sulzmann, Stan

☐ FEUDAL RABBITS
Elephant house / Spider / Feudal rabbits / Owens field / Feeling bettison / Review / Three quarters in the afternoon / Barry Diddle / Ken Blake - Ending
AHUM 011 / Nov '91 / Ah-Um

☐ NEVER AT ALL (Sulzmann, Stan & Marc Copland)
FMRCD 05 / Aug '82 / Future

☐ TREASURE TROVE (Sulzmann, Stan & Nikki Iles)
Since we met / Treasure trove / Story of a story / Little dog who loves the wood / Veils / Irish missed / I do it for your love / Poet / Midnight / Mtl
ASCCD 7 / Feb '96 / ASC

Sum

☐ I
CAI 2011 / 25 Jun '98 / Caipirinha

Sumac, Yma

☐ MAMBO AND MORE
CREV 048CD / Mar '97 / Rev-Ola

☐ VOICE OF THE XTABY AND OTHER DELIGHTS
CREV 034CD / Jul '95 / Rev-Ola

☐ YMA SUMAC
ECD 2116 / Jan '93 / Fresh Sound

Sumlin, Hubert

☐ BLUES ANYTIME
It's you baby / Love you woman / Every time I get to drinking / When I feel better / Blues anytime / I love / Levee camp moan / My babe / Hubert's blues / We gonna jump / Big legged woman / Too late for me to pray
ECD 260522 / Sep '94 / Evidence

☐ MY GUITAR AND ME
Happy with my french friends / Broke and hungry / Give the name Jacquot / My guitar and me / Groove / Easy, Hubert, easy / Don't forget / I wonder why / Broggin' all alone / Last boogie / I'll be home on Tuesday / Jerking in Paris
ECD 260452 / Mar '94 / Evidence

Summer, Daniel

☐ GLOBAL JOURNEY
M 45CD / Aug '96 / World Disc

Summer, Donna

☐ ANOTHER PLACE AND TIME
This time I know it's for real / I don't wanna get hurt / In another place and time / Whatever your heart desires / If it makes you feel good / When love takes over you / Only one / Sentimental / Breakaway / Love's about to change my heart
2559762 / Jan '89 / WEA

☐ ANTHOLOGY (2CD Set)
Love to love you baby / Could it be magic / Try me I know we can make it / Spring affair / Love's unkind / I feel love / Once upon a time / Rumour has it / I love you / Last dance / Macarthur Park / Heaven knows / Hot stuff / Bad girls / Dim all the lights / Sunset people
5181442 / Oct '93 / Casablanca

☐ BEST OF DONNA SUMMER, THE
I feel love / Macarthur park / Hot stuff / Wanderer / Love's unkind / On the radio / State of independence / Breakaway / Love is in control / Dinner with Gershwin / I don't wanna get hurt / This time I know it's for real / Love's about to change my heart
9031729092 / Nov '90 / WEA

☐ DONNA SUMMER
Love is in control / Mystery of love / Woman in me / State of independence / Livin' in America / Protection / (If it) hurts just a little / Love is just a breath away / Lush life
K2 99163 / Jul '82 / WEA

☐ DONNA SUMMER
12397 / Sep '94 / Laserlight

☐ ENDLESS SUMMER (The Best Of Donna Summer)
Melody of love (Wanna be loved) / Love to love you baby / Could it be magic / I feel love / Love's unkind / I love you / Last dance / MacArthur park / Hot stuff / Bad girls / No more tears (Enough is enough) / On the radio / Love is in control / State of independence / She works hard for the money / Unconditional love / This time I know it's for real / I don't wanna get hurt / Anyway at all
5262172 / 15 Sep '97 / Casablanca

☐ FOUR SEASONS OF LOVE
Spring affair / Summer fever / Autumn changes / Winter melody / Spring reprise
8262362 / Aug '91 / Casablanca

☐ FUNSTREET
Fun street / Shout it out / They can't take away our music / Nice to see you / Little marie / Back of boogaloo / Jeannie / Na na hey hey / Do what mother do
HADCD 196 / Nov '95 / Javelin

☐ I'M A RAINBOW
I believe (in you) / True love survives / You to me / Sweet emotion / Leave me alone / Melanie / Back where you belong / People talk / Turn the stone / Brooklyn / I'm a rainbow / Walk on (keep on movin') / Don't cry for me Argentina / Runner with the pack / Highway runner / Romeo / End of the week / I need time
5328692 / Nov '96 / Casablanca

☐ LOVE TO LOVE YOU BABY
Love to love you baby / Full of emptiness / Need-a-man blues / Whispering waves / Pandora's box / Full of emptiness (reprise)
8227922 / '93 / Casablanca

☐ LOVE TRILOGY
Try me I know we can make it better / Could it be magic / Wasted / Prelude to love / Come with me
8227932 / Feb '94 / Casablanca

☐ MISTAKEN IDENTITY
Get ethnic / Body talk / Work that magic / When love cries / Heaven's just a whisper away / Cry of a waking heart / Friends unknown / Fred Astaire / Say a little prayer / Mistaken identity / What is it you want / Let there be peace
9031751592 / Sep '91 / WEA

☐ SHOUT IT OUT
Fun Street / Little Marie / Shout it out / They can't take away our music / Back off boogaloo / Jeannie / Nice to see you / Na na hey hey / So what mothers do
CDBM 078 / Oct '89 / Blue Moon

Summer Hits

☐ BEACHES AND CANYONS
XARC 015 / Sep '97 / X-Mas

Summercamp

☐ PURE JUICE
Drawer / Nowhere near / Bright side / Pure juice / Should I walk away / Keep an eye on you / Play it by ear / Ninety nine / On her mind / Mountain size / Two shades of grey / With your blessing / Thing of the past
9362465282 / Aug '97 / Maverick

Summerfield, Saffron

☐ WHOSE LAND IS IT ANYWAY
My father was a carpenter / Sally free and easy / Small song for the world / Cruel mother / Farewell friends / Laszlo feher / Remember the days / Man on the Clapham omnibus / Seasons / Farmer, the fox and the rambler / Settlers
BHCD 9317 / Aug '94 / Brewhouse

Summers, Andy

☐ INVISIBLE THREADS (Summers, Andy & John Ethridge)
Broken brains / Moravia / Stoneless counts / Lolita / Nuages / Big gliss / Counting the days / Radiant lizards / Monk's mood / Archimedes / Heliotrope / Little transgressions
INAK 9024 / Jul '97 / In Akustik

☐ LAST DANCE OF MR.X, THE
Big thing / Three Marias / Strange earth / Afro blue / Last dance of Mr.X / Lonely woman / We see / Rumplestiltskin / Somnambulist / Footprints / Goodbye por pie hat
09026689372 / 6 Apr '98 / RCA Victor

☐ SYNAESTHESIA
CMPCD 1011 / Jan '96 / CMP

Summers, Gene

☐ SCHOOL OF ROCK 'N' ROLL
School of rock 'n' roll / Straight skirt / Nervous / Gotta lotta that / Twixteen / I'll never be lonely / Dance, dance, dance / Almost 12 O'clock / Alabama shake / Wine, wine, wine / I've had it / Leroy / Lover please / Mad mad world / Loco cat / Mr. Rock and roll / Floppin' / Turnip greens / Hey my baby / Baby are you kiddin' / You're gonna be sorry / Honey hush / Rock-a-boogie shake / Big blue diamonds / Rockin' Daddy / Who stole the marker / Blue Monday / Big river / Rebel Johnny yuma
CDCL 4420 / Aug '96 / Collector/White Label

Summit

☐ WEEDING THE CLIFF EDGE
SCANCD 19 / Oct '96 / Radarscope

Summit Meeting

☐ FULL OF LIFE
DRCD 205 / Jan '88 / Dragon

Summoning

☐ LUG BURZ
SPV 08423802 / Apr '95 / Napalm

Summumbonum

☐ DAVID DONSON
FFR 005CD / Feb '95 / Freek

Sumosonic

☐ THIS IS SUMO
CRECD 204 / 26 Jan '98 / Creation

SUN

☐ HYPNOTIKI
Xenon '88 / Dictorobotary / We love you / Spirality / LS dream / Vision / Hardware junky / Mezmorised / Hypnotiki / Big
OUTCD 003 / Jan '95 / Flat

Sun City Girls

☐ BOX OF CHAMELEONS (3CD Set)
ABTD 009 / 20 Oct '97 / ABTD

☐ TORCH OF THE MYSTICS
Blue mambo / Tarmac / Esoterica of Abyssynia / Space prophet dogon / Shining path / Flower / Cafe batik / Radar 1941 / Papa legba / Vinegar stroke / Burial in the sky
TUP 0442 / Oct '93 / Tupelo

☐ VALENTINES FROM THE MATAHARI
MAJ 7001 / 10 Nov '97 / Majora

Sun, David

☐ ETERNAL SPIRIT
CD 438 / 6 Jul '98 / New World

☐ TRANQUILITY
CD 204 / 6 Jul '98 / New World

Sun Electric

☐ 30.7.94 LIVE
Castor pollux / An atom of all suns / Northern lights no. 5
AMB 5938CD / Feb '95 / Apollo

☐ KITCHEN
UFO / Entrance / Pitcheon / Sarotti / R gent / Sonification / Up the drain / Osram 509 / Qwertz / Beauty o'locco / Licherfelde
RS 933CD / Nov '93 / R&S

☐ PRESENT
Spreewald / Stimpak / Eya / Parralax / Bagatto / Cristal bollore / Goldstruck / Quaila / Waitati post / Tassajara / Wassa / In vitro / Uschba
AMB 6943CD / 16 Feb '98 / Apollo

Sun Life Stanshawe Band

☐ AVONDALE
Avondale / Show me / Sorcerer's apprentice / Variations on a tyrolean song / Masaniello / Tom marches on / Prisms / From the shores of the mighty pacific / Angels guard thee
GRCD 41 / Nov '90 / Grasmere

Sun Project

☐ MACROPHAGE
EFA 028882 / 5 May '98 / Spirit Zone

Sun Ra

☐ ANGELS AND DEMONS AT PLAY/THE NUBIANS OF PLUTONIA (Sun Ra & His Myth Science Arkestra)
Tiny pyramids / Between two worlds / Music from the world tomorrow / Angels and demons at play / Urnack / Medicine for a nightmare / Call for all demons / Demon's lullaby / Plutonian nights / Golden lady / Star time / Nubia / Africa / Watusa / Aiethopia
ECD 220662 / Nov '93 / Evidence

☐ ATLANTIS (Sun Ra & His Arkestra)
Mu / Lemuria / Yucatan (Saturn version) / Yucatan (impulse version) / Bimini / Atlantis
ECD 220672 / Nov '93 / Evidence

☐ BIG UNIVERSE OF SUN RA, THE
KICJ 338 / 27 Apr '98 / King/Saturn

☐ BLUE DELIGHT
Blue delight / Out of nowhere / Sunrise / They dwell on other planes / Gone with the wind / Your guest is as good as mine / Nashira / Days of wine and roses
3952602 / Oct '94 / A&M

☐ CALLING PLANET EARTH (3CD Set)
3139776122 / 21 Apr '98 / FRD

☐ COSMIC TONES FOR MENTAL THERAPY
ECD 220362 / Nov '92 / Evidence

☐ DESTINATION UNKNOWN (Sun Ra & His Arkestra)
Carefree / Untitled (Echoes of the future) / Prelude to a kiss / Hocus pocus / Theme of the stargazers / Interstellar lo-ways / Calling planet earth / Satellites are spinning / 'S Wonderful / We travel the spaceways
ENJACD 70712 / Nov '94 / Enja

☐ FATE IN A PLEASANT MOOD/WHEN THE SUN COMES OUT (Sun Ra & His Myth Science Arkestra)
Others in their world / Space mates / Lights of a satelite / Distant stars / Kingdom of thunder / Fate in a pleasant mood / Ankhnation / Circe / Nile / Brazilian sun / We travel the spaceways / Calling planet earth / Dancing shadows / Rainmaker / When sun comes out / Dimensions in time
ECD 220682 / Nov '93 / Evidence

☐ FONDATION MAEGHT NIGHTS (Sun Ra & His Arkestra)
COD 006 / Mar '92 / Jazz View

☐ FUTURISTIC SOUNDS OF SUN RA, THE
Bassism / Of wounds and something / What's that / Where is tomorrow / Beginning / China gates / New day / Tapestry from an asteroid / Jet flight / Looking outward / Space jazz reverie
SV 0213 / May '98 / Savoy Jazz

☐ HOLIDAY FOR SOUL DANCE
ECD 220112 / May '92 / Evidence

☐ JAZZ IN SILHOUETTE
ECD 220122 / May '92 / Evidence

☐ LIVE AT THE HACKNEY EMPIRE (Sun Ra & The Year 2000 Myth Science Arkestra)
CDLR 214/5 / Feb '95 / Leo

☐ LIVE FROM SOUNDSCAPE (Sun Ra & His Arkestra)
DIW 388 / Feb '94 / DIW

☐ LIVE FROM SOUNDSCAPE/ POSSIBILITY OF ALTERED DESTINY (Sun Ra & His Arkestra)
DIW 388/2 / Feb '94 / DIW

☐ LIVE IN LONDON
BFFP 60CD / May '96 / Blast First

☐ LOVE IN OUTER SPACE (Sun Ra & His Arkestra)
CDLR 154 / Sep '88 / Leo

☐ MAGIC CITY, THE
Magic city / Shadow world / Abstract eye / Abstract 'I'
ECD 220692 / Nov '93 / Evidence

☐ MONORAILS AND SATELLITES
ECD 220132 / May '92 / Evidence

☐ MY BROTHER THE WIND VOL.2
ECD 220402 / Nov '92 / Evidence

☐ NIGHT IN EAST BERLIN, A (Sun Ra & His Cosmo Discipline Arkestra)
CDLR 149 / Sep '87 / Leo

☐ OTHER PLANES OF THERE
ECD 220372 / Nov '92 / Evidence

☐ OUT THERE A MINUTE
Love in outer space / Somewhere in space / Dark clouds with silver linings / Jazz and romantic sounds / When angels speak of love / Cosmo enticement / Song of tree and forest / Other worlds / Journey outward / Lights on a satelite / Starships and solar boats / Out there a minute
BFFP 42CD / Mar '89 / Blast First

☐ OUTER SPACEWAYS INCORPORATED
BLC 760191 / 1 Jun '98 / Black Lion

☐ QUIET PLACE IN THE UNIVERSE, A
CDLR 198 / Oct '94 / Leo

☐ SECOND STAR TO THE RIGHT (Salute To Walt Disney)
CDLR 230 / Oct '95 / Leo

☐ SINGLES, THE (2CD Set)
Foggy day / Daddy's gonna tell you no lie / Bye bye / Somebody's in love / Medicine for a nightmare / Saturn / Dreaming / Supersonic jazz / Happy New Year to you / It's Christmas time / Muck muck (matt matt) / Hot skillet Mama / Great balls of fire / Hours after / Teenager's letter of promises / I'm so glad you love me / Sun one / Sun man speaks / October / Adventure in space / Message to Earthman / State Street / Blue set / Big city blues / Tell her to come on home / I'm making believe / Bridge / Rocket no.9 / Blues on planet Mars / Saturn moon / Sky is crying / She's my baby / I'm gonna unmask the batman / I want an easy woman / Perfect man / Journey to Saturn / Enlightenment / Love in outer space / Disco 2100 / Sky blues / Rough house blues / Cosmo extensions / Quest / Outer space plateau
ECD 221642 / Oct '96 / Evidence

☐ SOUND OF JOY (Sun Ra & His Arkestra)
DD 414 / Dec '94 / Delmark

☐ SOUND SUN PLEASURE
ECD 220142 / May '92 / Evidence

☐ SPACE IS THE PLACE
It's after the end of the world / Under different stars / Discipline / Watusa / Calling planet Earth / I am the alter-destiny / Statelites are spinning / Cosmic forces / Outer spaceways incorporated / We travel the spaceways / Overseer / Blackman/Love in outer space / Mysterious crystal / I am the brother of the wind / We'll wait for you / Space is the place
ECD 220702 / Nov '93 / Evidence

☐ SPACE IS THE PLACE (Sun Ra Astro Intergalactic Infinity Arkestra)
Space is the place / Images / Discipline / Sea of sounds / Rocket number nine
IMP 12492 / 23 Mar '98 / Impulse Jazz

☐ SPACEWAYS INCORPORATED
BLCD 760191 / Feb '94 / Black Lion

☐ STARDUST FROM TOMORROW (2CD Set) (Sun Ra & His Intergalaxtic Arkestra)
CDLR 235/236 / May '97 / Leo

☐ SUN RA CAME DOWN TO THE EARTH
KICJ 315 / Nov '97 / King/Saturn

☐ SUN RA SEXTET AT THE VILLAGE VANGUARD
ROUCD 3124 / Jan '94 / Rounder

☐ SUN SONG
DD 411 / '84 / Delmark

☐ SUNRISE IN DIFFERENT DIMENSIONS
ARTCD 6099 / Dec '91 / Hat Art

☐ SUPER SONIC JAZZ (3CD Set)
ECD 220152 / May '92 / Evidence

☐ VISITS PLANET EARTH/ INTERSTELLAR LOW WAYS
ECD 220392 / Nov '92 / Evidence

☐ WE TRAVEL THE SPACE WAYS/BAD AND BEAUTIFUL
ECD 220382 / Nov '92 / Evidence

Sun Red Sun

☐ SUN RED SUN
I know a place / Hard life / Outrageous / Lock me up / Final curtain / Responsible / Deadly knightshade / Big understanding / Intoxication / How do you like those / Outrageous
SJPCD 018 / 6 Apr '98 / Angel Air

Sun Rhythm Section

☐ OLD TIME ROCK 'N' ROLL
Old time rock 'n' roll / Red hot / That's alright mama / Let it roll / Still rockin' / Don't send me no more drinks / You're a heartbreaker / Tutti frutti / Love my baby
CDMF 073 / Oct '89 / Magnum Force

Sun Sawed In Half

☐ FIZZY LIFT
NL 042 / 16 Feb '98 / Not Lame

Sunahara, Yoshinori

☐ CROSSOVER
MFRFM (Music For Robot For Music) / Stinger stingray / Whirlpool / Silver ripples / Long vowel / Huraloop / Muddy water / Elegant world / Clouds across the moon / Overtime work
BUNG 0322 / 26 Jan '98 / Bungalow

Sunamoto, Chiho

☐ MAMBO JAMBO
Moanin' / Ll'l darlin' / Misty / Jambo mambo / It's all right with me / Satin doll / Morning / In your eyes / Winter games / Birdland / Rhapsody in blue / Classics dance medley / Minute waltz (chopin) / Four seasons / Hungarian rhapsody / William tell overture (rossini) (galop and finale)
CDGRS 1248 / Feb '93 / Grosvenor

☐ TUXEDO JUNCTION
Over the rainbow / Tuxedo junction / Mas que nada / One note samba / Gentle rain / Tell me a bedtime story / Water fountain / Just in time / Go for it / Thunderbirds / Green dolphin street / Teach me tonight / Solveig's song / Waltz of the flowers / Chisai abi mitsuketa / Akimitsuketa / Yuyake koyake / Stars and stripes forever, the (sousa)
CDGRS 1233 / Feb '93 / Grosvenor

☐ WHAT'S NEW
Work song / When you wish upon a star / I'm beginning to see the light / What's new / One o'clock jump / Spring fairies / Colours of the wind / Do you know the way to San Jose / Speak low / Merry Christmas Mr. Lawrence / Alfie / Hard to say I'm sorry / Romeo and Juliet fantasy overture / Adagio / Warsaw concerto / Rhapsody on a theme by Paganini
CDGRS 1296 / May '97 / Grosvenor

Sunbeam

☐ OUT OF REALITY
CLP 9916 / Mar '97 / Hypnotic

Sunbrain

☐ GOOD SIDE
GROW 0142 / Jun '94 / Grass

Sunda

☐ MUSIQUE ET CHANTS CLASSIQUE (Music From Java)
C 580064 / Dec '95 / Ocora

Sunda Africa

☐ NO RISK NO FUN
Tanpa rintangan tak ada kegembiran / Tarian bidadari / Pengembara orang jipsi / Perjalanan ke India / Semua bersama-sama / Mengenang ilham leluhur / Rahasia rembulan / Raja / Khayalan yang tak dikenal / Sweet pain of sadness
CDORBD 095 / Apr '97 / Globestyle

Sunday Puncher

☐ LIVID EYE, THE
TB 007CD / 27 Oct '97 / Turnbuckle

Sundays

☐ BLIND
I feel / Goodbye / Life and soul / More / On earth / God made me / Love / What do you think / Twenty four hours / Blood on my hands / Medicine
CDPCSD 121 / Feb '94 / Parlophone

☐ READING, WRITING AND ARITHMETIC
Skin and bones / Here's where the story ends / Can't be sure / I won / Hideous towns / You're not the only one I know / Certain someone / I kicked a boy / My finest hour / Joy
CDPCS 7378 / May '96 / Parlophone

☐ STATIC AND SILENCE
Summertime / Homeward / Folk song / She / When I'm thinking about you / I can't wait / Another flavour / Leave this city / Your eyes / Cry / Monochrome
CDEST 2300 / 22 Sep '97 / Parlophone

Sunderland AFC

☐ ROKER ROAR (A Tribute To Sunderland AFC & Supporters) (Various Artists)
Sunderland all the way: *Sunderland AFC & Bobby Knoxall* / Gannin't Roker Park: *Ronnie Roker & The Black Cats* / Ticket fro the game: *Northeast* / Sunderland: *Fine Art* / Super Sunderland: *New City Sound* / Z Cars: *Rawlings, Brian Band* / Roker roar: *Hulme, Lloyd & The Supporters Squad* / Charley Hurley speaks: *Hurley, Charley* / Daydream believer: *Simply Red & White* / Ain't no stopping us now: *Sunderland AFC FA Cup Final Squad 1992* / Sunderland forever: *Universal* / Why can't you stay: *Shak Mad* / Dicky Ord song: *Simply Red & White* / We're the lads: *SR6* / Last roar at Roker: *ALS* / Twelve days of Sunderland: *Red & White Santas* / I left my heart in Roker Park: *Alfie*
CDGAFFER 18 / 6 Apr '98 / Cherry Red

Sundial

☐ ACID YANTRA
BBQCD 173 / Jun '95 / Beggars Banquet

☐ OTHER WAY OUT
UFO 1CD / Apr '91 / UFO

☐ OTHER WAY OUT
GAAS 2502 / Feb '97 / Clear Spot

☐ REFLECTOR
Reflecter / Easy for you / I don't mind / Slow motion / Tremelo / Never fade / Sunstroke / Mind train / Reflecter 2
UFO 008CD / Mar '92 / UFO

☐ RETURN JOURNEY
GAAS 2503 / Feb '97 / Clear Spot

Sundogs

☐ TO THE BONE
ROUCD 9044 / Apr '94 / Rounder

Sundown

☐ DESIGN 19
CMCD 77161 / Jun '97 / Century Media
CM 77194CD / 20 Oct '97 / Century Media

Sundowners

☐ BUSH TRACKS
8145742 / Mar '96 / Fable

Sunhouse

☐ CRAZY ON THE WEEKEND
Crazy on the weekend / Hurricaine / Chasing the dream / Spinning round the sun / Good day to die / Lips / Loud crowd / Monkey dead / Hard sun / Swing low / Animal
ISOM 4CD / 8 Jun '98 / Independiente

Sunkings

☐ HALL OF HEADS
GPRCD 7 / Aug '94 / GPR

☐ SOUL LIVING
BR 034CD / 7 Nov '97 / Blue Room

☐ SOUL SLEEPING
BR 044CD / 11 May '98 / Blue Room

Sunny

☐ COUNTRY PASSION
When love finds you / Power of love / How am I supposed to live without you / I'm still dancin' with you / Don't let love slip by / Little bit more / It's a heartache / Only one road / You cheated / Help me make it through the night / I've got to stay away from you / When I need you / Mention of your name / I want you completely / Love hurts / Why did I fall in love with you / (Everything I do) I do it for you
QED 173 / Nov '96 / Tring

Sunny Day Real Estate

☐ DIARY
SPCD 121302 / May '94 / Sub Pop

☐ SUNNY DAY REAL ESTATE
SPCD 316 / Nov '95 / Sub Pop

Sunnyland Blues Band

☐ MEAN DOG
Run for cover / Big easy woman / Fall to pieces / Time to think gain / Carry me / Helpless / Can't fight what you can't see / Move along / Pull me under / Dust my broom / Little by little / Bang for the buck / Little eden
INAK 9044 / Jul '97 / In Akustik

Sunnyland Slim

☐ CHICAGO JUMP (Sunnyland Slim Blues Band)
You used to love me / Halsted Street jump / Cryin' for my baby / Give you all my money / Calling out / I feel so bad / Got to stop this mess / From afar / Never picked no cotton / Chicago jump / Jammin' with Sam
ECD 26067 / Jul '95 / Evidence

☐ DECORATION DAY (Sunnyland Slim Blues Band)
Sun is going down / Past life / Decoration day / Boogie 'n' the blues / Depression blues / Tired of travelling / Canadian walk / Patience like Job / Sunnyland jump / Rock little Daddy / Every time I get to drinking / Sunnyland's New Orleans boogie / One room country shack / Tin pan alley / Dust my broom
ECD 260532 / Sep '94 / Evidence

☐ HOUSE RENT PARTY
I'm just a lonesome man / Sad old Sunday (Mother's Day) / Boogie man / Hard time (when Mother's gone) / Chicago woman / I'm in love / Bad times (cost of living) / Nervous breakdown / It keeps rainin' / Brown skin woman / Old age has got me / That's alright Mama / Sad old Sunday / I'm just a lonesome man / Bad times
DD 655 / Mar '97 / Delmark

☐ SUNNYLAND TRAIN
Sunnyland train / Be my baby / Sometime I worry / Decoration day / All my life / Tin pan alley / Unlucky one / Pinetop's boogie woogie / Worried about my baby / Highway 61 / Backwater blues / Sad and lonesome / She used to love me / Sittin' here thinkin' / I feel so good / Patience like Job / Goin' down slow
ECD 26066 / Jul '95 / Evidence

Suns Of Arqa

☐ CRADLE
CDE 04D / 23 Feb '98 / Arka Sound

☐ JAGGERNAUT WHIRLING DUB
Bilawal / Yaman kalyan / Misra pahvadi / Bhairavi / Bhupali
ARKA 2103CD / 8 Jun '98 / Arka Sound

☐ REMIXES (2CD Set)
EBSC 010 / 25 May '98 / Echo Beach

☐ SHABDA
Tomorrow never knows / There is no danger here / Bharavi alap / Through the gate we go / Bharavi live / Pure reality / Great invocation / Basant alap / Basant dhrupad / Beyond the beyond / Great unique / Waterloo / Fire of life / Hear the call
ARKA 2109CD / 8 Jun '98 / Arka Sound

Sunscreem

☐ 03
Portal / Pressure / B / Doved up / Love u more / Perfect motion / Chasing dreams / Your hands / Idaho / Walk on / Broken English / Release me / Psycho
4722182 / Sep '96 / Sony Soho2

☐ CHANGE OR DIE
Exodus / Ice screems / Something / When / Syclick / For maddened prophets / Looking at you / No angel / Secrets / Cheng cheng / White skies / Be of good heart
4813132 / Mar '96 / Sony Soho2

Sunset Heights
☐ TEXAX TEA
KGBCD 1 / Oct '94 / KGB

Sunset Stampede
☐ SUNSET STAMPEDE
WWRCD 6003 / Jun '95 / Wienerworld

Sunset Yellow
☐ AFTER SUNSET
CLP 9939 / Mar '97 / Hypnotic

Sunshine Kids
☐ TUBED
VOW 054CD / Feb '96 / Voices Of Wonder

Sunshine, Monty
☐ GOTTA TRAVEL ON
You tell me your dream / Pretty baby / Sleep my little Prince / Down in Honky Tonk Town / Goin' home / Martha / Sheikh of Araby / Careless love / Wise guy / Pallet on the floor / Gotta travel on / Burgundy St. Blues / Joe Avery's blues
CDTTD 570 / Nov '91 / Timeless Traditional

☐ GREAT MOMENTS WITH MONTY SUNSHINE
Sleep my little prince / Gotta travel on / Sheik of Araby / Old rugged cross / South / Bill Bailey won't you please come home / Isle of Capri / Weary blues / Savoy blues / If I had my life to live over / Just a closer walk with thee / Wreck of the old ninety seven / Dinah / You are my sunshine / Wildcat blues / Lover / Magnolia's wedding day
WWJ 3006 / 27 Apr '98 / World Wide Jazz

☐ IN LONDON
BLCD 760508 / Oct '93 / Black Lion

☐ JUST A CLOSER WALK WITH THEE
Weary blues / Old rugged cross / Salutation march / Spinning wheel / Savoy blues / Moose march / If I had my life to live over / East coast trot / Just a closer walk with thee / Marie / Chimes blues / Wreck of the old '97 / Does jesus care / Dinah / Saratoga swing
CDTTD 592 / Aug '95 / Timeless Traditional

☐ JUST A LITTLE WHILE TO STAY HERE (Sunshine, Monty Jazz Band)
Just a little while to stay here / Postman's lament / South / Old stag-o-lee blues / Ole Miss rag / My old Kentucky home / Jambalaya / Lily of the valley / You always hurt the one you love / Ma, he's making eyes at me / When I move to the sky / Corinne Corinna / Black cat on a fence / There's yes yes in your eyes
LACD 70 / Oct '96 / Lake

☐ NEW ORLEANS HULA (Great British Traditional Jazzband Vol.3) (Sunshine, Monty Jazz Band)
You tell me your dream / Wabash blues / In the sweet bye and bye / Beale street mama / New orleans hula / Memphis blues / Gettysburg march / When I grow too old to dream / Wildcat blues / Wise guy / Snag it / Bugle boy march / Far away blues / Magnolia's wedding day
LACD 47 / May '95 / Lake

☐ SOUTH (Sunshine, Monty Jazz Band)
It's tight like that / Memphis blues / Ice cream / Wabash blues / All the girls / South / Bill Bailey, won't you please come home / Bugle boy march / Ups and downs / Carry me back to old virginity / If I ever cease to love / Isle of Capri / When I grow too old to dream
CDTTD 583 / Jun '94 / Timeless Traditional

Sunship
☐ SUNSHIP
FILT 017CD / Apr '97 / Filter

Sunshot
☐ CAUGHT IN THE ACT OF ENJOYING OURSELVES
Nasties / She says / Big mistake / Stop me / Baby doll / Happy ever after / Play time / Twisting / Lose my grip / Brainstorm / Tank
DVAC 005 CD / Sep '92 / Deva

☐ IRON BALL DIRECTION
Nasties / Baby doll / Kill or be killed / Big mistake / Tank / She says / Lose my grip / Sally's ladders / Play time / Happy ever after
DVAC 007 / Jun '93 / NMC

Sunt
☐ TWEEZ
TG 138D / May '93 / Touch & Go

Suoni Moderni
☐ BEST OF MARC VOL.4
IRMA 481570CD / 13 Jul '98 / Irma

Suonsaari, Klaus
☐ REFLECTING TIMES (Suonsaari, Klaus Quintet)
STCD 4125 / Feb '89 / Storyville

☐ SOMETHING IN COMMON
Ritual / Jaska / Motion / Song for SR / Inseperable / Burning bridges / Serenity / Miles apart / Jab / If I were a bell / Happy people
STCD 4218 / 9 Mar '98 / Storyville

Sup
☐ ROOM 7
HOLY 030CD / 24 Nov '97 / Holy

Supahead
☐ CAULK
TOODAMNHY 42 / Feb '95 / Too Damn Hype

Super
☐ RENDEZVOUS WITH SUPER
Caramba wax / Girls go bravo / Bingo hostess goes beserk / People's democratic movement / Proposal / Misty hours / Tempted / True gentleman / Travelogue / Historical sights / Wicky wacky rodeo / Coup de soleil
ODOR 10 / 2 Mar '98 / Spinefarm

Super 400
☐ SUPER 400
TRDCD 1005 / 13 Jul '98 / Trade 2

Super 5 Thor
☐ FORD
ECHO 101 / Apr '97 / Echo Static

☐ GAZELLE
ECHO 103 / Jun '97 / Echo Static

Super Cat
☐ SI BOOPS DEH
WRCD 0021 / Nov '95 / Techniques

☐ STRUGGLE CONTINUES, THE
Dance / Girlstown / Turn / Warning / Forgive me Jah / My girl Josephine / 'A' Class rub-a-dub / Too greedy / South central / Ready back / Every nigger is a star / Settlement / I hear dem seh
4772922 / Oct '95 / Columbia

Super Deluxe
☐ FAMOUS
TK95CD 106 / 16 Feb '98 / Tim Karr

Super Discount
☐ SUPER DISCOUNT (The Album) (Various Artists)
Le patron est devenu fou: Minos Pour Main Basse (Sur La Ville) / Prix choc: De Crecy, Etienne / Super disco: Alex Gopher / Soldissimo: Air / Affaires a faire: La Chatte Rouge / Tout doit disparaitre: Minos Pour Main Basse (Sur La Ville) / Tout a 10 balles: DJ Tall / Liquidation totale: De Crecy, Etienne / Les 10 jours fous: Mooloodjee / Destoskage massif: Alex Gopher / Fermeture definitive: Mr. Learn
DIF 002CD / Mar '97 / Different

Super Furry Animals
☐ FUZZY LOGIC
God show me magic / Fuzzy birds / Something for the weekend / Frisbee / Hometown unicorn / Gathering moss / If you don't want me to destroy you / Bad behaviour / Mario man / Hangin' with Howard Marks / Long gone / For now and ever
CRECD 190 / May '96 / Creation

☐ RADIATOR
CRECD 214 / 25 Aug '97 / Creation

Super Rail Band
☐ MANSA
Silanide / Mansa / Kamalimba / Niamatoutou kono / Tolonte sebessa / Dounia / Kanou sale / Fourou kilon
LBLC 2520 / May '96 / Indigo

☐ NEW DIMENSIONS IN RAIL CULTURE (Super Rail Band of the Buffet de la Gare de Bamako, Mali)
Foliba / Bedianamogo / Tallassa / Konowale / Mali yo
CDORB 001 / Jul '90 / Globestyle

Super Star
☐ GREATEST HITS VOL.1
Barfly / Reason why / She's got everything I own / Let's get lost / Taste / After taste
CRECD 134 / May '96 / Creation

Superalmendrado
☐ GOTTA GIVE IT UP
DEDD 003CD / Feb '95 / Dedicated

Superbilk
☐ KONFITURE
TR 30060052 / 25 May '98 / Trocadero

☐ SUPERBILK
TR 30060012 / 29 Jun '98 / Trocadero

Supercharger
☐ GOES WAY OUT
ES 127CD / Jun '96 / Estrus

☐ SATURDAY NIGHT SPECIAL
Widemouth / Funkey dollar bill / Fuck the quality feel the width / Street gold baby / Ready to explode / Saturday night special / Pressure point / This punk's gonna self destruct / Dead Presidents / Tick like a bomb / Teenage gold / Rock the disco
ZEN 018CDN / 3 Aug '98 / Indochina

☐ SUPERCHARGER
ES 1240CD / Sep '97 / Estrus

☐ WALL TO WALL MOUSTACHE
Supercharger / We rock / Jim'll fix it / Boomer / Spacemaker deluxe / Airport '77 / Bouffant sisters / Return of the red eye / Filters / Wall to wall
ZEN 012CD / Jul '97 / Indochina

Superchunk
☐ ALBUM
EFA 049662 / Oct '95 / City Slang

☐ FOOLISH
Like a fool / First part / Water wings / Driveway to driveway / Saving my ticket / Kicked in / Why do you have to put a date on everything / Without blinking / Keeping track / Revelations / Stretched out / In a stage whisper
EFA 049382 / Apr '94 / City Slang

☐ INCIDENTAL MUSIC 1991-1995
EFA 049592 / Jul '95 / City Slang

☐ INDOOR LIVING
Unbelievable things / Burn last Sunday / Marquee / Watery hands / No bruises / Every single instinct / Song for Marion Brown / Popular music / Under our feet / European medicine / Martini's on the roof
EFA 049972 / 15 Sep '97 / City Slang

☐ ON THE MOUTH
Precision auto / From the curve / For tension / Mower package thief / Swallow that / I guess I remembered it wrong / New low / Untied / Question is how fast / Trash heap / Flawless / Only piece that you get
EFA 04915262 / Jan '93 / City Slang

Superconductor
☐ HIT SONGS FOR GIRLS
Scootin' / There goes Helen / For Kelly Freas / Nobody's cutie / Thorsen's eleven / Come on hot dog / E-Z bake oven / Lordy / I'm gonna knock your block off allstar / Feedbackin'
TUP 0482 / Aug '93 / Tupelo

Supereal
☐ ELIXIR
Body medusa / Aquaplane / Blue beyond belief / Mass motion / I almost love you / Terminal high rip / United state of love / One nation
GRCD 005 / Nov '92 / Guerilla

Supergrass
☐ I SHOULD COCO
CDPCS 7373 / May '95 / Parlophone

☐ IN IT FOR THE MONEY
In it for the money / Richard III / Tonight / Late in the day / G-song / Sun hits the sky / Going out / It's not me / Cheapskate / You can see me / Hollow little reign / Sometimes I make you sad
CDPCS 7388 / Jun '97 / Parlophone

Supergroove
☐ TRACTION
74321218462 / Oct '95 / RCA

Superior
☐ BEHIND
Truth ain't kind / Why / Tomorrow's eve / Nades / Escape from reality / Dreamtime / Tainted silence / Total void / Until the end
TT 00262 / Nov '96 / T&T

Supermodel
☐ CLUMBA MAR
FIRECD 56 / Apr '96 / Fire

Supermodel GT
☐ POPCALYPSE NOW
NOIR 007CD / 27 Apr '98 / God Bless

Supermorris
☐ MR. SLAM
RN 0030 / Nov '94 / Runn

Supernaturals
☐ IT DOESN'T MATTER ANYMORE
Please be gentle with me / Smile / Glimpse of the light / Lazy lover / I wish I was passed away / Dung beetle / Stammer / I don't think so / Pie in the sky / Day before yesterday's man / Prepeare to land / Trees
FOODCD 21 / Jun '97 / Food

☐ TUNE A DAY, A
You take yourself too seriously / Monday mornings / Submarine song / I wasn't built to get up / Country music / Motorcycle parts / Sheffield song / VW song / Idiot / Magnet / Still got that feeling / Let me know / It doesn't matter anymore / Everest
8568932 / 10 Aug '98 / Food

Supernova
☐ AGES 3 AND UP
ARRCD 65008 / Nov '95 / Amphetamine Reptile

Supersnazz
☐ DEVIL YOUTH BLUES, THE
TBI 35CD / May '97 / Time Bomb

Superstar
☐ 18 CARAT
CFAB 001CD / Mar '97 / Camp Fabulous

☐ PALM TREE
Monstermind / Superstar / Breathing space / Sparkle / Every day I fall apart / Once again / Palm tree / And when the morning comes / Two of a kind / Life is elsewhere / Teacher
CFAB 005XCD / 27 Apr '98 / Camp Fabulous

Supersuckers
☐ LA MANO CORUNDA
Creepy jackalope eye / Seventeen poles / High ya / On the couch / Clueless / Sugla / Mudhead / Gold top / How to maximize your kill count / I was born without a spine / Glad, damn glad / She's my bitch / Schmooze
SPCD 120301 / Apr '94 / Sub Pop

☐ MUST'VE BEEN HIGH
SPCD 380 / 8 Sep '97 / Sub Pop

☐ SACRILICIOUS
SPCD 303 / Sep '95 / Sub Pop

☐ SONGS ALL SOUND THE SAME, THE
EFA 11351 / Jul '92 / Musical Tragedies

Supertones
☐ SUPERTONES STRIKE BACK
BED 7401CD / 13 Apr '98 / BEC

Supertouch
☐ EARTH IS FLAT, THE
REV 021CD / Apr '92 / Revelation

Supertramp
☐ BREAKFAST IN AMERICA
Gone Hollywood / Logical song / Goodbye stranger / Breakfast in America / Oh darling / Take the long way home / Lord is it mine / Just another nervous wreck / Casual conversation / Child of vision
3937082 / May '97 / A&M

☐ CRIME OF THE CENTURY
School / Bloody well right / Hide in your shell / Asylum / Dreamer / Rudy / If everyone was listening / Crime of the century
3936472 / May '97 / A&M

☐ CRISIS, WHAT CRISIS
Easy does it / Sister moonshine / Ain't nobody but me / Soapbox opera / Another man's woman / Lady / Poor boy / Just a normal day / Meaning / Two of us
3945602 / May '97 / A&M

☐ EVEN IN THE QUIETEST MOMENTS
Give a little bit / Loverboy / Even in the quietest moments / Downstream / Babaji / From now on / Fool's overture
3946342 / May '97 / A&M

☐ FAMOUS LAST WORDS
Crazy / Put on your old brown shoes / It's raining again / Bonnie / Know who you are / My kind of lady / C'est le bon / Waiting so long / Don't leave me now
3937322 / May '97 / A&M

☐ INDELIBLY STAMPED
Your poppa don't mind / Travelled / Rosie had everything planned / Remember / Forever / Potter / Coming home to see you / Times have changed / Friend in need / Aries
3931292 / 2 Feb '98 / A&M

☐ SUPERTRAMP SONGBOOK, THE
From now on / Crime of the century / Hide in your shell / School / Dreamer / You started laughing / It's raining again / My kind of lady / Take the long way home / Goodbye stranger / Logical song / Give a little bit / Breakfast in america / Fool's overture
CCV 8919 / Apr '94 / Compact Club

☐ VERY BEST OF SUPERTRAMP, THE
39709125 / 15 Sep '97 / PolyGram TV

Supor Aeternus
☐ EHJEH ASCHER EHJEH
Ehjeh ascher ehjeh
EFA 015692 / Jun '96 / Apocalyptic Vision

Supperheads

☐ DINNER
On/off / Life bloody life / King Kong gang / Sweet nothings / Bang bang boom / Coffee girl / Valentine / Revolution / My green eyed monster / Lunar orbiter
RODO 002 / 16 Feb '98 / Odor/ Spinefarm

Supreme Chord Jesters

☐ HUNGRY FOR THE WORD
SCAT 1CD / Jul '96 / Scat

☐ PLAYGROUND
SCAT 3CD / Jul '96 / Scat

Supreme Dicks

☐ WORKINGMAN'S DICK
FFR 002CD / Aug '94 / Freek

Supremes

☐ HITS, THE
Stop in the name of love / Nathan Jones / Where did our love go / He's my man / Baby love / Love child / Someday we'll be together / Happening / Stoned love / Reflections / You can't hurry love / Automatically sunshine / I hear a symphony / Touch / Back in my arms again / Up the ladder to the roof / I guess I'll miss the man / My world is empty without you / I'm gonna let my heart do the walking / You keep me hangin' on
307742 / Jun '97 / Hallmark

Surf Creatures

☐ X-50
WIGCD 011 / Nov '96 / Alopecia

Surf Rats

☐ TROUBLES/STRAIGHT BETWEEN THE EYES
LMCD 1569 / 23 Mar '98 / Lost Moment

Surf Trio

☐ CURSE OF THE SURF TRIO
95030CD / Jun '97 / Blood Red Discs

☐ SAFARI IN A LIVING GRAVEYARD
BRCD 5002 / Mar '97 / Blood Red Discs

☐ SHOOK OUTTA SHAPE
SGCD 3 / Sep '97 / September Gurls

☐ SURF TRIO, THE
SGCD 2 / Sep '97 / September Gurls

Surface Of The Earth

☐ MUKWEP
HERMES 021 / Apr '97 / Corpus Hermeticum

Surfaris

☐ FUN CITY USA/WIPE OUT
REP 4118 / Aug '91 / Repertoire

☐ SURF PARTY
Wipeout / Tequila / Shake n' stomp / Surfer Joe / Point panic / Pipeline / Summertime blues / Surfbeat / Misirolu
GNPD 2239 / Aug '95 / GNP Crescendo

Surfin' Lungs

☐ HANG LOOSE
ACORDL 01 / 6 Nov '97 / Beechwood

Surgeon

☐ BALANCE
74321569992 / 25 May '98 / Filth

☐ BASIC TONAL VOCABULARY
74321473142 / Jun '97 / Tresor

☐ COMMUNICATIONS
DNCD 001 / Jun '97 / Downwards

Surgery

☐ SHIMMER
Bootywhack / Off the A list / Shimmer / Vibe out / Mr. Scientist / Low cut blues / D-Nice / Gulf coast / Nilla waif / Didn't I know you once / No l pistola
756782579 / '94 / East West

☐ TRIM, 9TH WARD HIGH ROLLER
ARRCD 35/225 / Jun '93 / Amphetamine Reptile

Surman, John

☐ ADVENTURE PLAYGROUND
Only yesterday / Figfoot / Quadraphonic question / Twice said once / Duet for no one / As if we knew / Twisted roots / Duet for one / Seven
5119812 / Sep '92 / ECM

☐ AMAZING ADVENTURES OF SIMON SIMON
Nestor's saga (the tale of the ancient) / Buccaneers / Kentish hunting (Lady Margaret's air) / Pilgrim's way (to the seventeenth walls) / Within the halls of Neptune / Phoenix and the fire / Fide et amore (by faith and love) / Merry pranks (the jester's song) / Fitting epitaph
8291602 / Aug '86 / ECM

☐ BIOGRAPHY OF REV ABSALOM DAWE
First light / Countess journeys / Monastic calling / Druid's circle / 'Twas but piety / Three aspects / Long narrow road / Wayfarer / Far corners / An image
5237492 / Sep '97 / ECM

☐ BRASS PROJECT, THE
Returning exile / Coastline / New one two / Special motive / Wider vision / Silent lake / Mellstock quire tantrum clangley / All for a shadow
5173622 / May '93 / ECM

☐ PROVERBS AND SONGS
Prelude / Sons / Kings / Wisdom / Job / No twilight / Pride / Proverbs / Abraham arise
5377992 / 13 Oct '97 / ECM

☐ ROAD TO SAINT IVES
Polperro / Tintagel / Trethevy quoit / Rame head / Mevagissey / Lostwithiel / Perranporth / Bodmin moor / Kelly Bray / Piperspool / Marazion / Bedruthan steps
8438492 / Oct '90 / ECM

☐ STORAAS NORDIC QUARTET
Traces / Unwritten letter / Offshore piper / Gone to the dogs / Double trouble / Ved sorevatn / Watching shadows / Illusions / Wild bird
5271202 / Mar '95 / ECM

☐ STRANGER THAN FICTION
Parce mihi domine / Primo tempore / Sanctus / Regnantem sempiterna / O salutaris hostia / Procedentem ponsorum / Pulcherrima rosa / Parce mihi domine / Beata viscera / De spineto nata rosa / Credo / Ave maris stella / Virgo flagellatur / Oratio Ieremiae / Parce mihi domine
5218502 / Sep '94 / ECM

☐ SURMAN FOR ALL SAINTS
Round the round / Twelve alone / Electric plunger / Cascadence / Walls / Satisfied air / Matador / Saints alive / Barcarolle
8254072 / Jan '89 / ECM

☐ UPON REFLECTION
Edges of illusion / Filigree / Caithness to Kerry / Beyond a shadow / Prelude and rustic dance / Lamp fighter / Following behind / Constellation
8254722 / '82 / ECM

Surman, Martin

☐ LIVE AT WOODSTOCK TOWN HALL (Martin, Stu & John Surman)
Harry Lovett - Man without a country / Are you positive you're negative / Wrested in mustard / Professor Goodly's implosion machine / Master of disaster / Don't leave me like this
BGOCD 290 / Nov '95 / Beat Goes On

Surprise Package

☐ FREE UP
FLASH 57 / 1 Jun '98 / Flash

Surrealists

☐ HEY BELIEVER
GRCD 349 / May '97 / Glitterhouse

Suso, Foday Musa

☐ DREAMTIME, THE
CMPCD 3001 / 30 Mar '98 / CMP

Suso, Jali Nyama

☐ ART OF THE KORA, THE
C 5580027 / Aug '96 / Ocora

Suso, Salieu

☐ GRIOT
LYRCD 7418 / Aug '93 / Lyrichord

Suspiral

☐ GREAT AND SECRET SHOW, THE
NIGHTCD 007 / Nov '95 / Nightbreed

Suspiria

☐ PRIMITIVE ATTENTIONS
NIGHTCD 017 / 27 Oct '97 / Nightbreed

Sussed

☐ ALL HAIL THE YOUNG ASSASSINS
GOODCD 13 / Sep '94 / Dead Dead Good

Sutch, Screaming Lord

☐ LIVE MANIFESTO
Roll over Beethoven / Jenny Jenny / Keep a knocking / Long tall Sally / I'm a hog for you baby / Bonie Maronie / Johnny B. Goode / Whole lotta shakin' / Good golly Miss Molly / Jack the ripper / All black and hairy / Bye bye Johnny
JETCD 1004 / Feb '98 / Jet

☐ ROCK AND HORROR
Scream and scream / All black and hairy / Jack the ripper / Monster rock / Rock and shock / Murder in the graveyard / London rocker / Penny penny / Rockabilly madman / Oh well / Loonabilly / Go Berry go
CDCHM 65 / Jul '91 / Ace

Sutherland Brothers

☐ LIFEBOAT
Lady like you / Lifeboat / Where do we go wrong / Ireland / All I got is you / Space hymn / Change the wind / Sailing / Love is my religion / Real love
4894502 / 28 Mar '98 / Columbia

☐ REACH FOR THE SKY (Sutherland Brothers & Quiver)
When the train comes / Dirty city / Arms of Mary / Something special / Love on the moon / Ain't too proud / Dr. Dancer / Reach for the sky / Moonlight lady / Mad trail
4805262 / May '95 / Columbia

Sutherland, Madge

☐ HOME FREE
CDJMI 2100 / Dec '95 / Jahmani

Sutherland, Nadine

☐ NADINE
VPCD 1500 / 18 Aug '97 / VP

Sutra

☐ MUMURES
Reflechir la lumiere / Touch the water / Tricky situation / Victime violent / VTL / Landing / La brulure de bruit / Dog food fetiches / Victime mad / Suicide / Victimes nothing
THECD 109 / 6 Apr '98 / Other

Sutton, Ralph

☐ ALLIGATOR CRAWL
SACD 92 / Feb '93 / Solo Art

☐ AT CAFE DES COPAINS
SKCD 2036 / Dec '97 / Sackville

☐ EASY STREET (Sutton, Ralph & Bob Barnard)
SKCD 2040 / Jul '96 / Sackville

☐ ECHOES OF SWING (The Complete Hamburg Concert/2CD Set) (Sutton, Ralph & The All Stars)
NHCD 038 / Nov '97 / Nagel Heyer

☐ EYE OPENER
Rippling waters / Viper's drag / Memories of you / Gone with the wind / June night / Old fashioned love / Cottage for sale / When I grow too old to dream / Clothes line ballet
SACD 122 / Mar '97 / Solo Art

☐ JAMMIN' AT RUDI'S (Sutton, Ralph & Pops Foster/Bob Wilber)
JCD 262 / Jun '96 / Jazzology

☐ LIVE AT MAYBECK RECITAL HALL VOL.30
Honeysuckle rose / In a mist / Clothes line ballet / In the dark / Ain't misbehavin' / Echo of Spring / Dinah / Love lies / Russian lullaby / St. Louis blues / Viper's drag / After you've gone
CCD 4586 / Dec '93 / Concord Jazz

☐ LIVE AT SUNNIE'S RENDEZVOUS (Sutton, Ralph Trio)
STCD 8288 / May '97 / Storyville

☐ MORE SOLO PIANO
SKCD 22036 / Aug '94 / Sackville

☐ PARTNERS IN CRIME (Sutton, Ralph & Bob & Len Barnard)
Swing that music / One morning in May / Old folks / Rain / I never knew / Slow boat to China / 'S wonderful / How can you face me / West End avenue blues / Diga diga doo
SKCD 22023 / Jun '93 / Sackville

☐ RALPH SUTTON & KENNY DAVERN (Sutton, Ralph & Kenny Davern)
That's a plenty / Old fashioned love / Jazz me blues / Am I blue / St. Louis blues / Black and blue / Take me to the land of jazz / All by myself / My honey's loving arms / T'ain't nobody's business if I do / My daddy rocks me / I would do most anything for you / Sweet Lorraine / Memphis blues / Porter's love song to a chambermaid
CRD 208 / 6 Jul '98 / Chiaroscuro

☐ RALPH SUTTON 1975 SOLO SIDES
Love lies / Eye opener / Echoes of spring / Morning / In the dark / Viper's drag / Cottage for sale / Old folks / T'ain't so honey, t'ain't so / Honeysuckle rose / Handful of keys / Somebody stole my gal / Ain't misbehavin' / Keeping out of mischief / My fate is in your hands / Alligator crawl / I found a new baby
FLYCD 911 / Jul '96 / Flyright

☐ RALPH SUTTON QUARTET, THE
STCD 8243 / Jan '97 / Storyville

☐ RALPH SUTTON QUARTET/TRIO
STCD 8210 / Jul '96 / Storyville

☐ SUNDAY SESSION (Sutton, Ralph & Milt Hinton/Butch Miles)
SKCD 2044 / Jul '96 / Sackville

Sutton, Tierney

☐ INTRODUCING TIERNEY SUTTON
Old country / You're nearer / Song is you / In love in vain / It never entered my mind / Caravan / I've never been in love before / Morning sun / My heart stood still / High wire / I'm a fool to want you / Footprints / My favourite things / If I were a bell / In the wee small hours of the morning
AL 73111 / Dec '97 / A

Sutton-Curtis, Barbara

☐ OLD FASHIONED LOVE
SKCD 2042 / Dec '97 / Sackville

☐ SOLO & DUETS (Sutton-Curtis, Barbara & Ralph Sutton)
SKCD 22027 / Jun '93 / Sackville

Suzuki, Damo

☐ VERNISSAGE
Date line today/yesterday / Ballad of a diver / Don't forget ya job / Weekend paradise
DNW 007 / 22 Jun '98 / CDS

Suzuki, Yoshio Chin

☐ MORNING PICTURE
Our sunday morning / What do you do when it's spring / Kane / Dancing snow / Meet me in the sheep meadow / Valpolicella / September walk / Bagel / Morning picture / Mirage
JD 3306 / Jul '88 / JVC

Svart Parad

☐ SVART PARAD 1984-1986
FINNREC 012 / Sep '96 / Distortion

Svelt

☐ SOUVENIR
TR 30060022 / 5 May '98 / Trocadero

Sven Gali

☐ IN WIRE
What you give / Keeps me down / Worms / Make me / Red moon / Tired of listening / Shallow truth / Rocking chair / Helen / Who said
74321282112 / May '95 / RCA

☐ SVEN GALI
Under the influence / Tie dyed skies / Sweet little gypsy in my garden / Freaxz / Love don't live here anymore / Stiff competition / Real thing / Whisper in the rain / Twenty five hours a day / Here today, gone tomorrow / Disgusture
74321114422 / Mar '93 / RCA

Svenne & Lotta

☐ VERY BEST OF SVENNE & LOTTA, THE
Sandy / Do you wanna dance medley / Can't stop myself from loving you / Little yellow aeroplane / Breaking up is hard to do / Bang a boomerang / All I have to do is dream / If we only had the time / Dance while the music still goes on / Tell Laura I love her / Save the last dance for me / Chapel of love / Extra extra read all about it / Let it be me / Be my baby / Take good care of my baby
10262 / Oct '97 / Go On Deluxe

Svuci, Kalsijki

☐ BOSNIAN BREAKDOWN
Oho ho sto je liepo / Ja te cekam milice / Crven fesic / Komsinice mila moja / Frula svira kosu kujem / Ramino kolo / Ako zelis mene / Inoco moja krivdoco / Vidate posta / Sanden puta lola se ozenio / Sota
CDORB 074 / Jan '92 / Globestyle

SW Storm

☐ NO FEAR
SWSCD 002 / 12 Jan '98 / SW Storm

SWA

☐ EVOLUTION 1985-1987
SST 157CD / Aug '88 / SST

☐ VOLUME
SST 282CD / May '93 / SST

☐ WINTER
SST 238CD / Mar '89 / SST

Swains

☐ ELECTRIC SOUL
KK 068CD / Jun '92 / KK

☐ SONIC MIND JUNCTION
KK 097 / Nov '93 / KK

Swainson, Neil

☐ FORTY NINTH PARALLEL (Swainson, Neil Quintet)
Forty ninth parallel / Port of Spain / Southern exposure / On the lam / Don't hurt yourself / Homestretch
CCD 4396 / Nov '89 / Concord Jazz

Swaleh, Zuhura

☐ JINO LA PEMBE (Swaleh, Zuhura & Maulidi Musical Party)
Shani / Bado basi / Safari / Singetema / Kisu chako / Humvui alovikwa / Parare / Jino la pembe / Nalia na jito / Mdudu
CDORBD 075 / Sep '92 / Globestyle

Swallow

☐ BLOW
Lovesleep / Tastes like honey / Sugar your mind / Mensurral / Peekaboo / Lacuna / Oceans and blue skies / Follow me down / Halo / Cherry stars collide / Head in a cave
GAD 2010CD / 6 Jul '98 / 4AD

Swallow

☐ BEST OF SWALLOW, THE
CR 003 / 13 Oct '97 / Charlie's

☐ SOCA KINGDOM
SCR 1075 / 13 Oct '97 / Charlie's

Swallow, Steve

☐ CARLA (Swallow, Steve Sextet)
Deep trouble / Crab alley / Fred and Ethel / Read my lips / Afterglow / Hold it against me / Count the ways / Last night
8334922 / Oct '87 / Watt

☐ DECONSTRUCTED
Running in the family / Babble on / Another fine mess / I think my wife is a hat / Bird world war / Bug in a rug / Lost in Boston / Name that tune / Viscous consistency / Deconstructed
5371192 / May '97 / Watt

☐ REAL BOOK
Bite your Grandmother / Second hand motion / Wrong together / Outfits / Thinking out loud / Let's eat / Better times / Willow / Muddy in the bank / Ponytail
5216372 / Jun '94 / Watt

☐ SWALLOW
Belles / Soca symphony / Slender thread / Thrills and spills / William and Mary / Doin' it slow / Thirty five / Ballroom / Playing with water
5119602 / Mar '92 / Watt

Swallows Tail Ceili Band

☐ HELL FOR LEATHER
SUNCD 28 / Dec '97 / Sound

Swamp Terrorists

☐ GROW - SPEED INJECTION
Ratskin / Hidden (crab) / Vault I / Skizzo pierce / Rebuff / Vault II / Green blood / Braintrash / Vault III / Rawhead / SSM / Drop the dig / Ratskin (floatmix) / Drip the dog
MA 0092 / Mar '92 / Machinery

Swamptrash

☐ IT DON'T MAKE NO NEVER MIND
FFUS 3301CD / '88 / Fast Forward

Swan, Billy

☐ BEST OF BILLY SWAN, THE
I can help / Shake rattle and roll / Stranger / Lover please / Number one / Don't be cruel / (You just) woman handled my mind / Everythings the same (ain't nothing changed) / I just want to taste your wine / Vanessa / You're the one / Do I have to draw a picture / I'm into lovin' you / Stuck right in the middle of your love / With their kind of money and our kind of love / Your picture still loves me (and I still love you)
4914492 / 10 Aug '98 / Monument

☐ BILLY SWAN/FOUR
I just want to taste your wine / Ms. Misery / I got it for you / Number one / Vanessa / Lucky / You're the one / Love you baby, to the bone / Your true love / Blue suede shoes / Swept away / Playing the game of love / Pardon me / Oliver Swan / Smokey places / Don't kill our love / Not everyone knows / Last call / California song (for Marlu) / Me and my honey
SEECD 471 / Jan '97 / See For Miles

☐ I CAN HELP
All shook up / Drivin' wheel / Rave on / When will I be loved / Hallelujah I love her so / Vanessa / Don't be cruel / My bucket's got a hole in it / I can help / Bright lights, big city / I'd rather go blind / Shake, rattle and roll / Lover please / Since I met you baby / Great balls of fire / Rock this joint / Me and Bobby McGee / Rockhouse
305082 / Jun '97 / Hallmark

☐ I CAN HELP/ROCK 'N' ROLL MOON
Lover please / I can help / I'm her foot / I'd like to work for you / Shake, rattle and roll / Queen of my heart / Don't be cruel / Wedding bells / Ways of a woman in love / PMS / Everything's the same (ain't nothin' changed) / You're the pain (in my heart) / (You just) woman handled my mind / Stranger / Baby my heart / Got you on my mind / Come by / Ubangi stomp / Home of the blues / Overnight thing (usually) / Rock 'n' roll moon blues
SEECD 470 / Jan '97 / See For Miles

Swan Death

☐ BLACK WOLF
9227966CD / Apr '97 / Nightbreed

Swan, Jimmy

☐ HONKY TONKIN' IN MISSISSIPPI
I had a dream / Juke joint mama / I love you too much / Trifflin' on me / Last letter / Little church / Mark of shame / Losers weepers / One more time / Lonesome daddy blues / Frost on my roof / Why did you change your mind / Hey baby, baby / It's your turn to cry / Good and lonesome / Country cattin' / Way that you're livin' / Lonesome man / I love you too much / Don't conceal you're wedding ring / No one loves a broken heart / It takes a lonesome man / Rattlesnakin' Daddy / Asleep in the deep / Walkin' my dog / Good and lonesome / Why did you change your mind
BCD 15758 / Nov '93 / Bear Family

Swan Silvertones

☐ HEAVENLY LIGHT
Jesus is all the world to me / Love lifted me / I'm sealed / How I got over / Have thine own way / Shine on me / Heavenly light shine on me / Jesus keep me near the cross / He won't deny me / Every day and every hour / Four and twenty elders / Shine on me medley / My rock / Lord's prayer / Medley / I'm coming home / After a while
CDCHD 482 / Jul '93 / Ace

☐ LOVE LIFTED ME AND MY ROCK
Trouble in my way / How I got over / After a while / Prayer in my mouth / Glory to his name / I'm a rollin' / Let's go / Jesus changed this heart of mine / I'm coming home / Love lifted me / Heavenly light shine on me / Day will surely come / My rock / Since Jesus came into my heart / I cried / What do you know about Jesus / Milky white way / He won't deny me / Jesus is a friend / Motherless child / Man in Jerusalem / Keep my heart / Oh how I love Jesus / This little light of mine
CDCHD 340 / May '91 / Ace

☐ SINGING IN MY SOUL
Oh Mary don't you weep / Great day in December / Singin' in my soul / At the cross / He saved my soul / Why I love him so / Jesus is alright with me / Lord is coming / Nobody but you / Love lifted me / Call him Jesus / Leave your burden there / Cross for me / I'll be satisfied / Send my child / I thank you Lord / Come to Jesus / Without a mother / Search me Lord / Bible days
CPCD 8089 / May '95 / Charly

Swana, John

☐ FEELING'S MUTUAL, THE
1090CD / Jan '95 / Criss Cross

☐ INTRODUCING JOHN SWANA
CRISS 1045CD / Apr '91 / Criss Cross

☐ JOHN SWANA AND FRIENDS
CRISS 1055CD / May '92 / Criss Cross

Swandive

☐ INTUITION
SD 003 / 13 Apr '98 / Stereo Deluxe

Swanee Quintet

☐ BEST OF THE SWANEE QUINTET, THE
NASH 4503 / Feb '96 / Nashboro

Swans

☐ CHILDREN OF GOD/WORLD OF SKIN (2CD Set)
New mind / In my garden / Over love lies / Sex, God, Sex / Blood and honey / Like a drug / You're not real girl / Beautiful child / Black mail / Trust me / Real love / Blind love / Children of God / Ill swallow you / 1000 years / Everything at once / Cry me a river / Breathing water / Blood on your hands / Nothing without you / We'll fall apart / I want to be your dog / My own hands / Turn to stone / Cold bed / 24 hours / Red rose / One small sacrifice / Still a sacrifice / Center of your heart
YGCD 02 / 13 Apr '98 / Young God

☐ FILTH
YGCD 1 / Jul '95 / Young God

☐ GREED
KCC 2CD / Mar '86 / K422

☐ HOLY MONEY
KCCD 3 / Feb '88 / Some Bizarre

☐ REAL LOVE
ALP 58CD / Jan '97 / Atavistic

☐ SWANS ARE DEAD (2CD Set)
Feel happiness / Low life form / Not alone / Blood on your hands / Hypogirl / I crawled / I am the sun / Blood promise / Final sac / Sound / I see them all lined up / Lavender / YR PRP / Yum yas / Helpless child / M/F
RR 69962 / 23 Feb '98 / Relapse

☐ WHITE LIGHT FROM THE MOUTH OF INFINITY
YGCD 3 / Jul '95 / Young God

Swans Of Avon

☐ WHEN HEAVEN FALLS
PANT 218CD / Apr '97 / Nightbreed

Swap

☐ SWAP
AMCD 735 / May '97 / Amigo

Swarbrick, Dave

☐ 50TH BIRTHDAY CONCERT (Various Artists)
Drowsy Maggie: *Swarbrick, Dave & Fairport Convention* / Heilanman: *Swarbrick, Dave & Fairport Convention* / 72nd's farewell to Aberdeen: *Marriot, Beryl Ceilidh Band* / 93rd's farewell to Gibraltar: *Marriot, Beryl Ceilidh Band* / Atholl highlanders: *Marriot, Beryl Ceilidh Band* / Hag with the money: *Marriot, Beryl Ceilidh Band* / Sleepy: *Marriot, Beryl Ceilidh Band* / Keech in the Creel: *Campbell, Ian Folk Group* / Viva la Quince Brigade: *Campbell, Ian Folk Group* / Oh dear oh: *Swarbrick, Dave & Martin Carthy* / Begging song: *Swarbrick, Dave & Martin Carthy* / Trip we took over the mountain: *Swarbrick, Dave & Martin Carthy* / Hens march: *Fairport Convention* / Four poster bed: *Fairport Convention* / Rosie: *Fairport Convention* / Hexamshire Lass: *Fairport Convention* / Dirty linen: *Fairport Convention*
MASHCD 001 / Jun '96 / Cooking Vinyl

☐ CLOSE TO THE WHITE BEAR (Swarbrick, Dave & Simon Nicol)
Young black cow / 'Appy 'ornpipe / Close of an Irish day / Si bheag si mhor / Democratic rage/ Constitution/President Garfield's / Close to the wind / Dark and slender boy / Humours of cappa / Pittengardner's rant / Time to ring some changes / Fiddlestix / Temptation rag / Lord Haddo's/Lady Mary Haye's scotch measure / 79th's farewell to Gibraltar / Three drunken maidens / Hen's march/4 Poster bed / Widow of westmoreland's daughter / Gravel path/Leighton Buzzard shuffle
WRCD 028 / 26 Jan '98 / Woodworm

☐ LIVE AT JACKSONS LANE
ATRAXCD 595 / Feb '96 / Bowsaw

☐ SMIDDYBURN/FLITTIN'
Wat ye wha I met the streen / Ribbons of the redheaded girl / Ril gan ainm / Sir Charles Coote / Smiths / I have a wife of my own / Lady Mary Haye's scotch measure / Wishing / Victor's return / Gravel walk / When the battle is over / Sword dance / Young black crow / Sean O'Dwyer of the glen / Hag with the money / Sleepy Maggie / It suits me well / Bride's march / Keelmans pertition / Show me the way to Sallingford / Sword dance / Parthenia / Pittnegardener's rant / Floggin / Grey daylight / Hawk / Ten pound fiddle / Jamaica / With all my heart / Nathaniel Gow's lament / Rory of the hills / Rakes of Sollohad / Dr. Isaacs Maggot / Cupids garden / Boadicea
RVCD 54 / Aug '96 / Raven
ESMCD 434 / Oct '96 / Essential

☐ SWARBRICK/SWARBRICK VOL.2
Heilanman/Drowsy Maggie / Carthy's march / White cockade/Doc Boyd's jig/Durham Rangers / My singing bird / Nightingale / Once I loved a maiden fair / Byker Hill / Ace and deuce of Pipering / Hole in the wall / Ben Dorian / Hullichans/Chorus jig / 79th's farewell to Gibraltar / Arthur McBride/Snug in the blanket / Athole highlanders / Shannon bells/Fairy dance/Miss McLeod's reel / King of the fairies / Chief O'Neil's favourite/Newcastle hornpipe / Sheebeg and Sheemore / Rocky road to Dublin/Sir Philip McHugh / Planxty Morgan Mawgan / Swallow's tail/ Rakes of Kildare/Blackthorn stick / Sheagh of Rye/ The friar's breeches / Derwentwaters farewell/The noble Squire Dacre / Teribus/Farewell to Aberdeen / Bonaparte's retreat / Coulin
ESMCD 355 / Jan '96 / Essential

Sward, Pierre

☐ JAZZ 'N' SOUL
FLCCD 147 / May '97 / Four Leaf Clover

Swarovski Musik Wattens

☐ NATIONAL ANTHEMS OF THE WORLD (2CD Set)
340872 / Sep '96 / Koch International

Swartalf

☐ CANDLES BURNING BLUE
MORI 002CD / 22 Jun '98 / Dark Vinyl

Swartz, Harvey

☐ IT'S ABOUT TIME (Swartz, Harvey & Urban Earth)
It's about time / Winthrop beach / Electric rainbow / Rv / Forever / Stang / Poem for a flower
1390112 / Feb '89 / Gaia

Swayzak

☐ SNOWBOARDING IN ARGENTINA
Speedboat / Burma heights / Blocks / Low rez skyline / Fukumachi / French dub / Redfarm / LO9VE / Bueno / Bluefarm / Evil dub / Skyline
PAGANCD 1006 / 27 Apr '98 / Pagan

Sweat, Keith

☐ GET UP ON IT
Interlude (how do you like it) / How do you like it / It gets better / Get up on it / Feels so good / How do you like it (part 2) / Intermission break / My whole world / Grind on you / When I give my love / Put your lovin' through the test / Telephone love / Come into my bedroom / For you (you got everything)
7559615502 / May '94 / Elektra

☐ I'LL GIVE ALL MY LOVE TO YOU
I'll give all my love to you / Make you sweat / Come back / Merry go round / Your love / Your love (part 2) / Just one of them thangs / I knew that you were cheatin / Love to love you
7559608612 / Jun '90 / Elektra

☐ JUST A TOUCH
I want her / Something just ain't right / Make it last forever / I'll give all my love to you / Make you sweat / How do you like it / Twisted / Nobody / Put your lovin' through the test / Why me baby / Just a touch / Just a touch (remix) / Nobody (remix)
7559621162 / 20 Oct '97 / Elektra

☐ KEITH SWEAT
Twisted / Funky dope lovin' / Yumi / Freak with me / Nature's rising / Just a touch / Whatever you want / Come with me / Show me the way / In the mood / Chocolate girl / Nobody
7559617072 / Jun '96 / Elektra

☐ MAKE IT LAST FOREVER
Something just ain't right / Right and a wrong way / Tell me it's me you want / I want her / Make it last forever / In the rain / How deep is your love / Don't stop your love
9607632 / Jul '88 / Elektra

SWED

☐ CROSSTALK
EFA 034072 / Oct '94 / Muffin

Swedish String Quartet

☐ LIVE AT SALSTA CASTLE
Poor butterfly / Avalon / Limehouse blues / I got rhythm / Tangerine / Have you met Miss Jones
NCD 8803 / '93 / Phontastic

☐ STOMPIN' AND FLYING
If I had you / Lover / Old folks / It could happen to you / Sweet Sue, just you / Flying home / Oh lady be good
NCD 8805 / '93 / Phontastic

Swedish Swing Society

☐ WHAT'S NEW
SITCD 9235 / May '97 / Sittel

☐ WINTER SWING
SITCD 9213 / Mar '95 / Sittel

Sweeney

☐ BINGO
Cummings family outing / Wannabe / Fish face / Zoo keeper / Compos mentis / Nostalgia rise / Rock / Kazoo song / Batman and Robin / Mrs Symmonds daughter / Twinkle toes / Outside / Wooden box
RRAD 113 / 3 Nov '97 / Rotator

☐ POP GUN
Shut up / This and that / England / Ticket void if scratched / Honey forever / Husbands and wives / Venus and fake furs / On stilts with feathers in her hair / Easy / Why / You belong to me / Big red
RRAD 107 / Aug '97 / Rotator

Sweeney's Men

☐ SWEENEY'S MEN/THE TRACKS OF SWEENEY
Rattlin' roarin' Willy / Sullivan's John / Sally Brown / My dearest dear / Exile's jig / Handsome cabin boy / Dicey Reilley / Tom Dooley / Willy o' Winsbury / Dance to your Daddy / House carpenter / Johnston / Reynard the fox / Dreams for me / Pipe on the hob / Brain jam / Pretty Polly / Standing on the shore / Mistake no doubt / Go by brooks / When you don't care / Afterthoughts / Hiram Hubbard / Hall of mirrors
ESMCD 435 / Oct '96 / Essential

Sweet

☐ A
AIM 1048 / Apr '95 / Aim

☐ ANSWER, THE (Scott, Andy/Sweet)
CDP 1029DD / Jun '97 / Pseudonym

☐ BALLROOM HITZ (The Best Of The Sweet)
5350012 / Jan '96 / PolyGram TV

☐ BEST OF SWEET, THE
Ballroom blitz / Blockbuster / Need a lot of lovin' / New York connection / Rock 'n' roll disgrace / Hellraiser / Burning / Done me wrong alright / Reflections / Little Willy / Funny funny / Co co / Chop chop / Alexander Graham Bell / Poppa Joe / Santa Monica sunshine / Tom Tom turnaround / Wig wam bam
74321476792 / Apr '97 / Camden

☐ ELECTRIC LANDLADY
RRCD 241 / Apr '97 / Receiver

☐ FIRST RECORDINGS 1968-1971
REP 4140 / Aug '91 / Repertoire

☐ GIVE US A WINK
REP 4084 / Aug '91 / Repertoire

☐ GREATEST HITS
290586 / Dec '92 / Ariola Express

☐ GREATEST HITS LIVE
AIM 1041 / Apr '95 / Aim

☐ HANOVER SESSIONS (4CD Set) (Scott, Andy/Sweet)
CDP 1028DD / Jun '97 / Pseudonym

☐ HARD CENTRES - THE ROCK YEARS
Set me free / Sweet FA / Restless / Yesterday's rain / White mice / Cockroach / Keep it in / Live for today / Windy city / Midnight to daylight
CDMZEB 11 / Sep '95 / Anagram

☐ HITZ, BLITZ, GLITZ (Andy Scott's Sweet)
Action / Blockbuster / Fox on the run / Teenage rampage / Love is like oxygen / Six teens / Ballraiser blitz / Hellraiser / Wig wam bam / Little Willy / Turn it down / Peppermint twist
CDEC 5 / Sep '96 / Out Of Time

☐ LET'S GO
Ballroom blitz / Rock 'n' roll disgrace / AC/DC / Burn on the flame / Fox on the run / Action / Cockroach / Windy City / Laura Lee (show me the way) / Are you coming to see me / Hard times / 4th of July / Live for today / Solid gold brass / Lady starlight / Lies in your eyes
EMPRCD 717 / Jun '97 / Emporio

☐ LEVEL HEADED
REP 4234 / Aug '91 / Repertoire

☐ LIVE AT THE MARQUEE
SPV 858826 / Mar '96 / SPV

☐ LOVE IS LIKE OXYGEN (The Singles Collection 1978-1982)
CDP 1009DD / Jun '97 / Pseudonym

☐ MASTERS, THE (Connolly, Brian/ Sweet)
Action / Hellraiser / Little Willy / Teenage rampage / Do it again / Ballroom blitz / Wig wam bam / Wait till morning comes / Burn on the flame / Fox on the run / Let's go / Blockbuster
EABCD 102 / 30 Mar '98 / Eagle

☐ OFF THE RECORD
Fever of love / Lost angels / Midnight to daylight / Windy city / Live for today / She gimme lovin' / Laura Lee / Hard times / Funk it up
REP 4085 / Aug '91 / Repertoire

☐ SOLID GOLD ACTION
RRCD 214 / Apr '96 / Receiver

☐ SWEET ARCHIVE
Eye gime / Strong love / White mice / Air on a tape loop / Healer / Windy city / Play all night / Distinct lack of ancient / Dream on / Why don't you do it to me / Cover girl / Sweet fa / California nights / Midnight to daylight / Stairway to the stars / Lady of the lake / Los angels
RMCD 215 / Nov '97 / Rialto

☐ SWEET LIVE 1973, THE
Ballroom blitz / Little Willie / Rock 'n' roll disgrace / Done me wrong alright / Hellraiser / You're not wrong for loving me / Burning/Someone else will / Man with the golden arm / Need a lot of lovin' / Wig wam bam / Teenage rampage / Blockbuster / Keep on knockin' / Shakin' all over / Lucille / Great balls of fire / Reelin' and rockin' / Peppermint twist / Shout
DOJOCD 89 / Mar '93 / Dojo

Sweet 75

☐ SWEET 75
GED 25140 / 25 Aug '97 / Geffen

Sweet Baby

☐ IT'S A GIRL
LOOKOUT 157CD / Oct '96 / Lookout

☐ SWEET BABY/BRENTS TV (Sweet Baby/Brents TV)
LOOKOUT 102CD / Sep '96 / Lookout

Sweet Betty

☐ THEY CALL ME SWEET BETTY
They call me Sweet Betty / It's all in the game / You're a two timing man / Brown liquor / I need my baby / Your tears become my tears / Bad company / Change is gonna come / These bills / I'm not your fool / I can find someone better / I still love you
JSPCD 2101 / Dec '97 / JSP

Sweet Daisy

☐ SLUDGE
GOD 021MCD / Sep '96 / Godhead

Sweet Diesel

☐ SEARCH AND ANNOY
GKCD 020 / Oct '96 / Go-Kart

☐ WRONGVILLE
VEL 79780 / 22 Jun '98 / Velvel

Sweet Exorcist

☐ CLONKS COMING
WARPCD 1 / Apr '96 / Warp

☐ SPIRIT GUIDE TO LOW TECH
T 3313 / Oct '95 / Touch

Sweet Heat

☐ BEST OF SWEET HEAT, THE
HTCD 116 / 20 Apr '98 / Hot Productions

Sweet Honey In The Rock

☐ BREATHS (The Best Of Sweet Honey In The Rock)
Breaths / Stranger blues / Joanne little / Ella's song / More than a paycheck / Mandiacapella / Study war no more / Waters of Babylon (rivers of Babylon) / Oughta be a woman / On children / Chile your waters run red through Soweto / Azanian freedom song
COOKCD 008 / Jan '97 / Cooking Vinyl

☐ FEEL SOMETHING DRAWING ME ON
Waters of Babylon (rivers of Babylon) / In the upper room / Leaning and depending on the Lord / Try Jesus / Feel something drawing on me
COOKCD 082 / Mar '95 / Cooking Vinyl

☐ GOOD NEWS
Breaths / Chile your waters run red through Soweto / Good news / If you had lived / On children / Alla that's all right, but / Echo / Oh death / Biko / Oughta be a woman / Time on my hands / Sometime
COOKCD 027 / Aug '89 / Cooking Vinyl

☐ IN THIS LAND
CDEB 2522 / May '93 / Earthbeat

☐ LIVE AT CARNEGIE HALL
Beautitudes / Where are the keys to the kingdom / Emergency / Are my hands clean / Peace / My lament / Run run mourner run / Letter to Dr. Martin Luther King / Ode to the international debt / Your worries ain' like mine / Song of the exile / Denko / Drinking of the wine / Wade in the water / Our side won
BAKECD 003 / May '90 / Cooking Vinyl
FF 70106 / Feb '97 / Flying Fish

☐ OTHER SIDE, THE
Mandiacapella / Step by step / Deportees / Moving on / Stranger blues / Venceremos / Other side / No images / Gift of love / Mae Frances / Let us go back to the old landmark / Tomorrow
COOKCD 083 / Mar '95 / Cooking Vinyl

☐ SACRED GROUND
9425802 / Jan '96 / Earthbeat

☐ SELECTIONS 1976-1988
CDFF 667668 / Aug '97 / Flying Fish

☐ STILL ON THE JOURNEY
EBCD 942536 / Nov '93 / Earthbeat

☐ SWEET HONEY IN THE ROCK
Sweet honey in the rock / Sun will never go down / Dream variations / Let us all come together / Joanne Little / Jesus is my only friend / Are there any rights I'm entitled to / Going to see my baby / You make my day pretty / Hey mann / Doing things together / Travelling shoes / Sweet honey in the rock
COOKCD 080 / Mar '95 / Cooking Vinyl

☐ WE ALL EVERYONE OF US
Study war no more / What a friend we have in Jesus / Sweet bird of youth / How long / More than a paycheck / Azanian freedom song / Listen to the rhythm / Testimony / Oh Lord hold my hand / Battle for my life / Ella's song / I'm gon' stand / We all everyone of us
COOKCD 081 / Mar '95 / Cooking Vinyl

Sweet Inspirations

☐ ESTELLE, MYRNA AND SYLVIA
Wishes and dishes / You roam when you don't get it at home / Slipped and tripped / All it takes is you and me / Pity yourself / Emergency / Call me when all else fails / Whole world is out / Why marry / Sweet inspiration / Why am I treated so bad
CDSXE 062 / Jul '92 / Stax

Sweet, Matthew

☐ 100% FUN
Sick of myself / Not when I need it / We're the same / Giving it back / Everything changes / Lost my mind / Come to love / Walk out / I almost forgot / Super baby / Get older / Smog moon
72445110812 / Mar '95 / Zoo Entertainment

☐ BLUE SKY ON MARS
Come back to California / Back to you / Where you get love / Hollow / Behind the smile / Until you break / Over it / Heaven and Earth / All over my head / Into your drug / Make believe / Missing time
614453113029 / Apr '97 / Zoo Entertainment

☐ BLUE SKY ON MARS (Japanese Issue)
Come back to California / Back to you / Where you get love / Hollow / Behind the smile / Until you break / Over it / Heaven and Earth / All over my head / Into your drug / Make believe / Missing time / If it's happening now / Close inside / Final hour
FHCP 1008 / Dec '97 / Funhouse

☐ GIRLFRIEND
Divine intervention / I've been waiting / Girlfriend / Looking at the sun / Winona / Evangeline / Day for night / Thought I knew you / You don't love me / I wanted to tell you / Don't go / Your sweet voice / Does she talk / Holy war / Nothing lasts
PD 90644 / Jun '92 / Zoo Entertainment

Sweet, Michael

☐ MICHAEL SWEET
CD 02231 / May '95 / Way Hey

Sweet People

☐ SUMMER DREAM
Et les oiseaux chantaient / Heartstring / Un ete avec toi / Elodie / Lake como / Santorini / Balladepoour tsi-co tsi co / Aria pour une voix / La foret enchantee / Barcarolle / Le grande large / Aria pour notre amour / Perce / Nuits blanche / Wonderful day
8312132 / Apr '94 / Polydor

Sweet, Rachel

☐ FOOL AROUND
REP 4218 / Aug '91 / Repertoire

☐ PROTECT THE INNOCENT
STIFFCD 10 / Jan '94 / Disky

Sweet Savage

☐ KILLING TIME
NM 011CD / Oct '97 / Neat Metal

☐ RUNE
NM 031 / 13 Jul '98 / Neat Metal

Sweet Talks

☐ HOLLYWOOD HIGHLIFE PARTY
ADC 301 / Feb '94 / PAM

Sweet Trip

☐ HALICA
DRL 057CD / 16 Mar '98 / Darla

Sweetback

☐ SWEETBACK
Gaze / Softly softly / Sensations / Au natural / Arabesque / You will rise / Chord / Walk of Ju / Hope she'll be happier / Come dubbing / Cloud people / Powder
4853902 / Nov '96 / Epic

Sweetbelly Freakdown

☐ SWEETBELLY FREAKDOWN
JT 1032CD / Apr '97 / Jade Tree

Sweetest Ache

☐ GRASS ROOTS
Love me gently / Something we can find / Carry me home / Good days gone / One more time / Jayne / Nothing ever ends / Never gonna say goodbye / Honey / Little angel
ASKCD 029 / Mar '94 / Vinyl Japan

Sweethearts Of The Rodeo

☐ BEAUTIFUL LIES
When love comes around the bend / Beautiful lies / When the morning comes / Catch the wind / I'll pass over thee / I won't cry / Inn at Innisfree / I know who you are / Pretty words / One more night / Muleskinner blues
SHCD 3857 / Mar '98 / Sugar Hill

☐ RODEO WALTZ
SHCD 3819 / Aug '96 / Sugar Hill

Sweetmouth

☐ GOODBYE TO SONGTOWN
Dangerous / Home to heartache / I know why the willow weeps / Forgiveness / Prayer to st valentine / Waltz continues / Don't be a stranger / Fear is the enemy of love / Goodbye to songtown / Broken by a breeze
PD 74971 / Apr '97 / RCA

Sweetpea

☐ CHICKS HATE WES
TR 51CD / May '96 / Trance

Swell

☐ FOR ALL THE BEAUTIFUL PEOPLE
Today / Oh my my / Make up your mind / I hate Christmas / Off in my head / Something to do / Pink pink rain / Blackmilk / Everything is good / Swill 9 / Tonight / Don't you know they love you
BBQCD 203 / 31 Aug '98 / Beggars Banquet

☐ TOO MANY DAYS WITHOUT THINKING
Throw the wine / What I always wanted / Make mine you / Fuck even flow / At Lennie's / When you come over / (I know) the trip / Going up (to Portand) / Bridgette, you love me / Sunshine everyday
BBQCD 187 / Mar '97 / Beggars Banquet

Swell Maps

☐ JANE FROM OCCUPIED EUROPE
Robot factory / Let's buy a fridge / Border country / Cake shop / Helicopter spies / Big maz in the desert / Big empty field / Mining villages / Collusion with a frogman / Mangrove delta plan / Secret island / Whatever happens next / Blenheim shots / Raining in my room / Let's build a car / Epic's trip / Uh / Secret island / Amphitheatres / Big empty field / Stairs are like an avalanche / Then Poland
MAPS 002CD / Jul '89 / Grey Area

☐ TRAIN OUT OF IT
MAPS 003CD / Aug '91 / Grey Area

☐ TRIP TO MARINEVILLE, A
HS art / Another song / Vertical slum / Spitfire parade / Harmony in your bathroom / Don't throw ashtrays at me / Midget submarines / Bridge head / Full moon in my pocket / Blam / Full moon reprise / Gunboats / Adventuring into basketry / My little shops / Ripped and torn / International rescue / Loin of the surf / Shoot the angels / Elephant flowers / Turn me on dead man / Bronze and baby shoes / Nevertoseeanotherway
MAPS 001CD / Jul '89 / Grey Area

Swelling Meg

☐ WELL
NGM 007 / Jul '96 / NGM

Swervedriver

☐ 99TH DREAM
SWD 099CD / 10 Aug '98 / Sonic Wave Discs

☐ EJECTOR SEAT RESERVATIONS
CRECD 157 / Aug '95 / Creation

☐ MEZCAL HEAD
For seeking heat / Duel / Blowin' cool / Mickey / Last train to Satansville / Harry and Maggie / Change is gonna come / Girl on a motorbike / Duress / You find it everywhere
CRECD 143 / Sep '93 / Creation

☐ RAISE
Sci-flyer / Pile-up / Son of mustang ford / Deep seat / Rave down / Sunset / Feel so real / Sandblasted / Lead me where you dare...
CRECD 093 / Oct '91 / Creation

SWF Orchestra

☐ VIVACE
ISCD 159 / Sep '96 / Intersound

Swift, Duncan

☐ BROADWAY CONCERT, THE
ESSCD 258 / Feb '95 / Essential

Swift, Jude

☐ COMMON GROUND
NOVA 9139 / Jan '93 / Nova

☐ MUSIC FOR YOUR NEIGHBOURHOOD
NOVA 8917 / Jan '93 / Nova

Swimmer

☐ PETITS POIS
SWEE 004CD / Jun '96 / Sweet

Swimwear Catalogue

☐ FNOPRX BOUTIQUE
APR 013CD / Oct '96 / April

☐ NTUNXUN
APR 005CD / 6 Oct '97 / April

Swindle

☐ BETTER OFF DEAD
CDGRL 007 / 1 Jun '98 / Grilled Cheese

☐ WITHIN THESE WALLS
GRL 003CD / Oct '96 / Grilled Cheese

Swing & Sway Orchestra

☐ ABSOLUT LEVANDE DANSMUSIK (Swing & Sway Orchestra & Arne Domnerus)
NCD 8853 / May '97 / Phontastic

Swing Out Sister

☐ GET IN TOUCH WITH YOURSELF
Get in touch with yourself / Am I the same girl / Incomplete without you / Everyday crime / Circulate / Who let the love out / Understand / Not gonna change / Don't say a word / Love child / I can hear you but can't see you (Inst.) / Everyday crime (Instrumental)
5122412 / May '92 / Fontana

☐ IT'S BETTER TO TRAVEL
Breakout / Twilight world (superb, superb mix) / After hours / Blue mood / Surrender / Fooled by a smile / Communion / It's not enough / It's better to travel / Breakout (Nad mix) / Surrender (Stuff gun mix) / Twilight world (Remix) / Communion (Instrumental)
8322132 / Jul '93 / Fontana

☐ KALEIDOSCOPE WORLD
You on my mind / Where in the world / Forever blue / Heart for fire / Tainted / Waiting game / Precious game / Masquerade / Between strangers / Kaleidoscope affair
8382932 / Jul '93 / Fontana

☐ LIVING RETURN, THE
Better make it better / Don't let yourself down / Ordinary people / Mama didn't raise no fool / Don't give up on a good thing / Making the right move / La la (Means I love you) / Feel free / Stop and think it over / That's the way it goes / All in your mind / O pesadelo dos autores / Low down dirty business
5226502 / Jun '94 / Fontana

Swinger

☐ HALF DAY ROAD
GR 1002 / Dec '97 / Ginger

Swingin' Haymakers

☐ FOR RENT
CCD 907 / Aug '95 / Circle

Swinging Blue Jeans

☐ 1960'S FRENCH EP COLLECTION, THE
519362 / Jul '97 / Magic

☐ 25 GREATEST HITS
Hippy hippy shake / It's too late now / Three little fishes / Good golly Miss Molly / Lawdy Miss Clawdy / Long tall Sally / Shakin' all over / Tutti frutti / Don't make me over / Crazy 'bout my baby / Shake rattle & roll / Don't worry about me / I've got a girl / You're no good / Angie / I'm gonna sit right down / It's all over now / Make me know you're mine / Promise you'll tell her / That's the way it goes / Do you know / Now the summer's gone / It isn't there / Tremblin' / Shaking feeling
4954832 / 6 Jul '98 / EMI Gold

☐ ALL THE HITS PLUS MORE
Tonight's the night / Angel / You're no good / Still the one / I'm an old rock'n'roller / Good golly miss molly / Hippy hippy shake / You win again / Banging in my head / Higher than a kite / Poets / Love machine / Whole lotta trouble / Way down yonder
CDPT 003 / Mar '94 / Prestige

☐ AT ABBEY ROAD 1963-1967
Old man mose / It's too late now / Hippy hippy shake / Good golly Miss molly / Shakin' feeling / Shakin' all over / Shake rattle and roll / You're no good / Don't worry about me / Promise you'll tell her / It's so right / Tutti frut / It isn't there / Ake me know you'e mine / Crazy about my baby / Good lovin' / Don't make me over / What can I do today / I'm gonna sit right down / Sandy / I'm gonna have you / You don't love me / Do you believe in magic / This boy / It's in her kiss / Rumours gossip word untrue / Tremblin' / Don't go out into the rain
4933272 / 23 Feb '98 / EMI

☐ BEST OF THE EMI YEARS, THE
CDP 7992352 / Aug '97 / EMI

☐ BEST OF THE SWINGING BLUE JEANS 1963-66, THE
Hippy hippy shake / It's too late now / Save the last dance for me / That's the way it goes / One of these days / Shakin' all over / Crazy about my baby / Shake, rattle and roll / Angie / Good golly Miss Molly / Don't worry 'bout me / Sandy / You're no good / Do you know / Long tall Sally / Don't make me over / Now the Summer's gone / Promise you'll tell her / It isn't there / Lawdy Miss Clawdy
CDSL 8254 / Jul '95 / EMI

☐ BLUE JEANS A' SWINGING
Ol' man Mose / Save the last dance for me / That's the way it goes / Around and around / It's all over now / Long tall Sally / Lawdy Miss Clawdy / Some sweet day / It's so right / Don't it make you feel good / All I want is you / Tutti Frutti / Ol' man Mose / Save the last dance for me / That's the way it goes / Around and around / It's all over now / Long tall Sally / Lawdy Miss Clawdy / Some sweet day / It's so right / Don't it make you feel good / All I want is you
DORIG 104 / Aug '97 / EMI

☐ BLUE JEANS ARE IN
MOGCD 007 / Dec '94 / Moggie

☐ HIPPY HIPPY SHAKE
Hippy hippy shake / Think of me / Angie / Now I must go / Shaking feeling / Don't you worry about me / It's so right / One of these days / I've got a girl / Good lovin' / What can I do today / I'm gonna have you
WB 885842 / 2 Feb '98 / Disky

☐ LIVE SHARIN'
Tulane / My life / Again and again / Good golly Miss Molly / Don't stop / I saw her standing there / She loves you / Caroline / You're no good / Heatwave / Shakin' all over / It's so easy / When will I be loved / Hard day's night / Hippy hippy shake
CDPT 502 / Jul '90 / Prestige

Swinging Ladies

☐ TAKE TWO
INAK 9039 / Oct '96 / In Akustik

Swinging Neckbreakers

☐ KICK YOUR ASS
TS 029CD / Sep '97 / Telstar

Swinging Utters

☐ FIVE LESSONS LEARNED
FAT 574CD / 29 Jun '98 / Fatwreck Chords

☐ JUVENILE PRODUCT OF THE WORKING CLASS, A
FAT 545CD / Sep '96 / Fatwreck Chords

Swingle Singers

☐ AROUND THE WORLD (A Folk Song Collection)
VC 7596162 / Jan '95 / Virgin Classics

☐ BACH HITS BACK (A Cappella Amadeus)
VBD 5614722 / Apr '98 / Virgin Classics

☐ BLUE SKIES, THE
Top hat, white tie and tails / How deep is the ocean / It's a lovely day/Isn't it a lovely day / Blue skies / Always / They say it's wonderful / No strings / Song is ended / Stepping out with my baby / White Christmas / Let yourself go / Cheek to cheek/Let's face the music and dance / Marrying for love/The girl that I marry / What'll I do / Puttin' on the Ritz / Abraham / Change partners / Heatwave / I've got my love to keep me warm / Count your blessings
RM 1503 / Aug '97 / BR Music

☐ NOTHING BUT BLUE SKIES (The Irving Berlin Songbook)
Top hat, white tie and tails / How deep is the ocean / Isn't it a lovely day / Blue skies / Always / They say it's wonderful / No strings / Song is ended / Steppin' out with my baby / Let yourself go / Cheek to cheek/Let's face the music and dance / Marrying for love/The girl that I marry / What'll I do / Puttin' on the ritz / Abraham / Change partners / Heatwave / I've got my love to keep me warm / Count your blessings / White Christmas
SUMCD 4054 / Nov '96 / Summit

Swingset Police

☐ KADICKADEE
BV 161962 / Nov '96 / Black Vinyl

Swirl

☐ PLUMPTUOUS
AMUSE 014CD / May '92 / Playtime

Swirlies

☐ STRICTLY EAST COAST SNEAKY FLUTE MUSIC
TAANG 132CD / 29 Jun '98 / Taang

☐ WHAT TO DO ABOUT THEM
TAANG 65CD / Oct '92 / Taang

Swish

☐ SUPERMAX
Pretty box / Game / Klauss / Spin / Rockstar / Shell / Marjorie song
IMAY 001 / May '96 / Instant Mayhem

Swiss Dixie Stompers

☐ PETITE FLEUR
JCD 184 / Oct '93 / Jazzology

☐ SWISS DIXIE STOMPERS, THE
CDTTD 611 / May '98 / Timeless Traditional

Swiss Family Orbison

☐ SWISS FAMILY ORBISON, THE
HAVENCD 9 / 12 Jan '98 / Haven

Switch Cru

☐ SWITCHED
SWITCHEDCD / 20 Jul '98 / Switch

Switchblade Symphony

☐ BREAD AND JAM FOR FRANCES
CLP 0098 / 12 Jan '98 / Cleopatra

Swoons

☐ YOUR ASS, EY
LRR 020 / Oct '96 / Last Resort

Swoosh

☐ BELIEVE THE HYPE (2CD Set)
B2BCD 2 / 23 Feb '98 / Back 2 Basics

Swordmaster

☐ DEATH RIDER
OPCD 058 / 8 Jun '98 / Osmose

☐ POSTMORTEM TALES
OPCD 055 / Jun '97 / Osmose

SWV

☐ IT'S ABOUT TIME
Anything / I'm so into you / Right here / Weak / You're always on my mind / Downtown / Coming home / Give it to me / Black pudd'n / It's about time / Think you're gonna like it / That's what I need / SWV (in the house) / Weak / Right here (Vibe mix)
74321166112 / Feb '97 / Arista

☐ NEW BEGINNING
New beginning / You're the one / Whatcha need / On and on / It's all about U / Use your heart / Where is the love / Fine time / Love so amazin' / You are my love / I'm so in love / When this feeling / What's it gonna be / Tha's what I'm here for / Don't waste your time / Soul intact
07863664872 / Apr '96 / Arista

☐ RELEASE SOME TENSION
Someone / Release some tension / Lose my cool / Love like this / Can we / Rain / Give it up / Come and get some / When U cry / Lose myself / Here for you / Gettin' funky
74321496162 / 1 Sep '97 / Arista

☐ REMIXES, THE
07863664012 / Jun '94 / Arista

Sybil

☐ GREATEST HITS
When I'm good and ready / Love I lost / Don't make me over / Walk on by / Make it easy on me / Beyond your wildest dreams / Falling in love / Let yourself go / My love is guarenteed / Oh how I love you / You're the love of my life / Love's calling / Open up the door / Crazy 4 U / Let it rain / Guarantee of love / Stronger together / Didn't see the signs / When I'm good and ready
NP 54929 / Jun '97 / Next Plateau

Sykes, Roosevelt

☐ ANN ARBOR JAZZ & BLUES FESTIVAL VOL.3 (Sykes, Roosevelt & Victoria Spivey)
Comments: *Sykes, Roosevelt* / Driving wheel: *Sykes, Roosevelt* / Night time is the right time: *Sykes, Roosevelt* / Run this bogie: *Sykes, Roosevelt* / St. James Infirmary: *Sykes, Roosevelt* / Dirty mother for you: *Sykes, Roosevelt* / Looka here (C'mon let's shake): *Sykes, Roosevelt* / Black snake blues: *Spivey, Victoria* / Detroit moan: *Spivey, Victoria* / Victoria Spivey comments: *Spivey, Victoria* / Low down man blues (you're a rank stud): *Spivey, Victoria* / Organ grinder blues: *Spivey, Victoria* / I'm tired: *Spivey, Victoria* / Brooklyn Bridge blues: *Spivey, Victoria*
NEXCD 284 / Aug '96 / Sequel

☐ BIG TIME WOMAN
IMP 311 / Feb '97 / IMP

☐ BLUES BY ROOSEVELT 'HONEYDRIPPER' SYKES
SFWCD 40051 / Nov '95 / Smithsonian Folkways

☐ FEEL LIKE BLOWING MY HORN
Feel like blowing my horn / My hamstring's poppin' / Blues will prank with your soul / Jubilee time / All days are good days / Sykes' gumboogie / Rock-a-bye birdie / Moving blues / Don't bat your eye / All days are good days / Eagle rock me baby / Jubilee time / Love the one you're with
DE 632 / Jul '97 / Delmark

☐ GOLD MINE
Big Ben / Boot that thing / Springfield blues / Henry Ford blues / I'm a dangerous man / True thing / You understand / Whole lot of children / Last laugh / Gold mine / 44 blues / Sugar cup
DD 616 / Mar '97 / Delmark

☐ HARD DRIVIN' BLUES
Kickin' motor scooter / Red-eye Jesse Bell / I like what you do (when you do what you did last night) / New fire detective blues / North Gulfport boogie / Watch your step (if you just can't be good) / Ho ho ho / Key to your heart / We gotta move / Dresser drawers / Living the right life / Run this boogie / Slidell blues / Mistake in life / You so small / Concentration blues / She's got me straddle a log
DD 607 / Mar '97 / Delmark

☐ HONEYDRIPPER, THE
SOB 35422 / Apr '93 / Story Of The Blues

☐ HONEYDRIPPER, THE (The Honeydripper's Duke's Mixture)
Goin' down slow / Ice cream freezer / Lost my boogie / Sweet Georgia Brown / St. James infirmary / Honeysuckle rose / Basin Street blues / Rock me / Woman is in demand / Dirty Mother for you
5197272 / Apr '93 / Verve

☐ HONEYDRIPPER, THE
OBCCD 557 / Jul '95 / Original Blues Classics

☐ HONEYDRIPPER, THE
STCD 8027 / Aug '97 / Storyville

☐ MUSIC IS MY BUSINESS
157702 / Feb '93 / Blues Collection

☐ MUSIC IS MY BUSINESS
Music is my business / Mistake in life / New York boogie / Dream woman / Stop stoppin' me / Look out for yourself / Some right, some wrong / Take time out / Hot pants / Good woman / Just smile / Last chance / Who's that pretty woman / How long
TBA 13010 / Dec '96 / Blues Alliance

☐ MUSIC IS MY BUSINESS
Music is my business / Mistake in life / New York boogie / Dream woman / Stop stoppin' me / Look out for yourself / Some right, some wrong / Take time out / Hot pants / Good woman / Just smile / Leavin' Chicago / Funky side / Last chance / Who's that pretty woman / How long
CPCD 8223 / Oct '96 / Charly

☐ RETURN OF ROOSEVELT SYKES, THE
Drivin' wheel / Long, lonesome night / Set the meat outdoors / Coming home / Stompin' the boogie / Number nine / Calcutta / Selfish woman / Hangover / Night time is the right time / Runnin' the boogie / Hey big momma
OBCCD 546 / Nov '92 / Original Blues Classics

☐ ROOSEVELT SYKES SINGS THE BLUES
Slave for your love / Gone with the wind / Wild side / Out on a limb / Honey child / Never loved like this before / Last chance / Casual friend / Your will is mine / Hupe dupe do
DIAB 854 / 6 Jul '98 / Diablo

☐ ROOSEVELT SYKES VOL.1 1929-1930
DOCD 5116 / Oct '92 / Document

☐ ROOSEVELT SYKES VOL.10 1951-1957
BDCD 6050 / Sep '94 / Blues Document

☐ ROOSEVELT SYKES VOL.2 1930-1931
DOCD 5117 / Oct '92 / Document

☐ ROOSEVELT SYKES VOL.3 1931-1933
DOCD 5118 / Oct '92 / Document

☐ ROOSEVELT SYKES VOL.4 1934-1936
DOCD 5119 / Oct '92 / Document

☐ ROOSEVELT SYKES VOL.5 1937-1939
DOCD 5120 / Oct '92 / Document

☐ ROOSEVELT SYKES VOL.6 1939-1940
DOCD 5121 / Nov '92 / Document

☐ ROOSEVELT SYKES VOL.7 1941-1944
DOCD 5122 / Oct '92 / Document

☐ ROOSEVELT SYKES VOL.8 1945-1947
BDCD 6048 / Sep '94 / Blues Document

☐ ROOSEVELY SYKES VOL.9 1947-1951
BDCD 6049 / Sep '94 / Blues Document

Sylk 130

☐ WHEN THE FUNK HITS THE FAN
Narration / Jimmy leans back / City / Reason / ERA / Gettin' into it / When the funk swings / Season's change / 13 / Red handed / Taggin' and baggin' / Incident on the couch / Gorgeous / Day in the life / New love / Uptown / Last night a DJ saved my life / When the funk hits the fan / Next
SYLKCD 1 / 20 Apr '98 / Ruff House/ Sony Soho2

Sylla, Macire

☐ MARIAMA (Sylla, Macire & Djembe-Fare)
3019492 / Feb '97 / Arcade

Sylva, Berthe

☐ LES ROSES BLANCHES
995882 / 24 Apr '98 / EPM

Sylvester

☐ LIVING PROOF
Overture / Body strong / Blackbird / Could it be magic / Song or you / Happiness / Lover man (oh where can you be) / Sharing something perfect between ourselves / You are my friend / Dance (Disco heat) / You make me feel (Mighty real)
CDSEWD 107 / Nov '96 / Southbound

☐ SELL MY SOUL/TOO HOT TO SLEEP
I need you / I'll dance to that / Change up / Sell my soul / Doin' it for the real thing / Cry me a river / My life is loving you / Fever / New beginings / Thinking right / Can't forget the love / Too hot to sleep / Give it up (Don't make me wait) / Here is my love / Can't you see / Ooo baby baby / I can't believe I'm in love / Ne beginnings
CDSEWD 106 / Jul '96 / Southbound

☐ STAR (The Best Of Sylvester)
Stars (everybody is one) / Dance / Down down down / I need somebody to love tonight / I who have nothing / You make me feel (mighty real) / My life is loving you / Can't stop dancing / Body strong / Over and over / Disco international
CDSEW 007 / Jun '89 / Southbound

☐ SYLVESTER/STEP VOL.2
Over and over / I tried to forget you / Changes / Tipsong / Down down down / Loving grows up slow / I been down / Never too late / You make me feel (Mighty real) / Dance (Disco heat) / You make me feel (Mighty real) / Grateful / I took my strength from you / Was it something that I said / Just you and me forever
CDSEWD 104 / Nov '95 / Southbound

Sylvestre, Anne

☐ 40 ANS DE CHANSONS
984442 / 24 Apr '98 / EPM

☐ CHANTE...AU BORD DE LA FONTAINE
984062 / Apr '97 / EPM

☐ LES ARBRES VERTS
984432 / 24 Apr '98 / EPM

Sylvestre, Randafison

☐ ART OF RANDAFISON SYLVESTRE, THE
VICG 50122 / Mar '96 / JVC World Library

Sylvia

☐ VERY BEST OF SYLVIA, THE
DEEPMC 013 / Mar '97 / Deep Beats

Sylvian, David

☐ BRILLIANT TREES
Pulling punches / Ink in the well / Nostalgia / Red guitar / Weathered wall / Back waters / Brilliant trees
CDV 2290 / Jun '84 / Virgin

☐ DAMAGE (Sylvian, David & Robert Fripp)
Damage / God's monkey / Brightness falls / Every colour you are / Firepower / Gone to earth / Twentieth Century dreaming (a shaman's song) / Wave / River man / Darshan (the road to Graceland) / Blinding light of heaven / First day
DAMAGE 1 / Sep '94 / Virgin

☐ DARSHAN (Sylvian, David & Robert Fripp)
Darshan (The road to Graceland) / Darshan
SLYCD 1 / Feb '94 / Virgin

☐ FLUX AND MUTABILITY
Flux (a big bright colour world) / Mutability (a new beginning in the offing)
CDVE 43 / Sep '89 / Venture

☐ GONE TO EARTH
Taking the veil / Laughter and forgetting / Before the bullfight / Gone to Earth / Wave / River man / Silver moon / Healing place / Answered prayers / Where the railroad meets the sea / Wooden cross / Silver moon over sleeping steeples / Campfire coyote country / Bird of prey vanishes into a bright blue / Home / Sunlight seen through towering trees / Upon this earth
CDVDL 1 / Apr '92 / Virgin

☐ PLIGHT AND PREMONITION (Sylvian, David & Holger Czukay)
Plight (the spiralling of winter ghosts) / Premonition
CDVE 11 / Mar '88 / Venture

☐ SECRETS OF THE BEEHIVE
September / Boy with the gun / Maria / Orpheus / Devil's own / When poets dreamed of angels / Mother and child / Let the happiness in / Waterfront / Forbidden colours
CDV 2471 / Jul '91 / Virgin

Symarip

☐ SKINHEAD CLASSICS (Skinhead Moonstomp/Monkey Business - 20 Skinhead Classics)
CDTRD 407 / Mar '94 / Trojan

☐ SKINHEAD MOONSTOMP
Skinhead moonstomp / Phoenix city / Skinhead girl / Try me best / Skinhead jamboree / Chicken merry / These boots are made for walking / Must catch a train / Skin flint / Stay with him / Fung shu / You're mine
CDTRL 187 / Jan '95 / Trojan

Sympathy Nervous

☐ ROUGH CAST
NZ 090CD / 10 Nov '97 / Nova Zembla

Symphonic Orchestra

☐ ORCHESTRA ROCK VOL.3 (The Love Classics)
With you I'm born again / Up where we belong / One day in your life / Three times a lady / Cavatina / You don't bring me flowers / Memory / One day I'll fly away / Imagine / Sun ain't gonna shine anymore / Hard to say I'm sorry / Miss you nights / I wish it would rain down / My funny valentine / It's raining again / All you need is love
MCCD 075 / Jun '92 / Music Club

Symphony X

☐ DAMNATION GAME, THE
SPV 08424402 / May '96 / SPV

☐ DIVINE WINGS OF TRAGEDY
SPV 08528332 / 2 Feb '98 / SPV

☐ SYMPHONY X
SPV 0844432 / May '96 / SPV

☐ TWILIGHT IN OLYMPUS
SPV 08528682 / 23 Mar '98 / SPV

Symposium

☐ ON THE OUTSIDE
Impossible / Answer to why I hate you / Bury you / Blue / End / Nothing special / Circles squares and lines / Stay on the outside / Paint the stars / Obsessive compulsive disorder / Natural / Way
INFECT 056CD / 18 May '98 / Infectious

☐ ONE DAY AT A TIME
Drink to the sunshine / Farewell to twilight / Puddles / Fairweather friend / One day at a time / Fizzy / Girl with the brains in her feet / Smiling
INFECT 49CD / 20 Oct '97 / Infectious

Syms, Sylvia

☐ SYLVIA SYMS SINGS/SONGS OF LOVE
Then I'll be tired of you / I'm the girl / Lilac wine / I don't want to cry anymore / Honey in the honeycomb / Woman's intuition / Experiment / Let me love you / We just couldn't say goodbye / I'm so happy I could cry / Down with love / He loves and she loves / Can't we be friends / Hands across the table / Isn't it romantic / Dancing in the dark / So far / When a woman loves a man / Alone too long / What's the use of won'drin' / I am loved / Don't ever leave me / I'll be seeing you
JASCD 606 / Oct '96 / Jasmine

☐ TORCH SONG
379362 / Aug '97 / Koch International

Symtpom

☐ TEMPORARY ALIEN RESIDENCE
LFCD 010 / Jul '97 / Little Fish

Synaesthesia

☐ EPHEMERAL
CDZOT 180 / 3 Nov '97 / Zoth Ommog

Synchro

☐ SCIENCE FRICTION
Science friction / Sync or swim / Kesh u later oscillator / Quake / Cyberphunk / Tamagotchi ki ller / Ace of space / Tip hop / This stuff is real / Drugs and babes / Kitchen sync / Human oscillator
TIPCD 18 / 6 Apr '98 / Tip

Syndicate

☐ SMILE SAYS IT ALL
SICD 255 / May '97 / Sticky

Syndicate Of Sound

☐ LITTLE GIRL
Big boss man / Almost grown / So alone / Dream baby / Rumours / Little girl / That kind of man / I'm alive / You / Lookin' for the good times / Witch / Is you is or is you ain't my baby / Upper hand / Mary / Keep it up / Good time music
SC 6120 / Aug '97 / Sundazed

Synergy

☐ TAIKO SYNERGY
150212 / Aug '97 / Black Sun

Synetics

☐ PURPLE UNIVERSE, THE
CAT 006CD / Mar '97 / Rephlex

Synopsis '77

☐ LIVE IN MITTWEIDA
SYN 01 / May '97 / Full Moon

Synthonic 2000

☐ CHARIOTS OF FIRE (2CD Set)
Oxygene IV / Theme from Antarctica / Twin Peaks / L'Opera Sauvage / Crockett's theme / Chariots of fire / Sadness part 1 / Tubular bells / Autobahn / Dances with wolves / Rotations logic / Theme from Rain Man / Equinoxe / Fanfare for the common man / Miami Vice theme / Mammagamma / Eve of war / Black hole / China / Boat / Theme from Battlestar Galactica / L'Apocalypse des Animaux / Conquest of paradise / To the unknown man / Rockit / Aurora / Magic fly / Tubbs and Valerie / Lucifer / Vienna / Omen / Midnight express / Blade runner / Chi Mai / Magnetic fields / Terminator 2
RCACD 208 / Jul '97 / RCA

SYPH

☐ PST
CTCD 093 / 27 Apr '98 / Captain Trip

☐ WIELEICHT
EFA 037622 / Apr '94 / Atatak

Syrinx

☐ KALEIDOSCOPE OF SYMPHONIC ROCK
CYBERCD 9 / Aug '94 / Cyber

System 01

☐ DRUGSWORK
74321250592 / Feb '95 / Tresor

System 360

☐ ACTIVE TECHNOLOGIES
EFA 006282 / 27 Apr '98 / Source

System 7

☐ 777
BFLCD 1 / 1 Sep '98 / Butterfly

☐ GOLDEN SECTION
Rite of Spring / Don Corleone / Y2K / Ring of fire / Exdreamist / Wave bender / Sinom X files / Merkaba / Y2K (back to the future) / Borobudor
BFLCD 27 / 1 Sep '98 / Butterfly

☐ POINT 3: FIRE ALBUM
BFLCA 11 / 1 Sep '98 / Butterfly

☐ POINT 3: WATER ALBUM
BFLCB 11 / 1 Sep '98 / Butterfly

☐ POWER OF 7
BFLCD 16 / 1 Sep '98 / Butterfly

☐ SYSTEM 7
Sunburst / Freedom fighters / Habibi / Altitude / Bon humeur / Fractal liaison / Dog / Thunderdog / Listen / Strange quotations / Miracle / Over and out
DIXCD 102 / Jun '91 / 10

☐ SYSTEM 7.3/FIRE & WATER (2CD Set)
ASW 61372 / 8 Jun '98 / Astralwerks

☐ SYSTEM EXPRESS
BFLCD 21 / Oct '96 / Butterfly
BFLCD 21X / 1 Sep '98 / Butterfly

Szabo, Gabor

☐ SORCERER, THE
Beat goes on / Little boat / Lou-ise / What is this thing called love / Space / Stronger than us
MCAD 33117 / Apr '90 / Impulse Jazz

☐ SORCERER, THE
Beat goes on / Little boat / Louise / What is this thing called love / Space / Stronger than us / Mizrab / Comin' back / Los matodoros / People / Corcovado
IMP 12112 / Apr '97 / Impulse Jazz

Szabo, Sandor

☐ SANCTIFIED LAND
Arrivers / Our presence and thirtyness / Equation of the existence / Ferdinandus / Miramare / Sikonda / Sanctified land / Departers
HWYLCD 6 / Jun '91 / Hwyl

Szaszcsavas Band

☐ FOLK MUSIC FROM TRANSYLVANIA
QUI 903072 / Mar '92 / Quintana

Szeki Kurva

☐ FEARLESS VAMPIRE KILLERS, THE
ILIGHT 006CD / 10 Aug '98 / Iris Light

☐ SOUND OF DEAD GOATS, THE
Beermonsters / Goat dance / Hunter killer / Did you spill my ghoulash / Flying manga attack
ILIGHT 004CD / 23 Feb '98 / Iris Light

Szelevenyi, Akosh

☐ PANNONIA (Szelevenyi, Akosh Ensemble)
EPC 891 / Jan '94 / European Music Production

Szemzo, Tibor

☐ RELATIVE THINGS (Selected Soundscapes For Films 1994-1997)
CDLR 250 / 1 Jun '98 / Leo

T

T-Bones

☐ 1960'S FRENCH EP COLLECTION, THE
(T-Bones & Gary Farr)
174792 / 21 Aug '97 / Magic

T-Connection

☐ BEST OF T-CONNECTION, THE (At Midnight)
Do what ya wanna do / Disco magic / Go back home / Got to see my lady / Peace line / At midnight / On fire (getting higher) / Ecstasy / Let's do it today / Choosing / That's love / Born to boogie / Midnight train / Love supreme
HTCD 32 / 20 Apr '98 / Hot Productions

☐ CONNECTION/MAGIC
CCLCD 62092 / 3 Aug '98 / Collectables

☐ MAGIC
Do what you wanna do / Disco magic / Go back home / Got to see my lady / Crazy mixed up world / Mother's love / Monday morning / Peace line
MUSCD 512 / May '95 / MCI Original Masters

T-Love

☐ RETURN OF THE B GIRL
PKR 004CD / 30 Mar '98 / Pickininny

T-Model Ford

☐ PEE-WEE GET MY GUN
Cut you loose / Been a long time / Turkey and the rabbit / Let me in / Sugar farm / Feels so bad / Where you been / T-model theme / I'm insane / Nobody gets me down / Can't be touched
03032 / Jun '97 / Fat Possum

T-Power

☐ SELF EVIDENT TRUTH OF AN INTUITIVE MIND, THE
SOURCDLP 3 / Oct '95 / SOUR

☐ WAVEFORM
TPOWCD 2 / Oct '96 / Anti-Static

Ta Ixiar, Maixa

☐ UHINEZ UHIN
KD 432CD / Nov '96 / Elkar

Tab Two

☐ FLAGMAN AHEAD
MBN Trumpet intro / No flagman ahead / Wanna lay (on your side) / Swingbridge / (There's) Not a lot / What'cha gonna do / Scubertplatz / Vraiment Paris / Tab jam / Curfew / Permanent protection
CDVIR 34 / Aug '95 / Virgin

Tabackin, Lew

☐ I'LL BE SEEING YOU (Tabackin, Lew Quartet)
I surrender dear / Wise one / I'll be seeing you / Ruby my dear / Chic lady / Perhaps / Isfahan / Lost in meditation / In walked bud
CCD 4528 / Oct '92 / Concord Jazz

☐ TENORITY
Soon / Autumn nocturne / Me and my shadow / Fashion's flower / Chasin' the carrot / Sentimental journey / Trinkel tinkle / Best thing for you / You stepped out of a dream / You don't know what love is
CCD 4733 / Nov '96 / Concord Jazz

☐ WHAT A LITTLE MOONLIGHT CAN DO
What a little moonlight can do / Easy living / I wished on the moon / Love letters / Poinciana / This time the dream's on me / Broken dreams / Leaves of absinthe / Dig
CCD 4617 / Oct '94 / Concord Jazz

Tabane, Philip

☐ UNH
7559792252 / Jan '95 / Nonesuch

Tabor, June

☐ AGAINST THE STREAMS
Shameless love / I want to vanish / False, false / Pavanne / He fades away / Irish girl / Apples and potatoes / Beauty and the beast / Turn off the road / Windy city / Waiting for the lark
COOKCD 077 / Aug '94 / Cooking Vinyl

☐ ALEYN
Great Valerio / I wonder what's keeping my true love tonight / No good at love / Bentley and Craig / Fiddler / April morning / Di nakht / Fair maid of Islington / Under the greenwood tree / Go from my window / Proper sort of gardener / Johnny O'Bredislee / Shallow brown
TSCD 490 / Jul '97 / Topic

☐ ANGEL TIGER
Hard love / Joseph cross / Sudden waves / Rumours of war / All our trades are gone / Happed in mist / Doctor calls / Let no man steal your thyme / All this useless beauty / 10,000 miles / Blind step away / Elephant
COOKCD 049 / Aug '97 / Cooking Vinyl

☐ ANTHOLOGY
Mississippi summer / Verdi cries / Strange affair / She moves among men / Lay this body down / Band played waltzing Matilda / Night comes in / King of Rome / Lisbon / Month of January / Hard love / Dark eyed sailor / Heather down the moor / Cold and raw / Sudden waves / No man's land/Flowers of the forest
MCCD 126 / Sep '93 / Music Club

☐ ASHES AND DIAMONDS
Reynard the fox / Devil and bailiff McGlynn / Streets of forbes / Lord Maxwell's last goodnight / Now I'm easy / Clerk Saunders / Earl of Aboyne / Lisbon / Easter tree / Cold and raw / No man's land / Flowers of the forest
TSCD 360 / Oct '92 / Topic

☐ CUT ABOVE, A
TSCD 410 / Nov '90 / Topic

☐ FREEDOM AND RAIN (Tabor, June & The Oyster Band)
Mississippi summer / Lullaby of London / Night comes in / Valentine's day is over / All tomorrow's parties / Dives and Lazarus / Dark eyed sailor / Pain or paradise / Susie Clelland / Finisterre
COOKCD 031 / Feb '95 / Cooking Vinyl

☐ SINGING THE STORM (Tabor, June & Danny Thompson/Savouma Stevenson)
Baker / Singing the storm / Dawn / Earth, wind, water / Witch of Fauldshope / Maybe then I'll be a rose / Gypsy Queen / Fleur de Lys / Broom of Cowdenknowes / Beyond ballad / Jean Gordon
COOKCD 102 / May '96 / Cooking Vinyl

☐ SOME OTHER TIME
Some other time / Night and day / You don't know what love is / Body and soul / This is always / Pork pie hat / Solitude / I've got you under my skin / Man I love / Meditation / Sophisticated lady / 'Round midnight
HNCD 1346 / Sep '89 / Hannibal

Tabor, Ty

☐ MOONFLOWER LANE
IOMCD 023 / 1 Jun '98 / InsideOut

Tabrizi-Zadeh, Mahmoud

☐ SCENES
ALCD 194 / Sep '96 / Al Sur

Tabuh Pacific

☐ MUSIC FOR GAMELAN
CDMANU 1514 / Sep '96 / Manu

Tabula Rasa

☐ EKKEDIEN TANSSI
Ekkedien tanssi / Uskollinen / Aamukasteen laiva / Omantunnon rukous / Lasihelmipeli / Rakastaa / Kehto / Babylo rasa / Saasta muu paa / Rakastatko viela kun on ilta / Yksin
LRCD 170 / May '97 / Love

☐ TABULA RASA
Lahto / Miks' ette vastaa vanhat puut / Tuho / Gryf / Tyhja on taulu / Nyt maalaan elamaa / Vuorellaistuja / Prinssi
LRCD 135 / May '97 / Love

Taburiente

☐ A TIERRA
68976 / Apr '97 / Tropical

Tackhead

☐ FRIENDLY AS A HAND GRENADE
WRCD 013 / Nov '89 / World

☐ POWER INC VOL.1
BLCCD 10 / Jun '95 / Blanc

☐ POWER INC. VOL.3 (Live)
BLCCD 17 / 3 Nov '97 / Blanc

☐ TACKHEAD TAPE TIME
Mind at the end of tether / Half cut again / Reality / MOVE / Hard left / Get this / Man in a suitcase / What's my mission now
NTCD 036 / Feb '88 / Nettwerk

Taco

☐ VERY BEST OF TACO, THE
Puttin' on the ritz / Singing in the rain / Encore / La vie en rose / Cheek to cheek / Let's face the music / In the mood / Winchester cathedral / La chambre separee / Mae west / Sayonara / Is it love / Nice weather / Chain reaction / Beautiful sailor / Night and day
10232 / Oct '97 / Go On Deluxe

Tacuma, Jamaaladeen

☐ DREAMSCAPE
DIW 904 / Feb '96 / DIW

☐ HOUSE OF BASS
GCD 79502 / Feb '95 / Gramavision

☐ RENAISSANCE MAN
Renaissance man / Flashback / Let's have a good time / Next stop / Dancing in your head / There he stood / Battle of images / Sparkle
GCD 79438 / Sep '95 / Gramavision

Tad

☐ 8-WAY SANTA
Jinx / Giant killer / Wired god / Delinquent / Hedge hog / Flame tavern / Trash truck / Stumblin' man / Jack Pepsi / Candi / 3-D witch hunt / Crane's cafe / Plague years
SPCD 8/122 / '91 / Sub Pop

☐ INFRARED RIDINGHOOD
Ictus / Emotional cockroach / Red eye angel / Dementia / Halcyon nights / Tool marks / Mystery copter / Particle accelerator / Weakling / Thistle suit / Bullhorn / Bludge
7559617892 / Apr '95 / Warner Bros.

☐ LIVE ALIEN BROADCAST
CDMFN 181 / Jan '95 / Music For Nations

☐ SALT LICK
Axe to grind / High on the hog / Loser / Hibernation / Glue machine / Potlatch / Wood goblins / Cooking with gas / Daisy
GRCD 76 / Apr '90 / Glitterhouse

Tad Morose

☐ LEAVING THE PAST BEHIND
BMCD 043 / May '94 / Black Mark

☐ PARADIGMA
BMCD 085 / Jan '96 / Black Mark

☐ SENDER OF...
BMCD 056 / Mar '95 / Black Mark

Tadpoles

☐ DESTROY TERRASTOCK
BKCD 9028 / 11 May '98 / Bakery

☐ SMOKE GHOST
BKCD 9018 / 13 Apr '98 / Bakery

Tafari, Judah Eskender

☐ RASTAFARI TELL YOU
GPCD 007 / Sep '95 / Gussie P

Taff, Russ

☐ WINDS OF CHANGE
Bein' happy / Love is not a thing / I'd fall in love tonight / Your face / Winds of change / Home to you / Once in a lifetime / Heart like yours / I cry / One and only love
9362456762 / Jun '95 / Warner Bros.

Tag Team

☐ WHOOMP (THERE IT IS)
Whoomp (There it is) / Funkey / Kick da flow / Get nasty / Bring it on / Wreck da set / Gettin' phat / Just call me DC / Rollerboard / Drop 'em / It's somethin' / You go girl / Free style
CLU 60062 / Feb '94 / Club Tools

Tagg, Larry

☐ ROVER
199641 / 2 Mar '98 / Psychoactive

Taggy Tones

☐ HEARTBREAK HOTEL
CDS 10156 / Mar '96 / Milkcow

☐ LIVE AT EIGENS BALLROOM
EIGEN 38 / Jan '97 / AGM

☐ LOST IN THE DESERT
I miss you / Monster bop / Big machine / People are strange / Wild girl / Double trouble / Saturday night / Trouble boys / Everybody's rockin' / Keep on waiting / Nose pickin' Mama / Lonely tonight / Baby I don't care / Champagne for breakfast / Blue train / My first guitar / Kinky Miss Pinky
NERCD 080 / Apr '95 / Nervous

☐ VIKING ATTACK
So fine, so kind / BC stomp / 501 / John and Mary / Pretty eyes / Rebel cat / To my bad / Paris, Copenhagen / Crazy love / Viking attack / Crazy kid / From me to you / C-mon Johnny / Sound of guns / Letter to my baby / Myggen svermer
NERCD 070 / Feb '93 / Nervous

Tah, Geggy

☐ GRAND OPENING
Last word (one for her) / Go / LA Lulah / Giddy up / P Sluff / Tucked in / Fasterhan / Who's in a hurry / Intro / Ovary / Bomb fishing / Crack of dawn / Ghost of P Sluff / Welcome to the world (Birthday song)
9362452542 / Jul '94 / Luaka Bop

Tahar, Samir

☐ TAQSIM OUD
AAA 165 / May '98 / Club Du Disque Arabe

Tahara, Tricia

☐ SECRETS
Follow my footprints / I ain't gonna let you break my heart again / Give all your love / Show me how to fly / L'arte notte in fondo al mare / Witness / Secrets / You are my sunshine
SAVCD 2006 / 16 Mar '98 / Savant

Tahitian Man Singers

☐ TOP 20 "TANE"
S 65813 / Nov '93 / Manuiti

Tahuantinsuyo

☐ MUSIC OF THE ANDES
GCD 3001 / Jan '98 / Genes

Taiko Drum Ensemble

☐ SOH DAIKO
LYRCD 7410 / '91 / Lyrichord

Tailgators

☐ IT'S A HOG GROOVE
UPSTART 019 / Feb '96 / Upstart

Taino, Joe

☐ HOODOO MAN
Dozer for a dime / Junkyard dog / Wide glide / Cold pillow / Loiza Aldea / Goin' to Chicago / Odd blues / Pickin' the blues / Hoodoo man / Lorraine / Cry of the warrior / Take me now / Annalee / Fortune woman
PRD 70902 / May '96 / Provogue

Taj, Dorian

☐ DORIAN TAJ
PP 003 / Oct '97 / Platypus

Taj Mahal

☐ BIG BLUES (Live At Ronnie Scott's)
Big Blues / Mail box blues / Stagger Lee / Come on in my kitchen / Local local girl / Soothin' / Fishin' blues / Statesboro blues / Everybody is somebody
CLACD 328 / Apr '94 / Castle

☐ DANCING THE BLUES
Blues ain't nothin' / Hardway / Strut / Goin' to the river / Mockingbird / Blue light boogie / Hoochie coochie coo / That's how strong my love is / Down home girl / Stranger in my own hometown / Sittin' on top of the world / I'm ready
01005821122 / Mar '94 / Private Music

☐ EVENING OF ACOUSTIC MUSIC, AN
T&M 004 / Nov '94 / Tradition & Moderne

☐ LIKE NEVER BEFORE
Don't call us / River of love / Scattered / Every wind (in the river) / Blues with a feeling / Squat that rabbit / Take all the time you need / Love up / Cake walk into town / Big legged mommas are back in style / Take a giant step
261679 / Jun '91 / Private Music

☐ LIVE AND DIRECT
Jorge Ben / Reggae no. 1 / You're gonna need somebody / Little brown dog / Take a giant step / LOVE Love / And who / Suva serenade / Airplay
CDTB 121 / Aug '95 / Thunderbolt

☐ MULEBONE
Jubilee / Graveyard mule (hambone rhyme) / Me and the mule / Song for a banjo dance / But I rode some / Hey hey blues / Shake that thing / Intermission blues / Crossing (lonely day) / Bound no'th blues / Final
GV 794322 / Mar '91 / Gramavision

☐ NATCH'L BLUES, THE
Good morning Miss Brown / Corine Corina / I ain't gonna let nobody steal my mail... / Done changed my way of living / She caught the Katy / Cuckoo / You don't miss your water / Lot of love
4836792 / Mar '96 / Columbia

☐ PHANTOM BLUES
Lovin' in my baby's eyes / Cheatin' on you / Hustle is on / Here in the dark / Fanning the flames / I need your loving / Ooh-poo-pah-doo / Lonely Avenue / Don't tell me / What am I living for / We're gonna make it / Let the four winds blow / (You've got to) Love her with a feeling / Car of your dreams
01005821392 / 2 Feb '98 / Private Music

☐ RISING SUN COLLECTION
RSCD 003 / Apr '94 / Just A Memory

☐ SENOR BLUES
Queen Bee / Think / Irresistable you / Having a real bad day / Senor blues / Sophisticated / Oh Lord, things are getting crazy up here / I miss you baby / You rascal you / Mind your own business / 21st century gypsy singin' lover man / At last (I found a love) / Mr. Pitiful
1005821512 / Jul '97 / Private Music

☐ TAJ MAHAL
Leaving trunk / Statesboro blues / Checkin' up on my baby / Everybody's got to change sometime / Ezy ryder / Dust my broom / Diving duck blues / Celebrated walkin' blues
4809682 / Aug '95 / Columbia

☐ TAJ MAHAL AND THE HULA BLUES
Calypsonians / Coconut man / Sacred island / Betty 'n' Dupree / New hula blues / No na mamo / Mailbox blues / Kanikapila
T&M 009 / Nov '97 / Tradition & Moderne

☐ TAJ'S BLUES
Leaving trunk / Statesboro blues / Everybody's got to change / Sometime / Bound to love me some / Frankie and Albert / East Bay woman / Dust my broom / Corinna / Jelly roll / Fishin' blues / Needed time / Curiosity blues / Horse shoes / Country blues
4716602 / Jul '92 / Columbia

Tajes, Juan Carlos

☐ TANGO CANCION (Tajes, Juan Carlos & Piet Capello)
La concion de Buenos Aires / Milonga de Albornoz / A Homero / Bailate un tango, Ricardo / Caseron de tejas / Milonga de la ganzua / Mil novecientos sesenta y cuatro / Los paraguas de Buenos Aires / Pequena nina mia / Oro y plata / Milonga en ay menor / Milonga de dos hermanos / Elegia / Y todavia te quiero / Pobre negra
AL 73029 / Nov '96 / A

Tajima, Tadashi

☐ SHAKUHACHI
CDT 124CD / Jul '94 / Music Of The World

Takadja

☐ DIYE
150252 / Aug '97 / Black Sun

☐ TAKADJA
130972 / Aug '97 / Black Sun

Takahashi, Ayuo

☐ PRIVATE TAPES
PSFD 64 / Dec '95 / PSF

Takahashi, Yukihiro

☐ NEUROMANTIC
Glass / Grand espoir / Connection / New (red) roses / Extraordinary / Drip dry eyes / Curtains / Charge / Something in the air
SPALAX 14501 / Oct '96 / Spalax

☐ WHAT, ME, WORRY
What...me worry / It's gonna work out / Sayonara / This strange obsession / Flashback / Real you / Disposable love / My highland home in Thailand / All you got to do / It's all too much
SPALAX 14502 / Oct '96 / Spalax

Takano, Max

☐ NEW YORK NEW YORK
Die fledermaus overture (johann strauss ii) / Puppet on a string / Walt disney (medley) / Night in tunisia (2nd version) / Somewhere out there / Sesame street / Annen polka / Tico tico / Tea for two / Just the two of us / Polonaise eroica / Birth of a band
CDGRS 1205 / Feb '93 / Grosvenor

Takara

☐ ETERNAL FAITH
NTHEN 007CD / Sep '95 / Now & Then

Takatina, He Toa

☐ AUTHENTIC MAORI SONGS
CDODE 1007 / Feb '90 / ODE

Take 6

☐ BROTHERS
9362462352 / Feb '97 / Reprise

☐ JOIN THE BAND
Can't keep goin' on and on / All I need (is a chance) / My friend / It's gonna rain / You can never ask too much (of love) / I've got life / Stay tuned (interlude) / Biggest part of me / Badiyah (interlude) / Harmony / Four Miles (interlude) / Even though / Why I feel this way / Lullaby
9362454972 / Jun '94 / Reprise

Take That

☐ EVERYTHING CHANGES
Everything changes / Pray / Wasting my time / Relight my fire / Love ain't here anymore / If this is love / Whatever you do to me / Meaning of love / Why can't I wake up with you / You are the one / Another crack in my heart / Broken your heart / Babe
74321169262 / Feb '97 / RCA

☐ GREATEST HITS
How deep is your love / Never forget / Back for good / Sure / Love ain't here anymore / Everything changes / Babe / Relight my fire / Pray / Why can't I wake up with you / Could it be magic / Million love songs / I found heaven / It only takes a minute / Once you've tasted love / Promise / Do what u like
74321355582 / Mar '96 / RCA

☐ INTERVIEW DISC
SAM 7007 / Nov '96 / Sound & Media

☐ NOBODY ELSE
Sure / Back for good / Everyguy / Sunday to Saturday / Nobody else / Never forget / Hanging onto your love / Holding back the tears / Hate it / Lady tonight / Day after tomorrow
74321279092 / 1 Sep '97 / RCA

☐ TAKE THAT AND PARTY
I found heaven / Once you've tasted love / It only takes a minute / Million love songs / Satisfied / I can make it / Do what you like / Promises / Why can't I wake up with you / Never want to let you go / Give good feeling / Could it be magic / Take That and party
74321109232 / Feb '96 / RCA

Takemura, Nobukazu

☐ CHILD'S VIEW
992157CD / Nov '96 / Ninetynine

Takeshita, Kazuhira

☐ FOLK SONGS OF AMAMI
VICG 53592 / Feb '96 / JVC World Library

Takfarinas

☐ LA COLLECTION
3024012 / 5 Jan '98 / Arcade

Takis & Anestos

☐ GREEK FOLK DANCES
MCD 71722 / Jun '93 / Monitor

Tala'i, Daryoush

☐ TRADITION CLASSIQUE DE L'IRAN VOL.2 (Tala'i, Daryoush & Djamchid Chemirani)
HMA 1901031 / Nov '93 / Musique D'Abord

Talamh, Sean

☐ TRADITIONAL IRISH MUSIC
EUCD 1252 / Mar '94 / ARC

Talbot, Mick

☐ OFF THE BEATEN TRACK (Talbot, Mick & Steve White)
Are we on / Sticks and stones / 'Til the cows come home / Out of my box / Off the beaten track / Hopes and fears / Riding the rapids / Sonny's prayer / Three's a crowd / Under my skin
NNCD 1002 / Sep '96 / New Note

Talila

☐ PAPIROSSN
LDX 274956 / Jan '93 / La Chant Du Monde

Talisman

☐ BEST OF TALISMAN, THE
ERCD 1031 / Feb '97 / Empire

Talisman

☐ LIFE
ERCD 1025 / 20 Apr '98 / Now & Then

Talk Show

☐ TALK SHOW
Ring twice / Hello hello / Everybody loves my car / Peeling an orange / So long / Wash me down / End of the world / John / Behind / Morning girl / Hide / Fill the fields
7567830402 / 20 Oct '97 / Atlantic

Talk Talk

☐ ASIDES AND BESIDES (2CD Set)
Talk talk / Today / My foolish friend / It's my life / Such a shame / Such a shame / Dum dum girl / Without you / Life's what you make it / Living in another world / Pictures of Bernadette / Happiness is easy / Talk talk / Mirror man / Candy / Strike up the band / Question mark / My foolish friend / Call in the night boys / Why is it so hard / Again a game...again... / Dum dum girl / It's getting late in the evening / For what it's worth / Pictures of Bernadette / Eden / John Cope
CDEMC 3670 / Nov '96 / EMI

☐ ASIDES AND BESIDES (2CD Set)
Talk talk / Today / My foolish friend / It's my life / Such a shame / Dum dum girl / Without you / Life's what you make it / Living in another world / Pictures of Bernadette / Hapiness is easy / Talk talk / Mirror man / Candy / Strike up the band / My foolish friend / Call in the night boys / Why is it so hard / Again a game again / Without you / Dum dum girl / It's getting late in the evening / For what it's worth / Pictures of Bernadette / Eden / John Cope
8548072 / 13 Apr '98 / EMI

☐ COLOUR OF SPRING, THE (Remastered)
Happiness is easy / I don't believe in you / Life's what you make it / April 5th / Living in another world / Give it up / Chameleon day / Time it's time
RETALK 102 / 1 Sep '97 / EMI

☐ HISTORY REVISITED (The Remixes)
Living in another world / Such a shame / Happiness is easy / Today / Dum dum girl / Life's what you make it / Talk Talk / It's my life / Living in another world (Curious world dub mix)
CDPCS 7349 / Feb '91 / Parlophone

☐ IT'S MY LIFE (Remastered)
Dum dum girl / Such a shame / Renee / It's my life / Tomorrow started / Last time / Call in the night boys / Does Caroline know / It's you
RETALK 101 / 1 Sep '97 / EMI

☐ PARTY'S OVER, THE (Remastered)
Talk talk / It's so serious / Today / Party's over / Hate / Have you heard the news / Mirror man / Another word / Candy
RETALK 100 / 1 Sep '97 / EMI

☐ SPIRIT OF EDEN (Remastered)
Rainbow / Eden / Desire / Inheritance / I believe in you / Wealth
RETALK 103 / 1 Sep '97 / EMI

☐ VERY BEST OF TALK TALK, THE
It's my life / Talk talk / Today / Dum dum girl / Have you heard the news / Such a shame / For what it's worth / Life's what you make it / Eden / April 5th / Living in another world / I believe in you / Give it up / John Cope / Wealth / Time it's time
CDEMC 3763 / Jan '97 / EMI

Talking Heads

☐ FEAR OF MUSIC
I Zimbra / Mind / Cities / Paper / Life during wartime / Memories can't wait / Air / Heaven / Animals / Electric guitar / Drugs
256707 / '94 / Sire

☐ LITTLE CREATURES
And she was / Give me back my name / Creatures of love / Lady don't mind / Perfect world / Stay up late / Walk it down / Television man / Road to nowhere
CDFA 3301 / Nov '93 / Fame

☐ MORE SONGS ABOUT BUILDINGS AND FOOD
Thank you for sending me an angel / With our love / Good thing / Warning sign / Girls want to be with the girls / Found a job / Artists only / I'm not in love / Stay hungry / Take me to the river / Big country
256531 / Jan '87 / Sire

☐ NAKED
Blind / Mr. Jones / Totally nude / Ruby dear / Nothing but flowers / Democratic circus / Facts of life / Mommy, daddy / Big daddy / Cool water / Bill
CDFA 3300 / Nov '93 / Fame

☐ ONCE IN A LIFETIME (The Best Of Talking Heads)
Psycho Killer / Take me to the river / Once in a lifetime / Burning down the house / This must be the place (Naive melody) / Life during wartime / And she was / Road to nowhere / Wild wild life / Nothing but flowers / Sax and violins / Lifetime piling up
CDEMD 1039 / Oct '92 / EMI

☐ REMAIN IN LIGHT
Great curve / Cross-eyed and painless / Born under punches (heat goes on) / Houses in motion / Once in a lifetime / Listening wind / Seen and not seen / Overload
256867 / '83 / Sire

☐ SPEAKING IN TONGUES
Burning down the house / Making flippy floppy / Swamp / Girlfriend is better / Slippery people / I get wild / Pull up the roots / Moon rocks / This must be the place (Naive melody)
9238832 / '83 / Sire

☐ STOP MAKING SENSE
Psycho Killer / Swamp / Slippery people / Burning down the house / Girlfriend is better / Once in a lifetime / What a day that was / Life during wartime / Take me to the river
CDFA 3302 / Nov '93 / Fame

☐ STOP MAKING SENSE/LITTLE CREATURES/TRUE STORIES (The Originals/3CD Set)
Psycho killer / Swamp / Slippery people / Burning down the house / Girlfriend is better / Once in a lifetime / What a day that was / Life during wartime / Take me to the river / And she was / Give me back my name / Creatures of love / Lady don't mind / Perfect world / Stay up late / Walk it down / Television man / Road to nowhere / Love for sale / Puzzlin' evidence / Hey now / Papa Legba / Wild wild life / Radio head / Dream operator / People like us / City of dreams
CDOMB 003 / 27 Jul '98 / EMI

☐ TALKING HEADS '77
Uh-oh, love comes to town / New feeling / Tentative decisions / Happy day / Who is it / No compassion / Book I read / Don't worry about the government / First week / Last week... carefree / Psycho killer / Pulled up
K 256647 / Feb '87 / Sire

☐ TRUE STORIES
Love for sale / Puzzlin' evidence / Hey now / Papa Legba / Wild wild life / Radio head / Dream operator / People like us / City of dreams / Wild wild life (remix)
CDFA 3231 / Sep '89 / Fame

Tall Guy Blues Band

☐ THEY CALL ME THE TALL GUY
TG 728525 / 19 Mar '98 / Tall Guy

Tallari

☐ KOMMIAMMASTI
KICD 45 / Nov '96 / Kansanmusiikki Instituutti

☐ KONSTA
KICD 31 / Dec '94 / Kansanmusiikki Instituutti

Talley, James

☐ AMERICAN ORIGINALS
Find somebody and love them / Bury me in New Orleans / Baby she loves a rocker / Whiskey on the side / Are they gonna make us outlaws again / Way to say I love you / New York town / Open all night / Montana song / Ready to please / We're all one family
BCD 15244 / '86 / Bear Family

☐ BLACKJACK CHOIR/ AIN'T IT SOMETHIN'
Bluesman / Alabama summertime / Everybody loves a love song / Magnolia boy / Mississippi river whistle town / Daddy just called it the blues / Up from Georgia / Migrant Jesse Sawyer / You know I've got to love her / When the fiddler packs his case / Ain't it somethin' / Only the best / We keep tryin' / Dixie blues / Not even when it's over / Nine pounds of hashbrowns / Richland, Washington / Middle C mama / Woman troubles / Old time religion / Poets of the West Virginia mines / What will there be for the children
BCD 15435 / Jul '89 / Bear Family

☐ GOT NO BREAD/ TRYIN' LIKE THE DEVIL
WLee O'Daniel and the Light Crust Dough Boys / Got no bread, no milk, no money / Red river memory / Give him another bottle / Calico gypsy / To get back home / Big taters in the sandy land / No openers needed / Blue eyed Ruth and my Sunday suit / Mehan, Oklahoma / Daddy's song / Take me to the country / Red river reprise / Forty hours / Deep country blues / Give my love to Marie / Are they gonna make us outlaws again / She tries not to cry / Tryin' like the devil / She's the one / Sometimes I think about Suzanne / Nothin' but the blues / You can't ever tell
BCD 15433 / Nov '93 / Bear Family

☐ LIVE
Tryin' like the devil / Woman trouble / Whiskey on the side / Dixie blues / W Lee O'Daniel and the light crust doughboys / Not even when it's over / Nothin' like love / Find somebody and love them / Survivors / Bluesman / I can't surrender / We keep tryin' / Are you gonna make us outlaws again / Give my love to Mary / Alabama summertime / Take me to the country / Take a whiff on me
BCD 15704 / Jun '94 / Bear Family

☐ LOVE SONGS AND THE BLUES
Your sweet love / Whatever gets you through your life / I can't surrender / He went back to Texas / Working girl / Little child / Up from Georgia / All because of you / Collection of sorrows / 'Cause I'm in love with you / May your dreams come true
BCD 15464 / Jul '89 / Bear Family

☐ ROAD TO TORREON
Maria / Ramon estevan / H John Tarragon / Demona / La rosa Montana / She was a flower / Rosary / Storm / Little child / Anna Maria / I had a love way out West
BCD 15633 / Jun '92 / Bear Family

Talulah Gosh

☐ BACKWASH
KLP 44CD / May '96 / K

☐ ROCK LEGENDS VOL.69
Beatnik boy / My best friend / Steaming train / Just a dream / Talulah gosh / Don't go away / Escalator over the hill / My boy says / Way of the world / Testcard girl / Bringing up baby / I can't get no satisfaction (Thank god) / Strawberry girl
ONLYCD 011 / May '91 / Avalanche

Talwalkar, Padma

☐ RAGAS BIHAG DURGA BASANT-KHYAL/DADRA
NI 5567 / Jun '98 / Nimbus

Tamalin

☐ RHYTHM AND RHYME
GRACD 227 / Jul '97 / Grapevine

Tamarack

☐ FIELDS OF ROCK AND SNOW
FE 1407 / Nov '94 / Folk Era

☐ FROBISHER BAY
FE 1409 / Nov '94 / Folk Era

Tamba Trio

☐ TAMBA TRIO CLASSICS (2CD Set)
Desafinado / Consolocao / Garota de Ipanema / Mas que nada / Sonho de Maria / So danco o samba / O Barquinho / Influenia do jazz / O morro nao tem vez / Batida diferente / O samba da minha terra / Nos e o mar / Tristeza de nos dois / Procissaco / Minha / Berimbau / Moca flor / Quem me dera / Agua de Beber / Cancao do nosso amor / Coreovado / Imagem / O amor que acabou / Nuvens / Tamba / Rio
5369582 / 15 Jun '98 / EmArCy

Tambastics

☐ TAMBASTICS
CD 704 / Apr '93 / Music & Arts

Tamburi Del Vesuvio

☐ TERRA E MOTUS
FT 02CD / Dec '97 / Robi Droli

Tamia

☐ SOLITUDES (Tamia & Pierre Favre)
8496454 / Feb '92 / ECM

Tammles

☐ SANS BAGAGE
BUR 832CD / '90 / Escalibur

Tampa Red

☐ BLUEBIRD RECORDINGS 1934-1936, THE (2CD Set)
I'll kill your soul (and dare your spirit to move) / If I let you get away with it (you'll do it all the time) / I'll find my way / You've got to do better / Kingfish blues / You don't want me blues / Nobody's sweetheart now / I'm just crazy 'bout you / I still got California on my mind / Grievin' and worryin' blues / Give it up Buddy and get goin' / Somebody's been usin' that thing / Mean mistreater blues / Happy Jack / I'm so disappointed in you / Worried devil blues / Christmas and New Year's blues / Sweet woman / I'll get a break someday / Witchin' hour blues / Stockyard fire / Worthy of you / If it ain't that gal of mine / Mean old Tom cat blues / Mean old Tom cat blues / Don't dog your woman / Singing and crying blues / Shake it up a little / My baby said yes / I'm betting on you / Rowdy woman blues / Keep on dealin' (play your hand) / (I could learn to love you) so good / When I take my vacation in Harlem / Drinkin' my blues away / Dark and stormy night / Good woman blues / You missed a good man / Wailing blues / When you were a gal of seven / Let's get drunk and truck / Maybe it's someone else you love / I wonder what's the matter / She don't know my mind / She don't know my mind
07863667212 / Feb '97 / Bluebird

☐ DON'T JIVE ME
OBCCD 549 / Nov '92 / Original Blues Classics

☐ DON'T TAMPA WITH THE BLUES
I'm a stranger here / Let me play with your poodle / Goodbye baby / Things about coming my way / Kansas city blues / You better do right / Louise blues / It's tight like that / You got to love her with a feeling / Boogie woogie woman
OBCCD 516 / Nov '92 / Original Blues Classics

☐ GREAT PIANO (Tampa Red & Big Maceo)
159072 / 24 Feb '98 / Blues Collection

☐ IT HURTS ME TOO
IGOCD 2004 / Oct '94 / Indigo

☐ TAMPA RED VOL.1 1928-1929
DOCD 5073 / '92 / Document

☐ TAMPA RED VOL.1 1934-1935
BDCD 6044 / May '93 / Blues Document

☐ TAMPA RED VOL.10
DOCD 5210 / Oct '93 / Document

☐ TAMPA RED VOL.11
DOCD 5211 / Oct '93 / Document

☐ TAMPA RED VOL.12
DOCD 5212 / Oct '93 / Document

☐ TAMPA RED VOL.13
DOCD 5213 / Oct '93 / Document

☐ TAMPA RED VOL.14
DOCD 5214 / Oct '93 / Document

☐ TAMPA RED VOL.15
DOCD 5215 / Oct '93 / Document

☐ TAMPA RED VOL.2 1929
DOCD 5074 / '92 / Document

☐ TAMPA RED VOL.2 1935-1936
BDCD 6045 / May '93 / Blues Document

☐ TAMPA RED VOL.3 1929-1930
DOCD 5075 / '92 / Document

☐ TAMPA RED VOL.4 1929-1930
DOCD 5076 / '92 / Document

☐ TAMPA RED VOL.5 1931-1934
DOCD 5077 / Oct '93 / Document

☐ TAMPA RED VOL.6
DOCD 5206 / Oct '93 / Document

☐ TAMPA RED VOL.7
DOCD 5207 / Oct '93 / Document

☐ TAMPA RED VOL.8
DOCD 5208 / Oct '93 / Document

☐ TAMPA RED VOL.9
DOCD 5209 / Oct '93 / Document

Tamplin

☐ IN THE WITNESS BOX
NTHEN 024CD / Jan '96 / Now & Then

Tamplin, Ken

☐ WE THE PEOPLE
A2Z 85006CD / Jul '96 / A-Z

Tams

☐ BEST OF THE TAMS, THE
I've been hurt / Go away little girl / Take away / Be young, be foolish, be happy / Hey girl don't bother me / You lied to your Daddy / Weep little girl / It's alright / Laugh it off / Shelter / What kind of fool / Letter / Greatest love / All my hard times
BGOCD 266 / Feb '95 / Beat Goes On

☐ BEST OF THE TAMS, THE
CDSGP 0110 / Sep '94 / Prestige

☐ HEY GIRL DON'T BOTHER ME (The Best Of The Tams)
HMNCD 032 / 22 Jun '98 / Half Moon

Tamson, Jock

☐ JOCK TAMSON'S BAIRNS (Tamson, Jock Bairns)
Lasses fashion / Robin / Merry nicht under the Tummel Brig / Braes o' Balquhidder / Greig's strathspey / Miss Wharton Duff / Lady Keith's lament / Gates of Edinburgh / O'er Bogie / Mrs. Gordon of Uvie / Tibbie Fowler / Shetland fiddler's society / Grant's reel / Gladstone's reel / Laird o' Drum / Kempy Kaye / Donald Willie and his dog / Peter MacKinnon of Skeabost / Arthur Bignold of Lochrosque / Hugh MacDonald / Sandy Duff / Birkin tree / Hieland soldier / Mullindhu / Skye man's jig / Jenny Dang the weaver / Brave Lewie Roy / Wantonness / Cathkin Braes / Miss Grace Hay's delight / Sheperdess / In dispraise of whisky / Hills of Perth / Mrs. MacDougall
CDTRAX 112 / Apr '96 / Greentrax

Tamulevich, David

☐ MUSTARD'S RETREAT (Tamulevich, David & Michael Hough)
RHRCD 72 / Aug '95 / Red House

Tamura, Natsuki

☐ HOW MANY (Tamura, Natsuki & Satoka Fujii)
LEOLABCD 029 / May '97 / Leo Lab

☐ SONG FOR JYAKI, A
LEOLABCD 039 / Feb '98 / Leo Lab

Tananas

☐ ORCHESTRA MUNDO
342602 / Dec '95 / Koch International
669712 / Mar '96 / Melodie

TanaReid

☐ BACK TO FRONT (Tana, Akira & Rufus Reid)
Mr. Brown: *TanaReid* / Dream catcher: *TanaReid* / Lazy afternoon: *TanaReid* / Back to front: *TanaReid* / But not for me: *TanaReid* / Embraceable you: *TanaReid* / When she smiles upon your face: *TanaReid* / Green grove: *TanaReid* / Perpetual stroll: *TanaReid* / McWorld: *TanaReid*
ECD 22206 / 7 Apr '98 / Evidence

☐ BLUE MOTION (Tana, Akira & Rufus Reid)
Day and night / Con alma / Blue motion / Tata's dance / It's the nights I like / I concentrate on you / Medley / With a song in my heart / Amy Marie / Elvinesque
ECD 220752 / Feb '94 / Evidence

☐ LOOKING FORWARD (Tana, Akira & Rufus Reid)
Billy / Gold minor / Duke / Skyline / Falling in love / Bell / Third eye / Reminiscing / Love dreams / Looking forward
ECD 22114 / Jun '95 / Evidence

☐ PASSING THOUGHTS (Tana, Akira & Rufus Reid)
Hotel le hot / City slicker / Heroes / Cheek to cheek / Sophisticated lady / Prelude to a kiss / Hope for now / Passing thoughts / Light blue / It's the magical look in your eyes / Scufflestyle
CCD 4505 / May '92 / Concord Jazz

Tanaw

☐ BLOAZ AN ERH DU
KMCD 73 / 21 Aug '97 / Keltia Musique

Tandu

☐ MULTIMOODS
20852 / 12 Jan '98 / Phonokol

Tanenbaum, David

☐ ASTOR PIAZZOLLA - EL PORTENO
NA 065 / May '94 / New Albion

Tangent

☐ SHADOW MAGIC (The Best Of Tangent)
ZRCD 1214 / 12 Jan '98 / Beat Goes On

Tangerine

☐ TANGERINE
CRECD 061 / May '94 / Creation

Tangerine Dream

☐ ALPHA CENTAURI
Sunrise in the third system / Fly and collision of comas sola / Alpha centauri
ESMCD 346 / Feb '96 / Essential

☐ ALPHA CENTAURI/ ATEM
Sunrise in the third system / Fly and collision of the comas sola / Alpha Centauri / Atem / Fauni-gena / Circulation of events / Wahn
8856180692 / Oct '87 / Relativity

☐ ANALOGUE SPACE YEARS 1969-1973 (2CD Set)
CLP 227 / 20 Apr '98 / Cleopatra

☐ ATEM
Atem / Fauni-gena / Consolation of events / Whan
ESMCD 348 / Feb '96 / Essential

☐ ATMOSPHERICS
EMPRCD 564 / Mar '95 / Emporio

☐ BEST OF TANGERINE DREAM, THE (The Blue Years)
CCSCD 824 / 30 Mar '98 / Castle

☐ COLLECTION VOL.1, THE
Genesis / Circulation of events / Fauni-gena / Alpha centauri / (Zeit first movement) Birth of liquid plejades / White clouds
CCSCD 815 / 26 Jan '98 / Castle

☐ CYCLONE
Bent cold sidewalk / Rising runner missed by endless sender / Madrigal meridian
TAND 9 / Apr '95 / Virgin

☐ DREAM ROOTS COLLECTION, THE (5CD Set)
Birth of liquid plejades / Journey through a burning brain / Alpha centauri / Zeit / Wahn / Fauni-gena / Green desert / White clouds / Astral voyager / Origin of supernatural probabilities / Indian summer / Ride on a ray / Livemiles / Tangent / Smile / Livemiles / Vigour / Central Park / Zen garden / Livemiles / Le parc / 21st century common man / Underwater sunlight / Livemiles / London / Gaudi Park / Barbakane / Alchemy of my heart / Horizon / Song of the whale / Yellowstone Park / Tyger / Bois de Boulogne / Tiergarten / Poland / Barbakane / Livemiles / Rarebird / Song of the whale / London / Valley of the sun / Beach bay bunker / Vanishing blue / Red morpho
ESFCD 420 / Nov '96 / Essential

☐ DREAM SEQUENCE (2CD Set)
Dream is always the same / Phaedra / Rubycon / Stratosfear / Choronzon / Cherokee Lane / Cinnamon Road / Kiew mission / Ricochet / Cloudburst flight / Force majeure / Tangram / Beach stone / Logos / White eagle / Dominion / Love on a real train
CDTD 1 / Apr '92 / Virgin

☐ ELECTRONIC MEDITATION
Genesis / Journey through a burning brain / Cold smoke / Ashes to ashes / Resurrection
ESMCD 345 / Feb '96 / Essential

☐ ENCORE (Live)
Cherokee lane / Monolight / Coldwater canyon / Desert dream
TAND 1 / Apr '95 / Virgin

☐ FORCE MAJEURE
Force Majeure / Cloudburst flight / Thru Metamorphic rocks
TAND 10 / Apr '95 / Virgin

☐ FROM DAWN TILL DUSK 1973-1988
Song of the whale (part 1: from dawn) / Song of the whale (part 2: from dusk) / Bois de Boulogne / Ride on the ray / Poland / London / Le parc / Live miles (extract) / Central Park / Zeit / Wahh
MCCD 034 / Sep '91 / Music Club

☐ GOBLINS CLUB
Towards the evening star / At Darwin's motel / On crane's passage / Rising haul in silence / United Goblins parade / Lamb with radar eyes / Elf June and the midnight patrol / Sad Merlin's Sunday
WENCD 011 / Sep '96 / When

☐ GREEN DESERT
Green desert / White clouds / Astral voyager / Indian summer
ESMCD 349 / Feb '96 / Essential

☐ HYPERBOREA
No man's land / Hyperborea / Cinnamon road / Sphinx lightning
TAND 4 / Jul '95 / Virgin

☐ LE PARC
Bois de Boulogne / Central Park / Gaudi Park / Tiergarten / Zen garden / Le Parc / Hyde Park / Cliffs of Sydney / Yellowstone Park
ESMCD 364 / May '96 / Essential

☐ LILY ON THE BEACH
Too hot for my chinchilla / Lily on the beach / Alaskan summer / Desert drive / Mount Shasta / Crystal curfew / Paradise cove / Twenty nine palms / Valley of the kings / Radio city / Blue Mango Cafe / Gecko / Long island sunset
260103 / Dec '89 / Private Music

☐ LIVE MILES
ESMCD 368 / May '96 / Essential

☐ LOGOS (Live At The Dominion, London 1982)
Logos / Dominion
TAND 3 / Jul '95 / Virgin

☐ OPTICAL RACE
Marrakesh / Atlas eyes / Mothers of rain / Twin soul tribe / Optical race / Cat scan / Sun gate / Turning of the wheel / Midnight trail / Ghazal (Love song)
259557 / Aug '88 / Private Music

☐ PERGAMON
ESMCD 413 / May '96 / Essential

☐ PHAEDRA
Phaedra / Mysterious semblance at the strand of nightmares / Movements of a visionary / Sequent C
TAND 5 / Feb '95 / Virgin

☐ POLAND (The Warsaw Concert)
Poland / Tangent / Barbarkne / Horizon
ESMCD 365 / May '96 / Essential

☐ PRIVATE MUSIC OF TANGERINE DREAM, THE
Melrose / Too hot for my chinchilla / Long Island sunset / Atlas eyes / Sun gate / Rolling down Cahuenga / Three bikes in the sky / After the call / Electric lion / Dolls in the shadow / Beaver town / Roaring of the bliss
01005821052 / Feb '93 / Private Music

☐ RICOCHET
TAND 7 / Feb '95 / Virgin

☐ ROCKOON
Big city of dwarves / Red roadster / Touchwood / Graffiti Street / Funky Atlanta / Spanish love / Lifted veil / Penguin reference / Body corporate / Rockoon / Girls on Broadway
ESMCD 403 / Jul '96 / Essential

☐ RUBYCON
TAND 6 / Feb '95 / Virgin

☐ STRATOSFEAR
Stratosfear / Big sleep in search of Hades / 3 a.m. at the border of the marsh / Invisible limits
TAND 8 / Feb '95 / Virgin

☐ TANGENTS 1973-1983 (5CD Set)
Mojave plan (Desert part) / No man's land / Kiew mission / Ricochet / Force majeure / Logos (blue part) / Stratosfear / Mysterious semblance at the strand of nightmares / Cinnamon road / Tangram (solution part) / White eagle / Phaedra / Logos (red part) / Sphinx lightning / Desert dream / Invisible limits / Exit / Mojave plan (canyon part) / Tangram (puzzle part) / Monolight / Rubycon (The Decision) / Cloudburst flight / Pilots of purple twilight / Logos (velvet part) / Monolight (yellow part) / Tangram (future part) / Rubycon (dice part) / Hyperborea / Rubycon (crossing part) / Dominion / Pergamon (piano part) / Going West / Dream is always the same / Alien goodbye / Call / Run / Betrayal (Sorceror theme) / Rainbirds move / Creation / Charly the kid / Journey / Scrap yard / Dirty cross roads / Search / Highway patrol / Grind / Risky business / Beach theme / Vulcano / Jogger / South Dakota / Coppercoast / Great barrier reef / Night at Ayers Rock / Afternoon on the Nile / Crane routing / Silver scale / Jamaican monk
CDBOX 4 / Oct '94 / Virgin

☐ TANGERINE AMBIENCE (A Tribute To Tangerine Dream) (Various Artists)
CLP 0048 / Aug '97 / Cleopatra

☐ TANGERINE DREAM
Phaedra / Mysterious semblance at the strand of nightmares / Movements of visionary / Sequent 'C' / Rubycon / Stratosfear
VI 873772 / Oct '96 / Disky

☐ TANGRAM
TAND 11 / Apr '95 / Virgin

☐ TIMESQUARE (Dream Mixes Vol.2)
Mobocaster / Jungle Jacula / Towards the evening star / Digital sister / Pixel pirates / Culpa levis / Timesquare
TDI 006CD / 10 Aug '98 / TDI

☐ TURN OF THE TIDES
Pictures at an exhibition (mussorgsky) / Firetongues / Galley slave's horizon / Death of a nightingale / Twilight brigade / Jungle journey / Midwinter night / Turn of the tides
CTCZ 108 / Nov '96 / Coast To Coast

☐ TYGER
Tyger / London / Alchemy of the heart / Smile / 21st century common man
ESMCD 367 / May '96 / Essential

☐ UNDERWATER SUNLIGHT
Song of the whale / Song of the whale / Dolphin dance / Ride on the Ray / Scuba Scuba / Underwater twilight
ESMCD 366 / May '96 / Essential

☐ WHITE EAGLE
Mojave plan / Midnight in Tula / Convention of the 24 / White Eagle
TAND 2 / Jul '95 / Virgin

☐ ZEIT
Birth of liquid plejades / Nebulous dawn / Origin of supernatural possibilities / Zeit
ESMCD 347 / Feb '96 / Essential

Tangle Edge

☐ EULOGY
DMCD 1029 / May '93 / Demi-Monde

☐ IN SEARCH OF A NEW DAWN
DMCD 1009 / Mar '95 / Demi-Monde

☐ TAKRA
DELECCD 065 / Jun '97 / Delerium

Tank

☐ HONOUR AND BLOOD
HV 1009 / Sep '97 / High Vaultage

☐ POWER OF THE HUNTER
REP 4150 / Aug '91 / Repertoire

☐ RETURN OF THE FILTH HOUNDS LIVE
This means war / Echoes of a distant battle / TWDAMO / And then we heard the thunder / Don't walk away / Honour and blood / Power of the hunter / Shellshock / In the last hour before dawn
RS 0082032CD / 17 Aug '98 / Rising Sun

☐ THIS MEANS WAR
HV 1008 / Sep '97 / High Vaultage

Tank, John

☐ SO IN LOVE
So in love / Address this issue / Snow place / West of the moon / Suite - peace / We'll say hello again / Vengeance / Uptown lex / Whipmarks
TCB 95602 / Dec '95 / TCB

Tankard

☐ DISCO DESTROYER
CM 77209CD / 13 Apr '98 / Century Media

☐ STONE COLD SOBER
Jurisdiction / Broken image / Mindwild / Ugly beauty / Centrefold / Behind the back / Stone cold sober / Blood guts and rock 'n' roll / Lost and found (tantrum part 2) / Sleeping with the past / Freibier / Of strange people talking under Arabian skies
N 01902 / Jun '92 / Noise

☐ TWO-FACED
N 02332 / Feb '94 / Noise

Tannahill Weavers

☐ BEST OF THE TANNAHILL WEAVERS 1979-1989, THE
Geese in the bog/Jig of slurs / Auld lang syne / Tranent muir / Highland laddie / Lucy Cassidy/ Bletherskate/Smith of Chilliechassie / Farewell to Fiunary/Heather Island / Roddie MacDonald's favourite / Gypsy laddie / Jamie Raeburn's farewell / Johnny Cope/Atholl Highlanders / I once loved a lass / Turf lodge/Cape Breton's fiddlers' welcome to the Shetlands / Lady Margaret Stewart/Flaggon
GLCD 1100 / Jul '92 / Green Linnet

☐ CAPERNAUM
GLCD 1146 / Aug '94 / Green Linnet

☐ COLLECTION, THE (Choice Cuts 1987-1996)
Blackbird set / Wild mountain thyme / Capernaum / Crann tara set / Joy of my heart/Kintail / Carls o' Dysart/The log splitter set / Hieland Harry / Braes o' Balouhidder / Are ye sleeping Maggie / Campbelton kiltie ball / Cuillins of rhum / Plooboy laddies/John Murray of Lochee / Good drying set / Braw burn the bridges
GLCD 1182 / Oct '97 / Green Linnet

☐ CULLEN BAY
GLCD 1108 / Mar '91 / Green Linnet

☐ DANCING FEET
Turf lodge / Tranent Muir / Isabeaux S'y Promene / Fisher row / Wild mountain thyme / Maggie's pancakes / Mary Morrison / Campbeltown kiltie ball / Final trawl
GLCD 1081 / Apr '92 / Green Linnet

☐ LAND OF LIGHT
Lucy Cassidy / Scottish settler's lament / Ronald Maclean's farewell to Oban / Dunrobin castle / Rovin' heilandman / Yellow haired laddie / Land of light / Queen amang the heather/Mairi Anne... / Bustles and bonnets / American stranger / Conon Bridge
GLCD 1067 / Jun '88 / Green Linnet

☐ LEAVING ST. KILDA
Good drying set / Hieland Harry / Rigs o' rye / Athol gathering / St. Kilda set / Shearin's no for you / Three healths / Crann Tara set / Wars o' Germany / Islay charms set / Last May a braw wooer / Fareweel you silver darlin's
GLCD 1176 / Nov '96 / Green Linnet

☐ MERMAID'S SONG
Greenwood side/Highland laddie/Pattie / Logie o' Buchan / Elspeth Campbell/Kenny Gilles of Portnalong/Skye/Malcolm Joh / Mermaid's song/ Herra boys/Captain Horn/Fourth floor / Are ye sleeping Maggie/Noose and the ghillie / A Bruxa / Come under my plaidie / Campbell's farewell to Redcastle / Flashmarket close / MacArthur/Colonel Fraser/Swallow's tale / Ass in the graveyard
GLCD 1121 / Feb '89 / Green Linnet

☐ PASSAGE
Roddie MacDonald's favourite / Jamie Raeburn's farewell / Harris and the mare / Duntroon/Trip to Alaska / Highland laddie / At the end of a pointed gun / Lady Dysie / Coach house reel/Marie Christina / Phuktiphanno/John MacKenzie's fancy / Drink a round
GLCD 3031 / Oct '93 / Green Linnet

Tannas

☐ HERITAGE
CDLDL 1217 / Nov '94 / Lochshore

☐ RU-RA
CDLDL 1231 / Oct '95 / Lochshore

Tannehill, Frank

☐ COMPLETE RECORDINGS 1932-1941
SOB 035262 / Feb '93 / Story Of The Blues

Tanner

☐ (GERMO) PHOBIC
HED 075 / Jun '97 / Headhunter

☐ ILL-GOTTEN GAINS
Hey jigsaw / Computers that breathe / Wig / Still a rat / Man below dim moon / Seiner / Catalogue / Kid / Purma Park / Guard dog / Noose / Spastic art / Not a fitting niche
CAROL 17892 / May '96 / Caroline

Tanrikorur, Cinucen

☐ CINUCEN TANRIKORUR
C 580045 / Feb '94 / Ocora

Tans, J.C.

☐ AROUND THE WORLD
BVHAASTCD 8905 / Sep '92 / Bvhaast

Tansads

☐ DRAG DOWN THE MOON (Tansads Live)
TRACD 118 / Apr '96 / Transatlantic

☐ FLOCK
Band on a rainbow / Fear of falling / She's not gone / God on a string / Iron man / Waiting for the big one / Dance / Sunlight in the morning / G Man / Ship of fools / I know I can (but I won't) / Heading for the heart / Separate souls
TRACD 1 / Apr '96 / Transatlantic

Tansey, Seamus

☐ BEST OF SEAMUS TANSEY, THE
PTICD 1007 / Jun '96 / Pure Traditional Irish

☐ EASTER SNOW
Josie McDermott's/Kitty gone a milking / Piper Anderson's delight / John Brennan's favourite/Ladd O'Beirne's favourite / Easter snow / Mick Flatley's delight/Ed Reavey's favourite / Dillon's favourite/ The bag o'spuds / Tribute to Peggy McGrath/John McKenna's jig / Dunphy's hornpipe/Sean Ryan's favourite / May morning dew / Jimeen Gannon's delight/Dowd's no.9 / Lament for the death of Staker Wallace / Maid in the cherry tree/Farewell to Ireland / Famine requiem / Ah surely/Maud Miller / Seannie Davey's reel/Alfie Joe Denning's reel
COMD 2063 / Mar '97 / Temple

Tanteeka

☐ NEW TRADITION, A
Laxity of morals / Pierre de Grenoble / Midnight feast / Ouvrez la porte / Day to day (up to here) / Mikenda / Claire Conner's lament / Laurel's retreat / Rossignolet / Thing / Watching the grass grow / Broomfield wager / Steel works / Le soir venu
OSMOCD 013 / Sep '97 / Osmosys

Tao

☐ ESOTERIC RED
Sleeping junk / Larvae / Esoteric red / Nocturnal / Kaleidoscope / Scarifice / Jinn and tonic / Radiance / Medium / Curvature/Overture / Sacred swell / Pharmacos / Astral circle / Green material / Riot in Lagos
WORDD 005 / Jul '97 / Language

Tapajos, Sebastiao

☐ AFFINITIES (Tapajos, Sebastiao & G. Peranzzetta)
68984 / Jul '97 / Tropical

☐ BRASILIDADE
Vila rica / Rancheira / Cancao para marisa / Olinda medieval / Repentes / O bonde das seis / Brinquedo pra o junior / Criancas da minha terra / Perere / Pelourinho / Frevo
68945 / Apr '97 / Tropical

☐ SAMBAS AND BOSSAS (Tapajos, Sebastiao & Friends)
Waves / Brasileiro and samba em Berlin / Cancao para marisa / Sertao / Ganga / Viajeiro / Tristeza / Vale do amanhecer / Xingu / Lua joa igarapes / Tocata para Billy Blanco / Chega de saudade / Asa branca / Sorriso da tristeza
68930 / Jul '97 / Tropical

☐ XINGU - GITARRE UND PERCUSSION
Xingu / Intoducao / Percutindo / Bacurau / Percussorongando / Odeon / Brasileiro and samba em Berlin / Escolado mar / Xadrez / Luz negra
68907 / Apr '97 / Tropical

Tapia Eta Leturia Band

☐ ERO
KD 466CD / Dec '97 / Elkar

☐ TAPIA ETA LETURIA BAND, THE
KD 412CD / Nov '96 / Elkar

Tapia, Oscar Moreno

☐ SONGS OF MEXICO VOL.2 (Tapia, Oscar Moreno & Los Mecateros)
VICG 53362 / Mar '96 / JVC World Library

Tappa Zukie

☐ DEEP ROOTS
RASCD 3224 / Sep '96 / Ras

☐ FROM THE ARCHIVES
RASCD 3135 / Jun '95 / Ras

☐ MASSIVE RESISTANCE (Various Artists)
RASCD 3142 / Jun '94 / Ras

☐ TAPPA ZUKIE IN DUB
BAFCD 8 / Sep '95 / Blood & Fire

Tapsi Turtles

☐ I WANNA HEAR THE SUNSHINE
TTT 001CD / Sep '96 / We Bite

Tar

☐ OVER AND OUT
TGCD 145 / Oct '95 / Touch & Go

Tar Babies

☐ DEATH TRIP
SON 0042 / Jan '93 / Sonic Noise

☐ HONEY BUBBLE
SST 236CD / Jul '89 / SST

Tara

☐ BOYS IN THE LANE
EUCD 1019 / '89 / ARC

☐ RIGS OF THE TIME
EUCD 1006 / '89 / ARC

Taraf De Carancebes

☐ MUSICIENS DU BANAT - ROUMANIA
Y225208 / Jun '93 / Silex

Taraf De Haidouks

☐ DYLAN PA NORSK (Taraf De Haidouks & Age Aleksandersen)
FX 183CD / Aug '97 / Kirkelig Kulturverksted

☐ HONOURABLE BRIGANDS, MAGIC HORSES AND EVIL EYE
CRAW 13 / Apr '95 / Crammed Discs

☐ MUSIQUE DES TZIGANES DE ROUMANIE
CRAW 2 / Jan '96 / Crammed World

Taralgatti, Shivu

☐ INDIA
927072 / 24 Feb '98 / BUDA

Taran

☐ MOD & MINI SPACE AGE
COMP 026CD / Oct '96 / Compost

Tardiff, Paul

☐ POINTS OF DEPARTURE
378002 / Oct '96 / Koch Jazz

Tardy, Gregory

☐ SERENDIPITY
Forgiveness / Blues for Professor Pickens / JL's wish / Ah-ite / Prisoner of love / Fractar question / Whenever wherever whatever / Serendipity / Ask me now
IMP 12582 / 23 Mar '98 / Impulse Jazz

Tarika

☐ BALANCE
FMSD 5028 / Jan '94 / Rogue

☐ BIBIANGO
GLCD 4028 / Jan '95 / Green Linnet

☐ FANAFODY
FMSD 5024 / Oct '92 / Rogue

☐ SON EGAL
Tsy kivy / Avelo / Voandalana / Zotra / Sonegaly / Rafrancois / Vavaka / Ady / Sento / Raha tiany / Forever / Diso be / Aza misy miteniteny
XEN 04042CD / Feb '97 / Xenophile

Tarika Sammy

☐ BENEATH SOUTHERN SKIES
SHCD 64067 / Jul '96 / Shanachie

Tarlton, Jeff

☐ ASTRAL YEARS
DELECCD 062 / 17 Nov '97 / Delerium

Tarmey, Bill

☐ AFTER HOURS
It's too late / Love don't live here anymore / Almaz / Everything I own / Wonderful tonight / Funny how time slips away / She's out of my life / Fool if you think it's over / What'll I do / Love on the rocks / I'm not in love / Never thought / I'm all out of love / Sandman's coming
PRMTVCD 2 / 16 Mar '98 / Premier/EMI

☐ DOWN HOME
Down home / I swear / She dreams / Come next Monday / One of those things / Why didn't I think of that / Too busy being in love / Wrong road again / Sure love / She believes in me / Cover to cover / When men were men / Letting go / Nobody knows / Doctor time
BILLCD 001 / 29 Sep '97 / Connoisseur Collection

☐ GIFT OF LOVE, A
Nobody loves me like you do / Somewhere out there / In your eyes / Tonight I celebrate my love / It might be you / That's all / Save the best for last / (Everything I do) I do it for you / She loves me / Right here waiting / Hundred ways / Weekend in New England / If we hold on together / Wind beneath my wings
CDEMC 3665 / 16 Mar '98 / EMI

☐ TIME FOR LOVE
Time for love / Don't it make my brown eyes blue / IOU / I'm the one / If I thought you'd ever change your mind / If this is what love can do / Don't know much / Dance of love / Some people / Perfect year / One shining moment / Belonging / You and I / As long as you are there
CDEMTV 85 / Oct '94 / EMI

Tarnation

☐ GENTLE CREATURES
Game of broken hearts / Halfway to madness / Well / Big o motel / Tell me it's not so / Two wrongs / Lonely lights / Gentle creatures / Listen to the wind / Hand / Do you fancy me / Yellow birds / Burn again / Stranger in the mirror / It's not easy
GAD 5010CD / 6 Jul '98 / 4AD

☐ MIRADOR
Awful shade of blue / Wait / Place where I know / Is she lonesome now / Your thoughts and mine / Christine / Destiny / There's someone / Like a ghost / Idly / Little black egg / You'll understand
GAD 7004CD / 6 Jul '98 / 4AD

Tarras, Dave

☐ YIDDISH AMERICAN KLEZMER MUSIC
Unzer toirele / Yiddisher march / Good luck / Polka 'strelotchek' / Chasidic in america / A yid bin ich geboiren / Dem monastrishter rebin's choisd't / Hopkele / Bridegroom special / Die goldene chasene / Pas d'espan / Mazel in liebe / A vaibele a tsnien / Zum gali gall / Die reize nuch amerika / Branas hassene / Kinos, tkios un ashrei / What can you mach / Oriental hora / Second avenue square dance / Freilachs / Dayeynu / Rumanian fantasy
YAZCD 7001 / Apr '92 / Shanachie

Tarres, Fernando

☐ OUTSIDER, THE
Luz mala / Astor's place / Evil dance / Alfonsina y el mar / Sketches of Markari / Nothing will take it away / La finadita / Quietude
SAVCD 2002 / Jan '98 / Savant

Tartan Amoebas

☐ EVOLUTION
He ro ho ro hi / Watergaw / Transcendental bru / Face to face / Infinite snack mode / Big sky / Once / Putting up shelves / Changing light / Study in scarlet / Easy peasy / Groovy wean / Reggalypso
IRCD 058 / Sep '97 / Iona

☐ IMAGINARY TARTAN MENAGERIE
Ska reggae / Sub heaven / Penguin blues / Road rage / New pipe order / Brief case shuffle / Clavershouse / I close my eyes / Adios amoebas
IRCD 034 / Nov '95 / Iona

☐ TARTAN AMOEBAS
Pinch of snuff / Reels of Tulloch / Lark in the morning / Miss Stewart / Loch Leven Castle / Funky pipes / Dubh / Alex's reels / Johnnie Cope / Kwela
CDTRAX 133 / May '97 / Greentrax

Tartan Lads

☐ ESSENTIAL COLLECTION FROM SCOTLAND, THE
Summer road / I've never kissed a bonnie lassie / Scottish selection / Triple hornpipes / You're my best friend / Bonnie lass o' Dundee / Waltz selection / Clarinet polka / Highlander's return / Bonnie Naver Bay / Son of the Scottish soldier / Annie's song / Highland gentleman / San Antonio rose / Waltz medley / She's mine / Farewell 51st / Almost persuaded / Alpine slopes / Galloway Hills
RECD 496 / Jan '98 / REL

☐ TARTAN LADS OF BONNIE SCOTLAND
Lads of bonnie scotland / Lovely glens of angus / Jacqueline waltz / Old meal mill / Rose of allandale / Skyline of skye / Bonnie wells o'wearie / Amazing grace / Morag's fairy glen / Dark island / Bonnie kirkwall bay
CDITV 540 / May '91 / Scotdisc

Tartaros

☐ GRAND PSYCHOTIC CASTLE
NR 6688CD / May '97 / Necropolis

Tarwater

☐ RABBIT MOON REVISITED
CR 9801CD / 13 Apr '98 / Capstack

Tasavallan Presidentti

☐ LAMBERT LAND
Lounge / Lambert Land / Celebration of the saved nine / Bargain / Dance / Last quarters
LRCD 60 / May '97 / Love

☐ MILKY WAY MOSES
Milky way Moses / Caught from the air / Jelly: confusing the issue / How to start a day / Piece of mind
LRCD 102 / Nov '96 / Love

Tasby, Finis

☐ PEOPLE DON'T CARE
SHCD 9007 / May '95 / Shanachie

Tasha Killer Pussies

☐ SHAKE & VAC
5503 BAG / Jan '97 / Bag

Tashan

☐ FOR THE SAKE OF LOVE
Tempted / Been a long time / Ecstatic / For the sake of love / Single and lonely / Still in love / Love is forever / Romantically inspired / Control of me / Insane / All I ever do / Love of my life
4724112 / Mar '94 / Columbia

Tashian, Barry

☐ HARMONY (Tashian, Barry & Holly)
It's too late to pray / I'll take my time / Don't kneel at my graveside / Wild wind / Power of love / Two ways to fall / Fools hall of fame / Blues for Dixie / Hello sorrow / Lonesome and blue / All I have to offer you is me / Love you give
ROUCD 0412 / Mar '97 / Rounder

☐ LIVE IN HOLLAND (Tashian, Barry & Holly)
SCR 27 / Jul '95 / Strictly Country

☐ READY FOR LOVE (Tashian, Barry & Holly)
Ready for love / Let me see the light / Heaven with you / Heart full of memories / Hearts that break / Highway 86 / Price of pride / Diamond / Ring of gold / Memories remain / If I knew then / This old love
ROUCD 0302 / May '93 / Rounder

☐ STRAW INTO GOLD (Tashian, Barry & Holly)
ROUCD 0332 / Nov '94 / Rounder

☐ TRUST IN ME (Tashian, Barry & Holly)
Trust in me / Home / Blue eyes / Ramona / Making a change / You're running wild / Party doll / My favourite memory / Poor woman's epitaph / Look both ways / Boy who cried love / I can't dance
CDRR 302 / Mar '92 / Request

Tassilli Players

☐ AT THE COWSHED
FISHNO 3CD / Jul '97 / Konkurrent

☐ OUTER SPACE
WWCD 21 / Sep '96 / Universal Egg

☐ WONDERFUL WORLD OF WEED IN DUB, THE
WWCD 11 / Sep '95 / Wibbly Wobbly

Taste

☐ LIVE AT THE ISLE OF WIGHT
What's going on / Sugar mama / Morning sun / Sinner boy / I feel so good / Catfish
8416022 / Apr '94 / Polydor

☐ ON THE BOARDS
What's going on / Railway and gun / It's happened before, it'll happen again / If the day was any longer / Morning sun / Eat my words / On the boards / If I don't sing I'll cry / See here / I'll remember
8415992 / Apr '94 / Polydor

☐ TASTE
Blister on the moon / Leaving blues / Sugar Mama / Hail / Born on the wrong side of time / Dual carriageway pain / Same old story / Catfish / I'm moving on
8416002 / Jul '94 / Polydor

Taste Of Fear

☐ TASTE OF FEAR
LF 118CD / Feb '95 / Lost & Found

Taste Of Honey

☐ INTERNAL BASS
IB 10CD / 16 Nov '97 / Internal Bass

Taste Of Joy

☐ TRIGGER FABLES
W 230089 / Mar '96 / Nettwerk
FAC 86442 / May '96 / Edel

Tate, Baby

☐ SEE WHAT YOU DONE
OBCCD 567 / Oct '95 / Original Blues Classics

Tate, Buddy

☐ BALLAD ARTISTRY OF BUDDY TATE, THE
SKCD 23034 / Oct '92 / Sackville

☐ BUDDY TATE AND HIS BUDDIES
CRD 123 / Mar '96 / Chiaroscuro

☐ BUDDY TATE, HUMPHREY LYTTELTON & RUBY BRAFF (Tate, Buddy & Humphrey Lyttelton/Ruby Braff)
Kansas City woman / One for me / Candyville / Outswinger / Steevos / Clarinet lemonade / Swinging scorpio / Mean to me / I surrender dear / My Monday date / Take the 'A' train / Pan Am blues
8747132 / Jul '96 / DA Music

☐ GROOVIN' WITH TATE
Me 'n' you / Idling / Blow low / Moon dog / No kiddin' / Miss Ruby Jones / Blues for Trix / Salt mines / I'm just a lucky so and so / East of the Sun and West of the moon / Makin' whoopee / Boardwalk / Overdrive
PCD 24152 / Jun '96 / Prestige

☐ JUMPING ON THE WEST COAST (Tate, Buddy & Friends)
BLCD 760175 / Mar '93 / Black Lion

☐ JUST JAZZ (Tate, Buddy & Al Grey)
RSRCD 110 / Dec '94 / Reservoir

☐ SWINGING SCORPIO (Tate, Buddy & Humphrey Lyttelton)
Kansas city woman / One for me / Pamela / Candyville / Outswinger / Steevos / Clarinet lemonade / Swinging scorpio
BLC 760165 / '92 / Black Lion

☐ TEXAS TWISTER, THE
Texas twister / Talk of the town / Take me back baby (parts 1 and 2) / Chicago / Boogie woogie / Topsy / Gee baby, ain't I good to you
NW 352 / '88 / New World

☐ WHEN I'M BLUE
BB 8662 / Apr '96 / Black & Blue

Tate, Grady

☐ BODY AND SOUL
This is all I ask / It might as well be spring / What a wonderful world / My romance / Dream love / You'll never walk alone / Body and soul / Little black samba / All the things you are / Everybody loves my baby
MCD 9208 / Jun '95 / Milestone

Tater Totz

☐ TATER COMES ALIVE
ROCK 60542 / Jul '93 / Rockville

Taters & Pie

☐ NO MORE PUTTING OFF
Let the white moon shine / Heather island/Catching flies / Where lies and land / Piskeflode / Sirens and screams / Fools never die out / Jamie foyers / East Anglian sunset / Sea fever / Chasing chickens / Highway to eternal night / Love is all he needs / Hands's have no tears to cry/Jonathan's hat / Farewell
GFMSCDS 6 / Nov '93 / Green Fingers

Tathak, Pandit Ashok

☐ COLOURFUL WORLD OF PANDIT ASHOK TATHAK, THE
CD 3301 / Aug '94 / Saraswati

Tati, Cheb

☐ DANS LA VIE
Dans la vie / Sada / Bled / Labsa / La moda / President / Henini / La moda jungle / Dans la vie
JVC 90072 / Oct '96 / JVC

Tatum, Art

☐ 20TH CENTURY PIANO GENIUS (2CD Set)
5317632 / Aug '96 / Verve

☐ ART OF TATUM (25 Great Solo Performances 1932-1944) (Various Artists)
Tiger rag / Sophisticated lady / (I would do) anything for you / After you've gone / Stardust / Shout / Liza / Gone with the wind / Stormy weather / Chloe / Sheikh of araby / Teas for two / Deep purple / Elegie / Humoresque / Get happy / Lullaby of the leaves / Moonglow / Love me / Cocktails for two / St. Louis blues / Begin the beguine / Rosetta / Sweet Lorraine
AIA 5164 / Apr '95 / ASV

☐ ART TATUM TRIO 1944, THE (Tatum, Art Trio)
I got rhythm / Cocktails for two / I ain't got nobody / After you've gone / Moonglow / Deep purple / I would do anything for you / Liza / Tea for two / Honeysuckle rose / Man I love / I know that you know / On the sunny side of the street / Flying home / Dark eyes / Body and soul / Topsy / If I had you / Soft winds / Boogie
CD 53295 / Apr '98 / Giants Of Jazz

☐ ART'S ART
(Back home again in) Indiana / Sheik of Araby / Sweet Lorraine / Get happy / St. Louis blues / Gone with the wind / Lullaby of the leaves / Elegie / Tiger rag / Chloe / Stormy weather / Humoresque / Moonglow / Coktails for two / Rosetta / Tea for two / Love me / Begin the beguine / Emaline / Deep purple
305042 / Jul '97 / Hallmark

☐ BODY AND SOUL
JHR 73514 / May '93 / Jazz Hour

☐ CLASSICS 1932-1934
CLASSICS 507 / Apr '90 / Classics

☐ CLASSICS 1934-1940
Liza / Take me back to my boots and saddle / Body and soul / With plenty of money and you (oh baby what I coul / What will I tell my heart / I've got my love to keep me warm / Gone with the wind / Stormy weather / Chloe / Sheik of araby / Tea for two / Deep purple / Elegie / Humoresque / Sweet lorraine / Get happy / Lullaby of the leaves / Tiger rag / Sweet emaline, my gal / Emaline / Moonglow / Love me / Cocktails for two / St. louis blues
CLASSICS 560 / Oct '91 / Classics

☐ CLASSICS 1940
CLASSICS 831 / Sep '95 / Classics

☐ CLASSICS 1940-1941
CLASSICS 800 / Mar '95 / Classics

☐ CLASSICS 1944
CLASSICS 825 / Sep '95 / Classics

☐ CLASSICS 1945-1947
CLASSICS 982 / 24 Feb '98 / Classics

☐ COMPLETE BRUNSWICK & DECCA SESSIONS 1932-1941 (3CD Set)
Strange as it seems / I'll never be the same / You gave me everything but love / This time it's love / Tea for two / St. Louis blues / Tiger rag / Sophisticated lady / Moonglow / (I would do) anything for you / When a woman loves a man / Emaline / Love me / Cocktails for two / After you've gone / Stardust / Ill wind / Shout / Beautiful love / Liza / I ain't got nobody / Boots and saddle / Body and soul / With plenty of money and you / What will I tell my heart / I've got my love to keep me warm / Gone with the wind / Stormy weather / Chloe / Sheikh of araby / Deep purple / Elegie / Humoresque / Sweet Lorraine / Get happy / Lullaby of the leaves / Begin the beguine / Rosetta / (Back home again in) Indiana / Wee baby blues / Stompin' at the Savoy / Last goodbye blues / Battery bounce / Lucille / Rock me mama / Corine Corina / Lonesome graveyard blues
CDAFS 10353 / Apr '93 / Affinity

☐ COMPLETE CAPITOL RECORDINGS, THE (2CD Set)
Willow weep for me / I cover the waterfront / Aunt Hagar's blues / Nice work if you can get it / Someone to watch over me / Dardanella / Time on my hands / Sweet Lorraine / Somebody loves me / Don't blame me / My heart stood still / You took advantage of me / I gotta right to sing the blues / How high the moon / Makin' whoopee / Going home / Blue skies / It's the talk of the town / Dancing in the dark / Tenderly / Melody in F / September song / Would you like to take a walk / Tea for two / Out of nowhere / Lover / Just one of those things / (Back home again in) Indiana
8213252 / 8 Dec '97 / Capitol Jazz

☐ COMPLETE PABLO GROUP MASTERPIECES 1954-1956, THE (6CD Set)
Blues in C / Undecided / Under a blanket of blue / Blues in B flat / Foggy day / Street of dreams / 'S wonderful / Makin' whoopee / Old fashioned love / Blues in my heart / My blue heaven / Hands across the table / You're mine you / Idaho / Night and day / I won't dance / In a sentimental mood / Moon is low / Moon song / You took advantage of me / This can't be love / I surrender dear / I won't dance / In a sentimental mood / What is this thing called love / I'll never be the same / Makin' whoopee / Hallelujah / Perdido / More than you know / How high the moon / This can't be love / Stars fell on Alabama / Lover man / Prisoner of love / Love for sale / Love for sale / Body and soul / Please be kind / This can't be love / Hallelujah / Verve blues / Plaid / Somebody loves me / September song / What is this thing called love / What is this thing called love / Just one of those things / More than you know / Some other Spring / If / Blue Lou / Love for sale / Isn't it romantic / I'll never be the same / I guess I'll have to change my plans / Trio blues / Deep night / This can't be love / Memories of you / Once in a while / Foggy day / Lover man / You're mine, you / Makin' whoopee / Deep night / Once in a while / This can't be love / Gone with the wind / All the things you are / Have you met Miss Jones / My one and only love / Night and day / My ideal / Where or when / Gone with the wind / Gone with the wind / Have you met Miss Jones
6PACD 4401 / Nov '96 / Pablo

☐ COMPLETE PABLO SOLO MASTERPIECES 1953-1956, THE (7CD Set)
Can't we be friends / This can't be love / Elegy / Memories of you / Over the rainbow / If you hadn't gone away / Body and soul / Man I love / Makin' whoopee / September song / Begin the beguine / Humouresque / Louise / Love for sale / Judy / I'm comin' Virginia / Wrap your troubles in dreams / Dixieland band / Embraceable you / Come rain or come shine / Just a-sittin' and a-rockin' / There will never be another you / Tenderly / What does it take / You took advantage of me / I've got the world on a string / Yesterdays / I hadn't anyone till you / Night and day / Jitterbug waltz / Someone to watch over me / Very thought of you / You're driving me crazy / I don't stand a ghost of a chance with you / I cover the waterfront / Where or when / Stay as sweet as you are / Fine and dandy / All the things you are / Have you met Miss Jones / In a sentimental mood / I'll see you again / I'll see you in my dreams / Ill wind / Isn't this a lovely day / Blue skies / Without a song / Stompin' at the Savoy / My last affair / I'm in the mood for love / Taboo / Would you like to take a walk / I've got a crush on you / Japanese sandman / Too marvellous for words / Aunt Hagar's blues / Just like a butterfly that's caught in the rain / Gone with the wind / Danny boy / They can't take that away from me / Tea for two / It's the talk of the town / Blue Lou / When a woman loves a man / Willow weep for me / Ain't misbehavin' / Smoke gets in your eyes / Mighty like a rose / Stars fell on Alabama / Blue moon / There's a small hotel / Caravan / Way you look tonight / You go to my head / Lover come back to me / Sophisticated lady / Dancing in the dark / Love me or leave me / Cherokee / These foolish things / Deep purple / After you've gone / I didn't know what time it was / Somebody loves me / What's new / Sweet Lorraine / Crazy rhythm / Isn't it romantic / You're blase / You're mine, you / That old feeling / Heatwave / She's funny that way / I surrender dear / Happy feet / Mean to me / Boulevard of broken dreams / Moonlight on the Ganges / Moon song / When your lover has gone / Moon is low / If I had you / S'posin' / Don't worry 'bout me / Prisoner of love / Moonglow / I won't dance / I can't give you anything but love / Lullaby of rhythm / Out of nowhere / I gotta right to sing the blues / It's only a paper moon / Everything I have is yours / I only have eyes for you / On the sunny side of the street / Do nothin' 'til you hear from me / So beats my heart for you / If you hadn't gone away / Please be kind / Someone to watch over me / Begin the beguine / Willow weep for me / Humouresque
7PACD 44042 / Nov '96 / Pablo

☐ IN PRIVATE
FSCD 127 / Jan '91 / Fresh Sound

☐ INTRODUCTION TO ART TATUM 1933-1944, AN
4022 / Jul '95 / Best Of Jazz

☐ JAZZ PORTRAITS
Tiger rag / St. Louis blues / Begin the beguine / (Back home again in) Indiana / Get happy / What will I tell my heart / Sheikh of Araby / Stormy weather / Tea for two / Sophisticated lady / I've got my love to keep me warm / Gone with the wind / Rosetta / Stompin' at the Savoy / Sweet Lorraine / I'll get by / Battery bounce / It had to be you
CD 14523 / May '94 / Jazz Portraits

☐ MASTERPIECES
158632 / Oct '96 / Jazz Archives

☐ MASTERPIECES OF ART TATUM, THE
393502 / Aug '94 / Music Memoria

☐ ON THE SUNNY SIDE 1944-1945
I know that you know / Man I love / Dark eyes / Body and soul / On the sunny side of the street / Flying home / Fine and dandy / It had to be you / Ja-da / Sweet and lovely / Boogie / If I had you / Topsy / Soft winds / Hallelujah / Poor butterfly / Song of the vagabonds / Lover / Memories of you / Runnin' wild / Yesterdays / Kerry dance
TPZ 1066 / Jun '97 / Topaz Jazz

☐ PIANO STARTS HERE
Tea for two / St. louis blues / Tiger rag / Sophisticated lady / How high the moon / Humoresque / Someone to watch over me / Yesterdays / I know that you know / Willow weep for me / Tatum-pole boogie / Kerry dance / Man I love
4765462 / May '94 / Sony Jazz

☐ QUINTESSENCE, THE (1933-1945/2CD Set)
FA 217 / Apr '96 / Fremeaux

☐ ROCOCO PIANO OF ART TATUM, THE
Gone with the wind / Stormy weather / Sheikh of araby / Tea for two / Rosetta / Humoresque / Sweet Lorraine / Get happy / Lullaby of the leaves / Tiger rag / Sweet Emmalina / Emaline / Moon glow / Love me / Cocktails for two / St. Louis blues / Begin the beguine / (Back home again in) Indiana / Stompin' at the savoy / Battery bounce / Rock me Mama / Corine Corina
PASTCD 7031 / Jan '94 / Flapper

☐ SOLOS 1937/CLASSIC PIANO SOLOS
Fine and dandy / Emaline / I guess I'll have to change my plans / Limehouse blues / I gotta right to sing the blues / Indiana / I've got the world on a string / What is this thing called love / I'm comin' Virginia / Can't we be friends / You took advantage of me / All God's chillun got rhythm / Come rain or come shine / Begin the beguine / Body and soul / I know that you know / Honeysuckle rose / Introspection / Memories of you / Kerry Dance
UCD 19010 / Sep '96 / Forlane

☐ ST. LOUIS BLUES
Tiger rag / Tea for two / St. Louis blues / Strange as it seems / Sophisticated lady / It'll never be the same / When a woman loves a man / Shout / You gave me everything but love / This time it's love / Liza / (I would do) anything for you / After you've gone / Stardust / I ain't got nobody / Beautiful love
GRF 085 / '93 / Tring

☐ STANDARD SESSIONS, THE
CD 919 / Feb '96 / Music & Arts

☐ STANDARD TRANSCRIPTIONS, THE (2CD Set)
CD 673 / Jul '91 / Music & Arts

☐ STANDARDS
BLCD 760143 / Nov '92 / Black Lion

☐ TATUM GROUP MASTERPIECES VOL.6
Just one of those things / More than you know / Some other Spring / If / Blue Lou / Love for sale / Isn't it romantic / I'll never be the same / I guess I'll have to change my plan / Trio blues
2405429 / Oct '93 / Pablo

TATUM, ART MAIN SECTION R.E.D. CD CATALOGUE

☐ TATUM GROUP MASTERPIECES VOL.7
Deep night / This can't be love / Memories of you / Once in a while / Foggy day / Lover man / You're mine / You / Makin' whoopee
24054302 / Nov '95 / Pablo

☐ TATUM GROUP MASTERPIECES VOL.8
Gone with the wind / All the things you are / Have you met Miss Jones / My one and only love / Night and day / My ideal / Where or when
24054312 / Jan '97 / Pablo

☐ TEA FOR TWO
BLCD 760192 / Feb '94 / Black Lion

☐ TEA FOR TWO 1933-1940
Tiger rag / St. louis blues / Begin the beguine / Indiana (back home again in) / Get happy / What will I tell my heart / Sheik of araby / Stormy weather / Tea for two / Sophisticated lady / I've got my love to keep me warm / Gone with the wind / Rosetta / Stompin' at the savoy / Sweet lorraine / I'll get by / Battery bounce / It had to be you
CD 56068 / Jul '95 / Jazz Roots

☐ TRIO DAYS
I got rhythm / Cocktails for two / I ain't got nobody / After you've gone / Moonglow / Deep purple / (I would do) anything for you / Liza / Tea for two / Honeysuckle rose / Man I love / Dark eyes / Body and soul / I know that you know / On the sunny side of the street / Flying home / Boogie / If I had you / Topsy / Soft winds
LEJAZZCD 43 / Jun '95 / Le Jazz

☐ V DISC YEARS 1944-1946, THE
BLCD 760114 / Apr '91 / Black Lion

Tauber, Richard

☐ COLLECTION, A
Without a song / Indian summer / Lover come back to me / One day when we were young / One alone / Plaisir d'amour / My moonlight madonna / Dearly beloved / Can I forget you / Pedro, the fisherman / Blue Danube / Perfect day / Serenade / We'll gather lilacs / English rose / Someday we shall meet again / Once there lived a fair lady / Beneath my window / First love is best love / Long ago and far away
307412 / Jul '97 / Hallmark

☐ GERMAN FOLK SONGS
BLA 103002 / Mar '95 / Belage

☐ GREAT ORIGINAL PERFORMANCES 1923-1929
Girls were made to love and kiss / Ich mocht einamal wieder / Bei einem tee 'a deux / Keiner schlafe / Can I forgive you / English rose / Ich kusse ihre hand madam / Nobody could love you more / On with the motley / Gruss mir mein wien / Flower song / O madchen, mein madcheni / Frohe botschaft / Di bist die welt fur mich / Wolgalied / Il mio tesoro / Vienna, city of my dreams / You are my heart's delight
RPCD 301 / Sep '96 / Robert Parker Jazz

☐ LEGENDARY RICHARD TAUBER, THE (2CD Set)
CMS 5666922 / 6 Apr '98 / EMI Classics

☐ MY LOVE FOR YOU
My love for you / English rose / Love everlasting / Can I forget you / World is waiting for sunrise / I know of two bright eyes / Sympathy / At the balalaika / Rosalie / Intermezzo / So deep is the night / Caprice Viennois / Liebestraum / Angels guard thee / Elegie / Love's last word is spoken / My heart and I / Jealousy / Little grey home in the West / Starlight serenade / Girls were made to love and kiss / Die Fledermaus
CDMOIR 433 / May '95 / Memoir

☐ OLD CHELSEA
BLA 103003 / Feb '95 / Belage

☐ ONLY A ROSE
Serenade / Little love, a little kiss / Rose marie / Lover come back to me / For you alone / Simple little melody / One alone / One day when we were young / Waltz of my heart / One night of love / Marcheta / Only a rose / All the things you are / Sweethearts / Kiss me again / Will you remember / Sleepy lagoon / You mean the world to me / Your love could be everything to me / Roses from the south / Vienna, city of my dreams (sieczyinski) / You are my heart's delight
CDMOIR 421 / Jun '93 / Memoir

☐ RARITIES
VA 1142 / 7 Nov '97 / Vocal Archive

☐ YOU ARE MY HEART'S DELIGHT
Dein ist mein ganzes herz / Gern hab'ich die frau'n gekusst (girls were made to love / O madchen, mein madchen (oh maiden, my maiden) / Wolgalied es steht ein soldat (volga song) / Schweig' zagendes herz / Serenade hab'ein blaues himmelbett / Schon wie die blau sommernacht (lovely as a night in june) / Beim tee en deux / Lippen schweigen..ballsirenen-walzer (love unspoken-the mer / Sah ein knab ein roslein steh'n / O wie schon / Frei und jung da bel / Zwei marchenaugen / Wie mein ahn'l zwanzig jahr (nightingale song) / Dieser anstand (watch duet) / Als flotter geist / Wer uns getraut (one day when we were young) / Im chambre separee / Du bist die welt fur mich (you are the world to me0 / Your love could be everything to me / Im prater bluh'n wieder die baume / Wien, du stadt meiner traume (vienna city of my dreams)
PASTCD 7042 / May '94 / Flapper

Taubkin, Daniel

☐ BRAZSIL
Swing dos Passaros / Grande Othelo / Brilho / Aurora de Verao / Valsa para Ninar Teresa / Lirio / Soma / Chuva de Manga / Velhos Camaradas / Girassol / Curva de Rio / Aipoke / Mein Lieve / Joao
BJAC 50182 / 29 Jun '98 / Blue Jackel

Taudi Symphony

☐ TAUDI SYMPHONY
Aujack swing / Africa soul / TODI / Caron style / Jam / Le lama el ritmo / Ludwig in the sunshine / Carcass / Royal Albert Hall / Loran's dance / Aktual / Africa soul (dub version)
FR 346CD / Apr '95 / Big Cheese

Tavares

☐ BEST OF THE TAVARES ON TOUR, THE
Bad times / Never had a love like this before / Medley / I hope you'll be very unhappy without me / You are the words, you are the music / Turn your love around / More than a woman / Heaven must be missing an angel
SUMCD 4074 / Nov '96 / Summit

☐ DANCE HEAVEN
Whodunnit / Don't take away the music / It only takes a minute / I hope you'll be very unhappy without me / Bad times / Turn your love around / More than a woman / You are the words, you are the music / Check it out / Remember what I told you to forget / She's gone / Heaven must be missing an angel
304152 / Jun '97 / Hallmark

☐ GOLD COLLECTION, THE
It only takes a minute / Heaven must be missing an angel / Slow train to paradise / Never had a love like this before / Check it out / She's gone / My ship / Don't take away the music / Whodunit / Mighty power of love / One step away / Ghost of love / Love I never had / I wanna see you soon / Bein' with you / More than a woman
CDGOLD 1016 / Mar '96 / EMI Gold

☐ HEAVEN MUST BE MISSING AN ANGEL (The Greatest Hits Live)
Heaven must be missing an angel / More than a woman / You are the words, you are the music / Bad times / She's gone / Whodunnit / Don't take away the music / Check it out / Remember what I told you to forget / I hope you'll be very unhappy without me / It only takes a minute girl / Never had a love like this before / Turn your love around
AIM 1062 / Sep '97 / Aim

☐ TAVARES LIVE IN CONCERT
Bad times / Never had a love like this before / Can't take the blame for losing you / You are the words / Motown philly / Turn you love around / More than a woman / Heaven must be missing an angel
JHD 104 / Aug '93 / Tring

Taxi

☐ CHOCOLATE
Want / Givin' up lovin' / Not important / Green eye / Killer / Guess my name / No way talk / Somebody loves you
TAXICD 001 / 2 Mar '98 / Golden Triangle

Tayfa

☐ TAYFA
GR 1191052 / 24 Feb '98 / Griffle

Taylor, Allan

☐ ALEX CAMPBELL TRIBUTE CONCERT, THE (2CD Set) (Taylor, Allan & Friends)
TCD 007 / May '98 / Living Tradition

☐ FADED LIGHT
T 005CD / Nov '95 / Living Tradition

☐ LINES
T 002CD / Aug '94 / Living Tradition

☐ LOOKING FOR YOU
Traveller / So long / Looking for you / Win or lose / Veteran / Dove / Restless / Joseph / Misty on the water / Cold hard town / Crazy man / Hard to tell
RTD 35760132 / Apr '97 / Stockfish

☐ SO LONG
T 004CD / Aug '94 / Living Tradition

☐ SOMETIMES/THE LADY
BGOCD 390 / 27 Apr '98 / Beat Goes On

Taylor, Art

☐ WAILIN' AT THE VANGUARD (Taylor, Art Wailers)
Street intro / AT's shout / Bridge theme/Mr. A.T. revisited / Band introductions / Dear old Stockholm / Stressed out / So sorry please / Bridge theme / Mr. A.T. revisited / Interchat / Sophisticated lady / In a sentimental mood / Chelsea Bridge / Harlem mardi gras / Bridge theme/Salt peanuts
5196772 / May '94 / Verve

Taylor, Billy

☐ BILLY TAYLOR TRIO WITH CANDIDO (Taylor, Billy Trio & Candido)
Mambo Inn / Bit of Bedlam / Declivity / Love for sale / Live one / Different bells
OJCCD 152 / May '97 / Original Jazz Classics

☐ MUSIC KEEPS US YOUNG (Taylor, Billy Trio)
AJ 71601 / 27 Apr '98 / Arkadia

☐ WHERE'VE YOU BEEN (Taylor, Billy Quartet & Joe Kennedy)
CCD 4145 / Jul '96 / Concord Jazz

Taylor, Bram

☐ FURTHER HORIZONS
FE 092CD / Oct '93 / Fellside

☐ PICK OF THE GRINNER
River run / Gin' I were a baron's heir / Feed the children / Language of the land / Thousand years / Harbour in the storm / High Germany / Low road / Why walk when you can fly / Banks of the Bann / Never be the sun / William Taylor / Katie / Picker and a grinner
FECD 120 / Sep '97 / Fellside

Taylor, Cecil

☐ 3 PHASIS
NW 303 / Aug '92 / New World

☐ AIR
Number one (take one) / Number one (take two) / Air (take nine) / Air (take 21) / Air (take 24) / Port of call (take 3)
CCD 79046 / Feb '97 / Candid

☐ CECIL TAYLOR UNIT
Idut / Serdab / Holiday en masque
NW 201 / '88 / New World

☐ CELL WALK FOR CELESTE
Cell walk for Celeste / Davis / Section C / Jumpin' punkins / Jumpin' punkins / Davis / Cell walk for Celeste
CCD 9034 / Feb '97 / Candid

☐ CHINAMPAS
CDLR 153 / Mar '88 / Leo

☐ CROSSING
Student studies / Niggle feuigle / Indent / Crossing / After all / Jitney
JHR 73505 / Sep '93 / Jazz Hour

☐ DARK TO THEMSELVES (Taylor, Cecil Unit)
ENJACD 20842 / 17 Oct '97 / Enja

☐ FONDATION MAEGHT NIGHTS VOL.1
COD 001 / Mar '92 / Jazz View

☐ FONDATION MAEGHT NIGHTS VOL.2
COD 002 / Jun '92 / Jazz View

☐ FONDATION MAEGHT NIGHTS VOL.3
COD 003 / Jul '92 / Jazz View

☐ GARDEN VOL.1
ARTCD 6050 / Nov '90 / Hat Art

☐ GREAT PARIS CONCERT, THE
Student studies / Student studies / Amplitude / Niggle feuigle
BLCD 760201 / Apr '95 / Black Lion

☐ INDENT
Indent: first layer / Indent: second layer / Indent: third layer
FCD 41038 / Dec '87 / Freedom

☐ IWONTUNWONSI
SSCD 8065 / Jan '96 / Sound Hills

☐ JAZZ ADVANCE
7844622 / 1 Jun '98 / EMI

☐ JUMPIN' PUNKINS
Jumpin' punkins / OP / I forgot / Things ain't what they used to be
CCD 79013 / Feb '97 / Candid

☐ LIVE IN BOLOGNA (Taylor, Cecil Unit)
CDLR 100 / Mar '88 / Leo

☐ LOVE FOR SALE
Get out of town / I love Paris / Love for sale / Little lees / Matie's trophies / Carol / Three points
4941072 / 22 Jun '98 / Pacific Jazz

☐ NEFERTITI THE BEAUTIFUL ONE HAS COME (2CD Set)
REV 202 / 15 Jun '98 / Revenant

☐ NEW YORK CITY RHYTHM AND BLUES (Taylor, Cecil & Buell Neidlinger)
OP / Cell walk for Celeste / Cindy's main mood / Things ain't what they used to be
CCD 79017 / Feb '97 / Candid

☐ ONE TOO MANY SALTY SWIFT AND NOT GOODBYE
ARTCD 26090 / Dec '91 / Hat Art

☐ SILENT TONGUES
Abyss / Petals and filaments / Jitney / Taylor crossing part one / Crossing / After all / Jitney No. 2 / After all No. 2
FCD 41005 / Sep '87 / Freedom

☐ SPRING OF TWO BLUE J'S (Taylor, Cecil Unit)
COD 008 / Aug '92 / Jazz View

☐ TRANCE
BLCD 760220 / Jun '97 / Black Lion

☐ TREE OF LIFE
FMPCD 98 / Jun '98 / Full Moon

☐ WINGED SERPENT (Taylor, Cecil Segments 11)
SNCD 1089 / '86 / Soul Note

☐ WORLD OF CECIL TAYLOR, THE
Air / This nearly was mine / Port of call / EB / Lazy afternoon
CCD 9006 / Feb '97 / Candid

Taylor, Chip

☐ HIT MAN
I can't make it with you / I can't let go / Angel of the morning / Wild thing / Anyway you want me / Try (just a little bit harder) / Storybook children / Country girl city man / Welcome home / Sweet dream woman / It's such a lonely time of year / Just a little bit later on down the line / Son of a rotten gambler
TW 002 / 20 Oct '97 / Train Wreck

☐ LAST CHANCE
(I want) the real thing / Son of a rotten gambler / I read it in a Rolling Stone / (The coal fields of) Shickshinny / I wasn't born in Tennessee / (Likes of) Louise / It's still the same / IOU in cash box / Family of one / Clean your own tables / Last chance / Real thing / Son of a rottenn agmbler / I read it in rollin' stone / Coal fields of skikshinny / I wasn't born in Tenessee / Louise / 101 in the cashbox / Clean your tables
GADFLY 237 / 9 Mar '98 / Train Wreck

☐ LIVING ROOM TAPES, THE
Something about losing it all / Same thing all over blues / Hell with her / Grandma's little LeBaron / Heroes of this song / Good love last night / Why Milwaukee / Only one Joan / Shut you down / Oh my Marie / Some hearts / Florence is the river
TW 101 / 20 Oct '97 / Train Wreck

☐ SEVEN DAYS IN MAY...A LOVE STORY
Seven days in May / I will be standing again / Through their Mother's eyes: *Taylor, Chip & Lucinda Williams* / If I don't know love: *Taylor, Chip & Lucinda Williams* / Just keep holding on / Florence the baby and me / One hell of a guy: *Taylor, Chip & Guy Clark* / Florence is the river / Oh Florence / Alexander / How can I get through this / Walk away from you / All my days
TW 007 / Jun '98 / Train Wreck

Taylor, Dave

☐ CADILLACS AND MOONLIGHT
MCD 705 / Jun '97 / Midnight Rock

☐ SHOTGUN BOOGIE
MCD 806 / Jun '98 / Midnight Rock

Taylor, David

☐ PAST TELLS
804362 / Feb '94 / New World

Taylor, Debbie

☐ STILL COMIN' DOWN ON YA
No if's, and's or but's / (I just make believe) I'm touching you / Too sad to tell / Second to none / Romance without finance / Leaving him tomorrow / No deposit, no return / Eye doctor / Jeremiah
NEMCD 941 / Jul '97 / Sequel

Taylor, Derek

☐ MY KIND OF JOLSON
CDOK 3008 / Dec '89 / OK

Taylor, Eddie

☐ BAD BOY (Charly Blues Masterworks Vol.35)
Bad boy / ET blues / Ride 'em on down / Big town playboy / You'll always have a home / Don't knock at my door / I'm gonna love you / Lookin' for trouble / Find my baby / Stroll out west / I'm sitting here / Do you want me to cry / Train fare / Leave this neighborhood / Somethin' for nothin'
CDBM 35 / Jan '93 / Charly

☐ BAD BOY (Taylor, Eddie 'Big Town Playboy' & Vera Taylor)
WCD 120711 / Jul '95 / Wolf

☐ I FEEL SO BAD
HCD 8027 / Sep '94 / Hightone

☐ LONG WAY FROM HOME
BPCD 5025 / Dec '95 / Blind Pig

☐ MY HEART IS BLEEDING (Taylor, Eddie Blues Band)
My heart is bleeding / Going to Virginia / So bad / Lexington breakdown / Blow wind blow / Wreck on 83 Highway / Soul brother / There'll be a day / Lawndale blues / Gamblin' woman / I got a little thing they call it swing / One day I get lucky / Dust my broom
ECD 260542 / Sep '94 / Evidence

Taylor, Eric

☐ ERIC TAYLOR
WWMCD 1040 / Nov '95 / Watermelon

Taylor, Eva

☐ EDISON LATERALS VOL.4, THE
DCP 303D / Jul '98 / Diamond Cut

☐ NOT JUST THE BLUES
Of all the wrongs you've done me / Everybody loves my baby / Mandy make up your mind / I'm a little blackbird / Cake-walking babies from home / Pickin' on your baby / Papa de da da / Just wait 'till you see my baby / Living high, sometimes / Coal cart blues / You can't shush Katie (the gabbiest girl in town) / Shake that thing / Get it fixed / I've found a new baby / Pile of logs and stone (called home) / When the red,

red robin comes bob, bob, bobbin along / (There's a blue ridge in my heart) Virginia / Nobody but my baby is getting my love / Morocco blues / Candy lips (I'm stuck on you) / Scatter your smiles / Where that old man river flows / Shout sister shout
TPZ 1044 / May '96 / Topaz Jazz

Taylor, Gary

☐ ONE DAY AT A TIME
In search of / Where do we go / Special / Think about me / Time has run out of time / Will you come back / One day at a time / I will be here / Who we are / Don't go there / Rest my lips
XECD 3 / Jun '95 / Expansion

☐ REFLECTIONS
Restless / Blind to it all / In and out of love / After effect / One love, one people / Time after time / Take control / Eye to eye / I need / Don't be so distant / APB / Irresistible love / Never too blue / Sign my life away
EXCDP 8 / Nov '94 / Expansion

☐ SQUARE ONE
Hold me accountable / Irresistible love / APB / Pieces / Square one / Read between the lines / Never too blue / I need you now / Eye to eye / One and only
EXCD 6 / Mar '93 / Expansion

☐ TAKE CONTROL
Take control / Whatever / I need / In and out of love / Wishful thinking / Don't be so distant / I live 4 U / Sign my life away / Time after time
EXCDP 5 / Jun '90 / Expansion

Taylor, 'Hound Dog'

☐ BEWARE OF THE DOG (Taylor, 'Hound Dog' House Rockers)
Give me back my wig / Sun is shining / Kitchen sink boogie / Dust my broom / Comin' around the mountain / Let's get funky / Rock me / It's alright / Freddie's blues
ALCD 4707 / May '93 / Alligator

☐ GENUINE HOUSEROCKING MUSIC (Taylor, 'Hound Dog' House Rockers)
Ain't got nobody / Gonna send you back to Georgia / Fender bender / My baby's coming home / Blue guitar / Sun is shining / Phillips goes bananas / What'd I say / Kansas City / Crossroads
ALCD 4727 / May '93 / Alligator

☐ HOUND DOG TAYLOR AND THE HOUSE ROCKERS (Taylor, 'Hound Dog' House Rockers)
She's gone / Walking the ceiling / Held my baby last night / Taylor's rock / It's alright / Phillip's theme / Wild about you baby / I just can't make it / It hurts me too / 44 blues / Give me back my wig / 55th Street boogie
ALCD 4701 / May '93 / Alligator

☐ LIVE AT JOE'S PLACE
422319 / Feb '92 / Last Call

☐ LIVE IN BOSTON (Taylor, 'Hound Dog' House Rockers)
Wild about you baby / Sky is crying / Dust my broom / Give me back my wig / Mama talk to your daughter / Gonna send you back to Georgia / Rock me baby / Jumping with Symphony Sid / I just can't take it / It hurts me too / Roll your money maker / Freddie's blues / Let's get funky / Take five / Goodnight boogie
CDGR 218 / 2 Feb '98 / Charly

☐ NATURAL BOOGIE (Taylor, 'Hound Dog' House Rockers)
Take five / Hawaiian boogie / See me in the evening / You can't sit down / Sitting at home alone / One more time / Roll your moneymaker / Buster's boogie / Sadie / Talk to my baby / Goodnight boogie
ALCD 4704 / May '93 / Alligator

☐ TRIBUTE TO 'HOUND DOG' TAYLOR, A (Various Artists)
Give me back my wig: *Allison, Luther* / Sadie: *Seals, Son* / Taylor's rock: *Landreth, Sonny* / Gonna send you back to Georgia: *Gov't Mule* / Freddie's blues: *Magic Slim & The Teardrops* / See me in the evening: *Margolin, Bob* / Let's get funky: *Bishop, Elvin* / It's alright: *Reid, Vernon* / Hawaiian boogie: *Hole, Dave* / She's gone: *Hills, Michael Blues Mob* / I just can't make it: *Thorogood, George* / Wayward angel: *Earl, Ronnie* / Take five: *Koda, Cub & The Houserockers*
ALCD 4855 / 19 Jan '98 / Alligator

Taylor, James

☐ BEST LIVE
Sweet baby James / Handyman / Your smiling face / Steamroller blues / Mexico / Walking man / Country road / Fire and rain / How sweet it is (to be loved by you) / Riding on a railroad / Something in the way she moves / Sun on the moon / Up on the roof / Copperline / Slap leather / You've got a friend / That lonesome road
4766572 / Apr '94 / Columbia

☐ DAD LOVES HIS WORK
Hard times / Her town too / Hour that the morning comes / I will follow / Believe it or not / Stand and fight / Only for me / Summer's here / Sugar trade / London Town / That lonesome road
4747632 / 26 Mar '98 / Columbia

☐ GREATEST HITS
Something in the way she moves / Carolina on my mind / Fire and rain / Sweet baby James / Country roads / You've got a friend / Don't let me be lonely tonight / Walking man / How sweet it is (to be loved by you) / Mexico / Shower the people / Steamroller
7599273362 / '94 / WEA

☐ HOURGLASS
Line 'em up / Enough to be your way / Little more time with you / Gaia / Ananas / Jump up behind me / Another day / Up er mei / Up from your life / Yellow and rose / Boatman / Walking my baby back home / Hangnail
4877482 / Jun '97 / Columbia

☐ JT
Your smiling face / There we are / Honey don't leave LA / Another grey morning / Bartender's blues / Secret o'life / Handyman / I was only telling a lie / Looking for love on Broadway / Terra nova / If I keep my heart out of sight / Traffic jam
4746802 / Feb '97 / Columbia

☐ LIVE
Sweet baby James / Traffic jam / Handyman / Your smiling face / Secret of life / Shed a little light / Everybody has the blues / Steamroller blues / Mexico / Millworker / Country road / Fire and rain / Shower the people / How sweet it is (to be loved by you) / New hymn / Walking man / Riding on a railroad / Something / Sun on the moon / Up on the roof / Don't let me be lonely tonight / She thinks I still care / Copperline / Slap leather / Only one / You make it easy / Carolina on my mind / I will follow / You've got a friend / That lonesome road
4742162 / Sep '93 / Columbia

☐ MUD SLIDE SLIM AND THE BLUE HORIZON
Love has brought me around / You got a friend / Places in my past / Riding on a railroad / Soldiers / Mud slide slim / Hey Mister, that's me upon the jukebox / Upon the jukebox / You can close your eyes / Machine gun Kelly / Long ago and far away / Let me ride / Highway song / Isn't it nice to be home again
256004 / '89 / WEA

☐ NEVER DIE YOUNG
Never die young / T-Bone / Baby boom baby / Runaway boy / Valentine's day / Sun on the moon / Sweet potato pie / Home by another way / Letter in the mail / First of May
4604342 / 16 Mar '98 / Columbia

☐ NEW MOON SHINE
Copperline / Down in the hole / (I've got to) stop thinkin' 'bout that / Shed a little light / Frozen man / Slap leather / Like everyone she knows / One more go round / Everybody loves to cha cha / Native son / Oh brother / Water is wide
4689772 / 16 Mar '98 / Columbia

☐ SALUTE TO JAMES TAYLOR, A (Various Artists)
Fire and rain / Country road / Handy man / How sweet it is / Copperline / Never die young / Up on the roof / Like everyone she knows / Don't let me be lonely tonight / Her town too / Sweet potato pie / You've got a friend
309182 / 13 Jul '98 / Hallmark

☐ SWEET BABY JAMES
Sweet baby James / Lo and behold / Sunny skies / Steam Roller / Country roads / Oh Susanna / Fire and rain blossom / Anywhere like heaven / Oh baby don't you lose your lip on me / Suite for 20G / Love has brought me around / You've got a friend / Places in my past / Riding on a railroad / Soldiers / Mud slide slim / Hey mister, that's me upon the jukebox / You can close your eyes / Machine gun Kelly / Long ago and far away / Let me ride / Highway song / Isn't it nice to be home again
246043 / Apr '84 / WEA

☐ THAT'S WHY I'M HERE
That's why I'm here / Song for you far away / Only a dream in Rio / Turn away / Going around one more time / Everyday / Limousine driver / Only one / Mona / Man who shot Liberty Valance / That's why I'm here (reprise)
4624912 / 16 Mar '98 / Columbia

Taylor, James

☐ BBC SESSIONS, THE (Taylor, James Quartet)
Blow up / Spyder / All about mine / Down by the river / Breakout / Bossa plante / Groovin' home / Mon oncle / Love the life / Tell it like it is
SFRSCD 043 / 8 Dec '97 / Strange Fruit

☐ BLOW UP (The JTQ Collection) (Taylor, James Quartet)
MCCD 333 / 16 Mar '98 / Music Club

☐ DO YOUR OWN THING (Taylor, James Quartet)
Love the life / Killing time / Money / JTQ theme / Ted's asleep / Always there / Oscar / Samba for Bill and Ben / Valhalla / Fat / Peace song
8437972 / Oct '90 / Polydor

☐ GET ORGANIZED (Taylor, James Quartet)
Grooving home / Electric boogaloo / Stretch / It doesn't matter / Riding high / Touchdown / Breakout / Brothers batucada / Bluebird / Bossa pilante
8394052 / May '89 / Polydor

☐ IN THE HAND OF THE INEVITABLE (Taylor, James Quartet)
Love will keep us together / Three mile island / Free your mind / Haitian breakdown / A good thing / Let's get together / Seque no. 1 / Steppin' into my life / Whole lotta love / Journey / Sounds of freedom / Keep on movin' / In the hands of the inevitable
JAZIDCD 115 / Feb '95 / Acid Jazz

☐ LIVE AT THE MANCHESTER ACADEMY (Taylor, James Quartet)
JTI 002CD / 25 May '98 / JTI

☐ LIVING UNDERGROUND (Taylor, James Quartet)
JAZIDCD 140 / Jun '96 / Acid Jazz

Taylor, John

☐ AMBLESIDE DAYS (Taylor, John & John Surman)
Lodore falls / Wandering / Ambleside days / Scale force / Coniston falls / Pathway / Clapperclowe / Dry stone
AHUM 013 / Oct '92 / Ah-Um

☐ BLUE GLASS (Taylor, John Trio)
Pure and simple / Spring is here / Q / Hermana guapa / Blue glass / How deep is the ocean / Fragment / Think before you think / Evansong / Clapperclowe
JHCD 020 / Jan '94 / Ronnie Scott's Jazz House

☐ PAUSE AND THINK AGAIN
FMRCD 24 / Dec '95 / Future

Taylor, John

☐ FEELINGS ARE GOOD AND OTHER LIES
B5 274747 / Dec '96 / B5
REVXD 215 / Apr '97 / Revolver

Taylor, John

☐ LIVE (Taylor, John & Andy Imbrie)
Roaring jelly / Flowers of Edinburgh / Sauchie Haugh / Pinewoods reel / Mrs. Stewart's jig / Neidpath Castle / Cadgers in The Canongate / Follow me home / Bonnie Ina Campbell / De'il among the tailors / Jennifer's jig / Mrs. MacLeod of Raasay
JA 102 / Dec '97 / Andy Imbrie

Taylor, Johnnie

☐ CHRONICLE
Who's making love / Take care of your homework / Testify / I could never be president / Love bones / Steal away / I am somebody / Jody's got your girl and gone / I don't wanna lose you / Hijackin' love / Standin' in for Jody / Doing my own thing (Part 2) / Doing my own thing / Stop doggin' me / I believe in you (You believe in me) / Cheaper to keep her / We're getting careless with our love / I've been born again / It's September / Try me tonight / Just keep on loving me
CDSXE 084 / Jul '93 / Stax

☐ JOHNNIE TAYLOR PHILOSOPHY CONTINUES/ONE STEP BEYOND
Testify / Separation line / Love bones / Love is a hurtin' thing / I had a fight with love / I could never be president / It's amazing / Who can I turn to / Games people play / It's your thing / Time after time / Party life / Will you love me forever / I am somebody / I don't wanna lose you / Don't take my sunshine / Jody's got your girl and gone / Fool like me
CDSXD 108 / Jul '94 / Stax

☐ RAW BLUES/LITTLE BLUEBIRD
Where there's smoke there's fire / Hello sundown / Pardon me lady / Where can a man go from here / That bone / That's where it's at / Part time love / If I had it to do all over / You're good for me / You can't keep a good man down / You can win with a losing hand / Little bluebird / Toe hold / I've got to love somebody's baby / Just the one (I've been looking for) / Outside love / You can't get away from it / I had a dream / Somebody's sleeping in my bed / I ain't particular / Steal away / Stop dogging me / Jody's got your girl and gone
CDSXD 051 / Jun '92 / Stax

☐ WANTED: ONE SOUL SINGER
I got to love somebody's baby / Just the one I've been looking for / Watermelon man / Where can a man go from here / Toe hold / Outside love / Ain't that lovin' you / Blues in the night / I had a dream / Sixteen tons / Little bluebird
7567822532 / Apr '95 / Atlantic

Taylor, Johnny

☐ 1960'S FRENCH EP COLLECTION, THE (Taylor, Johnny & The Strangers)
176252 / Sep '97 / Magic

Taylor, Koko

☐ AUDIENCE WITH THE QUEEN, AN (Live From Chicago)
Let the good times roll / I'm a woman / Going back to luka / Devil's gonna have a field day / Come to Mama / I'd rather go blind / Let me love you / Wang dang doodle
ALCD 4754 / May '93 / Alligator

☐ EARTH SHAKER
ALCD 4711 / May '93 / Alligator

☐ FORCE OF NATURE
Mother nature / If I can't be first / Hound dog / Born under a bad sign / Let the juke joint jump / 63 year old mama / Don't put your hands on me / Bad case of loving you / Fish in dirty water / Tit for tat / Put the pot on / Nothing takes the place of you / Spellbound / Greedy man
ALCD 4817 / Feb '94 / Alligator

☐ FROM THE HEART OF A WOMAN
Something strange is going on / I'd rather go blind / Keep your hands off him / Thanks but no thanks / If you got a heartache / Never trust a man / Sure had a wonderful time last night / Blow top blues / If walls could talk / It took a long time
ALCD 4724 / May '93 / Alligator

☐ JUMP FOR JOY
Can't let go / Stop watching your enemies / Hey baby / Tired of that / It's a dirty job / Jump for joy / Time will tell / Eyes don't lie / Fishing trip / I don't want no leftovers
ALCD 4784 / May '93 / Alligator

☐ QUEEN OF THE BLUES, THE
ALCD 4740 / Oct '93 / Alligator

☐ SOUTH SIDE LADY
ECD 260072 / Jan '92 / Evidence

☐ WHAT IT TAKES
Got what it takes / Don't mess with the messer / Whatever I am you made me / I'm a little mixed up / Wang dang doodle / (I got) All you need / Love me / What came first the chicken or the hen / Insane asylum / Fire / I don't care who knows / Twenty nine ways (to my baby's door) / Blue prelude / I need more and more / Um huh my baby / Bills, bills and more bills / I got what it takes
MCD 09328 / Apr '97 / Chess/MCA

Taylor, Lewis

☐ LEWIS TAYLOR
Lucky / Bittersweet / Whoever / Track / Song / Betterlove / How / Right / Damn / Spirit
CID 8049 / Aug '96 / Island

Taylor, Little Johnny

☐ GALAXY YEARS, THE
You'll need another favour / What you need is a ball / Part time love / Somewhere down the line / Since I found a new love / My heart is filled with pain / First class love / If you love me like you say / You win, I lose / Nightingale melody / I smell trouble / True love / For your precious love / I've never had a woman like you before / Somebody's got to pay / Help yourself / One more chance / Please come home for Christmas / All I want is you / Zig zag lightning / Things that I used to do / Big blue diamonds / I know you hear me calling / Drivin' wheel / Sometimey woman / Double or nothing
CDCHD 967 / Apr '91 / Ace

☐ UGLY MAN
Have you ever been to Kansas City / Never be lonely and blue / LJT / Ugly man / It's my fault, darlin' / I enjoy you / How can a broke man survive / King size souvenir / Have you ever been to Kansas City (Reprise)
ICH 1042CD / Oct '93 / Ichiban

Taylor, Livingston

☐ COLLECTION 1970-1980, THE
RE 21612 / 6 Apr '98 / Razor & Tie

☐ LIVINGSTON TAYLOR
JD 162 / 5 Jan '98 / Chesky

Taylor, Lynn

☐ I SEE YOUR FACE BEFORE ME
PS 0011CD / Sep '95 / P&S

Taylor, Martin

☐ ARTISTRY
Polka dots and moonbeams / Stella by starlight / Teach me tonight / Dolphin / Georgia on my mind / They can't take that away from me / Here, there and everywhere / Just squeeze me / Gentle rain / Cherokee / That certain smile
AKD 020 / Mar '93 / Linn

☐ CHANGE OF HEART
73 Berkeley street / Gypsy / You don't know me / After hours / Change of heart / I get along without you very well / Angels's camp
AKD 016 / Nov '91 / Linn

☐ DON'T FRET
I love you / Blue in green / I'm old fashioned / Laverne Walk / Moonlight in Vermont / Mugavero / Don't fret / You know it's true
AKD 014 / Feb '91 / Linn

☐ GOLD
Johnny and Mary / Sweet Sue just you / Sweet Lorraine / I'm old fashioned / Minor swing / It's only a paper moon / Undecided / In a mellow tone / I love you / Nuages / Gypsy / I get along without you very well / Angel's camp / I got rhythm
AKD 064 / Aug '97 / Linn

☐ GYPSY (The Spirit Of Django)
Gypsy medley / My vardo / Chicago / Chez Ferdinand / Tears / Kushti / Nuages / I can't give you anything but love / Dreaming of you / Sweet Sue just you / Musette for a magpie / Chillin' with Oscar / Squid kid
AKD 090 / 29 Jun '98 / Linn

☐ PORTRAITS
Shiny stockings / Like someone in love / Sweet Lorraine / I got rhythm / Why did I choose you / My funny valentine / Do you knwo what it means to Miss New Orleans / I remember Clifford / Ol'man river / Here, there and everywhere / In a mellow tone / My one and only love / Kiko / Very early
AKD 048 / Mar '96 / Linn

☐ SARABANDA
Mornin' / Call to sarabanda / They can't take that away from me / Jenna / Cherokee ridge / Holiday for two / I remember clifford / Deja vu / Don't blame me / I got rhythm / An eilen dhu (the dark island)
1390182 / Feb '89 / Gaia

☐ SPIRIT OF DJANGO
Chez Fernand / Minor swing / Night and day / Nuages / James / Django's dream / Swing '42 / Oh lady be good / Honeysuckle rose / Johnny and Mary
AKD 030 / Oct '94 / Linn

☐ TAYLOR MADE (Taylor, Martin & John Richardson/Peter Ind)
On Green Dolphin Street / Emily / Minor truth / Lady be good / St. Thomas / My Latin brother / Teach me tonight / Watch what happens / Scrapple from the apple
WAVE 17CD / 20 Jul '98 / Wave

☐ TRIPLE LIBRA (Taylor, Martin & Peter Ind)
Manhattan tea party / Senor Mouse / Ginger / Triple Libra / Windows / Bright size life / Waiting / Green eyes
WAVE 24CD / 20 Jul '98 / Wave

☐ TWO'S COMPANY
Bewitched / I've never been in love before / Skylark / Willow weep for me / Billie's bounce / Royal Garden blues / I thought about you / I'll never be the same / Triste / You're my everything / I'm beginning to see the light / You stepped out of a dream / When I fall in love / Gone with the wind / Everything happens to me / Don't blame me / My foolish heart
AKD 081 / 10 Nov '97 / Linn

Taylor, Matt

☐ RADIO CITY BLUES
MSECD 009 / Jun '95 / Mouse

☐ TROUBLE IN THE WIND
AIM 1034CD / Oct '93 / Aim

Taylor, Melvin

☐ BLUES ON THE RUN
Travellin' man / Lowdown dirty shame / Escape / Cold cold feeling / Just like a woman / Chitlins con carne
ECD 260412 / Mar '94 / Evidence

☐ DIRTY POOL (Taylor, Melvin & The Slack Band)
Too sorry / Dirty pool / I ain't superstitious / Kansas City / Floodin' in California / Born under a bad sign / Right place, wrong time / Telephone song / Merry Christmas baby
ECD 26088 / Sep '97 / Evidence

☐ MELVIN TAYLOR AND THE SLACK BAND (Taylor, Melvin & The Slack Band)
Texas flood / Depression blues / Grooving in New Orleans / Talking to Anna Mae / Tin pan alley / All your love / Don't throw your love on me so strong / T-bone shuffle / Voodoo chile (slight return) / Tequila
ECD 260732 / Oct '95 / Evidence

☐ PLAYS THE BLUES FOR YOU
Talking to Anna Mae, Part 1 / TV Mama / I'll play the blues for you / Born to lose / Tribute to Wes / Cadillac assembly line / Voodoo Daddy / Talking to Anna Mae, Part 2 / Groovin' in Paris
ECD 260292 / Feb '93 / Evidence

Taylor, Mick

☐ MICK TAYLOR AND CARLA OLSON LIVE (Taylor, Mick & Carla Olson)
Who put the sting in the honeybee / Slow rollin' train / Trying to hold on / Rubies and diamonds / See the light / You can't move in / Broken hands / Sway / Hartley quits / Midnight mission / Silver train
FIENDCD 197 / Oct '90 / Demon

☐ WITHIN AN ACE (Taylor, Mick & Carla Olson)
Justice / Dark horses / Why did you stop / World of pain / Fortune / Within an ace / Man once loved / How many days / Rescue fantasy / Is the lady gone
FIENDCD 726 / Jan '93 / Demon

Taylor, Neil

☐ TOOTHPICK'S PILLOW (Taylor, Neil & Dogwood)
Seek the blind / Once broken fool / Dancing strange / Everyday as it comes / Toothpick's pillow / In my soul / I just woke up tonight / Average man / White as a dove / Out of me / More that I can stand / In court of the crimson king
MSCDR 002 / 10 Nov '97 / Blueprint

Taylor, Rod

☐ LIBERATE
WSPCD 004 / Nov '93 / Word Sound & Power

Taylor, Roger

☐ FUN IN SPACE
Fun in space / No violins / Laugh or cry / Let's get crazy / Future management / My country / Good times are now / Magic is loose / Interlude in Constantinople / Airheads
CDPCS 7380 / May '96 / Parlophone

☐ HAPPINESS
Nazis 1994 / Happiness / Revelations / Touch the sky / Foreign sand / Freedom train / You had to be there / Key / Everybody hurts sometime / Loneliness / Dear Mr. Murdoch / Old friends
CDPCSD 157 / Sep '94 / Parlophone

☐ STRANGE FRONTIER
Strange frontier / Beautiful dreams / Man on fire / Racing in the street / Masters of war / Killing time / Abandonfire / Young love / It's an illusion / I cry for you
CDPCS 7381 / May '96 / Parlophone

Taylor, Rusty

☐ RUSTY TAYLOR & STEVE LANE'S RED HOT PEPPERS (Taylor, Rusty & Steve Lane's Red Hot Peppers)
Cake walkin' babies from home / Wrap your troubles in dreams (and dream your troubles away) / Trombone cholly / Just too bad / Do your duty / You've got to give me some / Baby, won't you please come home / Cheatin' on me / I've got what it takes / Alexander's ragtime band / There's a blue ridge 'round my heart, Virginia / Shine / I'm coming Virginia / Put it right here / Atlanta / Take me for a buggy ride / Spanish shawl / After you've gone
AZMC 17 / Apr '93 / Azure

Taylor, Sam

☐ BACK BEAT VOL.5 (The Rhythm Of The Blues) (Taylor, Sam 'The Man')
Big beat / Harlem nocturne / As time goes by / Hit the road / Taylor made / Oo wee / Look out / Fish roll / Let's ball / Sam's blues / Boss is home / Ride Sammy ride / Real gone / Blue suede shoes / O'ho oh yeah uh huh / To a wild rose
5112702 / Oct '94 / Mercury

Taylor, Simon

☐ IRISH GUITAR, THE
OSS 1CD / Jan '87 / Ossian

Taylor, Tot

☐ BOX OFFICE POISON
Australian / Arise Sir Tot / I was frank / Spoil her / Mr. Strings / Nevermore / Ballad of Jackie and Ivy / People will talk / I never rome / Babysitting / Mr. String's come back / My independant heart
TOTE 3 / Oct '88 / Soundcakes

☐ CLIVE BARKER'S A/Z HORROR/ WATERLAND
TWEEDCD 001 / 17 Nov '97 / Tweed

☐ INSIDE STORY, THE
TOTE 2 / Oct '88 / Soundcakes

☐ MY BLUE PERIOD
Wrong idea / It must have been a craze / It's good for you / It's all a blur / Wild scene / I'll wait / Compromising life / Young world / I'll miss the lads / It's not a bad old place / Girl did this
TOTE 4 / Oct '88 / Soundcakes

☐ PLAYTIME
TOTE 1 / Oct '88 / Soundcakes

Taylor, Tyrone

☐ REBIRTH
CRCD 81 / 20 Apr '98 / Charm

☐ REGGAE MAX
JSRNCD 20 / 1 Jun '98 / Jet Star

☐ WAY TO PARADISE
VPCD 1378 / Jan '95 / VP

Taylor, Vince

☐ I'LL BE YOUR HERO
842132 / Jun '94 / EVA

Taylor, Will

☐ TAYLOR MADE FOR SEQUENCE DANCERS
La golondrina/My thanks to you / Sometimes when we touch / Unforgettable/And I love you so / I won't send roses/A certain smile / Best of times / Nice people/Ready willing and able / Island of dreams/My ain folk / Things we did last summer/Count your blessings instead of sh / Cherry pink and apple blossom white/Like I do / I just want to dance with you / Softly as in the morning sunrise/Echo of a serenade / Kiss of fire/A woman in love / Just walking in the rain / On the sunny side of the street/Sonny boy / Slow boat to China/Black hills of Dakota / Mama Inez / Sweet muchacha / I've never been in love before/The gypsy / De corazon a corazon / Gentle maiden/Try to remember / Sweetest song in the world
CDVA 6 / Mar '97 / Tema

TC Hug

☐ PIE-MONDO
I'm doing fine / Go-go UFO / Greatest hour / Matters on the brain / So real / Hometruths / Find / Gunaway / Free lunch / Someone / Two heads / I will be well / Pie-mondo
AMUSE 34CD / Mar '97 / Playtime

TC Islam

☐ PLANET 2020 (TC Islam & The Phunky)
ANTICDLP 2 / Oct '96 / Anti-Static

TCG

☐ LARGER THAN LIFE
2665627972 / 14 Jul '98 / Warlock

Tchinar, Ashik Feyzullah

☐ SACRED CHANTS OF ANATOLIA
C 580057 / Jan '96 / Ocora

TDF

☐ RETAIL THERAPY
Blue rock / Angelica / Pnom-sen / Sno-god / Sienna / Seven / Angelica's dream / What she wants / Donna / Rip stop / What else
9362464892 / Mar '97 / Warner Bros.

Te Kanawa, Kiri

☐ CHRISTMAS SONGS (Te Kanawa, Kiri & Roberto Alagna/Thomas Hampson)
Toyland / I'll be home for Christmas / Silent night / Minuit / Chretiens (cantique de Noel) / O holy night / In dulci jubilo / Il est ne le divin enfant / Have yourself a merry little Christmas / Christmas song / Chestnuts roasting by an open fire / My Christmas song for you / Winter wonderland / O Christmas tree / In the bleak mid-winter / Sleigh ride / Twelve days of Christmas / White Christmas
CDC 5661762 / Nov '96 / EMI Classics

☐ HEAR MY PRAYER
4588672 / 16 Mar '98 / Decca

☐ KIRI SINGS BERLIN
Always / It only happens when I dance / Cheek to cheek / Easter parade / How deep is the ocean / I've got my love to keep me warm / It's a lovely day / Let's face the music and dance / Say it isn't so / Song is ended / They say it's wonderful / What'll I do / Isn't this a lovely day / I got the sun in the morning / Blue skies
CDC 55641526 / 3 Nov '97 / EMI Classics

☐ OUR CHRISTMAS SONGS FOR YOU (Te Kanawa, Kiri & Roberto Alagna/ Thomas Hampson)
Sleigh ride / Christmas song / Toyland / Il est ne ledivin' enfant / Winter wonderland / I'll be home for Christmas / Minuit wonderland / My Christmas song for you / Twelve days of Christmas / In dulci jublio / O tannen baum / Silent night / Have yourself a merry little Christmas / In the bleak midwinter / White Christmas
CDC 5561752 / Nov '97 / EMI

Te Track

☐ LET'S GET STARTED/EASTMAN DUB (Te Track & Augustus Pablo)
GRELCD 505 / Apr '90 / Greensleeves

Tea

☐ SHIP, THE
14929 / 22 May '98 / Spalax

Teacups

☐ THIS WILL COME BACK TO HAUNT YOU
KC 021CD / 13 Jul '98 / Kindercore

Teagarden, Jack

☐ ACCENT ON TROMBONE
FSRCD 138 / Dec '90 / Fresh Sound

☐ BIG T
TPZ 1001 / Jul '94 / Topaz Jazz

☐ BIG T JUMP 1944-1946
JCD 643 / Aug '95 / Jass

☐ CLASSIC YEARS, THE (Teagarden, Jack & His Orchestra)
My melancholy baby / Beale street blues / So many times / Peg o' my heart / Swingin' on the Teagarden gate / Can't we talk it over / I'll remember / Muddy river blues / Somewhere a voice is calling / Table in a corner / Wolverine blues / If what you say is true / Blues / Red wing / At least you could say hello / I wanna hat with cherries / United we swing / Stop kicking my heart around
CDSGP 0240 / 16 Feb '98 / Prestige

☐ CLASSICS 1930-1934 (Teagarden, Jack & His Orchestra)
CLASSICS 698 / Jul '93 / Classics

☐ CLASSICS 1934-1939
CLASSICS 729 / Dec '93 / Classics

☐ CLASSICS 1939-1940
CLASSICS 758 / Aug '94 / Classics

☐ CLASSICS 1940-1941
CLASSICS 839 / Sep '95 / Classics

☐ CLASSICS 1941-1943
CLASSICS 874 / Apr '96 / Classics

☐ CLEVELAND, OHIO 1958 (Teagarden, Jack Allstars)
JCD 199 / Oct '92 / Jazzology

☐ HAS ANYBODY SEEN JACKSON VOL.2
Fort knox jump / Sing a love song / Has anybody here seen jackson / Mr. jessie blues / Impressions of meade lux lewis / Prelude in g minor / Swing without words / Bashful baby blues / Soft as spring / Barcarolle / Get off on a fugue / Heaven is mine again / No need to be sorry / This is no laughing matter / Funiculi, funicula (denza) / Sherman shout / Barracks blues / Dig the groove / Salt on a devil's tail / You know (just as well as I do) / Time out / Pied piper / Octoroon / Rompin' and stompin' / Glass blues (theme song)
JCD 637 / Jan '93 / Jass

☐ I GOTTA RIGHT TO SING THE BLUES
That's a serious thing / I'm gonna stomp Mr. Henry Lee / Dinah / Never had a reason to believe in you / Tailspin blues / Dancing with tears in my eyes / Sheikh of Araby / Basin Street blues / (I'll be glad when you're dead) you rascal you / Two tickets to Georgia / I gotta right to sing the blues / Ain't cha glad / Texas tea party / Hundred years from today / Fare thee well to Harlem / Christmas night in Harlem / Davenport blues
CDAJA 5059 / Feb '89 / Living Era

☐ INDISPENSABLE JACK TEAGARDEN, THE
She's a great, great girl / I'm gonna stomp Mr. Henry Lee / That's a serious thing / Tailspin blues / Never had a reason to believe in you / Buy buy for baby (or baby will bye bye you) / Sentimental baby / Futuristic rhythm / Louise / My kinda love / Sweetheart we need each other / From now on / Two tickets to Georgia / Fare thee well to Harlem / Christmas night in Harlem / Ain't misbehavin' / At the Darktown strutter's ball / Every now and then / Barrel house music / I'se a muggin' / St. Louis blues / Blues after hours / Jam session at Victor / Say it simple / There'll be some changes made / I cover the waterfront / You took advantage of me
ND 89613 / Mar '94 / RCA

☐ INTRODUCTION TO JACK TEAGARDEN 1928-1943, AN
4025 / Sep '95 / Best Of Jazz

☐ IT'S TIME FOR T VOL.1:1941/HAS ANYBODY SEEN JACKSON (2CD Set) (Teagarden, Jack Orchestra)
Frenesi / Here's my heart / Accident'ly on purpose / It all comes back to me / Prelude in c# minor / Nobody knows the trouble I've seen / Casey Jones / Made up my mind / Afternoon of a faun 12blue mist / Anitra's dance / Yankee doddle / Off to the races / These things you left me / Rhythm hymn / I can't get away from the blues / Deep river / Blow the man down / Harlem jump / Well, of course / It's time for T / Star told a story / Fort Knox jump / Sing a love song / Has anybody here seen Jackson / Mr. Jessie blues / Impressions of Meade Lux Lewis / Prelude on G minor / Swing without words / Bashful baby blues / Soft as spring / Barcarolle / Get off on a fugue / Heaven is mine again / No need to be sorry / This is no laughing matter / Funiculi, funicula / Sherman shout / Barracks blues / Dig the groove / Salt on a Devil's tail / You know (just as well as I do) / Time out / Pied Piper / Octoroon / Rompin' and stompin' / Glass blues
JZCL 5012 / Nov '96 / Jazz Classics

☐ IT'S TIME FOR TEA VOL.1 1941
JASSCD 624 / '92 / Jass

☐ JACK TEAGARDEN & PEE WEE RUSSELL (Teagarden, Jack & Pee Wee Russell)
Shine / St. james infirmary / World is waiting for sunrise / Big eight blues / Baby won't you please come home / Dinah / Zutty's hooty blues / There'll be some changes made / I've found a new baby / Everybody loves my baby
OJCCD 1708 / Jun '95 / Original Jazz Classics

☐ MASTERS OF JAZZ VOL.10
STCD 4110 / Feb '89 / Storyville

☐ STARS FELL ON ALABAMA
I gotta right to sing the blues / My melancholy baby / Wolverine blues / Beale street blues / Somewhere a voice is calling / If I could be with you (one hour tonight) / Muddy river blues / Aunt Hagar's blues / Swingin' on the Teagarden gate / It's a hundred to one (I'm in love) / Peg o' my heart / United we swing / Blues / Stars fell on Alabama / Junk man / Sheik of Araby / You rascal you / China boy / Chances are / Tiger rag / Rockin' chair / I swung the election
CD 53287 / Jan '98 / Giants Of Jazz

☐ TEAGARDEN PARTY, A
Muddy river blues / Somewhere a voice calling / Swingin' on a teagarden gate / Wolverine blues / (I'll be glad when you're dead) you rascal you / Plantation moods / Shake your hips / Somebody stole Gabriel's horn / Love me / I just couldn't take it baby / Hundred years from today / Blue river / Ol' Pappy / Fare-thee well to Harlem / Stars fell on Alabama / Junk man / Gotta right to sing the blues / Ain't cha glad / Dr. Heckle and Mr. Jibe / Texas tea party
PAR 2013 / Apr '94 / Parade

☐ THINK WELL OF ME
Where are you / Guess I'll go back home this summer / I'm a fool about my mama / Don't smoke in bed / In a little waterfront cafe / Think well of me / Old folks / Country boy blues / T'ain't so honey t'ain't so / Round the old deserted farm
5571012 / 3 Aug '98 / Verve

Teallach Ceilidh Band

☐ CATCHING THE SUN RISE
Stool of repentance / Letham smiddy / Athol highlanders / Mountains of Pomeroy / Irish soldier laddie / Yellow's on the broom / John Barleycorn / Martin the Stout / All the blue bonnets are over the border / MacDonald's awa' tae the war / Rocks of bawn / David Ross of Rosehall / Major Manson at Clachantrushal / Rainy day / Lark in the morning / Mysteries of knock / Barrowburn reel / Jack broke da prison door / Donald Blue / Sleep sound ida morning / Arthur McBride / Athol and Breadalbane / Cameron highlanders / Old skibbereen / Sean O'Dwyer of the Glen / Royal Scots / Sleepy Maggie / Bessie McIntyre / All the way to Galway / Chris O'Callaghan / Hunting the hare / Shiramee / Back to the Haggard / Mo Dhachaidh (my home)
LCOM 5208 / '91 / Lismor

☐ DROPS OF BRANDY
SPRCD 1028 / Jan '90 / Springthyme

Team Dresch

☐ CAPTAIN MY CAPTAIN
CHSW 18CD / Dec '96 / Chainsaw

□ PERSONAL BEST
CHSW 11CD / Dec '96 / Chainsaw

Teape, Ronnie

□ ONE WAY TICKET
BRMCD 1 / 9 Feb '98 / Blue Rascal
Music

Tear Ceremony

□ HOURGLASS OF OPALS, AN
MA552 / Jun '94 / Machinery

Tear Garden

□ LAST MAN TO FLY, THE
Hipper form / Running man / Turn me on dead man /
Romulus and Venus / Great lie / Empathy with the
devil / Love notes and carnations / Ship named
despair / White coats and haloes / Isis veiled / Last
post / Thirty technicolour scrambled egg trip down
the hellhole
NET 027CD / Apr '92 / Nettwerk

□ TIRED EYES SLOWLY BURNING
Deja vu / Room with a view / Coma / Valium / You and
me and rainbows / Ooh ee oo ee
NTCD 034 / Feb '88 / Nettwerk

□ TO BE AN ANGEL BLIND
067003010726 / Nov '96 / Nettwerk

Teardrop Explodes

□ KILIMANJARO
Ha ha I'm drowning / Sleeping gas / Treason /
Second head / Reward poppies / Went crazy / Brave
boys keep their promises / Bouncing babies / Books
/ Thief of Baghdad / When I dream
8368972 / Jan '96 / Mercury

□ WILDER
Bent out of shape / Colours fly away / Seven views of
Jerusalem / Pure joy / Falling down around me /
Culture bunker / Tiny children / Passionate friend /
Like Leila Khaled said / Great dominions
8368962 / Jan '96 / Mercury

□ WILDER/KILIMANJARO (2CD Set)
Ha ha I'm drowning / Sleeping gas / Treason /
Second head / Reward poppies / Passionate friend
/ Tiny children / Like Leila Khaled said / And the
fighting takes over / Great dominions / Bent out of
shape / Colours fly away / Seven views of Jerusalem
/ Pure joy / Falling down around me / Culture bunker /
Went crazy / Brave boys keep their promises /
Bouncing babies / Books / Thief of Baghdad / When I
dream
5286012 / Aug '95 / Mercury

Tears For Fears

□ ELEMENTAL
5148752 / Jun '93 / Fontana

□ HURTING, THE
Mad world / Pale shelter / Ideas as opiates /
Memories fade / Suffer the children / Hurting / Watch
me bleed / Change / Prisoner / Start of the
breakdown
8110392 / Jan '88 / Fontana

□ HURTING, THE/SONGS FROM THE
BIG CHAIR (2CD Set)
Hurting / Mad world / Pale shelter / Ideas as opiates /
Memories fade / Suffer the children / Watch me
bleed / Change / Prisoner / Start of the breakdown /
Change (new) / Shout / Working hour / Everybody
wants to rule the world / Mother's talk / I believe /
Broken / Head over heels / Broken (live) / Listen
5285992 / Aug '95 / Fontana

□ SATURNINE, MARSHALL, LUNATIC
5281142 / Jun '94 / Fontana

□ SEEDS OF LOVE, THE
Badman's song / Sowing the seeds of love / Advice
for the young at heart / Standing on the corner of the
third world / Swords and knives / Famous last words
/ Woman in chains
8387302 / Sep '89 / Fontana

□ SONGS FROM THE BIG CHAIR
Shout / Working hour / Everybody wants to rule the
world / Mother's talk / I believe / Broken / Head over
heels / Broken (live) / Listen
8243002 / Mar '85 / Fontana

□ TEARS ROLL DOWN (Greatest Hits
1982-1992)
Sowing the seeds of love / Everybody wants to rule
the world / Woman in chains / Shout / Head over
heels / Mad world / Pale shelter / I believe / Laid so
low (tears roll down) / Mother's talk / Change /
Advice for the young at heart
5109392 / Mar '92 / Fontana

Teaser

□ TEASER
CDP 1045DD / 19 Jan '98 / Pseudonym

Teatre

□ ART
RRS 963CD / 11 May '98 / Diehard

Tebar, Ximo

□ SON MEDITERRANEO
Son mediterraneo / Bolero de rabet / Si te vas / En
aranjuez con tu amor / La moixeranga / Nosferatu / Si
te vas (instrumental) / Tarantza / Diana / Oda a
odalisca / Buleria / Mi pequeno girasol
0630109932 / Apr '96 / East West

Tebot Piws

□ Y GORE A'R GWAETHA
Yr hogyn pren / Dan ddwr oer y llyn / Llanfihangel /
Marwnad llon wili john / Blaenau ffestiniog / Lleucu
llwyd / Tyrd I ffwrdd / O arglwydd mae'n uffern yn y
pwll / Godro'r fuwch / Mae rhywun wedi dwyn fy
nhrwyn / Nwy yn y nen (breuddwyd) / Helo dymbo /
Ie, ie, ie, 'na fe' / dyn ni ddim yn mynd I birmingham /
Dilyn colomen / Mae gen I gariad / I ble rwyt ti'n
myned / Diferion o waelod y tebot
SCD 2049 / Dec '94 / Sain

Technical Jed

□ OSWALD CUP
SPART 51CD / Jan '97 / Spin Art

Technicolor

□ ONE TOUCH TEST STRIP
DRL 061CD / 18 May '98 / Darla

Techniques

□ CLASSIC VOL.2
WRCD 0019 / Nov '95 / Techniques

□ ROCK STEADY CLASSICS
RNCD 2078 / Dec '94 / Rhino

□ RUN COME CELEBRATE
Love is not a gamble / Queen majesty / I'm in the
mood / It's you I love / Festival '68 / Banana boat
song (day-o) / My girl / Traveling man / Out of many /
Heart of man / I wish it would rain / Bless you / Ol'
man river / I'm in love / Little did you know / My whole
life depends on you
HBCD 121 / Jun '93 / Greensleeves

□ TECHNIQUES IN DUB, THE
Born to love / Purify / Gambling / In the mood / I'll be
waiting / Man of my word / Find a fold / Fish mouth /
Marry me / Stalag / Stalag 18 / Ghetto / Once in a
life / Warboat / Watch out / Black man / Who is the
one / Top secret / Ready or not
PSCD 15 / 1 Sep '97 / Pressure Sounds

Techno Animal

□ RE-ENTRY
Flight of the hermaphrodite / Mighty atom smasher /
Mastadon Americanus / City heathen dub / Narco
Agent vs The Medicine Man / Demodex invasion /
Evil spirits/Angel dust / Catatonia / Needle Park /
Red Sea / Cape Canaveral / Resuscitator
AMBT 8 / May '95 / Virgin

□ VERSUS REALITY
Demonoid / Demonoid / Deceleration / Deceleration
/ Baka / Baka / Bionic beatbox / Bionic beatbox /
Atomic Buddha / Atomic Buddha
049912 / 30 Mar '98 / City Slang

Techno Army

□ TECHNO ARMY
WENCD 006 / Apr '96 / When

Technohead

□ HEADSEX
I wanna be a hippy / Headsex / Accelerator 2 /
Passion / Get high / Mary Jane / Get stoned / Keep
the party going / Sexhead / Gabba hop
DB 47919 / Feb '96 / Deep Blue

Technoise

□ TECHNOISE/HYWARE (Technoise/
Hyware)
IRE 1042 / Oct '96 / I

Technossomy

□ SYNTHETIC FLESH
AFRCD 2 / Mar '97 / Flying Rhino

Technotronic

□ GREATEST HITS
CCSCD 426 / May '95 / Castle

□ THIS BEAT IS TECHNOTRONIC
This beat is technotronic / Pump up the jam / Get up
(before the night is over) / Move this / Rockin' over
the beat / Hey yoh here we go / Work / Turn it up /
Move that body / Voices / One and one / Megamix
MCCD 297 / May '97 / Music Club

Technova

□ ALBUM
Firehorse one / Waiting / Sativa / Stalker /
Transcience / Pacific highways / Third party / Alwah /
Water margin / Yeah sister / Relentless / Forgotten
SOP 006CD / Nov '95 / Emissions

Tecnogod

□ 2000 BELOW ZERO
Get back: Technogod / Addition and subtraction:
Technogod / In this day and age: Technogod /
Kipple: Technogod / Technogod: Technogod / Wer
Wo Was: Technogod / Come to: Technogod / Class
thang: Technogod / (We don't need this) Facist
groove thang: Technogod / Wild appetites:
Technogod / Destiny manifesto: Technogod / Bone
swing: Technogod / Rhythm of Pam: Technogod /
Kaposi's last stand: Technogod / Silence=death:
Technogod / Luthering: Technogod
119602 / Nov '96 / Musidisc UK

Tedeschi, Susan

□ JUST WON'T BURN
Rock me right / You need to be with me / Little by little
/ It hurt so bad / Found someone new / Looking for
answers / Can't leave you alone / Just won't burn /
Mama he treats your daughter mean / Angel from
Montgomery / Friar's point
CDTC 1164 / Feb '98 / Tonecool

Tedio Boys

□ OUTER SPACE SHIT
ELM 016CD / 2 Mar '98 / Elevator

Tee, Richard

□ STROKIN'
First love / Everyday / Strokin' / I wanted it too /
Virginia Sunday / Jesus children of America / Take
the 'A' train
ESMCD 586 / 15 Sep '97 / Essential

Tee Set

□ 24 CARAT
Early in the morning / Believe what I say / Don't you
leave / Please call me / Now's the time / What can I do
/ Tea is famous / Rose in my hand / Mr. Music man /
Ma belle amie / Finally in love again / If you do believe
in love / She likes weeds / In your eyes / Little lady /
Sunny day in Greece / Shotguns / Mary Mary /
Bandstand / Do it baby / Linda Linda / Red red wine /
Magic lantern / Tribute to the Spencer Davis Group
SJPCD 014 / 15 Sep '97 / Angel Air

□ EMOTION
Just another hour / I go out of my mind / Don't you
leave / Midnight hour / Nothing can ever change / Jet
set / Willy nilly / Play that record / Can your monkey
do the dog / So fine / For Miss Caulker / You better
believe it / Early in the morning / Believe what I say /
Don't go mess with Cupid / Long ago / Please call me
/ So I came back to you / Now's the time / Bring a little
sunshine / What can I do / Colours of the rainbow /
When I needed you so
RPM 134 / Aug '94 / RPM

Teen Angels

□ DADDY
SPCD 330 / Jan '96 / Sub Pop

Teen Generate

□ SMASH HITS
ES 1222CD / Apr '96 / Vermiform

Teen Kings

□ ARE YOU READY (Unissued 1956
Recordings)
Ooby dooby / Racker tracker / Blue suede shoes /
Brown eyed handsome man / St. Louis Blues / All by
myself / Lawdy Miss Clawdy / Jam / Rock house /
Singin' the blues / Pretend / Rip it up / Trying to get to
you / TK Blues / Go go go / Bo Diddley / Do you
remember
RCCD 3012 / Mar '95 / Rollercoaster

Teen Queens

□ EDDIE MY LOVE
Eddie my love / Red top / All my love / Billy boy / Zig
zag / Till the day I die / Love sweet love / Just goofed /
Rock everybody / Baby mine / So all alone / Teenage
idol / Let's kiss / Riding / No other / Two loves and
two lives / I miss you / My heart's desire
CDCHD 581 / Feb '95 / Ace

Teenage Fanclub

□ BANDWAGONESQUE
Concept / Satan / December / What you do to me / I
don't know / Star sign / Metal baby / Pet rock /
Sidewinder / Alcoholiday / Guiding star / Is this
music
CRECD 106 / Oct '91 / Creation

□ GRAND PRIX
About you / Sparky's dream / Mellow doubt / Don't
look back / Verisimilitude / Neil Jung / Tears /
Discolite / Say no / Going places / I'll make it clear / I
gotta know / Hardcore/Ballad
CRECD 173 / May '95 / Creation

□ KING, THE
CRECD 096 / Aug '91 / Creation

□ SONGS FROM NORTHERN BRITAIN
Start again / Ain't that enough / I can't feel my soul / I
don't want control of you / Planets / Take the long
way round / Mount Everest / I don't care / Can we find
a place / It's a bad world / Your love is the place
CRECD 196
CRECD 196L / Jul '97 / Creation

□ THIRTEEN
Hang on / Cabbage / Radio / Norman 3 / Song to the
cynic / 120 mins / Escher / Commercial alternative /
Fear of flying / Tears are cool / Ret Liv Dead / Get
funky / Gene Clark
CRECD 144 / Oct '93 / Creation

Teenage Film Stars

□ BUY OUR RECORD
CRECD 177 / 26 Jan '98 / Creation

□ STAR
CRECD 111 / Jul '92 / Creation

Teenagers In Trouble

□ TEENAGERS IN TROUBLE/FAT PAUL
SF 007CD / Jan '97 / Swarf Finger

Teengenerate

□ GET ACTION
EFACD 11586 / Dec '94 / Crypt

□ SAVAGE
SFTRI 257CD / Nov '96 / Sympathy For
The Record Industry

Tees Valley Jazzmen

□ CREAM TEES
PKCD 069 / Mar '97 / PEK

Tehom

□ DESPIRITUALISATION OF NATURE
NERO 10CD / Oct '96 / Twilight
Command

Teitelbaum, Richard

□ SEA BETWEEN, THE (Teitelbaum,
Richard & Carlos Zingaro)
VICTOCD 03 / Nov '94 / Victo

Teixeira, Renato

□ AO VIVO NO RIO
KCD 100 / 14 Apr '98 / Sertanejo

Tejakula Gamelan
Ensemble

□ GAMELAN GONG KEBYAR VOL.3
VICG 53522 / Mar '96 / JVC World
Library

Tek 9

□ IT'S NOT WHAT YOU THINK IT IS (The
Oldies But Goodies 1991-1995 - 2CD
Set)
SSR 161CD / Mar '96 / SSR

Tekbilek, Omar Faruk

□ MYTHICAL GARDEN
130922 / Aug '96 / Celestial Harmonies

Tekton Motor Corporation

□ CHAMPIONS
CDKTB 19 / Nov '96 / Dreamtime

□ HUMAN RACE IGNITION
Cognitive magnitude / Ignition / Dreams / Horizon /
Interactive turbulence / Champion 1st part / Spiral
emotions / Champion 2nd part / Turning wheel /
Cyber transducing / Mechanical spirit / Alert on the
victory ahead / Dromologic mind
CDKTB 11 / Apr '95 / Dreamtime

Telefunken & Flying

□ DISTANT STATION
WIGCD 029 / Dec '96 / Domino

Telegraph

□ TEN SONGS AND THEN SOME
JUMP 007 / 15 Sep '97 / Jump Up

Telescopes

□ TASTE
CHEREE 009CD / Aug '90 / Cheree

□ UNTITLED
CRECD 79 / Nov '94 / Creation

Teletubbies

□ TELETUBBIES-THE ALBUM
Puddle dance / Ships / Dirty knees / Twisty dance /
Animals / Dipsy's fancy hat / Running away dance /
Teletubbies say eh-oh / Up and down dance /
Jumping for fun / Tree / Follow my leader / Clouds /
Lullaby
WMXU 00142 / 23 Mar '98 / BBC/
Teletubbies

Television

☐ ADVENTURE
Glory / Days / Foxhole / Careful / Carried away / Fire / Ain't that nothin' / Dream's dream
7559605232 / '92 / WEA

☐ BLOW UP, THE
Blow up / See no evil / Prove it / Elevation / I don't care / Venus De Milo / Foxhole / Ain't that nothin' / Knockin' on Heaven's door / Little Johnny Jewel / Friction / Marquee moon / Satisfaction
RE 114CD / Nov '94 / ROIR

☐ MARQUEE MOON
See no evil / Venus / Friction / Marquee moon / Elevation / Guiding light / Prove it / Torn curtain
9606162 / '89 / WEA

Television Personalities

☐ PRIMETIME 1981-1992
REMCD 529 / 1 Jun '98 / Reactive

Tell Tale Hearts

☐ HIGH TIDE ANTHOLOGY
VOXXCD 2027 / Oct '94 / Voxx

Tella, Sylvia

☐ REGGAE MAX
JSRNCD 15 / Jun '97 / Jet Star

☐ SPELL
JASCD 2 / Apr '97 / Sarge

Tellu

☐ SUDEN AIKA
KICD 43 / Aug '96 / Kansanmusiikki Instituutti

Telo

☐ RITUAL DEBATE
NZ 0062 / Apr '94 / Nova Zembla

Telstar Ponies

☐ IN THE SPACE OF A FEW MINUTES
FIRECD 52 / Oct '95 / Fire

☐ VOICES FROM THE NEW MUSIC
FIRECD 60 / Oct '96 / Fire

Tembang Sunda

☐ MUSIC FROM WEST JAVA
131342 / Aug '97 / Celestial Harmonies

☐ SUNDANESE TRADITIONAL SONGS
NI 5378CD / Oct '93 / Nimbus

Temiz, Okay

☐ FIS FIS TZIGANES
CDLLL 107 / Aug '93 / La Lichere

☐ ISTANBUL DA EYLUL
CDLLL 67 / Aug '93 / La Lichere

☐ MAGNET DANCE
Mus mus, mis mis / Ayiras / Komsu / Din din dina / Gulhane / Exmar / Namor / Izimirk / Gelen esme
8888192 / Aug '95 / Tiptoe

Tempchin, Jack

☐ AFTER THE RAIN (Tempchin, Jack & The Seclusions)
TX 2009CD / Jan '94 / Taxim

Temperance Seven

☐ 33 NOT OUT
After you've gone / Home in Pasadena / Saratoga shout / Me and Jane in a plane / Cecelia / Mooche / Black bottom / Deep Henderson / Happy feet / Royal garden blues / Varsity drag / Seven and eleven / Borneo / Ziggy / Chili bom bom / Thirty three not out / Mary / Button up your overcoat / You, you're driving me crazy
URCD 103 / Dec '90 / Upbeat

☐ PASADENA AND THE LOST CYLINDERS (Music From The Archives)
Charley my boy / You're driving me crazy / My baby just cares for me / Chilli bom bom / My Mama's in town / Words / China boy / Ukelele lady / My blue heaven / Oh, baby / I wonder what's become of Joe / Take me over / Carole / Mooche / Vo do do de o blues / Seven and eleven / East St.Louis toodle oo / Pleasant moments / Pasadena / Japanese dream / Deep Henderson / Ain't she sweet / Sugar / Sugar / Sugar / From Russia with love / Jimmy (Thompson) / Thoroughly modern Millie
LACD 77 / Jun '97 / Lake

☐ TEA FOR EIGHT
Waterloo Road / Charleston / Tea for two / Louisiana / Sahara / Running wild / Hard hearted Hannah / Charley my boy / My Momma's in town / Ukelele lady / Twelfth Street rag / 11.30 saturday night
URCD 101 / Mar '90 / Upbeat

☐ WRITING ON THE WALL
Dog bottom / I can't sleep / From Monday On / Writing on the wall / Crying for the Carolines / Man I Love / Everybody loves my baby / San / Mornington Crescent / My baby just cares for me / Drum crazy / Mississippi Mud / Brown eyes / Ain't she sweet / There Ain't No Sweet man Worth the Salt Of My Tears / My Blue heaven / 'S Wonderful
RRCD 108 / Sep '92 / Upbeat

Temperley, Joe

☐ CONCERTO FOR JOE
Hackensack / Snibor / Sentimental mood / Blues for Nat / East of the sun and west of the moon / Single petal of a rose / Cotton tail / Awright already / Blues / Slow for Joe / Day at a time / Sixes and sevens
HEPCD 2062 / Mar '95 / Hep

☐ NIGHTINGALE
Raincheck / Body and soul / Indian summer / Sunset and a mocking bird / Petite fleur / Nightingale / It's you or no one / Creole love / Action / My love is like a red red rose
HEPCD 2052 / Mar '92 / Hep

Tempest

☐ TEMPEST/LIVING IN FEAR
Gorgon / Foyers of fun / Dark house / Brothers / Up and on / Grey and black / Strange her / Upon tomorrow / Funeral empire / Paperback writer / Stargazer / Dance to my tune / Living in fear / Yeah yeah yeah / Waiting for a miracle / Turn around
NEXCD 159 / Dec '90 / Sequel

Tempest

☐ SUNKEN TREASURE (Unreleased Tracks 1989-1992)
FAM 10103CD / Jul '95 / Firebird

☐ SURFING TO MECCA
FAM 10105CD / Jul '95 / Firebird

Templars

☐ TEMPLARS 1118/1319
DMV / Land of the morning calm / Skins and punks / Glory it once was / Shades of grey / Chansons de geste / Police informer / War on the streets / Just another rebel
GKCD 027 / 15 Jun '98 / Go-Kart

Temple

☐ TEMPLE
PSCD 0006 / 5 Jan '98 / Psi-Fi

Temple, Johnny

☐ BLUES 1935-1940, THE (2CD Set)
FA 256 / Feb '97 / Fremeaux

☐ JOHNNY TEMPLE VOL.1 1935-1938
DOCD 5238 / May '94 / Document

☐ JOHNNY TEMPLE VOL.2 1938-1940
DOCD 5239 / May '94 / Document

☐ JOHNNY TEMPLE VOL.3 1940-1949
DOCD 5240 / May '94 / Document

Temple Roy

☐ DEAF AND DUMB
EB 012 / Mar '97 / Echo Beach

Temple, Shirley

☐ ON THE GOOD SHIP LOLLIPOP
On the good ship lollipop (bright eyes - 1934) / Baby take a bow / When I'm with you (poor little rich girl) / Laugh you son of a gun / At the codfish ball / Love's young dream / On accounta I love you / Goodnight my love / But definitely / In our little wooden shoes / Picture me without you / Get on board li'l children / Animal crackers in my soup / That's what I want for christmas / You gotta smile to be happy / Early bird / He was a dandy / Right somebody to love / Hey what did the blue jay say / Believe me if all those endearing young charms / When I grow up / Oh my goodness / World owes me a living / Dixie anna / Toy trumpet / Polly wolly doodle
PLCD 541 / Aug '95 / President

☐ SHIRLEY TEMPLE VOL.1 (America's Sweetheart)
On the good ship lollipop / Baby take a bow / On account-a I love you / Love's young dream / Lullaby to a doll / Animal crackers in my soup / When I grow up / Believe me, if all those endearing young charms / Song and dance / Polly wolly doddle / Early bird / At the codfish ball / Sextette from Lucia / Right somebody to love / Oh my goodness / Buy a bar of barry's/When I'm with you / But definitely / Peck's theme song / You've gotta each your spinach baby / I love a military man / Hey, what did the blue jay say / He was a dandy / Picture me without you / Get on board little children / Minstrel show introduction/ Dixie-Anna
PASTCD 7096 / Sep '96 / Flapper

☐ SHIRLEY TEMPLE VOL.2 (America's Sweetheart)
You've gotta S-M-I-L-E to be H-A-double-P-P-Y / Goodnight my love / That's what I want for Christmas / In our little wooden shoes / Hold God pray thy name / Silent night / Be optimistic and smile / How can I thank you / We should be together / If all the world were paper / When you were sweet sixteen / Courtroom scene / Old straw hat / Come and get your happiness / Rebecca's medley / Toy trumpet / This is a happy little ditty / I love to walk in the rain / Wot'cher (knock'd 'em in The Old Kent Road) / One, two, three / Lay-de-o / 5th Avenue / Young people / I wouldn't take a million / Tra-la-la-la / Leo is on the air / Kathleen
PASTCD 7097 / Sep '96 / Flapper

☐ SONGS OF SHIRLEY TEMPLE'S FILMS, THE (3CD Set)
CIN 024 / Nov '97 / IMP

Templebeat

☐ MEDIASICKNESS
CDWHIP 022 / Dec '96 / Sub/Mission

Templeton, Alec

☐ BACH GOES TO TOWN
Three little fishes / Blues in the night / Lost chord / Shortest Wagnerian opera / Tea for two / Body and soul / Music goes 'round and around
PASTCD 7057 / Feb '95 / Flapper

Temptations

☐ BEST OF THE TEMPTATIONS, THE
31272 / Oct '94 / Scratch

☐ BEST OF THE TEMPTATIONS, THE
My girl / I can't get next to you / Papa was a rolling stone / Ain't too proud to beg / Superstar (remember how you got where you are) / Beauty is only skin deep / I'm losing you (I know) / Cloud nine / Ball of confusion (that's what the world is today) / Runaway child (running wild) / Keep on trucking / Way you do the things you do / I wish it would rain / Get ready / Masterpiece / Psychedelic shack
WB 885922 / 2 Feb '98 / Disky

☐ FOR LOVERS ONLY
5305682 / 15 Sep '97 / Motown

☐ GREATEST HITS
I can't get next to you / I can't get next to you / Ain't too proud to beg / Superstar (remember how you got where you are) / Just my imagination (running away with me) / Beauty is only skin deep / (I know) I'm losing you / Cloud nine / Ball of confusion (that's what the world is today) / Runaway child, running wild / My girl / Keep on trucking / Way you do the things you do / I wish it would rain / Get ready / Masterpiece / Psychedelic shack
PA 7142 / Mar '94 / Paradiso

☐ MOTOWN EARLY CLASSICS
My girl / I'll be in trouble / (Girl) Why you wanna make me blue / Girl's alright with me / Get ready / (You're me dream) Come true / I couldn't cry If I wanted to / You're the one I need / You'll lose a precious love / Ain't too proud to beg / Who's lovin' you / Nobody but you / I gotta know now / Too busy thinking about my baby / You've got to earn it / Everybody needs love / It's growing / Don't look back
5523232 / Jul '96 / Spectrum

☐ MY GIRL
My girl / Ain't too proud to beg / Beauty is only skin deep / You're my everything / I could never love another / Get ready / Cloud nine / Ball of confusion / Just my imagination / Standing on the top / Way you do things to me / Please return your love to me / Girl / Runaway child running wild / Just one last look / Hello young lovers / How can I forget / It's summer / Psychedelic shack
5307952 / Apr '97 / Spectrum

☐ ONE BY ONE (The Best Of The Temptations/2CD Set)
My whole world ended (the moment you left me) / I've lost evrything I've ever loved / I'm so glad I fell for you / Which way to my baby / Double cross / It's so hard for me to say goodbye / This used to be the home of Johnnie Mae / Can I / If you left me / Girl you need a change of mind / Date with the rain / Eddie's love / Feel like givin' up / Once you had a heart / I miss you / Common man / Darling come back home / Keep on truckin' / Tell her love has felt the need / Boogie down / Shoeshine boy / Happy / Get the cream off the top / Walk away from love / Heavy love / Statue of a fool / He's a friend / When the lights come down on love / Everything's coming up love / Just let me hold you for a night / You're my peace of mind / Don't look any further / (You're my) Aphrodisiac / Coolin' out / Soulmate
5306152 / Jul '96 / Motown

☐ ORIGINAL LEAD SINGERS
Get ready / My girl / I can't get next to you / Papa was a rolling stone / Superstar (remember how you got where you are) / Just my imagination (running away with me) / Masterpiece / Ain't too proud to beg / Ball of confusion / Cloud nine / Runaway child (running wild) / Beauty is only skin deep / Keep on truckin' / Way you do the things you do / I wish it would rain / I'm losing you / Psychedelic shack
100212 / May '97 / A-Play Collection

☐ ULTIMATE COLLECTION
5308532 / 10 Aug '98 / Motown

Temptones

☐ TEMPTONES, THE
Girl I love you / Goodbye / Say these words of love / Something good / Baby, yes I do / Goodbye / Girl I love you / Say these words of love / I don't want to cry / I wish it would rain / I've been good to you / Meaning of existence / My girl / Voice your choice / I've been trying / So fine / Say it baby / I want a love I can see / So hard to be loved by you / Goodbye
BCD 15917 / May '96 / Bear Family

Ten

☐ NEVER SAY GOODBYE (2CD Set)
Robe / Bright on the blade / Wildest dreams / Torch / Yesterday lies in the flame / Rainbow / Crusades / Don't cry / Goodnight Saigon / Arcadia / You're in my heart / Lonliest place in the world / Ten fathoms deep / After the love has gone / Stay with me / Standing on the edge of time / Fly like an eagle / Drum solo / Battlelines / Pharoah's prelude / Wait for you / Name of the rose / Black moon rising / Venus and Mars / If only for a day / Gimme a piece of your heart
FRCD 001 / 13 Apr '98 / Frontier

☐ ROBE, THE
199635 / 13 Oct '97 / Made To Measure

☐ TEN
NTHEN 027CD / Jun '96 / Now & Then

Ten Benson

☐ 6 FINGERS OF BENSON
Evil heat / Bardot style / Claw / Transport overseas / Uncle Benson / City hoppers
BLUFF 063CD / 13 Jul '98 / Deceptive

Ten Foot Pole

☐ TEN FOOT POLE/SATANIC SURFERS (Split CD) (Ten Foot Pole & Satanic Surfers)
BTR 003CD / Nov '95 / Bad Taste

☐ UNLEASHED
Fiction / John / It's not me / Denial / What you want / Daddy / Damage / Too late / Excuses / Pride and shame / Regret / Hey Pete / ADD
64782 / Mar '97 / Epitaph

Ten Years After

☐ CRICKLEWOOD GREEN
Sugar the road / Working on the road / 50,000 miles beneath my brain / Year 3,000 blues / Me and my baby / Love like a man / Circles / As the sun still burns away
CDGOLD 1052 / Oct '96 / EMI Gold

☐ CRICKLEWOOD GREEN/WATT/A SPACE IN TIME (3CD Set)
Sugar the road / Working on the road / 50,000 miles beneath my brain / Year 3000 blues / Me and my baby / Love like a man / Circles / As the sun still burns away / I'm coming on / My baby left me / Think about the times / I say yeah / Band with no name / Gonna run / She lies in the morning / Sweet little sixteen / One of these days / Here they come / I'd love to change the world / Over the hill / Baby won't you let me rock 'n' roll you / Once there was a time / Let the sky fall / Hard monkeys / I've been there too / Uncle Jam
CDOMB 011 / Oct '95 / Chrysalis

☐ I'M GOING HOME
I'm going home / I'd love to change the world / It's getting harder / Love like a man / Woodchoppers ball / Rock 'n' roll music to the world / Me and my baby / I woke up this morning / Stoned women / Cho cho mama / Slow blues in 'c' / 50,000 miles beneath my brain / Positive vibrations / Hear me calling
DC 868782 / Nov '96 / Disky

☐ RECORDED LIVE
One of these days / You give me loving / Good morning little school girl / Hobbitt / Help me / Classical things / Scat thing / I can't keep from crying sometimes / Sometimes / Silly thing / Slow blues in 'C' / I'm going home / Choo choo Mama
BGOCD 341 / Mar '97 / Beat Goes On

☐ ROCK 'N' ROLL MUSIC TO THE WORLD
You give me loving / Convention prevention / Turned off TV blues / Standing at the station / You can't win them all / Religion / Choo choo mama / Tomorrow I'll be out of town / Rock 'n' roll music to the world
BGOCD 348 / May '97 / Beat Goes On

☐ SPACE IN TIME, A
One of these days / Here they come / I'd love to change the world / Over the hill / Baby won't you let me rock 'n' roll you / Once there was a time / Let the sky fall / Hard monkeys / I've been there too / Uncle Jam
BGOCD 351 / Jul '97 / Beat Goes On

☐ SSSSH
Bad scene / Two time Mama / Stoned woman / Good morning little school girl / If you should love me / I don't know that you don't know my name / Stomp / I woke up this morning
BGOCD 338 / Feb '97 / Beat Goes On

☐ STONEDHENGE
I can't live without you, Lydia / Woman trouble / Skoobly-oobly-doo-bob / Hear me calling / Sad song / Three blind mice / No title / Faro / Speed kills / Going to try
BGOCD 356 / Jul '97 / Beat Goes On

☐ WATT
I'm coming on / My baby left me / Think about the times / Band with no name / Gonna run / She lies in the morning / Sweet little sixteen
BGOCD 345 / Apr '97 / Beat Goes On

Tenaglia, Danny

☐ TOURISM
Baby do you feel me / Elements / Music is the answer / Turn me on / Read my lips / Better days / Roots / Headhunter / Do you remember / Dubhunter
TWCD 90006 / 20 Jul '98 / Twisted UK

Tendekist Wanganui Band

☐ CHAMPION BRASS
CDODE 1306 / Feb '90 / ODE

Tenebrae

☐ DYSANCHELIUM
SPI 17CD / Oct '94 / Spinefarm

Tenko

☐ DRAGON BLUE
SFCD 004 / Jun '97 / Sound Factory

Tennessee Rhythm Riders

☐ STEP IT UP AND GO
That's the way it's gonna be / Rockaway rock / Hillbily baby / Little red caboose / You won't believe this / Step it up and up / Truck driver's rock / Woman in town / Hot rod girl / Tennessee special / Kiss me quick and go / Good gosh girl / Kaw-liga / Ranch hand boogie / Road of sadness / Pistol boogie / When your house is not your home / Juke box boogie
FCD 3048 / May '97 / Fury

Tenney, Gerry

☐ LET'S SING A YIDDISH SONG (Tenney, Gerry & Betty Albert Schreck)
GV 134CD / Nov '93 / Global Village

Tenney, James

☐ BRIDGE & FLOCKING
ARTCD 6193 / Dec '96 / Hat Art

Tennille, Toni

☐ TENNILLE SWINGS BIG BAND
8605110192 / 7 Apr '98 / HNT

Tennors

☐ MOODS
73136319672 / 15 Jun '98 / Jamixal

Tenor, Jimi

☐ EUROPA
PUUCD 2 / Sep '95 / Still Bubbling

☐ INTERVISION
Outta space / Downtown / Sugardaddy / Never say it aloud / Can't stay with you baby / Tesla / Caravan / Wiping out / Wiping out / Shore Hotel / Nobody's perfect / Atlantis
WARPCD 48 / Mar '97 / Warp

Tenor Saw

☐ TENOR SAW LIVES ON
CD 005 / Jan '93 / Sky High

☐ WITH LOTS OF SIGN (Tenor Saw & Nitty Gritty)
BR 002CD / Nov '94 / Black Roots

Tenor Triangle

☐ AZTEC BLUES (Tenor Triangle & Melvin Rhyne Trio)
Cedar's blues / Nother fu'ther / Song is you / Ballad medley / Melvin's masquerade / Aztec blues
CRISS 1143CD / 9 Mar '98 / Criss Cross

Tenores Di Bitti

☐ AMMENTOS
NT 6746CD / Mar '96 / Newtone

☐ S'AMORE 'E MAMA
Lamentu / Monte seris / Anghelos cantade / Sa ballarina / S'amore 'e mama / T'amo / Sos ojos largimosos / Su manxanile / Sos artigianos / Satiras / S'annunziata / Sardinia soundscape
CDRW 60 / Jul '96 / Realworld

Tenpole Tudor

☐ EDDIE, OLD BOB, DICK & GARY
Swords of a thousand men / Go wilder / I wish / Header now / There are boys / Wunderbar / Tell me more / Judy annual / I can't sleep / Anticipation / What else can I do / Confessions
REP 4220 / Aug '91 / Repertoire

☐ LET THE FOUR WINDS BLOW
Let the four winds blow / Throwing my baby out with the bath water / Trumpeters / It's easy to see / What you doing in Bombay / Local animal / Her fruit is forbidden / Tonight is the night / Unpaid debt / King of Siam / Sea of thunder
STIFFCD 12 / Jan '94 / Disky

☐ SWORDS OF A THOUSAND MEN (2CD Set)
Swords of a thousand men / Go wilder / I wish / Header now / Here are the boys / Wunderbar / 3 bells in a row / Tell me more / Judy Annual / I can't sleep / Anticipation / What else can I do / Confessions / Love and food / There are the boys / Wunderbar / Let the four winds blow / Throwing my baby out with the bathwater / Trumpeters / It's easy to see / What you doing in Bombay / Local animal / Her fruit is forbidden / Tonight is the night / Unpaid debt / King of Siam / Sea of thunder / Conga tribe / Tenpole 45 / Fashion / Rock and roll music
SMDCD 144 / May '97 / Snapper

☐ WUNDERBAR (The Best Of Tenpole Tudor)
Three bells in a row / Swords of a thousand men / Go wilder / Header now / Wunderbar / What else can I do / I can't sleep / Confessions / Tell me more / Throwing my baby out with the bath water / Let the four winds blow / Tonight is the night / What you doing in Bombay / Her fruit is forbidden / Sea of thunder / Hayrick song
DOJOCD 76 / Nov '92 / Dojo

Tepper, Robert

☐ NO REST FOR THE WOUNDED HEART
MTM 199611 / Nov '96 / Made To Measure

Tequila Sisters

☐ OUT OF THE SHADOWS
MSPCD 9403 / Jul '94 / Mabley St.

Ter Veldhuis, Jacob

☐ DIVERSO IL TEMPO
BVHAASTCD 9308 / Oct '94 / Bvhaast

Terem Quartet

☐ CLASSICAL
Eine kleine nachtmusik / Ave Maria / Concerto grosso in G-minor / Waltz / Chardash / Oginsky's polonaise / Funeral march / Nocturne 'Separation' / Flea waltz
CDRW 49 / Oct '94 / Realworld

☐ TEREM
Lyrical dance / Fantasy / Legend of the old mountain man / Cossack's farewell / Toccata / Variations on Swan Lake / Simfonia lubova / Old carousel / Two-step Nadya / Tsiganka / Letni Kanikuli / Country improvisation / Valenki / Baryni
CDRW 23 / Mar '92 / Realworld

Terminal Cheesecake

☐ PEARLESQUE
WSCD 001 / Oct '96 / World Serpent

Terminals

☐ TERMINALS LIVE
MED 001 / Dec '96 / Medication

Terminator X

☐ TERMINATOR X AND THE VALLEY OF THE JEEP BEETS
Vendetta... the big getback / Buck whylin': *Chuck D & Sister Souljah* / Homey don't play dat: *Bonnie 'N' Clyde* / Juvenile delinquintz: *Juvenile Delinquintz* / Blues: *Andreas 13* / Back to the scene of the bass: *Interrogators* / Can't take my style: *Celo Of The Casino Brothers* / Wanna be dancin' / DJ is the selector: *Dub Master* / Run that go: *Spacey B Experience* / Power thang / No further: *Section 8* / High priest of turbulence: *Chief Groovy Loo* / Ain't got nuthin'
5234822 / Jan '96 / RAL

Termos Dubbel Expres

☐ DEATH DANCE OF PRINCIPLES
GEESTCD 16 / Aug '97 / Bvhaast

Ternent, Billy

☐ UNMISTAKABLE SOUND OF BILLY TERNENT VOL.3, THE (Ternent, Billy & His Orchestra)
SAV 241CD / Dec '95 / Savoy

☐ UNMISTAKABLE SOUND OF BILLY TERNENT VOL.4 (Ternent, Billy & His Orchestra)
SAV 242CD / Dec '95 / Savoy

Terra Ferma

☐ TURTLE CROSSING
Lunar surprise / Fire / Scream / Visions / Poet / Floating / Snakecharmer / Planet Ogo / Crazy people
PLAT 30CD / May '97 / Platipus

Terra Sul

☐ KINDNESS OF STRANGERS
Lands / Kindness of strangers / Mestico / Matatlantica / Caminhando / Incognito / Deus dara / Meia luz / KYZ / Debra Ann / Heavenly bodies
5303162 / Oct '94 / MoJazz

Terranova

☐ LIVIN' IT UP
NTHEN 039CD / 24 Nov '97 / Now & Then

Terranova

☐ DJ KICKS (Various Artists)
Five days: *Howie B* / Disorientation: *Priest* / Sex, sluts and heaven: *Depth Charge* / Galactic funk: *DJ Spooky* / Tried by 12: *East Flatbush Project* / Run the line: *Peanutbutter Wolf* / Devil's claw: *Stereo MC's* / Please stand by: *BFC* / City lights (city of starsings): *Pulsinger, Patrick* / Ladies and gentlemen: *69* / Definition of a track: *Backroom* / Who needs to sleep tonight: *Silicon Soul* / Modern funk beats: *Octagon Man* / Tokyo tower: *Terranova* / I love you: *DSL* / Stop it stop it stop it: *Stereo MC's* / Jungle brother: *Jungle Brothers* / Word: *Junkyard Band* / Spoonie rap: *Spoonie Gee* / Contact/DJ kicks: *Terranova*
K7 064CD / 19 Jan '98 / Studio K7

Terraplane

☐ BLACK AND WHITE
Don't walk away / When you're hot / I can't live without your love / Talking to myself / You can't hurt me anymore / I survive / Right between the eyes / Black and white / I'm the one / Get your face out of my dream / Couldn't handle the tears / Tough kind of life / Beginning of the end / All night and day
4894512 / 26 Jan '98 / Epic

Terrasson, Jacky

☐ ALIVE
Things ain't what they used to be / Cumba's dance / Sister things / Nature boy / Love for sale / For taking over Noe Valley theme / There's no disapointment
8596512 / 4 May '98 / Blue Note

☐ JACKY TERRASSON
I love Paris / Just a blues / My funny valentine / Hommage a lill boulanger / Bye bye blackbird / He goes on a trip / I fall in love too easily / Time after time / For once in my life / What a difference a day makes / Cumba's dance
CDP 8293512 / Feb '95 / Blue Note

☐ REACH
I should care / Rat race / Baby Plum / I love you for sentimental reasons / Reach/Smoke/Reach / Happy man / First affair / Just one of those things
CDP 8357932 / Jan '96 / Blue Note

☐ RENDEZVOUS (Terrasson, Jacky & Cassandra Wilson)
Old devil moon / Chan's song / Tennessee waltz / Little boy lost / Autumn leaves / It might as well be spring / My ship / I remember you / Tea for two / If ever I would leave you / Chicago
CDP 8554842 / 8 Sep '97 / Blue Note

Terre Thaemlitz

☐ COUTURE COSMETIQUE
CAI 20022 / May '97 / Caipirinha

Terrell

☐ ANGRY SOUTHERN GENTLEMAN
Let's go for a ride / Straw dogs (Before the fall) / Dreamed I was the devil / Newhope / Angry southern gentleman / Piece of time / Toystore / Redneck gigolo / Broken man / Blacktop runaways / Long train / Come down to me
VPBCD 23 / Apr '95 / Pointblank

☐ BEAUTIFUL SIDE OF MADNESS
Chant of faith / Hopeful sinner / Home / Convince myself / Hollywood drag / Pour our souls / Georgia O'Keefe / Black and white blues / Whitley Flats / Shotgun / Needle's kiss / Beautiful side of madness
VPBCD 37 / Oct '96 / Pointblank

Terremoto

☐ COSA NATURAL
En tus suenos / Me dio risa en el alma / Que te peredone / Al tiempo le pregunte / Sonaba el canto del gallo / A la del desamparo / Sigue cantando gitano / Camino de los juncales / Entre triana y Jerez
B 6847 / Jul '97 / Auvidis/Ethnic

Territory Singers

☐ TERRITORY SINGERS VOL.1 1922-1928
DOCD 5470 / Jul '96 / Document

☐ TERRITORY SINGERS VOL.2 1928-1930
DOCD 5471 / Jul '96 / Document

Terror Against Terror

☐ PSYCHOLIGICAL WARFARE
PA 001CD / May '95 / Paragoric

Terror Fabulous

☐ GLAMOROUS
NWSCD 7 / 5 May '98 / New Sound

☐ LYRICALLY ROUGH
Lyrically rough / Pum pum / Gun fool / Introduce your friend / Mi have fi ask / Old dog / We no mingle / Girls them motto / Position / Book of life / Jump and gwaan bad / Pop style
GRELCD 221 / Oct '95 / Greensleeves

☐ YAGA YAGA
Number 2 / Broke wine butterfly / Mr. Big Man / From birth / You must be a fool / Talk 'bout / If you know you're ready / You nuh kotch / Yaga yaga / Pretty teenager / Gangster's anthem / Action / Miss Goody Goody / Too bad / Water bed expert
7567923272 / Aug '94 / Warner Bros.

Terrorgruppe

☐ UBER AMERIKA
BYO 042CD / Feb '97 / Better Youth Organisation

Terrorizer

☐ WORLD DOWNFALL
After world obliteration / Tear of napalm / Corporation pull in / Resurrection / Need to live / Dead shall rise / Injustice / Storm of stress / Human prey / Condemned system / Enslaved by propaganda / Whirlwind struggle / World downfall / Ripped to shreds
MOSH 016CD / Sep '97 / Earache

Terrorvision

☐ HOW TO MAKE FRIENDS AND INFLUENCE PEOPLE
Alice, what's the matter / Oblivion / Stop the bus / Discotheque wreck / Middle man / Still the rhythm / Ten shades of grey / Stab in the back / Pretend best friend / Time o' the signs / What the doctor ordered / Some people say / What makes you tick
VEGASCD 2 / Apr '94 / Total Vegas
VEGASCDX 2 / Sep '97 / Total Vegas

☐ REGULAR URBAN SURVIVORS
Enteralterego / Superchronic / Perseverance / Easy / Hide the dead girl / Conspiracy / Didn't bleed red / Dog chewed the handle / Junior / Bad actress / If I was you / Celebrity hit list / Mugwump
VEGASCD 3 / Mar '96 / Total Vegas

Terry

☐ SILVERADO TRAIL (Terry & The Pirates)
Wish I was your river / Sweet emotions / I can't dance / Heartbeatin' away / Silverado trail / Follow her around / Risin' of the moon / Mustang ride / Gun metal blues / Inlaws and outlaws / Nighthawkin' the dawn
CDWIK 89 / Jan '90 / Big Beat

Terry & Gerry

☐ BEST EVER TERRY AND GERRY ALBUM IN THE WORLD...EVER, THE
Hello / Joey / Ballad of a nasty man / CARS / Thousand towns / Butter's the bread of a rich man's life / Independent's day / Last bullet in the gun / Banking on Simon / Pizza pie and junk / Reservation / Fashion rodeo / Percy Crusoe / Good, the bad, and the usherette / Wolfman's request / Kennedy says / Clothes shop closed
CDMRED 144 / Jun '97 / Cherry Red

Terry, Clark

☐ ALTERNATE BLUES (Terry, Clark/ Freddie Hubbard/Dizzy Gillespie/ Oscar Peterson)
Alternate one / Alternate two / Alternate three / Alternate four / Wrap your troubles in dreams (and dream your troubles away) / Here's that rainy day / Gypsy / If I should lose you
OJCCD 744 / May '93 / Original Jazz Classics

☐ CLARK AFTER DARK
5290882 / Mar '96 / MPS Jazz

☐ CLARK TERRY
5377542 / 22 Sep '97 / Verve Elite

☐ COLOR CHANGES
Blue waltz (la valse bleue) / Brother Terry / Flutin' and fluglin' / No problem / La rive gauche / Nahstye blues / Chat qui peche (A cat that fishes)
CCD 79009 / Jan '89 / Candid

☐ COLOUR CHANGES
CCD 9009 / Jul '87 / Candid

☐ DAYLIGHT EXPRESS (Terry, Clark & Paul Gonsalves)
Caravan / Candy / Clark's expedition / Trumpet mouthpiece blues / Phalanges / Blue for Daddy-O's jazz patio blues / Basin Street blues / Daylight express / Taking a chance on love / Festival / Clark's bars / Daddy-O's patio / Impeccable / Paul's idea / Phat Bach / Milli Terry / Funky / Girl I call baby
GRP 18192 / 8 Jun '98 / Chess Jazz

☐ EXPRESS
RR 73CD / Jul '96 / Reference Recordings

☐ IN ORBIT (Terry, Clark Quartet & Thelonious Monk)
OJCCD 302 / Apr '92 / Original Jazz Classics

☐ INTIMATE STORIES
Putte's patter / Brahm's lullaby / Out of nowhere / Perils of Pauline / What will I tell my heart / Blue moon / Simple waltz / Days of wine and roses
CHR 70050 / Jun '98 / Challenge

☐ LUCERNE 1978 (Terry, Clark & Chris Woods)
Hymn / Silly samba / I want a little girl / Straight no chaser / On the trail / Lemon drop / Somebody done stole my blues / God bless the child / Somewhere over the rainbow
TCB 02082 / Aug '97 / TCB

☐ MELLOW MOODS
Out in the cold again / Simple waltz / This is always / Lullabye / Among my souvenirs / In the alley / Michelle / As you desire me / What a country / Same language / If I were you / I've just seen her / Once upon a time / Nightlife / It's fun to think / Fight song
PCD 24136 / Jun '95 / Pablo

☐ OW (2CD Set)
My secret love / Ow / Just and old manuscript / Jingle bells / Georgia on my mind / Shaw 'nuff / Oh lady be good / Mack the knife / Rebecca / God bless the child / Straight, no chaser / On Green Dolphin Street / All blues / Take the 'A' train
JLR 103601 / May '96 / Live At EJ's

☐ SECOND SET, THE
One foot in the gutter / Opus ocean / Michelle / Serenade to a bus seat / Joonji / Ode to a flugelhorn / Funky Mama / Interview
JD 127 / Mar '95 / Chesky

☐ SHADES OF BLUE
CHR 70007 / Jun '95 / Challenge

☐ SPACEMEN, THE
CRD 309 / Mar '96 / Chiaroscuro

☐ TO DUKE AND BASIE
ENJA 50112 / 17 Nov '97 / Enja

☐ TOP AND BOTTOM (Live At The 1995 Floating Jazz Festival) (Terry, Clark Quintet & Red Holloway)
Quicksand / Opening remarks/Introductions / Mood indigo / Straight no chaser / My romance / Top and bottom / Love walked in / Medley / Closing remarks/ Empty bed blues
CRD 347 / 8 Nov '97 / Chiaroscuro

☐ TOP AND BOTTOM BRASS
Mili-Terry / Swinging Chemise / My heart belongs to Daddy / Blues for Etta / Top 'n' bottom / 127 / Sunday kind of love / Mardi Gras waltz
OJCCD 764 / Dec '96 / Original Jazz Classics

Terry, Gordon

☐ LOTTA LOTTA WOMEN
Lotta lotta women / It ain't right / I had a talk with me / Queen of the seasons / Gonna go down the river / Lonely road / Honky tonk man / You remembered me / Revenooer man / Long black limousine / Wild desire / Little ole you / How my baby can love / Fortune of love / Slow down old world / For old time's sake / You'll regret / Hook, line and sinker / Maybe / Keep on talking / Then I heard the bad news / I don't hurt anymore / Saddest day / All by my lonesome / Battle of New Orleans / Fifty stars / When they ring these wedding bells / Almost alone
BCD 15881 / Nov '95 / Bear Family

Terry, Iain

☐ ROCK TIL MIDNIGHT
PT 607001 / Jun '96 / Part

Terry, Keith

☐ SERPENTINE (Terry, Keith & Crosspulse)
De aquil pa'lla / Llevo llevo / Lamban Bali / Abran paso / Serpentine / Colo do rio / Bambu beat / Come together / Joropeando / What's up / Still waitin' for the buzz
CPRCD 001 / 24 Aug '98 / Cubop

Terry, Lillian

☐ DREAM COMES TRUE, A (Terry, Lillian & Tommy Flanagan)
Lover man / Lover man / Black coffee / Lush life / I remember clifford / 'round midnight / You've changed
1210472 / Oct '90 / Soul Note

☐ OO-SHOO-BE-DOO-BE....OO,OO
SN 1147 / '86 / Soul Note

Terry, Los

☐ FROM AFRICA TO CAMAGUEY
RWCD 9703 / 5 Jan '98 / Fresh Sound

Terry, Sonny

☐ AMERICAN BLUES LEGEND
CPCD 8336 / 29 Jun '98 / Charly

☐ AT SUGAR HILL (Terry, Sonny & Brownie McGhee)
OBCCD 536 / Nov '92 / Original Blues Classics

☐ BACK TO NEW ORLEANS (Terry, Sonny & Brownie McGhee)
Let me be your big dog / Pawn shop / You don't know / Betty and dupree / Back to New Orleans / Stranger here / Fox hunt / I'm prison bound / Louise Louise / Baby how long / Freight train / I got a woman / Hold me in your arms / CC and the O blues / Devil's gonna git you / Don't you lie to me / That's why I'm walking / Wrong track / Blue feeling / House lady / I know better
CDCH 372 / May '92 / Ace

☐ BLOWIN' THE FUSES (Terry, Sonny & Brownie McGhee)
TCD 1013 / May '96 / Tradition

☐ BLUES BROTHERS (Terry, Sonny & Brownie McGhee)
PLSCD 186 / Apr '97 / Pulse

☐ BLUES FOR THE LOWLANDS (Terry, Sonny & Brownie McGhee)
BN 035 / Apr '98 / Blue Nite

☐ BROWNIE MCGEE & SONNY TERRY SING (Terry, Sonny & Brownie McGhee)
SFCD 40011 / Sep '94 / Smithsonian Folkways

☐ CALIFORNIA BLUES (Terry, Sonny & Brownie McGhee)
I got fooled / No need of running / I feel so good / Thinkin' and worrying / I love you baby / California blues / Walkin' and lyin' down / First and last love / Christine / I have had my fun / Whoppin' and Squalin' / Waterboy cry / Motherless child / Sportin' life / John Henry / I'm a stranger / Cornbread and peas / Louise / I done done / Meet you in the morning / Poor boy from home / Hudy Leadbelly / Something's wrong at home / Take this home / Take this hammer / Baby's gone / Lose your money
CDCHD 398 / May '93 / Ace

☐ DUO, THE (Terry, Sonny & Brownie McGhee)
Mean old frisco blues / Woman is killing me / Lightnin's blues / Brownie's blues / Sonny's blues / I've been treated wrong / Climbing on top of the hill / Fox chase / Going down slow / Lost john / Can't help myself / Crow jane blues / Living with the blues / Back to new orleans / I'm prison bound / Freight train / Sweet woman blues / Key to the highway / Walk on / Rock island line
CD 52032 / May '94 / Blues Encore

☐ FOLKWAYS YEARS 1944-1963, THE
SFWCD 40033 / Dec '94 / Smithsonian Folkways

☐ GOING IT ALONE (Terry, Sonny & Brownie McGhee)
Cold wind blowing / Feel like robbin' the grave / Keep on lovin' you / Mean old woman / Blues had a baby / Selling out / That train and my woman / Rainy day / Cut off from my baby / Chicken when I'm hungry / Mean and evil / Black night road / Playing with the thing / Ask myself a question
TBA 130122 / Jun '97 / Blues Alliance

☐ JUST A CLOSER WALK WITH THEE (Terry, Sonny & Brownie McGhee)
OBCCD 541 / Nov '92 / Original Blues Classics

☐ LEGENDARY SONNY TERRY & BROWNIE MCGHEE, THE (Terry, Sonny & Brownie McGhee)
John Henry / Midnight special / Muddy water / Take this hammer whup / Sportin' life / Cornbread and peas / Louise, Louise / Hooray, hooray, this woman is killing me / Evil hearted me / Sonny's squall / Red river blues / Spread the news around / Just about crazy / Wholesale dealin' papa / Just a closer walk with thee / I shall not be moved / Back to New Orleans / Don't you lie to me / That's why I'm walking / Freight train
REMCD 510 / Feb '98 / Reactive

☐ LIVE AT THE NEW PENELOPE CAFE (Terry, Sonny & Brownie McGhee)
Hooray hooray (these women is killing me) / Cornbread, peas and black molasses / Sportin' life / Come on if you're coming / Blues medley / Easy rider / Pack it up and go / Hootin' the blues / Under your hood / Walking my blues away
JAM 91312 / 23 Feb '98 / Just A Memory

☐ LONDON SESSIONS 1958, THE (Terry, Sonny & Brownie McGhee)
Just a dream / I've been treated wrong / Woman's lover blues / Climbing on top of the hill / Southern train / Black horse blues / Gone but not forgotten / I love you baby / Cornbread, peas and black molassas / You'd better mind / Brownie blues / Change the lock on my door / Auto-mechanics blues / Sonny's blues / Wholesale and retail / Fox chase / Way I feel / Hooray (this woman is killing me)
NEXCD 120 / Apr '90 / Sequel

☐ MASTERS, THE (Terry, Sonny & Brownie McGhee)
What a beautiful city / Dirty mistreater / Don't dog your woman / Harmonica hop / Doggin' my heart around / Daisy / Blowin' the fuses / Right on that shore / Blues for the lowlands / Walk on / Down by the riverside / Trouble in mind / Everybody's blues / Po' boy / Drinkin' in the blues
EABCD 097 / 30 Mar '98 / Eagle

☐ MIDNIGHT SPECIAL (Terry, Sonny & Brownie McGhee)
Sonny's squall / Red river blues / Gone gal / Blues before sunrise / Blues of happiness / Understand me / Jealous man / Midnight special / East Coast blues / Muddy water / Beggin' and cryin'
CDCH 951 / Aug '90 / Ace

☐ ORIGINAL, THE (Terry, Sonny & Brownie McGhee)
What a beautiful city / Dirty mistreater / Don't dog your woman / Harmonica hop / Doggin' my heart around / Daisy / Blowin' the fuses / Right on that shore / Blues for the lowlands / Walk on / Down by the riverside / I'm a stranger here / Trouble in mind / Everybody's blues / Po' boy / Drinkin' in the blues
CDBM 122 / Jun '97 / Blue Moon

☐ PO' BOY (Terry, Sonny & Brownie McGhee)
IMP 306 / Sep '96 / IMP

☐ REAL FOLK BLUES, THE (Terry, Sonny & Brownie McGhee)
Walk on / Blues for the lowland / Down by the riverside / Drinking in the blues / Right on the shore / Blowing the fuses / Blues for the gamblers / Just rode in your town / Po'boy / Sun's gonna shine
CDSGP 0395 / 27 Jul '98 / Prestige

☐ SONNY AND BROWNIE (Terry, Sonny & Brownie McGhee)
People get ready / Bring it on home to me / You bring out the boogie in me / Sail away / Sonny's thing / White boy / Lost in the blues / Battle is over (but the war goes on) / Walkin' my blues away / Big wind (is a' comin') / Jesus gonna make it alright / God and man / On the road again
3972002 / Oct '94 / A&M

☐ SONNY IS KING
OBCCD 521 / Nov '92 / Original Blues Classics

☐ SONNY TERRY 1938-1945/ALONZO 1955 (Terry, Sonny & Alonzo Scales)
DOCD 5230 / Apr '94 / Document

☐ SONNY'S STORY
I ain't gonna be your dog no more / My baby done gone / Worried blues / High powered woman / Pepperheaded woman / Sonny's story / I'm gonna get on my feet after a while / Four o'clock blues / Telephone blues / Great tall engine
OBCCD 503 / Nov '92 / Original Blues Classics

☐ WHOOPIN' (Terry, Sonny & Johnny Winter/Willie Dixon)
ALCD 4734 / May '93 / Alligator

☐ WIZARD OF THE HARMONICA, THE
STCD 8018 / Jan '97 / Storyville

Terry, Todd

☐ BEST OF TODD TERRY'S UNRELEASED PROJECTS, THE
BB 042132CD / Jan '96 / Broken Beat

☐ DAY IN THE LIFE OF TODD TERRY
SOMCD 2 / Jul '96 / Ministry Of Sound

☐ MINISTRY OF SOUND - SESSIONS VOL.8 (2CD Set) (Various Artists)
MINCD 8 / Jul '97 / Ministry Of Sound

☐ READY FOR A NEW DAY
Preacher / Something's going on / I'm feelin' it / Ready for a new day / It's over love / Satisfaction guaranteed / Sax trac / Come on baby / Free yourself / Live without you / Keep on jumpin' / Rave / Something goin' on / Keep on jumpin'
5360762 / Jul '97 / Manifesto

☐ TODD TERRY PROJECT (Terry, Todd Project)
Put your hands together / Bolla / I'm goin' insane / Holdin' on / Definition wild side / Take me / Dee intermission / Day in the life part 11 / Do what you want / Popular demand / Don't get carried away / Day in the groove
CHAMPCD 1027 / May '92 / Champion

Terveet Kadet

☐ KUMIA JA VERTA 1987
AA 028 / Jul '97 / AA

☐ SIGN OF THE CROSS
AA 025 / Jul '97 / AA

Terzis, Michalis

☐ MAGIC OF THE GREEK BOUZOUKI
Dance of the dolphins / Near the sea / Dance of the fisherman / Trikimia / Olympus / Morning breeze / Trip with Alexandra / Nocturno / Flight of the seagull / South wind / Dance of Captain Michalis / Sea dream / Mermaid on the boat
EUCD 1206 / Sep '93 / ARC

☐ NOSTIMON IMAR
EUCD 1076 / '89 / ARC

Tesi, Riccardo

☐ ACCORDION CLARINET MANDOLIN (Tesi, Riccardo & Patrick Vaillant/ Gianluigi Trovesi)
Capelli neri / Nove di corporacions / La landiera / La balada de Felis Galean / Matelote / Notturno / Tarantella / Sestrina e perigurdino / Tricot marin / Polka / Lu ferolhs son fach per sautar / Monzuno e dintorni / Sirventes de catarina / Maienca dansa / Il funambolo / Promenade / Li barquetas de Sant Joan / Tarantella rouge et noire / Romance / Mazurcazione
Y 225068 / Nov '97 / Silex

☐ COLLINE (Tesi, Riccardo & Patrick Vaillant)
Y 225048CD / Apr '95 / Silex

☐ IL BALLO DELLA LEPRE
MWCD 4001 / Apr '93 / Music & Words

☐ UN BALLO LISCIO
Y 225056CD / Mar '96 / Silex

Tesla

☐ BUST A NUT
Gate / Invited / Solution / Shine away / Try so hard / She want she want / Need your lovin' / Action talks / Mama's fool / Cry / Earthmover / Lot to lose / Rubber band / Wonderful world / Games people play
GED 24713 / 2 Feb '98 / Geffen

☐ FIVE MAN ACOUSTICAL JAM
Comin' atcha live-truckin' / Heaven's trail (no way out) / Way it is / We can work it out / Signs / Gettin' better / Before my eyes / Paradise / Lodl / Mother's little helper / Modern day cowboy / Love song / Tommy's down-home / Down fo' boogie
GEFD 24311 / Feb '91 / Geffen

☐ GREAT RADIO CONTROVERSY
Hang tough / Lady luck / Heaven's trail / Be a man / Lazy days, crazy nights / Did it for the money / Yesterdaze gone / Making magic / Way it is / Flight to nowhere / Love song / Paradise / Party's over
GED 24224 / 8 Sep '97 / Geffen

☐ MECHANICAL RESONANCE
Ez come ez go / Cumin' atcha live / Gettin' better / 2 late 4 love / Rock me to the top / We're no good together / Modern day cowboy / Changes / Little Suzie's on the up / Love me / Cover queen / Before my eyes
GED 24120 / 8 Sep '97 / Geffen

☐ PSYCHOTIC SUPPER
Change in the weather / Edison's medicine / Don't de-rock me / Call it what you want / Song and emotion / Time / Government personnel / Freedom slaves / Had enough / What you give / Stir it up / Can't stop / Toke about it
GED 24424 / 8 Sep '97 / Geffen

Test Department

☐ BEATING A RETREAT
Fall from light / Kick to kill / Sweet sedation / Spring into action / Plastic / Inheritance / Cold witness / Compulsion / Total state machine
SBZCD 023 / 15 Sep '97 / Some Bizarre

☐ ECSTASY UNDER DURESS
RUSCD 8213 / Oct '95 / ROIR

☐ GOODNIGHT OUT, A
Goodnight / Milk of human kindness / Generous terms / Victory / We shall return no more / Demonomania / Voice of reason
MOP 003CD / Mar '94 / Some Bizarre

☐ LEGACY (1990-93)
FREUDCD 47 / Oct '94 / Jungle

☐ LIVE ATONAL
EFA 08438 / Jul '92 / Dossier

☐ MATERIA PRIMA
DEPTCD 1 / Jan '95 / Jungle

☐ PROVEN IN ACTION
DEPTCD 002 / Apr '96 / Sub Rosa

☐ TERRA FIRMA
Nadka / Siege / Current affairs / Dark eyes / Terra firma
SUBCD 00212 / '88 / Sub Rosa

☐ TOTALITY
KK 140CD / Nov '95 / KK

Testa, Gianmaria

☐ MONTGOLFIERES
Citta lunga / La traiettorie delle mongolfiere / Habanara / La donna del bar / Dento la tasca di un qualuque mattino / Un aeroplance a vela / Come le onde del mare / L'automobile / Senza titolo / La donne nelle stazione / Maria / Manacore / La terre delle colline
LBLC 2519 / Jun '96 / Indigo

Testament

☐ DEMONIC
Demonic refusal / Burning times / Together as one / Jun-jun / John Doe / Murky waters / Hatred's rise / Distorted lives / New eyes of old / Ten thousand thrones / Nostrovia
CDMFN 221
CDMFNX 221 / Jun '97 / Music For Nations

☐ LIVE AT THE FILLMORE
CDMFN 186 / Jul '95 / Music For Nations

☐ LOW
Low / Legions (in hiding) / Hail mary / Trail of tears / P c / All I could bleed / Dog faced gods / Last call / Ride / Chasing fear / Urotsukidoji / Shades of war
7567826452 / May '95 / Atlantic

☐ PRACTICE WHAT YOU PREACH
Practice what you preach / Perilous nation / Envy time / Time is coming / Blessed in contempt / Greenhouse effect / Sins of omission / Ballad, The (A song of hope) / Nightmare (coming back to you) / Confusion fusion
7820092 / Feb '95 / Atlantic

☐ RITUAL, THE
Sermon / As the seasons grey / Electric crown return to serenity / Ritual / Deadline / So many lies / Let go of my world / Agony / Troubled dreams / Signs of chaos / Electric crown / Return to serenity
7567823922 / May '92 / East West

☐ SIGNS OF CHAOS (The Best Of Testament)
Signs of chaos / Electric crown / New order / Alone in the dark / Dog faced Gods / Demonic refusal / Ballad / Souls of black / Trial by fire / Low / Practice what you preach / Over the wall / Legacy / Return to serenity / Perilous nation / Sails of Charon / Draw the line
908611120CD / 11 May '98 / Mayhem

Testify

☐ BALLROOM KILLER
RTD 19519192 / Jul '95 / Our Choice

☐ TESTIFY
RTD 19516392 / Oct '93 / Our Choice

☐ YOUR VISION
RTD 19515923 / Jul '93 / Our Choice

Testimony

☐ SATISFACTION WARRANTED
MABCD 006 / Jan '94 / MAB

Tetes Noires

☐ CLAY FOOT GODS
Reflections / Tell me when / Dear jane / Pour more water on her, george / Walk through the ruins / Bless me / Plain / Heading for a fall / World turning / Why are the farmers dying
ROUCD 9008 / '88 / Rounder

Tethered Moon

☐ FIRST MEETING
9100162 / Dec '97 / Winter & Winter

Tetreault, Martin

☐ LA NUIT OU J'AI DIT NON
AUDIO 003 / 30 Mar '98 / Audioview

Tew, Alan

☐ STRINGS GO LATIN (Tew, Alan & Tony Hatch)
PLSCD 230 / Jul '97 / Pulse

Tex, Joe

☐ AIN'T GONNA BUMP NO MORE
Ain't gonna bump no more / Be cool / Leaving you dinner / I mess eveything up / We held on / Music ain't got no colour / Loose caboose / Rub down / Congratulations / You can be my star / You might be diggin' the garden / Give the baby anything the baby wants / Takin' a chance / You're in too deep / God of love / Baby let me steal you / Woman cares / Love me right girl / I gotcha
CDSEWD 043 / Jun '93 / Southbound

☐ BUMP TO THE FUNK
Papa was too / Men are getting scarce / You need me, baby / Anything you wanna know / We can't sit down now / I can't see you no more / You're right, Ray Charles / Give the baby anything the baby wants / I gotcha / You said a bad word / King Thaddeus / Cat's got her tongue / My body wants you / I'm goin' back again / I don't want you to love me / Ain't gonna bump no more / I mess up everything I get my hands on / Loose caboose / Who gave birth to the funk / Stick your key in (and start your car)
CPCD 8081 / Mar '95 / Charly

☐ GREATEST HITS (2CD Set)
Hold what you've got / Only girl I've ever loved / Meet me in church / Woman can change a man / Same things it took to get me / I want to (do everything with you) / Don't make your children pay (for your mistakes) / Sweet woman like you / Love you save (may be your own) / SYSLJFM (the letter song) / I believe I'm gonna make it / Papa was too / Show me / All a man needs (is his woman's love) / Woman like that, yeah / Woman's hands / Skinny legs and all / Men are gettin' scarce / I'll never do you wrong / You need me / Baby / Buying a book / Anything you wanna know / She said yeah / I can't see everybody's baby / I gotcha / Bad feet / Takin' a chance / Woman stealer / Under your powerful love / I'm going back again / Have you ever / Baby it's raining / Time brings about a change / I don't want you to love me (if you're gonna talk about it) / Ain't gonna bump no more (with no big fat woman) / Hungry
CPCD 82662 / Dec '96 / Charly

☐ I GOTCHA (His Greatest Hits)
Hold what you've got / You got what it takes / Woman can change a man / One monkey don't stop no show / I want (to do everything for you) / Sweet woman like you / Love you save (may be your own) / SYSLJFM (The letter song) / I believe I'm gonna make it / I've got to do a little bit better / Papa was, too (Tramp) / Show me / Woman like that, yeah / Woman's hands / Skinny legs and all / Men are getting scarce / I'll never do you wrong / Keep the one you got / Buying a book / I gotcha
CPCD 8015 / Feb '94 / Charly

☐ MASTERS, THE
EABCD 070 / 24 Nov '97 / Eagle

☐ SHOW ME THE HITS AND MORE
ICH 1149CD / Jan '94 / Ichiban

☐ SKINNY LEGS AND ALL
SYSLJFM (The letter song) / Love you save (may be your own) / Show me / Hold what you've got / Heep see few know / Someone to take your place / One monkey don't stop no show / If sugar was as sweet as you / Meet me in church / You got what it takes / I had a good home but I left (part 1) / Don't let your left hand know / Woman can change a man / Skinny legs and all / I want to (do everything for you) / Sweet woman like you / I believe I'm gonna make it / Men are getting scarce / I'm a man / I've got to do a little bit better / Papa was too / Watch the one (that brings the bad news) / Truest woman in the world / Chicken crazy
CDKEND 114 / Mar '94 / Kent

☐ YOU'RE RIGHT (King Of Downhome Soul)
You're right, Ray Charles / You need me, baby / Dark end of the street / Woman like that, yeah / Keep the one you got / Same things it took to get me / I'll never do you wrong / Take the fifth amendment / Sweet sweet woman / We can't sit down now / Buying a book / Sure is good / That's the way / Anything you wanna know / Only way / Grandma Mary / Take my baby a little love / I can see everybody's baby / She said yeah / When a woman stops loving a man / Woman stealer / Funny how time slips away
CDKEND 117 / Jan '95 / Kent

Texabilly Rockers

☐ HONEY LET'S GO
Tennessee train / I'm gonna catch you baby / Feelin' blue / True love / Cadillac stomp / Who's that cat / Just because / Booze-a-billy bop / Honey let's go / Rockabilly bop / Wrong yo yo / Mystery baby / I was the one
RNRCD 002 / May '97 / Metralha

Texas

☐ SOUTHSIDE/RICK'S ROAD (2CD Set)
I don't want a lover / Tell me why / Everyday now / Southside / Prayer for you / Faith / Thrill has gone / Fight the feeling / Fool for love / One choice / Future is promises / So called friend / Fade away / Listen to me / You owe it all to me / Beautiful angel / So in love with you / You've got to give a little / I want to go to heaven / Hear me now / Fearing these days / I've been missing you / Winter's end
5286042 / Aug '95 / Vertigo

☐ WHITE ON BLONDE
0.30 / Say what you want / Drawing crazy patterns / Halo / Put your arms around me / Insane / Blacke eyed boy / Polo mint city / White on blonde / Postcard / 0.25 / Ticket to lie / Good advice / Breathless
5343152 / Feb '97 / Mercury

Texas Is The Reason

☐ DO YOU KNOW WHO YOU ARE
REV 051CD / Apr '96 / Revelation

Texas Kellys

☐ STAY ALL NIGHT
LUNMCD 058 / Dec '97 / Mulligan

Texas Lone Star

☐ DESPERADOS WAITING FOR A TRAIN
Good hearted woman / Here I am again / Friend of the devil / Desperados waiting for the train / Fast train / Me and my uncle / Wild horses / In my own way / Bluebirds are singing for you / Luckenbach, Texas (Back to the basics of love) / Painted ladies
BCD 15692 / Aug '92 / Bear Family

Texas Red

☐ WHAT KIND OF WOMAN IS THAT
BLRCD 034 / May '97 / Blue Loon

Texier, Henri

☐ LE COFFRET JMS (2CD Set)
Amir / Le sage/Le Singe/Et les petits enfants / Hommage / Le piroguier / Hommage rouge / Les korrigans / Quand tout s'arrete / Les La Bas / Terra-Basse / Quand le blues s'en Ira / L'elephant / Varech / Mr. Donald Cerise / Angele / L'ecluse / L'ultime danse / Luce D'alba / Kan al labour / Libertad / A cords et a cris / Hocoka / Exode / Blues urbain / Chemin de vie / Mektoub
JMS 186962 / 29 Jun '98 / JMS

☐ PARIS BATIGNOLLES (Texier, Henri Quartet)
LBLC 6506 / May '92 / Label Bleu

☐ RESPECT
Respect / Thingin / Too much, too often / Ladies waders / In the year of the dragon / Abacus / Lee and me / Idyll / Am(i)en / Marcello Mastroianni
LBLC 6612 / Aug '97 / Label Bleu

☐ SCENE IS CLEAN, THE (Texier, Henri Trio)
LBLC 6540 / Jun '91 / Label Bleu

Tez Fa Siyon

☐ P YOURNESS
CDLINC 010 / Dec '95 / Lion Inc.

Tezerdi

☐ TEZERDI
PAN 152 / Oct '94 / Pan

Thackeray, Jimmy

☐ DRIVE TO SURVIVE (Thackeray, Jimmy & The Drivers)
Drive to survive / You got work to do / That's how I feel / All about my girl / Play to win / Cool guitars / Slow down baby / Long, lean and lanky / Bruford's bop / Rub on up / Apache
BPCD 5035 / Nov '96 / Blind Pig

☐ EMPTY ARMS MOTEL
Paying the cost to be the boss / Rude mood / Empty arms motel / Lickin' gravy / I can't tell / Getting tired of waiting / Honey hush / Love to ride / Red house / Last night
BPCD 5001 / Jan '93 / Blind Pig

☐ PARTNERS IN CRIME (Thackeray, Jimmy & Tom Principato/The Assassins)
VDCD 112 / Jun '96 / Voodoo

☐ SIDEWAYS IN PARADISE (Thackeray, Jimmy & John Mooney)
BP 5006CD / Mar '94 / Blind Pig

☐ WILD NIGHT OUT (Thackeray, Jimmy & The Drivers)
BPCD 75021 / Jul '95 / Blind Pig

Tharpe, Sister Rosetta

☐ COMPLETE SISTER ROSETTA THARPE VOL.1, THE (2CD Set)
FA 1301 / 1 Jun '98 / Fremeaux

☐ SISTER ROSETTA THARPE VOL.1 1938-1941
DOCD 5334 / May '95 / Document

☐ SISTER ROSETTA THARPE VOL.2 1942-1944
DOCD 5335 / May '95 / Document

☐ SISTER ROSETTA THARPE VOL.3 1946-1947
DOCD 5607 / 27 Jul '98 / Document

That Dog

☐ THAT DOG
Old timer / Jump / Punk rock girl / Zodiac / You are here / She / Angel / Westside angst / She looks at me / Family functions / Raina / She looks at me (reprise) / Just like me / Paid programming / This boy
GU 6CD / 6 Jul '98 / Guernica

That Petrol Emotion

☐ CHEMICRAZY
Hey venus / Blue to black / Mess of words / Sensitize / Another day / Gnaw mark / Scum surfin' / Compulsion / Tingle / Head staggered / Abandon / Sweet shiver burn
CDV 2618 / Apr '90 / Virgin

☐ END OF THE MILLENNIUM PSYCHOSIS
Sooner or later / Every little bit / Cellophane / Candy love satellite / Here it is...take it / Price of my soul / Groove check / Bottom line / Tension / Tired shattered man / Goggle box / Under the sky
CDV 2550 / Oct '88 / Virgin

☐ MANIC POP THRILL
Fleshprint / Can't stop / Lifeblood / Natural kind of joy / It's a good thing / Circusville / Mouth crazy / Tightlipped / Million miles away / Lettuce / Cheapskate / Blindspot / V2 / Jesus says / Deadbeat / Mine / Non-alignment pact
DIAB 823 / Mar '97 / Diablo

That Uncertain Feeling

☐ 500/600
GOODCD 5 / May '95 / Dead Dead Good

Thatcher On Acid

☐ CURDLED/MOONDANCE
SKIP 55 / Mar '97 / Broken

☐ FRANK
SKIP 71 / 22 Jun '98 / Broken

☐ PRESSING 1984-91
DAR 013CD / Nov '94 / Desperate Attempt

Thau

☐ UTAH
FROG 0012 / Mar '95 / Pingo

THD

☐ MECHANICAL ADVANTAGE
HY 859210588 / Jun '94 / Hypnobeat

The The

☐ BURNING BLUE SOUL
Red cinders in the sand / Song without an ending / Time (again) for the golden sunset / Icing up / (like a) sun risin' thru my garden / Out of control / Bugle boy / Delirious / River flows east in spring / Another boy drowning
HAD 113CD / Jun '84 / 4AD

☐ DUSK
True happiness this way lies / Love is stronger than death / Dogs of lust / This is the night / Slow emotion replay / Helpline operator / Sodium light baby / Lung shadows / Bluer than midnight / Lonely planet
4724682 / Sep '96 / Epic

☐ HANKY PANKY
Honky tonkin' / Six more miles / My heart would know / If you'll be a baby to me / I'm a long gone daddy / Weary blues from waiting / I saw the light / Your cheatin' heart / I can't get you off my mind / There's a tear in my beer / I can't escape from you
4781392 / Feb '95 / Epic

☐ INFECTED
Infected / Out of the blue (into the fire) / Heartland / Sweet bird of truth / Slow train to dawn / Twilight of a champion / Mercy beat / Angels of deception / Disturbed
CD 26770 / May '87 / Epic
4886112 / 8 Sep '97 / Epic

☐ MIND BOMB
Good morning beautiful / Armageddon days are here (again) / Violence of truth / Kingdom of rain / Beat(en) generation / August and September / Gravitate to me / Beyond love
4633192 / Apr '94 / Epic

☐ SOUL MINING
I've been waiting for tomorrow / This is the day / Sinking feeling / Uncertain smile / Twilight hour / Soul mining / Giant / Perfect / Three orange kisses from Kazan / Nature of virtue / Mental healing process / Waitin' for the upturn / Fruit of the heart
4663372 / Mar '90 / Epic

Theard, Sam

☐ LOVIN' SAM THEARD 1929-1934
DOCD 5479 / Sep '96 / Document

Theatre Of Hate

☐ ACT 1 (Revolution/Live In Sweden - 2CD Set)
Legion / Original sin / Rebel without a brain / My own invention / Nero / Westworld / Propaganda / Hop / Incinerator / Eastworld and Americanos / Original sin / 63 / Wake / Love is a ghost / Klan / Nero / Conquistador / Westworld / Judgement hymn / Incinerator / Legion / Dreams of the poppy
TOH 001DCD / 9 Mar '98 / Eastworld

☐ ACT 2 (Ten Years After/Who Dares Wins/2CD Set)
Hop / Americana / Eastworld / Grapes of wrath / Solution / Omen / Arta / Murder of love / Black madonna / Flying Scotsman and the man tunes the drum / My own invention / Rebel without a brain / Original / Wake / Incinerator / Freaks / Propaganda / Legion / 63 / Incinerator
TOH 002DCD / 30 Mar '98 / Eastworld

☐ ARIA TO THE DEVIL
SMMCD 527 / 30 Mar '98 / Snapper

☐ COMPLETE SINGLES COLLECTION
Original sin / Legion / Rebel without a brain / My own invention / Nero / Incinerator / Do you believe in the Westworld / Propaganda / Hop / Conquistador / Eastworld / Assegai / Poppies / Brave new soldiers / Heathen / King of kings / Number twelve / Thalidomide / St Teresa / Abbatoir
CDMGRAM 93 / May '95 / Cherry Red

☐ HE WHO DARES WINS
LOMACD 35 / Jun '96 / Loma

☐ RETRIBUTION OVER THE WESTWORLD 1996
RRCD 229 / Aug '96 / Receiver

☐ RETRIBUTION/BINGLEY HALL (2CD Set)
TOH 003DCD / 6 Jul '98 / Eastworld

☐ TEN YEARS AFTER
Hop / Americana / East world / Grapes of wrath / Solution / Omen / Aria / Murder of love / Black Madonna / Flying Scotsman / Man who tunes the drums
DIAB 860 / 1 Jun '98 / Diablo

☐ WESTWORLD
Do you believe in the Westworld / Judgement hymn / 63 / Love is a ghost / Wake / Conquistador / New trail of tears / Freaks / Klan / Anniversary / Nero / Incinerator / Propaganda
DOJOCD 220 / Jan '96 / Dojo
SMMCD 511 / 29 Sep '97 / Snapper

Theatre Of Tragedy

☐ AEGIS
MASSCD 159
MASSDP 159 / 25 May '98 / Massacre

☐ CASSANDRA
MASSCD 166 / 13 Jul '98 / Massacre

☐ ROSE FOR THE DEAD
MASSCD 130 / Apr '97 / Massacre

☐ VELVET DARKNESS
MASSCD 107 / Oct '96 / Massacre

Theatricum Chemicum

☐ VERSO LA LUCE
EFA 148242 / Oct '95 / Glasnost

Theaudience

☐ THEAUDIENCE (2CD Set)
5587712
5588452 / 17 Aug '98 / Mercury

Thee Headcoatees

☐ BALLAD OF THE INSOLENT PUP
What once was / This heart / Pretend / Ballad of the insolent pup / You'll be sorry now / All my feelings denied / It's bad / When you stop loving me / Two hearts beating / No respect / Again and again / Now is not the best time / I was led to believe / You'll never do it baby
ASKCD 045 / Oct '94 / Vinyl Japan

☐ HAVE LOVE WILL TRAVEL
ASKCD 011 / Oct '92 / Vinyl Japan

☐ PUNK GIRLS
SFTRI 463CD / Mar '97 / Sympathy For The Record Industry

☐ SOUND OF THE BASKERVILLES (Thee Headcoatees & Thee Headcoats)
OVER 42CD / Dec '95 / Overground

Thee Headcoats

☐ BEACH BUMS MUST DIE
EFA 11563 D / Apr '93 / Crypt

☐ BROTHER IS DEAD...BUT FLY IS GONE
Louie Louie / Boredom / Diddy wah diddy / What's my name / Whatcha gonna do about it / Love comes in spurts / Don't gimme no lip / 1977 / Loathsome and wild / Punk rock ist might tot / You gotta lose / Viva la rock 'n' roll / Darling let's have another baby / Agitated
ASKCD 070 / 27 Apr '98 / Vinyl Japan

☐ CONUNDRUM
SCRAG 2CD / Sep '94 / Hangman's Daughter

☐ DEERSTALKING MEN (Thee Headcoat Sect)
SCRAG 8CD / Sep '96 / Hangman's Daughter

☐ HEAVENS TO MURGATROYD EVEN, IT'S THEE HEADCOATS
SPCD 6119 / May '93 / Sub Pop

☐ IN TWEED WE TRUST
DAMGOOD 96CD / Jun '96 / Damaged Goods

☐ LIVE IN LONDON (Thee Headcoats & Thee Headcoatees)
DAMGOOD 30CD / Mar '94 / Damaged Goods

☐ MESSERSCHMITT PILOT'S SEVERED HAND
DAMGOOD 140CD / 27 Apr '98 / Damaged Goods

Thee Hypnotics

☐ LIVER THAN GOD
All night long / Let's get naked / Revolution stone / Rock me baby / Justice in freedom
SITL 026CD / Oct '89 / Situation 2
SP 54B / Jan '94 / Sub Pop

☐ VERY CRYSTAL SPEED MACHINE, THE
Keep rollin' on / Heavy liquid / Phil's drum acropolis / Goodbye / If the good lord love ya / Ray's baudelaire / Caroline inside out / Tie it up / Down in the hole / Peasant song / Fragile / Look what you've done / Broken morning has
74321264512 / Jun '95 / American

Thee Madkatt Courtship

☐ BY DAWN'S EARLY LIGHT
Wet Wednesday / By dawn's early light / Tha' mental blowout / Panic 60466 / Lovetraxx 1990 / Who tha' critics / Revelation / Da mindfuck / Phuzon
SLIKCD 001 / Oct '95 / Deep Distraxion/ Profile

Thee Mighty Caesars

☐ ACROPOLIS NOW
I've got everything indeed / When the night comes / (Miss America) got to get you outside my head / Ask the dust / I don't need no baby / Dictator of love / Now I know / I can judge a daughter / Li'l Red Riding Hood / Loathsome 'n' wild / Despite all this / I feel like giving in / I was led to believe
SCRAG 9CD / Apr '97 / Hangman's Daughter

☐ CAESAR'S PLEASURE
Wily cayote / Miss Ludella Black / Death of a mighty caesar / Why don't you try my love / It ain't no sin / You'll be sorry now / All of your love / Give it to me / Baby please / Little by little / What you've got / I've got everything indeed / When the night comes / You make me die / Loathsome 'n' wild / I don't need no baby / I was led to believe / Man taken from guts / Devious means / I've been waiting / True to you / I can't find pleasure / Come into my life / Double axe / Neat neat neat / She's just 15 years old / Everything I've got to give / Lie detector / Why can't you see / Cowboys are square
CDWIKD 124 / Feb '94 / Big Beat

☐ SURELY THEY WERE THE SONS OF GOD
Wiley coyote / (Miss America) Got to get you outside my head / I don't need no baby / Stay the same / Double axe / I was led to believe / You make me die / Now I know / I've been waiting / Loathsome 'n' wild / You'll be sorry now / I can't find pleasure / Kinds of women / Lie detector / Confusion / Baby who mutilated everybody's heart / Suck the dog / Beat on the brat / Career opportunities / Because just because / Headcoats on / Somebody like you / Searching high and low / Don't wanna be ruled by women and money no more / Don't break my laws / Strange words / Signals of love / I've got everything indeed / Devious means / Why don't you try my love / Wise blood / It's you I hate to lose / Miss Loudella Black
CD 0141823 / Jul '93 / Crypt

Thee Phantom Creeps

☐ TEENAGE FINGERS
Sweetcorn / I love Lucy / Marty party / Prayer to overtaking / Do the dead / Churn it up / Long arm / Dirty love song / Head on backwards / Teenage fingers / Sign / Bad place / Strychnine / Teenage fingers / Bad place / Trance dance
FART 1 / Dec '96 / Armed & Fat

Thee Rayguns

☐ REBEL ROCKERS
RAUCD 013 / Feb '95 / Raucous

Thee Waltons

☐ DRUNK AGAIN
RAUCD 69 / May '94 / Raucous

☐ ESSENTIAL COUNTRY BULLSHIT
SPV 08476802 / Jun '94 / Steamhammer

☐ GET OUT YER VEGETABLES
Get out yer vegetables / Rubber chicken / Kings of veg-a-billy / Barking up the wrong tree / Elvis P / Devil in disguise / Hound dog / Famous / Devil's music / Drunk son / Tear it up
CDGRAM 90 / Feb '95 / Cherry Red

☐ LIK MY TRAKTER
Colder than you / Sunshine / Water well and the farmer's hand / In the meantime / I could care less / Truth and beauty / Living room / Look at me / Naked rain / (Don't let it) Slide / Fine line / Like my tractor
4509919512 / Mar '94 / WEA

☐ LOCK UP YER LIVESTOCK
RAUCD 007 / Aug '93 / Raucous

Theessink, Hans

☐ BABY WANTS TO BOOGIE
BG 1020CD / Apr '94 / Blue Groove

☐ CRAZY MOON
MWCD 2018 / Nov '95 / Music & Words

☐ HARD ROAD BLUES
SPINCD 155 / Dec '94 / Spindrift

☐ JOHNNY & THE DEVIL
BG 2020CD / Apr '94 / Blue Groove

☐ LIVE
SPINCD 150 / Dec '97 / Spindrift

☐ TITANIC
BG 3020CD / Apr '94 / Blue Groove

Theis & Nyegaard Jazzband

☐ THEIS/NYEGAARD JAZZBAND 1963/88 (The First 25 Years)
Chant / West End blues / Sidewalk blues / Sweet Georgia Brown / It don't mean a thing if it ain't got that swing / Blue turning grey over you / After you've gone / Someday you'll be sorry / Ain't misbehavin' / Willow weep for me / I found a new baby / Confessin' / Baby, won't you please come home / You can depend on me
STCD 4174 / Feb '90 / Storyville

☐ TONIGHT LIVE
MECCACD 2017 / May '97 / Music Mecca

Thelin, Eje

☐ POLYGLOT
1291 / Dec '92 / Caprice

Them

☐ STORY OF THEM & VAN MORRISON, THE
Story of them / Don't start crying now / Gloria / Philosophy / One two brown eyes / Baby please don't go / Here comes the night / All for myself / One more time / Little girl / I gave my love a dimond / Go on home baby / My little baby / Mystic eyes / Don't look back / I like it like that / I'm gonna dress in black / Route 66 / Just a little bit / You just can't win / Bright lights big city / Baby what do you want me to do / I'm gonna dress in black / One more time / How long baby / Half as much / Something you got / Call my name / Turn on your lovelight / I put a spell on you / I got a woman / Out of sight / It's all over now baby blue / Bad or good / Hello Josephine / Don't you know / Hey Girl / Bring 'em on in / Times getting tougher than tough / Stormy Monday / Friday's child / Richard Cory / My lonely sad eyes / I can only give you everything / Could you would you / Bring 'em on in / Richard Cory / Call my name
8448132 / Jun '98 / Deram

☐ THEM (Remastered)
Mystic eyes / If you and I could be as two / Little girl / Just a little bit / I gave my love a diamond / Gloria / You just can't win / Go on home baby / Don't look back / I like it like that / I'm gonna dress in black / Bright lights big city / My little baby / Route 66
8448242 / Jun '98 / Deram

☐ THEM AGAIN (Remastered)
Could you would you / Something you got / Call my name / Turn on your love light / I put a spell on you / I can only give you everything / My lonely sad eyes / I got a woman / Out of sight / It's all over now baby blue / Bad or good / How long baby / Hello Josephine / Don't you know / Hey girl / Bring 'em on in
8448252 / Jun '98 / Deram

Them Mushrooms

☐ THEM MUSHROOMS
RPM 0022 / 9 Mar '98 / Rags Productions

Themis, John

☐ ATMOSPHERIC CONDITIONS
Emily / Trick / Post-hypnotic suggestions / Cinderella's last waltz / Electric storm / Transition / Black mamba samba / Trouble
NAGE 1CD / Jan '86 / Art Of Landscape

☐ ENGLISH RENAISSANCE
Over the dark cloud / James I / Open Arms / Catrina / Cross crusader / English renaissance / Steed for a king / Don't wake the dragon George
NAGE 11CD / Jul '86 / Art Of Landscape

Then Jerico

☐ ELECTRIC
Big area / Word / Motive / Fault / Quiet place (apathy and sympathy) / Clank (countdown to oblivion) / Blessed days / Electric / Prairie rose / Reeling / You ought to know / Big sweep / One life / Darkest hour
5501932 / Mar '94 / Spectrum

☐ ORGASMAPHOBIA
EAGCD 012 / 5 May '98 / Eagle

☐ RADIO JERICO (2CD Set)
Let her fall / Muscle deep / Blessed days / Hitcher / Play dead / Quiet place / Electric / Searching / Big area / Muscle deep / Motive / Under fire / Reeling / Where you lie / What does it take / Sugarbox / Helpless / You ought to know / Blessed days / Hitcher / Where you lie / Sugarbox / What does it take / Reeling / Motive / Big area / Muscle deep
MURD 001CD / 15 Jun '98 / Murder

Theo

☐ SMOOTH LOVER
STPCD 1 / May '96 / Keeling

Theodorakis, Mikis

☐ BIRTHDAY CONCERT 1995, THE
68974 / Apr '97 / Tropical

☐ BOUZOUKIS OF MIKIS THEODORAKIS, THE
Sto parathiri stekoussoun / Myrtia / Tou mikou voria / Varka sto yialo / Marina / Yitonia ton anghelon / Balanda tou andrikou / To yelasto pedi / Apagoghi / To parathiro / Mana mou ke panayia
111 692 / May '90 / Musidisc

☐ CANTO GENERAL
INT 31142 / Jun '93 / Intuition

☐ CYCLADES MINOR
ML 3582 / 11 May '98 / Musurgia Graeca

☐ GOLD
MMB 10674 / 11 May '98 / Musurgia Graeca

☐ HOSTAGE, THE
ML 3702 / 11 May '98 / Musurgia Graeca

☐ TOGETHER IN CONCERT (Theodorakis, Mikis & Z. Livaneli)
68987 / Jul '97 / Tropical

☐ ZORBA - THE BALLET
Three zeibekikos songs (scene 1) / Zorba's entrance (scene 2 / Gran ballo (scene 3) / Madame hortense (scene 4) / Sta perivolia (scene 5) / Tsifteteli (scene 6) / Evin evan (scene 7) / Return of zorba (scene 8) / Veatriki (scene 9) / Asteraki (scene 10) / Marina (scene 11) / Death of hortense (scene 12) / Zorba's dance (scene 13)
INT 31032 / Jul '92 / Intuition

Theodore, Mike

☐ COSMIC WIND/HIGH ON MAD MOUNTAIN (Theodore, Mike Orchestra)
Belly boogie / Bull / Cosmic wind / Moon trek / Ain't nothing to it / Brazilian lullaby / I love the way you move / High on mad mountain / Wonder man / Disco people / Dragons of midnight
CDSEWD 120 / 29 Jun '98 / Westbound

Therapy

☐ BABYTEETH
185072 / Mar '93 / Southern

☐ INFERNAL LOVE
Epilepsy / Stories / Moment of clarity / Jude the obscene / Bowels of love / Misery / Bad mother / Me vs. you / Loose / Diane / Thirty seconds
5403792 / Jun '95 / A&M

☐ PLEASURE DEATH
Skinning pit / Fantasy bag / Shitkicker / Prison breaker / D.l.c. / Potato junkie
185082 / Apr '93 / Southern

☐ SEMI-DETACHED
Church of noise / Tightrope walker / Black eye purple sky / Lonely cryin' only / Born too soon / Stay happy / Safe / Straight life / Heaven's gate / Don't expect roses / Tramline / Boy's asleep
5408912 / 30 Mar '98 / A&M

☐ TROUBLEGUM
Knives / Screamager / Hellbelly / Stop it you're killing me / Nowhere / Die laughing / Unbeliever / Trigger inside / Lunacy booth / Isolation / Turn / Femtex / Unrequited / Brainsaw / You are my sunshine
5401962 / Nov '93 / A&M

Thergothon

☐ STEAM FROM THE HEAVENS
AV 001 / May '94 / Avantgarde

Therion

☐ BEAUTY IN BLACK, THE
NB 125CD / Mar '95 / Nuclear Blast

☐ BEYOND SANCTORIUM
CDATV 23 / Jul '92 / Active

☐ LEPACA KLIFFOTH
NB 216CD / Nov '96 / Nuclear Blast

☐ SIREN OF THE WOODS
NB 178CD / Jul '96 / Nuclear Blast

☐ THELI
NB 179CD / Sep '96 / Nuclear Blast

☐ VOVIN
Rise of Sodom and Gomorrah / Birth of Venus illegitima / Wine of Aluqah / Clavicula nox / Wild hunt / Eye of Shiva / Blacksun / Draconian / Draconian / Draconian / Raven of dispersion
NB 3172 / 1 Jun '98 / Nuclear Blast

These Animal Men

☐ ACCIDENT AND EMERGENCY
Life support machine / So sophisticated / When your hands are tied / Monumental moneymaker / Riverboat captain / New wave girl / 24 hours to live / Going native / Ambulance man / Light emitting electrical wave / April 7th
CDHUT 40 / Apr '97 / Hut

☐ COME ON JOIN THE HIGH SOCIETY
Sharp kid / Empire building / Ambulance / This year's model / You're always right / Flawed is beautiful / This is the sound of youth / Sitting tenant / Too sussed / Come on join the high society / We are living / High society
FLATCD 8 / Sep '94 / Hi-Rise

☐ TAXI FOR THESE ANIMAL MEN
You're always right / Nowhere faces / My human remains / False identification / Wait for it
FLATMCD 14 / Mar '95 / Hi-Rise

☐ TOO SUSSED
Too sussed (live) / Speed king / Jobs for the boys / Cjhhe daddy now / You're not my babylon
FLATMCD 4 / Jun '94 / Hi-Rise

These Immortal Souls

☐ GET LOST (DON'T LIE)
Marry me (lie lie) / Hide / These immortal souls / Hey little child / I ate the knife / Blood and sand she said / One in shadow one in sun / Open up and bleed / Blood and sand she said (alternate) / I ate the knife (alternate) / These immortal souls (alternate)
CD STUMM 48 / Oct '87 / Mute

☐ I'M NEVER GONNA DIE AGAIN
King of kalifornia / Shamed / Black milk / Hyperspace / So the story goes / Insomnicide / All the money's gone / Crowned
CDSTUMM 98 / Oct '92 / Mute

Thessalonians

☐ SOULCRAFT
PS 9334 / Oct '93 / Silent

They Might Be Giants

☐ APOLLO 18
Dig my grave / I palindrome I / She's actual size / My evil twin / Mammal / Statue got me high / Spider / Guitar (The lion sleeps tonight) / Dinner bell / Narrow eyes / Hall of heads / Which describes how you're feeling / See the constellation / If I wasn't shy / Turn around / Hypnotist of ladies / Fingertips / Space suit
7559612572 / Mar '92 / Elektra

☐ DON'T LET'S START
TPCD 14 / Nov '89 / One Little Indian

☐ FACTORY SHOWROOM
7559618622 / Feb '97 / Elektra

☐ FLOOD
Theme from flood / Lucky ball and chain / Dead / Particle man / We want a rock / Birdhouse in your soul / Istanbul (not Constantinople) / Your racist friend / Twisting
7559609072 / '89 / Elektra

☐ JOHN HENRY
Subliminal / Snail shell / Sleeping in the flowers / Unrelated thing AKA driver / I should be allowed to think / Extra savoir faire / Why must I be sad / Spy / O do not forsake me / No one knows my plan / Dirt bike / Destination moon / Self called nowhere / Meet James Ensor / Thermostat / Window out of jail / Stomp box / End of the tour
7559616542 / Sep '94 / Elektra

☐ LINCOLN
Ana ng / Cowtown / Lie still / Little bottle / Purple toupee / Cage and aquarium / Where your eyes don't go / Piece of dirt / MR. Me / Pencil rain / World's address / I've got a match / Santa's beard / You'll miss me / They'll need a crane / Shoehorn with teeth / Stand on your own head / Snowball in hell / Kiss me / Son of God
7559611452 / Jun '91 / Elektra

Thibodeaux, Donald

☐ FRED'S HOT STEP (Thibodeaux, Donald & Cajun Fever)
Fred's hot step / La bouteille / Pine grove blues / Chere petite / Fifi poncheaux / La valse de cajin / Lacassine special / Louisiana rambler's waltz / Old fashioned two-step / Quit making a fool of myself / Chere tout toute / Pardon waltz / J'ai ete au bal / Les flammes d'enfer
ARHCD 9006 / Nov '97 / Arhoolie

Thibodeaux, Jimmy

☐ CAJUN AND ZYDECO BOURBON STREET PARTY
SWALCD 6137 / Mar '98 / Swallow

Thielemans, 'Toots'

☐ BLUESETTE (Thielemans, Jean 'Toots')
CDCH 303 / Feb '91 / Milan

☐ BRASIL PROJECT, THE (Thielemans, Jean 'Toots')
Comecar de novo / Obi / Felicia and Bianca / O cantador / Joana Francesca / Coisa feita / Preciso aprender a so ser / Furta boa / Coracao vagabundo / Manha de carnaval / Casa forte / Moments / Bluesette
01005821012 / Jul '96 / Private Music

☐ CONCERTO FOR HARMONICA (Thielemans, Jean 'Toots')
Prelude to a new life / Toots / Mo blues / Song for Willy Graz / Ne me quitte pas / Passionement / Asco / You just forgot that I love you / Coda / Body and soul
TCB 94802 / Nov '94 / TCB

☐ EAST COAST, WEST COAST (Thielemans, Jean 'Toots')
01005821202 / Feb '95 / Private Music

☐ IMAGES (Thielemans, Jean 'Toots')
Days of wine and roses / I never told you / Dr.Pretty / Airegin / Images / Day dream / Giant steps / Snooze / Stella by starlight / Revol
CHCD 71007 / Jul '97 / Candid

☐ JAZZ MASTERS (Thielemans, Jean 'Toots')
Undecided / Body and soul / Flirt / Soldier in the rain / Hummin' / Brown ballad / You're my blues machine / Bluesette / Big bossa / Tenor madness / Nocturne / Vai passar / Killer Joe / Peacocks / C to G jam blues / For my lady
5352712 / 5 May '98 / Verve

☐ LIVE IN THE NETHERLANDS (Thielemans, Jean 'Toots' & Joe Pass/ N.H. Orsted Pederson)
Blues in the closet / Mooche / Thriving on a riff / Autumn leaves / Someday my Prince will come
CD 2308233 / Apr '94 / Pablo
OJCCD 9302 / Nov '97 / Original Jazz Classics

☐ MAN BITES HARMONICA (Thielemans, Jean 'Toots')
OJCCD 1738 / Oct '92 / Original Jazz Classics

☐ ONLY TRUST YOUR HEART (Thielemans, Jean 'Toots')
Speak no evil / Estate (ess-tah-tay) (in summer) / Three and one / Rain waltz / All of you / Dragon / Only trust your heart / Sophisticated lady / Hello young lovers / Sarabande / Little rootie tootie / We'll be together again
CCD 4355 / Sep '88 / Concord Jazz

☐ TWO GENERATIONS (Thielemans, Jean 'Toots')
Bluesette / Be be creole / Monologue / Two generations / Why did I choose you / Uncle Charlie / Friday night / T T / Inner journey / L'eternal mari
FCD 0003 / Nov '95 / Limetree

Thierry, Jacques

☐ HAWAIIAN GUITAR VOL.2, THE (Thierry, Jacques & Trio Kailus)
PS 65081 / Nov '91 / PlayaSound

Thievery Corporation

☐ SOUNDS FROM THE THIEVERY HI-FI
ESL 5CD / Sep '97 / 18th Street Lounge

☐ SOUNDS FROM THE THIEVERY HI-FI
Warning / 2001 spliff odyssey / Shaolin satellite / Vivid / Universal highness / Incident at gate 7 / Mnanha / Glass bead game / Foundation / Interlude / Oscillator / So vast as the sky / 38:45 (a thievery number) / Walking through babylon
CAD 8006CD / 8 Jun '98 / 4AD

Thieves

☐ THIEVES
Either / Not wiser / Unworthy (edit) / Misunderstood / Is it raining / Conversation / He loves you / Worn away / It's always this way / My grey boy / They hide
CDHUT 12 / May '94 / Hut

Thigpen, Ed

☐ MR. TASTE (Thigpen, Ed Trio)
JUST 432 / Oct '92 / Justin Time

☐ OUT OF THE STORM
Cielito lindo / Cloud break (up blues) / Out of the storm / Harper / Elbow and mouth / Heritage / Struttin' with some barbecue
5571002 / 3 Aug '98 / Verve

☐ YOUNG MEN AND OLD
Strike up the band / Yesterdays / Summertime / Night and day / Scramble / Shuffin' long / Oh my gosh / Dark before the dawn / I should care
CDSJP 330 / Aug '90 / Timeless Jazz

Thile, Chris

☐ LEADING OFF...
SHCD 3828 / Nov '94 / Sugar Hill

☐ STEALING SECOND
Ah spring / Stealing second / Kneel before Him / Bittersweet reel / Alderaanian melody / Hyperdrive / Leaves fall / Night in Mos Eisley / Hop the fence / Game is afoot / Clear the tracks / Golden pond / Road to Wrigley / Ryno's lament
SHCD 3863 / Mar '98 / Sugar Hill

Thilo, Jesper

☐ FLAT FOOT BOOGIE
MECCACD 1010 / Nov '94 / Music Mecca

☐ HALF NELSON (Thilo, Jesper Quartet)
MECCACD 1009 / Jul '93 / Music Mecca

☐ JESPER THILO & ANN FARHOLT/ THOMAS CLAUSEN (Thilo, Jesper & Ann Farholt/Thomas Clausen)
MECCACD 2025 / May '97 / Music Mecca

☐ JESPER THILO PLAYS BASIE AND ELLINGTON
MECCACD 2102 / May '97 / Music Mecca

☐ JESPER THILO QUARTET AND HARRY EDISON (Thilo, Jesper Quartet)
STCD 4120 / Feb '89 / Storyville

☐ JESPER THILO/CLARK TERRY (Thilo, Jesper & Clark Terry)
Just one of those things / Sophisticated lady / Save your love for me / Rose room / Wave / Ballad for Lester / Cherokee / Sunday / Did you call her today / Stardust / Frog eyes / Body and soul
STCD 8204 / Nov '94 / Storyville

☐ PLAYS BASIE
MECCACD 1035 / Nov '94 / Music Mecca

☐ SHUFFLIN'
MECCACD 1015 / Nov '94 / Music Mecca

☐ WE LOVE HIM MADLY (Thilo, Jesper Quintet)
MECCACD 1025 / Jul '93 / Music Mecca

Thin Lizzy

☐ BAD REPUTATION
Bad reputation / Dancin' in the moonlight / Dear Lord / Downtown sundown / Killer without cause / Opium train / Soldier of fortune / Southbound / That woman's gonna break your heart
5322982 / Mar '96 / Mercury

☐ BLACK ROSE
Do anything you want to / Toughest street in town / S and M / Waiting for an alibi / Sarah / Got to give it up / Get out of here / With love / Roisin dubh
5322992 / Mar '96 / Mercury

☐ CHINATOWN
We will be strong / Chinatown / Sweetheart / Sugar blues / Killer on the loose / Havin' a good time / Genocide / Didn't I / Hey you
8303932 / Jun '89 / Vertigo

☐ FIGHTING
Ballad of a hard man / Fighting my way back / For those who love to live / Freedom song / King's vengeance / Rosalie / Silver dollar / Spirit slips away / Suicide / Wild one
5322962 / Mar '96 / Mercury

☐ JAILBREAK
Angel from the coast / Boys are back in town / Cowboy song / Emerald / Fight or fall / Jailbreak / Romeo and the lonely girl / Running back / Warriors
5322942 / Mar '96 / Mercury

☐ JOHNNY THE FOX
Boogie woogie dance / Borderline / Don't believe a word / Fool's gold / Johnny / Johnny the fox meets Jimmy the weed / Massacre / Old flame / Rocky / Sweet Marie
5322952 / Mar '96 / Mercury

☐ LIFE
Thunder and lightening / Waiting for an alibi / Jailbreak / Baby please don't go / Holy war / Renegade / Hollywood / Got to give it up / Angel of death / Are you ready / Boys are back in town / Cold sweat / Don't believe a word / Killer on the loose / Sun goes down / Emerald / Black rose / Still in love with you / Rocker
8128822 / Aug '90 / Vertigo

☐ LIVE AND DANGEROUS - IN CONCERT
Boys are back in town / Dancin' in the moonlight / Massacre / I'm still in love with you / Me and the boys / Don't believe a word / Warriors / Are you ready / Sha la la la / Baby drives me crazy
5322972 / Mar '96 / Mercury

☐ RENEGADE
Angel of death / Renegade / Pressure will blow / Leave this town / Hollywood (down on your luck) / No one told him / Fats / Mexican blood / It's getting dangerous
8424352 / Jun '90 / Vertigo

☐ THIN LIZZY
Friendly ranger at Clontarf Castle / Honesty is no excuse / Diddy levine / Ray gun / Look what the wind blew in / Eire / Return of the farmer's son / Clifton Grange Hotel / Saga of the ageing orphan / Remembering part 1 / Dublin / Remembering part 2 / Old moon madness / Thing's ain't working out down at the farm
8205282 / Jan '89 / Vertigo

☐ THUNDER AND LIGHTNING
Thunder and lightning / This is the one / Sun goes down / Holy war / Cold sweat / Someday / She is going to hit back / Baby, please don't go / Bad habits / Heart attack / Thunder and lightening
8104902 / Jun '89 / Vertigo

☐ VAGABONDS OF THE WESTERN WORLD
Mama nature said / Hero and the madman / Slow blues / Rocker / Vagabond of the western world / Little girl in bloom / Gonna creep up on you / Song for while I'm away / Whiskey in the jar / Black boys on the corner / Randolph's tango / Broken dreams
8209692 / May '91 / Vertigo

☐ WHISKY IN THE JAR
Whiskey in the jar / Sarah / Look what the wind blew in / Return of the farmer's son / Old moon madness / Dublin / Shades of blue orphanage / Buffalo girl / Black boys on the corner / Rocker / Mama nature said / Broken dreams / Here I go again / Little darling / Vagabond of the western world / Remembering (part 2)
5520852 / Mar '96 / Spectrum

☐ WILD ONE (The Very Best Of Thin Lizzy)
Boys are back in town / Jailbreak / Don't believe a world / Waiting for an alibi / Rosalie/Cowgirl song / Cold sweat / Thunder and lightning / Out in the fields / Dancin' in the moonlight / Parisienne walkways / Sarah / Still in love with you / Emerald / Bad reputation / Killer on the loose / Chinatown / Do anything you want to / Rocker / Whiskey in the jar
5281132 / Jan '96 / Mercury

Thin White Rope

☐ EXPLORING THE AXIS/BOTTOM FEEDERS
Down in the desert / Disney girl / Soundtrack / Lithium / Dead grammas on a train / Three song / Eleven / Roger's tongue / Real West / Exploring the axis / Ain't that loving you baby / Macy's window / Waking up / Valley of the bones / Atomic imagery / Rocket USA
DIAB 824 / Mar '97 / Diablo

☐ IN THE SPANISH CAVE/RED SUN
Mr. Limpet / Ring / It's OK / Ahr-skidar / Red sun / Elsie crashed the party / Timing / Astronomy / Wand / July / Ain't that loving you baby / Macy's window / Waking up / Valley of the bones / Atomic imagery / Rocket USA / Munich eunuch / Town without pity / Man with the golden gun / They're hanging me tonight / Some velvet morning / Red sun
DIAB 826 / 26 Jan '98 / Diablo

☐ MOONHEAD...PLUS
Not your fault / Wire animals / Take it home / Thing / Moonhead / Wet heart / Mother / Come around / If those tears / Crawl piss freeze / Tina and Glen / Munich eunuch / God rest ye merry gentlemen / Here she comes now
DIAB 825 / Apr '97 / Diablo

☐ ONE THAT GOT AWAY, THE (2CD Set)
Down in the desert / Disney girl / Eleven / Not your fault / Wire animals / Take it home / Mr. Limpet / Elsie crashed the party / Red sun / Some velvet morning / Triangle song / Yoo doo right / Tina and Glen / Napkin song / Ants are cavemen / Fish song / Bartender's rag / Hunter's moon / Astronomy / Outlaw blues / It's OK / Wreck of the ol' 97 / Roadrunner / Munich eunuch / Silver machine / Clown song
DIAB 829 / 6 Jul '98 / Diablo

☐ RUBY SEA, THE/SQUATTER'S RIGHTS
Ruby sea / Tina and Glen / Puppet dog / Bartender's rag / Midwest flower / Dinosaur / Lady vanishes / Up to midnight / Hunter's moon / Christmas skies / Fish song / Clown song / Caravan / Film theme / Roadrunner / May this be love / Everybody's been burned / I knew I'd want you
DIAB 828 / 6 Jul '98 / Diablo

☐ SACK FULL OF SILVER...PLUS
Hidden lands / Sack full of silver / Yoo doo right / Napkin song / Americana / Ghost / Whirling dervish / Triangle / Diesel man / On the floe / Ants are cavemen / Little doll / Outlaw blues / Burn the flames / Eye / Skinhead
DIAB 827 / 26 Jan '98 / Diablo

☐ WHEN WORLDS COLLIDE
MRCD 047 / May '94 / Munster

Thine

☐ TOWN LIKE THIS, A
This town / Masque / Feathers and roses / Here tonight / My song / Pianoman / Miss Grey / Sonic showmen / Re-animate the
CDVILE 72 / 20 Jul '98 / Peaceville

Things To Come

☐ I WANT OUT
Sweetgina / Mississippi dealer / I want out / Your down / Speak of the devil / Smokestack lightnin' / Character of Caruso / Tell me why / Tomorrow / Pushin' too hard (instr.) / Show me a place / I'm a man / Home to you / Your down (instr.) / Icicles on the roof / Sweetgina (instr.) / Behold now behemoth / Darkness
CDSC 11017 / Jan '94 / Sundazed

Thingy

☐ SONGS ABOUT ANGELS, EVIL AND RUNNING AROUND ON FIRE
HED 067 / May '97 / Headhunter

Think About Mutation

☐ HELLRAVER
Ganglords / Overload / River / Lucky times / Rewinding seeds / Suffer / Warning / Psycho DJ / Nude / Try the way to move / View (what's this life) / Killing Zoe / 4 steps ahead
DY 162 / Jun '96 / Dynamica

☐ HOUSE GRINDER
DY 32 / Oct '93 / Dynamica

☐ HOUSEBASTARDS
DY 102 / Sep '94 / Dynamica

Think Floyd

☐ HOPE
Prologue / Brain rape / Circle / If I had power / Waiting for inspiration / Scanning for life / Hope / Home again / Reprise / Long dream
RP 0001 / 1 Mar '98 / Red

Think Out Loud

☐ SHELF LIFE
Castles on quicksand / Way beyond my reach / Don't throw it away / From where I stand / Answer to the way / Moonlight on water / Just like that / Let's talk about love / I'll find my way again / Calm before the storm / Dancing on a high wire / Invisible man
199629 / Sep '97 / Made To Measure

Think Twice

☐ JOY IS FREE
IBCD 1 / Feb '97 / Internal Bass

Thinking Fellas Union Local 282

☐ I HOPE IT LANDS
COMM 043CD / Dec '96 / Communion

☐ PORCELAIN ENTERTAINMENTS
RTS 21 / Jan '96 / Return To Sender

☐ STRANGERS FROM THE UNIVERSE
My pal the tortoise / Socket / Bomber pilot WWII / Hundreds of years / Guillotine / Uranium / February / Pull my pants up tight / Cup of dreams / Oxenmaster / Operation / Piston and the shaft / Communication / Noble experiment
OLE 1092 / Oct '94 / Matador

☐ WORMED BY LEONARD
THW 0022 / Dec '96 / Thwart

Thinking Plague

☐ IN THIS LIFE
RERTPCD / Apr '90 / ReR/ Recommended

Third & The Mortal

☐ PAINTING ON GLASS
VOW 051CD / Jan '96 / Voices Of Wonder

☐ TEARS LAID TO REST
VOW 041CD / Oct '96 / Voices Of Wonder

☐ THIRD & THE MORTAL
VOW 059CD / Mar '97 / Voices Of Wonder

Third Ear Band

☐ ALCHEMY
Mosaic / Ghetto raga / Druid one / Stone circle / Egyptian book of the dead / Area three / Dragon lines / Lark rise
DOCD 1999 / Apr '91 / Drop Out

☐ LIVE GHOSTS
Hope mosaic / Druid three / Ghetto raga / Live ghosts
MASO 90004 / '90 / Materiali Sonori

☐ MACBETH
Overture / Beach / Lady Macbeth / Inverness / Banquet / Dagger and death / At the well/Prince's escape/Coronation/Come sealing night / Court dance / Fleance groom's dance / Bear baiting / Ambush/Banquo's ghost / Going to bed/Blind man's buff / Requiescant/Sere and yellow leaf / Cauldron / Prophesies / Wicca way
BGOCD 61 / Jan '89 / Beat Goes On

☐ NECROMANCERS OF THE DRIFTING WEST (CD/Book Set)
SB 05 / 23 Feb '98 / Sonic Book

☐ NEW AGE MAGICAL MUSICAL
Gog and Magog / Flight of the coven / Dance of the elves / Atlantis rising / Midnight on mars
BP 257CD / Apr '97 / Blueprint

☐ THIRD EAR BAND
Air / Earth / Fire / Water
BGOCD 89 / Dec '90 / Beat Goes On

☐ VOICEPRINT RADIO SESSION
VPR 017CD / Oct '94 / Voiceprint

Third Eye

☐ ANCIENT FUTURE
NZ 0242 / Oct '94 / Third Eye

☐ DANCE OF CREATION
NZ 023CD / Nov '94 / Nova Zembla

Third Eye

☐ AWAKENING/SEARCHING
TOU 005 / 8 Jun '98 / Tou

Third Eye Blind

☐ SEMI-CHARMED LIFE
Losing a whole year / Narcolepsy / Semi-charmed life / Jumper / Graduate / How's it going to be / Thanks a lot / Burning man / Good for you / London / I want you / Background / Motorcycle drive by / God of wine
7559620122 / Jul '97 / Elektra

Third Eye Foundation

☐ GHOST
What to do but cry / Corpses as bedmates / Star's gone out / Out sound from way in / I've seen the light and it's dark / Ghosts / Donald Crowhurst
WIGCD 032 / Apr '97 / Domino

☐ IN VERSION
LSD 04CD / Oct '96 / Linda's Strange Day

☐ SEMTEX
LSD 02 / Oct '96 / Linda's Strange Day

Third Person

☐ BENDS, THE
KFWCD 102 / Nov '94 / Knitting Factory

☐ LUCKY WATER
Busy river / Cold call / Trick water / Bubble and crow / Bridge of a thousand tears / Globe trudgers / Old Grandad (doesn't smell too bad) / John Frum he come / Curlew's sad day / Cadillac bolero / Moro reflex / Hasten slowly
KFWCD 156 / Feb '95 / Knitting Factory

Third Sex

☐ CARD CARRYIN'
CHSW 15 / Dec '96 / Chainsaw

Third World

☐ GREATEST HITS
Try jah love / Dancing on the floor (hooked on love) / Rock the world / Spiritual revolution / You're playing us too close / Before you make your move (melt with everyone) / Inna time like this / Low key-jammin' / Lagos jump / Love is out to get you / Sense of purpose / One more time / World of uncertainty / Hold on to love / Spirit lives / We could be jammin' reggae
4805782 / 13 Jul '98 / Columbia

☐ REGGAE AMBASSADORS (20th Anniversary Collection)
Satta a masagana / Brand new beggar / Freedom song / Railroad track / 1865 / Rhythm of life / Dreamland / Now that we've found love / Journey to Addis / Cool meditation / Night heat / Talk to me / Irie ites / Always around / Uptown rebel / Jah glory / African woman / Breaking up is hard to do / Roots with quality / Dancing on the floor / Try Jah love / Lagos jump / Sense of purpose / Reggae radio station / Forbidden love / Reggae ambassador / DJ ambassador / Riddim haffe rule / Committed / Mi legal / Give the people what they need
CRNCD 3 / Feb '94 / Island

☐ REGGAE GREATS
Now that we've found love / Prisoner in the street / Always around / Talk to me / Cool meditation / Satta a masagana / Ninety six degrees in the shade / African woman / Rhythm of life
5527352 / Jul '97 / Spectrum

☐ ROCK THE WORLD
Rock the world / Spiritual revolution / Who gave you / Dub music / Shine like a blazing fire / Dancing on the floor / There's no need to question why / Peace and love / Standing in the rain / Hug it up
44879452 / Jul '97 / Columbia

☐ WORL'ERS
Now that we found love / Layla / Spare me the blues tonight / Conversation / Magnet and steel / Umbeyo / Live it up / Times hard / Getting on fire / Love devine / Papa was a rolling stone / Born in this time
336232 / 3 Aug '98 / Koch Dance Force

Third World War

☐ THIRD WORLD WAR VOL.1
14504 / Jul '97 / Spalax

☐ THIRD WORLD WAR VOL.2
14538 / Jul '97 / Spalax

Thirty Ought Six

☐ HAG SEED
CDSTUMM 86 / Apr '96 / Mute

This

☐ LETTUCE SPRAY
Grooverang (intro) / Mind's eye / Michael / Criss cross world / Kite / Mentholated head balm / Tighter / Chicken run / Destiny / Swimming against the tide / Sandwich
YM 002CD / Oct '93 / Yellow Moon

This Ascension

☐ LIGHT AND SHADE
EFA 064812 / Mar '94 / Tess

This Heat

☐ MADE AVAILABLE
THESE 010CD / Jun '97 / These

This Mortal Coil

☐ BLOOD
Lacemaker / Mr. Somewhere / Andialu / With tomorrow / Loose joints / You and your sister / Nature's way / I come and stand at every door / Bitter / Baby ray baby / Several times / Lacemaker II / Late night / Ruddy and wretched / Help me lift you up / Carolyn's song / DD and E / Till I gain control again / Dreams are like water / I am the cosmos / (Nothing but) Blood
DADCD 1005 / Apr '91 / 4AD

☐ FILIGREE AND SHADOW
Velvet belly / Jeweller / Ivy and neet / Meniscus / Tears / Tarantula / My father / Come here my love / At first and then / Strength of strings / Morning glory / Inch-blue / I want to live / Mama K / Filigree and shadow / Firebrothers / Thais / I must have been blind / Heart of glass / Alone / Mama K / Horizon bleeds and sucks its thumb / Drugs / Red rain / Thais
DAD 609 CD / Sep '86 / 4AD

☐ IT'LL END IN TEARS
Kangaroo / Song to the siren / Holocaust / Fyt / Fond affections / Last ray / Waves become wings / Another day / Barramundi / Dreams made flesh / Not me / Single wish
CAD 411 CD / '86 / 4AD

This Train

☐ MIMES OF THE OLD WEST
Hanger / We're getting nowhere / Missing link / Who's supporting you / Mimes of the old west / Million years / I saw the light / Seafoam green / I don't want to know / Sandee / Wailing wall / I've got half a mind / Goodbye
ORCD 9801 / Jun '98 / Pamplin

Thistlethwaite, Anthony

☐ CRAWFISH AND CAVIAR
Down in New Orleans / Best of all things / Sun rays / Come here to me now / Something better / All the way / Celestial ride / Welcome to the white nights / Embrasse moi / Tricky one / Dungarees / Enchanted rock / Stella / Faoilean / Colours
FIENDCD 937 / 3 Nov '97 / Demon

Thomas, Angelika

☐ LIEBLING DER SAISON (Thomas, Angelika & Orchestra Melange)
Overture / Jonny wenn du geburtstag hast / Ich wunsch mir zum geburtstag dich / Alles mit den beinen / Lass mich einmal deine Carmen sein / Baby / Black market / Illusions / Moonlight and shadows / Boys in the backroom / Ich bin von kopf bis fuss auf liebe eingestel / Reizend / Nimm dich in acht vor blonden Frau'n / Lola / Abschiednehmen mit musik
BCD 16015 / Dec '96 / Bear Family

Thomas, B.J.

☐ INSPIRATIONAL COLLECTION
VSD 5904 / 7 Apr '98 / Varese Sarabande

☐ RAINDROPS KEEP FALLIN' ON MY HEAD
CPCD 8228 / Aug '96 / Charly

Thomas, Bill

☐ PREACHER'S SON
422504 / May '95 / Last Call

Thomas, Buddy

☐ KITTY PUSS FIDDLER
Nine miles out of Louisville / Frankie / John Rawl Jamieson / Sheeps and hogs walking through the pasture / Georgia row / Briarpacker brown / Stillhouse branch / Blue goose / Yellow barber / Possum up a simmon tree / Kitty puss / Martha Campbell / Turkey in a pea patch / Big Indian hornpipe / Brown button shoes / Sweet sunny south
ROUCD 0032 / Feb '98 / Rounder

Thomas, Carla

☐ BEST OF CARLA THOMAS, THE
Where do I go / I've fallen in love / I like what you're doing (to me) / Strung out over you / Just keep on loving me: *Thomas, Carla & Johnnie Taylor* / My life: *Thomas, Carla & Johnnie Taylor* / I need you woman: *Thomas, Carla & William Bell* / I can't stop: *Thomas, Carla & William Bell* / Some other man (is beating your time) / Guide me well / Time for love / (I'm going back to) living in the City / All I have to do is dream: *Thomas, Carla & William Bell* / I loved you like I love my very life / Hi de ho (that old sweet roll) / You've got a cushion to fall on / Love means you never have to say you're sorry / Sugar / I may not be all you want (but I'm all you got) / Love among people / I have a God who loves / Gee whiz / I'll never stop loving you
CDSXD 093 / Aug '93 / Stax

☐ COMFORT ME
Comfort me / No time to lose / Yes I'm ready / Lover's concerto / I'm for you / What the world needs now / Let it be me / Woman's love / Will you love me tomorrow / Forever / Move on drifter / Another night without my man
SCD 706 / Apr '96 / Stax

☐ HIDDEN GEMS
I'll never stop loving you / I wonder about love / Little boy / Loneliness / (Your love is a) lifesaver / Sweet sensation / You'll lose a good thing / I've made up my mind / My man believes in me / I like it / Runaround / Good good lovin' / That beat keeps disturbing my sleep / If it's not asking too much / It ain't no easy thing / Toe hold / Good man / I can't hide it / Thump in my heart / Goodbye my love
CDSXD 039 / Oct '91 / Stax

☐ LOVE MEANS
Didn't we / Are you sure / What is love / Daughter, you're still your daddy's child / Love means you never have to say you're sorry / You've got a cushion to fall on / Il est plus doux que / Cherish / I wake up wanting you
CDSXE 060 / Jul '92 / Stax

Thomas, Charlie

☐ BIG CHARLIE THOMAS (Various Artists)
I'm gonna hoodoo you: *Martin, Sara* / Your going ain't giving me the blues: *Martin, Sara* / What more can a monkey do: *Martin, Sara* / Shake that thing: *Williams, Clarence* / Get it fixed: *Williams, Clarence* / I want plenty grease in my frying pan: *Carter, Margaret* / Come get me Papa before I faint: *Carter, Margaret* / Skunk: *Christian, Buddy's Jazz Rippers* / South Rampart Street Blues: *Christian, Buddy's Jazz Rippers* / Georgia Grind: *Morris, Thomas* / Ham gravy: *Morris, Thomas* / Look out, Mr Jazz: *Okeh Melody Stars* / Nobody but my baby is getting my love: *Brown, Bessie* / St Louis Blues: *Brown, Bessie* / Papa if you can do better (I'll let a better Papa move in): *Henderson, Rosa* / I'm saving it all for you: *Henderson, Rosa* / Dark eyes: *Dixie Washboard Band* / Gimme blues: *Dixie Washboard Band* / King of the Zulus: *Dixie Washboard Band* / Zulu blues: *Dixie Washboard Band* / What do you know about that: *Williams, Clarence & Joe Sims* / Shut your mouth: *Williams, Clarence & Joe Sims*
CBC 1030 / Aug '96 / Timeless Jazz

Thomas, Chris

☐ SIMPLE
HCD 8043 / Jun '94 / Hightone

Thomas, Clara

☐ CLARA THOMAS
5345192 / 20 Oct '97 / Mercury

Thomas, David

☐ EREWHON (Thomas, David & Two Pale Boys)
Obsession / Planet of fools / Nowheresville / Fire / Lantern / Morbid sky / Weird Cornfields / Kathleen / Highway 61 revisited
COOKCD 105 / Sep '96 / Cooking Vinyl

☐ GIANTS DANCE (Thomas, David & Ronnie Gunn)
Great Western / I get the feeling / Somewhere upon the way / Minor epic / I knw she danced / (Give my) Love to the future / Coolly I love you / Walk to the water / Bring back the old money / Falcon rise / Hillside / Memorium / Hey lady / Go get the girl / To my surprise / Fate is a dancer / Black rat sleepy tune / Giants dance
BP 223CD / Oct '96 / Blueprint

☐ MONSTER (5CD Set)
Birds are a good / Yiki tiki / Crickets in the flats / Sound of sand / New atom mine / Big dreams / Happy to see you / Crush this horn part 2 / Confuse did / Sloop John B / Man's best friend / Pedestrian walk / Bird town / Day at the Botaical gardens / Egga and I / Whi is it / Song of the hoe / Hurry back / Rain / Semaphore / Through the magnifying glass / Enthusiastic / Whale head king / Song of bailing man / Big breezy day / Farmer's wife / About true friends / My theory of spontaneous simultude/Run tin bus / What happened to me / Monster walks the winter lake / Bicycle / Coffee train / My town / Monster magee, King of the seas / Monster thinks about the good old days / My town / Fact about trains / King knut / When love is uneven / Storm breaks / Long rain / Having time / Fields of stone / Veilovsky 2-step / Obsession / Nobody knows / Red sky / Can't help falling in love / Nowheresville / Fire / Kathleen / Surfer girl/Around the fire / Beach boys / Weird cornfields / Busman's honeymoon
HR 110 / Jun '97 / Cooking Vinyl

Thomas, Doc

☐ ITALIAN JOB, THE/SHOTGUN EYES (Thomas, Doc Group/Silence)
I'll be doggone: *Thomas, Doc Group* / She was really saying something: *Thomas, Doc Group* / Steal your heart away: *Thomas, Doc Group* / My babe: *Thomas, Doc Group* / Please do something: *Thomas, Doc Group* / Shake: *Thomas, Doc Group* / I got you: *Thomas, Doc Group* / Harlem shuffle: *Thomas, Doc Group* / Talking about my baby: *Thomas, Doc Group* / Just can't go to sleep: *Thomas, Doc Group* / Barefootin': *Thomas, Doc Group* / Rescue me: *Thomas, Doc Group* / Leaving here: *Silence* / Shame shame shame: *Silence* / See you tomorrow: *Silence* / You can't judge a book by looking at the cover: *Silence* / Gunshot: *Silence* / Doctor Feelgood: *Silence* / I think of you: *Silence* / Let it rock: *Silence* / I'm not talking: *Silence* / Fortune teller: *Silence* / Don't start me to talkin': *Silence* / Farmer John: *Silence* / Route 66: *Silence* / We'll silence you: *Silence*
SJPCD 020 / 22 Apr '98 / Angel Air

Thomas, Evelyn

☐ BEST OF EVELYN THOMAS, THE (High Energy)
This is madness / No win situation / Weak spot / Doomsday / Sleaze / Love in the first degree / Summer on the beach / I wanna make it on my own / Have a little faith in me / High energy / Masquerade / Heartless / Reflections / How many hearts
HTCD 18 / 20 Apr '98 / Hot Productions

Thomas, Gary

☐ BY ANY MEANS NECESSARY
By any means necessary / Continuum / You're under arrest / Potential hazard / To the vanishing point / Screen gem / Janala / At risk / Out of harm's way
8344322 / Dec '94 / jMT

☐ EXILE'S GATE
5140092 / Dec '93 / jMT

☐ FOUND ON SORDID STREETS
9100022 / Oct '97 / Winter & Winter

☐ OVERKILL: MURDER IN THE WORST DEGREE
SOL / Guaranteed flow / Have hope / Outta tha game / Terror of the streets / Barrikade'll stop ya / Doomsday booty / Fuk tha massa / Godfather waltz / Just a villain / Soulja / It's on
5140242 / Mar '96 / jMT

☐ PARIAH'S PARIAH
9100332 / Jun '98 / Winter & Winter

Thomas, Guthrie

☐ MIDNIGHT TRAIN
TX 3006CD / Apr '96 / Taxim

☐ THROUGH THE YEARS
TX 3001CD / Jan '94 / Taxim

☐ WRITER, THE
TX 3002CD / Dec '93 / Taxim

Thomas, Henry

☐ COMPLETE RECORDINGS, THE
YAZCD 1080 / Apr '91 / Yazoo

Thomas, Hociel

☐ HOCIEL THOMAS & LILLIE DELK CHRISTIAN 1925-1928 (Thomas, Hociel & Lillie Delk Christian)
DOCD 5448 / May '96 / Document

Thomas, Irma

☐ LIVE - SIMPLY THE BEST
Breakaway / Time is on my side / Hip shakin' mama / That's what love is all about / Thinking of you / I need somebody / I've been loving you too long / Please please please / It's raining / I done got over/Iko iko/ Hey pocky way / Wish someone would care / You can have my husband / Oh me oh my (I'm a fool for you) / Simply the best
NETCD 25 / May '91 / Network

☐ NEW RULES, THE
New rules / Gonna cry till my tears run dry / I needed somebody / Good things don't come easy / Love of my man / One more time / Thinking of you / Wind beneath my wings / I gave you everything / Yours until tomorrow
ROUCD 2046 / '86 / Rounder

☐ SOUL QUEEN OF NEW ORLEANS
It's raining / Ruler of my heart / I did my part / Cry on / Look up / It's too soon to know / I done got over / That's all I ask / For goodness sake / Gone / Somebody told you / Two winters long / (You ain't) hittin' on nothing / Girl needs boy / In between tears / She'll never be your wife / These four walls / What's so wrong with you loving me / You're the dog (I do the barking myself) / Coming from behind / Wish someone would care / Turn my world around
CPCD 8010 / Feb '94 / Charly

☐ STORY OF MY LIFE, THE
No use talkin' / Story of my life / I count the teardrops / Cried too long / Love don't get no better than this / Hold me while I cry / I won't cry for you / All we need love / Get here / Keep the faith / Dr. Feelgood
ROUCD 2149 / Feb '97 / Rounder

☐ SWEET SOUL QUEEN OF NEW ORLEANS (The Irma Thomas Collection)
RAZCD 2097 / Apr '96 / Razor & Tie

☐ TIME IS ON MY SIDE...PLUS
Take a look / Time is on my side / Baby don't look down / Times have changed / I done got over it / It's raining / Somebody told you / Wait wait wait / Break-a-way / I haven't got time to cry / Some things you never get used to / Look up (when ever) / Ruler of my heart / I need your love so bad / Wish someone would care / (I want a) True true love / I did my part / You don't miss a good thing (until it's gone) / Anyone who knows what love is (will understand) / Straight from the heart / Gone / Two winters long / Without love (there is nothing) / It's a man's-woman's world
CDKEND 010 / Nov '96 / Kent

☐ WALK AROUND HEAVEN
Ask what you will / I know prayer changes things / Careful hands / Hold to god's unchanging hand / No not one / I will say yes lord / Walk around heaven all day / Oh holy night / Just a little while to stay here / Where we'll never grow old
ROUCD 2128 / Apr '94 / Rounder

Thomas Jefferson Slave Appartments

☐ BAIT AND SWITCH
My mysterious death / Is she shy / Down to High Street / Quarrel with the world / Cheater's heaven / Cyclotron / Negative guestlist / Fire in the swimming girl / You can't kill stupid / Rock 'n' roll hall of fame / Contract dispute / Wrong headed
74321279652 / Jul '95 / American

☐ STRAIGHT TO VIDEO
AW 44 / Jun '97 / Anyway

Thomas, Jay

☐ 360 DEGREES
Cheryl / Wlatz / All too soon / Wing span / Why not / Aisha / Valse / Peacocks / Whims of chambers / My ideal / Blues for McVouty / Isfahan
HEPCD 2060 / Feb '95 / Hep

☐ BLUES FOR MCVOUTY
Blues for mcvouty / Easy living / Hallucination / Django / Simple pleasures / Ev'rything I love / Lover man / Moose the mooche / Detour ahead / Big foot / Close enough for love / Love letters
STCD 562 / May '93 / Stash

Thomas, Jesse

☐ BLUE GOOSE BLUES
IMP 704 / Nov '95 / Iris Music

☐ LOOKIN' FOR THAT WOMAN
CDBT 1128 / Mar '96 / Black Top

Thomas, Joe

☐ JOE THOMAS 1945-1950
BMCD 1051 / Apr '97 / Blue Moon

Thomas, John Charles

☐ HOME ON THE RANGE
GEMMCD 9977 / Sep '92 / Pearl

Thomas, Kenny

☐ VOICES
Outstanding / Best of you / Tender love / Will I ever see your face / Something special / If you believe / Thinking about your love / Voices / Girlfriend / Were we ever in love
CCD 1890 / Sep '97 / Cooltempo

Thomas, Leon

☐ ANTHOLOGY
Prince of peace / Creator has a master plan (peace) / Song for my father / Bag's groove / CC rider / China doll / Just in time to see the sun / Shape your mind to die / It's my life I'm fighting for / Balance of life (peace of mind) / Little sunflower / Sun song
CDSBPJ 1 / 3 Aug '98 / Soul Brother

Thomas, Louise

☐ BEST OF LOUISE THOMAS, THE (I Can Fly)
HTCD 72 / 20 Apr '98 / Hot Productions

Thomas, Nicky

☐ DOING THE MOONWALK
Doing the moonwalk / God bless the children / Red eye / Love of the common people / Lonely feelin' / Watch that little girl / Yesterday / Tell it like it is / Images of you / If I had a hammer / Turn back the hands of time / Rainy night in georgia / Have a little faith / Deep in the morning / Lonely for your love / I can't stand it / New morning / I'll be waiting / Long gone / Mama's song
CDTRL 288 / Apr '91 / Trojan

Thomas, Nigel

☐ YOICHI (Thomas, Nigel Quintet)
OJIN 1 / May '97 / Ojin

Thomas, Pat

☐ REMEMBERING
NJC 003 / Jun '98 / NJC

☐ ST. KATHERINE
WSFASF 144 / May '94 / Normal

Thomas, Peter

☐ EASY LISTENING CLASSICS
5294912 / Apr '96 / Polydor

☐ FUTUREMUZIK (Thomas, Peter Soundorchester)
SCP 9724 / 20 Apr '98 / Scamp

☐ RAUMPATROUILLE (Thomas, Peter Soundorchester)
Space patrol / Shub a dooe / Lancet bossa nove / Love in space / Ballet / Bolero on the moon / Rocks / Song and sound the stars around / Landing on the moon / Piccicato in heaven / Outside atmosphere / Take sex / Jupiter's pop music / Sky life / Starlight party / Orion 2000 / Danger for the crew / Position overkill / Space patrol's return / Mars close up / Hedono / Moontown
RTD 34600092 / Nov '96 / City Slang
BUNG 009CD / 27 Apr '98 / Bungalow

Thomas, Ramblin'

☐ RAMBLIN' THOMAS 1928-1932
DOCD 5107 / Nov '92 / Document

Thomas, Rene

☐ GUITAR GENIUS
All the things you are / Body and soul / Deep purple / You go to my head / Just friends / B like Bud / 'Round midnight
CDSGP 009 / Jan '94 / Prestige

☐ GUITAR GROOVE (Thomas, Rene Quintet)
Spontaneous effort / Ruby, my dear / Like someone in love / MTC / Milestones / How long has this been going on / Greenstreet scene
OJCCD 1725 / Jun '96 / Original Jazz Classics

Thomas, Richard

☐ SHOES AND RADIOS ATTRACT PAINT
Horla / Occupying the distance / Echo locator / Darby tuff / Sumo groupies / Antelope valley high / Stanton ductile warrior / Valley of the interlocking spurs / Return to pow 7 / Gurl trivia / Ordure rechouffe / Waxy flexibility
LCD 006 / 2 Feb '98 / Lo Recordings

Thomas, Ruddy

☐ GREATEST HITS
RN 7029 / 15 Dec '97 / Rhino

☐ SINGS BOB MARLEY
I shot the sheriff / No woman no cry / One love / Iron lion zion / Is this love / Get up stand up / Kaya / Three little birds / Stir it up / Jammin' / Buffalo soldier / Trench town rock / Could you be loved / Exodus / Kinky reggae / Sleep on, your songs will live on
WB 877082 / Mar '97 / Disky

☐ WHEN I'VE GOT YOU
HLCD 010 / Jun '94 / Hawkeye

Thomas, Rufus

☐ BEST OF RUFUS THOMAS, THE (The Singles)
Funky Mississippi / So hard to get along with / Funky way / I want to hold you / Do the funky chicken / Preacher and the bear / Sixty minute man / Do the push and pull (part 1) / Do the push and pull (part 2) / World is round / Breakdown (part 1) / Breakdown (part 2) / Do the funky penguin (part 1) / Do the funky penguin (part 2) / 6-3-8 (that's the number to play) / Itch and scratch (part 1) / Funky robot (part 1) / I know (I love you so) / I'll be your santa baby / Funky bird / Boogie ain't nuttin' (but gettin' down) / Do the double bump / Jump back '75 (part 1) / Looking for a love (part 1)
CDSXD 094 / Oct '93 / Stax

☐ BLUES THANG
NEGCD 280 / Mar '96 / Sequel

☐ CAN'T GET AWAY FROM THIS DOG
Walking the dog / Can't get away from this dog / Forty four long / Strolling Beale no.1 / Cherry red blues / Carry me back to old Virginny / Barefootin' / Story that's never been told / Last clean shirt / Show me the way to go home / Jump back / My girl / We're gonna make it: *Thomas, Rufus & Carla* / Don't mess up a good thing: *Thomas, Rufus & Carla* / I want to hold you / Can your monkey do the dog / Stop kicking my dog around / Wang dang doodle / Reconsider baby: *Thomas, Rufus & Carla*
CDSXD 038 / Oct '91 / Stax

☐ CROWN PRINCE OF DANCE
Git on up and do it / I know you don't want me no more / Funkiest man alive / Tutti Frutti / Funky robot / I wanna sang / Baby it's real / Steal a little / I'm still in love with you / Funky bird
CDSXE 054 / Nov '92 / Stax

☐ DID YOU HEARD ME
Do the Push and pull (Parts 1 and 2) / World is round / (I love you) for sentimental reasons / Breakdown (part 1) / Breakdown (part 2) / Love trap / Do the funky penguin (part 1) / Do the funky penguin (part 2) / Ditch digging / 6-3-8 (That's the number to play)
CDSXE 050 / Nov '92 / Stax

☐ DO THE FUNKY CHICKEN
Do the funky chicken / Let the good times roll / Sixty minute man / Looking for a love / Bearcat / Old McDonald had a farm (parts 1 and 2) / Rufus Rastus Johnson Brown / Soul food / Turn your damper down / Preacher and the bear
CDSXE 036 / Mar '91 / Stax

☐ RUFUS THOMAS LIVE DOING THE PUSH AND PULL AT PJ'S
Monologue / Ooh-poo-pah-doo / Old McDonald had a farm / Walking the dog / Preacher and the bear / Night time is the right time / Push and pull / Do the funky chicken / Breakdown / Do the funky chicken / Do the funky penguin
CDSXE 121 / Jul '95 / Stax

☐ THAT WOMAN IS POISON
That woman is poison / Big fine hunk of woman / Somebody's got to go / Walk / I just got to know / Blues in the basement / Breaking my back / All night worker
ALCD 4769 / May '93 / Alligator

☐ WALKING THE DOG
Dog / Mashed potatoes / Ooh-poo-pah-doo / You said / Boom boom / It's aw'rite / Walking the dog / Ya ya / Land of 1000 dances / Can your monkey do the dog / Because I love you / I want to be loved
SCD 703 / Apr '96 / Stax

Thomas, Steve

☐ FISH GROOVES VOL.1
RIBCD 2002 / 14 Apr '98 / Tinrib

Thomas, Timmy

☐ WHY CAN'T WE LIVE TOGETHER (The Best Of The TK Years 1972-1981)
Why can't we live together / Funky me / I've got to see you tonight / You're the song I've always wanted to sing / People are changin' / One brief moment / What can I tell her / Sweet brown sugar: *Thomas, Timmy & Betty Wright* / Let me be your eyes / Ebony affair: *Thomas, Timmy & Betty Wright* / Dizzy dizzy world / Love shine / Stone to the bone / Freak in freak out / Take care of home / Fox with the box / Touch to touch / Drown in my own tears / Are you crazy / Why can't we live together
WESM 552 / 16 Feb '98 / Westside

Thompson

☐ GRAVITY SUIT
FIRECD 69 / 26 Jan '98 / Fire

Thompson Twins

☐ BEST OF THE THOMPSON TWINS, THE
In the name of love / Lies / Love on your side / Lay your hands on me / Gap / Hold me now / Doctor doctor / You take me up / King for a day / Get that love
261220 / Mar '91 / Arista

☐ COLLECTION, THE
Hold me now / Sister of mercy / Don't mess with Doctor Dream / Who can stop the rain / Perfect day / Day after day / Doctor doctor / You take me up / Lies / Follow your heart / Still waters / Emperor's clothes / Revolution / In the name of love
74321152212 / Sep '93 / Ariola Express

☐ SINGLES COLLECTION
Perfect game / Lies / Love on your side / We are detective / Watching / Hold me now / Doctor doctor / King for a day / You take me up / Sister of mercy / Don't mess with Doctor Dream / Get that love / Revolution / Lay your hands on me / In the name of love
74321393352 / Jan '97 / Camden

Thompson, Anthony

☐ EDGE OF THE SWAMP (Thompson, Anthony 'Packrat')
Them jelly blues / Creepin' blues / Son of a king / Hoodoo lover / Swamp junkin' / Haints in my house / Hoy hoy hoy / Credit card blues / Go down Moses / What's your flavour baby / Bisquit roller / 95 South (High sheriff from Hell)
KS 044 / May '98 / King Snake

Thompson, Barbara

☐ BARBARA THOMPSON'S SPECIAL EDITION
Country dance / Fear of spiders / City lights / Little Annie ooh / Fields of flowers / Dusk: Nightwatch / Listen to the plants / Out to lunch / Sleepwalker / Midday riser / Times past / Voices behind locked doors
VBR 20172 / Sep '93 / Vera Bra

☐ BREATHLESS (Thompson, Barbara Paraphernalia)
Breathless / Sax rap / Jaunty / You must be jokin' / Squiffy / Bad blues / Cheeky / Gracey / Breathless (short cuts) / Sax rap (short cuts) / Cheeky (short cuts)
VBR 20572 / Sep '93 / Vera Bra

☐ CRY FROM THE HEART, A (Live In London) (Thompson, Barbara Paraphernalia)
VBRCD 20212 / Sep '93 / Vera Bra

☐ EVERLASTING FLAME
Everlasting flame / Tatami / In the eye of a storm / Ode to sappho / Emerald dusky maiden / Night before culloden / Unity hymn / Ancient voices / So near, so far / Fanaid grove
VBR 20582 / Nov '93 / Vera Bra

☐ HEAVENLY BODIES
Le grand voyage / Extreme jonction / Requiem pour deux memoire / Entre les trous de la memoire / Les barricades mysterieuses / Heavenly bodies / Love on the edge of life / Elysian fields / Flights of fancy / Tibetan sunrise / Horizons new
VBR 20152 / Sep '93 / Vera Bra

☐ LADY SAXOPHONE
In memory / All in love is fair / Falling scars / I do it for your love / Rueben, Rueben / Out on a limb / Wastelands / Waiting for the rain / What am I here for / Lady S
VBR 21662 / May '96 / Vera Bra

☐ LIVE IN LONDON / A CRY FROM THE HEART (Thompson, Barbara Paraphernalia)
Joyride / L'extreme jonction / Cry from the heart / Entre les trous de la memoire / Out to lunch / Close to the edge / Voices behind locked doors / Eastern Western promise Part 1 / Eastern Western promise Part 11
VBR 20212 / Sep '93 / Vera Bra

☐ NIGHTWATCH (Thompson, Barbara Paraphernalia)
Fields of flowers / Coconut hurling game / Dusk / Nightwatch / Kafferinya / Chapter and verse / To Ceres / Listen to the plants / Pure fantasy / Firefly
VBR 21252 / Feb '97 / Vera Bra

Thompson, Bob

☐ EV'RY TIME I FEEL THE SPIRIT
D 2248772 / Apr '96 / Ichiban

☐ MAGIC IN YOUR HEART
ICH 1165CD / Apr '94 / Ichiban

Thompson, Bobby

☐ BOBBY THOMPSON COLLECTION, THE (3CD Set)
RUBCD 3238 / Dec '96 / Rubber

☐ BOBBY THOMPSON LAUGH-IN, THE
RUBCD 038 / Dec '96 / Rubber

☐ LITTLE WASTER, THE
RUBCD 032 / Dec '96 / Rubber

Thompson, Bruce

☐ BIBLE SINGERS, THE (Thompson, Bruce & The Black Roses)
Bible singers / Go down Moses / Sweet sweet spirit / How great thou art (O store gud) / Solid rock / I want Jesus to walk with me / When the saints go marchin' in / Sometimes I feel like a Motherless child / Oh happy day / Amazing grace
CD 12528 / Jun '96 / Music Of The World

Thompson, Butch

☐ BUTCH & DOC (Thompson, Butch & Doc Cheatham)
Reclining civilization / Je t'aime / Day by day by day / Dab in da mida / We're a family / Red army song / What has to be / Spirit / L'accordion / Gabriel's dreams
CD 3012 / Dec '94 / Daring

☐ BUTCH THOMPSON PLAYS JELLY ROLL MORTON
BCD 141 / Apr '96 / Biograph

☐ BUTCH THOMPSON PLAYS JOPLIN
CD 3033 / Jul '98 / Daring

☐ LINCOLN AVENUE BLUES
DARINGCD 3019 / Nov '95 / Daring

☐ LINCOLN AVENUE EXPRESS
Tom cat blues / Big lip blues / Basin Street blues / Weeping willow blues / New Orleans hop scop blues / Aunt Hagar's blues / Willow tree / Lincoln Avenue express / Arkansas blues / Careless love / Mr. Jelly Lord / Yellow dog blues / Atlanta blues / St. Louis blues
DARINGCD 3027 / Jun '97 / Daring

☐ MINNESOTA WONDER
DR 3004 / Mar '93 / Daring

☐ PLAYS FAVORITES (Thompson, Butch Trio)
SACD 113 / Feb '93 / Solo Art

☐ THOMPSON PLAYS JOPLIN
Maple leaf rag / Bethena (a concert waltz) / Swipesy cakewalk / Wall street rag / Ragtime dance / Solace (a Mexican serenade) / Pineapple rag / Heliotrope bouquet / Elite syncopations / Lily queen / Euphonic sounds / Cascades / Magnetic rag
DARINGCD 3033 / 16 Mar '98 / Daring

☐ YULESTRIDE
DARING 3010CD / Nov '94 / Daring

Thompson, Carroll

☐ COLLECTIVELY CARROLL THOMPSON
BSRCD 09 / 23 Mar '98 / Boot Street

☐ OTHER SIDE OF LOVE, THE
Other side of love / I go weak / Move me / Walk away / Unity / Show some love/ Where is love / Where were you / Natural woman / Lovers and strangers / Rock me gently
ARICD 077 / Dec '92 / Ariwa Sounds

Thompson, Dale

☐ TESTIMONY (Thompson, Dale & The Kentucky Cadillacs)
Better watch what you say / Hand me down religion / Business as usual / Who'll bell the cat / One man's opinion / Ain't no devil / Ain't done me no wrong / Don't judge the preacher / Road less travelled / If I plant a tree today
ORCD 9745 / May '98 / Pamplin

Thompson, Danny

☐ SONGHAI (Thompson, Danny/Toumani Diabate/Ketama)
Jarabi / Mani mani kuru / Caramelo / A toumani / Vente pa madrid / Africa / A mi tia marina / Ne ne koitaa
HNCD 1323 / May '89 / Hannibal

☐ SONGHAI VOL.2
Sute monebo / Niani / Pozo del deseo / Monte de los suspiros / Djamana djana / De jerez a mali / Ndia / De la noche a la manana / Mali sajio
HNCD 1383 / Aug '94 / Rykodisc

☐ WHATEVER
Idle Monday / Till Minne av jan / Yucateca / Lovely Joan / Swedish dance / Lament for Alex / Crusader / Minor escapade
HNCD 1326 / Jul '87 / Hannibal

☐ WHATEVER'S BEST
Dargal / Beanpole / Full english basket / Sadansko oro / Major escapade / Prayer-dance-thanksgiving (freedom) / Women in war / Fair isle friends / Musing mingus
WHAT 001CD / Feb '95 / Whatdisc

Thompson, Eddie

☐ AIN'T SHE SWEET (Thompson, Eddie Trio & Spike Robinson)
Surrey with the fringe on top / Cool blues / Cool blues / Ain't she sweet / Ain't he sweet / You are my sunshine / You are my sunshine / Easy does it / Easy does it / One morning in May / One morning in May / Nancy / Nancy / There is no greater love / There is no greater love / Just friends / Wave / Why don't you do right / I've got the world on a string / When the lights are low
HEPCD 2002 / Apr '98 / Hep

☐ AT CHESTERS (Thompson, Eddie Trio & Spike Robinson)
'S Wonderful / Flamingo / Emily / I'm getting sentimental over you / I should care / Ow / Everything happens to me / Please don't talk about me when I'm gone
HEPCD 2028 / Jan '92 / Hep

☐ AT CHESTERS VOL.2 (Thompson, Eddie Trio & Spike Robinson)
You'd be so nice to come home too / You'd be so nice to come home too / East of the sun / But beautiful / Way you look tonight / Skylark / I'm beginning to see the light / That's all
HEPCD 2031 / Jun '94 / Hep

☐ MEMORIES OF YOU (Thompson, Eddie Trio & Spike Robinson)
Rosetta / Memories of you / C Jam blues / Misty / Paris mambo / 'Round midnight / Love will find a way / Satin doll / Memories of you (alt. take) / Round midnight / Love will find a way (alt. take)
HEPCD 2021 / Aug '94 / Hep

☐ WHEN LIGHTS ARE LOW (Thompson, Eddie Trio & Roy Williams)
Lamp is low / Keepin' out of mischief now / Never say yes / When lights are low / Don't stop the carnival / I've got the world on a string / Mister Bojangles / Fred / It never entered my mind
HEPCD 2007 / Jan '97 / Hep

Thompson, Eric

☐ ADAM & EVE HAD THE BLUES (Thompson, Eric & Suzy)
ARHCD 5041 / Apr '95 / Arhoolie

Thompson, Gail

☐ JAZZ AFRICA
Long time in Togo / Burkina faso / Kamara river / Expedition / Stressless / Finale
ENJ 90532 / Sep '96 / Enja

Thompson, Gina

☐ NOBODY DOES IT BETTER
Rodalude / Things that you do / Nobody does it better / Can't go another minute / Angel / Freak on / Can't help myself / He'll make a way / Put me on / Into you / Strung out / I can't wait / Things that you do
5320602 / Sep '96 / Mercury Black Vinyl

Thompson, Hank

☐ HANK THOMPSON 1946-1964 (14CD Set) (Thompson, Hank & His Brazos Valley Boys)
Swing wide your gate of love / Whoa sailor / California women / What are we gonna do about the moonlight / Lonely heart knows / Starry eyed Texas gal / Humpty dumpty heart / Today / Don't flirt with me / Rock in the ocean / My heart is a jigsaw puzzle / Yesterday's mail / I find you cheatin' on me / Second hand gal / You broke my heart / Mary had a little lamb / You remembered me / Green light / What are we gonna do about he moonlight / All that goes up must come down / Standing on the outside looking in now / Tomorrow night / My front door is open / Soft lips / Grass looks greener over yonder / She's a girl without any sweetheart / Take a look at this broken heart of mine / Give a little, take a little / Cat has nine lives / Beautiful Texas / Daddy blues / How do you feel / New rovin' gambler / Humpty Dumpty boogie / Can't feel at home in the world anymore / When God calls his children home / If I cry / Broken heart and a glass of beer / Devil in my angels eyes / Playin' possum / Where is your heart tonight / Those things money can't buy / Hangover heart / I ain't cryin' over you / You were the cause / I'll be your sweetheart for a day / Love thief / Teardrops on the tea leaves / Wild side of life / Waiting in the lobby of your heart / Don't make me cry again / Cryin' in the deep blue sea / You're walking on my heart / It's better to have loved a little / How cold hearted can you get / Rub-a-dub-dub / I'd have never found somebody new / Where my sweet baby used to walk / I'll sign my heart away / Yesterday's girl / John Henry / Letter edged in black / Mother the queen of my heart / At the rainbow's edge / When you're lovin', you're livin' / You don't have the nerve / I saw my Mothers name / No help wanted / Go cry your heart out / Wake up, Irene / Fooler / Breakin' the rules / We've gone to far / If lovin' you is wrong / Tears are only rain / Annie over / This train / Little rosewood casket / Gloria / Honky tonk girl / Jersey bounce / Sunrise serenade / Johnson rag / Dardanella / When your love burns low / New deal of love / Baby I need lovin' / I'd do it again / Dusty skies / New green light / Simple Simon / Most of all / Breakin' in another heart / Too in love / String of pearls / Big beaver / Pandhandle rag / Wildwood flower / Honey, honey bee ball / Quicksand / You can give le rag / You can give me back my heart / Don't take it all out on me / Red skin girl / Westphalia waltz / Don't be that way / It makes no difference now / Anybody's girl / Taking my chances / I'm not mad, just hurt / Blackboard of my heart / Across the alley from the Alamo / Weeping willo / Prosperity special / Under the double eagle / You'll be the one / I don't want to know / Someone can steal your love from me / Old Napoleon / I was the first one / Rockin' in the Congo / Hang your head in shame / Gypsy / Don't get around much anymore / I didn't mean to fall in love / Girl in the night / Don't look now / Bubbles in my beer / Headin' down the wrong highway / Lawdy, what a girl / After all the things I've done / Make room in your heart / I wouldn't miss it for the world / Kishamo klingo / Li'l Liza Jane / If I'm not too late / Just and old flame / How do you hold a memory / Beaumont rag / Summit ridge drive / Woodchopper's ball / Bartender's polka / Wednesday's rag / Wednesday waltz / Gold and silver waltz / Skater's waltz / Fifty year ago waltz / La zindo waltz / Anniversary waltz / Let me call you sweetheart / What will I do on Monday / You're going back to your old ways again / I've run out of tomorrows / Shenandoah waltz / Signed, sealed and delivered / In the valley of the moon / Warm red wine / Squaws along the Yukon / Two hearts deep in the blues / Gathering flowers / Little blossom / Deep elem / Rovin' gambler / Cocaine blues / May I sleep in your barn tonight mister / I'll be a bachelor till I die / Three times seven / Bumming round / I left my gal in the mountains / Teach 'em how to swim / Drunkard's blues / Dry bread / Lost John / I guess I'm getting over you / What made her change / Total strangers / Just one step away / Coconut grove / Tuxedo junction / Give the world a smile / Gypsy and the tealeaves / Fooler, a faker / Six pack to go / We will start it all over again / She's just a whole lot like you / There my future goes / Teach me how to lie / It's got to be a habit / It's my fault / I'd like to tell you / I'll be around / Just an old faded photograph / I dreamed of an old love affair / Sing me something sentimental / Paying off the interest with my tears / I keep meeting girl's like you / My old flame / Just a little while / I've convinced everybody but myself / I gotta have my baby back / Oklahoma hills / Hangover tavern / Honky tonk town / I'd look forward to tomorrow / How many teardrops will it take / Drop me gently / That's the recipe for a heartache / Blue skirt waltz / I cast a lonesome shadow / Detour / I don't hurt anymore / Pick me up on your way down / Beer barrel polka / Wabash cannon ball / Then I'll keep on loving you / Shot gun boogie / Back street affair / You nearly lose your mind / Eyes of Texas / More in love your heart is / I wasn't even in the running / Luckiest heartache in town / Whatever happend to Mary / Twice as much / Just to ease the pain / Reaching for the moon / Stirring up the ashes / Paper doll / There's no you / You always hurt the one you love / September in the rain / Til then / That's all there is to that / Don't take it out on me / Just an old flame / Life's sweetest moment / I'm gonna practice freedom / Then I'll start believing in you / In the back of your mind / Here comes Santa Claus / Gonna wrap my heart in ribbons / It's Christmas everyday in Alaska / Santa Claus is coming to town / Blue Christmas / Silver bells / It's Christmas time / I'd like to have an elephant for Christmas / White Christmas / Little Christmas angel / Mr. and Mrs. Snowman / Rudolph the red nosed reindeer / We wish you a merry Christmas / Intro / Honky-tonk girl / I'll step aside / Orange blossom special / Nine pound hammer / Have I told you lately that I love you / Steel guitar rag / Lost highway / Forgive me / Rose city chimes / That's the recipe for heartache / Darling what more can I say / Cincinnati Lou / Deep in the heart of Texas / My heart is a playground / Charmaine / News wears off too fast / Will we start all over again / River road two step / There's a little bit of everything in Texas
BCD 15904 / Jul '96 / Bear Family

☐ HANK THOMPSON AND FRIENDS
CURCD 051 / 9 Mar '98 / Curb

☐ RADIO BROADCASTS 1952 (Thompson, Hank & His Brazos Valley Boys)
FLYCD 948 / Jul '97 / Flyright

☐ SOUNDS OF THE BRAZOS VALLEY
Whoa sailor / Home in San Antone / Boogieoo drag / Green light / Good man is hard to find / Down yonder / Tramp on the street / Crying in the deep blue sea / Farther on down the road / Sagebrush shuffle / That beautiful picture / I ain't cryin' over you / Devil's dream / When God dips his love in your heart / Always late / Grass looks greener over there / Silver bell / Heart full of pain / Piano boogie / Foggy river / Beaumont rag / Easy to please / Uvalde polka / Panhandle rag / This world is not my home / I'll take you to the picture show / Right or wrong / I'll be your sweetheart for a day / Baca's boogie / Broken heart and a glass of beer
RFDCD 19 / Jan '98 / Country Routes

Thompson, Johnny

☐ WAKE UP NOW (Thompson, Johnny Singers)
FA 420 / Apr '97 / Fremeaux

Thompson, Laurence A.

☐ CLASSIC ROMANCE
Le mistral / Rhapsody d'amour / You / My serenade for you / Bachanalia / Golden days / Champagne and bass / I can't help feeling blue / Winds of summer / Something would come of this / Jasmine / Lady is in love with me / Woman of the world / Lullaby to a star / Regency lace / Valley of dreams / Thought you didn't love me / Now all I got is the blues
CDRPM 0038 / 8 Jun '98 / RP Media

Thompson, Linda

☐ DREAMS FLY AWAY
Lonely hearts / Walking on a wire / I live not where I love / Sometimes it happens / For shame of doing wrong / Talking like a man / Sisters / Shay Fan Yan Ley / One clear moment / First light / Pavanne / Many dreams must fly away / I want to see the bright lights tonight / Great Valerio / Insult to injury / Poor boy is taken away / Blackwaterside / Telling me lies / I'm a dreamer / Dimming of the day
HNCD 1379 / Jul '96 / Hannibal

Thompson, Linval

☐ HAVE TO BE SURE
RN 7006 / Sep '96 / Rhino

☐ I LOVE MARIJUANA
I love marijuana / Dread are the controller / Children of the ghetto / Don't push your brother / Begging for apology / Not follow fashion / Roots lady / Big big girl / Just another girl / Starlight / Jamaican calley
CDTRL 151 / Feb '97 / Trojan

☐ LONG LONG DEADLINES
LG 21118 / Aug '96 / Lagoon

☐ LOOK HOW ME SEXY
Are you ready / You're young / Look how me sexy / Call me / Sure of the one you love / Baby mother / I spy / Things couldn't be the same / Holding on to my girlfriend / Lick up the chalice
GRELCD 515 / Aug '95 / Greensleeves

☐ SIX BABYLON
KPTSCD 1 / Mar '97 / Thompson Sound

☐ STRONG LIKE SAMSON
KPSLSCD 1 / Mar '97 / Strong Like Samson

Thompson, Lucky

☐ BEGINNING YEARS, THE
IAJRCCD 1001 / Jun '94 / IAJRC

☐ LORD LORD AM I EVER GONNA KNOW
Lord Lord am I ever gonna know / Love and respect / Say that to say this / Choose your own / Beautiful Tuesday / Warm inside / Our shared blessings / Scratching the surface
CCD 79035 / Mar '97 / Candid

☐ LUCKY MEETS TOMMY (Thompson, Lucky & Tommy Flanagan)
FSRCD 199 / Jan '93 / Fresh Sound

☐ LUCKY STRIKES
In a sentimental mood / Fly with the wind / Midnite oil / Reminiscent / Mumba Neua / I forgot to remember / Prey-loot / Invitation
OJCCD 194 / May '93 / Original Jazz Classics

Thompson, Malachi

☐ 47TH STREET
47th street / Is it not true simply because you cannot believe it / X / CJ's blues / Some freebop for monk / Miyako / African sundance / Discovery the house of jaaz / An elevated cry / Lamentation and the harmony of ya
DE 497 / Nov '97 / Delmark

☐ BUDDY BOLDEN'S RAG (Thompson, Malachi & Africa Brass)
Buddy Bolden's rag / World view / Chaser in Brazil / We bop / Nubian call / Chaser in America / Kojo time / Harold the great / Mouse in the house
DE 481 / Mar '97 / Delmark

☐ JAZZ LIFE, THE
In walked John / My romance / Drown in my own tears / Mystic trumpet man / Croquet ballet / Lucky seven
DD 453 / Mar '97 / Delmark

☐ LIFT EVERY VOICE (Thompson, Malachi & Africa Brass)
Elephantine island / Old man river / Tales of ancient Kemet / Transition / Lift ev'ry voice and sing / Nubian call / Trick of the trip / Nobody knows the trouble I've seen
DE 463 / Mar '97 / Delmark

☐ NEW STANDARDS (Thompson, Malachi Freebop Band)
Joshua / Pinnoccio / Crescent / Resolution / If I only had a brain / We speak / Dyhia Malika / Chicago soundscapes
DE 473 / Mar '97 / Delmark

☐ SPIRIT
Spirit of man / Back to the one / Rising daystar / Dhiya malika / I remember Clifford / Dearly beloved / No more hard times
DD 442 / Mar '97 / Delmark

Thompson, Mayo

☐ CORKY'S DEBT TO HIS FATHER
DC 49 / Dec '96 / Drag City

Thompson, Richard

☐ ACROSS A CROWDED ROOM
When the spell is broken / You don't say / I ain't going to drag my feet no more / Love is a faithless country / Fire in the engine room / Walking through a wasted land / Little blue number / She twists the knife again / Ghosts in the wind
BGOCD 139 / Mar '92 / Beat Goes On

☐ BBC LIVE IN CONCERT
WINCD 034 / May '93 / Windsong

☐ BEAT THE RETREAT (A Tribute To Richard Thompson) (Various Artists)
Shoot the light: *X* / Wall of death: *REM* / When the spell is broken: *Raitt, Bonnie* / Turning of the tide: *Mould, Bob* / For shame of doing wrong: *Straw, Syd & Evan Dando* / Down where the drunkards roll: *Los Lobos* / Beat the retreat: *Tabor, June* / Genesis hall: *Tabor, June* / I misunderstood: *Dinosaur Jr.* / Madness of love: *Parker, Graham* / Just the motion: *Byrne, David* / Valerie: *Beausoleil* / Heart needs a home: *Colvin, Shawn & Loudon Wainwright III* / Dimming of the day: *Five Blind Boys Of Alabama* / Farewell, farewell: *Prior, Maddy* / Great Valerio: *Prior, Maddy*
CDEST 2242 / Feb '95 / EMI

☐ DARING ADVENTURES
Bone through her nose / Valerie / Missie how you let me down / Dead man's handle / Long dead love / Lover's lane / Nearly in love / Jennie / Baby talk / Cash down never never / How will I ever be simple again / Al Bowlly's in heaven
BGOCD 138 / Mar '92 / Beat Goes On

☐ GUITAR/VOCAL
Heart needs a home / Free as a bird / Night comes in / Pitfall/Excursion / Calvary cross / Time will show the wiser / Throw away street puzzle / Mr. Lacey / Ballad of easy rider / Poor Will' and the jolly hangman / Sweet little Rock 'n' roller / Dark end of the street / It'll be me
HNCD 4413 / Mar '89 / Hannibal

☐ HAND OF KINDNESS
Poisoned heart and a twisted memory / Tear stained letter / How I wanted to / Both ends burning / Wrong heartbeat / Hand of kindness / Devonside / Two left feet
HNCD 1313 / Jun '86 / Hannibal

☐ HENRY THE HUMAN FLY
Roll over Vaughan Williams / Nobody's wedding / Poor ditching boy / Shaky Nancy / Angels took my racehorse away / Wheely down / New St George / Painted ladies / Cold feet / Mary and Joseph / Old changing way / Twisted
HNCD 4405 / May '89 / Hannibal

☐ HOKEY POKEY (Thompson, Richard & Linda)
Heart needs a home / Hokey pokey / I'll regret it all in the morning / Smiffy's glass eye / Egypt / Never again / Georgie on a spree / Old man inside a young man / Sun never shines on the poor / Mole in a hole
HNCD 4408 / May '89 / Hannibal

☐ I WANT TO SEE THE BRIGHT LIGHTS TONIGHT (Thompson, Richard & Linda)
When I get to the border / Calvary cross / Withered and died / I want to see the bright lights tonight / Down where the drunkards roll / We sing hallelujah / Has he got a friend for me / Little beggar girl / End of the rainbow / Great Valerio
IMCD 160 / Mar '93 / Island

☐ INDUSTRY (Thompson, Richard & Danny Thompson)
Chorale / Sweetheart on the barricade / Children of the dark / Big chimney / Kitty "quick get up I can hear clogs going up in the street" / Drifting through the days / Lotteryland / Pitfalls / Saboteur / Mew rhythms / Last shift
CDPCS 7383 / May '97 / Parlophone

☐ MIRROR BLUE
For the sake of Mary / I can't wake up to save my life / MGB GT / Way that it shows / Easy there, steady now / King of Bohemia / Shane and Dixie / Brando mumble, Mingus eyes / I ride in your slipstream / Beeswing / Fastfood / Mascara tears / Taking my business elsewhere
CDEST 2207 / Jan '94 / Capitol

☐ POUR DOWN LIKE SILVER (Thompson, Richard & Linda)
Streets of paradise / For shame of doing wrong / Poor boy is taken away / Night comes in / Jet plane is a rocking chair / Beat the retreat / Hard luck stories / Dimming of the day / Dargai
HNCD 4404 / May '88 / Hannibal

☐ SHOOT OUT THE LIGHTS (Thompson, Richard & Linda)
Man in need / Walking on a wire / Don't renage on our love / Just the motion / Shoot out the lights / Backstreet slide / Did she jump or was she pushed / Wall of death
HNCD 1303 / Mar '97 / Hannibal

☐ SMALL TOWN ROMANCE
Heart needs a home / Time to ring some changes / Beat the retreat / Woman or man / For shame of doing wrong / Honky tonk blues / Small town romance / I want to see the bright lights tonight / Down where the drunkards roll / Love is bad for business / Great Valerio / Don't let a thief steal into your heart / Never again / Wrong / Genesis hall / How many times do you have to fall / Roll over Vaughan Williams / Meet on the ledge
HNCD 1316 / Jun '86 / Hannibal
HNCD 1419 / 3 Nov '97 / Hannibal

☐ STRICT TEMPO
Banish misfortune / Dundee hornpipe / Do it for my sake / Rockin' in rhythm / Random jig / Grinder / Will ye no' come back again / Cam o'er the steam Charlie / Ye banks and braes o' bonnie Doon / Rufty tufty / Nonsuch a la mode de France / Andalus / Radio Marrakesh / Knife edge
TSCD 460 / Aug '92 / Topic

☐ SUNNYVISTA (Thompson, Richard & Linda)
Civilization / Borrowed time / Saturday rolling around / You're going to need somebody / Why do you turn your back / Sunnyvista / Lonely heart / Sisters / Justice in the streets / Traces of my love
HNCD 4403 / Oct '92 / Rykodisc

☐ WATCHING THE DARK (The History Of Richard Thompson 1969-1982/3CD Set)
Man in need / Can't win / Waltzing's for dreamers / Crash the party / I still dream / Bird in God's garden/ Lost and found / Now be thankful / Sailor's life / Genesis hall / Knife edge / Walking on a wire / Small town romance / Shepherd's march/Maggie Cameron / Wall of death / For the shame of doing wrong / Back street slide / Strange affair / Wrong heartbeat / Borrowed time / From Galway to Graceland / Tear stained letter / Keep your distance / Bogie's bonnie belle / Poor wee Jockey Clarke / Jet plane is a rocking chair / Dimming of the day / Old man inside a young man / Never again / Hokey pokey / Heart needs a home / Beat the retreat / Al Bowlly's in heaven / Walking through a wasted land / When the spell is broken / Devonside / Little blue number / I ain't going to drag my feet no more / Withered and died / Nobody's wedding / Poor ditching boy / Great valerio / Twisted / Calvary cross / Jennie / Hand of kindness / Two left feet / Shoot out the lights
HNCD 5303 / Apr '93 / Hannibal

☐ YOU ME US
Razor dance / She steers by lightning / Dark hand over my heart / Hide it away / Put it there pal / Business on you / No's not a word / Am I wasting my love on you / Bank vault in heaven / Ghost of you walks / Baby don't know what to do / She cut off her long silken hair / Burns supper / Train don't leave / Cold kisses / Sam Jones / Woods of Darney
CDEST 2282 / Apr '96 / Capitol

Thompson, Sheik

☐ COLOUR OF THE LIGHT (Thompson, Sheik 'Crystaltones')
Rainbow sunshine / On the bed / Colour of the light / London love train / Goodbye baby bye bye baby / River to the bank through the delta to the sea / Beyond the blue / That one / Blues walk/Don't get scared / Opening 'Fathia' the door
CUECD 36251 / Jan '98 / Cue

Thompson, Sir Charles

☐ TAKIN' OFF
DD 450 / Dec '89 / Delmark

Thompson, Sonny

☐ JAM SONNY JAM (Original Miracle & King Masters 1947-1956)
Fish / Jam Sonny jam / Long gone / Screamin' boogie / Creeping (late freight) / Walking / After sundown / I'm coming back home to stay / Harlem rug cutter / Uncle Sam blues / Smokestack blues / Clang clang clang / Flying home / Four thirty in the morning / Kenner cuts one / So-o-o-o good / Things ain't what they used to be / Cotton ball / Gum shoe
NEMCD 900 / Jan '97 / Sequel

Thompson, Tony

☐ SEXSATIONAL
74321276862 / Jul '95 / RCA

Thorazine

☐ VICIOUS CYCLE
HELL 45CD / 16 Mar '98 / Hell Yeah

Thorburn, Billy

☐ DON'T SWEETHEART ME
It's always you / Little steeple pointing to a star / What more can I say / It's foolish but it's fun / If I could paint a memory / Four buddies / I'd never fall in love again / It costs so little / I crossed the gypsy's hand with silver / Don't sweetheart me / Sometimes / My dreams are getting better all the time / I'm all alone / Echo of a serenade / Somebody else is taking my place / Journey to a star / I'll just close my eyes / There's a land of beginning again / There'll come another day / I hear bluebirds / I'll be waiting for you / Until you fall in love / Mem'ry of a rose
RAJCD 843 / Jul '97 / Empress

Thore, Francke

☐ ART OF RUMANIAN PAN FLUTE, THE
CDCH 021 / Feb '91 / Milan

☐ PIPE DREAMS
Mon amour / Greensleeves for pipes / Solvejg's song / Way he makes me feel / Entr'acte / Pipe dreams / Spain / Blue rondo a la Turk / Tretemps nippon / Thais meditation / Carillon / Thorn birds
CDSGP 9009 / Mar '95 / Prestige

Thorn, Paul

☐ HAMMER AND NAIL
Heart with 4 wheel drive / 800 pound Jesus / I bet he knows / Double wide paradise / Sure sign / Every little bit hurts / Heart like mine / Temporarily forever mine / Hammer and nail / Resurrection day
5407142 / Jun '97 / A&M

Thorn, Tracey

☐ DISTANT SHORE, A
Smalltown girl / Simply couldn't care / Seascape / Femme fatale / Dreamy / Plain sailing / New opened eyes / Too happy
CDMRED 35 / Jul '93 / Cherry Red

Thornhill, Claude

☐ CLAUDE THORNHILL & HIS ORCHESTRA
JH 1048 / Jul '96 / Jazz Hour

☐ CLAUDE THORNHILL 1947
Snowfall theme / Robbin's nest / Cabin in the sky / 'deed I do / Happy stranger / Just about this time / Donna lee / Poor little rich girl / Polka dots and moonbeams / I may be wrong / Adios / Sometimes I'm happy / Puttin' and takin' / Sunday drivin' / Anthropology
HCD 108 / Aug '94 / Hindsight

☐ TRANSCRIPTION PERFORMANCE 1984, THE
Poor little rich girl / Adios / Where or when / Spanish dance / Anthropology / Baia / Arab dance / Robbin's nest / Royal garden blues / Polka dots and moonbeams / There's a small hotel / I knew you when / Someone to watch over me / Sometimes I'm happy / I don't know why / April in Paris / Begin the beguine / Godchild / Song is you / La paloma / Lover man / To each his own / Elevation
HEPCD 17 / Oct '94 / Hep

Thornton, Phil

☐ ALIEN ENCOUNTER
CD 428 / 6 Jul '98 / New World

☐ ETERNAL EGYPT
CD 416 / 6 Jul '98 / New World

☐ SHAMAN
CD 293 / 6 Jul '98 / New World

Thornton, Willie Mae

☐ BALL AND CHAIN (Thornton, Willie Mae 'Big Mama' & Lightnin' Hopkins)
ARHCD 305 / Apr '95 / Arhoolie

☐ JAIL (Thornton, Willie Mae 'Big Mama')
Little red rooster / Ball 'n' chain / Jail / Hound dog / Rock me baby / Sherriff O E and me / Oh happy day
VMD 79351 / Oct '95 / Vanguard

☐ ORIGINAL HOUND DOG, THE
Hound dog / Walkin' blues / My man called me / Cotton pickin' blues / Willie Mae's trouble / Big change / I smell a rat / I just can't help myself / They call me Big Mama / Hard times / I ain't no fool either / You don't move me no more / Let your tears fall baby / I've searched the world over / Rock-a-bye baby / How come / Nightmare / Stop a hoppin' on me / Laugh laugh laugh / Just like a dog (barking up the wrong tree) / Fish / Mischievous boogie
CDCHD 940 / Jun '90 / Ace

☐ RISING SUN COLLECTION
RSNCD 002 / Apr '94 / Just A Memory

☐ SASSY MAMA (Thornton, Willie Mae 'Big Mama')
Rolling stone / Lost city / Mr. Cool / Big Mama's new love / Private number / Sassy Mama / Everybody's happy but me
VMD 79354 / Apr '96 / Vanguard

Thorogood, George

☐ BAD TO THE BONE (Thorogood, George & The Destroyers)
Back to Wentsville / Blue highway / Nobody but me / It's a sin / New boogie chillen / Bad to the bone / Miss Luann / As the years go passing by / No particular place to go / Wanted man
BGOCD 94 / Nov '90 / Beat Goes On

☐ BOOGIE PEOPLE (Thorogood, George & The Destroyers)
If you don't start drinkin' (I'm gonna leave) / Long distance lover / Madman blues / Boogie people / Can't be satisfied / No place to go / Six days on the road / Born in Chicago / Oklahoma sweetheart / Hello little girl
BGOCD 250 / Dec '94 / Beat Goes On

☐ BORN TO BE BAD
Shake your moneymaker / You talk too much / Highway 49 / Born to be bad / You can't catch me / I'm ready / Treat her right / I really like girls / Smokestack lightnin' / I'm movin' on
BGOCD 224 / May '94 / Beat Goes On

☐ GEORGE THOROGOOD AND THE DESTROYERS (Thorogood, George & The Destroyers)
ROUCD 3013 / '88 / Rounder

☐ LIVE - LET'S WORK TOGETHER (Thorogood, George & The Destroyers)
No particular place to go / Ride on Josephine / Bad boy / Cocaine blues / If you don't start drinkin' (I'm gonna leave) / I'm ready / I'll change my style / Get a haircut / Gear jammer / Move it on over / You talk to much / Let's work together / St. Louis blues / Johnny B Goode
CDEMC 3718 / Jul '95 / EMI

☐ MAVERICK (Thorogood, George & The Destroyers)
Gear jammer / I drink alone / Willie and the hand jive / What a price / Long gone / Dixie fried / Crawlin' kingsnake / Memphis Marie / Woman with the blues / Go go go / Ballad of Maverick
BGOCD 223 / Jun '94 / Beat Goes On

Thorpe, Billy

☐ CHILDREN OF THE SUN
Children of the sun / We're leaving / We welcome you / Solar anthem / Beginning / Wrapped in the chains of your love / Dream maker / Simple life / Goddess of the night
D 19773 / Oct '97 / Festival

☐ IT'S ALL HAPPENING (Thorpe, Billy & The Aztecs)
4770982 / Oct '97 / Albert

☐ LOCK UP YOUR MOTHERS (3CD Set) (Thorpe, Billy & The Aztecs)
D 80968 / Oct '97 / Festival

Thorpe, Richie

☐ FAIRY TALES CAN COME TRUE
Colombia / Let me be the one / Mi amorcito / Shake your body / Life is a jungle / Falling down / Count on me / Nothing is real / Need you more than life / Turn back the clock / South American girl / Fairy tale
CDRPM 0022 / Oct '97 / RP Media

Those Bastard Souls

☐ 20TH CENTURY CHEMICAL
DRL 011CD / Sep '97 / Darla

Those Darn Accordians

☐ SQUEEZE THIS
FF 70627 / Nov '94 / Flying Fish

Those Magnificent Men

☐ WHAT KIND OF COUNTRY IS THIS
What kind of country is this / Nine miles high / Kissing in the wind / Wrong side of the river / Little baby / Got a thing about you / Looks like rain / It's women thats killing me / I'm smoking again / On the rebound/ Sidesaddle / Call me a fool / This land
WOWCD 06 / May '98 / Way Out West

Those Norwegians

☐ KAMINZKY PARK
Kaminzky park / 39-38-39 / Dom B Sensi / Goulette / Da kingue da mazda / L'hybride fiasco / Molde / Hurdy burdy / Toons / Laika / Da kingue da mazda (S-Charge mix)
PAPCD 001 / 22 Sep '97 / Paper

Those Unknown

☐ THOSE UNKNOWN
GMM 109 / Oct '96 / GMM

Those X-Cleavers

☐ FIRST ALBUM/THE WAITING GAME
OW 29313 / Apr '94 / One Way

Thou

☐ UNE POUPEE POUR M'AMUSER
BRCD 061 / Jul '97 / Brinkman

Thou Shalt Suffer

☐ INTO THE WOODS OF BELIAL
ECLIPSE 007CD / 1 Dec '97 / Nocturnal Art

Thought Industry

☐ OUTER SPACE IS JUST A MARTINI AWAY
398414101CD / Jan '96 / Metal Blade

☐ RECRUITED TO DO GOOD DEEDS FOR THE DEVIL
398414161 CD / 11 May '98 / Metal Blade

Thoumire, Simon

☐ EXHIBIT A (Thoumire, Simon & Fergus MacKenzie)
By the right / Green man / Interaction / Topless / Totally tropical / Experience the real (stop imagining) / Starjumping / Down / Overcast / Art of non-resistance
IRCD 031 / May '95 / Iona

☐ MARCH, STRATHSPEY & SURREAL (Thoumire, Simon Three)
GLCD 1171 / Aug '96 / Green Linnet

☐ WALTZES FOR PLAYBOYS
ARADCD 102 / Mar '94 / Acoustic Radio

Thrall

☐ CHEMICAL WEDDING
VIRUS 189CD / Oct '96 / Alternative Tentacles

Threadbare

☐ FEELING OLDER FASTER
DOG 028CD / Jul '95 / Doghouse

Threadgill, Henry

☐ CARRY THE DAY
Come carry the day / Growing a big banana / Vivjanrondirkski / Between orchids, lillies, blind eyes and cricket / Hyla crucifer... silence of / Jenkins boys again / Wish somebody die / It's hot
4785062 / Apr '95 / Sony Music

☐ MAKIN' A MOVE
Noisy flowers / Like it feels / Official silence / Refined poverty / Make hot and give / Mockingbird sin / Dirty in the right
4811312 / 26 Jan '98 / Sony Jazz

☐ SPIRIT OF NUFF...NUFF
1201342 / May '91 / Black Saint

☐ WHERE'S YOUR CUP (Threadgill, Henry & Make A Move)
100 year old game / Laughing club / Where's your cup / And this / Feels like it / Flew / Go to far
4851392 / Aug '97 / Sony Jazz

Threats

☐ WASTED
GET 23CD / 17 Nov '97 / Get Back

Three

☐ DARK DAYS COMING
DIS 33CD / Jun '97 / Dischord

Three Baritone Saxophone Band

☐ PLAYS MULLIGAN
Line for lions / Blue port / I want to live / Walkin' shoes / Elevation / Black nightgown / Bernie's tune / Festive minor / Theme for Jobim / Five brothers / Lonesome boulevard / Waltz for Gerladus
FDM 365882 / 23 Mar '98 / Dreyfus

Three Blue Teardrops

☐ ONE PART FIRST
Sinner's spiritual / Rough and tumble world / Cadillac Jack / Switchblade pompadour / Wanted man / Red head gal / Ricochet rhythm rockabilly / In my own time / Jenny the generator / Vaporlock / Go, She devil / Rustbelt bop / Claimjumper blues / Another doggone Saturday night
NERCD 075 / Mar '94 / Nervous

Three Chord Wonder

☐ NOTHING MEANS NOTHING ANYMORE
LF 155CD / Sep '95 / Lost & Found

Three Degrees

☐ ALL THE HITS
Woman in love / My simple heart / When will I see you again / Heaven I need / Jump the gun / Get your love back / Dirty old man / Together / Take good care of yourself / Giving up giving in / Runner / TSOP / Long lost lover / Red light / Take me away / Year of decision
308572 / 20 Apr '98 / Hallmark

☐ ALL THE HITS PLUS MORE
Jump the gun / Long lost lover / Red light / Together / Take good care of yourself / Giving up giving in / Year of decision / When will I see you again / Woman in love / Take me away / My simple heart / TSOP / Dirty old man / Runner / Heaven I need / Get your love back
CDSGP 0383 / May '98 / Prestige

☐ BEST OF THE THREE DEGREES, THE
Givin' up givin' in / My simple heart / Golden lady / Runner / Out of love again / Without you / Magic in the air / Jump the gun / Starlight / Falling in love again / Hot summer night / Woman in love / Set me free / Bodycheck / Red light / Dirty old man / I'll never love this way again / When will I see you again
74321452032 / Feb '97 / Camden

☐ BEST OF THE THREE DEGREES, THE (New Recordings Of Their Greatest Hits...And More)
When will I see you again / Take good care of yourself / Woman in love / My simple heart / Dirty ol' man / Take me away / Together / Heaven I need / Runner / Givin' up givin' in / TSOP / Get your love back / Red light / Jump the gun / Long lost lover / Year of decision
ECD 3413 / 14 Apr '98 / K-Tel

☐ COLLECTION OF THEIR 20 GREATEST HITS, A
When will I see you again / Can't you see what you're doing to me / Toast of love / We're all alone / Long lost lover / Get your love back / I like being a woman / What I did for love / Standing up for love / Take good care of yourself / Dirty ol' man / Loving cup a woman needs / TSOP (The sound of Philadelphia) / Another heartache / Distant lover / Together / Here I am / Year of decision / Love train
4631882 / Oct '95 / Columbia

☐ COMPLETE SWAN RECORDINGS, THE
Gee baby (I'm sorry) / Do what you're supposed to do / Let's shindig / You're gonna miss me / How did that happen / Little red riding hood (that's what they call me) / I'm gonna need you / Just right for love / I'll weep for you / Don't (leave me lover) / Someone (who will be true) / Bongo's on the beach / Close your eyes / Gotta draw the line / Mine all mine / Are you satisfied / And in return / Heartbroken memories / Signs of love / Look in my eyes / Drivin' me mad / Maybe / Yours / Tales are true / I wanna be your baby / Love of my life
NEMCD 631 / Nov '92 / Sequel

☐ ROULETTE YEARS, THE
Ebb tide / Trade winds / Maybe / I turn to you / Collage / I won't let you go / I do take you / Through misty eyes / You're the fool / Find my way / Grass will sing for you / Sugar on Sunday / Melting pot / Who is she (and what is she to you) / You're the one / Requiem / Stardust / Isn't it a pity / There's so much love all around me / Shades of green / Lowdown / Macarthur park
NEMCD 753 / Sep '95 / Sequel

☐ THREE DEGREES, THE
Tie u up / Make it easy on yourself / After the night is over / Are you that kind of guy / When will I see you again / Midnight train / Dirty ol' man / Nigal Naminda / TSOP / I'm doin' fine now / I'm going to miss you / I'll be around / Do right woman do right man / Let's get it on
GFS 076 / Jul '97 / Going For A Song

☐ WHEN WILL I SEE YOU AGAIN
HADCD 188 / Nov '95 / Javelin

Three Deuces

☐ KEEP ON IT (Live At The Yardbird Suite)
Keep on it / Face to face / Is that all / Mr. Ed / Down at arts / Boogie on reggae woman
YBR 005 / Jun '97 / Yardbird Suite

Three Dog Night

☐ 20 GREATEST HITS
Try a little tenderness / One / Easy to be hard / Eli's coming / Celebrate / Mama told me not to come / Out in the country / One man band / Joy to the world / Liar / Old fashioned love song / Never been to spain / Family of man / Black and white / Pieces of april / Shambala / Let me serenade you / Show must go on / Sure as I'm sittin' here / Play something sweet (brickyard blues)
MPG 74015 / May '93 / Movieplay Gold

☐ THAT AIN'T THE WAY TO HAVE FUN
Try a little tenderness / One / Easy to be hard / Eli's coming / Celebrate / Mama told me not to come / Out in the country / One man band / Joy to the world / Liar / Old fashioned love song / Never been to Spain / Family of man / Black and white / Pieces of April / Shamballa / Let me serenade you / Show must go on / Sure as I'm sitting / Play something sweet (brickyard blues) / Till the world ends
VSOPCD 211 / Feb '95 / Connoisseur Collection

Three Hour Tour

☐ 1969
PARCD 011 / Dec '97 / Parasol

Three Johns

☐ BEST OF THE THREE JOHNS, THE
DOJOCD 225 / Jul '96 / Dojo

Three Man Army

☐ MAHESHA
REP 4057 / Aug '91 / Repertoire

☐ THIRD OF A LIFETIME, A
REP 4071 / Aug '91 / Repertoire

Three Mile Pilot

☐ ANOTHER DESERT ANOTHER SEA
HED 078CD / 10 Nov '97 / Headhunter

Three O'Clock

☐ SONGS AND NAILS
WB 1153CD / Sep '96 / We Bite

Three Peppers

☐ CLASSICS 1937-1940
CLASSICS 889 / Jul '96 / Classics

Three Sounds

☐ BLACK ORCHID
Black orchid / Foggy day / For alll we know / Oh well oh well / At last / Secret love / Don't go don't go / Saucer eyes / You dig it / Nature boy / Theme from M Squad / Azule serape / For dancers only / Back home / Tadd's delight
8212892 / 19 Jan '98 / Blue Note

☐ STANDARDS
Makin' whoopee / Cry me a river / Witchcraft / Again / Sometimes I'm happy / Saty as sweet as you are / Best things in life are free / Red sails in the sunset / Alone together / Lights out / Thinking of you / Good night ladies
8212812 / 2 Feb '98 / Blue Note

Three Suns

☐ THREE SUNS VOL.1 1949-1957, THE
CCD 075 / Oct '93 / Circle

☐ THREE SUNS VOL.2 1949-1953, THE
CCD 145 / Mar '95 / Circle

Threnody

☐ AS THE HEAVENS FALL
MASSCD 024 / Feb '94 / Massacre

☐ BEWILDERING THOUGHTS
MASSCD 065 / Aug '95 / Massacre

☐ THRENODY
MASSCD 120 / Apr '97 / Massacre

Threshold

☐ EXTINCT INSTINCT
Exposed / Somatography / Eat the unicorn / Forever / Virtual isolation / Whispering / Lake of despond / Clear / Life flow / Somatography
GEPCD 1019 / Mar '97 / Giant Electric Pea

☐ LIVEDELICA
GEPCD 1015 / Jun '95 / Giant Electric Pea

☐ PSYCHEDELICATESSEN
Sunseeker / Into the light / Under the sun / He is I am / Devoted / Tension of souls / Will to give / Babylon rising / Innocent
GEPCD 1014 / Feb '95 / Giant Electric Pea

☐ WOUNDED LAND
Consume to live / Days of dearth / Sanity's end / Paradox / Surface of air / Mother earth / Siege of Baghdad / Keep it with mine
GEPCD 1005 / Aug '93 / Giant Electric Pea

Thriller U

☐ BEST OF ME, THE
Groove my mind / Right time / Best of me / Missing you / Ebony eyes / Masterpiece / Why do I believe / Everything to me / Take this love / Moving on / Ebony eyes
WRCD 006 / Nov '97 / World

☐ LOVE RULE
VPCD 1439 / Oct '95 / VP

☐ THRILLER U & SANCHEZ (Thriller U & Sanchez)
RFCD 005 / Nov '96 / Record Factory

Thrillhammer

☐ GIFTLESS
Pretty dead girl / Suffocation time / Bad trip / Laughing / Happy anniversary / Motor / Bleed / Magret / Dread / Alice's place / Jinx / Bride
RTD 15714012 / Apr '93 / World Service

Throbbin Hoods

☐ AMBUSH
BMCD 076 / Jun '95 / Raw Energy

Throbbing Gristle

☐ 20 JAZZ FUNK GREATS
20 jazz funk greats / Beachy head / Still walking / Tanith / Convincing people / Exotica / Hot on the heels of love / Persuasion / Walkabout / What a day / Six six sixties / Discipline (berlin) / Discipline (manchester)
TGCD 4 / Apr '93 / Grey Area

☐ ASSUMING POWER FOCUS
PA 016CD / Jan '97 / Paragoric
TX 60010CD / 27 Apr '98 / Triple XXX

☐ BLOOD PRESSURE
DCD 9048 / Jan '97 / Dossier

☐ DOA - THIRD AND FINAL REPORT
I.b.m. / Hit by a rock / United / Valley of the shadow of death / Dead on arrival / Weeping / Hamburger lady / Hometime / Ab\7a / E-coli / Death threats / Walls of sound / Blood on the floor / Five knuckle shuffle / We hate you (little girls)
TGCD 3 / Apr '93 / Grey Area

☐ FUNK BEYOND JAZZ
EFA 08450CD / Nov '93 / Dossier

☐ GIFTGAS
DCD 9058 / Jan '97 / Dossier

☐ GRIEF
CDTG 24 / Oct '96 / NMC

☐ HEATHEN EARTH
Rhythms / Vocals and echo effects / Bass guitar / Cornet, tape / Cornet, lead guitar / Synthesisers / Binaural left / Binaural right
TGCD 5 / Apr '93 / Grey Area

☐ JOURNEY THROUGH A BODY
TGCD 8 / Oct '93 / Grey Area

☐ KREEME HORN
EFA 08490CD / 26 Aug '97 / Dossier

☐ LIVE VOL.1
TGCD 10 / Apr '93 / Grey Area

☐ LIVE VOL.2
TGCD 11 / Apr '93 / Grey Area

☐ LIVE VOL.3
TGCD 12 / Apr '93 / Grey Area

☐ LIVE VOL.4
TGCD 13 / Apr '93 / Grey Area

☐ MISSION OF DEAD SOULS
Dead souls / Guts on the floor / Circle of animals / Looking for the oto / Vision and voice / Funeral rites / Spirits flying / Persuasion u.s.a. / Process / Discipline (reprise) / Distant dreams (part two) / Something came over me
TGCD 6 / Apr '93 / Grey Area

☐ ONCE UPON A TIME
OBESSCD 2 / Oct '94 / Jungle

☐ SECOND ANNUAL REPORT
Industrial introduction / Slug bait (ica) / Slug bait - live at southampton / Slug bait - live at brighton / Maggot death (studio) / Maggot death - live at rat club / Maggot death - live at southampton / Maggot death - live at brighton / After cease to exist / Zyclon b zombie / United
TGCD 2 / Apr '93 / Grey Area

☐ THROBBING GRISTLE
TGCD 1 / '88 / Mute

☐ VERY FRIENDLY
CDTG 23 / Oct '96 / NMC

Throne Of Ahaz

☐ NIFELHEIM
NFR 008 / Oct '94 / No Fashion

☐ ON TWILIGHT ENTHRONED
NFR 016 / Jan '97 / No Fashion

Throneberry

☐ SQUINTING BEFORE THE DAZZLE
Squint before the dazzle / Summerschool / Let's hear it for decay / Guerilla skies / Shepherd song / Stolen / Down at the foundry / Shut up / Isn't it a pity / Quinnipac / See me off
A 1190 / 10 Aug '98 / Alias

Thrones

☐ ALRAUNE
COMM 42 / Dec '96 / Communion

Throw

☐ INVISIBLE DAYLIGHT
BUZ 010 / Feb '97 / Buzz

Throw That Beat In The Garbage Can

☐ LARGE MARGE SENT US
SGCD 1 / Sep '97 / September Gurls

Throwing Muses

☐ CURSE, THE
Manic depression / Counting backwards / Fish / Hate my way / Furious / Devil's roof / Snailhead / Firepile / Finished / Take / Say goodbye / Mania / Two step / Delicate cutters / Cotton mouth / Pearl / Vic / Bea
TAD 2019CD / Nov '92 / 4AD

☐ HOUSE TORNADO
Colder / Mexican women / River / Juno / Marriage tree / Run letter / Saving grace / Drive / Downtown / Giant / Walking in the dark / Garoux des larmes / Pools in eyes / Feeling / Soap and water / And a she-wolf after the war / You cage
CAD 802CD / Mar '88 / 4AD

☐ HUNKPAPA
Devil's roof / Dizzy / Dragonhead / Fall down / Angel / Burrow / Bea / No parachutes / Say goodbye / I'm alive / Mania / Take / Santa Claus
CAD 901CD / Jan '89 / 4AD

☐ LIMBO
Buzz / Ruthie's knocking / Freeloader / Field / Limbo / Tar kisser / Tango / Serene / Mr. Bones / Night driving / Cowbirds / Shark
CAD 6014CD / Aug '96 / 4AD

☐ REAL RAMONA, THE
Counting backwards / Him dancing / Red shoes / Graffiti / Golden thing / Ellen West / Dylan / Hook in her head / Not too soon / Honeychain / Say goodbye / Two step
CAD 1002CD / Feb '91 / 4AD

☐ RED HEAVEN
Furious / Firepile / Dio / Dirty water / Stroll / Pearl / Summer St. / Vic / Backroad / Visit / Dovey / Rosetta stone / Carnival wig
CAD 2013CD / Aug '92 / 4AD

☐ THROWING MUSES
Call me / Green / Hate my way / Vicky's box / Rabbits dying / America (she can't say no) / Fear / Stand up / Soul soldier / Delicate cutters
CAD 607CD / Nov '86 / 4AD

☐ UNIVERSITY
Bright yellow gun / Start / Hazing / Shimmer / Calm down, come down / Crabtown / No way in hell / Surf cowboy / That's all you wanted / Teller / University / Snakeface / Flood / Fever few
CADD 5002CD
CAD 5002CD / Jan '95 / 4AD

Thrown Ups

☐ SEVEN YEARS GOLDEN
AMREP 0552 / 24 Nov '97 / Amphetamine Reptile

Thulbion

☐ TWILIGHT BOUND
King's reel/The perfect host/Boys of portaferry/Trad reel / Twilight / St. Gilbert's hornpipe/The fiddler's wife/Chromatic hornpipe / Annie / John D Burgess/ Major Nickerson's fancy/Dick Gossip's reel / James F Dickie/JF Dickie's delight / Sheilis / Branden's centennial waltz / Waltz for Mary Ann / Raemona / Gravel walk / Andy Renwick's ferret / Old mountain road / Time for thought / Theodore Napier / Laird of Mackintosh / Earl of Lauderdale / Little daisy / North king street / Lady on the island / Killavil reel / Far from home / Paddy on the turnpike / Loretta / Frank and Maureen Robb / Grew's hill / Duncan Black's hornpipe / Doon hingin' tie / Eeles' dream
CDTRAX 088 / Jan '95 / Greentrax

Thule

☐ 321 NORMAL 2
While it lasts / Dynamo / Idiomatic / Murderball / Let it ring / Three legged race / 4/5 of 5/8 of F/A / King's English / Park keeper / Split / We is you AM / Skyscraper
CLAYCD 114 / Nov '92 / Clay

Thum, Pam

☐ BELIEVE
It's OK to cry / For the future of the world / Lazarus generation / Stand by the cross / I believe / As the angels sang / Down to the river / Victory in me / Age of faith
8441844532 / Oct '97 / Benson

Thum, Rick

☐ HAMMERED FIDDLE TUNES
RTA 2001CD / Mar '98 / RT Audio

☐ REASON TO DANCE
RTA 2002CD / Mar '98 / RT Audio

Thumbnail

☐ RED DEAD
HED 064CD / Feb '97 / Headhunter

Thumper

☐ HELLFIRE AND DAMNATION
ELM 022CD / 2 Mar '98 / Elevator

☐ NO ONE LEFT THE DISCO ALIVE
ELM 003CD / 2 Mar '98 / Elevator

Thunder

☐ BEHIND CLOSED DOORS
Moth to the flame / Fly on the wall / I'll be waiting / River of pain / Future train / Till the river runs dry / Stand up / Preaching from a chair / Castles in the sand / Too scared to live / Ball and chain / It happened in this town
CDEMD 1076 / Jan '95 / EMI

☐ LAUGHING ON JUDGEMENT DAY
Does it feel like love / Everybody wants her / Low life in high places / Laughing on judgement day / Empty city / Today the world stopped turning / Long way from home / Fire to ice / Feeding the flame / Better man / Moment of truth / Flawed to perfection / Like a satellite / Baby I'll be gone
CDEMD 1035 / Feb '94 / EMI

☐ LIVE (2CD Set)
EDGCD 016 / 16 Feb '98 / Eagle

☐ THEIR FINEST HOUR (AND A BIT)
Dirty love / River of pain / Love walked in / Everybody wants her / In a broken dream / Higher ground / Backstreet symphony / Better man / Gimme shelter / Like a satellite / Low life in high places / Stand up / Once in a lifetime / Gimme some lovin' / Castles in the sand / She's so fine
CDEMD 1086 / Sep '95 / EMI

☐ THRILL OF IT ALL, THE
Pilot of my dreams / Living for today / Love worth dying for / Don't wait up for me / Something about you / Welcome to the party / Thrill of it all / Hotter than the sun / This forgotten town / Cosmetic punk / You can't live your life
RAWCD 115
RAWPD 115 / Feb '97 / Raw Power

Thunderballs

☐ SUMMER HOLIDAY
SSHD 2 / Jul '94 / Hush

Thunderclap Newman

☐ HOLLYWOOD DREAM
REP 4065 / Aug '91 / Repertoire

Thunderdome

☐ CHAPTER XXI (2CD Set)
TDCD 99023 / 10 Jun '98 / Thunderdome

Thundermother

☐ NO RED ROWAN
KSG 003 / Jun '97 / Kissing Spell

Thunders, Johnny

☐ BELFAST ROCKS
Pipeline / Countdown love / Personality crisis / Little bit of whore / MIA / Too much junkie biz / Talk about you / Chinese rocks / Copy cat / In cold blood / Alone in a crowd / Eve of destruction / You can't put your arms / Sad vacation / Born to lose / Stepping stone / Pipeline / Chinese rock / Chinese rocks
CDMGRAM 117 / 20 Oct '97 / Anagram

☐ BOOTLEGGING THE BOOTLEGGERS
You can't put your arms around a memory / Personality crisis / Sad vacation / I can tell / Little queenie / Stepping stone / As tears go by
FREUDCD 30 / Jan '90 / Jungle

☐ COPY CATS (Thunders, Johnny & Patti Palladin)
FREUDCD 20 / Jun '88 / Jungle

☐ DAWN OF THE DOLLS
CD 0001 / 1 May '98 / Fab

☐ DTK (Thunders, Johnny & The Heartbreakers)
FREUDCD 4 / Oct '94 / Jungle

☐ HAVE FAITH (Live In Japan 1988)
Pipeline / Blame it on mom / Personality crisis / I can tell / Who do you love / Spoonful / Joey Joey / You can't put your arms around a memory / Play with five / I only wrote this song for you / Too much junkie business / Chinese rocks / Born to lose
ESMCD 453 / Nov '96 / Essential
800052 / Aug '97 / Mutiny

☐ HURT ME
Sad vacation / Eve of destruction / Too much too soon / Joey Joey / I'm a boy I'm a girl / Go back to go / I like to play games / Hurt me / Illagitammate song of Segovia / It ain't me babe / Diary of a lover / I'd rather be with the boys / You can't put your arms around a memory / She's so untouchable / Ask me no questions / She's so strange / Lonely planet boy / Mia / Cosa nostra
ESMCD 588 / Aug '97 / Essential

☐ I ONLY PLAY ROCK 'N' ROLL FOR KIDS (A Tribute To Johnny Thunders) (Various Artists)
622532 / 23 Feb '98 / Skydog

☐ I ONLY WROTE THIS SONG FOR YOU (A Tribute To Johnny Thunders) (Various Artists)
Leave me alone: *Palladin, Patti* / Disappointed in you: *Monroe, Michael* / In cold blood: *Kane, Arthur* / Children are people too: *Kramer, Wayne* / Some hearts: *Johansen, David* / Society makes me sad: *Sylvian Sylvian* / Just another girl: *Gordy, Alison* / Can't kick: *Filthy Lucre* / You can't put your arms around a memory: *De Ville, Willy* / Diary of a lover: *Die Toten Hosen* / I love you: *Ramones* / Let go: *Lure, Walter & The Waldoes* / So alone: *Monroe, Michael* / Help the homeless: *Screwballs* / Alone in a crowd: *Los Lobos*
ESMCD 401 / Jan '97 / Essential

☐ IN COLD BLOOD
In cold blood / Just another girl / Green onions / Diary of a lover / Look in my eyes / Intro/Just another girl / Too much junkiebusiness / Sad vacation / Louie Louie / Gloria / Treat me like a nigger / Do you love me / Green onions / Commandments
ESMCD 589 / Aug '97 / Essential

☐ LAMF (The Lost '77 Mixes) (Thunders, Johnny & The Heartbreakers)
FREUDCD 44 / Sep '96 / Jungle

☐ LIVE
Pipeline / Countdown live / Personality crisis / Little bit of whore / MIA / Stepping stone / So alone / Endless party / Copy cats (live) / Don't mess with cupid / Born to lose / Too much junkie business (live) / Chinese rocks / Pills
CDGRAM 70 / Mar '96 / Anagram

☐ LIVE AT MAX'S KANSAS CITY (Thunders, Johnny & The Heartbreakers)
Milk me / Chinese rocks / Get off the phone / London / Take a chance / One track mind / All by myself / Let go / I love you / Can't keep my eyes on you / I wanna be loved / Do you love me
RUSCD 8219 / Feb '96 / ROIR

☐ LIVE AT MOTHERS (Thunders, Johnny & The Heartbreakers)
422168 / May '94 / New Rose
422390 / Feb '97 / Last Call

☐ QUE SERA SERA
FREUDCD 49 / Nov '94 / Jungle

☐ STATIONS OF THE CROSS
Wipeout / In cold blood / Just another girl / Too much junkie business / Sad vacation / Who needs girls / Do you love me / So alone / Seven day weekend / Chinese rocks / Re-entry interlude / Voodoo dub / Surfer jam / Just because I'm white / One track mind (dub) / Little London boys / Stepping stone / I don't mind Mr. Kowalski / Creature from ET rap / Rather be with the boys
RE 146CD / Nov '94 / ROIR

☐ STUDIO BOOTLEGS, THE
DOJOCD 231 / May '96 / Dojo

☐ TOO MUCH JUNKIE BUSINESS
RE 118CD / Nov '94 / ROIR

Thundersteel

☐ THUNDERSTEEL
BMCD 53 / Aug '94 / Black Mark

Thuresson, Svante

☐ LIVE
SITCD 9203 / Aug '94 / Sittel

Thurston, Bobby

☐ YOU GOT WHAT IT TAKES/THE MAIN ATTRACTION
You got what it takes / I wanna do it with you / Check out the groove / I want your body / Sittin' in the park / Is something wrong with you / Main attraction / Love makes it complete / Keep it going / I know you feel like I feel / Very last drop / I really didn't mean it / Life is what you make it
DEEPM 026 / Apr '97 / Deep Beats

Thus Defiled

☐ WINGS OF THE NIGHTSTORM
To yearn that which shall be / Rapture of twilight burning / (Angelblood) Tears of an age now dead / Through eyes of fire / Illumination through darkness / Winter's dawn / Empire of souls bleeding / On ravenwings I fly / Final fall of the light
DTP 003CD / 20 Apr '98 / Dark Trinity

Thy Serpent

☐ CHRISTCRUSHER
Chambers of the shalwatcher / Curtain of treachery / Thou bade nothingness / So free are the wolves / Circle of pain / Christcrusher / Crystalcrusher / Crystalmoors / Calm blinking
SPI 56CD / 25 May '98 / Spinefarm

☐ FORESTS OF WITCHERY
Flowers of witchery abloom / Of darkness and light / Traveller of unknown plains / Only dust moves... / Like a funeral veil of melancholy / Wine from tears
SPI 36CD / 17 Nov '97 / Spinefarm

☐ LORDS OF TWILIGHT
SP 1042CD / 1 Sep '97 / Spinefarm

☐ THY SERPENT
SPI 036CD / Sep '96 / Spinefarm

Ti Jaz

☐ EN CONCERT
Y225027 / Jun '93 / Silex

☐ MUSIQUE BRETONNE AUJOURD 'HUI
Y 225027CD / Aug '93 / Silex

☐ MUSIQUES DE BASSE BRETAGNE
MWCD 4005 / Jul '94 / Music & Words

☐ REVES SAUVAGES
CD 834 / May '93 / Diffusion Breizh

Tia

☐ TIA
ICHI 11872 / Jul '96 / Ichiban

☐ TIA'S SIMCHA SONGS
GV 167CD / May '94 / Global Village

Tiajin Buddhist Music Ensemble

☐ BUDDHIST MUSIC OF TIANJIN
NI 5416 / Mar '95 / Nimbus

Tiamat

☐ ASTRAL SLEEP, THE
CM 97222 / Sep '94 / Century Media

☐ DEEPER KIND OF SLUMBER
CM 77180 / Apr '97 / Century Media

☐ SLEEPING BEAUTY, THE (Remix)
CM 770652 / May '94 / Century Media

☐ WILDHONEY
CM 77080CD / Oct '94 / Century Media

Tibbett, Lawrence

☐ SONG IS YOU, THE
I got plenty o' nuttin' / Song is you / And love was born / Without a song / Life is a dream / Rogue song / Narrative / When I'm looking at you / White dove / Oh that we two were maying / Thy beaming eyes / Tramps at sea / Cuban love song / Want you / Love come back to me / On the road to mandalay / Myself when young / A kingdom by the sea / Goin' home / My own united states / Battle hymn of the republic
CDMOIR 427 / Apr '95 / Memoir

Tibbetts, Steve

☐ BIG MAP IDEA
Black mountain side / Black year / Big idea / Wish / Station / Start / Mile 234 / 100 moons / Wait / Three letters
8392532 / Oct '89 / ECM

☐ EXPLODED VIEW
Name everything / Another year / Clear day / Your cat / Forget / Drawing down the moon / X festival / Metal summer / Assembly field
8311092 / Jan '87 / ECM

☐ FALL OF US ALL, THE
Dzogchen punks / Full moon dogs / Nyemma / Formless / Roam and spy / Hellbound train / All for nothing / Fade away / Drinking lesson / Burnt offering / Travel alone
5211442 / Apr '94 / ECM

☐ NORTHERN SONG
Form walking / Big wind / Aerial view / Nine doors, breathing space
8293782 / Oct '89 / ECM

☐ SAFE JOURNEY
Test / Climbing / Running / Night again / My last chance / Vision / Any minute / Mission / Burning up / Going somewhere
8174382 / Oct '89 / ECM

☐ YR
UR / Sphexes / Ten years / One day / Three primates / You and it / Alien lounge / Ten year dance
8352452 / Aug '88 / ECM

Tibet, David

☐ MUSICAL PUMPKIN COTTAGE (Tibet, David & Steven Stapleton)
UDORCD 1 / Oct '96 / United Durtro

☐ SADNESS OF THINGS, THE (Tibet, David & Steven Stapleton)
UD 037CD / Oct '96 / United Dairies

Tibetan Dixie

☐ NOTHING TOO SERIOUS
LRJ 263 / Oct '93 / Larrikin

Tibetan Institute Of Performing Arts

☐ DHAMA SUNA (Music Of Tibet)
0630190642 / 13 Oct '97 / Erato

Tickell, Kathryn

☐ BORDERLANDS
Mary the maid / David's hornpipe / Sidlaw Hills / Brafferton Village / Stellgreen / Loch rannoch / Gypsy's lullaby / Flowers of the forest / Alston flower show / Claudio's Polka / Tents hornpipe / Walker / Lord Gordon's reel / Robson / Roly gentle / Troy's wedding / Tartar frigate / Wark football team
CROCD 210 / Feb '89 / Black Crow

☐ COMMON GROUND
Walsh's hornpipe / Dorrington lads / Richard Moscrop's waltzes / Another knight / Mrs. Bolowski's / Neil Gow's lament / Andrew Knight's favourite / Shining pool / Outclassed / Glen Aln / Bill Charlton's fancy / Fenham / Catch a penny fox / Bowmont water / Geoff Heslop's reel / New rigged ship / Remember me / Rafferty's reel / Wild hills o' Wannies
CROCD 220 / Feb '89 / Black Crow

☐ GATHERING, THE
Raincheck / Lads of Alnwick / Sunderland lasses / Peacocks march / Redesdale / La bettaille dans le petit arbre acharavi waltz / Gathering / Kates house / Real blues reel / St. Kilda wedding pjotr / Green brechans O'Branton / I saw my love / Tune for Matt Robson / Kathleen / Mr Nelson's birthday waltz
PRKCD 39 / Mar '97 / Park

☐ KATHRYN TICKELL BAND
Holey ha'penny-tyne bridge hornpipe / Peacock followed the hen / Drop dead waltz-franklin river reel / Desperation / Nancy's waltz-200th birthday jig / Floating from skerry / Dargai-jockey stays long at the fair / Otterburn
CROCD 227 / Jun '91 / Black Crow

☐ NORTHUMBERLAND COLLECTION, THE
Rothbury hills / Old Morpeth rant/Morpeth rant/ Hesleyside reel / Felton lonnen / Whittingham green lane / Robin spraggon's old grey mare / Stagshaw bank fair/Shew's the way to Wallington/Mike to ride / Sir John Fenwick's the flower amang them / Sir Sidney Smith's march / Lindisfarne / Bonny at morn / Otterburn / Breamish/Warksburn/Elsey's waltz / Sair Fyel's hinny / Jockey lay up in the hayloft/ Bellingham boat / Northumberland air / Fareweel Regality
PRKCD 42 / 26 Jan '98 / Park

☐ NORTHUMBRIAN SMALL PIPES & FIDDLE
Joan's jig / Cut the file / Sweet hesleyside / Hesleyside reel / Skate / Beeswing / Ronell's reel / Bob thompson's crooked bawbee / J.b. milne / Carrick hornpipe / Peacock followed the hen / Da slockit light / Kielder jock / Matt's the stage / Jean's reel / Johnny cope / Tipsy sailor / Border spirit / A.b. hornpipe / Billy pigg's hornpipe
CDSDL 343 / Oct '92 / Saydisc

☐ SIGNS
CROCD 230 / Mar '94 / Black Crow

Tickell, Mike

☐ WARKSBURN (Tickell, Mike/Kathryn Tickell/Martin Simpson)
CROCD 229 / Dec '94 / Black Crow

Tickled Pink

☐ TICKLED PINK
PINK 9301CD / Jan '94 / Pink Kitten

Tickmayer Formatio

☐ WILHELM DANCES
RERTFCD / Oct '96 / ReR/ Recommended

Tied & Tickled Trio

☐ TIED & TICKLED TRIO, THE
PAYKS / Oct '97 / Payola/Kollaps

Tielman Brothers

☐ DIE SINGLES
Tahiti jungle / Fern am Amazonas / Java guitars / Warum wenst du, kleine Tamara / Little Hans'chen twist / Twistin' the Carioca / Hello Caterina / Say you are mine / No one but you / You are the one / Little lovely lady / Warte ab darling Rosmarie / Maria / I wonder / White Christmas / Exodus / Marabunta / Real love / Michelle / Du gehst voruber / Wanderer ohne Ziel / Viel zu spat / You've got too much going / Can't help falling in love
BCD 15918 / May '96 / Bear Family

Tieng Hat Que Huong Instrumental Ensemble

☐ FROM SAIGON TO HANOI
74321301092 / May '96 / Milan

Tiere Der Nacht

☐ EVERGREENS
CTCD 069 / 15 Dec '97 / Captain Trip

☐ HOT STUFF
CTCD 073 / 15 Dec '97 / Captain Trip

☐ WOLPERTINGER
CTCD 074 / 15 Dec '97 / Captain Trip

Tiermes

☐ TIERMES
SGA 011CD / Nov '96 / Misanthropy

Tierra Caliente

☐ MESTIZA
MWCD 3005 / Aug '94 / Music & Words

Tiger

☐ BAM BAM
Bam bam / Do it anyway / Rough and cool / Top the chart / Decent man / Carbon copy / Presto / Tiger don / Dreadie and baldhead / Nominee
RASCD 3042 / Sep '88 / Ras

☐ LOVE AFFAIR
RRTGCD 7787 / Jul '90 / Rohit

☐ ME NAME TIGER
RASCD 3021 / '88 / Ras

☐ RAM DANCEHALL
Get in a temper / Dig a hole / Save yu money / Jump up / Hide and seek / Ram dance hall / Jungle move / O.k. kids / Rock with me / Ride mi ninja
VPCD 1052 / '89 / VP

☐ RAS PORTRAITS
No wanga gut / Bam bam / Puppy love / Don't be greedy / Decent man / Rough and cool / Me name tiger / Tiger talking / Dreadie and baldhead / Do it anyway
RAS 3315 / Jul '97 / Ras

Tiger

☐ WE ARE PUPPETS
My puppet pal / Shamed all over / Race / Bollinger farm / Storm injector / Depot / On the rose / Sorry monkeys / Cateader reddle / She's ok / Ray Travey / Keep in touch
TRDCD 1002 / Nov '96 / Trade 2

Tiger B. Smith

☐ TIGER B. SMITH
SB 036 / Jun '97 / Second Battle

Tiger Lillies

☐ BIRTHS, DEATHS & MARRIAGES
Beatman / Hell / Normal / Heroin and cocaine / Prison house blues / Jackie / Despite / Autumn leaves / Lager lout / Open your legs / Down and out / Tears / Her room / Flowers / War / Obscene / You're world / Sense of sentiment / Wake up / Repulsion / Sodsville / Bones / Circle line / Haunting me / Lili Marlene
TIGER 1 / Jul '94 / Gee Street

Tiger Moth

☐ MOTHBALLS
OMM 2012CD / Aug '96 / Omnium

Tigerlilies USA

☐ SPACE AGE LOVE SONGS
ALP 307
TRUCK 07CD / Jun '97 / Truckstop

Tigertailz

☐ TIGERTAILZ LIVE IN CONCERT
MIN 06CD / Oct '96 / Minority/One

☐ YOUNG AND CRAZY
Star attraction / Hollywood killer / Living without you / Shameless / City kids / Shoot to kill / Turn me on / She's too hot / Young and crazy / Fall in love again
CDMFN 78 / Aug '89 / Music For Nations

Tight Fit

☐ BACK TO THE 60'S (60 Non Stop Dancing Hits)

Dancing in the street / I like it / (I can't get no) satisfaction / You really got me / All day and all of the night / Do wah diddy diddy / Pretty flamingo / Black is black / Bend me, shape me / High in the sky / Mr. tambourine man / Oh pretty woman / Proud mary / Letter / Baby let me take you home / Mony mony / Baby come back / How do you do it / Tossin' and turnin' / Let's hang on / Hippy hippy shake / Sherry / Stay / Big girls don't cry / Walk like a man / Rag doll / Dawn / Yes I will / Just one look / Here I go again / I'm alive / There's a kind of hush / No milk today / A must to avoid / Hold tight / Legend of xanadu / Sweets for my sweet / Sugar and spice / Needles and pins / When you walk in the room

CDMFP 6075 / Aug '89 / Music For Pleasure

☐ BEST OF TIGHT FIT, THE

Lion sleeps tonight / Dancing in the street/I can't get no satisfaction/really got / Do wah diddy diddy / Black is black / Bend me shape me / When you walk in the room / Mony mony / Fantasy island / Lovers concerto / Secret heart / I'm undecided / Just a moment away / Heart of stone break hearts of glass / Love the one you're with / One two three / One thing leads to another / Magic eyes / Baby I'm lost for words / Let's hang on / Sherry / Big girls don't cry / Walk like a man / Rag doll / Dawn (go away) / Yes I will / Stay / Just one look / Here I go again / I'm alive / There's a kind of hush (all over the world) / No milk today / Must to avoid / Hold tight / Legend of xanadu / Sweets for my sweet / Sugar and spice / When you walk in the room / Needles and pins

EMPRCD 570 / May '95 / Emporio

Tikaram, Tanita

☐ ANCIENT HEART

Good tradition / Cathedral song / Sighing Innocents / I love you / World outside your window / For all these years / Twist in my sobriety / Poor cow / He likes the sun / Valentine heart / Preyed upon

2438772 / Feb '95 / WEA

☐ BEST OF TANITA TIKARAM, THE

Good tradition / My love tonight / Happy taxi / I might be crying / Love don't need no tyranny / Men women / Trouble / You make the whole world cry / Only the ones we love / I think of you - e penso a te / Twist in my sobriety / Wonderful shadow / Lovers in the city / World outside your window / Twist in my sobriety / Cathedral song / Little sister leaving town

0630151062 / Sep '96 / East West

☐ CAPPUCCINO SONGS, THE

MUMCD 9801 / 7 Sep '98 / Mother

☐ EVERYBODY'S ANGEL

Only the ones we love / Deliver me / This story in me / To wish this / Mud in any water / Sunface / Never known / This stranger / Swear by me / Hot pork sandwiches / Me in mind / Sometime with me / I love the heaven's solo / I'm going home

9031733412 / Feb '91 / East West

☐ LOVERS IN THE CITY

I might be crying / Feeding the witches / My love tonight / Yodelling song / Lovers in the city / Leaving the party / Women who cheat on the world / Wonderful shadow / Happy taxi / Bloodlines

4509988042 / Dec '96 / East West

☐ SWEET KEEPER

Once and not speak / It all come back today / Sunset's arrived / I owe all to you / Harm in your hands / Thursday's child / We almost got it together / Little sister leaving town / Love story

9031708002 / '89 / East West

Tiki Tones

☐ SUBURBAN SAVAGES

ID 123348CD / Aug '97 / Dionysus

Til, Sonny

☐ SOLO FEATURING EDNA MCGRIFF

My prayer / I never knew (I could love anybody) / Fool's world / You never cared for me / For all we know / Blame it on yourself / Proud of you / No other love / Night has come / I only have eyes for you: *Til, Sonny & Edna McGriff* / Once in a while: *Til, Sonny & Edna McGriff* / Good: *Til, Sonny & Edna McGriff* / Pick-a-dilly: *Til, Sonny & Edna McGriff* / That's how I feel without you: *Til, Sonny & Edna McGriff* / Lovebirds: *Til, Sonny & Edna McGriff* / Congratulations to someone / (Danger) Soft shoulders / Have you heard / Lonely wine / Come on home / First of Summer / Panama Joe / Night and day / Shimmy time / So long

NEMCD 737 / Mar '95 / Sequel

Til Tuesday

☐ COMING UP CLOSE: A RETROSPECTIVE

Love in a vacuum / I could get used to this / Voices carry / You know the rest / No one is watching you now / On Sunday / Coming up close / Will she just fall down / David denies / What about love / Why must I / Other end of the telescope / J for Jules / (Believed you were) Lucky / Limits to love / Long gone buddy / Do it again

4851132 / Oct '96 / Epic

Tilbury, John

☐ DAVE SMITH'S FIRST PIANO CONCERT

MR 14 / '90 / Matchless

Tiles

☐ FENCE THE CLEAR

SPV 08528528512 / May '98 / SPV

Tilja

☐ TILJA

AMCD 734 / Aug '97 / Amigo

Tillery, Linda

☐ GOOD TIME A GOOD TIME

Hammer ring / Tampin' ties / Rock Island line / Boll weevil blues / How long watchman / Moses Moses / Yemaya / Another man done gone / Old lady come from Booster / Let's go huntin' / Fix me Jesus / Throw me down in the old field / What's the matter / Po' little Johnny / That's alright / Good time a good time

T&M 011 / Jun '98 / Tradition & Moderne

Tillet, Louis

☐ CAST OF ASPERSIONS, A

Carousel / Condemned to live / From me to you / Dig it up / Liferaft / Long walk home / Children of the cave / Midnight witch

CGAS 812CD / May '94 / Citadel

☐ EGO TRIPPING AT THE GATES OF HELL

Trip to kalu-ki-bar / Duet in blue minor / Swimming in the mirror / Dream well / Voluntary slavery / On your way down / Persephone's dance / Dead end street in the lucky country

CGAS 802CD / May '94 / Citadel

☐ LETTERS TO A DREAM

CGAS 816CD / May '94 / Citadel

☐ MIDNIGHT RAIN

RTS 18 / Aug '95 / Return To Sender

☐ RETURN TO SENDER FESTIVAL TOUR

NORMAL 175CD / Nov '94 / Normal

☐ UGLY TRUTH

RTS 5 / Jul '94 / Normal

Tillis, Pam

☐ ALL OF THIS LOVE

Deep down / Mandolin rain / Sunset red and pale moonlight / It's lonely out there / River and the highway / You can't have a good time without me / Betty's got a bass boat / Tequila mockingbird / No two ways about it / All of this love

07822187992 / Nov '95 / Arista

☐ EVERY TIME

I said a prayer / Every time / You put the lonely on me / Whisper and a scream / Lay the heartache down / Hurt myself / Not me / Whiskey on the wound / We must be thinking alight / After hours / Great disguise

07822188612 / 29 Jun '98 / Arista

☐ GREATEST HITS

Land of the living / All the good ones are gone / Don't tell me what to do / Maybe it was Memphis / Shake the sugar tree / Let that pony run / Cleopatra, queen of denial / Spilled perfume / When you walk in the room / In between dances / Mi vida loca (my crazy life) / River and the highway

07822188362 / May '97 / Arista

☐ HOMEWARD LOOKING ANGEL

How gone is goodbye / Shake the sugar tree / Do you know where your man is / Cleopatra, Queen of denial / Love is only human: *Tillis, Pam & Marty Roe* / Rough and tumble heart / Let that pony run / Fine, fine, very fine love / We've tried everything else / Homeward looking angel

07822186492 / Oct '93 / Arista

☐ SWEETHEART'S DANCE

07822187582 / Apr '95 / Arista

Tillotson, Johnny

☐ ALL HIS EARLY HITS - AND MORE

Poetry in motion / It keeps right on a-hurtin' / Send me the pillow that you dream on / Without you / You can never stop me loving you / We'll I'm your man / Dreamy eyes / True true happiness / Love is blind / Why do I love you so / Never let me go / Earth angel / Pledging my love / Princess, princess / Jimmy's girl / (Little sparrow) his true love said goodbye / Cutie pie / She gave sweet love to me / What'll I do / I can't help it (if I'm still in love with you) / I'm so lonesome I could cry / Out of my mind / Empty feeling / Judy Judy Judy / Funny how time slips away / Very good year for girls / Lonely street / I got a feeling / Lonesome town / I fall to pieces

CDCHD 946 / Jul '90 / Ace

☐ FABULOUS JOHNNY TILLOTSON, THE

Poetry in motion / It keeps right on a-hurtin' / Dreamy eyes / True true happiness / Why do I love you so / Jimmy's girl / Without you / Send me the pillow that you dream on / I can't help it (if I'm still in love with you) / Out of my mind / You can never stop me loving you / Funny how time slips away

CDFAB 003 / Aug '91 / Ace

☐ HIT SINGLE COLLECTABLES

DISK 4507 / Apr '94 / Disky

☐ SHE UNDERSTANDS ME/THAT'S MY STYLE

She understands me / That's love / Busted / Willow tree / Tomorrow / Little boy / To be a child again / That's when it hurts the most / More than before / Island of dreams / Yellow bird / Take this hammer / Heartaches by the number / Without your sweet lips on mine / Countin' my teardrops / You don't want my love / Just one time / Race is on / Things / Me, myself and I / Oh, lonesome me / Then I'll count again / I've seen better days / Your mem'ry comes along

CDCHD 345 / Feb '92 / Ace

☐ TALK BACK TREMBLING LIPS/THE TILLOTSON TOUCH

Talk back trembling lips / Blue velvet / Danke schon / What am I gonna do / My little world / I can't stop loving you / Worried guy / Another you / Rhythm of the rain / All alone am I / Please don't go away / Blowin' in the wind / I rise, I fall / On the sunny side of the street / Then you can tell me goodbye / This ole house / Suff'rin from a heartache / I've got you under my skin / Worry / I'm watching my watch / When I lost you / Always / Cold cold heart / Jailer bring me water

CDCHD 331 / Aug '91 / Ace

☐ YOU'RE THE REASON

Talk back trembling lips / Another you / Worried guy / Please don't go away / I rise, I fall / Worry / Heartaches by the number / She understands me / Angel / Suff'rin from a heartache / (Wait 'till you see) My gidget / No love at all / More than before / Blue velvet / You're the reason / Dreamy eyes / Red roses for a blue lady / When I lost you / Oh, lonesome me / Danke schoen / It keeps right on hurtin' / Then you can tell me goodbye / Things / All alone am I / Cold, cold heart / Always / Without you / Race is on / I can't stop loving you / Rhythm of the rain

CDCH 618 / Jan '96 / Ace

Tilston, Steve

☐ ACOUSTIC CONFUSION, AN

SCOFCD 1002 / 23 Mar '98 / Scenescof

☐ ALL UNDER THE SUN (Tilston, Steve & Maggie Boyle)

Let your banjo ring / Maid with the bonny brown hair / Here's to Tom Paine / Fair Annie / Man gone down (Fred's song) / Linden Lea / Cage / Navvy / Dark days of war / Willie the ploughboy / Threepenny bit / Fool such as I

CDFF 663 / Sep '96 / Flying Fish

☐ AND SO IT GOES

HR 01CD / Jul '95 / Hubris

☐ MUSIC OF O'CAROLAN, THE (Tilston, Steve & Duck Baker/Maggie Boyle/Ali Anderson)

O'Carolan's concerto / Planxty Irwin / O'Hara's cup / Thomas Leixlip the proud / Carolan's ramble to Cashel / O'Carolan's farewell to music / Princess royal / Blind Mary / Planxty Eleanor Plunkett / Hewlett / Squire Wood's lamentation on the refusal of his half pence / Planxty George brabazon / Bridget Cruise / Carolan's welcome

SHAN 97023CD / Mar '98 / Shanachie

☐ OF MOOR AND MESA (Tilston, Steve & Maggie Boyle)

GLCD 3087 / Feb '95 / Green Linnet

Tilt

☐ COLLECT 'EM ALL

FAT 567CD / 30 Mar '98 / Fatwreck Chords

☐ I PUT A SMELL ON YOU

EFA 125412 / Dec '95 / Celtic Circle

☐ TILL IT KILLS

FAT 521CD / Jun '95 / Fatwreck Chords

Timber

☐ PARTS AND LABOR

There's always 1 and 9 / At the same time / I'm 30, I'm having a heart attack / Evidence is shifting / Bad education / Belay that / Crankcase / Fatal flaw / Move / Real NY / Stupid reasons / Deer slayer / Reversivle fortune / Puddle / Robins make eggs blue / Passage from Pakistan / Acid test/Pads / Sugary peppery

R 3142 / Mar '94 / Rift

Timbuk 3

☐ LIVE

WM 1012 / Jun '93 / Watermelon

Time

☐ TIME/SMOOTH BALL

Take me along / Make it right / Let the colours keep on / Trippin' into sunshine / Love you, cherish you / You changed it all / Make love to you / Finders keepers / What can it be / I can't find it / Label it love / Preparation G / Leavin' my home / See me as i am / I think you'd cry / I'll write a song / Lazy day blues / Do you feel it / Flowers / Morning come / Trust in men everywhere

C5HCD 643 / Jun '96 / See For Miles

Time Bomb '77

☐ PROTECT AND SERVE

GMM 112 / Jun '97 / GMM

Time Control

☐ TIME CONTROL

SR 139 / 6 Jul '98 / Sub Rosa

Time Shard

☐ HUNAB KU

BARKCD 018 / May '96 / Planet Dog

Timebox

☐ TIMEBOX

8448072 / 1 Jun '98 / Deram

Timeless All Stars

☐ ESSENCE

DCD 4006 / '88 / Delos

Times

☐ ALTERNATIVE COMMERCIAL CROSSOVER

Obligatory grunge song / Finnegans break / How honest are Pearl Jam / Sweetest girl / Ballad of Georgie Best / Lundi bleu / Palace in the sun / Sorry, I've written a melody / Finnegans break (Corporate rock mix) / Whole world's turning scarface / All I want is you to care

CRECD 137 / Apr '93 / Creation

☐ BEAT TORTURE

Godevil / Heaven sent me an angel / I'll be your volunteer / Department store / Love like haze or rain / It had to happen / Chelsea green / How to start your own country / On the peace line / Scarlet and sapphire / Angel / Volunteer / Country / L-o-v-e

CRECD 038 / May '94 / Creation

☐ E FOR EDWARD

Manchester / Valvaline / Snow / Catherine wheel / Crashed on you / Count to five / All your life / French film bleurred / No love on haight st. / Acid angel of ecstasy / Gold / Sold / Life

CRECD 053 / Oct '89 / Creation

☐ ENJOY/UP AGAINST IT

CREV 029CD / Nov '93 / Rev-Ola

☐ ET DIEU CREA LA FEMME

Septieme ciel / Chagrin d'amour / Baisers voles / Sucette / Extase / Aurore boreale / Volupte / Pour Kylie / 1990 Anee erotique

CRECD 070 / May '94 / Creation

☐ I HELPED PATRICK MCGOOHAN ESCAPE

Big painting / Stranger than fiction / Danger man / I helped Patrick McGoohan escape / All systems are go / Up against it

CREV 006CD / Nov '92 / Rev-Ola

☐ LIVE AT THE ASTRADOME

Wellcome / Septieme ciel / Big painting / On the peace line / Valvaline / Crashed on you / All your life / No love on haight st. / Love and truth / Shoom / Manchester / Cloud over liverpool

CRECD 123 / Apr '92 / Creation

☐ PINK BALL, BROWN BALL, RED BALL

Manchester / Septieme ciel / How to start your own country / Snow / Confiance / Catherine wheel / Heaven sent me an angel / Extase / A girl called mersey / Five thirty / I've got all this and heaven too / Lundi bleu

CRECD 073 / Jul '91 / Creation

☐ PURE

From chelsea green to brighton beach / From chelsea green to brighton beach / Lundi bleu / From l.a. to edgebaston / Ours is a wonderlove world / Another star in heaven

CRECD 091 / Mar '91 / Creation

Timeshard

☐ CRYSTAL OSCILLATIONS

BARKCD 004 / Jun '94 / Planet Dog

Timewriter

☐ JIGSAW PIECES

PLACCD 012 / 15 Jun '98 / Plastic City UK

☐ LETTERS FROM THE JESTER

PLACCD 006 / Jun '97 / Plastic City UK

Timmons, Bobby

☐ BORN TO BE BLUE (Timmons, Bobby Trio)

Born to be blue / Malice towards none / Sometimes I feel like a Motherless child / Know not one / Sit-in / Namely you / Often Annie

OJCCD 873 / Jun '96 / Original Jazz Classics

☐ SOUL MAN, THE

Cut me loose Charlie / Tom Thumb / Ein bahn strasse / Damned I know / Tenaj / Little waltz

PRCD 7465 / Jun '96 / Prestige

☐ THIS HERE IS BOBBY TIMMONS

OJCCD 104 / Oct '92 / Original Jazz Classics

Timms, Sally

☐ COWBOY SALLY

BS 016 / 19 Jan '98 / Bloodshot

Timoteo, Chiquinho

☐ LA GUITARE BRESILIENNE DE CHIQUINHO TIMOTEO

KAR 988 / Nov '96 / IMP

Tin Machine

☐ TIN MACHINE

Heaven's in here / Tin machine / Prisoner of love / Crack city / I can't read / Under the God / Amazing / Working class hero / Bus stop / Pretty thing / Video crime / Run / Sacrifice yourself / Baby can dance / Bus stop (live country version)

4931012 / 19 Jan '98 / EMI

Tin Pots

☐ DREAMS & NIGHTMARES
TP 3 / Apr '95 / Tin Pot Productions

Tin Tin Out

☐ ALWAYS
Dealers to the dancefloor / Always something there to remind me / Strings for Yasmin / Dance with me / Strings for Yasmin / Here's where the story ends / This is for you: Tin Tin Out & Mansa / Always something there to remind me / All I wanna do / Feeling: Tin Tin Out & Sweet Tee
CDVCR 1 / 6 Apr '98 / Virgin

☐ ALWAYS (2CD Set)
Dance with me / Feeling: Tin Tin Out & Sweet Tee / Strings for Yasmin / Dance with me / Strings for Yasmin / Here's where the story ends / Always something there to remind me / Dealers to the dancefloor / This is for you / All I wanna do / Strings for Yasmin / Here's where the story ends / Feeling: Tin Tin Out & Sweet Tee / Here's where the story ends: Tin Tin Out & Sweet Tee / Strings for Yasmin / All I wanna do / Trance with me / Strings for Yasmin / Here's where the story ends / Always something there to remind me
CDVCRX 1 / 6 Apr '98 / Virgin

Tinandari Male Chorus

☐ GEORGIAN POLYPHONY VOL.3
VICG 52252 / Mar '96 / JVC World Library

Tindersticks

☐ CURTAINS
Another night in / Rented rooms / Don't look down / Dick's slow song / Fast one / Ballad of Tindersticks / Dancing / Let's pretend / Desperate man / Buried bones / Bearsuit / (Tonight) Are you trying to fall in love again / I was your man / Bathtime / Walking
5243442 / Jun '97 / This Way Up

☐ DONKEYS 1992-1997
Patchwork / Marbles / Her / City sickness / Travelling light / I've been loving you / Plus de liasons / Here / Tiny tears / Bathtime / Marriage made in heaven / For those / Feeling relatively good
CID 8074 / 14 Sep '98 / Island

☐ LIVE AT THE BLOOMSBURY
El diabolo en el ojo / Night in / Talk to me / She's gone / My sister / No more affairs / City slickers / Sleepy song / Jism / Drunktank / Mistakes / Tiny tears / Raindrops / For those
5285972 / Sep '95 / This Way Up

☐ NENETTE ET BONI (Original Soundtracks)
Ma souer / La Passerelle / Les gateaux / Camions / Nenette est la / Petites chiennes / Nosterfrau / Petites gouttes d'eau / Les Cannes a peche / La mort de Felix / Nenette s'en va / Les bebes / Les fleurs / Rumba
5243002 / Oct '96 / This Way Up

☐ SECOND ALBUM
El Diablo en El Ojo / Night in / My sister / Tiny tears / Snowy in F# minor / Seaweed / Vertrauen 2 / Talk to me / No more affairs / Singing / Travelling light / Cherry blossoms / She's gone / Mistakes / Vertrauen 3 / Sleepy song
5263032 / Jun '97 / This Way Up

☐ TINDERSTICKS, THE
Nectar / Tyed / Sweet sweet man / Whiskey and water / Blood / City sickness / Patchwork / Marbles / Walt blues / Milky teeth / Jism / Piano song / Tie dye / Raindrops / Her / Tea stain / Drunk tank / Paco de Renaldo's dream / Not knowing
5183062 / Jun '97 / This Way Up

Ting, Li Xiang

☐ SOUL OF CHINA
CDSV 1337 / Jun '93 / Voyager

Tingstad, Eric

☐ PASTORALE (Tingstad, Eric & Nancy Rumbel)
Elysian fields / Guinevere's lament / Jester / Savannah / Bouraree / Country dance / Roses and lace / Pastorale / Fisherman's dream / Chapel in the valley / Reverence
ND 61061 / May '97 / Narada

☐ SENSE OF PLACE, A
Appalachia calling / Monogahela / Sense of place / Spirit of Rydal Mount / Magnolia / Sovereign of the sea / Castle by the lough / Sissinghurst / American blend / Craftsman / Moonlight blue
ND 61048 / Jul '95 / Narada

☐ STAR OF WONDER (Tingstad, Eric & Nancy Rumbel)
ND 61043 / Oct '94 / Narada

Tintino

☐ SALSA PA' ABIDJAN
3021672 / Jul '97 / Arcade

Tiny Monroe

☐ LITTLE VOLCANOES
She / Cream bun / Love of the bottle / Open invitation / Snake in the grass / Vhf 850s / Drink bombs / Secret place / Skin bleach / Women in love / Bubble
8288042 / Jul '96 / Laurel

Tiny Monsters

☐ LIGHTING AT THE END
303233 / May '97 / TM

Tiny Tim

☐ CHRISTMAS ALBUM
Rudolph the red nosed reindeer / All I want for Christmas is my two front teeth / That's what I want for Christmas / Law Mommy kissing Santa Claus / White Christmas / Christmas song / O holy night / Silent night / Medley / Rainbow on the river / Mission bell / What a friend we have in Jesus
ROUCD 9054 / Nov '96 / Rounder
DURTRO 029CD / Oct '96 / Durtro

☐ IMPOTENT TROUBADOUR
DURTRO 026CD / Oct '96 / Durtro

☐ LIVE IN LONDON
DURTRO 034CD / Apr '97 / Durtro

☐ PRISONER OF LOVE
VRP 005 / Jul '97 / Vinyl Retent

☐ RESURRECTION - TIPTOE THROUGH THE TULIPS
Tiptoe through the tulips / Sweet Rosie O'Grady / Shine on harvest moon / Baby face / Till we meet again / It's a long way to Tipperary / Prisoner of love / Those were the days / Pennies from Heaven / When you wore a tulip / Tiny bubbles / When the saints go marching in / Just a gigolo / Happy days are here again / Bill Bailey, won't you please come home
BCD 15409 / Dec '87 / Bear Family

Tipico Oriental

☐ ETERNA MELODIA
262582 / 1 Jun '98 / Lusafrika

Tippa Irie

☐ IS IT REALLY HAPPENING TO ME
Unlucky burglar / It's good to have the feeling you're the best / You're the best / Telephone / Heartbeat / Robotic reggae / Married life / Football hooligan / Complain neighbour / Hello darling / Is it really happening to me
TIPCD 1 / Sep '86 / Greensleeves

☐ MR. VERSATILE
DTJCD 004 / 18 May '98 / Jammin'

☐ REBEL ON THE ROOTS CORNER
ARICD 091 / Dec '93 / Ariwa Sounds

Tippett, Keith

☐ COUPLE IN SPIRIT VOL.2 (Live At The Stadtgarten, Cologne) (Tippett, Keith & Julie)
Together / Rainbow
ASCCD 12 / Aug '97 / ASC

☐ DEDICATED TO YOU, BUT YOU WEREN'T
REP 4227 / Aug '91 / Repertoire

☐ FRAMES (Music For An Imaginary Film/ 2CD Set) (Tippett, Keith Ark)
OGCD 010/011 / May '96 / Ogun

Tipsy

☐ TRIP TEASE (The Seductive Grooves Of Tipsy)
ASP 0967CD / 22 Jun '98 / Asphodel

Tipton, Glenn

☐ BAPTIZM OF FIRE
Hard core / Paint it black / Enter the storm / Fuel me up / Extinct / Baptizm of fire / Healer / Cruise control / Kill or be killed / Voodoo brother / Left for dead
7567829742 / Mar '97 / Atlantic

Tir Na Nog

☐ STRONG IN THE SUN
Free ride / Teesside / Strong in the sun / Wind was high / In the morning / Love lost / Most magical / Fall of day
EDCD 336 / Oct '91 / Edsel

☐ TEAR AND A SMILE, THE
EDCD 334 / Sep '91 / Edsel

☐ TIR NA NOG
Time is like a promise / Mariner blues / Daisy lady / Tir na nog / Aberdeen Angus / Looking up / Boat song / Our love will not decay / Hey friend / Dance of years / Live a day / Piccadilly / Dante
BGOCD 53 / '89 / Beat Goes On

Tiramakhan Ensemble

☐ SONGS FROM GAMBIA
SOW 90128 / Sep '94 / Sounds Of The World

Tirta Sari Ensemble

☐ GAMELAN SEMARPEGULINGAN
VICG 50242 / Feb '96 / JVC World Library

Tiso, Wagner

☐ BRAZILIAN SCENES
KAR 079 / Nov '97 / IMP

Tit Wrench

☐ 8-11-96 (Live)
VC 106 / Jan '97 / Vinyl Communication

Titanic

☐ TITANIC
REP 4151 / Aug '91 / Repertoire

Titans

☐ INSTANT DISASTERS
LRR 030CD / 11 May '98 / Lance Rock

Titiyo

☐ THIS IS
This is / Back and forth / Hot gold / Deep down underground / Make my day / Way you make me feel / Spinnin' / Human climate / Defended / Never let me go / Man in the moon
74321188822 / Jan '94 / RCA

Tittle, Jimmy

☐ GREATEST HITS
473924 2 / Aug '93 / Dixie Frog

☐ IT'S IN THE ATTITUDE
DFGCD 8438 / Jun '96 / Dixie Frog

Titus Groan

☐ TITUS GROAN...PLUS
It wasn't for you / Hall of bright carvings / Liverpool / I can't change / It's all up with us / Fuschia / Open the door homer / Woman of the world
SEECD 260 / Sep '89 / See For Miles

Tiven, Jon

☐ BLUE GURU (Tiven, Jon Group)
He don't know / 24-7 / Midnight again / Inside information / River of no return / Let's think about it / 2nd hand paradise / Tricks of the trade / I smell smoke / Fool's gold / Laugh / Had to have it / Beginning of the blues / End of the blues
PRD 71102 / 16 Mar '98 / Provogue

Tjader, Cal

☐ A FUEGO VIVO
CCD 4176 / Jul '88 / Concord Jazz

☐ BLACK ORCHID
Mi china / Close your eyes / Mambo at the "M" / Contigo / Bonita / Lady is a tramp / Black orchid / Happiness is a thing called Joe / I've waited so long / Out of nowhere / Guajira at the blackhawk / I want to be happy / Nearness of you / Pete Kelly's blues / Minor goof / Undecided / Philadelphia mambo / Flamingo / Stompin' at the savoy / Laura / Lullaby of birdland
FCD 24730 / Jun '94 / Fantasy

☐ GOOD VIBES
Guarachi guaro / Doxy / Shoshana / Speak low / Broadway / Cuban fantasy / Good vibes
CCD 4247 / Apr '90 / Concord Picante

☐ HERE AND THERE
Guarabe / Where is love / This masquerade / Reza / Black orchid / El muchacho / Tu crees que / Liz Anne / Morning / Here / If
FCD 24743 / Aug '96 / Fantasy

☐ JAZZ MASTERS
5218582 / 5 May '98 / Verve

☐ LA ONDA VA BIEN
CCD 4113 / '88 / Concord Jazz

☐ MAMBO WITH TJADER
Mambues / Midnight sun / Sonny boy / Cherry / I'll remember april / This can't be love / Tonight / Dearly beloved / Chloe / Lucero / Bye bye blues / Autumn leaves
OJCCD 271 / Nov '95 / Original Jazz Classics

☐ MONTEREY CONCERTS
Doxy / Afro blue / Laura / Walkin' with wally / We'll be together again / 'round midnight / Love me or leave me / Tu crees que / S.s. groove / Night in tunisia / Bess, you my woman now / Lover come back to me / Tumbao
PCD 24026 / Oct '93 / Pablo

☐ SENTIMENTAL MOODS
Autumn leaves / Spring is here / Time was / Star eyes / Stella by starlight / Alone together / Ode to a beat generation / Skylark / Martha / Quizas quizas quizas / Running out / Raccoon Strait / Last luff / Sigmund Stern groove / Colt tower / Triple T blues / Union Square / Skyline waltz / Viva candela / Grant Avenue suite
FCD 24742 / Aug '96 / Fantasy

☐ SOUL SAUCE
Soul sauce / Soul bird / Spring is here / Tanya / Joao / Maramoor mambo / Pantano / Somewhere is the night / Afro blue / Triste / Whiffenpoof song / Leyte / Mambues / Curacao
CD 62073 / Jan '96 / Saludos Amigos

☐ TALKIN' VERVE (The Roots Of Acid Jazz)
5315622 / Jun '96 / Verve

TLC

☐ CRAZYSEXYCOOL
Intro-lude / Creep / Kick your game / Diggin' on you / Case of the fake people / Crazysexycool / Red light special / Waterfalls / Intermission-lude / Let's do it again / If I was your girlfriend / Sexy-interlude / Take our time / Can I get a witness / Switch / Sumthin' wicked this way comes
73008260092 / May '95 / Arista

☐ OOOOOOOH... ON THE TLC TIP
Ain't 2 proud 2 beg / Shock dat monkey / Intermission / Hat 2 da bak / Das da way we like / What about your friends / His story / Intermission 2 / Bad my myself / Somethin' you wanna know / Baby-baby-baby / This is how it should be done / Depend on myself / Conclusion
262 878 / Feb '97 / Arista

TLM

☐ I'VE GOT THE BATTERY...WHERE'S THE SLOT
DUKE 028CD
☐ LIVE
DUKE 028L / Jul '96 / Hydrogen Dukebox

☐ RE-CHARGED
DUKE 030CD / Nov '96 / Hydrogen Dukebox

Tmar, Ubar

☐ TRUE
MPCD 18 / 14 Sep '98 / Matsuri

TNT

☐ FIREFLY AND LIVE
SH 1109 / Oct '97 / Shrapnel

To Hell With Burgundy

☐ 3
STIGCD 07 / Aug '94 / Stig

☐ ONLY THE WORLD
STIGCD 05 / Jul '94 / Stig

To Live & Shave In LA

☐ TONAL HARMONY
TLASILA 001 / 29 Sep '97 / Bentley Welcomes Careful Drivers

To Rococo Rot

☐ TO ROCOCO ROT
KITTY 010 / Jul '97 / Kitty Yo

☐ VEICULO
Marchomaged / He loves me / Modern homes / Moto / Mit dir in der gegend / Leggiero / Geheimnis eines manfels / Extra / Fach / Lips / Merano / Allover dezent / Lift
EFA 049902 / Feb '97 / City Slang

Toad The Wet Sprocket

☐ FEAR
Walk on the ocean / Is it for me / Butterflies / Nightingale song / Hold her down / Pray your Gods / Before you were born / Something to say / In my ear / All I want / Stories I tell / I will not take these things for granted
4685822 / Mar '92 / Columbia

Toadies

☐ PLEATHER
ASS 001 2 / May '93 / Grass

Toast

☐ COLLECTION, THE
DAMGOOD 124 / May '97 / Damaged Goods

Toasters

☐ DUB 56
DOJOCD 214 / Jun '95 / Dojo

☐ FRANKENSKA
PHZCD 60 / Nov '93 / Unicorn

☐ LIVE IN LA
EFA 046072 / Dec '94 / Pork Pie

☐ NAKED CITY
PHZCD 55 / Oct '89 / Unicorn

☐ NEW YORK FEVER
EFA 046902 / Jan '93 / Pork Pie

☐ SKA BOOM
EFA 046052 / Apr '94 / Pork Pie

☐ TWO TONE ARMY
EFA 046322 / Sep '96 / Pork Pie

Tobias, Nancy

☐ BEAUTIFUL SOUNDS OF THE PANPIPE (Tobias, Nancy & Phil)
HADCD 178 / Nov '95 / Javelin

Tobin, Amon
☐ PERMUTATION
Like regular chickens / Bridge / Reanimator / Sordid / Nightlife / Escape / Switch / People like Frank / Sultan drops / Fast Eddie / Toys / Nova / Melody infringement
ZENCD 036 / 1 Jun '98 / Ninja Tune

Tobin, Christine
☐ AILILIU
BDV 9501 / Jul '95 / Babel
☐ HOUSE OF WOMEN
BVD 9820 / May '98 / Babel
☐ YELL OF THE GAZELLE
BDV 9613 / Aug '96 / Babel

Tobin, Penelope
☐ WHEN
When / Love of money / Paris romancing / Leave me in peace / La vendetta / Scaredy cat / Friend into lover / Melancholy / First day of spring / Only got the moment
DDG 001 / Jun '96 / Dodgem Discs

Tobruk
☐ PLEASURE AND PAIN
Rock 'n' roll casualty / Love is in motion / Alleyboy / No paradise in Heaven / Burning up / Two hearts on the run / Let me out of here / Cry out in the night / Set me on fire
WKFMXD 105 / May '88 / FM

Today Is The Day
☐ TEMPLE OF THE MORNING STAR
Temple of the morning star / Man who loves to hurt himself / Blindspot / High as the sky / Miracle / Kill yourself / Mankind / Pinnacle / Crutch / Root of all evil / Rabid lassie / Satan is alive / Friend is for life fuck off / My life is with you / I see you / Hemaphrodite
RR 69642 / 27 Oct '97 / Relapse
☐ TODAY IS THE DAY
ARR 71014CD / Apr '96 / Amphetamine Reptile
☐ WILLPOWER
AAR 57354CD / Nov '94 / Amphetamine Reptile

Todd, Dick
☐ CANADIAN CROSBY, THE (His Greatest Recordings 1938-1942)
All this and Heaven too / As long as we're together / Blue orchids / Blue evening / Change partner / Concerto for two / Deep purple / Gaucho serenade / Girl in the bonnet of blue / Goodnight Mother / Hi-yo silver / I can't get started / I can't believe / The world on fire / It's a hap-hap happy day / It's a hundred to one / It's the talk of the town / Lazy river / Little Sir Echo / Love doesn't grow on trees / Outside of that I love you: Todd, Dick & Dinah Shore / Penny serenade / Someday sweetheart / To you sweetheart aloha / When Paw was coutin' Maw / When the lights go on again / Why begin again / You can't brush me off: Todd, Dick & Dinah Shore
CDAJA 5179 / Dec '95 / Living Era

Todd, Mia Doi
☐ SWE AND THE EYE
XARC 016 / Sep '97 / X-Mas

Toe Fat
☐ TOE FAT VOL.1 & 2
That's my love for you / Bad side of the moon / Nobody / Wherefores and the whys / But I'm wrong / Just like me / Just like all the rest / I can't believe / Working nights / You tried to take it all / Stick heat / Indian summer / Idol / There'll be changes / New way / Since you've been gone / Three time loser / Midnight sun
BGOCD 278 / Sep '95 / Beat Goes On

Toe To Toe
☐ THREATS AND FACTS
KANG 006CD / Nov '95 / Kangaroo

Toenut
☐ INFORMATION
CDSTUMM 89 / Apr '96 / Mute
☐ TWO IN A PINATA
CDSTUMM 160 / 25 Aug '97 / Mute

Tofu Love Frogs
☐ VEGTABLE ATTACK
PROX 001 / 8 Sep '97 / Prox

Togashi, Masahiko
☐ COLOUR OF DREAM
TKOJ 1502 / Jan '96 / Take One
☐ ISOLATION (Togashi, Masahiko & Mototeru Takagi)
TKOJ 1503 / Jan '96 / Take One
☐ SONG OF SOIL
TKOJ 1501 / Jan '96 / Take One

Tognoni, Rob
☐ HEADSTRONG
Times change / Got yourself to blame / Stones and colours / Roosevelt and Ira Lee / Wanna be with you / Ain't that enough / Take me away / Dark angel / Everlasting lovin' boy / Jim Beam blues / Riverside / Keep your head above water / Baby please don't go
PRD 70982 / Mar '97 / Provogue
☐ STONES AND COLOURS
PRD 70832 / Oct '95 / Provogue

Tohama
☐ ETOILES DE LA CHANSON
8446732 / 24 Feb '98 / Music Memoria

Toho Sara
☐ KYOJINKAI
FDCD 58 / Apr '97 / Fourth Dimension

Toiling Midgets
☐ SON
Faux pony / Fabric / Slaughter of Summer St. / Mr. Foster's shoes / Process words / Clinging fire/Clams / Third chair / Listen / Chains
HUTCD 006 / Jan '93 / Hut

Token Women
☐ OUT TO LUNCH
NMCD 6 / Feb '96 / No Master's Voice
☐ RHYTHM METHOD, THE
NMCD 2 / Jun '97 / No Master's Voice

Tokens
☐ WIMOWEH - THE BEST OF THE TOKENS
Lion sleeps tonight / B'wanina (pretty girl) / La bamba / Hear the bells (ringing bells) / You're nothing but a girl / Tonight I met an angel / Sincerely / When I go to sleep at night / Thousand miles away / Please write / Dream angel good night / Somewhere there's a girl / I'll do my crying tomorrow / ABC 123 / Tonight, tonight / Dry your eyes / Sweet Laurie / My candy apple vette / My fiend's car / When summer is through
07863664742 / Nov '94 / RCA

Tokeya Inajin
☐ DREAM CATCHER
CDEB 2696 / May '93 / Earthbeat

Tokyo Blade
☐ BURNING DOWN PARADISE
SPV 08512122 / Mar '96 / SPV
☐ NIGHT OF THE BLADE
HV 1012 / Sep '97 / High Vaultage
☐ NIGHT OF THE BLADE (The Night Before)
HV 1013 / Sep '97 / High Vaultage
☐ TOKYO BLADE
HV 1011 / Sep '97 / High Vaultage

Tokyo Combo
☐ UH YEAH
APR 034CD / 8 Jun '98 / April

Tokyo's Coolest Combo
☐ TOKYO'S COOLEST COMBO
BOM 04CD / Jul '96 / Bomba

Tolbert, Skeets
☐ CLASSICS 1931-1940
CLASSICS 978 / 24 Feb '98 / Classics
☐ CLASSICS 1940-1942
CLASSICS 993 / 24 Apr '98 / Classics

Tollhouse Company
☐ BETWEEN THE FLAT LAND AND THE SKY (A Fenman's Life In Song & Narrative) (2CD Set)
Overture / End of an era / Entire man / Good life for a young man / Between the flat land and the sky / I wished myself at home / Guns of Italy / End of everything / Forty pounds / Return home / Welcome home / Living and the dead / Silent fen / Angel of mercy / Jerusalem Drove / Stepping back into life / Cock of the walk / Shooting butterflies / Out beneath the moon / That's progress / Man from the ministry / Plastic roses / Me and Ted and Harry / Back on the old fen / Old man's happy again / Last drop from the bottle / Between the flat land and the sky (reprise)
THCDCD 9701 / May '97 / Tollhouse

Tolliver, Charles
☐ GRAND MAX
Grand max / Truth / Prayer for peace / Our second father / Repetition
BLC 760145 / Apr '91 / Black Lion
☐ IMPACT
CDGR 231 / 30 Mar '98 / Charly

☐ LIVE AT HISTORIC SLUGS (Tolliver, Charles & Music Incorporation)
CDGR 232 / 27 May '98 / Charly
☐ LIVE IN TOKYO (Tolliver, Charles & Music Incorporation)
CDGR 248 / 1 Jun '98 / Charly
☐ RINGER, THE
Plight / On the nile / Ringer / Mother wit / Spur
BLCD 760174 / Oct '93 / Black Lion
☐ WITH MUSIC INC. AND ORCHESTRA
Impact / Mother Wit / Grand Max / Plight / Lynnsome / Mournin' variations
6605 1004 / Feb '91 / Strata East

Tolman, Russ
☐ ROAD MOVIE
422368 / May '94 / New Rose

Tolonen, Jukka
☐ HOOK/HYSTERICA
LRCD 113/149 / Dec '94 / Love

Tom Angelripper
☐ EIN TROPFOCHEN VOLLER
GUN 154CD / 9 Mar '98 / Gun

Tom Tom Club
☐ TOM TOM CLUB
Wordy rappinghood / Genius of love / Tom Tom theme / L'elephant / As above so below / Lorelei / On on on / Booming and zooming
IMCD 103 / Feb '90 / Island

Tom Wax
☐ TOM WAX MIX TRAX (Various Artists)
WAXCD 0092 / 2 Feb '98 / Phuture Wax

Tomelleri, Paolo
☐ FROM DUO TO BIG BAND
CD 53278 / May '98 / Giants Of Jazz

Tomita
☐ BEST OF TOMITA, THE
PD 89381 / '88 / RCA
☐ DIFFERENT DIMENSIONS
Snowflakes are dancing / Dawn chorus / Bolero / Ballet of the chicks in shells / Reverie / Gardens in the rain / Footprints in the snow / World of different dimensions / Arabesque no.1 / Infernal dance of king kastchei / Girl with the flaxen hair / Great gate of Kiev / Passepied / Old castle / Whistle train / Promenade / Golliwog's cakewalk / Canon of three stars
74321535812 / 22 Nov '97 / RCA
☐ FIREBIRD
Firebird suite / Prelude a l'apres midi d'un faune / Night on the bare mountain
GD 60578 / Oct '91 / RCA Victor
☐ GREATEST HITS
RD 85660 / Jul '94 / RCA Victor
☐ KOSMOS
Space fantasy / Unanswered question / Solvejg's song / Hora staccato / Sea named Solaris
GD 82616 / Oct '91 / RCA Victor
☐ PICTURES AT AN EXHIBITION
Gnome / Old castle / Tuileries / Bydlo / Ballet of the chicks in their shells / Samuel Goldenberg and Schmuyle / Limoges / Catacombs / Cum mortuis in lingua mortua / Hut of Baba Yaga / Great gate of Kiev
GD 60576 / Oct '91 / RCA Victor
☐ PLANETS, THE
Mars, the bringer of war / Venus, the bringer of peace / Mercury the winged messenger / Jupiter, the bringer of jollity / Saturn, the bringer of old age / Uranus, the magician / Neptune, the mystic
GD 60518 / Aug '85 / RCA Victor
☐ SNOWFLAKES ARE DANCING (Music Of Claude Debussy)
Snowflakes are dancing / Reverie / Gardens in the rain (estampes no 3) / Clair de Lune / Arabesque No.1 / Engulfed cathedral (preludes book no.8) / Golliwog's cakewalk / Footprints in the snow(preludes book no.6)
GD 60579 / Jul '85 / RCA Victor

Tommaso, Giovanni
☐ VIA GT (Tommaso, Giovanni Quintet)
1231962 / Apr '94 / Red

Tomney, Ed
☐ SAFE (Original Soundtrack)
IONIC 14CD / Aug '95 / The Fine Line

Tomokawa, Kazuki
☐ SHIBUYA APIA
PSFD 65 / Dec '95 / PSF
☐ YUME WA HIBI GENKI NI SHINDE YUKU
PSFD 96 / Aug '98 / PSF

☐ ZEINIKU NA ASA (Fat In The Morning Light)
PSFD 82 / May '97 / PSF

Tomorrow
☐ 50 MINUTE TECHNICOLOUR DREAM
Am I glad to see you / Blow up / Caught in a web / Revolution / Why / Real life permanent dream / Three jolly little dwarfs / Revolution / Caught in a web / Shotgun and the duck / My white bicycle / Real life permanent dream / Revolution / Why / Mr. Rainbow / Strawberry fields forever
RPM 184 / 6 Jul '98 / RPM
☐ TOMORROW
My white bicycle / Colonel Brown / Real life permanent dream / Shy boy / Claremount lake / Revolution / Incredible journey of Timothy Chase / Auntie Mary's dress shop / Strawberry fields forever / Three jolly little dwarfs / Now your time has come / Hallucinations
SEECD 314 / 1 Feb '97 / See For Miles

Tomorrow's Child
☐ ROCKY COAST
DCD 9630 / Nov '96 / Dream Circle

Tomorrow's Gift
☐ TOMORROW'S GIFT
SB 017 / Jun '97 / Second Battle

Tomorrowland
☐ SEQUENCE OF NEGATIVE SPACE CHANGES
KRANK 029CD / 10 Aug '98 / Kranky
☐ STEREOSCOPIC SOUNDWAVES
DRL 042CD / Jul '97 / Darla

Tompkins, Ross
☐ AKA THE PHANTOM
PCD 7090 / Jun '93 / Progressive
☐ CELEBRATES THE MUSIC OF HAROLD ARLEN
PCD 7107 / May '98 / Progressive
☐ CELEBRATES THE MUSIC OF JULES STYNE
PCD 7103 / Aug '95 / Progressive

Tomrerclaus
☐ TOMRERCLAUS
APM 9715 / 15 Dec '97 / APM

Toms
☐ TOMS
NLA 001 / 16 Feb '98 / Not Lame

Ton-Art
☐ MAL VU, MAL DIT
ARTCD 6088 / Jan '92 / Hat Art

Tonar, Tidlause
☐ TIMELESS TONES
LMP 196CD / May '96 / Laerdal Musik

Tone Float
☐ MUSIK VON TONE FLOAT
TB 007 / 27 Apr '98 / Tim's Brain

Tone Loc
☐ COOL HAND LOC
Funky westside / Pimp without a caddy / I adore you / All through the night / Fatal attraction / I joke but I don't pay / Freaky behaviour / Mean green / Why / Hip hop it is kinda different / Funky westside (reprise)
IMCD 247 / Mar '97 / Island
☐ LOC'ED AFTER DARK
On fire (remix) / Wild thing / Loc'ed after dark / I got it going on / Cutting rhythms / Funky cold medina / Cheeba cheeba / Don't get close / Loc'in on the shaw / Homies
IMCD 125 / Apr '91 / 4th & Broadway

Tone Rec
☐ PHOLCUS
SR 136 / 4 May '98 / Sub Rosa

Tone, Yasunao
☐ SOLO FOR THE WOUNDED
TZA 7212 / Jul '97 / Tzadik

Tones On Tail
☐ EVERYTHING
BEGA 200CD / 6 Apr '98 / Beggars Banquet

Toney, Kevin
☐ LOVESCAPE
Kings / Aphrodisiac / Winds of romance / Lovescape / Sweet whispers / Intimate persuasion / Body language / Deeper shade of love / African knights / Twylight 2053 / Someone / Carnival / King's reprise
ICH 1167CD / Jan '94 / Ichiban

Tongue Man
☐ COP THIS
DS 005CD / Oct '96 / Drunken Swan

Tonic
☐ LEMON PARADE
5310422 / Sep '97 / Polydor

Tonics
☐ LOOKING FOR THE GOOD TIME
LRR 028 / 5 May '98 / Lance Rock

Tonight At Noon
☐ DOWN TO THE DEVILS
John MacLean march / Hawks and eagles fly like doves / Travelling song / Wire the loom / People's will / Run run / Hell of a man / Down to the devils / Nae trust / Mission hall / Harry Wigwam's / Banks of marble / Jack the tanner / Rolling seas
LCOM 9041 / Nov '90 / Lismor

Tonnerre, Michel
☐ DOUCE BARBARIE
KMCD 78 / Nov '97 / Keltia Musique

☐ TI BEUDEFF - CHANT DE MARINS
KMCD 39 / Aug '93 / Keltia Musique

Tonooka, Sumi
☐ HERE COMES KAI
Giant steps / It must be real / At home / In the void / Warm valley / Upper Manhattan medical group / Mystery / Here comes Kai
CCD 79516 / Feb '97 / Candid

☐ TAKING TIME
Taking time / Yours and mine / Seriously speaking / Shadow waltz / Night and day / Out of the silence / Station levitation / In the night / One for Mary Lou
CCD 79502 / Feb '97 / Candid

Tons Of Tones
☐ COMPLETE CITATION SAGA, THE
DBM 2196 / Apr '97 / Fierce

☐ PLATINUM
DBM 33934 / 30 Mar '98 / Fierce

Tonto Irie
☐ JAMMY'S POSSE
792052 / Nov '92 / Greensleeves

Tony D
☐ GET YOURSELF SOME (Tony D Band)
TRCD 9919 / Nov '93 / Tramp

☐ POUND FOR POUND
Flavour / Back to the basics / Crystal maze (skit) / Come round here / Don't wanna lose you / All I have / Walk like a man / Phone beat / Erase the pain / Queen of my dreams / Crystal meth (skit) / Piano grand
GCCD 102 / 15 Sep '97 / Grand Central

Tony O
☐ TOP OF THE BLUES (Tony O Blues Band)
DELCD 3014 / Jan '96 / Deluge

Tony Rebel
☐ DANCEHALL CONFRENCE (Tony Rebel & Garnet Silk)
CDHB 152 / May '94 / Heartbeat

☐ IF JAH
VPCD 1506 / 24 Nov '97 / VP

☐ MEET IN A DANCEHALL CONFERENCE (Tony Rebel & Garnet Silk)
HBCD 152 / Jun '94 / Heartbeat

☐ REBELLIOUS
RASCD 3097 / May '92 / Ras

Tony Toni Tone
☐ HITS
If I had no loot / Boyz and girlz / Annie mae / Blues / Don't fall in love / Little walter / I've been thinking of you / Anniversary / Feels good / Let's get down / Lay your head on my pillow / It never rains / Baby doll / Whatever you want / X girl friend
5363682 / 10 Nov '97 / Mercury

☐ HOUSE OF MUSIC
Thinking of you / Top notch / Let's get down / Til last summer / Lovin' you / Still a man / Don't fall in love / Holy smoke and gee whiz / Annie May / Let me know / Tossin' 'n' turnin' / Wild child / Party don't cry / Lovin' you interlude
5342502 / Nov '96 / Mercury

☐ SONS OF SOUL
If I had no loot / What goes around comes around / My ex-girlfriend / Tell me mama / Leavin' / Slow wine (slow grind) / Lay your head on my pillow / I couldn't keep it to myself / Gangsta groove / Tonyies, In the wrong key / Dance hall / Time Square 2:30 AM (Segue) / Fun / Anniversary / Castleers
5149332 / Jul '93 / Polydor

Tony Tuff
☐ LINK UP
RN 7045 / 22 Jun '98 / Rhino

Tony Z
☐ KISS MY BLUES
CDTC 1161 / 19 Jan '98 / Tonecool

Tonyall
☐ NEW GIRL, OLD STORY
CRZ 016CD / May '93 / Cruz

Too Slim
☐ BLUES FOR EB (Too Slim & The Taildraggers)
BCD 00282 / Nov '97 / Burnside

Too Slim & The Taildraggers
☐ SWAMP OPERA
BCD 00212 / May '96 / Burnside

☐ WANTED: LIVE
BCD 00162 / Jun '96 / Burnside

Too Strong
☐ RABENSCHWARZE NACHT
HAUS 1 / Jan '94 / Tribehaus Recordings

Tool
☐ AENIMA
Stinkfist / Eulogy / H / Useful idiot / Forty six and 2 / Message to Harry Manback / Hooker with a penis / Intermission / Jimmy / Die Eier von Satarn / Push it
61422311442 / Oct '96 / Zoo Entertainment

Toop, David
☐ PINK NOIR
Mixed blood / Ultra-paste / Pink noir / Almost transparent blue / Sugar frosted charcoal scene / Mr. Lullaby should have rocked you / Mamba point / Slow Loris versus Poison Snail / Lime leaves / Spore divination
AMBT 18 / Sep '96 / Virgin

☐ SPIRIT WORLD
Ceremony viewed through a iron slit / Sunless / Haunted gate / Phantoms keep watching / Sleeping powder / Spirits shimmered among the live people / Writen by snakes / Snapshots of a ghost / Aether talk
AMBT 22 / 8 Sep '97 / Virgin

Toors, Wille
☐ FRAN LOGAR SKOGAR
KR 20 / Mar '98 / Hurv

Toothpaste 2000
☐ FINE COOL WITH LOVE BEST
PARCD 028 / 23 Feb '98 / Parasol

Toots & The Maytals
☐ AN HOUR LIVE
GCD 8924 / Jan '98 / Genes

☐ BLA BLA BLA
CC 2706 / Jan '94 / Crocodisc

☐ DON'T TROUBLE
RB 3017 / Jan '96 / Reggae Best

☐ FUNKY KINGSTON
Sit right down / Pomp and pride / Louie Louie / I can't believe / Redemption song / Daddy's home / Funky Kingston / It was written down
RRCD 21 / Nov '90 / Reggae Refreshers
CDTRL 201 / Mar '94 / Trojan

☐ IN THE DARK
Got to be there / In the dark / Having a party / Time tough / I see you / Take a look in the mirror / Take me home country roads / Fever / Love gonna walk out on me / Revolution / 54-46 (was my number) / Sailing on
CDTRL 202 / Mar '94 / Trojan

☐ JAMAICAN MONKEY MAN (2CD Set)
SMDCD 223 / 10 Aug '98 / Snapper

☐ NEVER GROW OLD (Maytals)
I'll never grow old / Sweet sweet Jenny / Are you mine / Matthew Mark / My destination / True love / Just got to be / Treat me bad / Hallelujah / Don't let / War no more / Tell me you love me / Six and seven books of Moses / Four seasons / I'm gonna sit right down and cry over you
CDHB 143 / Oct '97 / Heartbeat

☐ PRESSURE DROP (The Best Of Toots & The Maytals)
54-46 (was my number) / Revival reggae / African Doctor / Take me home country roads / Funky Kingston / I can't believe / Revolution / Pressure drop / Monkey man / Gold and silver / Redemption song / Pomp and pride / Time tough / In the dark / Peeping Tom / Love gonna walk out on me / She's my scorcher / One eyed Enos / Feel alright / Thy Kingdom come / It must be true love / It's you / If you act this way / Monkey girl
CDTRL 171 / Oct '97 / Trojan

☐ REGGAE GREATS
54-46 (was my number) / Reggae got sould / Monkey man / Just like that / Funky Kingston / Sweet and dandy / Take me home country oads / Time tough / Spititual healing / Pressure drop / Peace perfect peace / Bam bam
5525842 / Jul '97 / Spectrum

☐ ROOTS REGGAE
RNCD 2132 / Oct '95 / Rhino

☐ TIME TOUGH (The Island Anthology/ 2CD Set)
Six and seven books of Moses / Broadway jungle / It's you / Never you change / John and James / 54-46 (was my number) / Do the reggay / Desmond Dekker came first / Sweet and dandy / Monkey man / Peeping Tom / One eyed enos / She's my scorcher / Pressure drop / Pomp and pride / Funky Kingston / Take me home, country roads / Time tough / In the dark / Reggae got soul / Rastaman / Living in the ghetto / Hallelujah / Get up, stand up / My love is so strong / Chatty chatty / Gee whizz / Just like that / Careless Ethiopians / Never get weary / Spend the weekend / Beautiful woman / Bam bam / Spiritual healing / B for butter / Peace, perfect peace / You know / (I've got) dreams to remember / Precious precious / Hard to handle / Freedom train
5242192 / Jul '96 / Island Jamaica

☐ VERY BEST OF TOOTS & THE MAYTALS, THE
MCCD 332 / 16 Mar '98 / Music Club

Top 8 Band 1996
☐ LIVE (3CD Set)
Royal Garden blues / Someday you'll be sorry / I'm gonna sit right down and write myself a letter / Have you met Mis Jones / I believe in miracles / Way down yonder in New Orleans / At the Jazz Band ball / Savoy blues / Do you know what it means to miss New Orleans / Sweet Georgia Brown / Georgia grind / Shine / California here I come / Pennies from heaven / Flying high / Bourbon Street Parade / I wanna be like you / Muskrat ramble / I can't get started / Sheik of Araby / All of me / Ice cream / When the saints go marching in / That's a plenty / Auf wiedersehn
TTD 616 / 29 Jun '98 / Timeless

Top Cat
☐ 9 LIVES OF THE CAT
NLDCD 001 / Feb '95 / 9 Lives

☐ CAT O NINE TALES
NLDCD 002 / Dec '95 / 9 Lives

Top, Emmanuel
☐ ASTEROID
NOMU 51CD / Oct '96 / Nova Mute

Topham, Top
☐ ON TOP 1963-1969
Heart of stone / Anything for now / You're gonna ruin me / Long and lonely year / Spider drag / Globetrotter / Funkology / Mini minor mo / Sugar babe / How blue can you get / Tryin' hard / I'm in love with you babe / Ridin' the blinds / Tell me sweet Mama / Shakin' it all around / Mean old pullman / Hot ginger / On top
IGOCD 2080 / Oct '97 / Indigo

Topley, William
☐ BLACK RIVER
WFRCD 6 / 17 Nov '97 / World Famous

Topper
☐ SOMETHING TO TELL HER
ANKST 080CD / Jul '97 / Ankst

Topping, Steve
☐ TIME AND DISTANCE
Adrenalin / Amongst the leaves / Renewal / Blueways / Watercolour / Son of Spock / Fossil / Time and Distance / Life divine
BBJ 1003 / 10 Aug '98 / Black Box Jazz

Toquinho
☐ AMIGOS (Toquinho & Vinicius)
1917522 / Apr '97 / EPM

Toraia Orchestra Of Tangiers
☐ YA BAY
TCD 1043 / Mar '97 / Tradition

Toral, Rafael
☐ CHASING THE SONIC BOOMS
E 33 / 23 Mar '98 / Ecstatic Peace

Torch, Sidney
☐ SIDNEY TORCH
Dance of the blue marionettes / Hot dog / Bugle call rag / Le cygne (the swan) / Twelfth street rag (one step) / Rendezvous / In the mood / Night ride / Temptation rag / You're a sweetheart / In the still of the night / Orient express
PASTCD 9747 / Jun '91 / Flapper

Torch Song
☐ TOWARD THE UNKNOWN REGION
Shine on me / Blue night / Raphael / Gumbo ya ya / Ruler of my heart / Toward the unknown region / Ballad of pearl and john / Shine on me / Field of view / Kang kalika / Slip away
4509989692 / Dec '96 / Warner Bros.

Torero Band
☐ EASY TIJUANA
Lonely bull / Tijuana taxi / Guantanamera / I'll never fall in love again / From me to you / Walk in the black forest / Spanish flea / Hello Dolly / All my loving / Spanish Harlem / This guy's in love with you / Casino Royale / Yesterday / A banda / America / If I were a rich man / Our day will come / Acapulco 1922 / Man and a woman / Happening
CDMFP 6251 / Sep '96 / Music For Pleasure

Torino
☐ ROCK IT
Rock it / Nights on fire / Seven mountains / Baby blue / It takes a man to cry / Showdown / Dance all night / One in a million / Shine / Turn it up
WKFMXD 123 / Mar '89 / FM

Torkanowsky, David
☐ STEPPIN' OUT
Steppin' out / Melody for jaco / Love song / Spring can really hang you up the most / Conflict of colour / Patrocenio / Has anybody heard from mickey p / Big greaze / Dance farewell
ROUCD 2090 / '88 / Rounder

Torme, Bernie
☐ ARE WE THERE YET
Teenage kicks / Come the revolution / Let it rock / All around the world / Mystery train / Search and destroy / Shoorah shoorah / Wild west / Star / Turn out the lights / Lies / Chelsea girls
HMRXD 168 / Apr '91 / Heavy Metal

☐ BACK TO BABYLON
All around the world / Star / Eyes of the world / Burning bridges / Hardcore / Here I go / Family at war / Front line / Arabia / Mystery train / TVOD / Kerrap / Love, guns and money
CDZEB 6 / Jul '91 / Zebra

☐ DEMOLITION BALL (Torme)
Fallen angel / Black sheep / Action / Ball and chain / Slip away / Long time coming / Spinnin' your wheels / Don't understand / Industry / Draw the line / US made / Let it go / Walk it / Man o' means
CDBLEED 2 / Apr '93 / Bleeding Hearts

☐ DIE PRETTY, DIE YOUNG (Torme)
Let it rock / Real thing / Ready / Sex action / Ways of the East / Killer / Memphis / Louise / Crimes of passion / Ghost train
HMRXD 94 / Nov '89 / Heavy Metal

☐ ELECTRIC GYPSIES
Wild west / Twentieth century / Lightning / Strikes / Too young / Call of the wild / DISE / Presences / I can't control myself / Go go / Shoorah shoorah / Star / Search and destroy / Possession / New world
RETRK 102 / Jul '98 / Retrowreck

☐ OFFICIAL BOOTLEG
Front line / Turn out the lights / Hardcore / Star / Burning bridges / TVOD / My baby loves a vampire / New Orleans / Love, guns and money / All around the world / Mystery train / Front line 2
CDTB 112 / '91 / Thunderbolt

☐ PUNK OR WHAT
Anyway anyhow anywhere / Don't look back / One night stands / Secret sevice / It's alright / Rebel / City's falling / Tear it down / Instant impact / Weekend / Dance / All nite / Trying again / I'm not ready
RETRK 104 / Jun '98 / Retrowreck

☐ TURN OUT THE LIGHTS
Turn out the lights / Painter man / Lies / America / Getting there / Possession / No reply / Chelsea girls / India / Oh no / Try and stop me / What's next / Back with the boys
RETRK 101 / Jul '97 / Retrowreck

☐ WILD IRISH
Rat / Ghost walking / Follow the leader / Bad blood / Howling at the moon / River / Walk don't run / Lonesome train / One more heartache / Yesterday and nowhere
RETRK 103 / Jun '98 / Retrowreck

Torme, Mel

☐ A&E'S EVENING WITH MEL TORME
Just one of those things / On Green Dolphin Street / You make me feel so young / Nightingale sang in Berkeley Square / Pick yourself up / Star dust / Love for sale / Since I fell for you / Three little words / Slipped disc / Smooth one/Rachel's dream / I remember you / It's easy to remember / Lover come back to me / Stairway to the stars / Oh lady be good / Ev'ry time we say goodbye
CCD 4736 / Nov '96 / Concord Jazz

☐ AROUND THE WORLD
Frenesi / Blue moon / You're getting to be a habit with me / Skylark / Perfidia / Autumn leaves / It's delovely / Recipe for romance / South of the border / Vaya con dios / I wish I were in love again / Tenderly / I've got a feeling I'm falling / Oh you beautiful doll / Sonny Boy / Bewitched, bothered and bewildered / Lullaby of the leaves / I hadn't anyone 'til you / Piccolino / Black moonlight
CDMFP 6217 / Sep '96 / Music For Pleasure

☐ CHRISTMAS SONGS
Christmas song / Have yourself a merry little christmas-just look around / Glow-worm / Christmas feeling / Christmas waltz / Sleigh ride / White christmas / Silver bells / God rest ye merry gentlemen / It happened in sun valley / Christmastime is here / Good king wenceslas / What child is this / Christmas was made for children
CD 83315 / Sep '92 / Telarc

☐ EASY TO REMEMBER
Don't let that moon get away / Day in, day out / I'll be seeing you / It's easy to remember / 'round midnight / I could have told you / I concentrate on you / Moon was yellow / Night we called it a day / I'm gonna miss you / In love in vain / Swingin' on the moon / Where are you / Portia brown / Long ago and far away / All I need is the girl
HCD 253 / May '94 / Hindsight

☐ FUJITSU-CONCORD JAZZ FESTIVAL (Japan '90)
Shine on your shoes / Looking at you/Look at that face / Nightingale sang in Berkeley Square / Wave / Stardust / Don't cha go 'way mad/Come to baby do / Christmas song/Autumn leaves / You're driving me crazy / Sent for you yesterday / Swingin' the blues / New York state of mind
CCD 4481 / Oct '91 / Concord Jazz

☐ GREAT AMERICAN SONGBOOK, THE
Stardust / You make me feel so young / Riding high / All God's chillun got rhythm / I'm gonna go fishin' / Don't get around much anymore / Sophisticated lady/I dinn't know about you / Rockin' in rhythm / It don't mean a thing if it ain't got that swing / Lovely way to spend an evening / I'll remember April/I concentrate on you / Autumn in New York / You gotta try / Just one of those things/On Green Dolphin Street / Party's over / I let a song go out of my heart
CD 83328 / Dec '93 / Telarc

☐ IN CONCERT - TOKYO (Torme, Mel & Marty Paich Dektette)
It don't mean a thing if it ain't got that swing / Cotton tail / More than you know / Sweet Georgia Brown / Just in time / When the sun comes out / Carioca / Too close for comfort / City / Bossa nova pot pourri / On the street where you live
CCD 4382 / Jun '89 / Concord Jazz

☐ IT'S A BLUE WORLD (Bethlehem Jazz Classics)
I got it bad and that ain't good / Till the clouds roll by / Isn't it romantic / I know why / All this and Heaven too / How long has this been going on / Polka dots and moonbeams / You leave me breathless / I found a million dollar baby / Wonderful one / It's a blue world / Stay as sweet as you are
CDGR 135 / Apr '97 / Charly

☐ MAGIC OF MEL TORME, THE
Stranger in town / Day by day / You've laughed at me for the last time / Am I blue / My rose marie / Anything can happen mambo / Hut sut song / All of you / Hold tight / Blue skies / Rose o'day / Spellbound / That old black magic (live) / Blue moon (live) / County fair (live) / Christmas song (merry christmas to you) / Mountain greenery (live) / You're driving me crazy (live)
MCCD 198 / Mar '95 / Music Club

☐ MEL AND GEORGE 'DO' WORLD WAR II (Torme, Mel & George Shearing)
Lili Marlene / I've heard that song before / I know why / Love / Aren't you glad you're you / Ellington medley / Walk medley / I could write a book / Lovely way to spend an evening / On the swing shift/Five o'clock whistle / Accentuate the positive / This is the army Mister Jones / We mustn't say goodbye
CCD 4471 / Jul '91 / Concord Jazz

☐ MEL TORME/ROB MCCONNELL AND BOSS BRASS (Torme, Mel/Rob McConnell/Boss Brass)
Just friends / September song / Don't cha go 'way mad / House is not a home / Song is you / Cow cow boogie / Handful of stars / Stars fell on Alabama / It don't mean a thing if it ain't got that swing / Do nothin' 'til you hear from me / Mood indigo / Take the 'A' train / Sophisticated lady / Satin doll
CCD 4306 / Jan '87 / Concord Jazz

☐ MY NIGHT TO DREAM (The Ballads Collection)
This is my night to dream/It must be true / My foolish heart / More than you know / Here's to my lady / Moonlight becomes you / After the waltz is over / Angel eyes / How do you say auf wiedersehn / If you could see me now / House is not a home / I'll be seeing you / I'll be around
CCD 47902 / 17 Nov '97 / Concord Jazz

☐ NIGHT AT THE CONCORD PAVILION
Sing for your supper / Sing sing sing / Sing (sing a song) / You make me feel so young / Early Autumn / Guys and dolls medley / I could have told you / Losing my mind / Deep in a dream / Goin' out of my head / Too darn hot / Day in, day out / Down for double / You're driving me crazy / Sent for you yesterday
CCD 4433 / Nov '90 / Concord Jazz

☐ NOTHING WITHOUT YOU (Torme, Mel & Cleo Laine)
CCD 4515 / Jul '92 / Concord Jazz

☐ REUNION (Torme, Mel & Marty Paich Dektette)
Sweet Georgia Brown / I'm wishing / Blues / Trolley song / More than you know / For whom the bell tolls / When you wish upon a star / Walk between raindrops / Bossa nova pot porri / Get me to the church on time / Goodbye look / Spain (I can recall)
CCD 4360 / Jul '90 / Concord Jazz

☐ RIGHT NOW
Comin' home baby / Homeward bound / My little red book / Walk on by / If I had a hammer / Strangers in the night / Better use your head / Time / Secret agent man / Pretty flamingo / Red rubber ball / All that jazz / You don't have to say you love me / Dominique's discotheque / Power of love / Lover's roulette / Ciao baby / Molly Marlene / King / Lima lady / Wait until dark / Only when I'm lonely
CK 65164 / Jun '97 / Sony Jazz

☐ SINGS FRED ASTAIRE
CDGR 124 / Mar '97 / Charly

☐ SWINGIN' ON THE MOON
Swingin' on the moon / Moonlight cocktail / I wished on the moon / Moon song / How high the moon / Don't let the moon get away / Blue moon / Velvet affair / No moon at all / Moonlight in Vermont / Oh you crazy moon / Moon was yellow
5113852 / 3 Aug '98 / Verve

☐ THAT'S ALL
I've got you under my skin / That's all / What is there to say / Do I love you because you're so beautiful / Folks who live on the hill / Isn't it a pity / Ho ba la la / PS I love you / Nearness of you / My romance / Second time around / Haven't we met / I know you're heart / You'd better love me / I see it now / Once in a lifetime / Hang on to me / Seventeen / I remember Suzanne / Only the very young / Paris smiles / Ev'ry day's like a holiday / One little snowflake / Christmas song
CK 65165 / Jun '97 / Sony Jazz

☐ TORME
All in love is fair / First time ever I saw your face / New York state of mind / Stars / Send in the clowns / Ordinary fool / When the world was young / Yesterday when I was young / Bye bye blackbird
RHCD 3 / Jan '87 / Rhapsody

☐ TOUCH OF CLASS, A
Careless hands / Again / Four winds and the seven seas / Old master painter / Stranger in town / Blue moon / I've got a feeling I'm falling / Bewitched bothered and bewildered / Don't fan the flame / My buddy / On a little street in Singapore / Oh you beautiful doll / You're getting to be habit with me / Heart and soul / Lullaby of the leaves
TC 885732 / 2 Feb '98 / Disky

☐ TRIBUTE TO BING CROSBY (Paramount's Greatest Singer)
This is my night to dream / It must be true / Moonlight becomes you / I can't escape from you / With every breath I take / Man and his dream / Without a word of warning / May I / Please / Thanks / Don't let that moon get away / Soon / It's easy to remember / Love in bloom / Day you came along / Pennies from heaven / Learn to croon
CCD 4614 / Oct '94 / Concord Jazz

☐ VELVET AND BRASS
Liza / Swing shift / I'll be around / Sweety / Love walks in / These are the things / If you could see / High and low / Have you met Miss Jones / Nobody else / Autumn serenade / I get a kick out of you / Still of the night / I'm glad
CCD 4667 / Oct '95 / Concord Jazz

Torment

☐ HYPNOSIS
NERDCD 057 / Jul '90 / Nervous

Tormentors

☐ ANNO DOMINI
ECLIPSE 004CD / Nov '96 / Nocturnal Art

Torn Bloody Poetry

☐ HARD BOILED WONDERLAND
OCHOE 001CD / 1 Dec '97 / Ochre

Torn, David

☐ BEST LAID PLANS
Before the bitter wind / Best laid plans / Hum of its parts / Removable tongue / In the fifth direction / Two face flash / Angle of incidents
8236422 / Mar '85 / ECM

☐ CLOUD ABOUT MERCURY
Suyafhu skin..snapping the hollow reed / Mercury grid / Three minutes of pure entertainment / Previous man / Network of sparks
8311082 / Mar '87 / ECM

☐ DAVID TORN COLLECTION, THE
CMPCD 2502 / 1 Jun '98 / CMP

☐ POLYTOWN
Honey sweating / Palms for Lester / Open letter to the heart of Diaphora / Bandaged by dreams / Warrior horsemen... / Snail hair dune / This is the abduction scene / Red sleep / Res majuko / City of the dead
CMPCD 1006 / May '94 / CMP

☐ TRIPPING OVER GOD
CMPCD 1007 / Jan '95 / CMP

☐ WHAT MEANS SOLID TRAVELLER
CMPCD 1012 / Apr '96 / CMP

Tornados

☐ 1960'S FRENCH EP COLLECTION, THE
525732 / Jul '97 / Magic

☐ COMPLETE TORNADOS (2CD Set)
RR 4708 / Jul '98 / Repertoire

☐ EP COLLECTION, THE
Telstar / Popeye twist / Love and fury / Jungle fever / Ridin' the wind / Dreamin' on a cloud / Red rosesand a sky of blue / Rip it up / All the stars in the sky / Hot pot / Earthy / Chasing moonbeams / Summer place / Swinging beefeater / Breeze and I / Ready Teddy / My babe / Joy stick / Flycatcher / Costermonger / Blue moon of Kennedy / Long tall Sally / Globe trotter / Alan's tune / Night ride / Chattanooga choo-choo / Life on Venus / Robot / Locomotion with me
SEECD 445 / Jul '96 / See For Miles

☐ ORIGINAL 60'S HITS, THE
MCCD 161 / Jul '94 / Music Club

☐ TORNADOS ARCHIVE, THE
Telstar / Jungle fever / Love and fury / Popeye twist / Locomotion with me / Globetrotter / Robot / Life on Venus / Ice cream man / Scales of justice / Hymn for teenagers / Dragonfly / Joystick / Hot pot / Monte Carlo / Blue blue blue beat / Exodus / Blackpool rock / Granada / Early bird / Stingray / Pop art goes Mozart / Is that a ship I hear
RMCD 228 / Apr '98 / Rialto

Torner, Gosta

☐ TRUMPET PLAYER
PHONTCD 9301 / Jun '94 / Phontastic

Toro, Yomo

☐ CELEBREMOS NAVIDAD
ASHECD 2003 / Nov '96 / Ashe

☐ GOLDEN HANDS
Le pepita de mango - salsa / Usted - Bolero mejicano / Curame - Salsa / Danzon criollo - Danzon instrumental / Vereda tropical / La otra - Bachara / Three minus two - Jibaro / Country / Invitacion patria - Salsa boriqua / Mi pueblo / Que es eso i jene - Guaracha jibara / Bello amanecer - Salsa / Amor sincero - Bolero romantico
TWI 1001CD / Mar '96 / Les Disques Du Crepuscule

Torok, Mitchell

☐ MEXICAN JOE IN THE CARIBBEAN (4CD Set)
Nacogdoches county line / I'll get my lovin' from someone else / Clingin' heart / Piney Woods boogie / Yearnin' / Someday (when someone hurts you) / Table hoppin' blues / Sober up / Little Hoo-wee / Judalina / Caribbean / Weep away / Caribbean / Hootchy kootchy Henry / Gigolo / Edgar the eager Easter bunny / Living on love / Haunting waterfall / Dancerette / World keeps turning around / Peasant's guitar / Roulette / Havana huddle / Smooth talk / My silly old heart / Sit down you're rocking the boat / Too late now / My kind of woman / Little Hoo-wee / Marching my blues away / Country and western (that's for me) / Red light, green light / No money down / It'll be all right / Woman by your side / I wish I was a little bit younger / Memories of you haunting me night and day / When Mexico gave up the rhumba / Go ahead and be a fool / Drink up and go home / Take this heart / Pledge of love / Another love from now / What's behind the strange door / You never belonged to me / Sweet revenge / Love me like you mean it / You win again / I can't help it (if I'm still in love) / Love your touch (love you so much) / Two words (True love) / You're tempting me / You can't keep a good man down / Honolulu baby / Filipino baby / How much (Do I love you) / Be kind to me / These things I hold dear / Date with a teardrop / All over again, again / You can't get there from here / You drive Buddy / PTA rock 'n' roll / Here I come cruel world / Teenie weenie bikini / Cryin' honky tonk blues / Caribbean / New guitar / You are the one / Especially for you / Kish Leon / Johnny's gone away to college / Mexican Joe / Little Hoo-wee / Rig-a-jig-a-boom / You are the one / That's my desire / Guardian Angel / Rose covered garden / When the stars get in your eyes / I want to know everything / Guardian Angel / Pink chiffon / Seventeenth summer / What you don't know (won't hurt you) / Happy street / Little boy in love / King of Holiday Island / El Tigre / Eating my heart out / Comancheros / Rio Grande / Fool's disguise / Mighty, mighty man / For somebody who's supposed to be hurtin' / I'm not myself / Hawaiian sunset / Little secrets / I wish I Timid soul / El Tigre / Summer romance / Your love / Too bad / For your precious love / Tree / What goes on in your heart / Imagination / Hidin' the hurt / Little teenage heart / Country music I gave you the best years of my life
BCD 15906 / May '96 / Bear Family

Torque

☐ TORQUE
M 7019CD / Apr '96 / Mascot

Torr, Michele

☐ GRANDS SUCCES
MCD 339 207 / '88 / Accord

☐ LA COMPIL DES MES SUCCES
108692 / 1 Jun '98 / Musidisc

☐ MICHELE TORR
113552 / 1 Jun '98 / Musidisc

Torres, Eddie Lalo

☐ IS EVERYWHERE
Quiero / Las Lagrimas Rojas / Arriba San Antonio / Que te han Contado / Balando Cumbia / Mejor Sin Ti / Margarita / Vida de mi Vida / Munequita / Sandra / Te Seguire Queriendo / Popurri
ROUCD 6072 / Nov '96 / Rounder

Torres, Edwin

☐ HOLY KID
KRS 293CD / 20 Apr '98 / Kill Rock Stars

Torres, Jaime

☐ CHARANGO
Chimba chica / La diablada / Naupaj tiempos jinan tatay / Mambo de machahuay / Ch'isi / Caminos en la puna / La peregrinacion / El dia que me quieras / Chacarera del tiempo / Zamba de la candeleria / Sirvinaco / Milonga de mis amores
1115949 / Jan '87 / Messidor

Torres, Juan Pablo

☐ TROMBONE MAN
Sweet cherry pie / From John to Johnny / Who's smoking / Fiesta for Juan Pablo / Foot tapping / Samba for Carmen / At daybreak / Four and como fue / Memories / Banana split / For Elsa
66058085 / Feb '96 / Bellaphon

Torres, Marcelo

☐ EDAD LUZ
F 1037CD / Jun '94 / Sonifolk

Torres, Roberto

☐ EL CASTIGADOR
CDGR 156 / May '97 / Charly

☐ JUNTOS (Torres, Roberto & Chocolate)
CDGR 238 / 27 May '98 / Charly

Torriani, Vico

☐ BIEDERMANN UND COOL MAN
Waikiki / Vagliamoci Tanto Bene / Immer, immer wieder / Sieben junge madchen / Piano / Komm und tanz / Bambonella aus Turin / Hello Mary Lou / Sempre Amore / Je t'aime bien Pinocchio / Pepino O Suricillo / Bon soir, Herr Kommissar / Mister / Ave Maria no morro / De Granada a Seville / Glaub' meiner liebe / La Tua Piccola Mano / Calcutta / Lass uns mal ein Tanzchen wagen / Das ist die wahre Liebe / Chitarra Romana / Signorina Cappuccina / J'ai rendezvous avec Paris / Das hat mir keiner von dir gesagt / Come Sempre / Boa Legani / Die grossen haben grosse Sorgen / Cosi come sei / Piove
BCD 16111 / Nov '96 / Bear Family

☐ GRANADA
Das machen nur die Beine von Dolores / Isabella (Andalusisches madchen) / Granada / Spanisches Abenteuer / Blaue nacht in Sevilla / Haya Ole / Soir Espaniol / Es war einmal ein Matador / Maria Dolores / Malaguena / Komm, wir fahren nach Venedig / Rose im Garten der Liebe / Florentinische nachte / Simonetta / Carina / Carissima / Habanera / Kleine orangenverkauferin / Barcarole / D'Amore / Wie schade, dass Venedig noch so weit ist / Buona sera, Annabell / Wenn im Tal die Glocken lauten / Oh schone Heimat / Und fuhr' ich ein Madchen / Wo meine Wiege stand / Alle kleinen Englein jetzt sur Ruh'
BCD 16109 / Nov '96 / Bear Family

Torske, Bjorn

☐ BJORN TORKSE
FERCD 005 / 22 Jun '98 / Nedi Myra

Tortharry

☐ WHEN MEMORIES ARE FREE
TAGA 001CD / Nov '94 / MAB

Tortoise

☐ DIGEST COMPENDIUM OF...
TKCB 70932 / May '97 / Thrill Jockey

☐ MILLIONS NOW LIVING
EFA 049722 / Jan '96 / City Slang

☐ MILLIONS NOW LIVING (Japanese Version)
TKCB 70931 / May '97 / Thrill Jockey

☐ RHYTHMS, RESOLUTIONS AND CLUSTERS
EFA 049572 / Jun '95 / City Slang

☐ TNT
TNT / Swung from the gutters / Ten-day interval / I set my face to the hillside / Equator / Simple way to go faster than light that does not work / Suspension bridge at Iguazu Falls / Four-day interval / In Sarah Mencken Christ and Beethoven there were women and m / Almost always is never enough / Jetty / Everglade
087052 / 9 Mar '98 / City Slang

☐ TORTOISE
EFA 049502 / Jan '95 / Sub Pop

☐ TORTOISE REMIXED
TKCB 71016 / 20 Apr '98 / Thrill Jockey

Tortoise Corpse

☐ STANDARD OF MISERY
CMGCD 012 / 11 May '98 / Communique

Tosca

☐ FUCK DUB (Remixes)
GSCD 003 / 15 Sep '97 / G-Stone

Toscho

☐ SERIOUS FUN
INAK 9041 / Oct '96 / In Akustik

Tosh, Andrew

☐ MAKE PLACE FOR THE YOUTH
Stop what you doin' / Things I used to do / Why did you do it / Come together / Time is longer than rope / Message from Jah / One step to happiness / Small axe / Evil ones / Make place for the youth / Stop what you doin'
CPCD 8186 / Oct '96 / Charly

☐ ORIGINAL MAN, THE
Same dog bite / Too much rat / Heathen rage / My enemies / Maga dog / I'm the youngest / Poverty is a crime / Original man / My enemies (dub version) / Poverty is a crime (dub version) / Original man (dub version)
CDHB 140 / Apr '94 / Heartbeat

Tosh, Peter

☐ BUSH DOCTOR
You gotta walk don't look back / Pick myself up / I'm the toughest / Soon come / Moses the prophet / Bush doctor / Stand firm / Dem ha fe get a beatin' / Creation
CDTRP 100 / Nov '90 / Trojan

☐ CENTENARY COLLECTION, THE (The Best Of Peter Tosh)
(You gotta walk) don't look back / Mama Africa / Johnny B. Goode / Where you gonna run / Maga dog / Crystal ball / Mystic man / Coming in hot / Reggaemylitus / Bush doctor / Pick myself up / No nuclear war / Hag goa jail / In my sing / Vampire / Wanted dread and alive
CTMCD 334 / 8 Sep '97 / EMI

☐ EQUAL RIGHTS
Get up stand up / Downpressor man / I am that I am / Stepping razor / Equal rights / African / Jah guide / Apartheid
CDV 2081 / Nov '88 / Virgin

☐ GOLD COLLECTION, THE
Johnny B Goode / Bush doctor / (You gotta walk) don't look back / No nuclear war / Come together / Na goa jail / Coming in hot / Pick myself up / In my song / Reggaemylitis / Equal rights / Crystal ball / Vampire / Lesson in my life / Testify / Maga dog
CDGOLD 1007 / Mar '96 / EMI Gold

☐ HONORARY CITIZEN (3CD Set)
C3K 65064 / 22 Sep '97 / Columbia

☐ LEGALIZE IT
Legalize it / Burial / What'cha gonna do / No sympathy / Why must I cry / Igziabeher (Let Jah be praised) / Ketchy shuby / Till your well runs dry / Brand new secondhand
CDV 2061 / Aug '88 / Virgin

☐ TOUGHEST, THE
Coming in hot / Don't look back / Pick myself up / Crystal ball / Mystic man / Reggaemylitis / Bush doctor / Maga dog / Johnny B Goode / Equal rights / In my song
CDHB 150 / Mar '96 / Heartbeat

☐ WANTED DREAD AND ALIVE
Coming in hot / Nothing but love / Reggaemylitis / Rock with me / Oh bumbo klaat / Wanted dread and alive / Rastafari is / Guide me from my friend / Fools die
7916702 / 1 Jun '98 / EMI

Toss The Feathers

☐ AWAKENING
Fever / Sunset / Awakening / Lonely man / Heritage / Requiem for the innocent / Thorn and nail / Drifting apart / Seven / Dr. Jekyll and Mrs. Hyde / Sail away / Long forgotten line
FC 003CD / Feb '93 / Fat Cat
MMRCD 301 / Dec '97 / Magnetic

☐ COLUMBUS ECLIPSE
MMRCD 401 / Dec '97 / Magnetic

☐ NEXT ROUND, THE
MMRCD 1004 / Mar '96 / Magnetic

Total

☐ BUFFIN' THE CELESTIAL MUFFIN
REP 001 / Apr '97 / Rural Electrification Programme

☐ KASPAR HAUSER
METONYMIC 003CD / Jun '97 / Metonymic

Total

☐ TOTAL
78612730062 / Feb '96 / Arista

Total

☐ ETERNITY'S BEAUTIFUL FRONTISPIECE
VHF 34 / 30 Mar '98 / VHF

Total Chaos

☐ ANTHEMS FROM THE ALLEYWAY
64712 / Jun '96 / Epitaph

☐ PATRIOTIC SHOCK
864502 / May '95 / Epitaph

☐ PLEDGE OF DEFIANCE
E 864382 / Apr '94 / Epitaph

Total Eclipse

☐ DELTA AQUARIDS
BR 2CD / Feb '97 / Blue Room Released

☐ VIOLENT RELAXATION (2CD Set)
BR 015CD / Feb '97 / Blue Room Released

Totenmond

☐ FLEISCHWALD
MASSCD 157 / 4 May '98 / Massacre

☐ VATERCHEN FROST
MASSDP 145 / 24 Nov '97 / Massacre

Totennacht

☐ DER SCHWARZE PRINZ
SQD 001CD / 28 Jul '97 / Serpent Qui Danse

Toto

☐ IV/THE SEVENTH ONE/KINGDOM OF DESIRE (3CD Set)
Rosanna / Make believe / I won't hold you back / Good for you / It's a feeling / Afraid of love / Lovers in the night / We made it / Waiting for your love / Africa / Pamela / You got me / Anna / Stop loving you / Mushanga / Stay away / Straight for the heart / Only the children / Thousand years / These chains / Home of the brave / Gypsy train / Don't chain my heart / Never enough / How many times / 2 hearts / Wings of time / She knows the devil / Other side / Only you / Kick down the walls / Kingdom of desire / Jake to the bone
4853262 / 3 Nov '97 / Columbia

☐ PAST TO PRESENT 1977-1990
Love has the power / Africa / Hold the line / Out of love / Georgie Porgie / I'll be over you / Can you hear what I'm saying / Rosanna / I won't hold you back / Stop loving you / Ninety nine / Pamela / Animal
4659982 / Sep '90 / CBS

☐ TAMBU
Gift of faith / I will remember / Slipped away / If you belong to me / Baby he's your man / Other end of time / Turning point / Time is the enemy / Drag him to the roof / Just can't get to you / Dave's gone skiing / Road goes on / Hold the line / Africa / Rosanna / I won't hold you back / I'll be over you
4812029 / Jul '96 / Columbia

☐ TOTO IV
Rossana / Make believe / I won't hold you back / Good for you / It's a feeling / Afraid of love / Lovers in the night / We made it / Waiting for your love / Africa
4500882 / Mar '91 / CBS

☐ XX
Goin' home / Tale of a man / Last night / In a word / Modern eyes / Right part of me / Mrs. Johnson / Miss Sun / Love is a man's world / On the run / Dave's gone skiing / Baba Mnumzane / Africa
4899652 / 1 Jun '98 / Columbia

Toto Bissainthe

☐ TOTO BISSAINTHE
LDX 274014 / Oct '95 / La Chant Du Monde

Toto Coelo

☐ I EAT CANNIBALS (& Other Tasty Tracks)
I eat cannibals / Mucho mucho / Man o'war / Milk from the coconut / Spy versus spy / Dracula's tango / Hey rajah / (I may commit) Perfect crime / Weird / I eat cannibals / Milk from the coconut
RE 21062 / Jul '96 / Razor & Tie

☐ I EAT CANNIBALS
I eat cannibals / Milk from the coconut / Man o'war / (I may commit) the perfect crime / Spy versus spy / Dracula's tango / Mucho macho / Milk from the coconut / Hey rajah / I eat cannibals
301652 / Jun '97 / Hallmark

Totsiou, A.

☐ RUSSIAN MUSIC FOR TWO PIANOS (Totsiou, A. & L.)
ML 0183 / 11 May '98 / Musurgia Graeca

Tottenham Hotspur FC

☐ GLORY GLORY TOTTENHAM HOTSPUR (Various Artists)
Glory glory Tottenham / Ossie's dream / Hot shot Tottenham / Tottenham Tottenham / It's a grand old team to play for / When the year ends in one / We're off to Wembley / Nice one Cyril / One team in London / Tottenham win away / We are Tottenham / Tribute to Ardiles and villa / Tip top Tottenham Hotspurs / Spurs go Spurs boogie / Up the Spurs / Spurs go marching on / Cry Gazza cry / Gascoigne please / Nice one Gazza / New cockeral chorus / Ooh Gary / Gary Lineker a young girls dream / Diamond lights / It's goodbye / Fog on the Tyne / All you need is love / Happy Christmas (war is over)
CDGAFFER 2 / Nov '95 / Cherry Red

Touch

☐ TOUCH SAMPLER VOL.2
TZERO 2 / Dec '96 / Touch

Touch

☐ STREET SUITE
GF 105 / 9 Feb '98 / Gear Fab

Touchstone

☐ JEALOUSY
Mooncoin jig/High reel/Plover's wing / Cuach mo lonndubh bui/Three sea captains / Last chance / Lonely wanderer / Primrose lass/Keel row/Green grow the rushes o / Garcon a marier/Orgies nocturnes/Dans fisel / Jealousy / King's favourite/ Cook in the kitchen/Din Turrant's polka / Invisible wings/Faolean / Green gates/Pinch of snuff / White snow
GLCD 1050 / Feb '90 / Green Linnet

☐ NEW LAND, THE
Kilmoulis jig/The maid at the spinning wheel / Jack Haggerty / Flowing tide/Cooley's hornpipe / Susanna Martin / Flying reel/My Maryann/Game of love / Casadh cam na Feadarnaighe / Three polkas / Farewell to Nova Scotia / Song in F / Bolen's fancy/ Dunmore lasses/Glass of beer / New land
GLCD 1040 / Feb '88 / Green Linnet

Touff, Cy

☐ HIS OCTET AND QUINTET (Touff, Cy Octet & Quintet)
Keester parade / TNT / What am I here for / Groover wailin' / Prezence / Half past jumping three / Smooth one / Primitive cats / It's sand man / Smooth one
4931622 / 18 May '98 / Pacific Jazz

Toulouse

☐ WAY THE CITY STRETCHES
G 005CD / Mar '97 / Won't Go Flat

Toups, Wayne

☐ BACK TO THE BAYOU (Toups, Wayne & ZydeCajun)
I saw Johnny dance / Mine, mine, mine / Old fashioned two-step / Take my hand / Come on in / Oh what a night / 4.A.M Alone / Un autre biere / Ma belle / Rockin' Saturday night / Every man needs a woman / Back door
IRCD 036 / Jul '96 / Iona

Toure, Ali Farke

☐ RADIO MALI
Njarka / Yer mali gakoyoyo / Soko / Bandalabourou / Machengoidi / Samarya / Hani / Gambari / Gambari (Njarka) / Biennal / Arsany / Amadinin / Seygalore / Trei kongo / Radio mali / Njarka (excerpt)
WCD 044 / Apr '96 / World Circuit

☐ SOURCE, THE
Goye kur / Goye kur / Roucky / Dofana / Karaw / Hawa dolo / Cinquante six / I go ka / Yenna / Mahini me
WCD 030 / Jun '92 / World Circuit

☐ TALKING TIMBUKTU (Toure, Ali Farke & Ry Cooder)
Blonde / Soukora / Gomni / Sega / Amandrai / Lasidan / Keito / Banga / Ai du / Diarabi
WCD 040 / Mar '94 / World Circuit

Toure Kunda

☐ AMADOU TILO
CPCD 8296 / Jul '97 / Charly

☐ BEST OF TOURE KUNDA, THE
CDNEW 119 / 30 Mar '98 / Charly

☐ CASAMANCE AU CLAIR DE LUNE
CPCD 8269 / Mar '97 / Charly

☐ E'MMA AFRICA
E'mma / On vera ca / Samala / Kambe / Africa Lelly / Soye / Bounane / Mango / Touty yolle
CPCD 8297 / Oct '97 / Charly

☐ KARADINDI
CPCD 8298 / Nov '97 / Charly

☐ LES FRERES GRIOTS
Em'ma / On verra ca / Samala / Kambe / Africa lelly / Soye / Bounane / Mango / Touty yolle
MPG 74041 / Jun '97 / Movieplay Gold

☐ NATALIA
Toure Kunda / Duu nya / Santhiaba silo / Natalia / M'barring / Fode / Babacady
CPCD 8268 / Dec '96 / Charly

☐ OKUNAYA
MPG 74048 / 3 Mar '98 / Movieplay Gold

☐ TOURE KUNDA
Turu / Salaly Muhamed / Banny / Kano kano / Samba / Waar / Guedj / Hamidu / Yaya bah
CPCD 8295 / Apr '97 / Charly

☐ TOURE KUNDA LIVE
CPCD 8226 / Aug '96 / Charly

Tourists

☐ GREATEST HITS
Blind among the flowers / I only want to be with you / Useless duration of time / Ain't no room / Save me / Fools paradise / So good to be back home again / It doesn't have to be this way / Lonliest man in the world / In the morning (when the madness has faded) / All life's tragedies / Everywhere you look / Deadly kiss / Don't say I told you so / From the middle room / Nothing to do / One step nearer the edge / Angels and demons / So you want to go away now / Strange sky
74321523812 / 29 Sep '97 / Camden

Tournesol

☐ KOKOTSU
Imeat / Electric church / Henka / Orange planet / Draagmad Ultramarine / Cathedral / Holy cow
AMB 4931CD / Mar '94 / Apollo

☐ MOONFUNK
Inside angel / Chords of rhythm / Junglemovie / Sunny blow / Interplanetary zonecheck / Electrowaltz / Scapeland / Break 'n' space / Voltage / Mapping your mind / Beljeane / 2095 / Clockworking clockwork clock
RS 95074CD / Aug '95 / R&S

Tourniquet

☐ CRAWL TO CHINA
9219312262 / Oct '97 / Benson

Toussaint, Allen

☐ 20 GOLDEN LOVE THEMES (Movie Themes) (Toussaint, Allen Orchestra)
MU 5036 / Oct '92 / Musketeer

☐ 50'S MASTERS, THE
Whirlaway / Happy times / Up the crek / Tim tam / Me and you / Bono / Java / Wham tousan / Nowhere to go / Nashua / Po' boy walk / Pelican parade / Chico / (Back home again in) Indiana / Second liner / Cow cow blues / Moo moo / Sweetie pie (twenty years later) / You didn't know, did you / Up right / Blue mood / Lazy day / Naomi / Real churchy / Real church
BCD 15641 / Mar '92 / Bear Family

☐ ALLEN TOUSSAINT COLLECTION, THE
On your way down / Soul sister / Last train / You will not lose / Night people / Lover of love / Happiness / Viva la money / From a whisper to a scream / Am I expecting too much / With you in mind / Motion / Southern nights / Country john / What is success / What do you want the girl to do
7599265492 / May '95 / Reprise

☐ FROM A WHISPER TO A SCREAM
From a whisper to a scream / Chokin' kind / Sweet touch of love / What is success / Working in a coalmine / Everything I do gohn be funky / Either / Louie / Cast your fate to the wind / Number nine / Pickles
CDKENM 036 / Mar '91 / Kent

☐ MOTION
Night people / Just a kiss away / With you in mind / Lover of love / To be with you / Motion / Viva la money / Declaration of love / Happiness / Optimism blues
7599265972 / Jan '96 / Reprise

☐ SOUND OF MOVIES, THE (Toussaint, Allen Orchestra)
MU 5038 / Oct '92 / Musketeer

☐ WILD SOUND OF NEW ORLEANS PIANO, THE
Up the creek / Tim Tam / Me And You / Bono / Java / Happy Times / Nowhere to go / Nashua / Po' Boy Walk / Pelican parade / Whirlaway / Wham Tousan
EDCD 275 / Apr '91 / Edsel

Toussaint, Jean

☐ LIFE I WANT
Blue funk / It's for you / Island man / Life I want / Crouch End afternoon / Soho strut / Gangway / Short straw / Grooving at the hall / London / Red cross
NNCD 1001 / Oct '95 / New Note

☐ WHAT GOES AROUND
Transformer / What goes around / Lower bridge level / Rice head / Ruby my dear / Poo's shuffle / Brother joe / Autumn leaves (french version) / Trinkle tinkle / Transformer
WCD 029 / May '92 / World Circuit

☐ WHO'S BLUES
Opening gambit / Who's blues / London / Visiting / Body language / Yanar's dance / Soundtrack / Chameleon
JHCD 019 / Jan '94 / Ronnie Scott's Jazz House

Tovey, Frank

☐ CIVILIAN
New jerusalem / Ultramarine / From the city to the isle of dogs / Bridge st. shuffle / Brotherhood / Diana / Unknown civilian / Desperate dan
CDSTUMM 56 / Jun '88 / Mute

☐ FAD GADGET SINGLES
Back to nature / Box / Ricky's hand / Fireside favourite / Insecticide / Lady shave / Saturday night special / King of the flies / Life on the line / 4M / For whom the bells toll / Love parasite / I discover love / Collapsing new people / One man's meat
CDSTUMM 37 / '86 / Mute

☐ SNAKES AND LADDERS
Cutting edge / Snakes and ladders / Shot in the dark / Concrete / Collapsing new people / Luxury / Small world / Luddite joe / Megalomaniac / Coitus interruptus / Sheep look up / Ideal world
CDSTUMM 23 / '86 / Mute

☐ TYRANNY AND THE HIRED HAND
'31 depression blues / Hard times in the cotton mill / John Henry/Let your hammer ring / Blantyre explosion / Money cravin' folks / All I got's gone / Midwife song / Sam Hall / Dark as a dungeon / Men of good fortune / Sixteen tons / North country blues / Buffalo skinners / Black lung song / Pastures of plenty / Joe hill
CDSTUMM 73 / Aug '89 / Mute

Tower City

☐ ALL OR NOTHING
199650 / 25 May '98 / Made To Measure

☐ LITTLE BIT OF FIRE, A
19966 / Oct '96 / Made To Measure

Tower Of Power

☐ BUMP CITY
You got to funkifize / What happend to the world that day / Flash in the pan / Gone / You strike my main nerve / Down to the nightclub (bump city) / You're still a young man / Skating on thin ice / Of the earth
7599263482 / Sep '93 / Warner Bros.

☐ IN THE SLOT
Just enough and too much / Treat me like your man / If I play my cards right / As surely as I stand here / Fanfare-matanuska / On the serious side / Ebony jam / You're so wonderful, so marvelous / Vuela por noche / Essence of innocence / Soul of a child / Drop it in the slot
7599263502 / Sep '93 / Warner Bros.

☐ RHYTHM & BUSINESS
So I got the groove / Crazy for you / East bay way / Unconditional love / You do the math / More you know / Recapture the magic / What's your trip / Rhythm and business / Don't knock me down / That was then this is now / It really doesn't matter / Spank a dang
4887102 / 20 Oct '97 / Sony Jazz

☐ SOULED OUT
Souled out / Taxed to the max / Keep comin' back / Soothe you / Do you wanna (make love to me) / Lovin' you forever / Gotta make a change / Diggin' on James Brown / Sexy soul / Just like you / Once you get a taste / Undercurrent
4809422 / Sep '95 / Epic

☐ URBAN RENEWAL
Only so much oil in the ground / Come back baby / It's not the crime / I won't leave unless you want me to / Maybe it'll rub off / (To say the least) you're the most / Willing to learn / Give me the proof / It can never be the same / I believe in myself / Walkin' up hip street
7599263492 / Sep '93 / Warner Bros.

Tower Recordings

☐ FURNITURE MUSIC FOR EVENING SHUTTLES
SB 54CD / 18 May '98 / Siltbreeze

Towering Inferno

☐ KADDISH
Rose / Prayer / Dachau / 4 By 2 / Edvard Kiraly / Memory / Not me / Reverse field / Occupation / Sto Mondo Rotondo / Organ loop / Toll / Toll (II) / Ruin / Juden / Pogrom / Partisans / Modern times / Bell / Kaddish / Weaver
CID 8039
CIDX 8039 / Aug '95 / Island

Townend, Rick

☐ MAKE THE OLD TIMES NEW (Townend, Rick & Rosie Davis)
BOBB 001CD / Nov '95 / British Bluegrass

Towner, Ralph

☐ ANA
Reluctant bride / Tale of saverio / Joyful departure / Green and golden / I knew it was you / Les douzilles / Veldt / Between the clouds / Child on the porch / Carib crib (1 and 2) / Slavic blood / Toru / Sage brush rider
5370232 / Apr '97 / ECM

☐ BATIK
Waterwheel / Shades of Sutton Hoo / Trellis / Batik / Green room
8473252 / Oct '89 / ECM

☐ BLUE SUN
Blue sun / Prince and the sage / C.t. kangaroo / Mevlana etude / Wedding of the streams / Shadow fountain / Rumours of rain
8291622 / Oct '86 / ECM

☐ CITY OF EYES
Jamaica stopover / Cascades / Les douzilles / City of eyes / Sipping the past / Far cry / Janet / Sustained release / Tundra / Blue gown
8377542 / May '89 / ECM

☐ CLOSER VIEW, A (Towner, Ralph & Gary Peacock)
Opalesque / Viewpoint / Mingusiana / Creeper / Infrared / From branch to branch / Postcard to Salta / Toledo / Amber captive / Moor / Beppo / Closer view
5316232 / 2 Feb '98 / ECM

☐ DIARY
Dark spirit / Entry in a diary / Images unseen / Icarus / Mon enfant / Ogden road / Erg / Silence of a candle
8291572 / Aug '86 / ECM

☐ LOST AND FOUND
Harbringer / Trill ride / Elan vital / Summer's end / Col legno / Soft landing / Flying cows / Mon enfant / Breath away / Scrimshaw / Midnight blue...red shift / Moonless / Sco cone / Tattler / Taxi's waiting
5293472 / Feb '96 / ECM

☐ MATCHBOOK (Towner, Ralph & Gary Burton)
Drifting petals / Some other time / Brotherhood / Icarus / Song for a friend / Matchbook / 1x6 / Aurora / Goodbye pork pie hat
8350142 / Oct '88 / ECM

☐ OLD FRIENDS, NEW FRIENDS
8291962 / Oct '86 / ECM

☐ OPEN LETTER
Sigh / Wistful thinking / Adrift / Infection / Alar / Short 'n' stout / Waltz for Debby / I fall in love too easily / Magic touch / Magnolia Island / Nightfall
5119802 / Jun '92 / ECM

☐ SARGASSO SEA (Towner, Ralph & John Abercrombie)
Fable / Avenue / Sargasso sea / Over and gone / Elbow room / Staircase / Romantic descension / Parasol
8350152 / Sep '88 / ECM

☐ SLIDE SHOW (Towner, Ralph & Gary Burton)
Maelstrom / Vessel / Around the bend / Blue in green / Beneath an evening sky / Donkey jamboree / Continental breakfast / Charlotte's tangle / Innocenti
8272572 / Feb '86 / ECM

☐ SOLO CONCERT
Spirit lake / Ralph's piano waltz / Train of thought / Zoetrope / Nardis / Chelsea courtyard / Timeless
8276682 / Dec '85 / ECM

☐ SOLSTICE
Oceanus / Visitation / Drifting petals / Numbus / Winter solstice / Piscean dance / Red and black / Sand
8254582 / '82 / ECM

☐ SOUND AND SHADOWS
Distant hills / Balance beam / Along the way / Arion / Song of the shadows
8293862 / Oct '89 / ECM

☐ TRIOS AND SOLOS (Towner, Ralph & Glen Moore)
Brujo / Winter light / Noctuary / 1x12 / A belt of asteroids / Re: person i knew / Suite; 3x12 / Raven's wood / Reach me, friend
8333282 / Jul '88 / ECM

☐ WORKS
Oceanus / Blue sun / New moon / Beneath an evening sky / Prince and the sage / Nimbus
8232682 / Jun '89 / ECM

Townes, Billy

☐ LIVIN' FOR YOUR LOVE
Moroccan pasta / Minutes to go / Low gear / For my friend / Snowbound / Hypnotique / And the beat goes where / Sea breeze / Sun city at night / Dawn / Livin' for your love
101S 71422 / Nov '93 / 101 South

Townsend, Devon

☐ BIOMECH
USG 10212 / 6 Apr '98 / USG
REVXD 222 / Feb '98 / Revolver

Townshend, Emma

☐ WINTERLAND
Better than music / Last time I saw Sadie / Walk at night / Ghost kitchen / My angel of vertigo / Ambition of my heart / Groundswell / Five-a-side football / Wish finger / How gardens grow / Ladder
3984246852 / 2 Mar '98 / East West

Townshend, Pete

☐ ALL THE BEST COWBOYS HAVE CHINESE EYES
Stop hurting people / Sea refuses no river / Slit skirts / Somebody saved me / North country girl / Uniforms (crop d'esprit) / Stardom in Acton / Communication / Exquisitely bored / Face dances part two / Prelude
7567828122 / Jan '96 / Atco

☐ COOLWALKINGSMOOTHTALKING STRAIGHTSMOKINGFIRESTOKING
Rough boys / Little is enough / Let my love open the door / Slit skirts / Street in the city / Give blood / Let my love open the door / Sheraton gibson / Friend is a friend / Uneasy street / Pure easy / English boy / Face the face / Misunderstood / Sea refuses no river
7567827122 / May '96 / Atco

☐ EMPTY GLASS
Rough boys / I am an animal / And I moved / Let my love open the door / Jools and Jim / Keep on working / Cats in the cupboard / Little is enough / Empty glass / Gonna get ya
7567828112 / Nov '95 / Atco

☐ PSYCHODERELICT
English boy / Meher baba M3 / Let's get pretentious / Maher baba M4 (signal box) / Early morning dreams / I want that thing / Dialogue introduction to Outlive The Dinosaur / Outlive the dinosaur / Flame (demo) / Now and then / I am afraid / Don't try to make me real / Dialogue introduction to Predictable / Predictable / Flame / Meher baba m5 / Fake it / Dialogue introduction to Now And Then (Reprise) / Now and then (reprise) / Baba O'Riley / English boy (reprise)
7567824942 / Jun '93 / Atco

☐ WHITE CITY
Second hand love / Give blood / Brilliant blues / Crashing by design / Lonely words / White City fighting / Face the face / All shall be well / Hiding out / Closing sequence
2523922 / Apr '86 / Atco

☐ WHO CAME FIRST
Pure and easy / Evolution / Forever's no time at all / Let's see action / Time is passing / There's a heartache following me / Sheraton Gibson / Content / Parvardigar / His hands / Seeker / Day of silence / Sleeping dog / Loved man / Latern cabin
RCD 10246 / Mar '97 / Rykodisc

Township Express

☐ FISHBONE
JK 005 / 7 Jul '98 / Jika

Toxic Waste

☐ TOXIC WASTE/BLEEDING RECTUM (Toxic Waste/Bleeding Rectum)
REJ 1000018 / 8 Jun '98 / Rejected

Toy Dolls

☐ BARE FACED CHEEK
Bare faced cheek / Yul Bryner was a skinhead / How do you deal with Neal / Howza bouta kiss babe / Fisticuffs in Frederick Street / A Diamond / Quick to quit the Quentin / Nowt can compare to Sunderland Fine-Fare / Ashbrooke launderette
RRCD 232 / Mar '97 / Receiver

☐ ONE MORE MEGABYTE
RRCD 236 / May '97 / Receiver

☐ RECEIVER YEARS, THE
RRCDX 504 / Sep '95 / Receiver

☐ TEN YEARS OF TOYS
Florence is deaf (But there's no need to shout) / Glenda and the test tube baby / Idle gossip / Carol Dodds is pregnant / Tommy Knowey's car / Peter practise's practise place / Dierdre's a slag / Blue suede shoes / Dig that groove baby / Lambrusco kid / Doughy giro / Bless you my son / My girlfriend's Dad's a vicar / She goes to fino's / Firey Jack
RRCD 234 / Jan '97 / Receiver

Toyah

☐ ACOUSTIC ALBUM, THE
Vow / Moonlight dancing / Revive the world / I want to be free / It's a mystery / Danced / Good morning universe / Blue meanings / Jungles of jupiter / It's a mystery (up-tempo) / Leyla / Angels and demons / I am / Thunder in the mountain / It's a mystery(string version)
ANT 012 / Nov '96 / Tring

☐ BEST OF TOYAH, THE
It's a mystery / Good morning universe / I want to be free / Neon womb / Be proud, be loud, be heard / Bird in flight / Rebel run / Brave new world / Dawn chorus / Victims of the riddle / Vow / Tribal look / Thunder in the mountains / Angel and me / Danced / leya
CSAPCD 115 / Feb '94 / Connoisseur Collection

☐ LIVE AND MORE
Good morning universe / Warrior rock / Jungles of Jupiter / It's a mystery / Neon womb / Victims of the riddle / Angel and me / Brave new world / Urban tribesman / To the mountains high / Danced / Thunder in the mountains / We are / I want to be free / I believe in Father Christmas / Leya
CSAPCD 125 / 1 Jun '98 / Connoisseur Collection

☐ LOOKING BACK
I wanna be free / Obsolete / It's a mystery / We are / Thunder in the mountains / Good morning universe / Angel and me / Be proud, be loud / Danced / Rebel run / leya
QED 065 / Nov '96 / Tring

☐ PHOENIX
Now and then / Let me go / World of tension / Out of the blue / Unkind / Dreamchild / Lost and found / Over you / I don't know / Disappear / Tone poem / Now and then / Phoenix
RRCD 235 / Apr '97 / Receiver

☐ VERY BEST OF TOYAH, THE
It's a mystery / Good morning universe / I want to be free / Be proud be loud be heard / Bird in flight / Rebel run / Brave new world / Thunder in the mountains / leya / Street creature / Elusive stranger / Martian cowboy / Love me / Broken diamonds / Castaways / She / Jungles of Jupiter / We are
REMCD 501 / Feb '98 / Reactive

Toyama, Yoshio

☐ DUET (Toyama, Yoshio & Ralph Sutton)
JCD 226 / Apr '94 / Jazzology

Toyota Pipes & Drums

☐ AMAZING GRACE
March, strathspey and reel / Slow air, jig and hornpipe / 6/8 Marches / Amazing grace / By the rivers of Babylon / Mount Fuji / Greatest hits medley / Sands of time / Magnificent seven / Send in the clowns / Salute to America
LCOM 5133 / Jun '93 / Lismor

Toys

☐ LOVER'S CONCERTO/ATTACK
SC 6034 / 20 Jul '98 / Sundazed

T'Pau

☐ BRIDGE OF SPIES
Heart and soul / I will be with you / China in your hand / Friends like these / Sex talk / Bridge of spies / Monkey house / Valentine / Thank you for goodbye / You give up / China in your hand (reprise)
CDVIP 179 / Apr '97 / Virgin VIP

☐ GREATEST HITS
Place in my heart / I will be with you / Bridge of spies / Valentine / Secret garden / Promise / Hold on to love / Strange place / No sense of pride / Only the lonely / This girl / Road to our dream / Sex talk / Heart and soul / Only a heartbeat / China in your hand / Whenever you need me
CDVIP 221 / 3 Aug '98 / Virgin VIP

☐ HEART AND SOUL (The Best Of T'Pau)
Heart and soul / Valentine / Only a heartbeat / Whenever you need me / Secret garden / Sex talk / Road to our dream / This girl / Only the lonely / Bridge of spies / I will be with you / China in your hand
TPAUD 1 / Mar '93 / Virgin

☐ PROMISE, THE
Soul destruction / Whenever you need me / Walk on air / Made of money / Hold on to love / Strange place / One direction / Only a heartbeat / Promise / Place in my heart / Man and woman / Purity
CDVIP 124 / Mar '94 / Virgin VIP

Trace

☐ WHITE LADIES
4189 / 23 Feb '98 / Musea

Tracey, Clark

☐ FULL SPEED SIDEWAYS
Revenge of Sam Tracet / They're lovely / Sherman at the Copthorne / Sphere my dear / Mark nightingale song / Arnie's barnie / Chased out
33JAZZ 018 / Apr '95 / 33 Jazz

☐ WE'VE BEEN EXPECTING YOU (Tracey, Clark Quintet)
33JAZZ 007CD / Jun '93 / 33 Jazz

Tracey, Stan

☐ FOR HEAVEN'S SAKE
SGCCD 04 / May '96 / Cadillac

☐ LAUGHIN' AND SCRATCHIN' (Tracey, Stan Trio)
JHAS 608 / Mar '97 / Ronnie Scott's Jazz House

☐ SOLO TRIO
SGCCD 06 / Feb '98 / Cadillac

Tracii Guns

☐ KILLING MACHINE
SB 001 / 13 Apr '98 / Stand Back

Track Star

☐ COMMUNICATION BREAKS
DIE 002CD / 24 Nov '97 / Die Young Stay Pretty

Tractor

☐ TRACTOR
All ends up / Little girl in yellow / Watcher / Ravenscroft's 13 bar boogie / Shubunkin' / Hope in favour / Every time it happens / Make the journey
REP 4081 / Aug '91 / Repertoire

☐ WORST ENEMIES
Lost on the ocean / Average man's hero / Suicidal / Argument for one / Word games / Trick of the light / Scotch boulevard / No more rock 'n' roll / Peterloo
OZITCD 0019 / May '97 / Ozit

Tractors

☐ HAVE YOURSELF A TRACTOR CHRISTMAS
Santa Claus is coming to town / Jingle my bells / Shelter / Rockin' this Christmas / Santa looked a lot like Daddy / Christmas is coming / Santa Claus is comin' (in a boogie woogie choo choo train) / Baby wanna be by you / Swingin' home for Christmas / White Christmas / Santa Claus boogie / Silent night / Christmas blue
07822188052 / Nov '95 / Arista

☐ TRACTORS, THE
Tulsa shuffle / Fallin' apart / Thirty days / I've had enough / Little man / Baby likes to rock it / Badly bent / Blue collar rock / Doreen / Settin' the woods on fire / Tryin' to get to New Orleans / Tulsa shuffle (Revisited)
07822187282 / Aug '94 / Arista

Tracy, Arthur

☐ ALWAYS IN SONG
PLATCD 36 / Mar '95 / Platinum

☐ MARTA (The Return Of The One & Only Street Singer)
Across the great divide / Broken hearted clown / East of the sun and west of the moon / Greatest mistake of my life / I'll see you again / I'll sing you a thousand love songs / In a little gypsy tea room / Love's last word is spoken / My curly headed baby / Marta / Music, maestro, please / Old sailor / Red maple leaves / Roses of Picardy / September in the rain / Smilin' through / South Sea island magic / Stay awhile / When I grow too old to dream / Where are you / Whistling waltz / You are my heart's delight
CDAJA 5095 / Feb '98 / Living Era

☐ SPEAK TO ME OF LOVE
Speak to me of love / East of the Sun and West of the moon / Brokenhearted clown / September rain / Trees / Love's last word is spoken / In a little gipsy tea room / It looks like rain in Cherry Blossom Lane / Serenade / Whistling waltz / Give me a heart to sing to / Smoke gets in your eyes / Roses of Picardy / South of the border / (I'm afraid) The masquerade is over / Solitude / Where are you / Wheel of the wagon is broken / Farewell sweet senorita / It's a sin to tell a lie / Somewhere in the West / When I'm with you / Marta (rambling rose of the wild wood) / When I grow too old to dream
CDMOIR 517 / Aug '96 / Memoir

☐ STREET SINGER, THE
There's a goldmine in the sky / Waltz for those in love / Giannina mia / Water lilies in the moonlight / When the organ played 'O promise me' / Halfway to heaven / Song of songs / Smilin' through / Faithful forever / Just a wearyin' for you / Hills of old Wyomin' / Along the Santa Fe trail / We three (my echo, my shadow and me) / Breeze and I / Shepherd's serenade / Say it (over and over again) / Shrine of St. Cecilia / When the roses bloom again / Last time I saw Paris / Somewhere in France with you / White cliffs of Dover / Marta
PASTCD 7006 / Mar '93 / Flapper

☐ STREET SINGER, THE
Serenade / Marta / Little lady make believe / There's rain in my eyes / I won't tell a soul / Ol' man river / Goodnight angel / Roses of Picardy / Masquerade is over / San Antonio Rose / I shall always remember you smiling / Sweetest song in the world / Goodnight my love / In a little gypsy tea room / It's my mother's birthday today / It's a sin to tell a lie / When I grow too old to dream / Trees / Red sails in the sunset / Where are you / Little love, a little kiss / Home / Danny boy
SWNCD 016 / Oct '97 / Sound Waves

☐ VERY BEST OF THE STREET SINGER VOL.2
I'll see you again / Home town / Music maestro please / Little old lady / I shall be waiting / Choir boy / Halfway to heaven / Breeze and I / Song of songs / September in the rain / Delyse / White cliffs of dover / Shepherd's serenade / We three / Way you look tonight / Red maple leaves / Broken hearted clown / Say it / Faithful forever / Old pal of mine / Along the santa fe trail / Smoke gets in your eyes / Smilin' through
SWNCD 002 / May '95 / Sound Waves

Tracy, Jeanie

☐ IT'S MY TIME
PULSE 17CD / Nov '95 / Pulse 8

Tracy, Steve

☐ GOING TO CINCINNATI
BSCD 4707 / '92 / Blue Shadow

Trad Gras Och Stenar

☐ GARDET 12/6/1970
TILCD 01 / Jun '97 / Subliminal

Trader Horne

☐ MORNING WAY...PLUS
Jenny may / Children of oare / Three rings for eleven kings / Growing man / Down and out blues / Mixed up kind / Better than today / In my loneliness / Sheena / Mutant / Morning way / Velvet to atone / Luke that never was / Here comes the rain / Goodby mercy kelly
SEECD 308 / '90 / See For Miles

Tradia

☐ TRADE WINDS
Never gonna go / Let's not turn love away / Without you / Look away / No pain, no gain / Stand your ground / Don't play your ace / Take the chance / You've got me crying again / Exiles
WKFMXD 108 / Jul '88 / FM

Trafalgar

☐ FACEDOLL
SD 012 / 8 Jun '98 / Stereo Deluxe

Traffic

☐ BEST OF TRAFFIC, THE
Paper sun / Heaven is in your mind / No face, no name, no number / Coloured rain / Smiling phases / Hole in my shoe / Medicated goo / Forty thousand headmen / Feeling alright / Shanghai noodle factory / Dear Mr. Fantasy
IMCD 169 / Mar '93 / Island

☐ FAR FROM HOME
Riding high / Here comes a man / Far from home / Nowhere is their freedom / Holy ground / Some kinda woman / Every night, every day / This train won't stop / State of grace / Mozambique
CDV 2727 / May '94 / Virgin

☐ JOHN BARLEYCORN MUST DIE
Glad / Freedom rider / Empty page / Stranger to himself / John Barleycorn / Every mother's son
IMCD 40 / Sep '89 / Island

☐ LAST EXIT
Just for you / Shanghai noodle factory / Something's got a hold of my toe / Withering tree / Medicated goo / Feeling good / Blind man
IMCD 41 / Sep '89 / Island

☐ LOW SPARK OF HIGH-HEELED BOYS, THE
Hidden treasure / Low spark of high heeled boys / Light up or leave me alone / Rock 'n' roll stew / Many a mile to freedom / Rainmaker
IMCD 42 / Sep '89 / Island

☐ MR. FANTASY
Heaven is in your mind / Berkshire poppies / House for everyone / No face, no name, no number / Dear Mr. Fantasy / Dealer / Utterly simple / Coloured rain / Hope I never find me there / Giving to you
IMCD 43 / Sep '89 / Island

☐ ON THE ROAD
Glad/Freedom rider / Tragic magic / (Sometimes I feel so) Inspired / Shoot out at the fantasy factory / Light up or leave me alone / Low spark of high heeled boys
IMCD 183 / Mar '94 / Island

☐ SHOOT OUT AT THE FANTASY FACTORY
Shoot out at the fantasy factory / Roll right stones / Evening blue / Tragic magic / Sometimes I feel so uninspired
IMCD 44 / Sep '89 / Island

☐ TRAFFIC
You can all join in / Pearly queen / Don't be sad / Who knows what tomorrow may bring / Feeling alright / Vagabond virgin / Forty thousand headmen / Cryin' to be heard / No time to live / Means to an end
IMCD 45 / '89 / Island

☐ WELCOME TO THE CANTEEN (Recorded Live)
Medicated goo / Sad and deep / As you / Forty thousand headmen / Shouldn't have took more than you gave / Dear Mr. Fantasy / Gimme some lovin'
IMCD 39 / '89 / Island

☐ WHEN THE EAGLE FLIES
Something new / Dream Gerrard / Graveyard people / Walking in the wind / Memories of a rock and rolla / LOVE / When the eagle flies
IMCD 142 / Aug '91 / Island

Traffic Sound

☐ TRAFFIC SOUND
HBG 122/13 / Apr '94 / Background

☐ TRAFFIC SOUND 1968-1969
HBG 122/4 / Mar '94 / Background

Traffik

☐ SOCA SUMMER
CAR 004CD / 13 Jul '98 / Cariwak

Tragedy Divine

☐ VISIONS OF POWER
TT 00212 / Mar '96 / T&T

Tragert, Walter

☐ HEAVY JUST THE SAME
MRCD 1095 / Jun '96 / Club De Musique

Tragic Error

☐ KLATCH IN DIE HANDEN
WHOS 022CD / '90 / Who's That Beat

Tragically Hip

☐ DAY FOR NIGHT
Grace, too / Daredevil / Greasy jungle / Yawning or snarling / Fire in the hole / So hard done by / Nautical disaster / Thugs / Inevitability of death / Scared / Inch an hour / Emergency / Titanic terrarium / Impossibilium
MCD 11140 / 18 Aug '97 / MCA

☐ FULLY COMPLETELY
Courage / Looking for a place to happen / At the hundreth meridan / Pigeon camera / Lionized / Locked in the trunk of a car / We'll go too / Fully completely / Fifty mission cap / Wheat kings / Wherewithal / Eldorado
MCLD 19314 / Aug '97 / MCA

☐ LIVE BETWEEN US
UMD 81055 / 18 Aug '97 / Universal

☐ PHANTOM POWER
Poets / Something on / Save the planet / Bobcaygeon / Thompson girl / Membership / Fireworks / Vapour trails / Rules / Chagrin falls / Escape is at hand for the travellin' man / Emperor Penguin
4344310252 / 3 Aug '98 / Sire

☐ ROAD APPLES
MCD 10173 / 18 Aug '97 / MCA

☐ TROUBLE AT THE HENHOUSE
Gift shop / Springtime in Vienna / Ahead by a century / Don't wake daddy / Flamenco / 700 ft. ceiling / Butts wigglin / Apartment song / Coconut cream / Let's stay engaged / Sherpa / Put it off
MCD 81011 / Aug '97 / MCA

☐ UP TO HERE
Blow at high dough / I'll believe in you / New Orleans is sinking / 38 years old / She didn't know / Boots or hearts / Everytime you go / When the weight comes down / Trickle down / Another midnight / Opiated
MCD 06310 / Sep '97 / MCA

Trail Of Thebow

☐ ORNAMENTATION
RR 69122 / Jul '96 / Relapse

Trailer Hitch

☐ LONG TALL TALES, THE
MR 040 / 22 Jun '98 / Man's Ruin

Train Journey North

☐ FIRST TRACKS
Faca sibh mairi nighean Alisdair / Wha'll be King but Charlie/Galway Trolley/Double rise / Road to Drumlemon / Da new rigged ship/The chanter's tune/MacArthur Road / Hebridean reel/The trip to Windsord / Skyemans jig/Skylark ascension/Alex MacDonald/Echoes of Oban / Bobs of Balmoral/ Curlew / Glasgow city Police Pipe Band/Jenny Dang the weaver/Hogties / Domhnull ban nan gobhar / Melody O'Farrel / Far from home/The streaker/ Rodrigo / Coille an fhabach
CDLDL 1207 / Feb '97 / Lochshore

Training For Utopia

☐ PLASTIC SOUL IMPALEMENT
2629710992 / 3 Mar '98 / Tooth & Nail

Trains & Boats & Planes

☐ ENGULFED
RAIN 002 / Jan '94 / Cloudland

☐ HUM
UFO 010CD / Mar '92 / UFO

Traitors

☐ TRAITORS
JFR 041CD / 11 May '98 / Johann's Face

Trammell, Bobby Lee

☐ YOU MOSTEST GIRL
Shirley Lee / I sure do love you baby / You mostest girl / Uh oh / Should I make amends / My Susie Jane my Susie Jane / Martha Jane / Jenny Lee / It's all your fault / Couldn't believe my eyes / You stand a chance of losing what you've got / Love don't let me down / Twenty four hours / Am I satisfying you / I tried / Just let me love you one more time / Come on and love me / If you don't wanna you don't have to / Give me that good lovin' / New dance in France / Long Tall Sally
BCD 15887 / Nov '95 / Bear Family

Trammps

☐ LEGENDARY ZING ALBUM, THE
Penguin at the big apple/Zing went the strings of my heart / Pray all you sinners / Sixty minute man / Scrub board / Tom's song / Rubber band / Hold back the night / Penguin at the big apple
CDKENM 088 / Oct '88 / Kent

Tramp

☐ BRITISH BLUES GIANTS
Own up / What you gonna do when the road comes through / Somebody watching me / Baby, what you want me to do / On the scene / Hard work / Too late for that now / What you gonna do / You gotta move / Funky money / Maternity orders (keep on rolling in) / Same old thing / Too late now / Street walking blues / Month of Sundays / Another day / Now I ain't a junkie anymore / Like you used to do / Put a record on / Beggar by your side / It's over
SEECD 354 / Sep '92 / See For Miles

Tramp, Mike

☐ CAPRICORN
Already gone / Have you ever / Better off / Wait for me / Love will come and go / If I live tomorrow / Here I don't belong / Heart of every woman / Had I not complained / Running out of life
CDSINE 001 / 20 Oct '97 / Music For Nations

Trance Atlantic Air Waves

☐ ENERGY OF SOUND, THE
Lucifer / Axel F. / Crockett's theme / Dance with the devil / Addiction day / Magic fly / Chase / Twelve after midnight / L 42 / Pulstar
DGVIR 65 / 2 Mar '98 / Dindisc

Trance Groove

☐ PARAMOUNT
Dschang thang / Stone soup / Trainspotting / Ange gardien / Morning zoo / Hotel Clapham / In a field / Paramount / Paris / Wedding / Terje rypdal
CIA 40002 / Oct '96 / Call It Anything

☐ SOLID GOLD EASY ACTION
Reebop / Character / Bladerunner / Waiting man / Fireball / Driving south / Swamp / Air Afrique / Mamboo moon / Water / Low tide / Bladerunner II / Reebop radio edit
VBR 21432 / Jun '94 / Vera Bra

Trance Mission

☐ TRANCE MISSION
CDSGP 0303 / Jul '96 / Prestige

Trance To The Sun

☐ GHOST FOREST
EFA 064822 / Apr '94 / Tess

Trancendental Anarchists

☐ CLUSTER ZONE
SR 9462CD / Jan '95 / Silent

Tranquil

☐ TO REACH THE HEAVENS
CLOUD 14 / 24 Nov '97 / Colourful Clouds

Tranquility

☐ PACIFIC DAWN
Pacific dawn
307032 / 11 May '98 / Hallmark

☐ WHALES OF THE DEEP
Discovery / Whales of the deep / Dance of the deep / Farewell
307062 / 11 May '98 / Hallmark

Tranquility Bass

☐ BEEP
ASW 6237 / 4 May '98 / Astralwerks

☐ LET THE FREAK FLAG FLY
Five miles high / La la la / Bird / Soldiers sweetheart / We all want to be free / Never gonna end / I'll be here / Let the freak flag fly / Lichen me to Wyomin'
ASW 6200CD / Apr '97 / Astralwerks

Trans Am

☐ SURRENDER TO THE NIGHT
Motr / Cologne / Illegalize it / Love commander / Rough justice / Zero tolerance / Tough love / Night dreaming / Night dancing / Carboforce / Surrender to the night
EFA 0498826 / Feb '97 / City Slang

☐ TRANS AM
EFA 049772 / Apr '96 / City Slang

☐ TRANS AM (Japanese Issue)
TKCB 71017 / Dec '97 / Thrill Jockey

Trans Megetti

☐ STEAL THE JET KEYS
AMC 17 / 30 Mar '98 / Art Monk

Trans-Europe Express

☐ TRANS EUROPE EXPRESS
CLEO 5878CD / Jan '94 / Cleopatra

Trans-Lucid

☐ DREAM DUST
AQUACD 2 / Feb '97 / Aquarius

Transambient Communications

☐ MOONMEN
Moonmen (intro) / Radio friendly / Weightless / Bubble / V5 / Are we water / Special orgee / Armstrong / Moonbeams / Receiving transmission / Moonmen (outro)
STONE 025CD / 30 Mar '98 / 3rd Stone

☐ PRAZE-AN-BEEBLE
Seabeams / Ocean waves at sunset / They shoot geese don't they / Alaska / Arcades / Mauve / Iceman / Alaska / What is muzik / River
STONE 015CD / 30 Mar '98 / 3rd Stone

Transcend

☐ 2001-2008 FULL LENGTH
2001 / 2002 / 2003 / 2004 / 2005 / 2006 / 2007 / 2008
NTONECD 007 / Sep '95 / Ntone

☐ VERSION 8.5
SSR 005CD / Jul '95 / Stormstrike

Transcendental Love Machine

☐ ORGASMATRONIC
DUKE 032CD / Jan '97 / Hydrogen Dukebox

Transfinite

☐ BUGGED
KINXCD 5 / Feb '97 / Kinetix

Transglobal Underground

☐ DREAM OF 100 NATIONS
NRCD 021 / Oct '93 / Nation

☐ INNERNATION VOL.2 (Nation Records Peel Sessions) (Transglobal Underground/Fun-Da-Mental/Loop Guru)
This is the army of forgotten souls: Transglobal Underground / Yalla chant: Transglobal Underground / Shimmer: Transglobal Underground / Sirius B: Transglobal Underground / Justice or just defy: Fun-Da-Mental / Truth commission: Fun-Da-Mental / Mr. Bubbleman: Fun-Da-Mental / Front line: Fun-Da-Mental / Paradigm shuffle: Loop Guru / Dreaming with Kings: Loop Guru / Under influence: Loop Guru / Aphrodites shoe: Loop Guru
SFRSCD 041 / 8 Dec '97 / Strange Fruit

☐ INTERNATIONAL TIMES
NATCD 38 / Oct '94 / Nation

☐ INTERPLANETARY MELTDOWN
NATCD 57 / Oct '95 / Nation

☐ PSYCHIC KARAOKE
NRCD 1067 / May '96 / Nation

☐ REJOICE REJOICE
Nice little fish business and making money / Delta disco / Thousand year heat / Body machine / Imperial hippy / Rude buddah / Air giant / Ali Mullah / City of gold / Chemnitz / Shining iron face / Son of thingdrum / Sky giant
NRCD 1273 / 22 Jun '98 / Nation

Transient Waves

☐ TRANSIENT WAVES
IRE 2042 / Jun '97 / I

☐ WADING AND WAITING
DRL 046CD / 6 Oct '97 / Darla

Transistor

☐ TRANSISTER
What you are / Dizzy moon / Look who's perfect now / Day no.1 / Falling off the world / Then I walked away / Weather boy / Flow / Stars collide / I saw red / Head
CDV 2847
CDVX 2847 / 6 Jul '98 / Virgin

Transits Of Tone

☐ SYNTHESIZED THERAPY
Audio motive / Molecular structure / Dawning / Acid bunker / Sem X 4 / Wild life / Syncrone / Dawning / Cyborg remake / Computer / Dawning / Battle zone
INTCD 20 / Oct '96 / Intelligence

Transjoik

☐ MAHKALAHKE
BACH 007CD / Mar '98 / Atrium

Transmetal

☐ BURIAL AT SEA
GCI 89804 / Jun '92 / Plastic Head

Transmisia

☐ DUMBSHOW
INV 027CD / Jun '94 / Invisible
WD 010CD / Jul '97 / Wide

☐ FRIGID PROSE
WD 024CD / Apr '97 / Wide

☐ MINCING MACHINE
WD 019CD / Jul '97 / Wide

Transmission

☐ TRANSMISSION
ASH 018 / Mar '97 / Audible Hiss

Transvision Vamp

☐ BEST OF TRANSVISION VAMP, THE
MCLD 19376 / 8 Jun '98 / MCA

☐ POP ART
Trash city / I want your love / Sister moon / Psychosonic Cindy / Revolution baby / Tell that girl to shut up / Wild star / Hanging out with Halo Jones / Andy Warhol's dead / Sex kick
MCLD 19224 / Sep '93 / MCA

☐ VELVETEEN
Baby I don't care / Only one / Landslide of love / Falling for a goldmine / Down on you / Song to the stars / Kiss their sons / Born to be sold / Pay the ghosts / Bad valentine / Velveteen
MCLD 19215 / Aug '93 / MCA

Transwave

☐ PHOTOTROPIC
SUB 48092 / Dec '96 / Distance

Traore, Boubacar

☐ SA GOLO
Sa golo / Mouso teke soma ye / Yafa ma / Dounia / Ntaara diagnamogo fe / Ala ta deye tignaye / Je chanterai pour toi / Soundiata
LBLC 2534 / Jul '96 / Indigo

Traore, Rokia

☐ MOUNEISSA
Laidu / Mouneissa / Finini / Dianguina / Sabali / Tchiwara / Fatalite / Sakanto / Se
LBLC 2524 / 29 Jun '98 / Indigo

Trapeze

☐ HIGH FLYERS (The Best Of Trapeze)
8209572 / Jan '96 / Deram

☐ HOLD ON
Don't ask me how I know / Take good care / When you get to heaven / Livin' on love / Hold on / Don't break my heart / Running / You are / Time will heal
SEECD 450 / 10 Aug '98 / See For Miles

☐ LIVE IN TEXAS (Dead Armadillos)
Black cloud / You are the music, we're just the band / Way back to the bone / Back street love / Hold on / Midnight flyer
SEECD 462 / 10 Aug '98 / See For Miles

☐ MEDUSA
Black cloud / Jury / Your love is alright / Touch my life / Seagull / Mates you wanna cry / Medusa
8209552 / Feb '94 / London

☐ TRAPEZE
It's only a dream / Giants dead, hoorah / Over / Nancy Gray / Fairytale / Verily verily / It's my life / Am I / Suicide / Wings / Another day / Send me no more letters
8209542 / Feb '94 / London

☐ YOU ARE THE MUSIC, WE'RE THE BAND
Keepin' time / Coast to coast / What is a woman's role / Way back to the bone / Feelin' so much better now / Will our love end / Loser / We are the music
8209562 / Feb '94 / London

Trapezoid

☐ COOL OF THE DAY
SHCD 1132 / Jan '97 / Sugar Hill

☐ NOW AND THEN
FF 239CD / May '93 / Flying Fish

Trapp

☐ STOP THE GUNFIGHT
Stop the gunfight / Can I get your number / Standtall / 5th Ward / Don't drink and drive / History / Be the realist brick house / Monkey see monkey do / Swing that axx / When I come down / Recognize / Stone jam
0099242RAP / 10 Aug '98 / Edel

Trasante, Negrito

☐ UNTIL DAWN
972 / Aug '93 / Kardum

Trash

☐ INDUSTRIAL SAMPLE/COREGOUCH BEAT
EFA 000912 / 1 Dec '97 / Mille Plateau

Trash Can Sinatras

☐ CAKE
Obscurity knocks / Obscurity knocks / Thruppeny tears / Even the odd / Best man's fall / Circling the circumference / Funny / Only tongue can tell / You made me feel / January's little joke
8282012 / Jul '90 / Go Discs

☐ HAPPY POCKET, A
Make yourself at home / Twisted and bent / Main attraction / To Sir, with love / How can I apply / Unfortunate age / Outside / Pop place / Genius I was / Sleeping policeman / I must fly / I'll get them in / Safecracker / Therapist
8286962 / Sep '96 / Go Discs

Trashmen

☐ BIRD CALL 1961-1967 (The Twin City Stomp Of The Trashmen/4CD Set)
Cyclon / Sally Jo / Johnny B. goode / Malaguena / Suzie Q / Sweet little sixteen / Million reasons / Malaguena / Guitar boogie / Surfin' bird / King of the surf / This should go on forever / Yellow jacket / Rumble / Let's go trippin' / My woodie / Bird bath / Tube city / Farmer Louie / Goofy foot / Church key / Raw-hide / Bird dance beat / A-bone / Stick shift / Ghost rider in the sky / Think it over / Be true to your school / Too young / Greensleeves / Wild cat loose in town / Green onions / Walk don't run / We belong together / True true lovin' / Roll over Beethoven / Congratulations (to me) / Hava nigala / Drive in / Walkin' the dog / Break-up / Bad news / On the move / New generation / Whoa dad / Peppermint man / Baja / Long tall Texan / Great balls of fire / Lost angel / Bye bye Johnny / Slow down / Walkin' my baby / Keep your hands off my baby / Hi-heel sneakers / Summertime / Long tall Sally / Real live doll / Dancin' with Santa / Bird '65 / Ubangi stomp / That I love you / Loves made a fool of you / Same lines / Hangin' on to me / Hanging on to me / Pretty country girl / My your own business / Talk about love / Gloria / Tell me how / Bird Diddley beat / It takes two / Heartbeat / Well all right / Talk about love / I'm not your stepping stone / Breathless / What'd I say / Money
SC 11022 / 9 Mar '98 / Sundazed

☐ LIVE BIRD 1965-1967
Let's go trippin' / Baja / Lovin' up a storm / Malaguena / Green onions / Surfin' bird / Henrietta / Rumble / Bird dance beat / King of the surf / The Mashed potatoes / Ubangi stomp / Dai Winslow interview / Same lines / Keep your hands off my baby
CDSC 11006 / Jan '94 / Sundazed

Traum, Artie

☐ CAYENNE
Cayenne / Nod / Snippy man / Shambhala / Catskill thunder / Morning flight / Blue jay boogie / Robbie's mirage / Foolin' around / Overseas / Late night / Monhegan dream
ROUCD 3084 / ' / Rounder

☐ LETTERS FROM JOUBEE
SHAN 5008CD / Dec '93 / Shanachie

☐ VIEW FROM HERE, THE
SHCD 5016 / Mar '96 / Shanachie

Trauma Club

☐ HEADOLOGY
JCRACD 008 / 26 Jan '98 / Just Create

Travelin' Light

☐ CHRISTMAS WITH TRAVELIN' LIGHT
Let it snow, let it snow, let it snow / Sleigh ride / Frosty the Snowman / Twelve days of Christmas / Carol of the bells / Have yourself a merry little Christmas / We wish you a merry Christmas / Jingle bells / Rudolph the red nosed reindeer / Here comes Santa Claus / Winter wonderland / Christmas song / Silver bells / Silent night
CD 83330 / Nov '93 / Telarc

☐ COOKIN' WITH FRANK & SAM
Manior de mes beves / Monk's dream / Dark eyes / Deep purple / Say it's so / Under Paris skies / Dig / Mood indigo / Alice's fax / Nuages / FDR Jones / Smoke gets in your eyes / Song d'automne / Lover
CCD 4647 / Jun '95 / Concord Jazz

☐ MAKIN' WHOOPEE
Micro / Wabash blues / China boy / You are my sunshine / Bill bailey won't you please come home / Mack the knife / Alexander's ragtime band / Chasin' the antelope / New orleans / Up a lazy river / Little suede shoes / Makin' whoopee / Indiana / Jambalaya / Georgia on my mind / Carioca / What'll I do
CD 83324 / Feb '93 / Telarc

Traveling Wilburys

☐ TRAVELING WILBURYS VOL.1
Handle with care / Dirty world / Rattled / Last night / Not alone anymore / Congratulations / Heading for the light / Margarita / Tweeter and the monkey man / End of the line
9257962 / Oct '88 / Wilbury

☐ TRAVELING WILBURYS VOL.3
She's my baby / Inside out / If you belonged to me / Devil's been busy / Seven deadly sins / Poor house / Where were you last night / Cool dry place / New blue moon / You took my breath away / Wilbury twist
7599263242 / Nov '90 / Wilbury

Travers, Pat

☐ BEST OF PAT TRAVERS, THE
SHR 2037 / 10 Nov '97 / Shrapnel

☐ BLUES TRACKS VOL.1
Memory pain / Calling card blues / I can't quit you / Statesboro' blues / I've got news for you / I ain't superstitious / Built for comfort / Mystery train / Just got paid / Sitting on top of the world
RR 91472 / Sep '96 / Roadrunner

☐ BLUES TRACKS VOL.2
BB 20382 / 15 Jun '98 / Blues Bureau

☐ BORN UNDER A BAD SIGN
PATT 33 / 6 Jul '98 / Dressed To Kill

☐ HALFWAY TO SOMEWHERE
PRD 70842 / Oct '95 / Provogue

☐ JUST A TOUCH
RR 90452 / Sep '96 / Roadrunner

☐ LOOKIN' UP
PRD 70972 / Oct '96 / Provogue

☐ PAT TRAVERS BAND, THE
SFRSCD 038 / 15 Sep '97 / Strange Fruit

Travis

☐ GOOD FEELING
All I want to do is rock / U16 girls / Line is fine / Good day to die / Good feeling / Midsummer nights dreamin' / Tied to the 90's / I love you anyways / Happy / More than us / Falling down / Funny thing
ISOM 1CD / 8 Sep '97 / Independiente

Travis Cut

☐ SERIAL INCOMPETENCE
Electric retarder / Not to blame / Waking hours / Had a gun / Totally / Just a girl / Mailage / Open letter / Theme park / Acceptance / Wuss / No static
DAMGOOD 68CD / Apr '95 / Damaged Goods

Travis, Merle

☐ COUNTRY HOEDOWN SHOWS AND FILMS OF THE 1940S/50'S
RFDCD 14 / Feb '95 / Country Routes

☐ FOLKSONGS OF THE HILLS
Nine pound hammer / That's all / John Bolin / Muskrat / Dark as a dungeon / John Henry / Sixteen tons / Possum up a Simmon tree / I am a pilgrim / Over by number nine / Barbara Allen / Lost John / Black gold / Harlan County boys / Pay day comes too slow / Browder explosion / Bloody Brethitt County / Here's to the operators, Boys / Miner's wife / Courtship of second cousin Claude / Miner's strawberries / Paw walked behind us with a cabride lamp / Preacher lane / Dear old Halifax
BCD 15636 / May '93 / Bear Family

☐ GUITAR RAGS & A TOO FAST PAST (5CD Set)
You'll be lonesome too / Steppin' out kind / When Mussolini laid his pistol down / Two time Annie / What will I do / So long, farewell, goodbye / God put a rainbow in the clouds / It may be too late / Be on your way / Rainin' on the mountains / Give me your hand / Out on the open range / Ridin' down to Santa Fe / Hominy grits / That's all / Used to work in Chicago / Boogie woogie boy / Boogie woogie boy (Alt) / Merle's buck dance / Steel guitar stomp / I used to work in Chicago / I'm all thru trusting you / Weary lonesome me / No vacancy / Cincinnati Lou / Two is a couple (And three is a crowd) / What a shame / T For Texas (Blue yodel) / Missouri / Divorce me COD / Fool at the steering wheel / Nine pound hammer / Sixteen tons / Dark as a dungeon / Over by number nine / John Henry / Muskrat / I am a pilgrim / This world is not my home / Covered wagon rolled right along / Oh why oh why did I ever leave Wyoming / Little too far / When Rosie Riccoola do the Hoola Ma Boola / Steel guitar rag (Alt) / Honey bunch (Alt) / Sweet temptation / Don't hand me that line / Steel guitar rag / Honey bunch / So round, so firm, so fully packed / Alimony bound / Follow thru / Three time's seven / I'm sick and tired of you little darlin' / Sunshine's back in town / Devil to pay / Lawdy, what a gal / Sioux City Sue / Fat gal (False start) / Fat gal / I like my chicken fryin' size / Merle's boogie woogie (Alt) / Merle's boogie woogie / Dapper Dan / When my baby double talks to me / I'm pickin up the pieces of my heart / Information please / Any old time / Kentucky means paradise / Leave my honey bee alone / I'm a natural born gamblin' man / Get along blues / Too fast past / Crazy boogie / You better try another man / Deck of cards / Wabash cannonball / Blues stay away from me / Philosophy / I got a mean old woman / Petticoat fever / Start even / Cane bottom chair / I'm knee deep in trouble / Little Miss Sherlock Holmes / Too much sugar for a dime / Spoonin' moon / Trouble, trouble / El Reno / Won't cha be my baby / Dry bread / Lost John Boogie / Deep south / Boogie in minor / Let's settle down (To runnin' around together) / Done rovin' / Faithful fool / Love must be ketchin' / Kinfolks in Carolina / Rainy day feelin' / Ain't that a cryin' shame / I'll see you in my dreams / Cannonball rag / I'll have myself a ball / Bayou baby (Cajun lullaby) / Green Cheese / Louisiana boogie / Saturday night shuffle / Waltz you saved for me / Crazy about you / Re-enlistment blues / Dance of the golden road / Gambler's guitar / Shut up and drink your beer / Seminole drag / Jolie fille / I can't afford the coffee / Blue bell / Memphis blues / Sheikh of araby / On a bicycle made for two (Daisy Belle) / Black diamond blues / Blue smoke / Walking the strings / Sleepy time gal / Tuck me to sleep in my old 'Tucky home / Rock-a-bye rock / Bugle call rag / Cuddle up a little closer / Beer barrel polka / Turn my picture upside down / If you want it, I've got it / Lazy river / Hunky dory
BCD 15637 / Jun '94 / Bear Family

☐ MERLE TRAVIS 1944-1965
Old Joe Clark / Nine pound hammer / Down yonder / Blues / Rock-a-bye rag / Sugar Hill / Cincinati Lou / House of David blues / Memphis blues / Wildwood flower / Midnight special / Bugle call rag / Give me your hand / Fireball mail / Smoke on the water / Fox chase / Turn your radio on / Maple on the hill / Tiger rag / Mose Merle rag / Old guitar blues (in A) / I'll see you in my dreams / Sixteen tons / Cannonball rag / John Henry / Rock-a-bye rag / Under the double eagle / No vacancy/So firm so round so fully packed / Nine pound hammer / I'll see you in my dreams
RFDCD 20 / Jun '98 / Country Routes

Travis, Mike

☐ VIEW FROM WHERE, THE (Travis, Mike EH15)
Regarding Nelson: Travis, Mike / Grandfather clock menace: Travis, Mike / Cycle time: Travis, Mike / Forethought: Travis, Mike / L'allegria: Travis, Mike / Moonlight over joppa: Travis, Mike / Shall we Mr.Witherspoon: Travis, Mike / Backtalk: Travis, Mike
ECLCD 9105 / Apr '96 / Eclectic

Travis, Randy

☐ BEST OF RANDY TRAVIS, THE
On the other hand / Diggin' up bones / 1982 / Good intentions / Tonight we're gonna tear down the walls / Honky tonk moon / He walked on water / It's just a matter of time / Wind in the wire / If I didn't have you / This is me / Before you kill us all / Point of light / Hard rock bottom of your heart / Deeper than the holler / Forever and ever amen / Too gone too long / No place like home
9548334612 / Apr '95 / WEA

☐ GREATEST NO.1 HITS
1982 / Diggin' up bones / Forever and ever amen / Too gone too long / I told you so / Deeper than the holler / It's just a matter of time / Hard rock bottom of your heart / Look heart no hands
9362470282 / 24 Aug '98 / Warner Bros.

☐ HIGH LONESOME
Let me try / Oh what a time to be me / Heart of hearts / Point of light / Forever together / Better class of losers / I'd surrender all / High lonesome / Allergic to the blues / I'm gonna have a little talk
7599266612 / Oct '91 / WEA

☐ OLD 8 BY 10
Forever and ever, amen / Honky tonk moon / Deeper than a holler / It's out of my hands / Is it still over / Written in stone / Blues in black and white / Here in my heart / We ain't out of love yet / Promises
WX 162CD / Jul '88 / WEA

☐ YOU AND YOU ALONE
DRD 50034 / 20 Apr '98 / Dreamworks

Travis, Theo

☐ 2AM
33JAZZ 011 / Jun '93 / 33 Jazz

☐ SECRET ISLAND
Lulworth night / Crow road / After the storm / Waterlily / Details / Out of sight, out of mind / Three people / Full moon rising / Nostalgia in Times Square
33JAZZ 033 / Sep '96 / 33 Jazz

☐ VIEW FROM THE EDGE
Fort Dunlop / Love for sale / Ghosts of Witley Court / Freedom / View from the edge / Psychgroove / I'm coming home / Empathy / Purple sky
33JAZZ 019 / May '95 / 33 Jazz

Travis, Tom

☐ TOM TRAVIS BLUEGRASS BAND
BOBB 003CD / Nov '95 / British Bluegrass

Travolta, John

☐ 20 GREATEST HITS
Razzamatazz / Never gonna fall in love again / Let her in / Rainbows / I don't know what I like about you / Baby, I could be so good at loving you / It had to be you / Goodnight Mr. Moon / Slow dancin' / You set my dreams to music / Whenever I'm away from you / Settle down / Back doors crying / Moonlight / Can't let you go / What would they say / Sandy / Right time of the night / Easy evil / Greased lightnin'
12892 / May '97 / Laserlight

☐ BEST OF JOHN TRAVOLTA, THE
Sandy / Girl like you / Whenever I'm away from you / All strung out on you / Let her in / Never gonna fall in love again / Rainbows / Razzamatazz / I don't know what I like about you baby / Big trouble / Goodnight Mr. Moon / Baby, I could be so good at lovin' you / Greased lightnin' / It had to be you / Slow dancin' / Can't let you go / Easy evil / Back doors crying / What would they say / Right time of the night / Moonlight lady / Settle down / You set my dreams to music
3035900072 / Feb '96 / Essential Gold

☐ BEST OF JOHN TRAVOLTA, THE
Greased lightnin' / Sandy / I don't know what I like about you baby / What would they say / You set my dreams to music / Goodnight Mr. Moon / Back doors crying / Let her in / Baby I could be so good at lovin' you / Easy evil / Never gonna fall in love again / Razzamatazz / Settle down / Rainbows / Big trouble / Moonlight lady / Slow dancing / Can't let you go / It had to be you / Right time of the night
ECD 3259 / Jan '97 / K-Tel

☐ BEST OF JOHN TRAVOLTA, THE
HTCD 93 / 20 Apr '98 / Hot Productions

☐ GREASED LIGHTNIN'
PLSCD 123 / Apr '96 / Pulse

☐ GREASED LIGHTNIN'
CDPS 003 / Feb '96 / Pulsar

☐ GREASED LIGHTNIN'
Let her in / Never gonna fall in love again / Rainbows / Razzamatazz / I don't know what I like about you baby / Big trouble / Goodnight Mr. Moon / Sandy / Baby, I could be so good at lovin' you / It had to be you / Slow dancing / Can't let you go / Easy evil / Back doors crying / What would they say / Right time of the night / Moonlight lady / Greased lightnin' / Settle down / You set my dreams to music
MM 012 / 24 Aug '98 / MagMid

☐ JOHN TRAVOLTA
Let her in / Never gonna fall in love / Rainbows / Razzamatazz / I don't know what I like / Big trouble / Goognight Mr Moon / Sandy / Baby, I could be so good at lovin' you / It had to be you / Slow dancin' / Can't let you go / Easy evil / Back doors cryin' / What would they say / Right time of the night / Moon lightnin' / Greased lightnin' / Settle down / You set my dreams to music
EMPRCD 524 / Sep '94 / Empress

☐ SANDY
Sandy / Whenever I'm away from you / Moonlight lady / Baby, I could be so good at lovin' you / Rainbows / Girl like you / Slow dancing / Back doors crying / Let her in / Big trouble / It had to be you / Goodnight Mr. Moon / Never gonna fall in love again / You set my dreams to music / What would they say / I don't know what I like about you baby / Razzamatazz / All strung out on you / Settle down / Easy evil / Can't let you go
100472 / May '97 / A-Play Collection

☐ SINGS
VSD 5682 / 6 Apr '98 / Varese Sarabande

☐ VERY BEST OF JOHN TRAVOLTA, THE
Greased lightnin' / Sandy / Let her in / Never gonna fall in love again / Rainbows / Razzamatazz / I don't know what I like about you baby / Big trouble / Goodnight Mr. Moon / Baby I could be so good lovin' you / It had to be you / Slow dancin' / Can't let you go / Easy evil / Back doors cryin' / What would they say / Right time of the night / Moonlight lady / Settle down / You set my dreams to music / Sandy
SUMCD 4066 / Nov '96 / Summit

Trax Beyond Subconscious

☐ AMBIENT CUT-OUTS VOL.1
LABUKCD 3 / Oct '94 / Labworks

Tre & The Blueknights

☐ BLUES ROCKIN' BABY
WCD 120888 / Jun '97 / Wolf

Tre Martelli

☐ OMI E PAIZ
RD 5024CD / Mar '96 / Robi Droli

Treacherous Human Underdogs

☐ VICE
RGE 1032 / Nov '94 / Enemy

Treadway, Sonny

☐ JESUS WILL FIX IT
Jesus will fix it for you / Blessed assurance Jesus is mine / How I got over / Lord I put my trust in you / Create in me a clean heart / No never alone / Praise in rememberance of bishop Lorenzo Harrison / Hallelujah anyhow / When I've gone the last mile of the way / I read that letter / Precious Lord take my hand / Holy holy holy
ARHCD 462 / Nov '97 / Arhoolie

Treasure Land

☐ GATEWAY
King of all kings / Where tomorrow will remain / Dreams of reality / Rendez-vous / Winter's night / Heaven / Possessed / Voices are calling / Liar
TT 00372 / 30 Mar '98 / T&T

☐ QUESTIONS
Gift / Misery / Why / Demons / To live again / Miracle / Spirits / Kingdom / Let the rain
TT 00292 / Mar '97 / T&T

Treat Her Right

☐ ANTHOLOGY 1985-1990, THE
RE 821742 / 1 Sep '98 / Razor & Tie

Treatment

☐ CIPHER CAPUT
Hidden attack / Boing song / Risky / Dissolving / Designer / Cigarettes and starling / Doubt / Better future for Britain / Big I am / Decay / Damage / Holding on
DELECCD 026 / Nov '93 / Delerium

Trebunia Family Band

☐ POLAND
NI 5437 / Jul '95 / Nimbus

Tree Fort Angst

☐ KNEE DEEP
BUS 10072 / Mar '97 / Bus Stop

Treepeople

☐ GUILT, REGRET AND EMBARRASSMENT
KLP 69CD / Jun '97 / K

Trees

☐ ON THE SHORE
Soldiers three / Murdoch / Streets of Derry / Sally free and easy / Fool / Adams toon / Geordie / While the iron is hot / Little Sadie / Polly on the shore
4844352 / Jul '96 / Columbia

Trelik

☐ TRELIK VOL.1
TRCD 1 / Feb '97 / Trelik

Trelldom

☐ TIL EVIGHET
HNF 016CD / Jul '96 / Head Not Found

Tremble Kids All-Stars

☐ PLAY CHICAGO JAZZ
NHCD 043 / May '98 / Nagel Heyer

☐ TREMBLE KIDS ALL-STARS
JCD 254 / Jul '96 / Jazzology

Trembling Blue Stars

☐ HER HANDWRITING
SHINKANSEN 3CD / Dec '96 / Shinkansen

☐ LIPS THAT TASTE OF TEARS
SHINKANSEN 10CD / 26 Jan '98 / Shinkansen

Treme Brass Band

☐ GIMME MY MONEY BACK
ARHCD 417 / Jan '96 / Arhoolie

Tremeloes

☐ GOLD
GOLD 208 / Apr '94 / Disky

☐ GOLDEN HITS
Even the bad times are good / And then I kissed her / Call me number one / Never win / St Tropez / I like it that way / Once on a Sunday Morning / Here comes my baby / Silence is golden / Me and my life / Someone / Lean on me baby / Hello world / My little lady / African lullaby / Helule helule
306132 / Jan '97 / Hallmark

☐ GREATEST HITS
Silence is golden / Here comes my baby / Even the bad times are good / Suddenly you love me / Helule Helule / My little lady / I shall be released / Hello world / (Call me) Number one / By the way / Hello Buddy / Rag doll / Yellow river / Twist and shout / Do you love me / Me and my life / I swear / Ain't nothing but a house party / Be mine / Every little bit hurts
SELCD 501 / Mar '98 / Castle Select

☐ HELLO WORLD (2CD Set)
SMDCD 192 / 22 Sep '97 / Snapper

☐ SILENCE IS GOLDEN
Call me number one / Even the bad times are good / Here comes my baby / Alli-oop / Do you love me / Ain't nothing but a house party / Reach out, I'll be there / I shall be released / Yellow river / My little lady / Silence is golden / I like it that way / Cool jerk / Every day / Peggy Sue / Rag doll / Twist and shout / Every little bit hurts
5507422 / Jan '95 / Spectrum

☐ SINGLES, THE
Goodday sunshine / Here comes my baby / Silence is golden / Even the bad times are good / Be mine / Suddenly you love me / Helule helule / My little lady / I'm gonna try / I shall be released / Hello world / Once on a Sunday morning / (Call me) Number one / By the way / Me and my life / Right wheel, left hammer sham / Hello Buddy / Too late (to be saved) / I like it that way / Blue suede / Ride on / Make it break it / You can't touch Sue / Do I love you / Say OK / Be boppin boogie
BX 4572 / Dec '95 / BR Music

☐ STORY OF THE TREMELOES, THE
BS 80182 / Jul '94 / BR Music

☐ TREMENDOUS HITS
Silence is golden / Even the bad times are good / Here comes my baby / Me and my life / Helule helule / (Call me) number one / My little lady / Words / Hello world / Yellow river / Blue suede tie / Be mine / Hello Buddy / Once upon a Sunday morning / I like it that way / Before I sleep / By the way / Good day sunshine / Suddenly you love me / I shall be released
MCCD 303 / Jun '97 / Music Club

☐ WORLD OF BRIAN POOLE & THE TREMELOES, THE (Poole, Brian & The Tremeloes)
Do you love me / Candy man / Someone someone / Twist and shout / What do you want with my baby / Time is on my side / I can dance / Out of my mind / Medley / Three bells / I want candy / Rag doll / We know / It's alright / Mr. Bass Man / South Street / Hey girl / Well who's that / Medley / Twelve steps to love
5513212 / May '96 / Spectrum

Tremulis, Nicholas

☐ BLOODY SHOW
BV 170962 / Nov '96 / Black Vinyl

Trenchmouth

☐ BROADCASTING SYSTEM, THE
RUNT 21 / Mar '97 / Runt

☐ CONSTRUCTION OF NEW ACTION
SR 89222CD / Nov '92 / Skene

Trend

☐ BITCH
RRS 946CD / Nov '95 / Progress

Trenet, Charles

☐ ANTHOLOGIE
EN 521 / Feb '96 / Fremeaux

☐ BOUM
Fleur bleue / La polka du Roi / Y'a d'la Joie / Boum / Pigeon vole / En quittant le Ville / Le Grand Cafe / La Vielle / Miss Emily / Les Oiseaux de Paris / Beguine a Bagno / Vous Oubliez votre Cheval / Vous etes Jolie / Il Pleut dans ma Chambre / La Route Enchantee / Ah Dis, ah Dis, ah Bonjour / La Vie qui va / Annie-Anna / Tout me sourit / Hop hop / Jardin du Mois de Mai / Le Soleil et la Lune / Mam'zelle Clio
MDF 102604 / 1 Sep '97 / Mudisque

☐ CHANSONS DE MES FILMS 1937-1943
175102 / 21 Aug '97 / Musidisc

☐ COMPLETE CHARLES TRENET VOL.1, THE (Charles & Johnny/2CD Set) (Trenet, Charles & Johnny Hess)
FA 081 / May '96 / Fremeaux

☐ COMPLETE CHARLES TRENET VOL.2, THE (2CD Set)
FA 082 / Nov '96 / Fremeaux

☐ COMPLETE CHARLES TRENET VOL.3, THE (2CD Set)
FA 083 / Feb '97 / Fremeaux

☐ COMPLETE CHARLES TRENET, THE (4CD Set)
FA 084 / Nov '97 / Fremeaux

☐ DIAMOND COLLECTION, THE
3004452 / Jun '97 / Arcade

☐ EXTRAORDINARY GARDEN, THE (The Very Best Of Charles Trenet)
Boum / L'ame des poetes / Moi j'aime le music hall / Vous qui passez sans me voir / La jolie sardane / En Avril a Paris / Le jardin extraordinaire / Coin de rue / Mes jeunes annes / A la porte du garage / France Dimanche / Qur reste t'il de nos amours / Y'a d'la Joie / Douce France / La polka du roi / Revoir Paris / La folie complainte / Le grand cafe / La mer / Menilmontant / Vous oubliez votre cheval / La maison du poete / La famille musicienne / Le chante
CDP 7944642 / Jul '97 / EMI

☐ GOLD COLLECTION, THE (2CD Set)
R2CD 7001 / 13 Apr '98 / Deja Vu

☐ IL Y A D'LA JOIE
AC 75105 / 27 Apr '98 / Arkadia

☐ LE FOU CHANTANT
Que reste-t-il de nos amours / Les temps des cerises / Debit de l'eau..Bonsoir Jolie Madame / Un rien me fait chanter / Swing troubadour / La romance de Paris / Verlaine / Le jardin du mais de Mai / Meinilmontant / Le soleil et la lune / Vous oubliez votre cheval / J'ai ta main / Boum..Y'a de la joie / Fleur bleue / J echante
995752 / Apr '97 / EPM

☐ PORTRAIT OF CHARLES TRENET, A (2CD Set)
Boum / Je chante / Fleur bleue / J'ai ta main / Y'a d'la joie / Pigeon vole / Le grand cafe / La polka du roi / Vous obliez votre cheval / J'ai connu de vous / Biguine a bango / Vous etes jolie / Il pleut dans ma chambre / La route enchantee / Ah dis ah dis ah bonjour / La vie qui va / Quand j'etais petit je vous aimais / Les enfants s'ennuient le dimanche / Menilmontant / Tout me sourit / Les oiseaux de Paris / La vieille / Your hand in my hand / Boom / La mer / Jardin du mois de mai / Le soleil et la lune / Mam'zelle Clio / Pres de toi mon amour / Verlaine / Terre / Papa pique et maman coud / La chanson du jolie feu de bois / La cigale et la fourmis / Bonsoir jolie madame / La romance de Paris / Un rien me fait chanter / Swing troubadour / Tout ca c'est pour vous / Sur le fil / Devant la mer / Frederica / Le soleil a des rayons de pluie / DDebit de l'eau debit de lait / L'heritage infernal / Quand un facteur s'envole / On danse a Paris / Que reste-t-il de nos amours
GALE 417 / 6 Oct '97 / Gallerie

Treniers

☐ COOL IT BABY
You're killing me / Day old bread / Squeeze me / Flip our wigs / Rock bottom / Give a little time / Hey you / I got the blues so bad / Straighten up baby / Cool it baby / Drinkin' wine spo-dee-o-dee / Margie / Madune / Sorrento / Lover come back to me / We want a rock and roll president / Longest walk / Ain't nothing wrong with that baby
BCD 15418 / Dec '88 / Bear Family

☐ HEY SISTER LUCY
Hey sister Lucy / Buzz buzz buzz / But I'd rather / Hey boys better get yourself an extra / Oooh look a there ain't she pretty / Near to me / No baby no / Sometimes I'm happy / I'll follow you / It's a quiet town / Convertable cadillac / Ain't she mean / Sure had a wonderful time last night / I miss you so / Hey jacobia / Why / Lady luck / When you're finished talkin' (let's make some love)
BCD 15419 / Dec '88 / Bear Family

Trent, Jackie

☐ BEAT SINGLES VOL.1
RPM 161 / Jun '96 / RPM

☐ TWO OF US, THE (Trent, Jackie & Tony Hatch)
Downtown / Where are you now / My love / Joanna / What would I be / Call me / Who am I / Forget him / Colour my world / Thank you for loving me / I know a place / Opposite your smile / You're everything / Other man's grass / I couldn't live without your love / Let's do it again / Look for a star / Don't sleep in the subway / Sign of the times / Two of us
PRCD 144 / Nov '94 / President

Treorchy Male Choir

☐ 50 GOLDEN YEARS OF SONG
Cwm Rhondda / For the fallen / Men of Harlech / Soldiers' chorus from Faust / Llef / Myfanwy / Jacob's ladder / O Isi and Osiris / Gwahoddiad / Hava nagila / Softly as I leave you / Cavatina / With a voice of singing / Unwaith eto / My way
CDMFP 6214 / Feb '96 / Music For Pleasure

☐ TREORCHY SING QUEEN
Overture / We are the champions / Radio ga ga / Save me / Crazy little thing called love / Flash / You're my best friend / Play the game / Good old fashioned lover boy / Don't stop me now / We will rock you / Bohemian rhapsody
CDMFP 6365 / May '97 / Music For Pleasure

Triad

☐ THREE PIANOS FOR JIMI
ADC 14 / 23 Mar '98 / Douglas Music

Trial Of The Bow

☐ RITE OF PASSAGE
Father of the flower / Ubar / Promise / Serpent / Eyre of awakening / Ceilidh for the sallow ground / Muezin / Court of the servant / As night falls / Alizee
RR 69502 / Jun '97 / Relapse

Trian

☐ TRIAN VOL.2
GLCD 1159 / Dec '95 / Green Linnet

Triangle
☐ L'INTEGRALE (The Complete Works 1969-1973/4CD Set)
176302 / Oct '97 / Magic

Triarchy
☐ BEFORE YOUR VERY EARS
ETHEL 005CD / 2 Feb '98 / Vinyl Tap

Tribal Draft
☐ COLLECTIVE JOURNEYS
CHILLCD 006 / Nov '95 / Chillout

Tribal Drift
☐ PRIORITY SHIFT
ONUCD 88 / Nov '96 / On-U Sound

Tribe 8
☐ ROLE MODELS FOR AMERIKA
VIRUS 212CD / 9 Mar '98 / Alternative Tentacles

☐ SNARKISM
VIRUS 181CD / 10 Nov '97 / Alternative Tentacles

Tribe After Tribe
☐ PEARLS BEFORE SWINE
Boy / Lazurus / Ballad of winnie / Uh oh / Senor / Firedancers / Bury me / Pat on the back / Heart / Murder on the lee / Hopeless the clown
CDVEST 82 / Apr '97 / Bulletproof

Tribe Called Quest
☐ BEATS, RHYMES AND LIFE
Phony rappers / Get a hold / Motivators / Jam / Crew / Pressure / 1nce again / Mind power / Hop / Keeping it moving / Baby Phife's return / Seperate/Together / What really goes on / Word play / Stressed out
CHIP 170 / Jul '96 / Jive

☐ LOW END THEORY
Excursions / Buggin' out / Rap promoter / Butter / Verses from the abstract / Showbusiness / Vibes and stuff / Infamous date rape / Check the rhyme / Everything is fair / Jazz (We got the) / Sky pager / What / Scenario
CHIP 117 / Mar '97 / Jive

☐ MIDNIGHT MARAUDERS
Midnight marauders tour guide / Steve Biko (Stir it up) / Award tour / 8 million stories / Sucka nigga / Midnight / We can get down / Electric relaxation / Clap your hands / Oh my God / Keep it rollin' / Chase Part II / Lyrics to go / God lives through / Hot sex
CHIP 143 / Mar '97 / Jive

☐ PEOPLE'S INSTINCTIVE TRAVELS & THE PATHS OF RHYTHM
Push it along / Luck of Lucien / After hours / Footprints / I left my wallet in El Segundo / Public enemy / Bonita Applebum / Can I kick it / Youthful expression / Rhythm (Devoted to the art of moving butts) / Mr. Muhammad / Ham 'n' eggs / Go ahead in the rain / Description of a fool
CHIP 96 / Mar '97 / Jive

☐ REVISED QUEST FOR THE SEASONED TRAVELLER
Bonita applebum / I left my wallet in El Segundo / Description of a fool / Public enemy / Check the rhyme / Luck of Lucien / Can I kick it / Scenario / If the papes came / Jazz (we've got) / Butter
CHIP 130 / Mar '97 / Jive

Tribe Of Cro
☐ HYDROCULTURE
UFCRO 777 / 16 Mar '98 / UF Cro

Tribes Of Krom
☐ LOGICAL ILLUSION
DBM 33864 / 30 Mar '98 / Fierce

Tribes Of Neurot
☐ ADAPTATION AND SURVIVAL
MR 086CD / 25 May '98 / Man's Ruin

☐ SILVER BLOOD TRANSMISSION
Primordial uncarved block / Wolf lava / Fires of putrification / Accidental process / Fall back to stone / Manifestation / Achtwan / Continuous regression / Closing in
RR 69292 / 26 Jan '98 / Release

☐ STATIC MIGRATION (Tribes Of Neurot/ Walking Timebombs)
Unspoken path / Rust / Recurring birth / March to the sun / Origin unknown / Blood and water / Edgewood / Head of the scorpion
RR 69722 / 9 Mar '98 / Relapse

Tribulation
☐ CLOWN OF THORNS
Borka intro / Born bizarre / My world is different / Rise of prejudice / Everything's fluating / Safe murder of emotions / Angst / Decide (take a stand) / Angel in a winterpile / Beautiful views / Landslide of losers / Down my lungs / Pick an image (make sure it sells) / Herr Ober / Tiny little skeleton / Disgraceland / Dogmother
8410602 / Feb '92 / Black Mark

☐ SPICY
BHR 010CD / Oct '94 / Burning Heart

Tribulation All Stars
☐ DUB LIBERATION
WSPCD 005 / Apr '94 / Word Sound & Power

Tribute
☐ NEW VIEWS
EUCD 1042 / '89 / ARC

Tribute To Nothing
☐ STRAIGHT LINE
Straight line / Find it / Cecil / Could I / Think you should / Do something / How could things / Don't care
LJCD 002 / Jun '97 / Lockjaw

☐ WRENCH
Backdown / Time to see / Finding my own mind / Should the quiet / Two minutes of hate / RTA / Fight for life / Prevention / 212 / Catch your grip / Blue alloy / Timebomb
LJCD 004 / 27 Oct '97 / Lockjaw

Trick Babys
☐ FOOL AND HIS MONEY, A
GKCD 023 / 20 Oct '97 / Go-Kart

Tricky
☐ ANGELS WITH DIRTY FACES
Money greedy / Mellow / Singin' the blues / Broken homes / 6 minutes / Analyze me / Moment I feared / Talk to me (angels with dirty faces) / Carriage for two / Demise / Your eyes / Record companies / Peyote songs / Taxi
CID 8071 / 25 May '98 / Island

☐ MAXINQUAYE
Overcome / Ponderosa / Black steel / Hell is round the corner / Pumpkin / Aftermath / Abbaon fat track / Brand new you're retro / Suffocated love / You don't / Strugglin' / Feed me
BRCD 610 / Feb '95 / 4th & Broadway

☐ NEARLY GOD (Nearly God)
Tattoo / Poems / Together now / Keep your mouth shut / I be the prophet / Make a change / Black coffee / Bubbles / I sing for you / Yoga
DPCD 1001 / Apr '96 / Durban Poison

☐ PRE-MILLENNIUM TENSION
Vent / Christiansands / Tricky kid / Bad dreams / Makes me wanna die / Ghetto youth / Sex drive / Bad things / Lyrics of fury / My evil is strong / Piano
BRCD 623
BRCDX 623 / Nov '96 / 4th & Broadway

Triffids
☐ AUSTRALIAN MELODRAMA
D 31182 / Oct '94 / Mushroom

☐ BORN SANDY DEVOTIONAL
D 19457 / Mar '95 / Mushroom

☐ CALENTURE
Trick of the night / Bury me deep in love / Kelly's blues / Home town farewell kiss / Unmade love / Open for you / Holy water / Blinder by the hour / Vagabond holes / Jerdacuttup man / Calenture / Save what you can
D 19458 / Feb '95 / Mushroom

☐ IN THE PINES
Suntrapper / In the pines / Kathy knows / Twenty five to five / Do you want me near you / Once a day / Just might fade away / Better off this way / Only one life / Keep your eyes on the hole / One soul loss on your fiery list / Born Sandy Devotional / Love and affection
D 19480 / Feb '95 / Mushroom

☐ STOCKHOLM
D 30231 / Feb '95 / Mushroom

Trigger Happy
☐ KILLATRON 2000
BMCD 073 / Jun '95 / Raw Energy

Trigger Tha Gambler
☐ LIFE'S A 50/50 GAMBLE
5334142 / Oct '96 / Talkin' Loud

Triggering Myth
☐ SINS OF OUR SAVIOURS, THE
LE 1030 / 15 Jun '98 / Laser's Edge

☐ TWICE BITTEN
LE 1019 / 15 Jun '98 / Laser's Edge

Trikha, Pandit Kanwar Sain
☐ THREE SITAR PIECES
Bageshri in teental / Rag desh in dadra / Folk piece in kahrwa / Untitled sitar
SEECD 481 / Aug '97 / See For Miles

Trimble, Gerald
☐ CROSS CURRENTS
Bedding of the bride / Adieu my lovely Nancy / Rolling spey/Green hills of Tyrol/Bob Walters / Blessed be (the lady's token) / Frank Gilruth/Jack Danielson's reel / Trimble's compliments to the city of Philadelphia / Breakdown / Christina Marie / Shifting paradigms
GLCD 1065 / Jul '93 / Green Linnet

☐ FIRST FLIGHT
Paddy o'brien's-scatter the mud-arthur darley's / War hent kerrigouarch-gavotte de scrignac / York reel-dancing feet / Martin wynne's no. 2 / Sailor's return-the return to camdentown-the maid behi / Captain's hornpipe-the first flight of geese / Mr. webster-miss jane macinnes-dandeleith / Three men of brittany-the wild man of steel / Elizabeth's air / Pumpherston hornpipe-open the door to three-the judge'
GLCD 1043 / Nov '88 / Green Linnet

☐ HEARTLAND MESSENGER
Kail pot/Fisher's rant/Morayshire farmer's club/ General Long / Miss Wharton Duff's jig / Coates hall/ Amazon / Miss Stewart's jig/Mrs. Rose of Kilravock/ Donald MacLean / Ostinelli's reel/Miss Gunning's fancy / Heartland Messsenger trilogy
GLCD 1054 / Oct '93 / Green Linnet

Trin-i-tee 5:7
☐ TRIN-I-TEE 5:7
Respect yourself / God's grace / Call his name / Oh Mary / Pray for a while / With all my heart / Good for me / God's blessing / Sunshine / Thank you / Holy and righteous / I won't turn back / Call his name
701007271X / May '98 / Brite

Trinidad Steel Band
☐ CARIBBEAN HOLIDAY
ECD 3435 / 6 Jul '98 / K-Tel

Trinidad Steel Combo
☐ STEEL DRUMS FROM THE CARIBBEAN
Pantalones de vaquero / Panguin's walk / Sexy panties / Panorama / Pan American blues / Nice pants / You look pantastic / Panatonics forever / Let's pan out the gold / Pancratic body / Black panther blues / Max loves pancakes / Happy pans / Don't panic / Panthouse in Miami
QED 228 / Nov '96 / Tring

Trinity
☐ AFRICAN REVOLUTION
African revolution / Turn yu roll / Staff of life / Not the worst / Tan tudy / Righteous rock / Judgement day / Hard time reggae / A nuh so / Rain a fall
CDGR 116 / Jan '97 / Charly

☐ BIG BIG MAN
Big big man / Eastwood married / Babylon them sick ina them head / I live a dream / Kiss well swift / Family planning / Case eye thing / Simmer thing / Scrub it in all nation / Kendal crash / Going on a work site / Sams / Just because you are a star / Santa claus comes once a year
LG 21057 / May '93 / Lagoon

☐ CLASH (Trinity & Dillinger)
BFMCD 113 / 24 Nov '97 / Bushranger

Trinity College Choir
☐ CAROLS FROM TRINITY (2CD Set)
75605517542 / 10 Nov '97 / RCA Victor

Trio
☐ CONFLAGRATION
BGOCD 253 / Oct '95 / Beat Goes On

☐ TRIO, THE
Oh, Dear / Dousing Rod / Silvercloud / Incantation / Caractacus / Let's stand / Foyer hall / Portes des blais / Verifably / In between / Sixes and sevens / Green walnut / Billy the kid / Dee tune / Centering / Joachim / Drum
BGOCD 231 / Aug '94 / Beat Goes On

Trio Azteca
☐ BEST OF MEXICAN FOLK SONGS
EUCD 1109 / '91 / ARC

Trio Bulgarka
☐ FOREST IS CRYING
Zaplakala e gorata / Sedyankata ye na razvala / Sluntseto trepti zauda / Ot matze, matze / Prochula se moma nedelya / More, zazheni se gyuro / Mari tudoro / Pozaspo li yagodo / Raditze le / Oy zlato yanke / Az ti postudiam shergil / Taz vecher ne mi vesela / Ozdole ide devoiche / Sluntse zaide / Snoshti sem minal, kuzum elenke / Pilentse pel / Vuv pirina / Melai doina
HNCD 1342 / May '88 / Hannibal

☐ MISSA PRIMI - MUSIC OF PALESTRINA
669512CD / Apr '95 / Melodie

Trio Idea
☐ NAPOLI CONNECTION (Trio Idea & Jerry Bergonzi)
1232612 / Apr '94 / Red

Trio Los Panchos
☐ Y SUS VOCES 6
9944132032 / 3 Mar '98 / Orfeon

Trio Matamoros
☐ TRIO MATAMOROS
HQCD 69 / Apr '97 / Harlequin

Trio Mexico
☐ MEXICAN LANDSCAPES VOL.1
PS 65901 / Jan '92 / PlayaSound

Trio Pantango
☐ TANGO ARGENTINO
EUCD 1334 / Mar '96 / ARC

☐ TANGO ARGENTINO POPULAR
EUCD 1257 / Mar '94 / ARC

Trio Patrekatt
☐ ADAM
Farsans 50-Ars Polska / Perflektens favoriter / Neptun / Sa Flickan / Ornen / Polska efter Kopman / Adam i Paradis / Lappa Skor/Byggnan / Brudmarsch efter Byss-Calle / Goethe / Funderingar / Farden
XOUCD 119 / Sep '97 / Xource

Trio Pellen-Molard
☐ TRYPTICH
GWP 002CD / Aug '93 / Gwerz

Trio Pennec
☐ JAVADAO
CD 847 / Apr '94 / Diffusion Breizh

Trio Sautivet
☐ PARTIR REVENIR
495302CD / Apr '96 / Acousteak

Trio Toykeat
☐ SUSI
5365802 / 8 Dec '97 / EmArCy

Triple Fast Action
☐ CATTLEMEN DON'T
DER 364CD / 6 Jul '98 / Deep Elm

Triple X
☐ GOOD, THE BAD & THE UGLY, THE
UNION 057 / Aug '96 / Union

Tripmaster Monkey
☐ GOODBYE RACE
Albert's twisted memory bank / Pecola / Shutter's closed / Faster than Dwight / Valium / Roman catholic haircut / Is that my day / Gravity / Key / Night of day / Not quite sure / Depravation test
9362456742 / Jul '94 / Warner Bros.

Tripping Daisy
☐ I AM AN ELASTIC FIRECRACKER
Rocket pop / Bang / I got a girl / Piranha / Motivation / Same dress new day / Trip along / Raindrop / Step behind / Noose / Prick / High
5241122 / 15 Sep '97 / Island

☐ JESUS HITS LIKE THE ATOMIC BOMB
5245182 / 27 Jul '98 / Island

Tripsichord
☐ TRIPSICHORD
852124 / 1 Jun '98 / EVA

Triptych
☐ SLEEPLESS
GAP 031 / Nov '95 / Gap Recordings

Trisan
☐ TRISAN
Triangle / Big trouble in old ballymore E / May yo I / Dragon / Mother and son / Wintermoon / River of life / Tri le cheile
CDRW 32 / Nov '92 / Realworld

Trischka, Tony
☐ ALONE & TOGETHER
BRAM 1991242 / Nov '93 / Brambus

☐ DUST ON THE NEEDLE
Crossville breakdown / Twelve weeks at sea / Only way / Jerzy the peddler / Roll in my sweet baby's arms / Slapback / Soddy daisy / Heartaches / Roberto's dream / Dust on the needle-paddy kelly's jig / You won't know til you find out / Black mountain rag / His mouth is in his forehead / Evansbow / Divine nine / New york chimes / Looking for the light / Salt creek
ROUCD 11508 / '88 / Rounder

☐ FIRE OF GRACE (Trischka, Tony & Skyline)
FF 479CD / Jun '94 / Flying Fish

☐ GLORY SHONE AROUND
ROUCD 0354 / Oct '95 / Rounder

☐ ROBOT PLANE FLIES OVER ARKANSAS, A
ROUCD 0171 / May '94 / Rounder

☐ SOLO BANJO WORKS (Trischka, Tony & Bela Fleck)
Ruben's wah wah: Trischka, Tony / Fourteen: Trischka, Tony / Liberec: Trischka, Tony / Free improvision no.2: Trischka, Tony / Assunta: Trischka, Tony / Old Joe Clark/June Apple: Trischka, Tony / Max and Gus: Trischka, Tony / Beaumont rag: Trischka, Tony / Kingfisher's wing: Trischka, Tony / Earl Scrugg's medley: Nashville Skyline/Ground speed/Shuckin: Trischka, Tony / Jeff Davies medley: Jeff Davies/Fort Monroe/Danville Days: Trischka, Tony / Yaha yaha: Trischka, Tony / Beatles medley: Trischka, Tony / Rings of saturn: Trischka, Tony / Green Willis/Whiskey before breakfast: Trischka, Tony / Killer bees of caffeine: Trischka, Tony / Oma and Opa: Fleck, Bela / Solaris: Fleck, Bela / Flapperette/Red pepper - Spicy rag: Fleck, Bela / Triplet fever: Fleck, Bela / Bach violin partitain D minor: Fleck, Bela / Did you ever meet Gary Owen, Uncle Joe: Fleck, Bela / Middle Eastern medley: Improv/Hilmi rit/George and Gladys ka: Fleck, Bela / Twisted teen: Fleck, Bela / Au lait: Fleck, Bela
ROUCD 0247 / Feb '93 / Rounder

☐ WORLD TURNING
ROUCD 294 / Oct '93 / Rounder

Triskell

☐ CELTIQUE HARPES
Plangstigh Ewen / Dainty Davie / Dime ramo verde / Iona / Sun and shadow / Vincenta / Enezenn du / Planxty George Barbazon / Vieux chateau sous la lune / Boulavogue / King William's march / Dafydd y garreg wen / Pardon sant fiakr / Plijadur ha displijadur
3037200012 / Apr '96 / Carlton

☐ DAOU
KMCD 83 / 24 Apr '98 / Keltia Musique

☐ HARPES CELTIQUES
KMCD 60 / Jul '95 / Keltia Musique

☐ WAR VARC'H D'AH (Triskell & Mouez Armor)
KMCD 64 / Jul '96 / Keltia Musique

Trisomie 21

☐ DISTANT VOICES
Shine ola / Touch sweet pleasure / Again and again (what a regular world) / Perfect side of doubt / Badlands / Is anybody home / Distant voices / Soft brushing speed / Jazz / Long rider
BIAS 212 CD / Oct '92 / Play It Again Sam

☐ SONGS BY TRISOMIE 21 VOL.1, THE
Perfect side of doubt / Again and again (What a regular world) / New outset / Bamboo / Missing piece / Betrayed / Story so far / Sharing sensation / Sunken lives / Night flight / Last song / Waiting for / Moving by you / Is anybody home / Logical animals / Il se noie
BIAS 281CD / May '94 / Play It Again Sam

☐ T21 PLAYS THE PICTURES
BIAS 152CD / Apr '90 / Play It Again Sam

Trisquel

☐ AMANDI
20052CD / Dec '94 / Sonifolk

☐ O CHAPEU DE MERLIN
J 1023CD / Jun '94 / Sonifolk

Tristan Park

☐ LOOKING HOMEWARD
Memorial day / American Tragedy / Four freedoms / Ambition / Mistress / Cruelest month / American tragedy / Looking homeward
CYCL 070 / 17 Aug '98 / Cyclops

Tristano, Lennie

☐ CONTINUITY
Continuity / She's funny that way / My baby / Everything happens to me / Subconscious Lee / 317 East 32nd / Background music
JR 6CD / Sep '97 / Jazz

☐ JAZZ KEYBOARDS, THE (Tristano, Lennie & Marian McPartland)
Supersonic / On a planet / Air pocket / Celestia / Just one of those things / But beautiful / I married an angel / I love you madly / Squeeze me / Mean to me / Indian summer / (Back home again in) Indiana
SV 0224 / May '98 / Savoy Jazz

☐ LENNIE TRISTANO/THE NEW TRISTANO
Line up / Requiem / Turkish mambo / East 32nd / These foolish things / You go to my head / If I had you / I don't stand a ghost of a chance with you / All the things you are / Becoming / You don't know what love is / Deliberation / Scene and variations / Love lines / G minor complex
2715952 / Jun '94 / Atlantic

☐ LIVE AT BIRDLAND 1949
Remember / Pennies / Foolish things / Indiana / I'm no good without you / Glad am I / This is called love / Blame me / I found my baby
JR 1CD / Sep '97 / Jazz

☐ LIVE IN TORONTO 1952
Lennie's pennies / 317 East 32nd / You go to my head / April / Sound Lee / Back home
JR 5CD / Sep '97 / Jazz

☐ MANHATTAN STUDIO
Manhattan Studio / My melancholy baby / Lover man / I'll see you in my dreams / There will never be another you / Momentum / Mean to me / All the things you are / I'll remember April
JR 11CD / Sep '97 / Jazz

☐ NOTE TO NOTE
Just Prez / Palo Alto scene / It's personal / Note to note / There will always be you
JR 10CD / Sep '97 / Jazz

☐ WOW
Wow / Remembrance / April fool / Subconscious Lee / Fugue in D minor / Chord interlude / Sound Lee / Do the things you do / No figs
JR 9CD / Sep '97 / Jazz

Tristitia

☐ CRUCIDICTION
HOLY 021CD / Dec '96 / Holy

☐ ONE WITH DARKNESS
HOLY 011CD / May '95 / Holy

☐ WIDOW'S WEEDS
NPR 041CD / 22 Jun '98 / Napalm

Tritonus

☐ BETWEEN THE UNIVERSES
SB 046 / 26 Jan '98 / Second Battle

Tritt, Travis

☐ GREATEST HITS
Can I trust you with my heart / Tell me I was dreaming / Foolish pride / Drift off to dream / Sometimes she forgets / Country club / Only you (and you alone) / I'm gonna be somebody / Help me hold on / Whiskey ain't workin' / Put some drive in your country / Anymore / Here's a quarter (call someone who cares) / T-r-o-u-b-l-e / Ten feet tall and bulletproof
9362460012 / Oct '95 / Warner Bros.

☐ RESTLESS KIND
Restless kind / She's going home with me / Did you fall far enough / Where corn don't grow / Sack full of stones / More than you'll ever know / Helping me get over you / Back up against the wall / Double trouble / Draggin' my heart around / Still in love with you
9362463042 / Aug '96 / Warner Bros.

☐ TEN FEET TALL & BULLETPROOF
Ten feet tall and bulletproof / Walkin' all over my heart / Foolish pride / Outlaws like us / Hard times and misery / Tell me I was dreaming / Wishful thinking / Between an old memory and me / No vacation from the blues / Southern justice
9362456032 / May '94 / Warner Bros.

Troggs

☐ ALL THE HITS PLUS MORE
Wild thing / With a girl like you / Love is all around / Little pretty thing / Anyway that you want me / I can't control myself / I love you baby / Black bottom / Louie Louie / Save the last dance for me / I do do / Strange movies / Bass for my birthday / Last night / Hot days / I don't / Widge you / Feels like a woman
CDSGP 0337 / Apr '97 / Prestige

☐ ATHENS ANDOVER
Crazy Annie / Together / Tuned into love / Deja vu / Dust bowl / I'm in control / Don't you know / What's your game / Suspicious / Hot stuff
ESMCD 180 / Aug '96 / Essential

☐ ATHENS, GEORGIA & BEYOND
MCCD 242 / Jun '96 / Music Club

☐ AU
ROSE 186 CD / May '90 / New Rose

☐ BEST OF THE TROGGS, THE
Wild thing / I can't control myself / Save the last dance for me / Little pretty thing / Hot days / Bass for my birthday / Last night / I don't know why / I do do / With a girl like you / Louie Louie / Black bottom / Anyway you want me / I love you baby / Widge you / Strange movie / Feels like a woman / Love is all around
SUMCD 4002 / Nov '96 / Summit

☐ BLACK BOTTOM
ROSE 4CD / Mar '85 / New Rose

☐ CELLOPHANE/MIXED BAG
Little red donkey / Too much of a good thing / Butterflies and bees / All of the time / Seventeen / Somewhere my girl is waiting / It's showing / Her emotion / When will the rain come / My lady / Come the day / Love is all around / Surprise surprise / You can cry if you want to / Say darlin' / Marbles and some gum / Purple shades / Heads or tails / Hip hip hooray / Little girl / Maybe the madman / Off the record / We waited for someone / There's something about you
BGOCD 343 / Mar '97 / Beat Goes On

☐ DOUBLE HITS COLLECTION (Troggs/ Dave Dee, Dozy, Beaky, Mick & Tich)
PLATCD 3908 / Oct '89 / Platinum

☐ EP COLLECTION, THE
Wild thing / From home / Yella in me / With a girl like you / Our love will still be there / Jingle jangle / I want you / Can't control myself / Hi hi Hazel / Gonna make you / Anyway that you want me / Cousin Jane / 66.54.321 / You can't beat it / Give it to me / You're lying / I can only give you everything / Oh no / Night of the long grass / Girl in black / Love is all around / Little girl
SEECD 453 / Oct '96 / See For Miles

☐ FROM NOWHERE/ TROGGLODYNAMITE
Wild thing / Kitty cat song / Ride your pony / Hi hi Hazel / I just sing / Evil / Our love will still be there / Louie Louie / Jingle jangle / When I'm with you / From home / Jaguar and thunderbird / I can only give you everything / Last summer / Meet Jacqueline / Oh no / It's too late / 10 Downing Street / Mona / I want you to come into my life / Let me tell you babe / Little Queenie / Cousin Jane / You can't beat it / Baby come closer / It's over
BGOCD 340 / Feb '97 / Beat Goes On

☐ GREATEST HITS
Wild thing / Love is all around / With a girl like you / I want you / I can't control myself / Gonna make you / Good vibrations / Anyway that you want me / Give it to me / Night of the long grass / Girl in black / Hi hi Hazel / Little girl / Cousin Jane / Don't you know / Together / Nowhere Road / I'm in control / Summertime / Hot stuff / Dust bowl / I'll buy you an island / Crazy Annie / Jingle jangle / Deja vu
5227392 / Jul '94 / PolyGram TV

☐ GREATEST HITS
MU 5022 / Oct '92 / Musketeer

☐ LOVE IS ALL AROUND
Love is all around / Wild thing / Give it to me / Hi hi Hazel / Night of the long grass / Seventeen / Kitty cat song / Little girl / I just sing / Jingle jangle / When I'm with you / Let me tell you babe / You can cry if you want to / Ride your pony / Lost girl / Hip hip hooray / I can only give you everything / Louie Louie
5510452 / Jul '95 / Spectrum

☐ LOVE IS ALL AROUND
Love is all around / Wild thing / Black bottom / Widge you / Strange movies / Feels like a woman / Last night / Bass for my birthday / Hot days / Little pretty thing / I don't / With a girl like you / I can't control myself / Any way that you want me / I do do / Save the last dance for me / Louie Louie / Hang on Sloopy / Twist and shout / Game of love / Louie Louie (reprise)
QED 144 / Nov '96 / Tring

☐ LOVE IS ALL AROUND
Love is all around / Wild thing / Black bottom / Widge you / With a girl like you / Twist and shout / Louie Louie / Save the last dance for me / I do do / Last night / Feels like a woman / I can't control myself / Any way that you want me / Bass for my birthday / Hot days / Game of love / Little pretty thing
CD 6065 / Apr '97 / Music

☐ TROGGLODYNAMITE
TR 7708 / 10 Nov '97 / Gone Beat

☐ TROGGS AU ALBUM
HADCD 195 / Nov '95 / Javelin

☐ WILD THING
Wild thing / Love is all around / Little pretty thing / Any way that you want me / I can't control myself / With a girl like you / I love you baby / Black bottom / I do do / Strange movies / Bass for my birthday / Last night / Hot days / I don't care about you / Widge you / Feels like a woman
15081 / Aug '91 / Laserlight

☐ WILD THING
Wild thing / With a girl like you / I can't control myself / Any way that you want me / Give it to me / Night of the long grass / Love is all around / Little girl / Widge you / Strange movie / Feels like a woman / Last night / Bass for my birthday / Hot days / Game of love/Little pretty thing / I don't / I do do / Louie Louie/Hang on Sloopy / Twist and shout
PLATCD 203 / Feb '97 / Platinum

☐ WILD THING
322699 / Jul '97 / Koch Presents

☐ WILD THING (The Best Of The Troggs)
Wild thing / With a girl like you / Love is all around / Little pretty thing / Anyway that you want me / I can't control myself / I love you baby / Black bottom / Louie Louie / Save the last dance for me / I do do / Strange movie / Bass for my birthday / Last night / Hot days / I don't / Widge you / Feels like a woman
AIM 2017CD / Sep '97 / Aim

☐ WILD THINGS
I got lovin' if you want it / Good vibrations / No particular place to go / Summertime / Satisfaction / Full blooded band / Memphis Tennessee / Peggy Sue / Wild thing / Get you tonight / Different me / Down South in Georgia / After the rain / Rock 'n' roll lady / Walking the dog / We rode through the night / You could make you / Supergirl / I'll buy you an island / Rollin' stone
SEECD 256 / Feb '98 / See For Miles

Troika

☐ GODDESS
Venus / Diana / Oya / Zorya / Kuan yin / Gwenhwyfar / Athena / Inanna
ND 62804 / Oct '96 / Narada

Troise

☐ TROISE & HIS MANDOLIERS (Troise & His Mandoliers)
An 18th century drawing room / Beside my caravan / Spanish gypsy dance / Hawaiian paradise / Ballerina / Nights of gladness / Madonna mine / In the hills of colorado / King steps out / Wedding of the rose / Old monastery bell / Black eyes / Lonely linden tree / Classical medley / Lady sing your gypsy song / Hungarian dance / Havanna heaven / Grasshopper's dance / Waltz memories / Maruschka / Serenata
PASTCD 7051 / Feb '95 / Flapper

Trojans

☐ CELTIC SKA
GAZCD 011 / Nov '94 / Gaz's Rockin' Records

☐ COOL RULERS
GAZCD 014 / Jun '96 / Gaz's Rockin' Records

☐ EARTH FIRST
GAZCD 015 / Apr '97 / Gaz's Rockin' Records

☐ REBEL BLUES
GAZCD 010 / Oct '93 / Gaz's Rockin' Records

☐ SKALALITUDE
GAZCD 007 / Sep '91 / Gaz's Rockin' Records

☐ STACK-A-DUB
GAZCD 012 / Jul '95 / Gaz's Rockin' Records

☐ WICKED AND WILD
622382 / Mar '96 / Skydog

☐ WILD & FREE
Great british spliff / Great british spliff / Can't kill the spirit / Message to the sun / One world / Love life / Anam mana / Leabin' phairaig / Arn-afarl / Itchy feet / Cairo next giro / Horns to troy
GAZCD 008 / Jun '93 / Gaz's Rockin' Records

Troka

☐ TROKA
OMCD 54 / Dec '94 / Olarin Musiikki Oy

Troll

☐ DEEP DE KRISTINE
HNF 042CD / 29 Jun '98 / Head Not Found

☐ TROLLSTORM OVER NIDINGJUV
HNF 015CD / Oct '96 / Head Not Found

Troll

☐ ANIMATED MUSIC
FLASH 10 / 20 Apr '98 / Flashback

Trom

☐ EVIL
SR 9506CD / Sep '95 / Shiadarshana

Tron

☐ SYNDICATE
London labyrinth / It's about time / Fall angel fall / Never forever / Voices by the standing stones / Snowfall in Eden / Outside / Requiem / Kingdom of forbidden thoughts / Eternity (You are alone) / Nightfall (Chapter IV) / Syndicate / Gate number two / Death's cold glance
MYSCD 111 / Jul '97 / Mystic

Tronzo, David

☐ NIGHT IN AMNESIA (Tronzo, David & Reeves Gabrels)
UPSTART 018 / Jul '95 / Upstart

Tronzo Trio

☐ ROOTS
KFWCD 154 / Feb '95 / Knitting Factory

☐ YO HEY
Improvisation no.1/The consequences / Bakutsi/Yo hey / Improvisation no.2/Long distance blues / Monk's dream / Church waltz/Sailing the Chicarrone
T&M 006 / Nov '96 / Tradition & Moderne

Trooper, Greg

☐ EVERYWHERE
CBM 009CD / Mar '94 / Cross Border Media

Trotsky Icepick

☐ BABY
SST 197CD / Sep '88 / SST

☐ CARPETBOMB THE RIFF
SST 295CD / Sep '93 / SST

☐ DANNY AND THE DOORKNOBS
SST 254CD / Sep '90 / SST

☐ EL KABONG
SST 246CD / Jul '89 / SST

☐ HOT POP HELLO
SST 286CD / May '94 / SST

☐ POISON SUMMER
Gaslight / Nightingale drive / Just the end of the world / Clowns on fire / Ivory tour / Commissioner / Big dreams / Drawing fire / Hit parade / You look like something Goya drew
SST 239CD / Dec '89 / SST

☐ ULTRA-VIOLET CATASTROPHE, THE
SST 279CD / Oct '91 / SST

Trottel

☐ FINAL SALUTE
XM 028CD / Apr '92 / X-Mist

Troubador Squat

☐ TROUBADOR SQUAT
PRL 0002 / Nov '96 / Pleather

Trouble

☐ PLASTIC GREEN HEAD
CDVEST 45 / Apr '95 / Bulletproof

☐ PSALM 9
398414068CD / May '96 / Metal Blade

☐ RUN TO THE LIGHT
Misery show / Thinking of the past / Peace of mind / Born in a prison / Tuesdays child / Beginning
398414051CD / May '96 / Metal Blade

☐ SKULL, THE
398141069CD / May '96 / Metal Blade

Trouble Funk

☐ DROP THE BOMB
Hey fellas / Get on up / Let's get hot / Drop the bomb / Pump me up / Don't try to use me / My love (burning love) / Caravan to midnight / I'm out to get you / Lost in love / Fool / It's for you / Birthday boy / King of the dances / Sail on / Supergrit / Hey Fellas
NEBCD 663 / Oct '93 / Sequel

☐ GO-GO DANCE WITH TROUBLE FUNK (Live)
74321391742 / Oct '96 / Infinite Zero

Troubles

☐ TROUBLES
LARRCD 316 / Nov '94 / Larrikin

Troup, Bobby

☐ IN A CLASS BEYOND COMPARE
ACD 98 / Apr '93 / Audiophile

☐ KICKS ON 66
Route 66 / Girl talk / It happened once before / Please belong to me / For once in my life / Jack 'n' Jill / Watch what happens / Thou swell / Hungry man / Tangerine / Bright lights and you girl / (Back home again in) Indiana / Try a little tenderness / Lemon twist / Misty / Lulu's back in town
HCD 607 / Nov '95 / Hindsight

Trout, Jimbo

☐ JIMBO TROUT & THE FISH PEOPLE (Trout, Jimbo & The Fishpeople)
EFA 800382 / Sep '95 / Twah

Trout, Walter

☐ BREAKING THE RULES (Trout, Walter Band)
PRD 70762 / Jun '95 / Provogue

☐ LIFE IN THE JUNGLE (Trout, Walter Band)
Good enough to eat / Mountain song / Life in the jungle / Spacefosh / Red house / She's out there somewhere / Frederica (I don't need you) / In my mind / Cold cold feeling / Serve me right to suffer
PRD 70202 / '90 / Provogue

☐ NO MORE FISH JOKES (Trout, Walter Band)
Dust my broom / If you just try / False alarm / Life in the jungle / Girl from the north country / Victor the cajun / Earrings on the table / Motivation of love / Playing with gloves on / Love what we once knew / Prisoner of a dream / Going down
PRD 70512 / May '93 / Provogue

☐ POSITIVELY BEALE STREET (Trout, Walter Band)
PRD 71042 / May '97 / Provogue

☐ PRISONER OF A DREAM (Trout, Walter Band)
Prisoner of a dream / Love that we once knew / Sweet as a flower / Love in vain / Victor the cajun / Girl from the north country / False alarm / Say goodbye to the blues / You're the one / Earrings on the table / Tribute to muddy waters
PRD 70262 / Oct '91 / Provogue

☐ TRANSITION (Trout, Walter Band)
Motivation of love / Endless variety / Transition / Running in place / Deeper shade of blue / Got to kill the monkey / Face the night / Playing with gloves on / She's missing / Fast moving traffic
PRD 70442 / Nov '92 / Provogue

Trovesi, Gianluigi

☐ FROM G TO G (Trovesi, Gianluigi Octet)
1212312 / Nov '92 / Soul Note

☐ LES HOMMES ARMES (Trovesi, Gianluigi Octet)
1213112 / Feb '97 / Soul Note

Trower, Robin

☐ 20TH CENTURY BLUES
20th century blues / Prisoner of love / Precious gift / Whisper up a storm / Extermination blues / Step into the dark / Rise up like the sun / Secret place / Chase the bone / Promise you the stars / Don't lose faith in tomorrow / Reconsider baby
FIENDCD 753 / Aug '94 / Demon

☐ ANTHOLOGY
VSOPCD 197 / Apr '94 / Connoisseur Collection

☐ BBC LIVE IN CONCERT
Day of the eagle / Bridge of sighs / Gonna be more suspicious / Fine day / Lady love / Twice removed from yesterday / Daydream / Alethea / Little bit of sympathy / Rock me baby
WINCD 013 / Feb '92 / Windsong

☐ BLT/TRUCE
BGOCD 411 / 17 Aug '98 / Beat Goes On

☐ CARAVAN TO MIDNIGHT/VICTIMS OF THE FURY
My love (burning love) / I'm out to get you / Lost in love / Fool / It's for you / Birthday boy / King of the dance / Sail on / Jack and Jill / Roads to freedom / Victims of the fury / Ring / Only time / Into the flame / Shout / Mad house / Ready for the taking / Fly low
BGOCD 352 / Jun '97 / Beat Goes On

☐ LIVE/FOR EARTH BELOW
Too rolling stoned / Daydream / Rock me baby / Lady love / I can't wait much longer / Alethea / Little bit of sympathy / Shame the devil / It's only money / Confessin' midnight / Fine day / Alethea / Tale untold / Gonna be more suspicious / For earth below
BGOCD 347 / Mar '97 / Beat Goes On

☐ LONG MISTY DAYS/IN CITY DREAMS
Some rain falls / Long misty days / Hold me / Caledonia / Somebody calling / Sweet wine of love / Bluebird / Falling star / Farther on up the road / Pride / Sailing / SMO / I can't live without you / Messin' the blues
BGOCD 349 / Apr '97 / Beat Goes On

☐ SOMEDAY BLUES
Next in line / Feel so bad / Someday blues / Crossroads / I want you to love me / Inside out / Shining through / Looking for a true love / Extermination blues / Sweet little angel
FIENDCD 931 / Jun '97 / Demon

☐ TWICE REMOVED FROM YESTERDAY/BRIDGE OF SIGHS
I can't wait much longer / Daydream / Hannah / Man of the world / I can't stand it / Rock me baby / Twice removed from yesterday / Sinner's song / Ballerina / Day of the eagle / Bridge of sighs / In this place / Fool and me / Too rolling stoned / About to begin / Love / Little bit of sympathy
BGOCD 339 / Feb '97 / Beat Goes On

Towers, Robert

☐ POINT OF VIEW
Have you met Miss Jones / Minority / Riff / Statement / Spleen bop / St. Thomas / Holiday for strings / R 'n' B / 'Deed I do / Joint is jumpin' / End of a love affair
CCD 4656 / Jul '95 / Concord Jazz

Trubee, John

☐ WORLD OF LIVING PIGS
EFA 113362 / Feb '94 / Musical Tragedies

Truce

☐ NOTHING BUT THE TRUCE
BLRCD 29 / Oct '95 / Big Life

Truckadelic

☐ LIVE AT THE STAR BAR
TRCD 01 / 27 Jul '98 / Truckadelic

Trudell, John

☐ AKA GRAFFITI MAN
RCD 51028 / Sep '92 / Rykodisc

☐ JOHNNY DAMAS AND ME
Rant 'n' roll / See the woman / Raptor / Shadow over sisterland / Baby doll's blues / That love / Johnny Damas and me / Across my heart / Something about you / After all these years / All there is to it
RCD 10286 / Feb '94 / Rykodisc

Trudy

☐ TUNE-IN TO THE TRUDY LOVE-RAY
TDYCD 054 / May '90 / Planet Miron

True, Andrea

☐ MORE MORE MORE (True, Andrea Connection)
More more more / What's your name what's your number / You make love worthwhile / Life's what you make it / It's all up to you / NY you got me dancing / White witch / Sally can't dance / Party line / Keep it up longer / Call me / Fill me up (heart to heart)
74321558482 / 26 Jan '98 / Camden

True Believers

☐ HARD ROAD
Tell her / Ring the bell / So blue about you / Rebel kind / Train round the bend / Lucky moon / Hard road / We're wrong / I get excited / Sleep enough to dream / Rain won't help you when it's over / She's got / All mixed up / One moment to another / Who calls my name / Outside your door / Wild eyed and wound up / Nobody's home / Only a dream / Please don't fade away
RCD 40287 / Mar '94 / Rykodisc

True Playaz

☐ TRUE PLAYAZ IN THE MIX VOL.1 (Mixed By DJ Hype & DJ Zinc) (Various Artists)
Cool manoeuvre: *Pascal* / Load: *Swift* / Break the loop: *Dope Skillz* / Peace love and unity: *DJ Hype* / Reachout: *Zinc* / ATTACK: *Freestyles* / Soul: *Swift* / No diggedy: *Dope Skillz* / Vortex: *Pascal* / Play the game: *Freestyles* / Pranksters: *Zinc* / Learn from the mistakes: *Freestyles* / Dawn: *Zinc* / Feel: *Freestyles* / And remember folks: *DJ Hype*
TPRCD 001 / 9 Feb '98 / True Playaz

True West

☐ BIG BOOT, THE
BOYD 10032 / 22 May '98 / BOYD

☐ HOLLYWOOD HOLIDAY/ DRIFTERS
ROSE 23CD / Sep '90 / New Rose

Truffaz, Erik

☐ DAWN, THE
Bukowsky / Yuri's choice / Dawn / Wet in Paris / Slim pickings / Round trip / Mask / Free stylin'
4939162 / 4 May '98 / Blue Note

☐ OUT OF A DREAM
Down town / Out of a dream / Beaute bleue / Wet in Paris / Porta camollia / Indigo saisir / Elegie / Samara / Up town / Betty
CDP 8558552 / Jul '97 / Blue Note

Truly

☐ FEELING YOU UP
HUK 003CD / 23 Mar '98 / Headhunter

Truman's Water

☐ ACTION ORNAMENTS
RUNT 28 / Jun '97 / Runt

☐ APISTOGRAMMA
JME 006 / 20 Apr '98 / Justice My Eye

☐ FRAGMENTS OF A LUCKY LADY
EJ 23CD / 17 Aug '98 / Emperor Jones

☐ GOD SPEED THE PUNCHLINE
ELM 15CD / Feb '94 / Elemental

☐ MILKTRAIN TO PAYDIRT
HMS 2212 / Aug '95 / Homestead

☐ OF THICK TUM
HMS 1922 / Mar '93 / Homestead

☐ SPASM SMASH XXX OX OX OX & ASS
Aroma of gina arnold / Speeds exceeding / Good blood after bad / Rations / Death to dead things / Sun go out / Bludgeon elites and stagger / Limbs / Athlete who is suck / Top of morning / Lo priest / Soar ossinaxx at long last / Our doctor thinks were blind / Fingers / Steps ahead of our minds / La jolly my armpit / K-song / Mindstab, forklift to milktruck / Bladder stomp krautrack / Sad skinhead
ELM 9CD / Mar '93 / Elemental

Trumystic Sound System

☐ PRODUCT VOL.3
MSS 0030 / 20 Apr '98 / Mutant Sound System

Trunk Federation

☐ INFAMOUS HAMBURGER TRANSFER, THE
Quality burn / Original uptight / Sweet bread / Dog reject / Clyde suckfinger / Young cherry trees / Match / Alright / Over-rated / Gelatin / Pinhead / St. Francis / Beanie's soft toy factory
A 111D / Feb '97 / Alias

Trusty

☐ FOURTH WISE MAN, THE
DIS 104CD / Oct '96 / Dischord

☐ GOODBYE DR. FATE
DIS 93CD / May '95 / Dischord

Truth

☐ I 'N' I A DEAL WID ROOTS
GTCD 001 / 20 Oct '97 / Good Time

Tryolia Singers

☐ SOUND OF TYROL
321680 / Sep '92 / Koch

Tryphon

☐ ZOUAVES
500222 / 1 Jun '98 / Musidisc

Tryst

☐ OPEN FIELDS
RT 93112 / Feb '98 / Red Toucan

Tsahar, Assif

☐ AIN SOF (Tsahar, Assif Trio)
SHCD 148 / Oct '97 / Silkheart

Tsai-Ping, Professor Liang

☐ CHINESE CHENG - ANCIENT AND MODERN
4445773022 / 17 Mar '98 / Irma

Tsatthoggua

☐ HOSANNA BIZARRE
OPCD 035 / Jul '96 / Osmose

☐ TRANS CUNT WHIP
OPCD 061 / 25 May '98 / Osmose

Tschanz, Mark

☐ BLUE DOG
Love song / Time / Immortals / Life / Storm / Rattlesnake / Happy / Incubus / Rain / Windwalker
0630106062 / Dec '96 / East West

Tse Tse Fly

☐ MUD FLAT JOEY
M 1 / Jonah / Talk to me / Pog eared / On purpose / Lido / Roo mole suit / Itchy / Some pay soon / Non-ferrous / Kitchen / Hogwash
CDBRED 117 / Oct '94 / Cherry Red

Tsiboe, Nana

☐ ASEM NIL TROUBLE DAT
Bue bue / Kai onyame / Adum / Nana ewusi / Odumankumah boa mi / Kokofu hene mba / Ghana muntye
TD 8001 / Feb '94 / World Circuit

Tsinandali Choir

☐ TABLE SONGS OF GEORGIA
Kakhuri mravaljamieri / Makruli / Shashvi, Kakabi / Orovela / Turpani skhedan / Zamtari / Diambego / Shemodzakhili / Berikatsi var / Charkrulo
CDRW 28 / Jan '93 / Realworld

Tsitanis, Bellou & Ninou

☐ BELLOU AND NINOU TSITANIS
ML 0158 / 11 May '98 / Musurgia Graeca

Tsitsanis, Vassilis

☐ VASSILIS TITSANIS
ROUCD 1124 / Feb '97 / Rounder

TSOL

☐ DANCE WITH ME
Sounds of laughter / Core blue / Triangle / Eighty times / I'm tired of life / Love storm / Silent scream / Funeral march / Die for me / Peace thru power / Dance with me
64622 / Jan '97 / Epitaph

☐ THOUGHTS OF YESTERDAY
EFA 122142 / Nov '94 / Poshboy

☐ TSOL/WEATHERED STATUES
158142 / 24 Nov '97 / Nitro

Tsunami

☐ BRILLIANT MISTAKE, A
SMR 53 / 6 Oct '97 / Simple Machines

☐ DEEP END
SMR 13D / May '93 / Simple Machines

☐ HEART'S TREMOLO
SMR 25CD / Jun '94 / Simple Machines

☐ WHO IS IT
DYN 101 / Sep '93 / Nova

☐ WORLD TOUR AND OTHER DESTINATIONS
SMR 33CD / Apr '95 / Simple Machines

Tsurata, Kinshi

☐ PLAYS SATSUMA BIWA
C559067 / May '91 / Ocora

Tuatara

☐ TRADING WITH THE ENEMY
Streets of New Delhi / Smugglers cove / Night in the Emerald city / Bender / Negotiation / Fela the Conqueror / Wormwood / Koto song / L'Espionage de pomme de terre / Angel and the ass / PCH / Afterburner
4912142 / 22 Jun '98 / Epic

Tub

☐ WHY I DRINK
Charles Murray / Repeller / Life by beerlight / Ronald Reagan / Crash / Hardcore muscles and fitness / Teenagers from outer space / Rudy Giuliana / Two foot / Scoping / Static life
BLK 5001ECD / May '96 / Blackout

Tubb, Ernest

☐ LEGEND AND THE LEGACY, THE (Tubb, Ernest & Friends)
Waltz across Texas: *Tubb, Ernest & Willie Nelson* / When the world has turned you down: *Tubb, Ernest & Waylon Jennings/Vern Gosdin* / Let's say goodbye like we said hello: *Tubb, Ernest & Marty Robbins* / Walkin' the floor over you: *Tubb, Ernest & Merle Haggard/Charlie Daniels* / Half a mind: *Tubb, Ernest & George Jones* / Jealous loving heart: *Tubb, Ernest & Johnny Cash* / Rainbow at midnight: *Tubb, Ernest & Marty Robbins* / Set up two glasses Joe: *Tubb, Ernest & Ferlin Husky/Simon Crum* / You nearly lose your mind: *Tubb, Ernest & Willie Nelson/Waylon Jennings* / You're the only good thing: *Tubb, Ernest & Charlie Rich* / Filipino baby: *Tubb, Ernest & George Jones* / Jimmie Rodger's last blue yodel: *Tubb, Ernest & Conway Twitty* / Seaman's blues: *Tubb, Ernest & Merle Haggard* / Thanks a lot: *Tubb, Ernest & Loretta Lynn* / It's been so long darling: *Tubb, Ernest & Conway Twitty* / Blue eyed Elaine: *Tubb, Ernest & Justin* / Our baby's book: *Tubb, Ernest & Cal Smith* / Soldier's last letter: *Tubb, Ernest & Johnny Cash*
EDCD 517 / Mar '97 / Edsel

☐ LET'S SAY GOODBYE LIKE WE SAY HELLO (5CD Set)
You hit the nail right on the head / Two wrongs don't make a right / That wild and wicked look in your eye / Lonely heart knows / Don't your face look red / Answer to Rainbow At Midnight / Watching my past go by / Woman has wrecked many a good man / Headin' down the wrong highway / Let's say goodbye like we say hello / Takin' it easy here / Seaman's blues / How can I forget you / Yesterday's winner is a loser today / I'm with a crowd but so alone / Waiting for a train / Forever is ending today / Have you ever been lonely / Till the end of the world / Daddy, when is mommy coming home / Don't rob another man's castle / I'm biting my fingernails and thinking of you: *Tubb, Ernest & Andrews Sisters* / My Filipino rose / My Tennessee baby / Slippin' around / Warm red wine / Driftwood on the river / Tennessee border: *Tubb, Ernest & Red Foley* / Letters have no arms / I'll take a back seat for you / Throw your love my way / Don't be ashamed of your age: *Tubb, Ernest & Red Foley* / Stand by me / Old rugged cross / What a friend we have in Jesus / Wonderful city / When I take my vacation in heaven / Farther along / I love you because / Give me a little old-fashioned love / Unfaithful one / Hillbilly fever: *Tubb, Ernest & Red Foley* / Texas Vs Kentucky: *Tubb, Ernest & Red Foley* / G-I-R-L spells trouble / You don't have to be a baby to cry / Mother, the Queen of my heart / Goodnight Irene: *Tubb, Ernest & Red Foley* / Remember me, I'm the one who loves you / I need attention bad / I'm lonely and blue / Why did you give me your love / I'm free from the chain gang now / Why should I be lonely / Hobo's meditation / Good morning Irene: *Tubb, Ernest/Red Foley/Minnie Pearl* / Love bug itch: *Tubb, Ernest/Red Foley/Minnie Pearl* / Don't stay too long / I'm steppin' out of the picture / May the good lord bless and keep you / When it's prayer meetin' time in the hollow / Drunkard's child / Any old time / If you want some lovin' / So long (it's been good to know yuh): *Tubb, Ernest & Red Foley* / Chicken song: *Tubb, Ernest & Red Foley* / Strange little girl / Kentucky waltz / Hey la la / Rose of the mountains / Precious little baby / So many times / My mother must have been a girl like you / Somebody's stolen my honey / Heartsick soldier on a heartbreak ridge / I'm in love with Molly: *Tubb, Ernest & Red Foley* / Too old to cut the mustard: *Tubb, Ernest & Red Foley* / Missing in action / I will miss you when you go / Fortunes in memories / Dear judge / Don't brush them on me / I love everything you do / Somebody loves you / Don't trifle on your sweetheart / Hank, it will never be the same without you / Beyond the sunset / When Jimmie Rodgers said good-bye / Jimmie Rodgers' last thoughts / My wasted past / Counterfeit kisses / Honeymoon is over / No help wanted: *Tubb, Ernest & Red Foley* / You're a real good friend: *Tubb, Ernest & Red Foley* / Dear John letter: *Tubb, Ernest & Elaine 'Scooter Bill' Tubb* / Double datin': *Tubb, Ernest & Red Foley* / It's the mileage that's slowin' us down: *Tubb, Ernest & Red Foley* / Divorce granted / Honky tonk heart / I'm not looking for an angel / I met a friend / When Jesus calls / Too old to tango: *Tubb, Ernest & Red Foley* / Dr. Ketchum: *Tubb, Ernest & Red Foley* / Love lifted me / White Christmas / Blue Christmas / Christmas Island / C-H-R-I-S-T-M-A-S / We need God for Christmas / Merry Christmas you all / Blue snowflakes / I'm trimming my Christmas tree with teardrops
BCD 15498 / Feb '91 / Bear Family

☐ STARS OVER TEXAS
You nearly lose your mind / It's been so long darlin' / Have you ever been lonely (have you ever been blue) / Sweet thang / Tomorrow never comes / (When you feel like you're in love) don't just stand there / I'm with a crowd but so alone / Soldier's last letter / Blue eyed Elaine / Thanks a lot / Half a mind / Rainbow at midnight / Jimmy Rodger's last blue yodel / Journey's end / Waltz across Texas / Filipino baby / Walkin' the floor over you / You're the only good thing / Set up two glasses, Joe / Our baby's book / Driftwood on the river / Answer the phone / Jealous loving heart / Drivin' nails in my coffin / Let's say goodbye like we said hello / I'll step aside / There's a little bit of everything in Texas
3036001052 / Jun '97 / Carlton

☐ VERY BEST OF ERNEST TUBB, THE
HMNCD 024 / 3 Nov '97 / Half Moon

☐ WALKING THE FLOOR OVER YOU (8CD Set)
Passing of Jimmie Rodgers / Last thoughts of Jimmie Rodgers / Married man blues / Mean old red bug blues / My Mother is lonely / Right train to heaven / TB is whipping me / Since that black cat crossed my path / Blue eyed Elaine / I'll never cry over you / I'll get along somehow / You broke a heart / I ain't gonna love you anymore / I'm glad I met you after all / I cared for you more than I knew / You'll love me too late / I've really learned a lot / Swell San Angelo / I know what it means to be lonely / Please remember me / My rainbow trail / Last night I dreamed / I'm missing you / My baby and my wife / Walking the floor over you / When the world has turned you down / Our baby's book / I'll always be glad to take you back / Mean Mama blues / I wonder why you said goodbye / I ain't goin' honky tonkin' anymore / I hate to see you go / Time after time / First years blues / Just rollin' on / There's nothing more to say / Wasting my life away / You may have your picture / That same old story / Try me one more time / You nearly lose your mind / That's when it's coming home to you / I don't want you after all / I'm wandering how / Tomorrow never comes / Soldier's last letter / Careless Darlin' / Yesterday's tears / I'll never cry Over's last letter / Those simple things are worth a million now / Answer to walking the floor over you / You won't ever forget me / Keep my memory in your heart / I lost my ace of hearts / Though the days were only seven / With tears in my eyes (False starts) / With tears in my eyes / Are you waiting just for me / Blue eyes Elaine / I'll never lose you though you're gone / I'm too blue to worry over you / Too late to worry, too blue to cry / I'm wondering how / This time we're really through / I ain't goin honky tonkin' anymore / Have you changed your mind / That's all she wrote / Just crying to myself / I've lived a lie / Wondering if you're wondering to / When love turns to late / There's a new moon over my shoulder / Daisy may / I hung my head and cried / There's nothin' on my mind / Too late tp worry, to blue to cry / Love gone cold / You brought sorrow to my heart / Home in San Antone / Darling what more can I do / Blue bonnet lane / I believe I'm entitled to you / You're going to be sorry / My confession / That's why I'm crying over you / Gone and left me blues / When the tumble weeds come tumbling down / I'll be true while you're gone / End of the world / It just don't matter now / You're on my mind / I'm wasting my tears on you / Ten years / Old love letters / Low and lonely / Where the deep waters flow / It's coming back to you / Over the river / You don't care / Let me smile my last smile at you / I'm tired of you / You told me a lie / Frankie and Johnny / Jealous heart / Crying myself to sleep / Fort Worth Jail / You're breaking my heart / My hillbilly baby / Farther and farther apart / I loved you once / I'll step aside / Worried mind / Year ago tonight / Time changes everything / What good will it do / My time will come someday / Grey eyed darling / I never cross your mind / I told you so / I'm beginning to forget you / I'm gonna be long gone when I go away / I walk alone / Heart of stone / You'll want me back / Our baby boy / Hang your head in shame / Last goodbye / Pins and needles (In my heart) / Love I have for you / I'll never tell you I love you / I knew the moment I lost you / I wonder you feel the way I do / I'll have to live and learn (Alt) / National lament / Tweedle O'Twill / There's a rainbow on the Rio Colorado / Action speaks louder than words / Left all alone / Two more years (And I'll be free) / Trailing home to Mother / It's been so long darling / Sould I come back home to you / There's a little bit of everything in Texas / Darling, what more can I do / There's gonna be some changes made around / You were only teasing me / I'm free at last / Filipino baby / Rainbow at midnight / I don't blame you / Get in or get out of my heart / How can I be sure / Those tears in your eyes (Were not for me) / So round, so firm, so fully pakced / Don't look now / Hundred and sixty acres / Woman has wrecked many a good man / White Christmas / It's a lonely world / Mississippi gal / Trouble with me is trouble / Heart please be still / I hope I'm wrong / Those tears in your eyes / Don't talk to me about dames / You won't ever forget me / You could have said goodbye
BCD 15853 / Jul '96 / Bear Family

☐ WALTZ ACROSS TEXAS
Waltz across Texas / When the world has turned you down / Let's say goodbye like we say hello / Answer the phone / Journey's end / Walkin' the floor over you / Half a mind / Jealous loving heart / Rainbow at midnight / Set up two glasses, Joe / You nearly lose your mind / You're the only good thing / Filipino baby / Jimmie Rodgers' last blue yodel / Seaman's blues
PWKS 4217 / Jul '95 / Carlton

☐ YELLOW ROSE OF TEXAS, THE (5CD Set)
Till we two are one / Your Mother, your darling, your friend / Baby your mother (Like she babied you) / Jealous loving heart / Two glasses, Joe / Woman's touch / Journey's end / Kansas city blues / Lonely Christmas eve / I'll be walking the floor this Christmas / Have you seen my boogie woogie baby / It's a lonely world / I got the blues for Mammy / (I'm gonna make my home) A million miles from here / Yellow rose of Texas / Answer the phone / Honeymoon is over / Thirty days / Doorstep to heaven / Will you be satisfied that way / Steppin' out / If I never have anything else / So doggone lonesome / Old love letters (Bring memories of you) / Jimmie Rodgers' last blue yodel / Travellin' blues / You're the only good thing (that's happened to me) / I've got the blues for Mammy / I dreamed of an old love affair / (I know my baby loves me) in her own peculiar way / Mississippi gal / There's no fool like a young fool / I new the moment I lost you / You're breaking my heart / When a soldier knocks and finds nobody home / This troubled mind o'mine / My hillbilly baby / Daisy May / Loving you is my weakness / Treat her right / I want you know (I love you) / Don't forbid me / God's eyes / My treasure / Leave me / Mr. Love / I always went through / Go home / Hey Mr. Blubird / How do we know / House of glass / Heaven help me / Tangled mind / Home of the blues / I found my girl in the USA / Geisha girl / I wonder why I worry over you / Deep purple blues / Please keep me in mind / I'm a long gone Daddy / Your cheatin' heart / Don't trade your old fashioned sweetheart / It makes no difference now / San Antonio rose / I want you to know I love you / That, my darlin', is me / I'll get along somehow / Educated Mama / I'm waiting for the ships that never come in / Half a mind / Next time / Goodbye sunshine / Hello blues / It's the age that makes the difference / What am I living for / Next voice you hear / All of those yesterdays / Walking the floor over you / When the world has turned you down / I'll always be glad to take you back / It's been so long Darling / Careless Darlin' / Though the days were only seven / Last night I dreamed / Slippin' around / I love you because / There's nothing more to say / There's a little bit of everything in Texas / You nearly lose your mind / Blue Christmas / Don't rob another man's castle / What I don't know about her / I cried a tear / Let's say goodbye like we say hello / Driftwood on the river / I wonder why you said goodbye / Tomorrow never comes / Filipino baby / I'd rather be / Letters have no arms / Rainbow at midnight / Have you ever been lonely / I will miss you when you go / Live it up / (I've lost you) So why should I care / Accidently on purpose / Do it now / He'll have to go / Mr. Blues / Kind of love she gave to me / Pick me up on your way down / This ain't the blues (Instrumental) / You win again / I believe I'm entitled to you / Guy named Joe / Who will buy the wine / Why I'm walkin' / White silver sands / Am I that easy to forget / Everybody's somebody's fool / Let the little girl dance / Candy kisses / It happened when I really needed you / Wondering / Cold cold heart / Four walls / Bouquet of roses / Crazy arms / I love you so much it hurts / I walk the line / Little ole band of gold / Wabash cannonball / I'm movin' on / Tennessee Saturday night / Signed, sealed, delivered (I'm yours) / Thoughts of a fool / Girl from Abilene / Same thing as me / Christmas is just another day / I hate to see you go / I'm sorry now / What will you tell them / It is no secret / Don't just stand there / Big blue diamonds / I'll just have another cup of coffee
BCD 15688 / May '93 / Bear Family

Tubb, Justin

☐ ROCK ON DOWN TO MY HOUSE (2CD Set)
I'm a darn good man / Story of my life / Ooh la la / Give three cheers for my baby / Somebody ughed on you / Something called the blues / I'm looking for a date tonight / You're the prettiest thing that ever happend to me / Who will it be / Sufferin' heart / Looking back to see / Miss you so / My heart's not for little girls to play with / Little bit waltz / I'm sorry I stayed away so long / Sure fire kisses / Fickel heart / Waterloo / I gotta go get my baby / Chuga-chuga, chica maugal / I'm a damn good man / All alone / Within your arms / Pepper hot baby / Lucky lucky someone else / You nearly lose your mind / Oh how I miss you / Desert blues / Miss the Mississippi and you / It takes a lot of heart / I'm just fool enough / I'm a big boy now / Life I have to live / Bachelor man / Party is over (For me) / Tears of angels / If you'll be my love / Someday, you'll want me to want you / I saw your face in the moon / Try me one more time / I'd trade all of my tomorrows / Silver dew on the bluegrass / Bonaparte's retreat / There'll be no teardrops tonight / Gone and left my blues / My Mary / Into each life some rain must fall / I've gotta have my baby back / Hang your head in shame / Sugar lips / Rock it down to my house / Mine is a lonely life / Almost lonely / Giveway girl / Heart's command / Buster's gang / I wish I could love that much / I know you do
BCD 15761 / Jun '94 / Bear Family

Tube, Shem

☐ ABANA BA NASERY (Tube, Shem/ Justo Osala/Enos Okola)
Atisa wangu / Khwatsia ebunangwe / Servanus andai / Nilimwacha muke risavu / Mapenzi kama karata / Noah libuko / Omukhana meri / Abasiratsi muhulire / Ndakhomela / Ebijana bie bubayi / Mushalo ebutula / Rosey wangu / Willison oluhambo
CDORB 052 / Nov '89 / Globestyle

Tubes

☐ COMPLETION BACKWARD PRINCIPLE, THE
Talk to ya later / Let's make some noise / Matter of pride / Mr. Hate / Attack of the 50 foot woman / Think about me / Sushi girl / Don't want to wait anymore / Power tools / Amnesia / When I see you / Politics / Slave trade / Could be her...could be you / Make believe / Don't go away / Price / Animal laugh / Anything is good enough / Product of... / Perfect game / Vendredi saint
BGOCD 100 / Mar '91 / Beat Goes On

☐ DON'T WANT TO WAIT ANYMORE
Don't want to wait anymore / Tip of my tongue / Sushi girl / Let's make some noise / Think about me / Matter of pride / Mr. Hate / Attack of the fifty foot woman / She's a beauty / Amnesia / Muscle girls / When you're ready to come / Bora bora 2000/Love bomb / No not again / Talk to ya later / Monkey time / Keyboard kids
DC 886112 / 2 Feb '98 / Disky

☐ GOING DOWN...THE TUBES (2CD Set)
White punks on dope / Up from the deep / Malaguena salerosa / What do you want from life / Boy crazy / Tubes world tour / Don't touch me there / Slipped my disco / Smoke (la vie en fumer) / My head is my only house unless it rains / God-bird-change / I'm just a mess / This town / Pound of flesh / Drivin' all night / Love will keep us together / White punks on dope / Turn me on / TV is king / Prime time / I want it all now / No way out / Getoverture / No mercy / Only the strong survive / Be mine tonight / Love's a mystery (I don't understand) / Telecide / Overture / Mondo bondage / Crime medley / I was a punk before you were a punk / I saw her standing there / White punks on dope
5405642 / Oct '96 / A&M

☐ LOVE BOMB
Piece by piece / Stella / Come as you are / One good reason / Bora Bora 2000 / Love bomb / Night people / Say hey / Eyes / Muscle girls / Theme from a wooly place / For a song / Say hey (part 2) / Feel it / Night people (reprise)
BGOCD 188 / Jul '93 / Beat Goes On

☐ OUTSIDE/INSIDE
She's a beauty / Do not again / Out of the business / Monkey time / Glasshouse / Wild women of Wongo / Tip of my tongue / Fantastic delusion / Drums / Theme park / Outside looking in
BGOCD 133 / Mar '92 / Beat Goes On

Tubetop

☐ THREE MINUTE HERCULES
LRR 9606 / Dec '97 / Laundry Room

Tubilah Dog

☐ IN SEARCH OF PLAICE
CMGCD 023 / 11 May '98 / Communique

Tubuai Choir

☐ POLYNESIAN ODYSSEY
SHAN 64049CD / Dec '93 / Shanachie

Tuck & Patti

☐ BEST OF TUCK & PATTI, THE
01934111562 / Oct '94 / Windham Hill

☐ DREAM
Dream / One hand, one heart / Togetherness / Friends in high places / Voodoo music / From now on we're one / I wish / Sitting in limbo / High heel blues / All the love / As time goes by
01934101302 / Nov '93 / Windham Hill

☐ LEARNING TO FLY
Live in the light / Heaven down here / Learning how to fly / Strength / Woodstock / Drum / Up from the skies / Tossin' and turnin' / Getaway / In my life / Yeah yeah / Wide awake / Still tossin' and turnin
4783992 / Apr '95 / Sony Soho2

☐ LOVE WARRIORS
Love warriors / Honey pie / They can't take that away from me / Hold out hold up and hold on / Cantador (like a lover) / On a clear day (You can see forever) / Europa / Castles made of sand / Little wing / Glory glory / If it's magic
01934101162 / Jan '95 / Windham Hill

☐ TEARS OF JOY
Tears of joy / Takes my breath away / I've got just about everything / Time after time / Everything's gonna be alright / Better than anything / My romance / Up and at it / Mad mad me / Love is the key
01934101112 / Jan '95 / Windham Hill

Tucker, Johnny

☐ STRANDED (Tucker, Johnny & James Thomas)
HMG 1001 / Aug '97 / Hightone

Tucker, Junior

☐ DEEP INSIDE OF YOU
DTCD 001 / Jun '97 / Don't Test

☐ LOVE OF A LIFETIME
VPCD 1314 / Aug '93 / VP

☐ SECRET LOVER
CRCD 35 / Nov '94 / Charm

☐ TRUE CONFESSION
VPCD 1466 / May '96 / VP

Tucker, Leslie

☐ IN THIS ROOM
742282 / May '98 / Compass

Tucker, Luther

☐ LUTHER TUCKER & THE FORD BLUES BAND (Tucker, Luther & The Ford Blues Band)
CCD 11040 / Nov '95 / Crosscut

☐ SAD HOURS
ANT 0026CD / Apr '94 / Antones

Tucker, Marshall

☐ FINEST SOUTH ROCK (Tucker, Marshall Band)
Fire on the mountain / Searchin' for a rainbow / Virginia / Bob away the blues / Walkin' and talkin' / Take the highway / Can't you see / Losing you / Hillbilly band / See you later, I'm gone / Ramblin' / My jesus told me so / Ab's song
12363 / May '94 / Laserlight

Tucker, Mickey

☐ GETTIN' THERE
SCCD 31365 / Dec '95 / Steeplechase

Tucker, Moe

☐ DOGS UNDER STRESS
NR 422492 / Mar '94 / New Rose

☐ I SPENT A WEEK THERE THE OTHER NIGHT
422373 / May '94 / New Rose

☐ LIFE IN EXILE AFTER ABDICATION
CREV 011CD / Mar '93 / Rev-Ola

☐ OH NO, THEY'RE RECORDING THIS SHOW
422418 / May '94 / New Rose

Tucker, Sophie

☐ JAZZ AGE HOT MAMA 1922-1929
TT 404 / May '98 / Take Two

☐ LAST OF THE RED HOT MAMAS
Some of these days / After you've gone / I ain't got nobody / One sweet letter from you / Fifty million Frenchmen can't be wrong / There'll be some changes made / Man I love / My Yiddishe momme / I know my baby is cheatin' on me / He hadn't until yesterday / Aren't women wonderful / There's a blue ridge round my heart Virginia / He's tall dark and handsome / I'm the last of the red hot mommas / Moanin' low / That's where the south begins / Follow a star / I never can think of the words / Life begins at forty / When a lady meets a gentleman down south / Foolin' with the other woman's man / If you can't sing it you'll have to swing it / Lady is a tramp
CDMOIR 529 / Jul '98 / Memoir

☐ LEGENDARY SOPHIE TUCKER, THE
I'm the last of the red hot mammas / Some of these days / Aren't women wonderful / Louisville Lou / Oh you have no idea / Life begins at forty / 'Cause I feel low-down / You can't sew a button on a heart / What good am I without you / Older they get, the younger they want them / Fifty million Frenchmen can't be wrong / After you've gone / Washing the blues from my soul / Follow a star / Who wants them tell, Dard and Handsome / My Yiddishe momme / That man of my dreams / Man I love / He hadn't up 'til yesterday / Some of these days
PAR 2031 / Sep '94 / Parade

☐ SOME OF THESE DAYS
My Yiddishe Momme / Man I love / Fifty million Frenchmen can't be wrong / Life begins at forty / Complainin' / Some of these days / After you've gone / Oh you have no idea / He's a good man to have around / When a lady meets a gentleman down South / There'll be some changes made / Washing the blues from my soul / One I love (belongs to someone else) / You've got to see Mamma ev'ry night / Aren't women wonderful / 'Cause I feel lowdown / What'll I do / Makin' wickey wackey down in Waikiki / Moanin' low / My pet / I ain't got nobody / Man of my dreams / Foolin' with the other woman's man / (If you can't sing) you'll have to swing it
PASTCD 7807 / Oct '96 / Flapper

☐ SOME OF THESE DAYS
GO 3821 / 1 Dec '97 / Golden Options

Tucker, Tanya

☐ COUNTRY CLASSICS
Strong enough to bend / Love me like you used to / Just another love / One love at a time / Texas (when I die) / I won't take less than your love / San Antonio stroll / Would you lay with me (in a field of stone) / What's your mama's name / Child / Blood red and going down / Highway robbery / Walkin' shoes / Jamestown ferry / If it didn't come easy / Something
CDMFP 6323 / Apr '97 / Music For Pleasure

☐ LIZZIE AND THE RAINMAN
Lizzie and the rainman / I'm not lisa / Love of a rolling stone / San antonio stroll / Someday soon / Travelling salesman / Should I do it / Rodeo girls / You just loved the leaving out of me / I use the soap / Dancing the night away / It was always you / Texas (when I die) / Lover goodbye / All the way / My song / Can I see you tonight
CDCOT 108 / Mar '94 / Cottage

Tucker, Tommy

☐ TOMMY TUCKER & HIS ORCHESTRA 1941-1947
CCD 15 / Mar '95 / Circle

Tud

☐ DEUS KERNE
CD 851 / Jul '94 / Diffusion Breizh

☐ LA PLUME DE PAON
TUD 002CD / Aug '97 / Arfolk

Tudor, David

☐ RAINFOREST
MODE 64 / Jun '98 / Mode

Tudor Lodge

☐ IT ALL COMES BACK
SCOFCD 1005 / 20 Apr '98 / Scenescof

☐ LET'S TALK
CIRCD 010 / 23 Mar '98 / Cast Iron

☐ TUDOR LODGE
REP 4064 / Aug '91 / Repertoire
SRMC 0028 / Oct '97 / Siwan

Tuesday

☐ FREEWHEELIN'
AM 019CD / Nov '97 / Asian Man

Tuesday Weld

☐ HERSELF
SUPERCD 01 / Feb '97 / Supermodern

Tuff & Jam

☐ TUFF JAM PRESENTS UNDERGROUND FREQUENCIES VOL.1 (2CD Set) (Various Artists)
Gabrielle: *Davis, Roy Jr.* / Puch the love: *Edwards, Todd* / Rush: Tywanda / Tumblin' down: *Xavier* / Spin spin sugar: *Sneaker Pimps* / Closer than close: *Gaines, Rosie* / Moments in love: *D'Ambrosio, Bobby* / Harvest for the world: *Hunter, Terry* / Ripgroove: *Double 99* / Dreams: *Smokin' Beats* / Dangerous: *Mr. X* / Things are never: *Operator & Baffled* / Bliss: *Mutiny* / Runaway: *Nu Yorican Soul* / Jump: *Double 99* / Never let you go: *Moore, Tina* / Anytime: *Nu Birth* / Find a path: *New Horizons* / Just gets better: *TJR* / No.1: *Industry Standard*
74321494652
74321494672 / Jul '97 / Northwestside

☐ TUFF JAM PRESENTS UNDERGROUND FREQUENCIES VOL.2 (2CD Set) (Various Artists)
90% of me is you: *Powell, Samantha* / Boundaries: *Conquest, Leena* / Never far from you: *Edwards, Todd* / Flava fever: *Cole, MJ* / Somebody else's guy: *Peniston, Ce Ce* / Shake that ass: *Divine Soul* / Love shy: *Blond, Kristine* / Sweet love got me: *Ultymate* / Who taught you how: *Waters, Crystal* / Hallilujah: *Chandler, Kerri* / Find a way: *Mr. X* / Lost in space: *Lighthouse Family* / D-Dubs vol.2: *M-Dubs* / Nobody better: *Moore, Tina* / R U sleeping: *Indo* / New York city girl: *Tallman, Dawn* / Back to life: *Ragga's Revenge* / Buddy X: *Cherry, Neneh* / Need good love: *Tuff & Jam* / Freak me: *Another Level*
74321564462
74321564452 / 11 May '98 / Northwestside

Tuff, Mikey

☐ NAH LEF JAH JAH
RMCD 012 / Dec '92 / Roots Man

Tulku

☐ SEASONS OF SOULS
3145580072 / 24 Mar '98 / TRLK

☐ TRANCENDENCE
Life force / Golden era / Agua sante / Time dances slowly / Ghost dance / Orca song / Anni rose / Trancendence / Journey of the warrior / Sacred circle / Prayer to the protector
4444772152 / 24 Feb '98 / Triloka

Tulla Ceili Band

☐ CELEBRATION OF 50 YEARS, A
Concertina reel/Coffey's reel / Imelda Roland's/Cregg's pipes / Peacock's feather / Tatter Jack Walsh/Cook in the kitchen / Four courts/Tear the calico / Battering ram/Bill Harte's/Ward's jig / Lad O'Beirne's/Broderick's / Battle of Aughrim / Cooley's/The cup of tea/The wise maid / Hole in the hedge/Seamus Cooley's/Kerfunken jig / Jenny picking cockles/The Sligo maid / Castle Kelly/humours of Ballyconnell/The Duke of Leinster / Butcher's jig/The lark's march/Gander at the Pratie Hole / Joe's/The mountain lark
GLCD 1178 / Feb '97 / Green Linnet

Tullycraft

☐ CITY OF SUBARUS
DRL 055CD / 2 Mar '98 / Cher Doll/Darla

Tumbaito

☐ OTROS TIEMPOS
DEPCD 003 / May '98 / Deep South

Tumbao

☐ SALSA PA' GOZAR
EUCD 1188 / Apr '92 / ARC

Tumor Circus

☐ TUMOR CIRCUS
VIRUS 87CD / Oct '91 / Alternative Tentacles

Tungsten

☐ 183.85
IRSCD 981202 / 6 Oct '97 / Intercord

☐ TUNGSTEN SURVIVAL KIT, THE
LTR 004 / 15 Dec '97 / Lighttown

Tunic

☐ CONTROVERSIAL STINGER T-SHIRT
100GM 23 / 16 Feb '98 / 100 Guitar Mania

☐ WITHOUT LOVE, WHERE WOULD YOU BE NOW
RYPE 303 / May '97 / Project Rype

Tunjung, Gamelan Seker

☐ MUSIC OF K.R.T. WASITODININGRAT
Gending corobalen / Ketawang wedyasmoro / Ladrang sri-duhito / Lancaran orde baru / Ketawang gending purnomo sidhi / Lancaran penghijauan / Ketawang cokrowala / Ketawang angleng
CMPCD 3007 / Jul '92 / CMP

Tupaia, Andy

☐ HITS SELECTION VOL.2
S 65810 / Sep '92 / Manuiti

Tura Satana

☐ ALL IS NOT WELL
Hypocrite / Sickness / Kiss or kill / Break / Empty / Put your head out / Victim / Clean / Roughness / Six feet deep / Cycle of violence / Down / Down (reprise)
N 02682 / 12 Jan '98 / Noise

Turas

☐ IRISH TRADITIONAL MUSIC
DOL 001CD / Dec '97 / Dolmen

Turbinton, Earl

☐ AFRICAN COWBOY, THE
PCD 7067 / May '98 / Progressive

☐ BROTHERS FOR LIFE
All tied up / Real mccoy / Brothers for life / Fat blues / Neferdoris / Kingston town / Think of one / Upside down crescent
ROUCD 2064 / '88 / Rounder

Turbo AC's

☐ DAMNATION OVERDRIVE
Graveyard shifter / Eat my dust / No ieNo lie / Praise the lord / Righteous ruler / BBe fast / Superbad / Puff of smoke / Twistoflex / I don't care / Last mile
BLK 034ECD / Jan '97 / Blackout

Turbonegro

☐ APOCALYPSE DUDES
BOOMBA 002CD / 13 Apr '98 / Boomba

☐ ASS COBRA
BOOMBA 0012 / Jun '96 / Boomba
SFTRI 385CD / May '97 / Sympathy For The Record Industry

☐ HELTA SKELTA
EFA 15665CD / Jun '93 / Repulsion

Turbulent Force

☐ DISTURBING TRUTH, THE
Green sugar / Dreams / Media overdose / Voidcom / Metro city / Renegade / Shangri-la / Breathless / Paranoia
SOP 010CD / Feb '97 / Emissions

Turmoil

☐ CHOKE
CM 770752 / Sep '94 / Century Media

☐ FROM BLEEDING HEARTS
CMCD 77102 / May '96 / Century Media

Turn Ons

☐ TURN ONS
DS45CD 18 / Jul '97 / Duophonic 45's

Turner, 'Big' Joe

☐ BIG JOE TURNER RIDES AGAIN
Switchin' in the kitchen / Until the real thing comes along / Rebecca / Don't you make me high / Pennies from heaven / Nobody in mind / I get the blues when it rains / When I was young / Time after time / Here comes your iceman
RSACD 810 / Oct '94 / Sequel

☐ BIG THREE, THE (Turner, 'Big' Joe & Joe Houston/L.C. Williams)
CDBM 095 / Jul '93 / Blue Moon

☐ BLUES TRAIN (Turner, 'Big' Joe & Roomful Of Blues)
Crawdad hole / Red sails in the sunset / Cock-a-doodle-doo / Jumpin' for Joe / I want a little girl / I know you love me / Last night / I love the way (my baby sings the blues) / Blues train
MCD 5293 / Feb '87 / Muse

☐ BOSS OF THE BLUES (That's Jazz Vol.14)
Cherry red / Roll 'em Pete / I want a little girl / Low down dog / Wee baby blues / You're driving me crazy / How long blues / Morning glories / St. Louis blues / Piney Brown blues
7567814592 / Jun '93 / Atlantic

☐ BOSS OF THE BLUES 1939-1947
159112 / 24 Feb '98 / Blues Collection

☐ FLIP, FLOP AND FLY (Turner, 'Big' Joe & Count Basie Orchestra)
CD 23109372 / Jan '92 / Pablo

☐ GREATEST HITS
Chill is on / After my laughter came tears / Bump Miss Suzie / Chains of love / I'll never stop loving you / Sweet sixteen / Baby I still want you / Honey hush / Crawdad hole / Oke she moke she pop / Shake, rattle and roll / Well all right / Hide and seek / Flip flop and fly / Chicken and the hawk / Boogie woogie country girl / Corrine Corrina / Midnight special train / Red sails in the sunset / Feeling happy / Blues in the night
RSACD 809 / Oct '94 / Sequel

☐ HAVE NO FEAR, BIG JOE IS HERE
SK blues / Watch that jive / Howling wind / Low down dog / Mad blues / Playboy blues / My gal's a jockey / Sally Zu-Zazz / Oowee baby blues / Lucille Lucille / Careless love / Hollywood bed / Johnson and Turner blues / I got love for sale
SV 0265 / May '98 / Savoy Jazz

☐ HONEY HUSH
Shake, rattle and roll / Chains of love / Roll 'em Hawk / Piney Brown blues / Cherry red / Nothin' from nothin' / Honey hush / Corine Corina / TV Mama / Wee baby blues / Squeeze me baby
CDMF 064 / Mar '95 / Magnum Force

☐ JOE TURNER'S BLUES
Goin' away blues / Roll 'em Pete / Cherry red / Lovin' Mama blues / How long how long blues / Shake it and break it / Joe Turner blues / Beale Street blues / Piney brown blues / Careless love / Jumpin' down blues / Wee baby blues / Last goodbye blues / Lucille / Rock me mama / Corrine Corrina / Lonesome graveyard / It's the same old story / SK blues / Johnson and Turner blues / Watch that jive / My gal's a jockey / Sunday morning blues / Still in the dark / Miss Brown blues
TPZ 1070 / 24 Nov '97 / Topaz Jazz

☐ LA SELECTION 1938-1941
700102 / Nov '92 / Art Vocal

☐ LIFE AIN'T EASY
OJCCD 809 / Jan '95 / Original Jazz Classics

☐ ROCK 'N' ROLL SHAKEDOWN
Shake, rattle and roll / When the sun goes down / Jump for joy / Stormy Monday / Hide and go seek / How long blues / Morning, noon and night / Everyday I have the blues / Early one morning / Chains of love / Corrina Corrina / I hear you knockin'
CWNCD 2036 / Jun '97 / Crown

☐ ROOTS OF ROCK 'N' ROLL VOL.6, THE (Watch That Jive)
I gotta girl (for every day of the week) / Little bittie gal's blues / Rebecca / It's the same old story / SK blues / SK blues / Johnson and Turner blues / Watch that jive / Howlin' winds / Doggin' the blues / I got my discharge papers / Miss Brown Blues / I'm still in the dark / My gal's a jockey / I got love for sale / Sunday morning blues / Mad blues / It's a low down dirty shame / I'm still in the dark / Miss Brown Blues / Sally-zu-zazz / Rock of Gibraltar / Milk and butter blues / That's when it really hurts / I'm in sharp when I hit the coast / Ooh wee baby blues
PLCD 562 / May '97 / President

☐ STORMY MONDAY
Long way from home / Somebody loves me / Stormy Monday / Time after time / Love is like a faucet / Things that I used to do
CD 2310 943 / Jun '93 / Pablo

☐ TELL ME PRETTY BABY (Turner, 'Big' Joe & Pete Johnson Orchestra)
ARHCD 333 / Apr '95 / Arhoolie

☐ TEXAS STYLE
T.v. mama / T.v. mama / I've got a pocket full of pencil / Rock me baby / Texas style / Cherry red / Tain't nobody's business if I do / Money first
BLE 595472 / Oct '94 / Black & Blue

☐ TRUMPET KINGS MEET JOE TURNER, THE
Mornin', noon and night / I know you love me baby / TV momma / Ain't nobody's business if I do
OJCCD 497 / May '97 / Original Jazz Classics

☐ VERY BEST OF BIG JOE TURNER, THE
Chains of love / Sweet sixteen / Honey hush / TV mama / Oke she moke she pop / Shake rattle and roll / Well alright / Flip flop fly / Hide and seek / Midnight cannonball / Chicken and the hawk / Boogiw woogie country girl / Corrine Corrina / You're driving me crazy / Midnight special train / Tomorrow night
8122729682 / 4 May '98 / Rhino

Turner, 'Big' Joe

☐ JACKSON ON MY MIND (Turner, 'Big' Joe Memphis Blues Caravan)
Jackson on my mind / Evil / I am the blues / Travelling man / Right to love your woman / Just ain't enough / Some day / BJ / Target / Time to go
MYSCD 118 / 13 Oct '97 / Mystic

☐ LIVE (Turner, 'Big' Joe Memphis Blues Caravan)
Blue monk / Thing's ain't what they used to be / Woke up this morning / Bad luck / Take home pay / Aching heart / No response / Something about you / Blood on your hands / Somebody have mercy
MYSCD 109 / Jul '97 / Mystic

Turner, Bruce

☐ THAT'S THE BLUES, DAD
New orleans hop scop blues / Viper mad / Roses of picardy / Blue turning grey over you / Creole love call / On treasure island / Blues gone away / Mandy, make up your mind / Blueberry hill / I've got to sing a torch song / You're a heavenly thing / Imagination / Love is just around the corner / Farewell blues / Blue feeling / That's the blues, dad / Your eyes / Stop, look and listen / Jumpin' at the woodside / Donegal cradle song
LACD 49 / Nov '95 / Lake

Turner, Ike

☐ HEY HEY (Turner, Ike & The Rhythm Kings)
PCD 5321 / 27 Apr '98 / P-Vine

☐ MY BLUES COUNTRY
Get it get it / Baby baby let's get it on / Five long years / I'm blue / My babe / Fool in love / You're so / Sexy Ida / Sweet black angel / Get it get it / Love like yours / Early one morning
MYSCD 115 / 15 Sep '97 / Mystic

☐ RHYTHM ROCKIN' BLUES (Turner, Ike & The Kings Of Rhythm)
Rocket 88: *Brenston, Jackie* / Way you used to treat me: *Lover Boy* / I miss you so: *Binder, Dennis* / Nobody wants me: *Binder, Dennis* / Wild one: *Turner, Ike* / All the blues, all the time: *Turner, Ike* / Sitting and wondering: *Walker, J.W.* / Early times: *Binder, Dennis* / World is yours: *Wright, Johnny & Ike Turner's Orchestra* / Suffocate: *Wright, Johnny* / Talking about me: *Burton, Little Johnny* / Walk my way back home: *Burton, Little Johnny* / I ain't drunk:

Lonnie The Cat / Road I travel: *Lonnie The Cat* / Night howler: *Gayles, Billy* / Woman won't just do: *Gayles, Billy* / I'm tired of being dogged around: *Gayles, Billy* / You got me way down here: *Binder, Dennis* / Love is scarce: Lover Boy / Nobody seems to want me: *Lover Boy*
CDCHD 553 / Oct '95 / Ace

☐ **TRAILBLAZER (Turner, Ike & The Kings Of Rhythm)**
Big question / Just one more time / Mistreater / No coming back / You found the time / She made my blood run cold / I'm tore up / Trail blazer / You've changed my love / Let's call it a day / Much later / Miserable / Do you mean it / Gonna wait for my chance / If I never had known you / Rock-a-bucket / Sad as a man can be / What can it be / Do right baby / My baby's tops / Take your fine frame home
CDCHARLY 263 / Feb '91 / Charly

Turner, Ike & Tina

☐ **18 CLASSIC TRACKS**
Proud Mary / Nutbush city limits / Get back / Honky tonk women / Living for the city / I want to take you higher / Come together / Higher ground / Workin' together / Sexy Ida / I idolize you / Drift away / Sweet Rhodode Island Red / Early one morning / I'm yours / Love like yours / I heard it through the grapevine / I've been loving you too long
CDGOLD 1049 / Jul '96 / EMI Gold

☐ **BEST OF IKE & TINA TURNER, THE (18 Original Hits/3CD Set)**
Acid queen: *Turner, Tina* / Nutbush city limits / Higher ground / Get back / Pick me tonight / Bootsey Whitelaw: *Turner, Tina* / Proud Mary / Under my thumb: *Turner, Tina* / I can see for miles: *Turner, Tina* / Whole lotta love: *Turner, Tina* / Sweet Rhode Island red / Honky tonk woman / Let's spend the night together: *Turner, Tina* / Piece of my heart / Sexy Ida / Rockin' and rollin': *Turner, Tina* / Baby get it on / I've been loving you too long
LAD 873302 / Nov '96 / Disky

☐ **BOLD SOUL SISTER**
Bold soul sister / Mississippi rolling stone / Living for the city / Shake a hand / It's all over / Somebody (somewhere) needs me / Too much for one woman / Rockin' and rollin' / Sugar sugar / Crazy about you baby / I've been loving you too long / Fool in love / Something's got a hold on me / It sho' ain't me / Fool for you / It's gonna work out fine / I can't stop loving you / Cussin' cryin' and carryin' on / Push / Tina's prayer
PLATCD 211 / Feb '97 / Platinum

☐ **BOLD SOUL SISTER**
HIPD 40051 / 16 Feb '98 / Hippo

☐ **CUSSIN', CRYIN' AND CARRYIN' ON**
Black angel / Getting nasty / It sho' ain't me / Fool in love / Nothing you can do boy / I better get ta steppin' / Shake a tailfeather / We need an understanding / You're so fine / Too hot to hold / I'm fed up / You got what you wanted / Betcha can't kiss me (just one time) / Cussin', cryin' and carryin' on / Ain't nobody's business if I do / Funky mule / Thinking black / Black beauty / Ghetto funk / Black's alley
CDSB 014 / May '96 / Starburst

☐ **GOOD OLD TIMES**
Let's get it on / Mr. Right / Bootsie Whitelaw / Oh my my / Games people play / So fine / Something / Soul deep / You got to work it / I can't believe what you say / Stormy weather / Night time is the right time / It's gonna work out fine / Proud Mary / Endlessly
662171 / Dec '92 / FNAC

☐ **IT'S ALL OVER**
CDSGP 058 / Oct '93 / Prestige

☐ **LET THE GOOD TIMES ROLL**
I can't believe what you say / Sweet Rhode Island Red / I idolize you / Ooh poo pah do / I'm movin' on / I can't stop loving you / You are my sunshine / Early in the morning / Tell the truth / Let the good times roll / Keep on using me / Golden empire / I gotta man / Ain't got nobody / Sugar sugar / She belongs to me / Stormy weather / Twist and shout
PLSCD 253 / 27 Oct '97 / Pulse

☐ **LIVING FOR THE CITY**
Living for the city / Rockin' and rolling / Sugar sugar / Chicken / Mississippi rolling stone / Golden empire / I'm looking for my mind / Shake a hand / Bootsie whitelaw / Too much man for one woman / I know (you don't want me no more) / Never been to Spain / Push / Raise your hand / Tina's prayer / If you want it / You're up to something / You're still my baby / Jesus
101762 / May '97 / A-Play Collection

☐ **MASTERS, THE**
EABCD 072 / 24 Nov '97 / Eagle

☐ **MASTERS, THE (2CD Set)**
EDMCD 016 / 24 Nov '97 / Eagle

☐ **MRS**
Living for the city / Rockin' and rollin' / Sugar sugar / Chicken / Mississippi rolling stone / Golden empire / I'm looking for my mind / Shake a hand / Bootsie whitelaw / Too much man for one woman / I know (you don't want me no more) / Never been to spain / Push / Raise your head / Tina's prayer / If you want it / Keep getting it on / You're up to something / You're still my baby / Jesus
GRF 218 / Mar '93 / Tring

☐ **OLYMPIA 1971 (The Mythical Concert)**
472364 / Jul '96 / Flarenasch

☐ **PROUD MARY (Legendary Masters Series - The Best Of Ike & Tina Turner)**
Fool in love / I idolize you / I'm jealous / It's gonna work out fine / Poor fool / Tra la la la la / You shoulda treated me right / Come together / Honky tonk women / I want to take you higher / Workin' together / Proud Mary / Funkier than a mosquita' tweeter / Ooh-poo-pah-doo / I'm yours (use me anyway you wanna) / Up in heah / River deep, mountain high / Nutbush City Limits / Sweet Rhode Island Red / Sexy Ida (part 1) / Sexy Ida (part 2) / Baby - get it on / Acid Queen
CDP 7958462 / Jul '96 / Premier/EMI

☐ **RIVER DEEP, MOUNTAIN HIGH**
River deep, mountain high / I idolize you / Love like yours / Fool in love / Make 'em wait / Hold on baby / Save the last dance for me / Oh baby / Everyday I have to cry / Such a fool for you / It's gonna work out fine / I'll never need more than this
CDMID 134 / Oct '92 / A&M

☐ **ROCKIN' SOUL OF IKE & TINA TURNER, THE**
Living for the city / Rockin' and rolin' / Sugar sugar / Chicken / Mississippi rolling stone / Golden empire / I'm looking for my mind / Shake a hand / Bootsie whitelaw / Too much man for one woman / I know (you don't want me no more) / Never been to Spain / Push / Raise your hand / Tina's prayer / If you want it / You're up to something / You're still my baby / Jesus
QED 031 / Nov '96 / Tring

☐ **SENSATIONAL IKE & TINA TURNER, THE (2CD Set)**
Nutbush city limits / Golden Empire / Something / Oh my, my (can you boogie) / Stormy weather / You don't love me (yes I know) / Stand by me / Give me a chance / I idolise you / Put on your tight pants / Ain't that a shame / Rockin' and rollin' / Shake / I wish it would rain / If you can hully gully / Betcha can't kiss me (just one time) / I need a man / I wanna jump / I can't stop loving you / River deep, mountain high / Philadelphia freedom / You can't have your cake and eat it too / Baby get it on / Daily bread / Come together / He belongs to me / Ooh-poo-pah-do / I want to take you higher / We need an understanding / Never been to Spain / Country girl, city man / Ya ya / Why I sing the blues / Living for the city / Use me / Sweet Rhode Island Red / Locomotion / Stagger Lee / Sugar sugar / I'm movin' on
CPCD 82572 / Nov '96 / Charly

☐ **SHAKE**
MU 5068 / Oct '92 / Musketeer

☐ **SPOTLIGHT ON IKE & TINA TURNER**
It's gonna work out fine / Fool for you / Crazy about you baby / I can't stop loving you / Somebody somewhere needs you / Too hot to hold / Cussin', cryin' and carryin' on / I know / It sho' ain't me / You got what you wanted / Ain't nobody's business if I do / Betcha can't kiss me (Just one time) / I smell trouble / It's all over / Nothing you can do boy / All I do is cry
HADCD 127 / Feb '94 / Javelin

☐ **THOSE WERE THE DAYS**
Sugar sugar / Never been to Spain / Too much for one woman / Stormy weather / Into to it / Trying to find my mind / I want to take you higher / Fool in love / I idolize you / Poor fool / Lay it down / Freedom to stay / Loving him was easier / Rescue me / Father alone / What a friend / When the saints go marching in / Near the cross / Nutbush City Limits
662172 / Dec '92 / FNAC

☐ **WHAT YOU HEAR IS WHAT YOU GET (Live At Carnegie Hall)**
Piece of my heart / Everyday people / Doin' the Tina Turner / Sweet soul music / Ooh-poo-pah-doo / Honky tonk women / Love like yours / Proud Mary / I smell trouble / Ike's tune / I want to take you higher / I've been loving you too long / Respect
CTMCD 302 / Feb '97 / EMI

☐ **WORKIN' TOGETHER (3CD Set)**
Proud Mary / Nutbush city limits / Ooh poh pah doo / Workin' together / I'm your (use me anyway you wanna) / Living for the city / I love what you do to me / Piece of my heart (live) / Early in the morning / I wan to take you higher / What you don't see is better yet / Sexy Ida (part 1) / Way yoWay you love me / Respect (live) / Way you love me / Respect / Sweet Rhode island red / Sexy Ida (part 2) / Reconsider baby / Higher ground / Up in heah / I idolize you / I'm jealous / Dust my broom / Love like yours / Nuff said / That's my purpose / You can have it / Ike's tune / I've been loving you too long / Baby - get it on / Come together / Under my thumb / Funker than a mosquita's tweeter / Honky tonk woman / Drift away / Get back / Let it be / Let's spend the night together / She came in through the bathroom window / Baby (what you want me to do) / Doin' the Tina Turner (live) / Fool in love / I heard it through the grapevine (live)
SA 872702 / Sep '96 / Disky

Turner, Joe

☐ **CLASSICS 1941-1946**
CLASSICS 940 / Jun '97 / Classics

☐ **JOE TURNER**
SACD 106 / Oct '93 / Solo Art

Turner, Joe Lynn

☐ **NOTHING'S CHANGED**
Promise of love / Baby's got a habit / Nothing's changed / Knock knock / I believe / Satisfy me / Liviana / Bad blood / All or nothing / Last thing / Imagination / Save a place / Let me love you
CDMFN 189 / Oct '95 / Music For Nations

Turner, Ken

☐ **BEST OF THE DANSAN YEARS VOL.4, THE (Turner, Ken & His Orchestra)**
Cavatina (waltz) / Serenade (waltz) / Diane (waltz) / Ole guapa (tango) / Tango supreme (tango) / Where the rainbow ends (slow foxtrot) / September song-it had to be you (slow foxtrot) / What a difference a day made (slow foxtrot) / Mountain greenery-day in day out (quickstep) / One morning in may (quickstep) / King of dixieland (quickstep) / Cherry pink and apple blossom white (cha cha) / Patsy (cha cha cha) / Copacabana (samba) / Born free (rumba) / Temptation (rumba) / Opus one (jive)
DACD 004 / Jul '92 / Dansan

☐ **BEST OF THE DANSAN YEARS VOL.5, THE (Turner, Ken & His Orchestra)**
Fascination (waltz) / Tenderly (waltz) / Song for someone (waltz) / Blauer himmel (tango) / Jealousy (tango) / Poor butterfly (slow foxtrot) / Bye bye blackbird (slow foxtrot) / Hallelujah (slow foxtrot) / You are the sunshine of my life (quickstep) / Mrs. robinson (quickstep) / Good old bad old days (quickstep) / Teach me tonight (cha-cha) / More I see you (cha cha cha) / I love you and don't you forget it (samba) / I go to rio (samba) / Flamingo (rumba) / Serenata (rumba) / Amparito roca (pasodoble)
DACD 005 / Jul '92 / Dansan

Turner, Mark

☐ **YAM YAM**
CRISS 1094 / Apr '95 / Criss Cross

Turner, Mick

☐ **TREN PHANTASMA**
DC 138CD / 15 Sep '97 / Drag City

Turner, Nik

☐ **NEW ANATOMY (Turner, Nik & Inner City Unit)**
Young girls / Convoy / Beyond the stars / Help sharks / Birdland / Lonesome train (on a lonesome track) / Forbidden planet / Stop the city / Dr. Strange / Wildhunt
CDTB 096 / Mar '93 / Thunderbolt

☐ **PAST OR FUTURE**
CLP 96852 / May '97 / Cleopatra

☐ **PROPHETS OF TIME**
CLEO 69082 / Jun '94 / Cleopatra

☐ **SONIC ATTACK 200**
EFA 084802 / 23 Mar '98 / Dossier

☐ **SPACE RITUAL**
CLEO 95062 / Feb '95 / Cleopatra

☐ **SPHYNX**
CLEO 21352 / May '97 / Cleopatra

☐ **XITINTODAY**
NIKTCD 333 / 24 Nov '97 / Emergency Broadcast System

Turner, Ruby

☐ **BEST OF RUBY TURNER, THE**
I'd rather go blind / If you're ready come go with me / I'm in love / What becomes of the broken hearted / Just my imagination (running away with me) / Bye baby / In my life it's better to be in love / Signed sealed delivered I'm yours / I'm livin' a life of love / Still on my mind / Vibe is right / It's a cryin shame / It's gonna be alright / Paradise / Rumours / It's you my heart beats for
EMPRCD 566 / May '95 / Emporio

☐ **BEST OF RUBY TURNER, THE**
If you're ready (come go with me): *Turner, Ruby & Jonathan Butler* / What becomes of the broken hearted: *Turner, Ruby & Jimmy Ruffin* / Merry go round / Just my imagination (running away with me): *Turner, Ruby & The Temptations* / Ooo baby baby / I'd rather go blind / Leaves in the wind / It's gonna be alright / Vibe is right / It's a cryin' shame / Rumours / I'm livin' a life of love / It's you my heart beats for / I'm in love / Paradise / Signed, sealed, delivered I'm yours / In my life (It's better to be in love) / Still on my mind
QED 034 / Nov '96 / Tring

☐ **GUILTY**
You can't do that / There is something on your mind / You're pouring water on a drowning man / My oh my / Wang dang doodle / Don't mess up a good thing / Bring it on home to me / Love like blood / Ain't nobody / One time around / Guilty / Take it as it comes / That way / Over the edge / Rockin' good way / My eyes are weeping
IGOXCD 502 / Sep '96 / Indigo

☐ **LIVE IN CONCERT GLASTONBURY FESTIVAL**
Get on without you / Sexy / Feel my love / If you're ready / I'd rather go blind / Either way you lose / On fire / Easy on yourself / Only women bleed / Blue Monday
SFRSCD 062 / 18 May '98 / Strange Fruit

Turner, Tina

☐ **BREAK EVERY RULE**
What you get is what you see / Change is gonna come / Addicted to love / In the midnight hour / 634 5789 / Land of 1000 dances / Typical male / Two people / Till the right man comes along / Afterglow / Girls / Back where you started / Break every rule / Overnight sensation / Paradise is here / I'll be thunder
CDP 746 323 2 / Sep '86 / Capitol

☐ **COLLECTED RECORDINGS, THE (Sixties To Nineties - 3CD Set)**
Fool in love / It's gonna work out fine / I idolize you / Poor fool / Letter from Tina / Finger poppin' / River deep, mountain high / Crazy about you baby / I've been loving you too long / Bold soul sister / I want to take you higher / Come together / Honky tonk women / Proud Mary / Nutbush city limits / Sexy Ida / It ain't right (lovin' to be lovin') / Acid Queen / Whole lotta love / Ball of confusion / Change is gonna come / Johnny and Mary / Games / When I was young / Total control / Let's pretend we're married / It's only love: *Turner, Tina & Bryan Adams* / Don't turn around / Legs / Addicted to love / Tearing us apart: *Turner, Tina & Eric Clapton* / It takes two: *Turner, Tina & Rod Stewart* / Let's stay together / What's love got to do with it / Better be good to me / Private dancer / I can't stand the rain / Help / We don't need another hero / Typical male / What you get is what you see / Paradise is here / Back where you started / Best / Steamy windows / Foreign affair / I don't wanna fight
CDESTX 2240 / Nov '94 / Capitol

☐ **COUNTRY CLASSICS**
HADCD 166 / May '94 / Javelin

☐ **COUNTRY SIDE OF TINA TURNER**
ST 5009 / Apr '95 / Star Collection

☐ **IN PROFILE (Interview Disc)**
CDINPROF 002 / Aug '97 / EMI

☐ **INSTRUMENTAL MEMORIES (Various Artists)**
River deep mountain high / It takes two / Best / Can't stand the rain / We don't need another hero / Private dancer
306952 / Aug '97 / Hallmark

☐ **PRIVATE DANCER**
I might have been queen / What's love got to do with it / Show some respect / I can't stand the rain / Private dancer / Let's stay together / Better be good to me / Steel claw / Help
CDP 7460412 / Jun '84 / Capitol

☐ **PRIVATE DANCER (Added Value Centenary Edition)**
I might have been queen / What's love got to do with it / Show some respect / I can't stand the rain / Private dancer / Let's stay together / Better be good to me / Steel claw / Help / 1984 / I wrote a letter / Rock 'n' roll widow / Don't rush the good things / When I was young / What's love got to do with it / Better be good to me / I can't stand the rain
CDCNTAV 1 / Feb '97 / Capitol

☐ **ROUGH**
Fruits of the night / Bitch is back / Woman I'm supposed to be / Viva la money / Funny how time slips away / Earthquake hurricane / Root toot undisputable rock 'n' roller / Fire down below / Sometimes when we touch / Woman in a man's world / Night time is the right time
CDP 7952132 / Aug '95 / Capitol

☐ **TINA TURNER**
Golden empire / Tina's prayer / You're still my baby / Sugar sugar / Loving him was easier / Gonna have fun / Don't you blame it on me / I don't need / We need an understanding / Crazy 'bout you baby / Push / Good hearted woman / Chicken shack / You're so fine / Bootsie Whitelaw / Lay it down / Shake a hand / Let's get it on / You're up to something / Mississippi rolling stone / I'm looking for my mind / If this is our last time / Too much man for one women / Raise your hand / Rock me baby / If you want it / Rockin' and rollin' / We had it all / Living for the city / If it's alright with you / I know / Freedom to stay / Please love me / Stand by your man
399561 / May '97 / Koch Presents

☐ **TINA TURNER**
You're up to something / I know (you don't want me no more) / Living for the city / Rock me baby / If you want it / Please love me / Freedom to stay / Stand by your man / Soul deep / Rockin' and rollin' / I'm looking for my mind / Mississippi rolling stone / Raise your hand / We had it all / If this is our last time / You ain't woman enough to take my man / If it's alright with you / Too much man for one woman
399547 / Jun '97 / Koch Presents

☐ **TINA TURNER**
GFS 075 / Jul '97 / Going For A Song

☐ **TINA TURNER GOES COUNTRY**
74321534002 / 8 Nov '97 / Milan

☐ **WILDEST DREAMS**
Do what you do / Whatever you want / Missing you / On silent wings / Thief of hearts / In your wildest dreams / Golden eye / Confidential / Something beautiful remains / All kinds of people / Unfinished sympathy / Dancing in my dreams
CDEST 2279 / Apr '96 / Parlophone

Turner, Titus

☐ **JAMIE RECORDINGS, THE**
Never, never nothin' / Sound off (duckworth chant) / Me and my lonely telephone / I bet you shut your big mouth now / Day in, day out / Knock me a kiss / Sweet georgia brown / I'll always be in love with you / Left right out of your heart / Blue moon / Glory of love / Hey doll baby / I want a little girl / Pony train / Bla bla cha cha cha / Horsin' it around / Bull run / Chances go around / You stayed away too long / Build a bridge / Foolish pride / Beautiful stranger / Shake the hand of a fool / Walk on the wild side / Twist-twistin train
BCD 15532 / Feb '92 / Bear Family

Turning Point

☐ **FEW AND THE PROUD, THE**
LF 172CD / Jul '95 / Lost & Found

☐ **IT'S ALWAYS**
NA 004CD / Jul '96 / New Age

Turntable Symphony

☐ **MINI LP, THE**
Instructions of life (mixes) / Remix of life / Can't stop / It'll make you go ooh / Techno love
HAPPYCD 001 / May '93 / Happy Music

Turpentines

☐ **AMERICAN MUSIC FOR AMERICAN PEOPLE**
JAZZ 009CD / 6 Jul '98 / White Jazz

Turquoise

☐ TURQUOISE TRAIL, THE
TURQUOISE 1995 / Aug '95 / Turquoise

Turre, Steve

☐ STEVE TURRE
5371332 / Aug '97 / Verve

Turrentine, Stanley

☐ COMMON TOUCH
Buster brown / Blowin' in the wind / Lonely avenue / Boogaloo / Common touch / Living through it all / Ain't no way
CDP 8547192 / Feb '97 / Blue Note

☐ DEUCES WILD
Flipped out / Brown eyed woman / Yester-me / I only get this feeling / I'll take you all the way there / Deuces wild / My cherie amour / Wedding bell blues / Flipped / Let it be
CDSGP 0184 / Apr '98 / Prestige

☐ EASY (Stanley Turrentine Plays The Pop Hits)
Can't buy me love / Spooky / Return of the prodigal son Sunny / Light my fire / Look of love / Ain't no mountain high enough / MacArthur Park / Blowin' in the wind / Elusive butterfly / Hey Jude / Stone soul picnic / Wave / Fool on the hill / Little green apples
4939912 / 11 May '98 / Blue Note

☐ EASY WALKER
Meat wave / They all say I'm the biggest fool / Yours is my heart alone / Easy walker / What the world needs now is love / Alone together / Foggy day / Stan's shuffle / Watch what happens / Intermission walk / Wave
CDP 8299082 / Jan '97 / Blue Note

☐ LOOK OUT
Look out / Journey into melody / Return engagement / Little Sheri / Tin tin deo / Yesterdays / Tiny capers / Minor chant
CDP 7865432 / May '96 / Blue Note

☐ MORE THAN A MOOD
Thomasville / They can't take that away from me / In a sentimental mood / Easy walker / Triste / Pieces of a dream / Spirits up above / More than a mood
MM 65156 / 2 Apr '98 / Music Masters

☐ NEVER LET ME GO
7841292 / 1 Jun '98 / Blue Note

☐ PIECES OF A DREAM
Pieces of dreams / I know it's you / Deep in love / Midnight and you / Evil / Blanket on the beach / I'm in love
OJCCD 831 / Nov '95 / Original Jazz Classics

☐ SALT SONG
Gibralter / I told Jesus / Salt song / I haven't got anything better to do / Vera cruz
ZK 65126 / 8 Sep '97 / Sony Jazz

Turriff, Jane

☐ SINGIN IS MA LIFE
SPRCD 1038 / Apr '96 / Springthyme

Turtlehead

☐ BACK SLAPPING PRAISE
BTR 012CD / Nov '96 / Bad Taste

☐ GO
BTR 010CD / Jul '96 / Bad Taste

☐ I PREFERRED THE EARLIER STUFF
BTR 24 / 6 Apr '98 / Bad Taste

Turtles

☐ HAPPY TOGETHER (The Very Best Of The Turtles)
Happy together / She'd rather be with me / Too young to be one / Me about you / Think I'll run away / Can I get to know you better / Guide for the married man / Elenore / It ain't me babe / You baby / Let me be / She's my girl / You don't have to walk in the rain / You know what I mean / Lady O / You showed me / There you sit lonely / Outside chance / Buzz saw / Sound asleep
MCCD 046 / Sep '91 / Music Club

☐ TURTLE SOUP
Come over / House on the hill / She always leaves me laughing / How you loved me / Torn between temptations / Love in the city / Bachelor Mother / John and Julie / Hot little hands / Somewhere Friday night / Dance this dance / You don't have to walk in the rain / Lady O / Last thing I remember
SC 6086 / Aug '97 / Sundazed

☐ WOODEN HEAD
I can't stop / She'll come back / Get away / Wrong from the start / I get out of breath / We'll meet again / On a summer's day / Come back / Say girl / Tie me down / Wanderin' kind / Ain't gonna party no more / Who would ever think that I would marry
SC 6087 / Aug '97 / Sundazed

Tusen, Till

☐ JAZZIN' JACKS
FLCCD 151 / May '97 / Four Leaf Clover

Tuskegee Institute Singers

☐ COMPLETE RECORDING WORKS 1914-1927
DOCD 5549 / Jul '97 / Document

Tuu

☐ ALL OUR ANCESTORS
RBADCD 9 / Oct '94 / Beyond

Tuva

☐ ECHOES FROM THE SPIRIT WORLD
Audience welcome / Ogbeler / Kadararda khoyum charash / Dadyr - dodur / Kham algyzhy / Avtyng deril / Morgul / Sygyt / Toruktug dolgai tangdym / Oorzhak khunashtaar-ool bile / Ugbazhkylar ooldary / Ulug-khemim, sayan, tangdym / Aratyng yry / Sygyt / Sygyt no 3 / Potpourri of steppe melodies / Teve khaya
PANCD 2013 / May '93 / Pan

☐ VOICES FROM THE CENTRE OF ASIA
SFWCD 40017 / May '95 / Smithsonian Folkways

Tuxedo Junction

☐ BEST OF TUXEDO JUNCTION, THE
HTCD 91 / 20 Apr '98 / Hot Productions

Tuxedo Moon

☐ BEST OF TUXEDO MOON
What use / No tears / Cage / Some guys / Dark companion / In a manner of speaking / Atlantis / Waltz / L'etranger / Tritone (musica diablo) / East/ jinx / Desire / You
CBOY 1313 / Jan '94 / Crammed Discs

☐ GHOST SONATA, THE
Funeral of a friend / Ghost sonata / Catalyst / Affair at the soiree / Music number two / Drowning / Cascade / Mystic death / Basso pomade / Llicorice stick ostinato / Laboratory / Les odalisques / Unsigned postcard
CBOY 1414 / 20 Oct '97 / Cramboy

☐ TEN YEARS IN ONE NIGHT
MASOCD 90006 / 29 Jun '98 / Materiali Sonori

TV Personalities

☐ AND DON'T THE KIDS JUST LOVE IT
REF 33007 / Oct '91 / Fire

☐ CHOCOLAT-ART LIVE 1984
EFA 04320 CD / Jun '93 / Pastell

☐ CLOSER TO GOD
You don't know how lucky you are / Hard luck story no.39 / Little works of art / Razor blades and lemonade / Coming home soon / Me and my big ideas / Honey for the bears / I see myself in you / Goodnight Mr. Spaceman / My very first nervous breakdown / We will be your gurus / You are special and you always will be / Not for the likes of us / You're younger than you know / Very dark today / I hope you have a nice day / This heart's not made of stone / Baby, you're only as good as you should be / Closer to God
FIRECD 32 / Oct '92 / Fire

☐ I WAS A MOD BEFORE YOU WAS A MOD
OVER 41CD / Jul '95 / Overground

☐ MUMMY, YOU'RE NOT WATCHING ME
Adventure playground / Day in heaven / Scream quietly / Mummy you're not watching me / Brians magic ear / Where the rainbow ends / David hockneys diaries / Painting by numbers / Lichtenstein painting / Magnificent dreams / If I could write poetry
REF 33008 / Oct '91 / Fire

☐ PAINTED WORD THE
Stop and smell the roses / Painted word / Life of her own / Bright sunny smiles / Mentioned in dispatches / A sense of belonging / Say you won't cry / Someone to share my life with / You'll have to scream louder / Happy all the time / Girl who had everything / Paradise estates / Back to vietnam
REF 33010 / Oct '91 / Fire

☐ PRIVILEGE
Paradise is for the blessed / Conscience tells me no / All my dreams are dead / Man who paints the rainbows / Sad Mona Lisa / Sometimes I think you know me / Privilege / Good and faithful servant / My hedonistic tendencies / Salvador Dali's garden party / What if it's raining / Engine driver song / Better than I know myself
FIRE 33021 / Oct '91 / Fire

☐ THEY COULD HAVE BEEN BIGGER THAN THE BEATLES
Psychedelic holiday / David Hockney's diary / Boy in the paisley shirt / When Emily cries
REF 33009 / Oct '91 / Fire

☐ TOP GEAR
OVER 48CD / Mar '96 / Overground

Twain, Shania

☐ COME ON OVER
5580002 / 9 Mar '98 / Mercury

Tweed, Karen

☐ DROPS OF SPRINGWATER
DMP 9401CD / Jan '96 / DMP

☐ FYASCE (Tweed, Karen & Ian Carr)
FYAS 001CD / Aug '97 / Fyasce

☐ SILVER SPIRE, THE
DMP 9402CD / Jan '96 / DMP

☐ TUNES FOR THE ACCORDION VOL.1
PMCD 003 / Aug '94 / Punch Music

☐ TUNES FOR THE ACCORDION VOL.2
PMCD 004 / Aug '94 / Punch Music

Twelfth Night

☐ COLLECTORS ITEM
We are sane / Sequences / Art and illusion / First new day / Take a look / Blondon fair / Collector / Love song
CDGRUB 18 / Feb '91 / Food For Thought

☐ LIVE AND LET LIVE
Ceiling speaks / End of the endless majority / We are sane / Fact and fiction / Poet sniffs a flower / Sequences / Creepshow / East of eden / Love song
CYCL 050 / Feb '97 / Cyclops

Twenty Miles

☐ TWENTY MILES
Intro / Junkyard blues / Place called hell / She don't know / Fred McDowell / My back door / I'm not a man / Come right in / My little baby / Mississippi bolero
03022 / Jun '97 / Fat Possum

Twice A Man

☐ COLLECTION, THE
YELLOW 16 / Aug '88 / Yellow

☐ FROM THE NORTHERN SHORE
YELLOW 01CD / '89 / Yellow

Twiggy

☐ TWIGGY AND THE GIRLFRIENDS
14529 / Feb '97 / Spalax

Twiggy

☐ TWIGGY
PHCD 2056 / Jan '97 / Penthouse

Twilight

☐ EYE FOR AN EYE
35641 / Nov '96 / Seagull

Twilight Circus Dub Sound System

☐ BIN SHAKER DUB
MCD 150 / 6 Oct '97 / M

☐ DUB PLATE SELECTION
MCD 160 / 23 Mar '98 / M

☐ OTHER WORLDS OF DUB
MCD 127 / Aug '96 / M

Twilight Ophera

☐ SHADOWS EMBRACE THE DARK
Crown of thorns / Blessed to forget / Moon is your lover / Queen of the night / Shadowdancer / Oper 666-The whore / Wasted / Storms of silence
NIHIL 27CD / 16 Feb '98 / Cacophonous

Twin Obscenity

☐ FOR BLOOD HONOUR AND SOIL
CM 77228CD / 17 Aug '98 / Century Media

Twinkeyz

☐ ALIENS IN OUR MIDST
ANOLPHES 003 / 15 Jun '98 / Anopheles

Twinkle

☐ GOLDEN LIGHTS
Terry / Boy of my dreams / Golden lights / Ain't nobody home but me / Tommy / So sad / A lonely singing doll / Unhappy boy / Poor old johnny / I need your hand in mine / End of the world / Take me to the dance / What am I doing here with you / Now I have you / Micky / Darby and joan / Soldier's dream
RPM 108 / Jul '93 / RPM

Twinkle Brothers

☐ ALL THE HITS 1970-1988
NGCD 513 / 17 Aug '98 / Twinkle

☐ BABYLON RISE AGAIN
NGCD 528 / Apr '92 / Twinkle

☐ BURDEN BEARER
NGCD 501 / 17 Aug '98 / Twinkle

☐ CHANT DOWN BABYLON
NGCD 547 / Oct '95 / Twinkle

☐ COUNTRYMAN
I don't want to be lonely anymore / Pattoo / Never get burnt / Free us now / Kingdom come / Since I threw the comb away / One head / Bite me
NGCD 510 / 17 Aug '98 / Twinkle

☐ DJ SELECTION
NGCD 545 / Dec '94 / Twinkle

☐ DUB MASSACRE VOL.1 & 2
NGCD 7102 / Dec '94 / Twinkle

☐ DUB MASSACRE VOL.3 & 4
NGCD 505 / Jan '96 / Twinkle

☐ DUB MASSACRE VOL.6
NGCD 543 / Jun '94 / Twinkle

☐ DUB PLATE
NGCD 546 / Dec '94 / Twinkle

☐ DUB WITH STRINGS
Dub betrayal / Dub betrayal / Loving dub / Dub from the mountain / Don't foget the dub / Want more dub / Outlaw dub / Dub it for jah / Independent dub / Dub alone
NGCD 535 / Nov '92 / Twinkle

☐ ENTER ZION
NGCD 503 / Jan '96 / Twinkle

☐ EQUALITY AND JUSTICE
Equality and justice / Rejoice / Lamb to the slaughter / We nah go let Jah go / Blood on their hands / Wicked them a go run / Lightning and thunder / You're bound / I will praise Jah
NGCD 541 / 22 Dec '97 / Twinkle

☐ FINAL CALL
NGCD 552 / 24 Nov '97 / Twinkle

☐ FREE AFRICA
I don't want to be lonely anymore / Free Africa / Love / I love you so / Gone already / Solid as a rock / Come home / Shu be dub (you can do it too) / Patoo / Never get burn / Dread in the ghetto / Watch the hypocrites / Jahovah / Since I threw the comb away / One head / Free us
CDFL 9008 / Sep '90 / Frontline

☐ ME NO YOU
Me no you-you no me / Make everyone happy / Stealing / Africa for the africans / Dub / Longing for you / Constipated people / Stomack sick / Truble de yah / Beautiful jamaica
NGCD 632 / Jul '94 / Twinkle

☐ NEW SONGS FOR JAH
NGCD 518 / Jan '96 / Twinkle

☐ OTHER SIDE, THE (Twinkle Brothers & Ralston Grant)
RGCD 5805 / Oct '95 / Twinkle

☐ RASTA PON TOP
NGCD 532 / Apr '92 / Twinkle

☐ TWINKLE LOVE SONGS VOL.2
NGCD 536 / Feb '93 / Twinkle

Twinz

☐ CONVERSATION
Conversation / Round and round / Good times / Eyes 2 heads / Jump ta this / Eastside LB / Sorry I kept you / Conversation # 2 / Journey wit me / Hollywood / Pass it on / Don't get it twisted / 1st Round draft pick
5278832 / Aug '95 / RAL

Twisted Science

☐ SHARPEST TOOL IN THE BOX, THE
LCD 09 / 27 Jul '98 / Lo Recordings/Leaf

Twisted Sister

☐ BIG HITS AND NASTY CUTS
We're not going to take it / I wanna rock / I am (I'm me) / Price / You can't stop rock 'n' roll / Kids are back / Shoot 'em down / Under the blade / I'll never grow up now / Feel so fine / Let the good times roll / It's only rock 'n' roll / Tear it loose / What you don't know / Be chrool to your scuel
7567823802 / Mar '92 / Atlantic

☐ LIVE AT HAMMERSMITH (2CD Set)
What you don't know / Kids are back / Stay hungry / Destroyer / We're not gonna take it / You can't stop rock 'n' roll / Knife in the back / Shoot 'em down / Under the blade / Burn in hell / I am (I'm me) / I wanna rock / SMF / We're gonna make it / Jailhouse rock / Train kept a rollin'
CDMFN 170 / Oct '94 / Music For Nations
SPV 08518102 / 1 Sep '98 / SPV

Twisty Willow

☐ DARKNESS IN THE SKY
TW 1 / Nov '97 / ODE

Twitty, Conway

☐ BEST OF CONWAY TWITTY, THE
It's only make believe / Hello darlin' / Fifteen years ago / Danny boy / You've never been this far before / Touch of the hand / To see an angel cry / She needs someone to hold her (when she cries) / I'll try / After all the good is gone / After our last date / As soon as I

hang up the phone / Baby's gone / I can't see me without you / I'm not through loving you yet / I've hurt her more than she loves me / (Lying here with) Linda on my mind / Games that Daddies play / Don't cry Joni / (I can't believe) she gives it all to me
CD 3558 / Mar '96 / Cameo

☐ BEST OF CONWAY TWITTY, THE
HMNCD 036 / 22 Jun '98 / Half Moon

☐ CONWAY TWITTY
Guess my eyes were bigger than my heart / Look into my teardrops / I don't want to be with me / Image of me / To see my angel cry / Hello darlin' / I can't see me without you / (Lost her love) On our last date / You've never been this far before / I'm not through loving you yet / Linda on my mind / (I can't believe) She gives it all to me / I've already loved you in my mind / Boogie grass band / Don't take it away / I'd just love to lay you down / Tight fittin' jeans / Slow hand / Rose / I don't know a thing about love / Don't call him a cowboy / Desperado love / That's my job / Goodbye time / She's got a single thing in mind
MCLD 19236 / May '94 / MCA

☐ CONWAY TWITTY
LECD 043 / May '94 / Dynamite

☐ FINAL RECORDINGS OF HIS GREATEST HITS
PWKS 4263 / Jul '95 / Carlton

☐ HIGH PRIEST OF COUNTRY MUSIC, THE
Image of me / Next in line / Darlin' you know I wouldn't lie / I love you more today / Hello darlin' / Fifteen years ago / How much more can she stand / I wonder what she'll think about me leaving / On our last date / I can't stop loving you / She needs someone to hold her / You've never been this far before / There's a honky tonk angel / I see the want to in your eyes / Linda on my mind / This time I've hurt her more than she loves me / That games that daddies play / Play guitar play / I've always loved you in my mind / Don't take it away / I'd love to lay you down / Rest your love on me / Tight fittin' jeans / Red neckin' love makin' night
EDCD 500 / May '97 / Edsel

☐ ROAD THAT I WALK, THE
CDSGP 0170 / Sep '95 / Prestige

☐ ROCK 'N' ROLL WITH CONWAY TWITTY
Golly gosh oh gee / I wonder if you told her (About me) / Why can't I get through to you / This road that I walk / Crazy dreams / You made me what I am today / Born to sing the blues / Double talk baby / I need your lovin' / Maybe baby / Midnight / Shake it up baby
306792 / May '97 / Hallmark

☐ ROCK 'N' ROLL YEARS 1956-1964, THE (8CD Set)
Rock house / Crazy dreams / Give me some love / I need your lovin' kiss / Just in time / Born to sing the blues / Maybe baby / Shake it up / I need your lovin' / Golly gosh oh gee / Double talk baby / Why can't I get through to you / Crazy dreams / Give me some love / Born to sing the blues / Born to sing the blues / Born to sing the blues / Born to sing the blues / Crazy dreams / Crazy dreams / Crazy dreams / It's only make believe / I'll try / I vibrate / Will you love me then as you love me now / Story of my love / Don't you know / When I'm not with you / Judge of hearts / Yea yea boo hoo / Heavenly / Come on home / Nobody / Sputnik / Easy to fall in love / Goin' home / Big train / Teenage heart / One and only you / When I'm not with you / Don't you know / Story of my love / My one and only you / Goin' home / Make me know you're mine / Judge of hearts / First romance / I need you so / Mona Lisa / Sentimental journey / Hallelujah I love her so / You'll never walk alone / Hey little Lucy / Halfway to Heaven / Teasin' / Heavenly / Halfway to Heaven / Just because / Cry Jane cry / Blueberry Hill / Heartbreak Hotel / You win again / Danny boy / Hey Miss Ruby / Restless / She's mine / Lonely kind of love / Beachcomber / Easy to fall in love / Because you love me / Leonora my love / Rosaleena / My adobe hacienda / Hey little Lucy / Restless / Because you love me / My adobe hacienda / Star spangled Heaven / Huggin' and a kissin' / Can't we go steady / Lonely blue boy / Sorry / Blue moon / Eternal tears / Foggy river / Platinum high school / Trouble in mind / Pretty eyed baby / Rebound / Hurt in my heart / Maybe tomorrow we'll know / Tell me one more time / What am I living for / Fallen star / I'd still play the fool / Betty Lou / Knock three times / What a dream / Is a bluebird blue / Whole lotta shakin' goin' on / My heart cries / Sweet Georgia Brown / Lonely blue boy / Betty Lou / That's where my lovin' goes / Don't you dare let me down / Send her to me / Flame / C'est si bon / Long black train / Blue suede shoes / Great balls of fire / Jailhouse rock / Treat me nice / Handy man / Girl can't help it / Shake, rattle and roll / Diana / Splish splash / Reelin' and rockin' / Million teardrops / Next kiss (is the last goodbye) / Tree in the meadow / Above and beyond / I'm in a blue blue mood: *Twitty, Conway & Roy Orbison* / Live fast, love hard, die young / Man alone / Donna's dream / Tower of tears / I can hear my heart break / Million teardrops / Prisoner of love / Unchained melody / Sweet sorrow / Little bird told me / It's driving me wild / Turn around / Walk on by / Portrait of a fool / There is something on your mind / Don't cry no more / Mr. Jones / Hang up the phone / Little piece of my heart / She knows me like a book / Comfy n' cozy / Lookin' back / Pledging my love / Prisoner of love / Unchained melody / Unchained melody / Sweet sorrow / It's driving me wild / Walk on by / Mr. Jones / Little piece of my heart / Little piece of my heart / It's too late / I almost lost my mind / I got a woman / My babe / Let the good times roll / Fever / Boss man / Don't cry no more / City lights / Faded love / Don't let the stars get in your eyes / Ages and ages ago / I hope, I think, I wish / Pickup / Hound dog / She ain't no angel / Got my mojo working / Long tall Texan / Go on and cry / She loves me / I'm sorry heart / Talkin' about you / Walk proud / Such a night / My baby left me / Where your love leadeth me / Big town / This road that I walk / Bad man / Ever since you went away / Blue is the way I feel / Turn the other cheek / Treat me mean, treat me cruel / I'm checkin' out / Heartache just walked in / I wonder if you told her about me / Girl at the bar / You made me what I am / I'll get over losing you / Have I been away too long / Let me be the judge / Sound of an angel's wings / Highland rock: *Bruno, Al* / Midnite creep: *Bruno, Al*
BCD 16112 / May '97 / Bear Family

☐ SPOTLIGHT ON CONWAY TWITTY
Fifteen years ago / To see my angel cry / I see the want to in your eyes / I'm not through loving you yet / Linda on my mind / Don't cry Joni / I've already loved you in my mind / Play guitar, play / It's only make believe / Let me be the judge / Ever since you went away / Big town / Sitting in a dim cafe
HADCD 121 / Feb '94 / Javelin

☐ WORLD OF CONWAY TWITTY, THE
Unchained melody / Fever / Mona Lisa / Diana / Heartbreak hotel / Splish splash / I almost lost my mind / Lonely blue boy / Blue suede shoes / Great balls of fire / Shake, rattle and roll / Blue moon / Jailhouse rock / Handy man / Let the good times roll / Blueberry Hill / Treat me nice / What am I living for / Whole lotta shakin' goin' on / It's only make believe
5514322 / May '96 / Spectrum

Two

☐ VOYEURS
I am a pig / Stutter kiss / Water's leaking / My ceiling's low / Leave me alone / If / Deep in the ground / Hey sha la la / Wake up / Gimp / Bed of rust
3984220892 / 30 Mar '98 / East West

Two Lone Swordsmen

☐ FIFTH MISSION (RETURN TO THE FLIGHTPATH ESTATE) (2CD Set)
Little did we know / Best of Stealth / Slow drive West / Big man original / Spark / Lino Square / Search for a car / Gang sweep shuffling / King Mob file / Enemy haze / Beacon block / Two barb quickstep / Switch it / Rico's helly / Paisley dark
SOP 009CD / Aug '96 / Emissions

☐ STOCKWELL STEPPAS
Another heady cocktail / Plunge / Spin desire / Kicking in / Kicking in / Turn the filter off / Spray can attack / We love mutronics / Because I can
PT 040CD / Mar '97 / Emissions

☐ SWIMMING NOT SKIMMING
Swimming not skimming / Swimming not skimming (Obo 07 mix) / Swimming not skimming (Andy Sheriff mix) / Swimming not skimming (Pod mix) / Swimming not skimming (16b and Anthony Teasdale mix) / Glide by shooting / Bim, Jack and Florence / Don't call it jerk / Flossie wears Paco and Ralph / Swimming not skimming (ITN mix)
PT 035CD / Nov '96 / Emissions

Two Man Sound

☐ DISCO SAMBA
Charlie brown / So fla fla / Cha cha non stop / Brigitte bardot / Oye come va / Copacabana / Mambo no.5 / Capital tropical / Americano / Mariana / La musica latina / Vini vini / Samba samba / San salvador / Que tal america / Disco samba
12375 / Sep '97 / Laserlight

Two Timers

☐ TWO TIMERS
Harder you pull / Big bad lovin' / Footstompin' music / Do it / Childless mother / Blues fell this morning / Another story / One good reason / Crazy 'bout you / Long gone / Paradise lost / Whole lotta love
GRAND/MONKEYCD 1 / May '98 / Grand

Two Tons

☐ TWO TONS O'FUN/BACKATCHA
Do you wanna boogie huh / Just us / I got the feelin' / Gone away / Earth can be just like heaven / Make someone feel happy today / Taking away your space / One-sided love affair / Never like this / I depend on you / Your love is gonna see me through / It's true I do / Can't do it by myself / Cloudy with a chance of rain / I've got to make it on my own / I been down
CDSEWD 082 / Jul '93 / Southbound

Two Tunes

☐ RAINDROPS TALKING
BRAM 1991272 / Nov '93 / Brambus

Ty Gwydr

☐ 292 YMLAEN AT Y FILIWN
ANKST 045CD / Feb '94 / Ankst

Tycoon

☐ TYCOON/TURN OUT THE LIGHT
RMED 0163CD / 15 Dec '97 / Renaissance

Tygers Of Pan Tang

☐ CAGE, THE
Rendezvous / Lonely at the top / Letter from LA / Paris by air / Tides / Making tracks / Actor / Cage / Love potion no.9 / You always see what you want to see / Danger in paradise / Life of crime / Love's a lie / What you sayin' / Making tracks
EDGY 104 / 18 May '98 / Neat

☐ CRAZY NIGHTS
Slip away / Stormlands / Paradise drive / Do it good / Love don't stay / Never satisfied / Running out of time / Crazy nights / Down and out / Lonely man / Make a stand / Raised on rock
EDGY 103 / 18 May '98 / Neat

☐ SPELLBOUND
Gangland / Take it / Minotaur / Hellbound / Mirror / Silver and gold / Tyger Bay / Story so far / Black Jack / Don't stop by / All or nothing / Don't give a damn / Bad times / It ain't easy / Don't take nothing
EDGY 102 / 18 May '98 / Neat

☐ WILD CAT
Euthanasia / Slave to freedom / Don't touch me there / Money / Killers / Fireclown / Wild catz / Badger badger / Insanity / Suzie smiled / Rock and roll man / Alright on the night / Tush / Straight as a die / Don't take nothing / Bad times / Burning up / Don't touch me there
EDGY 101 / 18 May '98 / Neat

Tyketto

☐ SHINE
Jamie / Rawthigh / Radio Mary / Get me there / High / Ballad of Ruby / Let it go / Long cold winter / I won't cry / Shine
CDMFN 195 / Nov '95 / Music For Nations

☐ STRENGTH IN NUMBERS
Strength in numbers / Rescue me / End of the summer days / Ain't that love / Catch my fall / Last sunset / All over me / Write your name in the sky / Meet me in the night / Why do you cry / Inherit the wind / Standing alone
CDMFN 157 / Feb '94 / Music For Nations

☐ TAKE OUT AND SERVED UP
CDMFN 207 / Jul '96 / Music For Nations

Tyla

☐ GOTHIC
REVXD 218 / Aug '97 / Revolver

☐ LIFE AND TIMES OF A BALLAD MONGER
REVXD 197 / Nov '95 / Revolver

Tyla Gang

☐ BLOW YOU OUT
622392 / Apr '97 / Skydog

Tyle, Chris

☐ CHRIS TYLE AND HIS SILVER LEAF BAND (Tyle, Chris Silver Leaf Band)
SOSCD 1311 / Sep '97 / Stomp Off

☐ SUGAR BLUES (Tyle, Chris & His Silver Leaf Jazzband)
SOSCD 1298 / Jul '96 / Stomp Off

Tyler, Alvin 'Red'

☐ GRACIOUSLY
Count 'em / Cutie pie / Graciously / Here's that rainy day / If my shoes hold out / Greystoke / Like so many others / Dreamsville
ROUCD 2061 / '88 / Rounder

☐ HERITAGE
ROUCD 047 / '88 / Rounder

☐ SIMPLY RED (Tyler, Alvin 'Red' & The Gyros)
Stinky / Dippy / Drag race / Long ride / Peanut vendor / Walk on / Junk village / Tonking / Classy lassie / Lovely for you / Double whammy / Snake eyes / Hey Mama / Peanut vendor / Classy lassie / Walk on / Tonking / Hey Mama
WESM 529 / 15 Jun '98 / Westside

Tyler, Bonnie

☐ BEST, THE
Total eclipse of the heart / Faster than the speed of the night / Have you ever seen the rain / If you were a woman (and I was a man) / Here she comes / Loving you's a dirty job but someone's got to do it / Getting so excited / Save up all your tears / Best / Holding out for a hero / Married men / Rockin' good way / More than a lover / Don't turn around / Lovers again / Lost in France / It's a heartache / To love somebody
4735222 / Oct '94 / Columbia

☐ BONNIE TYLER LOVE SONGS
SSLCD 206 / Jun '95 / Savanna

☐ FASTER THAN THE SPEED OF NIGHT
Have you ever seen the rain / Faster than the speed of night / Getting so excited / Total eclipse of the heart / It's a jungle out there / Going through the motions / Tears / Take me back / Straight from the heart
CD 32747 / Oct '92 / CBS

☐ FREE SPIRIT
Bridge over troubled water / You're the one / Nothing to do with love / Two out of three ain't bad / Making love (out of nothing at all) / What you got / Sexual device / Driving me wild / All night to know you / Sexual device / Time mends a broken heart / Forget her / Make it right tonight / Given it all
0630121082 / Mar '96 / East West

☐ GOODBYE TO THE ISLAND
I'm just a woman / We danced on the ceiling / Wild love / Closer you get / Sometimes when we touch / Goodbye to the island / Wild side of life / Whiter shade of pale / Sitting on the edge of the ocean / I believe in your sweet love
CLACD 288 / Jul '92 / Castle

☐ HEAVEN AND HELL (Tyler, Bonnie & Meatloaf)
Bat out of hell: *Meat Loaf* / Faster than the speed of night: *Tyler, Bonnie* / You took the words right out of my mouth: *Meat Loaf* / Have you ever seen the rain: *Tyler, Bonnie* / Read 'em and weep: *Meat Loaf* / Total eclipse of the heart: *Tyler, Bonnie* / Two out of three ain't bad: *Meat Loaf* / Holding out for a hero: *Tyler, Bonnie* / Dead ringer for love: *Meat Loaf* / If you were a woman (and I was a man): *Tyler, Bonnie* / If you really want to: *Meat Loaf* / Straight from the heart: *Tyler, Bonnie* / Loving you's a dirty job but somebody's got to do it: *Tyler, Bonnie* / Heaven can wait: *Meat Loaf*
4736662 / 27 Jul '98 / Columbia

☐ IT'S A HEARTACHE
It's a heartache / Louisiana rain / Married men / Love of a rolling stone / Blame me / My guns are loaded / Heaven / If I sing you a love song / Whiter shade of pale / Piece of my heart / If you ever need me again / Eyes of a fool / I believe in your sweet love / Living for the city / Baby I remember you / Wild side of life
5507282 / Aug '94 / Spectrum

☐ LOST IN FRANCE
Sometimes when we touch / More than a lover / (You make me feel like) a natural woman / Goodbye to the island / Sitting on the edge of the ocean / Don't stop the music / Here I am / Get out of my head / Lost in France / Closer you get / Come on give me loving / I'm just a woman / Give me your love / Got so used to loving you / Here's Monday / Love tangle
5507292 / Mar '95 / Spectrum

☐ LOVE COLLECTION, THE (2CD Set)
Lost in France / Baby, I remember you / Give me your love / Love of a rolling stone / World starts tonight / Piece of my heart / Love tangle / Heaven / More than a lover / Got so used to loving you / It's about time / Louisiana rain / Yesterday dreams / Baby goodnight / Living for the city / Don't stop the music / (You make me feel like) a natural woman / World is full of married men / It's a heartache / Hey love (it's a feelin') / If I sing you a love song / Too good to last / Come on, give me loving / I believe in your sweet love / What a way to treat my heart / Baby I just love you / If you ever need me again / Words can change your life / Bye bye now my sweet love / I'm just a woman / Wild love / Closer you get / Sometimes when you touch / Whiter shade of pale / We danced on the ceiling / Goodbye to the island
SMDCD 104 / May '97 / Snapper

☐ NATURAL FORCE
It's a heartache / Blame me / Living for the city / If I sing you a love song / Heaven / Yesterday dreams / Hey love / (You make me feel like) a natural woman / Here I am / Baby goodnight
CLACD 232 / Apr '91 / Castle

☐ PIECE OF MY HEART
Lost in France / Whiter shade of pale / World starts tonight / Heaven / Here I am / More than a lover / Love tangle / Louisiana rain / My guns are loaded / Piece of my heart / Goodbye to the island / Living for the city / Love of a rolling stone / We danced on the ceiling / Bye bye now my sweet love / It's a heartache
21018 / Jul '97 / Laserlight

☐ STRAIGHT FROM THE HEART
CCSCD 801 / Aug '95 / Castle

☐ WORLD STARTS TONIGHT, THE
Got so used to loving you / Love of a rolling stone / Lost in France / Piece of my heart / More than a lover / Give me your love / World starts tonight / Here's Monday / Love tangle / Let the show begin
CLACD 231 / Apr '91 / Castle

Tyler, Chris

☐ SMILER, THE
SOSCD 1258 / Dec '93 / Stomp Off

Tyler, Kris

☐ WHAT A WOMAN KNOWS
RTD 53045 / 16 Feb '98 / Radioactive

Tymes

☐ GREAT SOUL HITS
379832 / Nov '97 / Koch

Tyndall, Nik

☐ AMBIENT MUSIC
SKYCD 3049 / Feb '95 / Sky

Tyner, McCoy

☐ 4 X 4 (Tyner, McCoy Quartets)
Inner glimpse / Manha de carnaval / Paradox / Backward glace / Forbidden land / Pannonica / I wanna stand over there / Seeker / Blues in the minor / Stay as sweet as you are / It's you or no one
MCD 55007 / Apr '94 / Milestone

☐ ASANTE
Malika / Asante / Goin' home / Fulfilment / Forbidden land / Asian lullaby / Hope
4933842 / 13 Apr '98 / Blue Note

☐ ATLANTIS
Atlantis / In a sentimental mood / Makin' out / My one and only love / Pursuit / Love samba
MCD 55002 / Aug '96 / Milestone

☐ AUTUMN MOOD
Natural bridge / Traces / Monster and the flower / Up jump Spring / Autumn mood
17121 / Oct '97 / Laserlight

☐ BEST OF MCCOY TYNER, THE (The Blue Note Years)
Passion dance / Search for peace / Man from Tanganyika / Peresina / Song for my lady / Wanderer / You taught my heart to sing / Blue Monk / My one and only love
CDP 8370512 / Apr '96 / Blue Note

☐ BLUE BOSSA
CDC 9033 / Jul '91 / LRC

☐ **BLUE BOSSA**
Blue bossa / Recife's blues / I'll take romance / Rotunda / We'll be together again
17120 / May '97 / Laserlight

☐ **BON VOYAGE**
Bon voyage / Don't blame me / Summertime / You stepped out of a dream / Jazz walk / How deep is the ocean / Blues for Max / Yesterdays
CDSJP 260 / Jul '91 / Timeless Jazz

☐ **EXTENSIONS**
Message from the Nile / Wanderer / Survival blues / His blessings
CDP 8376462 / Jun '96 / Blue Note

☐ **INCEPTION**
Inception / There is no greater love / Blues for Gwen / Sunset / Effendi / Speak low
IMP 12202 / Apr '97 / Impulse Jazz

☐ **INCEPTION/NIGHT OF BALLADS AND BLUES**
Inception / Blues for Gwen / Speak / We'll be together again / For heaven's sake / Blue monk / Days of wine and roses / There is no greater love / Sunset effendi / Satin doll / 'Round midnight / Star eyes / Groove waltz
MCAD 42000 / Jun '89 / Impulse Jazz

☐ **INFINITY (Tyner, McCoy & Michael Brecker)**
Flying high / I mean you / Where is love / Changes / Happy days / Impressions / Mellow minor / Good morning heartache
IMP 11712 / Sep '95 / Impulse Jazz

☐ **JAZZ PROFILE**
Four by five / High priest / Surrey with fringe on top / Smitty's place / Planet X / Goin' home / Hip toe
CDP 8332072 / 6 Oct '97 / Blue Note

☐ **LIVE AT WARSAW JAZZ FESTIVAL 1991**
CD 66050008 / Jul '93 / Bellaphon

☐ **MCCOY TYNER PLAYS ELLINGTON**
Duke's place / Caravan / Solitude / Searchin' / Mr. Gentle and Mr. Cool / Satin doll / Gypsy without a song / It don't mean a thing... / I got it bad / Gypsy without a song
IMP 12162 / Apr '93 / Impulse Jazz

☐ **NIGHTS OF BALLADS AND BLUES**
Satin doll / We'll be together again / 'Round midnight / For heaven's sake / Star eyes / Blue monk / Groove waltz / Days of wine and roses
IMP 12212 / Apr '97 / Impulse Jazz

☐ **PARIS BOSSA (Tyner, McCoy Quintet)**
MCD 0342 / Jan '92 / Moon

☐ **PLAYS ELLINGTON**
Duke's place / Caravan / Solitude / Searchin' / Mr. Gentle and Mr. Cool / Satin doll / Gypsy without a song / It don't mean a thing if it ain't got that swing / I got it bad and that ain't good / Gypsy without a song (Alternate take)
MCAD 33124 / Dec '90 / Impulse Jazz

☐ **PRELUDE & SONATA**
MCD 92442 / Feb '96 / Milestone

☐ **REACHING FOURTH**
Reaching fourth / Goodbye / Theme for Ernie / Blues back / Old devil moon / Have you met Miss Jones
IMP 12552 / 23 Mar '98 / Impulse Jazz

☐ **REAL MCCOY, THE**
Passion dance / Contemplation / Four by five / Search for peace / Blues on the corner
CDP 7465122 / Mar '95 / Blue Note

☐ **SAHARA**
Ebony queen / Prayer for my family / Valley of life / Rebirth / Sahara
OJCCD 311 / Apr '92 / Original Jazz Classics

☐ **SONG FOR MY LADY**
Native song / Night has a thousand eyes / Song for my lady / A silent tear / Essence
OJCCD 313 / Apr '92 / Original Jazz Classics

☐ **SUPER TRIOS**
Wave / Blues on the corner / I mean you / Greeting / Prelude to a kiss / Moment's notice / Hymn song / Consensus / Four by five / Stella by starlight / Lush life / Blues for ball
MCD 55003 / Oct '93 / Milestone

☐ **TOGETHER**
Nubia / Shades of light / Bayou fever / One of another kind / Ballad for Aisha / Highway one
OJCCD 955 / 26 Jan '98 / Original Jazz Classics

☐ **UPTOWN DOWNTOWN (Tyner, McCoy Big Band)**
Love surrounds us / Three flowers / Genesis / Uptown / Lotus flower / Blues for Basie
MCD 9167 / Apr '94 / Milestone

☐ **WHAT THE WORLD NEEDS NOW (The Music Of Burt Bacharach) (Tyner, McCoy Trio)**
(They want to be) Close to you / What the world needs now is love / Look of love / Alfie / (There's) Always something there to remind me / House is not a home / One less bell to answer / Windows of the world / You'll never get to heaven (If you break my heart)
IMP 11972 / May '97 / Impulse Jazz

Tyni, Seppo

☐ **NIIN AINA**
Asemalla / Kanssasi halki kaupungin / Sesaus / Kelmit / Silta / Aamujen hamara / Takapihan valo / Nakemin / Kuvakirja / Alkuun uudestaan / Viisi paivaa / Klubilla / Viiletys / Niin aina / Vanttaut
PELPCD 9 / Dec '97 / Pohjola

Type O Negative

☐ **OCTOBER RUST**
RR 88742 / Sep '96 / Roadrunner

☐ **ORIGIN OF THE FAECES**
RR 87622 / 24 Nov '97 / Roadrunner

☐ **SLOW DEEP AND HARD**
Unsuccessfully coping with the natural beauty of infidelity / Der untermensch / Xero tolerance / Prelude to agony / Glass walls of limbo / Misinterpretation of silence and its disastrous consequ / Gravitational constant g=6.67 x 10.8cm.3 gm.1 sec.2
RO 93132 / May '91 / Roadrunner

Tyran' Pace

☐ **LONG LIVE METAL**
N 00272 / 27 Jul '98 / Noise

☐ **WATCHING YOU**
N 00552 / 27 Jul '98 / Noise

Tyrell, Sean

☐ **CRY OF A DREAMER**
Mattie / Coast of Malabar / Demolition Dan / Isle of Inisfree / House of delight / November rain / Blue-green bangle / Message of peace / Cry of the dreamer / Only from day to day / No-go / Connie's song / Fortune for the finder / 12th Of July
LMCD 001 / Jun '94 / L-MCD

☐ ...
HNCD 1391 / Nov '95 / Hannibal

Tyrrall, Gordon

☐ **BRIDGE FLOWS, THE**
PM 001CD / Jun '94 / Punch Music

☐ **WHERE THE RIVER FLOWS**
PMCD 001 / Aug '94 / Punch Music

Tyson, Ian

☐ **AND STOOD THERE AMAZED**
SP 1168CD / Oct '93 / Stony Plain

☐ **COWBOYOGRAPHY**
Springtime / Navajo rug / Summer wages / Fifty years ago / Rockies turn rose / Claude Dallas / Own heart's delight / Cowboy pride / Old Cheyenne / Coyote and the cowboy
NC 002CD / Dec '97 / New Country

☐ **OLD CORRALS AND SAGEBRUSH & OTHER COWBOY CLASSIC**
Gallo del cielo / Alberta's child / Old double diamond / Windy Bill / Montana waltz / Whoopie ti yi yo / Leavin' Cheyenne / Old corrals and sagebrush / Old Alberta moon / Night rider's lament / Oklahoma hills / Tom Blasingame / Colorado trial / Hot summer tears / What does she see / Rocks begin to roll / Will James / Murder steer
BCD 15437 / Aug '88 / Bear Family

☐ **ONE JUMP AHEAD OF THE DEVIL**
What does she see / Beverly / Turning thirty / Nortonville waltz / Lone star and coors / One too many / Texas / I miss you / Goodness of Shirley / Freddie Hall / Half a mile to hell
SPCD 1177 / Oct '93 / Stony Plain

Tyson, Sylvia

☐ **YOU WERE ON MY MIND**
Pepere's mill / Slow moving heart / Rhythm of the road / Walking on the moon / Thrown to the wolves / Night the Chinese restaurant burned down / You were on my mind / Sleep on my mind / Trucker's cafe / River Road / Last call / Le Moulin a Pepere / Blind fiddler's waltz
RTMCD 77 / Jun '96 / Round Tower

Tytot, Angelin

☐ **GIITU**
MIPU 204CD / Dec '93 / Mipu

Tzuke, Judie

☐ **BEST OF JUDIE TZUKE**
New friends again / Black furs / Sukarita / Sports car / For you / These are the laws / Welcome to the cruise / Come hell or waters high / Higher and higher / Chinatown / Stay with me 'til dawn / Bring the rain
8113922 / Feb '94 / Phonogram

☐ **RITMO**
Face to face / Nighthawks / How do I feel / Another country / Joannie no / She don't live here anymore / Shoot from the heart / Walk don't walk / Push push / Chinatown / City of swimming pools
BGOCD 225 / Jun '94 / Beat Goes On

☐ **ROAD NOISE (The Official Bootleg)**
Heaven can wait / Chinatown / I'm not a loser / Information / Flesh is weak / Sports car / For you / Come hell or waters high / Southern smiles / Kateria Island / Love on the border / Black furs / City of swimming pools / Bring the rain / Sukarita / Stay with me 'til dawn / Hunter
BGOCD 212 / Dec '93 / Beat Goes On

☐ **SHOOT THE MOON**
Heaven can wait / Love on the border / Information / Beacon Hill / Don't let me sleep / I'm not a loser / Now funeral / Water in motion / Shoot the moon
BGOCD 226 / Oct '94 / Beat Goes On

☐ **STAY WITH ME TILL DAWN**
Stay with me till dawn / Bring the rain / Ladies night / Welcome to the cruise / We'll go dreaming / Let me be the pearl / Dominique / Turning stones / Choice you've made / Understanding / Living on the coast / Sports car / Higher and higher / I never know where my heart is / Come hell or waters high / Black furs
5508962 / Aug '95 / Spectrum

☐ **WONDERLAND**
Wonderland / I can read books / Man and a gun / Black furs / Higher / Vivien / Sara's gone / She loves his hands / Fly / Swimming
ESMCD 184 / Jan '97 / Essential

U

U-Brown

☐ **TRAIN TO ZION 1975-1978**
Watch this people / Big licking stick / Natty hold the handle / Let love shine along the way / Watch what is going on / News to the nation / Stop them jah / Live as one / Too much / Satta dread style / Jah give me strength / Train to Zion: *U-Brown & Linval Thopson* / Bits of paper / Nuh kill fi dunza / Hard times
BAFCD 020 / 1 Sep '97 / Blood & Fire

U-Men

☐ **STEP ON A BUG**
Whistlin' Pete / Three year old could do that / Flea circus / Willie Dong hurts dogs / Pay the bubba / Two times four / Juice party / Too good to be food / Papa doesn't love his children anymore
TUPCD 012 / Jun '90 / Tupelo

U-Roy

☐ **BABYLON KINGDOM MUST FALL**
ARICD 129 / Sep '96 / Ariwa Sounds

☐ **DREAD IN A BABYLON**
Runaway girl / Chalice in the palace / I can't love another / Dreadlocks dread / Great psalms / Natty don't fear / African message / Silver bird / Listen to the teacher / Trenchtown rock
CDFL 9007 / Sep '90 / Frontline

☐ **FLASHING MY WHIP**
RNCD 2130 / Nov '95 / Rhino

☐ **MUSIC ADDICT**
I originate / Come fe warn them / King Tubby's skank / Reggae party / I feel good / Music addict / Jah Jah call you / Haul and pull / Waterboat
RASCD 3024 / Aug '87 / Ras

☐ **MUSICAL VISION**
LG 21080 / Nov '93 / Lagoon

☐ **NATTY REBEL**
Babylon burning / Natty rebel / So Jah Jah say / Natty kung fu / If you should leave me / Do you remember / Travelling man / Have mercy / Badie boo / Go there natty / Fire in a Trench Town
CDFL 9017 / Apr '83 / Frontline

☐ **ORIGINAL DJ**
Babylon burning / Natty rebel / Evil doers / Jah Jah / Rule the nation / On the beach / Tide is high / Rock away / Peace and love in the ghetto / Say you / I can't love another / Trenchtown rock / Hot pop / Wear you to the ball / True confession / Everybody bawling / Words of wisdom / Great psalms / African message / Listen to the teacher / Control tower / Runaway girl / Natty don't fear / Chalice in the palace / Come home little girl
CDFL 9020 / Jun '95 / Frontline

☐ **RASTA AMBASSADOR**
Control tower / Wear you to the ball / Evil doers / Mr. Slave Driver / Small axe / Come home little girl / Say you / No more war / Tide is high / Jah Jah
CDFL 9016 / Jun '91 / Frontline

☐ **SMILE A WHILE (U-Roy & Yabby U)**
ARICD 085 / May '93 / Ariwa Sounds

☐ **SUPER BOSS**
What is catty (big boy and teacher) / Rock away (you'll never get away) / Wake the town / Rule de nation / Version galore / Wear you to the balls / True confession (true true true) / Things you love / On the beach / Everybody bawling / Ain't that lovin' you / Flashing my whip / Way back home / Drive her home / Hot pop / Your ace from outer space / Treasure isle skank / Words of wisdom / Super boss (do re mi) / Same song / Tide is high / Merry go round / Happy go lucky girl / My girl / Don't stay away / Honey come back / I can't lose
LG 21024 / Jul '93 / Lagoon

☐ **TEACHER MEETS THE STUDENT, THE (U-Roy & Josie Wales)**
SONCD 0028 / Apr '92 / Sonic Sounds

☐ **TRUE BORN AFRICAN**
AIRCD 071 / Sep '91 / Ariwa Sounds

☐ **VERSION GALORE**
444192 / 23 Mar '98 / Jet Set

☐ **VERSION OF WISDOM**
Your ace from outer space / Rule the nation / Honey come forward / Version galore / Things you love / Wear you to the ball / On the beach / Rock away / True confession / Everybody bawling / Wake the town / Words of wisdom / Treasure isle skank / Same song / Tide is high / Hot pop / Tom drunk / Drive her home / Merry go round / What is catty
CDFL 9003 / Jul '90 / Frontline

☐ **WAKE THE TOWN**
RNCD 2114 / Jul '95 / Rhino

☐ **WITH A FLICK OF MY MUSICAL WRIST (U-Roy & Friends)**
CDTRL 268 / Sep '94 / Trojan

☐ **YOUR ACE FROM SPACE**
CDTRL 359 / Aug '95 / Trojan

u-Ziq

☐ **BLUFF LIMBO (2CD Set)**
CAT 018CD / Apr '96 / Rephlex

☐ **IN PINE EFFECT**
Mr. Angry / Melancho / Wailing song / Iced jem / Funky pipecleaner / Phiescope / Old fun no.1 / Pine effect / Dauphine / Roy Castle / Within a sound / Rain / Tungsten carbide / Frank / Problematic / Green crumble
FLATCD 20 / Oct '95 / Hi-Rise

☐ **LUNATIC HARNESS**
Brace yourself Jason / Hasty boom alert / Mushroom compost / Blainville / Lunatic harness / Approaching menace / My little beautiful / Secret stair / Secret stair / Wannabe / Catkin and teasel / London / Midwinter log
CDPLU 005 / 12 Aug '97 / Planet U

☐ **TANGO N'VECTIF**
CAT 013CD / Aug '96 / Rephlex

☐ **URMER BILE TRAX VOL.1 & 2**
Urmer bile / Let let / M5 saabtone / Fine tuning / Hydrozone / 1 Hip 007 / Hornet / Phonic socks
PLUD 003 / Feb '97 / Planet U

U2

☐ **ACHTUNG BABY**
Zoo station / Even better than the real thing / One / Until the end of the world / Who's gonna ride your wild horses / So cruel / Fly / Mysterious ways / Tryin' to throw your arms around the world / Ultraviolet / Acrobat / Love is blindness
CIDU 28 / Oct '91 / Island

☐ **ALL I WANT IS (Interview Disc)**
3D 001 / Nov '96 / Network

☐ **BIOGRAPHY SERIES**
10013 / 3 Nov '97 / Metro Independent

☐ **BOY**
Twilight / An cat dubh / Out of control / Stories for boys / Ocean / Day without me / Another time another place / Electric Co / Shadows and tall trees / I will follow
IMCD 211 / Apr '95 / Island

☐ **INTERVIEW DISC**
SAM 7003 / Nov '96 / Sound & Media

☐ **JOSHUA TREE, THE**
Where the streets have no name / I still haven't found what I'm looking for / With or without you / Bullet the blue sky / Running to stand still / Red hill mining town / In God's country / Trip through your wires / One tree hill / Exit / Mothers of the disappeared
CIDU 26 / Mar '87 / Island

☐ **OCTOBER**
Gloria / I fall down / I threw a brick through a window / Rejoice / Fire / Tomorrow / October / With a shout (Jerusalem) / Stranger in a strange land / Scarlet / Is that all
IMCD 223 / Mar '96 / Island

☐ **ORIGINAL SOUNDTRACKS VOL.1 (Passengers)**
United colours / Slug / Your blue room / Always forever now / Different kind of blue / Beach sequence / Miss Sarajevo / Ito okashi / One minute warning / Corpse (These chains are way too long) / Elvis ate America / Plot 180 / Theme from The Swan / Theme from Lets Go Native
CID 8043 / Oct '95 / Island

☐ **PHILADELPHIA INTERVIEWS, THE**
CBAK 4006 / Apr '88 / Baktabak

☐ **POP**
Discotheque / Do you feel loved / Mofo / If God will send his angels / Staring at the sun / Last night on Earth / Gone / Miami / Playboy mansion / If you wear that velvet dress / Please / Wake up dead man
CIDU 210 / Mar '97 / Island

☐ **RATTLE AND HUM**
Helter skelter / Hawkmoon 269 / Van Diemen's land / Desire / Angel of Harlem / I still haven't found what I'm looking for / When love comes to town / God pt II / Bullet the blue sky / Silver and gold / Pride (in the name of love) / Love rescue me / Heartland / Star spangled banner / All I want is you / All along the watchtower
CIDU 27 / Oct '88 / Island

☐ **SHAPED CD INTERVIEW DISC/ADAM**
UFOADAM 1 / Apr '97 / UFO

☐ **SHAPED CD INTERVIEW DISC/BONO**
UFOBONO 1 / Apr '97 / UFO

☐ **SHAPED CD INTERVIEW DISC/LARRY**
UFOLARRY 1 / Apr '97 / UFO

☐ **SHAPED CD INTERVIEW DISC/THE EDGE**
UFOEDGE 1 / Apr '97 / UFO

☐ **TELLTALES (Interview Disc)**
TELL 15 / Jun '97 / Network

☐ **UNDER A BLOOD RED SKY (Live)**
Eleven o'clock tick tock / I will follow / Party girl / Gloria / Sunday Bloody Sunday / Electric Co / New Year's Day / 40
IMCD 248 / Mar '97 / Island

☐ **UNFORGETTABLE FIRE, THE**
Sort of homecoming / Pride (in the name of love) / 4th of July / Wire / Unforgettable fire / Promenade / Indian Summer sky / MLK / Elvis Presley and America
IMCD 236 / Sep '96 / Island

☐ **WAR**
Sunday bloody Sunday / Seconds / Like a song / New Year's Day / Two hearts beat as one / Refugee / Drowning man / Red light / 40 / Surrender
IMCD 141 / Aug '91 / Island

☐ **WIDE AWAKE IN AMERICA**
Bad / Sort of homecoming / Three sunrises / Love comes tumbling
IMCD 75 / Nov '89 / Island

☐ **ZOOROPA**
Zooropa / Babyface / Numb / Lemon / Stay (Faraway, so close) / Daddy's gonna pay for your crashed car / First time / Some days are better than others / Dirty day / Wanderer: *U2 & Johnny Cash*
CIDU 29 / Jun '93 / Island

☐ **ZOOVENIR (A Tribute To U2) (Various Artists)**
Where the streets have no name: *Nordahl, Tom* / Even better than the real thing: *Sharp Kiddie* / Mysterious ways: *Blue Plastic* / With or without you: *Apocalypse Cow* / One: *Straitjackets* / Sunday bloody Sunday: *Liar* / Bullet the blue sky: *Exit* / Fly: *Blake Carringtons* / Pride: *Inbetweendays* / Hold me thrill me kiss me kill me: *Groove Tunnel* / I still haven't found what I'm looking for: *Chosen* / Party girl: *Automobile*
TR 025CD / 8 Jun '98 / Tribute

Uakti

☐ **TRILOBYTE**
4540562 / Oct '96 / Point Music

UB40

☐ **BAGGARIDDIM**
King step / Buzz feeling / Lyric officer Mk2 / Demonstrate / Two in a one mk1 / Hold your position Mk3 / Hip hop lyrical robot / Style Mk4 / V's version / Don't break my heart / I got you babe: *UB40 & Chrissie Hynde* / Mi spliff / Fight fe come in Mk2
DEPCD 10 / Oct '85 / DEP International

☐ **BEST OF UB40 VOL.1, THE**
Red red wine / I got you babe / One in ten / Food for thought / Rat in mi kitchen / Don't break my heart / Cherry oh baby / Many rivers to cross / Please don't make me cry / If it happens again / Sing our own song / Maybe tomorrow / My way of thinking / King
DUBTV 1 / Oct '87 / DEP International

☐ **BEST OF UB40 VOL.2, THE**
Breakfast in bed / Where did I go wrong / I would do for you / Homely girl / Here I am (come and take me) / Kingston Town / Wear you to the ball / Can't help falling in love / Higher ground / Bring me your cup / C'est la vie / Reggae music / Superstition / Until my dying day
DUBTV 2 / Oct '95 / DEP International

☐ **DANCEHALL ALBUM, THE**
Magic carpet / Force ripe / Smile for me / Waw waw waw / Ladda bay / More opportunity / Oh no baby don't go / Love that I need / More love / Nuff love / Who point the gun / Hills and valley / No stray
DEPCD 17 / 27 Apr '98 / DEP International

☐ **GEFFREY MORGAN**
Riddle me / As always you were wrong again / If it happens again / DUB / Pillow / Nkomo a go-go / Seasons / You're not an army / I'm not fooled so easily / You're eyes were open
DEPCD 6 / Oct '84 / DEP International

☐ **GROOVIN' JAMAICA PAYS TRIBUTE TO UB40 (Various Artists)**
RNCD 2065 / Oct '94 / Rhino

☐ **GUNS IN THE GHETTO**
Always there / Hurry come up / I love it when you smile / I've been missing you / Oracabessa moonshine / Guns in the ghetto / Tell me is it true / Friendly fire / I really can't say / Lisa
CADEP 16 / Jun '97 / DEP International

☐ **LABOUR OF LOVE VOL.1**
Johnny too bad / Guilty / Sweet sensation / Many rivers to cross / Red red wine / Please don't make me cry / She caught the train / Keep on moving / Cherry oh baby / Version girl
DEPCD 5 / Jul '86 / DEP International

☐ **LABOUR OF LOVE VOL.1 & 2**
Cherry oh baby / Keep on moving / Please don't make me cry / Sweet sensation / Johnny too bad / Red red wine / Guilty / She caught the train / Version girl / Many rivers to cross / Here I am (come and take me) / Tears from my eyes / Groovin' / Way you do the things you do / Wear you to the ball / Singer man / Kingston town / Baby / Wedding day / Sweet cherrie / Stick by me / Just another girl / Homely girl / Impossible love
DEPDDX 1 / Oct '94 / DEP International

☐ **LABOUR OF LOVE VOL.2**
Here I am (come and take me) / Tears from my eyes / Groovin' / Way you do the things you do / Wear you to the ball / Singer man / Kingston town / Baby / Wedding day / Sweet cherrie / Stick by me / Just another girl / Homely girl / Impossible love
DEPCD 14 / Nov '89 / DEP International

☐ **PRESENT ARMS**
Present arms / Sardonicus / Don't let it pass you by / Wild cat / One in ten / Don't slow down / Silent witness / Lambs bread / Don't walk on the grass / Dr. X
DEPCD 1 / Apr '88 / DEP International

☐ **PRESENT ARMS IN DUB**
Present arms in dub / Smoke it / B line / King's row / Return of Dr. X / Walk out / One in ten / Neon haze
DEPCD 2 / '88 / DEP International

☐ **PRESENT ARMS/BAGGARIDDIM/ CCCP - LIVE IN MOSCOW (3CD Set)**
TPAK 20 / Nov '91 / Virgin

☐ **PROMISES AND LIES**
C'est la vie / Desert sand / Promises and lies / Bring me your cup / Higher ground / Reggae music / Can't help falling in love / Now and then / Things ain't like they used to be / It's a long, long way / Sorry
DEPCD 15 / Jul '93 / DEP International

☐ **RAT IN MI KITCHEN**
All I want to do / You could meet somebody / Tell it like this / Elevator / Watchdogs / Rat in mi kitchen / Looking down at my reflection / Don't blame me / Sing our own song
DEPCD 11 / Apr '92 / DEP International

☐ **SIGNING OFF**
Tyler / King / Twelve Bar / Burden of shame / Adella / I think it's going to rain again / 25% / Food for thought / Little by little / Signing off / Madame Medusa / Strange fruit / Reefer madness
CDOVD 439 / Oct '93 / DEP International

☐ **SIGNING OFF/RAT IN THE KITCHEN/ PRESENT ARMS IN DUB (3CD Set)**
TPAK 35 / Oct '94 / Virgin

☐ **UB40**
Dance with the devil / Come out to play / Breakfast in bed / You're always pulling me down / I would do for you / 'Cause it isn't true / Where did I go wrong / Contaminated minds / Matter of time / Music so nice / Dance with the devil (reprise)
DEPCD 13 / Jul '88 / DEP International

☐ **UB40 FILE, THE**
Tyler / King / Twelve bar / Burden of shame / Adella / I think it's going to rain today / 25% / Food for thought / Little by little / Signing off / Madame Medusa / Strange fruit / Reefer madness / My way of thinking / Earth dies screaming / Dream a lie
VGDCD 3511 / Jul '86 / DEP International

☐ **UB40 LIVE**
Food for thought / Sardonicus / Don't slow down / Folitician / Tyler / Present arms / Piper calls the tune / Love is all is alright / Burden of shame / One in ten
DEPCD 4 / '88 / DEP International

☐ **UB44**
So here I am / I won't close my eyes (remix) / Forget the cost / Love is all is alright (remix) / Piper calls the tune / Key / Don't do the crime / Folitician (remix) / Prisoner
DEPCD 3 / Apr '86 / DEP International

Ubik

☐ **JUST ADD PEOPLE**
World without end / Remedy / Transcendental devotion / Command you to lie / Let go / Non stop / 1991 / I can see the light / Evolution / Truth vibration / Rise / We jack the house / Float beyond desire / Rush hour / Bass generation / Techno prisoners
ZOOMCD 1 / Jul '92 / Zoom

UDO

☐ **NO LIMITS**
GUN 158CD / 18 May '98 / Gun

☐ **SOLID**
GUN 122CD / 22 Sep '97 / Gun

Uen, Jin Long

☐ **BUDDHIST CHANTS AND PEACE MUSIC**
MCCD 235 / Mar '96 / Music Club

UFO

☐ **AIN'T MISBEHAVIN'**
Between a rock and a hard place / Another Saturday night / At war with the world / Hunger in the night / Easy money / Rock boyz, rock / Lonely cities (of the heart)
WKFMXD 107 / Mar '88 / FM

☐ BEST OF UFO, THE
Doctor Doctor / Only you can rock me / Let it roll / Shoot shoot / Let it rain / When it's time to rock / Rock bottom / Love to love / High flyer / Can you roll her / Pack it up (and go) / Hot and ready / This time / Long gone / Young blood / Lonely heart
CDGOLD 1050 / Jul '96 / EMI Gold

☐ HEAVEN'S GATE LIVE
Heavens' gate / Chase / This time / Meanstreets / Name of love / Only ones / Wreckless / Night run / Only you can rock me / Doctor doctor
MNMCD 1 / Nov '95 / M&M
INDELCD 18 / 4 May '98 / Indelible

☐ MAKING CONTACT/MISDEMEANOUR
BGOCD 319 / Jul '96 / Beat Goes On

☐ NO HEAVY PETTING/LIGHTS OUT
Natural thing / I'm a loser / Can you roll her / Belladonna / Reasons love / Highway lady / On with the action / Fool in love / Martian landscape / Too hot to handle / Just another suicide / Try me / Lights out / Gettin' ready / Alone again or / Electric phase / Love to love
BGOCD 228 / Aug '94 / Beat Goes On

☐ OBSESSION/NO PLACE TO RUN
Only you can rock me / Pack it up (and go) / Arbory hill / Ain't no baby / Lookin' out for no.1 / Hot 'n' ready / Cherry / You don't fool me / Lookin' out for No.1 (Reprise) / One more for the rodeo / Born to lose / Alpha Centauri / Lettin' go / Mystery train / This fire burns tonight / Gone in the night / Young blood / No place to run / Take it or leave it / Money, money / Any day
BGOCD 229 / May '94 / Beat Goes On

☐ ON WITH THE ACTION (Live At The Roundhouse 1976)
ZCRCD 1 / 9 Feb '98 / Zoom Club

☐ PHENOMENON/FORCE IT
Too young to no / Crystal light / Doctor Doctor / Space child / Rock bottom / Oh my / Time on my hands / Built for comfort / Lipstick traces / Queen of the deep / Let it roll / Shoot shoot / High flyer / Love lost love / Out in the street / Mother Mary / Too much of nothing / Dance your life away / This kid's
BGOCD 227 / Oct '94 / Beat Goes On

☐ TOO HOT TO HANDLE (The Best Of UFO)
Only you can rock me / Too hot to handle / Long gone / Profession of violence / We belong to the night / Let it rain / Lonely heart / This time / Lettin' go / Lights out / Natural thing / Blinded by a lie / Wreckless / When it's time to rock / Shoot shoot / Young blood / Let it roll / Doctor doctor
MCCD 153 / Feb '94 / Music Club

☐ UNIDENTIFIED FLYING OBJECT
Unidentified flying object / Boogie / C'mon everybody / Shake it about / Melinda / Timothy / Follow you home / Treacle people / Who do you love / Evil / Silver bird / Star storm / Prince Kajuku / Coming of Prince Kajuku
WB 885952 / 2 Feb '98 / Disky

☐ WILD, THE WILLING AND THE INNOCENT/MECHANIX
Chains chains / Long gone / Wild, the willing and the innocent / It's killing me / Makin' moves / Lonely heart / Couldn't get it right / Profession of violence / Writer / Something else / Back into my life / You'll get love / Doing it all for you / We belong to the night / Let it rain / Terri / Feel it / Dreaming
BGOCD 230 / Sep '94 / Beat Goes On

☐ X-FACTOR - OUT THERE...AND BACK, THE (2CD Set)
Unidentified flying object / Boogie / C'mon everybody / Shake it about / (Come away) Melinda / Follow you home / Who do you love / Evil / Silver birdstar storm / Prince Kajaku / Loving cup / One of those nights / Ain't life sweet / Long gone / Borderline / She's the one / Running up the highway / Back door man / Let the good times roll / Cherry / Love to love / Only you can rock me / Lights out / Doctor doctor / Rock bottom / Shoot shoot
SMDCD 122 / May '97 / Snapper

Ugarte, Enrique 'Kike'

☐ ENRIQUE UGARTE, ACCORDION CHAMPION
Bolero / Sabre dance / Czardas
EUCD 1151 / Jun '91 / ARC

☐ FOLKLORE VASCO
EUCD 1157 / Jun '91 / ARC

☐ VALSE MUSETTE
EUCD 1114 / '91 / ARC

☐ VALSE MUSETTE VOL.2
EUCD 1200 / Sep '93 / ARC

Ugly Duckling

☐ 12 BARS
Ugly guys are cool / Devil's highway / Day I put the jukebox on the rails / Not that guy / Pulp fiction / What a drag / I love you for yourself / Dog eat dog / Rimbaud or Rambo / Dancing alone
BMCD 288 / Feb '97 / Munich

Ugly Kid Joe

☐ AMERICA'S LEAST WANTED
Neighbor / Goddamn devil / Come tomorrow / Panhandlin prince / Busy bee / Don't go / So damn cool / Same side / Cats in the cradle / I'll keep tryin' / Everything about you / Madman ('92 Re-mix) / Mr. Record man
5125712 / Nov '92 / Mercury

☐ AS UGLY AS IT GETS
5588672 / 3 Aug '98 / Mercury

☐ AS UGLY AS THEY WANNA BE
Madman / Whiplash / Too bad / Everything about you / Sweet leaf / Funky fresh country club / Heavy metal
8688232 / May '92 / Mercury

☐ MESSAGE TO SOBRIETY
Intro / God / Tomorrow's world / Clover / C.u.s.t. / Milkman's son / Suckerpath / Cloudy skies / Jesus rode a harley / Iq-iq / V.i.p. / Oompa / Candle song / Slower than nowhere
5282822 / Jun '95 / Mercury

☐ MOTEL CALIFORNIA (2CD Set)
It's a lie / Dialogue / Sandwich / Rage against the answering machine / Would you like to be there / Little red man / Bicycle wheels / Father / Undertow / Shine / Strange / 12 Cents / Sweeping up
RAWCD 113 / Oct '96 / Raw Power

UI

☐ LIFELIKE
185471 / 13 Apr '98 / Southern

☐ SIDELONG
185352 / Apr '96 / Southern

☐ TWO SIDED SHARPIE
CLP 42 / 27 Oct '97 / Southern

☐ UNLIKE
LUNAMOTH 05 / Sep '96 / Lunamoth

Ui Cheallaigh, Aine

☐ CUIMHNI CEOIL
CIC 077CD / Nov '93 / Clo Iar-Chonnachta

☐ IN TWO MINDS
CEFCD 158 / Jan '94 / Gael Linn

Uitti, Frances Marie

☐ IMPROVISATIONS (Uitti, Frances Marie & Elliot Sharp)
JDK 01 / 6 Jul '98 / JDK

UK Subs

☐ ANOTHER KIND OF BLUES
CID / I couldn't be you / I love in a car / Tomorrow's girls / Killer / World War / Rockers / IOD / TV blues / Blues / Lady esquire / All I wanna know / Crash course / Young criminals / BIC / Disease / Stranglehold
DOJOCD 226 / Jun '95 / Dojo

☐ ANOTHER KIND OF BLUES...PLUS
CID / I couldn't be you / I live in a car / Tomorrow's girls / Killer / World war / Rockers / IOD / TV blues / Blues / Lady esquire / All I wanna know / Crash course / Young criminals / BIC / Disease / Stranglehold / Scum of the Earth / Telephone numbers
DIAB 862 / 6 Jul '98 / Diablo

☐ DOWN ON THE FARM
CID / I live in a car / Bic / Down on the farm / Endangered species / Countdown / Plan of action / Living dead / Ambition / Fear of girls / Lie down and die / Sensitive boys / Ice age / I Robot / Flesh wound / I don't need your love / Motivator / Combat zone / Fascist regime
DOJOCD 117 / Apr '93 / Dojo

☐ ENDANGERED SPECIES/ HUNTINGDON BEACH
Endangered species / Living dead / Countdown / Ambition / Lie down and die / Fear of girls / Down on the farm / Sensitive boys / Ice age / I robot / Flesh wound / Rock 'n' roll savage / Between the eyes / Suicide taxi / Party animal / Unkown / Miss Teenage USA / Huntingdon / All the king's horses / Jukebox / SK8 tough / Death row / Bullshitter / Dirt boy / All change for Hollywood / Blinding stories
LOMACD 7 / Feb '94 / Loma

☐ EUROPE CALLING
Rock 'n' roll savage / Motivator / Combat zone / Emotional blackmail / Endangered species / I robot / New York state police / Streets on fire/Punk rap / Captain Scarlet / Sk8 tough / She's not there / Warhead / Rockers / You don't belong / CID / Stranglehold / Tomorrow girls / Teenage / Thunderbird wine / I couldn't be you / I live in a car / New barbarians / Limo life / Kicks / All I wanna know / Interview
PINCD 101 / 13 Jul '98 / PinHead

☐ FLOOD OF LIES/SINGLES 1982-85
FALLCD 18 / '95 / Fallout

☐ HUNTINGTON BEACH
Rock n roll savage / Between the eyes / Suicide taxi / Party animal / Unknown / Miss teenage usa / Huntington / All the king's horses / Juke box / Sk8 tough / Death row / Bullshitter / Dirt boy / All change for hollywood / Blinding stories
REVXD 150 / May '90 / FM

☐ IN ACTION (10 YEARS)
Emotional blackmail / Endangered species / Fear of girls / New york state police / Rock n roll savage / Organised crime / B.i.c. / You don't belong / Confrontation street / Barbie's dead / Keep on running / Warhead / Police state / Teenage / Telephone numbers / I couldn't be you / I live in a car / Party in paris / Crash course / Blues / Young criminals / Left for dead / Rockers / Between the eyes / Sk8 tough / C.i.d. / Tomorrow's girls / Stranglehold / New barbarians / Does she suck / Killer / Rat race
REVXD 142 / Mar '90 / FM

☐ LEFT FOR DEAD, ALIVE IN HOLLYWOOD
RE 412CD / Nov '94 / ROIR

☐ LIVE AT THE ROXY
B.i.c. / I couldn't be you / I live in a car / Tomorrow's girls / Stranglehold / Illegal 15 / C.i.d. / No rules (victim) / Lady esquire / Telephone numbers / World war / Disease
RRCD 146 / Jul '93 / Receiver

☐ OCCUPIED
FALLCD 052 / Apr '96 / Fallout

☐ PEEL SESSIONS, THE (1978-1979)
FALLCD 53 / Mar '97 / Fallout

☐ PUNK CAN TAKE IT VOL.2 (Self Destruct 1982-1988)
CLP 9826 / Oct '96 / Cleopatra

☐ PUNK IS BACK, THE
Organised crime / Bomb factory / Dirty girls / Waiting for the man / Rat race / Teenage / Warhead / Sensitive boys / CID / Tomorrow's girls / Left for dead / She's not here / Kicks / I don't need your love / Limo life / Cocaine
CD 430002 / Apr '95 / Voiceprint

☐ PUNK SINGLES COLLECTION, THE
CID / Stranglehold / Tomorrows girls / She's not there / Warhead / Teenage / Party in Paris / Keep on running / Countdown / Self destruct / Another typical city / Private army / Gun says / Motivator / Sabre dance / Hey Santa / Here comes Alex / Barmy London army / Freaked / New barbarians / Limo life
CDPUNK 66 / Aug '95 / Anagram

☐ QUINTESSENTIALS
FALLCD 054 / Apr '97 / Fallout

☐ RIOT
Cyberjack / Rebel radio / Power corrupts / Preacher / Riot / Chemical war / Paradise burning / House of cards / Human rights / Guilty man / Lost not found / Music for the deaf / Beggars and bums / My little red book / Flat earth society
CDMGRAM 113 / Jun '97 / Anagram

☐ SCUM OF THE EARTH
Stranglehold / Tomorrow's girls / Rockers / T.v. blues / Young criminals / Scum of the earth / Warhead / Teenage / Emotional blackmail / 500cc / New york state police / I'm waiting for the man / Party in paris / You don't belong / Violent city / Confrontation / Time and matter / Face the machine / Just another jungle / Collision cult
MCCD 120 / Aug '93 / Music Club

☐ SINGLES 1978-1982, THE
GBR 001 / Apr '93 / Get Back

☐ UK SUBS BOX SET (4CD Set)
SUBBOX 1 / Nov '96 / Abstract

Ukamau

☐ FOLKLORE DE BOLIVIA
EUCD 1023 / '91 / ARC

☐ MUSICA DE BOLIVIA
EUCD 1207 / Sep '93 / ARC

Ukrainians

☐ KULTURA
Polityka / Ukrain America / Kievskiy express / Smert / Horilka / Slava / Europa / Kinets / Tycha voda / Zillya zeleneke / Ya / Tsyhanochka / Dyakuyu i dobranich
COOKCD 070 / Sep '94 / Cooking Vinyl

☐ VORONY
Vorony / Chlib / Koroleva Ne Pomerla / Chi skriptsi hrayu / Sche Raz / Nadia Pishla / Doroha / Rospryahaite / Durak / Sertsem I dusheyu / Dvi Lebidky / De ye moya mila / Teper mi hovorymo / Chekannya (Venus in furs)
COOKCD 054 / Feb '95 / Cooking Vinyl

Ulan Bator

☐ ULAN BATOR VOL.2
DSA 54043 / Dec '96 / CDSA

Ullman, Tracey

☐ BOBBY'S GIRL (The Very Best Of Tracey Ullman)
Breakaway / They don't know / My guy / Shattered / Terry / Helpless / Falling in and out of love / Bobby's girl / Move over darling / Sunglasses / Bad motorcycle / (I'm always touched by your) presence dear / You caught me out / Alone / Thinking of running away / If I had you
12374 / Sep '94 / Laserlight

☐ HIT SINGLE COLLECTABLES
DISK 4513 / Apr '94 / Disky

☐ VERY BEST OF TRACY ULLMAN, THE
STIFFCD 19 / Jan '94 / Disky

☐ YOU CAUGHT ME OUT
You caught me out / Little by little / Bad motorcycle / Loving you is easy / Sunglasses / Helpless / If I had you / Where the boys are / I know what boys like / Give him a great big kiss / Baby I lied
STIFFCD 08 / Jan '94 / Disky

Ullmann, Gebhard

☐ BASEMENT RESEARCH
1212712 / Apr '95 / Soul Note

Ulloa, Francisco

☐ MERENGUE
La tijera / Agua de tu fuente / La situacion / El beso robao / Tongoneate / Ramonita / Manana por la manana / Los caballos / Linda Mujer / Lucas y radhames / La lengua / San Francisco / Homenaje a bolo
CDORB 020 / Jul '90 / Globestyle

Ullulators

☐ FLAMING KHAOS
Don't thump the hamster / Mustaffa vole / Mr. buddha geks / Special brew / Sunrise / Smi2le / Feel it / Do ya wanna
DMCD 1021 / Feb '92 / Demi-Monde

Ulman Brothers

☐ ACOUSTIC POWER
LZ 2122 / Aug '96 / RUM

Ulmer, Georges

☐ PIGALLE
995902 / 24 Apr '98 / EPM

Ulmer, James 'Blood'

☐ BLACK AND BLUES
DIW 845 / Jul '91 / DIW

☐ HARMOLODIC GUITAR WITH STRINGS
DIW 878 / Feb '94 / DIW

☐ MUSIC SPEAKS LOUDER THAN WORDS (James 'Blood' Ulmer Plays The Music Of Ornette Coleman)
DIW 910 / Dec '96 / DIW

☐ MUSIC SPEAKS LOUDER THAN WORDS
CD 378332 / Jul '97 / Koch Jazz

☐ ODYSSEY
Church / Little red house / Love dance / Are you glad to be in America / Election / Odyssey / Please tell her / Swing and things
4851012 / Sep '96 / Sony Jazz

Ulterior Motive Orchestra

☐ SPY TIME
TCD 1033 / Nov '96 / Tradition

Ultimate

☐ BEST OF ULTIMATE, THE (Love Is The Ultimate)
HTCD 103 / 20 Apr '98 / Hot Productions

Ultimate Buzz

☐ BEST OF ULTIMATE BUZZ, THE
On a mission / People stompin' / Rock da bass / Vibe / Flying high / Rofo's theme / In your dreams / Ultimate buzz / Bounce master / Ardcore / Back in business / Ultimate buzz megamix
DSCR 016 / 3 Nov '97 / Clubscene

☐ OFFICIAL ALBUM, THE
BEECD 001 / 1 Dec '97 / Beeswax

Ultimate Concern

☐ SHIELD BETWEEN
NLB 002CD / Mar '96 / No Looking Back

Ultimate Kaos

☐ ULTIMATE KAOS
Intro (Age ain't nuthin' but a number) / Hoochie booty / Some girls / This heart belongs to you / Skip to my Lou / Misdemeanour / Show a little love / Weekend girl / Cool out alley / Believe in us / Age ain't nuthin' but a number / Uptown / Falling in love / Right here
5274442 / May '95 / Wild Card

Ultimate Spinach

☐ BEHOLD AND SEE
Behold and see / Mind flowers / Where you're at / What you're thinking of / Fragmentary march of green / Genesis of beauty suite / Fifth horseman of the apocalypse
CDWIKD 148 / Oct '95 / Big Beat

☐ ULTIMATE SPINACH
Ego trip / Sacrifice of the moon (In four parts) / Plastic raincoats / Hung up minds / (Ballad of the) Hip death goddess / Your head is reeling / Dove in Hawk's clothing / Baarogue no.1 / Funny freak parade / Pamela
CDWIKD 142 / Apr '95 / Big Beat

☐ ULTIMATE SPINACH VOL.3
(Just like) Romeo and Juliet / Some days you just can't win / Daisy / Reasons / Eddie's rush / Happiness, child / Strange life tragicomedy / Back door blues / World has just begun
CDWIKD 165 / Jun '96 / Big Beat

Ultra Bide

☐ SUPER MILK
VIRUS 213CD / 30 Mar '98 / Alternative Tentacles

Ultra Living

☐ MONOCHROMATIC ADVENTURE
CRECD 211 / 22 Jun '98 / Creation

Ultramagnetic MC's

☐ B SIDES COMPANION
NP 54822 / 1 Dec '97 / Next Plateau

☐ SMACK MY BITCH UP
TUFCD 0624 / 22 Jun '98 / Tuff City

Ultra Nate

☐ BLUE NOTES IN THE BASEMENT
(Basement Boys)
Blue notes / Sands of time / Is it love / Deeper love (missing you) / You and me together / It's over now / Scandal / Rejoicing / Rain / Love hungover / It's my world / Funny (how things change)
9031747042 / Jun '91 / WEA

☐ ONE WOMAN'S INSANITY
How long / You're not the only one / Show me / I'm not afraid / Incredibly you / Joy / I specialize in loneliness / One woman's insanity / Feelin' fine / Love is a many splendoured thing
9362453302 / Oct '93 / WEA

☐ SITUATION CRITICAL
Situation critical / New kind of medicine / Free / Found a cure / It's crying time / Release the pressure / Any ole love / Love you can't deny / Every now and then / Divine love / Found a cure / Free / Free
5408242 / 27 Apr '98 / AM:PM

Ultra Vivid Scene

☐ JOY 1967-1990
It happens every time / Three stars / Grey turns white / Guilty pleasure / Beauty No. 2 / Praise the love / Staring at the sun / Special one / Poison / Extraordinary / Kindest cut / Lightning
GAD 005CD / 6 Jul '98 / 4AD

☐ REV
Candida / Cut throat / Mirror to mirror / Portion of delight / Thief's love song / How sweet / Medicating angels / Blood and thunder / This is the way
GAD 2017CD / 6 Jul '98 / 4AD

☐ ULTRA VIVID SCENE
She screamed / Crash / You didn't say please / Lynne-Marie 2 / Nausea / Mercy seat / Dream of love / Lynne-Marie / This isn't real / Whore of God / Bloodline / How did it feel / Hail Mary
GAD 809CD / 6 Jul '98 / 4AD

Ultrabide

☐ GOD IS GOD, PUKE IS PUKE
K 162C / Nov '95 / Konkurrel

Ultrabreakfast

☐ ICE CREAM TRICYCLE
CAT 012 / 13 Oct '97 / Catapult

Ultradolce

☐ COSMIC EXOTIC SEXTEASE PARTY
IRMA 491571CD / 13 Jul '98 / Irma

Ultrahigh

☐ VIEW OF ULTRAHIGH
FIM 1015 / Mar '95 / Force Inc.

Ultramarine

☐ BEL AIR
78 / K v / Welcome / Maxine / Mutant / Pioneer spirit / Rainbow brew / Escape velocity / Harmony street / Free radical / Alter ego / Citizen / Schmaltz / I got sane / Everyone in brazil / Fantasy filter / Buena vista
0630112062 / Dec '96 / Blanco Y Negro

☐ EVERY MAN AND WOMAN IS A STAR
R 2892 / Jun '92 / Rough Trade

☐ UNITED KINGDOMS
Source / Kingdom / Queen of the moon / Prince Rock / Happy land / Urf / English heritage / Instant kitten / Badger / Hooter / Dizzy fox / No time
4509934252 / Dec '96 / Blanco Y Negro

☐ USER'S GUIDE, A
All of a sudden / Surfacing / Sucker 4U / On the brink / Zombie / By turns / Ambush / 4U version / Ghost routine / What machines want
ELEC 36CD / 16 Feb '98 / New Electronica

Ultramarine

☐ DE
Djanea / U song / Dub it / Ivory coast / De / Bod kan'nal / Modakofa
500052 / Mar '90 / Musidisc

☐ E SI MALA
500242 / Nov '93 / Musidisc

Ultrasonic

☐ GLOBAL TEKNO (2CD Set)
1,2,3,4 / Out of control / Hey Mr. DJ / Make that move / 180 mph / Tic tok / Total break up / Let the muzik set you free / Dreamer of dreams / In the air tonight / There is no back-up / Do you believe in love / Joyriderz / We want one more / Star spangled tekno / Party people in the house / DJ ragga / US vs. bass baby / Annihilating rhythm / Check your head / Make that move / Tekno junkies in the mix
DCSR 007 / Oct '95 / Clubscene

☐ HOUR OF CHAOS, THE
USR 693533 / 25 May '98 / USR

☐ LIVE AT CLUB KINETIC
DCSR 010 / Sep '96 / Clubscene

☐ TECHNO JUNKIES 1992-94
DCSR 002 / Sep '94 / Clubscene

Ultravibe

☐ TRAVELS THROUGH THE ULTRAVIBE SPECTRUM
REVCC 008 / Jul '96 / Revco

Ultraviolence

☐ KILLING GOD
Dawn / Adultery / Paranoid / Still / Bombs in my head / Facilitator / Masochist / Killing God / Strangled / Horror / Immolation
MOSH 191CD / 30 Mar '98 / Earache

☐ LIFE OF DESTRUCTOR
I am destructor / Electric chair / Joan / Hardcore motherfucker / Digital killing / Only love / We will break / Hiroshima / Destructor's fall / Death of a child
MOSH 103CD / 1 Sep '97 / Earache

☐ PSYCHODRAMA
Birth - Jessica / Reject / Disco boyfriend / Pimp / Psychodrama / Birth hitman / Stone faced / Murder academy / Hitman's heart / Contract / Lovers / Suicide pact / God's mistake / Searching hell / Heaven is oblivion
MOSH 142CD / 1 Sep '97 / Earache

Ultravox

☐ COLLECTION, THE
Dancing with tears in my eyes / Hymn / Thin wall / Voice / Vienna / Passing strangers / Sleepwalk / Reap the wild wind / All stood still / Visions in blue / We came to dance / One small day / Love's great adventure / Lament
CCD 1490 / Mar '85 / Chrysalis

☐ DANCING WITH TEARS IN MY EYES
Sleepwalk / Waiting / Passing strangers / Vienna / Passionate reply / Voice / Hymn / Monument / We came to dance / Dancing with tears in my eyes / Reap the wild wind / Love's great adventure / White china / All fall down / Dreams / All in one day
CDGOLD 1078 / Feb '97 / Music For Pleasure

☐ EXTENDED (A Collection Of 12 Remixes)
All stood still / Reap the wild wind / We came to dance / Serenade / One small day / Dancing with tears in my eyes / Lament / Love's great adventure / Same old story / All fall down
4934652 / 16 Feb '98 / EMI Gold

☐ HA HA HA
Rock work / Frozen ones / Fear in the western world / Distant smile / Man who dies everyday / Artificial life / While I'm still alive / Hiroshima mon amour
IMCD 147 / Jul '92 / Island

☐ INGENUITY
Ingenuity / There goes a beautiful world / Give it all back / Future picture forever / Silent cries / Distance / Ideals / Who'll save you / Way out-a way through / Majestic
RES 109CD / 3 Aug '98 / Resurgence

☐ MONUMENT
Monument / Reap the wild wind / Voice / Vienna / Mine for life / Hymn / Passing strangers / Visions in blue
CDGOLD 1025 / Jul '96 / EMI Gold

☐ RAGE IN EDEN
Voice / We stand alone / I remember death in the afternoon / Thin wall / Stranger within / Accent on youth / Ascent / Rage in Eden / Your name has slipped my mind again
CDGOLD 1097 / 15 Sep '97 / EMI Gold

☐ RARE VOL.1
Waiting / Face to face / King's lead hat (live) / Passionate reply / Herr X / Alles klar / Keep talking / I never wanted to begin / Paths and angles / Private lives (live) / All stood still / Hosanna (In Excelsis deo) / Monument / Thin wall / Break your back / Reap the wild wind (live) / Overlook
CDCHR 6053 / Nov '93 / Chrysalis

☐ RARE VOL.2
Easterly / Building / Heart of the country / White china / Man of two worlds / Three / All in one day / Dreams / All fall down (instrumental) / All fall down (Live) / Dream on (Live) / Prize (Live) / Stateless / One small day (Final mix)
CDCHR 6078 / Aug '94 / Chrysalis

☐ THREE INTO ONE
Young savage / Rock work / Dangerous rhythm / Man who dies everyday / Wild, the beautiful and the damned / Slow motion / Just for a moment / Quiet men / My sex / Hiroshima mon amour
IMCD 30 / '89 / Island

☐ ULTRAVOX
Ultravox / Saturday night in the city of the dead / Life at rainbow's end / Slip away / I want to be a machine / Wide boy / Dangerous rhythm / Lonely hunter / Wild, the beautiful and the damned / My sex
IMCD 146 / Jul '92 / Island

☐ ULTRAVOX/HA HA HA/SYSTEMS OF ROMANCE (3CD Set)
Saturday night in the city of the dead / Life at the rainbow's end / Slip away / I want to be a machine / Wide boys / Dangerous rhythm / Lonely hunter / Wild, the beautiful and the damned / My sex / Rockwrok / Frozen ones / Fear in the Western world / Distant smile / Man who dies everyday / Artificial life / While I'm still alive / Hiroshima mon amour / Slow motion / Can't stay long / Someone else's clothes / Blue light / Some of them / Quiet men / Dislocation / Maximum acceleration / When you walk through me / Just for a moment
5241522 / Nov '95 / Island

☐ VIENNA
Astradyne / New Europeans / Private lives / Passing strangers / Mr. X / Sleepwalk / Western promise / Vienna / All stood still
CCD 1296 / Jul '94 / Chrysalis

Ulver

☐ BERGTATT
HNF 005CD / Aug '95 / Head Not Found

☐ KVELDSSANGER
HNF 014CD / Feb '96 / Head Not Found

☐ MADRIGAL OF RIGHT, THE
CM 77158CD / Mar '97 / Century Media

Umajets

☐ DEMOLITION
EFA 054052 / 2 Feb '98 / Clear Spot

Uman

☐ PURPLE PASSAGE
5243982 / 24 Feb '98 / Six Degrees

Umba, Mac

☐ DON'T HOLD YOUR BREATH
CDTRAX 113 / May '96 / Greentrax

Umbra Et Imago

☐ MACHINA MUNDI
CD 08562062 / 29 Jun '98 / SPV

☐ MYSTICA SEXUALS
SONO 195CD / Apr '97 / Spirit Production

Umbrella Heaven

☐ CHOSEN TO BE FROZEN
BWL 022 / 20 Oct '97 / Boogie Wonderland

☐ DO YOU HATE ME
BWL 017 / Sep '95 / Boogie Wonderland

Umezu, Kazutoki

☐ ECLECTICISM
KFWCD 130 / Feb '95 / Knitting Factory

Umiliani, Piero

☐ TO-DAY'S SOUND
ET 906CD / 16 Dec '97 / Easy Tempo

UMO

☐ UMO VOL.2
CA 12009 / 23 Mar '98 / Caipirinha

☐ UNIDENTICAL MUSICAL OBJECT
HE 013 / Dec '96 / Home Entertainment

Umo Jazz Orchestra

☐ UMO JAZZ ORCHESTRA, THE
860102 / Feb '98 / Naxos Jazz

Una Notte Speciale

☐ HITS FROM THE SAN REMO FESTIVAL 1998
ZYX 204542 / 26 May '98 / ZYX

Unaminated

☐ GOD OF EVIL
NFR 009CD / Mar '95 / No Fashion

☐ IN THE FOREST OF THE DREAMING DEAD
NFR 004 / Oct '94 / No Fashion

Unbelievable Truth

☐ ALMOST THERE
Stone / Settle down / Angel / Same mistakes / Be ready / Forget about me / Finest little space / Building / Almost here / Solved / Higher than reason
CDVX 2849 / 11 May '98 / Virgin

Unbroken

☐ LIFE LOVE REGRET
NA 022CD / Jul '96 / New Age

☐ RITUAL
NA 016CD / Jul '96 / New Age

Uncle Fish & The Cry

☐ DUSSELDORF PHILIPSHALLE 7.12.91
DDICK 17CD / Sep '96 / Dick Bros.

Uncle Ho

☐ SMALL IS BEAUTIFUL
SUBWAYS 1 / 15 Dec '97 / Subway

Uncle Sam

☐ FOURTEEN WOMEN
CMGCD 010 / Nov '93 / Communique

☐ HEAVEN OR HOLLYWOOD
Live for the day / Don't be shy / Alice D / No reason why / Candy man / Don't you ever / All alone / Peace of mind, piece of body / Under sedation / Heaven or Hollywood / Steppin stone / Train kept a rollin'
3MC3 / Nov '90 / Skeller

☐ UNCLE SAM
Can you feel it / You make me feel like / Throw your hands in the air / Leave well alone / Without lovin' you / Someone like you / Tender love / Think about me / Baby you are / Stop foolin' around / I don't ever want to see you again
4887132 / 5 Jan '98 / Epic

Uncle Tupelo

☐ ANODYNE
Slate / Acuff-Rose / Long cut / Give back the key to my heart / Chickamauga / New Madrid / Anodyne / We've been had / Fifteen keys / High water / No sense in lovin' / Steal the crumbs
9362454242 / Oct '93 / WEA

☐ MARCH 16-20 1992
Grindstone / Coalminers / Wait up / Criminals / Shaky ground / Satan your kingdom must come down / Black eye / Moonshiner / I wish my baby was born / Atomic power / Lilli Schull / Warfare / Fatal wound / Sandusky / Wipe the clock
ROCK 6090CD / Apr '97 / Rockville

☐ NO DEPRESSION
ROCK 6050CD / Apr '97 / Rockville

☐ STILL FEEL GONE
Gun / Looking For A Way Out / Fall Down Easy / Nothing / Still Be Around / Watch me fall / Punch Drunk / D Boon / True To Life / Cold shoulder / Discarded / If that's alright
BUFF 001CD / May '93 / Yellow Moon
ROCK 6070CD / May '97 / Rockville

Uncle Walt's Band

☐ AMERICAN IN TEXAS REVISITED, AN
SHCD 1034/5 / Jan '97 / Sugar Hill

☐ GIRL ON THE SUNNY SHORE, THE
SHCD 1032/3 / Jan '97 / Sugar Hill

Uncurbed

☐ MENTAL DISORDER
LF 094CD / Jan '95 / Lost & Found

☐ NIGHTMARE IN DAYLIGHT, A
FINNREC 010CD / Jun '96 / Finn

☐ STRIKE OF MANKIND
LF 061CD / Aug '93 / Lost & Found

☐ STRIKE OF MANKIND/MENTAL DISORDER
LF 237CD / Sep '96 / Lost & Found

Undeclinable Ambuscade

☐ ONE FOR THE MONEY
65372 / 31 Aug '98 / Epitaph

☐ THEIR GREATEST ADVENTURES
Growing older / Magic hairspray / Can't bring me down / Release the animals / I'm sorry / African song / Stick 'em up / Love story / Snowboard / Something she'll never have / World full of understanding / Why does a fly / Far away / Alcohol
65262 / 17 Nov '97 / Epitaph

Under The Church

☐ SPACE INVADERS
NLR 010CD / Apr '97 / New Life

Under The Noise

☐ OF GENERATION AND CORRUPTION
SPV 08434242 / Apr '96 / SPV

☐ REGENERATION
COPCD 024 / Nov '96 / Cop International

Under The Sun

☐ UNDER THE SUN
MARBEL 002CD / 2 Feb '98 / Vinyl Tap

Underbelly

☐ EVERYONE LOVES YOU WHEN YOU'RE DEAD
SEVE 003CD / Jul '95 / 7

☐ MUMBLY PEG
OUT 1142 / Sep '97 / Brake Out

Undergroove

☐ VIRTUAL
Wrapped in rage / Alright / Uncensored / Cruel way / No ground bait / Half-way up / Twisted / Gangster / Off the floor / Hyped / Back to insanity / Don't bring me down
PCOM 1149 / 26 Aug '97 / President

Underground Lovers

☐ LEAVES ME BLIND
Eastside stories / Promenade / I was right / Holiday / Got off on it / Daze / Waves / Your eyes / Ladies' choice / Get to know / Whisper me nothing
GU 2CD / 6 Jul '98 / Guernica

Underground Resistance

☐ X-101
EFA 01727CD / Oct '96 / Tresor

Undernation

☐ ANGER
OUT 1112 / Sep '97 / Brake Out

☐ SOMETHING ON THE TV
OUT 1062 / Sep '97 / Brake Out

Undertakers

☐ UNEARTHED
(Do the) Mashed potatoes / Everybody loves a lover / Money (that's what I want) / What about us / Just a little bit / Stupidity / If you don't come back back / Think / Be my little girl / She said yeah / I need your lovin' / Tell me what you're gonna do / Tricky Dicky / Irresistable you / Love is a swingin' thing / Hey hey hey hey / You're so fine and sweet / Leave my kitten alone / Watch your step / Throw your love away girl / I fell in love (for the very first time)
CDWIKD 163 / Feb '96 / Big Beat

Undertones

☐ HYPNOTISED
More songs about chocolate and girls / There goes Norman / See that girl / Whizz kids / Under the boardwalk / Way girls talk / Hard luck / My perfect cousin / Boys will be boys / Tearproof / Wednesday week / Nine times out of ten / Girls that don't talk / What's with Terry
DOJOCD 192 / May '94 / Dojo

☐ HYPNOTISED
More songs about chocolate and girls / There goes Norman / See that girl / Whizz kids / Under the boardwalk / Way girls talk / Hard luck / My perfect cousin / Boys will be boys / Tearproof / Wednesday week / Nine times out of ten / Girls that don't talk / What's with Terry / You've got my number (Why don't you use it) / Hard luck (Again) / Let's talk about girls / I told you so / I don't wanna see you again
ESMCD 486 / Mar '97 / Essential

☐ POSITIVE TOUCH
Fascination / Julie Ocean / Life's too easy / Crises of mine / You're welcome / His good looking girlfriend / Positive touch / When Saturday comes / It's going to happen / Sign and explode / I don't know / Hannah Doot / Boy wonder / Forever paradise
DOJOCD 193 / May '94 / Dojo

☐ POSITIVE TOUCH
Fascination / Julie Ocean / Life's too easy / Crisis of mine / You're welcome / Goodlooking girlfriend / Fairly in the money now / Beautiful friend / Kiss in the dark / Forever paradise / Boy wonder / Hannah Doot / I don't know / Sigh and explode / It's going to happen / When Saturday comes / Positive touch
ESMCD 485 / Mar '97 / Essential

☐ SIN OF PRIDE, THE
Got to have you back / Untouchable / Valentine's treatment / Love before romance / Luxury / Bye bye baby blue / Love parade / Soul seven / Conscious / Chain of love / Save me / Sin of pride
DOJOCD 194 / May '94 / Dojo

☐ SIN OF PRIDE, THE
Got to have you back / Valentine's treatment / Luxury / Love before romance / Untouchable / Bye bye baby blue / Conscious / Chain of love / Soul seven / Love parade / Save me / Sin of pride / Bittersweet / You stand so close (But you're never there) / Turning blue / Like that / I can only dream / Window shopping for new clothes
ESMCD 487 / Mar '97 / Essential

☐ TEENAGE KICKS (The Best Of The Undertones)
Teenage kicks / Get over you / Male model / Jimmy Jimmy / Mars bar / My perfect cousin / Tearproof / Hypnotised / Positive touch / It's going to happen / When Saturday comes / Love parade / Casbah rock / Family entertainment / Girls don't like it / Here comes the summer / You got my number / Let's talk about girls / Way girls talk / More songs about chocolate and girls / Wednesday week / You're welcome / Julie Ocean / Forever paradise / Soul seven
CCSCD 808 / Jan '97 / Renaissance Collector Series

MAIN SECTION

☐ UNDERTONES
Family entertainment / Girls don't like it / Male model / I gotta getta / Teenage kicks / Wrong way / Jump boys / Here comes the summer / Get over you / Billy's third / Jimmy Jimmy / True confessions / She's a runaround / I know a girl / Listening in / Casbah rock
DOLECD 101 / Jan '96 / Dojo

☐ UNDERTONES
Family entertainment / Girls don't like it / Male model / I gotta getta / Teenage kicks / Wrong way / Jump boys / Here comes the summer / Get over you / Billy's third / Jimmy Jimmy / True confessions / (She's a) Runaround / I know a girl / Emergency cases / Casbah rock / Smarter than U / Emergency cases / Top twenty / Really really / Mars bars / She can only say no / One way love
ESMCD 484 / Mar '97 / Essential

Undertow

☐ EDGE OF QUARREL
LF 152CD / May '95 / Lost & Found

Underworld

☐ DARK AND LONG
APR 002CD / 5 Jan '98 / April

☐ DUBNOBASSWITHMYHEADMAN
Dark and long / Mmm skyscraper I love you / Surfboy / Spoonman / Tongue / Dirty epic / Cowgirl / River of bass / M.e.
JBO 1001992 / 11 May '98 / Junior Boys Own

☐ PEARL'S GIRL
Pearl's girl / Puppies / Oich oich / Cherry pie / Mosaic / Deep arch
TVT 87482 / Jan '97 / TVT

☐ SECOND TOUGHEST IN THE INFANTS (2CD Set)
Juanita / Kiteless / To dream of love / Banstyle / Sappys curry / Confusion the waitress / Rowla / Pearl's girl / Air towel / Blueski / Stagger
U2 CDB / Dec '96 / Logic
JBO 1002002 / 11 May '98 / Junior Boys Own

Undish

☐ ACTA EST FABULA
MASSCD 126 / Jun '97 / Massacre

Undivided Roots

☐ HAND AND HEARTS TOGETHER
CRCD 55 / 11 Aug '97 / Charm

Unfolding

☐ HOW TO BLOW YOUR MIND...
3197 / Jun '97 / Head

Ungar, Jay

☐ CIVIL WAR CLASSICS (Ungar, Jay & Molly Mason)
FD 102CD / Mar '98 / Fiddle & Dance

Ungod

☐ CIRCLE OF THE 7 INFERNAL PACTS
MRCD 001 / Oct '94 / Merciless

Unholy

☐ SECOND RING OF POWER, THE
CDAV 005 / Aug '94 / Avantgarde

Uniform Choice

☐ STARING AT THE SUN
LF 176CD / Jul '95 / Lost & Found

☐ STARING INTO THE SUN
FLY 009CD / 18 Aug '97 / Tackle Box

☐ STRAIGHT AND ALERT
LF 175CD / Jul '95 / Lost & Found

Union

☐ UNION
Old man wise / Around again / Pain behind your eyes / Love (I don't need it anymore) / Heavy D... / Let it flow / Empty soul / October morning wind / Get off my cloud / Tangerine / Robin's song
908611124CD / 11 May '98 / Mayhem

Union

☐ UNION, THE
GROW 0422 / Feb '95 / Grass

Union 13

☐ EAST LOS PRESENTS UNION 13
Who are you / Regrets / Fuck society / Bonded as one / Todo es una política / Burocrata Estafador / Children's story / Falling down / Country full of lies / I can't stand it anymore / Govierno podrido / Realidad / Over the hill / Government / State of consciousness / Un muro por cruzar / Ronald's fuckhouse / Final approach
64942 / Jul '97 / Scooch Pooch

Union Avenue

☐ UNION AVENUE
I shot the sheriff / Other side / Bad moon rising / Ace of spades / Big river
RAUCD 029 / May '97 / Raucous

Union Carbide

☐ SWING (Union Carbide Productions)
FIST 014 / 6 Apr '98 / Fist Puppet

Union Jack

☐ THERE WILL BE NO ARMAGEDDON
PLAT 15CD / Jul '95 / Platipus

Uniques

☐ BEST OF THE UNIQUES 1967-1969, THE
CDTRL 340 / Jun '94 / Trojan

Unit 187

☐ LOADED
Loaded / Dick / Dead dogs / Nobody / Traces / Shape shifter / Rat trap / Planet Claire / Stillborn / Loaded / Stillborn
08543592 / 1 Sep '97 / Off Beat

Unit Moebius

☐ LIFE MOOD PARTS 1-8/REMIXES
SIRE 001 / Jul '96 / Silver Recordings

☐ STATUS
KKCD 150 / May '96 / KK

Unit Pride

☐ CAN I KILL A DREAM
LF 158CD / Jun '95 / Lost & Found

United

☐ NO IQ
398141107CD / Mar '96 / Metal Blade

United Future Organisation

☐ 3RD PERSPECTIVE
His name is... / Planet plan / Friends we'll be / Spy's spice(mon espionne) / Fool's paradise / Waltz (le serpent rouge) / Picaresque eye / Nica's dream / Cosmic gypsy / Dice for a chance / Moving shadows
5344872 / Jun '97 / Talkin' Loud

☐ NO SOUND IT TOO TABOO
Mistress of the dance / Stolen moments / Sunday folk tale / Future light / Make it better / Magic wand of love / Bar f out / Doopsylalolic / Tears of gratitude / United future airlines
5222712 / Sep '94 / Talkin' Loud

☐ SOUNDTRACK, THE
APR 003CD / May '95 / April

United Mutations

☐ UNITED MUTATIONS
LF 297CD / 27 Oct '97 / Lost & Found

United States Of America

☐ UNITED STATES OF AMERICA
American metaphysical / Circus / Hard coming love / Cloud song / Garden of earthly delights / I won't leave my wooden wife for you / Sugar / Where is yesterday / Coming song for the dead / Stranded in time / American way of love
EDCD 541 / 24 Nov '97 / Edsel

United States Of Existence

☐ COLLECTION, THE
0005 / Jul '97 / US Fidelit

Unitone Hi-Fi

☐ BOOMSHOT
INCCD 3314 / Sep '97 / Incoming

☐ REWOUND & RERUBBED
INCCD 3308 / Jun '97 / Incoming

Unitone Rockers

☐ MAGIC PLANET
BFRCD 010 / Apr '93 / Beat Farm

Unity

☐ BLOOD DAYS
LF 103CD / Aug '97 / Lost & Found

Universal Being

☐ ARCHIVES, THE
HOLCD 28 / Jun '97 / Holistic

☐ HOLISTIC RHYTHMS
HOLCD 23 / Jan '96 / Holistic

R.E.D. CD CATALOGUE

☐ JUPITER
HOLCD 025 / Jul '96 / Holistic

Universal Congress Of

☐ ELEVENTH HOUR SHINE ON
EMY 1362 / Sep '97 / Enemy

☐ MECOLODICS
SST 204CD / May '93 / SST

☐ SAD AND TRAGIC DEMISE OF THE BIG FINE HOT SALTY BLACK WIND
EMY 1172 / Sep '97 / Enemy

Universal Indicator

☐ COMPILATION VOL.1-4
MKS 80 / May '94 / Rephlex

Universal Order Of Armageddon

☐ UNIVERSAL ORDER OF ARMAGEDDON
KRS 224CD / Sep '96 / Kill Rock Stars

Universe Crew

☐ WHAT'S INSIDE YOUR AFRO
GTO 1CD / 27 Oct '97 / Green Tea

University Of Wisconsin Band

☐ UNIVERSITY OF WISCONSIN/EAU CLAIRE SYMPHONY BAND
SOSCD 1284 / Dec '94 / Stomp Off

UNKLE

☐ PSYENCE FICTION
Guns blazing / Unkle main title theme / Bloodstain / Unreal / Lonely soul / Getting ahead in the lucrative field of artist management / Nursery rhyme / Celestial annihilation / Knock / Chaos / Rabbit in your headlights
MW 085CD
MW 085CDS / 24 Aug '98 / Mo Wax

Unknown Factor

☐ GLOBAL FACTOR
DFDCD 008 / Apr '97 / Defender

Unleashed

☐ ACROSS THE OPEN SEA
CM 770552 / Nov '93 / Century Media

☐ EASTERN BLOOD
CM 771182 / Nov '96 / Century Media

☐ LIVE IN VIENNA
CM 770562 / Jan '94 / Century Media

☐ VICTORY
CM 770902 / May '95 / Century Media

☐ WARRIOR
CM 77124CD / Jun '97 / Century Media

☐ WHERE NO LIFE DWELLS
CM 97182 / '92 / Century Media

Unlimited Dream Company

☐ VOLTAGE
Up in dub heaven / Shore gardens / As one door closes / Potion takes effect / If I should step / Feel like I'm falling / Scenic root / Sandoz by moonlight / No headaches
CDTOT 24 / Apr '95 / Jumpin' & Pumpin'

Unlimited Sound Orchestra

☐ CHRISTMAS IN AMERICA
I 3885762 / Dec '96 / Galaxy

Unlord

☐ SCHWARZWALD
D 00048CD / 27 Oct '97 / Displeased

Unnatural Axe

☐ IS GONNA KICK YOUR ASS
LAWLESS 001 / Oct '97 / Lawless

Unorthodox

☐ ASYLUM
HELL 0021CD / '90 / Hellhound

☐ BALANCE OF POWER
HELL 0030CD / Apr '94 / Hellhound

Unrest

☐ FUCK PUSSY GALORE (AND ALL HER FRIENDS)
So you want to be a rock 'n' roll star / Scott and Zelda / Hill / Happy song / Rigor mortis / Can't sit still / Cats / Die grunen / Holiday in Berlin / 91st Century schizoid man / Hil, part 2 / Picnic at Hanging Rock / Live on a hot August night / Chastity ballad / Judy says / Tundra / Wild thang / Laughter / S Street shuffle / Over the life / Hope / Communist tart / She makes me free to be me / Sammy's mean mustard / Greg Hershey where are you / Egg cheer
OLE 0242 / Jan '94 / Matador

☐ IMPERIAL
Volume reference tone / Sukl / Imperial / I do believe you are blushing / Champion nines / Sugar shack / Isabel / Cherry cream on / Firecracker / June / Loyola / Yes she is my skinhead girl / Hydrofoil no.1 / Full frequency / Wednesday and proud
GU 1CD / 6 Jul '98 / Guernica

☐ PERFECT TEETH
Angel I'll walk you home / Cath carroll / So sick / Light command / Food and drink synthesizer / Soon it is going to rain / Make out club / Breather x.o.x.o. / West coast love affair / Six layer cake / Stylized ampersand
GAD 3012CD / 6 Jul '98 / 4AD

Unsane

☐ AMREP CHRISTMAS
MR 069CD / Jul '97 / Man's Ruin

☐ ATTACK IN JAPAN
SPV 08545912 / Mar '97 / SPV
ZIKSBB 022 / 9 Mar '98 / Z

☐ OCCUPATIONAL HAZARD
Committed / This pain / Over me / Take in the stray / Stop / Wait to lose / Sick / Hazmat / Smells like rain / Lead / Humidifier / Scan / Understand
LJCD 006 / 23 Feb '98 / Lockjaw
RR 67662 / 16 Mar '98 / Relapse

☐ SCATTERED, SMOTHERED AND COVERED
SPV 08445782 / Dec '95 / SPV

☐ SINGLES 1989-1992, THE
EFA 049132 / Nov '92 / City Slang

☐ TOTAL DESTRUCTION
EFA 049262 / Jan '94 / City Slang

Unsophisticates

☐ GUIDO
Riverbank / Maxi's dead / So long, Glasgow / Blow up / Pervert / Ain't got no life / Straitjacket / Almost normal / Ghost of tess renaudo / Israeli relations / Lie / Growth / Is it safe
SCANCD 23 / May '97 / Passion

Unsteady

☐ DOUBLE OR NOTHING
AM 017CD / 29 Sep '97 / Asian Man

Untamed Youth

☐ PLANET MACE
ES 1223CD / Jul '97 / Estrus

Untouchables

☐ AGENT DOUBLE O SOUL
Agent double o soul / Stripped to the bone / World gone crazy / Cold city / Education / Let's get together / Airplay / Under the boardwalk / Sudden attack / Shama lama ding dong
723422 / Feb '95 / Restless

☐ DECADE OF DANCE (Live)
725072 / Feb '95 / Restless

☐ WILD CHILD
HIPD 40118 / 30 Jun '98 / Hippo

Unun

☐ SUPER SHINY
BAD 001CD / Feb '96 / Bad Taste

UNV

☐ SOMETHING'S GOIN' ON
UNV thang / When will I know / Who will it be / Close tonight / Gonna give U what U want / Something's goin' on 2 B or not 2 B / Straight from my heart / Hold on / No one compares to you
93624528742 / Nov '93 / WEA

Unwound

☐ CHALLENGE FOR A CIVILIZED SOCIETY
KRS 289CD / 15 Jan '98 / Kill Rock Stars

☐ FUTURE OF WHAT
KRS 245CD / Jul '95 / Kill Rock Stars

☐ NEW PLASTIC IDEAS
Entirely different / Matters / What was wound / Envelope / Fiction friction / Abstrahtions / Arboretum / Usual dosage / All souls day / Hexenszene
KRS 223CD / Mar '94 / Kill Rock Stars

Up Bustle & Out

☐ LIGHT 'EM UP, BLOW 'EM OUT
Clandestine operation / Emerald alley / Rain in Tibet / Silks, perfume and gold / Beautiful lure / Apple strudle / Compared to what / Y ahora tu / Radio Madrid / Dance of Caravan summer / Lazy daze / Hearty do-lilies / Coca conga / Coffee at Senor Rudl's / Ilusion / Party with the Raj
ZENCD 027 / Jun '97 / Ninja Tune

☐ ONE COLOUR JUST REFLECTS ANOTHER
Aqui no ma / Revolutionary woman of the windmill, part 1 / Running rude / Bicycles, flutes and you / 1,2,3, Alto y fuera / African friendship / Twelve penny apples / Three drunk musicians / Poncho cafe / Hand of contraband / Mr. Pavement man / Ninja's principality / Unmarked grave / Discoursing drums / Street of Huangayo, Peru
ZENCD 019 / Apr '96 / Ninja Tune

Up Front

☐ PSALMS
RASCD 3093 / Oct '92 / Ras

Up There Trio

☐ PUSH IT
BVHAASTCD 9607 / Apr '98 / Bvhaast

Upchurch, Phil

☐ ALL I WANT
Poison / When we need it bad / 12/25 / 516 / Grace / What will I do / All I want from you / U god it gowin on
ICH 1127CD / Jan '94 / Ichiban

☐ LOVE IS STRANGE (Upchurch, Phil & Chaka Khan)
GOJ 60142 / 8 Jun '98 / Go Jazz

☐ WHATEVER HAPPENED TO THE BLUES
GOJ 60062 / 8 Jun '98 / Go Jazz

Upfront

☐ SPIRIT
LF 087CD / Jun '94 / Lost & Found

Upfront

☐ MOVEMENT
IJT 005 / 15 Sep '97 / Idjit
GOW 003CD / 20 Jul '98 / Grapes Of Wrath

Upper Crust

☐ LET THEM EAT ROCK
UPSTART 026 / Oct '95 / Upstart

Uppsala Big Band

☐ IN PROGRESS
SITCD 9208 / Jun '94 / Sittel

☐ RADIO UPPLAND BIG BAND 93
SITCD 9207 / Jun '94 / Sittel

Upright Citizens

☐ COLOUR YOUR LIFE
IRC 037 / Mar '97 / Impact

Upshaw, Dawn

☐ I WISH IT SO
7559793522 / Sep '94 / Elektra

Upsidedown Cross

☐ EVILUTION
TAANG 70CD / Jun '93 / Taang

Uptighty

☐ UPTIGHTY
MUDCD 003 / Feb '97 / Mud/Parasol

Upton, Barry

☐ 5678 (Upton, Barry & Wild At Heart)
STKCD 4 / 17 Aug '98 / Southern Tracks

Uralsky All Stars

☐ FRIENDS WITH PLEASURE
I'll be a friend with pleasure / Creole love call / Sweet Georgia Brown / New Orleans / Duet - blues / Runnin' wild / What's new / New York New York / Moonglow / Benny bugle / Rose room / Mack the knife
CDTTD 614 / 26 May '98 / Timeless

☐ RUSSIAN ROULETTE
Mishka, mishka / South Rampart Street Parade / C'est si bon / Cabaret / Fine flowers in the spring garden / I've been dreaming of you for three years / My blue heaven / Natasha / Midnight in Moscow / Stenjka razin / Ah, Odessa / Mjasoedowskaya uliza
CDTTD 597 / Sep '95 / Timeless Jazz

☐ WE'LL MEET AGAIN
Song of the Volga boatmen / Back home again in Indiana / Dream a little dream of me / Nobody's sweetheart / Just a gigolo / I ain't got nobody / Night train / Amapola / Night and day / Struttin' with some barbecue / Meet me tonight in dreamland / We'll meet again
CDTTD 595 / Sep '96 / Timeless Jazz

Uranium 235

☐ CULTURAL MINORITY
SPV 08518832 / 1 Jun '98 / SPV

Uranium 9 Volt

☐ WILD SEVEN
LK 181CD / 8 Sep '97 / Lookout

Urban City Mixers

☐ BEST OF DANCE, THE
PLSCD 252 / 27 Oct '97 / Pulse

Urban Cookie Collective

☐ HIGH ON A HAPPY VIBE
PULSE 13CD / Mar '94 / Pulse 8

Urban Dance Squad

☐ LIFE N' PERSPECTIVES OF A GENUINE CROSSOVER
longing / Friendship / Miracle / Rose / Urban samba / Forever more / Senegal
GRP 98152 / May '95 / GRP

☐ PERSONA NON GRATA
Demagogue / Good grief / No honestly / Alienated / Candy strip exp / Self sufficient snake / (Some) Chit chat / Burnt up cigarette / Self styled / Mugshot / Hangout / Downer
CDHUT 19 / Jun '94 / Hut

☐ PLANET ULTRA
Nonstarter / Temporarily expendable / Forgery / Planet Ultra / Dresscode / Totalled / Warzone 109 / Metaphore warfare / Ego / Carbon copy / Everyday blitzkrieg / Inside-outsider / Stark sharks and backlashes / Pass the baton right / Damn the quota / Grifter swifter / Tabloid say / Natural born communicator
CDVIR 53 / Sep '96 / Virgin

Urban Dogs

☐ URBAN DOGS/NO PEDIGREE
LOMACD 42 / Jun '96 / Loma

Urban Knights

☐ URBAN KNIGHTS
On the radio / Wanna be with you / Chill / Hearts of gold / Friendship / Miracle / Rose / Urban samba / Forever more / Senegal
GRP 98152 / May '95 / GRP

☐ URBAN KNIGHTS VOL.2
Scirroco / Get up / Come dance with me / South African jam / Brazilian rain / Interlude / Summer nights / Tell me why / Urban paradise / Drama / Step by step / Promise / Interlude / Dawn
GRP 98622 / Mar '97 / GRP

Urban Sax

☐ SPIRAL
FCD 1125 / Jul '91 / EPM

☐ URBAN SAX
FDC 1124 / Jul '91 / EPM

Urban Turban

☐ URBAN TURBAN
SRS 4722CD / Dec '94 / Silence

Urban Waste

☐ URBAN WASTE
LF 062 / Jan '94 / Lost & Found

Urbanator

☐ URBANATOR VOL.2
Urbanate the area II / Basia / New Yorker / Magic / Urbal tea / Moody's mood for love / Anytime anywhere / Mantra / Hi no silver / Polak
HIBD 8012 / Oct '96 / Hip Bop

Urbani, Massimo

☐ BLESSING, THE
1232572 / Nov '93 / Red

Urbaniak, Michal

☐ FRIDAY NIGHT AT THE VILLAGE VANGUARD
STCD 4093 / Feb '89 / Storyville

☐ TAKE GOOD CARE OF MY HEART
SCCD 31195 / Jul '88 / Steeplechase

Urd

☐ SOLO DIDGERIDOO - GINNUNGAGAP
URD 9701CD / Dec '97 / Urd

Ure, Midge

☐ BREATHE
Breathe / Fields of fire / Fallen angel / Free / Guns and arrows / Lay my body down / Sinnerman / Live forever / Trail of tears / May your good Lord / Maker
74321346292 / May '96 / Arista
74321547092 / 15 Dec '97 / Arista

☐ GIFT, THE
If I was / When the winds blow / Living in the past / That certain smile / Gift / Antilles / Wastelands / Edo / Chieftain / She cried / Mood music / Piano / Man who sold the world / Gift (Instrumental)
CDGOLD 1045 / Jul '96 / EMI Gold

☐ IF I WAS (The Very Best Of Midge Ure & Ultravox)
If I was / No regrets / Love's great adventure / Dear God / Cold cold heart / Vienna / Call of the wild / Dancing with tears in my eyes / All fall down / Yellow pearl / Fade to grey / Reap the wild wind / Answers to nothing / Do they know it's Christmas
CDCHR 1987 / Feb '93 / Chrysalis

☐ IF I WAS
If I was / That certain smile / When the winds blow / Living in the past / Wastelands / Antilles / Gift / brother / Hell to heaven / Take me home / Homeland / Edo
DC 868792 / Mar '97 / Disky

Urge Overkill

☐ 10 YEARS OF WRECKING (2CD Set)
86132RAD / Jul '95 / Edel

☐ AMERICRUISER
TGCD 52 / Nov '94 / Touch & Go

☐ EXIT THE DRAGON
Jaywalkin' / Break / Need some air / Somebody else's body / Honesty files / This is no place / Mistake / Take me / View of the rain / Last night / Tomorrow / Tin foil / Monopoly / You'll say / Digital black epilogue
GED 24818 / 2 Feb '98 / Geffen

☐ SUPERSONIC STORYBOOK
TG 70CD / Nov '94 / Touch & Go

Uriah Heep

☐ ABOMINOG (Remastered)
Too scared to run / Chasing shadows / On the rebound / Hot night in a cold town / Running all night / That's the way that it is / Prisoner / Hot persuasion / Sell your soul / Think it over / Tin soldier / Son of a bitch / That's the way that it is / Chasing shadows
ESMCD 571 / Aug '97 / Essential

☐ BEST OF URIAH HEEP VOL.1, THE
Gypsy / Bird of prey / Lady in black / Salisbury / July morning / Look at yourself / Easy livin' / Wizard / Sweet Lorraine / Stealin' / Suicidal man / Return to fantasy / Misty eyes / Easy livin' / Stealin'
ESMCD 418 / Oct '96 / Essential

☐ BEST OF URIAH HEEP VOL.2, THE
ESMCD 594 / 20 Oct '97 / Essential

☐ COLLECTION, THE
Love machine / Look at yourself / Firefly / Return to fantasy / Rainbow demon / That's the way it is / Love is blind / On the rebound / Easy livin' / July morning / Running all night / Been away too long / Gypsy / Wake up (set your sights) / Can't keep a good band down / All of my life
CCSCD 226 / Jul '89 / Castle

☐ CONQUEST (Remastered)
No return / Imagination / Feelings / Fools / Carry on / Won't have to wait too long / Out on the street / It ain't easy / Been hurt / Love stealer / Think it over / My Joanna needs tuning / Lying
ESMCD 570 / Aug '97 / Essential

☐ DEMONS AND WIZARDS
Wizard / Traveller in time / Easy livin' / Poet's justice / Circle of hands / Rainbow demon / All my life / Paradise / Spell / Why / Home again to you
ESMCD 319 / Jul '96 / Essential

☐ DIFFERENT WORLD (Remastered)
Blood on stone / Which way will the wind blow / All God's children / All for one / Different world / Step by step / Seven days / First touch / One by one / Cross that line / Stand back / Blood red roses / Hold your head up / Rockarama
ESMCD 614 / Mar '98 / Essential

☐ DREAM ON (2CD Set)
CDHTD 102 / Oct '95 / HTD

☐ FALLEN ANGEL (Remastered)
One more night / Falling in love / Woman of the night / I'm alive / Come back to me / Whad'ya say / Save it / Country of origin / Put your lovin' on me / Fallen angel / Cheater / Gimme love / Right to love / Been hurt
ESMCD 561 / Jul '97 / Essential

☐ FIREFLY (Remastered)
Hanging tree / Been away too long / Who needs me / Wise man / Do you know / Rollin' on / Sympathy / Firefly / Come of passion / Do you know / Far better way / Wise man
ESMCD 559 / Jul '97 / Essential

URIAH HEEP

☐ FREE ME
Wizard / Something or nothing / On the rebound / I'm so tired / Been away too long / One way or another / Return to fantasy / Free me / Woman of the world / Love or nothing / That's the way that it is / Wise man / Prima donna / Dreams
5507312 / Mar '95 / Spectrum

☐ HEAD FIRST (Remastered)
Other side of midnight / Stay on top / Lonely nights / Sweet talk / Love is blind / Roll-overture / Red lights / Rollin' the rock / Straight through the heart / Weekend warriors / Playing for time / Searching / Wizard
ESMCD 572 / Aug '97 / Essential

☐ HIGH AND MIGHTY
One way or another / Weep in silence / Misty eyes / Midnight / Can't keep a good band down / Woman of the world / Footprints in the snow / Can't stop singing / Make a little love / Confession / Name of the game / Sundown
ESMCD 468 / Jan '97 / Essential

☐ INNOCENT VICTIM
Keep on ridin' / Flyin' high / Roller / Free 'n' easy / Illusion / Free me / Cheat and lie / Dance / Choices / Illusion/Masquerade / River
ESMCD 560 / Jul '97 / Essential

☐ KING BISCUIT PRESENTS
880272 / Jun '97 / King Biscuit

☐ KING BISCUIT PRESENTS...
Easy livin' / Sweet Lorraine / Stealin' / July morning / Seven stars / Gypsy / Drum solo / Sweet freedom / Look at yourself / Love machine / Medley
KBFHCD 008 / 26 May '98 / King Biscuit

☐ LADY IN BLACK
Lady in black / Easy livin' / Gypsy / Spider man / Sympathy / Carry on / Think it over / Traveller in time / Shady lady / Lonely nights / Fallen angel / Come back to me / Love stealer / Stay on top
5507302 / Jan '95 / Spectrum

☐ LANSDOWNE TAPES
Born in a trunk / Simon the bullet freak / Here I am / Magic lantern / Why / Astranaz / What's within my heart / What should be done / Lucy blues / I want you babe / Celebrate / Schoolgirl / Born in a trunk (instrumental) / Look at yourself
RMCCD 0193 / Jun '96 / Red Steel

☐ LIVE AT SHEPPERTON '74 (Remastered)
Easy livin' / So tired / I won't mind / Sweet freedom / Something or nothing / Easy road / Stealin' / Love machine / Rock 'n' roll medley / Easy road/Sleazy/Easy livin'
ESMCD 590 / Aug '97 / Essential

☐ LIVE IN EUROPE,1979
Easy livin' / Look at yourself / Lady in black / Free me / Stealin' / Wizard / July morning / Falling in love / Woman of the night / I'm alive / Who needs me / Sweet Lorraine / Free'n'easy / Gypsy
RAWCD 030 / Mar '87 / Raw Power

☐ LIVE IN MOSCOW (Remastered)
Bird of prey / Stealin' / Too scared to run / Corina / Mister Majestic / WizaWizard / July morning / Easy livin' / That's the way that it is / Pacific highway / Gypsy / Rockarama / Heartache city
ESMCD 611 / Mar '98 / Essential

☐ LOOK AT YOURSELF
Look at yourself / I wanna be free / July morning / Tears in my eyes / Shadows of grief / What should be done / Love machine / Look at yourself / What's within my heart
ESMCD 318 / Jan '96 / Essential

☐ MAGICIAN'S BIRTHDAY, THE
Sunrise / Spider woman / Blind eye / Echoes in the dark / Rain / Sweet Lorraine / Tales / Magician's birthday / Silver white man / Crystal ball
ESMCD 339 / Jan '96 / Essential

☐ RAGING SILENCE (Remastered)
Hold your head up / Blood red roses / Voice on my TV / Rich kid / Cry freedom / Bad bad man / More fool you (more fool me) / When the war is over / Lifeline / Rough justice / Miracle child / Look at yourself / Too scared to run / Corina / Hold your head up / Blood red
ESMCD 612 / Mar '98 / Essential

☐ RARITIES FROM THE BRONZE AGE
Simon the bullet freak / Look at yourself / Gypsy / Why / Stealin' / Sunshine / What can I do / Shout it out / Crime of passion / Cheater / Been hurt / Love stealer / Think it over / My joanna needs tuning / Tin soldier / Son of a bitch / Playing for time / Time will come / Gimme love / Masquerade
NEXCD 184 / Feb '92 / Sequel

☐ RETURN TO FANTASY
Return to fantasy / Shady lady / Devil's daughter / Beautiful dream / Prima donna / Your turn to remember / Showdown / Why did you go / Year or a day
ESMCD 381 / May '96 / Essential

☐ SALISBURY
Bird of prey / Park / Time to live / Lady in black / High priestess / Salisbury / Simon the bullet freak / High priestess (single edit)
ESMCD 317 / Jan '96 / Essential

☐ SEA OF LIGHT
SPV 08576952 / Dec '96 / SPV

☐ SPELLBINDER LIVE
CD 08576992 / Jul '96 / SPV

☐ STILL 'EAVY, STILL PROUD (Remastered)
Gypsy / July morning / Mister Majestic / Lady in black / Easy livin' / Too scared to run / Corina / Split image / Playing for time / Valley of kings / I'm alive again / Pacific highway / Mr. Majestic / Corina
ESMCD 613 / Mar '98 / Essential

☐ SWEET FREEDOM
Dreamer / Stealin' / One day / Sweet freedom / If I had the time / Seven stars / Circus / Pilgrim / Sunshine / Stealin' / Seven stars
ESMCD 338 / Jan '96 / Essential

☐ TIME OF REVELATION, A (2CD Set)
ESFCD 298 / May '96 / Essential

☐ URIAH HEEP LIVE 1973
Sunrise / Sweet Lorraine / Traveller in time / Easy livin' / July morning / Tears in my eyes / Gypsy / Circle of hands / Look at yourself / Magician's birthday / Love machine / Rock 'n' roll medley
ESMCD 320 / Jun '96 / Essential

☐ VERY 'EAVY, VERY 'UMBLE
Gypsy / Walking in your shadow / Come away Melinda / Lucy blues / Dreammare / Real turned on / I'll keep on trying / Wake up (set your sights) / Gypsy / Come away Melinda / Born in a trunk
ESMCD 316 / Jan '96 / Essential

☐ WONDERWORLD
Wonderworld / Suicidal man / Shadows and the wind / So tired / Easy road / Something or nothing / I won't mind / We got we / Dreams
ESMCD 380 / May '96 / Essential

Uriel

☐ UNDER COMPULSION
Jazz funk conspiracy / Roof top sniper / Pimp strikes back / Under compulsion / Lazy days / Precinct 25 / On the run / Flight to Sao Paulo / Planet Samba / Jeune amour
BMCD 001 / Jun '97 / Beau Monde

Urinals

☐ NEGATIVE CAPABILITY
AMREP 0452 / 24 Nov '97 / Amphetamine Reptile

Urlich, Margaret

☐ CHAMELEON DREAMS
TIMBCD 604 / Aug '95 / Timbuktu

Urtreger, Rene

☐ MOVE
BB 647 / Nov '97 / Black & Blue

Urusei Yatsura

☐ ALL HAIL
SUPERCD 005 / 16 Mar '98 / Tiny Superhero

☐ SLAIN
3984222212 / 2 Mar '98 / Che

☐ WE ARE URUSEI YATSURA
CHE 54CD / 22 Sep '97 / Che

US 3

☐ HAND ON THE TORCH
Cantaloop (Flip fantasia) / I got it goin' on / Different rhythms, different people / It's like that / Just another brother / Cruisin' / I go to work / Tukka yoot's riddim / Knowledge of self / Lazy day / Eleven long years / Make tracks / Dark side
CDEST 2230 / Sep '97 / Capitol

US Bombs

☐ NEVER MIND THE OPENED MINDS
ALIVECD 033 / Sep '97 / Bomp

☐ PUT STRENGTH IN FINAL...
DIS 1 / Jun '97 / Disaster

☐ WAR BIRTH
That's life / Orange crush / Jaks / War storyville / 12 25 / Outta touch / US of hate / War birth / Hand me downs / Rocks in Memphis / Beetle boot / Her and me / Don't need you / No company town
804042 / 20 Oct '97 / Epitaph

US Chaos

☐ COMPLETE CHAOS ANTHOLOGY
GMM 140A / 20 Apr '98 / GMM

US Maple

☐ LONG HAIR IN 3 STAGES
GR 33CD / Nov '95 / Skingraft

☐ SANG PHAT EDITOR
GR 44CD / Jun '97 / Skingraft

US Saucer

☐ HELL, YES
ACM 606 / Jun '97 / Amarillo

☐ UNITED STATES SAUCER
Famous dogs / Fade / Devotional Sam / Ramblin' man / Size it up / Sweet chariot / God OD / Cindy / Tres mellow / Les Mardis Gras / Run shroud run / Born free / I'll always love you
RTS 22 / Oct '96 / Return To Sender

USA

☐ LITTLE BIRDS
DC 115CD / 23 Mar '98 / Drag City

USA All Stars

☐ IN BERLIN FEBRUARY 1955
EBCD 21132 / Feb '94 / Flyright

Used Carlotta

☐ WASTED WORDS
HYMN 5 / Aug '97 / Fundamental

Usher

☐ MY WAY
You make me wanna / Just like me / Nice and slow / One day / You make me wanna
73008260432 / 2 Feb '98 / Arista

☐ USHER
I'll make it right / Can you get wit it / Think of you / Crazy / Slow love / Many ways / I'll show you love / Love was here / Whispers / You took my heart / Smile again / Final goobye / Interlude / Interlude 2 (Can't stop)
73008260082 / Oct '94 / Arista

Ushna

☐ TWICE BREWED
Puffing Billy/The Rocket / Felton Ionnen / Joe's garden/Joe the quilter / William Jobling / Medley / Buy broom besoms / Water of Tyne / Blaydon flats / Doli a/Polka / Bonny at morn / Tramp / Elsie Marley / My Northumberland
FECD 132 / May '98 / Fellside

Usmanova, Yulduz

☐ ALMA ALMA
39840572 / 21 Aug '97 / Blue Flame

☐ BINAFSCHA
39840852 / 21 Aug '97 / Blue Flame

☐ JANNONA
39840772 / 21 Aug '97 / Blue Flame

☐ SELECTION ALBUM, THE
39850022 / 21 Aug '97 / Blue Flame

Usurper

☐ THRESHOLD OF THE USURPER
NR 6667CD / May '97 / Necropolis

Ut

☐ IN GUT'S HOUSE
BFFP 17CD / ' / Blast First

Utah Saints

☐ UTAH SAINTS
New Gold Dream / What can you do for me / Soulution / Believe in me / Too much to swallow / What can you do for me / Something good / I want you / States of mind / Trance Atlantic glide / Kinetic synthetic / My mind must be free
8283792 / 17 Aug '98 / FFRR

UTE

☐ FREE TO BE...FREE TO BREATHE
33JAZZ 009CD / Jun '93 / 33 Jazz

Uthanda

☐ GROOVE
Be my friend / Sweet soul salvation / Found out the hard way / Look away / Change in my world / Don't let me be misunderstood / To be loved / You groove / Mercy mercy / Way you are / Red September
CD 0794 / Jan '92 / Broken

Utica Institute Jubilee Singers

☐ COMPLETE RECORDED WORKS 1927-1929
DOCD 5603 / 15 Jun '98 / Document

Uttal, Jai

☐ BEGGARS AND SAINTS
Lake of exploits / Hara shiva shankara / Be with you / Gopala / Rama bolo / Radhe radhe / Menoka / Beggars and saints / Lake of exploits / Conductor / Coda
3202082 / Nov '94 / Triloka

☐ MONKEY
Monkey / Soldiers / Hooded serpent / I won't ask for more / Govinda / Ayodhya / A distant episode / Heaven (parts 1 and 2) / Petition to ram / Watching the signs
3201942 / Sep '92 / Triloka

☐ SHIVA STATION (Uttal, Jai & Pagan Love Orchestra)
5349112 / 24 Feb '98 / Triloka

Uum

☐ SAINIDA SILLA PUBLIC
VC 131CD / 2 Mar '98 / Vinyl Communication

UVX

☐ DOUBLE HELIX
EYECDLP 7 / Aug '94 / Magick Eye

☐ RAYS
MEYCD 11 / Apr '96 / Magick Eye

UX

☐ ULTIMATE EXPERIENCE
Ux part 1 / Life support technology / Chameleon / Outer reaches / Escape / Alien life activity / Pure intellect / Master of the universe / Nebula / Ux part 2
BFLCD 22 / 1 Sep '98 / Butterfly

Uxia

☐ ESTOU VIVINDO NO CEO
Alala das marinas / Laranxa / Volume eu Fermosa / Tua nai e meiga / Green God / Verdes sao os campos / Aquestas noites tan longas / Canto de nadal / Millo verde / Suite de bembibre / Senhora do Almortao
INT 31872 / 27 Oct '97 / Intuition

☐ LA SAL DE LA VIDA (Uxia, Rasha & Maria Salgado)
Trigo verde / N'na dau un beijo / A Lavandeira / Danra / Paso rios / Para la Habana / No le daba el sol / Arrolo / La sabiduria / Fibali / Cantadora / Ay gitano / Tu gitana
INT 32352 / 27 Jul '98 / Intuition

Uys, Tessa

☐ PIANO MUSIC
URCD 107 / Nov '92 / Upbeat

Uz Jsme Doma

☐ IN THE MIDDLE OF WORDS
MAM 29 / Jun '97 / Indies

Uzeb

☐ ENTRE CIEL ET TERRE
Apres les confidences / 4 P M Gate 26 / Good bye pork pie hat / Spacy country / Perrier citron / Home / Blue in green / Luna mars / Son song / Bella's lullaby / Entre ciel et terre
JMS 186842 / Jul '96 / Cream

☐ LIVE IN EUROPE
Time Square / Mile O / 4 p.m., gate 26 / Le baiser sale / 60 Rue Des Lombards / New Funk / Slinky / La ballade bleue / Bull's nostril blues
JMS 186282 / May '95 / JMS

Uzect Plaush

☐ MORE BEAUTIFUL HUMAN LIFE
Violet cell edit / Wind from nowhere / Wetzone rapture / Falling dream / Auto-radia / Boiling horizon / Discrete global / Sky rolled back
AMB 4932CD / Apr '94 / Apollo

Uzeda

☐ DIFFERENT SECTION WIRES
TG 186CD / 14 Apr '98 / Touch & Go

UZI

☐ SLEEP ASYLUM
Criminal child / Pale light / Gabrielle / Ha ha ha / Collections / Underneath
PILLMCD 4 / Feb '94 / Placebo

Uzzell Edwards, Charles

☐ OCTOPUS
PS 0879CD / Nov '95 / Fax

V

V Majestic
☐ V MAJESTIC
EDGY 001 / 24 Nov '97 / Edgy

V-Card
☐ THERE'S YOU
ALLIED 90CD / Oct '97 / Allied

V-Roys
☐ JUST ADD ICE
Guess I know I'm right / No regrets / Pounding heart / Sooner or later / Wind down / Goodnight looser / Cry / What's she found / Lie I believe / Around you / Kick me around / Cold beer hello
TRACD 240 / Aug '96 / Transatlantic

V2
☐ V2 (Anthology)
OVER 55CD / Aug '96 / Overground

V3
☐ PHOTOGRAPH BURNS
American face / Bristol girl / Harry / Horsekick / Photograph burns / Caucasian white / Adam twelve / Torch / End of the bar / Star artist / Split dog / Hating me hating you / Super human
74321312642 / Mar '96 / American

Vache Allred & Metz Family Jazz Band
☐ VACHE ALLRED & METZ FAMILY JAZZ BAND, THE
NHCD 042 / May '98 / Nagel Heyer

Vache, Allan
☐ ALLAN VACHE & HIS FLORIDA JAZZ ALLSTARS (Vache, Allan Florida Jazz Allstars)
NHCD 032 / Mar '97 / Nagel Heyer

☐ ATLANTA JAZZ PARTY
ACD 270 / Apr '93 / Audiophile

☐ INSPIRED BY BECHET AND SPANIER (Vache, Allan Big Four)
NHCD 044 / May '98 / Nagel Heyer

☐ JAZZ IN AMERIKA HAUS VOL.3 (Vache, Allan Quintet)
CD 013 / May '96 / Nagel Heyer

☐ ONE FOR MY BABY (Vache, Allan Quintet)
ACD 255 / '91 / Audiophile

☐ SWING AND OTHER THINGS (Vache, Allan Sextette)
ARCD 19171 / May '97 / Arbors Jazz

Vache, Warren Jr.
☐ AFFAIR TO REMEMBER, AN (Vache, Warren & Brian Lemon)
You'll never know / I only have eyes for you / I'll string along for you / You must have been a beautiful baby / Jeepers creepers / September in the rain / There will never be another you / Nagasaki (take 3) / Nagasaki (take 4) / Summer night / Serenade in blue / You're my everything / Lulu's back in town / You're getting to be a habit with me / I remember you from somewhere / At last
ZECD 8 / Sep '97 / Zephyr

☐ EASY GOING (Vache, Warren Sextet)
Little girl / Easy going bounce / Warm valley / You'd be so nice to come home to / Michelle / It's been so long / Was I to blame for falling in love with you / London by night / Mandy, make up your mind / Moon song (That wasn't meant for me)
CCD 4323 / Jul '87 / Concord Jazz

☐ FIRST TIME OUT
ACD 196 / Jan '94 / Audiophile

☐ LIVE AT THE VINEYARD THEATRE (Vache, Warren Trio)
CHR 70028 / Sep '96 / Challenge

☐ SHINE (Vache, Warren & Tony Coe/Alan Barnes Septet)
Shine / Drop me off in Harlem / Angel face / Stella by starlight / Just squeeze me / There we sweet blues / I want a little girl / Purple gazelle / Everytime we sat goodbye / Don't get around much anymore / Shine
ZECD 24 / 5 May '98 / Zephyr

☐ WARREN PLAYS WARREN (Vache, Warren Quintet)
CD 033 / Aug '97 / Nagel Heyer

☐ WARREN VACHE & DEREK WATKINS/ BRIAN LEMON QUARTET (Vache, Warren Jr. & Derek Watkins/Brian Lemon)
ZECD 9 / May '96 / Zephyr

☐ WARREN VACHE AND THE BEAUX-ARTS STRING QUARTET (Vache, Warren & The Beaux-Arts String Quartet)
With the wind and rain in your hair / You go to my head / Summer night / That old feeling / This is all I ask / He loves and she loves / All through the night / A flower is a lovesome thing / There with you / Beautiful friendship / Too late now / Spike's waltz / Day dream
CCD 4392 / '89 / Concord Jazz

Vache, Warren Sr.
☐ JAZZ IN AMERIKA HAUS VOL.2 (Vache, Warren Quintet)
CD 012 / May '96 / Nagel Heyer

☐ MUSIC OF ISHAM JONES, THE (Vache, Warren Sr. Syncopatin' Seven)
JCD 296 / May '98 / Jazzology

☐ WARREN VACHE & SYNCOPATIN' 7
CCD 57 / Apr '94 / Circle

Vada
☐ VADA
MASS 64CD / Jul '95 / Mass Productions

Vada, Anne
☐ SOLRENNING (Vada, Anne & Aki Fukakusa)
FX 185CD / Dec '97 / Kirkelig Kultuverksted

Vader
☐ BACK TO THE BLIND
IRC 104CD / 2 Mar '98 / Impact

☐ BLACK TO THE BLIND
SPV 08453042 / Dec '97 / SPV

☐ DARKEST AGE, THE (Live 1993)
MMPCD 055 / 8 Jun '98 / Metal Minds
SPV 08453132 / May '98 / SPV

☐ FUTURE OF THE PAST
Merciless death / Dethroned emperor / Death metal / Outbreak of evil / Storm of stress / Flag of hate / Deadness / IFY / We are the league / Black Sabbath / Silent scream
SPV 08453862 / Mar '97 / SPV

☐ KINGDOM
MMPCD 057 / 8 Jun '98 / Metal Minds

☐ REBORN IN CHAOS
MMPCD 054 / 8 Jun '98 / Metal Minds

☐ ULTIMATE INCANTATION
Creation (intro) / Dark age / Viscous circle / Crucified ones / Final massacre / Testimony / Chaos / One step to salvation / Demon's wind / Decapitated saints / Breath of centuries
MOSH 059CD / 1 Sep '97 / Earache

Vai, Steve
☐ ALIEN LOVE SECRETS
Mad horsie / Juice / Die to live / Boy from Seattle / Ya yo gakk / Kill the guy with the ball / Good eaters / Tender surrender
4785862 / Apr '95 / Relativity

☐ FIRE GARDEN
There's a fire in the house / Crying machine / Dyin' day / Whookam / Blowfish / Mysterious murder of Christian Tiera's lover / Hand on heart / Bangkok / Fire garden suite / Deepness / Little Alligator / All about Eve / Aching hunger / Brother / Damn you / When I was a little boy / Genocide / Warm regards
4850622 / Sep '96 / Relativity

☐ FLEX-ABLE
Little green men / Viv woman / Lovers are carzy / Salamanders in the sun / Boy/girl song / Attitude song / Call it sleep / Junkie / Bill's private parts / Next stop Earth / There's something dead in here / So happy / Bledsoe Blvd / Burnin' down the mountain / Chronic insomnia
4878712 / Jun '97 / Epic

☐ PASSION AND WARFARE
Liberty / Erotic nightmares / Animal / Answers / Riddle / Ballerina 12/24 / For the love of God / Audience is listening / I would love to / Blue powder / Greasy kids stuff / Alien water kiss / Sisters / Love secrets
4671092 / Oct '93 / Relativity

Vain
☐ FADE
REVXD 216 / Aug '97 / Revolver

☐ HELLSAU
INV 116CD / 26 Jan '98 / Invisible

☐ MOVE ON IT
Breakdown / Whisper / Long time ago / Ivy's dream / Hit and run / Family / Planets turning / Get up / Crumpled glory / Resurrection / Ticket outta here
HMRXD 194 / Sep '94 / Heavy Metal

Vainio/Vaisanen
☐ ENDLESS (Vainio/Vaisanen & Alan Vega)
Medal / Incredible criminals world thugs / Motor maniac / No home kings / Outrage for the front page / Endless / Desparate fa tha miracle / Red lights down / Fun in the wonderland / Baby lips / Sick sick USA / Disgrace
BFFP 147CD / 6 Jul '98 / Blast First

Vajra
☐ SICHISIKI
PSFD 88 / Sep '97 / PSF

Val, Joe
☐ DIAMOND JOE
ROUCD 11537 / Nov '95 / Rounder

☐ LIVE IN HOLLAND (Val, Joe & New England Bluegrass Boys)
All the good times are past and gone / Lonesome river / Blue moon of Kentucky / Molly and tenbrooks / Satan's jewelled crown / Prisoner's song / Teardrops in my eyes / Ocean of diamonds / Swing low, sweet chariot / Corey is gone / Rose of old Kentucky / Sunny side of the mountain / No Mother or Dad / Don't give your heart to a rambler / Going back to old Kentucky
SCR 29 / Feb '97 / Strictly Country

☐ ONE MORNING IN MAY (Val, Joe & New England Bluegrass Boys)
ROUCD 0003 / Jun '96 / Rounder

Valaida
☐ VALAIDA VOL.1 1935-1937
HQCD 12 / '92 / Harlequin

☐ VALAIDA VOL.2 1935-1942
HQCD 18 / Feb '94 / Harlequin

Valance, Ricky
☐ TELL LAURA I LOVE HER
Tell Laura I love her / Once upon a time / Movin' away / Lipstick on your lips / Jimmy's girl / Only the young / Say hello (to a new love) / Why can't we / Fisher boy / Bobby / I want to fall in love / I never had a chance / It's not true / Try to forget her / At times like these / Don't play no.9 / Til the final curtain falls / Six boys / Face in the crowd / My Summer love: Merryweather, Jason / Abigail: Merryweather, Jason
GEMCD 006 / Jan '97 / Diamond

Valavelsky, Alexandra
☐ TEN PAIRS OF KISSES (Valavelsky, Alexandra & The Bashava Band)
Polka / Rumania rumania / Rozhinkes mit mandlen / Verbunkos / Csardas / Sheyn vi di l'vone / Avreml der marvikher / Zog niy keyn mol / Mi am cusut / Ionel Ionelule / Hungarian gypsy suite / Vilja / In fata ocjinzii / Tum balalaika / Mit dir iz mir gut / Lakodalmus / Hore ich zigeunergeigen
CCP 221 / Mar '98 / Criss Cross

Valdes, Bebo
☐ BEDO RIDES AGAIN
MES 158342 / Jul '95 / Messidor

☐ DESCARGA CALIENTE (Valdes, Bebo Orchestra)
CCD 512 / Jul '96 / Caney

☐ SABOR DE CUBA (Valdes, Bebo Orchestra)
CCD 509 / Jul '96 / Caney

Valdes, Carlos
☐ MASTERPIECE
MES 158272 / Dec '93 / Messidor

Valdes, Chucho
☐ GRANDES MOMENTOS
74321327242 / May '96 / Milan

☐ LIVE
RMD 82251 / 24 Mar '98 / RMM

☐ LUCUMI
MES 158762 / Apr '93 / Messidor

☐ PIANISSIMO
3006040 / 1 Jun '98 / IMP

Valdes, Merceditas
☐ TUMI CUBA CLASSICS VOL.2 (Afro Cuban)
TUMICD 050 / Aug '95 / Tumi

Valdes, Miguelito
☐ HAVANA 1938-1940
HQCD 81 / Apr '97 / Harlequin

Valdespi, Armando
☐ EN NUEVA YORK 1935 VOL.1
TCD 073 / Jul '96 / Tumbao Cuban Classics

☐ EN NUEVA YORK 1935 VOL.2 (Valdespi, Armando Orchestra)
TCD 077 / Jan '97 / Tumbao Cuban Classics

Vale Of Tears
☐ PRECESSION BY SUNSET
FZ 001CD / 23 Feb '98 / Nightbreed

Valenca, Alceu
☐ SINO DE OURO
ML 51015 / 14 Apr '98 / Musica Latina

Valens, Ritchie
☐ BEST OF RITCHIE VALENS
Come on let's go / La bamba / Donna / Bluebirds over the mountain / Fast freight / Cry cry cry / That's my little Suzie / Stay beside me / Big baby blues / Little girl / Hurry up / Bony Moronie / We belong together / Malaguena / Framed / In a turkish town / Dooby dooby wah / Ooh my head
CDCHM 387 / Mar '92 / Ace

☐ COME ON LET'S GO (3CD Set)
DLF 2359 / 27 Apr '98 / Del-Fi

☐ LOST TAPES, THE
We belong together / Blues with drum / Ritchie's blues / Come on let's go / In a turkish town / Dooby dooby wah / Bluebirds over the mountain / That's my little Suzie / Let's rock 'n' roll / Donna / Blues instrumental / Cry cry cry / Malaguena / Blues - slow / Stay beside me / Ritchie's song / Guitar instrumental / Rock lil darlin' / La bamba / Ooh my head
CDCHD 317 / May '92 / Ace

☐ RICHIE VALENS STORY, THE
DFCD 71011 / Jan '97 / Del-Fi

☐ RITCHIE VALENS STORY, THE
Bony Moronie / Come on let's go / That's my little Suzie / Rock little Darlin' / Bluebirds over the mountain / La bamba / Let's rock 'n' roll / Donna / Summertime blues / In a Turkish town / Paddiwack song / Big baby blues / Malaguena / Stay beside me
CDCHD 499 / Jan '94 / Ace

☐ RITCHIE VALENS/RITCHIE
That's my little Suzie / In a Turkish town / Come on let's go / Donna / Bony Moronie / Ooh my head / La Bamba / Bluebirds over the mountain / Hi-tone / Framed / We belong together / Dooby dooby wah / Stay beside me / Cry cry cry / Big baby blues / Paddiwack song / My darling is gone / Hurry up / Little girl / Now you're gone / Fast freight / Ritchie's blues / Rockin' all night
CDCHD 953 / Oct '90 / Ace

Valente, Caterina
☐ INTERNATIONAL, THE
Guardando Il cielo / Zeeman / Koini tsukarete / Adam et eve / El bardo / Hava nagila / Nessuno mai / Tintarella di luna / Es mi amor / Tra-la-la-la-la / Das weisse hchzeitskleid / Diz me em setemro / Mijn souvenir / Leccion de twist / Weil die sehnsucht so gross war / Don Quixote / Dindi / Hana / Morgen wird's schoner sein / Me importas tu / Caro mio / Dammi retta / Oyedo nihonbashi / Una lagrima del yuo dolore / Parlez-moi d'amour / Napule ca se sceta / Ein stern ging verloren / Scandinavian folk song
BCD 15604 / Oct '91 / Bear Family

☐ ONE AND ONLY, THE
Ola, ola, ola / Un p 'tit beguine / Tornera / Das kommt vom kussen / Bruxeria / Ados Panama / Halbmne no Utah / Amo solo te / When in Rome / Und dann kam der Mondenschein / O Erotas pou makousse / Broadway conga / La otra cara / Fandwack song / Twist a Napoli / Zuviel tequila / Dia de fiesta / I Melenia / virtuposlu / Amor prohibido / Kom lat ons dansen / Im Kabarett der illusionen / Una sera di Tokyo / Cua cua cua / Israeli lullaby
BCD 15601 / Oct '90 / Bear Family

Valente, Dino
☐ DINO VALENTE
379302 / Mar '98 / Koch

Valentine 6
☐ VALENTINE 6
EFA 043912 / Jul '97 / Crippled Dick Hot Wax

873

Valentine Saloon

☐ SUPER DUPER
PIPECD 001 / Mar '93 / Pipeline

Valentine, 'Kid' Thomas

☐ DANCEHALL YEARS
AMCD 48 / Jan '94 / American Music

☐ KID THOMAS
AMCD 10 / Oct '93 / American Music

☐ KID THOMAS & HIS DIXIELAND BAND 1960
Milenburg joys / Just a closer walk with thee / Kid Thomas boogie / Just a little while to stay here / Just a little while to stay here / Milk cow blues / Smile darn ya smile / Smile darn ya smile / Mack the knife / St. Louis blues / Sister Kate / I believe I can make it by myself / Sheik of Araby / China boy / St. Louis blues boogie / Bourbon street parade / Chiri-biri-bin / When the saints go marching in
504CD 33 / Mar '98 / 504

☐ KID THOMAS AT THE MOOSE HALL
BCD 305 / Oct '93 / GHB

☐ KID THOMAS IN CALIFORNIA
BCD 296 / Jan '94 / GHB

☐ KID THOMAS' DIXIELAND BAND 1957
Darktown strutter's ball / Just take a closer walk with thee / Li'l Liza Jane / Milenberg joys / Kid thomas boogie / That's a plenty / That's a plenty / It's all over now / Sister Pnanama / AlexaKate / Nder's ragtime band / Alexander's ragtime band / St. Louis blues
504CD 37 / Mar '98 / 504

☐ KID THOMAS/EMANUEL PAUL/ BARRY MARTYN BAND
BCD 257 / Mar '95 / GHB

☐ NEW ORLEANS TRADITIONAL JAZZ LEGENDS
MG 9004 / Feb '95 / Mardi Gras

☐ SONNETS FROM ALGIERS
AMCD 53 / Jul '96 / American Music

☐ SPIRIT OF NEW ORLEANS, THE (Valentine, 'Kid' Thomas & Percy Humphrey)
MMCD 1059 / Dec '97 / Music Mecca

☐ TRUMPET KING
MG 9003 / Feb '95 / Mardi Gras

Valentine, Cal

☐ TEXAS ROCKER, THE
BMCD 9027 / Dec '94 / Black Magic

Valentine, Dickie

☐ BEST OF DICKIE VALENTINE, THE
Fool that I am / Teenager in love / Climb ev'ry mountain / Hold me in your arms / How unlucky can you be / I'll never fall in love again / My favourite song / Once, only once / One more sunrise / Roundabout / Shalom / Sometimes I'm happy / Standing on the corner / Venus / Where (in the old home town) / You touch my hand
SOW 704 / May '94 / Sound Waves

☐ MR. SANDMAN
Wanted / Stay awhile / Second time around / With these hands / For all we know / Lost dreams and lonely hearts / Wait for me / No such luck / My word / In times like these / Once in each life / Build yourself a dream / Mona Lisa / It's better to have loved / Nothing but the best / Free me / Old devil moon / Come another day another love / Dreams can tell a lie / Cry my soul / Something good / Song of the trees / Kiss to build a dream on / Mr. Sandman
C5MCD 625 / Jul '95 / See For Miles

☐ MY FAVOURITE SONGS
Fool that I am / Teenager in love / Climb ev'ry mountain / Hold me in your arms / How unlucky can you be / I'll never love again / My favourite song / Once, only once / One more sunrise (morgen) / Roundabout / Shalom / Sometimes I'm happy / Standing on the corner / Venus / Where (in the old home town) / You touch my hand
SSLCD 202 / Jun '95 / Savanna

☐ THIS IS DICKIE VALENTINE (2CD Set)
Venus / La Rosita / Song of the trees / You touch my hand / Sometimes I'm happy / Just in time / Teenager in love / King of dixieland / Hold me in your arms / Get well soon / Homecoming waltz / Dreams can tell a lie / Long before I knew you / Blossom fell / Broken wings / Climb every mountain / Roundabout / My favourite song / Finger of suspicion / Mr. Sandman / Fool that I am / All the time and ev'rywhere / Ronettes / One more sunrise / No such luck / Where (in the old hometown) / Old pi-anna rag / Clown who cried / I'll never love again / You belong to me / Chapel of the roses / Standing on the corner / Endless / How unlucky can you be / Once, only once / Shalom
CDDL 1224 / Apr '92 / Music For Pleasure

☐ VERY BEST OF DICKIE VALENTINE, THE
Finger of suspicion / Mr. Sandman / Blossom fell / Cleo and me-o / Many loves and penny loves / All the time and ev'rywhere / There'll be some changes made / Endless / Broken wings / Give me a carriage with eight white horses / Old pi-anna rag / Three sides to every story / I wonder / Runaround / Many times / Pine tree pine over me / Who's afraid (not I, not I) / Guessing / In a golden coach (there's a heart of gold) / My impossible castle
5520222 / Jan '97 / Spectrum

Valentino, Vinny

☐ VINNY VALENTINO & HERE NO EVIL
Distance between two lines / Venice / Don't blame me / Blues for a while / Secret hiding place / Full moon over the Mediterranean / Veins / Song is you / As you said / When the feeling moves you / Lu / Old folks
PAR 2016 / Aug '93 / PAR

Valera Miranda Family

☐ VALERA MIRANDA FAMILY, THE
Llora mi nena / Bambay / Tuna, mayari, guantanamo / Juramento / Que lindo bayamo / Basta ya / Rita la caimana / Retorna / Vuela como el aguila / Dulce embeleso / Murio Valera en San Luis / El misterio de tus ojos / El calvario de un poeta / El penqquito de Coleto
C 560107 / Jun '97 / Ocora

☐ VALERA MIRANDA FAMILY, THE
C 570600 / Mar '98 / Ocora

Valette, Thierry

☐ SCATLANDES
591132 / 1 Jun '98 / Musidisc

Valhal

☐ MOONSTONE
HNF 009CD / Mar '95 / Head Not Found

Vali, Justin

☐ TRUTH, THE (Vali, Justin Trio)
Malagasy intro / Ny marina (The truth) / Sova (Malagasy rap) / Sariaka (Joy) / Rambala / Tsondrao (Benediction) / Tsingy (Sacred mountain) / Bilo (Malagasy voodoo) / Relahy / Ray sy Reny (Mum and Dad) / Manga ny Lanitr'i / Kintana (The open roof) / Vato malaza / Sova (Repeat) / Bongo lava (The broad mountain range) / Malagasy folk dance medley / Surprise tunnel track
CDRW 51 / Jan '95 / Realworld

Valitsky, Ken

☐ SPECIES COMPATIBILITY
KFWCD 135 / Nov '94 / Knitting Factory

Valland, Asne

☐ DEN LJOSE DAGEN
FXCD 139 / Jan '95 / Musikk Distribujson

☐ JULEKVAD
FX 177CD / Aug '97 / Kirkelig Kultuverksted

Valle, Marcus

☐ ESSENTIAL MARCUS VALLE VOL.1, THE
MRBCD 003 / May '95 / Mr. Bongo

☐ ESSENTIAL MARCUS VALLE VOL.2, THE
Os grilos / Tiao branco forte / Previsao do tempo / Menitira carioca / Tanta andei / Seu encanto / Gente / Com mais de 30 / Gara / Dues Brasileiro / Amor de nada / A morte de um deus de sal / Wanda vidal / Revolucao organica / Batacuda surgiu / Azimuth
MRBCD 007 / Oct '96 / Mr. Bongo

☐ NOVO BOSSA NOVA
Novo visual / Abandonou / Cidade aberto / Bahia blue / Frieo aerodynamico / Mushi mushi / Nova bossa nova / Nordeste / Bar ingles / Vontade de rever voce
FARO 022CD / 11 May '98 / Far Out

Vallee, Rudy

☐ HEIGH-HO EVERYBODY, THIS IS RUDY VALLEE
Heigh ho everybody, heigh ho / Betty co-ed / If I had a girl like you / Let's do it / I still remember / Salaaming the rajah / My heart belongs to the girl who belongs to somebody else / One in the world / I'll be reminded of you / You'll do it someday, so why not now / Kitty from Kansas City / That's when I learned to love you / Outside / Dream sweetheart / Love made a gypsy out of me / Perhaps / Little kiss each morning a little kiss each night / Verdict is life with you / Lover come back to me / Stein song
PASTCD 7077 / Sep '95 / Flapper

☐ VOICE THAT HAD THEM FAINTING 1928-1937, THE
TT 405 / May '98 / Take Two

Vallenato

☐ PRE - LOG
TOPYCD 074 / May '94 / Temple

Valletti, Elisabeth

☐ INNOCENTI
Credis / Dance of sands / Innocenti / Dancing on the Nile / Il Tuo viso / Lili / Quiet days in vitro / Voices of sands / Troisieme
CDCOL 10001 / 29 Sep '97 / Colombe D'Or

Vallhall

☐ HEADING FOR MARS
HNF 018CD / Jun '97 / Voices Of Wonder

Valli, Frankie

☐ 20 GREATEST HITS (Valli, Frankie & Four Seasons)
Sherry / Big girls don't cry / Walk like a man / Dawn / Rag doll / Stay / Let's hang on / Working my way back to you / Opus 17 (Don't you worry about me) / I've got you under my skin / C'mon Marianne / You're ready now / Who loves you / December '63 (oh what a night) / Silver star / My eyes adored you / Swearin' to God / Fallen angel / Grease / Can't take my eyes off you
PLATCD 4902 / Dec '88 / Platinum

☐ AIN'T THAT A SHAME/LIVE ON STAGE (Four Seasons)
Candy girl / Happy, happy birthday baby / Honey love / Soon (I'll be home again) / Stay / Dumb drum / Marlena / Long lonely nights / New Mexican rose / That's the only way / Melancholy / Ain't that a shame / Silver wings / Starmaker / Blues in the night / Just in time / Little boy (In grown up clothes) / I can dream, can't I / How do you make a hit song / By myself / Jada / We three / Day in, day out / My mother's eyes / Mack the knife / Come si bella / Brotherhood of man
CDCHD 596 / Jun '95 / Ace

☐ BIG HITS/NEW GOLD HITS (Four Seasons)
What the world needs now is love / Anyone who had a heart / There's always something there to remind me / Make it easy on yourself / Walk on by / What's new pussycat / Queen Jane approximately / Mr. Tambourine man / Like a rolling stone / Don't think twice it's alright / All I really want to do / Blowin' in the wind / C'mon Marianne / Let's ride again / Beggin' / Around and around / Goodbye girl / I'm gonna change / Tell it to the rain / Dody (I dig you) / Puppet song / Lonesome road / Opus 17 (Don't you worry 'bout me) / I've got you under my skin
CDCHD 620 / Feb '96 / Ace

☐ CHRISTMAS ALBUM/BORN TO WANDER (Four Seasons)
We wish you a merry Christmas / Angels from the realms of glory / Hark the herald angels sing / It came upon a midnight clear / What child is this / Carol of the bells / Deck the walls / Excelsis deo / O come all ye faithful (adeste fidelis) / Little drummer boy / First Noel / O holy night / Silent night / Deck the halls with boughs of holly / God rest ye merry gentlemen / Away in a manger / Joy to the world / Santa Claus is coming to town / Christmas tears / I saw Mommy kissing Santa Claus / Christmas song / Jingle bells / White Christmas / Born to wander / Don't cry, Elena / Where have all the flowers gone / Cry myslef to sleep / Ballad for our time / Silence is golden / New town / Golden ribbon / Little pony get along / No surfin' today / Searching wind / Millie
CDCHD 615 / Oct '95 / Ace

☐ DAWN (GO AWAY)/RAG DOLL (Four Seasons)
Big man's world / You send me / Mountain high / Life is but a dream / Church bells may ring / Dawn / Only yesterday / Sixteen candles / Breaking up is hard to do / Earth angel / Don't let go / Do you want to dance / Save it for me / Touch of you / Danger / Marcie / No one cares / Rag doll / Angel cried / Funny face / Huggin' my pillow / Setting sun / Ronnie / On broadway tonight
CDCHD 554 / Sep '94 / Ace

☐ EDIZIONE D'ORO (Four Seasons)
Sherry / Big girls don't cry / Connie-o / Walk like a man / Candy girl / Marlena / Peanuts / Ain't that a shame / Dawn (go away) / Stay / Big man in town / Alone (why must I be alone) / Save it for me / Girl come running / Ronnie / Rag doll / Bye bye baby (baby goodbye) / Toy soldier / Let's hang on / Don't think twice it's alright / Working my way back to you / Opus 17 / I've got you under my skin / Beggin' / Silence is golden / C'mon Marianne
CDCHD 642 / 29 Sep '97 / Ace

☐ FOUR SEASONS ENTERTAIN YOU/ WORKING MY WAY BACK TO YOU (Four Seasons)
Show girl / Where is love / One clown cried / My prayer / Little Darlin' / Bye bye baby (baby goodbye) / Betrayed / Somewhere / Living just for you / Little angel / Big man in town / Sunday kind of love / Toy soldier / Girl come running / Let's hang on / Working my way back to you / Pity / I woke up / Beggar's parade / Can't get enough of you baby / Sundown / Too many memories / Comin' up in the world / Everybody knows my name
CDCHD 582 / Feb '95 / Ace

☐ GENUINE IMITATION LIFE GAZETTE (Valli, Frankie & Four Seasons)
American crucifixion resurrection / Mrs. Stately's garden / Look up look over / Something's on her mind / Saturday's father / Wall Street village day / Genuine imitation life / Idaho / Wonder what you'll be / Soul of a woman / Watch the flowers grow / Raven / Will you love me tomorrow / Electric stories
CDCHD 628 / Oct '96 / Ace

☐ GOLD
GOLD 212 / Apr '94 / Disky

☐ HALF AND HALF (Valli, Frankie & Four Seasons)
Emily / And that reminds me (my heart reminds me) / Singles game / Circles in the sand / Sorry / Girl I'll never know (angels never fly this low) / Face without a name / She gives me light / To make my father proud / Patch of blue / Morning after loving you / Any day now / Oh how happy / Dream of Kings / You've got your troubles / Lay me down (wake me up) / Where are my dreams
CDCHD 635 / Jun '96 / Ace

☐ HARMONY (Four Seasons)
Mystic Mr. Sam / Silver star / December '63 (oh what a night) / Storybook lovers / Slip away / Harmony perfect harmony / Emily's (saille de danse) / Who loves you
100572 / May '97 / A-Play Collection

☐ ORIGINAL HITS 1962-1972, THE (Four Seasons)
Sherry / Big girls don't cry / Walk a man / Ain't that a shame / Candy girl / Dawn (go away) / Stay / Ronnie / Alone / Rag doll / Save it for me / Big man in town / Bye bye baby (baby goodbye) / Let's hang on / Working my way back to you / Don't think twice / Opus 17 (don't you worry 'bout me) / I've got you under my skin / Tell it to the rain / Beggin' / C'mon marianne / Will you still love me tomorrow / Marlena / Girl come running / Watch the flowers grow / Silver star / Who loves you / December 1963 (oh what a night)
DCD 5367 / Apr '94 / Disky

☐ SHERRY & 15 OTHERS (Four Seasons)
DCD 5409 / Oct '94 / Disky

☐ SHERRY/BIG GIRLS DON'T CRY (Four Seasons)
Sherry / I've cried before / Yes sir that's my baby / Peanuts / La dee dah / Teardrops / You're the apple of my eye / Never on a Sunday / I can't give you anything but love / Girl in my dreams / Oh Carol / Lost lullabye / Walk like a man / Silhouettes / Why do fools fall in love / Tonite, tonite / Lucky ladybug / Alone / One song / Sincerely / Since I don't have you / My sugar / Hi Lili hi lo / Big girls don't cry
CDCHD 507 / Apr '94 / Ace

☐ SOLO/TIMELESS
My funny valentine / Cry for me / (You're gonna) Hurt yourself / Ivy / Secret love / Can't take my eyes off you / My Mother's eyes / This is goodbye / Sun ain't gonna shine anymore / Trouble with me / Proud one / You're ready now / By the time I get to Phoenix / Expression of love / For all we know / Sunny / Watch where you walk / To give (the reason I live) / Eleanor Rigby / September rain (here come's the rain) / Make the music play / Stop and say hello / Donnybrook / I make a fool of myself
CDCHD 538 / Jun '94 / Ace

☐ VERY BEST OF FRANKIE VALLI & THE FOUR SEASONS, THE (Valli, Frankie & Four Seasons)
Sherry / Big girls don't cry / Walk like a man / Ain't that a shame / Rag doll / Dawn / Silence is golden / Let's hang on / Working my way back to you / Who loves you / Opus 17 (Don't you worry about me) / I've got you under my skin / Can't take my eyes off you / Night / My eyes adored you / You're ready now / Swearin' to God / December '63 (oh what a night) / Silver star / Fallen angel / We can work it out / Sun ain't gonna shine anymore / Down the hall / Grease
5131192 / Feb '92 / PolyGram TV

☐ VERY BEST OF THE FOUR SEASONS, THE (Four Seasons)
MCCD 211 / Oct '95 / Music Club

Valramm

☐ LURE
AW 14CD / Aug '97 / Tongang

Value

☐ PULLING LEGS OFF FLIES
Drain my will / Hunchback / Naive / Grow your hair / Fly forever / Waiting for the rain / Domination / Shrink / Play / Ride / Mosquito buzz
BBA 10CD / Feb '94 / Big Cat

Vamp

☐ HORISONTER
MS 1121CD / Dec '94 / Musikk Distribujson

Vamvakaris, Markos

☐ BOUZOUKI PIONEER 1932-1940
Karadouzeni / Arap / Efoumaram ena vradhi / O hasapis / Prepi na xeris michani / Alanairis / I plimira / Ossi echoune polla lefta / Mavra matia mavra fridhia / Markos polytechnicis / Oli i rembettes tou douia / Echi omorfes afrates / Sto phaliro pou plenese / Mia galanomata stin athina / Nostimo trello mikro mou / Ta dhio sou heria pirane / Foras foustani vissini / An figoume ston polemo / Maroko / O koumbaros o psaras / Yia sas fandarakia mas
ROUCD 1139 / Feb '98 / Rounder

Van Der Graaf Generator

☐ 1ST GENERATION
Darkness / Killer / Man erg / Theme one / Pioneers over C / Pictures/Lighthouse / Eyewitness / SHM / Presence of the night / Kosmos tours / (Custards) last stand / Clot thickens / Land's end / We go now / Refugees
COMCD 2 / Feb '87 / Virgin

☐ AEROSOL GREY MACHINE, THE
Afterwards / Orthenthian Street / Running back / Into a game / Ferret and featherbird / Aerosol grey machine / Black smoke yen / Aquarian / Squid I / Octopus
REP 4647 / Dec '97 / Repertoire
FIE 9116 / May '97 / Fie

☐ GODBLUFF
Undercover man / Scorched earth / Arrow / Sleepwalkers
CASCD 1109 / Apr '88 / Charisma

☐ H TO HE, WHO AM THE ONLY ONE
Killer / With no door / Emperor in his war room / Lost / Pioneers over C
CASCD 1027 / Nov '88 / Charisma

☐ I PROPHESY DISASTER
Afterwards / Necromancer / Refugees / Boat of millions of years / Lemmings (Including cog) / Arrow / La rossa / Ship of fools / Medley
CDVM 9026 / Aug '93 / Virgin

☐ LEAST WE CAN DO IS WAVE TO EACH OTHER, THE
Darkness / Refugees / White hammer / Whatever would Robert have said / Out of my book / After the flood
CASCD 1007 / '87 / Charisma

☐ MAIDA VALE
SFRSCD 064 / 18 May '98 / Strange Fruit

☐ MASTERS, THE
Saigon roulette / Gentlemen prefer blues / Tropic of conversation / Tarzan / Rift valley / Liquidator / Coil night / Ronceceaux / It all went up / Faint and forsaken
EABCD 085 / 30 Mar '98 / Eagle

☐ NOW AND THEN
Liquidator / Gentlemen prefer blondes / Main slide / Spooks / Saigon roulette / Tropic of conversation / Tarzan the epilogue
CDTB 042 / 31 Jul '98 / Thunderbolt

☐ PAWN HEARTS
Lemmings (including Cog) / Man erg / Pictures/ Lighthouse / Eyewitness / SHM / Kosmos tours / Clot thickens / Land's end / We go now / Presence of the night / (Custards) last stand
CASCD 1051 / Apr '88 / Charisma

☐ QUIET ZONE PLEASURE DOME
Lizard play / Habit of the broken heart / Siren song / Last frame / Wave / Cat's eye, yellow fever (running) / Sphinx in the face / Chemical world / Sphinx returns
CASCD 1131 / '87 / Charisma

☐ STILL LIFE
Pilgrims / Still life / La Rossa / My room (waiting for wonderland) / Childlike faith in childhood's end
CASCD 1116 / Apr '87 / Charisma

☐ TIME VAULTS
Liquidator / Rift valley / Tarzan / Coil night / Time vaults / Drift / Roncevaux / It all went red / Faint and forsaken / (In the) Black room
CDTB 106 / Dec '92 / Thunderbolt
14847 / Feb '97 / Spalax

☐ VITAL
Ship of fools / Still life / Last frame / Mirror images / Medley / Plague of lighthouse keepers / Pioneers over C / Sci finance / Door / Urban / Killer / Urban (part 2) / Nadir's big chance
CVLCD 101 / '89 / Virgin

☐ WORLD RECORD
When she comes / Place to survive / Masks / Meurglys 111 (The songwriters guild) / Wondering
CASCD 1120 / Aug '88 / Charisma

Van Derrick, Johnny

☐ HOT CLUB (2CD Set)
Black eyes / Cecilia / 'Tis autumn / You are my heart's delight / Broken date / Hot lips / Until the real thing comes along / Pink champagne / Maybe you'll be there / Chemin de fer / Careless / Candy by the fireside / Night and day / Moon got in my eyes / In a little Spanish town / Nancy / Rhythm at the Ritz / Midnight on Broadway / All that jazz / Just for fun / Don't stop now / Table for two / Le weekend / Rendezvous / Still in my dreams / Joie de vivre / C'est bon / L'espionage / Nighttime in Paris / Members night / Jazz tango / Au revoir / Cafe de Paris / C'est la vie / Le Hot Club / Blackbird / How could I forget / Talkin' the blues / Naughty rhythm
PDSCD 545 / 13 Oct '97 / Pulse

Van Dieren, Bernard

☐ BERNARD VAN DIEREN COLLECTION
BML 001 / Feb '96 / British Music

Van Duser, Guy

☐ AMERICAN FINGER STYLE GUITAR
ROUCD 11533 / '88 / Rounder

☐ EVERY LITTLE MOMENT (Classic Jazz For Acoustic Guitar & Clarinet) (Van Duser, Guy & Billy Novick)
Let's dance / Every little moment / Wabash blues / Whose honey are you / Song is ended (but the melody lingers on) / Indian summer / Got a date with an angel / Wolverine blues / When my ship comes in / Linger awhile / I'll see you in my dreams / Moonlight serenade
DARINGCD 3026 / Oct '96 / Daring

☐ GUY & BILLY (Van Duser, Guy & Billy Novick)
CD 3014 / Dec '94 / Daring

Van Dyke, Leroy

☐ ORIGINAL AUCTIONEER, THE
Auctioneer / I fell in love with a pony tail / Leather jacket / I'm movin' on / My good mind (went bad on me) / Heartbreak cannonball / Chicken shack / Poor boy / What this old work needs / Every time I ask my heart / Pocketbook song / Down at the south end of town / Honky tonk song / One heart
BCD 15647 / Nov '93 / Bear Family

☐ WALK ON BY (Hits & Misses)
Walk on by / If a woman answers (Hang up the phone) / Black cloud / Happy to be unhappy / Night people / Big man in a big house / Faded love / Save me the moonlight / My world is caving in / Handful of friends / I got a conscience / Broken promise / Dim dark corner / I sat back and let it happen / Geh nicht vorbei / Just before dawn / Now I lay me down / Heartaches by the number / Sea of heartbreak / Love letters in the sand / Sugartime / Don't forbid me / Honeycomb / How long must you keep me a secret / Party doll / Conscience I'm guilty / Day the preacher comes / Fireball mail / If you don't, somebody else will / Put your little hand in mine
BCD 15779 / Jan '94 / Bear Family

Van Dyke, Paul

☐ 45 REVOLUTIONS PER MINUTE
Introjection / I'm coming / For an angel / Spannung / Emergency / Rushin' / Step right on / World full of DJ's / Magical moment / Love letter / Ejeculoutro
DVNT 025CD / 27 Apr '98 / Deviant

☐ SEVEN WAYS (2CD Set)
Home / Seven ways / I like it / Heaven / Come (and get it) / Forbidden fruit / Beautiful place / People / Greatness of Britain / I can't feel it / Words / Seven ways (beware the veil demo) / Don't imitate, innovate / Come / Sundae 6AM / Forbidden fruit / Don't imitate, innovate / I want you, I need you / Living for the night / Beautiful place
DVNT 014CD
DVNT 014DCD / May '97 / Deviant

Van Eps, George

☐ KEEPIN' TIME (Van Eps, George & Howard Alden)
Blue skies / Satin doll / It had to be you / Body and soul / How high the moon / Honeysuckle rose / I cover the waterfront / Chant / Willow weep for me / Kay's fantasy / More than you know / I got rhythm
CCD 4713 / Jul '96 / Concord Crossover

Van Halen

☐ 1984
1984 / Jump / Panama / Top Jimmy / Drop dead legs / Hot for teacher / I'll wait / Girl gone bad / House of pain
9239852 / Feb '95 / WEA

☐ 5150
Good enough / Why can't this be love / Get up / Dreams / Summer nights / Best of both worlds / Love walks in / 5150 / Inside
9253942 / Feb '95 / WEA

☐ BALANCE
Baluchitherium / Aftershock / Not enough / Feelin' / Take me back (deja vu) / Doin' time / Seventh seal / Amsterdam / Big fat money / Strung out / Don't tell me (what love can do) / Can't stop lovin' you
9362457602 / Jan '95 / WEA

☐ BEST OF VAN HALEN, THE
Runnin' with the devil / Eruption / Dance the night away / Unchained / Panama / Jump / Me wise magic / Can't get this stuff no more / Humans being / Can't stop lovin' you / Right now / Poundcake / When it's love / Dreams / Why can't this be love / And the cradle will rock / Ain't talkin' 'bout love
9362464742 / Oct '96 / WEA

☐ DIVER DOWN
Where have all the good times gone / Hang 'em high / Cathedral / Secrets / Intruder / Pretty woman / Dancing in the street / Little guitar (intro) / Little guitars / Big bad Bill is sweet William now / Bull bug / Happy trails
257003 / Jan '84 / WEA

☐ FAIR WARNING
Mean street / Dirty movies / Sinner's swing / Hear about it later / Unchained / Push comes to shove / So this is love / Sunday afternoon in the park / One foot out of the door
9235402 / Jun '89 / WEA

☐ FOR UNLAWFUL CARNAL KNOWLEDGE
Pound cake / Judgement day / Spanked / Runaround / Pleasure dome / In 'n' out / Man on a mission / Dream is over / Right now / 316 / Top of the world
7599265942 / Jun '91 / WEA

☐ LIVE - RIGHT HERE, RIGHT NOW
Right now / One way to rock / Why can't this be love / Give to live / Finish what ya started / Best of both worlds / 316 / You really got me / Won't get fooled again / Jump / Top of the world / Pound cake / Judgement day / When it's love / Spanked / Ain't talkin' 'bout love / In 'n' out / Dreams / Man on a mission / Ultra bass / Pleasure dome / Panama / Love walks in / Runaround
9362451982 / Feb '93 / WEA

☐ OU812
Mine all mine / When it's love / AFU (naturally wired) / Cabo wabo / Source of infection / Feels so good / Come back and finish what you started / Black and blue / Sucker in a 3 piece
9257322 / Jun '88 / WEA

☐ VAN HALEN II
You're no good / Dance the night away / Somebody get me a doctor / Bottoms up / Outta love again / Light up the sky / DOA / Women in love / Spanish fly / Beautiful girls
256616 / Mar '87 / WEA

☐ VAN HALEN III
Neworld / Without you / One I want / From afar / Dirty water dog / Once / Fire in the hole / Josephine / Year to the day / Primary / Ballot or the bullet / How many say I
9362466622 / 16 Mar '98 / WEA

☐ VAN HALEN VOL.1
You really got me / Jamie's cryin' / On fire / Runnin' with the Devil / I'm the one / Ain't talkin' 'bout love / Little dreamer / Feel your love tonight / Atomic punk / Eruption / Ice cream man
256470 / Feb '95 / WEA

☐ WOMEN AND CHILDREN FIRST
Tora tora / Cradle will rock / Romeo delight / Fools / In a simply rhyme / Could this be magic / Loss of control / Take your whiskey home / Everybody wants some
9234152 / Jun '89 / WEA

Van Helden, Armand

☐ COLLECTION, THE
ZYX 204302 / Feb '97 / ZYX

☐ OLD SCHOOL JUNKIES
HSCD 3005 / Mar '97 / Raging Bull

☐ SAMPLESLAYA: ENTER THE MEAT MARKET
Push 'em up / Hot butter / We came to party / Blakpeoplez / Daaboodaa munks / Crooklyn anthems / Ultrafunkula / Hood movie stars / Word up Doc / Pulling G-Spots / Puerto Rican handclap / Out of frame / This is it / Reservoir dogs / 6 minutes of funk / Bounce / Heh yah heh / Ballistic funk
8289402 / 3 Nov '97 / FFRR

Van Helsingen, Bart

☐ PERCUSSION DUO (Van Helsingen, Bart & Hans Hasebos)
HH 001 / Apr '92 / Bvhaast

Van Hoen, Mark

☐ FLOWERS FROM THE DARKNESS
TO 31 / Feb '97 / Touch

Van Hove, Fred

☐ SUITE FOR B CITY (Van Hove, Fred Nonet)
FMPCD 88 / Jan '98 / Full Moon

Van Lier, Bart

☐ TWILIGHT
369082 / 3 Aug '98 / Koch Jazz

Van Maasakkers, Gerard

☐ ZONDER TITEL
MWCD 1002 / Jun '92 / Music & Words

Van Meter, Sally

☐ ALL IN GOOD TIME
High country / Blues for your own / Tyson's dream / Crazy creek / Anne's waltz / Weary lonesome blues / Bird that I held in my hand / Amor de mi vida / Road to Columbus / Damien Miley/The idlers of Belltown / We're not over yet
SHCD 3792 / Jan '91 / Sugar Hill

Van Peebles, Melvin

☐ X-RATED BY AN ALL WHITE JURY (2CD Set)
Lilly done the zampoughi everytime I pulled her coat tail / Mirror mirror on the wall / Coolest place in town / You can get up before noon without being a square / Dozens / Tenth and Greenwich (women's house of detention) / Come raising your leg on me / Sera sera Jim / Catch that on the corner / Three boxes of longs please / You ain't no astronaut / Come on feet do your thing / Funky girl on Motherless Broadway / Put a curse on you / I got the blood / You gotta be holdin' out five dollars on me / Heh heh (chuckle) good morning sunshine / Salamaggi's birthday / Rufus and Ruby / Mother's prayer / Country brother and the city sister / Chippin' / Just don't make no sense / Dear Mistuh P / Love that's America / I remember / My pal Johnny
5406942 / Jun '97 / A&M

Van Pelt

☐ SULTANS OF SENTIMENT
GERN 025CD / 20 Oct '97 / Gern Blandsten

Van Ronk, Dave

☐ FOLKWAYS YEARS 1959-1961
SFCD 40041 / Sep '94 / Smithsonian Folkways

☐ LIVE AT SIR GEORGE WILLIAMS UNIVERSITY
Gambler's blues / That will never happen no more / Old man / St. Louis tickle / Frankie and Albert / Down and out / W.C. Fields routine / Mack the knife / Song of the wandering Angus / Mean world blues / Keep it clean / Statesboro blues / Cocaine
JAM 91322 / 23 Feb '98 / Just A Memory

Van Rossum, Jerome

☐ DIPLOMATIC IMMUNITY
78942847872 / 17 Mar '98 / Irma

Van Ruller, Jesse

☐ EUROPEAN QUINTET
Debits 'n credits / Bewitched / Ruler / De poesch / I'll be seeing you / Two walk / Green's greenery / Vienna night express / You're my everything / This could be the start of something big
BM 1002 / Feb '97 / Blue Music

Van Sant, Gus

☐ GUS VAN SANT
POP 010 / 23 Mar '98 / Pop Secret

Van Senger, Dominik

☐ FIRST, THE
VBR 20072 / Dec '90 / Vera Bra

Van Vliet, Winanda

☐ LUNA Y MAR
CHR 70037 / Sep '96 / Challenge

Van Zandt, Johnny

☐ BROTHER TO BROTHER
SPV 08518900 / Mar '98 / SPV

☐ JOHNNY VAN ZANDT
AGEK 2066 / Aug '97 / Unidisc

☐ KING BISCUIT PRESENTS...
88028 / May '97 / King Biscuit

Van Zandt, Townes

☐ ABNORMAL
If I needed you / Pancho and Lefty / Snake mountain blues / Two girls / Kathleen / Waiting around to die / Tecumseh valley / Dead flowers / Catfish song / Flying shoes / Blazes blues / Marie / Song for lungs / Old Shep
RTS 24 / Oct '96 / Return To Sender

☐ ANTHOLOGY 1968-1979 (2CD Set)
Be here to love me / Kathleen / Our Mother the mountain / St. John The Gambler / Snake Mountain blues / For the sake of the song / Waiting around to die / Don't take it too bad / Colorado girl / I'll be here in the morning / None but the rain / Delta Momma blues / Turnstyled junkpiled / Tower song / Come tomorrow / Brand new companion / Where I lead me / Two hands / Standin' / No deal / To live is to fly / Mr. Gold and Mr. Mud / High low and between / No lonesome tune / Don't let the sunshine fool ya / Honky tonkin' / Fraulein / Pancho and Lefty / If I needed you / Heavenly houseboat blues / Fraternity blues / Tecumseh Valley / Lungs / Only him or me / Loretta / No place to fall / Flyin' shoes / Who do you love / When she don't need me / Snake song
CDGR 2072 / 2 Feb '98 / Charly

☐ AT MY WINDOW
Snowin' on Raton / Blue wind blew / At my window / For the sake of the song / Ain't leavin' your love / Buckskin stallion blues / Little sundance / Still lookin' for you / Gone gone blues / Catfish song
SHCD 1020 / Jun '97 / Sugar Hill

☐ BEST OF TOWNES VAN ZANDT, THE
Kathleen / St John the gambler / Waiting around to die / Don't take it too bad / Colorado girl / I'll be here in the morning / Delta momma blues / Tower song / Brand new companion / Two hands / Standin' / No deal / To live is to fly / No lonesome tune / Honky tonkin' / Pancho and lefty / If I needed you / Heavenly houseboat blues / Loretta / No place to fall / Flyin' shoes
CPCD 8176 / Jun '96 / Charly

☐ DELTA MOMMA BLUES
FFV / Delta momma blues / Only him or me / Turnstyled, junkpiled / Tower song / Come tomorrow / Brand new companion / Rake / Nothin'
174042 / Nov '97 / Musidisc
CDGR 213 / 29 Jun '98 / Charly

☐ DOCUMENTARY
Waiting around to die / Tecumseh Valley / If I needed you story / Pancho and Lefty / Blaze's blues / Marie / Hole / Cowboy junkies lament / Lightnin' Hopkins / Brand new companion / I'll be here in the morning
NORMAL 211CD / Jul '97 / Normal

☐ FOR THE SAKE OF THE SONG
CDGR 241 / 1 Jun '98 / Charly

☐ HIGH LOW AND IN BETWEEN
Two hands / You are not needed now / Greensboro woman / Highway kind / Standin' / No deal / To live is to fly / When he offers his hand / Mr. Gold and Mr. Mud / Blue Ridge mountains / High low and in between
CDGR 214 / 24 Aug '98 / Charly

☐ HIGHWAY KIND, THE
Lost highway / My proud mountains / Highway kind / Dublin blues / Blaze's blues / Wreck on the highway / Hole / (I heard that) Lonesome whistle / Rake / Banks of the Ohio / Ira Hayes / Darcey Farrow / Song for / STill lookin' for you / Joke / No deal / At my window
SHCD 1056 / Apr '97 / Sugar Hill
NORMAL 201CD / May '97 / Normal

☐ LAST RIGHTS
GREGORCD 41290 / Mar '98 / Gregor

☐ LATE GREAT TOWNES VAN ZANDT, THE
CDGR 215 / Nov '97 / Charly

☐ LIVE AND OBSCURE (Live In Nashville 1985)
Dollar bill blues / Many a fine lady / Pueblo waltz / Talking Thunderbird blues / Loretta / Snake Mountain blues / Waitin' around to die / Tecumseh Valley / Pancho and Lefty / You are not needed now
SHCD 1026 / Jul '97 / Sugar Hill

☐ LIVE AT THE OLD QUARTER HOUSTON TEXAS (2CD Set)
Announcement / Pancho and Lefty / Mr. Mudd and Mr. Gold / Don't you take it too bad / Tow girls / Fraternity blue / If I needed you / Brand new companion / White freightliner blues / To live is to fly / She came and she touched me / Talking thunderbird blues / Rex's blues / Nine pound hammer / For the sake of the song / No place to fall / Loretta / Kathleen / Tower song / Waitin' around to die / Tecumseh valley / Lungs / Only him or me
CDCHARLY 183 / Oct '89 / Decal
CDGR 2162 / 24 Aug '98 / Charly

☐ MASTERS, THE
EABCD 043 / 24 Nov '97 / Eagle

☐ NO DEEPER BLUE
SHCD 1046 / Aug '95 / Sugar Hill
IRS 993151 / Jun '96 / Intercord

☐ OUR MOTHER THE MOUNTAIN
CDGR 211 / 17 Mar '98 / Charly

☐ PANCHO AND LEFTY (Live & Obscure)
Dollar bill blues / Many a fine lady / Nothin' / Pueblo waltz / Talking thunderbird blues / Rex's blues / White freightliner blues / Loretta / Snake Mountain blues / Waitin' round to die / Tecumseh Valley / Pancho and Lefty / You are not needed now
EDCD 344 / Mar '97 / Edsel

☐ REAR VIEW MIRROR
SHCD 1054 / Feb '97 / Sugar Hill
NORMAL 203 / Nov '97 / Normal

☐ ROADSONGS
Ira Hayes / Dead flowers / Automobile blues / Coo coo / Fraulein hello / Central Indian cowboy / Racing in the streets / My starter won't start this morning / Texas river song / Wabash cannonball / Short haired woman blues / Man gave names to all of the animals / Little Willie the gambler / Cocaine / You win again / High, low and in between / When he offers his hand
SHCD 1042 / Apr '94 / Sugar Hill
NORMAL 195 / Feb '97 / Normal

☐ TOWNES VAN ZANDT
For the sake of the song / Columbine / Waiting around to die / Don't take it too bad / Colorado girl / Lungs / I'll be here in the morning / Fare thee well, Miss Carousel / (Quick silver day dreams of) Maria / None but the rain
CDGR 212 / 30 Mar '98 / Charly

Van Zyl

☐ RELIC (2CD Set)
CENCD 013 / Feb '96 / Centaur

Vandalias

☐ MACH V
BD 9015 / Dec '97 / Big Deal

Vandals

☐ CHRISTMAS WITH THE VANDALS (Oi To The World)
Gun for Christmas / Grandpa's last Christmas / Thanks for nothing / Oi to the world / Nothing's going to ruin my holiday / Christmas time for my penis / I don't believe in Santa Claus / My first Christmas as a woman / Dance of the sugarplum fairies / Here I am Lord / Christmas / Hang myself from the tree
787622 / 15 Jun '98 / Kung Fu

☐ FEAR OF A PUNK PLANET
TX 51094CD / '95 / Triple X

☐ HITLER BAD VANDALS GOOD
158172 / 3 Aug '98 / Nitro

☐ LIVE FAST DIARRHOEA
158022 / Oct '96 / Nitro

☐ QUICKENING
158062 / Oct '96 / Nitro

☐ SWEATIN' TO THE OLDIES
TX 51154CD / Jul '95 / Triple X

Vanden Plas

☐ ACAULT
DCD 9629 / Nov '96 / Dream Circle

☐ GOD THING, THE
SPV 08528572 / Dec '97 / SPV

Vander, Christian

☐ 65 (Vander, Christian Trio)
A 10 / Nov '93 / Seventh

☐ OFFERING (Parts 1 & 2)
A 1/2 / Mar '93 / Seventh

☐ OFFERING
A 9 / Sep '93 / Seventh

☐ OFFERING VOL.3 & 4
A 5/6 / Mar '93 / Seventh

☐ SONS - DOCUMENT 1973 - LE MANOR (Vander/Top/Blasquiz/Garber)
AKT 2 / Jan '93 / AKT

Vander, Stella

☐ D'EPREUVES D'AMOUR
A 8 / Mar '93 / Seventh

Vanderhoof

☐ VANDERHOOF
SPV 08518792 / Mar '98 / SPV

Vandermark, Ken

☐ SINGLE PIECE FLOW (Vandermark Five)
Careen / Momentum / Fence / Data janitor / Mark inside / Wood-skin-metal / Billboard / Limited edition
ALP 47CD / Apr '97 / Atavistic

☐ STEEL WOOD TRIO
OD 12005 / Aug '95 / Okka Disk

Vanderveen, Ad

☐ BRAND NEW EVERYTIME
MWCD 1008 / Apr '96 / Music & Words

Vandoni, Chris

☐ RAIN FOREST, THE
BRAM 1991192 / Nov '93 / Brambus

Vandross, Luther

☐ BEST OF LUTHER VANDROSS, THE/ THE BEST OF LOVE (2CD Set)
Searching / Glow of love / Never too much / If this world were mine / Bad boy / Having a party / Since I lost my baby / Promise me / Till my baby comes home / In only for one night / Creepin' superstar / Until you come back to me / Stop to love / So amazing / There's nothing better than love / Give me the reason / Any love / I really didn't mean it / Love won't let me wait / Treat you right / Here and now
4658012 / 2 Feb '98 / LV

☐ BUSY BODY
I wanted your love / Busy body / I'll let you slide / Make me a believer / For the sweetness of your love / How many times can we say goodbye / Superstar (Don't you remember) / Until you come back to me
4879562 / Jul '97 / Epic

☐ FOREVER, FOR ALWAYS, FOR LOVE
Bad boy/Having a party / You're the sweetest one / Since I lost my baby / Forever, for always, for love / Better love / Promise me / She loves me back / Once you know how
4844602 / Aug '96 / Epic

☐ GIVE ME THE REASON
Stop to love / See me / I gave it up (when I fell in love) / So amazing / Give me the reason / There's nothing better than love / I really didn't mean it / Because it's really love / Anyone who had a heart
4501342 / Jan '87 / Epic

☐ GREATEST HITS 1981-1995
Never too much / Sugar and spice / She's a super lady / House is not a home / Give me the reason / So amazing / Stop to love / See me / I really didn't mean it / Any love / Here and now / Power of love (love power) / Best things in life are free: *Jackson, Janet & Luther Vandross* / Love the one you're with / Power of love (love power) (mix) / Thrill I'm in
4811002 / Oct '95 / LV

☐ I KNOW
Keeping my faith in you / Isn't there someone / Religion / Get it right / I know / I'm only human / Nights in Harlem / Dream lover / When I need you / Are you using me / Are you mad at me / Now that I have you / Nights in Harlem
8460892 / 10 Aug '98 / EMI

☐ NEVER TOO MUCH
Never too much / Sugar and spice / Don't you know that / I've been working / She's a super lady / You stopped loving me / House is not a home
32807 2 / May '90 / Epic

☐ NIGHT I FELL IN LOVE, THE
Till my baby comes home / Night I fell in love / If only for one night / Creepin' / It's over now / Wait for love / My sensitivity (Gets in the way) / Other side of the world
4624892 / Mar '90 / Epic

☐ ONE NIGHT WITH YOU
One night with you / When you call on me / Baby that's when I come running / It's all about you / I won't let you do that to me / Power of love / Power of love / Don't want to be a fool / Best things in life are free / Little miracles / Endless love / Always and forever / Love the one you're with / Your secret love / I can make it better / Love don't love you anymore / My favourite things
4888882 / 29 Sep '97 / LV

☐ SONGS
Love the one you're with / Killing me softly / Endless love: *Vandross, Luther & Mariah Carey* / Evergreen / Reflections / Hello / Ain't no stoppin' us now / Always and forever / Going in circles / Since you've been gone / All the woman I need / What the world needs now / Impossible dream
4766562 / 27 Jul '98 / LV

☐ THIS IS CHRISTMAS
With a Christmas heart / This is Christmas / Mistletoe jam (everybody kiss somebody) / Every year, every Christmas / My favourite things / Have yourself a merry little Christmas / I listen to the bells / Please come home for Christmas / Kiss for Christmas / O come all ye faithful (adeste fidelis)
4813122 / Dec '95 / LV

☐ YOUR SECRET LOVE
Your secret love / Love don't love you anymore / It's hard for me to say / Crazy love / I can make it better / Too proud to beg / I can't wait no longer (let's do this) / Nobody to love / Whether or not the world gets better: *Vandross, Luther & Lisa Fischer* / This time I'm right / Knocks me off my feet / Goin' out of my head
4843832 / Oct '96 / LV

Vanessa-Mae

☐ CHINA GIRL
Butterfly lovers concerto / Fantasy on Puccini's Turandot / Happy valley / Butterfly lovers violin concerto / Violin fantsy on Puccini's Turandot
CDC 5564832 / 26 Jan '98 / EMI Classics

☐ STORM
Summer haze / Storm / Retro / Bach street prelude / Leyenda / Can can (you) / Happy valley / Poet's quest (for a distant paradise) / Embrasses moi (fly me up) / Aurora / I'm a doun / I feel love / Hocus pocus / Blessed spirits
8218002 / 27 Oct '97 / EMI

Vangelis

☐ ALBEDO 0.39
Pulstar / Freefall / Mare tranquilitatis / Main sequence / Sword of Orion / Alpha / Nucleogenesis (part 2) / Albedo 039
ND 74208 / Sep '89 / RCA

☐ BEAUBOURG
ND 70010 / 2 Feb '98 / RCA

☐ CHARIOTS OF FIRE (The Music Of Vangelis)
MACCD 246 / Aug '96 / Autograph

☐ CHINA
Chung kuo (the long march) / Dragon / Himalaya / Little fete / Long march / Plum blossom / Summit / Tao of love / Yin and Yang / Chung kuo
8136532 / '83 / Polydor

☐ CITY
Dawn / Morning papers / Nerve centre / Side streets / Good to see you / Twilight / Red lights / Procession
9031730262 / Nov '90 / East West

☐ COLLECTION, THE
74321224152 / Aug '94 / RCA

☐ DIRECT
Motion of stars / Will of the wind / Metallic rain / Elsewhere / Glorianna (hymn a la femme) / Rotations logic / Oracle of Apollo / Message / Ave / First approach / Dial out / Intergalactic radio station
259149 / Feb '93 / Arista

☐ GALACTIC SOUNDS UNLIMITED PERFORM THE HITS OF VANGELIS (Galactic Sounds Unlimited)
Pulstar / Eric's theme / Italian song / Rotations logic / Will of the wind / Hymne / Elsewhere / L'apocalypse des animaux / Tao of love / To the unknown man / L'opera sauvage / I hear you now / Theme from Antarctica / I'll find my way home / Dervish D / Chariots of fire
QED 011 / Nov '96 / Tring

☐ GIFT (The Best Of Vangelis)
Cosmos theme / Pulstar / Page of life / Alpha / 12 o'clock / Sword of Orion / Motion of stars / Way / Heaven and hell suite / Will of the wind / Glorianna / Metallic rain / Shine for me / Intergalactic radio station
74321393372 / Jun '96 / Camden

☐ HEAVEN AND HELL
Heaven and hell / So long long ago so'clear
ND 71148 / Sep '89 / RCA

☐ L'APOCALYPSE DES ANIMAUX
Apocalypse des animaux / Generique / Petite fille de la mer (la) / Sing bleu (le) / Mort du loup / Ours musicien / Creation du monde / Mer recommencee
8315032 / '88 / Polydor

☐ MASK
8252452 / Apr '85 / Polydor

☐ MUSIC OF VANGELIS AND JEAN MICHEL JARRE, THE (Virtual Reality)
Oxygene / Apocalypse des animaux / Eric's theme / Tao of love / Calypso / Ethnicolour / Italian song / Zoolookologie / Antartica / Souvenir de Chine / I'll find my way home / L'opera sauvage / Chariots of fire / Equinoxe / Arpegiator / China / Magnetic fields / Fourth rendezvous
SUMCD 4018 / Nov '96 / Summit

☐ OCEANIC
Bon voyage / Songs of the seas / Spanish harbour / Islands of the orient / Fields of coral / Memories of blue / Aquatic dance / Dreams of surf / Siren's whispering
0630167612 / Oct '96 / East West

☐ PORTRAIT
5311542 / Apr '96 / Polydor

☐ SOIL FESTIVITIES
Movement / Movement 2 / Movement 3 / Movement 4 / Movement 5
8233962 / Sep '84 / Polydor

☐ SPIRAL
Spiral / Ballad / Dervish D / To the unknown man / Three plus three
ND 70568 / Oct '89 / RCA

☐ THEMES
Bladerunner (end titles) / Missing (main theme) / L'enfant / Hymn / Chung kuo / Tao of love / Antarctica / Bladerunner (love theme) / Mutiny on the bounty (opening titles) / Mutiny on the bounty (closing titles) / Memories of green / La petite fille de la mer / Chariots of fire / Five circles
8395182 / 23 Feb '98 / Polydor

☐ VOICES
Voices / Dream in an open place / P s / Ask the mountains / Prelude / Messages / Losing sleep (still my heart) / Come to me / Echoes
0630127862 / Feb '96 / East West

Vanguard Jazz Orchestra

☐ MUSIC OF JIM MCNEELY, THE
805342 / Jan '98 / New World

☐ TO YOU (A Tribute To Mel Lewis)
MM 5054 / Oct '94 / Music Masters

Vanian, Dave

☐ DAVE VANIAN & THE PHANTOM CHORDS
Voodoo doll / Screamin' kid / Big town / This house is haunted / You and I / Whiskey and me / Fever in my blood / Frenzy / Shooting Jones / Jezebel / Tonight we ride / Johnny Guitar / Chase the wild wind / Swamp thing
CDWIKD 140 / Mar '95 / Big Beat

Vanilla Fudge

☐ NEAR THE BEGINNING
REP 4127 / Aug '91 / Repertoire

☐ PSYCHEDELIC SUNDAE (The Best Of Vanilla Fudge)
You keep me hangin' on / Where is my mind / Look of love / Ticket to ride / Come by day, come by night / Take me for a little while / That's what makes a man / Season of the witch / Shotgun / Thoughts / Faceless people / Good good lovin' / Some velvet morning / I can't make it alone / Lord in the country / Need love / Street walking woman / All in your mind
8122711542 / Mar '93 / Atlantic

☐ RENAISSANCE
REP 4126 / Aug '91 / Repertoire

☐ ROCK 'N' ROLL
REP 4168 / Aug '91 / Repertoire

☐ VANILLA FUDGE
Ticket to ride / People get ready / She's not there / Bang bang (my baby shot me down) / You keep me hangin' on / Take me for a little while / Eleanor Rigby
7567903902 / Mar '93 / Atlantic

Vanilla Pod

☐ TRIGGER HAPPY
Come undone / Understand / Rebound / Who gives / Friendly / Problems / Greed / Dredger / Don't know / You / Corner of my mind / Fat Sam / Jingle jangle
GOOD 006CD / 3 Aug '98 / Them's Good

Vanishing Heat

☐ ITCH
TEQM 93005 / Jul '97 / TEQ

Vanity Fare

☐ SUN, THE WIND AND OTHER THINGS, THE
REP 4155 / Aug '91 / Repertoire

Vannelli, Gino

☐ BIG DREAMERS NEVER SLEEP
FDM 362112 / Oct '93 / Dreyfus

☐ BLACK CARS
Black cars / Other man / It's over / Here she comes / Hurts to be in love / Total stranger / Just a motion away / Imagination / How much
FDM 362102 / Oct '93 / Dreyfus

Van't Hof, Jasper

☐ AT THE CONCERTGEBOUW
CHR 70010 / Aug '95 / Challenge

☐ BLUE CORNER
Blue balls / Blauklang / U / Before birth / Blue corner / Two brothers / Gog / L'epoque bleue / Another night in Tunesia / Icarus / Fate / Black is the colour of my true love's hair
92292 / Jun '96 / Act

☐ EYEBALL
Bax / Viber snake / Eyeball I / Hyrax / Schwester Johanna / Laur / One leg missing / Eyeball II / Rev
FCD 0002 / Oct '95 / Limetree

☐ FREEZING SCREENS (Van't Hof, Jasper & Greetje Bijma/Pierre Favre)
Part 1 / Part 2 / Part 3 / Part 4 / Part 5
ENJ 90632 / Oct '96 / Enja

☐ TOMORROWLAND
Whoozit / Tomorrow land / Rutherford / Wildcard / Pilansberg / Ascot / Mr. Woof / Round about / Ma belle / Ballad for a lady / Ventre a terre / Quiet American
CHR 70040 / Mar '97 / Challenge

Vanwarmer, Randy

☐ EVERY NOW AND THEN
Stories, trophies and memories / Ain't nothin' coming / Every now and then / You were the one / Tomorrow would be better / She's the reason / Appaloosa night / Beautiful rose / Just when I needed you most / Love is a cross you bear / Safe harbour / I never got over you
ETCD 190 / Mar '96 / Etude

☐ I WILL WHISPER YOUR NAME
I guess it never hurts to hurt sometimes / I'm in a hurry / Vital spark / Used cars / Velvet vampire / Time and money / Just when I needed you most / Silence of her dreams / Echoes / There's a rhythm / Don't look back / I will whisper your name
KCD 377 / Jan '96 / Irish

☐ VITAL SPARK, THE
ALCD 194 / May '96 / Alias

☐ WARMER
Losing out on love / Just when I needed you most / Your light / Gotta get out of here / Convincing lies / Call me / Forever loving you / I could sing / Deeper and deeper / One who loves you
8122713982 / Jun '95 / Rhino

Vanzyl

☐ CELESTIAL MECHANICS
Moment of totally / Callisto / Valhalla / Celestial mechanics
CENCD 003 / Oct '93 / Centaur

Vapors

☐ TURNING JAPANESE (The Best Of The Vapors)
Turning Japanese / News at ten / Waiting for the weekend / Spring collection / Sixty second interval / Somehow / Trains / Bunkers / Cold war / America / Letter from Hiro / Jimmie Jones / Daylight titans / Isolated case / Wasted / Billy / Talk talk / Prisoners / Spiders / Here comes the judge
CDGO 2071 / Nov '96 / EMI Gold

Varathron

☐ HIS MAJESTY AT THE SWAMP
CYBERCD 8 / Mar '94 / Cyber

Vard Sisters

☐ HEAVENLY
Flower duet / Listen / Hiding place / Amazing grace / Be still my soul / Ag croist an siol / On eagles wings / I rejoiced / Song of ruth / Ave maria / Hermit song / Nearer my god / Pie jesu / How great thou art / Be not afraid / Lord is my sheperd / Here I am lord
4880922 / 3 Nov '97 / Columbia

Vardaro, Elvino

☐ EL VIOLIN MAYOR DEL TANGO
EBCD 94 / 24 Apr '98 / El Bandoneon

Vardis

☐ BEST OF VARDIS, THE
Situation negative / Let's go / 100 mph / Dirty money / If I were king / Destiny / Silver machine / Police patrol / Steamin' along / Blue rock / Jumping Jack flash / Do I stand accused / Where there's mods there's rockers / Gary glitter / Together tonight / Boogie blitz / Jeepster / Don't mess with the bet / Radio rockers / Bad company
CDMETAL 12 / Sep '97 / Anagram

Varela, Hector

☐ PATIO PORTENO
BMT 013 / 5 Jan '98 / Melodie

Varga

☐ PROTOTYPE
Unconscience / Greed / Wawnan mere / Freeze don't move / Self proclaimed / Thief / Bring the hammer down / Cast into the shade / Strong / Film at eleven / Goodbye boogaloo (Instrumental) / Freeze don't move (Krash's psycho mix)
74321190802 / Aug '94 / RCA

Varganvinter

☐ FROSTFOOD
IR 023CD / Nov '96 / Invasion

Vargas, Angel

☐ EL RUISENOR DE LAS CALLES PORTENAS
EBCD 79 / Jul '96 / El Bandoneon

Vargas, Pedro

☐ BOLERO MAMBO
ALCD 030 / Jul '97 / Alma Latina

☐ BOLEROS MEXICANOS VOL.1
ALCD 038 / Jul '97 / Alma Latina

☐ BOLEROS MEXICANOS VOL.2
ALCD 040 / Jul '97 / Alma Latina

☐ CANCIONES DE SIEMPRE
BMCD 2007 / Nov '97 / Blue Moon

☐ CANTA CANCIONES RANCHERAS
ALCD 035 / Jul '97 / Alma Latina

☐ CANTA CON GRANDES ORQUESTAS LATINA
ALCD 033 / Jul '97 / Alma Latina

☐ CANTA INOLVIDABLES BOLEROS CUBANOS
ALCD 027 / Jul '97 / Alma Latina

☐ TANGOS Y VALSES
BMCD 2008 / Nov '97 / Blue Moon

Varis, Tapani

☐ MUNNIHAPPUUNA
Gammal brollopspolska / Polska / Munnihappunna / Metsapelto d / Fanitullen / G taklax / Maanitus / Menuetti / Palkintopolska / Valssi / Tantsun paalle / Jesus din sode forening / Omsk avoin kaupunki / Sordolen
KICD 46 / Dec '97 / Kansanmusiikki Instituutti

Varley, Gez

☐ PRESENTS TONY MONTANA
Colombia / Political prisoner / World is yours / Tax trouble / Revenga / Cocoroach / Paranoia
K7R 023CD / 24 Aug '98 / Studio K7

Varnaline

☐ MAN OF SIN
Hammer goes down / Gary's paranoia / Lbs / Thorns and such / Little pills / Dust / No decision, no disciple / Want you / Green again / In the year of dope
RCD 10368 / Aug '96 / Rykodisc

☐ SHOT AND A BEER, A
Hear the birds cry / Only one / In your orbit / Bardust / Judges seventeen / Don't come home
ZERCD 3130 / 26 Jan '98 / Zero Hour

☐ SWEET LIFE
Gulf of Mexico / Northern lights / Now you're dirt / All about love / While you were sleeping / Saviours / This is the river / Underneath the mountain / Fuck and fight / Mare imbrium / Tonight / Sweet life
ZERC 0413D / 24 Aug '98 / Zero Hour

☐ VARNALINE
Lights / Meet me on the ledge / Sky's out / Why are you unkind / Empire blues / Really can't say / Velocity / My time / Understanding H / God in your eyes
ZERCD 2130 / 17 Nov '97 / Zero Hour

Varner, Tom

☐ MOTION/STILLNESS (Varner, Tom Quartet)
1210672 / Nov '97 / Soul Note

Varro, Johnny

☐ SAY YES
ARCD 19178 / Feb '98 / Arbors Jazz

Vartonki, Zsuzsanna

☐ I'M GOING AWAY
177572 / 24 Apr '98 / Musidisc

Varukers

☐ BLOODSUCKERS/PREPARE FOR THE ATTACK
Protest and survive / Nowhere to go / No masters no slaves / Don't conform / Android / March of the SAS / Nodda (contraceptive machine) / Government's to blame / Tell us what we all want to hear / Don't wanna be a victim / What the hell do you know / School's out (maybe) / Killed by man's own hands / Animals / Enter a new phase / Stop the killing now / Instrumental / Thatcher's fortress / Massacred millions / Nuclear / State enemy / Will they never learn / Bomb blast / Die for your government / Soldier boy
CDPUNK 56 / Oct '95 / Anagram

☐ DEADLY GAMES
ABBT 806CD / Sep '94 / Abstract

☐ LIVE IN LEEDS 1984
RRCD 002 / 13 Apr '98 / Retch

☐ MURDER
VARUKERS 003CD / Jul '97 / Varukers
WB 1165CD / 19 Jan '98 / We Bite

☐ ONE STRUGGLE ONE FIGHT
RRCD 004 / 13 Apr '98 / Retch

☐ SINGLES 1981-1985, THE
CDPUNK 74 / Apr '96 / Anagram

☐ STILL BOLLOX AND STILL HERE
WB 1136CD / Nov '95 / We Bite

Vas

☐ SUNYATA
Ningal / Saphyrro / Refuge / Sunyata / Apsara / Astrae / Iman / Rememberance / Arc of ascent / As siva's feet
ND 63039 / May '97 / Narada
VNDCD 3 / 11 May '98 / Virgin

Vas Deferens Organization

☐ TRANSCONTINENTAL
QU 02 / May '97 / Uaquaversal

Vasaria

☐ VASARIA
CM 77184CD / 3 Nov '97 / Century Media

Vasconcelos, Monica

☐ NOIS
MOVAS 001 / Jul '97 / Movas

Vasconcelos, Nana

☐ FRAGMENTS: MODERN TRADITION
TZA 7506 / Jul '97 / Tzadik

☐ STORYTELLING
Curtain (Cortina) / Fui fuio, na praca / Uma tarde no norte (An afternoon in the north) / Um dia no Amazonas (A day in the Amazon) / Clementina, no terreiro / Vento chamando vento / Tu nem quer saber (You don't want to know) / Nordeste (Northeast) / Tiroleo / Noite das estrelas (Night of stars)
CDEMC 3712 / Sep '97 / EMI

Vaselines

☐ ALL THE STUFF AND MORE
Son of a gun / Rory ride me raw / You think you're a man / Dying for it / Molly's lips / Teenage Jesus superstar / Jesus doesn't want me for a sunbeam / Let's get ugly / Sex sux (amen) / Dum dum / Oliver twisted / Monster pussy / Day I was a horse / Bitch / Slushy / No hope / Hairy / Dying for some blues / Lovecraft
ONLYCD 013 / Sep '95 / Avalanche

☐ COMPLETE HISTORY, A
SPCD 145 / Mar '94 / Sub Pop

Vasen

☐ ESSENCE
B 6787 / Oct '94 / Auvidis/Ethnic

☐ LEVANDE VASEN
DRCD 009 / Mar '96 / Drone

☐ VARLDENS VASEN
Kapten Kapsyl / Bambodansarna / Borjar du fatta / Shapons vindaloo / Nitti pomfritti / 30 ars jiggen / Anno / Tartulingen / Sald och solde / En timme i ungern / Till farmor
XOUCD 118 / Jul '97 / Xource

Vasilisk

☐ SIXTH DARSHAN
TRI 011CD / 6 Jul '98 / Trinity

Vasmalom

☐ VASMALOM VOL.2
MWCD 4012 / Nov '95 / Music & Words

Vasquez, Andrew

☐ KIOWA APACHE MUSIC
14996 / Jan '97 / Spalax

☐ WIND RIVER
14567 / Nov '97 / Spalax

Vasquez, Junior

☐ JUNIOR VASQUEZ LIVE VOL.2 (2CD Set) (Various Artists)
78067453032 / 19 May '98 / Drive Archive

☐ LIVE VOL.1 (2CD Set) (Various Artists)
Kimantana: *Life Force* / YDW: *S'N'S* / Excess: *X-Pact* / Burning up: *Moraes, Angel & Sally Cortes* / Mr. Fantast: *Hanson, Johnny* / Check this out: *Fisher, Cevin* / Dream drums: *Lectroluv* / Wombo lombo: *Kidjo, Angelique* / Wave speech: *Lazonby, Peter* / Come on home: *Lauper, Cyndi* / Clear: *Campbell, Sonny* / Live it cool (just do it): *Rhodes, Lydia* / Phunkee muzeek: *Shazzamm* / House of joy: *Robinson, Vickie Sue* / You got to pray: *Cardwell, Joi* / Storm in my soul: *Kamasutra* / No more I love you's: *Lennox, Annie* / If I were you: *Lang, k.d.* / Reap (what you sow): *Mitchell, Vernessa* / One by one: *Cher* / Ab fab: *Saunders, Jennifer & Joanna Lumley*
74321477692 / Apr '97 / Logic

Vath, Sven

☐ ACCIDENT IN PARADISE
Ritual of life / Caravan of emotions / L'esperanca / Sleeping invention / Mellow illusion / Merry go round somewhere / Accident in paradise / Drifting like whales in the darkness / Coda
4509911932 / May '93 / Eye Q

☐ FUSION
Fusion / Breakthrough / Sensual enjoyments / Discophon / Augenblick / Scorpio's movement / Trippy moonshine / Face it / Schubduse / Sounds control your mind / Blue spliff / Omen AM
CDVIR 71 / 2 Mar '98 / Virgin

☐ REMIX LP
Harlequin's meditation / Harlequin plays bells / Harlequin - the beauty and the beast / Birth of robby / Ballet-fusion / Ballet-dancer / Robot
4509997022 / Mar '95 / Eye Q

☐ ROBOT, THE HARLEQUIN & THE BALLETDANCER, THE
Intro / Harlequinn plays bells / Harlequin / Beauty and the beast / Harlequin's meditation / Birth of Robby / Robot / Ballet romance / Ballet fusion / Ballet dancer
4509975342 / Sep '94 / Eye Q

Vatten

☐ DIGGIN' THE ROOTS
You'll never know / Looking back / Status quo / Crossroads / Pretty woman / Stumble / First sight phenomenon / Black cat moan / Walkin' by myself / Don't try your jive on me / Prisons on the road / Little girl / Baby, baby, baby / Ervik boogie / Killing floor
GUTS 008CD / Mar '93 / Gutta

Vaucaire, Cora

☐ CORA L'INTEMPORELLA
112692 / 24 Apr '98 / Musidisc

☐ JACQUES PREVERT PAR...
113122 / 24 Apr '98 / Musidisc

☐ RECITAL AU THEATRE DE LA VILLE
101602 / 24 Apr '98 / Musidisc

Vaughan, Frankie

☐ BEST OF THE EMI YEARS, THE
There must be a way / So tired / Nevertheless / Happy days and lonely nights / Your nobody 'til somebody loves you / Mame / Red roses for a blue lady / There I've said it again / More I see you / My son my son / Unchained melody / Istanbul / If I had my way / With these hands / Look at that girl / Heartless / From the vine came the grape / My sweetie went away / Do do do do do do do it again / Hey Joe / Too marvellous for words / Good old bad old days / Girl talk
4961772 / 3 Aug '98 / Music For Pleasure

☐ GIVE ME THE MOONLIGHT (The Best Of Frankie Vaughan)
Give me the moonlight, give me the girl / Old piano roll blues / Tweedle dee / Happy go lucky / Seventeen / My boy Flat Top / Green door / Garden of Eden / These dangerous years / Man on fire / Wanderin' eyes / Gotta have somethin' in the bank Frank / Kisses sweeter than wine / Can't get along without you / We are not alone / Kewpie doll / Judy / Come softly to me / Heart of a man / Walkin' tall / M'Lord / Tower of strength / Don't stop twist / Loop de loop / Hello Dolly / Cabaret
5543172 / 20 Apr '98 / Spectrum

☐ THERE'S ONLY ONE FRANKIE VAUGHAN
Hello Dolly / Singin' in the rain / There's no business like show business / Mame / Smoke gets in your eyes / Give my regards to Broadway / Begin the beguine / Way we were / I just called to say I love you / Can't smile without you / It's all in the game / If you were the only girl in the world / I get a kick out of you / 42nd Street / Cabaret / Lullaby of Broadway / Stella by starlight / When I fall in love
HADCD 215 / Jun '97 / Spotlight On

☐ WORLD OF FRANKIE VAUGHAN, THE
Give me the moonlight, give me the girl / Tower of strength / Green door / Long time, no see / Gotta have something in the bank, Frank / Tweedle Dee / Wonderful things / Am I wasting my time on you / Hey Mama / Sometime somewhere / Hello Dolly / Man on fire / There'll be no teardrops tonight / I'm gonna clip your wings / Kewpie doll / Hercules / Judy / You're the one for me / Kookie little paradise / That's my doll
5520152 / May '96 / Spectrum

Vaughan, Jimmie

☐ OUT THERE
Like a king / Lost in you / Out there / Can't say no / New ironic twist / Positively meant to be / Motorhead baby / Kinky women / Astral projection blues / Little son big son
4912202 / 15 Jun '98 / Epic

Vaughan, Malcolm

☐ EMI PRESENTS THE MAGIC OF MALCOLM VAUGHAN
Chapel of the roses / Every day of my life / More than ever / My special angel / St. Therese of the roses / To be loved / Wait for me / With your love / World is mine / Hello young lovers / Heart of a child / Holy city / Lady of Spain / Love me as if there were no other / Love me as though there were no other / Wedding / You'll never walk alone / Only you (and you alone) / Oh my Papa / You were the only girl in the world / Miss you / Willingly / Bell is ringing / My foolish heart / Guardian angel / When the last rose has faded
CDMFP 6289 / May '97 / Music For Pleasure

Vaughan, Sarah

☐ 16 MOST REQUESTED SONGS
Black coffee / That lucky old sun (Just rolls around heaven all day) / Summertime / Nearness of you / Goodnight my love / Can't get out of this mood / It might as well be spring / Come rain or come shine / Thinking of you / These things I offer you (For a lifetime) / Vanity / Pinky / Sinner or saint / My tormented heart / Linger awhile / Spring will be a little late this year
4743992 / Feb '94 / Columbia

☐ **20 JAZZ CLASSICS**
Serenata / Baubles, bangles and beads / Star eyes / Wrap your troubles in dreams (and dream your troubles away) / My favourite things / Come spring / Taste of honey / Fly me to the moon / This can't be love / Goodnight sweetheart / On Green Dolphin Street / I'm gonna live till I die / Maria / Until I met you / Moonglow / I don't know about you / All I do is dream of you / Because
CDMFP 6160 / May '95 / Music For Pleasure

☐ **AFTER HOURS**
My favourite things / Every time we say goodbye / Wonder why / Easy to love / Sophisticated lady / Great day / Ill wind / If love is good to me / In a sentimental mood / Vanity / Through the years
CDP 8554682 / Mar '97 / Roulette

☐ **AT MISTER KELLY'S (Vaughan, Sarah Trio)**
September in the rain / Willow weep for me / Just one of those things / Be anything but darling be mine / Thou swell / Stairway to the stars / Honeysuckle rose / Just a gigolo / How high the moon / Dream / I'm gonna sit right down and write myself a letter / It's got to be love / Alone / If this isn't love / Embraceable you / Lucky in love / Dancing in the dark / Poor butterfly / Sometimes I'm happy / I cover the waterfront
8327912 / Mar '92 / EmArCy

☐ **BEST OF SARAH VAUGHAN, THE**
You're blase / I've got the world on a string / Midnight sun / I gotta right to sing the blues / From this moment on / Ill wind / All too soon / Lush life / In a sentimental mood / Dindi
CD 2405416 / Jun '93 / Pablo

☐ **BODY AND SOUL**
HADCD 187 / Nov '95 / Javelin

☐ **CLASSICS 1944-1946**
CLASSICS 958 / Nov '97 / Classics

☐ **CLASSICS 1946-1947**
CLASSICS 989 / 24 Apr '98 / Classics

☐ **COLLECTION, THE**
Whatever Lola wants / Thinking of you / Black coffee / Summertime / More I see you / My favourite things / In a sentimental mood / 'Round midnight / Hands across the table / I cried for you / Just friends / Lover man / Ooh, what-cha doin' to me / Perdido / Polka dots and moonbeams / Prelude to a kiss / Sophisticated / Star eyes / Nearness of you / You hit the spot / When sunny gets blue / When your lover has gone / You stepped out of a dream / It might as well be spring
COL 059 / Jul '96 / Collection

☐ **COPACABANA**
Copacabana / Smiling hour / To say goodbye / Dreamer / Gentle rain / Tete / Dindi / Double rainbow / Bonita
CD 2312125 / Jan '92 / Pablo

☐ **CRAZY AND MIXED UP**
I didn't know what time it was / That's all / Autumn leaves / Love dance / Island / In love in vain / Seasons / You are too beautiful
CD 2312137 / Apr '94 / Pablo

☐ **DIVINE MISS VAUGHAN, THE (2CD Set)**
September in the rain / Willow weep for me / Just one of those things / Be anything but darling be mine / Thou swell / Stairway to the stars / Honeysuckle rose / Just a gigolo / How high the moon / Detour ahead / Three little words / Speak low / Like someone in love / You'd be so nice to come home to / I'll string along with you / All of you / Thanks for the memory / Lover man / Shulie a bop / Polka dots and moonbeams / Body and soul / They can't take that away from me / Prelude to a kiss / You hit the spot / If I knew then what I know now / September song / Lullaby of birdland / I'm glad there is you / You're not the kind / Jim / He's my guy / April in paris / It's crazy / Embraceable you
JWD 102301 / Nov '94 / JWD

☐ **DIVINE SARAH**
BN 050 / Apr '98 / Blue Nite

☐ **DUKE ELLINGTON SONGBOOK VOL.1, THE**
In a sentimental mood / I'm just a lucky so and so / Solitude / I let a song go out of my heart / I didn't know about you / All too soon / Lush life / In a mellow tone / Sophisticated lady / Daydream
CD 2312111 / Oct '93 / Pablo

☐ **DUKE ELLINGTON SONGBOOK VOL.2, THE**
I ain't got nothin' but the blues / Black butterfly / Chelsea Bridge / What am I here for / Tonight I shall sleep / Rocks in my bed / I got it bad and that ain't good / Everything but you / Mood indigo / It don't mean a thing if it ain't got that swing / Prelude to a kiss
CD 2312116 / Oct '93 / Pablo

☐ **EASY LIVING (Vaughan, Sarah & Oscar Peterson)**
I've got the world on a string / Midnight sun / How long has this been going on / You're blase / Easy living / Body and soul / My old flame / More than you know / Teach me tonight / When your lover has gone
JWD 102219 / Jul '95 / JWD

☐ **EMBRACEABLE YOU**
Embraceable you / Scat blues / 'Round midnight / Sassy's blues / Misty / Just one of those things / Alfie / What now my love / I had a ball / Theme / Lover man
17110 / Mar '97 / Laserlight

☐ **ESSENTIAL SARAH VAUGHAN, THE**
Summertime / East of the sun (and west of the moon) / Black coffee / Come rain or shine / Can't get out of this mood / It might as well be spring / Ain't misbehavin' / Goodnight my love / Pinky / Nearness of you (take 3) / Ooh what cha doin' to me / Perdido / I cried for you / Just friends / Nice work if you can get it / Mean to me / Thinking of you
4671522 / Oct '93 / Columbia

☐ **GEORGE GERSHWIN SONGBOOK VOL.1, THE**
They can't take that away from me / 's wonderful / Embraceable you / Soon / Maybe / My ship / But not for me / Someone to watch over me / Foggy day / Bidin' my time / He loves and she loves / Love walked in / Looking for a boy / I've got a crush on you / Isn't it a pity
PRS 23021 / Jan '95 / Personality

☐ **GEORGE GERSHWIN SONGBOOK VOL.1, THE**
Embraceable you / I'm kinda glad we did / They all laughed / Looking for a boy / He loves and she loves / My man's gone now / I won't say I will / Foggy day / Let's call the whole thing off / Things are looking up / Do it again / Love walked in / They can't take that away from me / 'S wonderful / Soon
8468952 / Mar '91 / EmArCy

☐ **GEORGE GERSHWIN SONGBOOK VOL.2, THE**
Do it again / How long has this been going on / Aren't you kinda glad we did / Man I love / Let's call the whole thing off / They all laughed / Lorelei / I'll build a stairway to paradise / Summertime / Things are looking up / I won't say I will but I won't say I won't / Of thee I sing / My one and only / My man's gone now / Embraceable you
PRS 23022 / Jan '95 / Personality

☐ **GEORGE GERSHWIN SONGBOOK VOL.2, THE**
But not for me / Isn't it a pity / Of thee I sing / I'll build a stairway to paradise / Someone to watch over me / Bidin' my time / Man I love / How long has this been going on / My one and only / Lorelei / I've got a crush on you / Summertime / Fascinatin' rhythm / Maybe / Embraceable you
8468962 / Mar '91 / EmArCy

☐ **GITANES - JAZZ 'ROUND MIDNIGHT**
April in Paris / Lover man / I won't say I will but I won't say I won't / I'm glad there is you / Prelude to a kiss / Jim my man / (I'm afraid) this masquerade is over / It's easy to remember / But not for me / Darn that dream / I'll never smile again / Smoke gets in your eyes / September song / Over the rainbow
5100862 / Apr '91 / Verve

☐ **HOW LONG HAS THIS BEEN GOING ON**
I've got the world on a string / Midnight sun / How long has this been going on / You're blase / Easy living / More than you know / My old flame / Teach me tonight / Body and soul / When your lover has gone
CD 2310821 / Oct '92 / Pablo

☐ **IN THE LAND OF HI-FI**
Over the rainbow / Soon / Cherokee / I'll never smile again / Don't be on the outside / How high the moon / It shouldn't happen to a dream / Sometimes I'm happy / Maybe / Occasional man / Why can't I / Oh my
8264542 / Mar '94 / EmArCy

☐ **IRVING BERLIN SONGBOOK, THE**
PRS 23023 / Jan '95 / Personality

☐ **JAZZ MASTERS**
Cherokee / September song / Shulie a bop / My funny valentine / How high the moon / It shouldn't happen to a dream / Linger awhile / Poor butterfly / Just one of those things / Lonely woman / Lullaby of birdland / Say it isn't so / Sometimes I'm happy / All the things you are / Sassy's blues / Misty
5181992 / 5 May '98 / Verve

☐ **JAZZ MASTERS (The Jazz Sides)**
5268172 / 5 May '98 / Verve

☐ **JAZZ MASTERS**
Serenata / Baubles, bangles and beads / Star eyes / Wrap your troubles in dreams / My favourite things / Come spring / Taste of honey / Fly me to the moon / This can't be love / Because / All I do is dream of you / I didn't know about you / Moonglow / Trees / Invitation / Until I met you / Maria / I'm gonna live till I die / On green dolphin street / Goodnight sweetheart
CDMFP 6299 / Mar '97 / Music For Pleasure

☐ **LIVE IN CHICAGO**
September in the rain / Willow weep for me / Just one of those things / Be anything but darling be mine / Thou swell / Stairway to the stars / Honeysuckle rose / Just a gigolo / How high the moon / Detour ahead / Three little words / Speak low / Like someone in love / You'd be so nice to come home to / I'll string along with you / All of you / Thanks for the memory
JHR 73580 / Jun '94 / Jazz Hour

☐ **LIVE IN JAPAN**
557304 / Dec '89 / Accord

☐ **LOVER MAN**
I'll wait and pray / Signing off / Interlude / No smokes blues / East of the sun / Loverman / What more can a woman do / I'd rather have a memory than a dream / Mean to me / All too soon / Time and again / I'm scared / You go to my head / It might as well be Spring / We're through / Hundred years from today / If you could see me now / I can make you love me / My kinda love / You're blase / I'm through with love / Body and soul / Don't worry 'bout me / Time after time / September song
PLCD 556 / Feb '97 / President

☐ **LOVER MAN**
I cried for you / But not for me / What kind of fool am I / As long as he needs me / More I see you / Stormy weather / What is this thing called love / Trouble is a man / While you are gone / Tenderly / Lover man / Love me or leave me / Penthouse serenade / What a difference a day made / Everything I have is yours
CDMT 031 / Jul '97 / Meteor

☐ **MANY MOODS OF SARAH VAUGHAN, THE**
Love me or leave me / Don't worry about me / September song / I'm through with love / One I love belongs to somebody else / Lover man / I feel so smoochie / Trouble is a man / Gentleman friend / Hundred years from today
EMBCD 3333 / 30 Mar '98 / Ember

☐ **MASTERPIECES OF SARAH VAUGHAN**
Shulie a bop / Body and soul / Lullaby of Birdland / My funny valentine / Willow weep for me / Stardust / Summertime / Honeysuckle rose / Just a gigolo / Boy from Ipanema / Take the 'A' train / What is this thing called love / Everyday I have the blues / Padre / I feel pretty / Mist / Lover man
8463302 / Oct '93 / EmArCy

☐ **MASTERS, THE (2CD Set)**
EDMCD 032 / 30 Mar '98 / Eagle

☐ **MEMORIAL ALBUM, THE**
UAE 34112 / 27 Apr '98 / Memorial Album

☐ **MY FUNNY VALENTINE AND OTHER LOVE SONGS**
My funny valentine / I'm in the mood for love / Touch of your lips / All the things you are / That old black magic / Lover man / Misty / It's magic / All of me / They say it's wonderful / Prelude to a kiss / Man I love / Cheek to cheek / My romance / Love walked in / Body and soul / Just one of those things / Bewitched, bothered and bewildered / Thou swell / S'wonderful
PRS 23020 / Nov '95 / Personality

☐ **PLATINUM COLLECTION, THE (2CD Set)**
All too soon / I'm scared / September song / You got to my head / Time after time / It might as well be spring / Don't worry about me / We're through / Body and soul / Hundred years from today / I'm through with love / If you could see me now / You're blase / I can make you love me / Careless / Sweet affection / Mary Contrary / What so bad about it / Broken hearted melody / That old black magic / Misty / Seperate ways / Friendly enemies / I've got the world on a string / Are you certain / Lord's prayer / When your lover has gone / Round midnight / Nearness of you / When sunny gets blue / Sophisticated lady / Remember you / Star eyes / It's you or no-one else / Love me or leave me / East of the sun / One I love / (Sometimes I feel like) a motherless child / What a difference a day makes / Lover man
PC 620 / 10 Nov '97 / Platinum Collection

☐ **SARAH AND CLIFFORD (Vaughan, Sarah & Clifford Brown)**
Lullaby of Birdland / April in Paris / He's my guy / Jim / You're not the kind / Embraceable you / I'm glad there is you / September song / It's crazy
8146412 / May '85 / EmArCy

☐ **SARAH AND CLIFFORD (Vaughan, Sarah & Clifford Brown)**
Lover man / Shulie a bop / Polka dots and moonbeams / Body and soul / They can't take that away from me / Prelude to a kiss / You hit the spot / If I knew then what I know now / September song / Lullaby of birdland / I'm glad there is you / You're not the kind / Jim / He's my guy / April in paris / It's crazy / Embraceable you
JHR 73581 / Jun '94 / Jazz Hour

☐ **SARAH VAUGHAN**
CD 107 / Oct '94 / Timeless Treasures

☐ **SARAH VAUGHAN**
UAE 30052 / Jan '98 / Members Edition

☐ **SARAH VAUGHAN 1944-1950**
CD 14568 / May '95 / Jazz Portraits

☐ **SARAH VAUGHAN COLLECTOR'S EDITION**
DVAD 6012 / Apr '95 / Deja Vu

☐ **SARAH VAUGHAN IN HI-FI**
East of the sun / Nice work if you can get it / Come rain or come shine / Mean to me / It might as well be spring / Can't get out of this mood / Goodnight my love / Ain't misbehavin' / Pinky / Nearness of you / Spring will be a little late this year / Ooh whatcha doin' to me / It's all in the mind
CK 65117 / Jun '97 / Sony Jazz

☐ **SARAH VAUGHAN'S GOLDEN HITS**
Misty / Broken hearted melody / Make yourself comfortable / Autumn in New York / Moonlight in Vermont / How important can it be / Smooth operator / Whatever Lola wants / Lullaby of Birdland / Eternally / Poor butterfly / Close to you / Lover man / Tenderly / Passing strangers / C'est la vie / Experience unnecessary / Banana boat song
8248912 / Apr '91 / Mercury

☐ **SASSY 1950-1954**
Lullaby of birdland / September song / You're not the kind / April in paris / He's my guy / I'm glad there is you / It's crazy / Embraceable you / They can't take that away from me / Polka dots and moonbeams / If I knew then what I know now / Body and soul / Shulie a bop / Prelude to a kiss / Mean to me / Pinky / Ooh what cha doin' to me / Thinking of you
CD 53165 / Jan '94 / Giants Of Jazz

☐ **SASSY AT RONNIE'S**
Here's that rainy day / Like someone in love / I'll remember April / Sophisticated lady / If you could see me now / Foggy day / I cried for you / But not for me/Embraceable you / Man I love / My funny valentine / Passing strangers / Blue skies / More I see you / Early Autumn / Tenderly
JHCD 015 / Jan '94 / Ronnie Scott's Jazz House

☐ **SASSY SWINGS THE TIVOLI (Sarah Vaughan Live At The Tivoli, Copenhagen/2CD Set)**
I feel pretty / Misty / What is this thing called love / Lover man / Sometimes I'm happy / Won't you come home Bill Bailey / Tenderly / Sassy's blues / Polka dots and moonbeams / I cried for you / Poor butterfly / I could write a book / Time after time / All of me / I hadn't anyone till you / I can't give you anything but love / I'll be seeing you / Maria / Day in, day out / Fly me to the moon / Baubles, bangles and beads / Lady's in love with you / Honeysuckle rose / What is this thing called love / Lover man / I cried for you / More I see you / Say it isn't so / Black coffee / Just one of those things / On Green Dolphin Street / Over the rainbow
8327882 / Jul '90 / EmArCy

☐ **SEND IN THE CLOWNS**
Send in the clowns / Love don't live here anymore / That'll be johnny / Right in the next room / I need you more (than ever now) / On thinking it over / Do away with april / Wave / Got to see if I can't get daddy to come back home / Frasier (the sensuous lion)
4806822 / Jan '95 / Sony Jazz

☐ **SINGS THE MANCINI SONGBOOK**
How soon / Days of wine and roses / Dear heart / Charade / Too little time / Dreamsville / Peter Gunn / Moon river / I love you and don't you forget it / Slow how wind / Mr. Lucky / It had better be tonight
5584012 / 3 Aug '98 / Verve

☐ **SLOW AND SASSY**
No smoke blues / East of the sun / Don't blame me / All too soon / Lover man / What more can a woman do / I'd rather have a memory than a dream / Mean to me / Time and again / I'm scared / You go to my head / I can make you love me / It might as well be spring / We're through / If you could see me now / You're not the kind / My kinda love / I've got a crush on you / I'm through with love / Everything I have is yours / Body and soul / Penthouse serenade / Don't worry 'bout me / September song / Time after time
PASTCD 7809 / May '97 / Flapper

☐ **SNOWBOUND/THE LONELY HOURS**
Snowbound / I hadn't anyone 'til you / What's good about goodbye / Stella by starlight / Look to your heart / Oh you crazy moon / Blah blah blah / I remember you / I fall in love too easily / Glad to be unhappy / Spring can really hang you up the most / Lonely hours / I'll never be the same / If I had you / Friendless / You're driving me crazy / Always on my mind / Look for me, I'll be around / What'll I do / Solitude / These foolish things / Man I love / So long my love
CTMCD 109 / Jan '97 / EMI

☐ **SOFT AND SASSY**
Sometimes I'm happy / I cried for you / Out of this world / You're blase / Serenata / Over the rainbow / Say it isn't so / Stormy weather / All of me / How long has this been going on / Day in, day out / Tenderly / What is this thing called love / Summertime / Poor butterfly / I'll be seeing you
HCD 601 / Apr '94 / Hindsight

☐ **SONGS OF THE BEATLES, THE**
7567814832 / Jun '93 / Atlantic

☐ **SPOTLIGHT ON SARAH VAUGHAN**
That old black magic / Careless / Separate ways / Are you certain / Mary contrary / Broken hearted melody / I've got the world on a string / Friendly enemies / What's so bad about it / Sweet affection / Misty / Send in the clowns / If you could see me now
HADCD 108 / Feb '94 / Javelin

☐ **THAT OLD BLACK MAGIC (Vaughan, Sarah & Billy Eckstine)**
That old black magic / I'm beginning to see the light / I hear a rhapsody / Misty / I apologise / Cottage for sale / More I see you / Stormy weather / As long as he needs me / My favourite things / What kind of fool am I / I'll be seeing you
306492 / May '97 / Hallmark

☐ **THIS IS JAZZ**
Ain't misbehavin' / Summertime / Wave / Just friends / Thinking of you / East of the sun (and west of the moon) / So many stars / It might as well be spring / Nearness of you / I cried for you / Black coffee / Nothing will be as it was / Can't get out of this mood / You're mine you / Mean to me / My man's gone now
CK 64974 / Oct '96 / Sony Jazz

☐ **TIME AFTER TIME**
I feel so smoochie / Lover man / As long as he needs me / Gentleman friend / What a difference a day made / Sometimes I feel like a Motherless child / What kind of fool am I / Trouble is a man / It's you or no one else / Don't worry 'bout me / More I see you / East of the sun / September song / I'm through with love / My favourite things / Time after time
SUMCD 4006 / Nov '96 / Summit

☐ **TOUCH OF CLASS, A**
Serenata / Baubles, bangles and beads / Star eyes / Wrap your troubles in dreams / My favourite things / Goodnight sweetheart / On Dolphin Street / I'm gonna live till I die / Maria / Until I met you / Invitation / Trees / Moonglow / I didn't know about you / All I do is dream of you / Come spring / Taste of honey / Fly me to the moon / This can't be love / Because
TC 865232 / 2 Feb '98 / Disky

☐ **TOWN HALL CONCERT 1947 (Vaughan, Sarah & Lester Young)**
Lester leaps in / Just you just me / Jumpin' with symphony Sid / Sunday / Don't blame me / My kinda lover / I cover the waterfront / I don't stand a ghost of a chance with you / Lester's bebop boogie / These foolish things / Movin' with Lester / Man I love / Time after time / Mean to me / Body and soul / I cried for you
CDP 8321392 / Apr '97 / Parlophone

☐ **ULTIMATE DIVAS**
5390522 / 10 Nov '97 / Verve

☐ **YOU'RE MINE YOU (Vaughan, Sarah & Quincy Jones)**
You're mine you / Best is yet to come / Witchcraft / So long / Second time around / I could write a book / Maria / Baubles, bangles and beads / Fly me to the moon / Moonglow / Invitation / On green dolphin street / One mint julep / Mama he treats your daughter mean
CDP 8571572 / Jul '97 / Roulette

Vaughan, Stevie Ray

☐ **COULDN'T STAND THE WEATHER (Vaughan, Stevie Ray & Double Trouble)**
Scuttle buttin' / Couldn't stand the weather / Things that I used to do / Voodoo chile / Cold shot / Tin Pan Alley / Honey bee / Stang's swang
EK 64425 / Feb '95 / Epic

☐ **COULDN'T STAND THE WEATHER/ SOUL TO SOUL/TEXAS FLOOD (3CD Set)**
Scuttle buttin' / Couldn't stand the weather / Things that I used to do / Voodoo chile (slight return) / Cold shot / Tin pan alley / Honey bea / Stang's swang / Love struck baby / Pride and joy / Texas flood / Tell me / Testify / Rude mood / Mary had a little lamb / Dirty pool / I'm cryin' / Lenny / Say what / Lookin' out the window / Look at little sister / Ain't gone 'n' give up on love / Gone home / Change it / You'll be mine / Empty arms / Come on (part 3) / Life without you
4683362 / Jan '94 / Epic

☐ **GREATEST HITS (Vaughan, Stevie Ray & Double Trouble)**
Taxman / Texas flood / House is rockin' / Pride and joy / Tightrope / Little wing / Crossfire / Sky is crying / Cold shot / Couldn't stand the weather / Life without you
4810232 / Nov '95 / Epic

☐ **IN STEP**
House is rockin' / Tightrope / Leave my girl alone / Wall of denial / Love me darlin' / Crossfire / Let me love you baby / Travis walk / Scratch 'n' sniff / Riviera paradise
4633952 / Jul '89 / Epic

☐ **IN THE BEGINNING (Vaughan, Stevie Ray & Double Trouble)**
In the open / Slide thing / They call me guitar hurricane / All your love / I miss loving / Tin Pan alley / Love struck baby / Tell me / Shake for me / Live another day
4726242 / Sep '94 / Epic

☐ **LIVE ALIVE**
Say what / Ain't gonna give up on love / Pride and joy / Mary had a little lamb / Superstition / I'm leaving you (commit a crime) / Cold shot / Willie the wimp / Look at little sister / Texas flood / Voodoo chile / Lovestruck baby / Change it / Life without you
4668392 / Apr '93 / Epic

☐ **LIVE FROM CARNEGIE HALL**
Intro / Scuttle buttin' / Testifiyin / Love struck baby / Honey bee / Cold shot / Letter to my girl / Dirty pool / Pride and joy / Things that I used to do / COD / Iced over / Lenny / Rude mood
4882062 / Aug '97 / Epic

☐ **SKY IS CRYING, THE (Vaughan, Stevie Ray & Double Trouble)**
Boot Hill / Sky is crying / Empty arms / Little wing / Wham / May I have a talk with you / Close to you / Chitlins con carne / So excited / Life by the drop
4686402 / Nov '91 / Epic

☐ **SOUL TO SOUL**
Say what / Looking out the window / Look at little sister / Ain't gonna give up on love / Gone home / Change it / You'll be mine / Empty arms / Come on / Life without you
4663302 / Apr '91 / Epic

☐ **SOUL TO SOUL/TEXAS FLOOD/ COULDN'T STAND THE WEATHER (3CD Set)**
Say what / Lookin' out the window / Look at little sister / Ain't gone 'n' give up on love / Gone home / Change it / You'll be mine / Empty arms / Come on (part 3) / Life without you / Love struck baby / Pride and joy / Texas flood / Tell me / Testify / Rude mood / Mary had a little lamb / Dirty pool / I'm cryin' / Lenny / Scuttle buttin' / Couldn't stand the weather / Things (that) I used to do / Voodoo chile (slight return) / Cold shot / Tin Pin Alley / Honey bee / Stang's swang
4853272 / 3 Nov '97 / Epic

☐ **TEXAS FLOOD (Vaughan, Stevie Ray & Double Trouble)**
Lovestruck baby / Pride and joy / Texas flood / Tell me / Testify / Rude mood / Mary had a little lamb / Dirty pool / I'm cryin' / Lenny
4609512 / Jul '89 / Epic

☐ **TRIBUTE TO STEVIE RAY VAUGHAN, A (Various Artists)**
Pride and joy: *Raitt, Bonnie* / Texas flood: *Vaughan, Jimmie* / Telephone song: *King, B.B.* / Long way from home: *Guy, Buddy* / Ain't gone 'n give up on love: *Clapton, Eric* / Love struck baby: *Cray, Robert* / Cold shot: *Dr. John* / Six strings down-tick tock srv shuffle: *All*
4850672 / Aug '96 / Epic

Vaughn, Ben

☐ **MONO**
Daddy rollin' in your arms / Cross ties / Goin' down the road / Sundown sundown / Our favourite martian / Strange desire / Jailbait / Exploration in fear / Just a little bit of you / Dark glasses / Magdalena / I waited too long too late / Out of control / Skip a rope / I'll come runnin' / That's how I got to Memphis / Sheba / We belong together
7882772 / Sep '96 / Sky Ranch

☐ **RAMBLER '65**
7 Days without love / Levitation / Song for you / Heavy machinery / Boomerang / Only way to fly / Rock is dead / Beautiful self destruction / Perpetual motion machine / Soundtrack music from Rambler 65 / Main title / Piston search / Geator drive
MRCD 066 / Jun '95 / Rubble
8122724842 / Mar '97 / Rhino

Vaughn, Maurice John

☐ **GENERIC BLUES ALBUM**
ALCD 4763 / Apr '93 / Alligator

☐ **IN THE SHADOW OF THE CITY**
ALCD 4813 / May '93 / Alligator

Veagas Soul

☐ **PURE**
BLVSCD 01 / 23 Mar '98 / Bellboy

Veasley, Gerald

☐ **LOOK AHEAD**
Fanfare / Fly spy / Six pm / Country preacher / Just a word / Prayer I / Algeria (joy) / Heaven in your eyes / Sweet Mary / Shango / Fool's lullaby / Dream / Prayer II
101S 8771312 / Aug '94 / 101 South
INAK 30162CD / Nov '97 / In Akustik

☐ **SIGNS**
Marvin's mood / Lasting moment / Highway home / Exit to the street / Signs / Salamanca / Imani (faith) / Soul seduction / What are you doing for the rest of your life / Walking through walls / Tranquility
101S 8770522 / Oct '94 / 101 South
INAK 30272CD / Nov '97 / In Akustik

☐ **SOUL CONTROL**
Carolina / Love is the cure / Lady / Broad street / Quiet storm / Nobody knows / As blue as you / Deeper / Kyle's groove / But when she smiles / Earthworm
INAK 30382CD / Nov '97 / In Akustik

Ved Buens Ende

☐ **THOSE WHO CARESS THE PALE**
ALC 001 / Mar '97 / Misanthropy

☐ **WRITTEN IN WATERS**
AMAZON 006CD / 3 Nov '97 / Misanthropy

Vee, Bobby

☐ **EP COLLECTION, THE**
Little star / Rubber ball / Bo diddley / Peggy sue / Linda lu / At a time like this / Run to him / Sharing you / Devil or angel / Do you want to dance / Sincerely / Lollipop / Someday / Night has a thousand eyes / Walk right back / Take good care of my baby / More than I can say / A forever kind of love / Since I met you baby / On't you believe them / One last kiss / I can't say goodbye
SEECD 297 / 16 Mar '98 / See For Miles

☐ **NIGHT HAS A THOUSAND EYES/ MEETS THE VENTURES**
BGOCD 408 / 17 Aug '98 / Beat Goes On

☐ **ORIGINAL, THE**
Take good care of my baby / Night has a thousand eyes / Rubber ball / Devil or angel / Charms / Please don't ask about Barbara / Sharing you / More than I can say / How many tears / Punish her / Stayin' in / Be true to yourself / I'll make you mine / Look at me girl / Maybe just today / Beautiful people / My girl/Hey girl / Come back when you grow up
TO 860152 / 2 Feb '98 / Disky

☐ **TAKE GOOD CARE OF MY BABY (22 Greatest Hits)**
Devil or angel / Rubber ball / Stayin' in / More than I can say / How many tears / Take good care of my baby / Run to him / Walkin' with my angel / Please don't ask about barbara / Sharing you / Punish her / A forever kind of love / Night has a thousand eyes / Charms / Be true to yourself / Yesterday and you (armen's theme) / I'll make you mine / Look at me girl / Come back when you grow up / Beautiful people / Maybe just today / My girl-hey girl
RMB 75075 / Sep '94 / Remember

☐ **VERY BEST OF BOBBY VEE, THE**
Rubber ball / More than I can say / How many tears / Take good care of my baby / It doesn't matter anymore / True love ways / Run to him / Please don't ask about Barbara / Walkin' with my angel / Punish her / Taht'll be the day / Peggy Sue / Oh Boy / Heartbeat / Sharing you / Forever kind of love / Raining in my heart / Everyday / Bobby tomorrow / Night has a thousand eyes
CDMFP 6386 / 13 Oct '97 / Music For Pleasure

Vega, Alan

☐ **DUJANG PRANG**
213CD 008 / Oct '96 / 2.13.61

☐ **JUKEBOX BABE**
668532 / Mar '96 / Melodie

☐ **NEW RACEION**
Pleaser / Christ dice / Gamma pop / Viva the legs / Do the job / Junior's little sister dropped ta cheap / How many lifetimes / Holy skips / Keep it alive / Go trane go
110122 / May '93 / Musidisc

Vega, Chilton & Vaughn

☐ **CUBIST BLUES**
7422466 / May '97 / Last Call

Vega, Ray

☐ **RAY VEGA**
Greenhouse / Tahluchahchah / Afternoon in Paris / Islands / No two people / Partido Alto / It's a New York thing / Alone together / Psalm 150
CCD 4735 / Nov '96 / Concord Picante

Vega, Suzanne

☐ **99.9 F**
Rock in this pocket (Song of David) / Blood makes noise / In Liverpool / 99.9 F / Blood sings / Fat man and dancing girl / (If you were) in my movie / As a child / Bad wisdom / When heroes go down / As girls go / Song of sand / Private goes public
5400122 / 15 Sep '97 / A&M

☐ **DAYS OF THE OPEN HAND**
Tired of sleeping / Men in a war / Rusted pipe / Book of dreams / Institution green / Those whole girls (run in grace) / Room off the street / Big space / Predictions / Fifty-fifty chance / Pilgrimage
3952932 / Apr '95 / A&M

☐ **NINE OBJECTS OF DESIRE**
Birth-day (Love made real) / Headshots / Caramel / Stockings / Casual match / Thin man / No cheap thrill / World before Columbus / Lolita / Honeymoon suite / Tombstone / My favourite plum
5405832 / Feb '97 / A&M

☐ **SOLITUDE STANDING**
Tom's diner / Luka / Ironbound / Fancy poultry / In the eye / Night vision / Solitude standing / Calypso / Language / Gypsy / Wooden horse
SUZCD 2 / May '87 / A&M

☐ **SUZANNE VEGA**
Cracking / Freeze tag / Marlene on the wall / Small blue thing / Straight lines / Undertow / Some journey / Queen and the soldier / Night movies / Neighbourhood girls
CDMID 177 / Mar '93 / A&M

Vega, Tony

☐ **APARENTEMENTE**
Aparentemente / Donde estas / En resumen / Esposa / Me gusta que seas celosa / No me liames amor / Deja / Con su mejor amiga / Por fin
66058017 / Jun '93 / RMM

Vegas Beat

☐ **VEGAS BEAT**
CAR 21CD / Mar '97 / Candy Ass

Vei, Yiota

☐ **IONIA**
ML 4843 / 11 May '98 / Musurgia Graeca

Veil

☐ **WORDS VERSUS NOTHING**
CM 77222CD / 27 Apr '98 / Century Media

Veillon, Jean-Michel

☐ **E KOAD NIZAN**
GWP 004CD / Aug '93 / Gwerz

☐ **JEAN-MICHEL VEILLON**
GWP 009CD / Aug '95 / Gwerz

Vela, Rosie

☐ **ZAZU**
Fool's paradise / Magic smile / Interlude / Tonto / Sunday / Taxi / Second emotion / Boxes / Zazu
3950162 / 15 Sep '97 / A&M

Velaires

☐ **SCREAMERS TO FLAIRS TO VELAIRES FROM SIOUX CITY TO PHOENIX**
I dig / Roll over Beethoven / Brazil / Sticks and stones / Dream / Hey pretty baby / Scotch and soda / Ubangi stomp / Sweet little sixteen / Memories are made of this / Lotta lovin' / Mule train / Lovin' you / It's almost tomorrow / Yes it's me / Tragedy train / Don't wake me up / Locomotion / Johnny B Goode / Memory train / Summertime blues / Will I / I can never do enough for you / Sticks and stones / What did I do wrong / Ubangi stomp
BCD 16168 / May '97 / Bear Family

Velez, Glen

☐ **RHYTHMCOLOUREXOTICA**
ELLICD 4140 / May '97 / Ellipsis Arts

Velocette

☐ **SONORITIES**
REFCD 8 / May '96 / Reflective

Velocity Girl

☐ **6 SONG CD**
I don't care if you go / Always / Forgotten favorite / Why should I be nice to you / Not at all / I don't care if you go (accoustic)
SLUM 023 / Feb '93 / Slumberland

☐ **COPACETIC**
SPCD 75242 / Apr '93 / Sub Pop

☐ **GILDED STARS AND ZEALOUS HEARTS**
SPCD 340 / Mar '96 / Sub Pop

☐ **SIMPATICO**
SPCD 122/303 / Jul '94 / Sub Pop

Veloso, Caetano

☐ **CIRCULADO**
Fora de orem / Circulado de fulo / Itapua / Boas vindas / Ela ela / Santa Clara padroeira da telivisiao / Baiao da penha / Neide candolina / Terciera margem do rio / O cu do mundo / Lindeza
5106392 / Feb '94 / Philips

☐ **CIRCULADO VIVO**
A tua presence morena / Black or white / Americanos / Um Indio circulado de fulo / Queixe / Mano a mano / Chega de saudade / Disseram que eu voltei / Americanizade / Quando eu penso na Bahia / A terceira margem do rio / Oceano / Jokerman / Voce e Linda / O leaozinho / Itapua / Debaizo dos caracois dos seus / O mais doces barbaros / A filha da chiquita bacana / Chuve suor e cerveja / Sampa
5180702 / Oct '93 / Philips

☐ **FINA ESTAMPA AO VIVO**
5289182 / Mar '96 / Verve

Velvet Color

☐ **LET ME HOLD YOUR HEART**
EFA 128202 / Feb '96 / Hot Wire

☐ **NOW IS THE TIME**
EFA 128192 / Dec '95 / Hot Wire

Velvet Crush

☐ **HEAVY CHANGES**
AMCD 102 / 22 Jun '98 / Action Musik

☐ **IN THE PRESENCE OF GREATNESS**
Window to the world / Drive me down / Ash and earth / White soul / Superstar / Blind faith / Speedway baby / Stop / Asshole / Die a little every day
CRECD 109 / Oct '90 / Creation

☐ **TEENAGE SYMPHONIES TO GOD**
Hold me up / My blank pages / Why not your baby / Time wraps around you / Atmosphere / Ten / Faster days / Something's gotta give / This life is killing me / Weird summer / Star trip / Keep on lingerin'
CRECD 130 / Jun '94 / Creation

Velvet Energy

☐ **WHALES AND DOLPHINS**
AHLCD 49 / 18 May '98 / Hit

Velvet Monkeys

☐ **RAKE**
We call it rock / We call it rock / Ballad 'rake' / Something's in the air / Velvet monkey (theme song) / Rock the night / Harmonica hell house / Love to give / 7 angels / Rock party / Velvet monkey
DANCD 061 / Feb '95 / Danceteria

Velvet Sound Orchestra

☐ **INSTRUMENTAL SUMMER HITS (3CD Set)**
Mes emmeredes / L'amour c'est l'affaire des gens / She / Rosa / Cafe de la paix / L'important c'est la rose / Yesterday when I was young / Mefie toi / La maladie d'amour / Little love and understanding / Ne me quitte pas / Old fashioned way / La vie devant soi / Nathalie / La France / Milonga sentimental / Lady Laura / Quiereme mucho / Y como es el / Playa / Hey / Abrazame / Que canten los Ninos / Quiero / Un canto a Galicia / Comidas / Y te vas / Por el amor de una mujer / Mi querido mi viego mi amigo / Amor de mis Amores / Stani amori / Per lei / Se bastasse una canzone / Felicita / La solitudine / Mara / Ma che bello questo amore / Liberta / Lettera martedi / Amarti e l'immenso per me / Se stiamo insieme / Stracciatella / Sincerita / Musica e
HR 880392 / May '97 / Disky

Velvet Underground

☐ **1969 VOL.1**
Waiting for my man / Lisa says / What goes on / Sweet Jane / We're gonna have a real good time together / Femme fatale / New age / Rock 'n' roll / Beginning to see the light / Heroin
8348232 / '88 / Mercury

☐ **1969 VOL.2**
Ocean / Pale blue eyes / Heroin / Some kinda love / Over you / Sweet Bonnie Brown / It's just too much / White light / White heat / I can't stand it / I'll be your mirror
8348242 / '88 / Mercury

☐ **ANOTHER VIEW**
We're gonna have a real good time together / I'm gonna move right in / Hey Mr. Rain / Ride into the sun / Coney Island steeplechase / Guess I'm falling in love / Ferryboat Bill / Rock 'n' roll
8294052 / Jan '94 / Polydor

☐ **BEST OF THE VELVET UNDERGROUND, THE**
I'm waiting for the man / Femme fatale / Run run run / Heroin / All tomorrow's parties / I'll be your mirror / White light, white heat / Stephanie says / What goes on / Beginning to see the light / Pale blue eyes / I can't stand it / Lisa says / Sweet Jane / Rock 'n' roll
8411642 / Oct '89 / Polydor

☐ LIVE AT MAX'S KANSAS CITY
I'm waiting for the man / Sweet Jane / Lonesome Cowboy Bill / Beginning to see the light / I'll be your mirror / Pale blue eyes / Sunday morning / New age / Femme fatale / After hours
7567903702 / May '93 / Atlantic

☐ LIVE MCMXCIII
We're gonna have a real good time together / Venus in furs / Guess I'm falling in love / Afterhours / All tomorrow's parties / Some kinda love / I'll be your mirror / Beginning to see the light / Gift / I heard her call my name / Femme fatale / Hey Mr. Rain / Sweet Jane / Velvet nursery rhyme / White light, white heat / I'm sticking with you / Black angel's death song / Rock 'n' roll / I can't stand it / I'm waiting for the man / Heroin / Pale blue eyes / Coyote
9362454642 / Oct '93 / WEA

☐ LOADED
Who loves the sun / Sweet Jane / Rock 'n' roll / Cool it down / New age / Head held high / Lonesome Cowboy Bill / I found a reason / Train round the bend / Oh sweet nuthin'
7567903672 / May '93 / Atlantic

☐ LOADED (The Fully Loaded Edition/ 2CD Set)
Who loves the sun / Sweet Jane / Rock and roll / Cool it down / New age / Head held high / Lonesome cowboy Bill / I found a reason / Train round the bend / Oh sweet nuthin' / Ride into the sun / Ocean / I'm sticking with you / I love you / Rock and roll / Head held high / Who loves the sun / Sweet Jane / Rock and roll / Cool it down / New age / Head held high / Lonesome cowboy Bill / I found a reason / Trail round the bend / Oh sweet nuthin' / Ocean / I love you / Satellite of love / Oh gin / Walk and talk / Sad song / Love makes me feel 10 feet tall
8122725632 / Mar '97 / Rhino

☐ PEEL SLOWLY AND SEE (4CD Set)
5278872 / Sep '95 / Polydor

☐ VELVET DOWN UNDERGROUND, THE (Various Artists)
Sunday morning: *Painters & Dockers* / I'm waiting for the man: *Bored* / Femme fatale: *Nursery Crimes* / Venus in furs: *Glory Box* / Run run run: *Authohaze* / All tomorrow's parties: *Spleens* / Heroin: *Ripe* / There she goes again: *Cosmic Psychos* / I'll be your mirror: *Underground Lovers* / Black angel's death song: *Clowns Smiling Backwards* / European son: *Snark*
SUR 529CD / Jun '93 / Survival

☐ VELVET UNDERGROUND
Candy says / What goes on / Pale blue eyes / That's the story of my life / Beginning to see the light / Murder mystery / Jesus / After hours / Some kinda love / I'm set free
5312522 / Apr '96 / Polydor

☐ VELVET UNDERGROUND AND NICO, THE (Velvet Underground & Nico)
Sunday morning / I'm waiting for the man / Femme fatale / Venus in furs / Run run run / All tomorrow's parties / Heroin / There she goes again / I'll be your mirror / Black angel's death song / European son
5312502 / Apr '96 / Polydor

☐ WHITE LIGHT, WHITE HEAT
White light, white heat / Gift / Lady Godiva's operation / Here she comes now / I heard her call my name / Sister Ray
5312512 / Apr '96 / Polydor

Velvets

☐ COMPLETE VELVETS, THE
Tonight (Could be the night) / Time and again / Spring fever / That lucky old sun / Laugh / Lana / Love express / Let the good times roll / Light goes on, light goes off / Crying in the chapel / Dawn / Here comes that song again / Nightmare / If / Let the fool kiss you / Baby the magic is gone / Be ever mine / You done me bad / Kiss me / Alicia / Bird dog / My love / Who has the right / I'm trusting in you / Almost but not quite / Husbands and wives / I can feel it / Poison love / That's out of my line
CDCHD 625 / Mar '96 / Ace

Velvett Fogg

☐ VELVETT FOGG...PLUS
Yellow cave woman / New York mining disaster 1941 / Wizard of Gobsolod / Once among the trees / Lady Caroline / Come away Melinda / Owed to the dip / Within the night / Plastic man / Telstar '69
SEECD 259 / Sep '89 / See For Miles

Velvette, Lorette

☐ LOST PART OF ME
EFA 128622 / 13 Oct '97 / Veracity

Vendemian

☐ BETWEEN TWO WORLDS
ABCD 001 / May '94 / Resurrection

☐ ONE EYE OPEN
ABCD 014 / Apr '97 / Resurrection

☐ THROUGH THE DEPTHS
ABCD 002 / Jan '96 / Resurrection

☐ TRANSITION
ABCD 006 / Mar '96 / Resurrection

☐ TREACHEROUS
ABCD 003 / Jan '96 / Resurrection

Venerea

☐ BOTH ENDS BURNING
GIFT 052CD / Apr '97 / Gift Of Life

☐ SHAKE YOUR BOOTY
GIFT 048CD / Dec '96 / Gift Of Life

Venetsanou, Nena

☐ AGERON ECHOS THEATROU
MMB 10707 / 11 May '98 / Musurgia Graeca

☐ ICONES
MA 008 / 11 May '98 / Musurgia Graeca

Vengeance

☐ ARABIA (2CD Set)
CDP 1060 / 22 Jun '98 / Pseudonym

☐ BACK FROM FLIGHT 19
TM 011 / Nov '97 / Transmission

☐ WE HAVE WAYS TO MAKE YOU
CDP 1054 / 22 Jun '98 / Pseudonym

Veni Domine

☐ FALL BABYLON FALL
MASSCD 127 / Jun '97 / Massacre

☐ MATERIAL SANCTUARY
MASSCD 074 / Oct '95 / Massacre

Venom

☐ BLACK REIGN
RRCD 212 / Apr '96 / Receiver

☐ CAST IN STONE (2CD Set)
SPV 08818812 / Dec '97 / SPV

☐ EINE KLEINE NACHTMUSIK
Too loud for the croed / Seven gates of hell / Leave me in hell / Nightmare / Countess Bathory / Die hard / Schizo / Guitar solo by Mantas / In nomine Satanus / Witching hour / Black metal / Chanting of the priest / Satanchrist / Fly trap / Warhead / Buried alive / Love amongst / Bass solo Cronos / Welcome to hell / Bloodlust
NEATXSO 132 / Nov '87 / Neat

☐ FROM HEAVEN TO THE UNKNOWN (2CD Set)
Welcome to hell / Witching hour / Angel dust / Red light fever / Black metal / Buried alive / Teacher's pet / Countess Bathory / Don't burn the witch (at war with Satan-intro) / Rip ride / Cry wolf / Women, leather and hell / Satanachist / Possessed / Hellchild / Mystique / Too loud for the crowd / In league with Satan / Live like an angel / Bloodlust / In nomine satanas / Die hard / Acid queen / Bursting out / Warhead / Lady Lust / 7 gates of hell / Manitou / Dead of the night / Dead on arrival / Hounds of hell / Bitch bitch / Sadist / Black metal / Snots shit
SMDCD 120 / May '97 / Snapper

☐ IN MEMORIUM (The Best Of Venom)
Angel dust / Raise the dead / Red light fever / Buried alive / Witching hour / At war with satan / Warhead / Manitou / Under a spell / Nothing sacred / Dead love / Welcome to hell / Black metal / Countess bathory / 1000 Days in sodom / Prime evil / If you wanna war / Surgery
MCCD 097 / Mar '93 / Music Club

☐ LIVE OFFICIAL BOOTLEG
Leave me in hell / Countess bathory / Die hard / Seven gates of hell / Buried alive / Don't burn the witch / In nomine satanus / Welcome to hell / Warhead / Stand up and be counted / Bloodlust
CDTB 110 / '91 / Thunderbolt

☐ NEW LIVE AND RARE
CLEO 3052 / 30 Jun '98 / Cleopatra

☐ NEW LIVE AND RARE VOL.1 (2CD Set)
Harder than ever / Skeletal dance / Speed king / Welcome to Hell / Blackened are the priests / Playtime / Carnivorous / Die hard / Hall bent for leather / Burstin' out / Prime evil / Black metal / Meglamania / Faerie tale / Civilized / Clarrise / Temples of ice / Angel dust / Teachers pet / Witching hour
CDBLEED 22 / 1 Jun '98 / Bleeding Hearts

☐ POSSESSED
Powerdrive / Flytrap / Satanchist / Burn this place (to the ground) / Harmony dies / Possessed / Hellchild / Moonshine / Wing and a prayer / Suffer not the children / Voyeur / Mystique / Too loud for the croed
CLACD 402 / Jun '94 / Castle

☐ PRIME EVIL
Prime evil / Parasite / Blackened are the priests / Carnivorous / Skeletal dance / Megalomania / Insane / Harder than ever / Into the fire / Skool daze / Live like an angel, die like a devil
CDFLAG 36 / Oct '89 / Under One Flag

☐ TEAR YOUR SOUL APART
CDFLAG 50 / Sep '90 / Under One Flag

☐ TEMPLES OF ICE
Tribes / Even in heaven / Trinity mcmxlv 0530 / In memory of (paul miller 1964-90) / Faerie tale / Playtime / Acid / Arachnid / Speed king / Temples of ice
CDFLAG 56 / Jun '91 / Under One Flag

☐ WASTELAND, THE
Cursed / I'm paralysed / Back legions / Riddle of steel / Need to kill / Kissing the beast / Crucified / Shadow king / Wolverine / Clarisse
CDFLAG 72 / Nov '92 / Under One Flag

☐ WELCOME TO HELL
Sons of Satan / Welcome to hell / Schizo / Mayhem with mercy / Poison / Live like an angel / Witching hour / 1000 days in Sodom / Angel dust / In league with Satan / Red light fever
CLACD 255 / '91 / Castle

Venom P. Stinger

☐ TEARBUCKETER
SB 0512 / May '96 / Matador

Vent 414

☐ VENT
Fixer / Fits and starts / At the base of the fire / Last episode / Laying down with / Life before you / Correctional / Easy to talk / Night out with a foreign fella / Kissing the mirror / At one / 2113 / Guess my God
5330482 / Oct '96 / Polydor

Ventilators

☐ VENTILATORS, THE
EFA 046222 / Sep '95 / Pork Pie

Ventura, Ray

☐ DU JAZZ A LA CHANSON 1929-1946 (2CD Set)
984382 / 24 Feb '98 / EPM

☐ SUCCES ET RARETES 1930-1939
701592 / Sep '96 / Chansophone

Venturas

☐ GUITAR INSTRUMENTALS
DBM 1003CD / Sep '97 / Drum Boy

Ventures

☐ 10TH ANNIVERSARY ALBUM
OW 19385 / 15 Jun '98 / One Way

☐ ANOTHER SMASH/THE COLOURFUL VENTURES
Riders in the sky / Wheels / Lonely heart / Bulldog / Lullaby of the leaves / Beyond the reef / Rawhide / Meet Mister Callaghan / Trombone / Last date / Ginchy / Josie / Blue moon / Yellow jacket / Bluer than blue / Cherry pink and apple blossom white / Green leaves of summer / Blue skies / Green fields / Red top / White silver sands / Yellow bird / Orange fire / Silver city
C5HCD 619 / Aug '94 / See For Miles

☐ BATMAN/TV THEMES
Batman Theme / Zocko / Cape / Get Smart theme / Man from UNCLE / Hot Line / Joker's Wild / Up, Up, And Away / Green Hornet 1966 / 00-711 / Vampcamp / Secret Agent Man / Charlie's Angels / Medical Centre / Star Trek / Streets Of San Francisco / Starsky and Hutch / Baretta's Theme / Hawaii Five-0 / SWAT / Police Story / MASH / Policewoman / Nadia's Theme (The Young And The Restless)
C5HCD 653 / Jun '97 / See For Miles

☐ BEST OF POP SOUNDS/GO WITH THE VENTURES
Kyoto doll / Hokkaido skies / Blue chateau / Scat in the dark / Koyubino-Omoide / Sukiyake / Ginirono-Michi / Reflections in a palace lake / Ginza lights / Forbidden love / Wakareta-Hitoto / Kirino-Kanatani / Sometimes I feel longing for a motherless child / Kimito-Itsumademo / Green grass / These boots are made for walkin' / Frankie and Johnny / Ad-Venture / Monday, Monday / Good lovin' / Eight miles high / Escape / Sloop John B / Go / California dreamin'
C5HCD 642 / Jun '96 / See For Miles

☐ DON'T WALK RUN VOL.2/KNOCK ME OUT
House of the rising sun / Diamond head / Night train / Peach fuzz / Rap city / Blue star / Walk don't run '64 / Night walk / One mint julep / Pedal pusher / Creeper / Stranger on the shore / I feel fine / Love potion no.9 / Tomorrow's love / Oh pretty woman / Mariner no.4 / When you walk in the room / Gone gone gone / Slaughter on 10th avenue / She's not there / Lonely girl / Bird rockers / Sha la la
C5HCD 630 / Aug '95 / See For Miles

☐ EP COLLECTION VOL.2, THE
Walk don't run / Last night / Red river rock / You are my sunshine / Scratch / Action / No matter what / Wild thing / Wild cat / Walk don't run '64 / Running wild / Memphis / El cumbanchero / McCoy / Green onions / Lovesick blues / Penetration / Pipeline / Stop action / Little bit of action / Wolly and wild / Wild child / Cruel sea / Tall cool one / Tarantella / Skip to m'limbo
SEECD 363 / Jan '93 / See For Miles

☐ EP COLLECTION, THE
No trespassing / Night train / Ram bunk shush / Lonely heart / Ups 'n' downs / Torquay / Bulldog / Meet Mr. Callaghan / Trambone / Josie / Yellow jacket / Bluer than blue / Gringo / Moon dawg / Sunny river / Guitar twist / Telstar / Percolator / Silver city / Wildwood flower / Wabash cannonball / Secret agent man / Man from UNCLE / Hot line
SEECD 292 / Jan '90 / See For Miles

☐ FLIGHT OF FANTASY/IN SPACE
Mighty Quinn / Innermotion faze / Ballad of Bonnie and Clyde / Walking the carpet / Flights of fantasy / Soul coaxing / Green light / Cry like a baby / Fly away / Love shower / Summertime blues / Scarborough fair canticle / Out of limits / He never came back / Moon child / Fear / Exploration in terror / War of the satelites / Bat / Penetration / Love goddess of Venus / Solar race / Fourth dimension / Twilight zone
C5HCD 644 / Jul '96 / See For Miles

☐ GIANTS OF THE GUITAR
In crowd / Satisfaction / Sleepwalk / Telstar / Blue moon / Rebel rouser / Walk don't run / La bamba / Perfidia / I like it like that / Night stick / Secret agent man / Memphis Tennessee
HADCD 211 / Jun '97 / Spotlight On

☐ GUITAR FREAKOUT/SUPER PSYCHEDELICS
Good thing / High and dry / Standing in the shadow of love / Off in the 93rds / Cookout freakout on lookout mountain / Wack wack / Mod east / I'm a believer / Guitar freakout / Snoopy Vs. the Red Baron / Paper airline / Theme from the wild angels / Strawberry fields forever / Psychedelic venture / Western Union / Guitar psychedelics / Kandy koncoction / Reflections / Little bit me, a little bit you / Endless dream / Vibrations / Psyched out / 1999 A.D. / Happy together
C5MCD 627 / Jul '95 / See For Miles

☐ HORSE, THE/NEW TESTAMENT
OW 19387 / 15 Jun '98 / One Way

☐ IN THE VAULTS (Their Greatest Rarities Of The 1960's/1970's)
McCoy / Lady of Spain / Damaged goods / Way you look tonight / Gemini / Lawrence of Arabia / Green hornet / El Greco / Comin' home baby / Arabesque / Peace pipe / Pandora's box / Summer love / Too young to know my mind / Paint it black / Squaw man / Mercenary / Kern County line / Skylab (passport to the future) / Samovar / Joyride / Tora tora tora / Endless summer
CDCHD 651 / May '97 / Ace

☐ JOY/THE LATIN ALBUM
Beethoven's Sonata in C minor / One fine day / In a Persian market place / Swan Lake / Bach's Prelude / Peter and the wolf / Mozart Forty / Joy / Elise / Ravel's Pavane / Mozart's Minuet / Melody of joy / Breeze and I / Yours / Begin the beguine / Peanut vendor / Spanish eyes / Brazil / It's impossible / Poinciana / Green eyes / El Condor Pasa / Delicado / Guantanamera / Cuando caliente el Sol
C5HCD 638 / Apr '96 / See For Miles

☐ LET'S GO/COUNTRY CLASSICS
Memphis / Let's go / More / El watusi / Walk right in / Sukiyaki / New Orleans / So fine / Wipe out / Hot pastrami / Runaway / Over the mountain across the sea / Panhandle rag / Wabash cannonball / San Antonio rose / I walk the line / Wildwood flower / I can't stop loving you / Lovesick blues / Steel guitar rag / You are my sunshine / Oh, lonesome me / Sugarfoot rag / Born to lose
C5HCD 657 / Jul '97 / See For Miles

☐ LONELY BULL/ONE MILLION DOLLAR WEEKEND
Telstar / Lonely bull / Mexico / Calcutta / Apache / Never on Sunday / Tequila / Green onions / Percolator / Red river rock / Let there be drums / Last night / What now my love / Georgy girl / Ode to Billy Joe / Sunny / Respect / To Sir with love / Music to watch girls by / Groovin' / Windy / Sealed with a kiss / Uptight / Yesterday
C5HCD 663 / 6 Oct '97 / See For Miles

☐ MASHED POTATOES AND GRAVY/ GOING TO THE VENTURES DANCE PARTY
Lucille / Gravy (for mashed potatoes) / Hernando's hideaway / Mashed potato time / Summertime / Hot summer (Asian mashed) / Poison ivy / Wah-watusi / Instant mashed / Scratch / Hully gully (baby) / Spudnik / Mr. Moto / Theme from come September / Gully-ver / Loco-motion / Lolita ya ya / Limbo rock / Sweet and lovely / Gandy dancer / Intruder / Venus / Night drive / Ya ya wobble
C5HCD 635 / Jan '96 / See For Miles

☐ NEW TESTAMENT/MORE GOLDEN GREATS
Good mornin' captain / Testament / Oye como va / Wild world / Katana / Manchurian beat / Whole lotta love / What is love / What is life / Novios para siempre / Spirit / She's a lady Pesado / Good, the bad, and the ugly (Il buono, Il brutto, Il cattivo / Mission impossible / House of the rising sun / More / Torquay / Love is blue / Classical gas / Taste of honey / Green onions / Grazing in the grass / Raunchy / Hawaii five-o
C5HCD 652 / Jun '97 / See For Miles

☐ ON STAGE/SURFING
Wipe-out / Journey through the stars / Slaughter on 10th Avenue / Caravan / Pedal pusher / Apache '65 / Bumble bee / Driving guitars / Medley / Yellow jacket / Pipeline / Diamonds / Windy and warm / Ten over / Surf rider / Changing tides / Ninth wave / Party in Laguna / Barefoot venture / Heavies / Cruncher / Lonely sea
C5HCD 658 / Aug '97 / See For Miles

☐ ONLY HITS
OW 19391 / 15 Jun '98 / One Way

☐ ORIGINAL, THE
Walk don't run / Perfidia / Ram bunk shush / Lullabye of the leaves / Blue moon / Lolita ya ya / 2000 pound bee / Slaughter on tenth avenue / Diamond head / Secret agent man / Hawaii five o / Yellow jacket / Driving guitars / Road runner / Twisted / Dick Tracy / Pedal pusher / Walk don't run
TO 860962 / 2 Feb '98 / Disky

☐ PLAY GUITAR VOL.1-4 & 7 (3CD Set)
OW 19386 / Nov '97 / One Way

☐ PLAY GUITAR VOL.3/PLAY GUITAR VOL.7
Tuning the electric guitar and electric bass / Secret agent man / Diamond head / No matter what shape (your stomach's in) / Taste of honey / Honky tonk / Louie Louie / Night train / Peter Gunn
C5HCD 655 / Aug '97 / See For Miles

☐ PLAY THE CARPENTERS/THE JIM CROCE SONGBOOK
We've only just begun / Yesterday once more / It's going to take some time / Bless the beasts and children / Top of the world / Sing / Superstar / Close to you / Hurting each other / Rainy days and Mondays / Jambalaya / Goodbye to love / I got a

name / Bad, Bad Leroy Brown / I'll have to say I love you in a song / Lover's cross / It doesn't have to be that way / Age / Time in a bottle / Don't mess around with Jim / One less set of footsteps / Operator / Five short minutes / Speedball Tucker
C5HCD 620 / Oct '94 / See For Miles

☐ ROCK 'N' ROLL FOREVER/NOW PLAYING
OW 19388 / Jun '97 / One Way

☐ STARS ON GUITARS (2CD Set)
SMDCD 178 / 2 Mar '98 / Snapper

☐ SWAMP SONG/HAWAII FIVE-O
Carry me back / Honky tonk woman / Muddy Missisippi line / Jambalaya / Swamp rock / Niki Hoeky / Green river / Suspicious minds / Catfish mud dance / Proud Mary / Gumbo / Plaquemines parish / Hawaii Five-O / Lovin' things / Galveston / Letter / Don't give in to him / Theme from "A Summer Place" / Spooky / Traces / Stormy / Aquarius / Let the sunshine in / Games people play / I can hear music / Dizzy
C5HCD 647 / Jul '96 / See For Miles

☐ THEME FROM SHAFT, THE/ROCKY
OW 19389 / 15 Jun '98 / One Way

☐ THEME FROM SHAFT, THE/THE HORSE
Shaft / Peace train / Thunder cloud / Gimme some lovin' / Indian sun / Deep, deep in the water / Gypsys, tramps and thieves / Two divided by love / Tight fit / I'm a man / Never my love / Cherries jubilee / Horse / Here comes the judge / Licking stick, licking stick / Crazy horse / Gallop / Grazing in the grass / Walk don't run/Land of a 1000 dances / Jumpin' Jack flash / Choo choo train / Horse power / Tip toe thru' the tulips with me
C5HCD 651 / Oct '96 / See For Miles

☐ TV THEMES/THE VENTURES MEET BOBBY VEE
OW 19390 / Jun '97 / One Way

☐ TWIST WITH THE VENTURES/TWIST PARTY VOL.2
Driving guitars / Twist / Roadrunner / Gringo / Moon dawg / Guitar twist / Opus twist / Movin' and groovin' / Sunny river / Let's twist again / Shanghai'd / Bumble bee twist / My bonnie lies / Twisted / Twomp / Besame mucho / Blue tailed fly / Swanee River twist / Instant guitars / Dark eyes twist / Counterpoint / Kicking around / Bluebird / Red wing twist
C5HCD 621 / Oct '94 / See For Miles

☐ UNDERGROUND FIRE/HOLLYWOOD METAL DINAMIC SOUND 3000
Underground fire / Embers in E minor / Sea of grass / Higher than thou / Up, up and down / Country funk and the canned heat / Born to be wild / Sunshine of your love / Weight / Light my fire / Down on me / Fire / Johnny B Goode / Linda Lou / Diana / Hound dog / Goodbye rock'n'roll / House of the rising sun / Reddy teddy / Lucille / Rip it up / Dance the night away / When the saints go marching in / Lonesome town
C5HCD 636 / Feb '96 / See For Miles

☐ VENTURES A GO-GO/WHERE THE ACTION IS
Satisfaction / Go go slow / Louie Louie / Night stick / La bamba / In crowd / Woolly bully / Go go guitar / Go go dancer / Swingin' creeper / Whittier boulevard / I like it like that / Action / Lies / Fever / Stop action / Three's a crowd / Taste of honey / No matter what shape / Action plus / Hang on sloopy (my girl sloopy) / Nutty / Little bit of action / She's just my style
C5HCD 622 / Mar '95 / See For Miles

☐ VENTURES, THE
Driving guitars (Ventures twist) / Ups 'n' downs / Wailin' / Lonely heart / Perfidia / McCoy / Better than blue / Ram-bunk-shush / Trespassing / Lullaby of the leaves / Bulldog / Silver City / Lolita ya ya / 2000 pound bee / Ninth wave / Journey to the stars / Torquay / Walk don't run / Slaughter on 10th Avenue / Diamonds head / Ten seconds to heaven / Secret agent man / Blue star / Rap city / Walk don't run/ Land of a 1000 dances / Hawaii Five-O
CDSL 8257 / Jul '95 / EMI

☐ WALK DON'T RUN (The Best Of The Ventures)
PLSCD 203 / Apr '97 / Pulse

☐ WALK DON'T RUN/THE VENTURES
Morgen / Raunchy / Home / My own true love (Tara's theme) / Switch / Walk don't run / Night train / No trespassing / Caravan / Sleep walk / McCoy / Honky tonk / Shuck / Detour / Ram-bunk-shush / Hawaiian war chant / Perfidia / Harlem nocturne / Blue tango / Up's and downs / Lonesome tonight / Torquay / Wailin' / Moon of manakoora
C5HCD 618 / Aug '94 / See For Miles

☐ WILD THINGS/THE FABULOUS VENTURES
Wild thing / Fuzzy and wild / Sweet pea / Wild wooly / Wild child / Summer in the city / Pied Piper / Wild trip / Hanky panky / Wild cat / How now wild cow / Work song / Needles and pins / Runnin' wild / Eleventh hour / Cruel sea / Scratchin' tall cool one / Journey to the stars / Fugitive / Ravin' blue / Walkin' with pluto / Pink panther theme
C5HCD 662 / 6 Oct '97 / See For Miles

Venus & The Razorblades

☐ SONGS FROM THE SUNSHINE JUNGLE
Finer things in life / Big city / All right you guys / Midnight / Punk-a-rama / Workin' girl / I wanna be where the boys are / Dog food / Wrong kind of guy / Victim of my backstreet love
SEECD 444 / Aug '97 / See For Miles

Venus Fly Trap

☐ TOTEM
DANCD 024 / Jan '90 / Danceteria

Venuti, Joe

☐ ALONE AT THE PALACE (Venuti, Joe & Dave McKenna)
CRD 160 / Mar '96 / Chiaroscuro

☐ GEMS (Venuti, Joe & George Barnes)
I want to be happy / I'm coming Virginia / Almost like being in love / I'll never be the same / Oh baby / Hindustan / Lover / Humoresque / Poor butterfly / Oh lady be good
CCD 6014 / Nov '94 / Concord Jazz

☐ JAZZ PORTRAITS (Venuti, Joe & Eddie Lang)
Dinah / Wild dog / Sweet Sue, just you / I've found a new baby / Stringin' the blues / Black and blue bottom / Wild cat / Beatin' the dog / Sunshine / Goin' places / Doin' things / Cheese and crackers / Little girl / Wolf wobble / Penn beach blues / I'll never be the same / Raggin' the scale
CD 14515 / May '94 / Jazz Portraits

☐ JOE VENUTI AND EDDIE LANG VOL.1 (Venuti, Joe & Eddie Lang)
JSPCD 309 / Aug '89 / JSP

☐ JOE VENUTI AND EDDIE LANG VOL.2 (Venuti, Joe & Eddie Lang)
JSPCD 310 / Aug '89 / JSP

☐ JOE VENUTI AND ZOOT SIMS (Venuti, Joe & Zoot Sims)
CRD 142 / Mar '96 / Chiaroscuro

☐ PRETTY TRIX
IAJRCCD 1003 / Jun '94 / IAJRC

☐ STRINGIN' THE BLUES
TPZ 1015 / Apr '95 / Topaz Jazz

Verbal Abuse

☐ RED, WHITE AND VIOLENT
CM 77095CD / Aug '95 / Century Media

Verbena

☐ SOULS FOR SALE
Hot blood / Shaped like a gun / Junk for fashion / Song that ended your career / Desert / Hey come on / Me and Keith / So what / Postcard blues / Kiss yourself
SETCD 035 / May '97 / Setanta

Verdell, Jackie

☐ LAY MY BURDEN DOWN
Lay my burden down / Praise him / Can I get a witness / Storm is passing over / Walk all over God's heaven / When the saints go marching in / Let it be / I want Jesus to walk with me
CDCH 375 / Jun '93 / Ace

Vergelmer

☐ LIGHT THE BLACK FLAME
Hellstorms over holy ground / Blessed by Satan / Blackened rebirth / Her harvest is my prey / At war for his majesty / Purifying / In the dead of winter / Heaven in ruins lay / Light the black flame
NIHIL 20CD / Apr '97 / Cacophonous

Verheyen, Carl

☐ SLANG JUSTICE
Down like hail / Slang justice / Jet plane blues / Two trains running / Spotty Herbert / Little swamp / Passing through / Loud guy blues / Silence is golden / Lights out
PRD 71002 / Feb '97 / Provogue

Veritas

☐ MO SMO SOKEI
EUCD 1078 / '89 / ARC

Verlaine, Tom

☐ COVER
Five miles of you / Let go the mansion / Travelling / O foolish heart / Miss Emily / Rotation / Swim
CDV 2314 / Jun '89 / Virgin

☐ FLASH LIGHT
Cry mercy Judge / Say a prayer / Town called Walker / Song / Scientist / Bomb / 4 a.m. / Funniest thing / Annie's telling me / Sundown
8308612 / Jan '96 / Fontana

☐ MILLER'S TALE, THE (A Tom Verlaine Anthology)
Kingdom come (live) / Souvenir from a dream (live) / Clear it away (live) / Always (live) / Postcard from Waterloo (live) / Penetration (live) / Breakin' in my heart (live) / Marquee moon (live) / Days on the mountain (live) / Prove it (live) / Venus / Glory / Grip of love / Without a word / Words from the front / Let go the mansion / Lindi-Lu / O Foolish heart / Five miles of you / Your finest hour / Anna / Sixteen tulips / Call me / A 4AM / Stalingrad / Call Mr. Lee / No glamour for Willi / Revolution
CDVDM 9034 / Apr '96 / Virgin

☐ TOM VERLAINE
Grip of love / Souvenir from a dream / Kingdom come / Mr. Bingo / Yonki time / Flash lightning / Red leaves / Last night / Breakin' in my heart
7559605402 / Jan '97 / Elektra

☐ WARM AND COOL
Those harbor lights / Sleepwalkin' / Deep dark clouds / Saucer crash / Depot (1951) / Boulevard / Harley quinn / Sor juanna / Depot (1957) / Spiritual / Little dance / Ore / Depot (1958) / Lore
R 2882 / Apr '92 / Rough Trade

☐ WONDER, THE
Kaleidescopin' / August / Ancient Egypt / Shimmer / Stalingrad / Pillow / Storm / Five hours from Calais / Cooleridge / Prayer
8424202 / Jan '96 / Fontana

Verlaines

☐ WAY OUT WHERE
Mission of love / I stare out... / This valentine / Blanket over the sky / Cathedrals under the sea / Aches in whisper / Way out where / Lucky in my dreams / Black wings / Stay gone / Incarceration / Dirge
8283882 / Apr '94 / Slash

Vermenton Plage

☐ J'SUIS CONTENT D'ETRE UN CAJUN
VP 03CD / Jun '94 / Weaving

Vermin

☐ HELL OR LAS VEGAS
BET 21 / Jan '97 / Behemoth

☐ OBEDIENCE TO INSANITY
CHAOSCD 01 / Oct '94 / Chaos

Vernon, Nan

☐ MANTA RAY
Motorcycle / Tattoo tears / Elvis waits / No more lullabyes / Big picture / Lay down Joe / While my guitar gently weeps / Iron John / Treasure / Fisherman / Johnny's birthday / Manta ray
4509939432 / May '94 / WEA

Vernons Girls

☐ VERY BEST OF THE VERNONS GIRLS, THE
Hey lover boy / We love the Beatles / Don't wanna go / Dat's love / Funny all over / Do the bird / Mama doesn't know / Stay at home / Why why why / Stupid little girl / Just another girl / You know what I mean / Lover please / Locomotion / Be nice to him Mama / See for yourself / I'm gonna let my hair down / He'll never come again / Tomorrow is another day / Only you can do it / Do you know what I mean
C5CD 616 / May '96 / See For Miles

Veronica

☐ V...AS IN VERONICA
Without love / What I wanna do / Unnecessary trip / Lockdown / Can't stop loving you / Sista / Love to come home to / Really don't miss you / House party / Trippin' / Ova and ova / 4 U
5285482 / Oct '95 / Mercury

Verplanck, Billy

☐ DANCING JAZZ
Summer evening / On top of old mountie / I'll keep loving you / Day by day / Oh gee, oh me, oh my / Make up your mind / Embraceable you
SV 0235 / Oct '97 / Savoy Jazz

Verplanck, Marlene

☐ BREATH OF FRESH AIR, A
ACD 109 / Apr '93 / Audiophile

☐ EVERY BREATH I TAKE
With every breath I take / Accent on youth / Snuggled on your shoulder / Some other time / If I love again / We could make such beautiful music together / Deep in a dream / Two cigarettes in the dark / Without a word of warning / You leave me breathless
SV 0233 / Oct '97 / Savoy Jazz

☐ LIVE IN LONDON
ACD 280 / Jan '94 / Audiophile

☐ LOVES JOHNNY MERCER
ACD 138 / Apr '89 / Audiophile

☐ MARLENE VERPLANCK MEETS SAXOMANIA IN PARIS
ACD 288 / Apr '95 / Audiophile

☐ NEW YORK SINGER, A
ACD 160 / Jun '96 / Audiophile

☐ PURE AND NATURAL
ACD 235 / May '95 / Audiophile

☐ QUIET STORM, A
ACD 256 / Feb '91 / Audiophile

☐ SINGS ALEC WILDER
ACD 218 / Apr '93 / Audiophile

☐ YOU GOTTA HAVE HEART (The Songs Of Richard Adler)
I'm seeing ribbons / I ask myself / Hey there / Near to you / Whoever invented love / What's wrong with me / New town is a blue town / If I knew then / Whatever Lola wants / You gotta have heart / You knew what I needed / Another time another place / Christmas in your heart / No soap blues / If you win you lose / Put your money on me
VSD 5804 / 16 Feb '98 / Varese Sarabande

Vershki Da Koreshki

☐ AFRO RUSSIAN COLLABORATION
ALCD 204 / Jan '97 / Al Sur

☐ REAL LIFE OF PLANTS
CDLA 96020 / 21 Aug '97 / Long Arms
SH 64099 / Oct '97 / Shanachie

Versus

☐ DEAD LEAVES
RAIN 015CD / May '95 / Cloudland

☐ SECRET SWINGERS
Lose that dress / Yeah you / Glitter of you / Ghost story / Use as directed / Double suicide (mercy killing) / Jealous / Shower song / Angels rushing in / Heart is a diamond
CAROL 004CD / Sep '96 / Caroline

☐ STARS ARE INSANE, THE
RAIN 011CD / Feb '95 / Cloudland

Vertical Hold

☐ HEAD FIRST
Head first / Now that it's over / Let me break it down / Love today / Spend some time / You keep giving me / Sounds of New York / Well I guess you / Crash course to heartbreak / Morning after / Blue skies / Pray
5403332 / 15 Sep '97 / A&M

Vertical Slit

☐ TWISTED STEEL AND THE TITS OF ANGELS
SO 6 / Feb '97 / Spirit Of Orr

Vertinsky, Alexander

☐ ALEXANDER VERTINSKY
LDX 274939/40 / Jan '93 / La Chant Du Monde

Veruca Salt

☐ AMERICAN THIGHS
Get back / All hail me / Seether / Spiderman '79 / Forsythia / Wolf / Celebrate you / Fly / Number one blind / Victrola / Twinstar / Twenty five / Sleeping where I want
FLATCD 9 / Oct '94 / Rise

☐ EIGHT ARMS TO HOLD YOU
Straight / Volcano girls / Don't make me prove it / Awesome / One last time / With David Bowie / Benjamin / Shutterbug / Morning sad / Sound of the bell / Loneliness is worse / Stoneface / Venus man trap / Earthcrosser
OPD 30001 / Mar '97 / Outpost

Verve

☐ NO COME DOWN
No come down / Blue / Make it till Monday / Butterfly / Where the geese go / Six o'clock / One way to go / Gravity grave / Twilight
CDHUT 18 / May '94 / Hut
YARDCD 007 / 1 Jun '98 / Vernon Yard

☐ NORTHERN SOUL, A
New decade / This is music / On your own / So it goes / Northern soul / Brainstorm interlude / Drive you home / History / No knock on my door / Life's an ocean / Stormy clouds / Reprise
CDHUT 27
DGHUT 27 / Jul '95 / Hut

☐ STORM IN HEAVEN, A
Star sail / Slide away / Already there / Beautiful mind / Sun the sea / Virtual world / Make it 'til Monday / Blue / Butterfly / See you in the next one (have a good time)
CDHUT 10 / Jun '93 / Hut

☐ URBAN HYMNS
Bitter sweet symphony / Sonnet / Rollingn people / Drugs don't work / Catching the butterfly / Neon wilderness / Space and time / Weeping willow / Lucky man / One day / This time / Velevet morning / Come on / Deep freeze
CDHUT 45 / 29 Sep '97 / Hut

Verve Pipe

☐ VILLAINS
Barely (if at all) / Drive you mild / Villains / Reverend girl / Cup of tea / Myself / Freshmen / Photograph / Ominous man / Real / Penny is poison / Cattle / Veneer
07863668092 / Nov '96 / RCA

Very Secretary

☐ BEST POSSIBLE SOUVENIR
MUDCD 031 / 23 Feb '98 / Mud

Very Things

☐ BUSHES SCREAM WHILE MY DADDY PRUNES, THE
Conqueror / Down the final flight / Bushes scream while my daddy prunes / Information / Wall of fir / World of difference / Message from disney time / Shearing machine / Phillips world service / Message from disney time / Down the final flight / Wall of fir / World of difference / Information
REFIRECD 12 / Feb '94 / Fire

☐ IT'S A DRAG, IT'S A DRUG
Ag 1 / Mummy, you're a wreck / When father papered the parlour / Gong man / Ag 2 / Where's the rest of me (link) / Transfusion / Hole / Colours are speaking to me / Motorlogue / Ag 3 / Gong man / When mummy papered the wreck / Ag 4
REFIRECD 13 / Feb '94 / Fire

☐ MOTORTOWN
Let's go out / Let's go out / There's a ghost in my house / She's standing still / Walking in the sand / Motortown epilogue / Let's go out (pre-mix) / This is motortown (hot rod) / She's standing still (pre-mix) / Let's go out (a7e) / Let's go out (idm) / This is motortown (solid chrome)
REFIRECD 14 / Feb '94 / Fire

Vesala, Edward

☐ INVISIBLE STORM (Vesala, Edward's Sound & Fury)
Sheets and shrouds / Murming morning / Gordion's flashes / Shadows on the frontier / In the gate of another gate / Somnamblues / Sarastus / Wedding of all essential parts / Invisible storm / Haze of the frost / Caccaroo boohoo
5119282 / Mar '92 / ECM

☐ LUMI (Vesala, Edward's Sound & Fury)
Wind / Frozen melody / Calypso bulbosa / Third moon / Lumi / Camel walk / Fingo / Early messenger / Together
8315172 / Jul '87 / ECM

☐ NORDIC GALLERY (Vesala, Edward's Sound & Fury)
Bird in the high room / Fulflandia / Quay of meditative / Hadendas / Unexpected guest / Bluego / Lavender lass blossom / Steaming below the time / 1-2-3 or 4-5-6 / Significant look of birch grove / On the shady side of forty / Flavor lust
5232942 / Nov '94 / ECM

☐ ODE TO THE DEATH OF JAZZ
Sylvan swizzle / Infinite express / Time to think / Winds of Sahara / Watching for the signal / Glimmer of sepal / Mop mop / What? Where? Hum hum
8431962 / Jun '90 / ECM

Vetta, Patty

☐ LADDERS OF DAYLIGHT (Vetta, Patty & Alan Franks)
Jackie Lee / Look up look down / We're going to be revealed / Give me the samba / I'd rather be blind / Open secret / My influential friend / Getting restless / Martin's heron/Kate's 'air / Islands of oil / I try to fall in love / Take good care of your memories / I once loved a girl / PLease don't enquire about me / End of the line / Ladders of daylight
RGFVFCD 038 / 20 Oct '97 / Road Goes On Forever

☐ WILL (Vetta, Patty & Alan Franks)
RGFCD 023 / May '95 / Road Goes On Forever

Vetter, Michael

☐ ZEN KOTO
SM 10522 / Apr '97 / Wergo

Vex

☐ FRONTIERS AND NEW TECH
DELECCD 058 / 17 Nov '97 / Delerium

☐ NEW TECHNOLOGY EP
DELECCDS 057 / Jun '97 / Delerium

Vibe Tribe

☐ AFTER LIFE (THE JOURNEY)
VTP 001 / Mar '96 / Backs

Vibert & Simmons

☐ WIERS
CAT 016CD / Oct '94 / Rephlex

Vibert, Luke

☐ BIG SOUP
Intro - welcome / Rank rink ring / Voyage into the unknown / Fused into music / No turn unstoned / Reality check / MARS / Stern facials / Am I still dreaming / 2001 beats / Music called jazz / Space race / So long - outro / CORN / Fresh / Original soundmaster
MW 072CD / Jun '97 / Mo Wax

☐ PHAT LAB NIGHTMARE (Wagon Christ)
Mahadelic / Glass world / B.phat lab. nightmare / Aerhaart; from within / Aerhaart; ahead / Aerhaart; barrier / D.panorak / Dances with francis
RSNCD 18 / Jul '94 / Rising High

☐ THROBBING POUCH (Wagon Christ)
RSNCD 30 / Mar '95 / Rising High

Vibraphonic

☐ VIBRAPHONIC VOL.1
Trust me / I see you / Meter's runner / Lonnie's legacy / Bounce / Believe in me / Fall for you / So what / Tell me / Evidence
JAZIDCD 063 / Apr '93 / Acid Jazz

☐ VIBRAPHONIC VOL.2
Heavy vibes / Buck the system / Down home / Can't get enough / Strolling / To know you is to love you / Light and shade / True life / Funkly / Watch out for this one
JAZIDCD 118 / Mar '95 / Acid Jazz

Vibrasonic

☐ VIBRASONIC
YEPCD 01 / Mar '95 / Yep

☐ VIBRASONIC'S GUITAR PARTY
YEPCD 02 / Jun '97 / Yep

Vibrations

☐ MEDITERRANEN MOODS
EAGCD 005 / Aug '97 / Eagle

Vibrators

☐ BBC LIVE IN CONCERT (Vibrators/ Boys)
Wrecked on you / Wrecked on you / Stiff little fingers / Wake up / He's a psycho / Baby baby / Flying duck theory / Whips and furs / I need a slave / Keep it clean / Feel alright / Sex kick / Bad time / First time / Rue morgue / Kamikaze / Cop cars / New guitar in town / Brickfield nights / Worm song / Terminal love
WINCD 036 / Jul '93 / Windsong

☐ BEST OF THE VIBRATORS, THE
Guilty: Wolfman howl / Rocket to the moon / Sleeping / Parties / Jumpin' Jack Flash / Watch out baby / Do a runner / We name the guilty / Baby baby / Fighter pilot / Day they caught the killer / Kick it / Dot ain't a lot / Claws in my brain / Alaska: amphetamine blue / Somnambulist / Baby blue eyes / Peepshow / 4875 / 3-D Jesus / Jesus always lets you down / Flying home / Shadow love / MX America / Flash flash flash / Punish me with kisses
CDPUNK 43 / Jan '95 / Anagram

☐ DEMOS 1976-1977
DOLECD 102 / Jan '98 / Dojo

☐ FIFTH AMENDMENT/RECHARGED
Blown away by love / Rip up the city / Tomorrow is today / Wipe away / Too late for love / Demolishers / Running right into your heart / Frankenstein stomp / Crazy dream / Criminal / String him along / Hay little doll / I don't trust you / Go go go / Hey nonny no (Instrumental) / Picture of you / Every day I die a little / Too dumb / Rip it up tear it up / Someone stole my heart / Electricity / Tight black jeans / Reach for that star
CDPUNK 34 / May '94 / Anagram

☐ FRENCH LESSONS WITH CORRECTION
Tired of living with you / Girls screwed up / Shiver / Judy's killing herself / Cycle of violence / Cold cold cold / Party on / Rain must fall / Date with disaster / Juice on / Evil that men do / Don't you tell me / Johnny b bad / Money money / I hate blind date
CDMGRAM 114 / 15 Sep '97 / Anagram

☐ GUILTY & ALASKA 127
Wolfman howl / Rocket to the moon / Sleeping / Parties / Jumpin' jack flash / Watch out baby / Do a runner / We name the guilty / Baby baby / Fighter pilot / Day they caught the killer / Kick it / Dot ain't a lot / Claws in my brain / Amphetamine blue / Somnambulist / Baby blue eyes / Peepshow / 4875 / 3-D Jesus / Jesus always lets you down / Flying home / Shadow love / MX America / Flash flash flash / Punish me with kisses
CDPUNK 16 / Sep '93 / Anagram

☐ HUNTING FOR YOU
Hunting for you / Kids a mess / Fever (you gimma) / Please please please / No no no / Modern world / Another day without you / Goodbye you stupid cow / Keep away from me / She's the one you need / Hey hey / Radium city
DOJOCD 179 / Nov '94 / Dojo

☐ INDEPENDENT PUNK SINGLES COLLECTION
CDPUNK 76 / May '96 / Anagram

☐ MELTDOWN
Office girls / Don't cha lean on me / So young / Speedtrap / Other side of midnight / Cruel to you / (Na na na) U 238 / Dynamite / Letting you go / Danger Street / Let's go / Baby / Sally gardens / Don't trust anyone / Wasted life
REVCD 121 / Nov '88 / Revolver

☐ MELTDOWN/VICIOUS CIRCLE
Office girls / Don't cha lean on me / So young / Speed trap / Other side of midnight / Cruel to you / U2 38 / Dynamite / Letting you go / Danger streets / Let's go / Baby / Sally gardens / No getting over you / Poll tax blues / I don't wanna fall / Rocket ride to heaven / Count on me / Slow death / Fire / Halfway to paradise / Ruby's got a heart / Don't trust anyone / No mercy / Work
CDPUNK 58 / Jun '95 / Anagram

☐ VICIOUS CIRCLE
REVXD 135 / Nov '89 / FM

☐ VOLUME 10
REVXD 159 / Sep '90 / Revolver

☐ VOLUME 10/UNPUNKED
OVER 73CD / 22 Jun '98 / Overground

☐ WE VIBRATE (The Best Of The Vibrators)
CLP 0090 / 6 Oct '97 / Cleopatra

☐ YEAH YEAH YEAH
REP 4001 / Aug '91 / Repertoire

Vibrazioni Productions

☐ ESPRESSIONE GLOBALE
RR 101CD / Jul '96 / Roots

☐ NUOVA PROSPETTIVA
RR 104CD / Jul '96 / Roots

☐ SUONI NELLA NOTTE
MI 2007 / 16 Jul '97 / Milano 2000

Vicari, Andreas

☐ LUNAR SPELL
You're reported / Blue, green and space / Chequemate / Bedsprings / Way you treat people / Lunar spell / Birthday song / Voy a lomar / Last chair blues
33JAZZ 026 / Nov '95 / 33 Jazz

☐ SUBURBAN GORILLAS
Pegasus / Fly so high / Awakening / In Africa Maibouye / Pin stripe woman / Southern comfort / Danse vendange / L'orchestre de fous / Sverr / Whispering whales
33JAZZ 016CD / May '95 / 33 Jazz

Vice Barons

☐ FRIENDS IN LOW PLACES
NITR 001 / Jan '97 / Demolition Derby

☐ RARITEASE
NITR 006 / Jan '97 / Demolition Derby

Vice Squad

☐ BBC SESSIONS, THE
Coward / It's a sell out / 1981 / Times they are a-changing / Living on dreams / Coward / Evil / Still dying / Resurrection / Humane / Propaganda / No right to reply / Sterile / Saviour machine / You'll never know / Rest of your life / Scarred for life
CDPUNK 99 / Aug '97 / Anagram

☐ GET A LIFE
PREACH 004CD / 27 Apr '98 / Rhythm Vicar

☐ LAST ROCKERS
AABCD 805 / Oct '91 / Abstract

☐ LAST ROCKERS/SINGLES
AABT 805CD / Sep '94 / Abstract

☐ NO CAUSE FOR CONCERN
Young blood / Coward / Nothing / Summer fashion / 1981 / Saturday night special / Offering / Times they are a-changing / Evil / Angry youth / It's a sell-out / Still dying / Last rockers
DOJOCD 167 / Feb '94 / Dojo

☐ PUNK SINGLES COLLECTION
Last rockers / Living on dreams / Latex love / Resurrection / Young blood / Humane / Out of reach / So what for the eighties / Sterile / Stand strong stand proud / Tomorrow's soldier / Rock 'n' roll massacre / Darkest hour / Citizen / Scared for life / Faceless men / Black sheep / New blood / Pledge / You'll never know / What's going on / Times they are a changin' / Teenage rampage / High spirits
CDPUNK 89 / Mar '97 / Anagram

☐ SHOT AWAY
New blood / Take it or leave it / Out in the cold / Nowhere to hide / You'll never know / Rebels and kings / Playground / Rest of your life / What's going on / Killing time / Teenage rampage / Black sheep / Times they are a changin' / High spirits / New bond (Version) / Pledge / Nothing
CDPUNK 28 / Dec '93 / Anagram

☐ STAND STRONG STAND PROUD
Stand strong, stand proud / Humane / Cheap / Gutterchild / Rock 'n' roll massacre / Fist full of dollars / Freedom begins at home / Out of reach / Saviour machine / No right of reply / Deathwish / Propaganda
DOJOCD 170 / Nov '93 / Dojo

Viceroys

☐ AT STUDIO ONE: YA HO
CDHB 133 / Jun '95 / Heartbeat

Vicious Rumors

☐ CYBERCHRIST
MASSCD 142 / 18 May '98 / Massacre

☐ SOMETHING BURNING
MASSCD 091 / Jul '96 / Massacre

Vicious, Johnny

☐ NEW YORK IN THE MIX
SUB 12D / May '96 / Subversive

Vicious, Sid

☐ LIVE AT THE ELECTRIC BALLROOM (Vicious White Kids & Sid Vicious)
C'mon everybody / I'm not your stepping stone / (Don't gimme) no lip / I wanna be your dog / Belsen was a gas / Chatterbox / Tight pants / Something else / My way
RRCD 180 / Sep '95 / Receiver
STRCD 601 / Apr '96 / Delorean

☐ SID DEAD LIVE
CDPUNK 86 / Jan '97 / Anagram

☐ SID SINGS
Born to lose / I wanna be your dog / Take a chance on me / Stepping stone / My way / Belsen was a gas / Something else / Chatterbox / Search and destroy / Chinese rocks / I killed the cat
CDV 2144 / Feb '89 / Virgin

Victim's Family

☐ 4 GREAT THRASH SONGS
K 161CD / Jun '95 / Konkurrel

☐ GERM, THE
VIRUS 108CD / '92 / Alternative Tentacles

☐ HEADACHE REMEDY
K 151CD / Mar '94 / Konkurrel

Victor

☐ VICTOR
Don't care / At the end / Shut up shuttin' up / Sending a warning / I am the spirit / Victor / Big dance / Strip and go naked / Mr.X / Promise / Start today
7567828522 / Jan '96 / Atlantic

Victoria Kings

☐ MIGHTY KINGS OF BENGA, THE
VB Pod Wamol / Dick Ooro / Jack jack 2 / Jessica adhiambo / Akinyi / Eddo / Eddo / Yworo law kwach / Marine atiesh / Oluoch odalo / Wee juok / Yukabeth / Musa aloo / Ojowi telo
CDORBD 079 / Jun '93 / Globestyle

Victoria Police Pipe Band

☐ LIVE IN THE ROCKIES
Pipe solo / Strathspey and reels / Spirits of old pulteney / Major A. F MacGillivary / Doune of invernochty / Wasted journey / Am brematain tobbain dubh / Kenny Giles of Portnalong / Red Ken's jig / Acid piper / Bulgarian bandit / Adrian's obsession / Out of the air / Slick diamond back / New year in Noosa / Air / Girl from dungannon / Mrs. Donald MacPherson / Glayva kid / Riverbeat / Pumpkins fancy / Hen's march / Alan Macpherson of Mosspark
VPCD 001 / Dec '97 / Victoria Police
CDMON 829 / 24 Jul '98 / Monarch

☐ MASTERBLASTERS
CDMON 832 / Jul '98 / Monarch

☐ VICTORIA POLICE PIPE BAND LIVE IN IRELAND
MON 819CD / Dec '93 / Monarch

Victoria, Irma

☐ PHANTASMAGORIA
MM 3000CD / Dec '94 / Pingo

Victory

☐ DON'T GET MAD GET EVEN
MERD 2105 / Dec '93 / Mercenary

☐ EARLY SINGLES, THE
VE 18CD / Mar '95 / Victory

☐ VOICEPRINT
SPV 08460052 / Jun '96 / SPV

Vidal, Jorge

☐ TRES ESPERANZAS
BMT 019 / 5 Jan '98 / Blue Moon

Vidal, Lluis

☐ MILIKITULI (Vidal, Lluis Trio)
FSNT 009CD / Nov '95 / Fresh Sound New Talent

Vidalias

☐ MELODYLAND
UPSTART 014 / Feb '95 / Upstart

☐ STAYIN' IN THE DOGHOUSE
Misery loves company / Body and soul / Thunder and rain / Whole lotta doin' without / Fashion lasts forever / What a nice surprise / Whose side are you on / Such a mystery / Lonely sundown / Questioningly / All over me / Coffee break
UPSTART 034 / Feb '97 / Upstart

Vieja Trova Santiaguera

☐ GUSTO Y SABOR
How times change / Deception / Nengon, for you / Red lips / Desire / Samll casserole - Ofelia's dish / Description of the rumba / Doubts / For you to remember / Full-time / Beginnings of love / Sweet embellishment / Whispering / Taste and flavour
INT 31832 / Aug '96 / Intuition

☐ HOTEL ASTURIAS
Pregon santiaguero / No sangres corazon / Un meneito na' mas / El peluquero / La guinda / Yo son ganga / Me dieron la clave / Mi guantanamera / Un ano de amor / Las amargas verdades / Arrimese usted / Palma soriano / Zun zun paloma / Guarapo, pimienta y sal / Guajira guantanamera
INT 32152 / Jun '97 / Intuition

☐ VIEJA TROVA SANTIAGUERA
El tren / Ella y yo / El paralitico / Blancas azucenas / Que viste / Alma de roca / El huerfanito / Retorna / Capullito de alheli / Lagrimas negras / Dime, por que no me quieres / Olvido / Son de la loma / Mujer perjura / Esperanza
INT 31822 / Sep '96 / Intuition

Viellistic Orchestra

☐ IMAGINARY HISTORY OF THE HURDY GURDY, AN
245192 / Mar '96 / Musidisc

Vienna Art Orchestra

☐ 20TH ANNIVERSARY
5370952 / 3 Nov '97 / Amadeo

☐ BLUES FOR BRAHMS (2CD Set)
Punkt 1 / Festliche eroffnung / OK but who is Tober / Alphabet / Blues for Brahms / Break for connoisseurs / What was this thing called free jazz / Inspired by J.A. Poschiavo / Bars and stripes / Danke das wars
8391052 / 3 Nov '97 / Amadeo

☐ CHAPTER II
Sizilianische eroffnung / Chapter II / Blue loop play / Realta / Response from an outstanding horn / One fish why not / Aspect of social drumming / Incubi et succubi
8490662 / 3 Nov '97 / Amadeo

☐ EUROPEAN SONGBOOK
5276722 / 3 Nov '97 / Amadeo

☐ FE AND MALES (Vienna Art Special)
Schwarz / Grun / Rot / Turkis / Gelb / Sandelfarben / Weiss
5133282 / 3 Nov '97 / Amadeo

☐ FROM NO TIME TO RAG TIME
ARTCD 6073 / Nov '93 / Hat Art

☐ HIGHLIGHTS 1977-1990/LIVE IN VIENNA 1989 (2CD Set)
Opener is bizarre / Blue for two / Two little animals / Poschiavo / Liberate proposal / Haluk / Perpetuum mobile / K wie ikeda / His majesty's blues / Lady delay / Polish contrasts / Innocence of cliches / Charly's trauma / Blue loop play
5133252 / 3 Nov '97 / Amadeo

☐ INNOCENCE OF CLICHES (2CD Set)
Ouverture etrange / Aschera / Call your tribe / In a sentimental mood / Mental power of 13 children / Share your money and read fairytales / Souffleuse Saturnienne / Off minor / Secret of European heritage / Innocence of cliches
8416462 / 3 Nov '97 / Amadeo

☐ NOTION IN PERPETUAL MOTION, A
ARTCD 6096 / Sep '92 / Hat Art

☐ ORIGINAL CHARTS OF DUKE ELLINGTON & CHARLES MINGUS, THE
Hobo ho / Interlude / Shoes of the fisherman's wife are some jive ass slippers / Interlude / I of hurricane Sue / Don't be afraid the clown's afraid too / Interlude / Red shoes / Madness in great ones / Anitra's dance / Asphalt jungle / Come Sunday / El gato
5235712 / 3 Nov '97 / Amadeo

☐ PLAYS FOR JEAN COCTEAU
5292902 / 3 Nov '97 / Amadeo

☐ STANDING...WHAT
Search / CNPA / Maladie blanche melody blue / 1e XVIII Catalan / On the funny side / Flowers of friendship / Miss Ribbit / Friendly shaving / Les oiseaux extraordinaires / Comment from another generation
5198162 / 3 Nov '97 / Amadeo

Vienna City Ramblers

☐ SWINGIN' AGAIN
323539 / Mar '96 / Koch International

Vienna Symphony Orchestra

☐ ORCHESTRAL ROCK VOL.1
Sledgehammer / I wanna dance with somebody (who loves me) / They dance alone / Man in the mirror / Against all odds / Nothing's gonna stop us now / Prelude / VSOP / Mull of Kintyre / Groovy kind of love / One moment in time / Orinoco flow / First time / Looking for freedom / Phantom of the opera / Living years / Hand in hand / Beatles medley
MCCD 031 / Oct '91 / Music Club

☐ ORCHESTRAL ROCK VOL.2
Private dancer / Bohemian rhapsody / Radio ga ga / Power of love / St. Elmo's fire / Space oddity / Satisfaction / Brothers in arms / Bridge over trouble water / Kyrie / Rock me Amadeus / Heart on fire / Dreamer / Sailing / Stairway to heaven
MCCD 065 / '92 / Music Club

Vierny, Dina

☐ CHANTS DU GOULAG
LDX 274933 / Mar '92 / La Chant Du Monde

Viewfinder

☐ STARS ON ICE
MUDCD 024 / May '97 / Mud

Viewmaster

☐ VIEWMASTER
POOF 14CD / 18 May '98 / Pop Factory

Vigilantes Of Love

☐ KILLING FLOOR
SKYCD 5020 / Sep '94 / Sky

☐ TO THE ROOF OF THE SKY
VOL 1CD / 27 Jul '98 / Vol

Viglietti, Daniel

☐ CANCIONES PARA MI AMERICA
926912 / 5 Jan '98 / BUDA

Vignola, Frank

☐ APPEL DIRECT
Appel direct / Play fiddle play / Ready'n able / Indian love call / Jeannine / Whirly twirly / Jitterbug waltz / Love for sale / Rajah / I'll never smile again / It might as well be spring
CCD 4576 / Nov '93 / Concord Jazz

☐ LET IT HAPPEN
Let it happen / Tico tico / Diminishing blackness / String of pearls / Ligia / Spanish eyes / Quizas quizas quizas / Felche d'or / Seven minds / Unit seven / Lu Lu's trip / Ah so
CCD 4625 / Nov '94 / Concord Jazz

☐ LOOK RIGHT, JOG LEFT
Organized confusion / President Street / Jonathan's wine / Late night / Jog left / O Morro nao tern vez / Look right / Desert moon blues / Katrina / Tuxedo junction / Antidote / Jeff's dancing
CCD 4718 / Aug '96 / Concord Vista

Vikings

☐ GO BERSERK
1+2CD 090 / 26 Jan '98 / 1+2

Villa, Beto

☐ FATHER OF THE TEJANO ORQUESTA
ARHCD 364 / Apr '95 / Arhoolie

Village

☐ VILLAGE, THE
ER 1036 / Aug '97 / Elefant

Village Of Savoonga

☐ PHILIP SCHATZ
COMM 44CD / Nov '96 / Communion

☐ SCORE
COMM 48 / 30 Mar '98 / Communion

Village People

☐ GREATEST HITS
YMCA / In the navy / Can't stop the music / San Francisco / Macho man / Go west / Fire island / Ready for the 80's / Sex over the phone / New York City / Just a gigolo/I ain't got nobody / Five o'clock in the morning / In Hollywood / YMCA (remix)
74321178312 / Nov '93 / Arista

☐ VILLAGE PEOPLE: THE HITS
YMCA / Macho man / San Francisco (you've got me) / Can't stop the music / Megamix / In the navy / In Hollywood / Fire island / Go West / Village people / Ready for the 80's / Do you wanna spend the night
MCCD 004 / Feb '91 / Music Club

Villarroel, Edgar

☐ CLASSIC IRISH PAN PIPE MELODIES VOL.1
CHCD 1097 / May '96 / Chyme

☐ CLASSIC IRISH PAN PIPE MELODIES VOL.2
CHCD 1098 / Dec '96 / Chyme

Villarroel, Patricio

☐ IMPROVISATIONS
TE 015 / 24 Feb '98 / BUDA

Vincent, Gene

☐ 500 MILES
Oh lonesome me / Woman in black / 500 miles / Day the world turned blue / Boppin' the blues / How I love them old songs / Listen to the music / If you could only see me today / Million shades of blue / Sunshine / I need a woman's love / High on life / Our souls / You can make it if you try / Geese / Slow times comin' / There is something on your mind / Looking back / Danse Colinda / North Carolina line / Tush hog
74321558442 / 26 Jan '98 / Camden

☐ BE BOP A LULA (The 1960's Recordings)
Be bop a lula / Rocky road blues / Baby blue / Whole lotta shakin' goin' on / Day the world turned blue / Story of the rockers / Pickin' poppies / Say mama / Ain't that too much / Bird doggin' / Love is a bird / Lonely street / Hurtin' for your baby / Poor man's prison / Born to be a rolling stone / Hi lili hi lo / I'm a lonesome fugitive / I've got my eyes on you
QED 115 / Nov '96 / Tring

☐ BEST OF GENE VINCENT & HIS BLUE CAPS, THE (The Screaming End) (Vincent, Gene & The Bluecaps)
RE 2123 / Feb '97 / Razor & Tie

☐ EP COLLECTION VOL.1, THE
Race with the devil / Crazy legs / Hold me, hug me, rock me / Wayward wind / Somebody help me / Five feet of lovin' / Peace of mind / Look what you gone and done to me / Summertime / Keep it a secret / Rocky road blues / Dance to the bop / Baby blue / Dance in the street / Lovely Loretta / Important words / Gone gone gone / She she little Sheila / Weeping willow / Crazy beat / I'm gonna catch me a rat / If you want my lovin'
SEECD 253 / Jan '96 / See For Miles

☐ EP COLLECTION VOL.2, THE
Blue jean bop / Jezebel / Woman in love / Gonna back up baby / You belong to me / Should I ever love again / It's no lie / I got a baby / Over the rainbow / Yes I love you baby / Wear my ring / Lotta lovin' / Walkin' home from school / Bi-I-bickey-bi-bo-go / Five days five days / I got it / Say Mama / Pistol packin' Mama / Right now / Wild cat / Right here on Earth / I'm going home / Where have you been all my life / You are my sunshine / Spaceship to Mars / Be-bop-a-Lula
SEECD 492 / 22 Jun '98 / See For Miles

☐ GENE VINCENT
Say mama / Blue jean bop / Wild cat / Right here on earth / Who slapped John / Walkin' home from school / Five feet of lovin' / She-she little Sheila / Be bop a lula / Jump back / Dance in the street / Pistol packin' mama / Crazy beat / High blood pressure / Five days, five days / Bi bickey bi bo bo boo
LECD 038 / May '94 / Dynamite

☐ GENE VINCENT & CARL PERKINS (Vincent, Gene/Carl Perkins)
UAE 30002 / Jan '98 / Members Edition

☐ GREAT ROCKER, THE
Hold me, hug me, rock me / Who slapped John / You better believe it / Bop Street / Gonna back up baby / Jumps, giggles and shouts / Well I knocked and I knocked / Jump back honey / Double talking baby / B-I-bickey bi, bo bo go / Pink Thunderbird / Red blue jeans and a ponytail / Race with the devil / I flipped / Cat man / Five feet of lovin' / Pretty pretty baby / Blue jean bop / Cruisin' / Crazy legs / You told a fib / Say Mama / Lotta lovin' / Dance to the bop / Wildcat / Be bop a lula
CDMFP 6269 / Sep '96 / Music For Pleasure

☐ I'M BACK AND I'M PROUD
Rockin' Robin / In the pines / Be bop a lula / Rainbow at midnight / Black letter / White lightning / Sexy ways / Ruby baby / Lotta lovin' / Circle never broken / (I heard that) lonesome whistle / Scarlet ribbons
REP 4205 / Aug '91 / Repertoire
SEECD 415 / Oct '94 / See For Miles

☐ INTO THE SEVENTIES
Sunshine / I need woman's love / 500 miles away from home / Slow time's coming / Listen to the music / If only you could see me today / Million shades of blue / Tush hog / How I love them old songs / High on life / North Carolina line / There is something on your mind / Day the world turned blue / Boppin' the blues / Looking back / Oh lonesome me / Woman in black / Danse colinda / Geese / You can make it if you try / Our souls
SEECD 233 / Sep '88 / See For Miles

☐ LOST DALLAS SESSIONS 1957-1958, THE (Vincent, Gene & The Bluecaps)
My love / Hey Mama / Lonesome boy / In my dreams / Lotta lovin' / Lady bug / Night is so lonely / Blue jean bop / Whole lotta shakin' goin' on / Dance to the bop / Lotta lovin' / Nervous / On my mind / Who's pushing your swing: *Glenn, Darrell* / Git it: *Kelly, Bob* / Somebody help me: *Kelly, Bob* / I don't feel like rockin' tonight: *Owen, Grady*
RCCD 3031 / 7 Apr '98 / Rollercoaster

☐ MASTERS, THE (2CD Set)
EDMCD 028 / 30 Mar '98 / Eagle

☐ ORIGINAL, THE
Be bop a lula / Race with the devil / Bluejean bop / Lotta lovin' / Wear my ring / Dance to the bop / Wild cat / My heart / Pistol packin' mother / She she little Sheila / I'm going home / Maybelline / Rocky road blues / Say Mama / Crazy legs / Rollin' Danny / Over the rainbow / Git it
TO 860942 / 2 Feb '98 / Disky

☐ REBEL HEART VOL.1
Hound dog / Be bop a lula / Blue jean bop / Last word in lonesome / Pretty girls everywhere / Dance to the bop / Lonely street / Rainy day sunshine / Green grass / Mr. love / Roll over Beethoven / Rocky road blues / Say Mama / Pistol packin' Mama / (I heard that) Lonesome whistle / Maybellene / Whole lotta shakin' goin' on
CDMF 087 / Nov '92 / Magnum Force

☐ REBEL HEART VOL.2
Who slapped John / Dance to the bop / In my dreams / Lotta lovin' / Nervous / Ramble / Mr. Loneliness / Say Mama / Frankie and Johnny / Where have you been all my life / Temptation baby / Chicken feathers (Inst.) / Come on in / Downtown / Girl from Ipanema / Mean (Inst.) / Story of the rockers / Pickin' poppies / Whole lotta shakin' goin' on / Day the world turned blue / Say Mama / Rocky road blues / I'm movin' on / Say Mama
CDMF 093 / Apr '95 / Magnum Force

☐ REBEL HEART VOL.3
CDMF 096 / Apr '96 / Magnum Force

☐ REBEL HEART VOL.4
Rollin' Danny / Lady Bug / Lonesome boy / Be bop a Lula / High blood pressure / Baby blue / Blue jean bop / Lotta lovin' / Long tall Sally / Baby blue / Jenny Jenny / Where have you been / You are my sunshine / Say Mama / Hi Lilli, hi lo / Sad memories / Take it like a man / Be bop a Lula
CDMF 097 / Mar '97 / Magnum Force

☐ REBEL HEART VOL.5
Rocky road blues / Frankie and Johnny / Wild cat / Right here on Earth / Be-bop-a-Lula / Blue jean bop / Rocky road blues / Be-bop-a-Lula / If you want my lovin' / Mister Lonliness / Rocky road blues / Summertime / I'm goin' home / Tutti frutti / Crazy beat / Another Saturday night / I'm gonna catch me a rat / Long tall Sally / Suzie Q / Good golly Miss Molly / She she little Sheila / Roll over Beethoven
CDMF 099 / 27 Apr '98 / Magnum Force

☐ SHAKIN' UP A STORM (Vincent, Gene & The Shouts)
Hey hey hey / Lavender blue / Private detective / Shimmy shammy shingle / Someday you'll want me to want you / Another Saturday night / Slippin' and slidin' / Long tall Sally / Send me some lovin' / Love love love / Good golly Miss Molly / Baby blue / Suzie Q / You are my sunshine
DORIG 124 / Aug '97 / EMI

Vincent, Jean

☐ ROCK WITH ME BABY
RKCD 9103 / Mar '96 / Rockhouse

Vincent, Kyle

☐ KYLE VINCENT
62094 / 24 Nov '97 / Hollywood

Vincent, Rhonda

☐ TROUBLE FREE
74321309332 / Jun '96 / RCA

Vincent, Rick

☐ WANTED MAN, A
4747492 / Jan '94 / Curb

Vincent, Sunny

☐ PURE FILTH
OR 006CD / 10 Nov '97 / Overdose

Vindictives

☐ LEAVE HOME
L 378082 / 16 Mar '98 / Liberation

Vinegar Joe

☐ VINEGAR JOE
Rusty red armour / Early Monday morning / Ride me easy rider / Circles / Leg up / See the world / Never met a dog / Avinu malkenu / Gettin' out / Live a little get somewhere
EDCD 566 / 1 Jun '98 / Edsel

Vingerhoeds, Vera

☐ LIVE (Vingerhoeds, Vera & Lazybones)
BVHAASTCD 9208 / Jan '92 / Bvhaast

☐ WALL WORKS
BVHAASTCD 9405 / Oct '94 / Bvhaast

Vinnegar, Leroy

☐ WALKIN' THE BASSES
Blue 'n' boogie / Back on the farm / Love nest / Big shoes (for your feet) / Grandstand / Leroy's waltz / Blues on purpose / Ah que linda / Who has seen the wind / How insensitive / Me ho
CCD 14068 / Jun '95 / Pablo

Vinson, Eddie

☐ BLUES BOOGIE AND BEBOP (The Meat's Too High) (Vinson, Eddie 'Cleanhead')
Old maid boogie / Somebody's got to go / Travellin' / Home boy / Meat's too high / If you were my buddy / Investigation blues / That's all / Cleangead's thing / Roxanne / Fun in London / High class baby / Straight away
JSPCD 804 / 9 Mar '98 / JSP

☐ CLEANHEAD AND CANNONBALL (Vinson, Eddie & Cannonball Adderley)
LCD 13092 / Oct '88 / Landmark

☐ EDDIE 'CLEANHEAD' VINSON (Vinson, Eddie 'Cleanhead')
SCD 029 / Oct '93 / Southland

☐ EDDIE VINSON SINGS (Cleanhead's Back In Town/Original Bethlehem Classics)
CDGR 166 / Aug '97 / Charly

☐ FUN IN LONDON (Vinson, Eddie 'Cleanhead')
JSPCD 204 / Nov '87 / JSP

☐ JAMMING THE BLUES (Vinson, Eddie 'Cleanhead')
BLCD 760188 / Jul '93 / Black Lion

☐ KIDNEY STEW (Vinson, Eddie 'Cleanhead')
Kidney stew / Wait a minute baby / Old maid boogie / Somebody's got to go / Things ain't what they used to be / Wee baby blues / Juice head baby / I had a dream / I'm in an awful mood / Please send me someone to love / Person to person / Alimony blues / Hey little doggy / Totsy
BB 8782 / Feb '97 / Black & Blue

☐ ROOMFUL OF BLUES (Vinson, Eddie 'Cleanhead')
MCD 5282 / Sep '92 / Muse

Vinterland

☐ WELCOME TO MY LAST CHAPTER
NFR 017CD / Jan '97 / No Fashion

Vintersorg

☐ HEDNISKHJARTED
NPR 049CD / 3 Aug '98 / Napalm

Vinton, Bobby

☐ BEST OF BOBBY VINTON, THE
Blue velvet / Roses are red (my love) / Sealed with a kiss / Venus / Great pretender / Earth angel (will you be mine) / Only you / Unchained melody / When I fall in love / Mr Lonely / Take good care of my baby / Raindrops keep falling on my head / Rain rain go away / LONELY / Tell me why / There I've said it again / I love how you love me / My heart belongs to only you / True love
4871672 / 3 Aug '98 / Epic

Vinx

☐ STORYTELLER, THE
Forever yours / Moondance / Just one dance / Armida prelude / Armida / Living in the Metro / Grits and pate / Please come back / What's come over me / I will always care / East of away / Dial it / I know the way / Letter to the killer / I feel incredible
5401952 / Jan '94 / A&M

Vinyl Devotion

☐ FLOOR MODEL
PARCD 029 / 10 Nov '97 / Parasol

Vinyl Groover

☐ WORLD OF VINYLGROOVER VOL.3, THE
ALPHACD 4 / 16 Feb '98 / Alpha Projects

Vio-Lence

☐ NOTHING TO GAIN
Atrocity / Twelve gauge justice / Ageless eyes / Pain of pleasure / Virtues of vice / Killing my words / Psychotic memories / No chains / Welcoming party / This is system / Color of life
CDBLEED 4 / Mar '93 / Bleeding Hearts

Viogression

☐ PASSAGE
CORPSECD 006 / Sep '96 / Tombstone

Violation Of Trust

☐ RHYMES OF REDEMPTION
LF 306CD / 6 Jul '98 / Lost & Found

Violators

☐ NO FUTURE PUNK YEARS, THE
MOGCD 004 / 2 Mar '98 / Mog

Violent Children

☐ SPLIT SCENE
LF 108CD / Jan '95 / Lost & Found

Violent Femmes

☐ '3'
Nightmares / Just like my father / Dating days / Fat / Fool in the full moon / Nothing worth living for / World we're living in / Outside the palace / Telephone book / Mother of a girl / See my ships
8281302 / Jan '89 / Slash

☐ NEW TIMES
Don't start me on the liquor / Breakin' up / Key of 2 / Four Seasons / Machine / I'm nothing / When everybody's happy / Agamemnon / Island life / I saw you in the crowd / Mirror mirror (I see a damsel) / Jesus of Rio
7559615532 / May '94 / Warner Bros.

☐ VIOLENT FEMMES
Gone daddy gone / Add it up / To the kill / Kiss off / Good feeling / Confessions / Promises / Blister in the sun / Please do not go
8280352 / Aug '91 / Slash

Violent Green

☐ HANGOVERS
UP 056CD / 6 Jul '98 / Up

Violet Arcana

☐ IN THE SCENE OF MIND
CDZOT 112 / Jun '94 / Zoth Ommog

Violet Burning

☐ VIOLET BURNING, THE
Crush / Arabic tremelo radio / Blind / Fever / Sun and the sky / Underwater / Low / Silver / Goldmine / Waiting / Eleven / Feel
DOMO 710102 / Oct '96 / Domo

Violet Ultra

☐ DISTURBING JOY
Out of this world / Misfit / Blow me away / Caught under you / Slut magnet / Quiet day in Dunblane / Into the future / Teenage turbo / Turn away / Someone else / Siren
HTT 2002 / May '97 / Holier Than Thou

Viper

☐ LIVE MANIACS
MASSCD 046 / Feb '95 / Massacre

Vipers Skiffle Group

☐ 10,000 YEARS AGO (3CD Set) (Vipers Skiffle Group & Wally Whyton)
Ain't you glad / Pick a bale of cotton / It takes a worried man to sing a worried song / Don't you rock me daddy-o / 10,000 years ago / Hey Liley Liley-o / Jim Dandy / Cumberland gap / Maggie May / Sam Hall / Kevin Barry / Charlie is my darling / My bonnie lies over the ocean / I know where I'm going / Derby ram / Liverpool blues / Ash Grove / She was poor but she was honest / Wild colonial boy / Spinning wheel / Three lovely lasses / Greensleeves / Clementine / Darlin' / Streamline train / Railroad steamboat / This land is your land / Poor Lazarus / Glory land / Precious memories / Pay me my money down / I know the Lord laid his hands on me / Easy rider / Wanderin' / Old Joe Clark / Old Joe Clark / Homing bird / If I Had a hammer / I saw the light / John B Sails / Last train to San Fernando/Putting on the... / All shook up/Wandering eyes / Skiffle party medley / Skiffle party medley / Baby why / No other baby / Make ready for love / Nothing will ever change (my love for you) / Banks of the Ohio / Trouble in mind / Worried man blues / Experimental / Summertime blues / Cool good / Liverpool blues / Horror show / Don't tell me all your troubles / It's all over now / All over this world / Got me a girl / It's a rat race / Marriage of convenience / 95% of me loves you / You're going to be sorry
BCD 15954 / Dec '96 / Bear Family

VIP's

☐ BEAT CRAZY (The Best Of The VIP'S)
TANGCD 12 / Jan '97 / Tangerine

Virgin Prunes

☐ ARTFUCK
NR 422476 / Jan '94 / New Rose

☐ GREATEST HITS
PILOT 007 / Mar '97 / Burning Airlines

☐ HERESIE
NR 422475 / Jan '94 / New Rose

☐ HIDDEN LIE (Live In Paris)
Sweet home / Lady Day / God bless the child / Never ending story / Pagan love song / Love is danger / Moon looked down and laughed / Caucasian walk / Blues song
NR 422473 / Jan '94 / New Rose

☐ IF I DIE I DIE
NR 452043 / May '94 / New Rose

☐ MOON LOOKED DOWN AND LAUGHED, THE
NR 422474 / Jan '94 / New Rose

☐ NEW FORM OF BEAUTY, A
NR 452042 / Jan '94 / New Rose

☐ PAGAN LOVE SONG
NR 453041 / Jan '94 / New Rose

☐ SONS FIND DEVILS (The Best Of The Virgin Prunes)
CLP 0179 / 2 Feb '98 / Cleopatra

Virgin Steele

☐ AGE OF CONSENT, THE
Let it roar / Prelude to the evening / Lion in winter / Stranger at the gate / Perfect mansions / Coils of the serpent / Serpents kiss / On the wings of the night / Desert plains / Cry forever / We are eternal
TT 00322 / 8 Sep '97 / T&T

☐ INVICTUS
TT 00342 / 20 Apr '98 / T&T

☐ LIFE AMONG THE RUINS
TT 00062 / Nov '96 / T&T

☐ MARRIAGE OF HEAVEN AND HELL, THE
TT 00192

☐
TT 00122 / Nov '96 / T&T

☐ NOBLE SAVAGE
TT 00282 / Nov '96 / T&T

Virginia Squires

☐ BEST OF THE VIRGINIA SQUIRES, THE
Cold sheets of rain / Hard times in Kentucky / Chilly winds / I'm going to make heaven my home / No one to love me now / Late night cry of the whippoorwill / I'm working my way / Denver / You'd better be prepared / Fall after stranger / Sky is weeping / Cabin on the hill / I've just seen the rock of ages / Only a memory away / War between the hearts / When the roll is called up yonder
REBCD 1125 / Jun '98 / Rebel

Virtue

☐ VIRTUE
Let the redeemed / Your love lifted me / SO good to know / Greatest part of me / Quiet times / Lord you are worthy / Take it by force / Throught your name / I must tell Jesus / Cry no more / Be with you
CHIP 188 / 18 Aug '97 / Jive

Virus

☐ REVELATION
SB 015 / 26 Jan '98 / Second Battle

☐ THOUGHTS
SB 047 / 26 Jan '98 / Second Battle

☐ WARMONGER
MIA 001CD / Sep '94 / MIA

Visage

☐ ANVIL, THE
Anvil / Damned don't cry / Move up / Night train / Horseman / Look what they've done / Again we love / Wild life / Whispers
OW 34518 / Sep '97 / One Way

☐ FADE TO GREY (The Best Of Visage)
Anvil / Night train / Pleasure boys / Damned to cry / Love glove / Fade to grey / Mind of a toy / Visage / We move / Tar / In the year 2525
5210532 / Mar '96 / Polydor

☐ VISAGE
Visage / Blocks on block / Dancer / Tar / Fade to grey / Malpaso man / Mind of a toy / Moon over Moscow / Visa-age / Steps
8000292 / May '91 / Polydor
OW 34519 / Sep '97 / One Way

Visby Big Band

☐ FINE TOGETHER
DRCD 210 / Feb '87 / Dragon

Visceral Evisceration

☐ INCESSANT DESIRE
SPV 08407922 / Sep '94 / Napalm

Viscount Oliver

☐ I'M FOR REAL
FECD 16 / Apr '96 / First Edition

☐ JUST ONE MOMENT
FECD 13 / Apr '93 / First Edition

Viseur, Gus

☐ COMPOSITIONS 1934-1942
FA 010CD / Nov '95 / Fremeaux

Vision

☐ WAVEFORM TRANSMISSION VOL.2
EFA 1750D / Jun '93 / Tresor

Vision

☐ IN THE BLINK OF AN EYE
FLY 006CD / Jun '97 / Tackle Box

☐ KIDS STILL HAVE A LOT TO SAY, THE
GRL 006CD / 5 Jan '98 / Grilled Cheese

☐ ONE AND THE SAME
CI 012CD / 13 Apr '98 / Striving For Togetherness

Vision Of Disorder

☐ IMPRINT
What you are / Twelve steps to nothing / Landslide / By the river / Imprint / Colorblind / Rebirth of tragedy / Locust of the dead / Up in flow / Clone / Jada bloom
RR 87932 / 3 Aug '98 / Roadrunner

☐ STILL
FORCE 002CD / 11 Aug '97 / Sonic Rendezvous
SFT 10CD / Apr '98 / Striving For Togetherness

☐ VISION OF DISORDER
Element / Watering disease / Through my eyes / Viola / Liberation / Divide / Ways to destroy one's ambition / Suffer / Zone zero / DTO / Excess / Gloom
RR 88612 / Apr '97 / Roadrunner

Visionary

☐ POSITIVE TRAVELLER
Conflicity / Love defined / Speechless / Just / Dogfishpsyche / Tagmyzky / TEMPLE / Altered state / Sunday morning / Shame
SUCD 6 / 27 Oct '97 / Aura Surround Sounds

Visit Venus

☐ MUSIC FOR SPACE TOURISM
YO 40122 / Apr '96 / Yo Mama

Visitors

☐ IN MY YOUTH
In my youth / Juggler / Visit / Mood seekers / Giant steps
MCD 5024 / May '95 / Muse

Viswanathan, Tanjor

☐ SOUTH INDIAN CLASSICAL FLUTE
Karunmpa / Nivadanegana / Sankaracaryam / Paiyeda pamdala / Kanduha madakkariyai / Krishna ni begane baro
VICG 54532 / Oct '96 / JVC

Vital Information

☐ RAY OF HOPE
Clouds / Celebrate life / Rio-lize / Lorenzo's soul / Sacred treasure / Sixth sense / Ray of hope / Maxed out / All my love, always / Peace / Fit to be tired / Over and out
VBR 21612 / Jun '96 / Vera Bra

☐ WHERE WE COME FROM
Dr. Demento / Moby Dick / Craniac trilogy / Listen up / Swamp stomp / First thing this morning / Take eight / Bob / Cranial joy: Completion / Happy house / Cranial meltdown: Dementia / Blowfish blues / Sitting duck / Once in a lifetime / 008
INT 32182 / 29 Jun '98 / Intuition

Vital Remains

☐ FOREVER UNDERGROUND
OPCD 050 / Jun '97 / Misanthropy

☐ INTO COLD DARKNESS
Immortal crusade / Under the moons fog / Crown of the black hearts / Scrolls / Into cold darkness / Descent into hell / Angels / Dethroned emperor
CDVILE 48 / Nov '95 / Peaceville

☐ LET US PRAY
War in paradise / Of pure unholiness / Ceremony of the seventh circle / Uncultivated grave / Malevolent invocation / Isolated magick / Cult of the dead / Frozen terror / Amulet of the conquering
CDVILE 58 / Mar '95 / Peaceville

Vitale, Lito

☐ CUARTETO
El chupetin paleta / Estar entre / Nosotros / Ese amigo del alma / La enfermeria, sala cuatro / Manana es mejor / Himno coya / La luz sagrada
MES 159952 / Jun '93 / Messidor

Vitale, Richie

☐ LIVE AT SMALLS (Vitale, Richie Quintet)
Barry's blues / Mariko / Ballad medley / Sweet and lovely / Just one of those things / Time on my hands / Fuji mama
TCB 96402 / Feb '97 / TCB

Vitier, Jose Maria

☐ HABANA SECRETA
74321285942 / May '96 / Milan

Vitous, Miroslav

☐ ATMOS (Vitous, Miroslav & Jan Garbarek)
Pegasos / Goddess / Forthcoming / Atmos / Time out part I / Direvision / Time out part II / Helikon / Hippukrene
5133732 / Jun '93 / ECM

☐ EMERGENCE
Epilogue / Transformation / Atlantis suite / Atlantis suite: Emergence of the spirit / Atlantis suite: Matter and spirit / Atlantis suite: Choice / Atlantis suite: Destruction into energy / Wheel of fortune / Regards to Gershwin's honeyman / Alice in Wonderland / Morning lake for ever / Variations on Spanish themes
8278552 / Dec '86 / ECM

☐ FIRST MEETING
Silver lake / Beautiful place to / Trees / Recycle / First meeting / Concert in three parts / You make me so happy
5192802 / Mar '94 / ECM

☐ GUARDIAN ANGELS
His meaning/Rising resolution / Inner peace / Guardian angels / Off to buffalo / Eating it raw / Shinkansen
ECD 22055 / Jul '93 / Evidence

☐ JOURNEY'S END
U dunaje u prespurka / Tess / Carry on No. 1 / Paragraph Jay / Only one / Windfall
8431712 / May '91 / ECM

☐ MIROSLAV
Watching the sunset run / Bassamba / Tiger in the rain / Concerto in e minor / Pictures from moravia / Sonata for a dream
FCD 741040 / Sep '88 / Freedom

Vitro

☐ DISTORT
Mentally dull / Orange / Set it down / Bucket / Head / On it / Orange anorak / Too close / Liquid
ISOM 2CD / 16 Mar '98 / Independiente

Vitro, Roseanna

☐ PASSION DANCE
Out of this world / Long as you're livin' / Return to me / Freedom jazz dance / For Heaven's sake / Whisper not / Simone / Blue Monk / Passion / More than you know / Strollin'
CD 83385 / Mar '96 / Telarc

☐ SOFTLY
Falling in love with love / In summer / Song for all ages / Softly as in a morning sunrise / Moon and sand / So many stars / I'm through with love / Wild is the wind / Life I choose / Our love rolls on / Nothing like you / Why try to change me now / I ain't got nothin' but the blues
CCD 4587 / Feb '94 / Concord Jazz

Viva Brasil

☐ VIVA BRASIL
O bode Iemania / Dancing the Baiao / Turn to yourself / She / Skindo-le le / Voce abusou/Desabafo / Ronco da Cuica / Menina danada / Produto Nacional
CDSR 1000 / 6 Oct '97 / Sugar Loaf

Viva La Musica

☐ LA NAISSANCE DE L'ORCHESTRE 1977-1978 (Viva La Musica/Papa Wemba)
NG 026 / Jan '97 / Ngoyarto

Viva Satellite

☐ EXTRA EYE
TB 246 / Oct '97 / Teenbeat

Viva Saturn

☐ SOUNDMIND
NORMAL 139 / May '94 / Normal

Vivino, Jimmy

☐ DO WHAT, NOW (Vivino, Jimmy & The Rekooperators)
MM 65157 / Apr '97 / Music Masters

Vivona, Massimo

☐ CHRONICLES OF SOUND (2CD Set)
HEADZCD 001 / Jun '97 / Headzone

Vixen

☐ TANGERINE
EAGCD 028 / 18 May '98 / Eagle
86246 / 22 May '98 / CMC

Vizonto

☐ NEW WAVE
FYCD 8004 / Apr '98 / Robi Droli

Vlad

☐ SECRET LANGUAGE
In this world / Tell lies / Dead love / Believe / Taking / Something else / Burning / Everyone / Blindness / Anybody / Living in prison / Darkness
HYP 3910183CD / 13 Apr '98 / Hyperium

Vlad Tepes

☐ MARCH IN THE BLACK HOLOCAUST (Vlad Tepes/Belketre)
TE 02CD / Jul '96 / Embassy

Vloeimans, Eric

☐ BESTIARIUM
Mack truck / For Jacq / Rabbit, the fox / Hunter and the hole / Whirlpool / Je ne sais quoi / Uncle Theo / 2 For 1 / Ellen / Bedtime story / F for fun, funk and fumble / ZMDIHM / Elephant walk
CHR 70038 / Mar '97 / Challenge

☐ FIRST FLOOR
CHR 70011 / Aug '95 / Challenge

Voag, L.

☐ WAY OUT, THE
ALLVCD / Jun '97 / ReR/Recommended

Voci Del Lesima

☐ SPLENDE LA LUNA IN CIELO
RDC 5034CD / Nov '96 / Robi Droli

Vocokesh

☐ PARADISE REVISITED
DC 136CD / 23 Mar '98 / Drag City

Vodou

☐ HAITIAN VOODOO (Ritual Possession Of The Dead)
Ya te g / Por Pourre I / Por pourre II / St. Jaques / Ogou / En rezo / Negue nago
IN 5734 / Jan '98 / Interra

Voelz, Susan

☐ 13 RIBS
VDCD 106 / Jun '96 / Voodoo

☐ SUMMER CRASHING
DFGCD 8432 / Jun '96 / Dixie Frog

Vogel, Christian

☐ ABSOLUTE TIME
EFA 017832 / Jul '95 / BMG

☐ ALL MUSIC HAS COME TO AN END
EFA 292662 / Apr '97 / Tresor

☐ BEGINNING TO UNDERSTAND
EFA 006582 / Nov '94 / Mille Plateau

☐ SPECIFIC MOMENTS
EFA 006772 / Sep '96 / Mille Plateau

Vogel, Karsten

☐ SINDBILLEDE
MECCACD 1011 / Nov '94 / Music Mecca

Vogt, Michael

☐ TUBA INTIM
RERTUBA 1 / Oct '96 / ReR/Recommended

Voice

☐ PREDICTION
AFM 022CD / 17 Aug '98 / AFM

Voice Crack

☐ EARFLASH
DEX 4 / Dec '96 / Dexter's Cigar

Voice Of A Generation

☐ CLASSIC STUPIDITY
JABSCD 005CD / 17 Nov '97 / Burning Heart

☐ ODD GENERATION
JABSCD 010CD / 27 Apr '98 / Burning Heart

Voice Of Authority

☐ VERY BIG IN AMERICA RIGHT NOW
(Short intro) knock the house down / Very big in America right now / Middle East power station / In another world / Stopping and starting / Technical miracle / Slipped disco / Grand prix / Feeling wild
CDBRED 62 / 22 Sep '97 / Cherry Red

Voice Of The Beehive

☐ HONEY LINGERS
Monsters and angels / Adonis Blue / I think I love you / Look at me / Beauty to my eyes / Just like you / Little gods / I'm shooting Cupid / Say it / Perfect place
5521112 / Mar '96 / Spectrum

☐ LET IT BEE
Beat of love / Sorrow floats / Don't call me baby / Man in the moon / What you have is enough / Oh love / I walk the earth / Trust me / I say nothing / There's a barbarian in the back of my car / Just a city
8281002 / May '92 / London

☐ SEX AND MISERY
Scary kisses / Moonblind / So hard / Blue in paradise / Moon of dust / I'm still in love / Love locked inside / Heavenly / Playing house / Angel come down / New day
0630110042 / Dec '96 / East West

Voice Squad

☐ HOLLYWOOD
Coventry carol / Coventry carol / Sheepstealers / A stor mo chroi / Jimmy murphy / I am stretched on your grave / Good people all / Brown and the yellow ale / Sarah jane / Down in yon forest / A fond kiss / Annan waters / Parting glass
HBCD 0002 / Oct '93 / Hummingbird

☐ MANY'S THE FOOLISH YOUTH
When a man's in love / Bonny Irish maid / Willie Taylor / Banks of the Bann / Holly she bears a berry / Parting glass / Kilmore Carol / Annan waters / Shepherds arise / Ode to autumn / Oh good ale
TARACD 4004 / Nov '95 / Tara

Voice Stealer

☐ ALL ELECTRIC HOUSE, THE
Unintensional / Memorandrum / Moebius / Electromotive force / Motorola / Electronic eyes / Memorandum / Eventuality / Ordeal x / Evaluation
VERTCD 01 / 2 Feb '98 / Subvert

Voice Union

☐ VOICE UNION (Voice Union & Maddy Prior)
Bourrees du centre / Mal mariee / Ninna nana jam / Chanson a la mariee / La visite / Oh to be alone / Le moine complaisant / La puissance d'argent / La fille soldat / Allegra mi / Dans Paris y a t'une brune / La sentiment des filles / Nous coucherons ensemble / Jardin d'amour
FECD 119 / Jul '97 / Fellside

Voices Of East Harlem

☐ CAN YOU FEEL IT
UFOXY 6CD / May '95 / Vexfilms

☐ VOICES OF EAST HARLEM
UFOXY 5CD / May '95 / Vexfilms

Voices Of Kwahn AD

☐ OPERATION DISMANTLED SUN
SF 014 / 24 Nov '97 / Swarf Finger

☐ PENINSULAR ENCLOSURE
SF 015 / Apr '97 / Swarf Finger

☐ SILVER BOWL OF TRANSMISSION
VOK 100CD / Jul '96 / Abstract

Voices Of Silence

☐ VOICES OF SILENCE
74321236092 / Apr '95 / Arista

Voices Of Theory

☐ VOICES OF THEORY, THE
6119341016 / 21 Apr '98 / Hola

Void

☐ CONDENSED FLESH
LF 92CD / Nov '94 / Lost & Found

Void Section

☐ INSANITY PLEAD
IS 8898702CD / 15 Dec '97 / I Scream Music

Voivod

☐ NEGATRON
Insect / Project X / Nanoman / Reality / Negatron / Planet hell / Meteor / Cosmic conspiracy / Bio TV / Drift / DNA (Don't no anything)
HYP 001CD / Oct '95 / Hypnotic

☐ PHOBOS
HYPSD 1057CD / 11 Aug '97 / Mascot

☐ WAR AND PAIN
Voivod / Suck your bone / War and pain / Live for violence / Nuclear war / Warriors of ice / Iron gang / Blower / Black city
398414049CD / Jun '97 / Metal Blade

Volare

☐ UNCERTAINTY PRINCIPLE, THE
LE 1028 / Sep '97 / Laser's Edge

Volcano Suns

☐ FARCED
SST 210CD / Sep '88 / SST

☐ THINGS OF BEAUTY
Barracade / It's a conspiracy / Man outstanding / Courageous stunts / No place / Noodle on the couch / Ask the pundits / Arm and a leg / How to breathe / Rite of way / Soft hits / Malamonda / Deeply moved / Now file / Fill the void / Nightmare country / Needles in the camel's eye / Hung out / Suck out the jams / Redeye express / Mud / Veteran / Hang up
SST 257CD / Nov '89 / SST

Volcanos

☐ SURFQUAKE
ES 1230CD / Sep '96 / Estrus

Volitzer, Eva

☐ JEWISH SEPHARDIC SONGS
EUCD 1344 / Apr '96 / ARC

Volkaert, Redd

☐ TELEWACKER
Telewacker / Strangers / Tube'n / I hate you / It's a minor thing / Stumblin' / You're still on my mind / Breakneck / Home in San Antone / Buck stops here / That girl who waits on tables / Redd white and blue
HMG 3002 / 30 Mar '98 / Hightone

Volt Creations

☐ VOLT, THE
TVOLTCD 1 / Jun '96 / The Volt

Volume All Stars

☐ CLOSE ENCOUNTERS OF THE BUMP AND GRIND
SLABCO 37 / Jun '97 / Slabco

Volumen Cero

☐ ANDROMEDA
859600192 / 24 Mar '98 / GTA

Voluptuous Horror Of Karen Black

☐ NATIONAL HEALTHCARE
Neigherachie / Alaska / Dionetics / SunAshinin / King of the sea / Mr twilight / You sley me / One man lady / Shame / Isis water / Mother / Oh diane / Chopsley rabid bikini model / Feeling stronger everyday
GKCD 018 / 22 Sep '97 / Go-Kart

Vomacka, Sammy

☐ EASY RIDER
BLR 84 019 / May '91 / L&R

Vomiting Corpses

☐ SPHERES, THE
IR 013CD / Jun '95 / Invasion

Vomito Negro

☐ DARE
KK 009CD / '89 / KK

☐ HUMAN
Raise your power / Give him coke / In strict tempo (part 2) / Black power / Citydump / In strict tempo (part 3) / Meeting eyes / Future / Escape / Human / Needle / Feel the heat
KK 050CD / Sep '90 / KK

☐ SAVE THE WORLD
KKUK 002CD / '90 / KK

☐ SHOCK
KK 023CD / '89 / KK

Vomiturition

☐ LEFTOVER AGE, A
IR 014CD / Jun '95 / Invasion

Von Bulow, Christina

☐ SOLITUDE (Von Bulow, Christina Trio)
MECCACD 2039 / Jan '98 / Music Mecca

Von Daniken

☐ NEW WORLDS
CYCL 028 / Nov '95 / Cyclops

Von Groove

☐ MISSION MAN
AVCB 66002 / May '97 / Bareknuckle

☐ RAINMAKER
342122 / Oct '95 / No Bull

Von Hausswolff, Carl Michael

☐ TO MAKE THINGS HAPPEN IN THE BUNKER VIA THE MICRO WAY
F 14 / Sep '97 / Fire Inc.

Von Hermann, Heinz

☐ JAZZ AHEAD (Live In LA) (Von Hermann, Heinz Quintet)
Healer / Little peace / Samba for Carmen / Kathie's garden / Blues for Olla / Groovin' on Dr. John / Triolypso / Ground blues
MR 874810 / 8 Apr '98 / Mons

Von Magnet

☐ COMPUTADOR
HYPE 06CD / Nov '92 / Roughneck

Von Sneidern, Chris

☐ BIG WHITE LIES
HEY 037 / 30 Mar '98 / Heyday

☐ GO
MODLANG 3 / 27 Apr '98 / Mod Lang

☐ SIGHT AND SOUND
HEY 032 / 30 Mar '98 / Heyday

☐ WOOD AND FIRE
ML 005 / 16 Feb '98 / Modern Language

Von Stade, Frederica

☐ ACROSS YOUR DREAMS (Frederica Von Stade Sings Dave Brubeck)
Distance between us / La paloma azul / Strange meadowlark / Across your dreams / Summer song / Polly / Blue rondo / Autumn in our city / Weep no, you, thinking of me / It's a raggy waltz / Heart of Winter / In the grace of your room / Lonely on both ends of the road
CD 80467 / Sep '96 / Telarc

885

Von Trapp Family

☐ SOUND OF CHRISTMAS, THE
15466 / Nov '95 / Laserlight

Von Westernhagen, Thilo

☐ FORGOTTEN GARDENS (Von
Westernhagen, Thilo & Charlie
Mariano/Peter Weihe)
BEST 1011CD / Nov '93 / Acoustic
Music

Von Zamla

☐ ZAMLARANAMMA
Harujanta / Rainbox / Doppler / Clandestine /
Temporal you are / Original 13 11 / Ten tango /
Antsong / Tail of antsong
RES 511CD / Jul '97 / Resource

Von Zippers

☐ WOW 'EM DOWN AT FRANZL'S
ANDA 218CD / May '97 / Au-Go-Go

Vondur

☐ GALACTIC ROCK 'N' ROLL EMPIRE
NR 025CD / 17 Aug '98 / Necropolis

☐ STRIDSYFIRLYSING
NR 010CD / Oct '96 / Necropolis

Voodoo Glowskulls

☐ BAILE DE LOS LOCOS
64922 / Jun '97 / Epitaph

☐ BAND GEEK MAFIA, THE
Human piñata / Symptomatic / Love letter / They
always come back / Walkin' frustration / Yo no tengo
tiempo (para ti) / Left for dead / Band geek mafia /
Brodie Johnson weekend / Delinquent song /
Hieroglyphics / Misunderstood / Hit a guy with
glasses / Stranded in the jungle
65352 / 13 Jul '98 / Epitaph

☐ FIRME
864542 / Oct '95 / Epitaph

☐ WHO IS THIS IS
DSR 018CD / 16 Mar '98 / Dr. Strange

Voodoo Queens

☐ CHOCOLATE REVENGE
PURECD 030 / Dec '93 / Too Pure

Voodoo X

☐ AWAKENING, THE (Vol.1)
NTHEN 016CD / Apr '95 / Now & Then

Voorn, Orlando

☐ NIGHTVISIONS (2CD Set)
NV 010CD / Oct '96 / Abstract

Vorak

☐ TRIUMPH OF THE WILL
DSTK 7661CD / Dec '96 / Destruktive
Kommndoh

Vorhaus, David

☐ WHITE NOISE VOL.2
CDV 2032 / Jun '97 / Virgin

☐ WHITE NOISE VOL.4
AMPCD 010 / Feb '95 / AMP

Voss, Jochen

☐ ALTERATIONS
BEST 1029CD / Nov '93 / Acoustic
Music

Vow

☐ VOW
VOWCD 1 / Jun '96 / Vowcom

Vox Humana

☐ UNSAMPLED
ALIGCD 1 / Jan '95 / Alligator

Voyage

☐ BEST OF VOYAGE
Scotch machine: Voyager / From east to west:
Voyager / Point zero: Voyager / Orient express:
Voyager / Let's get started: Voyager / Latin
odyssesy: Voyager / Lady America: Voyager / Follow
the brightest star: Voyager / Souvenirs: Voyager /
Kechak fantasy: Voyager / I love you dancer:
Voyager / Tahiti tahiti: Voyager / I'm only human:
Voyager
EMPRCD 633 / Jun '96 / Emporio

☐ BEST OF VOYAGE, THE (Souvenirs)
From east to west / Souvenirs / Point zero / Orient
express / Latin odyssey / Lady America / Let's fly
away / Tahiti Tahiti / I love you dancer / I'm only
human / Let's get started / Follqw the brightest star /
Kechak fantasy
HTCD 12 / 20 Apr '98 / Hot Productions

Voyage

☐ SELAM
39850182 / 1 Jun '98 / Blue Flame

Voyager

☐ FUTURE RETRO
Desire / Hypersleep / Animal magic / Collect call /
Martian chronics / Jazzed out / Definition of love /
Waiting for me / Long distance / See forever
RS 97109CD / Apr '97 / R&S

Vranich, Mick

☐ CLOAK OF SKIN
NAR 092CD / Feb '94 / New Alliance

Vriends, Peter

☐ EMOTIONAL TRAVELLOG
Serenity / Joy / Fear / Anger / Envy / Lust / Jealousy /
Security / Greed / Love
SMCCD 8002 / Oct '96 / Smile
Communications

Vrod, Jean-Francois

☐ VOYAGE
Y 225036CD / Oct '94 / Silex

VSOP

☐ ORCHESTRAL ROCK
Queen medley / All you need is love / Sailing / Groovy
kind of love / Stairway to Heaven / Bridge over
troubled water / Orinoco flow / Space oddity /
Satisfaction / Beatles medley
MCCD 347 / 15 Jun '98 / MCI Music

VSS

☐ NERVOUS CIRCUITS
HB 15CD / May '97 / Honey Bear

Vujicsics

☐ VUJICSICS
HNCD 1310 / May '89 / Hannibal

Vulcheva, Kalinka

☐ CROSS THE DANUBE (Vulcheva/
Jenkins Incident)
Only laughter in her eyes / Cross the Danube /
Lazarski / Fisher's wife / Stano stankay / Blacksmith
/ Yankin brat / Same air / Goro zelena / Burying
ground
OSMOCD 009 / Mar '97 / Osmosys

Vulgar Boatmen

☐ YOU AND YOUR SISTER
SH 11712 / Nov '96 / Safe House

Vulgar Unicorn

☐ SLEEP WITH THE FISHES
CYCL 040 / Oct '96 / Cyclops

☐ UNDER THE UMBRELLA
House at fudge corner / By post-chaise to the prim
rose legue / Waiting under the umbrella / Thief of
clubs
CYCL 018 / Apr '95 / Cyclops

Vulpecula

☐ FONS IMMORTALIS
Astride the darklands / Fons immortalis / Down
among them / Phoenix of the creation / First points of
aries / Seven layers of light
MRCD 006 / 30 Sep '97 / Merciless

Vulva

☐ BIRDWATCH
CAT 035CD / Oct '96 / Rephlex

☐ FROM THE COCKPIT
CAT 021CD / Mar '95 / Rephlex

☐ YONIC VULVICATION
EFA 006262 / Jul '97 / Source

Vuust, Peter

☐ BIG VIEW, THE (Vuust, Peter Quartet)
Big view / Hey Fred / Homesick / Waving back at me /
Morning song / End of a perfect day / November
black / Face of an angel / Swiss sun in the 70's /
That's my dad mowing the lawn / Carl / Please
silently walk go
STCD 4219 / Feb '98 / Storyville

Vyas, Satish

☐ RAGA MARWA
NRCD 0074 / Nov '96 / Navras

☐ STRINGS OF YOUR SOUL
NRCD 0061 / Jul '96 / Navras

Vybe

☐ VYBE
Take it to the front / Warm Summer daze / I can't fight
anymore / I like it / I don't like it / All my love / Slow and
easy / Funky low down feeling / Mama's on the
phone / Stay / Tell me / Knocks me off my feet / Love
is all we need / If I cry
BRCD 618 / Oct '95 / 4th & Broadway

Vysniauskas, Petras

☐ LITHUANIA
ITM 1449 / Jan '91 / ITM

W

Waaberi

☐ NEW DAWN
Rogo rogosho / Cidlaan dareemaya / Heei yaa alahobalin hobalowa / Hafun / Shubahada / Ada bere chaelka / Indo ashak / Nin hun heloha modina / Ulimada / Kafiyo kaladeri
CDRW 66 / 14 Jul '97 / Realworld

Waby Spider

☐ SIDA
ADC 1001 / Feb '94 / PAM

Wachsmann, Philip

☐ CHATHUNA
BEADCD 3 / Aug '97 / Bead

☐ GUSH WACHS
BEADCD 2 / Sep '97 / Bead

Wackerman, Chad

☐ FORTY REASONS
Holiday insane / You came along / Forty reasons / Fearless / Quite life / Waltzing on jupiter / Tell me / House on fire / Hidden places / Go / Schemes
CMPCD 48 / 6 Apr '98 / CMP

Waco Brothers

☐ COWBOY IN FLAMES
BS 015CD / Jun '97 / Bloodshot

☐ DO YOU THINK ABOUT ME
BS 024 / 19 Jan '98 / Bloodshot

☐ TO THE LAST DEAD COWBOY
BS 006 / 19 Jan '98 / Bloodshot

Waddell, Steve

☐ ALONG THE ROAD (Waddell, Steve & His Creole Bells)
SOSCD 1301 / Jul '96 / Stomp Off

☐ EGYPTIAN ELLA (Waddell, Steve & His Creole Bells)
SOSCD 1230 / Oct '92 / Stomp Off

Wade, Stephen

☐ DANCING IN THE PARLOUR
Theme form Beethoven's mandolin / Bonaparte's retreat / Darling Cory / Feather bed / Coal creek march / Rocky Hill / Sunflower dance / Pretty Polly / Walking in the parlour / Ash groove / Ministrel medley / Flowery girls / Foxhunter's reel / Lost John / Greenback dollar / Malvern Hill / Hobart SMith wabash blues / Over the waterfall / Elzic's farewell / Train on the island / Oh my little darling / Reckless Rufus / Ratler tryied a possum / Banging breakdown
COCD 2721 / 9 Mar '98 / County

Wade, Wayne

☐ LADY
RNCD 2133 / Feb '96 / Rhino

Wagon

☐ ANNIVERSARY
GRCD 423 / 23 Mar '98 / Glitterhouse

☐ NO KINDER ROOM
HCD 8072 / Jul '96 / Hightone

Wagoner, Porter

☐ ESSENTIAL PORTER WAGGONER & DOLLY PARTON, THE (Wagoner, Porter & Dolly Parton)
Last thing on my mind / Holding on to nothin' / We'll get ahead someday / Yours love / Always always / Just someone I used to know / Tomorrow is forever / Daddy was an old time preacher man / Better move it on home / Right combination / Burning the midnight oil / Lost forever in your kiss / Together always / We've found it / Say forever you'll be mine / If teardrops were pennies / Please don't stop loving me / Is forever longer than always / If you go I'll follow you / Making plans
07863668582 / Aug '96 / RCA Nashville

☐ IN PERSON
Howdy neighbour howdy / Misery loves company / Head over heels in love with you / I didn't mean it / Foggy mountain top / Comedy / Sweet fern / Haven't you heard / Eat drink and be merry / Satisfied mind / I thought of God / Sally goodin' / Come on in (and make yourself at home) / My baby's not here (in town tonight) / Talk back trembling lips / Private little world / Comedy / Find out / Old log cabin for sale / John Henry
KOCCD 7987 / Mar '98 / Koch

☐ THIN MAN FROM WEST PLAINS (4CD Set)
Settin' the woods on fire / Headin' for a weddin' / Lovin' letters / I can't live with you (I can't live without you) / Bringing home the bacon / Angel made of ice / Takin' chances / All roads lead to love / That's it / Beggar for your love / Trademark / Don't play that song (You lied) / Flame of love / Dig that crazy moon / Trinidad / Bad news travels fast / Get out of here / My bonfire / Town crier / Love at first sight / Be glad you ain't me / Our shivaree / Company's coming / Tricks of the trade / Satisfied mind / Good time was had by all / Hey maw / How quick / I like girls / Itchin' for my baby / Eat, drink and be merry / I'm stepping out tonight / Let's squiggle / Living in the past / What would you do (if Jesus came to your house) / How can you refuse him now / Tryin' to forget the blues / Uncle pen / How I've tried / I've known you from somewhere / Seeing her only reminded me of you / Midnight / I guess I'm crazy / Born to lose / Ivory tower / I should be with you / Would you be satisfied / I'm day dreamin' tonight / I'll pretend / Who will he be / Good mornin' neighbor / My brand of blues / Thinking of you / I thought I heard you call my name / Turn it over in your mind / Payday / Big wheels / Wound time can't erase / As long as I'm dreaming / Your love / Doll face / I don't want this memory / Burning bridges / Five O'clock in the morning / Heaven's just a prayer away / Tomorrow we'll retire / Just before dawn / Dear lonesome / Tell her lies and feed her candy / Haven't you heard / Don't ever leave me / Who'll buy the wine / Me and Fred and Joe and Bill / Out of sight out of mind / I thought of God / I'm gonna sing / Our song of love / Battle of little big horn / Luannie Brown / Your kind of people / Girl who didn't need love / Legend of the big steeple / Wakin' up the crowd / Old log cabin for sale / Falling again / Old Jess / Your old love letters / Heartbreak affair / Everything she touches get the blues / I cried again / My name is mud / Sugarfoot rag / I thought I heard you calling my name / One way ticket (to the blues) / Take good care of her / I went out of my way / Tennessee border / I gotta find someone (who loves like I do) / Misery loves company / Cryin' loud / I wonder where you are tonight / Frosty the snowman / Cold dark waters / Ain't it awful / Wasted years / Private little world / I've enjoyed as much of this as I can stand / Blue house painted white
BCD 15499 / May '93 / Bear Family

Wahab, Mohamed Abdel

☐ FAKAROUNI
3106262 / 23 Mar '98 / Odeon

Wahls, Shirley

☐ DOWN BY THE RIVERSIDE (Wahls, Shirley Singers)
BB 1962 / Feb '96 / Black & Blue

Wai Fat, Chan

☐ FOO CUP KWAN NAN
FS 001 / Jun '97 / Fat Sound

Wai Wan

☐ DISTRACTION
Deep / Nightmare / Ain't easy / Yesterday / Goddess / Blue / Hindsight / Filtered funk / Revenge
4931682 / 30 Mar '98 / Autonomy

Wailer, Bunny

☐ BLACKHEART MAN
Blackheart man / Fighting against conviction / Oppressed song / Fig tree / Dreamland / Rastaman / Reincarnated soul / Amagideon / Bide up / This train
RRCD 6 / Jun '90 / Reggae Refreshers

☐ BUNNY WAILER SINGS THE WAILERS
Dancing shoes / Mellow mood / Dreamland / Keep on moving / Hypocrite / I'm the toughest / Rule this land / Burial / I stand predominate / Walk the proud land
RRCD 8 / Jun '90 / Reggae Refreshers

☐ CRUCIAL ROOTS CLASSICS
SHCD 45014 / Apr '94 / Shanachie

☐ GUMPTION
Sounds clash / Gumption / Dog war / Warrior / Don man / Reggae burden / See and blind / Piaka / Never grow old / Closer together
SMCD 014 / Jul '91 / Solomonic

☐ HALL OF FAME
RASCD 3502 / Jan '96 / Ras

☐ JUST BE NICE
RASCD 3121 / Jul '93 / Ras

☐ LIBERATION
SHANCD 43059 / Feb '89 / Shanachie

☐ MARKETPLACE
Stay with the reggae / Jump jump / Dance hall music / Cool and deadly / Ally worker / Dance the night away / Electric city / Tear in your eyes / Home sweet home (instrumental) / Together
SHCD 43071 / Jun '91 / Shanachie

☐ PROTEST
Moses children / Get up stand up / Scheme of things / Quit trying, follow fashion monkey / Wanted children / Who feels it / Johnny too bad
RRCD 7 / Jun '90 / Reggae Refreshers

☐ RETROSPECTIVE REGGAE CLASSICS
SHCD 45021 / Mar '98 / Shanachie

☐ ROOTS MAN SKANKING
SHANCD 43043 / Sep '87 / Shanachie

☐ ROOTS RADICS ROCKERS REGGAE
SHANCD 43013 / Jan '84 / Shanachie

☐ RULE DANCE HALL
SHANCD 43050 / Jun '88 / Shanachie

Wailers

☐ FABULOUS WAILERS, THE (The Original Golden Crest Masters)
Tall cool one / Roadrunner / Mau mau / Dirty robber / Wailin' / Shanghied / Beat guitar / Driftwood / Lucille / Scratchin' / Long gone / High wall / Gunnin' for Peter / Why did it happen to me / Swing shift / Snake pit / Driftwood / Dirty robber / Touch bounce
CDCHD 675 / 23 Feb '98 / Ace

Wailing Roots

☐ FEELINGS AND DUB
ACPCG 014 / Oct '95 / Melodie

Wailing Souls

☐ BEST OF THE WAILING SOULS, THE
JJCD 167 / 6 Jul '98 / Channel One

☐ FACE THE DEVIL
CDTRL 360 / Jun '95 / Trojan

☐ FIRE HOUSE ROCK
Firehouse rock / Run dem down / Oh what a feeling / Kingdom rise, kingdom fall / Act of affection / Busnah / Fool will fall / Bandits taking over / Who lives it / See Baba Joe
GRELCD 21 / Sep '89 / Greensleeves

☐ INCHPINCHERS
Inchpinchers / Things and time / Baby come rock / Mass charley ground / Oh what a lie / Ghetto of Kingston Town / Tom sprang / Don't get lost / Modern slavery / Infidels
GRELCD 47 / Sep '92 / Greensleeves

☐ LAY IT ON THE LINE
Lay it on the line / We won't succumb / Them a fret / No big thing / Informer / Bum rap / Good over evil / If I love you too much
LLCD 024 / 18 May '98 / Live & Learn

☐ ON THE ROCKS
Down on the rocks / Sticky stay / Stop red eye / Gun / Jah is watching you / Riddim of life / What is your meaning / Ishen tree / Don't burn baby
GRELCD 59 / Feb '96 / Greensleeves

☐ STRANDED
Stranded in L A / File for your machete / Thinking / Peace and love shall reign / Helmet of salvation / War deh round a John shop / Eyes of love / Divided and rule / Sunrise till sunset / Best is yet to come
GRELCD 73 / Aug '95 / Greensleeves

☐ TENSION
BSCD 8 / Mar '97 / Big Ship

☐ VERY BEST OF THE WAILING SOULS, THE
War / Jah give us life / Bredda / Old broom / Kingdom rise, Kingdom fall / Firehouse rock / Who no waan come / Things and time / Stop red eye / Sticky stay / They don't know Jah / War deh round a John shop
GRELCD 99 / Oct '95 / Greensleeves

☐ WILD SUSPENSE
Row fisherman / Slow coach / We got to be together / Feel the spirit / Bredda Gravilicious / Wild suspense / They never knew / Black rose / Something funny / Very well / Walk but mind you don't fall / Row fisherman (dub) / Bredda Gravilicious (dub) / Slow coach (dub) / Something funny (dub) / We've got to be together / Very well (dub)
RRCD 53 / Apr '95 / Reggae Refreshers

Wainapel, Harvey

☐ AMBROSIA (The Music Of Kenny Barron)
Anywhere / Ambrosia / Phantoms / Lunacy / Lullabye / Sambao / Belem / Sonia braga / If and when
AL 73060 / Nov '96 / A

Wainwright III, Loudon

☐ CAREER MOVES
Road ode / I'm alright / Five years old / Your mother and I / Westchester county / He said, she said / Christmas rap / Suddenly it's Christmas / Thanksgiving / Fine Celtic name / TSMNWA / Some balding guys / Swimming song / Absence makes the heart grow fonder / Happy birthday Elvis / Fabulous songs / Unhappy anniversary / I'd rather be lonely / Just say no / April fool's day morn / Man who couldn't cry / Acid song / Tip that waitress / Career moves
CDV 2718 / Jul '93 / Virgin

☐ FAME AND WEALTH
Reader and advisor / Grammy song / Dump the dog / Five years old / Westchester county / Saturday morning fever / April fools day morn / Fame and wealth / Thick and thin / Revenge / Ingenue / IDTTYWLM
ROUCD 3076 / Aug '88 / Rounder

☐ GROWN MAN
Birthday present / Grown man / That hospital / Housework / Cobwebs / Year / Father/Daughter dialogue / 1994 / Iwiwal / Just a John / I suppose / Dreaming / End has begun / Human cannonball / Treasures untold
CDV 2789 / Oct '95 / Virgin

☐ HISTORY
People In love / Men / Picture / When I'm At Your House / Doctor / Hitting You / I'd rather be lonely / Between / Talking New Bob Dylan / So many songs / Four times ten / Father And A Son / Sometimes I forget / Handful Of Dust
CDV 2703 / Sep '92 / Virgin

☐ I'M ALRIGHT
One man guy / Lost love / I'm alright / Not John / Cardboard boxes / Screaming issue / How old are you / Animal song / Out of this world / Daddy take a nap / Ready or not / Career moves
ROUCD 3096 / Aug '88 / Rounder

☐ LITTLE SHIP
Breakfast in bed / Four mirrors / Mr,. Ambivalent / OGM / Our own war / So damn happy / Primrose hill / Underwear / World / Waht are families for / Bein' a dad / Birthday present / I can't stand myself / Little ship / Song
CDV 2844 / 6 Oct '97 / Virgin

☐ LIVE ONE, A
Motel blues / Hollywood hopeful / Whatever happened to us / Natural disaster / Suicide song / School days / Kings and Queens / Down drinking at the bar / B side / Nocturnal stumblebutt / Red guitar / Clockwork chartreuse / Lullaby
ROUCD 3050 / Mar '96 / Rounder

☐ MORE LOVE SONGS
Hard day on the planet / Synchronicity / Your mother and I / I eat out / No / Home stretch / Unhappy anniversary / Man's world / Vampire blues / Overseas calls / Expatriot / Back nine
ROUCD 3106 / '88 / Rounder
DIAB 842 / 24 Nov '97 / Diablo

☐ ONE MAN GUY (The Best Of Loudon Wainwright III 1984-1989)
MCCD 166 / Jul '94 / Music Club

Wainwright, Rufus

☐ RUFUS WAINWRIGHT
DRD 50039 / 10 Aug '98 / Dreamworks

Wainwright, Sloan

☐ SLOAN WAINWRIGHT
WBG 0023CD / Aug '96 / Waterbug

Waistcoats

☐ SURFISTICATED SOUND OF THE WAISTCOATS, THE
WIGCD 014 / 20 Jul '98 / Alopecia

Waite, John

☐ NO BRAKES
Saturday night / Missing you / Dark side of the sun / Restless heart / Tears / Euroshima / Dreamtime / Shake it up / For your love / Love collision
NSPCD 514 / Jun '95 / Connoisseur Collection

☐ WHEN YOU WERE MINE
536207 / Sep '97 / Purr

Waiting For God

☐ DESIPRAMINE
REC 040 / 20 Oct '97 / Re-Constriction

☐ QUARTER INCH THICK
CDREC 030 / Jan '97 / Re-Constriction

Waiting For The Sun

☐ WAITING FOR THE SUN
KSCD 9508 / Jun '97 / Kissing Spell

Waits, Tom

☐ ASYLUM YEARS
Diamonds on my windshield / Looking for the heart of Saturday night / Martha / Ghosts of Saturday night / Grapefruit moon / Small change / Burma shave / I never talk to strangers / Tom Traubert's blues / Blue valentines / Potter's field / Kentucky Avenue / Somewhere / Ruby's arms
9604942 / Oct '86 / Asylum

☐ BEAUTIFUL MALADIES 1983-1993
Hang on St. Christopher / Temptation / Clap hands / Black rider / Underground / Jockey full of bourbon / Earth died screaming / Innocent when you dream / Straight to the top / Frank's wild years / Singapore / Shore leave / Johnsburg Illinois / Way down in the hole / Strange weather / Cold cold ground / November / Downtown train / 16 shells from a 30.6 / Jesus gonna be here / Good old world / I don't wanna grow up / Time
5245192 / 15 Jun '98 / Island

☐ BIG TIME
16 shells from a 30.6 / Red shoes / Underground / Cold cold ground / Straight to the top / Yesterday is here / Way down in the hole / Falling down / Strange weather / Big black Mariah / Rain dogs / Train song / Johnsburg Illinois / Ruby's arms / Telephone call from Istanbul / Clap hands / Gun street girl / Time
IMCD 249 / Mar '97 / Island

☐ BLACK RIDER
Lucky day overture / Black rider / November / Just the right bullets / Black box theme / 'tain't no sin / Flash pan hunter-intro / That's the way / Briar and the rose / Russian dance ('trepak') / Gospel train-orchestrra / I'll shoot the moon / Flash pan hunter / Crossroads / Gospel train / Knterlude / Oily night / Lucky day / Last rose of summer / Carnival
CID 8021 / Nov '93 / Island

☐ BLUE VALENTINE
Red shoes by the drugstore / Christmas card from a hooker in Minneapolis / Romeo is bleeding / Twenty nine dollars / Wrong side of the road / Whistlin' past the graveyard / Kentucky Avenue / Sweet little bullet from a pretty blue gun / Title track
7559605332 / Oct '94 / WEA

☐ BONE MACHINE
Earth died screaming / Dirt in the ground / Such a scream / All stripped down / Who are you this time / Ocean / Jesus gonna be here / Little rain / In the colosseum / Going out West / Murder in the red barn / Black wings / Whistle down the wind / I don't wanna grow up / Let me get up on it / That feel
CID 9993 / Aug '92 / Island

☐ CLOSING TIME
Ol' 55 / Hope that I don't fall in love with you / Virginia Avenue / Old shoes / Midnight lullaby / Martha / Rosie / Ice cream man / Little trip to heaven / Grapefruit moon / Closing time
9608362 / Feb '93 / WEA

☐ FOREIGN AFFAIRS
Cinny's waltz / Muriel / I never talk to strangers / Sight for sore eyes / Potter's field / Burma shave / Barber shop / Foreign affair
7559606182 / Feb '95 / WEA

☐ FRANKS WILD YEARS
Hang on St. Christopher / Straight to the top (Rhumba) / Blow wind blow / Temptation / I'll be gone / Yesterday is here / Please wake me up / Franks theme / More than rain / Way down in the hole / Straight to the top / I'll take New York / Telephone call from Istanbul / Cold cold ground / Train song / Innocent when you dream
IMCD 50 / Jun '89 / Island

☐ HEART OF SATURDAY NIGHT, THE
New coat of paint / San Diego serenade / Semi suite / Shiver me timbers / Diamonds on my windshield / Looking for the heart of Saturday night / Fumblin' with the blues / Please call me, baby / Depot depot / Drunk on the moon / Ghosts of Saturday night
7559605972 / Jan '89 / WEA

☐ NIGHTHAWKS AT THE DINER
Emotional weather report / On a foggy night / Eggs and sausages / Better off without a wife / Nighthawk postcards / Warm beer and cold women / Putnam county / Spare parts 1 / Nobody / Big Joe and Phantom 309
9606202 / '89 / WEA

☐ RAIN DOGS
Singapore / Clap hands / Cemetery polka / Jockey full of Bourbon / Tango till they're sore / Big black Maria / Diamonds and gold / Hang down your head / Time / Rain dogs / Midtown / Ninth and headpin / Gun Street girl / Union Square / Blind love / Walking Spanish / Downtown train / Bride of raindog / Anywhere I lay my head
IMCD 49 / Aug '89 / Island

☐ SMALL CHANGE
Tom Traubert's blues / Step right up / Jitterbug boy / I wish I was in New Orleans / Piano has been drinking / Invitation to the blues / Pasties and a G string / Bad liver and a broken heart / One that got away / Small change / I can't wait to get off work
9606122 / '89 / WEA

☐ STEP RIGHT UP (The Songs Of Tom Waits) (Various Artists)
Old shoes: *Drugstore* / Mockin' bird: *Tindersticks* / Better off without a wife: *Shelley, Pete* / Red shoes by the drugstore: *Wedding Present* / Step right up: *Violent Femmes* / Downtown: *Chilton, Alex* / Big Joe and the Phantom 309: *Archers Of Loaf* / You can't unring a bell: *These Immortal Souls* / Pasties and a G-string: *Pierce, Jeffrey Lee* / Christmas card from a hooker in Minneapolis: *Magnapop* / Ol' 55: *Alvin, Dave* / Jersey girl: *Pale Saints* / Martha: *Buckley, Tim* / Ruby's arms: *Frente* / I hope that I don't fall in love with you: *10,000 Maniacs*
CARCD 30 / Nov '95 / Caroline
PT 341101CD / 16 Mar '98 / Manifesto

☐ SWORDFISHTROMBONES
Underground / Shore leave / Dave the butcher / Johnsburg, Illinois / Sixteen shells from A 306 / Town with no cheer / In the neighbourhood / Just another sucker on the vine / Frank's wild years / Swordfishtrombones / Down down down / Soldier's things / Gin soaked boy / Trouble's braids / Rainbirds
IMCD 48 / Jun '89 / Island

Wake

☐ MASKED
CLEO 91872 / Mar '94 / Cleopatra

Wake Ooloo

☐ STOP THE RIDE
K 171CD / Sep '96 / Konkurrent

Wake RSV

☐ PRAYERS TO A BROKEN STONE
PLASCD 025 / Mar '90 / Plastic Head

Wakeford, Tony

☐ SELFISH SHELLFISH (Wakeford, Tony & Steven Stapleton)
TURSA 004CD / Oct '96 / Tursa

Wakely, Graham

☐ MANHATTAN SKYLINE
Winter games / Fascination / Solitaire / Orange coloured sky / Girl from Corsica / Devil's gallop / You make me feel brand new / Skylark / Mornings at seven / Blaze away / Missing / Love theme from St. Elmo's Fire / Manhattan skyline
MSKY 001 / Apr '94 / Wakely Graham

Wakeman, Adam

☐ 100 YEARS OVERTIME
See what you see / Too late to cry / Take my hand / 100 Years overtime / Hold on / Here with me / More to say / Too long dead / Only me missing / Someone / Sound of a broken heart / Lonely heart tonight
RWCD 26 / Nov '94 / President

☐ REAL WORLD TRILOGY (3CD Set)
Lonely wind cries / First dawn / Passing rain / Innocent world / Reflections on a river / Dying earth / Where eagles fly / Morning light / Endless sea / As the planets move / Mountain air / Nightfall / Ice / Springtime / Silent pleasures / Voices / Waiting for the sun / Beautiful place / Hunted / Endangered world / Barren land / Wild horses run / Clear skies / Forever / As the trees fall / Atlantis / Lost valley / Forgotten world / As winter comes / Echoes / Night skies / Waiting
RWCD 31 / 27 Oct '97 / President

☐ SOLILOQUY
Words of love / Don't say goodbye / There go the angels / One way down / Soliloquy / Little justice / Edge of my heart / Soliloquy part II: The act is over / No time for your love no more / Something strange / Save a tear for me
RWCD 15 / Nov '93 / President

Wakeman, Rick

☐ 2000 AD INTO THE FUTURE
Into the future / Toward peace / 2000 AD / ADRock / Time tunnel / Robot dance / New beginning / Forward past / Seventh dimension
RWCD 21 / Nov '93 / President

☐ AFRICAN BACH
African Bach / Message of mine / My homeland / Liberty / Anthem / Brainstorm / Face in the crowd / Just a game / Africa east / Don't touch the merchandise
RWCD 20 / Nov '93 / President

☐ ASPIRANT SUNRISE
Thoughts of love / Gentle breezes / Whispering cornfields / Peaceful beginnings / Dewy morn / Musical dreams / Distant thoughts / Dove / When time stood still / Secret moments / Peaceful
RWCD 17 / Nov '93 / President

☐ ASPIRANT SUNSET
Floating clouds / Still waters / Dream / Sleeping village / Sea of tranquility / Peace / Sunset / Dying embers / Dusk / Evening moods
RWCD 18 / Nov '93 / President

☐ ASPIRANT SUNSHADOWS
Nightwind / Churchyard / Tall shadows / Shadowlove / Melancholy mood / Mount Fuji by night / Hidden reflections / Evening harp / Moonraker pond / Last lamplight / Japanese sunshadows
RWCD 19 / Nov '93 / President

☐ BEST OF RICK WAKEMAN LIVE, THE
After Henry / Realisation/The prisoner / Elizabethan rock/Make me a woman / King Arthur
WB 885982 / 2 Feb '98 / Disky

☐ CAN YOU HEAR ME
HRHCD 005 / Mar '97 / Music Fusion

☐ CIRQUE SURREAL (Wakeman, Rick Band)
Gnash / Balance of power / Wings of fortune / Static / Party / Wired for sound / Juliet / Tubular bells / Carlos / Love that I know / Jig
MACD 075 / 30 Jan '98 / Magnum America

☐ CLASSIC TRACKS, THE
Journey to the centre of the Earth / Catherine Howard / Merlin the magician
305632 / Oct '96 / Hallmark

☐ CLASSIC, THE
CDSGP 115 / Apr '94 / Prestige

☐ CLASSICAL CONNECTION VOL.1, THE
Gone but not forgotten / After the ball / Elgin mansions / Sea horses / Merlin the magician / Catherine of Aragon / Catherine Howard / 1984 Overture / Hymn / Finale incorporating Julia
RWCD 13 / Nov '93 / President

☐ CLASSICAL CONNECTION VOL.2, THE
Eleanor Rigby / Birdman of Alcatraz / Day after the fair / Opus 1 / Painter / Summertime / Dancing in heaven / Garden of music / Mackintosh / Farandol / Pont Street / Art and soul
RWCD 14 / May '93 / President

☐ COST OF LIVING, THE
Twij / Pandamonia / Gone but not forgotten / One for the road / Bedtime stories / Happening man / Shakespeare run / Monkey nuts / Elegy written in a country churchyard
GCDWR 1892 / Jun '97 / Griffin

☐ COUNTRY AIRS
Lakeland walks / Wild moors / Harvest festival / Glade / Dandelion dreams / Ducks and drinks / Green to gold / Stepping stones / Morning haze / Waterfalls / Spring / Quiet valleys / Nature trails / Heather carpets
NAGE 10CD / Apr '86 / Art Of Landscape

☐ COUNTRY AIRS (1992 Version)
RWCD 10 / Nov '93 / President

☐ CRIMES OF PASSION
Shamas-ud-doha, badar-ud-doja / Allah, mohammed, char, yar / Nit khair mansan sohnia main terl / Kehna ghalat ghalat to chhupana sahi sahl / Kali kali zulfon ke phande nah dalo / Meri ankhon ko bakhshe hain aansoo
RWCD 3 / Nov '93 / President

☐ FAMILY ALBUM, THE
Adam (Rick's second son) / Black beauty (black rabbit) / Jemma (Rick and Nina's daughter) / Benjamin (Rick's third son) / Oscar (Rick and Nina's son) / Oliver (Rick's eldest son) / Nina (Rick's wife) / Wiggles (black and white rabbit) / Chloe / Kookie / Tilly / Mum / Dad / Day after the fair / MacKintosh
RWCD 4 / Nov '93 / President

☐ FIELDS OF GREEN
Election '97/Arthur / Starship trooper/wurm / Promise of love / Spanish wizard / Never ending road / Fighter / Tell me why / Rope trick / Nice man / Fields of green
MFCD 001 / Aug '97 / Music Fusion

☐ HERITAGE SUITE
Chasms / Thorwald's cross / St. Michael's isle / Spanish head / Ayres / Mona's isle / Dhoon / Bee orchid / Chapel hill / Curraghs / Painted lady / Peregrine falcon
RWCD 16 / Nov '93 / President

☐ KING BISCUIT PRESENTS...
Journey to the centre of the Earth / Catherine Howard / Lancelot and the black knight / Anne Boleyn / Forrest / Arthur and Guinevere / Merlyn the magician / Catherine Parr
KBFHCD 011 / 6 Jul '98 / King Biscuit

☐ LIGHT AT THE END OF THE TUNNEL
HRHCD 004 / Mar '97 / Music Fusion

☐ LIVE AT HAMMERSMITH
Arthur / Three wives / Journey / Merlin
RWCD 2 / Nov '93 / President

☐ LIVE ON THE TEST
Recollection / Part IV, the realisation / Sir Lancelot and the black knight / Part III, the spaceman / Catherine Parr / Prisoner / Merlin the magician
WHISCD 007 / Oct '94 / Windsong

☐ MYTHS AND LEGENDS OF KING ARTHUR, THE
Arthur / Lady of the lake / Guinevere / Sir Lancelot and the black knight / Merlin the magician / Sir Galahad / Last battle
CDMID 135 / Oct '92 / A&M

☐ NIGHT AIRS
RWCD 9 / Nov '93 / President

☐ NO EXPENSE SPARED (Wakeman, Rick & Adam)
No expense spared / Dylic / It's your move / No one cares / Luck of the draw / Dream the world away / Is it the spring / Nothing ever changes / Number 10 / Jungle / Children of Chernobyl / Find the time
RWCD 22 / Nov '93 / President

☐ PIANO ALBUM, THE
ESSCD 322 / Nov '95 / Essential

☐ PRIVATE COLLECTION, THE
Battle / Penny's piece / Pearl and dean piano concerto / Piece for granny / Steamhole dance (parts 1 and 2) / Mountain / Warmongers / Aberlady / Now a word from our sponsor
RWCD 23 / Apr '94 / President

☐ ROCK 'N' ROLL PROPHET...PLUS
Return of the prophet / I'm so straight I'm a weirdo / Dragon / Dark / Alpha sleep / Maybe '80 / March of the child soldiers / Early warning / Spy of '55 / Stalemate / Do you believe in fairies / Rock 'n' roll prophet
RWCD 12 / Nov '93 / President

☐ ROMANCE OF THE VICTORIAN AGE (Wakeman, Rick & Adam)
Burlington Arcade / If only / Last teardrop / Still dreaming / Memories of the Victorian age / Lost in words / Tale of love / Mysteries unfold / Forever in my heart / Days of wonder / Swans / Another mellow day / Dance of the elves
RWCD 25 / Nov '94 / President

☐ SEA AIRS
Harbour lights / Pirate / Storm clouds / Lost at sea / Mermaid / Waves / Fisherman / Flying fish / Marie Celeste / Time and tide / Lone sailor / Sailor's lament
RWCD 8 / Nov '93 / President

☐ SEVEN WONDERS OF THE WORLD, THE
Pharos of Alexandra / Colossus of Rhodes / Pyramids of Eygpt / Hanging gardens of Babylon / Temple of Artemis / Statue of Zeus / Mausoleum at Halicarnassus
RWCD 27 / Jun '95 / President

☐ SILENT NIGHTS
Tell 'em all you know / Opening line / Opera / Man's best friend / Glory boys / Silent nights / Ghost of a rock 'n' roll star / Dancer / Elgin mansions / That's who I am
RWCD 1 / Nov '93 / President

☐ SIX WIVES OF HENRY VIII, THE
Catherine of Aragon / Ann of Cleves / Catherine Howard / Jane Seymour / Anne Boleyn / Catherine Parr
CDMID 136 / Oct '92 / A&M

☐ SOFTSWORD
Magna charter / After prayers / Battle sonata / Siege / Rochester collage / Story of love (King John) / March of time / Don't fly away / Isabella / Softsword / Hymn of hope
RWCD 24 / Apr '94 / President

☐ SUITE OF GODS, A (Wakeman, Rick & Ramon Ramedios)
RWCD 5 / Nov '93 / President

☐ TAPESTRIES (Wakeman, Rick & Adam)
Fremiet's cat / Time will tell / Fountains of love / View from a window / Les Vendanges / Summer's end / Clair de Lune / Brighter dawn / Blue Lily / Tapestries / Garden party / Portraits in a gallery / Daydream / Storyteller
RWCD 29 / Jun '96 / President

☐ THEMES
Fanfare / Bassolla / Nothing left to say / AmbienLatin cycle / Without loop / t love / Section seven / Hall of fame / On our way / Forvever and ever / Freefall
RWCD 32 / 29 Jun '98 / President

☐ TIME MACHINE
Custer's last stand / Ocean city / Angel of time / Slaveman / Ice / Open up your eyes / Elizabethan rock / Make me a woman / Rock age
RWCD 7 / Nov '93 / President

☐ TRIBUTE (Beatles Covers)
Norweigan wood / You've got hide your love away / Fool on the hill / Eleanor Rigby / Come together / While my guitar gently weeps / We can work it out / Things we said today / Blackbird / She's leaving home
CDRPM 0018 / 11 May '98 / RP Media

☐ VIGNETTES (Wakeman, Rick & Adam)
Waiting alone / Wish I was you / Sun comes crying / A breath of heaven / Moment in time / Artist's dream / Change of face / Madman blues / A painting of our love / Riverside / Need you / Simply acoustic / Just another tear
RWCD 30 / Nov '96 / President

☐ VISIONS
Fantasy / Peace of mind / Innermost thoughts / Vision of light / Higher planes / Astral traveller / Dream on / Thought waves / Drifting patterns / Future memories / Levitation / Moondreams
RWCD 28 / Oct '95 / President

☐ VOYAGE (The Very Best Of Rick Wakeman/2CD Set)
Catherine of Aragon / Catherine Howard / Jane Seymour / Anne Boleyn / Arthur / Merlin the magician / Last battle / White rock / Searching for gold / After the ball / Ice run / March of the gladiators / Summertime / Temperament of mind / Journey / Recollection / Battle / Forest / Crime of passion / Judas Iscariot / Hibernation / Free song / Maker
5405672 / Oct '96 / A&M

☐ WAKEMAN WITH WAKEMAN (Wakeman, Rick & Adam)
Lure of the wild / Beach comber / Meglomania / Rage and rhyme / Sync or swim / Jiggajig / Caesarea / After the atom / Suicide shuffle / Past and present / Paint it black
RWCD 11 / Feb '93 / President

☐ ZODIAQUE (Wakeman, Rick & Tony Fernandez)
RWCD 6 / Nov '93 / President

Wakenius, Ulf

☐ DIG IN
SITCD 9230 / Aug '97 / Sittel

☐ ENCHANTED MOMENTS
DRCD 278 / Feb '98 / Dragon

☐ HEART OF MINE
Way you look tonight / I wanna be yours / Sweet lilacs / On second thought why can't I / Lester leaps in / Some other time / Rain sometimes / Whenever a soft rain falls / It's like reaching for the moon / Never let me go / In some other world / This heart of mine
DRGCD 91416 / Jul '94 / DRG

☐ NEW YORK MEETING
Bernie's tune / Way you look tonight / Crazy he calls me / Nature of business / Spartacus / New York meeting / Jet lag / Angel eyes / Georgia on my mind
CDLR 45082 / Jul '94 / L&R

Wakeooloo

☐ HEAR NO EVIL
EFA 262072 / Dec '94 / Pravda

☐ WHAT ABOUT IT
EFA 061972 / Jul '95 / House In Motion

Walcott, Collin

☐ GRAZING DREAMS
Song of the morrow / Gold sun / Swarm / Mountain morning / Jewel ornament / Grazing dreams / Samba tala / Moon lake
8278662 / Jun '86 / ECM

☐ WORKS
Scimitar / Song of the morrow / Like that of sky / Travel by night / Godumada / Hey da boom lullaby / Prancing / Cadona / Awakening / Padma / Travel by day
8372762 / Jun '89 / ECM

Walden, Lois

☐ TRAVELLER
1046770732 / 27 Jul '98 / PWL

Walden, Myron

☐ HYPNOSIS
My house / Telepathy / Dimensions / Hypnosis / Untitled in A flat minor / Marva / As the sun peaks / Dearted
NYC 60252 / Nov '96 / NYC

Walden, Narada Michael

☐ ECSTASY'S DANCE
White night / Delightful / First love / Rainbow sky / I cry, I smile / I don't want nobody else(to dance with you) / Awakening / I shoulda loved ya / Tonight I'm alright / Real thang / Blue side of midnight / Reach out / High above the clouds / Gimme, gimme, gimme / Divine emotions
8122725662 / Mar '97 / Rhino

Waldo, Elisabeth

☐ SACRED RITES
Serpent and the eagle / Within the temple of macuilzochitl / Papaganga lament / Ritual of the human scarifice / Festival of Texcatlipoca / Song for the mountain spirits / Penitente procession / Land of the sun kings / Song of the chasqui / Incan festival dance / Making chica / Balsa boat / Swinging the quipu / Saycuscal (weary stones) / Dance of the nustas
GNPD 2225 / Oct '95 / GNP Crescendo

Waldo, Terry

☐ TERRY WALDO AND THE GOTHAM CITY BAND VOL.2 (Waldo, Terry & The Gotham City Band)
SOSCD 1201 / Oct '92 / Stomp Off

Waldron, Cliff

☐ OLD FRIENDS AND MEMORIES (Waldron, Cliff & New Shades Of Grass)
Places and friends I once knew / Greenville trestle high / I'll never grow tired of you / You'll forget / In the good old days / Walk a mile iin my shoes / Heaven is holding my memories / Still right here in my heart / Legend / Reason to believe / Anchored in the fold / Blue bonnet lane
REBCD 1741 / 9 Mar '98 / Shanachie

Waldron, Mal

☐ BLACK SPIRITS ARE HERE AGAIN (Waldron, Mal & Roberto Ottaviano)
DIW 917 / Jan '97 / Ocora

☐ BLUES FOR LADY DAY (Personal Tribute To Billie Holiday)
Blues for Lady Day / Just friends / Don't blame me / You don't know what love is / Man I love / You're my thrill / Strange fruit / Easy living / Mean to me
BLC 760193 / Jun '94 / Black Lion

☐ CROWD SCENE (Waldron, Mal Quintet)
1212182 / Nov '92 / Soul Note

☐ FREE AT LAST (Waldron, Mal Trio)
Rat now / 1-3-234 / Willow weep for me / Balladina / Rock my soul / Boo
8313322 / Aug '89 / ECM

☐ LEFT ALONE (Plays The Moods Of Billie Holiday) (Waldron, Mal Trio)
BET 6024 / Jan '95 / Bethlehem

☐ MUCH MORE (Waldron, Mal & Marion Brown)
Soul mates / Soul mates / All god's chillun got rhythm / My funny valentine / I can't get started / Inch worm / My old flame
FRLCD 010 / Oct '92 / Freelance

☐ NO MORE TEARS (FOR LADY DAY)
Yesterdays / No more tears / Melancholy waltz / Solitude / Love me or leave me / All night through / As time goes by / Smoke gets in your eyes / Alone together
CDSJP 328 / Aug '90 / Timeless Jazz

☐ OUR COLLINE'S A TREASURE
1211982 / May '91 / Soul Note

☐ PEAK (Waldron, Mal & Steve Lacy)
ARTCD 6186 / Mar '97 / Hat Art

☐ QUEST, THE (Waldron, Mal & Eric Dolphy)
Status seeking / Duquility / Thirteen / We did it / Warm canto / Warp and woof / Fire waltz
OJCCD 82 / Jun '96 / Original Jazz Classics

☐ SONGS OF LOVE AND REGRET (Waldron, Mal & Marion Brown)
FRLCD 006 / Oct '92 / Freelance

☐ SOUL EYES
Soul eyes / Judy / God bless the child / From darkness into light / Fire waltz / Dee's dilemma / Straight ahead / Git go / What it is / No more tears
74321538872 / 6 Apr '98 / RCA Victor

☐ TWO NEW (Waldron, Mal & George Haslam)
I've got the world on a string / One for Steve / Tangled lawful bells / Let's do it over / Sakura / Steps in rhythm / Datura / From charleston till now / Come Sunday / I'm old fashioned / After the carnage / Thailand dance
SLAMCD 306 / Oct '96 / Slam

☐ WALDRON-HASLAM (Waldron, Mal & George Haslam)
I got it bad and that ain't good / If I were a bell / Catch as catch should / Somewhere / Variations on Brahms' Symphony no.3/movement no.3 / Time for Duke / Vortex / Motion in order
SLAMCD 305 / Oct '94 / Slam

☐ WHERE ARE YOU (Waldron, Mal Quintet)
1212482 / May '94 / Soul Note

Walk On Water

☐ SOLVENT BASED MELODIES
HWR 0082 / 17 May '98 / Small Stone

Walkabouts

☐ DEATH VALLEY DOLLS
GRCD 404 / Nov '96 / Glitterhouse

☐ DEVIL'S ROAD
Light will stay on / Rebecca wild / Stopping off place / Cold eye / Christmas valley / Blue head flame / When fortune smiles / For all this / Fairground blues / Leaving kind / Forgiveness song
CDVIR 46 / Mar '96 / Virgin

☐ JACK CANDY
SPCD 251 / Jan '93 / Sub Pop

☐ NEW WEST HOTEL
GRCD 252 / Nov '96 / Glitterhouse

☐ NIGHTTOWN
Follow me an angel / These proud streets / Tremble (Goes the night) / Unwind / Lift your burdens up / Prayer for you / Immaculate / Nocturno / Heartless / Nightbirds / Forever gone / Harbour lights / Slow red dawn
CDVIR 57 / Jun '97 / Virgin

☐ RAG AND BONE CATARACT
GRCD 85 / Nov '96 / Glitterhouse

☐ SATISFIED MIND
GRCD 294 / Nov '96 / Glitterhouse

☐ SCAVENGER
GRCD 161 / Nov '96 / Glitterhouse

☐ SEE BEAUTIFUL RATTLESNAKE GARDENS
GRCD 335 / Jun '97 / Glitterhouse

☐ SETTING THE WOODS ON FIRE
GRCD 319 / Nov '96 / Glitterhouse

Walker

☐ STRIKE WHILE THE IRON'S HOT
Strike while the iron's hot / Mon ami / Don't look over your shoulder / It all takes time / Ships that pass in the night / Everyone was a baby / Curacao - blue sky / Tender zone / Looking for an answer / Belong / Month of Sundays / Tudor sweet
ZYZ 077CD / Jan '94 / Zyzzle

Walker, Albertina

☐ I'M STILL HERE
01241430962 / Oct '97 / Benson

Walker Brothers

☐ AFTER THE LIGHTS GO OUT (The Best Of The Walker Brothers 1965-1967)
Love her / Make it easy on yourself / First love never dies / My ship is coming in / Deadlier than the male / Another tear falls / Baby you don't have to tell me / After the lights go out / Mrs. Murphy / In my room / Arcangel / Sun ain't gonna shine anymore / Saddest night in the world / Young man cried / Livin' above your head / Stay with me baby / Walking in the rain / Orpheus / I can't let it happen to you / Just say goodbye / Disc and Music Interview / Japanese Interview
8428312 / May '90 / Fontana

☐ COLLECTION, THE
Lights of Cincinatti / Jackie / Joanna / If I promise / Annabella / I'll be your baby tonight / Love her / Sun ain't gonna shine anymore / (Baby) You don't have to tell me / Stay with me baby / Here comes the night / Land of 1000 dances / Living above your head / In my room / Archangel / Stand by me / Everything under the sun / People get ready
5502002 / Mar '96 / Spectrum

☐ GALA
Make it easy on yourself / Summertime / My ship is coming in / Lonely winds / There goes my baby / Livin' above your head / Here comes the night / Stay with me baby / No sad songs for me / Sun ain't gonna shine anymore / Land of 1000 dances / (Baby) You don't have to tell me / Dancing in the street / In my rain / Walking in the rain / Just say goodbye
8302122 / Feb '89 / Phonogram

☐ IMAGES
5581812 / 22 Jun '98 / Fontana

☐ LINES
Lines / Taking it all in stride / Inside of you / Have you seen my baby / We're all alone / Many rivers to cross / First day / Brand new Tennessee waltz / Hard to be friends / Dreaming as one
4836742 / Mar '96 / Columbia

☐ NITE FLIGHTS
Shutout / Fat Mama kick / Nite flights / Electrician / Death of romance / Den Haague / Rhythms of vision / Disciples of death / Fury and the fire / Child of flames
4844382 / Jul '96 / Epic

☐ NO REGRETS
No regrets / Hold an old friend's hand / Boulder to Birmingham / Walkin' in the sun / Lover's lullaby / I've got to have you / He'll break your heart / Everything that touches you / Lovers / Burn our bridges
4773542 / Aug '94 / GTO

☐ PORTRAIT
5581802 / 22 Jun '98 / Fontana

☐ TAKE IT EASY WITH THE WALKER BROTHERS
Make it easy on yourself / There goes my baby / First love never dies / Dancing in the street / Lonely winds / Girl I lost in the rain / Land of 1000 dances / You're all around me / Love minus zero / I don't want to hear it anymore / Here comes the night / Tell the truth / Love her / Seventh dawn / But I do / My ship is coming in / Looking for me / Young man cried / Everything's gonna be alright / I need you
5581792 / 22 Jun '98 / Fontana

Walker, Billy

☐ CROSS THE BRAZOS AT WACO (6CD Set)
Headin' for heartaches / I'm gonna take my heart away from you / You're gonna pay with a broken heart / You didn't try and didn't care / Too many times / Dirt 'neath your feet / I guess I'll have to die / Anything your heart desires / Last kiss is the sweetest / Alcohol love / I ain't got no roses / Beautiful brown eyes / Don't tell a soul / She's got honky tonk blood in her veins / What would you do / Always think of you / Ting a ling a school pickney sing ting / Fifteen hugs past midnight / Millie darling / Anything your heart desires / What makes me love you (like I do) / One heart's beatin', one heart's cheatin' / If I should live that long / Stolen love / Who took my ring from your finger / True love's so hard to find / You have my heart now / You know what did / One you hurt / I can tell / I didn't have the nerve it took to leave / Don't let your pride break your heart / Mexican Joe / Time will tell / Headin' for heartaches / It hurts too much to laugh (and I'm too big) / I got lost along the way / I can't keep the girls away / Thank you for calling / Candlelight / Pretend you just don't know me / I'm a fool to care / Going going gone / Kissing you / You're the only good thing (that's happened to me) / Let me hear from you / Let me hear from you / Hey / Fool that I am / Record / Which one of us is to blame / Let's make memories tonight / Whirlpool / Go ahead and make me cry / Most important thing / Can't you love me just a little / Blue mountain waltz / Why does it have to be / So far / Little baggy britches / Leavin' on my mind / I'll never stand in your way / Untamed heart / Especially for fools / If you were happy (then I'm satisfied) / Headin' down the wrong highway / On my mind again / Viva la Matador / I care no more / Image of me / I need it / Where my baby goes she goes with me / Put your hand in mine / It'll take a while / It's doggone tough on me / Ghost of a promise / Love's got a hold on me / I dreamed of an old love affair / Mr. Heartache / I thought about you / Storm within my heart / One way give and take / Woman like you / I call it heaven / Forever / Farewell party / Changed my mind / Gotta find a way / I'll be true to you / Little lover / I wish you love / Yes, I've made it / Faded lights and lonesome people / Just call me lonesome / Let's think about living / Alone with you / They'll never take love from me / I take the chance / Guess things happen that way / Remember me, I'm the one who loves you / Molly darling / Rockin' alone in an old rocking chair / Gonna find me a bluebird / There stands the glass / Jambalaya / Charlie's shoes / Funny how time slips away / Joey's back in town / Charlie's shoes / Wild colonial boy / I know I'm lying / Next voice you hear / Willie the weeper / It's me, not them / Lovely hula hands / Beggin' for trouble / Plaything / I've got a new heartache / Give me back my heart / Ancient history / Man who had everything / These arms of mine / Throw me out / Storm of love / That would sure go good / Heart be careful / Circumstances / It's lonesome / Morning paper / Coming back for more / Cross the brazos at Waco / Down to my last cigarette / If it pleases you / I'm so miserable without you / Matamoros / Samuel Colt / Blue moonlight / Come a little bit closer / Gun, the gold, the girl / Blizzard / Pancho villa / Cattle call / Amigo's guitar / Lawman / Buy Juanita some flowers / I'm nothin' to you / Smoky memories / Nobody but a fool / Pretend you don't see me / Don't change
BCD 15657 / Oct '93 / Bear Family

Walker, Brett

☐ BRETT WALKER & THE RAILBIRDS (Walker, Brett & The Railbirds)
Look a little closer / Can't stay too long / Tell me why / What's still left / Drown in your ocean / Rain dance / It's a good thing / Yesterday has gone / Everything I want / I could be wrong / Take me to the river / American dreamer
WESTCD 9 / Nov '96 / West Coast

Walker, Clay

☐ CLAY WALKER
Dreaming with my eyes open / What's it to you / Silence speaks for itself / How to make a man lonesome / Next step in love / White palace / Money can't buy (the love we had) / Things I should have said / Where do I fit in the picture / Live until I die / I don't know how love starts
74321166762 / Aug '94 / Giant

☐ GREATEST HITS
What's it to you / you're begging to get to me / Live until I die / This woman and this man / Dreaming with my eyes open / Rumour has it / Hypnotize the moon / Then what / Where do I fit in the picture / If I could make a living / Ordinary people / Only on days that end in Y / Watch this / Who needs you baby
07599247002 / 4 Jul '98 / Giant

☐ IF I COULD MAKE A LIVING
If I could make a living / Melrose Avenue cinema / My heart will never know / What do you want for nothin' / This woman and this man / Boogie till the cows come home / Heartache highway / You make it look so easy / Lose your memory / Money ain't everything / Down by the river
74321250172 / Apr '95 / Giant

☐ RUMOUR HAS IT
Rumour has it / One, two, I love you / I'd say that's right / Heart over head over heels / Watch this / You'll never hear the end of it / Country boy and city girl / I need a Margarita / That's us / Then what
74321454772 / Apr '97 / Giant

Walker, Dee

☐ JUMP BACK
Jump back / My happy little heart / Tears on a rainy sunday / Dial 'I' for love / Swinging on a star / Every little moment / Oranges and lemons / Hey mr love / Goodbye song
TANGCD 6 / Aug '92 / Tangerine

Walker, Ian

☐ CROSSING THE BORDERLINES (Walker, Ian & Setanta)
FE 088CD / Apr '93 / Fellside

Walker Jazz Band

☐ BIG BAND STORY VOL.2
PV 785093 / Feb '86 / Disques Pierre Verany

Walker, Jerry Jeff

☐ CHRISTMAS GONZO STYLE
I'll be home for Christmas / White Christmas / Santa Claus is coming to town / Christmas song / Here comes Santa Claus / Rudolph the red nosed reindeer / Jingle bells / Walking in a winter wonderland / Frosty the snowman / Jingle bell rock / Twelve days of Christmas / We wish you a merry Christmas
RCD 10312 / Nov '94 / Rykodisc

☐ CIRCUS MAXIMUS
Travelin' around / Lost sea shanty / Oops I can dance / You know I've got the rest of my life to go / Bright light lover / Chess game / People's game / Time waits / Fading lady / Short haired fathers / Wind
VMD 79260 / 27 Jul '98 / Vanguard

☐ DRIFTIN' WAY OF LIFE
Driftin' way of life / Morning song to Sally / Shell game / Ramblin' scramblin' / No roots in ramblin' / Old road / North Cumberland blues / Let it ride / Fading lady / Gertrude / Dust on my boots
VMD 73124 / 27 Apr '98 / Vanguard

☐ GYPSY SONGMAN
Gypsy songman / David and me / Mr. Bojangles / Hands on the wheel / Ramblin' hearts / Then came the children / She knows her daddy sings / Long afternoons / Borderline / Driftin' way of life / Hard livin' / Railroad lady / Jaded lover / Rain just falls / Night rider's lament / We were kind of crazy then / Cadillac cowboy / Pass it on / Charlie Dunn / Hill country rain
RCD 20071 / May '92 / Rykodisc

☐ HILL COUNTRY RAIN
Rock and roll my baby / So bad last night / Singin' the dinosaur blues / Time to stay home / Last night I fell in love again / Man he used to be / Curly and lil / Dutchman / To the artist / Hill country rain
RCD 10241 / Jun '92 / Rykodisc

☐ LIVE AT GRUENE HALL
Lovin' makes livin' worthwhile / Pickup truck song / Long long time / I feel like Hank Williams tonight / Man with the big hat / Quiet faith of man / Little bird / Woman in Texas / Rodeo wind / Trashy wind
RCD 10123 / May '92 / Rykodisc

☐ NAVAJO RUG
Navajo rug / Just to celebrate / Blue mood / Lucky man / Detour / I'm all through throwing good love after bad / Rockin' on the river / Nolan Ryan (a hero to us all) / Flowers in the snow / If I'd loved you then
RCD 10175 / Jul '91 / Rykodisc

☐ VIVA LUCKENBACH
Gettin' by / Viva Luckenbach / Learning to p'like and Luckenbach women's lib / Keep Texas beautiful / What I like about Texas / I'll be here in the morning / Gift / Little man / Some phone numbers / I makes money (money don't make me) / Gonzo compadres / Movin' on
RCD 10268 / Mar '94 / Rykodisc

Walker, Jimmy

☐ ROUGH AND READY BOOGIE WOOGIE FOR 4 HANDS (Walker, Jimmy & Erwin Helfer)
TCD 5011 / Dec '94 / Testament

Walker, Joe

☐ I'M IN THE DOG HOUSE
I'm in the dog house / Couche couche and ky-yay / Bullet through my heart / Give me what I want / I left my home / Watch that black cat / Tante Sarah / I screwed up / I'd like to put my hand on that / Seen it for myself / Keep on pushing / Mom and pop waltz
ZNCD 1006 / Oct '95 / Zane

☐ ZYDECO FEVER
ZNCD 1004 / Oct '95 / Zane

Walker, Joe Louis

☐ BLUES SURVIVOR
Help yourself / Shake for me / My dignity / Young girl's eyes / Part of me / Bad thing / You just don't know / Put you down baby / Blues survivor / Rainy nights / Workin' blues
5190632 / Jan '93 / Verve

☐ GIFT, THE
One time around / Thin line / 747 / Gift / What about you / Shade tree mechanic / Quarter to three / Mama didn't raise no fools / Everybody's had the blues / Main goal
HCD 8012 / Jan '89 / Hightone

☐ GREAT GUITARS
5371412 / Mar '97 / Verve

☐ JLW
I can't get you off my mind / I need your lovin' everyday / Rain on my mind / Inner city man / On that powerline / Hold on / 12 step lovin' / Alone / Got to find my baby / Lost the will to love me / Going to Canada
5231182 / Sep '93 / Verve

Walker, John

☐ ADVENTURE/DEVOTED TO YOU
Once upon a time in the West / I know why / To a wild rose / Breaker on the side / Memory / April in Portugal / Blue moon / Prelude no.1 / How do I love thee / Moonlight serenade / Argentine melody / Tales of the unexpected / Clair de lune / Chariots of fire / Theme from Ice Castles / Again / Hooked on classics / Adventure / Swiss piece
C5CD 632 / Feb '96 / See For Miles

☐ JUST THE WAY YOU ARE
I believe / Copacabana / Night has a thousand eyes / Morning has broken / Goodbye yellow brick road / Raindance / Sing / Mornings at seven / Killing me softly with his song / Go West / I'll never fall in love again / Isn't she lovely / How deep is your love / End of the world / Time revisited / Softly as I leave you / Can't smile without you / Just the way you are / Could it be magic / Return to Glen Brae
C5JCD 656 / 10 Nov '97 / See For Miles

☐ MY FAVOURITE LENNON/ MCCARTNEY (Walker, John & The Digital Sunset)
Long and winding road / Michelle / Yellow submarine / She's leaving home / And I love her / Ob-la-di, ob-la-da / Maxwell's silver hammer / Imagine / Do you want to know a secret / Mull of kintyre / Girl / When I'm sixty-four / Norwegian wood (this bird has flown) / Fool on the hill / Yesterday / Goodnight / We all stand together / Can't buy me love
C5MCD 565 / Jun '91 / See For Miles

☐ MY FAVOURITE SINATRA (Walker, John & The Digital Sunset)
New York, New York / Something stupid / Strangers in the night / It's been a long, long time / Five minutes more / Saturday night is the loneliest night of the week / Love and marriage / Three coins in the fountain / It's nice to go travellin' / I'll be seeing you / Nancy with the laughing face / I'm a fool to want you / Come fly with me / Witchcraft / Nice 'n' easy / London by night / Tender trap / Begin the beguine / I've got you under my skin / Night and day / All the way / High hopes / If you never come to me / Hey jealous lover / Lady is a tramp / My kind of town (Chicago is) / Young at heart / My way
C5CD530 / May '89 / See For Miles

☐ PLAYS MY FAVOURITE JOHN WALKER ORIGINALS (Walker, John & The Digital Sunset)
Spring serenade / Walking in harmony / Shades of oriental / Adventure / People of the hills / Cair paravel / Village parade / First flight / Disco take / Vistabella / Tudor rose / Carol for christmas / Little swiss piece / Summer song / Alpine holiday / Seasons / Silhouettes / Eleanor waltz / Do the samba just like this / What a lovely day / Sunrise / Reflections / It's christmas in the morning / Evening calm
C5MCD 575 / '91 / See For Miles

☐ SUMMER SONG/BY SPECIAL REQUEST
Water babies / I got rhythm / S'wonderful / On the street where you live / Tritsch-tratsch polka / Island in the sun / Jamaica farewell / Mon amour / Jive alive / Forgotten dreams / Theme from "New York, New York" / Lonely shepherd / John and Julie / Chanson de matin / My favourite things / Ave Maria / Caribbean melody / In the mood / Little brown jug / American patrol / Chattanooga choo choo / Lambada / We'll be together again / Amor / If (they made me a king) / Weep they will / I left my heart in San Francisco
C5CD 629 / Oct '95 / See For Miles

☐ TIME TO RELAX/LIVE AT TURNER'S
Atlantis / Seasons / Elizabethan serenade / Thousand and one nights / Fleur de Paris / Pastoral symphony / Jesu joy of my soul / Minuet in G / Morning / Skater's waltz / Valse des fleurs / Morgenblaetter / Wiener blut / I know not where / Stars fell on Alabama / People on the hills / Hooked in space / 2001 / Close encounters of the third kind / Star Wars / Cair paravel / Blue danube / Liebestraum / Artist's life / Cuckoo waltz / Voices of spring / Nocturne in E flat / Wine, women and song / Coppelia valse / Tales from the Vienna Woods / March of the toys / Yellow bird / Stranger in paradise / Evening clam ski Sunday / Love changes everything / Till / Jesu joy of man's desiring / Village parade / Valentino / Classical romance / Aces high / Meditation / Tico tico / Valse romantique / Sunrise / In a monastery garden / May you always
C5CD 626 / Jul '95 / See For Miles

☐ UNCHAINED MELODIES
Unchained melody / Any dream will do / Wooden heart / Forever and ever / One day in your life / Ferry across the Mersey / Nothings gonna change my love for you / Annie's song / Clair / House of the rising sun / Puppet on a string / Take my breath away / Summer holiday / I just called to say I love you / Lady in red / Sacrifice / Those were the days / In the summertime / Hello / Dancing queen / Uptown girl / Wombling song
C5JCD 615 / Apr '95 / See For Miles

☐ YOUR FAVOURITE MELODIES (40 Timeless Romantic Moods - 2CD Set) (Walker, John & Digital Orchestra)
Titanic / True love always / Strangers in the night / Vila vella / I'll never fall in love again / Candle in the wind / Unchained melody / Michelle / Killing me softly with his song / Return to Glen Brae / I just called to say I love you / Norwegian wood / Something stupid / Love changes everything / Take my breath away / Cair paravel / Long and winding road / Forever and ever / May you always / My way / One day in your life / Born free / Vistabella / Softly as I need you / Imagine / Dream a little dream of me / Three coins in a fountain / Love me tender / Mornings at seven / Tudor rose / Lady in red / She's leaving home / Forgotten dreams / Goodbye yellow brick road / All the way / Lonely shepherd / Yesterday / Annie's song / Spring serenade / World in union
PNTVCD 1 / 3 Aug '98 / Tailormade

Walker, Johnny

☐ BLUE LOVE (Walker, Johnny 'Big Moose')
Mean ol' Frisco blues / Blue shadows / Lone wolf / I'm gonna tell my Mama / Georgia on my mind / One room country shack / Blackjack / Don't cry / Who's been foolin' with you / Hallelujah I love her so / Drown in my own tears
ECD 260822 / Sep '96 / Evidence

☐ LIVE AT THE RISING SUN (Walker, Johnny 'Big Moose')
RS 0008CD / Jul '95 / Rising Sun

Walker, Junior

☐ BEST OF JUNIOR WALKER & THE ALL STARS, THE (Walker, Junior & The All Stars)
5302932 / Apr '94 / Motown

☐ SHAKE AND FINGERPOP
Shotgun / How sweet it is (to be loved by you) / Home cooking / Money / Pucker up buttercup / What does it take (to win your love) / Come see about me / Hip city / Cleo's mood / Shake and fingerpop / Shoot your shot
CDBM 072 / Apr '89 / Blue Moon

Walker, Melissa

☐ MAY I FEEL
I'm a fool to want you / Time for love / Dancing in the wings / Love is / What a little moonlight can do / Ruby my dear / Never let me go / Miss Otis regrets / Little wishes / Old country
ENJ 93352 / 17 Nov '97 / Enja

Walker, Philip

☐ BIG BLUES FROM TEXAS (Walker, Philip & Otis Grand)
Dressin' trashy / Dressin' trashy / She's gone / Bluesmoore / Beatrice beatrice / Don't leave me baby / Play me some blues / Insomnia / Goodier train / So torture me / You're so fine / Big blues from texas
JSPCD 248 / Nov '92 / JSP

☐ BLUES SHOW
PCD 5330 / 27 Apr '98 / P-Vine

☐ I GOT A SWEET TOOTH
Drag me down / My name is misery / Rub some good luck on me / I got a sweet tooth / On my way / How could I be such a fool / I'd rather be blind crippled and crazy / Seemed like a good idea at the time / Laughin' and clownin' / It's all in your mind / Crying for my baby
CDBT 1146 / Jun '98 / Black Top

☐ SOMEDAY YOU'LL HAVE THESE BLUES
HCD 8032 / Sep '94 / Hightone

☐ WORKING GIRL BLUES
CDBT 117 / Aug '95 / Rounder

Walker, Pipe Sergeant Gordon

☐ PIPE BANDS OF DISTINCTION (Walker, Corporal Gordon)
Nethercraigs / Pm g.n.m. stoddart / 10th h.l.i. crossing the rhine / Tulgainn leums dean cabnaig / Rakes of kildare / Caber feidh / Cameronian rant / Lament for the children / Mr. john mccoll / Dora macleod / Broadford bay / An ataireachd ard / Humors of tulla / Famous ballymate / Traditional irish reel / Easy club / Wee man from skye / Duncan mckillop / Tulloch castle / Susan macleod / Lt. col. d.j.s. murray / John garroway / 74th slow march / Crossing the minch / Train journey north / Martin ainsborough / Jimmy young / Helen black of inveran / Donald cameron's powderhorn / Donella beaton / Troy's wedding / Glasgow city police pipers / Paps of glencoe / Knightswood ceilidh / Smith's a gallant fireman / Wiseman's exercise / A.a. cameron's strathspey / Prince of wales / A highland reel / Lintie
CDMON 804 / Dec '89 / Monarch

☐ WORLD'S GREATEST PIPERS VOL.13, THE
Crags of Stirling / 71st Highlanders / Atholl Cummers / Cameronian rant / Smith of Chilliechassie / Mrs. Macpherson of Inveran / My love my joy / Duncan Johnstone / Doctor MacInnes' fancy / Banks of the Allan water / Colin's cattle / Carbello crossing / Highland wedding / Piper's bonnet / John Morrison of Assynthouse / High level hornpipe / Tam Bain's lum / Sweet maid of Mull / Star of Kuwait / Mo Gra's lullaby / Freedom's cry / MacPhedran's strathspey / Stumpie / Thick lies the mist on yon hill / Brolum / Scots air reel / Jimmy Blue / Duke of Hamilton's reel / Row me home / Leaving Barra / Old wife of Mill Dust / John Patterson's mare / MacKay's banner
LCOM 5252 / Aug '96 / Lismor

Walker, Robert 'Bilbo'

☐ PROMISED LAND
Goin to the train station / Please love me / Just a country boy / Promised land / You took my love / Still a fool / Wild side of life / It wasn't God that made honky tonk angels / Everything gonna be alright / Baby, baby, baby / How much more / Mama talk to your daughter / Better lovin' man / Hold that train conductor / Got my mojo working / Berry pickin'
R 2632 / Mar '97 / Rooster

☐ ROMPIN' AND STOMPIN'
Baby how long / Take yo' hand off a me / Mustang Sally / Cut you loose / Something on your mind / Mel's hideaway / Shake for me / Moanin' at midnight / I've been a fool
FCD 5005 / 14 Apr '98 / Fedora

Walker, Sammy

☐ IN CONCERT
BRAM 1990162 / Nov '93 / Brambus

Walker, Scott

☐ BOY CHILD
Plague / Such a small love / Plastic palace people / Big Louis / Seventh seal / Old man's back again / Little things (that keep us together) / Girls from the streets / Copenhagen / War is over / Montague Terrace (in blue) / Amorous Humphrey Plugg / Bridge / We came through / Boy child / Prologue / Time operator / It's raining today / On your own again / Rope and the colt
8428322 / May '90 / Fontana

☐ CLIMATE OF HUNTER, THE
Rawhide / Dealer / Sleepwalkers woman / Blanket roll blues
CDV 2303 / Nov '89 / Virgin

☐ EARLY TEN YEARS
14566 / 8 Dec '97 / Spalax

☐ IT'S RAINING TODAY (The Scott Walker Story 1967-1970)
RE 21202 / Dec '96 / Razor & Tie

☐ LOOKING BACK WITH SCOTT WALKER
Too young / I don't want to know / Comin' home / Bluebell / Paper doll / Sunday / When I kiss you goodnite / Sing boy sing / Too young to know / Take this love / Till you return / When you see her / All I do is dream of you / Everybody but me
EMBCD 3393 / 2 Feb '98 / Ember

☐ NO REGRETS (The Best Of Scott Walker/Walker Brothers) (Walker, Scott & The Walker Brothers)
No regrets: *Walker Brothers* / Make it easy on yourself: *Walker Brothers* / Sun ain't gonna shine anymore: *Walker Brothers* / My ship is comin' in: *Walker Brothers* / Joanna: *Walker, Scott* / Lights of Cincinatti: *Walker, Scott* / Another tear falls: *Walker Brothers* / Boy child: *Walker, Scott* / Montague Terrace in blue: *Walker, Scott* / Jackie: *Walker, Scott* / Stay with me baby: *Walker Brothers* / If you go away: *Walker, Scott* / First love never dies: *Walker Brothers* / Love her: *Walker Brothers* / Walking in the rain: *Walker Brothers* / Baby you don't have to tell me: *Walker Brothers* / Deadlier than the male: *Walker Brothers* / We're all alone: *Walker Brothers*
5108312 / Jan '92 / Fontana

☐ SCOTT VOL.1
Mathilde / Montague Terrace in blue / Angelica / Lady came from Baltimore / When Joanna loved me / My death / Big hurt / Such a small love / You're gonna hear from me / Through a long and sleepless night / Always coming back to you / Amsterdam
5108792 / Feb '92 / Fontana

☐ SCOTT VOL.2
Jackie / Best of both worlds / Black sheep boy / Amorous Humphrey Plugg / Next / Girls from the streets / Plastic palace people / Wait until dark / Girls and the dogs / Windows of the world / Bridge / Come next Spring
5108802 / Feb '92 / Fontana

☐ SCOTT VOL.3
It's raining today / Copenhagen / Rosemary / Big Louise / We came through / Butterfly / Two ragged soldiers / 30 century man / Winter night / Two weeks since you've gone / Sons of / Funeral tango / If you go away
5108812 / Aug '92 / Fontana

☐ SCOTT VOL.4
Seventh seal / On your own again / World's strongest man / Angels of ashes / Boy child / Hero of the war / Old mans back again / Duchess / Get behind me / Rhymes of goodbye
5108822 / Aug '92 / Fontana

☐ SINGS JACQUES BREL
Mathilde / Amsterdam / Jackie / My death / Next / Girl and the dogs / If you go away / Funeral tango / Sons of
8382122 / Sep '92 / Fontana

☐ STRETCH/WE HAD IT ALL
BGOCD 358 / May '97 / Beat Goes On

☐ TIL THE BAND COMES IN
BGOCD 320 / Aug '96 / Beat Goes On

☐ TILT
Farmer in the city / Cockfighter / Bouncer see bouncer / Manhattan / Face on breast / Bolivia '95 / Patriot / Tilt / Rosary
5268592 / May '95 / Fontana

☐ TILT (US Version)
DC 134CD / Nov '97 / Drag City

Walker, Sylford

☐ LAMB'S BREAD
GRELCD 119 / May '90 / Greensleeves

Walker, T-Bone

☐ AMERICAN BLUES LEGEND
CPCD 8335 / 29 Jun '98 / Charly

☐ BEGINNING 1926-1946, THE
158852 / Feb '97 / Blues Collection

☐ BLUES T-BONE STYLE (Various Artists)
Strollin' with bones: *Brown, Clarence 'Gatemouth'* / T-Bone boogie: *Earl, Ronnie* / Dedication to the late T-Bone Walker: *Guy, Buddy* / Don't leave me baby: *Walker, Philip & Otis Grand* / Blues for T-Bone: *Houston, Joe* / When the rain starts fallin': *Copeland, Johnny* / Two bones and a pick: *Roomful Of Blues* / T-Bone jumps again: *Schultz, Alex & The Mighty Flyers* / Hustle is on: *Walker, Philip* / Duke's mood: *Robillard, Duke*
EDCD 7019 / Jul '97 / Easydisc

☐ FUNKY TOWN
Goin' to funky town / Party girl / Why my baby (keep on bothering me) / Jealous woman / Going to build me a playhouse / Long skirt baby blues / Struggling blues / I'm in an awful mood / I wish my baby (would come home at night)
BGOCD 116 / Sep '91 / Beat Goes On

☐ GOOD FEELIN'
Good feelin' / Every day I have the blues / Woman you must be crazy / Long lost lover / I wonder why / Vacation / Shake it baby / Poontang / Reconsider / Sail on little girl / When I grow up / See you next time
5197232 / Feb '94 / Verve

☐ I WANT A LITTLE GIRL
DD 633 / Nov '92 / Delmark

☐ LOW DOWN BLUES
Don't leave me baby / I'm gonna find my baby / It's a lowdown dirty deal / I know your wig has gone / T-Bone jumps again / Stormy Monday / She's my old time used to be / Midnight blues / Long skirt baby blues / Too much trouble blues / Hypin' woman blues / Natural blues / That's better for me / Lonesome woman blues / Inspiration blues / T-Bone shuffle / That old feeling is gone / I wish you were mine / She's the no sleepin 'est woman / Plain old down home blues / Go back to the one you love / You're my best poker hand
CPCD 8214 / Feb '97 / Charly

☐ STORMY MONDAY
Every day I have the blues / I woke up this morning / Stormy Monday blues / Why my baby (keep on bothering me) / Late blues / Sail on / T-Bone blues special / Treat me so low down / When I grow up / Long lost lover / Shake it baby
17103 / Jan '97 / Laserlight

☐ STORMY MONDAY
Left home when I was a kid / Glamour girl / (You'll never find anyone) to be a slave like me / When we are schoolmates / Got to cross the deep blue sea / My patience keeps running out / Stormy Monday blues / Lousiana bayou drive / Don't go back to New Orleans / That evening train / All night long / T-Bone's that way
305992 / Apr '98 / Hallmark

☐ STORMY MONDAY BLUES (The Essential Collection)
HMNCD 038 / 22 Jun '98 / Half Moon

☐ T-BONE BLUES
Papa ain't salty / T-bone shuffle / T-bone blues special / T-bone blues / Blues for marill / Evenin' / You don't know what you're doing / Why not / Play on little girl / Mean old world / Call it stormy monday / Shufflin' the blues / Two bones and a pick / How long blues / Blues rock
RSACD 811 / Oct '94 / Sequel

☐ T-BONE SHUFFLE (Charly Blues Masterworks Vol.14)
I got a break baby / No worry blues / Bobby Sox blues / I'm in an awful mood / Don't give me the runaround / Hard pain blues / Goodbye blues / I'm waiting for your call / First love blues / Born to be no good / Inspiration blues / Description blues / T-Bone shuffle / I want a little girl / I'm still in love with you / West side baby
CDBM 14 / Apr '92 / Charly

☐ WELL DONE
Back on the scene / Good boy / No do right / Please come back to me / Natural ball / Baby / She's a hit / Treat your Daddy well / Further on / Up the road / Why don't my baby treat me right / Afraid to close my eyes / She's my old time used to be / I used to be a good boy
CDBM 098 / Apr '94 / Blue Moon

Walker, Wailin'

☐ BUZZSAW BOOGIE (Walker, Wailin' Band)
PRLS 21497 / Jun '98 / Peerless

☐ WAILIN' WALKER
CD 3030 / Oct '92 / Double Trouble

Walking On Ice

☐ NO MARGIN FOR ERROR
Jealous hearts / Set me free / Today, tomorrow / Thinking man's friend / End of an era / Walk in the rain / What you see, what you hear / Footpump / Loser's waltz / Everyman / Rock
CYCL 009 / Aug '97 / Cyclops

Walking Timebombs

☐ WALKING TIMEBOMBS
CHCD 27 / Sep '97 / Channel

Walking Wounded

☐ HARD TIMES
TX 2005CD / Jan '94 / Taxim

Wall

☐ JAZZ IN SWEDEN 1985
1312 / Dec '90 / Caprice

Wall, Akure

☐ AFROMORPH TEXT
FSCD 0007 / 29 Sep '97 / Freak Street

Wall, Chris

☐ HONKY TONK HEART
Honky tonk heart / Rodeo wind / Empty seat beside me / Faithfully / Trashy women / Sure is smokey in here / He lives my dream / I wish john stetson made a heart / Entourage / Something to shoot
RCD 10179 / '92 / Hannibal

☐ NO SWEAT
RCD 10219 / Mar '92 / Rykodisc

Wall, Dan

☐ OFF THE WALL
13 Steps / Black ice / I didn't know what time it was / Electric ballroom / Carol's bridge / End of a love affair / Zakatak / Waltz for John / Off the wall
ENJ 93102 / Mar '97 / Enja

Wall Of Sleep

☐ WALL OF SLEEP
WO 24CD / Jun '95 / Woronzow

Wall Of Sound

☐ WALL OF SOUND
EBCD 2 / Jan '95 / Eightball

Wallace Brothers

☐ LOVER'S PRAYER (Classic Southern Soul)
Lover's prayer / Love me like I love you / Faith / I'll let nothing seperate me / Who's fooling who / I'll still love you / Precious words / You're mine / One way affair / Bye bye bye / Go on girl / She loves me not / I'll step aside / Hold my hurt for awhile / No more / Darlin' I love you so / Stepping stone / Girl's alright with me / These arms of mine / Talking about my baby / Thanks a lot / Line between love and hate
CDKEND 128 / Nov '95 / Kent

Wallace Collection

☐ VICTORIAN CHRISTMAS
Christmas tree quadrille / We wish you a merry christmas / In the bleak mid-winter / Hark the herald angels sing / On christmas night all christmas sing / Twelve days of christmas / Christmas tree quadrille / Boars head carol / O come all ye faithful / While shepherds watched their flocks by night / Now the holly bears a berry / Holly and the ivy / I saw three ships / Christmas tree quadrille / Gaudete / Christmas tree quadrille / Angels from the realms of glory / God rest you merry gentlemen / Away in a manger / Away in a manger / See amid the winter's snow / Three kings of Orient / Silent night holy night / It came upon the midnight clear
JVC 90282 / Nov '97 / JVC

Wallace, Bennie

☐ BIG JIM'S TANGO
ENJA 40462 / May '95 / Enja

☐ MYSTIC BRIDGE (Wallace, Bennie & Chick Corea)
ENJA 40282 / 17 Nov '97 / Enja

Wallace, Robert

☐ BREAKOUT
Barlinnie Highlander / Great is the cause of my sorrow / Mary Horne/Lewis jig / Etain / Barra marches / Lochaber no more/Dog in the bushes / King of lies / Ane ground / Broderick's bodhran / Old woman's lullaby / Below the belt / Strathspey and reel / Leaving Lochboisdale
LCOM 5253 / Aug '96 / Lismor

Wallace, Sippie

☐ WOMEN BE WISE
Women be wise / Trouble everywhere I roam / Lonesome hours blues / Special delivery blues / Murder gonna be my crime / Gambler's dream / Caldonia blues / You got to know how / Shorty George blues / I'm a mighty tight woman / Bedroom blues / Up the country blues / Suitcase blues
ALCD 4810 / May '93 / Alligator
STCD 8024 / Dec '94 / Storyville

Wallen, Byron

☐ EARTH ROOTS
Millenium / Mountains of the moon / Winds of change / Dream catcher / Eastern wind / Heritage / Reflections / Finery of the feast / Healing ceremony / Voices of the millennium
BW 090 / Jun '97 / Melt 2000

Wallenstein

☐ MOTHER UNIVERSE
20291132 / 16 Feb '98 / OHR

Waller, Fats

☐ AIN'T MISBEHAVIN'
CD 53078 / Mar '92 / Giants Of Jazz

☐ AIN'T MISBEHAVIN'
Crazy 'bout my baby / Hallelujah, things look rosy / Thousand dreams of you / I got rhythm / Old grand dad / Go down moses / Blues for two in b flat / Cash for your trash / Ain't misbehavin' / There's a girl in my life / Honeysuckle rose
17011 / Jan '95 / Laserlight

☐ AIN'T MISBEHAVIN'
Ain't misbehavin' / Flat foot floogie / A-tisket, a-tasket / All God's chillun got wings / Deep river / Go down, Moses / Water boy / Lonesome road / That old feeling: *Waller, Fats & Adelaide Hall* / Pent up in a penthouse / Music maestro please / Don't try your jive on me / I can't give you anything but love: *Waller, Fats & Adelaide Hall* / Not there, right there / Cottage in the rain / London suite / Smoke dreams of you / You can't have your cake and eat it
QED 015 / Nov '96 / Tring

☐ AIN'T MISBEHAVIN'
Ain't misbehavin' / Sweet Sue, just you / Joint is jumpin' / Handful of keys / Your feets too big / I've got my fingers crossed / Honeysuckle rose / Crazy 'bout my baby / Hallelujah things look rosy now / Serenade for a wealthy widow / I'm gonna sit right down and write myself a letter / Thousand dreams of you / Believe it, beloved / I wish I were twins / Christopher Columbus / How can you face me
SUMCD 4022 / Nov '96 / Summit

☐ AUDIO ARCHIVE
Pent-up in a penthouse / I can't give you anything but love / Smoke dreams of you / You can't have your cake and eat it / Don't try your jive on me / All God's chillun got wings / Ain't misbehavin' / Go down Moses / Not there, right there / Flat foot floogie / Cottage in the rain / Swing low, sweet chariot / Deep river / Waterboy / Music maestro please / Lonesome road / Tisket-a-tasket / That old feeling
CDAA 023 / Jun '92 / Tring

☐ CHANT OF THE GROOVE
BMCD 3070 / 24 Feb '98 / Blue Moon

☐ CLASSIC JAZZ FROM RARE PIANO ROLLS
18th street strut / If I could be with you one hour tonight / I'm coming Virginia / Ain't nobody's business if I do / Clearing house blues / Squeeze me / Snake hips / Laughin' cryin' blues / You can't do what my last man did / New kind of man with a new kind of love / Nobody but my baby / Got to cool my doggies now / Ain't misbehavin'
BCD 104 / Jul '91 / Biograph

☐ CLASSICS 1922-1926
CLASSICS 664 / Nov '92 / Classics

☐ CLASSICS 1926-1927
CLASSICS 674 / Nov '92 / Classics

☐ CLASSICS 1929
CLASSICS 702 / Jul '93 / Classics

☐ CLASSICS 1929-1934
CLASSICS 720 / Dec '93 / Classics

☐ CLASSICS 1934-1935
CLASSICS 732 / Jan '94 / Classics

☐ CLASSICS 1935 VOL.1
CLASSICS 746 / Aug '94 / Classics

☐ CLASSICS 1935 VOL.2
CLASSICS 760 / Jun '94 / Classics

☐ CLASSICS 1935-1936
CLASSICS 776 / Mar '95 / Classics

☐ CLASSICS 1936
CLASSICS 797 / Mar '95 / Classics

☐ CLASSICS 1936-1937
CLASSICS 816 / May '95 / Classics

☐ CLASSICS 1937 VOL.1
CLASSICS 838 / Sep '95 / Classics

☐ CLASSICS 1937 VOL.2
CLASSICS 857 / Feb '96 / Classics

☐ CLASSICS 1937-1938
CLASSICS 875 / Apr '96 / Classics

☐ CLASSICS 1938
CLASSICS 913 / Jan '97 / Classics

☐ CLASSICS 1938-1939
CLASSICS 943 / Jun '97 / Classics

☐ CLASSICS 1939
CLASSICS 973 / Jan '98 / Classics

☐ COMPLETE EARLY BAND WORKS 1927-1929
Fats Waller stomp / Savannah blues / Won't you take me home / He's gone away / Red hot Dan / Geechee / Please take me out of jail / Minor drag / Harlem fuss / Lookin' good but feelin' bad / I need someone like you / Lookin' for another sweetie / Ridin' but walkin' / Won't you get off it / When I'm alone
DHDL 115 / Sep '93 / Halcyon

☐ CREAM SERIES VOL.2
S'posin' / 'tain't good (like a nickel made of wood) / Nero / I'm sorry I made you cry / You run your mouth, I'll run my business / Everybody loves my baby (but my baby don't love nobody but / You're gonna be sorry / Stayin' at home / Rump steak serenade / You must be losing your mind / La-de-de, la-de-da / I'm at the mercy of love / Who's afraid of love / Georgia on my mind / My mommie sent me to the store / Hey stop kissin' my sister / I wanna hear swing songs / Oh baby, sweet baby (what are you doing to me) / Darktown strutters' ball / Moon is low (part 1) / Fats waller's original e flat blues / It's you who taught it to me
PASTCD 7020 / Sep '93 / Flapper

☐ DEFINITIVE FATS WALLER, THE
STCD 528 / Jan '93 / Stash

☐ DEFINITIVE FATS WALLER, THE (2CD Set)
Baby brown / Viper's drag / How can you face me / Down home blues / Dinah / Handful of keys / Solitude / Moon is low / Moon is low / Sheik of Araby / 'E' flat blues / 'E' Flat blues / Honeysuckle rose / Honeysuckle rose / Ain't misbehavin' / Sweet Sue, just you / Nagasaki / I'm crazy 'bout my baby / I'm crazy 'bout my baby / Spider and the fly / Lonesome me / After you've gone / After you've gone / Dinah / Poor butterfly / St. Louis blues / Hallelujah / Tea for two / Handful of keys / I'm crazy about my baby / Tea for two / Sweet Sue, just you / Somebody stole my gal / Honeysuckle rose / Night wind / African ripples / Because of once upon a time / Where were you on the night of June the third / Clothesline ballet / Don't let it bother you / 'E' flat blues / Alligator crawl / Zonky / Hallelujah / Do me a favour / California, here I come / I've got a feeling I'm falling / My fate is in your hands / Ain't misbehavin' / You're the top / Blue, turning grey over you / Russian fantasy / I'm crazy about my baby / Truckin' / You can't have your cake and eat it / Not there, right there / Theme and introduction / Hallelujah / By the light of the silvery moon
JZCL 5004 / Nov '96 / Jazz Classics

☐ EARLY YEARS VOL.1, THE (Breaking The Ice 1934-1935/2CD Set)
Porter's love song / I wish I were twins / Armful o'sweetness / De me a favor / Georgia May / Then I'll be tired of you / Don't let it bother you / Have a little dream on me / Serenade for a wealthy widow / How can you face me / Sweetie pie / Mandy / Let's pretend there's a moon / You're not the only oyster in the stew / Honeysuckle rose / Belive it, beloved / Dream man (make me dream some more) / I'm growing fonder of you / If it isn't love / Breakin' the ice / I'm 100% for you / Baby brown / Night wind / Because of once upon a time / I believe in miracles / You fit into the picture / Louisiana fairy tale / I ain't got nobody (and nobody cares for me) / Who's honey are you / Rosetta / Pardon my love / What's the reason / Cinders / Oh Suzannah / Dust off that old pianna / Lulu's back in town / Sweet and slow / You've been taking lessons in love / You're the cutest one
07863666182 / Aug '95 / RCA Victor

☐ EARLY YEARS VOL.3, THE (Fractious Fingering 1936)
Christopher Columbus (a rhythm cocktail) / Cross patch / It's no fun / Cabin in the sky / Us on a bus / Stay / More I know you / You're not the kind / Why do I lie to myself about you / Let's sing again / Big Chief de Sota / Black raspberry jam / Bach up to me / Fractious fingering / Paswonky / Lounging at the Waldorf / Latch on / I'm crazy 'bout my baby (and my baby's crazy 'bout me) / I just made up with that old girl of mine / (It will have to do) until the real thing comes along / There goes my attraction / Curse of an aching heart / Bye bye baby / S'posin' / Copper colored gal / I'm at the mercy of love / Floatin' down to Cotton Town / La-de-de la-de-da / Hallelujah / Things look rosy now / 'Tain't good (like a nickel made of wood) / Swingin' them jingle bells / Thousand dreams of you / Rhyme for love / I adore you
07863667472 / Apr '97 / RCA Victor

☐ FATS AT HIS FINEST (Waller, Fats & His Rhythm)
I'm gonna sit right down and write myself a letter / Dinah / My very good friend the milkman / Baby Brown / Whose honey are you / Blue because of you / 12th Street rag / You've been taking lessons in love / Somebody stole my gal / Breakin' the ice / I ain't got nobody / Just as long as the world goes round and round / I'm on a see-saw / I got rhythm / Sweet Sue, just you / Rhythm and romance / Sweet thing / Serenade for a wealthy widow
PAR 2003 / May '90 / Parade

☐ FATS AT THE ORGAN
Eighteenth Street strut / I'm coming Virginia / If I could be with you one hour tonight / Laughin' cryin' blues / Midnight blues / Papa better watch your step / Ain't nobody's business if I do / Your time now will be mine after a while / Nobody but my baby is getting my love / Do it Mr So-and-so / Clearing house blues / You can't do what my last man did / Don't try to take my loving man away / Squeeze me
CDAJA 5007 / Oct '88 / Living Era

☐ FATS WALLER
LECD 051 / May '94 / Dynamite

☐ FATS WALLER
887858 / Jul '94 / Milan

☐ FATS WALLER
DVX 08102 / May '95 / Deja Vu

☐ FATS WALLER
Let's sing again / I've got my fingers crossed / Tain't nobody's business if I do / Your time now / Bye bye baby / New kind of man with a new kind of love for me / Love me or leave me / Sheik of araby / Christopher columbus / 18th street stomp / I used to love you / Stardust / Papa, better watch your step / S'posin' / Sweet and slow
22712 / Nov '95 / Music

☐ FATS WALLER
Laughin' cryin' blues / Midnight blues / Papa better watch yourself / Tain't nobody's bizness if I do / You can't do what my last man did / Your time now / Clearing house blues / Do it mister so and so / Don't try to take my loving man away / 18th Street strut / If I could be with you one hour tonight / Just squeeze me
17061 / Aug '96 / Laserlight

☐ FATS WALLER
15711 / Apr '94 / Laserlight

☐ FATS WALLER 1935-1936
CD 14569 / May '95 / Jazz Portraits

☐ FATS WALLER AND HIS RHYTHM 1934-1935
Lulu's back in town / (Oh Susanna) Dust off that old pianna / Rosetta / Honeysuckle rose / I believe in miracles / Baby Brown / I'm gonna sit right down and write me a letter / Whose honey are you / What's the reason / Sweet and slow / Take it easy / Sweetie pie / How can you face me / Serenade for a wealthy widow / Mandy / Let's pretend there's a moon / Believe it beloved / I'm growing fonder of you / I'm a hundred percent for you / If it isn't love / Don't let it bother you / Do me a favour / I wish I were twins
CD 53264 / Nov '97 / Giants Of Jazz

☐ FATS WALLER IN LONDON
London suite / Don't try your jive on me / Ain't misbehavin' / Flat foot Floogie / Pent-up in a penthouse / Music maestro please / Tisket-a-tasket / That old feeling / I can't give you anything but love / Smoke dreams of you / You can't have your cake and eat it
CDXP 8442 / '88 / DRG

☐ HALLELUJAH
STCD 539 / Oct '92 / Stash

☐ HANDFUL OF KEYS 1929-1934
You're not the only oyster in the stew / African ripples / Honeysuckle rose / Alligator crawl / If it isn't love / Viper's drag / I'm growing fonder of you / Do me a favor / Handful of keys / Minor drag / Numb fumblin' / Mandy / Let's pretend there's a moon / Dream man (make me dream some more) / Have a little dream on me / Smashing thirds / I wish I were twins / Armful o' sweetness
CD 56049 / Nov '94 / Jazz Roots

☐ HONEYSUCKLE ROSE
JHR 73503 / '91 / Jazz Hour

☐ I'M 100% FOR YOU
My very good friend the milkman / Come down to Earth my angel / You must be losing your mind / Stop pretending / Shortnin' bread / Pantin' in the panther room / Twelfth street rag / Old grandad / I'm gonna salt away some sugar / Your socks don't match / Too tired / Your feet's too big / By the light of the silvery moon / Twenty four robbers / Bless you / Romance a la mode / Us on a bus / Pan pan / Sugar rose / I'm 100% for you / Imagine my surprise / Truckin' / Music maestro please / Ain't misbehavin'
RAJCD 824 / Feb '98 / Empress

☐ INTRODUCTION TO FATS WALLER 1928-1942, AN
4006 / Mar '94 / Best Of Jazz

☐ IRREPRESSIBLE HUMOUR OF FATS WALLER, THE
BMCD 3072 / Jan '98 / Blue Moon

☐ IT'S A SIN TO TELL A LIE (Waller, Fats & His Rhythm)
CDSGP 0168 / Nov '95 / Prestige

☐ IT'S A SIN TO TELL A LIE 1935-1936 (Waller, Fats & His Rhythm)
It's a sin to tell a lie / More I know you / Let's sing again / Bye-bye, baby / I've got my fingers crossed / All my life / There'll be some changes made / Somebody stole my gal / Christopher Columbus / It's no fun / There's going to be the devil to pay / Cabin in the sky / Sweet thing / Oooh, look-a there, ain't she pretty / Sugar rose / Paswonky / Until the real thing comes along / Big chief de sota / La-de-de, la-de-da / There goes my attraction / Curse of an aching heart / Truckin' / Blue because of you
CD 53269 / Jul '97 / Giants Of Jazz

☐ JAZZ GREATS
Ain't misbehavin' / Handful of keys / I'm crazy 'bout my baby / Honeysuckle rose / Keepin' out of mischief now / Tea for two / Joint is jumpin' / I ain't got nobody / Smashing thirds / Your feet's too big / Ring dem bells / Carolina shout / S'posin' / Lulu's back in town
74321499642 / 6 Oct '97 / RCA Victor

☐ JAZZ PORTRAITS
You're not the only oyster in the stew / African ripples / Honeysuckle rose / Alligator crawl / If it isn't love / Viper's drag / I'm growing fonder of you / Do me a favour / Handful of keys / Minor drag / Numb fumblin' / Mandy / Let's pretend there's a moon / Dream man / Have a little dream on me / Smashing thirds / I wish I were twins / Armful o'sweetness
CD 14516 / May '94 / Jazz Portraits

☐ JOINT IS JUMPIN', THE
Handful of keys / Minor drag / Numb fumblin' / Ain't misbehavin' / Smashing thirds / African ripples / Alligator crawl / Viper's drag / Lulu's back in town / Crazy about my baby / S'posin' / Blues / Tea for two / I ain't got nobody / Joint is jumpin' / Sheikh of Araby / Yacht club swing / Squeeze me / Your feet's too big / Carolina shout / Honeysuckle rose
ND 86288 / Apr '88 / Bluebird

☐ **JOINT IS JUMPIN', THE (The Music Of Thomas 'Fats' Waller) (Repertory Quartet)**
MECCACD 1097 / May '97 / Music Mecca

☐ **LOW DOWN PAPA**
I'm crazy 'bout my baby / Wild cat blues / Jailhouse blues / Do it Mr So-and-So / Don't try to take my man away / Your time now / Papa better watch your step / Haitian blues / Mama's got the blues / Midnight blues / Last go round blues / Cryin' for my used to be / Low down papa
BCD 114 / Jul '91 / Biograph

☐ **LULU'S BACK IN STORE**
HADCD 189 / Nov '95 / Javelin

☐ **MASTERPIECES 1929-1941**
158152 / Mar '94 / Masterpieces

☐ **MASTERPIECES OF FATS WALLER, THE**
393342 / Jul '96 / Music Memoria

☐ **MIDDLE YEARS VOL.1, THE (1936-1938/3CD Set) (Waller, Fats & His Rhythm)**
Havin' a ball / I'm sorry I made you cry / Who's afraid of love / Please keep me in your dreams / One in a million / Nero / You're laughing at me / I can't break the habit of you / Did anyone tell you / When love is young / Meanest thing you ever did was kiss me / Cryin' mood / Where is the sun / Old plantation / To a sweet pretty thing / You've been reading my mail / Spring cleaning / You showed me the way / Boo-hoo / Love bug will bite you / San Anton, San Anton / I've got a new lease of love / I've got a new lease on love / Sweet heartache / Sweet heartache (Instrumental) / Honeysuckle rose / Smarty (you know it all) / Don't you know or don't you care / Lost love / I'm gonna put you in your place / Blue turning grey over you / You've got me under your thumb / Beat it out / Our love was meant to be / I'd rather call you baby / I'm always in the mood for you / She's tall, she's tan, she's terrific / You're my dish / More power to you / How can I / Joint is jumpin' / Hopeless love affair / What will I do in the morning / How ya baby / Jealous of me / Everyday's a holiday / Neglected / My window faces the south / I'm in another world / Why do Hawaiians sing aloha / My first impression of you / On the sunny side of the street / Georgia on my mind / Something tells me / I love to whistle / You went to my head / Florida Flo / Lost and found / Don't try to cry your way back to me / Marie / In the gloaming / You had an ev'ning to spare / Let's break the good news / Skrontch / I simply adore you / Sheikh of Araby / Hold my hand / Inside
7863660832 / Dec '92 / RCA Victor

☐ **MIDDLE YEARS VOL.2, THE (A Good Man Is Hard To Find/3CD Set)**
In the gloaming / I simply adore you / Sheikh of araby / Hold my hand / Inside / There's honey on the moon tonight / If I were you / Wide open spaces / On the bumpy road to love / Fair and square / We the people / Two sleepy people / Shame shame (Everybody knows your game) / I'll never forgive myself (For not forgiving you) / You look good to me / Tell me with your kisses / I wish I had you / I'll dance at your wedding / Imagine my surprise / Yacht club swing / Love / I'd give my life for you / I won't believe it (Till I hear from you) / Spider and the fly / Patty cake, patty cake / Good man is hard to find / You outsmarted yourself / Last night a miracle happened / Good for nothin' but love / Hold tight, hold tight / Kiss me with your eyes / You asked for it - you got it / Some rainy day / T'ain't what you do (it's the way that you do it) / Got no time / Step up and shake my hand / Undecided / Remember who you're promised to / Honey hush / I used to love you (But it's all over now) / Wait and see / You meet the nicest people in your dreams / Anita / What a pretty Miss / Squeeze me / Bless you / It's the tune that counts / Abdullah / Who'll take my place / Bond Street / It's you who taught me / Suitcase Susie / Your feet's too big / You're lettin' the grass grow under your feet / Darktown strutters ball / I can't give you anything but love / Swinga-dilla street / At twilight / Oh frenchy / Cheatin' on me / Black Maria / Mighty fine / Moon is low
7863665522 / Jun '95 / RCA Victor

☐ **MISBEHAVIN'**
I can't give you anything but love / Your feet's too big / Let's swing again / Viper's drag / Joint is jumpin' / Ain't misbehavin'
BSTCD 9105 / May '92 / Best Compact Discs

☐ **MISBEHAVIN'**
Tain't nobody's biz-ness if I do / Keepin' out of mischief now / Abercrombie had a zombie / Buckin' the dice / Ain't misbehavin' / Honeysuckle rose / (You're a) square from Delaware / Mamacita / Your feet's too big / Handful of keys / Joint is jumpin' / Cash for your trash / Alligtor crawl / Min drag / Send me Jackson / Twenty four robbers / Viper's drag / Hey, stop kissing my sister / You must be losing your mind / Pantin' in the pather room / All that meat and no potatoes / Carolina shout / Scram / You run your mouth, I'll run my business
74321500202 / Jun '97 / Camden

☐ **OUR VERY GOOD FRIEND, FATS (Waller, Fats & His Rhythm)**
12th street rag / I ain't got nobody / Dinah / My very good friend the milkman / I'm on a see-saw / I'm gonna sit right down and write myself a letter / Basin Street blues / Why do hawaiians sing aloha / Paswonky / Lost love / Don't you know or don't you care / She's tall, she's tan, she's terrific / I'm always in the mood for you / St. Louis blues / Shortnin' bread / Sugar rose / That never to be forgotten night / After you've gone / Old plantation / Honeysuckle rose
DBCD 16 / Jul '89 / Dance Band Days

☐ **PEARL SERIES: FATS WALLER**
It's a sin to tell a lie / Your feet's too big / I'm crazy 'bout my baby / Draggin' my heart around / Music, maestro, please / Flat foot floogie / You're not the only oyster in the stew / Ain't nobody's business if I do / Viper's drag / My very good friend the milkman / Write myself a letter / Truckin' / I'm on a see-saw / Handful of keys / Joint is jumpin' / I wish I were twins / Minor drag / Sweet Sue, just you / Black raspberry jam / Tisket-a-tasket / Dinah / Clothes line ballet / Nagasaki / Ain't misbehavin'
PASTCD 9742 / Mar '91 / Flapper

☐ **PHENOMENAL FATS**
I'm gonna put you in your place / Patty cake, patty cake / Good for nothing (but love) / Last night a miracle happend / Twelfth street rag / Paswonky / Neglected / How ya babe / Lost love / She's tall, she's tan, she's terrific / Why do Hawaiians sing Aloha / Spider and the fly / Old plantation / I love to Whistle / That never to be forgotten night
PAR 2011 / Jul '94 / Parade

☐ **PIANO MASTERWORKS VOL.1**
158922 / Jun '97 / Jazz Archives

☐ **PIANO MASTERWORKS VOL.2 1929-1943**
158992 / Nov '97 / Jazz Archives

☐ **PIANO ROLLS & ORGAN 1923-1938 (4CD Set)**
Laughin' cryin' blues / Your time now / Tain't nobodies buziness if I do / Papa, better watch your step / You can't do what my last man did / Midnight blues / Don't try to take my loving man away / Clearing house blues / Do it, mister so and so / If I could be with you one hour tonight / Fats Waller stomp / Savannah blues / Won't you take me home / New kind of man with a new kind of love for me / I'm coming Virginia / Nobody but my baby / He's gone away / Red hot Dan / Gee chee / Please take me out of jail / Minor drag / Harlem fuss / Baby, oh where can you be / Lookin' good but felin' bad / I need someone like you / My fate is in your hands / Lookin' for another sweetie / Ridin' but walkin' / Won't you get off it, please / When I'm alone / I'm crazy 'bout my baby / Armful o'sweetness / Porter's love song to a chambermaid / I wish I were twins / Do me a favour / Don't let it bother you / Georgia May / Have a little dream on me / Then I'll be tired of you / Mandy / Sweetie pie / Serenade for a wealthy widow / You're not the only oyster in the stew / How can you face me / Let's pretend there's a moon / If it isn't love / Honeysuckle rose / I'm growing fonder of you / Dream man / Believe it, beloved / Breakin' the ice / African ripples / I'm a hundred percent for you / Baby brown / Baby brown / Oh Susannah / What's the reason / Who's honey are you / Lulu's back in town / Dinah / Somebody stole my gal / Take it easy / There's going to be the devil to pay / Christopher Columbus / Big chief De Sota / It's a sin to tell a lie / Curse of an aching heart / Bye bye baby / Swingin' them jingle bells / Hallelujah, things look rosy now / Thousand dreams of you / Every day's a holiday / I love to whistle / Something tells me / Hold my hand / In the gloaming / Let's break the good news
FBB 908 / 1 Dec '97 / Ember

☐ **PIANO SOLOS 1929-1941**
Blue black bottom / Handful of keys / Numb fumblin' / Ain't misbehavin' / Sweet savannah Sue / I've got a feeling I'm falling in love / Love me or leave me / Gladyse / Valentine stomp / Waiting at the end of the road / Baby, oh where can you be / Goin' about / My feelin's are hurt / Smashing thirds / My fate is in your hands / Turn on the heat / St. Louis blues / After you've gone / African ripples / Clothes line ballet / Alligator crawl / Viper's drag / Down home blues / E flat blues / Zonky / Keepin' out of mischief now / Stardust / Basin Street blues / Tea for two / I ain't got nobody / Georgia on my mind / Rockin' chair / Carolina shout / Honeysuckle rose / Ring dem bells
ND 89741 / May '94 / Jazz Tribune

☐ **PORTRAIT OF FATS WALLER, A**
GALE 412 / May '97 / Gallerie

☐ **QUINTESSENCE, THE (1929-1943/2CD Set)**
FA 207 / Oct '96 / Fremeaux

☐ **SWEET AND ROMANTIC MR. WALLER, THE**
BMCD 3066 / Jan '98 / Blue Moon

☐ **THOMAS 'FATS' WALLER (A Career Perspective 1922-1943)**
Birmingham blues / Red hot Dan / Henderson stomp / I'm crazy 'bout my baby / Royal Garden blues / (I'll be glad when you're dead) you rascal you / That's what I like about you / Chances are / Mean old bed bug blues / Porters love song to a chambermaid / I wish I were twins / Let's pretend there's a moon / You're not the only oyster in the sea / Baby Brown / Viper's drag/How can you face me/Down home blues / Yacht club swing / Hold my hand / Pent up in a penthouse / Honeysuckle rose / Yacht club swing / You look good to me / Hallelujah / That ain't right / Reefer man / That's what the bird said to me
CDMOIR 515 / Jan '97 / Memoir

☐ **ULTIMATE COLLECTION, THE (2CD Set)**
When somebody thinks you're wonderful / I'm on a see saw / Georgia rockin' chair / Sweet Sue / Rhythm and romance / Somebody stole my gal / Twelfth street rag / There'll be some changes made / My very good friend / Milkman / It's a sin to tell a lie / I'm crazy 'bout my baby / Until the real thing comes along / Bye bye baby / There goes my attraction / S'posin' / Copper coloured gal / Why do I lie to myself about you / Please keep me in your dreams / One in a million / Where is the sun / You've been reading my mail / Sheik of Araby / Hold my hand / Ain't misbehavin' / Two sleepy people / Joint is jumping / What will I do in the morning / Jealous of me / Boo hoo / Love bug will bite you / I can't give you anything but love / Honeysuckle rose / Smarty / Blue, turning grey over you / I'm always in the mood for you / She's tall, she's tan, she's terrific / Your feet's too big / Little bit independent / Sweet thing / Truckin' / Sugar rose / Moon rose / West wind / That never-to-be-forgotten night / All my life / Christopher Columbus / Cabin in the sky / Us on a bus / Cross patch
PDSCD 550 / 13 Oct '97 / Pulse

☐ **UNIQUE MR. WALLER, THE**
BMCD 3064 / Jan '98 / Blue Moon

☐ **YOU LOOK GOOD TO ME (Waller, Fats & His Rhythm)**
CDSGP 089 / Oct '93 / Prestige

☐ **YOU RASCAL, YOU**
Georgia May / I'm crazy 'bout my baby / Breakin' the ice / Baby, oh where can you be / If it isn't love / Won't you get up off it, please / I wish I were twins / Numb fumblin' / (I'll be glad when you're dead) you rascal you / Ain't misbehavin' / Porter's love song / Draggin' my heart around / Minor drag / My fate is in your hands / That's what I like about you / Harlem fuss / Believe it, beloved / Honeysuckle rose
CDAJA 5040 / Oct '88 / Living Era

Waller, Robert James

☐ **BALLAD OF MADISON COUNTY, THE**
Madison County waltz / Wabash cannonball / Dutchman / Steamer / Blue suspenders / Tangerine / Girl from the north country / Golden apples of the sun / Idaho rain / Autumn leaves
7567825112 / Mar '94 / WEA

Wallflowers

☐ **BRINGING DOWN THE HORSE**
One headlight / 6th avenue heartache / Bleeders / Three marlenas / Difference / Invisible city / Laughing out loud / Josephine / God don't make lonely girls / Angel on my bike / I wish I felt nothing
IND 90055 / Jun '97 / Interscope

Wallgren, Jan Edvard

☐ **RAGA BEBOP AND ANYTHING**
DRCD 303 / Feb '98 / Dragon

☐ **STANDARDS AND BLUEPRINTS**
DRCD 246 / Oct '94 / Dragon

Wallin, Bengt A.

☐ **BIRTH AND REBIRTH OF SWEDISH FOLK JAZZ, THE**
Down by the old well / Backwood mating / O'thy beautiful / Maid is pretty / Ruverbank air / Cow and the fiddle
ACT 92542 / 23 Mar '98 / Act

Wallin, Per Henrik

☐ **DOLPHINS, DOLPHINS, DOLPHINS**
DRCD 215 / Sep '89 / Dragon

☐ **ONE KNIFE IS ENOUGH**
1273 / Feb '90 / Caprice

☐ **TRIO**
1185 / May '89 / Caprice

Wallington, George

☐ **GEORGE WALLINGTON TRIO, THE (Wallington, George Trio)**
Twins / Polka dot / I'll remember April / High score / Hyacinth / Joy bell / I didn't know what time it was / Fine and dandy / Knockout / Igloo / Fairyland / Racing
SV 0136 / May '98 / Savoy Jazz

☐ **JAZZ AT HOTCHKISS (Wallington, George Quintet)**
Dance of the infidels / Strange music / Before dawn / Ow / 'S make 'T
SV 0119 / May '98 / Savoy Jazz

☐ **LIVE AT CAFE BOHEMIA (Wallington, George Quintet)**
Johnny one note / Sweet blanche / Monor march / Snakes / Jay Mac's crib / Bohemia after dark / Minor march (alternate)
OJCCD 1813 / Apr '93 / Original Jazz Classics

Wallis, Bob

☐ **GREAT BRITISH JAZZ BANDS, VOL.11 (Ol' Man River) (Wallis, Bob & His Storyville Jazz Men)**
Moose march / Big house blues / Chinatown / Flee as a bird/Didn't he ramble / New Orleans stomp / Confessin' / Louisian-i-ay / All for you Louis / Easy does it / Spooky takes a holiday / Martha / Algiers bounce / Ol' man river / Knocked 'em in the Old Kent Road / I'm shy Mary Ellen / Shanty in Old Shanty Town / Redwing / Perfect rag / When it's sleepy time down South / Gossip Jones / Cotten pickers congregation
LACD 91 / Apr '98 / Lake

Wallochmore Ceilidh Band

☐ **HIGHLANDERS COMPANION, THE (Dr Walloch's Fifth Prescription)**
Paddy's potion / Canadian barn dance / St. Bernard's waltz / Broon's reel / Eva three step / Jack Tarr two step / Gay gordons / Corn rigs / Welcome Christmas morning / Wee Todd / Polka / Retreat marches / Pride of Erin waltz / Hornpipe and reel / Final dose
LAPCD 111 / Dec '88 / Lapwing

☐ **LOOKING FOR A PARTNER**
LAPCD 101 / Dec '88 / Lapwing

Wallowitch, John

☐ **MY MANHATTAN**
My Manhattan / Cosmic surgery / Come a little closer / Oh wow / Bruce / I live alone again / None of your business / Florida / It's come true at last / Threepenny things / Tony and I / Cheap decadent drivel / This moment / Beekman place elegy / Night train to Chicago / Oy vey / Time to come home again / Old friends
DRGCD 91414 / Sep '93 / DRG

Wallpaper

☐ **MAGIC STATIC THREATS**
BBPTC 23 / Oct '96 / Black Bean & Placenta Tape Club

Wallumrod, Christian

☐ **NO BIRCH (Wallumrod, Christian Trio)**
She passes the house of her Grandmother / Birch / Royal garden / Somewhere East / Travelling / Birch / Ballimaran / Watering / Before church / Birch / Two waltzing one square and then / Fooling around / Gardener / Birch
5373442 / 6 Apr '98 / ECM

Walrath, Jack

☐ **HI JINX**
STCD 576 / Feb '94 / Stash

☐ **HIPGNOSIS (Walrath, Jack & The Masters Of Suspense)**
Sweet hip gnosis / Hip gnosis / Trane trip / Philosopher stone / Mingus piano / Blue sinistra / Games / Baby fat / Premature optomism / Eclipse / Love enough for everybody
TCB 01062 / Feb '96 / TCB

☐ **JOURNEY, MAN (Walrath, Jack & Hard Corps)**
Bouncin' with ballholzka / Ancient intrigues / When love has gone (it comes out like this) / Pete's steps / (I wanna be) out there somewhere / Butt (tails from the backside) / Sarah hurts / Song of everywhen / Orange has me down
ECD 221502 / Sep '96 / Evidence

☐ **OUT OF THE TRADITION**
Clear out this world / So long Eric / Stardust / Wake up and wash it off / Come Sunday / Brother can you spare a dime / Cabin in the sky / I'm getting sentimental over you
MCD 5403 / Sep '92 / Muse

☐ **SOLIDARITY (Walrath, Jack & Ralph Reichert)**
Azathoth / Hamburg concerto / Loneliness of a child / Solidarity / Hot-dog for lunch / Political suicide / Psychotic indifference / Pegasus
92412 / Oct '96 / Act

Walser, Don

☐ **ARCHIVES VOL.1 (Walser, Don & The Pure Texas Band)**
WM 1041CD / Nov '95 / Watermelon

☐ **ARCHIVES VOL.2 (Walser, Don & The Pure Texas Band)**
WM 1042CD / Nov '95 / Watermelon

☐ **DOWN AT THE SKY-VUE DRIVE-IN**
64344310172 / 27 Apr '98 / Watermelon

☐ **ROLLING STONE FROM TEXAS**
WMCD 1028 / Dec '94 / Watermelon

Walsh, Colin

☐ **ENGLISH ORGAN MUSIC FROM LINCOLN CATHEDRAL**
PRCD 379 / Jul '92 / Priory

Walsh, Danny

☐ **D'S MOOD (Walsh, Danny Quartet)**
SCCD 31428 / Jan '98 / Steeplechase

Walsh, Joe

☐ **BEST OF JOE WALSH, THE**
HMNCD 007 / Jun '97 / Half Moon

☐ **BUT SERIOUSLY FOLKS**
Over and over / Second hand store / Indian summer / At the station / Tomorrow / Inner tube / Boat Weirdos / Life's been good
7559605272 / Oct '93 / WEA

☐ **LOOK WHAT I DID**
Tuning, part 1 / Take a look around / Funk # 48 / Bomber / Tend my garden / Funk # 49 / Ashes the rain and I / Walk away / It's all the same / Midnight man / Here we go / Midnight visitor / Mother says / Turn to stone / Comin' down / Meadows / Rocky mountain way / Welcome to the club / All night laundry matt blues / Country fair / Help me thru the night / Life's been good / Over and over / All night long / Life of illusion / Theme from the island weirdos / I can play that rock and roll / ILBT'S / Space age whizz kids / Rosewood bitters / Shut up / Decades / Song for a dying planet / Ordinary average guy
MCD 11233 / Jul '95 / MCA

☐ **SMOKER YOU DRINK, THE PLAYER YOU GET, THE**
Rocky mountain way / Bookends / Wolf / Midnight moodies / Happy ways / Meadows / Dreams / Days gone by / (Daydream) prayer
MCLD 19020 / Apr '92 / MCA

☐ YOU CAN'T ARGUE WITH A SICK MIND/THE SMOKER YOU DRINK... (2CD Set)
Rocky mountain way / Bookends / Wolf / Midnight moodies / Happy ways / Meadows / Time out / Help me make it through the night / Turn to stone / Walk away / Dreams / Days gone by / (Daydream) prayer
MCD 33728 / Jul '96 / MCA

Walsh, John

☐ TIME TO SPARE
Donald maclean's farewell to oban-knightswood cellidh (24 / Balmforth's brigadoon-john walsh's walk (slow air and hornp
LCOM 5204 / Nov '91 / Lismor

Walsh, Sean

☐ HAYMAKER, THE
GTDCD 001 / Jan '95 / GTD

☐ WILL THE CIRCLE BE UNBROKEN
GTD 008 / Feb '95 / GTD

Walshe, Seamus

☐ CLARE ACCORDION
SW 003CD / Nov '96 / SW Music

Walt Mink

☐ COLOSSUS
DER 361 / Jul '97 / Deep Elm

Walter Elf

☐ HOMO SAPIENS
XM 027 CD / Apr '92 / X-Mist

Walter, Robert

☐ SPIRIT OF '70 (Walter, Robert & Gary Bartz)
Corry's snail and slug death / Bidi man / Palilalia / Little miss lover / Impervious / Jan Jan / Volcanic acne
GBR 004CD / Nov '96 / Greyboy

Waltham Forest Pipe Band

☐ TRADITIONAL SCOTTISH PIPES AND DRUMS
EUCD 1171 / '91 / ARC

Walton, Brenda

☐ MORTGAGED HEART, THE
HARTCD 002 / Apr '94 / Heartsongs

Walton, Cedar

☐ AMONG FRIENDS (Walton, Cedar Trio)
For all we know / Without a song / Off minor / My foolish heart / Midnight waltz / Ruby my dear / My old flame / I've grown accustomed to her face
ECD 220232 / Aug '92 / Evidence

☐ BLUES FOR MYSELF
RED 1232052 / Aug '95 / Red

☐ BLUESVILLE TIME (Walton, Cedar Quartet)
Rubberman / Naima / Bluesville / I remember clifford / Ojos de rojos / 'Round midnight / Without a song
CRISS 1017CD / Jul '97 / Criss Cross

☐ CEDAR WALTON PLAYS (Walton, Cedar & Ron Carter/Billy Higgins)
DCD 4008 / '88 / Delos

☐ CEDAR'S BLUES (Walton, Cedar Quintet)
1231792 / Apr '95 / Red

☐ COMPOSER
Martha's prize / Vision / Happiness / Minor controversy / Hindsight / Underground memoirs / Theme from jobim / Groove passage / Groundwork
TCD 4001 / Jul '96 / Astor Place

☐ EASTERN REBELLION (Walton, Cedar Quartet)
Bolivia / 5/4 thing / Mode for Joe / Naima / Bittersweet
CDSJP 101 / Jun '89 / Timeless Jazz

☐ FIRST SET
SCCD 31085 / Jul '88 / Steeplechase

☐ MANHATTAN AFTERNOON (Walton, Cedar Trio)
CRISS 1082CD / May '94 / Criss Cross

☐ NALMA (Walton, Cedar & Clifford Jordan)
412320462 / 17 Mar '98 / Thirty Two

☐ OFF MINOR (Walton, Cedar & David Williams/Billy Higgins)
1232422 / Mar '92 / Red

☐ SOUL CYCLE
OJCCD 847 / Nov '95 / Original Jazz Classics

Walton, Frank

☐ REALITY
Safari / Spongie / Waltz of the prophets / Shorter's vibes / Change of mode
DD 436 / Mar '97 / Delmark

Walton, Mercy Dee

☐ ONE ROOM COUNTRY SHACK
One room country shack / My woman knows the score / Misery blues / Great mistake / Save me some / Strugglin' with the blues / Lonesome cabin blues / Rent man blues / Fall guy / Drifter / Hear me shout / Love is a mystery / Winter blues / Pauline / Get to gettin' / Dark muddy bottom / What'cha gonna do / My woman and the devil / Big minded daddy / Perfect health / Problem child / Pull 'em and pop 'em / Eighth wonder of the world / Rock 'n' roll fever
CDCHD 475 / Jun '93 / Ace

☐ PITY AND SHAME
Pity and shame / Your friend and woman / Five card hand / Have you ever been out in the country / After the fight / One room country shack (a thousand miles from nowhere) / My little angel / Shady lane / Drunkard
OBCCD 552 / Jan '94 / Original Blues Classics

☐ TROUBLESOME MIND
ARHCD 369 / Apr '95 / Arhoolie

Walton, Peter

☐ DANCE GUITAR
DLD 1019 / '92 / Dance & Listen

Wamdue Kids

☐ THESE BRANCHING MOMENTS
Intro / Alasque / Optimistique / These branching moments / Reflection / Time we will never share / Full metal emotion
PF 059CD / Jan '97 / Peacefrog

☐ WAMDUE WORKS
K7R 006CD / May '96 / Studio K7

Wamdue Project

☐ PROGRAMME YOURSELF
King of my castle / Like this / Are you high / Walk with me / I acknowledge you / Giraffe / Where do we go / Spirit / You're the reason / Instrumentation / Diving for pills
ERUPTCD 001 / 15 Jun '98 / Eruption

☐ RESOURCE
SR 328CD / Sep '96 / Strictly Rhythm

Wamma Jamma

☐ SIX BY FOUR
Wotcha gonna tell me / Hanging on a string / Fairer slink / Slow walk / Down the track / Six-one-two
WAMMA 003CD / Dec '94 / Dr. Woolybach

Wammack, Travis

☐ THAT SCRATCHY GUITAR FROM MEMPHIS
Night train / Fire fly / It's karate time / Scratchy / Flip flop and bop / Your love / Louie Louie / Tech-nically speaking / Hallelujah, I love her so / Thunder road / I ain't lyin' / Upset / Super soul beat / Distortion part 2 / There's a UFO up there / Umm how sweet it is / Hideaway / Find another man / Fannie Mae / You are my sunshine / Memphis Tennessee
BCD 15415 / Nov '87 / Bear Family

Wampas

☐ CHAUDS SALES ET HUMIDES
ROSE 161CD / Mar '89 / New Rose

Wanamaker, Lisa

☐ SHIRIM
SYNCOOP 5754CD / Feb '95 / Syncoop

Wanda Chrome & The Leather Pharaohs

☐ DANGEROUS TIMES
35500542 / 30 Mar '98 / Subway

Wandering Eyes

☐ SONGS OF FORBIDDEN LOVE
It's a cheatin' situation / Lovin' on backstreets / Cheatin' traces / In some room above the street / Forbidden angel / Devil in Mrs. Jones / Unspoken kind / Even if I have to steal / When she does me right she does you wrong / Game of triangles / Hell yes I cheated / Me and Mr. Jones
LAZYSOB 04 / Jun '98 / Lazy SOB

Wandering Lucy

☐ LEAP YEAR
KLP 53CD / Sep '96 / K

Wanderley, Walter

☐ RAIN FOREST
Summer samba / Cried cried / Rain / Girl from Ipanema / Beloved melancholy / Taste of sadness / Beach samba / Call me / Cry out your sadness / Great love / Song of the jet
8255332 / 3 Aug '98 / Verve

☐ TALKIN' VERVE
Popcorn / Agua de Beber / Amazonas / Girl from Ipanema / Summer samba / Blue island / Taste of sadness / Crickets sing for Ana Maria / Canto de Ossanha / Different beat / Call me / Wave / Beach samba / Music to watch girls by / Goodbye sadness (Trizteza) / Batucada surgiu
5570802 / 29 Jun '98 / Verve

Wanderlust

☐ WANDERLUST
NLL 004 / 29 Jun '98 / Not Lame

Wangford, Hank

☐ HARD SHOULDER TO CRY ON (Wangford, Hank & The Lost Cowboys)
Dim lights / You're still on my mind / Jealousy / My lips want to stay (but my heart wants to go) / Birmingham hotel / Stormy horizons / My baby's gone / Gonna paint this town / Jalisco / What happens / Get rhythm / Prisoner song / Lay down my old guitar / I'm coming home / End of the road
HANKCD 001 / Mar '93 / Sincere Sounds

☐ WAKE UP DEAD (Wangford, Hank & The Lost Cowboys)
Wake up dead / Trail of lies / Get out / Counting the cost / Home sweet home / Wedding dress / In the palm of your hand / If you went away / Did you see me wave / Chaganuga / Johnny 55 / Mouth of the river / Simple pleasures
WOWCD 08 / Jul '97 / Way Out West

Wank

☐ GET A GRIP ON YOURSELF
Crime pays / Forgiven / Super normal / Fearless / Never / On the radio / Paranoid / Best friend / Mickey / Diana's haus / Larry Brown / White lightning
9362469432 / 17 Aug '98 / Maverick

Wannabes

☐ MOD FLOWER CAKE
DJD 3211 / Dec '94 / Dejadisc

☐ POPSUCKER
DJD 3222 / Nov '95 / Dejadisc

Wannadies

☐ AQUANAUTIC
Everything's true / Cherry man / Things that I would love to have undone / Love is dead / So happy now / Lucky you / 1.07 / December days / Something to tell / Suddenly I missed her / God knows / Never killed anyone / I love you love me love
SNAP 005 / Jan '93 / Soap

☐ SKELLEFTEA
XRESNAP 3 / 2 Mar '98 / Soap

Waorani Indians

☐ WAORANI WAAPONI
TUMICD 043 / '94 / Tumi

Wappat, Frank

☐ SONGS OF PRIMITIVE METHODISM, THE
PMCD 001 / Apr '98 / Heritage

War

☐ ALL DAY MUSIC
All day music / Get down / That's what love will do / There must be a reason / Nappy head / Slippin' into darkness / Baby brother
74321305202 / Sep '95 / Avenue

☐ BLACK MAN'S BURDON, THE
Paint it black / Spirit / Beautiful new born child / Nights in white satin / Bird and squirrel / Nuts, seeds and life / Out of nowhere / Sun / Moon / Pretty colors / Gun / Jimbo / Bare back ride/Home cookin' / They can't take away our music
74321307422 / Aug '96 / Avenue

☐ DELIVER THE WORLD
H2Overture / In your eyes / Gypsy man / Me and baby brother / Deliver the word / Southern part of Texas / Blisters
74321305222 / Sep '95 / Avenue

☐ PEACE SIGN
74321297662 / Jun '95 / Avenue

☐ WORLD IS A GHETTO
Cisco kid / City, country, city / Beetles in a bog / Four cornered room / Where was you at / World is a ghetto
74321305212 / Sep '95 / Avenue

War

☐ TOTAL WAR
NR 019MCD / 19 Jan '98 / Necropolis

War Collapse

☐ ROLLED OVER BY TANKS
DISTCD 018 / Nov '95 / Distortion

War Pipes

☐ WAR PIPES
BRGCD 20 / Jul '95 / Bridge

Ward, Anita

☐ ANITA WARD
GFS 069 / Jul '97 / Going For A Song

☐ RING MY BELL
Ring my bell / I'm ready for love / Curtains up / This must be love / Sweet splendour / There's no doubt about it / You lied / Make believe lovers / If I could feel that old feeling again / Spoiled by your love / I won't stop loving you / Ring my bell
CPCD 8311 / Oct '97 / Charly

Ward, Bill

☐ WHEN THE BOUGH BREAKS
CLP 9981 / Jun '97 / Cleopatra

Ward, Billy

☐ 21 HITS (Ward, Billy & The Dominoes)
KCD 5008 / Apr '97 / King

☐ SIXTY MINUTE MAN (Ward, Billy & The Dominoes)
Sixty minute man / Chicken blues / Don't leave me this way / Do something for me / That's what you're doing to me / Weeping willow blues / How long blues / I am with you / Have mercy baby / If I ever get to heaven / Pedal pushin' papa / I'd be satisfied / Deed I do / Bells / My baby's 3-D / Tenderly / I ain't gonna cry for you / You can't keep a good man down / I really don't want to know / I'm gonna move to the outskirts of town
CDCHARLY 242 / Oct '90 / Charly

Ward Brothers

☐ WAVE GOODBYE TO GRANDMA
Swing / Shadows / Take from u / Imelda / Step on it / Little boy / Shirt song / Falling / Find the groove / Footsteps / Friends
CDSGP 0242 / Apr '97 / Prestige

Ward, Clifford T.

☐ GAYE AND OTHER STORIES
Gaye / Wherewithal / Cellophane / Dubious circus company / Not waving, drowning / Time the magician / Home thoughts from abroad / Way of love / Open university / Jigsaw girl / Day to myself / Nightingale / We could be talking / Where's it going to end / Crisis / Scullery / Where would that leave me / To an air hostess / Sad affair
CDVM 9009 / Jun '92 / Virgin

☐ HIDDEN TREASURES
All that glitters is not gold / Jenny / My my what a day / I'd like to take you out tonight / Wait a minute you fool / Session singer / Learning my part / Love in the song / Mule / Sympathy / Gloria bosom show / Sylvie / Not to mention her smile / Got to get into your way of life / Trousers / Here's 'til then / There's no such thing / Attraction
CDRPM 0041 / 3 Aug '98 / RP Media

☐ JULIA AND OTHER NEW STORIES
Julia / Jackdaw / Dancer / Sunshine girl / New English bible / Marron's glance / Unmarried mother / I don't understand your logic / Heaven lend a hand / Taking the long way round / That's the way our love goes / This is the stuff / Water / Marble Arch / Give me one more chance / Sweetness and light / Weather / Lullaby
GRADCD 4 / 24 Mar '98 / Graduate

☐ SINGER SONGWRITER PLUS
Coathanger / Leader / Anticipation / Session singer / God help me / Sympathy / You knock when you should come in / Sam / Dream / Rayne / Carrie / Cause is good / Circus girl / Sidetrack
SEECD 418 / May '95 / See For Miles

Ward, John

☐ WATER ON THE STONE
Water on the stone / Free world market place / Paper chase / Stoney ground / Heart of the town / Status / I want to see your face / Leakin' minister / Rural vandals / Must I go bound / Way of the world / Only treasure / Binding light
IONGF 5 / Jun '92 / Green Fingers

Ward, Ray

☐ NEVER IN QUESTION (Ward, Ray Trio)
Linger awhile / Weaver of dreams / I'll never be the same / At sundown / Charade / Good morning heartache / Running wild / My blue heaven / There'll never be another you / Beautiful friendship / Caravan / Roll on blues / Secret love / Margie / On a slow boat to China
LOTCD 4308 / Jun '98 / Loose Tie

Ward, Robert

☐ BLACK BOTTOM
BT 1123CD / Nov '95 / Black Top

☐ FEAR NO EVIL (Ward, Robert & The Black Top All Stars)
Your love is amazing / Born to entertain / Forgive me darling / Your love is real / Something for nothing / Fear no evil / Trying my best (not to never do wrong) / Strictly reserved for you / So tired of wandering / Blessings / Newborn music / K-po-kee / Lord have mercy on me / Dry spell / Comfort table
ORECD 520 / Mar '94 / Silvertone

☐ RHYTHM OF THE PEOPLE
BT 1088CD / May '93 / Black Top

☐ TWIGGS COUNTRY SOUL MAN
Your love is amazing / Newborn music / Real deal / Something for nothing / White fox / You can't stop my loving now / Silver and gold / So tired of wandering / Lonely man / I'm gonna cry a river / Black bottom
CDBTEL 7003 / Mar '97 / Black Top

Ward, Robin

☐ STORY OF ROBIN WARD, THE
MISS 002 / 1 May '98 / Missing/Marginal

Warda

☐ WARDA
Batwanness beek (I feel safe with you) / Zarny fil dohah (He came to visit me in the morning) / Ya khsara (what a pity) / Hobak west madah (Your love reached its end) / Nar el ghera (Fire of jealousy) / Ya saeedy (Oh, my master)
HEMIMDCD 102 / Feb '97 / Hemisphere

Wardell, Anita

☐ WHY DO YOU CRY
UGCD 03 / Sep '97 / Future

Wardell, Dick

☐ STREET LIFE BLUES
Some of these days / Dream and change blues / It's too late / Birds are singing / Walking the blues / Future blues / Streeet life blues / Love will make you cry / Mean old Frisco / Midnight moon / Let's turn out the light / Katie Mae / Poor children dyin' / Play with your poodle / New day coming
FECD 108 / Jun '96 / Fellside

Warden, Monte

☐ HERE I AM
WMCD 1037 / Aug '95 / Watermelon

☐ MONTE WARDEN
WMCD 1015 / May '94 / Watermelon

Wardi, Mohammed

☐ LIVE IN ADDIS ABABA
RPM 0012 / 9 Mar '98 / Rags Productions

Wardog

☐ SCORCHED EARTH
398414112CD / Jul '96 / Metal Blade

Ware, Bill

☐ LONG & SKINNY (Ware, Bill & The Club Bird Allstars)
KFWCD 131 / Feb '95 / Knitting Factory

☐ VIBES
Bayla / Reunion / Carousel / Margarida / Joel / Sneaky Pete / So tired / Inner city blues / VCX
KFWCD 210 / 20 Apr '98 / Knitting Factory

Ware, David S.

☐ EARTHQUATION
DIW 892 / Jan '95 / DIW

☐ FLIGHT OF I
DIW 856 / May '92 / DIW

☐ GODSPELISED
DIW 916 / Dec '96 / DIW

☐ OBLATIONS AND BLESSINGS (Ware, David S. Quartet)
Rollin' over / Song of a baker / I feel much better / Talk to you / Tin soldier / Autumn stone / Become like you / I can't make it / Donkey rides, a penny a glass / Rene / I'm only dreaming / Hungry intruder / Red balloon / Just passing
SHCD 145 / Oct '97 / Silkheart

☐ WISDOM OF UNCERTAINTY (Ware, David S. Quartet)
AUM 001CD / 13 Apr '98 / Aum Fidelity

Ware, Leon

☐ TASTE THE LOVE
Come with me angel / Back to back / Meltdown / Love parts / Cream of love / Telepathy / Musical massage / Can't stop love / I got your recipe / I get weak / Yes / It was always you / Where do I stand / Taste the love
XECD 5 / Aug '95 / Expansion

Warfare

☐ CONFLICT OF HATRED
Waxworks / Revolution / Dancing in the flames of insanity / Evolution / Fatal vision / Death charge / Order of the dragons / Elite forces / Rejoice the feast of quarantine / Noise filth and fury
NEATCD 1044 / Mar '88 / Neat

☐ DECADE OF DECIBELS
CDBLEED 8 / Oct '93 / Bleeding Hearts

☐ HAMMER HORROR
Hammer horror / Plague of the zombies / Ballad of the dead / Phantom of the opera / Baron Frankenstein / Velvet rhapsody / Sold of shadows / Prince of Darkness / Tales of the gothic genre / Scream of the vampire
REVXD 147 / Jun '90 / FM
FILMCD 130 / Apr '93 / Silva Screen

Warfield, Derek

☐ LEGACY
SHCD 52042 / Apr '96 / Shanachie

☐ LIBERTE '98 (Erin Go Bragh)
Volunteers of Ireland / Ballad of Buddy McClean / Ballad of St. Colmcille / Henry Joy McCracken/The rising of the moon/Roddy McCorley / Ballad of Aidan McAnespie / Cead mile failte / Boys of Wexford/Who fears to speak / Kelly the boy from Killane / Ballad of Ann Devlin / John O'Neill Nebraska / King Alfred's tour of Ireland / Irish in Glasgow / Bantry Bay the French on the sea / Decent cup of tea / Michael Collins
SHANCD 5246 / Jul '98 / Shanachie

Warfield, Justin

☐ JUSTIN WARFIELD SUPERNAUT, THE
Glimmer / Crawl / In a mirrored ladybong / Everglide / Alice / Ritalan / Around about / Moontower / Come back again / Molasses the butterfly / Jesus candles / Rollerderby
9362458712 / May '95 / Qwest

Warfield, Tim

☐ COOL BLUE, A
CRISS 1102 / Oct '95 / Criss Cross

☐ WHISPER IN MIDNIGHT, A (Warfield, Tim Sextet)
Tin soldier / Soprano song / Speak low / I've never been blue before / Whisper in midnight / Bye bye blackbird / Prayer for Uthman
CRISS 1122CD / Mar '98 / Criss Cross

Wargasm

☐ FIREBALL
MASSCD 036 / Jul '94 / Massacre

☐ UGLY
MASSCD 020 / Nov '93 / Massacre

Warhead

☐ WARHEAD
CMGCD 011 / Nov '95 / Communique

Warhorse

☐ RED SEA
Red sea / Back in time / Confident but wrong / Feeling better / Sybilla / Mouth piece / I who have nothing
REP 4056 / Aug '91 / Repertoire

☐ WARHORSE
REP 4055 / Aug '91 / Repertoire

☐ WARHORSE STORY VOL.1 & 2, THE (2CD Set)
Vulture blood / No chance / Burning / St. Louis / Ritual / Solitude / Woman of the devil / Ritual / Miss Jane / Solitude / Woman of the devil / Burning / Red Sea / Back in time / Confident but wrong / Feeling better / Sybilla / Mouthpiece / I (who have nothing) / Ritual / Bad time / She was my friend / Gypsy dancer / House of dolls / Standing right behind you
RPM 501 / Jun '97 / RPM

☐ WARHORSE STORY VOL.1, THE
Vulture blood / No chance / Burning / St. Louis / Ritual / Solitude / Woman of the devil / Ritual / Miss Jane / Solitude / Woman of the devil / Burning
RPM 174 / Jun '97 / RPM

☐ WARHORSE STORY VOL.2, THE
Red sea / Back in time / Confident but wrong / Feeling better / Sybilla / Mouthpiece / I (who have nothing) / Ritual / Bad time / She was my friend / Gypsy dancer / House of dolls / Standing right behind you
RPM 175 / Jun '97 / RPM

Wariner, Steve

☐ BURNIN' THE ROADHOUSE DOWN
Burnin' the roadhouse down / Holes in the floor of heaven / Every little whisper / Six pack ago / Road trippin' / Love me like you love me / Smoke from an old flame / I don't know how to fix it / Big ol' empty house / Closer I get to you / Big tops / What If I said
4944822 / 10 Aug '98 / EMI

☐ FLOWER THAT SHATTERED THE STONE, THE
HMNCD 028 / 16 Mar '98 / Half Moon

☐ NO MORE MR. NICE GUY
No more Mr. Nice Guy / Big hero, little hero / Prelude/ Practice your scales / Somewhere else / Theme / Forever loving you / Next March / If you can't say something good / Hap Towne breakdown / For Chester B / Brickyard boogie / Don't call me Ray / Guitar talk
07822188142 / Apr '96 / Arista

Waring, Fred

☐ MEMORIAL ALBUM, THE
Farewell blues / Bolshevik / Helo Montreal / Stack O'Lee blues / What a night for spooning / Glorianna / Navy blues / Hello baby / Good for you bad for me / Red hot Chicago / How'm I doin / I heard / Old yazoo / Holding my honey's hand / Old man of the mountain / You'll get by / Fit as a fiddle / Young and healthly / Dance selections / Flying colours
VN 179 / Nov '96 / Viper's Nest

Waring, Steve

☐ GUITAR PICKING (Waring, Steve & Roger Mason)
LDX 274969 / Oct '94 / La Chant Du Monde

Warlock

☐ EARTH SHAKER ROCK
Burning the witches / Metal racer / Hellbound / Earth shaker rock / Time to die / Love in the danger zone / True as steel / All we are / 3 Minute warning / I rule the ruins / Metal tango / Fur immer / Hellraiser / Angels with dirty faces / Under the gun / Something wicked this way / Comes
VSOPCD 247 / 26 Jan '98 / Connoisseur Collection

Warlord

☐ MAXIMUM CARNAGE
NB 119CD / Apr '96 / Nuclear Blast

Warm Jets

☐ FUTURE SIGNS
Move away / Never never / Hurricane / Vapour trails / Future signs / Romero
5243542 / 23 Feb '98 / This Way Up

Warm Wires

☐ SEVERE COMFORT
BRCD 062 / Apr '97 / Brinkman

Warmers

☐ WARMERS, THE
DIS 102CD / Jun '96 / Dischord

Warner, Albert

☐ ALBERT WARNER & THE BROWN BUDDIES/ALBERT JILES ONZAGA OWLS (Warner, Albert & The Brown Buddies/Albert Jiles Onzaga Owls)
AMCD 66 / May '98 / American Music

Warner, Simon

☐ WAITING ROOMS
Keep it down / Decorating / Wake up the street / Jamboree / Moody / Doggy / Wrong girl / Hiding / Kitchen tango / Mrs Zaniewski / Ticket collector / Proper job / Waiting rooms / Simply marvellous / Coda
R 4132 / May '97 / Rough Trade

Warner, Tom

☐ LONG NIGHT BIG DAY
804102 / Jun '91 / New World

Warnes, Jennifer

☐ FAMOUS BLUE RAINCOAT
First we take Manhattan / Bird on the wire / Famous blue raincoat / Joan of Arc / Ain't no cure for love / Coming back to you / Song of Bernadette / Singer must die / Came so far for beauty
258418 / Feb '97 / RCA

☐ HUNTER, THE
Rock you gently / Somewhere, somebody / Big noise, New York / True emotion / Pretending to care / Whole of the moon / Light of Louisanne / Way down deep / Hunter / I can't hide
261974 / Feb '96 / Private Music

☐ JUST JENNIFER
Close the door / Sunny day blue / Here, there and everywhere / Chelsea morning / I want to meander in the meadow / I am waiting / Places everyone / Three hoouse of gold / It's hard to love a poet / Leaves / Park / Let the sunshine in / Easy to be hard / Saturday night the world / Time is on the run / Old folks (les vieux) / We're not gonna take it / Just like Tom Thumb's blues / Back street girl / Weather's better / Tell me again I love thee / Cajun train
8209892 / ' / Deram

☐ SHOT THROUGH THE HEART
Shot through the heart / I know a heartache when I see one / Don't make me over / You remember me / Sign on the window / I'm restless / Tell me just one more time / When the feeling comes around / Frankie in the rain / Hard times / Come again no more
74321197372 / Feb '97 / Arista

Warpath

☐ KILL YOUR ENEMY
SPV 085182852 / Mar '96 / SPV

Warpig

☐ WARPIG
HF 9552 / Oct '97 / Warpig

Warrant

☐ BELLY TO BELLY VOL.1
In the end / Feels good / Letter to a friend / AYM / Indian giver / Falling down / Interlude / Solid / All 4 U / Coffee house / Interlude / Vertigo / Room with a view / Nobody else
06076862002 / May '97 / CMC

☐ BEST OF WARRANT, THE
Down boys / 32 pennies in a ragu jar / Heaven / DRFSR / Big talk / Sometimes she cries / Cherry pie / Thin disguise / Uncle Tom's cabin / I saw red / Bed of roses / Mr. Rainmaker / Sure feels good to me / Hole in my wall / Machine gun / We will rock you
4840122 / Jul '96 / Columbia

☐ ULTRAPHOBIC
CDMFN 183 / Feb '95 / Music For Nations

Warren, Fran

☐ SOMETHING'S COMING
FSRCD 101 / Jan '98 / Fresh Sound

Warren G

☐ REGULATE G FUNK ERA
Regulate: Warren G & Nate Dogg / Do you see / Gangsta sermon / Recognize / Super soul sis / '94 Ho draft / So many ways / This DJ / This is the Shack / What's next / And ya don't stop / Runnin' wit no breaks
5233352 / Jul '94 / Island Red

☐ TAKE A LOOK OVER YOUR SHOULDER
Intro / Annie Mae / Smokin' me out / Reverend Eazy Dick / Reality / Interlude / Young fun / What we go through / We bring heat / Can you feel it / Transformers / Reel tight intro / Relax your mind / To all the DJ's / Back up / What's love got to do with it: *Warren G & Adina Howard* / I shot the sheriff
5334842 / Feb '97 / Def Jam

Warren, Huw

☐ BARREL ORGAN FAR FROM HOME
BDV 9718 / Nov '97 / Babel

Warren J 5

☐ COMPLETE DISCOGRAPHY
SAF 007 / 22 May '98 / Giallo

Warren, Nick

☐ BRAZIL (2CD Set) (Various Artists)
Marching powder: PMT / Lose it: *Desert* / Sequenza: *DJ Gogo* / India: *E-Razor* / All I am: *Capricorn* / Tequila flange: *PMT* / Rise and fall: *Yin & Yunk* / New sunset: *Stone Factory* / No one in the world: *Locust* / Acushla: *Origin* / Miralaca: *Junk Project* / Northern lights: *Conscious* / Trancelifusion: *VFR* / Psychout (thing): *Slacker* / Your beautiful: *Madagascar* / Kill city: *Hybrid* / Reality detached: *Forth* / Ya yae ya yo yo yo: *Forth* / Aquaphonic: *Nickelson* / Cafe del Mar: *Energy 52* / Breathe in: *Tekara* / Equilibrium: *Anthony & Georgio* / Indica: *Pink Bomb* / Dreamscape: *Serpico* / Pressure: *Propulsion* / Boiler: *POB*
GU 008CD
GU 008CDX / 20 Jul '98 / Global Underground

☐ DJ'S IN A BOX VOL.8 (Various Artists)
UCCD 008 / Nov '96 / Urban Collective

☐ NICK WARREN LIVE IN PRAGUE (2CD Set) (Various Artists)
Ohm sessions (coloured oxygen reprise): *Cruzeman* / Tech theme: *Cruzeman* / Nipple fish: *Coffee boys* / Schattenmund: *Mikerobenics* / Spirit: *Aquaplex System* / Noise shots: *Riot Rhythm* / Cut the midrange: *Watchman* / Boom: *LT Project* / Life on Mars: *Life On Mars* / Magic shop (fourth coded dub): *Pako, Stef & Frederik* / Credits: *Celysys, Tom* / Distant drum: *Distant Drums* / Gospel 2001: *16C+* / Pandamonia: *DJ Randy* / Ancient quest: *Dark Age* / Cafe del mar: *Energy 52* / Reach for it: *Chaser* / Seadog: *Clanger* / Submissions: *Freek & Mac Zimms* / Tempest: *Deepsky* / Sunrise: *Anjo* / Galaxia: *Moonman*
GU 003CD / Mar '97 / Boxed

Warrior

☐ ANCIENT FUTURE
Fight or fall / Pray / Who sane / Learn to love / Tonight we ride / Power / White mansions / rush / Tear it down / Ancient future
DCD 9839 / Jul '98 / Dream Circle

Warrior

☐ LET BATTLE COMMENCE
Let battle commence / Long stretch Broadmoor blues / Night time girl / Memories / Yesterday's hero / Invaders / Ulster bloody Ulster / Warrior
ETHEL 002CD / 2 Feb '98 / Vinyl Tap

Warrior River Boys

☐ SOUNDS LIKE HOME
ROUCD 310 / Jan '94 / Rounder

Warrior Soul

☐ FUCKER
NYC girl / Gimme some of this / Punk rock 'n' roll / Turn on / 5 ways to the gutter / Stun fun / My sky / Makin' it / Raised on riots / American / Kiss me / This joy / Can't fix / Come to me / Last decade dead cantury / If you think you're dead
CDMFN 204 / Sep '96 / Music For Nations

☐ LAST DECADE, DEAD CENTURY
I see the ruins / We cry out / Losers / Downtown / Trippin' on ecstasy / One minute years / Super power dreamland / Charlie's out of prison / Blown away / Lullaby / In conclusion / Four more years
GED 24285 / Jun '97 / Geffen

☐ SALUTATIONS FROM THE GHETTO NATION
Love destruction / Blown / Shine like it / Dimension / Punk and belligerent / Ass-kickin' / Party / Golden shore / Trip rider / I love you / Fallen / Ghetto nation
GED 24488 / Jun '97 / Geffen

☐ SPACE AGE PLAYBOYS
CDMFN 172 / Oct '94 / Music For Nations

Warsaw

☐ WARSAW
MPG 74034 / Feb '95 / Movieplay Gold

Warwick, Dionne

☐ AQUARELA DO BRASIL
Jobim medley / Virou areia / Oh Bahia / Piano na manquiera / Captives of the heart / Samba dobrado / Heart of Brasil / N'kosi sikelel'i - Afrika / So bashiya bahlala ekhaya / Brasil / Caravan / Flower of Bahia / 10,000 words
07822187772 / Jan '95 / Arista

☐ DIONNE
Who, what, when, where and why / After you / Letter / I'll never love this way again / Deja vu / Feeling old feelings / In your eyes / My everlasting love / Out of my hands / All the time
MCCD 169 / Sep '94 / Music Club

☐ DIONNE WARWICK SINGS COLE PORTER
Night and day / I love Paris / I get a kick out of you / What is this thing called love / So in love / You're the top / I've got you under my skin / Begin the beguine / It's all right with me / Anything goes / You'd be so nice to come home to / All of you / I concentrate on you / Night and day (jazz version) / Just one of those things
260918 / Oct '90 / Arista

☐ ESSENTIAL COLLECTION, THE (2CD Set)
Do you know the way to San Jose / Walk on by / Anyone who had a heart / Raindrops keep falling on my head / Reach out for me / I just don't know what to do with myself / Don't make me over / Always something there to remind me / This girl's in love with you / Wishin' and hopin' / House is not a home / I'll never fall in love again / I say a little prayer / Are you there with another girl / Message to Michael / Close to you / Make it easy on yourself / Promises promises / What the world needs now / Windows of the world / Alfie / Trains and boats and planes / You'll never get to heaven / Look of love / Only love can break a heart / Wives and lovers / Heartbreaker / All the love in the world / I'll never love this way again / That's what friends are for / Run to me / Love power / Yours / So your eyes / Our day will come / Night and day / So amazing / Begin the beguine / You're all I need to get by / You've lost that lovin' feelin' / Who can I turn to / (Theme from) Valley of the dolls
RADCD 48 / Nov '96 / Global TV

☐ FRIENDS CAN BE LOVERS
Where my lips have been / Sunny weather lover / Age of miracles / Love will find a way: Warwick, Dionne & Whitney Houston / Much to much / Till the end of time / Woman that I am / Fragile / Can't break this heart / Superwoman: *Warwick, Dionne & Gladys Knight/ Patti LaBelle*
07822186822 / Mar '93 / Arista

☐ GREAT SONGS OF THE SIXTIES
What the world needs now is love / Yesterday / Raindrops keep falling on my head / Promise, promise / You've lost that lovin' feelin' / I'm your puppet / Something / We've only just begun / Macarthur park / My way / Up, up and away / Going out of my head / People get ready / You're my world / Loving you is sweeter than ever / Put yourself in my place / Someday we'll be together / I've been loving you too long / Games people play / Windows of the world
3035900122 / May '96 / Essential Gold

☐ GREATEST HITS
259279 / Aug '95 / Arista

☐ HEARTBREAKER
All the love in the world / I can't see anything but you / You are my love / Just one more night / Our day will come / Heartbreaker / Yours / Take the short way home / It makes no difference / Misunderstood
258719 / Oct '87 / Arista

☐ HERE I AM/HERE WHERE THERE IS LOVE
In between the heartaches / Here I am / If I ever make you cry / Lookin' with my eyes / Once in a lifetime / This little light / Don't go breaking my heart / Window wishing / Long day, short night / Are you there / How can I hurt you / I loves you Porgy / Go with love / What the world needs now is love / I just don't know what to do with myself / Here where there is love / Trains and boats and planes / Alfie / As long as he needs me / I wish you love / I never knew what you were up to / Blowin' in the wind
NEMCD 762 / Oct '95 / Sequel

☐ JUST BEING MYSELF
JHD 002 / Jun '92 / Tring

☐ LOVE SONGS COLLECTION
I'll never fall in love again / Let it be me / Here where there is love / I love Paris / Hurt so bad / As long as he needs me / Blowin' in the wind / One hand, one heart / You can have him / People / This girl's in love with you / You're all I need to get by / Baubles, bangles and beads / Getting ready for the heartbreak / Who can I turn to / People got to be free / It's the good life / Somewhere / Unchained melody / Valley of the dolls
PWKS 525 / Feb '96 / Carlton

☐ MAKE WAY FOR DIONNE WARWICK/ THE SENSITIVE SOUND OF DIONNE
House is not a home / People / (They want to be) Close to me / Last one to be loved / Land of make believe / Reach out for me / You'll never get to heaven (if you break my heart) / Walk on by / Wishin' and hopin' / I smiled yesterday / Get rid of him / Make the night a little longer / Unchained melody / Who can I turn to / How many days of sadness / Is there another way to love him / Where can I go without you / You can have him / Wives and lovers / Don't say I didn't tell you so / Only the strong, only the brave / Forever my love
NEMCD 761 / Oct '95 / Sequel

☐ ORIGINAL HITS 1962-1972, THE
Theme from "valley of the dolls" / I'll never fall in love again / I say a little prayer / Walk on by / You've lost that lovin' feelin' / Alfie / Trains and boats and planes / You'll never get to heaven (if you break my heart) / Don't make me over / Reach out for me / I just don't know what to do with myself / April fools / This girl's in love with you / Do you know the way to san jose / Anyone who had a heart / Message to michael / Let me go to him / Promises, promises / Windows of the world / Who is gonna love me / Are you there with another girl / Green grass starts to grow / Make it easy on yourself / Odds and ends / Paper mache / Another night / (there's) always something there to remind me / House is not a home
DCD 5366 / Apr '94 / Disky

☐ PRESENTING DIONNE WARWICK/ ANYONE WHO HAD A HEART
This empty place / Wishin' and hopin' / I cry alone / Zip-a-dee-doo-dah / Make the music play / If you see Bill / Don't make me over / It's love that really counts (in the long run) / Inlucky / I smiled yesterday / Make it easy on yourself / Love of a boy / Anyone who had a heart / Shall I tell her / Gettin' ready for the heartbreak / Oh Lord what are you doing to me / Any old time of day / Mr. Heartbreak / Put yourself in my place / I could make you mine / Please make him love me
NEMCD 760 / Oct '95 / Sequel

☐ SINGS THE STANDARDS
I love Paris / Summertime / Baubles bangles and beads / Birth of the blues / Somewhere / I loves you Porgy / C'est si bon / For all we know / Good life / I believe in you / I cry alone / Impossible dream / La vie en rose / My favourite things / Taking a chance on love / Way you look tonight / You the night and the music / Something wonderful / One hand one heart
VSOPCD 255 / 17 Aug '98 / Connoisseur Collection

☐ SOULFUL
You've lost that lovin' feelin' / I'm your puppet / People got to be free / You're all I need to get by / We can work it out / Silent voices / Hard day's night / Do right woman, do right man / I've been loving you too long / People get ready / Hey Jude / What's good about goodbye
DCD 5401 / Oct '94 / Disky

Warzone

☐ FIGHT FOR JUSTICE
VR 062CD / 27 Oct '97 / Victory

☐ OLD SCHOOL VS. NEW
VR 015CD / Sep '96 / Victory

☐ OPEN YOUR EYES, DON'T FORGET THE STRUGGLE
Into bust / It's your choice / Crazy but not insane / Fuck your attitude / As one / We're the crew / Don't forget the struggle / In the mirror / Skinhead youth / Growing up - the next step / Judgement day / Fight for our country / Open up your eyes / Dance hard or die / Face up to it / Always - a friend for life / Racism - World history part 1 / Back to school again / American movement / Fight the oppressoh / Deceive us - no more / Striving for a better life
LF 109CD / Oct '94 / Lost & Found

☐ SOUND OF REVOLUTION, THE
VR 045CD / Oct '96 / Victory

Was Not Was

☐ WHAT UP DOG
Somewhere in America / Spy in the house of love / Out come the freaks / Earth to Doris / Love can be bad luck / Boy's gone crazy / Eleven miles an hour / What up dog / Anything can happen / Robot girl / Wedding vows in Vegas / Anytime Lisa / Walk the dinosaur / I can't turn you loose / Shadow and Jimmy / Dad I'm in jail
5504042 / May '96 / Spectrum

Wasa Express

☐ SAME
SLPCD 2594 / 5 Jan '98 / Sonet

Washboard Rhythm Kings

☐ WASHBOARD RHYTHM KINGS COLLECTION VOL.5 1930-1931
COCD 30 / Aug '97 / Collector's Classics

☐ WASHBOARD RHYTHM KINGS VOL.1 1931
Please don't talk about me / Minnie the moocher / One more time / Walkin' my baby back home / Porter's love song / Everyman for himself / Blues in my heart / Just one more chance / Many happy returns of the day / Shoot 'em / Wake 'em up / Georgia on my mind / Pepper steak / If you don't love me / Please tell me / (I'll be glad when you're dead) you rascal you / Crooked world blues / Call of the freaks / I'm crazy 'bout my baby / Because I'm yours sincerely / Stardust / You can't stop me from lovin' you / Boola boo / Who stole the lock
COCD 17 / Jul '96 / Collector's Classics

☐ WASHBOARD RHYTHM KINGS VOL.2 1932
COCD 18 / Jul '96 / Collector's Classics

☐ WASHBOARD RHYTHM KINGS VOL.3 1931-1932
COCD 25 / Jul '96 / Collector's Classics

☐ WASHBOARD RHYTHM KINGS VOL.4 1933
COCD 26 / May '97 / Collector's Classics

Washboard Sam

☐ GET DOWN BROTHER
Play your vendor / Flying crow blues / Soap and water blues / Laid my cards / I just can't help it / River hip mama / You can't have none of that / Hit the highway / Life is just a book / Rockin' my blues away / My feet jumped salty / Lover's lane blues / Evil blues / Do that shake dance / Down south woman blues / Good old cabbage greens / How can you love me / I've been treated wrong / She belongs to the devil / I'm feeling lowdown / Levee camp blues / Red river dam blues / Get down brother
74321535832 / 22 Nov '97 / RCA

☐ WASHBOARD SAM 1935-1941
158662 / Jun '97 / Blues Collection

☐ WASHBOARD SAM VOL.1 - 1935-36
DOCD 5171 / Oct '93 / Document

☐ WASHBOARD SAM VOL.2 - 1937-38
DOCD 5172 / Oct '93 / Document

☐ WASHBOARD SAM VOL.3 - 1938
DOCD 5173 / Oct '93 / Document

☐ WASHBOARD SAM VOL.4 - 1939-40
DOCD 5174 / Oct '93 / Document

☐ WASHBOARD SAM VOL.5 - 1940-41
DOCD 5175 / Oct '93 / Document

☐ WASHBOARD SAM VOL.6 - 1941-42
DOCD 5176 / Oct '93 / Document

☐ WASHBOARD SAM VOL.7 - 1942-49
DOCD 5177 / Oct '93 / Document

Washburn, Lalomie

☐ LALOMIE WASHBURN
Try my love / Use it / It's now or never / In my groove / Dream of me / I wanna be with you / Take me / If you got time / Part time love (part 2) / Part time love / Get over it
ME 00532 / 9 Feb '98 / Soulciety

Washer, Bill

☐ ASAP (Washer, Bill & Danny Gottlieb)
ITMP 970054 / Jan '91 / ITM

Washingmachine, George

☐ SWEET ATMOSPHERE (Washingmachine, George & Ian Date)
JH 2008 / Oct '93 / Jazz Hour

Washington, Baby

☐ SUE SINGLES, THE
No tears / Go on / Handful of memories / Careless hands / I've got a feeling / Hush heart / Standing on the pier / Clock / That's how heartaches are made / There he is / Leave me alone / Hey lonely / I can't wait until I see my baby's face / Who's gonna take care of me / It'll never be over for me / Move on drifter / Run my heart / Your fool / Only those in love / No time for pity / You and the night and the music / Doodlin' / Ballad of Bobby Dawn / You are what you are / Either you're with me (or either you're not) / I know / White Christmas / Silent night
CDKEND 136 / Jun '96 / Kent

Washington, Dinah

☐ 50 GREATEST HITS
Ain't misbehavin' / West side baby / Resolution blues / Walkin' and talkin' / I want to cry / Am I asking too much / It's too soon to know / You satisfy / Baby get lost / Long john blues / Good daddy blues / I only know / It isn't fair / I wanna be loved / I'll never be free / Time out for tears / Mad about the boy / Harbor lights / My heart cries for you / I won't cry anymore / Cold cold heart / Wheel of fortune / Tell me why / Trouble in mind / New blowtop blues / T.v. is the thing (this year) / Fat daddy / I don't hurt anymore / Dream / Teach me tonight / That's all I want from you / If it's the last thing I do / I concentrate on you / I'm lost without you tonight / You might have told me / Soft winds / Make me a present of you / What a difference a day makes / Unforgettable / Baby (you've got what it takes) / Rockin' good way (to mess around and fall in love) / This bitter earth / Love walked in / It could happen to you / We have love / September in the rain / Early every morning / Our love is here to stay / Tears and laughter / If I loved you
DBP 102004 / Nov '93 / Double Platinum

☐ BACK TO THE BLUES
Blues ain't nothing but a woman cryin' for her man / Romance in the dark / You've been a good old wagon / Let me be the first to know / How long how long blues / Don't come running back to me / It's a mean old man's world / Key to the highway / If I never get to heaven / Duck before you drown / No hard feelings / Nobody knows the way I feel this morning / Don't say nothing at all / No one man / Me and my gin
CDP 8543342 / Mar '97 / Roulette

☐ BALLADS AND LOVE SONGS
Stairway to the stars / How deep is the ocean / If I loved you / I wanna be loved / I apologize / I thought about you / Mad about the boy / My devotion / Am I blue / Our love is here to stay / If it's the last thing I do / Darn that dream / Teach me tonight / I concentrate on you / Make the man love me / Blue gardinia / You don't know what love is / My old flame / Easy living / If I had you / I'm lost without you tonight / Goodbye / Smoke gets in your eyes / Look to the rainbow / More than you know / Willow weep for me / You're crying / Every time we say goodbye / I'll close my eyes / Never let me go / I've got a feeling I'm falling / Cry me a river / It's magic / Time after time / This love of mine / Good morning heartache / Again / It shouldn't happen in a dream / I remember clifford
CPCD 83042 / Sep '97 / Charly

☐ CLASSIC DINAH WASHINGTON, THE (2CD Set)
Septmeber in the rain / Smoke gets in your eyes / All of me / This can't be love / I can't get started / Love is here to stay / Blue skies / Love letters / They didn't believe me / Stormy weather / Ain't misbehavin' / Ev'ry time we say goodbye / Teach me tonight / I get a kick out of you / Come rain or come shine / Love walked in / Mad about the boy / Dream / Everybody loves my baby / Manhattan / Unforgettable / It could happen to you / Stardust / This bitter Earth / I wanna be loved / Trouble in mind / You don't know what love is / What a difference a day made / Baby get lost / Since I fell for you / Love for sale / Evil gal blues / I don't hurt anymore / Feel like I wanna cry / Please send me someone to love / I won't cry anymore / Tears to burn / I could have told you / I'll never be there / Salty Papa blues / Am I blue / Cry me a river / Make the man love me / When a woman loves a man / More than you know / There is no greater love
CPCD 82472 / Oct '96 / Charly

☐ COLLECTION, THE
Mad about the boy / Ain't misbehavin' / What a difference a day made / Close to you / Smoke gets in your eyes / Willow weep for me / Unforgettable / I cried for you / Jitterbug waltz / Shoo shoo baby / All or nothing / And her tears flowed like wine / Look to the rainbow / Keepin' out of mischief / Wise woman blues / Blues for a day / Chewin' mama blues / No love, no nothin' / No voot is really you / My loving papa / No voot no boot / Mellow mama blues / Arkansas / Million dollar smile / Do nothing till you hear from me
COL 057 / Jun '95 / Collection

☐ DINAH AND CLIFFORD
JHR 73583 / Dec '94 / Jazz Hour

☐ DINAH JAMS
Lover come back to me / Alone together/ Summertime/Come rain or come shine / I've got you under my skin / There is no greater love / You go to my head / Darn that dream / Crazy he calls me / I'll remember April
8146392 / Apr '90 / EmArCy

☐ DINAH WASHINGTON SINGS THE BLUES
5378112 / 22 Sep '97 / Verve Elite

☐ FATS WALLER SONGBOOK, THE
Christopher Columbus / Ain't nobody's business if I do / Jitterbug waltz / Someone's rocking my dreamboat / Ain't cha glad / Squeeze me / Ain't misbehavin' / Black and blue / Everybody loves my baby / I've got a feeling I'm falling in love / Honeysuckle rose / Keepin' out of mischief now
8189302 / Apr '85 / EmArCy

☐ FIRST ISSUE (The Dinah Washington Story/2CD Set)
5148412 / Dec '93 / Verve

☐ FOR THOSE IN LOVE
I get a kick out of you / Blue gardenia / Easy living / You don't know what love is / This can't be love / My old flame / I could write a book / Make the man love me / Ask a woman who knows / If I had you
5140732 / Feb '93 / EmArCy

☐ GITANES - JAZZ 'ROUND MIDNIGHT
New blowtop blues / Jail house blues / Me and my gin / Trouble in mind / Postman blues / My song / When the sun goes down / Since I fell for you / Raindrops / Feel like I wanna cry / Willow weep for me / You don't know what love is / You're crying / I'll close my eyes / Our love is here to stay / Teach me tonight / Fine fat daddy / After you've gone / Light
5100872 / Apr '91 / Verve

☐ GREATEST HITS
Am I asking too much / It's too soon to know / Baby get lost / Long John blues / I only know / I wanna be loved / I'll never be free / Cold cold heart / Wheel of fortune / TV is the thing (this year) / I don't hurt anymore / Teach me tonight / What a difference a day makes / Unforgettable / Baby (you've got what it takes) / Rockin' good way / This bitter Earth / Love walked in / September in the rain / Mad about the boy
CPCD 8008 / Oct '93 / Charly

☐ HOW TO DO IT
PASTCD 7818 / Jun '97 / Flapper

☐ JAZZ MASTERS
5182002 / 5 May '98 / Verve

☐ JAZZ MASTERS (Dinah Washington Sings Standards)
5220552 / 5 May '98 / Verve

☐ JAZZ PROFILE
Destination moon / Blues ain't nothin' / Lover man / Don't say nothin' at all / Coquette / Man that got away / Funny thing / Just one more chance / Miss you / To forget about you / Handful of stars / I'll never stop loving you / I wanna be around / Stranger on Earth
CDP 8549072 / May '97 / Blue Note

☐ JAZZ SIDES OF MISS D, THE
Introduction / I've got you under my skin / No more / Darn that dream / You go to my head / Lover come back to me / Come rain or come shine / Crazy he calls me / There is no greater love / I'll remember april / I could write a book / Make the man love me / Blue gardenia / You don't know what love is / My old flame / Easy living / I get a kick out of you / This can't be love / Lover come back to me / Crazy love / Send me to the 'lectric chair / Me and my gin / Back water blues / All of me
JWD 102312 / Nov '94 / JWD

☐ LOW DOWN BLUES (20 Classics From Dynamic Dinah)
Mellow Mama blues / Evil gal blues / Pacific Coast blues / Embraceable you / Blow top blues / Mean and evil blues / Rich man blues / When a woman loves a man / Oowee walkie talkie / Salty Papa blues / Postman blues / Wise woman blues / How to do it / Homeward bound / Chick (on the mellow side) / I can't get started / All or nothing / That's why a woman loves a heel / Joy juice / No voot no boot
306502 / Jul '97 / Hallmark

☐ MAD ABOUT THE BOY
Mad about the boy / What a difference a day makes / Unforgettable / Baby, you got what it takes / Rockin' good way / September in the rain / Love for sale / Every time we say goodbye / Makin' whoopee / All of me / Let's do it / If I were a bell / Teach me tonight / Manhattan / Everybody loves somebody / Our love is here to stay / Cry me a river
5122142 / Apr '92 / Mercury

☐ MAD ABOUT THE BOY
MPV 5522 / May '92 / Movieplay

☐ MAD ABOUT THE BOY
Mad about the boy / I wanna be loved / It's too soon to know / Unforgettable / Wheel of fortune / I only know / Am I asking too much / Soft winds / What a difference a day makes / I don't hurt anymore / Dream / Time after time / Manhattan / Trust in me / Smoke gets in your eyes / Our love is here to stay
SUMCD 4015 / Nov '96 / Summit

☐ MAD ABOUT THE BOY
BN 051 / Apr '98 / Blue Nite

☐ MASTERS, THE
EABCD 053 / 24 Nov '97 / Eagle

☐ MASTERS, THE (2CD Set)
EDMCD 006 / 24 Nov '97 / Eagle

☐ MELLOW MAMA
DD 451 / Dec '87 / Delmark

☐ QUEEN OF THE BLUES 1943-1947, THE
159152 / 24 Apr '98 / Blues Collection

☐ QUEEN OF THE BLUES, THE (4CD Set)
Evil gal blues / Salty papa blues / Blow top blues / Wise woman blues / My lovin' papa / Rich man's blues / Blues for a day / Pacific coast blues / When a woman loves a man / Oo-wee walkie talkie / Slick chick (on the mellow side) / Stairway to the stars / Want to be loved / You satisfy / Since I fell for you / West side baby / You can depend on me / Walkin' and talkin' / Ain't misbehavin' / Am I asking too much / Resolution blues / I want to cry / Long John blues / It's too soon to know / Good daddy blues / Baby, get lost / I only know / Fast movin' mama / It isn't fair / Big deal / I'll never be free / I wanna be loved / Harbour lights / Time out for tears / Please send me someone to love / My heart cries for you / I apologize / I won't cry anymore / Cold cold heart / New blowtop blues / Wheel of fortune / Tell me why / Trouble in mind / When the sun goes down / Double dealing daddy / Half as much / I cried for you / Fat daddy / TV is the thing / Am I blue / I let a song go out of my heart / Blue skies / Dream / I don't hurt anymore / Soft winds / If it's the last thing I do / I've got you under my skin / Darn that dream / Teach me tonight / That's all I want from you / I concentrate on you / I could write a book / Make the man love me / Blue gardenia / Easy livin' / You might have told me / I'm lost without you tonight / Make me a present of you / Smoke gets in your eyes / Look to the rainbow / If I were a bell / Is you is or is you ain't my baby / Every time we say goodbye / I'll close my eyes / I've got a feelin' I'm fallin' / Keeping out of mischief now / It ain't nobody's business if I do / Backwater blues / What a difference a day made / Cry me a river / It could happen to you / Unforgettable / Baby (you've got what it takes): *Washington, Dinah & Brook Benton* / This bitter Earth: *Washington, Dinah & Brook Benton* / Love walked in: *Washington, Dinah & Brook Benton* / Rockin' good way (to mess around and fall in love): *Washington, Dinah & Brook Benton* / We have love: *Washington, Dinah & Brook Benton* / Early every morning (early every evening too) / Stardust / September in the rain / Our love is here to stay / Tears and laughter / Mad about the boy
CDDIG 20 / Nov '96 / Charly

☐ SLICK CHICK (ON THE MELLOW SIDE), A
Evil gal blues / I know how to do it / Salty Papa blues / Homeward bound / Blow top blues / Wise woman blues / Walking blues / No voot no boot / Chewin' Mama blues / My lovin' papa / Rich man's blues / All or nothing / Beggin' Mama blues / Mellow Mama blues / My voot is really vout / Blues for a day / Pacific coast blues / Embraceable you / I can't get started / When a woman loves a man / Oo-wee walkie talkie / Man I love / You didn't want me then / Slick chick (on the mellow side) / Postman blues
IGOCD 2073 / Sep '97 / Indigo

☐ TEACH ME TONIGHT
I've got you under my skin / Teach me tonight / I could write a book / Easy living / Make me a present of you / If I were a bell / Keeping out of mischief now / Back water blues / All of me / What a difference a day makes / Manhattan / I remember clifford / September in the rain / Salty papa blues / Trust in me / Time out for tears / Mad about the boy / Mixed emotions
JHR 73565 / Oct '92 / Jazz Hour

☐ TWO ON ONE: DINAH WASHINGTON & SARAH VAUGHAN (Washington, Dinah & Sarah Vaughan)
What a difference a day makes / Mad about the boy / September in the rain / Smoke gets in your eyes / Our love is here to stay / Dream / Such a night / I concentrate on you / Manhattan / Love walked in / More I see you / I'll be seeing you / What kind of fool am I / Stormy weather / My favourite things / As long as he needs me / East of the sun (and west of the moon) / Lover man / Time after time / September song
CDTT 4 / Apr '94 / Charly

☐ ULTIMATE DIVAS
5390532 / 10 Nov '97 / Verve

☐ UNFORGETTABLE
This bitter Earth / I understand / This love of mine / Alone / Somewhere along the line / Song is ended (but the melody lingers on) / Everybody loves somebody / Ask a woman who knows / Man who only does (what a woman makes him do) / Bad case of the blues / When I fall in love / Unforgettable / Lingering / Do you want it that way / Congratulations to someone / I'm in Heaven tonight / Our love is here to stay / Surprise party
5106022 / Apr '93 / Mercury

☐ WHAT A DIFFERENCE A DAY MAKES
I remember you / I thought about you / That's all there is to that / I'm through with love / Cry me a river / What a difference a day makes / Nothing in the world (could make me love you more than I do) / Manhattan / Time after time / It's magic / Sunday kind of love / I won't cry anymore
8188152 / Oct '84 / Mercury

☐ WHAT A DIFFERENCE A DAY MAKES
September in the rain / Dream / Such a night / Tell me why / I concentrate on you / Mad about the boy / Trust in me / Manhatten / What a difference a day makes / Harbour lights / I won't cry anymore / Soft winds / Our love is here to stay / That's all I want from you / If it's the last thing I do / Smoke gets in your eyes
308852 / 11 May '98 / Hallmark

Washington, Ernestine

☐ SISTER ERNESTINE WASHINGTON 1943-1948
DOCD 5462 / Jun '96 / Document

Washington, Geno

☐ GENO
I can't turn you loose / You left the water running / In the midnight hour / Gimme a little sign/Raise your hand/I get so excited / Knock on wood / Dirty, dirty / Bring it to me baby / Alison please / I can't let you go / Michael the lover / Hold on I'm comin' / Don't fight it / Land of 1000 dances / You don't know (like I know) / Tell it like it is / Put out the fire / All I need / Water / Whatever will be will be (Que sera sera) / Hi hi Hazel
5507692 / Mar '95 / Spectrum

☐ HAND CLAPPIN' FOOT STOMPIN' FUNKY BUTT...LIVE (Hipsters, Flipsters, Finger-poppin' Daddies) (Washington, Geno & The Ram Jam Band)
Philly dog / Up tight (everything's alright) / Hold on I'm comin' / Land of 1000 dances / Willy nilly / Michael / You don't know (like I know) / Day tripper / You left the water running / Hi-heel sneakers / Raise your hand / Things get better / She shot a hole in my soul / Ride your pony / Roadrunner / Don't fight it / Respect / Get down with it / Whatever will be will be (Que sera sera) / Herk's works / I can't turn you loose / In the midnight hour / Shotgun / Who's foolin' who / It's a wonder / Wild thing
C5CD 581 / Oct '96 / See For Miles

☐ HAND CLAPPIN'-FOOT STOMPIN'-FUNKY BUTT-LIVE (Washington, Geno & The Ram Jam Band)
Philly dog / Ride your pony / Up tight / Roadrunner / Hold on / Don't fight it / Land of 1000 dances / Respect / Willy nilly / Get down with it / Michael / Whatever will be will be (Que sera sera) / You don't know
REP 4189 / Aug '91 / Repertoire

☐ HIPSTERS, FLIPSTERS AND FINGER POPPIN' DADDIES
REP 4190 / Aug '91 / Repertoire

☐ WHAT'S IN THE POT
GENOCD 01 / 23 Mar '98 / Quantum Leap

Washington, Glen

☐ BROTHER TO BROTHER
SOCD 7789 / Mar '98 / Studio One

Washington, Grover Jr.

☐ ALL MY TOMORROWS
E preciso perdoar (one must forgive) / When I fall in love / I'm glad there is you / Happenstance / All my tomorrows / Nature boy / Please send me someone to love / Overjoyed / Flamingo / For heaven's sake / Estate (ess-tah-tay) (in summer)
4745532 / Jan '95 / Sony Jazz

☐ ANTHOLOGY VOL.1
Best is yet to come / East River drive / Be mine tonight / Can you dig it / In the name of love / Just the two of us / Jamming / Little black samba / Jetstream / Let it flow
9604152 / '89 / Elektra

☐ BEST OF GROVER WASHINGTON, THE (2CD Set)
I loves you Porgy / Where is the love / Inner city blues (make me wanna holler) / Georgia on my mind / Trouble man / Mercy mercy me (the ecology) / Ain't no sunshine/theme from man and boy / Lean on me / Lover man / Body and soul / No tears, in the end / Until it's time for you to go / Aubrey / All the king's horses / Reed seed (trio tune) / Black frost / Mister magic / Dolphin dance / Easy loving you / Juffure / Bright moments / Snake eyes / Santa cruzin' / It feels so good
5306202 / Jul '96 / Motown

☐ BREATH OF HEAVEN
Have yourself a merry little christmas / Breath of heaven / Love is in his infant eyes / Away in the manger / I wonder as I wander / Christmas time is here / Child is born / Jesu / Christmas song / Christmas waltz / Christmas day chant / Breath of heaven
CK 68527 / 3 Nov '97 / Sony Jazz

☐ COME MORNING
East River drive / Come morning / Be mine tonight / Reaching out / Jamming / Little black samba / Making love to you / I'm all yours
252337 / Apr '84 / Elektra

☐ INSIDE MOVES
Inside moves / Dawn song / Watching you watching me / Secret sounds / Jetstream / When I look at you / Sassy stew
7559603182 / Oct '94 / Elektra

☐ MISTER MAGIC
Earth tones / Passion flower / Mr. Magic / Black frost
5301032 / Jan '93 / Motown

☐ NEXT EXIT
Take five / Your love / Only for you (siempre para d'sers) / Greene street / Next exit / I miss home / Love like this / Summer chill / Till you return to me / Get on up / Check out Grover
4690882 / Jul '92 / Columbia

☐ SOULFUL STRUT
Soulful strut / Can you stop the rain / Play that groove for me / Bordertown / I can count the times / Village groove / Headman's haunt / Poacher man / Mystical force / Uptown
4851422 / Oct '96 / Sony Jazz

☐ THEN AND NOW
Blues for DP / Just enough / French connections / Something borrowed, something blue / Lullaby for Shana Bly / In a sentimental mood / Stella by starlight
CK 44256 / Aug '97 / Sony Jazz

☐ WINELIGHT
Winelight / Let it flow / In the name of love / Take me there / Just the two of us / Make me a memory
252262 / Nov '83 / Asylum

Washington, Isidore 'Tuts'

☐ NEW ORLEANS PIANO (The Larry Borenstein Collection Vol.3)
On the sunny side of the street / Muskrat ramble / Fast blues no.1 / Blue moon / Basin Street blues / Some of these days / Yancey special no.1 / After you've gone / Early one morning / Cow cow blues / Pinetop's boogie / Trouble trouble / Tack head blues / Yancey special no.2 / (Back home again in) Indiana / St. Louis blues
504CD 32 / Mar '98 / 504

☐ NEW ORLEANS PIANO PROFESSOR
ROUCD 11501 / '88 / Rounder

Washington, Keith

☐ YOU MAKE IT EASY
Let me make love to you / Stay in my corner / Don't leave me in the dark / You always gotta go / What it takes / We need to talk/Before I let go / Trippin' / Do what you like / Believe that / No one / You make it easy
9362453362 / Sep '93 / Warner Bros.

Washington, Peter

☐ WHAT'S NEW
DIW 605 / Jun '91 / DIW

Washington, Salim

☐ LOVE IN EXILE
Love in exile / Blossom / To know Yahweh / Time for living / Ask me now / Blessing from Oshun / Whispered fade / Sound pronounced / Where did you go / Chaos in America
AC 5028 / Jun '98 / Accurate

Washington, Toni Lynn

☐ BLUES AT MIDNIGHT
CDTC 1152 / Apr '95 / Tonecool

☐ IT'S MY TURN NOW
Just around the corner / You gotta know / It's my turn now / Ain't gonna cry no more / Paycheck in my pocket / Who will the next fool be / I'm leaving you / You can stay but the noise must go / It's too late / TeardrTeardrops from my eyes / Young men go wild / Down the drain / I don't need no doctor / Sugar in my bowl
CDTC 1163 / Nov '97 / Tonecool

Washington, Walter

☐ BEST OF NEW ORLEANS RHYTHM & BLUES VOL.2 (Washington, Walter 'Wolfman')
MG 9008 / Feb '95 / Mardi Gras

☐ FUNK IS IN THE HOUSE (Washington, Walter 'Wolfman')
Trials and tribulations / Funkyard / I stand accused / Mary Ann / Please come back to me / Wolf funk / When the answer is clear / Close the door / Big easy / I'm in love / Funk is in the house / Counsin Joe
CDBB 9599 / May '98 / Bullseye Blues

☐ GET ON UP (Charly Blues Masterworks Vol.9) (Washington, Walter 'Wolfman')
It's raining in my life / Good and juicy / Girl, don't ever leave me / Nobody's fault but mine / Honky tonk / Get on up (The Wolfman's song) / You got me worried / Sure enough it's you / Lovely day
CD BM 9 / Apr '92 / Charly

☐ OUT OF THE DARK (Washington, Walter 'Wolfman')
You can stay but the noise must go / On the prowl / Steal away / Out of the dark / Ain't that lovin' you / Feel so bad / Nobody's fault but mine / Save your love for me
ROUCD 2068 / '88 / Rounder

☐ WOLF TRACKS (Washington, Walter 'Wolfman')
I'm tiptoeing through / Thinking for yourself / Are you the lady / Sweet cakes / It was fun while it lasted / You got me worried / One way or another / Can I change my mind / Without you
ROUCD 2048 / '88 / Rounder

WASP

☐ CRIMSON IDOL (2CD Set)
SMDCD 145 / 1 Jun '98 / Snapper

☐ CRIMSON IDOL, THE
Titanic overture / Invisible boy / Arena of pleasure / Chainsaw Charlie / Gypsy meets the boy / Dr. Rockter / I am one / Idol / Hold on to my heart / Great misconception of me
SMMCD 507 / 2 Mar '98 / Snapper

☐ HEADLESS CHILDREN, THE
Heretic (the lost child) / Real me / Headless children / Thunderhead / Mean man / Neutron bomber / Mephisto waltz / Forever free / Maneater / Rebel in the FDG
CDEST 2087 / Jul '94 / Capitol
SMMCD 509 / 20 Apr '98 / Snapper

☐ INSIDE THE ELECTRIC CIRCUS
Big welcome / I don't need no doctor / 95 nasty / Shoot from the hip / I'm alive / Easy livin' / Sweet cheetah / Mantronic / King of Sodom and Gomorrah / Rock rolls on / Restless gypsy
CDEST 2025 / Jul '94 / Capitol
SMMCD 505 / 23 Feb '98 / Snapper

☐ KFD
Kill fuck die / Take the addiction / My tortured eyes / Killahead / Kill your pretty face / Foetus / Little death / U / Wicked death / Horror
RAWCD 114 / Apr '97 / Raw Power

☐ LAST COMMAND, THE
Wild child / Ballcrusher / Fistful of diamonds / Jack action / Widowmaker / Blind in Texas / Cries in the night / Last command / Running wild in the streets / Sex drive / Savage / Mississippi queen / Animal fuck like a beast / Helion / Love machine / On your knees / I want to be somebody
SMMCD 502 / 29 Sep '97 / Snapper

☐ LIVE IN THE RAW
Inside the electric circus / I don't need no doctor / LOVE machine / Wild child / 95 nasty / Sleeping (in the fire) / Manimal / I wanna be somebody / Harder faster / Blind in Texas / Scream until you like it
CDEST 2040 / Jul '94 / Capitol
SMDCD 506 / 1 Jun '98 / Snapper

☐ STILL NOT BLACK ENOUGH
RAWCD 103 / Apr '96 / Raw Power

☐ WASP
I wanna be somebody / LOVE machine / Flame / BAD / School daze / Hellion / Sleeping (in the fire) / On your knees / Tormentor / Torture never stops / Animal (fuck like a beast) / Show no mercy / Paint it black
SMMCD 501 / 29 Sep '97 / Snapper

Wasserman, Rob

☐ SOLO
Thirteen / Lima twist / Sunway / Punk sizzle / Clare / Lady be good / Strumming / Bass blue / Bass space / April aire / Freedom bass dance / Ode to casals / Sara's rainbow song
ROUCD 0179 / Apr '94 / Rounder

Wassy, Brice

☐ SHRINE DANCE
Footprints / Shrine dance / Frenet / Ta kish / Mevum for King Nfaleu / BMF / Ku jazz / Mr. BW / All blues / Danzi
BW 089 / 30 Jul '98 / Melt 2000

Wasteland

☐ DAYS OF THE APOCALYPSE
WASTE 003CD / Jun '95 / Nightbreed

Watanabe, Kazumi

☐ KILOWATT
100 mega / Capri / No one / Jive / Papyrus / Sunspin / Pretty soon / Bernard / Dolphin dance / Goodnight machines
794 152 / Mar '90 / Gramavision

☐ MOBO 2
Voyage / Yatokesa / Alicia / Shang hi / All beets are coming
GRCD 8406 / May '85 / Gramavision

☐ MOBO CLUB
1885062 / May '89 / Gaia

☐ MOBO SPLASH
1886022 / May '89 / Gaia

☐ PANDORA
Pandora / Peaking doll / Vega / Ashita tenki ni / Passy home / Dr. Manmbo X. / Firecracker / Kumpoo manman / Arahi no yoru kimi ni tsugu / Django 1953 / Winter swallow / Satisfaction / We got lost / Memories of Phonecia / Lady Jane / I mean you / Angie / Slippin' into the river / Continental drift
R2 79473 / Nov '92 / Gramavision

☐ SPICE OF LIFE TOO
Andre / Fu bu ki / Small wonder / Kaimon / We planet / Rain / Concrete cows / Men and angels
1888102 / Dec '88 / Gramavision

Watanabe, Sadao

☐ CALIFORNIA SHOWER
California shower / Duo-creatics / Desert ride / Seventh high / Turning pages of wind / Ngoma party / My country
JMI 20122 / Apr '94 / JVC

☐ IN TEMPO
5272212 / Feb '95 / PolyGram Jazz

☐ MORNING ISLAND
Morning island / Down south / Serenade / We are the one / Home meeting / Peter Vbalse pour sadao / Samba Do Marcos / Inner embrace
JMI 20132 / Aug '96 / JVC

Watchman

☐ PEACEFUL ARTILLERY
INTREPID 4202 / Nov '95 / Intrepid

Watchtower

☐ ENERGETIC DISASSEMBLY
RTD 3970002CD / 1 Dec '97 / Institute Of Art

Water Wheel

☐ PANCHROMA
AS 019CD / Mar '97 / Alley Sweeper

Waterboys

☐ DREAM HARDER
New life / Glastonbury song / Preparing to fly / Return of Pan / Corn circles / Suffer / Winter winter / Love and death / Spiritual city / Wonders of Lewis / Return of Jimi Hendrix / Good news
GFLD 19318 / Jul '96 / Geffen

☐ FISHERMAN'S BLUES
Fisherman's blues / Strange boat / Sweet thing / Has anybody seen Hank / When ye go away / We will not be lovers / World party / A bang on the ear / When will we be married / Stolen child
CCD 1589 / Oct '88 / Chrysalis

☐ PAGAN PLACE, A
Church not made with hands / All the things she gave me / Thrill is gone / Rags / Somebody might wave back / Big music / Red army blues / Pagan place
CCD 1542 / Jul '94 / Ensign

☐ ROOM TO ROAM
In search of a rose / Song from the end of the world / Man is in love / Kaliope House / Bigger picture / Natural bridge blues / Something that is gone / Star and the sea / Life of Sundays / Island man / Raggle taggle gipsies / How long will I love you / Upon the wind and waves / Spring comes to Spiddal / Trip to Broadford / Further up, further in / Room to roam
CCD 1768 / Sep '90 / Ensign

☐ SECRET LIFE OF THE WATERBOYS 1981-1985, THE
Medicine bow / That was the river / Pagan place / Billy Sparks / Savage earth heart / Don't bang the drum / Ways of men / Rags (Second amendment) / Earth only endures / Somebody might wave back / Going to Paris / Three day man / Bury my heart / Out of control / Love that kills
CDCHEN 35 / Sep '97 / Ensign

Watercress

☐ TRIPPED UP
Tripped up
WCHCD 003 / Jan '97 / Creeping Herb

Waterfall

☐ FLIGHT OF THE DAY, THE
ENG 1019CD / 10 Nov '97 / English Garden

Waterlillies

☐ ENVOLUPTUOUSITY
Sunshine like you / Hip to my way / Lie with you / Tired of you / Only one (I could stand) / Girl's affair / Nether nether / Day and age / Mermaid song
7599267292 / Oct '92 / Sire

☐ TEMPTED
Tempted / I wanna be there / Never get enough / Free / I don't want your love / Nolion doll / Take my breath away / Supersonic / She must be in love / How does it feel / Work it out / Close to you
9362455392 / Aug '94 / Warner Bros.

Waterman, Steve

☐ DESTINATION UNKNOWN
Changing places (prelude) / Mute retrieval / Long forgotten dreams / Ella's waltz / Changing places / Song for Annie / Changing places (interlude) / Reservations / Destination unkown / Changing places (epilogue)
ASCCD 4 / Oct '95 / ASC

Waters, Benny

☐ (SMALL'S) TO SHANGRI-LA
MCD 5340 / Sep '92 / Muse

☐ BENNY WATERS & BILL COLEMAN (Live in Paris 1972/1979) (Waters, Benny & Bill Coleman)
Calling the cats / Mini-minor / Silver case baby / Hot feet / My jungle baby / Butterfly valley / Pat it (but don't you take) / Poping the blues / Satin doll / On green dolphin street / Do you know what it means to miss New Orleans / S'wonderful
17153 / Sep '97 / Laserlight

☐ HURRY ON DOWN
STCD 8264 / May '97 / Storyville

☐ PLAYS SONGS OF LOVE
CDJP 1039 / May '94 / Jazz Point

☐ SWINGING AGAIN (Waters, Benny Quartet)
CDJP 1037 / Jan '94 / Jazz Point

☐ TAKE IT HOME
BMSTRCD 001 / Jun '94 / Blues Master

Waters, Crystal

☐ CRYSTAL WATERS
Momma told me / Love I found / On my mind / Uptown / Say if you feel alright / Easy / Female intuition / Let go my love / Just a freak / Body music / You spin me round / Passion / Who taught you how
5362902 / Aug '97 / Manifesto

☐ STORYTELLER
100% pure love / Ghetto day / Regardless / I believe I love you / Relax / What I need / Storyteller / Is it for me / Listen for my beep / Daddy do / Lover lay low / Piece of lonely
5223372 / Nov '95 / Manifesto

Waters, Ethel

☐ CABIN IN THE SKY
239772 / Mar '95 / Milan

☐ CLASSICS 1921-1923
CLASSICS 796 / Mar '95 / Classics

☐ CLASSICS 1923-1925
CLASSICS 775 / Feb '95 / Classics

☐ CLASSICS 1925-1926
CLASSICS 672 / Nov '92 / Classics

☐ CLASSICS 1929-1931
CLASSICS 721 / Dec '93 / Classics

☐ CLASSICS 1931-1934
CLASSICS 735 / Feb '94 / Classics

☐ CLASSICS 1935-1940
CLASSICS 755 / Aug '94 / Classics

☐ INTRODUCTION TO ETHEL WATERS 1921-1940, AN
4013 / Mar '95 / Best Of Jazz

Waters, Kim

☐ LOVE'S MELODY
Nightfall / Sunny / Possession / Easy going / Water's edge / Love's melody / Midnight at the oasis / 95 north / Two hearts of mine / Wonderama / Let's do this
SHANCD 5042 / May '98 / Shanachie

☐ SWEET 'N' SAXY/SAX APPEAL
FMJXD 188 / Dec '92 / FM Jazz

Waters, Muddy

☐ AUDIO ARCHIVE
Stuff you gotta watch / She's alright / Baby, please don't go / Iodine in my coffee / So glad I'm living / Sittin' here drinkin' / One more mile / Close to you / I can't call her sugar / Trainfare blues / You gonna miss me / You can't lose what you ain't never had / I got a rich man's woman / Mean red spider / Sad letter / Mean mistreater / I can't be satisfied / Diamonds at your feet / Rollin' stone / You gonna need my help
CDAA 034 / Jun '92 / Tring

☐ BABY PLEASE DON'T GO
IMP 305 / Apr '96 / IMP

☐ BEST OF MUDDY WATERS 1947-1955, THE
MCD 09370 / Jul '97 / Chess/MCA

☐ BLUES ANTHOLOGY
15719 / Jan '95 / Laserlight

☐ COMPLETE PLANTATION RECORDINGS, THE
Country blues / Interview 1 / I be's troubled / Interview 2 / Blur cover farm blues / Interview 3 / Ramblin' kid blues / Rosalie / Joe Turner / Pearlie May blues / Take a walk with me / Blu clover blues / Interview 4 / I be bound to write to you / You're gonna miss me when I'm gone / You got to take sick and / Why don't you live so God / Country blues / You're gonna miss me when I'm gone / 32-20
MCD 09344 / Apr '97 / Chess/MCA

☐ ELECTRIC MUD
I just want to make love to you / I'm your hoochie coochie man / Let's spend the night together / She's alright / Mannish boy / Herbert Harper's free press news / Tom cat / Same thing
MCD 09364 / Apr '97 / Chess/MCA

☐ ELECTRIC MUD AND MORE (Charly R&B Masters Vol.15)
I just want to make love to you / Hoochie coochie man / Let's spend the night together / She's alright / Herbert Harper's free press / Tom cat / Same thing / Mannish boy / Got my mojo working / I can't be satisfied / Rollin' stone
CDRB 15 / Mar '95 / Charly

☐ EP COLLECTION, THE (Waters, Muddy & Howlin' Wolf)
Howlin' for my baby: *Howlin' Wolf* / Tell me: *Howlin' Wolf* / Back door man: *Howlin' Wolf* / My country sugar Mama: *Howlin' Wolf* / Evil: *Howlin' Wolf* / Louise: *Howlin' Wolf* / You'll be mine: *Howlin' Wolf* / You gonna wreck my life: *Howlin' Wolf* / Going down slow: *Howlin' Wolf* / 300 pounds of joy: *Howlin' Wolf* / Spoonful: *Howlin' Wolf* / Smokestack lightnin': *Howlin' Wolf* / Louisiana blues: *Waters, Muddy* / Little brown bird: *Waters, Muddy* / I'm ready: *Waters, Muddy* / I just want to make love to you: *Waters, Muddy* / Messin' with the man: *Waters, Muddy* / Got my mojo working (Live): *Waters, Muddy* / Still a fool: *Waters, Muddy* / You need love: *Waters, Muddy* / She moves on: *Waters, Muddy* / I can't be satisfied: *Waters, Muddy* / Hoochie Coochie man: *Waters, Muddy* / Wee wee baby: *Waters, Muddy*
SEECD 379 / Oct '93 / See For Miles

☐ FATHER OF CHICAGO BLUES, THE
Sugar sweet / Twenty four hours / All abroad / Hoochie coochie man / I'm ready / Long distance call / I want you to love me / Honey bee / Gone to main street / She moves me / I can't call her sugar / I can't be satisfied / Rollin' stone / You gonna miss me / Baby, please don't go / Standing around crying / Got my mojo working / Still a fool / Louisiana blues / I just want to make love to you / You can't lose what you ain't never had / Blow wind blow / Forty days and forty night / Walkin' thru the park
CD 52001 / '92 / Blues Encore

☐ GOIN' HOME (Live in Paris 1970)
422405 / Jan '97 / Last Call

☐ GOIN' WAY BACK
Gypsy woman / Little Anna Mae / My home is on the delta / Take a little walk / Mean disposition / Laverne (why do you treat me so mean) / Leavin' in the mornin' / Got a sweet little girl / Bad lovin' trouble / Nothin' bother me / Crazy 'bout you
JAM 91302 / 23 Feb '98 / Just A Memory

☐ GOLD
GOLD 049 / Aug '96 / Gold

☐ GOODBYE NEWPORT BLUES
I got my brand on you / Hoochie coochie man / Baby, please don't go / Soon forgotten / Tiger in your tank / I feel so good / I've got my mojo working / I've got my mojo working / Goodbye Newport blues / Wee wee baby / Sittin' and thinkin' / Clouds in my heart / Nineteen years old / Long distance call / Same thing
CDBM 101 / May '93 / Blue Moon

☐ GOT MY MOJO WORKING
MACCD 193 / Aug '96 / Autograph

☐ HOOCHIE COOCHIE MAN
CDC 9050 / Jun '93 / LRC

☐ HOOCHIE COOCHIE MAN
Mannish boy / I'm ready / Champagne and reefer / I want to be loved / Baby, please don't go / Sad, sad day / I'm a king bee / Blues had a baby and they named it rock and roll / Screamin' and cryin' / I can't be satisfied / She's nineteen years old / Hoochie coochie man
4611862 / Aug '88 / Epic

☐ KING OF THE ELECTRIC BLUES
I'm a king bee / Champagne and reefer / Mean old 'frisco blues / Sad sad day / No escape from the blues / She's 19 years old / Nine below zero / Howling wolf / Baby please don't go / I'm your hoochie koochie man / Rock me / Good morning little school girl / I'm ready / Mannish boy / Blues had a baby and they named it rock and roll / I want to be loved / 33 years / Who do you trust
4878472 / 20 Oct '97 / Mojo Filter

☐ KINGS OF CHICAGO
CDDIG 9 / Feb '95 / Charly

☐ LIVE AT NEWPORT
BGOCD 314 / Jun '96 / Beat Goes On

☐ MANNISH BOY
BN 052 / Apr '98 / Blue Nite

☐ MISSISSIPPI ROLLIN' STONE
I can't call her sugar / You can't lose what you ain't never had / Sad letter / I can't be satisfied / Baby, please don't go / Walkin' thru the park / Train fare blues / Sittin' here drinkin' / I got a rich man's woman / Mean mistreater
CDBM 014 / Jul '89 / Blue Moon

☐ MUD IN YOUR EAR
Diggin' my potatoes / Watchdog / Sting it / Why d'you do me / Natural wig / Mud in your ear / Excuse me baby / Sad day uptown / Top of the boogaloo / Long distance call / Mini dress / Remember me / Snake / Comin' home baby / Blues for hippies / Chicken shack / Love u trouble / I'm so glad / Love without jealousy / Evil
600630 / Feb '91 / Muse

☐ MUDDY WATERS
Can't get no grindin' (What's the matter with the mill) / Trouble no more / Everything gonna be alright / Hoochie coochie man / Blues straight ahead / Rollin' and tumblin'
BSTCD 9104 / May '92 / Best Compact Discs

☐ MUDDY WATERS
Stuff you gotta watch / Iodine in my coffee / Close to you / You gonna miss me / Mean red spider / Diamonds at your feet / You gonna need my help / She's alright / So glad I'm living / One more mile / I can't call her sugar / You can't lose what you ain't never had / Sad letter / I can't be satisfied / Baby, please don't go / Walkin' through the park / Trainfare blues / Sittin' here drinkin' / I got a rich man's woman / Mean mistreater / Forty days and forty nights / Rollin' and tumblin' / All aboard / Rock me / Rollin' stone / I'm ready
GRF 025 / '93 / Tring

☐ MUDDY WATERS & HOWLIN' WOLF GOLD (2CD Set) (Waters, Muddy & Howlin' Wolf)
R2CD 4015 / 13 Apr '98 / Deja Vu

☐ MUDDY WATERS 1941-1946
DOCD 5146 / Mar '95 / Document

☐ MUDDY WATERS ANTHOLOGY (The Finest Recordings)
You shook me / I feel so good / Mannish boy / Rollin' stone / You need love / Stuff you gotta watch / Baby, please don't go / Still a fool / Evan's shuffle / Rollin' and tumblin' / Hoochie coochie man / She's into something / My home is in the Delta / I just want to make love to you / Gypsy woman / Elevate me mama / Got my mojo working / Twenty four hours / Honey Bee / Forty days and forty nights / I feel so go
PLATCD 3911 / May '91 / Platinum

☐ MUDDY WATERS BLUE BAND, THE
MCD 6004 / Sep '92 / Muse

☐ MUDDY WATERS BLUES BAND, THE (Waters, Muddy & Dizzy Gillespie)
Nicest blues / Harmonica rockin' / Down broke down / Baby rock and roll / So long / Kansas City / Luther's blues / Got my mojo working / Portnoy's blues / Hoochie coochie man / Baby please don't go / Key Little highway
17102 / Mar '97 / Laserlight

☐ MUDDY WATERS COLLECTOR'S EDITION
DVBC 9042 / Apr '95 / Deja Vu

☐ MUDDY WATERS IN CONCERT
Baby please don't go / Soon forgotten / Corrina, Corrina / Hoochie coochie man / Howlin' Wolf / Floyd's guitar blues / Blow wind blow / Caldonia / Screamin' and cryin' / I got my mojo working / Garbage man
CDSGP 0150 / Mar '95 / Prestige

☐ MUDDY WATERS SINGS BIG BILL/ FOLK SINGER
Tell me baby / Southbound train / When I get to thinking / Just a dream (on my mind) / Double trouble / I feel so good / I done got wise / Mopper's blues / Lonesome road blues / Hey hey / Cold weather blues / Big leg woman / Country boy / Feel like going home / My home is in the delta / Long distance / My captain / Good morning school girl / You gonna need my help
BGOCD 397 / 3 Aug '98 / Beat Goes On

☐ MY HOME IS IN THE DELTA
My home is in the delta / Country boy / Cold weather blues / Sad letter / Feel like going home / You don't have to go / County jail / Lonesome day / Deep down in my heart / Born lover / Smokestack lightnin' / Mean mistreater / Close to you / She's got it / Trouble no more / They call me muddy waters / Don't get no further / Rock me / Howling wolf / Crawlin' kingsnake
CD 52021 / Nov '92 / Blues Encore

☐ ONE MORE MILE
Hard days / Muddy jumps one / Burying ground / You gonna need help / Rollin' and tumblin' part 2 / Rollin' stone / Country boy / She's so pretty / Oh yeah / I don't know why / I want to be loved / I got to find my baby / Crawlin' kingsnake / Read way back / Tiger in you tank / EMeanest woman / I got my brand on you / Lonesome room blues / Messin' with the man / Five long years / You don't have to go / Elevate me mama / Thirteen highway / Early in the morning blues / One more mile / Come back baby (let's talk it over) / My dog can't bark / Roll me over baby / Trouble in mind / Trouble trouble / My pencil won't write no more / Cold up North / Streamline woman / Rock me / Standin' round cryin' / Hoochie coochie man / Baby please don't go / You can't lose what you ain't ever had / Feel like goin' home / Where's my woman been / Rollin' and tumblin'
MCD 09348 / Apr '97 / Chess/MCA

☐ PARIS 1972
PACD 5302 / Jul '97 / Pablo

☐ ROLLIN' STONE
Forty days and forty nights / Rollin' and tumblin' / All aboard / Rock me / Rollin' stone / I'm ready / Standing around crying / She moves me / I feel so good / Going home
CDBM 006 / Jan '89 / Blue Moon

☐ THEY CALL ME MUDDY WATERS
SUMCD 4173 / Jan '98 / Summit

☐ VERY BEST OF MUDDY WATERS, THE (& Roots Of the Blues No.2 Compilation/3CD Set)
Gypsy woman / I can't be satisfied / I feel like going home / You're gonna miss me / Rollin' and tumblin' (part 1) / Rollin' stone / Louisiana blues / Long distance call / Honey bee / She moves me / Still a fool / Stuff you gotta watch / Please baby don't go / Mad love / I'm your hoochie coochie man / I just want to make love to you / I'm ready / I want to be loved / Manish boy / Sugar sweet / Trouble no more / Forty days and forty nights / Don't go no further / I live the life I love / Got my mojo working / Close to you / You shook me / You need me / You need love / My love strikes light lightning / My john the conquer root / My dog can't bark / When the eagle flies / Let's spend the night together / I am the blues / Walkin' thru the park / Sugar sweet / Key to the highway / Who's gonna be your sweet man when I'm gone / Down main street / Let the good times roll / Kokomo blues / Nobody's dirty business / Pinetop's boogie woogie / Roll and tumble blues / I'm so glad / Black angel blues / When the sun goes down / Truckin' my blues away / You just as well let her go / I believe I'll dust my broom / Good morning, little school girl / That's alright baby / Nothin' in ramblin' / Catfish / Worried life blues / You got to take sick and die some of these days
VBCD 302 / Jul '95 / Charly

☐ YOU'RE GONNA MISS ME WHEN I'M DEAD AND GONE (Muddy Waters Tribute Band)
Trouble no more / Clouds in my heart / I don't know why / You can't lose what you never had (you can't spend what you / Don't go no further / Going to Main Street / Going down slow / Blow wind blow / Honey bee / Sugar sweet / Messin' with the man / Muddy's shuffle / Mean mistreater / Walking through the park
CD 83335 / Jul '96 / Telarc

Waters, Roger

☐ AMUSED TO DEATH
Ballad of Bill Hubbard / What God wants (pt 1) / Perfect sense / Bravery of being out of range / Late home tonight / Too much rope / What God wants (pt 2) / What God wants (pt 3) / Watching TV / Three wishes / It's a miracle / Amused to death
4687612 / Sep '92 / Columbia

☐ PROS AND CONS OF HITCH HIKING, THE
Apparently they were travelling abroad / Running shoes / Arabs with knives and West German skies / For the first time today (part 2) / Sexual revolution / Remains of our love / Go fishing / For the first time today (part 1) / Dunroamin' duncarin' dunlivin' / Pros and cons of hitch hiking / Every stranger's eyes / Moment of clarity
CDP 7460292 / May '84 / Harvest

☐ RADIO KAOS
Radio waves / Who needs information / Me or him / Powers that be / Sunset strip / Home / Four minutes / Tide is turning
CDKAOS 1 / Jun '87 / Harvest

☐ WALL, THE (Live In Berlin - 2CD Set) (Various Artists)
In the flesh: *Scorpions* / Thin ice: *Lemper, Ute* / Another brick in the wall pt 1: *Waters, Roger* / Happiest days of our lives: *Waters, Roger* / Another brick in the wall pt 2: *Lauper, Cyndi* / Mother: *O'Connor, Sinead* / Goodbye blue sky: *Mitchell, Joni* / Empty spaces: *Adams, Bryan* / What shall we do now: *Adams, Bryan* / One of my turns: *Waters, Roger* / Don't leave me now: *Waters, Roger* / Another brick in the wall pt 3: *Waters, Roger* / Goodbye cruel world: *Waters, Roger* / Hey you: *Carrack, Paul* / Is there anybody out there: *Waters, Roger* / Nobody home: *Waters, Roger* / Vera: *Waters, Roger* / Bring the boys back home: *Waters, Roger* / Comfortably numb: *Morrison, Van* / In the flesh: *Waters, Roger* / Run like hell: *Waters, Roger* / Waiting for the worms: *Waters, Roger* / Trial: *Waters, Roger/Marianne Faithfull/Thomas Dolby/Tim Curry* / Tide is turning: *Waters, Roger*
8466112 / Aug '90 / Mercury

Waterson, Lal

☐ ONCE IN A BLUE MOON (Waterson, Lal & Oliver Knight)
TSCD 478 / Feb '96 / Topic

Waterson, Norma

☐ COMMON TONGUE (Waterson, Norma & Martin/Eliza Carthy)
Rambleway/Valentine waltz / Cloudy banks / Rockabello / Lowlands of Holland / Medley / Meeting is a pleasure / Hares in the old plantation / Flash company / Maid lamenting / American stranger / French stroller / Polly's love / Stars in my crown
TSCD 488 / Mar '97 / Topic

☐ NORMA WATERSON
Black muddy river / St. Swithin's day / God loves a drunk / Birds will still be singing / There ain't no sweet man (who's worth the salt of my tears) / Rags and old iron / Pleasure and pain / Outside the wall / Anna Dixie / There is a fountain in Christ's blood / Hard times heart
HNCD 1393 / Sep '96 / Hannibal

☐ WATERSON:CARTHY (Waterson, Norma & Martin/Eliza Carthy)
TSCD 475 / Oct '94 / Topic

Watersons

☐ EARLY DAYS
TSCD 472 / Jul '94 / Topic

☐ FOR PENCE & SPICY ALE
Country life / Swarthfell rocks / Barney / Swinton May song / Bellman / Adieu adieu / Apple tree / Wassailing song / Sheep shearing / Three day millionaire / King Pharin / T stands for Thomas / Malpas wassail song / Chickens in the garden / Good old way
TSCD 462 / May '93 / Topic

☐ GREEN FIELDS
Stormy winds / Sedgefield fair / Fare thee well cold winter / Wensleydale lad / Young banker / While gamekeepers lie sleeping / Prickle holly bush / We'll all go a-hunting today / Unfortunate lass / Brisk lad / Hares in the old plantation / Rosebuds in June / Furze field / I went to the market / Three pretty maidens / Lincolnshire shepherd / Brave ploughboy
TSCD 500 / Jun '98 / Topic

Wates, Matt

☐ RELAXIN' AT THE CAT (Wates, Matt Sextet)
Long hot / East 34th Street / Stablemates / Relaxin' at The Cat / Rio summit / Arabesque / One for JG / Never will I marry / Weaver
ABCD 2 / Oct '96 / AB

☐ TWO (Wates, Matt Sextet)
Boat race / Blues from the royalty / Waltz for Frankie / Table for two / Serendipity / Jerusalem / Not forgotten / Way you look tonight
ABCD 5 / Oct '96 / AB

Watford, Michael

☐ MICHAEL WATFORD
Luv 4-2 / Love me tonight / First mistake / Holdin' on / Happy man / Interlude / So into you / Love to the world / Yesterday love / Michael's prayer
7567923232 / Jan '94 / East West

Watkins, Mitch

☐ HUMHEAD
DOS 7501 / Oct '95 / Dos

☐ STRINGS WITH WINGS
Zephyr / One lost love / Oh how we danced / May your sorrows pass / Map of the dark / Suspicion / October 7 / Cry / Wildest flame / Only one moment
8888142 / Nov '92 / Tiptoe

Watley, Jody

☐ FLOWER
Lovin' you so / Flower / Off the hook / Everything you do / Just one more time / If I'm not in love / Lifetime / No more tears / Never find a love / I don't want you back / Baby tonight / 16 / Off the hook
7567830872 / 30 Mar '98 / Atlantic

Watrous, Bill

☐ TIME FOR LOVE, A
Low life / Shadow of your smile / Time for love / Close enough for love / Emily / Where do you start / Shining sea / Zoot / Not really the blues
GNPD 2222 / Jun '95 / GNP Crescendo

Watson, Bobby

☐ ADVANCE
But not for me / Karita / Round midnight / You're lucky to me / ETA
ENJ 910752 / 27 Oct '97 / Enja

☐ BEATITUDES (Watson, Bobby & Curtis Lundy)
To see her face / Karita / Jewel / ETA / Minority / Orange blossom / Beatitudes / On the one / Karita / To see her face
ECD 22178 / Feb '97 / Evidence

☐ GUMBO
Unit seven / Point the finger / Luqman's dream / From east to west / Gumbo / Wheel within a wheel / Premonition
ECD 220782 / Feb '94 / Evidence

☐ JEWEL (Watson, Bobby Sextet)
To see her face / Orange blossom / Jewel / Karita / You're lucky to me / And then again
ECD 22043 / Mar '93 / Evidence

☐ URBAN RENEWAL
Lou B / Agaya / Hi-tech trap / If / Love/hate / Beattitudes / Here's to you babe / Back in the day / P D On Great Jones Street / Reachin' and searchin' / Welcome to my world
KOKO 1209 / Feb '96 / Kokopelli

☐ YEAR OF THE RABBIT, THE (A Tribute To The Music Of Johnny Hodges)
Jeep is jumpin' / Good Queen Bess / Things ain't what they used to be / Squatty roo / Blues for alto / Isfahan / Jeep's blues / Flower is a lovesome thing / Honey bunny / Daydream
ECD 222102 / 28 Apr '98 / Evidence

Watson, Chris

☐ OUTSIDE THE CIRCLE OF FIRE
TO 37 / 4 May '98 / Touch

☐ STEPPING INTO THE DARK
TO 27 / Jun '96 / Touch

Watson, Dale

☐ BLESSED OR DAMNED
HCD 8070 / May '96 / Hightone

☐ CHEATIN' HEART ATTACK
HCD 8061 / Jul '95 / Hightone

☐ I HATE THESE SONGS
HCD 8082 / May '97 / Hightone

Watson, Diz

☐ TONKY HONK
AM 91CD / May '96 / Amalthea

Watson, Doc

☐ DOC AND DAWG (Watson, Doc & David Grisman)
ACD 25 / Oct '97 / Acoustic Disc

☐ DOC WATSON
Nashville blues / Sitting on top of the world / Intoxicated rat / Country blues / Talk about suffering / Born about six thousand years ago / Black mountain rag / Little Omie Wise / Georgie Buck / Doc's guitar / Deep river blues / St. James' hospital / Tom Dooley
VMD 79152 / Oct '95 / Vanguard

☐ DOC WATSON FAMILY TRADITION, THE
ROUCD 0129 / Aug '95 / Rounder

☐ DOCABILLY
SHCD 3836 / May '95 / Sugar Hill

☐ DOWN SOUTH (Watson, Doc & Merle)
Solid gone / Bright sunny south / Slidin' delta / Coal miner's blues / Hesitation blues / What a friend we have in Jesus / Fifteen cents / Twin sisters / Hobo / Cotton eyed Joe / Hello stranger / Down south
SHCD 3742 / Mar '85 / Sugar Hill

☐ ELEMENTARY DOCTOR WATSON
SHCD 3812 / Jan '94 / Sugar Hill

☐ ELEMENTARY DOCTOR WATSON/ THEN AND NOW
COLCD 5839 / May '97 / Collectables

☐ GUITAR ALBUM, THE (Watson, Doc & Merle)
Sheeps in the meadow / Stoney fork / Talking to Casey / Liza / Oh lady be good / Black pine waltz / Guitar polka / Going to Chicago blues / Black mountain rag / Cotton row / John Henry / Worried blues / Twinkle twinkle / Take me out to the ball game / Gonna lay down my old guitar
FF 70301 / Nov '96 / Flying Fish

☐ HOME AGAIN
VMD 79239 / Oct '96 / Vanguard

☐ MEMORIES
SHCD 2204 / Apr '95 / Sugar Hill

☐ MY DEAR OLD SOUTHERN HOME
My dear old southern home / Ship that never returned / Your lone journey / My friend Jim / No telephone in heaven / Dream of the miner's child / Wreck of old no.9 / Grandfather's clock / Don't say goodbye if you love me / Sleep, baby, sleep / Signal light / That silver haired Daddy of mine / Life is like a river
SHCD 3795 / Jan '91 / Sugar Hill

☐ ON PRAYING GROUND
You must come in at the door / Precious Lord / On praying ground / I'll live on / Gathering buds / Beautiful golden somewhere / We'll work 'til Jesus comes / Ninety and nine / Farther along / Christmas lullaby / Did Christ o'er sinners weep / Uncloudy day
SHCD 3779 / Apr '90 / Sugar Hill

☐ ORIGINAL FOLKWAYS RECORDINGS 1960-1962 (Watson, Doc & Clarence Ashley)
SFWCD 40029 / Jun '94 / Smithsonian Folkways

☐ PICKIN' THE BLUES (Watson, Doc & Merle Watson)
Mississipppi heavy water blues / Sittin' hear pickin' the blues / Stormy weather / Windy and warm / St. Louis blues / Jailhouse blues / Freight train blues / Hobo Bill's last ride / Carroll county blues / Blue ridge mountain blues / I'm a stranger here / Honey babe blues
FF 352CD / Jul '92 / Flying Fish

☐ PORTRAIT
I'm worried now / Nobody knows but me / Leaving London / Stay in the middle of the road / Risin' sun blues / George Gudger's overalls / Tucker's barn / Storms on the ocean / Prayer bell of heaven / Tough luck man / My blue eyed Jane
SHCD 3759 / Jan '97 / Sugar Hill

☐ RED ROCKING CHAIR (Watson, Doc & Merle)
Sadie / Fisher's hornpipe / Devil's dream / Along the road / Smoke, smoke, smoke / Below freezing / California blues / John Hurt / Mole in the ground / Any old time / Red rocking chair / How long blues / Down yonder
FF 70252 / Nov '96 / Flying Fish

☐ REMEMBERING MERLE (Watson, Doc & Merle)
Frost morn / Nine pound hammer / Omie wise / Summertime / Frankie and Johnny / New river train / Honey babe blues / Black mountain rag / St. James infirmary / Southern lady / Honey please don't go / Mama don't allow / Nancy Rowland/Salt creek / Blue suede shoes / Miss the mississippi and you / Wayfaring stranger / Thoughts of never
DFGCD 8427 / Jun '96 / Dixie Frog
SHCD 3800 / Jan '97 / Sugar Hill

☐ RIDIN' THE MIDNIGHT TRAIN
I'm going back to the old home / Greenville high trestle / Highway of sorrow / Fill my way with love / We'll meet again sweetheart / Ridin' that midnight train / Stone's rag / Ramshackle shack / Midnight on the stormy deep / Blue baby eyes / What does the deep sea say / Let the church roll on / Sweet heaven when I die
SHCD 3752 / Dec '88 / Sugar Hill

☐ SONGS FOR LITTLE PICKERS
Talkin' guitar / Mole in the ground / Mama blues / Froggie went a-courtin' / Shady grove / Riddle song / Sing song kitty / John Henry / Sally Goodin / Crawdad song / Grass grew all around / Liza Jane / Tennessee stud
SHCD 3786 / Sep '90 / Sugar Hill

☐ SONGS FROM THE SOUTHERN MOUNTAINS (Watson, Doc & Family)
SHCD 3829 / Oct '94 / Sugar Hill

☐ SOUTHBOUND
Walk on boy / Blue railroad train / Sweet Georgia Brown / Alberta / Southbound / Windy and warm / Call of the road / Tennessee stud / That was the last thing on my mind / Little darling pal of mine / Nothing to it / Riddle song / Never no more blues / Nashville pickin'
VMD 79213 / Oct '95 / Vanguard

☐ THEN AND NOW/TWO DAYS IN NOVEMBER (Watson, Doc & Merle)
Bonaparte's retreat / Milkcow blues / Bottle of wine / Matchbox blues / Freight train boogie / If I needed you / Frankie and Johnnie / Summertime / That's all / Corrina Corrina / Meet me somewhere in your dreams / Old camp meetin' time / Rain crow Bill / Walk on boy / Poor boy blues / I'm going fishing / Kinfolks in Carolina / Last thing on my mind / Lonesome moan / Little beggar man / Old Joe Clark / Kaw-Liga / Three times seven / Train that carried my girl from town / Snow bird / Doc's rag
BGOCD 297 / Nov '95 / Beat Goes On
SHCD 2205 / Sep '96 / Sugar Hill

☐ TREASURES UNTOLD (Watson, Doc & Family)
Intro / Lights in the valley / Beaumont rag / I heard my mother weeping / Billy in the lowground / Omie wise / Rueben's train / Hick's farewell / Ramblin' hobo / White House blues / Jimmy Sutton / The old buck ram / I want him to love me more / Grandfather's clock / Chinese breakdown / Handsome Molly / Beaumont rag: *Watson, Doc & Clarence White* / Farewell blues: *Watson, Doc & Clarence White* / Lonesome road blues: *Watson, Doc & Clarence White* / Footprints in the snow: *Watson, Doc & Clarence White*
VCD 77001 / Jan '96 / Vanguard

☐ VANGUARD YEARS, THE (4CD Set)
Rambling hobo / Train that carried my girl from town / Coo coo / Reuben's train / Hick's farewell / Grandfather's clock / Beaumont rag / Farewell blues / Footprints in the snow / Intoxicated rat / Talk about suffering / Omie wise / Country blues / Black mountain rag / Doc's guitar / Deep river blues / Muskrat / Dream of the miner's child / Rising sun blues / Otto Wood the bandit / Little Sadie / Windy and warm / Tennessee stud / Blue railroad train / Down in the valley to pray / Dill pickle rag / FFV / Childhood play / Streamline cannonball / Old camp meeting time / I'm thinking tonight of my blue eyes / Girl in the blue velvet band / New river train / Rank stranger / Corrina Corrina / What does the deep sea say / There's more pretty girls than one / Way downtown / Brown's ferry blues / Spike driver blues / Roll on buddy / I am a pilgrim / Wabash cannonball / Roll in my sweet baby's arms / Lawson family murder / Cuckoo / Alabama bound / Bye bye bluebells / Kinfolks in Carolina / San Antonio Rose / Blow your whistle freight train / Cannonball rag / I am a pilgrim / Arrangement blues / I got a pig at home in the pen / My rough and rowdy ways / Deep river blues / Banks of the Ohio / A-roving on a Winter's night / Southbound / Memphis blues / Salt creek/Bill Cheatham / Brown's ferry blues / Windy and warm
VCD 4155 / Apr '96 / Vanguard

☐ WATSON COUNTRY (Watson, Doc & Merle)
FF 651CD / Aug '96 / Flying Fish

Watson, Eric

☐ BROADWAY BY TWILIGHT
500482 / May '94 / Musidisc

☐ MEMORY OF WATER, THE (Watson, Eric & John Lindberg)
LBLC 6535 / Jun '91 / Label Bleu

Watson Family

☐ WATSON FAMILY, THE
CDSF 40012 / Aug '94 / Smithsonian Folkways

Watson, Helen

☐ NOTES ON DESIRE
BUILD 001CD / Mar '96 / Building

☐ SOMERSAULT
Help you forget / Smoke signals / You'll never go away / Out of left field / Close to making sense / Ground floor flat / Value / Home before you know it / Flag / All weather girls / Kicking in my stall / Wasted on me / Lowish time
FLED 3013 / Nov '97 / Fledg'ling

Watson, Johnny 'Guitar'

☐ AIN'T THAT A BITCH
I need it / I want to ta ta you baby / Superman lover / Ain't that a bitch / Since I met you baby / We're no exception / Won't you forgive me baby
NEM 774 / Jan '96 / Sequel

☐ AND THE FAMILY CLONE
NEMCD 780 / Jun '96 / Sequel

☐ FUNK BEYOND THE CALL OF DUTY
Funk beyond the call of duty / It's all about the dollar bill / Give me my love / It's a damn shame / I'm gonna get you baby / Barn door / Love that will not die
NEM 776 / Jan '96 / Sequel

☐ GANGSTER OF LOVE
I got eyes / Motorhead baby / Gettin' drunk / Walkin' to my baby / Highway 60 / Space guitar / Sad fool / Half pint of whiskey / No I can't / Thinking / Broke and lonely / Cuttin' in / What you do to me / Those lonely, lonely nights / You can't take it with you / I just wants me some love / Gangster of love / Sweet lovin' mama
CDCHARLY 267 / Feb '91 / Charly

☐ GANGSTER OF LOVE
CCSCD 802 / Aug '95 / Castle

☐ GANGSTER OF LOVE
KCD 6004 / 17 Nov '97 / King

☐ GIANT
Miss Frisco (Queen of the disco) / Tu jours amour / Gangster of love / Guitar disco / Wrapped in black mink / You can stay but the noise must go / Baby face
NEMCD 777 / Feb '96 / Sequel

☐ HOT JUST LIKE TNT
Hot little Mama / I love to love you / Hot little Mama / Don't touch me (I'm gonna hit the highway) / Too tired / Lonely girl / Ain't gonna hush / These lonely, lonely nights / Oh baby / Someone cares for me / Ruben / Give a little / Love me baby / She moves me / Ruben / Three hours past midnight / Love bandit (gangster of love) / Telephone boogie / Dee's boogie / I got a girl (that lives over yonder) / Gangster of love / One room country shack / Deana baby / Honey / Come on baby / My baby and me / You've been gone too long / Come on baby
CDCHD 621 / Sep '96 / Ace

☐ LISTEN
If I had the power / You've got a hard head / Loving you / It's all about you / You're the sweetest thing I've ever had / I get a feeling / Like I'm not your man / You bring love / You stole my heart / I don't want to be a lone ranger / Your new love is a player / Tripping / Lonely man's prayer / You make my heart want to sing / It's way too late / Love is sweet misery / You can stay but the noise must go / Strong vibrations
CDCHD 408 / Sep '92 / Ace

☐ LOVE JONES
Booty ooty / Love Jones / Going up in smoke / Close encounters / Asante sana / Telephone bill / Lone Ranger / Jet plane / Children of the universe
NEMCD 779 / Feb '96 / Sequel

☐ REAL MOTHER FOR YA, A
Real Mother for you / Nothing left to be desired / Your love is my love / Real deal / Tarzan / I wanna thank you / Lover Jones
NEM 775 / Jan '96 / Sequel

☐ WHAT THE HELL IS THIS
Real mother for ya / Ain't that a bitch / Booty ooty / Mother In Law / Miss Frisco (queen of the disco) / I want to ta ta you baby / Your love is my love / It's all about the dollar bill / Lover Jones / What the hell is this / I need it / I don't want to be president / Wrapped in black mink / Strung out
NEMCD 778 / Feb '96 / Sequel

Watson, Junior

☐ LONG OVERDUE
Certainly all / Lonesome train / Biscuits / Frankie and johnny / Mojo boogie / That's what you do to me / Woodpecker / Want me some love / Big boy / Long time baby / Special lesson no.1 / Five long letters / Cool evening / I gotta go (back home) / Lump in my throat / Mule train / Don't leave me baby (the easy livin' plan)
BMCD 9021 / Apr '93 / Black Magic

Watson, Wayne

☐ WAY HOME, THE
There goes sundown / Here in this town / Wouldn't that be something / For such a time as this / Urgency / Growing / Long way home / Perception / What are you still doing here / Come home
7019972608 / Apr '98 / Word

Watt, Ben

☐ NORTH MARINE DRIVE
On Box Hill / Some things don't matter / Lucky one / Empty bottles / North Marine Drive / Waiting like mad / Thirst for knowledge / Long time no see / You're gonna make me lonesome when you go / Walter and John / Aquamarine / Slipping slowly / Another conversation with myself / Girl in winter
CDBRED 40 / Jun '87 / Cherry Red

Watters, Lu

☐ AIR SHOTS FROM THE DAWN CLUB 1941 (Yerba Buena Jazz Band)
MMRCCD 16 / Feb '98 / Merry Makers

☐ COMPLETE GOOD TIME JAZZ RECORDINGS, THE (4CD Set) (Watters, Lu & The Yerba Buena Jazz Band)
At a Georgia camp meeting / Irish black bottom / Original jelly roll blues / Smokey mokes / Maple leaf rag / Memphis blues / Black and white rag / Black and white rag / Muskrat ramble / High society / High society / Millenberg joys / Daddy do, Daddy do / Hot house rag / Muskrat ramble / Muskrat ramble / London cafe blues / Tiger rag / Fidgety feet / Fidgety feet / Come back sweet Papa / Sunset cafe stomp / Sunset cafe stomp / Terrible blues / Temptation rag / Riverside blues / Cake walkin' babies from home / Make me a pallet on the floor / Moose march / Jazzin' babies blues / Dippermouth blues / Fidgety feet / Kansas City stomp / Muskrat ramble / Trombone rag / Minstrels of Annie Street / Jazzin' babies blues / Easy winners / Ostrich walk / Pineapple rag / I'm goin' huntin' / Ain't gonna give nobody none o' this jelly roll / New Orleans blues / Original rag / Ory's creole trombone / Pastime rag / Canal Street blues / You can't shush Katie (the gabbiest girl in town) / Maple leaf rag / Annie Street rag / Big bear stomp / Antigua blues / Emperor Norton's hunch / Climax rage / Sage hen strut / Trombone strut / Down home rag / Harlem rag / Creole belles / Sunburst rag / That's a plenty / South / Chattanooga stomp / 1919 rag / Sunset cafe stomp / Copenhagen / Panama / Working man blues / Richard M Jones blues / Bienville blues / Triangle jazz blues / Weary blues / Friendless blues / That's a plenty / Original jelly roll blues / Muskrat ramble / Canal Street blues / Yerba buena strut / Oriental strut / Struttin' with some barbecue / Emperor Norton's hunch / Ory's creole trombone / Weary blues / Down home rag / Big bear stomp / Trombone rag / Annie Street rock / Get it right / Cake walkin' babies from home / Antigua blues / Pineapple rag / Beale Street blues / Chattanooga stomp / Jazzin' babies blues / Snake rag
4GTJCD 4409 / Nov '96 / Good Time Jazz

☐ DAWN CLUB FAVOURITES VOL.1 (Watters, Lu & The Yerba Buena Jazz Band)
Minstrels of annie street / Jazzin' babies blues / Easy winners / Ostrich walk / Pineapple rag / I'm goin' huntin' / I ain't gonna give nobody none of my jelly-roll / New orleans blues / Original rags / Ory's creole trombone / Pastime rag no. 5 / Canal street blues / You can't shush kaie (the gabbiest girl in town) / Maple leaf rag
GTCD 12001 / Nov '95 / Good Time Jazz

☐ HAMBONE KELLY (Watters, Lu & The Yerba Buena Jazz Band)
MMRCD 10 / Aug '95 / Merry Makers

☐ IN TOWN (Yerba Buena Celebration Jazz Band)
PKCD 094 / Apr '98 / PEK

☐ TOGETHER AGAIN (Watters, Lu & Turk Murphy)
MMRCD 8 / Mar '95 / Merry Makers

☐ YERBA BUENA JAZZ BAND VOL.12
BCD 97 / Mar '95 / GHB

Watts, Anne

☐ BOISTER
3036662 / 24 Apr '98 / Last Call

Watts, Bari

☐ SOULCATCHER
DSKCD 003 / 27 Oct '97 / Dark Skies

Watts, Charlie

☐ FROM ONE CHARLIE (Watts, Charlie Quintet)
UFO 002CD / May '91 / UFO Jazz

☐ LONG AGO & FAR AWAY
I've got a crush on you / Long ago and far away / More than you know / I should care / Good morning heartache / Someday you'll be sorry / I get along without you very well / What's new / Stairway to the stars / In the still of the night / All or nothing at all / I'm in the mood for love / Sentimental journey / Never let me go
VPBCD 36 / Jun '96 / Pointblank

Watts, Ernie

☐ ERNIE WATTS QUARTET, THE (Watts, Ernie Quartet)
Language of the heart / Continental blues / Echoes / My one and only love / On the border / Skylark / One in three / Body and soul
JVC 20052 / Nov '97 / JVC

☐ LONG ROAD HOME
Lover man / At the end of my rope / River of light / Nostalgia in Times Square / Bird's idea / Long road home / Goodbye pork pie hat / Willow weep for me / Moonlight and shadows
JVC 20592 / Oct '96 / JVC

☐ REACHING UP
Reaching up / Mr. Sums / I hear a rhapsody / Transparent sea / High road / Inward glance / You leave me breathless / Juice Lucy / Angels flight / Sweet solitude
JVC 20312 / Feb '94 / JVC

☐ TENOR TRIO (Watts, Ernie & Pete Christlieb/Rickey Woodard)
Blues up and down / Strollin' / Groovin' high / Love for sale / St. Thomas / Fried bananas / Here's to Alvy / Holy land / Moten swing / Eternal triangle / Little pony
JVC 90212 / Jul '97 / JVC

☐ UNITY
You say you care / In your own sweet way / Tricotism / Unity / Silver hollow / Some kind a blue / Don't look now / Joyous reunion / Lonely hearts / Sticky kisses / Soul eyes
JVC 20462 / Apr '95 / JVC

Watts, Jeff

☐ MEGAWATTS (Watts, Jeff 'Tain')
500552 / Aug '93 / Sunnyside

Watts, Noble

☐ RETURN OF THE THIN MAN
ALCD 4785 / May '93 / Alligator

Watts, Trevor

☐ MOIRE MUSIC (Watts, Trevor Moire Music)
Egugu / Ahoom mbram / Tetegramatan / Free flow / Tetegramatan reprise / Opening gambit / Otublohu / Bomsu / Hunter's song: Ibrumankuman / Rocky road to Dublin / Brekete takai / Southern memories / We are
5213512 / Feb '94 / ECM

☐ WIDER EMBRACE, A
ECM 1449 / May '94 / ECM

Waulk Elektrik

☐ HOUSE MUSIC
Brannvin / Miles / Vision / Eclipse / Futterat / Deer on the hill / Heltor / Cathal's cod / Been out with her / Lingerbay
WAULK 1 / 20 Apr '98 / Waulk Elektrik

☐ UPROOTED
West wind / Ud Nameh / Lendrick Hill / Green fingers / Uist / Breakout / Dreampad / Punch it / Stumpie / Madam Frederick's/Hunter's purse
DREXCD 102 / Apr '94 / Dangerous

Wave

☐ WAVE
EBCD 31 / Jan '95 / Eightball

Wax

☐ WAX FILES, THE
FLYCD 10 / Apr '97 / For Your Love

Wax Doctor

☐ SELECTED WORKS
RS 98095CD / 2 Mar '98 / R&S

Waxworth Industries

☐ ALIEN DISCO
WAX 100CD / Aug '94 / Abstract

Way, Anthony

☐ CHOIRBOY'S CHRISTMAS, THE
4550502 / Nov '96 / PolyGram TV

Way Out West

☐ WAY OUT WEST
Blue / Domination / Dancehall tornado / Questions never answered / Sequoia / Ajaere / Drive by / King of funk / Earth
74321501952 / 1 Sep '97 / De-Construction

Way We Live

☐ WAY WE LIVE, THE
REP 4204 / Aug '91 / Repertoire

Waybill, Fee

☐ DON'T BE SCARED BY THESE HANDS
I know you / Tall dark and harmless / Shut up and love me / Swing of things / Fools cry / Surprise yourself / I've seen this movie before / Dying of delight / What's wrong with that / Somewhere deep inside
WESTCD 11 / Nov '96 / West Coast

☐ READ MY LIPS
You're still laughing / Nobody's perfect / Who loves you baby / I don't even know your name (passion play) / Who said life would be pretty / Thrill of the kill / Saved my life / Caribbean sunsets / Star of the show / I could've been somebody
BGOCD 283 / Aug '95 / Beat Goes On

Waylander

☐ REAWAKENING PRIDE ONCE LOST
CM 77211CD / 13 Apr '98 / Century Media

Wayne, Chuck

☐ JAZZ GUITARIST, THE
Taking a chance on love / Sirod / Uncus / Stella by starlight / Prospecting / Tasty pudding / While my lady sleeps / Sidewalks of Cuba / Butterfingers / SS cool / Mary Ann / You brought a new kind of love
SV 0189 / May '98 / Savoy Jazz

☐ TASTY PUDDING (Wayne, Chuck & Brew Moore/Zoot Sims)
You brought a new kind of love to me / S S Cool / Mary Ann / Butterfingers / Taking a chance on love / Sirod / While my lady sleeps / Tasty pudding / Prospecting / Sidewalks of Cuba / Uncas / Stella by starlight
SV 0253 / Oct '97 / Savoy Jazz

Wayne, Jeff

☐ WAR OF THE WORLDS (Musical Version Of The War Of The Worlds)
Coming of the Martians / Eve of the war / Horsell Common and the heat ray / Artilleryman and the fighting machine / Forever autumn / Thunder child / Earth under the Martians / Red weed / Red weed / Spirit of man / Brave new world / Dead London / Epilogue (part 1) / Epilogue (part 2)
CD 96000 / Jul '86 / CBS

☐ WAR OF THE WORLDS (Highlights)
Eve of the war / Horsell Common and the heat ray / Forever autumn / Fighting machine / Thunderchild / Red weed / Spirit of man / Dead London / Brave new world
CDX 32356 / Feb '97 / Columbia
CD 32356 / 27 Jul '98 / Columbia

☐ WAR OF THE WORLDS (Coming Of The Martians/Earth Under The Martians/ 2CD Set)
Eve of the war / Horsell Common and the heat ray / Artillery man and the fighting machine / Forever Autumn / Thunder child / Red weed / Spirit of man / Red weed / Brave new world / Dead London / Epilogue / Epilogue / Spirit of man / Dark Autumn dub / Forever Autumn / Epilogue / Eve of the war / Epilogue #2/Eve of the war
CDX 96000 / Jun '96 / Sony Music

Wayne Wonder

☐ ALL ORIGINAL BOMBSHELL
PHRICD 27 / Jan '96 / Penthouse

☐ DON'T HAVE TO
PHCD 24 / Oct '93 / Penthouse

☐ WAYNE WONDER COLLECTION, THE
PICK 001CD / Jun '97 / Sprint Enterprise

Wayra, Pukaj

☐ BOLIVIA
LYRCD 7361 / '91 / Lyrichord

☐ MUSICA ANDINA
Condor pasa / Amorosa palomita / Tamalito / Wayra de los andes / Ya no puedo vivir / Wa ya yay / Amame / Leno verde / Silvanita / Wa ya yay / Ya no puedo vivir / Sin tl / Ya no puedo vivir
CD 12511 / Nov '92 / Music Of The World

Waysted

☐ GOOD, THE BAD AND THE WAYSTED, THE
Hang 'em high / Hi ho my baby / Heaven tonight / Manuel / Dead on your legs / Rolling out the pie / Land that's lost the love / Crazy about the stuff / Around and around / Won't get out alive / Price you pay / Rock steady / Hurt so good / Cinderella boys / Ball and chain
CDMFN 43 / Dec '92 / Music For Nations

☐ VICES
Love loaded / Sleazy / Night of the wolf / Toy with the passion / Can't take that love away / Hot love / All belongs to you / Somebody to love
ZCRCD 5 / 23 Mar '98 / Shadows

WC

☐ CURB SERVIN' (WC & The Maad Circle)
Intro / West up / Granny nuttin' up / One / Crazy break / Put on tha set / In a twist / Homesick / Feel me / Curb servin' / Stuckie mack / Taking ova / Kill a habit / Reality check / Creator
8286502 / Sep '95 / Payday

☐ SHADIEST ONE, THE
8289572 / 27 Apr '98 / London

Wckr Spgt

☐ EVERYBODY'S DEAD (OH NO)
SHR 95 / 20 Oct '97 / Shrimper

We

☐ AS IS
ASP 0971CD / 22 Jun '98 / Asphodel

☐ WOOFERWHEELS
VOW 063CD / 3 Aug '98 / Voices Of Wonder

We All Together

☐ WE ALL TOGETHER
HBG 122/8 / Apr '94 / Background
LZ 2422 / Jun '97 / Lazarus

We Are Going To Eat You

☐ EVERYWHEN
If I could / Heart in hand / This conspiracy / Each life a mystery / Glory / Ride upon the tide / Eye to eye / On a day like this / Just another one / Here always / If you believe / Her dreamworld
ABBCD 014 / Jan '90 / Big Cat

We Are The People

☐ MIRROR OF OUR MINDS (2CD Set)
SC 11056 / 1 Jun '98 / Sundazed

We The People

☐ DECLARATION OF INDEPENDENCE
EVA 842144 / Nov '94 / EVA

Weak Moments

☐ WEAK MOMENTS
BING 008 / Apr '97 / Ba Da Bing

Weakener

☐ WHAT DO YOU KNOW ABOUT IT
EFA 294712 / 24 Aug '98 / Word Sound Recordings

Weakerthans

☐ FALLOW
G7 003CD / 29 Jun '98 / G7 Welcoming Committee

Weather Girls

☐ DOUBLE TONS OF FUN
We're gonna party / Sweet thang / Can U feel it (dee ooh la la la) / We shall all be free / Sexy ghost / Still I'm free / Here goes my heart / Love somebody tonite / Happy, happy / I want to take you higher / Can't let you go / It's raining men
4509940182 / Mar '94 / WEA

Weather Prophets

☐ JUDGES, JURIES AND HORSEMEN
Always the light / Hollow heart / Poisons mind / Well done sonny / Born inbetween / Thursday seems a year ago / Bury them deep / You bring the miracles / Never been as good / Ostrich bed / Stepping lightly on the ancient path / Sleeping when the sun comes up / Joe shmo and the eskimo
CRECD 033 / May '94 / Creation

☐ TEMPERANCE HOTEL
Key to my love is green / Key to my love is green / Mayflower / Midnight mile / Why does the rain / Can't keep my mind off you / In my room / Odds and ends / Sleep / Chinese cadillac / Blue rooftop / I saw the light / Stepping lightly on the ancient path / Joe shmo and the eskimo / Hollow heart (live) / Chinese cadillac (live)
CRECD 50 / May '94 / Creation

☐ WEATHER PROPHETS LIVE
Why does the rain / Head over heels / Poison mind / Like frankie lymon / Worm in my brain / She comes from the rain / Mayflower / Your heartbeat breathes the life into me / Key to my love is green / Hollow heart / Almost prayed
CRECD 085 / May '94 / Creation

Weather Report

☐ 8.30 (2CD Set)
Black market / Scarlet woman / Teen town / Remark you made / Slang / In a silent way / Birdland / Thanks for the memory / Badia / Boogie woogie waltz medley / 8.30 / Brown Street / Orphan / Sightseeing
4769082 / Jan '95 / Sony Jazz

☐ BLACK MARKET
4682102 / Jan '95 / Sony Jazz

☐ DOMINO THEORY
Can it be done / D flat waltz / Peasant / Predator / Blue sound-note / Swamp cabbage / Domino theory
CD 25839 / Feb '84 / CBS

☐ HEAVY WEATHER
Birdland / Remark you made / Teen town / Harlequin / Rumba mama / Palladium / Juggler / Havona
4682092 / Jan '92 / Columbia
CK 65108 / 6 Oct '97 / Sony Jazz

☐ I SING THE BODY ELECTRIC
4682072 / Jan '95 / Sony Jazz

☐ LIVE IN TOKYO (2CD Set)
Medley / Vertical invader / Seventh arrow / TH / Doctor Honoris Causa / Surucucu / Lost / Early minor / Directions / Orange lady / Eurydice / Moors / Tears / Umbrellas
4892082 / 26 Jan '98 / Sony Jazz

☐ MR. GONE
Pursuit of the woman in the feathered hat / River people / Young and fine / Elders / Mr. Gone / Punk jazz / Pinocchio / And then
4682082 / Jan '95 / Sony Jazz

☐ MYSTERIOUS TRAVELLER
4718602 / Jan '95 / Sony Jazz

☐ NIGHT PASSAGE
Dream clock / Port of entry / Forlorn / Rockin' in rhythm / Fast city / Night passage / Three views of a secret / Madagascar
4682112 / Jan '95 / Sony Jazz

☐ SWEETNIGHTER
Boogie woogie waltz / Manolette / Adios / 125th Street congress / Will / Non-stop home
4851022 / Sep '96 / Sony Jazz

☐ TALE SPINNIN'
Man in the green shirt / Lusitanos / Between the thighs / Badia / Freezing fire / Five short stories
4769072 / Jan '95 / Sony Jazz

☐ THIS IS JAZZ
Birdland / Remark you made / Black market / Man in the green shirt / Young and fine / Teen town / Moors / Mysterious traveller / Orange lady
CK 64627 / May '96 / Sony Jazz

☐ THIS IS JAZZ (The Jaco Years)
Punk jazz / River people / Remark you made / Havona / Three views of a secret / Teen town / Speechless / Port of entry / Barbary coast / Slang
CK 65451 / 4 May '98 / Sony Jazz

☐ THIS IS THIS
This is this / Face the fire / I'll never forget you / Jungle stuff (part 1) / Man with the copper fingers / Consequently / Update / China blues
CD 57052 / Jan '95 / Sony Jazz

☐ WEATHER REPORT
Milky way / Umbrellas / Seventh arrow / Orange lady / Morning lake / Waterfall / Tears / Eurydice
4682122 / Jan '95 / Columbia

Weathersby, Carl

☐ DON'T LAY YOUR BLUES ON ME
Rock your town / Things the blues will make you do / Killing floor / Your love is everything / All your affection is gone / Don't lay your blues on me / Same thing / Poverty / Somebody help me / Fannie Mae
ECD 260752 / Apr '96 / Evidence

☐ LOOKING OUT OF MY WINDOW
If that ain't the blues / Feel so bad / Looking out of my window / Do you call that a buddy / Sweet music / Hipshakin' woman / Blues follow me around / Merry way / Whole story / Love shock / Feels like rain / Standing at the crossroads
ECD 26089 / 14 Oct '97 / Evidence

Weaver, Curley

☐ COMPLETE RECORDED WORKS 1933-35
DOCD 5111 / Nov '92 / Document

Weaver, Sylvester

☐ COMPLETE RECORDED WORKS VOL.1
DOCD 5112 / Nov '92 / Document

☐ COMPLETE RECORDED WORKS VOL.2
DOCD 5113 / Nov '92 / Document

Weavers

☐ ALMANAC
When the stars begin to fall / We're all dodgin' / Brother can you spare a dime / Jackhammer John / A walkin' and a talkin' / Rally round the flag / Fight on / Bill / Get along little doggies / True religion / Which are you side on / Bye bye bye
VMD 79100 / Oct '95 / Vanguard

☐ TOGETHER AGAIN
ROUCD 1681 / '88 / Rounder

☐ WASN'T THAT A TIME
HMNCD 012 / Jun '97 / Half Moon

Webb, Cassell

☐ HOUSE OF DREAMS
Cold wind at the sideshow / House of dreams / Do you believe / Waltz of the tennis players / Nightfall / Love will never let me down / Let me talk to you / Blue horizon / Saints and the blue-eyed girl / Further down the road
WOLCD 1025 / May '92 / China

Webb, Chick

☐ 'TAIN'T WHAT YOU DO, IT'S THE WAY THAT YOU DO IT (Webb, Chick & Ella Fitzgerald)
Strictly jive / If you can't sing it, you'll have to swing it (Mr. Paganini) / Gee boy you're swell / Liza / Moonlight and magnolias / Facts and figures / T'ain't what you do (it's the way that you do it) / Love you're just a laugh / Wacky dust / Midnight in Harlem / Dipsy doodle / Congo / Rusty hinge / I've got a guy / Down home rag / Tisket-a-tasket / Take another guess / Sweet Sue, just you / Rock it for me / Go Harlem / Holiday in Harlem / Azure
RAJCD 836 / Mar '97 / Empress

☐ CLASSICS 1929-1934
CLASSICS 502 / Apr '90 / Classics

☐ CLASSICS 1935-1938
CLASSICS 517 / Apr '90 / Classics

☐ INTRODUCTION TO CHICK WEBB 1929-1939, AN
4015 / Nov '94 / Best Of Jazz

☐ ON THE AIR 1939
TAX 37062 / Aug '94 / Tax

☐ QUINTESSENCE, THE (1929-1939/2CD Set) (Webb, Chick & Ella Fitzgerald)
FA 214 / Feb '96 / Fremeaux

☐ RHYTHM MAN 1931-1934 (Webb, Chick Orchestra)
Heebie jeebies / Blues in my heart / Soft and sweet / On the sunnyside of the street / At the Darktown strutter's ball / If dreams come true / Let's get together / I can't dance / Imagination / Why should I beg / Stompin' at the Savoy / Blue minor / True / Lonesome moments / If it ain't love / That rhythm man / On the sunnyside of the street / Lona / It's over because we're through / What a shuffle / Blue Lou
HEPCD 1023 / May '92 / Hep

Webb, Jimmy

☐ AND SOMEONE LEFT THE CAKE OUT IN THE RAIN (The Classic Songs Of Jimmy Webb) (Various Artists)
Up up and away: *Mann, Johnny Singers* / Wichita lineman: *Campbell, Glen* / Do what you gotta do: *Four Tops* / Still within the sound of my voice: *Ronstadt, Linda* / By the time I get to Phoenix: *Campbell, Glen* / Moon is a harsh mistress: *Collins, Judy* / It's a sin when you love somebody: *Cocker, Joe* / MacArthur Park: *Summer, Donna* / Someone is standin' outside: *Houston, Thelma* / Magic garden: *Springfield, Dusty* / All I know: *Garfunkel, Art* / Galveston: *Campbell, Glen* / Highwayman: *Highwaymen* / Didn't we: *Webb, Jimmy* / Where's the playground Susie: *Campbell, Glen* / If ships were made to sail: *Walker, Scott* / If this were the last song: *Medley, Bill* / MacArthur Park: *Harris, Richard*
5554302 / Feb '98 / Debutante

☐ ARCHIVE
PF Sloan / Love song / Three songs / Met her on a plane / All my love's laughter / One lady / If ships were made to sail / Galveston / Once in the morning / When can Brown begin / Piano / Highwayman / Christian no / Where the universes are / Moon is a harsh mistress / Feet in the sunshine / Lady fits her blue jeans / Just this one time / Crying in my sleep / Land's end/Asleep on the wind
9548320632 / Jun '93 / WEA

☐ SUSPENDING DISBELIEF
Too young to die / I don't know how to love you anymore / Elvis and me / It won't bring her back / Sandy cove / Friends to burn / What does a woman see in a man / Postcard from Paris / Just like always / Adios / I will arise
7559615062 / Oct '93 / WEA

☐ TEN EASY PIECES
Galveston / Highway man / Wichita lineman / Moon's a harsh mistress / By the time I get to Phoenix / If these walls could speak / Didn't we / Worst that could happen / All I know / MacArthur Park
8528262 / 27 Oct '97 / EMI

Webb, Natalie

☐ TAKE ME TO PARADISE
NATCD 1 / Jun '95 / Nation

Webb, Stan

☐ 40 BLUE FINGERS FRESHLY PACKED (Chicken Shack)
Letter / Lonesome whistle blues / When the train comes back / San-Ho-Zay / King of the world / See see baby / First time I met the blues / Webbed feet / You ain't no good / What you did last night
4773572 / Aug '94 / Columbia

☐ BLACK NIGHT
Management / So far so back / Don't want to see you anymore / Man of the road / Black night / High cost of living / Quick step / Dirty weekend / Mine all the time / Meeting on a hill / Sweet Delilah / Singer / Prisoner / Drinkng with redstone / Broken glass
IGOCD 2064 / Sep '97 / Indigo

☐ CHANGES (Webb, Stan & Chicken Shack)
These foolish things / Where you pushed or did you fall / Sweetest little thing / Will you dance with me / Don't you worry about a thing / I'd rather go blind / Have you seen my heart / Burning love / Poor boy
INAK 9008CD / Jul '97 / In Akustik

☐ COLLECTION, THE (Chicken Shack)
Letter / When the train comes back / Lonesome whistle blues / You ain't no good / Baby's got me crying / Right way is my way / Get like you used to be / Woman is blues / I wanna see my baby / Remmington ride / Mean ol' world / San-Ho-Zay / Way it is / Tears in the wind / Maudie / Some other time / Andalucian blues / Crazy about you baby / Close to me / I'd rather go blind
CCSCD 179 / Jan '94 / Castle

☐ FROM THE VAULTS (Chicken Shack)
Midnight hour / When the train comes back / Night life / It's OK with me baby / Tell me / Telling your fortune / Strange things happening / Side tracked / Lonesome whistle blues / Letter / Mean old world / Tired eyes / My mood / You've done lost your good thing now / Everyday I have the blues / Waiting for you / San ho zay / It'll be me / Hey hey hey hey
IGOXCD 508 / Jun '97 / Indigo

☐ IMAGINATION LADY (Chicken Shack)
Crying won't help you now / Daughter of the hillside / If I were a carpenter / Going down / Poor boy / Telling your fortune / Loser
IGOXCD 506 / May '97 / Indigo

☐ OK KEN (Chicken Shack)
Baby's got me crying / Right way is my way / Get like you used to be / Pony and trap / Tell me / Woman is the blues / I wanna see my baby / Remington ride / Fishing in your river / Mean ol' world / Sweet sixteen
4746082 / Mar '97 / Epic

☐ ON AIR (Chicken Shack)
Tired eyes / I'd rather go blind / Tears in the wind / Night is when it matters / Telling your fortune / You knew you did / Midnight hour / Hey baby / Things you put me through / Things you put me through / Get like you used to be / You done lost that good thing now / Look Ma I'm crying
SFRSCD 045 / 2 Mar '98 / Strange Fruit

☐ PLUCKING GOOD (Webb, Stan & Chicken Shack)
Reflections / Broken hearted melody / Look out / Talk about love / I'm not sorry / Crying again / For all your love / If only / Nothing I can do / Dr. Brown / Let me love you babe / Thrill has gone
INAK 9019CD / Jul '97 / In Akustik

☐ SIMPLY LIVE
848824 / Jan '90 / SPV

☐ STAN THE MAN LIVE
Going up, going down / Going up, going down / Love her with feeling / Look out / Lost the best friend I ever had / C.s. opera / Broken hearted melody / Poor boy / Oh well / Poor boy / Dr. brown / Reconsider baby
IGOCD 2053 / Nov '95 / Indigo

☐ STAN WEBB ARCHIVE
Going up going down / Hold on / Management / I'd rather go blind / Love her with a feeling / Drinking with Redbone / Every little bit of my heart / Sweet nuthin's / Man of the road / Evil / Webb's blues / Blues song / Every day I have the blues / Thrill has gone / Black night / Crying won't help you now / Loser / Broken glass
RMCD 230 / Apr '98 / Rialto

☐ WEBB'S BLUES (Webb, Stan & Chicken Shack)
IGOCD 2013 / Dec '94 / Indigo

Webber, Dave

☐ TOGETHER SOLO (Webber, Dave & Anni Fentiman)
DRGNCD 931 / Mar '94 / Dragon

Webber, Garth

☐ ON THE EDGE (Webber, Garth & Mark Ford)
CCD 11045 / Nov '94 / Crosscut

Weber, Eberhard

☐ CHORUS
Chorus, parts 1-7
8238442 / Oct '93 / ECM

☐ COLOURS OF CHLOE, THE
More colours / Colours of chloe / Evening with vincent van ritz / No motion picture
8333312 / Jul '88 / ECM

☐ FLUID RUSTLE
Quiet departures / Fluid rustle / A pale smile / Visible thoughts
8293812 / Oct '93 / ECM

☐ FOLLOWING MORNING, THE
T on a white horse / Moana I / Following morning / Moana II
8291162 / Jun '86 / ECM

☐ LATER THAT EVENING
8293822 / Oct '93 / ECM

☐ ORCHESTRA (Weber, Eberhard Orchestra)
Seven movements / Broken silence / Before dawn / Just a moment / Air / Ready out there / Too early to leave / One summer's evening (bass with keyboards) / A daydream / Trio / Epilogue
8373432 / Feb '89 / ECM

☐ PENDULUM
Bird out of a cage / Notes after an evening / Delirium / Children's song no.1 / Street scenes / Silent for a while / Pendulum / Unfinishsed self - portrait / Closing scene
5197072 / Oct '93 / ECM

☐ SILENT FEET (Weber, Eberhard Colours)
Seriously deep / Silent feet / Eyes that can see in the dark
8350172 / Sep '88 / ECM

☐ WORKS
Sand / Dark spell / More colours / Touch / Eyes that can see in the dark / Moana II
8254292 / Jun '89 / ECM

☐ YELLOW FIELDS
Touch / Sand glass / Yellow fields / Left lane
8432052 / May '91 / ECM

Webster, Ben

☐ AUTUMN LEAVES
152162 / Mar '94 / EPM

☐ BEN AND 'SWEETS' (Webster, Ben & Harry 'Sweets' Edison)
Better go / How long has this been going on / Kitty / My Romance / Did you call her today / Embraceable you
4606132 / Jan '95 / Sony Jazz

☐ BEN AND BUCK (Webster, Ben & Buck Clayton/Henri Chaix Quartet)
SKCD 2037 / Mar '97 / Sackville

☐ BEN AND BUCK ANTWERP 1967 (Webster, Ben & Buck Clayton)
STCD 8245 / Jan '97 / Storyville

☐ BEN AND THE BOYS
Teezol / Horn / Victory stride / Body and soul / Joshua / Talk to me / Concerto for Cozy / Nice and Cozy / Sleep / Memories of you / Linger awhile / Just a riff / Blues on the delta / Honeysuckle rose / I surrender dear / Blue skies / Kat's fur / Pick-up boys / My old flame / Sheik of Araby / Conversing in blue / Limehouse blues
PLCD 549 / Nov '96 / President

☐ BEN WEBSTER
Round horn / Moonglow / Satin doll / For Max / But not for me / For all we know / Sunday
BLCD 760141 / Apr '90 / Black Lion

☐ BEN WEBSTER MEETS DON BYAS (Webster, Ben & Don Byas)
Blues for Dottie Mae / Lullaby for Dottie Mae / Sundae / Perdido / When Ash meets Henry / Caravan
8279202 / Jun '86 / ECM

☐ BEN WEBSTER MEETS OSCAR PETERSON (Remastered) (Webster, Ben & Oscar Peterson)
5214482 / Oct '97 / Verve Master Edition

☐ BEN WEBSTER PLAYS BALLADS
71710141182 / 7 Apr '98 / Storyville

☐ BEN WEBSTER STORY 1937-1944
158612 / Oct '96 / Jazz Archives

☐ BIG BEN TIME (Webster, Ben Quartet)
Just a-sittin' and a-rockin': Webster, Ben / Exactly like you: Webster, Ben / How deep is the ocean: Webster, Ben / My one and only love: Webster, Ben / Honeysuckle rose: Webster, Ben / Jeep is jumpin': Webster, Ben / Where or when: Webster, Ben / Wrap your troubles in dreams (and dream your troubles away): Webster, Ben / Solitude: Webster, Ben / You forgot to remember: Webster, Ben
8144102 / Sep '84 / Philips

☐ DIFFERENT PATHS (Webster, Ben & Buck Clayton)
SKCD 22037 / Oct '94 / Sackville

☐ EVOLUTION
TPZ 1014 / Feb '95 / Topaz Jazz

☐ FOR THE GUV'NOR
I got it bad and that ain't good / Drop me off in Harlem / One for the guv'nor / Prelude to a kiss / In a sentimental mood / John Brown's body / Work song / Preacher / Straight no chaser / Rockin' in rhythm
LEJAZZCD 8 / Mar '93 / Le Jazz

☐ GONE WITH THE WIND
Perdido / Yesterday / I'm gonna sit right down and write myself a letter / Set call / That's all / Gone with the wind / Over the rainbow / (Back home again in) Indiana / Misty
BLCD 760125 / Apr '91 / Black Lion

☐ HORN, THE
PCD 7001 / Jun '93 / Progressive

☐ IN A MELLOW TONE (Archive Series - Live At Ronnie Scott's)
In a mellow tone / Over the rainbow / Gone with the wind / Someone to watch over me / C Jam blues / Perdido / Stardust / Ben's blues / My romance / Ben's theme tune
JHAS 601 / Jun '95 / Ronnie Scott's Jazz House

☐ JAMMIN'
Tea for two / Don't blame me / 'Nuff said / I surrender dear / Woke up clipped / Dirty deal / Teezol / Horn / Romp / Honeysuckle rose / Somebody loves me / Flying home
VN 1012 / Aug '97 / Viper's Nest

☐ JAZZ MASTERPIECES
BN 022 / Apr '98 / Blue Nite

☐ JAZZ MASTERS
5254312 / 5 May '98 / Verve

☐ JEEP IS JUMPING, THE
Stompy jones / Blue light / Brother john's blues / Nancy / Duke's in bed / My romance / What's I'm gotchere / Days of wine and roses / Jeep is jumping
BLC 760147 / Oct '90 / Black Lion

☐ KING OF THE TENORS
Tenderly / Jive at six / Don't get around much anymore / That's all / Bounce blues / Pennies from Heaven / Cotton tail / Danny boy / Poutin' / Jive at six / That's all
5198062 / Oct '93 / Verve

☐ LIVE AT THE HAARLEMSE JAZZCLUB
For all we know / Sunday / How long has this been going on / In a mellotone / Stardust / Perdido
MCD 0040 / Apr '96 / Limetree

☐ LIVE AT THE JAZZHUS VOL.1
Sunday / That's all / Gone with the wind / Over the rainbow / Indiana / Misty / Our love is here to stay / My romance / Blues for Herluf / Londonderry air / Set call
8747102 / Jul '96 / DA Music

☐ LIVE AT THE JAZZHUS VOL.2
Mack the knife / I can't get started / Friskin' the fog / Stormy weather / Teach me tonight / Perdido / Yesterdays / I'm gonna sit right down and write myself a letter / Set call
8747122 / Oct '96 / DA Music

☐ LIVE AT THE KING & QUEENS, PROVIDENCE, RHODE ISLAND 1963 (Webster, Ben Quartet)
Perdido / Danny boy / On green dolphin street / Go home / Bye bye blackbird / Lover come back to me / My romance / Wee dot / Tenderly / Sometimes I'm happy / How long has this been going on / Embraceable you / Theme
STCD 8237 / Mar '97 / Storyville

☐ LIVE IN PARIS
LEJAZZCD 29 / Aug '94 / Le Jazz

☐ LIVE IN VIENNA - 1972
RST 91529 / '91 / RST

☐ MASTERS OF JAZZ VOL.5
STCD 4105 / Feb '89 / Storyville

☐ SOULVILLE
Soulville / Late date / Time on my hands / Lover come back to me / Where are you / Makin' whoopee / Ill wind / Boogie woogie / Roses of Picardy
8335512 / Oct '93 / Verve

☐ STORMY WEATHER
BLCD 760108 / Dec '88 / Black Lion

☐ THERE IS NO GREATER LOVE
BLCD 760151 / Apr '91 / Black Lion

Webster, E.T.

☐ CHANGES
NGCD 527 / Apr '92 / Twinkle

☐ FREEDOM FIGHTER
RN 0053 / 27 Apr '98 / Runnetherlands

☐ LAMENT OF A DREAD
Reggae symphony / Cold sweat / Loner / Same, same, same / Dem say / Lament of a dread / Experience / What about I / Deeper love / Cry cry cry
NGCD 539 / Feb '94 / Twinkle

☐ MANKIND
NGCD 551 / Jul '96 / Twinkle

Webster, Gregory

☐ MY WICKED WICKED WAYS
Forever England / Water is wide / Blue eyes crying in the rain / Last night on earth / All the greatest stories / Winter / Clock chimes / Wonderland / Foolhardy / Lonesome town
MASKCD 055 / Apr '96 / Vinyl Japan

Webster, Joe

☐ I'M IN THE MOOD FOR BIG BAND MUSIC (Webster, Joe & Swing Fever Band)
LPCD 1025 / Apr '94 / Disky

☐ I'M IN THE MOOD FOR DIXIE MUSIC (Webster, Joe & His River City Jazzmen)
LPCD 1026 / Apr '94 / Disky

Webster, Katie

☐ I KNOW THAT'S RIGHT
ARHCD 393 / Apr '95 / Arhoolie

☐ NO FOOLIN'
Little meat on the side / I'm bad / No deposit, no return / Zydeco shoes and California blues / Too much sugar for a dime / Hard lovin' mama / It's might hard / Tangled in your web / Those lonely, lonely nights / Mama cat cuttin' no slack
ALCD 4803 / May '93 / Alligator

☐ SWAMP BOOGIE QUEEN
Who's making love / Sea of love / Black satin / After you get rid of me / Fa-fa-fa-fa-fa (sad song) / Try a little tenderness / Hold on to what you got / Somebody's on your case / On the run / Lord, I wonder / No bread, no meat / Whoo-wee sweet daddy
ALCD 4766 / Oct '93 / Alligator

☐ TWO FISTED MAMA
ALCD 4777 / May '93 / Alligator

Webster, Roger

☐ PIECES
Four variations on a theme of Domenico Scarlatti / Aria and Scherzo / Prelude op.8 no.11 / Allegro from Toot Suite / Sicilienne / Slavish fantasie / Nightsongs / Concerto scherzo / Reflections / Concerto (Arutiunian)
QPRZ 018D / Oct '97 / Polyphonic

☐ TWILIGHT DREAMS
Jubilance / I'd rather have Jesus / Russian dance / Twilight dreams / Concert study / Heavenly gales / Someone cares / Concerto for cornet and brass bands
QPRL 066D / Jul '94 / Polyphonic

Webster-Fabio, Sarah

☐ JUJUS (Alchemy Of The Blues)
Hand that rocks / Sweet songs / Juju for Grandma / Chromo / Still, a red hot axe / If we come as soft as rain / Jujus/Alchemy of the blues / Jujus/Alchemy of the blues
CDBGPD 112 / 27 Oct '97 / Beat Goes Public

Webstirs

☐ ROCKET TO THE MOON
GR 4005CD / 20 Apr '98 / Ginger

Weckl, Dave

☐ RHYTHM OF THE SOUL
Zone / 101 shuffle / Mud sauce / Designer stubble / Someone's watching / Transition jam / Rhythm dance / Access denied / Song for Claire / Big B little B / Good night
SCD 90162 / 16 Feb '98 / Stretch

Wedding Anniversary

☐ WEDDING ANNIVERSARY, THE
DANCD 010 / May '89 / Danceteria

Wedding Present

☐ BIZARRO
Brassneck / Crushed / No / Thanks / Kennedy / What have I said now / Granadaland / Bewitched / Take me / Be honest
PD 74302 / Oct '89 / RCA

☐ EVENING SESSIONS 1986-1994, THE
Everyone thinks he looks daft / Shatner / My favourite dress / I found that essence rare / Sticky / No Christmas / Lone slave / Queen of outer space / Click click / It's a gas / Hot pants / Catwoman
SFRSCD 029 / Jun '97 / Strange Fruit

☐ GEORGE BEST
Everyone thinks he looks daft / What did your last servant die of / Don't be so afraid / Million miles / All this and more / Getting nowhere fast / My favourite dress / Shatner / Something and nothing / It's what you want that matters / Give my love to Kevin / Anyone can make a mistake / You can't moan can you / All about Eve / Nobody's twisting your arm / Nothing comes easy / Don't laugh / I'm not always so stupid / Why are you being so reasonable now / Not from where I'm standing / Give my love to Kevin (acoustic) / Getting better / Pourquoi es tu devenue si raisonnable
COOKCD 134 / 13 Oct '97 / Cooking Vinyl

☐ HIT PARADE VOL.1
Blue eyes / Go-go dancer / Three / Silver shorts / Come play with me / California / Cattle and cane / Don't cry no tears / Think that it might / Falling / Pleasant valley Sunday / Let's make some plans
74321400732 / Sep '96 / RCA

☐ MINI
Drive / Love machine / Go, man, go / Mercury / Convertible / Sports car
COOKCD 094 / Aug '97 / Cooking Vinyl

☐ PEEL SESSIONS 1992-1995, THE
California / Come play with me / Flying saucer / Softly softly / Spangle / So long baby / Gazebo / Him or me (what's it gonna be) / Love machine / Go man go / Drive / Sports car
COOKCD 146 / 27 Apr '98 / Cooking Vinyl

☐ SATURNALIA
Snake eyes / Big boots / Spaceman / Skin diving / Real thing / Dreamworld / Kansas / Hula doll / Up / Venus / 50's / Montreal / 2,3 Go
COOKCD 099 / Sep '96 / Cooking Vinyl

☐ TOMMY
Go out and get 'em boy / Everything's spoiled again / Once more / At the edge of the sea / Living and learning / This boy can wait / You should always keep in touch with your friends / Felicity / What becomes of the broken hearted / Never said / Every mother's son / My favourite dress
COOKCD 135 / 13 Oct '97 / Cooking Vinyl

☐ WATUSI
So long baby / Click click / Yeah yeah yeah yeah yeah / Let him have it / Gazebo / Shake it / Spangle / It's a gas / Swimmimg pools, movie stars / Big rat / Catwoman / Hot pants
CID 8014 / Aug '94 / Island

Weddings, Parties & Anything

☐ DIFFICULT LOVES
Father's day / Taylor Square / Difficult loves / Old Ronny / Telephone in her car / Nothin' but time / Alone amongst savages / Rambling girl / Step in, step out / Four corners of the earth / For your ears only / Do not go gently
COOKCD 059 / Feb '95 / Cooking Vinyl

☐ KING TIDE
Monday's experts / Live it everyday / Money cuts you out / Rain in my heart / It wasn't easy / Keep talking to me / Island of humour / Easy money / In my lifetime / Always leave something behind / If you were a cloud / Year she spent in England / Stalactites
4509937732 / Mar '94 / WEA

☐ ROARING DAYS
Industrial town / Under the clocks / Gun / Brunswick / Tilting at windmills / Sergeant Small / Sisters of mercy / Roaring days / Say the word / Missing in action / Laughing boy / Big river / Summons in the morning / Morton (Song for Tex)
COOKCD 026 / Nov '89 / Cooking Vinyl

Wedgwood, Michael

☐ PLACES LIKE THESE
Lifeline / Places like these / Act like a dog / Loving and leaving / New man coming / Piece / Searching for a fantasy / Fundamental fool / Indigo / Cry nightly / Take me away / Looking forward to missing you / Take it as it comes / You and I combine
VP 143CD / Nov '93 / Voiceprint

Weed

☐ WEED
SB 018 / 26 Jan '98 / Second Battle

Weed, Joe

☐ JOE WEED AND THE VULTURES (Weed, Joe & The Vultures)
NCD 205 / Mar '96 / Highland

Weedon, Bert

☐ KING SIZE GUITAR/HONKY TONK GUITAR
Guitar boogie shuffle / Nashville boogie / King size guitar / Apache / Teenage guitar / Querida / I wonder where my baby is tonight / Pretty baby / Elmer's tune / Charleston / Chicago / Sweet Georgia Brown / Big beat boogie / Lonely guitar / Bongo rock / Blue guitar / Bert's boogie / Summer place / Bye bye blackbird / Varsity drag / Ma, he's making eyes at me / Carolina in the morning / Jealous / (In) a shanty in old Shanty Town
C5HCD 617 / Jan '97 / See For Miles

Weekenders

☐ THAT WAS NOW BUT THIS IS THEN
BLOWUP 5CD / Feb '96 / Blow Up

Weeks & Co.

☐ BEST OF WEEKS & CO, THE (Rock Your World)
HTCD 84 / 20 Apr '98 / Hot Productions

Weems, Ted

☐ BROADCAST RECORDINGS 1940-1941 (Weems, Ted & His Orchestra)
JH 1032 / Jul '93 / Jazz Hour

☐ MARVELLOUS (Weems, Ted & His Orchestra)
Marvellous / Oh if I only had you / From Saturday night to Sunday morning / She'll never find a fellow like me / Chick, chick, chick, chick, chicken / Cobblestones / You're the cream in my coffee / My troubles are over / Piccolo Pete / Man from the south / Come on baby / Harmonica Harry / Mysterious Mose / Slappin' the bass / Washing dishes with my sweetie / Egyptian Ella / Jig time / Play that hot guitar / Oh Mo'nah / My favourite band
CDAJA 5029 / May '84 / Living Era

Ween

☐ MOLLUSK, THE
MUSH 3CD / 1 Sep '97 / Mushroom

☐ PURE GUAVA
Little birdy / Tender situation / Stallim / Big Jim / Push little daisey's / Goin' gets tough / Reggae junkie jew / Play it off legit / Pumpin for the man / Sarah / Sprim theme / Flies on my dick / I saw Gene crying in her sleep / Touch my tooter smoocher / Morning glory / Lovin' you through it all / Her fatboy (Asshole) / Don't get to close to my fantasy / Poor ship destroyer
RUST 002CD / Dec '92 / Creation

Weezer

☐ PINKERTON
Tired of sex / Getchoo / No other one / Why bother / Across the sea / Good life / El scorcho / Pink triangle / Falling for you / Butterfly
GED 25007 / Sep '96 / Geffen

☐ WEEZER
My name is Jonas / On one else / World has turned and left me here / Buddy Holly / Undone / Sweater song / Surf wax America / Say it ain't so / In the garage / Holiday / Only in dreams
GED 24629 / 25 May '98 / Geffen

Wegmuller, Walter

☐ TAROT (2CD Set)
14900 / Jul '97 / Spalax

Weidman, James

☐ PEOPLE MUSIC
Raw deal / Petals / Hang with the gang / Bird alone / Limehouse blues / Up on the horizon / I can tell blues / Contessa's last dance / Jeannine
TCB 96302 / Apr '97 / TCB

Weiland, Scott

☐ 12 BAR BLUES
Desperation no.5 / Barbarella / About nothing / Where's the man / Divider / Cool kiss / Date / Son / Jimmy was a stimulator / Lady your roof brings me down / Mockingbird girl / Opposite octave reaction
7567830842 / 18 May '98 / Atlantic

Weiling, Paul

☐ NEW AMSTERDAM REFLECTIONS (Weiling, Paul Trio & David Tronzo)
New Amsterdam refections / Claro / Bohemian beguine / Wailin' / Sneakin' / Internet tango / Triads / Bird song / Hackensack / Strange flowers / Internet tango
9920282 / Apr '98 / Via Jazz

Wein, George

☐ METRONOME PRESENTS JAZZ AT THE MODERN (Live In The Sculpture Garden At the Museum Of Modern Art) (Wein, George & The Storyville Sextet)
BET 6025 / Jan '95 / Bethlehem

Weinert, Susan

☐ BOTTOM LINE, THE (Weinert, Susan Band)
Hombre / Triple X / Tribute T Fitzcarraldo / Don't smile to soon / Masters of the midiverse / That's for you / Kluski theory / Dakota kid / Nothing / Trabucco / Vinnie
VBR 21772 / Aug '96 / Vera Bra

☐ CRUNCH TIME (Weinert, Susan Band)
Don't try that again, MF / Hopeless case / Don't you guys know any nice songs / One for George / Member of the Syndicate / Crown / He knows / Pacific Palisades / Maybe / Guess who called
VBR 21442 / Aug '94 / Vera Bra

Weinstein, David

☐ PERFUME
AVANT 020 / Jul '98 / Avant

Weinstein, Georgina

☐ COME RAIN OR SHINE
FSNT 020 / Jan '98 / Fresh Sound New Talent

Weir, Bob

☐ ACE
Greatest story ever told / Walk in the sunshine / Looks like rain / One more saturday night / Black throated wind / Playing in the band / Mexicali blues / Cassidy
GDCD 4004 / Feb '89 / Grateful Dead

☐ KINGFISH
Lazy lightnin' / Supplication / Wild northland / Asia minor / Home to Dixie / Jump for joy / Goodbye yer honer / Big iron / This time / Hypnotize / Bye and bye
GDCD 4012 / Oct '89 / Grateful Dead

Weir, Frank

☐ MAN AND HIS MUSIC, THE
RAJCD 899 / 3 Aug '98 / Empress

Weird Little Boy

☐ WEIRD LITTLE BOY
63416400432 / 21 Apr '98 / Avant

Weird Lovemakers

☐ FLU SHOT
MTR 367CD / 26 May '98 / Empty

Weird Summer

☐ CRY FOR THE MOON
PARCD 012 / 16 Mar '98 / Parasol

☐ INCARNATA MYSTERICA
PARCD 009 / 16 Mar '98 / Parasol

☐ LSO
PARCD 017 / 16 Mar '98 / Parasol

Weiskopf, Walt

☐ SIMPLICITY (Weiskopf, Walt Sextet)
CRISS 1075CD / Nov '93 / Criss Cross

☐ SLEEPLESS NIGHTS (Weiskopf, Walt Sextet)
Inner loop / Come rain or come shine / Mind's eye / Jazz folk song / Wishing tree / Liberian lullaby / With you with me / Sleepless nights
CRISS 1147 / Jun '98 / Criss Cross

Weiss, Harald

☐ OTHER PARADISE, THE
SM 18112 / Sep '95 / Wergo

☐ TROMMELGEFLUSTER
8492852 / May '91 / ECM

Weiss, Klaus

☐ LA CALLING
Other side / LA calling / Spring passed / I've heard this before / Four four / Bad girl / I'll take it / All night through
CDLR 45033 / Jun '91 / L&R

Weiss, Marcus

☐ CONQUEST OF MELODY
ARTCD 6178 / Sep '97 / Hat Art

Weiss, Michael

☐ MICHAEL WEISS QUINTET FEATURING... (Tom Kirkpatrick/R. Lalama/R. Drummond)
CRISS 1022CD / May '91 / Criss Cross

☐ POWER STATION
DIW 924 / Mar '98 / DIW

Weissman, Dick

☐ NEW TRADITIONS
FE 1400CD / Dec '94 / Folk Era

Weizmann, Danny

☐ HOLLYWOODLAND
Hollywoodland part one / Jimmy the king of life / Actress / Teller / Grandpa's abbreviated movie reviews / Beat girl / Heatwave / Green sunlight / Pinball wizard / Hollywoodland part two
NAR 100CD / 29 Sep '97 / New Alliance

☐ WET DOG SHAKES, THE
NAR 065CD / May '93 / New Alliance

Welch, Bob

☐ FRENCH KISS/THREE HEARTS
Sentimental lady / Easy to fall / Hot love cold world / Mystery train / Lose my heart / Outskirts / Ebony eyes / Lose your / Carolene / Dancin' eyes / Danchiva / Lose your heart / Three hearts / Oh Jenny / I saw her standing there / Here comes the night / China / Ghost of flight 401 / Precious love / Church / Come softly to me / Devil wind / Don't wait too long / Little star
EDCD 538 / 26 Jan '98 / Edsel

☐ MAN OVERBOARD/THE OTHER ONE
Rebel rouser / Love came 2X / Watch the animals / Straight up / Hideaway / Future games / Oneonone / Don't let me fall / Spanish dancers / Old man of 17 / Man overboard / Justine / Nightmare / B666 / Don't rush the good things / Girl can't stop / Jealous / Fate decides / Reason / Those days are gone
EDCD 539 / 2 Mar '98 / Edsel

Welch, Elisabeth

☐ ELISABETH WELCH IN CONCERT
No time at all / Nearness of you (take 3) / To keep my love alive / Man I love / When I get you alone tonight / Such a night / Miss otis regrets / Love for sal / As time goes by / Solomon / Smoke gets in your eyes / La vie en rose / Song on the sand / My cousin in milwaukee / It had to be you / Bye bye blackbird / Experiment
OCRCD 6016 / Mar '96 / First Night

☐ SOFT LIGHTS AND SWEET MUSIC
PASTCD 7060 / Nov '95 / Flapper

☐ ULTIMATE ELISABETH WELCH, THE
313752 / Nov '92 / Koch

☐ WHERE HAVE YOU BEEN
It was worth it / I got it bad and that ain't good / My love is a wanderer / I always say hello (to a flower) / How little it matters, how little we know / Where have you been / Manhattan madness / He was too good to me / Little girl blue / You were there / Dancing in the dark / Mean to me / As long as I live / Come rain or come shine / Remember
CDSL 5202 / Jun '91 / DRG

Welch, Gillian

☐ HELL AMONG THE YEARLINGS
ALMCD 60 / 3 Aug '98 / Almo Sounds

☐ REVIVAL
ALMCD 011 / May '96 / Almo Sounds

Welch, Ian

☐ MUSIC FOR SHIATSU
MBSCD 900 / 6 Jul '98 / New World

Welch, Kevin

☐ LIFE DOWN HERE ON EARTH
Pushing up daisies / Troublesome times / Wilson's tracks / I feel fine today / Feast of bread and water / Wishing for you / Kicking back in Amsterdam / Love I have for you / One way rider / Life down here on Earth
DR 00032 / Dec '97 / Dead Reckoning

Welch, Mike

☐ AXE TO GRIND
Did she say / Palm of her hand / Axe to grind / Elkmont stomp / Every time you lie / Afriad of my own tears / Take your best shot / She couldn't know / Time stands still / That's my sin / My emptiness / Cruise control
CDTC 1159 / Feb '97 / Tonecool

☐ CATCH ME
As good as gone / Make up your mind / If I love you / Mole's blues / Changing of the guard / Catch me (nothing lasts forever) / Worried life blues / Can't reach you / My love belongs to you / Price to pay / Blues for Cara / Money (that's what I want) / Don't worry
CDTC 1167 / Jun '98 / Tonecool

☐ THESE ARE MINE
8425812 / Apr '97 / Sky Ranch

☐ THESE BLUES ARE MINE
CDTC 1154 / Feb '96 / Tonecool

Welcome

☐ BIEN VENUE
A 19 / Feb '96 / Seventh

Welcome

☐ LOW COST SOLUTION
RXR 009 / Nov '96 / RX Remedy

Weldon, Casey Bill

☐ CASEY BILL WELDON VOL.1-3 1935-1938
DOCD 5217/8/9 / Jan '94 / Document

☐ HAWAIIAN GUITAR WIZARD 1935-1938, THE
158292 / Jan '95 / Blues Collection

Weldon, Irvine Jr.

☐ BEST OF IRVINE WELDON JR, THE
CNM 01CD / 16 Jul '97 / Cool Note

Weldon, Nick

☐ LAVENDER'S BLUE
Mabs and tucker / Sonora / In the wee small hours of the morning / Alone together / Liffey / Never let me go / Some other time / Softly as in a morning sunrise / Lavender's blue
VERGE 001CD / May '96 / Verge

Well Oiled Sisters

☐ ALCOHOL AND TEARS
CYCLECD 001 / Apr '94 / Cycle

Weller, Don

☐ LIVE (Weller, Don Big Band)
33JAZZ 032 / Mar '97 / 33 Jazz

Weller, Paul

☐ HEAVY SOUL
Heavy soul / Peacock suit / Up in Suzie's room / Brushed / Driving nowhere / I should have been there to inspire you / Heavy soul (part two) / Friday street / Science / Golden sands / As you lean into the light / Mermaids
CID 8058 / Jun '97 / Island

☐ INTERVIEW DISC
SAM 7025 / Jan '97 / Sound & Media

☐ LIVE WOOD
8285612 / Sep '94 / Go Discs

☐ PAUL WELLER
Uh huh oh yeh / Bullrush / Remember how we started / Clues / Amongst butterflies / Into tomorrow / Strange museum / Above the clouds / Bitterness rising
8283432 / Sep '92 / Go Discs

☐ STANLEY ROAD
Changing man / Porcelein Gods / Walk on gilded splinters / You do something to me / Woodcutter's son / Time passes / Stanley Road / Broken stones / Out of the sinking / Pink on white walls / Whirlpool's end / Wings of speed
8286192
8286202 / May '95 / Go Discs

☐ WILD WOOD
Sunflower / Can you heal us (holy man) / Wild wood / Instrumental / All the pictures on the wall / Has my fire really gone out / Country / Fifth Season / Weaver / Instrumental / Foot of the mountain / Shadow of the sun / Holy man (reprise) / Moon on your pyjamas
8285132 / Sep '93 / Go Discs

Wellington, Sheena

☐ CLEARSONG
Women of dundee / Beirut / Christ child lullaby / Yellow on the broom / My ain countrie / Where are ye now / There was a lad / Dandy and the beano / Willie's fatal visit
DUNCD 012 / Jun '87 / Dunkeld

☐ KERELAW
Derwentwater's farewell / Newport braes / Death of Queen Jane / Irish boy / Last leviathan / Bunch of Thyme / Nicky tams / Aileen Aroon / Eh'll bide a wee o / Sheath and knife
DUNCD 005 / Feb '98 / Dunkeld

☐ STRONG WOMEN
Strong women rule us with their tears / Dark eyed Molly / Address the haggis / Mill O'Tifty's Annie / Tryst / False bride / Glasgow councillor / Slaves lament / Seattle / Great Silkie O'Sule Skerrie / Shearin' / Waulkrife Minnie / Silver tassie / My luv's like a red red rose / Little Sunday school
CDTRAX 094 / Oct '95 / Greentrax

Wellington, Valerie

☐ LIFE IN THE BIG CITY
GBW 002 / Feb '92 / GBW

☐ MILLION DOLLAR SECRET
R 2619 / Apr '95 / Rooster

Wellins, Bobby

☐ DON'T WORRY 'BOUT ME
SGCCD 05 / Sep '97 / Cadillac

☐ MAKING LIGHT WORK
Erco makes light work / Visionaire / Bossa Oseris / Logotec logarhythm / Track sound / Downright downlight / Take the 'A' train / Just friends / I'm beginning to see the light
HEPCD 2070 / Aug '97 / Hep

☐ NOMAD
HHCD 1008 / May '95 / Hot House

☐ SATIN ALBUM, THE
I'm a fool to want you / For heaven's sake / You don't know what love is / I get along without you very well / For all we know / Violets for your furs / You've changed / It's easy to remember / But beautiful / Glad to be unhappy / I'll be around / End of a love affair
JITCD 9607 / Feb '97 / Jazzizit

Wells Cathedral Choir

☐ CHRISTMAS CAROLS FROM WELLS CATHEDRAL
O come all ye faithful (adeste fidelis) / God rest ye merry gentlemen / Holly and the ivy / Unto us is born a son / Once in Royal David's City / Silent night / Away in a manger / It came upon a midnight clear / I saw three ships / O little town of Bethlehem / Ding dong merrily on high / Hark the herald angels sing / First Noel / Deck the hall / Coventry carol / While shepherds watch / Good King Wenceslas / In the bleak mid winter / Infant holy, infant lowly / We wish you a merry Christmas
XMAS 004 / Nov '96 / Tring

Wells, Carlene

☐ BE MY LOVER TONIGHT
36K7893 / 2 Feb '98 / Trinidad & Tobago

Wells, Dicky

☐ CLASSICS 1929-1946
CLASSICS 937 / Jun '97 / Classics

☐ DICKY'S BLUES
TPZ 1023 / Jul '95 / Topaz Jazz

☐ SWINGIN' IN PARIS (Wells, Dicky & Bill Coleman)
LEJAZZCD 20 / Jun '93 / Le Jazz

Wells, James

☐ BEST OF JAMES WELLS, THE (My Claim To Fame)
Double dose of love / Baby I'm still the same man / All I ever need is music / If you lead me into temptation / Parting is such sweet sorrow / My days are numbered / Never let go / My claim to fame / True love is my destiny / That's the way the wind blows / Explosion / RSVP / Mirror image / Great minds think alike / No cure for me
HTCD 55 / 20 Apr '98 / Hot Productions

Wells, Jean

☐ SOUL ON SOUL
Have a little mercy / I'll drown in my own tears / After loving you / Sit down and cry / Ease away a little bit at a time / Our sweet love turned bitter / Somebody's been loving you (but it ain't been me) / Keep your mouth shut and your eyes open / If you've ever loved someone / Broomstick horse cowboy / I couldn't love you (more than I do now) / I feel good / With my love and what you've got / Keep on doin' it / Take time to make time for me / Try me and see / Roll up your sleeves, come out lovin' (winner takes all) / What have I got to lose / Puttin' the best on the outside / He ain't doin' bad / Hello baby, goodbye too
CDKEND 113 / Jun '94 / Kent

Wells, Junior

☐ BETTER OFF WITH THE BLUES (Wells, Junior & Buddy Guy)
CD 83354 / Aug '93 / Telarc

☐ BLUES HIT BIG TOWN
Hoodoo man / Cut that out / Junior's wail / Tomorrow night / Ways like an angel / Eagle rock / Please throw this poor dog a bone / Blue hit big town / Lord Lord / 'Bout the break of day / So all alone / Can't find my baby / Please throw this poor dog a bone / Junior's wail / Eagle rock / Lord Lord / Blues hit big town
DD 640 / Jul '98 / Delmark

☐ COME ON IN THIS HOUSE
What my momma told me/That's all right / Why are people like that / Trust my baby / Million years blues / Give me one reason / Ships on the ocean / She wants to sell my monkey / So glad you're mine / Mystery train / I'm gonna move to Kansas City / King fish blues / You better watch yourself / Come on in this house / Goat
CD 83395 / Nov '96 / Telarc Blues

☐ COMING AT YOU
Stop breakin' down / Somebody's tippin in / Five long years / Mystery train / So sad this morning / When my baby left me / Little by little / Tobacco road / Worried life blues / I'm your hoochie coochie man / You don't love me
VMD 79262 / Jan '96 / Vanguard

☐ EVERYBODY'S GETTIN' SOME
Sweet sixteen / Everybody's gettin' them some / I can't stand no signifyin' shaky ground / Trying to get over you / Use me / You're tough enough / Get down / That's what love will make you do / Don't you lie to me / Last hand of the night / Back into the fold / Keep on steppin'
CD 83360 / May '95 / Telarc

☐ IT'S MY LIFE BABY
It's my life baby / Country girl / Stormy Monday blues / Checking on my baby / I got a stomach ache / Slow, slow / It's so sad to be lonely / You lied to me / Shake it baby / Early in the morning / Look how baby / Everything's gonna be alright
VMD 73120 / Oct '95 / Vanguard

☐ KEEP ON STEPPIN' (The Best Of Junior Wells)
Oh pretty woman / Sweet sixteen / Give me one reason / Get down / Keep on steppin' / Broke and hungry / Mystery train / Use me / King fish blues / Why are people like that / Train / Messin' with the kid
CD 83444 / Mar '98 / Telarc Blues

☐ LIVE AT BUDDY GUY'S LEGENDS
Broke and hungry / Messin' with the kid / Hoodoo man / Little by little / Train / Sweet sixteen / What my Momma done told me / Got my mojo working / Love her with a feeling / Help me / Today I started loving you again
CD 83412 / Aug '97 / Telarc Jazz

☐ ON TOP
DD 635 / Oct '86 / Delmark

☐ PLEADING THE BLUES (Wells, Junior & Buddy Guy)
Pleading the blues / It hurts me too / Cut out the lights / Quit teasing my baby / I'll take care of you / Take your time baby / I smell something
BLE 599012 / Dec '90 / Black & Blue
ECD 260352 / Sep '93 / Evidence
IS 9012 / Mar '96 / Isabel

☐ SOUTHSIDE BLUES JAM
DD 628 / Jan '93 / Delmark

Wells, Kitty

☐ GREATEST HITS VOL.1
It wasn't God who made honky tonk angels / Left to right / I don't claim to be an angel / Password / Wedding ring ago / Dust on the bible / Thank you for the roses / Whose shoulder will you cry on / Lonely street / Love makes the world go round / Loving you was all I ever needed / Amigo's guitar
SORCD 0046 / Oct '94 / D-Sharp

☐ QUEEN OF COUNTRY MUSIC 1949-1958, THE (4CD Set)
Death at the bar / Love or hate / Gathering flowers for the master's bouquet / Don't wait til the last minute to pray / How far is heaven / My mother / Make up your mind / I'll be all smiles tonight / I'm too lonely to smile / Things I might've been / I heard the jukebox playing / Wedding ring ago / Divided by two / Crying steel guitar waltz / Paying for that back street affair / Icicles hanging from your heart / I don't claim to be an angel / Honky tonk waltz / Life they live in songs / You said you could do without me / Whose shoulder will you cry on / Hey Joe / My cold cold heart is melting now / I'll love you 'til the day I die / I've kissed you my last time / I'm a stranger in my home / I gave my wedding dress away / Cheatin's a sin / You're not easy to forget / Satisfied, so satisfied / One by one / Release me / After dark / (Don't hang around) he's married to me / Thou shalt not steal / Lonely side of town / I hope my divorce is never granted / I'm in love with you / Make believe / You and me / As long as I live / No one but you / Making believe / I'd rather stay home / I was wrong / There's poison in your heart / Goodbye Mr. Brown / Mother hold me tight / Searching / Dust on the bible / Beside you / I'm counting on you / They can't take your love / I'm tired of pretending / Oh so many years / One week later / When I'm with you / Can I find it in your heart / Repenting / I guess I'll go on dreaming / Each day / Pace that kills / Change of heart / Stubborn heart / Standing room only / Mansion on the hill / Your wild life's gonna get you down / Right or wrong / Winner of your heart / Dancing with a stranger / Three ways (to love you) / She's no angel / Broken marriage vows / What about you / Sweeter than the flowers / You can't conceal a broken heart / Just when I needed you / Lonely street / That's me without you / Cheated out of love / Waltz of the angels / May you never be alone / If teardrops were pennies / Touch and go heart / My ued to be darling / Fraulein / Love me to pieces / What I believe dear (is all up to you) / I can't stop loving you / Slowly dying / I can't help wondering / He's lost his love for me / Jealousy / Mommy for a day / Hands you're holding now / Let me help you forget / All the time / (I've got my) one way ticket to the sky / I heard my saviour call / I dreamed I searched heaven for you / Great speckled bird / Matthew 24 / I need the prayers / My loved ones are waiting for me / Lord I'm coming home / He will set your fields on fire / Lonesome valley / We buried her beneath the willows
BCD 15638 / Jul '93 / Bear Family

☐ T'WASN'T GOD THAT MADE HONKY TONK ANGELS
Don't claim to be an angel / Release me / Making believe / Whose shoulder will you cry on / One by one / Lonely side of town / Searching / Mommy for a day / From left to right / After dark / Password / I'll repossess my heart / As long as I live / Honky tonk angels / This white circle
PRACD 4000 / Jun '97 / Prairie

Wells, Mary

☐ 22 GREATEST HITS
My guy / Bye bye baby / I don't want to take a chance / Only one who really loves you / You beat me to the punch / Two lovers / Your old standby / Old loe (let's try again) / Oh little boy (what you did to me) / What love has joined together / You lost the sweetness / What's easy for two is so hard for one / Two wrongs don't make a right / Everybody needs love / I'll be available / One block from heaven / When I'm gone / He's the one I love / Whisper you love me boy / Does he love me / Was it worth it
5301042 / '95 / Polydor

☐ MOTOWN EARLY CLASSICS
My guy / My baby just cares for me / I only have eyes for you / Shop around / When your lover comes back / Let your conscience be your guide / One who really loves you / (I guess there's) No love / You beat me to the punch / Two lovers / Together: *Wells, Mary & Marvin Gaye* / 'Deed I do: *Wells, Mary & Marvin Gaye* / Drop in the bucket / He's the one I love / After the lights go down low: *Wells, Mary & Marvin Gaye* / He holds his own / Does he love me / Whisper you love me boy
5521242 / Jul '96 / Spectrum

☐ MY GUY (The Best Of Mary Wells)
What love has joined together / Laughing boy / What's easy for two is so hard for one / My guy / Operator / Two lovers / One who really loves you / You beat me to the punch / Your old standby / You lost the sweetest boy / Old love (let's try again)
CDSGP 057 / May '93 / Prestige

☐ MY GUY (The Best Of Mary Wells)
Two lovers / You beat me to the punch / Oh little boy what did you do to me / What's easy for two is hard for one / What love has joined together / You lost the sweetest boy / My guy / One who really loves you / Old love let's try again / I'm a lady / Make up break up / I feel for you / To feel your love / Money talks
AIM 2015CD / 20 Oct '97 / Aim

☐ SISTERS OF SOUL
RSACD 806 / Oct '94 / Sequel

☐ ULTIMATE COLLECTION
5308592 / 13 Jul '98 / Motown

☐ VERY BEST OF MARY WELLS, THE (The Very Best Of The Motorcity Recordings)
My guy / Hold on a little longer / Walk on the city streets / Don't burn your bridges / What's easy for two is so hard for one / Keeping my mind on love / Stop before it's too late / You're the answer to my dreams / You beat me to the punch / Once upon a time
3035990122 / Feb '96 / Motor City

Wells, Susan

☐ BEST OF SUSAN WELLS, THE (Nightmare)
HTCD 66 / 20 Apr '98 / Hot Productions

Wellstood, Dick

☐ ALL STAR ORCHESTRA AND BLUE THREE (Wellstood, Dick & Kenny Davern)
CRD 129 / Mar '96 / Chiaroscuro

☐ ALONE
SACD 73 / Sep '97 / Solo Art

☐ LIVE AT THE STICKY WICKET (Live 1986/2CD Set)
ARCD 19188 / Sep '97 / Arbors Jazz

☐ STRETCHING OUT (Wellstood, Dick & Kenny Davern Quartet)
JCD 187 / Feb '91 / Jazzology

☐ THIS IS THE ONE...DIG
SACD 119 / Dec '95 / Solo Art

Wellwater Conspiracy

☐ DECLARATION OF CONFORMITY
3G 17 / 16 Mar '98 / Third Gear

Welsh, Alex

☐ CLASSIC CONCERT (Britain's Jazz Heritage)
BLCD 760503 / Oct '90 / Black Lion

☐ DIXIELAND TO DUKE/THE MELROSE FOLIO (Welsh, Alex & His Jazz Band)
Mandy make up your mind / I'm coming Virginia / Queen Bess / Up jumped you with love / Winin' boy blues / Cornet chop suey / Ostrich walk / Buddy's habit / Kansas City stomp / Sidewalk blues / Tia juana / Sugar babe / Dippermouth blues / Honey babe / King Porter stomp / Someday sweetheart
LACD 92 / Apr '98 / Lake

☐ DOGGIN' AROUND
BLCD 760510 / May '93 / Black Lion

☐ IF I HAD A TALKING PICTURE
BLC 760521 / Nov '97 / Black Lion

☐ LOUIS ARMSTRONG MEMORIAL CONCERT
Hear me talkin' to ya / Georgia on my mind / Ory's creole trombone / Rockin' chair / It's alright with me / Davenport blues / Dippermouth blues / Rose room / St. James Infirmary / Royal garden blues
BLCD 760515 / Nov '95 / Black Lion

☐ MUSIC OF THE MAUVE DECADE
Charleston / Black bottom / Lonesome and sorry / I cover the waterfront / Shimma sha wabble / Don't leave me Daddy / Nobody's sweetheart / Needle / Tell 'em bout me / I cried for you / Mammy o'mine / Down among sheltering palms / Please don't talk about me when I'm gone / Sleepy time gal / Bye bye blues
LACD 62 / Jun '96 / Lake

Welsh Guards Band

☐ BAND OF THE WELSH GUARDS, THE (Directed by Captain Andrew Harris)
Under the double eagle / Merry peal / Floradora / Cupid's army / Serenadeno / Voyage in a troopship / Rusticanella / London Scottish / Turkish patrol / Cavalcade of martial songs / Jungle drums / On the quarterdeck / Baby's sweetheart / Knightsbridge march / Silver stars / Children of the regiment / Bells of Shoreline / Maid of the mountains
PASTCD 9726 / Mar '91 / Flapper

☐ GILBERT AND SULLIVAN
Overture- The yeoman of the guard / Take a pair of sparkling eyes / Regular royal queen / When a wooer goes a wooing / Cheerily carols the lark / I am a courtier grave and serious / When the night wind howls / Hornpipe from Ruddigore / Man who would woo a fair maid / Refrain audacious tar / I hear the soft note / Long years ago / If you're anxious for to shine / Minerva / When the buds are blossoming / Strange adventure / Once more gondolieri
BNA 5022 / Jul '88 / Bandleader

☐ LAND OF MY FATHERS (HM Welsh Guards)
Bell a' peal / Casatschok / Tsarist anthem from War and Peace / British isles medley / Liberty bell / Eye level / Sentry's song from Iolanthe / Y viva Espana / Colditz march / Amazing grace / Jerusalem / Ar hyd y nos all through the night / God bless the prince of Wales / Land of my fathers / Evening hymn and last post / Colonel Bogey / Changing of the guard / Elizabethan serenade / Radetsky march
EMPRCD 572 / May '95 / Emporio

☐ MUSIC FROM THE CHANGING OF THE GUARD (Band Of The Welsh Guards)
To your guard / Empire / Birdcage walk / Guardsman / Long live Elizabeth / Royal review / Oxford street / Music of the night / Waterloo march / Welsh airs and fancies / Children's patrol / Gold and silver waltz / Spirit of pageantry / Welsh rhapsody / Great and glorious / Guard's parade / Lord Rothermere's march / Guards armoured division / King's guard / Welshman
BNA 5045 / '91 / Bandleader

Welt

☐ PARANOID DELUSION
PCD 14 / May '95 / Progress

Weltenbrand

☐ DAS RABENLAND
GIT 005CD / 6 Jul '98 / Trinity

Welti, Stephen

☐ TAKE OFF
Take off / Ocean dream / Alpine adventure / Riviera / Olympic arena / Another love / Russian vine / Stampede / Satellite / Chopper chase / Caribbean can can / Pacific paradise / Cochabamba / Return to mijas / Santa Monica freeway / Lights of Lugano / Hawaiian cocktail / Continental express
DLCD 107 / Jan '90 / Dulcima

Weltman, Sandy

☐ NEW WORLD HARMONICA
WILD 7272C / Mar '98 / Wildstone

Wenblom, Carolyn

☐ BEES TO THE HONEY
GRCD 385 / May '97 / Grasmere

Wench

☐ TIDY SIZE CHUNK OF SOMETHING, A
CORECD 5 / Apr '91 / Abstract

Wendholt, Scott

☐ FROM NOW ON
From now on / Magnolia tones / Solar / In a sentimental mood / At the falls / Times past / Dear old Stockholm / Promise / I remember you
CRISS 1123CD / Feb '97 / Criss Cross

☐ SCHEME OF THINGS, THE (Wendholt, Scott Quintet)
CRISS 1078CD / Nov '93 / Criss Cross

Wendt, Joja

☐ ART OF BOOGIE WOOGIE PIANO
Death ray boogie / Just for you / Mister Freddie's blues / Boogie woogie stomp / St. Louis blues / Boogie rocks / Bass gone crazy / Dupree blues / Bear cat crawl / Chapel blues / Honky tonk train blues / Meade's boogie / Jancey special / Sweet patootie blues / Barrelhouse boogie / Chicago in mind / Boogie woogie man / Blues on my mind / Dive bomber / Zero hour
QED 077 / Nov '96 / Tring

Wendy & Lisa

☐ ARE YOU MY BABY
Are you my baby / Lolly lolly / Waterfall / Satisfaction / Strung out / Rainbow lake / Tears of joy / Fruit at the bottom / Skeleton key / Staring at the sun / Everyday / Why wait for heaven / Are you my baby / Waterfall
VI 868812 / Nov '96 / Disky

☐ FRUIT AT THE BOTTOM
Lolly lolly / Satisfaction / Everyday / Tears of joy / Fruit at the bottom / Are you my baby / Always in my dreams / From now on / I think it was December / Someday
CDV 2580 / Apr '92 / Virgin

☐ RE-MIX-IN-A-CARNATION
Lolly Lolly / Waterfall / Are you my baby / Staring at the sun / Satisfaction / Sideshow
CDV 2676 / '91 / Virgin

Wenguang, Wu

☐ MUSIC OF THE QIN
VICG 52132 / Mar '96 / JVC World Library

Wennerstrom, Cecilia

☐ MINOR STOMP
FLCCD 157 / Oct '97 / Four Leaf Clover

Wentzel, Magni

☐ ALL OR NOTHING AT ALL
GMCD 150 / Oct '90 / Gemini

☐ MY WONDERFUL ONE
GMCD 157 / Oct '89 / Gemini

☐ NEW YORK NIGHTS
GMCD 174 / Oct '90 / Gemini

Wenzel, Rolf

☐ FREU' DICH JEDEN MORGEN
Freu' dich jeden morgen / Wer im norden wohnt / Gehst du in kur-Ole / Auf dem bremer freimarkt / Solang' uns diese blume bluht
BCD 17010 / Aug '97 / Bear Family

Werdell, Leonard

☐ MYSTO'S HOT LIPS
BCD 306 / Jul '93 / GHB

Werefrogs

☐ SWING
TOPPCD 3 / Jul '94 / Ultimate

Werner, Kenny

☐ DELICATE BALANCE, A (Werner, Kenny & Dave Holland/Jack DeJohnette)
Amonkst / Work song / Ivoronics / Footsteps / Trio imitation / Look of you / Lorraine / Melodies of 1997
74321516942 / Mar '98 / RCA Victor

☐ LIVE AT MAYBECK RECITAL HALL VOL.34
Roberta moon / Someday my prince will come / In your own sweet way / Naima / Autumn leaves / Try to remember / Guru / Child is born
CCD 4622 / Nov '94 / Concord Jazz

☐ LIVE AT VISIONES
Stella by starlight / Fall / All the things you are / Blue in green / There will never be another you / Blue train / Windows / Soul eyes / I hear a rhapsody
CCD 4675 / Dec '95 / Concord Jazz

☐ PRESS ENTER
SSC 1056D / May '92 / Sunnyside

Wernick, Pete

☐ I TELL YOU WHAT (Wernick, Pete Live Five)
Sky rider / Fire dance / Jobob rag / Dear old Dixie / D-Funk / Playground swing / Huckling the berries / Go cheetahs go / Free as the wind / June apple / Plain and fancy / Round the horn / Daybreak in Dixie
SHCD 3854 / Mar '98 / Sugar Hill

☐ ON A ROLL
SHCD 3815 / Mar '94 / Sugar Hill

Wernt

☐ WRECKING TEMPLES
CHOCROB 001 / 8 Dec '97 / Chocolate Roberts

Werup, Jacques

☐ PROVINSENS LJUS
DRCD 208 / Jul '87 / Dragon

Wes

☐ WELENGA
Awa / Alane / Kekeana / Wezale and transition 1 debita / Ken Mouka / Mawaza / Mindoulou / Mizobiya and transition 2 mizam / Degue wegue / Ramende / Woukase / Welenga
4851462 / 23 Feb '98 / St. George

Wesley, Fred

☐ BLOW FOR ME AND A TOOT TO YOU, A (Wesley, Fred & The Horny Horns)
Up for the down stroke / Blow for me, a toot to you / When in doubt vamp / Between two sheets / Four play / Peace fugue / Blow for me, a toot for you / Four play (new remix no. 1) / Four play / Interview
NEDCD 268 / May '94 / Sequel

☐ FINAL BLOW, THE (Wesley, Fred & The Horny Horns)
Fallen off the edge / Cookie monster / Westward ho / Oh I don't think sew / Lickity split / Discositdown / Bells
NEDCD 270 / May '94 / Sequel

☐ FULL CIRCLE
EAGCD 017 / 20 Apr '98 / Eagle

☐ SAY BLOW BY BLOW BACKWARDS (Wesley, Fred & The Horny Horns)
NEXCD 269 / May '94 / Sequel

Wess, Frank

☐ DEAR MR. BASIE (Wess, Frank & Harry Edison Orchestra)
Jumpin' at the woodside / Very thought of you / Blue on blue / All riled up / This is all I ask / I wish I knew / Whirly bird / Li'l darlin' / Dejection blues / Battle royal / One o'clock jump
CCD 4420 / Jul '90 / Concord Jazz

☐ OPUS DE BLUES
I hear ya talkin' / Liz / Boop-pe-doop / Opus de blues / Struttin' down blues / Broadway
SV 0137 / May '98 / Savoy Jazz

☐ SURPRISE SURPRISE (2CD Set) (Wess, Frank Quartet)
All or nothing at all / Beautiful friendship / My funny valentine / Estoril sol / One for amos / Firm roots / Nada mas / It could happen to you / All the things you are / On green dolphin street / Cottontail / Surprise surprise
CRD 350 / 6 Jul '98 / Chiaroscuro

☐ TRYIN' TO MAKE MY BLUES TURN GREEN
Come back to me / Tryin' to make my blues turn green / Listen to the dawn / So it is / Short circuit / Little Esther / Stray horn / Night lights / Surprise surprise / Blues in the car / Small talk / Alfie
CCD 4592 / Apr '94 / Concord Jazz

West Coast All Stars

☐ CELEBRATION OF WEST COAST JAZZ, A
CCD 79711/12 / Nov '95 / Candid

West Coast Pop Art Experimental Band

☐ WEST COAST POP ART EXPERIMENTAL BAND VOL.1
Something you got / Work song / Louie Louie / Don't break my balloon / You really got me / Don't let anything stand in your way / I won't hurt you / If you want this love / Insanity / It's all over now baby blue / She belongs to me / She surely must know / Sassafras / She may call you up tonight / One day / Funny how love can be / Obviously bad / Endless night / Tell me what you want to know / Just you and me / Chimes of freedom / Scuse me Miss Rose
SC 11047 / Aug '97 / Sundazed

☐ WEST COAST POP ART EXPERIMENTAL BAND VOL.1 & 2
POP 12CD / Jan '97 / Clear Spot
3096 / Jun '97 / Head

West, David

☐ ARCANE
TX 3003CD / Jan '94 / Taxim

West, Dottie

☐ DOTTIE WEST COLLECTION 1976-1984, THE (Are You Happy Baby)
RE 21602 / Dec '97 / Razor & Tie

West Ham United FC

☐ FOREVER BLOWING BUBBLES (20 Hammers Hits) (Various Artists)
I'm forever blowing bubbles: *1975 Cup Final Squad* / West ham united: *1975 Cup Final Squad* / Football mad: *Boleyn Boys* / Oh sweet England: *Boleyn Boys* / Sugar sugar: *Moore, Bobby & Friends* / West side boys: *Cockney Rejects* / Viva Bobby Moore: *Serious Drinking* / Bobby Moore was innocent: *Serious Drinking* / Leroy's boots: *Barmy Army* / Devo: *Barmy Army* / Blunted irons: *United Nations* / Billy bonds mbe: *Barmy Army* / Come on you irons (big beat centenary): *Rainbow's Quest* / Bobby Moore's legs: *Barmy Army* / Up the hammers: *Alf's Army* / Over land and sea: *Chicken Ron* / Julian Dicks: *Flat back four* / Terminator: *Flat back four* / I'm forever blowing bubbles: *Cockney Rejects* / I'm forever blowing bubbles: *Looking for a Rainbow*
CDGAFFER 7 / Aug '96 / Cherry Red

West Indies Jazz Band

☐ MEDLEY FOR MARIUS
LBLC 6542 / Oct '91 / Label Bleu

West, Keith

☐ EXCERPTS FROM GROUPS AND SESSIONS
Time is on my side / Don't lie to me / That's how strong my love is / Things she says / You're on your own / I don't mind / Am I glad to see you / Blow up / Three jolly little dwarfs / Revoloution / Excerpt from a teenage opera / Sam / Shy boy / Colonel Brown / On a Staurday / Kid was a killer / Visit / She / Little understanding / Power and the glory / West country / Riding for a fall / Having someone
RPM 141 / Jun '95 / RPM

West, Leslie

☐ BLOOD OF THE SUN 1969-1975 (West, Leslie & Mountain)
RVCD 49 / Mar '96 / Raven

☐ DODGIN' THE DIRT
Whiskey train / Daddy are you angry / New york state of mind / Sambuca / Juke joint jumpin' / Easy street / One last lick / Crosscut saw / Hang me out to dry / Wasted years / My friend sam / Thunderbird / Red house
RR 90262 / Sep '96 / Roadrunner

West Lothian Schools Brass Band

☐ CARTOON
Star Wars / Trumpet tune and air / La Bamba / Concertino for trumpet and brass band / Amazing grace / Charivari / Mr. Macintyre's march / Cartoon / Pastime with God company / Li'l darlin' / Harry James' trumpet concerto / Ruby Tuesday / Highland cathedral
QPRL 075D / Oct '97 / Polyphonic

West, Mae

☐ I'M NO ANGEL (The Original Commercial Recordings/The Film Soundtracks)
I like a guy what takes his time / Easy rider / I'm no angel / I found a new way to go to town / I want you, I need you / They call me Sister Honky Tonk / Willie of the valley / I like a guy what takes his time / Easy rider / Frankie and Johnny / They call me Sister Honky Tonk / That Dallas man / I found a new way to go to town / I want you, I need you / I'm no angel / When a St. Louis woman comes down to New Orleans / My old flame / Memphis blues / Troubled waters / He's a bad bad man / Mon coeur s'ouvre a ta voix / I'm an Occidental in an Oriental mood for love / Mister Deep Blue Sea / Little bar butterfly / On a typical tropical night / I was saying to the moon / Fifi / Now I'm a lady
JASCD 102 / Oct '96 / Jasmine

West, Mick

☐ FINE FLOWERS AND FOOLISH GLANCES
Bonnie jean cameron / Lassie lie near me / Chester city / Seasons / Fine flowers in the valley / Mission hall / Braw sailin on the sea / Twa bonnie boys / Rip the calico / Sean o'dhuibhir a 'gleanna / Blantyre explosion / Farewell to the gold
CDLDL 1229 / Jul '95 / Lochshore

☐ RIGHT SIDE O' THE PEOPLE... (West, Mick Band)
Young munro / Shift and spin / Highland muster roll / Ballad of John McLean / Jamie Foyers / Propeller song / Pipe tunes / Road to Dundee / January man / Lord Randall / MacCrimmons lament / Little cascade / Freedom come ye
CDLDL 1262 / 1 Dec '97 / Lochshore

West Section Line

☐ MAN DOWNSTAIRS, THE
RXR 006CD / Nov '96 / RX Remedy

West, Sonny

☐ RELENTLESS
Come on everybody / Come on let's go / Guitar attack / Relentless / Think it over baby / Almost grown / Jasmine / Icehouse / Take and give / Wyle E Coyote / Blue fire / I'm a man / So long baby / Doin' the boogie / Darlene / Hot choc / Runaway girl / I'll be there
NERCD 067 / Apr '92 / Nervous

West, Speedy

☐ FLAMIN' GUITARS (4CD Set) (West, Speedy & Jimmy Bryant)
Jelly beans Daddy / Just remember / Boogie barn dance / Gamblin' money / Steel strike / Bryant's boogie / Red headed polka / Railroadin' / Stainless steel / Hub cap roll / T-bone rag / Truck driver's ride / Liberty bell polka / Crackerjack / Bryant's shuffle / Roadside rag / Yodelling guitar / Georgie steel guitar / Pickin' the chicken / Midnight ramble / Comin' on / Lover / Skiddle dee boo / Serenade to a frog / Bryant's bounce / Opus I / Whistle stop / Speedin' West / Hometown polka / This ain't the blues / Jammin' with Jimmy / Two of a kind / Sunset / Steel guitar rag / Swingin' on the strings / Old Joe Clark / This is Southland / Arkansas traveller / Blue bonnet rag / Hop, skip and jump / Country capers / Low man on a totem pole / Sleepwalker's lullaby / Our paradise / Cotton pickin' / Bustin' thru / Flippin' the lid / Deep water / Stratosphere boogie / West of Samoa / Shuffleboard rag / Steelin' moonlight / Caffeine patrol / Yankee clover / Pickin' peppers / Chatter box / Frettin' fingers / Pushin' the blues / Sand canyon swing / Water baby blues / Shawnee trot / On the Alamo / Rolling sky / Night rider / Hillcrest / China boy / China boy / Hawaiian war chant / Song of the islands / On the beach of Waikiki / My tane / Drifting and dreaming / My little grass shack in Kealakekua, Hawaii / Sweet Hawaiian chimes / Blue Hawaii / Yaaka hula hickey dula / Moon of Manakoora / Ka lu a / Luna / Reflections from the moon / Spaceman in orbit / Lazy Summer evening / Double or nothing / Afternoon of a swan / Wild and woolly West / Rippling waters / Totem pole dance / Slow and easy / Speedy's special / Sunset at Waikiki / Tulsa twist / Candy kisses: *Kirk, Eddy* / Ain't nobody's business but my own: *Starr, Kay & Tennessee Ernie Ford* / I'll never be free: *Starr, Kay & Tennessee Ernie Ford* / Wild card: *Williams, Tex* / Okie boogie: *Morse, Ella Mae* / Down South: *Jones, Spike* / I've turned a gadabout: *Jones, Spike* / Stop your gamblin': *Jones, Spike* / There's a blue sky way out yonder: *Jones, Spike* / Okie boogie: *Morse, Ella Mae* / Twice the lovin' (in half the time): *Shepard, Jean* / Crying steel guitar waltz: *Shepard, Jean* / Nobody else can love you like I do: *Shepard, Jean* / Keep it a secret: *Shepard, Jean* / Y'all come: *Crosby, Bing* / Under the double eagle: *Jones, Spike* / Hot lips: *Jones, Spike* / Hotter than a pistol: *Jones, Spike* / Keystone kapers: *Jones, Spike* / Boys in the backroom: *Jones, Spike* / Whistle stop: *May, Billy* / This must be the place: *Hutton, Betty & Tennessee Ernie Ford*
BCD 15956 / Apr '97 / Bear Family

Westbam

☐ BAM BAM BAM
Acid sausage from Salzburgo / Wizards of the sonic / Celebration generation / Raving society / Strictly bam / Club canossa / Escapist / Track / Bam bam bam / After hours
5271122 / Jun '95 / Low Spirit/Polydor

☐ JOURNEYS BY DJ INTERNATIONAL VOL.4 (Various Artists)
JDJI 4CD / Oct '96 / JDJ

Westbrook, Mike

☐ BAR UTOPIA (Westbrook, Mike Orchestra)
Overture / Nowhere / Utopia blues / Honest love / Dialogue / Utopia ballad / Happy jazz singer / Bar Utopia
ASCCD 13 / Nov '96 / ASC
ENJ 93332 / 23 Mar '98 / Enja

☐ LOVE OR INFATUATION (The Hollywood Songs Of Friedrich Hollaender) (Westbrook, Mike & Kate)
Love or infatuation / Awake in a dream / Falling in love again / You've got that look / You leave me breathless / This is the moment / Moon's our home / Boys in the bathroom
ASCCD 20 / Oct '97 / ASC

☐ ON DUKE'S BIRTHDAY (Westbrook, Mike Orchestra)
ARTCD 6021 / Apr '94 / Hat Art

☐ ROSSINI (Studio)
ARTCD 6002 / Jul '88 / Hat Art

☐ ROSSINI - ZURICH LIVE 1986
ARTCD 26152 / May '94 / Hat Art

☐ STAGE SET (Westbrook, Kate & Mike)
September song / Private Jenny / Clio's cosmetics / Eto nepitiaai to kpyo / Une volta C'era un re / I got it bad / Nahe des geliebten / Un avenugle chant pour sa ville / Human abstract / L'egalite des sexes / Honest love / Don't explain / You've been a good old wagon / Casablanca / As time goes by
ASCCD 9 / Apr '96 / ASC

Westen, Eric

☐ WORKING DREAMER
BVHAASTCD 9212 / Dec '89 / Bvhaast

Westerberg, Paul

☐ 14 SONGS
Knockin' on mine / First glimmer / World class fad / Runaway wind / Dice behind your shades / Even here we are / Silver naked ladies / Few minutes of silence / Someone I once knew / Black eyed Susan / Things / Something is me / Mannequin shop / Down love
9362452552 / Jun '93 / Sire

☐ EVENTUALLY
Stain yer blood / Once around the weekend / Hide n seekin' / Time flies tomorrow / Good day / Angels walk / Trumpet clip / Century / Ain't got me / You've had it with you / Mamadaddydid / Love untold / These are the days
9362462512 / May '96 / Sire

Westercamp, Hildegard

☐ TRANSFORMATIONS
IMED 9631 / Jun '97 / Diffunzioni Musicali

Westerman, Floyd

☐ CUSTER DIED/THIS LAND
TRIK 017 / Oct '94 / Trikont

Western Vacation

☐ VIBRAUDOBLAST
EFA 034322 / Apr '97 / Muffin

☐ WESTERN VACATION
EFA 034312 / Apr '96 / Muffin

Western Wind Vocal Ensemble

☐ MY FUNNY VALENTINE (Classic Love Songs 1920-1990) (Western Wind Vocal Ensemble & Dick Hyman)
75199240042 / 7 Apr '98 / Western Wind

☐ PASSOVER STORY (Western Wind Vocal Ensemble & Theodore Bikel)
77220918002 / 7 Apr '98 / Western Wind

Western, Johnny

☐ GUNFIGHT AT OK CORRAL
Ghost riders in the sky / Gunfight at the OK Corral / Gunfighter / Don't take your guns to town / Ringo / Hangin' tree / Cross the Brazos at Waco / Johnny Yuma / Bonanza / Ballad of Paladin / Rawhide / Searchers / High noon / Song of the bandit / Hannah Lee / Lillies grow high / Ballad of Boot Hill / Cheyenne / Wyatt Earp / Bat Masterson
BCD 15429 / Jun '89 / Bear Family

☐ HEROES AND COWBOYS (3CD Set)
Ballad of Paladin / Guns of the Rio Muerto (and Richard Boone) / Gunfighter / Geronimo / Lonely man / Hannah Lee / Streets of Laredo / Cowpoke / Lillies grow high / Cotton wood tree / Rollin' dust / Searchers / Nineteen men / Long tall shadow / Last round-up / Streets of old dodge city / Mr. Rodeo cowboy / Singin' man / Big battle / Forty shades of green / Violet and a rose / Give me more, more, more (of your kisses) / Let old mother nature have her way / Little buffalo Bill / Love me love me love me / Honey, how sweet can you be / Echo of your voice / Ten years / Uh huh / Delia's gone / Time has run out on me / Willowgreen / Don't cry little girl / Darling Corey / Stranger drive away / I love you more / All by my lonesome / Just for the record / Kathy come home / Only the lonely / Light the fuse / Tender years / Turn around and look at me / Sincerely your friend / Ruby, don't take your love to town / Used to / I'll try hard to forget you if I can / Whoever finds this, I love you / Last time I saw phoenix / Hustler / You wouldn't know love / Arizona morning / Stay a little longer, stay all night / Lonely street / You weren't ashamed to kiss me last night / John Henry / Remember me / Wayward wind / Gotta travel on / Ghost riders in the sky / I still miss someone / I take a country girl for mine (Texas Bill strength) / I walk the line / Ballad of Paladin / Guns of Rio Muerto
BCD 15552 / May '93 / Bear Family

Western, Phil

☐ ESCAPIST
MAP 2042 / 20 Apr '98 / Map

Westfield, Steve

☐ BRAINWRECK
BS 20232 / Nov '96 / Pandemonium

☐ REJECT ME FIRST
PANNCD 11 / Mar '96 / Pandemonium

☐ UNDERWHELMED (Westfield, Steve Slow Band)
Lies / Happy birthday world / Underwhelmed / Nothing left to give / Monument / Leaving town / Riding with the flood / Have no fear / Life is too long / Friend
PANNCD 16 / May '97 / Pandemonium

Westlake, David

☐ WESTLAKE
Word around town / Dream come true / Rings on her fingers / Everlasting / She grew and she grew / Talk like that
CRECD 019 / Jul '93 / Creation

Weston

☐ GOT BEAT UP
GKCD 019 / Oct '96 / Go-Kart

☐ MATINEE
Opening chord / Record shop / My favourite mistake / Uninspired / Indie rock star / Lonely when I'm with you / Bus stop / Mrs. perfect girl / Next to you at night / Matinee / Eternally / In april sometime / Radio
GKCD 033 / 20 Oct '97 / Go-Kart

Weston, Arthur

☐ PEA VINE WHISTLE
TCD 6005 / Nov '97 / Testament

Weston, John

☐ GOT TO DEAL WITH THE BLUES
MCR 10022 / 7 Apr '98 / Midnight Creeper

☐ I'M DOIN' THE BEST I CAN
APCD 120 / Sep '96 / Appaloosa

☐ SO DOGGONE BLUE (Weston, John & Blues Force)
Leaving home / Because of love / Back to the country / So doggone blue / Coloration / I'd rather leave / Stuck with the blues / Squeeze play / So much in love / You didn't fool me / Younger days / Too jealous / Blue and lonesome
ECD 26092 / 17 Mar '98 / Evidence

Weston, Kim

☐ GREATEST HITS AND RARE CLASSICS
It takes two: *Weston, Kim & Marvin Gaye* / Take me in your arms (rock me a little while) / Helpless / Do like I do / Teach me tonight: *Weston, Kim & Marvin Gaye* / I'm still loving you / Little more love / It should have been me / Love me all the way / Looking for the right guy / What good am I without you: *Weston, Kim & Marvin Gaye* / Love like yours (don't come knocking everyday) / Another train coming / Feel alright tonight / Baby (don't you leave me) / I'll never see my love again / Thrill a moment / Just loving you / Don't compare me with her / Go ahead and laugh
5545132 / 3 Aug '98 / Spectrum

☐ KIM, KIM, KIM
You just don't know / Love I've been looking for / What could be better / When something is wrong with my baby / Love vibrations / Buy myself a man / Got to get you off my mind / Soul on fire / Brothers and sisters (get together) / Penny blues / Choice is up to you (Walk with me Jesus)
CDSXE 063 / Jul '92 / Stax

☐ VERY BEST OF KIM WESTON, THE
Somebody's eyes / Helpless / You hit me where it hurt me / Signal your intention / My heart's not made of stone / Doin' it for myself / Investigate / It's too late / Case of too much loves making / Talkin' loud / It should have been me / After the rain / Just one man for me / Riding on the crest of a wave / Restless feet / Oh no not my baby / Springtime in my heart / Baby I'm yours
3035990012 / Oct '95 / Carlton

Weston, Paul

☐ FLOATIN' LIKE A FEATHER/THE SWEET AND THE SWINGIN'
Breezin' along with the breeze / What can I say after I say I'm sorry / It's a lovely day today / You turned the tables on me / All of me / Just you, just me / At sundown / You took advantage of me / Keepin' out of mischief now / Cheatin' on me / Isn't it a lovely day / Floatin' like a feather / Thrill is gone / I love you / Time on my hands / I'll see you in my dreams / Lies / Dream / Blue moon / Bye bye blues / Linger awhile / All by myself / Sometimes I'm happy / Street of dreams
CTMCD 116 / Jun '97 / EMI

Weston, Randy

☐ BLUES TO AFRICA
African village / Bedford stuyvesant / Tangier Bay / Blues to Africa / Kasbah kids / Uhuru Kwanza / Call / Kucheza blues / Sahel
FCD 41014 / Sep '87 / Freedom

☐ CARNIVAL
Carnival / Tribute to Duke Ellington / Mystery of love
FCD 41004 / Sep '87 / Freedom

☐ EARTH BIRTH
5370882 / May '97 / Verve

☐ HOW HIGH THE MOON
Loose wig / Run Joe / Theme for Teddy / In a Spanish town / Don't blame me / JK blues / Well you needn't / How high the moon
BCD 147 / Jun '97 / Biograph

☐ MARRAKESH IN THE COOL OF THE EVENING
In the cool of the evening / Portrait of billie / Two different ways to play the blues / Portrait of dizzy / Lisa lovely / Uli shrine / Blues for elmo lewis / Ballad for t / Valse triste walse / Where / Let's climb a hill / Jitterbug waltz / Blues for five reasons / Lotus blossom
5215882 / May '94 / Verve

☐ MONTEREY 1966
Call / Afro black / Little Niles / Portrait of Vivian / Berkshire blues / Blues for Strayhorn / African cookbook
5196982 / May '94 / Verve

☐ SAGA
5292372 / Apr '96 / Verve

☐ SPIRITS OF OUR ANCESTORS, THE (2CD Set)
African village Bedford-Stuyvesant / Healers / African cookbook / La elaha elle Allah / Morad Allah / Call / African village Bedford-Stuyvesant / Seventh Queen / Blue Moses / African sunrise / Prayer for us all
5118572 / Feb '92 / Verve

☐ VOLCANO BLUES (Weston, Randy & Melba Liston)
Blue mood / Chalabati blues / Sad beauty blues / Nafs / Volcano / Harvard blues / In memory of / Blues for Strayhorn / Penny packer blues / JK blues / Mystery of love / Kucheza blues / Blues for Elma Lewis
5192692 / Feb '93 / Verve

Westside Connection

☐ BOW DOWN
World domination / Bow down / Gangsta's make the world go round / All the critics in New York / Do you like criminals / Gangstas don't dance / Gangsta, the killa and the dope dealer / Cross 'em out and out a 'K / King of the hill / 3 time felons / Westward ho / Pledge / Hoo-bangin'
CDPTY 134 / Nov '96 / Priority/Virgin

☐ GANGSTAS MAKE THE WORLD GO ROUND
PTYCD 119 / May '97 / Priority/Virgin

Westworld

☐ BEATBOX ROCK 'N' ROLL
Sonic boom boy / Where the action is / Beatbox rock 'n' roll / Rockulator / Psychotech / Silver mac / Ba-na-na-bam-boo / Mix me up / Injection / Cheap 'n' nasty / Joy rider / Painkiller / Johnny Blue / Everything good is bad / Dance on / Break your heart / Big Red Indian / Ultimate Westerner / Paper skyscraper / Whirlwind girls / Cadillac / Fly Westworld
74321487292 / May '97 / Camden

Wet Wet Wet

☐ 10 (2CD Set)
If I never see you again / Back on my feat / Fool for your love / Only sounds / If only I could be with you / I want you / Maybe I'm in love / Beyond the sea / Lonely girl / Strange / Theme from Ten / It hurts
5363192
5364622 / 1 Sep '97 / Precious

☐ END OF PART ONE - GREATEST HITS
Wishing I was lucky / Sweet little mystery / Temptation / Angel eyes / With a little help from my friends / Sweet surrender / Brokeaway / Stay with me heartache / Hold back the river / This time / Make it tonight / More than love / Put the light on / Goodnight girl / Lip service / Blue for you / Shed a tear / Cold cold heart
5184772 / Nov '93 / Precious

☐ HIGH ON THE HAPPY SIDE
More than love / Lip service / Put the light on / High on the happy side / Maybe tomorrow / Goodnight girl / Celebration / Make it tonight / How long / Brand new sunrise / Two days after midnite
5104272 / Jan '92 / Precious

☐ HOLDING BACK THE RIVER
Sweet surrender / Can't stand the night / Blue for you / Brokeaway / You've had it / I wish / Keys to your heart / Maggie May / Hold back the river
8420112 / Mar '92 / Precious

☐ MEMPHIS SESSIONS, THE
I don't believe / Sweet little mystery / East of the river / This time / Temptation / I remember / For you are / Heaven help us all
8366032 / Nov '88 / Precious

☐ PICTURE THIS
Julia says / After the love goes / Somewhere, somehow / Gypsy girl / Don't want to forgive me now / She might never know / Someone like you / Love is my shepherd / She's on my mind / Morning / Home tonight / Love is all around
5268512 / Apr '95 / Precious

☐ POPPED IN SOULED OUT
Wishing I was lucky / East of the river / I remember / Angel eyes / Sweet little mystery / Temptation / I can give you everything / Moment you left me
8327262 / Sep '87 / Precious

Wettling, George

☐ CLASSICS 1940-1944
CLASSICS 909 / Nov '96 / Classics

Wetton, John

☐ AKUSTIKA LIVE IN AMERICA
BP 226CD / Jul '96 / Blueprint

☐ ARKANGEL
Circle of St. Giles / Last thing on my mind / Desperate times / I can't lie anymore / Arkangel / You against the world / Be careful what you wish for / Emma / Nothing happens for nothing / All grown up / After all / Celtic cross / Take those tears
EAGCD 020 / 2 Mar '98 / Eagle

☐ BATTLE LINES
Right where I wanted to be / Battle lines / Jane / Crime of passion / Sand in my hand / Sea of mercy / Hold me now / Space and time / Walking on air / You're not the only one
BP 240CD / Nov '96 / Blueprint
CPCD 020 / Sep '96 / Cromwell

☐ CHASING THE DEER
BP 282CD / 6 Apr '98 / Blueprint

☐ CHASING THE DRAGON
Heat of the moment / Don't cry / Rendezvous / Crime of passion / Caught in the crossfire / Easy money / In the dead of the night / Thirty years / Only time will tell / Hold me now / Starless / Book of Saturday / Battle lines / Open your eyes / Smile has left your eyes
BP 227CD / Nov '96 / Blueprint

Whale

☐ PAY FOR ME
Pay for me / I think no / Darling Nikki / Buzzbox babe / Trying
DGHUTM 24 / May '95 / Hut

☐ WE CARE
Kickin' / That's where it's at / Pay for me / Eurodog / I'll do ya / Electricity / Hobo humpin' slobo babe / Tryzasnice / Happy in you / I miss me / Young, dumb and full of cum / I'm cold / Born to raise hell
CDHUT 25
DGHUT 25 / Jul '95 / Hut

Wham

☐ FANTASTIC
Bad boys / Ray of sunshine / Love machine / Wham rap / Club Tropicana / Nothing looks the same in the light / Come on / Young guns (go for it)
4500902 / '91 / Epic

☐ FINAL, THE
Wham rap / Young guns go for it / Bad boys / Club Tropicana / Wake me up before you go go / Careless whisper / Freedom / Last Christmas / Everything she wants / I'm your man / Blue (armed with love) / Different corner / Battlestations / Where did your heart go / Edge of heaven
CD 88681 / '86 / Epic

☐ IF YOU WERE THERE (The Best Of Wham)
If you were there / I'm your man / Everything she wants / Club tropicana / Wake me up before you go go / Like a baby / Freedom / Edge of heaven / Wham rap / Young guns / Last Christmas / Where did your heart go / Everything she wants / I'm your man
4890202 / 24 Nov '97 / Epic

☐ TWELVE INCH MIXES
Wham rap / Careless whisper / Freedom (long mix) / Everything she wants / I'm your man
4501252 / Nov '92 / Epic

Wharton Tiers

☐ BRIGHTER THAN LIFE
ALP 60CD / Jul '97 / Atavistic

Wharton, Bill

☐ SOUTH OF THE BLUES
KS 023 / Nov '94 / Flying Fish

☐ STANDING IN THE FIRE (Wharton, Bill & The Ingredients)
KS 036CD / Oct '96 / King Snake

What Noise

☐ FAT
Eventually / Change / Obliv / Zombic / Wobble / Core / Strange times / Vanilla / Pow / Anybody / Crash / Whip / Taste / Nob
BND 8 CD / Feb '90 / One Little Indian

Whatever

☐ LIES AND GOLD DUST
Stepping stone / Down on the up / Tin soldiers / Good time high / Suffer immaculate / All that remains / Hero's ego / No.1 / Back from the dead / Corrosion / Brain drain
CDMFN 220 / Jun '97 / Music For Nations

☐ SUGARBUZZ
CDMFN 193 / Mar '96 / Music For Nations

Whatnauts

☐ DEFINITIVE WHATNAUTS, THE (2CD Set)
I just can't lose your love / Tweedly dum dum / She's gone to another / What life to give (after giving it all) / Fall in love all over / Just can't leave my baby / I'll erase away your pain / Please make the love go away / Souling with the Whatnauts / Dance to the music / Message from a black man / You forgot too easy / Heads up / Hurry up and wait / I'm so glad I found you / Only people can save the world / Blues fly away / Why can people be colours too / Ooh baby baby / Try me (and I'll show you) / Friends by day (lovers by night) / Alibis and lies / I dig your act / You gave me true loving / World / We will always be together / My thing / Let me be that special one / Girls (part 1): *Whatnauts & Moments* / Girls: *Whatnauts & Moments* / Help is on the way / Genuine / Give a damn / Why can't we be together / Just passing / Strolling / Gotta be a love (somewhere)
DEEPD 005 / Nov '96 / Deep Beats

Wheat

☐ MEDEIROS
SF 004 / 24 Aug '98 / Sugar Free

Wheat Chiefs

☐ REDEEMER
BANG 10142 / Feb '97 / Bang On

Wheater, Paul

☐ ROCK OF AGES
Lead me gently home / I'd rather have Jesus / He'll understand / When God dips his love in my heart / He walked that lonesome road / God will / What a friend we have in Jesus / I saw a man
ALD 063 / Oct '96 / Alliance Music

Wheater, Tim

☐ HEARTLAND
ALMOCD 006 / Mar '96 / Almo Sounds

Wheatstraw, Peetie

☐ BLUES, THE (2CD Set)
FA 255 / Nov '96 / Fremeaux

☐ DEVIL'S SON-IN-LAW, THE
SOB 035412 / Apr '93 / Story Of The Blues

☐ PEETIE WHEATSTRAW VOL.1 1930-1941
DOCD 5241 / May '94 / Document

☐ PEETIE WHEATSTRAW VOL.2 1930-1941
DOCD 5242 / May '94 / Document

☐ PEETIE WHEATSTRAW VOL.3 1930-1941
DOCD 5243 / May '94 / Document

☐ PEETIE WHEATSTRAW VOL.4 1930-1941
DOCD 5244 / May '94 / Document

☐ PEETIE WHEATSTRAW VOL.5 1930-1941
DOCD 5245 / May '94 / Document

☐ PEETIE WHEATSTRAW VOL.6 1930-1941
DOCD 5246 / May '94 / Document

☐ PEETIE WHEATSTRAW VOL.7 1930-1941
DOCD 5247 / May '94 / Document

Wheeler, 'Golden Big'

☐ JUMP IN
DE 709 / Jan '98 / Delmark

Wheeler, Cheryl

☐ CIRCLES AND ARROWS
I know this town / Hard line to draw / Aces / Estate sale / Don't wanna / Northern girl / Soon as I find my voice / Miss you more than I'm mad / Moonlight and roses / When you're gone / Arrow
CDPH 1162 / May '95 / Philo

☐ DRIVING HOME
PH 1152CD / Jan '94 / Philo

☐ MRS. PINOCCI'S GUITAR
CDPH 1192 / Nov '95 / Philo

Wheeler, Ian

☐ IAN WHEELER AT FARNHAM MALTINGS
Easter parade / 2.19 blues / Gatemouth / Liberia rag / Higher ground / Honeysuckle rose / Curse of an aching heart / Tyrees blues / Ole miss rag / Hesitation blues / Sensation / Old fashioned love / Melt down
LACD 32 / Nov '94 / Lake

Wheeler, James

☐ READY
Ready / This old freight train / Gonna make some changes / My key won't fit that lock no more / Cold hearted woman / Blues at midnight / Good morning little schoolgirl / Bad girl / Extension / I'm just your fool / My baby's comin' home / Hound dog / Looking for my baby
DE 719 / Jul '98 / Delmark

Wheeler, Kenny

☐ ALL THE MORE
1212362 / May '98 / Soul Note

☐ ANGEL SONG
Nicolette / Present past / Kind folk / Unti / Angel song / Onmo / Nonetheless / Past present / Kind of gentle
5330982 / Feb '97 / ECM

☐ AROUND 6
Mai we go round / Solo one / May ride / Follow down / Riverrun / Lost woltz
5291242 / Feb '96 / ECM

☐ CALIFORNIA DAYDREAM (Wheeler, Kenny & Gardner/Van De Geyn/ Ceccarelli)
500292 / Nov '93 / Musidisc

☐ DOUBLE DOUBLE YOU
Foxy trot / Ma bel / W W / Three for D'reen / Blue for Lou / Mark time
8156752 / Jan '90 / ECM

☐ GNU HIGH
Heyoke / Smatter / Gnu suite
8255912 / Aug '85 / ECM

☐ KENNY WHEELER 1976
Hi-yo / Slofa / Quiso / Blues news / Kitts
JAS 95062 / May '96 / Just A Memory

☐ LIVE AT THE MONTREAL BISTRO TORONTO (Wheeler, Kenny & Sonny Greenwich)
Gentle piece / Memories of Miles / I love you / For Kenny Wheeler / Canticle / Summertime
JUST 1142 / 23 Feb '98 / Justin Time

☐ MUSIC FOR LARGE AND SMALL ENSEMBLES
Part I (opening) / Part II (For H) / Part III (for Jan) / Part IV (for PA) / Part V (know where you are) / Part VI (consolation) / Part VII (Freddy C) / Part VIII (closing) / Sophie / Sea lady / Gentle piece / Trio / Duet I / Duet II / Duet III / By myself
8431522 / Nov '90 / ECM

☐ SIREN'S SONG (Wheeler, Kenny & Norma Winstone)
Ticketeeboo / Little suite / Siren's song / Winter sweet / Heyoke / Quatorze / Sumother song
JTR 84652 / 23 Feb '98 / Justin Time

☐ TOUCHE (Wheeler, Kenny & Paul Bley)
Presto / Ouvre / Fausto / Doing time / Mystique / Double standard / Touche / Concours / Deja vu / Colour / Upscale / Prequel / Sortie
JUST 972 / Feb '97 / Justin Time

☐ WALK SOFTLY (Wheeler, Kenny & Guildhall Jazz Band)
Kayak / Walk softly / Widow in the window / Little suite / Who are you / Know where know how
WAVE 32CD / 20 Jul '98 / Wave

☐ WIDOW IN THE WINDOW (Wheeler, Kenny Trio)
Aspire / Ma balle Helene / Widow in the window / Ana / Hotel le hot / Now, and now again
8431982 / Jun '90 / ECM

Wheeler, Onie

☐ ONIE'S BOP
Jump right out of this jukebox / Tell em off / I wanna hold my baby / Onie's bop / Booger gonna getcha / Going back to the city / Long gone / Steppin' out / I'll love you for a lifetime / Beggar for your love / Walkin' shoes / That's all / Cut it out / That's what I like / She wiggled and giggled / I'm satisfied with my dreams / No, i don't guess i will / Would you like to wear a crown / I saw mother with God last night / My home is not a home at all / Little mama / Hazel / Closing time / Tried and tried, I / I'll swear you don't love me / Love me like you used to do / When we all fet there / Mother prays loud in her sleep / Million years in glory / Run 'em off / Bonaparte's retreat
BCD 15542 / May '91 / Bear Family

Wheelz

☐ AROUND THE WORLD VOL.1 (Wheelz & Ingrid Jensen)
Wheelz newz / Balkanamera / Allah / 52nd Street / Hot wheelz / Hungarian red house / Adria / Indian summer / Naked world / Ruth / Away from home
92472 / Feb '97 / Act

Whelan, John

☐ CELTIC CROSSROADS
Denis Dillon's square dance polka / Mabel Ruddy's the windy gap / Skimming the surface / Ceol nanolag / There were roses / Beautiful blackwater / Maggie K's / Father Maroney's 95 south Granny Barnes / Champs Elysees / Balkans / Grosse ile / Ian's return to Ireland / Yanik's / Denis Whelan's / Flower of Magherally / Passage of time
ND 61060 / Apr '97 / Narada
VNDCD 5 / 11 May '98 / Virgin

☐ CELTIC REFLECTIONS
Louise / Longing for home, longing for here / Dancing to a lot of time / Last dance / Road home / Sacred ground / From the heart / Mist-eyed morning / Breton gathering / Song for Hilary / Desaunay / Cape finisterre / Trip to Skye / My Ballingarry lady
ND 61052 / Apr '96 / Narada

☐ FRESH TAKES (Whelan, John & Eileen Ivers)
Castle kelly's / Tom fleming's-kitty's wedding-sean mcguire's / Lorraine's waltz / Blackberry blossom / Jenny's welcome to charlie-father francis cameron (reels) / Kevin burke's / Gypsy / Red-haired lass-paddy o'brien's-the scholar / Desaunay-the petticoat I bought in mullingar (hornpipe and r / Trip to skye-darach debrun's
GLCD 1075 / Feb '93 / Green Linnet

Whellans, Mike

☐ SWING TIME JOHNNY RED
COMD 2036 / Feb '94 / Temple

When

☐ BLACK, WHITE AND GREY
RERWHCD / Jan '94 / ReR/ Recommended

When Granny Sleeps

☐ PLANET CONSTRUCTION
STCD 4209 / May '97 / Storyville

Where Eagles Fly

☐ SCOTTISH FANTASIA
WEF 5 / May '95 / Glencoe

Whetstone, Dave

☐ RESOLUTION, THE
Rocky and the gopher / Bonavista 1 and 2 / Resolution / Emilia's angels/Jolly jolly demons / Black swan / Hotfoot 2 / Henry's moat / Fish pie polka/timberline / Sherborne rose / Fingers in the jam / Sweet ginger / Candlemas moon / Cummerbund/heads up / Hare in the long grass / Rachel's delight
MKRCD 410 / Nov '96 / Monkey's Knib

☐ WAZ (WAZ)
COOKCD 143 / Mar '98 / Cooking Vinyl

Whigfield

☐ WHIGFIELD
Think of you / Another day / Don't walk away / Big time / Out of sight / Close to you / Sexy eyes / Ain't it blue / I want to love / Saturday night
8286272 / Jun '95 / Systematic

☐ WHIGFIELD VOL.2
ZYX 204452 / Nov '97 / ZYX

While, Chris

☐ IN THE BIG ROOM
FLED 3009 / Mar '97 / Fledg'ling

☐ LOOK AT ME NOW
FAT 003CD / Aug '94 / Fat Cat

☐ PIECEWORK (While, Chris & Julie Matthews)
Class reunion / Starting all over again / This is your instant karma / Hard to be the way / Piecework / Factory floor / Seven years of rust / From this wood / White water running / Winter shines / Even the desert bears a seed
TWO 002 / Jan '98 / Fledg'ling

Whiplash

☐ CULT OF ONE
MASSCD 087 / Apr '96 / Massacre

☐ POWER AND PAIN/TICKET TO MAYHEM
D 00053CD / 11 May '98 / Displeased

☐ SIT STAND KNEEL PRAY
MASSCD 129 / 8 Dec '97 / Massacre

Whipped Cream

☐ ...& OTHER DELIGHTS
Explosion / Remember / Silver 1 / Let us try it out / Wishing / This time next time / Theodora wine / I know your mine / Whatever / Together / Come together / Explosion '93
RESNAP 001 / Jan '94 / Soap

☐ TUNE IN THE CENTURY
Yes / Tune in the century / Wait for a minute / Lay down beside / Give away / Sensational / Virtuosly / Observatory crest / Up the country / Come and find / Beyond the sun
SNAP 003 / Sep '92 / Soap

Whippersnapper

☐ FORTUNE
WPSCD 004 / Dec '97 / WPS

☐ PROMISES
Farewell my lovely Nancy / Whenever / Banks of the sweet primroses / Pride of Kildare / Rouge and the red shoes / An Sean bhean bhocht / I wandered by a brookside / John Gaudie / Seven keys / One way donkey ride / Hard times of old England / Romanitza / Downtown rodeo / Deneze sous doue (on the wall) / Frank Dempsey's lament and joy / Carolanning / My little fiddle / Loving Hannah / Lizzie Wan / There's a river / An Sean bhean bhocht / Gipsys rest / John broke the prison door
WPSCD 001 / Dec '97 / WPS

☐ STORIES
WPSCD 005 / Dec '97 / WPS

☐ TSUBO
Farewell my lovely Nancy / Pride of Kildare / Rouge and the red shoes / I wandered by a brookside / Seven keys / Romanitza / Deneze sous doue (on the wall) / Frank Dempsey's lament and joy / My little fiddle / There's a river
WPSCD 002 / May '88 / WPS

Whippersnapper

☐ AMERICA'S FAVOURITE PASTIME
LOB 10006CD / 11 May '98 / Lobster/ Fat Wreck Chords

Whirligig

☐ CELTIC DAWN
CDLDL 1227 / Mar '95 / Lochshore

☐ WHAT IF A DAY...
Galliard/Watkin's ale/Frog Galliard / Lord Lovat's lament / Scots canaries / Scotch times / Simon Brodie / Deutu Gamene/Soizic/Maharid / Piper's three/Coranto/Les poules houpees / Fayne would I wed/Giles Farnaby's dream / What if a day/A toy/ Wison's Wilde / Longmyno / Sanz canarios/Sanz jig / My lord of Marche Pavan / Quarter Brante
CDLDL 1248 / Sep '97 / Lochshore

Whirling Pope Joan

☐ SPIN
TAT 294CD / Aug '94 / Panic ATC

Whirlpool

☐ LIQUID GLASS
REV 052CD / Dec '96 / Revelation

Whirlpool Productions

☐ BRIAN DE PALMA
LAD 0201612 / May '95 / Ladomat

Whirlwind

☐ IN THE STUDIO
Hang loose (I've gotta rock) / Boppin' high school baby / My bucket's got a hole in it / My advice / Thousand stars / One more chance / Don't be crazy / Rockin' Daddy / Slow down / Blue moon of Kentucky / Together forever / Who's that knocking / Tore apart / Do what I do / Duck tail / I only wish (That I'd been told) / Midnight blue / Teenage cutie / You got class / Honey hush / Cruisin' around / Stay cool / Running wild / Okie's in the pokie / Heaven knows / Big Sandy / Such a fool / Nightmares / If it's all the same to you / Stayin' out all night
CDWIKD 147 / Jun '95 / Chiswick

Whiskey Town

☐ STRANGERS ALMANAC
OPD 30005 / 12 Jan '98 / Outpost

Whiskeytown

☐ RURAL FREE DELIVERY
MFR 0082 / Jun '97 / Mood Food

Whisky Before Breakfast

☐ MARY'S TEAPOT
WBBCD 1 / Jul '97 / Abacus

Whisky Priests

☐ BLEEDING SKETCHES
WPTCD 13 / Oct '95 / Whippet

☐ BLOODY WELL LIVE
WPT CD7 / May '93 / Whippet

☐ FIRST FEW DROPS, THE
WPTCD 10 / Oct '94 / Whippet

☐ LIFE'S TAPESTRY
WPTCD 14 / Sep '96 / Whippet

☐ NEE GUD LUCK
WPTCD 11 / Oct '94 / Whippet

☐ POWER & THE GLORY, THE
WPT 008CD / Apr '94 / Whippet

☐ THINK POSITIVE
Better man than you / Side by side / My ship / Alice in wonderland / Song for Ewan / Man who sold his town / Going to the mine / What I could have been / Car boot sale / Wherever you go / Brothers in arms again / Positive steps / Leave her Johnny leave her
IRONCD 001 / Jun '98 / Iron Man

☐ TIMELESS STREET
WPTCD 12 / Oct '94 / Whippet

Whispers

☐ 30TH ANNIVERSARY ANTHOLOGY (2CD Set)
Seems like I gotta do wrong / There's a love for everyone / Can't help but love you / I only meant to wet my feet / Somebody loves you / Mother for my children / Bingo / One for the money / Living together (In sin) / Make it with you / (Let's go) All the way / Lost and turned out / Can't do without love / Song for Donny / And the beat goes on / Lady my girl / It's a love thing / I'm the one for you / I can make it better / This kind of lovin' / In the raw / Emergency / Tonight / Keep on loving me / Contagious / Some kinda lover / Rock steady / Just gets better with time / In the mood / No pain no gain / Say yes / Special F/X
NEDCD 267 / Aug '94 / Sequel

☐ AND THE BEAT GOES ON
And the beat goes on / Lady / My girl / It's a love thing / I'm the one for you / Seems like I gotta do wrong / There's a love for everyone / Headlights / All the way / One for the money / Rock steady / Emergency / Some kinda lover / Keep on loving me / This kind of lovin' / In the mood
21045 / Jul '97 / Laserlight

☐ BEST OF THE WHISPERS, THE
And the beat goes on / My girl / Headlights / One for the money / I can make it better / It's a love thing / In the raw / Tonight / Some kinda lover / Contagious / Rock steady / Special FX / Lady / No pain, no gain / Make it with you / Let's go all the way / Out the box / Living together
CCSCD 804 / Sep '95 / Renaissance Collector Series

☐ ESSENTIAL SLOW GROOVE DANCEFLOOR CLASSICS
DGPCD 727 / May '95 / Deep Beats

☐ IMAGINATION
It's a love thing / Say you would love for me too / Continental shuffle / I can make it better / Imagination / Girl I need you / Up on soul train / Fantasy
NEBCD 793 / Jul '96 / Sequel

☐ LOVE IS WHERE YOU FIND IT
In the raw / Turn me out / Cruisin' in / Emergency / Say yes / Love is where you find it / Only you / Small talkin'
NEBCD 840 / Jul '96 / Sequel

☐ LOVE THING
It's a love thing / And the beat goes on / My girl / Can't do without your love / Cruisin' in / Welcome into my dreams / Only you / Rock steady / Lady / Emergency / Keep on lovin' me / Tonight / Imagination / I want to make it with you
5507562 / Mar '95 / Spectrum

☐ SONGBOOK VOL.1
INTD 90111 / 8 Dec '97 / Interscope

☐ WHISPERS
Song for Donny / My girl / Lady can you do the boogie / And the beat goes on / I love you / Out the box / Welcome into my dream
NEBCD 794 / Jul '96 / Sequel

Whistlebinkies

☐ ANNIVERSARY
Farewell to Nigg / Piper, the harper, the fiddler / Fiddle Strathspey and Reel / MacBeth / Island jigs / Whistlebinkies' reel / Ane ground / Sir John Fenwick / Ailein Duinn / MacDonald of the Isles / Dominic McGowan / Fiddlers' farewell / Winter it is past / Dogs among the bushes / Rattlin' roarin' Willie / Barlinnie Highlander / Change of tune
CC 54CD / Nov '92 / Claddagh

☐ INNER SOUND
Inner sound / Inner sound / Bonny at morn / Christening piece / Lost boys / Montrose 500 / Miss valerie wallace / Peter macleod's reel / Boston cuffes / Beloved gregor / Isle of barra march / Tryst / Piper's controversy / Theme from etain / Follow my highland soldier / 72nd farewell to aberdeen / Campbell's farewell to redcastle / Barren rocks of aden / Oran mor / Bright love of my heart
CDLOC 1063 / Feb '95 / Lochshore

☐ WANTON FLING, A
Piper's jig / Ay waulkin o / Whistlebinkies jig / Ho ro mo chuachag / Dunkeld Bridge / Cam' ye o'er frae France / Taladh / Farewell to Muirhead's / Deireadh leave 1940 / Wee Eddie reel / Wanton fling / A'bhalsa mu dheireadh
CDTRAX 095 / Feb '96 / Greentrax

Whitaker, Rodney

☐ HIDDEN KINGDOM
DIW 929 / Feb '98 / DIW

Whitcomb, Ian

☐ HAPPY DAYS ARE HERE AGAIN (Whitcomb, Ian Dance Band)
DAPCD 242 / Apr '89 / Audiophile

☐ IAN WHITCOMB & HIS BUNGALOW BOYS/REGINA WHITCOMB
ACD 267 / Jun '96 / Audiophile

☐ IAN WHITCOMB & HIS MERRY BAND 1967-1993
SOSCD 1276 / Apr '94 / Stomp Off

☐ LOTUS LAND
ACD 283 / Jun '95 / Audiophile

☐ RAGTIME AMERICA
ACD 277 / Aug '94 / Audiophile

☐ THIS SPORTING LIFE
This sporting life / Soho / Boney Maronie / Dance again / Turn a song (Test pressing version) / You turn me on (Turn a song) / Be my baby / That is rock 'n' roll / N-n-nervous / Good hard rock / Where did Robinson Crusoe go with Friday on Saturday night / Poor little bird / Your baby has gone down the plughole / Louie Louie / Lover's prayer / Naked ape / Kingfisher of the loving pack / Life has no reason / Sally sails the sky / Notable yacht club of staines / Star / When rock 'n' roll was young / Oh pretty woman / Rolling with the quake / Rocking the baby to sleep
CREV 032CD / Jul '94 / Rev-Ola

☐ TITANIC (Music As Heard On The Fateful Voyage) (Whitcomb, Ian White Star Orchestra)
REP 4685 / Oct '97 / Repertoire
ARTFULCD 11 / 19 Jan '98 / Artful

☐ YOU TURN ME ON/MOD MOD MUSIC HALL
You turn me on / River of no return / Be my baby / Nervous / Poor but honest / Fizz / This sporting life / Too many cars on the road / That is rock 'n' roll / Sugar babe / No tears for Johnny / Poor little bird / Got a date with an angel / Night I appeared as Macbeth / August 1914 / Coney Island washboard / Mother mother mother / Junkman rag / Sweetheart of Sigma Chi / Awful tale of Maggie May / Where did Robinson Crusoe go / Saucy seaside Sue / Reindeer / Ragtime two step / Ida sweet as apple cider / That ragtime suffragette / Oh Helen / Your baby has gone down the plughole
SC 11044 / Aug '97 / Sundazed

White, Alan

☐ RAMSHACKLED
7567803962 / Jan '96 / Atlantic

White, Aline

☐ JUST A LITTLE WHILE
BCD 292 / Oct '93 / GHB

White, Andy

☐ DESTINATION BEAUTIFUL
Street scenes from my heart / Thinking of change / John / Many's the time / Punk outside the secret police / She doesn't want to cry any more / Learning to cry / He's out there / Ciao baby / Looking into friends / I couldn't leave you / Government of love
COOKCD 072 / Aug '94 / Cooking Vinyl

☐ HIMSELF
In a groovy kinda way / 1,000,000 miles / Six string street / Freeze out / Just jumped out of a tree / Twenty years / Guildford four / Pale moonlight / Bird of passage / St. Patrick's good luck / Coup I / Whole love story / Six string street (30 mph) / Travelling circus
COOKCD 029 / Feb '95 / Cooking Vinyl

☐ OUT THERE
Palaceful of noise / Where's my home / Colour of love / Waiting for the 39 / La Rue Beaurepaire / Speechless / Berlin 6 am / James Joyce's grave / One last kiss / Na na na na / Placeful of noise
9031770122 / Jun '92 / East West

☐ TEENAGE
Acoustic guitar / Get back home / All the things I can bring / If you don't know by now / It's gonna be like this all the time / Jacqui / Because she loves it / Don't be afraid / My gay cousin / Between the man and a woman / I couldn't do it / It's gonna be like this in the rain / Whole thing
COOKCD 123 / Jan '97 / Cooking Vinyl

White, Artie

☐ BEST OF ARTIE WHITE, THE
Today I started loving you again / Nothing takes the place of you / Tore up / Tired of sneaking around / Jody / Dark end of the street / That's where it's at / Nobody wants you when you're old and grey / Funny how time slips away / Hattie Mae / Thangs got to change / I need someone
ICH 1131CD / Oct '93 / Ichiban

☐ THINGS GOT TO CHANGE
Things got to change / Rainy day / I ain't taking no prisoners / You upset me baby / Thank you pretty baby / Hattie Mae / I wonder why / Reconsider baby / Somebody's on my case
ICH 1044CD / Oct '93 / Ichiban

☐ TIRED OF SNEAKIN' AROUND
Today I started loving you / Thinking about making a change / Jody / Peeping Tom / Tired of sneaking around / Don't pet my dog / Can't get you off my mind / I can't seem to please you / Turn about is fair play / Nose to the grindstone
ICH 1061CD / Oct '93 / Ichiban

☐ WHERE IT'S AT
Too weak to fight / I dig my gig / One woman's man / That's where it's at / Love ain't been used / Nobody needs you when you're old and gray / God bless our love / Proud to be your man / Day or two
ICH 1026CD / Oct '93 / Ichiban

White, Barry

☐ BARRY WHITE AND FRIENDS (2CD Set)
America / Let me in and let's begin with love / High steppin', hip dressin' fella (you got it together) / Your love, your love / We can't get go of love / Our theme / Our theme / If you want me, say it / Don't forget, remember / I'm giving you a love (every man is searchin' for) / You make my life easy livin' / It ain't love babe (until you give up) / Take a good look (and what do you see) / I'm so glad that I'm a woman / Sheet music / Never, never say goodbye / Lady, sweet lady / Love makin' music / This love / Better love is (the worse it is when it's over) / Gotta be where you are / Free / You / Hung up in your love / Jamaican girl / Didn't we make it happen baby / Relax to the max / Bayou / Life / I did it for love / In the ghetto / Your the first, the last, my everything
24363 / May '97 / Laserlight

☐ BOSS SOUL
DLF 71255 / 23 Mar '98 / Del-Fi

☐ COLLECTION, THE
You're the first, the last, my everything / You see the trouble with me / Can't get enough of your love babe / I'll do for you anything you want me to / Just the way you are / Walking in the rain with the one I love / It may be Winter outside / Love's theme / Sho' you right / What am I gonna do with you / Never, never gonna give you up / Baby we better try and get it together / Let the music play / Don't make me wait too long / I'm gonna love you just a little more babe / Right night
8347902 / Feb '94 / PolyGram TV

☐ HEART AND SOUL OF BARRY WHITE, THE
Come on in love / I owe it all to you / Long black veil / Out of the shadows of love / I've got the world to hold me up / Your heart and soul / Where can I turn to / Under the influence of love / All in the run of a day / Fragile handle with care
305952 / Jan '97 / Hallmark

☐ I'M GONNA LOVE YOU
MPG 74030 / Nov '94 / Movieplay Gold

☐ ICON IS LOVE, THE
Practice what you preach / There it is / I only want to be with you / Time is right / Baby's home / Come on / Love is the icon / Sexy undercover / Don't you want to know / Whatever we had, we had
5402802 / Oct '94 / A&M

☐ JUST FOR YOU (2CD Set)
5141432 / Jan '93 / Phonogram

☐ LET THE MUSIC PLAY
What am I gonna do with you / Let the music play / You see the trouble with me / Sha la la means I love you / I've got so much to give / Love serenade / How did you know it was me / Bring back my yesterday / Right night / Theme from 'king kong' / Theme from 'together brothers' / It may be winter outside (but in my heart it's spring)
MPG 74032 / Nov '94 / Movieplay Gold

☐ LET THE MUSIC PLAY
Let the music play / I can't get enough of your love, babe / I love you more than anything (In this world girl) / Love serenade / I Hard to believe that I found you / September when I first met you / Don't make me wait too long / Look at her / I'm gonna love you just a little more, baby / Oh love, well we finally made it / Let me live my life lovin' you babe / Love serenade II
5515152 / Oct '95 / Spectrum

☐ LOVE ALBUM, THE
I've got the whole world to hold me up / Your heart and soul / Under the influence of love / All in the run of love / Out of the shadows of love / Long black veil / Come on in love / Where can I turn to / I owe it all to you / Fragile, handle with care / My buddy / I've got the whole world to hold me up
PLATCD 210 / Feb '97 / Platinum

☐ LOVE ALBUM, THE
Out of the shadows of love / I owe it all to you / Where can I turn / Come on in love / Under the influence of love / I've got the whole world to hold me up / Your heart and soul / I'm fragile handle with care / All in the run of the day / Long black veil
100252 / May '97 / A-Play Collection

☐ RIGHT NIGHT AND BARRY WHITE, THE
Sho' you right / For your love / There is a place / Love is in your eyes / Right night / I'm ready for love / Share / Who's the fool
CDMID 155 / Oct '92 / A&M

☐ SATIN AND SOUL VOL.2 (2CD Set)
Walking in the rain with the one I love / Don't make me wait too long / Don't tell me about heartaches / I won't settle for less than the best (You baby) / Didn't we make it happy baby / Let me in, let's begin with love / Let the music play / Lady sweet lady / I like you, you like me / Change / Gotta be where you are / What am I gonna do with you / You're the one I need / Life / Any fool could see / I found love / Our theme (part 2) / Baby we better try and get it together / She's everything to me / Let's make tonight an evening to remember / I can't let him down / You're the only one for me
DVSOPCD 154 / Dec '90 / Connoisseur Collection

☐ SOUL SEDUCTION
Never never gonna give ya up / Standing in the shadows of love / What am I gonna do with you / Honey please can't you see / Your sweetness is my weakness / I love to sing the songs I sing / It's only love doing it's thing / Bring back my yesterday / I've got so much to give / You see the trouble with me / Playing your game baby / You're so good, you're so bad / Oh me oh my (I'm such a lucky guy)
5500902 / Oct '93 / Spectrum

☐ SPOTLIGHT ON BARRY WHITE
My buddy / Long black veil / Where can I turn to / I've got the world to hold me up / Your heart and soul / Out of the shadows of love / Under the influence of love / Fragile hadnle with care / All in the run of love / Come on in love / I owe it all to you
HADCD 142 / Feb '94 / Javelin

☐ UNLIMITED LOVE COLLECTION, THE
Can't get enough of your love, babe / Just the way you are / It's ecstasy when you lay down next to me / I've got so much to give / Let the music play / Never, never gonna give you up / You see the trouble with me / You're the first, the last, my everything / I've found someone / Bring back my yesterday / Standing in the shadows of love / I'm gonna love you just a little more, baby
APH 102801 / Apr '96 / Audiophile Legends

☐ YOU'RE THE FIRST, THE LAST, MY EVERYTHING
Can't get enough of your love babe / You're the first, the last, my everything / I'll do for you anything you want me to / Baby we better try and get it together / It's ecstasy when you lay down next to me / Just the way you are / Honey please can't you see / Standing in the shadows of love / Rhapsody in white / My sweet summmer suite / Under the influence of love
MPG 74031 / Nov '94 / Movieplay Gold

☐ YOUR HEART & SOUL
JHD 001 / Jun '92 / Tring

White, Brian

☐ C'EST MAGNAFIQUE (White, Brian & His Magna Jazz Band)
JCD 248 / Jun '95 / Jazzology

☐ MUGGSY REMEMBERED
JCD 200 / Oct '92 / Jazzology

☐ PLEASURE MAD (White, Brian & His Magna Jazz Band)
JCD 178 / Oct '92 / Jazzology

☐ RAGTIMERS VOL.1 (White, Brian & Alan Gretsy)
JCD 116 / Aug '94 / Jazzology

White, Buck

☐ MORE PRETTY GIRLS THAN ONE
SHMC 3710 / Mar '89 / Sugar Hill

White, Bukka

☐ 1963 NOT 1962
Streamline special / Drunken leroy blues / Fixin' to die / Midnight twister / Aberdeen blues / Vaseline head woman / Jump / Jack o'diamonds / Chi chi boogie / 1963 is not 1962 / Blues / Boogie 'till dubuque / Driftin' and driftin' / Corina corina
EDCD 382 / Oct '94 / Edsel

☐ BIG DADDY
Gibson hill / Black cat bone blues / 1936 trigger toe / Cryin' Holy unto the Lord / Shake my hand blues / Sic em dogs on / Aberdeen Mississippi / Mama don low / Hot springs Arkansas / Jelly roll Morton man / Black crepe blues / Glory bound train / Hobo blues
BCD 145 / Jun '97 / Biograph

☐ BIG DADDY, MISSISSIPPI BLUES
BG 145CD / Dec '96 / Biograph

☐ COMPLETE SESSIONS 1930-1940
New Frisco train / Panama limited / I am in the heavenly way / Pine bluff Arkansas / Where can I change my clothes / Sleepy man blues / Parchman farm / Good gin blues / Special line
TMCD 03 / Apr '90 / Travellin' Man

☐ MISSISSIPPI BLUES
Shake 'em on down / I am in the heavenly way / Atlanta special / Drunk man blues / Army blues / Aberdeen, Mississippi blues / Baby please don't go / New Orleans, streamline / Parchman Farm blues / Poor boy long way from home / Remembrance of Charley Patton
AIM 0007CD / Aug '97 / Aim

☐ MISSISSIPPI BLUES
Aberdeen Mississippi blues / Baby please don't go / New Orleans streamline / Parchman farm blues / Poor boy long way from home / Rememberance of Charlie Patton / Shake 'em on down / I am in the heavenly way / Atlanta special / Drunk man blues / Army blues / World boogie / Midnight blue / Old man walking blues
CDTAK 1001 / Jun '98 / Takoma

☐ SHAKE 'EM ON DOWN
New 'frisco train / Panama limited / I am in the heavenly way / Promise true and grand / Pinebluff Arkansas / Shake 'em on down / Sic 'em dogs on / Po' boy / Black train blues / Strange place blues / When can I change my clothes / Sleepy man blues / Parchman farm blues / Good gin blues / High fever blues / District attorney blues / Fixin' to die blues / Aberdeen Mississippi blues / Bukka's jitterbug swing / Special streamline
KATCD 106 / 26 May '98 / Catfish

☐ SKY SONGS VOL.1-2
ARHCD 323 / Apr '95 / Arhoolie

White Caps

☐ BLOWN IN THE USA
F 003CD / Apr '97 / Fearless

White, Carla

☐ LISTEN HERE
Devil may care / Harlem nocturne / Dreamsville / It's you or no one / Lotus blossom / It's only a paper moon / Darn that dream / I've got your number / Listen here / Feelin' good / Dream
ECD 221092 / Jan '95 / Evidence

White Cockade

☐ TARTAN CAPERS
WHITECD 1 / Feb '98 / Sylvia Miskoe

White Devil

☐ REINCARNATION
LF 210CD / Jan '96 / Lost & Found

White Eagle Jazzband

☐ TRIBUTE TO PAUL BARBARIN, A
BCD 404 / Mar '97 / GHB

White, Ernie

☐ SCENES FROM AMERICA
199643 / 16 Mar '98 / Made To Measure

White, Georgia

☐ GEORGIA WHITE VOL.1 1930-1936
DOCD 5301 / May '95 / Document

☐ GEORGIA WHITE VOL.2 1936-1937
DOCD 5302 / May '95 / Document

☐ GEORGIA WHITE VOL.3 1937-1939
DOCD 5303 / May '95 / Document

☐ GEORGIA WHITE VOL.4 1939-1941
DOCD 5304 / May '95 / Document

☐ TROUBLE IN MIND 1935-1941
158322 / Apr '95 / Blues Collection

White Hassle

☐ NATIONAL CHAIN
Let me drive your car / Beating of my heart / What I said / Out of control / Tom the harlequin / Don't make a sound / Oh what a feeling / Oh it's so hard / I'm so lonesome I could cry / Great ship / Adventure / I lose again / Leave my woman alone / Another day passes
OLE 2622 / Aug '97 / Matador

White Heaven

☐ OUT
PSFD 11 / Sep '95 / PSF

White House

☐ DEDICATED TO PETER KURTEN
SLCD 013 / Nov '96 / Susan Lawley

☐ GREAT WHITE DEATH SPECIAL EDITION
SLCD 017 / Dec '96 / Susan Lawley

☐ NEW BRITAIN
SLCD 015 / Nov '96 / Susan Lawley

☐ QUALITY TIME
SLCD 012 / Nov '96 / Susan Lawley

☐ THANK YOUR LUCKY STARS
SLCD 018 / 22 Sep '97 / Susan Lawley

☐ WORTHLESS
SLCD 020 / 16 Mar '98 / Susan Lawley

White, Howard

☐ NASHVILLE SIDEMAN WITH FRIENDS
Jealous heart / Blue eyes cryin' in the rain / Roly poly / Deep water / Rose of ol' Pawnee / San Antonio rose / Faded love / Midnight / Columbus Stockade blues / Before I met you / Steel guitar dowve / Ensonata / Rosette / Steel guitar swallow
BCD 15575 / Apr '92 / Bear Family

☐ WESTERN SWING AND STEEL INSTRUMENTALS
Jealous heart / Blue eyes cryin' in the rain / Roly poly / Deep water / Rose of ol' Pawnee / San Antonio rose / Faded love / Midnight / Columbus stockade blues / Before I met you / Steel guitar dove / Ensonata / Rosette / Steel guitar swallow
BCD 15575 / Apr '93 / Bear Family

White, James

☐ BUY (White, James & The Contortions)
Design to kill / My infatuation / I don't want to be happy / Anesthetic / Contort yourself / Throw me away / Roving eye / Twice removed / Bedroom athlete / Throw me away (live) / Twice removed (live) / Jailhouse rock
74321327572 / Mar '96 / Infinite Zero

☐ FLAMING DEMONICS
Devil made me do it / Boulevard of broken dreams / Rantin' and ravin' / Natives are restless / Caravan/It don't mean a thing/Melt yourself down / I danced with a Zombie
74321391762 / Oct '96 / Infinite Zero

☐ OFF WHITE
74321318792 / Oct '95 / Infinite Zero

White, Jeff

☐ WHITE ALBUM, THE
Cold cold heart / Right before my eyes / I never know / Old Plank Road / Cabin among the trees / All prayed up / Leavin' town / Hannah / Little lies / Little Joe / Promises you made / I'm goin' on / When the night is near
ROUCD 0385 / Oct '96 / Rounder

White, Jim

☐ WRONG EYED JESUS
Book of angels / Burn the river dry / Still waters / When Jesus gets a brand new name / Sleepy town / Perfect day to chase tornados / Wordmule / Stabbed in the heart / Angel land / Heaven of my heart / Road that leaves to Heaven
9362464722 / Jun '97 / Luaka Bop

White, Joshua

☐ BLUES AND SPIRITUALS
How long blues / Careless love / Oh lula / St. Louis blues / Kansas city blues / I had to stoop to conquer you / I know how to do it / Dink's blues / One mint julep / Good morning blues
HILLCD 16 / Apr '97 / Wooded Hill

☐ FREE AND EQUAL BLUES
SFWCD 40081 / 6 Apr '98 / Smithsonian Folkways

☐ JOSH WHITE VOL.1 1929-1933
DOCD 5194 / Oct '93 / Document

☐ JOSH WHITE VOL.2 1933-1935
DOCD 5195 / Oct '93 / Document

☐ JOSH WHITE VOL.3 1935-1940
DOCD 5196 / Oct '93 / Document

☐ JOSH WHITE VOL.5 1944
DOCD 5571 / 21 Sep '97 / Document

☐ JOSH WHITE VOL.6 1944-1945
DOCD 5572 / 21 Sep '97 / Document

☐ LEGENDARY JOSH WHITE, THE
John Henry / Cotton eyed Joe / One meat ball / Careless love / Motherless children / Prison bound / Hard time blues / St. Jame's infirmary / Pure religion hallilu / Waltzing Matilda / Miss Otis regrets / Told my captain / Jerry / No.12 train / Trouble / Riddle song / House I live in / Joshua fit the battle of Jericho
CBCD 3 / 29 Jun '98 / Collector's Blues

☐ SOUTHERN EXPOSURE
John Henry / One meatball / Southern exposure / Did you ever love a woman / Billy boy / Beloved comrade / No more blues / Frankie and Johnny / Milkcow blues / Hard time blues / Lord Randall, my son / Jelly jelly / Watercress / Evil hearted man / Mean mistreatin' woman / Miss Otis regrets / Baby baby / Dupree / Left a good deal in mobile / Lass with the delicate air / Backwater blues / House I live in / Strange fruit / Jim Crow train / Outskirts of town
PASTCD 7810 / Jan '97 / Flapper

White, K.C.

☐ SIGNS AND WONDER
RN 7044 / 22 Jun '98 / Rhino

White, Karyn

☐ KARYN WHITE
Way you love me / Secret rendezvous / Slow down / Superwoman / Family man / Love saw it / Don't mess with me / Tell me tomorrow / One wish
K 9256372 / Mar '94 / WEA

☐ MAKE HIM DO RIGHT
Hungah / Nobody but my baby / I'm your woman / Weakness / One minute / Simple / Pleasure / I'd rather be alone / Thinkin' bout love / Make him do right / Can I stay / With you / Here comes the pain again
9362454002 / Sep '94 / WEA

☐ RITUAL OF LOVE
Romantic / Ritual of love / Way I feel about you / Hooked on you / Walking the dog / Love that's mine / How I want you / One heart / Tears of joy / Beside you / Do unto me / Hard to say goodbye
7599263202 / Sep '91 / WEA

White Knight

☐ WHITE KNIGHT
Twilite / Energy / Techno disco / Alarm / Gonna jack '96 / White Knight '96 / Hard drive / New world order
TRXUKCD 003 / Sep '96 / Trax UK

White, Lari

☐ BEST OF LARI WHITE, THE
Amazing Grace / Itty bitty little single solitary piece of my heart / Lay around and love on you / Lead me not / What a woman wants / That's what at Heart / Just thinking / That's my baby / That's how you know (when you're in love) / Now I know / Ready, willing and able / I've been waiting for your love / Helping me get over you: *White, Lari & Travis Tritt*
7863669942 / Jan '97 / RCA Nashville

☐ DON'T FENCE ME IN
74321339142 / Jun '96 / Camden

☐ WISHES
That's my baby / Somebody's fool / Wishes / Now I know / If I'm not already crazy / That's how you don't know / When it rains / Go on / It's love / If you only knew
7863663952 / Apr '95 / RCA

White, Lavelle

☐ MISS LAVELLE
ANT 0031CD / Sep '94 / Antones

White, Lenny

☐ RENDERERS OF SPIRIT
HIBD 8014 / Feb '97 / Hip Bop

White Light

☐ WHITE LIGHT/VELVET SANDPAPER
001 / Oct '97 / Two Of Us

White Lightning

☐ STRIKES TWICE
AA 066 / 24 Nov '97 / Arf Arf

White Lion

☐ BEST OF WHITE LION, THE
Wait / Radar love / Broken heart / Hungry / Little fighter / Lights and thunder / All you need is rock 'n' roll / When the children cry / Love don't come easy / Cry for freedom / Lady of the valley / Tell me / Farewell to you
7567824252 / Oct '92 / Atlantic

☐ FIGHT TO SURVIVE
CDMFN 130 / Jul '92 / Music For Nations

☐ MANE ATTRACTION
Lights and thunder / Leave me alone / Love don't come easy / You're all I need / Broken heart / Warsong / It's over / Till death do us part / Out with the boys / Farewell to you / She's got everything
7567821932 / Apr '91 / Atlantic

☐ PRIDE
Hungry / Lonely nights / Don't give up / Sweet little loving / Lady of the valley / Wait / All you need is rock 'n' roll / Tell me / All join our hands / When the children cry
7817682 / Jul '87 / Atlantic

White, Lily

☐ NO PORK LONG LINE
JFCD 017 / May '97 / Jazz Focus

☐ SOMEWHERE BETWEEN TRUTH AND FICTION
KFWCD 153 / Feb '95 / Knitting Factory

White, Michael

☐ EIGHTIES, THE (White, Michael & His New Orleans Music)
Shake it and break it / Am I blue / Please don't talk about me when I'm gone / In the upper garden / Mama Inez / It's a sin to tell a lie / Apex blues / Baby won't you please come home / Girl of my dreams / Exactly like you / Hindusthan / Streets of the city / Careless love / Sing on / Royal garden blues
504CDS 6 / Mar '98 / 504

☐ MOTION PICTURES (White, Michael & Bill Frisell)
You are too beautiful / Easy living / Night has a thousand eyes / Flamingo / My shining hour / Misterioso / My one and only love
INT 32122 / Aug '97 / Intuition

White Moon

☐ TRADITIONAL MUSIC FROM MONGOLIA
PANCD 2010 / May '93 / Pan

White Mountain Bluegrass

☐ ARAGON MILL
I've had a time / Church on the foot of the hill / Dobro chimes / Aragon mill / One you slip around with / Five miles to Winchester / Achin' heart / I thought I heard you calling my name / Ragtime Annie / You ain't woman enough to take my man / I wonder how the old folks are at home / Shuckin' the corn / Papa played the dobro / Stranger in my home / Old spinning wheel / Daddy for a day / Prisoner song / Pathway of teardrops / I love God's way of living
SCR 30 / Nov '97 / Strictly Country

White Noise

☐ ELECTRIC STORM, AN
Love without sound / My game of loving / Here comes the fleas / Firebird / Your hidden dreams / Visitation / Black mass / Electric storm in hell
3DCID1001 / '94 / Island

White Orange

☐ WHITE ORANGE
1215 / Dec '91 / Caprice

White Out

☐ RED SHIFT
E 96 / 23 Mar '98 / Ecstatic Peace

White, Peter

☐ CARAVAN OF DREAMS
Caravan of dreams: *White, Peter & Boney James* / Together again: *White, Peter & Boney James* / Venice beach / Soul embrace / Long ride home: *White, Peter & Rick Braun* / Just another day: *White, Peter & Basia* / City of lights / Cafe mystique: *White, Peter & Marc Antoine* / Bittersweet / Lullaby
4851362 / Aug '96 / Sony Jazz

☐ SONGS OF THE SEASON
Christmas song / Joy to the world/Hark the herald angels sing / Greensleeves / River / First Noel / O tannenbaum / O little town Bethlehem / Jingle bells / Silent night / White Christmas
CK 68493 / 3 Nov '97 / Sony Jazz

White Plains

☐ MY BABY LOVES LOVIN'
I've got you on my mind / When tomorrow comes tomorrow / Taffeta rose / Taffeta rose (I remember) / (I remember) Summer morning / Ecstasy / Julie Anne / Does anybody know where my baby is / Step into a dream / Dad you saved the world / I can't stop / Carolina's coming home / Gonna miss her missisippi / When you are a king / Every little move she makes / Julie do ya love me / Lovin' you baby / Honey girl / Young birds fly / Show me your hand / You've got your troubles / Today I killed a man I didn't know / My baby loves lovin' / In a moment of madness / To love you
8206222 / May '93 / London

White, Rodric

☐ NEW JAZZ DIRECTIONS
LB 9513 / Jul '98 / La Brava

White, Roland

☐ TRYING TO GET TO YOU
SHCD 3826 / May '95 / Sugar Hill

White, Saylor

☐ THAT'S JUST THE WAY IT GOES
422491 / Nov '94 / New Rose

White, Sheila G.

☐ NEW COUNTRY LINE 'N' KICKIN' (White, Sheila G. & Blueberry Hill)
SOW 528 / Sep '97 / Sound Waves

☐ ROCK 'N' COUNTRY DANCE PARTY (White, Sheila G. & Red River Boys)
Hello Mary Lou / Mystery train / Six days on the road / Blue days black nights / Well alright / Whole lotta shakin' / That's alright mama / Wild side of life / Blue moon of Kentucky / Wanderer / Rave on / Come on everybody/Summertime blues / Bye bye love / It doesn't matter anymore / Hound dog/Wipeout / You never can tell / Maybe baby / Hey good lookin' / Promised land / Nadine
SOW 531 / Apr '98 / Sound Waves

White Sister

☐ FASHION BY PASSION
Place in the heart / Fashion by passion / Dancin' on midnight / Save me tonight / Ticket to ride / April / Until it hurts / Troubleshooters / Lonely teardrops / Place in my heart
WKFMXD 76 / Mar '87 / FM

White, Snowy

☐ GOLDTOP (The Definitive Collection)
Carol / Modern times / Pigs on the wing: *Pink Floyd* / Drop in from the top: *Wright, Richard* / Renegade: *Thin Lizzy* / Memory pain / Slaybo day / In the skies: *Green, Peter* / Answer / Bird of paradise / Tailfeathers / Someone else is gonna love me / That certain thing / Out of order / Open for business / Highway to the sun / Time has come / Judgement day
RPM 154 / Nov '95 / RPM

☐ HIGHWAY TO THE SUN
Highway to the sun / Can't find love / Burning love / Loving man / Time has come / Heartful of love / Love, pain, and sorrow / Hot Saturday night / Keep on working / I loved another woman / I can't get enough of the blues
29007205 / Sep '95 / Bellaphon
CDMANU 1493 / Feb '97 / ODE

☐ LITTLE WING (White, Snowy & The White Flames)
Discoveri / Long distance loving / I'll be moving on / More you live / Little wing / That's when I'll stop loving you / Terpisah / First move / Like the sun / That ain't right / Melting
HYCD 298175 / Feb '98 / Hypertension

☐ MASTERS, THE
EABCD 103 / 30 Mar '98 / Eagle

White Stains

☐ WHY NOT FOREVER
EFA 112302 / Feb '94 / Danse Macabre

White, Tam

☐ KEEP IT UNDER YOUR HAT (White, Tam Band)
More / Dream / Coupe de Ville / Mad Sam / Good morning heartache / Street people / Stone mason's blues / Sleep-late Louie's / Woman in love / Nature of the beast / 36th Street mission blues
JHCD 018 / Jan '94 / Ronnie Scott's Jazz House

☐ MAN DANCIN'
DDICK 23CD / 6 Oct '97 / Dick Bros.

☐ REAL DEAL, THE
Pollution blues / Blue blue feeling / Born under a bad sign / This is the way we make a broken heart / Save me / Eyesight to the blind / Workin' class white boy / Home is where the hatred is / Stonemason's blues / Man dancin' / Long time comin'
G2CD 7002 / 1 Aug '98 / G2

White Town

☐ SOCIALISM, SEXISM AND SEXUALITY
PARCD 004 / Nov '96 / Parasol

☐ WOMEN IN TECHNOLOGY
Undressed / Thursday night at the Blue Note / Week next June / Your woman / White town / Shape of love / Wanted / Function of the orgasm / Going nowhere somehow / Theme for an early evening sitcom / Death of my desire / Once I flew
CDCHR 6120 / Feb '97 / Chrysalis

White, Tony Joe

☐ BEST OF TONY JOE WHITE, THE
Polk salad Annie / Willie and Laura Mae Jones / Soul Francisco / Don't steal my love / Roosevelt and Ira Lee / For Lee Ann / Elements and things / Rainy night in Georgia / High sheriff of Calhoun Parrish / Widow Wimberly / Stud spider / Old man Willis / Save your sugar for me / Polka salad Annie
9362453052 / Sep '93 / Warner Bros.

☐ BEST OF TONY JOE WHITE, THE (2CD Set)
Roosevelt and Ira Lee / Stockholm blues / High sheriff of Calhoun Parrish / Old man Willis / Train I'm on / If I ever saw a good thing / As the crow flies / Even trolls love to rock and roll / Backwood preacher man / Takin' the midnight train / Did somebody make a fool out of you / Caught the Devil and put him in jail in Eudor, Arkansas / Saturday night in Oak Grove , Louisiana / I've got a thing about you baby / For ol' time sake / Ol' Mother earth
MPG 74177 / Nov '94 / Movieplay Gold

☐ CLOSER TO THE TRUTH
5113862 / Mar '96 / Polydor

☐ COLLECTION, THE
D 31737 / Jun '97 / Festival

☐ GROUPIE GIRL
Stud-spider / High sheriff of calhoun parrish / Widow wimberly / Conjure woman / Save your sugar for me / Groupy girl / Hard to handle / What does it take (to win your love) / My friend / Stockholm blues / Boom boom
MPG 74023 / Nov '93 / Movieplay Gold

☐ LAKE PLACID BLUES
5275302 / 15 Sep '97 / Polydor

☐ LIVE
DFG 8407 / Sep '90 / Dixie Frog

☐ POLK SALAD ANNIE (Live In Europe 1971)
Roosevelt and Ira Lee / Night in the life of a swamp fox / Rainy night in Georgia / Lustful Earl and the married woman / Willie and Laura Mae Jones / My kind of woman / Mississippi river / Travelling bones / Back to the country / Polk salad Annie
WB 885972 / 2 Feb '98 / Disky

☐ POLKA SALAD ANNIE
Willie and laura mae jones / Soul francisco / Aspen colorado / Whompt out on you / Don't steal my love / Polk salad annie / Who's making love / Scratch my back / Little green apples / Wichita lineman / Look of love
MPG 74021 / Nov '93 / Movieplay Gold

☐ RAINY NIGHT IN GEORGIA
Rainy night in Georgia / Willie and Laura Mae Jones / Polk salad Annie / Groupie girl / Don't steal my love / Scratch my back / Roosevelt and Ira Lee (night of the Missacin) / I thought I knew you well / Elements and things / I want you / Save your sugar for me / Stud-spider / High Sherriff of Calhoun Parrish / Stockholm blues
APH 102803 / Apr '96 / Audiophile Legends

☐ ROOSEVELT AND IRA LEE
Elements and things / Roosevelt and ira lee (night of the mossacin) / Woodpecker / Rainy night in georgia / For le ann / Old man willis / Woman with soul / I want you / I thought I knew you well / Migrant
MPG 74022 / Nov '93 / Movieplay Gold

White Willow

☐ EX TENEBRIS
LE 1029 / 16 Feb '98 / Laser's Edge

☐ IGNIS FATUUS
LE 1021 / 15 Jun '98 / Laser's Edge

White Zombie

☐ ASTRO CREEP
Electric head (The agony) / Supercharger heaven / Real solution # 9 / Creature of the wheel / Electric head (2)(The ecstasy) / Grease paint and monkey brains / I zombie / More human than human / El phantasmo and the chicken run blast-o-rama / Blur the technicolor / Blood milk and sky
GED 24806 / May '95 / Geffen

☐ LA SEXORCISTO DEVIL MUSIC VOL.1
Welcome to planet motherfucker/Psychoholic slag / Knuckle duster (Radio 1-A) / Thunder kiss / Black sunshine / Soul crusher / Cosmic monsters inc / Spiderbaby (yeah yeah yeah) / I am legend / Knuckle duster (Radio 2-B) / Thrust / One big crunch / Grindhouse (A go-go) / Starface / Warp asylum
GEFD 24460 / Mar '92 / Geffen

☐ SUPER SEXY SWINGIN'
Electric head / More human than human / I, Zombie / Grease paint and monkey brains / Blur the technicolour / Super-charger / Heaven / El phantasmo and the chicken-run blasto-rama / Blood, milk and sky / Real solution / Electric head / I'm your boogie man
GED 24976 / 25 May '98 / Geffen

Whitehead Brothers

☐ SERIOUS
Forget I was a G / Your love is a 187 / Shaniqua / Change / Interlude / Late nite tip / Just a touch of love / Where ya at / Serious / Beautiful black princess / Sex on the beach / Turn U out / She needed me / Love goes on / Beautiful black princess (reprise)
5303462 / 15 Sep '97 / Motown

Whitehead, Tim

☐ AUTHENTIC
Falling grace / No more war / All I ever wanted / Neighbourly complaint / Aspiration / One view of Annet / Come on home / Gypsy
JHCD 017 / Jan '94 / Ronnie Scott's Jazz House

☐ SILENCE BETWEEN WAVES
Southend / Sky seas / Return / Third exposure / One view of Annet / Secret talks / Warners well / True to your word / 34 Cambrian road / These tears / Come on home
JHCD 033 / Nov '94 / Ronnie Scott's Jazz House

Whitehill, Johnny

☐ GUITAR SLINGER
Hold on / Easy / Guitar slinger / Since you've been gone / I'm tired / West End blues / Muddy's blues / Guitar swinger / No more trouble / Sun is shining / Bone picking / As the years go passing by / Guilty / Blow wind blow
IGOXCD 509 / Apr '98 / Indigo

Whitehurst, Gill

☐ GREEN AND LIVING CROWN
Life / Visions / Mirror / Garden / Choices / Shadow / Threads / Strength / Peace / Changes / Rainbow / Roadode / Idol / Miracle / Circus / Time / First / Fool
TERRCD 010 / Jan '98 / Terra Nova

Whiteleather, John

☐ GO RAT GO (Whiteleather, John & The King Rats)
PT 601001 / Jul '96 / Part

☐ HARD LUCK PLAN (Whiteleather, John & The King Rats)
PT 601003 / Jun '96 / Part

☐ TEQUILA HANGOVER (Whiteleather, John & The King Rats)
PT 601002 / Jun '96 / Part

☐ USED PARTS
PT 601004 / Jun '98 / Part

Whiteman, Paul

☐ 16 CLASSIC PERFORMANCES
Whispering / Wang wang blues / Rhapsody in blue / Washboard blues / When the day is done / Way down yonder in New Orleans / Muddy water / China boy / It's only a paper moon / Among my souvenirs / Man I love / Sugar / Mississippi mud / I'm coming, Virginia / Deep purple / Star dust
CWNCD 2030 / Jul '96 / Crown

☐ BIRTH OF RHAPSODY IN BLUE, THE (Historic 1924 Aeolian Hall Concert)
MM 65144 / Apr '96 / Music Masters

☐ GREAT COMBINATION, A
This can't be love / Simple and sweet / Mexican jumpin' bean / My melancholy baby / Cuckoo in the clock / Sing for your supper / Kiss your hand Madam
DAWE 45 / Sep '93 / Magic

☐ KING OF JAZZ, THE (His Greatest Recordings 1920-1936)
Rhapsody in blue: *Whiteman, Paul & George Gershwin* / Changes / Charleston / Darktown strutters ball / Happy feet / Louisiana / Makin' whoopee / Medley / Ol' man river / Slaughter on 10th Avenue / When it's sleepy time down South / Song of India / Three o'clock in the morning / Wang wang blues / Whispering / Whiteman stomp / You took advantage of me
CDAJA 5170 / Mar '96 / Living Era

☐ PAUL WHITEMAN AND HIS ORCHESTRA 1921-1934 (Whiteman, Paul & His Orchestra)
Southern Rose / Merry widow waltz / I'm a dreamer / Nola / Deep purple / Caprice futuristic / South Sea isles / Suite of serenades / It all depends on you / Parade of the tin soldiers / Liebestraum / Park Avenue fantasy / When you're in love / Night with Paul Whiteman at The Biltmore / Signature tune
PASTCD 9718 / '90 / Flapper

☐ RHAPSODY IN BLUE (& Concerto In F/ Grofe's Grand Canyon/Mississippi Suites) (Whiteman, Paul & His Orchestra)
GEM 0022 / May '98 / Pearl

Whiteout

☐ BIG WOW
YOLP 01 / 1 Jun '98 / Yo Yo

☐ BITE IT
ORECD 536 / Jun '95 / Silvertone

Whiteouts

☐ WHITEOUTS
E 119192 / Dec '93 / Vince Lombard

Whiteside, Taylor

☐ NEW ENGLAND FAVOURITES
FE 1406 / Nov '94 / Folk Era

Whitesnake

☐ 1987
Still of the night / Bad boys / Give me all your love / Looking for love / Crying in the rain / Is this love / Straight for the heart / Don't turn away / Children of the night / Here I go again / You're gonna break my heart again
CDEMS 1531 / Jul '94 / EMI

☐ COME AN' GET IT
Come an' get it / Hot stuff / Don't break my heart again / Lonely days, lonely nights / Wine, women and song / Child of Babylon / Would I lie to you / Girl / Hit and run / Till the day I die
CDEMS 1528 / Jul '94 / EMI

☐ FORKED TONGUE - THE INTERVIEW
CBAK 4064 / Feb '94 / Baktabak

☐ GREATEST HITS
Still of the night / Here I go again / Is this love / Love ain't no stranger / Looking for love / Now you're gone / Slide it in / Slow an' easy / Judgement day / You're gonna break my heart again / Deeper the love / Crying in the rain / Fool for your loving / Sweet lady luck
CDEMD 1065 / Jun '94 / EMI

☐ LIVE IN THE HEART OF THE CITY
Come on / Sweet talker / Walking in the shadow of the blues / Love hunter / Fool for your loving / Ain't gonna cry no more / Ready an' willing / Take me with you / Might just take your life / Lie down / Ain't no love in the heart of the city / Trouble / Mistreated
CDEMS 1525 / Jul '94 / EMI

☐ LOVEHUNTER
Long way from home / Walking in the shadow of the blues / Help me thro' the day / Medicine man / You 'n' me / Mean business / Love hunter / Outlaw / Rock 'n' roll women / We wish you well
CDEMS 1529 / Jul '94 / EMI

☐ READY AN' WILLING
Fool for your loving / Sweet talker / Ready an' willing / Carry your load / Blindman / Ain't gonna cry no more / Love man / Black and blue / She's a woman
CDEMS 1526 / Jul '94 / EMI

☐ RESTLESS HEART (Coverdale, David & Whitesnake)
Don't fade away / All in the name of love / Restless heart / Too many tears / Crying / Stay with me / Can't go on / You're so fine / Your precious love / Take me back again / Woman trouble blues
CDEMD 1104 / Jun '97 / EMI

☐ SAINTS AND SINNERS
Young blood / Rough and ready / Bloody luxury / Victim of love / Crying in the rain / Here I go again / Love and affection / Rock 'n' roll angels / Dancing girls / Saints and sinners
CDEMS 1521 / 6 Jul '98 / EMI Gold

☐ SLIDE IT IN/1987/SLIP OF THE TONGUE (The Originals/3CD Set)
Gambler / Slide it in / Standing in the shadow / Give me more time / Love ain't no stranger / Slow an' easy / Spit it out / All or nothing / Hungry for love / Guilty of love / Still of the night / Bad boys / Give me all your love / Looking for love / Crying in the rain / Is this love / Straight for the heart / Don't turn away / Children of the night / Slip of the tongue / Cheap and nasty / Fool for your loving / Now you're gone / Kitten's got claws / Wings of the storm / Deeper the love / Judgement day / Slow poke music / Sailing ships
CDOMB 016 / 27 Jul '98 / EMI

☐ SLIP OF THE TONGUE
Slip of the tongue / Cheap an' nasty / Fool for your loving / Now you're gone / Kitten's got claws / Wings of the storm / Deeper the love / Judgement day / Slow poke music / Sailing ships
CDEMS 1527 / Jul '94 / EMI

Whitfield, Barrence

☐ BARRANCE WHITFIELD & THE SAVAGES (Whitfield, Barrence & The Savages)
422393FC058 / Jan '95 / Fan Club

☐ HILLBILLY VOO DOO
RTMCD 55 / Sep '93 / Round Tower

☐ LET'S LOSE IT
422391 / May '94 / New Rose

☐ LIVE EMULSIFIED (Whitfield, Barrence & The Savages)
422392 / Jan '95 / New Rose

☐ OW OW OW (Whitfield, Barrence & The Savages)
Rockin' the mule / Madhouse / Apology line / I don't dig your noise / Living proof / Stop twisting' my arm / Girl from outer space / Runnin' and hidin' / Blues is a thief / Ain't she wild / Chillin'
ROUCD 9011 / '88 / Rounder

☐ SAVAGE TRACKS (Whitfield, Barrence & The Savages)
422402 / May '94 / New Rose

Whitfield, David

☐ FROM DAVID WITH LOVE
8209482 / Jan '96 / Deram

☐ GREATEST HITS
Cara mia / Santo natale / Book / Mama / Everywhere / Rags to riches / When you lose the one you love / My son John / Bridge of sighs / My September love / Answer me / Beyond the stars / Adoration waltz / On the Street where you live / Willingly / I'll find you / Right to love / Cry my heart / My unfinished symphony / I believe
8206432 / Nov '90 / Eclipse

☐ WORLD OF DAVID WHITFIELD, THE
I believe / Cara mia / My September love / Answer me / If ever I would leave you / Smile / Book / Trees / Who can I turn to (when nobody needs me) / Adoration waltz / Rags to riches / Ev'rywhere / You are too beautiful / I'll never stop loving you / Rose Marie / Marta / When you lose the one you love / Stranger in paradise / Rudder and the rock / Santo natale
5514052 / May '96 / Spectrum

Whitfield, Mark

☐ FOREVER LOVE
5339212 / Mar '97 / Verve

Whitfield, Norman

☐ I HEARD IT THROUGH THE GRAPEVINE (The Motor City Stars Sing The Songs Of Norman Whitfield) (Various Artists)
Needle in a haystack: *Velvelettes* / Just my imagination: *Cameron, G.C.* / Too busy thinking about my baby: *Cameron, G.C.* / It should have been me: *Weston, Kim* / Runaway child running wild: *Cameron, G.C.* / Smiling faces sometimes: *Vee* / I can't get next to you: *Satintones* / He was really saying something: *Velvelettes* / Lonely lonely girl am I: *Velvelettes* / Ain't too proud to beg: *Wylie, Richard 'Popcorn'* / You got the love I need: *Calvin, Billie* / I heard it through the grapevine: *Gaye, Frankie* / Law of the land: *Undisputed Truth* / Too many fish in the sea: *Marvelettes*
305762 / Oct '96 / Hallmark

Whitfield, Weslia

☐ LUCKY TO BE ME
Lucky to be me / Something to remember you by / Do I love you / Glad to be unhappy / Moments like this / My buddy / This funny world / He was too good to me / By myself / Be careful it's my heart / For all we know / Face like yours / Rhode Island is famous for you / Don't you know I care (or don't you care to) / Two for the road
LCD 15242 / Aug '90 / Landmark

☐ MY SHINING HOUR
Out of this world / Let's fall in love / My shining hour / Medley / Happy as the day is long / Moanin' in the mornin' / As long as I live / I wonder what became of me / Ill wind / Over the rainbow / Ding song the witch is dead / What good about goodbye / Let's take the long way home / Someone at last / One for my baby
HCD 7012 / 16 Mar '98 / Highnote

☐ TEACH ME TONIGHT
It's a most unusual day / I've heard that song before / Almost like being in love / Teach me tonight / Pick yourself up / Don't worry 'bout me / I fall in love too easily / I double dare you / It ain't necessarily so / When you wish upon a star / I wish I were in love again / All my tomorrows / Just in time / Until the real thing comes along / I should care
HCD 7009 / Jan '98 / Highnote

Whiting, Margaret

☐ GREAT LADIES OF SONG, THE
Day in, day out / But not for me / Gypsy in my soul / Like someone in love / He's funny that way / Time after time / My heart stood still / Nobody but you / I hadn't anyone till you / I've never been in love before / But beautiful / My foolish heart / I get a kick out of you / Let's fall in love / Someone to watch over me / I could write a book / Back in your own backyard
CDP 8303952 / Aug '95 / Capitol Jazz

☐ LADY'S IN LOVE WITH YOU, THE
ACD 207 / Feb '91 / Audiophile

☐ LOVE SONGS/SINGS FOR THE STARRY EYED
My ideal / Moonlight in Vermont / Bill you're an old smoothie / Younger than springtime / I've never been in love before / It might as well be spring / Tree in the meadow / He's funny that way / Wonderful guy / Come rain or shine / If I had you / Why shouldn't I / Like someone in love / Day in day out / Love can happen anytime / I got lost in his arms / They didn't believe me / Sometimes I'm happy / Remind me / I hadn't had anyone till you / Young man's fancy
4930642 / Jan '98 / Capitol

☐ MARGARET WHITING
ACD 173 / Aug '94 / Audiophile

☐ THEN AND NOW
I fought every step of the way / Moonlight in Vermont / That old black magic / It might as well be Spring / Lies of handsome men / Coffee shoppe / Hell of a way to run a love affair / I got lost in his arms / Best thing for you / Our little day / Blame it on my youth / Young and foolish / Can't teach my old heart new tricks / My best friend / What is a man / Bewitched, bothered and bewildered / Old devil moon / Now that I have everything
DRGCD 91403 / Mar '92 / DRG

☐ TOO MARVELLOUS FOR WORDS
ACD 152 / Jun '95 / Audiophile

Whitley, Keith

☐ ESSENTIAL KEITH WHITLEY, THE
Turn me to love / Living like there's no tomorrow (finally got to me tonight) / Hard act to follow / If a broken heart could kill / If you think I'm crazy now (you should have seen me when I w / Don't our love look natural / I wonder where you are tonight / I've got the heart for you / Ten feet away / Miami my Amy / Hard livin' / Homecoming / Don't close your eyes / I'm no stranger to the rain / Would these arms be in your way / When you ssay nothing at all / It ain't nothin' / I'm over you / I wonder do you think of me / I'm losing you all over again
07863668532 / Aug '96 / RCA Nashville

Whitman, Slim

☐ 50TH ANNIVERSARY COLLECTION (The Very Best Of Slim Whitman)
Indian love call / I pretend / Rose Marie / Unchained melody / My special angel / I'll Tumbling weeds / My heart has a mind of it's own / Love song of the year / Serenade / Old spinning wheel / When you and I were young Maggie / China Doll / More than yesterday / I'm thinking tonight of my blue eyes / I'm a fool / If I had my life to live over / Happy anniversary / Pearly shells / Love song of the waterfall
CDEMC 3772 / 15 Sep '97 / EMI

☐ COUNTRY CLASSICS
Rose Marie / Indian love call / Let me call you baby / Somewhere my love / My elusive dreams / When you were sweet sixteen / Love song of the waterfall / I'll take you home again Kathleen / Have I told you lately that I love you / Happy anniversary / Beautiful dreamer / When you wore a tulip and I wore a big red rose / Serenade / Roses are red (my love) / Girl of my dreams / Edelweiss / Oh my darlin' (I love you) / Twelfth of never / Can't help falling in love / You are my sunshine
CDMFP 6319 / Apr '97 / Music For Pleasure

☐ COUNTRY STYLE
Rhinestone cowboy / Red river valley / Tumbling tumbleweeds / Kentucky waltz / Home on the range / I can't stop loving you / Cattle call / Rose Marie / Riders in the sky / From a jack to a king / Broken wings / Paper roses / It keeps right on a-hurtin' / Wayward wind / Top of the world / Cool water
CDMFP 6035 / Nov '88 / Music For Pleasure

☐ HOW GREAT THOU ART
REMCD 524 / 27 Apr '98 / Reactive

☐ LEGENDARY SLIM WHITMAN, THE
PLSCD 287 / 1 Jun '98 / Pulse

☐ LOVE SONGS
Rose Marie / Indian love call / Let me call you sweetheart / Somewhere my love / My elusive dreams / When you were sweet sixteen / Love song of the waterfall / I'll take you home again Kathleen / HAve I told you lately that I love you / Happy Anniversary / Beautiful dreamer / When you wore a tulip / Serenade / Roses are red / Girl of my dreams / Edelweiss / Oh my darlin' (I love you) / Twelfth of never / Can't help falling in love / You are my sunshine
CDMFP 6113 / Mar '94 / Music For Pleasure

☐ MAGIC MOMENTS (Whitman, Slim & Byron)
I'll get by: *Whitman, Slim* / Back home again / Rose of cimarron: *Whitman, Byron* / Wabash waltz / If ever I see you again: *Whitman, Byron* / If you love me let me know / River road: *Whitman, Byron* / Before the next teardrop falls / What a fool I was: *Whitman, Slim* / Cowboy heaven / I wish I ws eighteen again / Blue eyes crying in the rain
ANT 002 / Nov '96 / Tring

☐ ROSE MARIE (1949-1959/6CD Set)
I'll do as much for you someday / I'll never pass this way again / Paint a rose on the garden wall / Tears can never drown the flame / I'm casting my lasso towards the sky / Wabash waltz / I'm crying for you / Birmingham Jail / Let's go to church / There's a rainbow in every teardrop / Love song of the waterfall / My love is growing stale / Bandera waltz / End of the world / In a hundred years or more / Why / Cold empty arms / Blue river / Indian love call / China doll / Amateur in love / Song of the old water wall / By the waters of Minnetonka / Keep it a secret / My heart is broken in three / All that I'm asking is sympathy / How can I tell / There's a rainbow in every teardrop / I'm casting my lasso towards the sky / Restless heart / There's a rainbow in every teardrop / Danny Boy / North wind / Darlin' don't cry / Stairway to heaven / Lord help me be as thou / Warm, warm lips / Ride away / Secret love / Why / We stood at the altar / There's a loveknot in my lariat / Too late now / I love the Milky Way / Rose Marie / Heart full of love / Cattle call / Beautiful dreamer / Singing hills / Haunted hungry heart / I hate to see you cry / You have my heart / When I grow too old to dream / Song of the wild / I talk to the waves / Blue eyes crying in the rain / When my blue moon turns to gold again / That silver haired Daddy of mine / Petal from a faded rose / I'll never take you back again / Lord protect my darling / Cryin' for the moon / Roll on silvery moon / Haunted hungry heart / I talk to the waves / At the end of nowhere / I'll never stop loving you / Song of the wild / Tumbling tumbleweeds / Tell me / I'll take you home again Kathleen / Serenade / First one to find the rainbow / Brahms lullaby / In the valley of the moon / Dear Mary / I'll take you home again Kathleen / Dear Mary / Cryin' for the moon / Whiffenpoof song / Curtain of tears / Smoke signals / Among my souvenirs / Tree in the meadow / At the close of a long, long day / I must have been blind / You're the only one / Riding the range for Jesus / Roundup in glory / At the end of nowhere / Careless love / Hawaiian cowboy / Warm, warm lips / I'll take you home again Kathleen / Since you've gone / Amateur in love / Lovesick blues / Many times / Forever / Unchain my heart / Once in a lifetime / Tormented / Candy kisses / Hush-a-bye / Careless hands / Very precious love / Put your trust in me / When it's springtime in the Rockies / At the end of nowhere / Mexicali rose / My best to you / Cowpoke / Wherever you are / I'll sail my ship alone / River of tears / Blues stay away from me / Fool such as I / Letter edged in black / Too tired to care / Prisoner's song / Tree in the meadow / Heartbreak hill / I'll never see Maggie alone / When I call on you / You're the only one / Blues stay away from me / I'll sail my ship alone / What kind of God (do you think you are) / Tree in the meadow / I'll walk with god / Whispering hope / I'm a pilgrim / Evening prayer / Jesus took my burden / Two loves have I / Sunrise / Walk beside me / Each step I take / Great Judgement morning / He lives on high / Today is mine / When I go to my garden / Twilla Lee / Roll river roll / Rose Marie / Indian love call / Amateur in love / Song of the old water wheel / All that I'm asking is sympathy / How can I tell / Danny Boy / Warm, warm lips / Ride away / Rose Marie / Haunted hungry heart / At the close of a long, long day / Unchain my heart / Tormented / Candy kisses / Hush-a-bye
BCD 15768 / May '96 / Bear Family

☐ UNDER HIS WINGS
CDC 5383 / May '94 / Disky

Whitney, Dave

☐ CREATIVE HORN OF DAVE WHITNEY, THE
JCD 68 / Jun '96 / Jazzology

Whitstein Brothers

☐ OLD TIME DUETS
Mansion on the hill / We parted by the riverside / There's an open door waiting / Sinner you'd better get ready / We met in the saddle / I'm troubled / That silver haired daddy / Seven year blues / Weary lonesome blues / Somewhere in Tennessee / Maple on the hill / If I could hear my mother pray again / Pitfall / Beautiful lost river valley
ROUCD 0264 / '89 / Rounder

☐ ROSE OF MY HEART
Rose of my heart / Highway headin' South / Kentucky / My curly headed baby / Weary days / Weary blues from waiting / Arkansas / Bridge over troubled water / Eighth wonder of the world / Scared of the blues / Where the old river flows / Smoky mountain memories
ROUCD 0206 / Oct '94 / Rounder

☐ SWEET HARMONY
ROUCD 0344 / Mar '96 / Rounder

☐ WHITSTEIN BROTHERS SING GOSPEL SONGS OF THE LOUVINS
ROUCD 0308 / Nov '94 / Rounder

Whittaker, Roger

☐ BEST OF ROGER WHITTAKER, THE
New world in the morning / I don't believe in 'if' anymore / River lady / Mexican whistler / Streets of london / Why / Mamy blue / Morning please don't come / Durham town / If I were a rich man / Sunrise, sunset / Morning has broken / Dirty old town / Mistral / Moon shadow / Last farewell
MATCD 326 / Feb '95 / Castle

☐ COLLECTION, THE
MACCD 186 / Aug '96 / Autograph

☐ DANNY BOY...& OTHER IRISH FAVOURITES
When Irish eyes are smiling / Down by the Sally gardens / Forty shades of green / Rose of Tralee / Giant land / Star of the county down / Irish whistler / Unicorn / Minstrel boy / I'll tell me Ma / Rooney / Rising of the lark / Believe me, if all those endearing young charms / Uncle Benny / Danny boy / Kilgarry mountain
09026619722 / Feb '97 / RCA

☐ EVENING WITH ROGER WHITTAKER, AN
PLATCD 3929 / May '94 / Platinum

☐ EVENING WITH ROGER WHITTAKER, AN
Last farewell / Hello good morning happy day / If I were a rich man / Elizabethan serenade / Changelip (African whistler) / All of my life / From the people / Durham town / Mexican whistler / New world in the morning / Mammy blue / Hold on / What love is / First hello last goodbye / Hound dog / Summer in the country / Summer days / Fire and rain / Both sides now / Streets of London / River lady / Sloop John B
EMPRCD 522 / Sep '94 / Emporio

☐ FEELINGS
Feelings / Time in a bottle / Harbour lights / For I loved you / Love me tender / Leavin' on a jet plane / Everytime is gonna be the last time / Send in the clowns / Honey / Gentle on my mind / Unchained melody / When I need you / Miss you nights / Before she breaks my heart / Have I told you lately that I love you
74321183302 / Jun '94 / RCA

☐ GREATEST HITS LIVE
Last farewell / Mexican whistler / Mammy blue / Both sides now / Streets of London / Hello good morning happy day / If I were a rich man / Elizabethan serenade / All of my life / From the people to the people / River lady / Sloop John B / New world in the morning / Hold on / What love is / First hello, last goodbye / Summer in the country / Summer days / Fire and rain
100232 / May '97 / A-Play Collection

☐ I DON'T BELIEVE IN IF ANYMORE
RMB 75077 / Sep '94 / Remember

☐ I WILL ALWAYS LOVE YOU
A whole new world / (Everything I do) I do it for you / When I fall in love / Somewhere my love / Beauty and the beast / Evergreen / Wind beneath my wings / Unchained melody / Somewhere out there / High / What a wonderful world / Sunrise, sunset / You've lost that loving feeling / Born free / I will always love you
09026626822 / Feb '97 / RCA

☐ IN CONCERT (2CD Set)
CPCD 82922 / Jul '97 / Charly

☐ LIVE
MU 5062 / Oct '94 / Musketeer

☐ LIVE
Last farewell / Hello good morning happy day / If I were a rich man / Elizabethan serenade / Changelip (african whistler) / All of my life / From the people / Durham town / Mexican whistler / New world in the morning / Mammy blue / Hold on / What love is / First hello, the last goodbye / Hound dog / Summer in the country / Summer days / Fire and rain / Both sides now / Streets of london / River lady / Sloop john b.
15089 / Aug '91 / Laserlight

☐ NEW WORLD IN THE MORNING
New world in the morning / Streets of London / Early one morning / Lemon tree / Morning please don't come / Last farewell / From both sides now / Waterboy / Special kind of man / Leaving of Liverpool / Mexican whistler
WMCD 5697 / Oct '94 / Disky

☐ NEW WORLD IN THE MORNING
Last farewell / Hello goodmorning happy day / If I were a rich man / Elizabeth serenade / Changelip (African whistler) / All of my life / From the people / Durham town / Mexican whistler / New world in the morning / Mammy blue / Hold on / What love is / First hello, last goodbye / Hound dog / Summer in the country / Summer days / Sloop John B / River lads / Streets of London / Both sides now / Fire and rain
306462 / May '97 / Hallmark

☐ PERFECT DAY
It's impossible / Smile / Hello young lovers / Raindrops keep falling on my head / There I've said it again / Anytime / Blueberry Hill / Perfect day / Whole new world / (Everything I do) I do it for you / When I fall in love / Beauty and the beast / Somewhere out there / I will always love you / Ol' man river / If ever I should leave you / Summertime / Make believe / Durham town / Last farewell / New world in the morning / I don't believe in if anymore
74321371562 / Apr '96 / RCA

☐ ROGER WHITTAKER
Last farewell / Hello good morning happy day / If I were a rich man / Elizabeth serenade / Changelip (African whistler) / All of my life / From the people / Durham Town / Mexican whistler / New World in the morning / Mammy blue / Hold on / What love is / First hello the last goodbye / Hound dog / Summer in the country / Summer days / Fire and rain / Both sides now / Streets of London / River lady / Sloop John B
GFS 066 / Jul '97 / Going For A Song

☐ ROGER WHITTAKER COLLECTION
New world in the morning / Sunrise, sunset / Imagine both sides now / Love lasts forever / Send in the clowns / Wind beneath my wings / I can see clearly now / She / What a wonderful world / Evergreen / Last farewell
74321339392 / Jan '96 / Camden

☐ ROMANTIC SIDE OF ROGER WHITTAKER
It's your love / One another / Love will / New love / Man without love / I would if I could / See you shine / Tall dark stranger / Goodbye / My world / Don't fight / Before she breaks my heart / Time / Summer days / Pretty bird of love / Let me be your sun / Indian lady / Here we stand / Newport Belle / For I loved you
CDMFP 5882 / Apr '90 / Music For Pleasure

☐ SINCERELY YOURS
New world in the morning / Before she breaks my heart / Say my goodbyes to the rain / I can't help it (if I'm still in love with you) / All the way to Richmond / Summer days / Imagine / Love will / My son / Feelings / I would if I could / Man without love / It's your love / Time / Weekend in New England / Pretty bird of love / Let me be your sun / New love / Here we stand / Don't fight / One another / For I loved you / Shoe you shine / What a wonderful world
VSOPCD 129 / Nov '88 / Connoisseur Collection

☐ WORLD OF ROGER WHITTAKER, THE
Durham Town / Last farewell / Morning has broken / Mamy blue / Skye boat song / Morning, please don't come / What a wonderful world / He ain't heavy, he's my brother / New world in the morning / I don't believe in if anymore / Streets of London / Mexican whistler / Dirty old town / Taste of honey / Good morning sunshine / By the time I get to Phoenix / From both sides now / Why
5517382 / May '96 / Spectrum

Whittaker, Sebastian

☐ ONE FOR BU
JR 02032 / Apr '94 / Justice

☐ SEARCHIN' FOR THE TRUTH (Whittaker, Sebastian & The Creators)
JR 002022 / Nov '92 / Justice

Who

☐ 30 YEARS OF MAXIMUM R'N'B (4CD Set)
I'm the face / Here 'tis / Zoot suit / Leaving here / I can't explain / Anyway anyhow anywhere / Daddy rollin' stone / My generation / Kids are alright / Ox / Legal matter / Substitute / I'm a boy / Disguises / Happy Jack / Boris the spider / So sad about us / Quick one / Pictures of Lily / Early morning cold taxi / Last time / I can't reach you / Girl's eyes / Bag o' nails / Call me lightning / I can see for miles / Mary Anne with the shaky hand / Armenia city in the sky / Tattoo / Our love was / Rael 1 / Rael 2 / Sunrise / Jaguar / Melancholia / Fortune teller / Magic bus / Little Billy / Dogs / Overture / Acid queen / Underture / Pinball wizard / I'm free / See me, feel me / Heaven and hell / Young man blues / Summertime blues / Shakin' all over / Baba O'Riley / Bargain / Pure and easy / Song is over / Behind blue eyes / Won't get fooled again / Seeker / Bony Moronie / Let's see action / Join together / Replay / Real me / 5.15 / Bell boy / Love reign o'er me / Long live rock / Naked eye / Slip kid / Dreaming from the waist (Live) / Blue, red and grey / Squeeze box / My wife / Who are you / Music must change / Sister disco / Guitar and pen / You better you bet / Eminence front / Twist and shout / I'm a man / Saturday night's alright for fighting
5217512 / Feb '94 / Polydor

☐ FACE DANCES (Remastered)
You better you bet / Don't let go the coat / Cache cache / Quiet one / Did you steal my money / How can you do it alone / Daily records / You / Another tricky day / I like nightmares / It's in you / Somebody save me / How can you do it alone / Quiet one
5376952 / 6 Apr '98 / Polydor

☐ IT'S HARD (Remastered)
Athena / It's your turn / Cook's country / Dangerous / Eminence front / I've known war / One life's enough / It's hard / One day at a time / Why did I fall for that / Man is a man / Cry if you want / It's hard / Eminence front / Dangerous / Cry if you want
5376962 / 6 Apr '98 / Polydor

☐ KIDS ARE ALRIGHT, THE (Original Soundtrack)
My generation / I can't explain / Happy Jack / I can see for miles / Magic bus / Long live rock / Anyway anyhow anywhere / Young man blue / Baba O'Riley / My wife / Quick one / Tommy can you hear me / Sparks / Pinball wizard / See me, feel me / Join together / Roadrunner / My generation blues / Won't get fooled again
5179472 / Jun '93 / Polydor

☐ LIVE AT LEEDS (25th Anniversary Edition)
Heaven and hell / I can't explain / Fortune teller / Tattoo / Young man blues / Substitute / Happy Jack / I'm a boy / Quick one / Amazing journey / Summertime blues / Shakin' all over / My generation / Magic bus / Sparks
5271692 / 6 Apr '98 / Polydor

☐ LIVE AT THE ISLE OF WIGHT FESTIVAL 1970
Heaven and Hell / I can't explain / Young man blues / I don't even know myself / Water / Shakin' all over / Spoonful/Twist and shout / Summertime blues / My generation / Magic bus / Overture / It's a boy / Eyesight to the blind (the hawker) / Christmas / Acid queen / Pinball wizard / Do you think it's alright / Fiddle about / Go to the mirror / Miracle cure / I'm free / We're not gonna take it / Tommy can you hear me
EDFCD 326 / Oct '96 / Essential

☐ MY GENERATION (The Very Best Of The Who)
I can't explain / Anyway, anyhow, anywhere / My generation / Substitute / I'm a boy / Boris the spider / Happy Jack / Pictures of Lily / I can see for miles / Magic bus / Pinball wizard / Seeker / Baba O'Riley / Won't get fooled again / Let's see action / 5:15 / Join together / Squeeze box / Who are you / You better you bet
5331502 / Aug '96 / Polydor

☐ ODDS AND SODS
Postcard / Now I'm a farmer / Put the money down / Little Billy / Too much of anything / Glow girl / Pure and easy / Faith in something bigger / I'm the face / Naked / Long live rock
5179462 / Jun '93 / Polydor

☐ QUADROPHENIA (Original Soundtrack - Remastered/2CD Set)
I am the sea / Real me / Cut my hair / Punk and the godfather / I'm one / Dirty jobs / Helpless dancer / Is it in my head / I've had enough / 5.15 / Sea and sand / Drowned / Bell boy / Dr. Jimmy / Rock / Love reign o'er me
5319712 / 6 Apr '98 / Polydor

☐ QUICK ONE, A (Remastered)
Run run run / Boris the spider / I need you / Whiskey man / Heatwave / Cobwebs and strange / Don't look away / See my way / Quick one / I've been away / So sad about us / Doctor doctor / Bucket T / Barbara Ann / Batman / Disguises / In the city / Man with money / Happy Jack / My generation/Land of hope and glory
5277582 / 6 Apr '98 / Polydor

☐ TALKIN' BOUT THEIR GENERATION
CBAK 4067 / Feb '94 / Baktabak

☐ TELLTALES (Interview Disc)
TELL 14 / Jun '97 / Network

☐ TOMMY (Remastered)
Overture / It's a boy / 1921 / Amazing journey / Sparks / Eyesight to the blind (the hawker) / Christmas / Cousin Kevin / Acid Queen / Underture / Do you think it's alright / Fiddle about / Pinball wizard / There's a doctor / Go to the mirror / Tommy / Can you hear me / Smash the mirror / Sensation / Miracle cure / Sally Simpson / I'm free / Welcome / Tommy's holiday camp / We're not gonna take it
5310432 / 6 Apr '98 / Polydor

☐ WHO ARE YOU (Remastered)
New song / Had enough / 905 / Sister disco / Music must change / Trick of the light / Guitar and pen / Love is coming down / Who are you / No road romance / Empty glass / Guitan and pen / Love is coming down / Who are you
5338452 / 6 Apr '98 / Polydor

☐ WHO BY NUMBERS, THE (Remastered)
Slip kid / However much I booze / Squeeze box / Dreaming from the waist / Imagine a man / Success story / They are all in love / Blue, red and grey / How many friends / In a hand or a face / Squeeze box / Behind blue eyes / Dreaming from the waist
5338442 / 6 Apr '98 / Polydor

☐ WHO COVERS WHO (Various Artists)
I can see for miles: *Hyperhead* / Kids are alright: *Revs* / Pictures of Lily: *McLagan, Ian & The Bump Band* / Bargain: *Buck Pets* / Good's gone: *Telescopes* / In the city: *Swervedriver* / Substitute: *Blur* / Glowgirl: *Mess* / Anyway, anyhow, anywhere: *Chilton, Alex* / Baba O'Riley: *Hinnies* / Good's gone: *Brilliant Corners*
CM 006CD / Sep '96 / NMC

☐ WHO SELL OUT, THE (Remastered)
Armenia City in the sky / Heinz baked beans / Mary Anne with the shaky hand / Odorono / Tattoo / Our love was / I can see for miles / Medac / Silas Stingy / Sunrise / I can't reach you / Relax / Rael #1/#2 / Glittering girl / Melancholia / Someone's coming / Jaguar / Early morning cold taxi / Hall of the mountain King / Girls eyes / Mary Anne with the shaky hand / Glow girl
5277592 / 6 Apr '98 / Polydor

☐ WHO'S LAST
My generation / I can't explain / Substitute / Behind blue eyes / Baba O'Riley / Boris the spider / Who are you / Pinball wizard / See me, feel me / Love reign o'er me / Long live rock / Long live rock (reprise) / Won't get fooled again / Dr. Jimmy / Magic bus / Summertime blues / Twist and shout
MCLD 19005 / Apr '92 / MCA

☐ WHO'S NEXT (Remastered)
Baba O'Riley / Getting in tune / Love ain't for keeping / My wife / Song is over / Bargain / Going mobile / Behind blue eyes / Won't get fooled again / Pure and easy / Baby don't you do it / Naked eye / When I was a boy / Too much of anything / I don't even know myself / Let's see action
5277602 / 6 Apr '98 / Polydor

Whole Thing

☐ WHOLE THING, THE
Another time / It's all in / Natural feeling / Missing you already / Who's got the makings / Rubberneckin' / Peer pressure / Rope walks
JAZIDCD 088 / Sep '93 / Acid Jazz

Whores Of Babylon

☐ METROPOLIS
CANDLE 006CD / Aug '94 / Candlelight

Whyte, Ronny

☐ ALL IN A NIGHT'S WORK
ACD 247 / '89 / Audiophile

☐ SOFT WHYTE
ACD 204 / Apr '94 / Audiophile

☐ WALK ON THE WEILL SIDE (Whyte, Ronny & Eddie Monteiro)
ACD 289 / Jun '96 / Audiophile

☐ WE LIKE A GERSHWIN TUNE (Whyte, Ronny & Travis Hudson)
ACD 54 / May '98 / Audiophile

Whyton, Wally

☐ CHILDREN SONGS OF WOODY GUTHRIE
Put your fingers in the air / Ocean go / Little seed / Pick it up / Why oh why / Race you down the mountain / One day old / My Daddy / Goodnight little Arlo / How di do / Swimmy swim / Ridin' my car / Cleano / Dance around / Mail myself to you / Bling blang / Don't you push me down / Sleep eye
BCD 16125 / May '97 / Bear Family

☐ LEAVE THEM A FLOWER MINUS 1/IT'S ME MUM
BCD 16158 / May '98 / Bear Family

Wichita Line Band

☐ CHRISTMAS LINE DANCE PARTY
Have yourself a merry little Christmas / White Christmas / Winter wonderland / Deck the halls / Frosty the snowman / God rest ye merry gentleman / Jingle bells / Jingle bell rock / Santa Claus is coming to town / Rockin' around the Christmas tree / Rudolph the red nosed raindeer / We three kings / Good king Wenceslas / Jolly old St. Nicholas / Mister Santa / I saw Mummy kissing Santa Claus / Happy holiday / I wish it could be Christmas every day / We wish you a merry Christmas
3036001182 / Sep '97 / Carlton

Wicked Lady

☐ AXEMAN COMETH, THE
KSCD 9307 / Jun '97 / Kissing Spell

☐ PSYCHOTIC OVERKILL
KSCD 9499 / Jun '97 / Kissing Spell

Wicklows

☐ OLD IRELAND (20 Traditional Irish Tunes)
Old Ireland / Old Dungannon oak / Rare old times / Mursheen Durkin / Galway shawl / Bold O'Donoghue / Fields of Athenry / Wicklow Hills / Dirty old town / Hometown on the Foyle / Do you want your old lobby washed down / Veil of white lace / Rose of Clare / Lovely Lectrim / Pretty little girls from Omagh / Cliffs of Dooneen / I'll tell me Ma / Forty shades of green / Spancil Hill / Wild Rover
CD 6059 / Jan '97 / Music

Wickman, Putte

☐ BEWITCHED (Wickman, Putte Trio)
ABCD 051 / Nov '96 / Bluebell

☐ IN SILHOUETTE (Wickman, Putte Quintet)
NCD 8848 / Aug '95 / Phontastic

☐ IN TROMBONES
NCD 8826 / Aug '94 / Phontastic

☐ INTERCHANGE (Wickman, Putte & Claes Crona)
NCD 8852 / Aug '97 / Phontastic

☐ SEARCHING & SWINGING 1945-1955
PHONTCD 9304 / Aug '94 / Phontastic

☐ SOME OF THIS AND SOME OF THAT (Wickman/Kellaway/Mitchell)
DRCD 187 / Jun '88 / Dragon

☐ VERY THOUGHT OF YOU, THE (Wickman, Putte & Red Mitchell)
DRCD 161 / Oct '88 / Dragon

Widespread Depression Orchestra

☐ DOWNTOWN UPROAR
STCD 540 / '91 / Stash

Widespread Panic

☐ BOMBS AND BUTTERFLIES
Radio child / Aunt Avis / Tall boy / Gradle / Glory / Rebirtha / You got yours / Hope in a hopeless world / Happy / Greta
5343962 / 30 Mar '98 / Mercury

☐ LIGHT FUSE GET AWAY (2CD Set)
5581452 / 22 Jun '98 / Mercury

Widmer, Barbara

☐ BARBARA WIDMER AND HER NEW REVIVAL BAND (Widmer, Barbara New Revival Band)
RSCD 672 / Jul '98 / Raymer

Widowmaker

☐ STAND BY FOR PAIN
CDMFN 175 / Oct '94 / Music For Nations

Wiegand, Roy

☐ WHATEVER FLOATS YOUR BOAT HOME (Wiegand, Roy Big Band)
SB 2081 / Jan '97 / Sea Breeze

Wierbos, Walter

☐ X-CALIBER (A Demonstration Of Extreme Solo Trombone Techniques)
ICP 032 / Apr '98 / ICP

Wiesel, Arnan

☐ DIARY FOR PIANO
BVHAASTCD 9613 / Apr '98 / Bvhaast

Wigan's Ovation

☐ NORTHERN SOUL DANCER
Northern soul dancer / Upon my soul / Let's get together / Be with me tonight / Stand in line / Ski-ing in the snow / Superlove / Sign on the dotted line / Personally / What's wrong with me baby / Ten miles high / My girl
C5CD 592 / Mar '97 / See For Miles

Wiggins, Gary

☐ TIME FOR SAXIN'
BEST 1012CD / Nov '93 / Acoustic Music

Wiggins, Gerald

☐ KING AND I, THE (Modern Jazz Rendition) (Wiggins, Gerald Trio)
FSRCD 53 / Jan '98 / Fresh Sound

☐ SOULIDARITY
Way you look tonight / You're mine you / Surprise blues / Some other spring / On Green Dolphin Street / Strip city / Child is born / What is there to say / Alexander's ragtime band / If it's the last thing I do / Lover
CCD 4706 / Jul '96 / Concord Crossover

☐ WIG IS HERE
You are the sunshine of my life / Edith is the sweetest / Lover / Oh give me something to remember you by / Lady is a tramp / On a clear day (You can see forever) / Stolen sweets / This is the end of a beautiful friendship
BLE 590692 / Dec '90 / Black & Blue

Wiggs, Johnny

☐ SOUNDS OF NEW ORLEANS VOL.2
STCD 6009 / Jul '96 / Storyville

Wiggs, Josephine

☐ BON BON LIFESTYLE (Wiggs, Josephine Experience)
Make me feel like Doris Day / Head to toe / Downward facing dog / Arizona / Like a cool breeze / Trieste / Going home / Vivi's fugue / Mr. B goes surfing / Til I die / Upward facing dog / Trieste reprise
GR 035CD / 27 Oct '97 / Grand Royal

Wights, Jamie

☐ SPREADING JOY
JCD 232 / Apr '94 / Jazzology

Wigsville Spliffs

☐ WIGSVILLE SPLIFFS, THE
RAUCD 018 / May '96 / Raucous

Wigwam

☐ HIGHLIGHTS
Eddie and the boys / Tramdriver / Freddie are you ready / Kite / Nuclear nightclub / Autograph / Just my situation / Cheap evening return / Frederick and Bill / Tombstone valentine / Do or die / June may be too late / Losing hold / Lost without a trace / Henry's highway code / Silver jubilee / Grass for blades / Prophet / Marvelry skimmer (friend from the fields)
LXCD 605 / May '97 / Love

☐ LIGHT AGES
WISHCD 46 / Jun '93 / Digelius

☐ LIVE MUSIC FROM THE TWILIGHT ZONE, THE
LXCD 517 / Dec '95 / Love

☐ NUCLEAR NIGHTCLUB
Nuclear nightclub / Freddie are you ready / Bless your lucky stars / Kite / Do or die / Simple human kindness / Save my money and name / Pig storm / Tram driver / Wardance / Bertha come back / Better hold (and a little view) / All over too soon / Masquerade at the white palace / Goddammadog
CDOVD 466 / Jan '96 / Virgin

Wiik, Kjersti

☐ STRILESOLV
H 7126CD / Aug '97 / Heilo

Wiklund/Svensson/Ekblad

☐ SURGE
DRCD 216 / Jun '88 / Dragon

Wilber, Bob

☐ BOB WILBER AND THE BECHET LEGACY
Down in Honky Tonk Town / Si tu vois ma mere / Stop shimmying sister / Lazy blues / If I let you get away with it / Roses of Picardy / Petite fleur / Rue des Champes Elysees / Chant in the night / I'm a little blackbird looking for a bluebird / Kansas City man blues / China boy
CHR 70018 / Jun '95 / Challenge

☐ BOB WILBER AND THE SCOTT HAMILTON QUARTET (Wilber, Bob & Scott Hamilton)
CRD 171 / Mar '96 / Chiaroscuro

☐ BOB WILBER/DICK WELLSTOOD DUET (Wilber, Bob & Dick Wellstood)
PCD 7080 / Mar '95 / Progressive

☐ BUFADORA BLOW UP (Wilber, Bob Big Band)
ARCD 19187 / May '97 / Arbors Jazz

☐ HAMBURG 1995 (Wilber, Bob & The Bechet Legacy)
CD 028 / May '96 / Nagel Heyer

☐ HORNS A-PLENTY
ARCD 19135 / Nov '94 / Arbors Jazz

☐ IN THE MOOD FOR SWING
I'm in the mood for swing / Talk of the town / Dinah / I'm confessin' that I love you / When lights are low / Ring dem bells / Memories of you / Bei mir bist du schon / Yours and mine / Chinatown
PHONTCD 7526 / Apr '88 / Phontastic

☐ JAZZ IN AMERIKA HAUS VOL.5
CD 015 / May '96 / Nagel Heyer

☐ MAN AND HIS MUSIC, A (Wilber, Bob Quintet)
World is waiting for the sunrise / Stalkin' the Bean / Do I love you / That old gang of mine / Django / I want to be happy / Chu / Freeman's way / Lazy afternoon / JJ Jump / Accent on youth / Lullaby in rhythm / Smoke rings / Bossa losada
J&MCD 503 / Aug '94 / J&M

☐ MEMORIES OF YOU/LIONEL AND BENNY (Wilber, Bob & Dany Doriz)
BB 897 / Apr '97 / Black & Blue

☐ MOMENTS LIKE THIS (Wilber, Bob & Antti Sarpila)
Rent party blues / CC rider / Estrellita / Lester's bounce / Snake charmer / I want a little girl / Moments like this
NCD 8811 / '93 / Phontastic

☐ ODE TO BECHET (Wilber, Bob & The Bechet Legacy)
Margie / Blues in the air / I can't believe that you're in love with me / I get the blues when it rains / Mooche / I ain't gonna give nobody none o' this jelly roll / When my dreamboat comes home / Ode to Bechet / Quincy Street stomp / Sailboat in the moonlight / High society / Bechet's fantasy / Shake it and break it
JCD 142 / Jul '96 / Jazzology

☐ RAPTUROUS REEDS
Jumpin' at the woodside / Chloe / Sherman shuffle / Sultry summer day / Stompin' at the Savoy / You are my lucky star / I've loved you all my life / I double dare you / Alone together / Linger awhile / Yours is my heart alone
PHONTCD 7517 / Apr '94 / Phontastic

☐ REUNION AT ARBORS (Wilber, Bob & Kenny Davern)
ARCD 19183 / 1 Jun '98 / Arbors Jazz

☐ SOPRANO SUMMIT (2CD Set) (Wilber, Bob & Kenny Davern)
Swing parade / Song of songs / Meet me tonight in dreamland / Penny rag / Mooche / Oh sister ain't that hot / Steal away / Egyptian fantasy / Fish vendor / Johnny was there / Please clarify / Where are we
CRD 148 / Mar '96 / Chiaroscuro

☐ SOPRANO SUMMIT 1977 (Wilber, Bob & Kenny Davern)
Strike up the band / Pubbles / Elsa's dream / How can you face me / Dreaming butterfly / Tracks in the snow / Lament / Panic is on / Panama rag
CCD 4052 / May '91 / Concord Jazz

☐ SOPRANO SUMMIT CONCERTO (Wilber, Bob & Kenny Davern)
CCD 4029 / Dec '90 / Concord Jazz

☐ SOPRANO SUMMIT LIVE (Wilber, Bob & Kenny Davern)
J&MCD 501 / May '96 / J&M

☐ SUMMIT REUNION (Wilber, Bob & Kenny Davern)
CRD 311 / Mar '96 / Chiaroscuro

☐ SUMMIT REUNION (Yellow Dog Blues) (Wilber, Bob & Kenny Davern)
CRD 339 / Jun '96 / Chiaroscuro

☐ TRIBUTE TO A LEGEND (The Bechet Legacy)
NHCD 028 / Jul '96 / Nagel Heyer

☐ WHAT SWING IS ALL ABOUT
Smiles/Tickle toe / Someday you'll be sorry / I gotta right to sing the blues / I want to be happy / You'd be so nice to come home to / Basic jump / Back home again in Indiana / Love comes along once in a lifetime / Song is you / Feeling I'm falling / I've got a crush on you/You do something to me / Bernfest '96/This is new / Goody goody / Billie's bounce/Doggin' around
CD 035 / Aug '97 / Nagel Heyer

Wilbur, Jason

☐ LOST IN YOUR HOMETOWN
FLT 111CD / 29 Jun '98 / Flat Earth

Wilburn Brothers

☐ TROUBLE'S BACK IN TOWN (The Hits)
Sparkling brown eyes / I wanna wanna wanna / I'm so in love with you / Mister love / Hey Mr.Bluebird / Which one is to blame / Knoxville girl / Somebody's back in town / Roll muddy river / Tell her so / I'm going to tie one on tonight / I had one too many / It's another world / Someone before me / I can't keep away from you / Hurt her once for me / Arkansas
EDCD 540 / 2 Mar '98 / Edsel

Wilce, Malcolm

☐ BEST OF FAMILY FAVOURITES (Wilce, Malcolm Duo)
She'll be coming round the mountain-the happy wanderer (qu / I can't begin to tell you-careless hands (foxtrot) / I've got you anything but love-sentimental journey (fo / In a shanty in old shanty town-home on the range (waltz) / Cockles and mussels-when irish eyes are smiling (waltz) / It's now or never (tango) / Strangers in the night-april in portugal (tango) / Albatross (rumba) / Love changes everything-i know him so well (rumba) / Star wars (cha cha) / Eye level (cha cha) / Bobbin' up and down-all by yourself in the moonlight (blue / Gilly gilly osenfeffer-chestnut tree (blues) / Pack up your troubles-it's a long way to tipperary (swing) / Bless you-don't laugh at me 'cos I'm a fool (saunter) / I see the moon-last night on the back porch (saunter) / Locomotion (jive) / Pennsylvania 6-5000-string of pearls (jive) / Lambada-riders in the sky (samba) / Pickin' a chicken-i yi yi yi (samba)
CDTS 004 / Aug '93 / Maestro

☐ DANCE GOES ON (Wilce, Malcolm Duo)
CDTS 039 / Nov '93 / Maestro

☐ DANCING ALL OVER THE WORLD (Wilce, Malcolm Duo)
CDTS 051 / Dec '95 / Maestro

Wilco

☐ BEING THERE (2CD Set)
Misunderstood / Forget the flowers / I got you (at the end of the century) / Red eyed and blue / (Was I) in your dreams / Dreamer in my dreams / Lonely one / Why would you wanna live / Kingpin / Someone else's song / Outta mind (outta sight) / Someday soon / Sunken treasure / Say you miss me / Hotel Arizona / What's the world got in store / Far far away / Monday
9362462362 / Feb '97 / Warner Bros.

Wilcox, David

☐ EAST ASHEVILLE HARDWARE
379202 / Dec '97 / Koch

☐ TURNING POINT
379422 / Dec '97 / Koch

Wilcox, Spiegle

☐ JAZZ KEEPS YOU YOUNG
CHR 70015 / Aug '95 / Challenge

Wilcoxson, Sheila

☐ BACKWATER BLUES
BCD 00272 / Jul '97 / Burnside

Wilczeks, Glenek

☐ MUSIC OF THE TATRA MOUNTAINS, POLAND (Wilczeks, Glenek Bukowina Band)
NI 5464 / Mar '96 / Nimbus

Wild

☐ GOOD TO GO
NERCD 085 / Apr '96 / Nervous

Wild Canyon

☐ 18 GUITAR TRACKS
Enchanted canyon / Raunchy / Teen scene / Trambone / Strollin' / Mexican lady / Corn pickin' / My memories / We were born with the music of rock / Dobro / Buffalo skip / Sunny river / Skip along / Poor boy jamboree / Flamingo shuffle / Snail pace / Take me back home / Blue steel blues
BCD 15538 / Nov '90 / Bear Family

Wild Ones

☐ WRITING ON THE WALL
Mr. meaner / That was then, this is now / Girl called crazy / My time has come / You make it right / Affected / Bring on the day / I need you / Hard times / Caught in the middle
HMRXD 171 / Apr '91 / Heavy Metal

Wild Planet

☐ BLUEPRINTS
Nurnberg / Hardware software / Headcleaner / Electron / Input output / Cabasa cabasa / 15 love
WARPCD 11 / Jun '93 / Warp

Wild Pumpkins At Midnight

☐ SECRET OF THE SAD TREE
Entertaining Lucy / Dear Michele / Chuck it out / Vale of tears / Fruit cake recipe / Dear Jane / Stranger in the house / 7 Sisters / She wolf / Johnny Zorra / Ma
HOT 1061CD / Mar '97 / Hot

Wild Spirit

☐ DO THAT THING
HMRXD 164 / May '91 / Heavy Metal

Wild Strawberries

☐ QUIVER
301192 / 23 Mar '98 / Nettwerk

Wild Swans

☐ SPIRITS
GRACD 237 / 3 Aug '98 / Grapevine

Wild Turkey

☐ BATTLE HYMN
EDCD 333 / Sep '91 / Edsel

☐ STEALER OF YEARS
HTDCD 58 / Apr '96 / HTD

☐ TURKEY
Good old days / Tomorrow's friend / Universal man / Eternal mother - the return / Ballad of Chuck Stallion and the Mustangs / Street / See you next Tuesday / Telephone
EDCD 424 / May '95 / Edsel

Wildchild

☐ ATMOSPHERIC DRUM & BASS VOL.1 (Mixed By Wildchild/2CD Set) (Various Artists)
MILL 031CD / Oct '96 / Millenium

☐ BEST OF WILDTRAX, THE (Wildchild Experience)
LOADW 1CD / Dec '96 / Loaded

Wilde, Eugene

☐ BEST OF EUGENE WILDE, THE (Got To Get You Home Tonight)
HTCD 101 / 20 Apr '98 / Hot Productions

Wilde Flowers

☐ WILDE FLOWERS, THE
Impotence / Those words they say / Memories / Don't try to change me / Parchman farm / Almost grown / She's gone / Slow walkin' talk / He's bad for you / It's what I feel (A certain kind) / Memories (instrumental) / Never leave me
BP 123CD / Sep '96 / Blueprint

Wilde, Kim

☐ BEST OF KIM WILDE, THE (18 Original Hits/3CD Set)
Cambodia / Water on glass / Young heroes / Falling out / Just a feeling / Can you come over / Kids in America / Everything we know / 2-6-5-8-0 / Words fell down / Chaos at the airport / Wendy said / Chequered love / View from a bridge / You'll never be so wrong / Action city / Take me tonight / Our town
LAD 873342 / Nov '96 / Disky

☐ GOLD COLLECTION, THE
Kids in America / Chequered love / Water on glass / Everything we know / Young heroes / 2-6-5-8-0 / You'll never be so wrong / Falling out / Tuning in tuning on / Ego / View from a bridge / Words fell down / Action city / Just a feeling / Chaos at the airport / Take me tonight / Can you come over / Wendy said / Our town / Cambodia
CDGOLD 1001 / Mar '96 / EMI Gold

☐ KIM WILDE/SELECT/CATCH AS CATCH CAN (3CD Set)
Water on glass / Our town / Everything we know / Young heroes / Kids in America / Chequered love / 2-6-5-8-0 / You'll never be so wrong / Falling out / Tuning in tuning out / Ego / Words fell down / Action City / View from a bridge / Just a feeling / Chaos at the airport / Take me tonight / Can you come over / Wendy Sadd / Cambodia / House of Salome / Back street Joe / Stay awhile / Love blonde / Dream sequence / Dancing in the dark / Shoot to disable / Can you hear it / Sparks / Sing it out for love
CDOMB 012 / 27 Jul '98 / EMI

☐ MORE OF THE BEST
Love blonde / Dancing in the dark / Sing it out for love / Child come away / Sparks / House of Salome / Stay awhile / Shane / Boys / Watching for shapes / Can you hear it / Backstreet Joe / Love blonde / Dancing in the dark
DC 886872 / 2 Feb '98 / Disky

☐ SINGLES 1981-1993, THE
Kids in America / Chequered love / Water on glass / Cambodia / View from bridge / Child come away / Love blonde / Second time / Rage to love / You keep me hangin' on / Another step (Closer to you) / You came / Never trust a stranger / Four letter word / Love is holy / If I can't have you / In my life
MCLD 19344 / Oct '96 / MCA

Wilde, Marty

☐ BEST OF MARTY WILDE, THE
Teenager in love / Donna / Sea of love / Endless sleep / Bad boy / Rubber ball / Put me down / Danny / Johnny Rocco / Ever since you said goodbye / Don't pity me / Splish splash / High school confidential / Wild cat / Blue moon of Kentucky / Teenage tears / Tomorrow's clown / Little girl / Are you sincere / Flight / Hide and seek / Jezebel / Honeycomb / Dream lover
5517942 / Nov '95 / Spectrum

Wildebeests

☐ WILDEBEEST
SFTRI 486CD / 26 Jan '98 / Sympathy For The Record Industry

Wilden, Gert

☐ I TOLD YOU NOT TO CRY (Swinging Themes From Thrilling Crime Films 1966-1972)
EFA 043802 / Jan '97 / Crippled Dick Hot Wax

☐ SCHULMADCHEN REPORT (Wilden, Gert & Orchestra)
EFA 043742 / Aug '96 / Crippled Dick Hot Wax

Wilder, Alec

☐ SUCH A TENDER NIGHT (The Music Of Alec Wilder) (Manhattan Chamber Orchestra)
Children met the train / Such a tender night / Nonet for brass instruments / Her old man was suspicious / Air for English horn and strings / Sea fugue Mama / Suite for brass quintet and strings / Little white samba / Amorous poltergeist / Songs for Patricia
NPD 85630 / Apr '98 / Newport

Wilder, Joe

☐ WILDER 'N' WILDER
Cherokee / Prelude to a kiss / My heart stood stil / Six bit blues / Mad about the boy / Darn that dream
SV 0131 / Oct '97 / Savoy Jazz

Wilder, Webb

☐ IT CAME FROM NASHVILLE (Wilder, Webb & The Beatnicks)
How long can she last / Horror hayride / I'm burning / Is this all there is / Devil's right hand / Move on down the line / One taste of the bait / I'm wise to you / It gets in your blood / Poolside / Ruff rider / Keep it on your mind
WM 1018CD / Feb '94 / Watermelon

☐ TOWN & COUNTRY (Wilder, Webb & Nashvegas)
WMCD 1032 / Apr '95 / Watermelon

Wildflowers

☐ NEW YORK JAZZ LOFT SESSIONS VOL.1
WILDFLOWER 1 / May '97 / Douglas Music

☐ NEW YORK JAZZ LOFT SESSIONS VOL.2
WILDFLOWER 2 / May '97 / Douglas Music

☐ NEW YORK JAZZ LOFT SESSIONS VOL.3
WILDFLOWER 3 / May '97 / Douglas Music

Wildhearts

☐ ANARCHIC AIRWAVES (The Wildhearts At The BBC)
Greetings from Shitsville / Nothing else changes (but the shoes) / Everlone / Shame on you / Love you 'til I don't / Suckerpunch / Drinking about life / Love you 'til I don't / I wanna go where the people go / Nita nitro / 29 x the pain / Sick of drugs / TV tan / Pump it up / Everlone / Something weird (going on in my head) / Liberty cap
KNEK 3 / 23 Mar '98 / Kuro Neko

☐ ENDLESS NAMELESS
MUSH 13CD / 27 Oct '97 / Mushroom

☐ FISHING FOR LUCKIES
Inglorious / Sick of drugs / Soul searching on planet earth (different kind of / Red light - green light / Nite songs / In like flynn / Mood swings and roundabouts / Sky babies / Schitzophonic / Do the channel bop
0630148559 / May '96 / East West

☐ PHUQ
I wanna go where the people go / V Day / Just in lust / Baby strange / Nita nitro / Jonesing for Jones / Woah shit you got through / Cold patootie tango / Caprice / Be my drug / Naivety play / In Lilly's garden / Getting it / Don't worry 'bout me
0630104042 / Dec '96 / East West

Wildkatz

☐ PINK 'N' BLACK
RAUCD 033 / 23 Mar '98 / Raucous

Wilen, Barney

☐ BARNEY WILEN
FSCD 48 / Oct '90 / Fresh Sound

☐ MOVIE THEMES FROM FRANCE (Wilen, Barney & Mal Waldron Trio)
Un homme et une femme / Julien dans l'ascenseur / Florence sur les Champs Elysees / Les parapluies de Cherbourg / No problem / Manha de Carnaval / Generique / Les feuilles mortes / Quiet temple
CDSJP 335 / Aug '90 / Timeless Jazz

Wiley, Fletch

☐ NIGHTWATCH
Fiesta / I am what I am / People get ready / Started right / Are you ready / Nightwatch / Joy dance
CDPM 6000 / Mar '90 / Prestige

Wiley, Lee

☐ ART VOCAL 1931-1940
AV 015 / Sep '95 / Art Vocal

☐ BACK HOME AGAIN
ACD 300 / May '95 / Audiophile

☐ DUOLOGUE 1954 (Wiley, Lee & Ellis Larkins)
BLCD 760911 / Jun '88 / Black Lion

☐ HOT HOUSE ROCK
TPZ 1047 / Jul '96 / Topaz Jazz

☐ LEE WILEY AT CARNEGIE HALL 1972
ACD 170 / Jul '96 / Audiophile

☐ LEE WILEY RARITIES
JASSCD 15 / Oct '91 / Jass

☐ LEE WILEY SINGS RODGERS & HART AND HAROLD ARLEN
ACD 10 / Feb '91 / Audiophile

☐ SINGS THE SONGS OF GEORGE/IRA GERSHWIN & COLE PORTER
ACD 1 / Feb '91 / Audiophile

Wilhelm, Michael

☐ LIVE IN TOKYO
PSFD 85 / 1 Jun '98 / PSF

☐ MIKE WILHELM
422394 / Feb '97 / New Rose

Wilhelm, Mick

☐ WOOD AND FIRE
NR 422457 / Feb '97 / New Rose

Wilhoite, Kathleen

☐ PITCH LIKE A GIRL
270082 / 10 Mar '98 / Daves

Wilkie, David

☐ COWBOY CEILIDH (Wilkie, David & Cowboy Celtic)
RHRCD 117 / 29 Jun '98 / Red House

☐ COWBOY CELTIC
RHRCD 95 / Sep '96 / Red House

Wilkins, Ernie

☐ KALEIDODUKE
Johnny come lately / Mooche / Sophisticated lady / Kinda Dukish / My little brown book / Things ain't what they used to be / Good Queen Bess / Don't get around much anymore / Isfahan
5193462 / Oct '94 / Birdology

Wilkins, Jack

☐ ALIEN ARMY (Wilkins, Jack Trio)
MM 5049 / Oct '94 / Music Masters

☐ CALL HIM RECKLESS (Wilkins, Jack Trio)
MM 5019 / Oct '94 / Music Masters

☐ KEEP IN TOUCH (Wilkins, Jack & Kenny Drew Jr.)
Short stories / Alice in wonderland / Third phase / If you could see me now / Smatter / Kiwi bird / Street of dreams / If I should lose you / Keep in touch / East coasting
501295 / Jun '96 / Claves

☐ MERGE
CRD 156 / Mar '96 / Chiaroscuro

Wilkins, Robert

☐ WILKINS, DICKSON AND ALLEN 1928-35 (Wilkins, Robert, Tom Dickson & Allen Shaw)
DOCD 5014 / Dec '81 / Document

Wilkinson, Jeff

☐ BALLADS IN PLAIN TALK
BRAM 1990102 / Nov '93 / Brambus

☐ BRAVE & TRUE
BRAM 1991212 / Nov '93 / Brambus

Will Haven

☐ EL DIABLO
CRISIS 015CD / 2 Mar '98 / Crisis

☐ WILL HAVEN
LS 001CD / 2 Mar '98 / Landspeed

Willard Grant Conspiracy

☐ FLYING LOW
Smile at the bottom of the ladder / Evening mass / August list / St.John street / House is not a home / Bring the monster inside / No such thing as clean / It doesn't matter / Ephus pitch / Water / Split tender
SRRCD 035 / 16 Mar '98 / Slow River

Willemark, Lena

☐ AGRAM (Willemark, Lena & Ale Moller)
Syster Glas / Agram / Sasom Fagelem / Fastan / Bjornen / Samsingen / Per Andsu lietjin / Josef fran Arimatea / Lager och Jon / Blamairi / Slangpolskor / Elvedansen / Simonpolskan
5330992 / Oct '96 / ECM

☐ NORDAN (Willemark, Lena & Ale Moller)
5231612 / Sep '94 / ECM

☐ SECRETS OF LIVING (Willemark, Lena & Elise Einarsdotter)
21377 / Jun '85 / Caprice

Willet, Slim

☐ BOPPIN' HILLBILLY SERIES
CLCD 2857 / 29 May '98 / Collector/ White Label

Willetts, Dave

☐ TIMELESS
HELPD 002 / Apr '96 / Big Help

William Davis Construction Group Band

☐ TOUCH MORE SPICE, A
America/Love on the rocks / Overture from 'Phantom of the opera' / Bring him home / Invictus / Party piece / Men of Harlech / Pie Jesu / Fidgety feet / Skye boat song / Rhapsody in blue
QPRL 042D / Jun '90 / Polyphonic

Williams, 'Big' Joe

☐ BABY PLEASE DON'T GO
CD 52035 / May '94 / Blues Encore

☐ BIG JOE WILLIAMS & SONNY BOY WILLIAMSON VOL.1 1935-1941
BDCD 6003 / '91 / Blues Document

☐ BIG JOE WILLIAMS & SONNY BOY WILLIAMSON VOL.2 1945-1949 (Williams, 'Big' Joe & Sonny Boy Williamson)
BDCD 6004 / '91 / Blues Document

☐ BIG JOE WILLIAMS AT FOLK CITY
OBCCD 580 / Jan '96 / Original Blues Classics

☐ BLUES ON HIGHWAY 49
DD 604 / Jul '93 / Delmark

☐ CLASSIC DELTA BLUES
OBCCD 545 / Nov '92 / Original Blues Classics

☐ DELTA BLUES 1951 (Williams, 'Big' Joe & Willie Love/Luther Huff)
ALCD 2702 / Oct '93 / Alligator

☐ FINAL YEARS, THE
Tailormade woman / Highway / Back door / Whistling pine blues / Sunny road blues / Change gotta be made / No special rider blues / Baby please don't go / I believe I'll make a change / You're dogging me / New car blues / Black rat blues / Mama don't allow me / Down on Mr. George Mace's Farm / Meet me in the bottom / Muscle shoals blues / Big road blues
5199432 / Mar '93 / Verve

☐ GIANT OF THE 9 STRING GUITAR 1935-1945, THE
158552 / Mar '96 / Blues Collection

☐ HAVE MERCY
TCD 1014 / May '96 / Tradition

☐ MALVINA MY SWEET WOMAN
Whistling pine blues / Mama don't allow no doggin' all night long / Thousand year blues / She's been shaking a little boogie / Strange girl blues / Early morning blues / Shake a little boogie / Early in the morning / New car blues / Taylor made stomp / You done me wrong / Black rat blues / Poor beggar / Everyday brings out a change / Baby don't you wanna go / Highway 61 blues / Rooster blues / Rollin' in your arms / You are my sunshine
OLCD 7004 / Nov '97 / Oldie Blues

☐ MISSISSIPPI'S BIG JOE WILLIAMS AND HIS NINE STRING GUITAR
SFWCD 40052 / Nov '95 / Smithsonian Folkways

☐ NINE STRING GUITAR BLUES
I got the best King Biscuit / Haunted house blues / I done hollering / I got a bad mind / Long tall woman, skinny Mama too / Stack of dollars / Indiana woman blues / My baby keeps hanging around / Jiving the blues / Jump baby jump
DE 627 / Mar '97 / Delmark

☐ PINEY WOOD BLUES
Baby please don't go / Drop down Mama / Mellow peaches / Tailor made babe / Big Joe talking / Some day baby / Good morning little school girl / Peach orchard Mama / Juanita / Shetland pony blues / Omaha blues
DE 602 / Jul '97 / Delmark

☐ SHAKE YOUR BOOGIE
ARHCD 315 / Apr '95 / Arhoolie

☐ STAVIN' CHAIN BLUES (Williams, 'Big' Joe & J.D. Short)
Stavin' chain blues / Roll and tumble / Mean stepfather / You got to help me some / You're gonna need King Jesus / Jumpin' in the moonlight / Rocks and gravel / Sweet old Kokomo / Nobody knows Chicago / Gonna check up on my baby / You're gonna need King Jesus / Rambled and wandered / Going back to Crawford, Miss / Stavin' chain blues / JD talks
DD 609 / Mar '97 / Delmark

☐ THESE ARE MY BLUES
TCD 6010 / 1 Jun '98 / Testament

Williams, Alanda

☐ KID DYNAMITE
Christina / You need to know / I want your love / Looking for my baby / Sailor sailor / Keep it in the groove / Out of bounds / Kid Dynamite / Big butt woman / Jacksboro highway / I wanna tell ya / One more river
JSPCD 292 / May '97 / JSP

Williams, Alyson

☐ RAW
Just call my name / We're gonna make it: *Williams, Alyson & Ted Mills* / I looked into your eyes / Not on the outside / Masquerade / I'm so glad: *Williams, Alyson & Chuck Stanley* / My love is so raw: *Williams, Alyson & Nikki D* / On the rocks / Still my No.1 / I need your lovin' / Sleep talk
5273632 / Jan '96 / Def Jam

Williams, Andy

☐ BEST OF ANDY WILLIAMS, THE
Moon river / Days of wine and roses / More I see you / Hawaiian wedding song / It's a most unusual day / Look of love / Music to watch the girls go by / I can't take my eyes off you / Solitaire / Happy heart / Can't get used to losing you / You lay so easy on my mind / Time for us / In the arms of love / Danny boy / May each day
4810372 / 12 Jul '98 / Columbia

☐ BUTTERFLY (His Greatest Hits 1956-1961)
Butterfly / Hawaiian wedding song / Canadian sunset / Unchained melody / I like your kind of love / Village of St. Bernadette / (In the Summertime) you don't want my love / Let it be me / Picnic / Look for the silver lining / Boom / This nearly was mine / Getting to know you / Dreamsville / Lonely Street / I'm so lonesome I could cry / In the wee small hours of the morning / Wake me when it's over / He's got the whole world in his hands / Sweet morning
3036000862 / Jul '97 / Carlton

☐ CADENCE COLLECTION (2CD Set)
SMDCD 200 / 30 Mar '98 / Snapper

☐ CAN'T GET USED TO LOSING YOU/ LOVE ANDY
Falling in love with love / I left my heart in San Francisco / You are my sunshine / What kind of fool am I / When you're smiling / Days of wine and roses / It's a most unusual day / My colouring book / Can't get used to losing you / I really don't want to know / Exactly like you / May each day / Somethin' stupid / Watch what happens / Look of love / What now my love / Can't take my eyes off you / Kisses sweeter than wine / Holly / When I look in your eyes / More I see you / There will never be another you / God only knows
4775912 / Oct '94 / Columbia

☐ GRANDES BALADES
31839 / Oct '96 / Divusca

☐ GREAT PERFORMANCES
DBP 102009 / Oct '95 / Double Platinum

☐ GREATEST HITS
L.o.v.e.-love is here to stay (opening medley) / Macarthur park / Born free / Canadian sunset / Hawaiian wedding song / Can't get used to losing you / Moon river / May each day
12351 / Aug '94 / Laserlight

☐ GREATEST LOVE CLASSICS (Williams, Andy & The Royal Philharmonic Orchestra)
Romeo and Juliet / Love made me a fool / Vino de amor / Different light / Another Winter's day / Vision / Journey's end / Twist of fate / Home / Brave new world / She'll never know / In my world of illusion / Words
CDMFP 6173 / Sep '95 / Music For Pleasure

☐ LOVE SONGS, THE
Can't take my eyes off you / Can't get used to losing you / Something stupid / Seasons in the sun / Strangers in the night / Fire and rain / You've got a friend / We've only just begun / Where do I begin (love story) / Way we were / Look of love / You are the sunshine of my life / Touch me in the morning / Without you / Solitaire / Unchained melody / Can't help falling in love / Hawaiian wedding song / I won't last a day without you / Music to watch girls by / Butterfly / Killing me softly / May each day
4879742 / 8 Sep '97 / Columbia

☐ PERSONAL CHRISTMAS COLLECTION
It's the most wonderful time of the year / My favourite things / Christmas song / Bells of St. Mary's / Christmas present / Winter wonderland / First Noel / O come all ye faithful (Adeste Fidelis) / Sleigh ride / Silver bells / Hark the herald angels sing / Christmas bells / Silent night / White Christmas / Happy holiday/The holiday season
4777702 / 3 Nov '97 / Columbia

☐ REFLECTIONS
Moon river / Both sides now / Home loving man / Seasons in the sun / Days of wine and roses / Happy heart / Born free / Love story / Almost there / Can't help falling in love / Can't get used to losing you / God only knows / Solitaire / Your song / Way we were / Can't take my eyes off you / My way / May each day of the year be a good one
4687812 / Jun '91 / Columbia

☐ TOUCH OF CLASS, A
Butterfly / Are you sincere / Lonely street / Canadian sunset / Village of St. Bernadette / I like your kind of love / Hawaiian love song / Lips of wine / Promise, me love / Baby doll / When your lover has gone / In the wee small hours of the morning / How wonderful to know / I'm so alone / Gone with the wind / Do you mind / You don't want my love / Walk hand in hand / Wake me when it's over / Bilbao song
TC 877022 / 2 Feb '98 / Disky

☐ WORLD OF LOVE, A
MCCD 218 / Oct '95 / Music Club

Williams, Bekki

☐ ELYSIAN FIELDS
Megaera / Elysian fields / Charon / Moons of Artemis / Hera / Secrets of the labyrinth / Icarus / In the arms of Morpheus / Glance from Medusa / Elysian fields
AD 13CD / Dec '96 / AD

Williams, Blind Connie

☐ PHILADELPHIA STREET SINGER
TCD 5024 / Jul '95 / Testament

Williams, Brooks

☐ INLAND SAILOR
GLCD 2114 / Apr '94 / Green Linnet

☐ KNIFE EDGE
GLCD 2121 / Aug '95 / Green Linnet

☐ SEVEN SISTERS
Seven sisters / Mother Earth / Rich tonight / Nothing at all / Hello heartbreak / Minor maybe / Jane / Miles away / Winter moon / Threadbare soul / Some fine day
GLCD 2125 / Sep '97 / Green Linnet

Williams, Bruce

☐ BROTHERHOOD
Our day will come / Brotherhood / Portrait of Jennie / Out of nowhere / Ichi-wuda / Memory of Waterford / My lady's tears / Jackie's tune / I can't get started / Adreena / Gemini minds / Spankin'
SAVCD 2004 / Jan '98 / Savant

Williams, Carol

☐ HAMMOND TODAY
Tico-tico / Fancy pants / Dizzy fingers / Unforgettable / What now my love / May you always / Jumpin' Jupiter / Rhapsody rag / Fools rush in / Red roses for a blue lady / We'll meet again / It's today / Kitchen rag / March: City of Chester / Bess you is my woman now / Promette / Brazil / White cliffs of Dover / Russian rag / In the news / You and the night and the music
MCTCD 002 / Feb '93 / Melcot

☐ JUST RAGS
Leicester Square rag / Tiger rag / Black and white rag / Brittania rag / Maple leaf rag / 12th Street rag / Barrel house rag / Root beer rag / Pineapple rag / Chatterbox rag / Tin Pan Alley rag / Spaghetti rag / Ivory rag / Entertainer / Fiddlesticks rag / Coronation rag / Jingles / Kitchen rag / Zig zag rag / Temptation rag / Bugle call rag / Rhapsody rag / Peacherine rag / Russian rag (Rockies rag) / Alexander's ragtime band
MCTCD 007 / Aug '93 / Melcot

Williams, Christopher

☐ NOT A PERFECT MAN
74321254552 / Jun '95 / RCA

Williams, Clarence

☐ CLARENCE WILLIAMS COLLECTION VOL.1 1927-1928
COCD 19 / Nov '94 / Collector's Classics

☐ CLARENCE WILLIAMS COLLECTION VOL.2 1928
COCD 28 / Mar '97 / Collector's Classics

☐ CLARENCE WILLIAMS COLLECTION VOL.3 1929-1930
COCD 29 / May '97 / Collector's Classics

☐ CLASSICS 1921-1924
CLASSICS 679 / Mar '93 / Classics

☐ CLASSICS 1924-1926
CLASSICS 695 / Jul '93 / Classics

☐ CLASSICS 1926-1927
CLASSICS 718 / Jul '93 / Classics

☐ CLASSICS 1927
CLASSICS 736 / Feb '94 / Classics

☐ CLASSICS 1927-1928
CLASSICS 752 / May '94 / Classics

☐ CLASSICS 1928-1929
CLASSICS 771 / Aug '94 / Classics

☐ CLASSICS 1929
CLASSICS 791 / Jan '95 / Classics

☐ CLASSICS 1929-1930
CLASSICS 810 / May '95 / Classics

☐ CLASSICS 1930-1931
CLASSICS 832 / Sep '95 / Classics

☐ CLASSICS 1933-1934
CLASSICS 871 / Apr '96 / Classics

☐ CLASSICS 1934
CLASSICS 891 / Sep '96 / Classics

☐ CLASSICS 1934-1937
CLASSICS 918 / Jan '97 / Classics

☐ CLASSICS 1937-1941
CLASSICS 953 / Nov '97 / Classics

☐ COLUMBIA RECORDINGS VOL.1 (Dreaming The Hours Away)
DGF 14 / Sep '97 / Frog

☐ COLUMBIA RECORDINGS VOL.2, THE (Whoop It Up)
DGF 17 / Dec '97 / Frog

Williams, Claude

☐ KING OF KANSAS CITY, THE
PCD 7100 / Sep '97 / Progressive

☐ LIVE AT J'S VOL.1
ARHCD 405 / Apr '95 / Arhoolie

☐ LIVE AT J'S VOL.2
ARHCD 406 / Apr '95 / Arhoolie

☐ MY SILENT LOVE
BB 901 / 24 Apr '98 / Black & Blue

Williams, Cootie

☐ CLASSICS 1941-1944
CLASSICS 827 / Sep '95 / Classics

☐ CLASSICS 1945-1946
CLASSICS 981 / 24 Feb '98 / Classics

☐ ECHOES OF HARLEM
Stompy Jones / Diga diga doo / I can't believe that you're in love with me / Blue reverie / My honey's loving arms / Alabamy home / Stompology / Watchin' / Ring dem bells / Echoes of Harlem / Chasin' chippies / Sharpie / Boys from Harlem / Gal-avantin' / She's gone / Black beauty / Toasted pickles / Concerto for Cootie (do nothin' till you hear from me) / Royal garden blues / You talk a little trash / Sweet Lorraine / 'Round midnight / Blue garden blues
TPZ 1042 / Apr '96 / Topaz Jazz

☐ INTRODUCTION TO COOTIE WILLIAMS 1930-1943, AN
4018 / Apr '95 / Best Of Jazz

☐ SEXTET AND BIG BAND 1941-1944
158382 / Sep '95 / Jazz Archives

Williams, Cunnie

☐ LOVE STARVED HEART
YO 4019CD / Jul '96 / Yo Mama

Williams, Danny

☐ BEST OF DANNY WILLIAMS, THE
CDSGP 006 / Aug '91 / Prestige

☐ ESSENTIAL COLLECTION, THE
Moon river / Love is a many splendoured thing / Portrait of my love / What kind of fool am I / I've got you under my skin / It might as well be spring / Steppin' out with my baby / With these hands / Stay as sweet as you are / In other words / Wonderful world of the young / Jeannie / O Danny boy / Story of a starry night / No love or nuthin' / All or nothing at all / AUtumn leaves / After you / I'm beginning to see the light / White on white / I talk to the trees / Stress of goodbyes / Boy I really didn't know what hit me / Everytime we say goodbye
CDMFP 6401 / 13 Oct '97 / Music For Pleasure

☐ GENTLE TOUCH, THE
Stay awhile / (With you I'm) Born again / Save the best for last / Beauty and the beast / Moon river / Where do you start / Gentle touch / Best time of my life / Maybe September / Always / Shadow of your smile / My funny valentine / Never let me go / Rainbow bridge / Someone to watch over me / Feelings / God only knows
URCD 121 / Jun '96 / Upbeat

Williams, Dar

☐ END OF THE SUMMER
828302 / 7 Sep '98 / Velvel

☐ HONESTY ROOM
GRACD 210 / Nov '96 / Grapevine

☐ MORTAL CITY
GRACD 212 / Nov '96 / Grapevine

☐ MORTAL CITY/THE HONESTY ROOM (2CD Set)
GRCDX 211 / Feb '96 / Grapevine

Williams, David

☐ DAVE 'FAT MAN' WILLIAMS (Williams, Dave 'Fat Man')
BCD 355 / Nov '96 / GHB

Williams, Delroy

☐ YOU SEXY THING
CDTRL 371 / Jul '96 / Trojan

Williams, Deniece

☐ GREATEST GOSPEL HITS
Fire inside my soul / So glad I know / My soul desire / His eye is on the sparrow / Healing / God made you special / Special love / They say / I surrender all / Every moment / God is amazing / We sing praises
SPD 1461 / May '95 / Alliance Music

☐ THIS IS MY SONG
Blessed assurance / Lover of my soul / Standing / Nothing but the blood / No never alone / Just as I am / Prodigal sons and daughters / It is well / I love him above all things / I come to the garden alone
6116552 / 6 Jul '98 / EMI

Williams, Dicky

☐ FULL GROWN MAN
ICH 1186CD / Dec '95 / Ichiban

☐ I WANT YOU FOR BREAKFAST
Weekend playboy / You hurt the wrong man / I've been loving you too long / Letter from a soldier / Need your love / Lost my woman to a woman / Good used man / I'm in love with two women / I want you for breakfast / Let me love you before we make love / Don't give your love to anyone but me / Little closer
ICH 1115CD / Oct '93 / Ichiban

Williams, Don

☐ AN EVENING WITH DON WILLIAMS (Best Of Live/Including Interview)
Introduction / Good ole boys like me / She's in love with a rodeo man / Some broken hearts never mend / Ties that bind / Louisiana saturday night / Till the rivers run dry / I recall a gypsy woman / It must be love / Lay down beside me / Lord I hope this day is good / Country boy / Tulsa time / Amanda / You're my best friend / Dialogue / I believe in you
30052 / Oct '97 / Go On Deluxe

☐ BEST OF DON WILLIAMS LIVE, THE
Good ole boys like me / She' in love with a rodeo man / Some broken hearts never mend / Ties that bind / Louisiana Saturday night / Till the rivers all run dry / I recall a gypsy woman / It must be love / Lay down beside me Lord, I hope this day is good / (I'm juts a) Country boy / Tulsa time / Amanda / You're my best friend / Dialogue / I believe in you
3036300072 / Apr '96 / Carlton

☐ BEST OF DON WILLIAMS, THE
Storybook children / Good ole boys like me / Amanda / Take my hand for a while / Tears / There's never been a time / Follow me back to Louisville / Coming apart / I believe in you / Spend some time with me / Where do I go from here / Ruby Tuesday / On her way to being a woman / I've been loved by the best / Tulsa time / Always something there to remind me / You're my best friend / Lord I hope this day is good
SUMCD 4179 / 23 Feb '98 / Summit

☐ BORROWED TALES
Fever / Crying in the rain / Lay down Sally / My rifle my pony and me / I'll be there if you ever want me / Reason to believe / Games people play / If you could read my mind / Peace train / Long black veil / Letter / You've got a friend / Pretend
3036300012 / Apr '96 / Carlton
30042 / Oct '97 / Go On Deluxe

☐ COUNTRY CLASSICS
Another time another place / Come from the heart / Desperately / Old coyote town / Running out of reasons / Looking back / I wouldn't be a man / Easy touch / Heartbeat in the darkness / I'll never be in love again / Senorita / Shot full of love / We've got a good fire goin' / Till I can't take it anymore / We got love / You love me through it all / Send her roses / Light in your eyes / It's about time / Then it's love
4949202 / 1 Jun '98 / EMI Gold

☐ COUNTRY LOVE SONGS
There's never been a time / (There's) always something there to remind me / Spend some time with me / In my life / Take my hand / Where do I go from here / On her way to being a woman / Follow me back to Louisville / Apartment no.9 / Ruby Tuesday / Tears / Storybook children / Ordinary / Long walk from childhood / Coming apart / There's no angel on my shoulder
100502 / May '97 / A-Play Collection

☐ CURRENTS
Only water (shining in the air) / Too much love / That song about the river / Catfish bates / Back on the street again / So far, so good / Gettin' back together tonight / In the family / Standing knee deep in a river (dying of thirst) / Lone star state of mind / Old trail / It's who you love
PD 90645 / Mar '92 / RCA

☐ DON WILLIAMS VOL.1 & 2
Come early morning / Too late to turn back now / Endless sleep / Shelter of your eyes / I recall a gypsy woman / No use running / How much time does it take / My woman's love / Don't you believe / Wish I was in Nashville / Amanda / Your sweet love / She's in love with a rodeo man / Atta way to go / We should be together / Loving you so long now / Oh misery / Miller's cave / I don't think about her no more / Down the road I go
EDCD 499 / Mar '97 / Edsel

☐ FLATLANDS
3036300132 / Sep '96 / Carlton

☐ GREATEST HITS VOL.1
Amanda / Come early morning / Shelter of your eyes / Atta way to go / Don't you believe / Down the road I go / I wouldn't want to live if you don't / Love me / We should be together / Ties that bind / Ghost story / She's in love with a rodeo man / I recall a gypsy woman
3036300052 / May '97 / Carlton

☐ I BELIEVE IN YOU
Good ole boys like me / Storybook children / Take my hand for a while / Amanda / There's never been a time / Tears / Coming apart / Follow me back to Louisville / Spend some time with me / I believe in you / Ruby Tuesday / Where do I go from here / I've been loved by the best / On her way to being a woman / (There's) Always something there to remind me / Tulsa time / Lord I hope this day is good / You're my best friend
300082 / Feb '98 / Hallmark

☐ IT'S GOTTA BE MAGIC
It's gotta be magic / I would like to see you again / Lay down beside me / Tears of the lonely / You've got a hold on me / Fallin' in love again / I need someone to hold me when I cry / Turn out the lights and love me tonight / Lovin' understandin' man / Fly away / Your sweet love / Tempted / No use running / Oh misery / Sweet fever / Missing you, missing me
3036300062 / Apr '96 / Carlton

☐ LOVE STORIES
74321432562 / Oct '96 / Camden

☐ MASTERS, THE
EABCD 026 / 24 Nov '97 / Eagle

☐ RUBY TUESDAY
HADCD 185 / Nov '95 / Javelin

☐ SHELTER OF YOUR EYES, THE
Shelter of your eyes / Come early morning / Amanda / Atta way to go / We should be together / Down the road I go / I wouldn't want to live if you didn't love me / I recall a gypsy woman / Playing around / Miller's cafe / She's in love with a rodeo man / He's a friend of mine / Bringing it down to you / There's never been a time / Coming apart / On her way to being a woman / Follow me back to Louisville / Always something there to remind me
CTS 55435 / Jan '96 / Country Stars

☐ SOME BROKEN HEARTS
Stay young / You're my best friend / I'm just a country boy / Listen to the radio / All I'm missing is you / Some broken hearts never mend / I believe in you / Turn out the lights (love me tonight) / Tulsa time / Years from now / Say it again / Till the rivers all run dry / Amanda / I wouldn't want to live if you didn't love me / We should be together / Come early morning
PLATCD 301 / Oct '92 / Platinum

☐ SPEND SOME TIME WITH ME
Spend some time / Follow me to Louisville / Storybook children / There's never been a time / Take my hand for a while / Ruby Tuesday / Coming apart / Tears / She walked out on her way to be a woman / Where do we go from here / Always something there to remind me
CDSGP 0396 / Jun '98 / Prestige

☐ VERY BEST OF DON WILLIAMS, THE
HMNCD 018 / 3 Nov '97 / Half Moon

☐ YOU'RE MY BEST FRIEND
You're my best friend / When I'm with you / It must be love / Till the rivers run dry / (Turn out the lights) And love me / Tonight / I'm just a country boy / All I'm missing is you / Don't you think it's time / Endless sleep / Some broken hearts never mend / I'm getting good at missing you / Goodbye isn't really good at all
3036300082 / Apr '96 / Carlton

☐ YOU'RE MY BEST FRIEND
Good ole boys like me / Storybook children / Take my hand for a while / Amanda / There's never been a time / Tears / Coming apart / Follow me back to Louisville / Spend some time with me / I believe in you / Ruby Tuesday / Where do I go from here / I've been loved by the best / On her way to being a woman / Always something there to remind me / Tulsa time / Lord I hope this day is good / You're my best friend
CD 6037 / Sep '96 / Music

☐ YOU'RE MY BEST FRIEND
CTS 55436 / Oct '95 / Country Stars

Williams, Elmo

☐ TAKES ONE TO KNOW ONE (Williams, Elmo & Hezekiah Early)
Mother's dead / Insane instrumental / Blue jumped the rabbit / Booster / Nothin' man / Hoopin' and hollerin' / Been here and gone / Natchez fire / Do your thing / Let it all go
03132 / 30 Mar '98 / Fat Possum

Williams, Ernie

☐ SISTER (Williams, Ernie & The Wildcats)
WC 1004 / 27 Jul '98 / Wildcats

Williams, Freddy

☐ BARBERSHOP FAVOURITES (Williams, Freddy Four)
Down by the riversdie / Whispering / Ragtime cowboy Joe / Carry me back to old Virginny / Heart of my heart / Drink to me only / Carolina moon / If you were the only girl in the world / Sweet Rosie O'Grady / Danny boy / Sweet sixteen / Mary Mary / Tea for two / Sixty seconds / Honeysuckle and the bee / Sleepy time girl / Genevieve / On the banks of the Wabash / If I had you / Whiffenpoof song / My evaline / When you wore a tulip / Bye bye blackbird / South Rampart Street Parade / Sweet adeline / In the good old summertime
3036000432 / May '96 / Carlton

Williams, Geoffrey

☐ DROP, THE
HORCD 1001 / Apr '97 / Hands On

Williams, George

☐ GEORGE WILLIAMS & BESSIE BROWN VOL.1 1923-1925 (Williams, George & Bessie Brown)
DOCD 5527 / Apr '97 / Document

☐ GEORGE WILLIAMS & BESSIE BROWN VOL.2 1925-1930 (Williams, George & Bessie Brown)
DOCD 5528 / Apr '97 / Document

☐ SHADES
CDSGP 0113 / Mar '94 / Prestige

Williams, Ginger

☐ GREATEST HITS
In my heart / Baby we're taking a chance / As long as you love me / Mad about you / Tenderly / Strange world / Oh baby come back / He's my honey boy / I'll still love you / Here we are / Please forgive me / Holding on / I'm crying I'm crying
WSRCD 103 / Sep '96 / World Sound

Williams, Hank

☐ 24 GREATEST HITS VOL.1
Your cheatin' heart / Move it on over / I'm so lonesome I could cry / Ramblin' man / My heart would know / Kaw-liga / Cold cold heart / Lovesick blues / Honky tonk blues / Honky tonkin' / Mind your own business / Jambalaya / Wedding bells / Hey good lookin' / Window shopping / Settin' the woods on fire / I can't help it (if I'm still in love with you) / Half as much / Why don't you love me / You win again / May you never be alone / Baby we're really in love / Take these chains from my heart / There'll be no teardrops tonight
8232932 / Jul '94 / Polydor

☐ 24 GREATEST HITS VOL.2
My bucket's got a hole in it / Crazy heart / I'll never get out of this world alive / Moanin' the blues / I could never be ashamed of you / Lost highway / You're gonna change (or I'm gonna leave) / House without love / I'd still want you / Dear John / Let's turn back the years / Howlin' at the moon / Mansion on the hill / I saw the light / (I heard that) lonesome whistle / I'm a long gone Daddy / Why should we try anymore / Long gone lonesome blues / Nobody's lonesome for me / My sweet love ain't around / I just don't like this kind of livin' / I won't be home no more / I'm sorry for you my friend
8232942 / Jul '94 / Polydor

☐ 40 GREATEST HITS (2CD Set)
Move it on over / Mansion on the hill / Lovesick blues / Wedding bells / Mind your own business / You're gonna change (or I'm gonna leave) / Lost highway / My bucket's got a hole in it / I'm so lonesome I could cry / I just don't like this kind of livin' / Long gone lonesome blues / My son calls another man Daddy / Why don't you leave me / Why should we try anymore / They'll never take her love from me / Moanin' the blues / Nobody's lonesome for me / Cold cold heart / Dear John / Howlin' at the moon / I can't help it (if I'm still in love with you) / Hey good lookin' / Crazy heart / (I heard that) Lonesome whistle / I saw the light / Weary blues from waiting / I won't be home no more / Take these chains from my heart / Your cheatin' heart / Kaw-liga / I'll never get out of this world alive / You win again / Settin' the woods on fire / Window shopping / Jambalaya / Half as much / I'm sorry for you my friend / Honky tonk blues / Ramblin' man / Baby we're really in love
8212332 / Apr '89 / Polydor

☐ ALONE AND FORSAKEN
5280372 / Jan '96 / Polydor

☐ AMERICAN LEGENDS (A Tribute To Hank Williams) (Various Artists)
My heart would know: *Osborne Brothers* / Why don't you love me: *Williams, Hank* / Singing waterfall: *O'Day, Molly* / Move it on over: *Maddox, Rose* / You win again: *Williams, Hank* / Mansion on the hill: *Glaser, Tompall & The Glaser Brothers* / On the banks of the old Ponchartrain: *Maddox, Rose* / Fool about you: *Williams, Hank* / My sweet love ain't around: *Osborne Brothers* / When God comes to gather up his jewels: *O'Day, Molly* / My son calls another man Daddy: *Williams, Hank*
12748 / Aug '97 / Laserlight

☐ BEST OF HANK WILLIAMS VOL.1, THE
8495752 / Jul '94 / Polydor

☐ BEST OF HANK WILLIAMS, THE
Cold cold heart / Hey good lookin' / Your cheatin' heart / Jambalaya (on the bayou) / Kaw-Liga / Take these chains / Half as much / Settin' the woods on fire / I can't help it (if I'm still in love with you) / You win again / Crazy heart / Love sick blues / Long gone lonesome blues / Why don't you love me / I'll never get out of this world alive / I'm so lonesome I could cry / Honky tonk blues / My bucket's got a hole in it / Moanin' the blues / Move it over
5543812 / 6 Apr '98 / Spectrum

☐ BEST RECORDINGS VOL.1, THE
BMCD 3052 / 5 Jan '98 / Blue Moon

☐ BEST RECORDINGS VOL.2, THE
BMCD 3053 / 5 Jan '98 / Blue Moon

☐ HANK WILLIAMS FAVOURITES (Various Artists)
74321378372 / Jul '96 / RCA

☐ I SAW THE LIGHT
I saw the light / Calling you / Dear brother / Wealth won't save your soul / I'm gonna sing / Message to my mother / How can you refuse him now / When God comes and gathers his jewels / Jesus remembered me / House of gold / Thank God / Angel of death
8119002 / Jul '94 / Polydor

☐ LEGEND OF COUNTRY MUSIC
Happy rovin' cowboy / Lovesick blues / Mansion on the hill / You're gonna change (or I'm gonna leave) / Tramp on the street / I'm a long gone Daddy / When God comes and gathers all his jewels / Lost highway / I'll have a new body (I'll have a new life) / I can't get you off my mind / Prodigal son / Pan American / There'll be no teardrops tonight / Mind your own business / Wedding bells / I've just told Mama goodbye / I'm so lonesome I could cry / Thy burdens are greater than mine / I saw the light / Sally Goodin
CD 6053 / Jan '97 / Music

☐ MEN WITH BROKEN HEARTS (Three Hanks)
CURCD 029 / Nov '96 / Curb

☐ RARE DEMOS: FIRST TO LAST
Won't you sometimes think of me / Why should I cry / Calling you / You break your own heart / Pan American / Mother is gone / I watched my dreamworld crumble like clay / In my dreams you still belong to me / Wealth won't save your soul / I told a lie to my heart / Singing waterfall / I'm goin' home / Jambalaya / Heaven holds all my treasures / You better keep it on your mind / Lost on the river / Your cheatin' heart / House of gold / Honky tonk blues / Help me understand / 'Neath a cold grey tomb of stone / There's nothing as sweet as my baby / Fool about you / Log train
CMFCD 067 / Jan '93 / Country Music Foundation

Williams, Hank Jr.

☐ WORLD OF HANK WILLIAMS JR, THE
Ring of fire / Bye bye love: *Williams, Hank Jr. & Connie Francis* / Make the world go away / I walk the line / So sad: *Williams, Hank Jr. & Lois Johnson* / Sweet dreams / North to Alaska / There goes my everything / Singin' the blues: *Williams, Hank Jr. & Connie Francis* / Folsom Prison blues / I love you a thousand ways / Please help me I'm falling: *Williams, Hank Jr. & Connie Francis* / Understand your man / Long black veil / Guess things happen that way / Together again: *Williams, Hank Jr. & Lois Johnson* / Blizzard / Window up above / Your cheatin' heart
5520212 / May '96 / Spectrum

Williams, Huw

☐ LIVE (Williams, Huw & Tony)
TCS 10005CD / Aug '97 / Tudor Crescent

☐ NEXT EXIT, THE (Williams, Huw & Tony)
TCS 1001CD / Oct '94 / Tudor Crescent

☐ PARADISE CIRCUS (Williams, Huw & Tony)
TCS 1002C / Oct '94 / Tudor Crescent

☐ ROSEMARY'S SISTER (Williams, Huw & Tony)
TCS 1003CD / Jul '95 / Tudor Crescent

Williams, James

☐ LIVE AT MAYBECK RECITAL HALL VOL.42
Polka dots and moonbeams / Footprints / Dreamsville / I fall in love to easily / New York / 'Round midnight / Inner urge / Sweet dreams / Blues etude / Holy, holy, holy / Sometimes I feel like a Motherless child / Blessed assurance / Why we sing
CCD 4694 / May '96 / Concord Jazz

☐ PROGRESS REPORT (Williams, James Sextet)
Progress report / Episode from a village dance / Affaire d'amour / Mr. Day's dream / Unconscious behaviour / Renaissance lovers
SSC 1012D / Feb '86 / Sunnyside

☐ TRUTH, JUSTICE & THE BLUES
Truth, justice and the blues / Self esteem / For old times sake / Yes, yes oh yes / For all intensive purposes / On his word / Take time for love / You're my alter ego / J's rhythm song / Just a feelin' / Be real special
ECD 221422 / Mar '96 / Evidence

☐ UP TO THE MINUTE BLUES
DIW 882CD / Apr '94 / DIW

☐ WE'VE GOT WHAT YOU NEED (Williams, James & ICU)
Beautiful friendship / Dat dere / Playin' the field / Dialogue: A few miles to Holland / You'll never walk alone / Vignette / Day by day / Deliverance / Lester left town / Vignette / Calvary / Praise song for the people
ECD 222072 / 28 Apr '98 / Evidence

Williams, Jerry Lynn

☐ PEACEMAKER
174512 / Apr '97 / XIII Bis
BLUECD 1001 / 11 May '98 / Bluemark

Williams, Jessica

☐ AND THEN, THERE'S THIS
Bemsha swing / And then, there's this / All alone / Nichol's bag / Child within / Elaine / House that Rouse, built / Newk's fluke / Swanee / I mean you
CDSJP 345 / Feb '91 / Timeless Jazz

☐ ARRIVAL
JFCD 001 / Nov '94 / Jazz Focus

☐ ENCOUNTERS
JFCD 021 / Apr '98 / Jazz Focus

☐ GRATITUDE
Sheikh / I cover the waterfront / Mr. Syms / Serenata / 'Round midnight / Nice work if you can get it / Last trane / Like Sonny / Justice
CCD 79721 / Feb '97 / Candid

☐ HIGHER STANDARDS
Get out of town / When your lover has gone / Mack the knife / Night in Tunisia / Don't take your love from me / East of the sun and West of the moon / Solitude / Midnight sun / My heart belongs to Daddy
CCD 79736 / May '97 / Candid

☐ IN THE POCKET
Weirdo / Gal in calico / I really love you / Driftin' / For you again / Cheek to cheek / I remember Bill / I don't stand a ghost of a chance with you / Pfrancing
HEPCD 2055 / Jun '94 / Hep

☐ JESSICA'S BLUES
JFCD 018 / Sep '97 / Jazz Focus

☐ MOMENTUM
Stonewall blues / Stonewall blues / We kiss in a shadow / Shuffle boil / Easy to remember / Little dog blues / You do something to me / Thembl's tune / Sherlock's lament / Autumn leaves
JFCD 003 / Nov '94 / Jazz Focus

☐ NEXT STEP, THE
Taking a chance on love / Stonewall blues / Easter parade / Bongo's waltz / I didn't know until you told me / Quilt / Clear blue Lou / I should care / Theme for Lester Young / Like someone in love / I'll always be in love with you / I got it bad and that ain't good / Little waltz
HEPCD 2054 / Sep '93 / Hep

☐ SONG THAT I HEARD, A
Make it so / Burning castle / I wish I knew / (Beautiful girl of my dreams) I love you / Geronimo / Kristen / Alone together / Blues not / Say not / Say it / Song that I heard somewhere / Blues for Mandela / I'll remember April
HEPCD 2061 / Mar '95 / Hep

Williams, Jessica

☐ BEST OF JESSICA WILLIAMS, THE (Queen Of Fools)
HTCD 87 / 20 Apr '98 / Hot Productions

Williams, Jett

☐ THAT REMINDS ME OF HANK
IG 5001 / Feb '96 / Copper Creek

Williams, Joe

☐ COME BACK
Come back / Hold it right there / Sent for you yesterday / Yesterday / Who she do
D/PC 2102 / '88 / Delos

☐ EVERY DAY (The Best Of The Verve Years/2CD Set)
5198132 / Mar '94 / Verve

☐ HERE'S TO LIFE
What a wonderful world / Save that time / I found a million dollar baby / When I fall in love / If I had you / Little Sir Echo / Young and foolish / I didn't know about you / Maybe September / Time for love / Here's to life
CD 83357 / Jan '94 / Telarc

☐ I JUST WANT TO SING (Williams, Joe & Friends)
Until I met you / After you've gone / Fat and forty / War no more / It's not easy being white / Dimples / Young and foolish / I was a fool / I got it bad / What a difference a day makes / Sawmill blues / Later than you think / All the things you are
DCD 4004 / May '94 / Delos

☐ JOE WILLIAMS SINGS
It's raining again / Detour ahead / Every day / They didn't believe me / Blow Mr. Low / Time for moving / When the sun goes down / Kansas city blues / Always on the blue side / Safe sane and single
SV 0199 / Oct '97 / Savoy Jazz

☐ LIVE AT ORCHESTRA HALL (Williams, Joe & The Count Basie Orchestra)
Sometimes I'm happy / Hurry on down / Sugar / Summertime / Lover come back to me / Little at a time / There will never be another you / Jimmy's blues / Honeysuckle rose / My baby upsets me / Comeback / Georgia rose / Roll 'em pete / I'd rather drink muddy water / One o'clock jump
CD 83329 / Mar '93 / Telarc

☐ NOTHIN' BUT THE BLUES
Who she do / Just a dream / Please send me someone to love / Alright, OK you win / Hold it right there / In the evening / Rocks in my bed / Sent for you yesterday / Goin' to Chicago blues / Ray Brown's in town
DCD 4001 / May '94 / Delos

☐ WAR NO MORE
War no more / What a difference a day makes / After you're gone / All the things you are
D/PC 2103 / '88 / Delos

Williams, John

☐ SUMMON THE HEROES (The Official Centennial Olympic Theme) (Williams, John & The Boston Pops Orchestra)
Summon the heroes / Olympic spirit / Olympic fanfare/theme / O fortuna / Bugler's dream / Ode to Zeus / Javelin / Olympic hymn / Overture festivo / Conquest of paradise / Chariots of fire / Parade of charioteers / Toward a new life
SK 62622 / Jun '96 / Sony Classical

Williams, John

☐ BEST OF JOHN WILLIAMS, THE
Cavatina / Horizon / Raga vilasakhani todi / Sarabande / Deer may safely graze / River God / Z / All at sea minor / Bach changes / Dance of the emperor's clothes / Dance of the living / El tuno / Good morning freedom / JSB / Lisa Larne / Lorelei / Spanish trip
MCCD 007 / Feb '91 / Music Club

☐ PORTRAIT
JHD 029 / Jun '92 / Tring

Williams, John

☐ JOHN WILLIAMS
GLCD 1157 / Dec '95 / Green Linnet

Williams, Juanita

☐ INTRODUCING
BIGMO 1024 / Jul '94 / Big Mo

Williams, Larry

☐ BEST OF LARRY WILLIAMS, THE
Short fat Fannie / Baby's crazy / Dizzy Miss Lizzy / Lawdy Miss Clawdy / Slow down / I was a fool to let you go / You bug me baby / Rockin' pneumonia and the boogie woogie flu / She said "yeah" / Hootchy-koo / Bony moronie / Little school girl / Just because / Hocus pocus / Took a trip / Jelly belly Nellie / Peaches and cream / Oh babe / Zing zing / Dummy / Bad boy
CDCH 917 / May '88 / Ace

☐ FABULOUS LARRY WILLIAMS
Short fat Fannie / Bony Moronie / Dizzy Miss Lizzy / Lawdy Miss Clawdy / Baby's crazy / Just because / Slow down / You dug me baby / Rockin' pneumonia and the boogie woogie flu / Little school girl / Hocus pocus / Peaches and cream
CDFAB 012 / Oct '91 / Ace

Williams, Leona

☐ LEONA WILLIAMS & EDNA WINSTON 1922-1927 (Williams, Leona & Edna Winston)
DOCD 5523 / Apr '97 / Document

Williams, Lester

☐ I CAN'T LOSE WITH THE STUFF I USE
I can't lose with the stuff I use / My home ain't here / Crawlin' blues / Lonely heart blues / When I miss her most / Trying to forget / Let me tell you a thing or two / Lost gal / Sweet lovin' daddy / Disgusted blues / Don't leave me baby / Brand new baby / If you knew how much I loved you / Balling blues / When you're tired of running / Crazy about a woman / You're the sweetest thing / 'Bout to put you down / Going away baby / Foolin' with my heart / My time is running out / Life's no bed of roses / Waking up baby
CDCHD 476 / Jun '93 / Ace

Williams, Lucinda

☐ CAR WHEELS ON A GRAVEL ROAD
Right in time / Car wheels on a gravel road / Too cool to be forgotten / Drunken angel / Concrete and barbed wire / Lake Charles / Can't let go / I lost it / Metal firecracker / Greenville / Still I long for your kiss / Joy / Jackson
5583382 / 6 Jul '98 / Mercury

☐ HAPPY WOMAN BLUES
Lafayette / I lost it / Maria / Happy woman blues / King of hearts / Rolling along / One night stand / Howlin' at midnight / Hard road / Louisiana man / Sharp cutting wings (song to a poet)
MRCD 149 / '90 / Munich
SFWCD 40003 / Dec '94 / Smithsonian Folkways

☐ LUCINDA WILLIAMS
380052 / 29 Jun '98 / Koch International

☐ RAMBLIN'
SFWCD 40042 / Oct '94 / Smithsonian Folkways

Williams, Marion

☐ BORN TO SING GOSPEL
SHCD 6009 / Mar '95 / Shanachie

☐ CAN'T KEEP IT TO MYSELF
SHCD 6007 / Dec '93 / Shanachie

☐ MY SOUL LOOKS BACK/THE GENIUS OF MARION WILLIAMS 1962-1992
SHCD 6011 / Dec '94 / Shanachie

☐ THROUGH MANY DANGERS (Classic Performances 1966-1993)
SH 6021 / Oct '96 / Shanachie

Williams, Mary Lou

☐ CLASSICS 1927-1940
CLASSICS 630 / Nov '92 / Classics

☐ CLASSICS 1944
CLASSICS 814 / May '95 / Classics

☐ FREE SPIRITS
SCCD 31043 / Jul '88 / Steeplechase

☐ KEY MOMENTS
TPZ 1016 / Apr '95 / Topaz Jazz

☐ LIVE AT THE COOKERY
CRD 146 / Mar '96 / Chiaroscuro

☐ MARY LOU WILLIAMS STORY 1930-1941, THE
159002 / Jan '98 / Jazz Archives

☐ ROLL 'EM
PCD 7016 / Nov '96 / Progressive

☐ ZODIAC SUITE
SFWCD 40810 / Nov '95 / Smithsonian Folkways

☐ ZONING
SFWCD 40811 / Nov '95 / Smithsonian Folkways

Williams, Mason

☐ CLASSICAL GAS (Williams, Mason & Mannheim Steamroller)
AGCD 800 / Oct '88 / American Gramophone

Williams, Maurice

☐ SPOTLIGHT ON MAURICE WILLIAMS
High heeled sneakers / Bare footin' / Spanish harlem / Up on the roof / On broadway / Corine Corina / Drift away / Save the last dance for me / Raindrops keep falling on my head / Mustang Sally / Running around / Little darlin' / This feeling / Stay
HADCD 120 / Feb '94 / Javelin

☐ STAY (Carolina Beach Music - The Best Of Maurice Williams) (Williams, Maurice & The Zodiacs)
Stay / Come along / Little darlin' / Don't you ever leave me / Golly gee / Do I / Return / So fine / Barefootin' / My baby's gone / Running around / Up on the roof / Mustang Sally / Hi heel sneakers / Surely / Oop oop pah doo / On Broadway / Corinna Corinna / Drift away / Raindrops keep falling on my head / Save the last dance for me / Spanish Harlem
AIM 2016CD / 20 Oct '97 / Aim

Williams, Midge

☐ CLASSICS 1937-1938
CLASSICS 745 / Aug '94 / Classics

Williams, Otis

☐ OTIS WILLIAMS & THE CHARMS (The Original Rockin' And Chart Masters) (Williams, Otis & His Charms)
Love love stick stov / Love's our inspiration / Heart of a rose / I offer you / Fifty five seconds / My baby dearest darling / Bye bye baby / Please believe in me / When we get together / Mambo sh-mambo / Heaven only knows / Happy are we / Come to me baby / Loving baby / Let the happening happen / Quiet please / This love of mine / It's you, you, you / One fine day / What do you know about that / First time we met / Boom diddy boom boom / I'll be true / Crazy crazy love / Hearts of stone / Two hearts
CDCHD 531 / Mar '94 / Ace

Williams, Pamela

☐ EIGHT DAYS OF ECSTASY
5336130432 / 24 Mar '98 / Hup

☐ SAXTRESS
Matter of time / I can love you like that / Castine / Secret garden/Sweet seduction suite / Natural woman / Ladies night / Matador and the maiden / Latin lullaby / Saxtress / Slow burn / Angels among us
INAK 30342CD / Nov '97 / In Akustik

Williams, Paul

☐ AIN'T GOD GOOD
Heaven's getting brighter / With the church I'll fly away / Jesus had rose from the dead / Ain't God good / Paul's ministry / I wasn't there / I just steal away and pray / Church will be home / Two coats / I don't know what I'd do / Saved through Jesus' blood / Jesus called it paradise
ROUCD 0414 / Sep '97 / Rounder

Williams, Paul

☐ IN MEMORY OF ROBERT JOHNSON (Williams, Paul & Friends)
Terraplane blues / Crossroads blues / Kind hearted woman blues / If I had possession over judgement day / Ramblin' blues / When you got a good friend / Come on in my kitchen
VSOPCD 259 / 17 Aug '98 / Connoisseur Collection

Williams, Paul

☐ BACK TO LOVE AGAIN
PICP 1132 / 22 Jun '98 / Pioneer

Williams, Richard

☐ NEW HORN IN TOWN
I can dream, can't I / I remember Clifford / Ferris wheel / Raucous notes / Blues in a quandry / Over the rainbow / Renita's bounce
CCD 79003 / Feb '97 / Candid

Williams, Robbie

☐ LIFE THRU A LENS
Lazy days / Life thru a lens / Ego a go go / Angels / South of the border / Old before I die / One of god's better people / Let me entertain you / Killing me / Clean / Baby girl window
CDCHR 6127 / 29 Sep '97 / Chrysalis

Williams, Robert Pete

☐ FREE AGAIN
OBCCD 553 / Jan '94 / Original Blues Classics

☐ I'M AS BLUE AS A MAN CAN BE
ARHCD 394 / Apr '95 / Arhoolie

☐ LOUISIANA BLUES
Somebody help poor me / Freight train blues / It's hard to tell / I'm going down slow / Motherless children have a hard time / Ugly / So long boogie / This is a mean old world to me / High as I want to be / It's a long old road
CDTAK 1011 / 29 Jun '98 / Takoma

☐ WHEN A MAN TAKES THE BLUES
ARHCD 395 / Apr '95 / Arhoolie

Williams, Robin

☐ ALL BROKEN HEARTS ARE THE SAME (Williams, Robin & Linda)
Rollin' and ramblin' / All broken hearts are the same / Baby rocked her dolly / Leaving this land / Annie / Riding on the Santa Fe / Pan handle wind / Pine country / Stone wall country / Across the blue mountains / After the flood
SHCD 1022 / Jan '97 / Sugar Hill

☐ CLOSE AS WE CAN GET/9 TILL MIDNIGHT (Williams, Robin & Linda)
FF 359CD / May '93 / Flying Fish

☐ DEVIL OF A DREAM (Williams, Robin & Linda)
Things I've learned / Five rooms / Green summertime / Rolling and rambling / Men with guns / Genius / I wonder if I care as much / Walking like a man / While I'm waiting for you / So it's like this man / Falls from the sky / At the crossroads again / Letter that I wrote
SHCD 1059 / 9 Mar '98 / Sugar Hill

☐ GOOD NEWS (Williams, Robin & Linda/ Their Fine Group)
SHCD 3832 / Apr '95 / Sugar Hill

☐ LIVE (Williams, Robin & Linda/Their Fine Group)
SHCD 1043 / Nov '94 / Sugar Hill

☐ RHYTHM OF LOVE, THE (Williams, Robin & Linda)
Rhythm of love / When I hear that whistle blow / House of gold / I'll remember you love in my prayers / Gone to the West / Hired gun / They all faded away / Six o'clock news / Hill county song / Devil is a mighty wind / Poor wayfaring stranger / You done me wrong
SHCD 1027 / Jul '90 / Sugar Hill

☐ SUGAR FOR SUGAR (Williams, Robin & Linda)
Sugar for sugar / Together all alone / Border bound / Cheapest kind / Brimming glass / Traffic light / High atmosphere / Talking too much / Honky tonk nation / Streets of gold / Old Wyatt / Edge of the world
SHCD 1052 / Mar '98 / Sugar Hill

☐ TURN TOWARD TOMORROW (Williams, Robin & Linda)
SHCD 1040 / Jan '94 / Sugar Hill

Williams, Rod

☐ HANGING IN THE BALANCE
MCD 5380 / Sep '92 / Muse

Williams, Roger

☐ COLLECTION, THE
VSD 5908 / 21 Apr '98 / Varese Sarabande

Williams, Roy

☐ ABSOLUTELY (Williams, Roy & Bill Allred)
CD 024 / Aug '97 / Nagel Heyer

☐ GRUESOME TWOSOME (Williams, Roy & John Barnes)
BLCD 760507 / Oct '93 / Black Lion

☐ ROYAL TROMBO
PHONTCD 7556 / '93 / Phontastic

☐ SOMETHING WONDERFUL (Williams, Roy & Eddie Thompson)
Like someone in love / Is'nt it romantic / Something wonderful / I'm comin' virginia / It never entered my mind / Cheek to cheek / I'm getting sentimental over you / Folks who live on the hill / Ind's out
HEPCD 2015 / Jul '96 / Hep

☐ WHEN YOU'RE SMILING (Williams, Roy & Benny Waters)
Broadway / When you're smiling / Things ain't what they used to be / Line for Lyons / Don't blame me / Just friends / Where or when / Know what I mean / Medley / Jumpin' at the woodside
HEPCD 2010 / Aug '97 / Hep

Williams, Rozz

☐ WHORSES MOUTH
600012 / Jul '97 / Hollows Hill

☐ WOUND OF EXIT (2CD Set) (Williams, Rozz Premature Ejaculation)
Alone with the devil / Head / At the end of every day / Rope trick / Two thirteen / Wound of exit / Alone with devil / Ruptured walls (7700 volts) / Sick swing / Purged and destroyed / Flesh and blood / End is here/Exit
TX 60004CD / 17 Aug '98 / Triple XXX

Williams, Steve

☐ FULL MOON ON BROADWAY
PLAN 008CD / Nov '97 / Planet

Williams, Sylvia

☐ FROM NEW ORLEANS
BCD 319 / Jan '94 / GHB

Williams, Tex

☐ TEX WILLIAMS ON THE AIR 1947-1949
Smoke smoke smoke / What's the matter with you / Texas playboy rag / Don't telephone don't telegraph / Spanish two step / Spanish fandango / Palace stomp / Careless love / Don't come crying to me / San Antonio rose / Theme / Covered wagon rolled right along / I found a new baby / Brush those tears / Who clipped Samson's hair / Swanee river / Caravan ride / Riverside stomp / One O'Clock jump / Steel guitar rag / Please don't leave me anymore / Three way boogie / She's a real gone Oakie / South / Smoke smoke smoke
RFDCD 17 / Oct '97 / Country Routes

Williams, Tom

☐ INTRODUCING TOM WILLIAMS (Williams, Tom Quintet)
CRISS 1064CD / Oct '92 / Criss Cross

☐ STRAIGHT STREET
1091CD / Jan '95 / Criss Cross

Williams, Tony

☐ EMERGENCY (Williams, Tony Lifetime)
Emergency / Games / Where / Vashkar / Via the spectrum road / Spectrum / Sangria for three / Something special
5391172 / 10 Nov '97 / Verve

☐ LIFETIME: THE COLLECTION
4689242 / Jan '95 / Sony Jazz

☐ SPRING
Extras / Echo / From before / Love song / Tee
CDP 7461352 / 1 Jun '98 / Blue Note

☐ TURN IT OVER (Williams, Tony Lifetime)
To whom it may concern / To whom it may concern / This night this song / Big Nick / Right on / Once I loved / Vuelta abajo / Famous blues / Allah be praised / One word
5391182 / 10 Nov '97 / Verve

☐ WILDERNESS
Wilderness rising / Chinatown / Infant wilderness / Harlem mist '55 / Night you were born / Wilderness voyager / Macchu picchu / China moon / Wilderness island / Sea of wilderness / Gambia / Cape wilderness
CDP 8545712 / Nov '96 / Ark/Blue Note

Williams, Valdo

☐ NEW ADVANCED JAZZ
Desert fox / Bad manners / Move faster / Conquerer
SV 0238 / Oct '97 / Savoy Jazz

Williams, Vanessa

☐ COMFORT ZONE, THE
Comfort zone / Running back to you / Work to do / You gotta go / Still in love / Save the best for last / What will I tell my heart / Stranger's eyes / Two of a kind / Freedom dance (get free) / Just for tonight / One reason / Better off now / Goodbye / Right stuff
5112672 / 15 Sep '97 / Wing

☐ NEXT
5360602 / 15 Sep '97 / Mercury

☐ SWEETEST DAYS
Intro-lude / Way that you love / Betcha never / Sweetest days / Higher ground / You dont' have to say you're sorry / Ellamental / Sister moon / You can't run / Long way home / Constantly / Moonlight over Paris
5261722 / Feb '95 / Mercury

Williams, Victoria

☐ LOOSE
What a wonderful world / Harry went to heaven / When we sing together / Love / Polish these shoes / Psalms / Waterfall / Get away / Hitchhikers smile / My ally / Happy to have known pappy / Sunshine country / Nature's way / Crazy mary / You r loved / Century plant
7567924302 / Jan '95 / Mammoth

☐ MUSINGS OF A CREEKDIPPER
Periwinkle sky / Rainmaker / Kashmir's corn / Train song (demise of the caboose) / Last word / Nature boy / Tree song (eucalyptus lullabye) / Let it be so / Allergic boy / Hummingbird / Grandpa in the cornpatch / Blackbirds rise
7567830722 / 30 Mar '98 / Atlantic

Williams, Willie

☐ ARMAGIDEON TIME
Masterplan / See you when I get there / People / Armagideon time / All the way / Turn on the power / Easy / Burn
CDHB 3509 / '90 / Heartbeat

☐ JAH WILL
DS 007 / Jun '95 / Drumstreet

☐ MESSENGER MAN (Williams, Willie & The Armagedions)
CRCD 42 / Sep '95 / Charm

☐ NATTY WITH A CAUSE
SHAKACD 922 / Nov '92 / Jah Shaka

☐ SEE ME
SHAKACD 949 / Jul '93 / Jah Shaka

Williams-Fairey Band

☐ ACID BRASS
Can u dance / Jibaro / Voodoo ray / Paciffic 202 / Stings of life / Groove won't stop / Let's get brutal / Cubik / Day in the life / Can you party / What time is love
BFFP 150CD / 10 Nov '97 / Blast First

☐ BRASS FROM THE MASTERS VOL.1 (Williams-Fairey Band & James Gourlay/Bryan Hurdley)
Life divine / Moor of Venice / Shining river / Energy / Variations / Severn suite op.87
CHAN 4547 / Aug '97 / Chandos

☐ FREEDOM (Williams-Fairey Engineering Band)
Silkstream / Scheherazade / Laughter in the rain / Brassmens holiday / Disney fantasy / Swiss air / Lass of Richmond Hill / Thoughts of love / Freedom
QPRL 038D / Sep '88 / Polyphonic

☐ GOLDEN JUBILEE (Williams-Fairey Engineering Band)
Tritsch Tratsch Polka / Swing low, sweet chariot / Kim / Piper in the meadow / Pie Jesu / Marching with Sousa / Carnival for brass / Scarecrow and Mrs. King / Serenade / Bohemian rhapsody / Folk festival
GRACC 17 / May '94 / Grasmere

☐ HYMNS ANCIENT AND MODERN (Williams-Fairey Engineering Band)
Praise my soul / Praise my soul / Blaenwern / Lloyd / Jerusalem (parry) / St. clement / All things bright and beautiful / Old rugged cross / Aurelia / Cwm rhondda / Old hundredth / Crimond / Ellacombe / Dear lord and father of mankind / Slane / Aberystwyth / What a friend we have in jesus / Rimington / Simple gifts / I vow to thee my country / Easter hymn / Onward christian soldiers
QPRL 054D / Mar '93 / Polyphonic

☐ JAZZ
Jazz / Unholy sonnets / Shadow songs / Dragons arise / Turba / Lord of the dance / White knuckle ride
DOYCD 068 / Oct '97 / Doyen

☐ PROCESSION TO THE MINSTER (Williams-Fairey Engineering Band)
Boys in blue / Tuesday blues / Concertino classico / Autumn leaves / Land of the mountain and the flood / Gladiator's farewell / Batman / Festival music / Caprice / Procession to the minster
GRCD 42 / Nov '90 / Grasmere

☐ SPANISH IMPRESSIONS (Williams-Fairey Engineering Band)
Amparito roca / Allorada del gracioso / Maids of Cadiz / Ritual fire dance / Carmen fantasy / Andalucia / La boda de luis alonso / Bonds of friendship / Spanish march / Evocations / Four Spanish impressions
CHAN 4554 / Apr '97 / Chandos

☐ TOURNAMENT FOR BRASS (Williams-Fairey Engineering Band)
President / Over the rainbow / Tournament for brass / Trouble with the tuba is... / Blenheim flourishes / Fest musik der stadt wien / Military overture / Ballycastle bay / Twin Peaks / Neapolitan scenes
GRCD 35 / May '90 / Grasmere

☐ WILLIAMS-FAIREY DIAMOND JUBILEE (2CD Set)
Beaufighters / Jubilee / Scottish cradle song / Jubilance / Cantilena / Russian sailors dance / Gaudete / Rondo / Carrickfergus / Londonderry air / Leonardo / Praeludium / Royal duchy / Five Greek sketches / Fantasy variations / Birdland / She moved through the fair / Bergamasca / Finale / Psalm of praise
DOYCD 052 / Apr '98 / Doyen

Williams-Holdings Band

☐ DOUBLE CHAMPIONS
Land of the long white cloud / Masquerade / Devil and the deep blue sea / Rhapsody for euphonium / Capriccio / Dance sequence / Variations on a welsh theme
QPRL 065D / Jan '94 / Polyphonic

☐ MIDNIGHT EUPHONIUM
Midnight euphonium / Euphonism / Arioso / How soon / On my own / Concerto No. 1 / Nessun dorma / Deep inside the sacred temple / Somewhere / Jeanie with the light brown hair / Your tiny hands are frozen / Carnival cocktail / Love is forever / Hail acient walls / Allegro / Ina / Pokarekareana
QPRL 064D / Jan '94 / Polyphonic

Williamson Brothers

☐ COMPLETE RECORDED WORKS (Williamson Brothers & Dick Justice/ Frank Hutchison)
DOCD 8004 / Jan '97 / Document

Williamson, Ann

☐ AMAZING GRACE
Once a day / Ae fond kiss / Wings of a dove / Roses in the winter / Old homing waltz / Gaelic selection / Wishes were fishes / Funny familiar / House with a spire / Amazing grace / Scottish waltz / She moves through the fair / Love me / Peace in the valley / Crystal chandelier
CDITV 600 / Mar '95 / Scotdisc

☐ FLOWER OF SCOTLAND
Water is wide / Forty shades of green / Flower of Scotland / Rose / Beyond the sunset / Crying time / Bluebells of Scotland / Wild mountain thyme / Mountains of mourne / Rowan tree / Picture of me / Star O'Rabbie Burns / Dark island / Bonnie Mary Of Argyll / Battle's o'er / Farewell my love
CDITV 590 / Aug '94 / Scotdisc

☐ VERY BEST OF ANN WILLIAMSON, THE
I can't stop loving you / I'll get over you / Tiny bubbles / Like strangers / Cryin' time / I can't help it if I'm still in / Pal of my cradle days / She's got you / Bonaparte's retreat / Maggie / Four in the morning / Invisible tears / Is it no secret / Don't it make my brown eyes / Send me the pillow / Foresaking all the rest / Tennessee waltz / Your cheating heart / I fall to pieces / Room full of roses / Dear John
MCVD 30003 / Nov '96 / Emerald Gem

Williamson, Claude

☐ MULLS MULLIGAN
FSRCD 54 / Jan '98 / Fresh Sound

☐ ROUND MIDNIGHT (Bethlehem Jazz Classics) (Williamson, Claude Trio)
CDGR 134 / Apr '97 / Charly

Williamson, Harry

☐ TARKA (Williamson, Harry & Anthony Philips)
Movement 1 / Movement 2 / Movement 3 / Anthem
BP 219CD / Jul '96 / Blueprint

Williamson, Robin

☐ AMERICAN STONEHENGE (Williamson, Robin & His Merry Band)
Port London early / Pacheco / Keepsake / Zoo blues / These Islands green / Man in the van / Sands and the glass / Her scattered gold / When evening shadows / Rab's last woollen testament
EDCD 389 / Jun '94 / Edsel

☐ BLOOMSBURY 1997 (Williamson, Robin & Mike Heron)
PWMD 5006 / Mar '98 / Pig's Whisker

☐ CELTIC HARP AIRS AND DANCE TUNES
Lude's supper / Meggie's fou / Mwynen mon / Galway rambler / Port Atholl / Rocks of pleasure / Scholar / Glan medd dod mwyn / Old frieze britches / Blackbird / Kimiad
CDTRAX 134 / Jun '97 / Greentrax

☐ DREAM JOURNALS 1966-1976
Dream journals foreword / There was no snow / Carefully folding my wings / On the way to the cathedral / On our holidays / Charlie the taxi driver / Turn again / These are dreams / Out with McClachan / Snah eer / From odin's tree / Welsh pavanes
PWMD 5004 / 16 Mar '98 / Pigs Whisker Music

☐ ISLAND OF THE STRONG DOOR
TMC 9504 / Feb '96 / Music Corporation

☐ JOURNEY'S EDGE
Border tango / Tune I hear so well / Red eye blues / Tomorrow / Mythic times / Lullaby for a rainy night / Rap city rhapsody / Maharajah of Mogador / Bells / Voices of the Barbary coast / Out on the water
EDCD 374 / Jun '93 / Edsel

☐ LEGACY OF THE SCOTTISH HARPERS
Scotch cap/Scotland / Flowers of the forest/ Cromlet's lilt/Chevy chase / Weel hoddled Lucky/ Lochmaben harper / Gilderoy/Cow the Gowan / MacGregor's lament/MacGregor's search / Kilt thy coat Maggie/Three sheepskins / Lord Dundee's lamentation/Brae's o'Killiecrankie / I'll mek ye fain to follow me / Lady Cassilis' lilt/Auld jew/Broom o'Cowdenknowes / MacDonald of the Isles salutation / Rushes/Birk and green hollin / Soor plooms / Jockey went to the wood / Banks of Helicon/Deil tak the wars
CCF 12CD / Nov '84 / Claddagh

☐ MERRY BANDS FAREWELL
Wassail / Her scattered gold / By weary well / Woodcutter's song / Flower of the Briar / Legend / Five denial's on Merlin's grave / Cadgers on the cannongate
PWMD 5001 / Apr '98 / Pig's Whisker

☐ MIRROR MAN SEQUENCES 1961-1966, THE (2CD Set)
Mirrorman's sequences / Oh Marie / Sheepish / Beat gadjies / Run run run / Kererra / Flat foot skiffle / Ironstone bit / Behold the Indian unicorn / Onion arc / To unmake demons / On the job / Hand of Fatima
PWMD 5002 / May '97 / Pig's Whisker

☐ RING DANCE
Ring dance / Veshengro / Back in Paris / My enemy is listening / Gaol for sure / Fine fingered dance / At Waverley Station / Lady with the book / Take a heed of me sometimes / Invocation / Lights of sweet St. Anne / I see us cross great waters
PWMD 5008 / 20 Apr '98 / Pig's Whisker

☐ SONGS OF LOVE & PARTING/5 BARDIC MYSTERIES
Versus in stewart street / For mr thomas / Fare thee well sweet mally / Return no more / Tarry wool / For three of us / Sigil / Flower of the briar / Forming of blodeuwedd / Gwydion's dream / Verses at balwearie tower / Night at ardpatrick / Parting glass / Spoils of annwn / Battle of the trees / Dialogue of the two sages / Voyage of bran, son of febal / Three celtic nature poems
TMC 9403 / Jan '96 / Music Corporation

☐ TEN OF SONGS, THE
Ancient song / Lammas / Political lies / Scotland yet / Skull and nettlework / Barley / Here to burn / Verses at Ellesmere / Innocent love / Verses at Powis
FF 70448 / Feb '97 / Flying Fish

☐ WINTER'S TURNING
Drive the cold winter away / Avant de s'en aller / Pastime with good company (Henry VIII)/Somerset wassail / Greensleeves morris/Green groweth the holly/Eagle's whistle / Past 1 o'clock/Great Tom's cast / Sheep under the snow/Welsh morris / Praetorius' courante clxxix/Drive the cold winter away / Blow blow thou winter wynd/Vivaldi's winter largo / Trip to the boar/Manage the miser / Carolan's quarrel with the landlady/Christmas eve / Hunting the wren / Corelli's sonato/Scottish country dance / Polka du tapis
FF 70407 / Feb '97 / Flying Fish

Williamson, Roy

☐ LONG JOURNEY SOUTH, THE
Long journey South / Laggan love / Skye boat song / Donald Og / Peggy Gordon / Nicky's theme / Number one / Tuscan / Long journey South (reprise)
MOICD 001 / Oct '91 / Moidart

Williamson, Sonny Boy

☐ ALL TIME BLUES CLASSICS
8420312 / Oct '96 / Music Memoria

☐ AMERICAN BLUES LEGEND
CPCD 8332 / 27 May '98 / Charly

☐ ANTHOLOGY 1937-1944
EN 519 / Sep '95 / Encyclopaedia

☐ BLUEBIRD BLUES, THE
Good morning little schoolgirl / Moonshine / Early in the morning / Project highway / You give an account / Susie Q / Little girl blues / Blue bird blues / Whiskey headed blues / Jackson blues / Got the bottle up and gone / You've been fooling around / Downtown / Deep down in the ground / Up the country blues / Worried me blues / Black gal blues / Collector man blues / You can lead me / Miss Louisa blues / I'm tired of trucking my blues away / Beauty parlour / Until my love come down / Sugar mama blues
743215696223 / 23 Mar '98 / Camden

☐ BLUEBIRD RECORDINGS 1937-1938, THE
Good morning little school girl / Blue bird blues / Jackson blues / Got the bottle up and gone / Sugar mama blues / Skinny woman / Up the country blues / Worried me blues / Black gal blues / Collector man blues / Frigidaire blues / Suzanna blues / Early in the morning / Project highway / My little Cornelius / Decoration blues / You can lead me / Moonshine / Miss Louisa blues / Sunny land / I'm tired of truckin' my blues away / Down South / Beauty parlor / Until my love come down
07863667232 / Feb '97 / Bluebird

☐ BLUES 1937-1945, THE
FA 253 / Jul '96 / Fremeaux

☐ GOOD MORNING LITTLE SCHOOLGIRL
Good morning little school girl / Bluebird blues / Sugar Mama blues / Skinny woman / Collector man blues / Early in the morning / Black gal blues / Suzie Q / Bad luck blues / Good gravy / Honeybee blues / Decoration blues / Train fare blues / Jivin' the blues / Welfare store blues / My black name blues / Check up on my baby blues / Stop breaking down / Hoodoo hoodoo / Shake the boogie / Better cut that out
CD 52044 / Oct '96 / Blues Encore

☐ KING OF BLUES HARMONICA 1938-1940
My baby I've been your slave / Christmas morning blues / Bluebird blues (part 2) / Doggin' my love around / Good for nothing blues / Sugar mama blues no. 2 / Good gravy / TB blues / Good gal blues / Thinking my blues away / I'm not pleasing you / New jailhouse blues / Life time blues / Miss ida lee / Tell me baby / Honey bee blues / I been dealing with the devil / Wartime blues / Train fare home blues / Decoration day blues / Welfare store blues / My little machine / Jivin' the blues
BLE 592512 / Dec '92 / Black & Blue

☐ MASTERS, THE
Good morning school girl / Jackson blues / I'm tired trucking my blues away / Moonshine / Whiskey headed blues / Little low woman blues / Good gravy / Thinking my blues away / Tell my baby / She don't love me that way / Life time blues / I been dealing with the devil / Western Union man / New early in the morning / Coal and iceman blues / Sonny boy's jump / Springtime blues / I have to go
EABCD 082 / 30 Mar '98 / Eagle

☐ NOTHING BUT THE BLUES
CBCD 11 / Jul '96 / Collector's Blues

☐ ORIGINAL SONNY
Bad luck blues / My baby I've been your slave / Whiskey headed blues / Susie Q / Low down ways / Insurance man blues / Good gravy / Collector man / Joe Louis and John Henry / Doggin' my love around / Until my love come down / Bad luck blues / Goodbye red / Right kind of life / Little low woman blues / Blue bird blues / Number five blues / You give an account
CDBM 113 / Feb '97 / Blue Moon

☐ PORTRAIT OF A BLUES MAN
APR 3017CD / Dec '96 / Analogue Revival

☐ SONNY BOY WILLIAMSON 1937-1939
157602 / Feb '93 / Blues Collection

☐ SONNY BOY WILLIAMSON 1940-1942
158102 / Dec '93 / Blues Collection

☐ SONNY BOY WILLIAMSON 1940-1947
DOCD 5521 / Mar '97 / Document

☐ SUGAR MAMA
Good morning little school girl / Blue bird blues / Got the bottle up and go / Sugar mama blues / Early in the morning / Black gal blues / Decoration blues / Whiskey headed woman blues / Lord oh lord / Good gravy / TB Blues / Tell me baby / I have been dealing with the devil / Welfare store blues / My little machine / Jivin' the blues / Shotgun blues / Million years blues / Sloppy drunk blues / You've got to step back / Ground hog blues / My black name / She don't love me that way / What's gettin' wrong with you
IGOCD 2014 / Feb '95 / Indigo

Williamson, Sonny Boy

☐ BLUES OF SONNY BOY WILLIAMSON, THE
STCD 4062 / Jun '87 / Storyville

☐ BOPPIN' WITH SONNY
Shuckin' woman / I'm not beggin nobody / Boppin' with Sonny / Empty bedroom / From the bottom / No nights by myself / Red hot kisses / Keep it to yourself / Going in your direction / Gettin' out of town / Sonny's rhythm / She's crazy / City of New Orleans / 309 Cat / Cat hop / Clownin' with the world
CDBM 088 / '90 / Blue Moon

☐ BUMMER ROAD
She got next to me / Santa Claus / Little village / Your funeral and my trial (alternate) / Lonesome cabin / I can't do without you / Temperature 110 / Unseen eye / Keep your hand out of my pocket / Open road / This old life
MCD 09324 / Apr '97 / Chess/MCA

☐ CLOWNIN' WITH THE WORLD
ALCD 2700 / Oct '93 / Alligator

☐ COLLECTION, THE
All my love in vain / Born blind / Cross my heart / 99 / Nine below zero / Got to move / Your funeral and my trial / Goat / Bring it on home / Keep it to yourself / Help me / I wonder why / Checkin' up on my baby / Decoration day / Don't start me talkin' / Fattening frogs for snakes / Lonesome cabin / One way out / Key (to your door) / Trust my baby / Work with me / Your imagination / Stop crying (all your throwing away is mine) / Santa claus / I don't know why
COL 044 / Feb '95 / Collection

☐ DOWN AND OUT BLUES
Don't start me talkin' / I don't know / All my love in vain / Key / Keep it to yourself / Dissatisfied / Fattenin' frogs for snakes / Wake up baby / Your funeral and my trail / Ninety nine / Cross my heart / Let me explain
CHLD 19106 / Oct '92 / Chess/MCA

☐ EP COLLECTION VOL.2, THE
Help me / Bring it on home / Checkin' up on my baby / Don't start me talkin' / Your funeral and my trial / Keep it to yourself / Cross my heart / Too old to think / One way out / Let your conscience be your guide / Temperature 110 / Tryin' to get back on my feet / You killing me / Ninety nine / I don't know / Too young to die / Dissatisfied / It's sad to be alone / Key / Trust my baby / Wake up baby / Bye bye bird / Hurts me so much / That's all I want / (I want you) close to me
SEECD 395 / Feb '94 / See For Miles

☐ ESSENTIAL SONNY BOY WILLIAMSON, THE
Good evening everybody / Don't start me to talkin' / All my love in vain / You killing me / Let me explain / Your imagination / Don't lose your eye / Keep it to yourself / Key (to your door) / Have you ever been in love / Fattening frogs for snakes / I don't know / Like Wolf / Cross my heart / Ninety nine / Born blind / Little village / Unseen eye / Your funeral and my trial / Keep your hands out of my pocket / Unseeing eye / Let your conscience be your guide / Goat / Cool disposition / Santa Claus / Checkin' up on my baby / Temperature 110 / Lonesome cabin / Somebody help me / Down child / Trust my baby / Too close together / Too young to die / She's my baby / Stop right now / Too old to think / One way out / Nine below zero / Help me / Bye bye bird / Bring it on home / Decoration day / Trying to get back on my feet / Close to me / I can't be alone
CHLDD 19330 / Sep '96 / Chess/MCA

☐ GOIN' IN YOUR DIRECTION
AL 2803 / Jul '94 / Alligator

☐ HARP FROM DEEP SOUTH, THE
Your funeral and my trial / Wake up baby / Checkin' up on my baby / Down child / Too young to die / Fattenin' frogs for snakes / Don't start me talkin' / Sky is crying / Got to move / Help me / Bring it on home / Story of Sonny Boy Williamson / When the light went out / Keep it to yourself / Sonny's rhythm / Bye bye bird / Work with me / Movin' down the river Rhine / I wonder do I have a friend / Eyesight to the blind / Mighty long time / Nine below zero
CD 52018 / '92 / Blues Encore

☐ HIS BEST
MCD 09377 / Jul '97 / Chess/MCA

☐ KEEP IT TO OURSELVES
ALCD 4787 / Aug '92 / Alligator

☐ KING BISCUIT TIME
ARHCD 310 / Apr '95 / Arhoolie

☐ LIVE IN ENGLAND
Bye bye bird: *Williamson, Sonny Boy & The Yardbirds* / Mr. downchild: *Williamson, Sonny Boy & The Yardbirds* / River Rhine: *Williamson, Sonny Boy & The Yardbirds* / Twenty three hours too long: *Williamson, Sonny Boy & The Yardbirds* / Lost care: *Williamson, Sonny Boy & The Yardbirds* / Take it easy: *Williamson, Sonny Boy & The Yardbirds* / Out of the water coast: *Williamson, Sonny Boy & The Yardbirds* / Western Arizona: *Williamson, Sonny Boy & The Yardbirds* / Slow walk: *Williamson, Sonny Boy & The Yardbirds* / Highway 69: *Williamson, Sonny Boy & The Yardbirds* / My little cabin: *Williamson, Sonny Boy & The Yardbirds* / Sonny's slow walk: *Williamson, Sonny Boy & The Animals* / Pontiac blues: *Williamson, Sonny Boy & The Animals* / My babe: *Williamson, Sonny Boy & The Animals* / I don't care no more: *Williamson, Sonny Boy & The Animals* / Baby don't you worry: *Williamson, Sonny Boy & The Animals* / Night time is the right time: *Williamson, Sonny Boy & The Animals* / I'm gonna put you down: *Williamson, Sonny Boy & The Animals* / Fattenin' frogs for snakes: *Williamson, Sonny Boy & The Animals* / Nobody but you: *Williamson, Sonny Boy & The Animals*
CDRB 21 / Apr '95 / Charly

☐ ROCK GENERATION (Williamson, Sonny Boy & Graham Bond)
14552 / 22 May '98 / Spalax

☐ SONNY BOY WILLIAMSON & YARDBIRDS 1963 (With Eric Clapton) (Williamson, Sonny Boy & The Yardbirds)
CDLR 42020 / Aug '87 / L&R

☐ VERY BEST OF SONNY BOY WILLIAMSON, THE (& Roots Of The Blues No.4 Compilation/3CD Set)
Work with me / Don't start me talkin' / All my love in vein / Don't lose your eye / Keep it to yourself / Key (to your door) / Have you ever been in love / Fattening frogs for snakes / I don't know / Cross my heart / Born blind / Ninety nine / Dissatisfied / Your funeral and my trial / Wake up baby / Let your conscience be your guide / Unseeing eye / Goat / It's sad to be alone / Checkin' up on my baby / Temperature 110 / Somebody help me / Down child / Trust my baby / Too close together / Too young to die / Hunt / Nine below zero / Got to move / Bye bye bird / Help me, bring it on home / One way out / Trying to get back on my feet / Decoration / Mister downchild / 23 Hours too long / Take it easy, baby / Highway 69 / My little cabin / Cool drink of water: *Johnson, Tommy* / Statesboroe blues: *McTell, 'Blind' Willie* / Candy man blues: *Hurt, 'Mississippi' John* / Nobody knows you (When you're down and out): *Smith, Bessie* / That's no way to get along: *Wilkins, Robert* / Broken hearted: *Estes, 'Sleepy' John* / Kingfisher blues: *Tampa Red* / Walking blues: *Johnson, Robert* / Sugar Mama blues: *Williamson, Sonny Boy* / Roll 'em Pete: *Turner, 'Big' Joe* / New 'shake 'em on down: *McClennan, Tommy* / Rockin' chair: *Broonzy, 'Big' Bill* / Take a little walk with me: *Lockwood, Robert Jr.* / I be's troubled: *Waters, Muddy* / Rock Island line: *Leadbelly* / Ramblin' mind blues: *Big Maceo*
VBCD 304 / Jul '95 / Charly

Willie & The Poor Boys

☐ WILLIE AND THE POOR BOYS
Baby, please don't go / Can you hear me / These arms of mine / Revenue man / You never can tell / Slippin' and slidin' / Saturday night / Let's talk it over / All night long / Chicken shack boogie / Sugar bee / Poor boy boogie
NEMCD 688 / Apr '94 / Sequel

☐ WILLIE AND THE POOR BOYS LIVE
High school confidential / Baby, please don't go / Mystery train / Chicken shack boogie / Stagger lee / Red hot / Poor boy boogie medley / Land of 1000 dances / Tear it up / Ooh-poo-pah-doo / Rockin' pneumonia and the boogie woogie flu / What'd I say / Lovin' up a storm / Hound dog / Shake, rattle and roll / Looking for someone to love
NEMCD 689 / Apr '94 / Sequel

Willimas, Derede

☐ WHY NOT TONIGHT
FECD 11 / Apr '93 / First Edition

Willis, Butch

☐ REPEATS (Willis, Butch & The Rocks)
TB 134CD / May '94 / Teenbeat

Willis, Chick

☐ BACK TO THE BLUES
Don't let success (turn our love around) / Goin' to the dogs / Bow legged woman / I ain't superstitious / Tell papa / Story of my life / My adorable one / I ain't jivin' baby / Strange things happening
ICH 1106CD / Oct '93 / Ichiban

☐ FOOTPRINTS ON MY BED
Love crazy / Use what you got / What's to become of the world / Roll the dice / Footprints in my bed / Big red caboose / Hello central / Jack you up / Voodoo woman / Nuts for sale
ICH 1054CD / Oct '93 / Ichiban

☐ I GOT A BIG FAT WOMAN
ICH 1171CD / May '94 / Ichiban

☐ NOW
I want a big fat woman / What have you got on me / I want to play with your poodle / I can't stop loving you / For your precious love / Stoop down '88 / It's all over / Garbage man
ICH 1029CD / Feb '89 / Ichiban

Willis, Gary

☐ NO SWEAT
No sweat / Knothead / Everlasting night / Stagger / Liquified / Easy street / Til the cows come home / Knothead II / Ancient promise / Hymn
ALCD 1009 / Apr '97 / Alchemy

Willis, Ike

☐ SHOULD' A GONE BEFORE I LEFT
EFA 034062 / Jul '94 / Muffin

Willis, Larry

☐ HEAVY BLUE (Willis, Larry Quartet)
SCCD 31269 / Oct '90 / Steeplechase

☐ SERENADE
SSCD 8063 / Jan '96 / Sound Hills

☐ TRIBUTE TO SOMEONE, A
King cobra / Wayman's way / Sensei / Tribute to someone / Maiden voyage / For Jean / Teasdale place
AQ 1022 / Jul '95 / Audioquest

Willis, Ralph

☐ RALPH WILLIS VOL.1 1944-1950
DOCD 5256 / May '94 / Document

☐ RALPH WILLIS VOL.2 1950-1953
DOCD 5257 / May '94 / Document

Willis, Robert

☐ DATE WITH THE DEVIL'S DAUGHTER
X 09829 / 6 Jul '98 / Casual Tonalities

Willis, Wesley

☐ FABIAN ROAD WARRIOR
Shoot my jam seesion down / Ward my rock music off / Tripping daisy / Alanis Morrisette / Rock Saddam Hussein's ass / Rock the nation / Porno For Pyros / Slow cars fast cars / Quaker youth ensemble / Solid state 11 / It's against the law / Empty bottle / Firewall the throttle / Spank wagon / Reid Hyams / Rock it to Russia / Pollo / Anni Vookman / Wesley Willis / Brutal juice / Silverchair / Loud Lucy / Rock 'n' roll superhighway / Dino Paredes
74321422762 / Feb '97 / American

☐ FEEL THE POWER
Fir throwing hell ride / Lonely kings / Play that rock 'n' roll / Shoot me in the ass / Thirsty whale / Rick Sims / Jello Biafra / Alice In Chains / Ice Cube / Snoop Doggy Dogg / Get me on the city bus / Rock 'n' roll power / Jason Dummeldinger / Hell me on the bus / Freak out hell bus / Shoot me down / Robin Miramontez / Greg Abramson / Mark Neiter / Scream Dracula scream / Rick Rubin / Melissa Dragich / Megan Shaw / Dust Brothers
74321422752 / Feb '97 / American

Willison, Christian

☐ BOOGIE WOOGIE AND SOME BLUES
10072 / Apr '91 / Blues Beacon

☐ HEART BROKEN MAN
Girl like you / Heart broken man / Congo square / Raven / New York city / Funeral / Unauthentic blues / Macho man / Drown in my own tears / On the bayou / Little voodoo baby / Man in your life
BLU 10262 / Dec '96 / Blues Beacon

Willoughby, Mike

☐ CRIMSON TROPHIES
RUCK 001CD / Nov '96 / Rucksack

Wills, Bob

☐ AMERICAN LEGENDS
Across the alley from the Alamo / I laugh when I think how I cried over you / New San Antonio rose / Faded love / When you leave Amarillo (turn off the lights) / Elmer's tune / Bottle baby boogie / Bubbles in my beer / Big balls in cow town / Stay all night, stay a little longer / Keeper of my heart / South of the border
12735 / May '97 / Laserlight

☐ BOB WILLS VOL.1 (Milk Cow Blues) (Wills, Bob & His Texas Playboys)
BMCD 3065 / Nov '97 / Blue Moon

☐ BOB WILLS VOL.2 (In The Mood) (Wills, Bob & His Texas Playboys)
BMCD 3068 / Nov '97 / Blue Moon

☐ COUNTRY'S LEGENDARY GUITAR GENIUS
All night long / Don't cry baby / C jam blues / If he's moving in, I'm moving out / Let's get it over and done with / Right or wrong / Cotton eyed Joe / Honeysuckle rose / Linda Lou / No disappointments in heaven / Roly poly / Beaumont rag / Oh Monah / Ida Red / Faded love / I'm gonna be boss from now on / Time changes everything / Wills junction
PRACD 4002 / Jun '97 / Prairie

☐ KING OF WESTERN SWING, THE (25 Hits 1935-1945) (Wills, Bob & His Texas Playboys)
New San Antonio rose / Osage stomp / Never no more hard times blues / Steel guitar rag / Sugar blues / Fan it / Right or wrong / Whoa baby / That's what I like about the south / Lone star rag / Corrine Corrina / Bob Wills special / Time changes everything / Big beaver / Take me back to Tulsa / Dusty skies / We might as well forget it / Home in San Antone / You're from Texas / Goodbye Liza Jane / Texas playboy rag / Roly poly / Stay a little longer / New Spanish two-step / I'm feelin' bad
CDAJA 5250 / Mar '98 / Living Era

☐ LONGHORN RECORDINGS, THE
Sooner or later / Buffalo twist / All night long / You can't break a broken heart / If he's movin' in / Let's get it over and done with / Big tater in the sandy land / Mayflower waltz / Billy in the lowground / Beaumont rag / Faded love / Dian waltz / Done gone / Put your little foot / Bob's first fiddle tune / Bob's schottische / Gone indian / No disappointments in heaven / Will's junction / You'll never walk out of my heart / Betty's waltz / San Antonio rose
BCD 15689 / Aug '93 / Bear Family

☐ ROOTS OF ROCK 'N' ROLL VOL.3, THE (The King Of Lone Star Swing) (Wills, Bob & His Texas Playboys)
Osage stomp / Cherokee maiden / Get with it / Twin guitar special / Roly poly / Take me back to Tulsa / New San Antonio Rose / Steel guitar rag / Texas Playboy Rag / Home in San Antone / Bob Wills special / Right or wrong / New Spanish two step / Time changes everything / Corrina Corrina / Big beaver / Red hot gal of mine / Whoa baby / That's what I like about the South / San Antonio Rose / Oklahoma rag / Lone star rag / Dusky skies / Bluin' the blues / No matter how she done it / Black rider / You're okay / Please don't leave me
PLCD 553 / Nov '96 / President

☐ SWING HI, SWING LOW (The Best Of Bob Wills & His Texas Playboys) (Wills, Bob & His Texas Playboys)
Red river valley / Along the navajo trail / You're from texas / New spanish two step / Across the alley from the alamo / Texarkana baby / Faded love / Take me back to tulsa / Time changes everything / Roly poly / San antonio rose / Corrine, corrina / Right or wrong / Ida red / Cherokee maiden / Stay a little longer / Maiden's prayer / Steel guitar rag / I can't go on this way / Worried mind / Oklahoma hills / Sally goodin (instrumental) / Sioux city sue / Ten years / Don't cry baby / If it's wrong to love you / Shame on you
MCCD 143 / Nov '93 / Music Club

Wills, Johnny Lee

☐ BAND'S A ROCKIN', THE
KKCD 18 / Nov '96 / Krazy Kat

Wills, Viola

☐ BEST OF VIOLA WILLS, THE (Gonna Get Along Without You Now)
HTCD 86 / 20 Apr '98 / Hot Productions

Wills, Warren

☐ ELEVEN ASPECTS
CDSGP 0321 / Oct '96 / Prestige

Willson, Michelle

☐ EVIL GAL BLUES
BB 9550CD / Aug '94 / Bullseye Blues

☐ SO EMOTIONAL
CDBB 9580 / Jun '96 / Bullseye Blues

Willson-Piper, Marty

☐ ART ATTACK
19273 / 22 May '98 / Festival

☐ I CAN'T CRY
RCD 51025 / Jul '92 / Rykodisc

Wilmot, Gary

☐ WIND BENEATH MY WINGS
Love situation / On a way to a dream / Unchained melody / And now she's gone / Take my breath away / Star without a soul / Wind beneath my wings / Expectation road / I won't forget you / Against all odds / Danny you're a loser / There's only room for the good girls
306042 / Jan '97 / Hallmark

Wilshire, Lori & Micah

☐ 10 TRACKS OF UNCONDITIONAL LOVE
Over my head / Ms. Innocence / Closer still / Can you see me / Face / Hear the sound / If I could / Deep / Medicine / In this moment
7011530029 / Mar '98 / Rocketown

Wilson, Al

☐ SHOW AND TELL
CDSGP 0160 / Nov '95 / Prestige

Wilson, Bo

☐ MAGIC MAN (Wilson, Bo Band)
Magic man / Chevrolet / I'm tore down / Trick bag / Boogie man / Stormy Monday / Don't take advantage of me / Statsboro blues / Shake the room / If you have to know / Hard time in the land of plenty / Madhouse
BMAC 0316 / 29 Sep '97 / BMA

Wilson, Brian

☐ BRIAN WILSON
Love and mercy / Walkin' the line / Melt away / Baby let your hair grow long / Little children / One for the boys / There's so many / Night time / Let it shine / Rio Grande / Meet me in my dreams tonight
7599256692 / Nov '95 / WEA

☐ I JUST WASN'T MADE FOR THESE TIMES
Meant for you / This whole world / Caroline, no / Let the wind blow / Love and mercy / Do it again / Warmth of the sun / Wonderful / Still I dream of it / Melt away / Till I die
MCD 11270 / 8 Sep '97 / MCA

☐ IMAGINATION
Your imagination / She says that she needs me / South American / Where has love been / Keep an eye on summer / Dream angel / Cry / Lay down burden / Let him run wild / Sunshine / Happy days
74321573032 / 15 Jun '98 / RCA

☐ ORANGE CRATE ART (Wilson, Brian & Van Dyke Parks)
Orange crate art / Sail away / My hobo heart / Wings of a dove / Hold back time / Movies is magic / Lullaby / This town goes down at sunset / My jeanine / San francisco / Summer in monterey / Palm tree and moon
9362454272 / Nov '95 / WEA

Wilson, Buster

☐ BUSTER WILSON 1947-1949
AMCD 89 / Mar '97 / American Music

Wilson, Callum

☐ SCOTTISH COUNTRY DANCING (Wilson, Callum Scottish Dancing Band)
CWSDCD 001 / Dec '97 / Callum Wilson

Wilson, Cassandra

☐ AFTER THE BEGINNING AGAIN
There she goes / 'Round midnight / Yazoo moon / Sweet black night / My corner of the sky / Baubles, bangles and beads / Redbone / Summer wind
5140012 / May '93 / jMT

☐ BLUE LIGHT 'TIL DAWN
You don't know what love is / Come on in my kitchen / Tell me you'll wait for me / Children of the night / Hellhound on my trail / Black crow / Sankofa / Estrellas / Redbone / Tupelo honey / Blue light 'til dawn / I can't stand the rain
CDP 7813572 / Jan '94 / Blue Note

☐ BLUE SKIES
Shall we dance / Polka dots and moonbeams / I've grown accustomed to his face / I didn't know what time it was / Gee baby ain't I good to you / I'm old fashioned / Sweet Lorraine / My one and only love / Autumn nocturne / Blue skies
8344192 / Feb '89 / jMT

☐ DAYS AWEIGH
Electromagnolia / Let's face the music and dance / Days aweigh / Subatomic blues / Apricots on their wings / If you only know how / You belong to you / Some other time / Black and yellow
8344122 / Mar '94 / jMT

☐ NEW MOON DAUGHTER
Strange fruit / Love is blindness / Solomon sang / Death letter / Skylark / Find him / I'm so lonesome I could cry / Last train to Clarksville / Until / Little warm death / Memphis / Harvest moon / 32.20
CDP 8371832 / Mar '96 / Blue Note

☐ POINT OF VIEW
Square roots / Blue in green / Never desperate move / Love and hate / I am waiting / I wished on the moon / I thought you knew
8344042 / Oct '93 / jMT

Wilson, Charles

☐ BLUES IN THE KEY OF C
Who it's going to be / Is it over / Leaning tree / You cut off my love supply / Let's have a good time / Selfish lover / It's a crying shame / I've got a good woman
ICH 1120CD / Oct '93 / Ichiban

Wilson, Damian

☐ COSMAS
VGCD 007 / 29 Sep '97 / Verglas Music

Wilson, Delroy

☐ 22 MAGNIFICENT HITS
BLCD 017 / Jan '96 / Graylan

☐ 36 GREAT MELODIES (Wilson, Delroy & Owen Gray)
SWCD 002 / 22 Dec '97 / S&WSK

☐ COOL OPERATOR
MCCD 281 / Dec '96 / Music Club

☐ DANCING MOOD
SOCD 50149 / Oct '96 / Studio One

☐ GOLDEN MEMORIES OF DELROY WILSON, THE
RNCD 2111 / Jul '95 / Rhino

☐ GOOD ALL OVER
CSL 8014 / May '97 / Studio One

☐ GREATEST HITS
I'm in a dancing mood / This heart of mine / Rain from the skies / Doing my thing / Cool operator / Who cares / Never will conquer me / Put yourself in my place / I'm yours / Let there be love / I'm in the mood for love / Might can't beat right
JMC 200102 / Dec '92 / Jamaican Gold

☐ MY SPECIAL LADY
CDSGP 069 / Oct '94 / Prestige

☐ ONCE UPON A TIME (The Best Of Delroy Wilson)
This old heart of mine / Once upon a time / I want to love you / Give love a try / This life makes me wonder / Put yourself in my place / It hurts / I'm the one that loves you / You're number one / I've tried my best / Run run / Show me the way / Gave you my love / Loving you is sweeter than ever / Got to get away / Better must come / Cool operator / Be my wife / Adisababa / Can I change my mind / Live and learn / Pretty girl / Ain't that perculiar / What is man / It's a shame
CDTRL 391 / Feb '98 / Trojan

☐ SARGE
CD 1 / May '95 / Chambers

☐ SING 26 MASSIVE HITS
RNCD 2138 / Apr '96 / Rhino

☐ SPECIAL
RASCD 3119 / Sep '93 / Ras

☐ STATEMENT
CDGR 253 / 29 Jun '98 / Charly

☐ TUNE INTO REGGAE MUSIC
RNCD 2061 / Jun '94 / Rhino

Wilson, Eddie

☐ DANKESCHON, BITTESCHON, WIEDERSEHEN (2CD Set)
Wabash cannonball / Strictly nothin' / Streets of Laredo / Mid the green fields of Virginia / It's OK / I wish I could / Johnny Reb / I found my girl in the USA / Show her lots of gold / Long time to forget
BCD 15615 / Mar '93 / Bear Family

Wilson, Edith

☐ EDITH & LENA WILSON 1924-1931
DOCD 5451 / Jun '96 / Document

☐ HE MAY BE YOUR MAN, BUT HE COMES TO SEE ME SOMETIMES (Wilson, Edith & Little Brother Montgomery/State St. Swingers)
Mistreatin' blues / Hesitating blues / He may be your man / Easin' away from me / That same dog / Hey hey boogie / Poppa-mama blues / My handy man ain't handy anymore / Lonesome / Twiddlin' / Slow creepin' blues / Put a little love in everything you do
DD 637 / Mar '97 / Delmark

Wilson, Elder Roma

☐ THIS TRAIN
ARHCD 429 / Sep '95 / Arhoolie

Wilson, Garland

☐ CLASSICS 1931-1938
CLASSICS 808 / Apr '95 / Classics

Wilson, Gerald

☐ CLASSICS 1945-1946
CLASSICS 976 / 24 Feb '98 / Classics

Wilson, Glenn

☐ BITTER SWEET (Wilson, Glenn & Stuart, Rory)
SSC 1057D / Aug '92 / Sunnyside

☐ BLUE PORPOISE AVENUE
SSC 1074 / Apr '97 / Sunnyside

Wilson, Greg

☐ PIPER OF DISTINCTION
CDMON 822 / Oct '94 / Monarch

Wilson, Hop

☐ HOUSTON GHETTO BLUES
BB 9538CD / Jan '94 / Bullseye Blues

☐ STEEL GUITAR FLASH (Wilson, Hop & His Two Buddies)
My woman has a black cat bone / I'm a stranger / I ain't got a woman / Merry christmas darling / Rockin' in the coconuts / Why do you twist / You don't move me anymore / You don't love me anymore / Feel so glad / Be careful with the blues / My woman done quit me / Dance to it / Fuss too much / Good woman is hard to find / Need your love to keep me warm / I done got over / Toot toot Tootsie goodbye / Your Daddy wants to rock / Broke and hungry / Always be in love with you / I met a strange woman / Love's got me all fenced in / Chicken stuff / Rockin' with Hop / That wouldn't satisfy
CDCHD 240 / Jun '94 / Ace

Wilson, Jack

☐ IN NEW YORK
DIW 615 / Jan '94 / DIW

☐ RAMBLIN'
FSRCD 152 / Dec '90 / Fresh Sound

Wilson, Jackie

☐ DYNAMIC JACKIE WILSON
Higher and higher / I get the sweetest feeling / Squeeze her, tease her (but love her) / She's alright / Think twice / I've got to get back (Country boy) / Whispers (gettin' louder) / Just be sincere / Since you showed me how to be happy / I don't want to lose you / I've lost you / Stop lying / Who am I / I believe / Even when you cry / (I can feel those vibrations) This love is real / You got me walking / No more goodbyes / Don't burn no bridges / Open the door to your heart
CPCD 8018 / Feb '94 / Charly

☐ HIGHER AND HIGHER
Soul galore / I've lost you / I don't want to lose you / Who who song / Nothing but blue skies / I get the sweetest feeling / You brought about a change in me / I'm the one to do it / Nobody but you / Higher and higher / Uptight / Whispers (gettin' louder) / You got me walking / Let this be a letter (to my baby) / Because of you / What'cha gonna do about love / (I can feel those vibrations) This love is real / Since you showed me how to be happy
CDKEN 901 / May '86 / Kent

☐ HIGHER AND HIGHER
Reet petite / Lonely teardrops / Come back to me / Danny boy / Why can't you be mine / If I can't have you / That's why (I love you so) / I'll be satisfied / You better know it / Talk that talk / I know I'll always be in love with you / Doggin' around / Woman / Lover, a friend / Am I the man / Tear of the year / Please tell me

why / I'm comin' on back to you / You don't know what it means / I just can't help it / Baby workout / Shake, shake, shake / No pity (in the naked city) / Whispers (gettin' louder) / Higher and higher / I get the sweetest feeling
CPCD 8005 / Oct '93 / Charly

□ HIT COLLECTION, THE
(Your love keeps lifting me) Higher and higher / Talk that talk / I'll be satisfied / That's why I love you so / I'm comin' on back to you / Am I the man / Woman, a lover, a friend / Doggin' around / Baby workout / Reet Petite / I get the sweetest feeling / Lonely teardrops / To be loved / Whispers getting louder / Shake shake shake / You better know it / All my love / Alone at last / My empty arms / Chain Gang: *Wilson, Jackie & Count Basie*
3036001002 / Apr '97 / Carlton

□ JACKIE WILSON STORY - THE CHICAGO YEARS VOL.1
Beautiful day / Pretty little angel eyes / I still love you / To change my love / I've learned about life / Just as soon as the feeling's over / Just be sincere / Tears will tell it all / That lucky old sun (just rolls around heaven all day) / Love is funny that way / Since you showed me how to be happy / My heart is calling / (Your love keeps lifting me) Higher and higher / I don't need you around / I need your loving / Let this be a letter (to my baby) / Hard to get a thing called love / Fountain / Don't you know I love you / Didn't I
JWCD 5 / Oct '95 / Charly

□ JACKIE WILSON STORY - THE CHICAGO YEARS VOL.2
I get lonely sometimes / Love changed her face / (I can feel those vibrations) This love is real / Because of you / Go away / Who am I / Whispers (gettin' louder) / Hum de dum de do / Somebody up there likes you / You left the fire burning / Think about the good times / Woman needs to be loved / Growin' tall / Light my fire / Try it again / Those heartaches / With these hands / Where is love / You got me wlaking / Don't burn no bridges
JWCD 6 / Oct '95 / Charly

□ JACKIE WILSON STORY - THE NEW YORK YEARS VOL.1
Etcetera / You better know it / Sazzle dazzle / Try a little tenderness / (You were made for) All my love / I'm wanderin' / I'll be satisfied / So much / Years from now / I apologize / Please tell me why / Crazy she calls me / To be loved / I'm comin' on back to you / Lonely teardrops / It's been a long time / My heart belongs to only you / Love is all / Keep smiling at trouble (trouble's a bubble) / Night
JWCD 1 / Oct '95 / Charly

□ JACKIE WILSON STORY - THE NEW YORK YEARS VOL.2
JWCD 2 / Jan '96 / Charly

□ JACKIE WILSON STORY - THE NEW YORK YEARS VOL.3
JWCD 3 / Jun '96 / Charly

□ JACKIE WILSON STORY - THE NEW YORK YEARS VOL.4
I just can't help it / Squeeze her, please her (but love her) / Kickapoo / No time out / You don't know me / To be loved / Hearts / There's nothing like this: *Wilson, Jackie & Linda Hopkins* / So you say you wanna dance / It's all my fault / Groovin' / I've got to get back (country boy) / I wanna be around / He's got the whole world in his hands: *Wilson, Jackie & Linda Hopkins* / Nobody knows the trouble I've seen: *Wilson, Jackie & Linda Hopkins* / Sing a little song / Soul time / Be my girl / Danny boy / You thing of beauty
JWCD 4 / Sep '96 / Charly

□ JACKIE WILSON STORY, THE (2CD Set)
Reet petite (The finest girl you ever want to meet) / To be loved / We have love / Lonely teardrops / That's why (I love you so) / I'll be satisfied / You better know it / Talk that talk / Doggin' around / Night / Woman, a love, a friend / Am I the man / Alone at last / Passin' through / Tear of the year / My empty arms / Please tell me why / I'm coming on back on you / Lonely life / Years from now / You don't know what it means / Way I am / My heart belongs only to you / Greatest hurt / There'll be no next time / Hearts / I just can't help it / Forever and a day / Baby workout / Shake a hand / Shake shake shake / Squeeze her, tease her (But love her) / Danny Boy / Whispers (Gettin' louder) / I don't want to lose you / Just be sincere / I've lost you / (Your love keeps lifting me) Higher and higher / Since you showed me how to be happy / For your precious love / Chain gang / I get the sweetest feeling / For once in my life / Let this be a letter (To my baby) / (I can feel those vibrations) This love is real / You got me walking
DBG 53035 / Jul '96 / Double Gold

□ MASTERS, THE
EABCD 064 / 24 Nov '97 / Eagle

□ MASTERS, THE (2CD Set)
EDMCD 007 / 24 Nov '97 / Eagle

□ PORTRAIT OF JACKIE WILSON, A
PWKS 4238 / Feb '95 / Carlton

□ REET PETITE
Shake, shake, shake / Why can't you be mine / I'm wanderin' / Lonely teardrops / Yeah yeah / It's so fine / Come back to me / Shake a hand / Reet petite / If I can't have you / All my love / So much / I know I'll always be in love with you / Danny boy / Doggin' around / Do Lord: *Wilson, Jackie & Linda Hopkins*
CDCH 902 / May '86 / Ace

□ VERY BEST OF JACKIE WILSON, THE
Reet petite / Lonely teardrops / To be loved / That's why / I'll be satisfied / Doggin' around / Lonely life / Night / You better know it / Talk talk talk / Am I the man / I'm comin' on back to you / Woman, a lover, a friend / Baby workout / Squeeze her, tease her (but love her) / No pity (in the naked city) / Whispers (gettin' louder) / I get the sweetest feeling / Since you showed me how to be happy / Love is funny that way / Just be sincere / Higher and higher / You got me walking / (I can feel those vibrations) this love is real
CDCHK 913 / Nov '94 / Ace

□ VERY BEST OF JACKIE WILSON, THE
Reet petite / Lonely teardrops / That's why I love you so / Night / You better know it / Talk that talk / To be loved / I'll be satisfied / Whispers (gettin' louder) / Higher and higher / I get the sweetest feeling / Doggin' around / Am I the man / I'm comin' on back to you / Woman, a lover, a friend / No pity (in the naked city)
MCCD 017 / Feb '91 / Music Club

□ VERY BEST OF JACKIE WILSON, THE
I get the sweetest feeling / In the midnight hour / Chain gang / I was made to love her / My empty arms / Please don't hurt me / Think twice / Alone at last / I'll be satisfied / For your precious love / Lonely teardrops / (You're love keeps lifting me) higher and higher / Doggin' around / Body workout / Uptight / Respect / Whispers (getting louder) / Shake a hand / Swing low, sweet chariot / He's got the whole world / Talk that talk / Reet petite
MOCD 3018 / Nov '96 / More Music

Wilson, Joemy

□ CELTIC TREASURES
DMCD 112 / Feb '96 / Dara

□ TURLOUGH O'CAROLAN
DMCD 102 / Jun '93 / Dargason Music

□ YOUNG TURLOUGH
DMCD 116 / Feb '96 / Dara

Wilson, John

□ TELL ME SOMETHING NEW
River of love / Rainbows and you / Jump back / We all wanna be in love / Jump / Tell me something new / Is this love / Everything I need / 24 Reasons / Little Mistreater / Daddy sang the blues
3036000182 / Mar '96 / Carlton

Wilson, John

□ WORLD'S GREATEST PIPERS VOL.5, THE
6/8 marches / Gaelic air and 2/4 marches / Hornpipe and jigs / Strathspeys and reels / Slow air, strathspey and reel / Lowland air and two Irish reels / March, strathspey and reel / Gaelic airs and jigs / Glengarry's march / 9/8 marches / Hornpipes and jigs
LCOM 5170 / Oct '96 / Lismor

Wilson, Kim

□ MY BLUES
BCM 7107 / Dec '97 / Blue Collar

□ THAT'S LIFE
ANTCD 0034 / Jul '95 / Antones

□ TIGERMAN
Tiger man / Don't touch me / Hustle is on / She moves me / Hush on hush / If I should lose you / Hunch rythm / When the lights go out / You got me / Come back baby / Boogie all night / Trust my baby / Reel eleven, take one
ANTCD 0023 / Nov '93 / Antones

Wilson, Lena

□ LENA WILSON VOL.1 1922-1924
DOCD 5443 / May '96 / Document

Wilson, Les

□ ON THE LOOSE (Wilson, Les & The Mighty Houserockers)
RLCD 0096 / Jun '97 / Red Lightnin'

Wilson, Mari

□ CRY ME A RIVER
MANTRA 058 / 1 Jun '98 / Mantra

Wilson, Nancy

□ BEST OF NANCY WILSON, THE (Jazz & Blues Sessions)
Like someone in love / I wish I didn't love you so / Dearly beloved / Just for a thrill / I've got your number / In a sentimental mood / Getting to know you / Call it stormy monday / He's my guy / You're gonna hear from me / People / Sufferin' with the blues / Wave / Unchain my heart / Never will I marry / Green dolphin street / You don't know me / Good man is hard to find
CDP 8539212 / Jan '97 / Capitol Jazz

□ IF I HAD MY WAY
Hello like before / Sweet love / If I had my way / Wish you were here / One more try / Not a day in your life / Anything for your love / Where do I go from you / Fool in love / Loving you loving me
CK 67769 / Aug '97 / Sony Jazz

□ LUSH LIFE
Free again / Midnight sun / Only the young / When the world was young / Right to love / Lush life / Over the weekend / You've changed / River shallow / Sunny / I stayed too long at the fair
CDP 8327452 / Aug '95 / Capitol Jazz

□ OUTTA SIGHT (Nancy Wilson Sings The Hits)
End of our love / Call me / Son of a preacher man / Willie and Laurie Mae Jones / Look of love / Mercy mercy mercy / For once in my life / Sunny / Come get to this / Spinning wheel / Ten years of tears / Power of love / Uptight / Ode to Billie Joe / You're all I need to get by / Long and winding road / Reach out for me / My love / You've lost that loving feeling / My babe
4939932 / 11 May '98 / Blue Note

□ TODAY, TOMORROW, FOREVER/A TOUCH OF TODAY
One note Samba / Go away, little boy / Unchain my heart / (I left my heart) in San Francisco / Wives and lovers / Good life / What kind of fool am I / Can't stop loving you / On Broadway / Our day will come / Call me irresponsible / Tonight may have to last me all my life / You've got your troubles / And I love him / Uptight (everything's allright) / Have a heart / Before the rain / Shadow of your smile / Call me / Yesterday / Wasn't it wonderful / You're gonna hear from me / No one else but you / Goin' out of my head
CTMCD 115 / Mar '97 / EMI

Wilson, Phillip

□ PHILLIP WILSON PROJECT, THE (Various Artists)
JD 1243 / Oct '96 / Jazz Door

Wilson, Reuben

□ BLUE BREAKBEATS
Hot rod / Orange peel / Ronnie's bonnie / Love bug / Bus ride / Blue mode
4947072 / 13 Jul '98 / Blue Note

□ BLUE MODE
Bambu / Knock on wood / Bus ride / Orange peel / Twenty five miles / Blue mode
CDP 8299062 / Feb '97 / Blue Note

□ LOVE BUG
Hot rod / I'm gonna make you love me / I say a little prayer / Love bug / Stormy / Back out / Hold on I'm comin'
CDP 8299052 / Jan '97 / Blue Note

□ ORGAN DONOR
EFA 063412 / 17 Nov '97 / Ausfahrt
JAZ 202982 / 23 Mar '98 / Jazzateria

Wilson, Rick

□ SUITABLE LANGUAGE
TFCD 001 / Feb '97 / ReR/ Recommended

Wilson, Robert

□ VERY BEST OF ROBERT WILSON, THE
Road to the isles / Bonnie Mary of Argyle / Eriskay love lilt / Uist tramping song / My love is like a red red rose / Westering home / Maid of Kenmore / Bonnie Strathyre / Lewis bridal song / Down the glen / Bonnie Scots lassie / Gordon for me / Scotland the brave / Northern lights of Aberdeen / Tobermory Bay / Marching through the heather / Rothesay Bay / Soft lowland tongue of the borders / Song of the Clyde / Haste ye back
CDSL 8268 / Sep '95 / Music For Pleasure

Wilson, Roger

□ STARK NAKED
WH 001CD / Apr '94 / Whiff

Wilson, Sean

□ 20 ALL-TIME FAVOURITES
Home to Aherlow / Pat Murphy's meadow / Medley / Molly malone/Cockles and mussels / Jig selection / Dirty old town / My native town Drumlish / Accordion selection / Will you visit me on Sunday / Galway hornpipe / Cuttin' the corn in creeslough / Town I love so well
SWCD 1014 / Sep '97 / Irish

□ 20 LOVELY HITS
For these are my mountains / I love you still / Medley / Aul lammas fair / Camden town / Give my love to rose / Your lovely Irish eyes / Instrumental medley / Moon behind the hill / Banks of the Ohio / Murshin durkin / Any dream will do / She's my girl / Galway bay
SWCD 1015 / Sep '97 / Irish

□ 25 ACCORDIAN FAVOURITES (A Musical Journey To Ireland)
Medley / Tom Dooley / Mother's love's a blessing / Fields of Athenry / Walk right back / Medley / Forever and ever amen / When I grow too old to dream / Wild colonial boy / Green fields of Ireland / One day at a time / Spanish lady / Medley / You are my sunshine / Take me to old Ireland
SWCD 1018 / Nov '97 / Irish

□ 30 NASHVILLE COUNTRY FAVOURITES
Medley / Medley / Medley / Medley / Medley / Medley
SWCD 1017 / Nov '97 / Irish

□ 50 ALL-TIME FAVOURITE SONGS
Medley / Medley / Medley / Medley / Medley / Medley / Medley / Medley / Medley / Medley (10) / Medley (11) / Medley (12)
SWCD 1003 / Nov '97 / Irish

□ 50 GREAT PARTY HITS
Medley / Medley / Medley / Medley / Medley / Medley / Medley / Medley / Medley / Medley (10)
SWCD 1020 / Sep '97 / Irish

□ 50 GREAT SONGS (King & Queen Of Irish Country) (Wilson, Sean & Susan McCann)
PLATCD 3927 / May '94 / Platinum

□ COUNTRY AND IRISH
Twenty-one acres of land / Don't trade your love for gold / Blackboard of my heart / Sweet moneymore / Moyola river / I'm so afraid of losing you again / December day / I wonder could I live there anymore / Love gets older / Sing a song for Jesus / Tipperary on my mind
SWCD 1002 / 31 Jan '98 / Irish

□ GREAT PARTY SINGALONG-50 SONGS
Lovely leitrim / Gentle mother / A mother's love / Give an irish girl to me / Old bog road / Cottage in the country / Cottage on the old dungannon road / Misty rollin' midlands / Home in tyrone / Four country roads / Village in co. tyrone / Among the wicklow hills / Wedding bells / Wild life of life / Some day you'll call / Drumlish / Three leaf shamrock / Rathlin island / Abbeyshrule / Pat murphy's meadow / Where the grass grows greenest / Gypsy woman / Love me tonight / Rambling fever / Jesus takes a hold / Cocky farmer / Fields of athenry / Long before your time / Rare ould times / Flight of earls / Bed of roses / Pull the covers over me / Nancy miles / Hello blues / Old dungarvan oak / Forever and ever / My wild irish rose / Goodnight irene / Wild rover / Far away in australia / Oh lonesome me / I still miss someone / Last thing on my mind / Old love letters / Too old to die young / Old pals / My side of the road / If those lips could only speak / These are my mountains / My lovely rose of clare
SWCD 1001 / Nov '92 / Irish

□ TURN BACK THE YEARS
Let's turn back the years / Back on my mind again / It's good to see you / Home to donegal / If I kiss you will you go away / Walking piece of heaven / Irish harvest day / Through the eyes of a child / Irish soldier boy / South of the border / Ring of fire / Old country church / Old ireland is the only place for me / Working man / Forever and ever amen
PLATCD 911 / Apr '93 / Platinum

□ WHEN IRISH EYES ARE SMILING
Medley / When Irish eyes are smiling / My own Donegal / Sprig of Irish heather / Peace song / Rosie O'Brien / Little pub in London / Old man / Medley / Daddy's girl / Titanic story / Goodbye good luck farewell
SWCD 1021 / Sep '97 / Irish

Wilson, Smokey

□ 88TH STREET BLUES
BPCD 5026 / Dec '95 / Blind Pig

□ MAN FROM MARS, THE
Thanks for making me a star / Something inside of me / Man from Mars / 44 blues / Louise / Too drunk to drive / You don't drink what I drink / Black widow / Just like a mountain / Don't want to tangle with me / Doctor blues / Easy baby
CDBB 9581 / Feb '97 / Bullseye Blues

□ REAL DEAL, THE
CDBB 9559 / Aug '95 / Rounder

□ SMOKE 'N' FIREFIRE
BB 9534CD / Jan '94 / Bullseye Blues

□ SMOKEY WILSON WITH THE WILLIAM CLARKE BAND
BMCD 9013 / Nov '93 / Black Magic

Wilson, Spanky

□ SINGIN' AND SWINGIN'
BBRC 9104 / Nov '92 / Big Blue

Wilson, Steve

□ BLUES FOR MARCUS (Wilson, Steve Quintet)
CRISS 1073CD / Nov '93 / Criss Cross

□ NEW YORK SUMMIT (Wilson, Steve Quintet)
CRISS 1062CD / Oct '92 / Criss Cross

□ STEP LIVELY
CRISS 1096 / Apr '95 / Criss Cross

Wilson, Teddy

□ AIR MAIL SPECIAL
BLCD 760115 / Oct '90 / Black Lion

□ ALONE
Tea for two / Body and soul / After you've gone / I can't get started (with you) / Moonglow / Sweet Georgia Brown / Shiny stockings / Li'l darlin' / One o'clock jump / Medley / But not for me / Sophisticated Lady / Medley / Medley
STCD 8211 / Mar '95 / Storyville

□ BLUES FOR THOMAS WALLER
Honeysuckle rose / My fate is in your hands / Ain't cha glad / I've got a feeling I'm falling in love / Stealin' apples / Blues for Thomas Waller / Handful of keys / Striding after Fats / Squeeze me / Zonky / Blue turning grey over you / Ain't misbehavin' / Black and blue
BLCD 760131 / Apr '90 / Black Lion

□ CLASSICS 1934-1935
CLASSICS 508 / Apr '90 / Classics

□ CLASSICS 1935-1936
CLASSICS 511 / Apr '90 / Classics

□ CLASSICS 1936-1937
CLASSICS 521 / Apr '90 / Classics

□ CLASSICS 1937
CLASSICS 531 / Dec '90 / Classics

□ CLASSICS 1937-1938
CLASSICS 548 / Dec '90 / Classics

□ CLASSICS 1938
CLASSICS 556 / Dec '90 / Classics

□ CLASSICS 1939
CLASSICS 571 / Oct '91 / Classics

☐ CLASSICS 1939-1941 (Wilson, Teddy & His Orchestra)
CLASSICS 620 / Nov '92 / Classics

☐ CLASSICS 1942-1945
CLASSICS 908 / Nov '96 / Classics

☐ CLASSICS 1946
CLASSICS 997 / 1 Jun '98 / Classics

☐ COLE PORTER CLASSICS
Get out of town / Just one of those things / I get a kick out of you / It's all right with me / Why shouldn't I / Love for sale
BLC 760166 / '92 / Black Lion

☐ COMPLETE ASSOCIATED TRANSCRIPTIONS 1944, THE (Wilson, Teddy Sextet)
Flying home / Indiana / Embraceable you / Touch of boogie woogie / B-flat swing / Don't be that way / Honeysuckle rose / Mop mop / I got rhythm / Rose room / Lady be good / Way you look tonight / Stompin' at the Savoy / You're my favourite memory / Sheik of Araby
STCD 8236 / Feb '98 / Storyville

☐ EARLY YEARS, THE (Wilson, Teddy & His Piano Band)
CDSGP 0159 / Sep '95 / Prestige

☐ FINE AND DANDY (Wilson, Teddy Orchestra & Billie Holiday)
Sentimental and melancholy / This is my last affair / Carelessly / Moanin' low / Fine and dandy / There's a lull in my life / It's swell of you / How am I to know / I'm comin' Virginia / Sun flowers / Yours and mine / I'll get by / Mean to me / Foolin' myself / Easy living / I'll never be the same / I've found a new baby / You're my desire / Remember me / Hour of parting / Cocquette
HEPCD 1029 / Oct '91 / Hep

☐ GOLDEN DAYS, THE
My melancholy baby / Rosetta / Mean to me: *Wilson, Teddy & Billie Holiday* / Now it can be told: *Wilson, Teddy & Nan Wynn* / China boy: *Wilson, Teddy & Nan Wynn* / Tisket-a-tasket / Them there eyes / If I were you: *Wilson, Teddy & Nan Wynn* / Jungle love / On treasure Island / Sugar plum / I know that you know / You let me down: *Wilson, Teddy & Billie Holiday* / Mary had a little lamb: *Wilson, Teddy & Roy Eldridge* / If you were mine: *Wilson, Teddy & Billie Holiday* / All my life: *Wilson, Teddy & Ella Fitzgerald* / Sailin' / Breakin' in a pair of shoes / Hour of parting: *Wilson, Teddy & Boots Castle* / Coquette / My last affair: *Wilson, Teddy & Billie Holiday* / You brought a new kind of love: *Wilson, Teddy & Frances Hunt*
PASTCD 7025 / Oct '93 / Flapper

☐ HOW HIGH THE MOON
TCD 1050 / May '97 / Tradition

☐ JAZZ PIANO (Wilson, Teddy & Mary Lou Williams/Mel Powell)
You're mine, you / I got rhythm / Someone to watch over me / Indiana / Time on my hands / Sweet Georgia Brown / I can't get started / Taking a chance on love / Melody maker / Musical express / Sometimes I'm happy / Monk's tune / Homage to Fats / Homage to Debussy / For Miss Blanc / Don't blame me
303062 / Jun '97 / Hallmark

☐ MEETS EIJI KITAMURA
STCD 4152 / May '96 / Storyville

☐ MOMENTS LIKE THIS
Alone with you / Moments like this / I can't face the music / Don't be that way / If I were you / You go to my head / I'll dream tonight / Jungle love / Now it can be told / Laugh and call it love / Tisket-a-tasket / Everybody's laughing / Here is tomorrow again / Say it with a kiss / April in my heart / I'll never fail you / They say / You're so desirable / You're gonna see a lot of me / Hello my darling / Let's dream in the moonlight / What shall I say / It's easy to blame the weather / Sugar / More than you know
HEPCD 1043 / May '95 / Hep

☐ OF THEE I SWING (Wilson, Teddy & Billie Holiday)
You turned the tables on me / Sing baby sing / Easy to love / With thee I swing / Way you look tonight / Who loves you / Pennies from Heaven / That's life / Sailin' / I can't give you anything but love / I'm with you (right or wrong) / Where the lazy river goes by / Tea for two / I'll see you in my dreams / He ain't got rhythm / This year's kisses
HEPCD 1020 / Jun '90 / Hep

☐ PARTNERS IN JAZZ (Classic Piano & Vocal Masterpieces) (Wilson, Teddy & Billie Holiday)
Somebody loves me / Why was I born / I've found a new baby / China boy / 711 / Wham be bop boom bam / Sailin' / Don't blame me / Way you look tonight / Blues in C sharp minor / Just a mood / More than you know / Why do I lie to myself about you / Jumpin' for joy / You can't stop me from dreaming / Jumpin' in the blacks and whites
307702 / Jul '97 / Hallmark

☐ PIANO SOLOS
Somebody loves me / Sweet and simple / Liza / Rosetta / Every now and then / It never dawned on me / I found a dream / On a treasure island / I feel like a feather in the breeze / Breakin' in a pair of shoes / Don't blame me / Between the devil and the deep blue sea / Sweat and simple
CDAFS 1016 / Sep '91 / Affinity

☐ REVISITS THE GOODMAN YEARS (1980 - Copenhagen) (Wilson, Teddy Trio)
STCD 4046 / Feb '89 / Storyville

☐ RUNNIN' WILD
One o'clock jump / Mood indigo / Take the 'A' train / Satin doll / Smoke gets in your eyes / Running wild / St James infirmary blues / After you've gone
BLCD 760184 / Apr '93 / Black Lion

☐ SOLO
Get out of town / Just one of those things / I get a kick out of you / It's all right with me / Love for sale / Too damn blue / Blue turning grey over you / Ain't cha glad / I've got a feeling I'm falling / Zonky / Black and blue / Ain't misbehavin' / Honeysuckle rose
8747152 / Jul '96 / DA Music

☐ STOMPING AT THE SAVOY
I can't get started (with you) / Sometimes I'm happy / Body and soul / I'll never be the same / Easy living
BLCD 760152 / Apr '91 / Black Lion

☐ TEDDY WILSON
CDC 9003 / Oct '90 / LRC

☐ TEDDY WILSON & HIS ALLSTARS (Wilson, Teddy Allstars)
CRD 150 / Jun '96 / Chiaroscuro

☐ TEDDY WILSON & HIS ORCHESTRA VOL.5 (Wilson, Teddy & His Orchestra)
Big apple / You can't stop me from dreaming / If I had you / You brought a new kind of love to me / Ain't misbehavin' / Ain't misbehavin' / Just a mood (pts 1 and 2) (blue mood / Honeysuckle rose / Nice work if you can get it / Things are looking up / My man (mon homme) / Can't help lovin' dat man / Don't blame me / Between the devil and the deep blue sea / My first impression / With a smile and a song / When you're smiling / I can't believe that you're in love with me / My first impression / When you're smiling / I can't believe that you're in love with me / If dreams come true
HEPCD 1035 / May '94 / Hep

☐ TEDDY WILSON SEXTET 1944
STCD 5236 / Jul '98 / Storyville

☐ TEDDY WILSON WITH BILLIE HOLIDAY (Wilson, Teddy & Billie Holiday)
Nice work if you can get it / Where the lazy river goes by / If you were mine / My last love affair / Why do I lie to myself about you / Mood that I'm in / I'm coming Virginia / Easy living / How am I to know / Hour of parting / Coquette / You let me down / I've found a new baby / All my life / Mary had a little lamb / Miss Brown to you / What a little moonlight can do / I wished on the moon
CDAJA 5053 / Jun '88 / Living Era

☐ THREE LITTLE WORDS
BB 8692 / Apr '96 / Black & Blue

☐ TOO HOT FOR WORDS (Wilson, Teddy Orchestra & Billie Holiday)
I wished on the moon / What a little moonlight can do / Miss Brown to you / Sun bonnet blue / It never dawned on me / Spreadin' rhythm round the world / You let me down / Sugar plum / Rosetta / Liza / Sweet Lorraine
HEPCD 1012 / Mar '90 / Hep

☐ WARMIN' UP
Life begins when you're in love: *Wilson, Teddy & Billie Holiday* / Rhythm in my nursery rhymes / Christopher Columbus / My melancholy baby: *Wilson, Teddy & Ella Fitzgerald* / All my life: *Wilson, Teddy & Ella Fitzgerald* / I found a dream / On treasure island / Mary had a little lamb: *Wilson, Teddy & Roy Eldridge* / Too good to be true / Warmin up / Blues in C sharp minor / It's like reaching for the moon: *Wilson, Teddy & Billie Holiday* / These foolish things: *Wilson, Teddy & Billie Holiday* / Why do I lie to myself about you / I cried for you: *Wilson, Teddy & Billie Holiday* / Guess who: *Wilson, Teddy & Billie Holiday* / I feel like a feather in the breeze / Breakin' in a pair of shoes / You came to my rescue: *Wilson, Teddy & Helen Ward* / Here's love in your eyes: *Wilson, Teddy & Helen Ward*
HEPCD 1014 / Oct '92 / Hep

☐ WITH BILLIE IN MIND
CRD 111 / Mar '96 / Chiaroscuro

Wilson, Tom

☐ TOM WILSON PRESENTS TONZ OF TEKNO (2CD Set) (Various Artists)
DBM 2026 / Aug '96 / Death Becomes Me

☐ TOM WILSON'S BOUNCIN' BEATS VOL.1 (Various Artists)
BNCCD 1 / Oct '94 / Rumour

☐ TOM WILSON'S BOUNCIN' BEATS VOL.2 (Various Artists)
BNCCD 2 / Jul '95 / Rumour

☐ TOM WILSON'S BOUNCIN' BEATS VOL.3 (Various Artists)
BNCCD 3 / Apr '96 / Rumour

☐ TOM WILSON'S TARTAN TECHNO VOL.1 (Various Artists)
TOONCD 101 / Oct '95 / Tempo Toons

☐ TOM WILSON'S TARTAN TECHNO VOL.2 (2CD Set) (Various Artists)
TOONCD 102 / Feb '97 / Tempo Toons

Wilson, Tony

☐ I LIKE YOUR STYLE
REP 4076 / Aug '91 / Repertoire

☐ SWEET AND SOULFUL/TONY WILSON SONGBOOK
GEMCD 023 / 30 Mar '98 / Diamond

Wilson, U.P.

☐ BOOGIE BOY
Tell me baby / Shakin' dem bones / Still with you / Boogie boy / Whiskey headed woman / Half step / 't' for texas / Need the need / Soul king shuffle / Too late to cry
JSPCD 255 / Jan '95 / JSP

☐ GOOD THE BAD AND THE BLUES, THE
JSPCD 2103 / Jun '98 / JSP

☐ WHIRLWIND
Roll over / Walk that walk / Your last chance / Juicin' / Going round in a daze / Who will your next fool be / Deep down inside / Bluesola / Come on baby, go home with me / If you don't know how to act (your place is at home)
JSPCD 277 / Feb '97 / JSP

Wimbledon FC

☐ SMELLS LIKE TEAM SPIRIT (Wimbledon FC/Supporters)
We are Wimbledon: *Wimbledon FC* / Dons song: *Wimbledon FC* / Wooly bully: *Jones, Vinnie* / Vinnie Jones is innocent: *Monty* / This is Vinnie Jones: *Monty* / When Irish eyes are smiling: *Kinnear, Joe & Friends* / Crazy games: *Jones, Vinnie* / Smells like team spirit: *Big Blue W* / Chant no.88: *Reservoir Dons & The West Bank* / All heroes (in yellow and blue): *Reservoir Dons* / Dons are coming: *Reservoir Dons* / Remember you're a Womble: *Plough Lane Boys*
CDGAFFER 13 / Apr '97 / Cherry Red

Wimme

☐ GIERRAN
Iras / Skittish / Havana / Whirlwind / Gierran / Rainbow / Snow grouse / Vision / Destiny / Draft reindeer / Haraly / Angelica / Importance of moss
ZENCD 2055 / Dec '97 / Rockadillo

☐ WIMME
ZENCD 2043 / May '95 / Rockadillo

Winans

☐ ALL OUT
Payday / It's not heaven if you're not there / If he doesn't come tonight / That extra mile / Tradewinds / All you ever been was good / Money motive / Love will never die / Heaven belongs to you / He said go
9362452132 / Aug '93 / Qwest

Winans, Bebe

☐ GREATEST HITS (Winans, Bebe & Cece)
Count it all joy / Addictive love / Lost without you / For always / Feels like heaven / It's ok / Meantime / Heaven / If ever happened to you / Celebrate new life / IOU / Up where we belong / Love said not so / I'll take you there
8370482 / 16 Feb '98 / EMI

☐ IN HARM'S WAY
In harm's way / So in love / Love is the reason / Thank you / This song / Did you know / If you stay / Love's coming / Stay / With all my heart / In the midst of the rain / Seeing for the very first time / Oh happy day / When you love someone
7567807482
7567830412 / 15 Jun '98 / Atlantic

☐ RELATIONSHIPS (Winans, Bebe & Cece)
Count it all joy / Love of my life / Don't let me walk down this road alone / Both day and night / Stay with me / He's always there / Right away / If anything ever happened to you / These what about's / (If I was only) Welcomed in / We can make a difference
CDEST 2237 / Sep '94 / Capitol

Winans, Cece

☐ ALONE IN HIS PRESENCE
Overture / Alone in his presence / I surrender all / Because of you / His strength is perfect / Every time / Great is thy faithfulness / Praise medley / Blessed assurance / Blood medley / He's always there / Alone in his presence (reprise)
SPD 1441 / Sep '96 / Alliance Music

Winans, Mario

☐ STORY OF MY HEART
5308022 / 29 Sep '97 / Polydor

Winans, Vickie

☐ VICKIE WINANS
We work it out / We shall overcome / Precious Lord / Stand up and praise him / We shall behold Him / Only one / Suddenly / I remember when / You never left me / Believing is seeing / Mary, did you know
CDK 9127 / Sep '95 / Alliance Music

Winchester Cathedral Choir

☐ CAROLS FOR CHRISTMAS
O come all ye faithful (Adeste Fidelis) / Unto us a boy is born / Rocking / God rest ye merry gentlemen / Away in a manger / First Noel / Once in Royal David's City / Silent night / In dulci jubilo / While shepherds watched their flocks by night / Coventry carol / O little town of Bethlehem / In the bleak midwinter / Hark the herald angels sing
261279 / Oct '94 / Arista

Winchester, Jesse

☐ HUMOUR ME
SHCD 1023 / Aug '96 / Sugar Hill

☐ JESSE WINCHESTER
SPCD 1198 / Dec '94 / Stony Plain

☐ LEARN TO LOVE IT
SPCD 1205 / May '95 / Stony Plain

☐ LET THE ROUGH SIDE DRAG
SPCD 1206 / May '95 / Stony Plain

☐ THIRD DOWN 10 TO GO
SPCD 1199 / Dec '94 / Stony Plain

Wind

☐ SEASONS
SB 016 / Oct '97 / Second Battle

Wind In The Willows

☐ WIND IN THE WILLOWS
Moments spent / Uptown girl / So sad (to watch good love go bad) / My uncle used to love me but she died / There is but one truth / Daddy / Friendly lion / Park Avenue blues / Djini Judy / Little people / She's fantastic and she's yours / Wheel of changes
DOCD 1985 / Aug '93 / Drop Out

Wind, Martin

☐ TENDER WAVES
There's a boat that's leaving shortly for New York / Quietly / Marc's moments / You're my everything / Tender waves / Make a new start / Coracao vagabundo / You and the night and the music / Too far from you
AL 73030 / Nov '96 / A

Winding, Kai

☐ CLEVELAND 1957 (Winding, Kai Septet)
DSTS 1012 / '94 / Status

☐ JAI AND KAI + 6 (Winding, Kai & J.J. Johnson)
Night in Tunisia / Piece for two tromboniums / Rise 'n' shine / All at once you love her / No moon at all / Surrey with the fringe on top / Peanut vendor / You're my thrill / Jeanne / Four plus four / You don't know what love is / Continental (you kiss while you're dancing)
4809902 / Dec '95 / Sony Jazz

☐ KAI WINDING & J.J. JOHNSON (Winding, Kai & J.J. Johnson)
Out of this world / Thous sweet / Lover / Lope city / Stolen bass / It's all right with me / Mad about the boy / Yes sir that's my baby / That's how I feel about you / Gong rock
BET 6026 / Jan '95 / Bethlehem

☐ NUF SAID (Bethlehem Jazz Classics) (Winding, Kai & J.J. Johnson)
CDGR 132 / Apr '97 / Charly

Windir

☐ SOKNARDAIR
HNF 037CD / 3 Aug '98 / Head Not Found

Windows

☐ BLUE SEPTMEBER
101S 70882 / Nov '92 / 101 South

Windracht Acht

☐ OP DE WILDE VAART
PAN 148CD / Aug '94 / Pan

Winds The Six

☐ MANESHAAL
BVHAASTCD 9706 / Apr '98 / Bvhaast

Windsor For The Derby

☐ CALM HADES FLOAT
TR 46CD / May '96 / Trance

☐ METROPOLITAN THEN POLAND
TR 54CD / Jan '97 / Trance Syndicate

☐ MINNIE GREUNZFELDT
TR 63CD / 17 Oct '97 / Trance Syndicate

Windy & Carl

☐ ANTARCTICA
DRL 0272CD / 5 Jan '98 / Darla

☐ DEPTHS
KRANK 024CD / 2 Feb '98 / Kranky

☐ PORTAL
BING 004 / Nov '97 / Ba Da Bing

Winfield, Roger

☐ WINDSONGS - THE SOUND OF THE AEOLIAN HARP
CDSDL 394 / Mar '94 / Saydisc

Winger, Kip

☐ MADE BY HAND
Another way / Down incognito / Under one condition / Miles away / Steam / Headed for a heartbreak / How far will you go / Naked son / Spell I'm under / Easy come easy go / Daniel
DOMO 710192 / 9 Feb '98 / Domo

☐ THIS CONVERSATION SEEMS LIKE A DREAM
Kiss of life / Monster / Endless circle / Angel of the underground / Steam / I'll be down / Naked son / Daniel / How far will we go / Don't let go / Here
DOMO 710152 / Feb '97 / Domo

Wingless Angels

☐ WINGLESS ANGELS
I write my name/Good morning / No dark there / Keyman / On Mount Zion I / Morning train / Roll Jordan roll / Rasta army / We shall overcome / Come in my little ones / Four and twenty / Rivers of Babylon / Ring out Mount Zion bells / Bright soul / Enjoy yourself / Love love love / Keyman acapella
5244472 / 15 Dec '97 / Island

Wings

☐ BAND ON THE RUN
Band on the run / Jet / Bluebird / Mrs. Vanderbilt / Let me roll it / Marmunia / No words / Picasso's last words / 1985
CDPMCOL 5 / Apr '93 / Parlophone

☐ BIOGRAPHY SERIES
10028 / 3 Nov '97 / Metro Independent

Winico

☐ BON VOYAGE
KRS 282CD / Aug '97 / Kill Rock Stars

Wink, Josh

☐ HEAR HERE
Intro / Back in tha day / Hard hit / Sixth sense / Black bomb (Jerry in the bag) / Young again / I'm on fire / Track 9 / Ah git up / Are you there / New groove / Simple man
WINK 2CD / 29 Jun '98 / Sony Soho2

☐ HIGHER STATE OF WINK'S WORKS, A
Unification: *E-Culture* / I'm ready: *Size 9* / Higher state of consciousness / How's the music: *Winx* / Thoughts of a tranced love: *Winc* / Tribal confusion: *E-Culture*
5340572 / Sep '96 / Manifesto

☐ LEFT ABOVE THE CLOUDS (Winx)
XLCD 119 / Sep '96 / XL

Winkler, Harold

☐ BORN WITH A KISS (Winkler, Harold & Norman Candler Orchestra)
ISCD 156 / Jun '95 / Intersound

Winkler, Mark

☐ CITY LIGHTS
0328110302 / 27 Apr '98 / Chartmaker

☐ HOTTEST NIGHT OF THE YEAR
Dancin' in the sunshine / Stain doll / Hottest night of the year / Tropical breezes / Beauty and the beast / Forward motion / Moon made me do it / Takin' chances / In a minor key
CDLR 45015 / Apr '90 / L&R

Winsborough, Richard

☐ SONGS OF PASSION
PMCD 002 / Nov '97 / Phoenix

Winski, Colin

☐ HELLDORADO
FCD 3027 / Sep '93 / Fury

Winsome

☐ STORY OF A BLACK WOMAN
SGCD 019 / Oct '94 / Sir George

Winston Groovy

☐ AFRICAN GIRL
African girl / Moving on / You keep me hangin' on / From we met / Please don't go / Lay back in the arms of someone / Girl, without you / So in love with you / All because of you / Give me time / Please don't make me cry / Am I a dreamer / Oh little darling / Dear mama / Black hearted woman / Midnight train / Can't stand the morning / Anything goes with me / Old rock 'n' roller / Don't wanna hear that song again / Sea of dreams
BRCD 3000 / Apr '92 / Blue Moon

☐ COME ROCK WITH ME
WGCD 009 / Nov '95 / Winston Groovy

☐ COMING ON STRONG
WGCD 007 / Oct '92 / Winston Groovy

☐ PLEASE DON'T MAKE ME CRY
Are we makin love-or just makin time / Look what lovin' you has done / Please don't make me cry / Secure and warm / Only good thing / I'll still be lovin you / I'm addicted to you baby / Game of making love / On the other hand
WGCD 005 / 12 Jan '98 / Winston Groovy

☐ VERY BEST OF WINSTON GROOVY, THE
RN 7036 / 15 Dec '97 / Rhino

Winston, George

☐ ALL THE SEASONS OF GEORGE WINSTON
All the seasons of George Winston colours/Dance / Venice dreamer / Living in the country / Cradle / Joy / Treat street / Variations on the Canon by Pachelbel / Thanksgiving / Miles city train / Corrina Corrina / Hummingbird / Longing / Cast your fate to the wind / Sandman / Snowman's music box dance / Northern plains song / Sleep baby mine / Evening song
01934126621 / 23 Mar '98 / Windham Hill

☐ AUTUMN
Colors/dance / Woods / Longing/love / Road / Moon / Sea / Stars
01934110122 / Jan '95 / Windham Hill

☐ BALLADS AND BLUES
08022340022 / Jun '94 / RCA

☐ DECEMBER
Thanksgiving / Jesus Jesus rest your head / Joy / Prelude / Carol of the bells / Night / Midnight (part 2) / Minstrels (part 3) / Variations on the kanon / Holly and the ivy / Some children see him / Peace / Snow
01934110252 / Jan '95 / Windham Hill

☐ FOREST
01934111572 / Oct '94 / Windham Hill

☐ LINUS AND LUCY (The Music Of Vince Guaraldi)
Cast your fate to the wind / Skating / Linus and Lucy / Great pumpkin waltz / Monterey / Charlie Brown thanksgiving / Treat Street / Eight five five / Masked marvel / Charlie brown and his All-Stars / You're in love / Charlie Brown / Peppermint Patty / Bon voyage / Young man's fancy / Remembrance / Theme to grace/Lament
01934111842 / Sep '96 / Windham Hill

☐ SUMMER
Living in the country / Loreta and desiree's bouquet (parts 1 and 2) / Fragrant fields / Garden / Spring creek / Lullaby / Black stallion / Hummingbird / Early morning range / Living without you / Goodbye montana-part 1 / Corina corina / Goodbye montanta-part 2 / Where are you
01934111072 / Jan '95 / Windham Hill

☐ WINTER INTO SPRING
January stars / February sea / Ocean waves (o mar) / Reflection / Raindance / Blossom meadow / Venice dreamer / Introduction (part 1) / Part 2
01934110192 / Jan '95 / Windham Hill

Winstone, Eric

☐ BY THE FIRESIDE (18 Intimate Easy Listening Classics) (Winstone, Eric & His Orchestra)
Me and my shadow / I'm in the mood for love / Rebecca / Kisses by candlelight / I'll close my eyes / That old feeling / Goodnight sweetheart / Very thought of you / You were meant for me / Unforgetaable / By the fireside / All my loving / Touch of your lips / Bye bye blues / You go to my head / Somewhere my love / Don't blame me / If I had you
306212 / Jan '97 / Hallmark

☐ EASY GOING SIXTIES (18 Superb Arrangements Of 1960's Standards) (Winstone, Eric Orchestra)
Monsieur Dupont / Please please me cha cha / Last waltz / Can't take my eyes off you / Joanna / Congratulations / Can't buy me love / By the time I get to Phoenix / Strangers in the night / Sabre dance / Bonnie and Clyde / You've got your troubles / Ob-la-di ob-la-da / Something / Good vibrations / San Francisco / I wish you love / Pontinental
307382 / Jul '97 / Hallmark

☐ TEACH ME TO DANCE (Winstone, Eric Orchestra)
Happy feet / You've got your troubles / Somewhere my love / From a window / Bye bye blues / I'll just close my eyes / Bonnie and Clyde / Pepito's tune / Green eyes / Cuban nights / Darling / Last waltz / Copacabana / Tico tico / Games that lovers play / Teach me to dance / International waltz / Rebecca / Thoughly modern Millie / Goodbye blues / (We're gonna) Rock around the clock / Can't buy me love / Congratulations / Girl about town
DNSN 903 / Apr '94 / President

Winstone, Norma

☐ MANHATTAN IN THE RAIN
Heather on the hill / Music that makes me dance / It never was you / Two kites / Manhattan in the rain / People will say we're in love / I have dreamed / Retrato em Branco e Preto / Lucky to be me / Baby don't you quit now / Shall we dance / Far away places / When the world was young
ENOCD 001 / 29 Jun '98 / Enodoc

☐ WELL KEPT SECRET (Winstone, Norma & Jimmy Rowles)
Where or when / Timeless place / I dream too much / It amazes me / Prelude to a kiss / Joy spring / Remind me / Flower is a lovesome thing / Dream of you / Morning star
378362 / Mar '97 / Koch Jazz

Winter

☐ ETERNAL FROST
NB 107 / Sep '94 / Nuclear Blast

☐ INTO DARKNESS
NB 064CD / Nov '92 / Nuclear Blast

Winter, Cathy

☐ NEXT SWEET TIME
FF 598CD / Feb '93 / Flying Fish

Winter, Edgar

☐ COLLECTION, THE
8122708952 / Jun '95 / Rhino

☐ HARLEM NOCTURNE
Searching / Tingo tango / Cry me a river / Save your love for me / Quiet gas / Satin doll / Jordu / Girl from Ipanema / Harlem nocturne / Come back baby / Before the sunset / Who dunnit / Please come home for Christmas
CDTB 089 / Dec '90 / Thunderbolt

☐ I'M NOT A KID ANYMORE
Way down south / I'm not a kid anymore / Against the law / Brothers keeper / I wanta rock / Crazy / Just like you / Big city woman / Innocent lust / Frankenstein
CDTB 152 / Jan '94 / Thunderbolt
SPV 08446642 / Aug '97 / SPV

☐ MASTERS, THE (Winter, Edgar & Rick Derringer)
Introduction / Keep playin' that rock 'n' roll / Teenage love affair / Free ride / Fly away / Blood from a stone / Undercover man / Jump jump jump / Hang on sloopy / Against the law / Play guitar / Rock and roll hoochie koo / Frankenstein
EABCD 078 / 30 Mar '98 / Eagle

☐ REAL DEAL, THE
Hoochie coo / Real deal / We can't win / Good ol' rock 'n' roll / Give me the will / Nitty gritty / Eye of the storm / Sanctuary / Hot passionate love / Music is you / What do I tell my heart
CDTB 182 / May '97 / Thunderbolt

Winter, Johnny

☐ BACK IN BEAUMONT (Winter, Johnny & Uncle John Turner)
Made in the shade / They call my lazy / Family rules / Ooh-poo-pah-doo / Drivin' wheel / Allons dancez / Struggle in Houston / You're humbuggin' me / Just a little bit / Rainin' breakdown
CDTB 077 / Apr '90 / Thunderbolt

☐ BLUE SUEDE SHOES
Don't drink whiskey / Hook you / Blue suede shoes / Ronettes / Voodoo twist / How do you live a lie / Lost without you / Jolie blon / Bring it on home / Hello my lover / Rockin' pneumonia and the boogie woogie flu / Ice cube / Gangster of love / Parchman farm / Bad news / Roadrunner
CDTB 108 / Feb '92 / Thunderbolt

☐ BROKE AND LONELY
CDTB 165 / Mar '96 / Thunderbolt

☐ EARLY WINTER
Ease my pain / That's what love does / Crying in my heart / Guy you left behind / Shed so many tears / Creepy / Gangster of love / Roadrunner / Leave my woman alone / I can't believe you want to leave / Broke and lonely / Oh my darling / By the light of the silvery moon / Five after four AM
PRCD 116 / Jan '87 / President

☐ EASE MY PAIN
That's what love does / Leave my wife alone / 5 after 4am / Roadrunner / Ease my pain / Guy you left behind / Kiss tomorrow goodbye / I can't believe you want to leave / By the light of the silvery moon / Easy lovin' girl / Shed so many tears / Creepy / Please come home for Christmas / Harlem nocturne
SC 6071 / Aug '97 / Sundazed

☐ ELECTRIC BLUES MAN (2CD Set)
My baby / Parchman farm / Night ride / One night of love / Thirty to twenty blues / Reelin' and rockin' / Tramp / Bad news / Bad news / Bad news / Suicide won't satisfy / Ice cube / Easy loving girl / We go back quite a ways / Hello my lover / Hook you / You'll be the death of me / Gonna miss me when I'm gone / Sloppy drunk blues / Goin' down slow / Low down gal of mine / Take my choice / Gangster of love / Eternally / Blue suede shoes / Ballad of Bertha Glutz / Living in the blues / Raindrops in my heart / Black cat bone / Talk to your daughter
CDTB 509 / Jan '97 / Thunderbolt

☐ FIVE AFTER FOUR AM
Oh my darling / Five after four AM / That's what love does / Shed so many tears / Roadrunner / Guy you left behind / Gangster of love / By the light of the silvery moon / Leave my woman alone / I can't believe you want to leave
CDTB 073 / Nov '89 / Thunderbolt

☐ FIVE AFTER FOUR AM
Oh my darling / Five after four / That's what love does / Road runner / Guy you left behind / Gangster of love / By the light of the silvery moon / Leave my woman alone / I can't believe you want to leave / Shed so many tears
MM 004 / 27 Apr '98 / MagMid

☐ GANGSTER OF LOVE
Gangster of love / Goin' down slow / That's what love does / Low down gal of mine / I can't believe you want to leave / Road runner / Out of sight / Five after four am / Leaving blues / Kind hearted woman / Leave my woman alone / Parchman farm
305702 / Oct '96 / Hallmark

☐ GUITAR SLINGER
It's my life baby / Iodine in my coffee / Trick bag / Mad dog / Boot Hill / I smell trouble / Lights out / Kiss tomorrow goodbye / My soul / Don't take advantage of me
ALCD 4735 / May '93 / Alligator

☐ HEY, WHERE'S YOUR BROTHER
Johnny Guitar / She likes to boogie real low / White line blues / Please come home for Christmas / Hard Way / You must have a twin / You keep sayin' that you're leavin' / Treat Me Like You Wanta / Sick and tired / Blues This Bad / No More Doggin' / Check out her mama / Got my brand on you / One step forward
VPBCD 11 / Sep '92 / Pointblank

☐ JOHNNY B. GOODE
E Z Rider / Black cat bone / Going down slow / Five after four AM / Made in the shade / Gonna miss me when I'm gone / 32-20 Blues / Parchman farm / Don't drink whiskey / Gangster of love / Bring it on home / Hook you / Living in the blues / Hoochie coochie man / Gangster of love (Instrumental) / Messin' with the kid / Walking by myself / Johnny B Goode
3036000852 / Apr '97 / Carlton

☐ JOHNNY WINTER
I'm yours and I'm hers / Be careful with a fool / Dallas / Mean mistreater / Leland Mississippi / When you got a good friend / I'll drown my tears / Back door friend
4712182 / Feb '97 / Columbia

☐ LIBERTY HALL SESSIONS
CDTB 175 / Jun '96 / Thunderbolt

☐ LIVE AT THE TEXAS OPRY HOUSE
Somethin' goin' on wrong / Come on in my kitchen / Brown eyed handsome man / In the wee wee hours / Wipeout / Hideaway / Diving duck blues / Mississippi blues / Last night
CDTB 185 / 24 Oct '97 / Thunderbolt

☐ LIVE IN HOUSTON, BUSTED IN AUSTIN
EZ rider / Walking by myself / Mother earth / Boney Maronie / Busted in Austin / Messin' with the kid / I can't make it by myself / Johnny B Goode / It's all over now / Jumpin' Jack flash
CDTB 100 / Jul '91 / Thunderbolt

☐ LIVE NYC '97
VPBCD 43 / 9 Mar '98 / Pointblank

☐ LIVIN' IN THE BLUES
Livin' in the blues / Leavin' blues / Parchman farm / Bad news / Birds can't row boats / World turns all around her / Take a chance on love / 32-20 blues / Kindhearted woman blues / Going down slow / Low down gal of mine / Out of sight / I had to cry / Avocado green
SC 6070 / Aug '97 / Sundazed

☐ LIVIN' IN THE BLUES
That's what love does / Leave my wife alone / 5 after 4am / Roadrunner / Ease my pain / Guy you left behind / Kiss tomorrow goodbye / I can't believe you want to leave / By the light of the silvery moon / Shed so many tears / Creepy / Harlem nocturne / Livin' in the blues / World turns all around her / 38 32 20 blues / Kind hearted woman / Going down slow / Low down gal of mine
WB 886012 / 2 Feb '98 / Disky

☐ LIVING IN THE BLUES
Goin' down slow / Kind hearted woman blues / 38-20-30 blues / Low down gal of mine / Avocado green / My world turns around her / Coming up fast / Living in the blues / Bad news / I had to cry / Kiss tomorrow goodbye / Parchman farm / Tramp / Harlem nocturne
CDTB 083 / '91 / Thunderbolt

☐ MASTERS, THE (2CD Set)
EDMCD 029 / 30 Mar '98 / Eagle

☐ NO TIME TO LIVE
Ain't that kindness / Stranger / Am I here / Self destructive blues / Golden days of rock and roll / Rock 'n' roll hoochie coo / Guess I'll go away / Rock 'n' roll people / Lay down your sorrows / Raised on rock / Let the music play / Prodigal son / Mind over matter / Pick up on my mojo / No time to live / On the limb
CDTB 136 / Mar '92 / Thunderbolt

☐ PROGRESSIVE BLUES EXPERIMENT
Rollin' and tumblin' / Tribute to Muddy / Got love if you want it / Bad luck and trouble / Help me / Mean town blues / Broke down engine / Black cat bone / It's my own fault / Forty four
CDLL 57350 / Jul '94 / One Way

☐ RAISED ON ROCK
Prodigal son / On the limb / Let the music play / Nothing left / Look up / Rock 'n' roll / Golden days of rock 'n' roll / Self destruction blues / Raised on rock / Stranger
CDSGP 0306 / 27 Oct '97 / Prestige

☐ RAW TO THE BONE (Winter, Johnny & Calvin Johnson)
Late on blues / They call me loudmouth / Line on your body / Once I had a woman / Take my choice / Unwelcome in your home / Gangster of love / Alone in my bedroom / Hoochie coochie man / Moth balls / She's mine / Unsatisfied mind / Rock me baby
CDTB 126 / Feb '92 / Thunderbolt
8400872 / May '96 / Sky Ranch

☐ ROCK 'N' ROLL COLLECTION (2CD Set)
Johnny B Goode / Good morning little school girl / I'll drown my tears / When you got a good friend / Be careful with a fool / Miss Ann / Hustled down in Texas / Rock 'n' roll / Hoochie koo / Rock me baby / Sitting in the jail house / Baby, watcha want me to do / Bony Moronie / It's all over now / TV Mama / Drinkin' blues / Walking thru the park / I'm not sure / Guess I'll go away / Thirty days / Come on in my kitchen / Highway 61 revisited
4838972 / Jun '96 / Columbia

☐ SAINTS AND SINNERS
Stone County / Blinded by love / Thirty days / Stray cat blues / Bad luck situation / Rollin' cross the country / Riot in cell block 9 / Hurtin' so bad / Bony Moronie / Feedback on Highway 101 / Dirty
CK 66420 / Mar '96 / Columbia

☐ SEARCHIN' BLUES
Walking by myself / Diving duck / One step at a time / Bladie Mae / Mad blues / It was rainin' / Man mistreater / Mother In Law Blues / Dallas / Mean town blues
4716612 / Jul '92 / Columbia

☐ SERIOUS BUSINESS
Master mechanic / Sound the bell / Murdering the blues / It ain't your business / Good time woman / Unseen eye / My time after awhile / Serious as a heart attack / Give it back / Route 90
ALCD 4742 / Oct '93 / Alligator

☐ SUICIDE WON'T SATISFY
My baby / Parchman farm / Night ride / One night of love / Thirty two twenty blues / Reelin' and rockin' / Tramp / Bad news / Bad news / Bad news / Suicide won't satisfy / Ice cube / Easy lovin' girl / We go back quite a way / Hello my lover / Hook you / You'll be the death of me
CDTB 192 / 31 Jul '98 / Thunderbolt

☐ TEXAS BLUES (2CD Set)
SMDCD 185 / 9 Feb '98 / Snapper

☐ THIRD DEGREE
Mojo boogie / Love life and money / Evil on my mind / See see baby / Tin Pan Alley / I'm good / Third degree / Shake your moneymaker / Bad girl blues / Broke and lonely
ALCD 4748 / May '93 / Alligator

☐ WHITE LIGHTNING
Mean town blues / Black cat bone / Mean mistreater / Talk to your daughter / Look up / I can love you baby
CDTB 149 / Oct '93 / Thunderbolt

☐ WINTER BLUES
Leavin' blues / Avocado blues / Parchman farm / Gangster of love / 38-32-20 / Kind hearted woman / Low down gal of mine / Goin' down slow / Ease my heart / Out of sight / Bad news / I can't believe you want to leave / I had to cry / That's what love does / Guy you left behind / Shed so many tears / Leave my woman alone / Broke and lonely / Creepy no.2 / By the light of the silvery moon / 5 after 4am / Spiders in my mind (birds can't row boats) / Easy lovin' girl
CCSCD 445 / May '97 / Castle

☐ WINTER HEAT
79567630372 / 14 Apr '98 / Multimedia

Winter, Kitty

☐ GYPSY ALBUM, THE (Winter, Kitty & Gipsy Nova)
BLDCD 539 / 6 Oct '97 / Boulevard

Winter, Paul

☐ CANYON LULLABY
LMUS 0033 / Oct '97 / Living Tradition

☐ EARTHBEAT
LD 0015 / Aug '88 / Living Music

Winter Rose

☐ WINTER ROSE
SPV 08528522 / Dec '97 / SPV

Winters, Ruby

☐ RUBY WINTERS
I will / For the good times / If this is our last time / I can't fake it any more / I won't mention it again / Every little bit hurts / I've had my share of broken hearts / Baby lay down / You lay so easy on my mind / Come to me / Treat me right / Neither one of us / Love me now / Lonely heartaches / I've been waiting for you all my life / Woman enough to take my man / I'm your woman / You won't see me anymore / Loving me is a full time job / You still got a place in my heart / Back to the love / Bluer days ahead
RNCD 1008 / Jun '93 / Rhino

Winther, Jens

☐ LOOKING THROUGH (Winther, Jens Quintet)
STCD 4127 / Feb '90 / Storyville

Winwood, Steve

☐ AIYE KETA (Third World)
Happy vibes / Irin Ajo / Black beauty / Afro super / Shango
EDCD 513 / Feb '97 / Edsel

☐ ARC OF A DIVER
While you see a chance / Second hand woman / Slowdown sundown / Spanish dancer / Night train / Dust / Arc of a diver
CID 9576 / Jan '87 / Island

☐ BACK IN THE HIGH LIFE
Higher love / Take it as it comes / Freedom overspill / Back in the high life / Finer things / Wake me up on judgement day / Split decision / My love's leavin'
CID 9844 / Jul '86 / Island

☐ FINER THINGS, THE (4CD Set)
Dimples: *Davis, Spencer Group* / I Can't stand it: *Davis, Spencer Group* / Every little bit hurts: *Davis, Spencer Group* / Strong love: *Davis, Spencer Group* / Keep on running: *Davis, Spencer Group* / Somebody help me: *Davis, Spencer Group* / When I come home: *Davis, Spencer Group* / I want to know: *Clapton, Eric & The Powerhouse* / Crossroads: *Clapton, Eric & The Powerhouse* / Gimme some lovin': *Davis, Spencer Group* / I'm a man: *Davis, Spencer Group* / Paper sun: *Traffic* / Dealer: *Traffic* / Coloured rain: *Traffic* / No face, no name, no number: *Traffic* / Heaven is in your mind: *Traffic* / Smiling phases: *Traffic* / Dear Mr. Fantasy: *Traffic* / Pearly Queen: *Traffic* / Forty thousand headmen: *Traffic* / No time to live: *Traffic* / Shanghai noodle factory: *Traffic* / Medicated goo: *Traffic* / Withering tree: *Traffic* / Had to cry today: *Blind Faith* / Can't find my way home: *Blind Faith* / Sea of joy: *Blind Faith* / Sleeping in the ground: *Blind Faith* / Under my thumb: *Blind Faith* / Stranger to himself: *Traffic* / John Barleycorn: *Traffic* / Glad: *Traffic* / Freedom rider: *Traffic* / Empty pages: *Traffic* / Low spark of high heeled boys: *Traffic* / Rainmaker: *Traffic* / Shoot out at the fantasy factory: *Traffic* / (Sometimes I feel so) Uninspired: *Traffic* / Happy vibes: *Winwood, Steve & Remi Kabaka/Abdul Lasisi Amao* / Something new: *Traffic* / Dream Gerrard: *Traffic* / Walking in the wind: *Traffic* / When the eagle flies: *Traffic* / Winner/Loser: *Winwood, Steve & Stomu Yamashta* / Crossing the line (Live): *Yamashta, Stomu & Steve Winwood* / Hold on: *Winwood, Steve & Jim Capaldi* / Time is running out: *Winwood, Steve & Jim Capaldi* / Vacant chair: *Winwood, Steve & Viv Stanshall* / While you see a chance / Arc of a diver / Spanish dancer / Night train / Dust / Valerie / Talking back to the night / Your silence is your song / Higher love / Freedom overspill / Back in the high life / Finer things / Roll with it / Don't you know what the night can do / One and only man
IBXCD 2 / Mar '95 / Island

☐ JUNCTION 7
Spy in the house of love / Angel of mercy / Just wanna have some fun / Let your love come down / Real love / Fill me up / Gotta get back to my baby / Someone like you / Family affair / Plenty lovin' / Lord of the Street
CDV 2832 / Jun '97 / Virgin

☐ KEEP ON RUNNING
Keep on running / Gimme some lovin' / Somebody help me / I'm a man / Every little bit hurts / Paper sun / Smiling phases / Heaven is in your mind / Here we go round the mulberry bush / No face, no name, no number / Well alright / Empty pages / John barleycorn (must die) / Happy vibes / Something new / Time is running out / Hold on
IMCD 224 / Mar '96 / Island

☐ REFUGEES OF THE HEART
You'll keep on searching / Every day (oh Lord) / One and only man / I will be here / Another deal goes down / Running on / Come out and dance / In the light of day
CDV 2650 / Nov '90 / Virgin

☐ ROLL WITH IT
Roll with it / Holding on / Morning side / Put on your dancing shoes / Don't you know what the night can do / Hearts on fire / One more morning / Shining song
CDV 2532 / Jun '88 / Virgin

☐ STEVE WINWOOD
Hold on / Time is running out / Let me make something in your life / Luck's in / Vacant chair / Midland maniac
IMCD 161 / Mar '93 / Island

Wipers

☐ FOLLOW BLIND
GIFT 024CD / 16 Feb '98 / Gift Of Life

☐ HERD
TK 95CD114 / Jul '97 / Tim Karr

☐ IS THIS REAL
SPOD 82/253 / Mar '93 / Sub Pop

☐ LAND OF THE LOST
GIFT 023CD / 16 Feb '98 / Gift Of Life

☐ LIVE
GIFT 021CD / 16 Feb '98 / Gift Of Life

☐ SILVER SAIL
Y I came / Back to basics / Warning / Mars / Prisoner / Standing there / Sign of the times / Line / On a roll / Never win / Silver sail
TK 92CD031 / Jun '94 / T/K

Wire

☐ 154
I should have known better / Two people in a room / 15th / Other window / Single KO / Touching display / On returning / Mutual friend / Blessed state / Once is enough / Map ref 41 degrees N 93 degrees W / Indirect enquiries / Forty versions
CDGO 2064 / Jul '94 / EMI

☐ BEHIND THE CURTAIN
Mary is a dyke / Too true / Just don't care / TV / New York City / After midnight / Pink flag / Love ain't polite / Oh no not so / It's the motive / Practice makes perfect / Sand in my joints / Stablemates / I feel mysterious today / Underwater experience / Dot dash / Options R / From the nursery / Finistaire / No romans / Another the letter / Forty Versions / Blessed state / Touching display / Once is enough / Stepping off too quick / Indirect inquiries / Map ref 41 degrees N 93 degrees W / Question of degree / Two people in a room / Former airline
CDGO 2066 / May '95 / EMI

☐ BELL IS A CUP UNTIL IT IS STRUCK, A
Silk skin paws / Finest drops / Queen's of Ur and The King of Um / Free falling divisions / It's a Bob / Boiling boy / Kidney bongos / Come back in two halves / Follow the locust / Public place
CDSTUMM 54 / Jun '88 / Mute

☐ CHAIRS MISSING
Practice makes perfect / French film blurred / Another the letter / Men 2nd / Marooned / Sand in my joints / Being sucked in again / Heartbeat / Mercy / Outdoor miner / I am the fly / I feel mysterious today / From the nursery / Used to / Too late
CDGO 2065 / Jul '94 / EMI

☐ FIRST LETTER, THE
CDSTUMM 87 / Oct '91 / Mute

☐ IDEAL COPY, THE
Point of collapse / Ahead / Madman's honey / Feed me / Ambitious / Cheeking tongues / Still shows / Over theirs / Ahead (II) / Serious of snakes / Drill / Advantage in height / Up to the sun / Ambulance chasers / Feed me (II) / Vivid riot of red
CDSTUMM 42 / Apr '87 / Mute

☐ IT'S BEGINNING TO AND BACK AGAIN
Finest drops / Eardrum buzz / German shepherds / Public place / It's a boy / Illuminated / Boiling boy / Over theirs / Offer / In vivo
CDSTUMM 66 / Apr '89 / Mute

☐ MANSCAPE
Life in the manscape / Stampede / Patterns of behaviour / Other moments / Small black reptile / Torch it / Morning bell / Where's the deputation / What can you see / Goodbye ploy / Sixth sense / Children of groceries / You hung your lights in the trees-a craftsman's touch
CDSTUMM 80 / Apr '90 / Mute

☐ ON RETURNING (Wire 1977-1979)
12XU / It's so obvious / Mr. Suit / Three girl rhumba / Ex lion tamer / Lowdown / Strange / Reuters / Feeling called love / I am the fly / Practice makes perfect / French film blurred / I feel mysterious today / Marooned / Sand in my joints / Outdoor miner / Question of degree / I should have known better / Other window / Forty versions / Touching display / On returning / Another the letter / Straight line / 106 beats that / Field day for the Sundays / Dot dash / Men 2nd / Two people in room / Blessed state
CDP 7925352 / Sep '96 / Harvest

☐ PINK FLAG
Reuters / Field day for the Sundays / Three girl rhumba / Ex lion tamer / Lowdown / Start to move / Brazil / It's so obvious / Surgeon's girl / Pink flag / Commercial / Straight line / 106 Beats that / Mr. Suit / Strange / Fragile / Mannequin / Different to me / Champs / Feeling called love / 12XU / Dot dash / Options R
CDGO 2063 / Jul '94 / EMI

☐ WIRE 1985-1990
Ahead / Kidney bingos / A serious of snakes / Eardrum buzz / Drill / Ambitious / In vivo / Finest drops / Madman's honey / Over theirs / Silk skin paws / Queen of ur and the king of um / Torch it / Advantage in height / Point of collapse / Feed me
CDSTUMM 116 / Jun '93 / Mute

Wired To The Moon

☐ PURE
Hold me / No way home / Pure / Same old story / Believes / Promises / This girl / World of stone / All the time / Harry's letter
COOKCD 104 / Jul '97 / Cooking Vinyl

Wiregrass Sacred Harp Singers

☐ COLORED SACRED HARP
804332 / Feb '94 / New World

☐ DESIRE FOR PIETY
805192 / Aug '97 / New World

Wireless

☐ WIRELESS
Banana tea / All the good ones have gone / I need you / How much I think of you / We all go slow sometimes / Stupid trend / Happy / In love with the familiar / I will be there / You're all I need / Timebomb / Lesson in life
4935712 / 20 Jul '98 / Chrysalis

Wirtz, Mark

☐ GO GO MUSIC OF MARK WIRTZ, THE (Wirtz, Mark Orchestra/Chorus)
Yeh yeh / If illusion met fantasy / Yellow spotted Capricorn / Come back and shake me / You didn't have to be so nice / Comin' home baby / Don't do it baby / Real Mr. Smith / Monday Monday / Touch of velvet / Sting of brass / Sunny / I can hear music / Sunday night / Riviera carnival / Chinese chequers / Watching a matchstick flight / Yesterday's laughter, today's tears / Dizzy / Ther's no business like monkey business / Thimble full of puzzles / Beyond the horizon / Dreamin' / Fantastic fair
RPM 172 / Dec '96 / RPM

Wirtz, Rev. Billy C.

☐ BACKSLIDER'S TRACTOR PULL
HCD 8024 / Feb '96 / Hightone

☐ DEEP FRIED AND SANCTIFIED
HCD 8017 / Feb '96 / Hightone

☐ PIANIST ENVY
HCD 8051 / Feb '96 / Hightone

☐ SONGS OF FAITH AND INFLAMMATION
HCD 8069 / Apr '96 / Hightone

☐ TURN FOR THE WIRTZ, A
HCD 8042 / Feb '96 / Hightone

Wisdom

☐ SIGNS OF THE TIME
WBM 2002 / Sep '93 / Wisdom Wise

Wisdom, Norman

☐ WISDOM OF A FOOL, THE
Don't laugh at me / Wisdom of a fool / Dream for sale / Up in the world / Narcissus: *Wisdom, Norman & Joyce Grenfell* / Beware / Me and my imagination / Skylark / Who can I turn to / Boy meets girl: *Wisdom, Norman & Ruby Murray* / You must have been a beautiful baby / Heart of a clown / I don't arf love you: *Wisdom, Norman & Joyce Grenfell* / By the fireside / Joker / Impossible / You're getting to be a habit with me / Happy ending / Make a miracle: *Wisdom, Norman & Pip Hinton* / Once in love with Amy / My darling, my darling / Leaning on a lampost / For me and my girl / Lambeth walk
SEECD 477 / Jun '97 / See For Miles

Wisdom Tooth

☐ MENTAL FLOSS
KFWCD 141 / Jun '97 / Knitting Factory

Wiseblood

☐ PEDAL TO THE METAL
ABB 030CD / Nov '91 / Big Cat

Wiseguys

☐ EXECUTIVE SUITE
WALLCD 008 / May '96 / Wall Of Sound

Wiseman Sextette

☐ WISEMAN SEXTETTE/QUARTET 1923
DOCD 5520 / Mar '97 / Document

Wiseman, Bob

☐ CITY OF WOOD
GRCD 324 / Sep '94 / Glitterhouse

Wiseman, Mac

☐ TEENAGE HANGOUT
Teenage hangout / Step it up and go / Sundown / I hear you knocking / Meanest blues in the world / Hey Mr. Bluesman / One mint julep / I'm waiting for the ships that never come in / Fool / I like this kind of music / Now that you have me / Talk of the town / Glad rags / I'm eatin' high on a hog / I want someone / Camptown races / I'll still write your name in the sand / Promise of things to come / Thinkin' about you / Because we are young / Be good baby / 'Tis sweet to be remembered / Running bear / Ballad of Davy Crockett / Tom Dooley / Sixteen tons / El Paso / Old lamplighter / Three bells / I'm movin' on
BCD 15694 / Jul '93 / Bear Family

Wishart, Trevor

☐ BEACH SINGULARITY
PD 03 / Mar '98 / Paradigm

Wishbone Ash

☐ ARGUS
Time was / Sometime world / Blowin' free / King will come / Leaf and stream / Warrior / Throw down the sword
MCLD 19085 / Nov '92 / MCA

☐ ARGUS/PILGRIMAGE (2CD Set)
Time was / Sometime world / Blowin' free / King will come / Leaf and stream / Warrior / Throw down the sword / Vas dis / Pilgrim / Jailbait / Alone / Lullaby / Valediction / Where were you tomorrow
MCD 33003 / Jul '96 / MCA

☐ BEST OF WISHBONE ASH, THE
Blind eye / Blowin' free / King will come / Persephone
MCAD 11620 / 16 Feb '98 / MCA

☐ DISTILLATION (4CD Set)
REP 4649WX / 22 Jun '98 / Repertoire

☐ ILLUMINATIONS
HTDCD 67 / Oct '96 / HTD

☐ JUST TESTING
Living proof / Haunting me / Insomnia / Helpless / Pay the price / New rising star / Master of disguise / Lifeline
MCLD 19375 / 4 May '98 / MCA

☐ LIVE DATES
King will come / Warrior / Throw down the sword / Lady whiskey / Phoenix / Rock 'n' roll widow / Ballad of the beacon / Baby, what you want me to do / Pilgrim / Blowin' free / Jailbait
BGOCD 293 / Sep '95 / Beat Goes On

☐ LIVE IN GENEVA
HNRCD 03 / Mar '96 / Hengest

☐ MOTHER OF PEARL
CP 1002 / 27 Apr '98 / Rhino

☐ NO SMOKE WITHOUT FIRE
You see red / Baby the angels are here / Ships in the sky / Stand and deliver / Anger in harmony / Like a child / Way of the world
MCLD 19374 / 4 May '98 / MCA

☐ PILGRIMAGE
Vas dis / Pilgrim / Jailbait / Alone / Lullaby / Valediction / Where were you tomorrow
MCLD 19084 / Nov '92 / MCA

☐ RAW TO THE BONE
Cell of fame / People in motion / Don't cry / Love is blue / Long live the night / Rocket in my pocket / It's only love / Don't you mess / Dreams (searching for an answer) / Perfect timing
CLACD 390 / Aug '93 / Castle

☐ THERE'S THE RUB
Silver shoes / Don't come back / Persephone / Hometown / Lady Jay / FUBB
MCLD 19249 / Oct '94 / MCA

☐ TIMELINE (Live)
RRCD 216 / Jan '97 / Receiver

☐ TRANCE VISIONARY
Numerology / Wonderful stash / Heritage / Interfaze / Powerbright / Remnants of a paranormal menagerie / Narcissus nervosa / Trance visionary / Flutterboy / Banner headlines / Loner / Powerbright volition / Gutterfly / Wronged by righteousness
IHCD 12 / 6 Apr '98 / Invisible Hands

☐ TWIN BARRELS BURNING
Engine overheat / Can't fight love / Genevieve / Me and my guitar / Hold on / Streets of shame / No more lonely nights / Angels have mercy / Wind up
CLACD 389 / Aug '93 / Castle

☐ WISHBONE ASH
Blind eye / Lady whisky / Errors of my ways / Queen of torture / Handy / Phoenix
BGOCD 234 / Oct '94 / Beat Goes On

☐ WISHBONE ASH ARCHIVE
Vas dis / Phoenix / Where were you tomorrow / Blowin' free / Leaf and stream / King has come / Lost cause in paradise / Standing in the rain / Strange affair / Throw down the sword / Time was / Wings of desire / In the skin
RMCD 224 / Nov '97 / Rialto

☐ WISHBONE ASH IN CONCERT
WINCCD 4 / Sep '91 / Windsong

☐ WISHBONE FOUR
So many things to say / Ballad of the beacon / No easy road / Everybody needs a friend / Doctor / Sorrel / Sing out the song / Rock 'n' roll widow
MCLD 19149 / Aug '94 / MCA

Wishdokta

☐ POST MODERN BREAKS (Wishdokta & James Hyman)
KICKCD 2 / Apr '93 / Kickin'

Wishing Stones

☐ WILDWOOD
HVNCD 004 / Nov '91 / Creation

Wishplants

☐ COMA
WOLCD 1033 / Oct '93 / China

☐ DADDY LONGLEGS
WOLCD 1070 / Jul '96 / China

Witch Hazel Sound

☐ IT'S ALL TRUE
CAM 012CD / 13 Jul '98 / Camera Obscura

Witchcraft

☐ AS I HIDE
Mindfire wish / Open ways / Liquid air / X-position / Absentia / Return to me / Invocation / Iridescent / We rest / Cathedral / Love on a battleship
AD 24CD / Oct '96 / AD

Witchdoktors

☐ ASWAT HEALIN' RITUAL
INTD 90146 / 31 Aug '98 / Interscope

☐ BRAIN MACHINE
LOUDEST 18 / Mar '97 / One Louder

☐ BRAIN MACHINE
LOUDEST 18X / 20 Jul '98 / One Louder

Witches

☐ LET'S GO TO THE...
PUSH 001 / 11 May '98 / Pushover

Witchfinder General

☐ FRIENDS OF HELL
HMRXD 13 / Feb '98 / Heavy Metal

Witchfynde

☐ BEST OF WITCHFYNDE, THE
CDMETAL 1 / Feb '97 / British Steel

Witchkiller

☐ DAY OF THE SAXONS
047554 / '89 / Steamhammer

Witchman

☐ EXPLORIMENTING BEATS
Viper flats / Amok / Stone def / Hammerhead / Chemical noir / Order of the dragon / Post trauma blues / NY 23 / No place like chrome / Palace of angels / Light at the edge
DVNT 019CD / Apr '97 / Deviant

☐ HEAVY TRAFFIC (2CD Set)
Mutha lode / Bullet head / Heavy mental / Bone music / AMok II / Chemical noir / Kada nostra / Light at the edge / Hammer head / Primal skin / Offbeat / Arcane radio / Red demon loco / Offworld / Hand of God / Destiny
DVNT 027CD / 20 Oct '97 / Deviant

Withered Beauty

☐ WITHERED BEAUTY
NB 3162 / 22 Jun '98 / Nuclear Blast

Withers, Bill

☐ LEAN ON ME (The Best Of Bill Withers)
Ain't no sunshine / Grandma's hands / Lean on me / Use me / Kissing my love / Who is he and what is he to you / I don't want you on my mind / Same love that made me laugh / Hello like before / Lovely day / Let me be the one you need / I want to spend the night / Stepping right along / Whatever happens / Watching you watching me / Heart is your life / You try to find a love / Just the two of uus
4805062 / May '95 / Columbia

☐ LIVE AT CARNEGIE HALL
Use me / Friend of mine / Ain't no sunshine / Grandma's hands / World keeps going around / Let me in your life / Better off dead / For my friend / I can't write left handed / Lean on me / Lonely town / Lonely street / Hope she'll be happier / Let us love / Harlem / Cold baloney
4889872 / 3 Nov '97 / Columbia

Witherspoon, Jimmy

☐ AIN'T NOTHIN' NEW ABOUT THE BLUES (Witherspoon, Jimmy & Robben Ford)
AIM 1050 / Apr '95 / Aim

☐ BABY-BABY-BABY
OBCCD 527 / Nov '92 / Original Blues Classics

☐ BIG BLUES
You got me running / Whiskey drinking woman / Once there lived a fool / Just a dream / Lotus blossom / Big boss man / Nobody knows you when you're down and out / That's the one / Let's think awhile / Swing on it / Point / Snow was falling
JSPCD 285 / Jul '97 / JSP

☐ BLOWIN' IN FROM KANSAS CITY
Love my baby / There ain't nothing better / Love and frendship / TB blues / Goin' around in circles / She's evil / I'm just a country boy / Good jumping aka jump children / Blowing the blues / It's raining outside / I'm just a lady's man / I'm just wandering / Who's been jivin' you / Sweet lovin' baby / Thelma Lee blues / Slow your speed / Dr. Knows His Business aka Dr. Blues / Rain rain rain / Baby baby
CDCHD 279 / Feb '91 / Ace

☐ BLUES AROUND THE CLOCK
OBCCD 576 / Jan '96 / Original Blues Classics

☐ BLUES FOR EASY LIVERS
Lotus blossom / Gee baby ain't I good to you / Travellin' light / PS I love you / I'll always be in love with you / Don't worry 'bout me / Easy living / Embraceable you / Blues in the night / Trouble in mind / How long will it take to be a man / I got it bad and that ain't good
OBCCD 585 / Oct '96 / Original Blues Classics

☐ BLUES THE WHOLE BLUES AND NOTHING BUT THE BLUES
You got a hold of my heart / It never rains but it pours / Real bad day / Sooner or later / Killing time / Blues the whole blues and nothing but the blues / Help me operator / Would man be satisfied / Two sides to every story / Wake up call / Think / You ain't foolin' me
IGOCD 2001 / Jul '95 / Indigo

☐ EVENIN' BLUES
Money's gettin' cheaper / Grab me a freight / Don't let go / I've been treated wrong / Evening / Cane River / Baby how long / Good rockin' man / Kansas City / Drinking beer
OBCCD 511 / Apr '94 / Original Blues Classics

☐ JIMMY WITHERSPOON
Time's gettin' tougher than tough / St. Louis blues / Trouble in mind / Goin' to Kansas city / Outskirts of town / Every day / Roll 'em Pete / CC rider / Corina Corina / How long
17069 / Aug '96 / Laserlight

☐ JIMMY WITHERSPOON & JAY MCSHANN (Witherspoon, Jimmy & Jay McShann)
BLCD 760173 / Mar '93 / Black Lion

☐ JIMMY WITHERSPOON SINGS THE BLUES
AIM 1005CD / Oct '93 / Aim

☐ KANSAS CITY
Kansas City / Ain't nobody's business / Gee baby ain't I been good to you / Nobody knows you / Goin' to Chicago / CC Rider / Sweet lotus blossom / Trouble in mind / Roll 'em Pete
CDSGP 0359 / 17 Nov '97 / Prestige

☐ LIVE AT CONDON'S, NEW YORK
Goin' to Chicago / Gee baby ain't I good to you / You got me runnin' / Big boss man / Sweet lotus blossom / I'm gonna move to the outskirts of town / If I didn't get well no more / Money's getting cheaper / In the dark / I'm knocking out your teeth tonite / Ain't nobody's business if I do / Trouble in mind / Don't you miss your baby
CDGATE 7023 / Nov '90 / Kingdom Jazz

☐ LIVE AT MONTEREY
M&MJ 421 / Feb '88 / Fresh Sound

☐ MIDNIGHT LADY CALLED THE BLUES
New York City blues / Barber / Blinded by love / Happy hard times / Something rotten in East St Louis / Midnight lady called the blues / Blues hall of fame
MCD 5327 / Sep '92 / Muse

☐ ROCKIN' WITH SPOON (Charly Blues Masterworks Vol.25)
Good rockin' tonight / When I been drinkin' / Big fine girl / No rollin' blues / Ain't nobody's business if I do / Times gettin' tougher than tough / How long / Corine / CC rider / Roll 'em Pete / Everyday / Outskirts of town / Kansas City / Trouble in mind / St. Louis blues
CDBM 25 / Apr '92 / Charly

☐ SINGIN' THE BLUES
SK blues / When I've been drinkin' / Then the lights go out / All that's good / Spoon's blues / It ain't what you're thinkin' / 'Taint nobody's business / Wee baby blues / Times are changing / Sweet's blues / There's a good rockin' tonight / Midnight blues
4941082 / 22 Jun '98 / Pacific Jazz

☐ SPOON & GROOVE (Witherspoon, Jimmy & Richard 'Groove' Holmes)
TCD 1015 / May '96 / Tradition

☐ SPOON SO EASY
It ain't no secret / Ain't nobody's business / Live so easy / Congratulations / I can make it without you / Goin' down slow / When the lights go out / Crying / TWA / Danger / I don't know why (why do I love you like I do) / Garfield Avenue / Mack and Jay / Just to prove my love to you
MCD 93003 / Apr '97 / Chess/MCA

☐ SPOON'S LIFE
Night life / Help me / Big boss man / Cold cold feeling / Worried life blues / Did you ever / Blues with a feeling / Big leg woman
ECD 260442 / Mar '94 / Evidence

☐ SPOONFUL
Big boss man / Nothing's changed / Sign on the building / Reds and whiskey / Moon is rising / Inflation blues / Take out some insurance / Pearly whites / Spoonful / Gloomy Sunday
74321332932 / Feb '97 / RCA

☐ TOUGHER THAN TOUGH
Time's getting tougher than tough / How long / Corrina Corrina / CC rider / Roll 'em Pete / Everyday / Outskirts of town / Kansas City / Trouble in mind / St. Louis blues / In blues / Loser's blues / Please send me someone to love / Life's highway / Cry the blues / Out blues
CDBM 123 / Jun '97 / Blue Moon

Within Reach

☐ SOMETHING'S NOT RIGHT
JABSC 002CD / Jan '97 / Burning Heart

☐ STRENGTH THROUGH DIVERSITY
JABSCD 004CD / 17 Nov '97 / Burning Heart

Without Warning

☐ STEP BEYOND
IOMCD 024 / 29 Jun '98 / InsideOut

Witthuser & Westrupp

☐ DER JESUSPILZ
2021098 / 16 Feb '98 / OHR

☐ TRIPS UND TRAUME
OHRCD 556016 / 23 Feb '98 / OHR

Wizards Of Twiddly

☐ MAN MADE SELF
FFPCD 2 / Jan '94 / Fracture For Pleasure

Wizo

☐ KRAUT AND RUBEN
FAT 571CD / 13 Apr '98 / Fatwreck Chords

☐ UUAARRGH
FAT 527CD / Jun '95 / Fatwreck Chords

Wob

☐ I CAN'T STAY LONG
Poacher / Legacy / Sometimes / Dancing for sixpence / Rapunzel / Goodbye Twyford / Mole / Kings clearing / Dusty corners / Mother Earth / London / Hardest part
CYCLECD 002 / Feb '96 / Cycle

☐ STRAIGHT ON 'TILL MORNING
Cradled / Hopeless / Butterfly / Berlin / Kite / Cultureless / Big sun big sky / Fishing / New day / Nowadays / Into you / Go well / Slipping
CYCLECD 006 / May '98 / Cycle

Wobbling Woodwinds

☐ SOLO FLIGHT (Wobbling Woodwinds & Ulf Johansson)
NCD 8829 / Mar '94 / Phontastic

Wofa

☐ GUINEA/MARTINIQUE ENCOUNTER (Wofa/Tambou Bo Kannal)
926502 / Oct '96 / BUDA

Wofford, Mike

☐ LIVE AT MAYBECK RECITAL HALL VOL.18
Tonk / Too marvellous for words (vocal george melachrino) / Stablemates / For woff-one to one / Rose of the rio grande / Little girl blue / Duke's placemainstem / Topsy / Impressions intimas no.1 / Lullaby of rhythm
CCD 4514 / Jul '92 / Concord Jazz

Woggles

☐ GET TOUGH
TR 023CD / May '97 / Telstar

☐ WAILIN' WITH THE WOGGLES
LOUDEST 29 / 15 Jun '98 / One Louder

Wogram, Nils

☐ SPEED LIFE
Morphing / Hotel blues / King of trash / Circle / Newsed / Alien's earworm / Beauty of meat / Annoying neighbour / Speed life
ENJ 93462 / 29 Jun '98 / Enja

Wojtasik, Piotr

☐ QUEST
PB 00147 / Jul '97 / Power Bros.

Wolde, Teshome

☐ SONGS FROM ETHIOPIA (2CD Set) (Wolde, Teshome & The Ethio-Stars)
RPM 0112 / 9 Mar '98 / Rags Productions

Wolf, Kate

☐ BACKROADS (Wolf, Kate & Wildwood Flower)
Lately / Emma Rose / Sitting on the porch / Redtail hawk / Telluride / Goodbye babe / It ain't in the wine / Tequila and me / Legend in his time / Riding in the country / Oklahoma going home / Back roads
R 27142 / Oct '94 / Rhino

☐ BREEZES
GAD 210 / Mar '96 / Gadfly

☐ CARRY IT ON
Then came the children / September song / Both sides now / We were strangers / Sweet love / Carry it on / Old and lonely sound / Boy from Oklahoma / One by one / Forsaken lover / Highway in the wind / Muddy roads
FR 301 / May '97 / Flat Rock

☐ CLOSE TO YOU
Across the great divide / Legget serenade / Like a river / Unfinished life / Friend of mine / Love still remains / Eyes of a painter / Here in California / Stone in the water / Close to you
R 271482 / Oct '94 / Rhino

☐ EVENING IN AUSTIN, AN
Eyes of a painter / Green eyes / Carolina pines / Give yourself to love / Let's get together / Friend of mine
R 271487 / Oct '94 / Rhino

☐ GIVE YOURSELF TO LOVE VOL.1 & 2
R 271483 / Oct '94 / Rhino

☐ LOOKING BACK AT YOU
R 71613 / Jul '94 / Rhino

Wolf Soup

☐ QUESTION, THE
Little one / Herman's holiday / Question / Chicken pie / Grey / Frog legs / In a sentimental mood / What / Inside the river / Current / Breathe
AL 73106 / Dec '97 / A

Wolf Spider

☐ KINGDOM OF PARANOIA
Manifestants / Pain / Black'n'white / Foxes / Waiting for sense / Desert / Sickened nation / Nasty-ment / Survive / Weakness
CDFLAG 49 / Nov '90 / Under One Flag

Wolf, Thilo

☐ SWINGING HOUR IN NEW YORK, A (Wolf, Thilo Trio)
Last blues / Late summernight / Fascinating rhythm / When I fall in love / Another sunburn / Teach me tonight / Riffifi / First step / Sizzle whizzle / Days in Paris / They can't take away / Nice toys / Little white lies / In the wee small hours of the morning / Sing sing sing
MR 874801 / 8 Nov '97 / Mons

Wolfe, Ben

☐ 13 SKETCHES
Poet (speaks) / Bad bellows / Blind seven / Ursula's dance / Charlie cool Charles / Who was left / Sweet beautiful / 888 Montgomery / Albert's no / Bronzed blue / Waiter / Dr. Jack and Mr. Hylen / Bonnie and Bonnie / Morgan's soundtrack
MR 874791 / 8 Nov '97 / Mons

Wolfe, Robert

☐ ANY DREAM WILL DO
It's the natural thing to do / Gal in Calico / It only happens when I dance with you / Take these chains from my heart / Nobody's child / Your cheatin' heart / Crystal chandeliers / Jardin secret / Dolannes melodie / Oh lady be good / Our love is here to stay /

Liza / Embraceable you / Fascinating rhythm / They can't take that away from me / Somebody loves me / Someone to watch over me / Golden wedding day (La Cinquantaine) / From a distance / Mr. Mistoffelees / Tell me on a Sunday / Close every door / Any dream will do / Chanson de Matin / I'm beginning to see the light / I've got a gal in Kalamazoo / It don't mean a thing if it ain't got that swing / Romantica / At the Cafe Continental / Serenade in the night / Florentiner march
GRCD 51 / '92 / Grasmere

☐ BLACKPOOL REVISITED
High school cadets march / Wind beneath my wings / Meditation / South American Joe / Tequila / As I love you / Once in a while / Sentimental journey / She didn't say 'yes' / I'm old fashioned / Make believe / Smoke gets in your eyes / Song is you / Somewhere out there / Spanish flea / Wedding samba / Cumana / Unchained melody / True love ways / Money is the root of all evil / We're in the money / At the end of the day / Castle on a cloud / I dreamed a dream / Master of the house / Empty chairs at empty tables / On my own / Do you hear the people sing
CDGRS 1238 / '91 / Grosvenor

☐ EVERYTHING'S IN RHYTHM
Household Brigade / If you love me / Vilia / All I do is dream of you / Hold me / Have you ever been lonely / Summer of '42 / Happy whistler / Stumbling / Nearness of you / Under the double eagle / Head over heels in love / When you've got a little springtime in your heart / Everything's in rhythm / Over my shoulder / When the midnight choo choo leaves for Alabama / Blackfoot walk / Crazy words crazy tune / Can you feel the love tonight / Oliver selection / You've got to pick a pocket or two / I'd do anything / Oom-pah-pah / As long as he needs me / Nights of gladness / Gimme dat ding / Bare necessities / Bring me sunshine / One moment in time
GRCD 69 / Nov '95 / Grasmere

☐ FRIENDS FOR LIFE
Royal Air Force march past / Silver threads among the gold / When your old wedding ring was new / Till we meet again / Parade of the tin soldiers / Songs my mother taught me / My fair lady / Gymnopedie No.1 / Mona Lisa / Orange coloured sky / Those lazy-hazy-crazy days of summer / Aces high / Gold and silver waltz / I've got a pocketful of dreams / Zing went the strings of my heart / Painting the clouds with sunshine / Sanctuary of the heart / Friends for life (Amigos para siempre) / Mairzy doats and dozy doats / We're gonna hang out the washing on the siegfried line / Don't fence me in / When you tell me that you love me / Me and my girl
GRCD 56 / Mar '93 / Grasmere

☐ GOLDEN WURLITZER FAVOURITES (2CD Set) (Wolfe, Robert & Nicholas Martin)
Medley / Medley / Golden wedding day / Tiger rag / Medley / Medley / Chanson de matin / Medley / Medley / Florentiner march / Medley / Medley / Medley / Medley (10) / Our director / Medley (11) / Bless this house / Medley (12) / Parade of the tin soldiers / Medley (13) / Waltz of the flowers / Kitten of the keys / Medley (14) / Leap year waltz / Aces high / Medley (15) / Songs my Mother taught me / Medley (16) / Blaze of glory
MUCD 9501 / May '96 / Musketeer

☐ HEAR MY SONG
Holyrood / Rose / Mack and Mabel / Hoagy Carmichael medley / Somewhere my love/My own true love / Whistling waltz/Gladrag doll/My blue heaven / Hear my song, Violetta / Amapola/ Guaglione / History of love/Here's that rainy day / Il silenzio / Yakety sax / Smilin' through/Always / How high the moon / It's only a paper moon / Moonlight in Vermont / Stranger on the shore/La Mer / I'm crazy 'bout my baby / On a slow boat to China / Pagan love song / That's my weakness / Don't be cross / Sons of the brave
GRCD 79 / Feb '97 / Grasmere

☐ SPREAD A LITTLE HAPPINESS
Blaze of glory / Im chambre separee / Bless this house / With one look / Leap year waltz
GRCD 61 / May '94 / Grasmere

☐ WONDERFUL DAY LIKE TODAY, A
Espana / Candle in the wind / Ja da/Mambo jambo / Medley / Delicado / Medley / El Chico / Don't cry for me Argentina / Great little army / Affair to remember / Medley / Trees / Borsalino theme / Elvira Madigan theme/Cactus polka / Don't it make my brown eyes blue/Crazy / How great thou art
GRCD 86 / Jan '98 / Grasmere

☐ WURLITZER MAGIC
Children of the regiment / Around the world / Poeme / (Why does my heart go) Boom / 'Deed I do / Keep young and healthy / Sweet Sue, just you / Best things in life are free / Continental / Guilty / Confessin' (that I love you) / Harbour lights / Wedding of the painted doll / My heart and I / March militaire / Fascination / Under the linden tree / Mr. Sandman / Crazy people / Brown eyes, why are you blue / Rosalie / September in the rain / September song / (We're gonna) Rock around the clock / Opus one / In the mood / Pokare kareana / I still call Australia home / Now is the hour / Waltzing Matilda
CD 6021 / Apr '96 / Music

Wolfetones

☐ 25TH ANNIVERSARY (2CD Set)
Celtic symphony / Merry ploughboy / Women of Ireland / Rock on Rockall / Foggy dew / James Connolly / Man from Mullingar / Flow Liffey waters / First of May / Piper that played before Moses / Janie Mac I'm nearly forty / Give me your hand / Boys of the old brigade / Dingle bay / Big strong man / Monsignor Horan / Boston rose / Zoological gardens / Broad black brimmer / Newgrange (bru na boinne) / Treat me daughter kindly / Come out ye black and tans / Slieve na mban / Far away in Australia / Goodbye / Helicopter song / An dord feinne (oro se do bheatha abhaile) / Merman / Teddy bear's head / Banna strand / Many young men of twenty / West's awake
SH 52024 / Mar '98 / Shanachie

☐ BELT OF THE CELTS
SHAN 52035CD / Aug '93 / Shanachie

☐ IRISH TO THE CORE
SHAN 52033CD / Aug '93 / Shanachie

☐ SING OUT FOR IRELAND
TRCD 1015 / '88 / Triskel

Wolfgamme, Nani

☐ 20 GOLDEN HITS OF HAWAII
MCD 71804 / Jun '93 / Monitor

Wolfgang Press

☐ BIRD WOOD CAGE
King of soul / Raintime / Bottom drawer / Kansas / Swing like a baby / See my wife / Holy man / Hang on me / Shut that door
GAD 810CD / 6 Jul '98 / 4AD

☐ FUNKY LITTLE DEMONS
Going south / 11 years / Blood satisfaction / Chains / Christianity / Derek the confessor / So long dead / Executioner / She's so soft / New glass / Fallen not broken / People say
GAD 4016CD / 6 Jul '98 / 4AD

☐ LEGENDARY WOLFGANG PRESS AND OTHER TALL STORIES
Tremble (my girl doesn't) / Heart of stone / Respect / My way / I'm coming home (mama) / Deserve / Sweatbox / Fire eater / Ecstasy / Deep briny / Muted
GAD 514CD / 6 Jul '98 / 4AD

☐ MAMA TOLD ME NOT TO COME
BAD 1007 CD / May '91 / 4AD

☐ QUEER
Birmingham / Mama told me not to come / Heaven's gate / Riders on the heart / Question of time / Louis XIV / Fakes and liars / Honey tree / Birdie song / Dreams and light / Sucker / Mother valentine
GAD 1011CD / 6 Jul '98 / 4AD

☐ STANDING UP STRAIGHT
Dig a hole / My life / Hammer the halo / Bless my brother / Fire-fly / Rotten fodder / Forty days, thirty nights / I am the crime
GAD 606CD / 6 Jul '98 / 4AD

Wolfhound

☐ HALLELUJA
BLR 84 024 / May '91 / L&R

☐ NEVER ENDING STORY, THE (Wolfhound & Anne Haigis)
BLR 84 025 / May '91 / L&R

Wolfhounds

☐ LOST BUT HAPPY (The Wolfhounds 1986-1990)
CDMRED 126 / Apr '96 / Cherry Red

Wolfpack

☐ HELLHOUND WARPIG
DISTEP 29CD / 1 Sep '97 / Distortion

☐ LYCANTHRO PUNK
DISTCD 041 / 26 Jan '98 / Distortion

Wolfsbane

☐ MASSIVE NOISE INJECTION
Protect and survive / Load me down / Black lagoon / Rope and ride / Kathy Wilson / Loco / End of the century / Steel / Temple of rock / Manhunt / Money to burn / Paint the town red / Wild thing
ESMCD 193 / Aug '96 / Essential

☐ WOLFSBANE
Wings / Lifestyles of the broke and obscure / My face / Money talks / See how it's done / Beautiful lies / Protect and survive / Black machine / Violence / Die again
ESMCD 396 / Jan '97 / Essential

Wolfstone

☐ CHASE, THE
Tinnie Run / Glass And The Can / Prophet / Appropriate Dipstick / Flames And Hearts / Ten pound float / Close it down / Jake's Tune / Early Mist / Cannot Lay Me Down
IRCD 018 / Aug '92 / Iona

☐ HALF TAIL, THE
GLCD 1172 / Aug '96 / Green Linnet

☐ PICK OF THE LITTER (The Best Of Wolfstone)
Baffle / Tall ships / Glass and the can / Heart and soul / White gown / Glen lass / Brave foot soldiers / Dinner's set / Sleepy toon / 10 pound float / Holy ground
IRCD 056 / Jul '97 / Iona

☐ THIS STRANGE PLACE
GLCD 1188 / 9 Mar '98 / Green Linnet

☐ UNLEASHED
Cleveland park / Song for yesterday / Silver spear / Sleepy toon / Hector the hero / Howl / Here is where the heart is / Hard heart / Erin
IR 014 CD / Nov '91 / Iona

☐ WOLFSTONE VOL.1
CMCD 072 / Apr '94 / Celtic Music

☐ WOLFSTONE VOL.2
CMCD 073 / Dec '97 / Celtic Music

☐ YEAR OF THE DOG
GL 1145CD / Jul '94 / Green Linnet

Wolpe, Stefan

☐ PASSACAGLIA - FIRST RECORDINGS
ARTCD 6182 / Oct '96 / Hat Art

Wolstenholme, Woolly

☐ SONGS FROM THE BLACK BOX
Has to be a reason / Down the line / All get burned / Too much, too loud, too late / Even the night / Deceivers all / Will to fly / Sunday bells / Open / Sail away / Quiet islands / Prospect of Whitby / Lives on the line / Patriots / Gates of heaven (14/18) / American excess / Maestoso / Waveform
BP 174CD / May '97 / Blueprint

Woltz, Da Costa

☐ COMPLETE RECORDED WORKS, THE (Woltz, Da Costa Southern Broadcasters)
DOCD 8023 / 24 Mar '98 / Document

Wolverines

☐ WOLVERINES OF BERNE AT 35
ARCD 19196 / 1 Jun '98 / Arbors Jazz

Wolverton Brothers

☐ LIARMAN
AW 09D / 17 Oct '97 / Atavistic

Wolz, Christian

☐ COR
EFA 112342 / Nov '94 / Danse Macabre

☐ INTUS MESTRA DE LA FORE
EFA 112282 / Jan '94 / Danse Macabre

Woma, Bernard

☐ LIVE AT THE PITO BAR
AVAN 063 / Mar '98 / Avant

Womack & Womack

☐ CONSCIENCE
Conscious of my conscience / MPB / Friends / Slave / Teardrops / Good man monologue / Life's just a ball game / I am love / Celebrate the world
IMCD 213 / Mar '96 / Island

☐ TEARDROPS
Teardrops / Celebrate the world / Slave / Conscious of my conscience / Good man monologue / MPB / Life's just a ball game / Friends (so called) / I am love / Love wars / Take me home country roads / Family / Rejoice
5500672 / May '93 / Spectrum

☐ TRANSFORMATION TO THE HOUSE OF ZEKKARIYAS
Drive (first gear) / Fiesta / Understanding / Passion and pain / Long time / Second gear / Candy world / Land of odd / Pie in the sky / Secret star / Focus
9362450752 / May '93 / Warner Bros.

Womack, Bobby

☐ ACROSS 110TH STREET (Original Soundtrack) (Womack, Bobby & Peace)
Across 110th Street / If you don't want my love give it back / Quicksand / Do it right / Hang on in there / Across 110th Street / Harlem clavinette: *Johnson, J.J. Orchestra* / Harlem love theme: *Johnson, J.J. Orchestra*
CPCD 8340 / May '98 / Charly

☐ FACTS OF LIFE/I DON'T KNOW WHAT THE WORLD IS COMING TO
CDGR 208 / 16 Mar '98 / Charly

☐ FLY ME TO THE MOON/MY PRESCRIPTION
Fly me to the moon / Baby / You oughta think it's over / I'm a midnight mover / What is this / Somebody special / Take me / Moonlight in Vermont / Time is now / I'm in love / California dreamin' / No money in my pocket / Lillie mae / How I miss you babe / More than I can stand / It's gonna rain / Everyone's gone to the moon / I can't take it like a man / I left my heart in San Fransisco / Arkansas state prison / I'm gonna forget about you / Don't look back / Tired and convicted / Thank you
CDGR 165 / Sep '97 / Charly

☐ GREATEST HITS
CDGR 255 / 29 Jun '98 / Charly

☐ I FEEL A GROOVE COMIN' ON
Let's get together / Broadway walk / What is this / I'm a midnight mover / Communication / I can understand it / Hang on in there / Can't stop a man in love / Let it hang out / Check it out / Daylight / I feel a groove comin' on / So many sides of you / Secrets / Stand up / Tryin' to get over you / Tell me why / Falling in love again
CPCD 8294 / Apr '97 / Charly

☐ LOOKIN' FOR A LOVE (The Best Of Bobby Womack 1968-1975)
RE 2009 / Jun '96 / Razor & Tie

☐ LOOKIN' FOR A LOVE AGAIN/BW GOES CW
Lookin' for a love / I don't wanna be hurt by ya love again / Doing it my way / Let it hang out / Point of no return / You're welcome, stop on by / You're messing up a good thing / Don't let me down / Copper kettle / There's one thing that beats failing / Don't make this the last date for you and me / Behind closed doors / Bouquet of roses / Tired of living in the country / Tarnished rings / Big bayou / Song of the mocking bird / I'd be ahead if I could quit while I'm behind / You / I take it on home
CDGR 179 / Nov '97 / Charly

☐ MASTERS, THE
EABCD 044 / 24 Nov '97 / Eagle

☐ MASTERS, THE (2CD Set)
EDMCD 020 / 24 Nov '97 / Eagle

☐ ONLY SURVIVOR (The MCA Years)
I wish he didn't trust me so much / Wanna make love to you / That's where it's at / Truth song / Let me kiss it where it hurts / Woman likes to hear that / So many rivers / World where no-one cries / Living in a box / I ain't got nobody else / When the weekend comes / Only survivor / Inherit the wind / (No matter how high I get) I'll still be lookin' up to you
MCLD 19355 / Apr '97 / MCA

☐ POET TRILOGY, THE (3CD Set)
CPCD 80803 / Jul '94 / Charly

☐ POET VOL.1, THE
So many sides of you / Lay your lovin' on me / Secrets / Just my imagination / Stand up / Games / If you think you're lonely now / Where do we go from here
MUSCD 505 / Sep '94 / MCI Original Masters
RE 2029 / Jun '96 / Razor & Tie

☐ POET VOL.2, THE
Love has finally come at last / It takes a lot of strength to say goodbye / Through the eyes of a child / Surprise surprise / Tryin' to get over you / Tell me why / Who's foolin' who / I wish I had someone to go home to / American dream
MUSCD 506 / Sep '94 / MCI Original Masters
RE 2030 / Jun '96 / Razor & Tie

☐ ROADS OF LIFE
RE 2140 / Aug '97 / Razor & Tie

☐ SAFETY ZONE/WOMACK LIVE
CDGR 237 / 1 Jun '98 / Charly

☐ SOUL SENSATION
Womack's groove / Baby I'm back / Nobody knows you when you're down and out / Daylight / Woman's gotta have it / That's the way I feel about cha / Inherit the wind / If you think you're lonely now / World where no one cries / Ain't nothing like the love we got / Trying to get over you / I wanna make love to you / It's all over now / When the weekend comes / No matter how high I get / How can it be
NEMCD 996 / 26 Jan '98 / Sequel

☐ UNDERSTANDING/COMMUNICATION
I can understand it / Woman's gotta have it / And I love her / Got to get you back / Simple man / Ruby Dean / Thing called love / Sweet Caroline / Harry hippie / Communication / Come l'amore / Fire and rain / (If you don't want my love) give it back / (They long to be) close to you / Everything is beautiful / That's the way I feel about cha / Yield not to temptation
CDGR 183 / 2 Feb '98 / Charly

☐ VERY BEST OF BOBBY WOMACK, THE
I can understand it / Harry hippie / I'm a midnight mover / What is this / Somebody special / That's the way I feel about cha / Communication / California dreamin' / If you don't want my love, give it back / I wish it would rain / Nobody wants you when you're down and out / Across 110th street / If you want my love, put something down on it / Lookin' for a love / I don't wanna be hurt by ya love again / Got to get you back / Woman's gotta have it / There's one thing that beats failing / You're messing up a good thing / Love ain't something you can get for free
MCCD 018 / May '91 / Music Club

☐ VERY BEST OF BOBBY WOMACK, THE (2CD Set)
What is this / Fly me to the moon / California dreamin' / I'm a midnight mover / I left my heart in San Francisco / It's gonna rain / How I miss you baby / Don't look back / I'm gonna forget about you / Preacher / More than I can stand / Communication / That's the way I feel about cha / If you don't want my love, give it back / Woman's gotta have it / I can understand it / Sweet Caroline / Nobody wants you when you're down and out / I'm through trying to prove my love to you / You're welcome / Stop on by / Harry Hippie / Across 110th Street / All along the watchtower / That's heaven to me / Lookin' for a love / I don't know what the world is coming to / I don't wanna be hurt by ya love again / If you want my love, put something down on it / Check it out / It's all over now / Where there's a will there's a way / Daylight / So many sides of you / Just my imagination / If you think you're lonely now / Love has finally come at last: *Womack, Bobby & Patti Labelle* / Tell me why / I wish I had someone to go home to
CPCD 82552 / Nov '96 / Charly

Womack, Lee Ann

☐ LEE ANN WOMACK
MCD 11585 / Jul '97 / MCA

Womack, Tommy

☐ POSITIVELY NA NA
CPR 007 / 27 Jul '98 / Checkered Past

Womack/Warden

☐ RANDOM ACTS OF SENSELESS VIOLENCE (4CD Set)
213CD 007 / Oct '96 / 2.13.61

Womb

☐ BELLA
DCD 9624 / Nov '96 / Dream Circle

Wombles

☐ BEST WOMBLES ALBUM SO FAR, THE
Wombling song (underground overground) / Remember you're a womble / Wombling white tie and tails / Orinoco kid / To Wimbledon with love / Wombles on parade / Down at the barber shop (singing in harmony) / Empty tidy bag blues / Wellington goes to Waterloo / Nashville wombles / Invitation to the Ping Pong ball / Non stop wombling summer party / Underground overture / Merton Womble and his journey to the centre of the Earth / Hall of the mountain Womble / Banana rock / Womble of the universe
4895622 / 6 Apr '98 / Columbia

Wonder Stuff

☐ CONSTRUCTION FOR THE MODERN IDIOT
Change every light bulb / I wish them all dead / Cabin fever / Hot love now / Full of life (happy now) / Storm drain / On the ropes / Your big assed Mother / Swell / Sing the absurd / Hush / Great drinker
5198942 / Mar '96 / Polydor

☐ IF THE BEATLES HAD READ HUNTER (The Singles)
Welcome to the cheap seats / Wish away / Caught in my shadow / Don't let me down gently / Size of a cow / Hot love now / Dizzy / Unbearable / Circlesquare / Who wants to be the Disco King / Golden green / Give give give me more more more / Coz I luv you / Sleep alone / Full of life (happy now) / It's yer money I'm after baby / On the ropes / It's not true
5213972 / Sep '96 / Polydor

Wonder, Stevie

☐ CONVERSATION PEACE
Rain your love down / Edge of eternity / Taboo to love / Take the time out / I'm new / My love is with you / Treat myself / Tomorrow Robins will sing / Sensuous whisper / For your love / Cold chill / Sorry / Conversation peace
5302382 / Mar '95 / Motown

☐ FULFILLINGNESS FIRST FINALE
Smile please / Heaven is ten zillion light years away / Too shy to say / Boogie on reggae woman / Creepin' / You haven't done nothin' / It ain't no use / They won't go when I go / Bird of beauty / Please don't go
5301052 / Jan '93 / Motown

☐ HOTTER THAN JULY
Did I hear you say you love me / All I do / Rocket love / I ain't gonna stand for it / As if you read my mind / Masterblaster / Do like you / Cash in your face / Lately / Happy birthday
5300442 / Jan '93 / Motown

☐ IN SQUARE CIRCLE
Part time lover / I love you too much / Whereabouts / Stranger on the shore of love / Never in your sun / Spiritual walkers / Land of la la / Go home / Overjoyed / It's wrong (la la) / I wish he didn't trust me so much / Baby don't leave home without it / So many rivers / Got to be with you tonight / Whatever happened to those times / Let me kiss it where it hurts / Only survivor / That's where it's at / Check it out
5300462 / Mar '96 / Motown

☐ INNERVISIONS
Too high / Visions / Living for the city / Golden lady / Higher ground / Jesus children of America / All in love is fair / Don't you worry about a thing / He's misstra know it all
5300352 / Jan '93 / Motown

☐ INSTRUMENTAL MEMORIES (Various Artists)
I just called to say I love you / Superstition / My cherie amour / Signed sealed delivered I'm yours / Don't you worry about a thing / Isn't she lovely / Master blaster (jammin') / Sir Duke / Happy birthday / For once in my life / Part time lover / Lately / Ebony and ivory / You are the sunshine of my life
306962 / Jun '97 / Hallmark

☐ JOURNEY THROUGH THE SECRET LIFE OF PLANTS (2CD Set)
Earth's creation / First garden / Voyage to India / Same old story / Venus flytrap and the bug / Ai no, sono / Seed's a star and treed medley / Secret life of plants / Finale / Seasons / Power flower / Send one your love (instrumental) / Race babbling / Outside my window / Black orchid / Ecclesiastes / Kesse ye lolo de ye / Come back as a flower / Send one your love
5301062 / Jan '93 / Motown

☐ LOVE SONGS - 20 CLASSIC HITS
Contract on love / My cherie amour / Until you come back to me / Yester-me, yester-you, yesterday / Never had a dream come true / If you really love me / Heaven help us all / Never dreamed you'd leave in Summer / Place in the sun / Alfie / Hey love / For once in my life / We can work it out / I was made to love her / Don't know why I love you / Blowin' in the wind / Shoo-be-doo-be-doo-da-day / I'm wondering / Nothing's too good for my baby / Signed, sealed, delivered (I'm yours)
5300372 / Jan '93 / Motown

☐ MUSIC OF MY MIND
Love having you around / Superwoman / I love every little thing about you / Sweet little girl / Happier than the morning sun / Girl blue / Seems so long / Keep on running / Evil
5300282 / Jan '93 / Motown

☐ NATURAL WONDER - LIVE IN CONCERT (2CD Set)
Love's in need of love today / Master blaster (Jammin') / Higher ground / Rocket love / Ribbon in the sky / Pastime paradise / If it's magic / Village ghetto land / Tomorrow Robins will sing / Overjoyed / My cherie amour / Signed, sealed, delivered I'm yours / Living for the city / Sir Duke / I wish / You are the sunshine of my life / Superstition / I just called to say I love you / For your love / Another star / Stevie Ray blues / Ms. and Mr. Little Ones / Stay gold
5305462 / Oct '95 / Motown

☐ SONG REVIEW (The Very Best Of Stevie Wonder)
Isn't she lovely / I just called to say I love you / Superstition / Sir Duke / Master blaster (jammni') / Ebony and ivory / Happy birthday / Living for the city / He's Misstra know it all / You are the sunshine of my life / Lately / Part-time lover / My cherie amour / Yester-me, yester-you, yesterday / Uptight (everything's alright) / I was made to love her / For once in my life / Signed, sealed, delivered, I'm yours / For your love / Kiss lonely goodbye / Redemption song
5307572 / 10 Aug '98 / Motown

☐ SONGS IN THE KEY OF LIFE (2CD Set)
Love's in need of love today / Have a talk with God / Village ghetto land / Confusion / I am singing / If it's magic / As / Another star / I wish / Knocks me off my feet / Pastime paradise / Summer soft / Ordinary pain / Isn't she lovely / Joy inside my tears / Black man / Sir Duke / Ngiculela es una historia
5300342 / Jan '93 / Motown

☐ STEVIE WONDER SONGBOOK (Various Artists)
I was made to love you: *Khan, Chaka* / It's a shame: *Detroit Spinners* / Until you come back to me: *Franklin, Aretha* / Heaven is ten zillion light years away: *Johnson, Paul* / Try Jah love: *Third World* / Buttercup: *Anderson, Carl* / Creepin': *Vandross, Luther* / You are the sunshine of my life: *Washington, Grover Jr.* / Pastime paradise: *Barretto, Ray* / Perfect angel: *Riperton, Minnie* / Too shy to say: *Jackson, Walter* / Never said: *Reeves, Dianne* / You haven't done nothin': *Robinson, Orphy* / Do I do: *Morrissey-Mullen* / Girl blue: *Main Ingredient* / Don't you worry 'bout a thing: *Irvin, Weldon* / Tell me something good: *Rufus* / Signed, sealed, delivered I'm yours: *Gadd Gang* / Another star: *Sledge, Kathy*
VSOPCD 216 / Apr '95 / Connoisseur Collection

☐ TALKING BOOK
You are the sunshine of my life / Maybe your baby / You and I / Tuesday heartbreak / You've got it bad, girl / Superstition / Big Brother / Blame it on the sun / Lookin' for another pure love / I believe
5300362 / Jan '93 / Motown

Wondermints

☐ WONDERFUL WORLD OF...
TFCK 88799 / May '97 / Toys Factory

☐ WONDERMINTS
BD 9033 / Jun '97 / Big Deal

Wong, Francis

☐ PILGRIMAGE (Wong, Francis Quartet)
CD 974 / Jul '97 / Music & Arts

Wongraven

☐ HELLTRONEN
FOG 006CD / Jun '95 / Moonfog

Wonky Alice

☐ ATOMIC RAINDANCE
Linar Adam / Radius / Sirius / Son of the sun / Sundance / Captain paranoia / Astronauts / Moon / Atomic raindance
ONA 001 CD / Jan '93 / Pomona

Wood Brothers

☐ HOOKED ON COUNTRY (Wood Brothers & The Nashville Greats)
Hooked on country love / Hooked on Randy Travis / Hooked on Willie Nelson / Hooked on trains / Hooked on Merle Haggard / Hooked on George Strait / Hooked on Marty Robbins / Hooked on a waltz / Hooked on Johnny Cash / Hooked on a country party
ECD 3072 / Jan '95 / K-Tel

☐ I'M IN THE MOOD FOR COUNTRY MUSIC
LPCD 1027 / Apr '94 / Disky

Wood, Charlie

☐ SOUTHBOUND
One kind word / Back to where it was before / It all and everything / Man on the money / I believe I could fall in love again / Southbound / River of jive / Lucky charm / That note costs a dollar / After all
GOJ 60232 / 29 Jun '98 / Go Jazz

Wood, Chris

☐ LISA (Wood, Chris & Andy Cutting)
RUF 002CD / Sep '92 / RUF

☐ LIVE AT SIDMOUTH (Wood, Chris & Andy Cutting)
RUF 003CD / Feb '95 / RUF

☐ LUSIGNAC (Wood, Chris & Andy Cutting)
RUF 004CD / Nov '95 / RUF

Wood, Clynt

☐ TEARS OF SUCCESS
WINK 1994 / Oct '94 / Wink

Wood, Diana

☐ BEST SAX EVER
Street life / Put it where you want it / Smooth operator / Inherit the wind / Your latest trick / Morning dance / This means so much to me / Lily was here / In the mood / Take five / Yakety sax / Heaven is in your heart / Girl from Ipanema / Slam / Roadblaster / Songbird / Baker street / Careless whisper / Pick up the pieces
QED 083 / Nov '96 / Tring

☐ SAXUAL HEALING
PLSCD 280 / 1 Jun '98 / Pulse

Wood, Lauren

☐ CAT TRICK
7599268722 / Jan '96 / WEA

☐ LAUREN WOOD
7599268712 / Jan '96 / WEA

Wood, Richard

☐ CELTIC TOUCH, THE
Jigs / Strathspeys and reels / Lament/The Celtic touch / Jigs / Clog and reels / Jigs / Lament/ Memories of Dot Mackinnon / Clog reels hornpipe / Strathspeys and reels / Slow air and reels / Reels
IRCD 042 / Feb '97 / Iona

☐ FIRE DANCE
IRCD 060 / Feb '98 / Iona

Wood, Ronnie

☐ MAHONEY'S LAST STAND (Wood, Ronnie & Ronnie Lane)
Tonights number / From the late to the early / Chicken wire / Chicken wired / I'll fly away / Title one / Just for a moment / Mona the blues / Car radio / Hay tumble / Woody's thing / Rooster funeral
CDTB 067 / '88 / Thunderbolt

☐ SLIDE ON LIVE, PLUGGED IN AND STANDING
74321518072 / 18 May '98 / Arista

☐ SLIDE ON THIS
Somebody else might / Ain't rock and roll / Testify / Josephine / Knock yer teeth out / Ragtime Annie / Must be love / Fear for your future / Show me / Always wanted more / Thinkin' / Like it / Breath on me
332802 / May '98 / Koch

Wood, Roy

☐ BOULDERS
Songs of praise / Wake up / Rock down low / Nancy sing me a song / Dear Elaine / All the way over the hill / Irish loafer (and his hen) / Miss Clarke and the computer / When Gran'ma plays the banjo / Rockin' shoes / She's too good for me / Locomotive
BGOCD 219 / Mar '94 / Beat Goes On

☐ DEFINITIVE ALBUM, THE
Night of fear / I can hear the grass grow / Flowers in the rain / Fire brigade / Here we go 'round the lemon tree / Blackberry way / Curly / Beautiful daughter / Tonight / Chinatown / 10538 overture / Ball park incident / See my baby jive / Angel fingers (a teen ballad) / I wish it could be christmas every day / Forever / Dear elaine / Songs of praise / Nancy sing me a song
BRCD 50 / May '94 / BR Music

☐ ROY WOOD & WIZZARD (16 Greats) (Wood, Roy & Wizzard)
Are you ready to rock / Look thru the eyes of a fool / Marathon man / You sure got it now / This is the story of my love (baby) / Indiana rainbow / I can't help my feelings / Mustard / Why does such a pretty girl sing / Such sad songs / Rattle snake roll / Any old time will do / Rain came down on everything / This is this / Get on down home / Benjal jig / Dream of unwin
EMPRCD 573 / Jul '95 / Emporio

☐ ROY WOOD & WIZZARD ARCHIVE (Wood, Roy & Wizzard)
Oh what a shame / Eddy's rock / Crazy jeans / Look thru the eyes of a fool / Rattlesnake and roll / Any old time will do / Rain came down on everything / Marathon man / Are you ready to rock / This is the story of my love / You sure got it now / Why does such a pretty girl sing those sad songs / Song / Get on down home / Strider / Dream of unwin / Bengal jig / Rock and roll winter / Everyday I wonder / Come back Karen
RMCD 219 / Nov '97 / Rialto

☐ ROY WOOD SINGLES (Various Artists)
Night of fear: *Move* / I can hear the grass grow: *Move* / Flowers in the rain: *Move* / Fire brigade: *Move* / Blackberry way: *Move* / Curly: *Move* / Brontosaurus: *Move* / Tonight: *Move* / Chinatown: *Move* / California man: *Move* / Ball park incident: *Wizzard* / See my baby jive: *Wizzard* / Dear Elaine: *Wood, Roy* / Angel fingers: *Wizzard* / Forever: *Wood, Roy* / I wish it could be Christmas every day: *Wizzard* / Rock 'n' roll winter: *Wizzard* / Going down the road: *Wood, Roy* / This is the story of my love: *Wizzard* / Are you ready to rock: *Wizzard* / Oh what a shame: *Wood, Roy*
VSOPCD 189 / Aug '93 / Connoisseur Collection

☐ THROUGH THE YEARS
Tonight / Chinatown / Down on the bay / California man / 10538 overture / Ball park incident / Carlsberg Special / See my baby jive / Bend over Beethoven / Angel fingers / I wish it could be Christmas very day / Dear Elaine / Forever / Music to commit suicide to / Going down the road / Premium bond theme / Green glass windows / It's not easy
CDGOLD 1070 / Oct '96 / EMI Gold

Wood That Sings

☐ INDIAN FIDDLE MUSIC OF THE AMERICAS
SFWCD 40472 / Dec '97 / Smithsonian Folkways

Wood, Victoria

☐ REAL LIFE - THE SONGS
Baby boom / It would never have worked / Andrea / Reincarnation / Love song / Pam / Real life / Music and movement / Litter bin / Crush / Saturday night / Go with it / Alternative tango / Barry and Freda
OMCD 1212 / 27 Oct '97 / PNE Video

Woodard, Rickey

☐ CALIFORNIA COOKING
Wilbur's idea / When I fall in love / This I dig of you / Jeannine / Jet lag / Day by day / Sashay / Jake's place / My one and only love / Take your pick
CCD 79509 / Feb '97 / Candid

☐ SILVER STRUT, THE
Silver strut / Grizzly / Quick flash / Kerstin / Take your pick / Stardust / Lover man / Firm roots / Sashay
CCD 4716 / Aug '96 / Concord Jazz

☐ TOKYO EXPRESS, THE
Recorda-me / Very thought of you / Just friends / Sand dance / Easy living / Groovy samba / Polka dots and moonbeams / Tokyo express
CCD 79527 / Feb '97 / Candid

☐ YAZOO
Icicle / Fried bananas / Abell / Turbulence / Portrait of Jennie / Holy land / 14th and Jefferson / Tadd's delight / September in the rain / Yazoo City blues
CCD 4629 / Jan '95 / Concord Jazz

Woodland, Nick

☐ LIVE FIREWORKS
Rock 'n' roll man / Train (23 stops) / Worried / Freight train / Race is on / I loved another woman / Cross my heart / My babe / Got a mind to give up living / Hip shake / Double trouble
BLU 10272 / Mar '97 / Blues Beacon

Woodruff, Bob

☐ DESIRE ROAD
CURCD 37 / Mar '97 / Curb

Woods, Chris

☐ SOMEBODY DONE STOLE MY BLUES
DD 434 / Sep '87 / Delmark

Wood's Famous Blind Jubilee Singers

☐ WOOD'S FAMOUS BLIND JUBILEE SINGERS 1925
DOCD 5039 / May '96 / Document

Woods, Mitch

☐ SHAKIN' THE SHACK (Woods, Mitch & His Rocket 88's)
BP 5008CD / Mar '94 / Blind Pig

☐ STEADY DATE (Woods, Mitch & His Rocket 88's)
BP 1784CD / Mar '94 / Blind Pig

Woods, Phil

☐ BOP STEW (Woods, Phil Quintet)
Dreamsville / Bop stew / Poor Butterfly / Yes there is a Coya
CCD 4345 / Jul '88 / Concord Jazz

☐ CELEBRATION
Reet's neet / Nefertiti / Banja Luka / Goodbye Mr. Evans / Willow weep for me / All bird's children / My man Benny / Perils of Poda / How's your Mama
CCD 47702 / Aug '97 / Concord Jazz

☐ ELSA (Woods, Phil & Enrico Pieranunzi)
W 2062 / Aug '92 / Philology

☐ EUROPEAN TOUR
1231632 / Apr '95 / Red

☐ EVOLUTION (Woods, Phil Little Big Band)
Alvin G / Black flag / Hal mallet / Miles ahead / Rain go away / Song for Sisyphus / Thaddeus / Which way is uptown
CCD 4361 / Nov '88 / Concord Jazz

☐ FLOWERS FOR HODGES (Woods, Phil & Jim McNeely)
Lost / Hodges / Day dream / Dutch morning / Flowers / Warm valley-star crossed lovers-isfahan (medley) / I didn't know about you / Paul / Lotus / Dekooning
CCD 4485 / Nov '91 / Concord Jazz

☐ FULL HOUSE
Samba de be-bop / Empty house / Pensive / Here's to alvy / Hindsight / Mr. daijobn
MCD 9196 / Oct '93 / Milestone

☐ HEAVEN (Woods, Phil Quintet)
I'm getting sentimental over you / Heaven / Duke / Azure / 222 / Occurrence
ECD 221482 / Sep '96 / Evidence

☐ INTO THE WOODS
All bird's children / Hal mallet / Bop brew / Misirlou / Tune of the unknown / Samba / I didn't know about you / Just you just me / Weaver
CCD 4699 / Jun '96 / Concord Jazz

☐ JAZZ 1968 (Woods, Phil & Slide Hampton)
7812532 / Aug '93 / Jazztime

☐ JAZZ LIFE, A
W 742 / Sep '92 / Philology

☐ LIVE AT THE CORRIDONIA JAZZ FESTIVAL (Woods, Phil & Space Jazz Trio)
W 2112 / Aug '92 / Philology

☐ LIVE AT THE WIGMORE HALL (The Complete Concert/2CD Set) (Woods, Phil & Gordon Beck)
Quill / Everything I love / Goodbye Mr Evans / Solar / Little D / For Keith / Isotope / Petite chanson / In your own sweet way / Harlem nocturne / Re: Person I knew / How deep is the ocean / Core of the apple / Alone together
JMS 186862 / Oct '96 / JMS

☐ MILE HIGH JAZZ (Woods, Phil Quintet)
Blues for KB / Song for Sass / Harlem nocturne / Godchild / Walkin' thing / Clairevoyance
CCD 4739 / Nov '96 / Concord Jazz

☐ MORE LIVE (Woods, Phil Quartet)
GCD 6010 / Jan '98 / Genes

☐ MUSIC OF JIM MCNEELY, THE
Perfect six / If I'd only / Paper spoons / Baby faced / Hey you / New waltz / Don't even ask
TCB 95402 / Apr '96 / TCB

☐ MUSIQUE DU BOIS
MCD 5037 / Sep '92 / Muse

☐ ORNITHOLOGY
PHIL 692 / Oct '94 / Philology

☐ PHIL WOODS & LEW TABACKIN (Woods, Phil & Lew Tabackin)
Limehouse blues / Sweet and lovely / Lew blew / Petite chanson / Theme of no repeat / Sittin' here / Theme of no repeat
ECD 222092 / 28 Apr '98 / Evidence

☐ PHIL WOODS QUARTET LIVE 1979 VOL.1 (Woods, Phil Quartet)
Bloomdido / Everything I love / Along came Betty / Hallucinations / Phil's theme
CCD 702 / Nov '96 / Clean Cuts

☐ RIGHTS OF SWING
Prelude and part 1 / Part 2 (ballad) / Part 3 (waltz) / Part 4 (scherzo) / Part 5 (presto)
CCD 79016 / Feb '97 / Candid

☐ STOLEN MOMENTS (Woods, Phil Quartet)
JMY 10122 / Aug '91 / JMY

☐ WOODLORE (Woods, Phil Quartet)
OJCCD 52 / '92 / Original Jazz Classics

Woods, Rosemary

☐ WALKING TOGETHER
SP 1027CD / Feb '93 / Spring

Woods, Terry

☐ GAY AND TERRY WOODS IN CONCERT (Woods, Terry & Gay)
WIN 071CD / Jul '95 / Windsong

Woods, Tony

☐ HIGH SEAS (Woods, Tony Project)
FMRCD 44 / Jul '98 / Future

Woodwork

☐ GRADE A JOINERY
LIQ 010CDL / 6 Jul '98 / Liquid Bubble

Woodys

☐ WOODYS, THE
ROUCD 3149 / 19 Jan '98 / Rounder

Wooley, Sheb

☐ RAWHIDE/HOW THE WEST WAS WON
Rawhide / Goodnight loving trail / Shifting whispering sands / Indian maiden / Story of Billy Bardell / Enchantment of the prairie / Lonley man / Wayward wind / Bars across the widow / Cattle call / How the west was won / Gotta pull up stakes (and move on west) / High lonesome / Wagonmaster's diary / Buffalo stampede / Rosie the queen of California / Building a railroad / Plowin' in new ground / Papa's old fiddle / Silver target / I belong / Big land
BCD 15899 / Nov '95 / Bear Family

☐ THAT'S MY PA (4CD Set)
I can't live without you / Oklahoma honky tonk girl / Lazy Mazy / Wooley's polka / Peepin' through the keyhole (watching jole blon) / Time won't heal an achin' heart / Too long with the wrong woman / Your Papa ain't steppin' anymore / Cherokee waltz / Texas rose / Spanish darling / Freight train cinders in my eyes / Heart bound in chains / Indian maiden / Romance / Jole quadroon / Rover scoot over / Sun is going down upon my heart / That mean feeling / You're the cat's meow / (Now you're) changing your name / Wha' happen to me baby / Mule boogie / Over the barrel / Country kisses / Hoot owl boogie / Aircastles / Boogie woogie waltz / Down in the toolies / Whatcha gonna do / Backroom boogie / You never can tell / Goodbye Texas hello Tennessee / I'll return the letters / Cowboy ought to be single / Knew I had lost / Don't stop kissing me goodnight / Texas tango / Love is just another merry-go-round / White lightnin' / Fool about you / Panama Pete / Blue guitar / I go outta my mind / 38-24-35 / I flipped / Hillbilly mambo / Listening for your footsteps / Speak of the devil / Love at first sight / Love is a fever / Humdinger / It takes a heap of livin' / Tom the boogie woogie tomcat / First day of school / Lonely man / Memories are made of this / That's my Pa / That's my Ma / Daddy kiss and make it well / Sally's arms / Ten chances to one / Only for you / Juarez / Wildwood flower on the autoharp / Anchor's aweigh (my love) / Will / Cowboy hero / Big blizzard / Four walls / Tonight's the night my angel's halo fell / Letter to daddy / Daddy's home / Number one on the survey / She called me baby / Laughin' the blues / Roughneck / Tennessee walkin' horse / Legend of Echo Mountain / Natchez landing / Recipient / Nobody's child / You still turn me on / Answer my love / Somebody please (say something funny) / Place to be lonely / Love-in / One man band / Good time Charlie / I don't belong in her arms (devil don't tempt me) / Land of no love / I remember loving you / Not once but a hundred times / Sittin' and thinkin' / New kind of lonesome / Juarez / I'll leave the singing to the bluebirds / Joy / Tie a tiger down / Cheap hotel / Sun also rises / Whirlpool of love / Old rag Joe / Not since Adam / Make 'em laugh / Life is a fountain / It's gold / Goodbye Wabash cannonball / Kick in the head / Right is right and left is lonely / Draggin' the river / Wrap me up some hurt / Doin' my thing
BCD 15902 / Mar '98 / Bear Family

Woolpackers

☐ EMMERDANCE
Hillbilly rock, Hillbilly roll / Chatahoochee / Line dancing / Boot scootin' boogie / Two chilli dogs / Footloose / On my radio / Horses / Baby likes to rock it / Blue rodeo / You're gonna be blue / 2 left feet / Down on the farm
74321444052 / Dec '96 / RCA

Wooten, Victor

☐ SHOW OF HANDS, A
742312 / 30 Mar '98 / Compass

☐ WHAT DID HE SAY
742452 / 16 Mar '98 / Compass

Wootton, Brenda

☐ VOICE OF CORNWALL, THE
KM 67CD / Aug '96 / Keltia Musique

Worcester Cathedral Choir

☐ CHRISTMAS BY THE FIRESIDE (Best Loved Christmas Carols/2CD Set) (Worcester Cathedral & Tewkesbury Abbey Choirs)
8551036/37 / Nov '96 / Naxos

Word Of Life

☐ FURTHER AHEAD
SATORI 3001 / 27 Apr '98 / Satori

Wordsound & Powa

☐ PLANET CROOKLYN
RUSCD 8224 / Apr '97 / ROIR

Work

☐ RUBBER CAGE
PYO 314116 / Oct '95 / Woof

☐ SLOW CRIMES
MEGA 001 / Oct '95 / Woof

Work, Jimmy

☐ MAKING BELIEVE (2CD Set)
That's the way it's gonna be / Rock Island line / Puttin' on the dog / When she said you all / Digging my own grave / Don't give me a reason to wonder why / Blind heart / You've got a heart like a merry-go-round / That cold, cold look in your eyes / Hands away from my heart / That's the way the juke box plays / There's only one you / Making believe / Blind heart / Let 'em talk / Just like downtown / My old stomping ground / Don't knock just come on in / Those Kentucky bluegrass hills / You're gone, I won't forget / Rainy rainy blues / Hear that steamboat whistle blow / Tennessee border / Your jealous heart is broken now / Bluegrass ticklin' my feet / Please don't let me love you / I would send you roses (but they cost too much) / Surrounded by water and bars / Smoky mountain moon / Who's been here since I've been gone / Mr. and Mrs. Cloud / Hospitality / Pickup truck / Do your honky tonkin' at home / Southern fried chicken / Let's live a little / If I should lose you / Don't play with my heart / I'm lonesome for someone / Puttin' on the dog (Tom cattin' around) / Crazy moon / Little popcorn man / How can I love you / Out of my mind / That's what makes the jukebox play / Don't knock, just come in / Blind heart / Let me be alone / I never thought I'd have the blues / I dreamed last night
BCD 15651 / Aug '93 / Bear Family

Working Week

☐ PAYDAY (Collection)
Soul train / Venceremos / South Africa / King of the night / Touching heaven / Doctor / Friend / Largo / Knocking on your door / Strut / Apocalypse / I thought I'd never see you again / Storm of light / Sweet nothin's / Who's foolin' who / We will win
CDVE 19 / Jul '88 / Venture

Workman, Reggie

☐ SYNTHESIS (Workman, Reggie Ensemble)
CDLR 131 / Feb '89 / Leo

Workshop

☐ TALENT
LADO 17030 / Jan '95 / Ladomat

Workshop

☐ WELCOME BACK THE WORKSHOP
CTCD 054 / Jul '97 / Captain Trip

☐ WORKSHOP
CTCD 053 / Jul '97 / Captain Trip

Workshy

☐ COAST
Something sweeter / Never the same / Ghost train / All in the mind / Finding the feeling / Heaven sent / All is fair in love / On the inside / True to life / Breakdown / Blue murder / Too late
CI 001CD / Mar '96 / Pony Canyon

World Of Leather

☐ JESUS CHRIST SUPERSTORE
CAKECD 17 / Sep '95 / Soundcakes

World Of Silence

☐ MINDSCAPES EP
BMCD 127 / 6 Apr '98 / Black Mark

World Of Twist

☐ QUALITY STREET
Lose my way / Sons of the stage / This too shall pass away / Jellybaby / Speed wine / Lights / On the scene / Sweets / Spring / Storm / She's a rainbow / Life and death
CIRCD 17 / Nov '91 / Circa

World Party

☐ EGYPTOLOGY
It is time / Beautiful dream / Call me up / Vanity fair / She's the one / Curse of the mummy's tomb / Hercules / Love is best / Rolling off a log / Strange groove / Whole of the night / Piece of mind / This world / Always
CDCHR 6124 / Jun '97 / Chrysalis

☐ GOODBYE JUMBO
Is it too late / Way down now / When the rainbow comes / Put the message in the box / Ain't gonna come til I'm ready / And I fell back alone / Take it up / God on my side / Show me to the top / Love street / Sweet soul dream / Thank you world
CCD 1654 / Apr '90 / Ensign

☐ PRIVATE REVOLUTION
Private revolution / Making love (to the world) / Ship of fools / All come true / Dance of the happy lads / It can be beautiful (sometimes) / Ballad of the little man / Hawaiian island world / All I really want to do / World party / It's all mine
CCD 1552 / Apr '87 / Ensign

World Sax Orchestra

☐ WORLD SAX ORCHESTRA
BVHAASTCD 8902 / Oct '85 / Bvhaast

World Saxophone Quartet

☐ BREATH OF LIFE (World Saxophone Quartet & Fontella Bass)
Jest a little / Jest a little / Suffering with the blues / You don't know me / Picasso / Song for camille / Breath of life / Deb
7559793092 / Nov '94 / Nonesuch

☐ FOUR NOW
JUST 832 / May '96 / Justin Time

☐ LIVE IN ZURICH
Funny paper / Touchic / My first winter / Bordertown / Steppin' / Stick / Hattie wall
BSR 0077 / '86 / Black Saint

☐ METAMORPHOSIS (World Saxophone Quartet & African Drums)
7559792582 / Jul '94 / Nonesuch

☐ MOVING RIGHT ALONG
1201272 / May '94 / Black Saint

☐ SELIM SIVAD (A Tribute To Miles Davis) (World Saxophone Quartet & Jack DeJohnette)
Seven steps to heaven / Selim / Freddie freeloader / Road to Nefertiti / Tutu / Blue in green / All blues
JUST 1192 / 24 Aug '98 / Justin Time

☐ STEPPIN'
BSR 0027 / '86 / Black Saint

☐ TAKIN' IT 2 THE NEXT LEVEL
Wiring / Soft landing / Rio / Peace before / Blues for a warrior spirit / Desegregation of our children / When the monarchs come to town / Endless flight / Ballad after us / Australopithecus
JUST 932 / Jan '97 / Justin Time

☐ WORLD SAXOPHONE QUARTET PLAYS DUKE ELLINGTON, THE
7559791372 / Jul '94 / Nonesuch

World Standard

☐ COUNTRY GAZETTE
Introduction / Good red road / Lonely driver 1952 / Country sad ballad man / Loser's lounge / Old man blues / Loving spoonful / Billy strange country / My low chuned banjo / 900 miles from home / Silent homecoming / Hollyville train / Montage/Lonesome hobo-land / Cowboys don't cry
ASP 0982CD / 29 Jun '98 / Asphodel

World Trio

☐ WORLD TRIO
Palantir / Whirling dervish / Over there / Will o' the wisp / Dr. Do-Right / Arch mage / Billy Jean / Seven rings / Eulogy
VBR 21522 / Aug '95 / Vera Bra

World Turtle

☐ WILDERNESS OF EDEN
Let go / Hereos / Wilderness of Eden / Last unicorn / Kickback / Queen's gambit / Stalemate / Vertigo / Long sleep / Rip Van Winkle / Wolf / Wave / Human / One day
CYCL 056 / 20 Oct '97 / Cyclops

World Wide Message Tribe

☐ HEATSEEKER
Messiah / Tell the world hypocrite / Everything I need / Cuckoo land / Make a change / Love / Precious angel / Heatseeker / When the day is over
1908092 / 27 Oct '97 / Alliance Music

World/Inferno Friendship Society

☐ TRUE STORY OF THE BRIDGEWATER ASTRAL LEAGUE, THE
Night in the woods / Evil dance of Nostiw Pilf / Incendiarism / Lust for timing / Millicent didn't want to wait for it to get better / One for the witches / Tarot Americane / Joe Tennis redeemed
GERNCD 35 / 2 Feb '98 / Gern Blandsten

Worlds Apart

☐ TOGETHER
Could it be I'm falling in love / Papa wouldn't understand / Beggin' to be written / Everlasting love / Come back and stay / Arnold Schwarzenegger / Heaven must be missing an angel / Same old promises / Experienced / Wonderful world / September / Like it was, like it is
74321198122 / Feb '97 / Arista

Worlds Collide

☐ ALL HOPE ABANDON
LF 120 / Mar '95 / Lost & Found

World's Greatest Jazz Band

☐ PLAY GERSHWIN/RODGERS & HART
JCD 300 / Dec '97 / Jazzology

☐ WAY OUT WEST
TCD 1030 / Aug '96 / Tradition

Worm

☐ AGOGO
NZ 069CD / Oct '96 / Nova Zembla

Worms, Marcel

☐ JAZZ IN 20TH CENTURY PIANO MUSIC
BVHAAST 9403 / Oct '94 / Bvhaast

☐ JEAN WIENER WORKS FOR PIANO
BVHAASTCD 9614 / Apr '98 / Bvhaast

Worst Case Scenario

☐ TOTAL DISCOGRAPHY
VMFM 26 / Feb '97 / Vermiform

Worth Abbey Choir

☐ WESTMINSTER HYMNAL, THE
HAVPCD 207 / Jan '98 / Herald

Would-Be-Goods

☐ CAMERA LOVES ME
Camera loves me / Velazquez and I / Cecil Beaton's scrapbook / Pinstriped rebel / Rose Du Barry / Marvellous boy / Young man from Caracas / Amaretto / Motor bike girl / Death a la carte / Perfect dear / Wrong way around / End of the world / Bayswater blues / By the light of the cynical moon
MONDE 13CD / 9 Mar '98 / Richmond

Wraith

☐ RIOT
Russian roulette / Human zoo / Get what I want / Shattered/Cursed/Riot/Pride of youth/You've got it comin' / Down on me / Shove it
NM 007CD / Oct '97 / Neat Metal

☐ SCHIZOPHRENIA
NM 014CD / Oct '97 / Neat Metal

Wrathchild

☐ BIZ SUXX (BUT WE DON'T CARE), THE
Biz suxx / Millionaire / Hooked / (Na na) nukklear rokket / Wild wild honey / Ring my bell / Hooligunz / She'z no angel / OK UK / Noo sensation / Stikky fingerz
HMRXD 116 / Nov '88 / Heavy Metal

☐ DELIRIUM
Delirium / Watch me shake it / That's what U get / My girlz / Long way 2 go / Good girlz / Do what you wanna / Kid pusher / She's high on luv / Rock me over / Only 4 the fun / Drive me krazy
WKFMXD 137 / Dec '89 / FM

☐ STAKK ATTAKK
Stakk attakk / Too wild to tame / Trash queen / Sweet surrender / Kick down the walls / Tonight / Law abuzer / Shokker / Alrite with the boyz / Wreckless
HMRXD 18 / Apr '89 / Heavy Metal

Wray, Link

☐ APACHE/WILD SIDE OF THE CITY LIGHTS
Wild one / Dallas blues / Big boss man / Shawnee / Joker / Apache / Beautiful brown eyes / Stars and stripes forever / Green hornet / Dick Tracy / Private eye / Hotel Loneliness / Raunchy / Flying wedge / Don't leave me / American sunset / Little sister / Love me tender / Wild side of the city lights / Viva zapata / As long as I have you / Street beat
CDCHD 931 / Jun '90 / Ace

☐ GUITAR PREACHER (The Polygram Years/2CD Set)
La de da / Take me home Jesus / Juke box Mama / Rise and fall of Jimmy Stokes / Fallin' rain / Fire and brimstone / Ice people / Go out West / Crowbar / Black river swamp / Tail dragger / Hobo man / I'm so glad, I'm so proud / Georgia pines / Water boy / Alabama electric circus / Take my hand (precious Lord) / Walkin' in the Arizona sun / Scorpio woman / All because of a woman / On the run / Days before Custer / Be what you want to / All cried out / Tuscon, Arizona / River bend / You walked by / Walk easy, walk slow / Morning / It was a bad scene / Good time Joe / Walkin' bulldog / I got to ramble / Backwoods preacher man / She's that kind of woman / Super / Rumble
5277172 / Apr '96 / Polydor

☐ INDIAN CHILD
SHED 001CD / Jun '93 / Creation

☐ LIVE AT THE PARADISO
Blue suede shoes / Ace of spades / Walk away from love / I saw her standing there / Run chicken run / She's no good / Rumble / Rawhide / Subway blues / Money / Shake, rattle and roll / Be bop a lula
CDMF 008 / Apr '91 / Magnum Force

☐ LIVE IN 85/GROWLING GUITAR
Rumble / It's only words / Fire / Mystery train / I got a woman / Baby let's play house / Jack the ripper / Love me / King Creole / I'm counting on you / Rawhide / Born to be wild
CDWIK 972 / Apr '91 / Big Beat

☐ MISSING LINKS VOL.4 (Streets Of Chicago)
CED 253 / Sep '97 / Norton

☐ MR. GUITAR (Wray, Link & His Raymen)
CED 242 / Sep '97 / Norton

☐ ORIGINAL RUMBLE, THE
Rumble / Swag / Batman / Ace of spades / Jack the ripper / I'm branded / Fat back / Run chicken run / Turnpike USA / Dueces wild / Mustang / Blueberry Hill / Bow nun run / Sweeper / Hound dog / That'll be the day / Fuzz / Rawhide / Draggin' / Aces wild / Bull dawg / Rumble man / Copenhagen boogie
CDCH 924 / Nov '89 / Ace

☐ ROCK AND RUMBLE
Rumble / Jack the ripper / Ace of spades / Black widow / Shadow knows / My Alberta / Sweeper / Good rockin' tonight / I'll do anything for you / Deuces wild / Rawhide / Hound dog / Mustang / Steel trap / Bo Diddley / Turnpike USA
309162 / 13 Jul '98 / Hallmark

☐ RUMBLE PLUS
CDWIK 924 / Feb '89 / Big Beat

☐ SHADOWMAN
Rumble on the docks / Heartbreak hotel / Geronimo / Young love / Moped baby / Run through the jungle / I can't help it (if I'm still in love with you) / Night prowler / It was so easy / Timewarp/Strider / Listen to the drums / Shadowman
CDCHD 638 / Jan '97 / Ace

☐ SWAN SINGLES COLLECTION, THE (Wray, Link & His Raymen)
Jack the ripper / Black widow / Weekend / Turnpike USA / Sweeper / Run chicken run / Shadow knows / My Alberta / Deuces wild / Summer dream / Good rockin' tonight / I'll do anything for you / Branded / Hang on / Please please me / Rumble '65 / Girl from the North Country / You hurt me so / Fuzz / Ace of spades / Batman / Ace of spades / Hidden charms / Let the good times roll / Soul train
CDROLL 3011 / Oct '97 / Rollercoaster

☐ THEY'RE OFF AND RUMBLIN' (Wray, Link & His Raymen)
RCCD 3032 / May '98 / Rollercoaster

☐ WALKING DOWN A STREET CALLED LOVE
Walking down a street called love / Batman / Mystery train/My babe / That's alright / I got a woman / Jailhouse rock / Mr. Guitar / Born to be wild / Rumble / Sweeper / Jack the ripper / Deuces wild / Tiger man / King Creole / Fire / I can't help it if I'm still in love with you / Run chicken run / Ace of spades / Young and beautiful
VICD 010 / Feb '97 / Visionary/ Jettisoundz

Wreckless Eric

☐ AT THE SHOP
Big old world / Waiting for the shit (to hit the fan) / Bony Moronie / Our neck of the woods / If it makes you happy / Depression / Semaphore signals / You're the girl for me
422395 / Jun '94 / New Rose

☐ BIG SMASH
Pop song / Tonight / Too busy / Broken doll / Can I be your hero / Back in my hometown / Whole wide world / Take the cash / Let's go to the pictures / Walking on the surface of the moon / Hit and miss Judy / I wish it would rain / It'll soon be the weekend / Strange towns / Excuse me / Break my mind / Good conversation / Out of the blue / Reconnez cherie / Veronica / Brain thieves / Semaphore signals / I need a situation / Final taxi / There isn't anything else
STIFFCD 13 / Jan '94 / Disky

☐ DONOVAN OF TRASH
SFTRI 230 / Jul '98 / Sympathy For The Record Industry

☐ LE BEAT GROUP ELECTRIQUE
Tell me I'm the only one / Wishing my life away / Depression / It's a sick sick world / Just for you / Sarah / Sun is pouring down / I'm not going to cry / You sweet big thing / Fuck by fuck / Parallel beds / True happiness
422396 / Jun '94 / New Rose

☐ WRECKLESS ERIC
Reconnez cherie / Rags 'n' tatters / Waxworks / Grown ups / Telephone home / Whole wide world / Rough kids / Personal hygiene / Brain thieves / There isn't anything
REP 4217 / Aug '91 / Repertoire

Wreckx n' Effect

☐ HARD OR SMOOTH
New jack swing II (Hard version) / Wreckx shop / Rump shaker / Knock-n-boots / Tell me how you feel / Wreckx-N-Effect / Here we come / Ez come ez go (what goes up must come down) / Hard (short) / Smooth (Short) / My cute
MCD 10566 / 8 Sep '97 / MCA

☐ WRECKS 'N' EFFECT
Go for what you know / We be Mafia / I need money / Let's do it again / Wreckx-n-effect
K 781 860 2 / Jul '94 / Atlantic

Wrench, David

☐ BLOW WINDS BLOW
ANKST 078CD / Jul '97 / Ankst

Wrens

☐ SILVER
GROW 0102 / Apr '94 / Grass

Wretched

☐ LIFE OUT THERE
HELL 024 / Sep '93 / Hellhound

☐ LOTTA PER VIVERE
AD 3 / Oct '96 / Anti-Christ

☐ PSYCHOSMATIC MEDICINE
H 00312 / May '94 / Hellhound

Wretched Ones

☐ WRETCHED ONES
HR 022 / 30 Mar '98 / Headache

Wright, Andrew

☐ PIPERS OF DISTINCTION
Lament for the son of king aro / Clan campbell's gathering / Macleod's controversy / Men went to drink / Aged warriors sorrow / A glase / Gordon's salute / Battle of balladruishaig
CDMON 802 / Dec '89 / Monarch

Wright, Betty

☐ 4U2 NJOY
4 U 2 NJOY / It's been real / Quiet storm / Keep love new / From pain to joy / Valley of lonely / Lightning / We "down" / Won't be long now
SDCD 2 / Jul '89 / Sure Delight

☐ BEST OF BETTY WRIGHT, THE
Shoorah shoorah / Tonight is the night pts 1 and 2 / Where is the love / That's when I'll stop loving you / Ooh la la / Slip and do it / If I ever do you wrong / Life / Do right girl / I think I'd better think about it / Smother me / You can't see for looking / Loving is really my game / That man of mine / If you abuse my love / Sometime kind of thing / Room at the top / My love is
NEMCD 671 / May '94 / Sequel

☐ MOTHER WIT
MSBCD 3301 / Oct '89 / Ms. B

Wright, Billy

☐ GOIN' DOWN SLOW
If I didn't love you so / Sad hour blues / Goin' down slow / After a while / Four cold cold wails / Live the life / I remember / Will you need me / Billy's boogie blues / This love of mine / If I had my life to live over / Every evenin' / Drinkin' and thinkin' / Restless blues
SV 0257 / Oct '97 / Savoy Jazz

Wright, Charles

☐ EXPRESS YOURSELF (Wright, Charles & The Watts 103rd St. Rhythm Band)
Express yourself / Express yourself / 'Till you get enough / Joker (on a trip thru the jungle) / Sweet Lorene / Keep saying / Do your thing / Your love (means everything to me) / Tell me what you want to do / Spreadin' honey / Doin' what comes naturally / 90 day cycle people / One lie / 65 bars and a taste of soul / I got love / Love land / Comment
9362453062 / Jul '96 / Warner Bros.

Wright, Chely

☐ LET ME IN
MCD 70003 / 27 Sep '97 / RCA

Wright, Clyde

☐ OH WHAT A DAY
FA 417 / Feb '97 / Fremeaux

Wright, Danny

☐ BLACK AND WHITE
72810209842 / 7 Apr '98 / NWR

Wright, David

☐ BETWEEN REALITIES
Eastern innersense / Between realities / Strange liaisons / Over the edge / Taiga / Illusions
AD 5CD / Mar '97 / AD

☐ DISSIMILAR VIEWS
Legend of the tundra / Beijing / Rysheara / Cosmicon / Albania / Smiling shadows lie / Koroe / Room of dolphins / Borders of colour / Transformation / Benny's theme / Albania / Love remembered / Returning tides / Dissimilar views
AD 9CD / Mar '97 / AD

☐ LIVE AT THE LONDON PLANETARIUM
Landings / Enchantress / Rysheara / Images / London / Love theme / Running cloud / Bridge to the sun / Buffalo run / Berlin / Nomad / Legend of the Tundra
AD 17CD / Nov '96 / AD

☐ MARILYNMBA
Confused encounters / Marilynmba / Syntasia / Walkin' the sand / Colours of the night / Marilynmba
AD 4CD / Mar '97 / AD

☐ MOMENTS IN TIME
Ancient dreams / Spirit of the plains movements 1-5
AD 7CD / Mar '97 / AD

☐ OCEAN WATCH
Dream maker / Ocean watch / Nomad / Glass mountains / Seven seas / Desert storm / Reflections / Beyond the airwaves
AD 6CD / Mar '97 / AD

Wright, Gary

☐ DREAM WEAVER
Love is alive / Let it out / Can't find the judge / Power of love / Blind feeling / Dream weaver / Feel for me / Much higher / Made to love you
7599272942 / Nov '94 / Warner Bros.

Wright, John

☐ OTHER ROADS (Wright, John Band)
Naked to the eyes / What's the use of wings / Winds of freedom / Ghost of the chair / All the answers / Snows of France and Holland / Keep your distance / What you do with what you got / Weakness in me / Bigg market lasses / Queen of Argyll / Keep it up / Angel flying too close to the ground / All used up / Family
FECD 121 / 1 Nov '97 / Fellside

☐ RIDE THE ROLLING SKY
FE 097CD / Jan '94 / Fellside

☐ THINGS WE'VE HANDED DOWN, THE (Wright, John Band)
FE 106CD / May '96 / Fellside

Wright, Kevin

☐ OUT OF THE BLUE
RSCD 227 / Nov '97 / Keltia Musique

Wright, Marva

☐ BLUESIANA MAMA
Let the good times roll / Boogie song / Little red rooster / Driving wheel / Bluesiana mama / Got my mojo working / Members only / I'd rather go blind / Go tell it on the mountain / Never make your move too soon / Mama he treats your daughter mean / CC rider / Shake, shake
12863 / May '97 / Laserlight

☐ I STILL HAVEN'T FOUND WHAT I'M LOOKING FOR
AIMA 2CD / Oct '95 / Aim

Wright, Michelle

☐ FOR ME IT'S YOU
Nobody's girl / Answer if yes / We've tried everything else / I'm not afraid / What love looks like / You owe me / For me it's you / Cold kisses / Crank my tractor / Love has no pride
74321417232 / Aug '96 / Arista

Wright, O.V.

☐ HI MASTERS, THE
Into something (can't shake it loose) / I feel love growin' / Precious precious / Trying to live my life without you / Your good thing is about to end / Bottom line / I don't do windows / Time we have / You gotta have love / Rhymes / Without you / No easy way to say goodbye / That's the way I feel / Fool can't see the light / I don't know why
HEX 39 / 4 Aug '98 / Hi

☐ O.V. WRIGHT 45'S
Rhymes / Without you / Into something (can't shake loose) / Time we have / Precious, precious / You gotta have love / I don't do windows / I feel love growin' / No easy way to say goodbye / Bottom line / We're still together / I don't know why
HILOCD 2 / Nov '93 / Hi

☐ SOUL OF O.V. WRIGHT, THE
MCD 10670 / 16 Feb '98 / MCA

Wright, Rev. Robert

☐ REMEMBER ME
Jesus said if you go / (jesus will fix it) alright / You gotta move / Streamline 'frisco limited / Pray for me / Don't let nobody turn you around / Why don't you do it / Just a closer walk with thee / Rock of ages / Remember me / You've got to stand your test in judgement / When the saints go marching in / In the army of the lord
EDCD 380 / Dec '93 / Edsel

Wright, Rick

☐ BROKEN CHINA
Breaking water / Night of a thousand furry toys / Hidden fear / Runaway / Unfair ground / Satellite / Woman of custom / Interlude / Black cloud / Far from the harbour wall / Drowning / Reaching for the rail / Blue room in Venice / Sweet July / Along the shoreline / Breakthrough
CDEMD 1098 / Sep '97 / EMI

Wright, Stephen

☐ INTERNATIONAL CHANGE
ROTCD 003 / Nov '94 / Reggae On Top

Wrigley, Jennifer

☐ DANCING FINGERS (Wrigley, Jennifer & Hazel)
ATCD 026 / Dec '97 / Attic

☐ HULDRELAND (Wrigley, Jennifer & Hazel)
Eynhallow Sound / Halloween flit / Rohan/Keenan's welcome / Peedie Sophie / Meg's hornpipe / Reel O'Colster / Giants party/Stoned giants / Hills of Hoy / Shannandah Falls / Barbara's wedding/Irene's reel / Ingi / Light fight/Chi cha / Whistlebinkies ghost / Dougal's sustain / Horse of Copinsay / Orkney Isles hornpipe/Toe Reid / Ba' rag / Huldreland / Eynhallow sound / Keenan's welcome / Stoned giants
CDTRAX 148 / 1 Nov '97 / Greentrax

☐ WATCH STONE, THE (Wrigley, Jennifer & Hazel)
ATCD 038 / Jan '95 / Attic

Wu Man

☐ CHINESE MUSIC FOR THE PIPA
NI 5368CD / Oct '93 / Nimbus

Wu Tang Clan

☐ ENTER THE WU TANG (36 CHAMBERS)
Shaolin sword / Bring da ruckus / Shame on a nigga / Clan in da front / Wu-tang / Seventh Chamber / Can it be so simple / Wu-tang sword / Da mystery of chessboxin' / Wu-tang ain't nuthing ta taf' wit / CREAM / Method man / Protect ya neck / Tearz / Seventh Chamber
74321203672 / Apr '94 / Loud

☐ WU TANG FOREVER (2CD Set)
Wu revolution: *Wu Tang Clan & Poppa Wu/Uncle Pete* / Reunited / For Heaven's sake: *Wu Tang Clan & Cappadonna* / Cash still rules/Scary hours (still don't nothing move but t / Visions / As high as Wu Tang gets / Severe punishment / Older Gods / Maria: *Wu Tang Clan & Cappadonna* / Better tomorrow / It's yours / Triumph: *Wu Tang Clan & Cappadonna* / Impossible: *Wu Tang Clan & Tekitha* / Little ghetto boys: *Wu Tang Clan & Cappadonna* / Deadly melody: *Wu Tang Clan & Cappadonna* / City / Projects international / Bells of war / MGM / Dog shit / Duck season / Hells wind staff / Heaterz: *Wu Tang Clan & Cappadonna* / Black shampoo / Second coming / Sunshower
74321457682 / May '97 / Loud

Wubble-U

☐ WHERE'S WUBBLE-U
Theme from Wubble-U / Jellied eels / Petal / I like the future / Wow man / Name Czech / Europhobix / Realitea break / Down / Theme reprisal / Giantkillaz / Kazum / Ambient bingo nuns / Time / Stanley clears the throakus / Angel in Bermondsey (pt 1)
8286662 / Oct '95 / Go Discs

Wumpscut

☐ BORN AGAIN
Is it you / Womb / Angel / Embryodead / Golgotha / Wumpsex / Womb / War / Man's complete video / Thorns / Down where we belong / Embryodead / Vaporize / Die in the winter
9060622 / 2 Mar '98 / Nova Tekk

☐ MUSIC FOR A SLAUGHTERING TRIBE
SPV 08484782 / Mar '96 / SPV

Wunderlich, Klaus

☐ GOLDEN SOUNDS OF KLAUS WUNDERLICH, THE
GS 864362 / Mar '96 / Disky

☐ KEYS FOR LOVERS
NSPCD 507 / Mar '95 / Connoisseur Collection

☐ PLAYS ABBA - THE WINNER TAKES IT ALL
Money, money, money / Dancing queen / Super trouper / Fernando / I do, I do, I do, I do / I have a dream / Take a chance on me / Lay all your love on me / Knowing me, knowing you / Mamma mia / S.o.s. / Waterloo / Thank you for the music / Winner takes it all
NSPCD 506 / Jan '94 / Connoisseur Collection

☐ TRIBUTE TO FRANK SINATRA, A
Lady is a tramp / Strangers in the night / I only have eyes for you / Something / From here to eternity / I've got you under my skin / My way / Downtown / New York, New York / Something stupid / Someone to watch over me / What now my love / Autumn in New York / Night and day / I'm gettin' sentimental over you / Just one of those things
NSPCD 502 / Apr '91 / Connoisseur Collection

Wurzel

☐ CHILL OUT OR DIE
Electric wave / Anubis / Barewires / Supertrev / Space debris / Karma for Katy / Bliss in the sack and the hat / Surfing the waveband / Final waveband
BAH 34 / 10 Aug '98 / Humbug

WWF

☐ WE GOTTA WRESTLE
0089622CTR / Jul '97 / Concrete

Wyands, Richard

☐ ARRIVAL, THE (Wyands, Richard Trio)
DIW 611 / Nov '92 / DIW

☐ GET OUT OF TOWN
SCCD 31401 / Apr '97 / Steeplechase

☐ REUNITED (Wyands, Richard Trio)
Moment to moment / Easy living / Lady's in love with you / Estate / Afternoon in Paris / How long has this been going on / Blues for Pepper / I'm just a lucky so and so / Moon and sand / Yesterdays / Alone together
CRISS 1105CD / 20 Oct '97 / Criss Cross

☐ THEN HERE AND NOW
Yes it is / Lament / As long as there's music / Leonara / Never let me go / Yesterdays / Blue rose / Leonara / Blue rose
STCD 8269 / Jul '98 / Storyville

Wyatt, Robert

☐ DONESTAN
Costa / Sight of the wind / Catholic architecture / Worship / Shrink rap / Cp jeebies / Left on man / Lisp service / N.i.o. (new information order) / Dondestan
R 2742 / Sep '91 / Rough Trade

☐ FLOTSAM AND JETSAM
R 3112 / Aug '94 / Rough Trade

☐ GOING BACK A BIT (A Little History Of Robert Wyatt)
Moon in June / Alifib / Alifie / Soup song / Calyx / Sonia / All she wanted / I'm a believer / Yesterday man
CDVM 9031 / Jul '94 / Virgin

☐ MID EIGHTIES
Yolanda / Te recuerdo amanda / Biko / Amber and the amberines / Memories of you / 'round midnight / Pigs...(in there) / Chairman mao / Alliance / United states of amnesia / East timor / Speechless / Age of self / Vandalusia / British road / Mass medium / Gharbzadegl / P.l.a.
R 2952 / Jan '93 / Rough Trade

☐ NOTHING CAN STOP US
Born again cretin / At last I am free / Caimanera / Grass / Stalin wasn't stallin' / Red flag / Strange fruit / Arauco / Trade union / Stalingrad
HNCD 1433 / 8 Jun '98 / Hannibal

☐ OLD ROTTENHAT
Alliance / United States Of Amnesia / East Timor / Speechless / Age of self / Vandalusia / British road / Mass medium / Gharbzadegi / PLA
HNCD 1434 / 8 Jun '98 / Hannibal

☐ ROCK BOTTOM
Sea song / Last straw / Little Red Riding Hood hit the road / Alifib / Little Red Robin Hood hit the road
CDV 2017 / Feb '89 / Virgin
HNCD 1426 / 27 Apr '98 / Hannibal
70043570452 / 5 May '98 / Thirsty Ear

☐ RUTH IS STRANGER THAN RICHARD
Soup song / Sonia / Team spirit / Song for Che / Muddy mouse / Solar flares / Muddy mouse / Five black notes and one white note / Muddy mouse / Muddy mouth
CDV 2034 / Feb '89 / Virgin
HNCD 1427 / 27 Apr '98 / Hannibal
70043570442 / 5 May '98 / Thirsty Ear

☐ SHLEEP
Heaps of sheeps / Duchess / Maryan / Was a friend / Free will and testament / September the ninth / Alien / Out of season / Sunday in Madrid / Blues in Bob minor / Whole point of no return
HNCD 1418 / 29 Sep '97 / Hannibal

☐ SHORT BREAK, A
Short break / Tubab / Kutcha / Ventilatir / Unmasked
BP 108CD / Apr '96 / Blueprint

Wycherley, Ellen

☐ SCOTTISH CANTICLE, A
EWCD 004 / Jul '94 / Auldgate

Wyclef Jean

☐ CARNIVAL, THE
Intro/Court/Clef/Intro / Apocalypse / Guantanamera / Pablo diablo / Bubblegoose / Prelude/To all the girls / Down lo ho / Anything can happen / Gone till November / Words of wisdom / Year of the dragon / Sang Fezi / Fresh interlude / Mona Lisa / Street jeopardy / Killer MC / We trying to stay alive / Gunpowder / Closing arguments / Enter the Carnival / Jaspora / Yele / Carnival
4874422 / 11 May '98 / Ruff House

Wylie & The Wild West Show

☐ WAY OUT WEST
Hello heartache / Jingle, jangle, jingle / Heaven / Rain, rain / Sidewalks of LA / Girl on the billboard / Give me a pinto pal / I remember you / I'm your man / Heartaches, tears and misery / Fill it up / I still get a thrill
ROUCD 3152 / Sep '97 / Rounder

☐ WYLIE AND THE WILD WEST SHOW
DFGCD 8436 / Feb '96 / Dixie Frog

Wylie-Hubbard, Ray

☐ LOCO GRINGO'S LAMENT
DJD 3213 / Dec '94 / Dejadisc

☐ LOST TRAIN OF THOUGHT
DJD 3223 / Nov '95 / Dejadisc

Wyman, Bill

☐ BILL WYMAN
Ride on baby / New fashion / Nuclear reactions / Visions / Jump up / Come back Suzanne / Rio de Janeiro / Girls / Seventeen / Si si, je suis un rock star
NEMCD 848 / Jun '96 / Sequel

☐ MONKEY GRIP
I wanna get me a gun / Crazy woman / Pussy / Mighty fine time / Monkey grip glue / What a blow / White lightnin' / I'll pull you thro' / It's a wonder
NEMCD 846 / Jun '96 / Sequel

☐ STONE ALONE
Quarter to three / Gimme just one chance / Soul satisfying / Apache woman / Every sixty seconds / Get it on / Feet / Peanut butter time / Wine and wimmen / If you wanna be happy / What's the point / No more foolin'
NEMCD 847 / Jun '96 / Sequel

Wyndham, Tex

☐ YOU'RE BOUND TO... (Wyndham, Tex Rent Party Revellers)
BCD 386 / Dec '97 / GHB

Wyndham-Read, Martyn

☐ BENEATH A SOUTHERN SKY (Wyndham-Read, Martyn & No Man's Band)
Shearer's lament/Orotaba waltz / Emu plains / Colonial / My eldorado / Lambs on the green hills / Heel and toe polka / Sailor home from the sea / Faithful Emma / Goorianawa / Lily/Exercise 77 / Best of Autumn / Banks of the Tees / Off to the shearing / Swaggie snake and frog/Ebb wren's schottische
FE 115CD / May '97 / Fellside

☐ MUSSELS ON A TREE
Bold Reynolds / Hills are clad / Irish lords / Reunion / Flash stockman / Bunch of red roses / Valley of tees / Smokestack land / Jim Jones / 'ard tack / Cockleshells / Springtime it brings on the shearing / Ginny on the moor / Van Diemen's land / Shelter
FE 084CD / '92 / Fellside

☐ SUNLIT PLAINS
FE 102CD / Jan '95 / Fellside

☐ UNDISCOVERED AUSTRALIA
MP 10002CD / Mar '98 / Musica Panagaea

Wynette, Tammy

☐ BEST OF TAMMY WYNETTE, THE
Stand by your man / Lonely street / DIVORCE / Gentle on my mind / Take me to your world / Almost persuaded / Your good girl's gonna go bad / Apartment no. 9 / Hey good lookin' / I don't wanna play house / My arms stay open late / There goes my everything
CD 32015 / Jun '91 / CBS

☐ BEST OF TAMMY WYNETTE, THE
DIVORCE / There goes my everything / Ode to Billy / No charge / Honey / Crying in the chapel / Ways to love a man / Sometimes when we touch / Stand by your man / Help me make it through the night / Hey good lookin' / I don't want to play house / Crying in the rain / Another lonely song / Funny face / Your good girl's gonna go bad / Please come to Boston / Apartment no.9
4840462 / May '96 / Epic

☐ COUNTRY STARS (Wynette, Tammy & George Jones)
No show jones: Jones, George / Race is on: Jones, George / Bartender blues: Jones, George / I always get lucky with you: Jones, George / She's my rock: Jones, George / Chicken reel: Jones, George / He stopped loving her today: Jones, George / Who's gonna fill their shoes: Jones, George / One I loved back then: Jones, George / Welcome to my world: Wynette, Tammy / Another chance: Wynette, Tammy / You good girl's gonna go bad: Wynette, Tammy / DIVORCE: Wynette, Tammy / Singing my song: Wynette, Tammy / Till I can make it on my own: Wynette, Tammy / Womanhood: Wynette, Tammy / Fairy tales: Wynette, Tammy / When the grass grows over me: Wynette, Tammy / Amazing grace: Wynette, Tammy / I'll fly away: Wynette, Tammy / Will the circle be unbroken: Wynette, Tammy / I saw the light: Wynette, Tammy / Stand by your man: Wynette, Tammy / Crying in the rain: Wynette, Tammy
PLATCD 351 / May '91 / Platinum

☐ DIVORCE
There's fire in your heart / Legend of Bonnie and Clyde / Gentle on my mind / Honey/All night long / Kiss away / Lonely street / Come on home / Yesterday / Sweet dreams / D-I-V-O-R-C-E
379452 / Sep '97 / Koch

☐ I'LL FLY AWAY (Wynette, Tammy & George Jones)
MU 5048 / Oct '92 / Musketeer

☐ SINGING HER SONG (In Concert)
My man (understands) / Another chance / 'Til I can make it on my own / Rocky top / Alive and well / What a difference you've made in my life / (They call it) making love / You and me / Take me to your world / Womanhood / Crying in the rain / Medley no.1 / I still believe in fairy tales / Stand by your man / Medley no.2 / Let's call it a day, today / Heart over mind
CTS 55440 / Feb '97 / Country Stars

☐ STAND BY YOUR MAN
You make me want to be a mother / Another lonely song / Kids say the darndest things / Love's the answer / Woman to woman / Bedside story / Stand by your man / Good lovin' / Reach out your hand / Please come to Boston / Till I get it right / My man (understands) / There goes that old steel guitar / Help me make it through the night
379462 / Aug '97 / Koch

☐ TAKE ME TO YOUR WORLD/I DON'T WANNA PLAY HOUSE
I don't wanna play house / JJackson ain't a very big town / Broadminded / Cry / Phone call / It's my way / Take me to your world / (Or) is it love / Fuzzy wuzzy ego / Good / Ode to Billy Joe
KOCCD 7944 / Mar '98 / Koch

☐ TEARS OF FIRE (The 25th Anniversary Collection/3CD Set)
You can steal me / Apartment no. 9 / She didn't color daddy / Your good girl's gonna go bad / Walk through this world with me / My elusive dreams: Wynette, Tammy & David Houston / I don't wanna play house / Take me to your world / DIVORCE / Sweet dreams / Lonely street / I believe / He / Stand by your man / You'll never walk alone / Great thou art / Singing my song / Too far gone / Ways to love a man / I'll see him through / Kids say the darndest things / He loves me all the way / We sure can love each other / Deepening snow / Good lovin' / Bedtime story / Till I get it right / My man understands / We're gonna hold on: Wynette, Tammy & George Jones / We're not the jet set: Wynette, Tammy & George Jones / Another lonely song / I don't think about him no more / No charge / Woman to woman / This time I almost made it / Near you: Wynette, Tammy & George Jones / I still believe in fairytales / Till I can make it on my own / Golden ring: Wynette, Tammy & George Jones / Did you ever: Wynette, Tammy & George Jones / You and me / Let's get together (One last time) / One of a kind / Southern California: Wynette, Tammy & George Jones / Dear daughters / They call it making love / Two story house: Wynette, Tammy & George Jones / Cowboys don't shoot straight (like they used to) / Crying in the rain / Another chance / You still get to me in my dreams / Unwed fathers / (I'm not) A candle in the wind / Sometimes when we touch: Wynette, Tammy & Mark Gray / Between twenty-nine and danger / Alive and well / Talkin' to myself again: Wynette, Tammy & The O'Kanes / I wasn't meant to live my life alone: Wynette, Tammy & Vince Gill / Beneath painted sky: Wynette, Tammy & Emmylou Harris / Your love: Wynette, Tammy & Ricky Skaggs / Higher ground: Wynette, Tammy & Larry, Steve & Rudy Gatlin / Liars roses / We're strangers again: Wynette, Tammy & Randy Travis / Suddenly single / It could've been so good / Justified and ancient: KLF & Tammy Wynette / Precious memories: Wynette, Tammy & Masters Five
E3K 52741 / 18 May '98 / Columbia

☐ WITHOUT WALLS
It's the last thing I do / Woman's needs / Every breath you take / If you were to wake up / Glasshouses / What do they know / All I am to you / I second that emotion / This love / Girl thang
4748002 / Apr '95 / Epic

Wyngarde, Peter

☐ WHEN SEX LEERS IT'S INQUISITIVE HEAD
Come in / You wonder how these things begin / Rape / La ronde de l'amour / Jenny kissed me / Way I cry over you / Unknown citizen / It's when I touch you / Hippie and the skinhead / Try to remember to forget / Jenny kissed me and it was... / Widdecombe fair / Neville Thumbcatch / Once again (flight number ten) / Pay no attention / April
RPM 187 / 13 Jul '98 / RPM

Wynn, Steve

☐ FLUORESCENT
OUT 1162 / Nov '94 / Brake Out

☐ MELTING IN THE DARK
OUT 1242 / Aug '96 / Brake Out

☐ SWEETNESS AND LIGHT
Silver lining / Black magic / Sweetness and light / This strange effect / This deadly game / How's my little girl / Ghosts / Blood from a stone / In love with everyone / Great divide / That's the way love is / If my life was an open book
ZEROCD 2160 / 15 Sep '97 / Zero Hour

☐ TAKE YOUR FLUNKY AND DANGLE
RTS 13 / Dec '94 / Return To Sender

Wynona Ryders

☐ JD SALINGER
LOOKOUT 104CD / Sep '95 / Lookout

Wyzards

☐ FINAL CATASTROPHE
MR 3001 / 16 Feb '98 / Mandrake Root

X

X-103
☐ ATLANTIS
E 01740CD / Mar '93 / Tresor

X-ASP
☐ TERRA FIRMA
CAT 028CD / Oct '96 / Rephlex

X-Cabs
☐ CHEMISTRY
HKCDXY 03 / 24 Aug '98 / Hook

X-Cops
☐ YOU HAVE THE RIGHT TO REMAIN SILENT
140802 / Oct '95 / Metal Blade

X-Dream
☐ RADIO
BRO 66CD / 20 Apr '98 / Blue Room

X-Ecutioners
☐ X-PRESSIONS
Out takes / Get started / Word play / Out takes / Raida's theme / Pianos from hell / Cipher / Turntablast anthem / Out takes / One man band / Countdown / Solve for X / Out takes / Turntable exhibition / Bare treats / Musical intaction / Mad flava / Out takes / Poetry in motion / Scratch to this / Musica negra / Table talk
ASP 0977CD / 26 Jan '98 / Asphodel

X-Hausted
☐ X-IST
TM 010 / 22 Jun '98 / Transmission

X-Legged Sally
☐ LAND OF THE GIANT DWARVES
KFWCD 182 / Oct '96 / Knitting Factory

X-Mal Deutschland
☐ FETISCH
Qual / Geheimnis / Young man / In der nacht / Orient / Hand in hand / Kaempfen / Danghem / Boomerang / Stummes kind / Qual / Sehnsucht / Zeit
GAD 302CD / 6 Jul '98 / 4AD

☐ TOCSIN
Mondicht / Eiland / Reigen / Tag fur tag (day by day) / Augen blich / Begrab / Mein herz / Nacht schatten / Christmas in Australia / Der wisch / Incubus succubus / Vifo
GAD 407CD / 6 Jul '98 / 4AD

X Marks The Pedwalk
☐ AIR BACK TRAX
CDZOT 118 / Aug '94 / Zoth Ommog

☐ DRAWBACK
ZOTH 196CD / 3 Nov '97 / Zoth

☐ KILLING HAD BEGUN
CDZOT 107 / Mar '94 / Zoth Ommog

☐ PARANOID ILLUSIONS
CDZOT 29 / Aug '93 / Zoth Ommog

X-Men
☐ MUSICA NEGRA
EFA 710072 / 29 Sep '97 / Asphodel

X-Rated
☐ TIGHT PUM PUM
LG 21077 / May '93 / Lagoon

X-Ray Spex
☐ CONSCIOUS CONSUMER
Cigarettes / Junk food junkie / Crystal clear / India / Dog in Sweden / Hi chaperone / Good time girl / Melancholy / Sophia / Peace meal / Prayer for peace / Party
RRCD 205 / Oct '95 / Receiver

☐ GERM FREE ADOLESCENTS
Day the world turned dayglo / Obsessed with you / Genetic engineering / Identity / I live off you / Germfree adolescents / Art I ficial / Let's submerge / Warrior in woolworths / I am a poseur / I can't do anything / Highly inflammable / Age / Plastic bag / I am a cliche / Oh bondage up yours
CDVM 9001 / Jun '92 / Virgin

X-Rays
☐ DOUBLE GODZILLA WITH CHEESE
MTR 350CD / Oct '96 / Empty

X-Seed
☐ DESOLATION
CDBLEED 19 / Jul '96 / Bleeding Hearts

X-Specials
☐ COZ I LUV YOU
RRSCD 1010 / Feb '94 / Receiver

X-Tal
☐ BITING THE UGLY BISCUIT
Family jewels / Dear friends / White rat / Lullaby / Happy Americans / I'll believe / Cheap holiday / Encore / Kansas song / Through you (Emotional consumerism) / Your fragile mind / Dub rat / Goldfish bowl / Fatal distractions / You're not saved yet / Daddy auction / Smells like smoke / Black Russian
RTS 25 / Mar '97 / Return To Sender

Xenakis
☐ ENSEMBLE MUSIC VOL.2
MODE 56 / Dec '96 / Mode

☐ REBONDS/AKEA/EPICYLES
BVHAASTCD 9219 / Jun '89 / Bvhaast

Xenakis, Iannis
☐ KRAANERG (Xenakis, Iannis & DJ Spooky)
ASP 0975CD / 22 Jun '98 / Asphodel

Xentrix
☐ SCOURGE
HMRXD 198 / Nov '95 / Heavy Metal

Xerox
☐ HUMAN RACE (Xerox & Freeman)
HMCD 2 / 27 Jul '98 / Hom-Mega

Xhol-Caravan
☐ MOTHER FUCKERS GMBH
14531 / Feb '97 / Spalax

Xiame
☐ PENSA
Pensa / Tokyoto / Arastape pe / Falando / Anduva / Kleiner bar / Carioca / Nossa doce lia / Hickyoung / Dois berlinese in Rio / Goodbye, pork pie hat / Dor da floresta
VBR 21072 / Aug '92 / Vera Bra

☐ XIAME (OUR EARTH)
Xiame / Nosso destino / Minha rua / Guaratiba / Rio De Janeiro / Um brasileiro em Berlin / Mutio swer / Gone but still here / 'Round midnight / Choro de crainza / I can't stand the pain / Flor da terra
VRB 20362 / Jul '90 / Vera Bra

Xid
☐ XID
RTD 19519182 / Nov '94 / Our Choice

XIII
☐ SALT
342712 / Nov '95 / No Bull

☐ SERPENTINE
50540 / 29 Sep '97 / Semaphore

Xingu Hill
☐ MAPS OF THE IMPOSSIBLE
NZ 035CD / May '95 / Nova Zembla

☐ RELAY
NZ 081 / 6 Oct '97 / Nova Zembla

Xistra De Coruxo
☐ ADICADO
DF 008CD / Dec '97 / Do Fol

XL
☐ XLENT
OCTO 4042 / Aug '95 / Ondine

XLNC
☐ R U READY
DMUT 1254 / Apr '96 / Multitone

Xolton, Blake
☐ COOL ON MY SKIN
ROSE 166CD / Mar '89 / New Rose

Xscape
☐ OFF THE HOOK
Do your thang / Feels so good / Hard to say goodbye / Can't hang / Who can I run to / Hip hop barber shop request line / Do you want to / What can I do / Do like lovers do / Work me slow / Love's a funny thing / Keep it on the real
4896442 / Jul '95 / Columbia

☐ TRACES OF MY LIPSTICK
All about me / My little secret / Softest place on Earth / Do you know one of those love songs / Arms of the one that loves you / I will / Your eyes / All I need / Am I dreamin' / Runaraound / Hold on
4894172 / 18 May '98 / So So Def

Xtasy
☐ XTASY
1385328962 / 17 Mar '98 / Caiman

XTC
☐ BIG EXPRESS, THE
Wake up / All you pretty girls / Shake you donkey up / Seagulls screaming kiss her kiss her / This world over / Everyday story of smalltown / I bought myself a liarbird / Reign of blows / You're the wish (you are) I had / I remember the sun / Train running low on soul coal / Red brick dream / Washaway / Blue overall
CDV 2325 / '84 / Virgin

☐ BLACK SEA
Respectable street / Generals and majors / Living through another Cuba / Love at first sight / Rocket from a bottle / No language in our lungs / Towers of London / Paper and iron (notes and coins) / Burning with optimism's flame / Sgt. Rock (is going to help me) / Travels in nihilon / Smokeless zone / Don't lose your temper / Somnambulist
CDV 2173 / Jun '88 / Virgin

☐ COMPACT XTC, THE (The Singles 1978-1985)
Science friction / Making plans for Nigel / Sgt. Rock (is going to help me) / Senses working overtime / Love on a farmboy's wages / Wake up / Statue of Liberty / This is pop / Are you receiving me / Life begins at the hop / Wait till your boat goes down / Generals and majors / Towers of London / Ball and chain / Great fire / Wonderland / All you pretty girls / This world over
CDV 2251 / '86 / Virgin

☐ DRUMS AND WIRES
Making plans for Nigel / Helicopter / Day in, day out / When you're near me I have difficulty / Ten feet tall / Roads girdle the globe / Real by reel / Millions / That is the way / Outside world / Scissor man / Complicated game
CDV 2129 / Jun '88 / Virgin

☐ ENGLISH SETTLEMENT
Runaways / Ball and chain / Senses working overtime / Jason and the Argonauts / No thugs in our house / Yacht dance / All of a sudden (it's too late) / Melt the guns / Leisure / It's nearly Africa / Knuckle down / Fly on the wall / Down in the cockpit / English roundabout / Snowman
CDV 2223 / Dec '81 / Virgin

☐ EXPLODE TOGETHER (The Dub Experiments 1978-1980)
Part 1 (go) / Dance with me Germany / Beat the bible / Dictionary of modern marriage / Clap clap clap / We kill the beast / Part II (take away) / Commerciality / Day they pulled the North Pole down / Forgotten language of light / Steam fist futurist / Shore leave ornithology (another 1950) / Cairo / Part III (the lure of the salvage) / Rotary / Madhatter / I sit in the snow / Work away / Tokyo day / New broom
CDOVD 308 / Jul '93 / Virgin

☐ FOSSIL FUEL (The XTC Singles Collection 1977-1992)
Science friction / Statue of Liberty / This is pop / Are you receiving me / Life begins at the hop / Making plans for Nigel / Ten feet tall / Wait till your boat goes down / Generals and Majors / Towers of London / Sgt. Rock (is going to help me) / Love at first sight / Respectable Street / Senses working overtime / Ball and chain / No thugs in our house / Great fire / Wonderland / Love on a farmboy's wages / All you pretty girls / This world over / Wake up / Grass / Meeting place / Dear God / Mayor of Simpleton / King for a day / Loving / Disappointed / Ballad of Peter Pumpkinhead / Wrapped in grey
CDVD 2811
CDVDX 2811 / Sep '96 / Virgin

GO 2
Meccanik dancing / Crowded room / Battery brides (Andy paints Brian) / Buzzcity talking / Rhythm / Beattown / Life is good in the greenhouse / I am the audience / Ted / My weapon / Jumping in Gomorrah / Super tuff / Are you receiving me
CDV 2108 / Jul '87 / Virgin

☐ MUMMER
Beating of hearts / Wonderland / Love on a farmboy's wages / Great fire / Deliver us from the elements / Human alchemy / Ladybird / In loving memory of a name / Me and the wind / Funk pop a roll
CDV 2264 / Jun '88 / Virgin

☐ ORANGES AND LEMONS
Garden of earthly delights / King for a day / Loving / Across the antheap / Pink thing / Chalkhills and children / Mayor of Simpleton / Here comes President kill again / Poor skeleton steps out / Hold me daddy / Minature sun / One of the millions / Scarecrow people / Merely a man / Cynical days
CDV 2581 / Apr '92 / Virgin

☐ RAG 'N' BONE BUFFET (Rarities & Out-Takes)
Extrovert / Ten feet tall / Mermaid smiled / Too many cooks in the kitchen (the colonel) / Respectable street / Looking for footprints / Over rusty water / Heaven is paved with broken glass / World is full of angry young men / Punch and Judy / Thanks for Christmas (the three wise men) / Tissue tigers / I need protection (the colonel) / Another satellite / Strange tales / Officer blue / Scissor man / Cockpit dance mixture / Pulsing pulsing / Happy families / Countdown to Christmas party time / Blame the weather / Take this town / History of rock 'n' roll
CDOVD 311 / Jul '93 / Virgin

☐ SKYLARKING
Summer's cauldron / Grass / Meeting place / That's really super, supergirl / Ballet for a rainy day / 1000 umbrellas / Season cycle / Earn enough for us / Big day / Another satellite / Mermaid smiled / Man who sailed around his soul / Dying / Sacrificial bonfire
CDV 2399 / Jul '93 / Virgin

☐ TESTIMONIAL DINNER, A (A Tribute To XTC) (Various Artists)
Earn enough for us: Johnston, Freedy / Senses working overtime: Spacehog / All you pretty girls: Crash Test Dummies / Wake up: Verve Pipe / Making plans for Nigel: Rembrandts / Dear God: McLachlan, Sarah / Man who sailed around his soul: Blades, Ruben / Another satellite: P-Hux / 25 O'Clock: They Might Be Giants / Good things: Terry & The Lovemen / Statue of Liberty: Jackson, Joe
COOKCD 145 / 30 Mar '98 / Cooking Vinyl

☐ WHITE MUSIC
Radios in motion / Crosswires / This is pop / Do what you do / Statue of Liberty / All along the watchtower / Into the atom age / I'll set myself on fire / I'm bugged / Spinning top / Neon shuffle / New town animal in a furnished cage / Science friction / She's so square / Dance band / Hang on to the night / Heatwave / Traffic light rock / Instant tunes
CDV 2095 / Jun '88 / Virgin

Xterminator
☐ XTERMINATOR DUB
RASCD 3195 / Apr '96 / Ras

☐ XTERMINATOR PRESENTS THE AWAKENING (Various Artists)
RASCD 3165 / Sep '96 / Ras

Xtraverts
☐ SO MUCH HATE
RUBBISHCD 001 / May '97 / Bin Liner

Xymox
☐ CLAN OF XYMOX
Day / No words / Stumble and fall / Cry in the wind / Stranger / Equal ways / Seventh time / No human can drown
GAD 503CD / 6 Jul '98 / 4AD

☐ MEDUSA
Themes 1 and 2 / Medusa / Michelle / Louise / Lorretine / Agonised by love / Masquerade / After the call / Back door
GAD 613CD / 6 Jul '98 / 4AD

☐ REMIX ALBUM
340372 / Dec '94 / Koch

☐ SUBSEQUENT PLEASURES
CDP 1013DD / Jun '97 / Pseudonym

Xysma

☐ DELUXE
SP 1020 / Jul '94 / Spinefarm

Xytras

☐ PASSAGE
CM 77202CD / 2 Feb '98 / Century Media

XYZ

☐ TAKE WHAT YOU CAN
3025502 / 13 Oct '97 / Axe Killer

XYZ

☐ COMPAS-ZOUK
STCD 1379 / Jan '91 / Stern's

Xzibit

☐ AT THE SPEED OF LIFE
Grand opening / At the speed of life / Just maintain / Eyes may shine / Positively negative / Don't hate me / Paparazzi / Foundation / Mrs. Crabtree / Bird's eye view / Hit and run (part 2) / Carry the weight / Plastic surgery / Enemies and friends / Last words
07863668162 / Oct '96 / Loud

Y

Y&T

☐ ENDANGERED SPECIES
Hello hello / Black gold / God only knows / Summthin 4
nuthin' / Can't stop the rain / Sail on by / Still fallin' / I
wanna cry / Gimme the beat / Voices / Try to believe /
Rocco
CDMFN 229 / 6 Oct '97 / Music For
Nations

☐ LIVE ON THE FRIDAY ROCK SHOW
SFRSCD 071 / 7 Sep '98 / Strange Fruit

☐ MUSICALLY INCORRECT
Long way down / I've got my own / 21st Century / Fly
away / Nowhere land / I'm lost / Quicksand / Pretty
prison / Confusion / Cold day in hell / Don't know
what to do / No regrets
CDMFN 191 / Sep '95 / Music For
Nations

☐ YESTERDAY AND TODAY LIVE
398417017CD / May '96 / Metal Blade

Y Cyrff

☐ MAE DDOE YN DDOE
ANKCD 30 / Oct '92 / Ankst

Y-Live

☐ Y ON EARTH
Humanity takes over / Who owns your soul / I want
you all / Vortex vision / Don't buy it / Killing the
innocents / Earthquake at Sellafield / Death of a
nation / Logo of love / Humanity (reprise)
ICACD 001 / Dec '93 / CyberArts

Ya Ho Wha 13

☐ PENETRATION: AQUARIAN
SYMPHONY
001CD / Jul '97 / Higher Key

Yabby You

☐ BEWARE DUB
RE 188CD / Feb '95 / Danceteria

☐ DELIVER ME FROM MY ENEMIES
YVJ 006 / Apr '92 / Vivian Jones

☐ JESUS DREAD 1972-1977 (2CD Set)
Love thy neighbour: Jackson, Vivian & The
Defenders / Conquering lion: Jackson, Vivian & The
Defenders / Fisherman special: McCook, Tommy &
Don D Jr. / Yabby Youth: Big Youth & Vivian Jackson
/ Big youth fights against capitalism: King Tubby /
Covetous man: Jackson, Vivian & The Prophets /
Run come rally: Jackson, Vivian & The Prophets /
Rally dub: Perry, Lee 'Scratch' / Anti christ: Jackson,
Vivian & The Prophets / God is watching you: Burton,
Dicky / Pablo dread in a red: Pablo, Augustus &
Vivian Jackson / King Tubby's rock: King Tubby /
Warn the nation: Prophets / Warning version: King
Tubby / Carnal mind: Jackson, Vivian & The
Prophets / Love of jah: Jackson, Vivian & The
Prophets / Love of jah version: King Tubby / Man who
does the work: Jackson, Vivian & The Prophets / Jah
vengeance: Jackson, Vivian & The SOns Of Jah /
REvenge: McCook, Tommy / Freshly: Dillinger /
Natty dread on the mountain top: Tappa Zukie /
Gwan and let me: Trinity / Tubby's vengeance: King
Tubby / Death trap: McCook, Tommy & VJ / Man of
living: Wade, Wayne / King Tubby's special: King
Tubby / Lord of Lords: Wade, Wayne / Lord Dub:
King Tubby / Walls of Jerusalem: Jackson, Vivian &
The Prophets / Jersulalem dub: Jackson, Vivian &
The Prophets / Ing Pharaohs plague discomix:
Prophets & Trinity / Plague of horn: McCook, Tommy
/ King Pharaoh Dub: King Tubby / Jesus dread:
Trinity & Dillinger / Chant down Babylon kingdom
mix: Prophets & Trinity / Chanting dub: King Tubby /
Hornsman chant: McCook, Tommy / Fire in a
kingston: Jackson, Vivian & The Prophets / Fire
version: King Tubby / Judgement on the land:
Jackson, Vivian & The Prophets / Repatriation rock:
King Tubby / Deliver me from my enemies: Jackson,
Vivian & The Prophets / Born free extended mix:
Rose, Michael & King Tubby / Love thy neighbour:
King Tubby
BAFCD 021 / 27 Oct '97 / Blood & Fire

☐ KING TUBBY'S PROPHECY OF DUB
Version dub / Conquering dub / Jah love dub / Anti-
Christ rock / Beware of God / Robber rock / Rock
vibration / Zion is here / Hungering dub / Love and
peace / Homelessness / Creations and versions
BAFCD 5 / Jan '95 / Blood & Fire

☐ YABBY YOU & MICHAEL PROPHET
MEET SCIENTIST (Yabby You &
Michael Prophet)
YVJ 008 / May '95 / Yabby You

☐ YABBY YOU MEETS MAD
PROFESSOR/BLACK STEEL
ARICD 083 / Apr '93 / Ariwa Sounds

☐ YABBY YOU MEETS TOMMY MCCOOK
IN DUB (Sounds Of The 70's) (Yabby
You & Tommy McCook)
CD 1275 / 29 Jun '98 / Peacemaker

Yacoub, Gabriel

☐ BABEL
BPCD 3186 / Dec '97 / Boucherie
Productions

☐ BEL
KMCD 15 / '91 / Red Sky

☐ QUATRE
BP 3182CD / Apr '95 / Chantons Sous
La True

Yage

☐ INTEGRATION
MRCD 068 / Mar '97 / Munster

Yah Congo

☐ YAH CONGO MEETS KING TUBBY/
MAD PROFESSOR AT DUB TABLE
(Yah Congo & King Tubby/Mad
Professor)
RUSCD 8217 / Oct '95 / ROIR

Yahel, Sam

☐ SEARCHIN'
860042 / Jun '97 / Naxos Jazz

Yahowha 13

☐ I'M GONNA TAKE YOU HOME
HIGHERKEY 20 / Nov '97 / Higher Key

Yakutia

☐ EPICS AND IMPROVISATIONS
925652 / Aug '93 / BUDA

Yamada, Norman

☐ BEING AND TIME
TZA 7035 / 1 Jun '98 / Tzadik

Yamaha International Allstar Band

☐ YAMAHA INTERNATIONAL ALLSTAR
BAND
CD 005 / May '96 / Nagel Heyer

Yamashita, Yosuke

☐ ASIAN GAMES (Yamashita, Yosuke &
Bill Laswell/Ryuichi Sakamoto)
Melting pot / Chasin' the air / Asian games / Ninja
drive / Napping on the bamboo / Parade of rain /
Moon and a bride
5183442 / Feb '94 / Verve

☐ CANVAS IN QUIET (Homage To Morio
Matsui)
5370072 / Feb '97 / Verve

☐ CANVAS IN VIGOR (Yamashita, Yosuke
New York Trio & Ravi Coltrane)
5370082 / 10 Nov '97 / Verve

☐ DAZZLING DAYS
5213032 / May '94 / Verve

☐ KURDISH DANCE
Kurdish dance / Back yard / Act 3-8 / Brooklyn
express / Tiny square / Subway gig / 4th street up /
K's gift
5177082 / Oct '93 / Verve

☐ SAKURA
Sakura / Yurikago / Haiku / Amefuri / Ano machi /
Dobarada / Sasa no ha / Sunayama / Tsuki no
sabaku / Usagi no dance / Nenkorori
8490652 / Oct '93 / Verve

☐ SPIDER
5312712 / Jun '96 / Verve

☐ STONE FLOWER
Surfboard / So danco samba / Eu te amo / Chovendo
na roseira / Meu amigo Radames / Stone flower /
Felicidade / Homage to Jobim
JVC 90142 / Aug '97 / JVC

☐ WAYS OF TIME
5328412 / Jun '95 / Verve

☐ WIND OF CHANGE
For David's sake / 10th theme / JG bird / Double
sides / Fuga de la liberation / Brick busters / My one
and only love / My favourite things
5570082 / 3 Aug '98 / Verve

Yamashta, Stomu

☐ RED BUDDHA
SPALAX 14512 / Nov '96 / Spalax

Yamato Ensemble

☐ ART OF THE JAPANESE
BAMBOOFLUTE AND KOTO
EUCD 1248 / Nov '93 / ARC

☐ ART OF THE JAPANESE KOTO,
SHAKUHACHI AND SHAMISEN, THE
EUCD 1364 / Nov '96 / ARC

Yami Bolo

☐ BORN AGAIN
RASCD 3174 / Sep '96 / Ras

☐ COOL AND EASY
DSRCD 442 / Aug '93 / Tappa

☐ FIGHTING FOR PEACE
RAS 3141 / Jun '94 / Ras

☐ JAH LOVE
VPCD 1523 / 6 Jul '98 / VP

☐ NO SURRENDER
RFCD 009 / 26 Jan '98 / Record Factory

☐ RANSOM
Ransom of a man's life / Take time to know / What
make the world taste good / Definitely / Memories /
She loves me so / World of confusion / Jah is life /
Star time - fun time / One has to be real strong
GRELCD 125 / Apr '89 / Greensleeves

☐ WAR MONGER
Johanna / Warmonger / Show me / Call me / African
woman / Satr of love / Mind games / Maximum
greedium / Spread jah love / Mr. Big and in crime
RFCD 002 / Sep '95 / Record Factory

☐ WONDERS & SIGN
SPCD 0129 / 13 Oct '97 / Jammy's

Yami Sari Ensemble

☐ GAMELAN GONG KEBYAL
Yami Sari / Ratna gurnita / Puspa raga / Giri kenaka /
Legong jobog / Kapi raja
VICG 54172 / Oct '96 / JVC

Yamo

☐ TIME PIE
011925 / Sep '97 / Cleopatra

Yanagisawa, Rie

☐ KUROKAMI - THE MUSIC OF JAPAN
(Yanagisawa, Rie & Clive Bell)
Hari no umi (Sea in spring) / Kurokami / Disguised as
a silverer of mirrors / Midare rinzetsu / Yugao (The
moon-flower) / Esashi Oiwake / Aki no shirabe (Tune
of Autumn)
CDSDL 367 / Mar '94 / Saydisc

Yancey, Jimmy

☐ ETERNAL BLUES
Two o' clock blues / Lucille's lament / Steady rock
blues / South side stuff / Yancey's getaway /
Yancey's special / Salute to pinetop / Blues for albert
/ Monkey woman blues / Santa fe blues / Yancey's
bugle call / Four o'clock blues / 35th and dearborne /
How long blues / White sox stomp / Make me a pallet
on the floor / Eternal blues / Shave 'em dry
CD 52031 / May '94 / Blues Encore

☐ IN THE BEGINNING
SACD 1 / Jul '93 / Solo Art

☐ JIMMY YANCEY VOL.1 1939-1940
DOCD 5041 / Feb '92 / Document

☐ JIMMY YANCEY VOL.2 1940-1943
DOCD 5042 / Feb '92 / Document

☐ JIMMY YANCEY VOL.3 1943-1950
DOCD 5043 / Feb '92 / Document

☐ PRIVATE PARTY 1951 (The Unissued
Yancey Wire Recordings)
DOCD 1007 / May '97 / Document

Yancey, Mama

☐ MAYBE I'LL CRY
Trouble in mind / Santa Fe blues / Monkey woman
blues / How long, how long blues / Maybe I'll cry /
Pallet on the floor / Weekly blues / Baby, won't you
please come home / Four o'clock blues / Kitchen
sink blues
ECD 260782 / Apr '96 / Evidence

Yankee Brass Band

☐ YANKEE BRASS BAND, THE
Arizona quickstep / Bond's serenade / No one to
love / Blondinette polka / Mabel waltz / Helene
Schottisch / American hymn / Red stocking
quickstep / Mockingbird quickstep / Memories of
home-waltz / Schottische / Moon is above us / Brin
d'amour polka / Goodnight my angel / Firemen's
polka
NW 312 / Aug '92 / New World

Yankovic, Weird Al

☐ OFF AT THE DEEP END
Smells like nirvana / Trigger happy / I can't watch this
/ Polka your eyes out / I was only kidding / White stuff
/ When I was your age / Taco grande / Airline amy /
Plumbing song / You don't love me anymore
5125062 / Jan '94 / Polydor

Yannatou, Savina

☐ SONGS OF THE MEDITERRANEAN
ML 4900 / 11 May '98 / Musurgia Graeca

Yanni

☐ CHAMELEON DAYS
Swept away / Marching season / Chasing shadows /
Rain must fall / Days of summer / Reflections of
passion / Walkabout / Everglade run / Word in
private
259644 / May '89 / Private Music

☐ DARE TO DREAM
262667 / Aug '95 / Private Music

☐ DEVOTION
Once upon a time / Within attraction / Song for
Antarctica / Aria / Love for life / Reflections of
passion / To take...to hold / Only a memory / Flight of
fantasy / To the one who knows / End of August /
Marching season / Santorini / Nice to meet you /
Night to remember
01005821532 / 6 Apr '98 / Private Music

☐ IN CELEBRATION OF LIFE
Santorini / Song for Antarctica / Marching season /
Walkabout / Keys to imagination / Looking glass /
Someday / Within attraction / Standing in motion /
Sand dance
262342 / Jan '92 / Private Music

☐ IN THE MIRROR
In the mirror / In the morning light / Love for life / One
man's dream / Within attraction / Forbidden dreams
/ Once upon a time / Chasing shadows / Aria / Quiet
man / Enchantment / Song long my friend / Before I
go / End of August
74321471252 / 2 Feb '98 / Private Music

☐ KEYS TO IMAGINATION
North shore of Matsushima / Looking glass /
Nostalgia / Santorini / Port of mystery / Keys to
imagination / Forgotten yesterdays / Forbidden
dreams
259960 / Nov '89 / Private Music

☐ LIVE AT THE ACROPOLIS
Santorini / Keys to imagination / Until the last
moment / Rain must fall / Acroyali/Standing in
motion / One man's dream / Within attraction /
Nostalgia / Swept away / Reflections of passion /
Aria
01005821222 / Jul '95 / Private Music

☐ NIKI NANA
Niki nana (We're one) / Dance with a stranger /
Running time / Someday / Human condition / First
touch / Nightbird / Quiet man
260208 / Oct '89 / Private Music

☐ OUT OF SILENCE
Sand dance / Standing in motion / Mermaid / With
attraction / Street level / Secret vows / Point or origin
/ Acroyali / Paths on water
259965 / Nov '89 / Private Music

☐ PORT OF MYSTERY
Sphynx / You only live once / Port of mystery /
Butterfly dance / Farewell / Street level / Magus /
Looking glass
1934112412 / 1 Sep '97 / Windham Hill

☐ REFLECTIONS OF PASSION
After the sunrise / Reflections of passion / Nostalgia /
Adbout a whisper / Acrorali / Rain must fall / Swept
away / Farewell / Secret vow / Flight of fantasy /
Word in private / First touch / Reflections
260652 / Feb '90 / Private Music

☐ TRIBUTE
Deliverance / Adagio in c minor / Renegade / Dance
with a stranger / Tribute / Prelude / Love is all /
Southern exposure / Waltz in 7/8 / Nightingale / Niki
nana
CDVUS 135 / 9 Mar '98 / Virgin

Yano, Akiko

☐ AKIKO YANO
7559792052 / Jan '95 / Nonesuch

☐ LOVE LIFE
7559792792 / Jan '95 / Nonesuch

☐ PIANO NIGHTLY
7559794162 / Jun '96 / Nonesuch

Yarborough, Glenn

☐ FAMILY PORTRAIT (Yarborough, Glenn & Holly)
FE 1416 / Dec '94 / Folk Era

☐ LIVE AT THE TROUBADOUR
FE 1704 / Dec '94 / Folk Era

Yardbirds

☐ BEST OF THE YARDBIRDS, THE (2CD Set)
I wish you would / Certain girl / Good morning little school girl / I ain't got you / For your love / Got to hurry / Heart full of soul / Steeled blues / Evil hearted you / Still I'm sad / Shapes of things / Mister you're a better man than I / I'm a man / New York City blues / Train kept a rollin' / Paff...burn / Mr. Zero / Sweet music / Someone to love / Stroll on / Too much monkey business / Got love if you want it / Smokestack lightning / Five long years / Louise / Baby what's wrong / Boom boom / Honey in your hips / Talkin' 'bout you / Let it rock / Take it easy baby: *Yardbirds & Sonny Boy Williamson* / Highway 69: *Yardbirds & Sonny Boy Williamson* / Putty (in your hands) / I'm not talking / I ain't done wrong / My girl sloopy / Jeff's blues / Like Jimmy Reed again / What do you want / Here 'tis
CPCD 82452 / Dec '96 / Charly

☐ BEST OF THE YARDBIRDS, THE
For your love / Heart full of soul / Ha ha said the clown / Goodnight sweet Josephine / Shape of things / Honey in your hips / Boom boom / Train kept a-rollin' / Ten little Indians / Certain girl / Still I'm sad / Putty / Pafff...bum / Good morning little school girl / I wish you would / I'm a man
12900 / Jul '97 / Laserlight
REMCD 509 / Feb '98 / Reactive

☐ COLLECTION, THE
I wish you would / Good morning little school girl / I ain't got you / Boom boom / Good morning little school girl / Got to hurry / For your love / Too much monkey business / Got love if you want it / Here 'tis / Pontiac blues / Twenty three hours too long / Let it rock / Smokestack lightnin' / Honey in your hips / Heart full of soul / Evil hearted you / Still I'm sad / I'm a man / Jeff's blues / You're a better man than I / Shapes of things / Stroll on
CCSCD 141 / '88 / Castle

☐ COMPLETE YARDBIRDS, THE (4CD Set)
DTKBOX 85 / 23 Mar '98 / Dressed To Kill

☐ GOOD MORNING LITTLE SCHOOLGIRL
I wish you would / Trains kept a-rollin' / New York city blues / I ain't got you / Baby what's wrong / Who do you love / I ain't done wrong / Rock my mind / I'm not talking / Good morning little school girl / Smokestack lightning / 23 hours too long / Mister you're a better man than I / Jeff's blues / You can't judge a book (by looking at the cover) / I'm a man / Let it rock / Boom / Stroll on / Too much monkey business
3036000902 / Feb '97 / Carlton

☐ HEART FULL OF SOUL
Heart full of soul / Still I'm sad / For your love / Putty / Evil hearted you / I'm a man / I'm not talking / You're a better man than I / Shapes of things / Goodnight sweet josephine / Train kept a rollin' / I wish you would / I ain't done wrong / A certain girl / Got to hurry / Honey in your hips
12206 / May '94 / Laserlight

☐ LITTLE GAMES
Little games / Puzzles / Smile on me / White Summer / Tinker tailor / Glimpses / Ten little indians / Ha ha said the clown / Drinking muddy water / No excess baggage / Stealing stealing / Only the black rose / Little soldier boy / Think about it / I remember the night / Goodnight sweet Josephine / Together now
CDGOLD 1068 / Oct '96 / EMI Gold

☐ LIVE AND IN THE STUDIO
472155 / May '96 / Flarenasch

☐ MASTERS, THE
EABCD 066 / 24 Nov '97 / Eagle

☐ MASTERS, THE (2CD Set)
EDMCD 015 / 24 Nov '97 / Eagle

☐ ON AIR
I ain't got you / For your love / I'm not talking / I wish you would / Heart full of soul / I've been wrong / Too much monkey business / Love me like I love you / I'm a man / Evil hearted you / Still I'm sad / Hang on sloopy / Smokestack lightnin' / Mister, you're a better man than I / Train kept a rollin' / Shapes of things / Dust my blues / Scratch my back / Over under sideways down / Sun is shining / Most likely you'll go your way / Little games / Drinking muddy water / Thnik about it / Goodnight sweet Josephine / My baby
BOJCD 20 / May '91 / Band Of Joy

☐ OVER UNDER SIDEWAYS DOWN (The Yardbirds 1963-1968)
RVCD 12 / May '91 / Raven

☐ RARITIES
PRCDSP 501 / Aug '92 / Prestige

☐ ROGER THE ENGINEER
RR 4681 / 20 Apr '98 / Repertoire

☐ ROGER THE ENGINEER
Happenings ten years time ago / Psycho daisies / Lost women / Over under sideways down / Nazz are blue / I can't make tour way / Rack my mind / Farewell / Hot house of Omagararshid / Jeff's boogie / He's always there / Turn into earth / What do you want / Ever since the world began / Mr. Zero: *Relf, Keith* / Knowing: *Relf, Keith* / Shapes in my mind: *Relf, Keith* / Shapes in my mind: *Relf, Keith* / Blue sands: *Relf, Keith*
DIAB 852 / 6 Apr '98 / Diablo

☐ TRAIN KEPT A ROLLIN' (The Complete Georgio Gomelsky Productions/4CD Set)
CDLIKBOX 3 / Nov '95 / Decal

☐ VERY BEST OF THE YARDBIRDS, THE
For your love / Heart full of soul / Good morning little school girl / Still I'm sad / Evil hearted you / Certain girl / Jeff's blues / I wish you would / New York City / I'm not talking / You're a better man than I / Shapes of things / I'm a man / Boom boom / Smokestack lightnin' / Let it rock / You can't judge a book by the cover / Who do you love / Too much monkey business / Pretty girl / Stroll on / Respectable
MCCD 023 / May '91 / Music Club

☐ VERY BEST OF THE YARDBIRDS, THE
Heartful of soul / I'm a man / Baby what's wrong / New York city blues / Got to hurry / Putty in your hands / Still I'm sad / Honey in your hips / Got love if you want it / You're a better man than I / Good morning little school girl / Evil hearted you / Like Jimmy Reed again / Jeff's blues / For your love
SUMCD 4115 / May '97 / Summit

☐ WHERE THE ACTION IS (Radio Sessions 1965-1968/2CD Set)
I ain't got you / For your love / I'm not talking / I wish you would / Heart full of soul / I ain't done no wrong / Too much monkey business / Love me like I love you / I'm a man / Evil hearted you / Still I'm sad / Hang on Sloopy / Smokestack lightnin' / Mister you're a better man than I / Train kept a rollin' / Shapes of things / Dust my blues / Scratch my back / Over under sideways down / Sun is shining / Shapes of things / Most likely you'll go your way / Little games / Drinking muddy water / Think about it / Goodnight sweet Josephine / My baby / Shapes of things / Heart full of soul / Mister you're a better man than I / You go your way / Over under sideways down / Little games / My baby / I'm a man
PILOT 010 / Jul '97 / Burning Airlines

☐ YARDBIRDS AVEC ERIC CLAPTON
842148 / May '94 / EVA

☐ YARDBIRDS WITH ERIC CLAPTON (Yardbirds & Eric Clapton)
305222 / Apr '98 / Hallmark

Yared, Gabriel

☐ MAP OF THE HUMAN HEART
5149002 / Jan '94 / Polydor

Yasnaia

☐ ONIRO
LILITH 1CD / Oct '96 / Lilith

Yasus Afari

☐ MENTAL ASSASSIN
CDTZ 015 / Aug '93 / Tappa

Yat-Kha

☐ YENESEL PUNK
Solun chaagai sovet churtum / Karangailyg kara hovaa / Kaachem / Kuula khashtyn baaryndan / Kamgalanyr kuzhudaa bar / Irik chuduk / Chashpykhem / Kadarchy / Chokla kizhi / Een kurug kagbanna men / Toorugtug taiga / Kargtram
GMCD 9504 / Dec '97 / Global Music Centre

Yates, Billy

☐ BILLY YATES
ALMCD 45 / 29 Sep '97 / Almo Sounds

Yawar

☐ DESDE LOS ANDES A LIVERPOOL
4301120582 / 27 Apr '98 / ANS

Yawp

☐ EXCUSES FOR HATE
KANG 005CD / Aug '95 / Kangaroo

Yazbek, David

☐ LAUGHING MAN
Welcome to my world / Monkey in the middle / Mississippi honeymoon / Black cowboys on the beach / Wind / No more / Pinnochio's nose / Tomorrow / Fight the one-armed man / Surface tension (bug on the water) / 666 / Only dreaming
BAH 22 / Mar '95 / Humbug

Yazoo

☐ UPSTAIRS AT ERIC'S
Don't go / Too pieces / Bad connection / Midnight / In my room / Only you / Goodbye 70's / Tuesday / Winter kills / Bring your love down / Situation / Other side of love / I before e except after c)
CDSTUMM 7 / May '95 / Mute

☐ YOU AND ME BOTH
Nobody's diary / Softly over / Sweet thing / Mr. blue / Good times / Walk away from love / Ode to boy / Unmarked / Anyone / Happy people / And on
CDSTUMM 12 / May '95 / Mute

Yazz

☐ ONE ON ONE
Have mercy / Calling 2 U / Child / One on one / How long / Back in love again / Baby talk / Everybody's gotta learn sometime / Look of love / Live your life / That's just the way that it is
5219892 / Aug '94 / Polydor

Ybarra, Eva

☐ A MI SAN ANTONIO (Ybarra, Eva Y Su Conjunto)
ROUCD 6056 / Apr '94 / Rounder

☐ ROMANCE INOLVIDABLE (Ybarra, Eva Y Su Conjunto)
ROUCD 6062 / Jun '96 / Rounder

Year Zero

☐ CREATION
H 00382 / Jul '95 / Hellhound

☐ NIHIL'S FLAME
Prefall (Intro) / Planetfall / Headache station / Harsh believing / Civilisation dreaming / Wishing horse / Year zero / Evergreen / Shining violet / Invention of God / Eternal dawn
H 00272 / Aug '94 / Hellhound

Yearwood, Trisha

☐ EVERYBODY KNOWS
I want to live again / It's alright / Even a cowboy can dream / Believe me baby / I need you / Little hercules / Under the rainbow / Everybody knows / Hello, I'm gone / Find a river / Chance I take / Maybe it's love / Lover is forever
MCD 11512 / Aug '96 / MCA

☐ HEARTS IN ARMOUR
You say you will / Woman before me / When goodbye was a word / Walkaway Joe / Down on my knees / That's what I like about you / Woman walk the line / You don't have to move that mountain / Hearts in armour / Wrong side of Memphis / Like we never had a broken heart / Fools like me / Nearest distant shore / She's in love with the boy / Lonesome dove
MCLD 19323 / Sep '96 / MCA

☐ SONG REMEMBERS WHEN, THE
Song remembers when / Better your heart than mine / I don't fall in love so easy / Hard promises to keep / Mr. Radio / Nightingale / If I ain't got you / One in a row / Here comes temptation / Lying to the moon / Walkaway Joe / New kid in town
MCLD 19324 / Sep '96 / MCA

☐ SONGBOOK
UMD 80407 / 1 Sep '97 / Universal

☐ THINKIN' ABOUT YOU
Thinkin' about you / Xxx's and ooo's (an american girl) / You can sleep while I drive / Restless kind / Two days from knowing / On a bus to st. cloud / Fairytale / Those words we said / O mexico / Jackie's house / I wanna go too far / Bartender blues / 'til I get it right
MCD 11226 / Feb '95 / MCA

☐ TRISHA YEARWOOD
She's in love with the boy / Woman before me / That's what I like about you / Like we never had a broken heart / Fools like me / Victim of the game / When goodbye was a word / Whisper of your heart / You done me wrong (and that ain't right) / Lonesome dove
MCLD 19322 / Sep '96 / MCA

☐ WHEREVER YOUR ROAD GOES
UMD 80513 / 13 Jul '98 / Universal

Yeats, Grainne

☐ BELFAST HARP FESTIVAL, THE
CEFCD 156 / Jan '94 / Gael Linn

Yela

☐ SWING LOW SANGOLO
Nobody knows / Sometimes I feel like a motherless child / Mwana zwambi / Swing low sangolo / Go down Moses / Okileou / City called heaven / Ote mi lookaou / Liyaimauo / Nkembo na yawe
FA 423 / 21 Aug '97 / Fremeaux

Yell

☐ LET'S GO
Let's go round again / One thing leads to another / Instant replay / Give me a little more time / One touch too much / Surrender / Nothing comes for nothing / I got the feeling / What u do to me / Let's go round again (extended) / One thing leads to another (extended) / Instant replay (extended)
FARECD 102 / Oct '92 / Fanfare

Yello

☐ BABY
Intro / Rubber band man / Sticky jungle / Ocean club / Who's groove / Capri calling / Lazy / On the run / Blender / Sweet thunder
8487912 / Jun '91 / Mercury

☐ CLARO QUE SI
Daily disco / No more Roger / Take it all / Evening's young / She's got a gun / Ballet mechanique / Quad el habib / Lorry / Homer hossa / Pinball cha cha
8183402 / Mar '88 / Mercury

☐ ESSENTIAL YELLO
Oh yeah / Race / Rubberband man / Vicious games / Tied up / Lost again / I love you goodbye / Of course I'm lying / Pinball cha cha / Bostitch / Desire / Jungle Bill / Goldrush / Rhythm divine
5123902 / Sep '92 / Phonogram

☐ FLAG
Tied up / Of course I'm lying / 3rd of June / Blazing saddles / Race / Alhambra / Tied up in gear / Otto di catania
8367782 / Aug '90 / Mercury

☐ HANDS ON YELLO
Lost again / Excess / La habenera / L'hotel / I love you / Live at the Roxy / Oh yeah / Vicious circle / Crash dance / Dr. Van Steiner / Bostich / Ciel Ouvert / You gotta say yes to another excess / Great mission
5273832 / Mar '95 / Urban

☐ NEW MIX IN ONE GO 1980-1985, THE
Daily disco / Swing / Evening's young / Pinball cha cha / I love you / Sometimes (Dr. Hirsch) / Base for Alec / Oh yeah / Lost again / Tub dub / Angel no / Desire / Bananas to the beat / Koladiola / Domingo / Bostich / Live at the Roxy
8267732 / Jun '89 / Mercury

☐ ONE SECOND
Habanera / Moon on ice / Call it love / Le secret farida / Hawaiian chance / Rhythm divine / Santiago / Gold rush / Dr. Van Steiner / Si senor and the hairy grill
8309562 / Jun '89 / Mercury

☐ POCKET UNIVERSE
5343532 / May '97 / Mercury

☐ SOLID PLEASURE
Bimbo / Night flanger / Reverse lion / Downdown samba / Magneto / Massage / Assistant's cry / Bostich / Rock stop / Coast to polka / Blue green / Eternal legs / Stanztrigge / Bananas to the beat
8183392 / Mar '88 / Mercury

☐ STELLA
Desire / Vicious games / Oh yeah / Desert inn / Stalakdrama / Koladiola / Domingo / Sometimes (Dr. Hirsch) / Let me cry / Ciel ouvert / Angel no
8228202 / Mar '88 / Mercury

☐ YOU GOTTA SAY YES TO ANOTHER EXCESS
I love you / Look again / No more words / Crash dance / Great mission / You gotta say yes to another excess / Swing / Heavy whispers / Smile on you / Pumping velvet / Salut mayoumba
8121662 / Mar '88 / Mercury

☐ ZEBRA
5224962 / Nov '94 / Mercury

Yellow Balloon

☐ YELLOW BALLOON, THE
How can I be down / Stained glass window / Baby baby it's you / Panama red / I've got a feeling for love / Yellow balloon / Good feelin' time / Follow the sunshine / Springtime girl / Can't get enough of your love / Junk maker shoppe / Yellow balloon / Children of St. Monica / Good man to have around the house / Impressions with Syvonne / Leaving it up to you / Can't get enough of your love / Follow the sunshine / How can I be down / Gary Zekley interview
CDSC 11069 / May '98 / Sundazed

Yellow Jackets

☐ PRICELESS JAZZ
Oz / River waltz / Evan song / Downtown / Spirits / 1998 / Storytellers / Peace / Homecoming
GRP 98932 / 23 Mar '98 / GRP

Yellow Monkey

☐ PUNCH DRUNKARD
74321582202 / 13 Jul '98 / RCA

☐ SICKS
Rainbow man / I can be shit / Mama / Love love show
74321515792 / Aug '97 / RCA

Yellow Note

☐ WE'RE NOT THE BEATLES
JSK 134 / 6 Jul '98 / Jungle Sky

Yellowcake

☐ HARD TRAX
RA 019 / 6 Apr '98 / Radikal Ambience

☐ INNER STATE STATIONS
RA 017CD / Oct '96 / Radikal Ambience

Yellowman

☐ 20 SUPER HITS
SONCD 0006 / Oct '90 / Sonic Sounds

☐ BEST OF YELLOWMAN LIVE IN PARIS, THE
503562
503552 / Apr '95 / Blue Silver
8412162 / Oct '96 / Declic

☐ BEST OF YELLOWMAN, THE
794502 / Dec '95 / Melodie

☐ BLUEBERRY HILL
Blueberry Hill / Letter to Rosey / Jean a miss follow fashion / Who say yellow don't go hotel / Nah pay no tax / Anything me say / Young girl be wise / Another Saturday night
GRELCD 107 / Sep '92 / Greensleeves

☐ DON'T BURN IT DOWN
Don't burn it down / Stop beat woman / Diseases / Nuh tie me / Hold a girl / Want a woman / Free africa / Want a virgin / Scorpio crew / Dry head adassa
GRELCD 110 / May '88 / Greensleeves

☐ FANTASTIC YELLOWMAN
LG 21091 / Nov '93 / Lagoon

☐ FREEDOM OF SPEECH
Weed dem / Run cum-cum / Warn dem / Hip hip hurray / Chant / Abortion / Freedom of speech / Visa / Sugar darling / Here I come / African drum / Fed up / Nice to be important / Girls in the ring / Bump and whine
RASCD 3179 / 6 Oct '97 / Ras

☐ FREEDOM OF SPEECH
BSCCD 019 / 22 Jun '98 / Black Scorpio

☐ GALONG GALONG GALONG
Galong galong galong / Beat it / Under mi fat thing / Cus cus / Reggae get the grammy / Throw me corn / Skank quadrille / Blow saxophone / Money make friend / Bubble with mi ting
GRELCD 87 / Nov '87 / Greensleeves

☐ GOOD SEX GUIDE
GRELCD 217 / Oct '95 / Greensleeves

☐ IN BED WITH YELLOWMAN
GRELCD 179 / Feb '93 / Greensleeves

☐ KING OF THE DANCE HALL
Hot fe me / Full metal jacket / Monkey time / Good to have feeling / Greatest lover / New york / Fling it up / Have fun / Starting all over again / Sexy yellowman
RRTGCD 7717 / '88 / Rohit

☐ KISS ME
Kiss me / Dicky / Hot again / Jordan river / Thanks and praise / Murderer / Hek she gwan / Love is a splendid thang / Woman / Slow motion
113862 / Jul '95 / Musidisc UK

☐ LIVE IN ENGLAND
SON 0024 / Apr '92 / Greensleeves

☐ MAN YOU WANT, A
SHCD 45011 / Mar '94 / Shanachie

☐ MESSAGE TO THE WORLD
RASCD 3185 / Jan '96 / Ras

☐ MISTER YELLOWMAN
Natty sat upon the rock / Lost mi love / Mr. Chin / Two to six super mix / Morning ride / How you keep a dance / Jamaica a little Miami / Yellowman get's married / Duppy or gunman / Cocky did a hurt me
GRELCD 35 / '87 / Greensleeves

☐ NEGRIL CHILL (Yellowman & Charlie Chaplin)
Arrival / Feeling sexy / Don't sell yourself / Nuff punany / Naw breed again / Undergal frock / Blueberry Hill / Reason with entertainers / Gone a South Africa / Jah mi fear / Trouble Rosie / Old lady / Listen Charlie / Same way it taste / Calypso jam / Don't drop yu pants / Rent a dread
RE 155CD / Jul '97 / ROIR

☐ NOBODY MOVE - NOBODY GET HURT
Nobody move nobody get hurt / Strictly mi belly / Bedroom mazurka / Body move / Good lovin' / Wreck a pum pum / Hill and gully rider / Yellowman a lover boy / Watch your words / Why you bad so
GRELCD 71 / Jul '89 / Greensleeves

☐ ONE YELLOWMAN AND FATMAN
JJCD 067 / Apr '96 / Channel One

☐ OPERATION RADICATION
11 and 11 / Shorties / Morning ride / Eventide fire / Operation radication / Couchie / Out a hand / Mad over me / Lovers corner / Bim and Bam / Badness / My possie
REMCD 520 / 27 Apr '98 / Reactive

☐ PARTY
Party / Oldies but goodies / Still got it / 100 sexy girls / Freedom / Gone up / World of girls / Original love / My girl friend
RASCD 3073 / Aug '96 / Ras

☐ PRAYER
Prayer / Carolina / Romance / Dancehall / Reggae music / Guantanamera / Crowd / Africa / Girlfriend / Politician: *Yellowman & Daddy Snake*
DREAD 331322 / Nov '97 / Dread Beat

☐ RAS PORTRAITS
Reggae on the move / Party / Yellow like cheese / Prayer / God alone / AIDS / Love King Yellowman / I'm ready / Wild wild West / Gone up / Dancehall / Reggae music / Maximum / War / Got the rammer / No touch ya so
RAS 3314 / Jul '97 / Ras

☐ REGGAE CALYPSO ENCOUNTER
RMJLCD 0101 / '88 / Rohit

☐ REGGAE ON THE MOVE
RASCD 3094 / Sep '93 / Ras

☐ SATURDAY NIGHT
RB 3009 / Jul '94 / Reggae Best

☐ THEM A MAD OVER ME
78249700060 / Apr '95 / Channel One

☐ THIS IS YELLOWMAN
RN 7009 / Sep '96 / Rhino

☐ TWO GIANTS CLASH (Yellowman & Josey Wales)
Society party / Strictly bubbling / Mr. Big shot / King of the crop / Wrong girl to play with / Bobo dread / Mi have Fi get you / Cure for the fever / Jah a mi guiding star / Sorry to say
GRELCD 63 / '89 / Greensleeves

☐ YELLOW LIKE CHEESE
Budget / Easy me ting / Gaze / Want a woman / To touch ya so / Yellow like cheese / No get nuthin' / Ain't no meaning / Na no lyrics / Mi mother love, my father love
RASCD 3019 / Nov '97 / Ras

☐ YELLOWMAN GOING TO THE CHAPEL
Look in a me eye / Rub-a-dub / Going to the chapel / Hunnu fi move / Come back to Jamaica / No lucky in gambling / Ready fe them / Amen / To the bump
GRELCD 97 / '86 / Greensleeves

☐ YELLOWMAN RIDES AGAIN
Aids / Ease up President Botha / Wild, wild west / Boys want to have fun / Girl you're too hot / In the army / I'm ready / In memory of / Pretty girl / Want a virgin
RASCD 3034 / Nov '97 / Ras

☐ ZUNGGUZUNGGUGUZUNGGUZENG
Zungguzungguguzungguzeng / Good, the bad and the ugly / Rub-a-dub a play / Dem sight the boss / Can't hide from Jah / Who can make the dance ram / Yellowman wise / Take me to Jamaica / Friday night jamboree / Jah Jah are we guiding star
GRELCD 57 / Feb '87 / Greensleeves

Yelvington, Malcolm

☐ TENNESSEE SATURDAY NIGHT
CLCD 4403 / Oct '96 / Collector/White Label

Yelworc

☐ COLLECTION 1988-1994, THE
EFA 125252 / Apr '95 / Celtic Circle

Yemm, Bryn

☐ HEART 'N' SOUL (The Best Of Bryn Yemm)
Haffron / Say a little prayer / Soul of my saviour / Why me Lord / Cleanse me / Since I laid my burden down / Amazing grace / I have a dream / Old rugged cross / When a child is born / Anna Marie / Let me live / End of the day / How great thou art / Holy city / It's no secret / One day at a time / I'll fly away
CD 101 / Mar '96 / Bay

Yes

☐ 90125
Owner of a lonely heart / Hold on / It can happen / Changes / Cinema / Leave it / Our song / City of love / Hearts
7901252 / Nov '83 / Atlantic

☐ AFFIRMATIVE (The Yes Solo Family Album) (Various Artists)
VSOPCD 190 / Sep '93 / Connoisseur Collection

☐ ANDERSON, BRUFORD, WAKEMAN, HOWE (Anderson Bruford Wakeman Howe)
Sound / Second attention / Soul warrior / Fist of fire / Brother of mine / Big dream / Nothing can come between us / Birthright / Meeting / I wanna learn / She gives me love / Who was the first / I'm alive / Teakbois / Order of the universe / Order theme / Rock gives courage / It's so hard to grow / Universe / Let's pretend
262155 / Jan '92 / Arista

☐ BEYOND AND BEFORE (BBC Recordings 1969-1970)
CLEO 2462 / 27 Apr '98 / Cleopatra

☐ BIG GENERATOR
Rhythm of love / Big generator / Shoot high aim low / Almost like love / Love will find a way / Final eyes / I'm running / Holy lamb
7905222 / Aug '87 / Atlantic

☐ CLASSIC YES
Heart of the sunrise / Wonderous stories / Yours is no disgrace / Starship trooper / Long distance runaround / Fish / And you and I
7567826872 / Sep '94 / Atlantic

☐ CLOSE TO THE EDGE
Solid time of change / Total mass retain / I get up, I get down / Seasons of man / And you and I / Cord of life / Eclipse / Preacher / Teacher / Siberian Khatru
7567826662 / Aug '94 / Atlantic

☐ DRAMA
Machine messiah / White car / Does it really happen / Into the lens / Run through the light / Tempus fugit
7567826852 / Sep '94 / Atlantic

☐ EVENING OF YES, AN (Anderson Bruford Wakeman Howe)
DC 865762 / Mar '96 / Disky

☐ FRAGILE
Roundabout / Cans and Brahms / We have heaven / South side of the sky / Five per cent of nothing / Long distance runaround / Fish / Mood for a day / Heart of the sunrise
7567826672 / Aug '94 / Atlantic

☐ GOING FOR THE ONE
Going for the one / Turn of the century / Parallels / Wonderous stories / Awaken
7567826702 / Aug '94 / Atlantic

☐ KEYS TO ASCENSION VOL.2 (2CD Set)
All good people / Going for the one / Time and a word / Close to the edge / Turn of the century / And you and I / Mind drive / Foot prints / Bring to the power / Lightning / Children of the light / Lifeline / Sign language
EDFCD 457 / 1 Nov '97 / Essential

☐ KEYS TO ASCENSION, THE (2CD Set)
Siberia / Revealing science / America / Onward / Awaken / Roundabout / Starship trooper / Be the one / That, that is
EDFCD 417 / Oct '96 / Essential
ESFCD 635 / 9 Mar '98 / Essential

☐ OPEN YOUR EYES
EAGCD 013 / 24 Nov '97 / Eagle

☐ OPEN YOUR EYES (Limited Edition Surround Sound)
36985730752 / 5 May '98 / Beyond

☐ RELAYER
Gates of delirium / Sound chaser / To be over
7567826642 / Sep '94 / Atlantic

☐ SOMETHING'S COMING (2CD Set)
PILOT 025 / 19 Jan '98 / Burning Airlines

☐ SYMPHONIC MUSIC OF YES (Featuring Yes) (London Philharmonic Orchestra/David Palmer)
Roundabout: *Yes* / Wonderous stories: *Yes* / I've seen all good people: *Yes* / Mood for a day: *Yes* / Owner of a lonely heart: *Yes* / Survival: *Yes* / Heart of the sunrise: *Yes* / Soon: *Yes* / Lifeseeker-warm (starship trooper): *Yes*
09026619382 / Jan '94 / RCA Victor

☐ TALES FROM TOPOGRAPHIC OCEANS
Revealing science of God / Remembering / Ancient / Ritual
7567826832 / Sep '94 / Atlantic

☐ TALES FROM YESTERDAY (A Tribute To Yes) (Various Artists)
Roundabout: *Berry, Robert* / Siberian khatru: *Stanley Snail* / Mood for a day: *Morse, Steve* / Don't kill the whale: *Magellan* / Turn of the century: *Howe, Steve* / Release release: *Shadow Gallery* / Wondrous stories: *World Trade* / South of the sky: *Cairo* / Soon: *Moraz, Patrick* / Changes: *Enchant* / Astral traveller: *Banks, Peter* / Clap: *Morse, Steve* / Starship trooper: *Jeronimo Road*
RR 89142 / Oct '95 / Roadrunner

☐ TIME AND A WORD
No opportunity necessary / No experience needed / Then / Everdays / Sweet dreams / Prophet / Clear days / Astral traveller / Time and a word
7567826812 / Sep '94 / Atlantic

☐ TORMATO
Future times / Rejoice / Don't kill the whale / Madrigal / Release release / Arriving UFO / Circus of heaven / Onward / On the silent wings of freedom
7567826712 / Aug '94 / Atlantic

☐ UNION
I would have waited forever / Shock to the system / Masquerade / Lift me up / Without hope you cannot start the day / Saving my heart / Miracle of life / Silent talking / More we live-let go / Angkor Wat / Dangerous / Holding on / Evensong / Take the water to the mountain / Give and take
261558 / Apr '94 / Arista

☐ VERY BEST OF YES, THE (Highlights)
Survival / Time and a word / Starship trooper / Life seeker / Disillusion / Wurm / I've seen all good people / Your move / All good people / Roundabout / Long distance runaround / Soon / Wonderous stories / Going for the one / Owner of a lonely heart / Leave it / Rhythm of love
7567825172 / Sep '93 / Atlantic

☐ YES
Beyond and before / I see you / Yesterday and today / Looking around / Harold land / Every little thing / Sweetness / Survival
7567826802 / Aug '94 / Atlantic

☐ YES ALBUM, THE
Yours is no disgrace / Clap / Starship trooper / Life seeker / Disillusion / Wurm / I've seen all good people / Your move / All good people / Venture / Perpetual change
7567826652 / Sep '94 / Atlantic

☐ YES FRIENDS AND RELATIVES (2CD Set)
Owner of a lonely heart: *Anderson, Jon* / ICE: *Wakeman, Rick* / Red and white: *Howe, Steve* / Zone of O: *Esquire* / Up North: *Bruford, Bill Earthworks* / Pyramids of Egypt: *Wakeman, Rick* / Roundabout: *Howe, Steve* / Sync or swim: *Wakeman, Rick & Adam* / Close to the edge / No expense spared: *Wakeman, Rick & Adam* / Say: *Anderson, Jon* / Walk don't run: *Howe, Steve* / Tron Thomi: *Esquire* / 10 million: *Anderson, Jon* / Tales of topographic oceans: *Howe, Steve* / More you know: *Anderson, Jon* / Journey: *Wakeman, Rick* / America
EDGCD 034 / 22 Jun '98 / Eagle

☐ YES YEARS, THE (4CD Set)
Something's coming / Survival / Every little thing / Then / Everydays / Sweet dreams / No opportunity necessary, no experience needed / Time and a word / Starship trooper / Yours is no disgrace / I've seen all good people / Long distance runaround / Fish (schindleria praematurus) / Roundabout / Heart of the sunrise / America / Close to the edge / Ritual / Sound chaser / Soon / Amazing grace / Vevey (part 1) / Wonderous stories / Awaken / Montreux's theme / Vevey (part 2) / Going for the one / Money / Abilene / Don't kill the whale / On the silent wings of freedom / Does it really happen / Tempus fugit / Run with the fox / I'm down / Make it easy / It can happen / Owner of a lonely heart / Hold on / Shoot high aim low / Rhythm of love / Love will find a way / Changes / And you and I / Love conquers all
7567916442 / Aug '91 / Atlantic

☐ YESSHOWS
Parallels / Time and a word / Going for the one / Gates of Delirium
7567826862 / Sep '94 / Atlantic

☐ YESSONGS (2CD Set)
Opening: Excerpt from the firebird suite / Siberian Khatru / Heart of the sunrise / Perpetual change / And you and I / Cord of life / Eclipse / Preacher and the teacher / Apocalypse / Mood for a day / Excerpts from the six wives of Henry VIII / Roundabout / Your move / I've seen all good people / Long distance runaround / Fish / Close to the edge / Solid time of change / Total mass retain / I get up, I get down / Seasons of man / Yours is no disgrace / Starship trooper / Life seeker / Disillusion / Wurm
7567826822 / Sep '94 / Atlantic

☐ YESSTORY (2CD Set)
Survival / No opportunity necessary, no experience needed / Time and a word / Starship trooper / I've seen all good people / Roundabout / Heart of the sunrise / Close to the edge / Ritual / Soon / Wonderous stories / Going for the one / Don't kill the whale / Does it really happen / Make it easy / Owner of a lonely heart / Rhythm of love / Changes
7567917472 / Sep '91 / Atlantic

☐ YESTERDAYS
America / Looking around / Time and a word / Sweet dreams / Then / Survival / Astral traveller / Dear father
7567826842 / Sep '94 / Atlantic

Yeshuah

☐ KNOWLEDGE IS KING
81085175993 / 23 Mar '98 / Imani

Yesterday's Children

☐ YESTERDAY'S CHILDREN
LSDBY 5002 / 8 Jun '98 / LSD

Yesteryear

☐ UNDER THE RUG
MES 006 / Feb '97 / Magick Eye

Yetties

☐ COME TO THE YETTIES BARN DANCE
Gay Gordons / Hello / Family waltz / Clopton bridge / Swanee river / Strip the willow / Cumberland square eight / Barn dance / Timber salvage reel / Swedish masquerade / Tom Pate / Devil's dream / Circassian circle
GRCD 53 / May '92 / Grasmere

☐ FIDDLER KNOWS, THE
Sicilian dance / Come rouze brother sportsman / Negro's complaint / Braes of busbie / Mill in the wad / Carravan gigs / Mr. witts favourit jig / Mrs. george derring's waltz / Dorchester hornpipe / Jack's alive / Spanish dance / Ladies play thing / Paddy carry / Sociable / Rosebud in summerlass of richmond hill / Ploughboy / Rose tree / March / Rosline castle / Comet waltz / Turk / John de paris / Lucklian / Jockey to the fair / Poor but honnist soldier or the blue-eyed strainger / Woodpecker / Legisey / Barth waltz / Waltz / White joke / Plains of vittoria or roast beef of old england / Go to the devel and shake your self / Irish row dow dow / Waltz / Wonded hussar / Miss platoff
CDALA 3010 / '89 / ASV

☐ FOLK MUSIC OF ENGLAND
John Peel / Turmit hoeing / Medley / Foggy, foggy dew / Jolly waggoner / Lincolnshire poacher / Cuckoo's nest / Sailor cut down in his prime / South Australia / Medley / Lilliburleo / Trelawney / Leaving of Liverpool / No sir no / Medley / Brigg fair / Spanish ladies / Fox / Medley / Derby ram / Home dearest home
GRCD 82 / Jul '97 / Grasmere

☐ MUSICAL HERITAGE OF THOMAS HARDY
CDALD 4010 / Feb '88 / ASV

☐ SINGALONG PARTY
GRCD 72 / Oct '95 / Grasmere

☐ SINGING ALL THE WAY
Over the hills and far away / Ball of yarn / Grey hawk / Polka medley / Rabbit / John Barleycorn / Winter / Poor, poor farmer / Ee weren't all bad / Man at the nore / Bread and cheese and kisses / We've got oil / Beggar's song / Beaumont rag / Back 'n' back yer you / Scarlet and the blue / Carolina moon / Beautiful dreamer / Early one evening / Linden lea / Bell ringing / Levi Jackson's rag / Wave over wave / Last rose of Summer / Praise o'Dorset
CDALA 3009 / Jul '89 / ASV

☐ TOP OF THE CROPS
GRCD 68 / Oct '95 / Grasmere

Yiladi Trio

☐ SONGS IN YIDDISH & LADINO VOL.3
YILADI 9103 / Sep '94 / Yiladi

Yips

☐ BONFIRE IN A DIXIE CUP
SB 49 / Nov '96 / Siltbreeze

YN-Vee

☐ YN-VEE
Even when U sleep / All I wanna do / 4 play / I'm goin' down / Sceamin' / Sonshine's groove / Chocolate / Stra8 hustler / Tricks-n-trainin' / YN-Vee / Real G / Gangsta's prayer / We got a good thing
5235852 / Oct '94 / Island

YO 3

☐ BITTER SWEET
GPRCD 5 / Jun '94 / GPR

Yo La Tengo

☐ GENIUS + LOVE = YO LA TENGO (2CD Set)
Evanescent psychic pez drop / Demons / Fog over Frisco / Too late / Hanky panky nohow / Something to do / Ultra-powerful short wave radio picks up music from Venus / Up to you / Somebody's baby / Walking away from you / Artificial heart / Cast a shadow / I'm set free / Barnaby, hardly working / Some kinda fatigue / Speeding motorcycle / Her Grandmother's gift / From a motel 6 / Gooseneck problem / Surfin' with the Shah / Ecstasy blues / Too much, part 1 / Blitzkreig bop / One self : fish girl / Enough / Drum solo / From a motel 6 / Too much, part 2 / Sunsquashed
OLE 1942 / Nov '96 / Matador

☐ I CAN HEAR THE HEART BEATING AS ONE
Return to hot chicken / Moby octopad / Sugarcube / Damage / Deeper into movies / Shadows / Stockholm syndrome / Autumn sweater / Little honda / Green arrow / One PM again / Lie and how we told it / Center of gravity / Spec bebop / We're an American band / My little corner of the world
OLE 2222 / Apr '97 / Matador

☐ I CAN HEAR THE HEART BEATING AS ONE (Japanese Issue)
APCY 8425 / 27 Apr '98 / Apollon

☐ PAINFUL
EFA 049272 / Sep '93 / City Slang

☐ THAT IS YOURS
EFA 0406805 / Jan '95 / City Slang

Yo Yo

☐ YOU BETTER ASK SOMEBODY
IBWin' wit my crewin' / Can you handle it / Westside story / Mackstress / Twenty Sack / You better ask somebody / They shit don't stink / Letter to the pen / Givin' it up / Pass it on / Girl's got a gun / Bonnie and Clyde theme
7567922522 / Jun '93 / East West

Yoakam, Dwight

☐ BUENOS NOCHES FROM A LONELY ROOM
I got you / One more name / What I don't know / Home of the blues / Buenos noches from a lonely room / She wore red dresses / I hear you knocking / I sang Dixie / Streets of Bakersfield / Floyd county / Send me the pillow that you dream on / Hold onto God
9257492 / Jan '89 / Reprise

☐ DWIGHT LIVE
Suspicious minds / This time / Thousand miles from nowhere / It only hurts when I cry / Nothing's changed here / Heart that you own / Streets of bakersfield / Little ways / Please please baby / Rocky road blues / Lonesome roads / Wild ride / Fast as you / Two doors down / Little sister / Miner's prayer / Long white cadillac
9362459072 / May '95 / Reprise

☐ GONE
Sorry you asked / This much I know / One more night / Heart of stone / Baby why not / Never hold you / Don't be sad / Gone (that'll be me) / Nothing / Near you
9362460512 / Nov '95 / Reprise

☐ GUITARS CADILLACS ETC ETC
Honky tonk man / It won't hurt / I'll be gone / South of cincinati / Bury me / Guitars and Cadillacs / Twenty years / Ring of fire / Miner's prayer / Heartache by the number
9253722 / Feb '93 / Reprise

☐ HILLBILLY DELUXE
Little ways / Smoke along the track / Johnson's love / Please please baby / Readin', ritin' RT23 / Always late / 1000 miles from nowhere / Throughout all times / Little sister / This drinking will kill me
9255672 / Jun '87 / Reprise

☐ IF THERE WAS A WAY
Distance between you and me / Heart that you own / Takes a lot to rock you / Nothing's changed here / Sad, sad music / Since I started drinkin' again / If there was a way / Turn it on, turn it up, turn me loose / It only hurts when I cry / Send a message to my heart / I don't need it done / You're the one
7599263442 / Nov '90 / Reprise

☐ LA CROIX D'AMOUR
Things we said today / Truckin' / If there was a way / Hey little girl / What I don't know / Here comes the night / Dangerous man / Let's work together / Doin' what I did / Takes a lot to rock you / Suspicious minds / Long white cadillac
9362451362 / Nov '92 / Reprise

☐ LONG WAY HOME, A
Same fool / Curse / Things change / Yet to suceed / I wouldn't put it past me / These arms / That's okay / Only want you more / I'll take just these / Long way home / Listen / Traveler's lantern / Maybe you like it maybe you don't
9362469182 / 22 Jun '98 / Reprise

☐ UNDER THE COVERS
Claudette / Train in vain / Tired of waiting for you / Good time Charlie's got the blues / Baby don't go / Playboy / Wichita lineman / Here comes the night / Last time / Things we said today / North to Alaska / T is for Texas
9362466902 / Aug '97 / Reprise

Yockamo All Stars

☐ DEW DROP OUT A NEW ORLEANS SECOND LINE R AND B JAM
Blow blow tenor / Rich woman / Dew drop out / Falling in love / Talk to me baby / Jambolero / Ice cool / Ain't got no home / I hear you knockin' / Bhang bhang / Gravel grinder / Rat cheer
HNCD 1422 / 27 Apr '98 / Hannibal

Yodellers In Gold

☐ BEST YODELLERS, THE
323010 / Sep '93 / Koch

Yogeswaran, Manickam

☐ TAMIL CLASSICS
Sapthaswaram en jeevane / Aanai muga / Ammah umah / Sri lalita - shakti
EXIL 55342 / Jun '97 / Exil

Yokota

☐ FRANKFURT/TOKYO CONNECTION
In the beginning / Panicwaves / Source of soul / Tune for a replicant / A sonic fairy-tale / Spacious house / Judgement day / Follow the sonic leader / Japanese therapy / Wicked city / Trancewheel
HHCD 003 / Apr '94 / Harthouse

Yokoyama, Katsuya

☐ ART OF THE SHAKUHACHI (Yokoyama, Katsuya & Yoshikazu Iwamoto)
C 560114 / Jul '97 / Ocora

Yole

☐ A LA SOURCE
SCD 711 / Nov '95 / Several

☐ L'AMOUR D'ELOISE
SCD 709 / Nov '95 / Several

Yona Kit

☐ YONA KIT
GR 20CD / Sep '95 / Skingraft

York, Clive

☐ HYPERBOLE TRIO, THE (York, Clive & Dave Fowler/Julia Doyle)
SLAMCD 226 / Jan '98 / Slam

York Minster Choir

☐ CHRISTMAS AT YORK MINSTER
Away in a manger / Noel / See amid the winter's snow / I saw three ships / I sing of a maiden / Offertoire sur des Noels / O come, O come Emmanuel / Babe is born / Holy boy / Tomorrow shall be my dancing day / I sing the birth / Bendicamus domino / Great and mighty wonder / Child is born in Bethlehem / O little town of Bethlehem / Three Kings / Unto us a boy is born / Carillon de Longpont
YORKCD 846 / Nov '97 / York Ambisonic

☐ ON CHRISTMAS NIGHT
CHAN 6520 / Nov '97 / Chandos

York, Pete

☐ STEAMING (York, Pete & Brian Auger/ Colin Hodgkinson)
No one / Freedom jazz dance / Catcote rag / San Francisco bay blues / Take the A-train / Prelude to a kiss / Hawk talk / Season of the witch / All about my girl / Going down slow / Compared to what
INAK 855CD / Nov '97 / In Akustik

☐ STRING TIME IN NEW YORK
BLR 84 015 / May '91 / L&R

☐ SWINGING LONDON
341172 / Apr '94 / Koch

York Waites

☐ 1588 - MUSIC FROM THE TIME OF THE SPANISH ARMADA
Queene's visiting of the campe at Tilsburie / Spanish pavan / Galliard / Crimson velvet / La doune cella / La shy myze / La bounette / Obtaining of the great galleazzo / Browninge my dere / Browninge fantasy / Les bransles gays / Delight pavan / Galliard to delight pavan / Staines morris / Quarter brawles / Pavana / Galiarda / Coranto / Watkin's ale / Robin is to the greenwood gone / Wilson's fantasie / Spanish lady / Cushion dance / Dulcina / All you that love good fellowes / Eighty eight or Sir Francis drake / Les bransles de Champagne / Carman's whistle / Under and over / Pepper is black / Millfield / Roowe well ye marynors
CDSDL 373 / May '97 / Saydisc

☐ CHRISTMAS MUSICKE (1400-1800) (York Waits & Deborah Caterall)
Personent hodie / O jesulien suss o jesulein mild / Angelus ad pastores / Von himmel hoch / Resonet in laudibus / Thys endere nyghth / As I lay on a night / Als y lay on yoolis night / Piva ferrarese / O hac quam mundam / El noi de la mare / el desembre congelat/oi betleem/birjina g / De matin ai rescoutra lou train / Quando nascette ninno / Doux pommier/faisans rejoussance / Bergers, j'ai ouy la nouvelle / Quelle est cette odeur agreable / Bergers, par les plus doux accords / Born is the babe / Thus angels sing / Christmas cheer / Little barley corn / St Day carol / I saw three ships come sailing in / Sussex carol / Yorkshire wassail / Wexford wassail / Wexford carol / While sheperds watched / Waits(London) / Waits wassail / Ding dong merrily on high
BHCD 9607 / Dec '96 / Brewhouse

☐ CITY MUSICKE, THE
BH 9409CD / Jul '94 / Brewhouse

☐ MUSIC FROM THE TIME OF RICHARD III
Quene note / La spanga / Mater ora filium / L'hom arme / Danse de Cleves / Le souvenir / Tuba Gallicalis / Noel nouvelet / Anxi bon youre delabonestren / Nous voici dans la ville dit le Bourguinon / Allez a la fougere / In feuers hitz / Auf rief ein huebsches freulein / Der neue bauernschwanz / Die katzen pfote / Ein vrouleen edel von naturen / Das jaegerhorn / Mercantia / Anello / Amoroso / L'amor donna ch'io te porta / Bassa con misurias danza alta / Todos los biennes del mundo dindirin dindirin
CDSDL 364 / May '97 / Saydisc

☐ OLD CHRISTMAS RETURN'D
CDSDL 398 / Oct '92 / Saydisc

☐ PUNK'S DELIGHT, THE
HUNTSUPCD 1 / Dec '97 / Huntsup

Yorke, Peter

☐ GLAMOROUS NIGHTS
Anchors away / Songs to remember / Make mine music / Centennial summer / London town / Songs to remember no.2 / Songs to remember no.3
CDEA 6005 / Feb '98 / Vocalion

Yorkshire Building Society Band

☐ CRY OF THE CELTS
Riverdance / Demelza / Aye waukin' / Reel McCoy / Ye banks and braes / Wee cooper of Fife / Londonderry air / Alloway tales / Mull of the cool bens / Macushla / Cry of the Celts / Nightmare / Lord of the dance / Stolen kiss / Suil a ruin / Breakout / Lament / Finale
QPRL 091D / Oct '97 / Polyphonic

☐ ESSAYS FOR BRASS
Call of the righteous / Rhapsodic variations / My strength, my tower / Meditation / Light of the world / Lord is king / Meditation / Just as I am / Tone poem / Kingdom triumphant / Victorian snapshots / On Ratcliff Highway
QPRL 080D / Oct '96 / Polyphonic

☐ EUROPEAN BRASS BAND CHAMPIONSHIP 1996 (Yorkshire Building Society Band/Black Dyke Mills Band)
DOYCD 057 / Nov '96 / Doyen

☐ INTRODUCTION
Introduction / Chablis / March / Swedish hymn / Dance / Time for peace / Procession to the cathedral / Facilita / Country scene / Variations on laudate dominum / Maids of cadiz / King's herald / Cortege / Jousts
QPRL 074D / Oct '97 / Polyphonic

Yorkshire Imperial Band

☐ FAR AND AWAY
Imperial echoes / Keel row / None shall asleep / Far and away / Somewhere over the rainbow / Thunderer / Nun's chorus / James Bond collection / Indian summer / Let's face the music and dance / With one look / Mack and Mabel / Granada / Deep inside the sacred temple / Boys of the old brigade / Crimond / William Tell
QPRL 077D / Oct '97 / Polyphonic

☐ PAGEANTRY
Strike up the band / Chelsea bridge / Homage march / On the way home / Can can / Girl with the flaxen hair / March: Le coq d'or / Pageantry / Arnhem / Toccata from 'Organ symphony No. 5' / Drink to me only with thine eyes / Entry of the huntresses from 'Sylvia' / Country scene / Sandpaper ballet / Norwegian wood / Downfall of lucifer
QPRL 040D / Oct '97 / Polyphonic

Yoshizawa, Motoharu

☐ PLAY UNLIMITED
PSFD 95 / Feb '98 / PSF

Yothu Yindi

☐ FREEDOM
TVD 93380 / Mar '94 / Mushroom

You Am I

☐ FOURTH RECORD, THE
9362468752 / 27 Apr '98 / East West

☐ HOURLY DAILY
9362465202 / Feb '97 / East West

You Fantastic

☐ PALS
GR 42CD / Jun '97 / Skingraft

☐ RIDDLER
GR 38CD / Oct '96 / Skingraft

You Slosh

☐ GLORIOUS RACKET
Break / Time to laugh / Hearthquake above leaves / Up in the slosh / When worlds collide / Dust
ONTHCD 1 / Dec '97 / On Them

☐ LIFT ME UP
Lift me up / Last swim / Source / At rest
ONTHCD 2 / Dec '97 / On Them

Youcef

☐ SALAM
AL 006 / 21 Aug '97 / Night & Day

Yougourthen

☐ MODERN BERBER SONGS
AAA 148 / Sep '97 / Club Du Disque Arabe

Youla, Fode

☐ BASIKOLO (Youla, Fode & African Djole)
FMPCD 44 / Feb '98 / Full Moon

Youmans, Vincent

☐ VINCENT YOUMANS
ACD 089 / Oct '93 / Audiophile

Young, Bob

☐ IN QUO COUNTRY
Down down / Caroline / Living on an island / Mean girl
SPRAYCD 104 / Dec '97 / Making Waves

Young, Claude

☐ DJ KICKS (Various Artists)
K7 045CD / May '96 / Studio K7

Young, Dave

☐ FABLES AND DREAMS (Young, Dave & Phil Dwyer Quartet)
JUST 532 / Nov '93 / Justin Time

☐ INNER URGE
Inner urge / Our waltz / It don't mean a thing / Sir William / Zingaro / Bolivia / Psalm for EM / Three in one / Irie
JUST 1102 / 27 Apr '98 / Justin Time

☐ PIANO-BASS DUETS VOL.1
JUST 762 / Sep '95 / Justin Time

☐ PIANO-BASS DUETS VOL.2
Dolphin dance / Blowin' the blues away / Make me a pallet on the floor / Moment to moment / Bass blues / Self portrait in three colors / One finger snap / Loverman / Nascimento / Pendulum at Falcon's lair / I'm all smiles / Peaceful
JUST 812 / May '96 / Justin Time

☐ PIANO-BASS DUETS VOL.3
In a mellow tone / Joshua / Milestones / Is that so / Soul eyes / Juicy lucy / Lament / Count two / Think of one / Don't blame me / Marie Antoinette
JUST 912 / Jan '97 / Justin Time

Young, Dougie

☐ SONGS OF DOUGIE YOUNG, THE
AIAS 19CD / Nov '94 / Larrikin

Young Dubliners

☐ ALIVE ALIVE O
CRGO 85018 / 16 Mar '98 / Earth Music

Young, Faron

☐ 18 ORIGINAL COUNTRY CLASSICS
Four in the morning / Little green apples / City lights / Walk tall / Yellow bandana / He'll have to go / Is it really over / Welcome to my world / Four walls / I'm gonna change everything / You don't know me / Am I that easy to forget / She thinks I still care / Faded love / I can't stop loving you / San Antonio rose / Linda on my mind / Drinking champagne
5525542 / Sep '96 / Spectrum

☐ ALONE WITH YOU
Hello walls / Four in the morning / Alone with you / Heartache for keepsake / Live fast, live hard and die young / Face to the wall / Unmitigated gall / Goin' steady / Some of these memories / Three days / Cryin' time / I could never be ashamed of you / Country girl / Apartment no.9 / Memphis Tennessee
PRACD 4001 / Jun '97 / Prairie

☐ CAPITOL YEARS, THE (5CD Set)
If you ain't lovin' (you ain't livin') / I've got five dollars and it's Saturday night / Place for girls like you / I can't tell my heart that / In the chapel in the moonlight / If that's the fashion / Forgive me, Dear / Just married / Baby my heart / What's the use to love you / That's what I do for you / I'm gonna tell Santa Claus on you / You're the angel on my christmas tree / I hardly knew it was you / That's what it's like to be lonesome / You're right (but I wish you were wrong) / Down Lover's Lane alone / So I'm in love with you / Goin' steady / Just out of reach / I can't wait (for the sun to go down) / Have I waited too long / Tattle tale tears / What can I do with my sorrow / Good Lord must have sent you / I knew you when / Saving my tears for tomorrow / Foolish pride / Live fast, love hard, die young / Go back, you fool / All right / For the love of a woman like you / It's a great life / Better things than these / Turn her down / You're still mine /

Sweet dreams / Till I met you / I'm gonna live some before I die / Candy kisses / Have I told you lately that I love you / I'll be satisfied with love / I can't help it / Your cheatin' heart / I'll be yours / Sweethearts or strangers / Shame on you / Worried mind / I miss you already / I'm a poor boy / You call everybody darlin' / You are my sunshine / Moonlight mountain / Anything your heart desires / Vacation's over / Shrine of St. Cecilia / Love has finally come my way / Face of love / The way it's gotta be / We're talking it over / I made a fool of myself / I'll be all right / You old used to be / Out of my heart / Every time I'm kissing you / Alone with you / That's the way I feel / I hate myself / Last night all the party / Long time ago / Hey good lookin' / Tennessee waltz / Let old Mother Nature have her way / Making believe / Almost / Mom and Dad's waltz / Don't let the stars get in your eyes / Bouquet of roses / Slowly / Bimbo / Chattanooga shoe shine boy / I don't hurt anymore / I'll go on alone / Honey stop / Locket / Snowball / When it rains it pours / Rosalie (is gonna get married) / I can't dance / Once in a while / Riverboat / Country girl / Face to the wall / There's not any like you left / Forget the past / World so full of love / Hello walls / Is she will you thought she'd be / Congratulations / Three days / Safely in love again / Down by the river / Part where I cry / I hear you talkin' / Big shoes / Believing in yourself / Come back / Overtonely and underkissed / Things to remember / I fail to please / Moment isn't very long / Moments to remember / Lifetime isn't long enough / I can't find the time / Trail of tears / I let it slip away / Let's pretend we're lovers again / Backtrack / How can I forget you / I'll fly away / Mansion over the hilltop / He was there / How long has it been / Beautiful garden of prayer / My home sweet home / Suppertime / May the good Lord bless and keep you / What can he do / He knows just what I need / When I've learned enough to live / Now I belong to Jesus / I won't have to cross Jordan alone / Travelling on / My wonderful Lord / I know who holds tomorrow / Where could I go but to the Lord / God bless God / Don't take your love from me / If I had you / Stay as sweet as you are / My darling, my darling / Who wouldn't love you / I can't believe that you're in love with me / Object of my affection / It all depends on you / Thank you for a lovely evening / Everything I have is yours / Nearness of you / Sweet and lovely

☐ **BCD 15493 / Mar '92 / Bear Family**

☐ **FOUR IN THE MORNING**
If you ain't lovin' (you ain't livin') / All right / Three days / Sweet dreams / Going steady / Hello walls / Backtrack / Wine me up / Your times comin' / I miss you already / This little girl of mine / Four in the morning / Seasons come, seasons go / Alone with you / Heartache for a keepsake / Apartment no. 9 / Live fast, love hard, die young / Your cheatin' heart / Satisfied mind / As far as I'm concerned / Is it really over / Chapel in the moonlight / Some of those memories / There goes my everything / Crying time / Swingin' doors / Tiger by the tail / Here comes my baby back again / Once a day / Sweet thang / I could never be ashamed of you / Are you sincere / Memphis

☐ **GRF 073 / Feb '93 / Tring**

☐ **GREATEST HITS**
PWKS 4221 / Nov '94 / Carlton

☐ **GREATEST HITS**
Four in the morning / Sweet dreams / I miss you already / Hello walls / Riverboat / Country girl / All right / Goin' steady / Backtrack / Live fast, love hard, die young / Wine me up / Your time's comin' / This little girl of mine / If you ain't lovin' / Comeback / Alone with you / That's the way it's gotta be / I've got five dollars / Three days / Yellow bandana

ECD 3301 / Mar '97 / K-Tel

☐ **HELLO WALLS**
CDSGP 0166 / Oct '95 / Prestige

Young Fresh Fellows

☐ **SOMOS LOS MEJORES**
MR 015CD / Apr '92 / Munster

Young, Gary

☐ **HOSPITAL**
Plant man / First impression / Mitchell / Foothill blud / Real crill (no video) / Warren / Hospital for the chemically insane / Birds in traffic / Where you are at / Ralph the vegetarian robot / Missing in action / Wipeout / Twentieth day / Gari / Hooks of the highway
ABB74CD / Aug '95 / Big Cat

Young, George

☐ **OLD TIMES**
CRD 307 / Mar '96 / Chiaroscuro

☐ **SPRING FEVER**
It might as well be Spring / All of me / Imagination / Bernie's tune / Mysticize / Garden of desire / Kid stuff / Little O's / Domingo en la tarde / Don't stay away / Spring fever
66055009 / Nov '91 / Sweet Basil

Young Ginns

☐ **YOUNG GINNS**
HB 20 / 8 Jun '98 / Honey Bear

Young Gods

☐ **LIVE SKY TOUR**
Intro / TV sky / Jimmy / Envoye/chanson rouge / L'eau rouge / Skinflowers / She rains / Summer eyes / Pas mal / Longue route / September song / Seerauber Jenny
BIAS 241CD / Jul '93 / Play It Again Sam

☐ **ONLY HEAVEN**
Outside / Strangel / Speed of night / Donnez les esprits / Moon revolutions / Kissing the sun / Dreamhouse / Lointaine / Grdez les esprits / Child in the tree
BIAS 301CD / Jun '95 / Play It Again Sam

☐ **RED WATER, THE**
BIAS 130CD / Aug '89 / Play It Again Sam

☐ **TV SKY**
Our house / Gasoline man / TV sky / Skinflowers / Dame chance / Night dance / She rains / Summer eyes
BIAS 201CD / Feb '92 / Play It Again Sam

☐ **YOUNG GODS PLAY KURT WEILL, THE**
BIAS 188CD / Apr '91 / Play It Again Sam

Young Jazz

☐ **SITTEL FROM SWEDEN**
SITCD 9237 / May '97 / Sittel

Young, James

☐ **SONGS THEY NEVER PLAY ON THE RADIO**
Mystery of love / Long wooden box / For the sunrise / Mr. Misterioso / Listen to the rain / Aphro gypsia / Curious / Tall tales / Der leiermann / Planet pussy / Silver sweet siren / Songs they never play on the radio
CREDCD 158 / Dec '93 / Creation

Young Jessie

☐ **I'M GONE**
Mary Lou / Lonesome desert / Rabbit on a log / Don't think I will / Well baby / Nothing seems right / Down at Hayden's / I smell a rat / Why do I love you / Pretty soon / Oochie coochie / Don't happen no more / Hit, git and split / Here comes Henry / Hot dog / Do you love me / This is young Jessie / Maybelline - Fragment / I hear you knocking - Fragment
CDCHD 607 / Nov '95 / Ace

Young, Jesse Colin

☐ **GREATEST HITS**
Get together / Darkness darkness / Light shine / Ridgetop / Songbird / T-bone shuffle / Sunlight / Lovely day / Grey day / Sugar babe / Song for Julie / Workin' / Peace song / Ramblin' on my mind
EDCD 542 / 6 Apr '98 / Edsel

☐ **HIGHWAY IS FOR HEROES, THE**
Highway is for heroes / When you dance / Master / Dreams take flight / Do it slow / T-bone shuffle / Before you came / Young girls / Erica
EDCD 479 / Jun '96 / Edsel

☐ **LOVE ON THE WING**
EDCD 477 / Jun '96 / Edsel

☐ **PERFECT STRANGER**
EDCD 478 / Jun '96 / Edsel

☐ **TOGETHER**
Good times / Sweet little child / Together / Sweet little sixteen / Peace song / Six days on the road / Lovely day / Creole belle / 1000 miles from nowhere / Born in Chicago / Pastures of plenty
EDCD 491 / Jul '96 / Edsel

☐ **YOUNGBLOOD**
Rider / Doc Geiger / Lullabye / Brother can you spare a dime / Trouble in mind / Little Suzie / Nobody's dirty business / Green Hill Mountain home / Summer rain / Walkin' off the blues / Cotton eyed Joe / Another strange town / Sometime / Hey babe / No more pain
EDCD 476 / 29 Sep '97 / Edsel

Young, John

☐ **WATER OF LIFE, THE (Young, John & Dougie Pincock)**
ADLCD 01 / Jun '96 / Kilmahew Music

Young, John

☐ **SERENATA**
I don't wanna be kissed / Baby doll / Circus / Cubana chant / In love in vain / Bones / Serenata / When I fall in love / Circus / Baby doll / I don't wanna be kissed
DD 403 / Mar '97 / Delmark

Young, John Paul

☐ **GREATEST HITS**
Love is in the air / Lost in your love / Here we go / Hot for your baby / Yesterday's hero / St. Louis / Pasadena / Love game / Heaven sent / Standing in the rain / Day that my heart caught fire / 6 5 33 5 4 / Where the action is / I wanna do it with you / Don't sing that song / Birmingham
12896 / Feb '97 / Laserlight

☐ **LOVE IS IN THE AIR**
Love is in the air / Standing in the rain / Lost in your love / Yesterday's hero / St. louis / Heaven sent / Pasadena / Love game / I hate the music / I wanna do it with you / Here we go / Keep on smilin' / Birmingham / Where the action is / Day that my heart caught fire / Hot for your baby
12212 / '93 / Laserlight

☐ **VERY BEST OF JOHN PAUL YOUNG, THE**
Walk in the park / Don't come back / Little bit of jazz / Straight ahead / Leaving on a midnight train / You know I like it / Way of life / Come over / Last goodbye / Information / Sleeping alone / Crazy nights / Like dust / Another night in jail / Modern music / Walk in the park
10152 / Oct '97 / A-Play Collection

Young, Johnny

☐ **CHICAGO BLUES**
ARHCD 325 / Apr '95 / Arhoolie

☐ **JOHNNY YOUNG AND HIS FRIENDS**
TCD 5003 / Aug '94 / Testament

Young, Karen

☐ **BEST OF KAREN YOUNG, THE (Hot Shot)**
Hot shot / Bring on the boys / Baby you ain't nothin' without me / Detour / Expressway to your heart / Hot for you / Dynomite / God bless America / Ain't gettin' better / You don't know what you got / Don't say goodbye / One sure way / Change is gonna come
HTCD 45 / 20 Apr '98 / Hot Productions

Young, 'Lady' Linda

☐ **GOOD MORNING TO HEAVEN (Young, 'Lady' Linda & 'Tuba Fats' Lacen Band)**
MECCACD 2001 / May '97 / Music Mecca

Young, La Monte

☐ **JUST STOMPIN'**
Stompin' / Young Dorian's blues in G
R2 71262 / Aug '93 / Gramavision

☐ **SECOND DREAM OF...**
GRV 74672 / Oct '91 / Gramavision

☐ **WELL TUNED PIANO, THE**
1887012 / Jul '90 / Gramavision

Young, Larry

☐ **GROOVE STREET**
Groove street / I found a new baby / Sweet Lorraine / Gettin' into it / Talkin' 'bout JC
OJCCD 1853 / Apr '97 / Original Jazz Classics

☐ **INTO SOMETHIN'**
Tyrone / Plaza des tores / Paris eyes / Back up / Ritha / Ritha
8217342 / 2 Feb '98 / Blue Note

☐ **LOVE CRY WANT (Young, Larry & Nicholas/Joe Gallivan)**
Peace / Tomorrow, today will be yesterday / Great medicine dance / Angel place / Ancient place / Love cry
NJC 001 / Jun '97 / NJC

Young, Leo

☐ **COSMIC LAND**
EFA 019572 / Mar '97 / KTM

Young, Lester

☐ **ALTERNATIVE LESTER, THE**
Way down yonder in New Orleans / Countless blues / I want a little girl / Pagin' the devil
TAXCDS 6 / Apr '91 / Tax

☐ **AN INTRODUCTION TO LESTER YOUNG**
4042 / Apr '97 / Best Of Jazz

☐ **BLUE LESTER**
I don't stand a ghost of a chance with you / Crazy over jazz / Ding dong / Back home in Indiana / These foolish things / Exercise in swing / Blues 'n' bells / Salute to Fats / June bug / Blue Lester / Jump Lester jump / Basie English / Circus in rhythm / Poor little plaything / Tush
SV 0112 / Oct '97 / Savoy Jazz

☐ **CLASSICS 1943-1946**
CLASSICS 932 / Apr '97 / Classics

☐ **CLASSICS 1946-1947**
CLASSICS 987 / 24 Apr '98 / Classics

☐ **COMPLETE ALADDIN RECORDINGS, THE (2CD Set)**
Indiana / I can't get started / Tea for two / Body and soul / DB blues / Lester blows again / These foolish things / Jumpin' at Mesner's / It's only a paper moon / After you've gone / Lover come back to me / Jumpin' with Lester / You're driving me crazy / New Lester leaps in / Lester's be bop boogie / She's funny that way / Sunday / SM blues / Jumpin' with me / symphony Sid / No eyes blues / Sax-o-be-bop / On the sunny side of the street / Easy does it / Bass blues it / Movin' with Lester / One o'clock jump / Jumpin' at the Woodside / I'm confessin' / Lester smooths it out / Just cooling / East of the sun and West of the moon / Sheik of Araby / Something to remember you by / Untitled / Please let me forget / He don't love me anymore / Pleasing man blues / CC rider / It's better to give than receive
CDP 8327872 / Oct '95 / Blue Note

☐ **EASY DOES IT 1936-1940**
Shoe shine boy / Boogie woogie / Oh lady be good / Sailboat in the moonlight / Every tub / Blue and sentimental / Jumpin' at the woodside / Way down yonder in New Orleans / Countless blues / Them there eyes / I want a little girl / Pagin' the devil / You can depend on me / Jive at five / Taxi war dance / Twelfth Street rag / Clap hands / Here comes Charlie / Dickie's dream / Lester leaps in / I left my baby / I never knew / Tickle-toe / Easy does it / Broadway
IGOCD 2036 / Sep '96 / Indigo

☐ **IN WASHINGTON DC 1956**
Talk of the town / I cover the waterfront / Pennies from Heaven / G's if you please / Almost like being in love / I'm confessin' that I love you / DB blues
OJCCD 963 / Jul '98 / Original Jazz Classics

☐ **IN WASHINGTON DC VOL.1**
Foggy day / When you're smiling / I can't get started (with you) / Fast Bob blues / DB blues / Tea for two / Jeepers creepers
OJCCD 782 / Apr '94 / Original Jazz Classics

☐ **JAZZ ARCHIVES 1941-1944**
158352 / May '95 / Jazz Archives

☐ **JAZZ MASTERS**
Love me or leave me / Sometimes I'm happy / I've found a new baby / Polka dots and moonbeams / On the sunny side of the street / (Back home again) In Indiana / Prisoner of love / In a little Spanish town / Just you, just me / Peg o' my heart / Too marvellous for words / All of me / I'm confessin' that I love you / Mean to me / I never knew
5218592 / 5 May '98 / Verve

☐ **KANSAS CITY SESSIONS**
Way down yonder in New Orleans / Countless blues / Them there eyes / I want a little girl / Pagin' the devil / Three little words / Jo-Jo / I got rhythm / Four o'clock drag / Laughing at life / Good mornin' blues / I know you know / Love me or leave me
CMD 14022 / Feb '97 / Commodore Jazz

☐ **LESTER LEAPS AGAIN**
Up 'n' at 'em / (Back home again in) Indiana / Too marvellous for words / Mean to me / Sweet Georgia Brown / I'm confessin' that I love you / Neenah / I cover the waterfront / Lester leaps in / I don't stand a ghost of a chance with you / How high the moon / Be bop boogie / DB blues / Lavender blues / These foolish things / Just you, just me / Lester leaps again
LEJAZZCD 4 / Mar '93 / Le Jazz

☐ **LESTER LEAPS IN**
Shoe shine boy / Lady be good / Boogie woogie / I found a new baby / A sailboat in the moonlight / When you're smiling / I can't believe that you're in love with me / Every tub / Jumpin' at the woodside / Way down yonder in new orleans / Countless blues / Them there eyes / I want a little girl / Shorty george / Taxi war dance / China boy / Dickie's dream / Lester leaps in / Tickle toe
JHR 73571 / Nov '93 / Jazz Hour

☐ **LESTER YOUNG 1936-1944**
CD 14551 / Jul '94 / Jazz Portraits

☐ **LESTER YOUNG 1943-1947**
CD 53073 / Mar '92 / Giants Of Jazz

☐ **LESTER YOUNG IN WASHINGTON DC 1956, VOL.3**
Just you just me / Sometimes I'm happy / Indiana (back home again in) / Up'n Adam / There will never be another you / G's if you please
OJCCD 9012 / May '98 / Original Jazz Classics

☐ **LESTER-AMADEUS**
Moten swing / Shout and feel it / You and me that used to be / Count steps in / They can't take that away from me / I'll always be in love with you / Swing brother swing / Bugle blues / I got rhythm / Allez oop / Blues with Helen / I ain't got nobody / Don't be that way / Song of the wanderer / Mortgage stomp
PHONTCD 7639 / Apr '94 / Phontastic

☐ **MASTER TAKES WITH COUNT BASIE (Young, Lester & Earle Warren/Johnny Guamieri)**
Circus in rhythm / Poor little plaything / Tush / These foolish things / Exercise in swing / Salute to Fats / Basie English / Lester / I don't stand a ghost of a chance with you / Black home again in) Indiana / Jump Lester jump / Crazy over jazz / Ding dong / Blues 'n' bells / June bug
SV 0250 / Oct '97 / Savoy Jazz

☐ **MASTER'S TOUCH**
Crazy over jazz / I don't stand a ghost of a chance with you / Ding dong / Blues 'n' bells / (Back home again in) Indiana / Basie English / Salute to Fats / Exercise in swing / Circus in rhythm / Tush / Poor little plaything
SV 0113 / Oct '97 / Savoy Jazz

☐ **MASTERPIECES OF LESTER YOUNG, THE**
393462 / Aug '94 / Music Memoria

☐ **MASTERS OF JAZZ (2CD Set)**
R2CD 8010 / 13 Apr '98 / Deja Vu

☐ **MEMORIAL**
Crazy over jazz / Crazy over jazz / Ghost of a chance / Ding dong / Ding dong / Blues 'n' bells / Blues 'n' bells / Indiana / Basie English / Salute to Fats / Salute to Fats / Exercise in swing / Exercise in swing / Circus in rhythm / Circus in rhythm / Tush / Poor little plaything / Exercise in swing / Salute to Fats / Salute to Fats
CY 18056 / 13 Apr '98 / Savoy Jazz

☐ **PRES, THE**
Lester warms up / I can't get started / Lester's blues / Lester's blues / Body and soul / Up and atom / How high the moon / Pennies from heaven
CY 18064 / Jun '98 / Savoy Jazz

☐ **PRESIDENT PLAYS WITH THE OSCAR PETERSON TRIO, THE (Young, Lester & Oscar Peterson Trio)**
Ad lib blues / Just you, just me / Tea for two / Indiana / These foolish things / I can't get started / Stardust / On the sunny side of the street / Almost like being in love / I can't give you anything but love / There will never be another you / I'm confessin' / It takes two to tango
8316702 / Feb '93 / Verve

☐ **PRESIDENT PLAYS WITH THE OSCAR PETERSON TRIO, THE (Remastered) (Young, Lester & Oscar Peterson Trio)**
5214512 / Oct '97 / Verve Master Edition

☐ **PRESIDENT VOL.1, THE**
COD 029 / Mar '92 / Jazz View

☐ **PRESIDENT VOL.2, THE**
COD 039 / Jul '92 / Jazz View

☐ **PRESIDENT VOL.4, THE**
COD 038 / Jun '92 / Jazz View

☐ **PRESIDENT VOL.6, THE**
COD 040 / Aug '92 / Jazz View

☐ **PREZ (Jazz Immortal Series Vol.2)**
Lester warms up / I can't get started (with you) / Lester's blues #1 and 2 / Body and soul / Up and atom / How high the moon / Pennies from Heaven / One o'clock jump / Jumpin' with Symphony Sid
SV 0180 / Oct '97 / Savoy Jazz

☐ **PREZ AND SWEETS (Young, Lester & Harry 'Sweets' Edison)**
Mean to me / Red boy blues / Pennies from Heaven / That's all / One o'clock jump / She's funny that way / It's the talk of the town / I found a new baby
8493912 / Mar '91 / Verve

☐ **PREZ CONFERENCES**
JASSCD 18 / Oct '91 / Jass

☐ **QUINTESSENCE, THE (1936-1943/2CD Set)**
FA 210 / Oct '96 / Fremeaux

☐ **RARITIES**
MCD 0482 / Nov '93 / Moon

☐ **SUPER SESSIONS, THE**
(Back home again in) Indiana / I can't get started (with you) / Tea for two / Body and soul / Just you / Just you, just me / I never knew / Afternoon of Basie-ite / Sometimes I'm happy / After theatre jump / Six cats and a prince / Lester leaps again / Destination KC
LEJAZZCD 36 / May '95 / Le Jazz

☐ **TENOR KING**
CDSGP 0280 / Jul '97 / Prestige

☐ **THIS IS JAZZ**
Shoe shine boy / Boogie woogie / He ain't got rhythm / I must have that man / Honeysuckle rose / Live and love tonight / Pound cake / Exactly like you / Clap hands / Here come Charlie / Dickie's dream / Lester leaps in / Ham 'n eggs / Man I love / Easy does it / Five o'clock whistle / All of me / I got rhythm
CK 65042 / May '97 / Sony Jazz

☐ **ULTIMATE LESTER YOUNG, THE**
5397722 / 16 Mar '98 / Verve

Young Lions

☐ **YOUNG LIONS**
VJ 001 / 24 Feb '98 / Vee Jay

Young Marble Giants

☐ **COLOSSAL YOUTH**
Searching for Mr. Right / Include me out / Taxi / Eating noddemix / Constantly changing / NITA / Colossal youth / Music for evenings / Man amplifier / Choci loni / Wurlitzer jukebox / Salad days / Credit in the straight world / Brand new life / Wind in the rigging / This way / Posed by models / Clock / Clicktalk / Zebra trucks / Sporting life / Final day / Radio silents / Cake walking / Ode to Booker T
TWI 9842 / Apr '94 / Les Disques Du Crepuscule

Young MC

☐ **STONE COLD RHYMIN'**
Come off / Bust a move / Name is Young / Roll with the punches / Stone cold buggin' / Principal's office / Fastest rhyme / Know how / I let 'em know / Just say no
IMCD 122 / Apr '91 / 4th & Broadway

Young, 'Mighty' Joe

☐ **BLUES WITH A TOUCH OF SOUL**
I walked all night / Somebody loan me a dime / Every man needs a woman / Why, baby / Things I used to do / Got a bad case of loving you / Honk tonk
DD 629 / Jul '98 / Delmark

☐ **BLUESY JOSEPHINE**
Teasing the blues / Five long years / Sweet home chicago / Wisefool express / Take money / Take a fool's advice / Need a friend
BLE 595212 / Oct '94 / Black & Blue

☐ **LIVE AT THE WISE FOOLS PUB**
AIM 1052CD / Oct '95 / Aim

☐ **MIGHTY MAN**
Starvation / Mighty man / Turning point / Got my mind on my woman / Got a hold on me / Bring it on / End of the line / Ain't goin' for that / Wishy washy woman / On the move again
BPCD 5040 / May '97 / Blind Pig

Young Neal

☐ **ONE'S ENOUGH (Young Neal & The Vipers)**
KS 045 / 1 Sep '98 / King Snake

Young, Neil

☐ **AFTER THE GOLDRUSH**
Tell me why / After the goldrush / Only love can break your heart / Southern man / Till the morning comes / Oh, lonesome me / Don't let it bring you down / Birds / When you dance I can really love / I believe in you / Cripple Creek ferry
244088 / Mar '93 / Reprise

☐ **AMERICAN STARS AND BARS**
Old country waltz / Saddle up the palomino / Hey babe / Hold back the tears / Bite the bullet / Star of Bethlehem / Will to live / Like a hurricane / Homegrown
7599272342 / Dec '96 / Reprise

☐ **BRIDGE SCHOOL CONCERTS VOL.1, THE (Various Artists)**
Intro: *Young, Neil* / I am a child: *Young, Neil* / Shadow of a doubt: *Petty, Tom* / All that you have is your soul: *Chapman, Tracy* / Sense of purpose: *Pretenders* / It's all in your mind: *Beck* / Road's my middle name: *Raitt, Bonnie* / Yes it is: *Henley, Don* / Friend of the devil: *Ministry* / America: *Simon & Garfunkel* / Heroes: *Bowie, David* / Nothingman: *Pearl Jam* / Battle of evermore: *Lovemongers* / Believe: *Lofgren, Nils* / Alison: *Costello, Elvis* / People have the power: *Smith, Patti*
9362468242 / 17 Nov '97 / Reprise

☐ **BROKEN ARROW (Young, Neil & Crazy Horse)**
Big time / Music arcade / This town / Baby what you want me to do / Loose change / Slip away / Changing highways / Scattered (let's think about livin')
9362462912 / Jun '96 / Reprise

☐ **COMES A TIME**
Goin' back / Comes a-time / Look out for my love / Peace of mind / Lotta love / Human highway / Already one / Field of opportunity / Motorcycle mama / Four strong winds
7599272352 / Jun '93 / Reprise

☐ **DECADE (2CD Set)**
Down to the wire / Burned / Mr. Soul / Broken arrow / Expecting to fly / Sugar mountain / I am a child / Loner / Old laughing lady / Cinnamon girl / Down by the river / Cowgirl in the sand / I believe in you / After the goldrush / Southern man / Helpless / Ohio / Soldier / Old man / Man needs a maid / Heart of gold / Star of Bethlehem / Needle and the damage done / Tonight's the night / Turnstiles / Winterlong / Deep forbidden lake / Like a hurricane / Love is a rose / Cortez the killer / Campaigner / Long may you run / Harvest
7599272332 / Jun '93 / Reprise

☐ **EVERYBODY KNOWS THIS IS NOWHERE (Young, Neil & Crazy Horse)**
Cinnamon girl / Everybody knows this is nowhere / Round and round / Down by the river / Losing end / Running dry (Requiem for the rockets) / Cowgirl in the sand
244073 / Jun '89 / Reprise

☐ **FREEDOM**
Rockin' in the free world / Crime in the city / Don't cry / Hangin' on a limb / Eldorado / Ways of love / Someday / On Broadway / Wrecking ball / No more / Too far gone
9258992 / Feb '95 / Reprise

☐ **HARVEST**
Out on the weekend / Harvest / Man needs a maid / Heart of gold / Are you ready for the country / Old man / There's a world / Alabama / Needle and the damage done / Words (between the lines of age)
244131 / '92 / Reprise

☐ **HARVEST MOON**
Unknown legend / From Hank to Hendrix / You and me / Harvest moon / War of man / One of these days / Such a woman / Old king / Dreamin' man / Natural beauty
9362450572 / Nov '92 / Reprise

☐ **HAWKS AND DOVES**
Little wing / Homestead / Lost in space / Captain Kennedy / Staying power / Coastline / Union man / Comin' apart at every nail / Hawks and doves
9362457022 / Dec '96 / Reprise

☐ **JOURNEY THROUGH THE PAST**
For what it's worth / Mr. Soul / Rock 'n' roll woman / Find the cost of freedom / Ohio / Southern man / Alabama / Are you ready for the country / Words / Soldier
7599261232 / Jun '94 / Reprise

☐ **LANDING ON WATER**
Weight of the world / Violent side / Hippie dream / Bad news beat / Touch the night / People on the street / Hard luck stories / I got a problem / Pressure / Drifter
GED 24109 / Nov '96 / Geffen

☐ **LIFE (Young, Neil & Crazy Horse)**
Mid East vacation / Long walk home / Around the world / Inca Queen / Too lonely / Prisoners of rock'n'roll / Crying eyes / When your lonely heart breaks / We never danced
GED 25154 / 16 Feb '98 / Geffen

☐ **LIVE RUST (Young, Neil & Crazy Horse)**
Sugar mountain / I am a child / Comes a-time / After the goldrush / My my, hey hey (out of the blue) / When you dance I can really love / Loner / Needle and the damage done / Lotta love / Sedan delivery / Powder finger / Cortez the killer / Cinnamon girl / Like a hurricane / Hey hey, my my (into the black) / Tonight's the night
7599272502 / Jun '93 / Reprise

☐ **LUCKY THIRTEEN**
Sample and hold / Transformer man / Depression blues / Get gone / Don't take your love away from me / Once an angel / Where is the highway tonight / Hippie dream / Pressure / Around the world / Mid East vacation / Ain't it the truth / This note's for you
GFLD 19328 / Sep '96 / Geffen

☐ **MIRROR BALL**
Song X / Act of love / I'm the ocean / Big green country / Truth be known / Downtown / What happened yesterday / Peace and love / Throw your hatred down / Scenery / Fallen angel
9362459342 / Jun '95 / Reprise

☐ **NEIL YOUNG**
Emperor of Wyoming / Loner / If I could have her tonight / I've been waiting for you / Old laughing lady / String quartet from whiskey boot hill / Here we are in the years / What did you do to my life / I've loved her so long / Last trip to Tulsa
244059 / Mar '93 / Reprise

☐ **OLD WAY**
GFLD 19356 / Apr '97 / Geffen

☐ **ON THE BEACH**
Walk on / See the sky about to rain / Revolution blues / For the turnstiles / Vampire blues / On the beach / Motion pictures / Ambulance blues
9362456992 / Dec '96 / Reprise

☐ **PICKIN' ON NEIL YOUNG (Various Artists)**
2729780252 / 19 May '98 / CMH

☐ **RAGGED GLORY (Young, Neil & Crazy Horse)**
Country home / White line / Fuckin' up / Over and over / Love to burn / Farmer John / Mansion on the hill / Days that used to be / Love and only love / Mother Earth (natural anthem)
7599263152 / Feb '95 / Reprise

☐ **RE-AC-TOR**
Opera star / Surfer Joe and Moe the sleaze / T-Bone / Get back on it / Southern Pacific / Motor city / Rapid transit / Shots
7599258692 / Jun '94 / Reprise

☐ **RUST NEVER SLEEPS (Young, Neil & Crazy Horse)**
My my, hey hey (out of the blue) / Thrasher / Ride my llama / Pocohontas / Sail away / Powder finger / Welfare mothers / Sedan delivery / Hey hey, my my (into the black)
7599272492 / Jun '93 / Reprise

☐ **SLEEPS WITH ANGELS**
My heart / Prime of life / Drive-by / Sleeps with angels / Western hero / Change your mind / Blue Eden / Safeway cart / Train of love / Trans Am / Piece of crap / Dream that can last
9362457492 / Aug '94 / Reprise

☐ **THIS NOTE'S FOR YOU (Young, Neil & The Blue Notes)**
Ten men workin' / This note's for you / Coupe de ville / Life in the city / Twilight / Married man / Sunny inside / Can't believe your lyin' / Hey hey / One thing
9257192 / Feb '95 / Reprise

☐ **TIME FADES AWAY**
Time fades away / LA / Journey through the past / Bridge / Love in mind / Don't be denied / Last dance / Yonder stands the sinner
7599259342 / Jun '94 / Reprise

☐ **TONIGHT'S THE NIGHT**
Tonight's the night / Speakin' out / World on a string / Borrowed tune / Come on baby let's go downtown / Mellow my mind / Roll another number (for the road) / Albuquerque / New mama / Look out, Joe / Tired eyes / Tonight's the night pt 2
7599272212 / Jun '93 / Reprise

☐ **TRANS**
Little thing called love / Computer age / We R in control / Transformer man / Computer cowboy (aka Skycrusher) / Hold on to your love / Sample and hold / Mr. Soul / Like an Inca
GFLD 19357 / Apr '97 / Geffen

☐ **UNPLUGGED**
Old laughing lady / Mr. Soul / World on a string / Pocahontas / Stringman / Like a hurricane / Needle and the damage done / Helpless / Harvest moon / Transformer man / Unknown legend / Look out for my love / Long may you run / From Hank to Hendrix
9362453102 / Jun '93 / Reprise

☐ **WELD (2CD Set) (Young, Neil & Crazy Horse)**
Hey hey, my my (into the black) / Crime in the city / Blowin' in the wind / Welfare mothers / Love to burn / Cinnamon girl / Mansion on the hill / Fuckin' up / Cortez the killer / Powder finger / Love and only love / Rockin' in the free world / Like a hurricane / Farmer John / Tonight's the night / Roll another number (for the road) / Arc
7599266712 / Nov '91 / Reprise

☐ **YEAR OF THE HORSE, THE (Neil Young Live)**
When you dance / Barstool blues / When your lonely heart breaks / Mr. Soul / Big time / Pocahontas / Human highway / Slip away / Scattered / Danger bird / Prisoners / Sedan delivery
9362466522 / Jun '97 / Reprise

☐ **ZUMA (Young, Neil & Crazy Horse)**
Don't cry no tears / Danger bird / Pardon my heart / Looking for a love / Barstool blues / Stupid girl / Drive back / Cortez the killer / Through my sails
7599272262 / Jun '93 / Reprise

Young, Paul

☐ **FROM TIME TO TIME (The Singles Collection)**
Every time you go away / Come back and stay / I'm only foolin' myself / Senza una Donna / I'm gonna tear your playhouse down / Broken man / Everything must change / Wonderland / Don't dream it's over / Love of the common people / Wherever I lay my hat (that's my home) / Both sides now / Oh Girl / Softly whispering I love you / Some people
4688252 / Aug '91 / Columbia

☐ **LOVE SONGS**
Everytime you go away / Don't dream it's over / Broken man / Softly whispering I love you / Wonderland / It will be you / Senza una Donna (without a woman): Young, Paul & Zucchero / Now I know what made Otis blue / Love will tear us apart / Everything must change / Half a step away / This means anything / Won't look back / Calling you / Wherever I lay my hat (that's my home) / Follow on / Love hurts
4783122 / 27 Jul '98 / Columbia

☐ **NO PARLEZ**
Come back and stay / Love will tear us apart / Wherever I lay my hat (that's my home) / Ku-ku kurama / No parlez / Love of the common people / Oh women / Iron out the rough spots / Broken man / Tender trap / Sex
4609092 / '91 / CBS

☐ **NO PARLEZ/THE SECRET OF ASSOCIATION (2CD Set)**
Come back and stay / Love will tear us apart / Wherever I lay my hat (that's my home) / Ku-ku kurama / No parlez / Love of the common people / Oh women / Iron out the rough spots / Broken man / Tender trap / Sex / Bite the hand that feeds / Everytime you go away / I'm gonna tear your playhouse down / Standing on the edge / Soldier's things / Everything must change / Tomb of memories / One step forward / Hot fun / This means anything / I was in chains / Man in the iron mask
4784812 / Mar '95 / Columbia

☐ **OTHER VOICES**
Heaven can wait / Little bit of love / Softly whispering I love you / Together / Stop on by / Our time has come / Oh girl / Right about now / It's what she didn't say / Calling you
4844702 / Jul '97 / Columbia

☐ **PAUL YOUNG**
Ball and chain / I wish you love / Tularosa / Vanish / Hard cargo / Say goodbye / In a dream gone by / You'd better run away / Across the borderline / It was a very good year / Window world
0630186192 / May '97 / East West

☐ **PAUL YOUNG AND THE Q-TIPS (Young, Paul & The Q-Tips)**
JHD 031 / Jun '92 / Tring

☐ **SECRET OF ASSOCIATION, THE**
Bite the hand that feeds / Everytime you go away / I'm gonna tear your playhouse down / Standing on the edge / Soldier's things / Everything must change / Tomb of memories / One step forward / Hot fun / This means anything / I was in chains
4655772 / 11 May '98 / Columbia

☐ **SOME KIND OF WONDERFUL (Young, Paul & The Q-Tips)**
SYSLJFM (the letter song) / Tracks of my tears / You are the life inside of me / Man can't lose what he don't have / Some kind of wonderful / Love hurts / I wish it would rain / Sweet talk / You're gonna love me / Empty bed
101172 / May '97 / A-Play Collection

☐ **TRACKS OF MY TEARS (Young, Paul & The Q-Tips)**
Tracks of my tears / Love hurts / Hi-fidelity / Man can't lose (What he don't have) / Sweet have / I wish it could rain / We are the life inside of me / SYSLJFM (The letter song) / Link / Broken man / Raise your hand / Get 'em up Joe / Empty bed / You're gonna love me
306582 / May '97 / Hallmark

Young Pioneers

☐ **1ST VIRGINIA VOLUNTEERS**
VMFM 21CD / Jul '95 / Lookout

☐ **CRIME WAVE**
VMFM 27CD / May '97 / Vermiform

☐ **FIRST VIRGINIA VOLUNTEERS**
VMFM 212 / May '95 / Vermiform

Young Rascals

☐ **TIME PEACE (Greatest Hits) (Rascals/ Young Rascals)**
7567814412 / Jun '95 / Atlantic

Young, Steve

☐ **ROCK, SALT & NAILS**
That's how strong my love is / Rock, salt and nails / I'm a one woman man / Coyote / Gonna find me a bluebird / Love in my time / Seven Bridges Road / Kenny's song / Holler in the swamp / Hoboin' / My sweet love ain't around
EDCD 193 / Feb '91 / Edsel

YOUNG, STEVE

☐ **SOLO/LIVE**
White trash song / Tobacco road / Seven bridges road / Don't miss your water / River and the swan / Long way to hollywood / Don't think twice, it's alright / Ballad of william sycamore / We've been together on this earth before / Montgomery in the rain / Go to sea no more / All her lovers want to be the hero / Drift away
WM 1004 / Jun '93 / Watermelon

Young Tradition

☐ **GALLERIES/NO RELATION (Young Tradition/Royston & Heather Wood)**
Intro/Ductia: Young Tradition / Barleystraw: Young Tradition / What if a day: Young Tradition / Loyal lover: Young Tradition / Entracte/Stones in my passway: Young Tradition / Idumea: Young Tradition / Husbandman and servingman: Young Tradition / Rolling of the stones: Young Tradition / Bitter withy: Young Tradition / Banks of the Nile: Young Tradition / Wondrous love: Young Tradition / Medieval mystery tour: Young Tradition / Divertissement: Upon the bough: Young Tradition / Ratcliff highway: Young Tradition / Brisk young widow: Young Tradition / Interlude/The Pembroke unique ensemble: Young Tradition / John Barleycorn: Young Tradition / Agincourt carol: Young Tradition / Chicken on a raft: Young Tradition / Randy-dandy-o: Young Tradition / Shanties: Young Tradition / Shepherd of the downs: Wood, Royston & Heather / Come ye that fear Lord: Wood, Royston & Heather / Foolish incredibly foolish: Wood, Royston & Heather / Bold Benjamin-o: Wood, Royston & Heather / Bold astrologer: Wood, Royston & Heather / St. Patrick's breastplate: Wood, Royston & Heather / Cutty wren: Wood, Royston & Heather / Will you miss me: Wood, Royston & Heather / Gloria laus: Wood, Royston & Heather
ESMCD 461 / Jan '97 / Essential

☐ **HOLLY BEARS THE CROWN, THE**
FLED 3006 / Nov '95 / Fledg'ling

☐ **YOUNG TRADITION/SO CHEERFULLY ROUND**
ESMCD 409 / Jul '96 / Essential

Young, Zora

☐ **TRAVELIN' LIGHT**
Travellin' light / Queen bee / Football widow / Mama jama / Key to the highway / Daughter of a son-of-a-gun / Stumbling blocks and stepping stones / Girlfriend / Brain damage / Can't take nothin out
DEL 3003 / Dec '95 / Deluge

Youngblood, Sydney

☐ **FEELING FREE**
Feelin' free / If only I could / I'd rather go blind / Sit and kiss and say goodbye / Ain't no sunshine / I'm your lover / Not just a lover but a friend / Congratulations / Could it me (I'm in love) / That was yesterday / Good times, bad times
CIRCD 9 / Apr '92 / Circa

☐ **HOOKED ON YOU (The Best Of Sydney Youngblood)**
If only I could / Spookey / Sit and wait / Feeling free / Hooked on you / Body and soul / Wherever you go / Feels like forever / I'm your lover / I'd rather go blind / Could it be (I'm in love) / Ain't no sunshine
CDVIP 129 / Apr '95 / Virgin VIP

Youngblood-Hart, Alvin

☐ **TERRITORY**
Tallacatcha / Illinois blues / Quachita run / Sallie queen of pines / Countrycide / Ice rose / Dancing with tears in my eyes / Mama don't allow / John Hardy / Underway at seven / Just about to go
HNCD 1431 / 22 Jun '98 / Hannibal

Youngbloods

☐ **DARKNESS DARKNESS**
Darkness darkness / Grizzly bear / Statesboro blues / Get together / Four in the morning / C.C. Rider / On Sir Francis Drake / Sunlight / Beautiful / Quicksand / Sham / Ride the wind / Euphoria / Too much monkey business / Sugar babe / Don't play games / Fool me / Wine song / Reason to believe
EDCD 561 / 4 May '98 / Edsel

☐ **EARTH MUSIC**
White trash song / Tobacco road / Seven bridges road / Don't miss your water / River and the swan / Euphoria / All my dreams blue / Monkey Business / Dreamer's dream / Sugar Babe / Long and tall / I Can Tell / Don't Play Games / Wine song / Fool me / Reason to believe
EDCD 274 / Apr '91 / Edsel

☐ **ELEPHANT MOUNTAIN**
Darkness darkness / Smug / On Sir Frances Drake / Sunlight / Double sunlight / Beautiful / Turn it over / Rainsong / Trillium / Quicksand / Black mountain breakdown / Sham / Ride the wind
EDCD 276 / Apr '91 / Edsel

☐ **YOUNGBLOODS**
Grizzly bear / All over the world / Statesboro Blues / Get Together / One note man / Other side of this life / Tears Are Falling / Four In The Morning / Foolin' Around / Ain't that lovin' you / CC rider
EDCD 271 / Jul '91 / Edsel

Younger, Dave

☐ **WESTERN HERO**
CCD 1011 / Jul '98 / Clarity

Youngs, Richard

☐ **ADVENT**
NIOBIUM 41 / 4 Nov '97 / Table Of The Elements

☐ **PULSE OF THE ROOSTERS (Youngs, Richard & Simon Wickham Smith)**
VHF 35 / 27 Apr '98 / VHF

☐ **RED AND BLUE BEAR - THE OPERA (Book/CD Set) (Youngs, Richard & Simon Wickham Smith)**
VHF 27 / Mar '97 / VHF

Youth Of Today

☐ **BREAKDOWN THE WALLS**
REV 008CD / 11 Nov '97 / Revelation

☐ **CAN'T CLOSE MY EYES**
Expectations / Crucial times / I have faith / Youth of today / Take a stand / Positive out / Can't close my eyes / We just.... / Youth crew
REV 062CD / 10 Nov '97 / Revelation

☐ **TAKE A STAND**
LF 044CD / Sep '95 / Lost & Found

☐ **WE'RE NOT IN THIS ALONE**
REV 059CD / 10 Nov '97 / Revelation

Yr Hergwd

☐ **YR HERGWD**
FFLACH 173CD / Aug '97 / Fflach

Yu, Chung

☐ **CLASSICAL CHINESE PIPA**
EUCD 1176 / '91 / ARC

Yu, Zhou

☐ **HOMELAND**
EUCD 1260 / Mar '94 / ARC

Yuan, Lily

☐ **ANCIENT ART MUSIC OF CHINA**
LYRCD 7409 / '91 / Lyrichord

Yugar, Zulma

☐ **TIERRA SIN MAR**
TUMICD 059 / Sep '96 / Tumi

Yulara

☐ **COSMIC TREE**
Riksha heaven / Deep hop / All the way / Tribute to Allah / Narayana / Wren peace / Atanka the sun / Rain on fire / Horizon / Desert to jungle
VHOCD 1 / 25 May '98 / Higher Octave

Yulya

☐ **RUSSIAN ROMANTIC SONGS**
MCD 71597 / Jun '93 / Monitor

Yum Yum

☐ **REMIXES, THE (Various Artists)**
SPERM 1002 / 20 Apr '98 / Sperm

Yumiko, Sato

☐ **ELFISH ECHO PRESENTS**
KM 2002 / Oct '96 / KM20

Yummy Fur

☐ **KINKY CINEMA**
GUIDE 22CD / 29 Sep '97 / Guided Missile

☐ **MALE SHADOW AT 3 O'CLOCK**
POMP 012CD / 2 Feb '98 / Vesuvius

☐ **NIGHT CLUB**
GUIDE 10CD / Mar '97 / Guided Missile

Yumuri Y Sus Hermanos

☐ **PROVOCACION**
AJA 1204 / Jun '96 / JVC World Library

Yupanqui, Atahualpa

☐ **CAMINO DEL INDIO**
BMCD 2010 / Nov '97 / Blue Moon

☐ **DON ALTA**
68956 / Apr '97 / Tropical

☐ **L'INTEGRALE**
LDX 274948/52 / Jan '93 / La Chant Du Monde

☐ **LA ZAMBA PERDIDA**
BMF 005 / Nov '97 / Blue Moon

☐ **SE POBLABAN DE MUSICA LOS ANDES**
BMF 006 / Nov '97 / Blue Moon

Yuro, Timi

☐ **18 HEARTBREAKING SONGS**
RMB 75061 / Oct '95 / Remember

☐ **HURT**
WMCD 5668 / May '94 / Disky

☐ **LOST VOICE OF SOUL, THE**
Hurt / Just say I love him / Trying / Smile / Let me call you sweetheart / Count everything / I know (I love you) / What's the matter baby / Only love me / That's right, walk on by / Should I ever love again / Love of a boy / I ain't gonna cry no more / Insult to injury / Make the world go away / Leavin' on your mind / She's got you / Are you sure / I'd fight the world / Gotta travel on / Down in the valley / Permanently lonely / Legend in my time / Call me / Something bad on my mind / It'll never be over for me
RPM 117 / Oct '93 / RPM

Yulara
(continued) ☐ **ORIGINAL, THE**
Hurt / Love of a boy / Let me call you / Make the world go away / I apologize / Smile / She really loves you / What's a matter babe (is it hurting you) / Insult to injury / Gotta travel on / I ain't gonna cry no more / I'm confessin' (that I love you) / I'll never fall in love again / My prayer / Hey girl (hey boy) / Cry / If I never get to love you / Just say I love him
TO 860972 / 2 Feb '98 / Disky

☐ **TIMI YURO SINGS WILLIE NELSON**
Did I ever love you / Crazy / There's a way / Will you remember mine / Permanently lonely / Touch me / My own peculiar way / You took my happy away / I never cared for you / Once alone / Opportunity to cry / On the road again / You / If you don't know by now
PLSCD 247 / 27 Oct '97 / Pulse

☐ **UNIQUE SOUND OF TIMI YURO, THE**
Hurt / Smoke gets in your eyes / You've lost that loving feeling / All alone am I / Little things mean a lot / Let me go lover / Make the world go away / Cry / Only you (and you alone) / Only love can break a heart / Tears on my pillow / It's only make believe / What's a matter baby (is it hurts to be in love / It must be him / I'm Sorry / Thank you for calling / I can't stop loving you
SUMCD 4141 / Sep '97 / Summit

☐ **VOICE THAT GOT AWAY**
Interlude / It's just a matter of time / I'll never fall in love again / When something is wrong with my baby / Nothing takes the place of my baby / Hey boy / Hallelujah I love him so / I must have been out of my mind / When he wants a woman / Loving you is all I ever had / I just got back from there / So ashamed / I apologise / All my love belongs to you / Put them aside / Wall / If you gotta make a fool of somebody / Thirteenth hour / Wrong / When you were mine / Guess who / It's too soon to know / She really loves you / I waited too long / If I never get to love you / Interlude
RPM 167 / Aug '96 / RPM

Yuzuru Syogase

☐ **YUZURU SYOGASE/KAISER NIETZSCHE (Yuzuru Syogase/Kaiser Nietzsche)**
ARTWARE 18 / Sep '97 / Artware

Yvert, Jean Pierre

☐ **NORD SUD (Yvert, Jean Pierre & J. Mayoud)**
829532 / 5 Jan '98 / BUDA

☐ **SPELA SALGFLOYT**
AW 13CD / Aug '97 / Tongang

Yvert, Oller

☐ **FUNAMBULES (Yvert, Oller & Trio)**
ARN 64235 / Jun '93 / Arion

Yves Choir

☐ **BY PRESCRIPTION ONLY**
Rush hour / After the rain / Rocky Road / D B / By prescription only / Mad about town / Far side / Follow me to the edge / Bianca / Morocco junction
103 254 / Mar '90 / Musidisc

YWFC

☐ **UP ON IT**
Rap 'n' read / This time / Up on it / How I'm feelin / Tears of a child / Gave me what I got / Heaven is my high / Master plan / Gotta get it back / Dancin' / Rap 'n' read
BDR 3211 / 24 Nov '97 / Big Doggie

Z

Z-Rock Hawaii

☐ Z-ROCK HAWAII
NIPP 12142 / Jul '97 / Nipp Guitar

Zabaleta

☐ INFERNUKO HAUSPOA (Zabaleta & Kepa Junkera)
KDCD 152 / May '97 / Elkar

☐ TRIKI UP (Zabaleta & Imanol)
KDCD 241 / May '97 / Elkar

Zaboitzeff, Thierry

☐ HEARTBEAT
EFA 129812 / 13 Oct '97 / Atonal

Zabrina

☐ Z = MC2
Take a minute / Nu sound / Sunsister / Philosophy of fiction / Tell me something good / Irresistible / Housework / Keystone groove / This gun's for hire / Killer is with me / Chosen one / Godmother / Fellas from the Southside / You can make it / Sucker for a man with a body
ICH 1122CD / Oct '93 / Ichiban

Zacharias, Helmut

☐ SWING PARTY
Ich kusse ihre hand, Madame / Dark eyes / Those little white lies / Swing '48 / Kosaken patrouille / Man I love / You made me love you / Mob mob / Embraceable you / What is this thing called love / Presto / How high the moon / Tigerjagd (tiger rag) / Blue moon / C jam blues / Swing party / Schwips boogie / Ich habe rhythmus (I got rhythm) / Mr. Callahan / Carioca / Sabeltanz boogie (sabre dance) / Boogie tur Geige / Fiddler's boogie / Blue blues / China boogie / Smoky / Minne minne ha ha
BCD 15642 / Jun '92 / Bear Family

Zachrisson, Johan

☐ RITMO DE ESTORNINHOS
Fado da liha / No comboio descendente / Dream ourselves away / Maneno Mataamu / Chegal / Ritmo de Estorninhos / Anda Maria / Danca da Serra
XOUCD 102 / May '97 / Xource

Zachze

☐ HIMMEL, ARSCH & ZWIRN
BEST 1008CD / Nov '93 / Acoustic Music

Zadeh, Aziza Mustafa

☐ ALWAYS
4738852 / Jan '95 / Sony Jazz

☐ AZIZA MUSTAFA ZADEH
Quiet alone / Tea on the carpet / Cemetry / Inspiration / Reflection / Oriental fantasy / Blue day / Character / Aziza's dream / Chargah / My ballad / I cannot sleep / Moment / Exprompt / Two candles
4682862 / Apr '94 / Columbia

☐ DANCE OF FIRE
Boomerang / Dance of fire / Sheherezadeh / Aspiration / Bana bana gel (Bad girl) / Shadow / Carnival / Passion / Spanish picture / To be continued / Father
4803522 / Jun '95 / Sony Jazz

☐ JAZZIZA
Lover man / Sunny rain / My funny valentine / Scrapple from the apple / Character / Nature boy / You've changed / Butterflies / Black orpheus / How insensitive / Take five / I can't sleep
4878972 CD / 1 Sep '97 / Sony Jazz

☐ SEVENTH TRUTH
Ay dilber / Lachin / Interlude 1 / Fly with me / F sharp / Desperation / Daha (again) / I am sad / Interlude 2 / Wild beauty / Seventh truth / Sea monster
4842382 / Jul '96 / Sony Jazz

Zaffarano, Marco

☐ HE WAS ONCE A BEAUTIFUL WOMAN
SILVER 1CD / 26 Jan '98 / Silver Planet

☐ MINIMALISM (2CD Set)
SILVER 15CD / 25 May '98 / Silver Planet

Zagraj Kapela

☐ MUSIQUES DE EUROPE
829262 / Nov '96 / BUDA

Zahar

☐ LIVE AT THE KNITTING FACTORY
KFWCD 112 / Oct '92 / Knitting Factory

Zahouani, Cheb

☐ FATIMA
DECLI 50633 / 3 Mar '98 / Munich

Zaiko Langa L

☐ SANS ISSUE
3018212 / Feb '97 / Arcade

Zamagni, Tony

☐ GET DOWN WITH THE BLUES
CDTC 1153 / Jul '95 / Tonecool

Zamfir, Gheorghe

☐ GHEORGHE ZAMFIR COLLECTION, THE
Anna / Joe de doi / Breaza de la dragodana / Invirtita / Rustemul de la listeava / Coragheasca / Balada lui costea pacurarul / Sirba lui pomieru and an o mindra mititica / Miertlita cind e bolnava / Flora / Asta e poteca mea / Cintec de nunta / Bocet / Mindra mea din badulesti / Hora ca din caval / Briu oltenesc / Muntinlor cu brazi inalti si / Cintecul-lui Iancu jianu / Frunzulita lemn adus / Hora din muntenia and cimpulung oras de munte / Mindrele / Sirba batrineasca / Briul de la faget / Mult ma-ntreaba inima
COL 075 / May '97 / Collection

☐ HEART OF ROMANIA, THE (Zamfir, Gheorghe & Marcel Cellier)
Inima ci venin muit / Doina din banat / Ca din banat / Cintec muntenesc / Ciorcilia / Doina Sus pe cilmea dealului / Joc dins oas / Joc de dai din banat / In memoriam Maria Lataretu / Geampara "Lelita I Oana" / Doina Gheoghe mina boll bine / Doina Lui efta botoca / Balada sarpelui / Doina da jale
PV 750002 / Jul '94 / Disques Pierre Verany

☐ LIVE IN CONCERT FROM THEIR AMERICAN TOUR (Zamfir, Gheorghe & Marcel Cellier)
Balada sarpelui / Doina de la domasnea / Doina din jebel / Joc dins oas / Doina Sus pe culmea dealului / Doina oltului / Doina lui petru unc / Doina Rugulet cu negra mure / Doina da jale
PV 750001 / Jul '94 / Disques Pierre Verany

☐ MAGIC OF THE MOMENTS
DCD 5358 / Apr '94 / Disky

☐ MAGIC OF THE PAN PIPES, THE (27 Haunting Melodies/2CD Set)
Dormasnea / Jebel / Arad / Sarmis and trefia / Flora / Anna / Oltera / Doina de la visina / Muntilor cu brazi inalti si / Mult ma-ntreaba inima / La cules de cucuruz / Am doi frati Severin / Hora din muntenia / Suita olteneasca / Doina/Hora lautareasca / Doina de jale/ Ciro cirlia / Hora din muntenia e cimpulung oras de munte / Balada lui costea Pacuraral / Coragheasca / Rustemul de la listeava / Bocet / Sirba de la gaesti / Invirita / Cintee de nunita / Breaza de la Dragodana / La marginea padurii / Asra iarna era iarna / Sirba de la comana / Joe de doi
SUDCD 4503 / Nov '96 / Summit

☐ MASTER OF THE PAN PIPES
11016 / '86 / Laserlight

☐ MELODIES OF THE HEART
DCD 5327 / Apr '94 / Disky

☐ MOMENTS OF MY DREAMS
DCD 5356 / Apr '94 / Disky

☐ NAMES IN MY LIFE
DCD 5352 / May '94 / Disky

☐ PAN FLUTES & ORGAN
323123 / Feb '94 / Koch

☐ PAN PIPE DREAMS
Love changes everything / Unchained melody / Somewhere / Theme from 'Limelight' / Chariots of fire / Just the way you are / Don't cry for me Argentina / Black rose / Memory / Beautiful dream / Endless dream / Your song / Bilitis / Chanson d'amour / Rose / Run to me / Serenade / Only love
5518212 / Nov '95 / Spectrum

☐ PAN PIPE MELODIES (2CD Set)
Suite de sirbe oltenesti / Sapte vai si-o vale-adinca / Invirtita / Asta e poteca mea / Joc de doi / Mult ma-ntreaba inima / Hora ca la caval / Doina de jale / Cintec de nunta / Caragheasca / Balada lui costea pacurarul / Rustemul de la listeava / Bocet / Briul oltenoso / Ca la breaza / Sirba lui pomieru si am o mindra mititica / Breaza de la dragodana / Muntilor cu brazi inalti si ferice codre de tine / Briul de la faget / Frunzulita lemn adus / Mierlita cind e bolnava / Pascui calcul pe razoare / Cintecul lui Iancu jianu / Hora din muntenia si cimpulung oras de munte / Sirba batrineasca / Doina de la visina / Mindrele / Mindra mea din Badulesti / Ciocirlia / Suite Transsilvana / Cintec de nunta de la Cotorca/Hora munteneasca/Briul / Sirba et coragheasca / Suite olteneasca / Doina din Arges/Hora ca la caval
24358 / Nov '97 / Laserlight

☐ PAN PIPES FOR CHRISTMAS
O du frohliche / Jingle bells / O tannenbaum / Six colours / Hark the herald angels sing / Noels Roumains / White Christmas / Little drummer boy / Ave Maria / Petit Papa Noel / Pour toi Jesus / Silent night / Notre Pere / Angels we have heard on high
5525812 / Nov '96 / Spectrum

☐ SPOTLIGHT ON GHEORGHE ZAMFIR
Stranger on the shore / Don't cry for me Argentina / Chanson d'amour / Rose / She / Yesterday / Just the way you are / Annie's song / Tema da un'estate del '42 (the summer knows) / Till / Run to me / I know him so well / If you go away / Sleepy shores / Memory / Lonely shepherd / Sleepy shores (tema da luci della rabalta) (limelight) / What now my love
8483732 / Mar '91 / Phonogram

☐ TRANQUIL SOUND OF THE PANPIPES
MCCD 285 / Mar '97 / Music Club

☐ WONDERFUL WORLD OF PANPIPES
MCCD 202 / May '95 / Music Club

Zaney Janey

☐ ZANEY JANEY
SGCD 14 / Sep '97 / September Gurls

Zao

☐ WHERE BLOOD AND FIRE BRING REST
TNR 1107CD / 25 May '98 / Tooth & Nail

Zap Mama

☐ 7
Jogging a Timbouctou / New world / Baba hooker / Belgo Zairoise / African sunset / Damn your eyes / Poetry man / Warmth / Telephone / Nostalgie / Timidity / Ele buma / Kesia Yanga / Illiol
CDVIR 62 / May '97 / Virgin

☐ SABSYLMA
Fusahi / Sabsylma / Mais qu'est ce / India / De la vie a la most / Citoyen 120 / Locklat Africa / Mr. Brown / Reveil en Australie / Fi dunia / Mamadit / For no one / Mamas of the Mamas / Adjosio omonie
CRAW 12 / Aug '95 / Crammed Discs

Zapak, Ali

☐ MY FIRST SUICIDE
SMART 1CD / Mar '97 / Fundamental

Zapp

☐ ALL THE GREATEST HITS (Zapp & Roger)
More bounce to the ounce / Be alright / I heard it through the grapevine / So ruff, so tuff / Do it Roger / Dance floor / Doo wa ditty (Blow that thing) / I can make you dance / Heartbreaker / In the mix / Midnight hour / Computer love / Night and day / I want to be your man / Curiosity / Slow and easy / Mega medley
9362451432 / Dec '93 / Reprise

☐ NEW ZAPP IV U, THE
It doesn't really matter / Computer love / Itchin' for your twitchin' / Radio people / I only have eyes for you / Rock 'n' roll / Cas-ta-spellome / Make me feel good / Ja ready to rock
7599253272 / May '94 / Warner Bros.

☐ ZAPP VOL.3
7599238752 / Jan '96 / Reprise

Zappa, Dweezil

☐ CONFESSIONS
Earth / Bad girl / F.w.a.k. / Kiss (aura resurrects flash) / Anytime at all / Helpless / Shoogagoogagunga / Stayin' alive / Maybe tonight / Confessions of a deprived youth / Gotta get to you / Pain of love / Obviously influenced by the devil / Return of the son of shoogagoogagunga / Vanity
CDGRUB 19 / Mar '91 / Food For Thought

☐ HAVIN' A BAD DAY
RCD 10057 / May '92 / Rykodisc

☐ SHAMPOOHORN (Z)
CDGRUB 25 / May '93 / Food For Thought

Zappa, Frank

☐ 200 MOTELS (2CD Set)
Semi fraudulent/Direct from Hollywood overture / Mystery roach / Dance of the rock'n'roll interviewers / This town is a sealed tuna sanwich / Tuna fish promenade / Dance of the just plain folks / This town is a sealed tuna sandwich (reprise) / Sealed tuna bolero / Lonesome cowboy Burt / Touring can make you crazy / Would you like a snack / Redneck eats / Centerville / She painted up her face / Janet's big dance number / Half a dozen provocative squats / Mysterioso / Shove it right in / Lucy's seduction of a bored violinist and postlude / I'm stealing the towels / Dental hygiene dilemma / Does this kind of life look interesting to you / Daddy, daddy, daddy / Penis dimension / What will this evening bring me this morning / Nun suit painted on some old boxes / Magic fingers / Motorhead's midnight ranch / Dew on the newts we got / Lad searches the night for his newts / Girl wants to fix him some broth / Girl's dream / Little green scratchy sweaters and corduroy ponce / Strictly genteel (the finale)
RCD 10513/14 / 13 Oct '97 / Rykodisc

☐ ABSOLUTELY FREE (Zappa, Frank & The Mothers Of Invention)
Plastic people / Uncle Bernie's farm / Brown shoes don't make it / Status back baby / America drinks and goes home / Invocation and ritual dance of the young pumpkin / Call any vegetable / Big Leg Emmas / Why don'tcha do me right / Son of Suzy Creamcheese / Duke of prunes / Amnesia vivace / Duke regains his chops / Soft sell conclusion
RCD 10502 / May '95 / Rykodisc

☐ AHEAD OF THEIR TIME (Zappa, Frank & The Mothers Of Invention)
Prologue / Progress / Like it or not / Jimmy Carl Black philosophy lesson / Holding the group back / Holiday in Berlin / Rejected Mexican Pope leaves the stage / Undaunted the band plays on / Agency man / Epilogue / King Kong / Help I'm a rock / Transylvania boogie / Pound for a brown / Sleeping in a jar / Let's make the water turn back / Harry you're a beast / Orange County lumber truck / Oh no
RCD 10559 / 27 Apr '98 / Rykodisc

☐ APOSTROPHE
Don't eat the yellow snow / Nanook rubs it / St. Alfonzo's pancake breakfast / Father O'Blivion / Cosmik debris / Excentrifugal forz / Apostrophe / Uncle Remus / Stinkfoot
RCD 10519 / Apr '95 / Rykodisc

☐ APOSTROPHE (Au20 Version)
Don't eat the yellow snow / Nanook rubs it / St. Alfonzo's pancake breakfast / Father O'Blivion / Cosmik debris / Excentrifugal forz / Apostrophe / Uncle Remus / Stink foot
RCD 80519 / Jun '96 / Rykodisc

☐ BABY SNAKES
Intro rap / Baby snakes / Titties 'n' beer / Black page / Jones crusher / Disco boy / Dinah moe humm / Punky's whips
RCD 10539 / May '95 / Rykodisc

☐ BEST BAND YOU NEVER HEARD IN YOUR LIFE, THE (2CD Set)
Heavy duty Judy / Ring of fire / Cosmik debris / Find her finer / Who needs the peace corps / I left my heart in San Francisco / Zomby woof / Zoot allures / Mr. Green Genes / Florentine pogen / Andy / Inca roads / Sofa / Purple haze / Sunshine of your love / Let's move to Cleveland / When Irish eyes are smiling / Godfather part II / Few moments with Brother AWest / Torture never stops (Part one) / Theme from Bonanza / Lonesome cowboy Burt (Swaggart version) / Torture never stops (Part two) / More trouble every day (Swaggart version) / Penguin in bondage (Swaggart version) / Eric Dolphy memorial barbeque / Stairway to heaven
RCD 10653/54 / Apr '96 / Rykodisc

☐ BONGO FURY
Debra Kadabra / Carolina hard-core ecstasy / Sam with the showing scalp flat top / Poofter's Froth Wyoming plans ahead / 200 years old / Cucamonga / Advance romance / Man with the woman head / Muffin man
RCD 10522 / Feb '96 / Rykodisc

☐ BROADWAY THE HARD WAY
Elvis has just left the building / Elvis has just left the building / Planet of the baritone women / Planet of the baritone women / Any kind of pain / Any kind of pain / Dickie's such an asshole / Dickie's such an asshole / When the lie's so big / When the lie's so big / Rhymin' man / Rhymin' man / Promiscuous / Promiscuous / Untouchables / Untouchables / Why don't you like me / Why don't you like me / Bacon fat / Bacon fat / Stolen moments / Stolen moments / Murder by numbers / Murder by numbers / Jezebel boy / Jezebel boy / Outside now / Outside now / Hot plate heaven at The Green Hotel / Hot plate heaven at the green hotel / What kind of girl / What kind of girl / Jesus thinks you're a jerk / Jesus thinks you're a jerk
RCD 10552 / 27 Apr '98 / Rykodisc

☐ BURNT WEENY SANDWICH (Zappa, Frank & The Mothers Of Invention)
WPLJ / Igor's boogie phase one / Overture to A Holiday In Berlin / Theme from Burnt Weeny Sandwich / Igor's boogie phase two / Holiday in Berlin full-blown / Aybe sea / Little house I used to live in / Valarie
RCD 10509 / May '95 / Rykodisc

☐ CHEAP THRILLS
I could be a star now / Catholic girls / Bobby Brown goes down / Youa re what you is / We are not alone / Cheap thrills / Mudshark interview / Hot plate heaven at the green hotel / Zomby woof / Torture never stops / Original version / Joe's garage / My guitar wants to kill your mama / Going for the money
RCD 10579 / 27 Apr '98 / Rykodisc

☐ CHUNGA'S REVENGE
Transylvania boogie / Road ladies / Twenty small cigars / Nancy and Mary music / Tell me you love me / Would you go all the way / Chunga's revenge / Clap / Rudy wants to buy yez drink / Sharleena
RCD 10511 / May '95 / Rykodisc

☐ **CRUISING WITH RUBEN & THE JETS (Zappa, Frank & The Mothers Of Invention)**
Cheap thrills / Love of my life / How could I be such a fool / Deserei / I'm not satisfied / Jelly roll gum drop / Anything / Later that night / You didn't try to call me / Fountain of love / No no no / Anyway the wind blows / Stuff up the cracks
RCD 10505 / 27 Apr '98 / Rykodisc

☐ **CUCAMONGA**
DFCD 7126 / 20 Apr '98 / Del-Fi

☐ **DOES HUMOR BELONG IN MUSIC**
Zoot allures / Tinsel Town rebellion / Trouble every day / Penguin in bondage / Hot-plate heaven at the green hotel / What's new in Baltimore / Cocksuckers' ball / WPLJ / Let's move to Cleveland / Whipping post
RCD 10548 / Feb '96 / Rykodisc

☐ **FILLMORE EAST - JUNE 1971 (Zappa, Frank & The Mothers Of Invention)**
Little house I used to live in / Mud shark / What kind of girl do you think we are / Bwana dik / Latex solar beef / Willie the pimp / Do you like my new car / Happy together / Lonesome electric turkey / Peaches en regalia / Tears begin to fall
RCD 10512 / May '95 / Rykodisc

☐ **FRANCESCO ZAPPA (Barking Pumpkin Digital Gratification Consort)**
RCD 10546 / 25 May '98 / Rykodisc

☐ **FRANK ZAPPA MEETS THE MOTHERS OF PREVENTION**
We're turning again / Alien orifice / Yo cats / What's new in Baltimore / I don't even care / One man, one vote / HR 2911 / Little beige sambo / Aerobics in bondage
RCD 10547 / 27 Apr '98 / Rykodisc

☐ **FRANK ZAPPA: INTERVIEW PICTURE DISC**
CBAK 4012 / Apr '88 / Baktabak

☐ **FREAK OUT (Zappa, Frank & The Mothers Of Invention)**
Hungry freaks Daddy / I ain't got no heart / Who are the brain police / Go cry on somebody else's shoulder / Motherly love / How could I be such a fool / Wowie zowie / You didn't try to call me / Anyway the wind blows / I'm not satisfied / You're probably wondering why I'm here / Trouble everyday / Help I'm a rock / It can't happen here / Return of the son of monster magnet
RCD 10501 / May '95 / Rykodisc

☐ **GRAND WAZOO, THE**
For Calvin (and his next two hitch-hikers) / Grand wazoo / Cletus awreetus-awrightus / Eat that question / Blessed relief
RCD 10517 / May '95 / Rykodisc

☐ **GUITAR (2CD Set)**
Sexual harassment in the workplace / Republicans / That's not really reggae / When no one was no one / Once again, without the net / Outside Now / Jim and Tammy's upper room / Were we ever really safe / That ol' G minor thing again / Move it or park it / Sunrise redeemer / But who was Fulcanneli / Winos do not match / Systems of edges / Things that look like meat / Watermelon in Easter hay
RCD 10550/51 / May '95 / Rykodisc

☐ **HAVE I OFFENDED SOMEONE**
Bobby Brown goes down / Disco boy / Goblin girl / In France / He's so gay / Sex / Titties 'n' beer / We're turning again / Dumb all over / Catholic girls / Dinah-moe humm / Tinsel-town rebellion / Valley girl / Jewish princess / Yo cats
RCD 10577 / Apr '97 / Rykodisc

☐ **HOT RATS**
Peaches en regalia / Willie the pimp / Son of Mr. Green Genes / Little umbrellas / Gumbo variations / It must be a camel
RCD 10508 / May '95 / Rykodisc

☐ **JAZZ FROM HELL**
Night school / Beltway bandits / While you were out / Jazz from hell / G spot tornado / Damp ankles / St. Etienne / Massaggio galore
RCD 10549 / May '95 / Rykodisc

☐ **JOE'S GARAGE ACTS I, II & III (2CD Set)**
Central scrutinizer / Joe's garage / Catholic girls / Crew slut / Wet t-shirt nite / Toad-O-Line / Why does it hurt when I pee / Lucille has messed my mind up / Token of his extreme / Stick it out / Sy Borg / Dong work for Yuda / Keep it greasy / Outside now / He used to cut the grass / Packard goose / Watermelon in Easter hay / Little green rosetta
RCD 10530/31 / May '95 / Rykodisc

☐ **JUST ANOTHER BAND FROM LA (Zappa, Frank & The Mothers Of Invention)**
Billy the mountain / Call any vegetable / Eddie, are you kidding / Magdalena / Dog breath
RCD 10515 / May '95 / Rykodisc

☐ **LATHER (3CD Set)**
Re-gyptian strut / Naval aviation in art / Little green Rosetta / Duck duck goose / Down in de dew / For the young sophisticate / Tryin' to grow a chin / Broken hearts are for assholes / Legend of the Illinois enema / Bandit / Lemme take you to the beach / Revised music for guitar and low / Budget orchestra / RDNZL / Honey, don't you want a man like me / Black page no.1 / Big leg Emma / Punky's whips / Flambe / Purple lagoon / Pedro's dowry / Lather / Spider of destiny / Duke of orchestral prunes / Filthy habits / Titties 'n' beer / Ocean is the ultimate solution / Adventures of Greggery Peccary / Re-gyptian strut / Lather goods / Revenge of the knick-knack people / Time is money
RCD 10574/76 / Sep '96 / Rykodisc

☐ **LONDON SYMPHONY ORCHESTRA VOL.1 & 2 (2CD Set) (London Symphony Orchestra)**
RCD 10540/41 / 25 May '98 / Rykodisc

☐ **LOST EPISODES, THE**
Blackouts / Lost ina whirlpool / Ronnie sings / Kenny's booger story / Mount St. Mary's concert excerpt / Take your clothes off when you dance / Tiger roach / Run home slow theme / Fountain of love / Run home cues / Any way the wind blows / Run homes cues / Charva / Dick Kunc story / Wedding dress song / Handsome cabin boy / Cops and buns / Big Squeeze / I'm a band leader / Alley cat / Grand wazoo / Wonderful wino / Kung fu / RDNZL / Basement music / Inca roads / Lil' Clanton shuffle / I don't wanna get drafted / Sharleena
RCD 40573 / Feb '96 / Rykodisc

☐ **LUMPY GRAVY**
Lumpy gravy
RCD 10504 / Apr '95 / Rykodisc

☐ **MAKE A JAZZ NOISE HERE (2CD Set)**
Stinkfoot / When yuppies go to hell / Fire and chains / Let's make the water turn black / Harry, you're a beast / Orange county lumber truck / Oh no / Lumpy gravy / Eat that question / Black napkins / Big swifty / King Kong / Star Wars won't work / Black page / T'mershi duween / Dupree's paradise / City of tiny lites / Royal March (L'Histoire du Soldat)/Theme from Bartok's 3rd / Sinister footwear / Stevie's spanking / Alien orifice / Cruisin' for burgers / Advance romance / Strictly genteel
RCD 10555/56 / May '95 / Rykodisc

☐ **MAN FROM UTOPIA, THE**
Cocaine decisions / Dangerous kitchen / Tink walks amok / Radio is broken / Moggio / Man from Utopia meets Mary Lou / Stick together / Sex / Jazz discharge party hats / We are not alone
RCD 10538 / 27 Apr '98 / Rykodisc

☐ **ONE SIZE FITS ALL (Zappa, Frank & The Mothers Of Invention)**
Inca roads / Can't afford no shoes / Sofa No. 1 / Po-jama people / Florentine / Pogen / Evelyn, a modified dog / San Ber'dino / Andy / Sofa No. 2
RCD 10521 / May '95 / Rykodisc

☐ **ONE SIZE FITS ALL (Au20 Version) (Zappa, Frank & The Mothers Of Invention)**
Inca roads / Can't afford no shoes / Sofa No.1 / Po-jama people / Florentine Pogen / Evelyn, a modified dog / San ber'dino / Andy / Sofa No.2
RCD 80521 / Jun '96 / Rykodisc

☐ **ORCHESTRAL FAVORITES**
Strictly genteel / Pedro's dowry / Naval aviation in art / Duke of prunes / Bogus pomp
RCD 10529 / 25 May '98 / Rykodisc

☐ **OVERNITE SENSATION**
Camarillo brillo / I'm the slime / Dirty love / 50/50 / Zomby woof / Dinah-Moe Humm / Montana
RCD 10518 / Apr '95 / Rykodisc

☐ **PERFECT STRANGER, THE (Boulez Conducts Zappa) (Barking Pumpkin Digital Gratification Consort)**
Dupree's paradise: *Ensemble Intercontemporain* / Girl in the magnesium dress / Jonestown / Love story / Naval aviation in art: *Ensemble Intercontemporain* / Outside now, again / Perfect stranger: *Ensemble Intercontemporain*
RCD 10542 / 25 May '98 / Rykodisc

☐ **PLAYGROUND PSYCHOTICS (2CD Set) (Zappa, Frank & The Mothers Of Invention)**
Here comes the gear lads / Living garbage truck / Typical soundcheck / This is neat / Motel lobby / Getting stewed / Motel room / Don't take me down / Dressing room / Learning penis dimension / You there with the hard on / Zanti serenade / Divan / Sleeping in a jar / Don't eat there / Brixton still life / Super grease / Wonderful wind / Sharleen A4 / Cruisin' for burger / Diptheria blues / Well / Say please / Aawk / Scumbag / Small eternity / Beer shampoo / Champagne lecture / Childish perversions / Playground psychotics / Mud shark interview / There's no lust in jazz / Botulism on the hoof / You got your armies / Spew king / I'm doomed / Status back baby / London cab tape / Concentration moon / Sanzini Brothers / It's a good thing we get paid to do this / Mom and Dad / Intro to music for low budget orchestra / Billy the mountain / He's watching us / If you're not a professional / He's right / Going for the money / Jeff quits / Bunch of adventures / Martin Lickert's story / Great guy / Bad acting / Worst reviews / Version of himself / I could be a star now
RCD 10557/58 / 27 Apr '98 / Rykodisc

☐ **PROPHETIC ATTITUDE (Le Concert Impromptu Play Frank Zappa) (Le Concert Impromptu)**
ED 13071 / Oct '97 / L'Empreinte Digitale

☐ **ROXY AND ELSEWHERE (Zappa, Frank & The Mothers Of Invention)**
Preamble / Penguin in bondage / Pygmy twylyte / Dummy up / Village of the sun / Echidna's arf (of you) / Don't you ever wash that thing / Cheepnis / Son of Orange County / More trouble every day / Be bop tango (of the old jazzmen's church)
RCD 10520 / May '95 / Rykodisc

☐ **SHEIK YERBOUTI**
I have been in you / Flakes / Broken hearts are for assholes / I'm so cute / Jones crusher / Whatever happened to all the fun in the world / Rat tomago / We gotta get into something real / Bobby Brown / Rubber shirt / Sheik Yerbouti tango / Baby snakes / Tryin' to grow a chin / City of tiny lites / Dancin' fool / Jewish princess / Wild love / Yo mama
RCD 10528 / May '95 / Rykodisc

☐ **SHIP ARRIVING TOO LATE TO SAVE A DROWNING WITCH**
No not now / Valley girl / I come from nowhere / Drowning witch / Envelopes / Teenage prostitute
RCD 10537 / 27 Apr '98 / Rykodisc

☐ **SHUT UP 'N PLAY YER GUITAR (3CD Set)**
Five, five, five / Hog Heaven / Shut up 'n' play yer guitar / While you were out / Treacherous cretins / Heavy duty Judy / Soup 'n' old clothes / Variations on the Carlos Santana / Gee I like your pants / Canarsie / Ship ahoy / Deathless horsie / Pink napkins / Beat it with your fist / Return of the son of shut up 'n play / Pinocchio's furniture / Why Johnny can't read / Stucco Homes / Canard du Jour
RCD 10533/34/35 / May '95 / Rykodisc

☐ **SLEEP DIRT**
Filthy habits / Flambay / Spider of destiny / Regyption strut / Time is money / Sleep dirt / Ocean is the ultimate solution
RCD 10527 / 25 May '98 / Rykodisc

☐ **STRICTLY COMMERCIAL (The Best Of Frank Zappa)**
Peaches en regalia / Don't eat the yellow snow / Dancin' fool / San Ber'dino / Dirty love / My guitar wants to kill your Mother / Cosmik debris / Trouble every day / Disco boy / Fine girl / Sexual harassment in the workplace / Let's make the water turn black / I'm the slime / Joe's garage / Bobby Brown goes down / Montana / Valley girl / Be in my video / Muffin man / Tell me you love me / Planet of the baritone women
RCD 40600 / Aug '95 / Rykodisc

☐ **STRICTLY GENTEEL (A Classical Introduction To Frank Zappa)**
Uncle meat (main title theme) / Regyptian strut / Pedro's dowry / Outrage at Valdez / Little umbrellas / Run home slow theme / Dwarf nebula processional march and dwarf nebula / Dupree's paradise / Opus 1, No.3, 2nd movement, presto / Duke of prunes / Aybe sea / Naval aviation in art / G spot tornado / Bob in dacron, first movement / Opus 1, no.4, 2nd movement, allegro / Dog breath variations / Uncle meat / Strictly genteel
RCD 10578 / May '97 / Rykodisc

☐ **STUDIO TAN**
Adventures of greggery peccary / Revised music for guitar and low-budget orchestra / Lemme take you to the beach / Rdnzl
RCD 10526 / 25 May '98 / Rykodisc

☐ **THEM OR US**
Closer you are / In France / Ya hozna / Sharleena / Sinister footwear II / Truck driver divorce / Stevie's spanking / Baby take your teeth out / Marque - son's chicken / Planet of my dreams / Be in my video / Them or us / Frogs with dirty little lips / Whipping post
RCD 10543 / May '95 / Rykodisc

☐ **THING FISH (2CD Set)**
Prologue / Mammy nuns / Harry and Rhonda / Galoot up-date / Torchum never stops / That evil prince / You are what you are / Mud club / Meek shall inherit nothing / Clowns on velvet / Harry as a boy / He's so gay / Massive improve'lence / Artificial Rhonda / Crabbgrass baby / White boy troubles / No not now / Brief case boogie / Brown Moses / Wistful wit a fist-full / Drop dead
RCD 10544/45 / 25 May '98 / Rykodisc

☐ **TINSELTOWN REBELLION**
Fine girl / Easy meat / For the young sophisticate / Love of my life / I ain't got no heart / Panty rap / Tell me you love me / Now you see it, now you don't / Dance contest / Blue light / Tinseltown rebellion / Pick me, I'm clean / Bamboozled by love / Brown shoes don't make it / Peaches III
RCD 10532 / May '95 / Rykodisc

☐ **TRIBUTE TO THE MUSIC OF FRANK ZAPPA (Various Artists)**
EFA 034202 / Jul '95 / Muffin

☐ **UNCLE MEAT (2CD Set) (Zappa, Frank & The Mothers Of Invention)**
RCD 10506/7 / May '95 / Rykodisc

☐ **WAKA/JAWAKA**
Big Swifty / Your mouth / It might just be a one-shot deal / Waka / Jawaka
RCD 10516 / May '95 / Rykodisc

☐ **WE'RE ONLY IN IT FOR THE MONEY (Zappa, Frank & The Mothers Of Invention)**
Are you hung up / Who needs the peace corps / Concentration moon / Mom and Dad / Bow tie Daddy / Harry, you're a beast / What's the ugliest part of your body / Absolutely free / Flower punk / Hot poop / Nasal retentive calliope music / Mother people
RCD 10503 / Apr '95 / Rykodisc

☐ **WEASELS RIPPED MY FLESH (Zappa, Frank & The Mothers Of Invention)**
Didja get any onya / Directly from my heart to you / Prelude to the afternoon of a sexually aroused gas mask / Toads of the short forest / Get a little / Eric Dolphy memorial barbecue / Dwarf Nebula processional march/Dwarf nebula / Oh no / Orange county lumber truck / Weasels ripped my flesh / Charles Ives
RCD 10510 / Feb '96 / Rykodisc

☐ **YELLOW SHARK (Ensemble Modern)**
Intro / Dog breath variations / Uncle meat / Outrage at valdez / Times beach il / Iii revised / Girl in the magnesium dress / Be bop tango / Ruth is sleeping / None of the above / Pentagon afternoon / Questi cazzi di piccione / Times beach iii / Food gathering in post industrial america 1992 / Welcome to the united states / Pound for a brown / Exercise 4 / Get whitey / G-spot tornado
RCD 40560 / May '95 / Rykodisc

☐ **YOU ARE WHAT YOU IS**
Teenage wind / Harder than your husband / Doreen / Goblin girl / Third movement of sinister footwear / Society pages / I'm a beautiful guy / Beauty knows no pain / Charlie's enormous mouth / Any downers / Conehead / You are what you is / Mudd club / Meek shall inherit nothing / Dumb all over / Heavenly bank account / Suicide chump / Jumbo go away / If only she woulda / Drafter again
RCD 10536 / May '95 / Rykodisc

☐ **YOU CAN'T DO THAT ON STAGE ANYMORE VOL.1 (2CD Set) (Zappa, Frank & The Mothers Of Invention)**
Florida airport tape / Once upon a time / Sofa no.1 / Mammy anthem / You didn't try to call me / Diseases of the band / Trying to grow a chin / Let's make the water turn back / Harry you're a beast / Orange County lumber truck / Groupie routine / Ruthie Ruthie / Babbette / I'm the slime / Big swifty / Don't eat the yellow snow / Plastic people / Torture never sleeps / Fine girl / Zombie woof / Sweet Leilani / Oh no / Be in my video / Deathless horsie / Dangerous kitchen / Dumb all over / Heavenly bank account / Suicide chump / Tell me you love me / Sofa no.2
RCD 10561/62 / 27 Apr '98 / Rykodisc

☐ **YOU CAN'T DO THAT ON STAGE ANYMORE VOL.2 (2CD Set)(The Helsinki Tapes)**
Tush tush tush / Stinkfoot / Inca roads / RDNZL / Village of the sun / Echidna's arf (of you) / Don't you ever wash that thing / Pygmy twylyte / Room service / Idiot bastard son / Cheepnis / Approximate / Dupree's paradise / Satumaa / T'mershi duween / Dog breath variations / Uncle meat / Building a girl / Montana (whipping floss) / Big swifty
RCD 10563/64 / 27 Apr '98 / Rykodisc

☐ **YOU CAN'T DO THAT ON STAGE ANYMORE VOL.3 (2CD Set)**
Sharleena / Bamboozled by love / Lucille has messed my mind up / Advance romance / Bobby Brown / Keep it greasy / Honey, don't you want a man like me / In France / Drowning witch / Ride my face to Chicago / Carol you fool / Chana in the Bushwah / Joe's garage / Why does it hurt when I pee / Dicky's such an asshole / Hands with a hammer / Zoot allures / Society pages / Beautiful guy / Beauty knows no pain / Charlie's enormous mouth / Cocaine decisions / Nigger biznis / King Kong / Cosmik debris
RCD 10565/66 / 27 Apr '98 / Rykodisc

☐ **YOU CAN'T DO THAT ON STAGE ANYMORE VOL.4 (2CD Set)**
Little rubber girl / Stick together / My guitar / Willie the pimp / Montana / Brown Moses / Evil prince / Approximate / Love of my life / Let's move to Cleveland / You call that music / Pound for a brown on the bus / Black page 2 / Take me out to the ball game / Filthy habits / Torture never stops / Church chat / Stevie's spanking / Outside now / Disco boy / Teenage wind / Truck driver divorce / Florentine pogen / Tiny sick tears / Smell my beard / Booger man / Carolina hard-core ecstasy / Are you upset / Little girl of mine / Closer you are / Johnny darling / No no cherry / Man from Utopia meets Mary Lou
RCD 10567/68 / 25 May '98 / Rykodisc

☐ **YOU CAN'T DO THAT ON STAGE ANYMORE VOL.5 (2CD Set)**
Downtown talent scout / Charles Ives / Here lies love / Piano and drum duet / Mozart ballet / Chocolate halvah / Jimmy Carl Black and Kansas on the bus 1 / Run home slow / Little march / Right there / Where is Johnny Velvet / Return of the hunchback duke / Trouble every day / Proto-minimalism / Jimmy Carl Black and Kansas on the bus 2 / My head / Meow / Baked bean boogie / Where's our equipment / Drum duet / No waiting for the peanuts to dissolve / Game of cards / Underground freak-out music / German lunch / My guitar wants to kill your mama / East meat / Dead girls of London / Shall we take ourselves seriously / What's new in Baltimore / Moggio / Dancing fool / RDNZL / Advance romance / City of tiny lites / Pound for a brown / Doreen / Black page 2 / Geneva farewell
RCD 10569/70 / 25 May '98 / Rykodisc

☐ **YOU CAN'T DO THAT ON STAGE ANYMORE VOL.6 (2CD Set)**
Mothers Of Invention Anti-Smut Loyalty Oath / Poodle lecture / Dirty love / Magic fingers / Madison panty-sniffing festival / Honey, don't you want a man like me / Farther Oblivion / Is that guy kidding or what / I'm so cute / White person / Lonely person devices / Ms. Pinky / Shove it right in / Wind up workin' in a gas station / Make a sex noise / Tracy is a snob / I have been in you / Emperor of Ohio / Dinah-Moe Humm / He's so gay / Camarillo brillo / Muffin man / NYC Halloween audience / Illinois enema bandit / 13 / Lobster girl / Black napkins / We're turning again / Alien orifice / Catholic girls / Crew slut / Tryin' to grow a chin / Take your clothes off when you dance / Lisa's life story / Lonesome Cowboy Nando / 200 Motels finale / Strictly genteel
RCD 10571/72 / 25 May '98 / Rykodisc

☐ **ZAPPA IN NEW YORK**
Titties and beer / Cruisin' for burgers / I promise not to come in your mouth / Punky's whips / Honey, don't you want a man like me / Illinois enema bandit / I'm the slime / Pound for a brown / Manx needs women / Black page / Big leg Emma / Sofa no.1 / Black page 2 / Torture never stops / Purple lagoon
RCD 10524/25 / May '95 / Rykodisc

☐ **ZOOT ALLURES**
Wind up workin' in a gas station / Black napkins / Torture never stops / Ms. Pinky / Find her finer / Friendly little finger / Wonderful wino / Zoot allures / Disco boy
RCD 10523 / Feb '96 / Rykodisc

Zarathustra

☐ **ZARATHUSTRA**
SB 029 / Jun '97 / Second Battle

Zariz, Jose
☐ EL CONDOR PASA
Amanecer / Woman in love / Sweet yasmin / Interludio - tierra / La paloma / Mi bahia / Besame mucho / Interludio - el llano / El condor pasa / Alfonsina / Guantanamera / Interludio - fuego / Adagio (albinoni) / Hora azul
12411 / Jul '95 / Laserlight

Zart
☐ ZART
MILL 029CD / 29 Sep '97 / Millenium

Zawinul, Joe
☐ BEGINNING, THE (Zawinul, Joe Trio)
FSRCD 142 / Dec '90 / Fresh Sound

☐ BLACK WATER (Zawinul Syndicate)
Carnavalito / Familial / In the same boat / Little rootie tootie / Black water / Medicine man / Monk's mood / They had a dream
4653442 / Jan '95 / Sony Jazz

☐ JOE ZAWINUL & AUSTRIAN ALLSTARS/SWINGING NEPHEWS 1954-1957
RST 91549 / Mar '95 / RST

☐ MY PEOPLE
Bimoya / Mi Gente / In an island way / Waraya: Talbot, Mick & Steve White / Many churches / Midnight rainbow / Sultan / Erdapfee blues / Otzi / Do you want to drink tea, Grandpa / Africama
ESC 036512 / Sep '96 / Escapade

☐ RISE AND FALL OF THE THIRD STREAM/MONEY IN POCKET
Baptismal / Soul of a village (part 1) / Soul of a village (part 2) / Fifth canto / From Vienna with love / Lord, lord, lord / Concerto retitled / Money in the pocket / If / My one and only love / Midnight mood / Some more of dat / Sharon's waltz / Riverbed / Del sasser
8122716752 / Jul '94 / Atlantic

☐ STORIES OF THE DANUBE (Czech State Philharmonic Choir/Caspar Richter)
4541432 / Jul '96 / Philips

☐ WORLD TOUR (2CD Set) (Zawinul, Joe & The Zawinul Syndicate)
Patriots / Sunday morning / Indiscretions / Untitled / Bimoya / Zansa II / Bona fortuna / N'awleans / Lost tribes / Gypsy / Three postcards / Slivovitz trail / When there was royalty / Success / Two lines / Carnavalito
ESC 036562 / 18 May '98 / Escapade

☐ ZAWINUL
Dr. Honoris Causa / In a silent way / His last journey / Double image / Arrival in New York
7567813752 / Apr '95 / Atlantic

Zawose, Hukwe
☐ CHIBITE
Sisitizo la amani duniani / Chilumi / Ibarikiwe mungu yupo duniani / Munyamaye / Nyangawuya / Nghanga msakuzi / Jende chiwuyaje kukaya / Sauti za kigogo / Safari na muziki / Twendeni sote na mwanga wa amani
CDRW 57 / Jun '96 / Realworld

☐ MATESO
TERRACD 104 / Jul '98 / Triple Earth

Zayas, Edwin Colon
☐ Y SU TALLER CAMPESINO BIEN JIBARO
ROUCD 5056 / May '94 / Rounder

Zazou, Hector
☐ GEOGRAPHIES
Cine citta: Gare centrale / Denise a venise / Sidi bel abbes / Vera C / Pali kao / Motel du sud / Sous les bougainvilliers / Des cocotiers
MTM 5 / Jun '96 / Made To Measure

☐ GEOLOGIES
Peresphone (Nue) / Enoch arden / Livia / Tanis a tunis / Plurabelle / Al sirat / Tout l'ete (Sans Toi) / Peresphone (Suite) / In the box / Deianira (Legato) / Anna / Etudes (Strates) / Brandan
MTM 20 / Jun '96 / Made To Measure

☐ GUILTY (Zazou, Hector & Bony Bikaye)
Guilty / No secret / Binagwe / Ba wela / Kinshasa / My shoes / Sans musik / It's a man's man's man's world / Zuwa / Na kenda
CRAM 062 / Nov '96 / Crammed Discs

☐ I'LL STRANGLE YOU (Zazou, Hector & Depardieu)
CRAM 80 / Oct '92 / Crammed Discs

☐ LIGHTS IN THE DARK
An realt / Seven joys of the Virgin Mary / Song of the dead / Keening of the three Marys / Lament of the three Marys / Song of the passion / In the name of the Father may we gain victory / Seven sorrows of the Virgin Marys / Little song to the heart of Jesus / Mary's lament / Requests of love / Tomb of every hope
3984216622 / 18 May '98 / Erato

☐ NOIR ET BLANC (Zazou, Hector & Bony Bikaye)
M'pasi ya m'pamba / Mangungu / Dju ya feza / Munipe wa kati / Eh yaye / Mama lenvo / Lamuka / Keba / Woa / M'pasi ya m'pamba / Eh yaye
CRAM 2534 / Nov '96 / Crammed Discs

☐ REIVAX AU BONGO
Opening theme / In the commandant's office / Crossing the border / Chief bingo's village / Reivax in a black mood / Apparition / Bongolese song / Reivax and his horse pepito / How beautiful bongo is / Hero / Chase / Reivax's theme / By the sea / Pier / Royal bath
MTM 2 / Jun '96 / Made To Measure

☐ SAHARA BLUE
I'll strangle you / First evening / Ophelie / Lines / Youth / Hapolot kenym / Hunger / Sahara blues (Brussels) / Amdyaz / Black stream / Harar Et Les Gallas / Lettre au directeur des messageries maritimes
MTM 32 / Apr '96 / Made To Measure

Ze, Tom
☐ BRAZIL CLASSICS VOL.4
Ma / O riso e a faca / Toc / To / Um "oh" e um "ah", ui (voce inventa) / Cademar / So (solidao) / Hein / Augusta / Doi / Complexo de epico / A felicidade / Vai (menina, amanha de manha)
7599263962 / Dec '90 / Sire

☐ BRAZIL CLASSICS VOL.5 (The Hips Of Tradition)
Ogodo, ano 2000 / Sem a letra / Fiera de santana / Sofro de juventude / Cortina 1 / Tai / Iracema / Fliperama / O amor e velho-menina / Cortina 2 / Taturamba / Jingle do disco / Lua-gira-sol / Cortina 3 / Multiplicar-se unica / Cortina 4 / O pao nosso de cada mes / Amor
9362451182 / Feb '93 / Luaka Bop

Zebra
☐ NO TELLIN' LIES
Wait until the summer's gone / I don't like it / Bears / I don't care / Lullaby / No tellin' lies / Takin' a stance / But no more / Little things / Drive me crazy
7567801592 / Jan '96 / Atlantic

Zeek Sheck
☐ GOOD LUCK SUCKERS
GR 53CD / 29 Jun '98 / Skingraft

☐ I LOVE YOU
GR 47CD / 17 Nov '97 / Skingraft

Zeigler, Diane
☐ STING OF THE HONEYBEE
CDPH 1174 / Apr '95 / Philo

Zein Musical Party
☐ STYLE OF MOMBASA
Mtindo wa mombasa / Maneno tisiya / Wanawake wa kiamu / Taksim bayati / Baina macho na moyo / Mwiba wa kujitoma / Binti mombasa / Nataka rafiki / Mwana hasahau mana / Taksim jirka
CDORBD 066 / Nov '90 / Globestyle

Zeitlin, Denny
☐ CONCORD DUO SERIES VOL.8 (Zeitlin, Denny & David Friesen)
All of you / Echo of a kiss / Night has a thousand eyes / Old folks / Oleo / Turn around / Island / Signs and wonders
CCD 4639 / Apr '95 / Concord Jazz

☐ IN CONCERT (Zeitlin, Denny & David Friesen)
ITM 970068 / Nov '92 / ITM

☐ LIVE AT MAYBECK RECITAL HALL VOL.27
Blues on the side / Girl next door / My man's gone now / Lazy bird / 'Round midnight / Love for sale / And then I wondered if you knew / Country fair / Sophisticated lady / End of a love affair / Just passing by / What is this thing called love / Fifth house
CCD 4572 / Sep '93 / Concord Jazz

Zeke
☐ FLAT TRACKER
T-5000 / Eddie Hill / Chiva Knievel / Overkill / Mystery chain / Viva agnostic / Hate / Wanna fuck / Fight in the storeroom / Flat truck / Bitch / Daytona / Super six / Eliminator
206162 / Jul '97 / Epitaph

☐ KICKED IN THE TEETH
God of GSXR / Telepath boy / Rodney / Twisted / Dogfight / Kicked in the teeth / Fuck all night / Revolution / Killer inside / Lawson / Revolution reprise / Goggle boy / Zeke you / Porked / Ages high / Shout it out loud / Mert
65132 / 30 Mar '98 / Epitaph

☐ SUPER SOUND RACING
Slut / Tuned out / Relapse / Chiva / Quicksand / Runnin' shine / Wreckin' machine / Eroded / Holley 750 / Incest / West Seattle acid party / Action / Mainline / 302 cubic inch V-8 / Powered blues / Hemicuda / Maybe someday / Galaxie 500 / Highway star / Schmidt value pack / Rid
206202 / Jul '97 / Scooch Pooch

Zellar, Martin
☐ BORN UNDER
Lie to me / Something's gotta happen / East side boys / Falling sky / Problem solved / Cross my heart / Lay this down gently / Summer kind of sad / Force a smile / Let's go
RCD 10318 / Mar '95 / Rykodisc

☐ MARTIN ZELLAR & THE HARDWAYS (Zellar, Martin & The Hardways)
Haunt my dreams / Ten year coin / Brown-eyed boy / I can't believe / Hammer's gonna fall / George and Tammy / Lullaby / Big sandals / Guilty just the same / We were young
RCD 10359 / Aug '96 / Rykodisc

Zelmani, Sophie
☐ SOPHIE ZELMANI
I'd be broken / Stand by / There must be a reason / So good / Always you / Thousand times / Tell me you're joking / Woman in me / You and him / Until dawn / I'll remember you / I'll see you (In another world)
4809556 / Jun '96 / Columbia

Zelwer
☐ LA FIANCEE AUX YEUX DE BOIS
Foire a kamenka / J'ai vu un ange / Le reve de la fiancee / Les montreurs d'ours sont partis / Grand-pere klonimus / Le soldat tufaiev se marie / Roulette russe / Igor l'innocent mort en poche / Dikanka (le soupirant) / Le tourment de vassilissa la belle / Repose toi un moment
MTM 24 / May '96 / Made To Measure

Zen Frisbee
☐ EAT AT THE BURRITO BUNKER
APR 3 / 20 Jul '98 / American Primitive

Zen Guerrilla
☐ POSITRONIC RAYGUN
Sauceships to ragtime / Trouble shake / Roachman / She's radar / Tomato cup / Fingers / Empty heart / Swamp / 54 stars and stripes / Healing in the water / 2000 watts over the south side / Frequency out
VIRUS 211CD / 10 Feb '98 / Alternative Tentacles
LJCD 009 / 18 May '98 / Lockjaw

☐ ZEN GUERILLA
OPS 8 / Mar '93 / Compulsive

Zen Men
☐ MEN FROM MARS
NOOMCD 0092 / 27 Apr '98 / Noom

Zen Paradox
☐ CATHARSIS
NZCD 051 / Oct '96 / Nova Zembla

☐ FROM THE SHORE OF A DISTANT LAND
NZCD 014 / Oct '94 / Nova Zembla

☐ INTO THE ABYSS
NZCD 011 / Jun '94 / Nova Zembla

☐ VOYAGE, THE
NZCD 041 / Oct '95 / Nova Zembla

Zeni Geva
☐ DESIRE FOR AGONY
Stigma / Dead sun rising / Desire for agony / Heathen blood / Disgraceland / Whiteout / Love bite / Autopsy love / Body
VIRUS 135CD / Feb '94 / Alternative Tentacles

Zenith Brass Band
☐ ECLIPSE ALLEY
AMCD 75 / Aug '94 / American Music

Zenith Hot Stompers
☐ SILVER JUBILEE
SOSCD 1191 / Aug '90 / Stomp Off

☐ ZENITH HOT STOMPERS PLAYS JELLY ROLL MORTON
BCD 012 / Oct '93 / GHB

Zenkl, Radim
☐ GALACTIC MANDOLIN
ACD 5 / May '97 / Acoustic Disc

☐ STRINGS & WINGS
SH 5021 / May '96 / Shanachie

Zeno
☐ ZENOLOGY
A2Z 0023CD / Jan '96 / A2Z

Zentner, Michael
☐ PRESENT TIME
EFA 132472 / May '94 / Ozone

Zephaniah, Benjamin
☐ BACK TO ROOTS
DUBI 01CD / Jun '95 / Acid Jazz

☐ BELLY OF THE BEAST
ARICD 113 / Jun '96 / Ariwa Sounds

Zephyr
☐ LIVE
TBACD 6 / Sep '97 / Tommy Brolin Archives

☐ ZEPHYR
Sail on / Sun's a-risin' / Raindrops / Boom-ba-boom / Somebody listen / Cross the river / St. james infirmary / Huna buna / Hard chargin' woman
BGOCD 41 / '89 / Beat Goes On

Zerbe-Blech, Hannez
☐ RANDO A LA FRIED (Zerbe-Blech, Hannez Band)
BVHAASTCD 9207 / Mar '86 / Bvhaast

Zero
☐ ZERO
PM 010 / Oct '97 / Pop Mafia

Zerouki, Charef
☐ GHOZALI - MY GAZELLE
Ma andaklah tgoulili kalma / Al wa'ad arrmani / Al 'achaq / Ghozali / Al 'adra / Yamra
CDORB 047 / Aug '89 / Globestyle

Zeus
☐ TRANSCENDENTAL COMPASSION (Zeus & The Spiritual Traders)
39850142 / 24 Apr '98 / Blue Flame

Z'Ev
☐ ONE FOOT IN THE GRAVE (1968-1990/ 2CD Set)
TO 13 / Mar '91 / Touch

Zevon, Warren
☐ MUTINEER
74321276852 / Jun '95 / RCA

☐ SENTIMENTAL HYGIENE
Sentimental hygiene / Boom boom Mancini / Factory / Trouble waiting to happen / Reconsider me / Detox mansion / Bad karma / Even a dog can shake hands / Heartache / Leave my monkey alone
CDV 2433 / Jul '93 / Virgin

☐ TRANSVERSE CITY
Transverse city / Run straight down / Long arm of the law / Turbulence / They moved the moon / Splendid isolation / Networking / Gridlock / Down in the mall / Nobody's in love this year
CDVUS 9 / Jan '90 / Virgin

ZGA
☐ END OF AN EPOCH
RERZGACD 2 / Oct '96 / ReR/ Recommended

☐ ZGAMONIUMS
RERZGACD / Jan '93 / ReR/ Recommended

Zhane
☐ PRONOUNCED JAH-NAY
5302832 / 15 Sep '97 / Motown

☐ SATURDAY NITE
5307512
5305882 / May '97 / Motown

Zhihou, Hu
☐ MUSIC OF THE GUANZI
VICG 52602 / Mar '96 / JVC World Library

Ziegler, Anne
☐ ANNE ZIEGLER AND WEBSTER BOOTH (Ziegler, Anne & Webster Booth)
Song of paradise / Only a rose / Paradise for two / Will you remember / Wanting you / Deep in my heart dear / Someday my heart will awake / Swing high swing low / Ah sweet mystery of life / Love steals your heart / Fruits of the Earth / Trot here trot there / I'll see you again / You just you / Fold your wings / Lift up your hearts / Dearest of all / Lover come back to me / Indian love call / Such lovely things / Gates of paradise / Throw open wide your window / Love's garden of roses / Love's last word is spoken / Hear my song, Violetta
CDMFP 6353 / Jun '97 / Music For Pleasure

☐ LOVE'S OLD SWEET SONG (Ziegler, Anne & Webster Booth)
Love's old sweet song / One alone / Second minute / Song of the vagabonds / If you were the only girl in the world / A paradise for two / Lover come back to me / Sweethearts / Keys of heaven / Macushla / Deep in my heart dear / Fold your wings / Ah sweet mystery of life / I'll see you again / Wanting you / Only a rose / You, just you / When we are married / So deep is the night / Hindu song / Medley
PASTCD 7034 / Aug '94 / Flapper

Ziegler, Finn

☐ ANDERSEN, NIELSEN OG DEN UKENDTE
MECCACD 1044 / Nov '94 / Music Mecca

Zig Zag

☐ ZIG ZAG'S FAMILY FUN ALBUM (Memorable Tunes For Everyone)
DUOCD 89025 / Dec '93 / Meridian

Zilch

☐ PLATINUM
Good / Here we go / Christiana / Everything / Surfer psalm / In the sky / BAP / Into Heaven
7013834882 / Nov '97 / Gotee

Zimmermann, Tabea

☐ CREAM OF VICTOR SYLVESTER, THE (Zimmermann, Tabea & Thomas Zehetmair)
You're dancing on my heart / Give a little whistle / So deep is the nigth / I shall be waiting / Love bells / Fragrant flowers / It's a hap-hap-happy day / When you wish upon a star / I'm in love for the last time / Love everlasting / Blue orchids / Mist is over the moon / If I were sure of you / In the middle of a dream / Lonely sweetheart / Love never grows old / Little rain must fall / Summer sweetheart / Summer evening in Santa Cruz / Dear Madam / Where of when / Don't say goodbye
PASTCD 9786 / Apr '92 / Flapper

Zineladbidine, Mohamed

☐ OUD
AAA 137 / Nov '96 / Club Du Disque Arabe

Zingaro, Carlos

☐ WESTERN FRONT VANCOUVER 1996 (Zingaro, Carlos & Peggy Lee)
HATOLOGY 513 / May '98 / Hatology

Zinn, Rusty

☐ SITTIN' AND WAITIN'
CDBT 1134 / Jul '96 / Black Top

Zion Harmonizers

☐ NEVER ALONE
FA 411 / Jul '96 / Fremeaux

Zion Train

☐ GREAT SPORTING MOMENTS IN DUB
WWCD 3 / Dec '93 / Wibbly Wobbly

☐ GROW TOGETHER
Seed / Space / La madrugada / Procession / Rise / Grow together / Babylon's burning / Stand up and fight / Harvest / Tubby's garden / Dutch flowers / Peace / Roots
WOLCD 1071
WOLCD 1071N / Jul '96 / China

☐ HOMEGROWN FANTASY
Dance of life / Free the bass / Healing of the nation / Universal communication / Venceremos / Get ready / For the revolution / Why should we have to fight / Live good (IV) / Better day / Love the earth / One world, one heart / One conscience
WOLCD 1060 / Jun '95 / China

☐ NATURAL WONDERS OF THE WORLD IN DUB
WOLCD 1055 / Jan '95 / China

☐ PASSAGE TO INDICA
WOLCD 1054 / Jan '95 / China

☐ SINGLE MINDED/ALIVE (2CD Set)
Get ready/We got to be together / Power One / Zimbabwe / Power Two / Legalise it (all around the world) / Dutch flowers/Need more love / Universal communication / Dance of life / Do anything you want to do / La Madrugada / Rise/Exodus / Follow like wolves / Fuck the Nazis / Babylons burning / Dance of life / Babylons burning / Do anything you want to do / Healing of the nation / Follow like wolves / Hovercraft / Rise / Stand up and fight / Get ready / Procession
WOLCD 1073 / Jun '97 / China

☐ SIREN
WOLCD 1056 / Jan '95 / China

Zion Travellers

☐ DOOTONE MASTERS, THE
Bye and bye / Down by the river / Packing up / Every time I feel the spirit / I dreamed of a city / Jesus said / I want to go to Heaven and rest / Blood / I must tell Jesus / God I'll live / Even me / I've started / Two little fishes / Death of Jesus / Close to thee / Soldier of the cross / Since he lightened my heavy load / I won't have to cross Jordan alone / Just a little talk with Jesus / Lord hold my hand / Bless me / I'm gonna wait on Jesus / You gotta reap what you so / I got to move / Lord I'll go
CDCHD 637 / Aug '96 / Ace

Zior

☐ ZIOR...PLUS
I really do / Za za za Zilda / Love's desire / New land / Now I'm sad / Give me love / Quabala / Oh Mariya / Your life will burn / I was fooling / Before my eyes go blind / Rolling thunder / Dudi Judy / Evolution / Cat's eyes / Strange kind of magic / Ride me baby / Entrance of the devil (the Chicago spine) / Every inch a man / Angel of the highway
SEECD 276 / Oct '89 / See For Miles

Zip

☐ GETTIN' X-PERIMENTAL
5294662 / Feb '97 / Verve

Zipci, Ferdi

☐ NAZOUNI
087942 / Nov '96 / Fresh Sound

Zipoli, Domenico

☐ MUSICA SAGRADA DE LOS MISIONES
74321476182 / Jun '97 / Jade

Zipper Spy

☐ WATCH YOUR DAMAGE
VC 114 / Jun '97 / Vinyl Communication

Ziryab Trio

☐ MASHREQ CLASSICS
Longa riad / Sihr al-sharq / Chutwat habibi / Tawsim qanoun in homayun mode / Sama'i shat araban / Zikrayati / Sama'i nahawand / Riqq solo / Sama'i farahfaza / Suzinak sakiz kasap oyun havasi
CRAW 18 / Jan '97 / Cramworld

Zlatne Uste Blakan Brass Band

☐ NO STRINGS ATTACHED
Simplon cocek / Simplon cocek / Zvonce kolo / Majko, majko-ekremov cocek / Kojcovata / Camceto / Zikino kolo / Ninetov cocek / Aman, aman, momce bre / Durdevdan / Sametov cocek / Papasov cocek / Kozarica kolo / Vranjanka / Zlatni prsti cocek
ROUCD 6054 / Aug '93 / Rounder

ZNR

☐ BARRICADE 3
RERZNR 1 / Oct '96 / ReR/ Recommended

Zoar

☐ CASSANDRA
4563152 / 15 Sep '97 / Point Music

Zodiac Mindwarp

☐ HOODLUM THUNDER (Zodiac Mindwarp & The Love Reaction)
Elvis / Tblr / Feed my frankenstein / Trash madonna / Airline highway / Chainsaw / President / Doctor jekyll / Hoodlum thunder / Mean streak
108642 / Jan '92 / Musidisc

☐ MY LIFE STORY
Porno movies / Porno movies / I love you, goodbye / Holy gasoline / Slut freak / My life story
109832 / Nov '92 / Musidisc

Zodiac Youth

☐ DEVIL'S CIRCUS
BFLCD 25 / Aug '97 / Butterfly

Zoic

☐ TOTAL LEVEL OF DESTRUCTION
PLRCD 001 / Nov '96 / Powerline

Zoinks

☐ PANORAMA
DSR 61CD / Jun '97 / Dr. Strange

☐ WELL AND GOOD
DSR 66CD / Sep '97 / Dr. Strange

Zollar, James

☐ SOARING WITH THE BIRD
860082 / Feb '98 / Naxos Jazz

Zoller, Attila

☐ WHEN IT'S TIME
Joy for hoy / Lu and Shu / After the morning / Song is you / When it's time / Homage to OP / Voyage / Meant to be
ENJ 90312 / Aug '95 / Enja

Zombies

☐ BEST OF THE ZOMBIES, THE
She's not there / Time of the season / I must move / I got my mojo working / I remember how I loved her / Summertime / What more can I do / Can't nobody love you / Can't make up my mind / Tell her no / I don't want to know / I love you / You really got a hold on me / Whenever you're ready / You make me feel good / Roadrunner
MCCD 002 / Feb '91 / Music Club

☐ ODESSEY AND ORACLE (Stereo/ Mono)
Care of cell 44 / Rose for Emily / Maybe after he's gone / Beechwood park / Brief candles / Hung up on a dream / Changes / I want her she wants me / This will be our year / Butcher's tale / Friends of mine / Time of the season / Rose for Emily / Time of the season / Prison song
CDWIKD 181 / 27 Apr '98 / Big Beat

☐ SINGLES A'S AND B'S
She's not there / Leave me be / Tell her no / She's coming home / I want her back / Whenever you're ready / Is this the dream / Remember you / Indication / Gotta get a hold on myself / Goin' out of my head / You make me feel good / Woman / What more can I do / I must move / I remember when I loved her / I love you / Don't go away / Just out of reach / How we were before / Way I feel inside / She does everything for me
SEECD 30 / Apr '97 / See For Miles

☐ ZOMBIE HEAVEN (4CD Set)
She's not there / You make me feel good / Leave me be / Woman / Tell her no / What more can I do / Road runner / Summertime / I can't make up my mind / Way I feel inside / Work 'n' play / You've really got a hold on me/Bring it on home to me / Sticks and stones / Can't nobody love you / I don't want to know / I remember when I loved her / I got my mojo working / She's coming home / I must move / I want you back again / Whenever you're ready / I love you / Is this the dream / Don't go away / Remember you / Just out of reach / Indication / How we were before / Gotta get a hold of myself / Goin' out of my head / She does everything for me / Care of cell 44 / Rose for Emily / Maybe after he's gone / Beechwood Park / Brief candles / Hung up on a dream / Changes / I want her she wants me / This will be her year / Butcher's tale (western front 1914) / Friends of mine / Time of the season / I'll call you mine / Imagine the swan / Conversation off Floral Street / If it don't work out / Don't cry for me / I know she will / Walking in the sun / I'll keep trying / I'll call you mine / Smokey day / She loves the way they love her / Girl help me / I could spend the day / Rose for Emily / This will be our year / Time of the season / Kind of girl / I'm going home / Sometimes / Sometimes / It's alright with me / Kind of girl / Walking in the sun / Way I feel inside / Way I feel inside / I want you back again / Nothing's changed / Nothing's changed / Remember you / I'll keep trying / Whenever you're ready / You'll go away from me / I know she will / Don't cry for me / If it don't work out / One day I'll say goodbye / I don't want to worry / Love that never was / Call of the night / Out of the day / This will be our year / Bunny Lake is missing / You make me feel good / Early one morning / She's not there / Tell her no / Soulville / Rip it up / Can't nobody love you / You must believe me / She's coming home / Just out of reach / I must move / Whenever you're ready / It's alright / Will you love me tomorrow / When the lovelight starts shining through her eyes / Just a little bit / Sitting in the park / Gotta get a hold of myself / Goin' out of my head / This old heart of mine / Friends of mine / Look of love / Kenny Everett jingle / Summertime / Woman
ZOMBOX 7 / 3 Nov '97 / Big Beat

☐ ZOMBIES 1964-1967, THE
She's not there / Rose for Emily / I can't make up my mind / You make me feel good / Tell her no / Kind of girl / Leave me be / Sometimes / It's all right with me / I don't want to know / I love you / Indication / Nothing's changes / Hung up on a dream / Whenever you're ready / Hold your head up: *Argent, Rod* / She's not there (live): *Argent, Rod* / Time of the season (Live): *Argent, Rod* / I'm in the mood: *Argent, Rod*
MOCD 3009 / Feb '95 / More Music

Zone

☐ BORN OF FIRE
ZONECD 3 / Oct '96 / Zone

☐ DIVINE SIMPLICITY, THE
ZONECD 4 / Oct '96 / Zone

Zoo

☐ ZOO PRESENTS CHOCOLATE MOOSE, THE
Chocolate moose / Written on the wind / I've been waiting too long / Soul drippin's / Get some beads / Ain't nobody / Try me / Love machine / Have you been sleepin' / From a camel's hump
CDWIKM 123 / Oct '93 / Big Beat

Zoo

☐ SHAKIN' THE CAGE
Reach out / God created woman / Night life / Shakin' the cage / Voodoo / How does it feel / Night and you / Takin' it out to the people / Breakin' up / In your hands
9362420042 / Jun '92 / WEA

Zoogz Rift

☐ MURDERING HELL'S HAPPY CRETINS
SST 21CD / Feb '89 / SST

☐ NONENTITY WATER 3 (FAN BLACK DADA)
SST 184CD / May '93 / SST

☐ TORMENT
SST 251CD / May '93 / SST

☐ VILLAGERS
EFA 11372 CD / May '93 / Musical Tragedies

☐ WATER : AT A SAFE DISTANCE
SST 137CD / May '93 / SST

Zoom

☐ HELIUM OCTIPEDE
Balboa's kitchen / Can fighting / Five fingers and a thumb / Ephedrine breakfast / Extrano / Letter from Allan / Bottle king / Mynr / Cycle of fifths
TK 93CD053 / Aug '94 / T/K

Zoom

☐ BIG DADDY
APCD 112 / Sep '96 / Appaloosa

Zoomer, George

☐ SPACE RADIO
300012 / Sep '97 / Magnatube

Zoot

☐ ZOOTLOCKER
8141832 / Oct '97 / Axis

Zorn, John

☐ CIRCLE MAKER, THE (2CD Set) (Zorn, John Masada String Trio & Bar Kokhba Sextet)
TZA 7122 / 2 Mar '98 / Tzadik

☐ COBRA (2CD Set)
ARTCD 26040 / '91 / Hat Art

☐ DURAS: DUCHAMP
TZA 7023 / Jul '97 / Tzadik

☐ FILM MUSIC VOL.7 (Cynical Hysterie Hour)
TZA 7315 / Jul '97 / Tzadik

☐ FILM WORKS 1986-1990
7559792702 / Jan '95 / Nonesuch
TZA 7314 / Jul '97 / Tzadik

☐ HARRAS (Zorn, John & Derek Bailey/ William Parker)
AVAN 056 / Jan '96 / Avant

☐ IN MEMORY OF NIKKI ARANE (Zorn, John & Eugene Chadbourne)
INCUSCD 23 / Jan '97 / Incus

☐ JOHN ZORN'S COBRA LIVE AT THE KNITTING FACTORY
KFWCD 124 / Feb '95 / Knitting Factory

☐ MASADA LIVE
JD 1293 / 26 Jan '98 / Jazz Door

☐ MASADA VOL.1
DIW 888 / Mar '95 / DIW

☐ MASADA VOL.4
DIW 923 / Feb '97 / DIW

☐ MASADA VOL.5
DIW 899 / Dec '95 / DIW

☐ MASADA VOL.6
DIW 900 / Feb '96 / DIW

☐ MASADA VOL.7
DIW 915 / Dec '96 / DIW

☐ MASADA VOL.8
DIW 925 / Oct '97 / DIW

☐ MASADA VOL.9
DIW 933 / Mar '98 / DIW

☐ MORE NEWS FOR LULU (Zorn, John/ Bill Frisell/George Lewis)
ARTCD 6055 / Feb '92 / Hat Art

☐ NAKED CITY
7559792382 / Jan '94 / Nonesuch

☐ NEWS FOR LULU (Zorn, John/Bill Frisell/George Lewis)
ARTCD 6005 / Jul '88 / Hat Art

☐ PARACHUTE YEARS 1977-1980, THE (7CD Set)
TZ 73167 / Sep '97 / Tzadik

☐ SPILLANE
9791722 / Mar '88 / Nonesuch

☐ SPY VS. SPY (The Music Of Ornette Coleman)
W.r.u. / W.r.u. / Word for bird / Good old days / Disguise / Enfant / Rejoicing / Blues connotation / C and d / Chippie / Peace warriors / Ecars / Feet music / Broad way blues / Space church / Zig zag / Mob job
9608442 / Aug '89 / Nonesuch

☐ TOKYO OPERATIONS 1994
AVAN 049 / Feb '96 / Avant

☐ TORTURE GARDEN (Zorn, John & Naked City)
MOSH 028CD / Sep '90 / Earache

☐ YANKEES (Zorn, John & Derek Bailey)
CDGR 221 / 16 Mar '98 / Charly

Zounds

☐ CURSE OF ZOUNDS
Fear / Did he jump / My Mummy's gone / Little bit more / This land / New band / Dirty squatters / Loads of noise / Target / Mr. Disney / War goes on / Can't cheat karma / War / Subvert / Demystification / Great white hunter / Dancing / True love / More trouble coming every day / Knife / Not me / Biafra / Wolves
SEEP 006 / Jan '94 / Rugger Bugger

Zubiria, Amaia

☐ TASOGARE (2CD Set) (Zubiria, Amaia & Pascal Gaigne)
BELLE 96284 / Jun '97 / Belle Antique

Zubop

☐ CYCLE CITY
33JAZZ 006CD / Jun '93 / 33 Jazz

☐ FREEWHEELING
33JAZZ 015CD / Oct '94 / 33 Jazz

☐ HIPTODISIAC
Gamelanaskankabopolus / Aardvark / George Formby / We come from universal life / Song of snape / Letter to vololoninrina / M'aidez juldeh / Fervour fever / Canigou / Nhema musasa / Cantina panorama
33JAZZ 038 / Feb '98 / 33 Jazz

Zucchero

☐ BEST OF ZUCCHERO, THE
5338222 / Jun '97 / Polydor

☐ MISERERE
5170972 / Jan '93 / London

☐ SPIRITO DI VINO
5277852 / Aug '95 / London

☐ ZUCCHERO
Diamante / Wonderful world: Zucchero & Eric Clapton / Il mare / Mama / Dunes of mercy / Senza una Donna: Zucchero & Paul Young / You're losing me / Solo una sana / You've chosen me / Diavolo in me / Overdose (d'amore) / Nice (nietzsche) che dice
8490632 / May '91 / London

Zugasti, Olatz

☐ KANTU BATEN BILA NABIL
KDCD 270 / May '97 / Elkar

Zulu, Philomon

☐ HOW LONG
SHCD 434048 / Apr '92 / Shanachie

Zulutronic

☐ BACK TO BOMMERSHIME
EFA 089202 / 26 May '98 / Pharma

☐ MISSION ZULU ONE
PHARMA 10CD / Apr '97 / Pharma

Zumaque, Francisco

☐ BAILA CARIBE BAILA
Chucu chucu / Cando / Salvaje amor / Sera / Adios amour / Colombia caribe / Dorotea / Fantasia caribe / Macumbia
68947 / Apr '97 / Tropical

☐ CUMBIALMA
68982 / 5 Jan '98 / Tropical

☐ RITUALES - AFROAMERINDIAN SUITE
68967 / Apr '97 / Tropical

☐ VOCES CARIBES
Cuentero / Enganadora / Cafe / Con amor / La danza / Falta tiempo / New morning / Baila caribe / Arde roma / Paginas de mujer / Balas
68960 / Apr '97 / Tropical

☐ VOICES CARIBES (Zumaque, Francisco, & Super Macumbia)
SH 64051 / Dec '94 / Shanachie

Zumi-Kai

☐ KOTO MUSIC OF JAPAN
12184 / Aug '95 / Laserlight

Zumpano

☐ GOIN' THROUGH CHANGES
SPCD 372 / Sep '96 / Sub Pop

☐ LOOK WHAT THE ROOKIE DID
SPCD 140344 / Jan '95 / Sub Pop

Zumzeaux

☐ BLAZING FIDDLES
PUG 010CD / Mar '96 / Black Pig

Zunomen

☐ PEOPLE
CP 03 / Feb '97 / Coop

Zuphall, Rufus

☐ WEISS DER TEUFEL
LW 1035 / 2 Mar '98 / Little Wing

Zuvuya

☐ SHAMANIA (Zuvuya & Terence McKenna)
Shaman I am / FX return / Black sun yadaki / Whisper in trees / Into the future / Shamania
DELECCD 021 / Sep '94 / Delerium

Zydeco Travelers

☐ Z-FUNK
H-Town zydeco / We will never know / Baby let me kiss you / Bad time woman / Z-Funk / Packin' up / I don't know why / Back up and try it again / Tang the hump / Keeping me out of the storm / You got me crying / Sunday walk / Back up and try it again
ROUCD 2146 / Feb '97 / Rounder

Zydecomotion

☐ ARE YOU READY FOR THIS
Bernadette / Dangerous man / Why you want to leave me / Joli blond / Are you ready for this / No sad songs / Rainbow / Zydecomotion theme / I done got over it / I'm a farmer / You worry me / Everybody knows / Everybody knows / Why you want to leave me
CDBCAT 06 / Nov '96 / Bearcat

Zygmuntowicz, Sam

☐ JUMP (A Southern Fiddle Suite)
DSMCD 102 / Mar '98 / DSM

Zyklon B

☐ ZYKLON B
MR 005CD / Nov '95 / Malicious

Zyklus

☐ VIRTUAL REALITIES
AMPCD 017 / Feb '95 / AMP

ZZ Top

☐ AFTERBURNER
Sleeping bag / Stages / Woke up with wood / Rough boy / Can't stop rockin' / Planet of women / I got the message / Velcro fly / Dipping low / Delirious
9253422 / Mar '94 / WEA

☐ ANTENNA
Pincushion / PCH / Breakaway / Lizard life / Cover your rig / Antenna head / Fuzzbox voodoo / World of swirl / T-shirt / Deal goin' down / Cherry red / Everything
74321182602 / Jan '94 / RCA

☐ DEGUELLO
I thank you / She loves my automobile / I'm bad I'm nationwide / Fool for your stockings / Manic mechanic / Dust my broom / Lowdown in the street / Hi-fi mama / Cheap sunglasses / Esther be the one
K 256701 / Mar '94 / WEA

☐ ELIMINATOR
Gimme all your lovin' / Got me under pressure / Sharp dressed man / I need you tonight / I got the six / Legs / Thug / TV dinners / Dirty dog / If I could only flag her down / Bad girl
W 37742 / Mar '94 / WEA

☐ FANDANGO
Thunderbird / Jailhouse rock / Backdoor medley / Backdoor love affair / Mellow down easy / Backdoor love affair no.2 / Long distance boogie / Nasty dogs and funky kings / Blue jean blues / Balinese / Mexican blackbird / Heard it on the X / Tush
K 256604 / Mar '94 / WEA

☐ GREATEST HITS
Gimme all your lovin' / Sharp dressed man / Rough boy / Tush / My head's in Mississippi / Viva Las Vegas / Legs / Doubleback / Gun love / Got me under pressure / Give it up / Sleeping bag / La grange / Tube snake boogie
7599268462 / Apr '92 / WEA

☐ ONE FOOT IN THE BLUES
I need you tonight / If I could only flag her down / Fool for your stockings / Heaven hell or houston / Apologies to pearly / Sure got cold after the rain fell / Old man / Just got back from baby's / Certified blues / 2000 blues / My head's in mississippi / Brown sugar / Bar b q / Hi fi mama / Lowdown in the street / She loves my automobile / Hot blue and righteous
9362458152 / Nov '94 / WEA

☐ RECYCLER
Concrete and steel / Love thing / Penthouse eyes / Tell it / My head's in Mississippi / Decision or collision / 2000 blues / Burger man / Doubleback
7599262652 / Mar '94 / WEA

☐ RHYTHMEEN
Rhythmeen / Bang band / Black fly / What's up with that / Vincent Price blues / Zipper job / Hairdresser / She's just killing me / My mind is gone / Loaded / Prettyhead / Hummbucking part 2
74321394662 / Sep '96 / RCA

☐ RIO GRANDE MUD
Francine / Just got paid / Mushmouth shoutin' / Koko blue / Chevrolet / Apologies to pearly / Bar B Q / Sure got cold after the rain fell / Whisky 'n' mama / Down brownie
7599273802 / Mar '94 / WEA

☐ RIO GRANDE MUD/TRES HOMBRES/ FANDANGO/TEJAS/EL LOCO/FIRST LP (ZZ Top's Sixpack/3CD Set)
(Somebody else been) shaking your tree / Brown sugar / Squank / Goin' down to Mexico / Old man / Neighbour, neighbour / Certified blues / Bedroom thang / Just got back from baby's / Backdoor love affair / Francine / Just got paid / Mushmouth shoutin' / Koko blue / Chevrolet / Apologies to Pearly / Bar B Q / Sure got cold after the rain fell / Whisky 'n' mama / Down brownie / Waitin' for the bus / Jesus just left Chicago / Beer drinkers and hell raisers / Master of sparks / Hot, blue and righteous / Move me on down the line / Precious and grace / La grange / Sheik / Have you heard / Thunderbird / Jailhouse rock / Mellow down easy / Back door love affair No.2 / Long distance boogie / Nasty dogs and funky kings / Blue jean blues / Balinese / Mexican blackbird / Heard it on the X / Tush / It's only love / Arrested for driving while blind / El diablo / Snappy kakkie / Enjoy and get it on / Ten dollar man / Pan am highway blues / Asleep in the desert / Tube snake boogie / I wanna drive you home / Ten foot pole / Leila / Don't tease me / It's so hard / Pearl necklace / Groovy little hippy pad / Heaven, hell or Houston / Party on the patio
9256612 / Dec '87 / WEA

☐ TEJAS
It's only love / Arrested for driving while blind / El diablo / Snappy kakkie / Enjoy and get it on / Ten dollar man / Pan Am highway blues / Avalon hideaway / She's a heartbreaker / Asleep in the desert
7599273832 / Mar '94 / WEA

☐ TRES HOMBRES
Waitin' for the bus / Jesus just left Chicago / Beer drinkers and hell raisers / Master of sparks / Hot, blue and righteous / Move me on down the line / Precious and grace / La grange / Sheik / Have you heard
K 256603 / Mar '94 / WEA

☐ ZZ TOP'S FIRST ALBUM
(Somebody else been) shaking your tree / Brown sugar / Squank / Goin' down to Mexico / Old man / Neighbour, neighbour / Certified blues / Bedroom thang / Just got back from my baby's / Backdoor love affair
K 256601 / Mar '94 / WEA

Compilations

☐ 1 IN THE JUNGLE (2CD Set)
Warning: DJ Stretch / Mash up yer know: Aladdin / Valley of the shadows: Origin Unknown / Feel: Guyver / Summer someting: Rude Bwoy Monty / R-Type: Jo / Funkula: B-Jam / Who runs tings: Shy FX & David Leboom / Living in darkness: Top Buzz / DNA: DNA / Set speed: DJ Krust / Music box: Roni Size & DJ Die / I like it: Da Intalex / Cold mission: Dreamers / London sometin': Tek 9 / Roughest: DJ Rap / Chopsticks: Special K & Roughcut / Spiritual aura: Engineers Without Fears / Angel fell: Dillinja / Follow me: Dillinja / Here comes the drums: DJ Doc Scott
CDTAKE 1 / Jan '96 / Take One

☐ 1+2 SAMPLER
1+2E 4394 / 20 Jul '98 / 1+2

☐ 1-2-3 MUSETTE VOL.1 (2CD Set)
R2CD 4037 / 13 Apr '98 / Deja Vu

☐ 1-2-3 MUSETTE VOL.2 (2CD Set)
R2CD 7004 / 13 Apr '98 / Deja Vu

☐ 2AM SMOKE DOWN (2CD Set)
DCID 002 / 16 Mar '98 / Dance Club International

☐ 3 BEAT HIGH & RISING
3BTTCD 1 / Jun '93 / 3 Beat

☐ 3 MINUTE BLUNTS VOL.1 (The Sound Of Detroit Instrumental Hip Hop)
Home coming: Parker, Terrence / Flexin': AW / Woodward avenue: Kanabis The Edit Assassin / Act a fool: Madd Phlavor / Crystal funk: Kanabis The Edit Assassin / Whodunnit: Papa Willie / Walk under a full moon's light: Kanabis The Edit Assassin / Too damn cool: Johnson, Andre Project / Soul searchin': Kanabis The Edit Assassin / Outland: DJ Slym Fas / Daze of native noise: Kanabis The Edit Assassin / Play time's over: AW / Unique: Johnson, Andre Project / Make it real: DJ Slym Fas / Reunion in Tennesse: Kanabis The Edit Assassin / Fun at the Belle Isle zoo: DJ Slym Fas / Romancing da drum: Parker, Terrence
K7 052CD / Jan '97 / Studio K7

☐ 3 VOCAL GREATS OF THE 50'S (Lita Roza/Petula Clark/Marion Ryan) (3CD Set)
That's the beginning of the end: Roza, Lita / I've got my eyes on you: Roza, Lita / Oh dear what can the matter be: Roza, Lita / I'll never say Never Again again: Roza, Lita / End of a love affair: Roza, Lita / Not mine: Rosa, Lita / As children do: Rosa, Lita / There's nothing rougher than love: Rosa, Lita / Somewhere, somehow, someday: Rosa, Lita / Allentown jail: Rosa, Lita / Once in a while: Rosa, Lita / Nel blu dipinto di blu: Rosa, Lita / This is my town: Rosa, Lita / Maybe you'll be there: Rosa, Lita / Sorry, sorry, sorry: Roza, Lita / I could have danced all night: Roza, Lita / All alone (by a telephone): Roza, Lita / Other woman: Roza, Lita / Love can change the stars: Roza, Lita / I Yi Yi Yi: Clark, Petula / You are my lucky star: Clark, Petula / Afraid to dream: Clark, Petula / It's the natural thing to do: Clark, Petula / As tiem goes by: Clark, Petula / Slumming on Park Avenue: Clark, Petula / I wish I knew: Clark, Petula / Goodnight my love: Clark, Petula / Alone: Clark, Petula / Zing went the strings of my heart: Clark, Petula / Sonny boy: Clark, Petula / Love me forever: Ryan, Marion / Stairway of love: Ryan, Marion / Hit the road to dreamland: Ryan, Marion / Jeepers creepers: Ryan, Marion / Mr. Wonderful: Ryan, Marion / I'm beginning to see the light: Ryan, Marion / Cry me a river: Ryan, Marion / That's happiness: Ryan, Marion / There will never be another you: Ryan, Marion / Oh oh, I'm falling in love again: Ryan, Marion / I'll take romance: Ryan, Marion / World goes round and round: Ryan, Marion / If I can't take it with me: Ryan, Marion / My heart belongs to Daddy: Ryan, Marion / It might as well be spring: Ryan, Marion / I need you: Ryan, Marion / Make the man love me: Ryan, Marion / Always and forever: Ryan, Marion / High life: Ryan, Marion / Why do fools fall in love: Ryan, Marion / Wait for me: Ryan, Marion / Hot diggity (dog diggity boom): Ryan, Marion / Chantez chantez: Ryan, Marion / Please don't say goodnight: Ryan, Marion / Sailor boy: Ryan, Marion
MAGPIE 7 / Sep '95 / See For Miles

☐ 3D COMPILATION, THE
TIPCD 12 / May '97 / Tip

☐ 4 BEAT (The New Happy Hardcore Phenomena)
Unity: Jack 'n' Phil / Seventh way: Beatmen / 7th Heaven: Fast Floor / Stomper: Format / Everybody can be: Higher Level / Emotions: Sy Project / Spiced up: Frantic & Impulse / Fantasy wonderland: Wendy / It's all over: Motiv 8 / Baby baby: Pooch & Hurse / Peaked up: S&A / Higher spirits: Higher Level
CDTOT 32 / Sep '95 / Jumpin' & Pumpin'

☐ 4 ON 1
DBMTRCD 19 / Sep '95 / Rogue Trooper

☐ 4 PLAY
DIMECD 1 / Sep '97 / Dimension

☐ 4-2-4 (The El Football Scrapbook)
Nice one Cyril / I'm forever blowing bubbles / Onward Sexton soldiers / Canaries / Football football / World Cup Willie / Good old Arsenal / Back home / We are Wimbledon / Belfast boy / We are the owls / Hibernian / Going back to Derby / Boys in blue / Viva el Fulham / Sunderland
MONDE 15CD / Aug '93 / Cherry Red

☐ 4TH ANNUAL FLAMENCO COMPETITION OF NIMES
172592 / Jan '97 / Musidisc

☐ 4TH DIMENSION (2CD Set)
Dominion: UX / Peaceful turbulence: Wasabe / Delerium: Manmademan / Lum bum bashi: Der Stern Von Afrika / Warriors of light: Evolution / Intrigue: Blue Planet Co-operation / Electeaser: Rave Base / Snake dance: Nemesis / Answer: NDMA / Earth medicine: Laughing Buddha / Men on the moon: Digital Sun / Silence: OOOD / Silicon trip: Shakta / Witching hour: Mok Systems / Sensory deception: Tristan / Wierd egg: For Cary Nuts / Slow motion: Hara Gobi
SPV 08947462 / Sep '97 / SPV

☐ 4TH PARIS GOSPEL FESTIVAL
FA 422 / Jun '97 / Fremeaux

☐ 4TH PARIS GOSPEL FESTIVAL (2CD Set)
FA 421 / Jun '97 / Fremeaux

☐ 5 YEARS
TIMECD 0332 / 2 Feb '98 / Time Unlimited

☐ 007 LICENSE TO PARTY
RUMCD 007 / Aug '92 / Rumble

☐ 7 HILLS CLASH (Deeper Signals)
What you want: Bouncing Bomb / Evil star: Tocsin / Medium: Celsius / 15 inches plus: Wad / Lethargy/ Apathy: Tonka Toi / Chickenfoot: Obeah / Giant: I Monster / Where's the love: Screwface / Welfare: Extra Breaks / Moonstomp: Mig / Fashioned by convenience: Fashioned For Convenience / Rude: Rude
DRC 1 / Jun '97 / Break Butt
DRC 2 / 11 May '98 / Break Butt

☐ 9.30 LIVE (2CD Set)
GCD 4930 / Jan '98 / Genes

☐ 10 METER OHNE KOPF
EFA 15179CD / Sep '92 / Fishcore

☐ 10 YEARS AND STILL NO HIT
NOHITCD 020 / Feb '97 / No Hit

☐ 10 YEARS OF NUCLEAR BLAST (3CD Set)
NB 280CD / 8 Dec '97 / Nuclear Blast

☐ 10% - FILE UNDER BURROUGHS (2CD Set)
SR 93 / Apr '96 / Sub Rosa

☐ 10TH ANNIVERSARY COLLECTION (2CD Set)
CHE 10 / Jun '97 / Chesky

☐ 10TH NEW ORLEANS JAZZ FESTIVAL
FF 099CD / May '93 / Flying Fish

☐ 11 PHASES
Roots: K-Hand / Flip flop: Lark Daddy / Gusto: Fowlkes, Eddie 'Flashin' / Losmic kung-fu funk: Web, Will / Mystique: Hood Scientific / Bad luck kid: De-Yang Crew / Ravish: Barnett, Thomas / Graffotots theme: Graffiti / In the park: Bell, Daniel / Can't turn back: Shakir, Anthony / Hip hop jazz: Deason, Sean
SBLCD 5023UK / 9 Feb '98 / Sublime

☐ 12 SALSA COCKTAIL MIXES
Los sitios entero: Ng La Banda / Takà taka ta: Irakere / Mi chiquita: Bennymore / Pare cochero: Orchestra Aragon / Cogel el cameron: La Origina De Manzanillo / Se muere la tia: Los Van Van / Lo que me paso en la: Adalberto Alvarez / Yo soy el punto cubana: Gonzalez, Celina / Longina: Burke, Malena / Yo no quiero oue seas celosa: Reve Y Su Charangon / La chica mamey: Reve Y Su Charangon / Mi son mi son mi son: Migelito Cuni Con Chappottin
ALPCD 103 / 8 Sep '97 / Alpha Entertainments

☐ 12 X 12 - VOL.3 (The Third Impression)
Can I kick it: Tribe Called Quest / Blame it on the bassline: Cook, Norman / Roadblock: Stock/Aitken/ Waterman / Get busy: Mr. Lee / Touch me (Sexual version): 49ers / Wee rule: Wee Papa Girl Rappers / I'm a wonderful thing, baby: Kid Creole & The Coconuts / Can I get a witness: Brown, Sam / Too good to be forgotten: Amazulu / Love's crashing waves: Difford & Tillbrook / Sweetest smile: Black / Lies: Butler, Jonathan
5501252 / Oct '93 / Spectrum

☐ 12 YEARS IN NOISE (Metal & Beyond/ 2CD Set)
Oernst of life: Helloween / Prisoner of our time: Running Wild / Back from the war: Gravedigger / Maniac forces: Tankard / Flag of hate: Kreator / Revolution command: Vendetta / Don't you fear the winter: Rage / I want you: Helloween / Not alone: Scanner / Lust for life: Gamma Ray / Observer from above: Secrecy / Spinning Jenny: Skyclad / My decision: Conception / Reaper: Mind Odyssey / Under permission: Sanvoisen / Proud nomad: Kamelot / Horus/Aggressor: Hellhammer / Into the crypts of rays: Celtic Frost / Innocence and wrath: Celtic Frost / Circle of the tyrants: Celtic Frost / Ravenous medicine: Voivod / Purple haze: Coroner / I want you: Coroner / Der Mussolini: Coroner / Everyday is a holiday: Mordred / Falling away: Mordred / Eldritch: Watchtower / Shout: Humungous Fungus / Identity: Punishable Act / Let da streetz burn: Gunjah / Bitter: Shihad / Kiss or kill: Manhole
N 02642 / Jun '96 / Noise

☐ 12" 80'S DANCE GROOVE CLASSICS (2CD Set)
Got to have your love: Mantronix / I wanted your love: Vandross, Luther / Who's zoomin' who: Franklin, Aretha / Push it: Salt n' Pepa / Midas touch: Midnight Star / I'm in love: King, Evelyn 'Champagne' / Band AKA: Grace / Rockit: Hancock, Herbie / Mr. Magician: Mystic Merlin / Circles: Atlantic Starr / Teardrops: Womack & Womack / Trapped: Colonel Abrams / Beat dis: Bomb The Bass / S'Express: S'Express / Wait: Howard, Robert & Kym Mazelle / Alice: Full Force / Come into my life: Sims, Joyce / Roses are red: Mac Band / Candy: Cameo / Tossing and turning: Windjammer / Friends: Stewart, Amii / You to me are everything: Real Thing / Lover in you: Shalamar / Love supreme: Downing, Will
NEDCD 293 / 1 Jun '98 / Sequel

☐ 12" JAZZ FUNK CLASSICS (2CD Set)
Special lady: Second Image / Groove: Franklin, Rodney / Blackjack: Locksmith / Can't you see me: Ayers, Roy / Black is the colour: Longmire, Wilbert / Love till the end of time: Da Costa, Paulino / Pick up the pieces: Average White Band / Hard work: Handy, John / Morning dance: Spyro Gyra / Brasilia: Klemmer, John / Sign of the times: James, Bob / Bottle: Scott-Heron, Gil / Saturday night: Hancock, Herbie / Fifty four: Sea Level / Glide: Pleasure / Love on a summer night: McCrarys / Ms. Cheryl: Banda Black Rio / Just can't give you up: Mystic Merlin / Love meeting love: Level 42 / Watchin' life: LA Boppers / Last summer in Ritz: Azymuth / Watermelon man: Santamaria, Mongo / First love: Tee, Richard
NEDCD 294 / 1 Jun '98 / Sequel

☐ 12" OF PLEASURE VOL.2
ALMYCD 14 / Jun '95 / Almighty

☐ 14 GRANDES EXITOS DE LA SALSA
76754213002 / 12 May '98 / Vedisco

☐ 14 YEARS OF ELECTRONIC CHALLENGE
COPCD 032 / 22 Sep '97 / Cop International

☐ 15 YEARS IN AN OPEN BOAT (A History Of On-U-Sound)
Virgin: Prince Far-I & Singers & Players / Language and mentality: African Headcharge / Jerusalem: Stewart, Mark & Maffia / Breaking down the pressure: Roy, Congo A. & Singers & Players / Watch yourself: Akabu & The Circuit / Doctor Who: Dr. Pablo & Dub Syndicate / African space: Creation Rebel / State assembly: New Age Steppers / Sharp as a needle: Barmy Army / Slumy ghetto: Sherman, Bim / Wadada: Dub Syndicate / Dervish chant: African Headcharge / Jack the biscuit: Fairley, Andy / I think of you: Little Annie / Jungle: Perry, Lee 'Scratch' / Free the marijuana: Audio Active / Weed specialist: 2 Bad Card / 15 to 4: Little Axe / Children of the future: Jalal / New song: Little Roy
CDV 2833 / 4 Aug '97 / Virgin

☐ 16 FAVOURITE LINE DANCE COUNTRY SONGS
I 3885832 / Nov '96 / Galaxy

☐ 17 DUB SHOTS FROM STUDIO ONE
CDBH 142 / Aug '95 / Heartbeat

☐ 17 NORTH PARADE
PSCD 17 / 26 Jan '98 / Pressure Sounds

☐ 18 GEMS OF THE GIANTS OF JAZZ CD COLLECTION
Milestones: Davis, Miles & Charlie Parker/John Lewis / Night in Tunisia: Gillespie, Dizzy & Milt Jackson/Don Byas/Ray Brown / Move: Navarro, Fats & Max Roach / Taps miller: Basie, Count & His Orchestra / 'Round midnight: Monk, Thelonius & Art Blakey / It don't mean a thing (if it ain't got that swing): Ellington, Duke Orchestra / Oh lady be good: Fitzgerald, Ella & Bob Haggart Orchestra / Pastel: Garner, Errol & Red Callender / Homeward bound: Washington, Dinah & Lionel Hampton Septet / Once in a while: Vaughn, Sarah & John Collins/Kenny Clarke / Poor butterfly: Peterson, Oscar Trio / Get your kicks (on route 66): Cole, Nat 'King' & Oscar Moore/Johnny Miller / Harlem folk dance: Kenton, Stan & His Orchestra/Art Pepper / Rockin' chair: Armstrong, Louis & Jack Teagarden / Man I love: Holiday, Billie & Lester Young / Ain't misbehavin': Waller, Fats & Benny Carter/Slam Stewart/Zutty Singleton / Doctor jazz: Morton, Jelly Roll & Kid Ory / Singin' the blues: Beiderbecke, Bix & Frankie Trumbauer/Eddie Lang
CD 53305 / Apr '98 / Giants Of Jazz

☐ 18 NORTHERN SOUL FLOOR SHAKERS
Makin' up time: Holidays / I can't get away: Bob & Earl / Going to a happening: Neal, Tommy / All of a sudden: Incredibles / Dreamin' up a world of fantasy: Charades / Run baby run: Hot Shots / Papa oom mow wow: Sharonettes / Blowing my mind to pieces: Roussel, Paula / Six by six: Floor Shakers / My sugar baby: Matthews, Sherlie / Thumb a ride: Soul Fox Orchestra / Lookin' for you: Garnett & The Soul Masters / Duck: Lee, Jackie / Somebody somewhere (needs you): Banks, Darrell / Hit and run: Owens, Gwen / Hold on: Soul Masters / Bounce: Olympics / Soul time: Ferguson, Helena
308092 / 13 Oct '97 / Hallmark

☐ 18 SOUSA FAVOURITES
Stars and stripes / Semper fields / Diplomat march / Invincible eagle / Liberty bells / Hands across the sea / King Cotton / Bells of Chicago / Crusader / Bride elect / Gladiator march / Manhattan beach / High school cadets / Elcapitano / Washington Post / Hail to the spirit of liberty / Thunderer / US field artillery
GRF 157 / Apr '93 / Tring

☐ 18 STOMPIN' ROCK 'N' ROLL HITS
CWNCD 2022 / Jul '96 / Javelin

☐ 18 TRAILBLAZING CLASSICS
We'll rest at the end of the trail: Wakely, Jimmy / Have I told you lately that I love you: Autry, Gene / Bummin' around: Williams, Tex / Great speckled bird: Acuff, Roy & His Crazy Tennesseans / South of the border: Autry, Gene / I'm casting my lasso towards the sky: Wakely, Jimmy / Any old time: Rodgers, Jimmie / Back in the saddle again: Autry, Gene / New San Antonio Rose: Willis, Bob & His Texas Playboys / Night train to Memphis: Acuff, Roy & His Smokey Mountain Boys / Hillbilly heaven: Acuff, Roy & His Smokey Mountain Boys / It makes no difference: Autry, Gene / Mule skinner blues: Monroe, Bill & His Bluegrass Boys / Along the Santa Fe Trail: Wakely, Jimmy / Wreck on the highway: Acuff, Roy & His Smokey Mountain Boys / Prodigal Son: Sunset Carson / Waiting for a train: Rodgers, Jimmie / You are my sunshine: Autry, Gene
CWNCD 2026 / Jul '96 / Javelin

☐ 18TH STREET LOUNGE SOUNDTRACK VOL.1
ESL 9 / 27 Oct '97 / 18th Street Lounge

☐ 20 ALL STAR R&B CLASSICS
I want to hug you: Hooker, John Lee / I'll be gone: Hooker, John Lee / I wish you would: Arnold, Billy Boy / Please be cool: Magic Sam / I ain't got nobody: Sly & The Family Stone / I smell trouble: Turner, Ike & Tina / Honest I do: Reed, Jimmy / Shakin' and shoutin': Magic Sam / Shake it baby: Hopkins, Lightnin' / Dragging my tail: Clapton, Eric / Louie louie: Kingsmen / I just got some: Stewart, Rod / Watermelon man: Sly & The Family Stone / Onions: Hooker, John Lee / Just pickin': Magic Sam / Don't you lie to me: Bloomfield, Mike / Catfish: Arnold, Billy Boy / Send me your pillow: Hooker, John Lee / Bullet blues: Magic Sam / I'll put a spell on you: Hawkins, Screamin' Jay
CWNCD 2012 / Jul '96 / Javelin

☐ 20 ALL TIME GREATS (Coasters And More)
Charlie Brown: Coasters / Little Egypt: Coasters / Why do fools fall in love: Diamonds / Poetry in motion: Tillotson, Johnny / Rubber ball: Vee, Bobby / Smoke gets in your eyes: Platters / Rock 'n' roll: Coasters / Hats off to Larry: Shannon, Del / Sealed with a kiss: Hyland, Brian / Night has a 1000 eyes: Vee, Bobby / Lion sleeps tonight: Tokens / Yakety yak: Coasters / Will you still love me tomorrow: Shirelles / Peggy Sue: Crickets / La Bamba: Tokens / Poison Ivy: Coasters / Tell Laura I love her: Peterson, Ray / Party doll: Knox, Buddy / At the hop: Original Juniors / Young blood: Coasters
HADCD 155 / May '94 / Javelin

☐ 20 BEST LOVED HYMNS
MCCD 214 / Oct '95 / Music Club

☐ 20 BEST OF BLUEGRASS
EUCD 1333 / Feb '96 / ARC

☐ 20 BEST OF TODAYS FOLK AND WORLD MUSIC VOL.2
EUCD 1141 / '91 / ARC

☐ 20 CLASSIC IRISH LOVE BALLADS
CDIRISH 006 / Oct '95 / Outlet

☐ 20 CLASSIC SONGS OF LOVE
True: Spandau Ballet / Room in your heart: Living In A Box / Man with the child in his eyes: Bush, Kate / Dreamin': Burnette, Johnny Rock 'N' Roll Trio / Missing you: Waite, John / Tonight I celebrate my love: Flack, Roberta & Peabo Bryson / More than I can say: Vee, Bobby / Why do fools fall in love: Lymon, Frankie & The Teenagers / Tears on my pillow: Imperials / God only knows: Beach Boys / Air that I breathe: Hollies / Love changes everything: Climie Fisher / Is there something I should know: Duran Duran / I apologise: Proby, P.J. / I only have eyes for you: Flamingos / I honestly love you: Newton-John, Olivia / When you're in love with a beautiful woman: Dr. Hook / Honey: Goldsboro, Bobby / Tell Laura I love her: Valance, Ricky / Crying: McLean, Don
CDMFP 5974 / Dec '92 / Music For Pleasure

☐ 20 COUNTRY LOVE SONGS
It's only make believe: Campbell, Glen / When I dream: Gayle, Crystal / There'll be no teardrops tonight: Nelson, Willie / July you're a woman: Stewart, John / Come to me: Newton, Juice / Summer wind: Newton, Wayne / Will you still love me tomorrow: Ronstadt, Linda / You're the reason I'm living: Darin, Bobby / Misty blue: Spears, Billie Jo / For the good times: Ford, Tennessee Ernie / Sharing the night together: Dr. Hook / Let it be me: Campbell, Glen & Bobbie Gentry / I'll take you home again Kathleen: Whitman, Slim / Stand by your man: Jackson, Wanda / It doesn't matter anymore: Anka, Paul / Give me your word: Ford, Tennessee Ernie / Everything a man could ever need: Campbell, Glen / Think I'll go somewhere and cry myself to sleep: Shepard, Jean / Minute you're gone: James, Sonny / We must believe in magic: Gayle, Crystal / Don't it make my brown eyes blue: Gayle, Crystal
CDMFP 6036 / Oct '87 / Music For Pleasure

☐ 20 EXPLOSIVE DYNAMIC SUPER SMASH HIT EXPLOSIONS VOL.1
EFA 201152 / May '95 / Pravda

☐ 20 EXPLOSIVE DYNAMIC SUPER SMASH HIT EXPLOSIONS VOL.2
EFA 201162 / May '95 / Pravda

☐ **20 FAVOURITE IRISH PUB SONGS VOL.1**
DOCD 2024 / Sep '96 / Dolphin

☐ **20 FAVOURITE IRISH PUB SONGS VOL.2**
DOCD 2029 / Oct '93 / Koch

☐ **20 FILM AND STAGE CLASSICS JAMAICAN STYLE**
People will say we're in love: *Spence, Trenton Orchestra* / Summertime: *Clarke, Lloyd* / Guns of Navarone: *Skatalites* / Bonanza ska: *Malcolm, Carlos & Afro Caribs* / Shot in the dark: *Soul Brothers* / From Russia with love: *Alphonso, Roland* / Dr. Zhivago: *McCook, Tommy & The Supersonics* / To sir with love: *Taitt, Lynn & The Jetts* / Ol' man river: *Silvertones* / Get me to the church on time: *McCook, Tommy & The Supersonics* / Hang 'em high: *Ace, Richard* / Zip a dee doo dah: *Smith, Slim* / Magnificent seven: *Wright, Winston* / Hello Dolly: *Pat Satchmo* / Summer place: *Charmers, Lloyd* / Try to remember: *Kelly, Pat* / Shaft: *Chosen Few* / I'm in the mood for love: *Chosen Few* / Moon river: *Ellis, Alton* / There's no business like show business: *Ellis, Alton*
CDTRL 319 / Mar '94 / Trojan

☐ **20 GERMAN FOLK SONGS**
MCD 71398 / Jun '93 / Monitor

☐ **20 GOLDEN GREATS FROM THE BIG BAND ERA**
Trumpet blues and cantabile / One o'clock jump / Yes indeed / Intermission riff / You made me love you / Four brothers / Artistry in rhythm / I've got a gal in Kalamazoo / I'll never smile again / Jeeps blues / Solitude / Don't be that way / Midnight sun / Red bank boogie / La paloma / Stardust / Skyliner / Goosey gander / Well, get it
HRM 7005 / Jun '87 / Hermes

☐ **20 GOLDEN NO.1'S VOL.2**
Whiter shade of pale: *Procol Harum* / This is my song: *Clark, Petula* / Sweets for my sweet: *Searchers* / Have I the right: *Honeycombs* / Always something there to remind me: *Shaw, Sandie* / Sunny afternoon: *Kinks* / Michelle: *Overlanders* / Let the heartaches begin: *Baldry, Long John* / Blackberry Way: *Move* / (If paradise is) half as nice: *Amen Corner* / In the Summertime: *Mungo Jerry* / Baby, now that I've found you: *Foundations* / Kung fu fighting: *Douglas, Carl* / Matchstalk men and matchstalk cats and dogs: *Brian & Michael* / Sad sweet dreamer: *Sweet Sensation* / Out of time: *Farlowe, Chris* / Israelites: *Dekker, Desmond* / Mouldy old dough: *Lieutenant Pigeon* / Double barrel: *Barker, Dave & Ansell Collins* / Everything I own: *Boothe, Ken*
CDMFP 5898 / Oct '90 / Music For Pleasure

☐ **20 GOSPEL GREATS VOL.1**
Love of God: *Taylor, Johnnie* / Trouble in my way: *Swan Silvertones* / My rock: *Swan Silvertones* / Get away Jordan: *Love Coates, Dorothy* / You better run: *Love Coates, Dorothy* / Ninety nine and a half (won't do): *Love Coates, Dorothy* / Straight Street: *Pilgrim Travellers* / Jesus hits like the atom bomb: *Pilgrim Travellers* / I'm determined to run this race: *Cleveland, Rev. James* / Living for my Jesus: *Five Blind Boys Of Alabama* / Alone and motherless: *Five Blind Boys Of Alabama* / This may be the last time: *Five Blind Boys Of Alabama* / Ball game: *Carr, Sister Wynona* / Touch the hem of his garment: *Cooke, Sam & The Soul Stirrers* / Prayer for the doomed: *Chosen Gospel Singers* / Holy ghost: *Bradford, Alex* / Lifeboat: *Bradford, Alex* / Whosoever will: *Griffin, Bessie* / Wade in the water: *Original Gospel Harmonettes*
CDROP 1017 / May '90 / Cascade

☐ **20 GOSPEL GREATS VOL.2**
I'm climbing higher mountains: *Echoes Of Zion* / New walk: *Swanee Quintet* / Tell the angels: *Angelic Gospel Singers* / Let the church roll on: *Barbee, Lucille* / Building a home: *Radio Four* / Go devil, go: *Littlejohn, Madame Ira Mae* / Wake me, shake me: *May, Brother Joe* / Yea Lord: *Trumpet Kings* / Lord bring me down: *Consolers* / Earnest prayer: *Radio Four* / I want to see jesus: *Littlejohn, Madame Ira Mae* / Fadeless days: *Smith Jubilee Singers* / How I got over: *Swanee Quintet* / Bible is right: *Gospel Songbirds* / Dark hours of distress: *Littlefield, Sister Lillie Mae* / No room at the inn: *Fairfield Four* / On my way (part one): *Chapman, Rev CC* / You got to be born again: *Christland singers* / Mother's advice: *Taylor Brothers* / Father I stretch my arms to thee: *Killens, Rev GW*
CDROP 1019 / Oct '93 / Cascade

☐ **20 GREAT BLUES RECORDINGS OF THE 50'S AND 60'S**
Rolling and rolling: *Hopkins, Lightnin'* / Drifting: *Bland, Bobby* / Gone with the wind: *Sykes, Roosevelt* / Me and my chauffeur: *Thornton, Willie Mae* / No rollin' blues: *Witherspoon, Jimmy* / No nights by myself: *Williamson, Sonny Boy* / Cool little car: *Hooker, John Lee* / Dark and dreary: *James, Elmore* / Ain't drunk: *Turner, Ike's Rhythm Kings* / Crying at daybreak: *Howlin' Wolf* / Three hours past midnight: *Watson, Johnny 'Guitar'* / Talking woman: *Fulson, Lowell* / Moon is rising: *Littlefield, 'Little' Willie* / Tease me baby: *Hooker, John Lee* / Dedicating the blues: *Crayton, Pee Wee* / Ten years long: *King, B.B.* / Beer drinking woman: *McCracklin, Jimmy* / Sunnyland: *James, Elmore* / Cow town: *Dixon, Floyd* / Heartache baby: *Hill-Louis, Joe*
CDROP 1005 / Jan '90 / Cascade

☐ **20 GREAT CRUISING FAVOURITES OF THE 50'S AND 60'S VOL.1**
Wake up little Susie / Nut rocker / Lonely teenager / Over and over / Church bells may ring / In the mood / Short fat Fanny / Tall Paul / Poetry in motion / Runaround Sue / I'll come back to you / I cried a tear / Tick tock / Girl of my dreams / Take a message to Mary / She say / He's so fine / Pink shoe laces / Tra la la la Suzy
CDROP 1014 / Jan '90 / Cascade

☐ **20 GREAT CRUISING FAVOURITES OF THE 50'S AND 60'S VOL.2**
Wanderer: *Dion* / Party girl: *Carroll, Bernadette* / Chattanooga choo choo: *Fields, Ernie Orchestra* / Dizzy Miss Lizzy: *Williams, Larry* / Rockin' robin: *Day, Bobby* / Angel baby: *Rosie & The Originals* / Sunday kind of love: *Mystics* / Will you still love me tomorrow: *Shirelles* / Bandit of my dreams: *Hodges, Eddie* / Baby face: *Little Richard* / Denise: *Randy & The Rainbows* / Chantilly lace: *Big Bopper* / Pretty girls everywhere: *Church, Eugene* / No wheels: *Chordettes* / Problems: *Everly Brothers* / Way you look tonight: *Jarmels* / It's my party: *Gore, Lesley* / Heart: *Chandler, Kenny* / Rockin' pneumonia and the boogie woogie flu: *Neville, Art* / I got a feeling: *Tillotson, Johnny*
CDROP 1015 / Jan '90 / Cascade

☐ **20 GREAT CRUISING FAVOURITES OF THE 50'S AND 60'S VOL.3**
Lovers who wander / Rock everybody / When will I be loved / She said "yeah" / Hickory dickory dock / Little star / My boyfriend's back / One fine day / I cried a tear / Lawdy Miss Clawdy / Mary Lou / Lucille / Hey doll baby / Forever / My block / Please don't tell me know / Little bitty pretty one / Buzz buzz buzz / Hey boy, hey girl / Bama lama bama loo
CDROP 1016 / Oct '88 / Cascade

☐ **20 GREAT DOOWOP RECORDINGS**
Pennies from Heaven: *Skyliners* / Hush-a-bye: *Mystics* / Automobile: *Stickshifts* / Dearest darling: *Smith, Huey 'Piano'* / Penalty of love: *Velvetones* / Cool baby cool: *Flairs* / Way you look tonight: *Lonely Guys* / Under stars of love: *Carlos Brothers* / Stay where you are: *Olympics* / Saturday night fish fry: *Blue dots* / These golden rings: *Strangers* / Just for you and I: *Supremes* / Why don't you write me: *Jacks* / Love only you: *Meadowlarks* / All I do is rock: *Robins* / I believe: *Twilighters* / Please understand: *Milton, Buddy & Twilighters* / Please don't tell 'em: *Blue dots* / Cold chills: *Sounds* / When I fall in love: *Skyliners*
CDROP 1008 / Jan '92 / Cascade

☐ **20 GREAT LOVE SONGS OF THE ROCK 'N' ROLL ERA**
CDROP 1018 / Apr '92 / Cascade

☐ **20 GREAT RHYTHM & BLUES OF THE 50'S**
Rockin' pneumonia and the boogie woogie flu: *Smith, Huey 'Piano' & The Clowns* / Ain't a better story told: *Littlefield, 'Little' Willie* / BB boogie: *King, B.B.* / Good rockin' daddy: *James, Etta* / Rock house boogie: *Hooker, John Lee* / Let the good times roll: *Shirley & Lee* / Bop hop: *Crayton, Pee Wee* / Don't you know Yockomo: *Smith, Huey & The Clowns* / Oop shoop: *Queens* / Reelin' and rockin': *McCracklin, Jimmy* / Who's been jivin' with you: *Witherspoon, Jimmy* / Road I travel: *Turner, Ike's Rhythm Kings* / Morning at midnight: *Howlin' Wolf* / Is everything alright: *King, Earl* / Love bandit: *Cadets* / Goodbye baby: *James, Elmore* / No more doggin': *Gordon, Rosco* / Early times: *Turner, Ike's Rhythm Kings* / Gee baby: *Joe & Ann* / Kansas City blues: *Turner, 'Big' Joe*
CDROP 1001 / Oct '88 / Cascade

☐ **20 GREATEST LINE DANCE PARTY HITS**
I 3885822 / Nov '96 / Galaxy

☐ **20 IRISH SONGS YOU KNOW**
Isle of Innisfree: *Dan The Street Singer* / I'll take you home again Kathleen: *Dan The Street Singer* / Wild colonial boy: *McCann, Susan* / Irish rover: *McCann, Susan* / Boys from Killybegs: *O'Neill, Steven* / Sweet sixteen: *Hara, Dano* / Bunch of thyme: *Hara, Dano* / Forty shades of green: *Hara, Dano* / Fields of Athenry: *Kennedy, Jerome* / My wild Irish rose: *McGuigan, Pat* / If You're Irish: *Shamrock Man* / Agricultural Irish girl: *Shamrock Man* / Hannigan's hooley: *Shamrock Man* / Galway shawl: *Swingin' Paddy* / Murphy and the bricks: *Big O* / Black velvet band: *Duncan, Hugo* / Carrickfergus: *Shannon Brothers* / Dan the street singer: *Golden Jubilee* / Three leaf shamrock: *O'Neill, Steven* / Danny Boy: *Kennedy, Jerome*
RBCD 532 / Jun '97 / Sharpe

☐ **20 ITALIAN SONGS OF LOVE**
Come prima / Tu scienda dalle stelle (Christmas song) / Quando, quando, quando / To the door of the sun / Speak softly love / Angelina / Sicilia bedda / Instrumento italiano / Tell me that you love me tonight / Il nostro concerto / Sorriento / Eh cumpare / Mamma / Santa Lucia / Il cielo in una stanza / Viva Italia / Italian wedding song / Strings of my heart (se avessi un mandolino) / Dormi dormi / Amor, mon amor
305732 / May '97 / Hallmark

☐ **20 NO.1'S OF THE 70'S**
In the summertime: *Mungo Jerry* / Sad sweet dreamer: *Sweet Sensation* / Matchstalk men and matchstalk cats and dogs: *Brian & Michael* / Heart of glass: *Blondie* / Love grows (Where my Rosemary goes): *Edison Lighthouse* / When you're in love with a beautiful woman: *Dr. Hook* / When I need you: *Sayer, Leo* / Kung fu fighting: *Douglas, Carl* / Without you: *Nilsson, Harry* / Oh Boy: *Mud* / Bye bye baby: *Bay City Rollers* / Blockbuster: *Sweet* / So you win again: *Hot Chocolate* / Yes sir, I can boogie: *Baccara* / I love you love me love: *Glitter, Gary* / See my baby jive: *Wizzard* / Make me smile (come up and see me): *Harley, Steve & Cockney Rebel* / Can the can: *Quatro, Suzi* / Seasons in the sun: *Jacks, Terry* / Ms. Grace: *Tymes*
CDMFP 5985 / Apr '93 / Music For Pleasure

☐ **20 NO.2'S OF THE 70'S**
Air that I breathe: *Hollies* / American pie: *McLean, Don* / Kissin' in the back row of the movies: *Drifters* / Do you wanna touch me (Oh yeah): *Glitter, Gary* / Don't let it die: *Smith, Hurricane* / Denis: *Blondie* / Moonlighting: *Sayer, Leo* / Lola: *Kinks* / Let's work together: *Canned Heat* / When I'm dead and gone: *McGuinness Flint* / Cat crept in: *Mud* / Shang-a-lang: *Bay City Rollers* / Goodbye my love: *Glitter Band* / Hellraiser: *Sweet* / Little bit more: *Dr. Hook* / You sexy thing: *Hot Chocolate* / Some girls: *Racey* / Loving you: *Riperton, Minnie* / Rock me gently: *Kim, Andy* / Can't get by without you: *Real Thing*
CDMFP 5986 / Apr '93 / Music For Pleasure

☐ **20 ORIGINAL COUNTRY GREATS**
Southern nights: *Campbell, Glen* / Wichita lineman: *Campbell, Glen* / Don't it make my brown eyes blue: *Gayle, Crystal* / Talking in your sleep: *Gayle, Crystal* / When you're in love with a beautiful woman: *Dr. Hook* / Sexy eyes: *Dr. Hook* / Ode to Billy Joe: *Gentry, Bobbie* / I'll never fall in love again: *Gentry, Bobbie* / Blanket on the ground: *Spears, Billie Jo* / Sing me an old fashioned song: *Spears, Billie Jo* / Lucille: *Rogers, Kenny* / Coward of the county: *Rogers, Kenny* / Snowbird: *Murray, Anne* / You needed me: *Murray, Anne* / Games people play: *South, Joe* / Hello walls: *Nelson, Willie* / There'll be no teardrops tonight: *Nelson, Willie* / It keeps right on a-hurtin': *Shepard, Jean* / Angel of the morning: *Newton, Juice* / July you're a woman: *Stewart, John*
CDMFP 6084 / Jun '90 / Music For Pleasure

☐ **20 ORIGINAL DOO WOP CLASSICS**
Daddy's home: *Shep & The Limelites* / Sunday kind of love: *Harptones* / Pretty little angel eyes: *Lee, Curtis* / I'm not a juvenile delinquent: *Lymon, Frankie & The Teenagers* / I only have eyes for you: *Flamingoes* / Maybe: *Chantels* / Heart and soul: *Cleftones* / Blue moon: *Marcels* / Chains: *Cookies* / Little star: *Elegants* / Thousand miles away: *Heartbeats* / Barbara Ann: *Regents* / Priscilla: *Cooley, Eddie* / Don't ask me to be lonely: *Dubs* / Tears on my pillow: *Little Anthony & The Imperials* / Why do fools fall in love: *Lymon, Frankie & The Teenagers* / Gee: *Crows* / Just to be with you: *Passion* / My melancholy baby: *Marcels* / Two people in the world: *Little Anthony & The Imperials*
CDMFP 6207 / Nov '95 / Music For Pleasure

☐ **20 ORIGINAL RADIO STARS**
399236 / Feb '94 / Koch

☐ **20 R 'N' B DANCE FLOOR FILLERS**
Harlem shuffle: *Traits* / Show me: *Tex, Joe* / Higher and higher: *Wilson, Jackie* / Don't mess up a good thing: *Bass, Fontella & Bobby McClure* / Gonna send you back to Georgia: *Shaw, Timmy* / Hi-heel sneakers: *Tucker, Tommy* / Shame shame shame: *Reed, Jimmy* / Soulful dress: *Desanto, Sugar Pie* / Put on your tight pants: *Turner, Ike & Tina* / Boom boom: *Hooker, John Lee* / Barefootin': *Parker, Robert* / We're gonna make it: *Little Milton* / Holy cow: *Dorsey, Lee* / Something's got a hold on me: *James, Etta* / You left the water running: *Maurice & Mac* / Gettin' mighty crowded: *Everett, Betty* / Everybody come clap your hands: *Moody & The Deltas* / (Down at) Papa Joe's: *Dixiebells* / Ain't love good: *Clarke, Tony* / Land of 1000 dances: *Cannibal & The Head Hunters*
CDRB 23 / May '95 / Charly

☐ **20 R 'N' B DIVAS**
My baby just cares for me: *Simone, Nina* / It's in his kiss (The shoop shoop song): *Everett, Betty* / Hello stranger: *Lewis, Barbara* / Oh no not my baby: *Brown, Maxine* / I didn't mean to hurt you: *Shirelles* / Do right woman, do right man: *James, Etta* / Woman will do wrong: *Thomas, Irma* / You don't know: *Greenwich, Ellie* / No stranger to love: *Foxx, Inez* / Take me for a little while: *Sands, Evie* / There's gonna be trouble: *Desanto, Sugar Pie* / Selfish one: *Ross, Jackie* / Recovery: *Bass, Fontella* / I don't want to cry: *Big Maybelle* / Love of my man: *Kilgore, Theola* / Let me down easy: *Lavette, Bettye* / Sit down and cry: *Washington, Ella* / You're gonna miss me: *Sexton, Ann* / Do I make myself clear: *James, Etta & Sugar Pie DeSanto* / Shame shame shame: *Shirley & Company*
CDRB 20 / Apr '95 / Charly

☐ **20 REGGAE BLOCKBUSTERS**
CDTRL 176 / Mar '94 / Trojan

☐ **20 REGGAE CLASSICS VOL.1**
Red red wine: *Tribe, Tony* / Sweet sensation: *Melodians* / Love of the common people: *Thomas, Nicky* / Johnny too bad: *Slickers* / Pressure drop: *Toots & The Maytals* / Liquidator: *Harry J All Stars* / Skinhead moonstomp: *Simaryp* / Longshot kick de bucket: *Pioneers* / Please don't make me cry: *Winston Groovy* / Many rivers to cross: *Cliff, Jimmy* / 007: *Dekker, Desmond & The Aces* / Rudie, a message to you: *Livingstone, Dandy* / Version girl: *Friday, Boy* / Cherry oh baby: *Donaldson, Eric* / Fattie fattie: *Eccles, Clancy* / Keep on moving: *Marley, Bob* / Rivers of Babylon: *Melodians* / Train to Skaville: *Ethiopians*
CDTRL 222 / Mar '94 / Trojan

☐ **20 REGGAE CLASSICS VOL.2**
54-46 (was my number): *Toots & The Maytals* / Phoenix city: *Alphonso, Roland* / Love I can feel: *Holt, John* / Java: *Pablo, Augustus* / Reggae in your jeggae: *Livingstone, Dandy* / Pop a top: *Andy Capp* / Double barrel: *Barker, Dave & Ansell Collins* / Wear you to the ball: *U-Roy & John Holt* / Herbsman shuffle: *King Stitt & The Dynamites* / Small axe: *Marley, Bob* / Battle axe: *Upsetters* / Israelites: *Dekker, Desmond & The Aces* / Law: *Andy Capp* / Fat man: *Morgan, Derrick* / So easy: *Winston Groovy* / Whip: *Ethiopians* / Pomp and pride: *Toots & The Maytals* / Further you look: *Holt, John* / Return of Django: *Upsetters* / Soul shakedown party: *Marley, Bob & The Wailers* / Fire corner: *King Stitt* / Next corner: *Dynamites*
CDTRL 224 / Mar '94 / Trojan

☐ **20 REGGAE CLASSICS VOL.3**
CDTRL 256 / Mar '94 / Trojan

☐ **20 REGGAE CLASSICS VOL.4**
CDTRL 284 / Mar '94 / Trojan

☐ **20 REGGAE HOT SHOTS VOL.1**
PWKS 4226 / Jun '98 / Carlton

☐ **20 REGGAE HOT SHOTS VOL.2**
Wonderful world, beautiful people: *Cliff, Jimmy* / Everything I own: *Boothe, Ken* / Longshot kick de bucket: *Pioneers* / You can get it if you really want: *Dekker, Desmond* / Dollar in the teeth: *Upsetters* / Help me make it through the night: *Holt, John* / Small axe: *Marley, Bob & The Wailers* / Black magic woman: *Brown, Dennis* / Hypocrite: *Heptones* / Band of gold: *Griffiths, Marcia* / My time: *Isaacs, Gregory* / Enter into his gates with praise: *Clarke, Johnny* / Singer man: *Kingstonians* / Hit the road Jack: *Big Youth* / Blame it on the sun: *Inner Circle* / Hurt so good: *Cadogan, Susan* / Kingston Town: *Lord Creator* / If you're ready (come go with me): *Richard, Cynthia* / Beat down Babylon: *Byles, Junior* / Barber saloon: *Mikey Dread*
3037350012 / Jun '98 / Hallmark

☐ **20 SONGS OF LOVE FROM THE 70'S**
All by myself: *Carmen, Eric* / Living next door to Alice: *Smokie* / Daytime friends: *Rogers, Kenny* / Emma: *Hot Chocolate* / There goes my first love: *Drifters* / Torn between two lovers: *McGregor, Mary* / Love is in the air: *Young, John Paul* / I can't stop loving you (Though I try): *Sayer, Leo* / I don't want to put a hold on you: *Flint, Bernie* / Romeo: *Mr. Big* / Give a little love: *Bay City Rollers* / Heaven must be missing an angel: *Tavares* / Where do I begin: *Bassey, Shirley* / And I love you so: *Como, Perry* / It's only make believe: *Child* / You're my everything: *Garrett, Lee* / I don't wanna lose you: *Kandidate* / If not you: *Dr. Hook* / If you go away: *Jacks, Terry* / Softly whispering I love you: *Congregation*
CDMFP 5987 / Apr '93 / Music For Pleasure

☐ **20 SOUL SENSATIONS**
Knock on wood: *Floyd, Eddie* / Backfield in motion: *Mel & Tim* / Don't play that song (you lied): *King, Ben E.* / My guy: *Wells, Mary* / Rescue me: *Bass, Fontella* / Got to get you off my mind: *Burke, Solomon* / Dancing in the street: *Reeves, Martha* / Raindrops: *Clark, Dee* / Um um um um um um: *Major Lance* / Tell it like it is: *Neville, Aaron* / Soul man: *Sam & Dave* / Hey girl don't bother me: *Tams* / Stay in my corner: *Dells* / What becomes of the broken hearted: *Ruffin, Jimmy* / Cool jerk: *Capitols* / I'm doin' fine now: *New York City* / Tell mama: *James, Etta* / Wake up everybody: *Melvin, Harold & The Bluenotes* / BABY: *Thomas, Carla* / Drift away: *Gray, Dobie*
308752 / 11 May '98 / Hallmark

☐ **20 SUPERSONIC MEGA HITS**
RUNT 04CD / Aug '95 / Runt

☐ **20 WELSH FOLK DANCES**
SCD 2094 / Mar '95 / Sain

☐ **20TH ANNIVERSARY COLLECTION (2CD Set)**
Give me back my wig / No cuttin' loose / Black cat bone / Big chief / That's why I'm crying / Double eyed whammy / I'm free / These blues is killing me / Rain / Look but don't touch / Fannie Mae / Serves me right to suffer / Leaving / Born in Louisiana / Leaving your town / Drowning on dry land / If I hadn't been high / Trouble in mind / Brick / Pussy cat moan / You don't exist anymore / Second hand man / I've got dreams to remember / Going down to Big Mary's / 300 pounds of heavenly joy / Going back home / Strike like lightning / Middle aged blues boogie / Eyeballin' / Full moon on Main Street / Crow Jane blues / I'm the Zydeco Man / You don't know what love is / Blues after hours / Boot Hill
ALCD 1056 / May '93 / Alligator

☐ **20TH ANNIVERSARY OF THE NEW YORK SALSA FESTIVAL, THE (2CD Set)**
Por eso yo cnato salsa / Pedro navaja / Azucar negra / El cantante / Sonora pa'l balladore / Dejame sonar / Mi primera rumba / Mentiras / Salsa caliente / Los tenis / Sonambulo / Si tu no te fueras / Experto en ti / Otra noche calente / Que manera de quererte / Salsumba / Una adventura / Torero / Sisculpeme senora / Puerto rico
6758001 / Jan '96 / Bellaphon

☐ **20TH ANNIVERSARY TOUR**
ALCD 1078 / May '93 / Alligator

☐ **20TH CONCORD FESTIVAL ALL STARS**
Blues for Sam Nassi / Time after time / I wish I knew / Just a closer walk with thee / Sophisticated lady / Bye bye blackbird / I got it bad and that ain't good
CDD 366 / Jan '89 / Concord Jazz

☐ **21 SWING BAND ALL-TIME GREATS**
Cherokee: *Barnet, Charlie* / One o'clock jump: *Basie, Count* / I can't get started (with you): *Berigan, Bunny* / Honky tonk train blues: *Crosby, Bob & Bob Zurke* / Amapola: *Dorsey, Jimmy* / Besame mucho: *Dorsey, Jimmy* / Boogie woogie: *Dorsey, Tommy* / I'm gettin' sentimental over you: *Dorsey, Tommy* / Don't get around much anymore: *Ellington, Duke* / Take the 'A' train: *Ellington, Duke* / Sing sing sing: *Goodman, Benny* / Why don't you do right: *Goodman, Benny & Peggy Lee* / Flying home: *Hampton, Lionel & Illinois Jacquet* / Body and soul: *Hawkins, Coleman* / At the woodchoppers' ball: *Herman, Woody* / All or nothing at all: *James, Harry & Frank Sinatra* / Ciribiribin: *James, Harry & Frank Sinatra* / Chattanooga choo choo: *Miller, Glenn* / In the mood: *Miller, Glenn* / Back bay shuffle: *Shaw, Artie* / Begin the beguine: *Shaw, Artie*
CDAJA 5141 / Sep '94 / Living Era

☐ **21 YEARS OF ALTERNATIVE RADIO 1**
Hey Joe: *Hendrix, Jimi* / Whiter shade of pale: *Procol Harum* / Delta lady: *Cocker, Joe* / My father's gun: *John, Elton* / Fat man: *Jethro Tull* / Mandolin king: *Lindisfarne* / Keep yourself alive: *Queen* / No love for free: *Armatrading, Joan* / New rose: *Damned* / Dancin' in the moonlight: *Thin Lizzy* / Overground: *Siouxsie & The Banshees* / Read it in books: *Echo & The Bunnymen* / Can't stand losing you: *Police* / It's better this way: *Associates* / 5-8-6: *New Order* / What difference does it make: *Smiths* / Sally MacLennane: *Pogues* / Inside me: *Jesus & Mary Chain* / My favourite dress: *Wedding Present* / Ruby red lips: *Gaye Bykers On Acid* / Strong enough to change: *Unseen Terror*
SFRCD 200 / Oct '88 / Strange Fruit

☐ **21ST CENTURY DUB**
RE 147CD / Jul '97 / ROIR

☐ **21ST CENTURY SOUL**
Falange dos tambores: *Silva, Robertinho* / Loveless: *4 Hero* / I am the black gold of the sun: *Nu Yorican Soul* / Living on the edge: *Darnell, Jeffrey* / Digital: *Roni Size & Reprazent* / Don't xplain: *Pine, Courtney* / No government: *Nicolette* / Future unknown: *DJ Krust* / Kamikaze: *Watkiss, Cleveland* / His name is: *UFO* / Sakara: *Boland, Clarke*
5347422 / Jun '97 / Talkin' Loud

☐ **24 ALL TIME VOCAL GREATS**
Zing went the strings of my heart: *Garland, Judy* / Last time I saw Paris: *Martin, Tony* / Pennsylvania 6-5000: *Andrews Sisters* / Begin the beguine: *Hutchinson, Leslie 'Hutch'* / Amapola: *Durbin, Deanna* / Wanderer: *Tracy, Arthur* / Atumn nocturne: *Carless, Dorothy* / Can't get Indiana out of my mind: *Crosby, Bing* / I yi yi yi yi (I like you very much):

24 ALL TIME VOCAL GREATS
COMPILATIONS
R.E.D. CD CATALOGUE

Miranda, Carmen / Autumn nocturne: Carless, Dorothy / Can't get Indiana off my mind: Crosby, Bing / You are too beautiful: Jolson, Al / I'll be with you in apple blossom time: Lynn, Vera / I'm so used to you now: Bowlly, Al / Boulevard of broken dreams: Langford, Frances / You were never lovelier: Astaire, Fred / Jim: Fitzgerald, Ella / In a moment of weakness: Powell, Dick / Let's do it: Martin, Mary / Do I worry: Ink Spots / Wrap yourself in cotton wool: Shelton, Anne / That lovely week end: Brown, Issy / Room 504: Hall, Adelaide / Nagasaki: Mills Brothers / I got rhythm: Merry Macs / Sweethearts: Jones, Alan

RAJCD 831 / Jul '94 / Empress

☐ 24 BELLES CHANSONS DE PARIS

995102 / Jun '93 / EPM

☐ 24 CARAT VOL.1

AGCD 1 / Aug '95 / Ore

☐ 24 NO.1'S OF THE 60'S

I like it: Gerry & The Pacemakers / Bad to me: Kramer, Billy J. & The Dakotas / Young ones: Richard, Cliff / You're my world: Black, Cilla / Pretty flamingo: Manfred Mann / Apache: Shadows / Shakin' all over: Kidd, Johnny & The Pirates / Poor me: Faith, Adam / World without love: Peter & Gordon / How do you do it: Gerry & The Pacemakers / Bachelor boy: Richard, Cliff / House of the rising sun: Animals / Do wah diddy diddy: Manfred Mann / Lily the pink: Scaffold / I remember you: Ifield, Frank / Anyone who had a heart: Black, Cilla / I'm alive: Hollies / Where do you go to my lovely: Sarstedt, Peter / Wonderful land: Shadows / Little children: Kramer, Billy J. & The Dakotas / Summer holiday: Richard, Cliff / I'm into something good: Herman's Hermits / Walkin' back to happiness: Shapiro, Helen / You'll never walk alone: Gerry & The Pacemakers

CDMFP 6006 / Oct '87 / Music For Pleasure

☐ 25 ALL THE BEST IRISH PUB SONGS

CDIRISH 004 / Jan '95 / Outlet

☐ 25 CONTINENTAL ALL-TIME GREATS

Lili Marlene: Andersen, Lale / Voulez vous de la canne a sucre: Baker, Josephine & Adrien Lamy / Due chitarre: Buti, Carlo / Maria La-O: Celis, Elyane & Lecuona Cuban Boys / Louise: Chevalier, Maurice / Night and day: Comedy Harmonists / Ich bin vom kopf bis fuss: Dietrich, Marlene / Mama: Gigli, Beniamino / Girl like Nina: Hendrik, John / Darling je vous aime beaucoup: Hildegarde / Es lebte einst in Hamburg: Igelhoff, Peter / Von der puszta will ich Traumen: Leander, Zarah / Bir mir bist du schoen: Marjane, Leo / La partie de bridge: Mireille & Jean Sablon/Pills & Tabet / Au fond de tes yeux: Mistinguett / Rosa da Madrid: Piquer, Conchita / Nuages: Reinhardt, Django / Guitare d'amour: Rossi, Tino / J'attendrai and Je sais que vous etes jolie: Sablon, Jean & Django Reinhardt / Andiamo a Napoli: Serra, Daniele / Guter mann im mond: Serrano, Rosita / La canzone del domani: Del Signore, Gino / Lamento Borinqueno: Supervia, Conchita / J'ai ta main: Trenet, Charles

CDAJA 5129 / May '94 / Living Era

☐ 25 FAVOURITE IRISH DRINKING SONGS

CDIRISH 003 / Jan '95 / Outlet

☐ 25 GREATEST HITS VOL.1

SPCD 355 / Nov '93 / Disky

☐ 25 GREATEST HITS VOL.2

SPCD 356 / Nov '93 / Disky

☐ 25 GREATEST HITS VOL.3

SPCD 357 / Nov '93 / Disky

☐ 25 GREATEST HITS VOL.4

SPCD 358 / Nov '93 / Disky

☐ 25 GREATEST HITS VOL.5

SPCD 359 / Nov '93 / Disky

☐ 25 IRISH REBEL SONGS

KOL 600CD / Jul '95 / Outlet

☐ 25 IRISH REPUBLICAN SONGS

Ireland's 32 / Gra mo chroi / Take me home to Mayo / Lonely woods of Upton / They were soldiers everyone / Four green fields / Fields of Athenry / Dying rebel / Lid of me granny's bin / IRELAND / Sean South / Ireland united / West awake / Shall my soul pass through old Ireland / Boys of the old brigade / Off to Dublin in the green / Lough Sheelin eviction / Little armalite / James Connolly / Broad black brimmer / Kevin Barry / Sniper's promise / Patriot game / Only our rivers run free / Nation once again

KOL 602CD / Jul '95 / Outlet

☐ 25 SWEETHEARTS OF YESTERYEAR 1927-1945

Let me call you sweetheart: Crosby, Bing / Magnolia: Marvin, Johnny / Ramona: Austin, Gene / Sweet Sue just you: Metaxa, George / Louise: Chevalier, Maurice / Liza: Jolson, Al & Brunswick Studio Orchestra / Oh Donna Clara: Layton & Johnstone / Sally: Fields, Gracie / Dinah: Crosby, Bing & The Mills Brothers / Marta: Tracy, Arthur / Mah Lindy Lou: Robeson, Paul / Sweet Georgia Brown: Mills Brothers / Honeysuckle rose: Waller, Fats / Rose Marie: Eddy, Nelson / Marie: Dorsey, Tommy / Diane: Novis, Donald / Cecilia: Todd, Dick / Hear my song Violetta: Martin, Tony & Ray Sinatra Orchestra / Chloe: Shore, Dinah / Sweet Lorraine: Cole, Nat 'King' / Lili Marlene: Shelton, Anne / Margie: Cantor, Eddie / Laura: Haymes, Dick / Nancy with the laughing face: Sinatra, Frank / Goodnight sweetheart: Bowlly, Al

CDAJA 5243 / Nov '97 / Living Era

☐ 25 YEARS OF LOVE

ONECD 22 / Jun '97 / Connoisseur Collection

☐ 25 YEARS OF NO.1 HITS (Country)

Hello darlin': Twitty, Conway / Four in the morning: Young, Faron / It's not love (but it's not bad): Haggard, Merle / (Old dogs, children and) watermelon wine: Hall, Tom T. / Before the next teardrop falls: Fender, Freddy / Rhinestone cowboy: Campbell, Glen / Together again: Harris, Emmylou / One piece at a time: Cash, Johnny / Don't it make your brown eyes blue: Gayle, Crystal / Lady lay down: Conlee, John / Devil went down to Georgia: Daniels, Charlie Band / I was country when country wasn't cool: Mandrell, Barbara / All my rowdy friends (have settled down): Williams, Hank Jr. / Don't cheat in our hometown: Skaggs, Ricky / On the other hand: Travis, Randy / I sang Dixie: Yoakam, Dwight / Some girls do: Brown, Sawyer / Achy breaky heart: Cyrus, Billy Ray / I still believe in you: Gill, Vince / She don't know she's beautiful: Kershaw, Sammy

ONECD 20 / Mar '97 / Connoisseur Collection

☐ 25 YEARS OF NO.1 HITS (Soul)

Thank you (falletinme be mice elf again): Sly & The Family Stone / Don't play that song: Franklin, Aretha / I'll take you there: Staple Singers / Get on the good foot: Brown, James / LOVE (love): Green, Al / Fight the power: Isley Brothers / This will be: Cole, Natalie / Best of my love: Emotions / It's ecstasy when you lay down next to me: White, Barry / Too much, too little, too late: Mathis, Johnny & Deniece Williams / One in a million you: Graham, Larry / Don't stop the music: Yarbrough & Peoples / She's strange: Cameo / Rock me tonight: Jackson, Freddie / Do me baby: Morgan, Meli'sa / Nite and day: Sure, Al B. / I can't wait another minute: Hi-Five / Back and forth: Aaliyah

ONECD 21 / Mar '97 / Connoisseur Collection

☐ 25 YEARS OF NO.1 HITS (Instrumentals)

TSOP: MFSB / Telstar: Tornados / Tequila: Champs / Popcorn: Hot Butter / Apache: Shadows / Hustle: McCoy, Van / Albatross: Fleetwood Mac / Sleepwalk: Santo & Johnny / Classical gas: Williams, Mason / Hoots mon: Lord Rockingham's XI / Stranger on the shore: Bilk, Acker / Diamonds: Harris, Jet & Tony Meehan / Nut rocker: B Bumble & The Stingers / Wonderland by night: Kaempfert, Bert / Cherry pink and apple blossom white: Calvert, Eddie

ONECD 23 / Jun '97 / Connoisseur Collection

☐ 25 YEARS OF NO.1 HITS (REGGAE)

Amigo: Black Slate / Sweat: Shinehead / No no no: Penn, Dawn / Point of view: Matumbi / Rumours: Isaacs, Gregory / Try jah love: Third World / Little Walter: Paul, Frankie / Don't look back: Tosh, Peter / Police officer: Smiley Culture / Day dreaming: Delgado, Junior / Cherry oh baby: Donaldson, Eric / 54-46 (was my number): Toots & The Maytals / Many rivers to cross: Cliff, Jimmy / Champion lover: Glasgow, Deborahe / Money in my pocket: Brown, Dennis / Up town top ranking: Althia & Donna / Good thing going: Lewis, C.J. & Philip Leo / Pirates anthem: Home T & Cocoa T/Shabba Ranks / Zungguzungguguzungguzeng: Yellowman

ONECD 24 / Jul '97 / Connoisseur Collection

☐ 25 YEARS OF NO.1 HITS VOL.1

I hear you knocking: Edmunds, Dave / All kinds of everything: Dana / War: Starr, Edwin / Maggie may: Stewart, Rod / Coz I love you: Slade / Yellow river: Christie / Family affair: Sly & The Family Stone / Spirit in the sky: Greenbaum, Norman / Make it with you: Bread / Mama told me not to come: Three Dog Night / Hey girl don't bother me: Tams / Gypsies, tramps and thieves: Cher / Shaft: Hayes, Isaac / Brand new key: Melanie / In the summertime: Mungo Jerry / Woodstock: Matthew's Southern Comfort / Venus: Shocking Blue / Hot love: T-Rex

ONECD 01 / Aug '96 / Connoisseur Collection

☐ 25 YEARS OF NO.1 HITS VOL.10

Sleeping satellite: Archer, Tasmin / Would I lie to you: Charles & Eddie / Stay: Shakespears Sister / Young at heart: Bluebells / Saturday night: Whigfield / Here comes the hot steppa: Kamoze, Ini / I like the way: Hi-Five / Take a chance: Erasure / Jump: Kriss Kross / Inside: Stiltskin / Mr. Vain: Culture Beat / Deeply dippy: Right Said Fred / Unbelievable: EMF / Set adrift on memory bliss: PM Dawn / Sadness: Enigma / Boom, shake the room: DJ Jazzy Jeff & The Fresh Prince / Ebeneezer good: Shamen

ONECD 10 / Aug '96 / Connoisseur Collection

☐ 25 YEARS OF NO.1 HITS VOL.2

American pie: McLean, Don / See my baby jive: Wizard / Can the can: Quatro, Suzi / Delta dawn: Reddy, Helen / Crocodile rock: John, Elton / Keep on truckin': Kendricks, Eddie / Morning after: McGovern, Maureen / Cum on feel the noize: Slade / I can see clearly now: Nash, Johnny / Me and Mrs Jones: Paul, Billy / School's out: Cooper, Alice / You're so vain: Simon, Carly / Oh girl: Chi-Lites / Rubber bullets: 10cc / Lean on me: Withers, Bill / Midnight train to Georgia: Knight, Gladys / Metal guru: T-Rex / I'll take you there: Staple Singers

ONECD 02 / Aug '96 / Connoisseur Collection

☐ 25 YEARS OF NO.1 HITS VOL.3

Angie baby: Reddy, Helen / Rhinestone cowboy: Campbell, Glen / Lovin' you: Riperton, Minnie / Can't get enough of your love: White, Barry / Can't give you anything but my love: Stylistics / Philadelphia freedom: John, Elton / Love will keep us together: Captain & Tennille / When will I see you again: Three Degrees / I can help: Swan, Billy / Shining star: Earth, Wind & Fire / Cat's in the cradle: Chapin, Harry / Pick up the pieces: Average White Band / Hey eyes adored you: Valli, Frankie / Sad sweet dreamer: Sweet Sensation / Make me smile: Harley, Steve / You're no good: Ronstadt, Linda / January: Pilot / Rock your baby: McCrae, George

ONECD 03 / Aug '96 / Connoisseur Collection

☐ 25 YEARS OF NO.1 HITS VOL.4

When I need you: Sayer, Leo / So you win again: Hot Chocolate / Kiss and say goodbye: Manhattans / Play that funky music: Wild Cherry / Free: Williams, Deniece / Best of my love: Emotions / December '63: Four Seasons / Don't cry for me Argentina: Covington, Julie / Float on: Floaters / Car wash: Royce, Rose / Let your love flow: Bellamy Brothers / Blinded by the light: Manfred Mann / You to me are everything: Real Thing / Love rollercoaster: Ohio Players / Rock 'n' me: Miller, Steve Band / I just want to be your everything: Gibb, Andy / Mississippi: Pussycat / Southern nights: Campbell, Glen

ONECD 04 / Aug '96 / Connoisseur Collection

☐ 25 YEARS OF NO.1 HITS VOL.5

Wuthering heights: Bush, Kate / Heart of glass: Blondie / When you're in love: Dr. Hook / We don't talk anymore: Richard, Cliff / My sharona: Knack / What a fool believes: Doobie Brothers / Good times: Chic / Brass in pocket: Pretenders / Geno: Dexy's Midnight Runners / I will survive: Gaynor, Gloria / I don't like Mondays: Boomtown Rats / Video killed the radio star: Buggles / Going underground: Jam / Baby come back: Player / Reunited: Peaches & Herb / Babe: Styx / Funkytown: Lipps Inc. / Do that to me one more time: Captain & Tennille

ONECD 05 / Aug '96 / Connoisseur Collection

☐ 25 YEARS OF NO.1 HITS VOL.6

Tide is high: Blondie / Bette Davis eyes: Carnes, Kim / Model: Kraftwerk / Centrefold: Geils, J. Band / Tainted love: Soft Cell / Celebration: Kool & The Gang / Fame: Cara, Irene / Town called malice: Jam / Come on Eileen: Dexy's Midnight Runners / Keep on loving you: REO Speedwagon / Down under: Men At Work / Total eclipse of the heart: Tyler, Bonnie / Wherever I lay my hat: Young, Paul / Give it up: KC & The Sunshine Band / Africa: Toto / Arthur's theme: Cross, Christopher / Baby come to me: Austin, Patti & James Ingram / Too shy: Kajagoogoo

ONECD 06 / Aug '96 / Connoisseur Collection

☐ 25 YEARS OF NO.1 HITS VOL.7

Missing you: Waite, John / Power of love: Lewis, Huey & The News / Everybody wants to rule the world: Tears For Fears / I should've known better: Diamond, Jim / 99 red balloons: Nena / Can't fight this feeling: REO Speedwagon / Every time you go away: Young, Paul / I feel for you: Khan, Chaka / Owner of a lonely heart: Yes / I want to know what love is: Foreigner / Move closer: Nelson, Phyllis / If I was: Ure, Midge / Take on me: A-Ha / Relax: Frankie Goes To Hollywood / 19: Hardcastle, Paul / Kharma chameleon: Culture Club

ONECD 07 / Aug '96 / Connoisseur Collection

☐ 25 YEARS OF NO.1 HITS VOL.8

Stuck with you: Lewis, Huey & The News / Don't leave me this way: Communards / La bamba: Los Lobos / Venus: Bananarama / Final countdown: Europe / Walk like an Egyptian: Bangles / Glory of love: Cetera, Peter / Always: Atlantic Starr / Mony mony: Idol, Billy / You keep me hanging on: Wilde, Kim / Rock me Amadeus: Falco / Sun always shines on TV: A-Ha / Caravan of love: Housemartins / At this moment: Era, Billy & The Beaters / Everything I own: Boy George / Died in your arms: Cutting Crew

ONECD 08 / Aug '96 / Connoisseur Collection

☐ 25 YEARS OF NO.1 HITS VOL.9

Nothing's gonna change my love: Medeiros, Glenn / Only way is up: Yazz / First time: Beck, Robin / Eternal flame: Bangles / Black velvet: Myles, Alannah / I don't have the heart: Ingram, James / I think we're alone now: Tiffany / Wishing well: D'Arby, Terence Trent / Something's gotten hold of my heart: Almond, Marc & Gene Pitney / My perogative: Brown, Bobby / Killer: Adamski / Joker: Miller, Steve Band / Roll with it: Winwood, Steve / Right here waiting: Marx, Richard / Ice ice baby: Vanilla Ice / Tears on my pillow: Minogue, Kylie / Sealed with a kiss: Donovan, Jason / Dub be good to me: Beats International

ONECD 09 / Aug '96 / Connoisseur Collection

☐ 25 YEARS OF RHYTHM 'N' BLUES HITS

Long gone: Thompson, Sonny / Tomorrow night: Johnson, Lonnie / I'm waiting just for you: Millinder, Lucky / Baby I'm doin' it: Allen, Annisteen / Moaning blues: Hooker, John Lee / Dissatisfied: Waters, Muddy / Sixty minute man: Ward, Billy & The Dominoes / Soft: Bradshaw, Tiny / Slow walk: Doggett, Bill / Good rockin' tonight: Harris, Wynonie / Hard luck blues: Brown, Roy / Trying: Baker, LaVern / Guess who: Hunter, Ivory Joe / Me and my mule: Dupree, 'Champion' Jack / Only you: Platters / Harlem nocturne: Bostic, Earl

EMBCD 3359 / 27 Apr '98 / Ember

☐ 25 YEARS OF TROJAN

CDTRD 413 / Mar '94 / Trojan

☐ 25TH FUJITSU CONCORD JAZZ FESTIVAL

You're lucky to me: Alden, Howard Trio / Very thought of you: Alden, Howard Trio / Nobody else but me: Alden, Howard Trio / Crazy she calls me: Alden, Howard Trio / All alone/Tango el bongo: Alden, Howard Trio / Kung fu willie: Harris, Gene Quartet / Grass is greener: Harris, Gene Quartet / Sweet Georgia Brown: Harris, Gene Quartet / Just a closer walk with thee: Harris, Gene Quartet / Robbin's nest: Harris, Gene Quartet / Tenderly: Harris, Gene Quartet / This one's for Scott: Harris, Gene Quartet / There is no greater love: McPartland, Marian Trio / Prelude to a kiss: McPartland, Marian Trio / There will never be another you: McPartland, Marian Trio / Gone with the wind: McPartland, Marian Trio / My foolish heart: McPartland, Marian Trio / I'll remember April: McPartland, Marian Trio

CCD 7002 / Mar '94 / Concord Jazz

☐ 26 ALL TIME COUNTRY CLASSICS

Cotton eyed Joe / I'll hold you in my heart / Walkin' the floor over you / Runaway train / I'm thinking tonight of my blue eyes / Waiting for a train / Wabash cannon ball / Shame on you / I want to be a cowboy's sweetheart / Tumbling tumbleweeds / New San Antonio rose / Sioux City Sue / Orange blossom special / You are my sunshine / Teardrops in my heart / Born to lose / Move it on over / Time changes everything / Be honest with me / Honky tonkin' / Brown's ferry blues / Long tall mama blues / Cain's stomp / Pan American / Hillbilly boogie / My chickashay girl

PASTCD 7827 / 25 May '98 / Flapper

☐ 26TH FUJITSU CONCORD JAZZ FESTIVAL

CCD 7003 / Apr '95 / Concord Jazz

☐ 27TH FUJITSU-CONCORD JAZZ FESTIVAL

No more blues / You'd be so nice to come home to / Stardust / In love in vain / It might as well be spring / Blues capers / Easy living / Sweet Georgia Brown / Tenderly / Swing until the girls come home / Buhaina buhaina / Love you madly / Song is you / Owl / Just friends / Portrait of Jenny / What's new / Skylark / Donna Lee

CCD 7004 / Apr '96 / Concord Jazz

☐ 30 CLASSIC ORIGINAL SOUL HITS (2CD Set)

Mr. Big Stuff: Knight, Jean / Do the funky penguin: Thomas, Rufus / Ain't gonna bump no more with no big fat woman: Tex, Joe / Shoorah shoorah: Wright, Betty / Walking in rhythm: Blackbyrds / Why can't we live together: Thomas, Timmy / I'll take you there: Staple Singers / Be thankful for what you've got: DeVaughan, William / Midnight train to Georgia: Knight, Gladys & The Pips / Give your baby a standing ovation: Dells / Misty blue: Moore, Dorothy / Daddy's home: Toots & The Maytals / God blessed our love: Brimmer, Charles / It's lying time again: LaSalle, Denise / Leaving me: Independents / Theme from Shaft: Hayes, Isaac / Time is tight: Booker T & The MG's / Groove me: Floyd, King / I will: Winters, Ruby / Ain't no woman like the one I got: Four Tops / I've got to use my imagination: Knight, Gladys & The Pips / First time we met: Independents / Funny how time slips away: Moore, Dorothy / That's how strong my love is: Brimmer, Charles / Members only: Bland, Bobby / It's you that I need: Enchantment / You'll never get your hooks in one man: LaSalle, Denise / Together we are beautiful: Kinney, Fern / Rock your baby: McCrae, George / Loose caboose: Tex, Joe

DOU 882462 / 2 Feb '98 / Disky

☐ 30 ITALO DANCE CLASSICS (2CD Set)

Tarzan boy: Baltimora / Another life: Kano / Step by step: Silver Pozzoli / Self control: DJK / All night long: BB Band / First true love affair: Ross, Jimmy / Can't we go: Electric Mind / Be my life: Cruisin' Gang / Maybe one day: Creatures / Love is gonna be on your side: Firefly / Talk with your body: Hooker, Tom / I'm going to: Jago / No escape: Max Him / I'm in love: Johnson, Patty / Boys boys boys: Sabrina / Black is black: Bell Epoque / Disco band: Scotch / Funky be-bop: Vin-Zee / Gringo: Benvenuto, Roby / America: Cruisin' Gang / Hit mix: Fun Fun / Woody boogie: Baltimora / I feel you: Harrow, Den / Stop bajon: De Piscopo, Tulio / You are a dancer: Low, Gary / I'm ready: Kano / Turn the music on: Johnson, Orlando / Crazy family: Hattle, John / Shame: Stephany / Only one: Hooker, Tom

DOU 882562 / 2 Feb '98 / Disky

☐ 30 SECONDS BEFORE CALICO WALL

AA 050 / Jul '97 / Arf Arf

☐ 30 YEARS OF DUB MUSIC

RNCD 2046 / Mar '94 / Rhino

☐ 30 YEARS OF DUB MUSIC ON THE GO

RNCD 2094 / Mar '95 / Rhino

☐ 30 YEARS OF JAMAICAN MUSIC ON THE GO

RNCD 2034 / Jan '94 / Rhino

☐ 30 YEARS OF JAMAICAN MUSIC VOL.2

RNCD 87 / Feb '95 / Rhino

☐ 30 YEARS OF NO.1'S VOL.7 (1972-1975)

You wear it well: Stewart, Rod / Mouldy old dough: Lieutenant Pigeon / Clair: O'Sullivan, Gilbert / Blockbuster: Sweet / See my baby jive: Wizzard / Can the can: Quatro, Suzi / Rubber bullets: 10cc / Welcome home: Peters & Lee / I'm the leader of the gang (I am): Glitter, Gary / Angel fingers: Wizzard / Daydreamer: Cassidy, David / You won't find another fool like me: New Seekers / Tiger feet: Mud / Devil gate drive: Quatro, Suzi / Seasons in the sun: Jacks, Terry / Sugar baby love: Rubettes / Streak: Stevens, Ray / Always yours: Glitter, Gary / Kung fu fighting: Douglas, Carl / Sad sweet dreamer: Sweet Sensation / Everything I own: Boothe, Ken / You're the first, the last, my everything: White, Barry / Down down: Status Quo / Ms. Grace: Tymes

TYNOCD 106 / Dec '89 / Connoisseur Collection

☐ 30'S GIRLS, THE

Second hand man / Rhythm for sale / Doin' the Suzie Q / All God's chillun got rhythm / Summertime / My castles rockin'

CBC 1026 / Sep '95 / Timeless Jazz

☐ 32 MASTERPIECES OF ROCK (2CD Set)

24003 / Jun '96 / Delta Doubles

☐ 35 YEARS OF THE BEST IN BLUEGRASS 1960-1995 (Rebel Record's Anniversary Collection/4CD Set)

REB 4000CD / Jul '97 / Rebel

☐ 36 IRISH LOVE BALLADS

CHCD 3202 / Oct '95 / Chyme

☐ 36 MASTERPIECES OF JAZZ VOL.2 (2CD Set)

FA 059 / Apr '97 / Fremeaux

☐ 36 SUCCES CHANSON FRANCAISE VOL.1 (2CD Set)

FA 970 / May '96 / Fremeaux

☐ 36 SUCCES CHANSON FRANCAISE VOL.2

Vous oubliez votre cheval: Trenet, Charles / Coches dans le foin: Pils Et Tabet / La mome caoutchouc: Gabin, Jean / C'est vrai: Mistinguett / Cette petite femme la: Simon, Michel / Mon amant de la St Jean: Delyle, Lucienne / La cucaracha: Rossi, Tino / Sombre dimanche: Damia / Toulon: Alibert /

Confessin': Baker, Josephine / Le vieux chateau: Pills & Tabet / Priere de la Charlotte: Dubas, Marie / Qui craint le grand mechant loup: Adison, Fred / Le fiancee du pirate: Gauty, Lys / Maman ne vend pas le maison: Petit Mirscha / Le fils de la femme poisson: Frehel / Ca sent si bon la France: Chevalier, Maurice / Tout est au duc: Trenet, Charles / Barnabe: Fernandel / Ou sont-ils tous mes copains: Piaf, Edith / Vous n'etes pas venue Dimanche: Rossi, Tino / Lily Marlene: Solidor, Suzy / Le marche de menilmontant: Solidor, Suzy / On m'suit: Mistinguett / On m'appelle simplet: Fernandel / Le chacal: Piaf, Edith / O corse ile d'amour: Rossi, Tino / Papa n'a pas voulu: Mireille / Vous qu'avez-vous fait de mon amour: Ventura, Ray & Guy Berry / La guinguette a ferme ses volets: Damia / Avec ma p'tit gueule: Gabin, Jean / Seule ce soir: Marjane, Leo / Folatrerie: Fernandel / Vous qui passez sans me voir: Sablon, Jean / Un seul regard: Bauge, Andre & Sim Viva / J'ai te main: Trenet, Charles

FA 975 / Apr '97 / Fremeaux

☐ **40 COMPLETE FAVOURITE IRISH BALLADS**

CDBALLAD 002 / Jan '95 / Outlet

☐ **40 COMPLETE IRISH PUB SONGS**

CDBALLAD 001 / Jan '95 / Outlet

☐ **40 CONCURSO DE GAITA GALEGA**

AB 001CD / Mar '98 / Areabrava

☐ **40 DEGREES C CARNAVAL TROPICAL**

74321459732 / Feb '97 / Milan

☐ **40 DRUM 'N' BASS FLOORBURNERS (4CD Set)**

CDBTOT 4 / 2 Feb '98 / Jumpin' & Pumpin'

☐ **40 FOLK BALLADS OF IRELAND (2CD Set)**

CHCD 1042 / Mar '96 / Chyme

☐ **40 IRISH LOVE SONGS**

CHCD 1069 / Oct '95 / Chyme

☐ **40 OLD SKOOL HIP HOP AND ELECTRO CLASSICS (2CD Set)**

SONYTV 53CD / 10 Aug '98 / Sony TV

☐ **40 UK TOP 10 HITS OF THE 1960'S (2CD Set)**

Tobacco road: Nashville Teens / Midnight in Moscow: Ball, Kenny & His Jazzmen / Candy man: Poole, Brian / He's in town: Rockin' Berries / Roses are red: Carroll, Ronnie / Bobby's girl: Maughan, Susan / Save the last dance for me: Drifters / Sheila: Roe, Tommy / Tell him: Davies, Billie / Diamonds: Harris, Jet / Mirror mirror: Pinkerton's Assorted Colours / Wimoweh: Denver, Karl / Tell me when: Applejacks / Juke like Eddie: Heinz / You've got your troubles: Fortunes / I think of you: Merseybeats / Juliet: Four Pennies / Winchester Cathedral: New Vaudeville Band / Come back and shake me: Rodgers, Clodagh / I'll pick a rose for my rose: Johnson, Marv / Tossin' and turnin': Ivy League / Hello little girl: Fourmost / When a man loves a woman: Sledge, Percy / Build me up buttercup: Foundations / Walkin' back to happiness: Shapiro, Helen / But I do: Henry, Clarence 'Frogman' / Are you sure: Allisons / Game of love: Fontana, Wayne / Where do you go to my lovely: Sarstedt, Peter / You were made to love me: Freddie & The Dreamers / Cradle of love: Preston, Johnny / Wild thing: Troggs / Baby love: Supremes / Good timin': Jones, Jimmy / My guy: Wells, Mary / Ain't misbehavin': Bruce, Tommy / Little children: Kramer, Billy J. / Picture of you: Bruvvers / I'm into something good: Herman's Hermits / Love is all around: Troggs

330002 / Jul '96 / Hallmark

☐ **40 UK TOP 10 HITS OF THE 1970'S (2CD Set)**

Angel face: Glitter Band / Heaven must have sent you: Elgins / Billy don't be a hero: Paper Lace / Big seven: Judge Dread / Have you seen her: Chi-Lites / Son of my father: Chicory Tip / Hang on in there baby: Bristol, Johnny / Love grows (where my Rosemary goes): Edison Lighthouse / Feel the need in me: Detroit Emeralds / Patches: Carter, Clarence / Yellow river: Christie / Wishing on a star: Rose Royce / Storm in a teacup: Fortunes / Goodbye my love: Glitter Band / Love machine: Miracles / Oh girl: Chi-Lites / J'taime: Judge Dread / Night Chicago died: Paper Lace / Freedom come freedom go: Fortunes / Rose garden: Anderson, Lynn / Rock your baby: McCrae, George / Standing in the road: Blackfoot Sue / Car wash: Rose Royce / My ding-a-ling: Berry, Chuck / Don't let it die: Smith, Hurricane / That same old feeling: Pickettywitch / He's the greatest dancer: Sister Sledge / Pepperbox: Peppers / Sky high: Jigsaw / Stoned love: Supremes / We are family: Sister Sledge / Heaven must be missing an angel: Tavares / I'm a man: Chicago / More than a woman: Tavares / Honey honey: Sweet Dreams / Nathan Jones: Supremes / Band of gold: Payne, Freda / Oh babe what would you say: Smith, Hurricane / With you I'm born again: Syreeta / Love don't live here anymore: Rose Royce

330012 / Jul '96 / Hallmark

☐ **40 VERY BEST IRISH PUB SONGS**

CDPUB 026 / Mar '97 / Outlet

☐ **48 GOLDENE INSTRUMENTALS DER VOLKSMUSIK (3CD Set)**

Hoch drob'n auf dem berg: Schultheiss, Fred / Gamser: Leizachter Musikanten / Es war im Bohmerwald: Leizachter Musikanten / Zauberzither: Wolf, Hubert / Brotzeitpolka: Hot Dogs / Vergissmeinnicht: Gustl's Frohliche Dorfmusik / Der witzbold: Kalina, Herbert / Das kufsteinlied: Fritz & Freddy / Blue Hawaii: Pokuhako, Carlos / Marianka: Greger, Max / Western saloon: Lambert, Franz / Heizelmannchens wachtparade: Lambert, Franz / Greensleeves: Schachtner, Heinz / Dorftratsch: Kittl, Franz / Es schmettern die Horner: Kittl, Franz / Mondnacht am Konigsee: Knabl, Rudi / Hohe tannen: Duo Aribert Korbel / 'S kammerfensterlin: Schultheiss, Fred / Im fruhtau zu Berge: Rheinische Waldhornquartett / Klarinettenwilderer: Leizachter Musikanten / Konig-ludwig-lied: Konig-Ludwig-Musikanten / Du bist die Rose vom: Alpenvorlandler / Kirchweih in Tirol: Knabl, Rudi / Wo die Musikanten sind: Fritz & Freddy / Im Gansemarsch: Graff, Willi / Tolzer schutzenmarsch: Graff, Willi / Herbert's posaunenwalzer: Kalina, Herbert / Echo polka: Gustl's Frohliche Dorfmusik / Hawaii tatoo: Pokuhako, Carlos / O sole mio: Schachtner, Heinz / Libellentanz: Kittl, Franz / Der zither-muckl: Wolf, Hubert / Herzerl fur's Herzerl: Leizachter Musikanten / Santo Domingo: Fritz & Freddy / Annchen von Tharau: Schultheiss, Fred / Kaiserjager Marsch: Knabl, Rudi / Quecksilber: Graff, Willi / Ambosspolka: Hot Dogs / Weinberg polka: Gustl's Frohliche Dorfmusik / Erinnerung an Rheinbach: Kalina, Herbert / Mitternachtblues: Strasser, Hugo / Mitternachtsblues: Strasser, Hugo / Erinnerung au Zirkus Renz: Lambert, Franz / Neopolitanisches Stanchen: Barny, Wal / Alo ahe: Pokuhako, Carlos / Klarinettenklamauk: Kittl, Franz / Dudlsackrischer: Wolf, Hubert / Der mond halt seine Wacht: Duo Aribert Korbel / Waldandacht: Rheinische Waldhornquartett

HR 867772 / Sep '96 / Disky

☐ **49 GOLDEN TREASURES (2CD Set)**

Mad dogs and Englishmen: Coward, Sir Noel / Nobody love's a fairy: O'Shea, Tessie / Home town: Flanagan & Allen / Physician: Lawrence, Gertrude / Auf weidersehen sweetheart: Bowlly, Al / Funny face: Astaire, Fred / St.Louis blues: Robeson, Paul / Everything's in rhythm with my heart: Matthews, Jessie / Little Betty Bouncer: Flotsam & Jetsam / Walter Walter: Fields, Gracie / Window cleaner: Formby, George / That old feeling: Hall, Adelaide / Don't have anymore Mrs. Moore: Hall, Adelaide / Dancing in the dark: Hutchinson, Leslie / When the poppies bloom again: Lynn, Vera / Man who broke the bank at Monte Cristo: Coburn, Charles / Soloman: Welch, Elisabeth / All the things you are: Tauber, Richard / I'll see you again: Laye, Evelyn / We saw the sea: Dawson, Peter / Jubilee baby: Driver, Betty / Teddy bears picnic: Hall, Henry Orchestra / Your heart and mine: Nicholas Brothers / There's a small hotel: Daniels, Bebe & Ben Lyon / Way you look tonight: Astaire, Fred / Why don't you do right: Lee, Peggy / Sonny boy: Jolson, Al / It's a great day for the Irish: Garland, Judy / I couldn't sleep a wink last night: Sinatra, Frank / 42nd Street: Boswell Sisters / Let's spring one: Cole, Nat 'King' Trio / I'm putting all my eggs in one basket: Rogers, Ginger / Without a song: Tibbett, Lawrence / I'd rather be blue: Brice, Fanny / Bob White: Crosby, Bing / Serenata: Swanson, Gloria / Hong Kong blues: Carmichael, Hoagy / Ah sweet mystery of life: Eddy, Nelson & Jeanette MacDonald / Darling Nellie Grey: Armstrong, Louis / I'm keeping this red red nose: Etting, Ruth / Minnie the moocher: Calloway, Cab / I'm the last of the red hot mammas: Tucker, Sophie / Joint is jumping: Waller, Fats / My heart belongs to daddy: Martin, Mary / Granny's old armchair: Crumit, Frank / Cow cow boogie: Fitzgerald, Ella / Making whoppee: Cantor, Eddie / We just couldn't say goodbye: Hanshaw, Annette / I can't help loving that man: Aunt Jemima (Tess Gardella)

SD 885602 / 2 Feb '98 / Disky

☐ **50**

COMPOST 50 / 3 Aug '98 / Compost

☐ **50 BEST IRISH REBEL BALLADS VOL.1**

IRB 1798CD / Oct '95 / Outlet

☐ **50 BIG BAND CLASSICS**

PDSCD 512 / Sep '97 / Pulse

☐ **50 CLASSIC PUB SONGS**

PUBCD 50 / Nov '97 / Primetime

☐ **50 COMPLETE IRISH REBEL SONGS VOL.2**

IRBCD 1916 / Jun '96 / Outlet

☐ **50 CONCURSA DE GAITA GALEGA**

AB 002CD / Mar '98 / Areabrava

☐ **50 COUNTRY NO.1'S**

DBG 53033 / Jun '94 / Double Gold

☐ **50 IRISH SINGALONG FAVOURITES**

Come back home to Erin / Whistling Phil McHugh / Gipsy Rover / Let him go let hime tarry / Flower of sweet Strabane / Give an Irish girl to me / I never will marry / Slaney valley / Delaney's donkey Mary Mack / Maggie Pickens / Some say the devil's dead Johnny / When you die / Highland / Keel row / Have a drink of whisky Ballyhoe / Where the River Shannon flows / Erin's green shore / Cutting the corn in creeslough / Lovely Derry / If I were a blackbird / Hills of Kerry / Homes of Donegal / County Mayo / Aloysius Magee Eileen / Oge agricultural Irish girl / Take me back to Castlebar / Blue hills of Breffni / Connemara bus / Dear Doctor John / I don't mind if I do / I'll take you home again Kathleen / Bunch of thyme / Rathlin island / Westering home / Where the blarney roses grow / Abbeyshrule / Brian oge and Molly Bawn / Johnny I hardly knew ye dear / Old Donegal / Peggy O'Neil / Nora Malone / My wild Irish rose / Nellie Kelly / Kitty Kelly / Maid of Fyvie / Drunken sailor / Rattling bog / Reel / Turkey in the straw

EMPRCD 553 / Nov '94 / Emporio

☐ **50 MILLION SELLERS (2CD Set)**

CPCD 82792 / Apr '97 / Charly

☐ **50 NUMBER ONE'S OF THE 60'S**

Young ones: Richard, Cliff / Wonderful land: Shadows / Oh pretty woman: Orbison, Roy / Baby love: Ross, Diana & The Supremes / It's not unusual: Jones, Tom / Sun ain't gonna shine anymore: Walker Brothers / (There's) always something there to remind me: Shaw, Sandie / Everlasting love: Love Affair / Baby come back: Equals / Sweets for my sweet: Searchers / Silence is golden: Tremeloes / With a little help from my friends: Cocker, Joe / Blue moon: Marcels / Three steps to heaven: Cochran, Eddie / You really got me: Kinks / I like it: Gerry & The Pacemakers / I'm alive: Hollies / Young girl: Puckett, Gary / Yeh yeh: Fame, Georgie / I'm into something good: Herman's Hermits / Walkin' back to happiness: Shapiro, Helen / Go now: Moody Blues / Pretty flamingo: Manfred Mann / Out of time: Farlowe, Chris / Whiter shade of pale: Procol Harum / You've lost that loving feeling: Righteous Brothers / Reach out I'll be there: Four Tops / You don't have to say to love me: Springfield, Dusty / Bad to me: Kramer, Billy J. & The Dakotas / World without love: Peter & Gordon / Do it again: Beach Boys / Sunny afternoon: Kinks / All or nothing: Small Faces / Blackberry way: Move / With a girl like you: Troggs / Mony mony: James, Tommy & The Shondells / Baby, now that I've found you: Foundations / Where do you go to my lovely: Sarstedt, Peter / Je t'aime, moi non plus: Birkin, Jane & Serge Gainsbourg / Fire: Crazy World Of Arthur Brown / Long live love: Shaw, Sandie / Michelle: Overlanders / Green green grass of home: Jones, Tom / I'll never find another you: Seekers / Don't throw your love away: Searchers / Mr. Tambourine Man: Byrds / San Francisco: McKenzie, Scott / Keep on running: Davis, Spencer Group / Make it easy on yourself: Walker Brothers / Albatross: Fleetwood Mac / Something in the air: Thunderclap Newman

RADCD 08 / Apr '95 / Global TV

☐ **50 ORIGINAL DANCE GOLDEN OLDIES**

55525 / Nov '94 / Laserlight

☐ **50 ROMANTIC LOVE SONGS (2CD Set)**

Somewhere my love / Love me tonight / What is this thing called love / Young love / Love's been good to me / Have I told you lately that I love you / Old fashioned way / You're just in love / Be my love / And I love you so / Our love affair / Secret love / Lover come back to me / Hello young lovers / When I fall in love / Love me tender / Let's fall in love / Love is blue / Love story / Love letters / Je t'aime / Why do I love you / Falling in love with love / No other love / Man and a woman / You've lost that loving feeling / Let there be love / What the world needs now / Love is here to stay / I'm in the mood for love / If I loved you / Fallin' in love / Goodbye to love / I can't stop loving you / LOVE / True love / Almost like being in love / I'll never fall in love again / I wish you love / So in love / She / Easy to love / Love grows / Love letters in the sand / Man I love / Puppy love / Can't help falling in love / Somebody loves me / People will say we're in love / This guy's in love with you

330422 / Mar '97 / Hallmark

☐ **50'S - JUKE JOINT BLUES, THE**

Three o'clock blues: King, B.B. / Long tall woman: James, Elmore / Ramblin' on my mind: Gilmore, Boyd / Gonna let you go: Turner, Babyface / Love my baby: Bland, Bobby & Junior Parker / Riding in the moonlight: Howlin' Wolf / 44 blues: Curtis, James Peck / Step back baby: Blair, Sunny / This is the end: Reed, James / Jake head boogie: Hopkins, Lightnin' / Down in New Orleans: Smith, Little George / Monte Carlo: Dixie Blues Boys / Doin' the town: Dixon, Floyd / Just got in from Texas: Gordon, Rosco / Big mouth: Nelson, Jimmy 'T-99' / Have you ever: Walton, Mercy Dee / Sputterin' blues: Robertson, Walter / Prowling blues: Fuller, Johnny / Going to New Orleans: Tanner, Kid / Good morning little angel: Hill-Louis, Joe / Panic's on: McCracklin, Jimmy / What's the matter with you: Horton, Big Walter

CDCH 216 / Jul '87 / Ace

☐ **50'S - R & B VOCAL GROUPS, THE**

Rock bottom: Rams / Hold me, thrill me, chill me: Flairs / My darling, my sweet: Flairs / I made a vow: Robins / Please remember my heart: Five Bells / My cutie pie: Five Bells / Girl in my dreams: Cliques / Even since you've been gone: Hawks / It's all over: Hawks / Please don't go: Chanters / Tick tock: Marvin & Johnny / Why did I fall in love: Jacks / Sweet thing: Maye, Arthur Lee & The Crowns / Hands across the table: Cadets / Hey Rube: Rocketeers / It won't take long/Native girl: Native Boys / Farewell: Relf, Bobby & The Laurels / At last: Berry, Richard & the Dreamers / Please please baby: Five Hearts / Love me love me love me: Chimes / I love you, yes I do: Marvin, Johnny

CDCH 212 / Jul '87 / Ace

☐ **50'S - ROCKABILLY FEVER, THE**

I guess it's meant that way: Cupp, Pat / Long gone daddy: Cupp, Pat / Don't do me no wrong: Cupp, Pat / Everybody's movin': Glenn, Glen / If I had me a woman: Glenn, Glen / I don't know when: Harris, Hal / True affection: Johnson, Byron / Be boppin' daddy: Cole, Les & The Echoes / Rock little baby: Cole, Les & The Echoes / My big fat baby: Hall, Sonny & The Echoes / Rock my warriors rock: Jackson, Joe / Snake eyed mama: Cole, Don / Nuthin' but a nuthin': Stewart, Jimmy & His Nighthawks / Wild wild party: Feathers, Charlie / Pink cadillac: Todd, Johnny / Slippin' and slidin': Davis, Link / All the time: LaBeef, Sleepy / Go home letter: Barber, Glen / Boppin' wigwam Willie: Scott, Ray / I can't find the doorknob: Jimmy & Johnny / Jitterbop baby: Harris, Hal / Little bit more: LaBeef, Sleepy

CDCH 218 / Jul '87 / Ace

☐ **52 SHADES OF ORANGE (2CD Set)**

CDULSTER 001 / Apr '96 / Outlet

☐ **52ND STREET (The Street Of Jazz/2CD Set)**

Tea for two: Tatum, Art / Let's have a jubilee: Prima, Louis & His New Orleans Gang / Honeysuckle rose: Norvo, Red / Liza: Wilson, Teddy / I'm coming Virginia: Berigan, Bunny / Music goes 'round and around: Dorsey, Tommy & His Clambake Seven / Swingin' on that famous door: Delta Four / I'se a-muggin': Smith, Stuff & His Onyx Club Boys / Swingin' for joy: Williams, Mary Lou / Fine romance: Holiday, Billie / Loch Lomond: Sullivan, Maxine / Morning air: Smith, Willie 'The Lion' / Flat foot floogie: Slim & Slam / Jim jam stomp: Marsala, Joe / Jumpin' at the Woodside: Basie, Count & His Orchestra / Yacht club swing: Waller, Fats & His Rhythm / At the Woodchopper's ball: Herman, Woody & His Orchestra / Cherokee: Barnet, Charlie Orchestra / Ja-Da: Watson, Leo / Let's fly away: Wiley, Lee / Hot and bothered: Profit, Clarence / Front and centre: Kirby, John Sextet / Body and soul: Hawkins, Coleman / South: Page, Hot Lips / Hit that jive, Jack: Cole, Nat 'King' Trio / Flying home: Hampton, Lionel / Desert sands: Smith, Stuff Trio / Moonglow: Tatum, Art Trio / Fiesta in brass: Eldridge, Roy / I surrender dear: Webster, Ben / Loverman: Holiday, Billie / Blue Harlem: Quebec, Ike Quintet / I may be wrong: Brown, Pete / Seven come eleven: Norvo, Red Quintet / Fast company: Garner, Erroll / Gutbucket blues: Hodes, Art Blue Five / I want to talk about you: Eckstine, Billy & His Orchestra / Hot house: Gillespie, Dizzy / Three blind micesky: Stewart, Slam / Blue and sentimental: Byas, Don / Spotlite: Hawkins, Coleman / Long tall Dexter: Gordon, Dexter / 52nd Street theme: Gillespie, Dizzy / All too soon: Vaughan, Sarah

CDGR 1812 / Nov '97 / Charly

☐ **55 MILES FROM TEXACO**

EFA 06187CD / Jul '93 / House In Motion

☐ **60 GREAT BLUES RECORDINGS (3CD Set)**

Jealous woman: Walker, T-Bone / I'm sinking: Fulson, Lowell / Same old lonesome day: Fulson, Lowell / Rocks in my pillow: Brown, Roy / We can't make it: King, B.B. / Time to say goodbye: King, B.B. / Please love me: King, B.B. / Past day: King, B.B. / My own fault darlin': King, B.B. / TB blues: Witherspoon, Jimmy / I'm going around in circles: Witherspoon, Jimmy / Telephone blues: Smith, George / Women in my life: Hooker, John Lee / Boogie chillun: Hooker, John Lee / Crawlin' kingsnake: Hooker, John Lee / Heartache baby: Hill-Louis, Joe / Walkin' talkin' blues: Hill-Louis, Joe / Going down slow: Hill-Louis, Joe / When night falls: Carter, Goree / Sinful woman: James, Elmore / I believe: James, Elmore / Dust my blues: James, Elmore / Sho' nuff I do: James, Elmore / That's all I care: Dixon, Floyd / Houston jump: Dixon, Floyd / Draftin' blues: Dixon, Floyd / Hey Mr. Porter: Smith, George / Good lovin': Bland, Bobby / Summertime: King, Saunders / Everything about midnight: King, Saunders / I'm so worried: King, Saunders / I ain't in the mood: Humes, Helen / Central Avenue blues: Crayton, Pee Wee / If that's the way you feel: Champion, Mickey / Best friend: Champion, Mickey / Gene's guitar blues: Phillips, Gene / Gene jumps the blues: Phillips, Gene / Jockey blues: Turner, 'Big' Joe / Playful baby: Turner, 'Big' Joe / Johnny's lowdown blues: Fuller, Johnny / Riding in the moonlight: Howlin' Wolf / How many more times: Wilson, Smokey / Straighten up baby: Wilson, Smokey / Standing in the backdoor crying: Thomas, Lafayette / Tired of everybody: Parker, Johnny / Dr. Brown: Reed, James / Lonesome dog blues: Hopkins, Lightnin' / Jake Head boogie: Hopkins, Lightnin' / Mississippi blues: Dixon, Floyd Trio / John Henry: Pinetop Slim / Thrill is gone: Hawkins, Roy / Tennessee woman: Robinson, Fenton / Applejack boogie: Pinetop Slim / Hardhearted woman: Horton, Big Walter / Black gal: Horton, Big Walter / Big chested mama: Cotton, Sylvester / Love me baby: Bland, Bobby & Junior Parker / I may be crazy baby but (I ain't no fool): Smith, Geechie / Cold blooded woman: Great Gates / I cried: Ace, Johnny

CBOXCD 3 / Jan '92 / Cascade

☐ **60 HITS OF THE 1960'S (2CD Set)**

You'll never walk alone: Gerry & The Pacemakers / Silence is golden: Tremeloes / Runaway: Shannon, Del / Happy birthday sweet sixteen: Sedaka, Neil / Wild thing: Troggs / I'm into something good: Herman's Hermits / Rubber ball: Vee, Bobby / Something's gotten hold of my heart: Pitney, Gene / I'm sorry: Lee, Brenda / Da doo ron ron: Crystals / When a man loves a woman: Sledge, Percy / I'm telling you now: Freddie & The Dreamers / Because they're young: Eddy, Duane / Little town flirt: Shannon, Del / It's my party: Gore, Lesley / Breaking up is hard to do: Sedaka, Neil / Walkin' back to happiness: Shapiro, Helen / Wishin' and hopin': Merseybeats / Rescue me: Bass, Fontella / Dancing in the street: Reeves, Martha / Do you want to know a secret: Kramer, Billy J. / Tossing and turning: Ivy League / Little loving: Fourmost / Um um um um um um: Fontana, Wayne / You were made for me: Freddie & The Dreamers / Just like eddie: Heinz / Do you love me: Poole, Brian / Pied piper: St. Peters, Crispian / Bobby's girl: Maughan, Susan / Save the last dance for me: Drifters / Juliet: Four Pennies / Hello little girl: Fourmost / Little children: Kramer, Billy J. / My guy: Wells, Mary / But I do: Henry, Clarence 'Frogman' / Crying game: Berry, Dave / Wimoweh: Denver, Karl / Tell me when: Applejacks / Baby now that I've found you: Foundations / Jesamine: Casuals / Let's have a party: Jackson, Wanda / My boyfriend's back: Angels / Tobacco road: Nashville Teens / With a girl like you: Troggs / Hats off to larry: Shannon, Del / Ferry 'cross the mersey: Gerry & The Pacemakers / Coming on strong: Lee, Brenda / Ob la di ob la da: Marmalade / Viva bobby joe: Equals / Then he kissed me: Crystals / He's so fine: Chiffons / Hippy hippy shake: Swinging Blue Jeans / Swiss maid: Shannon, Del / If I were a carpenter: Darin, Bobby / (Dance with) The guitar man: Eddy, Duane / Sea of heartbreak: Gibson, Don / Love is all around: Troggs / Only sixteen: Cooke, Sam / I heard it through the grapevine: Gaye, Marvin / Leader of the pack: Shangri-Las

55173 / 29 Sep '97 / Music

☐ **60'S - IN SEARCH OF SPACE (3CD Set)**

DTKBOX 73 / 13 Oct '97 / Dressed To Kill

☐ **60'S APOCALYPSE (2CD Set)**

AOP 51 / Apr '97 / Age Of Panik

☐ **60'S ARCHIVES VOL.1 - SOUND OF THE SIXTIES**

842039 / Jun '94 / EVA

☐ **60'S ARCHIVES VOL.2 - SCARCE GARAGE RECORDS**

842634 / May '94 / EVA

☐ **60'S ARCHIVES VOL.2 - TEXAS PUNK**

842040 / Jun '94 / EVA

☐ **60'S ARCHIVES VOL.3 - LOUISIANA PUNK**

842041 / Jun '94 / EVA

☐ **60'S ARCHIVES VOL.4 - FLORIDA & NEW MEXICO PUNK**

842042 / Jun '94 / EVA

☐ **60'S ARCHIVES VOL.5 - US PUNK FROM THE 60'S**

842043 / Jun '94 / EVA

☐ **60'S ARCHIVES VOL.6**

EVA 8420448 / Nov '94 / EVA

☐ **60'S ARCHIVES VOL.7 - MICHIGAN PUNK**

842045 / Jun '94 / EVA

☐ **60'S ARCHIVES VOL.8 - ACID TRIPS & HEAVY SOUNDS**

842046 / May '94 / EVA

☐ 60'S BEAT ITALIANO VOL.1
GHAS 5004CD / 15 Dec '97 / Get Hip

☐ 60'S CLASSICS
PDSCD 505 / Sep '97 / Pulse

☐ 60'S COLLECTION (3CD Set)
You really got me: *Kinks* / Sweets for my sweet: *Searchers* / (There's) always something there to remind me: *Shaw, Sandie* / Here comes my baby: *Tremeloes* / Catch the wind: *Donovan* / Downtown: *Clark, Petula* / 24 hours from Tulsa: *Pitney, Gene* / Go now: *Moody Blues* / Ain't nothin' but a house party: *Showstoppers* / Baby, now that I've found you: *Foundations* / Pictures of matchstick men: *Status Quo* / Summer in the city: *Lovin' Spoonful* / Even the bad times are good: *Tremeloes* / Here comes the nice: *Small Faces* / Out of time: *Farlowe, Chris* / That girl belongs to yesterday: *Pitney, Gene* / Sugar and spice: *Searchers* / Michelle: *Overlanders* / This is my song: *Clark, Petula* / First cut is the deepest: *Arnold, P.P.* / Needles and pins: *Searchers* / Silence is golden: *Tremeloes* / All day and all of the night: *Kinks* / I couldn't live without your love: *Clark, Petula* / Build me up buttercup: *Foundations* / Let the heartaches begin: *Baldry, Long John* / Colours: *Donovan* / Itchykoo park: *Small Faces* / Girl don't come: *Shaw, Sandie* / I'm gonna be strong: *Pitney, Gene* / Man of the world: *Fleetwood Mac* / Daydream: *Lovin' Spoonful* / Lazy sunday: *Small Faces* / Sunny afternoon: *Kinks* / Ice in the sun: *Status Quo* / Suddenly you left me: *Tremeloes* / When you walk in the room: *Searchers* / Don't sleep in the subway: *Clark, Petula* / Only love can break your heart: *Pitney, Gene* / America/Second amendment: *Nice* / Waterloo sunset: *Kinks* / Susannah's still alive: *Davies, Dave* / Tomorrow: *Shaw, Sandie* / (Call me) number one: *Tremeloes* / Universal: *Small Faces* / Other man's grass (is always greener): *Clark, Petula* / Something's gotten hold of my heart: *Pitney, Gene* / I'm gonna make you mine: *Christie, Lou* / Make me an island: *Dolan, Joe* / It's too late now: *Baldry, Long John* / Judy in disguise: *Fred, John & The Playboys* / Simon says: *1910 Fruitgum Company* / Oh happy days: *Hawkins, Edwin Singers* / Just one smile: *Pitney, Gene* / Puppet on a string: *Shaw, Sandie* / In the bad, bad old days (before you loved me): *Foundations* / Green tambourine: *Lemon Pipers* / Death of a clown: *Davies, Dave* / Let's go to San Francisco: *Flowerpot Men* / Don't throw your love away: *Searchers*
PBXCD 501 / Nov '96 / Pulse

☐ 60'S COLLECTION VOL.1
Runaway / He's so fine / Will you love me tomorrow / 24 Hours from Tulsa / Leader of the pack / Every beat of my heart / Fools rush in / Under the boardwalk / Rubber ball / Harbour lights / Walk - don't run / Mr. Bass Man / Judy in disguise / I believe / Tossin' and turnin' / Don't let the sun catch you crying / Silhouettes / Tobacco road / Baby, now that I've found you / Love is all around
QED 001 / Nov '96 / Tring

☐ 60'S COLLECTION VOL.2
Remember (walkin' in the sand) / Surfin' safari / I'm gonna be strong / Chapel of love / Duke of Earl / Oh no, not my baby / Barefootin' / Soldier boy / Hats off to Larry / Save the last dance for me / Ramona / Hippy hippy shake / You'll never walk alone / There's a kind of hush / Wild thing / Here it comes again / Tell Laura I love her / Walkin' back to happiness / Hurt / Dizzy
QED 002 / Nov '96 / Tring

☐ 60'S COLLECTION, THE (3CD Set)
KBOX 368 / Aug '97 / Collection

☐ 60'S COLLECTION, THE (4CD Set)
SUMBX 4005 / Jan '98 / Summit

☐ 60'S DANCE PARTY: LET'S DANCE
MU 5002 / Oct '92 / Musketeer

☐ 60'S DECADE, THE (3CD Set)
TTP 002 / Nov '92 / Tring

☐ 60'S HIT BOX, THE (3CD Set)
How do you do it: *Gerry & The Pacemakers* / Twist: *Checker, Chubby* / Save the last dance for me: *Drifters* / Let's think about living: *Luman, Bob* / Will you love me tomorrow: *Shirelles* / Are you sure: *Allisons* / Blue moon: *Marcels* / Dizzy: *Roe, Tommy* / If I had a hammer: *Lopez, Trini* / Keep searchin' (we'll follow the sun): *Shannon, Del* / Tobacco road: *Nashville Teens* / My Guy: *Wells, Mary* / We gotta get out of this place: *Animals* / I'm telling you now: *Freddie & The Dreamers* / Birds and the bees: *Akens, Jewel* / She's not there: *Zombies* / What becomes of the broken hearted: *Ruffin, Jimmy* / Baby now that I've found you: *Foundations* / Indian reservation: *Fardon, Don* / Games people play: *South, Joe* / Let's twist again: *Checker, Chubby* / Poetry in motion: *Tillotson, Johnny* / But I do: *Henry, Clarence* / Telstar: *Tornados* / Da do ron ron: *Crystals* / Runaway: *Shannon, Del* / Surf city: *Jan & Dean* / Little children: *Kramer, Billy J.* / Leader of the pack: *Shangri-Las* / House of the rising sun: *Animals* / Mr. Tambourine man: *Byrds* / Hold me: *Proby, P.J.* / Wild thing: *Troggs* / Letter: *Box Tops* / Judy in disguise: *Fred, John & His Playboy Band* / Happy together: *Turtles* / Those were the days: *Hopkin, Mary* / Young girl: *Puckett, Gary & The Union Gap* / You were on my mind: *St. Peters, Crispian* / Crying game: *Berry, Dave* / Rubber ball: *Vee, Bobby* / Hey baby: *Channel, Bruce* / Sheila: *Roe, Tommy* / Hippy hippy shake: *Swinging Blue Jeans* / It's my party: *Gore, Lesley* / I'm in love: *Fourmost* / With a girl like you: *Troggs* / When a man loves a woman: *Sledge, Percy* / Build me up buttercup: *Foundations* / Here comes my baby: *Tremeloes* / Elenore: *Turtles* / Jesamine: *Casuals* / Ob la di ob la da: *Marmalade* / Good morning starshine: *Oliver* / Baby come back: *Equals* / Soul man: *Sam & Dave* / You've got your troubles: *Fortunes* / Dancing in the street: *Reeves, Martha*
390532 / Aug '97 / Hallmark

☐ 60'S HITS COLLECTION: AT THE HOP
Leader of the pack: *Shangri-Las* / Let's twist again: *Checker, Chubby* / Then he kissed me: *Crystals* / Runaround Sue: *Dion* / Good golly Miss Molly: *Little Richard* / Blueberry Hill: *Domino, Fats*
MU 8006 / Nov '93 / Musketeer

☐ 60'S HITS COLLECTION: DA DOO RON RON
Sweet talking guy: *Chiffons* / Tell Laura I love her: *Valance, Ricky* / Rhythm of the rain: *Cascades* / Will you still love me tomorrow: *Shirelles* / Chapel of love: *Dixie Cups* / Surfin' safari: *Beach Boys*
MU 8005 / Dec '93 / Musketeer

☐ 60'S HITS COLLECTION: DOWNTOWN
Downtown: *Clark, Petula* / Ferry 'cross the Mersey: *Gerry & The Pacemakers* / Happy together: *Turtles* / Young girl: *Puckett, Gary* / Calender girl: *Sedaka, Neil* / Hold me: *Proby, P.J.*
MU 8002 / Nov '93 / Musketeer

☐ 60'S HITS COLLECTION: EVERLASTING LOVE
Wild thing: *Troggs* / Breaking up is hard to do: *Sedaka, Neil* / Everlasting love: *Love Affair* / Walkin' back to happiness: *Shapiro, Helen* / Crying game: *Berry, Dave* / California dreamin': *Mamas & The Papas*
MU 8001 / Nov '93 / Musketeer

☐ 60'S HITS COLLECTION: SILENCE IS GOLDEN
Don't take your love to town: *Rogers, Kenny* / Silence is golden: *Tremeloes* / Save the last dance for me: *Drifters* / No milk today: *Herman's Hermits* / Wishin' and hopin': *Merseybeats* / Bobby's girl: *Maughan, Susan*
MU 8004 / Nov '93 / Musketeer

☐ 60'S HITS COLLECTION: UP ON THE ROOF
I'm into something good: *Herman's Hermits* / Do you love me: *Poole, Brian* / Sugar sugar: *Archies* / Hello Mary Lou: *Nelson, Rick* / Night has a thousand eyes: *Vee, Bobby* / Moon river: *Williams, Danny*
MU 7003
MU 8003 / Nov '93 / Musketeer

☐ 60'S LOVE SONGS: DRIFT AWAY
MU 5001 / Oct '92 / Musketeer

☐ 60'S MEGAMIXES VOL.1
MACCD 303 / Aug '96 / Autograph

☐ 60'S MEGAMIXES VOL.2
MACCD 304 / Aug '96 / Autograph

☐ 60'S MIXES
JHD 085 / Mar '93 / Tring

☐ 60'S POP CLASSICS
Everybody's talking: *Nilsson, Harry* / In the year 2525: *Zager & Evans* / If paradise is half as nice: *Amen Corner* / Light my fire: *Feliciano, Jose* / Go now: *Moody Blues* / Come back and shake me: *Rodgers, Clodagh* / Daydream: *Lovin' Spoonful* / Letter: *Box Tops* / Captain of your ship: *Reparata & The Delrons* / Aquarius: *Fifth Dimension* / Let the sunshine in: *Fifth Dimension* / Ain't got no...I got life: *Simone, Nina* / Breaking up is hard to do: *Sedaka, Neil* / Didn't I blow your mind this time: *Delfonics* / Working in a coalmine: *Dorsey, Lee* / Keep on: *Channel, Bruce* / Itchycoo park: *Small Faces* / Grazing in the grass: *Friends Of Distinction* / Ice in the sun: *Status Quo*
74321449232 / Feb '97 / Camden

☐ 60'S POP CLASSICS VOL.2
Go now: *Moody Blues* / Man of the world: *Fleetwood Mac* / In the year 2525: *Zager & Evans* / Captain of your ship: *Reparata & The Delrons* / Yeah yeah: *Fame, Georgie* / Out of time: *Farlowe, Chris* / I'm a believer: *Monkees* / (If paradise is) half as nice: *Amen Corner* / Light my fire: *Feliciano, Jose* / Harlem shuffle: *Bob & Earl* / Leader of the pack: *Shangri-Las* / I'm believer: *Monkees*
74321339252 / Jan '96 / Camden

☐ 60'S POP CLASSICS VOL.3
Good bad and the ugly: *Montenegro, Hugo* / Ain't got no - I got life: *Simone, Nina* / Eve of destruction: *McGuire, Barry* / I'm your puppet: *Purify, James & Bobby* / Simon says: *1910 Fruitgum Company* / Waterloo sunset: *Kinks* / Catch the wind: *Donovan* / Needles and pions: *Searchers* / Yummy yummy yummy: *Ohio Express* / First cut is the deepest: *Arnold, P.P.* / Let the heartache begin: *Baldry, Long John* / Aquarius/Let the sun shine: *5th Dimension*
74321339262 / Jan '96 / Camden

☐ 60'S SMASH HITS VOL.1 (2CD Set)
Let it be me: *Everly Brothers* / There goes my heart again: *Domino, Fats* / Keep searching (we'll follow the sun): *Shannon, Del* / It keeps on a-hurtin': *Tillotson, Johnny* / Birds and the bees: *Akens, Jewel* / I'm gonna knock on your door: *Hodges, Eddie* / It's in his kiss (shoop shoop song): *Everett, Betty* / My girl: *Temptations* / Twist and shout: *Isley Brothers* / Foolish little girl: *Shirelles* / Only love can break a heart: *Pitney, Gene* / Bend it: *Dave Dee, Dozy, Beaky, Mick & Tich* / Reflections of my life: *Marmalade* / Green tambourine: *Lemon Pipers* / Will you still love me tomorrow: *Shirelles* / Happy together: *Turtles* / Hats off to Larry: *Shannon, Del* / Legend of Xanadu: *Dave Dee, Dozy, Beaky, Mick & Tich* / When will I be loved: *Everly Brothers* / Hold what you got: *Tex, Joe* / Hooked on a feeling: *Thomas, B.J.* / Red sails in the sunset: *Thomas, B.J.* / Ob la di ob la da: *Marmalade* / 24 hours from Tulsa: *Pitney, Gene* / Talk back tremblin' lips: *Tillotson, Johnny* / King of the road: *Miller, Roger* / Gitarzan: *Stevens, Ray* / Yakety sax: *Randolph, Boots*
SD 885362 / 2 Feb '98 / Disky

☐ 60'S SMASH HITS VOL.2 (2CD Set)
It hurts to be in love: *Pitney, Gene* / Runaway: *Shannon, Del* / Poetry in motion: *Tillotson, Johnny* / Let's dance: *Montez, Chris* / I'm gonna make you mine: *Christie, Lou* / Yummy, yummy, yummy: *Ohio Express* / Simon says: *1910 Fruitgum Company* / Sugar sugar: *Archies* / Daydream: *Lovin' Spoonful* / Raindrops keep falling on my head: *Thomas, B.J.* / Ahab the Arab: *Stevens, Ray* / You got what it takes: *Tex, Joe* / Ain't too proud to beg: *Temptations* / Dedicated to the one I love: *Shirelles* / All I have to do is dream: *Everly Brothers* / Heartbreak Hill: *Domino, Fats* / Only a fool: *Lee, Byron & Mighty Sparrow* / Detroit city: *Bare, Bobby* / Always something there to remind me: *Shaw, Sandie* / Don't throw away all those teardrops: *Avalon, Frankie* / String along: *Fabian* / Without you: *Tillotson, Johnny* / Louie Louie: *Kingsmen* / Zabadak: *Dave Dee, Dozy, Beaky, Mick & Tich* / Light my fire: *Feliciano, Jose* / Summer in the city: *Lovin' Spoonful* / House of the rising sun: *Animals* / Oh happy day: *Hawkins, Edwin Singers*
SD 885442 / 2 Feb '98 / Disky

☐ 60'S SUMMER MIX VOL.1 (2CD Set)
TCD 2908 / Jun '97 / Telstar

☐ 60'S SUMMER MIX VOL.2 (2CD Set)
It's not unusual: *Jones, Tom* / I'm a believer: *Monkees* / (I got you) I feel good: *Brown, James* / Think: *Franklin, Aretha* / Everybody needs somebody: *Burke, Solomon* / These boots are made for walking: *Sinatra, Nancy* / Guaglione: *Prado, Perez* / All or nothing: *Small Faces* / Waterloo sunset: *Kinks* / Monday Monday: *Mamas & The Papas* / Dream a little dream of me: *Mama Cass* / More I see you: *Montez, Chris* / In the midnight hour: *Pickett, Wilson* / Soul finger: *Bar-Kays* / Funky nassau: *Beginning Of The End* / Aquarius: *5th Dimension* / Needles and pins: *Searchers* / Move on up: *Mayfield, Curtis* / Wonderful world: *Armstrong, Louis* / You can get it if you really want: *Dekker, Desmond* / In the summertime: *Mungo Jerry* / Something stupid: *Sinatra, Frank & Nancy* / Puppet on a string: *Shaw, Sandie* / First cut is the deepest: *Arnold, P.P.* / Born to be wild: *Steppenwolf* / Wipe out: *Surfaris* / Bullit: *Schifrin, Lalo* / For what it's worth: *Buffalo Springfield* / I got you babe: *Sonny & Cher* / What I'd say: *Charles, Ray* / Shapes of things: *Yardbirds* / Louie Louie: *Kingsmen* / Mas que nada: *Sounds Orchestral* / Can't take my eyes off of you: *Williams, Andy* / 54321: *Manfred Mann* / Higher and higher: *Wilson, Jackie* / As tears go by: *Faithfull, Marianne* / 123: *Lewis, Ramsey* / Twist and shout: *Isley Brothers* / I only want to be with you: *Springfield, Dusty* / Do you know the way to San Jose: *Warwick, Dionne* / California girls: *Beach Boys* / Summer holiday: *Richard, Cliff* / Turn turn turn: *Byrds*
TTVCD 2972 / 3 Aug '98 / Telstar TV

☐ 60'S SUMMER OF LOVE
Daydream: *Lovin' Spoonful* / Sunny afternoon: *Kinks* / Whiter shade of pale: *Procol Harum* / Itchycoo park: *Small Faces* / Death of a clown: *Davies, Dave* / Blackberry way: *Move* / Lady Jane: *Garrick, David* / Man of the world: *Fleetwood Mac* / Elenore: *Turtles* / Summer in the city: *Lovin' Spoonful* / Green tambourine: *Lemon Pipers* / For your love: *Yardbirds* / Handbags and gladrags: *Farlowe, Chris* / Waterloo sunset: *Kinks* / Happy together: *Turtles* / Let's go to San Francisco: *Flowerpot Men* / Woodstock: *Matthew's Southern Comfort*
PWKS 4182 / Feb '96 / Carlton

☐ 60'S THE HITS GO ON: LOVE IS ALL AROUND
MU 5050 / Oct '92 / Musketeer

☐ 60'S UK HITS COLLECTION: TWIST AND SHOUT
MU 5053 / Oct '92 / Musketeer

☐ 60'S USA HITS
MACCD 116 / Aug '96 / Autograph

☐ 60'S USA HITS COLLECTION: SWEET TALKIN' GUY
MU 5052 / Oct '92 / Musketeer

☐ 60'S VOL.1, THE
Speedy gonzales: *Boone, Pat* / Twist: *Checker, Chubby* / Wild one: *Rydell, Bobby* / Swingin' school: *Rydell, Bobby* / Good golly miss molly: *Swinging Blue Jeans* / Let's have a party: *Jackson, Wanda* / Pipeline: *Chantays* / Hats off to Larry: *Shannon, Del* / Let's twist again: *Checker, Chubby* / Bread and butter: *Newbeats* / Here comes my baby: *Tremeloes* / One fine day: *Chiffons* / I'm the one: *Gerry & The Pacemakers* / Peppermint Twist: *Joey Dee and the Starliters* / Mr. Bass man: *Cymbal, Johnny* / You were on my mind: *Crispin St Peters* / Up on the roof: *Drifters* / Volare: *Rydell, Bobby* / Deep Purple: *Tempo, Nino* / Sheila: *Roe, Tommy* / Corina, corina: *Peterson, Ray* / Hey baby: *Channel, Bruce* / Do you want to know a secret: *Kramer, Billy J.* / Saturday night at the movies: *Drifters* / Keep searchin' (we'll follow the sun): *Shannon, Del* / Save the last dance for me: *Drifters* / Runaway: *Shannon, Del* / Hippy hippy shake: *Swinging Blue Jeans* / Surf city: *Jan & Dean* / Little old lady from Pasadena: *Jan & Dean*
ECD 3142 / Mar '95 / K-Tel

☐ 60'S VOL.2, THE
Dizzy: *Roe, Tommy* / Silence is golden: *Tremeloes* / Don't let the sun catch you crying: *Gerry & The Pacemakers* / (Don't know why) but I do: *Henry, Clarence 'Frogman'* / Trains and boats and planes: *Kramer, Billy J.* / Sweet pea: *Roe, Tommy* / Ob-la-di, ob-la-da: *Marmalade* / Because they're young: *Eddy, Duane* / I think of you: *Merseybeats* / Under the boardwalk: *Drifters* / Good morning starshine: *Oliver* / Little town flirt: *Shannon, Del* / Pied Piper: *St. Peters, Crispian* / Chapel of love: *Dixie Cups* / Blue moon: *Marcels* / Those oldies but goodies (remind me of you): *Little Caesar & The Romans* / Hey Paula: *Paul & Paula* / Devil or angel: *Vee, Bobby* / So much in love: *Tymes* / Forget him: *Rydell, Bobby* / Someone someone: *Poole, Brian* / Down in the boondocks: *Royal, Billy Joe* / Games people play: *South, Joe* / Everybody: *Roe, Tommy* / Those were the days: *Hopkin, Mary* / Groovy kind of love: *Fontana, Wayne* / Goin out of my head: *Little Anthony & The Imperials* / Zip a dee-doo-dah: *Soxx, Bob B. & The Blue Jeans* / More than I can say: *Vee, Bobby* / Run to him: *Vee, Bobby*
ECD 3143 / Mar '95 / K-Tel

☐ 60'S YEARS VOL.1
519382 / Jul '97 / Magic

☐ 60'S YEARS VOL.2
523302 / Jul '97 / Magic

☐ 60'S YEARS VOL.3
176162 / Jul '97 / Magic

☐ 60'S YEARS VOL.5
177022 / 1 Dec '97 / Magic

☐ 60'S YEARS VOL.6
176892 / 5 Jan '98 / Magic

☐ 60S COLLECTION (3CD Set)
TBXCD 501 / Jan '96 / TrueTrax

☐ 65 RAP AND HARDCORE DANCE ORIGINALS (4CD Set)
Don't stop the music: *Carroll, Dina & Simon Harris* / Respect due: *Daddy Freddie & Heavy D/Frankie Paul* / Cooling in paradise: *Thrashpack* / These are the breaks: *DJ Hanway* / Style wars: *Hijack* / Give it a rest: *She Rockers & Betty Boo* / Powerplay megamix: *Harris, Simon* / My whole life: *Spyder D* / Whole lotta love: *Vicious Rumour Club* / Shake it up: *Duke* / Burial proceedings in the course of three nights: *3 Knights* / Go freddy go: *Daddy Freddie* / Untitled: *Hardnoise* / Boingsville: *Thrashpack* / Coronation: *Royal Rhymes* / DC Jail: *DJ Daddy* / Movement: *SL Troopers* / Back 2 tha bass: *Harris, Simon* / Ill tip: *Einstein* / Free: *MC Duke* / Lyrical culture: *Demon Boyz* / Megamix: *Sirrah, Nomis* / Ragamuffin hip hop: *Asher D & Daddy Freddie* / Who's in the house: *45 King* / Trigger happy: *Thrashpack* / Tame 1 unleashed: *Lady Tame* / Theme from disturbing the peace: *Harris, Simon* / I'm riffin': *Duke* / My beat: *Father MC* / Sparky's in the place: *Sparky D* / Hits from small arms fire: *First Frontal Assault* / Every nigga's a star: *Einstein* / Return of the dread 1: *Duke* / Dancehall clash: *Tenor Fly & Daddy Freddy* / Runaway love: *Harris, Simon & Einstein* / Summertime: *Asher D & Daddy Freddie* / Onslaught: *Standing Ovation* / Bite of love doomsday of rap: *Hijack* / Shok da house: *Harris, Simon* / This is a jam: *Demon Boyz* / Rhymes unlimited: *Einstein* / Like a bike: *Asher D* / Roughneck nuh ramp: *Daddy Freddie & Tenor Fly* / Freestyle part 1: *Duke & Merlin* / Freestyle part 2: *Duke & Merlin* / Brutality: *Asher D & Daddy Freddie* / Silk smooth: *Monte Luv & DJ Rob* / Freddy's back: *Daddy Freddie & Duke* / Ragga house: *Harris, Simon & Daddy Freddy* / Shotgun wedding: *Leslie Lyrics* / Can I get a witness: *Einstein* / My policy: *Sharkey* / Live jam: *Daddy Freddie* / Rougher than an animal: *Demon Boyz* / Never made me a man: *Big Kraze* / Friday night Saturday morning: *Einstein* / This is serious: *Harris, Simon* / Dog catcher: *Duke* / Power of evil: *Predator* / Hypnotic FX: *Infamix* / Rhymes are smokin': *Einstein* / Ragamuffin duo take charge: *Asher D & Daddy Freddie* / Final conflict: *Duke*
TFP 041 / Apr '95 / Tring

☐ 67/97 NOVOPHONIC
NPH 697CD / 16 Jul '97 / Novophonic

☐ 70'S BLOCKBUSTERS
Blockbuster: *Sweet* / Rivers of Babylon: *Boney M* / All by myself: *Carmen, Eric* / Bye bye baby: *Bay City Rollers* / Native New Yorker: *Odyssey* / Seasons in the sun: *Jacks, Terry* / Ms Grace: *Tymes* / Woman in love: *Three Degrees* / New York, New York: *Kenny, Gerard* / Ready or not here I come: *Delfonics* / Every day hurts: *Sad Cafe* / Without you: *Nilsson, Harry* / Like sister and brother: *Drifters* / If you think you know how to love me: *Smokie* / Torn between two lovers: *McGregor, Mary* / It's a heartache: *Tyler, Bonnie* / I can't stand the rain: *Eruption* / Yes sir I can boogie: *Baccara*
74321449242 / Feb '97 / Camden

☐ 70'S COLLECTION (3CD Set)
TBXCD 502 / Jan '96 / TrueTrax

☐ 70'S COLLECTION (3CD Set)
Down the dustpipe: *Status Quo* / Apeman: *Kinks* / After the goldrush: *Prelude* / In the summertime: *Mungo Jerry* / (It's like a) sad old kind of movie: *Pickettywitch* / You don't mess around with Jim: *Croce, Jim* / Why did you do it: *Stretch* / This flight tonight: *Nazareth* / Swing your daddy: *Gilstrap, Jim* / Midnight train to Georgia: *Knight, Gladys & The Pips* / Natural born boogie: *Humble Pie* / Love's gotta hold on me: *Dollar* / Beach baby: *First Class* / Bad, bad Leroy Brown: *Croce, Jim* / Me and my life: *Tremeloes* / Sky high: *Jigsaw* / Man who sold the world: *Lulu* / You'll never know what your missing: *Real Thing* / Egyptian reggae: *Richman, Jonathan* / Summer of my life: *May, Simon* / It's a heartache: *Tyler, Bonnie* / Sunshine day: *Osibisa* / Operator (that's not the way it feels): *Croce, Jim* / Best thing that ever happened to me: *Knight, Gladys & The Pips* / Shooting star: *Dollar* / Making up again: *Goldie* / You to me are eveything: *Real Thing* / Girls: *Moments* / Show me you're a woman: *Mud* / Isn't she lovely: *Parton, David* / Lady rose: *Mungo Jerry* / So sad the song: *Knight, Gladys & The Pips* / Purely by coincidence: *Sweet Sensation* / In my chair: *Status Quo* / In Zaire: *Wakelin, Johnny* / Broken down angel: *Nazareth* / Now is the time: *James, Jimmy* / I'll have to say I love you with a song: *Croce, Jim* / Car 67: *Driver 67* / Can't get by without you: *Real Thing* / I wanna hold your hand: *Dollar* / Long legged woman dressed in black: *Mungo Jerry* / L-I-lucy: *Mud* / Mean girl: *Status Quo* / Love hurts: *Nazareth* / Roadrunner: *Richman, Jonathan* / Come back and finish what you started: *Knight, Gladys & The Pips* / Do you wanna dance: *Blue, Barry* / Lost in France: *Tyler, Bonnie* / This is it: *Moore, Melba* / I'm doin' fine now: *New York City* / Lean on me: *Mud* / Jack in the box: *Moments* / More, more, more: *True, Andrea Connection* / I got a name: *Croce, Jim* / Baby don't change your mind: *Knight, Gladys & The Pips* / That same old feeling: *Pickettywitch* / My white bicycle: *Nazareth* / Lola: *Kinks* / (Dancing) on a saturday night: *Blue, Barry*
PBXCD 502 / Nov '96 / Pulse

☐ 70'S COLLECTION VOL.1
Band of gold: *Payne, Freda* / I can do it: *Rubettes* / Angel face: *Glitter Band* / I only wanna be with you: *Bay City Rollers* / I love to love (but my baby just loves to dance): *Charles, Tina* / I wanna dance wit' choo: *Disco Tex & The Sexolettes* / Greased lightnin': *Travolta, John* / (Dancing) on a Saturday night: *Blue, Barry* / Hitchin' a ride: *Vanity Fare* / Baby jump: *Mungo Jerry* / Love really hurts without you: *Ocean, Billy* / Here comes that rainy day feeling again: *Fortunes* / I will survive: *Gaynor, Gloria* / Juke box jive: *Rubettes* / Goodbye my love: *Glitter Band* / Shang-a-lang: *Bay City Rollers* / Now is the time: *James, Jimmy & The Vagabonds* / Run back: *Douglas, Carl* / If you don't know me by now: *Melvin, Harold & The Bluenotes* / Woman in love: *Three Degrees*
QED 024 / Nov '96 / Tring

☐ 70'S COLLECTION VOL.2
Hey there lonely girl: *Holman, Eddie* / Dance little lady dance: *Charles, Tina* / Black and white: *Greyhound* / People like you and people like me: *Glitter Band* / Sandy: *Travolta, John* / In the summertime: *Mungo Jerry* / Get dancin': *Disco Tex & The Sexolettes* / Summerlove sensation: *Bay City Rollers* / Never can say goodbye: *Gaynor, Gloria* /

Kung fu fighting: *Douglas, Carl* / I'm on fire: *5000 Volts* / Ring my bell: *Ward, Anita* / Hold back the night: *Trammps* / Indiana wants me: *Taylor, R. Dean* / Yellow river: *Christie* / Freedom come, freedom go: *Fortunes* / I'll go where your music takes me: *James, Jimmy & The Vagabonds* / Wake up everybody: *Melvin, Harold & The Bluenotes* / Dirty ol' man: *Three Degrees* / Me and Mrs Jones: *Paul, Billy*

QED 025 / Nov '96 / Tring

☐ **70'S DISCO CLASSICS**

TSS 102 / 28 Feb '98 / BMG

☐ **70'S MEGAMIXES VOL.1**

MACCD 305 / Aug '96 / Autograph

☐ **70'S MIXES**

JHD 086 / Mar '93 / Tring

☐ **70'S POP CLASSICS**

TSS 103 / 28 Feb '98 / BMG

☐ **70'S SMASH HITS VOL.1 (2CD Set)**

Greased lightnin': *Travolta, John* / Swing your daddy: *Gilstrap, Jim* / Jeans on: *Dundas, David* / Love grows where my Rosemary goes: *Edison Lighthouse* / Something old something new: *Fantastics* / Sweet inspiration: *Johnson, Johnny & Bandwagon* / Indian reservation: *Fardon, Don* / Long tall glasses (I can dance): *Sayer, Leo* / Tie a yellow ribbon 'round the ole oak tree: *Orlando, Tony* / Sugar me: *De Paul, Lynsey* / I'm doin' fine now: *New York City* / Man who sold the world: *Lulu* / Don't let me be misunderstood: *Esmeralda, Santa* / Ride a wild horse: *Clark, Dee* / Ain't gonna bump no more with no big fat woman: *Tex, Joe* / Do it: *BT Express* / Sandy: *Travolta, John* / You make me feel like dancing: *Sayer, Leo* / Daughter of darkness: *Jones, Tom* / Knock three times: *Orlando, Tony* / Sugar candy kisses: *Kissoon, Mac & Katie* / Highwire: *Carr, Linda* / Show and tell: *Wilson, Al* / Only you can: *Fox* / Be thankful for what you've got: *DeVaughan, William* / Don't give up on us: *Soul, David* / Won't somebody dance with me: *De Paul, Lynsey* / Take your mama for a ride: *Lulu*

SD 885372 / 2 Feb '98 / Disky

☐ **70'S SMASH HITS VOL.2 (2CD Set)**

Get dancing: *Disco Tex & The Sexolettes* / Thunder in my heart: *Sayer, Leo* / Rock and roll: *Glitter, Gary* / Don't do it baby: *Mac & Katie Kissoon* / Where is the love: *Delegation* / Dreams are ten a penny: *Kincaid* / Cocaine: *Dillinger* / Reflections of my life: *Marmalade* / Lay down: *Melanie* / Clap for the wolfman: *Guess Who* / Put your hand in my hand: *Ocean* / Brother Louie: *Stories* / Papa was a rollin' stone: *Temptations* / Only you can: *Fox* / Everything is beautiful: *Stevens, Ray* / You won't find another fool like me: *New Seekers* / Beach baby: *First Class* / La la (peace song): *Wilson, Al* / I love you love love: *Glitter, Gary* / Midnight train to Georgia: *Knight, Gladys & The Pips* / Brand new key: *Melanie* / This is it: *Moore, Melba* / I gotcha: *Tex, Joe* / Sideshow: *Biggs, Barry* / Two of us: *Mac & Katie Kissoon* / Angel face: *Glitter Band* / Precious and few: *Geraci, Sonny* / Midnight rider: *Davidson, Paul*

SD 885412 / 2 Feb '98 / Disky

☐ **72 TRAD JAZZ CLASSICS**

MBSCD 413 / Jul '95 / Castle

☐ **80'S COLLECTION, THE (3CD Set)**

KBOX 370 / Aug '97 / Collection

☐ **80'S DANCE CLASSICS**

TSS 104 / 28 Feb '98 / BMG

☐ **80'S SUPER HITS (2CD Set)**

Kayleigh: *Marillion* / Do you really want to hurt me: *Culture Club* / Temptation: *Heaven 17* / Died in your arms tonight: *Cutting Crew* / Wishful thinking: *China Crisis* / Wishing: *Flock Of Seagulls* / Dancing with tears in my eyes: *Ultravox* / Kids in America: *Wilde, Kim* / Too shy: *Kajagoogoo* / Only when you leave: *Spandau Ballet* / Nineteen: *Hardcastle, Paul* / Golden brown: *Stranglers* / Are you my baby: *Wendy & Lisa* / Centrefold: *Geils, J. Band* / It's my party: *Stewart, Dave & Barbara Gaskin* / Vienna: *Ultravox* / We close our eyes: *Go West* / Karma chameleon: *Culture Club* / Love is a battlefield: *Benatar, Pat* / Words: *David, F.R.* / Only you: *Flying Pickets* / Turn back the clock: *Johnny Hates Jazz* / Let me go: *Heaven 17* / If this is it: *Lewis, Huey & The News* / Gimme hope Jo'anna: *Grant, Eddy* / View from a bridge: *Wilde, Kim* / Dolce vita: *Paris, Ryan* / Turn your back on me: *Kajagoogoo* / Showing out: *Mel & Kim* / Living in a box: *Living In A Box*

DOU 878252 / 2 Feb '98 / Disky

☐ **90'S COLLECTION, THE**

CDTRAX 5004 / Oct '95 / Greentrax

☐ **95 NORTH PRESENTS STIP ESSENTIAL**

CDSTIPMX 1 / Apr '97 / Blue Music

☐ **98.1**

ASHADOW 0CD / 5 May '98 / Moving Shadow

☐ **98.2**

ASH 982CD / 24 Aug '98 / Moving Shadow

☐ **100 BLUES AND SOUL GREATS (4CD Set)**

Dimples: *Hooker, John Lee* / You'll be mine: *Howlin' Wolf* / My babe: *Little Walter* / I got it bad and that ain't good: *Holiday, Billie* / Stuff you gonna watch: *Waters, Muddy* / Born blind: *Williamson, Sonny Boy* / Boogie chillun: *Williamson, Sonny Boy* / Catfish blues: *King, B.B.* / Who's been talkin': *Howlin' Wolf* / Early in the morning: *Milton, Roy* / Please don't talk about me when I'm gone: *Holiday, Billie* / Poor Howard Green corn: *Holiday, Billie* / Sad hours: *Little Walter* / Dust my broom: *James, Elmore* / Iodine in my coffee: *Waters, Muddy* / Tupelo: *Hooker, John Lee* / Nice work if you can get it: *Holiday, Billie* / Wang dang doodle: *Howlin' Wolf* / Say: *Simon, Joe* / You're so fine: *Little Walter* / Little baby: *Howlin' Wolf* / Drug store woman: *Hooker, John Lee* / BB boogie: *King, B.B.* / Work with me: *Williamson, Sonny Boy* / Close to you: *Waters, Muddy* / Little red rooster: *Howlin' Wolf* / Boom boom: *Hooker, John Lee* / God bless the child: *Holiday, Billie* / You gonna miss me: *Waters, Muddy* / Last night: *Little Walter* / You killing me: *Williamson, Sonny Boy* / Walkin' and cryin': *King, B.B.* / Boll weevil blues: *Leadbelly* / Shake for me: *Howlin' Wolf* / Frisco blues: *Howlin' Wolf* / Don't explain: *Holiday, Billie* / Look on yonder wall: *James, Elmore* / Mean red spider: *Waters, Muddy* / Blues with a feeling: *Little Walter* / Spoonful: *Howlin' Wolf* / Please love me: *King, B.B.* / No shoes: *Hooker, John Lee* / I loves you Porgy: *Holiday, Billie* / Gallis pole: *Leadbelly* / Keep it to yourself: *Leadbelly* / Diamonds at your feet: *Waters, Muddy* / Can't hold out much longer: *Little Walter* / I'm in the mood: *Hooker, John Lee* / Goin' down slow: *Howlin' Wolf* / Little rain: *Reed, Jimmy* / Baby, please don't go: *Waters, Muddy* / Hobo blues: *Hooker, John Lee* / Down in the bottom: *Howlin' Wolf* / Fine and mellow: *Holiday, Billie* / Don't lose your eye: *Williamson, Sonny Boy* / Joke: *Little Walter* / Blue tail fly: *Leadbelly* / Walkin' and talkin': *Charles, Ray* / Baby Lee: *Hooker, John Lee* / Trainfare blues: *Waters, Muddy* / Back door man: *Howlin' Wolf* / It hurts me too: *James, Elmore* / Fooling myself: *Holiday, Billie* / Everyday I have the blues: *King, B.B.* / Mean ol' world: *Little Walter* / Trouble blues: *Hooker, John Lee* / Howlin' for my baby: *Howlin' Wolf* / Where can you be: *Reed, Jimmy* / One way out: *Williamson, Sonny Boy* / Hey now: *Charles, Ray* / Easy to remember: *Holiday, Billie* / Settin' here drinkin': *Holiday, Billie* / Old time shimmy: *Hooker, John Lee* / Tell me: *Howlin' Wolf* / How long: *Leadbelly* / I got a rich man's woman: *Waters, Muddy* / When your lover has gone: *Holiday, Billie* / My baby has walked off: *Howlin' Wolf* / Little wheel: *Hooker, John Lee* / How blue can you get: *King, B.B.* / Off the wall: *Little Walter* / Cool disposition: *Williamson, Sonny Boy* / I'm wonderin' and wonderin': *Charles, Ray* / Big fat woman: *Charles, Ray* / Whiskey and wimmen: *Hooker, John Lee* / Killing floor: *Howlin' Wolf* / Easy to remember: *Holiday, Billie* / Mean mistreater: *Waters, Muddy* / Coming home: *James, Elmore* / You better watch yourself: *Little Walter* / Moanin' at midnight: *Little Walter* / Process: *Hooker, John Lee* / In New Orleans: *Leadbelly* / Commit a crime: *Howlin' Wolf* / Dusty road: *Hooker, John Lee* / Sad letter: *Waters, Muddy* / Ain't nobody's business if I do: *Holiday, Billie* / I wonder who's kissing her now: *Charles, Ray* / What do you say: *Hooker, John Lee* / Hand in hand: *James, Elmore*

TFP 006 / Nov '92 / Tring

☐ **100 COUNTRY CLASSICS (4CD Set)**

Reuben James: *Rogers, Kenny* / I believe: *Laine, Frankie* / You'll always have someone: *Nelson, Willie* / Wasted days and wasted nights: *Fender, Freddy* / Burning memories: *Jennings, Waylon* / Daddy: *Fargo, Donna* / Your tender years: *Jones, George* / Come on in: *Cline, Patsy* / Take these chains from my heart: *Drusky, Roy* / Slippin' away: *Fairchild, Barbara* / Shine on Ruby Mountain: *Rogers, Kenny* / Ol' blue: *Jackson, Stonewall* / Ragged but right: *Jones, George* / Sticks and stones: *Fargo, Donna* / High noon: *Laine, Frankie* / Last letter: *Drusky, Roy* / Wild side of life: *Fender, Freddy* / Should I go home: *Jackson, Stonewall* / Dream baby: *Jennings, Waylon* / Crazy love: *Fairchild, Barbara* / Cry not for me: *Cline, Patsy* / Ruby, don't take your love to town: *Rogers, Kenny* / Luckenbach, Texas (Back to the basics of love): *Drusky, Roy* / Wishful thinking: *Fargo, Donna* / Money: *Jennings, Waylon* / Singin' the blues: *Mitchell, Guy* / Hello walls: *Drusky, Roy* / I've lost at love again: *Cline, Patsy* / Mule train: *Laine, Frankie* / Kaw-liga: *Mandrell, Barbara* / Wedding bells: *Jones, George* / Four in the morning: *Young, Faron* / Blue eyes cryin' in the rain: *Drusky, Roy* / Sally was a good old girl: *Jennings, Waylon* / It wasn't God who made honky tonk angels: *Parton, Dolly* / Touch me: *Nelson, Willie* / Release me: *Mandrell, Barbara* / Heartaches by the number: *Mitchell, Guy* / Shake 'em up roll 'em: *Jackson, Stonewall* / Sunshine: *Rogers, Kenny* / Things have gone to pieces: *Jones, George* / 9,999,999 Tears: *Bailey, Razzy* / I let my mind wander: *Nelson, Willie* / Crying: *Jennings, Waylon* / Honky tonk merry go round: *Cline, Patsy* / Ticket to nowhere: *Rogers, Kenny* / Keep off the grass: *Jackson, Stonewall* / Daddy sang bass: *Perkins, Carl* / Ghost: *Nelson, Willie* / If you ain't lovin' (you ain't livin'): *Young, Faron* / Kentucky means paradise: *Mandrell, Barbara* / Stop, look and listen: *Cline, Patsy* / I can't escape from you: *Jones, George* / Making believe: *Wells, Kitty* / Honky tonk angels: *Parton, Dolly* / Abilene: *Jennings, Waylon* / Ruby Tuesday: *Williams, Don* / Elvira: *Rogers, Kenny* / Maybellene: *Robbins, Marty* / Dream baby: *Jennings, Waylon* / Good rockin' tonight: *Lewis, Jerry Lee* / Little blossom: *Parton, Dolly* / From a Jack to a King: *Miller, Ned* / I can't find the time: *Nelson, Willie* / Love's gonna live here: *Jennings, Waylon* / Jambalaya: *Jones, George* / Where do we go from here: *Williams, Don* / Homemade lies: *Rogers, Kenny* / Turn the cards slowly: *Cline, Patsy* / Things to talk about: *Jackson, Stonewall* / Your song: *Lee, Johnny* / I didn't sleep a wink: *Nelson, Willie* / Cold cold heart: *Jones, George* / Town without pity: *Pitney, Gene* / Send me the pillow that you dream on: *Locklin, Hank* / Six days on the road: *Dudley, Dave* / Rose garden: *Anderson, Lynn* / Rawhide: *Laine, Frankie* / Walkin' after midnight: *Cline, Patsy* / Rhythm and booze: *Owens, Buck* / Wings of a dove: *Husky, Ferlin* / Always leaving, always gone: *Rogers, Kenny* / Ramblin' rose: *Lee, Johnny* / I feel sorry for him: *Nelson, Willie* / In care of the blues: *Cline, Patsy* / Have I stayed away too long: *Ritter, Tex* / I'll repossess my heart: *Wells, Kitty* / Waterloo: *Jackson, Stonewall* / Last day in the mines: *Dudley, Dave* / Moonlight gambler: *Laine, Frankie* / This ole house: *Perkins, Carl* / Candy store: *Lee, Johnny* / Don't think twice, it's alright: *Jennings, Waylon* / I can't get enough of you: *Jackson, Stonewall* / Heart you break may be your own: *Cline, Patsy* / Hey good lookin': *Cash, Johnny* / Open pit mine: *Jones, George* / If I don't understand: *Nelson, Willie* / Please don't let that woman get me: *Jones, George*

TFP 003 / '88 / Tring

☐ **100 CRUISIN' GREATS (4CD Set)**

TFP 018 / Nov '92 / Tring

☐ **100 GREATEST JAZZ & SWING HITS 1917-1942 (4CD Set)**

CDAFS 10364 / Jun '93 / Affinity

☐ **100 HITS OF THE FIFTIES (4CD Set)**

TFP 015 / Nov '92 / Tring

☐ **100 HITS OF THE SEVENTIES (4CD Set)**

TFP 021 / Nov '92 / Tring

☐ **100 HITS OF THE SIXTIES VOL.1 (4CD Set)**

Save the last dance for me: *Drifters* / Sweet talking guy: *Chiffons* / Let's twist again: *Checker, Chubby* / It's in his kiss (The shoop shoop song): *Everett, Betty* / Let it rock: *Berry, Chuck* / Surfin' safari: *Beach Boys* / Blueberry Hill: *Domino, Fats* / Ride the wild surf: *Jan & Dean* / Every beat of my heart: *Knight, Gladys* / Hats off to Larry: *Shannon, Del* / When a man loves a woman: *Sledge, Percy* / Venus: *Avalon, Frankie* / Limbo rock: *Checker, Chubby* / Then he kissed me: *Crystals* / Leader of the pack: *Shangri-Las* / Venus in blue jeans: *Clanton, Jimmy* / Hold on I'm comin': *Sam & Dave* / On Broadway: *Drifters* / Sixteen candles: *Crests* / Rubber ball: *Vee, Bobby* / Sugar sugar: *Archies* / My guy: *Wells, Mary* / There's a kind of hush: *Herman's Hermits* / So sad the song: *Knight, Gladys* / Runaway: *Shannon, Del* / Judy in disguise: *Fred, John & His Playboy Band* / Up on the roof: *Drifters* / Surfin': *Beach Boys* / No particular place to go: *Berry, Chuck* / Letter full of tears: *Knight, Gladys* / Soul man: *Sam & Dave* / He's so fine: *Chiffons* / Devil or angel: *Vee, Bobby* / Twist: *Checker, Chubby* / You beat me to the punch: *Wells, Mary* / Da doo ron ron: *Crystals* / Tequila: *Champs* / Drag City: *Jan & Dean* / Chapel of love: *Dixie Cups* / No milk today: *Herman's Hermits* / Duke of Earl: *Chandler, Gene* / Groovy kind of love: *Fontana, Wayne* / Under the boardwalk: *Drifters* / Behind closed doors: *Sledge, Percy* / Night has a thousand eyes: *Vee, Bobby* / Pony time: *Checker, Chubby* / Bobby sox to stockings: *Avalon, Frankie* / Ain't that a shame: *Domino, Fats* / Little old lady from Pasadena: *Jan & Dean* / Build me up buttercup: *Foundations* / There goes my baby: *Drifters* / Operator: *Knight, Gladys* / My boyfriend's back: *Angels* / Little town flirt: *Shannon, Del* / Johnny B Goode: *Berry, Chuck* / I thank you: *Sam & Dave* / Oh no not my baby: *Brown, Maxine* / Knock on wood: *Floyd, Eddie* / Run to him: *Vee, Bobby* / Surfer girl: *Beach Boys* / Give him a great big kiss: *Shangri-Las* / Rockin' Robin: *Day, Bobby* / Corine Corina: *Peterson, Ray* / Promised land: *Berry, Chuck* / GTO: *Regents* / Hucklebuck: *Checker, Chubby* / Rescue me: *Bass, Fontella* / Dead man's curve: *Jan & Dean* / He's a rebel: *Crystals* / Backfield in motion: *Mel & Tim* / Why do fools fall in love: *Diamonds* / Memphis: *Berry, Chuck* / Can't you hear my heartbeat: *Herman's Hermits* / Some kind of wonderful: *Drifters* / Soul sister brown sugar: *Sam & Dave* / Drift away: *Gray, Dobie* / Remember (walkin' in the sand): *Shangri-Las* / Rhythm of the rain: *Cascades* / Itchycoo Park: *Small Faces* / Dance with me: *Drifters* / Barefootin': *Parker, Robert* / Cry baby cry: *Angels* / It's my party: *Gore, Lesley* / Letter: *Box Tops* / Wooly bully: *Sam The Sham & The Pharaohs* / Yakety yak: *Coasters* / Little darlin': *Diamonds* / In crowd: *Gray, Dobie* / Ferry 'cross the Mersey: *Gerry & The Pacemakers* / Tell Laura I love her: *Peterson, Ray* / Barbara Ann: *Regents* / Maybellene: *Berry, Chuck* / Deep purple: *Tempo, Nino & April Stevens* / I don't know why (I just do): *Henry, Clarence 'Frogman'* / Wild thing: *Troggs* / Mrs. Brown you've got a lovely daughter: *Herman's Hermits* / Surf city: *Jan & Dean* / Don't let the sun catch you crying: *Gerry & The Pacemakers* / Nadine: *Berry, Chuck*

TFP 004 / Nov '92 / Tring

☐ **100 HITS OF THE SIXTIES VOL.2**

TFP 016 / Nov '92 / Tring

☐ **100 NON STOP PARTY HITS (4CD Set)**

Let's have a party: *Jackson, Wanda* / Dyna-mite: *Mud* / Be bop a lula: *Vincent, Gene & The Bluecaps* / Some girls: *Racey* / Denis: *Blondie* / Gimme hope Jo'anna: *Grant, Eddy* / Breakaway: *Ullman, Tracey* / Can the can: *Quatro, Suzi* / My Sharona: *Knack* / Bus stop: *Hollies* / You were made for me: *Freddie & The Dreamers* / Runaway: *Shannon, Del* / Forever, forever: *Domino, Fats* / Pretend: *Stardust, Alvin* / Kids in America: *Wilde, Kim* / If this is it: *Lewis, Huey & The News* / Darlin': *Miller, Frankie* / Right back where we started from: *Nightingale, Maxine* / Showing out: *Mel & Kim* / Sex drugs and rock and roll: *Dury, Ian* / Call me: *Blondie* / Dancing in the city: *Hain, Marshall* / Don't worry be happy: *McFerrin, Bobby* / Geno: *Dexy's Midnight Runners* / Bring it on home: *Animals* / Party doll: *Knox, Buddy* / Do wah diddy diddy: *Manfred Mann* / C'mon everydogy: *Cochran, Eddie* / Hippy hippy shake: *Swinging Blue Jeans* / Barbara Ann: *Beach Boys* / Mony mony: *James, Tommy & The Shondells* / Hi ho silver lining: *Beck, Jeff* / Tiger feet: *Mud* / See my baby jive: *Wizzard* / Long tall glasses: *Sayer, Leo* / This little girl: *Bonds, Gary 'US'* / On the road again: *Canned Heat* / Roll over Beethoven: *ELO* / My girl Josephine: *Domino, Fats* / I'm into something good: *Herman's Hermits* / Surf city: *Jan & Dean* / I get around: *Beach Boys* / Rock your baby: *McCrae, George* / Don't take away the music: *Tavares* / Oh baby what would you say: *Smith, Hurricane* / Sixteen tons: *Ford, Tennessee Ernie* / Baby let me take you home: *Animals* / All around my hat: *Steeleye Span* / American pie: *McLean, Don* / You sexy thing: *Hot Chocolate* / I hear you knockin': *Edmunds, Dave* / Rubber ball: *Vee, Bobby* / Boat that I row: *Lulu* / Runaround Sue: *Dion* / Morning train: *Easton, Sheena* / Magic: *Pilot* / Cat crept in: *Mud* / Teenager in love: *Dion & The Belmonts* / I like it: *Gerry & The Pacemakers* / Buona sera: *Prima, Louis* / Mississippi: *Pussycat* / Walking back to happiness: *Shapiro, Helen* / Pretty flamingo: *Manfred Mann* / Good golly Miss Molly: *Swinging Blue Jeans* / Nutbush city limits: *Turner, Ike & Tina* / Coming on strong: *Broken English* / That's the way I like it: *KC & The Sunshine Band* / We've gotta get out of this place: *Animals* / No more heroes: *Stranglers* / Hanging on the telephone: *Blondie* / It ain't what you do: *Fun Boy Three & Bananarama* / Blue moon: *Marcels* / Kisses sweeter than wine: *Rodgers, Jimmie* / Big spender: *Bassey, Shirley* / Lily the pink: *Scaffold* / Summertime blues: *Cochran, Eddie* / Lay your love on me: *Racey* / Don't let me be misunderstood: *Animals* / World without love: *Peter & Gordon* / Baker street: *Rafferty, Gerry* / Boogie oogie oogie: *Taste Of Honey* / Heaven must be missing an angel: *Tavares* / Chequered love: *Wilde, Kim* / Oh boy: *Mud* / Tom Tom turnaround: *New World* / No milk today: *Herman's Hermits* / Devil gate drive: *Quatro, Suzi* / Stuck with you: *Lewis, Huey & The News* / Centerfold: *Geils, J. Band* / Stop stop stop: *Hollies* / Freedom come freedom go: *Fortunes* / You'll never walk alone: *Gerry & The Pacemakers* / I'm telling you now: *Freddie & The Dreamers* / Seven drunken nights: *Dubliners* / Sloop John B: *Beach Boys* / Oh Marie: *Prima, Louis* / If you can't give me love: *Quatro, Suzi* / Blueberry Hill: *Domino, Fats* / Do you want to know a secret: *Kramer, Billy J. & The Dakotas* / Thank u very much: *Scaffold*

HR 877362 / May '97 / Disky

☐ **100 OF THE GREATEST LOVE SONGS (4CD Set)**

Then he kissed me: *Crystals* / It's in his kiss (The shoop shoop song): *Everett, Betty* / Girls: *Moments* / Remember (walkin' in the sand): *Shangri-Las* / Let there be love: *Lee, Peggy* / I'm in the mood for love: *Day, Doris* / My boyfriend's back: *Angels* / Every beat of my heart: *Knight, Gladys & The Pips* / Venus in blue jeans: *Clanton, Jimmy* / Groovy kind of love: *Fontana, Wayne* / I can't find the time: *Nelson, Willie* / Don't let the sun catch you crying: *Gerry & The Pacemakers* / Sixteen candles: *Crests* / Warm and tender love: *Sledge, Percy* / Ain't no sunshine: *Jarreau, Al* / I'm so lonesome I could cry: *Spears, Billie Jo* / Night has a thousand eyes: *Vee, Bobby* / Love walked in: *Benson, George* / Embraceable you: *Day, Doris* / Where were you on our wedding day: *Price, Lloyd* / Release me: *Mandrell, Barbara* / Shelter of my arms: *Nelson, Willie* / Ruby, don't take your love to town: *Rogers, Kenny* / Portrait of my love: *Clark, Dee* / What is this thing called love: *Lee, Peggy* / Behind closed doors: *Sledge, Percy* / Lean on me: *Jarreau, Al* / Run to him: *Vee, Bobby* / Singin' in the rain: *Day, Doris* / Oh no not my baby: *Bass, Fontella* / There goes my baby: *Drifters* / He's a rebel: *Crystals* / Letter full of tears: *Knight, Gladys* / But I do: *Henry, Clarence 'Frogman'* / My guy: *Wells, Mary* / 'S wonderful: *Day, Doris* / I've loved and lost again: *Cline, Patsy* / Save the last dance for me: *Drifters* / Home is where you're happy: *Nelson, Willie* / Kisses sweeter than wine: *Rodgers, Jimmie* / Leader of the pack: *Shangri-Las* / Just a dream: *Clanton, Jimmy* / Best thing that ever happened to me: *Knight, Gladys* / Uptown: *Crystals* / Come what may: *Crosby, Bing* / Do I love you: *Garland, Judy* / Chapel of love: *Dixie Cups* / Runaway: *Shannon, Del* / Young and in love: *Dick & Deedee* / Just one of those things: *Lee, Peggy* / Rock your baby: *McCrae, George* / When a man loves a woman: *Sledge, Percy* / Operator: *Knight, Gladys & The Pips* / Dream baby: *Shannon, Del* / Stardust: *Day, Doris* / Do it love you: *Garland, Judy* / Give him a great big kiss: *Shangri-Las* / While I dream: *Sedaka, Neil* / High noon: *Laine, Frankie* / Let your love flow: *Burke, Solomon* / So sad the song: *Knight, Gladys & The Pips* / Why do fools fall in love: *Diamonds* / Rainy night in Georgia: *Benton, Brook* / World without you: *Shannon, Del* / Rhythm of the rain: *Cascades* / I can't give you anything but love: *Garland, Judy* / Love we had: *Dells* / Make it easy on yourself: *Butler, Jerry* / Just you, just me: *Day, Doris* / So many ways: *Benton, Brook* / It coulda been me: *Spears, Billie Jo* / Sh-boom: *Crew Cuts* / Tender years: *Jones, George* / Build me up buttercup: *Foundations* / Girls: *Moments* / Stormy weather: *Horne, Lena* / If ever I should fall in love: *Knight, Gladys & The Pips* / Deep purple: *Tempo, Nino & April Stevens* / Crying my heart out for you: *Day, Doris* / When my little girl is smiling: *Drifters* / Spanish Harlem: *King, B.B.* / Lyin' eyes: *Jones, Jack* / Single girl: *Posey, Sandy* / Tell Laura I love her: *Peterson, Ray* / Under the moon of love: *Lee, Curtis* / Everything I have is yours: *Crosby, Bing* / Little darlin': *Diamonds* / You and me against the world: *Knight, Gladys & The Pips* / One who really loves you: *Wells, Mary* / Why do fools fall in love: *Diamonds* / Closer you are: *Channel* / Just the two of us: *Jones, Jack* / What a man in love won't do: *Posey, Sandy* / Because you're mine: *Day, Doris* / Young and in love: *Dick & Deedee* / Up on the roof: *Drifters* / Please love me forever: *Edwards, Tommy* / When the red roses grow: *Crosby, Bing* / Earth angel: *Penguins* / Fools rush in: *Benton, Brook*

TFP 008 / Nov '92 / Tring

☐ **100 ROCK 'N' ROLL HITS (4CD Set)**

Roll over Beethoven: *Berry, Chuck* / Blueberry Hill: *Domino, Fats* / Yakety yak: *Coasters* / (We're gonna) Rock around the clock: *Haley, Bill & The Comets* / Venus: *Avalon, Frankie* / Reelin' and rockin': *Berry, Chuck* / Let's twist again: *Checker, Chubby* / My boyfriend's back: *Angels* / Keep a knockin': *Little Richard* / Sweet talking guy: *Chiffons* / Personality: *Price, Lloyd* / Hats off to Larry: *Shannon, Del* / Blue Monday: *Domino, Fats* / Sweet little rock 'n' roller: *Berry, Chuck* / Tequila: *Champs* / Tutti frutti: *Little Richard* / Rock 'n' roll is here to stay: *Danny & The Juniors* / Rockin' pneumonia and the boogie woogie flu: *Smith, Huey 'Piano'* / Crossfire: *Johnny & The Hurricanes* / Then he kissed me: *Crystals* / Rubber ball: *Vee, Bobby* / Be bop a lula: *Vincent, Gene* / Runaround Sue: *Shannon, Del* / Promised land: *Berry, Chuck* / Good golly Miss Molly: *Little Richard* / Twist: *Checker, Chubby* / Duke of Earl: *Chandler, Gene* / No particular place to go: *Berry, Chuck* / Ain't that a shame: *Domino, Fats* / Da doo ron ron: *Crystals* / At the hop: *Danny & The Juniors* / Shake, rattle and roll: *Haley, Bill* / School day: *Berry, Chuck* / Long tall Sally: *Little Richard* / Stagger Lee: *Price, Lloyd* / Charlie Brown: *Coasters* / Runaway: *Shannon, Del* / Book of love: *Monotones* / Beatnik fly: *Johnny & The Hurricanes* / Night has a thousand eyes: *Vee, Bobby* / Great balls of fire: *Lewis, Jerry Lee* / Too much monkey business: *Berry, Chuck* / Little Egypt: *Coasters* / Cry baby cry: *Angels* / Rockin' Robin: *Day, Bobby* / Rip it up: *Little Richard* / I go to pieces: *Shannon, Del* / Back in the USA: *Berry, Chuck* / Cool jerk: *Capitols* / Nadine: *Berry, Chuck* / See you later alligator: *Haley, Bill & The Comets* / Red river rock: *Johnny & The Hurricanes* / Hucklebuck: *Checker, Chubby* / Johnny B Goode: *Berry, Chuck* / Ooh my soul: *Little Richard* / Whole lotta shakin' goin' on: *Lewis, Jerry Lee* / Chapel of love: *Dixie Cups* / Little town flirt: *Shannon, Del* / Sweet little sixteen: *Berry, Chuck* / Jambalaya: *Domino, Fats* / Sea cruise: *Ford, Frankie* / He's a rebel: *Crystals* / Leader of the pack: *Shangri-Las* / Poison ivy: *Coasters* / Because they're young: *Eddy, Duane* / Whole lotta shakin' goin' on: *Little Richard* / Angels listened in: *Crests* / Let it rock: *Berry, Chuck* / Matchbox: *Perkins, Carl* / Kansas City: *Harrison, Wilbert* / Brown eyed handsome man: *Lewis, Jerry Lee* / Little bitty pretty one: *Day, Bobby* / I'm walkin': *Domino, Fats* / Short fat Fanny: *Little Richard* / Almost grown: *Berry, Chuck* / Maybellene: *Berry, Chuck* / Lucille: *Little Richard* / Shout: *Dee, Joey* / Limbo rock: *Checker, Chubby* / Reveille rock: *Johnny & The Hurricanes* / Why do fools fall in love: *Diamonds* / Brown eyed handsome man: *Berry, Chuck* / Baby blue: *Vincent, Gene* / Hello Josephine: *Domino, Fats* / She's got it: *Little Richard* / Mr. Bass Man: *Cymbal, Johnny* / Say man: *Diddley, Bo* / Rock 'n' roll music: *Berry, Chuck* / Handyman: *Shannon, Del* / He's so fine: *Chiffons* / This ole house: *Perkins, Carl* / Wooly bully: *Sam The Sham & The Pharaohs* / Pony time: *Checker, Chubby* / Girl can't help it: *Little Richard* / Rebel rouser: *Eddy, Duane* / Stroll: *Diamonds* / Under the moon of love: *Lee, Curtis* / Domino twist: *Domino, Fats* / Memphis: *Berry, Chuck* / Guitar man: *Eddy, Duane*

TFP 002 / Nov '92 / Tring

☐ **100 SOUL HITS (4CD Set)**
Soul man: *Sam & Dave* / Papa's got a brand new bag: *Brown, James* / Knock on wood: *Floyd, Eddie* / Under the boardwalk: *Drifters* / Rescue me: *Bass, Fontella* / It's just a matter of time: *Benton, Brook* / In crowd: *Gray, Dobie* / Oh no not my baby: *Brown, Maxine* / Every beat of my heart: *Knight, Gladys* / Rock your baby: *McCrae, George* / Barefootin': *Parker, Robert* / When a man loves a woman: *Sledge, Percy* / Backfield in motion: *Mel & Tim* / You don't know what you mean to me: *Sam & Dave* / Expressway to your heart: *Soul Survivors* / Save the last dance for me: *Drifters* / When something is wrong with my baby: *Sam & Dave* / If you need me: *Pickett, Wilson* / Do the funky chicken: *Thomas, Rufus* / Please please please: *Brown, James* / Rainy night in Georgia: *Benton, Brook* / Hold on I'm comin': *Burke, Solomon* / Bring it on home to me: *Floyd, Eddie* / Stand by me: *King, Ben E.* / I got the feelin': *Brown, James* / On broadway: *Drifters* / Hold on I'm comin': *Sam & Dave* / It's a man's man's man's world: *Brown, James* / Oh what a night: *Drells* / California girl: *Floyd, Eddie* / Spanish Harlem: *King, Ben E.* / True love: *Drifters* / Soul man: *Lewis, Ramsey* / So many ways: *Benton, Brook* / Letter full of tears: *Knight, Gladys* / Walking the dog: *Thomas, Rufus* / Hi-heel sneakers: *Lewis, Ramsey* / All in my mind: *Brown, Maxine* / Best thing that ever happened to me: *Knight, Gladys* / Turn it loose: *Brown, James* / Said I wasn't gonna tell nobody: *Sam & Dave* / I who have nothing: *King, Ben E.* / My guy: *Wells, Mary* / Sweets for my sweet: *Drifters* / Georgia on my mind: *Knight, Gladys* / Boll weevil song: *Benton, Brook* / You don't know like I know: *Sam & Dave* / Get up offa that thing: *Brown, James* / Warm and tender love: *Sledge, Percy* / Challenge: *Butler, Jerry* / It's too funky here: *Brown, James* / Kiddio: *Benton, Brook* / Tighten up: *Bell, Archie & The Drells* / I thank you: *Sam & Dave* / Lovin' arms: *Gray, Dobie* / Supernatural thing: *King, Ben E.* / Dancing in the street: *Lewis, Ramsey* / There goes my baby: *Drifters* / Operator: *Knight, Gladys & The Pips* / I wanna go home: *Drells* / Try me: *Brown, James* / Uptight: *Lewis, Ramsey* / So sad the song: *Knight, Gladys & The Pips* / Fools rush in: *Benton, Brook* / Girls: *Moments* / This magic moment: *Drifters* / Behind closed doors: *Sledge, Percy* / Listen: *Impressions* / Hard day's night: *Lewis, Ramsey* / Duke of Earl: *Chandler, Gene* / You got me hummin': *Sam & Dave* / Think twice: *Benton, Brook* / Since you've been gone: *Lewis, Ramsey* / Cold sweat/I can't stand myself (medley): *Brown, James* / I who have nothing: *King, Ben E.* / Soul sister brown sugar: *Sam & Dave* / (Get up I feel like being a) sex machine: *Brown, James* / Love me again: *Knight, Gladys & The Pips* / Up on the roof: *Drifters* / Look at me (I'm in love): *Moments* / Drift away: *Gray, Dobie* / It's too late: *Pickett, Wilson* / She does it right: *King, Ben E.* / Hotel happiness: *Benton, Brook* / Louie Louie: *Kingsmen* / Get on the good foot: *Brown, James* / Soul twist: *King Curtis* / Never found a girl: *Floyd, Eddie* / Don't pull your love out on me baby: *Sam & Dave* / Dance with me: *Drifters* / If ever I should fall in love: *Knight, Gladys & The Pips* / In crowd: *Lewis, Ramsey* / Love on a two way street: *Moments* / Take time to know her: *Sledge, Percy* / I need your love: *Impressions* / Can't you find another way: *Sam & Dave* / Some kind of wonderful: *Drifters* / Thank you pretty baby: *Benton, Brook* / What shall I do: *Knight, Gladys & The Pips* / I feel good: *Brown, James*
TFP 001 / Nov '92 / Tring

☐ **100 WATTS: SONGS FROM WPHK'S 'PURE HYPE'**
HPK 01 / Jul '97 / Atavistic

☐ **100% BRITISH MOD (2CD Set)**
Blood splattered with guitars: *Accidents* / One way street: *Aces* / Can we go dancing: *Amber Squad* / Mary Jane: *Blue Movies* / They're back again: *Cigarettes* / Circles: *Circles* / When the lights go out: *Clerks* / No vacancies: *Clueless* / Modern boys: *Crooks* / Choose you: *Deadbeats* / Three bands tonite: *Directions* / Fashion plague: *Exits* / Kids just wanna dance: *Fast Cars* / You: *Just Frank* / Statik motion: *Justin Case* / Why should it happen to me: *Killermeters* / Nobody loves me: *Letters* / 1970's boy: *Long Tall Shorty* / Back on the beach again: *Media* / Fuck art let's dance: *Name* / I saw her with another guy: *Nightriders* / Saturday night: *Odds* / Plane crash: *Purple Hearts* / I believe you: *Reputations* / Soho: *Run 229* / Wild about you: *Same* / Hey girl: *Scene* / You can do it: *Scoop* / Sema 4 messages: *Sema 4* / First impressions: *Small World* / Know what i want: *Split Screen* / Livin' in the city: *Squire* / One out all out: *Straight Up* / One step ahead: *Stripes* / I've got me parka: *Sussed* / I apologise: *Teenage Film Stars* / Just a little Mod: *Tonik, Terry* / Bank holiday: *Vandells* / Just can't let you go: *VIP's* / East coast kids: *What*
MODSKADCD 008 / 9 Mar '98 / Captain Mod

☐ **100% BRITISH OI (2CD Set)**
Don't mess with the SAS: *ABH* / Victory in Poland: *Angelic Upstarts* / 1980's: *Anti Establishment* / Official hooligan: *Anti Social* / Today's generation: *Attak* / Age that didn't care: *Barbed Wire* / Warriors: *Blitz* / Such fun: *Blood* / Friday night: *Burial* / Product: *Business* / Beginning of the end: *Cockney Rejects* / Chip on my shoulder: *Cock Sparrer* / Poseur: *Combat 84* / Oi ain't dead: *Condemned 84* / Going out: *Crack* / Fighting the system: *Criminal Class* / CIA: *Crux* / Have you got 10p: *Ejected* / Dr.Crippins: *Five O* / Sorry: *4 Skins* / Jobs not jails: *Gonads* / Addicted to love: *Guttersnipes* / Riot riot: *Infa Riot* / Ghost town: *Intensive Care* / Resort bootboys: *Last Resort* / Screwed up: *Menace* / White flag: *Menace* / 17 years of hell: *Partisans* / Up yer bum: *Peter & The Test Tube Babies* / Generation landslide: *Prole* / Take no prisoners: *Red Alert* / For the love of oi: *Section 5* / Borstal breakout: *Sham 69* / Football violence: *Skin Deep* / Situations: *Slaughter & The Dogs* / Pathetique: *Splodgenessabounds* / Skinhead: *Strike* / Loud and clear: *Subculture* / Anytime day or night: *Vicious Rumors* / Horror show: *Warriors*
AHOYDCD 083 / 2 Feb '98 / Captain Oi

☐ **100% BRITISH SKA (2CD Set)**
Pink slippers: *AK Band* / Spyderman: *Akrylykz* / Smart boy: *Akrylykz* / Blue lagoon: *Ammonites* / Shuffle shuffle: *Army* / Trendy: *Army* / I like bluebeat: *Cairo* / Moviestars: *Cairo* / Oh: *Case* / Wolly bully: *Gangsters* / We are the gangsters: *Gangsters* / Dambusters march: *JJ Allstars* / Lovers rock: *Judge Dread* / Ska fever: *Judge Dread* / Play my record: *Kay, Arthur Originals* / Sooty is a rudie: *Kay, Arthur Originals* / Yesterday man: *Odds* / Dread in bed: *Odds* / No one but you: *Originals* / High flyer: *Originals* / How many more: *Papers* / Reggae on the radio: *Papers* / Breaking up new ground: *Parrots* / In the midnight hour: *Pharaohs* / Fiddling while Babylon burns: *Piranhas* / Getting beaten up: *Piranhas* / Plastic gangsters: *Plastic Gangsters* / Phoenix City: *Rockers Express* / Never gonna lose me: *Sax Maniacs* / Let's twist again: *Sax Maniacs* / Time is tight: *Ska City Rockers* / You don't know like I know: *Ska City Rockers* / Road burner: *Ska City Rockers* / Yes yes yes: *Ska-Dows* / Twice: *Ska-Dows* / Odd man out: *Teenage Film Stars* / Shooting: *Thrillers* / To the top: *Thrillers* / Ska trekking: *Tigers* / Kidding stops: *Tigers*
MODSKACD 007 / 2 Feb '98 / Captain Mod

☐ **100% CHRISTMAS & NEW YEAR (2CD Set)**
TCD 2878 / Nov '96 / Telstar

☐ **100% DETROIT WORKOUT (4CD Set)**
CDFIT 5 / Nov '95 / Music For Pleasure

☐ **100% HARDCORE PUNK (2CD Set)**
AHOYDCD 84 / 16 Mar '98 / Captain Oi

☐ **100% PURE DANCE**
CDRPM 0012 / Apr '97 / RP Media

☐ **100% PURE FUNK VOL.2**
CS 8539 / 20 Apr '98 / C&S/Pure

☐ **100% PURE GROOVE VOL.1 (2CD Set)**
TCD 2818 / Mar '96 / Telstar

☐ **100% PURE GROOVE VOL.2 (2CD Set)**
TCD 2840 / Jun '96 / Telstar

☐ **100% PURE UNDERGROUND DANCE**
XCLU 001CDC / Sep '94 / X-Clusive

☐ **100% RAI VOL.1**
952052 / Jul '97 / Pomme

☐ **100% RAI VOL.2**
952192 / 5 Jan '98 / Pomme

☐ **100% SUMMER MIX '97 (2CD Set)**
Ecuador: *Sash* / Freed from desire: *Gala* / Fairground: *Simply Red* / Closer than close: *Gaines, Rosie* / Saturday night: *Whigfield* / All that she wants: *Ace Of Base* / Macarena: *Los Del Rio* / Bamboleo: *Gipsy Kings* / Fresh: *Gina G* / Sweets for my sweet: *Lewis, C.J.* / Things can only get better: *D:Ream* / Boom boom boom: *Outhere Brothers* / Bomb (These sounds fall into my mind): *Bucketheads* / Professional widow: *Amos, Tori* / Missing: *Everything But The Girl* / Lovefool: *Cardigans* / Parklife: *Blur* / Riverboat song: *Ocean Colour Scene* / Breakfast at Tiffany's: *Deep Blue Something* / Good enough: *Dodgy* / Turn on tune in cop out: *Freakpower* / Midnight at the oasis: *Brand New Heavies* / Remember me: *Blueboy* / Back to life: *Soul II Soul* / Boombastic: *Shaggy* / Mr. Loverman: *Shabba Ranks* / Cecilia: *Suggs* / Don't make me wait: *911* / I can make you feel good: *Kavana* / Horny: *Morrison, Mark* / Hey DJ (play that song): *N-Tyce* / Encore une fois: *Sash* / Keep warm: *Jinny* / I'm alive: *Stretch n' Vern* / Where love lives: *Limerick, Alison* / Ain't nobody: *Course* / Get up (everybody): *Stingily, Byron* / Let me be your fantasy: *Baby D* / I love you stop: *Red 5* / Stepping stone: *PJ & Duncan*
TTVCD 2906 / Jul '97 / Telstar TV

☐ **100% SUMMER MIX '98 (2CD Set)**
Three lions: *Lightning Seeds & David Baddiel/Frank Skinner* / Vindaloo: *Fat Les* / Tubthumping: *Chumbawamba* / World in motion: *New Order* / Sunchyme: *Dario G* / Feel it: *Tamperer* / Freed from desire: *Gala* / It's like that: *Run DMC* / Keep warm: *Jinny* / Megamix: *Sash* / I love you stop: *Red 5* / Naked in the rain 98: *Blue Pearl* / Kung fu fighting: *Bus Stop* / Gypsy woman: *Waters, Crystal* / Things can only get better: *D:Ream* / Stayin' alive: *N-Trance* / That's the way (I like it): *Clock* / Boom boom: *N-Tyce* / Here comes the hotstepper: *Kamoze, Ini* / Lovely daze: *DJ Jazzy Jeff & The Fresh Prince* / Doctor Jones: *Aqua* / Dance the night away: *Mavericks* / You make me feel like dancing: *Groovy Corporation* / Maria: *Martin, Ricky* / Ooh aah just a little bit: *Gina G* / Last thing on my mind: *Steps* / Saturday night: *Whigfield* / Girls just wanna have fun: *Lauper, Cyndi* / Guaglione: *Prado, Perez* / Macarena: *Los Del Mar* / Coco jamboo: *Mr. President* / Twist and shout: *Chaka Demus & Pliers* / Sweat: *Inner Circle* / Mr. Loverman: *Shabba Ranks* / Whine and grine: *Prince Buster* / Funkin' for Jamaica: *Browne, Tom* / Sweets for my sweet: *Lewis, C.J.* / Hot hot hot: *Arrow* / Everybody needs somebody to love: *Burke, Solomon* / Californian dreamin': *Mamas & The Papas*
TTVCD 2968 / 6 Jul '98 / Telstar TV

☐ **101 + 303 + 808 = NOW FORM A BAND**
Metamorphic structures: *Turbulent Force* / Alpha acid: *Point Alpha* / Steel mill: *THD* / Spalding: *THD* / Mollusk: *POD* / Untitled: *Turbulent Force* / Data blast: *Point Alpha* / Street stomper: *Psyche* / Geodesic dome: *POD* / Untitled: *Lords Of Afford* / Adrenalin rush: *Psyche*
SBR 004CD / Oct '95 / Sabrettes Of Paradise

☐ **101 IRISH BALLADS (4CD Set)**
Black Velvet Band: *Dubliners* / Medley: *Barnbrack* / John O'Dreams: *Dublin City Ramblers* / She moved thro' the fair: *Blackthorn* / Follow me up to Carlow: *Aran folk* / Ramblin' Irishman: *Corrib Folk* / Mary from Dungloe: *Spiceland, Emmet* / Free the people: *Kelly, Luke* / Nancy Spain: *Tara Folk* / Orange and green: *Corrib Folk* / James Connoly: *O'Neill, Terry* / Castle of Droriore: *O'Se, Sean* / Oul triangle: *Drew, Ronnie* / Time has come: *Moore, Brian* / Wild colonial boy: *Cane, Oliver* / Michael Davitt: *O'Neill, Terry* / Patriot game: *Irish Ramblers* / Ferryman: *Dublin City Ramblers* / Mursheen Durkin: *McEvoy, Johnny* / Carrickfergus: *Reilly, Paddy* / Slan Libh: *Moore, Brian* / James Larkin: *Drew, Ronnie* / Danny boy: *Locke, Josef* / Soldiers song: *Irish Ramblers* / Danny Farrell: *Drew, Ronnie* / Cavan girl: *Barnbrack* / Medley: *Brier* / Lough Sheelin eviction: *McIlhorne, Margaret* / Arthur McBride: *Corrib Folk* / God save Ireland: *Freedom Sons* / Steal away: *Fureys* / Streets of New York: *Brier* / Banna strand: *Shaskeen* / Ojos negros: *Dubliners* / Medley: *Barnbrack* / Galway shawl: *Brier* / Johnston's motor car: *Dubliners* / Dirty old town: *Kelly, Luke* / City of Chicago: *Close, John* / Nation once again: *Dubliners* / Farewell to my own native land: *Barry, Margaret* / Old bog road: *Locke, Josef* / McAlpine's fusiliers: *Dubliners* / Michael Collins: *Moore, Brian* / Fiddler's green: *Mark's Men* / Medley: *Dubliners* / Whiskey in the jar: *Dubliners* / Delaney's donkey: *Barnbrack* / Peggy Gordon: *Blackthorn* / Old Claddagh ring: *Corrib Folk* / Barry's column: *Irish Ramblers* / Take me back to Castlebar: *Brier* / Guinness song: *Barry, Margaret* / Will ye go lassie go: *Barnbrack* / My lagan flows softly: *Tara Folk* / Only our rivers run free: *Corrib Folk* / Belfast hornpipe: *Dubliners* / Foggy dew: *O'Brien, Jackie* / Flight of the Earls: *Brier* / Belfast: *Barnbrack* / Joe Hill: *Dubliners* / Back home in Derry: *Close, John* / Riverdance: *Innisfree Ceoil* / Fairytale of New York: *Brier* / As I roved out: *Blackthorn* / Grace: *Shamrog* / Boys of Barra sriade: *Moore, Brian* / West's awake: *Dubliners* / Belfast mill: *Dublin City Ramblers* / Raglan Road: *Kelly, Luke* / Four poster bed: *Dubliners* / Sick note: *Brier* / Lovely Armagh: *Woods, Pat* / Galway races: *McCann, Jim* / Monto: *Kelly, Luke* / Town I loved so well: *Brier* / Medley: *Barnbrack* / Spancil hill: *Corrib Folk* / Paddy lie back: *Blackthorn* / Boys of the old Brigade: *Wolfhound* / Four green fields: *Dubliners* / Ireland boys hurrah: *O'Brien, Dermot* / Lovely rose of Clare: *Barnbrack* / Irish rover: *Drew, Ronnie* / Galtee mountain boy: *Paddy's Dream* / La quinta brigada: *Close, John* / Boys of Killybegs: *Brier* / Rocky road to Dublin: *Reilly, Paddy* / Shanagolden: *Shaskeen* / Biddy Mulligan: *Dubliners* / Off to Dublin in the green: *Wolfhound*
ECD 3345 / Feb '98 / K-Tel

☐ **101% COUNTRY**
Mama tried: *Haggard, Merle* / Lonesome number one: *Gibson, Don* / City lights: *Price, Ray* / Lonely street: *Cline, Patsy* / Folsom Prison blues: *Cash, Johnny* / A moment isn't very long: *Jones, George* / I love you because: *Jackson, Stonewall* / If you ain't lovin': *Young, Faron* / Carroll county accident: *Wagoner, Porter* / Drunken driver: *Husky, Ferlin* / I don't believe you've met my baby: *Louvin Brothers* / If you can't bite don't growl: *Collins, Tommy* / I recall a gypsy women: *Thompson, Hank* / Sing me back home: *Haggard, Merle* / Blue blue day: *Gibson, Don* / Crazy arms: *Price, Ray* / Alone with you: *Young, Faron* / Stranger in my arms: *Cline, Patsy* / Waterloo: *Jackson, Stonewall* / Healing hands of time: *Nelson, Willie* / I love you so much it hurts: *Lewis, Jerry Lee* / Tender years: *Jones, George* / Little rosa: *Sovine, Red & Webb Pierce* / Thanks a lot: *Cash, Johnny* / Lookin' for love: *Lee, Johnny* / Let's think about living: *Luman, Bob* / Engine engine #9: *Miller, Roger* / Dream baby: *Dalton, Lacy J.* / Help me make it through the night: *Bare, Bobby* / Never ending song of love: *Lee, Dickey* / Tie a yellow ribbon 'round the old oak tree: *Carver, Johnny* / Before the next teardrop falls: *Fender, Freddy* / Oaklahoma hills: *Bandy, Moe* / Almost persuaded #2: *Houston, David* / You can have her: *Brown, Jim Ed* / Rhinestone cowboy: *Campbell, Glen* / Hearts aren't made to break: *Greenwood, Lee* / Take me: *Jones, George* / My shoes keeep walking back to you: *Price, Ray* / Little black book: *Price, Ray* / Yesterday when I was young: *Clark, Roy* / What does it take: *Davis, Skeeter* / Wishful thinking: *Stewart, Wynn* / Skip a rope: *Cargill, Bill* / When I stop dreaming: *Louvin Brothers* / I'll have another cup of coffee then I'll go: *Gray, Claude* / Another: *Drusky, Roy* / Rose and a baby ruth: *Hamilton, George IV* / It tickles: *Collins, Tommy* / Walking in the sunshine: *Miller, Roger* / Me and Bobby McGee: *Bare, Bobby* / 16th Avenue: *Dalton, Lacy J.* / Dixie road: *Greenwood, Lee* / Heartaches by number: *Price, Ray* / Before I met you: *Anderson, Bill* / Giddiup go: *Husky, Ferlin* / Six days on the road: *Dudley, Dave* / Hitchin' a ride: *Reno, Jack* / Take a letter Miss Grey: *Tubb, Justin* / I can't stay mad at you: *Davis, Skeeter* / Bridge washed out: *Mack, Warner* / Gentle on the mind: *Campbell, Glen* / San Antonio rose: *Bandy, Moe* / She's mine: *Paycheck, Johnny* / When you say love: *Luman, Bob* / Why don't they understand: *Hamilton, George IV* / Jambalaya: *Russell, Johnny* / I don't love you anymore: *Louvin, Charlie* / Family bible: *Gray, Claude* / Hello out there: *Belew, Carl* / Love's gonna happen to me: *Belew, Carl* / Watcha gonna do now: *Collins, Tommy* / Peel me a nanner: *Collins, Tommy* / They call me country: *Clark, Sanford*
ECD 3190 / Jun '97 / K-Tel

☐ **101% MOODS (4CD Set)**
Aria on air: *Brooks, Paul* / Oxygene 4: *Brooks, Paul* / La serenissima: *Brooks, Paul* / Forbidden colours: *Brooks, Paul* / Road: *Brooks, Paul* / Streets of Philadelphia: *Brooks, Paul* / Wonderful life: *Brooks, Paul* / Howards way: *Brooks, Paul* / Sadness: *Brooks, Paul* / Crockett's theme: *Brooks, Paul* / Lily was here: *Brooks, Paul* / Moonlighting: *Brooks, Paul* / Killing fields: *Brooks, Paul* / Here comes the sun: *Brooks, Paul* / Love changes everything: *Brooks, Paul* / Bilitis: *Brooks, Paul* / Chi mai: *Brooks, Paul* / Fernando: *Brooks, Paul* / Wedding song: *Brooks, Paul* / Summer love: *Brooks, Paul* / Song for guy: *Brooks, Paul* / To the unknown man: *Brooks, Paul* / Private investigations: *Brooks, Paul* / Twin peaks theme: *Brooks, Paul* / Colours of the wind: *Brooks, Paul* / Sailing: *Belmonde, Pierre* / Stranger on the shore: *Bilk, Acker* / We've only just begun: *Belmonde, Pierre* / Think twice: *Belmonde, Pierre* / Love hurts: *Belmonde, Pierre* / Sacrifice: *Belmonde, Pierre* / Rose: *Starsound Orchestra* / Can you feel the love tonight: *Belmonde, Pierre* / Greatest love of all: *Starsound Orchestra* / Happy ever after: *Belmonde, Pierre* / Miss you nights: *Belmonde, Pierre* / Stay another day: *Belmonde, Pierre* / Never my love: *Bilk, Acker* / Local hero: *Belmonde, Pierre* / Let it be me: *Starsound Orchestra* / Windmills of your mind: *Belmonde, Pierre* / Wind beneath my wings: *Starsound Orchestra* / Eternal flame: *Belmonde, Pierre* / Love story: *Starsound Orchestra* / Annie's song: *Starsound Orchestra* / Nobody does it better: *Starsound Orchestra* / I'm not in love: *Belmonde, Pierre* / Evergreen: *Starsound Orchestra* / Take my breath away: *Starsound Orchestra* / Without you: *Belmonde, Pierre* / Harry's Game: *Light Shadows* / Long and winding road: *Hill & Wiltchinsky* / Chariots of fire: *Masterworks* / Cacharpaya: *Interlude Orchestra* / Aria: *Belmonde, Pierre* / Walking in the air: *Hill & Wiltchinsky* / Flying: *SRE Band* / Meditation: *Royal Philharmonic Orchestra* / Concierto de arajuez: *Belmonde, Pierre* / Cavatina: *Hill & Wiltchinsky* / Clair de lune: *Allis, Julie* / Morning: *London Symphony Orchestra* / Spring song: *London Symphony Orchestra* / Morning has broken: *London Symphony Orchestra* / Canon in D major: *London Symphony Orchestra* / Brighteyes: *Belmonde, Pierre* / Whiter shade of pale: *Belmonde, Pierre* / Forever autumn: *Belmonde, Pierre* / Nights in white satin: *Belmonde, Pierre* / Feelings: *Belmonde, Pierre* / I can't stop loving you: *Belmonde, Pierre* / Light of experience: *Belmonde, Pierre* / We have all the time in the world: *Brooks, Paul* / If I could turn back time: *Starsound Orchestra* / When I fall in love: *Starsound Orchestra* / What a wonderful world: *Brooks, Paul* / Imagine: *Starsound Orchestra* / China in your hand: *Starsound Orchestra* / You don't bring me flowers: *Starsound Orchestra* / Leaving on a jet plane: *Starsound Orchestra* / No more I love yous: *Brooks, Paul* / Do that to me one more time: *Starsound Orchestra* / Nothing compares 2 U: *Brooks, Paul* / Albatross: *Dream Circle* / Caravan of love: *Starsound Orchestra* / Shadow of your smile: *Starsound Orchestra* / Lady in red: *Brooks, Paul* / Vincent: *Starsound Orchestra* / Three times a lady: *Starsound Orchestra* / Liebstraum: *Starsound Orchestra* / Greensleeves: *Starsound Orchestra* / Mandy: *Starsound Orchestra* / Parisean walkways: *Dream Circle* / Killing me softly: *Starsound Orchestra* / Sleepwalk: *Dream Circle* / Groovy kind of love: *Starsound Orchestra*
ECD 3180 / Aug '97 / K-Tel

☐ **101% REGGAE**
Sing a little song: *Dekker, Desmond* / We play record: *In Crowd* / Work all day: *Biggs, Barry* / Mad about you: *Ruffin, Bruce* / Island music: *Calendar, Phil* / Girlie girlie: *George, Sophia* / Do you really want to hurt me: *Heptones* / Sweet cherrie: *Honey Boy* / Keep on riding: *Donaldson, Eric* / Side show: *Biggs, Barry* / Take care of my heart: *Gardiner, Boris* / Blue moon: *Francis, Winston* / Come back Charlie: *Charlie Chaplin* / Rock my soul: *Pioneers* / It burn mi belly: *George, Sophia* / Happy anniversary: *Schloss, Cynthia* / Busted land: *Dekker, Desmond* / Kool and deadly: *Clint Eastwood & General Saint*
ECD 3074 / Jan '95 / K-Tel

☐ **101% REGGAE (4CD Set)**
ECD 3170 / Jun '96 / K-Tel

☐ **101% ROCK 'N' ROLL**
Rockin' good way (to mess around and fall in love): *Benton, Brook* / Lucille: *Little Richard* / Magic moment: *Drifters* / Coasters: *Coasters* / Rockin' robin: *Day, Bobby* / Love letters in the sand: *Boone, Pat* / Teen beat: *Nelson, Sandy* / Come softly to me: *Fleetwoods* / Smoke gets in your eyes: *Platters* / Come go with me: *Del-Vikings* / Purple people eater: *Wooley, Sheb* / Sea of love: *Phillips, Phil* / Little darlin': *Diamonds* / Sleep walk: *Santo & Johnny* / For your precious love: *Impressions* / Mr. Lee: *Bobbettes* / Love potion no.9: *Clovers* / You always hurt the one you love: *Henry, Clarence 'Frogman'* / Susie Darlin': *Luke, Robin* / Alley oop: *Hollywood Argyles* / Earth angel: *Crew Cuts* / Down the line: *Lewis, Jerry Lee* / Happy organ: *Cortez, Dave 'Baby'* / I'll make it all up to you: *Lewis, Jerry Lee* / My special angel: *Helms, Bobby* / Hula love: *Knox, Buddy* / Primrose lane: *Wallace, Jerry* / Ain't that a shame: *Boone, Pat* / Stagger lee: *Price, Lloyd* / Tell Laura I love her: *Peterson, Ray* / Teen angel: *Dinning, Mark* / Red river rock: *Johnny & The Hurricanes* / What in the world's come over you: *Scott, Jack* / Rebel rouser: *Eddy, Duane* / Will you love me tomorrow: *Shirelles* / Good golly Miss Molly: *Little Richard* / Bongo rock: *Epps, Preston* / He will bvreak your heart: *Butler, Jerry* / Lavender blue: *Turner, Sammy* / Western movies: *Olympics* / Dixie fried: *Perkins, Carl* / Hey little girl: *Clark, Dee* / My heart is an open book: *Dobkins, Carl Jr.* / Mr Blue: *Fleetwoods* / Why: *Avalon, Frankie* / Lonely street: *Vincent, Gene* / Only you (and you alone): *Platters* / Finger poppin' time: *Ballard, Hank & The Midnighters* / Razzle dazzle: *Haley, Bill & The Comets* / Sven little girls: *Evans, Paul* / Charlie Brown: *Coasters* / Walk don't run: *Ventures* / Do you wanna dance: *Freeman, Bobby* / Willie and the hand jive: *Otis, Johnny* / Lets go lets go lets go: *Ballard, Hank & The Midnighters* / Forty miles of bad road: *Eddy, Duane* / Let there be drums: *Nelson, Sandy* / Wonderful time up there: *Boone, Pat* / Sorry (I ran all the way home): *Impalas* / Keep a knockin': *Little Richard* / Rock 'n' roll is here to stay: *Little Richard* / Reveille rock: *Johnny & The Hurricanes* / Ooby dooby: *Orbison, Roy* / Blue suede shoes: *Perkins, Carl* / At the hop: *Danny & The Juniors* / Honky tonk: *Doggett, Bill* / Personality: *Price, Lloyd* / Little bitty pretty one: *Day, Bobby* / Jenny Jenny: *Little Richard* / This ole house: *Clooney, Rosemary* / Green door: *Lowe, Jim* / Party doll: *Knox, Buddy* / Searchin': *Coasters* / Raunchy: *Justis, Bill* / Tutti frutti: *Little Richard* / Rock around the clock: *Haley, Bill & The Comets* / Runaway: *Shannon, Del* / Blue moon: *Marcels* / Rubber ball: *Vee, Bobby* / Baby face: *Little Richard* / Wild one: *Rydell, Bobby* / Because they're young: *Eddy, Duane* / Speedy Gonzales: *Boone, Pat* / Singing the blues: *Mitchell, Guy* / Tiger: *Fabian* / Endlessly: *Benton, Brook* / Along came Jones: *Coasters* / Venus: *Avalon, Frankie* / Poetry in motion: *Tillotson, Johnny* / Devil or angel: *Vee, Bobby* / Corrina corrina: *Peterson, Ray* / Beatnik fly: *Johnny & The Hurricanes* / Hats off to Larry: *Shannon, Del* / Let's have a party: *Jackson, Wanda* / Venus in blue jeans: *Jackson, Wanda* / Hawaii five-o: *Ventures* / Swingin' school: *Rydell, Bobby* / Let's go: *Routers* / Hey baby: *Channel, Bruce* / Endless sleep: *Reynolds, Jody*
EMC 2165
ECD 3165 / Jun '96 / K-Tel

☐ **101% SPEED GARAGE VOL.1 (3CD Set)**
MMCCD 004 / 10 Nov '97 / Massive

☐ **101% SPEED GARAGE VOL.2 (3CD Set)**
MMCCD 011 / 13 Apr '98 / Massive

☐ **102% REGGAE**
OK Fred: *Dunkley, Errol* / Three ring circus: *Biggs, Barry* / Back a yard: *In Crowd* / Love again: *George, Sophia* / Starvation: *Pioneers* / Stick by me: *Holt, John* / Night like this: *Biggs, Barry* / Baby my love: *Calendar, Fip* / Eighteen yellow roses: *Gardiner, Boris* / Maga dawg: *George, Sophia* / Everybody join hands: *Dekker, Desmond* / Uptown Sharron: *Isaacs, Gregory* / I think I love you: *Donaldson, Eric* / You are my destiny: *Gardiner, Boris* / Please don't make me cry: *Winston Groovy* / Everything to me: *Holt, John* / One big happy family: *Ruffin, Bruce* / Elizabethan reggae: *Gardiner, Boris*
ECD 3103 / Jan '95 / K-Tel

☐ **0161**
Town owt: *Mild Man Jan* / Grated chicken: *Jackfear* / Two of: *Gescom* / Powderkex: *Fall* / 01706: *Bola* / Joking apart: *Bola* / Whore: *Jega* / Asymetric: *V/VM* / Destination tomorrow: *Renegades* / Probe: *Audiomontage* / Night raid: *Datathief* / Mood swingz: *O'Natural* / Cyclomethicone: *Yunx* / Flat slab: *Professor Broxburn*
0161 / 1 Sep '98 / Skam

☐ **200 PROOF COMPILATION**
DESTINY 100CD / Oct '96 / Destiny

☐ 300 YEARS OF SCOTLAND'S MUSIC
MMSCD 951 / Apr '95 / Scott Music

☐ 313 DETROIT
War of the worlds: *Dark Comedy* / Distance: *Reel By Reel* / Baby can: *KELSEY* / Unconscious world: *Subterfuge* / Electricity: *Santonio* / Warwick: *Fowlkes, Eddie* / Desire: *69* / Free Your Mind: *Piece*
INF 01CD / Nov '92 / Infonet

☐ 500 MILES TO GLORY
MR 098CD / Sep '97 / Man's Ruin

☐ 706 UNION INSTRUMENTALS
CPCD 8302 / May '97 / Charly

☐ 1000 VOLTS OF STAX
Hideaway: *Booker T & The MG's* / (Sittin' on the) dock of the bay: *Booker T & The MG's* / Don't you lie to me: *King, Albert* / Cupid: *Redding, Otis* / I've got dreams to remember: *Redding, Otis* / Don't worry about tomorrow: *Marchan, Bobby* / Walking the dog: *Thomas, Rufus* / Runaround: *Thomas, Carla* / Floyd's beat: *Newman, Floyd* / When my love comes down: *Johnson, Ruby* / She won't be like you: *Bell, William* / Never let me go: *Bell, William* / Sweet devil: *John, Mable* / Cloudburst: *Mad Lads* / Hippy dippy: *Mar-Keys* / Don't mess up a good thing: *Thomas, Rufus & Carla* / Just enough to hurt me: *Astors* / Knock on wood: *Floyd, Eddie*
CDSXD 042 / Sep '91 / Stax

☐ 1943-1947
22026 / Feb '89 / Caprice

☐ 1960'S FRENCH EP COLLECTION, THE
176152 / Sep '97 / Magic

☐ 1991 TRIANGLE JAZZ PARTYBOYS
FINCD 101 / Nov '94 / Arbors Jazz

☐ 1993 PORTLAND WATERFRONT BLUES FESTIVAL
BCD 00142 / Jul '96 / Burnside

☐ 1998 CALYPSO COMPILATION
JWMM 002CD / 9 Feb '98 / JW

☐ 1998 DOVE AWARDS NOMINEES
8306104812 / 7 Apr '98 / BWO

☐ 2000 VOLTS OF STAX
Kinda easy like: *Booker T & The MG's* / Ride your pony: *Thomas, Rufus* / You don't know like I know: *Taylor, Johnnie* / Pain in my heart: *Redding, Otis* / It's not that easy: *Johnson, Ruby* / How about you: *Parker, Deanie* / Hotshot: *Bar-Kays* / Come out tonight: *Astors* / Bark at the moon: *Floyd, Eddie* / I found a brand new love: *Kirk, Eddie* / Please don't go: *Tonettes* / Try me: *Thomas, Carla* / Slinky: *Mar-Keys* / Crosscut saw: *King, Albert* / She's the one: *Mad Lads* / You don't miss your water: *Bell, William* / I say a little prayer: *Booker T & The MG's* / Try a little tenderness: *Redding, Otis*
CDSXD 074 / Oct '92 / Stax

☐ 2001: A GRASS ODYSSEY
GROW 0272 / May '95 / Grass

☐ 3000 SERIES CMPLER VOL.1
CMPCD 5003 / 30 Mar '98 / CMP

☐ 3000 VOLTS OF STAX
Spoonful: *Booker T & The MG's* / Come to me: *Redding, Otis* / I'd rather fight than switch: *Johnson, Ruby* / Sixty minutes of your time: *Taylor, Johnnie* / Quittin' time: *Bell, William* / Good good lovin': *Thomas, Carla* / I got everything I need: *Floyd, Eddie* / Count your many blessings: *Stars Of Virginia* / Big bad wolf: *Jenkins, Johnny* / Rotation: *Tonettes* / Wee little bit: *Marchan, Bobby* / Juanita: *Prince Conley* / Win you over: *Porter, David* / Hunter: *King, Albert* / Per-culating: *Mar-Keys* / Patch my heart: *Mad Lads* / Remember me: *Redding, Otis* / Water: *Taylor, Johnnie* / Sock soul: *Bar-Kays* / Big bird: *Floyd, Eddie* / All I need is some sunshine in my life: *Dixie Nightingales*
CDSXD 102 / Mar '94 / Stax

☐ 4000 VOLTS OF STAX AND SATELLITE
Home grown: *Booker T & The MG's* / Woman who needs the love of a man: *Astors* / Just to hold your hand: *Marchan, Bobby* / Ain't that good: *Prince Conley* / All that I am: *Prince Conley* / As you can see: *Chips* / Shake up: *Cobras* / I'll never give her up (My friend): *Canes* / Somewhere along the line: *Canes* / Popeye the sailor man: *Del-Rios* / Any other way: *Bell, William* / Strut this Sally: *Astors* / Uncle Willie good time: *Astors* / I wish I were that girl: *Rene, Wendy* / Hawg: *Kirk, Eddie* / I see my baby coming: *Mack, Oscar* / Please don't leave: *Drapels* / Someday: *Veltones* / All the way: *Prince Conley* / Hard times (Every dog's got his day): *Prince Conley* / About noon: *Mar-Keys* / Something is worrying me: *Redding, Otis*
CDSXD 107 / May '95 / Stax

☐ 6000 OHM (2CD Set)
No good (Start the dance): *Prodigy* / I need your love: *Microwave Prince* / Signs of life: *Meteor Seven* / Feel the melodee: *Komakino* / Sacred cycles: *Lazonby* / Cybertrance: *Blue Alphabet* / My: *Van Dyke, Paul* / Bagdad: *Paragliders* / Perpetuum mobile: *Luxor* / Filterside: *Dimitri From Paris* / Phraser: *Bionic Boom* / Self immolation: *Hiroshima* / Torwart: *Deep Piece* / Mono 1: *Nervous Project* / Amphetamine: *Drax* / Drag: *Titan & Red Acid Jack* / Mongolian rider: *Phoenixx* / Asita: *Source T-10* / Let there by rhythm: *Mason, Steve* / Two full moons: *Union Jack*
SUCK CD6 / Oct '94 / Suck Me Plasma

☐ $10,000 WORTH OF DOO WOP
Pretty, pretty girl: *Timetones* / Where are you: *Bel Aires* / Why be a fool: *Nobles* / My life's desire: *Verdicts* / Ride away: *Revalons* / Tight skirt and sweater: *Versatones* / Tell me: *Mastertones* / Bang bang shoot 'em Daddy: *Emblems* / Crying for you: *Centuries* / My love: *Timetones* / Poor rock and roll: *Nobles* / Can I come over tonight: *Velours* / Tomorrow: *Decoys* / Sindy: *Squires* / Bila: *Versatones* / Oh darling: *Jaytones* / My love: *Revalons* / I love you: *4 Mosts* / Jerry: *Minors* / In my heart: *Timetones*
FICD 1 / Dec '93 / Finbarr Internationa

A

☐ A IS FOR ACTIV (2CD Set)
So bad: *Hagen, Nina* / American pie: *Just Luis* / Show me: *Taff, Joe* / I'll do my best: *Ritchie Family* / Always: *MK* / My sweet liar: *With It Guys* / Addicted: *Plutonic* / Hide-a-way: *Nu Soul* / Burning: *MK* / Unconditionally: *Williams, Sandra* / You shine so bright: *Dennis, Julie* / Always: *MK* / Addicted: *Plutonic* / I want it, I need it: *Williams, Sandra* / Hide-a-way: *Nu Soul* / I'll do my best: *Ritchie Family* / Burning: *MK* / Pleasure voyage: *X-Form*
ACTIVCD 8 / Oct '97 / Activ

☐ A NOS IDOLES
Une meche de cheveux: *Adamo* / Dominique: *Soeur Sourire* / Nous on s'aime: *Chelon, Georges* / Premier baiser, premiere larme: *Reggan, Jacky* / Come comedie: *Mars, Betty* / Les yeux d'un ange: *Fernandel, Franck* / La gendarmerie: *Topaloff, Patrick* / Mathias: *Gribouille* / C'est ma fete: *Antony, Richard* / Les ballons rouge: *Lama, Serge* / Les gens qui s'aiment: *Dumont, Charles* / Ensemble: *Sullivan, Art* / Adieu jolie Candy: *Michael, Jean Francois* / Parle mon maman: *Miras, Robert* / Souviens toi de moi: *Marie* / Comme j'ai toulours envie d'aimer: *Hamilton, Marc* / Le sud: *Ferrer, Nino* / Tout nu, tout bronze: *Carlos*
DC 863932 / Nov '96 / Disky

☐ A TODA CUBA LE GUSTA
CCD 505 / Nov '95 / Caney

☐ A&M RECORDS SAMPLER (2CD Set)
If it makes you happy: *Crow, Sheryl* / Everyday is a winding road: *Crow, Sheryl* / Good enough: *Dodgy* / If you're thinking of me: *Dodgy* / Marblehead Johnson: *Bluetones* / Let's make a night to remember: *Adams, Bryan* / Star: *Adams, Bryan* / I'm so happy I can't stop crying: *Sting* / Midnight in a perfect world: *DJ Shadow* / Stereo: *Spooky* / It's a sad sad planet: *Evil Superstars* / No cheap thrill: *Vega, Suzanne* / Heaven: *Washington, Sarah* / Sticky rock: *Bawl* / All gone away: *Joyrider* / 3000: *Dr. Octagon* / Berry mediatation: *UNKLE*
ARS 96 / Oct '96 / A&M

☐ A-SIDES VOL.1
CATNO 8CD / Nov '92 / Crass

☐ A-SIDES VOL.2
CATNO 9CD / May '93 / Crass

☐ A-Z OF JAZZ (2CD Set)
R2CD 4032 / 13 Apr '98 / Deja Vu

☐ ABORIGINAL MUSIC OF THE WANDJINA
EUCD 1341 / Apr '96 / ARC

☐ ABRACADABRA
1212012 / Nov '90 / Soul Note

☐ ABSOLUTE BLUES
JAZZFMCD 2 / Feb '97 / Jazz FM

☐ ABSOLUTE COUNTRY GOLD (2CD Set)
Walkin' after midnight: *Cline, Patsy* / Wishful thinking: *Fuller, Jerry & Wynn Stewart* / Husbands and wives: *Miller, Roger* / Let me be the one: *Locklin, Hank* / Dixie road: *Greenwood, Lee* / My friends are gonna be strangers: *Haggard, Merle* / In the misty moonlight: *Wallace, Jerry* / This time: *Shondell, Troy* / No charge: *Barrie, J.J.* / Hot rod Licoln: *Ryan, Charlie* / Stay away from the apple tree: *Spears, Billie Jo* / Detroit city: *Bare, Bobby* / I tell it like it used to be: *Brown, T. Graham* / To see my angel cry: *Twitty, Conway* / Heaven's just a sin away: *Kendalls* / Baby's got her blue jeans on: *McDaniel, Mel* / Okie from Muskogee: *Haggard, Merle* / All I have to do is dream: *Everly Brothers* / Primrose lane: *Wallace, Jerry* / All American boy: *Bare, Bobby* / Brilliant conversationalist: *Brown, T. Graham* / Crazy: *Spears, Billie Jo* / IOU: *Greenwood, Lee* / Your cheatin' heart: *Boxcar Willie* / Baby's gone: *Twitty, Conway* / Honky tonk merry go round: *Cline, Patsy* / My uncle used to love me but she died: *Miller, Roger* / Pittburg stealers: *Kendalls*
SD 885392 / 2 Feb '98 / Disky

☐ ABSOLUTE COUNTRY VOL.2
74321279242 / Apr '95 / RCA

☐ ABSOLUTE DANCE MIX
XTR 3002 / Feb '97 / X-Treme

☐ ABSOLUTE GOLD (2CD Set)
Heaven for everyone: *Queen* / Because you loved me: *Dion, Celine* / Missing: *Everything But The Girl* / Breakfast at Tiffany's: *Deep Blue Something* / Drive: *REM* / I'd lie for you (and that's the truth): *Meat Loaf* / Father and son: *Stevens, Cat* / How deep is your love: *Take That* / Where do broken hearts go: *Houston, Whitney* / Father figure: *Michael, George* / You don't understand me: *Roxette* / Always tomorrow: *Estefan, Gloria* / Missing you: *De Burgh, Chris* / Anywhere is: *Enya* / Where the wild roses grow: *Cave, Nick & Kylie Minogue* / Let it rain: *Marshall, Amanda* / Day we caught the train: *Ocean Colour Scene* / Don't look back in anger: *Oasis* / I just can't stop loving you: *Jackson, Michael* / Killing me softly: *Fugees* / Never never love: *Simply Red* / Earth, the sun, the rain: *Color Me Badd* / Open arms: *Carey, Mariah* / Anything: *3T* / I don't wanna fight: *Turner, Tina* / I'll never break your heart: *Backstreet Boys* / You're the star: *Stewart, Rod* / Secret garden: *Springsteen, Bruce* / Leningrad: *Joel, Billy* / Rocket man (I think it's going to be a long, long time): *John, Elton* / Help me: *Mike & The Mechanics* / Belfast child: *Simple Minds* / Love so beautiful: *Bolton, Michael* / All I wanna do is make love to you: *Heart* / Believer: *Glen, Marla* / You and I: *Scorpions*
SONYTV 22CD / Jan '97 / Sony TV

☐ ABSOLUTE PARTY PARTY
C'mon everybody: *Cochran, Eddie* / Locomotion: *Little Eva* / Shakin' all over: *Kidd, Johnny & The Pirates* / Do wah diddy diddy: *Manfred Mann* / Barbara Ann: *Beach Boys* / See my baby jive: *Wizzard* / That's the way I like it: *KC & The Sunshine Band* / Heaven must be missing an angel: *Tavares* / Devil gate drive: *Quatro, Suzi* / Kids in America: *Wilde, Kim* / Respectable: *Mel & Kim* / Whatever I do: *Dean, Hazell* / T'ain't what you do (it's the way that you do it): *Fun Boy Three & Bananarama* / Gangsters: *Specials* / Heart of glass: *Blondie* / Unbelievable: *EMF* / Geno: *Dexy's Midnight Runners* / Tiger feet: *Mud* / I'm the leader of the gang (I am): *Glitter, Gary* / Hi ho silver lining: *Beck, Jeff*
CDMFP 6239 / Nov '97 / Music For Pleasure

☐ ABSOLUTE REGGAE
Everything I own: *Boothe, Ken* / Let your yeah be yeah: *Pioneers* / You make me feel: *Gardiner, Boris* / Eighteen with a bullet: *Harriott, Derrick* / Return of Django: *Upsetters* / Love of the common people: *Thomas, Nicky* / Cherry oh baby: *Donaldson, Eric* / Black and white: *Greyhound* / Reggae man: *Dekker, George* / Walk away: *Pierre, Marie* / Rain: *Ruffin, Bruce* / Young, gifted and black: *Bob & Marcia* / Lively up yourself: *Marley, Bob & The Wailers* / Then he kissed me: *Marvels* / Heart made of stone: *Hall, Audrey* / Johnny too bad: *Slickers* / Many rivers to cross: *Cliff, Jimmy* / Israelites: *Dekker, Desmond & The Aces* / Oh what a feeling: *Simon, Tito* / Hurt so good: *Cadogan, Susan* / Rivers of Babylon: *Melodians* / First time ever I saw your face: *Griffiths, Marcia* / Help me make it through the night: *Holt, John* / Suzanne beware of the devil: *Livingstone, Dandy*
VSOPCD 104 / Nov '87 / Connoisseur Collection

☐ ABSOLUTE REGGAE (2CD Set)
Lady: *Wade, Wayne* / Midnight rider: *Davidson, Paul* / Cocaine: *Dillinger* / OK Fred: *Dunkley, Errol* / Please don't make me cry: *Winston Groovy* / Sideshow: *Biggs, Barry* / Israelites: *Dekker, Desmond* / Sister love: *Isaacs, Gregory* / Place in the sun: *Winjama* / So much things to say: *Marley, Rita* / Putting on the Ritz: *Mighty Diamonds* / Stir it up: *Thomas, Ruddy* / No woman no cry: *Marley, Kymani* / Nightshift: *Winston Groovy* / Girlie girlie: *George, Sophia* / I want to wake up with you: *Gardiner, Boris* / Try again: *Wade, Wayne* / Rock me tonight: *Winston Groovy* / Work all day: *Biggs, Barry* / Cherry oh baby: *Donaldson, Eric* / Ire feelings: *Edwards, Rupie* / This is reggae music: *Hammond, Beres & Mikey Zappow* / Wet dream: *Max Romeo* / Iron lion Zion: *Thomas, Ruddy* / Kinky reggae: *Marley, Kymani* / Wear you to the ball: *Holt, John* / Do you really want to hurt me: *Heptones* / Blue moon: *Francis, Winston*
SD 885322 / 2 Feb '98 / Disky

☐ ABSOLUTELY (The Very Best Of Prelude Records/2CD Set)
You're the one for me: *D-Train* / Beat the street: *Redd, Sharon* / Go with the flow: *Weeks & Co.* / Love fever: *Adams, Gayle* / Gonna get over you: *Joli, France* / You'll never know: *Hi-Gloss* / I wish you would: *Brown, Jocelyn* / Just let me do my thing: *Sine* / Come on dance, dance: *Saturday Night Band* / Keep on jumpin': *Musique* / Inch by inch: *Strikers* / I hear music in the streets: *Unlimited Touch* / Somebody else's guy: *Brown, Jocelyn* / Can you handle it: *Redd, Sharon* / Check out the groove: *Thurston, Bobby* / Feed the flame: *Johnson, Lorraine* / Music: *D-Train* / What I got is what you need: *Unique* / On a journey (I sing the Funk Electric): *Electrik Funk* / All I need is you: *Electrik Funk* / You are the one: *Pilot* / Come let me love you: *Day, Jeanette 'Lady'* / Must be the music: *Secret Weapon* / Love how you feel: *Redd, Sharon* / Ain't no mountain high enough: *Brown, Jocelyn* / I'm caught up (in a one night love affair): *Inner Life* / Come to me: *Joli, France* / In the bush: *Musique* / Body music: *Strikers* / Dyin' to be dancin': *Empress* / Give it to me (if you don't mind): *Conquest* / Searching to find the one: *Unlimited Touch* / Music got me: *Visual*
DEEPBOX 1 / Feb '97 / Deep Beats

☐ ABSOLUTELY (The Very Best Of Disco/3CD Set)
Jazzy rhythm: *Wallace, Michelle* / You can't run from my love: *Singleton, Maxine* / Harder they come: *Rockers Revenge & Donnie Calvin* / We got the funk: *Positive Force* / Check out the groove: *Thurston, Bobby* / Wastin' my love: *Sticky Fingers* / Sure shot: *Weber, Tracy* / There but for the grace of God go I: *Machine* / Don't bring back memories: *Passion* / Keep giving me love: *D-Train* / Weekend: *Class Action & Chris Wiltshire* / Happiness is just round the bend: *Gooding, Cuba* / Hit 'n' run lover: *Jiani, Carol* / Ain't no mountain high enough: *Brown, Jocelyn* / I don't want to be a freak (But I can't help myself): *Dynasty* / Do you wanna funk: *Sylvester* / Night fever: *Douglas, Carol* / Ain't no need for crying: *Silk* / I'll cry for you: *Kumano* / Let's start the dance: *Bohannon, Hamilton* / Jerky rhythm: *Erotic Drum Band* / Dancin' the night away: *Voggue* / I need you: *Sylvester* / You're gonna lose my love: *Jiani, Carol* / Making love: *Todd, Pam & Love Exchange* / Your love: *Silk, Satin & Lace* / Perfect love affair: *Constellation Orchestra* / Disco stomp: *Bohannon, Hamilton* / Double dutch bus: *Smith, Frankie* / Lay it down on me: *Mallory, Gerald* / In the name of love: *Redd, Sharon* / Nice and soft: *Wish & La-Rita Gaskin* / We fell in love while dancing: *Brandon, Bill*
DEEPBOX 2 / Mar '97 / Deep Beats

☐ ABSOLUTELY (The Very Best Of Electro/3CD Set)
White lines (Don't do it): *Grandmaster Flash & Melle Mel* / Give me tonight: *Shannon* / Uphill (Peace of mind): *COD* / Hungry for your love: *Hanson & Davis* / Crash goes love: *Holloway, Loleatta* / Boogie down bronx: *Man Parrish* / Break dancin' (Electric boogie): *West Street Mob* / Nunk: *Warp 9* / Soul makossa: *Nairobi* / Jungle rock: *Tribe* / Let the music play: *Shannon* / In the bottle: *COD* / Rock the box: *Sylvester* / And the beat goes on: *Orbit* / Mirda rock: *Griffin, Reggie & Technofunk* / Freak-a-zoid: *Midnight Star* / On journey (I sing the funk electric): *Electric Funk* / Feel the force: *G-Force* / Scorpio: *CD III* / Rotation: *Sine* / Hip hop be bop (Don't stop): *Man Parrish* / On the upside: *Xena* / Mosquito (Aka hobo scratch): *West Street Mob* / Jump back (Set me free): *Braxton, Dhar* / Your life: *Konk* / Message II (Survival): *Melle Mel & Duke Bootee* / Light years away: *Warp 9* / I'm the boss: *Amazing Kid & Cut Master Lee* / (I'm just a sucker) For a pretty face: *Phillips, West* / It's out of sight: *Lefturno*
DEEPBOX 3 / Mar '97 / Deep Beats

☐ ABSOLUTELY (The Very Best Of Solar Records Vol.1/3CD Set)
Night to remember: *Shalamar* / It's a love thing: *Whispers* / Wet my whistle: *Midnight Star* / It's all the way live: *Lakeside* / I've just begun to love you: *Dynasty* / In the raw: *Whispers* / I gotta keep dancin' (keep smiling): *Lucas, Carrie* / Make that move: *Shalamar* / Come back lover, come back: *Sylvers* / Can-U-dance: *Deele* / Operator: *Midnight Star* / I wanna be rich: *Calloway* / Romeo where's Juliet: *Collage* / Second time around: *Shalamar* / I can make it better: *Whispers* / Headlines: *Midnight Star* / Fantastic voyage: *Lakeside* / Does that ring a bell: *Dynasty* / Friends: *Shalamar* / Show me where you're coming from: *Lucas, Carrie* / Rock steady: *Whispers* / Groove control: *Dynasty* / Get in touch with me: *Collage* / Call me: *Wolfer, Bill* / And the beat goes on: *Whispers* / Wet my whistle: *Midnight Star* / Take that to the bank: *Shalamar* / Freak-a-zoid: *Midnight Star* / There it is: *Shalamar* / Headlines: *Midnight Star* / Romeo where's Juliet: *Collage* / Night to remember: *Shalamar* / Snake in the grass: *Midnight Star* / Fantastic voyage: *Lakeside* / Scientific love: *Midnight Star* / Can-U-dance: *Deele* / Special: *Lakeside* / Restrictions: *Lakeside* / Circumstantial evidence: *Shalamar* / Hot spot: *Midnight Star* / Alien Zzz: *Collage* / Rock steady: *Whispers* / Do me right: *Dynasty* / Wet my whistle: *Midnight Star* / Midas touch: *Midnight Star* / Flavour: *Just Ice & Grandmaster Flash* / I've got it good: *Tricky Tee*
DEEPBOX 4 / Jun '97 / Deep Beats

☐ ABSOLUTELY (The Very Best Of Solar Records Vol.2/3CD Set)
And the beat goes on: *Whispers* / I don't want to be a freak (but I can't help myself): *Dynasty* / Dance with you: *Lucas, Carrie* / Soul Train '75: *Soul Train Gang* / Papa was a rollin' stone: *Wolfer, Bill* / Engine no.9: *Midnight Star* / Take that to the bank: *Shalamar* / Tonight: *Whispers* / Raid: *Lakeside* / Take it to the top: *Sylvers* / Winners and losers: *Collage* / Let's get smooth: *Calloway* / There it is: *Shalamar* / Contagious: *Whispers* / Midas touch: *Midnight Star* / Do me right: *Dynasty* / I can make you feel good: *Shalamar* / Hello stranger: *Lucas, Carrie* / Shoot 'em up movies: *Deele* / I want to hold your hand: *Lakeside* / Curious: *Midnight Star* / I'm the one for you: *Whispers* / Adventures in the land of music: *Dynasty* / Groovin': *Collage* / Right in the socket: *Shalamar* / I owe you one: *Shalamar* / Take that to the bank: *Shalamar* / Second time around: *Shalamar* / Your piece of the rock: *Dynasty* / I've just begun to love you: *Dynasty* / I don't want to freak (but I can't help myself): *Dynasty* / Given in to love: *Lakeside* / It's all the way live: *Lakeside* / Two occasions: *Deele* / Lady: *Whispers* / Song for Donny: *Whispers* / And the beat goes on: *Whispers*
DEEPBOX 5 / Aug '97 / Deep Beats

☐ ABSOLUTELY (The Very Best Of Old School Rap/3CD Set)
Rapper's delight: *Sugarhill Gang* / Adventures of Grandmaster Flash: *Grandmaster Flash* / Super-Wolf can do it: *Super-Wolf* / Cold gettin' dumb: *Just Ice* / Hey fellas: *Trouble Funk* / Yes we can can: *Treacherous Three* / Monster jam: *Spoonie Gee & The Sequence* / Sucker DJ: *Dimples D & Marley Marl* / Outta control: *Miracle Mike & The Ladies Of The 80's* / Ooh baby: *West Street Mob* / Message: *Grandmaster Flash & The Furious Five* / Eighth wonder: *Sugarhill Gang* / That's the joint: *Funky 4+1* / Success is the word: *12:41* / Showdown: *Furious Five & Sugarhill Gang* / Funk you up: *Sequence* / Busy Bee's groove: *Busy Bee* / Breaking bells (take me to the Mardi Gras): *Crash Crew* / Leave it to the drums (here come the drums): *Tricky Tee* / All night long (waterbed): *Kevie Kev* / Apache: *Sugarhill Gang* / It's nasty (genius of love): *Grandmaster Flash & The Furious Five* / I've got it good: *Tricky Tee* / New York New York: *Grandmaster Flash & The Furious Five* / B-boy style: *Little Jazzy Jay* / Xmas rap: *Treacherous Three* / Making cash money: *Busy Bee* / Don't rock the boat: *Midnight Star & Ecstasy* / Johnny the fox: *Tricky Tee*
DEEPBOX 7 / Aug '97 / Deep Beats

☐ ABSOLUTELY FABULOUS DIVAS
IFTYCDL 2 / 4 May '98 / Infinity

☐ ABSTRACT EXPRESSION VOL.1
FLAGCD 107 / Jun '95 / Flagbearer

☐ ABSTRACT PHAZE
MPCD 004 / Nov '96 / Masturi

☐ ABSTRACT PUNK SINGLES COLLECTION
48 Crash: *Gymslips* / Big sister: *Gymslips* / Robot man: *Gymslips* / Self destruct: *UK Subs* / Police state: *UK Subs* / War of the roses: *UK Subs* / Vengence: *New Model Army* / Nowhere to run: *Outcasts* / Denise: *Joolz* / Three Johns: *AWOL* / Great expectations: *New Model Army* / Price: *New Model Army* / Armchair: *Hagar The Womb* / Evil eye: *Gymslips* / Drink problem: *Gymslips* / Daddy's been working: *Downbeats* / Lean on me: *Redskins* / Unionise: *Redskins* / Kick out the tories: *Newtown Neurotics* / Mindless violence: *Newtown Neurotics*
CDPUNK 52 / Apr '95 / Anagram

☐ ABSTRACT VIBES
5242522 / Jun '96 / Quango

☐ ABUSE YOUR FRIENDS
ABUSE 001 / 3 Nov '97 / Abuse

☐ ACADEMY AWARD LOSERS
MACCD 355 / 26 Jan '98 / Autograph

☐ ACCESS ALL AREAS VOL.1 (VIP)
Seven days and one week: *BBE* / Passion: *Amen UK* / Bellissima: *DJ Quicksilver* / Outragous: *Stix 'N' Stoned* / Let's groove: *Morel, George* / Party: *Fletch* / Move your body (mueve la cadera): *Reel 2 Real* / Groovebird: *Natural Born Groovers* / Techno solutions: *DJ Philip* / La batteria (the drum track): *Baby Doc* / Flash: *BBE* / Nightmare: *Brainbug* / Come with me: *Quattara* / Do that to me: *Lisa Marie Experience* / Freedom: *Black Magic* / Real vibration (want love): *Black Magic* / Stamp: *Healy, Jeremy & Amos*
CDTIVA 1015 / Apr '97 / Positiva

☐ ACCORDEON - LA COLLECTION A SUIVRE
174522 / Jun '97 / ARB

☐ **ACCORDEON - PARIS TANGO**
175692 / Jun '97 / ARB

☐ **ACCORDEON JAZZ 1911-1944 (2CD Set)**
FA 038 / Nov '95 / Fremeaux

☐ **ACCORDEON VOL.1 1913-1941 (2CD Set)**
DH 002CD / Nov '95 / Fremeaux

☐ **ACCORDEON VOL.2 1942-1952 (2CD Set)**
FA 005CD / Nov '95 / Fremeaux

☐ **ACCORDEON: NOSTALGIC POET OF PARIS (Poete Nostalgique De Paname)**
Sous les toits de Paris: *Alexander, Maurice & His Musette Orchestra* / La mattchiche: *Vacher, Emile* / T'aimer, c'est la folie: *Vacher, Emile* / On m'suit: *Vacher, Emile* / Les momes de la cloche: *Piaf, Edith/ Jean & Jacques Medinger* / Marionettes: *Marceau & His Musette Orchestra* / Napoli: *Marceau & His Musette Orchestra* / Le bonheur n'est plus un reve: *Daron, Robert & Ronaldo/Musette Orchestra* / Tel qu'il est il me plait: *Frehel & Maurice Alexander Musette Orchestra* / C'est un bureaucrate: *Alexander, Maurice & His Musette Orchestra* / Les patineurs: *Vela, Louis & Appennini* / La Java de doudoune: *Vela, Louis & Appennini* / Radieuse radiant: *Vacher, Emile* / Tant que la femme mentira: *Vacher, Emile* / Pouet poet: *Vacher, Emile* / La Java de cezigue: *Piaf, Edith/Jean & Jacques Medinger* / Souvenir de la varenne: *Marceau & His Musette Orchestra* / Athletic: *Marceau & His Musette Orchestra* / Lina: *Marceau & His Musette Orchestra* / Souvenir de Clichy: *Marceau & His Musette Orchestra* / Amusez-vous: *Gardoni, Fredo & Manuel Puig Musette Orchestra/Jean Cyrano* / Sur le plancher des vaches: *Gardoni, Fredo & Manuel Puig Musette Orchestra/Jean Cyrano* / Musette folie: *Pesenti, Rene* / Cascadeuse: *Pesenti, Rene* / L'accordeoniste: *Lebas, Renee Orchestra*
CDAJA 5203 / Oct '96 / Living Era

☐ **ACCORDEONS DIATONIQUES**
CVPV 1391CD / Apr '96 / CVPV

☐ **ACCORDION AND FIDDLES**
LBP 2026CD / Jun '96 / Lochshore

☐ **ACCORDIONS OF THE WORLD**
KAR 992 / Apr '97 / IMP

☐ **ACCOUNTABILITY**
I'm in a rush: *Joseph, Phil* / Street party: *Trampas* / Free for love: *Nelson, CJ* / No.1: *Nelson, CJ* / Precious love: *Richards, Maxine* / Gimme that love: *Ray Half Penny* / Life time: *Richards, Maxine* / Get it right: *Ray Half Penny*
FUNXD 228 / Aug '97 / Future Underground Nation

☐ **ACE BLUES MASTERS VOL.2, THE (4th & Beale And Further South)**
4th and Beale: *Louis, Joe* / Ruthie Mae: *Louis, Joe* / Joe Hill boogie: *Louis, Joe* / Going down to Louisiana: *Louis, Joe* / Get up off it: *Louis, Joe* / Sweetest woman I ever knew: *Louis, Joe* / Mean old world: *Crudup, Arthur 'Big Boy'* / Baby I've been mistreated: *Crudup, Arthur 'Big Boy'* / My baby boogies all the time: *Crudup, Arthur 'Big Boy'* / I wonder: *Crudup, Arthur 'Big Boy'* / What will Lucy do: *Sims, Frankie Lee* / Misery blues: *Sims, Frankie Lee* / Hey little girl: *Sims, Frankie Lee* / Walking with Frankie: *Sims, Frankie Lee* / My talk didn't do no good: *Sims, Frankie Lee* / I warned you baby: *Sims, Frankie Lee* / She likes to boogie real low: *Sims, Frankie Lee* / Well goodbye baby: *Sims, Frankie Lee* / How long: *Sims, Frankie Lee* / Marked deck: *Baby, Mercy* / Rock 'n' roll baby: *Baby, Mercy* / Pleadin': *Baby, Mercy* / Don't lie to me: *Baby, Mercy*
WESM 554 / 16 Mar '98 / Westside

☐ **ACID AND FLOWERS**
TB 1004 / Nov '97 / Tim's Brain

☐ **ACID ATTACK VOL.3**
Times fade: *Phuture The Next Generation* / Acid bites 1: *Acid Warrior* / Blanche: *Purple Plejade* / We call it acid: *Purple Plejade* / Full mane: *Laux & Olsson* / Acid code: *Beyer, Adam* / Acid marathon 1 and 2: *Acid Scout* / Hump around: *Rezzq* / Liquid: *Stoll, Steve* / Acid kraut: *Acidkraut* / Ride the rat: *Two On Acid* / Exorcisten: *Terric Krom* / Get my bearings: *Finnie, Mark* / Serial killer: *DJ Skull* / Utmosfear: *Yanni* / Hear and move: *Reich, Max* / Eazy 2 use: *Reich, Max* / Uplifting: *Prologue* / Trail: *Junk Project* / Angstman: *Metacosm* / Inside out: *Verbos, Mark* / Torn apart: *Singularity* / Dax: *Encephaloid Disturbance* / Reality: *Morant, Andrei*
MILL 042CD / Jul '97 / Millenium

☐ **ACID BOX VOL.1**
ENT 3CD / Oct '96 / Abstract

☐ **ACID COCKTAIL (2CD Set)**
Prison de L'espace: *Masala* / Box: *Blunt* / Sajut mission: *Victims Of Lobotomie* / HDA: *Stigma* / Necrotron: *Silent Room* / Bass junkies: *Loke* / Electroghost: *Edge & Dentist* / Soul mantra: *Chris Liberator* / Fiesta: *Aircraft* / Acidkraut: *Acidkraut* / Koka group: *Dance Therapy* / This is now: *Naked Ape* / Bomb: *Lochi* / Jay-Jay: *Blunt* / Kataplasma: *New Moon* / Freakee: *Til n' Ron* / Vibrations: *Off Beats* / Liquid: *Stoll, Steve* / Power of a darkside: *Brain* / Sportflugzeug: *Devlin, Roger*
560132 / 29 Sep '97 / Nova Tekk

☐ **ACID DREAMS EPITAPH**
HEAD 2696 / 20 Apr '98 / Head

☐ **ACID DREAMS TESTAMENT**
HEAD 2596 / 20 Apr '98 / Head

☐ **ACID FELCH**
SMTCD 003 / 25 May '98 / Smitten

☐ **ACID FLASH VOL.1 (2CD Set)**
SPV 08938422 / Jan '96 / SPV

☐ **ACID FLASH VOL.2 (2CD Set)**
Heulender Wolf: *Future Breeze* / Synaesthesia: *Synaesthesiacs* / Cell: *Parts Of Console* / Southern hemisphere: *Dual Mount* / Input transformer: *Komatsu* / Upside down: *Interrupt* / Go ahead London: *Tesox* / Touch me: *Kenton Connection* / It's hot: *Brainvibe* / Evolution: *Acut Genius* / Leak: *Naomi* / Acid train: *Asys* / Inertia: *Fast Trac* / Walking: *Mo, Kevin*
SPV 08938672 / May '96 / SPV

☐ **ACID FLASH VOL.3 (21 Acid Underground Traxx/2CD Set)**
Acid NRG: *NRG Jams* / Braintool: *Junk Project* / Secret pattern: *Riot Rhythm* / Lash v 11: *Rubicon Massacre Ltd.* / Enjoy the creation: *Assym* / Reality: *Morant, Andrei* / Turn it up: *Huntemann* / Track 1 side A: *Nip Collective* / Hip: *SPAX* / Arp impression: *Driver, Jan* / Search for experience: *Noodle Project* / Strong fish taste: *Plural* / Acid house...acid: *Nostrum* / Exceed: *Junk Project* / Fusion drive: *Baj Ram* / We are not: *Jet Set* / Accent: *Acid Device* / Get out: *Terratropin* / Blame groove: *Titan & Red Acid Jack* / Countbasic: *Cellblockx* / Berlin: *Rob Acid*
SPV 08947082 / Sep '96 / SPV

☐ **ACID FLASH VOL.4 (2CD Set)**
Humanoid: *N-Son-X* / I know what U R thinking: *New Moon* / Subway: *Spick & Span* / Unicum: *DJ Tomicraft* / One and only: *Lumo* / Racha: *TB-Tuner* / Running man: *Nuclear Hyde* / Guinean folks: *Patchwork* / Sentimental circuit: *Repulsor* / Dark side of light: *Framic* / Destruction: *D-Fense & Confusion* / House muzik: *Victims Of Lobotomie* / Brain1: *Brain1* / Phuture power: *Chevalier, John* / Pattern war: *18-DB* / Girl he's fine: *Nectar* / Eject: *Acid Device* / Fear of death: *Oddball* / Streichholz: *Laux & Olsson* / Switch board: *Church Windows* / So high: *Dennmarque* / Piquant: *A Dreams A*
SPV 08947322 / Feb '97 / SPV

☐ **ACID FLASH VOL.5**
SPV 08947552 / Jul '97 / SPV

☐ **ACID FLASH VOL.8 (2CD Set)**
SPV 08939032 / 1 Jun '98 / SPV

☐ **ACID FLASH VOL.9 (2CD Set)**
Acid techno: *Immersion, Lawrie & Dirtbag* / Black star rising: *Chris Liberator* / Fuckin' avin it 'ere: *Lochi & Dirtball* / Will I dream: *Tibet Team Frankfurt* / Dead can dance: *Alder, Andy & DJ Choci* / Mystique: *Brain 11* / 303 fever: *Indigo* / Sioux war dance: *Shawnie* / Acid machines: *Brain 13* / Vibrate: *OS/2 & Underground Cyber Movement* / Pathfinder: *Crude Infinity* / Seafroth: *Rob Acid* / No cure: *Rude 66* / Search: *Trancesetters* / Krypton FX: *Urhian* / Honey nut loop: *Latex Empire* / Shi ou: *Khan, Reysan* / Revolve: *Junh Project* / Extra jetzt: *Trach a Lula* / Heln traum: *Hopfus Resonator* / Glaol: *Foxxers*
SPV 08939082 / 1 Sep '98 / SPV

☐ **ACID FLASHBACK**
TRIPCD 1 / Mar '95 / Rumour

☐ **ACID JAZZ BREAKS**
Mission impossible: *Taylor, James Quartet* / Lesson one: *Stone Cold Boners* / I see you: *Vibraphonic* / Something in my eye: *Corduroy* / Unsettled life: *Emperor's New Clothes* / Price You Pay: *Emperor's New Clothes* / Watch my garden grow: *Emperor's New Clothes* / Solid: *New Jersey Kings* / Hippy cowboy: *Mister Exe* / Sunship: *Sunship* / Jesse: *Mother Earth* / Mini: *Corduroy* / Try me: *Isaacs, Gregory* / Doctor bang: *Greenfinger* / Girl overboard: *Snowboy*
EAMCD 004 / Apr '98 / Eagle

☐ **ACID JAZZ CLASSICS**
4892662 / 23 Feb '98 / Irma

☐ **ACID JAZZ JAZZ**
JAZIDCD 038 / Jul '91 / Acid Jazz

☐ **ACID JAZZ MO' JAZZ**
JAZIDCD 051 / Jun '92 / Acid Jazz

☐ **ACID JAZZ ON THE ROCKS**
IAM 801CD / 16 Sep '97 / Irma

☐ **ACID JAZZ VOL.1**
Better half: *Funk Inc.* / Got myself a good man: *Pucho* / Houston Express: *Person, Houston* / Grits and gravy: *Kloss, Eric* / Hoochie coo chickie: *Jones, Ivan 'Boogaloo Joe'* / Lady Mama: *Ammons, Gene* / Hip shaker: *Spencer, Leon* / *Psychedelic Sally*
CDBGP 1015 / Oct '91 / Beat Goes Public

☐ **ACID JAZZ VOL.2**
Super bad: *Muhammad, Idris* / Cold sweat: *Purdie, Bernard* / Wildfire: *Bryant, Rusty* / Hot barbecue: *McDuff, Jack* / Reelin' with the feelin': *Kynard, Charles* / Spinky: *Earland, Charles* / Who's gonna take the weight: *Sparks, Melvin*
CDBGP 1017 / Oct '91 / Beat Goes Public

☐ **ACID JAZZ VOL.3**
I want you back: *Mabern, Harold* / Psychedelic Pucho: *Pucho* / Zebra walk: *Kynard, Charles* / Akilah: *Sparks, Melvin* / What it is: *Jones, Ivan 'Boogaloo Joe'* / Bad Montana: *Parker, Maynard* / Dig on it: *Smith, Johnny 'Hammond'* / Bowlegs: *Funk Inc.*
CDBGP 1025 / Oct '91 / Beat Goes Public

☐ **ACID JAZZ VOL.3**
Whole lotta love: *Goldbug* / Lovesick: *Night Trains & Marcia Johnson* / Apple green: *Mother Earth* / Exe marks the spot: *Mister Exe* / Good thing: *Taylor, James Quartet* / Rising to the top: *Blacknuss Allstars & Lisa Nilsson/Desmond Foster* / Use me: *Raw Stylus* / Up to our necks in it: *Skunkhour* / How can you forget: *Dread Flimstone & Michael Prophet* / Try me: *Isaacs, Gregory* / Unsettled life: *Emperor's New Clothes* / World peace: *African Headcharge* / Living life your own way: *Windross, Rose* / Can't get enough: *Vibraphonic* / Mambito: *Snowboy* / Hip hop beat: *Nu Perspective* / Asteroid: *Goldbug*
JAZIDCD 141 / May '96 / Acid Jazz

☐ **ACID JAZZ VOL.4**
Soul dance: *Person, Houston* / Sing a simple song: *Earland, Charles* / Twang thang: *Butler, Billy* / Shaft: *Purdie, Bernard* / Sure nuff sure nuff: *Phillips, Sonny* / Mamblues: *Tjader, Cal & Bernard Purdie* / Haw right now: *Rushen, Patrice* / Life is funky: *Round Robin Monopoly*
CDBGP 1029 / Oct '91 / Beat Goes Public

☐ **ACID RANCH 2000**
UBR 05 / Sep '97 / Uncle Buzz

☐ **ACID RELIGION (2CD Set)**
TSU 74002CD / 1 Jun '98 / Tsunami

☐ **ACID RESISTANT VOL.1**
EFA 262332 / May '95 / Smile

☐ **ACID RESISTANT VOL.2**
SM 80282 / Nov '96 / Profile

☐ **ACID TUNES (2CD Set)**
560052 / Mar '97 / Westcom

☐ **ACID VISIONS VOL.3 (3CD Set)**
COLCD 8811 / 16 Mar '98 / Collectables

☐ **ACOUSTIC AID**
Is this the world we created: *Mercury, Freddie* / To be with you: *Mr. Big* / Melissa: *Allman Brothers* / Blood and roses: *Allman Brothers* / Bouree: *Jethro Tull* / When I'm gone: *Schenker, Michael Group* / From the beginning: *Lake, Greg* / Prove it every night: *Money, Eddie* / Keith don't go: *Lofgren, Nils* / She talks to angels: *Black Crowes* / Tuesday afternoon: *Hayward, Justin* / Lunatic fringe: *Cochrane, Tom* / Hands of time: *Y&T* / Rad gumbo: *Little Feat* / Your love: *Outfield* / Turn turn turn: *McGuinn, Roger*
399780 / Jun '97 / Koch Presents

☐ **ACOUSTIC DISC SAMPLER VOL.1, THE (100% Handmade Music)**
ACD 8 / Apr '97 / Acoustic Disc

☐ **ACOUSTIC DISC SAMPLER VOL.2, THE (100% Handmade Music)**
ACD 16 / Jul '97 / Acoustic Disc

☐ **ACOUSTIC DREAMS**
If you leave me now / Tears in heaven / You are not alone / Back for good / Think twice / How 'bout us / Unchained melody / Just the way you are / Kiss from a rose / Sacrifice / All by myself / Always and forever / Me and Mrs Jones / One sweet day / Three times a lady / You are the sunshine of my life / And I love her / How deep is your love
CDVIP 152 / Jan '97 / Virgin VIP

☐ **ACOUSTIC FREEWAY**
5257352 / Aug '95 / PolyGram TV

☐ **ACOUSTIC HEART (The Passion & Romance Of Acoustic Guitar Masters)**
SHCD 5030 / Apr '97 / Shanachie

☐ **ACOUSTIC MOODS**
Endless love: *In Tune* / Back for good: *In Tune* / Think twice: *In Tune* / La isla bonita: *In Tune* / Scarborough fair: *In Tune* / (Love theme from) Romeo and Juliet: *In Tune* / Get here: *In Tune* / Love is all around: *In Tune* / Save the best for last: *In Tune* / (Everything I do) I do it for you: *In Tune* / And I love her: *In Tune* / Promise me: *In Tune* / Take my breath away: *In Tune* / End of the road: *In Tune* / Gymnopedie no.1: *In Tune* / Summertime: *In Tune* / Don't let the sun go down on me: *In Tune*
RADCD 13 / Jun '95 / Global TV

☐ **ACOUSTIC MOODS (2CD Set)**
Old English / Jeanne / Under ground / Ar Soudarded / First interlude / Ways / In Pappa's garden / Childhood days / King of the fairies / Romanian dance / Keel row/John Peel / Double lead through/ Give us some treacle and bread / Reel of Pickering-Pick / Second interlude / Times of celebration / Mother Sea-Father Sun / Koh-I-Noor / Long Island / Slide mama / Snake river blues / Kalahari / Third interlude / Sic'e ceya ce / Fourth interlude / Calling / Sh'Dematy / Refleo del agua / Little ponies / L'isle de re / Tennessee moonlight / O ye yai quai faire / Jack hardy / Big blues / Fifth interlude / Convergence / Last stop
330112 / Jul '96 / Hallmark

☐ **ACOUSTIC MOODS (40 Timeless Instrumental Classics) (2CD Set)**
Yesterday / Fool on the hill / Eleanor Rigby / Wonderful tonight / Hello / Vincent / Suicide is painless / Nobody does it better / Just the two of us / No woman, no cry / Yesterday once more / Bridge over troubled water / Still crazy after all these years / Every breath you take / Just the way you are / Time after time / One more night / Raining in Ginza / Many rivers to cross / Wrapped around your finger / Smoke gets in your eyes / I only have eyes for you / Ain't misbehavin' / That ole devil called love / Strangers in the night / Blue moon / Autumn leaves / Night and day / Whispering grass / Nightingale sang in Berkeley Square / Ol' man river / Some day my prince will come / When you wish upon a star / Isn't this a lovely day / Back to the mountain / Moon river / I could / Harry Lime / Deja vu / Yatau
SUDCD 4506 / Nov '96 / Summit

☐ **ACOUSTIC ROCK**
Wild wood: *Weller, Paul* / Weather with you: *Crowded House* / Heal the pain: *Michael, George* / Prettiest eyes: *Beautiful South* / 74-75: *Connells* / Mmm mmm mmm mmm: *Crash Test Dummies* / Driving with the brakes on: *Del Amitri* / How men are: *Aztec Camera* / Is it like today: *World Party* / You and me song: *Wannadies* / Run baby run: *Crow, Sheryl* / Linger: *Cranberries* / Jennifer she said: *Cole, Lloyd* / Julie: *Levellers* / High and dry: *Radiohead* / Only living boy in New York: *Everything But The Girl* / It's about time: *Lemonheads* / You have place a chill in my heart: *Eurythmics* / Walk this world: *Nova, Heather* / Let it grow: *Clapton, Eric*
5258962 / Sep '95 / PolyGram TV

☐ **ACOUSTIC ROUTES**
NINETY 7 / Oct '93 / Code 90

☐ **ACOUSTICS SAMPLER, THE**
Arrival of the Queen of Sheba: *Mandolin Allstars* / Musette a Teresa: *Daniels, Luke* / Laughing with the moon: *James, Hilary* / Dance of the water boatmen: *Mayor, Simon* / Plum blossoms in the snow: *Mayor, Simon & Gerald Garcia* / Sail away: *James, Hilary* / Capriol suite: *Mayor, Simon* / Green man: *Marriott, Beryl* / All hallows dance: *Mayor, Simon* / Looking after business: *Slim Panatella & The Mellow Virginians* / Apres un reve: *Mayor, Simon & Gerald Garcia* / Gipsy dance from Carmen: *Mayor, Simon Quintet* / John Watt Henry set: *Daniels, Luke* / Buttermere waltz: *Mayor, Simon* / Jump the gun/ Reelin' over the rooftops: *Mayor, Simon* / Corn rigs: *James, Hilary* / Eine kleine nachtmusik: *Mandolin Allstars*
ACS 030CD / Jun '97 / Acoustics

☐ **ACROBATES ET MUSICIENS**
Lo ceu n'a creat / Deux nuits au palais ideal / Neols de limoges / Angels-satins blancs / La madeleine / Borjon, susato / Be ia longtemps joenessa / Une nuit de premier mal
SHAN 21009CD / Nov '95 / Shanachie

☐ **ACROSS THE GREAT DIVIDE**
DJD 3203 / May '94 / Dejadisc

☐ **ACROSS THE TRACKS VOL.1 (Nashville R&B/Rock'n'Roll)**
She can rock: *Little Ike* / Every night in the week: *Birdsong, Larry* / Let's rock'n'roll: *'Little Shy Guy' Douglas* / Now do you hear: *Gaines, Earl* / I understand: *Allison, Gene* / Somebody somewhere: *Birdsong, Larry* / Let your will be done: *Fairfield Four* / Pipe dreams: *Beck, Jimmy* / Jump, jump hi-ho: *Gant, Clenest* / Do you love me: *Birdsong, Larry* / You gonna be sorry: *Allison, Gene* / Best of luck baby: *Gaines, Earl* / Since you left me behind: *Birdsong, Larry* / Oh baby: *Green, Rudy* / I want to be a part of you: *Chellows* / For you my love: *Lucille & The Strangers* / I know Johnny loves me: *Lucille & The Strangers* / Small town girl: *Tig, Jimmy & The Rounders* / They wanna fight: *Harrod, Chuck* / Twistin' USA: *Keaton, Johnny* / Let's twist (slow and easy): *Jarett, Ted* / Doctor Feelgood: *Hunter, Herbert* / I'm going home: *Allison, Levert* / Yesterday's mistake: *Shelton, Roscoe* / Thank God things are as well as they are: *Consolers* / Now that we're together: *Allison, Gene* / I'm just what you're looking for: *Kittrell, Christine* / Young and fancy free: *Birdsong, Larry*
CDCHD 493 / Sep '96 / Ace

☐ **ACROSS THE TRACKS VOL.2**
Three times seven: *Birdsong, Larry* / Live the life I sing about: *Birdsong, Larry* / Six days a week (and sundays too): *Kinglets* / You gotta go: *Kinglets* / No fool no more: *Walker, Charles & The Daffodils* / Slave to love: *Walker, Charles & The Daffodils* / If things don't change: *Allison, Gene* / Sittin' here drinkin': *Gaines, Earl* / Blue night: *Beck, Jimmy Orchestra* / Real good man: *Garner, Alan* / Oh my love: *Garner, Alan* / Scooter poofin': *Birdsong, Larry* / Lord you know: *Fairfield Four* / I thank him: *Kittrell, Christine* / Kiss away: *Clips* / Let me get close to you baby: *Clips* / You're my baby: *Birdsong, Larry* / Love you so: *Gaines, Earl* / Hallelujah: *Gant, Clenest & Don Q* / Rent's too high: *Butler, Cliff Group* / Love me a long time: *Jarrett, Ted* / My little baby: *Little Shy Guy* / Crawdad hole: *Harrod, Chuck & The Anteaters* / Goofin' off: *Paul, Joyce* / Let me down easy: *Gaines, Earl* / Same thing: *Adams, Arthur* / You are my sunshine: *Gaines, Earl & Lucille Johns* / Stay a little longer: *Allison, Gene* / It's almost sundown: *Shelton, Roscoe* / You can make it if you try/Have faith: *Allison, Gene*
CDCHD 672 / 29 Sep '97 / Ace

☐ **ACROSS THE WATERS (Irish Traditional Music From England)**
NI 5415CD / Oct '94 / Nimbus

☐ **ACTION**
BB 2812 / Oct '95 / Blue Beat

☐ **ADAM PARFREY PRESENTS AN EVENING OF SONIC...**
MR 066 / Jun '97 / Man's Ruin

☐ **ADDICTED TO LOVE**
Addicted to love: *Palmer, Robert* / Eye of the tiger: *Survivor* / Power of love: *Lewis, Huey & The News* / I'm still standing: *John, Elton* / Missing you: *Waite, John* / Bette Davis eyes: *Carnes, Kim* / Kayleigh: *Marillion* / Wind of change: *Scorpions* / Womankind: *Little Angels* / St. Elmo's fire: *Parr, John* / Hey you: *Quireboys* / Dirty love: *Thunder* / Everything about you: *Ugly Kid Joe* / Gypsy Road: *Cinderella* / Centrefold: *Geils, J. Band* / Get on it: *Power Station* / Obsession: *Animotion* / Wonderland: *Big Country* / Spirit of radio: *Rush* / Caroline: *Status Quo*
5529202 / Oct '97 / Spectrum

☐ **ADDITIVE VOL.1**
Journey: *Bliss 'n' Tumble* / Nightmare: *Brainbug* / Black hill: *Little Jam* / Space: *Fletch* / Disco mirror: *Plastika* / Good time: *Hipgrinders* / 104 dub: *Dub Tractor* / Acid people: *White Trash* / Techno solution: *DJ Philip* / Neuro: *X-Cabs* / Are am eye: *Commander Tom* / Space is the place: *Svenson, Johan* / Furyo: *Kayashi*
CDADA 1002 / Jun '97 / Additive

☐ **ADRENALIN VOL.3 (2CD Set)**
EDM 47098 / 8 May '98 / EDM

☐ **ADULTS ONLY VOL.1**
Rub and sqeeze: *Perry, Lee 'Scratch' & The Soulettes* / Sexy Sadie: *Max Romeo* / Don't touch me tomato: *Dillon, Phyllis* / Wet dream: *Inspirations* / Adults only: *Lynch, Dermot* / Rub up push up: *Termites* / Push it in: *Versatiles* / Khaki: *Tennors* / Wreck a buddy: *Soul Sisters* / Hold the pussy: *Kid Gungo* / Birth control: *Lloydie & The Lowbites* / Barbwire: *Dean, Nora* / Open up: *Eccles, Clancy* / She want it: *Barker, Dave & The Gaylads* / Fat fat girl: *Lloydie & The Lowbites* / International pum pum: *Observers* / Punanny: *Charlie Ace & Fay* / Pussy cat: *Lloydie & The Lowbites*
CDTRL 305 / Mar '94 / Trojan

R.E.D. CD CATALOGUE
COMPILATIONS
AIN'T NUTHIN' BUT A SHE THING

☐ **ADULTS ONLY VOL.2**
Rub up, push up: *Hinds, Justin* / Want me cock: *Owen & Leon* / Pussy cat: *Cole, Stranger* / Dr. Dick: *Perry, Lee 'Scratch'* / Push it up: *Termites* / Adults only: *Calypso Joe* / Push push: *Itals* / Mr. Rhya: *Charmers, Lloyd* / Satan girl: *Ethiopians* / Pussy catch a fire: *Soulmates* / Big boy and teacher: *U-Roy* / Rough rider: *U-Roy* / Play with your pussy: *Max Romeo* / Papa do it sweet: *Lloyd & Patsy* / In a de pum pum: *Flowers & Alvin* / Mr. Whittaker: *Charlie Ace & Fay* / Hole under crutches: *Max Romeo* / Yum yum pussy: *Lloydie & The Lowbites*
CDTRL 308 / Mar '94 / Trojan

☐ **ADVANCE TECHNIQUES**
04 INPUTCD / 17 Nov '97 / Input

☐ **ADVENTURES IN AND BEYOND DUB**
Throw away your gun: *Prince Far-I* / No more war: *Prince Far-I* / Must must: *Khan, Nusrat Fateh Ali* / Requiem: *Khan, Nusrat Fateh Ali* / City heathen dub: *Techno Animal* / Radiation ruling the nation: *Massive Attack* / Acream: *Mantronix* / Swan lake: *Public Image Ltd.* / Cuutuzen as a peaceful dub: *Culture* / Command cousel dub: *Poet & The Roots* / Betrayal: *Jah Wobble* / I want to kill somebody: *Jah Wobble* / Dance with me: *XTC*
CDOVD 494 / 29 Sep '97 / Virgin

☐ **AFRICA - NEVER STAND STILL**
CT 3300 / Aug '94 / Ellipsis Arts

☐ **AFRICA CALLING**
They talk about / Ghetto cry / Down down (babylon walls) / Africa calling / Set jah people free / Life's road / Whoe whoe / I wish we'll be ready
RRTGCD 7734 / Mar '89 / Rohit

☐ **AFRICA DANCE**
CDCH 366 / Apr '90 / Milan

☐ **AFRICA IN AMERICA**
MT 115/7 / Jan '94 / Corason

☐ **AFRICAN MOVES VOL.3**
STCD 105 / Mar '96 / Stern's

☐ **AFRICA STAND ALONE**
Sidike/Gorel megamix: *Maal, Baaba* / Zine a zine: *Khaled, Hadj Ibrahim* / Nyanama: *Keita, Salif* / Africa unite: *Bayete* / Akwaba: *Kidjo, Angelique* / Je ne sais pas: *Positive Black Soul* / Kelma: *Taha, Rachid* / Nafanta: *Lo, Ismael* / Sama duniya: *Maal, Baaba* / Return of da jelly: *Positive Black Soul*
CDMNS 2 / Aug '96 / Mango

☐ **AFRICA: THE MUSIC OF A CONTINENT**
PS 66006 / Oct '95 / PlayaSound

☐ **AFRICAN ANGELS**
ARNR 0397 / Apr '97 / Amiata

☐ **AFRICAN BLUES**
Talibe: *Lo, Ismael* / Mounaissa: *Traore, Rokia* / A vasafy va lomo: *Orchestra Marrabenta Star De Mocambique* / Mansa: *Super Rail Band* / Balla et ses balladins: *Paulette* / Maggie: *Nkhata, Alick* / Omulanga wamuka: *Makobi, Henry* / Heygana: *Farka Toure, Ali* / Ndinderere: *Rambisai Chiweshe, Stella* / Shams esh'shamusa: *El Din, Hamza* / N'sangou: *El Din, Hamza* / Mouso teke soma ye: *Traore, Boubacar* / Kankan blues: *Manfila, Kante & Balia Kalia* / Miss Perfumado: *Evora, Cesaria* / Saa magni: *Sangare, Oumou*
RGNET 1019CD / 18 May '98 / World Music Network

☐ **AFRICAN DUB SERIES VOL.3 & 4**
RGCD 024 / Jan '95 / Rocky One

☐ **AFRICAN HORNS**
Next stop Soweto / Tshona / Black and brown cherries / Tegeni / Msunduza / Mafuta
CDN 1003 / 23 Mar '98 / Camden

☐ **AFRICAN MELODICA DUB**
ROTCD 008 / Jan '96 / Reggae On Top

☐ **AFRICAN MOVES**
ROUCD 11513 / Jan '88 / Rounder

☐ **AFRICAN MOVES VOL.2**
Pole mama: *Somo Somo* / Amilo: *Ley, Tabu* / Boya ye: *M'Bilia Bell* / Sanza Misato: *Orchestra Africa* / Mon couer balance: *Daouda* / Gbebe mi: *Obey, Chief Ebenezer* / Segun Adewale: *Adewale, Segun* / Yeme breoo: *African Brothers*
STCD 1029 / Nov '89 / Stern's

☐ **AFRICAN MUSEUM SELECTION**
HBCD 19 / May '90 / Heartbeat

☐ **AFRICAN RHYTHMS AND INSTRUMENTS VOL.1 (Mali, Niger, Ghana, Nigeria, Upper Volta, Senegal)**
LYRCD 7328 / '91 / Lyrichord

☐ **AFRICAN RUBBER DUB VOL.1**
CENCD 800 / Oct '96 / Century

☐ **AFRICAN RUBBER DUB VOL.2**
CEND 1400 / Oct '96 / Century

☐ **AFRICAN RUBBER DUB VOL.3**
CEND 1200 / Sep '94 / Century

☐ **AFRICAN TRANQUILITY**
SHCD 64076 / Nov '96 / Shanachie

☐ **AFRICAN TRIBAL MUSIC AND DANCES**
12179 / Aug '95 / Laserlight

☐ **AFRICAN TROUBADOURS (Best of African Singer/Songwriters)**
SHCD 64092 / Jul '97 / Shanachie

☐ **AFRICAN VOICES - SONGS OF LIFE**
Kothbiro: *Ogada, Ayub* / Dala: *Ogada, Ayub* / Ondiek: *Ogada, Ayub* / Sutu Kun: *Diop, Vieux* / Jali: *Diop, Vieux* / Ekibobo: *Samite* / Ndere: *Samite* / Wasuze Otya: *Samite* / Ngak: *Diop, Lucky* / Igne: *Diop, Lucky* / Mamadi: *Diop, Lucky* / Woza Azania: *Nathaniel, Kevin* / Tatenda: *Nathaniel, Kevin*
ND 63930 / Nov '96 / Narada

☐ **AFRICOLOUR**
092802 / 5 Jan '98 / Melodie

☐ **AFRIQUE DU SUD - JIVE TOWNSHIP**
669982 / 24 Apr '98 / Melodie

☐ **AFRIQUE PARADE VOL.3**
829042CD / Jul '95 / BUDA

☐ **AFRIQUE PARADE VOL.4**
829342CD / Jan '97 / Melodie

☐ **AFRIQUE PARADE VOL.5**
829592 / 24 Apr '98 / BUDA

☐ **AFRIQUE PARADE-TOP DU SOUKOUS**
828672 / Jun '93 / BUDA

☐ **AFRO BLUE VOL.1**
Afro blue: *Reeves, Dianne* / Capoeira: *Pullen, Don* / Home is Africa: *Parlan, Horace* / Mystery of love: *Blakey, Art* / Tin tin deo: *Moody, James* / Night in Tunisia: *Powell, Bud* / O'tinde: *Blakey, Art* / Man from Tanganyika: *Tyner, McCoy* / Appointment in Ghana: *McLean, Jackie* / Feast: *Blakey, Art* / Mr. Kenyatta: *Morgan, Lee* / Message from Kenya: *Silver, Horace* / Rhapsodia del marisillio: *Martinez, Sabu*
BNZ 304 / Nov '92 / Blue Note

☐ **AFRO BLUE VOL.2 (The Roots & Rhythms Of Jazz)**
Appointment in Ghana: *Jazz Crusaders* / Katanga: *Amy, Curtis & Dupree Bolton* / Message from Kenya: *Blakey, Art & Afro Drum* / Woman of Africa: *Blakey, Art & Afro Drum* / Yaba e: *Ilori, Simon & Afro Drum* / Follow me to Africa: *Ilori, Simon & Afro Drum* / Black Nile: *Shorter, Wayne* / Niger mambo: *Turrentine, Stanley* / Zambia: *Morgan, Lee* / Zulu: *Weston, Randy* / Blue dashiki: *Blue Mitchell* / Malika: *Tyner, McCoy* / Ghana spice: *Candido* / Marabi: *Adderley, Cannonball*
4940310 / 22 Jun '98 / Blue Note

☐ **AFRO CENTRICA**
Mama / Okunaya / Black man's cry / Makassi again / Mona opusi / Makhombo / Explorations / Woza sihambe / Pon moun paka bouge / Ama gents
MPG 74037 / Apr '97 / Movieplay Gold

☐ **AFRO CUBA: MUSICAL ANTHOLOGY**
ROUCD 1088 / Feb '94 / Rounder

☐ **AFRO CUBAN GROOVES VOL.1**
325042 / Apr '96 / Melodie

☐ **AFRO CUBAN GROOVES VOL.2**
325082 / 21 Aug '97 / Melodie

☐ **AFRO CUBAN GROOVES VOL.3**
325113 / 5 Jan '98 / Melodie

☐ **AFRO CUBAN JAZZ**
CLP 9017 / Jan '98 / Fresh Sound

☐ **AFRO CUBAN ROOTS VOL.1 (50 Years Of Cuban Music)**
78887220612 / 19 May '98 / Max Music

☐ **AFRO CUBAN ROOTS VOL.2 (Cuban Feelings - Bolera Era)**
78887220622 / 19 May '98 / Max Music

☐ **AFRO LATINO**
79024801392 / 19 May '98 / Putumayo

☐ **AFRO LIMONESE: MUSIC FROM COSTA RICA**
LYRCD 7412 / '91 / Lyrichord

☐ **AFRO MANIA CARIBE**
America latina / Hoy es viernes / El cumbanchero / Mentiras / Rumba sandunguera / La guayaba / Cafe con leche / Matilda / Eva pa've / Echao pa'lante / Dance this dance / No la dejare
68937 / Apr '97 / Tropical

☐ **AFRO MANIA VOL.3 (Afro Dance Music)**
Follow the drums: *Jambola* / Rasta: *African Vibes* / Fanfarissimo: *Ethnica* / Spirit of Africa: *SOP* / Wrassaroumba: *Mamukata* / White man, black heart: *Djibooti* / Strange: *Spacefront* / My rain: *L'Arabo, Mada & Max* / Camel song: *DJ Congano* / Cocain: *Cosmic Vibrations* / Sen culpa mare: *Papaya* / We need double light: *Mongawa*
MNF 05252 / Apr '97 / Manifold

☐ **AFROLUSAMERICA (Africa/Brazil Pop)**
68980 / Apr '97 / Tropical

☐ **AFROMANIA VOL.6**
MNF 05402 / 26 May '98 / Manifold

☐ **AFRS JUBILEE VOL.10**
JUBCD 1010 / Jan '97 / RST

☐ **AFRS JUBILEE VOL.11**
JUBCD 1011 / Jan '97 / RST

☐ **AFRS JUBILEE VOL.12**
JUBCD 1012 / Jan '97 / RST

☐ **AFRS JUBILEE VOL.13**
JUBCD 1013 / Jan '97 / RST

☐ **AFRS JUBILEE VOL.14**
JUBCD 1014 / Jan '97 / RST

☐ **AFRS JUBILEE VOL.15**
JUBCD 1015 / Jan '97 / RST

☐ **AFRS JUBILEE VOL.16**
JUBCD 1016 / Jan '97 / RST

☐ **AFRS JUBILEE VOL.7**
JUBCD 1007 / Jul '96 / RST

☐ **AFRS JUBILEE VOL.8**
JUBCD 1008 / Jul '96 / RST

☐ **AFRS JUBILEE VOL.9**
JUBCD 1009 / Jul '96 / RST

☐ **AFTER DARK (Jazz Ballads For The Wee Small Hours/2CD Set)**
I'll be around: *Braff, Ruby* / Hanid: *Freeman, Bud* / Moonlight in Vermont: *Brown, Pete* / Isn't it romantic: *Torme, Mel* / Stardust: *Charles, Teddy* / Smoke gets in your eyes: *Mariano, Charlie* / Polka dots amd moonbeams: *Fontana, Carl* / I can't get started: *Candoli, Conte* / You are so easy to love: *McRae, Carmen* / You are too beautiful: *Davis, Eddie 'Lockjaw'* / Embraceable you: *Williamson, Claude* / These foolish things: *Ortega, Anthony* / But beautiful: *Garcia, Russell* / Don't blame me: *McGhee, Howard* / Why shouldn't I: *Connor, Chris* / Out of nowhere: *Hardaway, Bob* / Echoes of spring: *Burns, Ralph* / What's new: *McKusick, Hal* / Autumn in New York: *Gordon, Dexter* / Flamingo: *Rosolino, Frank* / Something to live for: *Roche, Betty* / I'll take romance: *Socolow, Frank* / Mad about the boy: *Johnson, J.J. & Kai Winding* / Ruby my dear: *Levey, Stan* / Last time for love: *Rouse, Charlie & Paul Quinichette* / You don't know what love is: *Waldron, Mal* / If I should lose you: *Little, Booker* / I'll remember April: *Hartman, Johnny* / Memories of you: *Mingus, Charles* / Easy living: *Kirk, Rahsaan Roland* / For minors only: *Blakey, Art* / Bohemia after dark: *Pettiford, Oscar*
CDGR 2012 / Nov '97 / Charly

☐ **AFTER HOURS**
Tempus fugue-it: *Powell, Bud* / Six cats and a prince: *Young, Lester* / I've never been in love before: *Peterson, Oscar* / Bemsha swing: *Evans, Bill* / Relaxing with Lee: *Parker, Charlie* / Is you is or is you ain't my baby: *Garner, Erroll* / After hours: *Brown, Patti* / Swingin' the blues: *Bryant, Ray* / Way you loook tonight: *Keynoters & Nat 'King' Cole* / Stompin' at the Savoy: *Wilson, Teddy* / Father co-operates: *Cole, Cozy* / Love for sale: *Tatum, Art* / Carioca: *Gillespie, Dizzy* / Believe it, beloved: *Jones, Hank* / Blue boy: *Tristano, Lennie* / September in the rain: *Shearing, George* / Oh, lady, be good: *Flanagan, Tommy* / Buttercorn lady: *Blakey, Art & The Jazz Messengers*
5526432 / Mar '97 / Spectrum

☐ **AFTER HOURS VOL.1**
JDJAH 1CD / Jan '96 / JDJ

☐ **AFTER HOURS VOL.2 (Ultimate Deep Section)**
Brooklyn heights: *Down To The Bone* / Hey hey: *Riviera Traxx Vol.1* / Dangerous jazz: *Ferry Ultra & Roy Ayers* / A2 step: *Damier, Chez* / Ignorance is bliss: *Colour Climax* / Feelin' dub-e: *Miller, D. & C. Checkley* / Sun dance: *Fade 2 End* / Unification: *Doctors Of Dub* / Carreras: *MAP* / Unification II: *E-Culture* / Was I here before: *Owens, Robert* / Lonely winter: *Watergate* / Happiness: *Forthright* / Mystical journey: *Fontana, Lenny & Galaxy People* / It's music: *Century Falls & Philip Ramirez* / Gotta lotta luv: *Williams, Lenny*
JDJAH 2CD / Mar '97 / JDJ

☐ **AFTER HOURS VOL.3**
EX 3492 / Apr '97 / Instinct

☐ **AFTER MIDNIGHT**
Midnight at the Oasis: *Muldaur, Maria* / Sweet love: *Baker, Anita* / Feeling good: *Simone, Nina* / Nature boy: *Cole, Nat 'King'* / Let's face the music and dance: *Fitzgerald, Ella* / Dream a little dream of me: *Fygi, Laura* / Rockin' good way: *Washington, Dinah* / Mack the knife: *Darin, Bobby* / Cry me a river: *London, Julie* / Good morning heartache: *Holiday, Billie* / Tenderly: *Vaughan, Sarah* / Look of love: *Washington, Grover Jr.* / Like dreamers do: *Paris, Mica* / Razzamatazz: *Jones, Quincy* / Running away: *Ayers, Roy* / Cantaloop (Flip fantasia): *US 3* / Love supreme: *Downing, Will* / Time after time: *Davis, Miles* / Children of the ghetto: *Pine, Courtney* / Wrong side of town: *BBM*
5168712 / Sep '94 / Polydor

☐ **AFTER THE FLOOD**
WDM 10069 / 2 Mar '98 / World Domination

☐ **AFTER THE SEPULTURE**
RAD 003CD / Nov '95 / Radiation

☐ **AFTERBURNER (Your Gabba Nightmare)**
CLP 9984 / Jun '97 / Cleopatra

☐ **AGE OF NEW WAVE, THE**
25 Years: *Catch* / Doot doot: *Freur* / Stand or fall: *Fixx* / Wait a long time for you: *Thoughts* / I can't stop: *Numan, Gary* / I want to be free: *Toyah* / Bird song: *Lovich, Lena* / Louise (we get it right): *Lewie, Jona* / Ca plane pour moi: *Plastic Bertrand* / Butcher baby: *Plasmatics* / Destination Zululand: *King Kurt* / Disco in Moscow: *Vibrators* / Wonder woman: *County, Jayne* / Teenage: *UK Subs* / Nightmare continues: *Discharge* / If the kids are united: *Sham 69*
12841 / May '96 / Laserlight

☐ **AGE OF SEARCH AND DESTRUCTION (2CD Set)**
PLAC 0052 / Jun '97 / Plastic City UK

☐ **AGE OF SWING, THE (4CD Set)**
In the mood / Very thought of you / Let's dance / American patrol / Artistry in rhythm / Begin the beguine / Big John special / Skyliner / What is this thing called love / Hamp's boogie woogie / I've got a gal in Kalamazoo / Cherokee / Opus in pastels / Pinetop's boogie / Snowfall / One o'clock jump / Song of India / Perdido / Sing sing sing / King Porter stomp / Little brown jug / Solitude / Eager beaver / Serenade in blue / I know why / On the Alamo / Hornet / Listen to my music / Wrappin' it up on the Lindy slide / Chatanooga choo choo / Apple honey / I'm getting sentimental over you / Harlem nocturne / Leave us leap / You made me love you / Boogie woogie Maxine / Moonlight sonata / South Rampart Street Parade / St. Louis blues march / Mood indigo / Intermission riff / Jersey bounce / Hot toddy / 'S Wonderful / Oh lady be good / Chloe / Leapfrog / Pennsylvania 6-5000 / Opus / I got it bad and that ain't good / String of pearls / Sweet Georgia Brown / I'll never smile again / Stardreams / I get a kick out of you / Long John Silver / Down South camp meeting / Don't be that way / Anvil chorus / Moonlight serenade / After you've gone / Pompton turnpike / On the sunny side of the street / Do nothin' 'til you hear from me / At last / Flying home / Cotton tail / Body and soul / Painted rhythm / Tuxedo junction / Take the 'A' train / Swanee river / Don't sit under the apple tree / Sophisticated lady / Swingin' the blues / Memories of you / I can't get started (with you) / Poor butterfly / Song of the Volga boatmen / At the woodchoppers' ball
TFP 020 / Nov '92 / Tring

☐ **AGENDA 23**
Sensitivity room: *East Island* / Phantom: *Keyprocessor* / Metamorpheus: *2000 & One* / Disappointment: *Wladimir M.* / Flashback: *Ballet Mechanique* / Stroke: *Terrace* / Far away: *Keyprocessor* / Mother G: *TV 99 AD* / Recharge: *Moellhoven* / Caught by starlight: *Caron, David*
ELEC 35CD / 26 Jan '98 / New Electronica

☐ **AGGRO AND ATTITUDE (40 Punk Classics/2CD Set)**
Whips and fur: *Vibrators* / How much longer: *Alternative TV* / Kill the poor: *Dead Kennedys* / Questions: *Suburban Studs* / Solidarity: *Angelic Upstarts* / Never surrender: *Blitz* / City invasion: *Red Alert* / Killing machine: *Partisans* / Jerusalem: *One Way System* / Six guns: *Anti Pasti* / Howard Hughes: *Tights* / Animal bondage: *Art Attacks* / Ruby (don't take your love to town): *Outcasts* / Summertime now: *Erazerhead* / Bomb scare: *Dead Man's Shadow* / Nicely does it: *Instant Agony* / Violent society: *Special Duties* / Will they never learn: *Varukers* / In the future: *Riot Squad* / Do anything you wanna do: *Eddie & The Hot Rods* / Biggest prize in sport: *999* / Walk like a superstar (talk like a zombie): *Lurkers* / Where's Captain Kirk: *Spizz Energi* / Thinking of the USA: *Eater* / Just want to be myself: *Drones* / I am the bishop: *Not Sensibles* / I spy: *Rudi* / Wanna world: *Urban Dogs* / Times they are-a changin': *Vice Squad* / Little Miss Mystery: *Guitar Gangsters* / Up yer bum: *Peter & The Test Tube Babies* / Rich and hated: *Resistance 77* / Ambassador of fear: *English Dogs* / Rockers in rags: *Adicts* / What about a future: *Chaos UK* / Time is right: *Fits* / Go to hell: *Threats* / Violent world: *Disorder* / Anarchy in Woolworths: *Chaotic Dischord* / Personality crisis: *Thunders, Johnny*
SUDCD 4502 / Nov '96 / Summit

☐ **AGITPOP (The Politics Of Punk/3CD Set)**
DTKBOX 53 / 1 Jun '98 / Dressed To Kill

☐ **AH FEEL TO PARTY (2CD Set)**
ROUCD 506667 / Feb '96 / Rounder

☐ **AI CONFINI/INTERZONE**
NT 6714 / Jan '94 / Robi Droli

☐ **AICHA MINT CHIGALY (Mauritius)**
W 260078 / Oct '97 / Inedit

☐ **AIN'T NOTHIN' BUT A HOUSE PARTY**
Bless your soul: *Dreamlovers* / You gave me somebody to love: *Dreamlovers* / You ain't sayin' nothin' new: *Virgil, Henry* / You fooled me: *Virgil, Henry* / Ain't nothing but a house party: *Showstoppers* / What a man can do: *Showstoppers* / Eeeny meeny: *Showstoppers* / How easy your heart forgets me: *Showstoppers* / Suddenly: *Cherry People* / Father's angels: *Cherry People* / Bok to bak: *Cherry People* / I've been hurt: *Deal, Bill & The Rhondells* / Baby show it: *Festival* / Green grow the lilacs: *Festival* / You're gonna make it: *Devonnes* / Mob: *Devonnes* / I dig everything about you: *Devonnes* / Loan shark: *Chapter One* / Money won't do it, love will: *Chapter One* / I'll get by without you: *Gamble, Kenny & Tommy Bell* / Someday you'll be my love: *Gamble, Kenny & Tommy Bell*
NEMCD 678 / Apr '94 / Sequel

☐ **AIN'T NOTHIN' BUT THE BLUES (2CD Set)**
Lovin' in my baby's eyes: *Taj Mahal* / Smokestack lightin': *Howlin' Wolf* / My babe: *Little Walter* / Blue collar: *Scott-Heron, Gil* / Good morning little school girl: *Winter, Johnny* / First time I met the blues: *Guy, Buddy* / Grits ain't groceries: *Blues Band* / I'm your hoochie coochie man: *Waters, Muddy* / Christo redemptor: *Musselwhite, Charley* / Little red rooster: *Howlin' Wolf* / Snake drive: *Clapton, Eric* / Need your love so bad: *Fleetwood Mac* / Every day I have the blues: *King, B.B.* / Baby please don't go: *Williams, 'Big' Joe* / Daytime song: *Korner, Alexis* / Bleeding heart: *Hendrix, Jimi* / I'd rather go blind: *James, Etta* / Sun is shining: *James, Elmore* / I'm your witchdoctor: *Mayall, John* / Boogie chillen': *Hooker, John Lee* / Gangster of love: *Watson, Johnny 'Guitar'* / Stormy Monday: *Korner, Alexis* / Dust my broom: *James, Elmore* / Reconsider baby: *Fulson, Lowell* / Let me love you baby: *Guy, Buddy* / Worried life blues: *Big Maceo* / When the lights go out: *Witherspoon, Jimmy* / John the revelator: *House, Son* / Draggin' my tail: *Clapton, Eric & Jimmy Page* / Cruel little number: *Healey, Jeff Band* / Stealin': *Beck, Jeff* / Cold emotions, frozen hearts: *Blues Band* / Madison blues: *Thorogood, George & The Destroyers* / Bad luck blues: *Broonzy, 'Big' Bill*
RCACD 214 / Jul '97 / RCA

☐ **AIN'T NOTHIN' BUT A SHE THING**
Ain't nuthin' but a she thing: *Salt n' Pepa* / Mama: *Lennox, Annie* / 69 annee erotique: *Luscious Jackson* / Weakness in me: *Etheridge, Melissa* / Woman of the ghetto: *Oliver, Andi* / Open your eyes, you can fly: *Williams, Vanessa* / Hard times: *Queen Latifah* / Cimarron: Come / Don't smoke in bed: *Smith, Patti* / Women of Ireland: *O'Connor, Sinead*
8286742 / Feb '96 / London

☐ AIN'T TIMES HARD (A Modern Blues Anthology - 4CD Set)
CDDIG 3 / Feb '95 / Charly

☐ AIR BORN
Biological manipulation: Manipulators / Dealing with demons: *Process & Tristan* / Cyclothymic: *Process & Tristan* / Wizard: *Slinky Wizard* / Not now I've got a plane to catch: *Stripper* / Morphogenesis: *SYB Unity Nettwerk Experience* / Tranceformation: *Darshan* / Dense dawn: *Psychaos* / Beyond the internal horizon: *Process* / James Bond Theme: License To Slink: *Slinky Wizard*
AFRCD 3 / Jun '97 / Flying Rhino

☐ AIR MAIL - AFRICAN DRUMS
SA 141021 / Jul '98 / Air Mail

☐ AIR MAIL - AMERICAN WEST
SA 141002 / Nov '97 / Air Mail

☐ AIR MAIL - ANDEAN FLUTES
SA 141008 / Nov '97 / Air Mail

☐ AIR MAIL - BRAZIL
SA 141014 / Mar '98 / Air Mail

☐ AIR MAIL - CARIBBEAN STEEL BANDS
SA 141022 / Jul '98 / Air Mail

☐ AIR MAIL - CHINA
SA 141012 / Nov '97 / Air Mail

☐ AIR MAIL - COLOMBIA
SA 141010 / Nov '97 / Air Mail

☐ AIR MAIL - CUBA
SA 141024 / Jul '98 / Air Mail

☐ AIR MAIL - IRELAND
SA 141015 / Mar '98 / Air Mail

☐ AIR MAIL - LOUISIANA
SA 141004 / Nov '97 / Air Mail

☐ AIR MAIL - MEXICO
SA 141013 / Mar '98 / Air Mail

☐ AIR MAIL - MONGOLIA
SA 141006 / Nov '97 / Air Mail

☐ AIR MAIL - NORTH INDIA
SA 141001 / Nov '97 / Air Mail

☐ AIR MAIL - PARIS ACCORDEON
SA 141017 / Mar '98 / Air Mail

☐ AIR MAIL - PORTUGAL
SA 141003 / Nov '97 / Air Mail

☐ AIR MAIL - ROMANIA
SA 141009 / Nov '97 / Air Mail

☐ AIR MAIL - SCOTLAND
SA 141020 / Aug '98 / Air Mail

☐ AIR MAIL - SENEGAL
SA 141005 / Nov '97 / Air Mail

☐ AIR MAIL - SPAIN
SA 141019 / Aug '98 / Air Mail

☐ AIR MAIL - TAHITI
SA 141016 / Mar '98 / Air Mail

☐ AIR MAIL - TANZANIA
SA 141007 / Nov '97 / Air Mail

☐ AIR MAIL - THAILAND
SA 141023 / Jul '98 / Air Mail

☐ AIR MAIL - TOGO
SA 141011 / Nov '97 / Air Mail

☐ AIR MAIL - TUNISIA
SA 141018 / Mar '98 / Air Mail

☐ AKA DUB
Dub reaction: *Black Roots* / Wipe away the tears: *Dub Judah* / Breaking barrier dub: *Jah Woosh* / We do not want them dub: *Maximillian, D.* / *Blakamix* country: *Mixman* / Angelic dub: *Dub Wizard* / Conscious man: *Eastwood, Kevin* / Step inside dub: *Armagideon* / Twilight circus: *Dub Frequency* / Zion: *I-Dub* / Hannibal's journey: *Dub Addxx* / Green banana: *Abeng*
LRCD 006 / May '97 / Lush

☐ AKASHA - THE JILALA
BKA 009 / 22 Jun '98 / Baraka Foundation

☐ ALABADOS Y BAILES
80292 / Sep '95 / New World

☐ ALABAMA STRINGBANDS 1924-1937
DOCD 8032 / 27 Jul '98 / Document

☐ ALABAMA: BLACK COUNTRY DANCE BANDS 1924-1949
DOCD 5166 / May '93 / Document

☐ ALABAMA: SECULAR AND RELIGIOUS MUSIC
DOCD 5165 / May '93 / Document

☐ ALADDIN RECORDS STORY, THE (2CD Set)
Flying home: *Jacquet, Illinois & His Orchestra* / Be baba leba: *Humes, Helen* / Driftin' blues: *Moore, Johnny B. & Three Blazers* / When I'm in my tea: *Davis, Maxwell* / I don't stand a ghost of a chance with you: *Harris, Wynonie* / Mother Fuyer: *Dirty Red* / He may be your man: *Humes, Helen* / Milky white way: *Trumpeteers* / Guitar in my hand: *Brown, Clarence 'Gatemouth'* / Too late: *Five Keys* / Chicken shack boogie: *Milburn, Amos* / Loch Lomond: *Rockets* / Shotgun blues: *Hopkins, Lightnin'* / 'Round midnight: *Robins* / Glory of love: *Five Keys* / Safronia B: *Boze, Calvin* / Trouble blues: *Brown, Charles* / I got loaded: *Harris, Peppermint* / Sad journey blues: *Dixon, Floyd Orchestra* / Dad gum ya hide boy: *Jordan, Louis* / Hucklebuck with jimmy: *Five Keys* / Way down boogie: *Burrage, Harold* / Blue turning grey over you: *Holiday, Billie* / Feels so good: *Shirley & Lee* / Telephone blues: *Dixon, Floyd* / Kokomo: *Gene & Eunice* / Let the good times roll: *Shirley & Lee* / How long: *Five Keys* / I need you, I want you: *Parker, Jack* / Don't let go (hold me, hold me): *Cookies* / Messy Bessy: *Jordan, Louis & His Tympany Five* / This is my story: *Gene & Eunice* / Don't leave me baby: *Fulson, Lowell* / Call operator 210: *Dixon, Floyd* / Ding dong ding: *Bip & Bop* / Remember: *Aladdins* / Rockin' with the clock: *Shirley & Lee* / Honest I do: *Foster, Cell* / Rockin' at Cosmo's: *Allen, Lee* / Be cool my heart: *Allen, Lee* / I'm so high: *Five Keys* / I'm in the mood for love: *King Pleasure* / Ray Pearl: *Jivers* / Dreamy eyes: *Squires* / Yak, yak: *Marvin & Johnny* / Darling it's wonderful: *Lovers* / Our love is here to stay: *Sharps* / King Kong: *Tyler, Big T.* / Smack, smack: *Marvin & Johnny* / Little girl in the cabin: *Sloan, Flip* / Sugar doll: *Belvin, Jesse* / Little bitty pretty one: *Harris, Thurston*
ALADDIN 1 / Jan '95 / EMI

☐ ALAN FREED'S ROCK & ROLL DANCE PARTY
Pretzel / Rock rock rock / Maybellene / Ruby baby / Tear it up / (We're gonna) Rock around the clock / My prayer speedo / Be bop a lula / Why don't you write me / Little girl of mine / Rip it up
CDMF 075 / '91 / Magnum Force

☐ ALAN LOMAX COLLECTION - SOUTHERN JOURNEY VOL.1, THE (Voices From The American South)
D Day: *Jones, Bessie* / Katy went fishing with her hook and line: *Smith, Hobart* / Walk in the parlour: *Hemphill, Sid & Lucius Smith* / Mama's gonna buy: *Hall-Ward, Vera* / Wished I was in heaven sitting down: *McDowell, Fred* / Po' lazarus: *Bright Light Quartet* / Lass of Loch Royale: *Morris, Neil* / Three nights drunk: *Mainer, J.E.* / Turkey in the straw: *Everidge, Charley & Neil Morris* / Pharaoh: *Carter, Sydney* / Cripple creek: *Higgins, Uncle Charlie & Wade Ward* / Diver boy: *Gilbert, Ollie* / Pretty Polly: *Ball, E.C.* / Sweet Roseanne: *Bright Light Quartet* / Sink 'em low: *Jones, Bessie* / Dollar Mamie: *Lewis, Ed* / I wonder will we meet again: *Crenshaw, Rev. & The Congregation* / Poor wayfaring stranger: *Riddle, Almeda* / Testimony: *Beck, I.D.* / Guide me o thou great jehovah: *Claudill, Ike* / Last words of Copernicus: *Sacred Harp Singers* / Gospel train: *Belleville A Capella Choir* / Beulah land: *Davis, John & Bessie Jones* / It just suits me: *Smith, Hobart*
ROUCD 1701 / May '97 / Rounder

☐ ALAN LOMAX COLLECTION - SOUTHERN JOURNEY VOL.2, THE (Ballads And Breakdowns)
Old Joe Clark: *Ward, Wade* / Poor Ellen Smith: *Ball, E.C.* / Sourwood mountain: *Smith, Hobart* / Girl I left behind: *Moore, Spencer* / John Henry: *Stoneman, Glen* / Three little babes: *Gladden, Texas* / Bonaparte's retreat: *Edmonds, Norman* / June apple: *Higgins, Charlie & Wade Ward* / Peg an'awl: *Smith, Hobart* / Sally Anne: *Stoneman, George* / Fox chase: *Ward, Wade & Bob Carpenter* / Banks of the Ohio: *Vass, Ruby* / Willow garden: *Higgins, Charlie & Wade Ward* / Graveyard blues: *Smith, Hobart* / Uncle Charlie's breakdown: *Higgins, Charlie & Wade Ward* / Burglar man: *Carpenter, Bob* / Fly around my blue eyed girl: *Smith, Hobart* / Single girl: *Vass, Ruby* / Parson Burrs: *Smith, Hobart* / Piney woods gal: *Higgins, Charlie & Wade Ward* / Hick's farewell: *Gladden, Texas* / Black Annie: *Smith, Hobart* / Little schoolboy: *Smith, Hobart* / Breaking up Christmas: *Edmonds, Norman* / Whole heap of little hors: *Gladden, Texas* / Cluck old hen: *Ward, Wade*
ROUCD 1702 / May '97 / Rounder

☐ ALAN LOMAX COLLECTION - SOUTHERN JOURNEY VOL.3, THE (61 Highway Mississippi)
Louisiana: *Ratcliff, Henry* / Jim and John: *Young, Ed* / 61 Highway blues: *McDowell, 'Mississippi' Fred* / Stewball: *Lewis, Ed* / Po' boy blues: *Dudley, John* / God's unchanging hand: *Burton, A. & Congregation* / Keep your lamps trimmed and burning: *McDowell, Fred* / Emmaline, take your time: *Hemphill, Sid & Lucius Smith* / I'm gonna live anyhow 'till I die: *Pratcher, Miles & Bob* / Little Sally Walker: *Gardner, Mattie* / Old devil's dream: *Hemphill, Sid & Lucius Smith* / Rolled and tumbled: *Hemphill, Rose & Fred McDowell* / Mama Lucy: *Gary, Leroy* / Soon one mornin': *McDowell, Fred* / I'm goin' home: *Webb, Ervin* / Fred McDowell's blues: *McDowell, Fred* / Tryin' to make heaven my home: *James, Viola* / Berta, Berta: *Miller, Leroy* / Germany blues: *McDowell, Fred* / Clarksdale Mill blues: *Dudley, John* / If it's all night long: *Pratcher, Miles & Bob* / Lord have mercy: *McDowell, Fred* / Didn't leave nobody but the baby: *Carter, Mrs. Sidney*
ROUCD 1703 / May '97 / Rounder

☐ ALAN LOMAX COLLECTION - SOUTHERN JOURNEY VOL.4, THE (Brethren, We Meet Again)
Sardinia: *Alabama Sacred Harp Singers* / Testimony on pioneer religion: *Asher, D.N.* / Amazing grace: *Adams, Howard* / Lonely tombs: *Smith, Preston & Hobart* / Guide me, o thou great jehovah: *Spangler, George* / Old gospel ship: *Vass, Ruby* / Little family: *Gilbert, Ollie* / When the stars begin to fall: *Smith, Preston & Hobart* / Testimony: *Beck, I.D.* / When Jesus Christ was here on earth: *Beck, I.D.* / Northport: *Alabama Sacred Harp Singers* / Why must I wear this shroud: *Spangler, George* / See that my grave is kept clean: *Smith, Hobart* / My Lord keeps a record: *Mountain Ramblers* / I am a poor wayfaring stranger: *Riddle, Almeda* / Brethren, we have met again: *Spanger, George* / Jim and me: *Smith, Preston* / *Joseph Looney*: *Gilbert, Ollie* / Poor pilgrims of sorrow: *Beck, I.D.* / I'm on my journey home: *Alabama Sacred Harp Singers* / Closing prayer: *Alabama Sacred Harp Singers*
ROUCD 1704 / May '97 / Rounder

☐ ALAN LOMAX COLLECTION - SOUTHERN JOURNEY VOL.5, THE (Bad Man Ballads)
Jesse James: *Riddle, Almeda* / Po' Lazarus: *Bright Light Quartet* / Railroad Bill: *Smith, Hobart* / John Henry: *Lewis, Ed* / Willie Brennan: *Morris, Neil* / Hangman tree: *Riddle, Almeda* / Columbus stockade: *Mainer, J.E. Band* / Early in the mornin': *Moore, Johnny Lee* / Pretty Polly: *Ball, Estil C.* / Lazarus: *Morrison, Henry* / Claude Allen: *Smith, Hobart* / Cole Younger: *Gilbert, Oscar* / Lawson murder: *Moore, Spencer & Everett Blevins* / Tom Devil: *Lewis, Ed* / Hawkins County jail: *Smith, Hobart* / Dangerous blues: *Batts, Floyd* / Po' Lazarus: *Carter, James*
ROUCD 1705 / May '97 / Rounder

☐ ALAN LOMAX COLLECTION - SOUTHERN JOURNEY VOL.6, THE (Sheep, Don'tcha Know The Road)
Sheep, sheep, don'tcha know the road: *Jones, Bessie & The Sea Island Singers* / Juice of the forbidden fruit: *Morris, Neil* / Devil's dream: *Smith, Hobart* / You got dimples in your jaws: *Jones, Willie & Others* / Drunken hiccups: *Smith, Hobart* / You don tol' everybody: *McDowell, Fred* / House carpenter: *Riddle, Almeda* / Straighten 'em: *Bright Light Quartet* / Corn dodgers: *Morris, Neil* / I wished I was in heaven: *Gardner, Denise & Mattie/Fred McDowell* / Tribulations: *Ball, E.C. & Lacy Richardson* / No room at the inn/Last month of the year: *Hall-Ward, Vera* / My mother died and left me: *Shorty, James & Fred McDowell* / Buttermilk: *Pratcher, Miles & Bob* / Prayer wheel: *Bright Light Quartet* / Guide me o thou great Jehovah: *Caudill, Ike & Congregation*
ROUCD 1706 / May '97 / Rounder

☐ ALAN LOMAX COLLECTION SAMPLER
Interview: *Lomax, Alan* / I'm going home: *Webb, Ervin* / Girl I left behind: *Moore, Spencer* / Titanic: *Jones, Bessie* / Sherburne: *Alabama Sacred Harp Singers* / Early in the mornin': *22 & Group* / Roll roll roll and go / Luce-o, Luce Mauvais / Sambo Caesar: *Smith, Cyprus* / War: *Growling Tiger & Lord Airey* / Religious Bhajan: *Gopaul, Ram* / Mulad tha mulad: *Nicholson, Annie* / As I roved out: *Ennis, Seamus* / Sister's lament: *McNeill, Flora* / Four loom weaver: *MacColl, Ewan* / Jovial tradesman: *Copper, Bob & Ron* / Jota manchega: *Ordonez, Jesus Orchestra* / Fandango de comares: *Munoz, Inez* / Saeta: *Radio Nacional Madrid* / Pastores de Bormujo: *Campanilleros De Bormujo* / La partenza: *Genoese Longshoreman* / O giglio e beni constrastatu: *Pingitore Family* / Stornello: *Pila, Eugenio* / Canto di carrettiere: *Lanza, Domenico* / Ballo del tamburo: *Pasquale, Aristide* / Ma uitai spre rasarit: *Lataretu, Mari* / Esashi oiwake: *Unknown Fisherman* / Gender wayang: *Ubud Gamelan* / Rain dance: *Buck, George* / John Henry: *Hemphill, Sid* / Devil's dream: *Hemphill, Sid* / Ten pound hammer: *SC Ditch Diggers* / Mailheureuse negre: *Benoit, Cleveland* / My son David: *Robertson, Jeannie* / Hawkins County jail: *Smith, Hobart* / 61 Highway: *McDowell, 'Mississippi' Fred* / Low down dirty blues: *House, Son* / Bound to lose: *Guthrie, Woody*
ROUCD 1700 / May '97 / Rounder

☐ ALANTE DI MUSICA TRADIZIONALE
NT 6736CD / Apr '95 / Robi Droli

☐ ALBA (New And Traditional Music From Scotland)
Alba: *British Caledonian* / Hornpipes: *British Caledonian* / Slow airs: *British Caledonian* / Cradle song: *British Caledonian* / 6/8 marches: *British Caledonian* / America - the beautiful medley: *British Caledonian* / Intercontinental gathering: *British Caledonian* / Competition medley: *British Caledonian* / Waltz and march: *British Caledonian* / 4/4 marches: *British Caledonian* / Amazing grace: *British Caledonian* / Farewell medley: *British Caledonian* / Reprise drum salute: *British Caledonian*
LCOM 6017 / Feb '97 / Lismor

☐ ALBANIA: SONGS AS OLD AS THE EARTH
T 3312 / Mar '91 / Touch

☐ ALFAGURT LJODER MIN TUNGA (Traditional Music Of The Faroe Islands)
SHD 16 / 2 Apr '98 / Tutl

☐ ALIEN AMBIENT GALAXY
CLEO 9683CD / May '96 / Cleopatra

☐ ALIEN UNDERGROUND VOL.1
Excursions: *Floppy Sounds* / Overdrive: *Club Illusions* / Cut the midrange: *Watchman* / Rescue: *Omegaman* / Higher: *Mathumatix* / Kool kat: *Top Kat* / Soul freak: *Timewriter* / Tamburi: *Tamburi Project* / Basketball heroes: *McBride, Woody* / Alien funk: *DJ Hyperactive* / Jack in the bed: *DJ Silver*
KICKCD 50 / Apr '97 / Kickin'

☐ ALIENS ON ACID (2CD Set)
CLP 9941 / Mar '97 / X-Ray

☐ ALIVE DOWN SOUTH (From The Vaults Of Capricom Studios)
WHITECLAY 715 / 15 Jun '98 / Icehouse

☐ ALIVE IN IRELAND
REJ 1000019 / 29 Jun '98 / Rejected

☐ ALIVE IN THE LIVING ROOM
CRECD 01 / May '94 / Creation

☐ ALL ABOUT SOUL
Divine emotions: *Narada* / Love supreme: *Downing, Will* / There's nothing like this: *Omar* / Sexual healing: *Gaye, Marvin* / How do you stop: *Brown, James* / Sha la la (make me happy): *Green, Al* / Wishing on a star: *Rose Royce* / Rainy night in Georgia: *Crawford, Randy* / Always: *Atlantic Starr* / That lady: *Isley Brothers* / Shake you down: *Abbott, Gregory* / Me and Mrs Jones: *Jackson, Freddie* / Love I lost: *Melvin, Harold* / Ain't no sunshine: *Withers, Bill* / You'll never know: *Hi-Gloss* / Cherish: *Kool & The Gang* / Softly whispering I love you: *Congregation* / I'm doing fine now: *New York City*
RENCD 108 / Oct '95 / Renaissance Collector Series

☐ ALL AMERICAN COUNTRY
Thing called love: *Cash, Johnny* / Here comes my baby again: *Posey, Sandy* / Green green grass of home: *Miller, Roger* / Four in the morning: *Young, Faron* / Crystal chandeliers: *Drusky, Roy* / Walk on by: *Van Dyke, Leroy* / I love you because: *Jones, George* / I threw away the rose: *Williams, Hank Jr.* / Jambalaya: *Williams, Hank* / Love at the Five and Dime: *Mattea, Kathy* / Snowbird: *Glaser, Tompall & The Glaser Brothers* / Me and Bobby McGee: *Dudley, Dave* / Release me: *Lewis, Jerry Lee* / Ruby don't take your love to town: *Perkins, Carl* / Convoy: *McCall, C.W.* / I take a lot of pride in what I am: *Rodriguez, Johnny* / Make the world go away: *Arnold, Eddy* / Homecoming: *Hall, Tom T.*
5525572 / Sep '96 / Spectrum

☐ ALL AMERICAN ROCK 'N' ROLL FROM FRATERNITY RECORDS
Rock-a-bop: *Moore, Sparkle* / Flower of my heart: *Moore, Sparkle* / Killer: *Moore, Sparkle* / She's neat: *Wright, Dale* / Take hold of my hand: *Dobkins, Carl Jr.* / That's why I'm asking: *Dobkins, Carl Jr.* / Makin' love with my baby: *Turley, Richard* / That's my girl: *Turner, Jesse Lee* / Absolutely nothin': *Parsons, Bill* / Dance, dance, dance: *Parsons, Bill* / Hand me down my rockin' shoes: *Parsons, Bill* / Jungle bandstand: *Parsons, Bill* / Try it no more: *Marcum, Gene* / That's showbiz: *Wright, Dale & The Wright Guys* / You're the answer: *Wright, Dale & The Wright Guys* / Buddies with the blues: *Bare, Bobby & The All American Boys' Orchestra* / Teardrops from the eyes: *Jeffers, Jimmy & The Jokers* / Rubber dolly: *Bare, Bobby* / All American boy: *Bare, Bobby*
CDCHD 316 / Jul '91 / Ace

☐ ALL BOUNDARIES ARE ILLUSION
TO3CD 001 / Jun '97 / 21-3 Productions

☐ ALL FRUITS RIPE VOL.1
VPCD 1242 / Jul '92 / Shocking Vibes

☐ ALL IRELAND SONGS AND HEROES (A Musical Tribute To The 32 Counties - 2CD Set)
GAELD 1 / 26 Jan '98 / Dara

☐ ALL KINDSA GIRLS
MRCD 108 / Nov '96 / Munster

☐ ALL MIXED UP
TRX 001CDS / 15 Dec '97 / Trax UK

☐ ALL NIGHT LONG
Love supreme: *Downing, Will* / All night long: *Mary Jane Girls* / My one temptation: *Paris, Mica* / Rock me tonight: *Jackson, Freddie* / Rain: *Jones, Oran 'Juice'* / Treat her like a lady: *Temptations* / Thinking about your love: *Thomas, Kenny* / Come in to my life: *Sims, Joyce* / Joy and pain: *Maze & Frankie Beverly* / I want your lovin': *Hairston, Curtis* / Secret lovers: *Atlantic Starr* / Could it be I'm falling in love: *Grant, David & Jaki Graham* / Dancing tonight: *Galaxy & Phil Fearon* / You're lying: *Lynx* / Medicine song: *Mills, Stephanie* / She's strange: *Cameo* / Respect: *Adeva* / Good life: *Inner City* / Nights of pleasure: *Loose Ends* / Love town: *Newberry, Booker III*
5529222 / Oct '97 / Spectrum

☐ ALL NIGHT LONG THEY PLAY THE BLUES
Part time love / Country boy / I know you hear me calling / Little green house / Hey hey baby's gone / I'm serving time / Life goes on / Mama Rufus
CDCHD 440 / Jan '93 / Ace

☐ ALL OF MY APPOINTED TIME (40 Years Of Gospel)
Standing by the bedside of a neighbour: *Acapella Gospel Golden Gate Quartet* / Listen to the lambs: *Acapella Gospel Golden Gate Quartet* / Precious Lord: *Kings Of Harmony* / God shall wipe all tears away: *Kings Of Harmony* / I'm bound for Canaan land: *Blue Jay Singers* / Standing out on the highway: *Blue Jay Singers* / Well well well: *Soul Stirrers* / I'm gonna tell God: *Soul Stirrers* / Here I am, do Lord send me: *Peach, Georgia & the Harmonaires* / Where the sun will never go down: *Peach, Georgia & the Harmonaires* / Lord will make a way: *Griffin, Bessie* / Any stars in my crown: *Golden Harps* / I'll make it somehow: *Golden Harps* / They led my Lord away: *Williams, Marion* / All my appointed time: *Williams, Marion* / Groves show intro: *Golden Gate Quartet* / Polly wolly doodle: *Golden Gate Quartet* / Old Kentucky home: *Golden Gate Quartet* / On a mornin': *Golden Gate Quartet* / Take your time Miss Lucy: *Golden Gate Quartet* / Oh Noah: *Golden Gate Quartet* / Stewball: *Golden Gate Quartet* / Grove show sign off: *Golden Gate Quartet* / Hit the road to dreamland: *Charioteers* / I've got a home in that rock: *Charioteers* / Caledonia: *Charioteers* / Open the door Richard: *Delta Rhythm Boys* / Sittin' and a-rockin': *Delta Rhythm Boys*
JCD 640 / Aug '93 / Jass
CDMOJO 308 / Nov '96 / Mojo

☐ ALL OVER THE MAP
ROUCDAN 26 / Jun '96 / Rounder

☐ ALL PLATINUM FUNK
You got it (talkin' bout my love): *Youngblood, Lonnie* / I got a suspicion: *Patterson, Bobby* / This is it: *First Class* / In the bottle: *Brother To Brother* / Funk you: *BBP* / Stay: *Moments* / Let your mind be free: *Brother To Brother* / Thump and bump: *Fisher, Eddie* / (I'm in) The prime of love: *BBP* / On top: *Youngblood, Lonnie* / I'm gonna take your love: *Brother To Brother* / Is it funky enough: *Communications & Black Experiences Band* / Cosmic blues: *Fisher, Eddie* / Chance with you: *Brother To Brother* / Walter's inspiration: *Rimshots* / Music makes me feel good: *Fisher, Eddie* / I may be right, I may be wrong: *Mill Street Depo* / Gotta get it back: *Mother Freedom Band* / Give me, lend me, loan me (let me have): *Fisher, Eddie* / 7-6-5-4-3-2-1 Blow your whistle: *Rimshots*
CPCD 8082 / Mar '95 / Charly

☐ ALL PLATINUM/UNDISCOVERED GEMS (2CD Set)
7-6-5-4-3-2-1: *Rimshots* / Shame shame shame: *Shirley & Co.* / Sending out an SOS: *Young, Retta* / Where did our love go: *Elbert, Donnie* / Pillow talk: *Sylvia* / Girls: *Moments & Whatnauts* / 3 minutes 2 hey girl: *Kerr, George* / Me and my Gemini: *First Class* / Bottle: *Brother To Brother* / I'm needing you,

wanting you: Jackson, Chuck / Dolly my love: Moments / Your precious love: Jones, Linda / Sweet stuff: Sylvia / My funny Valentine: Benton, Brook / I got a suspicion: Patterson, Bobby / More shame: Powell, Seldon / Unaddressed letter: Cortez, Dave 'Baby' / What do you do: Elbert, Donnie / You send me: Ponderosa Twins / Because of you: Mickey & Sylvia / Don't you know a true love: O'Jays / Fascinating devastating man: Mills, Eleonore / You won't support me: Mill Street Depo / I can't help it: Sylvia / So this is our goodbye: Moments / Hey girl: Ponderosa Twins / Coward's way out: Valentine, Lezli / Reachin' for a dream: Youngblood, Lonnie / Distant lover: Keys, Kevin / I'm so glad I found you: Englewood Symphony / Do we have a love: Kerr, George

NEMCD 970 / 1 Jun '98 / Sequel

☐ **ALL SPICE**

Never like this: Two Tons Of Fun / I think I love you: Shock / Slipped away: Allspice / Give it up (don't make me wait): Sylvester / Rainy day stormy nights: Impact / Hungry for your love: Allspice / Keep it up: Everett, Betty / Lovin': Hurtt, Phil / Just us: Two Tons Of Fun / I ain't into that: Rappin' Reverend / SOS: Side Effect / Feel good all over: McWilliams, Paulette / For you: Reason, Johnny / I believe in you: Muhammad, Idris / Love's such a wonderful sound: Reason, Johnny / Finally found someone: Side Effect / Never been here before: McWilliams, Paulette

CDBGPD 074 / Oct '93 / Beat Goes Public

☐ **ALL STAR CHA CHA CHA**

New cha-cha: Puente, Tito / Ay, Jose: Graciela & Machito / Flanco's cha-cha: Cuba, Joe Sextet / St. Louis blues cha-cha-cha: Gutierrez, Julio Orchestra / El bodeguero: O'Farrill, Chico All Star Orchestra / No me quieras tanto: Lupe, Tito-La / Sabroso cha cha: Cuba, Joe Sextet / Improvisando cha-cha: Morales, Obdulio Cuban Orchestra & Peruchin / Almendra: Candido / Tea for two: Puente, Tito / Los parqueadores: Fajardo, Jose & His Orchestra / Holiday: Machito

12912 / May '97 / Laserlight

☐ **ALL STAR CHICAGO BLUES SESSION**

JSPCD 214 / '88 / JSP

☐ **ALL STAR YARD STYLE VOL.2**

2098730232 / 22 Dec '97 / Joe Gibbs

☐ **ALL THAT BLUES**

OBCCD 5001 / Nov '92 / Original Blues Classics

☐ **ALL THAT JAZZ (3CD Set)**

EMTBX 301 / Aug '97 / Emporio

☐ **ALL THAT JAZZ (Remix Project/2CD Set)**

APR 028CD / 3 Aug '98 / April

☐ **ALL THAT JAZZ IS BACK**

Things are getting better: Adderley, Cannonball / How high the moon: Baker, Chet / Jumpin' at the Woodside: Basie, Count / Afro jaws: Davis, Eddie 'Lockjaw' / There is no greater love: Davis, Miles New Quintet / Latin American sunshine: Ellington, Duke Orchestra / Waltz for Debby: Evans, Bill Trio / I ain't got nothin' but the blues: Fitzgerald, Ella & Tommy Flanagan Trio / Foggy day: Garland, Red / Birk's works: Gillespie, Dizzy / My funny valentine: Jackson, Milt Quartet / Bearcat: Jordan, Clifford Quartet / Spring is here: Kessel, Barney/Ray Brown/Shelly Manne

OJCCD 1001 / Oct '93 / Original Jazz Classics

☐ **ALL THAT SAX (The Magic Of The Saxophone)**

Black velvet / Lovely day / Knock on wood / One moment in time / Missing you / Piano in the dark / Don't it make my brown eyes blue / Nothing's gonna change my love for you / With a little help from my friends / Billie Jean / Groovy kind of love / Something's gotten hold of my heart / Isn't she lovely / Like dreamers do / Too much heaven / Fly robin fly / If you think you know how to love me / Way you make me feel

ECD 3146 / Mar '95 / K-Tel

☐ **ALL THE BEST FROM SCOTLAND VOL.1**

Rowan tree / Scotland again / Dark Lochnagar / Aye ready / Ae fond kiss / Work o' the weavers / Caledonia / Skye boat song / Amazing grace / Contentment / Lord's my shepherd / Man'a man / Ye banks and braes o' bonnie Doon / Massacre of Glencoe / Auld lang syne

LBP 2018CD / Oct '94 / Klub

☐ **ALL THE BEST FROM SCOTLAND VOL.2**

Bonnie Aberdeen / Highland bridge depot / Major J McGillvary / My ain folk / Loch Lomond / Dark island / Sweet afton / Bonnie lass o'Fyvie / Jessie's hornpipe / Kirk's hornpipe / Drumlees / Island spinning song / Banjo breakdown / Fiddlers choice / Scotland your a lady / Flowers of Edinburgh / Wee dug Tim / Lucky Scaup / Rose of Allendale / Skye boat song / Morag of Dunvegan / When you and I were young Maggie / Twa racruiting sergeants

LBP 2019CD / Oct '94 / Klub

☐ **ALL THE PRESIDENT'S MEN**

CRECD 140 / Jul '92 / Creation

☐ **ALL THE WORLD IN AN EGG**

WWCD 16 / Mar '96 / Universal Egg

☐ **ALL THROUGH THE YEAR**

HPRCD 2002 / Oct '93 / Hokey Pokey

☐ **ALL TIME COUNTRY GREATS**

Streets of Baltimore: Pride, Charley / Welcome to my world: Reeves, Jim / I'm movin' on: Snow, Hank / I'm a ramblin' man: Jennings, Waylon / Funny how time slips away: Nelson, Willie / I will always love you: Parton, Dolly / Send me the pillow you dream on: Locklin, Hank / Yakety axe: Atkins, Chet / Sea of heartbreak: Gibson, Don / End of the world: Davis, Skeeter / Once a day: Smith, Connie / She's a little bit country: Hamilton, George IV / Is anybody going to San Antone: Pride, Charley

7432144685 2 / Feb '97 / Camden

☐ **ALL TIME COUNTRY HALL OF FAME**

Jambalaya: Lewis, Jerry Lee / Sylvia's mother: Bare, Bobby / Stand by your man: Wynette, Tammy / Then she's a lover: Clarke, Roy / I walk the line: Cash, Johnny / I love you honey: Cline, Patsy / Geisha girl: Locklin, Hank / Above and beyond: Owens, Buck / There never was a time: Riley, Jeannie C. / Allons a lafayette: Newman, Jimmy C. / Rhinestone cowboy: Campbell, Glen / Crazy dreams: Twitty, Conway / My arms stay open late: Spears, Billie Jo / From a jack to a king: Miller, Ned / Little green apples: Miller, Roger / My last date with you: Davis, Skeeter / Ruby (don't take your love to town): Rogers, Kenny & The First Edition / Boy named Sue: Cash, Johnny / Poor man's roses: Page, Patti / Don't think twice it's alright: Jennings, Waylon

309082 / 13 Jul '98 / Hallmark

☐ **ALL TIME GREATEST COUNTRY SONGS (2CD Set)**

Ruby don't take your love to town: Rogers, Kenny / Everybody's talkin': Nilsson, Harry / Behind closed doors: Rich, Charlie / Angel of the morning: Newton, Juice / Lay lady lay: Dylan, Bob / If not for you: Newton-John, Olivia / Crazy: Cline, Patsy / He'll have to go: Reeves, Jim / Blue bayou: Ronstadt, Linda / Silver threads and golden needles: Parton, Dolly & Loretta Lynn/Tammy Wynette / I will survive: Spears, Billie Jo / Bye bye love: Everly Brothers / Cathy's clown: Everly Brothers / Language of love: Loudermilk, John D. / Love hurts: Harris, Emmylou / Me and Bobby McGee: Kristofferson, Kris / Take me home, country home: Denver, John / I don't know why: Colvin, Shawn / By the time I get to Phoenix: Campbell, Glen / Crying: Orbison, Roy / Don't it make my brown eyes blue: Gayle, Crystal / Always on my mind: Nelson, Willie / Islands on my mind: Nelson, Willie / Islands in the stream: Rogers, Kenny & Dolly Parton / Jolene: Parton, Dolly / Down to my last teardrop: Tucker, Tanya / Blue: Rimes, Leann / Let me into your heart: Carpenter, Mary-Chapin / Love can build a bridge: Judds / Good year for roses: Costello, Elvis & The Attractions / I'm just a country boy: Williams, Don / From a distance: Griffith, Nanci / Detroit city: Bare, Bobby / Ode to Billie Joe: Gentry, Bobbie / If I said you had a beautiful body (would you hold it agains: Bellamy Brothers / I will always love you: Rogers, Kenny / Memories: Davies, Mac / Kentucky woman: Diamond, Neil / King of the road: Miller, Roger / Jackson: Cash, Johnny & June Carter / Riders in the sky: Cash, Johnny / Polk salad Annie: White, Tony Joe / Achy breaky heart: Cyrus, Billy Ray / Devil went down to Georgia: Daniels, Charlie Band / Duelling banjos based on Feudin banjos: Weisberg, Eric & Steve Mandell

SONYTV 24CD / Mar '97 / Sony TV

☐ **ALL TIME GREATEST LOVE SONGS, THE (2CD Set)**

Julia says: Wet Wet Wet / Think twice: Dion, Celine / How deep is your love: Bee Gees / Always: Atlantic Starr / So amazing: Vandross, Luther / Oh baby I: Eternal / Soul provider: Bolton, Michael / On silent wings: Turner, Tina / Love and affection: Armatrading, Joan / Sexual healing: Gaye, Marvin / Show me heaven: McKee, Maria / I just want to make love to you: James, Etta / Wherever I lay my hat (that's my home): Young, Paul / (You make me feel like) A natural woman: King, Carole / What a wonderful world: Armstrong, Louis / Nothing compares 2 U: O'Connor, Sinead / Eternal flame: Bangles / Don't let the sun go down on me: Michael, George & Elton John / Chains: Arena, Tina / Back for good: Take That / Ocean Drive: Lighthouse Family / No more I love yous: Lennox, Annie / Your song: John, Elton / Love on the rocks: Diamond, Neil / Promise me: Craven, Beverley / Without you: Nilsson, Harry / If I could turn back time: Cher / Mandy: Manilow, Barry / Time after time: Lauper, Cyndi / Miss you nights: Richard, Cliff / Rose: Midler, Bette / I say a little prayer: Franklin, Aretha / Stand by me: King, Ben E. / Don't wanna lose you: Estefan, Gloria / I want to know what love is: Foreigner / Power of love: Rush, Jennifer / Unchained melody: Robson & Jerome

SONYTV 21CD / Oct '96 / Sony TV

☐ **ALL TIME GREATEST LOVE SONGS, THE (2CD Set)**

Love is all around: Wet Wet Wet / Because you loved me: Dion, Celine / 7 seconds: Cherry, Neneh / Say what you want: Texas / Forever love: Barlow, Gary / All I think about is you: Nilsson, Harry / I only have eyes for you: Garfunkel, Art / Anything: 3T / Everytime I close my eyes: Babyface / Don't know much: Rondstadt, Linda & Aaron Neville / Words: Boyzone / Anything for you: Estefan, Gloria / Lady in red: De Burgh, Chris / If you ever: East 17 & Gabrielle / Quit playing games with my heart: Backstreet Boys / Always and forever: Vandross, Luther / Perfect year: Carroll, Dina / Endless love: Ross, Diana & Lionel Richie / I still haven't found what I'm looking for: Chimes / I believe I can fly: Kelly, R / Will you be there: Jackson, Michael / One: John, Elton / All cried out: Moyet, Alison / Remembering the first time: Simply Red / Together we are beautiful: Kinney, Fern / Greatest love of all: Benson, George / Forever Autumn: Hayward, Justin / What becomes of the broken hearted: Robson & Jerome / You've lost that loving feeling: Righteous Brothers / I'm not in love: 10cc / Beautiful goodbye: Marshall, Amanda / She's always a woman: Joel, Billy / If not for you: Dylan, Bob / Don't dream it's over: Crowded House / If you know what I mean: Diamond, Neil / Glory of love: Cetera, Peter / Tonight: Michael, George

SONYTV 34CD / 20 Oct '97 / Sony TV

☐ **ALL TIME GREATEST ROCK SONGS**

Dancing in the dark: Springsteen, Bruce / Tonight's the night: Stewart, Rod / Go your own way: Fleetwood Mac / Love the one you're with: Stills, Stephen / Everybody hurts: REM / More than words: Extreme / Not where it's at: Del Amitri / Over my shoulder: Mike & The Mechanics / I'll stand by you: Pretenders / She's gone: Hall & Oates / Take my breath away: Berlin / One by one: Cher / Stay: Shakespears Sister / In the air tonight: Collins, Phil / Alone: Heart / November rain: Guns n' Roses / I want to know what love is: Foreigner / I'll do anything for love but I won't do that: Meat Loaf / Wonderful tonight: Clapton, Eric / China girl: Bowie, David / You're in my heart: Stewart, Rod / Kayleigh: Marillion / Walking in Memphis: Cohn, Marc / Drive: Cars / Fool if you think it's over: Rea, Chris / Knockin' on heavens door: Dylan, Bob / Real gone kid: Deacon Blue / What a fool believes: Doobie Brothers / Black velvet: Myles, Alannah / Hazard: Marx, Richard / Broken wings: Mr. Mister / Ride like the wind: Cross, Christopher / House of the rising sun: Animals / More than a feeling: Boston / Love is a battlefield: Benatar, Pat / Are you gonna go my way: Kravitz, Lenny / Running on empty: Brown, Jackie

MOODCD 53 / 27 Oct '97 / Sony TV

☐ **ALL TIME GREATEST SAMBA SCHOOL SONGS COLLECTION, THE**

7432146705 2 / May '97 / Milan

☐ **ALL TIME GREATS**

Puttin' on the ritz: Astaire, Fred / No man is ever going to worry me: Tucker, Sophie / April showers: Johnson, Al / That's the kind of baby for me: Cantor, Eddie / Eadie was a lady: Merman, Ethel / Tisket a tasket: Fitzgerald, Ella / Change partners: Astaire, Fred / Somebody stole Gabriel's horn: Crosby, Bing / I come from a musical family: Armstrong, Louis / Man I love: Tucker, Sophie / Rock a bye your baby with a dixie melody: Jolson, Al / It never rains but it pours: Garland, Judy / I used to be colour blind: Astaire, Fred / Gotta pebble in my shoe: Fitzgerald, Ella / Washing the blues from my soul: Tucker, Sophie / Little lady make believe/Says my heart: Cantor, Eddie / Bob White: Crosby, Bing & Connie Boswell / Please: Crosby, Bing / I got rhythm: Hall, Adelaide / Solitude: Armstrong, Louis / Crazy feet: Astaire, Fred / You are too beautiful: Jolson, Al / Canoe song: Robeson, Paul

300462 / Jun '98 / Hallmark

☐ **ALL TIME NUMBER ONE SONGS (2CD Set)**

I believe: Laine, Frankie / Moulin rouge: Mantovani & His Orchestra / Singin' the blues: Mitchell, Guy / This ole house: Clooney, Rosemary / It's only make believe: Twitty, Conway / I'll be home: Boone, Pat / My old man's a dustman: Donegan, Lonnie / Smoke gets in your eyes: Platters / Great balls of fire: Lewis, Jerry Lee / Poetry in motion: Tillotson, Johnny / Blue moon: Marcels / Tell Laura I love her: Valance, Ricky / Runaway: Shannon, Del / Walkin' back to happiness: Shapiro, Helen / Moon river: Williams, Danny / Nut rocker: B-Bumble & The Stingers / How do you do it: Gerry & The Pacemakers / Sweets for my sweet: Searchers / Little children: Kramer, Billy J. / Juliet: Four Pennies / I'm into something good: Herman's Hermits / Silence is golden: Poole, Brian & The Tremeloes / Baby now that I've found you: Foundations / Everlasting love: Ellis, Steve Love Affair / Dizzy: Roe, Tommy / Sugar sugar: Archies / Yellow river: Christie / Band of gold: Payne, Freda / Son of my Father: Chicory Tip / Blockbuster: Sweet / Billy, don't be a hero: Paper Lace / January: Pilot / Stand by me: King, Ben E. / Rock your baby: McCrae, George / I'd like to teach the world to sing: New Seekers / Bye bye baby: Bay City Rollers / Telstar: Tornados / Love grows: Edison Lighthouse / Diane: Bachelors / Needles and pins: Searchers

MUCD 9511 / May '96 / Musketeer

☐ **ALL TIME REGGAE HITS**

CPCD 8028 / Feb '94 / Charly

☐ **ALL WOMAN VOL.4**

ALLWOCD 4 / Oct '94 / Quality

☐ **ALLEZ OLA OLE (The Music Of The World Cup)**

Cup of life: Martin, Ricky / Top of the world (ole ole ole): Chumbawamba / Don't come home too soon: Del Amitri / Rise up: Jamaica United / Go west: Sash / I love football: Wes / Do you mind if I play: N'Dour, Youssou / Samba e gol: Bellini / It's only a game: Jam & Spoon / Rendez-vous 98: Jarre, Jean Michel / Oh eh oh eh: Gipsy Kings / Pais tropical: Mercury, Daniela / Tamborada: Fey / Los suenos de todo el mundo: Soledad / Mawe: M'du / Colours of the world: Coco Lee / Il bello della vita: Spagna / Together now: Jarre, Jean Michel / E uma partida de futebol: Skank / Three lions: Lightning Seeds & David Baddiel/Frank Skinner / Vindaloo: Fat Les

SONYTV 46CD / 15 Jun '98 / Sony TV

☐ **ALLIGATOR MAKES THE BLUES COME ALIVE**

ALCD 0007 / Jan '93 / Alligator

☐ **ALLIGATOR RECORDS 25TH ANNIVERSARY COLLECTION (2CD Set)**

ALL 110/11CD / Apr '96 / Alligator

☐ **ALLIGATOR RECORDS CHRISTMAS COLLECTION, THE**

Christmas song: Bishop, Elvin / Christmas on the bayou: Brooks, Lonnie / Let me be your Santa Claus: Clarke, William / Santa Claus wants some lovin': Ellis, Tinsley / Santa Claus Boogie: Brown, Charles / Christmas: Brown, Clarence 'Gatemouth' / I'm your santa: Lil' Ed & The Blues Imperials / Santa Claus: Little Charlie & The Nightcats / Silent night: Musselwhite, Charley / Christmas in the country: Neal, Kenny / One parent christmas: Saffire / Lonesome christmas: Seals, Son / Merry merry Christmas: Taylor, Koko / Deck the halls boogie: Webster, Katie

ALCDXMAS 9201 / Oct '93 / Alligator

☐ **ALLIGATOR SAMPLER**

ACDS 3657 / Aug '90 / Alligator

☐ **ALLONS CAJUN ROCK 'N' ROLL**

Lafayette two-step: Roger, Aldus / Lacassine special: Roger, Aldus / Mardi gras dance: Roger, Aldus / La valse d'ennui: Roger, Aldus / Diga ding ding dong: Roger, Aldus / Allons rock 'n' roll: Roger, Aldus / La valse de reno: Roger, Aldus / Mamou two step: Roger, Aldus / Hip et taiau: Abshire, Nathan / Cush cush: Forester, Blackie / Just because: Forester, Blackie / Hang your hat: Forester, Blackie / La fille de la ville: Bruce, Vin / Le sud de la Louisianne: Bruce, Vin / Lake Arthur stomp: Thibodeaux, Rufus / Les veuves de la coulee: Happy Fats / Married life: Cormier, Louis / Boil them cabbages down: Guidry, Doc / Grand mamou: Newman, Jimmy C. / Creole stomp: Breaux, Jimmy / Bosco stomp: Breaux, Jimmy / La valse de KLFY: Doucet, Michael / Ma belle Evangeline: Doucet, Michael / La maison a deux portes: Doucet, Michael

CDCHD 367 / Apr '91 / Ace

☐ **ALMIGHTY CLASSICS VOL.1 (Now & Then/2CD Set)**

ALMYCD 17 / 2 Feb '98 / Almighty

☐ **ALMIGHTY CLASSICS VOL.2 (Now & Then/2CD Set)**

ALMYCD 20 / 2 Feb '98 / Almighty

☐ **ALMIGHTY DEFINITIVE VOL.1**

Chains: Rochelle / Young hearts run free: Respect & Hannah Jones / Only wanna be with you: Obsession / Think twice: Rochelle / Let me feel it: Gilles, Samantha / Never been to me: Rainbow Nation / Back for good: Lipstick / You spin me round: Kinky Boyz / Until the night: Bianca / You are the music: Roman Holliday / Feels like heaven: Jones, Hannah / Baby don't cha leave me this way: Royal T / You keep me hangin' on: Hannah & Her Sisters / Can you feel the love tonight: Harakuku

ALMYCD 15 / 2 Feb '98 / Almighty

☐ **ALMIGHTY DEFINITIVE VOL.2**

ALMYCD 19 / 2 Feb '98 / Almighty

☐ **ALMIGHTY DEFINITIVE VOL.3**

ALMYCD 23 / 23 Feb '98 / Almighty

☐ **ALPINE SPIRIT (A Magical Blend Of Music And The Sounds Of Nature)**

57782 / May '97 / Nature's Harmony

☐ **ALT FREQUENCIES**

WI 007 / Oct '96 / Worm Interface

☐ **ALT. NOISE**

WIT 019CD / 8 Sep '97 / Switch

☐ **ALTER EGO**

CDSOR 002 / Nov '96 / Sound Of Rome

☐ **ALTERED STATES OF AMERICA**

LCD 07 / 16 Feb '98 / Lo Recordings

☐ **ALTERNATIVE AMERICA**

REVXD 210 / Feb '98 / Revolver

☐ **ALTERNATIVE CURRENT VOL.1**

CDACV 2002 / Nov '94 / ACV

☐ **ALTERNATIVE CURRENT VOL.2**

CDACV 2008 / Jan '96 / ACV

☐ **ALTERNATIVE FREQUENCIES VOL.3**

WI 015 / 3 Aug '98 / Worm Interface

☐ **ALTERNATIVE MEDITATIONS VOL.1**

MASOCD 90095 / 29 Jun '98 / Materiali Sonori

☐ **ALTERNATIVE NATION - MUSIC OF THE 90'S (Interview Disc)**

12941 / Oct '97 / Laserlight

☐ **ALTERNATOR (2CD Set)**

SYNCHRO 007CD / 1 Jun '98 / NMC

☐ **ALWAYS AND FOREVER VOL.1**

Baby I'm a want you: Bread / When a man loves a woman: Sledge, Percy / Sexual healing: Gaye, Marvin / True: Spandau Ballet / Tonight I celebrate my love: Bryson, Peabo & Roberta Flack / Your body's callin': Kelly, R / Missing you: Waite, John / More than I can say: Sayer, Leo / You might need somebody: Crawford, Randy / There'll be sad songs (to make you cry): Ocean, Billy / Caravan of love: Isley-Jasper-Isley / Please don't go: KC & The Sunshine Band / Glory of love: Cetera, Peter / If you don't know me: Melvin, Harold & The Bluenotes / Zoom: Fat Larry's Band / After the love has gone: Earth, Wind & Fire / Solid: Ashford & Simpson / Always and forever: Heatwave

MUSCD 029 / Jan '97 / MCI Music

☐ **ALWAYS AND FOREVER VOL.2**

Love don't live here anymore: Rose Royce / Cherish: Kool & The Gang / So amazing: Vandross, Luther / I'll never fall in love again: Deacon Blue / For your eyes only: Easton, Sheena / Words: Christians / Darlin': Miller, Frankie / Hurry home: Wavelength / Lovin' you: Riperton, Minnie / Love won't let me wait: Harris, Major / Me and Mrs. Jones: Paul, Billy / Sailing: Cross, Christopher / I don't wanna lose you: Kandidate / Through the barricades: Kandidate / All of my heart: ABC / Cry for help: Astley, Rick / Love is the answer: England Dan

MUSCD 035 / May '97 / MCI Music

☐ **AM I DREAMING**

They talk about us: Williams, Cindy / I deserve it: Jones, Samantha / Town I live in: Lee, Jacky / You've got that hold on me: Hillery, Jane / I can't stop thinking about you: Kaye, Linda / Baby let me be your baby: Deano / You'd think he didn't know me: Browne, Sandra / Sour grapes: Noble, Patsy Ann / Am I dreaming: Tiffany / Softly in the night: Three Bells / Snakes and snails: Cogan, Alma / Wait 'til my Bobby gets home: Jones, Beverley / Breakaway: Marsden, Beryl / You don't love me no more: Bell, Madeline / Don't come any closer: Jones, Samantha / Cry to me: Track / Be his girl: Sloan, Sam / Too young to go steady: Siver, Andee / You kissed me boy: Duncan, Lesley / Biggity big: Cope, Suzie / Some people: Deene, Carol / I gotta be with you: Rede, Emma / Once more with feeling: Wonder, Alison / I didn't love him anyway: Peanut

RPM 137 / Aug '94 / RPM

☐ **AMAZING GRACE**

MU 3012 / Oct '92 / Musketeer

☐ **AMAZING GRACE AND OTHER SCOTTISH FAVOURITES**

CC 266 / May '91 / Music For Pleasure

☐ **AMAZON RAIN FOREST**

DC 879522 / Oct '97 / Disky

☐ **AMAZON SOUNDSCAPE, AN (The Wayapi Of Guyane)**
CNR 2741102 / May '98 / Le Chant Du Monde

☐ **AMAZONIA**
LYRCD 7300 / Feb '94 / Lyrichord

☐ **AMBASSADORS OF RHYTHM**
CDHOT 602 / Jun '96 / Charly

☐ **AMBERDELIC SPACE VOL.1 (3CD Set)**
DTKBOX 55 / 1 Jun '98 / Dressed To Kill

☐ **AMBERDELIC SPACE VOL.2 (Angels Of Ecstasy/4CD Set)**
DTKBOX 74 / 1 Jun '98 / Dressed To Kill

☐ **AMBIANCES DU SAHARA (Desert Blues)**
58774CD / Apr '96 / World Network

☐ **AMBIENCE DUB VOL.1**
APCCD 7003 / 18 Sep '97 / APC Tracks

☐ **AMBIENCE DUB VOL.2**
APCCD 7004 / 18 Sep '97 / APC Tracks

☐ **AMBIENT AMAZON**
TMCD 1 / Nov '95 / Tumi Dance

☐ **AMBIENT ANTHOLOGY**
1970052 / 6 Jul '98 / Fairway

☐ **AMBIENT AURAS**
CDRAID 519 / Sep '94 / Rumour

☐ **AMBIENT BABYLON (2CD Set)**
AOP 53 / 1 Jun '98 / Age Of Panik

☐ **AMBIENT COMPILATION VOL.4**
SR 9753 / Mar '95 / Silent

☐ **AMBIENT COOKBOOK, THE (4CD Set)**
AW 007 / Mar '96 / Ambient World

☐ **AMBIENT DUB VOL.4**
Oracle: *Space Time Continuum* / Solar prophet: *Insanity Sect* / Callacop: *Deep Space Network* / Regina from the future: *Starseeds* / Sign: *Coldcut* / In 7: *Another Fine Day* / Warehouse 5AM: *Positive Life* / White darkness: *Sandoz* / Triangle: *Sounds From The Ground*
RBADCD 11 / Jun '95 / Beyond

☐ **AMBIENT FANTASY VOL.1 (L'Espirit De Ambience/2CD Set)**
Morphic resonance: *Encens* / Cosmic carrot: *Timeshard* / Mystical experience: *Infinity Project* / Ether: *Neill, Ben* / Slapback: *Node* / ...From Heaven: *Manna* / Bosphoressence: *Echo System* / 3am outside here: *Elysium* / Into the void: *Mandrake* / Wobbling in space: *Optic Eye* / Sound without time: *Further* / Alien patrol: *Infinity Project* / Lady burning sky: *Neutron 9000* / Hashidity: *Optica* / 5am sunrise: *Loop Guru*
SPV 08938782 / Sep '96 / SPV

☐ **AMBIENT IBIZA**
Tell me what you dream: *Sergio* / Light at heart: *Bindu* / Woman is like a fruit: *Lucky People Center* / Manifest your love: *DOP* / Perimitive: *Van Basten* / Overheated living room: *Dub Tractor* / Journey: *Gentle People* / Big warm glo (Planet Love): *Mind Over Rhythm* / Autumn has begun: *Fluff* / You are my desire: *Toney D & The Love Trip* / Come with me: *Affinity*
CDEMC 3752 / Sep '96 / Additive

☐ **AMBIENT JOURNEYS**
Ending: *Eno, Brian* / Mountain goat: *Amorphous Androgynous* / Pendulum man: *Bark Psychosis* / Abysmal evenings: *Schutze, Paul* / Dance: *Laraaji* / Needle park: *Techno Animal* / Earth floor: *Brook, Michael* / Gift of life: *Hassell, Jon* / Slow loris versus poison snail: *Toop, David* / Gringatcho demento: *Orbit, William* / Red earth: *Rain Tree Crow*
CDOVD 495 / 29 Sep '97 / Virgin

☐ **AMBIENT MOODS**
Play dead: *Bjork & David Arnold* / Protection: *Massive Attack* / Stars: *Dubstar* / Evangeline: *Cocteau Twins* / Visions of you: *Jah Wobble's Invaders Of The Heart* / Original: *Leftfield & Toni Halliday* / Missing: *Everything But The Girl* / Inner city life: *Goldie* / Little fluffy clouds: *Orb* / Sensual world: *Bush, Kate* / Sun rising: *Beloved* / Isobel: *Bjork* / Only love can break your heart: *St. Etienne* / Sadeness: *Enigma* / Raindance: *Raindance* / Moments of love: *Art Of Noise* / Ghosts: *Japan*
5259522 / Feb '96 / PolyGram TV

☐ **AMBIENT RITUALS**
CLEO 9516CD / Jun '95 / Cleopatra

☐ **AMBIENT SENSES (20 Contemporary Instrumentals)**
Forbidden colours / Winter ceremony / Jesus to a child / Light of experience / Albatross / Twin Peaks theme / X-Files / Inspector Morse theme / Sadness part 1 / Crockett's theme / Play dead / Earth song / Concierto de Aranjuez / Bilitis / Parisienne walkways / Wedding song / Book of days / Love theme from the Thorn Birds / Samba Pa Ti / Chariots of fire
ECD 3291 / Jan '97 / K-Tel

☐ **AMBIENT SENSES VOL.1 (The Vision)**
Towers of dub: *Orb* / Papua New Guinea: *Future Sound Of London* / Joyrex J9 ii: *Caustic Window* / Dreams of children: *Slater, Luke* / Earthdance: *Mandragora* / Ageispolis: *Aphex Twin* / Ready for dead: *Ready For Dead* / Minky starshine: *Seefeel* / O Locco: *Sun Electric* / Alqa: *Alien Mutation* / Galapagos: *Sunkings*
CDTOT 12 / Jun '94 / Jumpin' & Pumpin'

☐ **AMBIENT SENSES VOL.2 (The Feeling)**
Underground: *Irresistable Force* / My travels: *Larkin, Kenny* / Naiad: *Ishii, Ken* / Lean on me: *Moby* / Listening (Aural sculpture): *Optic Eye* / Path: *El Mal* / Moist mass: *Locust* / Stoned: *Golden Claw Music* / AM: *Wagon Christ* / Manuel versus the apaches: *Deep Secret*
CDTOT 16 / Oct '94 / Jumpin' & Pumpin'

☐ **AMBIENT SENSES VOL.3**
Next: *Skylab* / Batukau: *System 7* / Potion takes effect: *Unlimited Dream Company* / Planet D: *Sabres Of Paradise* / Self perpetuating myth: *Geiom* / Lifewish: *Optica* / Polynomial-C: *Aphex Twin* / Hovering glows: *Thaemlitz, Terre* / Dust (At the crossroads): *Psychik Warriors Ov Gaia* / Spaced nature: *Omicron* / Rainforest: *Trauma Club*
CDTOT 23 / Mar '95 / Jumpin' & Pumpin'

☐ **AMBIENT SYSTEMS VOL.3**
AMB 60072 / Apr '97 / Cleopatra

☐ **AMBIENT WAY TO DUB**
CLEO 9705CD / May '96 / Cleopatra

☐ **AMBITION VOL.1 & 2 (The History Of Cherry Red)**
CDBRED 140 / Feb '97 / Cherry Red

☐ **AMBITION VOL.2 (A History Of Cherry Red)**
Jest set junta / Night and day / From a to b / Something sends me to sleep / Plain sailing / If she doesn't smile (It'll rain) / Letter from America / Xoyo / Walter and John / Your holiness / On my mind / Mating game / Spain / Talking glamour / Foreign correspondent / Penelope tree / Taboos / Simply couldn't care / You frighten / Paraffin brain / Departure / How to die with style / English rose
CDBRED 96 / Oct '91 / Cherry Red

☐ **AMBO: TIBETAN MONASTERY OF LABRANG**
C 560101 / Mar '97 / Ocora

☐ **AMEN**
Curtain: *Marden Hill* / I bloodbrother be: *Shock Headed Peters* / Vallari: *King Of Luxembourg* / Nice on the ice: *King Of Luxembourg* / You Mary you: *Philippe, Louis* / Nicky: *Momus* / O come all ye faithful (Adeste fidelis): *Monochrome Set* / Cecil beaton's scrapbook: *Would-Be-Goods* / Blue shinin' quick star: *Flippers Guitar* / Curry crazy: *Bad Dream Fancy Dress* / It's love: *Hunki-Dori* / Andy Warhol: *Fisher-Turner, Simon* / Mystery stone: *Fisher-Turner, Simon* / Maria Celesta: *Adverse, Anthony* / Whoops what a palaver: *Bid* / Belfast boy: *Fardon, Don* / Fruit paradise: *Would-Be-Goods* / My cherie amour: *Philippe, Louis* / Trial of Dr. Fancy: *King Of Luxembourg* / Diary of a narcissist: *Momus* / Temptation of the angel / Amen: *Great Chefs Of Europe*
MONDE 1CD / Feb '92 / Richmond

☐ **AMERICAN BANJO: THREE FINGER & SCRUGGS STYLE**
SFWCD 40037 / Nov '94 / Smithsonian Folkways

☐ **AMERICAN BIG BANDS (2CD Set)**
You're driving me crazy: *May, Billy* / Little brown jug: *May, Billy* / I guess I'll have to change my plan: *May, Billy* / Rose Marie: *May, Billy* / Tenderly: *May, Billy* / When I take my sugar to tea: *May, Billy* / Diane: *May, Billy* / Do you ever think of me: *May, Billy* / Unforgettable: *May, Billy* / Cocktails for two: *May, Billy* / Charmaine: *May, Billy* / Artistry in rhythm: *Kenton, Stan* / Printed rhythm: *Kenton, Stan* / I told ya I love ya, now get out: *Kenton, Stan* / Eager beaver: *Kenton, Stan* / Artistry in percussion: *Kenton, Stan* / Lover: *Kenton, Stan* / Spider and the fly: *Kenton, Stan* / Laura: *Kenton, Stan* / How high the moon: *Kenton, Stan* / How am I to know: *Kenton, Stan* / Harlem nocturne: *Brown, Les & His Band Of Renown* / Continental: *Brown, Les & His Band Of Renown* / Riding high: *Brown, Les & His Band Of Renown* / On a little streeet in Singapore: *Brown, Les & His Band Of Renown* / Hit the road to dreamland: *Brown, Les & His Band Of Renown* / Lover's leap: *Brown, Les & His Band Of Renown* / Johnson rag: *Brown, Les & His Band Of Renown* / Leapfrog: *Brown, Les & His Band Of Renown* / That certain feeling: *Brown, Les & His Band Of Renown* / Sentimental journey: *Brown, Les & His Band Of Renown* / I've got my love to keep me warm: *Brown, Les & His Band Of Renown* / I wonder what's become of Sally: *Anthony, Ray Orchestra* / Rockin' through Dixie: *Anthony, Ray Orchestra* / Skip to my Lou: *Anthony, Ray Orchestra* / Did he do right by you: *Anthony, Ray Orchestra* / Wanted: *Anthony, Ray Orchestra* / Tuxedo junction: *Anthony, Ray Orchestra* / It's de-lovely: *Anthony, Ray Orchestra* / Mr. Anthony's boogie: *Anthony, Ray Orchestra* / When the saints go marching in: *Anthony, Ray Orchestra* / Struggle bunny: *Oliver, Joe 'King' Orchestra*
CDDL 1284 / Nov '94 / EMI

☐ **AMERICAN BIG BANDS (3CD Set)**
These foolish things: *Carter, Benny* / Drummin' man: *Krupa, Gene* / Nola: *Hampton, Lionel* / One o'clock jump: *Basie, Count* / Sunny side of the street: *Dorsey, Tommy* / Dinah: *Hampton, Lionel* / Mississippi mud: *Beiderbecke, Bix* / Jersey bounce: *Nelson, Ozzie* / Dippermouth blues: *Dorsey, Jimmy* / Christopher columbus: *Goodman, Benny* / Begin the beguine: *Shaw, Artie* / South Rampart Street Parade: *Shaw, Artie* / Wrap your troubles in dreams: *Gray, Glen* / Honeysuckle rose: *Basie, Count* / In a sentimental rose: *Jurgens, Dick* / In the mood: *Miller, Glenn* / Sugarfoot stomp: *Henderson, Fletcher* / Perdido: *Ellington, Duke* / Ciribirbin: *James, Harry* / At the woodchoppers ball: *Herman, Woody* / Yes indeed: *James, Harry* / Drop me off at Harlem: *Ellington, Duke* / Unsophisticated sue: *Lunceford, Jimmie* / Sweet lorraine: *Shaw, Artie* / More than you know: *Wilson, Teddy* / I can't give you anything but love baby: *Armstrong, Louis* / Nearness of you: *Miller, Glenn* / All of me: *Dorsey, Jimmy* / Stop look and listen: *Dorsey, Tommy* / Mean to me: *Napoleon, Phil* / King porter stomp: *Henderson, Fletcher* / California here I come: *Hampton, Lionel* / All or nothing at all: *James, Harry* / Creole love song: *Ellington, Duke* / May I never love again: *Weems, Ted* / Deep purple: *Shaw, Artie* / I'm coming virginia: *Henderson, Fletcher* / Happy feet: *Whiteman, Paul* / Boogie woogie man: *Casa Loma Orchestra* / Jitney man: *Hines, Earl 'Fatha' Orchestra* / American patrol: *Miller, Glenn* / Take the 'A' train: *Ellington, Duke* / Dipsy doodle: *Clinton, Larry* / Jazz me blues: *Basie, Count* / Dr. Jazz: *Morton, Jelly Roll* / Alligator crawl: *Armstrong, Louis* / Singin' the blues: *Trumbauer, Frankie* / Maple leaf bag: *Hines, Earl 'Fatha' Orchestra* / Struggle buggy: *Oliver, Joe 'King' Orchestra* / East st louis: *Ellington, Duke* / Minnie the moocher: *Calloway, Cab Orchestra* / Taking a chance on love: *Dorsey, Tommy* / Jumping at the woodside: *Basie, Count* / Caledonia: *Herman, Woody* / Skyliner: *Barnet, Charlie* / I'll never be the same: *Krupa, Gene* / My blue heaven: *Lunceford, Jimmie* / I wonder whose kissing her now: *Lunceford, Jimmie*
390182 / Jul '96 / Hallmark

☐ **AMERICAN CLAVE - AN ANTHOLOGY**
AMCL 1020/26 / Jan '94 / American Clave

☐ **AMERICAN DINER (18 Rock 'n' Roll Greats)**
Only you: *Platters* / Little darlin': *Diamonds* / Duke of Earl: *Chandler, Gene* / Tutti frutti: *Little Richard* / He's a rebel: *Crystals* / Charlie Brown: *Coasters* / My boyfriend's back: *Angels* / It's my party: *Gore, Lesley* / Run to him: *Vee, Bobby* / Sh-boom: *Crew Cuts* / Baby it's you: *Shirelles* / Poetry in motion: *Tillotson, Johnny* / Get a job: *Silhouettes* / Love potion no.9: *Clovers* / Maybe: *Chantels* / Wild one: *Rydell, Bobby* / Baby (you got what it takes): *Benton, Brook* / It's in his kiss (the shoop shoop song): *Everett, Betty*
SUMCD 4067 / Nov '96 / Summit

☐ **AMERICAN DREAM**
COA 70001CD / Feb '96 / North South

☐ **AMERICAN FOGIES, THE**
ROUCD 0379 / Mar '96 / Rounder

☐ **AMERICAN FOLK BLUES FESTIVAL 1970**
Introduction / Hard hearted woman / That ain't it / Maggie Lee / World boogie / Old lady / Going to Louisiana / Blues before sunrise / Hootin' the blues / Back water blues / Walk on / When I was drinking / Juanita / After hours / Crazy for my baby / Sittin' and cryin' the blues
CDLR 42021 / Jul '91 / L&R

☐ **AMERICAN FOLK BLUES FESTIVAL 1972**
CDLS 42018 / Jul '92 / L&R

☐ **AMERICAN GRAFFITI (2CD Set)**
R2CD 4047 / 13 Apr '98 / Deja Vu

☐ **AMERICAN INDIAN - WOUNDED KNEE**
SM 10882CD / Nov '95 / Wergo

☐ **AMERICAN INDIAN DANCE THEATRE**
824312 / Jan '90 / BUDA

☐ **AMERICAN INDIAN DANCES**
EUCD 1317 / Jul '95 / ARC

☐ **AMERICAN INDIAN, THE (2CD Set)**
R2CD 4031 / 13 Apr '98 / Deja Vu

☐ **AMERICAN LIVIN' BLUES FESTIVAL 1982**
157742 / Feb '93 / Blues Collection

☐ **AMERICAN PENSIONERS ON ECSTASY**
CRECD 095 / Apr '91 / Creation

☐ **AMERICAN PIE (2CD Set)**
American pie: *McLean, Don* / Both sides now: *Collins, Judy* / Maybe: *Pace, Thom* / Universal soldier: *Sainte-Marie, Buffy* / City of New Orleans: *Guthrie, Arlo* / Farewell Angelina: *Baez, Joan* / Catch the wind: *Donovan* / Baker street: *Rafferty, Gerry* / Leaving of Liverpool: *Clancy Brothers* / Some day soon: *Clancy Brothers* / Rain: *Feliciano, Jose* / Weight: *Band* / Morning of my life: *Ofarim, Esther & Abi* / If I were a carpenter: *Hardin, Tim* / Old you hear John Hurt: *Paxton, Tom* / Pancho and Lefty: *Harris, Emmylou* / Cat's in the cradle: *Chapin, Harry* / Night they drove old dixie down: *Baez, Joan* / Horse with no name: *America* / Colours: *Donovan* / Everybody's talkin': *Nilsson, Harry* / Streets of london: *McTell, Ralph* / Banks of the Ohio: *Newton-John, Olivia* / Seven drunken nights: *Dubliners* / Vincent: *McLean, Don* / After the goldrush: *Prelude* / Anchorage Alaska: *Shocked, Michelle* / Guantanamera: *Sandpipers* / You were on my mind: *Ian & Sylvia* / Walk right in: *Rooftop Singers* / I'd really love to see you tonight: *England Dan & John Ford Coley* / Ode to Billy Joe: *Gentry, Bobbie* / Goodnight Irene: *Weavers* / Eve of destruction: *McGuire, Barry* / Me and you and a dog named Bee: *Lobo*
ZYX 811322 / 26 Jan '98 / ZYX

☐ **AMERICAN PRIMITIVE VOL.1 (Raw Pre-War Gospel 1926-1936)**
REV 206 / 17 Nov '97 / Revenant

☐ **AMERICAN RHYTHM 'N' BLUES**
CDRB 27 / Aug '95 / Charly

☐ **AMERICAN ROCKABILLY**
NERCD 048 / Sep '95 / Nervous

☐ **AMERICAN ROOTS MUSIC**
This soul is mine: *Castro, Tommy* / Georgia on a fast train: *Shaver* / Heartattack and wine: *Popa Chubby* / Forever: *McMahan, Ken* / It's in the attitude: *Tittle, Jimmy* / Big Bill: *Ramsey, Bo* / Drive to survive: *Thackeray, Jimmy* / Every minute every hour: *Principato, Tom* / Midnight at a redlight: *Hamilton, George V* / Self sabotage: *Jason & The Scorchers* / Just like a fish: *Garrett, Amos* / Monterey: *Burch, Paul* / Still called the blues: *Solberg, James Band* / Big girl blues: *Connor, Joanna* / Lighting a torch: *Shaver, Eddy* / Everything that glitters: *Seals, Dan* / Honeydew: *Wylie & The Wild West Show* / Seven desires: *Montoya, Coco*
DFGCD 8464 / Aug '97 / Dixie Frog

☐ **AMERICAN WARRIORS**
War paint/Soldier boy / In the South the birds are flying / Lakota (Sioux) Little Bighorn victory songs / Carnegie War Mothers' Chapter (Kiowa) veterans songs / World War I and II / Canadian (Lakota) flag song / American (Lakota) flag song / Four Hochunk (Winnebago) service songs / Menominee Vietnam veterans song / Indian boys from Desert Storm
RCD 10370 / May '97 / Rykodisc

☐ **AMERICAN WILDS**
12148 / May '94 / Laserlight

☐ **AMERICANS IN PARIS VOL.2**
2512772 / Mar '90 / Jazztime

☐ **AMERICANS IN PARIS VOL.7 (1946-50)**
8274142 / Jan '95 / Jazztime

☐ **AMOUR (The Ultimate Love Collection) (2CD Set)**
Love is all around: *Wet Wet Wet* / Walk on by: *Gabrielle* / Breathe again: *Braxton, Toni* / Sexual healing: *Gaye, Marvin* / Goodbye heartbreak: *Lighthouse Family* / If you love me: *Brownstone* / Tired of being alone: *Texas* / Hey child: *East 17* / Don't be a stanger: *Carroll, Dina* / Forever: *Damage* / Nobody knows: *Rich, Tony Project* / Touch me in the morning: *Ross, Diana* / Betcha by golly, wow: *Stylistics* / Don't wanna lose you: *Estefan, Gloria* / One day in your life: *Jackson, Michael* / Dreaming: *MN8* / Single: *Everything But The Girl* / Manchild: *Cherry, Neneh* / What's love got to do with it: *Turner, Tina* / Flame: *Fine Young Cannibals* / Back for good: *Take That* / If you ever: *East 17 & Gabrielle* / You're gorgeous: *Baby Bird* / Quit playing games: *Backstreet Boys* / I feel you: *Andre, Peter* / Words: *Boyzone* / Child: *Owen, Mark* / One more chance: *One* / Forever love: *Barlow, Gary* / Don't dream it's over: *Crowded House* / Sacrifice: *John, Elton* / In too deep: *Carlisle, Belinda* / Wonderful tonight: *Clapton, Eric* / Chains: *Arena, Tina* / Woman in chains: *Tears For Fears* / Without you: *Nilsson, Harry* / So far away: *King, Carole* / Unchained melody: *Righteous Brothers* / Don't cry for me Argentina: *Covington, Julie*
5533322 / Feb '97 / PolyGram TV

☐ **AMP**
Block rocking beats: *Chemical Brothers* / Atom bomb: *Fluke* / Pearl's girl: *Underworld* / We have explosive: *Future Sound Of London* / Ni ten ichi ryu: *Photek* / Girl boy: *Aphex Twin* / Box: *Orbital* / We all want to be free: *Tranquility Bass* / Inner city life: *Goldie* / Voodoo people: *Prodigy* / Are you there: *Wink, Josh* / Busy child: *Crystal Method* / Sick to death: *Atari Teenage Riot*
CAR 7550 / May '97 / Astralwerks

☐ **AMPLIFIED VOL.1**
AABT 807CD / Apr '95 / Abstract

☐ **AMSTERDAM SMOKERS**
BDRCD 14 / May '96 / Breakdown

☐ **AN CEOL AGAINN FHEIN**
DUAL 3CD / Aug '95 / Macmeanmna

☐ **AN DROICHEAD BEAG/A MIGHTY SESSION**
DBCD 001 / Feb '96 / Dingle Pub

☐ **ANAGRAM PUNK SINGLES COLLECTION**
Give us a future / Just another hero / You talk we talk / Woman in disguise / Lust for glory / Baby baby / Dragnet / Jerusalem / Pressure / Solidarity / Five flew over the cuckoo's nest / Guilty / Hang ten / Cum on feel the noize / Breakin' in / Nowhere left to run / Not just a name / This is the age / Black sheep / Children of the night / You'll never know / Legacy / Teenage rampage
CDPUNK 37 / Sep '94 / Anagram

☐ **ANAKIN**
Ain't no lie: *His Name Is Alive* / To whom should I write: *Mojave 3* / Say what you came to say: *Scheer* / Reptile: *Germano, Lisa* / Dreamt U in a dream: *Starry Smooth Hound* / Foundation: *Thievery Corporation* / Blue mug: *Gus Gus* / Dagger: *Hope Blister* / Sacrifice: *Gerrard, Lisa & Peter Bourke* / Gazebo tree: *Hersh, Kristin*
TAD 8001CD / 2 Feb '98 / 4AD

☐ **ANALOGUE ELEMENTS VOL.1**
NEUCD 1 / May '94 / Neuton

☐ **ANALOGUE ELEMENTS VOL.2**
NEUCD 2 / 6 Oct '97 / Neuton

☐ **ANANYA**
Raga yaman / Raga hamsadhwani / Raga puriya / Rga abhogi
NRCD 0091/2 / Feb '98 / Navras

☐ **ANCIENT CELTIC ROOTS**
TSCD 704 / Aug '96 / Topic

☐ **ANCIENT EGYPT**
LYRCD 7347 / '91 / Lyrichord

☐ **AND I LOVE YOU SO (2CD Set)**
Feelings: *Albert, Morris* / And I love you so: *Bassey, Shirley* / Why can't we live together: *Thomas, Timmy* / What a difference a day makes: *Washington, Dinah* / I you don't know me by now: *Melvin, Harold & The Bluenotes* / Only love can break a heart: *Pitney, Gene* / Stand by your man: *Anderson, Lynn* / Most beautiful girl: *Rich, Charlie* / Will you love me tomorrow: *Shirelles* / Only a fool (Breaks his own heart): *Mighty Sparrow* / I'd rather go blind: *James, Etta* / Never my love: *Association* / Hurt: *Yuro, Timi* / When something is wrong with my baby: *Sam & Dave* / Ruby Tuesday: *Melanie* / Rainy night in Georgia: *White, Tony Joe* / When you wish upon a star: *Little Anthony & The Imperials* / Words of love: *Mamas & The Papas* / Three steps to heaven: *Cochran, Eddie* / Surfer girl: *Beach Boys* / It's just a matter of time: *Benton, Brook* / Daddy's home: *Shep & The Limelites* / Tonight is the night: *Wright, Betty* / If you need me: *Burke, Solomon* / Lovers concerto: *Toys* / Everybody loves somebody: *Martin, Dean* / Only you: *Platters* / Love you most of all: *Cooke, Sam* / You've lost that lovin' feelin': *Bass, Fontella* / You've

got a friend: Whittaker, Roger / Oh girl: Chi-Lites / Midnight train to Georgia: Knight, Gladys & The Pips / Warm and tender love: Sledge, Percy / Remember (Walkin' in the sand): Shangri-Las / It's all in the game: Edwards, Tommy / He's so fine: Chiffons / Bring back my yesterday: White, Barry / Summer (The first time): Goldsboro, Bobby / Sealed with a kiss: Hyland, Brian / Spies and specks: Bee Gees / Give up your guns: Buoys / Raindrops keep falling on my head: Thomas, B.J.
DBG 53047 / Jul '96 / Double Gold

☐ AND I LOVE YOU SO
When I need you: Sayer, Leo / When you're in love with a beautiful woman: Dr. Hook / Impossible dream: Jones, Tom / Crazy: Nelson, Willie / Red sails in the sunset: Domino, Fats / Greatest love of all: Bassey, Shirley / Love me with all your heart: Humperdinck, Engelbert / Vaya con dios: Orlando, Tony / Unforgettable: Rawls, Lou / It started with a kiss: Hot Chocolate / McLean, Don: Hot Chocolate / My special angel: Campbell, Glen / That's amore: Martin, Dean / Spanish eyes: Martino, Al
DC 879442 / Mar '97 / Disky

☐ AND I WRITE THE SONGS (2CD Set)
I want to see the bright lights tonight: Thompson, Richard & Linda / Say it ain't so: Head, Murray / Every kinda people: Palmer, Robert / Lova and affection: Armatrading, Joan / Breakaway: Gallagher & Lyle / Diamonds and rust: Baez, Joan / Daniel: John, Elton / Mandolin wind: Stewart, Rod / Shine silently: Lofgren, Nils / When you see a chance: Winwood, Steve / Spiders and snakes: Stafford, Jim / Gold: Stewart, John / Achy breaky heart: Cyrus, Billy Ray / Train leaves this morning: Dillard & Clark / Real fine love: Hiatt, John / Magic smile: Vela, Rosie / Yellow pearl: Lynott, Phil / Broken English: Faithfull, Marianne / It's different for girls: Jackson, Joe / Steel claw: Brady, Paul / There's a guy works down the chip shop swears he's Elvis: MacColl, Kirsty / Don't pay the ferryman: De Burgh, Chris / Charlotte Street: Cole, Lloyd & The Commotions / If love was like guitars: McNabb, Ian / Lady came from Baltimore: Hardin, Tim / Our last song together: Sedaka, Neil / King of the road: Miller, Roger / Over the hill: Martyn, John / It'll take a long time: Denny, Sandy / Bryter later: Drake, Nick / Cold cold heart: Williams, Hank / Lake Placid blues: White, Tony Joe / Sunny: Hebb, Bobby / High flying bird: Havens, Richie / Let's get it on: Gaye, Marvin / I'll go crazy: Brown, James
5530622 / Jan '97 / Debutante

☐ AND STILL NO HITS
NRCD 1100 / 25 Aug '97 / Nation

☐ AND STILL WE SAY NO SURRENDER
CDUCD 18 / Apr '97 / Ulster Music

☐ AND THE ANGELS SING OVER THE RAINBOW - 1939
Jeepers creepers: Armstrong, Louis / Jive at five: Basie, Count / Undecided: Webb, Chick / Zigeuner: Shaw, Artie / Moonlight serenade: Miller, Glenn / When lights are low: Hampton, Lionel / Ain't she sweet: Lunceford, Jimmie / At the woodchoppers' ball: Herman, Woody / I'm checkin' out (goodbye): Ellington, Duke / Body and soul: Hawkins, Coleman / And the angels sing: Goodman, Benny / I wish I could shimmy like my sister Kate: Spanier, Muggsy / Lady's in love with you: Miller, Glenn / Over the rainbow: Garland, Judy / Sugar: Wilson, Teddy / Lester leaps in: Basie, Count / I've got my eyes on you: Dorsey, Tommy / Opus 5: Kirby, John / Flyin' home: Goodman, Benny / T'ain't what you do (it's the way that you do it): Lunceford, Jimmie / I'm coming Virginia: Shaw, Artie
PHONTCD 7667 / Apr '90 / Phontastic

☐ AND THE BEAT GOES ON VOL.1 (42 Classics Of The 50's And 60's/2CD Set)
Um, um, um, um: Fontana, Wayne & The Mindbenders / Pamela, Pamela: Fontana, Wayne / Juliet: Four Pennies / I think of you: Merseybeats / Groovy kind of love: Fontana, Wayne & The Mindbenders / I only want to be with you: Springfield, Dusty / Say I won't be there: Springfields / Concrete and clay: Unit 4+2 / Tell me when: Applejacks / Mirror, mirror: Pinkerton's Assorted Colours / Do you love me: Poole, Brian & The Tremeloes / Ain't she sweet: Beatles / Bobby's girl: Maughan, Susan / Well I ask you: Kane, Eden / Crying game: Berry, Dave / (Fool's errand) Do you really love me too: Fury, Billy / Leave a little love: Lulu / Secret love: Kirby, Kathy / What's new pussycat: Jones, Tom / Diamonds: Harris, Jet & Tony Meehan / Are you sure: Allisons / It's my party: Gore, Lesley / Passing strangers: Vaughan, Sarah & Billy Eckstine / Mack The Knife: Fitzgerald, Ella / My happiness: Francis, Connie / Good timin': Jones, Jimmy / As I love you: Bassey, Shirley / Chantilly lace: Big Bopper / It's all in the game: Edwards, Tommy / It's only make believe: Twitty, Conway / Stranger on the shore: Bilk, Acker / Wedding: Rogers, Julie / Rubber ball: Wilde, Marty / Fings ain't what they used to be: Bygraves, Max / Strawberry fair: Newley, Anthony / Sorry: Impalas / Smoke gets in your eyes: Platters / Diane: Bachelors / Walk on by: Van Dyke, Leroy / Morere I see you: Montez, Chris / Unchained melody: Righteous Brothers
5356932 / Jul '96 / Debutante

☐ AND THE BEAT GOES ON VOL.1 & 2 (81 Classics Of the 1950's/1960's - 4CD Set)
5552822 / Aug '98 / Debutante

☐ AND THE BEAT GOES ON VOL.2 (40 Classics Of The 60's/2CD Set)
All or nothing: Small Faces / Beggin': Timebox / Matthew and son: Stevens, Cat / Sitting in the park: Fame, Georgie / Sun ain't gonna shine anymore: Walker Brothers / Jesamine: Casuals / You've got your troubles: Fortunes / In thoughts of you: Fury, Billy / Bend me, shape me: Amen Corner / She's not there: McArthur, Neil / Bend it: Dave Dee, Dozy, Beaky, Mick & Tich / Lightning strikes: Christie, Lou / From the underworld: Herd / Remember: Shangri-Las / Rain and tears: Aphrodite's Child / 98.6: Keith / Single girl: Posey, Sandy / Boys cry: Kane, Eden / Winchester Cathedral: New Vaudeville Band / I was Keiser Bill's batman: Smith, Whistling Jack / Rainbow chaser: Nirvana / Hole in my shoes: Traffic / San Franciscan nights: Burdon, Eric & The Animals / Mighty Quinn: Manfred Mann / I can't control myself: Troggs / Fire: Crazy World Of Arthur Brown / Something in the air: Thunderclap Newman / This wheel's on fire: Driscoll, Julie & Brian Auger / Son of a preacher man: Springfield, Dusty / Somebody help me: Davis, Spencer Group / Si tu dois partir: Fairport Convention / Hang onto a dream: Hardin, Tim / I put a spell on you: Simone, Nina / It's a man's man's man's world: Brown, James / Here comes the judge: Long, Shorty / Long shot kick de bucket: Pioneers / Wonderful world, beautiful people: Cliff, Jimmy / Foggy mountain breakdown: Flatt, Lester & Earl Scruggs / River deep, mountain high: Turner, Ike & Tina / Ride my seesaw: Moody Blues
5356682 / Jul '96 / Debutante

☐ AND THE BEAT GOES ON VOL.3 (2CD Set)
I can hear the grass grow: Move / I don't want our lovin' to die: Herd / My mind's eye: Small Faces / Get away: Fame, Georgie & The Blue Flames / Here it comes again: Fortunes / It's good news week: Hedgehoppers Anonymous / Everyone's gone to the moon: King, Jonathan / Go now: Moody Blues / Ha ha said the clown: Manfred Mann / Here we go round the mulberry bush: Traffic / With a girl like you: Troggs / Let's go to San Francisco: Flowerpot Men / Save me: Dave Dee, Dozy, Beaky, Mick & Tich / High in the sky: Amen Corner / Toy: Casuals / Creeque Alley: Mamas & The Papas / Game of love: Fontana, Wayne & The Mindbenders / Keep on running: Davis, Spencer Group / Pleasant Valley Sunday: Monkees / Rain, the park and other things: Cowsills / Woolly bully: Sam The Sham & The Pharaohs / Handy man: Jones, Jimmy / Let's dance: Montez, Chris / I'm gonna get me a gun: Stevens, Cat / My ship is coming in: Walker Brothers / You don't have to say you love me: Springfield, Dusty / Well I ask ya: Kane, Eden / It's not unusual: Jones, Tom / Only one woman: Marbles / Come and stay with me: Faithfull, Marianne / King of the road: Miller, Roger / I'm just a baby: Cordet, Louise / Love is blue: Mauriat, Paul / My boyfriend's back: Angels / Island of dreams: Springfields / Joanna: Walker, Scott / When will you say I love you: Fury, Billy / Finchley Central: New Vaudeville Band
5530652 / Jul '98 / Debutante

☐ AND THE BEAT GOES ON VOL.3 & 4 (72 Classics Of The 1960's/1970's - 4CD Set)
5552652 / Aug '98 / Debutante

☐ AND THE BEAT GOES ON VOL.4 (35 Classics Of The 1960's/2CD Set)
Be bop a lula: Vincent, Gene / Whole lotta woman: Rainwater, Marvin / Little darlin': Diamonds / Lonely blue boy: Twitty, Conway / Bad boy: Wilde, Marty & his Wildcats / Do you mind: Newley, Anthony / Get lost: Kane, Eden / Hoots man: Lord Rockingham's XI / Lipstick on your collar: Francis, Connie / Like I've never been gone: Fury, Billy / You know what I mean: Vernons Girls / Lover please: McPhatter, Clyde / Hey baby: Channel, Bruce / Rockin' good way: Benton, Brook & Dinah Washington / Silver threads and golden needles: Springfields / Great pretender: Platters / Rock island line: Donegan, Lonnie & his Skiffle Band / Rag mama rag: Band / Games people play: South, Joe / Ode to Billie Joe: Gentry, Bobbie / Feelin' alright: Traffic / Well alright: Blind Faith / Wrapping paper: Cream / Wild thing: Troggs / I got you: Brown, James / If you gotta go go now: Manfred Mann / Walk away renee: Left Banke / If I were a carpenter: Hardin, Tim / Don't mess with the bill: Marvelettes / Groovy kind of love: Mindbenders / I think of you: Merseybeats / Yeh yeh: Fame, Georgie & The Blue Flames / Tobacco road: Nashville Teens / I'm waiting for my man: Velvet Underground
5550002 / Jul '98 / Debutante

☐ AND THE CRAIC WAS GOOD
I want to live: Friday, Gavin / Emotional time: Hothouse Flowers / Religious persuasion: White, Andy / Munster hop: Shannon, Sharon / Rambling Irishman: Dannan, De / May morning dew: Moving Hearts / Saturday night: Dowdall, Leslie / Send me a river: Lohan, Sinead / Adam at the window: Black, Mary / Island: Brady, Paul / Slipside: Stockton's Wing / From Clare to here: Furey Brothers & Davy Arthur / She moved through the fair: Shades of McMurrough / Mna na heireann: Na Connerys / Take my hand: In Tua Nua / Dark hill: Hinterland / November november: Auto Da Fe / End titles (theme from Miller's Crossing): Burwell, Carter
5533272 / Feb '97 / Debutante

☐ AND THE HEAVENS CRIED (36 Progressive Rock Classics/2CD Set)
Tales of brave Ulysses: Cream / Mr. Fantasy: Traffic / Weight: Spooky Tooth / Meet on the ledge: Fairport Convention / It's only a dream: Trapeze / Place of my own: Caravan / I can take you to the sun: Misunderstood / Hold me back: Patto / Sing a song of summer: Martyn, John / Time has told me: Drake, Nick / Tiny Goddess: Nirvana / Strangely strange, but oddly normal: Dr. Strangely Strange / Breathless: Camel / Time goes by: Chicken Shack / Born to die: Hartley, Keef Band / Money can't save your soul: Savoy Brown / Jig a jig: East Of Eden / Those about to die: Colosseum / Fire: Crazy World Of Arthur Brown / Season of the witch: Driscoll, Julie & Brian Auger / House of the rising sun: Frijid Pink / Sky pilot: Burdon, Eric & The Animals / Country comfort: Stewart, Rod / Cry me a river: Cocker, Joe / Travelling man: Dummer, John Blues Band / Thunderback ram: Mott The Hoople / Room to move: Mayall, John / Born on the wrong side of time: Taste / Living in the past: Jethro Tull / Time seller: Davis, Spencer / Gungamai: Quintessence / Ride my seesaw: Moody Blues / I'm a mover: Free / Moon is down: Gentle Giant / I keep singing that same old song: Heavy Jelly
5356962 / Jul '96 / Debutante

☐ AND THE HITS KEEP COMING (22 Popular US Classics Of The 1960's)
5537902 / Sep '97 / Debutante

☐ AND THE ROAD GOES ON FOREVER VOL.1 (36 Hard Rock Classics/2CD Set)
You wear it well: Stewart, Rod / Benny and the Jets: John, Elton / You ain't seen nothin' yet: Bachman-Turner Overdrive / Come together in the morning: Free / Whiskey in the jar: Thin Lizzy / Down down: Status Quo / Love like a man: Ten Years After / Joy bringer: Manfred Mann's Earthband / Bad case of lovin' you: Palmer, Robert / Just a day away (forever tomorrow): Barclay James Harvest / I'm just a singer (in a rock and roll band): Moody Blues / Second chance: .38 Special / Wind of change: Scorpions / Nobody's fool: Cinderella / Rock'n'roll children: Dio / Tell Mama: Savoy Brown / Closer to the heart: Rush / St. Elmo's fire: Parr, John / Ramblin' man: Allman Brothers / Fooled around and fell in love: Bishop, Elvin / Show me the way: Frampton, Peter / Night games: Bonnet, Graham / Perfect strangers: Deep Purple / Since you been gone: Rainbow / 5-7-0-5: City Boy / Wonderland: Big Country / Valerie: Winwood, Steve / External exile: Fish / She's a little angel: Little Angels / Obsession: Animotion
5357172 / Jul '96 / Debutante

☐ AND THE ROAD GOES ON FOREVER VOL.1 & 2 (72 Legendary Rock Masterpieces/4CD Set)
5551832 / Aug '98 / Debutante

☐ AND THE ROAD GOES ON FOREVER VOL.2 (2CD Set)
Jessica: Allman Brothers / Blinded by the light: Manfred Mann's Earthband / Look away: Big Country / Addicted to love: Palmer, Robert / Lessons in love: Level 42 / Good thing: Fine Young Cannibals / Street of dreams: Rainbow / Show me the way: Styx / Eye of the tiger: Survivor / Caught up in you: .38 Special / Shelter me: Cinderella / Rock you like a hurricane: Scorpions / Roll on down the highway: Bachman-Turner Overdrive / Spirit of radio: Rush / Take me home: Cher / Womankind: Little Angels / Ballad of Jane: LA Guns / I'll see you in my dreams: Giant / One and one is one: Medicine Head / Stuck in the middle with you: Stealer's Wheel / Heart on my sleeve: Gallagher & Lyle / Walkin' in the Arizona sun: Wray, Link / Sweet dreams: Buchanan, Roy / Perfect skin: Cole, Lloyd & The Commotions / Dancin' in the moonlight: Thin Lizzy / All right now: Free / I know I'm losing you: Stewart, Rod / Question: Moody Blues / I got a line on you: Spirit / No mercy: Lofgren, Nils / Standing in the road: Blackfoot Sue / Webb's boogie: Chicken Shack / Restless: Status Quo / Philadelphia freedom: John, Elton / Walk the dinosaur: Was Not Was / Annie I'm not your Daddy: Kid Creole & The Coconuts
5530542 / Jul '98 / Debutante

☐ AND THE TRAIN KEPT A-ROLLIN' (19 Rockabilly Classics)
Train kept a rollin': Burnette, Johnny Rock 'N' Roll Trio / Rootie tootie: Williams, Hank / Rave on: Holly, Buddy & The Crickets / C'mon everybody: Cochran, Eddie / Race with the devil: Vincent, Gene & The Bluecaps / Rockin' bones: Dawson, Ronnie / Let's have a party: Jackson, Wanda / Be bop baby: Nelson, Ricky / Chantilly lace: Big Bopper / High school confidential: Lewis, Jerry Lee / Rumble: Wray, Link / Red cadillac and a black moustache: Gordon, Robert / Runaway boys: Stray Cats / Marie marie: Blasters / 6 nights a week: Burgess, Sonny / Little green men: Riley, Billy Lee / Jumpin' from 6 to 6: Big Sandy & The Flyrite Trio / Dixie doll: George, Sonny / Tired of toein' the line: Burnette, Rocky
5538682 / Sep '97 / Debutante

☐ AND THE WORLD'S ALL YOURS (An Essential Selection Of World Music/ 2CD Set)
No sant: Diop, Wasis & Lena Fiagbe / African soul: Baroudi, Hamid / 10th commandment: Papa Wemba / La ruinas en mi mente: Soroya / Boule fale: Positive Black Soul & Aminata Fall / Must must: Khan, Nusrat Fateh Ali / What do you want, life: Boine, Mari / Mansa: Super Rail Band / Carizzi r'amuri: Agricantus / Blow on my soul: Arvanitaki, Eleftheria / Rumba Arglina: Radio Tarifa / Comme un chien: Taha, Rachid / Sama du miya: Maal, Baaba / Feel ire: Lucky Dube / OS: Timba Lada / Tekere: Keita, Salif / Tshikunda: Muana, Tshala / Life: Dreamcatcher / LOVE: UFO / Mammou ayni: Amina / Elligibo: Menezes, Margareth / Alech taadi: Khaled, Cheb / Lakh bi: Africando / No no no: Roach, Archie / Not an easy road: Buju Banton / Un aeroplane a vela: Testa, Gianmaria / Zan'j yo: Boukman Experyans / Orca's song: Tulku / Chimes of freedom: N'Dour, Youssou
5359492 / Jul '98 / Debutante

☐ AND THEN SHE KISSED ME VOL.1 (38 Classic Love Songs/2CD Set)
Look of love: ABC / She drives me crazy: Fine Young Cannibals / I didn't mean to turn you on: Palmer, Robert / Don't go: Hothouse Flowers / I'm in love with a German film star: Passions / I got you: Split Enz / Will you: O'Connor, Hazel / No more I love you's: Lover Speaks / I should have known better: Diamond, Jim / Sweetest smile: Black / Pilot of the airwaves: Dore, Charlie / Love hurts: Capaldi, Jim / Captain of her heart: Double / We don't cry out loud: Brooks, Elkie / I wanna stay with you: Gallagher & Lyle / Song for Guy: John, Elton / Cry: Godley & Creme / I'm not in love: 10cc / Oh no, not my baby: Stewart, Rod / How can I be sure: Springfield, Dusty / Up where we belong: Cocker, Joe & Jennifer Warnes / Do that to me one more time: Captain & Tennille / Oh Lori: Alessi / Words: Coolidge, Rita / Me myself I: Armatrading, Joan / I'm your puppet: Purify, James & Bobby / Betcha by golly wow: Stylistics / On the radio: Summer, Donna / Just the way you are: White, Barry / Love's theme: Love Unlimited Orchestra / Love town: Newberry, Booker III / Cherish: Kool & The Gang / Secret lovers: Atlantic Starr / Never gonna let you go: Mendes, Sergio / Piano in the dark: Russell, Brenda / Get here: Adams, Oleta / Love is just the great pretender: Animal Nightlife / You can do magic: Limmie & Family Cooking
5356722 / Jul '96 / Debutante

☐ AND THEY DANCED THE NIGHT AWAY VOL.1 (39 Classic Disco Hits/2CD Set)
Word up: Cameo / Ladies night: Kool & The Gang / If I can't have you: Elliman, Yvonne / Hustle: McCoy, Van & Soul City Symphony / Let's put it all together: Stylistics / British hustle: Hi-Tension / Ain't nothin' goin' on but the rent: Guthrie, Gwen / Strawberry letter 23: Brothers Johnson / Never, never gonna give you up: White, Barry / Chase: Moroder, Giorgio / Do it again/Billy Jean: Club House / There's a ghost in my house: Taylor, R. Dean / Dr. Kiss Kiss: 5000 Volts / I love the nightlife: Bridges, Alicia / Behind the goove: Marie, Teena / Mama used to say: Junior / It should have been me: Fair, Yvonne / Fire: Ohio Players / In the thick of it: Russell, Brenda / Never knew love like this: Mills, Stephanie / Night birds: Shakatak / Breakin'...there's no stopping us now: Ollie & Jerry / Get down: Chandler, Gene / Don't stop the music: Yarbrough & Peoples / Hang on in there baby: Bristol, Johnny / Get up I feel like being a sex machine: Brown, James / Funky town: Lipps Inc. / I feel love: Summer, Donna / Oops upside your head: Gap Band / You can't hide (your love from me): Joseph, David / Let the music play: White, Barry / I will survive: Gaynor, Gloria / Now that we've found love: Third World / Teardrops: Womack & Womack / Ain't nothing gonna keep me from you: De Sario, Terri / Burning love: Con Funk Shun / Dancin' the night away: Voggue / Shake your groove thing: Peaches & Herb / I was made for dancing: Garrett, Leif / Check this out: LA Mix
5356802 / Jul '96 / Debutante

☐ AND THEY DANCED THE NIGHT AWAY VOL.1 & 2 (72 Pure Disco Classics From The 70's & 80's/4CD Set)
Word up: Cameo / Ladies night: Kool & The Gang / If I can't have you: Elliman, Yvonne / Hustle: McCoy, Van & Soul City Symphony / Let's put it all together: Stylistics / British hustle: Hi-Tension / Ain't nothin' goin' on but the rent: Guthrie, Gwen / Strawberry letter: Brothers Johnson / Never never gonna give you up: White, Barry / Chase: Moroder, Giorgio / Do it again/Billy Jean: Clubhouse / There's a ghost in my house: Taylor, R. Dean / Dr. Kiss Kiss: 5000 Volts / I love the nightlife: Bridges, Alicia / Behind the groove: Marie, Teena / Mama used to say: Junior / It should have been me: Fair, Yvonne / Fire: Ohio Players / In the thick of it: Russell, Brenda / Never knew love like this: Mills, Stephanie / Night birds: Shakatak / Breakin' there's no stopping us: Ollie & Jerry / Get down: Chandler, Gene / Don't stop the music: Yarbrough & Peoples / Hang on in there baby: Bristol, Johnny / (Get up I feel like being a) Sex machine: Brown, James / Funky town: Lipps Inc. / I feel love: Summer, Donna / Oops upside your head: Gap Band / You can't hide (your love from me): Joseph, David / Let the music play: White, Barry / I will survive: Gaynor, Gloria / Now that we've found love: Third World / Teardrops: Womack & Womack / Ain't nothing gonna keep me from you: De Sario, Terri / Burning love: Con Funk Shun / Dancin' the night away: Voggue / Shake your groove thing: Peaches & Herb / I was made for dancing: Garrett, Leif / Check this out: LA Mix / I want you back: Jackson Five / Good times: Chic / We are family: Sister Sledge / Rasputin: Boney M / Disco inferno: Trammps / Lady Marmalade: Labelle / Feel the need: Garrett, Leif / You to me are everything: Real Thing / Don't leave me this way: Melvin, Harold & The Bluenotes / Yes sir I can boogie: Baccara / Dance yourself dizzy: Liquid Gold / I'm on fire: 5000 Volts / You can't hide your love: Joseph, David / Instant replay: Hartman, Dan / Big fun: Gap Band / That's the way I like it: KC & The Sunshine Band / Upside down: Ross, Diana / Celebration: Kool & The Gang / Boogie wonderland: Earth, Wind & Fire / Never can say goodbye: Gaynor, Gloria / Play that funky music: Wild Cherry / Rock the boat: Hues Corporation / Jump to the beat: Lattisaw, Stacy / Night to remember: Shalamar / Just an illusion: Imagination / Somebody's watching me: Rockwell / IOU: Freeze / Down on the street: Shakatak / Medicine song: Mills, Stephanie / MacArthur Park: Summer, Donna / Ain't nobody: Khan, Chaka / It's raining men: Weather Girls
5551592 / Aug '98 / Debutante

☐ AND THEY DANCED THE NIGHT AWAY VOL.2 (36 Classic Disco Hits/2CD Set)
5551052 / Jul '98 / Debutante

☐ AND THIS IS A SKA EXPLOSION
Whine and grine: Prince Buster / Girls town Ska next: Brooks, Baba & Band / Ark: Hinds, Justin & The Dominoes / Frankenstein ska: Lee, Byron & The Dragonaires / Soon you will be gone: Blues Busters / Mood I am in: Reid, Duke / Oil in my lamp: Morris, Monty / James Bond: Alphonso, Roland / Rukumbine: Duffus, Shenley / Allepon: Drummond, Don / First session: Brooks, Baba / Girl next door: Blues Blenders / El pussy cat: Alphonso, Roland / I won't let you: Keith & Ken / Vitamin A: Brooks, Baba / Door neighbour: Grey, Owen and Leon Silvera / Independent anniversary ska: Skatalites / Don de lion: Skatalites / Tide is high: Paragons / Perfidia: Dillon, Phyllis
5651262 / 6 Jul '98 / Debutante

☐ AND THIS TIME IT'S FOR REAL (36 Classic R'n'B Standards - 2CD Set)
Soulful dress: Desanto, Sugar Pie / First I look at the purse: Contours / He was really saying something: Velvelettes / Don't mess up a good thing: Bass, Fontella & Bobby McClure / Hey Leroy your Mama's calling you: Castor, Jimmy / Cleo's mood: Walker, Junior / Devil with the blue dress: Long, Shorty / Mohair Sam: Rich, Charlie / Thread your needle: Dean & Jean / Out of sight: Brown, James / Uptight good woman: Lee, Laura / Ain't nobody home: Tate, Howard / Got to get you off my mind: Burke, Solomon / Every little bit hurts: Holloway, Brenda / Baby I'm for real: Originals / Hey Western Union man: Butler, Jerry / Nowhere to run: Martha & The Vandellas / It's better to have and don't need: Covay, Don / Stealing in the name of the Lord: Kelly, Paul / Who's gonna help brother get further: Dorsey, Lee / I'll take you there: Staple Singers / Buffalo soldiers: Flamingos / War: Starr, Edwin / Bring the boys back home: Payne, Freda / Tell me what you want: Ruffin, Jimmy / Got to get enough: Roy C / Groovy situation: Chandler, Gene / Think (about it): Collins, Lyn / Rubberband man: Detroit Spinners / Deception: Dynamic Superiors / Sneakin' Sally through the alley: Palmer, Robert / Rock steady: Franklin, Aretha / Meet de boys on teh battlefront: Wild Tchoupitoulas / 18 with a bullet: Wingfield, Pete
5531002 / Jul '98 / Debutante

☐ ANDALUSIAN FLAMENCO SONG AND DANCE
LYRCD 7388 / '91 / Lyrichord

☐ ANDEAN LEGACY
Tempestad: Andina, Savia / Encuentros: Alturas / Pueblo Lejano: Viento De Los Andes / Aranjuez: Echoes Of Incas / Cieldo Y Montana: Rumillajta / Kalasasaya: Inkuyo / Na Yachanichu: Imbaya / Tema De La Quebrada de Humahuaca: Inti-Illimani / Sombrero de Paja y Quina: Andes Manta / Ajawasi: Inkuyo / Akullicu: Rumillajta / La Samaritana: Ancient Winds / Concepcion: Sukay / El Pillan: Caliche
ND 63927 / Nov '96 / Narada

☐ ANDEAN MASTERPIECES
4301121012 / 27 Apr '98 / ANS

☐ ANGEL AIR SAMPLER
Demon rose: McCoys / Live wire: Guitar Orchestra / Talkin' 'bout you: Pirates / Restless: Gillan / Give or fake: Roussos, Demis / Always and forever: Mammoth / Clear air turbulence: Gillan, Ian Band / Poem about a gnome: Gustafson, John / Here I go again: D'Abo, Mike & Paul Jones / In my room: Musicians Union Band / It's over: Harrison, Bobby / I won't be there: Graham, Mike / Back USA: Fenwick, Ray / Ma belle Amie: Tee Set / Lonely: Hyams, Steve
SJPCDSIN 501 / 17 Nov '97 / Angel Air

☐ ANGEL CHILD VOL.3
MACDL 594 / 27 Apr '98 / Resurrection

☐ ANGEL OF THE MORNING (Rock & Pop Ballads)
CD 12202 / Aug '93 / Laserlight

☐ ANGELFOOD ELECTRONICS VOL.1 & 2
KMR 010CD / 17 Nov '97 / Kake Mix

☐ ANGELICA '91
CAICA 1001 / Jun '98 / ReR/ Recommended

☐ ANGELICA '92
CAICA 1003 / Jun '98 / ReR/ Recommended

☐ ANGELICA '93
CAICA 1004 / Jun '98 / ReR/ Recommended

☐ ANGELICA '94
CAICA 1006 / Jun '98 / ReR/ Recommended

☐ ANGELICA '95
CAICA 1007 / Jun '98 / ReR/ Recommended

☐ ANGELICA '96
CAICA 1011 / Jun '98 / ReR/ Recommended

☐ ANGER, FEAR, SEX AND DEATH
E 86402CD / Nov '92 / Epitaph

☐ ANGIE FOLK GUITAR
PLSCD 150 / Jan '97 / Pulse

☐ ANGOLA PRISONERS' BLUES
Prisoner's talking blues: Williams, Robert Pete / Stagger Lee: Maxey, Hogman / Electric chair blues: Welch, Guitar / Some got six months: Williams, Robert Pete / I'm gonna leave you Mama: Welch, Guitar / I'm lonesome blues: Williams, Robert Pete / Angola bound: Acapella Group / Worried blues: Maxey, Hogman / Josephine: Welch, Guitar / Soldier's plea: Young, Clara / Moon is rising: Mathews, Odea / I'm still in love with you: Joseph, Thelma Mae / I miss you so: Vocal Group / Hello Sue: Butterbeans & Susie / Fast life woman: Maxey, Hogman / Careless love: Webster, Otis / Have you ever heard the church bells tone: Charles, Roosevelt & Otis Webster / 61 Highway: Welch, Guitar / Strike at camp 1: Charles, Roosevelt
ARHCD 419 / Nov '96 / Arhoolie

☐ ANNIE ON ONE
Theme: Sabres Of Paradise / Age of love: Age Of Love / Lookee here: Transglobal Underground / Rocks: Primal Scream / Vision: Prophecy / Da funk: Daft Punk / Liberation: T-Power / What's that sound: Sever, Sam & The Raiders Of The Lost Art / Clubbed to death: Rob D / North south east west: Black Sheep / Weekender: Flowered Up
HVNCD 11 / Feb '96 / Heavenly

☐ ANNUAL VOL.3, THE (2CD Set)
ANNCD 97 / 3 Nov '97 / Ministry Of Sound

☐ ANOTHER PERFECT DAY
High: Lighthouse Family / Dance the night away: Mavericks / Life: Des'ree / Summer breeze: Isley Brothers / Wonderful life: Black / Kokomo: Beach Boys / Right by your side: Eurythmics / Rhythm is gonna get you: Estefan, Gloria / Wake me up before you go go: Wham / Shoop shoop song: Cher / I'm still standing: John, Elton / I'm a believer: Monkees / Baby I love your way/Freebird: Will To Power / Can you feel it: Jacksons / I can make you feel good: Shalamar / Only to be with you: Roachford / Last thing on my mind: Steps / Perfect: Fairground Attraction / Dancing in the Street: Martha & The Vandellas
SONYTV 51CD / 27 Jul '98 / Sony TV

☐ ANOTHER ROUND OF GOLF
CDHOLE 009 / Jun '96 / Golf

☐ ANOTHER SATURDAY NIGHT
Before I grow too old: McLain, Tommy / Cajun fugitive: Belton, Richard / Try to find another man: McLain, Tommy & Clint West / Jolie blon: Bruce, Vin / I cried: Cookie & The Cupcakes / Oh Lucille: Belton, Richard / Who needs you so bad: Walker, Gary / Don't mess with my man: White, Margo / Another Saturday night: White, Margo / Un auter soir d'ennui: Belton, Richard / Promised land: Allan, Johnnie / Two steps de bayou teche: Pitre, Austin / Sweet dreams: McLain, Tommy / Breaking up is hard to do: Cookie & The Cupcakes / Laisser les cajun danser: Belton, Richard / Down home music: Jangeaux, Rufus
CDCH 288 / Feb '90 / Ace

☐ ANOTHER SENTIMENTAL JOURNEY THROUGH THE 50'S (2CD Set)
Nina never knew: Brent, Tony / Undecided: Beverley Sisters / When you lose the one you love: Martin, Ray / Finger of suspicion points at you: Jupp, Eric Orchestra / Only yesterday: Campbell, Jean / How wonderful to know: Carr, Pearl / Roulette: Conway, Russ / Moon is blue: Cogan, Alma / I'm yours: Hughes, David / Now and forever: Warren, Alma / Hold my hand: Harris, Ronnie / Sing little birdie: Carr, Pearl / Gypsy in my soul: Boswell, Eve / So deep my love: Dean, Alan / Holiday affair: Day, Jill / Hey there: Hockridge, Edmund / Donna: Calvert, Eddie / It's not for me to say: Cordell, Frank / Cinco Robles (Five oaks): Day, Jill / Just say I love her: Hockridge, Edmund / Long long ago: Buxton, Sheila & Ronnie Harris/Ray Martin Orchestra / Way I feel: Brent, Tony / If you love me: Brennan, Rose / I may never pass this way again: Lotis, Dennis / Give her my love when you meet her: Day, Jill / Tammy: Brown, Jackie / Meet me on the corner: Jupp, Eric Orchestra / Charm: Buxton, Sheila & Ronnie Harris/Ray Martin Orchestra / Have you heard: Brent, Tony / No one will ever know: Campbell, Jean / Surprisingly: Harris, Ronnie / Hurry home to me: Beverley Sisters / Tear fell: Day, Jill / Royal event: Conway, Russ / From the time you say goodbye: Miller, Gary / My lucky number: Coronets / Lonely ballerina: Lawrence, Lee / How lucky you are: Carr, Pearl / Give me the right to be wrong: Brent, Tony / In-between age: Buxton, Sheila & Ronnie Harris/Ray Martin Orchestra / Erica: Calvert, Eddie / Where can I go without you: Campbell, Jean / No one could love you (more than I do): Carr, Pearl / Birds and the bees: Lyon, Barbara / Make me love you: Hughes, David / Unsuspecting heart: Brown, Fay / My darling, my darling: Miller, Gary / I'd rather take my time: Anthony, Billie / Waltzing the blues: Brent, Tony / Take me in your arms and hold me: Carr, Pearl
CDDL 1296 / Jun '95 / EMI

☐ ANOTHER SHADE OF LOVERS
RNCD 2109 / Jun '95 / Rhino

☐ ANOTHER TASTE OF TRANSIENT (2CD Set)
TRANR 615CD / 20 Apr '98 / Transient

☐ ANOTHER WORLD DOMINATION SAMPLER
Soft focus am: Lizard Music / Carolida: Latimer / Life and death: Low Pop Suicide / Deal: Psyclone Rangers / Scapegoat: Sky Cries Mary / Supermonkey: Stanford Prison Experiment / Caxton Vs the fourth estate: Elastic Purejoy / Drug groove: Crack Babies
WDOM 018CD / Jul '95 / World Domination

☐ ANSWER IS VOL.1, THE (The Great Answer Songs Of The 1950's)
Wild side of life: Thompson, Hank / It wasn't God who made honky tonk angels: Wells, Kitty / Back street affair: Pierce, Webb / Paying for that back street affair: Wells, Kitty / There stands the glass: Pierce, Webb / Please throw away the glass: Cody, Betty / Yesterday's girl: Thompson, Hank / I'm yesterday's girl: Hill, Goldie / I forgot more than you'll ever know: Davis Sisters / I found out more than you'll ever know: Cody, Betty / I really want you to know: Cody, Betty / I really don't want to know: Arnold, Eddy / Don't let the stars get in your eyes: McDonald, Skeets / I let the stars get in my eyes: Hill, Goldie / Long black veil: Frizzell, Lefty / My long black veil: Wilkin, Marijohn / I fall to pieces: Cline, Patsy / Mexican Joe: Reeves, Jim / Marriage of Mexican Joe: Bradshaw, Carolyn / Jambalaya: Williams, Hank / I'm Yvonne: Hill, Goldie / Dear John letter: Husky, Ferlin / Forgive me, John: Husky, Ferlin / Geisha girl: Locklin, Hank / Lost to a geisha girl: Davis, Skeeter / Fraulein: Helms, Bobby / I'll always be your fraulein: Wells, Kitty
BCD 15791 / Nov '94 / Bear Family

☐ ANSWER IS VOL.2, THE (Great Answer Songs Of The 1950's)
Burning bridges: Scott, Kjack / You burned the bridges: Jean, Bobbie / Bobby's girl: Blane, Marcie / Stay away from Bobbie: Sherry's Sisters / Diana: Anka, Paul / Remember Diana: Anka, Paul / Roses are red: Vinton, Bobby / As long as the rose is red: Darlin, Florraine / Tell Laura I love her: Peterson, Ray / Tell Tommy I need him: Michaels, Marilyn / Who's sorry now: Francis, Connie / I'm sorry now: Shields / Wooden heart: Dowell, Joe / You know your hearts not made of wood: Marie Ann / Take good care of my baby: Vee, Bobby / I'll take good care of you: Emery, Ralph / Mr. Lonely: Vinton, Bobby / Little Miss Lonely: Harris, Mike / Is it true what they say about Barbara: Regal, Mike / Honey: Goldsboro, Bobby / Honey (I miss you too): Lewis, Margaret / Are you lonesome tonight: Boone, Pat / Yes I am lonesome tonight: Carpenter, Thelma / Fool # 1: Lee, Brenda / No you're the fool: Stewart, Mark / Who put the bomp: Mann, Barry / I put the bomp: Lymon, Frankie
BCD 15792 / Jun '95 / Bear Family

☐ ANSWER IS VOL.3, THE (Great Answer Songs Of The 1960's)
Ballad of a teenage queen: Cash, Johnny / Return of the teenage queen: Tucker, Tommy / Charlie's shoes: Walker, Billy / Answer to Charlie's Shoes: Mosby, Johnny & Jonie / He'll have to go: Reeves, Jim / He'll have to stay: Black, Jeanne / She's got you: Cline, Patsy / She can have you: Judy / Almost persuaded: Houston, David / Almost persuaded: Harris, Donna / Detroit city: Bare, Bobby / Why don'cha come home: Ray, Shirley / Wolverton mountain: King, Claude / I'm the girl from Wolverton: Campbell, Jo Ann / Walk on by: Van Dyke, Leroy / I'll just walk on: Singleton, Margie / Ruby, don't take your love to town: Rogers, Kenny / Billy, I've got to go to town: Stevens, Geraldine / King of the road: Miller, Roger / Queen of the house: Miller, Jody / 5000 Miles away from home: Bare, Bobby / He's coming home: Taylor, Mary / Evil on your mind: Howard, Jan / Evil off my mind: Ives, Burl / Please help me, I'm falling: Locklin, Hank / (I can't help you) I'm fallin' too: Davis, Skeeter / Good hearted woman: Nelson, Willie / Good hearted man: Cato, Connie / Only Daddy that'll walk the line: Shepard, Jean / Only Mama that'll walk the line: Shepard, Jean
BCD 15793 / Nov '94 / Bear Family

☐ ANSWERS TO THE QUESTION, THE
KUCD 116 / Mar '97 / Kufe

☐ ANTHEMS (2CD/3CD Set)
Love is the icon: White, Barry / Saturday: East 57th Street / Harder they are: Sounds Of Blackness / What you want: Future Force / Heaven: Washington, Sarah / Ain't nobody's business if I do: H2O & Billie / Best things in life are free: Jackson, Janet / Voices inside my head: Police / Movin': Mone / I believe: Absolute / Love don't live: Urban Blues Project / Bring me love: Mendez, Andrea / I can't get no sleep: Masters At Work / I like it: Moraes, Angel / Can I get a witness: Nesby, Ann / We can make it: Mone / Ultra flava: Heller & Farley Project / Feel like singing: Taktix / Stand up: Love Tribe / Satisfied: H2O & Billie / Everything: Washington, Sarah / Giv me luv: Alcatraz / Jus' come: Cool Jack / I believe: Sounds Of Blackness / Puttin' a rush on me: Future Force
5406542
5406552 / Dec '96 / A&M

☐ ANTHEMS & CEREMONIALS
IMCD 3021 / Feb '96 / Image

☐ ANTHEMS VOL.1 (2CD Set)
UNCDL 003
UNCD 003 / Jan '97 / United Dance

☐ ANTHEMS VOL.2 1988-1992 (Mixed By Slipmatt/2CD Set)
You got the love: Source & Candi Staton / Sueno let me love you tonite: Kariya / Sueno Latino: Sueno Latino / Break 4 love: Raze / Rescue me: Malone, Debbie / Come get my lovin': Dionne / I can dance: Fast Eddie / Acid thunder: Fast Eddie / Monkey say monkey do: Westbam / Airport 89: Allen, Woody / Phantom: Renegade Soundwave / Humanoid: Stakker / Bring forth the guilotine: Silver Bullet / 20 to get in: Shut Up & Dance / Total confusion: Homeboy, A Hippy & A Funki-Dred / Mr. Kirk's nightmare: 4 Hero / What have you done: One Tribe & Gem / Papua New Guinea: Future Sound Of London / Dextrous: Nightmares On Wax / LFO: LFO / Give me the energy: Pink Noise / Pure: GTO / Kaos: Dr. Baker / Sound clash: Kick Squad / Go: Moby / Cubes: Modular Expansion / Just let go: Petra & Co / Stratosphere: Trigger / Quadrophonia: Quadrophonia / Take it easy: Winkleburger, Cedric / Bomb scare: 2 Bad Mice / DJ's unite: Seduction & Fantasy / Compounded/Edge 1: Edge / Hurt you so: Jonny L / Hypnosis: Psychotropic / Panic: Rabbit City
UMCD 04 / Jun '97 / United Dance

☐ ANTHOLOGIE DE LA CHANSON FRANCAISE (14CD/Book Set)
983992 / Jul '96 / EPM

☐ ANTHOLOGIE DE LA CHANSON FRANCAISE VOL.1 (From Troubadours To The Pleiades)
983152 / Jul '96 / EPM

☐ ANTHOLOGIE DE LA CHANSON FRANCAISE VOL.2 (French History)
983162 / Jul '96 / EPM

☐ ANTHOLOGIE DE LA CHANSON FRANCAISE VOL.3 (Ballads, Complaintes & Legends)
983172 / Jul '96 / EPM

☐ ANTHOLOGIE DE LA CHANSON FRANCAISE VOL.4 (Rites, Magic & Miracles)
983182 / Jul '96 / EPM

☐ ANTHOLOGIE DE LA CHANSON FRANCAISE VOL.5 (Soldiers, Conscripts & Deserters)
983192 / Jul '96 / EPM

☐ ANTHOLOGIE DE LA CHANSON FRANCAISE VOL.6 (The Sea, Ports & Sailors)
983202 / Jul '96 / EPM

☐ ANTHOLOGIE DE LA CHANSON FRANCAISE VOL.7 (Songs Of Labour & Toil)
983212 / Jul '96 / EPM

☐ ANTHOLOGY (2CD Set)
5553132 / 22 Dec '97 / A&M

☐ ANTHOLOGY OF AMERICAN FOLK MUSIC (6CD Set)
SFWCD 40090 / Sep '97 / Smithsonian Folkways

☐ ANTHOLOGY OF ARAB-ADALUSIAN MUSIC OF ALGERIA VOL.3
C 560004 / Jan '94 / Ocora

☐ ANTHOLOGY OF BALI MUSIC VOL.4 (2CD Set)
926032 / Apr '96 / BUDA

☐ ANTHOLOGY OF BRETON TRADITIONS - ACCORDIAN
SCM 034CD / Apr '95 / Diffusion Breizh

☐ ANTHOLOGY OF BRETON TRADITIONS - BOMBARDE & BINIOU
SCM 032CD / Apr '95 / Diffusion Breizh

☐ ANTHOLOGY OF BULGARIAN FOLK MUSIC VOL.2 (Music From Rhodope/ Dobroudja)
LDX 274975 / Jun '94 / La Chant Du Monde

☐ ANTHOLOGY OF COLUMBIANA
7992342 / Jan '95 / Hispavox

☐ ANTHOLOGY OF CUBAN MUSIC
Mi son, mi son, mi son: Miguelito Cuni Con Chappottin / Trae rumbavana: Conjunto Rumbavana / Bacalao con pan: Irakere / Unicornio: Rodriguez, Silvio / Cantido Celina: Gonzalez, Celina / Ese sentimiento que se llama amor: Alonso, Pacho Y Su Orquestra / La chica mamey: Orquesta Ritmo Oriental / El diapason: Orquesta Original De Manzanillo / Que es lo que hace ud: Gomez, Tito Con Su Conjunto / De mis recuerdos: Burke, Elena / A bayomo en coche: Son 14 / Por encima del nivel: Los Van Van
PSCCD 1010 / Feb '95 / Pure Sounds From Cuba

☐ ANTHOLOGY OF CUBAN MUSIC
Mi son, mi son, mi son: Cuni, Miguelito & Chappottin / Lo que te trae Rumbavana: Conjuncto Rumbavana / Bacalao con pan: Grupo Irakere / Unicornio: Rodriguez, Silvio / Cantido Celina: Gonzalez, Celina / Ese sentimiento que se llama amor: Alonso, Pacho / La chica mamey: Orquesta Ritmo Oriental / El diapason: Orquesta Original De Manzanillo / Que es lo que hace ud: Gomez, Tito & Jorrin / De mis recuerdos: Burke, Elena / A bayomo en coche: Son 14 / Por encima del nivel: Orquesta Los Van Van
CD 12542 / May '97 / Music Of The World

☐ ANTHOLOGY OF FLAMENCO
7992362 / Jan '95 / Hispavox

☐ ANTHOLOGY OF FLAMENCO SONGS
7914562 / Jan '95 / Hispavox

☐ ANTHOLOGY OF HOT R 'N' B FROM BATON ROUGE, AN
FLYCD 41 / Oct '91 / Flyright

☐ ANTHOLOGY OF INDIAN CLASSICAL MUSIC, AN (A Tribute To Alain Danielou/3CD Set)
D 88270 / Aug '97 / Auvidis UNESCO

☐ ANTHOLOGY OF MEXICAN SONES VOL.1 (Tierra Caliente, Jalisco Y Rio Verde)
CO 101 / Jan '94 / Corason

☐ ANTHOLOGY OF MEXICAN SONES VOL.1-3
MT 01/03 / Jan '94 / Corason

☐ ANTHOLOGY OF MEXICAN SONES VOL.2 (Tixtla, Costa Chica, Istmo Y Veracruz)
CO 102 / Jan '94 / Corason

☐ ANTHOLOGY OF MEXICAN SONES VOL.3, AN (Huasteca)
CO 103 / Jan '94 / Corason

☐ ANTHOLOGY OF MUSIC OF BALI VOL.3 (2CD Set)
926022 / Jan '97 / BUDA

☐ ANTHOLOGY OF RUMBA
7992642 / Jan '95 / Hispavox

☐ ANTHOLOGY OF SOLEA
7995412 / Feb '95 / Hispavox

☐ ANTHOLOGY OF TARANTA
7992662 / Jan '95 / Hispavox

☐ ANTHOLOGY OF WESTERN AUSTRALIAN TRADITIONAL JAZZ, AN
RQCD 1601 / Nov '96 / Request

☐ ANTHOLOGY OF WORLD MUSIC - AFRICA (The Ba-Benzele Pygmies)
Whistle solo / Djokolo / Nbu / Kongo asseka / Djokoko / Lullaby / Lullaby / Muya / E yimba e / Bondo / First stroy / Second story / Third story / Fourth story / Fifth story
ROUCD 5107 / Feb '98 / Rounder

☐ ANTHOLOGY OF WORLD MUSIC - AFRICA (The Dan)
Festival music / Solo song of a woman / Drum rhythms / Music for a chieftain / Singing at a wrestling match / Sword dance of the young girls / Sanza / Song to encourage the rice sowers / Singing game of small girls / Rice harvest / Music for the mask race / Mask baego / Trumpet orchestra / Dance of the woman / Hunters song from the Savannah / Hunter's song from the forest
ROUCD 5105 / Feb '98 / Rounder

☐ ANTHOLOGY OF WORLD MUSIC - CHINA
Haiquing na tian / Great ambuscande / Geese landing on a sandy beach / Flowering waters / Fisherman's song / Ode to the plum blossom / Song of guanling
ROUCD 5150 / Feb '98 / Rounder

☐ ANTHOLOGY OF WORLD MUSIC - IRAN (2CD Set)
Chahargah / Segah / Klashti / Poem of saadi / Bayote ispahan / Dombak / Tat / Mystic poem / Bhatriyati / Abu ata
ROUCD 5122/23 / Feb '98 / Rounder

☐ ANTHOLOGY VOL.1 (Come Organisation Archives/2CD Set)
SLCD 0019 / 12 Jan '98 / Susan Lawley

☐ ANTOLOGIA DE LA MUSICA CUBANA VOL.1
472190 / Nov '97 / Flarenasch

☐ ANTOLOGIA DE LA MUSICA CUBANA VOL.2
472191 / Nov '97 / Flarenasch

☐ ANTOLOGIA DEL TANGO
BM 519 / Jan '97 / Blue Moon

☐ ANTOLOGIA DEL TANGO ARGENTINO (4CD Set)
BMCD 99902 / Jul '96 / Palladium

☐ **ANTONES ANNIVERSARY ANTHOLOGY VOL.2**
Chicago bound / Trouble blues / Shake for me / Everything is going to be alright / Natural ball / Sloppy drunk / Moanin' at midnight / Evan's shuffle / Black cat bone / Same thing could happen to you / High Jack
ANTCD 0016 / Mar '92 / Antones

☐ **ANTWERPEN 93**
KK 087CD / Oct '93 / KK

☐ **ANYWAY SINGLES 1992-1993**
GH 1023CD / Jun '97 / Get Hip

☐ **APOCALYPSE NOW VOL.1 (2CD Set)**
SPV 08838752 / Oct '96 / SPV

☐ **APOLLO VOL.2**
Number readers: *Subsurfing* / Seal and the hydrophone: *Biosphere* / Skank: *Manna* / Too good to be strange: *Two Sandwiches Sort Of A Lunchbox* / Incidental harmony: *Global Communication* / Sick porter: *u-Ziq* / Agraphobia: *LA Synthesis* / First floor: *Morley, David* / Epique: *Felman, Thomas* / Blue orgasmic light: *Tournesol* / Like old movies: *Word Up* / Patashnik: *Biosphere* / Autophia: *Leiner, Robert* / Nine to five: *Global Communication* / Aural grey: *Meditation YS* / I feel cold inside because of the things you say: *Locust* / Stampede: *Andie* / Stardance: *Morley, David* / Traveller's dream: *Aedena Cycle*
AMB 5933CD / May '95 / Apollo

☐ **APPALOOSA ALL STARS**
APCD 095 / Nov '95 / Appaloosa

☐ **APPOINTMENT WITH FEAR**
CYBERCD 11 / Aug '94 / Cyber

☐ **APPROACHING INCANDESCENCE**
CANDRCD 8010 / Oct '94 / Candor

☐ **AQUADELIC TRANCE FLOW**
CLP 9972 / Apr '97 / Cleopatra

☐ **AQUARHYTHMS (Greetings From Deepest America)**
Experience remix: *Craig, Carl* / Spiritool: *Ether* / Done fukt me: *Aquarian* / Distilled: *Hydroelectric* / Ether's whisper: *Deep Dish* / Hydroelectronics: *Hydroelectric* / Who is the aquarian: *Gigi Galaxy* / Sage: *Phenom* / Deep in the feeling: *Hydronaut* / Hydr: *DJ Joost & Flux*
PHONOCD 2 / Feb '97 / Phonography

☐ **AQUI ESTA LA BACHATA**
75811550782 / 14 Apr '98 / Platano

☐ **AR-TI-FAKTS**
BONESCD 01 / Aug '97 / No Bones

☐ **ARAB CLASSICAL MUSIC VOL.1**
AAA 133 / Apr '96 / Club Du Disque Arabe

☐ **ARAB CLASSICAL MUSIC VOL.2**
AAA 134 / Apr '96 / Club Du Disque Arabe

☐ **ARAB-ANDUKUSIAN ANTHOLOGY**
C 560055 / Oct '94 / Ocora

☐ **ARABIAN JAM**
MHCD 0005 / Apr '95 / Madhouse

☐ **ARBORS SAMPLER VOL.1**
ARCD 19192 / Oct '97 / Arbors Jazz

☐ **ARC (Artists Remix Collective)**
PLAT 45CD / 29 Jun '98 / Platipus

☐ **ARCANE**
My mother is not the white dove: *Gifford, Alex* / Ginger: *Kennedy, Nigel* / Chinese canon: *Gifford, Alex & Simon Jeffes* / Yodel 3: *Gifford, Alex & Simon Jeffes* / Youth and age: *Gifford, Alex* / Which way out/Esmerelda Pia Fini: *Sheppard, Andy & Nana Vasconcelos* / Thoughts on the departure of a lifelong friend: *Gifford, Alex* / Cage dead (Word version): *Gifford, Alex & Simon Jeffes* / Morecambe Bay: *Gifford, Alex*
CDRW 40 / Oct '94 / Realworld

☐ **ARCHIVES OF SPACE**
CLP 0064 / Jul '97 / Cleopatra

☐ **ARCHIVES OF TURKISH MUSIC VOL.1**
C 560081 / Jul '95 / Ocora

☐ **ARCHIVES OF TURKISH MUSIC VOL.2 (Historic Recordings 1903-1935)**
C 560082 / Jan '96 / Ocora

☐ **ARCTIC REFUGE**
SP 7159CD / Aug '96 / Soundings

☐ **ARE (Panpipe Ensembles From The Solomon Islands)**
LDX 274961/62 / Feb '94 / La Chant Du Monde

☐ **ARE**
GR 4100CD / Nov '95 / Grappa

☐ **AREA 51 (The Roswell Incident/2CD Set)**
IS 88979CD / 13 Apr '98 / I Scream Music
CLP 0172 / 2 Feb '98 / Purple Pyramid

☐ **AREA CODE 212**
CRECD 114 / Nov '91 / Creation

☐ **ARF ARF SAMPLER**
AA 068 / 15 Dec '97 / Arf Arf

☐ **ARGENTINE TANGO BANDS IN SPAIN 1927-1941**
HQCD 88 / Nov '96 / Harlequin

☐ **ARHOOLIE AMERICAN MASTERS VOL.1 (15 Down Home Country Blues Classics)**
ARHCD 101 / Nov '96 / Arhoolie

☐ **ARHOOLIE AMERICAN MASTERS VOL.10 (16 Down Home Country Classics)**
Single girl: *Maddox, Rose* / No never no: *Strange Creek Singers* / Run mountain: *Mainer, J.E.* / Spanish Fandango: *Jenkins, Snuffy* / Eight thirty blues: *Armstrong Twins* / Hey hey bartender: *McCoury, Del* / Sam McGhee stomp: *McGhee, Sam* / Old Dan Tucker: *Louisiana Honeydrippers* / You turned your back: *Brown, Toni* / Carroll county blues: *Thompson, Suzy & Eric* / George's playhouse boogie: *Maddox Brothers & Rose Maddox* / John Barleycorn: *Baker, Kenny* / Black land farmer: *Neely, Bill* / Turkey buzzard/Chinquapin hunting: *Neely, Bill* / Hello stranger: *Carter Family* / Bogue chito fling ding: *Hodges Brothers*
ARHCD 110 / 16 Mar '98 / Arhoolie

☐ **ARHOOLIE AMERICAN MASTERS VOL.11 (15 Down Home Gospel Classics)**
Just a closer walk with thee: *Ghent, Aubrey & Friends* / There's a leak in this old building: *Paramount Singers* / I want my crown: *Big Joe & Mary Williams* / Sinner don't you know: *Williams, Robert Pete* / I feel good: *Campbell Brothers & Katie Jackson* / I'm going over the hill: *Mae, Annie & Fred McDowell* / Gonna wait till a change come: *Wilson, Elder Roma* / Farther along: *Black Ace* / I've got religion: *Smith, Rebecca & Tom Miller/Ruth Miller* / Motherless children: *Lipscomb, Mance* / Jesus will fix it for you: *Treadway, Sonny* / I'm working on a building: *Overstreet, Rev. Louis* / Keep your lamp trimmed and burning: *McDowell, Fred & Johnny Woods* / Amazing Grace: *Fuller, Jesse* / Praise music: *Ghent, Aubrey*
ARHCD 111 / 16 Mar '98 / Arhoolie

☐ **ARHOOLIE AMERICAN MASTERS VOL.2 (15 Down Home Urban Blues Classics)**
Pontiac blues: *Williamson, Sonny Boy* / Big Mama's bumble bee: *Thornton, Willie Mae 'Big Mama'* / Cincinnati stomp: *Duskin, 'Big' Joe* / Anna Lee: *Hooker, Earl* / Up and down the avenue: *Musselwhite, Charley* / Been around the world: *Littlejohn, Johnny* / Wine-o-baby boogie: *Turner, 'Big' Joe & Pete Johnson* / I know that's right: *Webster, Katie* / Raven: *Shariff, Omar* / You think I'm your good thing: *Houston, Bee Bee* / Going back to the country: *Bonner, Weldon 'Juke Boy'* / Ups and downs: *Robinson, L.C. 'Good Rockin'* / Atlanta bounce: *Piano Red* / Wild wild woman: *Young, Johnny* / Gibson Creek shuffle: *Ford, Charles Band*
ARHCD 102 / Nov '96 / Arhoolie

☐ **ARHOOLIE AMERICAN MASTERS VOL.3 (15 Louisiana Cajun Classics)**
Le jig Francais: *Beausoleil* / Chere te mon: *Abshire, Nathan* / Port Arthur blues: *Fruge, Wade* / J'ai passe devant ta porte: *Balfa, Dewey & Marc Savoy/D.L. Menard* / Fiddle stomp: *Read, Wallis 'Cheese'* / Chicot two step: *California Cajun Orchestra* / Poor hobo: *Choates, Harry* / Jolie blonde: *Hackberry Ramblers* / Two step d'amede: *Savoy-Doucet Cajun Band* / Bernadette: *Fontenot, Canray* / Bosco stomp: *Pitre, Austin* / La robe: *Magnolia Sisters* / Basile breakdown: *Balfa, Dewey & Nathan Abshire* / Grand tasso: *Doucet, Michael* / Flames de'enfer: *Falcon, Joseph*
ARHCD 103 / Nov '96 / Arhoolie

☐ **ARHOOLIE AMERICAN MASTERS VOL.4 (15 Tex Mex Conjunto Classics)**
Ay te dejo en San Antonio: *Jimenez, Flaco* / Connie: *Conjunto Bernal* / Cuando se pierde le Madre: *Mendoza, Lydia* / Cada vez que cae la tarde: *Jimenez, Santiago Jr.* / Zulema: *Jimenez, Don Santiago* / Alejamiento y regreso: *Los Pavos Reales* / Atotonilco: *De La Rosa, Tony* / El canoero: *Longoria, Valerio* / Corrido de Cesar Chavez: *Los Pinguinos Del Norte* / Pasos cortos: *Lopez, Juan* / No me estorbes: *Zimmerle, Fred Rio San Antonio* / Luzita: *Martinez, Narciso* / El Mexicano-Americano: *Los Cenzontles* / Hazme caso: *Jordan, Steve* / Negra traicion: *Jimenez, Flaco*
ARHCD 104 / Nov '96 / Arhoolie

☐ **ARHOOLIE AMERICAN MASTERS VOL.5 (15 Louisiana Zydeco Classics)**
Zydeco sont pas sale: *Chenier, Clifton* / Lafayette special: *Sam Brothers 5* / Rag around your head: *Delafose, John* / Old time zydeco: *Sam, Ambrose* / I'm coming home: *Chenier, C.J.* / Les blues du voyager: *Ardoin, Boisec* / Tante na na: *Preston Frank's Swallow Band* / I'm on a wonder: *Chenier, Clifton* / Cofair: *Ardoin, Lawrence* / Aimez moi ce soir: *Ardoin, Amade* / Oh negresse: *Delafose, John* / Lafayette zydeco: *King, Peter & Lester Herbert* / Bee de la manche: *Fontenot, Canray* / She's my woman: *Chenier, C.J.* / Je me reveiller le matin: *Chenier, Clifton*
ARHCD 105 / May '97 / Arhoolie

☐ **ARHOOLIE AMERICAN MASTERS VOL.6 (15 Regional Music Classics Of Mexico)**
La chileca: *Conjunto Alma De Apatzingan* / Bala perdida: *Los Cenzontles* / La leva: *Los Caimanes* / No compro amores: *Mariachi Los Gavilanes De Oakland* / Mi texana: *Los Pinguinos Del Norte* / La guacamaya: *Conjunto alma jarocha* / El gustito: *Los Caporales De Panuco* / No es culpa mia: *Mendoza, Lydia* / La mariquita: *Mariachi De La Sierra Del Nayer* / Noes culpa mia: *Mendoza, Lydia* / Corrido de andres lopez: *Mariachi Tapatio De Jose Marmolejo* / La petenera: *Los Caimanes* / La peineta: *Los Campesinos De Michocan* / Tristeza de quertert: *Silva, Chelo* / El tilingolingo: *Conjunto alma jarocha*
ARHCD 106 / May '97 / Arhoolie

☐ **ARHOOLIE AMERICAN MASTERS VOL.7 (15 World Music Classics)**
Manana me voy: *Conjunto Los Amigos Del ANde* / Zmirneikos balos: *Papagika, Marika* / La tinajita: *Cuesta, Ivan* / Acuerdate bien, chaleco: *Sexteto Munamar* / El caballito: *Los Caimanes* / Di zilberne khasene: *Klezmorim* / Kozaczka szumka: *Swystum, Theodore J.* / Eldest of all: *Damessae, Seleshe* / Poor but ambitious: *Houdini, Wilmouth* / Medley of hulas: *Kalamas Quartette* / I bid you goodnight: *Spence, Joseph* / Icek w kolomej: *Orkiestra Majkuta* / Amnatine amantine: *Stellio & Son Orchestre Creole* / Irrarra hayanh gurigiya: *Chatuye* / Chareiti kaharwa: *Aziz Herawi*
ARHCD 107 / May '97 / Arhoolie

☐ **ARHOOLIE AMERICAN MASTERS VOL.8 (15 Piano Blues & Boogie Classics)**
Dollar Bill Boogie: *Duskin, 'Big' Joe* / Have you ever been out in the country: *Dee, Mercy* / Whistling Alex Moore's blues: *Moore, Alex* / Moaning and groaning: *Young, Johnny* / Katie's boogie woogie: *Young, Johnny* / Cruel hearted woman: *Smith, Thunder* / Ma grinder: *Shaw, Robert* / Why did you go last night: *Chenier, Clifton* / Pinetop's boogie woogie: *Robinson, L.C.* / San Francisco can be such a lonely town: *Sharriff, Imam Omar* / Rocket boogie 88: *Johnson, Pete* / Sugar hill: *White, Bukka* / You ain't got a chance: *Piano Red* / Cold chills: *Piano Red* / On the spot boogie: *Musselwhite, Charley*
ARHCD 108 / May '97 / Arhoolie

☐ **ARHOOLIE AMERICAN MASTERS VOL.9 (15 Early Tejano Classics)**
Quien va a pensar: *Lopez, Isidro & Su Orquestra* / No pidas olvido: *Carmen Y Laura/Orquestra De Juan Colorado* / Rio grande: *Villa, Beto & Su Orquestra* / Para que quiero un amor: *Conjunto Bernal* / Mi morena: *Gonzalez, Balde & Su Orquestra* / Una cualquiera: *De La Rosa, Tony* / Dime: *Fender, Freddy* / Con alma chiquitia: *Zuniga, Agapito* / Amor en duda: *Mendoza, Lydia* / Besos de amor: *Martinez, Oscar Y Su Orquestra* / Quiereme vidita: *Silva, Chelo* / Delgadina: *Las Hermanas Mendoza* / Rosita vals: *Villa, Beto & Su Orquestra* / Una noche vacillando: *Sandoval, Chris* / Las gaviotas: *Nunez, Tomas Orquesta*
ARHCD 109 / 16 Mar '98 / Arhoolie

☐ **ARISTOCRAT OF BLUES (Early Chicago Blues - The Best Of Aristocrat Blues/2CD Set)**
MCD 09387 / 23 Feb '98 / Chess/MCA

☐ **ARIWA 12TH ANNIVERSARY ALBUM, THE**
Together we're beautiful: *Cadogan, Susan* / Country living: *Cross, Sandra* / If I gave my heart to you: *McLean, John* / Proud of Mandela: *Macka B* / Daydreaming: *Brown, Jocelyn & Robotiks* / True born african: *U-Roy & Sister Audrey* / Show some love: *Thompson, Carroll* / Runaround girl: *Mclean, John & Dego Ranks* / Don't drink too much: *Macka B* / Creator: *Aisha* / Lonely/Love on a mountain top: *Stone, Davina & Ranking Ann* / True loving: *Aquizim* / Stylers: *Delena* / Ganga smuggling: *Mother Nature* / Six million dub: *Mad Professor/Mafia/Fluxy*
ARICD 067 / Nov '92 / Ariwa Sounds

☐ **ARIWA HITS '89**
I'm in love with a dreadlock: *Kofi* / At the dance: *Simmons, Leroy* / Don't sell your body: *Macka B* / You'll never get to heaven (If you break my heart): *Annette B* / Let's make a baby: *Tajah, Paulette* / Midnight train to Georgia: *McLean, John* / Stop chat: *Lorna G.* / On my mind: *Intense* / Best friend's man: *Cross, Sandra* / Sheba's verandah: *King, Allan*
ARICD 050 / Oct '89 / Ariwa Sounds

☐ **ARKADIA JAZZ**
AJ 70001 / 27 Apr '98 / Arkadia

☐ **ARMENIAN FOLK MUSIC**
SOW 90126 / Sep '94 / Sounds Of The World

☐ **ARMY, THE NAVY & THE AIR FORCE, THE**
Army, Navy and Airforce: *Central Band of The Royal Air Force* / Royal Air Force march past: *Central Band of The Royal Air Force* / Aces high: *Central Band of The Royal Air Force* / Battle of Britain: *Central Band of The Royal Air Force* / Evening hymn: *Central Band of The Royal Air Force* / Last post: *Central Band of The Royal Air Force* / Sunset: *Central Band of The Royal Air Force* / British Grenadiers: *Band Of The Grenadier Guards* / Old comrades: *Band Of The Grenadier Guards* / Liberty bell: *Band Of The Grenadier Guards* / Scipio march: *Band Of The Grenadier Guards* / Life on the ocean wave: *Royal Marines* / National emblem: *Royal Marines* / Sailing: *Royal Marines* / Heart of oak: *Royal Marines* / Les Huguenots: *Bandsmen From Grenadier Guards* / Radetsky march: *Bandsmen From Grenadier Guards* / Trumpet tunes: *Bandsmen From Grenadier Guards* / Amazing grace: *Regimental Band, Pipes & Drums of Royal Scots Dragoon Band* / Holyrood: *Regimental Band, Pipes & Drums of Royal Scots Dragoon Band* / Flower of Scotland: *Regimental Band, Pipes & Drums of Royal Scots Dragoon Band* / Flowers of the forest: *Regimental Band, Pipes & Drums of Royal Scots Dragoon Band*
CDPMFP 6131 / Sep '94 / Music For Pleasure

☐ **ARNHEM LAND (Aboriginal Songs & Dances)**
CDLRH 288 / Jun '97 / Knock On Wood

☐ **AROUND THE DAY IN 80 WORLDS**
SSR 130 / Feb '95 / SSR

☐ **AROUND THE WORLD (FOR A SONG)**
RCD 00217 / Sep '91 / Rykodisc

☐ **ARRIVA LA BOMBA**
Arriva bomba / Baruba snake: *Brunetta* / To sat domant che taremo: *Quattro Ai Tocca* / Torse mai: *Gloris Paul* / Basta: *Samson, Patrick* / Il gatto nero: *Auger, Brian & The Trinity* / Hush: *I-Colour* / Sono un umomo: *Samson, Patrick* / Il baccara: *Terrell, Dino* / Soul finger: *I-Baronetti* / Mah na mah na: *Moroder, Giorgio* / Faru faru: *Moroder, Giorgio*
IRMA 489686 / 6 Apr '98 / Irma La Douce

☐ **ART OF BAGPIPES FROM THRACE, THE**
ARN 60369 / 24 Apr '98 / Arion

☐ **ART OF FINGER STYLE GUITAR, THE**
Stagefright: *Evans, Dave* / Dance for two people: *Graham, Davey* / Bridge: *Jansch, Bert* / New New nothynge: *Renbourn, John* / Wishbone ash: *Finger, Peter* / Elephant march: *Wijnkamp, Leo Jr.* / Sad pig: *Evans, Dave* / Happy meeting in glory: *Graham, Davey* / Feet on the ground: *James, John* / Sun and moon: *Evans, Dave* / When I'm sixty four: *Wijnkamp, Leo Jr.* / Return of Dr. Hakenbush: *Wijnkamp, Leo Jr.* / Forty ton parachute: *Graham, Davey* / Sabine: *Finger, Peter* / Guitar jump: *James, John & John Renbourn* / Steppenwolf: *Evans, Dave* / Lashtal's room: *Graham, Davey* / Hannah's skipping song: *James, John* / Whistlin' milkman: *Evans, Dave* / Pavane for the sleeping beauty: *Wijnkamp, Leo Jr.* / Blues for Gino: *Graham, Davey* / Braziliana: *Evans, Dave* / Trio: *James, John* / Hope and memory: *Finger, Peter* / Willie me: *Evans, Dave*
SH 98009 / Mar '98 / Shanachie

☐ **ART OF FLAMENCO VOL.12, THE (El Cante En Cordoba)**
MAN 4885 / Dec '96 / Mandala

☐ **ART OF FLAMENCO VOL.13, THE (Nostalgia)**
MAN 4890 / Feb '97 / Mandala

☐ **ART OF FLAMENCO VOL.14, THE (After The War)**
MAN 4893 / Feb '97 / Mandala

☐ **ART OF FLAMENCO VOL.2, THE**
MAN 4878CD / Aug '96 / Mandala

☐ **ART OF FLAMENCO VOL.9, THE (El Cante En Sevilla)**
MAN 4868 / Feb '96 / Mandala

☐ **ART OF FLAMENCO, THE**
Jaleo / Solea / Tanguillo / Solo guitarra / Tangos / Nuevo flamenco / Alegrias / Buleria / Siguiriyas / Buleria rancheros / Fandango de huelva / Cantinas / Martinetes / Sevillana
893002 / May '94 / Emocion

☐ **ART OF FRANCE**
PIAS 343000212CD / Sep '96 / Play It Again Sam

☐ **ART OF HARP, THE**
Wind: *Windharp* / Boy in the bush: *Hambly, Grainne* / Kid on the mountain: *Hambly, Grainne* / Kelefa: *Jobarteh, Malamini* / Coqueta / Tina Ye: *Naguru Adungu Troupe* / Berceuse: *Nogues, Kristen* / Prelude: *Mowery, Cynthia* / Kerzhadenn: *Nogues, Kristen* / Vers la source dans le bois: *Mowery, Cynthia* / Nigra sum: *Kirchner, Almut* / Blue diamonds: *Krimmel, Margot & Mark Miller* / Diatta Dinke: *Jobarteh, Malamini* / Dance with me: *Henson-Conant, Deborah* / Ambhan na leabhor/The bucks of Oranmore: *Hambly, Grainne* / Water is wide: *Krimmel, Margot* / Oro ma wangini bimu ubombo: *Naguru Adungu Troupe*
R 272496 / Nov '96 / Earthbeat

☐ **ART OF HUKWE ABI ZAWOSE**
VICG 50112 / Mar '96 / JVC World Library

☐ **ART OF JAZZ SAXOPHONE, THE (5CD Set)**
Blue Lester: *Young, Lester* / Jump Lester jump: *Young, Lester* / Body and soul: *Hawkins, Coleman* / Uptown lullaby: *Hawkins, Coleman & Ben Webster* / Pennies from heaven: *Webster, Ben* / Blue Lou: *Carter, Benny & Coleman Hawkins* / Blue Lou II: *Carter, Benny* / Back home again in Indiana: *Byas, Don & Coleman Hawkins/Stan Getz* / All the things you are: *Byas, Don* / Street beat: *Parker, Charlie* / Hot house: *Parker, Charlie* / Donna Lee: *Parker, Charlie* / Still takin' to ya: *Adderley, Cannonball* / Settin' the pace: *Gordon, Dexter* / There will never be another you: *Stitt, Sonny* / Duty free: *Stitt, Sonny* / Masquerade is over: *Stitt, Sonny* / Out of nowhere: *Woods, Phil* / Loot to boot: *Jacquet, Illinois* / It don't mean a thing: *Jacquet, Illinois* / I got it bad and that ain't good: *Hodges, Johnny* / Things ain't what they used to be: *Hodges, Johnny* / Leapin' on Lennox: *Davis, Eddie 'Lockjaw'* / Body and soul: *Davis, Eddie 'Lockjaw'* / Blues for BB: *Mobley, Hank* / Tonight I shall sleep: *Getz, Stan* / Desafinado: *Getz, Stan* / Soul lullaby: *Thompson, Lucky* / Fillet of soul: *Thompson, Lucky* / Come rain or come shine: *Sims, Zoot* / Nirvana: *Sims, Zoot* / Wells Fargo: *Coltrane, John* / EFFPH: *Coltrane, John* / Jeru: *Mulligan, Gerry* / Festive minor: *Mulligan, Gerry* / Blu-a-round: *Shihab, Sahib* / Patricia: *Pepper, Art* / Me and my baby: *Konitz, Lee* / Yusef: *Lateef, Yusef* / Left alone: *Shepp, Archie* / Apex: *Lovano, Joe* / Impressions: *Lovano, Joe* / Up jumped spring: *Golson, Benny* / Magic number: *Farrell, Joe* / OC-DC: *Barbieri, Gato* / Autumn leaves: *Berg, Bob* / Wayne's tune: *Garrett, Kenny* / No scratch: *Henderson, Joe* / Hero with a thousand faces: *Brecker, Michael*
15977 / Oct '97 / Laserlight

☐ **ART OF LANDSCAPE VOL.1**
ALC 11CD / Aug '92 / Art Of Landscape

☐ **ART OF LANDSCAPE VOL.2**
ALC 12CD / Aug '92 / Art Of Landscape

☐ **ART OF MECHANICAL MUSIC VOL.1, THE**
ARN 60359 / Nov '97 / Arion

☐ **ART OF MECHANICAL MUSIC VOL.2, THE**
ARN 60406 / 24 Feb '98 / Arion

☐ **ART OF MECHANICAL MUSIC VOL.3, THE**
ARN 60407 / 24 Feb '98 / Arion

☐ **ART OF THE BALATON, THE**
ARN 60403 / 5 Jan '98 / Arion

☐ **ART OF THE BERIMBAU, THE**
926782 / 21 Aug '97 / BUDA

☐ **ART OF THE CORNEMUSE VOL.2, THE**
ARN 60378 / 5 Jan '98 / Arion

☐ **ART OF THE DOTAR, THE (Music From Uzbekistan)**
C 560111 / Aug '97 / Ocora

☐ **ART OF THE FINNISH KANTELE**
EUCD 1342 / Apr '96 / ARC

☐ **ART OF THE HURDY GURDY VOL.2, THE**
ARN 60373 / 24 Apr '98 / Arion

☐ **ART OF THE SARANGI**
C 580067 / May '98 / Ocora

☐ **ART OF THE STEEL BAND, THE**
ARN 60399 / 5 Jan '98 / Arion

☐ **ART RUPE IN HIS OWN WORDS (The Specialty Story/2CD Set)**
Good golly Miss Molly: *Little Richard* / Dizzy Miss Lizzy: *Williams, Larry* / Hop skip and jump: *Milton, Roy & His Solid Senders* / Touch the hem of his garment: *Cooke, Sam & The Soul Stirrers* / Cadillac boogie: *Liggins, Jimmy & His Drops Of Joy* / Junior jives: *Milton, Roy & His Solid Senders* / Voo-it voo-it: *Blues Woman* / Boogie no.1: *Sepia-Tones* / RM blues: *Milton, Roy & His Solid Senders* / X-temporaneous boogie: *Howard, Camille* / Standing on the highway: *Pilgrim Travellers* / Too close to Heaven: *Bradford, Alex* / Ball game: *Carr, Sister Wynona* / Pink champagne: *Liggins, Joe & His Honey Drippers* / Please send me someone to love: *Mayfield, Percy* / One room country shack: *Walton, Mercy Dee* / Born on the 13th: *Hogg, Smokey* / Lawdy Miss Clawdy: *Price, Lloyd* / Things that I used to do: *Guitar Slim* / Long tall Sally: *Little Richard* / Tutti frutti: *Little Richard* / Ready Teddy: *Little Richard* / Girl can't help it: *Little Richard* / Keep a-knockin': *Little Richard* / Baby face: *Little Richard* / Bony Moronie: *Williams, Larry* / Short fat Fannie: *Williams, Larry* / Wonderful: *Cooke, Sam & The Soul Stirrers* / Loveable: *Cook, Dale* / I'll come running back to you: *Cooke, Sam* / I'm leavin' it (all) up to you: *Don & Dewey* / Lights out: *Byrne, Jerry* / Junior jives: *Milton, Roy & His Solid Senders*
CDCH2 542 / 27 Apr '98 / Ace

☐ **ARTCORE VOL.1 - AMBIENT JUNGLE**
Greater love: *Soundman & Don Lloydie* / Living for the future: *Omni Trio* / We enter: *Alladin* / Tranquility: *Reynolds, Austin* / Jazz note: *DJ Krust* / Jazz juice: *Jazz Juice* / Currents: *Sounds Of Life* / Sweet dreams: *DJ Crysti* / Soothe my soul: *Justice* / Dance of the saroes: *Rogue Unit* / Atmosphere: *DJ Phantasy* / Sparkling: *Little Matt* / Amenity: *Link* / Phat and phuturistic: *Little Matt* / Inhabitants of pandemonium: *Spirits From An Urban Jungle* / Deep in the jungle: *Amazon II* / Second heaven: *Atlas* / Angels in dub: *Code Blue* / Natural high: *Chaos & Julia Set*
REACTCD 059 / Apr '95 / React

☐ **ARTCORE VOL.2 - THE ART OF DRUM 'N' BASS**
Circles: *Adam F* / I'll fly away: *Balistic Brothers* / Total control: *Foulplay* / Sleepless: *Optical* / Drums '95: *DJ Doc Scott* / Mutante remix: *T-Power* / I wanted it more and more: *Aphrodite* / Lush life: *J-Majik* / Find me: *Skanna* / Another dream world: *Nemeton* / Three days: *Eugenix* / Can't deal with this: *Cool Breeze* / Enchanted: *Adam F* / London nights: *Dominion* / Cab Colombie: *Arteq* / Break it down: *Atomic Dog* / Fast and loose: *Bliss 'n' Tumble*
REACTCD 075
REACTCDX 075 / Apr '96 / React

☐ **ARTCORE VOL.3 - EXPRESSIONS IN DRUM 'N' BASS (2CD Set - Mixed By Peshay)**
Stretch: *Ishii, Ken* / F jam: *Adam F* / Journey: *Bliss 'n' Tumble* / Milk: *Garbage* / Electric soul: *Icon* / Reincarnation: *DJ Die* / Skylab: *Ed Rush* / On the nile: *Peshay* / Sea: *St. Etienne* / Expressions: *Wallace, Dave* / Motions: *Intense* / Pulse: *Zed* / Ave Maria: *A-Sides & Nathan Haines* / Crossing part 2 (words): *Underwolves* / Bear: *Danny Breaks* / Solar glide: *Spirit* / Death by sax: *Tribe zero 2* / Shadow boxing: *Doc Scott* / Mysterious people: *Nookie & Larry Heard* / Homeland, xpressive journey: *Wayward Mind*
REACTCDX 099
REACTCD 099 / Mar '97 / React

☐ **ARTCORE VOL.4 - DRUM 'N' BASS TECHNOLOGY (2CD Set)**
Essential 4 life: *Justine & Tertius* / Tides: *Forest Mighty Black* / Mystical flyte: *Subject 13* / Fluid motion: *Matrix* / Soul in motion: *DJ Krust* / Mind control: *Boymerang* / TPC: *Optical* / Spring box: *Dilemma* / Genetix: *Shimmon & Andy C* / Shockwave: *Digital & Spirit* / Piper: *Jonny L* / Searchin' for a beat: *Future Passed* / Spirit: *Kitachi* / LED: *Q Project & Spinback* / Sunstroke: *Chicain* / Nu reeze: *Smoke Screen* / Technologik: *State Logik* / Fountain: *Blu Mar Ten* / Pac 3: *Override* / Vapour dub: *Coda*
REACTCDX 112
REACTCD 112 / 22 Sep '97 / React

☐ **ARTE FLAMENCO**
MAN 4873CD / Apr '96 / Mandala

☐ **ARTE FLAMENCO VOL.1**
MAN 4828 / May '94 / Mandala

☐ **ARTE FLAMENCO VOL.2**
MAN 4829 / May '94 / Mandala

☐ **ARTE FLAMENCO VOL.3**
MAN 4832 / May '94 / Mandala

☐ **ARTIFICIAL INTELLIGENCE**
WARPCD 6 / Apr '96 / Warp

☐ **ARTISTRY IN JAZZ (Black Lion Jazz sampler)**
BLCD 760100 / '88 / Black Lion

☐ **ARTISTS FOR THE ENVIRONMENT**
0029292 / Oct '95 / Edel

☐ **AS IN MUSIC SO IN LIFE**
HOMCD 7086 / 10 Nov '97 / Higher Octave

☐ **AS SEEN ON TV**
SPARE 001 / May '97 / Spare Me

☐ **AS TIME GOES BY (2CD Set)**
Lili Marlene: *Anderson, Lale* / Moonlight serenade: *Miller, Glenn* / As time goes by: *Vallee, Rudy* / At the woodchopper's ball: *Herman, Woody* / Swinging on a star: *Crosby, Bing* / I've heard that song before: *James, Harry* / You'll never know: *Haymes, Dick* / Don't fence me in: *Andrews Sisters & Bing Crosby* / It's a lovely day tomorrow: *Lynn, Vera* / For me and my gal: *Garland, Judy & Gene Kelly* / I don't want to set the world on fire: *Geraldo* / Paper doll: *Mills Brothers* / Don't get around much anymore: *Ellington, Duke* / All or nothing at all: *Sinatra, Frank* / Tangerine: *Dorsey, Jimmy* / I don't want to walk without you: *Rhodes, Betty Jane* / Whispering grass: *Ink Spots* / Blues in the night: *Shore, Dinah* / Stardust: *Shaw, Artie* / Over the rainbow: *Garland, Judy* / You made me love you: *James, Harry* / Last time I saw Paris: *Martin, Tony* / In the mood: *Miller, Glenn* / Why don't you do right: *Lee, Peggy* / White cliffs of Dover: *Lynn, Vera* / Rum and coca cola: *Andrews Sisters* / Chattanooga choo choo: *Miller, Glenn* / I'll walk alone: *Shore, Dinah* / Waiter and the porter and the upstairs maid: *Martin, Mary & Jack Teagarden* / Yours: *Lynn, Vera* / Night and day: *Sinatra, Frank* / Begin the beguine: *Shaw, Artie* / Nightingale sang in Berkeley Square: *Shelton, Anne* / You are my sunshine: *Roy, Harry* / If I didn't care: *Ink Spots* / I know why: *Miller, Glenn* / Boogie woogie bugle boy: *Andrews Sisters* / I'll be seeing you: *Shelton, Anne* / Frenesi: *Shaw, Artie* / Moonlight becomes you: *Crosby, Bing* / Little on the lonely side: *Geraldo* / Long ago and far away: *Haymes, Dick & Helen Forrest* / Take the 'A' train: *Ellington, Duke* / You always hurt the one you love: *Mills Brothers* / Cow cow boogie: *Fitzgerald, Ella & Ink Spots* / I'll never smile again: *Sinatra, Frank* / When the lights go on again: *Monroe, Vaughan* / I had my way: *Crosby, Bing* / I've got a gal in Kalamazoo: *Miller, Glenn* / We'll meet again: *Lynn, Vera*
CPCD 8105 / Jun '95 / Charly

☐ **AS TIME GOES BY**
MACCD 327 / Aug '96 / Autograph

☐ **AS TIME GOES BY**
You are my sunshine: *Crosby, Bing* / For me and my gal / Nightingale sang in Berkeley square: *Layton, Turner* / Tangerine: *Dorsey, Jimmy* / Do I worry: *Ink Spots* / Sailor with the navy blue eyes: *Roy, Navy* / Never took a lesson in my life: *Gonella, Nat* / I hear a dream: *Lynn, Vera* / Apple for the teacher: *Roy, Harry* / It's foolish but it's fun: *Durbin, Deanna* / Don't get around much anymore: *Ink Spots* / Humpty dumpty heart: *Geraldo* / Our love affair: *Garland, Judy* / If I had my way: *Ambrose* / Mister meadow: *Crosby, Bing* / It had to be you: *Roy, Harry* / Where or when: *Hutch* / We three: *Gonella, Nat* / Begin beguine: *Hall, Adelaide* / You made me care: *Ambrose & His Orchestra* / As time goes by: *Winstone, Eric*
SWNCD 019 / Nov '97 / Sound Waves

☐ **ASANA**
Devabandha: *Makyo* / Om namah shiva: *Jah Wobble's Invaders Of The Heart* / Hear no evil: *Laswell, Bill* / Mantra: *Material*
ADC 7 / Jul '97 / Douglas Music
DM 10007 / 15 Jun '98 / Douglas Music

☐ **ASCENSION COLLECTION, THE**
It's all we know: *OBX* / Another kind of find: *Red Red Groovy* / That's how my heart sings: *Dial 4 FX* / Freak you: *Euphoria* / Nebula: *Positive Science* / Soul feel free: *Positive Science* / Caspar ound: *House* / Eternal prayer: *OBX* / Tangled in my thoughts: *RHC & Plavka* / Maximum motion: *Plavka*
ASCCD 1 / Apr '95 / Ascension

☐ **ASHTRAY HEART**
SRCD 1 / May '97 / Sorted

☐ **ASIAN THEATRE AND DANCE (Cambodia/India/Indonesia/3CD Set)**
C 570303 / Mar '97 / Ocora

☐ **ASSASSINATION**
Assassination: *Dixie Nightingales* / Safety zone: *Dixie Nightingales* / There's not a friend: *Dixie Nightingales* / Hush, hush: *Dixie Nightingales* / Swing low, sweet chariot: *Revelators* / Lady called Mother: *Revelators* / In the middle of the air: *Revelators* / God is using me: *Harps Of Melody* / I'll go, send me: *Harps Of Melody* / Walk in Jerusalem: *Harps Of Melody* / Press on: *Gospel Writers* / Blind Barnabus: *Gospel Writers* / Wonderful Jesus: *Gospel Writers* / What do you know about Jesus: *Gospel Writers*
CDZ 2019 / May '96 / Zu Zazz

☐ **ASSORTMENT, AN**
Surfer Baby: *Blind Mr. Jones* / Hey: *Blind Mr. Jones* / Brad: *Tse Tse Fly* / On purpose: *Tse Tse Fly* / PDF: *Prolapse* / Screws: *Prolapse* / Jack: *Monochrome Set* / House of God: *Monochrome Set* / Humtone 4: *Fisher, Morgan* / Humtone 4 (remix): *Fisher, Morgan*
CDMRED 107 / Feb '94 / Cherry Red

☐ **ASSUMPTION OF DABRA GANNAT, THE (Ethiopian Orthodox Church of Jerusalem)**
C 560027/28 / Mar '92 / Ocora

☐ **ASTURIES - CAMIN DE COMPOSTELLA**
FA 8738CD / Nov '96 / Fono Astur

☐ **ASURINI (Music From Brazil)**
C 560084 / Dec '95 / Ocora

☐ **AT THE COURT OF CHERA KING**
WLACS 34CD / Nov '95 / Waterlily Acoustics

☐ **AT THE DARKTOWN STRUTTER'S BALL**
DCD 8000 / Jan '95 / Disky

☐ **ATHLETICO COMPILATION VOL.1**
JAZIDCD 131 / Nov '95 / Acid Jazz

☐ **ATHLETICO SPEAK**
Fixy jointy: *Psychedeliasmith* / Wede man: *Selectah* / Summertime: *Lewis, Monk* / Let's get some girls: *Sir Drew* / I work the whole city: *Subsonic Legacy* / Take it back: *Athletico Borough Upsetters* / Get on it: *Berrios, Carlos* / Wired up: *Jeep Beat Collective* / Stump juice: *Capoeira Twins & KYO* / 3 wishes: *Dubz Deluxe*
ATHCD 001 / 2 Mar '98 / Athletico

☐ **ATLANTA GOSPEL 1925-1931**
DOCD 5485 / Nov '96 / Document

☐ **ATLANTE DI MUSICA TRADIZIONALE VOL.2**
RDC 5042CD / Mar '98 / Robi Droli

☐ **ATLANTIC BLUES MASTERS**
Ain't nobody's business if I do: *Witherspoon, Jimmy* / T-bone blues: *Walker, T-Bone* / Laundromat blues: *King, Albert* / Rollin' and tumblin': *Leroy, Baby Face* / All your love (I miss loving): *Rush, Otis* / Little by little: *Wells, Junior* / Evening sun: *Shines, Johnny* / Short haired woman: *Hopkins, Lightnin'* / Freeze: *Collins, Albert* / Stumble: *King, Freddie* / Flood down in Texas: *Vaughan, Stevie Ray* / Sugar coated love: *Lazy Lester* / Steady: *McCain, Jerry* / Got love if you want it: *Harpo, Slim* / Shake, rattle and roll: *Turner, 'Big' Joe* / Hoy hoy: *Jones, Little Johnny* / Hello little boy: *Brown, Ruth* / I'm a woman: *Taylor, Koko* / Master charge: *Collins, Albert* / Mojo boogie: *Winter, Johnny* / Feelin' good: *Parker, Junior & The Blue Flames* / Bear cat: *Thomas, Rufus*
8122713862 / Mar '94 / Atlantic

☐ **ATLANTIC BLUES: CHICAGO**
Chicago blues: *Jones, Johnny* / Hoy hoy: *Jones, Johnny* / Play on little girl: *Walker, T-Bone* / T-Bone blues special: *Walker, T-Bone* / Poor man's plea: *Guy, Buddy & Junior Wells* / My baby she left me: *Guy, Buddy & Junior Wells* / T-Bone shuffle: *Guy, Buddy & Junior Wells* / I wonder why: *King, Freddie* / Play it cool: *King, Freddie* / Woke up this morning: *King, Freddie* / Gambler's blues: *Rush, Otis* / Feel so bad: *Rush, Otis* / Reap what you sow / Highway 49 / Honey bee: *Waters, Muddy* / Wang dang doodle: *Taylor, Koko* / Dust my broom: *Shines, Johnny* / Going down: *King, Freddie* / Please send me someone to love: *Allison, Luther* / Walking the dog: *Allison, Luther* / Feel so good: *Hutto, J.B.*
7567816972 / Jan '97 / Atlantic

☐ **ATLANTIC BLUES: GUITAR**
Broke down engine: *McTell, 'Blind' Willie* / Shake 'em on down: *McDowell, 'Mississippi' Fred* / My baby don't love me: *Hooker, John Lee* / Tall pretty woman: *McGhee, Stick* / Blues rock: *Brown, Texas Johnny* / There goes the blues: *Brown, Texas Johnny* / Bongo boogie: *Brown, Texas Johnny* / Two bones and a pick: *Walker, T-Bone* / Mean ol' world: *Walker, T-Bone* / Let me know: *Norris, Chuck* / It hurts to love someone: *Guitar Slim* / Down through the years: *Guitar Slim* / Okie dokie stomp: *Dupree, Cornell* / Blues nocturne: *Dupree, Cornell* / TV mama: *Turner, 'Big' Joe* / Reconsider baby: *King, Al* / Midnight midnight: *Baker, McHouston 'Mickey'* / I smell trouble: *Turner, Ike & Tina* / Why I sing the blues: *King, Albert* / Crosscut saw: *King, Albert* / Angels of mercy: *King, Albert* / Can't be satisfied: *Hammond, John* / Flood down in Texas: *Vaughan, Stevie Ray*
7567816952 / Jan '97 / Atlantic

☐ **ATLANTIC BLUES: PIANO**
Yancey special: *Yancey, Jimmy* / Talkin' boogie: *Montgomery, Little Brother* / Mournful blues: *Yancey, Jimmy* / Farish street jive: *Montgomery, Little Brother* / Salute to pinetop: *Yancey, Jimmy* / Vicksburg blues: *Montgomery, Little Brother* / Shave 'em dry: *Yancey, Jimmy* / Frankie and Johnny: *Walker, T-Bone* / T B blues: *Walker, T-Bone* / Strollin': *Walker, T-Bone* / Boogie woogie: *Professor Longhair* / Tipitina: *Professor Longhair* / Blue sender: *Walls, Van* / After midnight: *Walls, Van* / Roll 'em Pete: *Turner, 'Big' Joe* / 'Fore day rider: *McShann, Jay* / Cherry red: *Turner, 'Big' Joe* / My chile: *McShann, Jay* / Cow cow blues: *Atlantic* / Albert's blues: *Lewis, Meade 'Lux'* / Honky tonk train blues: *Lewis, Meade 'Lux'* / Ray's blues: *Charles, Ray* / Low society: *Charles, Ray* / Bit of soul: *Charles, Ray* / Hey bartender: *Dixon, Floyd* / Floyd's blues: *Dixon, Floyd* / After hours blues: *Brown, Texas Johnny* / Junco partner: *Jordan, Louis* / I don't know: *Mabon, Willie*
7567816942 / Jan '97 / Atlantic

☐ **ATLANTIC BLUES: VOCALISTS**
You got to know how: *Wallace, Sippie* / Suitcase blues: *Wallace, Sippie* / Mighty tight woman: *Wallace, Sippie* / How long blues: *Witherspoon, Jimmy* / In the evening: *Witherspoon, Jimmy* / Gimme a pigfoot and a bottle of beer / Make me a pallet on the floor: *Yancey, Mama* / St. Louis blues: *Turner, 'Big' Joe* / Oke-she-moke-she-pop: *Turner, 'Big' Joe* / I've got that feeling: *Green, Lil* / Destination love: *Harris, Wynonie* / Tell a whale of a tale: *Harris, Wynonie* / Rain is a bringdown: *Brown, Ruth* / RB blues: *Brown, Ruth* / I don't want to be president: *Mayfield, Percy* / Nothing stays the same: *Mayfield, Percy* / River's invitation: *Taylor, Ted* / Just like a fish: *Phillips, Esther* / Pouring water on a drowning man: *Clay, Otis* / Did you ever love a woman: *Thomas, Rufus* / Baby girl (parts 1 and 2): *Turner, Titus* / Ain't that lovin' you: *Bland, Bobby* / It's my own tears that's being wasted: *Copeland, Johnny* / Cheatin' woman: *Holmes, Eldridge* / I had a dream / Takin' another mans place: *Franklin, Aretha* / It's a hang up baby: *Hill, Z.Z.* / Home ain't home at suppertime: *Hill, Z.Z.*
7567816962 / Jan '97 / Atlantic

☐ **ATLANTIC GROOVES - THE FUNK 'N' JAZZ EXPERIENCE VOL.1**
Rock steady / Captain Buckles / Drunk man / But I was cool / Bishop school / Wild man on the loose / Little ghetto boy / Dealing with hard times / No more / Behold the day / Groovin' time / Right on / Jive Samba / Backlash / Can't git enough / Motherless child / Well I'll be white black / Funky how time can change the meaning of a word
9548327712 / Aug '94 / Atlantic

☐ **ATLANTIC JAZZ - AVANT GARDE**
Black mystery has been revealed / Wednesday night prayer meeting / Eventually / Lonely woman / Cherryco / Countdown / Inflated tear / Nonaah
7817092 / Dec '87 / Atlantic

☐ **ATLANTIC JAZZ - BEBOP**
Our love is here to stay / Evidence / Be bop / Koko / Salt peanuts / Almost like me / Allen's alley (be bop tune)
7817022 / Dec '87 / Atlantic

☐ **ATLANTIC JAZZ - FUSION**
Freedom jazz dance / Beaux JPooboo / Quadrant four / Beneath the earth / Homunculus / Egocentric molecules
7817112 / Dec '87 / Atlantic

☐ **ATLANTIC JAZZ - INTROSPECTION**
Yoruba / Tones for Joan's bones / Forest flower-sunrise / In a silent way / Standing outside / Chega de saudade / Fortune smiles
7817102 / Dec '87 / Atlantic

☐ **ATLANTIC JAZZ - KANSAS CITY**
You're driving me crazy / Lamp is low / Hootie blues / E flat boogie / Confessin' the blues / Jumpin' at the woodside / Until the real thing comes along / Undecided / Evening / Buster's tune / Piney brown blues
7817012 / '88 / Atlantic

☐ **ATLANTIC JAZZ - MAINSTREAM**
I'll be seeing you / Ain't misbehavin' / Stuffy / Django / Daphne / Perdido / Embraceable you / Four brothers / Everything happens to me / Speedy reeds
7817042 / '87 / Atlantic

☐ **ATLANTIC JAZZ - NEW ORLEANS**
Bourbon street parade / Burgundy St. Blues / My bucket's got a hole in it / Cielito lindo / Salty dog / Eh la bas / Maple leaf rag / Joe Avery's blues / Nobody knows the way I feel this morning / Shreveport stomp / Sing on / Shake it and break it / Tiger rag
7817002 / '88 / Atlantic

☐ **ATLANTIC JAZZ - POST BOP**
Lydian M-1 / I can't get started (with you) / Bag's groove / This 'n' that / Giant steps / Sister salvation / White sand / Misty (instrumental version) / Thoroughbred
7817052 / Dec '87 / Atlantic

☐ **ATLANTIC JAZZ - SOUL**
Think / Twist city / How long blues / Comin' home baby / Russell and Eliot / Listen here / With these hands / Compared to what / You're the one / Jive samba / Money in the pocket
7567817082 / '88 / Atlantic

☐ **ATLANTIC JAZZ - WEST COAST**
Sa-frantic / Not really / Paradox / Chermoya / Martians go home / You name it / Tripin' awhile / Topsy / Song is you
7567817032 / Feb '94 / Atlantic

☐ **ATLANTIC JAZZ CLASSICS**
Sweet sixteen bars: *Charles, Ray* / Golden striker: *Modern Jazz Quartet* / In walked bud: *Blakey, Art & Thelonious Monk* / Hard times: *Newman, David 'Fathead'* / Wednesday night prayer meeting: *Mingus, Charles* / Ramblin': *Coleman, Ornette* / My favourite things: *Coltrane, John* / Comin' home baby: *Mann, Herbie* / Your mind is on vacation: *Allison, Mose* / Sweet slumber: *Crawford, Hank & The Marty Paich Orchestra* / Old country: *Adderley, Nat* / Inflated tear: *Kirk, Rahsaan Roland* / Compared to what: *McCann, Les & Eddie Harris*
8122729652 / 1 Jun '98 / Atlantic

☐ **ATLANTIC JAZZ GALLERY - FLUTES**
Ain't no sunshine / Laugh for Rory / Night of Nisan / Thirteenth floor / Memphis underground / Little girl of mine / Nubian lady / Stay with me / All soul / If you knew / Sombrero Sam / Journey within
8122716372 / May '94 / Atlantic

☐ **ATLANTIC JAZZ GALLERY - KEYBOARDS**
How long blues / Way you look tonight / Evidence / Little girl blue / C minor complex / Genius after hours / Rockin' chair / Sweet Georgia Brown / Catbird seat / Doin' that thing / My one and only love / Everything I love / Straight up and down
8122715962 / Feb '94 / Atlantic

☐ **ATLANTIC JAZZ GALLERY - LEGENDS VOL.1**
Hard times / Compared to what / Whispering grass / Golden striker / Inflated tear / Comin' home baby / Ramblin' / Your mind is on vacation / Sweet sixteen bars / Nubian Lady / Wednesday night prayer meeting
8122712572 / Jun '93 / Atlantic

☐ **ATLANTIC JAZZ GALLERY - SAXOPHONES VOL.1**
If I loved you / Freedom jazz dance / Willow weep for me / Russell and Eliot / Lorelei's lament / Confirmation / Giant steps / Lonely woman / Forest flower-sunrise / Forest flower-sunset
8122712562 / Jun '93 / Atlantic

☐ **ATLANTIC JAZZ GALLERY - SAXOPHONES VOL.2**
Blues shout / I wish you love / Old rugged cross / Don't get around much anymore / Topsy / Love theme from the Sandpiper / Down in Atlanta / September song / Senor blues / Parker's mood / Mr. PC / Embraceable you
81227177262 / Aug '94 / Atlantic

☐ **ATLANTIC JAZZ GALLERY - THE BEST OF THE 50'S**
Django / All about Ronnie / Martians go home / Evidence / Backwater blues / Cousin Mary / Train and the river / Wee baby blues / Come rain or come shine / You go to my head / Fathead / Pithecanthropus erectus
8122712822 / Feb '94 / Atlantic

☐ **ATLANTIC JAZZ GALLERY - THE BEST OF THE 60'S VOL.1**
Comin' home baby / Equinox / Una muy bonita / Volunteered slavery / In the evening / Stop this world / Groovin' / Summertime / Yesterday / With these hands / Listen here / Ecclusiastics / Sombrero Sam
8122715542 / Feb '94 / Atlantic

☐ **ATLANTIC JAZZ GALLERY - THE BEST OF THE 60'S VOL.2**
Creole love call / Silver cycles / Chained no more / Soul of the village part II / Hey Jude / One note samba / You can count on me to do my part / Dervish dance / Dream weaver / Stardust / Buddy and Lou / Dick's Holler / Eat that chicken / When I fall in love / Bagpipe blues
8122717272 / Aug '94 / Atlantic

☐ **ATLANTIC JAZZ GALLERY - THE BEST OF THE 70'S**
Samia / Come Sunday / Freaks for the festival / Ladies man / Missy / Dedicated to you / Moonchild / In your quiet place / Blues in A minor / Birdland (Vocal) / Yoruba / Egocentric molecules / Funky thide of sings
8122716102 / Feb '94 / Atlantic

☐ **ATLANTIC JAZZ VOCAL CLASSICS**
Tarvellin' light: *Hibbler, Al* / Moon ray: *Connor, Chris* / On a slow boat to China: *Paris, Jackie* / Don't let the sun catch you cryin': *Charles, Ray* / Easy livin': *Darin, Bobby* / Round midnight: *Carter, Betty* / Broadway: *Torme, Mel* / Every time we say goodbye: *Phillips, Esther* / Day by day: *McRae, Carmen* / Your molecular: *Allison, Mose* / With these hands: *McCann, Les* / Crazy he calls me: *Franklin, Aretha* / Exodus: *Scott, Jimmy* / Birdland: *Manhattan Transfer*
8122729662 / 1 Jun '98 / Atlantic

☐ **ATLANTIC R & B VOL.1 (1947-1952)**
Lowe groovin': *Morris, Joe* / That old black magic: *Grimes, Tiny* / Annie Laurie: *Grimes, Tiny* / Midnight special: *Grimes, Tiny* / Applejack: *Morris, Joe* / Drinkin' wine spo-dee-o-dee: *McGhee, Stick* / Coleslaw: *Culley, Frank* / So long: *Brown, Ruth* / I'll get along somehow: *Brown, Ruth* / Hey little girl: *Professor Longhair* / Mardi Gras in New Orleans: *Professor Longhair* / Tee nah nah: *Van Walls, Harry* / Anytime anyplace anywhere: *Morris, Joe* / Teardrops from my eyes: *Brown, Ruth* / One monkey don't stop no show: *McGhee, Stick* / Don't you know I love you: *Clovers* / Shouldn't I know: *Cardinals* / Chill is on: *Turner, 'Big' Joe* / Chains of love: *Turner, 'Big' Joe* / Fool, fool, fool: *Clovers* / One mint julep: *Clovers* / Wheel of fortune: *Cardinals* / Sweet sixteen: *Turner, 'Big' Joe* / 5-10-15 hours: *Brown, Ruth* / Ting a ling: *Clovers* / Gator's groove: *Jackson, Willis* / Daddy Daddy: *Brown, Ruth* / Midnight hour: *Charles, Ray*
7812932 / Feb '95 / Atlantic

☐ **ATLANTIC R & B VOL.2 (1952-1955)**
Beggar for your kisses: *Diamonds* / Mama he treats your daughter mean: *Brown, Ruth* / Good lovin': *Clovers* / Wild wild young men: *Brown, Ruth* / Mess around: *Charles, Ray* / Hush hush: *Turner, 'Big' Joe* / Soul on fire / Money honey: *McPhatter, Clyde & The Drifters* / Such a night: *McPhatter, Clyde & The Drifters* / Tipitina: *Professor Longhair* / White Christmas: *McPhatter, Clyde & The Drifters* / Honey love: *McPhatter, Clyde* / What'cha gonna do: *McPhatter, Clyde* / Shake, rattle and roll: *Turner, 'Big' Joe* / Sh-boom: *Chords* / Jam up: *Ridgley, Tommy* / Tomorrow night / Tweedlee dee / I got a woman: *Charles, Ray* / Door is still open: *Cardinals* / Flip flop and fly: *Turner, 'Big' Joe* / Fool for you: *Charles, Ray* / This little girl of mine: *Charles, Ray* / Play it fair / Adorable: *Drifters* / Smoky Joe's cafe: *Robins*
7812942 / Feb '95 / Atlantic

☐ **ATLANTIC R & B VOL.3 (1955-1958)**
Ruby baby: *Drifters* / In paradise: *Cookies* / Chicken and the hawk: *Turner, 'Big' Joe* / Devil or angel: *Clovers* / Drown in my own tears: *Charles, Ray* / Hallelujah, I love her so: *Charles, Ray* / Jim Dandy: *Baker, LaVern* / Down in Mexico: *Coasters* / Corine Corina: *Turner, 'Big' Joe* / Treasure of love: *McPhatter, Clyde* / Love love love: *Clovers* / It's too late: *Willis, Chuck* / Lonely avenue: *Charles, Ray* / Since I met you baby: *Hunter, Lloyd Serenaders* / Lucky lips: *Brown, Ruth* / Without love: *McPhatter, Clyde* / Fools fall in love: *Drifters* / Midnight special train: *Turner, 'Big' Joe* / Empty arms: *Hunter, Ivory Joe* / C.C. rider: *Willis, Chuck* / Betty and Dupree: *Bobbettes* / What am I living for: *Willis, Chuck* / Hang up my rock 'n' roll shoes: *Willis, Chuck* / Yakety yak: *Coasters* / Lover's question: *McPhatter, Clyde* / I cried a tear: *Charles, Ray* / Right time: *Charles, Ray* / What'd I say (parts 1 and 2): *Charles, Ray* / There goes my baby: *Drifters*
7812952 / Feb '95 / Atlantic

☐ **ATLANTIC R & B VOL.4 (1958-1962)**
Along came Jones: *Coasters* / Let the good times roll: *Charles, Ray* / Poison ivy: *Coasters* / Dance with me: *Drifters* / Just for a thrill: *Charles, Ray* / This magic moment: *Charles, Ray* / Save the last dance for me: *Charles, Ray* / Shopping for clothes: *Coasters* / Spanish Harlem: *King, Ben E.* / Young boy blues: *King, Ben E.* / Stand by me: *King, Ben E.* / Gee whiz: *Thomas, Carla* / Saved / Just out of reach: *Burke, Solomon* / Little Egypt: *Coasters* / Amor: *King, Ben E.* / Last night: *Mar-Keys* / I'm blue (the gong-gong song): *Ikettes* / You don't miss your water: *Bell, William* / I found a love: *Falcons* / Cry to me: *Burke, Solomon* / Don't play that song (You lied): *King, Ben E.* / Green onions: *Booker T & The MG's*
7812962 / Feb '95 / Atlantic

☐ **ATLANTIC R & B VOL.5 (1962-1966)**
Up on the roof: *Drifters* / CC rider / I who have nothing: *King, Ben E.* / If you need me: *Burke, Solomon* / These arms of mine: *Redding, Otis* / Hello stranger: *Lewis, Barbara* / On Broadway: *Drifters* / Just one look: *Troy, Doris* / Do the mashed potato: *Kindricks, Nat & The Swans* / Land of 1000 dances: *Kenner, Chris* / Walking the dog: *Kenner, Chris* / Release me: *Phillips, Esther* / Mercy mercy: *Covay, Don* / Under the boardwalk: *Drifters* / And I love him: *Phillips, Esther* / Hold what you've got: *Tex, Joe* / Mr. Pitiful: *Redding, Otis* / Baby, I'm yours: *Lewis, Barbara* / Teasin' you: *Tee, Willie* / I've been loving you too long: *Redding, Otis* / In the midnight hour: *Pickett, Wilson* / See saw: *Covay, Don* / Respect: *Redding, Otis* / You don't know like I know: *Sam & Dave* / When a man loves a woman: *Sledge, Percy* / Hold on I'm comin': *Sam & Dave* / Cool jerk: *Capitols* / Neighbour, neighbour: *Hughes, Jimmy*
7812972 / Feb '95 / Atlantic

☐ **ATLANTIC R & B VOL.6 (1966-1969)**
Land of 1000 dances: *Pickett, Wilson* / Knock on wood: *Floyd, Eddie* / Try a little tenderness: *Redding, Otis* / Mustang Sally: *Pickett, Wilson* / When something is wrong with my baby: *Sam & Dave* / Sweet soul music: *Conley, Arthur* / Soul man: *Sam & Dave* / I never loved a man (the way I love you): *Franklin, Aretha* / Do right woman, do right man: *Franklin, Aretha* / Show me: *Tex, Joe* / Tramp: *Redding, Otis & Carla Thomas* / Funky Broadway: *Pickett, Wilson* / Hip hug-her: *Booker T & The MG's* / Respect: *Franklin, Aretha* / (You make me feel like) a natural woman: *Franklin, Aretha* / Soul finger: *Bar-Kays* / Baby I love you: *Franklin, Aretha* / Skinny legs and all: *Tex, Joe* / Chain of fools: *Franklin, Aretha* / I'm in love: *Pickett, Wilson* / Memphis soul stew: *King Diamond* / (Sittin' on the) dock of the bay: *Redding, Otis* / Tighten up: *Redding, Otis* / Slip away: *Carter, Clarence* / Think: *Franklin, Aretha* / First time ever I saw your face: *Flack, Roberta* / Take a letter, Maria: *Greaves, R.B.* / Rainy night in Georgia: *Charles, Ray* / Ghetto: *Hathaway, Donny*
7812982 / Feb '95 / Atlantic

☐ **ATLANTIC R & B VOL.7 (1969-1974)**
Turn back the hands of time: *Davis, Walter* / Compared to what: *McCann, Les* / Don't play that song (You lied): *Franklin, Aretha* / Groove me: *Floyd, King* / Patches: *Carter, Clarence* / Funky Nassau (parts 1and2): *Beginning Of The End* / Thin line between love and hate: *Persuaders* / Rock steady: *Franklin, Aretha* / You've got a friend: *Flack, Roberta & Donny Hathaway* / Clean up woman: *Wright, Betty* / Could it be I'm falling in love: *Spinners* / Killing me softly: *Flack, Roberta* / Where is the love: *Flack, Roberta & Donny Hathaway* / I'll be around: *Spinners* / Feel like makin' love: *Flack, Roberta* / Mighty love: *Spinners* / Love won't let me wait: *Harris, Major*
7812992 / Feb '95 / Atlantic

☐ **ATLANTIC SOUL BALLADS**
Try a little tenderness: *Redding, Otis* / I say a little prayer: *Franklin, Aretha* / Save the last dance for me: *Drifters* / I'm in love: *Pickett, Wilson* / Warm and tender love: *Sledge, Percy* / Patches: *Carter, Clarence* / Thin line between love and hate: *Persuaders* / Spanish Harlem: *King, Ben E.* / When something is wrong with my baby: *Sam & Dave* / My girl: *Redding, Otis* / Love won't let me wait: *Harris, Major* / On Broadway: *Drifters* / Baby, I'm yours: *Lewis, Barbara* / Rainy night in Georgia: *Benton, Brook* / Hey Jude: *Pickett, Wilson*
2411362 / Jun '88 / Atlantic

☐ **ATLANTIC SOUL CLASSICS**
Sweet soul music: *Conley, Arthur* / In the midnight hour: *Pickett, Wilson* / Knock on wood: *Floyd, Eddie* / Soul man: *Sam & Dave* / Respect: *Franklin, Aretha* / See saw: *Covay, Don* / Everybody needs somebody to love: *Burke, Solomon* / Soul finger: *Bar-Kays* / Stand by me: *King, Ben E.* / B-A-B-Y: *Thomas, Carla* / Under the boardwalk: *Drifters* / Tramp: *Redding, Otis & Carla Thomas* / Green onions: *Booker T & The MG's* / When a man loves a woman: *Sledge, Percy* / Tribute to a king: *Bell, William* / (Sittin' on the) dock of the bay: *Redding, Otis*
2411382 / May '87 / Atlantic

☐ **ATLANTIC STORY, THE (2CD Set)**
Drinkin' wine spo-dee-o-dee: *McGhee, Stick* / 5-10-15 hours: *Brown, Ruth* / One mint julep: *Clovers* / Shake, rattle and roll: *Turner, 'Big' Joe* / Jim Dandy: *Baker, LaVern* / Lover's question: *McPhatter, Clyde* / What'd I say: *Charles, Ray* / Mack the knife: *Darin, Bobby* / Giant steps: *Coltrane, John* / Poison ivy: *Coasters* / Save the last dance for me: *Drifters* / Stand by me: *King, Ben E.* / Deep purple: *Tempo, Nino & April Stevens* / I got you babe: *Sonny & Cher* / Green onions: *Booker T & The MG's* / Hold on I'm comin': *Sam & Dave* / Knock on wood: *Floyd, Eddie* / When a man loves a woman: *Sledge, Percy* / Got to get you off my mind: *Burke, Solomon* / In the midnight hour: *Pickett, Wilson* / I say a little prayer: *Franklin, Aretha* / Sweet soul music: *Conley, Arthur* / (Sittin' on the) dock of the bay: *Redding, Otis* / Groovin': *Young Rascals* / You keep me hangin' on: *Vanilla Fudge* / In-A-Gadda-Da-Vida: *Iron Butterfly* / For what it's worth: *Buffalo Springfield* / Sweet Jane: *Velvet Underground* / Rock 'n' roll: *Led Zeppelin* / Can't get enough: *Bad Company* / Could it be I'm falling in love: *Detroit Spinners* / Such a night: *Dr. John* / Chanson d'amour: *Manhattan Transfer* / Soul man: *Blues Brothers* / Good times: *Chic* / We are family: *Sister Sledge* / Gloria: *Branigan, Laura* / I want to know what love is: *Foreigner* / Casanova: *Levert* / From a distance: *Levert* / Black velvet: *Myles, Alannah* / Walking in Memphis: *Cohn, Marc* / It's a shame about Ray: *Lemonheads* / Silent all these years: *Amos, Tori* / Hold on: *En Vogue*
9548324242 / Dec '92 / Atlantic

☐ **ATLAS EARTHED**
Nod to N20: *Rainer* / Don't judge the silence: *Edge Of Motion* / Luna swell: *Simmonds, Ian* / Scoobs in Columbia: *Plaid* / Work hard: *Charizmatix* / Infusion: *Yama & Kenny Future* / Chicken feed: *Bushflange* / Lovin' the version: *Pressure Drop* / Haze: *Rising Sons* / Dirty Kay: *Fusion*
CDTOT 50 / 24 Nov '97 / Jumpin' & Pumpin'

☐ **ATMOSPHERIC**
GAMBCD 0042 / 2 Mar '98 / Global Ambition

☐ **ATMOSPHERIC DRUM 'N' BASS VOL.2**
Rhode tune: *Flytronix* / Sweet mind: *Aphrodite* / Raucous grin: *Ratman* / Reaching out: *Natural Born Chillers* / Brand new heavy: *Plastic Soul* / State of grace: *Dead Calm* / Phuture subject: *Subject 13* / Abyss: *Slipstream* / We can make it happen: *Nookie* / Necessities: *Trip Wire* / Mediteranean falls: *DJ SS* / Men who fell to earth: *Marr, Leon* / Spice: *Aphrodite* / Chase: *Foulplay* / Flutes: *Alpha* / Bells of love: *DJ Special* / Something: *Sirens* / To ya: *Flytronix* / Flight: *Wallace, Dave* / Parallel life: *Starseeds* / Deep control: *Spectre* / Undefined divisions: *Nishki* / Horn section: *Rogue Unit* / True belivers: *Spectre* / Summer fresh: *Mastermind* / Biome: *Tundra* / Sly: *Shogun*
MILL 38CD / May '97 / Millenium

☐ **ATMOSPHERIC DRUM 'N' BASS VOL.3**
Shadow: *Rob & Goldie* / Soul beat runna: *Boymerang* / Twin town karaoke: *Omni Trio* / Fever: *E-Z Rollers* / Moments in space: *Nookie* / City lights: *Nishki* / Bridge: *Recoil* / Watercolours: *Parallax* / Hot rock tea: *Odd Toot* / Little black boxes: *Mission Control* / Nu breeze: *Smoke Screen* / One day: *Smoke Screen* / Savage times: *Justice* / Tension: *Justice* / Surrender: *Zohar* / Vibes: *Tertius* / Midnight voyager: *Universal Traveller* / Space walking: *Organic Synthetic* / Starseeds: *Starseeds* / Gary Strange: *One True Doc* / Noodles: *Big Bud* / Lose her now: *Gurley, S.* / Night accoustic: *Nishki* / Dream deferred: *Hydraflow*
MILL 052CD / 10 Nov '97 / Millenium

☐ **ATMOSPHERIC DRUM 'N' BASS VOL.4 (2CD Set)**
MILL 063CD / 20 Apr '98 / Millenium

☐ **ATMOSPHERIC SYNTHESIZER**
Theme from Antarctica / Eve of the war / Equinoxe part 5 / Tubular bells / Autobahn / Aurora / Magnetic fields part 2 / Las vegas theme from rainman / Tubbs and valerie / To the unknown man / Electrica salsa / Model / Rockit / Chariots of fire / Living on video / I'll find my way home
QED 113 / Nov '96 / Tring

☐ **ATMOSPHERIC SYNTHESIZER SPECTACULAR**
TFP 012 / Nov '92 / Tring

☐ **ATOMIC (The Sounds Of The Suburbs)**
Cool for cats: *Squeeze* / Geno: *Dexy's Midnight Runners* / Ever fallen in love: *Buzzcocks* / 2-4-6-8 motorway: *Robinson, Tom Band* / Into the valley: *Skids* / Turning Japanese: *Vapors* / Reward: *Teardrop Explodes* / Video killed the radio star: *Buggles* / My Sharona: *Knack* / Back of my hand: *Jags* / Is she really going out with him: *Jackson, Joe* / Atomic: *Blondie* / Eighth day: *O'Connor, Hazel* / Do anything you wanna do: *Eddie & The Hot Rods* / Down at the Doctors: *Dr. Feelgood* / Spanish stroll: *Mink Deville* / Young Parisians: *Adam & The Ants* / Peaches: *Stranglers* / Too much too young: *Specials* / Eton rifles: *Jam*
5529152 / Oct '97 / Spectrum

☐ **ATTACK OF THE NEW KILLER SURF GUITARS**
SH 5719 / Mar '97 / Shanachie

☐ **ATTITUDE**
RR 87832 / 20 Oct '97 / Roadrunner

☐ **AU COEUR DE LA MUSIQUE BRETONNE**
BUR 874CD / Dec '97 / Escalibur

☐ **AUDIO ALCHEMY VOL.1**
URCD 020 / Mar '97 / Ubiquity

☐ **AUDIO ALCHEMY VOL.2**
URO 26CD / 16 Sep '97 / Ubiquity

☐ **AUDIO COMPILATION VOL.1**
AUDIOCD 02 / 27 Apr '98 / Audio

☐ **AUDIOPHILE SAMPLER**
ASCD 1 / May '95 / Audiophile

☐ **AUDIUM CAPSULE VOL.1**
BLCCD 14 / Oct '96 / Blanc

☐ **AURA SURROUND SOUNDBITES VOL.2 (Access All Areas)**
SUSCD 3 / Sep '95 / Aura Surround Sounds

☐ **AURA SURROUND SOUNDBITES VOL.3 (3CD Set)**
Gotta get loose: *Must* / Scrumble: *DJ Misjah & Tim* / Dreamlab: *MLO* / Midsummer's dream: *Blokka* / Eternal: *Epik* / Axiom: *Arcana* / What is going on: *Dex* / Deltoid: *Hardline 2* / Dig deep: *Blokka* / Driver: *Epik* / Moonbase: *Sinus* / Samarkand: *MLO* / Bouncy castle: *Talisman* / Temple of acid: *Temple Of Acid* / Ice station zebra: *Temple Of Acid*
SUSCD 4 / Apr '96 / Aura Surround Sounds

☐ **AURAL GRATIFICATION VOL.1**
EFA 063522 / May '96 / Roundtrip

☐ **AURAL PLEASURE**
IAAPCD 1 / Oct '96 / Inter Aspect

☐ **AUSPICIOUS WEDDING**
NRCD 3003 / 20 Apr '98 / Navras

☐ **AUSTIN COUNTRY NIGHTS**
WMCD 1039 / Dec '95 / Watermelon

☐ **AUSTRALIA - A MUSICAL LANDSCAPE**
IMCD 3023 / Mar '96 / Image

☐ **AUSTRALIAN STARS OF THE INTERNATIONAL MUSIC HALL VOL.1 (Boiled Beef & Cabbage)**
LARRCD 325 / Nov '94 / Larrikin

☐ **AUSTRALIAN STARS OF THE INTERNATIONAL MUSIC HALL VOL.2 (Is 'E An Aussie, Is 'E Lizzie)**
LARRCD 324 / Nov '94 / Larrikin

☐ **AUSTRIA FOLKLORE**
399426 / Jul '91 / Koch

☐ **AUSTRIAN ZITHER CLASSICS**
995562 / Mar '96 / EPM

☐ **AUTENTICO IBIZA (4CD Set)**
Spirit of the sun: *Fontana, Lenny & Harvest* / Party people: *Baltimore Soul Train & Sande* / Blackboy whiteboy: *Dockins, Charles Heritage* / Do it: *DJ Rick Lenoir & The Disco Clique* / Move your body: *Reel 2 Real* / Plastic dreams: *Jaydee* / Dancin': *Mateo & Matos* / Mans love: *Crockpot Cookers* / White powder dreams: *Fire Island* / Anytime: *Nu Birth* / Harvest for the world: *Hunter, Terry* / Sunstroke: *Chicane* / Cafe del mar: *Energy 52* / Show me love: *Fruit Loop* / Age of love: *Age Of Love* / Schoneberg: *Marmion* / Blue fear: *Armin* / Dark and long: *Underworld* / Pacific melody: *Airscape* / Arc 3: *Spacer IV* / Offshore: *Chicane* / Living in ecstasy: *Rae, Fonda* / Manic jazz day: *DJ Anthony & Georgio* / Spin spin sugar: *Sneaker Pimps* / This is the only way: *Love Beads* / Testify: *Williams, Jay* / Live your life with me: *Joseph, Corrina* / Mama: *Restless Soul* / Past silence: *DJ Restyle* / Pull me up: *Ground 96* / Boogie: *Dive* / Automatic: *Continious Cool* / Remember me: *Blueboy* / Second coming: *Livin' Large* / You better: *Mount Rushmore & The Knack* / I'm ready for a good time: *Revelation* / Falling like dominoes: *Johan S. & Jazzheads* / Midnight: *Prelude & Co.* / Make you feel: *E-N* / I luv u baby: *Original* / Harmonics track '97: *Soul Boy* / Black people have rhythm: *Leaders* / Jumping and pumping: *Son* / Erotic fantasy: *Brutal Bill & Plan B* / RIP groove: *Double 99*
AUTIBCD 1 / Jul '97 / Beechwood

☐ **AUTHENTIC EXCELLO RHYTHM & BLUES**
I'm evil: *Lightnin' Slim* / You're gonna ruin me baby: *Lazy Lester* / Got love if you want it: *Harpo, Slim* / Going through the park: *Anderson, Jimmy* / I'm warning you baby: *Lightnin' Slim* / Lonesome lonely blues: *Lonesome Sundown* / Wild cherry: *Washington, Leroy* / You're too late baby: *Hogan, Silas* / I'm a lover not a fighter: *Lazy Lester* / I love the life I'm livin': *Harpo, Slim* / Naggin': *Anderson, Jimmy* / I'm gonna quit you pretty baby: *Hogan, Silas* / I'm glad she's mine: *Lonesome Sundown* / I'm a king bee: *Harpo, Slim* / Mean woman blues: *Smith, Whispering* / Loving around the clock: *Lightnin' Slim* / Tell me pretty baby: *Lazy Lester* / Hoodoo party: *Thomas, Tabby* / Lonesome la la: *Hogan, Silas* / Wake up old maid: *Smith, Whispering* / I'm tired waitin' baby: *Lightnin' Slim* / Gonna stick to you baby: *Lonesome Sundown* / No naggin' no draggin': *Gunter, Arthur* / I'm doin' alright: *Shy Guy Douglas*
CDCHD 492 / Oct '93 / Ace

☐ **AUTHENTIC JAMAICA SKA**
AJSCD 001 / Jul '93 / K&K

☐ **AUTHENTIC MUSIC OF THE AMERICAN INDIAN, THE**
SPALAX 14889 / Oct '96 / Spalax

☐ **AUTHENTIC NATIVE AMERICAN MUSIC**
12551 / Nov '95 / Laserlight

☐ **AUTOMATIC BOP VOL.1 (31 Rockabilly Burners)**
CLCD 4433 / Nov '96 / Collector/White Label

☐ **AUTOMATIC BOP VOL.2 (For Cats On The Go)**
CLCD 4441 / Nov '97 / Collector/White Label

☐ **AUTUMN RECORDS STORY, THE**
C'mon and swim: *Freeman, Bobby* / S-W-I-M: *Freeman, Bobby* / Scat swim: *Stewart, Sly* / Buttermilk: *Stewart, Sly* / Somebody to love: *Great Society* / Free advice: *Great Society* / She's my baby: *Mojo Men* / Jerk: *Beau Brummels & B. Freeman Band* / Sad little girl: *Beau Brummels* / No 1: *Charlatans* / Anything: *Vejtables* / Pay attention to me: *Tikis*
EDCD 145 / May '86 / Edsel

☐ **AVANT GARDISM (2CD Set)**
LAANGE 1CD / Jan '97 / Law & Auder/ Blue Angel

☐ **AVANT KNITTING TOUR**
KFWCD 142 / Nov '94 / Knitting Factory

☐ **AVANTGARDISM VOL.2 (2CD Set)**
LA 3CD / 27 Oct '97 / Law & Auder/Blue Angel

☐ **AVANTI VOL.2**
FILERCD 432 / Jul '92 / Profile

☐ **AVID JAZZ & VOCAL SAMPLER**
AMSC 568 / May '96 / Avid

☐ **'AVIN IT IN TENERIFE (2CD Set)**
Music sounds better: *Stardust* / Horny: *Mousse T* / Space Mac: *Space Mac* / Burnin': *Baby Bumps* / Ultimate: *Funky Choad* / We need energy: *Astro Teem* / I can't help myself: *Lucid* / Everybody dance: *Tucker, Barbara* / About you: *Clubbers Delight* / Can you feel it: *QED* / Touch me: *Full Frequency* / Independence: *Jonesey* / Futuro: *Wag & YONC* / Let me hear the DJ: *Miss Peppermint* / Sugar: *Mr. Pink* / Work it: *Junk Food Junkies* / Only me: *Hyperlogic* / Nervous breakdown: *Shrink* / OO theme: *Shrink* / Get with it: *Quench* / No me gustah: *Partision* / Disco tec: *Disco Tec* / Monkey way: *Tyrone* / Rockafella skank: *Fatboy Slim* / Jupiter: *Karma* / Just like

tomorrow: Invisible Man / Give a little love: Invisible Man / Deeper: Serious Danger / Follow me: Mental Madness Productions / Spank: D Menace / Dance with it: Boy Foy & Airtight / Shattered: Billy Wizz / Baby baby: Bump & Hustle
MMCCD 009 / 7 Sep '98 / Massive

☐ **AZERBAIJAN - INSTRUMENTAL AND VOCAL MUSIC**
SM 1518 / May '96 / Wergo

☐ **B IS FOR BROCCOLI**
KUDCD 007 / Jan '96 / Kudos

☐ **BABBLING BROOK**
DC 879572 / Oct '97 / Disky

☐ **BABEL**
E 10001CD / 27 Apr '98 / Electrolux

☐ **BABY BOOMERS (4CD Set)**
MBSCD 418 / Nov '93 / Castle

☐ **BABY DOLL**
OK doll it's a deal: King, Jack / Lou Lou knows: Wallace, Fonda / Rock baby rock: Tonnant, Barbara / Give a little take a little: Meyers, Orella / I'll never love again: Nickel, Betty / I've been thinking it over: Three Notes / Teach me how to dance: Miller, Pinky / Sugar doll: Mao, Doltje / Ask Lucille: Meyers, Orella / Go get the shotgun Grandpa: Castles, Ann / Rockin' lady: Candy, Penny / I'm in love with Elvis: Lowe, Virginia / Gonna be loved: Linda & The Eplos / Love me love me honey do: Cline, Patsy / Money honey: Morgan, J. / Breakin' your heart for fun: Forrest, Jackie / Peace in mind: Love, Joyce / I'm your slave: Allen, Jeannie / Rock doc: Casey, Patti / Big bounce: Caddell, Shirley / That's it: Bain, Babette / Rollercoaster: Grant, Janie / Pink shoe laces: Stevens, D. / Just wait: Frederick, Dotty / Paper boy: Lou, Norman / Where's the law: Gaudet, Dee Dee / Who baby how: Turzy, Jane / Starlight starbright: Johnson, Jackie / Rovin' gal: McCrory, Susan / Chilli dippin' baby: Reynolt, Joyce
BB 55053 / Aug '97 / Buffalo Bop

☐ **BABYLON A FALL DOWN**
CDTRL 290 / Apr '91 / Trojan

☐ **BABY'S GOT THE BLUES (2CD Set)**
AOP 55 / 25 May '98 / Age Of Panik

☐ **BACHELOR IN PARADISE**
Apartment: Ferrante & Teicher / Noche de Rhonda: Puente, Tito / Little Rachmaninoff and a single rose: Benet, Andre / El bimbo: Faith, Percy & His Orchestra / Fields of wonder: Greenslade, Arthur / Capriccorn - 3.30 am: Jacobs, Dick & His Orchestra / Bo mambo: Sumac, Yma / Spellbound concerto: Heindorf, Ray / Snowfall: Esquivel, Juan Garcia / Libra - Mediterranean: Jacobs, Dick & His Orchestra / Oh: King, Pee Wee / Dancing in the dark: Pinza, Enzio / Beautiful swallow: Cugat, Xavier / Lisbon Antigua: Riddle, Nelson / L'Aube se dur jour: Cinema Sound Stage Orchestra / Like blue: Previn, Andre
12801 / Aug '97 / Laserlight

☐ **BACHELOR'S LITTLE BLACK BOOK, THE**
Patricia: Pedro, Perez / Ruby: Haymann, Richard Orchestra / Jean: Kaempfert, Bert Orchestra / Celito linda: Faith, Percy Orchestra / His Kelly and me: Greenslade, Arthur & His Orchestra / Charmaine: Mantovani & His Orchestra / Melina: Stanyon Strings / Sweet Leilani: Crosby, Bing / Vanessa: Winterhalter, Hugo Orchestra / Main title from Joanna: Greenslade, Arthur / Anna: Mangano, Silvana / Gemini, summer song: Jacobs, Dick & His Orchestra / Hummingbird: Paul, Les & Mary Ford / Nola: Paul, Les / Virgo, blue lady: Jacobs, Dick & His Orchestra / Adios Marquita linda: Esquivel, Juan Garcia
12803 / May '97 / Laserlight

☐ **BACK FROM THE GRAVE VOL.1**
EFACD 11566 / 16 Mar '98 / Crypt

☐ **BACK FROM THE GRAVE VOL.2**
EFACD 11521 / 16 Mar '98 / Crypt

☐ **BACK FROM THE GRAVE VOL.3**
EFACD 11520 / 16 Mar '98 / Crypt

☐ **BACK FROM THE GRAVE VOL.4 (Mid-60's Garage Punk Screamers)**
EFA 115252 / Sep '95 / Crypt

☐ **BACK FROM THE GRAVE VOL.8**
EFACD 11592 / 16 Mar '98 / Crypt

☐ **BACK IN THE SADDLE AGAIN**
Old Chisholm trail: McClintock, Harry 'Haywire Mac' / Pot wrassler: Jackson, Harry / Gol-durned wheel: Holyoak, Van / When the work's all done this fall: Sprague, Carl T. / Streets of Laredo: Prude, John G. / Sioux Indians: Williams, Marc / Dying cowboy: Allen, Jules Verne / Tyin' knots in the devil's tail: Jack, Powder River & Kitty Lee / Strawberry Road: Arizona Wranglers / Lone star trail: Maynard, Ken / Ridge runnin' road: Rice, Glenn & His Beverly Hill Billies / Whoopie ti yi yo: White, John / Cowhand's last ride: Little old log shack I always call my home: Carter, Wilf / A-ridin' old paint: Ritter, Tex / I want to be a cowboy's sweetheart: Montana, Patsy / Cattle call: Owens, Tex / One more ride: Sons Of The Pioneers / Dim narrow trail: Ruby, Texas / I want to be a real cowboy girl: Girls Of The Golden West / Back in the saddle again: Autry, Gene / My dear old Arizona home: Allen, Hav / Cowboy stomp / O-Sar-2 horse wrangler: Critchlow, Slim / City boarders: Agins, Sam / Cowboys: Ohrlin, Glenn / Rusty spurs: Doux, Chris Le / Cowboy song: Riders In The Sky
NW 314/315 / Aug '92 / New World

☐ **BACK ON 52ND STREET**
DIW 406 / Mar '97 / DIW

☐ **BACK PORCH BLUES**
CDBM 099 / Apr '96 / Blue Moon

☐ **BACK PORCH BLUES**
Sugar Mama: Nelson, Bob / Arthritis: Miles, Floyd / Standing in the fire: Wharton, Bill / Credit card blues: Smokehouse / Dead cat luck: Culberson, Eric / Head in the bottle: Moreland, Ace / Whole lotta ash: Turner, Troy / Flyright: Hodgson, Mark / Short hair woman: Nelson, Bob / Way off in that jazz: Howell, Jeff / Cocky rooster: Miles, Floyd / Screamin' woman: Wharton, Bill / Them jelly blues: Smokehouse / Big foot woman: Hodgson, Mark / Gates of Hell: Moreland, Ace
KS 041CD / May '98 / King Snake

☐ **BACK TO LOVE**
RENCD 115 / Mar '96 / Renaissance Collector Series

☐ **BACK TO MONO**
WALLCD 002 / Sep '95 / Wall Of Sound

☐ **BACK TO THE 50'S**
Love letters in the sand: Boone, Pat / Old cape cod: Page, Patti / Hernando's hideaway: Ray, Johnnie / Standing on the corner: Four Lads / Most of all: Cornell, Don / To each his own: Ink Spots / Little shoemaker: Gaylords / Honeycomb: Rodgers, Jimmie / My prayer: Platters / Singin' the blues: Mitchell, Guy / Green door: Lowe, Jim / 26 miles: (Santa Catalina): Four Preps / Rose, Rose I love you: Laine, Frankie / Wayward wind: Grant, Gogi / Caribbean: York, Mitchell / Dark moon: Guitar, Bonnie / Marianne: Hilltoppers / This ole house: Clooney, Rosemary
ECD 3118 / Jan '95 / K-Tel

☐ **BACK TO THE 50'S - A BETTY PAGE TRIBUTE**
CLP 9964 / Jun '97 / Cleopatra

☐ **BACK TO THE 60'S VOL.1**
Love grows (Where my rosemary goes): Edison Lighthouse / With a girl like you: Troggs / Lightning strikes: Christie, Lou / Build me up buttercup: Foundations / How do you do it: Gerry & The Pacemakers / Love on a mountain top: Knight, Robert / Little arrows: Lee, Leapy / Yellow river: Christie / She's not there: Zombies / Dizzy: Roe, Tommy / Happy together: Turtles / It's my party: Gore, Lesley / Da doo ron ron: Crystals / Gimme little sign: Wood, Brenton / Letter: Box Tops / You've got your troubles (I've got mine): Fortunes / Groovy kind of love: Fontana, Wayne / Young girl: Puckett, Gary & The Union Gap
ECD 3046 / Jan '95 / K-Tel

☐ **BACK TO THE 60'S VOL.2**
Ob-la-di ob-la-da: Marmalade / I'm gonna make you mine: Christie, Lou / Here it comes again: Fortunes / The go-go: Detroit Sound / Your personality: Lee, Jackie / What good am I: Champion, Mickey / Just like you did me: Vernee, Yvonne / Baby don't you weep: Hamilton, Edward / King for a day: Ames, Stuart / Look at what I almost missed: Lewis, Pat / Baby I'm here just to love you: Stagemasters / This thing called love: Wyatt, Johnny / Save my lovin' for you: People's Choice / That's why I love you: Professionals / Never, never: Nettle / You'll never make the grade: Sunlovers / Running wild: Exsayvions / Quit twistin' my arm: Mitchell, Stanley / Bad adios: As long as you love me: Ronnie & The Airedales
ECD 3051 / Jan '95 / K-Tel

☐ **BACK TO THE 60'S VOL.3**
Here comes my baby: Tremeloes / Concrete and clay: Unit 4+2 / Those were the days: Hopkin, Mary / Little things: Berry, Dave / Tomorrow: Concrete and clay: Unit 4+2 / Those were the days: Hopkin, Mary / Little things: Berry, Dave / Tomorrow: Good morning sunshine: Oliver / Games people play: South, Joe / Bread and butter: Newbeats / Wooly bully: Sam The Sham & The Pharaohs / You'll never walk alone: Gerry & The Pacemakers / Hippy hippy shake: Swinging Blue Jeans / Hello little girl: Fourmost / Hitchin' a ride: Vanity Fare / Google eyes: Nashville Teens / You were on my mind: St. Peters, Crispian / Woman, woman: Puckett, Gary & The Union Gap / You were made for me: Freddie & The Dreamers / Game of love: Fontana, Wayne
ECD 3123 / Jan '95 / K-Tel

☐ **BACK TO THE 70'S**
Midnight at the oasis: Muldaur, Maria / Love won't let me wait: Harris, Major / Love I lost: Melvin, Harold & The Bluenotes / Peaches: Carter, Clarence / Hey girl don't bother me: Tams / You little trustmaker: Tymes / Something old something new: Fantastics / More more more: True, Andrea / Do it any way you wanna: People's Choice / My baby loves lovin': White Plains / Beg steal or borrow: New Seekers / Do you wanna dance: Blue, Barry / Let's get together: Rubettes / Band / I can do it: Rubettes / In Zaire: Wakelin, Johnny / Baby jump: Mungo Jerry / Fox on the run: Connolly, Brian / Pepper box: Peppers
ECD 3122 / Jan '95 / K-Tel

☐ **BACK TO THE 70'S (40 Chart Busting Seventies Hits - 2CD Set)**
Killer queen: Queen / Make me smile (come up and see me): Harley, Steve & Cockney Rebel / Maggie May: Stewart, Rod / Band on the run: McCartney, Paul & Wings / Lola: Kinks / American pie: McLean, Don / You're so vain: Simon, Carly / Never let him go: Gold, Andrew / Goodbye to love: Carpenters / Without you: Nilsson, Harry / Baker Street: Rafferty, Gerry / Rocket man: John, Elton / I don't like Mondays: Boomtown Rats / Hit me with your rhythm stick: Dury, Ian & The Blockheads / Oliver's army: Costello, Elvis & The Attractions / You ain't seen nothin' yet: Bachman-Turner Overdrive / All right now: Free / Everything I own: Bread / In the summertime: Mungo Jerry / Ride a white swan: T-Rex / Coz I luv you: Slade / I'm the leader of the gang (I am): Slade / Ballroom blitz: Sweet / Tiger feet: Mud / Heart of glass: Blondie
CDEMTV 77 / Sep '93 / EMI

☐ **BACK TO THE 70'S (4CD Set)**
MBSCD 432 / Jan '95 / Castle

☐ **BACK TO THE BLUES**
157152 / Feb '93 / Blues Collection

☐ **BACK TO THE BLUES (2CD Set)**
Easy rider: Leadbelly / Black train blues: White, Bukka / Dust my broom: Johnson, Robert / Mean mistreater Mama: Carr, Leroy / Four hands are better than two: Johnson, Lonnie / Georgia rag: McTell, 'Blind' Willie / My brownskin sugar plum: Fuller, 'Blind' Blind Boy / Walkin' blues: Johnson, Robert / Sun risin' blues: Turner, 'Big' Joe / Warehouseman blues: Dupree, 'Champion' Jack / Got the bottle up and go: Williamson, Sonny Boy / Born for bad luck: McGhee, Brownie / Rebecca: Turner, 'Big' Joe / I'm calling: Daisy: McGhee, Brownie / Sugar Mama blues: Williamson, Sonny Boy / Stomp down rider: McTell, 'Blind' Willie / Mean old bed bug blues: Johnson, Lonnie / Strange place blues: White, Bukka / Mean ol' frisco: Crudup, Arthur 'Big Boy' / Rock Island line: Leadbelly / Rocks in my bed: Turner, 'Big' Joe / Midnight hour blues: Carr, Leroy / You can't get that stuff no more: Tampa Red / Bull cow blues: Broonzy, 'Big' Bill / Gamblin' man blues: Dupree, 'Champion' Jack / Phonograph blues: Johnson, Robert / Broke down engine: McTell, 'Blind' Willie / Bluebirds blues: Williamson, Sonny Boy / Baby you gotta change your mind: Fuller, 'Blind' Boy / Good morning blues: Leadbelly / Preaching blues: Johnson, Robert / Gonna follow my baby: Crudup, Arthur 'Big Boy' / Mr. Johnson's swing: Johnson, Lonnie / Picking my tomatoes: McGhee, Brownie / 15 cents a day: Sykes, Roosevelt / I'm a rattlesnakin' Daddy: Fuller, Blind Boy / Worrying you off my mind: Broonzy, 'Big' Bill / Good woman blues: Carr, Leroy / You know I got a reason: Broonzy, 'Big' Bill / When you got a friend: Johnson, Robert
MUCD 9508 / May '96 / Musketeer

☐ **BACK TO THE STREETS**
SHACD 9006 / Nov '93 / Shanachie

☐ **BACKBEAT ALLSTARS COMPILATION VOL.1**
Funky loisaida: B Side / Talk to your man: Common Cause / Ven a gozar: Intergalactic Love Communication / Funk what: Exodus Quartet / Slippin' and sliddin': Exodus Quartet / Crusader: Fishbelly Black / Time is on our side: Shadow Boxers / Catwoman: Shadow Boxers / Mellow mode: DJ Hakim
BBCD 721232 / 16 Sep '97 / Backbeat

☐ **BACKDROP (The Very Essence Of Northern Soul 1974)**
Where there's a will: Thomas, Jimmy / I got love: Wills, Viola / Same old thing: Olympics / Jumping at the go-go: Detroit Sound / Your personality: Lee, Jackie / What good am I: Champion, Mickey / Just like you did me: Vernee, Yvonne / Baby don't you weep: Hamilton, Edward / King for a day: Ames, Stuart / Look at what I almost missed: Lewis, Pat / Baby I'm here just to love you: Stagemasters / This thing called love: Wyatt, Johnny / Save my lovin' for you: People's Choice / That's why I love you: Professionals / Never, never: Nettle / You'll never make the grade: Sunlovers / Running wild: Exsayvions / Quit twistin' my arm: Mitchell, Stanley / Carroll, Vivian / Just because of you: Rocky Roberts & The Airedales / As long as you love me: Ronnie & Robyn
GSCD 073 / Feb '97 / Goldmine

☐ **BACKSTREETS OF AMERICAN OI**
STEPCD 115 / 8 Jun '98 / Step 1

☐ **BACKTRACKIN' TO THE 70'S (4CD Set)**
MBSCD 437 / Nov '95 / Castle

☐ **BACKWATER VOL.2**
NBX 004 / Jun '94 / Noisebox

☐ **BAD, BAD WHISKEY (The Galaxy Masters)**
She's looking good: Collins, Rodger / Rufus Jr: Merced Blue Notes / I got to tell somebody: Everett, Betty / Chicken heads: Rush, Bobby / Get your lie straight: Cody, Bill / Why do you have to lie: Right Kind / You better stop: Rhodes, Sonny / Nightingale melody: Taylor, Little Johnny / I pity the fool: Saunders, Merl / It's a shame: Malone, J.J. / Rainbow 71: Holloway, Loleatta / Foxy girls in Oakland: Collins, Rodger / When you find a fool bump his head: Cody, Bill / Mama Rufus: Merced Blue Notes / For your precious love: Taylor, Little Johnny / Abraham, Martin and John: Brown, Charles / Bad bad whiskey: Merced Blue Notes / Have I done something to make you mad: forget you: Williams, Lenny / Ain't nothing gonna change me: Everett, Betty / Woman rules the world: Cody, Bill / Why did our love go: Huey, Claude
CDCHD 516 / Jan '94 / Ace

☐ **BAD BOY**
Screamin' Mimi Jeanie: Hawks, Mickey / Bip bop boom: Hawks, Mickey / Rock 'n roll rhythm: Hawks, Mickey / Hich hich hidi: Hawks, Mickey / I'm lost: Hawks, Mickey / Cotton pickin': Night Raiders / Bad boy: France, Steve & The Airgems / Don't hang around me anymore: Ford, Jimmy / You're gonna be sorry: Ford, Jimmy / Bad bad boy: McCulloch, Gordeanna / Lord Bateman: Knevett, Arthur / Bonnie banks of Fordie: Jones, Nic / Tam Lin: Carthy, Martin / Dame Durden: Waggy John / Croodin Doo: Anderson, Alisdair / Keys of Canterbury: Boden, Jon / Bonnie Bunch of Roses: McColl, Ewan / Famous flower of serving men: Wyndham-Read, Martyn / Robin Hood rescuing the three Squires: Kirkpatrick, John / Death of Queen Jane: Tabor, June / Sir shines tair: Adams, Linda / Bonnie house of Airlie: Eaglesham, Bobby
FECD 110 / Feb '97 / Fellside

☐ **BAD TASTE - THE ULTIMATE PUNK PARTY**
BTR 013CD / Nov '96 / Bad Taste

☐ **BADABOOM GRAMAPHONE VOL.3**
BBG 3CD / 3 Aug '98 / Ba Da Bing

☐ **BADAKHSHAN: MUSIC FROM THE TAJIK PAMIR MOUNTAINS**
PAN 2024CD / Mar '94 / Pan

☐ **BAG O' BLUES**
KS 201 / May '98 / King Snake

☐ **BAG OF GOODIES**
LHCD 001 / Jul '96 / Luv n' Haight

☐ **BAGAD DU MOULIN VERT - QUIMPER**
GRI 190842 / Sep '96 / Griffe

☐ **BAGPIPE, THE**
LYRCD 7327 / Dec '94 / Lyrichord

☐ **BAGPIPES AND DRUMS OF SCOTLAND, THE**
Inverness gathering / Australian ladies / Braig Lock Lall / Stool of repentance / Wandering away / Inglenuek / Ye jacobites by name / Boys of blue hill / Sporting Jamie / Gallant fireman / Devil in the kitchen / Highland train / Kilt is my delight / Kate dalymple / Bluebells of Scotland / Scotland the brave / Green hills of Tyrol / Sheepwife / Brogan Lochan / Braes of Badenoch / Skye boat song / My home / Glasgow police marchpast / Black bear / Greenwoodside / Pigeon on the gate / Cockney jocks / Bonnie lass O'Fyvie / Drum fanfare / Salute / To max rayne / Dundeach / Going to Plltlochry / Murdo's wedding / City of Hastings / Muir of Ord / Faded cabbage / Bannana fingers / Jim Tweedies sea leg
12713 / Feb '96 / Laserlight

☐ **BAGPIPES AND HURDY GURDY**
B 6830 / May '96 / Auvidis/Ethnic

☐ **BAGPIPES OF BRITAIN AND IRELAND**
CDSDL 416 / Mar '96 / Saydisc

☐ **BAHAMAS - ISLANDS OF SONG, THE**
SFWCD 40405 / Aug '97 / Smithsonian Folkways

☐ **BAILA MI AMOR**
DCD 5392 / Jul '94 / Disky

☐ **BALAFONS OF BOBO DIOULASSO, THE**
PS 65172 / Nov '96 / PlayaSound

☐ **BALI - COURT MUSIC AND BANJAR MUSIC**
BCD 8059 / Jan '95 / Auvidis/Ethnic

☐ **BALI - GAMELAN & KECAK**
7559792042 / Jan '95 / Nonesuch

☐ **BALI - MUSIC FROM THE MORNING OF THE WORLD**
7559791962 / Jan '95 / Nonesuch

☐ **BALI - SUITE OF MUSIC AND SOUNDS**
58397 / Mar '96 / World Network

☐ **BALI - THE CLASH OF THE GONGS**
122119 / Jul '95 / Long Distance

☐ **BALI - THE GREAT GONG KEBYAR**
C 560057 / Aug '94 / Ocora

☐ **BALI MUSIC ANTHOLOGY VOL.2 (2CD Set)**
926012 / Feb '95 / BUDA

☐ **BALL TONIGHT, A**
That's what I call a ball: Donn, Larry / Honey bun: Donn, Larry / Girl next door: Donn, Larry / Wild wild party: Vincent, Darryl / Ball tonight: Campbell, Ray / Rockin' spot: Coldtron, Curley / I've got love: Deckleman, Sonny / Party nine women: Irby, Jerry / There'll be a rockin' party tonight: Volk, Val / I fell for your line baby: Faire, Johnny / Bertha Lou: Faire, Johnny / Big ole: Curtin, Lee / Is the shoe pinchin': Queen's Royal Lancers / Long pony tail: Tom & Tornados / Saturday night party: Perkins, Reggie / Pretty Kitty: Perkins, Reggie / Party time: Noris, Bob / Stop at the hop: Dean, D / My queen and me: Lenny & The Star Chiefs / Rockin' bonie: Dietzel, Elroy / Teenage bait: Dietzel, Elroy / Pretty baby rock: Mayo, Danny / Chicken walk: Adkins, Hasil / She's mine: Adkins, Hasil / Betcha I getcha: Faire, Johnny / Bo peep rock: Vinyard, Eddie / Wildwood fun: Lefty & Leadsmen / There's gonna be a party: Gray, Bobby
CDBB 55007 / Apr '94 / Buffalo Bop

☐ **BALLADS**
ENJ 93052 / Jul '96 / Enja

☐ **BALLADS**
Seven gypsies: Tyrrall, Gordon / Mill O'Tifty's Annie: McCulloch, Gordeanna / Lord Bateman: Knevett, Arthur / Bonnie banks of Fordie: Jones, Nic / Tam Lin: Carthy, Martin / Dame Durden: Waggy John / Croodin Doo: Anderson, Alisdair / Keys of Canterbury: Boden, Jon / Bonnie Bunch of Roses: McColl, Ewan / Famous flower of serving men: Wyndham-Read, Martyn / Robin Hood rescuing the three Squires: Kirkpatrick, John / Death of Queen Jane: Tabor, June / Sir shines tair: Adams, Linda / Bonnie house of Airlie: Eaglesham, Bobby
FECD 110 / Feb '97 / Fellside

☐ **BALLADS FOR TENOR**
Lover man / Lotus blossom / I can't get started / Stormy weather / Body and soul / You leave me breathless / Yesterdays / Sur les quais du vieux Paris
8747092 / Oct '96 / DA Music

☐ **BALLADS FROM THE HEART (2CD Set)**
Show me heaven: *McKee, Maria* / Dedicated: *Carrack, Paul* / Every rose has its thorn: *Poison* / Room in your heart: *Living In A Box* / Mary's prayer: *Danny Wilson* / Tonight I celebrate my love: *Bryson, Peabo & Roberta Flack* / How can I fall: *Breathe* / Classic: *Gurvitz, Adrian* / I found someone: *Cher* / Could've been: *Tiffany* / Kayleigh: *Marillion* / Should've known better: *Marx, Richard* / You're in love: *Wilson Phillips* / You could have been with me: *Easton, Sheena* / Where does the time go: *Fordham, Julia* / These dreams: *Heart* / Carry the blame: *River City People* / Road to our dream: *T'Pau* / Dum dum girl: *Talk Talk* / Only when you leave: *Spandau Ballet* / Jessie: *Kadison, Joshua* / Follow my rainbow: *Easton, Sheena* / Would I lie to you: *Charles & Eddie* / Better part of me: *Graham, Jaki* / More than I can say: *Sayer, Leo* / Missing you: *Waite, John* / New kid in town: *Frey, Glenn* / China in your hand: *T'Pau* / Rush rush: *Abdul, Paula* / Don't want to wait anymore: *Tubes*
DOU 882432 / 29 Aug '97 / Disky

☐ **BALLANISLOE FAIR**
TRAC 4284CD / Mar '98 / Trad Crossroads

☐ **BALLERMAN GOES APRES SKI**
ZYX 550882 / Nov '97 / ZYX

☐ **BALLERMANN 6**
ZYX 550792 / Jul '97 / ZYX

☐ **BALLERMANN 6 BALNEARIO**
ZYX 550724 / Dec '96 / ZYX

☐ **BALLISTIC**
Withered: *Earthtone 9* / Silver spoon: *Seizure* / Tribe: *Fourwaykill* / Human killing kind: *Fourwaykill* / You may call me: *Sidewinder* / Ingredients: *Tipa Gore* / Some things: *Deadbolt* / Remanufacture the fracture: *Stress* / Screem: *Graven Image* / Queer fuck: *Split Seed* / Rage in pain: *Fracture* / Mental incarnation: *Parricide* / Dreaming in limbo: *Mortavik* / Drain the skies: *As She Screams* / Rise from the lake of the dreamer: *Doomflight*
COP 02 / 11 May '98 / Copro

☐ **BALLOS SARDOS**
TA 015CD / Dec '97 / Robi Droli

☐ **BALLROOM DANCING**
Dr. Quick / Hallo Susi / Swingtime medley / Lambada / I concentrate on you / El toro ballade / I've seen that face / Cheim chiem cheree / Saving all my love for you / Wie ein wunder / Chattanooga cha cha / Tango noir / Severin / Only you
22519 / Feb '96 / Music

☐ **BALLROOM NIGHTS**
Most beautiful girl in the world / Save the best for last / Whole new world / Endless love / Constant craving / Loco in Acapulco / September / Smooth operator / Best years of our lives / Johnny's mambo / That's the way / Amor amor amor / If you leave me now / Hero / Dancing queen / Moonlighting / Look of love / Girl from Ipanema / Wave / You are the sunshine of my life / Here we are / Walk on by / Meditation / Corcovado / All night long / Don't worry about a thing / Half a minute / Get on your feet / Fragile / Copacabana / Brazil / One note samba
CDVDB 2 / 4 Aug '97 / Virgin

☐ **BALOUTCHISTAN: THE INSTRUMENTAL TRADITION**
C 560105 / Mar '97 / Ocora

☐ **BALTIMORE'S TEENBEAT A GO GO**
GHAS 5009 / Nov '97 / Dome

☐ **BAM BAM**
VPCD 1237 / Jul '92 / VP

☐ **BAMBOO FENCE**
BS1CD 50 / 10 Aug '98 / Jackpot

☐ **BANANAS (14 Fruity Hardcore Anthems)**
Another day: *Sub State* / Gonna be alright: *DJ Vibes & Wishdokta* / Yee haa: *Forbes, Davie* / Watch me dance: *El Bruto* / I got something: *Kidz* / Everybody here tonight: *Speed, Jack* / Your love (get down): *Force & Styles* / I want your love: *Infernus* / Close your eyes: *Jimmy J & Cru-L-T* / Take me up: *Sub State* / Bassline kickin': *MC Lust* / Motorway madness: *DJ Vibes & Wishdokta* / Touch of klass: *DJ Happy Raver & The Smile-E* / Mind warp: *El Bruto*
DBM 2141 / Apr '97 / Death Becomes Me

☐ **BANDLEADER DIGITAL SPECTACULAR (Various Military & Brass Bands)**
Berne patrol / Thunderbird / Royal salute / Regimental slow march / Motorcycle display / Chocolate dancing / Shepherd's song / Music box dancer / Canter / St. Louis blues march / Caesar's romp / Concerto for clarinet in A / Mount Longden / Drumbeatings / Rule Britannia / Jerusalem / Last post / Auld lang syne / Colonel Bogey / Artillery salvo and opening fanfare / Fanfare / God save the Queen / Bugle flute and drum calls / Precision in percussion / Tornado
BNA 5000 / Feb '85 / Bandleader

☐ **BANDONEON PURE - DANCES OF URUGUAY**
SF 40431CD / Jan '94 / Smithsonian Folkways

☐ **BANDSTAND FAVOURITES (36 Timeless Performances/2CD Set)**
Strike up the band: *Life Guards Band* / Knightsbridge march: *Blues & Royals Band* / Westminster waltz: *Blues & Royals Band* / Calling all workers: *Royal Yeomanry* / Rhapsody in blue: *Central Band Of Royal British Legion* / Army of the Nile: *Gloucestershire Regiment* / It's a long way to Tipperary: *Royal Irish Rangers* / Anything goes: *Royal Marines* / London pubs medley: *Blues & Royals Band* / Le rejouissance: *Coldstream Guards* / British grenadiers: *Cheshire Regiment* / Golden mile: *Queen's Lancashire Regiment* / Sabre dance: *Royal Marines* / Street pictures medley: *Blues & Royals Band* / Stage centre: *Coldstream Guards* / Yankee doodle dandy: *Royal British Legion Band* / Alexander's ragtime band: *Royal British Legion Band* / On Richmond hill baht 'at: *Duke Of Wellington Regiment* / Czardas: *Coldstream Guards* / Radetsky march: *Royal British Legion Band* / Glenn Miller memories: *Royal British Legion Band* / Pageantry of Gilbert and Sullivan: *Blues & Royals Band* / Colonel Bogey: *Royal British Legion Band* / Nessun Dorma: *Royal British Legion Band* / Blaze away: *Blues & Royals Band* / Tie a yellow ribbon: *Royal British Legion Band* / Greensleeves: *Blues & Royals Band* / Bells across the meadow: *Blues & Royals Band*
330492 / Mar '97 / Hallmark

☐ **BANGING HOUSE (14 Seriously Clubbing Chuggers)**
FIRMCD 3 / Mar '96 / Firm

☐ **BANJO FESTIVAL**
Banjo cantata: *McGuinn, Jim* / Banjo workout: *Maphis, Joe* / Holston valley breakdown: *Seeger, Mike* / Little boxes: *Rosmini, Dick* / There's a meeting here tonight: *Helms, Jimmy* / Cripple creek: *Cheatwood, Billy* / Goodman coonhound: *Faier, Billy* / Clinch Mountain backstop: *Lindley, David* / Johnson boys: *Lindley, David* / Red apple juice: *Rosmini, Dick* / Hundreds of miles: *Cheatwood, Billy* / Old Joe Clark: *Weissman, Dick* / Movin' down the line: *Helms, Jimmy* / Hindu stomp: *Podell, Art* / Whistle while you work: *Williams, Mason* / Mad mountain medley: *Lindley, David* / Hooka tooka: *Helms, Jimmy* / Trail ridge road: *Weissman, Dick* / Joe's breakdown: *Maphis, Joe* / Banjo tune: *Darling, Erik* / Greenback dollar: *Rosmini, Dick & Jimmy Helms* / Rumblin' on: *McGuinn, Jim* / Fast and loose: *Rosmini, Dick* / Goin' down there: *Seeger, Mike* / Earle's breakdown: *Weissberg, Eric & Marshall Brickman* / Green corn: *Faier, Billy* / Banjo hello: *Williams, Mason*
CD 12550 / May '97 / Music Of The World

☐ **BANJO JAMBOREE**
TCD 1019 / May '96 / Tradition

☐ **BANKLANDS**
FE 100CB / Jan '95 / Fellside

☐ **BAR RAM TOP 20 HITS**
SONCD 0071 / Sep '94 / Sonic Sounds

☐ **BARA COUNTRY (Music From Madagascar)**
C 560089 / Feb '96 / Ocora

☐ **BARBADOS SWEET FUH DAYS**
CCD 0026 / Apr '96 / CRS

☐ **BARBECUE PARTY**
Macarena: *Los Del Rio* / La danse de Zorba: *Trio Helenique* / Drink drink drink: *Baker, George Selection* / Beach baby: *First Class* / Summerwine: *Roussos, Demis & Nancy Boyd* / Amor: *McKuen, Rod* / Hello summertime: *Goldsboro, Bobby* / There goes my heart again: *Domino, Fats* / Let's have a party: *Jackson, Wanda* / Poetry in motion: *Tillotson, Johnny* / Till I kissed you: *Everly Brothers* / La colegiala: *Low, Gary* / Belimbombero: *Los Reyes* / Music in the air: *US* / I'm your son South America: *Silvio* / Shame and scandal in the family: *Elliot, Shawn*
DC 880802 / May '97 / Disky

☐ **BARDES FROM THE MAKRAM (Traditional Music From Baluchistan, Iran/Pakistan)**
926332 / Feb '96 / BUDA

☐ **BARDS OF THE HIMALAYAS, THE (Epics & Trance Music)**
CNR 2741080 / Aug '97 / Le Chant Du Monde

☐ **BARNBRACK: 22 IRISH FOLK PUB SONGS**
HRL 199CD / Aug '94 / Outlet

☐ **BARONG**
VICG 52172 / Mar '96 / JVC World Library

☐ **BARRELHOUSE BLUES AND BOOGIE WOOGIE VOL.1**
Gravier Street rag / Night owl blues / Joe Martin blues / You ain't no good / My mother is gone / Boogie woogie for piano and celeste / I just want to be free / Get further little brother / My own blues / Bertha May / Drive 'em down special / Funky (slow and easy) blues / 41 Highway / Drivin' me mad / You're gonna worry too / Honky tonk boogie
STCD 8030 / Jul '98 / Storyville

☐ **BARRELHOUSE PIANO BLUES**
DOCD 5193 / Oct '93 / Document

☐ **BARRELHOUSE WOMEN VOL.2 (1924-1928)**
DOCD 5497 / Nov '96 / Document

☐ **BASEMENT BOP (British Jazz In The 1950's/2CD Set)**
Mike's choice: *Melody Maker New Stars* / Ten bar gait: *Whittle, Tommy Quintet* / Nemo: *Scott, Ronnie & His Orchestra* / Mango walk: *Graham, Kenny & His Afro Cubists* / For voters only: *Melody Maker All Stars* / Bremavin: *Dankworth, Johnny Quartet* / Smoke gets in your eyes: *Scott, Ronnie Quintet* / 52nd Street theme: *Scott, Ronnie Boptet* / Mop mop: *Feldman, Victor* / Flat foot: *Laurie, Cy* / It's a pity to say goodnight: *Laine, Cleo & John Dankworth* / Weaver of dreams: *Branscombe, Alan* / I can't get started: *All Star Sextet* / Not so fast: *Scott, Ronnie & Kenny Graham* / Night in Tunisia: *Dankworth, Johnny Quartet* / Close as pages in a book: *Deaucher, Jimmy* / All the things you are: *Scott, Ronnie & His Orchestra* / Fifth man: *Melody Maker New Stars* / Cotton tail: *Christie, Keith Quartet* / Scrapple from the apple: *Scott, Ronnie Boptet* / It was a lover and his lass: *Laine, Cleo & John Dankworth* / Battle royal: *Scott, Ronnie & Kenny Graham* / Pina colada: *Graham, Kenny & His Afro Cubists* / Gershwin ballad medley: *Melody Maker All Stars* / Jelly roll: *Laurie, Cy* / Stars fell on Alabama: *Whittle, Tommy Quintet* / Avalon: *Scott, Ronnie Boptet* / Oop pop a da: *All Star Sextet* / On green dolphin street: *Branscombe, Alan* / Ladybird: *Feldman, Victor*
330412 / Mar '97 / Hallmark

☐ **BASIC PRINCIPLES OF SOUND**
Beginnings: *Gilberto, Astrud* / Sunny: *O'Day, Anita* / Blues for Hari: *Richards, Emil* / Chewing gum delerium: *Free Pop Electronic Experiment* / Coming home baby: *Bernard, Bob* / Come together: *Cicero* / Little green apples: *Fat Sadi* / Lady Montego: *Ayers, Roy* / My love is a monster: *Bradford, Clea* / Pobodiznia: *Prazky big band* / Mambo del norte: *San Francisco Lmt* / Cochise: *Collins, Edmond* / Berimbau: *Black, Stanley*
SSCD 1 / 9 Mar '98 / Soundsational

☐ **BASIC TECHNO VOL.1**
7700684 / Oct '96 / Omnisonus

☐ **BASIC TECHNO VOL.2**
7702000 / Jun '97 / Omnisonus

☐ **BASS GENERATOR SINGLES COLLECTION VOL.1**
GTX 017CD / Jan '96 / Bass Generator

☐ **BASS GENERATOR SINGLES COLLECTION VOL.2**
GTX 018CD / Jan '96 / Bass Generator

☐ **BASS TALK VOL.4**
EFA 128222 / Feb '96 / Hot Wire

☐ **BASS TALK VOL.5 - PLAY DA BASS**
EFA 128322 / 29 Sep '97 / Hot Wire

☐ **BASS-IC ELEMENTS**
It's a dope thang: *HED UK* / Chronicles in dub: *2 Dreds In A Dub* / Sax'n'ting: *Ruf Intelligence* / Phat and phuturistic: *Little Matt* / Future now: *Atomic Dog* / Whole world: *Endemic Void* / Deeply: *Universal Love* / T power: *Mutant Jazz* / Lid: *Eugenix* / Atmosphere: *DJ Phantasy* / Taken over: *Fallen Angels* / Phone me in the morning: *Sub Sequence*
CDTOT 33 / Sep '95 / Jumpin' & Pumpin'

☐ **BASSA MUSICA**
CT 0001CD / Apr '95 / Robi Droli

☐ **BASSIC INSTINCT**
SD 010 / 13 Apr '98 / Stereo Deluxe

☐ **BASTA/INSITU ANNIVERSARY (3CD Set)**
IS 167/168/169 / Aug '97 / Basta/Insitu

☐ **BATAK OF NORTH SUMATRA**
NA 046 / Oct '92 / New Albion

☐ **BATAZOS DEL ANO**
RMD 811782 / 7 Apr '98 / RMM

☐ **BATTERY POINT**
Dirty mags: *Blueboy* / He gets me so hard: *Boyracer* / Autobiography: *Hit Parade* / Fran: *Aberdeen* / River: *Blueboy* / Last September's farewell kiss: *Northern Picture Library* / Wish you would: *Ivy* / Reproduction is pollution: *Shelley* / Mustard gas: *Action Painting* / Avenge: *Ivy* / Deep thinker: *Secret Shine* / Top 40 sculpture: *Sugargliders* / Paris: *Northern Picture Library* / Fireworks: *Aberdeen* / Toulouse: *Blueboy* / Hero: *Shelley*
SARAH 359CD / Jul '95 / Sarah

☐ **BATTLE OF BOSWORTH, THE**
BARKED 3CD / 9 Mar '98 / Trunk

☐ **BATTLE OF THE GARAGES VOL.1, THE**
VOXXCD 2067 / Oct '93 / Voxx

☐ **BATTLE OF THE GARAGES VOL.2, THE**
VOXXCD 2068 / Oct '93 / Voxx

☐ **BATTLE OF THE SAXES**
TCD 1026 / Aug '96 / Tradition

☐ **BATTLE OF THE SAXES (The Great Jazz Saxophonists 1927-1946)**
Battle of the saxes: *Hawkins, Coleman Sax Ensemble* / Esquire swank: *Hodges, Johnny & Duke Ellington Orchestra* / Favour of a fool: *Carter, Benny Orchestra* / Willow weep: *Jefferson, Hilton & Cab Calloway Orchestra* / Willow weep for me: *Smith, Willie Orchestra* / Ornithology: *Parker, Charlie Septet* / You need coachin': *Bostic, Earl & Don Byas/Hot Lips Page Orchestra* / Lullaby: *Hawkins, Coleman Trio* / Tea for two: *Freeman, Bud Orchestra* / I don't stand a ghost of a chance with you: *Berry, Leon 'Chu' & Cab Calloway Orchestra* / Afternoon of a Basie-ite: *Young, Lester Quartet* / Lotta sax appeal: *Wilson, Dick & Andy Kirk Orchestra* / Call me a taxi: *Miller, Eddie & The Bob Cats* / Concerto for tenor: *Auld, Georgie & His Orchestra* / Have you changed: *Webster, Ben & Harry Carney/Duke Ellington Orchestra* / Stompin' at The Savoy: *Philips, Flip Fliptet* / Trumbology: *Trumbauer, Frankie Orchestra* / Pompton Turnpike: *Barnet, Charlie Orchestra* / Indian summer: *Bechet, Sidney New Orleans Feetwarmers* / Tired socks: *Hodges, Johnny Orchestra* / Prelude to a kiss: *Carney, Harry & Duke Ellington Orchestra* / Humouresque in swing time: *Caceras, Ernie & Emilio Trio* / Beatin' the dog: *Rollini, Adrian & Joe Venuti Blue Four*
CDAJA 5247 / Aug '97 / Living Era

☐ **BATUCADA - THE SOUND OF THE FAVELAS**
Ritmo no.1: *De Costa, Paulinho* / Batumata: *Fernando* / So no apito: *Padre, Miguel* / Otao e eu: *Jaritz, Nicos* / Repimar: *De Castro, Jadir & Dom Um* / Vibrando com a selecao: *Amarelo, Verde* / Ba-tu-ca-da: *Pas Ney De Castro* / Communic - Ritmo: *De Castro, Jadir & Dom Um* / Mulata Faceira: *Fernando* / Rapido: *Bateria Nota* / Pai Bene Queimou o Pe: *Fantastica Bateria* / Ozonia: *De Castro, Jadir & Dom Um* / Quando: *Fernando*
MRBCD 005 / Mar '96 / Mr. Bongo

☐ **BATUCADA AND CAPOEIRA**
Samba Quente: *Perrone, Luciano* / Ensaio de escola: *Welcome To Rio* / Demonstrago: *Bateria Fantastica Da Porteia* / Sao bente grande: *Mestre Bimba* / Mistura no.2: *Geraldo* / Morte de Capoeira: *Suassuna* / Ritmo du Brasil: *Welcome To Rio* / Cavalaria: *Suassuna* / Demonstragao no.2: *Bateria Fantastica Da Briela* / Santa Maria: *Biyba* / Samba vocalizado: *Perrone, Luciano* / Hora de rezar: *Fillio, Bene* / Repique reza forte: *Padre, Miguel* / Berimbau and percussao: *Perrone, Luciano* / Som and andameuto: *Bateria Fantastica Da Porteia*
SJRCD 037 / 1 Jun '98 / Soul Jazz

☐ **BATUCADA POR FAVOR**
MRBCD 012 / 14 Apr '98 / Mr. Bongo

☐ **BATUQUE AND FINACON (Cape Verde)**
C5 60132 / Jul '98 / Ocora

☐ **BAULE VOCAL MUSIC FROM THE IVORY COAST**
AUD 008048 / Nov '93 / Auvidis/Ethnic

☐ **BAWDY BLUES**
OBCCD 544 / Nov '92 / Original Blues Classics

☐ **BAYERN: VOLKSMUSIK 1906-1941**
US 0196 / Jul '95 / Trikont

☐ **BAYOU BEAT**
Beau's cajun two step: *Jocque, Beau & The Zydeco Hi-Rollers* / Petite ou la grosse: *Berard, Al & The Basin Brothers* / El Sid O's zydeco boogaloo: *Nathan & Zydeco Cha Cha's* / Joli coeur: *Mamou* / Tanten nana: *August, Lynn* / Old time two step: *Delafose, John & The Eunice Playboys* / Louisiana playboys theme: *Louisiana Playboys* / Bernadette: *Arceneaux, Fernest* / Danse carre/Reel de Dennis McGee: *Daigrepont, Bruce* / Modern waltz: *Zydeco Force*
EDCD 7053 / Nov '97 / Easydisc

☐ **BAYOU BLUES MASTERS - GOLDBAND BLUES**
I'm a country boy / Purty little dolly / Going crazy baby / Broke and hungry / Make up my mind / Need shorter hours / It ain't right / Just got to (take a) ride / Wanna do me wrong / Tin pan alley / I got fever / Life's journey / Honey bee / Sunday morning / Trouble in my home / Oh Ramona / Highway back home / I'm going / Please stand by me / Too tired / Let me hold your hand / What in the world are you gonna do / Something working baby / Pretty little red dress / C-Key blues / Catch that morning train
CDCHD 427 / Aug '93 / Ace

☐ **BAYOU DANCE PARTY**
EDCD 7014 / Aug '96 / Easydisc

☐ **BAYOU HOT SAUCE**
New Orleans beat: *Riley, Steve & Mamou Playboys* / Hot tamale baby: *Ball, Marcia* / Zydeco la Louisiane: *Buckwheat Zydeco* / Valse bebe: *Beausoleil* / I'm here: *Chenier, Clifton* / Saturday night special: *Louisiana Playboys* / Tous le temps en temps: *August, Lynn* / Allons a Tepatate: *Balfa Toujours* / Pere et garcon zydeco: *Delafose, John & The Eunice Playboys* / You used to call me: *Chenier, Clifton & His Red Hot Louisiana Band*
EDCD 7044 / Sep '97 / Easydisc

☐ **BAZOOKA EXPLOSION, THE**
SONCD 0061 / Mar '94 / Sonic Sounds

☐ **BBC SONGS OF PRAISE FROM OLD TRAFFORD**
All people that on earth do dwell / Guide me o thou great redeemer / Amazing Grace / Thorns in the straw / Rejoice rejoice / When the saints go marching in / Mine eyes have seen the glory / Oh happy day / Shine, Jesus, shine / Alleluia / Sing to Jesus / Abide with me / You'll never walk alone
ALD 026 / Jun '95 / Alliance Music

☐ **BBE SAMPLER**
Bodyfusion: *Starvue* / Ravi's thing: *Harris, Bill 'Ravi' & The Prophets* / Got to get back to Louisiana: *Parker, Elmer & Brenda* / I wanna be loved by you: *Family of Eve* / Hunk of heaven: *Lemuria* / Sittin' on chrome: *Master Ace* / Trinidad: *Gibbs, John & US Steel Orchestra* / Mystery of ages: *Garnett, Carlos* / Blueberry Hill: *Washington, Joe* / Collect / Path of the blazing sarong: *Harris, Bill 'Ravi' & The Prophets* / It's time to party: *Murray, Jolynn* / Circus 97: *Aydin* / The Funky Chile / Do it some more: *Brains Unchained* / Love call: *Ramsey & Co.*
BBECDS 01 / 1 Jun '98 / Barely Breaking Even

☐ **BE BOP**
What is this thing called love: *Esquire Five* / Gone with the wind: *Feldman, Victor Quartet* / Buzzy: *Jazz At The Town Hall Ensemble* / Fallonology: *All Star Sextet* / Wee dot: *Scott, Ronnie Boptet* / Too marvellous for words: *Scott, Ronnie Quartet* / Little Willie leaps: *Scott, Ronnie Boptet* / Compus mentos: *Scott, Ronnie & His Orchestra* / Loverman: *Dankworth, John* / Gone with the windmill: *Dean, Alan Bebopers* / I hear music: *Dankworth, John*

Seven / Our delight: Dankworth, John Seven / Over the rainbow: Graham, Kenny & His Afro Cubists / Stars fell on Alabama: Burns, Norman Quartet / Johnny come lately: Burns, Tito Sextet / Why do I love you: Burns, Tito Sextet
305052 / Jun '97 / Hallmark

☐ **BE BOP 1945-1953**
CD 53029 / Mar '90 / Giants Of Jazz

☐ **BE BOP IN PARIS VOL.1**
2512882 / Mar '90 / Jazztime

☐ **BE BOP STORY 1944-1945, THE (3CD Set)**
152362 / Sep '96 / EPM

☐ **BEACH HITS - SONGS OF SUMMER**
JHD 013 / Jun '92 / Tring

☐ **BEACH 'N' BOOGIE VOL.1**
Shakin' dem bones: Wilson, U.P. / She's the one for me: Parker, Kenny / Here we go: Rawls, Johnny / Fine as wine: Coronado, Joe / Talkin' about love: Butler Twins / How much longer: Farr, Deitra / They killed crazy horse: Houston, Joe & Otis Grand / In all of my life: Ray, Kenny 'Blue' / Hey brother: Morello, Jimmy / Aunt Nancy's ball: Griswalds / Hoochie Mama: Jones, Andrew 'Jr. Boy' / Hot and saucy short and grand: Guitar Shorty & Otis Grand / You must be crazy: Brown, Nappy / Down and out: Sayles, Charlie / Bluesmobile: Walker, Philip & Otis Grand / Mo's stroll: Buford, Mojo / Roll over: Wilson, U.P. / You need to know: Williams, Alanda
JSPCD 2100 / Jul '97 / JSP

☐ **BEACH 'N' BOOGIE VOL.2**
Talk to me baby: Payne, Jackie / Search is over: Farr, Deitra / You're a two timin' man: Sweet Betty / Can't get enough: Martin, Mick / On my way to Memphis: Marshall, Johnnie / Drown in the gutter: McAllister, Randy / What's on your mind: Ray, Kenny 'Blue' / True what they say: Edwards, Willie / Kick out: Guitar Shorty / Hit the ground running: Payne, Jackie / Every man needs a good woman: Shields, Lonnie / You're a dog: Jones, Andrew / She gives me good lovings: Strother, Percy / Know who your friends are: Coronado, Joe / Foot Stompin': Griswalds / Are you stickin' with me baby: Wynne, J.B.
JSPCD 2107 / Jul '98 / JSP

☐ **BEACH PARTY**
Beach baby: First Class / Sunshine reggae: Laidback / Barbados: Typically Tropical / Red sails in the sunset: Domino, Fats / Mexico: Humphries, Les Singers / Tropicana bay: Roussos, Demis & Nancy Boyd / Little green bag: Baker, George Selection / Volare: Martino, Al / It never rains in Southern California: Hammond, Albert & Albert West / Cara mia: Jay & The Americans / Big bamboo: Merry Men / Sunglasses: Ullman, Tracey / Santa maria: Tatjana / Daydream: Lovin' Spoonful / Little old lady from Pasadena: Jan & Dean / Do wah diddy diddy: Manfred Mann
DC 880772 / May '97 / Disky

☐ **BEACH PARTY**
DLF 71263 / 17 Aug '98 / Del-Fi

☐ **BEACH, SUN AND SURFIN'**
12541 / Jul '95 / Laserlight

☐ **BEAN STALK ALL STARS**
793032 / Jul '97 / Melodie

☐ **BEAT AT ABBEY ROAD 1963-1965**
Love of the loved: Black, Cilla / I'm in love: Dakotas / Cruel Sea: Dakotas / If you gotta make a fool of somebody: Freddie & The Dreamers / Roll over Beethoven: Wayne, Pat & The Beachcombers / Answer is no: Powell, Keith & The Valets / Please Mr. Postman: Sheridan, Mike & The Nightriders / Shake shake shake: Rivers, Tony & The Castaways / 54321: Manfred Mann / Bad time: Roulettes / Come on back: Hollies / You're no good: Swinging Blue Jeans / I should have known better: Naturals / She's my girl: Shafto, Bobby / When you walked in the room: Kramer, Billy J. & The Dakotas / Look at me: Whirlwinds / I'm the one who loves you: Paramounts / Things will never be he same: Four Just Men / What a sweet thing that was: Sheridan, Mike & The Nightriders / I'll wait for you: Gerry & The Pacemakers / I gotta woman: Black Knights / I'd much rather be with the boys: Toggery Five / Blue ribbons: Paramounts / Tired of trying bored with lying scared of dying: Manfred Mann / Name game: Ford, Dean & The Gaylords / Candy to me: Raynor, Martin & The Secrets / Break a way: Marsden, Beryl / Day will come: Stewart, Rod
CDABBEY 100 / 13 Oct '97 / EMI

☐ **BEAT BOMBS VOL.1**
EFA 129602 / Mar '97 / Catch-a-Groove

☐ **BEAT CLASSIC**
B-Beat classic: B+ / Something fresh to swing to: Levi 167 / It's your rock: Fantasy Three / It's life: Rock Master Scott / Shout: MC Craig G / Just call us def: Steady B / Never satisfied: Hi-Fidelity Three / Throwdown: Disco Four / Triple threat: Z-3 Mc's / Funky: Ultramagnetic MC's / Beat bop: Rammelzee & K-Rob
DC 10CDX / Jun '97 / DC Recordings

☐ **BEAT FROM THE STAR CLUB, THE (2CD Set)**
OTR 1100031 / Jun '97 / Metro Independent

☐ **BEAT GENERATION AND THE ANGRY YOUNG MEN, THE**
That's what I want: Long Tall Sally / Underground: Small Arrows / I'll make you mine: Purple Hearts / Frustration: Les Elite / I do: Long Tall Sally / Dangerous Man: Merton Parkas / Get a job: Les Elite / Weekend dancers: Directions / Concrete mixer: Purple Hearts / Career girl: Les Elite / All by Myself: Long Tall Sally / It may be too late: Directions / You say you will: Merton Parkas / Kid: Small Hours / Hurry darkness: Purple Hearts
MODSKACD 003 / 3 Nov '97 / Captain Mod

☐ **BEAT MERCHANTS**
Man of the moment: Clayson, Alan & The Argonauts / Call of the wild: Overlanders / Pigtails in Paris: MacBeth, David / PFB: Fabulous Flee Rekkers / Come on baby (to the floral dance): Eagles / I could write a book: Chants / If you don't come back: Takers / Lies: Sandon, Johnny & The Remo Four / Show you mean it too: Me & Them / He's telling you lies: Kingpin / Think it over: Hellions / Funny how love can be: Rockin' Berries / Bags groove: Sheffields / Stage door: Jackson, Tony / Harry rag: Kinks / Lady Jane: Garrick, David / What a world: Hill, Benny / End of the season: Uglys / Popcorn double feature: Searchers / Everything's funny: Troggs / Born to be wild: Nashville Teens / Break up: Downliners / I'm still raving: Sutch, Screaming Lord / Heavy weather: British Invasion / Moonlight skater: Berry, Dave
SEECD 430 / Sep '95 / See For Miles

☐ **BEAT OF NEW SOUTH AFRICA, THE**
Laduma: Ngema, Mbonegeni / Usemncane: Soul Brothers / South Africa: New South Africa / Cry the beloved country: Free At Last / African solution: Ngema, Mbonegeni / Ndlondlo bashise: Ngema, Mbonegeni / Siyagiya: Dark City Sisters / Bazodlani: Soul Brothers / Daar is green: Kerkorrel, Johannes / Impedulo: Elimhlophe, Ihashi / Tumelo: IPCC / World: Jambo / Awuwa: Kerkorrel, Johannes / Ungakohlwa: New South Africa / Thwathwa: Phale, Thomas
LBLV 2521 / Jul '96 / Indigo

☐ **BEAT OF SOWETO VOL.5**
STEW 34CD / Mar '96 / Earthworks

☐ **BEAT SEEKING MISSILES**
PPV 9801D / 1 Jun '98 / Polyrhythmic

☐ **BEAT THE SYSTEM PUNK SINGLES COLLECTION**
Stab the judge: One Way System / Riot torn city: One Way System / Youth of today: External Menace / Someday: External Menace / Die for me: Uproar / Better off dead: Uproar / Sad society: Chaotic Youth / No future UK: Chaotic Youth / I hate: Fits / Time is right: Fits / Official hooligan: Anti Social / No views: External Menace / Poor excuse: External Menace / Backstreet boys: Anti Social / Death and pure destruction: Death Sentence / Death sentence: Death Sentence / Too many people: Anti Social / Rebel youth: Uproar / Victims: Uproar / IRA: Post Mortem / Day by day: Post Mortem / Me and you: One Way System / Arms race: Chaotic Youth / Victims of war: Death Sentence / Listen to me: Fits
CDPUNK 61 / Aug '95 / Anagram

☐ **BEATING PUNK, PAST**
REM 20 / May '93 / Released Emotions

☐ **BEATS BY DOPE DEMAND (3CD Set)**
KICKCD 63 / 23 Mar '98 / Kickin'

☐ **BEATS BY DOPE DEMAND VOL.1**
KICKCD 28 / Mar '96 / Kickin'

☐ **BEATS BY DOPE DEMAND VOL.2**
KICKCD 33 / Mar '96 / Kickin'

☐ **BEATS BY DOPE DEMAND VOL.3 (2CD Set)**
KICKCD 46 / Oct '96 / Kickin'

☐ **BEATS BY DOPE DEMAND VOL.4 (2CD Set)**
KICKCD 58 / 27 Oct '97 / Kickin'

☐ **BEATS MELT DOWN**
Dust bucket: Freddie Fresh / Freshmess: Hookian Mindz / Freshmess on wax: Riots / Flava unit: Playa / Aphrodite: King Of The Beats / Freashmess on wax: Lyca Journey / Interpret: Atkins, Juan / Citation: Tons Of Tones / Chiswick days: Spectral Emotions / Phunk=phunk: Stalker / Matter: Sunrise Society / Hayfever: Speedy J / System address: ISM / Squelch: Finitribe
DBM 2943 / Jun '97 / Fierce

☐ **BEATSERVICE EP COLLECTION, THE**
BSCD 011 / 18 May '98 / BeatService

☐ **BEATSVILLE DADDY-O**
DADDY-OCD 001 / Feb '97 / No Hit

☐ **BEATZ BUMPS & AFROS**
FSCD 0005 / Oct '96 / Freak Street

☐ **BEAUTIFUL IRISH BALLADS**
Galway bay / Only our rivers run free / Dirty old town / Flight of Earls / Sullivan's John / Luke a tribute / Cliffs of Dooneen / Sick note (Paddy on the bricks) / Fields of Athenry / Spancil Hill / Rose of Mooncoin / Green fields 'round Ferbane / Wild rover / Mary from Dunloe / Paddy's green shamrock shore / Old Dungarvan oak
21127 / Aug '97 / Laserlight

☐ **BEAUTY AN OILEAN**
Seainin Mhicil O Suilleabhain / Muiris O Dalaigh / Sean O Dunnshleibhe / Sean O Cearnaigh / Padraig O Cearnaigh / Eibhlin Ni Chearna / Thomas O Dalaigh / Peaiti O Duinnshleibhe / Sean Cheaist O Cathain / Aine Ui Laoithe / Breanndan O Beaglaoich
CC 56 CD / Oct '92 / Claddagh

☐ **BEAUTY IN DARKNESS VOL.1**
NB 166CD / May '96 / Nuclear Blast

☐ **BEAUTY IN DARKNESS VOL.2**
NB 256CD / May '97 / Nuclear Blast

☐ **BEAVIS & BUTTHEAD DO AMERICA**
Two cool guys: Hayes, Isaac / Love rollercoaster: Red Hot Chili Peppers / Ain't nobody: LL Cool J / Ratfinks, suicide tanks and cannibal girls: White Zombie / I wanna riot: Rancid / Walk on water: Osbourne, Ozzy / Snakes: No Doubt / Pimp'n ain't ez: Madd Head / Lord is a monkey (Rock version): Butthole Surfers / White trash: Southern Culture On The Skids / Gone shootin': AC/DC / Lesbian seagull: Humperdinck, Engelbert
GED 25002 / Feb '97 / Geffen

☐ **BEC RECORDINGS SAMPLER VOL.1**
BED 006CD / 13 Apr '98 / BEC

☐ **BECAUSE I LOVE YOU (Favourite Irish Love Songs)**
She moved through the fair / My Lagan love / My Mary of the curling hair / Eileen og / Down by the Sally gardens / Snowy breasted pearl / Love thee dearest / Down by the green bushes / Love's old sweet song / Maggie / Nancy Spain / Bunch of thyme / Wild Irish rose / Trottin' to the fair / I'll walk beside you / How are things in Glocca Morra / Spinning wheel / Old Claddagh ring
CDLOVE 200 / Jun '98 / Outlet

☐ **BEDOUIN SONGS (Jordan)**
Bedouin songs / Wedding songs / Fishermen's songs
W 260083 / Jul '98 / Inedit

☐ **BEDROOM TENORS**
Don't explain: Gordon, Dexter / God bless the child: Turrentine, Stanley / Gone with the wind: Getz, Stan / Infant eyes: Shorter, Wayne / Nature boy: Quebec, Ike / Spring can really hang you up the most: Sims, Zoot / Sweet and lovely: Jackson, Javon / Namely you: Rollins, Sonny / Laura: Henderson, Joe / Someone to watch over me: Hawkins, Coleman / Love you to the letter: Harp, Everette / Good life: Mobley, Hank
CDP 8348732 / Apr '96 / Blue Note

☐ **BEFORE THE BLUES VOL.1 (Early American Black Music Scene 1920's/ 1930's)**
YAZ 2015 / Mar '96 / Yazoo

☐ **BEFORE THE BLUES VOL.2**
YAZ 2016 / Mar '96 / Yazoo

☐ **BEFORE THE BLUES VOL.3**
YAZ 2017 / Mar '96 / Yazoo

☐ **BEFORE THE TANGO (Argentina's Folk Tradition 1905-1936)**
El carretero: De Nava, Arturo / El taita: De Nava, Arturo / Decimas del sargento: De Nava, Arturo / Atamisqueria: Aguirre, Domingo / El gato de Aguirre: Aguirre, Domingo / Silencio de las tumbas: Silva, Jose Maria / Recuerdos: Cazon, Higinio / Cosmopolisimo: Ezeiza, Gabino / El guacho en el ascensor: Barrios, Evaristo / Mi dulce soledad: Pelaia, Alfredo / Chinita: Pelaia, Alfredo / Venga conmigo gato: Paolantonio, Medero / Pericon por Maria: Pesoa, Iriarte / Vamos pa'l rancho: Pesoa, Iriarte / Caranitos: Pesoa, Iriarte / La tabla cayo clavada: Trio Los Nativos / Nubes que pasan: Trio Los Nativos / La tropilla: Pardo, Mario / Ausencia: Magaldi, Augustin / Rosas portenas: Pizzaro, Pelaia / Uruguayita: Paolantonio, Pelaia / Mate amargo: Trio Ciriaco Ortiz / Adios adios: Gomez, Vila / No digas que no: Magaldi & Noda / La buena ventura: Montes, Ramon / El cantar de los reseros: Charlo / A' raxada: Rondalla Cauvilla Prim
HQCD 114 / Apr '98 / Harlequin

☐ **BEFORE YOU WERE PUNK**
I melt with you: Good Riddance / Turning Japanese: No Use For A Name / In between days: Face To Face / Happy loving couples: Guttermouth / Pretty in pink: Automatic 7 / Goody two shoes: Unwritten law / Dancing with myself: Blink 182 / Crash: Mr. T Experience / Peace love and understanding: Down By Law / Walking in LA: Hagfish / Young Turks: Jughead's Revenge / 8675309 Jenny: Bracket
VR 330CD / 3 Aug '98 / Vagrant

☐ **BEGGARS BANQUET PUNK COLLECTION, THE**
Shadow: Lurkers / Freak show: Lurkers / Don't tango on my heart: Doll / Trash: Doll / That's too bad: Tubeway Army / Ain't got a clue: Lurkers / Bombers: Tubeway Army / I don't need to tell her: Tubeway Army / Desire me: Doll / Just 13: Lurkers / Out in the dark: Lurkers / Cinderella with a husky smile: Doll / I don't mean it: Carpettes / New guitar in town: Lurkers / You used to be my hero: Doll / Johnny won't hurt me: Carpettes / Nothing ever changes: Carpettes / Last lone ranger: Carpettes / Laugh at me: Stride, Pete & John Plain / Winkers song: Biggun, Ivor
CDPUNK 73 / Mar '96 / Anagram

☐ **BEGIN THE BEGUINE - 1938**
Begin the beguine: Shaw, Artie / Tisket-a-tasket: Webb, Chick / Ring dem bells: Hampton, Lionel / Sweet Georgia Brown: Goodman, Benny Quartet / I can't give you anything but love: Armstrong, Louis / Flat foot floogie: Gaillard, Slim & Slam Stewart / Music maestro please: Dorsey, Tommy / March of the bob cats: Crosby, Bob / When you're smiling: Wilson, Teddy / Swingin' the blues: Basie, Count / Louise: Goodman, Benny / Margie: Lunceford, Jimmie / Really the blues: Ladnier, Tommy / Little Joe from Chicago: Kirk, Andy / Back in your own backyard: Holiday, Billie / Back bay shuffle: Shaw, Artie / I let a song go out of my heart: Ellington, Duke / Jeepers creepers: Krupa, Gene / You must have been a beautiful baby: Crosby, Bing / Lullaby in rhythm: James, Harry
PHONTCD 7665 / Apr '90 / Phontastic

☐ **BEGINNERS GUIDE TO THE GALAXY OF PSI-TRANCE (2CD Set)**
ACTIVCD 9 / Sep '96 / Activ

☐ **BEGINNERS GUIDE TO TRADITIONAL SCOTTISH MUSIC**
My fair young love/Father John MacMillan's farewell to Barra: MacKay, Rhona / Lude's supper: Ossian / Flame of wrath for squinting Patrick: Livingstone, Pipe Major Bill / Ewe wi'the crooked horn/Mrs. Mcpherson of Inveran: Strathclyde Police Pipe Band / Cradle song: Gonnella, Ron / Little pickle/Hare among the corn/Money in both pockets: Glasgow Caledonian Strathspey & Reel Society / Duke of Perth/Hunter's hill/Rakes of Mallow: Ellis, John & His Highland Country Band / Island of heather/Ciaro (Oran na Ciaoro): Ellis, John & His Highland Country Band / Puirt a beul: MacInnes, Mairi / Dh'theidhinn a dh'uibhist: MacDonald Sisters / Renfrewshire Militia/Tenpenny bit: Stewart, Belle / Chi mi'n geamhradh: Runrig / Battle of Harlaw: Hunter, Andy / Nicky Tams: Stewart, Andy / Flower o'the Quern: Redpath, Jean / Skye boat song: McKellar, Kenneth / Tartan: Alexander Brothers / Freedom come all ye: Johnstone, Arthur / Flying haggis/Peacock/ MacArthur Road/Kiss the train goodbye: Mathieson, Pipe Major Robert / Journey to Skye: Mathieson, Pipe Major Robert / Ca' the yowes: Gaelforce Orchestra / Boys of Ballymoat: Wolfstone
LCOM 5227 / Mar '94 / Lismor

☐ **BEGINNING, THE (Jazz At The Philharmonic)**
Lester leaps in / Tea for two / Blues / Body and soul / I've found a new baby / Rosetta / Bugle call rag / How high the moon
LEJAZZCD 41 / Jun '95 / Le Jazz

☐ **BEGINNING, THE (An Introduction To Irish Dancing)**
Roddy McCorley / Rakes of Mallow / Father Kelly's reel/Jackie Coleman's / Haste to the wedding/ Leslie's hornpipe/The German beau / Lilting fisherman/Father Kelly's jig / Foxhunters / Maggie Pickens / Saint Patrick's day / Boys of blue hill / Blackbird / Garden of daisies / Jockey to the fair / Trip to the cottage
21128 / Aug '97 / Laserlight

☐ **BEGUINE A LA CANNE A SUCRE 1946-1949**
FA 051 / Oct '96 / Fremeaux

☐ **BEHIND THE EYE VOL.2**
Alienated / Symmetry / Capriole three / Desire / V s / Superstring / Franky's / Firedance / Blue illusion / Orange theme
4509990922 / Feb '95 / Eye Q

☐ **BELFAST BEAT - MARITIME BLUES**
Don't start crying now: Them / Philosophy: Them / I can tell: Mad Lads / I'm leaving: Wheels / Road block: Wheels / Send me your pillow: Wheels / It's a cruel world: Luvin' Kind / Well don't that beat them all: Just Five / On the waterfront: Bats / Strangers: Mad Lads / Bad little woman: Wheels / Call my love: Wheels / Don't you know: Wheels / I'm with you: People / Well...alright: People / Little Queenie: Mad Lads / You got me dizzy: Wheels / Kicks: Wheels / Tell me (I'm gonna love gain): Wheels / I went out with my baby tonight: Moses K & The Prophets / Answer your phone: Mad Lads / I will have you: Just Five / Answers please: Luvin' Kind / Chicago calling: Alleykatz / Mona: Wheels / Gloria: Wheels / Bad little woman: Wheel-a-ways
CDWIKD 152 / Apr '97 / Big Beat

☐ **BELIEVE IN THE FREQUENCY POWER**
Eternal: Organisation / Gotham City: Animism / Day of return: Drawing Future Life / Vermillion: Suzukiski / Colona: Solaire / Prussian blue smog: Ultra AA / Deep inside of me: Ken Inaoka / Halo: Palomatic / Dawn in the rainland: Hazemato, Kiyoshi / Phonetic: Mind Design
JAP 100CD / May '94 / North South

☐ **BELLEVUE**
MFCD 004 / Jan '94 / Mafia/Fluxy

☐ **BELLISSIMO VOL.1 (The El Records Story)**
La pluie fait des claquettes: Philippe, Louis / Ruling class: Adverse, Anthony / Straits of Malacca: King Of Luxembourg / St. Lucy: Gol Gappas / Nicky: Momus / Reach for your gun: Bid / It's a beautiful game: Cavaliers / Southern fields: Rosemary's Children / Our fairy tale: Adverse, Anthony / Valleri: King Of Luxembourg / Like nobody do: Philippe, Louis / Dreams of leaving: Always / Fire: Underneath / Curtain: Marden Hill / Montague terrace (In blue): Mayfair Charm School / Never underestimate the ignorance of the rich: Klaxon 5 / West 14: Gol Gappas / Libera me: Cagliostra / You Mary you: Philippe, Louis / Picture of Dorian Gray: King Of Luxembourg
MONDE 11CD / 6 Apr '98 / Richmond

☐ **BELLISSIMO VOL.2 (The El Records Story)**
Man of mine: Florentines / Whoops what a palaver: Raj Quartet / Metroland: Always / Fruit paradise: Would-Be-Goods / Imperial violets: Adverse, Anthony / Robe: Marden Hill / Another day: Philippe, Louis / Trial of Dr. Fancy: King Of Luxembourg / Curry crazy: Bad Dream Fancy Dress / Thames Valley leather club: Always / Red shoes waltz: Adverse, Anthony / Oh Constance: Marden Hill / Pop up man: Ambassador 277 / Flirt bliss love kiss: King Of Luxembourg / Camera loves me: Would-Be-Goods / Guess I'm dumb: Philippe, Louis / Supremes: Bad Dream Fancy Dress / Flair: Bad Dream Fancy Dress / Paradise lost: Adverse, Anthony / Sean Connery: James Dean Driving Experience
MONDE 12CD / 6 Apr '98 / Richmond

☐ **BELLY DANCE IN CAIRO**
PS 65141CD / Apr '95 / PlayaSound

☐ **BEN & JERRY'S NEWPORT FESTIVAL**
RHRCD 36 / Jul '95 / Red House

☐ **BEND IT '94 VOL.1**
Goal - world cup 1966: Hawksworth, Johnny Sound / Pele: Cornelius / Sampdoria formazione: Cornelius / Brazil Brazil: Narraga O De Waldir Amaral / World Cup football jazz: Karie, Kahimi / World Cup cha-cha: Silvester, Victor / Roberto Baggio - Non e un miraggio: Il General & Ludus Pinski / George Best - Belfast boy: Romaine / Georgie you've broken my heart: Her / George Best: El Beatle / World Cup chit-chat: Magnificent Andersons / Carioca maracana: Dreamers / Tip top Tottenham Hotspurs: Totnamites / Roger Milla - My number 9 dream: Rainbow Choir / Ryan Giggs we love you: Rainbow Choir / Diego Armando Maradona: Baggini, Francesco / 1-0 For your love: Bekenbaur, Franz / Eusebio: Philippe, Louis / Johan Cruyff - Flying Dutchman: Bridge / Pele - El Rey: Alberto, Luis / Manchestr United calypso: Connor, Edric & Ken Jones / Blackpool Blackpool: Nolans / World Cup doo wop: Rosettes / Back home - England 1970: Stewart, Ed / Soccer boppers: Posh
HARP 013 / 18 May '98 / Exotica

☐ **BENEATH THE ICY FLOW VOL.4**
PROJEKT 14CD / Apr '97 / Metal Blade

☐ BENTO BOX
CAI 20042 / 22 Sep '97 / Caipirinha

☐ BERKELEY EP'S
Bass strings: Country Joe & The Fish / Thing called love: Country Joe & The Fish / Section 43: Country Joe & The Fish / Hearts to cry: Fruminous Bandersnatch / Misty cloud: Fruminous Bandersnatch / Cheshire: Fruminous Bandersnatch / Gazelle: Mad River / Orange fire: Mad River / Windchimes: Mad River / Where does love go: Notes From The Underground / Down in the basement: Notes From The Underground / What am I doing here: Notes From The Underground / Got to get out of this dream: Notes From The Underground / You don't love me: Notes From The Underground / Let yourself fly: Notes From The Underground / Where I'm at today: Notes From The Underground
CDWIKD 153 / Jun '95 / Big Beat

☐ BERLIN ALWAYS
Cheek to cheek: Astaire, Fred / This year's kisses: Faye, Alice / Alexander's ragtime band: Goodman, Benny Orchestra / Slumming on Park Avenue: Lunceford, Jimmie & Orchestra / I'm putting all my eggs in one basket: Armstrong, Louis / Waiting on the edge of the road: Waters, Ethel / Isn't this a lovely day (to be caught in the rain): Ambrose & His Orchestra / Shakin' the blues away: Etting, Ruth / When I lost you: Crosby, Bing / Always: Goodman, Benny Orchestra / He ain't got rhythm: Holiday, Billie / I've got my love to keep me warm: Tatum, Art / Blue skies: Dorsey, Tommy Orchestra / I want to be in Dixie: American Ragtime Octette / Let yourself go: Astaire, Fred / How's chances: Hall, Henry & The BBC Dance Orchestra / Harlem on my mind: Waters, Ethel / Russian lullaby: Berigan, Bunny & His Orchestra / How deep is the ocean: Crosby, Bing / When the midnight choo choo leaves for Alabam': Dorsey, Tommy Orchestra / Now it can be told: Bowlly, Al
AVC 517 / Apr '93 / Avid

☐ BERLIN BY NIGHT
Ungarwein (gipsy wine): Von Geczy, Barnabas & His Orchestra / Ich tanze mit dir in den himmel hinein: Harvey, Lilian & Willi Fritsch / Gruss und kuss Veronika: Die Weintraubs / Regentropfen: Ruth, Ludwig Orchestra & Metropol Vocalists / Musik Stenzel, Otto Dance Orchestra / Arpanetta: Gaden, Robert Orchestra / Abends in der taverne: Strienz, Wilhelm / Du hast glück bei den frau'n bei ami: Waldmuller, Lizzi / Wochenend und sonnenschein: Comedy Harmonists / Liebling mein herz lasst dich grussen: Harvey, Lilian & Willi Fritsch / Rosamunde: Glahe, Will Orchestra / Liebe is ein geheimnis: Hildebrand, Hilde & Orchestra / O mia bella Napoli: Schuricke, Rudi / Lili Marlene: Andersen, Lale / Schones weiter heute: Zacharias, Helmut / Sing: Kunneke, Evelyn / Liebe, kleine schaffnerin: Carl, Rudolf / Es geht alles voruber, es geht alles vorbei: Andersen, Lale / Das alte spinnrad: Groh, Herbert Ernst & Odeon-Kunstler Orchester / Sag' beim abschied leise "servus": Forst, Willi
CDEMS 1395 / May '91 / EMI

☐ BERSERKLEY
CREV 010CD / Mar '93 / Rev-Ola

☐ BESERK
DBM 2141 / Sep '96 / Happy Trax

☐ BEST 60'S MEGAMIX, THE
My friend Jake: Smoke / Take a heart: Sorrow / Don't stop the carnival: Price, Alan / Long shot kick de bucket: Pioneers / Red red wine: Tribe, Tony / Train to Skaville: Ethiopians / Melting pot: Blue Mink / Up in a spell on you: Price, Alan / She's not in my race: Christian, Neil / Wonderful world, beautiful people: Cliff, Jimmy / It mek: Dekker, Desmond / Israelites: Dekker, Desmond / Shame: Price, Alan / More than I can say: Vee, Bobby / Hey baby: Quarrymen / Louie Louie: Fontana, Wayne / Love letters: Proby, P.J. / Tell Laura I love her: Valance, Ricky / Money: Fontana, Wayne / Groovy kinda love: Fontana, Wayne / Up on the roof: Valance, Ricky / Unchained melody: Quarrymen / Hold me: Proby, P.J. / Chains: Four Pennies / Johnny remember me: Leyton, Johnny / Crying: Shannon, Del / Lonesome drums: Nelson, Sandy / 007: Dekker, Desmond / Return of Django: Upsetters / Liquidator: Harry J All Stars
306812 / May '97 / Hallmark

☐ BEST 70'S MEGAMIX, THE
If I had you: Korgis / Rock 'n' roll winter: Wizzard / Knock on wood: Stewart, Ami / Hellraiser: Sweet / Tomorrow night: Atomic Rooster / Clog dance: Violinski / Moody old clough: Lieutenant Pigeon / Are you ready to rock: Wizzard / 7 Teen: Regents / Something better change: Stranglers / Do anything you wanna do: Eddie & The Hot Rods / Banana splits: Dickies / Silver Machine: Hawkwind / (Dancing) on a Saturday night: Blue, Barry / Chirpy, chirpy, cheep, cheep: Kissoon, Mac & Katie / Oh what a shame: Wood, Roy / Teenage depression: Eddie & The Hot Rods / Nice one Cyril: Cockerel Chorus / Snoopy and the red baron: Hot Shots / No honestly: De Paul, Lynsey / Indian reservation: Fardon, Don / You can get it if you really want: Dekker, Desmond / Young, gifted and black: Bob & Marcia / Everything I own: Boothe, Ken / Irie feelings: Edwards, Rupie / Double barrel: Barker, Dave & Ansell Collins / Pied piper: Bob & Marcia / Jarrow song: Price, Alan / Banner man: Blue Mink / Ballroom blitz: Sweet / Block buster: Sweet / Randy: Blue Mink / Help me make it through the night: Holt, John
306352 / Jun '97 / Hallmark

☐ BEST 80'S ALBUM IN THE WORLD...EVER, THE
Don't you want me: Human League / There must be an angel (playing with my heart): Eurythmics / Sledgehammer: Gabriel, Peter / Don't you forget about me: Simple Minds / Never too young: Dire Straits / Gimme all your lovin': ZZ Top / Dead ringer for love: Meat Loaf / Good heart: Sharkey, Feargal / Every breath you take: Police / Faith: Michael, George / If I could turn back time: Cher / Girls just wanna have fun: Lauper, Cyndi / Relax: Frankie Goes To Hollywood / House of fun: Madness / Going underground: Jam / She drives me crazy: Fine Young Cannibals / Golden brown: Stranglers / What's love got to do with it: Turner, Tina / I can't go for that (no can do): Hall & Oates / Wherever I lay my hat (that's my home): Young, Paul / Take on me: A-Ha / Freedom: Wham / Only way is up: Yazz / Hole on (I'm coming): Bluebells / Temptation: Heaven 17 / Ain't nobody: Rufus & Chaka Khan / Back to life: Soul II Soul / All around the world: Stansfield, Lisa / Look of love: ABC / Stop: Erasure / Only you: Yazoo / Song

<hr>

for whoever: Beautiful South / You got it: Orbison, Roy / Heaven is a place on earth: Carlisle, Belinda / Alone: Heart / Moonlight shadow: Oldfield, Mike / China in your hand: T'Pau / Drive: Cars / Vienna: Ultravox / Enola Gay: OMD
VTDCD 68 / Oct '95 / Virgin

☐ BEST ALBUM IN THE WORLD...EVER VOL.1, THE (2CD Set)
Alright: Supergrass / Girls and boys: Blur / Waking up: Elastica / Girls from mars: Ash / Whatever: Oasis / Girl like you: Collins, Edwyn / Only one I know: Charlatans / Do you remember the first time: Pulp / Yes: McAlmont & Butler / Everyday is like Sunday: Morrissey / High and dry: Radiohead / Zombie: Cranberries / Today: Smashing Pumpkins / La tristesse durera (Scream to a sigh): Manic Street Preachers / Sit down: James / Wake up boo: Boo Radleys / Animal nitrate: Suede / This is music: Verve / I want you: Inspiral Carpets / Screamager: Therapy / This charming man: Smiths / April skies: Jesus & Mary Chain / Supersonic: Oasis / Fools gold: Stone Roses / Connected: Stereo MC's / Out of space: Prodigy / Destination eschaton: Shamen / True faith '94: New Order / Leave home: Chemical Brothers / Bullet: Fluke / Loaded: Primal Scream / Unbelievable: EMF / Real real real: Jesus Jones / Personal Jesus: Depeche Mode / Chemical world: Blur / Fifteen years: Levellers / Lenny Valentino: Auteurs / I can dream: Skunk Anansie / Captain Dread: Dreadzone / Lifeforms: Future Sound Of London
VTDCD 58 / Sep '95 / Virgin

☐ BEST ALBUM IN THE WORLD...EVER VOL.2, THE (2CD Set)
Wonderwall: Oasis / Wild wood: Weller, Paul / Creep: Radiohead / Fine time: Cast / Common people: Pulp / Life of riley: Lightning Seeds / Parklife: Blur / He's on the phone: St. Etienne / What do I do now: Sleeper / Hope street: Levellers / Caught by the fuzz: Supergrass / Hobo humpin' slobo babe: Whale / Angel interceptor: Ash / Single girl: Lush / Connection: Elastica / Queer: Garbage / She bangs the drum: Stone Roses / Blue Monday: New Order / How soon is now: Smiths / It's oh so quiet: Bjork / Little Britain: Dreadzone / Country house: Blur / Size of a cow: Wonder Stuff / Stardust: Menswear / Cigarettes and alcohol: Oasis / Kicky door: Mondays / Movin on up: Primal Scream / More you ignore me, the closer I get: Morrissey / History: Verve / Stay together: Suede / Just when you're thinking things over: Charlatans / Far gone and out: Jesus & Mary Chain / Great things: Echobelly / Might be right: Wannadies / Weak: Skunk Anansie / Life is sweet: Chemical Brothers / Tosh: Fluke / Protection: Massive Attack / You do: McAlmont & Butler
VTDCD 76 / Jan '96 / Virgin

☐ BEST ALBUM IN THE WORLD...EVER VOL.3, THE (2CD Set)
Firestarter: Prodigy / Open up: Leftfield / Lust for life: Iggy Pop / Caught out: Supergrass / Don't look back in anger: Oasis / Sandstorm: Cast / You've got it bad: Ocean Colour Scene / Stupid girl: Garbage / Pure: Lightning Seeds / What the world is waiting for: Stone Roses / Street spirit (fade out): Radiohead / Stars: Dubstar / Universal: Blur / Only love can break your heart: St. Etienne / Temptation: New Order / Garden: Levellers / Weirdo: Charlatans / Kung fu: Ash / Born slippy: Underworld / Changing man: Weller, Paul / Around we way: Oasis / Step on: Happy Mondays / Inbetweener: Sleeper / Ladykillers: Lush / Perseverance: Terrorvision / Whole lotta love: Goldbug / Spaceman: Babylon Zoo / Sleeping in: Menswear / Time: Marion / King of the kerb: Echobelly / My legendary girlfriend: Pulp / Stutter: Elastica / Selling Jesus: Skunk Anansie / Chemical beats: Chemical Brothers / Stay: 60ft Dolls / Sparky's dream: Teenage Fanclub / For the dead: Gene / Life, love and unity: Dreadzone / Sly: Massive Attack
VTDCD 84 / Apr '96 / Virgin

☐ BEST ALBUM IN THE WORLD...EVER VOL.4, THE (2CD Set)
Some might say: Oasis / Alright: Cast / Day we caught the train: Ocean Colour Scene / Design for life: Manic Street Preachers / Trash: Suede / Goldfinger: Ash / Sale of the century: Sleeper / In a room: Dodgy / Sense: Lightning Seeds / Female of the species: Space / One to another: Charlatans / Loops of fury: Chemical Brothers / Born slippy: Underworld / No good part time lover: Dubstar / Army of me: Bjork / Inner city life: Goldie / Walking wounded: Everything But The Girl / Step it up: Stereo MC's / Not so manic now: Dubstar / Sunflower: Weller, Paul / Orange crush: REM / Panic: Smiths / Charmless man: Blur / Fast: Teenage Fanclub / Presidents Of The USA / On a rope: Rocket From The Crypt / All I want: Skunk Anansie / Love spreads: Stone Roses / Only happy when it rains: Garbage / Oh yeah: Ash / You're gorgeous: Baby Bird / If you don't want me to destroy you: Stone Roses / Far: Longpigs / Stripper vicar: Mansun / Where have you been tonight: Shed Seven / Just the one: Levellers / Teenage angst: Placebo / Safe from harm: Massive Attack / 6 underground: Sneaker Pimps / Masterplan: Oasis
VTDCD 96 / Oct '96 / Virgin

☐ BEST ALBUM IN THE WORLD...EVER VOL.5, THE (2CD Set)
Sorted for E's and whizz: Pulp / Tattva: Kula Shaker / Live forever: Oasis / Everything must go: Manic Street Preachers / Beetlebum: Blur / Nancy boy: Placebo / Ain't talkin' 'bout dub: Apollo 440 / Breathe: Prodigy / Scooby snacks: Fun Lovin' Criminals / Wide open space: Mansun / Female of the species: Space / Return of the Mack: Morales, Mark / Garage / Hedonism: Skunk Anansie / Beautiful ones: Suede / Day before yesterday's man: Supernaturals / Ahm's gone: Mansun / Bentnel: Nice guy Eddie: Sleeper / Getting better: Shed Seven / Lump: Presidents Of The USA / Into the blue: Geneva / Pearl's girl: Underworld / Out of the sinking: Weller, Paul / Roll with it: Oasis / Riverboat song: Ocean Colour Scene / What's the frenzy: Kenneth / REM / Hush: Deep Purple / Flying: Cast / Dark clouds: Space / Lucky you: Lightning Seeds / There she goes: La's / Good enough: Dodgy / Your woman: White Town / Candy girl: Baby Bird / Lopez: 808 State & James Dean Bradfield / One night stand: Aloof / Fake plastic trees: Radiohead / Lost myself: Longpigs / Easy / Terrorvision / I am the resurrection: Stone Roses
VTDCD 120 / Mar '97 / Virgin

<hr>

☐ BEST ALBUM IN THE WORLD...EVER VOL.6, THE (2CD Set)
Paranoid android: Radiohead / Song 2: Blur / Richard III: Supergrass / This is a call: Foo Fighters / Novocaine for the soul: Eels / North country boy: Charlatans / Free me: Cast / Australia: Manic Street Preachers / Hey dude: Kula Shaker / Disco 2000: Pulp / What do you want from me: Monaco / Smile: Supernaturals / Sun: Lydon, John / Copper girl: 3 Colours Red / King of New York: Fun Lovin' Criminals / 6 underground: Sneaker Pimps / Home: Depeche Mode / Star: Primal Scream / Ready to go: Republica / Place your hands: Reef / Swallowed: Bush / Ain't that enough: Teenage Fanclub / Made of stone: Stone Roses / Lazy: Suede / If you really want to know: Ether / Tranquilizer: Geneva / She makes my noise bleed: Mansun / Strumpet: My Life Story / Just another illusion: Hurricane / Bruise Pristine: Placebo / OPunka: Kenickie / We have explosive: Future Sound Of London / Absurd: Fluke / Hermann loves Pauline: Super Furry Animals / On your own: Verve / Staying out for the summer: Dodgy
VTDCD 136 / Jul '97 / Virgin

☐ BEST ANTHEMS IN THE WORLD...EVER VOL.1, THE (2CD Set)
VTDCD 154 / 13 Oct '97 / Virgin

☐ BEST ANTHEMS IN THE WORLD...EVER VOL.2, THE (2CD Set)
Ballad of Tom Jones: Space / Sexy boy: Air / Local boy in the photograph: Stereophonics / Nanny in Manhattan: Lilys / Brimful of Asha: Cornershop / It's like that: Run DMC & Jason Nevins / Common people: Pulp / Everything must go: Manic Street Preachers / Lump: Presidents Of The USA / Karma police: Radiohead / Blinded by the sun: Seahorses / Step on: Happy Mondays / Loaded: Primal Scream / Here's where the story ends: Sundays / She bangs the drum: Stone Roses / This charming man: Smiths / Live forever: Oasis / Riverboat song: Ocean Colour Scene / Out of the sinking: Weller, Paul / Passenger: Iggy Pop / In the name of the father: Black Grape / Richard III: Supergrass / One to another: Charlatans
VTDCD 183 / 6 Apr '98 / Virgin

☐ BEST BANDS IN COUNTRY, THE
DC 886022 / 2 Feb '98 / Disky

☐ BEST CHOICE
DCD 5388 / Jul '94 / Disky

☐ BEST CHRISTMAS ALBUM IN THE WORLD...EVER, THE (2CD Set)
Happy Christmas (war is over): Lennon, John & Yoko Ono / Wonderful Christmas time: McCartney, Paul / I wish it could be Christmas everyday: Wizzard / Merry Christmas everybody: Slade / Do they know it's christmas: Band Aid / Fairytale of New York: Pogues & Kirsty MacColl / I believe in Father Christmas: Lake, Greg / 2000 miles: Pretenders / Spaceman came travelling: De Burgh, Chris / Power of love: Frankie Goes To Hollywood / Driving home for Christmas: Rea, Chris / Step into Christmas: John, Elton / Merry Christmas everyone: Stevens, Shakin' / Another rock 'n' roll Christmas: Glitter, Gary / Little Saint Nick: Beach Boys / Santa Claus is coming to town: Jackson Five / In dulce jubilo: Oldfield, Mike / Stop the cavalry: Lewie, Jona / Christmas wrapping: Waitresses / Ring out, solstice bells: Jethro Tull / Peace on earth/Little drummer boy: Crosby, Bing & David Bowie / White Christmas: Crosby, Bing / Christmas song: Cole, Nat 'King' / Let it snow, let it snow, let it snow: Martin, Dean / Mary's boy child: Belafonte, Harry / When a child is born: Mathis, Johnny / Mistletoe and wine: Richard, Cliff / Walking in the air: Jones, Aled / I believe: Robson & Jerome / Winter wonderland: Dors, Doris / Lonely pup (in a Christmas shop): Faith, Adam / Rockin' around the Christmas tree: Mel & Kim / Last Christmas: State Of The Heart / Happy holiday: Williams, Andy / Santa baby: Kitt, Eartha / Lonely this Christmas: Mud / Pretty paper: Orbison, Roy / Silver bells: Reeves, Jim / God rest ye merry gentlemen: Como, Perry / We wish you a merry christmas: Weavers / Twelve days of Christmas: Sinners / Gaudete: Steeleye Span / In the bleak midwinter: Jansch, Bert / What are you doing New Year's eve: O'Hara, Mary Margaret
VTDCD 103 / 3 Nov '97 / Virgin

☐ BEST CHRISTMAS ALBUM...EVER, THE (2CD Set)
Do they know it's Christmas: Band Aid / Last Christmas: Wham / Step into Christmas: John, Elton / Santa Claus is coming to town: Jackson Five / Merry Christmas everybody: Slade / In dulci jubilo: Oldfield, Mike / Stop the cavalry: Lewie, Jona / Another rock 'n' roll Christmas: Glitter, Gary / Mary had a little boy: Snap / Ring out, solstice bells: Jethro Tull / Saviour's day: Richard, Cliff / Wall of Kintyre: Wings / Spaceman came travelling: De Burgh, Chris / Winter's tale: Essex, David / Keeping the dream alive: Freiheit / Peace on earth - little drummer boy: Bowie, David & Bing Crosby / White Christmas: Crosby, Bing / Let it snow, let it snow, let it snow: Martin, Dean / Christmas song: Fitzgerald, Ella / Winter wonderland: Day, Doris / Warm December: London, Julie / Merry Christmas darling: Carpenters / Santa baby: Kitt, Eartha / Happy holiday: Williams, Andy / Lonely pup (in a Christmas shop): Faith, Adam / Blue Christmas: Nelson, Willie / Silver bells: Reeves, Jim / Mary's boy child: Belafonte, Harry / Twelve days of Christmas: Daugherty, Jack / Gaudete: Steeleye Span / Winter Wonderland: Temptations / Only you: Flying Pickets / Walking in the air: Jones, Aled / Christmas wrapping: Waitresses / Sadness part 1: Enigma / Merry Christmas everyone: Stevens, Shakin'
VTDCD 23 / Oct '95 / Virgin

☐ BEST CLUB ANTHEMS...EVER VOL.1, THE (2CD Set)
Professional widow: Amos, Tori / Where love lives: Limerick, Alison / Don't you want me: Felix / I'm alive: Stretch 'n' Vern / I fairground: Simply Red / Klubhopping: Klubb Heads / Jumpin': Lisa Marie Experience / Scared: Slacker / Higher state of consciousness: Wink, Josh / Pearl river: Darryl Pandy / Born slippy: Underworld / Bolland, C.J. / Nightmare: Brainbug / Argentina: Healy, Jeremy & Amos / Bellissima: DJ Quicksilver / Children: Miles, Robert / Seven days and one week: BBE / Nighttrain: Kadoc / People of love: Amen UK / Turn on tune in cop out: Freakpower / Baby come back: Pato Banton / Right in the night (fall in love with music): Jam & Spoon / Run away: Real McCoy / Whoomp (there it is): Tag Team / Firestarter: Prodigy / If you want me: Human League / Baby: Corona / Ready or go: Papa's got a brand new

pig bag): Perfecto All Stars / Cry India: Umboza / Fee fi fo fum: Candy Girls / Sweet harmony: Liquid / U sure do: Strike / Not over yet: Grace / Your loving arms: Martin, Billie Ray / Set you free: N-Trance / Axel F: Clock / Keep warm: Jinny / Shoot me with your love: D:Ream / I need you: Deuce / Freedom: Gayle, Michelle / Mary Jane (all night long): Blige, Mary J. / My prerogative: Brown, Bobby / La luna (to the beat of the drum): Ethics / I'm ready: Size 9

VTDCD 67 / Oct '95 / Virgin

☐ BEST DANCE ALBUM IN THE WORLD...EVER VOL.5, THE

Right in the night: Jam & Spoon / Excited: M-People / Dreamer: Livin' Joy / Don't give me your life: Alex Party / Scatman: Scatman John / Don't stop (Wiggle wiggle): Outhere Brothers / Bomb: Bucketheads / Humpin' around: Brown, Bobby / Push the feeling on: Nightcrawlers / Another night: Real McCoy / Zombie: ADAM & Amy / Whoomp (There it is): Clock / Cotton eye Joe: Rednex / Got to get it: Culture Beat / Baby baby: Corona / What's up: DJ Miko / Call it love: Deuce / Set you free: N-Trance / Reach up: Perfecto All Stars

VIDCD 55 / Jul '95 / Virgin

☐ BEST DANCE ALBUM IN THE WORLD...EVER VOL.7, THE (2CD Set)

Free: Ultra Nate / Closer than close: Gaines, Rosie / Professional widow: Amos, Tori / Ecuador: Sash / Bellissima: DJ Quicksilver / Freed from desire: Gala / Who do you think you are: Spice Girls / Fastlove: Michael, George / I'm alive: Stretch n' Vern / Keep on jumpin': Terry, Todd / Remember me: Blueboy / One and one: Miles, Robert / Ready or not: Course / Lovefool: Cardigans / Belo horizonti: Heartists / Not over yet: Grace / Block rockin' beats: Chemical Brothers / Saint: Orbital / Higher state of consciousness: Wink, Josh / Seven days and one week: BBE / Nightmare: Brainbug / Piece of my heart: Shaggy / I wanna be the only one: Eternal / Everybody: Backstreet Boys / Bodyshakin': 911 / Flava: Andre, Peter / Fresh: Gina G / Macarena: Los Del Rio / Ain't nobody: Course / Encore une fois: Sash / You got the love: Source & Candi Staton / People hold on: Stansfield, Lisa / Let the veat hit 'em: Shena / Blurred: Pianoman / Shake your body down: Full Intention / Give me love: Diddy / Stamp: Healy, Jeremy & Amos / Rock da house: Tall Paul / Passion: Amen UK / Somebody like you: Elate

VTDCD 138 / 4 Aug '97 / Virgin

☐ BEST DANCE ALBUM IN THE WORLD...EVER VOL.8, THE (2CD Set))

VTDCD 196 / 13 Jul '98 / Virgin

☐ BEST DANCE ALBUM OF THE YEAR, THE (2CD Set)

No way: Freakpower / Feel it: Ultra Nate / Rose is still a rose: Franklin, Aretha / Angel st.: M-People / So good: Roberts, Juliet / It's like that: Run DMC & Jason Nevins / Fight for your right (to party): NYCC / Renegade master '98: Wildchild / Sounds of wickedness: Tzant / Superstar: Novy, Tom & Eniac / Can you feel it: CLS / Treat infamy: Rest Assured / Don't play dead: Vapourheadz Zone / Brimful of asha: Cornershop / Uh la la la: Alexia / Lovin' you: UBM / Choose life: PF Project & Ewan McGregor / Never ever: All Saints / Bamboogie: Bamboo / Get up stand up: Phunky Phantom / Move on up: Trickster / Kung fu: 187 Lockdown / Anytime: Nu Birth / London Town: JDS / Another groove: Another Level & Double 99 / Nobody better: Moore, Tina / R U sleeping: Indo / Ready for a new day: Terry, Todd / This is it: State Of Mind / More: De'Lacy / Word is love: Voices Of Life / Fun: Da Mob & Jocelyn Brown / Slide: Junkster / It's tricky: Run DMC & Jason Nevins / Show me love: Robyn

RADCD 97 / 5 May '98 / Global TV

☐ BEST DANCE HALL

RNCD 2053 / Mar '94 / Rhino

☐ BEST DISCO ALBUM IN THE WORLD...EVER VOL.1, THE (2CD Set)

I feel love: Summer, Donna / Funky town: Lipps Inc. / Shake your body (down to the ground): Jacksons / Boogie wonderland: Earth, Wind & Fire/The Emotions / Upside down: Ross, Diana / Le freak: Chic / Ladies night: Kool & The Gang / Young hearts run free: Staton, Candi / Jump to the beat: Lattisaw, Stacy / I'm every woman: Khan, Chaka / He's the greatest dancer: Sister Sledge / Get down tonight: KC & The Sunshine Band / Disco inferno: Trammps / Use it up, wear it out: Odyssey / Lady Marmalade: Labelle / Working my way back to you: Detroit Spinners / Boogie oogie oogie: Taste Of Honey / Shame: King, Evelyn 'Champagne' / Boogie nights: Heatwave / More than a woman: Tavares / Rock your baby: McCrae, George / Never never gonna give you up: White, Barry / I will survive: Gaynor, Gloria / YMCA: Village People / Instant replay: Hartman, Dan / Best disco in town: Ritchie Family / Stars on 45 Abba medley: Starsound / Stayin' alive: N-Trance / Get up and boogie: Silver Convention / Shame shame shame: Shirley & Company / Feels like I'm in love: Marie, Kelly / Black is black: La Belle Epoque / DISCO: Ottawan / Rasputin: Boney M / Spacer: Sheila B. Devotion / Love sensation: Holloway, Loleatta / Let's all chant: Zager, Michael Band / I can make you feel good: Shalamar / And the beat goes on: Whispers / Car wash: Rose Royce / I shoulda loved ya: Walden, Narada Michael / Can you feel the force: Real Thing / You make me feel (Mighty real): Sylvester / Knock on wood: Stewart, Amii

VTDCD 143 / 9 Feb '98 / Virgin

☐ BEST DISCO ALBUM IN THE WORLD...EVER VOL.2, THE (2CD Set)

Hot stuff: Summer, Donna / Good times: Chic / More than more: True, Andrea Connection / Strut your funky stuff: Frantique / I'm coming out: Ross, Diana / Theme from Shaft: Hayes, Isaac / Native New Yorker: Odyssey / Get up I feel like being a sex machine: Brown, James / We are family: Sister Sledge / Don't let me be misunderstood: Santa Esmerelda & Leroy Gomez / Is it love your after: Rose Royce / Forget me nots: Rushen, Patrice / Armed and extremely dangerous: First Choice / From east to west: Voyage / Heaven must be missing an angel: Tavares / Da ya think I'm sexy: N-Trance & Rod Stewart / Never can say goodbye: Gaynor, Gloria / Relight my fire: Hartman, Dan / TSOP: MFSB / Ain't no stoppin' us now: McFadden & Whitehead / Shake your booty: KC & The Sunshine Band / Keep on jumpin': Musique / Best of my love: Emotions / That's the way I like it: KC & The Sunshine Band / Night on broadway: Staton, Candi / This is it: Moore, Melba / Rock me gently: Kim, Andy / Ain't nobody: Rufus & Chaka Khan / Don't stop the music: Yarbrough & Peoples / If I can't have you: Elliman, Yvonne / Do what you wanna do: T-Connection / Oops upside your head: Gap Band / You to me are everything: Real Thing / Kung fu fighting: Douglas, Carl / In the navy: Village People / Pick up the pieces: Average White Band / You sexy thing: Hot Chocolate / Love machine: Miracles / Celebration: Kool & The Gang / Ma Baker: Boney M

VTDCD 191 / 18 May '98 / Virgin

☐ BEST EVER COLLECTION OF IRISH PUB SONGS VOL.1, THE

On Raglan road: Kelly, Luke / Irish Rover: Drew, Ronnie / Ferryman: Dublin City Ramblers / Sweet sixteen: Fureys / Lonesome boatman: Innisfree Ceoil / Town I love so well: Reilly, Paddy / Steal away: Fureys / Holy ground: Dubliners / Song for Ireland: Kelly, Luke / Streets of New York: Brier Folk / Follow me up to Carlow: McCann, Jim / Spanish lady: Dubliners / Danny Boy: Locke, Josef / Dicey Riley: Drew, Ronnie / Mary from Dungloe: Spiceland, Emmet / Boolavogue: Dubliners / Auld triangle: Drew, Ronnie / Fiddler's green: Marks Men / Fairmoyle lasses/Sportin' Paddy: Dubliners / God save Ireland: Dubliners

CDIRL 506 / May '97 / Outlet

☐ BEST EVER COLLECTION OF IRISH PUB SONGS VOL.2, THE

Fields of Athenry: Reilly, Paddy / Sick-note: Dubliners / Dublin in the rare auld times: Kelly, Luke / Green fields of France: Fureys & Davey Arthur / Cliffs of Dooneen: Innisfree Ceoil / Grace: Shamrog / Carrickfergus: Reilly, Paddy / Wild rover: Drew, Ronnie / Spancil hill: Reilly, Paddy / Flight of the Earls: Brier Folk / John O'Dreams: Dublin City Ramblers / Johnston's motor car: Drew, Ronnie / Galway races: Reilly, Paddy / Crack was ninety: Dublin City Ramblers / Wild colonial boy: Cane, Oliver / Black velvet band: Kelly, Luke / Belfast Mill: Dublin City Ramblers / Rose of Allendale: Reilly, Paddy / Mursheen Durkin: McEvoy, Johnny / A nation once again: Dubliners

CDIRL 507 / May '97 / Outlet

☐ BEST EVER SUMMER ALBUM, THE

Beach boys: Beach Boys / Let's got to San Francisco: Flowerpot Men / Summer breeze: Isley Brothers / Long hot summer: Style Council / Summer: Goldsboro, Bobby / Albatross: Fleetwood Mac / Bamboleo: Gipsy Kings / La bamba: Los Lobos / Diggin' your scene: Blow Monkeys / Sunny afternoon: Kinks / Sitting in the park: Fame, Georgie / Perfect day: Reed, Lou / San Francisco: McKenzie, Scott / Surf city: Jan & Dean / Surfin' USA: Astronauts / Walking on sunshine: Katrina & The Waves / In the summertime: Mungo Jerry / Here comes summer: Keller, Jerry / Summer holiday: Richard, Cliff / Dream a little dream of me: Mamas & The Papas

74321383162 / Jun '97 / RCA

☐ BEST EVER TRADITIONAL IRISH PUB SESSION VOL.1, THE

CDIRL 508 / 19 Jan '98 / Outlet

☐ BEST FOOTIE ANTHEMS IN THE WORLD...EVER VOL.1, THE (2CD Set)

We are the champions: Queen / World in motion: New Order & England World Cup Squad / Three lions: Lightning Seeds & David Baddiel/Frank Skinner / Back home: England 1970 World Cup Squad / Match of the day: Offside / Life of Riley: Lightning Seeds / Fog on the Tyne: Gazza & Lindisfarne / Anfield rap: Liverpool FC / You'll never walk alone: Gerry & The Pacemakers / Wonderwall: Oasis / Sportsnight: Hatch, Tony / Belfast boy: Fardon, Don / Come on you reds: Manchester United FC / Move move move (The Red Tribe): Manchester United FC/Stryker / Ooo aah Eric Cantona: 1300 Drums / Grandstand: Mansfield, Keith / Football crazy: Hall, Robin & Jimmy MacGregor / Alright: Hall, Robin & Jimmy MacGregor / Parklife: Blur / Blue is the colour: Chelsea FC / Diamond lights: Glenn & Chris / Ossie's dream: Tottenham Hotspur FC / Nice one Cyril: Cockerel Chorus / Nessun dorma: Pavarotti, Luciano / Ode to joy / Always look on the bright side of life: Monty Python

VTCD 94 / Jun '96 / Virgin

☐ BEST FOOTIE ANTHEMS IN THE WORLD...EVER VOL.2, THE (2CD Set)

VTDCD 193 / 15 Jun '98 / Virgin

☐ BEST FUNK ALBUM IN THE WORLD...EVER VOL.1, THE

(Get up I feel like being a) Sex machine: Brown, James / Funky stuff: Kool & The Gang / Oops upside your head: Gap Band / She's strange: Cameo / My lovin': En Vogue / If you're ready (come go with me): Staple Singers / Family affair: Sly & The Family Stone / Inner city blues: Gaye, Marvin / Green onions: Booker T & The MG's / Papa was a rollin' stone: Was Not Was / Cloud 9: Temptations / Yum yum (gimme some): Fatback Band / Give up the funk: Parliament / Which way is up: Starguard / Ain't nothin' goin' on but the rent: Guthrie, Gwen / I gotcha: Tex, Joe / Got to get you into my life: Earth, Wind & Fire / Fire: Ohio Players / Use me: Withers, Bill / Good times: Chic / Strut your funky stuff: Frantique / Get down tonight: KC & The Sunshine Band / Pick up the pieces: Average White Band / Papa's got a brand new pigbag: Pigbag / Higher ground: Red Hot Chili Peppers / Rockit: Hancock, Herbie / Theme from S'Express: S'Express / Something got me started: Simply Red / Once you get started: Rufus / Atomic dog: Clinton, George / I feel sanctified: Commodores / Sunshine day: Osibisa / Hard work: Handy, John / Never, never gonna give you up: White, Barry / Mr. Big Stuff: Knight, Jean / Ain't gonna bump no more (with no big fat woman): Tex, Joe / Where is the love: Wright, Betty / Right place, wrong time: Dr. John

VTDCD 44 / Feb '95 / Virgin

☐ BEST FUNK ALBUM IN THE WORLD...EVER VOL.2, THE (2CD Set)

Funky stuff: Kool & The Gang / Word up: Cameo / Atomic dog: Clinton, George / (Get up I feel like being a) Sex machine: Brown, James / Shaft: Hayes, Isaac / Superfly: Mayfield, Curtis / That lady: Isley Brothers / Use me: Withers, Bill / Funky Nassau: Beginning Of The End / Dance to the music: Sly & The Family Stone / Lady Marmalade: Labelle / Brick house: Commodores / Funkin' for Jamaica: Browne, Tom / Behind the groove: Marie, Teena / Which way is up: Starguard / Carwash: Rose Royce / Shoorah Shoorah: Wright, Betty / Shack up: Banbarra / Le freak: Chic / Tell me something good: Rufus / Oops upside your head: Gap Band / Give up the funk (tear the roof off the sucker): Parliament / Mr. Big Stuff: Knight, Jean / If you're ready (come go with me): Staple Singers / Wicky wacky: Fatback Band / Saturday nite: Earth, Wind & Fire / Fire: Ohio Players / Get down tonight: KC & The Sunshine Band / Nutbush City limits: Turner, Ike & Tina / Play that funky music: Wild Cherry / War: Starr, Edwin / Pick up the pieces: Average White Band / Move on up: Mayfield, Curtis / Green onions: Booker T & The MG's / Do what you wanna do: T-Connection / I gotcha: Tex, Joe / Rockit: Hancock, Herbie / Movin': Brass Connection / Expansions: Smith, Lonnie Liston / Revolution will not be televised: Scott-Heron, Gil

VTDCD 126 / Aug '97 / Virgin

☐ BEST GIRL POWER ALBUM EVER, THE (2CD Set)

Who do you think you are: Spice Girls / Professional widow: Amos, Tori / Sisters are doing it for themselves: Eurythmics & Aretha Franklin / Ready to go: Republica / Weak: Skunk Anansie / Free your mind: En Vogue / Lady marmalade: Labelle / I'm every woman: Khan, Chaka / Give me a little more time: Gabrielle / Dancing in the street: Reeves, Martha & The Vandellas / Respect: Franklin, Aretha / Slowhand: Pointer Sisters / What's love got to do with it: Turner, Tina / Woman: Cherry, Neneh / Superwoman: White, Karyn / I will survive: Savage, Chantay / If you love me: Brownstone / Back and forth: Aaliyah / Mary Jane (All night long): Blige, Mary J. / Freak like me: Howard, Adina / Let's talk about sex: Salt n' Pepa / Wannabe: Spice Girls / (Hey now) Girls just want to have fun: Lauper, Cyndi / Shy guy: King, Diana / Buffalo stance: Cherry, Neneh / Ain't nothin' goin' on but the rent: Guthrie, Gwen / None of your business: Salt n' Pepa / Creep: TLC / Right here: SWV / We are family: Sister Sledge / Heart of glass: Blondie / Heaven is a place on earth: Carlisle, Belinda / Manic Monday: Bangles / Alisha rules the world: Alisha's Attic / You're history: Shakespears Sister / You lied to me: Dennis, Cathy / Supermodel: Rupaul / Short short man: 20 Fingers / It's raining men: Weather Girls / Naked eye: Luscious Jackson / Extremis: Hal & Gillian Anderson

VTDCD 123 / May '97 / Virgin

☐ BEST HIP-HOP ANTHEMS IN THE WORLD...EVER, THE (2CD Set)

Rappers delight: Sugarhill Gang / Rain: Missy Elliot / hand of the dead body: Scarface & Ice Cube / C u when you get there: Coolio / Renegade master 98: Wildchild / Message: Grandmaster Flash & The Furious Five / Say no go: De La Soul / Jump around: House Of Pain / Adventures of flash on the wheels of steel: Grandmaster Flash / It's like that: Run DMC & Jason Nevins / I got 5 on it: Luniz / That's how I'm livin': Ice-T / Wear your love like heaven: Definition Of Sound / Who is it: Mantronix / Buffalo gals: McLaren, Malcolm / Rockit: Hancock, Herbie / It takes two: Rob Base & DJ E-Z Rock / Talkin' all that jazz: Stetsasonic / Don't believe the hype: Public Enemy / Regulate: Warren G / Woo ha (got you all in check): Busta Rhymes / 900 number: 45 King / Tha crossroads: Bone Thugs n' Harmony / It's a shame (my sister): Monie Love / Express yourself: NWA / Eye know: De La Soul / People everyday: Arrested Development / Planet rock: Bambaataa, Afrika & The Soul Sonic Force / OPP: Naughty By Nature / Gangsta's paradise: Coolio & LV / White lines (don't do it): Grandmaster Flash & Melle Mel / It's tricky: Run DMC / Gotta be movin' on up: PM Dawn / Mr. Wendall: Arrested Development / Paid in full: Eric B & Rakim / Walk this way: Run DMC & Aerosmith / I ain't going out like that: Cypress Hill / King of New York: Fun Lovin' Criminals

VTDCD 184 / 13 Apr '98 / Virgin

☐ BEST HOLIDAY ALBUM UNDER THE SUN, THE

Macarena / Saturday night / YMCA/In the navy / Locomotion / DISCO / Walking on sunshine / Lambada / Barbados / Rock the boat / Rivers of Babylon / Una paloma blanca / Hands up / Spirit in the sky / Time warp / In the summertime / Y viva Espana / Itsy bitsy teenie weenie yellow polkadot bikini / Do the conga

ECD 3373 / Jun '97 / K-Tel

☐ BEST IRISH ALBUM IN THE WORLD...EVER, THE (2CD Set)

Harry's Game: Clannad / Riverdance: Anderson, John Concert Orchestra / Island: Keane, Dolores / Rock'n'roll kids: Harrington, Paul & Charlie McGettigan / Maggie: Foster & Allen / Summerfly: O'Connell, Maura / She moved through the fair: Sharkey, Feargal / Song for Ireland: De Danann / When you were sweet sixteen: Fureys & Davey Arthur / Hold me now: Logan, Johnny / Whatever happened to old fashioned love: O'Donnell, Daniel / All kinds of everything: Dana / What's another year: Logan, Johnny / In your eyes: Kavanagh, Niamh / Voice: Quinn, Eimaer / Through the eyes of an Irishman: Kirwan, Dominic / Bunch of thyme: Foster & Allen / Danny boy: O'Donnell, Daniel / Galway bay: Locke, Josef / Hear my song Violetta: Locke, Josef / Whiskey in the jar: Thin Lizzy / Irish rover: Pogues & The Dubliners / Seven drunken nights: Dubliners / Blackbird: Shannon, Sharon / Brown eyed girl: Morrison, Van / Good heart: Sharkey, Feargal / Against the wind: Brennan, Maire / Place among the stones: Spillane, Davy / Homes of Donegal: Brady, Paul / Ride on: Moore, Christy / Carrickfergus: Kennedy, Brian / Thank you for hearing me: O'Connor, Sinead / Manannan/Tir Tairngiri: Breathnach, Maire / Dark haired lass/Biddy from Muckross/Sean Maguire's reels: Altan / Never mind the strangers: Saw Doctors / Black velvet band: Dubliners / Laziest gal in town: Coughlan, Mary / Bee in the bottle: Lohan, Sinead

VTDCD 102 / Oct '96 / Virgin

☐ BEST IRISH PUB SONGS IN THE WORLD

ARCD 028 / May '98 / Ainm

☐ BEST IRISH REQUESTS

DH 002 / Jul '94 / Outlet

☐ BEST JAZZ ALBUM IN THE WORLD...EVER, THE (3CD Set)

Let there be love: Cole, Nat 'King' & George Shearing / I get a kick out of you: Fitzgerald, Ella / Mad about the boy: Washington, Dinah / Fever: Lee, Peggy / Cry me a river: London, Julie / That ole devil called love: Holiday, Billie / Take the 'A' train: Ellington, Duke / Minnie the moocher: Calloway, Cab / Five guy's named Moe: Jordan, Louis / Hello Dolly: Armstrong, Louis / Ain't misbehavin': Waller, Fats / Relax: Redbone, Leon / Summertime: Vaughan, Sarah / Misty: Garner, Erroll / Foggy day: Kessel, Barney / Night and day: Reinhardt, Django / Let's get lost: Baker, Chet / I wish I knew: Taylor, Billy Trio / Kid from Red Bank: Basie, Count / Take five: Brubeck, Dave / Birdland: Weather Report / Running away: Ayers, Roy / Watermelon man: Santamaria, Mongo / Moondance: Fame, Georgie & Van Morrison / Do nothin' 'til you hear from me: Allison, Mose / Wade in the water: Lewis, Ramsey Trio / Dropping bombs on the Whitehouse: Style Council / Blue rondo a la Turk: Jarreau, Al / So what: Jordan, Ronny / Breezin': Benson, George / Morning dance: Spyro Gyra / Last night at danceland: Crawford, Randy / Girl from Ipanema: State Of The Heart / Travels: Metheny, Pat / So what: Davis, Miles / Cantaloupe island: Hancock, Herbie / 'Round midnight: Monk, Thelonious / Song for my Father: Andy, Horace / Sidewinder: Morgan, Lee / Moanin': Blakey, Art / Midnight blue: Burrell, Kenny / Eleanor Rigby: Jordan, Stanley / Goodbye Pork Pie Hat: Mingus, Charles / Ornithology: Parker, Charlie / Blue train: Coltrane, John

VTDCD 93 / Aug '96 / Virgin

☐ BEST JOVENES FLAMENCOS, THE

El vito cante / Jaleo pa las flamencas / Vengo del mora / Mi tio el nini miguel / El reloj del carino / Lo bueno y lo malo / Vuela, vuela pajarito / Chana / Venta zoraida / Chicuelina / Nubes de colores / De perdidos al rio / Anonimo jerezano / Que no quiero dinero / Piel de habichuela / Refrito

93042 / Feb '95 / Emocion

☐ BEST LATINO CARNIVAL IN THE WORLD...EVER, THE (2CD Set)

Bamboleo: Gipsy Kings / La bamba: Los Lobos / Lambada: Kaoma / Macarena: Los Del Rio / Samba de Janeiro: Bellini / Ecuador: Sash / Oye como va: Puente, Tito Jr. & The Latin Rhythm / Belo horizonti: Heartists / Cuba: Gibson Brothers / Guaglione: Prado, Perez 'Prez' / Tequila: Champs / Soul limbo: Booker T & The MG's / Hot hot hot: Arrow / Beginning of the end: Funky Nassau / Namorada: Brown, Carlinhos / Samba magic: Summer Daze / Latinos del mundo: Latin Thing / Healy Argentina: Healy, Jeremy & Amos / Rhythm of the night: Corona / Spiller from Rio: Corona / I go to Rio: Allen, Peter / Desafinado: Michael, George & Astrud Gilberto / Oye mi canto: Estefan, Gloria / Don't let me be misunderstood: Estefan, Gloria / Al nagalisa: Cortes, Joaquin / Soul bossa nova: Jones, Quincy / Mas que nada: Mendes, Sergio & Brasil '66 / Guantanmera: Sandpipers / More I see you: Montez, Chris / Gonna get along without ya now: Lopez, Trini / Spanish flea: Mexicans / La colegiala: Rodolfo Y Su Tipica RA 7 / Watermelon man: Mongo Santamaria / Light my fire: Feliciano, Jose / No chore mais: Gil, Gilberto / Cravo e canela: Nascimento, Milton / Samba pa ti: Santana / Atlantic avenue: Average White Band / Afro blue: Santamaria, Mongo / Volare: Martin, Dean

VTDCD 152 / 4 Aug '97 / Virgin

☐ BEST LOVE SONGS EVER, THE (2CD Set)

Just when I needed you / Only a fool: Lee, Byron & Mighty Sparrow / Move closer: Nelson, Phyllis / Can I get there by candlelight: McWilliams, David / Feelings: Albert, Morris / Only you: Flying Pickets / Rock me tonight: Jackson, Freddie / Cryin': McLean, Don / Classic: Gurvitz, Adrian / When I need you: Sayer, Leo / Tonight I celebrate my love: Bryson, Peabo & Roberta Flack / Suddenly: Ocean, Billy / Time in a bottle: Croce, Jim / Have you seen her: Chi-Lites / I will: Winters, Ruby / Sharing the night together: Dr. Hook / Love don't live here anymore: Nail, Jimmy / True: Spandau Ballet / Sad eyes: John, Robert / You could have been with me: Easton, Sheena / Loving you: Riperton, Minnie / No regrets: Ure, Midge / Orchard road: Sayer, Leo / Everybody's gotta learn sometime: Korgis / You make my life so beautiful: Harvey, Alex / Kayleigh: Marillion / Everytime I think of me: Babys / Air that I breathe: Babys / Missing you: Waite, John / Emma: Hot Chocolate

DOU 882452 / 2 Feb '98 / Disky

☐ BEST LOVED CHRISTMAS CAROLS

Hark the herald angels sing / Unto us is born a son / O little town of Bethlehem / Holly and the ivy / Away in a manger / Three Kings / O come all ye faithful (adeste fidelis) / First Noel / I saw three ships / Deck the hall / Ding dong merrily on high / Tomorrow shall be my dancing day / Of the father's heart / Cherry tree carol / I came upon a midnight clear / O come, O come Emmanuel / Once in Royal David's City / Sussex carol / As with gladness men of old / Hail blessed Virgin Mary / Jesus Christ the apple tree / Seven songs of Mary

XMAS 010 / Nov '96 / Tring

☐ BEST LOVED IRISH SONGS, THE

ARAN 3608 / 5 May '98 / Dara

☐ BEST MIX...EVER, THE (2CD Set)

Pump up the volume: MARRS / Theme from S'Express: S'Express / Boombastic: Shaggy / Groove is in the heart: Deee-Lite / Killer: Adamski / Fastlove: Michael, George / One night in heaven: M-People / Rhythm is a dancer: Snap / Pump up the jam: Technotronic / Push the feeling on: Nightcrawlers / Things can only get better: D:Ream / I like to move it: Reel 2 Real / Dreamer: Livin' Joy / Real thing: Di Bart, Tony / Rhythm of the night: Corona / Give it up: Goodmen / My love is for real: Strike / Don't you want me: Human League / Stamp: Healy, Jeremy & Amos / Born slippy (Nuxx): Underworld / All that she wants: Ace Of Base / Boom shake the room: DJ Jazzy Jeff & The Fresh Prince / Walk this way: Run DMC / Oh what a night (December '63): Clock / Gonna make you sweat (everybody dance now): C&C Music Factory / She's got that vibe: Kelly, R / Crazy: Morrison, Mark / What is love: Haddaway / It's my life: Dr. Alban / I luv U baby: Original / Don't give me your life: Alex Party / Son of a gun: JX / Temptation: Heaven 17 / Wannabe: Spice Girls / Mr. Vain: Culture Beat / Boom boom boom: Outhere Brothers / U got 2 let the music: Cappella / Right in the night (fall in love with music): Jam & Spoon / Reach up (Papa's got a brand new Pigbag): Perfecto All Stars / Seven days and one week: BBE

VTDCD 108 / Nov '96 / Virgin

☐ **BEST OF 2-TONE, THE**
Ghost town: *Specials* / On my radio: *Selecter* / Too much too young: *Special AKA* / Do nothing: *Specials* / People do rock steady: *Bodysnatchers* / Stereotype: *Specials* / Prince: *Madness* / Rat race: *Specials* / Boiler: *Rhoda & Special A.K.A.* / I can't stand up for falling down: *Costello, Elvis* / Nelson Mandela: *Special AKA* / Missing words: *Selecter* / Message to you Rudy: *Specials* / Selecter: *Selecter*
CDCHRTT 5012 / Nov '93 / Chrysalis

☐ **BEST OF 90'S COUNTRY, THE**
If tomorrow never comes: *Brooks, Garth* / Shotgun: *Tucker, Tanya* / Never ending song of love: *Gayle, Crystal* / On a good night: *Campbell, Glen* / I'm a survivor: *Dalton, Lacy J.* / My side of the story: *Bogguss, Suzy* / Race is on: *Brown, Sawyer* / On the bayou: *Wild Rose* / Moonshadow Road: *Brown, T. Graham* / Other side of love: *Davies, Gail* / Do you know where your man is: *Mandrell, Barbara* / Good times: *Seals, Dan* / Everything: *Chapman, Cee Cee* / What would you do about you (if you were me): *Osmond, Marie* / Country girl heart: *Gatlin, Larry & The Gatlin Brothers* / Tear it up: *Harms, Jonie*
CDMFP 5912 / Apr '91 / Music For Pleasure

☐ **BEST OF ACID JAZZ VOL.1, THE**
JAZIDCD 029 / Jan '91 / Acid Jazz

☐ **BEST OF ACID JAZZ VOL.1, THE (2CD Set)**
Cantaloop: *US 3 & rashaan* / Space cowboy: *Jamiroquai* / Midnight at the oasis: *Brand New Heavies* / Everyday: *Incognito* / Turn on tune in cop out: *Freakpower* / People in the middle: *Spearhead* / Feel so high: *Des'ree* / Rebirth of slick: *Digable Planets* / Feel the music: *Guru* / Been thinking about you: *Girault, Martine* / So what: *Jordan, Ronny* / Real love: *Driza Bone* / Never stop: *Brand New Heavies* / Spiritual love: *Urban Species* / Green Screen: *New Jersey Kings* / Mission impossible: *Taylor, James Quartet* / Keep steppin': *Omar* / Heavy vibes: *Vibraphonic* / Boundaris: *Conquest, Leena* / Take the L train: *Brooklyn Funk Essentials* / Whole lotta love: *Goldbug* / Apparently nothin': *Young Disciples* / Masterplan: *Sharpe, Barrie K. & Diana Brown* / Something in my eye: *Corduroy* / Venceremos: *Working Week* / Whirl keeps turning: *Jhelisa* / Dream come true: *Brand New Heavies* / Good lover: *D-Influence* / Promise me nothing: *Repercussions* / Creator has a masterplan: *Brooklyn Funk Essentials* / Now is the time: *D-Note* / Find our love: *City Lix* / 24 for betty page: *Snowboy* / Follow that arab: *Corduroy* / Turn it all around: *This I dig* / Watcha gonna do: *Xan* / Watchugot: *Groove Collective* / Funky guitar: *TC 1992* / Jesse: *Mother Earth* / Let it last: *Anderson, Carleen*
RADCD 35 / Jun '96 / Global TV

☐ **BEST OF ACID JAZZ VOL.2, THE**
Don't let it go to your head: *Brand New Heavies* / Masterplan: *Brown, Diana & Barrie K Sharpe* / Peace and love: *Sewell, Janette* / Watch my garden grow: *Humble Souls* / Jazz Jupiter: *A-Zel* / Hope you're feeling better: *Mother Earth* / E-type: *Corduroy* / Lucky fellow: *Snowboy* / Ain't no use: *Pure Wildness* / Girl overboard: *Snowboy* / Living life your own way: *Windross, Rose*
JAZIDCD 066 / May '93 / Acid Jazz

☐ **BEST OF ACID JAZZ VOL.2, THE**
EX 3412 / Jan '97 / Instinct

☐ **BEST OF ACID JAZZ VOL.2, THE (2CD Set)**
Virtual insanity: *Jamiroquai* / Dream on dreamer: *Brand New Heavies* / Remember me: *Blueboy* / There's nothing like this: *Omar* / Revival: *Girault, Martine* / Love the life: *Taylor, James Quartet* / High havoc: *Corduroy* / One temptation: *Paris, Mica* / Don't you worry 'bout a thing: *Incognito* / Brightest star: *Driza Bone* / Brother: *Urban Species* / Inner city blues: *Working Week* / Pushing against the flow: *Raw Stylus* / Long time gone: *Galliano* / Jackal: *Jordan, Ronny* / My definition of a bombastic style: *Definition Of Sound* / Can I kick it: *Tribe Called Quest* / Summertime: *Rebello, Jason* / Mercy mercy me: *Jazz Apostles* / Apparently nothing: *Anderson, Carleen* / Jazz in the house: *Count Basic* / You gotta be: *Des'ree* / Outside: *Omar* / Stay this way: *Brand New Heavies* / Dream warriors: *New Jersey Kings* / Friendly pressure: *Jhelisa* / Garden of earthly delight: *D-Note* / Bad as weed: *Mother Earth* / Love will keep us together: *Taylor, James Quartet* / Greenfinger: *Dr. Bong* / Beached: *Milk* / Got to be: *High Steppers* / Big city: *Outside* / Bad trip: *Night Trains* / Ain't no sunshine: *Beaujolais Band* / Corduroy orgasm club: *Corduroy* / It only gets better: *Society Of Soul* / Love supreme: *Downing, Will* / Time after time: *Tuck & Patti*
RADCD 52 / Jan '97 / Global TV

☐ **BEST OF ACID JAZZ, THE**
Chicken lickin': *Funk Inc.* / Zebra walk: *Kynard, Charles* / Reelin' with the feelin': *Kynard, Charles* / Dig on it: *Smith, Johnny 'Hammond'* / Got myself a good man: *Pucho* / Super bad: *Muhammad, Idris* / Who's gonna take the weight: *Sparks, Melvin* / Sure nuff sure nuff: *Phillips, Sonny* / Cold sweet: *Purdie, Bernard* / Psychedelic Sally: *Jefferson, Eddie* / Soul dance: *Person, Houston* / Houston Express: *Person, Houston* / Smokin' at Tiffany's: *Funk Inc.*
CDBGP 921 / Jun '89 / Beat Goes Public

☐ **BEST OF ACID JAZZ, THE**
London England: *Corduroy* / From the ghetto: *Dread Flimstone* / You don't know: *Colonel Abrams* / Sunship: *Sunship* / Calibra: *Incognito* / Spiritual love: *Urban Species* / Season of the witch: *Anger, Brian* / Get yourself together: *Young Disciples* / Reachin' (for the vibe): *Galliano* / Institution man: *Mother Earth* / Don't let it go to your head: *Brand New Heavies* / Eating me alive: *Brown, Diana & Barrie K Sharpe* / Nothing: *Sandals* / Swinging Foot: *Limerick, Alison* / Nine to five: *Isaacs, Gregory* / Wave: *Night Trains* / Creation: *Taylor, James Quartet* / Real love: *Driza Bone* / Love will bring us back together: *Ayers, Roy*
5651392 / 6 Jul '98 / Debutante

☐ **BEST OF AFRICA, THE**
Gerant: *Kalle, Pepe* / Loi de la nature: *4 Etoiles* / Odile: *Somo Somo* / Foolish harp: *Bhundu Boys* / Mbira jive: *Mohamed, Pops* / Bazobuya: *Soul Brothers* / Tarihinda: *Kayirebwa, Cecile* / Guy Yah: *Diabate, Sona* / Diewo: *Seck, Mansour* / Yedi Gosh: *Aweke, Aster* / Marimba song: *Amampondo*
RGNET 1005CD / Sep '96 / World Music Network

☐ **BEST OF AIM, THE**
AIM 005CD / Oct '95 / Aim

☐ **BEST OF AVI RECORDS, THE**
Cocomotion: *El Coco* / Le spank: *Le Pamplemousse* / Miami heat wave: *7th Avenue* / I've got to dance: *Destinations* / Disco train: *Rix, Jerry* / My destination is love: *Johnson, LJ* / Have a little faiyh in me: *Thomas, Evelyn* / Never let go: *Eastbound Expressway* / My claim to fame: *Wells, James* / Let's get it together: *El Coco* / Willie and the hand jive: *Rinder, Laurin & Michael Lewis* / Automatic lover: *Jackson, Dee D* / Mondo disco: *El Coco* / Keep it on ice: *Croisette*
HTCD 7 / 20 Apr '98 / Hot Productions

☐ **BEST OF BALLROOM, THE (Strict Tempo)**
Waterloo / Paperback jive / Everybody needs somebody / I'm a believer / Half a minute / All night long / One note samba / Hustle / Loco in acapulco / Boogie wonderland / Easy lover / When will I see you again / Annie's song / True love / Edelweiss / Chanson d'amour / Any dream will do / Moonlight serenade
QED 230 / Nov '96 / Tring

☐ **BEST OF BELLYDANCE FROM EGYPT AND LEBANON, THE**
EUCD 1320 / Nov '95 / ARC

☐ **BEST OF BELLYDANCE, THE**
EUCD 1211 / Sep '93 / ARC

☐ **BEST OF BGP, THE**
Always there: *Side Effect* / Got myself a good man: *Pucho* / Black whip: *Jones, Ivan 'Boogaloo Joe'* / So what: *Jefferson, Eddie* / Sister Janie: *Funk Inc.* / Nuther'n like thuther'n: *Jackson, Willis* / Rock Creek Park: *Blackbyrds* / Ban montana: *Parker, Maynard* / O baby I believe I'm losing you: *Hawks, Billy* / Ping pong: *Blakey, Art & The Jazz Messengers* / Selim: *Lytle, Johnny* / Milestones: *Murphy, Mark* / Jungle strut: *Ammons, Gene* / Jazz carnival: *Azymuth*
CDBGP 1030 / Oct '90 / Beat Goes Public

☐ **BEST OF BLUE NOTE VOL.1**
Blue train: *Coltrane, John* / Maiden voyage: *Hancock, Herbie* / Christo redemptor: *Byrd, Donald* / Moanin': *Blakey, Art* / Blues walk: *Donaldson, Lou* / Song for my Father: *Silver, Horace* / Back to the chicken shack: *Smith, Jimmy* / Chitlins con carne: *Burrell, Kenny* / Sidewinder: *Morgan, Lee*
CDP 7961102 / Oct '91 / Blue Note

☐ **BEST OF BLUE NOTE VOL.2**
Senor blues: *Silver, Horace* / Decision: *Rollins, Sonny* / Three o'clock in the morning: *Gordon, Dexter* / Blues march: *Blakey, Art* / Wadin': *Parlan, Horace* / Rumproller: *Morgan, Lee* / Something else: *Adderley, Cannonball* / Blue bossa: *Henderson, Joe* / Watermelon man: *Hancock, Herbie*
CDP 7979602 / Feb '93 / Blue Note

☐ **BEST OF BLUE NOTE, THE (A Selection From 25 Best Albums)**
Moanin': *Blakey, Art* / Midnight blue: *Burrell, Kenny* / Caravan: *Ellington, Duke* / Atomic Mr. Basie: *Basie, Count* / Un poco loco: *Powell, Bud* / Ornithology: *Parker, Charlie* / Rocker: *Davis, Miles* / I guess I'll hang my tears out to dry: *Gordon, Dexter* / Let's get lost: *Baker, Chet* / Tune up: *Rollins, Sonny* / Criss cross: *Monk, Thelonious* / Blue train: *Coltrane, John* / Maiden voyage: *Hancock, Herbie* / Song for my Father: *Silver, Horace*
CDP 8299642 / Mar '95 / Blue Note

☐ **BEST OF BLUES, THE (2CD Set)**
Boogie chillen: *Hooker, John Lee* / Roll and tumble: *Memphis Slim* / Tutti frutti: *Hawkins, Screamin' Jay* / Pinetop is just top: *Perkins, Willie 'Pinetop'* / I hate to see you go: *Walker, T-Bone* / Sweet home Chicago: *Brooks, Lonnie* / Things that I used to do: *Johnson, Luther 'Guitar Junior'* / Hands off: *McShann, Jay* / Take a lesson from your teacher: *Cousin Joe* / I can't quit my baby: *Rush, Otis* / Somebody please help me: *Clearwater, Eddy* / Every day I have the blues: *Guy, Buddy & Junior Wells* / Sloppy drunk: *Rogers, Jimmy* / So many days: *Perkins, Willie 'Pinetop'* / Highway is my home: *Magic Slim* / Impressions from France: *Johnson, Luther 'Georgia Snake Boy'* / Hey little girl: *Baker, McHouston 'Mickey'* / Railroad porter blues: *Cousin Joe* / Get back home in USA: *Hooker, John Lee* / Boogie for Meade: *Memphis Slim* / Looking back: *Rush, Otis* / Boogie woogie baby: *Clearwater, Eddy* / Country girl: *Magic Slim* / Got my mojo working: *Guy, Buddy & Junior Wells* / Slim's blues: *Memphis Slim* / Pretty baby: *Rogers, Jimmy* / Long gone blues: *Holiday, Billie* / Looking up at down: *Broonzy, 'Big' Bill* / Good morning little school girl: *Williamson, Sonny Boy* / Blues on Central Avenue: *Turner, 'Big' Joe* / Mean old world: *Walker, T-Bone* / Stop breaking down: *Johnson, Robert* / That's all: *Tharpe, Rosetta* / Rich man's blues: *Washington, Dinah* / Me and my chauffeur blues: *Memphis Minnie* / Empty bed blues: *Smith, Bessie*
FA 972 / Oct '96 / Fremeaux

☐ **BEST OF BOOGIE WOOGIE, THE**
158482 / Feb '96 / Jazz Archives

☐ **BEST OF BOOGIE WOOGIE, THE**
Boogie woogie stomp: *Ammons, Albert* / Pine Top's boogie woogie: *Smith, Pine Top* / Yancey stomp: *Yancey, Jimmy* / Cow cow blues: *Davenport, Cow Cow* / Boogie woogie: *Basie, Count Quintet* / State street jive: *Davenport, Cow Cow* / Chicago breakdown: *Big Maceo* / Honkt tonk train blues: *Lewis, Meade 'Lux'* / Pine Top's blues: *Smith, Pine Top* / Mr. Freddie blues: *Williams, Mary Lou* / Detroit rocks: *Taylor, Montana* / Dearborn St. Breakdown: *Avery, Charles* / Yancy special: *Lewis, Meade 'Lux'* / Boogie woogie: *Basie, Count* / No.29: *Wallace, Wesley* / Head rag hop: *Nelson, Romeo* / Dirty dozen: *Speckled Red* / Shout for joy: *Ammons, Albert* / Roll 'em: *Johnson, Pete* / Right string but the wrong yo-yo: *Speckled Red*
304062 / Jun '97 / Hallmark

☐ **BEST OF BOTH WORLDS, THE**
HNCD 8304 / Oct '94 / Hannibal

☐ **BEST OF BOUZOUKI, THE**
321889 / Jul '97 / Koch International

☐ **BEST OF BRASIL, THE**
JD 157 / May '97 / Chesky

☐ **BEST OF BREAKDANCE AND ELECTRIC BOOGIE, THE**
ZYX 550992 / 23 Mar '98 / ZYX

☐ **BEST OF BRITISH BE-BOP, THE**
Wee dot: *Scott, Ronnie* / Coquette: *Scott, Ronnie* / 52nd Street Theme: *Scott, Ronnie* / Ow: *Scott, Ronnie* / Don't blame me: *Scott, Ronnie* / Scrapple from the scrapple: *Scott, Ronnie* / Donna Lee: *Scott, Ronnie* / Too marvellous for words: *Scott, Ronnie* / Have you met Miss Jones: *Scott, Ronnie* / September song: *Scott, Ronnie* / Flamingo: *Scott, Ronnie* / Chasin' the bird: *Scott, Ronnie* / Little Willie leaps: *Scott, Ronnie* / El sino: *Scott, Ronnie* / Crazy rhythm: *Scott, Ronnie* / Lover come back to me: *Scott, Ronnie* / Compos mentos: *Scott, Ronnie* / Body beautiful: *Scott, Ronnie* / Stompin' at the Savoy: *Scott, Ronnie* / Oh lady be good: *Esquire Jazz All Stars* / Boppin' at the esquire: *Esquire Jazz All Stars* / Idapop: *Esquire Jazz All Stars* / What is this thing called love: *Esquire Jazz All Stars* / Mop mop: *Feldman, Victor* / Lady bird: *Feldman, Victor* / Quaternity: *Feldman, Victor* / Moonlight in Vermont: *Feldman, Victor* / Gone with the wind: *Feldman, Victor* / Buzy: *Jazz At The Town Hall Ensemble* / How high the moon: *Jazz At The Town Hall Ensemble* / Galaxy: *All Star Sextet* / I can't get started: *All Star Sextet* / First gear: *All Star Sextet* / Confirmation: *All Star Sextet* / My baby like to bebop: *All Star Sextet* / Disc jocky jump: *All Star Sextet* / Fallonology: *All Star Sextet* / Jack Fiddles while Norman Burns: *All Star Sextet*
3037300037 / Apr '96 / Carlton

☐ **BEST OF BRITISH BLUES, THE**
CD IMB 502 / Mar '93 / Charly

☐ **BEST OF BRITISH FOLK ROCK, THE**
Waiting for the wheel to turn: *Capercaillie* / Golden vanity: *Steeleye Span* / When I'm up I can't get down: *Oyster Band* / Lay down: *Strawbs* / Jewel in the crown: *Fairport Convention* / Breaking the chains: *Runrig* / Blacksmith: *Pentangle* / Lady Eleanor: *Lindisfarne* / Johnny: *New Celeste* / Pige ruadh: *Capercaillie* / One green hill: *Oyster Band* / Surfeit of lampreys: *Fairport Convention* / So early in the Spring: *Pentangle* / Tir an airm: *Runrig* / All around my hat: *Steeleye Span* / Meet me on the corner: *Lindisfarne* / Morrisons jig: *New Celeste* / Part of the union: *Strawbs*
PRKCD 36 / Oct '96 / Park

☐ **BEST OF BRITISH FOLK, THE**
TRTCD 156 / Oct '94 / TrueTrax

☐ **BEST OF BRITISH FOLK, THE**
PLSCD 149 / Feb '97 / Pulse

☐ **BEST OF BRITISH FOLK, THE**
PDSCD 516 / Sep '97 / Pulse

☐ **BEST OF BRITISH HARDCORE, THE**
I can live without you: *Vinyl Groover* / Pretty green eyes: *Force & Styles* / Divine inspiration: *DJ Slam* / Techno harmony: *DJ Sy & Unknown* / Take my breath away: *Go Mental* / Thoughts of you: *DJ Dougal* / Stay: *DJ Dougal* / Vol.4: *Unknown Artist* / Wanting to get high: *DJ Hixxy* / Setting you free: *DJ Unknown* / It's not over: *Seduction & Dougal* / Nothing better: *DJ Fade* / Phantasm: *Vinyl Groover* / Boom boom bang bang: *Sharkey* / Fly forever: *Midas & Fade* / Love inside: *DJ Supreme & UFO* / Doesn't have to be like that: *Ikan* / Take it from the groove: *Midas*
MMCCD 003 / 20 Oct '97 / Massive

☐ **BEST OF BRITISH JAZZ FROM THE BBC JAZZ CLUB VOL.1, THE**
URCD 118 / Oct '95 / Upbeat

☐ **BEST OF BRITISH JAZZ FROM THE BBC JAZZ CLUB VOL.2, THE**
Memphis shake / Last smile blues / Chicago buzz / Blues for an unkown gypsy / Elephant stomp blues / Under the double eagle / My gal Sal / Small hour fantasy / It's a lowdown dirty shame / March hare / Here today / PTQ Rag / Oh Dad / Sweet muscatel / Randolph Turpin / Steal away blues / Quincey Street stomp / Squatty Roo / Hard hearted Hannah / African Queen
URCD 119 / Feb '96 / Upbeat

☐ **BEST OF BRITISH JAZZ FROM THE BBC JAZZ CLUB VOL.3, THE**
Stockyard strut / If I ever cease to love / Down home rag / Chinatown, my Chinatown / Sweet Lorraine / Lil Liza Jane / Alligator hop / Beautiful dreamer / Blue blood blues / Shout 'em aunt Tillie / Pasadena / Oh, baby / Farewell blues / I've got a feeling for Orphelia / My sweetie went away / St. Louis rag / Do you know what it means to Miss New Orleans / Boodle-Am-Shake / Madeira / 20 Wang wang blues
URCD 120 / May '96 / Upbeat

☐ **BEST OF BRITISH JAZZ FROM THE BBC JAZZ CLUB VOL.4, THE**
'S wonderful: *Welsh, Alex Band* / Blue turning grey over you: *Welsh, Alex Band* / Chinatown, my Chinatown: *Welsh, Alex Band* / Preacher: *Welsh, Alex Band* / Sidewalk blues: *Welsh, Alex Band* / As long as I live: *Welsh, Alex Band* / On the Alamo: *Welsh, Alex Band* / Everybody loves my baby: *Welsh, Alex Band* / Exactly like you: *Welsh, Alex Band* / There'll be a hot time in the old town tonight: *Welsh, Alex Band* / Between the devil and the deep blue sea: *Disley, Diz & The Soho Quintette* / Oui: *Disley, Diz & The Soho Quintette* / Shine: *Disley, Diz & The Soho Quintette* / Crying the blues: *Disley, Diz & The Soho Quintette* / Ding dong daddy from Dumas: *Mulligan, Mick Magnolia Jazz Band & George Melly* / Hesitation blues: *Mulligan, Mick Magnolia Jazz Band & George Melly* / Muddy water: *Mulligan, Mick Magnolia Jazz Band & George Melly* / Wolverine blues: *Mulligan, Mick Magnolia Jazz Band & George Melly* / It's only a shanty in Old Shanty Town: *Mulligan, Mick Magnolia Jazz Band & George Melly* / Shim-me-sha-wobble: *Mulligan, Mick Magnolia Jazz Band & George Melly*
URCD 122 / Sep '96 / Upbeat

☐ **BEST OF BRITISH JAZZ FROM THE BBC JAZZ CLUB VOL.5, THE**
Hiawatha rag: *Sunshine, Monty Jazz Band* / South: *Sunshine, Monty Jazz Band* / All the girls go crazy about the way I walk: *Sunshine, Monty Jazz Band* / Saturday night function: *Sunshine, Monty Jazz Band* / Boyfriend/Song of the Swanee: *Stewart, Graham Seven* / Tears: *Stewart, Graham Seven* / Keyhole blues: *Stewart, Graham Seven* / Down South Camp meeting: *Turner, Bruce Quartet* / Stop, look and listen: *Turner, Bruce Quartet* / One o'clock jump: *Turner, Bruce Quartet* / That's a plenty: *Ashman, Micky & His Jazzband* / London blues: *Ashman, Micky & His Jazzband* / Give me your telephone number: *Ashman, Micky & His Jazzband* / Careless love: *Barber, Chris & His Jazz Band* / As long as I live: *Barber, Chris & His Jazz Band* / Too busy: *Barber, Chris & His Jazz Band* / Tell me is fancy bred: *Barber, Chris & His Jazz Band*
URCD 125 / Mar '97 / Upbeat

☐ **BEST OF BRITISH MELODIC TRANCE, THE**
Introduction / Northern light / Paradise / Tribute Remix / Gower Peninsular / Now and zen / Bells of Brixton / Telephonique / Aural intercourse / Bob Km / Interlude
TLCCD 4 / 6 Oct '97 / Lush

☐ **BEST OF BRITISH SOUL VOL.1, THE**
Boogie Nights: *Heatwave* / Hi tension: *Hi-Tension* / Can you feel the force: *Real Thing* / You're lying: *Linx* / Love games: *Level 42* / Nights: *Ocean, Billy* / Body talk: *Imagination* / I can't turn away: *Savannah* / Easier said than done: *Shakatak* / Mama used to say: *Junior* / Round and round: *Graham, Jaki* / Choose me/Hangin' on a string: *Loose Ends* / Say I'm your number one: *Princess* / Fair play: *Soul II Soul* / My one temptation: *Paris, Mica* / Tribute (right on): *Pasadenas* / Cuddly toy: *Roachford* / People hold on: *Coldcut & Lisa Stansfield* / There's nothing like this/Don't mind: *Omar* / It's gonna be alright: *Turner, Ruby*
5653102 / 10 Aug '98 / Debutante

☐ **BEST OF BRITISH STEEL, THE (2CD Set)**
Tales of destruction: *Dogs D'Amour* / Clerical conspiracy: *Sabbat* / (Na na) nukklear rokket: *Wrathchild* / Seventh church of the apocalyptic lawnmower: *Lawnmower Deth* / Low life: *Trixx* / Federation / Read my lips: *Tattooed Love Boys* / Goddess: *Acid Reign* / Rock 'n' roll lady: *Dominique, Lisa* / I'm on fire: *Mantas* / Deny reality: *Re-Animator* / Surrender: *Midnight Blue* / Queen of the night: *Deathtrash* / Prey to the Lord: *Deathwish* / Living without you: *Tigertailz* / Looking for a lady: *Last Of The Teenage Idols* / Testify to me: *Virus* / Nights on fire: *Torino* / Spirit cry: *Sacrilege* / Love attack: *After Hours* / One way ride: *Lixx* / Madman: *Metal Messiah* / So alone: *Soho Roses*
WKFMXD 128 / Jul '89 / FM

☐ **BEST OF BRITISH VOL.1, THE**
Battle hymn of the republic / When you're smiling / Baker's bounce / When your lover has gone / Whispering / Groovin' high / Big noise from Winnetka / Mood indigo / Pick yourself up / Pennies from heaven / Seven come eleven / When it's sleepy time down south / Trouble with you is me / Flintstones theme / Baker's blues
CDSIV 6146 / May '95 / Horatio Nelson

☐ **BEST OF BRITISH, THE**
When I'm cleaning windows: *Formby, George* / It's a lovely day tomorrow: *Lynn, Vera* / Sun has got its hat on: *Ambrose* / Run rabbit run: *Flanagan & Allen* / Sally: *Fields, Gracie* / Smoke gets in your eyes: *Mantovani* / Stately homes of England: *Coward, Sir Noel* / Parade of tin soldiers: *Dixon, Reginald* / Everything stops for tea: *Buchanan, Jack* / Man who comes around: *Cotton, Billy* / My yiddishe momma: *Shelton, Anne* / When I see an elephant fly: *Loss, Joe* / Albert and the lion: *Holloway, Stanley* / No one else will do: *Geraldo* / Laughing policeman: *Penrose, Charles* / Biggest aspidistra in the world: *Fields, Gracie* / Leaning on a lampost: *Formby, George* / Are you having any fun: *Flanagan & Allen* / Spider of the night: *Mantovani* / Nightingale sang in Berkeley Square: *Shelton, Anne* / You can't blame me for that: *Miller, Max* / Let him go, let him tarry: *Loss, Joe* / Mad dogs and Englishmen: *Coward, Sir Noel* / We'll meet again: *Lynn, Vera*
CD 6034 / Sep '96 / Music

☐ **BEST OF BUTTERFLY RECORDS, THE**
Boogie down and messaround: *Blackwell* / Chatanooga choo choo: *Tuxedo Junction* / Fill my life with love: *St. Tropez* / Tattoo man: *McCann, Denise* / Too hot for love: *THP Orchestra* / One more minute: *St. Tropez* / Superstar: *McGilpin, Bob* / Don't turn your back on love: *Whitaker, E* / Inferno and ice: *Fire & Ice* / Je t'aime: *St. Tropez* / Toot toot tootsie goodbye: *Tuxedo Junction* / Weekend two step: *THP Orchestra* / Move on up suite: *Destination* / Flight from Versailles: *Grand Tour*
HTCD 9 / 20 Apr '98 / Hot Productions

☐ **BEST OF CAPITAL GOLD, THE**
Something in the air: *Thunderclap Newman* / Waterloo sunset: *Kinks* / Out of time: *Farlowe, Chris* / Daydream: *Lovin' Spoonful* / Son of a preacher man: *Springfield, Dusty* / I don't want our love to die: *Herd* / I hear you knocking: *Edmunds, Dave* / Green tambourine: *Lemon Pipers* / (If paradise is) Half as nice: *Amen Corner* / This wheel's on fire: *Driscoll, Julie & The Brian Auger Trinity* / Concrete and clay: *Unit 4+2* / Jesamine: *Casuals* / Israelites: *Dekker, Desmond* / In the summertime: *Mungo Jerry* / With a little help from my friends: *Cocker, Joe* / Whiter shade of pale: *Procol Harum* / Get it on: *T-Rex* / Sweets for my sweet: *Searchers* / First cut is the deepest: *Arnold, P.P.* / Will you still love me tomorrow: *Shirelles* / Only one woman: *Marbles* / Rescue me: *Bass, Fontella* / Judy in disguise: *Fred, John & His Playboy Band* / Itchycoo Park: *Small Faces*
AHLCD 2 / Oct '92 / Hit

☐ **BEST OF CARNIVAL IN RIO VOL.1, THE**
EUCD 1097 / '91 / ARC

☐ **BEST OF CARNIVAL IN RIO VOL.2, THE**
EUCD 1136 / '91 / ARC

☐ **BEST OF CEILI BANDS VOL.2, THE**
Reels medley: *Blarney Ceili Band* / Marches: *Ballinamere Ceili Band* / Jigs: *Ballinamere Ceili Band* / Hornpipes: *St. Brendan's Ceili Band* / Reels: *Brophy Brothers Ceili band* / Set dance: *Ryan, Sean & Don Coughlan Ceili Band* / Marches: *Tuohy Radio Ceili Band* / Hornpipes: *Tuohy Radio Ceili Band* / Reels: *Tuohy Radio Ceili Band* / Jigs: *St. Peters Ceili Band* / Set dance: *St. Peters Ceili Band* / Polka: *Liam Ivory Ceili Band* / Reels: *Mulhaire Ceili Band* / Hornpipes: *Graiguenamanagh Ceili Band* / Marches: *Kearney Ceili Band* / Jigs: *Inisfail Ceili Band* / Reels: *Inisfail Ceili Band*
EMPRCD 756 / 8 Sep '97 / Emporio

☐ **BEST OF CELTIC INSPIRATION, THE**
REACD 002 / 20 Apr '98 / Reactive

☐ **BEST OF CHARLY GROOVE, THE**
Little soul party: *Ohio Players* / If she won't (find someone who will): *Dorsey, Lee* / Big legged woman: *Hobbs, Willie* / Good old funky music: *Meters* / Working in a coal mine: *Dorsey, Lee* / Give the baby anything the baby wants: *Tex, Joe* / Chokin' kind: *Toussaint, Allen* / It takes two to do wrong: *Patterson, Bobby* / Is it funky enough: *Communications & Black Experiences Band* / Thank you for letting me be myself again: *Maceo & All The King's Men* / All I do everyday: *Meters* / Full speed ahead: *Jungle Band* / Gone too far: *Toussaint, Allen* / Move on up: *Mayfield, Curtis* / Medley: *Brown, James* / It's too funky in here: *Payback* / (I got) so much trouble in my mind: *Quarterman, Sir Joe & Free Soul* / Ain't gonna bump no more: *Tex, Joe* / Soul music: *Mayfield, Curtis* / Tell me why: *Womack, Bobby* / Shine it on: *Sly & The Family Stone* / Cholly (funk getting ready to roll): *Funkadelic* / Mother's son: *Mayfield, Curtis* / Oh I: *Funkadelic* / Thump and bump: *Fisher, Eddie* / If it's not addin' up: *Sly & The Family Stone* / Tripping out: *Mayfield, Curtis* / One nation under a groove: *Funkadelic* / (Get up I feel like being a) sex machine: *Brown, James* / 7-6-5-4-3-2-1 Blow your whistle: *Rimshots* / Mambo mongo: *Santamaria, Mongo*
CPCD 8085 / Jun '95 / Charly

☐ **BEST OF CHESS BLUES VOL.1, THE**
CHLD 19093 / Oct '92 / Chess/MCA

☐ **BEST OF CHESS BLUES VOL.2, THE**
CHLD 19094 / Oct '92 / Chess/MCA

☐ **BEST OF CHESS R & B VOL.1**
CHLD 19160 / Nov '91 / Chess/MCA

☐ **BEST OF CHESS R & B VOL.2**
CHLD 19161 / Nov '91 / Chess/MCA

☐ **BEST OF CHESS RHYTHM, THE (2CD Set)**
CHD 29376 / Mar '97 / Chess/MCA

☐ **BEST OF CHESS VOL.1, THE**
Maybellene: *Berry, Chuck* / Bo Diddley: *Diddley, Bo* / Rocket 88: *Brenston, Jackie & The Delta Cats* / See you later alligator: *Charles, Bobby* / Suzie Q: *Hawkins, Dale* / Oh oh: *Bo, Eddie* / Johnny B Goode: *Berry, Chuck* / Sincerely: *Moonglows* / Ain't got no home: *Henry, Clarence 'Frogman'* / Most of all: *Moonglows* / I'll be home: *Flamingos* / Who do you love: *Diddley, Bo*
CHLD 19221 / Jul '93 / Chess/MCA

☐ **BEST OF CHESS VOL.2, THE**
Happy, happy birthday baby: *Tune Weavers* / I'm so young: *Students* / Book of love: *Monotones* / Teardrops: *Andrew, Lee & The Hearts* / Ten commandments of love: *Harvey & The Moonglows* / Let me in: *Sensations* / Over the mountain across the sea: *Johnnie & Joe* / Hi-heel sneakers: *Tucker, Tommy* / Rinky dink: *Cortez, Dave 'Baby'* / Sally go round the roses: *Jaynetts* / No particular place to go: *Berry, Chuck* / Roadrunner: *Diddley, Bo*
CHLD 19222 / Jul '93 / Chess/MCA

☐ **BEST OF CHOCI'S CHEWNS VOL.2 (Alternative Chunks) (2CD Set)**
CCLP 001 / Mar '97 / Choci's Chewns

☐ **BEST OF CHURCH STREET STATION VOL.1, THE (Country Stars Live)**
DIVORCE: *Wynette, Tammy* / Four in the morning: *Young, Faron* / Behind closed doors: *Rich, Charlie* / Mamas don't let your babies grow up to be cowboys: *Bruce, Ed* / This land is your land: *Allen, Rex Sr. & Rex Allen Jr.* / Duellin' banjos: *Devol, Skip* / Texas when I die: *Tucker, Tanya* / Before the next teardrop falls: *Fender, Freddy* / He stopped loving her today: *Jones, George* / Love in the hot afternoon: *Watson, Gene* / Detroit city: *Tillis, Mel* / He ain't heavy, he's my brother: *Osmond Brothers* / Cheating situation: *Bandy, Moe* / Wabash cannonball: *Boxcar Willie* / Big bad John: *Dean, Jimmy* / Teddy bear: *Fairchild, Barbara* / Tequila sunrise: *Bare, Bobby*
PLATCD 359 / '91 / Platinum

☐ **BEST OF CHURCH STREET STATION VOL.2, THE (Country Stars Live)**
Delta town: *Tucker, Tanya* / Mr. Bojangles: *Nitty Gritty Dirt Band* / Heart of the country: *Mattea, Kathy* / Let your love flow: *Bellamy Brothers* / Mexico rose: *Fender, Freddy* / Secret love: *Fender, Freddy* / Who's gonna fill their shoes: *Jones, George* / Door is always open: *Dave & Sugar* / Lonely days, lonely nights: *Loveless, Patty* / Key Largo: *Higgins, Bertie* / Carmen: *Watson, Gene* / Chains of gold: *Sweethearts Of The Rodeo* / Auctioneer: *Van Dyke, Leroy* / I like beer: *Hall, Tom T.* / Love don't care: *Conley, Earl Thomas* / Please Mr. Please / God bless America: *Greenwood, Lee* / Harper Valley PTA: *Riley, Jeannie C.* / Okie from Muskogee: *Haggard, Merle*
PLATCD 360 / May '91 / Platinum

☐ **BEST OF COUNTRY AND IRISH, THE**
RZCD 0072 / Apr '94 / Ritz

☐ **BEST OF COUNTRY, THE**
Harper Valley PTA: *Riley, Jeannie C.* / From a jack to a king: *Miller, Ned* / You are my sunshine: *Davis, Jimmie* / Angel of the morning: *Remington, Rita* / Honky tonk song: *Pierce, Webb* / I walk the line: *Cash, Johnny* / Born to lose: *Lewis, Jerry Lee* / It's four in the morning: *Young, Faron* / Teardrop falls: *Fender, Freddy* / End of the world: *Davis, Skeeter* / Please help me I'm falling: *Locklin, Hank* / CB Savage: *Hart, Rod* / Got you on my mind: *Coe, David Allan* / Good year for the roses: *Jones, George* / I fall to pieces: *Jackson, Wanda* / Auctioneer: *Van Dyke, Leroy* / Jambalaya (on the bayou): *Newman, Jimmy C.* / Dreaming: *Travis, Randy* / Nightlife: *Nelson, Willie* / Six days on the road: *Dudley, Dave*
304772 / Feb '98 / Hallmark

☐ **BEST OF COVER VERSIONS, THE**
ZYX 810992 / May '97 / ZYX

☐ **BEST OF CROONERS 1929-1946, THE**
BOC 23 / Nov '97 / Best Of Crooners

☐ **BEST OF CUBA, THE**
3028722 / 5 Jan '98 / Arcade

☐ **BEST OF CUBAN MUSIC VOL.1, THE**
76754212942 / 7 Apr '98 / Vedisco

☐ **BEST OF CUBAN MUSIC VOL.2, THE**
76754212952 / 7 Apr '98 / Vedisco

☐ **BEST OF DANCE '97, THE (44 Massive Hits Of The Year - 2CD Set)**
Sunchyme: *Dario G* / Stay: *Sash* / Professional widow: *Amos, Tori* / You're not alone: *Olive* / Breathe: *Prodigy* / Freed from desire: *Gala* / Remember me: *Blueboy* / Fix: *Blackstreet* / Oh la la: *Coolio* / Samba de Janeiro: *Carrilio* / Ready or not: *Course* / Joy: *Staxx* / Get up go insane: *Stretch n' Vern* / Don't give up: *Weeks, Michelle* / On and on: *Badu, Erykah* / We come to party: *N-Tyce* / Deep in you: *Livin' Joy* / My father's son: *Reeves, Conner* / Tremendous: *Mama Mystique* / Oh la la la: *2 Eivissa* / Offshore: *Chicane* / Encore une fois: *Sash* / Belissima: *DJ Quicksilver* / Do ya think I'm sexy: *N-Trance & Rod Stewart* / Everybody (Backstreet's back): *Backstreet Boys* / You sexy thing: *Clock* / You got the love: *Source & Candi Staton* / Get up everybody: *Stingily, Byron* / People hold on: *Stansfield, Lisa* / James Bond: *Moby* / I love you...stop: *Red 5* / Flash: *BBE* / Nightmare: *Brainbug* / Plastic dreams: *Jaydee* / Gabriel: *Davis, Roy Jr.* / One and one: *Miles, Robert* / Fly life: *Basement Jaxx* / Show me love: *Robin S* / Just gets better: *TJR & Xavier* / Oh boy: *Fabulous Baker Boys* / Fired up: *Funky Green Dogs* / Amour: *Porn Kings* / Ain't talking about dub: *Apollo 440*
TTVCD 2929 / 27 Oct '97 / Telstar TV

☐ **BEST OF DANCE BAND DAYS VOL.1, THE**
Moonlight serenade / Clarinade / Jumpin' at the woodside / Sweet Georgia Brown / Stars fell on Alabama / Angry / Stardust / Song of India / Caldonia / Airmail stomp / Rockin' in rhythm / Bei mir bist du schon / Little brown jug / Don't be that way / Tweet tweet / Button up your overcoat / Some people / 'S wonderful / Opus one / At the woodchoppers' ball / Blue moon / I got a girl named Netty
DBCD 20 / Oct '87 / Dance Band Days

☐ **BEST OF DANCE BAND DAYS VOL.2, THE**
Symphony / King Porter stomp / Rockin' in rhythm / I'll be seeing you / Down the road apiece / Man with a horn / Begin the beguine / Cheek to cheek / There, I've said it again / Everybody eats when they come to my house / Newport up / Lullaby of Broadway / Seven-o-five / All the cats join in / King size blues / Fare thee well to Harlem / Bedford drive / Blue skies / Goosey gander / Cruisin' with cab / St. Louis blues / Rum and coca cola
DBCD 21 / Oct '87 / Dance Band Days

☐ **BEST OF DISCO ONE HIT WONDERS, THE (16 Dance Floor Classics)**
Shame shame shame: *Shirley & Company* / Pillow talk: *Sylvia* / I don't know what it is but it sure is funky: *Ripple* / Where did our love go: *Elbert, Donnie* / Get dancin': *Disco Tex & The Sexolettes* / I'm doin' fine now: *New York City* / Be thankful for what you've got: *De Vaughn, William* / We're on the right track: *Ultra High Frequency* / Let her in: *Travolta, John* / Girls: *Moments* / Love on a two-way street: *Moments* / El bimbo: *Bimbo Jet* / I'll be holding on: *Downing, 'Big' Al* / Popcorn: *Hot Butter* / Just as long as you need me: *Independents* / I've been watching you: *South Side Movement*
HTCD 25 / 20 Apr '98 / Hot Productions

☐ **BEST OF DISCO ROCK, THE (2CD Set)**
ZYX 811002 / May '97 / ZYX

☐ **BEST OF DISTINCTIVE, THE**
Mystic motion: *Datura* / House forever: *Billabong* / Take me away: *Westbrook* / Feel good: *B-Code* / Madness: *Nights At The Round Tables* / Get into music: *DJ's Rule* / King cone: *X-Odus* / Lellenda el espiritu: *Nights At The Round Tables* / Fall out of love: *Hybrid* / Switchead: *Marshal Stax* / Feeling: *Endive* / I could be this: *Androgeny & Michael M*
DISNCD 10 / Apr '96 / Distinctive

☐ **BEST OF DWARF VOL.2, THE**
DWARFCD 002 / 29 Apr '98 / Dwarf

☐ **BEST OF EAST EUROPEAN SONGS AND DANCES**
EUCD 1148 / '91 / ARC

☐ **BEST OF EASY STREET RECORDS, THE (Body Work)**
Go deh yaka: *Monyaka* / Body work: *Hot Streak* / Share the night: *World Premiere* / Treat her sweeter: *Simpson, Paul* / Ma foom bey: *Cultural Vibe* / In and out of my life: *Adeva* / This way that way: *Pandella* / What I wouldn't do: *Townes, Carol Lynn* / Tomorrow: *Rodgers, Keith* / Pickin' up promises: *Brown, Jocelyn* / Automatic lover: *Hudson, Laurice* / You don't know: *Serious Intention* / Monster rap: *Pickett, Bobby*
HTCD 40 / 20 Apr '98 / Hot Productions

☐ **BEST OF ELECTRO VOL.1, THE**
Jam on it: *Newcleus* / Smurf: *Brunson, Tyrone* / Light years away: *Warp 9* / Breakin' in space: *Key-Matic* / Egypt, Egypt: *Egyptian Lover* / Party scene: *Russel Brothers* / Clear: *Cybotron* / One for the treble (fresh): *Davy DMX* / Wild style: *Timezone* / Al-naafiysh: *Hashim* / Hip hop be bop: *Man Parrish* / Break dancin' electric boogie: *Wet Street Mob*
SOUNDSCD 8 / Oct '95 / Street Sounds

☐ **BEST OF ENJOY RECORDS, THE**
Super rappin': *Grandmaster Flash* / Love rap: *Spoonie Gee* / Bodyrock: *Treacherous Three & Kool Moe Dee* / At the party: *Treacherous Three* / It's magic: *Fearless Four* / Move to the groove: *Disco Four* / Funky boy party: *Masterdon Committee* / Feel the heartbeat: *Treacherous Three & Kool Moe Dee* / Just having fun: *Fresh, Doug E* / New rap language: *Spoonie Gee* / Rappin' and rockin' the house: *Funky Four & Plus* / Rockin' it: *Fearless Four*
HTCD 5 / 20 Apr '98 / Hot Productions

☐ **BEST OF ERIC RECORDS, THE (We Are Invincible)**
Maybe this time: *Lewis, Norma* / I'm gonna love you forever: *Ruffin, Jimmy & Jackson Moore* / I believe in dreams: *Rawe, Jackie* / We are invincible: *501's* / Hold on to my love: *Ruffin, Jimmy* / Satellites: *Warren, Ellie* / Searching: *Faces* / Love fire: *James, Jimmy* / Reach out: *James, Jimmy* / Commumix / Hit mix / Let the night take the blame: *501's* / Haven't stopped dancing yet: *Faces* / Young heart: *Ruffin, Jimmy*
HTCD 47 / 20 Apr '98 / Hot Productions

☐ **BEST OF EVOLUTION, THE**
EVGCD 1 / Apr '96 / Evolution

☐ **BEST OF EXCELLO GOSPEL, THE**
Step by step: *Boyer Brothers* / Oh Lord stand by me: *Boyer Brothers* / On the beautiful shore: *Hendrix Singers* / Jesus be my keeper: *Silvertone Singers* / Since Jesus came into my heart: *Silvertone Singers* / I can call Jesus anytime: *Young Gospel Singers* / I got a home in that rock: *Silvertone Singers* / In my heart: *Silvertone Singers* / In the sweet bye and bye: *Sermonairs* / Is there anybody else like Jesus: *Edwards, Brother Henry* / Run on to the end: *Silvertone Singers* / Way bye and bye: *Silvertone Singers* / Just tell Jesus: *Waldo Singers* / Trust him today: *Waldo Singers* / In my Saviour's care: *Sons Of The South* / Didn't it rain children: *Sons Of The South* / Jesus my saviour: *Silvertone Singers* / Rescue the perishing: *Silvertone Singers* / I'm waiting and watching: *Sons Of The South* / One day: *Sons Of The South* / God is alright: *Sons Of The South* / Travelin' down this road: *Sons Of The South* / Oh Lord guide the way: *Jewel Gospel-Aires* / After a while with Jesus: *Jewel Gospel-Aires*
CDCHD 687 / 29 Jun '98 / Ace

☐ **BEST OF EYE Q CLASSICS (2CD Set)**
Summerbreeze: *Summerbreeze* / 4 Monks: *Virtual Symmetry* / Vernon's wonderland: *Vernon* / No fate: *Zyon* / Magnifica: *Sonic Infusion* / Sun down: *Volunteers* / Airborn: *Mirage* / Synfonica: *Brainchild* / Troya mix '93: *Odysee Of Noises* / Cosmos: *Java* / Alienated: *Earth Nation* / Superstring: *Cygnus X* / Goahead: *Freebeach* / Symmetry: *Brainchild* / Firedance: *Odysee Of Noises* / VS: *Virtual Symmetry* / El sueno: *Aquaform* / Orange theme: *Cygnus X*
EYEUKCD 011 / Jul '96 / Eye Q

☐ **BEST OF FLAMENCO, THE**
EUCD 1158 / Jun '91 / ARC

☐ **BEST OF FURY ROCKABILLY VOL.1, THE**
FCD 3049 / 20 Apr '98 / Fury

☐ **BEST OF GAY PRIDE COLOGNE, THE**
Samba de Janeiro: *Carrilio* / Free gay and happy: *Coming Out Crew* / You spin me round: *Ly, Kim* / Power of love: *Beverlee* / Just can't get enough: *Walker, Sam* / Can you feel the love tonight: *O'Hara, Stephanie* / Ooo lalala: *Earp, Justine* / It's raining men: *Weather Girls* / Safe: *Somerville, Jimmy* / I will always love you: *Grant, Natalie* / Day by day: *Regina* / Somewhere over the rainbow: *Ott, Stefanie* / Schoner fremder mann: *Ginger* / Wir sind die manner der nacht: *Manner Der Nacht* / Mein coming out: *Hella Von Sinnen*
DST 085702512 / Sep '97 / Dance Street

☐ **BEST OF GOA TRANCE VOL.1, THE (4CD Set)**
CDBTOT 6 / 9 Mar '98 / Jumpin' & Pumpin'

☐ **BEST OF GOA TRANCE VOL.2, THE (4CD Set)**
CDBTOT 7 / 22 Jun '98 / Jumpin' & Pumpin'

☐ **BEST OF GOSPEL, THE (2CD Set)**
3014342 / Feb '97 / Arcade

☐ **BEST OF GOTHAM RHYTHM AND BLUES, THE**
KKCD 04 / Oct '90 / Krazy Kat

☐ **BEST OF GREECE VOL.2**
EUCD 1159 / Jun '91 / ARC

☐ **BEST OF GRENADA 1995, THE**
JW 1017CD / Jan '96 / JW

☐ **BEST OF HARD HOUSE, THE (4CD Set)**
DAM 002 / Dec '96 / Tring

☐ **BEST OF HAREM RECORDS, THE**
Mr. Big shot: *Simon Orchestra* / Love and desire: *Arpeggio* / Let the music play: *Arpeggio* / Fighter: *Arpeggio* / After dark: *Brooks, Patti* / Queen of fools: *Williams, Jessica* / Gamblin' on your love: *Williams, Jessica* / Tie me down: *Romance & Jessica Williams* / Panic: *French Kiss* / Dance my way to your heart: *Romance* / You're my fantasy: *Charisma* / You killed the magic: *Arpeggio*
HTCD 6 / 20 Apr '98 / Hot Productions

☐ **BEST OF HI-NRG, THE**
Don't leave me this way: *Jiani, Carol* / Queen of fools: *Williams, Jessica* / Love fire: *James, Jimmy* / Satellites: *Warren, Ellie* / I'm living my own life: *Bentley, Earlene* / Whiplash: *Eastbound Expressway* / High energy: *Thomas, Evelyn* / I am what I am: *La Cage* / Love's gone mad: *Seventh Avenue* / Panic: *French Kiss* / Love and desire: *Arpeggio* / We are invincible: *501's* / Fight: *Lewis, Norma* / I'm gonna love you forever: *Ruffin, Jimmy & Jackson Moore*
303862 / Jun '97 / Hallmark

☐ **BEST OF HIP HOP (2CD Set)**
ZYX 811102 / Jul '97 / ZYX

☐ **BEST OF HTD, THE**
Down in the bottom: *Terraplane* / Shake for me: *Terraplane* / We lie: *Albion Band* / Thank Christ for the bomb/Soldier: *Groundhogs* / Land of my fathers (Hen wlad fy nhadau): *Caravan* / Foolish pride: *McPhee, Tony* / Railway station: *Tylor* / Children of the stones: *Rose Among Thorns* / Fogbound: *Banks, Peter* / Why: *Sister Mary Elephant*
HTDCD 20 / Aug '96 / HTD

☐ **BEST OF IMMEDIATE RECORDS, THE**
I'm your witch doctor: *Mayall, John* / Think: *Farlowe, Chris* / Baby don't you do it: *Poets* / Going back: *Goldie* / Sittin' on a fence: *Twice As Much* / Though it hurts me baby: *Arnold, P.P.* / Snake drive: *Clapton, Eric* / Ride on baby: *Farlowe, Chris* / Tell me have you ever seen me: *Apostolic Intervention* / Backstreet girl: *Scott, Nicky* / Here comes the nice: *Small Faces* / Would you believe: *Nicholls, Billy* / Come home baby: *Stewart, Rod & P.P.Arnold* / Handbags and gladrags: *Farlowe, Chris* / On the bombsite: *Browne, Duncan* / Half as nice: *Amen Corner* / Man of the world: *Fleetwood Mac* / Steelin': *All Stars & Jeff Beck* / I feel much better: *Small Faces* / First cut is the deepest: *Arnold, P.P.* / You baby: *Turtles* / She was perfection: *Head, Murray* / Universal: *Small Faces* / Circles: *Les Fleurs De Lys*
RENCD 124 / 29 Sep '97 / Renaissance Collector Series

☐ **BEST OF INDIE METAL, THE**
I survive: *Terraplane* / Take it all away: *Girlschool* / All the time: *Spider* / All around the world: *Torme, Bernie* / Motorhead: *Hawkwind* / Hit it: *Tygers Of Pan Tang* / Wind of change: *Lloyd-Langton, Huw Group* / We got the edge: *Savage* / Gimme the money: *Terraplane* / Too different: *Persian Risk* / Time for you: *Scrubs* / It could be better: *Girlschool* / Hurry on sundown: *Hawkwind* / Feel like a man: *Spider* / Star: *Torme* / Are you there: *Tygers Of Pan Tang*
EMPRCD 552 / Nov '94 / Emporio

☐ **BEST OF INDIE, THE**
BOTT 003CD / May '96 / Beechwood

☐ **BEST OF IRELAND, THE (Celtic Graces)**
Midnight walker: *Spillane, Davy* / Ballymun regatta: *Whelan, Bill* / Plains of Kildare: *Brady, Paul* / Maids of Mitchelstown: *Bothy Band* / Wee weaver: *Keane, Dolores & John Faulkner* / Aaron's key: *Stockton's Wing* / Arthur McBride: *Brady, Paul* / Eigigh suas a stoirin: *Clannad* / Rip the calico: *Bothy Band* / Mr. O'Connor: *De Danann* / Scar an nollaig sinn/It takes two: *King, Philip & Peter Browne* / Pursuit of Farmer Michael Hayes: *Planxty & Christy Moore* / Maid of Coolmore: *Bothy Band* / Declan: *Lunny, Donal* / Lord Franklin: *Burke, Kevin & Michael O'Dohmnhaill*
CDEMC 3693 / Feb '97 / Hemisphere

☐ **BEST OF IRELAND, THE (20 Tracks Of Traditional Irish Music)**
Galway bay: *Locke, Josef* / Whiskey in the jar: *Dubliners* / Trottin' to the fair: *Murray, Ruby* / Irish lullaby: *Shannonside Ceili Band* / When Irish eyes are smiling: *Jones, Sansie* / Dear old Donegal: *Locke, Josef* / Queen of Connemera: *Ardellis ceili band & John Bennet* / Danny boy: *O'Se, Sean* / Jigs: *Ardellis Ceili Band* / Mountains of Mourne: *O'Dowda, Brendan* / Galway races: *Dubliners* / When you were sweet sixteen: *Locke, Josef* / Reels: *Gallowglass Ceili Band* / Pretty Irish girl: *O'Dowda, Brendan & Ruby Murray* / Flower of sweet Strabane: *Gallagher, Bridie* / It's a great day for the Irish: *Murray, Ruby* / Rose of Tralee: *O'Dowda, Brendan* / Ireland my home: *Father Sydney MacEwan* / Bantry bay: *O'Se, Sean* / Isle of Innisfree: *Locke, Josef*
CDMFP 6231 / Jun '96 / Music For Pleasure

☐ **BEST OF IRISH BALLADS, THE**
DOCDS 2003 / 20 Apr '98 / Dara

☐ **BEST OF IRISH FOLK**
PDSCD 503 / Sep '97 / Pulse

☐ **BEST OF IRISH FOLK FEST, THE**
CDTUT 727478 / '89 / Wundertute

☐ **BEST OF IRISH FOLK, THE**
Rocky road to Dublin: *Dubliners* / Curragh of Kildare: *Furey, Finbar & Eddie* / Glenside polka: *Glenside Ceilidh Band* / Henry joy: *Grehan Sisters* / Handsome cabin boy: *Sweeney's Men* / Frog's wedding: *Johnstons* / Exile's jig: *Sweeney's Men* / Lambs on the green hills: *Johnstons* / Spanish cloak: *Furey, Finbar & Eddie* / Golden jubilee: *Glenside Ceilidh Band* / Cook in the kitchen: *Dubliners* / Orange and the green: *Grehan Sisters* / St. Patrick's breastplate: *Wood, Royston & Heather* / Inis dhun ramha: *Na Fili* / Foggy dew: *Imlach, Hamish* / Three pieces by O'Carolan: *Renbourn, John* / Madame Bonaparte: *Furey, Finbar* / Rakish Paddy: *Furey, Finbar* / Roisin dubh: *Dubliners* / Chanters tune: *Na Fili* / Spanish lady: *Johnstons* / Killarney boys of pleasure: *Swarbrick, Dave*
CCSCD 221 / Jun '89 / Castle

☐ **BEST OF IRISH FOLK, THE**
HMCD 064 / Aug '90 / Harmac

☐ **BEST OF IRISH FOLK, THE**
PLSCD 133 / Apr '96 / Pulse

☐ **BEST OF IRISH SHOWBANDS, THE**
EMPRCD 806 / 18 May '98 / Emporio

☐ **BEST OF IRISH TRADITIONAL MUSIC, THE (2CD Set)**
2CHDHX 807 / May '95 / Outlet

☐ **BEST OF ISRAEL VOL.4, THE**
AT 911 / 1 Mar '98 / Atoll

☐ **BEST OF JAMAICA GOLD VOL.1, THE**
JMC 200219 / May '94 / Jamaican Gold

☐ **BEST OF JAMAICA GOLD VOL.2, THE**
JMC 200220 / May '94 / Jamaican Gold

☐ **BEST OF JAZZ ORGANS, THE**
CDC 9006 / Oct '90 / LRC

☐ **BEST OF JAZZ SAXOPHONES VOL.3, THE**
CDC 9009 / Oct '90 / LRC

☐ **BEST OF JAZZ SINGERS VOL.2, THE**
CDC 9008 / Oct '90 / LRC

☐ **BEST OF JDC RECORDS, THE (Spin It)**
Too tough to Cry: *Tyrants in therapy* / Beyond the clouds: *Q-Boys* / My forbidden lover: *Tapps* / Spin it: *Sunbelt* / Cha cha cha: *Kontini, Finzy* / Holiday rap: *MC Miker G & DJ Sven* / LA party mix / Hurricane: *Tapps* / Tequila: *Mo Boss* / Feel the energy: *Jeanette & The New Dance* / Samba: *Chingas, Johnny* / Mr. DJ: *Glass Family* / Bonus: *JDC Mixer*
HTCD 27 / 20 Apr '98 / Hot Productions

☐ **BEST OF JUNGLE MASSIVE, THE (2CD Set)**
SMDCD 112 / Jul '97 / Snapper

☐ **BEST OF JUNGLE VOL.1, THE**
PNCCA 2 / Aug '94 / Production House

☐ **BEST OF JUNGLE VOL.3, THE**
PNCCA 4 / Jan '95 / Production House

☐ **BEST OF JUNGLE VOL.4, THE**
PNCCA 6 / May '95 / Production House

☐ **BEST OF LATIN AMERICA - CHANGE THE RULES, THE**
La noche: *Arroyo, Joe* / Sobre las olas: *Latin Brothers* / Descarge de hoy: *Alemany, Jesus* / EL patillero: *Fruko* / Me tenian amarrado con fe: *Saquito, Nico* / Juana pena: *Maestra, Sierra* / Pregoes do rios: *De Rua, Moleque* / Eu quero sossego: *Reiner, A* / Floreaux: *Os Ingenuos* / Negra presuntuosa: *Baka, Susana* / El puente de los suspiros: *Freundt, Julie* / Duele: *Kjarkas* / Mi corazon en la ciudad: *Junaro, Emma* / Me gusta todo: *Los Nemus Del Pacifico* / La tarde: *Estudiantina Invasora* / Mil horas: *La Sonora Dinamita* / El indio sinuano: *Jiminez, Maximo* / Bordoneo Y 900: *Mosalini, Juan Jose* / Alma de loca: *Varela, Adriana*
RGNET 1013CD / May '97 / World Music Network

☐ **BEST OF LATIN AMERICA - EL CONDOR PASA, THE**
El condor pasa / Tres bailecitos / Mburucya nostalgia Colombiana / Frederico / Reccuerdo del puno / Que nadie sepa mi sufrir / Noche del Paraquay despedida / Burrerita / Estampa Panamena / Alde viejo companario / La tropilla / Pastor de nubes Asuncion del Paraguay
PV 793093 / Oct '93 / Disques Pierre Verany

☐ **BEST OF LATIN AMERICA - LA COLEGIALA, THE**
La colegiala / La Peregrinacion / Palmeras / Concierto en la llanura / Sueno de angelita / Cascada la baguala / El arriero / Porque / Cruzando el dulce / Zamponas / Reservista purajhei / Villa guillermina / Paraguay pe el Indio muerte / Misionera / La danza del colibri
PV 793094 / Oct '93 / Disques Pierre Verany

☐ **BEST OF LATIN AMERICA - MOLIENDO CAFE, THE**
Moliendo cafe / Pajaro campana / Madrecita / Indiecita Linda / Cerro cora / Che picazu mi / Kantu / Itagua poti / Guesta de pampa azui / Virginia / Sanz del destino / Estancia ava ne-e / Genoveva / Recuerdos de ipacarai / Angela Rosa / Esperanza mia
PV 793095 / Oct '93 / Disques Pierre Verany

☐ **BEST OF LATIN AMERICA VOL.1, THE**
EUCD 1115 / '91 / ARC

☐ **BEST OF LATIN AMERICA VOL.2, THE**
EUCD 1147 / '91 / ARC

☐ **BEST OF LATIN JAZZ, THE**
Nica's dream: *Burrell, Kenny* / Sambop: *Adderley, Cannonball* / Gunky: *Lytle, Johnny* / Baion baby: *Stitt, Sonny* / Mambo inn: *Taylor, Billy* / Caravan: *Pucho & His Latin Soul Brothers* / Montuneando: *Santamaria, Mongo & La Lupe* / Ping pong: *Blakey, Art & The Jazz Messengers* / Mau mau: *Farmer, Art Septet* / Manteca: *Garland, Red Trio* / Seafood Wally: *Rodriguez, Willie* / Screamin': *McDuff, 'Brother' Jack* / Fatman: *Montego Joe* / Mambo ricci: *Dolphy, Eric & Latin Jazz 5*
CDBGP 1034 / Mar '92 / Beat Goes Public

☐ **BEST OF LATIN JAZZ, THE**
EMPRCD 707 / Mar '97 / Emporio

☐ **BEST OF LEGGO, THE**
504012 / Nov '95 / Declic

☐ **BEST OF LIQUID VOL.4, THE (2CD Set)**
LQ 0052 / 27 Apr '98 / Liquid

☐ **BEST OF LISTEN TO THE BAND VOL.1, THE**
Mephistopheles / Carmen suite / Laura / Batman / Molly on the shore / Bolero / Overture 'Tancredi' / Over the rainbow / Rhythm and blues / Festive prelude / Pastime with good company / Music from 'Ballet Russe' / March 'Le Reve Passe' / Capriccio Espagnol / Skye boat song / Fiorentiner march / Soldiers in the park
DOYCD 016 / Oct '92 / Doyen

☐ **BEST OF LIVING BEAT, THE**
Bass (how low can you go): *Harris, Simon* / Ragga house: *Daddy Freddie* / Grab the mike: *Wildman / SuperMarioland: Ambassadors Of Funk* / I'm in the mood for dancing: *Nolans* / Back for good: *Real Emotion* / Time: *Leslie Lyrics* / Armed and extremely damgerous: *M-Brace & Angie* / Who's crying now: *Sims, Joyce* / (I've got your)pleasure control: *Harris, Simon & Lonnie Gordon* / Go for the heart: *Fox, Samantha* / French Kiss: *Big Louis* / Sexy Lady: *Big Dipper* / Better move quick: *Bassman* / Don't stop the music: *Harris, Simon & Dina Carroll* / Boom boom boom(say what ho): *Inhere sisters* / Do it now: *Bailey, Louise*
ANT 004 / Nov '96 / Tring

☐ **BEST OF LOADING BAY VOL.1, THE**
LBAYCD 1 / Jan '93 / Loading Bay

☐ **BEST OF LOLLIPOP RECORDS, THE**
Boogie woogie dancin' shoes: *Barry, Claudja* / Space ranger: *Galaxie* / At the discoteque: *Lipstique* / Witch queen of New Orleans: *Proby, P.J.* / Dancin' fever: *Barry, Claudja* / Over and over: *Disco Circus* / I'm coming home baby: *Mascara* / California sun: *Rock, Johnny* / Sweet dynamite: *Barry, Claudja* / I'm a man: *Rowley, Mick* / Video games: *Jones, Ronnie* / Sing sing: *M Machine* / Why must a girl like me: *Barry, Claudja* / Work me over: *Barry, Claudja*
HTCD 10 / 20 Apr '98 / Hot Productions

☐ **BEST OF LOUISIANA MUSIC, THE**
ROUANCD 08 / Jun '93 / Rounder

☐ **BEST OF LOVE IS IN THE AIR, THE**
REACD 004 / Jun '98 / Reactive

☐ **BEST OF LOVERS ROCK VOL.1, THE**
RNCD 2018 / Feb '94 / Rhino

☐ **BEST OF LOVERS ROCK VOL.2, THE**
RNCD 2039 / Jan '94 / Rhino

☐ **BEST OF LOVERS ROCK VOL.3, THE**
RNCD 2062 / Jun '94 / Rhino

☐ **BEST OF LOVERS ROCK, THE (2CD Set)**
RN 7063 / 31 Aug '98 / Rhino

☐ **BEST OF LUV 'N' HAIGHT VOL.1, THE**
LHCD 011 / Jul '96 / Luv n' Haight

☐ **BEST OF MEMPHIS ROOTS, THE**
RZRCD 537 / Dec '93 / Ritz

☐ **BEST OF MOBY DICK RECORDS, THE (Jump Shout)**
HTCD 85 / 20 Apr '98 / Hot Productions

☐ **BEST OF MONTAGE RECORDS, THE (Love Town/A Collection Of 16 Rare Philly Classics)**
Love town: *Newbury, Booker* / Shake and pop: *Shotgun* / New love: *Royce, Rose* / Caught in the middle of goodbye: *LTD* / Get up and shake it: *Parker, Cecil* / Put your money where the funk is: *Mandrill* / Flashback: *Lord, C.M.* / Video reaction: *Green, Steve* / My world is empty without you: *Brown, Yvonne* / Want ads: *Cafe* / I'm going to love him: *Sanctuary* / It's hot: *Ultimate Choice* / New Wave: *Patterson Twins* / I need a freak: *Sexual Harassment* / I think I want to dance with you: *Rumple-Stilts-Skin* / Strike while the iron is hot: *Rumple-Stilts-Skin*
HTCD 54 / 20 Apr '98 / Hot Productions

☐ **BEST OF MOUNTAIN STAGE VOL.1, THE**
Such a night: *Dr. John* / Hell I'd go: *Acoustic Warriors* / Twilight: *Danko, Rick* / Bill of goods: *Wainwright III, Loudon* / O'Marie: *Lanois, Daniel* / Home is where the heart is: *Gregson, Clive* / Songbird: *Winchester, Jesse* / Yes, yes, yes: *NRBQ* / Shoot out the lights: *Thompson, Richard* / Bird on the wire: *Groce, Larry* / What you gonna do when the zydeco turn on you: *Buckwheat Zydeco*
BPM 001CD / May '97 / Blue Plate

☐ **BEST OF MOUNTAIN STAGE VOL.2, THE**
God is a real estate developer: *Shocked, Michelle* / It's a big old goofy world: *Prine, John* / Arms of love: *Hitchcock, Robyn* / Red wine and promises: *Tabor, June* / Losing my religion: *REM* / Tank park salute: *Bragg, Billy* / Summerfly: *O'Connell, Maura* / You're no good: *Harding, John Wesley* / Where've you been: *Mattea, Kathy* / These blues: *Gilmore, Jimmie Dale* / Simply: *Hickman, Sara* / Standing on shaky ground: *McClinton, Delbert*
BPM 002CD / May '97 / Blue Plate

☐ **BEST OF MOUNTAIN STAGE VOL.3, THE**
Border crossing: *Timbuk 3* / Guantan Amerika: *Chilton, Alex* / Superman's song: *Crash Test Dummies* / Never had it so good: *Carpenter, Mary-Chapin* / Waiting for a miracle: *Cockburn, Bruce* / Soy de San Louis: *Texas Tornados* / Misguided angel: *Cowboy Junkies* / Lewis: *Yo La Tengo* / Shelter: *McLachlan, Sarah* / Renegade: *Zevon, Warren* / Cynical girl: *Crenshaw, Marshall* / Romance is a slow dance: *Fabulous Twister Sisters* / Tear stained letter: *Sonnier, Jo El*
BPM 003CD / May '97 / Blue Plate

☐ **BEST OF MOUNTAIN STAGE VOL.4, THE**
Big boss man: *Holmes Brothers* / That's enough of that stuff: *Ball, Marcia* / You're so fine: *Hammond, John* / What do you want the girl to do: *Toussaint, Allen* / My tears: *Robillard, Duke* / Crazy horse blues: *Thompson, Bob* / My God called me this morning: *Fairfield Four* / Sweet home Chicago: *Edwards, David 'Honeyboy'* / Move on: *Nelson, Tracy* / Purple haze: *Bobs* / It's getting warm in here: *Musselwhite, Charley* / Why am I treated so bad: *Staples, Pops*
BPM 004CD / May '97 / Blue Plate

☐ **BEST OF MOUNTAIN STAGE VOL.5, THE**
Angels: *Holsapple, Peter & Chris Stamey* / Early summer rain: *Welch, Kevin* / Walkin' for your love: *Widespread Panic* / Particle man: *They Might Be Giants* / Peace: *Los Lobos* / Loves recovery: *Indigo Girls* / Responsibility: *Forbert, Steve* / Goodnite Irene: *Pere Ubu* / Any cure: *Subdudes* / Rockin' in the res: *Trudell, John*
BPM 005CD / May '97 / Blue Plate

☐ **BEST OF MOUNTAIN STAGE VOL.6, THE**
Girl from the north country: *Hornsby, Bruce* / Mister wrong: *Cracker* / World leader pretend: *REM* / Outbound plane: *Griffith, Nanci* / Black sunshine: *Me Phi Me* / Headmasters of mine: *Gaines, Jeffrey* / After you're gone: *DeMent, Iris* / Blue world: *Brady, Paul* / What a good boy: *Barenaked Ladies* / Working on a building: *Hampton, Bruce & The Aquarium Rescue Unit*
BPM 006CD / May '97 / Blue Plate

☐ **BEST OF MOUNTAIN STAGE VOL.7, THE**
Mama's got a girlfriend now: *Harper, Ben* / American music: *Violent Femmes* / Praise the lord and pass the snakes: *Hot Tuna* / You look like rain: *Morphine* / Moonshiner: *Uncle Tupelo* / Good things: *BoDeans* / Magic finger: *Fleck, Bela* / Being simple: *Judybats* / Pale sun: *Cowboy Junkies* / Mr Jones: *Counting Crows*
BPM 007CD / May '97 / Blue Plate

☐ **BEST OF MOUNTAIN STAGE VOL.8, THE**
Buildings and bridges: *Di Franco, Ani* / Dominique: *Pilgrim, Billy* / Find yourself a door: *Droge, Pete* / Happy home: *Cole, Paula* / Gypsy life: *Gorka, John* / I know better now: *Croce, A.J.* / Do not disturb: *Larkin, Patty* / Trampoline: *Lloyd, Bill* / Golden dreams: *Straw, Syd* / Howling wind: *Parker, Graham* / Mama's arms: *Kadison, Joshua* / Woman on the floor: *Band De Soleil*
BPM 008CD / May '97 / Blue Plate

☐ **BEST OF MUSIC OF LIFE, THE**
MOLCD 029 / Apr '93 / Music Of Life

☐ **BEST OF NASHBORO GOSPEL, THE**
Touch me Lord Jesus: *Angelic Gospel Singers* / I've fixed it with Jesus: *Boggs, Professor Harold* / Family prayer: *Bright Stars* / Milky white way: *CBS Trumpeteers* / Give me my flowers: *Consolers* / Stop gambler: *Cook, Madame Edna Gallmon* / Bible is right: *Gospel Songbirds* / Wake me, shake me: *May, Brother Joe* / Roll Jordan roll: *Famous Skylarks* / How I got over: *Swanee Quintet* / Mother's advice: *Taylor Brothers* / Step by step: *Boyer Brothers* / In my saviours care: *Sons Of The South* / Jesus be my keeper: *Silvertone Singers* / I'm a soldier: *Jordan River Singers* / If you miss me from praying: *Radio Four* / Sell out to the master: *Christland singers* / Since Jesus came into my heart: *Silvertone Singers* / Didn't it rain children: *Sons Of The South* / My life is in his hands: *Jordan River Singers* / Let the church roll on: *Barbee, Lucille* / You got to be born again: *Christland singers* / Earnest prayer: *Radio Four* / Don't drive your children away: *Fairfield Four* / I want to be just like him: *Supreme Angels* / No cross no crown: *Brooklyn Allstars* / Step by step (#2): *Swanee Quintet*
CDCHD 373 / Jan '93 / Ace

☐ **BEST OF NEW BRITISH COUNTRY, THE**
Lost highway: *Hollywood Cowboys* / Can can do: *Hayes, Lynda* / I looked a little closer: *Mitchell, Glen & The Troubleshooters* / I didn't mean to do it: *Mitchell, Glen & The Troubleshooters* / Wasting my time: *Plain Loco* / Mouth: *Well Oiled Sisters* / Divorce over easy: *Wangford, Hank & The Lost Cowboys* / Raising heaven: *Page, Stu Band* / Rio Grande: *Greaves, M.C. & The Lonesome Too* / Truck off the road: *Lemon Grass* / Someone to watch over me: *De Jongh, Julie* / Cherokee boogie: *Cool, Ricky & The Western Swing All Stars* / Bitter tear: *Rockingbirds* / In all the right places: *Trading With The natives* / Emma: *Paradise Canyon* / Sisters, best of friends: *Haley Sisters* / Go the hog: *52 Pick-Up* / Blood on the honky tonk floor: *Los Pistoleros* / Dixie's in Alabama: *Wishbone* / Ring around the roses: *Meuross, Reg* / Hard luck story line: *Johnson, Kenny* / Ride on: *Cross Country* / I'm smoking again: *Those Magnificent Men* / Thank you for the memories: *Newman, Syd & Pick Of The Bunch*
WOWCD 01 / Sep '97 / Way Out West

☐ **BEST OF NEW COUNTRY LINE DANCE VOL.1, THE**
One step forward / There goes my heart / Wild one / Elvira / All you ever do is bring me down / Boys and me / Achy breaky heart / Bring it on down to my house / Cotton eye Joe / My baby loves me / Anyway the wind blows / Gone country
305932 / Jan '97 / Hallmark

☐ **BEST OF NEW COUNTRY LINE DANCE VOL.2, THE**
308302 / Jun '98 / Hallmark

☐ **BEST OF NEW COUNTRY, THE**
Could have been me: *Cyrus, Billy Ray* / Lonesome standard time: *Mattea, Kathy* / Third rate romance: *Kershaw, Sammy* / Should have been a cowboy: *Kershaw, Sammy* / When boy meets girl: *Clark, Terri* / Has anybody seen Amy: *Wiggins, John & Audrey* / Oh lonesome me: *Kentucky Headhunters* / This hat ain't no act: *Dennis, Wesley* / Oh no not love again: *Comeaux, Amie* / Nobody but a fool: *Wright, Chely* / Small town: *Anderson, John* / Hard Luck Cafe: *Stegall, Keith* / Out here sits the King: *Daniel, Davis* / New faces in the fields: *Allen, Harley* / More I learn (the less I understand about love): *Reeves, Ronna* / Goin' by the book: *Cash, Johnny* / Everybody wants to be Hank Williams: *Boone, Larry* / Dance: *Twister Alley*
5543782 / 6 Apr '98 / Spectrum

☐ **BEST OF NEW WELSH FOLK MUSIC, THE (Goreuon Canu Gwerin Newydd)**
Y gog lwydlas: *James, Sian* / Hyd y frwynen/Rhuad teirw'r dyffryn: *Saith Rhyfeddod* / Os ymadael: *Bob Delyn* / Fflat huw puw: *Gwerinos* / Cefn du/ Ymdeithgan gwyr dyfi/Y derwydd: *Gwerinos* / Adar man y mynydd: *Ogam* / Jig poltague/Gyrru'r byd o'mlaen/Neidod twm bach: *Ogam* / Taflwn yr hosan: *Ogam* / Mon a Menai: *Pigyn Clust* / Hoffter menna/ Ffair y borth: *Pigyn Clust* / Taith madoc: *Aberjaber* / Y march glas: *Cusan Tan* / Jigolo/Harri Morgan: *Ar-Log* / Seidir ddoe: *Plethyn* / Cariad fach tirderi: *Rodge, John* / Ysbryd y werin/Mae'r ddaer yn glasu: *Carreg Lafar* / Marwnad yr ehedydd/Ymdaith gwyr dyfnaint: *Branwen* / Suo gan/Y gelynnen/Llantony Abbey: *Calennig* / Fe drawodd yn fy meddwl: *Iwan, Dafydd*
SCD 2146 / Jun '97 / Sain

☐ **BEST OF NIGHTMARE RECORDS, THE**
My heart keeps beating faster: *Rocq-E-Harrell* / Bad connection: *Glenn, Bobby* / I can fly: *Thomas, Louise* / Do you know the way to San Jose: *Croisette* / I got you covered: *Bentley, Earlene* / Turning my back and walking away: *Jiani, Carol* / I can't stay mad at you: *Clarke, Sharon Dee* / Backtrack: *Powell, Shezwae* / There are brighter days: *Pennington, Barbara* / Let's not say goodbye: *Jigsaw* / Visitors: *Moonstone* / You spin my world around: *Moore, Kevin* / Whatever happened to our melody: *Holman, Eddie* / Reaching for the best: *Exciters*
HTCD 20 / 20 Apr '98 / Hot Productions

☐ **BEST OF NORTHERN SOUL, THE**
Twenty four hours a day / Weak spot / Your magic put a spell on me / Breakin' down the walls of heartache / Key to my happiness / Ain't no soul left in these old shoes / Let me down easy / With this ring / Reaching for the best / Baby I'm still the same man / Our love is in the pocket / You're gonna love my baby / That's when the tears start / Doomsday / What's wrong with me baby / Goodbye cruel love / Out on the floor / There's nothing else to say / Skiing in the snow / Nothing's worse than being alone
QED 062 / Nov '96 / Tring

☐ **BEST OF NORTHSOUND VOL.1, THE (Harmonising Nature With Music)**
2456 / Aug '96 / NorthSound

☐ **BEST OF NUGGETS, THE**
BONCD 1 / 4 May '98 / Bon

☐ **BEST OF O RECORDS VOL.1, THE**
Desire: *Griffith, Roni* / Passion: *Flirts* / Native love: *Divine* / Just a gigolo: *Barbie & The Kens* / Make it on my own: *Free Enterprise* / Whisper to a scream: *Bobby O* / Danger: *Flirts* / These memories: *Oh Romeo* / Love reaction: *Divine* / Ready or not: *Hot Line* / Sensitive: *Bad South* / You and me: *Flirts*
HTCD 1 / 20 Apr '98 / Hot Productions

☐ **BEST OF O RECORDS VOL.2, THE**
Helpless: *Flirts* / She has a way: *Bobby O* / Shoot your shot: *Divine* / Lust or love: *Malibu* / Take a chance on me: *Waterfront Home* / Saving myself: *Girly* / Best part of breaking up: *Griffith, Roni* / How to pick up girls: *Bobby O* / Calling all boys: *Flirts* / Once is not enough: *Oh Romeo* / Who's your boyfriend: *Eric* / Love attack: *Caso, Tony* / West end girls: *Pet Shop Boys*
HTCD 2 / 20 Apr '98 / Hot Productions

☐ **BEST OF OI VOL.1, THE**
Suburban rebels: *Business* / Someone's gonna die: *Blitz* / George Davis is innocent: *Sham 69* / GLC: *Menace* / Police oppression: *Angelic Upstarts* / England belongs to me: *Cock Sparrer* / One law for them: *4 Skins* / King of the jungle: *Last Resort* / SPG: *Red Alert* / Summer of '81: *Violators* / Police story: *Partisans* / Smash the discos: *Business* / Runnin' riot: *Cock Sparrer* / Right to choose: *Combat 84* / Working class kids: *Last Resort* / Yesterday's heroes: *4 Skins* / Police car: *Cockney Rejects* / Razors in the night: *Blitz* / Meglomania: *Blood* / Maniac: *Peter & The Test Tube Babies* / Tuckers ruckers ain't no suckers: *Gonads* / Two pints of lager: *Splodge* / Kids of the 80's: *Infa Riot* / They don't understand: *Sham 69* / England: *Angelic Upstarts*
DOJOCD 94 / Apr '93 / Dojo

☐ **BEST OF OI VOL.2, THE**
Harry May: *Business* / Nation on fire: *Blitz* / Evil: *4 Skins* / Johnny Barden: *Last Resort* / Chip on my shoulder: *Cock Sparrer* / I'm civilised: *Menace* / Such fun: *Blood* / I wanna be a star: *Cockney Rejects* / Transvestite: *Peter & The Test Tube Babies* / I lost my love to a UK sub: *Gonads* / What am I gonna do: *Ejected* / For the love of oi: *Section 5* / Real enemy: *Business* / Rapist: *Combat 84* / Each dawn I die: *Infa Riot* / I don't wanna: *Sham 69* / Take 'em all: *Cock Sparrer* / Take the blame: *Vicious Rumors* / Arms race: *Partisans* / Don't you ever let me down: *Crack* / Violence in our minds: *Last Resort* / On the streets: *4 Skins* / Action man: *Strike* / Emergency: *Infa Riot* / Kids on the streets: *Angelic Upstarts*
DOJOCD 134 / Jan '96 / Dojo

☐ **BEST OF OI VOL.3, THE**
DOJOCD 207 / Mar '95 / Dojo

☐ **BEST OF OPEN, THE (2CD Set)**
OPENCD 1 / May '96 / Ministry Of Sound

☐ **BEST OF OUT OF THE COOL VOL.1, THE**
OOCD 001CD / 16 Sep '97 / Family Affair

☐ **BEST OF P&P RECORDS, THE**
HTCD 99 / 20 Apr '98 / Hot Productions

☐ **BEST OF PAN PIPES, THE (2CD Set)**
Killing me softly / Lifted / Whole new world / How deep is your love / Love is all around / (Everything I do) I do it for you / Careless whisper / Drive / Mysterious girl / I will always love you / Unchained melody / Tears in heaven / I swear / Without you / First time ever I saw your face / You don't bring me

flowers / Goodbye to love / Power of love / Walking in the air / Ev'ry time we say goodbye / Sacrifice / When I fall in love / Change the world / Forever love / Jesus to a child / Earth song / Think twice / El Condor Pasa / Yesterday / Back for good / Don't cry for me Argentina / Beauty and the beast / Riverdance / Orinoco flow / All by myself / Danny boy / Someday / Nothing compares 2 U / Wind beneath my wings / Memory

TCD 2845 / Sep '96 / Telstar

☐ BEST OF PARIS INTERNATIONAL RECORDS, THE

HTCD 92 / 20 Apr '98 / Hot Productions

☐ BEST OF PERSONAL RECORDS, THE

Din daa daa: *Kranz, George* / Touch me: *Wish & Fonda Rae* / Chinese eyes: *Fancy* / Come inside: *Fancy* / Push push: *Hicks, Claire & Love Exchange* / Check it out: *Fancy* / Dr. Music: *Jacobs Rock, Debbie* / In the heat of the night: *Jones, Klinte* / Set it out: *Midway* / Born to love: *Barry, Claudja* / Let's change it up: *Inner Life*

HTCD 3 / 20 Apr '98 / Hot Productions

☐ BEST OF PHILLY WORLD RECORDS, THE

HTCD 104 / 20 Apr '98 / Hot Productions

☐ BEST OF PIANO JAZZ, THE

Sept a dire / Force tranquille / Agripaume III / Bouillie bordelaise / Adi / Valse no.2 / Sep petits jeux / Beeing sincere / Leila / E si...si...si / Voice of Zak / Trio du porto / E H F T B

TCB 01042 / Sep '95 / TCB

☐ BEST OF RADAR RECORDS, THE (Makin' Music)

Knock me out: *Gary's Gang* / Reach up: *Lee, Tony* / You ain't really down: *Status IV* / Breakin' in space: *Key-Matic* / Under my thumb: *Fast Radio* / Break: *Scotti, Ritchie* / I'm out of your life: *Arnie's Love* / Lovin' you: *Status IV* / Makin' music: *Gary's Gang* / Runaway: *Gary's Gang* / Come and get my lovin': *Fowler, Barbara*

HTCD 39 / 20 Apr '98 / Hot Productions

☐ BEST OF RECORD SHACK RECORDS, THE

So many men so little time: *Brown, Miquel* / High energy: *Thomas, Evelyn* / Star gazing: *Bentley & Sylvester* / He's a saint he's a sinner: *Brown, Miquel* / On a crowded street: *Pennington, Barbara* / Caught in the act: *Bentley, Earlene* / Boys come to town: *Bentley, Earlene* / Heartless: *Thomas, Evelyn* / I'm living my own life: *Bentley, Earlene* / Reflections: *Thomas, Evelyn* / Fan the flame: *Pennington, Barbara* / Primitive desire: *Eastbound Expressway*

HTCD 4 / 20 Apr '98 / Hot Productions

☐ BEST OF REGGAE SUNSPLASH, THE

Ital love: *Chalice* / Revival time: *Chalice* / Calling you: *Sandi & The Sunsetz* / Do you feel like dancing: *Bloodfire Posse* / Can't stop rocking tonight: *Bloodfire Posse* / It's magic: *Brown, Dennis* / Wild fire: *Brown, Dennis & John Holt* / Botha: *Cocoa T* / Medley: *Charlie Chaplin & Yellowman* / Oh what a feeling: *Isaacs, Gregory* / Let off: *Josey Wales* / Ram jam dance: *Wailer, Bunny* / Jolly session: *Wailer, Bunny* / Sabotage: *Wailer, Bunny*

CDCHARLY 235 / Sep '90 / Charly

☐ BEST OF REGGAE VOL.1, THE

3885932 / Jun '97 / Galaxy

☐ BEST OF REGGAE VOL.1, THE (Roots & Toots)

Guns of Navarone: *Skatalites* / Red red wine: *Tribe, Tony* / Take me home country roads: *Toots & The Maytals* / 007 (Shanty town): *Dekker, Desmond & The Aces* / Love of the common people: *Thomas, Nicky* / Crying over you: *Boothe, Ken* / Long shot kick de bucket: *Pioneers* / Liquidator: *Harry J All Stars* / To be young gifted and black: *Bob & Marcia* / Double barrel: *Barker, Dave & Ansell Collins* / Small axe: *Marley, Bob & The Wailers* / Cherry oh baby: *Donaldson, Eric* / Oh baby (sick and tired): *Techniques* / Return of Django: *Upsetters* / Black and white: *Greyhound* / Reggae in your jeggae: *Dandy* / Montego bay: *Notes, Freddie & The Rudies* / Phoenix city: *Alphonso, Roland*

SELCD 503 / 2 Mar '98 / Castle Select

☐ BEST OF RIC RECORDS VOL.1, THE (Carnival Time)

Carnival Time: *Johnson, Al* / Cotton candy: *Capello, Lenny* / Check Mr. Popeye: *Bo, Eddie* / I don't talk too much: *Nelson, Martha* / Let's stop and talk it over: *Ridgley, Tommy* / Lena: *Johnson, Al* / Ninety pound weakling: *Capello, Lenny* / Losing battle: *Adams, Johnny* / Let's Get It: *Blanchard, Edgar* / She's got what it takes: *Ridley, Tommy* / Feeling right Sat: *Velvetiers*

ROUCD 2075 / '88 / Rounder

☐ BEST OF RIO CARNIVAL, THE

CDEB 2224 / May '93 / Earthbeat

☐ BEST OF ROCK 'N' ROLL VOL.2 1938-1946, THE (2CD Set)

FA 352 / Feb '97 / Fremeaux

☐ BEST OF ROCK ON STAGE VOL.1, THE

Come together: *MC5* / What goes on: *Velvet Underground* / Somebody to love: *Jefferson Airplane* / Shape I'm in: *Band* / Sweet Jane: *Reed, Lou* / Only women bleed: *Cooper, Alice* / It's all over now: *Faces* / Highway star: *Deep Purple* / Rosalie/ Cowgirl's song: *Thin Lizzy* / I want to go to the sun: *Frampton, Peter* / All in it together: *Pirates* / All through the city: *Dr. Feelgood* / Junior's wailing: *Status Quo* / Long train runnin': *Doobie Brothers* / In trance: *Scorpions* / Messin' with the kid: *Gallagher, Rory*

VSOPCD 202 / Aug '94 / Connoisseur Collection

☐ BEST OF ROCK ON STAGE VOL.2, THE

Pinball wizard: *Who* / Kill the king: *Rainbow* / Stealin': *Uriah Heep* / Too old to rock 'n' roll, too young to die: *Jethro Tull* / I'm going home: *Ten Years After* / Woke up this morning and found myself dead: *Hendrix, Jimi* / Voodoo chile: *Vaughan, Stevie Ray* / Black magic woman: *Santana* / Full moon boogie: *Beck, Jeff & Jan Hammer Group* / Born to be wild: *Blue Oyster Cult* / Do the strand: *Roxy Music* / This flight tonight: *Nazareth* / Breaking the law: *Judas Priest* / Ace of spades: *Motorhead* / Parisienne walkways: *Moore, Gary*

VSOPCD 208 / Nov '94 / Connoisseur Collection

☐ BEST OF ROTTERDAM RECORDS, THE

ROF CD1 / Mar '93 / Rotterdam

☐ BEST OF SALSA, THE

EUCD 1319 / Nov '95 / ARC

☐ BEST OF SAN FRANCISCO LIVE, THE

White rabbit: *Jefferson Airplane* / Morning dew: *Grateful Dead* / I want to be near you: *Scaggs, Boz* / Who do you love: *Hammond, John* / Early morning rain: *Lightfoot, Gordon* / Diggy liggy lo: *Commander Cody* / White bird: *It's A Beautiful Day* / So fine: *Bishop, Elvin* / Brand new Tennessee waltz: *Winchester, Jesse* / Stagger Lee: *Taj Mahal* / Turn on your lovelight: *Grateful Dead & Janis Joplin* / Plastic fantastic lover: *Jefferson Airplane* / Time has come today: *Chambers Brothers* / Hellbound train: *Town Cryers & Marty Balin*

3036000702 / Feb '97 / Carlton

☐ BEST OF SAXON WORLD WIDE VOL.1, THE

SAXCD 002 / Mar '95 / Saxon Studio

☐ BEST OF SAXON WORLD WIDE VOL.2, THE

SAXCD 0032 / Oct '95 / Saxon Studio

☐ BEST OF SAXON WORLD WIDE VOL.4, THE

SAXCD 007 / Jun '97 / Saxon Studio

☐ BEST OF SAXON WORLD WIDE VOL.5, THE

SAXCD 009 / 5 May '98 / Saxon Studio

☐ BEST OF SCORPGEMI RECORDS, THE (Keep In Touch Body To Body)

HTCD 80 / 20 Apr '98 / Hot Productions

☐ BEST OF SCOTLAND, THE (20 Tracks Of Traditional Scotish Music)

Bluebells of Scotland: *Corries* / Donald where's your troosers: *Stewart, Andy* / Scotland the brave: *Wilson, Robert* / Mairi's wedding: *Anderson, Moira* / Bluebell polka: *Shand, Jimmy* / Black Douglas: *Corries* / Rowan tree: *McKellar, Kenneth* / Road to the Isles: *Stewart, Andy* / Flower of Scotland: *Royal Scots Dragoon Guards* / Roamin' in the gloamin': *Logan, Jimmy* / Sound the pibroch: *Corries* / Westering home: *Wilson, Robert* / Mull of Kintyre: *Royal Scots Dragoon Guards* / I love a lassie: *Logan, Jimmy* / Gay Gordons medley: *Shand, Jimmy* / Dancing in Kyle: *Anderson, Moira* / Campbeltown loch: *Stewart, Andy* / I belong to Glasgow: *Fyffe, Will* / Amazing grace: *Royal Scots Dragoon Guards* / Haste ye back: *Wilson, Robert*

CDMFP 6230 / Jun '96 / Music For Pleasure

☐ BEST OF SCOTTISH FOLK, THE

PLSCD 148 / Feb '97 / Pulse

☐ BEST OF SCOTTISH PIPES AND DRUMS, THE

EUCD 1306 / Jul '95 / ARC

☐ BEST OF SIOUX VOL.1, THE

Wave of war: *Higgs, Joe* / Pharoah's walk: *Exodus & Jam Rock* / Funny man: *King Reggie* / In the ghetto: *Dillon, Phyllis* / With these hands: *Wayne, Mark* / African people (Indian Reservation): *Brown, Funky* / Super bad: *JD* / I don't know: *Smith, Junior* / Train (Engine 54): *Lloyd The Matador* / Lay a foundation: *Higgs, Joe* / You just gotta get ready: *Jackson, Pooch* / Cool girl: *King Reggie* / Mammy blue: *Circles* / Julia sees me: *Exodus* / I'm in a dancing mood: *Smith, Junior* / World is spinning around: *Higgs, Joe* / Happy song: *Twinkle Brothers* / Young, gifted and black: *King Reggie* / Vietnam: *Smith, Sammi* / Heavy reggae: *Roosevelt Singers*

PRCD 602 / Jun '95 / President

☐ BEST OF SKA LIVE, THE

Train to skaville: *Selecter* / Gangsters: *Specials* / Tears of a clown: *Special Beat* / On my radio: *Selecter* / Nite club: *Specials* / Mirror in the bathroom: *Special Beat* / Missing words: *Selecter* / Monkey man: *Specials* / Ranking full stop: *Special Beat* / Too much pressure: *Selecter* / Longshot kick the bucket: *Specials* / Rat race: *Special Beat* / James Bond: *Selecter* / Skinhead moonstomp: *Specials* / Enjoy yourself: *Special Beat*

EMPRCD 579 / Jul '95 / Emporio

☐ BEST OF SOCIETY HILL RECORDS, THE

HTCD 98 / 20 Apr '98 / Hot Productions

☐ BEST OF SOLAR, THE

I can make you feel good: *Shalamar* / And the beat goes on: *Whispers* / Midas touch: *Midnight Star* / I don't want to be a freak (but I can't help myself): *Dynasty* / Fantastic voyage: *Lakeside* / Dance with you: *Lucas, Carrie* / Romeo where's Juliet: *Collage* / Take that to the bank: *Shalamar* / Come back lover: *Sylvers* / Body talk: *Deele* / It's a love thing: *Whispers* / Headlines: *Midnight Star* / I wanna be rich: *Calloway* / I gotta keep dancin': *Lucas, Carrie* / Make that move: *Shalamar* / Rock steady: *Whispers*

RENCD 106 / Sep '95 / Renaissance Collector Series

☐ BEST OF SOUL STREET RECORDS, THE

HTCD 94 / 20 Apr '98 / Hot Productions

☐ BEST OF SPLATCH, THE

STOAT 006 / May '97 / Mother Stoat

☐ BEST OF STRAKER'S SOCA CALYPSO 1998, THE

GS 2416 / 8 Jun '98 / Strakers

☐ BEST OF SUGAR HILL GOSPEL VOL.1, THE (Everytime I Feel The Spirit)

SHCD 9102 / Jan '97 / Sugar Hill

☐ BEST OF SUGAR HILL GOSPEL VOL.2, THE (Way Down Deep In My Soul)

SHCD 9103 / Jan '97 / Sugar Hill

☐ BEST OF SUMMER JAM, THE

Introduction: *Sinbad* / Cisco kid: *War* / Pick up the pieces: *Average White Band* / For the love of money: *O'Jays* / Fire: *Ohio Players* / Lovegirl: *Marie, Teena* / Joy and pain: *Maze* / Midnight train to Georgia: *Knight, Gladys* / That's the way of the world: *Earth, Wind & Fire* / Celebration: *Kool & The Gang* / Shake and dance with me: *Con Funk Shun* / What is hip: *Tower Of Power* / Outstanding: *Gap Band* / Oops upside your head: *Gap Band* / I'm every woman: *Khan, Chaka* / Fantastic voyage: *Lakeside* / Love and happiness: *Green, Al*

RENCD 123 / Jun '97 / Renaissance Collector Series

☐ BEST OF SUN ROCKABILLY VOL.1, THE

Ten cats down: *Cantrell & Claunch* / Jump right out of this jukebox: *Wheeler, Onie* / Gonna romp and stomp: *Rhodes, Slim* / Domino: *Phillips, Sam* / Rakin' and scrapin': *Beard, Dean* / Slow down: *Earls, Jack* / Red cadillac and a black moustache: *Thompson & May* / Break up: *Rich, Charlie* / Greenback dollar / Red headed woman: *Burgess, Sonny* / Flyin' saucer rock 'n' roll: *Scott, Ray* / Crawdad hole: *Lewis, Jerry Lee* / Love my baby: *Parker, Herman* / Red hot: *Emerson, Billy 'The Kid'* / We wanna boogie: *Burgess, Sonny* / Come on little mama: *Harris & Cogswell* / Right behind you baby: *Rich, Charlie* / Ubangi stomp: *Underwood, Charles* / Let's bop: *Earls, Jack* / Rabbit action: *Thompson, Junior* / Put your cat clothes on: *Perkins, Carl* / Rockin' with my baby: *Yelvington, Malcolm*

CPCD 8202 / Feb '97 / Charly

☐ BEST OF SUN ROCKABILLY VOL.2, THE

Got love if you want it: *Smith, Warren* / That don't move me: *Perkins, Carl* / Itchy: *Burgess, Sonny* / Drinkin' wine: *Simmons, Gene* / How come you do me: *Thompson, Junior* / Gimme some lovin': *Jenkins, Harold* / Johnny Valentine: *Anderson, Andy* / Baby, please don't go: *Riley, Billy Lee* / Sentimental fool: *Pittman, Barbara* / Rebound: *Rich, Charlie* / Miss Froggie: *Smith, Warren* / Rock around the town: *Beard, Dean* / Wild one: *Lewis, Jerry Lee* / My baby don't rock: *McDaniel, Luke* / Find my baby for me: *Burgess, Sonny* / My gal Mary Ann: *Earls, Jack* / Me and my rhythm guitar: *Powers, Johnny* / All night rock: *Honeycutt, Glenn* / Your loving man: *Taylor, Vernon* / Madman 1: *Wages, Jimmy* / Fairlane rock: *Thompson, Hayden* / I need your loving kiss: *Jenkins, Harold* / Perkin's wiggle: *Perkins, Carl* / Ain't got a thing: *Burgess, Sonny*

CPCD 8209 / Feb '97 / Charly

☐ BEST OF SYNTHESIZER HITS, THE

EMPRCD 506 / Apr '94 / Emporio

☐ BEST OF TANGO, THE (2CD Set)

3020312 / Jun '97 / Arcade

☐ BEST OF TELESCOPE RECORDINGS, THE

Touch and go lover: *Jiani, Carol* / Razzle dazzle: *EVE* / I am what I am: *Le Cage* / Take a little chance: *EVE* / Don't leave me this way: *Jiani, Carol* / Dancing in the rain: *Jiani, Carol* / Pretty boy: *Charles, Elaine* / Stranded: *Charles, Elaine* / Build me up buttercup: *Davina* / Victim: *Kevin K* / In the night: *Totetda, Louis* / My heart: *Lace* / Love now play later: *Jiani, Carol* / Letter: *Charles, Elaine*

HTCD 21 / 20 Apr '98 / Hot Productions

☐ BEST OF THE '60S BRITISH BEAT VOL.2, THE

Build me up buttercup: *Foundations* / Little children: *Kramer, Billy J.* / Baby make it soon: *Marmalade* / Twist and shout: *Poole, Brian* / You were on my mind: *St. Peters, Crispian* / I understand: *Freddie & The Dreamers* / Um um um um um um: *Fontana, Wayne* / Pied piper: *St. Peters, Crispian* / Baby now that I've found you: *Foundations* / He's in town: *Rockin' Berries* / If you gotta make a fool of somebody: *Freddie & The Dreamers* / Do you love me: *Poole, Brian* / Reflections of my life: *Marmalade* / Poor man's son: *Rockin' Berries* / I'll keep you satisfied: *Kramer, Billy J.* / Game of love: *Fontana, Wayne*

305472 / Oct '96 / Hallmark

☐ BEST OF THE 1960'S GOLDEN OLDIES VOL.1, THE

Monday Monday: *Mamas & The Papas* / Eve of destruction: *McGuire, Barry* / Honey: *Goldsboro, Bobby* / Tracy: *Cuff Links* / Hush, not a word to Mary: *Rowles, John* / Magic carpet ride: *Steppenwolf* / Bend me, shape me: *American Breed* / Summertime: *Stewart, Billy* / Mama told me not to come: *Three Dog Night* / Dizzy: *Roe, Tommy* / Livin' next door to Alice: *Smokie* / I'm a believer: *Monkees* / White rabbit: *Jefferson Airplane* / Letter: *Box Tops* / Deep water: *Grapefruit* / Lion sleeps tonight: *Tokens*

MCD 30204 / Mar '94 / Ariola Express

☐ BEST OF THE BANDS, THE

Take the 'A' train: *Ellington, Duke* / Perdido: *Ellington, Duke* / Amercan patrol: *Miller, Glenn* / In the mood: *Ellington, Duke* / Litte brown jug: *Miller, Glenn* / String of pearls: *Miller, Glenn* / Caldonia: *Herman, Woody* / Woodchopper's ball: *Herman, Woody* / King Porter stomp: *Goodman, Benny* / On the sunny side of the street: *Dorsey, Tommy* / Begin the beguine: *Shaw, Artie* / Stardust: *Shaw, Artie* / Texas chatter: *James, Harry* / One o'clock jump: *Basie, Count* / Jeepers creepers: *Basie, Count* / Mack the knife: *Armstrong, Louis* / High society: *Armstrong, Louis* / Stompin' at the Savoy: *Armstrong, Louis* / Royal garden blues: *Dorsey, Tommy* / After you've gone: *Hampton, Lionel*

CD 6007 / Apr '96 / Music

☐ BEST OF THE BARBER SHOP QUARTET, THE

Michelle / You'll never know (just how much I love you) / Sixteen tons / Carolina I'm coming back to you / Dear little boy of mine / You can't be a beacon (if your light don't shine) / Turn on your light / How are things in Glocca Morra / You're in style when you're wearing a smile / Sweetheart of Sigma Chi / If you can't get a girl in the summertime / Chase the rain away / Looking at the world thru' rose coloured glasses / When you wish upon a star / One rose that's left in my heart / You're some pretty doll / Tennessee waltz / I miss mother most of all / Darkness on the delta / In the good old summertime / If you were the only girl in the world / Alabama jubilee / Albamy bound

QED 120 / Nov '96 / Tring

☐ BEST OF THE BEST VOL.2, THE

RASCD 3133 / Feb '94 / Ras

☐ BEST OF THE BEST VOL.3, THE

RASCD 3149 / Jun '95 / Ras

☐ BEST OF THE BEST VOL.4, THE

RASCD 3153 / Jun '95 / Ras

☐ BEST OF THE BIG BANDS, THE

DCD 5337 / Dec '93 / Disky

☐ BEST OF THE BIG BANDS, THE (36 Legendary Classics - 2CD Set)

Jumpin' at the woodside: *Basie, Count* / Do nothin' 'til you hear from me: *Herman, Woody* / Cherokee: *Barnet, Charlie* / It's the talk of the town: *Henderson, Fletcher* / Hamp's boogie woogie no.1: *Hampton, Lionel* / Tuxedo junction: *Hawkins, Erskine* / Christopher Columbus: *Kirk, Andy & His Twelve Clouds of Joy* / Jumpin' blues: *McShann, Jay* / King porter stomp: *Goodman, Benny* / One o'clock jump: *James, Harry* / Blue Lou: *Carter, Benny* / All the things you are: *Dorsey, Tommy* / Drumboogie: *Krupa, Gene* / Chattanooga choo choo: *Miller, Glenn* / There's a small hotel: *Thornhill, Claude* / Artistry in rhythm: *Kenton, Stan* / If dreams come true: *Webb, Chick* / Take the 'A' train: *Ellington, Duke* / Stompin' at the savoy: *Goodman, Benny* / Until the real thing comes along: *Kirk, Andy* / Nightmare: *Shaw, Artie* / One o'clock jump: *Basie, Count* / Snowfall: *Thornhill, Claude* / Let me off uptown: *Krupa, Gene* / I can't get started: *Berigan, Bunny* / For dancers only: *Lunceford, Jimmie* / At the woodchoppers ball: *Herman, Woody* / In the mood: *Miller, Glenn* / I'm getting sentimental over you: *Dorsey, Tommy* / Flying home: *Hampton, Lionel* / Undecided: *Webb, Chick* / Begin the beguine: *Shaw, Artie* / Rockin' in rhythm: *Ellington, Duke* / Fidgety feel: *Henderson, Fletcher* / Skyliner: *Barnet, Charlie* / Organ grinders swing: *Lunceford, Jimmie*

330052 / Jul '96 / Hallmark

☐ BEST OF THE BIG DANCE BANDS, THE

CDC 9010 / Oct '90 / LRC

☐ BEST OF THE BLUES SINGERS VOL.2

CDC 9007 / Oct '90 / LRC

☐ BEST OF THE CAMBRIDGE FOLK FESTIVAL, THE

CAFECD 001 / 27 Jul '98 / Strange Fruit

☐ BEST OF THE CEILI BANDS, THE

EMPRCD 706 / Mar '97 / Emporio

☐ BEST OF THE DELTA BLUES, THE

303652 / Apr '98 / Hallmark

☐ BEST OF THE DJ'S BOUT YA, THE

SONCD 0048 / Jul '93 / Sonic Sounds

☐ BEST OF THE EIGHTIES VOL.1, THE

West End girls: *Pet Shop Boys* / Mickey: *Basil, Toni* / Special brew: *Bad Manners* / Feels like I'm in love: *Marie, Kelly* / Swing the mood: *Jive Bunny* / High energy: *Thomas, Evelyn* / Transfer affection: *Flock Of Seagulls* / Bass (how low can you go): *Harris, Simon* / Touch me (I want your body): *Fox, Samantha* / Can't shake the feeling: *Big Fun* / You think you're a man: *Divine* / Fantasy Island: *Tight Fit* / Hands of she's mine: *Rankin' Roger* / Jack mix IV: *Mirage* / On a crowded street: *Pennington, Barbara*

QED 181 / Nov '96 / Tring

☐ BEST OF THE EIGHTIES VOL.2, THE

Kiss: *Jones, Tom & Art Of Noise* / Blame it on the boogie: *Big Fun* / That's what I like: *Jive Bunny* / Wishing (If I had a photograph of you): *Flock Of Seagulls* / Can can: *Bad Manners* / Lion sleeps tonight: *Tight Fit* / If you're ready (come go with me): *Turner, Ruby & Jonathan Butler* / Nothing's gonna stop me now: *Fox, Samantha* / Jack mix II: *Mirage* / Close to perfection: *Brown, Miquel* / Mirror in the bathroom: *Rankin' Roger* / Fan the flame: *Pennington, Barbara* / I eat cannibals: *Toto Coelo* / Wee rule: *Wee Papa Girl Rappers* / Walk like a man: *Divine* / Saddle up: *Christie, David* / Here comes that sound: *Harris, Simon*

QED 182 / Nov '96 / Tring

☐ BEST OF THE EIGHTIES, THE (4CD Set)

West end girls: *Pet Shop Boys* / High energy: *Thomas, Evelyn* / More you live the more you love: *Flock Of Seagulls* / Hey there lonely girl: *Big Fun* / You think you're a man: *Divine* / Mucho macho: *Toto Coelo* / That's what I like: *Jive Bunny* / Secret heart: *Tight Fit* / Special brew: *Bad Manners* / Don't try to stop it: *Roman Holliday* / Feels like I'm in love: *Marie, Kelly* / All of me: *Sabrina* / Heaven must be missing an angel: *Tavares* / Jack mix 4: *Mirage* / Lies: *Butler, Jonathan* / Fan the flame: *Pennington, Barbara* / Here comes that sound: *Harris, Simon* / Soulmate: *Wee Papa Girl Rappers* / Swing the mood: *Jive Bunny* / Missing words: *Black, Pauline* / We are family: *Sister Sledge* / Jack mix 2: *Mirage* / I eat cannibals: *Toto Coelo* / Kiss: *Jones, Tom & Art Of Noise* / Wishing (if I had a photograph of you): *Flock Of Seagulls* / Like a yo yo: *Sabrina* / If you're ready (come go with me): *Turner, Ruby & Jonathan Butler* / Hands off she's mine: *Rankin' Roger* / Heat it up: *Wee Papa Girl Rappers* / Don't stop till you get enough: *Faye, Ash* / Lip up fatty: *Bad Manners* / Nothing's gonna stop me now: *Fox, Samantha* / Saddle up 1990: *Christie, David* / I'm what I am: *Gaynor, Gloria* / Nightmares: *Flock Of Seagulls* / Nobody: *Basil, Toni* / Car wash: *Royce, Rose* / Lion sleeps tonight: *Tight Fit* / Boys: *Sabrina* / Blame it on

the boogie: Big Fun / Walk like a man: Divine / Cover plus (we're all grown up): O'Connor, Hazel / Bass (how low can you go): Harris, Simon / French kiss: Big Louie / Sunshine: Mills, Warren / Can't shake the feeling: Big Fun / I love to love: Charles, Tina / He's a saint he's a sinner: Brown, Miquel / Frankie: Sister Sledge / Dracula's tango: Toto Coelo / Faith: Wee Papa Girl Rappers / Handful of promises: Big Fun / I'd rather be blind: Turner, Ruby / Magic's wand: Whodini / Is it love you're after: Royce, Rose / Back to the sixties: Tight Fit / Mickey: Basil, Toni / Space age love song: Flock Of Seagulls / I'm in love: Turner, Ruby / Fantasy island: Tight Fit / Move closer: Jones, Tom / Mirror in the bathroom: Rankin' Roger / Wee rule: Wee Papa Girl Rappers / Touch me (I want your body): Fox, Samantha / Twistin' the night away: Divine / Italo house mix: Rococo / Three minute hero: Black, Pauline / Who's that girl (she's got it): Flock Of Seagulls / On a crowded street: Pennington, Barbara / Blow the house down: Wee Papa Girl Rappers / Magic touch: Royce, Rose / I surrender to the spirit of the night: Fox, Samantha / Close to perfection: Brown, Miquel / Can can: Bad Manners

QUAD 008 / Nov '96 / Tring

☐ BEST OF THE GUARDS, THE

Fanfare for a genial occasion: Life Guards Band / Knightsbridge march: Blues & Royals Band / Pomp and circumstance no.4: Coldstream Guards Band / Borough and bayonet: Life Guards Band / Pipe medley: Irish Guards Band / Royal star and garter march: Welsh Guards Band / Verdi airs: Coldstream Guards Band / Strike up the band: Life Guards Band / Duke of Cambridge: Coldstream Guards Band / Amazing grace: Blues & Royals Band / Old comrades: Blues & Royals Band / Tribute to pageantry: Welsh Guards Band / Pipe medley: Irish Guards Band / Czardas: Coldstream Guards / Royal salute: Welsh Guards Band / Radetsky: Blues & Royals Band / Crown imperial: Life Guards Band

306992 / Jul '97 / Hallmark

☐ BEST OF THE REST VOL.6

RASCD 3187 / Feb '96 / Ras

☐ BEST OF THE SOUND OF SUNSHINE, THE (TK Records)

Rock your baby: McCrae, George / Get down tonight: KC & The Sunshine Band / Do you wanna get funky with me: Brown, Peter / Get off: Foxy / Ring my bell: Ward, Anita / Dance with me: Brown, Peter / At midnight: T-Connection / Do what you wanna do: T-Connection / Spank: Horne, Jimmy 'Bo' / Where is the love: Wright, Betty / Party boys: Foxy / That's the way (I like it): KC & The Sunshine Band / Gimmie some: Horne, Jimmy 'Bo'

HTCD 11 / 20 Apr '98 / Hot Productions

☐ BEST OF THUNDERDOME, THE (3CD Set)

9902278 / Nov '96 / Arcade

☐ BEST OF TK DISCO, THE (All Day All Night)

Come into my heart: USA-European Connection / That's the meaning: Beautiful Bend / If there is love: Amant / Girl you need a change of mind: Lewis, Paul / Break: Kat Mandu / All day all night: Reynolds, Margaret / Star cruisin': Diamond, Greg / Black water gold: Sunshine Band / Plato's retreat: Thomas, Joe / Love machine: Tempest Trio / Full tilt boogie: Full Tilt / Beyond the clouds: Quartz / Odyssey: Harris, Johnny / Dance to the drummer's beat: Kelly, Herman & Life

HTCD 17 / 20 Apr '98 / Hot Productions

☐ BEST OF TK SOUL, THE (Party Down)

Why can't we live together: Thomas, Timmy / Clean up woman: Wright, Betty / Baptize me in your love: Reid, Clarence / Funky nassau: Beginning Of The End / Best part of man: Pickett, Wilson / Rockin' chair: McCrae, Gwen / Jazz freak: Reeves, Paulette / Party down: Little Beaver / What you won't do for love: Caldwell, Bobby / Party freaks: Miami / Hey sexy dancer: Mizzell, Rocky / Let's straighten it out: Latimore / Honey: Hudson, David / Dreams: Tropea, John / Shotgun shuffle: Sunshine Band / Make me feel like a woman: Moore, Jackie / Oh that's my man: Moore, Jackie / Ain't nothing wrong: Revere, Paul & The Raiders

HTCD 33 / 20 Apr '98 / Hot Productions

☐ BEST OF TODAY'S BLACK AFRICAN FOLK MUSIC, THE

EUCD 1205 / Sep '93 / ARC

☐ BEST OF TOMMY QUICKLY, JOHNNY SANDON, GREGORY PHILLIPS, THE

Tip of my tongue: Quickly, Tommy & The Remo Four / Heaven only knows: Quickly, Tommy & The Remo Four / Lies: Sandon, Johnny & The Remo Four / On the horizon: Sandon, Johnny & The Remo Four / Yes: Sandon, Johnny & The Remo Four / Magic potion: Sandon, Johnny & The Remo Four / Kiss me now: Quickly, Tommy & The Remo Four / No other love: Quickly, Tommy & The Remo Four / Prove it: Quickly, Tommy & The Remo Four / Haven't you noticed: Quickly, Tommy & The Remo Four / I wish I could shimmy like my sister Kate: Remo Four / Peter Gunn: Remo Four / You might as well forget him: Quickly, Tommy & The Remo Four / It's simple as that: Quickly, Tommy & The Remo Four / Sally go round the roses: Remo Four / I know a girl: Remo Four / Wild side of life: Quickly, Tommy & The Remo Four / Forget the other guy: Quickly, Tommy & The Remo Four / Humpty dumpty: Quickly, Tommy & The Remo Four / I go crazy: Quickly, Tommy & The Remo Four / Everybody knows: Phillips, Gregory & The Remo Four / Closer to me: Phillips, Gregory & The Remo Four / Angie: Phillips, Gregory / Please believe me: Phillips, Gregory / Don't bother me: Phillips, Gregory / Make sure that you're mine: Phillips, Gregory / Sixteen tons: Sandon, Johnny / Donna means heartbreak: Sandon, Johnny / Some kinda wonderful: Sandon, Johnny / Legend in my time: Sandon, Johnny

SEECD 349 / Apr '92 / See For Miles

☐ BEST OF TRANSIENT, THE (2CD Set)

NTD 9050224 / 3 Nov '97 / Transient

☐ BEST OF TVI RECORDS, THE (Dance The Night Away)

HTCD 83 / 20 Apr '98 / Hot Productions

☐ BEST OF UNDERGROUND DANCE, THE

Don't stop the music: Carroll, Dina & Simon Harris / Theme from disturbing the peace: Harris, Simon / These are the breaks: DJ Hanway / Ragga house (all night long): Harris, Simon & Daddy Freddy / Freddy's back: Daddy Freddie & Duke / This is serious: Harris, Simon / I'm riffin': MC Duke / Back 2 tha bass: Harris, Simon / Summertime: Asher D & Daddy Freddie / Boingsville: Thrashpack / Shok da house: Harris, Simon / In the house: Asher D / Runaway love: Harris, Simon & Einstein / Vibes: Demon Boyz / Right here right now: Harris, Simon / Gotstago: Einstein

QED 054 / Nov '96 / Tring

☐ BEST OF UNITED DANCE, THE (Mixed By Force & Styles/Slipmatt & Vibes/ 2CD Set)

Muzik: Happy Rollers / Jump around: Slippery Project / Ruffneck: DJ Vibes / Sincerely yours: DJ Kaos / Sensation: Sy & Demo / On and on: DJ Brisk / Forever more: DJ Sniper & Phase / Real world: Bang The Future / Shooting star: Bang / Sweet desire: DJ Kaos / Love so deep: DJ Huxley / You belong to me: Kingsize & Eternity / Devotion: Sy & Demo / Hardcore tour: DJ Vibes / Complete lovin': Assassins / Deeper: Sy & Demo / Surrender: Eruption / Wonderland: Force & Styles / I'm gonna get ya: Eruption / Heart of gold: Force & Styles / Party time: Dougal & Eruption / Reach out: Eruption / Harmony: Force & Styles / Let the music: Eruption / Don't you want me: Eruption / Pretty green eyes: Force & Styles / Shining down: Force & Styles / Sunshine: Slipmatt & Eruption / United in dance: Force & Styles / Paradise and dreams: Force & Styles

FBRCD 339 / 20 Apr '98 / United Music

☐ BEST OF VENTURE RECORDS, THE (Murphy's Law/A Collection Of 14 Disco Jems)

Murphy's law: Cheri / Up on the hill: Trammps / Rock the night away: Bazooka / Year of the child: Givens Family / Treasure chest: Rising Love / I will survive: Creme D'Cocoa / You don't know like I know: genty / If you want it you got it: Feva, Sandra / Space queen: King Errisson / Fantasy: Fifth Dimension / Big fat bottom: Redd Hott / Star struck: Cheri / Dynomite: Bazooka / Baby don't you know: Creme D'Cocoa

HTCD 53 / 20 Apr '98 / Hot Productions

☐ BEST OF WALES, THE (20 Tracks Of Traditional Welsh Music)

We'll keep a welcome: Morriston Orpheus & Treorchy Male Choirs / Men of Harlech: Morriston Orpheus & Treorchy Male Choirs/Welsh Guards / Myfanwy: Cwm Rhondda Morriston Orpheus Choir / How great thou art: Cwm Rhondda Morriston Orpheus Choir / Bugeilio'r Gwenith Gwyn: Cwm Rhondda Morriston Orpheus Choir / Gwahoddiad: Cwm Rhondda Morriston Orpheus Choir / Llanfair: Cwm Rhondda Morriston Orpheus Choir / Sospan fach: Treorchy Male Choir & The Band Of The Welsh Guards / Battle hymn of the republic: Treorchy Male Choir / Morte Christe: Treorchy Male Choir / Eli Jenkins Prayer: Treorchy Male Choir / Ar hyd y nos: Treorchy Male Choir / Medley: Welsh/Scots/Irish/ Coldstream/Grenadier Guards / Lily of the valley: Monmouthshire Massed Choir / Jacob's ladder: Monmouthshire Massed Choir / Speed your journey: Thousand Welsh Male Voices / Chorus of the Hebrew slaves: Thousand Welsh Male Voices / Kumbaya: Thousand Welsh Male Voices / Sanctus: Thousand Welsh Male Voices / Hen wlad fy nhadau: Morriston Orpheus Choir & The Band of the Welsh Guards

CDMFP 6232 / Jun '96 / Music For Pleasure

☐ BEST OF WMOT RECORDS, THE (Watch Out)

Double Dutch bus: Smith, Frankie / Act like you know: Fat Larry's Band / Watch out: Wells, Brandi / Will they miss: Simmons, David / Zoom: Fat Larry's Band / Motown review: Philly Cream / It's good to be the king: Brooks, Mel / Be thankful for what you got: DeVaughan, William / She's got the papers: Mason, Barbara / Everybody here tonight must party: Direct Current / Everybody's singing: Sweet Thunder / Sexy cream: Slick / Yes I'm Ready: Mason, Barbara

HTCD 38 / 20 Apr '98 / Hot Productions

☐ BEST OF WOODSTOCK, THE

Wooden ships / I had a dream / Going up the country / Joe hill / With a little help from my friends / I'm going home / Star spangles banner purple haze instrumental so / The / Volunteers / Soul sacrifice / We're not gonna take it / Freedom

7567826182 / Jun '94 / Warner Bros.

☐ BEST PARTY ALBUM IN THE WORLD...EVER, THE (2CD Set)

Wake me up before you go go: Wham / Good times: Chic / Staying alive: N-Trance / YMCA: Village People / Stars on 45 Abba medley: Star Sounds Orchestra / Saturday night: Whigfield / What is love: Haddaway / Rhythm of the night: Corona / It's my life: Dr. Alban / Relight my fire: Take That / Hey now (girls just wanna have fun): Lauper, Cyndi / All that she wants: Ace Of Base / Here comes the hotstepper: Kamoze, Ini / Boombastic: Shaggy / One step beyond: Madness / Baby come back: Pato Banton / Twist and shout: Chaka Demus / Give it up: Goodmen / Moving on up: M-People / Ride on time: Black Box / Come on Eileen: Dexy's Midnight Runners / Young at heart: Bluebells / Love shack: B-52's / It's in his kiss (The shoop shoop song): Cher / Crocodile rock: John, Elton / La bamba: Los Lobos / Reet petite: Wilson, Jackie / Baby love: Supremes / I will survive: Gaynor, Gloria / I'm in the mood for dancing: Nolan Sisters / Locomotion: Minogue, Kylie / Only way is up: Yazz & The Plastic Population / Stars on 45 disco medley: Starsound / Groove is in the heart: Deee-Lite / December '63 (oh what a night): Four Seasons / Let's dance: Montez, Chris / Shout: Lulu & The Luvvers / DISCO: Ottawan / I'm too sexy: Right Said Fred / Can can: Bad Manners / Time warp: Damian / Cotton eye Joe: Rednex / Always look on the bright side of life: Monty Python

VTDCD 71 / Nov '95 / Virgin

☐ BEST PARTY IN THE WORLD...EVER, THE (2CD Set)

Do ya think I'm sexy: N-Trance & Rod Stewart / Tubthumping: Chumbawamba / Spice up your life: Spice Girls / Ecuador: Sash / Samba de Janeiro: Bellini / Freed from desire: Gala / You sexy thing: Hot Chocolate / Stayin' alive: N-Trance / YMCA: Village People / Stars on 45 Abba medley: Starsound / Don't you want me: Human League / Jean Genie: Bowie, David / Best: Turner, Tina / Walk this way: Run DMC & Aerosmith / Get down tonight: KC & The Sunshine Band / Celebration: Kool & The Gang / Everybody dance: Chic / DISCO: Ottawan / Lambada: Kaoma / Macarena: Los Del Mar / Miami hit mix: Estefan, Gloria / Wannabe: Spice Girls / I wanna be the only one: Eternal & Bebe Winans / Everybody (backstreet's back): Backstreet Boys / Party people...friday night: 911 / Fastlove: Michael, George / Baby come back: Pato Banton & Ali Campbell/Robin Campbell / Baggy trousers: Madness / Boombastic: Shaggy / Girls just wanna have fun: Lauper, Cyndi / Stars on 45 Beatles medley: Starsound / I get around: Beach Boys / Reet petite: Wilson, Jackie / Locomotion: Little Eva / Daydream believer: Monkees / Hi ho silver lining: Beck, Jeff / Oh pretty woman: Orbison, Roy / Respect: Franklin, Aretha / Come on over to my place: Drifters / I only want to be with you: Springfield, Dusty / Time warp: Damian / Ooh aah...just a little bit: Gina G / 5,6,7,8: Steps / Cotton eye Joe: Rednex / Always look on the bright side of life: Idle, Eric

VTDCD 161 / 24 Nov '97 / Virgin

☐ BEST PUNK ALBUM IN THE WORLD...EVER VOL.1, THE

Anarchy in the UK: Sex Pistols / Ever fallen in love: Buzzcocks / Teenage kicks: Undertones / Into the valley: Skids / New rose: Damned / Babylon's burning: Ruts / Sheena is a punk rocker: Ramones / Sound of the suburbs: Members / All around the world: Jam / Another girl another planet: Only Ones / Passenger: Iggy Pop / Making plans for Nigel: XTC / Peaches: Stranglers / Sex and drugs and rock 'n' roll: Dury, Ian & The Blockheads / (I don't want to go to) Chelsea: Chelsea / Denis: Blondie / 2-4-6-8 motorway: Robinson, Tom Band / Milk and alcohol: Dr. Feelgood / Looking after no.1: Boomtown Rats / Deutscher girls: Adam & The Ants / Christine: Siouxsie & The Banshees / Identity: X-Ray Spex / C30 C60 C90 Go: Bow Wow Wow / Public Image: Public Image Ltd. / My way: Vicious, Sid / God save the queen: Sex Pistols / Neat neat neat: Damned / Gary Gilmore's eyes: Adverts / Top of the pops: Rezillos / Dancing the night away: Motors / What do I get: Buzzcocks / Jilted John: Jilted John / I am the fly: Wire / Mongoloid: Devo / Roadrunner: Richman, Jonathan & Modern Lovers / White punks on dope: Tubes / Blank generation: Hell, Richard & The Voidoids / Marquee moon: Television / Psycho killer: Talking Heads / Stop your sobbing: Pretenders / Is she really going out with him: Jackson, Joe / Ready steady go: Generation X / (Get a) grip (on yourself): Stranglers / Shot by both sides: Magazine / Alternative Ulster: Stiff Little Fingers / Eighties: Killing Joke / Money: Flying Lizards / Kung fu international: Cooper Clarke, John

VTDCD 42 / Jan '95 / Virgin

☐ BEST PUNK ALBUM IN THE WORLD...EVER VOL.2, THE (2CD Set)

Pretty vacant: Sex Pistols / Lust for life: Iggy Pop / No more heroes: Stranglers / Hong Kong garden: Siouxsie & The Banshees / Where's Captain Kirk: Spizz Energi 2 / Orgasm addict: Buzzcocks / Do anything you wanna do: Eddie & The Hot Rods / Eton rifles: Jam / My perfect cousin: Undertones / Hanging on the telephone: Blondie / This perfect day: Saints / Staring at the rude boys: Ruts / Day the world turned day-glo: X-Ray Spex / King rocker: Generation X / I want candy: Bow Wow Wow / Kings of the wild frontier: Adam & The Ants / Rock lobster: B-52's / Pump it up: Costello, Elvis & The Attractions / Sweet Gene Vincent: Dury, Ian & The Blockheads / So it goes: Lowe, Nick / Spanish stroll: Mink Deville / Brass in pocket: Pretenders / Pretty in pink: Psychedelic Furs / Rat trap: Boomtown Rats / Holiday in the sun: Sex Pistols / Something better change: Stranglers / If the kids are united: Sham 69 / Turning Japanese: Vapors / I don't mind: Buzzcocks / Don't dictate: Penetration / Saints are coming: Skids / She does it right: Dr. Feelgood / Love comes in spurts: Hell, Richard & The Voidoids / Sonic reducer: Dead Boys / Rock 'n' roll nigger: Smith, Patti Group / Suspect device: Stiff Little Fingers / Smash it up: Damned / Don't touch me there: Tubes / Shake some action: Flamin' Groovies / Little girl: Banned / Whole wide world: Wreckless Eric / Treason (It's just a story): Teardrop Explodes / Outdoor miner: Wire / Satisfaction: Devo / Death disco: Public Image Ltd. / Love will tear us apart: Joy Division / Beasley Street: Cooper Clarke, John

VTDCD 79 / Mar '96 / Virgin

☐ BEST PUNK ANTHEMS...EVER, THE (2CD Set)

Sound of the suburbs: Members / 2-4-6-8 motorway: Robinson, Tom Band / Eton rifles: Jam / Jilted John: Jilted John / Do anything you wanna do: Eddie & The Hot Rods / New rose: Damned / If the kids are united: Sham 69 / Teenage kicks: Undertones / Lust for life: Iggy Pop / Into the valley: Skids / Sex and drugs and rock 'n' roll: Dury, Ian & The Blockheads / Orgasm addict: Buzzcocks / I am the fly: Wire / Blank generation: Hell, Richard & The Voidoids / Shot by both sides: Magazine / Milk and alcohol: Dr. Feelgood / Mongoloid: Devo / Emergency: 999 / Outdoor miner: Wire / Top of the pops: Rezillos / Money: Flying Lizards / Ever fallen in love: Buzzcocks / Hanging on the telephone: Blondie / Peaches: Stranglers / C30 C60 C90 go: Bow Wow Wow / Alternative Ulster: Stiff Little Fingers / My way: Vicious, Sid / Sheena is a punk rocker: Ramones / Kung fu international: Cooper Clarke, John / Neat neat neat: Damned / Gary Gilmore's eyes: Adverts / Making plans for Nigel: XTC / Jimmy Jimmy: Undertones / Turning Japanese: Vapors / Dancing the night away: Motors / Saints are coming: Skids / Public image: Public Image Ltd. / (Get a) grip (on yourself): Stranglers / Don't dictate: Penetration / Identity: X-Ray Spex / (I don't want to go to) Chelsea: Costello, Elvis / Passenger: Iggy Pop / God save the Queen: Sex Pistols / Another girl another planet: Only Ones / Babylon's burning: Ruts / Marquee moon: Television / Roadrunner: Richman, Jonathan & Modern Lovers

VTDCD 198 / 22 Jun '98 / Virgin

☐ BEST RAP ALBUM IN THE WORLD...EVER, THE (2CD Set)

I got 5 on it: Luniz / Gangasta's paradise: Coolio / Regulate (album version): Warren G / Mr. Wendel: Arrested Development / White lines (don't do it): Grandmaster Flash & Melle Mel / I wish (radio edit): Skee Lo / Boombastic: Shaggy / Jump around: House Of Pain / Boom shake the room: DJ Jazzy Jeff & The Fresh Prince / U can't touch this: MC Hammer / (You gotta) Fight for your right (to party): Beastie Boys / Walk this way: Run DMC / No fronts (clean greene edit): Dog Eat Dog / Come back baby: K7 / Boom shack-a-lak (edit): Apache Indian / Hip hip hooray: Naughty By Nature / Whatta man: Salt n' Pepa & En Vogue / Gimme that body (radio edit): Q-Tee / Ain't no time to play: Guru / I'll be around: Rappin' 4-Tay / Rapper's delight: Sugarhill Gang / Message: Grandmaster Flash & The Furious Five / That's how I'm livin': Ice-T / Don't believe the hype: Public Enemy / Me, myself and I: De La Soul / Too hot (Clean version): Coolio / Getto jam: Domino / Round the way girl: LL Cool J / Love sick (upbeat mix): Gang Starr / Set adrift on memory bliss (Radio mix): PM Dawn / Karmacoma: Massive Attack / Brown sugar: D'Angelo / One shot: Brotherhood / Can't you see: Total F Notorious Big / Can I kick it: Tribe Called Quest / Wash your face in my sink (radio mix): Dream Warriors / It's a shame: Monie Love / Hand of the dead body: Scarface

VTDCD 75 / Apr '96 / Virgin

☐ BEST RAVE ANTHEMS IN THE WORLD...EVER, THE (2CD Set)

VTDCD 203 / 3 Aug '98 / Virgin TV

☐ BEST REGGAE ALBUM IN THE WORLD...EVER VOL.1, THE (2CD Set)

Tease me: Chaka Demus & Pliers / Boombastic: Shaggy / Mr. Loverman: Shabba Ranks / Close to you: Priest, Maxi / Don't turn around: Aswad / Good thing going: Minott, Sugar / Amigo: Black Slate / Keep on movin': Marley, Bob & The Wailers / I shot the sheriff: Inner Circle / Now that we've found love: Third World / Baby come back: Pato Banton & Ali Campbell/Robin Campbell / I don't wanna dance: Grant, Eddy / You can get it if you really want: Dekker, Desmond / Shine: Aswad / Compliments on your kiss: Red Dragon / Searchin': China Black / Silly games: Kay, Janet / (You gotta walk) don't look back: Tosh, Peter / On a ragga tip: SL2 / No no no (world a respect) / Oh Carolina: Shaggy / Israelites: Dekker, Desmond / Double barrell: Barker, Dave & Ansell Collins / Return of Django: Upsetters / Liquidator: Harry J All Stars / Rudi's in love: Locomotive / Message to you Rudi: Specials / On my radio: Selecter / One step beyond: Madness / Tears of a clown: Beat / Uptown top ranking: Althia & Donna / Wonderful world beautiful people: Cliff, Jimmy / Love of the common people: Thomas, Nicky / Pressure drop: Toots & The Maytals / Young, gifted and black: Bob & Marcia / Hurt so good: Cadogan, Susan / Help me make it through the night: Holt, John / I can see clearly now: Nash, Johnny / Everything I own: Boothe, Ken / Many rivers to cross: Cliff, Jimmy / Every little thing she does is magic: Chaka Demus & Pliers / Every breath you take: Wright, Betty

VTDCD 127 / Aug '97 / Virgin

☐ BEST ROCK 'N' ROLL ALBUM IN THE WORLD...EVER, THE

(We're gonna) Rock around the clock: Haley, Bill & The Comets / Ain't that a shame: Domino, Fats / Sweet little sixteen: Berry, Chuck / Bye bye love: Everly Brothers / La bamba: Valens, Ritchie / Peggy Sue: Holly, Buddy / That'll be the day: Crickets / Tutti frutti: Little Richard / Be bop a lula: Vincent, Gene / At the hop: Danny & The Juniors / Reet petite: Wilson, Jackie / Let's twist again: Checker, Chubby / Runaway: Shannon, Del / Summertime blues: Cochran, Eddie / Move it: Richard, Cliff / Locomotion: Little Eva / Why do fools fall in love: Lymon, Frankie & The Teenagers / Lipstick on your collar: Francis, Connie / Sealed with a kiss: Hyland, Brian / Teenager in love: Wilde, Marty / Rubber ball: Vee, Bobby / Wanderer: Dion / You're 16: Burnette, Johnny / Oh Carol: Sedaka, Neil / Chantilly lace: Big Bopper / Little darlin': Diamonds / Halfway to paradise: Fury, Billy / Let's dance: Montez, Chris / Red river rock: Johnny & The Hurricanes / Nutrocker: B-Bumble & The Stingers / Will you still love me tomorrow: Shirrelles / Poetry in motion: Tillotson, Johnny / Do you love me: Poole, Brian & The Tremeloes / Little bitty pretty one: Harris, Thurston / But I do: Henry, Clarence 'Frogman' / Bony moronie: Williams, Larry / That's alright Mama: Crudup, Arthur / Get a job: Silhouettes / Twist and shout: Isleys / Shake, rattle and roll: Haley, Bill & The Comets / Wake up little Susie: Everly Brothers / Golly Miss Molly: Little Richard / C'mon everybody: Cochran, Eddie / Happy birthday sweet sixteen: Sedaka, Neil / Blueberry Hill: Domino, Fats

VTDCD 37 / Oct '94 / Virgin

☐ BEST ROCK 'N' ROLL ALBUM IN THE WORLD...EVER, THE (2CD Set)

Tutti frutti: Little Richard / Chantilly lace: Big Bopper / At the hop: Danny & The Juniors / C'mon everybody: Cochran, Eddie / Wake up little Susie: Everly Brothers / That'll be the day: Crickets / Shakin' all over: Kidd, Johnny & The Pirates / Move it: Richard, Cliff / Lipstick on your collar: Francis, Connie / Bony Moronie: Williams, Larry / Red River rock: Johnny & The Hurricanes / Shake, rattle and roll: Haley, Bill & The Comets / Locomotion: Little Eva / Let's dance: Montez, Chris / Why do fools fall in love: Lymon, Frankie & The Teenagers / Little bitty pretty one: Harris, Thurston / Party doll: Knox, Buddy / Pretty little angel eyes: Lee, Curtis / Night has a thousand eyes: Vee, Bobby / Tequila: Champs / La bamba: Valens, Ritchie / Wipeout: Surfaris / Brand new cadillac: Taylor, Vince & Playboys / Promised land: Allan, Johnnie / Sweet little sixteen: Berry, Chuck / Be bop a lula: Vincent, Gene / Summertime blues: Cochran, Eddie / Rave on: Holly, Buddy / Rock around the clock: Haley, Bill & The Comets / Runaway: Shannon, Del / Poetry in motion: Tillotson, Johnny / Halfway to paradise: Fury, Billy / Will you still love me tomorrow: Shirelles / Hello Mary Lou (goodbye heart): Nelson, Rick / Bye bye love: Everly Brothers / Ain't that a shame: Domino, Fats / Teenager in love: Wilde, Marty / Twist and shout: Isley Brothers / Rett petite: Wilson, Jackie / Good golly Miss Molly: Little Richard / Get a job: Silhouettes / (I don't know why I love you) but I do: Henry, Clarence 'Frogman' / Personality: Price, Lloyd / Nutrocker: B Bumble & The Stingers / Oh Carol: Sedaka, Neil / Born too late: Poni-Tails / Sealed with a kiss: Hyland, Brian / Sea of love: Phillips, Phil / Blue velvet: Vinton, Bobby / Only the lonely: Orbison, Roy / Tutti fruiti: Little Richard

VTDCD 128 / Aug '97 / Virgin

☐ BEST ROCK ALBUM IN THE WORLD...EVER VOL.1, THE (2CD Set)

Are you gonna go my way: Kravitz, Lenny / Paradise City: Guns n' Roses / Walk this way: Run DMC & Aerosmith / Boys are back in town: Thin Lizzy / 20th Century Boy: Bolan, Marc & T-Rex / Gimme all your lovin': ZZ Top / Born to be wild: Steppenwolf / Al right now: Free / Simply the best: Turner, Tina / Girl like you: Collins, Edwyn / Inside: Stiltskin / Since you've been gone: Rainbow / Here I go again: Whitesnake / Turn it on again: Genesis / Do the Strand: Roxy Music / Passenger: Iggy Pop / Silver machine: Hawkwind /

Ace of spades: Motorhead / Paranoid: Black Sabbath / Another brick in the wall: Pink Floyd / Owner of a lonely heart: Yes / Strange brew: Cream / Smoke on the water: Deep Purple / Can't get enough: Bad Company / In a broken dream: Python Lee Jackson / Mannish boy: Waters, Muddy / All day and all of the night: Kinks / Stay with me: Faces / You ain't seen nothing yet: Bachman-Turner Overdrive / Cum on feel the noize: Slade / No more heroes: Stranglers / She sells sanctuary: Cult / Free bird: Lynyrd Skynyrd / Hard rain's a-gonna fall: Ferry, Bryan / More than a feeling: Boston / (Don't fear) the reaper: Blue Oyster Cult / In the air tonight: Collins, Phil / I'd do anything for love: Meat Loaf

VTDCD 125 / Aug '97 / Virgin

☐ **BEST ROCK ALBUM IN THE WORLD...EVER VOL.2, THE (2CD Set)**
Seven seas of Rhye: Queen / Desire: U2 / Why can't this be love: Van Halen / Bad love: Clapton, Eric / All night long: Rainbow / Here I go again: Whitesnake / Two princes: Spin Doctors / Viva Las Vegas: ZZ Top / Stay with me: Stewart, Rod & The Faces / Elected: Cooper, Alice / Rock 'n' roll dreams come through: Meat Loaf / Turn it on again: Genesis / Waterfront: Simple Minds / Rocks: Primal Scream / Wishing well: Free / Crossroads: Cream / Join together: Who / Rocky Mountain way: Walsh, Joe / Let love rule: Kravitz, Lenny / Losing my religion: REM / Solsbury Hill: Gabriel, Peter / Whole of the moon: Waterboys / Street life: Roxy Music / We gotta get out of this place: Animals / Cum on feel the noize: Slade / Pretty vacant: Sex Pistols / Blockbuster: Sweet / Telegram Sam: T-Rex / Cigarettes and alcohol: Oasis / Wild thing: Troggs / You really got me: Kinks / No more heroes: Stranglers / Down down: Status Quo / Don't believe a word: Thin Lizzy / Out in the fields: Moore, Gary & Phil Lynott / Black night: Deep Purple / She's not there: Santana / Feel like makin' love: Bad Company / All the young dudes: Mott The Hoople / Walk on the wild side: Reed, Lou

VTDCD 47 / Mar '95 / Virgin

☐ **BEST ROCK ANTHEMS IN THE WORLD...EVER, THE (2CD Set)**
We are the champions: Queen / Best: Turner, Tina / Addicted to love: Palmer, Robert / I found someone: Cher / Behind the mask: Clapton, Eric / Living years: Mike & The Mechanics / Everybody hurts: REM / Let's dance: Bowie, David / Bat out of hell: Meat Loaf / Are you gonna go my way: Kravitz, Lenny / All right now: Free / Inside: Stiltskin / Final countdown: Europe / Long train runnin': Doobie Brothers / Need you tonight: INXS / Don't you (forget about me): Simple Minds / Is this love: Whitesnake / In the air tonight: Collins, Phil / Should I stay or should I go: Clash / You could be mine: Guns n' Roses / Walk this way: Run DMC & Aerosmith / School's out: Cooper, Alice / Pinball wizard: Who / Changing man: Weller, Paul / All or nothing: Small Faces / 20th century boy: T-Rex / Cum on feel the noize: Slade / Slide away: Oasis / Life of Riley: Lightning Seeds / Goldfinger: Ash / Pretty vacant: Sex Pistols / Just for life: Iggy Pop / Gimme all your lovin': ZZ Top / Paper plane: Status Quo / Satellite: Hooters / Since you've been gone: Rainbow / Can't get enough: Bad Company / Love is the drug: Roxy Music

VTDCD 83 / May '96 / Virgin

☐ **BEST ROCK BALLADS IN THE WORLD...EVER VOL.1, THE (2CD Set)**
Kind of magic: Queen / Girl like you: Collins, Edwyn / Over my shoulder: Mike & The Mechanics / Stuck in the middle with you: Stealer's Wheel / Turn It Up: Fleetwood Mac / Heaven is a place on earth: Carlisle, Belinda / Dignity: Deacon Blue / Road to hell: Rea, Chris / I wish it would rain down: Collins, Phil / Romeo and Juliet: Dire Straits / Don't dream it's over: Crowded House / Waiting for a girl like you: Foreigner / I'll stand by you: Pretenders / Show me heaven: McKee, Maria / Eternal flame: Bangles / Oh yeah (on the radio): Roxy Music / Drive: Cars / Wind of change: Scorpions / To be with you: Mr. Big / Heaven help: Kravitz, Lenny / I'd do anything for love (but I won't do that): Meat Loaf / I'll find my way back home time: Cher / Is this love: Whitesnake / Black velvet: Myles, Alannah / Days: MacColl, Kirsty / Pure: Lightning Seeds / Mary's prayer: Danny Wilson / Valerie: Winwood, Steve / Every little thing she does is magic: Police / Rosanna: Toto / Keep on loving you: REO Speedwagon / Hard to say I'm sorry: Chicago / Follow you follow me: Genesis / Walking in Memphis: Cohen, Marc / Missing you: Waite, John / (I just) died in your arms: Cutting Crew / Kayleigh: Marillion / Babe: Styx / Listen to your heart: Roxette / Right here waiting: Marx, Richard

VTDCD 60 / Aug '95 / Virgin

☐ **BEST ROCK BALLADS IN THE WORLD...EVER VOL.2, THE (2CD Set)**
We are the champions: Queen / I want to know what love is: Foreigner / Against all odds: Collins, Phil / Living years: Mike & The Mechanics / Bad love: Clapton, Eric / Whole of the moon: Waterboys / Brown eyed girl: Morrison, Van / I drove all night: Orbison, Roy / Sweet child of mine: Guns n' Roses / Best: Turner, Tina / All I wanna do is make love to you: Heart / Breakfast at Tiffany's: Deep Blue Something / Day we caught the train: Ocean Colour Scene / Don't you forget about me: Simple Minds / Let's dance: Bowie, David / Roll with it: Winwood, Steve / Roll to me: Del Amitri / Itchycoo Park: Small Faces / Hazard: Marx, Richard / Bitch: Brooks, Meredith / All I wanna do: Crow, Sheryl / Don't speak: No Doubt / High and dry: Radiohead / Wonderwall: Oasis / Golden brown: Stranglers / Weather with you: Crowded House / You're the best thing: Style Council / Africa: Toto / In too deep: Genesis / More than words: Extreme / Avalon: Roxy Music / It must have been love: Roxette / Life in a northern town: Dream Academy / Forever Autumn: Hayward, Justin / Little lies: Fleetwood Mac / China in your hand: T'Pau / I'd lie for you (and that's the truth): Meat Loaf / Brothers in arms: Dire Straits

VTDCD 159 / 17 Nov '97 / Virgin

☐ **BEST SCOTTISH ALBUM IN THE WORLD...EVER, THE (2CD Set)**
Letter from America: Proclaimers / Every beat of my heart: Stewart, Rod / Sailing: Sutherland Brothers / Wild mountain thyme: Silencers / Mull of Kintyre: McCartney, Paul & Wings / Caledonia: Miller, Frankie / I should have known better: Diamond, Jim / Heart on my sleeve: Gallagher & Lyle / Perfect: Fairground Attraction / Stuck in the middle with you: Stealer's Wheel / Young at heart: Bluebells / Oh Ia-di, ob-la-da: Marmalade / Shout: Lulu / Shang-a-lang: Bay City Rollers / Magic: Pilot / Donald where's your troosers: Stewart, Andy / Bluebell polka: Shand, Jimmy / Stop yer tickling Jock: Lauder, Harry / Amazing Grace: Royal Scots Dragoon Guards / Over the sea to Skye: Celtic Spirit / Rabbie Burns trilogy:

Monroes / Auld lang syne: Festival Singers / Baker Street: Rafferty, Gerry / Mary's prayer: Danny Wilson / Dignity: Deacon Blue / Whole of the moon: Waterboys / Girl like you: Collins, Edwyn / Let's go round again: Average White Band / Somewhere in my heart: Aztec Camera / I was: Ure, Midge / Shoeshine boy: Humblebums / I'm gonna be (500 miles): Proclaimers / Fields of fire (400 miles): Big Country / Battle: Wolfstone / An ubhal as airde: Runrig / Tinseltown in the rain: Blue Nile / Patience of angels: Reader, Eddi / Breislach: Capercaillie / Flower of Scotland: Corries / Knockin' on heaven's door

VTDCD 137 / 17 Nov '97 / Virgin

☐ **BEST SELLERS OF THE 1960'S AND 1970'S (4CD Set)**
Let it be me: Everly Brothers / Walking to New Orleans: Domino, Fats / Reflections of my life: Marmalade / She'd rather be with me: Turtles / My girl: Temptations / It's in his kiss (the shoop shoop song): Everett, Betty / Bend it: Dave Dee, Dozy, Beaky, Mick & Tich / It keeps right on a-hurtin': Tillotson, Johnny / I'm gonna knock on your door: Hodges, Eddie / Clementine: Jan & Dean / Birds and the bees: Akens, Jewel / Surfin' safari: Beach Boys / Harlem shuffle: Bob & Earl / Moon river: Butler, Jerry / Happy together: Turtles / Duke of Earl: Chandler, Gene / Moody river: Boone, Pat / Legend of xanadu: Dave Dee, Dozy, Beaky, Mick & Tich / When will I be loved: Everly Brothers / Hold what you got: Tex, Joe / Oh what a night: Dells / Sound of silence: Bachelors / Ob la di ob la da: Marmalade / Surfin': Beach Boys / Talk back tremblin' lips: Tillotson, Johnny / Baby talk: Jan & Dean / Hey Paula: Paul & Paula / Leader of the pack: Shangri-Las / Greased lightnin': Travolta, John / Swing your daddy: Gilstrap, Jim / Jeans on: Dundas, David / Love grows where my Rosemary goes: Edison Lighthouse / Something old something new: Fantastics / Sweet inspiration: Johnson, Johnny & Bandwagon / Indian reservation: Fardon, Don / Long tall glasses (I can dance): Sayer, Leo / Tie a yellow ribbon 'round the ole oak tree: Orlando, Tony / Sugar me: De Paul, Lynsey / I'm doin' fine now: New York City / Man who sold the world: Lulu & David Bowie / Don't let me be misunderstood: Esmeralda, Santa / Wake up and make love with me: Dury, Ian / Breakaway: Ullman, Tracey / Wunderbar: Tenpole Tudor / Sandy: Johansen, Glen / You make me feel like dancing: Sayer, Leo / Daughter of darkness: Jones, Tom / Knock three times: Dawn / Little arrows: Lee / Tears of a clown: Higwire: Carr, Linda / Show and tell: Wilson, Al / Only you can: Fox / Be thankful for what you've got: DeVaughan, William / Don't give up on us: Soul, David / Won't somebody dance with me: De Paul, Lynsey / Take your mama for a ride: Lulu

HR 871392 / Jul '97 / Disky

☐ **BEST SELLERS VOL.1**

DCD 5354 / Apr '94 / Disky

☐ **BEST SELLERS VOL.2**

DCD 5355 / Apr '94 / Disky

☐ **BEST SELLERS VOL.3**

DCD 5379 / Apr '94 / Disky

☐ **BEST SEVENTIES ALBUM IN THE WORLD...EVER, THE (2CD Set)**
We will rock you: Queen / Starman: Bowie, David / See my baby jive: Wizzard / American pie: McLean, Don / Band on the run: McCartney, Paul & Wings / You wear it well: Stewart, Rod / Baker Street: Rafferty, Gerry / Mr. Blue Sky: ELO / You're so vain: Simon, Carly / Heart of glass: Blondie / Let's stick together: Ferry, Bryan / School's out: Cooper, Alice / Since you've been gone: Rainbow / Rockin' all over the world: Status Quo / Cum on feel the noize: Slade / Nutbush city limits: Turner, Ike & Tina / Spirit in the sky: Greenbaum, Norman / Ride a white swan: T-Rex / Rock 'n' roll: Glitter, Gary / One step beyond: Madness / You sexy thing: Hot Chocolate / You to me are everything: Real Thing / Tears of a clown: Robinson, Smokey & The Miracles / Band of gold: Payne, Freda / Boogie wonderland: Earth, Wind & Fire / Harvest for the world: Isley Brothers / Ain't no mountain high enough: Ross, Diana / Joy: Hurdy gurdy man: Donovan / How do you do it: Gerry & The Pacemakers / Mony mony: James, Tommy & The Shondells / Summertime holiday: Richard, Cliff & The Shadows / Something in the air: Thunderclap Newman / Kites: Dupree, Simon & The Big Sound / Lady Eleanor: Lindisfarne / Knockin' on heaven's door: Dylan, Bob / When you're in love with a beautiful woman: Dr. Hook / Show must go on: Sayer, Leo / Rubberneckin: Bush, Kate / Follow you, follow me: Genesis / Love is the drug: Roxy Music / I'm not in love: 10cc

VTDCD 157 / 10 Nov '97 / Virgin

☐ **BEST SIXTIES ALBUM IN THE WORLD...EVER VOL.1, THE (2CD Set)**
I'm a believer: Monkees / I got you babe: Sonny & Cher / It might as well rain until September: King, Carole / Young ones: Richard, Cliff & The Shadows / Runaway: Shannon, Del / Let's hang on: Four Seasons / I only want to be with you: Springfield, Dusty / Price of love: Everly Brothers / Mony mony: James, Tommy & The Shondells / Hi ho silver lining: Beck, Jeff / Flowers in the rain: Move / Waterloo sunset: Kinks / Good vibrations: Beach Boys / She's not there: Zombies / Pretty flamingo: Manfred Mann / Love is all around: Troggs / Anniversary waltz: Ringo Starr / Everyone's having a party: Otis & The Pacemakers / Whiter shade of pale: Procol Harum / Wichita lineman: Campbell, Glen / He ain't heavy, he's my brother: Hollies / Sun ain't gonna shine anymore: Walker Brothers / Downtown: Clark, Petula / Can't get used to losing you: Williams, Andy / Silence is golden: Tremeloes / I heard it through the grapevine: Gaye, Marvin / (Sittin' on the) dock of the bay: Redding, Otis / I say a little prayer: Franklin, Aretha / Do you know the way to San Jose: Warwick, Dionne / You can't hurry love: Supremes / Reach out, I'll be there: Four Tops / Dancing in the street: Reeves, Martha & The Vandellas / Uptight (everything's alright): Wonder, Stevie / Soul man: Sam & Dave / It's not unusual: Jones, Tom / Yeh yeh: Fame, Georgie / The Blue Flames / Sha la la la lee: Small Faces / Got to get you into my life: Beach Boys / Young ones: Richard, Cliff & The Rebel Rousers / In the midnight hour: Pickett, Wilson / Knock on wood: Floyd, Eddie / I got you (I feel good): Brown, James / Rescue me: Bass, Fontella / Go now: Moody Blues / Brown eyed girl: Morrison, Van / Mr. Tambourine Man: Byrds / House of the rising sun: Animals / When a man loves a woman: Sledge, Percy / Crazy: Cline, Patsy / We have all the time in the world: Armstrong, Louis / Stand by me: King, Ben E.

Withers, Bill / Groovin': Young Rascals / Weather with you: Crowded House / Back to life: Soul II Soul / Pray: Take That / Days: MacColl, Kirsty / Do it again: Beach Boys / This summer: Squeeze / Echo beach: Martha & The Muffins / Summertime blues: Cochran, Eddie / Macarena: Los Del Rio / Guaglione: Prado, Perez 'Prez' / Bamboleo: Gipsy Kings / Now that we've found love: Third World / Summertime: DJ Jazzy Jeff & The Fresh Prince / Love shack: B-52's / Walking on sunshine: Katrina & The Waves / California girls: Beach Boys / Summer holiday: Richard, Cliff & The Shadows / Summertime: Gerry & The Pacemakers

VTDCD 140 / Jun '97 / Virgin

☐ **BEST SUMMER PARTY IN THE WORLD...EVER, THE (2CD Set)**
La primavera: Sasha / Give me love: DJ Dado / Lazy days: Williams, Robbie / Eat my goal: Collapsed Lung / Rockafeller skank: Fatboy Slim / Driving in my car: Madness / Free: Ultra Nate / I luv u baby: Original / Se a vida e: Pet Shop Boys / Dance the night away: Mavericks / Summertime blues: Cochran, Eddie / Mony mony: James, Tommy & The Shondells / Strutt: Bamboo / Top of the world: Chumbawamba / One day I'll fly away: Crow, Sheryl / Spice girl: UB40 & Chrissie Hynde / Wannabe: Spice Girls / Samba de Janeiro: Bellini / Spice up your life: Spice Girls / Everybody (backstreet's back): Backstreet Boys / Horny: Mousse T / Tubthumping: Chumbawamba / Hot in herre: Cochran, Eddie / Everlasting love: Love Affair / Elenore: Turtles / Make it easy on yourself: Walker Brothers / First cut is the deepest: Arnold, P.P. / Walk on by: Warwick, Dionne / Groovy kind of love: Mindbenders / Something in the air: Thunderclap Newman / Albatross: Fleetwood Mac

VTDCD 106 / Nov '96 / Virgin

☐ **BEST SIXTIES ALBUM IN THE WORLD...EVER VOL.3, THE (2CD Set)**
Only the lonely: Orbison, Roy / Walk right back: Supremes / Loco-Motion: Little Eva / Breaking up is hard to do: Sedaka, Neil / Hippy hippy shake: Swinging Blue Jeans / Wouldn't it be nice: Beach Boys / It takes two: Gaye, Marvin & Kim Weston / Wanderer: Dion / What becomes of the broken hearted: Ruffin, Jimmy / Under the boardwalk: Drifters / Twenty four hours from Tulsa: Pitney, Gene / San Francisco: McKenzie, Scott / Everybody's talkin': Nilsson, Harry / More than I can say: Vee, Bobby / I'll never fall in love again: Gentry, Bobbie / True love ways: Holly, Buddy / You'll never walk alone: Gerry & The Pacemakers / Tracks of my tears: Robinson, Smokey & The Miracles / Dream a little dream of me: Mama Cass / Space oddity: Bowie, David / Night in white satin: Moody Blues / With a little help from my friends: Cocker, Joe / Gimme some lovin': Davis, Spencer Group / Out of time: Farlowe, Chris / Blackberry way: Move / Sunny afternoon: Kinks / Son of a preacher man: Springfield, Dusty / Hard to handle: Redding, Otis / Sweet soul music: Small Faces / Don't let me be misunderstood: Animals / Subterranean homesick blues: Dylan, Bob / So you wanna be a rock n roll star: Byrds / If you gotta go go now: Manfred Mann / I'm alive/Stay: Hollies / Shakin all over: Kidd, Johnny & The Pirates / Little bit of me a little bit of you: Monkees / (If Paradise is) half as nice: Amen Corner / Baby now that I've found you: Foundations / Wonderful land: Shadows / Silhouettes: Herman's Hermits / You're sixteen: Burnette, Johnny / Can't take my eyes off you: Williams, Andy / One fine day: Chiffons / Do you want to know a secret: Kramer, Billy J. & The Dakotas / Mrs. Robinson: Simon & Garfunkel / California dreamin': Mamas & The Papas

VTDCD 160 / 10 Nov '97 / Virgin

☐ **BEST SIXTIES SUMMER ALBUM...EVER, THE (2CD Set)**
Pretty flamingo: Manfred Mann / Got to get you into my life: Bennett, Cliff & The Rebel Rousers / Hi ho silver lining: Beck, Jeff / Do wah diddy diddy: Manfred Mann / Sun ain't gonna shine anymore: Walker Brothers / It's all over now: Rolling Stones / Hold tight: Dave Dee, Dozy, Beaky, Mick & Tich / Under the boardwalk: Drifters / Up on the roof: Kinks / Happy together: Turtles / Sea cruise: Beach Boys / She's a rainbow: Rolling Stones / Good morning little schoolgirl: Yardbirds / Summer in the city: Lovin' Spoonful / Itchycoo park: Small Faces / Waterloo sunset: Kinks / California dreamin': Mamas & The Papas / I get the sweetest feeling: Wilson, Jackie / Reach out I'll be there: Four Tops / Mony mony: James, Tommy & The Shondells / I'm a believer: Monkees / Day tripper: Beatles / Mony mony: James, Tommy & The Shondells / Everyday people: Sly & The Family Stone / Dedicated to the one I love: Mamas & Papas / Under the boardwalk: Drifters / Up and away: Mann, Johnny Singers / Living in the past: Jethro Tull

VTDCD 200 / 15 Jun '98 / Virgin

☐ **BEST SKA ALBUM IN THE WORLD...EVER, THE (2CD Set)**

VTDCD 199 / 10 Aug '98 / Virgin TV

☐ **BEST SUMMER ALBUM IN THE WORLD...EVER, THE (2CD Set)**
I wanna be the only one: Eternal & Bebe Winans / Closer than close: Gomes, Rosie / Lovefool: Cardigans / Wannabe: Spice Girls / Se a vida e (that's the way life is): Pet Shop Boys / Good enough: Dodgy / Alright: Supergrass / Girls and boys: Blur / Say you'll be there: Spice Girls / I'll be there: Mariah Carey / Freak me: Silk / Fever: Peggy Lee

VTDCD 194 / 22 Jun '98 / Virgin

☐ **BEST SUMMER...EVER, THE**
In the summertime: Shaggy / Compliments on your kiss: Red Dragon / Boom boom boom: Outhere Brothers / Wipeout: Fat Boys & The Beach Boys / hot hot: Arrow / Saturday night: Whigfield / Dreamer: Livin' Joy / Sweets for my sweet: Lewis, C.J. / Don't turn around: Aswad / You don't love me (no no no): Dawn Penn / Sweat (a la la la la long): Inner Circle / Humpin' around: Brown, Bobby / Love city Groove / Grease megamix: Travolta, John & Olivia Newton John / Give it up: KC & The Sunshine Band / Wake up Boo: Boo Radleys / Walking on sunshine: Katrina & The Waves / Beach baby: First Class / Barbados: Typically Tropical / Y viva Espana: Sylvia / Days: MacColl, Kirsty / Long hot summer: Style Council / Summer breeze: Isley Brothers / Back to life: Soul II Soul & Caron Wheeler / Summer nights: Withers, Bill / Summertime: DJ Jazzy Jeff & The Fresh Prince / In the around: Rappin' 4-Tay / Searching: China Black / Now that we've found love: Third World / Club Tropicana: Wham / Do it again: Beach Boys / Echo beach: Martha & The Muffins / Somewhere in my heart: Aztec Camera / Carlisle, Belinda / On the beach: Rea, Chris / Under the boardwalk: Drifters / Summertime: Gerry & The Pacemakers / Summer (The first time): Goldsboro, Bobby / Spanish wine: White, Chris

VTDCD 57 / Jul '95 / Virgin

☐ **BEST SWING ALBUM IN THE WORLD...EVER VOL.1, THE (2CD Set)**
Lifted: Lighthouse Family / This is how we do it: Jordan, Montell / Return of the Mack: Morrison, Mark / Whoo ha got you all in check: Busta Rhymes / Brown sugar: D'Angelo / If you love me: Brownstone / Stay: Eternal / Mary Jane (All night long): Blige, Mary J. / Flavour of the old school: Knight, Beverley / She's got that vibe: R Kelly / I wish: Skee Lo / You got a little something for you: MN8 / I got 5 on it: Luniz / Boombastic: Shaggy / I must stand: Ice-T / Regulate: Warren G / I wanna see you up: Color Me Badd / Don't walk away: Jade / Every little thing I do: Soul For Real / My prerogative: Brown, Bobby / Poison: Bel Biv Devoe / Rough with the smooth: Nelson, Shara / Right here: SWV / Freak like me: Howard, Adina / Real love: Driza Bone / Ghetto heaven: Family Stand / Search for the hero: M-People / Sensitivity: Tresvant, Ralph / Freek'n you: Jodeci / Undercover lover: Smooth / You love is a 187: Whitehead Brothers / Dance: Whitehead Brothers / I care: Soul II Soul / Hey Mr. DJ: Zhane / Back and forth: Aaliyah / Summertime: DJ Jazzy Jeff & The Fresh Prince / Sweetness: Gayle, Michelle / Can't stop: After 7 / U.3.4.3 /Bumpin' new): Coolio / Hangin' on a string (Contemplation): Loose Ends

VTCD 86 / Jun '96 / Virgin

☐ **BEST SWING ALBUM IN THE WORLD...EVER VOL.2, THE (2CD Set)**
Crazy: Morrison, Mark / Bump 'n' grind: Kelly, R / Good thing: Eternal / Love II love: Damage / Say you'll be there: Spice Girls / Give me one more time: Gabrielle / Ocean drive: Lighthouse Family / Spinning the wheel: Michael, George / Keep on moving: Soul II Soul & Caron Wheeler / Two can play that game: Brown, Bobby / Don't look any further: M-People / Down that road: Nelson, Shara / You gotta be: Des'ree / I'm gon down: Blige, Mary J. / Girlfriend: Pebbles / Anything: SWV / Everyday of the week: Jade / Happy just to be with you: Gayle, Michelle / Tuff act to follow: MN8 / Gangsta's paradise: Coolio & LV / Something for da honeyz: Jordan, Montell / Around: Tribe Called Quest & Faith Evans / Lone: Ice-T / Golden brown: Kaleef / Feel the music: Guru / Age ain't nothing but a number: Aaliyah / I wanna be down: Brandy / Throw on up (on the right side): Knight, Beverley / Throw your hands: Up: LV / Apparently nothin': Young Disciples / Special kind of love: Nu Colours / Who do u love: Nu Colours / Who do you love: Crew, Deborah / There's nothing like this: Omar / All the things (your man won't do): Joe / Mind blowin': Smooth / So good: Mica, Marshall / Wayne / Freak me: Silk / Feelin': Jodeci

VTDCD 111 / Nov '96 / Virgin

☐ **BEST...ALBUM IN THE WORLD...EVER VOL.1, THE (2CD Set)**
Don't you want me: Human League / Mirror man: Human League / Love action: Human League / Human League / Open your heart: Human League / Do you really want to hurt me: Culture Club / Karma chameleon: Culture Club / Time (clock of the heart): Culture Club / Church of the poison mind: Culture Club / Victims: Culture Club / True: Spandau Ballet /

Gold: Spandau Ballet / Chant no.1 (I don't need this pressure on): Spandau Ballet / Temptation: Heaven 17 / (We don't need this) fascist groove thang: Heaven 17 / Come live with me: Heaven 17 / Dancing with tears in my eyes: Ultravox / If I was: Ure, Midge / Vienna: Ultravox

VTCD 177 / 16 Feb '98 / Virgin

☐ **BEST...ALBUM IN THE WORLD...EVER VOL.2, THE (2CD Set)**

VTDCD 204 / 6 Jul '98 / Virgin

☐ **BETHLEHEM SAMPLER, THE**

CDBETH 1 / Mar '97 / Charly

☐ **BETIKO TRIKITIXA**

KD 383CD / Aug '97 / Elkar

☐ **BETSILEO LALANGINA (Madagascar)**

926622 / Feb '97 / BUDA

☐ **BETWEEN FATHER SKY AND MOTHER EARTH**

Ancient ground: Nakai, R. Carlos / Amazing grace: Nakai, R. Carlos / Wind spirit: Miller, Bill / Moonlit Stallions: Native Flute Ensemble / Riding with thunder: Native Flute Ensemble / Holy people: Douglas Spottedd Eagle / Snow geese: Douglas Spottedd Eagle / Ashne ate: Silverbird, Perry / Happy shepherd: Silverbird, Perry / Zuni friendship song: Manhooty, Chester / 500 Drums: Adams, Mel / Enchanted forest: Tsa'ne Dos'e / Kiowa hymn (III): Pewewardy, Cornel / Healing song: Primeaux, Mike & Attson

ND 63915 / Aug '95 / Narada

☐ **BETWEEN THE GROOVES - RHYTHM 'N' BLUES**

Mom's apple pie: Davis, Tyrone / You still love me: King, Ben E. / Check in the mail: Jackson, Millie / Strokin': Carter, Clarence / For your precious love: Reed, Francine / You're gonna come back to me: Mitchell, Prince Phillip / There's a change: Chi-Lites / Funny how time slips away: White, Artie / So tied up: Clayton, Willie / Mr. Mailman: Graham, Jesse

D 2248792 / Sep '96 / Ichiban

☐ **BEVERLEY HILLS - WILD, YOUNG AND RICH VOL.1**

DCD 5287 / Feb '93 / Disky

☐ **BEVERLEY HILLS - WILD, YOUNG AND RICH VOL.2**

DCD 5288 / Feb '93 / Disky

☐ **BEWARE OF THE TEXAS BLUES VOL.1**

I'm a stepper: Fritz, Joe 'Papoose' / Can't sleep tonight: Moore, Henry & Guitar Slim / Workin' man blues: Copeland, Johnny / Life's highway: Big Walter / Empty house of so many tears: Green, Clarence / Drowning on dry land: Eastwood Revue / Rock of Gibraltar / Farther on up the road / Line your body / Freeze / That's fat / Rock me baby / It's alright / Good as old time religion

CDBM 064 / Apr '91 / Blue Moon

☐ **BEWARE OF THE TEXAS BLUES VOL.2**

CDBM 085 / May '92 / Blue Moon

☐ **BEWARE THE CAT ISSUE**

BWC 07 / 22 Jun '98 / Beware The Cat

☐ **BEYOND BOUNDARIES**

CDEB 2552 / May '93 / Earthbeat

☐ **BEYOND COLOUR**

1.3 crumbs: GMS / Stoned: E-Rection / Blizzard of ooze: Snake Thing / Spastic elastic: Organic Noise / Godzilla: System Busters / Friagram: Psychopod / Magik: Hallucinogen / Wormhole: Doof / Seriaf: Psychopod

TIPCD 19 / 6 Jul '98 / Tip

☐ **BEYOND MAN'S MIND (The Mystery Of Trance) (2CD Set)**

Underground: Free Inside / Nosedive: Boom Generation / Best kept secrets: Ambergriz / Event: Upgrade 1.2 / Key spiracy: Zeromen / Devil in Heaven: Upgrade 1.2 / Bird of dawning: Cyberheads / Blue memories: West & Storm / Rich: Paradise In Dubs / Feel me: Angeldust / Fallen angel: Cyber Prince / Magic of light: Ambergriz / Mind butterflies: Bai Oo / Don't you like music: Clusia Icrtal / Nightvisions: Dr. M / Got to learn: Bi Boys Action Squad / Hostile takeover: Foam People / Freakin' the trance: Upgrade 1.2 / One of the frightened: Angeldust / Style shifting: Shape Shifter / Low key scenes: Zeromen 2

SPV 08938802 / Aug '96 / SPV

☐ **BEYOND PLANET DUB**

Irie stepper: Revolutionary Dub Warriors / Creation: Rhythmiques / Burning sun: Ullulators / Passin' Passin thru: Beathead / Let me out: Groove Corporation / Lugubrium dub: Eat Static / Casting out: Jah Free / Zion dub: Silicon Drum / Sounds from the ground: Silicon Drum / Abdromeda: Mad Professor / Ital breakfast: Dub Syndicate / Headmesh: V-Neck / Kallalau valley: Transequence / Counting chickens: Another Green World / Ilooli dub: Woodshed / Vecotr dub: Kaleidoscope

BARKCD 031 / 30 Mar '98 / Planet Dog

☐ **BEYOND THE BEACH**

UPSTARTCD 12 / Jan '95 / Upstart

☐ **BEYOND THE CALICO WALL**

VOXXCD 2051 / Feb '94 / Voxx

☐ **BEYOND THE FRONTLINE**

Looks is deceiving: Gladiators / Message from the king: Prince Far-I / Right time: Mighty Diamonds / Wear you to the ball: U-Roy / If I don't have you: Isaacs, Gregory / Lightning flash weak heart: Drop Big Youth / Behold: Culture / Great psalms: U-Roy / Never get burn: Twinkle Brothers / Declaration of rights: Clarke, Johnny / Universal tribulation: Isaacs, Gregory / Natty rebel: U-Roy / Civilisation: Hudson, Keith / Freedom fighters: Washington, Delroy

FRONT 1 / Jul '90 / Frontline

☐ **BEYOND THE RIVER (Seasonal Songs Of Latvia)**

Es redzeju jurina / Puke puke roze roze / Oki / Leitins leiti nemoceja / Gustavs biju karaviris / Sajaja svesiaud's / Kakitei / Berns nomira / Mezins dag / Milas dziesma / Janit's sedei kalnina / Miega del es raudaju / No jurinas izpeldeja / Es jums ludzu saimenieki / Joneits joja vyse godu / Ai dievini augustu saule / Garais dancis / Szie pa prieksu / Bralu masa / Tolka boiss

4933412 / 2 Mar '98 / Hemisphere

☐ **BGP PRESENTS: BACK TO FUNK (Selection Of Killer Cuts From East/ Westbound Collective)**

Back to funk: Lowe, Robert / Hicky burr: Frazier, Caesar / Monkey hips 'n' rice: 19th Whole / Pain: Person, Houston / Rainy day fun: Austin, Donald / Stone thing: Cash, Alvin / Gettin' off: Mason, Bill / Slippin' into darkness: 19th Whole / Whip whop: Sparks, Melvin / Kaleidoscope: Chandler, Gary / Stone thing: Cash, Alvin

CDBGPD 096 / Sep '95 / Beat Goes Public

☐ **BHAJANAM MADHURAM**

NRCD 3001 / Feb '98 / Navras

☐ **BHANGRA - EAST 2 WEST**

MCCD 121 / Aug '93 / Music Club

☐ **BHANGRA BEAT**

Gora chitta wrang: Ragga-Blasters / Umbhi: Amar / Nukhe chakhee javana: Achanak / Gem song: DJ Gem / Tappe: Achanak / Ambersaria: Eshara / Bhangra paa: Achanak / Kina sona: Achanak / Ena akian: Infinity / Veh sajna: Vocals Unlimited / Yaada: Amar / Boliyan: Anakhi / Westworld: East West Connection / Mirza (Here I come junglist): Punjabi MC

SUMCD 4125 / Jun '97 / Summit

☐ **BHANGRA FEVER (2CD Set)**

Rahaye rahaye / Anakhist / Aiy mausam rangeely sohaney / Mele chalia noo / Nashe diye bandhe bothle / Doabe dia jatta / Nukhe chakhee javana / Kudiye punjab diye / Chargiye / Aag / Yaar nach la doh chariye / Lala lala / Akain / Punjabe shere / Hai lachea long da lishkara / Kamlee yaar dhe khamlee / Bachke putt sardara de / O mere yaaro / Sun beliyo / Putt jattan de mere yaar ne / Shakin' shankar / Boliyaan

PDSCD 548 / 13 Oct '97 / Pulse

☐ **BHANGRA TOP TEN VOL.12**

CDSR 016 / Aug '90 / Star

☐ **BIER KELLER (Ultimate German Drinking Songs/2CD Set)**

336332 / 3 Aug '98 / Koch

☐ **BIG BAD BLUES (25 Sun Blues Classics)**

Before long: Jimmy & Walter / We all gotta go sometime: Hill-Louis, Joe / Bear cat: Thomas, Rufus / Carry my business on: Bolnes, Houston / Baby I'm coming home: Booker, Charlie / Juiced: Love, Billy / My real gone rocket: Brenston, Jackie / Greyhound blues: Hunt, D.A. / Wolf call boogie: Hot Shot Love / Prison bound blues: Nix, Willie / Blues train: Randolph, Tot / Mystery train: Parker, Junior & The Blue Flames / Beggin' my baby: Little Milton / Red hot: Emerson, Billy 'The Kid' / Cotton crop blues: Cotton, James / I'm gonna murder my baby: Hare, Pat / Rattlesnakin' mama: Stewart, William / Tiger man: Vinson, Mose / Gonna leave you baby: Lewis, Sammy & Willie Johnson / Cool down mama: Hunter, Long John / Come back home: Howlin' Wolf / Come back baby: Ross, Dr. Isiah / I feel so worried: Lewis, Sammy & Willie Johnson / Let's get high: Gordon, Rosco / Ain't that right: Snow, Eddie

CPCD 8100 / Jun '95 / Charly

CPCD 8272 / Apr '97 / Charly

☐ **BIG BAND BALLADS**

You made me love you: James, Harry / Adios: Miller, Glenn / If dreams came true: Webb, Chick / It never entered my mind: Goodman, Benny / These foolish things: Carter, Benny / I was doing all right: Norvo, Red / There's a small hotel: Norvo, Red / Skylark: Krupa, Gene / I'll never smile again: Dorsey, Tommy / I've got you under my skin: Herman, Woody / Mellow bit of rhythm: Kirk, Andy / Deep forest: Kirk, Andy / After hours: Hawkins, Erskine / I don't stand a ghost of a chance with you: Calloway, Cab / 'round midnight: Williams, Cootie / Moon mist: Ellington, Duke / Yesterdays: Shaw, Artie / Blue and sentimental: Basie, Count / Skyliner: Barnet, Charlie

307252 / 15 Sep '97 / Hallmark

☐ **BIG BAND BASH (2CD Set)**

CDB 1209 / Apr '92 / Giants Of Jazz

☐ **BIG BAND BLUES**

Loose wig: Hampton, Lionel Orchestra / Things ain't what they used to be: Ellington, Duke Orchestra / Lonesome lover blues: Eckstine, Billy & His Orchestra / Uptown blues: Lunceford, Jimmie Orchestra / Big Jim blues: Kirk, Andy & His Twelve Clouds of Joy / Deep in the blues: Krupa, Gene & His Orchestra / Sobbin' blues: Berigan, Bunny & His Orchestra / Gulf coast blues: Barnet, Charlie Orchestra / Feet draggin' blues: James, Harry Orchestra / Sent for you yesterday: Goodman, Benny Orchestra / Swingin' the blues: Basie, Count & His Orchestra / Gin mill blues: Crosby, Bob & His Orchestra / My favourite blues: Carter, Benny & His Orchestra / Sepian bounce: McShann, Jay & his Orchestra / Little jazz boogie: Eldridge, Roy Orchestra / St. James Infirmary: Shaw, Artie Orchestra / Basin Street blues: Teagarden, Jack Orchestra / Blue garden blues: Williams, Cootie & His Orchestra / Down your alley blues: Ellington, Duke / Blowin' up a storm: Herman, Woody & His Orchestra

304502 / Jun '97 / Hallmark

☐ **BIG BAND BOOGIE 1939-1942**

RACD 7107 / May '96 / Aerospace

☐ **BIG BAND BOX (3CD Set)**

TBXCD 512 / Jan '96 / TrueTrax

☐ **BIG BAND BOX (2CD Set)**

PBXCD 512 / Nov '96 / Pulse

☐ **BIG BAND CLASSICS**

In the mood: Miller, Glenn / Little brown jug: Miller, Glenn / American patrol: Miller, Glenn / Moonlight serenade: Miller, Glenn / Tuxedo junction: Miller, Glenn / Pennsylvania 6-5000: Miller, Glenn / String of pearls: Miller, Glenn / Take the 'A' train: Ellington, Duke / Perdido: Ellington, Duke / Creole love call: Ellington, Duke / Black and tan fantasy: Ellington, Duke / Mood indigo: Ellington, Duke / Caravan: Ellington, Duke / Solitude: Ellington, Duke / Stompin' at the Savoy: Goodman, Benny / Avalon: Goodman, Benny / King Porter stomp: Goodman, Benny / Moonglow: Goodman, Benny / One o' clock jump: Goodman, Benny / And the angels sing: Goodman, Benny / Sing sing sing: Goodman, Benny / Pinetop's boogie: Dorsey, Tommy / Night and day: Dorsey, Tommy / After you've gone: Dorsey, Tommy / Song of India: Dorsey, Tommy / Blue skies: Dorsey, Tommy / I'm getting sentimental over you: Dorsey, Tommy / Marie: Dorsey, Tommy

KAZCD 106 / Nov '89 / Kaz

☐ **BIG BAND CLASSICS VOL.2**

KAZCD 107 / Feb '92 / Kaz

☐ **BIG BAND COLLECTION (2CD Set)**

DEMPCD 011 / Mar '96 / Emporio

☐ **BIG BAND ERA (4CD Set)**

CDDIG 15 / Jun '95 / Charly

☐ **BIG BAND ERA VOL.1**

MICH 5601 CD / Sep '92 / Hindsight

☐ **BIG BAND ERA VOL.10**

MICH 5610 CD / Sep '92 / Hindsight

☐ **BIG BAND ERA VOL.2**

MICH 5602 CD / Sep '92 / Hindsight

CDB 103 / Jan '96 / Giants Of Jazz

☐ **BIG BAND ERA VOL.3**

MICH 5603 CD / Sep '92 / Hindsight

☐ **BIG BAND ERA VOL.4**

MICH 5604 CD / Sep '92 / Hindsight

☐ **BIG BAND ERA VOL.5**

MICH 5605 CD / Sep '92 / Hindsight

☐ **BIG BAND ERA VOL.6**

MICH 5606 CD / Sep '92 / Hindsight

☐ **BIG BAND ERA VOL.7**

MICH 5607 CD / Sep '92 / Hindsight

☐ **BIG BAND ERA VOL.8**

MICH 5608 CD / Sep '92 / Hindsight

☐ **BIG BAND ERA VOL.9**

MICH 5609 CD / Sep '92 / Hindsight

☐ **BIG BAND JAZZ - TULSA TO HARLEM**

DD 439 / Mar '89 / Delmark

☐ **BIG BAND JUMP**

VN 163 / Mar '96 / Viper's Nest

☐ **BIG BAND LATIN**

Christopher Columbus: Machito & His Afro-Cubans / Un conga me dio la lettra: Mendoza, Celeste / La reina: Morales, Noro / Partio y pelao: Orquesta Oriental / Que te parece cholito: Campo, Pupi / Memoria a Beny More: Orquesta Oriental / Cha cha cha flamenco: Valle, Joe Y Su Orquesta / Dispierta Emilia: Orquesta Riverside / Gozanda la salve: Cotto, Joe Y Su Orqesta / Echa pa' aca: Morales, Noro / Mamboscope: Machito & His Afro-Cubans / TNT: Grand, Rene / El eco y el carretero: Cruz, Celia & Rene Hernandez / El agua del pon pon: Orquesta Riverside / Pomme la mano: Mendoza, Celeste / Paraiso sonado: Valle, Joe Y Su Orquesta / Undecided: Puente, Tito / La culpa tiene el gallo: Cotto, Joe Y Su Orqesta / How high the moon: Campo, Pupi / Piel canela: Cruz, Celia & Rene Hernandez

CDHOT 611 / Sep '96 / Charly

☐ **BIG BAND SELECTION, THE (3CD Set)**

In the mood: Miller, Glenn / Temptation: Shaw, Artie / Tea for two: Armstrong, Louis / September song: Brown, Les / Blowing up a storm: Herman, Woody / One o'clock jump: Goodman, Benny / Take the 'A' train: Ellington, Duke / Basie boogie: Basie, Count / Imagination: Dorsey, Jimmy / Cherokee: Barnet, Charlie / Songs of India: Dorsey, Tommy / Little brown jug: Dorsey, Tommy / Moon glow: Dorsey, Tommy / Stompin' at the Savoy: Armstrong, Louis / Love me or leave me: Brown, Les / Caldonia: Herman, Woody / Sing sing sing: Goodman, Benny / Mooche: Ellington, Duke / April in Paris: Ellington, Duke / Nightmare: Shaw, Artie / Lover: Armstrong, Louis / Nutcracker suite: Brown, Les / Jersey bounce: Goodman, Benny / Caravan: Ellington, Duke / Lester leaps in: Basie, Count / Nearness of you: Dorsey, Jimmy / Skyliner: Barnet, Charlie / On the sunny side of the street: Dorsey, Tommy / Chattanooga choo choo: Miller, Glenn / Donkey serenade: Shaw, Artie / Jeepers creepers: Armstrong, Louis / How about you: Brown, Les / Northwest passage: Herman, Woody / Frankie and Johnny: Goodman, Benny / Pretty woman: Ellington, Duke / Moonlight serenade: Miller, Glenn / Stardust: Shaw, Artie / C'est si bon: Armstrong, Louis / It's all right with me: Brown, Les / Early autumn: Herman, Woody / There's a small hotel: Herman, Woody / I'll never be the same: Krupa, Gene / Goin' to Chicago: Krupa, Gene / Just you, just me: Krupa, Gene / Good for nothin' Joe: Barnet, Charlie / This love of mine: Dorsey, Tommy / Pennsylvania 6-5000: Miller, Glenn / Frenesi: Shaw, Artie / Tiger rag: Armstrong, Louis / Cabin in the sky: Brown, Les / After glow: Herman, Woody / Get happy: Goodman, Benny / Uptown blues: Barnet, Charlie / All the things you are: Barnet, Charlie / Blue and sentimental: Basie, Count / It started all over again: Dorsey, Tommy / Sleepy lagoon: Dorsey, Tommy / That old black magic: Miller, Glenn / Blues in the night: Shaw, Artie / When the saints go marching in: Armstrong, Louis / Sentimental journey: Brown, Les / Bijou: Herman, Woody / Stompin' at the Savoy: Goodman, Benny / Do nothin' 'til you hear from me: Ellington, Duke / Red bank boogie: Basie, Count / Fools rush in: Dorsey, Jimmy / East side, West side: Barnet, Charlie / Marie: Dorsey, Tommy / Tuxedo junction: Miller, Glenn / I can't get started (with you): Miller, Glenn / Ain't misbehavin': Miller, Glenn / I'm forever blowing bubbles: Brown, Les / At the woodchoppers' ball: Herman, Woody / Down south camp meeting: Goodman, Benny / Perdido: Ellington, Duke / I've got rhythm: Dorsey, Jimmy / Jumpin' at the woodside: Basie, Count / Taking a chance on love: Dorsey, Tommy / Trumpet blues: James, Harry

TFP 007 / Nov '92 / Tring

☐ **BIG BAND SOUND (2CD Set)**

American patrol: Miller, Glenn / Take the 'A' train: Ellington, Duke / Back bay shuffle: Shaw, Artie / Flying home: Hampton, Lionel / Dipsy doodle: Dorsey, Tommy / Spinning the web: Webb, Chick / Pennies from heaven: Kemp, Hal / Beat me daddy eight to the bar: Bradley, Will / My cousin in Milwaukee: Duchin, Eddie / Jumpin' at the woodside: Basie, Count / Boog it: Krupa, Gene / While the music plays on: Brown, Les / Wake up and live: Calloway, Cab / Get your boots laced papa: Herman, Woody / Jumpin' blues: McShann, Jay / Old man Harlem: Dorsey Brothers / Two o'clock jump: James, Harry / I'm in the mood for swing: Carter, Benny / What's new: Goodman, Benny / Yours: Dorsey, Jimmy / Contrasts: Dorsey, Jimmy / Air mail special: Goodman, Benny / One clock jump: Basie, Count / Rhythm is our business: Lunceford, Jimmie / It's winter again: Kemp, Hal / Period: Ellington, Duke / 12th street rag: Hampton, Lionel / Blue rhythm fantasy: Krupa, Gene / Dig it: Brown, Les / Blue frame: Herman, Woody / Mood Hollywood: Dorsey Brothers / Flight of the bumble bee: James, Harry / Swingmatism: McShann, Jay / Dixie lee: Gray, Glen / Blue minor: Webb, Chick / Hungarian dance no.5: Thornhill, Claude / Swingin' the blues: Carter, Benny / Get out of town: Duchin, Eddie / At last: Miller, Glenn / Bye bye blues: Calloway, Cab

PC 609 / 3 Nov '97 / Platinum Collection

☐ **BIG BAND SOUND VOL.1, THE**

Jeepers creepers: Armstrong, Louis / Does your heart beat for me: Morgan, Russ / Tiger rag: Dorsey, Jimmy / Cherokee: Barnet, Charlie / Magenta haze: Ellington, Duke / (In) a shanty in old Shanty Town: Long, Johnny / Sophisticated lady: Ellington, Duke / Harlem nocturne: Barnet, Charlie / Northwest passage: Herman, Woody / Let's dance: Goodman, Benny / Begin the beguine: Shaw, Artie / So rare: Dorsey, Jimmy / Night and day: Shaw, Artie / Oh Johnny: Fitzgerald, Ella & Chick Webb / Opus one: Dorsey, Tommy / One o'clock jump: Basie, Count / C'est si bon: Armstrong, Louis / (Back home again in) Indiana: Ellington, Duke / When the saints go marching in: Armstrong, Louis / Woodchopper's ball: Herman, Woody / Summit ridge drive: Pastor, Tony / They can't take that...: Basie, Count

GRF 012 / '93 / Tring

☐ **BIG BAND SOUND VOL.2, THE**

Pompton turnpike: Barnet, Charlie / What is this thing called love: Shaw, Artie / Ain't misbehavin': Ellington, Duke / Take the 'A' train: Ellington, Duke / Frenesi: Pastor, Tony / My heart belongs to dad: Shaw, Artie / Count steps in: Basie, Count / Sultry sunset: Ellington, Duke / Dipsy doodle: Clinton, Larry / I want the waiter: Webb, Chick / Flat foot floogie: Basie, Count / St. Louis blues: Dorsey, Jimmy / Skyliner: Barnet, Charlie / Bijou: Herman, Woody / Mame: Armstrong, Louis / Tip toe topic: Ellington, Duke / Old rocking chair: Armstrong, Louis / Caldonia: Herman, Woody / Margie: Lunceford, Jimmie / I'm just wild about Harry: Dorsey, Jimmy / Just a gigolo: Armstrong, Louis / Body and soul: Armstrong, Louis / Linger awhile: Morgan, Russ

GRF 013 / '93 / Tring

☐ **BIG BAND SOUND, THE**

April in Paris: Miller, Glenn / Begin the beguine: Shaw, Artie / Oh Johnny, oh Johnny Oh: Webb, Chick & Ella Fitzgerald / Does your heart beat for me: Morgan, Russ / In a shanty in old Shanty Town: Long, Johnny / Harlem nocturne: Barnet, Charlie / North West passage: Herman, Woody / Let's dance: Goodman, Benny / So rare: Dorsey, Jimmy / Opus one: Dorsey, Tommy / Indiana: Ellington, Duke / Something new: Basie, Count / Love me or leave me: Day, Doris & Les Brown / I'll never be the same: Krupa, Gene / Dipsy doodle: Clinton, Larry / Margie: Lunceford, Jimmie / Night and day: Shaw, Artie / Count steps in: Basie, Count / Sultry sunset: Ellington, Duke

QED 168 / Nov '96 / Tring

☐ **BIG BAND, THE**

CD 56032 / Nov '94 / Jazz Roots

☐ **BIG BANDS**

Dragnet: Anthony, Ray / Early autumn: Herman, Woody / Satin doll: Ellington, Duke / Creep: MacKintosh, Ken / Brother John: Riddle, Nelson / September song: Kenton, Stan / Man with golden arm: May, Billy / Don't be that way: Goodman, Benny / All the things you are: Barnet, Charlie / No name jive: Gray, Glen & The Casa Loma Orchestra / Staccato's theme: Bernstein, Elmer / Sleepy lagoon: James, Harry / Younger than springtime: Brown, Les / Up a lazy river: Zentner, Si / Experiments with mice: Dankworth, John / Mama's talking soft: Basie, Count / Once around: Jones, Thad & Mel Lewis / Nightmare: Shaw, Artie / Midnight sleighride: Sauter-Finegan Orchestra / Diabolus: Rich, Buddy

CDMFP 6164 / May '95 / Music For Pleasure

☐ **BIG BANDS OF THE SWINGING YEARS**

CD 104 / Oct '94 / Timeless Treasures

☐ **BIG BANDS OF THE SWINGING YEARS**

TCD 1035 / Nov '96 / Tradition

☐ **BIG BANG, THE**

BANG 01 / 20 Jul '98 / Big Bang

☐ **BIG BEAT ELITE (3CD Set)**

CERBAD 3 / 26 Jan '98 / Lacerba

☐ **BIG BEAT ROYALE**

KICKCD 83 / 14 Sep '98 / Kickin'

☐ **BIG BEATS**
Intro: *Plastic Scene* / Underground gets deep: *Unsung Heroes* / Hitman 2/Love song for a hitman: *Funky Monkey* / We're not playing God: *Mellowtrons* / Red: *Mother Nature's Cloud & Shower Show* / Bulldozer: *Moog* / Voice: *Van Cleef, Lee* / I say: *From A Dozen* / Silent partner: *Red Myers* / Get yourself organised: *Headrillaz* / Buss: *Puff* / This is the end: *Mr. Dan*
SPECCD 502 / May '97 / Dust II Dust

☐ **BIG BEATS VOL.1**
UE 701503 / 12 Jan '98 / Urban Essentials

☐ **BIG BLUES - BLUES MUSIC FOR KIDS**
Flying lesson / Zip a dee doo dah / Skip to my blues / Candy store blues / Pancake man / Late for school blues / Pick a bale o' cotton / Funky bluesy ABC's / Rainy day blues / Waggy tailed dog / Fishin' blues / There wouldn't be a me
R 272534 / Nov '96 / Music For Little People

☐ **BIG BLUES EXTRAVAGANZA**
Travellin' south: *Collins, Albert* / Rock me baby: *Hopkins, Lightnin'* / Lovestruck baby: *Vaughan, Stevie Ray* / Six strings down: *Vaughan, Jimmie* / I've never found a man: *White, Lavelle* / Tell everybody I know: *Keb Mo'* / Born in Lousiana: *Brown, Gatemouth* / Since I fell for you: *Dr. John* / Mary had a little lamb: *Guy, Buddy* / Queen bee: *Taj Mahal* / Yellow moon: *Neville Brothers* / Big road blues: *Block, Rory* / Ain't it funny how time slips away: *Clark, W.C.* / Night life: *King, B.B.* / Leap of faith: *McClinton, Delbert*
4899282 / 22 Jun '98 / Legacy

☐ **BIG CHILL PRESENTS PIPEDREAMS**
Poa alpina: *Biosphere* / Isolation: *Pulusha* / Dr1: *Dome* / Dope moves: *Nautilus* / Pipedreams: *Hoax* / Your consciousness goes bip: *Snooze* / Harp of gold: *Nice, Peter Trio* / Asteroid: *Pearl & Dean* / Mr. Excitement: *Tipsy* / NYC: *Khan, Shere* / Q-Flutes: *Aphrodite* / Finding: *Outside* / Last picture show: *Heavyshift* / Afterlife: *Jedi Knights* / Epilogue: *Stringtronix*
CDRAID 537 / 15 Sep '97 / Rumour

☐ **BIG CITY BLUES EAST COAST STYLE**
If the blues were whiskey: *Johnson, Luther 'Guitar Junior'* / Down in Virginia: *Holmes Brothers* / Full court press: *Magic Dick & Jay Geils* / That will never do: *Roomful Of Blues* / Eddie's gospel groove: *Earl, Ronnie & The Broadcasters* / What can I do (somebody tell me): *Little Buster & The Soul Brothers* / Better left unsaid: *Willson, Michelle* / Gimme a break: *Levy, Ron* / Life is a ballgame: *Persuasions*
EDCD 7018 / Mar '97 / Easydisc

☐ **BIG CITY BLUES WEST COAST STYLE**
Working man: *Fulson, Lowell* / Boogie on down: *McCracklin, Jimmy* / This is the thanks I get: *Lynn, Barbara* / Goin' out West: *Davis, Larry* / Don't burn down LA: *Wilson, Smokey* / Rebop jump: *Nocturne, Johnny* / My last goodbye: *Hawkins, Ted* / Can't stop these teardrops: *Strehli, Angela* / Help the bear: *McCracklin, Jimmy & Smokey Wilson/Larry Davis* / Go down sunshine: *Nelson, Tracy*
EDCD 7017 / Mar '97 / Easydisc

☐ **BIG CITY SOUL VOL.1**
Looking for you: *Mimms, Garnet* / Love is not a game: *Soul, Sam E* / My Dear heart: *Robinson, Shawn* / Mend my broken heart: *St. John, Rose & The Wonderettes* / Hold on: *O'Jays* / Ready, willing and able: *Holiday, Jimmy & Clydie King* / Lot of love: *Banks, Homer* / Hooked by love: *Banks, Homer* / I lost a true love: *Wagner, Danny & The Kindred Soul* / Then came heart break: *Jive Five* / Strange neighbourhood: *McDaniels, Gene* / Stick close: *Brown, Estelle* / Be careful girl: *Turner, Betty* / I'll never forget you: *O'Jays* / It's what's underneath that counts: *Jackson, June* / Working on your case: *O'Jays* / My heart is in danger: *Ray, Alder* / Honest to goodness: *Diplomats* / Are you trying to get rid of me baby: *Crystals* / Breakaway (part 1): *Karman, Steve* / I only get this feeling: *Irwin, Dee* / Livin' above your head: *Jay & The Americans* / Don't: *Josie, Marva* / It's a sad thing: *Pollard, Ray* / Walk with a winner: *McDaniels, Gene* / Drifter: *Pollard, Ray* / It'll never be over for me: *Yuro, Timi*
GSCD 042 / Jul '94 / Goldmine

☐ **BIG CITY SOUL VOL.2**
Stop and think it over: *Mimms, Garnet* / I love you baby: *Ambers* / Pretty little face: *Four Hi's* / You can split: *Youngblood Smith* / What would I do: *Superiors* / Living a lie: *High Keys* / Stop and take a look at yourself: *Shalimars* / Take a step in my direction: *Little Eva* / Real jive guy: *Ahres, Dajh* / Walkin' the duck: *Triumphs* / I can't make it without you baby: *Banks, Bessie* / Just a fool: *Gainey, Jerry* / I watched you slowly slip away: *Guyton, Howard* / Mighty good way: *Banks, Robert* / Right direction: *Ward, Clara* / My heart belongs to you: *Pickett, Wilson* / I don't want to lose your love: *Woods, Billy* / Love I give: *Murray, Louise* / (You'd better) Straighten up and fly right: *Bryant, Terry* / Born to please: *Prince Harold* / Baby I love you: *Tate, Howard* / I'm a practical guy: *Gardner, Don* / Backfield in motion: *Poindexter Brothers* / I don't need no doctor: *Ashford, Nick* / Can't deny the hurt: *Rakes, Pal & The Prophets* / Picture me gone: *Brooks, Diane* / Let's take a chance: *High Keys* / Let me be your boy: *Pickett, Wilson*
GSCD 044 / Sep '94 / Goldmine

☐ **BIG CITY SOUL VOL.3**
I'm alive with the love feeling: *Turner, Spyder* / Street talk: *Tymes* / To the ends of the earth: *Middleton, Tony* / I'm gonna change: *Velours* / (Love) You can't just walk away: *Courtney, Dean* / I can't make it anymore: *Turner, Spyder* / Key to my happiness: *Charades* / I got what you need: *Weston, Kim* / My heart took a licking: *Jackson, Millie* / Everything you always wanted to know about love: *Roberts, Lou* / I'm gonna hold on (to your love): *Mars, Marlina* / Can't make it without you: *Superiors* / At the top of the stairs: *Formations* / Watch out girl: *Embers* / You fooled me: *Roberts, Lou & The Marks* / You're just the kind of guy: *Weston, Kim* / We got togetherness: *Jewels* / What would I do: *Tymes* / Cry your eyes out: *Cambridge, Dottie* / Wanting you: *Stevens, April* / You just don't know: *Broadways* / Weeping cup: *Charades* / Betcha can't change my mind: *Courtney, Dean* / You never know: *Nash, Johnny* / Fool that I am: *Solitaires* / You can count on me: *Hamilton, Roy* / Panic is on: *Hamilton, Roy*
GSCD 047 / Jan '95 / Goldmine

☐ **BIG CITY SOUL VOL.4 (2CD Set)**
Fell in love with you baby: *Charts* / Wait til I give the signal: *Shirelles* / When it comes to my baby: *Mislap, Ronnie* / Not my girl: *Platters* / You can't fight love: *Shirley & Jessie* / Call on Billy: *Soul, Billy T.* / I feel better: *Bruce, Alan* / To get your love back: *Dodds, Nella* / Bricks, broken bottles and sticks: *Parish, Dean* / Never in a million years: *Honey Bees* / Glamour girls: *Hopkins, Harold* / How much pressure (do you think I can stand): *Robinson, Roscoe* / Mr. Creator: *Candy & The Kisses* / Change: *Eady, Ernestine* / Think twice before you walk away: *Porgy & The Monarchs* / Never love a robin: *Foxx, Inez & Charlie* / Tonight I'm gonna see my baby: *Hughes, Freddie* / I've got to be strong: *Jackson, Chuck* / Three rooms: *Freeman, Audrey* / Jerkin' time: *Diplomats* / Ain't that the truth: *Troy, J B* / If I'm hurt you'll feel the pain: *Barbara & Brenda* / You lie so well: *Knight, Marie* / I've got love for you: *Intruders* / First date: *Dodds, Nella* / Woman: *Esquires* / Hey girl: *Porgy & The Monarchs* / You've got my love: *Wells, Donnie* / Upset my heart (got me upset): *Clay, Judy* / Lover: *Hunt, Tommy* / Tonight's the night: *Candy & The Kisses* / Since you've been gone: *Anglos* / Magic touch: *Moore, Melba* / Try some soul: *Crossen, Ray* / You could be my remedy: *Shirelles* / No stranger to love: *Foxx, Inez & Charlie* / In the long run: *Blandon, Curtis* / Live on: *Troy, J B* / Hand it over: *Wand Orchestra* / I've got to find someone to love: *Fisher, Jerry & The Nightbeats* / Honey boy: *Dodds, Nella* / There goes a forgotten man: *Radcliffe, Jimmy* / That's no way to treat a girl: *Knight, Marie* / Fear of losing you: *Platters* / Just one more time: *Barnes, J.J.* / Silencer: *Jackson, Chuck* / There's still a tomorrow: *Diplomats* / Are you trying to get rid of me baby: *Candy & The Kisses* / Words can never tell it: *Hunt, Tommy* / Nobody made you love me: *Charts* / Keep a hold on me: *Porgy & The Monarchs* / Doesn't it ring a bell: *Platters* / Way to a woman's heart: *Soul, Billy T.* / All the way from heaven: *Chancellors* / Nobody knows: *Williams, Maurice* / Anything you do is right: *Brown, Maxine* / No doubt about it: *Shirelles* / Your kind of lovin: *Clay, Judy* / My little plaything: *Watts, Glen* / If I had you: *Big Maybelle*
GSCD 065 / Oct '95 / Goldmine

☐ **BIG COUNTRY ALBUM (40 Country Music Greats/2CD Set)**
DEMPCD 015 / Mar '96 / Emporio

☐ **BIG DANCE HITS 1992**
Ebeneezer Goode: *Shamen* / Rhythm is a dancer: *Snap* / Jump: *Kriss Kross* / Rock your baby: *KWS* / Don't talk just kiss: *Right Said Fred* / Are you ready to fly: *Rozalla* / I don't care: *Shakespears Sister* / Baker Street: *Undercover* / Expression: *Salt n' Pepa* / I feel love: *Messiah* / Too funky: *Michael, George* / Twilight zone: *2 Unlimited* / MASH (Suicide is painless): *Manic Street Preachers* / Blue room: *Orb* / Reality used to be a friend of mine: *PM Dawn* / I'm doing fine now: *Pasadenas* / It only takes a minute: *Take That* / Humpin' around: *Brown, Bobby* / Mutations (Chime): *Orbital* / Love makes the world go round: *Don-E* / I'm gonna get you: *Bizarre Inc.* / It's a fine day: *Opus III* / Hypnotic st8: *Altern 8* / Dream come true: *Brand New Heavies* / Make it on my own: *Limerick, Alison* / Love U more: *Sunscreem* / Everybody in the place: *Prodigy* / Crucified: *Army Of Lovers* / Kings of the ring: *Du Berry, Steve & Born 2 B* / Different strokes: *Isotonik*
AHLCD 4 / Nov '92 / Hit

☐ **BIG DIXIE**
TCD 1036 / Nov '96 / Tradition

☐ **BIG FIX, THE**
ALLIED 82CD / May '97 / Allied

☐ **BIG FOLK AND PROTEST HITS OF THE 60'S**
Walk right in / Puff the magic dragon / Go tell it on the mountain / If I had a hammer / Tom Dooley / Michael / House of the rising sun / Blowin' in the wind / Cotton fields / Where have all the flowers gone / San Francisco Bay blues / Little boxes / Freight train / Subterranean homesick blues / Green green / Catch the wind / Times they are a changin'
306032 / Jan '97 / Hallmark

☐ **BIG HIT MIX, THE**
Mysterious girl: *Andre, Peter* / Get down (You're the one for me): *Backstreet Boys* / Three lions: *Lightning Seeds & David Baddiel/Frank Skinner* / Lifted: *Lighthouse Family* / I got 5 on it: *Luniz* / Craz chance: *Kavana* / Love me for a reason: *Boyzone* / Light of life: *Louise* / Could it be forever: *Gemini* / Blue moon: *Alford, John* / Don't stop movin': *Livin' Joy* / Can't help it: *Happy Clappers* / Missing: *Everything But The Girl* / Thunder: *East 17* / What do I do now: *Sleeper* / Female of the species: *Space* / Stupid girl: *Garbage* / I wanna be a hippy: *Technohead* / Move move move (The Red Tribe): *Manchester United FC* / Good day: *Maguire, Sean*
VTCD 95 / Jun '96 / Virgin

☐ **BIG HITS (2CD Set)**
RADCD 88 / 8 Dec '97 / Global TV

☐ **BIG HITS FROM SWELL GUYS**
Chicago: *Bennett, Tony* / How about you: *Sinatra, Frank* / Nightingale sang in Berkeley square: *Crosby, Bing* / Wheel of fortune: *Laine, Frankie* / Someday: *Charles, Ray* / Think twice: *Benton, Brook* / Kiss to build a dream on: *Armstrong, Louis* / Love letters in the sand: *Boone, Pat* / Pennies from heaven: *Crosby, Bing* / Night and day: *Sinatra, Frank* / Mona Lisa: *Cole, Nat 'King'* / Diane: *Lanza, Mario* / My true confession: *Benton, Brook* / Little white cloud that cried: *Ray, Johnnie* / Friendly persuasion: *Boone, Pat* / It's magic: *Haymes, Dick*
300872 / Jun '98 / Hallmark

☐ **BIG IN WIGAN - 20 NORTHERN MAMMOTHS FROM THE WHEEL TO KEELE (A Collection Of Northern Soul Oldies From 1968-1996)**
It's a woman's world (you'd better believe it): *Gypsies* / Baby reconsider: *Haywood, Leon* / That's loving you: *Wiggins, Percy* / Sweet sherry: *Barnes, J.J.* / I wanna be (your everything): *Pretenders* / Happy: *Bell, William* / My man, a sweet man: *Jackson, Millie* / Little Miss Soul: *Lovettes* / I'll never fall in love again: *Freeman, Bobby* / Hey sah-lo-ney: *Lane, Mickey Lee* / Till you give: *Patterson, Bobby* / With my love and what you've got: *Wells, Jean* / Mother of shame: *Holloway, Loleatta* / Running away from love: *Mahoney, Skip & The Casuals* / You've come a long way baby: *Flower Shoppe* / Ain't that good enough: *Edwards, John* / You turned my bitter into sweet: *Love, Mary* / Baby I need you: *Lorraine & The Delights* / Can it be me: *Williams, Mel* / Our love will grow: *Showmen*
CDKEND 129 / Aug '96 / Kent

☐ **BIG KAHUNA KICKS VOL.1**
KCUTSCD 009 / 24 Aug '98 / Kahuna Cuts

☐ **BIG MIX '97 (2CD Set)**
Who do you think you are: *Spice Girls* / Fresh: *Gina G* / Fly like an eagle: *Seal* / Ready or not: *Course* / Horny: *Morrison, Mark* / Don't you love me: *Eternal* / Professional widow: *Amos, Tori* / Dance with me: *Tin Tin Out* / Spinning the wheel: *Michael, George* / Things can only get better: *D:Ream* / Lopez: *808 State* / Nightmare: *Brainbug* / Encore une fois: *Sash* / Tha wildstyle: *DJ Supreme* / Bellissima: *DJ Quicksilver* / Theme from The Professionals: *Johnson, Laurie London Big Band* / Passion: *Amen UK* / Flash: *BBE* / Ain't talkin' 'bout dub: *Apollo 440* / I believe I can fly: *R Kelly* / You might need somebody: *Ama, Shola* / Virtual insanity: *Jamiroquai* / Remember me: *Blueboy* / MFEO: *Kavana* / Bodyshakin': *911* / You got the love: *Source & Candi Staton* / Boss: *Braxtons* / Where can I find love: *Livin' Joy* / Flame: *Crustation* / Absurd: *Fluke* / Say my name: *Zee* / Scared: *Slacker* / Just playin': *JT Playaz* / Rock da house: *Tall Paul* / Groove Bird: *Natural Born Groovers* / Extremis: *Hal & Gillian Anderson* / Come with me: *Qattara*
VTDCD 130 / Jun '97 / Virgin

☐ **BIG NOISE VOL.2 (Another Mambo Inn Compilation)**
Beija flor: *Timbalada* / Que pena: *Costa, Gal & Caetano Veloso* / Aquela esquina: *Negrocan* / Ningirikiri: *Masuka, Dorothy* / Hamady Boiro: *Maal, Baaba* / African soul: *Baroudi, Hamid* / Sweet mother: *Gu, Wagadu* / Lakou-A: *Guillaume, Jephte* / Sama Thiel: *Africando* / El Pregunton: *Cubanismo* / A gozar con mi combo: *Cachao* / Pump me up: *Krosfyah* / Skaravan: *Jazz Jamaica*
HNCD 1400 / 22 Sep '97 / Hannibal

☐ **BIG NOISE: A MAMBO INN COMPILATION**
Dub lion (remake): *DJ Food* / Kinna sohna: *Khan, Nusrat Fateh Ali* / Did-funk club: *Khaled, Hadj Ibrahim* / Angelina: *Sweet Talks* / Zing zong: *Kanda Bongo Man* / Ussak ndja: *Tchando* / Mango mangue: *Mambomania* / El swing: *Montanez, Andy* / Elena Elena: *Libre* / Samba de flora: *Airto* / Wack wack: *Young-Holt Trio* / Do what you wanna: *Lewis, Ramsey* / You're the one: *McGriff, Jimmy* / My God can do anything: *Barnes, Luther & The Red Budd Gospel Choir*
HNCD 1382 / Nov '94 / Hannibal

☐ **BIG PEOPLE MUSIC VOL.1**
CRCD 56 / Nov '96 / Jet Star

☐ **BIG PEOPLE MUSIC VOL.2**
CRCD 65 / Mar '97 / Charm

☐ **BIG PEOPLE MUSIC VOL.3**
CRCD 76 / 24 Nov '97 / Charm

☐ **BIG ROCK 'N' BEATS**
TVT 72512A / 4 Nov '97 / TVT

☐ **BIG SCORE, THE (A Soundtrack To The Black Films Of The Seventies)**
Call me Mr.Tibbs: *Jones, Quincy* / Superfly: *Mayfield, Curtis* / Cleopatra Jones: *Simon, Joe* / Brothers gonna work it out: *Hutch, Willie* / Across 100th Street: *Womack, Bobby* / Freddie's dead: *Mayfield, Curtis* / Easing in: *Starr, Edwin* / People get up and drive your funky soul: *Brown, James* / Mama Feelgood: *Collins, Lyn* / Shaft: *Hayes, Isaac* / Sweetback's theme: *Hayes, Isaac* / Final comedown: *Green, Grant* / Foxy brown: *Hutch, Willie* / Are you man enough: *Four Tops* / Coffy is the colour: *Ayers, Roy* / Together brother: *White, Barry* / Flying machine: *War* / Car wash: *Rose Royce*
4936292 / 30 Mar '98 / Cooltempo

☐ **BIG SHIP OLE FUNG REGGAE SKA**
Reggae ska: *McGregor, Freddie* / Do the ska: *Papa San* / Dawn Karen and Gwen: *Cutty Ranks* / Old time ska: *Tyrical & Bobby Treasure* / Come ya mi darling come: *Chaka Demus* / One family: *Boy Ken* / Mek she bawl: *Mad Cobra* / Jack and Jill: *Buckley, Michael & Bugle Banton* / It's a wonderful thing: *Davis, Carlene* / Sammy: *Rappa Robert & Delta* / Girls need pleasure: *Ricky General & Yeshemabeth* / Mamma said: *Galaxy P* / Dance with me: *TOK & Winston Wheeler* / Higher inna life: *Captain Barkey & Angel Doolas* / My true love: *Brown, Richie* / Big ship ole fung ska: *Forde, Jermaine & Robbie Lyn*
GRELCD 242 / 18 Aug '97 / Greensleeves

☐ **BIG SQUEEZE, THE**
Johnny Allen's reel/Sporting Nell: *McComiskey, Billy & Sean McGlynn* / Miller of Draughin/Humours of Castlefin: *O'Brien, Paddy* / High reel/Geoghegan's reel: *Burke, Joe* / Maids of Selma/Larry Redican's/Dancing tables: *Keane, James* / Crossing the Sahannon/Lad O'Beirne's reel/Rough road: *Keane, James* / Andy Stewart's reel/Harsh February: *Cunningham, Phil* / Desaunay/Petticoat I bought in Mullingar: *Cunningham, Phil* / Sweeney's reel: *Daly, Jackie* / Bucks of Oranmore: *Burke, Joe* / Spike Island lassies/Humours of Tulla: *McComiskey, Billy* / Strathspey and reel: *O'Brien, Paddy* / La Bastringue: *Daly, Jackie* / Connaught man's rambles/Cat in the corner: *Burke, Joe* / Master Crowley's reels: *Keane, James* / Lament from Eoin Rhua/March of the Gaelic order: *O'Brien, Paddy* / Yellow tinker/Sally Gardens: *McComiskey, Billy* / Tom Fleming's reel/Kitty's wedding/Sean McGuire's reel: *Whelan, John* / Jackson's reel/Jean's reel/Moving cloud: *Cunningham, Phil*
CELT 9014 / Jul '98 / Celtophile

☐ **BIG SURF**
Pipeline: *Lively Ones* / Scratch: *Lively Ones* / Misirlou: *Lively Ones* / Surfbeat: *Lively Ones* / High tide: *Lively Ones* / Baja: *Lively Ones* / Torquay: *Lively Ones* / Soul surfer: *Lively Ones* / Rik-a-tik: *Lively Ones* / Church key: *Myers, Dave & The Surftones* / Moment of truth: *Myers, Dave & The Surftones* / Bullwinkle (part 2): *Centurions* / Sano: *Centurions* / Surfin' at Mazatland: *Centurions* / Body surfin': *Centurions* / Vesuvius: *Centurions* / Latin'ia: *Centurions* / Intoxica: *Centurions* / Steel pier: *Impacts* / Impact: *Impacts* / Blue surf: *Impacts* / Wipeout: *Impacts* / Fort Lauderdale: *Impacts* / Exotic: *Sentinals* / Pipe: *Sentinals* / Latin soul: *Sentinals* / Tor chula: *Sentinals* / Big surf: *Sentinals*
CDCHD 319 / Aug '91 / Ace

☐ **BIG TIMES IN A SMALL TOWN**
PH 1155CD / Oct '93 / Philo

☐ **BIG TRANCE JESUS HEAD (2CD Set)**
AOP 54 / 1 Jun '98 / Age Of Panik

☐ **BIG WHEELS OF AZULI (1991-1995)**
Bring me love: *Mendez, Andrea* / R U sleeping: *Indo* / Ministry of love: *Romanthony* / Anthem: *Black Shells* / Feeling: *Jasper Street Family* / Place called Heaven: *Tension* / In a fantasy: *Chocolate Fantasy* / Running: *Disco Elements* / Heaven: *KCC & Emile* / Falling from grace: *Romanthony* / Summer groove: *Sensory Elements*
AZNYCD 1 / Nov '95 / Azuli

☐ **BIGGEST BAND SPECTACULAR IN THE WORLD (1985 Military Musical Pageant Wembley Stadium/2CD Set)**
General salute and opening fanfare / By beat of drum / Light of foot / Pipes and drums / Queen's guards / Massed bands / Royal military band of The Netherlands / War and peace / Finale
BNW 9002 / '89 / Bandleader

☐ **BIGSHOT MIXES**
DBCD 506 / May '90 / Debut

☐ **BILL HANEY'S BROTHERHOOD OF SOUL**
I'm a dreamer: *Wilburn, Bobby* / Something wrong with our love: *Graham, Joe* / I've been blessed by your love: *Christian, Al* / Got my plans squared away: *Walker, Randolph* / You better listen to me: *Alexander, Arthur* / Pride and soul: *Allen, Gary* / Something I ain't never had: *Jackson, Jarvis* / Come back son: *Woodard, Jerry* / Like the wind: *Clark, Dee* / Don't let me know: *Thomas, Charlie* / Who are you fooling: *Graham, Joe* / Frozen love: *Meadows, Gay* / Sweet sweet woman: *Woodard, Jerry* / I know: *Dino & Doc* / Workin' on a new love: *Marlin, Matt* / Steppin' stone: *Graham, Joe* / Achin' all over: *Walker, Randolph* / What you don't know: *Jackson, Jarvis* / You got love: *Five Jays* / Nothing's going to change the way I feel: *Five Jays* / Hurt girl: *Dino & Doc* / Do me wrong: *Walker, Randolph* / My peaceful forest: *Hamilton, Roy*
CDKEND 159 / Jun '98 / Kent

☐ **BIND HER GAG HER AND DRINK HER BLOOD (2CD Set)**
AOP 61 / 23 Feb '98 / Dressed To Kill

☐ **BINN BLASTA**
CDTCD 008 / 1 Jun '98 / Gael Linn

☐ **BIONIC DUB**
LG 21114 / Aug '95 / Lagoon

☐ **BIRD IN THE BUSH, THE (Traditional Songs Of Love & Lust)**
Two magicians / Old man from over the sea / Wanton seed / Gathering rushes in the month of May / Bonnie black hare / Whirly whorl / Pretty Polly / Old bachelor / Stonecutter boy / Mower / Bird in the bush / Pegging awl / Mortinmas time / Widow of the Westmorland's daughter
TSCD 479 / Jun '96 / Topic

☐ **BIRTH OF BE BOP, THE (Wichita-New York 1940-1945/2CD Set)**
FA 046 / Feb '96 / Fremeaux

☐ **BIRTH OF BE BOP, THE (2CD Set)**
Hot mallets: *Hampton, Lionel Orchestra* / Dameron stomp: *Leonard, Harlan & His Rockets* / Pitter panther patter: *Ellington, Duke & Jimmy Blanton* / I never knew: *Young, Lester & Charlie Christian* / Swing to bop: *Christian, Charlie* / Hootie blues: *McShann, Jay & his Orchestra* / Gasser: *Eldridge, Roy Orchestra* / Moose: *Barnet, Charlie Orchestra* / Sometimes I'm happy: *Young, Lester Quartet* / Honeysuckle rose: *Williams, Cootie Sextet* / Woody 'n' you: *Hawkins, Coleman Orchestra* / Disorder at the border: *Hawkins, Coleman Orchestra* / Tiny's tempo: *Grimes, Tiny Quintet* / Red cross: *Grimes, Tiny Quintet* / Flyin' Hawk: *Hawkins, Coleman Quartet* / Blowing the blues away: *Eckstine, Billy & His Orchestra* / Opus X: *Eckstine, Billy & His Orchestra* / Interlude: *Vaughan, Sarah* / East of the sun: *Vaughan, Sarah* / Sometimes for you: *Pettiford, Oscar & His 18 All Stars* / Good bait: *Gillespie, Dizzy All Stars* / Be bop: *Gillespie, Dizzy All Stars* / Night in Tunisia: *Raeburn, Boyd Orchestra* / Groovin' high: *Gillespie, Dizzy Sextet* / Blue 'n' boogie: *Gillespie, Dizzy Sextet* / All the things you are: *Gillespie, Dizzy* / Dizzy atmosphere: *Gillespie, Dizzy* / Riff tide: *Hawkins, Coleman Orchestra* / Lover man: *Vaughan, Sarah* / Salt peanuts: *Gillespie, Dizzy & His All Star Quintet* / Shaw nuff: *Gillespie, Dizzy & His All Star Quintet* / Slam slam blues: *Norvo, Red* / Congo blues: *Norvo, Red* / Good Earth: *Herman, Woody Orchestra* / Super session: *Byas, Don Quartet* / Why not: *Thompson, Lucky All Stars* / Air mail special: *Auld, Georgie & His Orchestra* / Blow Mr. Dexter: *Gordon, Dexter All Stars* / Dexter's minor mad: *Gordon, Dexter All Stars* / Now's the time: *Parker, Charlie Reboppers* / Ko ko: *Parker, Charlie Reboppers* / Slim's jam: *Gaillard, Slim*
CPCD 81942 / Sep '96 / Charly

☐ **BIRTH OF BRITPOP, THE (Where It All Began/4CD Set)**
SUMBX 4014 / Jan '98 / Summit

☐ BIRTH OF SKA, THE

Carry go bring home: *Hinds, Justin & The Dominoes* / River bank: *Brooks, Baba* / Musical communion: *Brooks, Baba* / Feeling fine: *Alphonso, Roland* / Strongarm Sampson: *Hinds, Justin & The Dominoes* / Over the river: *Hinds, Justin & The Dominoes* / Next door neighbour: *Silvera, Owen & Leon & The Skatalite Band* / When I call your name: *Brooks, Baba* / Yeah yeah baby: *Stranger & Patsy/Baba Brooks/Skatalite Band* / Hog in a cocoa: *Skatalite Band* / Musical storeroom: *Anderson, Frank & Skatalite Band* / Corner stone: *Hinds, Justin & The Dominoes*

CDTRL 274 / Mar '94 / Trojan

☐ BIRTH OF SOUL VOL.1, THE

You're not the guy for me: *Anderson, Ernestine* / Sound of my man: *Kilgore, Theola* / Hey girl don't bother me: *Tams* / Ain't nothing you can do: *Bland, Bobby* / Pain in my heart: *Redding, Otis* / Cry baby: *Mimms, Garnet & Enchanters* / How can I forget: *Holiday, Jimmy* / You don't have to be a tower of strength: *Lynne, Gloria* / He will break your heart: *Butler, Jerry* / Have fun: *Cole, Ann* / Oh my angel: *Tillman, Bertha* / Something's got a hold on me: *James, Etta* / Daddy rollin' stone: *Martin, Derek* / Mockingbird: *Foxx, Inez & Charlie* / Snap your fingers: *Henderson, Joe* / I'll come running to you: *Cooke, Sam* / Merry go round: *Johnson, Marv* / Goin' out of my head: *Little Anthony & The Imperials* / Hey girl: *Scott, Freddie* / You'll lose a good thing: *Lynn, Barbara* / Part time love: *Taylor, Little Johnny* / I'm qualified: *Hughes, Jimmy* / Any other way: *Bell, William* / She ain't ready: *Barnes, J.J.* / I do: *Marvelows* / Telephone game: *Clark, Claudine* / Mama didn't lie: *Bradley, Jan* / Gypsy woman: *Impressions*

CDKEND 123 / Apr '96 / Kent

☐ BIRTH OF SOUL VOL.2, THE

Walk around heaven all day: *Caravans* / Heart full of love: *Invincibles* / Man's temptation: *Chandler, Gene* / Here's a heart: *Diplomats* / There goes my baby: *Drifters* / Two lovers make one fool: *Serenaders* / I never dreamed: *Cookies* / Come tomorrow: *Knight, Marie* / I'll give my life: *Holloway, Brenda* / Sad girl: *Wiggins, Jay* / I'm counting on you: *Freeman Brothers* / I found a love: *Falcons* / What'd I say: *Charles, Ray* / Wrong girl: *Showmen* / Lipstick traces (on a cigarette): *Showmen* / Down in the valley: *Burke, Solomon* / Always accused: *Tee, Willie* / Call somebody please: *Manhattans* / Lover's prayer: *Wallace Brothers* / This is my prayer: *Kilgore, Theola* / Time waits for no-one: *Eddie & Ernie* / Cry to me: *Harris, Betty* / Long haired daddy: *Hill, Vernell* / Spring: *Birdlegs & Pauline/Their Versatility Birds* / Standing in the shadows: *Birdlegs & Pauline/Their Versatility Birds* / Um um um um um: *Major Lance* / It's no good for me: *Nash, Johnny* / All in my mind: *Brown, Maxine*

CDKEND 147 / 26 Jan '98 / Kent

☐ BIRTH OF THE GROOVE

September 13: *Deodato, Eumir* / Canned funk: *Farrell, Joe* / Hurtin' house: *Phillips, Esther* / Rock steady: *Hammond, Johnny* / Sugar free: *Crawford, Hank* / Storm: *Turrentine, Stanley* / I'm not so sure: *Jackson, Milt* / I remember Wes: *Benson, George* / Shoogie wanna boogie: *Mathews, Dave* / Hard to face the music: *Muhammad, Idris*

ZK 65134 / 8 Sep '97 / Sony Jazz

☐ BIRTH OF THE THIRD STREAM

Three little feelings / Poem for brass / All about Rosie / Revelations / Suspensions / Symphony for brass and percussion / Transformation / Pharoah

4851032 / Sep '96 / Sony Jazz

☐ BISTRO EROTICA ITALIA

74321541932 / 9 Mar '98 / Bistro

☐ BITE HARD THE MUSIC (De Wolfe Studio Sampler 1972-1980)

Hard hitter / Hawk / Power surge / Spiro / Collect / Main chance / Hogan's thing / Night moves / Sunken ship / Rock bed 1 / Hold back / Trip wire / Condition red / Hot ice / Sounds unusual / Mantaray

BBECD 010 / 16 Feb '98 / Barely Breaking Even

☐ BITING BACK

WOWCD 35 / Jan '94 / Words Of Warning

☐ BITTER & TWISTED (Mrs. Wood & Blu Peter) (2CD Set)

Don't stop: *Mark NRG* / Hybrid oral: *Random Generator* / Smokin' Jesus: *Summer Skool* / Tribal steps: *Kaltenbrunner* / Side on: *Space DJ's* / Phreaks: *Huntemann* / Cachka: *Bulkhead* / Ignition: *Madame Dubois* / Universal spirit: *Freak Force* / Straight forward: *Secret Cinema* / Equilibrum: *Tranquilizer* / File 003tmp: *Gravital Force II* / Trip beat: *Wave Captain* / Secret spice: *Gargano, Pablo* / Mystery: *Code 16* / Automorphism: *RND Technologies* / Darkbag: *Kool World* / Famous: *Rubicon Massacre Ltd.* / Shi du: *Khan, Reysan* / Rhythm state 2: *Prussic Acid Rhythm* / Who's gettin' it: *Naked Ape* / Be silent: *Dr. Mu* / Homecoming: *Troop* / Here is justice: *Judge S* / Magnitude 7: *Sonic Animation* / Limits: *V-Tracks* / Diadora: *Mikerobenics* / Wake up: *Mark NRG* / Starburst: *Razors Edge* / Timerunner: *16C+* / 4 times: *Racoon* / My time is yours: *LSG* / Bruised: *Spira* / Weeping waste: *Renegade Legion*

REACTCD 086 / Aug '96 / React

☐ BITTER FRUITS

IUKCD 002 / Apr '95 / Harthouse

☐ BIWA AND SHAKUHACHI

C 580059 / Jan '95 / Ocora

☐ BIX MIX 1997

Closer than close: *Gaines, Rosie* / Free: *Ultra Nate* / Star people: *Michael, George* / Sunchyme: *Dario G* / Samba de Janeiro: *Bellini* / Ecuador: *Sash* / Freed from desire: *Gala* / Plastic dreams: *Jaydee* / Every little time: *Poppers & Aura* / Wannabe: *Spice Girls* / Joy: *Staxx* / All I wanna do: *Minogue, Dannii* / Nine ways: *JDS* / Home: *Chakra* / Strings for Yasmin: *Tin Tin Out* / Squirt Fluke: *Chakra* / Circles: *Adam F*

VTDCD 172 / 29 Sep '97 / Virgin

☐ BLACK & WHITE BLUES

MBSCD 431 / Oct '94 / Castle

☐ BLACK AND BLUE

BN 045 / Apr '98 / Blue Nite

☐ BLACK AND BLUES (Sweet Little Angel)

12207 / Jul '93 / Laserlight

☐ BLACK AND BLUES

VGCD 660510 / Oct '93 / Vogue

☐ BLACK AND SOUL

12403 / Feb '95 / Laserlight

☐ BLACK AND TAN CLUB, THE

NAR 060CD / May '93 / New Alliance

☐ BLACK AND WHITE BLUES (2CD Set)

John Lee's original boogie: *Hooker, John Lee* / Hoochie coochie man: *Waters, Muddy* / Death letter blues: *House, Son* / Mam don't like me runnin' around: *Williams, 'Big' Joe* / Rollin' and tumblin': *Memphis Slim* / Blues jumped over the rabbit: *Turner, 'Big' Joe* / Stormy monday blues: *Lewis, Smiley* / Shotgun blues: *Hopkins, Lightnin'* / Drop down mama: *McDowell, 'Mississippi' Fred* / Key to the highway: *McGhee, Brownie & Sonny Terry* / Shrewsbury blues: *Ridgley, Tommy* / Mean old world: *Walker, T-Bone* / Drifting blues: *Moore, Johnny B. & Three Blazers* / Trouble blues: *Brown, Charles Trio* / Trian time blues: *Milburn, Amos* / Call operator 210: *Dixon, Floyd* / How many more years: *King, Freddie* / Laughnin' and clownin': *Womack, Bobby* / New boogie chillun: *Thorogood, George* / Dust my broom: *Canned Heat* / Rollin' and tumblin': *Winter, Johnny* / Groundhog blues: *Groundhogs* / Dimples: *Animals* / Shotgun blues: *Dr. Feelgood* / Egg or the hen: *Rockpile* / Got my mojo working: *Manfred Mann* / I'm tore down: *Korner, Alexis* / Mistreated: *Groundhogs* / 3 O'clock blues: *Love Sculpture* / Parchment farm: *Nashville Teens* / Eddie's blues: *Cochran, Eddie* / You shook me: *Beck, Jeff* / Come on in my kitchen: *Miller, Steve* / TV mama: *Canned Heat* / Bluest blues: *Lee, Alvin*

CDEM 1624 / Jul '97 / EMI

☐ BLACK AND WHITE PIANO VOL.1 1923-1931

DOCD 5596 / 24 Mar '98 / Document

☐ BLACK AND WHITE PIANO VOL.2 1929-1942

DOCD 5597 / 24 Mar '98 / Document

☐ BLACK BOX (2CD Set)

9010552 / Mar '97 / Immediate

☐ BLACK BOX OF JAZZ (4CD Set)

MBSCD 450 / Aug '96 / Castle

☐ BLACK, BROWN & REGGAE

D 31516 / Oct '96 / Far I

☐ BLACK DANCE VOL.2

ZYX 550632 / Oct '96 / ZYX

☐ BLACK GOLD

HRCD 8047 / Jul '94 / Disky

☐ BLACK HOLLAND

Saramaka: *Snijders, Ronald Acoustic Band* / Mangrove: *Dandare, Cedric Group* / Cumbia: *Surinam Music Ensemble* / Story of Salia: *Fra Fra Sound* / Kaya grande: *Grupo Zamanakitoki* / Designs: *Alvorada* / Stroop: *Sedoction* / Camina: *Douglas, Franky Sunchild* / Bari odi: *Surfive*

AL 73104 / Dec '97 / A

☐ BLACK MARK ATTACK VOL.2

BMCD 130 / 6 Apr '98 / Black Mark

☐ BLACK MARK TRIBUTE VOL.2

Black celebration: *World Of Silence* / War pigs: *Bathory* / You can't stop rock and roll: *Divine Sin* / I'm only sleeping: *Quorthon* / It's alright for you: *Purity* / Moonchild: *Necrophobic* / Money: *Mental Crypt* / To heaven back again: *Memento Mori*

BMCD 138 / 27 Apr '98 / Black Mark

☐ BLACK MEETS HOUSE

HMC 100072 / 8 Jun '98 / Happy Music

☐ BLACK OUT

REVXD 166 / Feb '91 / Black

☐ BLACK RHINO

AFRCD 9 / 3 Nov '97 / Flying Rhino

☐ BLACK ROCK/CYBERFUNK/FUTURE BLUES

RCD 10313 / Oct '94 / Rykodisc

☐ BLACK SECULAR VOCAL GROUPS VOL.1 (1921-1929)

DOCD 5546 / Jul '97 / Document

☐ BLACK SECULAR VOCAL GROUPS VOL.2 (1931-1939)

DOCD 5550 / Jul '97 / Document

☐ BLACK SECULAR VOCAL GROUPS VOL.3

DOCD 5064 / 15 Jun '98 / Document

☐ BLACK TOP BAYOU STATE BOOGIE

Make a better world: *King, Earl* / Hey hey baby's gone: *Walker, Philip* / Love at first sight: *August, Lynn* / About my past: *Ridgley, Tommy* / Case of love: *Davis, James 'Thunderbird' & Earl King* / A ma maison: *Simien, Terrance* / Lookin' for that woman: *Thomas, Jesse* / Emmitt Lee: *Fran, Carol* / Second line: *Muldaur, Maria* / Buck's nouvelle jole blon: *Buckwheat Zydeco* / Mama and Papa: *Eaglin, Snooks*

CDBTEL 7005 / May '97 / Black Top

☐ BLACK TOP BLUES COSTUME PARTY

BT 1116CD / Jun '95 / Black Top

☐ BLACK TOP BLUES VOCAL DYNAMITE

BT 1124CD / Nov '95 / Black Top

☐ BLACK TOP BLUES-A-RAMA (Budget Sampler)

BT 002CD / Dec '90 / Black Top

☐ BLACK TOP BLUES-A-RAMA VOL.2

BT 1045CD / '92 / Black Top

☐ BLACK TOP BLUES-A-RAMA VOL.3 (Live From Tipitinas)

BT 1056CD / '92 / Black Top

☐ BLACK TOP BLUES-A-RAMA VOL.4 (Down And Dirty)

BT 1057CD / '92 / Black Top

☐ BLACK TOP BLUES-A-RAMA VOL.5

BT 1058CD / '92 / Black Top

☐ BLACK TOP BLUES-A-RAMA VOL.6

BT 1073CD / May '92 / Black Top

☐ BLACK TOP BLUES-A-RAMA VOL.7

BT 1089CD / May '93 / Black Top

☐ BLACK VOCAL GROUPS 1935-44

RFDCD 10 / Feb '92 / Country Routes

☐ BLACK VOCAL GROUPS VOL.1

DOCD 5340 / May '95 / Document

☐ BLACK VOCAL GROUPS VOL.2

DOCD 5347 / May '95 / Document

☐ BLACK VOCAL GROUPS VOL.3 1925-1943

DOCD 5551 / Jul '97 / Document

☐ BLACK VOCAL GROUPS VOL.4 1927-1939

DOCD 5552 / Jul '97 / Document

☐ BLACK VOCAL GROUPS VOL.5 1923-1941

DOCD 5553 / Jul '97 / Document

☐ BLACK VOCAL GROUPS VOL.6 1924-1937

DOCD 5554 / Jul '97 / Document

☐ BLACK VOCAL GROUPS VOL.7 1927-1941

DOCD 5555 / Jul '97 / Document

☐ BLACK VOCAL GROUPS VOL.8 1926-1935

DOCD 5556 / Jul '97 / Document

☐ BLACK VOCAL GROUPS VOL.9 1929-1942

DOCD 5606 / 27 Jul '98 / Document

☐ BLACK WHOLE STYLES

Dadaism: *Beyond There* / My experience is...: *Abstract Rude & Tribe Unique* / Misanthropic: *Alpha Pryme* / Feel da panic: *Roots Manuva* / Variations: *New Flesh For Old* / Elohim (1972): *Williams, Saul* / Duration 14: *Taylor, Toastie* / Twice the first time: *Williams, Saul* / Triple intruder: *Part 2 & Juice Aleem* / Uranium-235: *Drunken Immortals & New Flesh/Roots Manuva* / Gemini Twins: *Asylum* / Something about the music: *Abstract Rude & Tribe Unique* / Nanotech pilots: *Part 2 & Juice Aleem* / Elohim (1972): *Williams, Saul*

BDCD 007 / 25 May '98 / Big Dada

☐ BLACKEND VOL.1 (2CD Set)

BLACK 001DCD / Jul '96 / Blackend

☐ BLACKEND VOL.2 (2CD Set)

BLACK 003DCD / Jul '96 / Blackend

☐ BLACKPOOL MECCA STORY, THE

Love factory: *Laws, Eloise* / Seven day lover: *Fountain, James* / Bet if you ask around: *Velvet* / Get it off my conscience: *Lovelites* / I need you: *Jenkins, Dianne* / Time passes by: *Bynum, James* / Make up your mind: *Connelly, Earl* / Payback's a drag: *Smith Bros* / Destination unkown: *Delrey's Incorporated* / Ladies choice (part 1): *Franklin, Boby* / Wash and wear love: *Varnado, Lynn* / Cashing in: *Voices Of East Harlem* / Woman is hard to understand: *Mack, Jimmy* / Alone with no love: *Rock Candy* / I don't know what foot to dance on: *Tolliver, Kim* / Tow-a-way love: *Jenkins, Dianne* / Lord what's happening to your people: *Smith, Kenny* / You made me this way: *Vann, Ila* / Don't you care anymore: *Mathis, Jodi* / I can see him loving you: *Anderson Brothers* / Let our love grow higher: *Cooper, Eula* / You've been gone too long: *Sexton, Ann*

GSCD 068 / Oct '95 / Goldmine

☐ BLACKPOOL TOWER CENTENARY, THE (2CD Set)

Tiger rag: *Dixon, Reginald* / Little girl: *Dixon, Reginald* / As time goes by: *Dixon, Reginald* / When I take my sugar to tea: *Dixon, Reginald* / Happy feat: *Dixon, Reginald* / Sabre dance: *Dixon, Reginald* / Symphonic poem: *Dixon, Reginald* / Samum: *Dixon, Reginald* / I love the sunshine of your smile: *Dixon, Reginald* / When I grow too old to dream: *Dixon, Reginald* / Let's have another one: *Dixon, Reginald* / Oh you beautiful doll: *Dixon, Reginald* / Have you ever been lonely: *Dixon, Reginald* / Happy wanderer: *Dixon, Reginald* / Over the waves: *Dixon, Reginald* / Ma, he's making eyes at me: *Dixon, Reginald* / We'll keep a welcome: *Dixon, Reginald* / Blaydon races: *Dixon, Reginald* / Maybe it's because I'm a Londoner: *Dixon, Reginald* / I belong to Glasgow: *Dixon, Reginald* / I do like to be beside the seaside: *Dixon, Reginald* / Quicksteps: *Kelsall, Phil* / Mr. Sandman: *Kelsall, Phil* / Avalon: *Kelsall, Phil* / Crazy rhythm: *Kelsall, Phil* / Viennese waltz: *Kelsall, Phil* / Skater's waltz: *Kelsall, Phil* / Bossa novas: *Kelsall, Phil* / Girl from Ipanema: *Kelsall, Phil* / Destination love: *Kelsall, Phil* / Barn dance: *Kelsall, Phil* / Tip toe through the tulips: *Kelsall, Phil* / I don't know why (I just do): *Kelsall, Phil* / My mammy: *Kelsall, Phil* / Cha cha cha: *Kelsall, Phil* / Cherry pink and apple blossom white: *Kelsall, Phil* / Por favor: *Kelsall, Phil* / Slow rhumbas: *Kelsall, Phil* / Here's that rainy day: *Kelsall, Phil* / La Golondrina: *Kelsall, Phil* / St. Bernard's waltz: *Kelsall, Phil* / Bless 'em all: *Kelsall, Phil* / Band played on: *Kelsall, Phil* / Ash grove: *Kelsall, Phil* / Daisy bell: *Kelsall, Phil* / Mayfair quicksteps: *Kelsall, Phil* / Little white lies: *Kelsall, Phil* / Happy feet: *Kelsall, Phil* / It's just the time for dancing: *Kelsall, Phil* / Tango: *Kelsall, Phil* / La Camparsita: *Kelsall, Phil* / Jive: *Kelsall, Phil* / Nagasaki: *Kelsall, Phil* / Sweet Georgia Brown: *Kelsall, Phil* / Gay Gordons: *Kelsall, Phil* / Scotch mist: *Kelsall, Phil* / Rosetta: *Barlow, Charles & His Orchestra* / Apple for the teacher: *Barlow, Charles & His Orchestra* / Waltzes: *Barlow, Charles & His Orchestra* / Coppelia: *Barlow, Charles & His Orchestra* / Maria Elena: *Barlow, Charles & His Orchestra* / Sambas: *Barlow, Charles & His Orchestra* / El cumbanchero: *Barlow, Charles & His Orchestra* / Hawaiian samba: *Barlow, Charles & His Orchestra* / Cha chas: *Barlow, Charles & His Orchestra* / Something stupid: *Barlow, Charles & His Orchestra* / Swingin' shepherd blues: *Barlow, Charles & His Orchestra* / Paso dobles: *Barlow, Charles & His Orchestra* / For you, Rio Rita: *Barlow, Charles & His Orchestra* / March of the matadors: *Barlow, Charles & His Orchestra* / Annientamento: *Barlow, Charles & His Orchestra* / Foxtrots: *Barlow, Charles & His Orchestra* / Vilia: *Barlow, Charles & His Orchestra* / Red roses for a blue lady: *Barlow, Charles & His Orchestra* / Quaker girl: *Turner, Ken & His Orchestra* / Dollar princess: *Turner, Ken & His Orchestra* / Two-steps: *Turner, Ken & His Orchestra* / Semper fidelis: *Turner, Ken & His Orchestra* / Namur: *Turner, Ken & His Orchestra* / Saunters: *Turner, Ken & His Orchestra* / Oh my papa: *Turner, Ken & His Orchestra* / Trust in me: *Turner, Ken & His Orchestra* / Waltz: *Turner, Ken & His Orchestra* / Biberacher-waltzer: *Turner, Ken & His Orchestra* / Gavottes: *Turner, Ken & His Orchestra* / Country gardens: *Turner, Ken & His Orchestra* / I leave my heart in an English garden: *Turner, Ken & His Orchestra* / Way to the heart: *Turner, Ken & His Orchestra* / Tangos: *Turner, Ken & His Orchestra* / Midnight in Malaga: *Turner, Ken & His Orchestra* / Madame: *Turner, Ken & His Orchestra* / Modern waltz: *Turner, Ken & His Orchestra* / Peyton Place theme: *Turner, Ken & His Orchestra* / Manhattan: *Dixon, Reginald* / Boo hoo: *Dixon, Reginald*

CDDL 1272 / Mar '94 / Music For Pleasure

☐ BLANKET ON THE GROUND

MU 5056 / Oct '92 / Musketeer

☐ BLASTA (The Irish Traditional Music Special - A Gael Linn Sampler)

Cameronian wheel: *De Danann* / Doon reel: *De Danann* / Ansacht na nansacht: *Ni Fhearraigh, Aoife* / Mason's apron: *Murphy, Colm* / Coinleach ghlas an fhomhair: *Clannad* / Maids of Castlebar: *McMahon, Tony & Noel Hill* / Collier's reel: *McMahon, Tony & Noel Hill* / Is fada liom uaim i: *Ni Dhomhnaill, Maighread* / Danish quadrille: *Buttons & Bows* / We venerate thy cross: *Ni Riain, Noirin & Monks Of Glenstal Abbey* / Cucanandy/The jug of brown ale: *Clannad* / Floggin reel: *Bergin, Mary* / Ivy leaf: *Bergin, Mary* / Trim the velvet: *Bergin, Mary* / Jimmy mo mhile stor: *Keane, Dolores* / John Stewart's: *Glackin, Paddy* / James Byrne's pretty peg: *Glackin, Paddy* / Miss Patterson's supper: *Glackin, Paddy* / Wee lass on the brae: *Ni Dhomhnaill, Triona* / Ballintore jig: *Keenan, Paddy*

CDTCD 007 / May '97 / Gael Linn

☐ BLAXPLOITATION VOL.1 (Soul, Funk & Jazz From The Inner City) (2CD Set)

Ghetto: *Hathaway, Donny* / Inner city blues: *Washington, Grover Jr.* / Woman of the ghetto: *Shaw, Marlena* / Pusherman: *Mayfield, Curtis* / Home is where the hatred is: *Phillips, Esther* / Stone to the bone: *Brown, James* / Expansions: *Smith, Lonnie Liston* / Also sprach zarathustra: *Deodato, Eumir* / Stratus: *Cobham, Billy* / Shaft: *Hayes, Isaac* / He's a superstar: *Ayers, Roy* / Superfly: *Mayfield, Curtis* / Summer in the city: *Jones, Quincy* / For what it's worth: *Mendes, Sergio* / Stepping stones: *Harris, Johnny* / Nubian lady: *Lateef, Yusef* / I'd rather be with you: *Collins, Bootsy* / Straussmania: *Salinas, Daniel* / Children of the ghetto: *Pine, Courtney* / Other side of town: *Joseph, Julian* / By all means: *Mouzon, Alphonse* / Look of love: *Hayes, Isaac* / If you want me to stay: *Stone, Sly* / Why can't we live together: *Thomas, Timmy*

RADCD 43 / Sep '96 / Global TV

☐ BLAXPLOITATION VOL.2 (2CD Set)

RADCD 54 / Feb '97 / Global TV

☐ BLAXPLOITATION VOL.3 (2CD Set)

RADCD 76 / 1 Nov '97 / Global TV

☐ BLAXPLOITATION VOL.4 (Harlem Hustle - 2CD Set)

Law of the land: *Temptations* / Am I black enough for you: *Paul, Billy* / Death wish: *Hancock, Herbie* / (Don't worry)if there's a hell below we're all going to go: *Mayfield, Curtis* / September 13th: *Deodato, Eumir* / Grandma's hands: *Scott-Heron, Gil* / Who is he and what is he up to: *Withers, Bill* / Truck turner: *Hayes, Isaac* / Son of shaft: *Bar-Kays* / Mister magic: *Washington, Grover Jr.* / Theme from Cleopatra Jones: *Simon, Joe & The Mainstreeters* / Flying machine: *War* / Sweet sweetback's theme: *Earth, Wind & Fire* / I want you: *Gaye, Marvin* / Theme from savage: *Julian, Don* / For the love of money: *O'Jays* / Strawberry letter 23: *Brothers Johnson* / Natural high: *Bloodstone* / Inside my love: *Riperton, Minnie* / One gun salute: *Byrd, Donald* / Always there: *Laws, Ronnie* / God made me funky: *Headhunters* / Get up I feel like being a sex machine: *Brown, James* / Harlem shuffle: *Bob & Earl* / Didn't I (blow your mind this time): *Delfonics*

RADCD 92 / 4 May '98 / Global TV

☐ BLECH VOL.2

WARPCD 44 / Sep '96 / Warp

☐ BLESS MY BONES (Memphis Gospel Radio: The Fifties)

ROUCD 2063 / '88 / Rounder

☐ BLIND PIG - 20TH ANNIVERSARY COLLECTION (2CD Set)
Monkey see, monkey do: Montoya, Coco / Drive to survive: Thackeray, Jimmy & The Drivers / Think: Magic Slim & The Teardrops / That spot right there: Bell, Carey / Howlin' at the moon: Davies, Debbie / Tricky woman: Rogers, Jimmy / She's as cold as ice: Rogers, Roy / Terraplane blues: Hooker, John Lee / Don't move the mountain: Gospel Hummingbirds / I need a real man: Scott, E.C. / Had enough: Castro, Tommy / Right place, wrong time: Rush, Otis / Messin' with the kid: Guy, Buddy & Junior Wells / Wastin' time: Carrier, Chubby / Big girl blues: Connor, Joanna / Worried life blues: Perkins, Willie 'Pinetop' / Take me back: Cotton, James / Should I wait: Allison, Luther / Two time boogie: Studebaker John & The Hawks / My heart bleeds blue: Coleman, Deborah / Hey sweet baby: Cain, Chris / Harpin' on a riff: Musselwhite, Charley / Cold chills: Gray, Henry / La vierge: Rapone, Al / I won't be there: Preacher Boy / Blues come to Texas: Shines, Johnny / I got something on you baby: Wilson, Smokey / I been thinkin': Campbell, Eddie C. / That's my baby: Clearwater, Eddy / Bad thing: Brown, Sarah / If I could reach out (and help somebody): Clay, Otis / Old time shuffle: Boogie Woogie Red / Crazy 'bout my baby: Pryor, Snooky / I wonder: Sykes, Roosevelt / If I get lucky: Horton, Walter / Let's rock: Commander Cody
BPCD 2001 / May '97 / Blind Pig

☐ BLIND/FRAGMENT
ASH 14 / Jan '95 / Ash International

☐ BLISS
Mekong: Jam Nation / Inion: Afrocelt Sound System / Orovela: Tsinandali Choir / Zaar: Gabriel, Peter / Chinese cannon / Abonecronedrone 3 / Kothbiro: Ogada, Ayub / Svetasvatar upanisad: Roy, Sarmila / Think: Srinivas, U. & Michael Brook / Soldiers of the long march: Guo Brothers & Shung Tian / Fault lines: Khan, Nusrat Fateh Ali / Angel tech: Grid
CDRW 69 / 1 Jun '98 / Realworld

☐ BLOODSTAINS ACROSS BELGIUM VOL.1
BSB 1103 / 22 May '98 / Bloodstains

☐ BLOODSTAINS ACROSS BELGIUM VOL.1 & 2
BBB 1/2 / 19 Jan '98 / Bloodstains

☐ BLOODSTAINS ACROSS DENMARK
BSDK 1109 / 19 Jan '98 / Bloodstains

☐ BLOODSTAINS ACROSS EUROPE
BSEU 1 / 19 Jan '98 / Bloodstains

☐ BLOODSTAINS ACROSS FINLAND
BSF 1105 / 19 Feb '98 / Bloodstains

☐ BLOODSTAINS ACROSS NORWAY
BSN 1104 / 19 Jan '98 / Bloodstains

☐ BLOODSTAINS ACROSS SWEDEN
BSSW 1 / 19 Jan '98 / Bloodstains

☐ BLOODSTAINS ACROSS SWITZERLAND
BSCH 107 / 19 Jan '98 / Bloodstains

☐ BLOODSTAINS ACROSS THE UK VOL.1
BSUK 1101 / 19 Jan '98 / Bloodstains

☐ BLOODSTAINS ACROSS THE UK VOL.2
BSUKUK 2 / 19 Jan '98 / Bloodstains

☐ BLOODSTAINS ON THE WALL
Bloodstains on the wall: Honey Boy / You better move on away from here: Honey Boy / Have you a match: Honey Boy / Uncle Sam blues: Pine Blues Pete / Woman acts funny: Pine Blues Pete / Going back to Mama: Pine Blues Pete / Got a letter this morning: Pine Blues Pete / Want to boogie woogie: Pine Blues Pete / Ride my new car with me: Williams, 'Big' Joe / Rather be sloppy drunk: Williams, 'Big' Joe / Dial 110 blues: Bledsoe, Country Jim / Hollywood boogie: Bledsoe, Country Jim / One thing my baby likes: Bledsoe, Country Jim / Stormin' and rainin': Bledsoe, Country Jim / I ate the wrong part: Little Temple / What a mistake: Little Temple / Mean and evil: Little Temple / Cold love: Little Temple / Black snake blues: McKinley, Pete / Cryin' for my baby: McKinley, Pete / Look-a-here boy: McKinley, Pete / Whistlin' blues: McKinley, Pete / Don't want me blues: McKinley, Pete / David's boogie: McKinley, Pete / Sail on little girl, sail on: McKinley, Pete
CDCHD 576 / Jul '94 / Ace

☐ BLOW MR. HORNSMAN
Jumpin' Jack / Super Special / Death rides / Run for your life / On the moon / Undertaker's burial / Roll On / Franco Nero / Leaving Rome / Ghost capturer / Nightmare / Judgement warrant / East of the River Nile / Harvest in the East / Va Va Voom / Broken Contract / Butter sefish / If you're ready
CDTRL 257 / Mar '94 / Trojan

☐ BLOW MY BLUES AWAY VOL.1
ARHCD 401 / Apr '95 / Arhoolie

☐ BLOW MY BLUES AWAY VOL.2
ARHCD 402 / Apr '95 / Arhoolie

☐ BLOW THE MAN DOWN: SEA SONGS & SHANTIES
Wild goose: Killen, Louis / Lovely Nancy: Campbell, Ian / Black ball line: MacColl, Ewan / Nightingale: Tawney, Cyril / Blow the man down: Corbett, Harry H. / Heave away, my Johnny: Killen, Louis / Lofty tall ship: Larner, Sam / Row bullies row: Campbell, Ian / Flying cloud: Killen, Louis / Fireship: Tawney, Cyril / Tom's gone to Hilo: Tawney, Cyril / Greenland whale fishery: Watersons / Ship in distress: Killen, Louis / Lowlands low: Campbell, Ian / Cod banging: Hart, Bob / Hilo Johnny Brown: Killen, Louis / Bonny ship the Diamond: Lloyd, A.L. / Bold Princess Royal: Killen, Louis / Billy boy: Davenport, Bob / Windy old weather: Roberts, A.V. 'Bob' / Bold Benjamin: Tawney, Cyril / Hog eye man: Campbell, Ian / Goodbye fare thee well: Killen, Louis
TSCD 464 / May '93 / Topic

☐ BLOW THE WHOLE JOINT UP
I think I'm paranoid: Garbage / Bug powder dust: Bomb The Bass / Jail bird: Primal Scream / Bass lines: Semi Detached / No way: Freakpower / Gettin' it on: Freaky Jalepeno / Policeman skank: Audioweb / Rude boy rock: Lion Rock / Long as I can see the light: Monkey Mafia / Twisted ska: Pick & Mixed / Jimmy's jam: Soundlab / Bently's gonna sort it out: Bentley Rhythm Ace / Angry young man: Soundlab / Brown paper bag: Size, Roni / Digital: Goldie & KRS1 / Disappear: Exponential / Dive: Propellerheads / Oh la la: Wise Guys / Ruffneck: Freestylers / Rocco: Death In Vegas / Miracle: Olive
5652882 / 10 Aug '98 / Debutante

☐ BLOW UP PRESENTS EXCLUSIVE BLEND VOL.1
BLOWUP 006CD / 30 Sep '97 / Blow Up

☐ BLOW UP PRESENTS EXCLUSIVE BLEND VOL.2
Wild elephants / Close shave / Soul skimmer / Underlay no.3 / Powerboat / Boss man / Lucky seven / Heavy bopper / Funky fanfare / Trip wire / Second cut / Born / Teenage chase / Fast back / This way up / Raggers / Cult and colour / New project
BLOWUP 011CD / 30 Sep '97 / Blow Up

☐ BLOWIN' UP A STORM (Jazz Sax Classics)
One for the guv'nor: Webster, Ben / Charity rag: Shank, Bud / Sunny moon for two: Rollins, Sonny / Like someone in love: Rollins, Sonny / Stan's blues: Getz, Stan / Ben's blues: Webster, Ben / Sweet Lorraine: Webster, Ben / Here's that rainy day: Getz, Stan / Tonight I sleep with a smile on my face: Getz, Stan / Harlem nocturne: Bostic, Earl / Ain't misbehavin': Bostic, Earl / Blowin' up a storm: Herman, Woody / Caldonia: Herman, Woody / Goodnight sweetheart: Bostic, Earl / Woodchopper's ball: Herman, Woody / Dizzy atmosphere: Parker, Charlie
SUMCD 4113 / May '97 / Summit

☐ BLOWING MY HORN
Fiesta in brass: Eldridge, Roy / Mid-forte: Baker, Chet / Moon song: Armstrong, Louis / I'll take romance: Dorham, Kenny / It's a wonderful world: Butterfield, Billy / Where's art: Eldridge, Roy / La divorce de Leo Fall: Morgan, Lee / Si si: Rodney, Red / Sermonette: Adderley, Nat / What's new: Brown, Clifford / Hymn to her: Ferguson, Maynard / Squeaky's blues: Terry, Clark / I'm true to you: Stewart, Rex / Diner' au motel: Davis, Miles / Dizzy's business: Gillespie, Dizzy / Someone to love: Newman, Joe / Weather bird: James, Harry / Gee, baby, ain't I food to you: Edison, Harry
5526412 / Mar '97 / Spectrum

☐ BLOWOUT (16 Of The Best Indie Sounds)
Planet telex: Radiohead / Wild horses: Sundays / Persuasion: Finn, Tim / Mr. Tambourine man: Crowded House / Raggle taggle: Waterboys / Ship of fools: World Party / Jump in the river: O'Connor, Sinead / I am the fly: Wire / Ever fallen in love: Buzzcocks / Sheena is a punk rocker: Ramones / No more heroes: Stranglers / King rocker: Generation X / Psycho killer: Red Hot Chili Peppers / Sheriff Fatman: Carter USM / Well did you ever: Harry, Deborah & Iggy Pop / Mr. Briggs: Blur / Caught by the fuzz: Supergrass
4935852 / 9 Mar '98 / EMI Gold

☐ BLUE
CDSTUMM 49 / Oct '93 / Mute

☐ BLUE
CDBV 001 / Jun '96 / Blue Village

☐ BLUE 45'S (The Ultimate Jukebox)
Dat dere: Jazz Messengers / Camp meetin': Wilkerson, Don / Funky mama: Donaldson, Lou / Wavy gravy: Burrell, Kenny / Blind man blind man: Hancock, Herbie / I know: Roach, Freddie / Brother Isaac: Byrd, Donald / Fat Judy: Patton, 'Big' John / Jody grind: Silver, Horace / Rev Moses: Donaldson, Lou / Psychedelic Sally: Silver, Horace / Fungii mama: Mitchell, Blue / Bucket: Smith, Jimmy / Move your hand: Smith, Lonnie / Spanish harlem: Humphrey, Bobbi / Turnaround: Mobley, Hank / Rumproller: Morgan, Lee / Trouble: Turrentine, Stanley / Blue bossa: Henderson, Joe 'Mr. Piano' / Aligator boogaloo: Donaldson, Lou
4940300 / 22 Jun '98 / Blue Note

☐ BLUE BLUER BLUEST
Bluesman for life: Gaines, Roy / You're a dog: McGhee, Cookie / Get out of my house: Strother, Percy / They call me sweet Betty: Sweet Betty / Sweetest thing I know: Marshall, Johnnie / I don't like it: McAllister, Randy / Hit the ground running: Payne, Jackie / Walkin': Wilson, U.P. / Love hound: Martin, Mick Bluesrockers / I don't want no woman tying me down: Rawls, Johnny / Strange bed: Gilmore, Bobby / Insomnia: Grand, Otis / Blues is on fire: Shields, Lonnie / No time to waste: Ray, Kenny 'Blue' / You ain't all that: Beard, Chris / Looking for my baby: Williams, Alanda / Bad company: Farr, Deitra
JSPCD 55 / Jul '98 / JSP

☐ BLUE BOP (Great Goatees & Blazing Berets)
Bird feathers: Evans, Gil / Professor Bop: Gonzales, Babs / Now's the time: Clarke, Kenny / I got rhythm: Mulligan, Gerry / Groovin' high: Parker, Charlie / Criss cross: Jackson, Milt / Ornithology: Powell, Bud / Squirrel: Navarro, Fats & Tadd Dameron / Cherokee: Brown, Charlie Sextet / Fuller bop man: Moody, James & His Bop Men / Bop alley: Blakey, Art & The Jazz Messengers / Boperation: McGhee, Howard / Tune up: McLean, Jackie / Yardbird suite: Pepper, Art / Coast to coast: Gillespie, Dizzy / Mo is on: Hope, Elmo / Epistrophy: Monk, Thelonious / Tempus Fugit: Davis, Miles / I'm in the mood for love: Stitt, Sonny
CDP 8577422 / 1 Sep '97 / Blue Note

☐ BLUE BRAZIL VOL.1 (Blue Note In A Latin Groove)
Upa neguinho: Paez, Luiz Arrunda / Catavento: Costa, Alaide / Berimbau: Som, Mandrake / Vim de santana: Quarteto Novo / Deus Brasiliero: Ribiero, Perry & Bossa 3 / Primitivo: Banana, Milton Trio / Noa noa: Banana, Milton Trio / Viola fora de moda: Lobo, Edu / Nao me diga adeus: Bossa 3 / Batucada Sergiu: Valle, Marcus / Aldeia de ogum: Joyce / Tudo que voce podia ser: Lo Borges / Homenagem a mongo: Som Tres / Deixa isso pra la: Soares, Elza / Misturada: Quarteto Novo / Bebe: Deodato, Eumir / Um tema p'ro Simon: Alf, Johnny / Cala boca menino: Donato, Joao / Me deixa: Donato, Joao / Night and day: Brasil, Victor Assis
CDP 8291962 / Jun '94 / Blue Note

☐ BLUE BRAZIL VOL.2
Transamazonica: Adolfo, Antonio / Samba do Carioca: Cezar, Silvio & Meirelles / Nana: Simonal, Wilson / Freio aerodinamico: Os Tres Morais / Reflexos: Qunteto Villa Lobos / Deixa a negra gincar: Soares, Elza / Tudo que voce podia ser: Quarteto Em Cy / A vida em seus metoddos diz calma: Di Melo / Moleque: Gonzaga, Luiz Jr. / Procissao: Banana, Milton Trio / Mas que nada: Soares, Elza / Jungle: Som Tres / Vento bravo: Lobo, Edu / Also sprach Zarathustra: Meirelles / Estamos Al: Andrade, Leny / Ponteio: Quarteto Novo / Libero nos: Lobo, Edu
CDP 8577412 / 1 Oct '97 / Blue Note

☐ BLUE BREAK BEATS VOL.1 (You Gotta Hear Blue Note To Dig Def Jam)
Grooving with Mr G: Holmes, Richard 'Groove' / Sookie sookie: Green, Grant / Who's making love: Donaldson, Lou / Weasil: Byrd, Donald / Kudu: Henderson, Eddie / Harlem River Drive: Humphrey, Bobbi / Blue juice: McGriff, Jimmy / Final comedown: Green, Grant / Turtle walk: Donaldson, Lou / Your love is too much: Three Sounds / Black Jack: Byrd, Donald / Olilloqui Valley: Hancock, Herbie
BNZ 288 / Apr '92 / Blue Note

☐ BLUE BREAK BEATS VOL.2
Street lady: Byrd, Donald / Jasper country man: Humphrey, Bobbi / Kumquat kids: Henderson, Eddie / Higga boom: Harris, Gene / Orange peel: Wilson, Reuben / Worm: McGriff, Jimmy / Caterpillar: Donaldson, Lou / Ain't it funky now: Green, Grant / Ummh: Hutcherson, Bobby / Good humour man: Mitchell, Blue / Beale Street: Byrd, Donald / Viva Tirado: Wilson, Gerald / Pot belly: Donaldson, Lou / Spinning wheel: Smith, Lonnie Liston / Phantom: Pearson, Duke
BNZ 311 / Jul '93 / Blue Note

☐ BLUE BREAK BEATS VOL.3
Walk tall: Adderley, Cannonball / You've made me so very happy: Rawls, Lou / Ode to Billy Joe: Donaldson, Lou / Sho' nuff nelon: Wilson, Reuben / Howling for Judy: Steig, Jeremy / Light my fire: Bassey, Shirley / It's your thing: Donaldson, Lou / Put on train: Three Sounds / Don't call me nigger whitey: Harris, Gene / Dominoes: Byrd, Donald / Mystic brew: Foster, Ronnie / Get out of my life woman: Williams, Joe & Thad Jones/Mel Lewis Orchestra / Ground hog: Pearson, Duke / Soul, soul, soul: McLean, Jackie / Flat backing: Mitchell, Blue / Down here on the ground: Green, Grant / Blacks and blues: Humphrey, Bobbi / Going down south: Hutcherson, Bobby
CDP 8543602 / Oct '96 / Blue Note

☐ BLUE BREAK BEATS VOL.4
Prelude: Harris, Gene / Holy Thursday: Axlerod, David / Sitting duck: Harris, Gene & Three Sounds / Beat goes on: Rich, Buddy / Three is the magic number: Durrough, Bob / Shack up: Banbarra / Boomp boomp chomp: Sons / Capricorn: Adderley, Cannonball / Little green apples: Higgins, Monk / Bring down the birds: Hancock, Herbie / Whole lotta love: Turner, Ike & Tina / Repeat after me: Three Sounds / We're in love: Wilson, Rueben / Inside you: Henderson, Eddie / Woman of the ghetto: Shaw, Marlena / Here we go: Ripperton, Minnie / People sure act funny: Smith, Lonnie / This is soul: Nero, Paul Trio / Everyman's your brother: Fourth Way
4940270 / 22 Jun '98 / Blue Note

☐ BLUE BULL (A Trip To Happy Techno)
SPV 08938572 / Mar '96 / SPV

☐ BLUE CAT BLUES
Just messin' around: Wilson, Smokey / Animator's convention: Radcliff, Bobby / Chicken fried snake: Levy, Ron & Wild Kingdom/Ronnie Earl/Jimmie Vaughan / 102nd street blues: Davis, Larry / Blue cat blues: Crawl / Jr boy's jam: Jones, Andrew 'Jr. Boy' / On the prowl: Washington, Walter 'Wolfman' / Mardi gras alley: Nocturne, Johnny Band / Jack potato boogie: Buford, Mojo / Down at JJ's: Funderburgh, Anson & The Rockets
EDCD 7057 / Nov '97 / Easydisc

☐ BLUE EYED BLUES
303612 / Apr '98 / Hallmark

☐ BLUE EYES CRYING IN THE RAIN
Blue eyes cryin' in the rain: Drusky, Roy / Shine on Ruby mountain: Rogers, Kenny / I didn't sleep a wink: Nelson, Willie / Daddy: Fargo, Donna / Your song: Lee, Johnny / Stop, look and listen: Cline, Patsy / Making believe: Wells, Kitty / Slippin' away: Fairchild, Barbara / Abilene: Jennings, Waylon / Ruby, don't take your love to town: Rogers, Kenny / I feel sorry for him: Nelson, Willie / Where do we go from here: Williams, Don / Turn the cards slowly: Cline, Patsy / Moonlight gondolier: Laine, Frankie / From a Jack to a King: Miller, Ned / Elvira: Rogers, Kenny / Have I stayed away too long: Ritter, Tex / Ghost: Nelson, Willie / 9,999,999 tears: Baily, Razzy / Sticks and stones: Fargo, Donna / Shake 'em up roll 'em: Jackson, Stonewall / Heartaches by the number: Mitchell, Guy / Homemade lies: Rogers, Kenny / Hello walls: Drusky, Roy / I let my mind wander: Nelson, Willie
GRF 121 / Feb '93 / Tring

☐ BLUE GIRLS VOL.1 (1924-1930)
DOCD 5503 / Nov '96 / Document

☐ BLUE GIRLS VOL.2 (1925-1930)
DOCD 5504 / Nov '96 / Document

☐ BLUE HAWAII (A Vintage Anthology)
Little heaven of the seven seas: Coral Islanders / Moon of Manakoora: Coral Islanders / Blue Hawaii: Crosby, Bing & Lani McIntire & Hawaiians / Palace in paradise: Crosby, Bing & Lani McIntire & Hawaiians / Sweet Leilani: Crosby, Bing & Lani McIntire & Hawaiians / Love dreams of Lula Lu: Ferera, Frank / For you: Fillis, Len / Goodbye Hawaii: Hall, Henry & The BBC Dance Orchestra / Pua Kealoha: Hoopii, Sol & Novelty Trio/Quartet / Weave a lei: Hoopii, Sol & Novelty Trio/Quartet / Hawaiian paradise: Iona, Andy & Islanders / Night is young: Iona, Andy & Islanders/Cliff Edwards / St. Louis blues: Jim & Bob / Tomi, Tomi: Kanui & Lula / Makalapua O Kamakeaha: Klein, Manny & Hawaiians / Hawaiian gems: Mendelssohn, Felix & His Hawaiian Serenaders / I got rhythm: Mendelssohn, Felix & His Hawaiian Serenaders / Sing me a song of the Islands: Mendelssohn, Felix & His Hawaiian Serenaders / Song of the rose: Mendelssohn, Felix & His Hawaiian Serenaders / Where the waters are blue: Mendelssohn, Felix & His Hawaiian Serenaders / Palms of paradise: Johnny Kaonohi Pineapple & Native Islanders / On the beach at Waikiki: Sharpe, A.P. & Honolulu Hawaiians / O muki, muki O: Shaw, Al & Hawaiian Beachcombers / Lullaby of the leaves: Smeck, Roy & Vita Trio / Paradise beside the sea: Tauber, Richard
CDAJA 5121 / Feb '94 / Living Era

☐ BLUE HIGHWAY
BT 003CD / Aug '94 / Black Top

☐ BLUE HORIZON STORY VOL.1 1965-1970 (3CD Set)
4889922 / 17 Nov '97 / Columbia

☐ BLUE JUICE
Streets of Calcutta: Shankar, Anandar / Soul mission: Bennett, Brian / EVA: Perry, Jean Jacques / For what it's worth: Rawls, Lou / Willie and Laura Mae Jones: Wilson, Nancy / Mississippi delta: Gentry, Bobbie / Sookie sookie: Britt, Tina / Tighten up: Gordon, Benny / Grits and gravy: Fame Gang / Uptight: Preston, Billy / Look into the flower: Caravan, Jimmy / Give it up or turn it loose: Hyman, Dick / Dancing drums: Shankar, Anandar / Killiano: Lyttle, Johnny / No problema: Richardson, Jerome / Samba for Maria: Connors, Norman & Freddie Hubbard / Mas que nada: Soares, Elza / Cala boca menino: Donato, Joao / Never come closer: Doris / Ode to Billie Joe: Wilson, Nancy / Hey girl: Harris, Gene & Three Sounds / MSP: Hamilton, Chico
CDP 8543472 / Oct '96 / Blue Note

☐ BLUE LADIES 1934-1941
DOCD 5327 / Mar '95 / Document

☐ BLUE MOODS
Chi chi: Parker, Charlie / You'r mine, you: Webster, Ben / Pick yourself up: Carter, Benny / Limehouse blues: Adderley, Cannonball & John Coltrane / Chalmeau: Carney, Harry / World is waiting for the sunrise: Hawkins, Coleman / I never has seen snow: Woods, Phil / That old feeling: Mulligan, Gerry & Stan Getz / Over the rainbow: Byas, Don / Just friends: Konitz, Lee / Baby won't you please come home: Bechet, Sidney / Cheek to cheek: Phillips, Flip / Bemoanable lady: Dolphy, Eric / I want to be happy: Young, Lester / I didn't know about you: Hodges, Johnny / I know that you know: Rollins, Sonny & Sonny Stitt / Flying home: Jacquet, Illinois
5526422 / Mar '97 / Spectrum

☐ BLUE MOON (20 Doo Wop Delights)
Blue moon: Marcels / Come go with me: Del Vikings / What's your name: Don & Juan / Thousand stars: Young, Karen & The Innocents / Little darlin': Diamonds / Earth angel: Penguins / Little star: Elegants / Denise: Randy & The Rainbows / Heartaches: Marcels / Glory of love: Roomates / Hushabye: Mystics / Diamond and pearls: Paradons / Mr. Bass man: Cymbal, Johnny / Barbara Anne: Regents / Alley oop: Hollywood Argyles / Papa oom mow mow: Rivingtons / Those oldies but goodies: Little Caesar & The Romans / Please love me forever: Jean, Cathy & The Roomates / Heart and soul: Cleftones / Duke of Earl: Chandler, Gene
308612 / 20 Apr '98 / Hallmark

☐ BLUE MOVIES (Scoring For The Studio)
I wish I knew how: Taylor, Billy / James Bond Theme: Holmes, Leroy / Kojak: Bobo, Willie / Bullit: Felder, Wilton / From Russia with love: Basie, Count / Shadow of your smile: Donaldson, Lou / Down here on the ground: Green, Grant & Dianne Reeves / Blow up: Hutcherson, Bobby / Star Trek: Three Sounds / Mission Impossible: May, Billy / Alfie's theme: Patton, 'Big' John / Midnight cowboy: Morgan, Lee / Last tango in Paris: Shaw, Marlena / Moon river: Wilson, Nancy / Love story: Holmes, Richard 'Groove' / MASH: Hutcherson, Bobby / Windmills of your mind: Shank, Bud
CDP 8577482 / 1 Sep '97 / Blue Note

☐ BLUE 'N' GROOVY VOL.1 (Blue Note Connects With The Good Vibes)
Chili peppers: Pearson, Duke / On children: Wilson, Jack / Hi-heel sneakers: Mitchell, Blue / Senor blues: Silver, Horace / Meat wave: Turrentine, Stanley / Dem tambourines: Wilkerson, Don / Sidewinder: Morgan, Lee / Cantaloupe island: Hancock, Herbie / Ping pong: Blakey, Art / True blue: Brooks, Tina / Jeannine: Byrd, Donald / My favourite things: Green, Grant / 8/4 Beat: Hutcherson, Bobby / Tom Thumb: Shorter, Wayne
BNZ 300 / Oct '92 / Blue Note

☐ BLUE 'N' GROOVY VOL.2 (Mostly Modal)
Flip: Mobley, Hank / And satisfy: Turrentine, Stanley / Dixie Lee: Byrd, Donald / Greasy: McLean, Jackie / Little busy: Blakey, Art & The Jazz Messengers / Mambo de la pinta: Pepper, Art / Mamacita: Mitchell, Blue / Senorita Eula: Wilkerson, Don / Afreaka: Morgan, Lee / Una muy Bonita: Hutcherson, Bobby / Wahoo: Pearson, Duke / Message from the Nile: Tyner, McCoy / Congaleegre: Parlan, Horace
CDP 8577452 / 1 Sep '97 / Blue Note

☐ BLUE NOTE BOX, THE (4CD Set)
Blue train: Coltrane, John / Maiden voyage: Hancock, Herbie / Cristo redentor: Byrd, Donald / Moanin': Blakey, Art & The Jazz Messengers / Blues walk: Donaldson, Lou / Song for my Father: Silver, Horace / Back at the Chicken Shack: Smith, Jimmy / Chitlins con carne: Burrell, Kenny / Sidewinder: Morgan, Lee / Senor blues: Silver, Horace /

Decision: Rollins, Sonny / Three o'clock in the morning: Gordon, Dexter / Blues march: Blakey, Art / Wadin': Parlan, Horace / Rumproller: Morgan, Lee / Somethin' else: Adderley, Cannonball / Blue bossa: Henderson, Joe / Watermelon man: Hancock, Herbie / Hold on I'm comin': Wilson, Reuben / It's your thing: Green, Grant / Scorpion: Donaldson, Lou / Village lee: Patton, 'Big' John / Spooky: Turrentine, Stanley / Dancin' in an easy groove: Smith, Lonnie Liston / You want me to stop loving you: Turrentine, Stanley / Do like Eddie: Scofield, John / Blue monk: Tyner, McCoy & Bobby Hutcherson / Immediate left: Hagans, Tim / I waited for you: Jackson, Javon / Take the D flat train: Hays, Kevin / One of another kind: Green, Benny / Reflections: Fortune, Sonny / Donna Lee: Rubalcaba, Gonzala / Rounders mood: Lovano, Joe / I love Paris: Terrasson, Jacky

CDP 8360542 / Nov '95 / Blue Note

☐ BLUE NOTE CLUB CULTURE

Emotionalise: Interference / Dark lady: DJ Food / Able semen: Parlour Talk / Time bomb: Funky Finger / Reel DJ's: Reel DJ's / Dirty beatniks: Roger & Andre / Moonwalk: Blaze / Drumz: Doc Scott / Tillana: FSOI / Comparsa enowoy: MFOS / Putting heads to bed: Hightower Set / Shanti-ites: Jericho Walls / Club cleaners: Paint

EYECD 1 / Dec '96 / Blue Note/Acid Jazz

☐ BLUE NOTE RARE GROOVES

Bus ride: Wilson, Reuben / Hunk o'funk: McDuff, Jack / Hot rod: Wilson, Reuben / Bird wave: McGriff, Jimmy / Boogaloo: Turrentine, Stanley / Heaven on Earth: Young, Larry / Black rhythm happening: Gale, Eddie / String bean: Patton, 'Big' John / Groovin' for Mr. G: Holmes, Richard / Round town: Jones, Elvin / Soul special: Hill, Andrew / Blackjack: Byrd, Donald / Serenade to a savage: Candido

CDP 8356362 / Mar '96 / Blue Note

☐ BLUE PACIFIC FUNK (Walkin' On The West Coast)

East Dallas special: Ervin, Booker / Gone into it: Amy, Curtis & Frank Butler / Done it again: Lytle, Johnny / This here: Pass, Joe / Sack o' woe: Pass, Joe / Sad march: Jones, Carmell & Harold Land / Spanish castles: McCann, Les & Jazz Crusaders / Where's it at: Kynard, Charles & Clifford Scott / Paco: Wilson, Gerald / Uptight (everything's alright): Jazz Crusaders / Pygmy: Larkin, Billy & The Delegates / Coming to Atlantis: Robinson, Freddie / All blue: McCann, Les & Jazz Crusaders / Turkish black: Jazz Crusaders / Soul sisters: McBrowne, Lenny & Four Sisters / Montgomeryland funk: Montgomery, Wes & Harold Land / Burnin': Bryant, Paul & Jim Hall / LA after dark: Ervin, Booker

4940320 / 22 Jun '98 / Blue Note

☐ BLUE RIBBON BANJO

Adams county breakdown: Adams, Tom / Sleepy eyed John/Tom and Jerry: Smith, Craig / Clinging vine: Keith, Bill / Clarinet polka: Evans, B / Moving out: Schatz, Mark / Shelton special: Shelton, Allen / Maple leaf rag: Whisnant, Johnnie / Fortune: Cockerham, Fred / Boat's up the river: Reed, Ola Belle / Pea patch jig: Hartford, John / Jenny's wedding/Rakish Paddy: Furtado, Tony / Robot plane flies over Arkansas: Trischka, Tony / Perplexed: Fleck, Bela / Wired: Vestal, Scott / Runaround: Crowe, J.D. & The New South

EDCD 7001 / Aug '96 / Easydisc

☐ BLUE RIBBON BLUEGRASS

AN 11CD / Jan '94 / Rounder

☐ BLUE RIBBON FIDDLE

EDCD 7004 / Aug '96 / Easydisc

☐ BLUE RIBBON GUITAR

Blackberry blossom: O'Connor, Mark / Tarnation: Grier, David / Salt Creek: Blake, Norman & Tony Rice/Doc Watson / Shake your hips: McCoury Brothers / Cooley's reel: Barenberg, Russ / Bury me beneath the willow: Nygaard, Scott / Huckleberry hornpipe: Crary, Dan / Back up and push: Rice, Wyatt / Fisher's hornpipe/Devil's dream: Watson, Doc & Merle / Big mon: Rice, Tony / Fiddler's dram/ Whiskey before breakfast: Blake, Norman / Old, old house: Country Cooking

EDCD 7006 / Nov '96 / Easydisc

☐ BLUE RIDGE OLD-TIME SAMPLER

CUY 2701CD / Apr '96 / County

☐ BLUE SAX (20 Instrumental Sax Mood Classics)

Baker Street / Just the way you are / Body and soul / I dream / Wonderful world / Unforgettable / True / Think twice / All that I need / Ev'ry time we say goodbye / Misty blue / Killing me softly / I just called to say I love you / Lily was here / Kiss from a rose / Songbird / Holding back the years / Careless whisper / How deep is your love / Don't let the sun go down on me

308882 / 11 May '98 / Hallmark

☐ BLUE YORK, BLUE YORK

New York times: Humphrey, Bobbi / On Broadway: Wilson, Reuben / Hackensack: Smith, Jimmy / Stomping at the Savoy: Hall, Jim / Lullaby of Birdland: Shearing, George / Skating in Central Park: Modern Jazz Quartet / Blue Harlem: Quebec, Ike / Take the 'A' train: Kings Sisters / 52nd Street theme: Powell, Bud / Broadway: Staton, Dakota / City lights: Morgan, Lee / 116th and Lenox: McLean, Jackie / Jersey girl: Cole, Holly / Sugar hill: Three Sounds / Harlem River Drive: Humphrey, Bobbi

CDP 8543632 / Oct '96 / Blue Note

☐ BLUE-EYED RHYTHM AND BLUES

CDRB 25 / Aug '95 / Charly

☐ BLUEBEAT, SKA & REGGAE REVOLUTION VOL.1

SEECD 319 / May '91 / See For Miles

☐ BLUEBEAT, SKA & REGGAE REVOLUTION VOL.2

SEECD 353 / Sep '92 / See For Miles

☐ BLUEFUNKERS VOL.1 (Pitchers, Leftfielders & Flipsiders)

ZEN 002CD / Jan '95 / Indochina

☐ BLUEGRASS ALBUM VOL.4

Age / Cheyenne / Cora is gone / Old home town / Talk it all over with him / Head over heels / Nobody loves me / When you are lonely / I might take you back again / Lonesome wind blues

ROUCD 0210 / Feb '95 / Rounder

☐ BLUEGRASS ALBUM VOL.5 (Sweet Sunny South)

Rock hearts / Big black train / Thinking about you / Out in the cold war / On the old Kentucky shore / Preaching, praying, singing / Someone took my place with you / Foggy mountain rock / My home's across the Blue Ridge Mountains / Along about daybreak / Sweet sunny South

ROUCD 0240 / '89 / Rounder

☐ BLUEGRASS BREAKDOWN

New broom: Berline, Lue & Byron / Old Logan: Berline, Lue & Byron / Crazy creek: Berline, Lue & Byron / Dusty Miller: Berline, Lue & Byron / How mountain girls can love: Stanley Brothers / Man of constant sorrow: Stanley Brothers / Big Tildy: Stanley Brothers / Orange blossom special: Stanley Brothers / Leather britches: Smith, Arthur / Blackberry blossom: Smith, Arthur / Levee breakin' blues: Greenbriar Boys / At the end of a long lonely day: Greenbriar Boys / Old Joe Clark: Dillards / Ground hog: Dillards / Banjo in the hollow: Dillards / Polly Vaughn: Dillards / Duelling banjos: Dillards / Alabama jubilee: McMichen, Clayton / Sourwood mountain: McMichen, Clayton / You better get right little darlin': New York City Ramblers / I'm coming back but I don't know when: New York City Ramblers / Cedar hill: New York City Ramblers / Tell it to me: New York City Ramblers / Mule skinner blues: Monroe, Bill & His Bluegrass Boys / Blue moon of Kentucky: Monroe, Bill & His Bluegrass Boys / Walls of time: Monroe, Bill & His Bluegrass Boys / Somebody touched me: Monroe, Bill & His Bluegrass Boys / Bluegrass breakdown: Monroe, Bill & His Bluegrass Boys

VCD 77006 / Oct '95 / Vanguard

☐ BLUEGRASS BREAKDOWN

Cluck old hen: Krauss, Alison & Union Station / John Henry: Furtado, Tony / Back up and push: Carter, Jason / Bluegrass breakdown: Adams, Tom / Katy Hill: Hicks, Bob / Goodbye Liza Jane: Evans, Bill / Sally Ann: Dreadful Snakes / Shuckin' the corn: McCoury Brothers / Orange blossom special: Johnson Mountain Boys / Foggy mountain chimes: Bluegrass Album Band / Whistlin' Rufus: Duncan, Stuart / Crazy creek: Keith, Bill / Fishers hornpipe: Rice, Wyatt / Carroll County blues: Nashville Bluegrass Band

EDCD 9014 / Jun '98 / Easydisc

☐ BLUEGRASS COMPACT DISC VOL.1

Blue ridge cabin home / Blue ridge cabin home / A hundred years from now / On my way back to the old home / Cora is gone / Old home town / Take me in the lifeboat / Sitting alone in the moonlight / Head over heels / Ocean of diamonds / I'll never shed another tear / Unfaithful one / Is it too late now / Chalk up another one / One tear / Cheyenne / Devil in disguise / Age / Talk it all over with him / Model church

ROUCD 11502 / '88 / Rounder

☐ BLUEGRASS COMPACT DISC VOL.2

ROUCD 11516 / '88 / Rounder

☐ BLUEGRASS COUNTRY

Pike county breakdown / Stoney point / Lady Madonna / Washington county / Chereokee shuffle / Katy Hill / Lonesome whistle / Clinch mountain backstep / Cry cry darlin' / Caravan / Angeline the baker / Darlin' corey / Wheel hoss / Stone fox chase / Fireball mail / Ground speed / Gold rush / Don't think twice / Big country / Salt creek / Rebecca / Highway of regret

EURCD 002 / 24 Aug '98 / Eureka

☐ BLUEGRASS FROM THE GOLD COUNTRY

ROUCD 0131 / Sep '96 / Rounder

☐ BLUEGRASS GREATS

Trainwreck of emotion: McCoury, Del / Lost and I'll never find the way: Skaggs, Ricky & Peter Rowan / In my time of dying: Stevens, Beth & April / I never knew: White, Jeff / There's a brighter mansion over there: Longview / Mama's hand: Morris, Lynn / Picture in a tear: Rice, Wyatt & Santa Cruz / Everybody's reaching out for someone: Cox Family / Hard hearted: Jim & Jesse/The Virginia Boys / Indecision: King, James / I'm working on the road to gloryland: Illrd Tyme Out / My better years: Johnson Mountain Boys

EDCD 7007 / Jun '97 / Easydisc

☐ BLUEGRASS REUNION

ACD 4 / May '97 / Acoustic Disc

☐ BLUEGRASS SPECTACULAR

CTS 55424 / Sep '94 / Country Stars

☐ BLUEGRASS SPIRIT (12 Songs Of Faith)

EDCD 7021 / Nov '96 / Easydisc

☐ BLUEGRASS TODAY - THE HITS

EDCD 9001 / Aug '96 / Easydisc

☐ BLUEPRINT (The Definitive Moving Shadow Album - 3CD Set)

Shadow: Goldie & Rob / Rhode tune: Flytronix / Out there: Higher Sense / Helicopter tune: Deep Blue / Images '84: Aquasky / Analysis: Dom & Roland / Let the hustler's play: Pulse & Tango / Funked up flavas: E-Z Rollers / Distorted dreams: Dom & Roland / Conscious: Technical Itch / Incident on main street: Hoax / Free la funk: JMJ & Richie / Dezires: E-Z Rollers / Retro: E-Z Rollers / Valves: Neotek / Pipe dreams: Hoax / Dreamer: Technical Itch / In too deep: JMJ & Flytronix / Searchin': Dead Calm / Storm: Dom & Roland / So this is love: Essence Of Aura / Flight: Wallace, Dave / Nylon roadster: Aquasky / Retransitions: Deep Blue & Blame / Turbulence: Current Affairs / Slow waves: Natural Mystic / Virus: Technical Itch

8289522 / 13 Oct '97 / FFRR

☐ BLUES - CHICAGO STYLE (4CD Set)

What have I done: Smith, Byther / Going back to Louisiana: Bell, Lurrie / DJ play my blues: Guy, Buddy / If you got to love somebody: Dawkins, Jimmy / Where the hell were you: Lefty Dizz / Run don't walk: Sumlin, Hubert / Mean red spider: Rogers, Jimmy / Tina Nu: Guy, Phil / Ain't no sunshine: Smith, Byther / Addressing the nation: Smith, Byther / Moon is rising: Taylor, Eddie & KC Red / As the years go passing by: Allen, Pete & Carey Bell/Lurrie Bell / I need you so bad: Bell, Lurrie / All I can do: Sumlin, Hubert / Hoochie coochie: Bell, Carey / Minnie Sue: Burks, JT / Partnership woman: Burks, JT / Now darlin': Wrencher, Big John / Good morning blues: Easy Baby / That's alright in the dark: Bell, Carey & Lefty Dizz / Little Walter's blues: Sayles, Charlie / Watchdog: Buford, Mojo / Reconsider baby: Bell, Carey & Lurrie / Lamp post: Sayles, Charlie / Automobile: Sayles, Charlie / Rambling woman: Harmonica Hinds & Big Moose Walker / Burying ground: Harmonica Hinds & Big Moose Walker / New harp in town: Bell, Steve / Two old maids: Horton, Walter / Good lovings: Evans, Lucky Lopez / Tail draggin': Evans, Lucky Lopez / Oh baby: Left Hand Frank / Strange woman: Bell, Carey / Mighty Mars: Mars, Johnny / Rocket 88: Mars, Johnny / Same things: Campbell, Eddie C. / Cha cha in blues: Campbell, Eddie C. / I'm going upstairs: Bell, Carey / Extra extra: Evans, Lucky Lopez / Jack potato boogie: Buford, Mojo / Jealous of my baby: Buford, Mojo / Desert Island: Mars, Johnny / Best place: Louisiana Red / Valerie: Louisiana Red / Mama talk to your daughter: Carter, Joe / You're the one: Carter, Joe / Rock me: Carter, Joe / If you don't want me: Littlejohn, Johnny / Keep on running: Littlejohn, Johnny / I feel like jumping: Lefty Dizz / Take a walk with me: Rogers, Jimmy / Wee little room: Frank JR / Mojo: Littlejohn, Johnny / Looking for a woman: Smith, Byther / You got to help me: Sumlin, Hubert / It could be you: Sumlin, Hubert / Whisky headed woman: Philips, Brewster / Poison Ivy: Philips, Brewster / Bottleneck blues: Smith, Big Red

PBXCD 403 / Jul '97 / Pulse

☐ BLUES - THE CHICAGO YEARS

MACCD 195 / Aug '96 / Autograph

☐ BLUES 4 YOU

BN 044 / Apr '98 / Blue Nite

☐ BLUES 60'S

I have a dream: Hancock, Herbie / Cease the bombing: Green, Grant / Acid, pot and pills: Silver, Horace / Psychedelic: Morgan, Lee / Black heroes: Hutcherson, Bobby / There is the bomb: Cherry, Don / Black rhythm happenning: Gale, Eddie / Watts happening: Jazz Crusaders / Blowing in the wind: Turrentine, Stanley / I wish I knew how it'd feel to be free: Taylor, Billy / Say it loud (I'm black and I'm proud): Donaldson, Lou

CDP 8354722 / Oct '95 / Blue Note

☐ BLUES 88'S (Boogie Woogie Instrumentals)

Buzzin': Alexander, Honey / Walk the walk: Maxwell, David / My bonnie rocks: Copley, Al / C.Q boogie: Webster, Katie / Keep it rollin': Crawford, David / Albi's boogie: Roomful Of Blues / Backstage boogie: Bogart, Deanna / Yancey's bugle call: Preacher Jack / Honky tonk train: McShann, Jay / Three keys: Booker, James

EDCD 7060 / May '98 / Easydisc

☐ BLUES AFTER HOURS

Baby doll blues: Earl, Ronnie / They killed crazy horse: Houston, Joe & Otis Grand / 4811 Wadsworth (Blues for George): Piazza, Rod & The Mighty Flyers / Get down with the blues: Tony Z / Sanctified: Connors, Gene 'Mighty Flea' / Down at PJ's place: Maxwell, David / Blues for Al and Peggy: Morgan, Mike & The Crawl / I'm not ashamed to play the blues: Jones, Tutu / Blues for Henry: Sumlin, Hubert / John Henry: Rishell, Paul & Annie Raines

EDCD 7027 / Jul '97 / Easydisc

☐ BLUES ALBUM, THE (2CD Set)

Mannish boy: Waters, Muddy / Boom boom: Hooker, John Lee / Crossroads: Cream / When love comes to town: U2 & B.B. King / Mustang Sally: Guy, Buddy / Born under a bad sign: King, Albert / Need your love so bad: Fleetwood Mac / Somewhere down the crazy river: Robertson, Robbie / Black magic woman: Santana / Piece of my heart: Franklin, Erma / Dixie chicken: Little Feat / On the road again: Canned Heat / Smokestack lightnin': Howlin' Wolf / I'd rather go blind: James, Etta / Try a little tenderness: Commitments / Right next door (because of me): Cray, Robert Band / Fade to black: Dire Straits / Nineties blues: Rea, Chris / Bell bottom blues: Derek & The Dominoes / Cocaine: Cale, J.J. / Still got the blues: Moore, Gary / Hunter: Free / Thrill is gone: King, B.B. / Hoochie coochie man: Waters, Muddy / Muddy waters blues (acoustic version): Rodgers, Paul / I'm a king bee: Harpo, Slim / I'm in the mood: Hooker, John Lee / Dust my broom: James, Elmore / Help me: Williamson, Sonny Boy / Love in vain: Johnson, Robert / I'm a man: Diddley, Bo / My head's in Mississippi: ZZ Top / Shake your moneymaker: Fleetwood Mac / Shame shame shame: Winter, Johnny / I'm leaving you (commit a crime): Vaughan, Stevie Ray / Walkin' to my baby: Fabulous Thunderbirds / All your love: Mayall, John & The Bluesbreakers / You shook me: Beck, Jeff / Greeny: Blues Breakers / Little red rooster: Howlin' Wolf

VTDCD 54 / Jun '95 / Virgin

☐ BLUES AND BOOGIE - EXPLOSION

BLR 84003 / May '91 / L&R

☐ BLUES AND SOUL BIBLE (3CD Set)

DTKBOX 93 / 6 Jul '98 / Dressed To Kill

☐ BLUES AND SOUL COLLECTION

MU 5054 / Oct '92 / Musketeer

☐ BLUES AND SOUL LEGENDS

MACCD 185 / Aug '96 / Autograph

☐ BLUES ANTHOLOGY (2CD Set)

Boom boom: Hooker, John Lee / Shame: Reed, Jimmy / Grandma told grandpa: Hopkins, Lightnin' / Kansas City: Memphis Slim / I'm a stranger here: McGhee, Brownie & Sonny Terry / In New Orleans: Leadbelly / Rock me baby: James, Etta / You're so fine: Little Walter & Otis Rush / Bad luck blues: Lightnin' Slim / Got to move: McDowell, 'Mississippi' Fred / Comeback: Memphis Slim / Things I used to do: Turner, Joe / My babe: Lightnin' Slim / Baby what you want me to do: Reed, Jimmy / Blues for the lowalnds: McGhee, Brownie & Sonny Terry / Shake yo bottle: James, Etta / Mojo hand: Hopkins, Lightnin' / Frankie and albert: Hurt, 'Mississippi' John / Walk on: McGhee, Brownie & Sonny Terry / Boogie chillun: Hooker, John Lee / Sassy Mae: Memphis Slim / Chains of love: Turner, Joe / Goodnight Irene: Leadbelly / Wabash blues: Bechet, Sidney

SD 886362 / 2 Feb '98 / Disky

☐ BLUES ANYTIME VOL.1 (An Anthology Of British Blues)

I'm your witch doctor / Snake drive / Ain't gonna cry no more / I tried / Tribute to Elmore / I feel so good / Telephone blues / You don't love me / West coast idea / Ain't seen no whisky / Flapjacks / Cold blooded woman

CDIMM 008 / Nov '93 / Immediate

☐ BLUES ARCHIVE

Alabama born: Leadbelly / Hellhound on my trail: Johnson, Robert / Walking blues: Hooker, John Lee / How blue can you get: Collins, Albert / Country girl: Guy, Buddy & Junior Wells / Coming I'm coming: Green, Peter / Step at a time: Fulson, Lowell / Help me operator: Witherspoon, Jimmy / River's invitation: Korner, Alexis / Morning star: Bennett, Duster / Work song: Jones, Paul / Boom boom boom boom: Price, Alan / Fine condition: Price, Alan / I wonder who: Blodwyn Pig / Going up going down: Webb, Stan & Chicken Shack / Wang dang doodle: Turner, Ruby

RMCD 204 / Nov '97 / Rialto

☐ BLUES AT XMAS VOL.3

ICH 1173CD / Oct '94 / Ichiban

☐ BLUES BAR-B-QUE

Meat off the bone: Ward, Robert / BBQ at JD's: Dyer, Johnny / Mama's cooking: Ball, Marcia / Pigmeat on the line: Bishop, Elvin / Hot sauce: Seals, Son / Greasy gravy: Clarke, William / Smoke n' fire: Wilson, Smokey / Smells like bar-b-q: Big Joe & The Dynaflows / Heartburn: Heartsman, Johnny / Too much barbecue: Big Twist & The Mellow Fellows

EDCD 7030 / Sep '97 / Easydisc

☐ BLUES BEFORE SUNRISE: LIVE VOL.1

I'm ready: Big Wheeler / Down in Virginia: Big Wheeler / She loves another man: Big Wheeler / Got a feeling (I got the blues): Big Wheeler / I gotta go: Big Wheeler / Be careful: Brim, John / Lonesome man blues: Brim, John / Tough times: Brim, John / Ice cream man: Brim, John / Streetwise advisor: Arnold, Billy Boy / Billy Boy medley: Arnold, Billy Boy / You're the one: Burns, Jimmy / Leaving here walking: Burns, Jimmy

DE 699 / Jun '97 / Delmark

☐ BLUES BEHIND THE WALL (East Berlin 1966)

Running the boogie: Sykes, Roosevelt / All your love: Sykes, Roosevelt / I keep drinking: Little Brother Montgomery / You shouldn't do it: Sleepy John Estes & Yank Rachell / Roll 'em Pete: Turner, 'Big' Joe / Sheckin' on my baby: Wells, Junior / Vietnam blues: Wells, Junior / Suitcase blues: Wallace, Sippie / Midnight boogie: Williams, Robert Pete / Flip flop and fly: Turner, 'Big' Joe / It takes time: Turner, 'Big' Joe / Night time is the right time: Sykes, Roosevelt / My own fault: Rush, Otis / Pinetop's boogie woogie: Smith, Clarence 'Pinetop' / Yelow jam blues: Estes, 'Sleepy' John & Yank Rachell / Over yonder walls: Wells, Junior / Women keep your mouth shut: Wallace, Sippie / Tribute to Sonny Boy Williamson: Wallace, Sippie / Louise: Williams, Robert Pete / Feeling happy: Turner, 'Big' Joe

CDMOJO 309 / Nov '96 / Mojo

☐ BLUES BLUES BLUES (3CD Set)

EMTBX 303 / Aug '97 / Emporio

☐ BLUES BLUES BLUES (2CD Set)

Rocks in my bed: Turner, Joe / Midnight hours blues: Carr, Leroy / You can't get that stuff no more: Tampa Red / Denver blues: Tampa Red / Gamblin' man blues: Champion Blues Dupree / Phonograph blues: Johnson, Robert / Broke down engine: McTell, 'Blind' Willie / Blue birds blues: Williamson, Sonny Boy / Baby you gotta change your mind: Fuller, Blind Boy / Good morning blues: Leadbelly / Preaching blues: Johnson, Robert / Gonna follow my baby: Crudup, Arthur 'Big Boy' / Mr Johnson's swing: Johnson, Lonnie / Picking my tomatoes: McGhee, Brownie / 15c a day: Roosevelt Skyes / I'm a rattlesnakin' daddy: Fuller, Blind Boy / Worrying you off my mind: Broonzy, 'Big' Bill / Good woman blues: Car, Leroy / You know I got a reason: Broonzy, 'Big' Bill / When you got a friend: Johnson, Robert / Easy rider: Leadbelly / Black train blues: White, Bukka / Dust my broom: Johnson, Robert / Mean mistreater mama: Carr, Leroy / Four hands are better than two: Johnson, Lonnie / Georgia rag: McTell, 'Blind' Willie / My brownskin sugar plum: Fuller, Blind Boy / Walkin' blues: Johnson, Robert / Sun risin' blues: Turner, 'Big' Joe / Warehouse man blues: Dupree, 'Champion' Jack / Got the bottle up and go: Williamson, Sonny Boy / Born for bad luck: McGhee, Brownie / Rebecca: Turner, 'Big' Joe / I'm calling Daisy: McGhee, Brownie / Sugar mama blues: Williamson, Sonny Boy / Stomp down rider: McTell, 'Blind' Willie / Mean old bed bug blues: Johnson, Lonnie / Strange place blues: White, Bukka / Mean old frisco blues: Crudup, Arthur 'Big Boy' / Rock island line: Leadbelly

PC 604 / 10 Nov '97 / Platinum Collection

☐ BLUES BOX

308642 / Feb '96 / Scratch

☐ BLUES, BOOGIE & BOP (The 1940's Mercury Sessions/7CD Set)

5256092 / Feb '96 / Mercury

☐ BLUES BROTHERS

Bad luck shadow: Otis, Johnny / Wee baby blues: Turner, Joe / Kidney stew: Vinson, Eddie 'Cleanhead' / Louie Louie: Berry, Richard / Beans and cornbread: Jordan, Louis / Pink champagne: Liggins, Joe / Country girl: Otis, Johnny / Doin' it: Berry, Richard / Squeeze me baby: Turner, Joe / Midnight creeper: Vinson, Eddie 'Cleanhead' / Oh baby I love you: Berry, Richard / Honey dipper (part one): Liggins, Joe / Honey dipper (part two):

Liggins, Joe / Evening shadows coming down: Milburn, Amos / Cherry red: Vinson, Eddie 'Cleanhead' / Nothin' from nothin' blues: Turner, Joe / One scotch, one bourbon, one beer: Milburn, Amos / Boom chick a boogie: Liggins, Joe / Let the good times roll: Jordan, Louis / Person to person: Vinson, Eddie 'Cleanhead' / Chick shack a boogie: Milburn, Amos / I'm a good thing: Jordan, Louis / Bye bye baby: Otis, Johnny
3035900082 / Apr '96 / Essential Gold

☐ **BLUES BUSTERS VOL.2**
MSA 008CD / Apr '94 / Munich

☐ **BLUES BUSTERS VOL.3 (Classic Blues Rock)**
MSACD 010 / Aug '96 / Munich

☐ **BLUES CHICAGO STYLE**
PLSCD 181 / Apr '97 / Pulse

☐ **BLUES CLASSICS (2CD Set)**
R2CD 4033 / 13 Apr '98 / Deja Vu

☐ **BLUES COCKTAIL PARTY**
BT 1066CD / '92 / Black Top

☐ **BLUES COLLECTION (3CD Set)**
TBXCD 508 / Jan '96 / TrueTrax

☐ **BLUES COLLECTION (3CD Set)**
Snake drive: Clapton, Eric / Dust my broom: Waters, Muddy / I'm in the mood: Hooker, John Lee / Step back baby: King Biscuit Boy / Telephone blues: Mayall, John & The Bluesbreakers / First time I met the blues: Guy, Buddy / Hold that train: Smith, Byther / LA breakdown: All Stars & Jimmy Page / Looking for my baby: Johnson, Jimmy / You upset me baby: Allison, Luther / I've got a mind to travel: Collins, Albert / Came up the hard way: Clearwater, Eddy / You don't love me: McPhee, Tony / Stormy monday blues: Korner, Alexis / Dimples: Hooker, John Lee / Howlin' wolf: Waters, Muddy / On top of the world: Mayall, John & Eric Clapton / Don't let my baby ride: Scott, Isaac / Good rockin' mama: Hooker, John Lee / Red hot mama: Fleetwood Mac / Red house: Hendrix, Jimi / How can one woman be so mean: Guy, Buddy & Junior Wells / Leave me alone: Benton, Buster / Hoochie coochie man: Waters, Muddy / Cold blooded woman: Savoy Brown / No shoes: Hooker, John Lee / Easy: Horton, Big Walter / Walking blues: Waters, Muddy / Somebody loan me a dime: Robinson, Fenton / I wish you would: Arnold, Billy Boy & Tony McPhee / Foxtrot: Hooker, Earl / Can't hold out: Sharpville, Todd / She's mine (keep your hands to yourself): Hooker, John Lee / Bad news: Moore, Gary / Steelin': Clapton, Eric & Jimmy Page / Crosstown link: Lee, Albert / All my money gone: De Lay, Paul Band / End of the blues: Hooker, Earl / Born with the blues: Bell, Carey & Buster Benton / Blue light: Mighty Houserockers / Blow wind blow: Waters, Muddy / Hobo blues: Hooker, John Lee / Don't stay out all night: Arnold, Billy Boy & Tony McPhee / I gotta new car/Framed: Key, Troyce & J.J. Malone / I'm leaving: Hooker, John Lee / I had it so hard: Sunnyland Slim
PBXCD 508 / Nov '96 / Pulse

☐ **BLUES COLLECTION VOL.1 (Dust My Broom)**
Dust my broom: James, Elmore / Everyday: King, B.B. / I got it bad and that ain't good: Holiday, Billie / Boogie woogie papa: Moore, Gatemouth / Cole's bob blues: Cole, Nat 'King' Trio / I wonder who's kissing her now: Charles, Ray / Dimples: Hooker, John Lee / Shake that thing: Hopkins, Lightnin' / Look on yonder wall: James, Elmore / Catfish blues: King, B.B. / Fine and mellow: Holiday, Billie / Say: Simon, Joe / Hobo blues: Waters, Muddy / Tupelo: Hooker, John Lee / Early in the morning: Milton, Roy / In New Orleans: Leadbelly
101572 / May '97 / A-Play Collection

☐ **BLUES COLLECTION VOL.2**
Step it up and go: Fuller, Blind Boy / Diddie wa diddie: Blake, Arthur 'Blind' / Spoonful blues: Patton, Charlie / Nobody's fault but mine: Johnson, 'Blind' Willie / New someday baby: Estes, 'Sleepy' John / Billie's blues: Holiday, Billie / Boogie woogie: Young, Lester / Down the road apiece: Sanchez, Michael / Cry to me: Beaker, Norman Band / Act like you love me: Detonators / Mai Lee: Hooker, John Lee / It's a man down there: Bennett, Buster / Sonny Boy Williamson: Bruce, Jack & Paul Jones / Married men: McPhee, Tony & The Groundhogs / My baby she don't look like that: Lamb, Paul & The King Snakes / Look out: Webb, Stan & Chicken Shack / Time to love: Abrahams, Mick / Have a little faith in me: Farlowe, Chris / Rockin' good way: Turner, Ruby / Some change: Price, Alan & Electric Blues Company
IGOCD 2061 / Feb '97 / Indigo

☐ **BLUES COLLECTION VOL.2 (Boom Boom)**
Boom boom: Hooker, John Lee / Walkin' and talkin': Charles, Ray / Don't explain: Holiday, Billie / Forty days and forty nights: Waters, Muddy / Bring me my shotgun: Hopkins, Lightnin' / How blue can you get: King, B.B. / Did you ever love a woman: Moore, Gatemouth / How long: Leadbelly / Where can you be: Reed, Jimmy / Wee baby blues: Turner, Joe / It hurts me too: James, Elmore / I love you porgy: Holiday, Billie / Dusty road: Hooker, John Lee / Information blues: Milton, Roy / Please love me: King, B.B. / Ain't superstitious: Howlin' Wolf
101582 / May '97 / A-Play Collection

☐ **BLUES COLLECTION VOL.3 (She Moves Me)**
She moves me: Waters, Muddy / Red light: Milton, Roy / I'm wonderin' and wonderin': Charles, Ray / When your lover has gone: Holiday, Billie / BB boogie: King, B.B. / Comong home: James, Elmore / Little wheel: Hooker, John Lee / Don't cry cry baby: Cole, Nat 'King' Trio / Big fat woman: Leadbelly / Basin street blues: Fitzgerald, Ella / Little rain: Reed, Jimmy / Walkin' and cryin': King, B.B. / Somebody got to go: Moore, Gatemouth / Just pickin': Hopkins, Lightnin' / Easy to remember: Holiday, Billie / Hey now: Charles, Ray
101592 / May '97 / A-Play Collection

☐ **BLUES CROSSROADS (Acoustic Blues Old And New)**
Big road blues: Black, Rory / Trouble everywhere I go: McDowell, 'Mississippi' Fred / Friend like me: Bookbinder, Roy / Lonesome whistle: Shines, Johnny & Robert Lockwood / Automobile mechanic: Ball, Tom & Kenny Sultan / Police dog blues: James, Etta / Suckin' sugar blues: Geremia, Paul / Going to the city: Strehli, Angela / John Hardy: Thorogood, George / Mudville: Furtado, Tony / Stagerlee: Cephas, John 'Bowling Green' & Phil Wiggins
EDCD 7066 / Jul '98 / Easydisc

☐ **BLUES CRUISE (10 For The Highway)**
Bluesmobile: Walker, Philip & Otis Grand / Step on it: Kubek, Smokin' Joe Band & Bnois King / Body and fender man: Adams, Johnny / U turn: Hughes, Joe / Destination unknown: Sansone, Jumpin' Johnny / Let's ride: Roomful Of Blues / Cruise control: Welch, Mike / Automobile: Sayles, Charlie / '56 Eldorado: Ray, Kenny 'Blue' / Gas station man: Boyack, Pat & The Prowlers
EDCD 7056 / Nov '97 / Easydisc

☐ **BLUES DELUXE**
Clouds in my heart: Blues Deluxe / Hey bartender: Taylor, Koko / Wang dang doodle: Dixon, Willie / Sweet home Chicago: Brooks, Lonnie / Don't throw your love on me so strong: Seals, Son / You too might need a friend: Young, 'Mighty' Joe
XRTCD 9301 / Oct '93 / Alligator

☐ **BLUES ESSENTIAL**
CDNEW 123 / 27 May '98 / Charly

☐ **BLUES EXPERIENCE VOL.1**
CDRR 301 / May '92 / Request

☐ **BLUES FIREWORKS**
CAD 465 / Apr '95 / Blues Collection

☐ **BLUES FOR HIPPIES**
Things I used to do: Dawkins, Jimmy / Five minutes more: Friday, Charles / Boogie chillun: Harpo, Slim / Bloody murder: Spann, Otis / Fine drivin' machine: Watkins, Tiny / Keep on trying: Thomas, Tabby / Give me your love: James, Marion / Baby I'm stickin' to you: Friday, Charles / I've waited so long: Woodard, Mildred / High cost of living: Dawkins, Jimmy / Don't let nobody know: Baker, Willie / Mr. Buzzard: Thomas, Tabby / Sittin' and drinking: Davis, Rose / Make my way in this world: Dawkins, Jimmy / Thank you: Powell, Bobby / Right one: Friday, Charles / Think twice before you speak: Dawkins, Jimmy / I believe: Friday, Charles / I'm so sorry: Harpo, Slim / I say I: Thomas, Tabby / Chicago on my mind: Dawkins, Jimmy / Jimmy's blues: Stewart, James / All for business: Dawkins, Jimmy / Blues for hippies: Spann, Otis
CDCHD 504 / 29 Sep '97 / Ace

☐ **BLUES FOR LOVERS**
DCD 5272 / Nov '92 / Kenwest

☐ **BLUES FOR YOU**
ALSCD 7958 / Jul '89 / Alligator

☐ **BLUES FOR YOU (2CD Set)**
I'm in the mood: Hooker, John Lee / Red rooster: Howlin' Wolf / Bring it on home to me: Williamson, Sonny Boy / I just want to make love to you: James, Etta / Jinglin' baby: Burns, Eddie / I'm mad: Mabon, Willie / Cold cold feeling: Walker, T-Bone / Dirty work goin' on: Blue, Little Joe / Baby please don't go: McGhee, Brownie & Sonny Terry / Drivin' wheel: Parker, Junior / Blue Monday: Davis, James / Wrinkles: Big Three Trio / My time after a while: Guy, Buddy / Shame shame shame: Guy, Buddy / WOMAN: James, Etta / Hoochie coochie man: Waters, Muddy / One bourbon, one scotch, one beer: Hooker, John Lee / Help me: Williamson, Sonny Boy / Baby what you want me to do: James, Etta / Livin' with the blues: McGhee, Brownie & Sonny Terry / My babe: Little Walter / Stormy Monday: Little Milton / Shakedown: Glenn, Lloyd / What kind of man is that: Taylor, Koko / Your funeral my trial: Williamson, Sonny Boy / Boom boom: Hooker, John Lee / Brownie's guitar blues: McGhee, Brownie & Sonny Terry / Goin' down slow: Howlin' Wolf / Walking the blues: Dixon, Willie / Got my mojo working: Waters, Muddy
DOU 882502 / 2 Feb '98 / Disky

☐ **BLUES FROM CHICAGO**
Sweet home Chicago / Big boss man / Low down funk / I'm losing you / Lost love / Hoochie koochie man / You go me cryin' / I got to love my woman / Mess ada blues
CDTB 174 / Feb '96 / Thunderbolt

☐ **BLUES FROM DOLPHIN'S OF HOLLYWOOD**
Darkest hour: Crayton, Pee Wee / Forgive me: Crayton, Pee Wee / Crying and walking: Crayton, Pee Wee / Pappy's blues: Crayton, Pee Wee / Baby, pat the floor: Crayton, Pee Wee / I'm your prisoner: Crayton, Pee Wee / Lovin' John: Crayton, Pee Wee / Fillmore Street blues: Crayton, Pee Wee / Boogie bop: Crayton, Pee Wee / You can't bring me down: Little Caesar / Cadillac baby: Little Caesar / WDIA station ID: Mayfield, Percy / Look the whole world over: Mayfield, Percy / Monkey song: Mayfield, Percy / Treat me like I treat you: Mayfield, Percy / My country girl: Mayfield, Percy / Worried life blues: Mayfield, Percy / Pete's boogie: Mayfield, Percy / Big family blues: Witherspoon, Jimmy / Cain River blues: Witherspoon, Jimmy / Teenage party: Witherspoon, Jimmy / SK blues: Witherspoon, Jimmy / Never know when a woman changes her mind: Dixon, Floyd / Oh baby: Dixon, Floyd / Cadillac funeral: Harris, Peppermint
CDCHD 357 / Nov '91 / Ace

☐ **BLUES GIANTS**
PLSCD 172 / Apr '97 / Pulse

☐ **BLUES GIANTS IN CONCERT**
Blues everywhere: Memphis Slim / John Henry: Memphis Slim & Willie Dixon / Captain captain: Waters, Muddy / Catfish blues: Waters, Muddy / In the city: Waters, Muddy / I feel like cryin': Waters, Muddy / Your love for me is true: Williamson, Sonny Boy / Don't misuse me: Williamson, Sonny Boy / I'm getting tired: Williamson, Sonny Boy / Getting down slow: Spann, Otis / Careless love: Johnson, Lonnie / CC rider: Johnson, Lonnie / TB blues: Spivey, Victoria / Big roll blues: Williams, 'Big' Joe / Back in the bottom: Williams, 'Big' Joe / Baby, please don't go: Williams, 'Big' Joe
92052 / Aug '94 / Act

☐ **BLUES GOLD COLLECTION (2CD Set)**
D2CD 4008 / Jun '95 / Deja Vu

☐ **BLUES GREATS (3CD Set)**
159092 / Jan '98 / EPM

☐ **BLUES GUITAR**
PLSCD 155 / Apr '97 / Pulse

☐ **BLUES GUITAR BLASTERS**
After hours: Nolan, Jimmy / Killing floor: King, Albert / You threw your love on me too strong: King, Albert / Talkin' woman: Fulson, Lowell / Everytime it rains: Fulson, Lowell / Early in the morning: King, B.B. / Talkin' the blues: King, B.B. / Dust my blues: James, Elmore / Elmo's shuffle: James, Elmore / Hawaiian boogie: James, Elmore / Jumpin' in the heart of town: Thomas, Lafayette / Certainly all: Guitar Slim / Things that I used to do: Guitar Slim / Twistin' the strings: Turner, Ike / Three hours past midnight: Watson, Johnny 'Guitar' / Twinky: Crayton, Pee Wee / Mistreated so bad: Crayton, Pee Wee / Hey hey baby: Walker, T-Bone / I had a good girl: Hooker, John Lee
CDCH 232 / Jan '88 / Ace

☐ **BLUES GUITAR DUELS**
Girl you're nice and clean: Guy, Buddy & Phil / West side soul: Sumlin, Hubert Blues Party & Ronnie Earl / Corn palace: Kubek, Smokin' Joe Band / You're fine: Morgan, Mike & Jim Suhler / She's gone: Walker, Philip & Otis Grand / Backstroke: Earl, Ronnie & Duke Robillard / Full gain: Gaines, Grady & Texas Upsetters/Roy Gaines/Clarence Hollimon / Wasp: Coronado, Joe & Texas Beat/Mark Pollock/Ray Jimenez / Kick out: Guitar Shorty & Otis Grand / You got to help me: Sumlin, Hubert & Richard Studholme
EDCD 7049 / Nov '97 / Easydisc

☐ **BLUES GUITAR GREATS**
Move it on over: Thorogood, George & The Destroyers / Kings crosstown shuffle: King, Little Jimmy / Robert Nighthawk stomp: Earl, Ronnie & The Broadcasters / Don't stop by the creek son: Copeland, Johnny / Too hot to handle: Robillard, Duke / One way or another: Washington, Walter 'Wolfman' / Trouble: Shannon, Preston Band / Alligator boogaloo: Brown, Clarence 'Gatemouth' / Payback: Lynn, Barbara / Just for a little while: Kubek, Smokin' Joe Band
EDCD 7016 / Aug '96 / Easydisc

☐ **BLUES GUITAR GREATS**
Down in the bottom: Williams, 'Big' Joe / Government money: Estes, 'Sleepy' John / I don't want no woman: Magic Sam / Five long years: Allison, Luther / If you change your mind: Hutto, J.B. / Chitlins con carne: Dawkins, Jimmy / I walked all night: Young, 'Mighty' Joe / Lockwood's boogie: Lockwood, Robert Jr. / Trouble don't last always: Wells, Junior & Buddy Guy / So many roads: Rush, Otis / Crash head on into love: Brooks, Lonnie / Strange how I miss you: Johnson, Jimmy / Why's life got to be this way: McDaniel, Floyd & Blues Swingers / Someday after awhile: Barkin' Bill & Steve Freund / West side stroll: Specter, Dave & The Bluebirds / West side woman: Bell, Lurrie / Mean mistreater: Moore, Johnny B.
DE 697 / Jun '97 / Delmark

☐ **BLUES GUITAR HEROES**
Don't let my baby ride: Scott, Isaac / Leave me alone: Benton, Buster / Looking for my baby: Johnson, Jimmy / You upset me baby: Allison, Luther / Hold that train: Smith, Byther / Red house: Hendrix, Jimi / Somebody loan me a dime: Robinson, Fenton / End of the blues: Hooker, Earl / I've got a mind to travel: Collins, Albert / How can one woman treat a man so mean: Guy, Buddy & Junior Wells / Don't stay out all night: Arnold, Billy Boy & Tony McPhee / First time I met the blues: Guy, Buddy / Hoochie coochie man: Waters, Muddy / I had it so hard: Sunnyland Slim
TRTCD 154 / 16 Feb '98 / TrueTrax

☐ **BLUES GUITAR MASTERS (2CD Set)**
CDGR 1422 / Apr '97 / Charly

☐ **BLUES GUITAR POWER**
Give me my blues: Collins, Albert / Freeze: Piccolo, Greg / Can't see for looking: Kubek, Smokin' Joe / Guitar boogie shuffle twist: Holmstrom, Rick / Somebody's got a tail: King, Earl & Roomful Of Blues / Homesick boy: Thorogood, George & The Destroyers / Bluesola: Wilson, U.P. / You haven't hurt me: Radcliff, Bobby / Chronic late arriver: Jones, Tutu / For Jannie Ray: Ray, Kenny 'Blue'
EDCD 7046 / Sep '97 / Easydisc

☐ **BLUES GUITARISTS**
CLACD 431 / Mar '97 / Castle

☐ **BLUES GUMBO**
Your kind of love: Sansone, Jumpin' Johnny / Don't you make me act ig'nunt: Porter, George Jr. / My baby's gonna wash me down: Walker, Philip / More you got: Reed, Dalton / Stomp house blues: Gaines, Grady & The Texas Upsetters / Door poppin': Fran, Carol & Clarence Holliman / Handy wrap: King, Earl / Louisiana love shack: Boyack, Pat & The Prowlers / Just jammin': Rockin' Sidney / Hold me: Wilson, U.P.
EDCD 7063 / Jun '98 / Easydisc

☐ **BLUES HARMONICA SPOTLIGHT**
BT 1083CD / Jan '93 / Black Top

☐ **BLUES HARP BOOGIE**
MCCD 124 / Jan '92 / Music Club

☐ **BLUES HARP BOSSES**
Good morning little school girl: Williamson, Sonny Boy / I just keep loving her: Little Walter / Easy: Horton, Walter / Keep you arms around me: Hill-Louis, Joe / Wolf call boogie: Hot Shot Love / Chicago breakdown: Ross, Dr. Isiah / Baker shop boogie: Nix, Willie & James Cotton / So long baby goodbye: Johnson, Willie & Sammy Lewis / Floyd's blues: Jones, Floyd & Snooky Pryor / Blue Carnegie: Reed, Jimmy / I wish you would: Arnold, Billy Boy / Harmonica hop: Terry, Sonny / Fannie Mae: Brown, Buster / You don't have to go: Myers, Sam / Ain't broke ain't hungry: Polka Dot Slim / Take it easy baby: Williamson, Sonny Boy / Drinking again: Jones, Birmingham / Texas (wherever the action is): McCain, Jerry / My back scratcher: Frost, Frank / Best of wild child: Butler, George 'Wild Child'
CDGR 220 / 2 Feb '98 / Charly

☐ **BLUES HARP GREATS**
Three harp boogie: Cotton, James & Paul Butterfield/Billy Boy Arnold / (I shoulda did) What my Mama told me: Bell, Carey / Come back baby: Treat Her Right / Oven is on: Montgomery, James Band / Jumpin' blues: Magic Dick & Jay Geils / Ol' heartbreak: Raines, Annie & Paul Rishell / Hey baby (Don't you know your Daddy loves you so): Butler Twins / Rockin' at th eRiverside: Hummel, Mark / Pickin' rags: Buford, Mojo / Lamp post: Sayles, Charlie
EDCD 7023 / Feb '97 / Easydisc

☐ **BLUES HARP POWER**
Superharp: Cotton, James / Mouth on fire: Sugar Ray & The Bluetones / Vivienne: Louisiana Red / Deep fried: Piazza, Rod & The Mighty Flyers / Talkin' is over (the walkin' has begun): Sansone, Jumpin' Johnny / War is over: Clarke, William / Rack 'em up: Funderburgh, Anson & The Rockets / Made for one another: Hoy, Johnny & The Bluefish / Orange soda: Nulisch, Darrell & Texas Heat / Sweet Lolita: McBee, Lee & Mike Morgan
EDCD 7048 / Sep '97 / Easydisc

☐ **BLUES HOLLERIN' BOOGIE**
Help: Scott, Isaac / Hoochie coochie man: Waters, Muddy / I wouldn't treat a dog (the way you treated me): Big Twist & The Mellow Fellows / Just a dream: Arnold, Billy Boy & Tony McPhee / Never let me go: Tucker, Tommy / Wandering blues: Hooker, John Lee / Lowdown and funky: Gaines, Ropy & The Crusaders / Sorry: Benton, Buster & Carey Bell / Oh what a feeling: Ricks, Jimmy & the Ravens / War is starting: Hopkins, Lightnin' / That's alright Mama: Turner, Titus / Cut you loose: Smith, Byther / Whammy: Hawkins, Screamin' Jay / Don't you feel my leg: Muldaur, Maria / Hey hey: Turner, Ike & Jimmy Thomas / Insane asylum: Baldry, Long John & Kathi McDonald / Trouble all my days: Louisiana Red / Touch of your love: Sharpville, Todd / Mayor Daley's blues: Clearwater, Eddy / Walk right in: Musselwhite, Charley
MCCD 173 / Sep '94 / Music Club

☐ **BLUES IN CONCERT**
301792 / Apr '98 / Hallmark

☐ **BLUES IN JAZZ, THE**
CD 56002 / Aug '94 / Jazz Roots

☐ **BLUES IN THE MISSISSIPPI NIGHT**
RCD 10206 / Feb '92 / Rykodisc

☐ **BLUES IN THE NIGHT NO.1 (Newport Jazz Festival 1958 July 3rd-6th)**
NCD 8815 / '93 / Phontastic

☐ **BLUES IN THE NIGHT NO.2 (Newport Jazz Festival 1958 July 3rd-6th)**
NCD 8816 / '93 / Phontastic

☐ **BLUES IS A TRAMP - LIVE PARADISO**
TRCD 99122 / Nov '93 / Tramp

☐ **BLUES JAM IN CHICAGO**
Watch out / Ooh baby / South Indiana / Last night / Red hot jam / I'm worried / I held my baby last night / Madison blues / I can't hold out / I need your love / I got the blues / World's in a tangle / Talk with you / Like it this way / Someday soon baby / Hungry country girl / Black jack blues / Rockin' boogie / Sugar mama / Homework
4805272 / May '95 / Columbia

☐ **BLUES JOINT**
Life is hard: King, Jimmy & The King James Version / Can't get that stuff no more: Piazza, Rod & The Mighty Flyers / Treat you like a queen: Zinn, Rusty / I'll be the joker: Boyack, Pat & The Prowlers / Blues joint: Jones, Andrew 'Jr. Boy' / You don't drink what I drink: Wilson, Smokey / Lock doctor: Harman, James / Check out time: Davis, James 'Thunderbird' / Live and let live: King, Bobby & The Soul Brothers / Engines and wings: Little Buster & The Soul Brothers
EDCD 7058 / 19 Jan '98 / Easydisc

☐ **BLUES LADIES, THE**
CC rider blues: Rainey, Gertrude 'Ma' / Blame it on the blues: Rainey, Gertrude 'Ma' / Don't advertise your man: Smith, Clara / Nobody knows the way I feel this mornin': Hunter, Alberta / How long daddy, how long: Cox, Ida / Black snake blues: Spivey, Victoria / Bedroom blues: Wallace, Sippie / Trouble in mind: Hill, Chippie / Gin house blues: Smith, Bessie / Nobody knows you when you're down and out: Smith, Bessie / I need a little sugar in my bowl: Smith, Bessie / My Georgia grind: Bogan, Lucille / Black angel blues: Bogan, Lucille / Ice man (come on up): Memphis Minnie / You done lost your good thing now: White, Georgia / Blues ain't nothin' but: White, Georgia / Hot nuts (get them from the peanut man): Johnson, Lil / Don't you make me high: Johnson, Merline / Rock me: Tharpe, Rosetta / I'm tired of fattein' frogs for snakes: Crawford, Rosetta / Romance in the dark: Green, Lil / Why don't you do right: Green, Lil / Evil gal blues: Washington, Dinah / Salty papa blues: Washington, Dinah
IGOCD 2042 / Nov '96 / Indigo

☐ **BLUES LEGENDS (4CD Set)**
MBSCD 416 / Mar '93 / Castle

☐ **BLUES LEGENDS (4CD Set)**
MCBX 009 / Apr '94 / Music Club

☐ **BLUES LEGENDS**
MACCD 196 / Aug '96 / Autograph

☐ **BLUES LEGENDS VOL.1**
901592 / May '91 / FM

☐ **BLUES LEGENDS VOL.2**
901602 / May '91 / FM

☐ **BLUES LEGENDS VOL.3**
901612 / May '91 / FM

☐ **BLUES LIVE FROM THE MOUNTAIN STAGE**
Leave my woman alone: Nighthawks / It hurts me too: Nelson, Tracy / Slidell blues: Geremia, Paul / That's the way to do it: Pryor, Snooky / My Daddy was a jockey: Hammond, John / Blues why do you worry me: Musselwhite, Charley / Devil's real: Smither, Chris / Black cat on the line: Cephas, John 'Bowling Green' & Phil Wiggins / Lonesome bedroom blues: Clarke, William / Louisiana blues: Jackson, John / You got love if you want it: Legendary Blues Band / That'll work: Johnson, Johnnie / Quicks and blues: Brown, Charles / Gee I wish: Robillard, Duke
BPMCD 305 / May '97 / Blue Plate

☐ **BLUES MASTERS**
Can't get you off my mind: Jones, Lloyd / Kansas city monarch: Earl, Ronnie / Too proud: Mighty Sam / Bring it on home: MacLeod, Doug / Feel like going home: Lucas, Robert / Down in Mississippi: Evans, Terry / Feets out in the hallway: Beard, Joe / I'm so lonely: Mighty Sam / Moonshine 2: Lucas, Robert
AQCD 1034 / Feb '96 / Audioquest

☐ **BLUES MEN, THE**
Down at the corner grocery store: Reed, Jimmy / Goin' mad blues: Hooker, John Lee / Dust my broom: Waters, Muddy / I wish you would: Arnold, Billy Boy & Tony McPhee / Your gonna need me, baby: Louisiana Red / Major Daley's blues: Clearwater, Eddy / Come on in this house: Smith, Byther / Still a fool: Edwards, Clarence / In my younger days: Guy, Buddy & Junior Wells / Soft and mellow Stella: Sunnyland Slim / Somebody loan me a dime: Robinson, Fenton / Mona: Diddley, Bo / Neighbour neighbour: King Biscuit Boy & Ronnie Hawkins Band / War is starting again: Hopkins, Lightnin' / When my first wife quit me: Johnson, Jimmy / Ship made of paper: Magic Slim
ECD 3315 / May '97 / K-Tel

☐ **BLUES MISTLETOE & SANTA'S LITTLE HELPER**
BT 1122CD / Oct '95 / Black Top

☐ **BLUES MOODS**
Must I holler: Bell, Carey / Soul that's been abused: Sumlin, Hubert Blues Party & Margret Sam McClain / Learned to live without you: Love Dogs / Find another fool: Ball, Marcia / Ships passing in the night: Earl, Ronnie & The Broadcasters / Taking the long way home: Farr, Deitra / Moment of passion: Sugar Ray & The Bluetones / 35 long years: Smith, Byther / I let her slip right through my hands: Morgan, Mike & The Crawl / You left me dreaming: Guitar Shorty
EDCD 7050 / Nov '97 / Easydisc

☐ **BLUES NOTES - AND BLACK (A Blues Survey From 1920-1960)**
PHONTNCD 8827 / '93 / Phontastic

☐ **BLUES OBSCURITIES 1923-1931**
DOCD 5481 / Nov '96 / Document

☐ **BLUES ON FIRE**
Man and the blues: Bell, Lurrie / Blues at my baby's house: Guy, Buddy / She torture me: Walker, Philip & Otis Grand / Small room: Sayles, Charlie / Down so long: Louisiana Red / Bad day blues: Wilson, U.P. / Pursue your dreams: Butler Twins / Why don't you let me be: Wilson, Smokey / Devil send blues: Johnny / I can't live happy: Walker, Victor / It's so easy to love you: Bell, Carey / Fix the blues in Paris: Smith, Byther
EDCD 9007 / Feb '97 / Easydisc

☐ **BLUES ON THE HIGH SEAS (King Snake Live)**
KS 038 / 1 Sep '98 / King Snake

☐ **BLUES ORGAN GROOVES**
CC rider: Levy, Ron / Heart attack: Maxwell, David / Tone-cool: Tony Z / Let me love you baby: Heartsman, Johnny / Jaywalkin': August, Lynn / Cat: Crawford, David / Down thru' the years: Guitar Shorty & Otis Grand
EDCD 7061 / Jun '98 / Easydisc

☐ **BLUES PIANO ORGY**
Blues hurt my tongue to talk: Speckled Red / Dresser drawers: Sykes, Roosevelt / Concentration blues: Sykes, Roosevelt / Kickin' motor scooter: Sykes, Roosevelt / (New Year's) resolution blues: Sykes, Roosevelt / My baby's coming with a marriage license: Sunnyland Slim / Poor boy: Sunnyland Slim / Every time I get to drinkin': Sunnyland Slim / Depression blues: Sunnyland Slim / Stendahl stomp: Little Brother Montgomery / Tremblin' blues: Little Brother Montgomery / No special rider: Little Brother Montgomery / Bass key boogie: Little Brother Montgomery / Five o'clock blues: Memphis Slim / Nat Dee special: Memphis Slim / Lonesome bedroom blues: Jones, Curtis / Takin' off: Jones, Curtis / Three-in-one blues: Spann, Otis
DE 626 / Nov '96 / Delmark

☐ **BLUES ROAD TRIP (City To City)**
Goin' to New York: Ealey, Robert / One way ticket to Memphis: King, Bobby & Terry Evans / Back to New Orleans: Mohally, Jimmy / Mobile: Ball, Marcia / Full moon over Dallas: Crawl / Sittin' in Jackson: Wilson, Smokey / Hollywood girls: Harman, James / Little Rock: Davis, Larry / Chicago to Chicago: Boyack, Pat & The Prowlers / St. Louis blues: Brown, Clarence 'Gatemouth'
EDCD 7059 / May '98 / Easydisc

☐ **BLUES ROUND MIDNIGHT**
Three o'clock blues: Davis, Larry / Old man blues: Copeland, Johnny / Something about you: Davis, Larry / Blues around midnight: Fulson, Lowell / Love will lead you right: Walker, T-Bone / You're breaking my heart: King, B.B. / Shattered dreams: Fulson, Lowell / T-99 blues: Nelson, Jimmy 'T-99' / I'm wonderin' and wonderin': Charles, Ray / Second hand fool: Nelson, Jimmy 'T-99' / Quit hanging around: King, Saunders / Dragnet blues: Ervin, Frankie / Crazy with the blues: Jones,

---

☐ **BLUES SAX POWER**
Hammer: Piccolo, Greg / Go girl: Tri-Saxual Soul Champs / Skunky: Watts, Noble / Swing on it: Singer, Hal / Just good lovin': Love Dogs / Let's ball: Nocturne, Johnny / Miami strut: Reed, A.C. / GG shuffle: Gaines, Grady & The Texas Upsetters / Down but not out: Houston, Joe / Tater diggin': Copley, Al & Hal Singer
EDCD 7047 / Sep '97 / Easydisc

☐ **BLUES SHAKERS (20 Original Blues Grooves)**
Shake your moneymaker: James, Elmore / Left handed woman: Reed, Jimmy / Jennie Mae: Brown, Country girl blues: Memphis Willie B / Big road blues: Douglas, K.C. / Levee camp blues: Williams, Big Joe / Catfish: Smith, Robert Curtis / San Quentin blues: Maiden, Sidney / Big fat mama: Wilton, Wade / Grievin' me: Franklin, Pete / Dyin' crapshooters blues: McTell, 'Blind' Willie / Fine booze and heavy blues: McGhee, Brownie / Blues before sunrise: Blackwell, Scrapper / You got to move: Davis, Rev. Gary / Brown skin woman: Eaglin, Snooks / Pawn shop: McGhee, Brownie & Sonny Terry / T-model blues: Hopkins, Lightnin' / You is one black rat: Quattlebaum, Doug / Highway 61: Memphis Willie B / Shake 'em on down: Lewis, Walter 'Furry' / Hand me down baby: Maiden, Sidney / Alberta: Eaglin, Snooks / See what you have done: Tate, Baby / Goin' where the moon crosses the yellow dog: Blackwell, Scrapper
CDCH 247 / Jun '88 / Ace

☐ **BLUES, THE (2CD Set)**
R2CD 4008 / 13 Apr '98 / Deja Vu

☐ **BLUES, THE**
RENCD 114 / Mar '96 / Renaissance Collector Series

☐ **BLUES, THE**
Screamin' and cryin': Waters, Muddy / Seventh son: Dixon, Willie / Texas flood: Vaughan, Stevie Ray / Death letter: House, Son / Merry go round blues: Big Bill Broonzy / She's real: Big Bill Broonzy / Give me an old old lady: White, Bukka / Baby don't I know: Shines, Johnny / Blues before sunrise: Dupree, 'Champion' Jack / It was rainin': Winter, Johnny / Everybody's got to change sometime: Taj Mahal
4875302 / 29 Sep '97 / Sony Jazz

☐ **BLUES TRAIN (Railroad Songs)**
There's a train: Holmes Brothers / Fast train: Parker, Bobby / Boogie woogie choo choo train: Nocturne, Johnny Band / Railroad man: Johnson, Larry / Railroadin' some: Blake, Rory / That same old train: Eaglin, Snooks / Meet me at the station: Garbo, Chuck / Goodie train: Walker, Philip / Mystery train: Preacher Jack / Take the 'A' train: Brown, Clarence 'Gatemouth'
EDCD 7062 / May '98 / Easydisc

☐ **BLUES WITH A DIFFERENCE**
CDS 4 / '88 / Rounder

☐ **BLUES WITH A FEELING (2CD Set)**
Introduction: House, Son / Preaching blues: House, Son / Death letter blues: House, Son / Empire state express: House, Son / Devil got my woman: James, Skip / Aberdeen Mississippi blues: White, Bukka / Levee camp blues: Williams, Robert Pete / Louise McDowell, 'Mississippi' Fred / Don't let nobody turn you round: Wilkins, Rev. Robert / Keep your lamp trimmed and burning: Brown, Rev. Pearly & Christine / What do you think about Jesus: McDowell, 'Mississippi' Fred & Annie Mae/Rev. Robert Wilkins / Woman I'm loving she's taken my appetite: Hopkins, Lightnin' / Come on baby: Hopkins, Lightnin' / Baby please don't go: Hopkins, Lightnin' / Freddie: Lipscomb, Mance / So different blues: Lipscomb, Mance / God moves on the water (The sinking of the Titanic): Lipscomb, Mance / Freight train: Cotten, Elizabeth / Here I am Lord send me: Hurt, 'Mississippi' John / Pallet on your floor: Hurt, 'Mississippi' John / San Francisco Bay blues: Fuller, Jesse Lone Cat / I can't quit you baby: Hooker, John Lee / Stop now baby: Hooker, John Lee / Waters, Muddy / Five long years: Boyd, Eddie & Willie Dixon / Cocaine: Wrinkles: Lafayette, Leake & Willie Dixon / Cocaine: Van Ronk, Dave / Drop down mama: Hammond, John / Grizzly bear: Von Schmidt, Eric / Travelling blues: Koerner, 'Spider' John / CC rider: Chambers Brothers / Blues with a feeling: Butterfield, Paul Blues Band / Look over yonder wall: Butterfield, Paul Blues Band / Born in Chicago: Butterfield, Paul
VCD2 77005 / Oct '95 / Vanguard

☐ **BLUES WITH A FEELING**
MACCD 199 / Aug '96 / Autograph

☐ **BLUES WITH THE GIRLS**
157582 / Feb '93 / Blues Collection

☐ **BLUES WOMEN TODAY**
Two bit Texas town: Strehli, Angela / Don't let it end: Washington, Toni Lynn / Girlfriend says: Willson, Michelle / Blue house: Ball, Marcia / I'll take care of the: Thomas, Irma / Fear no evil: Peebles, Ann / Fool ain't gonna let you go: Boykin, Brenda / Come with me: Honeycutt, Miki / My blue mood: Bogart, Deanna / God's gift to women: Block, Rory
EDCD 7010 / Oct '96 / Easydisc

☐ **BLUES YOU HATE TO LOSE (16 Classic Blues Performances)**
Country boy blues: Span, Otis / Have a little walk with me: Lockwood, Robert Jr. / El capitan: Memphis Slim / How long blues: Price, Sammy / It's your so the highway: Gillum, Bill 'Jazz' / Bad luck and troubles: Stidham, Arbee / In the evening: Witherspoon, Jimmy / Mamie's blues: Hooker, John / CC rider: McGhee, Brownie & Sonny Terry / I've been drinkin': Smith, Jimmy / Mistreatin' mama: Smith, Jimmy

---

☐ **BLUESIANA HOT SAUCE**
SHCD 5009 / Apr '94 / Shanachie

☐ **BLUESIANA HURRICANE**
SHCD 5014 / Oct '95 / Shanachie

☐ **BLUESMEN & RHYTHM KINGS**
It's so cold and mean (drug scene): Johnson, L.V. / Something's mighty wrong: Davis, Tyrone / Strange: Haddix, Travis / You've got all of me: King, Ben E. / my baby: Graham, Jesse / Let love take care (of the rest): Brown, Nappy / You don't know nothing about love: Garrett, Vernon / Where is Leroy: Blues Boy Willie / I've been loving you too long to stop now: Clayton, Willie
ICH 11912 / Jun '96 / Ichiban

☐ **BLUESVILLE VOL.1**
Judge Boushay blues: Lewis, Walter 'Furry' / Country girl blues: Memphis Willie B / Big road blues: Douglas, K.C. / Levee camp blues: Williams, Big Joe / Catfish: Smith, Robert Curtis / San Quentin blues: Maiden, Sidney / Big fat mama: Wilton, Wade / Grievin' me: Franklin, Pete / Dyin' crapshooters blues: McTell, 'Blind' Willie / Fine booze and heavy blues: McGhee, Brownie / Blues before sunrise: Blackwell, Scrapper / You got to move: Davis, Rev. Gary / Brown skin woman: Eaglin, Snooks / Pawn shop: McGhee, Brownie & Sonny Terry / T-model blues: Hopkins, Lightnin'
CDNEW 102 / Dec '96 / Charly

☐ **BLUESVILLE VOL.1 (Big Blues Honks & Wails)**
PRCD 9905 / Feb '96 / Prestige

☐ **BLUESVILLE VOL.2**
Train done gone: Kirkland, Eddie / Down on my knees: Kirkland, Eddie / Homesick's blues: Homesick James / Stones in my passway: Homesick James / Rack 'em back Jack: Memphis Slim / Happy blues for John Glenn: Hopkins, Lightnin' / My baby jumped the black man: Hopkins, Lightnin' / My baby done gone: Terry, Sonny / School time: Arnold, Billy Boy / Big legged woman: Johnson, Lonnie / I have to worry: King Curtis / Calcutta: Sykes, Roosevelt / Show down: Lucas, Buddy / How long blues: Witherspoon, Jimmy / You better out that out: Arnold, Billy Boy / Drivin' wheel: Sykes, Roosevelt / It's a lonesome old world: Witherspoon, Jimmy / Jelly roll baker: Johnson, Lonnie
CDCH 250 / Oct '88 / Ace

☐ **BLUESVILLE VOL.2 (Feelin' Down On The South Side)**
PRCD 9906 / Feb '96 / Prestige

☐ **BLUESVILLE VOL.3 (Beale Street Get-Down)**
PRCD 9907 / Feb '96 / Prestige

☐ **BLUESVILLE VOL.4 (In The Key Of Blues)**
PRCD 9908 / Feb '96 / Prestige

☐ **BLUESVILLE VOL.6**
Meet me in the bottom: Anderson, Pink / Baby I'm going away: Anderson, Pink / Mama where did you stay last night: Anderson, Pink / Baby please don't go: Anderson, Pink / See what you done: Tate, Baby / Baby you just don't know: Tate, Baby / Hey mama hey pretty girl: Tate, Baby / What have I done to you: Tate, Baby / Callin' my mama: Terry, Sonny / slip mae: Terry, Sonny / Trucking them blues: Tate, Baby / Lonesome over there: Tate, Baby / Dupree blues: Tate, Baby / That's no way to do: Anderson, Pink / Weeping willow blues: Anderson, Pink / My baby left me this morning: Anderson, Pink / Ain't nobody home but me: Anderson, Pink / Boy was kissing the girl: Davis, Gary / Candyman: Davis, Gary / Tell you woman 'bout me: Johnson, Larry / Whiskey store blues: Johnson, Larry / Take these blues off my mind: Johnson, Larry / One thing for sure: McGhee, Brownie
PRCD 9914 / 30 Mar '98 / Prestige

☐ **BLUNT SPECIAL BLENDS**
TVT 10102 / Jun '97 / Blunt

☐ **BLUNTED VOL.2**
SDW 0242CD / 16 Sep '97 / Shadow

☐ **BOAT TO PROGRESS**
GRELCD 602 / May '90 / Greensleeves

☐ **BOATS AGAINST THE CURRENT**
CAKE 012CD / Dec '96 / Hedonist

☐ **BOCHIT BREAKS (2CD Set)**
BOSCD2LP 04 / 1 Sep '98 / Botchit & Scarper

☐ **BODY AND SOUL (2CD Set)**
I say a little prayer: Franklin, Aretha / River deep, mountain high: Turner, Ike & Tina / Only sixteen: Cooke, Sam / Stand by me: King, Ben E. / Have you seen her: Chi-Lites / My guy: Wells, Mary / Dancing in the street: Martha & The Vandellas / Harlem shuffle: Bob & Earl / If you don't know me by now: Melvin, Harold & The Bluenotes / When a man loves a woman: Sledge, Percy / (If loving you is wrong) I don't want to be right: Ingram, Luther / Tell it like it is: Neville, Aaron / Doggin' around: Wilson, Jackie / If you need me: Pickett, Wilson / Soul man: Sam & Dave / For your precious love: Butler, Jerry / On broadway: Drifters / This old heart of mine: Isley Brothers / Endless love: Ross, Diana & Lionel Richie / Nobody but me: foolish, be happy: Tams / Love don't live here anymore: Rose Royce / My special prayer: Sledge, Percy / Chain of fools: Franklin, Aretha / Wonderful world: Cooke, Sam / Spanish Harlem: King, Ben E. / Daddy's home: Shep & The Limelites / Down to my last heartbeat: Pickett, Wilson / Nowhere to run: Reeves, Martha / Release me: Phillips, Esther / Alone at last: Wilson, Jackie / One fine day: Chiffons / Holman, Eddie / Letter full of tears: Knight, Gladys & The Pips / Show and tell: Wilson, Al / Soul sister,

---

brown sugar: Sam & Dave / Love I lost: Melvin, Harold & The Bluenotes / Why can't we live together: Thomas, Timmy / Something old, something new: Fantastics / Hold on I'm coming: Burke, Solomon / It's a man's man's man's world: Brown, James
TNC 96236 / Aug '96 / Natural Collection

☐ **BODY HEAT**
Unbelievable: EMF / Your mama don't dance: Poison / Hot in the city: Idol, Billy / Hold on: Wilson Phillips / Coast to coast: Shaffer, Paul / Hot child in the city: Gilder, Nick / C'est la vie: Nevil, Robbie / We don't have to take our clothes off: Stewart, Jermaine / I touch myself: Divinyls / Right here right now: Jesus Jones / Land of a thousand dances: Geils, J. Band / Ice ice baby: Vanilla Ice / Some like it hot: Power Station / When you walk in the room: Carrack, Paul / I won't let the sun go down on me: Kershaw, Nik / So hot: Heights / Love blonde: Wilde, Kim
DC 880752 / Aug '97 / Disky

☐ **BODY RAPTURES VOL.3**
CDZOT 110 / Sep '94 / Zoth Ommog

☐ **BOGLE AT LARGE**
EWCD 01 / Oct '92 / Teams

☐ **BOGLE FEVER**
WRCD 003 / Jun '97 / World

☐ **BOGLE MANIA**
GRELCD 180 / Apr '93 / Greensleeves

☐ **BOLERO - THE COOL COMPILATION**
Popurri de boleros - si mi comprendieras: Faz, Roberto Y Su Conjunto / Como pienso en ti: Alonso Y Los Bocucos / Amor fugaz: More, Beny / Sabra a su manera (Comme d'habitude): Alvarez, Adalberto & Su Son / Si me pudieras querer: Faz, Roberto Y Su Conjunto Casino / Frenesi: Faz, Roberto Y Su Conjunto / Tu me entiendes: Faz, Roberto Y Su Conjunto Casino / Me talabas tu: Alonso, Pacho Y Su Orquestra / Popurri de boleros - Irremediablemente solo: Faz, Roberto Y Su Conjunto
PSCCD 1008 / Feb '95 / Pure Sounds From Cuba

☐ **BOLERO MANIA (4CD Set)**
BM 99906 / Apr '97 / Blue Moon

☐ **BOLLOCKS TO CHRISTMAS**
Christmas time again: Bad Manners / Christmas is really fantastic: Sidebottom, Frank / Step into Christmas: Business / Snowman: Anti Nowhere League / Blue Christmas: Frantic Flintstones / Merry Christmas everybody: 4 Skins / O come all ye faithful (adeste fideles): Sidebottom, Frank / Jingle bells: Judge Dread / Hey Santa: UK Subs / Twelve days of Christmas: Splodge / Stuff the turkey: Alien Sex Fiend / Another Christmas: Yobs / I wish it could be Christmas: Sidebottom, Frank / Jingle bells: Macc Lads / Christmas in Dreadland: Judge Dread / Turkey stomp: Hot Knives / Santa bring my baby back: Frantic Flintstones / Auld Lang Syne: UK Subs / C-h-r-i-s-t-m-a-s: Yobs / White Christmas: Gonads / Drinking and driving: Business / Christmas medley: Sidebottom, Frank / White Christmas (live): Stiff Little Fingers
DOJOCD 204 / Dec '94 / Dojo

☐ **BOMB WORLDWIDE**
BOMB 20042 / 27 Oct '97 / Bomb

☐ **BOMBA**
MCD 71355 / Jun '93 / Monitor

☐ **BOMBARDES ET BINIOUS DE BRETAGNE**
ARN 64243 / Aug '93 / Arion

☐ **BONANZA SKA**
CDTRL 309 / Mar '94 / Trojan

☐ **BOND BEAT AND BASS**
CLP 0182 / 16 Mar '98 / Hypnotic

☐ **BONE TONE COMPILATION**
BTCD 972 / Jun '98 / Bone Tone

☐ **BONESHAKERS VOL.1 (12 Superb Funky Boneshaking Grooves)**
IBCD 2 / Jun '97 / Internal Bass

☐ **BONESHAKERS VOL.2**
IBCD 5 / Jun '97 / Internal Bass

☐ **BONESHAKERS VOL.3**
Astral space: Quiet Boys / Jazz potato: Mr. Scruff / Jazz thing: Reminiscence Quartet / Dastaki: Dasta / Step / Get up get down: Fishbelly Black / Mo bounce: Lee, Tim / Future homosapiens: Future Homosapiens / Moonbeamz: Abacus / Jazz with attitude: Belair Project / Winds of change: Wallen, Byron
IBCD 11 / 27 Apr '98 / Internal Bass

☐ **BONNIE SCOTLAND**
PASTCD 9800 / Nov '92 / Flapper

☐ **BONNIE SCOTLAND**
GCMD 506 / Jun '97 / GCM

☐ **BOO**
Mountaineering in Belgium: Attila The Stockbroker / Charm: Shoulders / Oh Marie: Tender Trap / Muscle Brown: Tarquin's Party / Save me: drives my mind: Train: Rasque / Shotgun: Bleach / Turpentine: Newcranes / On Sunday: Shoulders / Polishing your mate: Stranglmartin / Eye of the average: Tarakata / Elevenses through: Tender Trap / Trash Madonna: Zodiac Mindwarp & The Love Reaction / Nature's love: Newcranes
10062 / Jan '93 / Musidisc

☐ **BOOGIE DOWN**
BWCD 0016 / 22 Jun '98 / Brickwall

☐ **BOOGIE WOOGIE**
CD 14552 / Jul '94 / Jazz Portraits

☐ **BOOGIE WOOGIE (2CD Set)**
Cavalcade of boogie: *Ammons, Albert* / Boogie woogie stomp: *Ammons, Albert* / Boogie woogie blues: *Ammons, Albert* / Suitcase blues: *Ammons, Albert* / Chicago in mind: *Ammons, Albert* / Shout for joy: *Ammons, Albert* / Boogie woogie: *Ammons, Albert* / Bass goin' crazy: *Ammons, Albert* / Derborn street breakdown: *Avery, Charles* / Henry Brown blues: *Brown, Henry* / Deep Morgan blues: *Brown, Henry* / Eastern chimes blues: *Brown, Henry* / Slow drag: *Davenport, Cow Cow* / Chimes blues: *Davenport, Cow Cow* / Atlanta rag: *Davenport, Cow Cow* / Barrelhouse woman: *Ezell, Will* / Heifer dust: *Ezell, Will* / Chain em down: *Garnett, Blind Leroy* / Louisiana glide: *Garnett, Blind Leroy* / Honky tonk train blues: *Lewis, Meade 'Lux'* / Fanny Lee blues: *Wallace, Wesley* / No. 29: *Wallace, Wesley* / Jab blues: *Williams, Jabo* / Pratt city blues: *Williams, Jabo*
24321 / Feb '96 / Laserlight

☐ **BOOGIE WOOGIE AND BARRELHOUSE PIANO VOL.1**
DOCD 5102 / Nov '92 / Document

☐ **BOOGIE WOOGIE AND BARRELHOUSE PIANO VOL.2**
DOCD 5103 / Nov '92 / Document

☐ **BOOGIE WOOGIE BEAT**
CWNCD 2008 / Jun '95 / Javelin

☐ **BOOGIE WOOGIE BLUES**
Cow cow blues: *Davenport, Cow Cow* / 5th street blues: *Davenport, Cow Cow* / Hurry and bring it home blues: *Davenport, Cow Cow* / Harlem choc'late babies on parade: *Johnson, James P.* / Birmingham blues: *Johnson, James P.* / Sugar blues: *Williams, Clarence* / Papa de da da: *Williams, Clarence* / Gulf coast blues: *Johnson, Clarence* / You're always messin' 'round with my man: *Johnson, Clarence* / Low down papa: *Johnson, Clarence* / Chicago stomp: *Blythe, Jimmy* / Society blues: *Blythe, Jimmy* / Boogie woogie blues: *Blythe, Jimmy* / Hard luck blues: *Robbins, Everett* / Fives: *Thomas, Hersal* / Down and out blues: *Fowler, Lemuel*
BCD 115 / Jul '91 / Biograph

☐ **BOOGIE WOOGIE GIANTS, THE**
JHR 73533 / May '93 / Jazz Hour

☐ **BOOGIE WOOGIE GOLD COLLECTION, THE (2CD Set)**
R2CD 7006 / 20 Apr '98 / Deja Vu

☐ **BOOGIE WOOGIE PIANO**
CD 14525 / Jan '94 / Jazz Portraits

☐ **BOOGIE WOOGIE PIANO**
CD 56001 / Aug '94 / Jazz Roots

☐ **BOOGIE WOOGIE RIOT (Piano & Guitar Boogie Blues)**
Tribute / Rocket 88 / Wine-o baby boogie / Rattler / Earl's boogie woogie / Cows / Lightnin's boogie / Atlanta bounce / Rock 'n' roll bed / Throw the boogie woogie / Down the road apiece / Fast Santa Fe / Boogie all the time / Right string baby, but the wrong yo-yo / Half tight boogie / Hammond boogie / Red light / Walter's boogie / Houston boogie / Pine top's boogie woogie / I know that's right / Fillmore street boogie / Skid row boogie
CDCHD 526 / Feb '95 / Ace

☐ **BOOGIE WOOGIE SPECIAL**
TPZ 1025 / Aug '95 / Topaz Jazz

☐ **BOOGIE WOOGIE STOMP**
Boogie woogie stomp: *Ammons, Albert* / Foot pedal boogie: *Ammons, Albert & Pete Johnson* / Boogie woogie prayer: *Ammons, Albert & Pete Johnson/ Meade 'Lux' Lewis* / Boogie woogie: *Basie, Count* / Boogie woogie: *Brown, Cleo* / Fat fanny stomp: *Clarke, Jim* / Yancey special: *Crosby, Bob & Bob Zurke* / Rocks: *Custer, Clay* / Boogie woogie: *Dorsey, Tommy & Howard Smith* / Chain 'em down: *Garnett, Blind Leroy* / Roll 'em: *Goodman, Benny & Jess Stacy* / After hours: *Hawkins, Erskine & Avery Parrish* / Chip's boogie woogie: *Herman, Woody & Tommy Linehan* / Indian boogie woogie: *Herman, Woody & Tommy Linehan* / Boogie woogie on St. Louis blues: *Hines, Earl 'Fatha'* / Boo-woo: *James, Harry & Pete Johnson* / Bear cat crawl: *Lewis, Meade 'Lux'* / Honky tonk train blues: *Lewis, Meade 'Lux'* / Vine Street boogie: *McShann, Jay* / No special rider: *Montgomery, Little Brother* / Pinetop's boogie woogie: *Smith, Pine Top* / Wilkins Street stomp: *Speckled Red* / Roll 'em Pete: *Turner, 'Big' Joe & Pete Johnson* / Crying in my sleep: *Yancey, Jimmy* / Slow and easy blues: *Yancey, Jimmy*
CDAJA 5101 / Feb '93 / Living Era

☐ **BOOGIE WOOGIE VOCALISTS**
CD 14541 / Jan '94 / Jazz Portraits

☐ **BOOGIE WOOGIE VOL.1 (Piano Soloists)**
Pinetop's boogie woogie: *Smith, Clarence 'Pinetop'* / Jump steady blues: *Smith, Clarence 'Pinetop'* / Detroit rocks: *Taylor, Montana* / Indiana Avenue stomp: *Taylor, Montana* / Dirty dozens: *Speckled Red* / Wilkins Street stomp: *Speckled Red* / Head rag hop: *Nelson, Romeo* / Cow cow blues: *Davenport, Cow Cow* / State Street jive: *Davenport, Cow Cow* / Yancey special: *Yancey, Jimmy* / Midnight stomp: *Yancey, Jimmy* / Streamline train: *Loften, Cripple Clarence* / I don't know: *Loften, Cripple Clarence* / Shout for joy: *Ammons, Albert* / Bass goin' crazy: *Ammons, Albert* / Yancey special: *Lewis, Meade 'Lux'* / Honky tonk train blues: *Lewis, Meade 'Lux'* / Blues on the downbeat: *Johnson, Pete* / Kaycee on my mind: *Johnson, Pete* / Ross Tavern boogie: *Hodes, Art*
JASMCD 2538 / Feb '95 / Jasmine

☐ **BOOGIE WOOGIE VOL.2 (The Small Groups)**
Boogie woogie stomp: *Ammons, Albert & His Rhythm Kings* / Boogie woogie: *Basie, Count* / Down the road apiece: *Bradley, Will* / Basin Street boogie: *Bradley, Will* / St. Louis blues: *Butterfield, Erskine* / Grand slam: *Goodman, Benny Sextet* / Munson Street breakdown: *Hampton, Lionel & His Orchestra* / Bouncing at the beacon: *Hampton, Lionel & His Orchestra* / We're gonna pitch a boogie woogie: *Harlem Hamfats* / Chip's boogie woogie: *Herman, Woody* / Boo woo: *James, Harry* / Boogie woogie's mother-in-law: *Johnson, Budd Orchestra* / Cherry red: *Johnson, Pete & Joe Turner* / Baby look at you: *Johnson, Pete & Joe Turner* / Far away blues: *Johnson, Pete & Joe Turner* / Bye bye baby: *Big Maceo* / Anytime for you: *Big Maceo* / Dirty dozen: *Price, Sammy* / Lead me Daddy: *Price, Sammy* / Straight to the bar: *Price, Sammy* / Rock it in rhythm: *Tampa Red* / She's love crazy: *Tampa Red*
JASMCD 2539 / Apr '95 / Jasmine

☐ **BOOGIE WOOGIE VOL.3 (The Big Bands)**
Scrub me Mama with a boogie beat / Basie boogie / Beat me, Daddy, eight to the bar / Rock-a-bye boogie / Back to boogie / Yancey special / Honky tonk train blues / Boogie woogie / Roll 'em / Indian boogie woogie / Boogie woogie bugle boy / Boogie woogie on St. Louis blues / Back beat boogie / Little Joe from Chicago / Drum boogie / Teddy bear boogie / Bluebird boogie woogie / Meade lux special / Cuban boogie woogie / Rum boogie
JASMCD 2540 / Jun '95 / Jasmine

☐ **BOOM REGGAE HITS VOL.5**
VPCD 1449 / Nov '95 / VP

☐ **BOOMING ON PLUTO (Electro For Droids - 2CD Set)**
Night drive: *Model 500* / I like to watch: *Freefall 68* / Dead cities: *Future Sound Of London* / Landslide: *Cabaret Voltaire* / Planet rock: *Bambaataa, Afrika & The Soul Sonic Force* / Angry dolphin: *Plaid* / Watermelon man: *Hancock, Herbie* / Bassline: *Mantronix* / Was a dog a doughnut: *Stevens, Cat* / Organic mango barbed: *HAT* / Salsa smurf: *Special Request* / Punjabi sher: *Safri Boys* / I didn't know I loved you: *Planet Patrol* / Solina: *Jedi Knights* / Extra: *To Rococo Rot* / Apartment: *Moroder, Giorgio* / Silicon based predator: *Sidewinder* / Let's get brutal: *Nitro Deluxe* / Olivine: *Black Dog* / Ear candy: *Tales From The Hardside* / Pack jam: *Jonzun Crew* / Computer games: *Clinton, George* / Nocturnal resort: *Prime, Michael* / Digicality: *Unique 3* / Running: *Information Society* / Al-naafiysh (The soul): *Hashim* / Genki: *Bleep & Booster* / Tootak, tootak, tootiyan: *Singh, Malkit* / Automannik: *Guy Called Gerald*
AMBT 20 / Apr '97 / Virgin

☐ **BOOT SCOOTIN' BOOGIE (The Nashville Line Dancing Album)**
Chattahoochie: *Jackson, Alan* / Mama don't get dressed up: *Brooks & Dunn* / Cherokee boogie: *BR5-49* / Big guitar: *Blackhawk* / Laid back stone cold: *Wright, Michelle* / We all get lucky sometimes: *Parnell, Lee Roy* / Betty's got a bass boat: *Tillis, Pam* / It's all in your head: *Diamond Rio* / Chain of this town: *BR5-49* / Boot scootin' boogie: *Brooks & Dunn* / Little Bitty: *Jackson, Alan* / Hammer and nails: *Foster, Radney* / House is rockin': *Parnell, Lee Roy* / Cleopatra, Queen of denial: *Tillis, Pam* / Baby likes to rock it: *Tractors* / Wake up and smell the whiskey Houdini: *Graham, Tammy* / Rock my world: *Brooks & Dunn* / You owe me: *Wright, Michelle*
74321461802 / Feb '97 / Arista

☐ **BOOTIN' THE BOOGIE (2CD Set)**
Reet petite: *Jordan, Louis & His Tympany Five* / It's just the blues: *Four Jumps Of Jive* / Beulah's boogie: *Hampton, Lionel & His Orchestra* / Come back to me baby blues: *Walker, T-Bone* / Honeydripper: *Liggins, Joe & His Honey Drippers* / I'm in town: *Thomas, Frantic Fay* / My gal's a jockey: *Turner, 'Big' Joe* / Bring 'em down front: *Williams, Cootie & His Orchestra* / 1280 Stomp: *Johnson, Pete* / Cement mixer: *Slim Gaillard Trio* / Voo it: *Humes, Helen* / Tiny's boogie woogie: *Grimes, Tiny Swingtet* / Voodoo woman blues: *Witherspoon, Jimmy* / Johnny's boogie: *Moore, Johnny B. & Three Blazers* / Hey ba ba re bop: *Harris, Wynonie* / What's the matter with me: *Jones, Albinia* / Blow Mr. Jackson: *Liggins, Joe & His Honey Drippers* / Red light: *Milton, Roy & His Solid Senders* / Big fat mama: *Millinder, Lucky Orchestra* / That's the stuff you've gotta watch: *Johnson, Budd Orchestra* / Slim's boogie: *Memphis Slim* / If it's good: *Lee, Julia* / No sale: *Jordan, Louis & His Tympany Five* / Doin' the boogie woogie: *Ammons, Albert* / Around the clock: *Harris, Wynonie* / Oo wee walkie talkie: *Washington, Dinah* / Jockey blues: *Samuels, Bill* / Too many women blues: *Vinson, Eddie* / Bobby sox blues: *Moore, Johnny B. & Three Blazers* / Tell your best friend nothing: *Taylor, Myra* / I ain't mad at you pretty baby: *Brown, Clarence 'Gatemouth'* / She's gonna ruin me: *Walker, T-Bone* / Drippers boogie: *Walker, T-Bone* / Laguna: *Gaillard, Slim* / Frantic boogie: *McVea, Jack* / Crown prince blues: *Crown Prince Waterford* / Be bop boogie: *Carter, Benny* / Bootin the boogie: *Chatman, Christine* / Mistake in life: *Memphis Slim* / Romance without finance: *Grimes, Tiny Swingtet* / Sally zu zazz: *Turner, 'Big' Joe* / Rock woogie: *Big Jim* / Texas and Pacific: *Jordan, Louis & His Tympany Five* / All the time: *Millinder, Lucky Orchestra*
CPCD 83002 / Sep '97 / Charly

☐ **BOOTLEGGERS**
Dynamics: *DJ Red* / Enta da dragon: *DJ Red* / Energise: *DJ Red* / Asylum: *Maldini* / Transmission: *IQ Collective* / Mode One: *IQ Collective* / Enta da dragon: *DJ Red* / Nasty: *DJ Red*
TOVBLCD 01 / 10 Aug '98 / Trouble On Vinyl

☐ **BOP BEGINS**
TPZ 1051 / Nov '96 / Topaz Jazz

☐ **BOPPIN' THE BLUES**
CPCD 8271 / Apr '97 / Charly

☐ **BOPPIN' TONIGHT**
Let's go boppin' tonight: *Ferrier, Al* / Honey baby: *Ferrier, Al* / No no baby: *Ferrier, Al* / What is that thing called love: *Ferrier, Al* / My baby done gone away: *Ferrier, Al* / Couple in the car: *Earl, Little Billy* / Who's baby are you: *Earl, Little Billy* / Go dan tucker: *Earl, Little Billy* / I never had the blues: *Earl, Little Billy* / Honey baby o: *Earl, Little Billy* / Freight train: *Hart, Larry* / Oh Nellie: *Hart, Larry* / I'm just a mender: *Hart, Larry* / Coffins have no pockets: *Hart, Larry* / Come on baby: *Hart, Larry* / Flashiest classiest: *Hart, Larry* / Never run out of love: *Hart, Larry* / Hold me baby: *Bill & Carroll* / Bluff city rock: *Bill & Carroll* / Bop stop rock: *Victorian, Ray* / Oh baby: *Jano, Johnny* / Mabel's gone: *Jano, Johnny* / High voltage: *Jano, Johnny* / Castro rock: *Chevalier, Jay*
CDCHD 442 / Feb '93 / Ace

☐ **BORDER MUSIC**
Laissez-faire: *Daigrepont, Bruce* / Kolinda: *Beausoleil* / La Viejito: *Jimenez, Flaco* / Allons a Lafayette: *Sonnier, Jo El* / This little girl: *Menard, D.L.* / Big chief: *Richard, Zachary* / Hundred Ladrones: *Los Linces* / Corrido el aceite: *Jordan, Steve* / J'etais au bal: *Doucet, David* / Someone else is steppin' in: *Buckwheat Zydeco* / High point two step: *Riley, Steve* / La otra modesta: *Jimenez, Santiago Jr.* / Cuando me miraste: *Salvidar, Mingo* / Tennis shoes: *Newman, Jimmy C.* / Aquella noche: *Hinojosa, Tish*
NETCD 1004 / Oct '92 / Network

☐ **BORDERLANDS - FROM CUNJUNTO TO CHICKEN SCRATCH**
SF 40418CD / Jan '94 / Smithsonian Folkways

☐ **BORED TO HELL**
35351423 / 22 Sep '97 / Viceroy

☐ **BOREDOM IS DEEP AND MYSTERIOUS VOL.1**
APR 001CD / 3 Oct '97 / April

☐ **BOREDOM IS DEEP AND MYSTERIOUS VOL.2**
APR 007CD / 6 Oct '97 / April

☐ **BOREDOM IS DEEP AND MYSTERIOUS VOL.3**
APR 023CD / Jul '97 / April

☐ **BORN BAD VOL.1**
BB 001CD / 1 Jun '98 / Born Bad

☐ **BORN BAD VOL.2**
BB 002CD / 1 Jun '98 / Born Bad

☐ **BORN BAD VOL.3**
BB 003CD / 1 Jun '98 / Born Bad

☐ **BORN BAD VOL.4**
BB 004CD / 1 Jun '98 / Born Bad

☐ **BORN BAD VOL.5**
BB 005CD / 1 Jun '98 / Born Bad

☐ **BORN BAD VOL.6**
BB 006CD / 1 Jun '98 / Born Bad

☐ **BORN TO BE WILD**
Born to be wild: *Steppenwolf* / Reelin' and rockin': *Berry, Chuck* / Big road blues: *Canned Heat* / C C Ryder: *Charles, Ray* / Keep on running: *Davis, Spencer* / Hell raiser: *Sweet*
DS 2303 / Aug '96 / BR Music

☐ **BORN TO BE WILD**
PLSCD 200 / Apr '97 / Pulse

☐ **BORN TO BE WILD**
GFS 088 / Nov '97 / Going For A Song

☐ **BORN TO BE WILD VOL.4**
Since you've been gone: *Rainbow* / Killer on the loose: *Thin Lizzy* / Young blood: *Thin Lizzy* / Bomber: *Motorhead* / Down down: *Status Quo* / Never say die: *Black Sabbath* / Hush: *Deep Purple* / United: *Judas Priest* / More tha a feeling: *Boston* / Gimme all your lovin': *ZZ Top* / Feels like the first time: *Foreigner* / Run to the hills: *Iron Maiden* / God gave rock 'n' roll to you: *Argent* / You ain't seen nothing yet: *Bachman-Turner Overdrive* / These dreams: *Heart* / No more Mr. Nice Guy: *Cooper, Alice* / Owner of a lonely heart: *Yes* / Holding out for a hero: *Tyler, Bonnie*
MUSCD 036 / May '97 / MCI Music

☐ **BORN TO CHOOSE**
Photograph: *REM & Natalie Merchant* / She said she said: *Sweet, Matthew* / Running out of time: *Sugar* / Born to choose: *Mekons* / Rant 'n' roll: *Trudell, John* / Box spring hog: *Waits, Tom* / Pancakes: *Williams, Lucinda* / Greenlander: *Pavement* / Don't talk about my music: *NRBQ* / Lost my driving wheel: *Cowboy Junkies* / HIV Baby: *Soundgarden* / Distracted: *Helmet*
RCD 10256 / Nov '93 / Rykodisc

☐ **BORN TO SWING (4CD Set)**
MBSCD 444 / Jul '96 / Castle

☐ **BORN UNDER A BAD SIGN**
VSOPCD 205 / Oct '94 / Connoisseur Collection

☐ **BORN WITH THE BLUES (4CD Set)**
391012 / Apr '98 / Hallmark

☐ **BORN WITH THE BLUES VOL.1**
Neighbour neighbour: *King Biscuit Boy & Ronnie Hawkins Band* / Sometimes I wonder: *Louisiana Red* / Cool drink of water: *Stackhouse, Houston* / Foxtrot: *Hooker, Earl* / She put the wammee on me: *Hawkins, Screamin' Jay* / Born with the blues: *Benton, Buster & Carey Bell* / Got me a Louisiana woman: *Hopkins, Lightnin'* / Things I used to do: *Collins, Albert* / Rode myself crazy: *Delay, Paul Band* / Honey bee: *Waters, Muddy* / Sweet Miss Bea: *Arnold, Billy Boy* / Down at the corner grocery store: *Reed, Jimmy* / Taking off: *Murphy, Matt* / Play the blues for you: *Mighty Houserockers* / Loaded: *Butterfield, Paul* / He sure could hypnotize: *Clovers* / Came up the hard way: *Clearwater, Eddy*
EMPRCD 525 / Sep '94 / Emporio

☐ **BORN WITH THE BLUES VOL.1**
Stomp boogie: *Hooker, John Lee* / I wish you would: *Arnold, Billy Boy & Tony McPhee* / Road runner: *Diddley, Bo* / Hard walking Hanna: *Reed, Jimmy* / When my first wife quit me: *Johnson, Jimmy* / Lonesome: *Memphis Slim* / Born with the blues: *Benton, Buster & Carey Bell* / Alabama train: *Louisiana Red* / I had it so hard: *Sunnyland Slim* / Don't stay out all night: *Arnold, Billy Boy & Tony McPhee* / Let the good times roll creole: *Memphis Slim* / Rent house boogie: *Hooker, John Lee* / Cry before I go: *Reed, Jimmy* / Don't know where I've been: *Diddley, Bo*
300932 / Apr '98 / Hallmark

☐ **BORN WITH THE BLUES VOL.2**
Can't hold out: *Sharpville, Todd* / Sinner's prayer: *Arnold, Billy Boy* / Bad news: *Sykes, Roosevelt* / St. Louis sunset twist: *Sharp, Benny* / Rocky mountains: *Edwards, Clarence* / Lightnin' bug: *Louisiana Red* / Sloppy drunk: *Williams, 'Big' Joe* / Hey hey: *Turner, Ike* / Bye bye bird: *Williamson, Sonny Boy* / Rialto rock: *Reed, Buddy* / Leg woman: *King, Willie* / I don't know why: *Clearwater, Eddy* / In my younger days: *Guy, Buddy & Junior Wells* / You better be sure: *Gibson, Lacy* / Daddy rollin' stone: *Ricks, Jimmy & the Ravens* / Late one evening: *Lamb, Paul & The Blues Burglars* / Babe: *Orta, Paulo* / End of the blues: *Hooker, Earl*
EMPRCD 526 / Sep '94 / Emporio

☐ **BORN WITH THE BLUES VOL.2**
304812 / Apr '98 / Hallmark

☐ **BORSALINO**
74321579612 / 8 Jun '98 / Milan

☐ **BOSNIA - ECHOES FROM AN ENDANGERED WORLD**
SF 40407CD / Nov '94 / Smithsonian Folkways

☐ **BOSSA BEACH**
DOUCE 802CD / Nov '96 / Irma La Douce

☐ **BOSSA BRAVA VOL.2**
EX 3452 / Mar '97 / Instinct

☐ **BOSSA NOVA**
CD 62029 / Oct '93 / Saludos Amigos

☐ **BOSSA NOVA & SAMBA IN CONCERTO**
CD 62011 / Oct '93 / Saludos Amigos

☐ **BOSSA NOVA AND SAMBA GOLD COLLECTION, THE (2CD Set)**
R2CD 4063 / 20 Apr '98 / Deja Vu

☐ **BOSSA NOVA VOL.2**
GLO 143 / Aug '93 / RGE

☐ **BOSSTOWN SOUND 1968 (The Music & The Time/2CD Set)**
Ballad of the hip death goddess: *Ultimate Spinach* / Baroque no.1: *Ultimate Spinach* / Fragmentary march of green: *Ultimate Spinach* / Can't find the time to tell you: *Orpheus* / Walk away Renee: *Orpheus* / Brown arms in Houston: *Orpheus* / Tomorrow man: *Orpheus* / Maybe more than you: *Lost* / Everybody knows: *Lost* / Mystic (seven starry skies): *Lost* / Violet gown: *Lost* / Everybody knows: *Bagatelle* / Back on the farm: *Bagatelle* / Off with the old: *Chameleon Church* / In a kindly way: *Chameleon Church* / Hapiness child: *Ultimate Spinach* / Eddie's rush: *Ultimate Spinach* / Born under a bad sign: *Apple Pie Motherhood Band* / Gypsy: *Apple Pie Motherhood Band* / Goodbye girl: *Eden's Children* / Just let go: *Eden's Children* / Come in it's all for free: *Eagle* / Kickin' it back: *Eagle* / Separated: *Eagle* / Vacuum: *Puff* / Go with you: *Puff* / Looking in my window: *Puff* / Bright lit blue skies: *Rockin' Ramrods* / Can't you see: *Rockin' Ramrods* / Prophecies/ Morning blue: *Front Page Review* / Silver children: *Front Page Review* / Valley of eyes: *Front Page Review* / In my dark world: *Front Page Review* / In my dark world: *Ill Wind* / High flyin' bird: *Ill Wind* / American eagle tragedy: *Earth Opera* / Red Sox are winning: *Earth Opera*
CDWIK2 167 / Oct '96 / Big Beat

☐ **BOSTON BLUES BLAST VOL.1**
CDTC 1146 / May '94 / Tonecool

☐ **BOSTON COLLEGE - GAELIC ROOTS (2CD Set)**
KMCD 9514 / Dec '97 / Kells

☐ **BOTTLENECK BLUES**
TCD 5021 / Oct '95 / Testament

☐ **BOUNCY TECHNO ANTHEMS VOL.1**
DBMTRCD 21 / Dec '95 / Rogue Trooper

☐ **BOUNCY TECHNO ANTHEMS VOL.2 (2CD Set)**
DBMPCHCD 2A / Jun '96 / Punch

☐ **BOURBON COUNTY**
I gotta get drunk: *Jones, George & Willie Nelson* / Sittin' and thinkin': *Rich, Charlie* / You're still on my mind: *Byrds* / Drinking my baby goodbye: *Daniels, Charlie Band* / Bottle: *Wynette, Tammy* / Power of positive drinking: *Gilley, Mickey* / Drunk and crazy: *Bare, Bobby* / Swinging doors: *Price, Ray* / Liquor emotion: *Bandy, Moe* / Pop a top: *Campbell, Stacy Dean* / There stands the glass: *Smith, Carl* / Jack Daniels if you please: *Coe, David Allan* / Red red wine: *Duncan, Johnny* / What made Milwaukee famous (has made a loser out of me): *Anderson, Lynn* / She's more to be pitied: *Skaggs, Ricky* / Why am I drinkin': *Haggard, Merle* / Whiskey river: *Nelson, Willie* / Just one more: *Cash, Johnny*
4878742 / 26 Jan '98 / Columbia

☐ **BOUYON RASIN**
68988 / 5 Jan '98 / Tropical

☐ **BOUZOUKIS & SIRTAKIS**
995142 / Jun '93 / EPM

☐ BOX HITS 1998 VOL.1, THE (2CD Set)
Brimful of Asha: *Cornershop* / Dr. Jones: *Aqua* / Spice up your life: *Spice Girls* / Torn: *Imbruglia, Natalie* / All I have to give: *Backstreet Boys* / Avenging angels: *Space* / Old before I die: *Williams, Robbie* / When I need you: *Mellor, Will* / Ain't that just the way: *McNeal, Lutricia* / Never gonna let you go: *Moore, Tina* / Renegade master: *Wildchild* / Good enough (la vache): *Milk Inc.* / Telefunkin': *N-Tyce* / 5678: *Steps* / That's the way: *Clock* / Le disc jockey: *Encore* / Stay: *Sash* / All cried out: *Allure* / Sunchyme: *Dario G* / All around the world: *Oasis* / Halo: *Texas* / It's a beautiful thing: *Ocean Colour Scene* / Nanny in Manhattan: *Lilys* / Too real: *Levellers* / Walking on the sun: *Smash Mouth* / B boy stance: *Freestylers* / Loveshy: *Blond, Kristine* / Give me the rhythm: *Black Connection* / You've got a friend: *Brand New Heavies* / My fathers son: *Reeves, Conner* / Man behind the music: *Queen Pen* / Rewind: *Celetia* / All night all right: *Andre, Peter* / Crazy little party girl: *Carter, Aaron* / Da ya think I'm sexy: *N-Trance* / Let a boy cry: *Gala* / Santa Maria: *DJ Milano & Sam Fox* / It's raining men: *Wash, Martha & Ru Paul* / Make the world go around: *Sandy B*
TTVCD 2951 / 9 Mar '98 / Telstar TV

☐ BOX HITS 1998 VOL.2, THE (2CD Set)
Turn back time: *Aqua* / Stop: *Spice Girls* / Dance the night away: *Mavericks* / Stranded: *McNeal, Lutricia* / Never ever: *All Saints* / Feel it: *Tamperer & Maya* / Megamix: *Sash* / Surfin' USA: *Carter, Aaron* / Kung fu fighting: *Bus Stop* / Cleopatra's theme: *Cleopatra* / No no no: *Destiny's Child* / Boom boom: *N-Tyce* / Angel St.: *M-People* / All my life: *K-Ci & Jo Jo* / Raincloud: *Lighthouse Family* / Kiss the rain: *Myers, Billie* / Last thing on my mind: *Steps* / Words: *Boyzone* / Ballad of Tom Jones: *Space* / Beat goes on: *All Seeing I* / Fight for your right: *NYCC* / Vindaloo: *Fat Les* / Naked in the rain: *Blue Pearl* / Treat infamy: *Rest Assured* / It's like that: *Run DMC & Jason Nevins* / Been a long time: *Fog* / All my love: *Queen Pen* / Be alone no more: *Another Level* / Read my mind: *Reeves, Conner* / Seven days: *Blige, Mary J.* / Kick it: *Reggae Boyz* / Who am I: *Beenie Man* / Jungle brother: *Jungle Brothers* / Ruffneck: *Freestylers* / Cherish: *Pappa Bear* / Rock your body: *Clock* / Girls just want to have fun: *Happy Nation* / Deeper love: *Ruff Driverz* / Sounds of the wickedness: *Tzant* / La primavera: *Sash*
TTVCD 2974 / 1 Jun '98 / Telstar TV

☐ BOX OF TRASH (Pebbles Box Set/5CD Set)
CDBOXX 1 / 17 Nov '97 / Ubik

☐ BOX OR BE BOXED
EFA 123662 / 22 Sep '97 / Empty

☐ BOXING CLEVER
DRGNCD 943 / May '94 / Dragon

☐ BOYD IN THE VOID
D 1392 / Feb '96 / Distance

☐ BOYS
Forever girl: *OTT* / I need you: *3T* / Flava: *Andre, Peter* / Wishes: *Human Nature* / Love me for a reason: *Boyzone* / Shout: *Ant & Dec* / Love guaranteed: *Damage* / I can make you feel good: *Kavana* / Quit playing games: *Backstreet Boys* / Hey child: *East 17* / Day we find love: *911* / I feel you: *Andre, Peter* / Forever love: *Barlow, Gary* / Horny: *Morrison, Mark* / Let me here you say ole ole: *Outhere Brothers* / Good day: *Maguire, Sean* / Last night: *Az Yet* / Twelth of never: *Carter Twins* / I've got a little something for you: *MN8* / Pray: *Take That*
SONYTV 27CD / May '97 / Sony TV

☐ BOYZ OF SWING VOL.1
Return of the Mack: *Morrison, Mark* / Hey lover: *LL Cool J* / I got 5 on it: *Luniz* / Lifted: *Lighthouse Family* / Runnin': *Pharcyde* / Somethin' for the honeyz: *Jordan, Montell* / Pathway to the moon: *MN8* / Down low (nobody has to know): *R Kelly* / I'm in love: *Joe* / Candy rain: *Soul For Real* / Your love is a 187: *Whitehead Brothers* / Water runs dry: *Boyz II Men* / I'll never break your heart: *Backstreet Boys* / Freak in you: *Jodeci* / Freak me: *Silk* / Tell me what you want me to do: *Campbell, Tevin* / Feel the music: *Guru* / Do it for love: *4Mandu* / Throw your hands up: *LV* / 1,2,3,4 (Sumpin' new): *Coolio*
5354232 / Apr '96 / PolyGram TV

☐ BOYZ OF SWING VOL.2
One for the money: *Brown, Horace* / Ocean Drive: *Lighthouse Family* / Hit me off: *New Edition* / I can't sleep baby (if I): *R Kelly* / On bended knee: *Boyz II Men* / Love U 4 life: *Jodeci* / Tell me what you like: *Guy* / Housekeeper: *Men Of Vizion* / You want this party started: *Somethin' For The People* / Feel your pain: *Whitehead Brothers* / Hooked on you: *Silk* / Process of elimination: *Gable, Eric* / We've got it goin' on: *Backstreet Boys* / Let's get down: *Morrison, Mark* / Thank God it's Friday: *R Kelly* / Every little thing I do: *Soul For Real* / Happy: *MN8* / Flava: *Andre, Peter* / We got it: *Immature* / Baby don't go: *4Mandu* / This is how we do it: *Jordan, Montell* / Two can play that game: *Brown, Bobby* / Sensitivity: *Tresvant, Ralph* / So in love with you: *Duke* / Grave and the constant: *Fun Lovin' Criminals* / Doin' it: *LL Cool J* / She said: *Pharcyde* / Playa hata: *Luniz* / It's all the way live (now): *Coolio* / I must stand: *Ice-T*
5357552 / Sep '96 / PolyGram TV

☐ BOYZ WHO SOULED THE WORLD, THE
AHLCD 18 / Feb '94 / Hit

☐ BRABANTS VOLKSORKFEST (Flemish Folk Music From Belgium)
B 6827CD / Apr '96 / Auvidis/Ethnic

☐ BRAIN SMASHERS VOL.1 (2CD Set)
AUM 975002 / 1 Sep '97 / 80 AUM

☐ BRAIN TICKET - ADRENALIN TRIP
SPV 08992302 / Jul '95 / Subterranean

☐ BRAINDEAD VOL.3 (Hardcore Cyberspace)
EFA 008752 / Jan '96 / Shockwave

☐ BRAINDEAD VOL.4 (2CD Set)
ZYX 810872 / Nov '96 / ZYX

☐ BRAINDEAD VOL.5 (2CD Set)
EFA 008802 / 26 Jan '98 / Shockwave

☐ BRAND NEW SECONDHAND
D'yer mak'er: *Eek-A-Mouse* / Bed's too big without you: *Hylton, Sheila* / On and on: *Aswad* / Hey Joe: *Black Uhuru* / Around the world: *Krystal* / Everday people: *Brown, Rula* / Best of my love: *Aswad* / Walk on by: *I-Tones & Ram* / Just my imagination: *Murvin, Junior* / Some guys have all the luck: *Tucker, Junior* / Groovin': *Killer Bees* / Take me home country roads: *Toots & The Maytals*
RCD 10247 / Feb '93 / Rykodisc

☐ BRASIL
Batucada 1 / Zanzibar / Amazon river / Berimbau / Capoeira / Magika / Forro / Misturada / Batucada 2
SJRCD 022 / Nov '94 / Soul Jazz

☐ BRASIL DO FERRO E CORDA
SP / Viola vadio / Fieira / Mulher rendeira / O sertao e o mar / Ginga / Trois amis a Paris / Suingue moreno / Campeao / Ferro e corda / Jangada a Toa / Vera
X 55524 / Feb '98 / Aspic

☐ BRASIL: A CENTURY OF SONG (Folk And Tradition/Carnaval/Bossa Nova/Musica/4CD/Book Set)
CD 50002 / Mar '97 / Blue Jackel

☐ BRASILEIRO
CD 62038 / Nov '93 / Saludos Amigos

☐ BRASILIAN CHRISTMAS, A
Ave Maria / Christmas song / Air on a six string / Have yourself a merry little christmas / O little town of Bethlehem / I'll be home for Christmas / Dance Natahl / O Velhinho / Santa Claus is coming to town / White Christmas / Jingle bells / What child is this
TCD 4006 / Nov '96 / Astor Place

☐ BRASILICA
After sunrise: *Mendes, Sergio* / Barumba: *Tamba Trio* / Birimbau: *Dom Um Romao* / Vera Cruz: *Nascimento, Milton* / Roda: *Gil, Gilberto* / Solo: *Meirelles E Os Copa 5* / Crickets sing for Anamaria: *Valle, Marcus* / Blues Avolente: *Powell, Baden* / Adam Adam: *Joyce* / Tereza Sabe Sambar: *Regina, Elis* / Tamba: *Tamba Trio* / Zanzibar: *Mendes, Sergio* / Upa neguinho: *Mendes, Sergio* / Mas que nada: *Jorge, Ben* / Tudo Tom: *Donato, Joao* / Vig=digal: *Resende, Marcos*
5168532 / Aug '94 / Talkin' Loud

☐ BRASS BAND
PDSCD 524 / Aug '96 / Pulse

☐ BRASS BAND FAVOURITES
Guns of Navarone / Magnificent seven / Over the rainbow / Trouble with the tuba is / Headless horseman / Men of Harlech / Marche militaire / Death of glass / Tea for two / Puttin' on the Ritz / Coronation Street / March of the cobblers / My way / Ein schnapps / Swan / Sailing by / Tango taquin / Can can / Semper sousa / Colonel Bogey
CC 257 / Oct '90 / Music For Pleasure

☐ BRASS BAND SPECTACULAR
PLSCD 233 / Jul '97 / Pulse

☐ BRASS BAND WALTZES AND POLKAS
PS 65154 / Sep '95 / PlayaSound

☐ BRASS FIDDLE, THE
Muilleann Na Maidi / Vincent Campbell's mazurkas / Marine / Drowsy Maggie / Doodley doodley dank / Frost is all over / Low Highland / Mary o' The Wisp / King George IV / Bagpipe March / Wild Irishman / Johnny Boyle's Jig / Biddy of Muckross / Jackson's bean a'ti ar lar / Lancers / Johnny Ward's Paddy Bartley's / La Marseillaise / Miss Drummond of Perth / Rakish Paddy / Cat that kittled in Jamie's wig / Kilcar Mazurka / On the road from glen to carrick / Old wheel of fortune / James Byrne's mazurka / Seamas O'Beirn's Highland / Ri Mhim Na Salach / Curly haired boy
CC 44CD / Aug '96 / Claddagh

☐ BRAVE HEARTS (New Scottish Music)
Landlords walk: *Douglas, Blair* / Walking nightmare: *Old Blind Dogs* / South Park House: *Murray, Anne* / Walking the plank: *Murray, Anne* / Skyedance: *Murray, Anne* / Shopgirl: *Old Blind Dogs* / Ailean Duinn: *Capercaillie* / Bob Parsons strathspey: *Tannas* / Mairead nan cuiread: *Tannas* / Auld lang syne: *MacLean, Dougie* / Tarruing an crios: *Murray, Anne* / Nelson Mandela's welcome to the city of Glasgow: *Douglas, Blair* / Jenny's chicken/Glasgow reel: *Leahy* / An fhideag airgid: *Matheson, Karen* / E horo: *Lamond, Mary Jane* / Sleepy Maggie: *MacIsaac, Ashley* / Croix rousse: *Old Blind Dogs* / Kevin's celtic chasm: *Murray, Anne*
VNDCD 9 / 11 May '98 / Virgin

☐ BRAVE NEW WORLD VOL.6 (2CD Set)
ZYX 810922 / Mar '97 / ZYX

☐ BRAVE NEW WORLD VOL.7 (2CD Set)
ZYX 811132 / 18 Aug '97 / ZYX

☐ BRAVEHEARTS (Traditional Songs From Scotland)
Campbells are coming / Annie Laurie / Bluebells of Scotland / Charlie is my darling / My heart is in the highlands / Flow gently sweet Afton / John Anderson / Wi' a hundred pipers / Comin' thro' the rye / Blythe Blythe and merry was she / Bonnie Dundee / I have heard the Mavis singing / My love she's but a lassie yet / Loch Lomond / Ye banks and braes o' bonnie doon / Rowan tree / Miss Dairymple / Weel may the Keel Row / O my love is like a red red rose / Skye boat song / Highland fling / Sword dance three and one / Sword dance four and one / March of the Cameron men / Highland fling / Robin Adair / Whistle and I'll come to you / Come o'er the stream Charlie / Scots wha' hae wi' wallace bled / Wha'll buy caller herrin / Belles o' Edinboro' / My Jo and dearie o / Moon had climbed / Years awa' / Soldier's return / Duncan Gray / Birks o' Aberfeldy / I lo'e na a laddie but Ane / Come under my plaidie / Jock o' Hazeldean / Highland lad my love was born / Man's a man for a that / Auld lang syne / Danny boy / Wee highland glen
SUMCD 4071 / Nov '96 / Summit

☐ BRAZIL
Samba triste / Samba triste / Samba de una nota so (one note samba) / O amore e a rosa (love is a rose) / O menino desce do morro (little brown boy) / Manha de carnaval / Chora tua tristeza (cry your sadness) / So um amor (only one love) / Chega de saudade (no more blues) / Samba do lorinho (lorito's samba) / Bim bom / Samba do empashgi (empashgl's samba) / Balanco no samba (street dance) / Brazil
CD 62031 / Oct '93 / Saludos Amigos

☐ BRAZIL (Manha De Carnaval)
Mas que nada: *Oliveira, Valdeci* / Meia lua inteira: *Banda Brasil Corcovado* / Danca de Ana: *Da Silva, Jorginho* / Agua de beber: *Oliveira, Valdeci* / Paraiso: *Banda Brasil Corcovado* / Garot ada Ipanema: *Oliveira, Valdeci* / Bachianas Brasileiras no.5: *Braganca, Maria* / Nino de Vespa: *Da Silva, Jorginho* / Misterio do Som: *Banda Brasil Corcovado* / Noites caiocas: *Braganca, Maria* / Quebrando: *Martins, Zeduardo* / Aique saudade voce: *Banda Brasil Corcovado* / Manha de Carneval: *Braganca, Maria* / Batucada: *Banda Brasil Corcovado*
12548 / Aug '96 / Laserlight

☐ BRAZIL
3003742 / Jan '97 / IMP

☐ BRAZIL BLUE
Regra tres: *Monteiro, Doris* / *Nereci* (A name): *Djavan* / Cidade vazia (Empty city): *Banana, Milton Trio* / Sarau para radames: *Da Viola, Paulinho* / O cantador (The street singer): *Brasil, Victor Assis* / Comecar de novo: *Lins, Ivan* / Sao Tome (St Thomas): *Venturini, Flavio* / Vento de maio: *Regina, Elis* / Bate-papo (Shoot the breeze): *Os Choroes & Radames Gnattali* / Chorando baixinho (Crying low): *Ferreira, Abel* / Copacabana: *Sete, Bola* / Samba de uma nota so: *Joyce* / Corcovado: *Gilberto, Joao* / Emotiva no.1: *Delmiro, Helio* / Ecos (Echoes): *Nascimento, Joel* / Fica mal com deus (Be bad with God): *Quarteto Novo & Hermeto Pascoal* / Milage dos peixes (Miracle of the fishes): *Nascimento, Milton* / Cantareiro (Dish rack): *Mariano, Cesar Camargo* / Choro de Mae (Mother's choro): *Tiso, Wagner* / Nem uma lagrima (Not one tear): *Caymmi, Nana*
CDEMC 3676 / May '94 / Hemisphere

☐ BRAZIL CLASSICS VOL.1 (Beleza Tropical)
Ponta de lanca Africano: *Ben, Jorge* / Sonho meu: *Bethania, Maria e Gal Costa* / So quero um xodo: *Gil, Gilberto* / Um canto de afoxe para o bloco do ile / Leaozinho: *Veloso, Caetano* / Cacada: *Buarque, Chico* / Calice: *Buarque, Chico & Milton Nascimento* / Equatorial: *Borges Lo* / San Vincente / Quilombo, O el dorado negro: *Gil, Gilberto* / Caramba...galileu de galileia: *Ben, Jorge* / Caixa de sol: *Pereira, Nazare* / Maculele: *Pereira, Nazare* / Queixa: *Veloso, Caetano* / Andar com fe: *Gil, Gilberto* / Fio maravilha: *Ben, Jorge* / Anima: *Nascimento, Milton* / Terra: *Veloso, Caetano*
7599258052 / May '94 / Sire

☐ BRAZIL IS BACK
CDNEW 111 / Aug '97 / Charly

☐ BRAZIL NOW
Mares de ti: *Brown, Carlinhos* / Ambar: *Bethania, Maria* / Sem nao: *Lo Borges & Caetano Veloso* / Novo amore: *Caymmi, Nana* / An up dawn: *Elias, Elaine* / Ijexa: *Nunes, Clara & Gilberto Gil* / Vem me saciar: *Bragada* / La bella luna: *Os Paralamas Do Sucesso* / Irremediaves mortais: *Marina* / Pra quem quisir me visitar: *Pinheiro, Leila* / Ser boemio: *Melodia, Luiz* / Danca da solidao: *Da Viola, Paulinho* / Amor meuzinho: *Guedes, Bueto* / Fazenda: *Nascimento, Milton* / Seduzir: *Djavan* / Vento de maio: *Regina, Elis*
4931572 / 2 Mar '98 / Hemisphere

☐ BRAZILIAN EXPLOSION
Felix: *Faze Action* / Carlos Alberta: *Soul Generation* / Eder: *Arakatuba* / Pele: *Balistic Brothers* / Jarzinho: *Arakatuba* / Rivelinho: *Beats & Pieces* / Junior: *Box Saga* / Josimar: *Fila Brazillia* / Dunga: *Arakatuba* / Zico: *Arakatuba* / Riva: *Lilliana*
MRBCD 006 / Jan '97 / Mr. Bongo

☐ BRAZILIAN INSTRUMENTAL MUSIC
PS 66405 / Aug '98 / PlayaSound

☐ BRAZILIAN NIGHTS
CDCH 539 / Sep '91 / Milan

☐ BRAZILIAN NIGHTS
Samba de verao: *Valle, Marcus* / Triste: *Klugh, Earl* / Garota de impanema: *Banana, Milton Trio* / Conversa de botequim: *Monteiro, Doris* / Samba do aviao: *Neco* / How insensitive: *Lagrene, Birelli* / Nereci: *Djavan* / Cidade vazia: *Banana, Milton Trio* / Regra tres: *Monteiro, Doris* / Ecos: *Nascimento, Joel* / Emotiva no.1: *Delmiro, Helio* / Chorando baixinho: *Ferreira, Abel* / Bate Papo: *Os Choroes* / Quem e voce: *Razao Brasileira*
DC 880862 / May '97 / Disky

☐ BRAZILIAN THOROUGH
LHCD 019 / Jul '96 / Luv n' Haight

☐ BRAZILICA VOL.2
Falange dos tambores: *Silva, Robertinho* / Taureg: *Costa, Gal* / Cravo e canela: *MPB4* / Queremos guerica: *Gil, Gilberto* / Agua de beber: *Quarteto Em Cy* / Carcara: *Nara* / Os grilles: *Soares, Claudette* / Amor no samba: *Pitman, E. & B.* / Mas que nada: *Mendes, Sergio* / Feitinho pro poeta: *Soares, Claudette* / Mano Joao: *Wanderlea* / Relance: *Costa, Gal* / Ponta de lanca Africano: *Ben, Jorge* / Consolacao: *Powell, Baden* / Imprevisto: *Bossa Tres* / Casa forte: *Regina, Elis* / Mara ton leblon: *Vaz, Celia* / Camtemplacao: *Meirelles*
5350272 / Jul '97 / Talkin' Loud

☐ BREAD AND ROSES (Festival of Acoustic Music, Greek Theatre)
CDWIK 103 / Mar '92 / Big Beat

☐ BREAKAGE VOL.1
Covert operations: *Insync* / Lazy summer nights: *French, Robert* / Mind games: *Cloud 9* / Prelude: *Nookie* / Woodsnake: *Twisted Anger* / 8 Ball: *Twisted Anger* / 9277: *Twisted Anger* / Rare groove: *Keith, Ray* / Heavy metal: *Decoy* / Dragon: *Decoy*
PBLRCD 001 / 23 Feb '98 / Penny Black

☐ BREAKBEAT ODYSSEY, A
SM 80412 / 2 Mar '98 / Profile

☐ BREAKBEAT SAMPLER VOL.1
BBC 004CD / 14 Apr '98 / Breakbeat Culture

☐ BREAKIN' RECORDS PRESENTS VOL.1
BRK 11CD / 22 Jun '98 / Breakin'

☐ BREAKING MOULDS (Jazz Dance Live)
JAGZCD 001 / Nov '96 / Jagz

☐ BREAKING THE BARRIERS WITH SOUND (Captured By The Vibes)
Captured by the vibes: *Robotiks* / Didn't I: *Kofi* / I just want to love you: *Simmons, Leroy* / Dancing time: *Aisha* / Roots and culture: *Macka B* / Let's make it work: *Cross, Sandra* / And now you're gone: *McLean, John* / Baby, baby, my love's all for you: *Tajah, Paulette* / Mellow: *Intense* / Daylight and darkness: *Sister Audrey* / Captured by the dub: *Mad Professor*
ARICD 040 / Sep '88 / Ariwa Sounds

☐ BREAKING THE ICE VOL.1
MOLECD 022 / Jun '97 / Mole

☐ BREAKING THE ICE VOL.2
MOLECD 0092 / 30 Mar '98 / Listening Pearls

☐ BREAKPOINT
LSCD 02 / Aug '97 / London Something

☐ BREIZH & ROLL
062049 / Jul '96 / Wotre Music

☐ BRESIL 1914-1945
FA 077 / 24 Feb '98 / Fremeaux

☐ BRESIL '90
824882 / Nov '90 / BUDA

☐ BRESIL EN FETE: BRAZILIAN FOLK FESTIVITIES
PS 65098 / Nov '92 / PlayaSound

☐ BRESIL ESCALE PARIS
KAR 991 / Feb '97 / IMP

☐ BRETAGNE - LEGEND CELTE (2CD Set)
3037362 / 1 Jun '98 / Arcade

☐ BRIEF HISTORY OF AMBIENT VOL.1, A (152 Minutes 33 Seconds/2CD Set)
Flowered knife shadows: *Budd, Harold* / Thru metamorphic rock (edit): *Tangerine Dream* / Evening star: *Fripp, Robert & Brian Eno* / Mountain goat: *Amorphous Androgynous* / Sea of vapours: *Khan, Nusrat Fateh Ali* / Forge of volcan: *Hawkwind* / Requiem: *Killing Joke* / Ending (ascent): *Eno, Brian* / Marnia's tent: *Horowitz, Richard* / Rapido de noir: *Schmidt, Irmin & Bruno Spoerri* / Kazoo: *Ashra* / Their memories: *Budd, Harold & Brian Eno* / Leave your body: *Grid* / Electric becomes eclectic: *Franke, Christopher* / Phaedra (edit): *Tangerine Dream* / Delta rain dream: *Eno, Brian & Jon Hassell* / Monkey king: *Orbit, William* / Castle in the clouds: *Gong* / Life form: *Hawkwind* / Dance: *Laraaji* / Sacred stones: *Chandra, Sheila* / Earth floor: *Earth Floor* / Gift of fire: *Hassell, Jon* / End of words: *Material* / Panorphelia: *Froese, Edgar* / Voices: *Eno, Roger* / Traum mal wieder: *Czukay, Holger* / Home: *Sylvian, David*
AMBT 1 / Aug '93 / Virgin

☐ BRIEF HISTORY OF AMBIENT VOL.2, A (Imaginary Landscapes/2CD Set)
Call to prayer: *Maal, Baaba* / Tal coat: *Eno, Brian* / In mind: *Amorphous Androgynous* / Rubicon: *Tangerine Dream* / Healing place: *Sylvian, David* / Crystal clear: *Grid* / Nuages: *Sakamoto, Ryuichi* / Wind on water: *Fripp, Robert & Brian Eno* / Wildlife: *Penguin Cafe Orchestra* / When things dream: *Jansen, Steve & Richard Barbieri* / Magick mother invocation: *Gong* / Bringing down the light: *Sylvian, David & Robert Fripp* / Not another: *Jah Wobble* / One flower: *Goo Brothers* / Black Jesus: *God* / Mountain of needles: *Eno, Brian & David Byrne* / You are here: *Manzanera, Phil* / Bendel dub: *Prince Far-I* / Slow kaliuki: *Pokrovsky, Dmitri Ensemble* / Euterpe gratitude piece: *Allen, Daevid* / Water music: *Fripp, Robert* / New moon at red deer wallow: *Rain Tree Crow* / Attack of the 50 foot drum demon: *Bass-O-Matic* / Mekong: *Jam Nation* / Endless life: *Verve* / Nachtmusik schattenhaft: *Schulze, Klaus* / Arrival: *Voyager* / Specific gravity of smile: *Froese, Edgar* / Orovela: *Tsinandali Choir* / Dance no. 3: *Laraaji* / Premonition: *Sylvian, David & Holger Czukay* / Island: *Grid*
AMBT 2 / Dec '93 / Virgin

☐ BRIEF HISTORY OF AMBIENT VOL.3, A (The Music Of Changes/2CD Set)
Sygyt khoomei kargyraa: *Shu-De* / When the waters came to life: *Schmidt, Irmin* / Gringatcho demento: *Orbit, William* / Red earth (As summertime ends): *Rain Tree Crow* / Last emperor (Theme variation 1): *Sakamoto, Ryuichi* / 1988: *Fripp, Robert* / Epiphany: *Sylvian, David* / Study of six guitars: *Amorphous Androgynous* / Amy yo I: *Trisan* / Kingdom come: *Laswell, Bill* / You will be all right: *Ono, Seigen* / Meditation: *Laraaji* / Pendulum man: *Bark Psychosis* / Distant village: *Brook, Michael* / Mystery R.P.S. (No.8): *Jah Wobble* / Throw away your gun (Dub): *Prince Far-I* / Wind and lonely fences: *Fripp, Robert & Brian Eno* / Nuages (That which passes, passes like clouds): *King Crimson* / Mustt mustt: *Khan, Nusrat Fateh Ali* / Concert for gender: *Shakuhachi &*

Zither / Healthy colours: Fripp, Robert & Brian Eno / Cascade parts 2 and 3: Future Sound Of London / Summer storm: Quine, Robert & Fred Maher / Rising thermal: Hassell, Jon & Brian Eno / Mutability (A new begining is in the offing): Sylvian, David
AMBT 3 / May '94 / Virgin

☐ BRIEF HISTORY OF AMBIENT VOL.4, A (Isolationism/2CD Set)
Lost: KK Null / Flat without a back: O'Rourke, Jim / Dredger: Ice / Strangers: Bjorkenheim, Raoul / Daisy gun: Soviet France / Air lubricated free axis trainer: Labradford / Self strangulation: Techno Animal / Hallucinations (In memory of Reinaldo Arenas): Schutze, Paul / Silver rain fell: Scorn / Lost in fog: Disco Inferno / Six: Total / Once again I cast myself into the flames of atonement: Nijiumu / Aphex airlines: Aphrodisiac / Vandoevre: AMM / Lief: Seefeel / O'rang: Little Sister / Hydroponic: Experimental Audio Research / Desert flower: Sufi / Burial rites: Toop, David & Max Eastley / Crater scar (Adrenochrome): Main / Hide: Final / Thoughts: Lull / Kamom (Part one: Brohuk): Koner, Thomas
AMBT 4 / Aug '94 / Virgin

☐ BRILLIANCE FOR A BETTER FUTURE
SR 9455 / Nov '94 / Silent

☐ BRILLIANT 80'S, THE
Ball of confusion: BEF / Close but no cigar: Dolby, Thomas / Open your heart: Human League / Wood beez: Scritti Politti / Ghosts: Japan / Enola gay: OMD / Sexcrime: Eurythmics / Dancing with tears in my eyes: Ultravox / Is it a dream: Classix Nouveaux / Chant no.1: Spandau Ballet / Wishful thinking: China Crisis / Echo beach: Martha & The Muffins / Together in electric dreams: Oakey, Philip & Giorgio Moroder / Promised you a miracle: Simple Minds / Temptation: Heaven 17
CDVIP 199 / 13 Apr '98 / Virgin

☐ BRING DA RUCKUS (A Loud Story)
Bring da rukus: Wu Tang Clan / Lump lump: Sadat X / When eyes may shine: Xzibit & Mobb Deep / Love what I feel: April / Protect ya neck: Wu Tang Clan / Everyday and everynight: Michelle, Yvette / Pass out: Alkaholiks / Paparazzi: Xzibit / Reality: Evans, Adriana / Glaciers of ice: Raekwon The Chef / Advance to boardwalk: Cella Dwellas / I don't know: Next Level / Drop a gem on 'em: Mobb Deep / Only when I'm drunk: Alkaholiks / Lower Eastside: Delinquent Habits / CREAM: Wu Tang Clan / Survival of the fittest: Mobb Deep
743214421628 / Jan '97 / Loud

☐ BRINGING IT ALL BACK HOME (2CD Set)
HBCD 0010 / Feb '97 / Hummingbird

☐ BRINGING IT ALL BACK HOME - GUINNESS TOUR '92
HBCD 0001 / Oct '93 / Hummingbird

☐ BRISTOL SESSIONS, THE
Skip to my Lou: Dunford, Uncle Eck / O Molly dear: Shelton, B.F. / Walking in the way of Jesus: Shelton, B.F. / Newmarket wreck: Barker, J.W. / Soldier's sweetheart: West Virginia Coon Hunters / Greasy string: West Virginia Coon Hunters / Are you washed in the blood: Stoneman, Ernest V. / Henry Whitter's fox chase: Whitter, Henry / Bury me beneath the willow: Carter Family / Jealous sweetheart: Johnson Brothers / Will they ring the golden bells: Karnes, Alfred G. / Sandy river belle: Dad Blackard's Moonshiners / Sleep: Rodgers, Jimmie / Johnny Goodwin: Bull Mountain Moonshiners / I'm redeemed: Alcoa Quartet / Little log cabin by the sea: Carter Family / Old time corn shuckin': Blue Ridge Corn Shuckers / I want to go where Jesus is: Phipps, Ernest / Midnight on the stormy deep: Stoneman, Ernest V. & Irma Frost/Erk Dunford / Wandering boy: Carter Family / To the work: Karnes, Alfred G. / Blackeyed Susie: Nestor, J.P. / Passing Policeman: Johnson Brothers / Tell mother I will meet her: Stoneman, Ernest V. / Single girl, married girl: Carter Family / Potlicker blues: Watson, El / Longest train I ever saw: Tenneva Ramblers / Resurrection: Stoneman, Ernest V. / Storms are on the ocean: Carter Family / Wreck of the Virginian: Reed, Blind Alfred / Billy Grimes, the Rover: Shellor family / Standing on promises: Tennessee mountaineers / Mountaineer's courtship: Stoneman, Ernest V. & Irma Frost/Erk Dunford / Poor orphan child: Carter Family / I am bound for the promised land: Karnes, Alfred G.
CMFCD 011 / Jan '93 / Country Music Foundation

☐ BRIT BEAT (16 Swingin' Hits)
Hippy hippy shake: Swinging Blue Jeans / You were made for me: Freddie & The Dreamers / Concrete and clay: Unit 4+2 / Hello little girl: Fourmost / Do you want to know a secret: Kramer, Billy J. / I think of you: Merseybeats / You've got your troubles: Fortunes / I like it: Gerry & The Pacemakers / Do you love me: Poole, Brian & The Tremeloes / Tossing and turning: Ivy League / Game of love: Fontana, Wayne / He's in town: Rockin' Berries / Baby now that I've found you: Foundations / Tell me when: Applejacks / Little things: Berry, Dave / You were on my mind: St. Peters, Crispian
SUMCD 4070 / Nov '96 / Summit

☐ BRIT FUNK
AHLCD 40 / Aug '96 / Hit

☐ BRIT HOP & AMYL HOUSE
What's that sound: Sever, Sam & The Raiders Of The Lost Art / Real shit: Fried Funk Food / Dirt: Death In Vegas / Don't die foolish: Lionrock / Shaolin Buddha finger: Depth Charge / Voodoo people: Prodigy / Leave home: Chemical Brothers / Santa Cruz: Fatboy Slim / Blow the whole joint up: Monkey Mafia / Beat bastik: Hard Hop Heathen / Flow: Model 500 / Higher state of consciousness: Wink, Josh / Lobotomie: Top, Emmanuel / Renegade Soundwave: Renegade Soundwave / Bug powder dust: Bomb The Bass
HARD 10LPCD / Jun '97 / Concrete

☐ BRIT PACK BRAT PACK (16 Transatlantic Hits)
Itchycoo park: Small Faces / For your love: Yardbirds / Wild thing: Troggs / Baby come back: Equals / Letter: Box Tops / Bend me, shape me: American Breed / Gimme some loving: Davis, Spencer Group / Young girl: Puckett, Gary & The Union Gap / Happy together: Turtles / You've got your troubles: Fortunes / Reflections of my life: Marmalade / Here comes my baby: Tremeloes / Sugar sugar: Archies / 98.6: Keith / Judy in disguise: Fred, John & His Playboy Band / Woolly bully: Sam The Sham & The Pharaohs
SUMCD 4065 / Nov '96 / Summit

☐ BRITISH 60'S HIT COLLECTION, THE
Jesamine: Casuals / Just like Eddie: Heinz / Diamonds: Harris, Jet / Bobby's girl: Maughan, Susan / Tell him: Davies, Billie / Tell me when: Applejacks / Tossing and turning: Ivy League / Tobacco Road: Nashville Teens / Baby now that I've found you: Foundations / Pied piper: St. Peters, Crispian / You don't have to: Caravelles / Ain't misbehavin': Bruce, Tommy / Juliet: Four Pennies / Are you sure: Allisons / Walking back to happiness: Shapiro, Helen / Early in the morning: Vanity Fair / Moon river: Williams, Danny
PLATCD 209 / Feb '97 / Platinum

☐ BRITISH 60'S VOL.1, THE
I'm telling you now: Freddie & The Dreamers / I understand: Freddie & The Dreamers / If you gotta make a fool of somebody: Freddie & The Dreamers / You were made for me: Freddie & The Dreamers / Sorrow: Merseybeats / I think of you: Merseybeats / Wishing and hoping: Merseybeats / Don't turn around: Merseybeats / It's love that really counts: Merseybeats / I love you, yes I do: Merseybeats / He's in town: Rockin' Berries / Poor man's son: Rockin' Berries / Little children: Kramer, Billy J. / I'll keep you satisfied: Kramer, Billy J. / Bad to me: Kramer, Billy J. / Do you want to know a secret: Kramer, Billy J.
PLATCD 207 / Feb '97 / Platinum

☐ BRITISH 60'S VOL.2, THE
Here it comes again: Fortunes / You've got your troubles: Fortunes / Freedom come freedom go: Fortunes / Storm in a teacup: Fortunes / This gold ring: Fortunes / Twist and shout: Poole, Brian / Do you love me: Poole, Brian / Someone someone: Poole, Brian / Candy man: Poole, Brian / Little loving: Fourmost / Hello little girl: Fourmost / I'm in love: Fourmost / Game of love: Fontana, Wayne / Um um um um um: Fontana, Wayne / Pamela Pamela: Fontana, Wayne / Groovy kind of love: Fontana, Wayne
PLATCD 208 / Feb '97 / Platinum

☐ BRITISH BLUEGRASS VOL.1
BBMA 1001CD / Nov '95 / British Bluegrass

☐ BRITISH BLUES HEROES
MCCD 194 / Mar '95 / Music Club

☐ BRITISH BLUES INVASION
MACCD 150 / Aug '96 / Autograph

☐ BRITISH DANCE BANDS
AVC 539 / May '94 / Avid

☐ BRITISH DUB FUNK VOL.1
XEN 004CD / Jul '96 / Funky Xen

☐ BRITISH DUB FUNK VOL.2
XEN 005CD / Jul '96 / Funky Xen

☐ BRITISH INVASION, THE
TFP 025 / Nov '92 / Tring

☐ BRITISH POP HISTORY
16103 / May '94 / Laserlight

☐ BRITISH POP HISTORY - THE 60'S
16081 / Nov '93 / Laserlight

☐ BRITISH PUNK ROCK 1977
How much longer: Alternative TV / Radio wunderbar: Carpettes / Runnin' riot: Cock Sparrer / Corgi crap: Ooonies / Thinking of the USA: Eater / Johnny won't get to heaven: Killjoys / Insane society: Menace / Mucky pup: Puncture / Let's go: Blitzkrieg Bop / Questions: Suburban Studs / Withdrawel: Unwanted / Baby baby: Vibrators / Living on dreams: Depressions / Sick of you: Users / Chelsea '77: Maniacs / Hungry: Zeros / I can't come: Snivelling Shits / College girls: Cane / Nasty nasty: 999 / Can't wait until '78: Wasps
CDPUNK 500 / 26 May '98 / Anagram

☐ BRITISH R 'N' B INVASION, THE
Stay: Eternal / Back to life: Soul II Soul / Living in the light: Wheeler, Caron / It's a shame (my sister): Monie Love / Hanging on a string (contemplating): Loose Ends / Let me be the one: Five Star / Tell me (how it feels): 52nd Street / Say I'm your number one: Princess / Love zone: Ocean, Billy / All woman: Stansfield, Lisa / Never stop: Brand New Heavies / Tribute (right on): Pasadenas / Mama used to say: Junior / It's gonna be alright: Turner, Ruby
DOMECD 8 / Sep '96 / Dome

☐ BRITISH SOUL NATION (2CD Set)
5575182 / 3 Aug '98 / PolyGram TV

☐ BRITISH SOUL VOL.1
This beautiful day: Jackson, Levi / Serving a sentence of life: Douglas, Carl / Beautiful night: Thomas, Jimmy / What love brings: Bernard, Kenny / I'll hold you: Frankie & Johnny / Don't pity me: Lynn, Sue / Lost summer love: Silva, Lorraine / Our love is getting stronger: Night, Jason / Love is wonderful: Parfit, Paula / Stop and you'll become aware: Shapiro, Helen / Nobody knows: St. John, Tammy / Everything's gonna be alright: Arnold, P.P. / Invitation: Band Of Angels / If you knew me: Keyes, Ebony / Number one in your heart: Goins, Herbie / Need your love: Notations / Movin' away: Lynch, Kenny / Baby I don't need your love: Chants / Stand accused: Colton, Tony / Never ever: Clements, Soul Joe / Tears of joy: Merrell, Ray
GSCD 049 / Feb '95 / Goldmine

☐ BRITISH SOUL VOL.2
It'll never be over for me: Yuro, Timi / You're absolutely right: Aldo, Steve / It's just love: Andrews, John / Drifter: Baldry, Long John / You're ready now: Bennett, Bobby / He's gotta love me: Brooks, Elkie / What greater love: Hammer, Jack / Surrounded by a ray of sunshine: Jones, Samantha / One in a million: Keyes, Karol / Sweet music: Koobas / Can't stop talkin' 'bout my baby: Patto, Michael / He knows how to love me: Shapiro, Helen / On the brink: Vickers, Mike / Stay a little while: Benson, Barry / That's the tune: Proby, P.J. / Lying awake: Chandelle, Dany / And suddenly: Jones, Samantha / Too late to say you're sorry: Soulmates / Just like Romeo and Juliet: West Five / Everything I touch turns to tears: St. John, Barry / My own two feet: Lynch, Kenny / What about the music: Spice / When I'm gonna find her: Loyd, Mark / Too busy thinking about my baby: Latter, Gene / Marble and iron: James, Jimmy / Sell my soul to the devil: Douglas, Carl
GSCD 079 / Oct '96 / Goldmine

☐ BRITISH TRADITIONAL JAZZ COLLECTIONS VOL.2
8307882 / Mar '93 / Philips

☐ BRITJAZZ
MCCD 290 / Mar '97 / Music Club

☐ BRITS - THE AWARDS 1995 (2CD Set)
What's the frequency, Kenneth: REM / My heart: Young, Neil & Crazy Horse / Patience of angels: Reader, Eddi / Mmm mmm mmm mmm: Crash Test Dummies / Red shoes: Bush, Kate / Kiss from a rose: Seal / Cornflake girl: Amos, Tori / Sulky girl: Costello, Elvis / Run to you: Adams, Bryan / Hung up: Weller, Paul / You gotta be: Des'ree / Love town: Gabriel, Peter / More you ignore me, the closer I get: Morrissey / Thank you for hearing me: O'Connor, Sinead / Zombie: Cranberries / Motherless child: Clapton, Eric / I believe: Detroit, Marcella / Circle of life: John, Elton / Seven seconds: N'Dour, Youssou / Searching: China Black / Sweetness: Gayle, Michelle / Half the man: Jamiroquai / Just a step from heaven: Eternal / Midnight at the oasis: Brand New Heavies / Love the one you're with: Vandross, Luther / Sight for sore eyes: M-People / Mama said: Anderson, Carleen / If I only knew: Jones, Tom / So natural: Stansfield, Lisa / Sly: Massive Attack / Stay another day: East 17 / Things can only get better: D:Ream / Girls and boys: Blur / Insomniac: Echobelly / Wild ones: Suede / Numb: Portishead / Live forever: Oasis
MOODCD 39 / Feb '95 / Columbia

☐ BRITS - THE AWARDS 1996
Wonderwall: Oasis / Common people: Pulp / Universal: Blur / Lucky you: Lightning Seeds / Basket case: Green Day / Alright: Supergrass / Kelly's heroes: Black Grape / High and dry: Radiohead / Girl like you: Collins, Edwyn / Alright: Cast / Queer: Garbage / Afroride: Leftfield / Pumpkin: Tricky / Kung Fu: Ash / Down by the water: PJ Harvey / Stutter: Elastica / Isobel: Bjork / Roll with it: Oasis / Changing man: Weller, Paul / Perfect: Lightning Seeds / Hold me, thrill me, kiss me, kill me: U2 / Hand in my pocket: Morissette, Alanis / Gangsta's paradise: Coolio / Kiss from a rose: Seal / Circus: Kravitz, Lenny / Missing: Everything But The Girl / Itchycoo Park: M-People / Rough with the smooth: Nelson, Shara / Protection: Massive Attack / Raindrops keep falling on my head: Manic Street Preachers / Strangers when we meet: Bowie, David / Sentimental fool: Cole, Lloyd / If I were you: Lang, k.d. / Shapes and sizes: Armatrading, Joan
SONYTV 10CD / Feb '96 / Sony TV

☐ BRITS - THE AWARDS 1997 (2CD Set)
Australia: Manic Street Preachers / Govinda: Kula Shaker / Marblehead Johnson: Bluetones / Sugar coated iceberg: Lightning Seeds / Fun lovin' criminals: Fun Lovin' Criminals / Oh yeah: Ash / You're gorgeous: Baby Bird / Neighbourhood: Space / Circle: Ocean Colour Scene / If it makes you happy: Crow, Sheryl / I am, I feel: Alisha's Attic / She said: Longpigs / Twisted (everyday hurts): Skunk Anansie / Good enough: Dodgy / Bittersweet me (Memphis soundcheck): REM / Mile End: Pulp / Stripper vicar: Mansun / Peaches: Presidents Of The USA / Lust for life: Iggy Pop / Don't look back in anger: Oasis / Breathe: Prodigy / Cosmic girl: Jamiroquai / No woman, no cry: Fugees / Return of the mack: Morrison, Mark / Angel: Simply Red / Say you'll be there: Spice Girls / Give me a little more time: Gabrielle / Nobody knows: Rich, Tony Project / You're makin' me high: Braxton, Toni / Ocean drive: Lighthouse Family / Gangsta's paradise: Coolio / Talk to me: Babyface / One and one: Miles, Robert & Maria Naylor / Kootchi: Cherry, Neneh / Born slippy: Underworld / Christiansands: Tricky / Loops of fury: Chemical Brothers / Final hit: Leftfield / Theme from mission: impossible: Mullen, Larry & Adam Clayton
SONYTV 23CD / Feb '97 / Sony TV

☐ BRITS - THE AWARDS 1998
Stand by me: Oasis / Diesel power: Prodigy / Karma police: Radiohead / Block rockin' beats: Chemical Brothers / Good good people: Embrace / Brown paper bag: Size, Roni / Tubthumping: Chumbawamba / High times: Jamiroquai / Black eyed boy: Texas / Even after all: Quaye, Finley / Beetlebum: Blur / You're the one I love: Ama, Shola / Bachelorette: Bjork / I know where it's at: All Saints / Got 'til it's gone: Jackson, Janet / Novocaine for the soul: Eels / On and on: Badu, Erykah / She's a good girl: Sleeper / Shelter: Brand New Heavies / Traffic: Stereophonics / My father's son: Reeves, Conner / Best: Orton, Beth / Real thing: Stansfield, Lisa / Tied to the 90's: Travis / I wanna be the only one: Eternal / Bitch: Brooks, Meredith / Phenomenon: LL Cool J / Spice up your life: Spice Girls / Ooh la la: Coolio / Old before I die: Williams, Robbie / Drop dead gorgeous: Republica / Just a girl: No Doubt / Outlaw: Olive / Arms around the world: Louise / Sunchyme: Dario G / You and me song: Wannadies / Equador: Sash / I'm kissing you: Des'ree / Choose life: PF Project
SONYTV 36CD / 26 Jan '98 / Sony TV

☐ BROKEN BEATEN SCRATCHED (Big Beat Breaks For The Chemical Generation)
Levy break / Shiver / Cold sweat / Dubism / Bassity roller / Loud break grooves / You know it / Shake / Beat freak / Secret beats / Memphis groove / Bad break / Smokin' / Bad young beats / Watcha sayin / Juiced / Apache / Buggin' beat / Voodoo / Garibaldi beats / Congetto / Sciene loop / Rumble riddim / Mighty break / Big blue / Assembly rhythm / Lower east loop / Drum culture / Get up get down / Bongola / Who can drum / Rolling thunder / Ensnared / Laid back / Take it to the bridge / Protest break / Don't mess / Skaville / Friday feeling / Neoclassical
SUMCD 4171 / 26 Jan '98 / Summit

☐ BROKEN BEATS & DIRTY PROMISES
TRPHOP 2002CD / Nov '96 / North South

☐ BROKEN DREAMS (18 Classic Tearjerkers)
What becomes of the broken hearted: Ruffin, Jimmy / When a man loves a woman: Sledge, Percy / Stand by me: King, Ben E. / If you don't know me by now: Melvin, Harold & The Bluenotes / Just walking in the rain: Ray, Johnnie / Love letters in the sand: Boone, Pat / Only you (and you alone): Platters / End of the world: Davis, Skeeter / Tell Laura I love her: Peterson, Ray / Hey Paula: Paul & Paula / (Hey there) Lonely girl: Holman, Eddie / Young girl: Puckett, Gary & Union Gap / Groovy kind of love: Fontana, Wayne / Ferry cross the Mersey: Gerry & The Pacemakers / Crying game: Berry, Dave / To know him is to love him: Teddy Bears / Chapel of love: Dixie Cups / Rhythm of the rain: Cascades
SUMCD 4193 / 11 May '98 / Summit

☐ BROKEN HEARTED
Just walking in the rain: Ray, Johnnie / Love letters in the sand: Boone, Pat / Only you (and you alone): Platters / End of the world: Davis, Skeeter / Tell Laura I love her: Peterson, Ray / Hey Paula: Paul & Paula / Hey there lonely girl: Holman, Eddie / Young girl: Puckett, Gary & The Union Gap / Groovy kind of love: Fontana, Wayne / Ferry 'cross the Mersey: Gerry & The Pacemakers / Cryin' game: Berry, Dave / To know him is to love him: Teddy Bears / Chapel of love: Dixie Cups / Rhythm of the rain: Cascades / What becomes of the broken hearted: Ruffin, Jimmy / When a man loves a woman: Sledge, Percy / Stand by me: King, Ben E. / If you don't know me by now: Melvin, Harold & The Bluenotes
ECD 3049 / Jan '95 / K-Tel

☐ BROKEN HEARTED (18 Bittersweet Love Songs)
Sad sweet dreamer: Sweet Sensation / Who were you with in the moonlight: Dollar / Be thankful for what you've got: De Vaughn, William / Way we were: Knight, Gladys & The Pips / I'm doin' fine now: New York City / Somebody else's guy: Brown, Jocelyn / Where did our love go: Elbert, Donnie / Goodbye nothing to say: Javells / I couldn't live without your love: Clark, Petula / Don't throw your love away: Searchers / Funny how love can be: Ivy League / Same old feeling: Pickettywitch / Let the heartaches begin: Baldry, Long John / Tired of waiting for you: Kinks / Sandy: Travolta, John / Making up again: Goldie / I'll have to go away: Jigsaw / Rainin' through my sunshine: Real Thing
SUMCD 4106 / Nov '96 / Summit

☐ BROOKLYN'S DOO WOP VOL.3
Goodbye: Carousels / Local city: Donnie & The Chapells / I want only you: Decoys / Mother nature: Del-Counts / I wonder: Stylists / Since you went away: Fascinations / Happy honeymoon: Four Fellows / Without a song: Junior & The Saharas / My inspiration: Inspirations / Crazy feeling: Riley, Russ & The Five Sounds / Whisper: Concepts / I'll pray: Bronay, Johnny & The Magics / Hey hey baby: Moonlights / I found my love: Fabutones / Why do fools fall in love: Decoys / Never let me go: Verdicts / My Juanita: Vel-Tones / Out in the cold again: Decoys / Don't say goodbye: Vel-Tones / Miracle of love: Myles, Donnie & The Dukes / This is my love: Jive Chords / Travelling stranger: Jive Chords / Fool was I: Vel-Tones / Jungle: Concepts
BB 55055 / Aug '97 / Buffalo Bop

☐ BROTHER, CAN YOU SPARE A DIME
Were you there / Maledetto / Lungi da te / Bist du bei mir / Hear de lambs/Plenty good room / Go down Moses / Bye and bye / Steal away / Crucifixion / Roun' about de mountain / Standin' in the need of prayer / Negro spiritual medley / Heav'n heav'n / Waterboy / Go down Moses/Deep river / Couldn't hear nobody pray / Every time I feel the spirit / Swing low, sweet chariot / Goin' to shoot all over God's heaven / Ol' man river / Street cries of New Orleans / Cobbler's song / Brother can you spare a dime
GEMMCD 9484 / Mar '91 / Pearl

☐ BROTHERHOOD
NLB 003CD / Mar '96 / No Looking Back

☐ BROTHERHOOD
LHCD 018 / Jul '96 / Luv n' Haight

☐ BROTHERS IN BLUES, SISTERS IN SOUL (18 Classic Tracks)
(Sittin' on the) Dock of the bay: Sledge, Percy / B-A-B-Y: Thomas, Carla / Harlem shuffle: Bob & Earl / Dancing in the street: Reeves, Martha / Green onions: Cortez, Dave 'Baby' / Ride Captain ride: Blues Image / It's in his kiss (the shoop shoop song): Everett, Betty / Knock on wood: Floyd, Eddie / My guy: Wells, Mary / Rescue me: Bass, Fontella / Soul man: Sam & Dave / I say a little prayer: Reeves, Martha / Tell it like it is: Neville, Aaron / Drift away: Gray, Dobie / Stand by me: King, Ben E. / All I could do was cry: James, Etta / Wake up everybody: Melvin, Harold & The Bluenotes / When a man loves a woman: Sledge, Percy
ECD 3066 / Jan '95 / K-Tel

☐ BROWN GIRL IN THE RING
ROUCD 1716 / Sep '97 / Rounder

☐ BROWNSWOOD WORKSHOP MULTI-DIRECTION VOL.2
Spontaneity: Jazz Brothers / April in Tokyo: Pronoia / Hug: Tiny Voice Production / La lune: Naoyuki Honzawa / Return of the space ape: Audio Active / Seasons change: Sylk 130 / Deep water: Trio Da Lata / Por El: Diet Music / Tune for us: Kruder & Dorfmeister / Rock 'n' roll philosophy: Love TKO / Is it worth it: DJ Milo
5286792 / Mar '96 / Talkin' Loud

☐ BROWSER
SCHTUMM 001CD / Sep '96 / Jealous

☐ BRUM BEAT
MBRCD 0002 / Nov '97 / Merseybeat

☐ **BUBBLED UP ON DUB (Natural Progression)**
Wild flower: *Herb* / In the valley: *Arkology* / Dusk till dawn: *Steff* / Sticks and stones: *Doof* / World today: *Arkology* / Blow up dub: *Blow Up* / Zero gravity: *Steff* / Many lands: *Herb* / Celebration: *Steff*
GLISSCD 004 / 23 Feb '98 / Gliss

☐ **BUBBLIN' UNDER VOL.1 (2CD Set)**
Tears: *Underground Solution & Colour Girl* / Tribute: *Gerideau* / Thinking about you: *Lady M* / Countdown: *Frontline* / Joy: *Wood, Cathy* / Groovin': *Garcia, Si & MC Rusty* / Contagious love: *Dockins, Charles* / Step to it: *Brown, Everton* / It's your love: *LZ Love* / Jazz light: *Spanish Inquistion* / 6 million ways to die: *Event* / Swing Lo: *United Club Artists* / Watch the flex: *Flex Kru* / Muzik: *Northbank* / Right before my: *N&G* / Freestylin': *Alex Hustler* / Get happy: *Underground Solution* / Inner city: *George E* / Duster: *Wiseguys & Dave Courtney* / Manor experience: *Manor Boys* / One more time: *Evelyn Divas Of Colour* / Extra large: *Global*
DSRCD 003 / 1 Jun '98 / Dreamscape

☐ **BUDAL LARDIL**
LARRCD 285 / Jun '94 / Larrikin

☐ **BUDDHIST CHANT 1/MAHA PIRIT - THE GREAT CHANT**
JD 6512 / Nov '90 / Jecklin Disco

☐ **BUDDHIST CHANT VOL.1**
VICG 50392 / Mar '96 / JVC World Library

☐ **BUENAVENTURA DURRUTI (2CD Set)**
777733 / Apr '97 / Nato

☐ **BUENOS AIRES 30'S TANGOS**
995222 / Jun '93 / EPM

☐ **BUENOS AIRES BANONEON ORCHESTRA**
CDCH 702 / Feb '91 / Milan

☐ **BUENOS AIRES BY NIGHT**
La cumparsita: *Basso, Jose* / El firulete: *Basso, Jose* / El choclo: *Sexeto Mayor* / Adios nonino: *Sexeto Mayor* / De vuelta y media: *Varela, Hector* / Paloma blanca: *Varela, Hector* / Quejas de bandoneon: *Troilo, Anibal* / Danzarin: *Troilo, Anibal* / Verano porteno: *Garello, Paul* / Margarita de agosto: *Garello, Paul* / La Cachila: *Pugliese, Osvaldo* / La Yumba: *Pugliese, Osvaldo* / El dia que me quieras: *Gardel, Carlos* / Mi buenos aires querido: *Gardel, Carlos* / Grisel: *Mores, Mariano* / Taquito militar: *Mores, Mariano* / La punalada: *Canaro, Francisco* / La tablada: *Canaro, Francisco* / Yira yira: *Sassone, Florindo* / Adios muchachos: *Sassone, Florindo*
CDEMS 1487 / May '93 / EMI

☐ **BUENOS AIRES TO PARIS 1924-1938**
Una noche en El Garron: *Pizarro, Manuel* / La jira: *Pizarro, Manuel* / Hay puchera a la criolla: *Pizarro, Manuel* / Siempre: *Pizarro, Manuel* / Araca: *Pizarro, Manuel* / Bandonean arrabalero: *Lucchesi, Jose M.* / Pebeta de arrabal: *Lucchesi, Jose M.* / Esta noche me emborracho: *Bachicha* / Anoche a las dos: *Pizzaro, Salvador* / Queja indianna: *Pizzaro, Salvador* / Zaraza: *Pizzaro, Salvador* / Aquella espanola: *Pizzaro, Salvador* / Mama...yo quiero un novio: *Du Perron, Rolando* / Suerta loca: *Perron, S* / Tahiti: *Pesenti, A.J* / La viruta: *Orlando* / Beautiful: *Tiny Quentin* / Alma del bandoneon: *Mateo, Juan* / La melodie de notre adieu: *Canaro, Rafael* / Un violon en la noche: *Melfi, Mario* / Mala junta: *Alemany, Bernardo*
HQCD 99 / Oct '97 / Harlequin

☐ **BUILT**
RI 039 / Sep '96 / Rather Interesting

☐ **BULERIAS 1930-1940 (Music From Spain)**
995792 / Sep '96 / EPM

☐ **BULGARIA - MUSIC OF SHOPE COUNTY**
LDX 274970 / Apr '94 / La Chant Du Monde

☐ **BULGARIAN BRASS**
PAN 153CD / Mar '95 / Pan

☐ **BULGARIAN FOLK MUSIC**
SOW 90115 / Sep '93 / Sounds Of The World

☐ **BULLDOG AT NIGHT**
USCD 3043 / Jun '97 / Urban Sound Of Amsterdam

☐ **BULLERENGUE, THE (Colombia)**
C 560129 / Jul '98 / Ocora

☐ **BULLSEYE BLUES CHRISTMAS**
CDBB 9567 / Oct '95 / Bullseye Blues

☐ **BULLSHIT - PUNK (6CD Set)**
DTKBOX 5859 / 25 May '98 / Dressed To Kill

☐ **BUMP 'N' HUSTLE**
New London alliance: *Savonne, Maxim & Dean* / Give it to me: *Fontaine, Miles* / Gunman: *187 Lockdown* / House clash: *Wildcat* / Show ya love: *Soft Butter Productions* / Jazz in the house: *Smokin' Beats* / Bad boys: *Baffled Republic* / Keep it warm: *Mowatt, Andy* / London thing: *Garcia, Scott & MC Styles* / Let me tell you: *Jump Up Crew* / Things are never: *Operator & Baffled* / Nu London alliance: *Nu London Alliance* / One more time: *Divas Of Color* / Nu London bassline: *Nu London Alliance*
CDHIGH 10 / 15 Dec '97 / High On Rhythm

☐ **BURGHERS VOL.1**
BW 1 / Sep '97 / Big Wink

☐ **BURIED ALIVE VOL.1**
BCD 4052 / Feb '96 / Bomp

☐ **BURIED ALIVE VOL.2 - THE BEST OF SMOKE VOL.7**
BCD 4058 / Jan '97 / Bomp

☐ **BURLINGTON COFFEEHOUSE VOL.1**
ALC 127CD / Aug '96 / Alcazar

☐ **BURN ONE YP**
RR 88382 / 24 Nov '97 / Roadrunner

☐ **BURNING AMBITIONS (A History Of Punk)**
Boredom: *Buzzcocks* / Bingo masters breakout: *Fall* / 12XU: *Wire* / Life: *Alternative TV* / Keys to your heart: *101'ers* / I'm alive: *999* / Gary Gilmore's eyes: *Adverts* / (Get a) grip (on yourself): *Stranglers* / Baby baby: *Vibrators* / Oh bondage up yours: *X-Ray Spex* / I'm stranded: *Saints* / Chinese rocks: *Thunders, Johnny & The Heartbreakers* / Love song: *Damned* / In a rut: *Ruts* / Stranglehold: *UK Subs* / Flares and slippers: *Cockney Rejects* / Wait: *Killing Joke* / Holiday in Cambodia: *Dead Kennedys* / Last rockers: *Vice Squad* / Someone's gonna die: *Anti Pasti* / City baby attacked by rats: *GBH* / Russians in the DHSS: *Attila The Stockbroker* / Lust for glory: *Angelic Upstarts*
CDBRED 3 / Jun '96 / Anagram

☐ **BURNING AMBITIONS VOL.2 (A History Of Punk)**
Then he kissed me: *Hollywood Brats* / I don't care: *Boys* / Thinkin' of the USA: *Eater* / Safety pin stuck in my heart: *Fitzgerald, Patrick* / Automatic lover: *Vibrators* / Action time vision: *Alternative TV* / Murder of Liddle Towers: *Angelic Upstarts* / CID: *UK Subs* / Police car: *Cockney Rejects* / Teenage kicks: *Undertones* / Totally wired: *Fall* / Kill the Poor: *Dead Kennedys* / Exploited barmy army: *Exploited* / So what: *Anti Nowhere League* / Seventeen years of hell: *Partisans* / Stab the Judge: *One Way System* / Run like hell: *Peter & The Test Tube Babies* / Smash the discos: *Business* / Warriors: *Blitz* / Dozen girls: *Damned* / Summer of '81: *Violators* / Megalomania: *Blood* / Vengeance: *New Model Army* / You'll never know: *New Model Army*
CDPUNK 81 / Jun '96 / Anagram

☐ **BURNING AMBITIONS VOL.3**
If the kids are united: *Sham 69* / Warhead: *UK Subs* / Greatest cockney rip off: *Cockney Rejects* / Another dead soldier: *Anti Pasti* / Decontrol: *Discharge* / Too drunk to fuck: *Dead Kennedys* / Transvestite: *Peter & The Test Tube Babies* / Ramrton song: *Disorder* / Puppets of war: *Chron Gen* / Let's break the law: *Anti Nowhere League* / No survivors: *GBH* / Stand strong stand proud: *GBH* / Everybody jitterbug: *Toy Dolls* / Viva la revolution: *Adicts* / Burn 'em down: *Abrasive Wheels* / Jerusalem: *One Way System* / Farmyard boogie: *Chaos UK* / Die for your government: *Varukers* / Fuck religion, fuck politics, fuck the lot of you: *Chaotic Dischord* / Decapitated: *Broken Bones*
CDPUNK 98 / Jun '97 / Anagram

☐ **BURNING BRIGHTLY**
CDRPM 0021 / Sep '97 / RP Media

☐ **BURNING LOVE**
HRCD 8045 / Dec '93 / Disky

☐ **BURNING UP**
CDTRL 336 / Mar '94 / Trojan

☐ **BURNING UP VOL.3**
CDBS 563 / Jan '97 / Burning Sounds

☐ **BURNLEY BLUES FESTIVAL '89**
JSPCD 228 / Jun '89 / JSP

☐ **BURRO PRESENTS BEATSPERIMENTS**
EMCD 1 / Oct '96 / Elephant Music

☐ **BUSTIN' OUT**
VPRC 1046 / May '89 / Steely & Cleevie

☐ **BUSTIN' SURFBOARDS**
Surf jam: *Beach Boys* / Out of limits: *Marketts* / Fast freight: *Valens, Ritchie* / Our man Flint: *Challengers* / Curl rider: *Surf Raiders* / Our favorite Martian: *Fuller, Bobby* / Perfect wave: *Norman, Neil* / Wild weekend: *Rockin' Rebels* / Victor: *Dale, Dick & His Del-Tones* / Bustin' surfboards: *Tornadoes* / Yang bu: *Messina, Jim* / Surf rider: *Lively Ones* / Lonely surfer: *Nitzsche, Jack*
GNPD 2152 / Jul '95 / GNP Crescendo

☐ **BUYAKA (The Ultimate Dancehall Collection)**
923722 / Mar '94 / Big Beat

☐ **BY THE FIRESIDE**
RFLCD 218 / 6 Oct '97 / Reflection

☐ **BY THE RIVERS OF BABYLON (Timeless Hymns Of Rastafari)**
SH 45031 / Mar '97 / Shanachie

C

☐ **C IS FOR CHERRIES**
KUDCD 008 / Jul '96 / Kudos

☐ **CABARET CHRISTMAS, A**
Winter wonderland: *Hampton Callaway, Ann & Billy Stritch* / Christmas love song: *Hampton Callaway, Ann* / I'll be home for Christmas: *Stritch, Billy* / Merry Christmas to me/Hard candy Christmas: *Sullivan, K.T.* / Let it snow, let it snow, let it snow: *Carroll, Barbara* / It must be Christmas: *Mulligan, Gerry* / After the holiday: *Marcovicci, Andrea* / Silent night: *Akers, Karen & Andrea Marcovicci* / I don't remember Christmas: *Akers, Karen* / Christmas waltz: *Whiting, Margaret* / What are you doing New Year's Eve: *Haran, Mary Cleere* / Christmas in the city: *Leonhart, Jay* / Have yourself a merry little Christmas: *Loudon, Dorothy* / White Christmas: *Cook, Barbara*
DRGCD 91415 / Nov '93 / DRG

☐ **CABARET'S GOLDEN AGE VOL.1**
Lili Marlene: *Andersen, Lale* / Suppose: *Baker, Josephine* / Just once for all time: *Garat, Henri* / La cucaracha: *Niessen, Gertrude* / Solomon: *Welch, Elisabeth* / Luxury cruise: *Andersen, Inga* / I'm one of the queens of England: *Byng, Douglas* / Il m'a vue nue: *Mistinguett* / I want yer, ma honey: *Guilbert, Yvette* / I should like to be really in love: *Ahlers, Anny* / 2-2-22 Timbuctoo: *Blaney, Norah* / Pretty little baby: *Baker, Josephine* / I'm just a poor little woman: *Leander, Zarah* / Folies musicales: *Betove* / Under the red lamps: *Andersen, Lale* / Je voudrais vous dire en Francais: *Serrano, Rosita* / Is your heart still free: *Ahlers, Anny* / Nymph errant: *Lawrence, Gertrude* / Hollyhollyhollyhollyhollywood: *Hansen, Max* / Ca c'est Paris: *Mistinguett* / Symphonie: *Dietrich, Marlene* / Spring: *Byng, Douglas* / When lights are low: *Welch, Elisabeth* / La Conga: *Niessen, Gertrude* / Falling in love again: *Dietrich, Marlene*
PASTCD 9727 / '90 / Flapper

☐ **CABARET'S GOLDEN AGE VOL.2**
Night and day: *Hutchinson, Leslie 'Hutch'* / Darling je vous aime beaucoup: *Hildegarde* / Button up your shoes and dance: *Wall, Max* / Wistaria: *Mayerl, Billy* / Stately homes of England: *Coward, Sir Noel* / La paloma: *Serrano, Rosita* / Drei rote rosen: *Andersen, Lale* / You've got to pay for everything you get: *Frankau, Ronald* / Hold 'em Joe: *Lili-Verona* / Je ne dis pas non: *Chevalier, Maurice* / Come and join the no-shirt party: *Long, Norman* / Am I blue: *Anona Winn* / Le chanson des rues: *Sablon, Jean* / Thank you so much, Mrs Lowsborough-Goodby: *Porter, Cole* / Where are the songs: *Coward, Sir Noel* / Sombreros et mantillas: *Ketty, Rina* / Paddlin' Madelin' home: *Layton & Johnstone* / Room with a view: *Hildegarde* / Mon coeur: *Chevalier, Maurice* / Two little babes in the wood: *Porter, Cole* / I'm shooting high: *Marsh, Carolyn* / Her mother came too: *Buchanon, Jack* / Le potpourri d'Alain Gerbault: *Printemps, Yvonne*
PASTCD 9737 / Mar '91 / Flapper

☐ **CABARETS AND CHANSONNIERS (3CD Set)**
984072 / Jun '97 / EPM

☐ **CADENCE STORY, THE**
Butterfly / All I have to do is dream / Poetry in motion / Lollipop / I'm gonna knock on your door / Rumble / Forty five men in a telephone booth / Dead Don / Bye bye love / Ballad of Davy Crockett / Mr. Sandman / Hernando's hideaway / I like your kind of love / Born to be with you / Lighthouse / Message from James Dean / Wake up little Susie / Baby doll / I love my girl / Swag / Cherry berry wine / Without you / (Girls, girls, girls) Made to love / Since I fell for you / IT keeps right on a-hurtin' since I left / Ain't gonna wash for a week / Ebb Tide / Eh, cumpari
CDCHD 550 / Aug '95 / Ace

☐ **CAFE CLASSICS**
74321263432 / Mar '95 / RCA

☐ **CAFE DE PARIS 1930-1941 (24 Accordian Classics From The Boulevards of Paris)**
Falmbee montalbanaise / L'accordeoniste / El ferrero / Enivrante / Strange harmony / Mado / Matelotte / Quand on se promene / Sporting java / Pepee / La guinguette a ferme ses volets / Swing valse / Brise napolitaine / Soir de dispute / Le charmeur de serpents / Les triolets / Gallito / Swing '39 / Pinsonnette / Rosetta / Melancolie / Jeanette
MCCD 096 / Mar '93 / Music Club

☐ **CAFE DEL MAR IBIZA VOL.2**
Haunted dancehall: *Sabres Of Paradise* / Making of Jill: *Mark & Henry's* / Tarenah: *Lab* / Moment scale: *Silent Poets* / Entre dos aguas: *De Lucia, Paco* / Sunset: *TBMP* / Eugene: *Salt Tank* / Devotion: *D-Note* / Blue eyes sunrise: *Woodshed* / Easter song: *Man Called Adam* / Unity: *Antoine, Marc* / Everybody loves the sunshine: *Ramp* / La mar: *Atlas*
REACTCD 062 / May '97 / React

☐ **CAFE DEL MAR IBIZA VOL.3**
Blue bar: *After Life* / Dusk: *Pressure Drop* / Emotions of paradise: *Miro* / Sueno Con Mexico: *Metheny, Pat* / Nights interlude: *Nightmares On Wax* / Tones: *Nova Nova* / Asia: *Neri, Alex* / Dust of life: *Fazed Idjuts* / Walking on air: *Padilla, Jose* / My freedom: *Beat Foundation* / Redemption song: *Moodswings* / Panama bazaar: *Eighth Wave* / Last picture show: *Heavy Shift* / Spells and angels: *Minister Of Noise*
REACTCD 084 / May '97 / React

☐ **CAFE DEL MAR IBIZA VOL.4**
Que bonito: *Padilla, Jose* / Sun shines better: *Martyn, John* / Leo leo: *Indo Aminata* / Grillos: *Fernandez, Paco* / Return journey: *Voices Of Kwahn AD* / Miracle Road: *Les Jumeaux* / No sant: *Diop, Wasis & Lena Fiagbe* / Out of time: *Levitation* / Place De La Concorde: *Fila Brazillia* / Offshore: *Chicane* / Fifth and avenida: *Afterlife* / Troubled girl: *Ramirez, Karen* / Lula: *Mison, Phil* / Street tattoo: *Getz, Stan*
5539072 / Aug '97 / Manifesto

☐ **CAFE DEL MAR IBIZA VOL.5**
Mumbai theme tune: *Rahman, A.R.* / More than ever people: *Levitation* / Appreciation: *Jelly & Fish* / Paradise: *Nookie* / Penelope: *4 Wings* / Tout est bleu: *Strong, Ame* / Uschi's groove: *Ballistic Brothers* / Lubumba: *New Funky Generation* / Face a la mer: *Les Negresses Vertes* / Talking with myself: *Electribe 101* / Pojo pojo: *Cyberfit* / Transfatty acid: *Lamb* / Angels landing: *Salt Tank* / Mani: *Fernandez, Paco* / Close cover: *Mertens, Wim*
5652282 / 13 Jul '98 / Manifesto

☐ **CAFE LATINO**
TCD 2841 / Jun '96 / Telstar

☐ **CAFE LATINO VOL.1**
TTTCD 004 / 1 Jun '98 / Two To Tango

☐ **CAFE LATINO VOL.2**
TTTCD 005 / 1 Jun '98 / Two To Tango

☐ **CAFE LOCAL VOL.1**
PIAS 015560120 / Sep '96 / Play It Again Sam

☐ **CAFE LOCAL VOL.2**
PIAS 015561520 / Nov '96 / Play It Again Sam

☐ **CAFE MAMBO VOL.1 (3CD Set)**
VTDCD 150 / Aug '97 / Virgin

☐ **CAFE MAMBO VOL.2 (3CD Set)**
VTDCD 206 / 10 Aug '98 / Virgin TV

☐ **CAFE SOCIETY 1939**
DOCD 1003 / Apr '97 / Document

☐ **CAINED AND ABLE**
PUSHCD 1 / Jul '97 / Push

☐ **CAJUAL RELIEF**
SOMCD 3 / Jul '95 / Sound Of Ministry

☐ **CAJUN AND CREOLE MASTERS**
T 138 / Aug '96 / Music Of The World

☐ **CAJUN AND ZYDECO FESTIVAL**
Homme a pitier: *Mamou* / Little love always makes it bettah: *Jocque, Beau & The Zydeco Hi-Rollers* / Zydeco boogaloo: *Doucet, Michael & Cajun Brew* / H-Town: *Li'l Brian & Zydeco Travelers* / Dans la Louisiane: *Berard, Al & The Basin Brothers* / Gon' be jus' fine: *Ardoin, Chris & Double Clutchin'* / Quoi faire: *File* / Hey Geno: *Delafose, Geno* / Bonjour Dimanche: *Diagrepont, Bruce* / Zydeco road: *Nathan & Zydeco Cha Cha's*
EDCD 7067 / Jun '98 / Easydisc

☐ **CAJUN CLASSICS VOL.1**
Back door: *Louisiana aces* / Pine grove blues: *Abshire, Nathan* / Saturday night special: *Cormier, Lesa & The Sundown Playboys* / Jolie blon: *Bruce, Vin* / Sugar bee: *Cleveland Crochet* / Lafayette two-step: *Roger, Aldus* / Cher cherie: *Guidry, Doc* / Fumes d'enfer: *Pitre, Austin* / Step it fast: *Bonsall, Joe & the orange playboys* / Parlez vous francais: *Matte, Bill* / I'll take you home: *Bertrand, Robert* / Equand j'etais pauvre: *Balfa, Dewey* / Lemonade song: *Broussard, Leroy* / Grande bosco: *Lejeune, Iry* / Mamou two step: *Walker, Lawrence* / Hippy ti yo: *Newman, Jimmy C.* / Sha ba ba: *Brown, Sidney* / Cajun stripper: *Richard, Belton* / J'ai fait mon idee: *Bergeron, Shirley* / Choupique two step: *Greely, David* / La pointe aux pins: *Jambalaya Cajun Band & Reggie Matte* / Creole stomp: *Breaux, Jimmy* / J'ai ve le loup: *Beausoleil* / Hee haw breakdown: *Cormier, Nolan & the LA Aces*
CDCHM 431 / Mar '93 / Ace

☐ **CAJUN CLASSICS VOL.2 (The Kings Of Cajun At Their Very Best)**
Lacassine special / Madam boso / Sur la courtableau / La valse de reno / Les veuves de la coulee / Jolie fille / Mamou blues / Louisiana aces special / Jolie blon / Grand nuit special / I passed by your door / Cajun pogo / Starvation waltz / Mowater blues / Hippy ti yo / Les traces de mon bogue / Hold my false teeth / Hey jolie / Makes me feel like dancing / Valse de cypriere / La vie de cadjin / Le ti-mouchoir / Tu peux cogner / Going back to Louisiana
CDCHM 519 / May '94 / Ace

☐ **CAJUN COLLECTION**
Good time two step / Old sharecropper's house / Whatever boils your crawfish / Enterre moi pas / Une deuxieme chance / Ossum blues / Tous les jours / Bernadette / Gone gone gone / Let the meatball roll / Where will I find another you / One last song / Blues a bebe / Cette la j'aime / Quand j'etais pauvre
SUMCD 4183 / 23 Feb '98 / Summit

☐ **CAJUN COOKIN'**
Jambalaya: *Sonnier, Jo El* / Danse sur le bayou: *Mamou* / Cochon de lait: *Beausoleil* / He Madeleine: *Newman, Jimmy C.* / J'ai vu le loup, le renard et la belette: *Balfa Toujours* / Hey yie yie: *Williams, Nathan & Michael Doucet* / Parlez-nous a boire: *Riley, Steve & Mamou Playboys* / Marksville two-step: *Daigrepont, Bruce* / Les flames d'enfer: *Le Trio Cadien* / Creole jam: *Berard, Al & The Basin Brothers* / Donnez-moi la: *LeJeune, Eddie* / Les bons temps rouler: *Doucet, David*
EDCD 7043 / Sep '97 / Easydisc

☐ **CAJUN COUNTRY**
EDCD 7013 / Oct '96 / Easydisc

☐ **CAJUN COUNTRY KICKERS**
Rave on / Cotton eye Joe / Lovin' all night / Summertime blues / Down at the Twist and Shout / Oh lonesome me / I couldn't leave you if I tried / Louisiana Saturday night / Kinda Cajun / One more last chance / Poor boy blues / One step away / That's alright Mama / Chattahoochee / All you ever do is bring me down / Wild side of life / There goes my heart
SOWCD 527 / 15 Sep '97 / Sound Waves

☐ **CAJUN DANCE HALL**
Couer des cajuns: *Daigrepont, Bruce* / Les grands bois: *Sonnier, Jo El* / La pointe aux pins: *Riley, Steve & Mamou Playboys* / J'aurais du t'aimer (I should have loved you): *Newman, Jimmy C.* / Rolling pin: *Beausoleil* / Balfa Waltz: *Doucet, David* / Grande bosco: *LeJeune, Eddie* / La danse de Mardi Gras: *Mamou* / Lafayette two step: *Menard, D.L.* / Bayou pon pon: *Doucet, Michael & Cajun Brew*
EDCD 7011 / Aug '96 / Easydisc

☐ **CAJUN DANCE HALL SPECIAL**
ROUCD 11570 / Feb '93 / Rounder

☐ **CAJUN FAIS DO-DO**
ARHCD 416 / Jan '96 / Arhoolie

☐ CAJUN GREATS
La chere toute-toute: *Sonnier, Jo El* / La porte d'en arriere: *Newman, Jimmy C.* / Midland special: *Berard, Al & The Basin Brothers* / Jolie blon: *LeJeune, Eddie* / Chez Seychelles: *Beausoleil* / Jeune filles de la campagne: *Balfa Toujours* / J'ai passe devant ta porte: *Menard, D.L.* / Mamou two step: *Trio Cadien* / Madeleine: *LeJeune, Eddie & The Morse Playboys* / Petit mamou: *Daigrepont, Bruce* / French blues: *Doucet, David* / Jongle a moi: *Riley, Steve & Mamou Playboys*
EDCD 7012 / Jun '97 / Easydisc

☐ CAJUN HONKY TONK
ARHCD 427 / Apr '95 / Arhoolie

☐ CAJUN HOT SAUCE
Mosquito that ate up my sweetheart in New Iberia: *Beausoleil* / Kaplan waltz: *Savoy-Doucet Cajun Band* / Monsieur Leonard: *California Cajun Band* / Port Arthur blues: *Balfa, Dewey* / Two step d'amende: *Savoy-Doucet Cajun Band* / En bas du chene vert: *Menard, D.L.* / Shoo black: *Fontenot, Canray & Beausoleil* / Bosco stomp: *Clark, Octa & Hector Duhon* / Jolie blonde: *Guillory, Chuck* / Allons a lafayette: *Choates, Harry* / Bayou pom pom: *Read, Wallis 'Cheese'* / Crowley waltz: *Hackberry Ramblers* / Hey Ma: *Breaux Brothers* / Grand Texas: *Guillory, Chuck* / Valse criminelle: *Clark, Octa & Hector Duhon* / Keep a knocking: *Read, Wallis 'Cheese'* / Catch my hat: *Fruge, Wade* / Je veux me marier: *Hackberry Ramblers* / Valse du mariage: *California Cajun Orchestra* / One step d'amende: *Doucet, Michael* / Basile waltz: *Choates, Harry* / Osson two step: *Falcon, Joseph*
CDCHD 591 / Feb '96 / Ace

☐ CAJUN LOUISIANA 1928-1929 (2CD Set)
FA 019CD / Nov '95 / Fremeaux

☐ CAJUN MAGIC (Instrumentals From Louisiana)
Amedee two step: *Sonnier, Jo El* / Galop a wade fruge: *Balfa Toujours* / O ye yai quoi faire: *Balfa Brothers* / Perrodin two step: *File* / Bruce's two step: *Daigrepont, Bruce* / Mulberry waltz: *Basin Brothers* / Deux valses a Wayne Perry: *Riley, Steve & Mamou Playboys* / Ugly day stomp: *Mamou* / Wagonwheel special: *Louisiana Playboys* / Valse a Thomas Ardoin: *Menard, D.L & Ken Smith* / Chez Seychelles: *Beausoleil*
EDCD 7031 / 19 Jan '98 / Easydisc

☐ CAJUN MOON (The Best Of The Bayou)
Tous les temps en temps (every now and then): *Reneaux, J.J. Band* / Cajun moon: *Deadweights & Memphis Roots* / Gumbo: *Milteau, J.J.* / Ye yai quoi faire: *Milteau, J.J.* / By you on the bayou tonight: *Reneaux, J.J. Band* / Crawdaddy stomp: *McCoy, Charlie & The United* / Bayou lafayette: *McCoy, Charlie & The United* / Flames d'enfer: *Reneaux, J.J. Band* / Louise (like sweet wine): *Buddy & Ghost Riders* / All you ever do is bring me down: *Deadweights & Memphis Roots* / Julie: *Ann Americana* / Down in lafayette: *Dobson, Richard & State Of The Heart* / Louisville: *Milteau, J.J.* / Julie jean bad bad girl: *Reneaux, J.J. Band* / Bootleggin': *Americana* / Leve tes fenetres haut (raise your windows high): *Reneaux, J.J. Band* / Cajun moon (reprise): *Deadweights & Memphis Roots*
306072 / Jan '97 / Hallmark

☐ CAJUN MUSIC ANTHOLOGY VOL.1 (Le Gran Mamou)
Basile: *Soileau, Leo & Mayuse Lafleur* / Saut' crapaud: *Fruge, Columbus* / Quelqu' un est jaloux: *Guilory, Delin T. & Lewis Lafleur* / Les blues de voyage: *Ardoin, Amedee & Dennis McGee* / Mon vieux D'Autrefois: *Falcon Trio* / Je vais jouer celea por tois: *Guidry, Bixy & Percy Babineaux* / L'abandoner: *Montet, Bethmost & Joswell Dupois* / Trois jours apres ma most: *Soileau Couzens* / O' bebe': *Doucet, Oscar & Alius Soileau* / Ma cherie: *Doucet, Oscar & Alius Soileau* / La valse j'aime: *Falcon Trio* / Grosse mama: *Soileau, Leo & Moise Robin* / Belle of Point Claire: *Mistric, Arteleus* / One stepde Lacassine: *Abshire, Nathan & The Rayn-Bo Ramblers* / Jolie blon: *Hackberry Ramblers* / Il y a pas la Claire de Lune: *Joe's Acadians* / Lake Charles waltz: *Four Aces* / Valse de maralis bulleur: *Rayne-Bo Ramblers* / La two-step a Erby: *Thibodeaux Boys* / Le gran mamou: *Soileau, Leo & His Three Aces* / Alberta: *Walker, Lawrence* / Je va t'aimer quand meme: *Hackberry Ramblers* / Viens donc me rejoindre: *Fusilier, J.B. & His Merrymakers* / Barroom blues: *Dixie Ramblers* / La veuve da la coulee: *Happy Fats & His Rayne-Bo Ramblers*
CMFCD 013 / Jan '93 / Country Music Foundation

☐ CAJUN MUSIC ANTHOLOGY VOL.2 (Raise Your Window)
Mama where are you at: *Soileau, Leo & Mayuse Lafleur* / Alone at home: *Guilory, Delin T. & Lewis Lafleur* / Je me suis en alle: *Montet, Bethmost & Joswell Dupois* / You belong to me: *Mistric, Arteleus* / When I meet you at the gate: *Doucet, Oscar & Alius Soileau* / Stop that: *Guilory, Delin T. & Lewis Lafleur* / Waltz of the bayou: *Guidry, Bixy & Percy Babineaux* / La fille que j'aime: *Creduer, Joe & Albert Babindeaux* / Sur le chemin chez moi: *Couzens, Soileau* / Pauvre garcon: *Falcon Trio* / La valse de Riceville: *Abshire, Nathan & The Rayn-Bo Ramblers* / Raise your window: *Falcon Trio* / Lake Arthur stomp: *Miller's Merrymakers* / La vieux vals an' onc mack: *Thibodeaux Boys* / Si voux moi voudrais ame: *Soileau, Leo & His Three Aces* / En route chez moi: *Falcon Trio* / Si tu vondroit marriez avec moi: *Joe's Acadians* / Lonesome blues: *Shreve, Floyd & the Three Aces* / Crowley waltz: *Hackberry Ramblers* / Joilie schvr rouge: *Happy Fats & His Rayne-Bo Ramblers*
CMF 017D / Aug '93 / Country Music Foundation

☐ CAJUN MUSIC ANTHOLOGY VOL.3 (Gran Prairie - Victor Bluebird Sessions 1935-1940)
One step de morse: *Abshire, Nathan & The Rayn-Bo Ramblers* / Noveau grand gueydan: *Rayne-Bo Ramblers* / Et la bas: *Hackberry Ramblers* / Les blues de bosco: *Rayne-Bo Ramblers* / Two step du la tell: *Fusilier, J.B. & His Merrymakers* / Jolie petite fille: *Hackberry Ramblers* / Rayne breakdown: *Rayne-Bo Ramblers* / Ta oblis de nernier: *Happy Fats & His Rayne-Bo Ramblers* / Pine island: *Miller's Merrymakers* / Las vas de la prison: *Hackberry Ramblers* / Les escrives dan plantin: *Rayne-Bo Ramblers* / Crap shooters hop: *Werner, Joe & Ramblers* / Ma chere bouclett: *Fusilier, J.B. & His Merrymakers* / Tickle her: *Hackberry Ramblers* / La response de blues de bosco: *Happy Fats & His Rayne-Bo Ramblers* / Hackberry hop: *Soileau, Leo* / La place mon coeur desire: *Rayne-Bo Ramblers* / La breakdown a Pete: *Hackberry Ramblers*
CMF 018D / Aug '93 / Country Music Foundation

☐ CAJUN SATURDAY NIGHT
Tipitina two step: *Daigrepont, Bruce* / Madame Bozo: *Beausoleil* / Hathaway one step: *Louisiana Playboys* / Cajun Saturday night: *Menard, D.L.* / Mamou hot step: *Riley, Steve & Mamou Playboys* / Huppets Taiauts 1935: *Sonnier, Jo El* / Opelousas Sostan: *Mamou* / Like a real cajun: *Doucet, Michael & Cajun Brew* / Chameaux one step: *Collet, Danny* / Le reel de Nonc Will: *Balfa Toujours* / My true love: *Basin Brothers* / La valse de Samedi au soir: *LeJeune, Eddie*
EDCD 7054 / Sep '97 / Easydisc

☐ CAJUN SOCIAL MUSIC
SFCD 40046 / Sep '94 / Smithsonian Folkways

☐ CAJUN SPICE
ROUCD 11550 / Oct '93 / Rounder

☐ CAJUN STRING BANDS (The 1930's Cajun Breakdown)
Ma jolie petite fille: *Soileau, Leo & His Three Aces* / La bonne valse: *Soileau, Leo & His Three Aces* / La blues de port Arthur: *Soileau, Leo & His Three Aces* / Quand je suis bleu: *Soileau, Leo & His Three Aces* / Chere tu tu: *Fusilier, J.B.* / Round up hop: *Fusilier, J.B.* / Anna Mae waltz: *Fusilier, J.B.* / Cajun breakdown: *Fusilier, J.B.* / Ma julie noir: *Fusilier, J.B.* / Redell breakdown: *Fusilier, J.B.* / Ma chere basett: *Fusilier, J.B.* / Ponce a moir: *Fusilier, J.B.* / Elton two step: *Fusilier, J.B.* / La valse de robot: *Fusilier, J.B.* / Gueydan two step: *Fusilier, J.B.* / Pourquoi que tu laise moi: *Breaux, Clifford* / Continuez de sonner: *Breaux, Clifford* / Dixie's hottest: *Dixie Ramblers* / Ma chere belle: *Darbone, Luderin & The Harberry Ramblers* / Shreve breakdown: *Darbone, Luderin & The Harberry Ramblers* / Rambling: *Darbone, Luderin & The Harberry Ramblers* / Oh Josephine my Josephine: *Darbone, Luderin & The Harberry Ramblers* / Se pas la pan: *Darbone, Luderin & The Harberry Ramblers* / French two step: *Darbone, Luderin & The Harberry Ramblers* / My little girl: *Darbone, Luderin & The Harberry Ramblers*
ARHCD 7014 / 16 Mar '98 / Arhoolie

☐ CAJUN VOL.2 (Fais Do Do)
Ma blonde est partie: *Breaux, Amedee* / Les tracas du hobo: *Breaux, Amedee* / Two step de Mama: *Ardoin, Amade* / Two step de eunice: *Ardoin, Amade* / Two step de pararie soileau: *Ardoin, Amade* / Rasalia: *Segura, Dewey* / You're small and sweet: *Segura, Dewey* / Far away from home blues: *Segura, Dewey* / Fais do-do negre: *Freres Breaux* / Tiger rag blues: *Freres Breaux* / One step a Marie: *Freres Breaux* / Mazurka de la louisiane: *Freres Breaux* / Le vieux soulard et sa femme: *Breaux, Cleoma* / Marie buller: *Breaux, Cleoma* / Mon coeur t'apelle: *Breaux, Cleoma* / C'est si triste san lui: *Breaux, Cleoma* / Madam atchen: *Ardoin, Amade* / Taunt aline: *Ardoin, Amade* / Le blues du petit chien: *Freres Breaux* / La valse d'auguste: *Freres Breaux* / La valse d'utah: *Freres Breaux*
4757032 / May '94 / Columbia

☐ CALANAIS
CD 001 / May '95 / An Lanntair

☐ CALBMELAN
DATCD 22 / Nov '95 / Dat

☐ CALEDONIAN COMPANION, THE (Instrumental Music From Scotland)
Lady Madeline Sinclair / High road to Linton / White cockade / Neil Gow's farewell to whiskey / Miss Jean Milligan / Muckin' o' Geordie's byre / Kinnegad slashers / Bugle horn / Brig o'Perth / Reel of Tulloch / Forbes Morrison / Ten pound fiddle / Smith's gallant fireman / Jenny dang the weaver / Bonnie Dundee / Hot punch / Kenmore's up and awa' / JB Milne / Lovat scouts / Breakdown / Caddam Woods / Polka / Smith's a gallant fireman / Soldier's joy / Kirrie debbuck / Sir David Davidson of Cantray / Tam Bain's lum / Blue bonnets o'er the border / Far frae Scotia's shores / Alley crocker / Orange and blue / Mrs. MacLeod of Raasay / Highland wedding / Dr. MacDonald / Lady Charlotte Campbell / Mason's apron / Timour the tartar
CDTRAX 9051 / 5 May '98 / Greentrax

☐ CALENDAR MUSIC IN THE CENTRAL VALLEYS
LDX 274938 / Sep '92 / La Chant Du Monde

☐ CALI KINGS MIX TAPE VOL.1
61426800172 / 5 May '98 / V-Wax

☐ CALIENTE - HOT
NW 244 / Aug '92 / New World

☐ CALIENTE GOLD COLLECTION (2CD Set)
D2CD 4021 / Jun '95 / Deja Vu

☐ CALIFORNIA COOL (Hip Sounds Of The West Coast)
This could be the start of something: *Murphy, Mark* / Man with the golden arm: *May, Billy & His Orchestra* / Black nightgown: *Mulligan, Gerry & Shelly Manne* / Squimp: *Hamilton, Chico* / But not for me: *Baker, Chet Quartet* / Ironic: *Guiffre, Jimmy & Jack Sheldon Quartet* / I hear music: *Hawes, Hampton Trio* / Lover man: *Konitz, Lee & Gerry Mulligan Quartet* / Hey Bellboy: *Woods, Gloria & Peter Candoli* / Diablo's dance: *Pepper, Art & Shorty Rogers* / Our love is here to stay: *Edwards, Teddy & Les McCann Ltd* / Route 66: *Troup, Bobby* / Two can play: *Gordon, Bob & Jack Montrose Quintet* / Take five: *Shank, Bud* / Jimmy's theme: *Baker, Chet & Bud Shank Orchestra* / Something cool: *Christy, June* / Mambo de la pinta: *Pepper, Art Quartet* / Do I love you: *Lee, Peggy & George Shearing* / Katanga: *Amy, Curtis & Dupree Bolton* / Handful of stars: *Chaloff, Serge* / West coast blues: *Criss, Sonny*
BNZ 303 / Feb '93 / Blue Note

☐ CALIFORNIA DRAMIN'
10512 / Jun '97 / A-Play Collection

☐ CALIFORNIA DREAMIN'
California dreamin': *Mamas & The Papas* / Little deuce coupe: *Beach Boys* / Summer in the city: *Lovin' Spoonful* / Let's go to San Francisco: *Flowerpot Men* / Little old lady from Pasadena: *Jan & Dean* / California girls: *Beach Boys* / Place in the sun: *Hammond, Albert* / Happy together: *Turtles* / Hello summertime: *Goldsboro, Bobby* / Walking on sunshine: *Katrina & The Waves* / Surf city: *Jan & Dean* / San Franciscan nights: *Burdon, Eric* / Dedicated to the one I love: *Mamas & The Papas* / Mama told me not to come: *Three Dog Night*
DC 880482 / May '97 / Disky

☐ CALIFORNIA DREAMIN' (Jazz Exotica)
IMP 12412 / 24 Aug '98 / Impulse Jazz

☐ CALL DAT GEORGE
JWIG 002CD / Jan '96 / JW

☐ CALL OF NATURE (3CD Set)
KBOX 374 / Aug '97 / Collection

☐ CALL ON THE DARK VOL.1
NB 233CD / Apr '97 / Nuclear Blast

☐ CALL ON THE DARK VOL.2
Beyond the Earthly: *Mundanus Imperium* / How it came to be this way: *Autumn* / Bondage song: *London After Midnight* / Wolf moon: *Type O Negative* / Black sun: *Therion* / Sacred: *Moonspell* / Worn away: *Left Hand Solution* / On lucid wings: *Evereve* / Not every pain hurts: *Lacrimosa* / Funnel: *Switchblade Symphony* / Phrases: *Love Like Blood* / When the sun hits: *Gathering* / Whores of Babylon: *Tiamat* / Blade of doom: *Dreams Of Sanity* / Child in me: *Clan Of Xymox* / Die with you: *Christian Death*
NB 3112 / 13 Jul '98 / Nuclear Blast

☐ CALLING ALL WORKERS
FDR Jones / Bandwagon / Mrs. Bagwash / Ernie Bagwash / Bell / It's that man again / Lambeth walk / Calling all workers / I'm one of the Whitehall warriors / It's foolish but it's fun / All over the place / Chattanooga choo choo / I l-love you so / Out in Indiah / Blues in the night / Take the world exactly as you find it / Why don't you do it right / Warsaw concerto / People will say we're in love / My heart and I / This is the army / Dark music / I couldn't sleep a wink last night
CDCHD 302 / Aug '94 / Happy Days

☐ CALMAGE
PIAS 59100228CD / 24 Nov '97 / 9MM

☐ CALYPSO CALALOO (Early Carnival Music From Trinidad 1914-50)
ROUCD 1105 / Apr '94 / Rounder

☐ CALYPSO CARNIVAL
ROUCD 1077 / Feb '93 / Rounder

☐ CALYPSO COSTA RICA
926462 / Jul '96 / BUDA

☐ CALYPSO FAVOURITES
304352 / Jun '98 / Hallmark

☐ CALYPSO LADIES 1926-1941
HTCD 06 / Feb '91 / Heritage

☐ CALYPSOCA 1998 HITS
JW 157CD / 14 Apr '98 / JW

☐ CALYPSOCA HITS VOL.1
JW 012 / Jan '96 / JW

☐ CAMBODIA - MUSIC OF THE ROYAL PALACES
C 5560034CD / Jul '94 / Ocora

☐ CAMDEN CRAWL, THE
PUBE 07CD / Nov '95 / Love Train

☐ CAMINO AL SOL
TUMICD 044 / Apr '95 / Tumi

☐ CAMP SKINGRAFT
GR 50CD / 22 Aug '97 / Skingraft

☐ CAMPUS CUTIE
That's all right: *Louis, Dwain* / How I love you: *Speck, Darrell* / Queen bee: *Orbits* / Suzanne: *Reed, Ken* / She's mine: *Monarchs* / Get a little: *St. Clair, Butch* / Please pretty baby: *Shadle, Bobby* / Only two me and you: *Goodspeed, Skip* / Blond headed woman: *Lee, Harold* / Ummm: *Ken & Roy* / Rockin' baby: *Fretts* / Come on baby: *Shadle, Bobby* / UT: *Sparkles* / That's my baby: *Shea, Johnny* / Rockin' blues: *Del-Tones* / Lover boy: *Dove, Ronnie* / Barnyard rock: *Hunt, Chuck* / Don't you go chicken: *Preston, Rudy* / My Rosa Lee: *Orbits* / Humpty Dumpty: *Deans* / Campus cutie: *Perkins, Billy* / Teen doll: *Starr, David* / Moonlight party: *Del-Tones* / Rock 'n' roll mama: *James, Roy* / For you: *Rock 'N' Rollers* / Romeo's teacher: *Duncan, Lanny* / So real: *Franklin Brothers* / World can't roll without love: *Perkins, Billy* / I can't live without you: *Popiel, Joe* / I'll keep your heart forever: *Cameos*
CDBB 55072 / Mar '98 / Buffalo Bop

☐ CAN SODOM (2CD Set)
AOP 63 / 6 Apr '98 / Dressed To Kill

☐ CAN YOU FEEL THE FORCE
PLSCD 135 / Apr '96 / Pulse

☐ CAN YOU HANDLE IT
Zoom: *Fat Larry's Band* / Purely by coincidence: *Sweet Sensation* / Jack in the box: *Moments* / No one can love you more: *Hyman, Phyllis* / Midas touch: *Midnight Star* / Friends: *Shalamar* / You to me are everything: *Real Thing* / Part time love: *Knight, Gladys & The Pips* / My girl: *Whispers* / Where did our love go: *Elbert, Donnie* / Lean on me: *Moore, Melba* / Can you handle it: *Redd, Sharon* / Best thing that ever happened to me: *Knight, Gladys & The Pips* / You'll never know what you're missing: *Real Thing* / Still in love: *Lucas, Carrie* / Homely girl: *Chi-Lites* / Casanova: *Coffee* / You are my starship: *Connors, Norman*
TRTCD 141 / Oct '94 / TrueTrax

☐ CANDID JAZZ
28th and 8th: *Hawkins, Coleman & Pee Wee Russell* / Wrap your troubles in dreams: *Eldridge, Roy* / Lord, Lord am I ever gonna know: *Thompson, Lucky* / Hard sock dance: *Bailey, Benny* / Brother Terry: *Terry, Clark* / Deep river: *Akiyoshi, Toshiko & Charlie Mariano Quartet* / Sallie: *Ellis, Don* / Ferris Wheel: *Williams, Richard* / African lady: *Lincoln, Abbey & Max Roach* / Man of words: *Little, Booker* / Boo: *Ervin, Booker* / Criss cross: *Lacy, Steve* / Port of call: *Taylor, Cecil* / Lock 'em up: *Mingus, Charles*
CCD 79000 / Feb '97 / Candid

☐ CANDLE IN THE WIND (A Unique Selection Of Moving Saxophone Instrumentals)
Candle in the wind / How deep is your love / Long and winding road / Lean on me / As tears go by / Holding back the years / Forever young / Everlasting love / Can you feel the love tonight / Heal the world / Seven seconds / Without you / Always on my mind / I guess that's why they call it the blues / Don't dream it's over / Love is all around / Close to you / Greatest love of all
CD 6109 / Nov '97 / Music

☐ CANDLELIGHT BOX SET VOL.1 (3CD Set)
CANDLEBOX 1 / 15 Dec '97 / Candlelight

☐ CANDLELIGHT BOX SET VOL.2 (3CD Set)
CANDLEBOX 2 / 24 Nov '97 / Candlelight

☐ CANDLELIGHT SAMPLER
CANDLE 011CD / Oct '96 / Candlelight

☐ CANNABIS WEEKEND
EFA 127022 / Mar '95 / Dope

☐ CANNED BLUES
HRCD 8036 / Jul '94 / Disky

☐ CAN'T GET ENOUGH
LHCD 006 / Jul '96 / Luv n' Haight

☐ CAN'T KEEP FROM CRYING (Blues From The Death Of President Kennedy)
TCD 5007 / Oct '94 / Testament

☐ CAN'T LIVE WITHOUT IT
Can't live without it: *Tucker, Luther* / Voodoo man: *White, Lavelle* / Why'd you have to say that I'word: *Kane, Candye* / Bird nest on the ground: *Bramhall, Doyle* / Baby please don't lie to me: *Wilson, Kim* / Give me time: *Foley, Sue* / Slow down baby: *Pryor, Snooky* / She put the hurt on me: *Sahm, Doug* / It won't be long: *Kane, Candye* / Itchy and scratchy: *Cowdrey, Lewis* / Keep on drinking: *Tucker, Luther* / Stop these teardrops: *White, Lavelle*
ANTCD 9905 / Jul '95 / Antones

☐ CANTE ANDALUZ (Flamenco Song Live In Seville)
NI 5554 / Jun '98 / Nimbus

☐ CANTE DE LAS MINAS VOL.1
BB 423CD / 1 Jun '98 / Karonte

☐ CANTE EN PRISON
BB 420CD / 1 Jun '98 / Karonte

☐ CANTE FLAMENCO
NI 5251 / Sep '94 / Nimbus

☐ CANTE GITANO
NI 5168 / Jun '98 / Nimbus

☐ CANTICLE OF THE PLAINS
There you are / Cry for freedom / If I could make it work / In your hands / Heaven is waiting / Things even angels / Buenas noches from nacogdoches / Love's as strong / Oh my Lord / You are all
RR 1010 / May '98 / Word

☐ CAPE BRETON ISLAND
NI 5383 / Sep '94 / Nimbus

☐ CAPE-VERDE ISLANDS (The Roots)
PS 65061 / Nov '90 / PlayaSound

☐ CAPITOL COUNTRY MUSIC CLASSICS - 1940'S
Jingle jangle: *Ritter, Tex* / Texas blues: *Willing, Foy* / I'm wastin' my tears on you: *Ritter, Tex* / Oklahoma hills: *Guthrie, Jack* / With tears in my eyes: *Tuttle, Wesley* / Divorce me COD: *Travis, Merle* / So round, so firm: *Travis, Merle* / Oakie boogie: *Guthrie, Jack* / Silver stars, purple sage, eyes of blue: *Stone, Cliffie* / Smoke, smoke, smoke: *Williams, Tex* / Humpty dumpty heart: *Thompson, Hank* / Peepin' through the keyhole: *Stone, Cliffie* / Rye whiskey: *Ritter, Tex* / Cigareets, whusky and wild, wild women: *Ingle, Red & The Natural Seven* / Cocaine blues: *Hogsed, Roy* / One has my name (the other has my heart): *Wakely, Jimmy* / Dear Oakie: *Rivers, Jack* / Life gits tee-jus, don't it: *Williams, Tex* / Candy kisses: *Kirk, Eddy & The String Band* / Tennessee border: *Ford, Tennessee Ernie* / Gamblin' polka dot blues:

Duncan, Tommy / Slippin' around: Whiting, Margaret & Jimmy Wakely / Whoa sailor: Thompson, Hank / Give me a hundred reasons: Jones, Ann / I love you because: Payne, Leon / Mule train: Ford, Tennessee Ernie

CDEMS 1412 / Jul '97 / Capitol

☐ CAPITOL COUNTRY MUSIC CLASSICS - 1950'S

Broken down merry-go-round: Whiting, Margaret & Jimmy Wakely / I'll never be free: Ford, Tennessee Ernie & Kay Starr / Shot gun boogie: Ford, Tennessee Ernie / Hot rod race: Dolan, Jimmy / Mockin' Bird Hill: Paul, Les & Mary Ford / Wild side of life: Thompson, Hank & His Brazos Valley Boys / High noon: Ritter, Tex / Don't let the stars get in your eyes: McDonald, Skeets / Goin' steady: Young, Faron / That's me without you: James, Sonny / Dear John letter: Shepard, Jean & Ferlin Husky / Forgive me, John: Shepard, Jean & Ferlin Husky / Wake up, Irene: Thompson, Hank / Release me: Heap, Jimmy & The Melody Mastg / You better not do that: Collins, Tommy / What'cha gonna do now: Collins, Tommy / Satisfied mind: Shepard, Jean / When I stop dreamin': Louvin Brothers / Sixteen tons: Ford, Tennessee Ernie / Waltz of the angels: Stewart, Wynn / I gotta know: Jackson, Wanda / I don't believe you've met my baby: Louvin Brothers / Young love: James, Sonny / Gone: Husky, Ferlin / Alone with you: Young, Faron / Country music is here to stay: Husky, Ferlin

CDEMS 1413 / Jul '97 / Capitol

☐ CAPITOL COUNTRY MUSIC CLASSICS - 1960'S

Six pack to go: Thompson, Hank / He'll have to stay: Black, Jeanne / Wings of a dove: Husky, Ferlin / Hello walls: Young, Faron / Right or wrong: Jackson, Wanda / In the middle of a heartache: Jackson, Wanda / I dreamed of a hillbilly heaven: Ritter, Tex / Sing a little song of heartache: Maddox, Rose / Must you throw dirt in my face: Louvin Brothers / Tips of my fingers: Clark, Roy / Second fiddle (to an old guitar): Shepard, Jean / I don't love you anymore: Louvin, Charlie / Just between the two of us: Owens, Bonnie & Merle Haggard / You're the only world I know: James, Sonny & the Southern Gentleman / Born to be with you: James, Sonny & the Southern Gentleman / Strangers: Haggard, Merle / Tombstone every mile: Curless, Dick / Queen of the house: Miller, Jody / Hicktown: Ford, Tennessee Ernie / Yodel, sweet Molly: Louvin, Ira / I'll take the dog: Shepard, Jean & Ray Pillow / Burning bridges: Campbell, Glen / Gentle on my mind: Campbell, Glen / It's such a pretty world today: Stewart, Wynn / Just hold my hand: Mosby, Johnny & Jonie / Mr. Walker, it's all over: Spears, Billie Jo / Okie from Muskogee: Haggard, Merle & the Strangers

CDEMS 1422 / Jul '97 / Capitol

☐ CAPITOL COUNTRY MUSIC CLASSICS - 1970'S

Fightin' side of me: Haggard, Merle & the Strangers / Cherokee maiden: Haggard, Merle & the Strangers / All I have to do is dream: Campbell, Glen & Bobbie Gentry / Big wheel cannonball: Curless, Dick / Snowbird: Murray, Anne / Something to brag about: Louvin, Charlie & Melba Montgomery / Empty arms: James, Sonny / I'm a truck: Simpson, Red / She's my rock: Edwards, Stoney / Comin' after Jenny: Ritter, Tex / Fiddle man: Stegall, Red / Bonparte's retreat: Campbell, Glen / Rhinestone cowboy: Campbell, Glen / Get on my love train: La Costa / I'm not Lisa: Colter, Jessi / What's happened to blue eyes: Colter, Jessi / Hurt: Connie Cato / Letter that Johnny Walker read: Asleep At The Wheel / Miles and miles of Texas: Asleep At The Wheel / Couple more years: Dr. Hook / Bluest heartache of the year: Dale, Kenny / Paper Rosie: Watson, Gene / Gambling polka dot blues: Texas Playboys / I cheated on a good woman's love: Craddock, Billy / Gambler: Schitz, Don / Ain't life hell: Cochran, Hank & Willie Nelson

CDEMS 1423 / Jul '97 / Capitol

☐ CAPITOL COUNTRY MUSIC CLASSICS - 1980'S

Nothing sure looked good on you: Watson, Gene / Something 'bout you baby I like: Campbell, Glen & Rita Coolidge / Could I have this dance: Murray, Anne / (You say you're) a real cowboy: Craddock, Billy / Louisiana Saturday night: McDaniel, Mel / Sweetest thing (I've ever know): Newton, Juice / Step that step: Brown, Sawyer / Meet me in Montana: Osmond, Marie & Dan Seals / I tell it like it used to be: Brown, T. Graham / Darlene: Brown, T. Graham / Heartbeat in the darkness: Williams, Don / Old coyote town: Williams, Don / Just another love: Tucker, Tanya / I don't want to set the world on fire: Bogguss, Suzy / Unconditional love: New Grass Revival / I won't take less than your love: Tucker, Tanya/Paul Davis & Paul Overstreet / I didn't (every chance I had): Rodriguez, Johnny / New never wore off my sweet baby: Dilon, Dean / Addicted: Seals, Dan / I wish I could fall in love today: Mandrell, Barbara / Much too young (to feel this damn old): Brooks, Garth / If tomorrow never comes: Brooks, Garth

CDEMS 1424 / Jul '97 / Capitol

☐ CAPITOL RARE VOL.1 (Funky Notes From The West Coast)

Music is my sanctuary: Bartz, Gary / Sky islands: Caldera / Annie Mae: Cole, Natalie / Sunshine: Wilson, Nancy / As: Harris, Gene / Genie: Lyle, Bobby / I love you: Taste Of Honey / While I'm alone: Maze / Peace of mind: Allen, Rance Group / Inside you: Henderson, Eddie / Every generation: Laws, Ronnie / She's my summer breeze: Reflections / Losalamitos (Latinfunklovesong): Harris, Gene / About love: Sidran, Ben / Dindi: Lawson, Janet / Woman of the ghetto: Shaw, Marlena / Cheshire cat: Foster, Ronnie

CDP 8298652 / Jun '94 / Capitol

☐ CAPITOL RARE VOL.2

It's a pleasure: Brown, Sheree / Before you break my heart: Dunlap, Gene / La Costa: Cole, Natalie / Carnival de L'esprit: Bartz, Gary / Sunshower: Mouzon, Alphonse / Abdullah and Abraham: Hamilton, Chico / Tidal wave: Laws, Ronnie / Can't hide love: McRae, Carmen / Space spiritual: Adderley, Nat Sextet / Expressway to your heart: Thunder, Margo / Beggar for the blues: Drew, Patti / Windy C: 100% Pure Poison / Theme for Relana: Harris, Gene / Inside my love: Riperton, Minnie / Nightfall: Stratavarious

CDP 8356072 / Oct '95 / Capitol

☐ CAPTAIN OF YOUR SHIP (New Dancehall Shots)

SHCD 45006 / Sep '93 / Shanachie

☐ CARAT VOL.2

PIAS 015561623 / Apr '97 / Play It Again

☐ CARIBBEAN BEAT VOL.1

La ki ni nano: Dixie Band / No dji m'en nouille: Caribbean Combo / Sally Brown: Aitken, Laurel / Bailando: Orlando, Ramon / Sans cesse di nouille: Cabrimol, Jean Michel / No dance: Imagination Brass / Argent: Amoro, Rene Paul / Sabor y pena: Roque, Victor / Pa kita' m: Vega Band / Lajan mwe: Reasons Orchestra / Gozolinn: Rosier, Piar / Wasmashin: Prudencia, Macorio / Agua: Vargas, Wilfred

INT 31122 / Aug '92 / Intuition

☐ CARIBBEAN BEAT VOL.2

Bayoe: Imagination Brass / On et yo: Toumpak / El emneito: La Fuerza Mayor / Sinking ship: Gypsy / Bayo bayo: Dixie Band / Doux doux cherrie: Heartbeat / Enojado: Huracan / Which one is me home: Exile One / Sa ki di sa: Dede Saint Prix / Guns of Navarone: Skatalites / Party feeling: Massive Chandelier / Musica latina: Fernadito Villalona / Hot hot hot: Arrow

INT 31262 / Nov '93 / Intuition

☐ CARIBBEAN BEAT VOL.3

El bailabien / La pachanga del futbol / Pimpele / Tafia / Mata shimaraya / Hickee / La pachanga / Pitaste / Pajaro loco / La negra quiere / No le crea / Zap zap / Laissez passer

INT 31472 / Oct '94 / Intuition

☐ CARIBBEAN BEAT VOL.4

Baila / Quien ha visto por ahi mi sombrero de yarey / Moon hop / El baile del perrito / Que seria de cali / Tipico caliente / El merengue / Karayib leve / Echao pa 'lante / Para que aprendan / SOS Maya / Beberte / Losd sitio entera

INT 31532 / Oct '95 / Intuition

☐ CARIBBEAN BEAT VOL.5

Pica pica: Mendez, Kinito / Para el llanto: Charanga Habanera / Soukwe: Reasons Orchestra / La flaca: Coco band / No me llores mas: Sierra Maestra / E alo: Taxi Kreol / Jugadita de engano...no: Origina De Manzanillo / La noche: Arroyo, Joe / Roots: Palacio, Andy / Anacaona by: Anacaona / Dos mujeres: Gitierrez, Alfredo / Cali Aji: Gripo Niche / We different: Arrow

INT 31722 / Jul '97 / Intuition

☐ CARIBBEAN BEAT VOL.6

Fenomene tabou: Tabou Combo / 17 Y 48: Son Damas / La cambia Pela: Gutierrez, Alfredo / Souwke: Reasons Orchestra / Yay boy: Africando / Una forma mas: Sampling / Lo que me falto por hacerte: Klimax / Tu no hablas conmigo: La India Canela / Music hot: David, Bredda / Doudou amnoin: Dixie Band / Viejo lazaro: Alfonso, Juan Carlos Orchestra Dan Den / Rude gyul wine: Blue Ventures

INT 31972 / 27 Oct '97 / Intuition

☐ CARIBBEAN CARNIVAL SOCA PARTY VOL.5

CSS 020 / 15 Sep '97 / Nuff

☐ CARIBBEAN CARNIVAL SOCA PARTY VOL.6

CSS 024 / 13 Jul '98 / Coral

☐ CARIBBEAN COCKTAIL

Caribbean surfer / Island in the sun / Rivers of Babylon / America / Sloop John B / Montego Bay / Yellow bird / Coconut woman / Soul limbo / Underneath the mango tree / Brown girl in the ring / Jamaican coffee / Don't stop the carnival / Banana boat song / Jamaica farewell / La bamba / Guantanamera

EMPRCD 580 / Jul '95 / Emporio

☐ CARIBBEAN CROSSOVER

CMBCD 36 / 15 Jun '98 / Caribbean

☐ CARIBBEAN DREAM

JWCRO 94CD / Jan '96 / JW

☐ CARIBBEAN FEELING (2CD Set)

Cumple anos: Mandingo Y Su Familia / Todo me gusta de ti: America, Ima / Salsa Caribeno: Camino De Lobo / Te distes cuenta: Mandingo, Felipe / Vals para mayra: Teran, Sergio / Tu y las nubes: Alvarez, Rosario / Sourie: De Souza, George / El gavilan: Mandingo Y Su Familia / Entre palmeras: Vesga, Jose Luis / Amor de mis amores: Alvarez, Rosario / Merengue pasion: Camino De Lobo / Kimbiza: Mi Orquesta / Juan Jose: Mandingo Y Su Familia / Parrandero: Mandingo Y Su Familia / Seis por derecho: Mandingo Y Su Familia / Destapa el ron: Mandingo Y Su Familia / Son Carebeno: Malaquias, Aldo / Guantanamera: Alvarez, Rosario / A pedir su mano: Caribbean Orchestra / Culo e pulla: Mandingo Y Su Familia / Mucho mucho: Jerez, Mauricio / Orgullo de ti: Conquistador / Teresa: Mandingo Y Su Familia / Olo lai lo: Mandingo Y Su Familia / El cumaco de San Juan: Mandingo Y Su Familia / Guadalajara: Mexican Mariachi Band / Correveula: Maipu / La Billirubina: Caribbean Orchestra / Extrano camino: Conquistador / Chorinho: Teran, Sergio

24331 / Jul '96 / Laserlight

☐ CARIBBEAN ISLAND MUSIC

7559720472 / 26 Jan '98 / Nonesuch

☐ CARIBBEAN MAGIC (A Magical Blend Of Music And The Sounds Of Nature)

57862 / May '97 / Nature's Harmony

☐ CARIBBEAN PARTY

L'histoire du zouk: Kali / Chale lanmou: Tabou Combo / Serjyo: Bago / Pump me up: Krosfyah / Ice cream: Coalishun / Roots rock reggae: Wailer, Bunny / Pa fe mwen la pen: Virgal, Eric / Chayew ale: Geremy, Patsy / Dokte: Thamar, Ralph / Don't touch my tempo: Arrow

PUTU 1322 / 29 Sep '97 / Putumayo

☐ CARIBBEAN PARTY RHYTHMS VOL.3

CO 4498 / 27 Jul '98 / Rituals Music

☐ CARIBBEAN SHORES

DC 879512 / Oct '97 / Disky

☐ CARIBBEAN TROPICAL DANCE PARTY - 20 HOT CARIBBEAN RHYTHMS

Marinero: Los Latinos / Quiero un sombrero: Carcamo, Pablo / Consigueme eso: Musica Latina / O cana sordi: Tumbao / Chapa'lante Catalina: Carcamo, Pablo / El pescador: Carcamo, Pablo / Un, dos, tres: Musica Latina / Mensaje de mi Colombia: Carcamo, Pablo / Villa carino: Carcamo, Pablo / Candela y tumbao: Tumbao / Fantasia caribena: Carcamo, Pablo / Los pirulos: Musica Latina / Mi alegre serenata: Carcamo, Pablo / Vuela paloma: Tumbao / Solo quedo: Carcamo, Pablo / Suave: Carcamo, Pablo / El Africano: Musica Latina / Ojala que llueva cafe: Carcamo, Pablo / Sol y arena: Carcamo, Pablo

EUCD 1209 / Sep '93 / ARC

☐ CARIBBEAN UNCOVERED (2CD Set)

VTDCD 175 / 23 Feb '98 / Virgin

☐ CARIBE TROPICAL

El superticioso: Orquesta La Super 'C' / Cambia el tumbao: Beltran, Alberto / El ano viejo: Valdes, Vicentico / Empezo la cumbia: Penaranda, Jose Maria / Todo para ti: Gonzalez, Cheito / Merengue colorao: Hernandez, Mario / Linda Calenita: Alvarez, Tony / Mi regreso: Los Admirables / Que te coma un chivo: Capo, Bobby / Canonazo: Laito & Rogelio/Caito / Sabina: Beltran, Alberto / Papa Boco: Machito & Graciela/La 'Serie / Cumbia de buenaventura: Caito, Elliot & Rogelio Justo / Ya se peino Maria: Santos, Daniel / El merengue de san juan: Granda, Bienvenido / El amor de carmela: Penaranda, Jose Maria / Mi cholita: Ticas, Oscar / El regalito: Lopez, Anardy / Bailando Abrazao: Conjunto Tipico Cibaeno / El Aguacero: Trio Maravilla

CDHOT 628 / Oct '97 / Charly

☐ CARIBEAN STEEL DRUMS

GRF 201 / Jan '93 / Tring

☐ CARILLON - THE COMPLETE PRELUDES

A 6230 / Dec '96 / Tempo

☐ CARMINA LATINA

74321544382 / 27 Apr '98 / Milan

☐ CARNEGIE HALL SALUTES THE JAZZ MASTERS (Verve 50th Anniversary)

Tea for two / Tangerine / Shiny stockings / Willow weep for me / I must have that man / Desafinado / Manteca / Parisian thoroughfare / How high the moon / Turn out the stars / Eternal triangle / How insensitive / Down by the riverside / Yellowstone / It's about that time / Now's the time

5231502 / Oct '94 / Verve

☐ CARNIVAL

Waters of Tyne: Sting & Jimmy Nail / Winds from the South: Chieftains / Dream Angus: Lennox, Annie / Va pensiero: Zucchero / Sweet and low: Midler, Bette / Tu scendi dalle stelle: Pavarotti, Luciano / Abide with me: John, Elton / All through the night: Colvin, Shawn / Lapwony: Oryema, Geoffrey / Freedom: Madonna / No voy a dejarte arder: Blades, Ruben / Ufomeni uyangithanda: Clegg, Johnny / Ten years: Simon, Paul / Nkosi sikelel' i Afrika: Katz, Sharon & The Peace Train / I bought me a cat: Taylor, James / Le carnival des animaux

74321447692 / 22 Sep '97 / RCA Victor

☐ CARNIVAL FEVER VOL.1

PD 006 / Mar '96 / Ebony

☐ CARNIVAL JUMP-UP

DE 4014 / Feb '94 / Delos

☐ CARNIVAL OF SOUL VOL.1 (Wishes)

Wishes: Metrics / She's so fine: Topics / All I need is your love: Manhattans / Me, myself and I: Jenkins, Norma / I need a guy: Lovettes / Forget him: Brown, Barbara / Nobody loves me (like my baby): Caldwell, Harry / I love you more: Williams, Lee & The Cymbals / I'll keep holding on: Ruffin, Kenneth / Nothing will ever change (this love of mine): Jules, Jimmy / My love is yours tonight: Turner Brothers / It's everything about you (that I love): Williams, Lee & The Cymbals / I wanna be (your everything): Pretenders / Love has passed me by: Terrell, Phil / I say yeah: Pets / I'll catch you on the rebound: Leon & The Metronomes / Can I come in: Terrell, Phil / Come home to Daddy: Goggins, Curby / I can tell: Little Royal / I'm gonna be missing you: Bailey, Rene / My baby's gone: Tren-Teens / I call it love: Pretenders / Until you come back to me: Manhattans / Go right on: Three Reasons

CDKEND 108 / Oct '94 / Kent

☐ CARNIVAL OF SOUL VOL.2 (Feelin' Good)

I'm just a young boy: Terrell, Phil / So in love: Brown, Barbara / Hey girl (where are you going): Topics / There goes a fool: Manhattans / Please come back: Caldwell, Harry / Peeping through the window: Williams, Lee & The Cymbals / I found you: Metrics / That's what love will do: Symphonies / I'm the one love forgot: Pretenders / Sometimes I wonder: Brown, Barbara / Don't let yourself go: Jules, Jimmy / Boogaloo party: Harold & Connie / Little Miss Soul: Lovettes / Love is breaking out all over: Manhattans / Broken heart: Pretenders / Warm and tender love: Bailey, Rene / Don't you run away: Terrell, Phil / Need someone to love: Jenkins, Norma / I don't have to cry: Topics / I'm afraid (to say I love you): Lovettes / New world (is just beginning): Caldwell, Harry / Lost love: Williams, Lee & The Cymbals / Leave me if you want to: Goggins, Curby / Feelin' good: Carnival Kings

CDKEND 118 / Mar '95 / Kent

☐ CARNIVAL OF SOUL VOL.3 (I Wanna Be)

I need you baby: Williams, Lee & The Cymbals / I'll be gone: Williams, Lee & The Cymbals / I'll erase you: Terrell, Phil / I wanna be (your everything): Manhattans / I call it love: Pretenders / If love comes knockin': Topics / Send him to me: Brown, Barbara / I'm the man for you baby: Turner Brothers / Just one more time: Jules, Jimmy / What kind of man are you: Johnson, Dolores / Try me one time: Johnson, Dolores / Oh why: Mays, Curly / You made me love you: Little Royal / Git go: Simon, Maurice & The Pie Men / Just be yourself: Pretenders / April lady: Perry, James / Take me back: Three Reasons / Lonely girl: Lovettes / Cry, cry, cry: Ruffin, Kenneth / Buy this record for me: Leon & The Metronomes / Your yah-yah is gone: Trenteens / It's too late for tears: Bailey, Rene / I don't wanna go: Manhattans / Groove in G: Bascomb, Wilbur & The Blue Zodiact / Love don't come easy: New Jersey Connection

CDKEND 124 / Oct '95 / Kent

☐ CARNIVAL RHYTHMS

Mango mangue: Parker, Charlie / Luxo so: Getz, Stan & Charlie Byrd / Arinanara: Valdes, Miguelito / Nague: Valdes, Miguelito / Agueas de marco (Waters of March): Jobim, Antonio Carlos / Evolution of Mann: Mann, Herbie / Doralice: Getz, Stan & Joao Gilberto / Tin tin deo: Gillespie, Dizzy / Felicidade: Gilberto, Astrud / Ritmo uni: Tjader, Cal & Eddie Palmieri / So danco samba (I only dance samba): Getz, Stan & Luiz Bonfa / Manteca: O'Farrell, Chico / Amor em paz (Once I loved): Jobim, Antonio Carlos / Mambo is here to stay: Machito / Um abraco no bonfa (Am embrace to bonfa): Gilberto, Joao / Ponce: Morales, Noro / Boto: Henderson, Joe / Elation: Bobo, Willie / Tristeza: Powell, Baden

5526512 / Mar '97 / Spectrum

☐ CAROLINA BLUES 1926-1929

DOCD 5168 / May '93 / Document

☐ CAROLINA BLUES AND GOSPEL 1945-1951

DOCD 5588 / 5 Feb '98 / Document

☐ CAROLINA GOSPEL QUARTETS VOL.2 1936-1939

DOCD 5562 / 21 Sep '97 / Document

☐ CAROLINA MY DARLING

VPCD 1290 / May '93 / VP

☐ CARRY ON OI

United: Johnson, Gary / Dambusters: JJ Allstars / Suburban rebels: Business / Each dawn I die: Infa Riot / Arms race: Partisans / East End kids: Ejected / Transvestite: Peter & The Test Tube Babies / Nation on fire: Blitz / King of the jungle: Last Resort / Tuckers ruckers ain't no suckers: Gonads / Evil: 4 Skins / Product: Business / SPG: Red Alert / Maniac: Peter & The Test Tube Babies / What am I gonna do: Ejected / No U-turn: Partisans / Youth: Blitz / Mob chorus

STEPCD 018 / 23 Mar '98 / Step 1

☐ CARRY ON SKA VOL.1

STEPCD 017 / 24 Nov '97 / Step 1

☐ CARRY ON SKA VOL.2

STEPCD 038 / 23 Feb '98 / Step 1

☐ CARWASH EXPERIENCE (2CD Set)

We are family: Sister Sledge / Let's start the dance: Bohannon, Hamilton / Do what you want to do: T-Connection / Shoot me with your love: Thomas, Tasha / Love sensaton: Hartman, Dan & Loleatta Holloway / Rappers delight: Sugar Hill Gang / Last night a DJ saved my life: In Deep / Dance across the floor: Horne, Jimmy 'Bo' / 7654321 blow your whistle: Toms, Gary Empire / You can do it: Hudson, Al & The Partners / Delirium: McGhee, Fancine / Let no man put asunder: First Choice / Contact Starr, Edwin: Starr, Edwin / Carwash: Rose Royce / Starsky and Hutch: Taylor, James Quartet / Soul power '74: Maceo & The Macks / Party time: Fatback Band / All this love that I'm giving: McCrae, Gwen / War: Starr, Edwin / Me and baby brother: War / Rose Royce express: Rose Royce / Funky man: Brown, James / Think: Collins, Lyn / Rock me again and again: Collins, Lyn / Blackwater gold: Sunshine Band / Ot to be reel: Lynn, Cheryl / Long train burning: Doobie Brothers / Give it up or turn it loose: Brown, James / Starting too fast: HT's / Machine gun: Commodores / Bite your granny: Morning, Noon & Night

CDEM 1614 / Jul '97 / EMI

☐ CASA DE LA TROVA: SANTIAGO DE CUBA

COCD 120 / Oct '94 / Corason

☐ CASA DE SAMBA VOL.1 (10 Latin House Anthems)

What a sensation: Kenlou III / Sykodelik: Restless Soul / Fiesta de defriteus: H-Man / Brazil: Master Builders / Eu Nao: Basement Jaxx / Carnival: Bah Samba / Breaking point: Crime / Escucha mi funk: High Tower Set / Resolution: Canto Azul / Constant ariba: MPQ

CDHIGH 5 / Mar '97 / High On Rhythm

☐ CASA DE SAMBA VOL.2

Urban haze: Basement Jaxx / Look who's loving me: Smokin' Beats / Latin seoul: DJ Sneak / Congo: River Plate Samba Orchestra / Red raw latino shakedown: Atlanta / Montayo: Agora / Spy in Rio: Laj, Leo & Mr. Beef / Symphony del ritmo: Pascal's Bongo Massive / Latin track: Second Nature / New York New York: Master Builders

CDHIGH 6 / Jun '97 / High On Rhythm

☐ CASA DE SAMBA VOL.3

Sueno Latino: Sueno Latino / Chilli in Rio: No Tenshun / Ashewo ara: Kabbala / Wish tonite: Joseph, Corrina / Reach inside: Bah Samba / Esta lal vida: El Cubano / Moods shift: Dark Night Trippers / Lazzy jating: Transfusion / Wholemeal: Groove Armada / Ola-Le: Takada

CDHIGH 9 / 1 Dec '97 / High On Rhythm

☐ CASA DE SAMBA VOL.4

CDHIGH 11 / 30 Mar '98 / High On Rhythm

☐ CASSEOPAYA RECORDINGS VOL.2
CSRCD 002 / 15 Jun '98 / Casseopaya

☐ CASTLE IN THE AIR (Scottish Country Dancing)
MU 3005 / Oct '92 / Musketeer

☐ CAT MUSIC
HMG 6607 / 30 Mar '98 / Hightone

☐ CATFISH BLUES
CDBM 090 / Jun '93 / Blue Moon

☐ CATTLE CALL
ROUCD 1101 / Feb '96 / Rounder

☐ CAUGHT IN THE CYCLONE
CYCD 102 / Dec '96 / Cyclone

☐ CAVA SESSIONS
TLV 003 CD / May '90 / Tennants Live Vinyl

☐ CD 2000 (Electrecord)
2000: *Third Electric* / Drop in: *Kit Builders* / Wireless intercom: *Artificial Material* / Elastisch: *Klys-Tron* / On it: *Invisible Man* / Infanticide: *Infanticide Inc.* / Give up the funk: *Synapse* / Celestial crawlers: *Spacepawn Masters* / Foreign motel: *Artificial Material* / My melody: *Rootpowder* / EXEL: *Klys-Tron* / Defcon: *Third Electric*
K7 058CD / Jun '97 / Studio K7

☐ CEILI CELEBRATION
Reels / Waltzes / Jigs / Reels / Military two step / Reels / Jigs / Set dance / Military two step / Hornpipes / Jigs / Reels / Jigs / Marches / Marches / Reels
21211 / Nov '97 / Laserlight

☐ CEILI TIME IN IRELAND
CDC 016 / Feb '97 / Ceol

☐ CEILIDH HOUSE SESSIONS (From The Tron Tavern Edinburgh)
Maggie Lauder / Full rigged ship / Turnpike / Trowie burn / Shady grove / Reel of tulla / Tron blues / Pottinger's reel / Mountain road / Lark in the morning
CDTRAX 5002 / May '94 / Greentrax

☐ CEILIDH IN THE PARK
CDITV 635 / 2 Oct '97 / Scotdisc

☐ CELEBRATE THIS LOVE (2CD Set)
NSCD 006 / Feb '95 / Newsound

☐ CELEBRATION (25 Years Of The Organist Entertains)
CDGRS 1273 / Feb '95 / Grosvenor

☐ CELEBRATION
IMCD 3013 / Feb '96 / Image

☐ CELEBRATION OF DUBLIN, A (24 Street Ballads From The Fair City/ Dublin Millennium)
DOLCD 1988 / Aug '96 / Dolphin

☐ CELEBRATION OF SCOTTISH MUSIC, A
COMD 2003 / Feb '94 / Temple

☐ CELEBRATION OF SOUL VOL.1, A
VSD 5488 / Oct '94 / Varese Sarabande

☐ CELEBRATION OF SOUL VOL.2, A
VSD 5494 / Jan '95 / Varese Sarabande

☐ CELLAR FULL OF SOUL
Open the door to your heart: *Banks, Darrell* / How do you like it: *Sheppards* / Oh my darlin': *Lee, Jackie* / Peace lovin' man: *Laskey, Emmanuel* / Love is the only solution: *Starr, Martha* / Recipe: *Johnson, L.V.* / Baby please let me in: *Barnes, J.J.* / No one to love: *Lewis, Pat* / When you lose the one you love: *Smith, Buddy* / He stole the love that was mine: *Mancha, Steve* / I need my baby: *Beavers, Jackie* / Got to get rid of you: *Johnson, L.V.* / Girl crazy: *Soul, Sharon* / I need you: *Henry, Andrea* / I'll never forget you: *O'Jays* / I must love you: *Davis, Melvin* / Headache in my heart: *Debonaires* / Mine exclusively: *Olympics* / Don't pretend: *Belles* / That beatin' rhythm: *Temple, Richard* / You're my mellow: *Starr, Edwin* / That's why I love you: *Professionals*
JAZZFMCD 11 / 20 Jul '98 / Jazz FM

☐ CELLO SOLO - ALL DIGITAL
CDLR 301 / Apr '89 / Leo

☐ CELLULOID FUNK
CDNEW 116 / Dec '97 / Charly

☐ CELLULOID INSTRUMENTAL MUSIC
668302 / Nov '97 / Melodie

☐ CELTIC
TSS 111 / 9 Mar '98 / BMG

☐ CELTIC ALBUM, THE
HMNCD 040 / 22 Jun '98 / Half Moon

☐ CELTIC ANGELS
ARNR 1397 / 29 Jun '98 / Amiata

☐ CELTIC CHRISTMAS COLLECTION
CND 002 / Dec '97 / Word

☐ CELTIC CHRISTMAS, A
Calennig / Taladh Chriosdahb / Wren hornpipe/ Christmas eve/Winter apples / Oikan ayns Bethlehem / Hunting the wren / Kanomp Nouel / Dublin tune / Mari Lwyd / Da day dawns/Christmas day i da mornin/Papa Stour sword danc / Tree of life / Carval ny drogh vraane / Gower Wassail / Plygain: Wel dyma'rborau gorau i gyd / Arise and hail the glorious star / Seven rejoices of Mary / Ffarwel gyr Aberffraw / Lenabh an aigh / Highland pipe medley
CDSDL 417 / Oct '96 / Saydisc

☐ CELTIC CIRCLE SAMPLER VOL.3
EFA 125322 / Oct '95 / Celtic Circle

☐ CELTIC COLLECTION, A
PUTU 1252 / Oct '96 / Putumayo

☐ CELTIC COLLECTION, THE (4CD Set)
SUMBX 4002 / Jan '98 / Summit

☐ CELTIC CONNECTIONS
LTCD 001 / Jan '95 / Living Tradition

☐ CELTIC DANCES (Jigs & Reels From Ireland)
Diplodocus/Gandy dancer/New leaf: *Trian* / Hunter's house: *Donnelly, Maeve* / In memory of Coleman: *Cronin, Paddy & Mick Moloney* / Packy's place/Castleblarney piper: *O'Donnell, Eugene & Mick Moloney* / Reilly of the white hill: *McComiskey, Billy & Andy O'Brien* / Road to the glen: *Carroll, Liz & Armin Barnett* / Shoemaker's daughter: *Donnelly, Maeve* / Battering ram: *Shannon, Joe* / McGlinchey's/New ivy leaf: *Keane, James & Liz Carroll* / Reavy's no.9: *Mulvihill, Brendan & Andy O'Brien* / Maudebawn chapel: *Fitzpatrick, Maureen* / Catherine McEvoy's/Arklow mountains: *Keane, James & Liz Carroll* / Scatter the mud/Fasten the leggin: *Shannon, Joe & John McGreevy* / Wild swans at Coole: *Carroll, Liz & Mick Maloney* / Flock of wild geese: *Mulvihill, Brendan & Billy McComiskey* / Pat Clark's/Shanvaghara: *Quinn, Louis & Mick Moloney* / Green mountain/Eddie Kelly/Love at the endings: *Carroll, Liz*
EDCD 9010 / 19 Jan '98 / Easydisc

☐ CELTIC DAWN
HCD 128 / Apr '95 / GTD

☐ CELTIC DREAM
Orinoco flow / Saw you running / As I leave behind Neidin / My Irish Molly / Teddy O'Neill / Tickle her leg / Nothing compares 2 U / Only a woman's heart / No frontiers / Carolina Rua / All the lies that you told me / Summerfly / After the ball
21113 / Aug '97 / Laserlight

☐ CELTIC DREAMS
Riverdance / Celtic spirit medley / Ta muid / How can I keep from singing / Fear is the enemy / Last crossing / Martha's harbour / Earthjig / Le coeur / Mystic lipstick / Ailein duinn / Will ye go lassie go / Daire's dream / Air song / Song for Ireland / Lord of the dance
5399992 / 12 Jan '98 / PolyGram TV

☐ CELTIC EVOLUTION (2CD Set)
Roger O'Hehir: *Planxty* / Drowsey Maggie: *Altan* / Undertow: *Spillane, Davy* / Venezuela: *Connolly, Rita* / Boys of Ballinafad: *Derrane, Joe* / Bulgarian bash: *Reeltime* / Henry Joy: *De Danann* / Peggy's waltz: *Hayes, Martin & Dennis Cahill* / James Connolly: *Irvine, Andy* / Rossclogher jigs: *Stockton's Wing* / Trip to Tokyo: *Casey, Nollaig & Arty McGlynn* / Man of the house: *Keenan, Paddy & Arty McGlynn* / Tinkerman's daughter: *Parsons, Niamh* / Chocolate biscuit set: *Rock Salt & Nails* / Storm: *Moving Hearts* / Chetvorno horo: *Irvine, Andy & Davy Spillane* / Tailor's twist: *Planxty* / I'm looking through you: *Rock Salt & Nails* / White petticoat/Kerry jig/Katy is waiting: *Patrick Street* / Jimmy Mo mhile stor: *Keane, Dolores & John Faulkner* / On horseback: *Ivers, Eileen* / Seamus O Caoimh/Ath trasna: *Daly, Jackie & Seamus Creagh* / Little musgrave: *Planxty* / Titanic: *Moving Hearts* / Aisling gheal: *O'Lionaird, Iarla* / Aly's waltz: *McGuire, Seamus* / Bantry girl's lament: *Reeltime* / Elanor Plunkett: *Buttons & Bows* / Sweet Lisbweemore: *Patrick Street* / When I was a fair maid: *Triona Ni Dhomnaill* / Factory girl/Same old man: *Connolly, Rita* / Lois na Banriona/Fort of the fairy queen: *Casey, Nollaig & Arty McGlynn* / Mac's fancy/Mist covered mountain: *De Danann* / Lucy Farr's: *Hayes, Martin* / Planxty Johnson: *O'Riada, Sean* / O'Carolan's farewell to music: *Triona Ni Dhomnaill*
SOVSOPCD 253 / 27 Apr '98 / Connoisseur Collection

☐ CELTIC EXPERIENCE VOL.1 (Haunting Themes From Scotland And Ireland)
Braveheart theme / My Laggan love / Ca the yowes / Cadal cha dean me / Star of County Down / Rocky road / Women of Ireland / Hebridean prayer / Sally gardens / Skye boat song / Silkie / She moved thro' the fair / Four green fields / My home town / Carrick Fergus / Raggle taggle gypsies
AKD 080 / 6 Oct '97 / Linn

☐ CELTIC EXPERIENCE VOL.2, THE
Flower of Scotland / Brian Boru's march / My Lagan love / Kintail / Ossian's lament / Will you go lassie go / Young girl / Glen of Copsewood / O'Carolan's farewell to music / Sally gardens / Sitting in the stern of a boat / Mary Scott, flower of yarrow / Flower o' the Quern / Coilsfield House / Lochanside, Magersfontain
AKD 082 / 29 Jun '98 / Linn

☐ CELTIC FAVOURITES
Ramblin' Irishman / Rising of the moon / Road to Sligo / Ashplant / 10 Franc piece / O'Carolan's dream / White, orange and green / High road to Linton/Mrs. McLeod's reel / Foxhunters / Fiddler's green / Rocky road to Dublin / Arthur McBride / Cherish the ladies/Paddy's Clancey's jig medley / Gravelwalk / Couragie / Bold O'Donaghue / Paddle me own canoe / Molly Malone / Doherty's reel / Ferryman / Cod-liver oil / Home boys home / Father O'Flynn / Lannigan's ball / All for me grog / Wild rover / Galway races medley / Muirsheen duirkin / Paddy Fathy's reel/Dinny's fancy / Spanish lady / Maid behind the bar/Gravel walk / Holy ground / Finnegan's wake / Irish rover/Rakes of mallow / Seven drunken nights
DCD 3011 / Jun '97 / Music

☐ CELTIC FIDDLE
REWCD 350 / Feb '98 / Reactive

☐ CELTIC FIDDLE
Mahoney's fancy / Sligo maid/Tommy Gunn / Excelsior and mason's apron / Two reevy's / Bank/ Gauger / Banks / Old grey goose / Farewell to Kilroe / Chief O'Neills fancy/Cuckoo / Pullet want a cock / Kesh/Morrison / Caroan's concerto / Harvest home and high level / Centenary
EURCD 004 / 24 Aug '98 / Eureka

☐ CELTIC FINGERSTYLE GUITAR VOL.1 (Ramble To Cashel)
Believe me if all these endearing young charms: *Simpson, Martin* / Waters of Tyne: *Simpson, Martin* / Shepherd's delight: *Simpson, Martin* / Lowlands of Holland: *Simpson, Martin* / Pony crossing the alps: *Baughman, Steve* / Ramble to Cashel: *Baughman, Steve* / Cullen Bay: *Baughman, Steve* / Murtagh McKann: *Bensusan, Pierre* / Flamorgan air: *Bensusan, Pierre* / Merrily kissed the quaker/Cunta: *Bensusan, Pierre* / Duke of Fife's welcome to Deeside: *Baker, Duck* / Golden keyboard: *Baker, Duck* / Faerie Queen: *Baker, Duck* / Planxty Kelly: *Baker, Duck* / Hardiman the fiddler: *Long, Tom* / Butterfly: *Long, Tom* / Banish misfortune: *Long, Tom* / Morgan Magan: *Kirtley, Pat* / Fanny Power: *Kirtley, Pat* / Chase the weasel: *Kirtley, Pat* / Finn MacCool's reel: *Kirtley, Pat* / Danny boy: *McMeen, El* / Star of County Down: *McMeen, El*
ROUCD 3156 / Jun '98 / Rounder

☐ CELTIC FINGERSTYLE GUITAR VOL.2 (Blarney Pilgrim)
Planxty Irwin: *Kirtley, Pat* / Rodney's glory: *Kirtley, Pat* / Rosie Anderson/The shearing's not for you: *Simpson, Martin* / Bogie's bonny belle: *Simpson, Martin* / Bill Malley's barndance: *Baughman, Steve* / Fanny Power: *Baughman, Steve* / Blarney pilgrim: *Baker, Duck* / Rakes of Waterloo: *Baker, Duck* / Sergeant Early's dream/Chief O'Neill's favourite: *Baker, Duck* / Miss Forbe's farewell/Poll halfpenny: *Baker, Duck* / Pure drop/The flax in bloom: *Bensusan, Pierre* / Sheebeg an sheemor: *Bensusan, Pierre* / Heman dubh: *Bensusan, Pierre* / Jenny picking cockles: *Long, Tom* / Broken pledge: *Long, Tom* / Moran's return: *Kirtley, Pat* / South wind: *Kirtley, Pat* / Jock O'Hazeldean/The castle of Dromore: *Kirtley, Pat* / Carolan's farewell to music: *Kirtley, Pat*
ROUCD 3157 / Jun '98 / Rounder

☐ CELTIC FLUTE MAGIC
ZZCD 9804 / 1 Jun '98 / Zah Zah

☐ CELTIC FOLK FESTIVAL
MRCD 183 / Aug '96 / Munich

☐ CELTIC HARP
Tri-coloured ribbon: *Soazig* / O'Carolan's concerto: *Waxie's Dargle* / Fields of Athenrey: *Heaney, Gerry* / Marv Pontkalleg: *Soazig* / Childhood days: *Skovbye, Kim* / Currah of Kildare: *Blarney Lads* / Into the rain: *Waxie's Dargle* / Ar soundarded: *Soazig* / Tipping it up to Nancy/Swallow's tail: *Waxie's Dargle* / Come all ye young and tender maidens: *Waxie's Dargle & Berni O'Sullivan* / Sleivenamon: *Royal Irish Rangers & Anne Marie O'Farrell* / Salt hill: *Waxie's Dargle* / Dancer and the moon: *Skovbye, Kim* / Geese in the bog/Wind that shakes the barley: *Waxie's Dargle* / Skibbereen: *Heaney, Gerry* / King of the fairies: *Waxie's Dargle*
12857 / Oct '96 / Laserlight

☐ CELTIC HARP
REWCD 357 / Feb '98 / Reactive

☐ CELTIC HARP
Bridget's cruis / White Snowdon / Ruisg a bhean na tabairne / Cliff's branch / Last rose of summer / Minstrel boy / Londonderry air / Drowsy Maggie please strae the wind that shakes the barley / Harp that once through Tara's halls / Johnny has gone a soldier / Severn / Reaper's branch / Lamb's fold hollow / Gaolan's nightcap ode to whiskey / Blind Mary / Siain's mantle / Ieuan's the blind harpists delight / Frailty of life/Blacksmith's song / David of the white rock / Greensleeves / Scottish love song / Cumba nan gillean / Ashgrove afton grove / Eriskay love lilt / Leezie Lindsay / Sleep my pretty little lady
EURCD 001 / 24 Aug '98 / Eureka

☐ CELTIC HEARTBEAT CHRISTMAS
Na hu o ho: *Kennedy, Fiona* / Snowy path: *Altan* / Dream in the night: *Clannad* / Snowy birch trees: *Loefke, Thomas* / Maria matrem virginem: *Anuna* / Wexford carol: *Nightnoise* / Night before christmas (the devil in the kitchen): *MacIsaac, Ashley* / No sandman, no santa: *Dunning, Brian* / Winter, fire and snow: *Hill, Benita* / Oiche nollaig: *Breatnach, Cormac* / Christmas pipes: *Celtia* / Fairy child: *Masterson, Declan* / Oiche chuain: *Minogue, Aine* / Angels are singing: *Minogue, Aine*
7567829292 / Oct '96 / Warner Bros.

☐ CELTIC HEARTBEAT COLLECTION, THE
Mairseail righ lir (king lir's march) / All the lies that you told me / Blue bird / Caracena / Hazel woods / Blackbird / Winter's end / Chetvorno horo / Inis sui / Road to glory / Storm / Down by the sally gardens
7567806102 / Apr '95 / Atlantic

☐ CELTIC HEARTBEAT COLLECTION, THE
Caracena: *Whelan, Bill* / Blackbird: *Shannon, Sharon* / All the lies that you told me: *Black, Frances* / Harry's Game: *Clannad* / Hazel woods: *Masterson, Declan* / Storm: *Moving Hearts* / Road to glory: *Shanely, Elenor* / Inis sui: *Breathnach, Maire* / Chetvorno horo: *Irvine, Andy & Davy Spillane* / Down by the Sally Gardens: *Finn, Alec* / Blue bird: *Anuna* / Winter's end: *O'Flynn, Liam*
UND 53082 / Jun '97 / Celtic Heartbeat

☐ CELTIC LEGENDS (Traditional Music/ Instrument Of War OST)
RECD 507 / Jun '98 / REL

☐ CELTIC LOVE
AHLCD 56 / 10 Aug '98 / Hit

☐ CELTIC LOVE SONGS
Galway rover: *Cherish The Ladies* / Flower of Magherally: *Altan* / Lover's heart: *Silly Wizard* / Gathering pace: *Relativity* / I once knew a little girl: *Trian* / Lakes of Pontchartrain: *Deanta* / Bonny blue eyed Nancy: *Moloney, Mick & Eugene O'Donnell* / When she sleeps: *Relativity* / Carrigdhoun: *Cherish The Ladies* / Night visitor's song: *Tannahill Weavers* / Ta mo chleamhnas a dheanamh: *Altan* / Take her in your arms: *Stewart, Andy M. & Manus Lunny* / Todd's sweet rural shade: *Boys Of The Lough* / All things are quite silent: *Steeleye Span* / Banks of the Lee: *Arcady* / Black waterside: *Renbourn, John Group* / Bridget O'Malley: *Silly Wizard* / Ned of the hill: *Ryan, Cathie* / Cocks are crowing: *Voice Squad* / As I roved out: *Planxty* / Courting is a pleasure: *Jones, Nic* / I live not where I love: *Prior, Maddy* / Unquiet grave: *Solas* / Erigh suas a stoirin: *Clannad* / Dark eyed sailor: *Steeleye Span* / Fair and tender ladies: *Makem & Clancy* / Fond kiss: *Voice Squad*
SHANCD 78162 / 9 Mar '98 / Shanachie

☐ CELTIC MAGIC (Eleven Irish Instrumentals)
Lorraine's waltz: *Whelan, John & Eileen Ivers* / Inisheer: *Cherish The Ladies* / Bright hollow fog: *Williams, John* / I'll always remember you: *Connolly, Seamus* / If ever you were mine: *O'Sullivan, Jerry* / Farewell my gentle harp: *O'Donnell, Eugene & Rosalyn Briley* / Planxty gan ainm: *Faulkner, John* / Dobbin's flowery vale: *Altan* / Sligo lament: *McGann, John* / Whistle on the wind/Jug of punch/Dogs among the bushes: *Madden, Joanie* / Derry air (Danny boy): *O'Donnell, Eugene & James MacCafferty*
EDCD 9008 / Jun '97 / Easydisc

☐ CELTIC MOODS (Musical Reflections Of Ireland)
DOCD 105 / Apr '94 / Dolphin

☐ CELTIC MOODS
Riverdance: *Whelan, Bill* / Only a woman's heart: *McEvoy, Eleanor* / New grange: *Clannad* / She moved through the fair: *Sharkey, Feargal* / Strange boat: *Waterboys* / Sarah: *Thin Lizzy* / Abhainn an t-aluaigh: *Runrig* / Grace and pride: *Capercaillie* / Three babies: *O'Connor, Sinead* / Ride on: *Moore, Christy* / Pair of brown eyes: *Pogues* / Blackbird: *Shannon, Sharon* / Against the wind: *Brennan, Maire* / Heroine: *Edge & Sinead O'Connor* / Invisible to you: *Coughlan, Mary* / Can't help falling in love: *Bloom, Luka* / Always travelling: *Spillane, Davy* / Island: *Brady, Paul* / Woodbrook: *O'Suilleabhain, Micheal*
VTCD 52 / Jun '95 / Virgin

☐ CELTIC MOODS
Swallowtail reel: *Northrop, Kate* / Kenavo cill airne: *Soazig* / Wedding gift: *Skovbye, Kim & Gabrielle Reger* / Strings in the earth and air: *Skovbye, Kim & Klaus Schonning* / Planxty brabazon: *Northrop, Kate* / Miss MacDermott: *Soazig* / Robin's tune: *Skovbye, Kim & Gabrielle Reger* / Eastbound: *Skovbye, Kim & Gabrielle Reger* / Storm clouds: *Northrop, Kate* / Pennherez keroulaz: *Soazig* / Stranger: *Skovbye, Kim & Klaus Schonning* / Portrait no.1: *Skovbye, Kim & Gabrielle Reger* / Crystal: *Skovbye, Kim & Gabrielle Reger* / Portrait no.2: *Skovbye, Kim & Gabrielle Reger* / Marche de Brian Boru: *Soazig*
12858 / May '97 / Laserlight

☐ CELTIC MOODS
Easy and slow / Teddy O'Neil / Rose of Tralee / She moved through the fair / Gartan's lullaby / Mountains of Mourne / Avondale / Fields of Athenry / Inisheer / Coolin / Derry air / Raglan road / Mna na heireann / Pat Murphy's meadow / Winter's end
DOCDK 105 / 30 Mar '98 / Dolphin

☐ CELTIC MORNING
Brezhoneg / Al labous marv / Seoladh na ngamhna / As I roved out / Skartinglas / Lonely banna strand / Orpiian / Earth dance / Mountain streams / Mo ghile near / Ul lizher d'eus paris / Suite gavotte / Danny boy / Silkie / Streets of derry / Trip we took over the mountains / Courting is a pleasure / Rain
12853 / Sep '97 / Laserlight

☐ CELTIC MUSIC (3CD Set)
PS 360502 / Sep '96 / PlayaSound

☐ CELTIC MUSIC LIVE FROM MOUNTAIN STAGE
Trooper and the maid: *Tannahill Weavers* / Devil whiskey: *Battlefield Band* / Choill choill: *Altan* / Dreams in America: *Bloom, Luka* / Struggle on: *Four Men & A Dog* / Only a woman's heart: *McEvoy, Eleanor* / Never tire of the road: *Irvine, Andy* / Little red bird: *Christian, Emma* / Different drummer: *Black 47* / Eternity: *MacLean, Dougie* / Here's to you: *Oyster Band*
BPM 311 / Dec '97 / Blue Plate

☐ CELTIC MUSIC TODAY
Music for a found harmonium: *Patrick Street* / Whiskey from the field: *Kilbride, Pat* / Calliope house: *Reeltime* / Heart and soul: *Wolfstone* / Ready for the storm: *Deanta* / On horseback: *Ivers, Eileen* / Golden grove/The hop down reel/An occasional flutter: *House Band* / An seanduine doite: *Relativity* / Broken wings: *Cherish The Ladies* / John's got school tomorrow/The North Sea Chinaman: *Thoumire, Simon Three* / Bus spotter's reel: *Thoumire, Simon Three* / Dulaman: *Altan* / Morning star/Caolite Mountains: *Hayes, Martin* / Beam me up: *Rare Air* / Alasdair mhic cholla ghasda: *Capercaillie*
CELT 9007 / Oct '97 / Celtophile

☐ CELTIC MYSTIC (2CD Set)
ZYX 811452 / 27 Apr '98 / ZYX

☐ CELTIC ODYSSEY
Carolan's ramble to Chashel: *Coulter, Steve & Harris Moore* / Butterfly: *Orison* / Donal Agus Morag/the new rigged ship: *Altan* / Calliope house/the cowboy jig: *Fraser, Alasdair & Paul Machlis* / Chuaigh me 'na Rosann: *Scartaglen* / Trip to Skye: *Whelan, John & Eileen Ivers* / Are ye sleeping Maggie: *Fraser, Alasdair* / Tribute to Peadar O'Donnell: *Moving Hearts* / Siun ni dhuibhir: *Relativity* / Alasdair Mhic cholla ghasda: *Capercaillie* / Puirt a buel: *Sileas* / York reel, The/dancing feet: *Trimble, Gerald* / Morghan meaghan: *Riley, Laurie & Bob McNally* / Strathgarry: *Wynberg, Simon*
ND 63912 / Jul '93 / Narada

☐ CELTIC PRAISE AND WORSHIP COLLECTION

CND 003 / Apr '98 / Word

☐ CELTIC ROCK

To you I bestow: Mundy / Ro Ro Rosey: Morrison, Van / Fairytale of New York: Pogues & Kirsty MacColl / Dirty old town: Pogues / Ride on: Moore, Christy / Mandinka: O'Connor, Sinead / Fisherman's blues: Waterboys / Kid gloves: Gallagher, Rory / Mustang Sally: Commitments / Good heart: Sharkey, Feargal / Over the hills: Moore, Gary / What's going on: Taste / Dear Miss Lonely Hearts: Lynott, Phil / Waiting for an alibi: Thin Lizzy / Big decision: That Petrol Emotion / Wasted: Energy Orchard / Teenage kicks: Undertones

RENCD 117 / Jun '97 / Renaissance Collector Series

☐ CELTIC ROOTS (2CD Set)

Fisherman's blues: Waterboys / Fergus sings the blues: Deacon Blue / Love is a stranger: Eurythmics / Robin (the hooded man): Clannad / Big yellow taxi: Brennan, Maire / Take the floor: Capercaillie / Captured: Kennedy, Brian / All or mothing: Reader, Eddi / Bring 'em all in: Scott, Mike / Van Diemens' land: Dickson, Barbara / Blues for Buddah: Silencers / First months of summer: Four Men & A Dog / Madame George: Energy Orchard / Caislean air: Clannad / When the ship come in: Dickson, Barbara / Newry highway men: Johnstons / Rocky road to Dublin: Dubliners / Kilarmey boys of pleasure: Swarbrick, Dave / Whole of the moon: Waterboys / Walk: Eurythmics / Hello in there: Reader, Eddi / Romeo's twin: Kavanagh, Niamh / Intuition: Kennedy, Brian / Painted moon: Silencers / Letter from America: Proclaimers / When you return: Capercaillie / My Johnny was a shoemaker: Dickson, Barbara / In your eyes: Kavanagh, Niamh / Handsome cabin boy: Sweeney's Men / Healer in your heart: Runrig / Perfect: Fairground Attraction / Modern girl: Easton, Sheena / Lets go round again: Average White Band / Can I have my money band: Rafferty, Gerry / Black velvet band: Dubliners / Hermit: Renbourn, John

RCACD 218 / Jul '97 / RCA

☐ CELTIC ROOTS

Crazy love: Kennedy, Brian / In a lifetime: Clannad & Bono / Take the floor: Capercaillie / Perfect: Fairground Attraction / Romeo's twin: Kavanagh, Niamh / Blues for buddah: Silencers / Fear is the enemy of love: Sweetmouth / Robin: Clannad / Madame George: Energy Orchard / All or nothing: Reader, Eddi / Against the wind: Brennan, Maire / When you return: Capercaillie / Hello in there: Reader, Eddi / First months in Summer: Four Men & A Dog / Can I have my money back: Rafferty, Gerry / Black is the colour: McNally, James / Jennifer: Eurythmics / No other words: Kennedy, Brian

74321603362 / 27 Jul '98 / Camden

☐ CELTIC SONGS OF LOVE (Traditional Airs & Ballads)

Boatman / Siubhan ni dhuibhir / Ploughboy lads / Bugeiliar Gwenith Gwyn / Sweet nightingale / Two magicians / Banks of the Lee / Graih my cheree / Ffarwel i Aberystwyth / Waly waly / Irree seose / Deus ganin me d'am bro / Well below the valley / How can ye gang lassie / Nee caillinyin roie / Merched / False love / Tam lin / Moorlough shore / Lloer dirion / Red top knots / Will ye go love / Bess o'bedlam

BEJOCD 16 / May '97 / Beautiful Jo

☐ CELTIC SOUNDSCAPE

She moved through the fair / St. Kevin's dream / Lullaby / Rites of man / Knockaphuca / Baidin fheilimi / Lake / Glendalough

21217 / Nov '97 / Laserlight

☐ CELTIC SPIRIT

Ubi Caritas: Dover, Connie / Seacht Suailci na Maighdine Muire: Ni Fhearraigh, Aoife / Kyrie Eleison, An Ghloir, An Phaidir: Minogue, Aine / Be thou my vision: Anjali Quartet / Salve splendor: Jackson, William / Noeleen Brehed: Groupe Vocal Jef Le Penven / Mo ghra thu: Ni Fhearraigh, Aoife / Bi, a losa, im Chroi-se: Coulter, William / Our Father, God celestial: Baltimore Consort / Puer Natus: Minogue, Aine / Christ Child's lullaby: Wellington, Sheena / Rosa Mystica: Schroeder-Sheker, Terese

ND 63929 / Nov '96 / Narada

VNDCD 11 / 25 May '98 / Virgin

☐ CELTIC SPIRIT

Danny boy / Wild mountain thyme / Dark island / She moved through the fair / Caledonia / Whiskey in the jar / Rowan tree / When you were sweet sixteen / Ae fond kiss / Amazing grace / Loch Lomond / My love is like a red, red rose / Bunch of thyme / Island song / Brides of Glenshiel / Will ye no come back again / Over the sea to Skye

RECD 513 / Dec '97 / REL

☐ CELTIC TAPESTRY VOL.2, A

Rocks of Bawn: Arcady / Garden valley: De Danann / Fisherman's song: Silly Wizard / Crested hens: Solas / Fear a' bhata: MacKenzie, Talitha / Longing for peace: Nugent, Laurence / One I love: Casey, Karan / Erin ni neosainn ce hi: De Danann / Banks of Sullane: Arcady / Cumba eoghain rua ui neill: Clannad / Oro mo bhaidin: Ryan, Cathie / Taimse im' chodladh: Planxty / Mary Rush theme: Out Of Ireland

SH 78062 / 23 Mar '98 / Shanachie

☐ CELTIC TWILIGHT VOL.3

HS 11107CD / Nov '96 / Hearts Of Space

☐ CELTIC VISIONS

ARCD 005 / May '98 / Ainm

☐ CELTIC VOICES: WOMEN OF SONG

Sealwoman: McLaughlin, Mary / Yundah: McLaughlin, Mary / Bring the peace: McLaughlin, Mary / You saw his eyes: McLaughlin, Mary / Little red bird: Christian, Emma / Birth in Bethlehem: Christian, Emma / O Kirre, thou wilt leave me: Christian, Emma / Goodnight song: Christian, Emma / Cantus: Dover, Connie / Wishing well: Dover, Connie / In aimsir bhaint an fheir: Dover, Connie / Siuil a ruin: Dover, Connie / Colour me: Sullivan, Maireid / She moved through the fair: Sullivan, Maireid / Waly waly: Sullivan, Maireid

ND 63921 / Oct '95 / Narada

☐ CELTIC WINDS (Irish Music In America)

Maid in the cherry tree/Wexford lassies / Barrel Rafferty's reel / Widow's daughter/Flogging reel / Ballinakill hornpipe/Bridge hornpipe / Sligo reel / Stranger hornpipe/Golden slipper / Buckley's reel/ Copper plate / Clare hornpipe / Coal miner's/ Farewell to Kilroe / Boys of Ballisodare/Duke of Leinster / Congress reel / Oak tree / Rookery/Saddle of the pony / Money musk/Keel row / Pigeon on the gate/Boys of the laugh / Banks of Newfoundland/ Woodford jig

EDCD 9011 / May '98 / Easydisc

☐ CELTIC WOMAN

CWRCD 7001 / May '96 / Celtic Woman

☐ CELTIC WORLD (2CD Set)

Swallowtail reel: Northrop, Kate / Church of Kildare: Blarney Lads / Tears in heaven: Hamilton, C. & J. Spencer / (Everything I do) I do it for you: Hamilton, C. & J. Spencer / On your shore: Hamilton, C. & J. Spencer / Al labous marv: Soazig / Seoladh na ngamhna: Campbell, D. / Storm clouds: Northrop, Kate / Pennherez keroulaz: Soazig / Falling: Hamilton, C. & J. Spencer / Against all odds: Hamilton, C. & J. Spencer / Silkie: Northrop, Kate / Streets of Derry: Campbell, D. / O'Carolan's concerto: Dargle, W. / Fields of Athenrey: Dargle, W. / Tipping it up to Nancy/Swallow's tail: Dargle, W. / Ar soundarded: Soazig / Miss McDermott: Soazig / Dancer and the moon: Skovbye, Kim Band / Portrait no.1: Skovbye, Kim & Gabrielle Reger / Tri-coloured ribbon: Soazig / Skartinglas: Campbell, D. / Earth dance: Northrop, Kate / In the air tonight: Hamilton, C. & J. Spencer / I will always love you: Hamilton, C. & J. Spencer / Robin the hooded man: Hamilton, C. & J. Spencer / Stranger: Skovbye, Kim & Klaus Schonning / Lonely banna strand: Soazig / King of the fairies: Dargle, W. / Childhood days: Skovbye, Kim Band / Brezhoneg: Soazig / Mountain streams: Campbell, D. / Mo ghile near: Campbell, D. / Eastbound: Skovbye, Kim & Gabrielle Reger / Wedding gift: Skovbye, Kim & Gabrielle Reger / Courting is a pleasure: Campbell, D. & M. Sands / Danny boy: Keaney, C.

24343 / Jul '97 / Laserlight

☐ CELTS RISE AGAIN, THE

CELT 9013 / Jul '98 / Celtophile

☐ CENTENARY VOL.2

SZCD 004 / Apr '96 / Surr Zema Musik

☐ CENTRAL AFRICAN REPUBLIC: MUSIQUE GBAYA/CHANTS A PENSER

C 580008 / Nov '92 / Ocora

☐ CENTRAL HEATING (2CD Set)

Central introduction: Tony D / Loop dreams: Aim / Spellbound: Rae & Christian / Its time 2: Tony D & Chubby / When we get: Tony D / Original Stuntmaster: Aim / How sweet it is: Mr. Scruff & Mr. Rae / Got to have her: Mr. Rae & Mr. Scruff / Like rain: Only Child / Pourquoi: Only Child / Good advice: Rae & Chris / Hemlocka: Votel / Hand of doom: Votel / Through these veins: Funky Fresh Few & Afu Ra / You mean fantastic: Funky Fresh Few / 2nd Street go go: Tony D

GCCD 101 / Nov '96 / Grand Central

☐ CENTRAL RESERVATIONS

Phantasm: Aim / Pourquoi: Only Child / Don't want to lose you: Tony D & Veba / Walk like a man: Tony D & Lorna Harris / Through these veins: Funky Fresh Few & Afu Ra / Is it worth it: Mr. Scruff & Spikey T. / Spellbound: Rae & Christian / Jersey MC's: Tony D & Lowkey / Queen of my dreams: Tony D & Lowkey / Don't want to lose you: Tony D & Veba / Blind mice: Votel, Andy / Rain: Only Child & Buffy Brox

GCCD 103 / 25 May '98 / Grand Central

☐ CEOL TIGH NEACHTAIN (Music From Galway)

CEFCD 145 / Jan '94 / Gael Linn

☐ CEREMONIAL

IMCD 3014 / Feb '96 / Image

☐ CEREMONIAL AND WAR DANCES (Native American Music)

Navahoe boy / Prisoner song / Girl and many boys / Mountain by the sea / Mescalero trail / Montana grass song / Mountain spirit song / Lightning song / Song of the Black Mountain / Song of the Green Rainbow / Yei-be-chai chant / Our father's thoughts / War dance / War dance / War dance (slow/fast) / Warrior song / Honoring song / Glory song / Memorial song

12552 / Nov '95 / Laserlight

☐ CHA CHA CABARET

KLP 66CD / Jun '97 / K

☐ CHA-CHA-CHA

CD 62030 / Oct '93 / Saludos Amigos

☐ CHAINSPOTTING

RAP 031 / 27 Apr '98 / Rapido

☐ CHAMAME - MUSIC OF THE PARANA

C 560052CD / Jul '94 / Ocora

☐ CHAMAME - RURAL MUSIC / ARGENTINA

KAR 989 / Apr '97 / IMP

☐ CHAMPION BRASS

King cotton: Fairey Engineering Works Band / Perpetuum mobile: Fairey Engineering Works Band / Send in the clowns: Fairey Engineering Works Band / Lohengrin intro: Fairey Engineering Works Band / Girl I left behind: Fairey Engineering Works Band / If: Fairey Engineering Works Band / Round the clock: Fairey Engineering Works Band / Queen of Sheba: Fairey Engineering Works Band / Can can: Fairey Engineering Works Band / Don't cry for me Argentina: Fairey Engineering Works Band / Polly wolly doodling: Fairey Engineering Works Band / Hustle: Fairey Engineering Works Band / Peace: Fairey Engineering Works Band / Fanfare and soliloquy: Fairey Engineering Works Band

EMPRCD 568 / May '95 / Emporio

☐ CHAMPION DJ'S FROM STUDIO ONE

SOCD 50151 / Oct '96 / Studio One

☐ CHAMPIONS OF ROCK (2CD Set)

Fireball: Deep Purple / Cry for the nations: Schenker, Michael Group / Radar love: Golden Earring / Race with the devil: Girlschool / And the band played on: Saxon / Caledonia: Trower, Robin / Silver machine: Hawkwind / Wild child: WASP / Overkill: Motorhead / Hair of the dog: Nazareth / Love like a man: Ten Years After / (Don't fear) the reaper: Blue Oyster Cult / Easy livin': Uriah Heep / Tomorrow night: Atomic Rooster / Some kinda wonderful: Grand Funk Railroad / Face down in the gutter: XYZ / I'm the urban spaceman: Bonzo Dog Band / I like to rock: April Wine / These dreams: Heart / Paranoid: Black Sabbath / Gypsy: Uriah Heep / Doctor doctor: UFO / 747 (Strangers in the night): Saxon / Roll over Beethoven: ELO / On the road again: Canned Heat / Trouble: Gillan / Who do you love: Juicy Lucy / Heroes: Meat Loaf / Ace of spades: Motorhead / Don't do that: Geordie / I'm going home: Ten Years After / Armed and ready: Schenker, Michael Group / Beck's bolero: Beck, Jeff & Rod Stewart / Back home: Golden Earring / Willie and the hand jive: Thorogood, George / Clap for the wolfman: Guess Who

SP 871942 / Nov '96 / Disky

☐ CHAMPIONS OF ROCK VOL.1

Fireball: Deep Purple / Cry for the nations: Schenker, Michael Group / Radar love: Golden Earring / Race with the devil: Girlschool / And the band played on: Saxon / Caledonia: Trower, Robin / Silver machine: Hawkwind / Wild child: WASP / Overkill: Motorhead / Hair of the dog: Nazareth / Love like a man: Ten Years After / (Don't fear) the reaper: Blue Oyster Cult / Easy livin': Uriah Heep / Tomorrow night: Atomic Rooster / Some kinda wonderful: Grand Funk Railroad / Everybody wants her: Thunder / I like to rock: April Wine / Face down in the gutter: XYZ

CR 871292 / Mar '97 / Disky

☐ CHAMPIONS OF ROCK VOL.2

These dreams: Heart / Paranoid: Black Sabbath / Gypsy: Uriah Heep / Doctor doctor: UFO / 747 (strangers in the night): Saxon / Roll over Beethoven: ELO / On the road again: Canned Heat / Trouble: Gillan / Who do you love: Juicy Lucy / Heroes: Meat Loaf / Ace of spades: Motorhead / Don't do that: Geordie / I'm going home: Ten Years After / Armed and ready: Schenker, Michael Group / Beck's bolero: Beck, Jeff / Back home: Golden Earring / Willie and the hand jive: Thorogood, George / Clap for the wolfman: Guess Who

CR 871302 / Mar '97 / Disky

☐ CHANSONS A MENER ET A DANSER

983252 / Oct '96 / EPM

☐ CHANSONS GAILLARDES ET LIBERTINES

983282 / Oct '96 / EPM

☐ CHANSONS INTROUVABLES, CHANSONS RETROUVEES VOL.3

171272 / Jul '95 / Musidisc

☐ CHANTONS FRANCAIS 1937-1944 GOLD COLLECTION, THE (2CD Set)

R2CD 7008 / 20 Apr '98 / Deja Vu

☐ CHANTONS FRANCAIS VOL.1 (2CD Set)

R2CD 4038 / 13 Apr '98 / Deja Vu

☐ CHANTONS FRANCAIS VOL.2 (2CD Set)

R2CD 7005 / 13 Apr '98 / Deja Vu

☐ CHANTS

GFS 084 / Nov '97 / Going For A Song

☐ CHANTS AND MUSIQUES DE PROVENCE

PV 782 112 / '88 / Disques Pierre Verany

☐ CHANTS DES ALBANAIS DE CALABRE

ARN 64404 / 5 Jan '98 / Arion

☐ CHANTS ET DANCES DE THRACE, BULGARIA

ARN 64343 / Sep '96 / Arion

☐ CHANTS ET DANSES

ARN 64244 / Aug '93 / Arion

☐ CHANTS ET MUSIQUES DE CORSE (2CD Set)

CDR 130 / 24 Apr '98 / MMED

☐ CHANTS ET TAMBOURS (Music From Venezuala)

C 560085 / Dec '95 / Ocora

☐ CHANTS IN PRAISE OF KRISHNA

VICG 50342 / Mar '96 / JVC World Library

☐ CHANTS TZIGANES

QUI 903028 / Nov '91 / Quintana

☐ CHARETTE

CH 9601 / May '96 / Eden

☐ CHARLESTON CHASERS VOL.2

SOSCD 1314 / Nov '96 / Stomp Off

☐ CHARLESTON DAYS, THE

Let's all go to Mary's house: Whidden, Jay & His New Midnight Follies Band / After I say I'm sorry: Mackey, Percival & His Band / Laugh clown laugh: Schubert, Adrian Dance Orchestra / Charleston: Bell, Edison & His Dance Orchestra / I've never seen a straight banana: Happiness Boys / What did I tell ya: Savoy Orpheans / Where's that rainbow: Baker, Edythe Piano / How could Red Riding Hood: Royal Automobile Club Orchestra / Chinese moon: Douglas, Fred / High up in the sky: Maddison, Bert & Dance Orchestra / Under the moon: Radio Imps / Latest dance hits of 1926: Coliseum Dance Orchestra / Julian: Denza Dance Band / Thanks for the buggy ride: Mackey, Percival & His Band / Breezin' along with the breeze: Revelers / Hitch up the horses: Savoy Orpheans / If I had a talking picture of you: Alfredo & His Band / Russian lullaby: Bidgood, Harry & His Broadcasters / Seven and eleven: Corona Dance Orchestra / Dainty Miss: Da Costa, Raie / Molly: Hylton, Jack & His Orchestra / My wife is on a diet: Hudson, Harry Melody Men / Barcelona: Savoy Orpheans / Electric flashes of 1926: Munro, Ronnie & His Dance Orchestra

PASTCD 9706 / '90 / Flapper

☐ CHARLESTON OF THE TWENTIES

995362 / Dec '93 / EPM

☐ CHARLOTTE GOSPEL 1920-1938

DOCD 5486 / Nov '96 / Document

☐ CHARLY'S EXTRAORDINARY SENSATIONS (20 Mod Soul Classics)

CDNEW 128 / 29 Jun '98 / Charly

☐ CHARLY'S RHYTHM CHANGES

CDNEW 118 / 27 May '98 / Charly

☐ CHARLY'S SOUL TEMPO (A Soulful Experience)

CDNEW 108 / May '97 / Charly

☐ CHARM RAGGA SAMPLER VOL.1

MPCCD 1 / Jul '94 / Charm

☐ CHART '96 (2CD Set)

Wannabe: Spice Girls / Spaceman: Babylon Zoo / I am blessed: Eternal / Going out: Supergrass / Charmless man: Blur / Naked: Louise / Se a vida e: Pet Shop Boys / Nighttrain: Kadoc / Seven days and one week: BBE / Stamp: Healy, Jeremy & Amos / Jazz it up: Reel 2 Real / Freedom: Williams, Robbie / Missing: Everything But The Girl / Not a dry eye in the house: Meat Loaf / I got 5 on it: Luniz / Don't stop moving: Livin' Joy / Day we caught the train: Ocean Colour Scene / I just wanna make love to you: James, Etta / Breakfast at Tiffany's: Deep Blue Something / Don't look back in anger: Oasis / I wanna be a hippy: Technohead / Firestarter: Prodigy / Whole lotta love: Goldbug / It's oh so quiet: Bjork / Female of the species: Space / We've got it goin' on: Backstreet Boys / Thank god it's Friday: R Kelly / Born Slippy: Underworld / Gangsta's paradise: Coolio / Trash: Suede / In too deep: Carlisle, Belinda / Stars: Dubstar / Goldeneye: Turner, Tina / You're gorgeous: Baby Bird / Where love lives: Limerick, Alison / Insomnia: Faithless / No Diggity: Blackstreet & Dr. Dre / Creep: TLC / I will survive: Savage, Chantay / Sale of the century: Sleeper / Mysterious girl: Andre, Peter

CDEMTVD 153 / Nov '96 / EMI TV

☐ CHART BUSTERS (2CD Set)

Back for good: Take That / Unchained melody: Robson & Jerome / No more I love you's: Lennox, Annie / Independent love song: Scarlet / Girl like you: Collins, Edwyn / Right in the night: Jam & Spoon / Baby baby: Corona / Scatman: Scatman John / Total eclipse of the heart: French, Nicki / U sure do: Strike / Tell me when: Human League / Wake up boo: Boo Radleys / Some might say: Oasis / Waking up: Elastica / Fool's gold '95: Stone Roses / In betweener: Sleeper / Guaglione: Prado, Perez / Reach up (papa's got a brnd new pig bag): Perfecto All Stars / Open your heart: M-People / Love City Groove: Love City Groove / I've got a little something: MN8 / Two can play that game: Brown, Bobby / Dreamer: Livin' Joy / Don't stop (wiggle wiggle): Outhere Brothers / Here comes the hotstepper: Kamoze, Ini / It's in his kiss (the shoop shoop song): Kikitup / Let's get it on: Shabba Ranks / Run away: Real McCoy / Set you free: N-Trance / Bump 'n' grind: Kelly, R / Cotton eye Joe: Rednex / Hands up, hands up: Zig & Zag / Surrender your love: Nightcrawlers / Not over yet: Grace / Always something there to remind me: Tin Tin Out / Any time you need a friend: New Jersey Gospel Choir / Freedom: Gayle, Michelle / Your loving arms: Martin, Billie Ray / White cliffs of Dover: Robson & Jerome

RADCD 15 / Jun '95 / Global TV

☐ CHART HIT HISTORY (3CD Set)

U can't touch this: MC Hammer / Feels like I'm in love: Marie, Kelly / Rock your baby: McCrae, George / Too shy: Kajagoogoo / So you win again: Hot Chocolate / Living in a box: Living In A Box / Just an illusion: Imagination / Solid: Ashford & Simpson / Loverboy: Ocean, Billy / Respectable: Mel & Kim / Some girls: Racey / Dancing with tears in my eyes: Ultravox / I don't wanna dance: Grant, Eddy / Dolce vita: Paris, Ryan / Breakaway: Ullman, Tracey / Denis: Blondie / Love changes (everything): Fisher, Climie / We belong: Benatar, Pat / China in your hand: T'Pau / Baker street: Rafferty, Gerry / Walking on sunshine: Katrina & The Waves / He ain't heavy he's my brother: Hollies / She's a lady: Jones, Tom / Road to nowhere: Talking Heads / True: Spandau Ballet / When I need you: Sayer, Leo / Kids in America: Wilde, Kim / Never ending story: Limahl / Love is a battlefield: Benatar, Pat / Radar love: Golden Earring / Heroes: Meat Loaf / Every rose has it's thorn: Poison / My sharona: Knack / Roll over Beethoven: ELO / Kayleigh: Marillion / Centrefold: Geils, J. Band / This flight tonight: Nazareth / Missing you: Waite, John / Power of love: Lewis, Huey & The News / Nutbush city limits: Turner, Ike & Tina / Ride like the wind: Saxon / (I just) died in your arms tonight: Cutting Crew

HR 873902 / Nov '96 / Disky

☐ CHART MACHINE

Dreamer: Livin' Joy / Love city groove: Love City Groove / Not over yet: Grace / Your body's calling: R Kelly / I'm going down: Blige, Mary J. / Don't stop (wiggle wiggle): Outhere Brothers / Two can play that game: Brown, Bobby / Turn on tune in cop out: Freakpower / One night stand: Let Loose / Baby baby: Corona / Love me for a reason: Boyzone / Whatever: Oasis / Stay another day: East 17 / Don't give me your life: Alex Party / Call it love: Deuce / Another day: Whigfield / Crazy: Morrison, Mark / Hoochie booty: Ultimate Kaos / Axel F: Ace Of Base / Living in danger: Ace Of Base

5250392 / May '95 / Polydor

☐ CHART SHOW DANCE ALBUM, THE

5257682 / Jul '95 / PolyGram TV

☐ **CHART SHOW ROCK ALBUM, THE**
5354892 / Jun '96 / PolyGram TV

☐ **CHART SHOW ULTIMATE BLUES ALBUM**
AHLCD 19 / Jun '94 / Hit

☐ **CHARTBUSTERS (2CD Set)**
I believe I can fly: *R Kelly* / Your woman: *White Town* / I have peace: *Strike* / Ready or not: *Course* / Encore une fois: *Sash* / Sometimes: *Brand New Heavies* / Underwater love: *Smoke City* / You're gorgeous: *Baby Bird* / Spaceman: *Babylon Zoo* / Hearing to go: *Republica* / Missing: *Everything But The Girl* / Good enough: *Dodgy* / Flying: *Cast* / Alright: *Supergrass* / Tattva: *Kula Shaker* / Riverboat song: *Ocean Colour Scene* / I'm alive: *Stretch n' Vern* / You got the love: *Source & Candi Staton* / Ain't talkin' 'bout dub: *Apollo 440* / X-Files: *DJ Dado* / Remember me: *Blueboy* / Unbreak my heart: *Braxton, Toni* / If you ever: *East 17 & Gabrielle* / Quit playing games: *Backstreet Boys* / Flava: *Andre, Peter* / Father and son: *Boyzone* / Just a little bit: *Gina G* / Back for good: *Take That* / Macarena: *Los Del Rio* / Clementine: *Owen, Mark* / Waterfalls: *TLC* / Nobody knows: *Rich, Tony* / Children: *Miles, Robert* / Forever: *Damage* / Don't make me wait: *911* / I can make you feel good: *Kavana* / Forvever love: *Barlow, Gary* / Search for the hero: *M-People* / Cecilia: *Suggs* / Female of the species: *Space* / Call around: *Livingstone* / Three lions: *Lightning Seeds & David Baddiel/Frank Skinner*
RADCD 65 / May '97 / Global TV

☐ **CHARTBUSTERS VOL.1 (4CD Set)**
MBSCD 422 / Nov '93 / Castle

☐ **CHARTBUSTERS VOL.1**
Tokyo blues / No room for squares / If ever I would leave you / So tired / Blues in a jiff / Una mas / Down under / Blues on the corner
NYC 60172 / Jul '95 / NYC

☐ **CHARTBUSTERS VOL.2 (4CD Set)**
MBSCD 423 / Nov '93 / Castle

☐ **CHARTS PUR X-TRA LARGE (2CD Set)**
ZYX 811242 / 13 Oct '97 / ZYX

☐ **CHE GUEVARA (Hasta Siempre)**
TUMICD 077 / Nov '97 / Tumi

☐ **CHEAP SHOTS VOL.1**
BHR 022CD / Mar '95 / Burning Heart

☐ **CHEAP SHOTS VOL.2**
BHR 043CD / Apr '96 / Burning Heart

☐ **CHEAP SHOTS VOL.3**
AKA idiot: *Hives* / Full on: *Samiam* / Catch me running around: *No Fun At All* / Shape of punk to come: *Refused* / Twenty two: *Millencolin* / Truth the whole truth and nothing but the truth: *Business* / Don't belong here: *59 Times The Pain* / Kick the bucket: *Liberator* / Don't fade away: *Satanic Surfers* / Petroleum: *Puffball* / You've taken everything: *Bodyjar* / Untruth: *Raised Fist* / Bring it down: *Chickenpox* / Walk a mile for you: *No Fun At All* / Replenish the empty: *Breach* / Flares n' slippers: *59 Times The Pain* / Girls I had: *Liberator* / Rather be dead: *Refused* / Start skanking: *Skalatones* / Unity company: *Within Reach* / Makin' babies: *Ducksoup* / Futureshock: *Nine* / Ultra special: *Voice Of A Generation*
BHR 070CD / 2 Mar '98 / Burning Heart

☐ **CHECK ONE (Mixed By Kirk DeGeorgio/2CD Set)**
XTR 22CDM / 6 Apr '98 / X-Treme

☐ **CHECK OUT THE GROOVE**
MCCD 203 / May '95 / Music Club

☐ **CHECK OUT THE GROOVE**
PLSCD 134 / Apr '96 / Pulse

☐ **CHECK THIS OUT VOL.1**
37463405 / Apr '97 / One Foot

☐ **CHECK THIS OUT VOL.2**
OFR 20031CD / 20 Jul '98 / One Foot

☐ **CHEMICAL BEATS VOL.2**
UE 01502 / 17 Nov '97 / Urban Essentials

☐ **CHEMICAL DANCE CULTURE VOL.2 (Heavenly Break Beats)**
TJAM 0002 / 2 Mar '98 / Tecnojam

☐ **CHEMICAL REACTION**
ORCD 033 / 3 Nov '97 / One

☐ **CHEMISTRY SET, THE**
EFA 063482 / 22 Jun '98 / Ausfahrt

☐ **CHEN ZHONG (The Traditions Of Shanghai For Lute, Fiddle & Zither)**
C 560090 / Dec '96 / Ocora

☐ **CHERNOBYL ENDLESS TRAGEDY**
REZ 420CD / 1 Sep '97 / Rezervation

☐ **CHERRY RED PUNK SINGLES COLLECTION**
Bad hearts / It / Cracked / Howard Hughes / China's eternal / Bored / You're gonna die / Then he kissed me / Sick on you / November 22nd 1963 / Meet the creeper / Right now / Black leather / No body knows / What do I get / Holiday in Cambodia / Police truck / Kill the poor / In sight / Too drunk to fuck / Prey
CDPUNK 51 / Apr '95 / Anagram

☐ **CHESS 50TH ANNIVERSARY COLLECTION (2CD Set)**
Smokestack lightnin': *Howlin' Wolf* / Hoochie coochie man: *Waters, Muddy* / Let me love you baby: *Guy, Buddy* / Boom boom (out go the lights): *Little Walter* / Tell mama: *James, Etta* / I had a talk with my man last night: *Collier, Mitty* / Summertime: *Stewart, Billy* / I'm a man: *Diddley, Bo* / If walls could talk: *Diddley, Bo* / Entertainer: *Clark, Tony* / Flat foot Sam: *TV Slim* / Ama talk to your daughter: *Lenoir, J.B.* / TWA: *Witherspoon, Jimmy* / Dirty old man: *Witherspoon, Jimmy* / Wang dang doodle: *Taylor, Koko* / So mnay roads: *Rush, Otis* / Seventh son: *Mabon, Willie* / Jock-a-mo: *Crawford, Sugar Boy* / Walk: *McCracklin, Jimmy* / Reconsider baby: *Fulson, Lowell* / One bourbon, one scotch, one beer: *Hooker, John Lee* / Roadrunner: *Diddley, Bo* / Reelin' and rockin': *Berry, Chuck* / That's all right: *Rogers, Jimmy* / My time after a while: *Guy, Buddy* / Don't know why I love you (but I do): *Henry, Clarence 'Frogman'* / Rescue me: *Bass, Fontella* / 'In' crowd: *Lewis, Ramsey Trio* / Soulful dress: *Desanto, Sugar Pie* / Stay in my corner: *Dells* / Voice your choice: *Radiants* / Talk to me baby: *James, Elmore* / Good to me: *Thomas, Irma* / Rocket 88: *Brenston, Jackie & The Delta Cats* / Selfish cone: *Ross, Jackie* / Juke: *Little Walter & His Night Cats* / Grit's ain't groceries: *Little Milton* / 29 ways: *Dixon, Willie* / Help me: *Williamson, Sonny Boy* / Rollin' stone: *Waters, Muddy*
CHD 29382 / Apr '97 / Chess/MCA

☐ **CHESS BLUES (The Rock Songbook/ 2CD Set)**
MCD 09389 / 23 Feb '98 / Chess/MCA

☐ **CHESS BLUES GUITAR**
MCD 09393 / 23 Feb '98 / Chess/MCA

☐ **CHESS CLUB RHYTHM AND SOUL**
Mellow fellow: *James, Etta* / Messin' with the man: *Waters, Muddy* / Get out: *Collier, Mitty* / Summertime: *Stewart, Billy* / Ooh baby: *Diddley, Bo* / You left the water running: *Maurice & Mac* / Hey Mr DJ: *Moore, Bobby & The Rhythm Aces* / Can't make it without you: *Hughes, Freddie* / Ain't it: *McDuff, 'Brother' Jack* / Let's wade in the water: *Shaw, Marlena* / Fire: *Taylor, Koko* / Do I make myself clear: *James, Etta & Sugar Pie DeSanto* / Knife and a fork: *Anderson, Kip* / My babe: *Little Walter* / Help me: *Williamson, Sonny Boy* / Good morning little school girl: *Don & Bob* / Who's that guy: *Kolettes* / Here comes the judge: *Markham, Pigmeat* / Function at the junction: *Lewis, Ramsey* / Grits ain't groceries (all around the world): *Little Milton* / Must I holler: *Thomas, Jano* / Every day I have to cry: *Alaimo, Steve* / Musty rusty: *Donaldson, Lou* / I don't want a fuss: *Desanto, Sugar Pie* / High heel sneakers: *Tucker, Tommy*
CDKEND 134 / Jun '96 / Kent

☐ **CHESS EP COLLECTION, THE**
Long tall shorty: *Tucker, Tommy* / Suzie Q: *Hawkins, Dale* / Ain't got no home: *Henry, Clarence 'Frogman'* / Rescue: *Bass, Fontella* / You all green: *Diddley, Bo* / I got to find my baby: *Little Walter* / Good morning little school girl: *Don & Bob* / Oh baby: *Williams, Larry* / Walk: *McCracklin, Jimmy* / I don't want 'cha: *Tucker, Tommy* / When the lights go out: *Witherspoon, Jimmy* / Entertainer: *Clarke, Tony* / Summertime: *Stewart, Billy* / I had a talk with my man: *Collier, Mitty* / Sitting in the park: *Stewart, Billy* / Who's cheating who: *Little Milton* / In crowd: *Lewis, Ramsey Trio* / Leave my baby alone: *Guy, Buddy* / Hi-heel sneakers: *Tucker, Tommy* / Soulful dress: *Desanto, Sugar Pie* / Crazy for my baby: *Dixon, Willie* / I can tell: *Diddley, Bo* / You gonna wreck my life: *Howlin' Wolf* / Messin' with the man: *Waters, Muddy* / Promised land: *Berry, Chuck*
SEECD 380 / Oct '93 / See For Miles

☐ **CHESS SOUL (A Decade Of Chicago's Finest/2CD Set)**
MCD 09388 / 23 Feb '98 / Chess/MCA

☐ **CHESS UPTOWN SOUL**
Entertainer: *Clarke, Tony* / Love ain't nothin': *Nash, Johnny* / Jerk and twine: *Ross, Jackie* / Oh what a feeling: *Phelps, James* / It ain't no big thing: *Radiants* / Sitting in the park: *Stewart, Billy* / Temptation 'bout to get me: *Knight Brothers* / Everything to me: *Elbert, Donnie* / Nothing but you: *Chessmen* / I won't need you: *Chandler, Gene* / Wear it on our face: *Dells* / Do you wanta go: *Mack, Andy* / Pushover: *James, Etta* / Believe in me baby: *Little Milton* / Searching for my love: *Moore, Bobby & The Rhythm Aces* / I had a talk with my man: *Collier, Mitty* / I believe she will: *Eddie & Ernie* / So much love: *Maurice & Mac* / Hurt so bad: *Lewis, Ramsey* / Here you come running: *De Santo, Sugar Pie* / Mama didn't lie: *Bradley, Jan* / Go away little boy: *Shaw, Marlena* / Soul of man: *Bass, Fontella* / Two in the morning: *Spooner's Crowd*
CDKEND 140 / Feb '97 / Kent

☐ **CHIARASCURO CHRISTMAS, A**
CRD 332 / Nov '95 / Chiaroscuro

☐ **CHICAGO - THAT TOODLIN' TOWN (2CD Set)**
DCD 8002 / Jan '95 / Disky

☐ **CHICAGO 1935**
CJR 1001 / Nov '95 / Gannet

☐ **CHICAGO BLUES**
CLACD 425 / Mar '97 / Castle

☐ **CHICAGO BLUES (The Golden Era/2CD Set)**
CDGR 1432 / Apr '97 / Charly

☐ **CHICAGO BLUES (The Chance Era/ 2CD Set)**
Miss Lorraine: *Hooker, John Lee* / I love to boogie: *Hooker, John Lee* / That's alright (ora nelle blues): *Little Walter* / Lonesome old james: *Homesick James* / Williamson shuffle: *Homesick James* / About to lose my mind: *Big Boy Spires* / My baby left me: *Big Boy Spires* / Some day little darling: *Big Boy Spires* / She got me walkin': *Lucas, Lazy Bill* / I had a dream: *Lucas, Lazy Bill* / Price of love: *Hutto, J.B.* / Pet cream man: *Hutto, J.B.* / Lovin' you: *Hutto, J.B.* / Whiskey headed woman: *Homesick James* / 12th street station: *Homesick James* / Wartime: *Homesick James* / Silver haired woman: *Williams, Johnny* / Fat mouth: *Williams, Johnny* / Nervous wreck: *Nix, Willie* / No more love: *Nix, Willie* / Woman I love (my home is in Georgia): *Homesick James* / Dirty rat: *Homesick James* / Baby please don't throw mw down: *Eager, Jimmy* / Should have loved her more: *Eager, Jimmy* / Graveyard blues: *Hooker, John Lee* / Road trouble: *Hooker, John Lee* / Talkin' boogie: *Hooker, John Lee* / I just keep loving her: *Little Walter* / Homesick: *Homesick James* / Williamson boogie: *Homesick James* / Which one do I love: *Big Boy Spires* / Rhythm rock boogie: *Big Boy Spires* / Tired of being mistreated: *Big Boy Spires* / Just can't say: *Nix, Willie* / All by myself: *Nix, Willie* / My baby's gone: *Lucas, Lazy Bill* / I can't eat can't sleep: *Lucas, Lazy Bill* / Combination boogie: *Hutto, J.B.* / Dim lights: *Hutto, J.B.* / Things are so slow: *Hutto, J.B.* / Johnnie mae: *Homesick James* / Farmer's blues: *Homesick James* / Lonesome blues: *Homesick James* / Roll tumble and slip (I cried): *Sunnyland Slim* / Train time (4 o'clock blues): *Sunnyland Slim* / Long lonesome day: *Homesick James* / Late hours at midnight: *Homesick James* / Now she's gone: *Hutto, J.B.* / Please Mr. Doctor: *Eager, Jimmy* / 609 boogie: *Eager, Jimmy*
CDGR 1462 / Oct '97 / Charly

☐ **CHICAGO BLUES (The Vee Jay Era/ 2CD Set)**
Goin' back (going back home): *Williams, 'Big' Joe* / Baby left town: *Williams, 'Big' Joe* / Every woman I know: *Emerson, Billy* / Don't be careless: *Emerson, Billy* / Comeback: *Memphis Slim* / Steppin' out: *Memphis Slim* / Someone to love me: *Pryor, Snooky* / You tried to ruin me baby: *Pryor, Snooky* / Oh baby: *Lenoir, J.B.* / Blue evening: *McKinley, L.C.* / I'm so satisfied: *McKinley, L.C.* / Gotta find my baby: *Memphis Slim* / Messin' around: *Memphis Slim* / Kissing at midnight: *Arnold, Billy Boy* / Don't stay out all night: *Arnold, Billy Boy* / Schooldays (on my mind): *Jones, Floyd* / Ain't times hard: *Jones, Floyd* / Tomorrow never comes: *Emerson, Billy* / Don't start me lyin': *Emerson, Billy* / If you won't stay home: *Emerson, Billy* / Blue and lonesome: *Memphis Slim* / Slim's blues: *Memphis Slim* / Goin' by the river: *Reed, Jimmy* / You'll always have a home: *Taylor, Eddie* / King's highway: *Williams, 'Big' Joe* / Eula Mae: *Williams, 'Big' Joe* / You never miss your water: *Emerson, Billy* / Somebody show me: *Emerson, Billy* / Mother Earth: *Memphis Slim* / Wish me well: *Memphis Slim* / No more doggin': *Gordon, Rosco* / Just a little bit: *Gordon, Rosco* / Down with it: *McKinley, L.C.* / Lonely: *McKinley, L.C.* / Lend me your love: *Memphis Slim* / Sassy Mae: *Memphis Slim* / Here's my picture: *Arnold, Billy Boy* / Prisoner's plea: *Arnold, Billy Boy* / Judgement day: *Pryor, Snooky* / Floyd's blues: *Jones, Floyd* / Any old lonesome day: *Jones, Floyd* / Pleasure is all mine: *Emerson, Billy* / Do yourself a favour: *Emerson, Billy* / (Do the) chicken: *Emerson, Billy* / Rockin' the house (beer drinkin' woman): *Memphis Slim* / My gal keeps me crying: *Memphis Slim* / Wheel and deal: *Hooker, John Lee* / Crawlin' black spider: *Hooker, John Lee* / Ride 'em on down: *Taylor, Eddie*
CDGR 1452 / 2 Feb '98 / Charly

☐ **CHICAGO BLUES 1940-1947 (2CD Set)**
FA 150 / 24 Apr '98 / Fremeaux

☐ **CHICAGO BLUES AT BURNLEY**
JSPCD 247 / '91 / JSP

☐ **CHICAGO BLUES AT HOME**
TCD 5028 / Oct '95 / Testament

☐ **CHICAGO BLUES FESTIVAL**
Buddy's blues: *Guy, Buddy* / Blue monday: *Guy, Buddy* / Everyday I have the blues: *Guy, Buddy* / Woman blues: *Guy, Buddy* / Satisfaction: *Guy, Buddy* / Messin' with the kid: *Guy, Buddy & Junior Wells* / No use cryin': *Guy, Buddy & Junior Wells* / Just to be with you: *Guy, Buddy & Junior Wells* / Junior's shuffle: *Guy, Buddy & Junior Wells* / Out of sight: *Guy, Buddy & Junior Wells* / It's hard for me to believe baby: *Rush, Otis* / May be the last time: *Rush, Otis* / I feel good: *Rush, Otis* / Otis' blues: *Rush, Otis* / Goin' down slow: *Little Walter* / Walter's blues: *Little Walter* / Lovin' you all the time: *Little Walter* / Blue mood: *Little Walter*
CDBM 125 / 2 Mar '98 / Blue Moon

☐ **CHICAGO BLUES FROM CJ RECORDS VOL.1**
WCD 120281 / Dec '96 / Wolf

☐ **CHICAGO BLUES FROM CJ RECORDS VOL.2**
WCD 120282 / 5 Feb '98 / Wolf

☐ **CHICAGO BLUES JAM**
Had it so hard: *Sunnyland Slim & Lacy Gibson* / Soft and mellow Stella: *Sunnyland Slim & Lacy Gibson* / Bessie Mae: *Sunnyland Slim & Lacy Gibson* / You went away baby: *Bell, Carey & Willie Williams* / Alcoholic man: *Bell, Carey & Willie Williams* / Showing off my car: *Bell, Carey & Willie Williams* / In the dark (that ain't right): *Magic Slim* / Cummins Prison farm: *Magic Slim* / Pretty baby: *Johnson, Jimmy* / When my first wife quit me: *Johnson, Jimmy* / Came up the hard way: *Clearwater, Eddy* / Muddy water's gonna run clear: *Clearwater, Eddy* / I don't know why: *Clearwater, Eddy* / Boogie my blues away: *Clearwater, Eddy* / Mayor Daley's blues: *Clearwater, Eddy*
NEBCD 852 / Aug '96 / Sequel

☐ **CHICAGO BLUES LIVE VOL.1**
WCD 120871 / Jul '97 / Wolf

☐ **CHICAGO BLUES NIGHT**
GBW 001 / Feb '92 / GBW

☐ **CHICAGO BLUES TODAY VOL.1**
Help me: *Wells, Junior Chicago Blues Band* / It hurts me too (when things go wrong): *Wells, Junior Chicago Blues Band* / Messin' with the kid: *Wells, Junior Chicago Blues Band* / Vietcong blues: *Wells, Junior Chicago Blues Band* / All night long: *Wells, Junior Chicago Blues Band* / Going ahead: *Hutto, J.B. & His Hawks* / Please help: *Hutto, J.B. & His Hawks* / Too much alcohol: *Hutto, J.B. & His Hawks* / Married woman blues: *Hutto, J.B. & His Hawks* / That's the truth: *Hutto, J.B. & His Hawks* / Marie: *Spann, Otis Southside Piano* / Burning fire: *Spann, Otis Southside Piano* / SP blues: *Spann, Otis Southside Piano* / Sometime I wonder: *Spann, Otis Southside Piano* / Spann's stomp: *Spann, Otis Southside Piano*
VMD 79216 / Oct '95 / Vanguard

☐ **CHICAGO BLUES TODAY VOL.2**
Cotton crop blues: *Cotton, Jimmy Blues Quartet* / Blues keep falling: *Cotton, Jimmy Blues Quartet* / Love me or leave: *Cotton, Jimmy Blues Quartet* / Rockett: *Cotton, Jimmy Blues Quartet* / West Helena blues: *Cotton, Jimmy Blues Quartet* / Everything's going to turn out alright: *Rush, Otis Blues Band* / It's a mean old world: *Rush, Otis Blues Band* / I can't quit you baby: *Rush, Otis Blues Band* / Rock: *Rush, Otis Blues Band* / It's my own fault: *Rush, Otis Blues Band* / Dust my broom: *Homesick James & His Dusters* / Somebody been talkin': *Homesick James & His Dusters* / Set a date: *Homesick James & His Dusters* / So mean to me: *Homesick James & His Dusters*
VMD 79217 / Oct '95 / Vanguard

☐ **CHICAGO BLUES TODAY VOL.3**
One more time: *Young, Johnny South Side Blues Band* / Kid man blues: *Young, Johnny South Side Blues Band* / My black mare: *Young, Johnny South Side Blues Band* / Stealin' back: *Young, Johnny South Side Blues Band* / I got mine in time: *Young, Johnny South Side Blues Band* / Tighten up on it: *Young, Johnny South Side Blues Band* / Dynaflow blues: *Shines, Johnny Blues Band* / Black spider blues: *Shines, Johnny Blues Band* / Layin' down my shoes and clothes: *Shines, Johnny Blues Band* / If I get lucky: *Shines, Johnny Blues Band* / Rockin' my boogie: *Horton, Big Walter Blues Harp & Memphis Charlie* / Mr. Boweevil: *Horton, Big Walter Blues Harp & Memphis Charlie* / Hey hey: *Horton, Big Walter Blues Harp & Memphis Charlie*
VMD 79218 / Oct '95 / Vanguard

☐ **CHICAGO BLUES VOL.1 (2CD Set)**
Where the hell where you when I got home: *Lefty Dizz* / Ain't it nice to be loved: *Lefty Dizz* / Keep on running: *Littlejohn, Johnny* / If you don't want me: *Littlejohn, Johnny* / You got to help me: *Sumlin, Hubert* / Tell me why: *Linkchain, Hip* / You must be shampoo baby: *Linkchain, Hip* / Good kookamaloo: *Louisiana Red* / Little boy blue: *Horton, Walter* / Cha cha in blues: *Campbell, Eddie C.* / Hello Mrs. Brown: *Smith, Byther* / Brought up the hard way: *Bell, Carey* / One eyed man: *Tre* / Young girl: *Evans, Lucky Lopez* / Good lovings: *Evans, Lucky Lopez* / Fishing in my pond: *Rogers, Jimmy* / Crazy woman blues: *Rogers, Jimmy* / Dr. Boogie: *Terry, Doc* / Things can't stay the same: *Terry, Doc* / So good to me: *Dawkins, Jimmy* / Swear to tell the truth: *Walker, Johnny 'Big Moose'* / Low down dog: *Burks, JT* / Must I holler: *Burks, JT* / From Greenwood Mississippi to Chicago: *Burks, JT* / Operator: *Burks, JT* / I'm very superstitious: *Tre* / Pickin' rags: *Buford, Mojo* / Jack potato boogie: *Buford, Mojo* / Once a gambler: *Guy, Phil* / Leaving town: *Louisiana Red* / Lonesome blues: *Granderson, John Lee* / Grease me baby: *Louisiana Red*
JSPCD 401 / Jul '97 / JSP

☐ **CHICAGO BLUES VOL.2 (2CD Set)**
You gave me the blues baby: *Guitar Shorty* / No educated woman: *Patterson, Jordan & Bobby Rush* / You don't love poor me no more: *Lefty Dizz* / Valerie: *Louisiana Red* / I'm leaving: *Louisiana Red* / Rambling woman: *Walker, Johnny 'Big Moose'* / Highway man blues: *Dawkins, Jimmy* / All I can do: *Sumlin, Hubert* / Sometimes I'm right: *Sumlin, Hubert* / Mean red spider: *Rogers, Jimmy* / Mighty Mars: *Mars, Johnny* / Teardrops on my pillow: *Lefty Dizz* / Baby please: *Left Hand Frank* / Crazy woman blues: *Rogers, Jimmy* / Rollin' and tumblin': *Granderson, John Lee* / Whisky drinking woman: *Phillips, Brewer & The Houserockers* / Poison ivy: *Phillips, Brewer & The Houserockers* / Poor boy blues: *Phillips, Brewer & The Houserockers* / Partnership woman: *Burks, JT* / Minnie Sue: *Burks, JT* / Cadillac driven woman: *Burks, JT* / Racetrack blues: *Burks, JT* / Take a walk with me: *Rogers, Jimmy* / Little Walter's blues: *Sayles, Charlie* / Tail draggin': *Evans, Lucky Lopez* / Extra extra: *Evans, Lucky Lopez* / Rocket 88: *Mars, Johnny* / This I know to be true: *Farr, Deitra* / Who do blues: *Terry, Doc* / Talk to your daughter: *Carter, Joe*
JSPCD 405 / Jun '98 / JSP

☐ **CHICAGO GARAGE BAND GREATS (The Best Of Rembrandt Records 1966-1968)**
Hassle: *Nite Owls* / Boots are made for talking: *Nite Owls* / Open up your mind: *Nuchez* / No reservations: *Circus* / Come on back: *Nickel Bag* / Woods: *Nickel Bag* / Games we play: *Circus* / Sands of mind: *Circus* / Long lost friend: *Monday's Child* / It's a hassle: *Nickel Bag* / I live in the springtime: *Lemon Drops* / Listen girl: *Lemon Drops* / Nobody for me: *Lemon Drops* / Flowers on the hillside: *Lemon Drops* / Trilogy: *Watermelon* / Ocean song: *Watermelon* / I can make you happy: *Buzzsaw* / Nowhere to go: *Buzzsaw* / Roll on Angeline: *Buzzsaw* / Walking through a rainbow: *Buzzsaw*
CDTB 164 / Mar '95 / Thunderbolt

☐ **CHICAGO GOSPEL**
HTCD 08 / '92 / Heritage

☐ **CHICAGO HOT BANDS 1924-1928**
Copenhagen / Riverboat shuffle / My Mama's in town / Blue bonnet you make me feel blue / Ace in the hole / Cryin' for the moon / Mandy / You don't like it, not much / Zulu wail / I ain't got nobody / Weary blues / I wish I could shimmy like my sister Kate / Sorry / Mama's gone goodbye / Lady of Havana / Voice of the Southland / Starlight and tulips / When sweet Susie goes steppin' by / Dusky Stevedore / Skinner's sock / When you're smiling / Hallucinations / I'm sorry Sally / My Gal Sal
CBC 1041 / 23 Feb '98 / Timeless Historical

☐ **CHICAGO HOUSE JAM**
We can make it: *UBQ & Kathy Summers* / My underground: *Vision* / Project 3: Two Men On A Struggle / Feel my soul: *UBQ & Kathy Summers* / Bubbles: *Tikkle* / Seduction: *Vision* / Cosmic rhythm: *UBQ Project* / Reachin': *LNR* / Project 1: Two Men On A Struggle / When I fall in love: *UBQ & Kathy Summers*
SLIPCD 57 / Mar '97 / Slip 'n' Slide

☐ **CHICAGO JUMP BANDS 1945-1953**
RST 915772 / Jun '94 / RST

☐ CHICAGO RADIO SOUL
Rescue me: Bass, Fontella / Don't mess up a good thing: Bass, Fontella & Bobby McClure / We got the winning hand: Little Milton / Selfish one: Ross, Jackie / Thousand miles away: Garrett, Jo Ann / Shy guy: Radiants / No faith, no love: Collier, Mitty / I can't help myself: Gems / Love is a five letter word: Phelps, James / This heart of mine: Clarke, Tony / Lonely girl: Davis, Andrea / (Don't it make you) feel kinda bad: Radiants / La de da, I'm a fool in love: Phelps, James / Only time will tell: James, Etta / Peak of love: McClure, Bobby / Bossa nova bird: Dells / Creeper: Robinson, Freddie / Heartbreak society: Radiants / Strange feeling: Stewart, Billy / Try my love again: Moore, Bobby & The Rhythm Aces / Sharing you: Collier, Mitty / Take me for a little while: Ross, Jackie / One day I'll show you: Radiants / Stay by my side: Garrett, Jo Ann / Love reputation: LaSalle, Denise / Happy new love: Gems
CDKEND 133 / Apr '96 / Kent

☐ CHICAGO SOUND VOL.1
CSDCD 1 / May '95 / Chicago Sound

☐ CHICAGO SOUND VOL.2
CDCS 002 / Sep '96 / Chicago Sound

☐ CHICAGO SOUNDS
CSCD 001 / Dec '94 / ACV

☐ CHICAGO TRAX (3CD Set)
CLP 0032 / 20 Oct '97 / Cleopatra

☐ CHICAGO TRAX VOL.1 (3CD Set)
TXCD 7001 / 15 Sep '97 / Trax

☐ CHICAGO'S BEST WEST AND SOUTH SIDE BLUES SINGERS VOL.1
WCD 120862 / 28 Oct '97 / Wolf

☐ CHICANO POWER (Latin Rock In The USA 1968-1975/2CD Set)
Been had: Sapho / It's too late: Black Sugar / Mira pa ca: Chango / Cayuco: Averne, Harvey Barrio Band / Ran kan kan: El Chicano / Fools are you: Mother Night / Soul sacrifice: Santana / Sapo's montuno: Sapho / Sun God: Tierra / Azteca theme: Azteca / Night flight: Benitez / Higher ground: Haze / Via jecito: Black Sugar / Ramona: Toro / Batuka: Antiques / Descartaga: Ascarrunz, Cesar
SJRCD 039 / 20 Jul '98 / Soul Jazz

☐ CHIKY(U)U
ASH 36 / May '97 / Ash International

☐ CHILDLINE
One: Automatic Baby / Feelin' alright: Weller, Paul / Huckleberry Grove: Ocean Colour Scene / Still life: Alisha's Attic / Punk boy: Ash / Ski jump nose: Mansun / Lazy: Suede / Whiskey in the jar: Pulp / Better man: Cast / Ocean Drive: Lighthouse Family / Can't smile without you: Menswear / Back street luv: Salad / Witchita lineman: These Animal Men / Dance of the bad angel: Booth, Tim & Angelo Badalamenti / Chaos: Tricky / Possibly maybe: Bjork / Looking for: East 17 / Your song: Boyzone
5530302 / Nov '96 / PolyGram TV

☐ CHILDREN - 100% KIDS
TCD 2798 / Nov '95 / Telstar

☐ CHILDREN - A TRADITIONAL CHRISTMAS
CD 251 / Jul '94 / CYP Children's Audio

☐ CHILDREN - CHANTEFABLES, CHANTEFLEURS (French Children's Songs, Poems & Music) (Desnos/ Tardieu/Mechin)
LDX 200314 / Jan '93 / La Chant Du Monde

☐ CHILDREN - CHRISTMAS HOUSE PARTY FOR KIDS
Jingle bells / Rudolph the red-nosed reindeer / White Christmas / O little town of Bethlehem / Oh Christmas tree / God rest ye merry gentlemen / Deck the halls / Jingle bell rock / Mary's boy child / Let it snow, let it snow, let it snow / Feliz navidad / Gloria in excelsis Deo / Away in a manger / Oh come all ye faithful / We wish you a merry Christmas
KI 880922 / 29 Aug '97 / Disky

☐ CHILDREN - CHRISTMAS PARTY POPS
CD 250 / Oct '93 / CYP Children's Audio

☐ CHILDREN - JUNIOR CHOICE VOL.1
Nellie the elephant: Miller, Mandy / Runaway train: Dalhart, Vernon / Gilly gilly ossenfeffer katzenellenbogen by the sea: Bygraves, Max / You're a pink toothbrush: Bygraves, Max / Robin Hood: James, Dick / I taut I taw a puddy tat: Blanc, Mel / Woody Woodpecker: Blanc, Mel / Ernie (the fastest milkman in the West): Hill, Benny / I've lost my mummy: Harris, Rolf / Jake the peg: Harris, Rolf / My boomerang won't come back: Drake, Charlie / Mr. Custer: Drake, Charlie / Little boy fishin': Abicair, Shirley / Laughing policeman: Penrose, Charles / Ragtime Cowboy Joe: Chipmunks / Buckingham Palace: Stephens, Anne / Hippopotamus song: Flanders & Swann / Ballad of Davy Crockett: Ford, Tennessee Erie / Grandad: Dunn, Clive
CDMFP 5890 / Oct '90 / Music For Pleasure

☐ CHILDREN - JUNIOR CHOICE VOL.2
Ugly ducking: Kaye, Danny / King's new clothes: Kaye, Danny / Little white duck: Kaye, Danny / Tubby the tuba: Kaye, Danny / Little red monkey: Nicols/ Edwards/ Bentley / Grandfather's clock: Radio Revellers / Kitty in the basket: Dekker, Diana / I know an old lady: Ives, Burl / Big Rock Candy Mountain: Ives, Burl / There's a friend for little children: Uncle Mac / All things bright and beautiful: Uncle Mac / Three billy goat gruff: Luther, Frank / Owl and the pussycat: Hayes, Elton / Puffin' Billy: Melodi Light Orchestra / (How much is that) doggie in the window: Roza, Lita / Mr. Cuckoo (sing your song): Ross, Edmundo / Typewriter: Anderson, Leroy / Little shoemaker: Michael Twins / Bimbo: Miller, Suzi / Swedish rhapsody: Mantovani
CDMFP 5891 / Oct '90 / Music For Pleasure

☐ CHILDREN - JUNIOR PARTY POPS VOL.1
CD 249 / May '93 / CYP Children's Audio

☐ CHILDREN - JUNIOR PARTY POPS VOL.2
PT 249CD / Mar '93 / CYP Children's Audio

☐ CHILDREN - JUNIOR PARTY POPS VOL.2
PT 247CD / Mar '93 / CYP Children's Audio

☐ CHILDREN - MR. BOOM IS OVER THE MOON
MB 007CD / Nov '95 / Moonbeam Music

☐ CHILDREN - MUSICAL FUN AND GAMES
Children's games / Sorcerer's apprentice / Dolly Suite: Academy Of St. Martin in the Fields/Neville Marriner / Musical box / Nutcracker suite: Royal Philharmonic Orchestra / Pied piper: MacDonald, George & Northern Sinfonia of England / Themes for Narnia: Robles, Marisa Ensemble & Christopher Hyde-Smith / Scaramouche-Braziliera: Johnson, Emma & Gordon Back
CDDCA 673 / Oct '89 / ASV

☐ CHILDREN - SONGS AND NURSERY RHYMES OF THE WORLD
Le furet / Une souris verte / Chant de deux petites filles / Los mamones / Oi cotou cotou cototchok / Barati baratin / Tutu marambaia / London Bridge / Madeira lullaby / Monday's child / Head and shoulders / Las Abejas / Grun grun grun / Assalalaa de la terre de Baffin / Simon says / Estaba el Senor Don Gato / Je te tiens par la barbichette / Alle meine entchen / Nick nack paddy wack / Savez vous planter les choux / ABCD / Pussy cat / Water drum / Lullaby / Eenie meenie minie moe / Der wettstreit / Chicken never shows its nest / Ikh agsal / Ihumke / Bingo
U 310110 / May '97 / Auvidis Jeunesse

☐ CHILDREN - THE COMPLETE JUNIOR CHOICE
Nellie the elephant / Who's afraid of the big bad wolf / Puff the magic dragon / Old Macdonald had a farm / Runaway train / Jake the peg / Splish splash / I taut I taw a puddy-tat / I've lost my mummy / Ugly bug ball / Owl and the pussycat / Puffin' Billy / (How much) Is that doggy in the window / You're a pink toothbrush / Woody woodpecker / Whistle while you work / Winnie The Pooh / All things bright and beautiful / Teddy bears picnic / My boomerang won't come back / Laughing policeman
CDLFPK 2000 / May '96 / Listen For Pleasure

☐ CHILDREN - THE WORLD OF KIDS' FAVOURITE HITS (2CD Set)
ZYX 111042 / Jan '98 / ZYX

☐ CHILDREN - YOUNG AT HEART
Christopher Robin: Lee, Mary / Animal crackers: BBC Dance Orchestra / Little man you've had a busy day: Rosing, Val & Jay Wilbur Band / Horsey horsey: Campbell, Big Bill & His Rocky Mountain Rhythm / Mickey Mouse's birthday party: Marcellion, Muzzy & Ted Fiorito Band / Little drummer boy: Robins, Phyllis & Jay Wilbur Band / On the good ship Lollipop: Geraldo & His Orchestra / Mommy I don't want to go to bed: Gonella, Nat & His Georgians / Wedding of Jack and Jill: Wilbur, Jay & his band / Runaway train: Dalhart, Vernon / Trains: Gardiner, Reginald / Bee song: Askey, Arthur / Teddy bears' picnic: Hall, Henry Orchestra / It's my mother's birthday today: Yates, Hal & His Orchestra / Three little fishes: Gonella, Nat & His Georgians / When the circus comes to town: Kyser, Kay Orchestra / Hush hush hush, here comes the bogeyman: Hall, Henry Orchestra / Laughing policeman: Penrose, Charles / Lion and Albert: Holloway, Stanley / Buckingham Palace: Stephens, Anne
PASTCD 9769 / Oct '93 / Flapper

☐ CHILDREN'S CHRISTMAS COLLECTION
PTCD 232 / Sep '97 / CYP Children's Audio

☐ CHILDREN'S FAVOURITES - YOU MUST REMEMBER THIS
Puffin' Billy: McLodi Light Orchestra/Ole Jensen / Teddy bear's picnic: Rosing, Val & Henry Hall/BBC Dance Orchestra / Swinging on a star: Crosby, Bing / I've got no strings: Kemp, Hal Orchestra / Grandfather's clock: Williams, Harold & BBC Male Chorus / One little raindrop: Ovaltineys & George Melachrino/Tessa Deane / Policeman's holiday: New Light Symphony Orchestra / Dicky bird hop: Fields, Gracie / Laughing policeman: Penrose, Charles / One, two, button your shoe: Swingettes & Jack Hylton Orchestra / Buckingham Palace: Stephens, Anne / Rhythm in the alphabet: Formby, George / Little boy bubbles: Doyle, Jack 'Trump' Aces Of Rhythm / Animal crackers in my soup: Robins, Phyllis & The Corona Babes / Parade of the tin soldiers: New Light Symphony Orchestra / Runaway train: Robinson, Carson & His Pioneers / Pied piper of Hamelin: Bowlly, Al & Ray Noble/His New Mayfair Orchestra / Owl and the pussy cat: Robertson, Stuart / I'm Popeye the sailor man: Costello, Billy / Three little fishes: Denham, Maurice / Wedding of the painted doll: Layton & Johnstone / Ragtime cowboy Joe: Carless, Dorothy & Johnny Green/Geraldo / Portrait of a toy soldier: Sandler, Albert & His Orchestra / Balloons: Ovaltineys & Monte Rey / Little man, you've had a busy day: Carlisle, Elsie / Everything stops for tea: Lorenzi, Mario 'Harp' & His Rhythmics / Goodnight children eveywhere: Lynn, Vera & Ambrose
75605522812 / Feb '97 / Happy Days

☐ CHILDREN'S SONGS FROM SOUTH INDIA
ARN 6428 / Oct '94 / Arion

☐ CHILDREN'S SONGS FROM SW CHINA
ARN 64365 / Feb '97 / Arion

☐ CHILD'S CELEBRATION OF FOLK MUSIC, A
9425852 / Aug '96 / Music For Little People

☐ CHILIK: SONGS AND MELODIES OF THE NAGAYBAKS (Recordings From Russian Tartar Province Of Chelyabinsk)
PAN 7003CD / Feb '95 / Pan

☐ CHILL FM
MR 14CD / Apr '96 / Massive Respect

☐ CHILL OUT
9548345492 / Aug '96 / East West

☐ CHILL OUT (2CD Set)
Floating over Calcutta: Exis / Rain train: Silent Persuasion / Islamabad calling: Ais / Sultry sultana: Nanga Parbat / In the temple of Masari Sharif: Oleum / Sun train in Alexandria: Nota Bene / Talking to Zalmoxe: Andromeda / Bad weekend: Modulator 27 / Sun train: Sulphur Sky / Top of Kilimandscharo: Total Recall / Haschisch: THC Project / Total Taliban: Mesmerized / Desert rumble: Stratos / Le retour du Abdul El Karim: Exorbitant Species / Nastratin hogea: Equilibrium / Trapped in Baghdad: Karanitant / Richard runs the voodoo down: Interrupted Transmission / See the sulphur sky: Sulphur Sky
9050524 / 24 Nov '97 / Nova Tekk

☐ CHILL OUT - THE ALBUM
XPS 3CD / Feb '97 / X-Treme

☐ CHILL OUT FREE (2CD Set)
AVEXCD 51 / Nov '96 / Avex

☐ CHILLIN' (The Best Of Jazz Funk)
Sun goddess: Lewis, Ramsey / Expansions: Smith, Lonnie Liston / Keep that same old feeling: Crusaders / Morning dance: Spyro Gyra / Always and forever: Jordan, Stanley / School days: Clarke, Stanley / Mystic voyage: Ayers, Roy / Mr. Magic: Washington, Grover Jr. / Feels so good: Mangione, Chuck / Sneakin' up behind you: Brecker Brothers / Funkin' for Jamaica: Browne, Tom / Action speaks louder than words: Chocolate Milk / Jaws: Schifrin, Lalo / Black cow: Connors, Norman
74321288852 / Jun '95 / Ariola

☐ CHILLOUT CLASSICS (Classical Music Mixed By Jonothan Moore)
39101822 / Jun '97 / Hyperium

☐ CHILLOUT FOUREVER
XTR 38CDM / Jun '97 / X-Treme

☐ CHINA - IT'S TIME TO LISTEN
5229635902 / 27 Apr '98 / Ellipsis Arts

☐ CHINESE BAMBOO FLUTE MUSIC
12183 / Aug '95 / Laserlight

☐ CHINESE HAN MUSIC
117052 / Jan '97 / Musidisc

☐ CHISWICK SAMPLER, THE (Good Clean Fun)
Beautiful Delilah: Count Bishops / Sweet revenge: 101'ers / Gatecrasher: Gorillas / Groovy Ruby: Moped, Johnny / Enemies: Radiators From Space / Tear it up/Teenage cutie: Whirlwind / Train kept a rollin': Motorhead / I want candy: Bishops / Radio stars/Buy Chiswick records: Radio Stars / Smash it up: Damned / Romford girls: Riff Raff / Dead vandals: Johnny & The Self Abusers / Come on let's go: Sharpe, Rocky & The Replays / Driver's seat/Poison pen mail: Sniff 'n' The Tears / Let's talk about the weather: Radiators / There's a boy on our street: Disguise / Addicts of the first night: Albania / Swim the Indian ocean: 2-2 / Over the top: Motordamn
CDWIKX 162 / Oct '95 / Chiswick

☐ CHISWICK STORY, THE (2CD Set)
Route 66: Count Bishops / Teenage letter: Count Bishops / Train train: Count Bishops / Keys to your heart: 101'ers / She's my gal: Gorillas / Gorilla got me: Gorillas / Drip drop: Sharpe, Rocky & The Razors / I'm crying: Story, Little Bob / Dirty pictures: Radio Stars / No Russians in Russia: Radio Stars / Nervous wreck: Radio Stars / Real me: Radio Stars / Television screen: Radiators From Space / Motorhead: Motorhead / I wanna be free: Rings / No one: Moped, Johnny / Darling let's have another baby: Moped, Johnny / Little queenie: Moped, Johnny / I want you to dance with me: Hill, Jeff / Common truth: Amazorblades / Saints and sinners: Johnny & The Self Abusers / Hang loose (I've gotta rock): Whirlwind / I only wish (that I'd been told): Whirlwind / Heaven knows: Whirlwind / Million dollar hero: Radiators / Dancing years: Radiators / Cosmonaut: Riff Raff / I want candy: Bishops / Gay boys in bondage: Drug Addix / Rama lama ding dong: Sharpe, Rocky & The Replays / Imagination: Sharpe, Rocky & The Replays / Shout shout (knock yourself out): Sharpe, Rocky & The Replays / Heart: Sharpe, Rocky & The Replays / Driver's seat: Sniff 'n' The Tears / Hey baby: Disguise / I couldn't help but cry: Kelleher, Dan / Automobile: Stickshifts / Love song: Damned / Smash it up: Damned / Gabrielle: Nips / That driving beat: Red Beans & Rice / I can't fight it: Textones / Albania (are you all mine): Albania / Go go go: Albania / Tomahawk cruise: Smith, TV's Explorers / Tennessee stud: Woods, Terry / Radioactive kid: Meteors / Insufficient data: 2-2 / Kwagayo: 2-2 / Desire: Radiation, Roddy & Tearjerkers / Grab what you can (biez co mozesz): Jakko
CDWIK2 100 / Mar '92 / Chiswick

☐ CHOIR MUSIC FROM WALES
Land of my fathers / Home / Welsh rapsody / Suo gan / God bless the Prince of Wales / Ash grove / When I survey the wonderous cross / All through the night / Arwelfa / Bells of Aberdovey / Tretswer court / Lisa Land and the ballad of Roke's drift / Welsh medley / David of the white rock / Cwm rhondda / How great thou art / Soldiers chorus / Abide with me
3036100162 / May '96 / Pearls

☐ CHOP CHOP BOOM
DE 703 / Jan '98 / Delmark

☐ CHOROS FROM BAHAI
NI 5404 / Feb '95 / Nimbus

☐ CHRISTMAS ALBUM, THE
VPCD 15182 / 22 Dec '97 / VP

☐ CHRISTMAS BLUES
White Christmas / Far away Christmas blues / Love for Christmas / Trim your tree / Wonderful Christmas night / Rudolph the red nosed reindeer / Silent night / Mr. Santa's boogie / Christmas blues / Frosty the snowman / I want to spend Christmas with Elvis / Santa's secret
SV 0241 / Oct '97 / Savoy Jazz

☐ CHRISTMAS CAROLS
God rest ye merry gentlemen / While shepherds watched their flocks by night / See amid the winter's snow / Silent night / Good King Wenceslas / O little town of Bethlehem: Guildford Cathedral Choir / Unto us is born a son / Away in a manger / Rocking / In dulci jubilo: Westminster Abbey Choir / Ding dong merrily on high / Coventry carol / I saw three ships: St. Paul's Cathedral Choir / Holly and the ivy / Angels from the realms of glory: St. Paul's Cathedral Choir / First Noel / O come all ye faithful (Adeste Fidelis) / Once in Royal David's City: Exeter Cathedral Choir / Hark the herald angels sing: Exeter Cathedral Choir
CC 224 / Dec '94 / Music For Pleasure

☐ CHRISTMAS CAROLS (3CD Set)
Once in royal David's city: Gloucester Cathedral Choir / O come all ye faithful (adeste fidelis): Wells Cathedral Choir / Hark the herald angels sing: Nottingham Harmonic Choir / Star carol: Beechwood Park School Choir / Adam lay y-bounden: Gloucester Cathedral Choir / God rest ye merry gentlemen: Wells Cathedral Choir / Ding dong merrily on high: Nottingham Harmonic Choir / O little town of Bethlehem: Beechwood Park School Choir / Three kings: Gloucester Cathedral Choir / Holly and the ivy: Wells Cathedral Choir / Joy to the world: Nottingham Harmonic Choir / Silent night: Beechwood Park School Choir / Cherry tree carol: Gloucester Cathedral Choir / Unto us a son is born: Wells Cathedral Choir / Jingle bells: Nottingham Harmonic Choir / O tannenbaum: Beechwood Park School Choir / Twelve days of Christmas: Gloucester Cathedral Choir / It came upon the midnight clear: Wells Cathedral Choir / Sleigh ride: Nottingham Harmonic Choir / In the winter darkness: Beechwood Park School Choir / Past three o'clock: Gloucester Cathedral Choir / First Noel: Wells Cathedral Choir / Gallery carol (rejoice and be merry): Nottingham Harmonic Choir / Here comes christmas: Beechwood Park School Choir / Shepherd's pipe carol: Gloucester Cathedral Choir / I saw three ships: Wells Cathedral Choir / Sussex carol: Nottingham Harmonic Choir / Carol of the children: Beechwood Park School Choir / Infant king: Gloucester Cathedral Choir / Deck the halls: Wells Cathedral Choir / Masters in the hall: Nottingham Harmonic Choir / Sans day carol: Gloucester Cathedral Choir / We wish you a merry Christmas: Wells Cathedral Choir / When a child is born: Nottingham Harmonic Choir / Christmas cheer: Beechwood Park School Choir / See amid the winter's snow: Gloucester Cathedral Choir / While shepherds watched their flocks by night: Wells Cathedral Choir / Santa claus - trophobia: Nottingham Harmonic Choir / Mary had a baby: Beechwood Park School Choir / Quelle est cette odeur agreable: Gloucester Cathedral Choir / Away in a manger: Wells Cathedral Choir / Good king Wenceslas: Nottingham Harmonic Choir / Infant holy infant lowly: Beechwood Park School Choir / As with gladness of old: Gloucester Cathedral Choir / In the bleak mid-winter: Wells Cathedral Choir / Auld lang syne: Nottingham Harmonic Choir / Child in a manger: Beechwood Park School Choir
120232 / Oct '97 / Jingle

☐ CHRISTMAS CAROLS VOL.1 (O Come All Ye Faithful)
Once in royal David's city: Gloucester Cathedral Choir / O come all ye faithful (adeste fidelis): Wells Cathedral Choir / Hark the herald angels sing: Nottingham Harmonic Choir / Star carol: Beechwood Park School Choir / Adam lay y-bounden: Gloucester Cathedral Choir / God rest ye merry gentlemen: Wells Cathedral Choir / Ding dong merrily on high: Nottingham Harmonic Choir / O little town of Bethlehem: Beechwood Park School Choir / Three kings: Gloucester Cathedral Choir / Holly and the ivy: Wells Cathedral Choir / Joy to the world: Nottingham Harmonic Choir / Silent night: Beechwood Park School Choir / Cherry tree carol: Gloucester Cathedral Choir / Unto us a son is born: Wells Cathedral Choir / Jingle bells: Nottingham Harmonic Choir / O tannenbaum: Beechwood Park School Choir
120242 / Oct '97 / Jingle

☐ CHRISTMAS CAROLS VOL.2 (It Came Upon A Midnight Clear)
Twelfth day of Christmas: Gloucester Cathedral Choir / It came upon a midnight clear: Wells Cathedral Choir / Sleigh ride: Nottingham Harmonic Choir / In the winter darkness: Beechwood Park School Choir / Past three o' clock: Gloucester Cathedral Choir / First Noel: Wells Cathedral Choir / Gallery carol (rejoice and be merry): Nottingham Harmonic Choir / Here comes Christmas: Beechwood Park School Choir / Shepherd's pipe carol: Gloucester Cathedral Choir / I saw three ships: Wells Cathedral Choir / Sussex carol: Nottingham Harmonic Choir / Carol of the children: Beechwood Park School Choir / Infant king: Gloucester Cathedral Choir / Deck the halls: Wells Cathedral Choir / Masters in the hall: Nottingham Harmonic Choir / Nativity carol: Beechwood Park School Choir
120252 / Oct '97 / Jingle

☐ CHRISTMAS CAROLS VOL.3 (We Wish You A Merry Christmas)
Sans day carol: *Gloucester Cathedral Choir* / We wish you a merry Christmas: *Wells Cathedral Choir* / When a child is born: *Nottingham Harmonic Choir* / Christmas cheer: *Beechwood Park School Choir* / See amid the winter's snow: *Gloucester Cathedral Choir* / While shepherds watched their flocks by night: *Wells Cathedral Choir* / Santa Claus - trophobia: *Nottingham Harmonic Choir* / Mary had a baby: *Beechwood Park School Choir* / Quelle est cette oduer agreable: *Gloucester Cathedral Choir* / Away in a manger: *Wells Cathedral Choir* / Good king Wenceslas: *Nottingham Harmonic Choir* / Infant holy infant lowly: *Beechwood Park School Choir* / As with goodness of old: *Gloucester Cathedral Choir* / In the bleak mid-winter: *Wells Cathedral Choir* / Auld lang sein: *Nottingham Harmonic Choir* / Child in a manger: *Beechwood Park School Choir*
120262 / Oct '97 / Jingle

☐ CHRISTMAS COLLECTION, A
Christmas song: *Cole, Nat 'King'* / O come all ye faithful (Adeste fidelis): *Cole, Nat 'King'* / Walking in the air: *Jones, Aled* / Santa Claus is coming to town: *Lee, Peggy* / Christmas waltz: *Lee, Peggy* / Rudolph the red nosed reindeer: *Martin, Dean* / White Christmas: *Martin, Dean* / Jingle bells: *Paul, Les & Mary Ford* / Silent night: *Paul, Les & Mary Ford* / When a child is born: *Rogers, Kenny* / Christmas is my favourite time of year: *Rogers, Kenny* / Little drummer boy: *Lynn, Vera* / Mary's boy child: *Lynn, Vera* / Have yourself a merry little Christmas: *Campbell, Glen* / Christmas is for children: *Campbell, Glen* / O' holy night: *Rodgers, Jimmie* / I'll be home for Christmas: *Beach Boys* / Winter wonderland: *Mercer, Johnny* / What child is this: *Rodgers, Jimmie* / We three kings of Orient are: *Beach Boys*
CDMFP 5903 / Nov '97 / Music For Pleasure

☐ CHRISTMAS COUNTRY COLLECTION
MCCDX 004 / Nov '94 / Music Club

☐ CHRISTMAS CROONERS
MCCDX 003 / Nov '93 / Music Club

☐ CHRISTMAS FAVOURITES
15463 / Nov '95 / Laserlight

☐ CHRISTMAS FOR BRASS
Deck the halls / Silent night / Holly and the ivy / Away in a manger / Once in Royal David's City / In the bleak midwinter / It came upon a midnight clear / While shepherds watched their flocks by night / First Noel / We three Kings / Ding dong merrily on high / Coventry carol / God rest you merry gentlemen / Christmas piece / O come all ye faithful (adeste fidelis) / Addolwn ef / Hark the herald angels sing
GRACC 85 / Oct '97 / Grasmere

☐ CHRISTMAS IN MARAMURES
926902 / 5 Jan '98 / BUDA

☐ CHRISTMAS IN STEREO
KC 014CD / 8 Dec '97 / Kindercore

☐ CHRISTMAS LINE DANCE
PLSCD 262 / 29 Sep '97 / Pulse

☐ CHRISTMAS LOUNGE
PLSCD 263 / 29 Sep '97 / Pulse

☐ CHRISTMAS MOODS
Deck the halls / First Noel / God rest ye merry gentlemen / Hark the herald angels sing / It came upon a midnight clear / Jingle bells / Joy to the world / O little town of Bethlehem / O Christmas tree / O come all ye faithful (adeste fidelis) / Silent night / We wish you a merry Christmas / We three Kings / Angels from the realms of glory / Away in a manger
XMAS 011 / Nov '96 / Tring

☐ CHRISTMAS PAN PIPES
ROJOC 1026 / Oct '96 / Hit

☐ CHRISTMAS PRESENCE
In the bleak midwinter / Oh come all ye faithfull / First Noel / Once in Royal David's city / It came upon a midnight clear / Silent night / Angels from the realms of glory / See amid the winter snow / O little town of Bethlehem / Hark the herald angels sing / See him lying on a bed of straw / Away in a manger / Love came down at Christmas / While shepherds watched their flocks by night
CDMFP 6408 / 6 Oct '97 / Music For Pleasure

☐ CHRISTMAS REFLECTIONS
MCCDX 005 / Nov '94 / Music Club

☐ CHRISTMAS SAX
Christmas song / Do you hear what I hear / I believe in Father Christmas / O Christmas tree / Mary's boy child / Last Christmas / Winter wonderland / When a child is born / Mistletoe and wine / White Christmas / Silver bells / Have yourself a merry little Christmas / Let it snow, let it snow, let it snow / Silent night
CDMFP 6245 / Nov '97 / Music For Pleasure

☐ CHRISTMAS SOUL SPECIAL
Jingle bells / Silent night / Drummer boy / Oh holy night / Jingle bell rock / Christmas song / Santa Claus is coming to town / Noel / Winter wonderland / O come all ye faithful (Adeste Fidelis) / Frosty the snowman / Silver bells
CDVR 015 / '88 / Varrick

☐ CHRISTMAS TIME WITH THE STARS
White Christmas / Jingle Bells / Santa Claus is coming to town / Siberian sleigh ride / Snow White and the seven dwarfs / Christmas bells at eventide / Sitting on the ice at the ice rink / Say it with carols / Kiddies go carolling / Christmas day in the cookhouse / Hansel and Gretel dance duet / Christmas dinner / Christmas swing / March of the toys / Christmas night in Harlem / It happened in sun valley / O little town of Bethlehem / Christmas song / Ghost of the turkey / Snowman / Fairy on the Christmas tree / I'm going home for Christmas / Don't wait till the night before Christmas
CDYULE 300 / Oct '94 / Happy Days

☐ CHRISTMAS WITH THE STARS (3CD Set)
Christmas song: *Cole, Nat 'King'* / When a child is born: *Monro, Matt* / Let it snow, let it snow, let it snow: *Martin, Dean* / Little Saint Nick: *Beach Boys* / Blue Christmas: *Campbell, Glen* / Santo natale: *Locke, Josef* / Christmas waltz: *Lee, Peggy* / Jingle bells: *Paul, Les & Mary Ford* / Little donkey: *Lynn, Vera* / See amid the winter's snow: *Morriston Orpheus & Treorchy Male Choirs* / Happiest Christmas of all: *Morecambe & Wise* / O' holy night: *Rogers, Jimmy* / Do you hear what I hear: *Adams, Cliff Singers* / Wassail song: *Mitchell, George Minstrels* / Christmas wish: *Lynn, Vera* / Christmas blues: *Martin, Dean* / Mary's boy child: *Monro, Matt* / Little boy that Santa Claus forgot: *Cole, Nat 'King'* / Walking in the air: *Jones, Aled* / Frosty the snowman: *Beach Boys* / Rudolf the red nosed reindeer: *Martin, Dean* / It must be getting close to Christmas: *Campbell, Glen* / Santa Claus is coming to town: *Lee, Peggy* / Deck the halls: *Treorchy & Morriston Orpheus/Pontarddulais Choirs* / Winter wonderland: *Mercer, Johnny* / Little drummer boy: *Lynn, Vera* / Star of Bethlehem: *Locke, Josef* / Twelve days of Christmas: *Adams, Cliff Singers* / Christmas medley: *Treorchy & Morriston Orpheus/Pontarddulais Choirs* / What child is this (Greensleeves): *Rogers, Jimmy* / Shepherds lay on a lonely hill: *Mitchell, George Minstrels* / We three kings of Orient are: *Beach Boys* / White Christmas: *Martin, Dean* / O come all ye faithful (adeste fidelis): *Cole, Nat 'King'* / I'll be home for Christmas: *Beach Boys* / Silent night: *Paul, Les & Mary Ford* / Holy city: *Locke, Josef* / Christmas alphabet: *Adams, Cliff Singers* / Happy holiday: *Lee, Peggy* / Sleigh ride: *Lynn, Vera & The Mike Sammes Singers* / Firts noel: *Fitzgerald, Ella* / Ding dong merrily on high: *Treorchy & Morriston Orpheus/Pontarddulais Choirs* / Happiest Christmas tree: *Cole, Nat 'King'* / Christmas is for children: *Campbell, Glen* / Silver bells: *Whiting, Margaret & Jimmy Wakely* / Sing we now of Christmas: *Ford, Tennessee Ernie* / Christmas bells: *Mitchell, George Minstrels* / A-wassailing: *Morecambe & Wise*
CDTRBOX 332 / 6 Oct '97 / EMI Gold

☐ CHRISTMAS WITH THE STARS (3CD Set)
White Christmas: *Crosby, Bing* / Santa Claus is coming to town: *Sinatra, Frank* / Mary's boy child: *Nina & Frederick* / Have yourself a merry little Christmas: *Clooney, Rosemary* / Silent night: *Jackson, Mahalia* / Christmas in New Orleans: *Armstrong, Louis* / Christmas song: *Cole, Nat 'King'* / This Christmas: *Adams, Johnny* / Frosty the snowman: *Autry, Gene* / You're all I want for Christmas: *Benton, Brook* / Ding dong merrily on high: *Mantovani & His Orchestra* / Please come home for Christmas: *Platters* / Suzy snowflake: *Clooney, Rosemary* / Mistletoe and holly: *Sinatra, Frank & Midnight Strings* / Away in a manger: *Jackson, Mahalia* / Auld lang syne: *Drifters* / Merry Christmas to you: *Sinatra, Frank* / Let it snow let it snow: *Crosby, Bing* / Zat you Santa Claus: *Armstrong, Louis* / Rudolph the red-nosed reindeer: *Clooney, Rosemary* / O little town of Bethlehem: *Jackson, Mahalia* / Deck the halls: *Sinatra, Frank & Bing Crosby* / Jingle bells: *Cole, Nat 'King'* / Blue Christmas: *Platters* / C-h-r-i-s-t-m-a-s: *Wells, Kitty* / O holy night: *Butler, Jerry* / Hitch a ride with Santa Claus: *Crosby, Bing* / Sleigh ride: *Mantovani & His Orchestra* / Silver bells: *Autry, Gene* / Lonesome Christmas: *Adams, Johnny* / This time of year: *Benton, Brook* / Little drummer boy: *Sinatra, Frank & Midnight Strings* / God rest ye merry gentlemen: *Sinatra, Frank & Bing Crosby* / Count your blessings: *Clooney, Rosemary* / What child is this: *Jackson, Mahalia* / Canticle Noel: *Mantovani & His Orchestra* / Snowman: *Crosby, Bing* / O holy night: *Drifters* / Bell of St. Mary's: *Adams, Johnny* / Sleigh bells: *Autry, Gene* / O come all ye faithful: *Sinatra, Frank & Midnight Strings* / Adeste fideles: *Sinatra, Frank & Bing Crosby* / I saw mummy kissing Santa Claus: *Sherman, Bobby* / Santa's on his way: *Wells, Kitty* / Hark the herald angels sing: *Jackson, Mahalia* / Joy to the world: *Vaughn, Billy* / That Christmas feeling: *Crosby, Bing* / Jesu joy of mans desiring: *Mantovani & His Orchestra*
CD 120152 / Nov '97 / Jingle

☐ CHRISTMAS WITH THE STARS
Christmas song (Merry Christmas to you): *Cole, Nat 'King'* / When a child is born: *Monro, Matt* / Let it snow let it snow let it snow: *Martin, Dean* / Little Saint Nick: *Beach Boys* / Blue Christmas: *Campbell, Glen* / Santo Natale: *Locke, Josef* / Christmas waltz: *Lee, Peggy* / Jingle bells: *Paul, Les & Mary Ford* / See amid the winters snow: *Paul, Les & Mary Ford* / Happiest Christmas of all: *Morecambe & Wise* / O holy night: *Rogers, Jimmy* / Do you hear what I hear: *Adams, Cliff Singers* / Wassail song: *Mitchell, George Minstrels* / Christmas wish: *Lynn, Vera* / Christmas blues: *Martin, Dean* / Mary's boy child: *Monro, Matt* / Little boy that Santa Claus forgot: *Cole, Nat 'King'* / Walking in the air: *Jones, Aled* / Frosty the snowman: *Beach Boys* / Rudolph the red nose reindeer: *Martin, Dean* / It must be getting close to Christmas: *Campbell, Glen* / Santa Claus is coming to town: *Lee, Peggy* / Deck the halls: *Treorchy & Morriston Orpheus/Pontarddulais Choirs* / Winter wonderland: *Mercer, Johnny* / Little drummer boy: *Lynn, Vera* / Star of Bethlehem: *Locke, Josef* / Twelve days of Christmas: *Adams, Cliff Singers* / Do they know it's Christmas/Savior's Day/Mistletoe and Wine/: *Treorchy & Morriston Orpheus/Pontarddulais Choirs* / What child is this: *Rogers, Jimmy* / Shepherds lay on a lonely hill: *Mitchell, George Minstrels* / We three kings of Orient are: *Beach Boys* / White Christmas: *Martin, Dean* / Adeste fidelis: *Cole, Nat 'King'* / I'll be home for Christmas: *Beach Boys* / Silent night: *Paul, Les & Mary Ford* / Holy city: *Locke, Josef* / Christmas alphabet: *Adams, Cliff Singers* / Happy holiday: *Lee, Peggy* / Sleigh ride: *Lynn, Vera & The Mike Sammes Singers* / First Noel: *Fitzgerald, Ella* / Ding dong merrily on high: *Treorchy & Morriston Orpheus/Pontarddulais Choirs* / Happiest Christmas tree: *Cole, Nat 'King'* / Christmas is for children: *Campbell, Glen* / Silver bells: *Whiting, Margaret & Jimmy Wakely* / Sing we now of Christmas: *Ford, Tennessee Ernie* / Christmas bells: *Mitchell, George Minstrels* / A-wassailing: *Morecambe & Wise*
HR 877322 / 30 May '97 / Disky

☐ CHRISTMAS WITH THE STARS OF THE 70'S (3CD Set)
So near to Christmas: *Stardust, Alvin* / It won't be Christmas: *Smokie* / Happy Christmas (war is over): *Christie* / Silent night: *Rubettes* / Santa Claus is coming to town: *Racey* / Hey Mr. Christmas: *Showaddywaddy* / Let the children sing: *Quatro, Suzi* / Let's ring the bell: *Fortunes* / Christmas at sea: *Goombay Dance Band* / She'll be home for Christmas: *Swinging Blue Jeans* / All I want for Christmas: *Gerry & The Pacemakers* / Happiest Christmas of all: *Searchers* / Mary's boy child: *Equals* / I believe in Father Christmas: *Dee, Dave* / I saw Mummy kissing Santa Claus: *New Seekers* / White Christmas: *Sally Carr's Middle Of The Road* / Winter's tale: *Smokie* / Don't forget at Christmas: *Stardust, Alvin* / When a child is born: *Fortunes* / Wonder of Christmas: *Mungo Jerry* / It's Christmas again: *Sailor* / Rockin' and rollin' with Santa Claus: *Showaddywaddy* / Big big Christmas: *Racey* / Sleigh ride: *Herman's Hermits* / Oh holy night: *Marmalade* / Jingle bells: *Andrews, Chris* / Frosty the snowman: *Quatro, Suzi* / Ave Maria no morro: *Goombay Dance Band* / God rest ye merry gentlemen: *Searchers* / Jerusalem: *Tremeloes* / All over the world: *Glitter Band* / Christmas lullaby: *Sally Carr's Middle Of The Road* / Rocking around the Christmas tree: *Glitter Band* / Light a candle: *Smokie* / Winter wonderland: *Swinging Blue Jeans* / Christmas tune: *New Seekers* / Yuletide lights: *Christie* / Noel: *Stardust, Alvin* / We three kings: *Mungo Jerry* / Santa Claus is coming: *Marmalade* / I believe in Father Christmas: *Dee, Dave* / Christmas tree: *Andrews, Chris* / All these things: *Herman's Hermits* / Lemon meringue: *Rubettes* / What a shame it's Christmas once a year: *Equals* / Magical time: *Goombay Dance Band* / Peace on Earth: *Christmas All Stars*
120112 / Oct '97 / Jingle

☐ CHRISTMAS WITH THE STARS OF THE 70'S VOL.1 (So Near To Christmas)
So near to Christmas: *Stardust, Alvin* / It won't be Christmas: *Smokie* / Happy Christmas (war is over): *Christie* / Silent night: *Rubettes* / Santa Claus is coming to town: *Racey* / Hey Mr. Christmas: *Showaddywaddy* / Let the children sing: *Quatro, Suzi* / Let's ring the bell: *Fortunes* / Christmas at sea: *Fortunes* / She'll be home for Christmas: *Swinging Blue Jeans* / All I want for Christmas: *Gerry & The Pacemakers* / Happiest Christmas of all: *Searchers* / Mary's boy child: *Equals* / I believe in Father Christmas: *Dee, Dave* / I saw Mummy kissing Santa Claus: *New Seekers* / White Christmas: *Sally Carr's Middle Of The Road*
120122 / Oct '97 / Jingle

☐ CHRISTMAS WITH THE STARS OF THE 70'S VOL.2 (Wonder Of Christmas)
Winters tale: *Smokie* / Don't forget at Christmas: *Stardust, Alvin* / When a child is born: *Fortunes* / Wonder of Christmas: *Mungo Jerry* / It's Christmas again: *Sailor* / Rockin' and rollin' with Santa Claus: *Showaddywaddy* / Big big Christmas: *Racey* / Sleigh ride: *Herman's Hermits* / Oh holy night: *Marmalade* / Jingle bell: *Andrews, Chris* / Frosty the snowman: *Quatro, Suzi* / Ave maria no morro: *Goombay Dance Band* / God rest ye merry gentlemen: *Searchers* / Jerusalem: *Tremeloes* / All over the world: *Glitter Band* / Christmas Lullaby: *Sally Carr's Middle Of The Road*
120132 / Oct '97 / Jingle

☐ CHRISTMAS WITH THE STARS OF THE 70'S VOL.3 (Rockin' Around The Christmas Tree)
Rocking around the Christmas tree: *Glitter Band* / Light a candle: *Smokie* / All I want for Christmas: *Gerry & The Pacemakers* / Winter wonderland: *Swinging Blue Jeans* / Christmas tune: *New Seekers* / Yueltide lights: *Christie* / Noel: *Stardust, Alvin* / We three kings: *Mungo Jerry* / Santa Claus is coming: *Marmalade* / I believe in Father Christmas: *Dee, Dave* / Christmas time: *Andrews, Chris* / All these things: *Herman's Hermits* / Lemon meringue: *Rubettes* / What a shame it's Christmas once a year: *Equals* / Magical time: *Goombay Dance Band* / Peace on earth: *Christmas All Stars*
120142 / Oct '97 / Jingle

☐ CHRISTMAS WITH THE STARS VOL.1 (Santa Claus Is Coming To Town)
White Christmas: *Crosby, Bing* / Santa Claus is coming to town: *Sinatra, Frank* / Mary's boy child: *Nina & Frederick* / Have yourself a merry little Christmas: *Clooney, Rosemary* / Silent night: *Jackson, Mahalia* / Christmas in New Orleans: *Armstrong, Louis* / Christmas song: *Cole, Nat 'King'* / This Christmas: *Adams, Johnny* / Frosty the snowman: *Autry, Gene* / You're all I want for Christmas: *Benton, Brook* / Ding dong merrily on high: *Mantovani Orchestra* / Please come home for Christmas: *Platters* / Suzy snowflake: *Clooney, Rosemary* / Mistletoe and holly: *Sinatra, Frank & Midnight Strings* / Away in a manger: *Jackson, Mahalia* / Auld lang syne: *Drifters*
120162 / Oct '97 / Jingle

☐ CHRISTMAS WITH THE STARS VOL.2 (Merry Christmas To You)
Merry Christmas to you: *Sinatra, Frank* / Let it snow let it snow: *Crosby, Bing* / Zat you Santa Claus: *Armstrong, Louis* / Rudolph the red-nosed reindeer: *Clooney, Rosemary* / O little town of Bethlehem: *Jackson, Mahalia* / Deck the halls: *Sinatra, Frank & Bing Crosby* / Jingle bells: *Cole, Nat 'King'* / Blue Christmas: *Platters* / C-h-r-i-s-t-m-a-s: *Wells, Kitty* / O holy night: *Butler, Jerry* / Hitch a ride with Santa Claus: *Crosby, Bing* / Sleigh ride: *Mantovani & His Orchestra* / Silver bells: *Autry, Gene* / Lonesome Christmas: *Adams, Johnny* / This time of year: *Benton, Brook* / Little drummer boy: *Sinatra, Frank & Midnight Strings*
120172 / Oct '97 / Jingle

☐ CHRISTMAS WITH THE STARS VOL.3 (That Christmas Feeling)
God rest ye merry gentlemen: *Sinatra, Frank & Bing Crosby* / Count your blessing: *Clooney, Rosemary* / What child is this: *Jackson, Mahalia* / Canticle Noel: *Mantovani & His Orchestra* / Snowman: *Crosby, Bing* / O holy night: *Drifters* / Bell's of St.Mary's: *Adams, Johnny* / Sleigh bells: *Autry, Gene* / O come all ye faithful (adeste fidelis): *Sinatra, Frank & Midnight Strings* / Adeste fideles: *Crosby, Bing & Frank Sinatra* / I saw Mummy kissing Santa Claus: *Sherman, Bobby* / Santa's on his way: *Wells, Kitty* / Hark the herald angels sing: *Jackson, Mahalia* / Joy to the world: *Vaughn, Billy* / That Christmas feeling: *Crosby, Bing* / Jesu joy of man's desire: *Mantovani & His Orchestra*
120182 / Oct '97 / Jingle

☐ CHRISTMAS WITH THE STARS, A
MCCDX 008 / Nov '94 / Music Club

☐ CHRONICLE OF JAZZ, THE (2CD Set)
Harlem strut: *Johnson, James P.* / Bill Bailey won't you please come home: *Ory, Kid* / There ain't no land like dixieland to me: *Beiderbecke, Bix* / Potato head blues: *Armstrong, Louis* / St. Louis blues: *Smith, Bessie* / Lester leaps in: *Basie, Count* / Prelude to a kiss: *Ellington, Duke* / In the mood: *Miller, Glenn Orchestra* / Air mail special: *Goodman, Benny* / Night and day: *Holiday, Billie* / My melancholy baby: *Fitzgerald, Ella* / Summertime: *Vaughan, Sarah* / Solo flight: *Christian, Charlie* / Tea for two: *Tatum, Art* / Embraceable you: *Webster, Ben & Harry 'Sweets' Edison* / Night in Tunisia: *Parker, Charlie* / 'Round midnight: *Monk, Thelonious* / Goodbye pork pie hat: *Mingus, Charles Trio* / Hullo bolinas: *Evans, Bill* / Django: *Lewis, John* / Blue rondo a la turk: *Brubeck, Dave* / Aguas de marco: *Getz, Stan* / You don't know what love is: *Baker, Chet* / Just in time: *Mulligan, Gerry* / Human nature: *Davis, Miles* / Black market: *Weather Report* / Common mama: *Jarrett, Keith* / April in Paris: *Carter, James* / Oleo: *Marsalis, Wynton* / Another rainy day: *Wilson, Cassandra* / Africa y las americas: *Sanchez, David* / Bemsha swing: *Parker, Leon*
4853609 / 3 Nov '97 / Sony Jazz

☐ CHUNKLET VOL.12
CH 12 / Sep '97 / Chunklet

☐ CHUNKS OF THE CHOCOLATE FACTORY (Best Of Choc's Chewns Vol.1/2CD Set)
SUSCD 2 / Jan '95 / Aura Surround Sounds

☐ CHURCH CHOIRS GOSPEL SINGERS AND PREACHERS VOL.1 1926-1948
DOCD 5585 / 28 Oct '97 / Document

☐ CHURCH CHOIRS GOSPEL SINGERS AND PREACHERS VOL.2 1925-1955
DOCD 5589 / 5 Feb '98 / Document

☐ CHURCH CHOIRS VOCAL GROUPS AND PREACHERS 1923-1931
DOCD 5605 / 27 Jul '98 / Document

☐ CHURCHICAL CHANTS OF THE NYABINGI (Live Field Recordings)
Got to move / Tell them wherever I go / Weeping and moaning / I I I / Fire man / Fire burn / White boy a follower / Keep cool Babylon / Think I never know / Armagiddion
CDHB 20 / Feb '97 / Heartbeat

☐ CHUTNEY CARNIVAL
JMC 1124 / May '96 / JMC

☐ CIAO ITALIA
Se bastasse una canzone / Il mondo / Grande grande grande / Come vorrei / Amore amore amore mio / Sara perche ti amo / Volare / L'italiano / Che sara / Guarde che luna / Gloria La mia California / Una lacrima sul viso / Sereno E' / Insieme / Vado via / Margherita / A chi
SP 881012 / Jul '97 / Disky

☐ CICADELIC 60'S VOL.1, THE
COLCD 0515 / Jun '97 / Collectables

☐ CICADELIC 60'S VOL.2, THE
COLCD 0525 / Jun '97 / Collectables

☐ CICADELIC 60'S VOL.3, THE
COLCD 0543 / Jun '97 / Collectables

☐ CICADELIC 60'S VOL.4, THE
COLCD 0544 / Jun '97 / Collectables

☐ CICADELIC 60'S VOL.5, THE
COLCD 0574 / Jun '97 / Collectables

☐ CIGARETTE MACHINE FROM GOD
It's gonna happen: *Enormous* / Something in my heart: *Enormous* / When you do: *Enormous* / Happy birthday asshole: *Enormous* / Terry: *Swells* / Confessions of Roger G: *Swells* / Oh no (summer days): *Swells* / Lipstick lover: *Ease* / Worser man: *Ease* / Over and under: *Ease* / Supernatural groover: *Kerrys* / Who are we: *Kerrys* / Different world: *Kerrys*
BTIFIC 001 / 24 Nov '97 / Beatific

☐ CINCOS ANOS
TR 38CD / Oct '95 / Trance

☐ CINEMA BEER NUTS
It's a fact: *Vandals* / Doing time: *MXPX* / You: *Mustard Plug* / Automatic: *Less Than Jake* / Embrace: *Ignite* / Don't want you: *Lunachicks* / Don't back down: *Queers* / Girl like you: *Nobodys* / Fighting fists: *Hi-Standard* / Bulletproof: *Voodoo Glowskulls* / No time: *Assorted Jelly Beans* / He who laughs last: *Afi* / Blistered: *Strife* / Biggest joke: *Goober Patrol* / Tainted love: *Shades Apart* / Girl on the bus: *Marshes* / Pop can park: *Pinker, Horace* / Verbal kint: *Link 80* / Lozin must: *Millencolin*
HR 6232 / 1 Sep '97 / Hopeless

☐ CINEMA ORGAN
Savoy hunting medley / Wedegwood blue / Mexican hat dance / Sleighride / Smoke gets in your eyes / Diane you're just in love / Royal command / Festival in Valencia / When I fall in love / Hunagry / Bluebell polka / Swingin' sleigh bells / Nola / Kitten on the keys / Always / Windows of Paris / Punch and Judy polka
EMPRCD 560 / Mar '95 / Emporio

☐ CINEMA ORGAN VOL.1
PASTCD 9722 / Jul '91 / Flapper

☐ CINEMA ORGAN VOL.2
PASTCD 7052 / Oct '94 / Flapper

☐ CIRCLE DANCE (Hokey Pokey Charity Compilation)
CONED 1 / Oct '90 / Hokey Pokey

☐ CITY LIMITS
TMPMC 016 / Oct '95 / Temple

☐ CITY SOUL FROM PHILLY
Didn't I blow your mind: Philly Groove Orchestra / Have I sinned: Labelle, Patti & The Bluebells / La la means I love you: Philly Groove Orchestra / Are you ready for me: Philly Groove Orchestra / Love freeze: Philly Groove Orchestra / Armed and extremely dangerous: First Choice / Smarty pants: First Choice / Guilty: First Choice / This is the house (where love died): First Choice / When will I see you again: Three Degrees / I'm doing fine now: Three Degrees / Dirty ol' man: Three Degrees / I'll be around: Three Degrees / Seems like I gotta do wrong: Whispers / I walked right in: Labelle, Patti & The Bluebells / Decatur Street: Labelle, Patti & The Bluebells
HADCD 218 / Jun '97 / Spotlight On

☐ CITY SPACE VOL.2
E 3759CD / Nov '93 / Atatak

☐ CLAMCHOWDER & ICE
EFA 11374 / Apr '93 / Musical Tragedies

☐ CLARE TRADITION, THE
GTDHCD 082 / Jul '93 / GTD

☐ CLARINET MARMALADE
Dizzy debutante: Bailey, Buster & Rhythm Busters / Blues in thirds: Bechet, Sidney Trio / Barney's concerto: Bigard, Barney & Duke Ellington / Dee blues: Carter, Benny & Chocolate Dandies / Too tight: Dodds, Johnny / Praying the blues: Dorsey, Jimmy / My inspiration: Fazola, Irving & Bob Crosby / Sweet Georgia Brown: Goodman, Benny Quartet / Sheikh of araby: Hamilton, Jimmy & Teddy Wilson / Woodsheddin' with Woody: Herman, Woody / Climax rag: Lewis, George & New Orleans Stompers / Reunion in Harlem: Marsala, Joe & Delta Four / Can't we be friends: Matlock, Matty & Bob Crosby / Bobcats / Everybody loves my baby: Mezzrow, Mezz & Mezzrow-Ladnier Quartet / High society: Miller, Eddie & Muscat City Blues Blowers / Chinatown, my Chinatown: Mince, Johnny & Tommy Dorsey / Clambake Seven / Monday date: Noone, Jimmie / Apex Club Orchestra / Stratton Street strut: Polo, Danny & Swing Stars / She's crying for me blues: Roppolo, Leon & Original New Orleans Rhythm Kings / Friars Point Shuffle: Russell, Pee-Wee & Eddie Condon/Chicagoans / Summit Ridge Drive: Shaw, Artie & His Gramercy Five / Clarinet marmalade: Shields, Larry / Beau Koo Jack: Simeon, Omer / Back home again in Indiana: Teschemacher, Frank & Eddie Condon / Pagin' the devil: Young, Lester & The Kansas City Six
CDAJA 5132 / May '94 / Living Era

☐ CLARITY COLLECTION, THE
CCD 1010 / Jul '98 / Clarity

☐ CLASH OF THE IRIES
VPCD 1235 / Jul '92 / VP

☐ CLASH OF THE TITANS (The Reggae Giants Meet)
Holy Mount Zion: McGregor, Freddie / Show us the way: Brown, Dennis / Take my breath away: Paul, Frankie / Rock on: Isaacs, Gregory / Better days: Heptones / Sister Maggie Brest: I-Roy / Dice cup: Don Carlos / Brandy: McGregor, Freddie / He can't spell: Brown, Dennis / Lay your head: Paul, Frankie / Bad da: Isaacs, Gregory / Land of love: Heptones / Dub and come: I-Roy / Open up the gates: Brown, Dennis / On a Sunday night: Don Carlos / No war in the ghetto: McGregor, Freddie / Concentration: Brown, Dennis / How I care for you: Paul, Frankie
CDGR 115 / Jan '97 / Charly

☐ CLASS & RENDEZVOUS STORY, THE
Rockin' Robin: Day, Bobby / Nut rocker: B-Bumble & The Stingers / Miami: Church, Eugene / In the mood: Fields, Ernie Orchestra / Little bitty pretty one: Day, Bobby & The Satellites / Hey girl, hey boy: Local Idol, Oscar & Jeanette Baker / Bear: Watson, Johnny 'Guitar' / That's my desire: Bob & Earl / Pretty girls everywhere: Church, Eugene & the Fellows / Texas twister: Fields, Ernie Orchestra / When that I love you: Belvin, Jesse / Bluebird, the buzzard and the oriole: Day, Bobby / No time: Titans / Ez: Rene, Google / You made a boo boo: Bob & Earl / One more kiss: Watson, Johnny 'Guitar' / Wow wow baby: Searchers / Good news: Church, Eugene / Alley oop: Dyna-sores / Let me know, let me know: McLollie, Oscar & Jeanette Baker / Mama Julie: Terry & Gerry / I ain't goin' for that: Church, Eugene / Chattanooga choo choo: Fields, Ernie Orchestra / Over and over: Day, Bobby
CDCHD 461 / Jun '93 / Ace

☐ CLASSIC 80'S GROOVE MASTERCUTS VOL.1
Do it to the music: Raw Silk / So fine: Johnson, Howard / After the dance is through: Krystol / (I'll be a) freak for you: Royalle Delite / Main thing: Shot / You used to hold me so tight: Houston, Thelma / Fool's paradise: Morgan, Meli'sa / Who do you love: Carey, Mariah / Hangin' on a string: Loose Ends / Change of heart: Change / Settle down: Thomas, Lillo / Encore: Lynn, Cheryl
CUTSCD 15 / Nov '93 / Beechwood

☐ CLASSIC 80'S GROOVE MASTERCUTS VOL.2
I am somebody: Jones, Glenn / Serious: Serious Intention / She's strange: Cameo / You ain't really down: Status IV / I'm in love: Thomas, Lillo / Twilight: Maze / Let's groove: Earth, Wind & Fire / I wonder if I take you home: Lisa Lisa & Cult Jam/Full Force / Thinking about your love: Skipworth & Turner / Stomp: Brothers Johnson / Breakin' down: Julia & Co. / Act like you know: Fat Larry's Band
CUTSCD 26 / Mar '95 / Beechwood

☐ CLASSIC 80'S GROOVE MASTERCUTS VOL.3
CUTSCD 36 / Feb '97 / Beechwood

☐ CLASSIC 80'S SOUL
TSS 105 / 9 Mar '98 / BMG

☐ CLASSIC ACID MASTERCUTS VOL.1
Poke: Endless Poker's / Acid tracks: Phuture / I've lost control: Sleazy D / Dream girl: Pierre's Pfantasy Club / Acid thunder: Fast Eddie / Lack of love: Charles B / Machines: Laurent X / Groove that won't stop: Saunderson, Kevin / Acid over: Tyree / Fantasy girl: Pierre's Pfantasy Club / Land of confusion: Armando / Magic feet: Dunn, Mike
CUTSCD 32 / Feb '96 / Beechwood

☐ CLASSIC BALEARIC MASTERCUTS
Barefoot in the head: Man Called Adam / Snappiness: BBG & Dina Taylor / La passionara: Blow Monkeys / Josephine: Rea, Chris / Talking with myself: Electribe 101 / Flotation: Grid / Wax the van: Lola / Spiritual high: Moodswings / Cascades: Sheer Taft / Sueno latino: Sueno Latino / Primavera: Tullio De Piscopo / Hoomba hoomba: Voice Of Africa
CUTSCD 34 / Jun '96 / Beechwood

☐ CLASSIC BANDS OF TANGO'S GOLDEN AGE
El arranque: De Caro, Julio / Sueno azul: De Caro, Julio / Cancion del olvido: De Caro, Julio / Alla en el bajo: De Caro, Julio / Chinquilina: De Caro, Julio / Obrerita: De Caro, Julio / Amurado: De Caro, Julio / Tierra querida: De Caro, Julio / Maula: De Caro, Julio / Ronda de ases: Fresedo, Osvaldo / Derecho viejo: Fresedo, Osvaldo / Pensando en ti: Fresedo, Osvaldo / Despues del canaval: Fresedo, Osvaldo / Hasta cuando: Fresedo, Osvaldo / Si no me engana el corazon: Fresedo, Osvaldo / Mas alla: Fresedo, Osvaldo / De buen aguero: Fresedo, Osvaldo / En un beso...la vida: Di Sarli, Carlos / Mi refugio: Di Sarli, Carlos / El estagiario: Di Sarli, Carlos / Cortando camino: Di Sarli, Carlos / Manana no estaras: Di Sarli, Carlos / Clavel del aire: Di Sarli, Carlos
HQCD 91 / Oct '97 / Harlequin

☐ CLASSIC BANDS OF THE THIRTIES
Song of india: Dorsey, Tommy Orchestra / South Rampart Street Parade: Crosby, Bob & His real: Lynn, Cheryl / Begin the beguine: Shaw, Artie and me tonight: Aurra / Good lovin': Belle, Regina / Heaven: Chimes / Can't stop: After 7
CDUBC 01 / Jan '94 / Debut

☐ CLASSIC BIG BAND JAZZ
AVC 540 / May '94 / Avid

☐ CLASSIC BLUES (3CD Set)
Boom boom: Hooker, John Lee / Blues is my middle name: Charles, Ray / You step out of my dream: Vaughan, Sarah / Please come back to me: Burke, Solomon / Poor boy: Howlin' Wolf / How blue can you get: King, B.B. / Goodnight Irene: Leadbelly / Don't let the sun catch you cryin': Big Maybelle / They call it stormy Monday: Turner, 'Big' Joe / My wanted is my baby treat me right: Walker, T-Bone / Little red blues: Mills Brothers / My man: Holiday, Billie / Baby, won't you please come home: Hines, Earl 'Fatha' / Jelly Roll blues: Morton, Jelly Roll / It's hard to believe you: Rush, Otis & Little Walter / Don't want no Rock Island line: Cash, Johnny / King of the road: Williams, 'Big' Joe / Good morning little school girl: Chicago Breakdown / Every day I have the blues: King, B.B. / I'll never fall in love again: Brown, Ruth / Old piano plays the blues: Cole, Nat 'King' / I wonder what my baby's doing tonight: Big Maybelle / There's good rockin' tonight: Hopkins, Lightnin' / These four walls: Thomas, Irma / I'm gonna home: Diddley, Bo / Billie's blues: Holiday, Billie / Birmingham blues: Hooker, John Lee / Nothing can stop me: Houston, Cissy / It may be the last time: Rush, Otis & Little Walter / El Dorado blues: Lightnin' Slim / Love for sale: Brown, Roy / How long blues: Turner, 'Big' Joe / Wang dang doodle: Howlin' Wolf / I put a spell on you: Hawkins, Screamin' Jay / I'm so glad: I'm in love again: Houston, Cissy / When the saints go marching in: Hines, Earl 'Fatha' / Lover come back to me: Holiday, Billie / I guess I'm a fool: Memphis Slim / Hey Bo Diddley: Diddley, Bo / Let the four winds blow: Brown, Roy / When the sun goes down: Turner, 'Big' Joe / Good morning little school girl: Chicago Breakdown / Every day I have the blues: King, B.B. / I'd rather go blind: James, Etta / Crazy 'bout you baby: Lightnin' Slim / If loving you is wrong: Mason, Barbara / Red rooster: Howlin' Wolf / I need you so bad: Comes, James / Goodnight sweetheart, goodnight: Spaniels
101562 / May '97 / A-Play Collection

☐ CLASSIC BLUES AND VAUDEVILLE SINGERS (Alternate Takes 1921-1927)
DOCD 5573 / 21 Sep '97 / Document

☐ CLASSIC BLUES JAZZ & VAUDEVILLE SINGERS VOL.2
DOCD 5602 / 15 Jun '98 / Document

☐ CLASSIC BLUESMEN (3CD Set)
Rocks in my bed: Turner, 'Big' Joe / Midnight hour blues: Carr, Leroy / I ain't gonna be worried no more: Estes, 'Sleepy' John / She's coming back some cold rainy day: Barbeque Bob / You can't get that stuff no more: Tampa Red / Blue coat blues: Broonzy, 'Big' Bill / Pine Bluff Arkansas: White, Bukka / Gamblin' man blues: Dupree, 'Champion' Jack / It's your time now: Broonzy, 'Big' Bill / Phonograph blues: Johnson, Robert / Blues from engine: McTell, 'Blind' Willie / Blue disco blues: Williamson, Sonny Boy / I know his blood can make me whole: Johnson, 'Blind' Willie / Baby you gotta change your mind: Fuller, Blind Boy / Good morning blues: Johnson / Preaching blues (up jumped the devil): Johnson, Robert / Gonna follow my baby: Crudup, Arthur 'Big Boy' / Mr.Johnson's swing: Johnson, Lonnie / Picking my tomatoes: McGhee, Brownie / 15 cents a day: Sykes, Roosevelt / Junie blues: the: Sykes, Roosevelt / CC rider: Leadbelly / Keys to the highway: Broonzy, 'Big' Bill / Black train blues: Broonzy, 'Big' Bill / Mean mistreater mama: Carr, Leroy / Four hands are better than one: Broonzy, 'Big' Bill / Denver blues: Tampa Red / Lonnie's blues: satisfied: Broonzy, 'Big' Bill / Motherless child blues:

Barbeque Bob / Death valley blues: Crudup, Arthur 'Big Boy' / Georgia rag: McTell, 'Blind' Willie / Dark was the night: McTell, 'Blind' Willie / My brownskin sugarplum: Fuller, Blind Boy / Walking blues: Johnson, Robert / Sun risin' blues: Turner, 'Big' Joe / Warehouse man blues: Dupree, 'Champion' Jack / Get the bottle up and go: Williamson, Sonny Boy / Born for bad luck: McGhee, Brownie / Little Laura blues: Estes, 'Sleepy' John / I'm a rattlesnakin' Daddy: Fuller, Blind Boy / Worryin' you off your mind: Broonzy, 'Big' Bill / I had my way I'd tear the building down: Johnson, 'Blind' Willie / Working man blues: Estes, 'Sleepy' John / Good woman blues: Carr, Leroy / You know I got a reason: Broonzy, 'Big' Bill / When you got a friend: Johnson, Robert / morning blues: Turner, 'Big' Joe / I'm calling: Daisy: McGhee, Brownie / Chain gang blues: Dupree, 'Champion' Jack / Sugar mama blues: Williamson, Sonny Boy / Western bound blues: Tampa Red / Stomp down rider: McTell, 'Blind' Willie / Keep your lamp trimmed and burning: Johnson, 'Blind' Willie / California blues: Barbeque Bob / Mean old bedbug blues: Johnson, Lonnie / Strange place blues: White, Bukka / Trouble and whiskey: Sykes, Roosevelt / Mean old Frisco blues: Crudup, Arthur 'Big Boy' / Rock Island line: Leadbelly
390042 / Apr '98 / Hallmark

☐ CLASSIC CEILI BANDS
MACCD 203 / Aug '96 / Autograph

☐ CLASSIC CHARTBUSTERS (4CD Set)
SUMBX 4021 / Jan '98 / Summit

☐ CLASSIC CHRISTMAS, A
DCD 5311 / Dec '93 / Disky

☐ CLASSIC CLUB COLLECTIVE (A Classic Collection Of Club Anthems)
Got to have your love: Mantronix / Let the beat hit 'em: Lisa Lisa & Cult Jam / Optimistic: Sounds Of Blackness / Love under moonlight: Graham, Jaki / Twilight: Maze & Frankie Beverly / Secret rendezvous: Rene & Angela / Laughin' at you: Dazz Band / Come into my life: Sims, Joyce / Got to be real: Lynn, Cheryl / Sleep talk: Williams, Alyson / You
CDUBC 01 / Jan '94 / Debut

☐ CLASSIC COUNTRY
Don't think twice its alright / Sam stone / American trilogy / Little ways / I'm for Wind beneath my wings / Thirty-nine and holding / I love a rainy night / Wonderful tonight / Shotgun willie / Don't forget to remember / Release me / Little unfair / My dixie darlin' / Forever and ever amen / Dance of a stranger / Jambalaya (on the bayou) / Love hurts / I will always love you / My tennessee mountain home
9548330072 / Nov '93 / WEA

☐ CLASSIC COUNTRY
MACCD 289 / Aug '96 / Autograph

☐ CLASSIC COUNTRY (4 In The Morning/Heartbreak USA/Fall To Pieces/3CD Set)
It wasn't God who made Honky Tonk Angels: Wells, Kitty / Ruby don't take your love to town: Rogers, Kenny / Baby on my mind: Spears, Billie Jo / Rose garden: Anderson, Lynn / Harper Valley: Riley, Jeannie C / No tomorrow in sight: Nelson, Willie / When two worlds collide: Miller, Roger / Walking the floor over you: Tubb, Ernest & his Texas Troubadours / Jackson: Lewis, Jerry Lee & Linda Gail / Big town: Twitty, Conway / Lonely women doing good lovers: Luman, Bob / Music City, U.S.A.: Jennings, Waylon / other side of life: Thompson, Hank / Rhinestone cowboy: Campbell, Glen / Satisfied mind: Wagoner, Porter / Rock Island line: Cash, Johnny / King of the road: Miller, Roger / Big bad John: Dean, Jimmy / Take me home: Bob / Me and Bobby McGhee: Rogers, Kenny / Race is on: Jones, George / Dang me: Miller, Roger / Indiana wants me: Taylor, R. Dean / Tom Dooley: You and me together: Haggard, Merle / is anybody going to San Antone: Nelson, Willie / Crystal chandeliers: Pride, Charley / Early morning rain: Martin, George IV / Foggy mountain breakdown: Hall, Tom T. / Cry me a river: Gayle, Crystal / It ain't me baby: Cash, Johnny & June Carter / Night life: Nelson, Willie / Ode to Billie Joe: Gentry, Bobbie / I got stripes: Cash, Johnny / I will always love you: Parton, Dolly / You're my best friend: Williams, Don / Good hearted woman:

Jennings, Waylon & Willie Nelson / Jambalaya: Jackson, Wanda / By the time I get to Phoenix: Campbell, Glen / Mr. Bojangles: Hall, Tom T. / Storms never last: Jennings, Waylon / Delta dawn: Tucker, Tanya / Amanda: Jennings, Waylon / Coat of many colours: Parton, Dolly / Queen of the silver dollar: Dave & Sugar / Crazy: Cline, Patsy / My heart: Milsap, Ronnie / My elusive dreams: Rich, Charlie / I can't stop loving you: Reeves, Jim
RCACD 217 / Jul '97 / RCA

☐ CLASSIC CROONERS
Anything goes: Bennett, Tony / Granada: Laine, Frankie / Love letters: Como, Perry / Blue skies: Haymes, Dick / So many ways: Benton, Brook / Hello Dolly: Armstrong, Louis / Come fly with me: Sinatra, Frank / My heart is saying: Crosby, Bing / Bambino: Mona Lisa: Cole, Nat 'King' / Cry: Ray, Johnnie / Life is a song: Bennett, Tony / Woman in love: Laine, Frankie / Song of songs: Como, Perry / Night and day: Haymes, Dick / Kiddio: Benton, Brook / Cabaret: Armstrong, Louis / East side of heaven: Crosby, Bing / Hernando's hideaway: Ray, Johnnie / Unforgettable: Cole, Nat 'King' / I've got you under my skin: Sinatra, Frank
MUCD 9012 / Apr '95 / Musketeer

☐ CLASSIC DANCE COLLECTION VOL.1, THE (Ain't No Getting Over You)
Ain't no getting over you: Roel, Charlotte / Groovin': Out Of Mind / 24 days: Run 4 Fun / Love me or leave me: Marian / Give me your love: Factual Beat / Night fever: New Soul / On Broadway: Dance Society / Paradise: Out Of Mind / I swear: Lulu & The Luvvers / Every beat of my heart: Marian / I shot the sheriff: Marian / What's love got to do with it: Buttercups / All I wanna do: Factual Beat / Hands up: Q-Generation / Someday we'll be together: Jackson, Latoya / Grease: Hairstyle 55
101002 / May '97 / A-Play Collection

☐ CLASSIC DANCE COLLECTION VOL.2, THE (You & Me Together)
If lovin' you is wrong: Marian / Sugar sugar: Kissin' Cousins / I keep gettin' higher: Corinne / Stop in the name of love: Jackson, Latoya / I believe: Factual Beat / Fly away: Toolex / Fame: Celebrity / Please don't talk to Jessica: Run 4 Fun / Kung fu fighting: Hadiza / Locomotion: Tax 'n' Tips / You and me together: Jampack & Bee / Destination nowhere: Out Of Mind / Celebration: Global Dance Party / Groove your soul: Factual Beat / Surrender: Levi Tuesday / Stumblin' in: Cash 'n' Carry
101012 / May '97 / A-Play Collection

☐ CLASSIC DANCE COLLECTION VOL.3, THE (Dancing With Somebody)
Dancing with somebody: Run 4 Fun / Summerdream: Out Of Mind / Born to be alive: Street Gang / Reminds me of you: Marian / Farewell my summer love: Jampack & Bee / Open your heart: Toolex / I was made to love her: Big Lovers / Groove your soul: Factual Beat / I'm 4 real: Corinne / Substitute: Nouveau Sisters / Baby love: Jackson, Latoya / Ma Baker: Black On White / Take me (beyond reality): Simon / Wild thing: Hadiza / He ain't heavy (he's my brother): Gray & Co. / Why: Little C
101022 / May '97 / A-Play Collection

☐ CLASSIC DANCE COLLECTION, THE (3CD Set)
Ain't no getting over you: Roel, Charlotte / Groovin': Out Of Mind / 24 days: Run 4 Fun / Love me or leave me: Marian / Give me your love: Factual Beat / Night fever: New Soul / On Broadway: Dance Society / Paradise: Out Of Mind / I swear: Lulu & The Luvvers / Every beat of my heart: Marian / I shot the sheriff: Hadiza / What's love got to do with it: Buttercups / All I wanna do: Factual Beat / Hands up: Q-Generation / Someday we'll be together: Jackson, Latoya / Grease: Hairstyle 55 / If lovin' you is wrong: Marian / Sugar sugar: Kissin' Cousins / I keep gettin' higher: Corinne / Stop in the name of love: Jackson, Latoya / I believe: Factual Beat / Fly away: Toolex / Fame: Celebrity / Please don't talk to Jessica: Run 4 Fun / Kung fu fighting: Hadiza / Locomotion: Tax 'n' Tips / You and me together: Jampack & Bee / Destination nowhere: Out Of Mind / Celebration: Global Dance Party / Groove your soul: Factual Beat / Surrender: Tuesday, Levi / Stumblin' in: Cash 'n' Carry / Dancing with somebody: Run 4 Fun / Summerdream: Out Of Mind / Born to be alive: Street Gang / Reminds me of you: Marian / Farewell my summer love: Jampack & Bee / Open your heart: Toolex / I was made to love her: Big Lovers / Groove your soul: Factual Beat / Surrender: Substitute: Nouveau Sisters / Baby love: Jackson, Latoya / Ma Baker: Black On White / Take me (beyond reality): Simon / Wild thing: Hadiza / He ain't heavy (he's my brother): Gray & Co. / Why: Little C
100992 / May '97 / A-Play Collection

☐ CLASSIC DEEP HOUSE VOL.2
GR 101014 / Dec '96 / Gravity

☐ CLASSIC DISCO MASTERCUTS VOL.1
Vertigo/Relight my fire: Hartman, Dan / Can't live without your love: Jones, Tamiko / I need you: Sylvester / This time baby: Brown, Jackie / Disco nights: GQ / Sure shot: Weber, Tracy / Body music: Strikers / Delirium: McGee, Francine / Casanova: Coffee / Dance with you: Rigby, Evelyn 'Champagne' / Do what you wanna do / I connection / I hear music in the street: Unlimited Touch
CUTSCD 25 / Feb '95 / Beechwood

☐ CLASSIC DOO WOP
You promise me love: Lewis, Earl & The Channels / Come back to me: Sylvia, Margo & The Tune Weavers / Sweetest one: Joel & The Dimensions / At the altar: Staton, Johnny & The Feathers / Miracle of love: Crew, Herb & The Five Keys / My angel lover: Cox, Herb & The Cleftones / Heaven and Cindy: Five Boroughs & Brian Daly / Wherever you are: Blandon, Richard & The Dubs / One little teardrop: Grant, George & The Castelles / Heaven's for real / Alice from dallas: Reede, Leon & The Bluejays / Whispering bells: Joel & The Dimensions / I've tried: Sylvia, Margo & The Tune Weavers / Play a new song: McGee, Francine / I've got to lose the game of love: Cox, Herb & The Cleftones / One too many nights: Five Boroughs & Siobhan Daly / That's the way it goes: Joel & The Dimensions / Why can't I marry: Winn, Henry & The Moonglows / Surrender to love: Grant, George & The Castelles / Moonlight: Mayer, Arthur / Our love: Julian, Don & The Meadowlarks / Accept me for what I am: Green, Vernon & The Medallions / My junaita: Joel & The Dimensions / This time baby: Blandon, Richard & The Dubs
CDCHD 417 / Sep '92 / Ace

☐ **CLASSIC EASY (Instrumental/The Very Best Of Easy Listening)**
Strangers in the light: Freeman, Stan / Moon river: *Starlight Strings* / This guy's in love with you: Goodwin, Ron & His Orchestra / Bright eyes: Manuel / String of pearls: Loss, Joe Orchestra / Continental: Love, Geoff & His Orchestra / What the world needs now is love: Goodwin, Ron & His Orchestra / Theme from 'A Man And A Woman': Love, Geoff & His Orchestra / Rodrigo's guitar concerto de aranjeuz: Manuel / Walk in the black forest: Love, Geoff & His Orchestra / Say it with music: Payne, Jack / Unforgettable: Starlight Strings / Goodnight: Loss, Joe Orchestra / Can't take my eyes off you: Henriques, Basil & The Wakiki Islanders / Blarney's stoned: Hawkshaw, Alan / Music to drive by: Loss, Joe Concertium / Countdown: Fahey, Brian / Sucu sucu: Jaramillo, Pepe / Wheels: Loss, Joe Orchestra / At the sign of the swinging cymbal: Fahey, Brian
CDMFP 6257 / Nov '96 / Music For Pleasure

☐ **CLASSIC EASY (Vocal/The Very Best Of Easy Listening)**
Unforgettable: Cole, Nat 'King' / True love: Crosby, Bing & Grace Kelly / Magic moments: Hilton, Ronnie / Folks who live on the hill: Lee, Peggy / Spanish eyes: Martino, Al / Memories are made of this: Martin, Dean / Where do I begin (love story): Bassey, Shirley / Why do fools fall in love: Cogan, Alma / It might as well rain until September: King, Carole / Galveston: Campbell, Glen / Edelweiss: Hill, Vince / Cry me a river: London, Julie / From Russia with love: Monro, Matt / Don't make my brown eyes blue: Gayle, Crystal / I don't know how to love him: Reddy, Helen / Very thought of you: Wilson, Nancy / When I fall in love: Cole, Nat 'King' / Nightingale sang in Beverley Square: Darin, Bobby / Vincent: McLean, Don / Carnival is over: Seekers
CDMFP 6258 / Nov '96 / Music For Pleasure

☐ **CLASSIC ELECTRO MASTERCUTS VOL.1**
Walking on sunshine: Rockers Revenge & Donnie Calvin / Don't make me wait: Peech Boys / White lines (don't don't do it): Grandmaster Flash & Melle Mel / Hip hop be bop (Don't stop): Man Parrish / Rockit: Hancock, Herbie / Smurf: Brunson, Tyrone / In the bottle: COD / London bridge is falling down: Newtrament / Al-Naafiysh (The soul): Hashim / Magic's wand: Whodini / Wildstyle: Time Zone / Adventures of Grandmaster Flash on the wheels of steel: Grandmaster Flash & The Furious Five
CUTSCD 19 / May '94 / Beechwood

☐ **CLASSIC ELEMENTS**
KLP 79CD / 13 Apr '98 / K

☐ **CLASSIC FOLK FIDDLE**
Cold wet and rainy night: Carthy, Eliza / Bonaparte's retreat: Swarbrick, Dave / Spanish cloak: Contraband / Byker hill: Carthy, Martin & Dave Swarbrick / Dr.Gilbert: Gorman, Michael / Rocky road to Dublin: Campbell, Ian Folk Group / Sally gardens: Four Men & A Dog / Da day dawn: Bain, Aly & Tom Anderson / Mason's apron: Dubliners / Mrs.Bermingham: Carthy, Martin & Dave Swarbrick / Blacksmith: Dransfield, Barry / Grand march in the battle of Prague: Carthy, Martin / Mrs.Jamieson's favourite: Bain, Aly & Tom Anderson / Sword dance: Swarbrick, Dave / Midnight on the water: Carthy, Martin
HILLCD 24 / Jan '98 / Wooded Hill

☐ **CLASSIC FOLK GUITAR**
San Francisco Bay blues: Elliott, Ramblin' Jack / Guitar train: Pearse, John / Anji: Jansch, Bert / Tic tocative: Jansch, Bert & John Renbourn / Goat island: Renbourn, John / Molly Oxford: Carthy, Martin / Swaggering boney: Carthy, Martin / Return to Camden Town: Carthy, Martin / Orange in bloom: Carthy, Martin & Eliza Carthy / Blind Blake's rag: McTell, Ralph / Maple leaf rag: Laibman, David & Eric Schoenberg / Roll and tumble blues: Grossman, Stefan / Conquistador: James, John & Pete Berryman / Head in the clouds: James, John / Saturday girl: Giltrap, Gordon / For Jessica sad or high kicking: Simpson, Martin / Keel row: Simpson, Martin / Planxty row: Simpson, Martin / Scojun waltz: Gaughan, Dick / Alan Macpherson of mosspark: Gaughan, Dick
HILLCD 23 / Jan '98 / Wooded Hill

☐ **CLASSIC FUNK**
MCCD 200 / May '95 / Music Club

☐ **CLASSIC FUNK MASTERCUTS VOL.1**
Who is he and what is he to you: Creative Source / Wicky wacky: Fatback Band / Gimme some more: JB's / For the love of money: O'Jays / Fire: Ohio Players / Pusherman: Mayfield, Curtis / Blow your head: Wesley, Fred & The JB's / Fencewalk: Mandrill / Pick up the pieces: Average White Band / Rock creek park: Blackbyrds / NT Pts 1 and 2: Kool & The Gang / Stone to the bone: Brown, James
CUTSCD 6 / May '92 / Beechwood

☐ **CLASSIC FUNK MASTERCUTS VOL.2**
Movin': Brass Construction / Express yourself: Wright, Charles & The Watts 103rd St. Rhythm Band / You can have your Watergate: JB's / It's alright now: Harris, Eddie / Funky stuff/More funky stuff: Kool & The Gang / Keep on steppin': Fatback Band / Jive turkey: Ohio Express / Ghetto: Hathaway, Donny / Baby let me take you (in my arms): Detroit Emeralds / Boss: Brown, James / Do it fluid: Blackbyrds / Stomp and buck dance: Crusaders
CUTSCD 14 / Sep '93 / Beechwood

☐ **CLASSIC FUNK MASTERCUTS VOL.3**
Just kissed my baby: Meters / Goin' to see my baby: Fatback Band / Turn off the light: Young, Larry / Hands of time: Perfect Circle / Let a man come in and do the popcorn: Brown, James / (I've got) So much trouble in my mind: Quarterman, Sir Joe & Free Soul / Sideway shuffle: Lewis, Linda / Miss Fatback: Philips, Saundra / This is it: Davis, Betty / Stop the rain: Average White Band / Can you get it: Mandrill / Who's in town: Nature Boys
CUTSCD 24 / Jan '95 / Beechwood

☐ **CLASSIC G-FUNK MASTERCUTS VOL.1**
Alwayz into somethin': NWA / Indo smoke: Mista Grimm / Keep their heads ringin': Dr. Dre / Regulate: Warren G & Nate Dogg / Dirty B side: Da Brat & Notorious BIG / Black superman: Above The Law / Gangsta's boogie: LV / Summer breeze: DJ Quik / Hand of the dead body: Scarface & Ice Cube / Guerilla funk: Paris / Ghetto jam: Domino / 12 pacofdoja: Lil' Half Dead
CUTSCD 39 / Jul '97 / Beechwood

☐ **CLASSIC HI-NRG VOL.1 (4CD Set)**
Catch me I'm falling in love: Raven, Marsha / Love trap: Astaire / Evergreen: Fantasia / Somebody to love: Cafe Society / Eat you up: Gold, Angie / Men in my life: Lee, Miriam / American love: Astaire / Deliverence: People Like Us / Got to get you: Astaire / Power of love: Astaire / Sun ain't gonna shine anymore: Quantize / You've lost that lovin' feelin': Quantize / Sunset people: Williams, Jessica / Burning: Sapphire / Strange desire: Gable, Nicci / Break me: Charade / Take my body: Ackerman, Tracy / Give me back my heart: Lewis, Norma / I'd do it for you: Astaire / Instant love: Quantize / Lover come back to me: Alexander, Ross / I don't give a damn: Gable, Nicci / Male stripper: Man To Man / Summernight city: Astaire / Ressurrection: People Like Us / There'll always be a place for you in my heart: Quantize / High sex drive: Astaire / What's up: Julia / Energy is eurobeat: Man To Man / Feels like love: Thomas, Love / I was tired of being alone: Klodya / Jackie: Touch Tone / Can't say no: Alexander, Ross / I want to know what love is: Astaire / Thunder and lightning: Heat-X-Change / Queen of fools: Williams, Jessica / Don't let the flame die out: Marie, Kelly
CDBBX 1 / 20 Oct '97 / Passion

☐ **CLASSIC HI-NRG VOL.2 (4CD Set)**
CDBBX 2 / 9 Feb '98 / Passion

☐ **CLASSIC HIGHLIFE**
AIM 1053 / Oct '95 / Aim

☐ **CLASSIC HIP HOP MASTERCUTS VOL.1**
My philosophy: Boogie Down Productions / It's my beat: Sweet Tee & Jazzy Joyce / Peter Piper: Run DMC / Strong island: JVCFORCE / Eric B for president: Eric B & Rakim / Have a nice day: Shante, Roxanne / Serious: Steady B / Jimbrowski: Jungle Brothers / Description of a fool: Tribe Called Quest / Talkin' all that jazz: Stetsasonic / King of the beats: Mantronix
CUTSCD 29 / Jul '95 / Beechwood

☐ **CLASSIC HIP HOP MASTERCUTS VOL.2**
It's yours: TLA Rock & Jazzy Jay / Chorus line part 1: Ultramagnetic MC's / It's a new style: Beastie Boys / Humpty dance: Digital Underground / Buddy: De La Soul / Rebel without a pause: Public Enemy / Paper thin: MC Lyte / Wrath of Kane: Big Daddy Kane / Peace is not the word to play: Main Source / Letter to the better: Master Ace / Uptown: Dope On Plastic / Choice is yours: Black Sheep
CUTSCD 35 / Sep '96 / Beechwood

☐ **CLASSIC HOUSE MASTERCUTS VOL.1**
Someday: Rogers, Cece / Tears: Knuckles, Frankie / Let the music (use you): Night Writers / Give it to me: Bam Bam / Big fun: Inner City / You used to hold me: Rosario, Ralphi / Baby wants to ride: Principle, Jamie / Break 4 love: Raze / Voodoo Ray: Guy Called Gerald / Devotion: Ten City / It's alright: Sterling Void / Promised land: Smooth, Joe
CUTSCD 20 / Jun '94 / Beechwood

☐ **CLASSIC HOUSE MASTERCUTS VOL.2**
Music is the key: Silk, J.M. / Strings of life: Rythim Is Rythim / Open our eyes: Jefferson, Marshall / I'm in love: Sha-Lor / Love will find a way: Romeo, Victor / Morning after: Fallout / Let's get busy: McClaine, Curtis & On The House / Make my body rock: Jomanda / Take some time out: Jarvis, Arnold / If you should need a friend: Blaze / Definition of a track: Back Room / Musical freedom: Simpson, Paul
CUTSCD 22 / Oct '94 / Beechwood

☐ **CLASSIC HOUSE MASTERCUTS VOL.3**
Ma foom bey: Cultural Vibe / Give me back the love: On The House / Can U dance: Jason, Kenny 'Jammin' & Fast Eddie / Night moves: Rickster / Forever together: Raven Maize / String free: Phortune / Can you party: Royal House / Who's gonna ease the pressure: Thornhill, Mac / Sound: Reese & Santonio / Release your party: Bang The Party / Can you feel it: Mr. Fingers
CUTSCD 28 / Jun '95 / Beechwood

☐ **CLASSIC IRISH LOVE SONGS**
ARAN 3607 / 5 May '98 / Dara

☐ **CLASSIC JAZZ-FUNK MASTERCUTS VOL.1**
Expansions: Smith, Lonnie Liston / Always there: Laws, Ronnie / Bottle: Scott-Heron, Gil / Change (makes you want to hustle): Byrd, Donald / Inherit the wind: Felder, Wilton / Shaker song: Spyro Gyra / Jazz carnival: Azymuth / Los conquistadores chocolates: Smith, Johnny 'Hammond' / Say you will: Henderson, Eddie / Brasilia: Klemmer, John / Till you take my love: Mason, Harvey / Unicorn: Gillespie, Dizzy
CUTSCD 2 / Sep '91 / Beechwood

☐ **CLASSIC JAZZ-FUNK MASTERCUTS VOL.2**
Could heaven ever be like this: Muhammad, Idris / Brazilian love affair: Duke, George / Easy: Jarreau, Al / Dominoes: Byrd, Donald / To prove my love: Doheny, Ned / Snowblower: Baker, B. / Poo poo la la: Ayers, Roy / Come with me: Maria, Tania / Rotation: Alpert, Herb / Chicago song: Sanborn, David / New killer Joe: Golson, Benny / Keep that same old feeling: Crusaders
CUTSCD 4 / Nov '91 / Beechwood

☐ **CLASSIC JAZZ-FUNK MASTERCUTS VOL.3**
Feel the real: Bendeth, David / Roller jubilee: Di Meola, Al / Saturday night: Hancock, Herbie / Love has come around: Byrd, Donald / Spring high: Lewis, Ramsey / Love will bring us back together: Ayers, Roy / Westchester lady: James, Bob / Summer madness: Kool & The Gang / Sun goddess: Lewis, Ramsey & Earth, Wind & Fire / Darlin' darlin' baby: Khan, Steve / You're a star: Aquarian Dream / Best of friends: White, Lenny
CUTSCD 7 / Jun '92 / Beechwood

☐ **CLASSIC JAZZ-FUNK MASTERCUTS VOL.4**
Birdland: Weather Report / I thought it was you: Hancock, Herbie / Can't you see me: Ayers, Roy / Dancing in outer space: Atmosfear / You got the floor: Adams, Arthur / Whistle bump: Deodato, Eumir / Real thing: Mendes, Sergio / Magic fingers: Hamilton, Chico / Strawberry letter 23: Brothers Johnson / Chief inspector: Badarou, Wally / Funkin' for Jamaica: Browne, Tom / Street life: Crusaders
CUTSCD 16 / Jan '94 / Beechwood

☐ **CLASSIC JAZZ-FUNK MASTERCUTS VOL.5**
Countdown (Captain Fingers): Ritenour, Lee / Grand prix: Fuse One / Freeze thaw: Basia / Sausalito: Washington, Grover Jr. / Intro (The River Niger): Ayers, Roy / Dreamin': Heath Brothers / Keep smiling: Szabo, Gabor / Watching life: LA Boppers / Boulevard: White, Peter / Let's funk tonight: Blue Feather / La Cuna: Barretto, Ray / African bird: OPA
CUTSCD 23 / Nov '94 / Beechwood

☐ **CLASSIC JAZZ-FUNK MASTERCUTS VOL.6**
Friends and strangers: Grusin, Dave / Deja vu: AB's / Mi mi Africa: Yagi, Nobuo / Nice shot: Watanabe, Sadao / Mid Manhattan: Casiopea / Antes de mais nada: Pacific Jam / Lament: Honda, Toshiyuki / From the lonely afternoon: Mukai, Shigeharu / Send me your feelings: Hino, Terumasa / Music inside you: Kazu Matsui Project / Cadillac kid: Morizono, Katsutoshi / Trinkets and things: Kawaski, Ryo
CUTSCD 31 / Jan '96 / Beechwood

☐ **CLASSIC JAZZ-FUNK MASTERCUTS VOL.7**
El bobo: Lewis, Webster / Valdez in the country: Hathaway, Donny / Family: Laws, Hubert / Black is the colour: Longmire, Wilbert / Deja vu: Da Costa, Paulino / Sweet power your embrace: Mason, James / Harlem boys: Rollins, Sonny / Life is like a samba: Benoit, David / Fifty four: Sea Level / Tequila mockingbird: Lewis, Ramsey / Straight to the bank: Summers, Bill
CUTSCD 37 / Mar '97 / Beechwood

☐ **CLASSIC LOVE**
0630150082 / May '96 / Warner Bros.

☐ **CLASSIC LOVE DUETS**
CDMOIR 430 / Jul '95 / Memoir

☐ **CLASSIC LOVE SONGS (Heartbeat/ You Are So Beautiful/Sharing The Night/3CD Set)**
If I said you had a beautiful body: Bellamy Brothers / Will you still love me tomorrow: Smokie / Heartbeat: Showaddywaddy / Thousand pieces: Goombay Dance Band / Only sixteen: Dr. Hook & Ray Sawyer / If you can't give me love: Quatro, Suzi / Time for a change of heart: Charles, Tina / Always and forever: Rogers, Kenny / Let it grow: Clout / Feel it all over: Andrews, Chris / Day that my heart caught fire: Young, John Paul / I feel love: Smokie / Suddenly: Stardust, Alvin / Funny how love can be: First Class / All I have to do is dream: Svenne & Lotta / Girl like you: Mungo Jerry / Rainbow: Marmalade / Adios, auf wiederschen: Humphries, Les Singers / Missing you takes up most of my time: Dr. Hook & Ray Sawyer / When your in love with a beautiful woman: Dr. Hook & Ray Sawyer / I wanna do it with you: Young, John Paul / Stumblin' in: Quatro, Suzi / Take good care of my baby: Smokie / Nickelodeon nights: Sailor / Why do lovers break each others hearts: Showaddywaddy / You are so beautiful: Rogers, Kenny / Let it be me: Svenne & Lotta / Day after day: Goombay Dance Band / Reflections of my life: Marmalade / Just to hear your voice: Stardust, Alvin / Always crying over you: Dr. Hook & Ray Sawyer / My guy: Surprise Surprise / For you my love: Gaynor, Gloria / Give a little love: Bay City Rollers / When will you be mine: Clout / Let a good thing die: Marian / Are you looking for someone: Andrews, Chris / I'm still lovin' you: Goombay Dance Band / I'll never get over you: Showaddywaddy / Midnight lady: Norman, Chris / Just when I needed you most: Vanwarmer, Randy / Three steps to heaven: Showaddywaddy / Sharing the night together: Dr. Hook & Ray Sawyer / I can't help falling in love: Rogers, Kenny / Every beat of my heart: Marian / Midnight blue: Tucker, Louise / Love is in the air: Young, John Paul / Everybody's got to learn sometime: Korgis / Guardian angel: Masquerade / Streets of London: McTell, Ralph / If you think you know how to love me: Smokie / It's only make believe: Showaddywaddy / Substitute: Clout / Hello baby: Marmalade / You were on my mind: Crispin St Peters / Aloha oe until we meet again: Goombay Dance Band / Love me for a reason: As We Speak / If we only had the time: Svenne & Lotta
10862 / Oct '97 / Go On Deluxe

☐ **CLASSIC LOVE SONGS PERFORMED ON PAN PIPES**
If you leave me now / Killing me softly / Feelings / How deep is your love / Love is all around / When I fall in love / Hello / Endless love / Love changes everything / First man you remember / It must have been love / Eternal flame / I need to be in love / Groovy kind of love / Hopelessly devoted to you
SUMCD 4097 / Feb '97 / Summit

☐ **CLASSIC MASTERCUTS (The Best Of Classic Mastercuts - 2CD Set)**
Boops (here to go): Sly & Robbie / Ain't nothin' goin' on but the rent: Guthrie, Gwen / Who's zoomin' who: Franklin, Aretha / Love comes down: King, Evelyn / Big fun: Gap Band / Going back to my roots: Odyssey / Night to remember: Shalamar / Trapped: Colonel Abrams / And the beat goes on: Whispers / Yah mo b there: Ingram, James / I feel for you: Khan, Chaka / Never knew love like this before: Mills, Stephanie / Jazz carnival: Azymuth / Morning dance: Spyro Gyra / Groove: Franklin, Rodney / Night birds: Shakatak / To prove my love: Doheny, Ned / Sign of the times: James, Bob / Garden party: Mezzoforte / Can't you see me: Ayers, Roy / Pick up the pieces: Average White Band / Space Princess: Smith, Lonnie Liston / I thought it was you: Hancock, Herbie / Love on a summer night: McRary's / This feeling is killing me: Jones Girls / You know how to love me: Hyman, Phyllis / Don't look any further: Edwards, Dennis / Keep on movin': Soul II Soul / See me: Vandross, Luther / Unfinished sympathy: Massive Attack / Whole town's laughing: Pendergrass, Teddy / Flesh of my flesh: Hudson, Lavine / Between the sheets: Isley Brothers / (You make me feel like) A Natural woman: Blige, Mary J. / Love don't live here anymore: Rose Royce / Don't be a fool: Loose Ends
VTDCD 101 / Sep '96 / Virgin

☐ **CLASSIC MELLOW MASTERCUTS VOL.1**
She's so good to me: Vandross, Luther / Risin' to the top (give it all you got): Burke, Keni / Outstanding: Gap Band / Joy and pain: Maze / Give me the sunshine: Leo's Sunshipp / Hold me tighter in the rain: Griffin, Billy / I'm out of your life: Arnie's Love / You'll never know: Hi-Gloss / What you won't do for love: Caldwell, Bobby / I'm back for more: Johnson, Al & Jean Carn / Fruit song: Reynolds, Jeannie / Mellow mellow right on: Lowrell
CUTSCD 3 / Sep '91 / Beechwood

☐ **CLASSIC MELLOW MASTERCUTS VOL.2**
Don't look any further: Edwards, Dennis / Baby I'm scared of you: Womack & Womack / Mind blowing decisions: Heatwave / I don't think that man should sleep alone: Parker, Ray Jr. / All night long: Mary Jane Girls / Sweet sticky thing: Ohio Players / It's ecstasy when you lay down next to me: White, Barry / Juicy fruit: Mtume / What'cha see is what'cha get: Dramatics / Yu-ma/Go away little boy: Shaw, Marlena / I choose you: Paris / So delicious: Fatback Band
CUTSCD 8 / Jul '92 / Beechwood

☐ **CLASSIC MELLOW MASTERCUTS VOL.3**
Never too much: Vandross, Luther / You're gonna get next to me: Kirkland, Bo & Ruth Davis / Nights over Egypt: Jones Girls / Now that we've found love: O'Jays / Don't let it go to your head: Carne, Jean / Do you get enough love: Jones, Shirley / You are my starship: Connors, Norman / Reasons (Live): Earth, Wind & Fire / Rock me tonight: Jackson, Freddie / Gotta get you home tonight: Jackson, Freddie / Wilde, Eugene: Jackson, Freddie / Sweet love: Baker, Anita / We're in this love together: Jarreau, Al
CUTSCD 17 / Feb '94 / Beechwood

☐ **CLASSIC MELLOW MASTERCUTS VOL.4**
Love is contagious: Sevelle, Taja / Headline news: Bell, William / Heaven sent you: Clark, Stanley / She's got the papers: Fields, Richard 'Dimples' / She's got the papers (I got the man): Mason, Barbara / Promise me: Dayton / Feel so free (won't let go): Rushen, Patrice / Stay: Controllers / Sugar free: Juicy / Do me baby: Morgan, Meli'sa / It's just the way I feel: Dunlap, Gene & The Ridgeways / I wish he didn't trust me so much: Womack, Bobby
CUTSCD 33 / Apr '96 / Beechwood

☐ **CLASSIC MIX MASTERCUTS VOL.1**
Yah mo be there: Ingram, James / Medicine song: Mills, Stephanie / You're the one for me: D-Train / Seventh heaven: Guthrie, Gwen / You don't know: Serious Intention / Searchin' to find the one: Unlimited Touch / Beat the street: Redd, Sharon / You can't hide (your love from me): Joseph, David / Ain't nothin' goin' on but the rent: Guthrie, Gwen / Thinking of you: Sister Sledge / Searching: Change / Running away: Ayers, Roy
CUTSCD 1 / Sep '91 / Beechwood

☐ **CLASSIC NEW JACK SWING MASTERCUTS VOL.1**
Rub you the right way: Gill, Johnny / Her: Guy / I got the feelin': Today / New Jack swing: Wreckx n' Effect / She's got that vibe: R Kelly / Do me right: Guy / Sensitivity: Tresvant, Ralph / So you like what you see: Samuelle / Poison: Bel Biv Devoe / Treat them like they want to be treated: Father MC / Another like my lover: Guy, Jasmine / Mama told me: Jackson, Keisha
CUTSCD 5 / Mar '92 / Beechwood

☐ **CLASSIC NEW JACK SWING MASTERCUTS VOL.2**
Is it good to you: Lucas, Tammy & Teddy Riley / Don't be afraid: Hall, Aaron / Yo that's a lot of body: Ready For The World / I like your style: Bubba / Whatever it takes: Basic Black / Swinging single: Groove B Chill / Just got paid: Kemp, Johnny / My fantasy: Guy / Why you get funky on me: Today / Coool aid express card: Nation Funktasia / Serious: La Rue / My prerogative: Brown, Bobby
CUTSCD 9 / Oct '92 / Beechwood

☐ **CLASSIC NEW JACK SWING MASTERCUTS VOL.3**
Ain't too proud to beg: TLC / I want her: Sweat, Keith / I just can't handle it: Hi-Five / Judy had a boyfriend: Riff / Somebody for me: Heavy D & The Boyz / I'm dreaming: Williams, Christopher / DOG me out: Guy / Rump shaker: Wreckx n' Effect / 69: Father MC / I'm so into you: SWV / Real love: Blige, Mary J. / Love thang: Intro
CUTSCD 18 / Mar '94 / Beechwood

☐ **CLASSIC NEW JACK SWING MASTERCUTS VOL.4**
Anything: SWV / Do me: Bell Biv Devoe / Do the right thing: Redhead Kingpin & The FBI / I found love: Redd, Jeff / I'm in luv: Joe / It's alright: Jodeci / Lisa baby: Father MC / Listen closely (bozack): Father MC / New jack city: Tamrock / She's mine: Basic Black / Wanna get with u: Guy / We've got our own thang: Heavy D & The Boyz
CUTSCD 27 / Apr '95 / Beechwood

☐ CLASSIC P-FUNK MASTERCUTS VOL.1
Disco to go: Brides Of Funkenstein / Dog talk: K-9 Corporation / Four play: Wesley, Fred & The Horny Horns / Funk funk: Cameo / Funken town: Slave / Get lucky: Well Red / Hollywood: Red Hot Chili Peppers / Loopzilla: Clinton, George / Shake: General Caine / Tweakin': Clinton, George / We came to funk ya: Wesley, Fred & The Horny Horns / Work that sucker to death: Xavier
CUTSCD 12 / Jan '93 / Beechwood

☐ CLASSIC PAN PIPES (Romantic Pan Pipes/For Lovers/Play Love Songs - 3CD Set)
I have a dream / Strawberry fields forever / Dark side of the sun / Scarborough fair / Sailing / Unchained melody / Amazing Grace / If you leave me now / Something / Feelings / Here comes the sun / Sara / Yesterday / MacArthur park / Bird of Paradise / House of the rising sun / Don't cry for me Argentina / Banks of the Ohio / Autumn dream / Let it be / Power of love / I've had the time of my life / We've got tonight / Eternal flame / You light up my life / Up where we belong / (Everything I do) I do it for you / Heartbreaker / For ever and ever / Do that to me one more time / When you're in love with a beautiful woman / Love changes everything / And I love her / Groovy kind of love / Have you ever really loved a woman / Light my fire / Woman in love / For your eyes only / I can't help falling in love with you / I will always love you / I don't wanna cry / Wind beneath my wings / Ebony and ivory / Fernando / I'll be there / Bridge over troubled water / Always on my mind / Can you feel the love tonight / Phantom Of The Opera / Music of the night / Orinoco flow / Flashdance...what a feeling / Top of the world / Norwegian Wood / Tears in heaven / Moonlight shadow / He ain't heavy, he's my brother / Michelle / Just when I needed you most / Begin the beguine / Take my breath away
55158 / Oct '96 / Music

☐ CLASSIC PARTY HITS VOL.1
Let's have a party: Jackson, Wanda / Yellow river: Christie / Sugar baby love: Rubettes / Hippy hippy shake: Swinging Blue Jeans / Da doo ron ron: Crystals / I'm into something good: Herman's Hermits / Baby come back: Equals / Walkin' back to happiness: Shapiro, Helen / Silence is golden: Tremeloes / You'll never walk alone: Gerry & The Pacemakers / Runaway: Shannon, Del / Just walkin' in the rain: Ray, Johnnie / Something's gotten hold of my heart: Pitney, Gene / Speedy Gonzales: Boone, Pat / Coasters: Brown, Charlie / Papa oom mow mow: Rivingtons / Ob-la-di ob-la-da: Marmalade / Nut rocker: B-Bumble & The Stingers
11980 / Feb '96 / Music

☐ CLASSIC PARTY HITS VOL.2
Words: David, F.R. / Under the moon of love: Showaddywaddy / Tonight: Rubettes / In the bad, bad old days (before you loved me): Foundations / Keep searchin' (we'll follow the sun): Shannon, Del / Walk don't run: Ventures / Viva Bobby Joe: Equals / I'm telling you now: Freddie & The Dreamers / Ferry cross the Mersey: Gerry & The Pacemakers / When a man loves a woman: Sledge, Percy / Someone: Tremeloes / Windy: Association / Wishin' and hopin': Merseybeats / Sheila: Roe, Tommy / Mr. Bassman: Cymbal, Johnny / It's my party: Gore, Lesley
11981 / Apr '96 / Music

☐ CLASSIC PERFORMERS
When the saints go marching in: Armstrong, Louis / Shall we dance: Astaire, Fred / One o'clock jump: Basie, Count / Where the blue of the night meets the gold of the day: Crosby, Bing / Boogie woogie: Dorsey, Tommy / It don't mean a thing if it ain't got that swing: Ellington, Duke / Tisket-a-tasket: Fitzgerald, Ella / Stompin' at the savoy: Goodman, Benny / Easy living: Holiday, Billie / Moonlight serenade: Miller, Glenn / Begin the beguine: Shaw, Artie / Honeysuckle Rose: Waller, Fats / Boogie woogie bugle boy: Andrews Sisters / Two sleepy people: Geraldo & His Orchestra / It's a sin to tell a lie: Ink Spots / Woodchopper's ball: Herman, Woody / Over the rainbow: Garland, Judy / March of the bob cats: Crosby, Bob & His Bobcats / There's a small hotel: Baker, Josephine / April showers: Jolson, Al / Thanks for the memory: Hope, Bob & Shirley Ross / Swingin' with Django: Quintette Du Hot Club De France / Rose Marie: Eddy, Nelson / Time on my hands: Bowlly, Al
HADCD 170 / May '94 / Javelin

☐ CLASSIC PIANO RAGS BLUES AND STOMPS 1928-1935
Trenches: Parrish, Turner / Mama don't allow no easy riders here: Davenport, Cow Cow / Atlanta rag: Davenport, Cow Cow / Avenue strut: Duerson, Herve / Mixed up rag: Ezell, Will / Louisiana glide: Garnett, Blind Leroy / Windy city: Wiley, Arnold / Slum Gullion stomp: Davenport, Cow Cow / Old Mill blues: Ezell, Will / Wilkins Street blues: Speckled Red / Easy drag: Duerson, Herve / Texas shout: Davenport, Cow Cow / Fives: Parrish, Turner / Arnold Wiley rag: Wiley, Arnold / Playing the dozen: Ezell, Will / Chain 'em down: Garnett, Blind Leroy / Alabama strut: Davenport, Cow Cow / Heifer dust: Ezell, Will / Walking blues: Barrow, Raymond / Dirty dozen: Speckled Red / Chimin' the blues: Davenport, Cow Cow / Oh you devil you: Brown, Olive
YAZCD 2034 / Apr '98 / Yazoo

☐ CLASSIC PIANO RAGS BLUES AND STOMPS 1928-1943
Head rag hop: Nelson, Romeo / Pine Top's boogie woogie: Smith, Pine Top / Pine Top's blues: Smith, Pine Top / Back in the alley: Davenport, Cow Cow / I'm so glad I'm 21 years old today: Dean, Joe / Pitchin' boogie: Ezell, Will / Honky tonk train blues: Lewis, Meade 'Lux' / Dearborn Street breakdown: Avery, Charles / Fat Fanny stomp: Clarke, Jim / Cow Cow blues: Davenport, Cow Cow / Hip shakin' strut: Hokum Boys & Jane Lucas / House rent scuffle: Johnson, Lil / Gettin' dirty just shakin' that thing: Nelson, Romeo / Jump steady blues: Smith, Pine Top / Detroit rocks: Taylor, Montana / Whoop and holler stomp: Taylor, Montana / Indiana Avenue stomp: Taylor, Montana / I'm sober now: Smith, Pine Top / Stomp 'em down to the bricks: Brown, Henry / Hokum stomp: Hokum Boys & Jane Lucas / Jimmy's rocks: Yancey, Jimmy / Mooch piddle: Davenport, Cow Cow / Tight whoopee: Alderson, Mozelle
YAZCD 2035 / Apr '98 / Yazoo

☐ CLASSIC PLANT
Autumnal: Boymerang / Silence go boom: Sons Of Silence / Field: Four Tet / Pass agent: Luger / Manicougan no.5: Thomas, Richard / 4am on point: Witchman / Horn: Small Good Thing / Cold fusion: Twisted Science / Chicken dinner: Ronnie & Clyde / Grain of sand: Sons Of Silence / Don: Boymerang
BAY 3CD / 11 May '98 / Leaf

☐ CLASSIC R&B MASTERCUTS
All or nothing: Joe / I just can't: Evans, Faith / Waiting for you: Tony Toni Tone / Believe in love: Pendergrass, Teddy / Be happy: Blige, Mary J. / I like the way you work it: Blackstreet / Where I wanna be boy: Miss Jones / Me and those dreaming eyes of mine: D'Angelo & Redman / You're makin' me high: Braxton, Toni & Foxy Brown / Only you: 112 & Notorious BIG / You should be mine: McKnight, Brian & Mase / Get on up: Jodeci
CUTSCD 40 / 23 Feb '98 / Beechwood

☐ CLASSIC RAGTIME (Roots And Offshoots)
African 400 (an educated rag): Prior, Arthur Band / Fo'de lawd's sake play a waltz: Victor Orchestra & Elsie Janis / Belle of the barber's ball: Murray, Billy & Ada Jones / Operatic rag: Moscowitz, Joseph / Brother Noah gave out checks for rain: Collins, Arthur / Moanin' saxophone rag: Six Brown Brothers / Trolley car swing: Victor Orchestra & Elida Morris / King of the bungaloos: Greene, Gene / Laughing rag: Moore, Sam / House rent rag: Dixieland Jug Blowers / South Street stomp: South Street Trio / Hot notes: Savoy Bearcats / 12th Street rag: Moten, Bennie Kansas City Orchestra / Tom's rag: Watkin's Band / Dew drop alley stomp: Underwood, Sugar / Pearls: Morton, Jelly Roll & His Red Hot Peppers / Ragtime Annie: Solomon & Hughes / Gladyse: Waller, Fats / Memphis kick-up: Lamar, Slim Orchestra / Maori: Green Brothers Marimba Orchestra / Bigay na pagibig: Manila String Circle / Beaumont Rag: Boyd, Bill & His Cowboy Ramblers / Maple leaf rag: Bluebird Military Band / Canadian Capers: Dorsey, Tommy & His Orchestra / Eccentric: Spanier, Muggsy & His Ragtimers
090266320622 / Aug '98 / RCA Victor

☐ CLASSIC RARE GROOVE MASTERCUTS VOL.1
Turned on to you: 80's Ladies / Riding high: Faze-O / Why I came to California: Ware, Leon / Say you love me girl: Break Water / Movin' in the right direction: Parks, Steve / Number one: Rushen, Patrice / Good love: Jeffries, Rome / So different: Kinky Foxx / Much too much: Sass / All I want is my baby: Gilliam, Roberta / Moonshadow: Labelle, Patti / It's your love: Beatty, Ethel
CUTSCD 11 / Apr '93 / Beechwood

☐ CLASSIC RARE GROOVE MASTERCUTS VOL.2
Caveman boogie: Wilson, Lesette / LA nights: Agawa, Yasuko / No.1 girl: Light Of The World / You need a change of mind: Brooklyn Express / There's a reason: Hi-Tension / Work it out: Break Water / Barely breaking even: Universal Robot Band / I'd like to get into you: Kelly, Denise & Fame / Windy city theme: Davis, Carl / Bump and hustle music: Stewart, Tommy / God made me funky: Head Hunters / Give me some: LA Boppers
CUTSCD 21 / Sep '94 / Beechwood

☐ CLASSIC REGGAE IN 90'S STYLE
RASCD 3104 / Jan '95 / Ras

☐ CLASSIC REGGAE MASTERCUTS
Very well: Wailing Souls / Chalice in the palace: U-Roy / I don't want to be left outside: Andy, Horace / Conscious man: Andy, Horace / War ina Babylon: Max Romeo / Nice time (late night blues): Don Carlos / Jah no dead: Burning Spear / Keep on knocking: Miller, Jacob / Hardtimes: Gad, Pablo / Warrior charge: Aswad / Prophecy: Fabian / Love and only love: Fred Locks
CUTSCD 30 / Oct '95 / Beechwood

☐ CLASSIC ROCK 'N' ROLL (2CD Set)
Gingerbread: Avalon, Frankie / Sally was a good old girl: Domino, Fats / La bamba: Valens, Ritchie / Hippy hippy shake: Romero, Chan / Talk back tremblin' lips: Tillotson, Johnny / Lollipop: Chordettes / Breathless: Lewis, Jerry Lee / Mama said: Shirelles / Teddy bear: Jordanaires / Please don't cry over me: Williams, Jimmy / Little town flirt: Shannon, Del / Donna: Valens, Ritchie / Lazy lady: Domino, Fats / Raunchy: Justis, Bill / Come on let's go: Valens, Ritchie / Twist and shout: Isley Brothers / Runaway: Shannon, Del / Venus: Avalon, Frankie / Reelin' and rockin': Domino, Fats / Ain't that too much: Vincent, Gene / What'd I say: Lewis, Jerry Lee / Without you: Tillotson, Johnny / Red hot: Riley, Billy Lee / Rip it up: Everly Brothers / Return to sender: Jordanaires / I think of you: Grayzell, Rudy / Soldier boy: Shirelles / De De Dinah: Avalon, Frankie
SD 885472 / 2 Feb '98 / Disky

☐ CLASSIC ROCKERS
Baby, I love you so: Miller, Jacob / King Tubby meets the rockers uptown: Pablo, Augustus / Isn't it time to see / Jah in the hills: Pablo, Augustus / Can't keep a good man down: Immortals / Earth, wind and fire: Blackman, Paul / Love won't be easy: Sibbles, Leroy / Changing world: Earl 16 / Blackman's heart: Delgado, Junior / Jah says the time has now come: Mundell, Hugh / You never know: Williams, Delroy / You never know dub: Rockers All Stars / Stop the fighting: Williams, Delroy / Stop the fighting dub: Rockers All Stars / Sukiyaki: Pablo, Augustus / Eastern promise: Pablo, Augustus
RRCD 52 / Apr '95 / Reggae Refreshers

☐ CLASSIC ROCKERS VOL.2
CDRP 0121 / Mar '97 / Rockers International

☐ CLASSIC SALSOUL MASTERCUTS VOL.1
Dreaming: Holloway, Loleatta / Heartbreaker: Burgess, Leroy / I got my mind made up: Instant Funk / Jingo: Candido / Let no man put asunder: First Choice / Love sensation: Holloway, Loleatta / Nice and nasty: Salsoul Orchestra / Runaway: Salsoul Orchestra & Loleatta Holloway / Ten percent: Double Exposure / Beat goes on and on: Ripple / Bottle: Bataan, Joe / You're just the right size: Salsoul Orchestra
CUTSCD 10 / Feb '93 / Beechwood

☐ CLASSIC SALSOUL MASTERCUTS VOL.2
First choice: Dr. Love / My love is free: Double Exposure / Ain't no mountain high enough: Inner Life / This will be a night to remember: Holman, Eddie / Just as long as I got you: Love Committee / Helplessly: Moment Of Truth / Spring rain: Silvetti / Moment of my life: Inner Life / Sing, sing: Gaz / Hit and run: Holloway, Loleatta / Ooh, I love it (love break): Salsoul Orchestra / Dancin' and prancin': Candido
CUTSCD 13 / Jun '93 / Beechwood

☐ CLASSIC SIXTIES BEAT GROUPS
Louie Louie: Kingsmen / You tell me why: Beau Brummels / How love was true: Bee Gees / He's in town: Rockin' Berries / I'm the one: Gerry & The Pacemakers / Jesamine: Casuals / Love is all around: Troggs / Don't want you no more: Davis, Spencer Group / Here it comes again: Fortunes / Can't you hear my heartbeat: Herman's Hermits / Dandy: Herman's Hermits / Mr. Moonlight: Merseybeats / When it comes to your love: Beau Brummels / Anyway that you want me: Troggs / How do you do it: Gerry & The Pacemakers / Walk in the room: Searchers
HADCD 220 / Jun '97 / Spotlight On

☐ CLASSIC SOUL
PLSCD 116 / Aug '96 / Pulse

☐ CLASSIC SOUL
Harlem shuffle: Bob & Earl / Rescue me: Bass, Fontella / B-A-B-Y: Thomas, Carla / Knock on wood: Floyd, Eddie / Green onions: Cortez, Dave 'Baby' / Dancing in the street: Reeves, Martha / My guy: Wells, Mary / (Sittin' on) The dock of the bay: Sledge, Percy / Tell it like it is: Neville, Aaron / Drift away: Gray, Dobie / Stand by me: King, Ben E. / All I could do was cry: James, Etta / When a man loves a woman: Sledge, Percy / Wake up everybody: Melvin, Harold & The Bluenotes / I'll say a little prayer: Reeves, Martha / Ride captain ride: Blues Image / It's in his kiss (The shoop shoop song): Everett, Betty / Soul man: Sam & Dave
SUMCD 4151 / Sep '97 / Summit

☐ CLASSIC SOUL MASTERCUTS VOL.1
Paradise: Hutson, Leroy / My sensitivity: Vandross, Luther / When love calls: Atlantic Starr / Love you anyway: Cameo / Much too much: Miller, Marcus / Feels like I'm falling in love: Bar-Kays / Try love again: Natural Four / Annie May: Cole, Natalie / My destiny: McClain, Alton & Destiny / Wanna hold on to you: Loose Change / How can you live without love: Terrel, Jean / Never like this: Weather Girls
CUTSCD 38 / Jun '97 / Beechwood

☐ CLASSIC SOUL MIX
Satisfaction guaranteed: Melvin, Harold & The Bluenotes / Love on a mountain top: Knight, Robert / Jimmy Mack: Reeves, Martha / It's in his kiss (the shoop shoop song): Everett, Betty / Soul man: Sam & Dave / In crowd: Gray, Dobie / My guy: Wells, Mary / Saturday night at the movies: Drifters / Knock on wood: Floyd, Eddie / Stand by me: King, Ben E. / Hey girl don't bother me: King, Ben E. / BABY: Thomas, Carla / Duke of Earl: Chandler, Gene / Harlem shuffle: Bob & Earl
ECD 3071 / Jan '95 / K-Tel

☐ CLASSIC SUBBASE (Hard To Find Old School Breakbeat Anthems)
Far out: Sonz Of A Loop Da Loop Era / Slammer: Krome & Time / Tell me why: Wallace, Rachel / Future sound: Phuture Assassins / I feel this way: M&M/ Rachel Wallace / This sound is for the underground: Krome & Time / Hardcore will never die: Q-Bass / Weird energy: DJ Hype / Life (hands to heaven): D'Cruze & Rachel Wallace / Fireball: Timebase / Bad boy: Mad Ragga Jon / Funky hardcore: Q-Bass
SUBBASECD 5 / Apr '97 / Suburban Base

☐ CLASSIC TO THE CORE VOL.2
BSECD 2 / May '96 / Bass Section

☐ CLASSICA
39101632 / Jan '97 / Hyperium

☐ CLASSICAL INSTRUMENT TRADITIONS
VICG 52622 / Feb '96 / JVC World Library

☐ CLASSICAL SWING
My reverie: Crosby, Bing / Hungarian dance no.5: Thornhill, Claude & His Orchestra / Anitra's dance: Kirby, John Sextet / Anvil chorus: Miller, Glenn Orchestra / Prelude in c sharp minor: Cole, Nat 'King' / None but the lonely heart: Sinatra, Frank / Interpretation swing de Bach: South, Eddie/Django Reinhardt/Stephane Grappelli / Flight of the bumble bee: James, Harry Orchestra / Till the end of time: Como, Perry / Lamp is low: Dorsey, Tommy & His Orchestra / Elegie: Tatum, Art / Mexican hat dance: Brown, Les & His Orchestra / If you are but a dream: Dorsey, Jimmy & His Orchestra / Story of a starry night: Miller, Glenn Orchestra / Boyd meets Stravinsky: Raeburn, Boyd & His Orchestra / Who is Sylvia: Sullivan, Maxine / Bach up to me: Waller, Fats / I'm always chasing rainbows: Garland, Judy / I love you: Sinatra, Frank / Moon love: Bailey, Mildred
308672 / 20 Apr '98 / Hallmark

☐ CLASSICAL TRADITIONS (Music From Central Asia/2CD Set)
C 56003536 / Nov '93 / Ocora

☐ CLASSICAL TURKISH MUSIC
CMT 2741013 / Sep '95 / La Chant Du Monde

☐ CLASSICS FROM THE TERRACES (Passionate Music For A Passionate Game)
3984234862 / 18 May '98 / Warner Bros.

☐ CLASSICS OF 1975
RNCD 2048 / Apr '94 / Rhino

☐ CLASSICS OF SUPERSTITION, THE (2CD Set)
SUPER 2816CD / Dec '96 / Superstition

☐ CLASSICS SAMPLER
CLASSICS 99 / Apr '95 / Classics

☐ CLASSIQUES DES CLUBS (2CD Set)
TRC 1012 / 13 Oct '97 / Total Recall

☐ CLASSIX ALBUM, THE (2CD Set)
Trancemission: Genetic / LSD: Hallucinogen / Aliens: Hallucinogen / Teleport: Man With No Name / Space Midi: Omputer / Double dragons: Doof / Fat Buddha: Black Sun / Optimum creakage: Green Nuns Of The Revolution / Tornado: Phreaky / Butterfly: Avi & Rami / DMT: Psychedelic Masters / Tantra mantra: Spacetribe / Utopia: Mandala / Time and space: Infinity Project / Time and space: Infinity Project / Blue psychopumbs: Elysium / Dig a jig: Baba G
BFLCD 28 / 12 Jan '98 / Butterfly

☐ CLEETHORPES STORY, THE
Can you imagine that: Jenkins, Norma / If I was a kid: Kennedy, Billy / SOS: Today's People / I'm your pimp: Skull Snaps / Your autumn of tomorrow: Crow / Gig: Raw Soul / I've got the need: Spooky & Sue / Spring rain: Silvetti / Boogie with your baby: Willie J / Cut your motor off: Black Nasty / Summer in the parks: East Coast Connection / Girl you better wake up: Liberty / Broadway sissy: Roscoe & Friends / Lady lady lady: Boogie Man Orchestra / You're the cream of the crop: Maurice, Andre / What took you so long: Woodruff, Stanley / Never gonna let you go: Jobell Orchestra / Hipit: Hosanna / If you really need a friend: Foster, Bobby / If I had my way: Troy Keys / What makes her a woman: Reed, Danny / What's happening to this love affair: Hunt, Danny / Soon everything's gonna be alright: 3rd Time Around / What about love: Marboo / Long gone: Flemming, Debbie
GSCD 086 / Mar '97 / Goldmine

☐ CLIMAX (Hi Energy Anthems From Start To Finish)
You think you're a man / Action / Feels like I'm in love / Male stripper / Jump, jump (a little higher) / Gimme gimme gimme (a man after midnight) / Let me feel it / Stand by your man / Rhinestone cowboy / These boots are made for walking / I feel the earth move / Relax
ECD 3200 / Mar '95 / K-Tel

☐ CLOAK AND DAGGER
SVCD 6 / 11 Aug '97 / Shocking Vibes

☐ CLOCKWORK ORANGE (Ibiza Experience)
HF 48CD / Nov '95 / PWL

☐ CLOSE TO THE HEART
Through Bucky's eyes: Gettel, Michael / Gabriel's dream: Mann, Brian / Portraits: Brewer, Spencer / Gemina: Illenberger, Ralf / Jonathan's lullaby: Stein, Ira / Summer's child: Lanz, David / Back home: Lauria, Nando / Je t'aime: Mann, Brian / Old house is silent: Gettel, Michael / Memory: Rumbel, Nancy / Another star in the sky: Arkenstone, David / Return to the heart: Lanz, David / Shape of her face: Whalen, Michael
ND 63918 / Apr '95 / Narada

☐ CLOSE TO THE HEART
NSCD 019 / May '95 / Newsound

☐ CLOSED ON ACCOUNT OF RABIES (A Musical Tribute To Edgar Allan Poe)
5364802 / 26 Jan '98 / Mercury

☐ CLOSET CLASSICS VOL.2
Everything starts with an E: Ezee Posse / Satan's butterfly ball: Boy George / Deliverance: Ezee Posse / Let love shine: Amos / You can have it all: Gallagher, Eve / Misunderstood: Gallagher, Eve / Dreamtime: Zee / Love on love: Ezee Posse / Same thing in reverse: Boy George / Love is leaving: Boy George / Generations of love: Jesus Loves You / Broadway: Kinky Roland / Church of freedom: Amos / Come away: Amos
IMPCD 002 / Apr '97 / More Protein

☐ CLOSET POP FOLK
PYCD 2 / Jul '97 / Pop Psycle

☐ CLOSET POP FREAK
PYCD 1 / Jul '97 / Pop Psycle

☐ CLOUDS (21 Instrumental Moods)
Windmills of your mind / Just for you / Someone to watch over me / You've got a friend / This masquerade / Amanda / Cavatina / What are you doing for the rest of your life / Laura Jane / Gymnopedie / Nearness of you / Clouds / Shadow of your smile / Secret love / Air on a g-string / This guy's in love with you / Till there was you / Very thought of you / Moon river / Another suitcase in another hall
EMPRCD 605 / Jun '96 / Emporio

☐ CLOUDWATCH VOL.1
SCS 001 / May '97 / Sonic Soul

☐ CLUB - JUST DANCE IT (2CD Set)
560012 / Jan '97 / Westcom

☐ CLUB 2 DEF (4CD Set)
BDRCD 13 / Apr '96 / Breakdown

☐ CLUB 4 CLUB (4CD Set)
ZYX 740052 / 26 May '98 / ZYX

☐ CLUB 4 LIFE (2CD Set)
AVEXCD 49 / Aug '96 / Avex

☐ CLUB ACID
BB 035244CD / May '96 / Broken Beat

☐ CLUB BOMBERS VOL.2
ZYX 811042 / May '97 / ZYX

☐ CLUB BUZZ '95
CUTZCD 95
CUTZBX 95 / Nov '95 / Rumour

☐ CLUB BUZZ VOL.1
CUTZCD 1 / Feb '95 / Rumour

☐ CLUB BUZZ VOL.2
CUTZCD 2 / Aug '95 / Rumour

☐ CLUB CLASS (2CD Set)
U sure do: Strike / Don't give me your life: Alex Party / Push the feeling on: Nightcrawlers / Always something there to remind me: Tin Tin Out / Reach up (papa's got a brand new pig bag): Perfecto All Stars / Two can play at that game: Brown, Bobby / Another night: MC Sar & The Real McCoy / Yeke yeke: Kante, Mory / Axel F (short stab): Clock / Shelter me: Circuit / You bring me joy: Rhythm Factor / Another star: Sledge, Kathy / What hope have I: Sphinx / Respect: Cheeks, Judy / Message of love: Love Happy / Spirit inside: Spirits / Sight for sore eyes: M-People / Rockin' my body: 49ers / Climax: Paperclip People / Embracing the sunshine: BT / Every time you touch me: Moby / Poison: Prodigy
RADCD 10 / Apr '95 / Global TV

☐ CLUB CLASS (2CD Set)
3984245692 / 3 Aug '98 / Warner ESP

☐ CLUB CLASSICS (2CD Set)
ZYX 811532 / 22 Jun '98 / ZYX

☐ CLUB CLIMAX
NRCDCOM 1 / 6 Apr '98 / Neoteric

☐ CLUB CONNECT (2CD Set)
Timber: Coldcut / Deep menace: D'Menace / Spin spin sugar: Sneaker Pimps / What would we do: DSK / Hideaway 1998: De'Lacy / Shout to the top: Fire Island & Loleatta Holloway / Don't stop: Ruff Driverz / Feeling good: Huff & Herb / High noon: Serious Danger / Disco tr-amba: Mistericky / Phunkee Muzeek: Shazzam / Voulez vous: Philly Beats / This is it: State Of Mind / Ajare: Way Out West / Fortunes: Dominion / Floribunda: Mothers Pride / 14 hours to save the world: Tomski / Hey: Rainey, Fatima / Don't play dead: Vapourheadz / Yim: Jez & Choopy / Peak time: Gold, Graham / Medusa: Arrakis / Horns of Jericho: DJ Supreme / Get ready to bounce: Brooklyn Bounce / Windows 98: SIL / Timber: Coldcut / Don't stop: Ruff Driverz / Feeling good: Huff & Herb / Ajare: Way Out West / Horns of Jericho: DJ Supreme / Get ready to bounce: Brooklyn Bounce
FSVC 0001 / 6 Jul '98 / Future Sound & Vision

☐ CLUB CULTURE
STRSCD 3 / May '94 / Stress

☐ CLUB CULTURE UNCOVERED (2CD Set)
It's like that: Run DMC & Jason Nevins / Brimful of Asha: Cornershop / Never gonna let you down: Moore, Tina / Hideaway: De'Lacy / So good: Roberts, Juliet / Meet her at the love parade: Da Hool / Stay: Sash / Sunchyme: Dario G / Free: Ultra Nate / Renegade master: Wildchild / Another groove: Another Level / Rip groove: Double 99 / Make the world go round: Sandy B / Rude boy rock: Lionrock / Angel street: M-People / Wishing on a star: Jay Z & Mary J. Blige / Nobody better: Moore, Tina / Back to life: Ragga's Revenge / R U sleeping: Indo / Superstar: Novy, Tom & Eniac / Give me rhythm: Black Connection / Remember: BT / Gunman: 187 Lockdown / Don't stop: Ruff Driverz / Theme: Dreem Teem / Funny angels: Rob D / Ajare: Way Out West / Love love love here I come: Rollo Goes Mystic / Twister: Viper / Freedom: Miles, Robert / Naked and scared: Nayler, Maria / People hold on: Stansfield, Lisa & Dirty Rotten Scoundrels / Boundaries: Leena Conquest / Bullit: Schifrin, Lalo
RADCD 93 / 21 Mar '98 / Global TV

☐ CLUB EUROPA
PHAZE 1 / Jul '96 / Music Factory

☐ CLUB FORCE (2CD Set)
HMC 100022 / 10 Nov '97 / Happy Music

☐ CLUB HITS '98 (2CD Set)
TIMECD 0422 / 2 Mar '98 / Time Unlimited

☐ CLUB HITS 1997-1998 (Soundtrack To A Season)
Absurd: Fluke / Loaded: Primal Scream / Fools gold: Stone Roses / You're not alone: Olive / 6 underground: Sneaker Pimps / Bentley's gonna sort you out: Bentley Rhythm Ace / Three little birdies down beats: Chemical Brothers / Voodoo people: Prodigy / Ain't talkin' 'bout dub: Apollo 440 / Eat my goal: Collapsed Lung / Going out of my head: Fatboy Slim / We have explosive: Future Sound Of London / Elektrobank: Chemical Brothers / Toxygene: Orb / Risingson: Massive Attack / Strings for Yasmin: Tin Tin Out / Magic carpet ride: Mighty Dub Katz / Your face: Slacker / Belo horizonti: Heartists / Closer than close: Gaines, Rosie / Where love lives: Limerick, Alison / Dirty cash: Adventures Of Stevie V / Don't you want me: Felix / Higher state of consciousness: Winx / Spiller from Rio: Laguna / Seven days and one week: BBE / Offshore: Chicane & Power Circle / Nightmare: Brainbug / Free: DJ Quicksilver / Hold your head up high: Dlugosch, Boris / Partay feeling: B Crew / Naked and ashamed: Dylan Rhymes / Squirt: Fluke
VTDCD 167 / 8 Sep '97 / Virgin

☐ CLUB HITS 1998 (2CD Set)
Feel it: Tamperer & Maya / It's like that: Run DMC & Jason Nevins / La primavera: Sash / Sounds of wickedness: Tzant / Kiss the rain: Myers, Billie / Move on up: Trickster / Renegade master: Wildchild / To the world: Organ / Word is love: Voices Of Life / Make the world go round: Sandy B / Deeper love: Ruff Driverz / Somebody else's guy: Peniston, Ce Ce / Give me rhythm: Black Connection / Dreams: Smokin' Beats & Lyn Eden / Meet her at the love parade: Da Hool / Prix choc: De Crecy, Etienne / Brimful of Asha: Cornershop / Marbles: Black Grape / Shout to the top: Fire Island / Love shy: Blond, Kristine / All my life: K-Ci & Jo Jo / You make me feel: Stingily, Byron / Mama used to say: Azure / Let's get down: JT Playaz / Read my mind: Reeves, Conner / This is it: State Of Mind / Troubled girl: Ramirez, Karen / Stop by: Patterson, Rashsaan / Ain't that just the way: McNeal, Lutricia / Spend the night: Lewis, Danny J. / Club lonely: Groove Connektion / Gotta keep pushin': Z-Factor / Been a long time: Fog / Yim: Jez & Choopy / Blue fear: Armin / Planet violet: Nalin INC
TTVCD 2953 / 20 Apr '98 / Telstar TV

☐ CLUB HITS 1998
TIMECD 0452 / 3 Aug '98 / Time Unlimited

☐ CLUB IBIZA VOL.1 (3CD Set)
QPMCD 1 / Oct '95 / QPM

☐ CLUB IBIZA VOL.1 (Silver Edition - 3CD Set)
QPMXCD 1 / Apr '96 / QPM

☐ CLUB IBIZA VOL.2 (3CD Set)
QPMCD 6 / Sep '96 / QPM

☐ CLUB JAM VOL.1
STATION 01 / 1 Sep '98 / Station 1

☐ CLUB JAZZ
Curro's: Hancock, Herbie & Donald byrd / Chantized: Hubbard, Freddie / Confined few: Little, Booker / There will never be another you: Benson, George / Soul power: Hancock, Herbie / Prophecy: Byrd, Donald / Out of this world: Hancock, Herbie & Donald byrd / Invitation: Hancock, Herbie & Donald byrd / Stop look and listen: Terry, Clark & Miles Davis / Handbags and gladrags: Farlowe, Chris / That's what a friend will do: Lynn, Barbara / Our soul brothers: Dickens, Charles
CWNCD 2015 / Jul '96 / Javelin

☐ CLUB MASTERS VOL.1 (2CD Set)
Play my track: DJ Cook / Bass loud: DJ Yann / Keep on dreaming: Lisa Marie Experience / Wait a minute: DJ EBO / Shelford road (remodelled): Schumacher, Thomas / Cocaine kiss: Snowman / Do u wanna work it: XFunkshun / Moon man: Locate One / Wicked: Unreal & Mr. DJ Dario / Minifunk: Massimo Vivona / Beachball: Nalin & Kane / Raumpatrouille: Kosmonova / Tribe a go go: DJ Spice P / Funny walker: Difference / Got to be paid: Two Phunky People / System feedback: Phasis / Watch me dance: Liquid For Plastics / I say it again: Loving Loops / Move your body: Casseopaya / Triptronic: Static Rhythm / Ambulance: Attila
560123 / 1 Sep '97 / Legoan/Nova Tekk

☐ CLUB MEETS DUB VOL.1
ZD 5CD / Oct '95 / Zip Dog

☐ CLUB MEETS DUB VOL.2
ZD 8CD / Sep '96 / Zip Dog

☐ CLUB MEETS DUB VOL.3
One chill: Dub War / Green dub: Xenos / Toker smoker: Salvo Jets / Dis power: Digital Science / Dolphinalysis: Emperor Sly / Actions = reactions dub: One Love Sound / Earth a biosphere: Salt Tank & Australasia / Cold blooded hot head: Ha-Lo / Road to Basra: Shotgun Rockers / Smokin' weed: Scar'd For Life / Prophet a man: Bloomfield, Alan / Didgeridogs: Emperor Sly
ZD 14CD / Jul '97 / Zip Dog

☐ CLUB MEETS DUB VOL.4
ZD 19CD / 8 Jun '98 / Zip Dog

☐ CLUB MIX '96 VOL.1
State of independence: Summer, Donna / Ultra flava: Heller & Farley Project / Got myself together: Bucketheads / Passion (Do you want it right now): Gat Decor / Give me luv: Alcatraz / Movin': Mone / Keep the music strong: Bizarre Inc. / Higher state of consciousness: Wink, Josh / I'm ready: Size 9 / I wish: Skee Lo / Innocent: Addis Black Widow / Klubhopping: Klubb Heads / Your love: Inner City / America: Full Intention / Disco's revenge: Gusto / And I'm telling you I'm not going: Giles, Donna / Are you gonna be there: Up Yer Ronson / Mr. Friday night: Moorish, Lisa / Tell it to my heart: Q-Club / Disco 2000: Pulp / Naughty north and the sexy south: E-Motion / I've got the vibration: Black Box / I'll be there: 99th Floor Elevators / Wham bam: Candy Girls & Sweet Pussy Pauline / I feel love: Summer, Donna / Renegade master: Wildchild / I believe: Happy Clappers / Nighttrain: Kadoc / To the beat of the drum (la luna): Ethics / Get into the music: DJ's Rule / Electronic pleasure: N-Trance / I wanna be a hippy: Technohead
5354122 / Mar '96 / PolyGram TV

☐ CLUB MIX '96 VOL.2
5357652 / Jul '96 / PolyGram TV

☐ CLUB MIX '97 VOL.1 (2CD Set)
Breathe: Prodigy / Seven days and one week: BBE / Real vibration (want love): Express Of Sound / So in love with you: Duke / Blue skies: BT / I'm alive: Stretch n' Vern & Maddog / Keep pushin': Dlugosch, Boris & Booom / Not over yet: Grace / Don't go: Third Dimension & Julie McDermott / Cuba: El Mariachi / Believe in me: Mankey / Pearl's girl: Underworld / Help me make it: Huff & Puff / Run to you: Carroll, Dina / It's just another groove: Mighty Dub Katz / Follow the rules: Livin' Joy / Offshore: Chicane / Arkham asylum: Sasha / Move any mountain: Shamen / Survive: Brutal Bill & Saundra Marquez / Tall 'n' handsome: Outrage / Yeke yeke: Kante, Mory / United nations of house: United Nations Project / Stamp: Healy, Jeremy & Amos / Waterfall: Atlantic Ocean / Access: DJ Misjah & Tim / Jump to my beat: Wildchild / Floor-essence: Man With No Name / Closer to you: JX / Groovebird: Natural Born Groovers / Ultimate: Antic / 100%: Kiani, Mary / Second coming: Libido / Floor space: Our House / Wizard's of the sonic: Westbam
5532012 / Dec '96 / PolyGram TV

☐ CLUB MIX '97 VOL.2 (2CD Set)
Discoteque: U2 / Toxygene: Orb / Inferno: Souvlaki / Barrel of a gun: Depeche Mode / Rez: Underworld / You got the love: Source & Candi Staton / Take me by the hand: Submerged / Close to your heart: JX / Life's too short: Hole In One / Bellisima: DJ Quicksilver / Party people: Pianoman / Just playin': JT Playaz / Get up: Stingily, Byron / Sugar is sweeter: Bolland, C.J. / Runaway: Nu Yorican Soul & India / One and one: Miles, Robert / 7 days and one week: BBE / Zoe: Paganini Traxx / All I wanna do: Tin Tin Out / Love is all you need: 99 All Stars / Girls and boys: Hed Boys / Up to no good: Porn Kings / Resonance: Magic Alec / Ultra Flava: Heller & Farley Project / Have fun: Coma B / Beat is over: Basco / Amber groove: SAS / Antheum: Digital Blondes / London x-press: X-Press 2 / Remember me: Blueboy / Brooklyn beats: Deep, Scotti / Drive me crazy: Partizan / Mystery land: Y-Traxx / Wiggly world: Mr. Jack / Open up: Leftfield & John Lydon
5533642 / Feb '97 / PolyGram TV

☐ CLUB MIX '97 VOL.3 (2CD Set)
Free: Ultra Nate / Closer than close: Gaines, Rosie / Something's going on: Terry, Todd / Spin spin sugar: Sneaker Pimps / Naked and ashamed: Dylan Rhymes / Heaven on earth: Spellbound / My love is deep: Parker, Sara / Fly life: Basement Jaxx / Satisfied (take me higher): H2O / Misbehavin': Booth, Buddy / Invader: Koolworld Productions / Break it: Mr. Spring / Legends: Sacred Spirit / I love you...stop: Red Five / Difference: Funny Walker / Snow: ORN / Nightmare: Brainbug / Hondy (no access): Hondy / Deep (I'm falling deeper): Ariel / To be loved: Drayton, Lucas / Scared: Slacker / Flash: BBE / Go with da flow: Loop Da Loop / Hand in hand: Grace / Love on and on: Cato, Lorraine / Rock da house: Tall Paul / Cafe del mar: Energy 52 / With or without you: Kiani, Mary / Shine: Space Brothers / Never lost his hardcore: NRG / Can you feel the heat: Carle Younge Project / Someone: Ascension / Flowtation: De Moor, Vincent / Prophet: Bolland, C.J. / Catch: Sunscreem
5536912 / Jun '97 / PolyGram TV

☐ CLUB MIX '98 VOL.1 (2CD Set)
Renegade master: Wildchild / Never ever: All Saints / 187 lockdow: Gunman / Somebody else guy: Peniston, Ce Ce / Plastic dreams: Jaydee / Sugar is sweeter: Bolland, C.J. / Dreams: Smokin' Beats / Free: Ultra Nate / Spin spin sugar: Sneaker Pimps / It's over love: Terry, Todd / Digital: Goldie & KRS1 / Hideaway: De'Lacy / Nightbird: Convert / Let me be your fantasy: Baby D / You make me feel: Stingily, Byron / That's the way: Clock / Insomnia: Faithless / Meet her at the love parade: Da Hool / Sunchyme: Dario G / Jumpin': Lisa Marie Experience / Where love lives: Limerick, Alison / Push the feeling on: Nightcrawlers / Bomb: Bucketheads / I feel love: Summer, Donna / Disco'c revenge: Gusto / Naksaki EP: Doh, Ken / U girlds: Nush / Passion: Gat Decor / Don't want you me: Felix / I reuse: Somore & Damon Trueitt / Gift: Way Out West / Not over yet: Grace / Higher state of consciousness: Wink, Josh / There's nothing I won't do: JX / I'm alive: Stretch n' Vern / Seven days and one week: BBE / Bellissima: DJ Quicksilver / Loving you more: BT & Vincent Covello / Born slippy: Underworld
5550962 / 26 Jan '98 / PolyGram TV

☐ CLUB NATION (2CD Set)
Shout to the top: Fire Island & Loleatta Holloway / Professional widow: Amos, Tori / Want love: Hysteric Ego / All that matters: Louise / Bellissima: DJ Quicksilver / Choose life: PF Project & Ewan McGregor / Love shy: Blond, Kristine / Give me rhythm: Black Connection / Let me show you: Camisra / I'm alive: Stretch n' Vern / Stop: Spice Girls / Promise: Essence / Plastic dreams: Dee, Jay / You make me feel (mighty real): Stingily, Byron / Brimful of asha: Cornershop / Somebody else's guy: Peniston, Ce Ce / Anytime: Nu Birth / Free: Ultra Nate / Closer than close: Gaines, Rosie / Music of my mind: Adam F / Make the world go round: Sandy B / Never ever: All Saints / Fusion: Vath, Sven / Meet her at the love parade: Da Hool / Here's where the story ends: Nelson, Shelley / Who am I: Beenie Man / It's like that: Run DMC & Jason Nevins / Sunchyme: Dario G / Insomnia: Faithless / Renegade master 98: Wildchild / Gotta keep pushin': Z-Factor / Bamboogie: Bamboo / Keep on dancin': Perpetual Motion / Seven days and one week: BBE / Let me entertain you: Williams, Robbie
VTDCD 180 / 23 Mar '98 / Virgin

☐ CLUB PARTY, THE (Midtown 10th Anniversary)
MIDCD 02 / Jun '97 / Midtown

☐ CLUB SALSA
Maracaibo: Morales, Noro / Babarabatiri: Prado, Perez & Benny More / Mambo inn: Ruiz, Hilton / Cao cao mani picao: Puente, Tito & Vicentico Valdes / De la rumba al cha cha cha: More, Benny / Mi tierra es asi: Raduenda Lima / Y su banda gigante pongan atencion: More, Benny / Te confundo: Ng La Banda / Take the 'A' train: Puente, Tito / Mambo Parisienne: Mancini, Henry / Raindrops in Rio: Mancini, Henry / Cherry pink and apple blossom white: Prado, Perez / Me sube la fiebre: Calzado, Ruben & His Latin Orchestra / Que bueno baila usted: More, Benny / Por eso te llaman gil: Alvarez, Adalberto / Adorado Guajira: Gonzalez, Celina / Facundo: Valdes, Merceditas / Ayudame protegeme la musica nuestra musica: Alonso, Pacho
74321578192 / 27 Apr '98 / Camden

☐ CLUB SATURN
BDRCD 17 / Oct '96 / Breakdown

☐ CLUB SKA '67 (Whine & Grine)
Guns of Navarone: Skatalites / Phoenix city: Alphonso, Roland / Shanty town: Dekker, Desmond / Broadway jungle: Flames / Contact: Richards, Roy / Guns fever: Brooks, Baba / Rub up, push up: Hinds, Justin / Dancing mood: Wilson, Delroy / Stop making love: Gaylads / Pied piper: Marley, Rita / Lawless Street: Soul Brothers / Ska-ing West: Sir Lord Comic / Copasetic: Rulers
IMCD 254 / 20 Apr '98 / Island

☐ CLUB SKA 1996
Shame and scandal: Skanga / Split personality: Skatalites / Move it girl and swank: Buru, Mento / Jungle beat: Rico / Polvora Negra: Publico, Desorden / One Day: Maroon Town / Fits: International Beat / Birthday Girl: Nutty Boys / Maxwell Smart: Toasters / Save a bread save a toast: Dr. Ring Ding / Look pon you: Intensified / Only 16: Golding, Lynval & Neville Staples / Mr.D: Ngobo ngobo / Makin' whopie: Allstonians / Conquering ruler: Morgan, Derrick / Hand in hand: Forest Hillbillies / Alcohol: Porkers / Madness: Selecter / Set me up another one: Bim Skala Bim
JAMDCD 001 / 3 Aug '98 / Jamdown

☐ CLUB TOGETHER IBIZA
CDEMTVD 134 / Sep '96 / EMI TV

☐ CLUB TRIBUNE, THE (Compiled By DJ Moguai) (2CD Set)
Sound: Humate / Cum on: DJ HMC / Jack the beat: Wicked Wipe / Substance: Incisions / Fuck up: Caunos / Da phonk: Elektrochemie UK / Excitement: Saturday Night Life / Metrum reflex: Norman / Tryout: Dit / Chord memory: Pooley, Ian / Siren: DJ Misjah / Our music: FEOS & MSO / Shogun: Direct Drive / Watchman's theme: Watchmen 2 / Torqueflight: DJ Moguai / Sulk: Encephaloid Disturbance / Toggle: Tan Ru / To the sky: Pump Panel / Take over: Oshawa / Forerunner: Natural Born Groovers
SPV 08938762 / Aug '96 / SPV

☐ CLUB UK (Mixed By Biko & Steve Harvey/2CD Set)
Crazy man: Blast / Feel so right: Solution / Do that to me: Lisa Marie Experience / Want love: Hysteric Ego / Let's groove: Morel, George / Up to no good: Porn Kings / Sound of Eden: Shades Of Rhythm / Question: Seven Grand Housing Authority / So in love with you: Duke / Into your heart: 6 By 6 / I feel so good: Totalis / Love resurrection: Floor Federation / Klubhopping: Klubb Heads / Tall 'n' handsome: Outrage / Le voie de soleil: Subliminal Cuts / Jus' come: Cool Jack / Ultra flava: Farley & Heller / Keep pushing: Dlugosch, Boris & Booom / Blue skies: BT & Tori Amos / Huff 'n' puff: Puff Dogs / Curse of voodoo ray: May, Lisa / Dirty games: Groove Committee / Two fatt guitars: Direckt / Cangica: Mighty Dub Katz / Blue: LaTour / U can abuse my body: Bruno, Tony / Access: DJ Misjah & Tim / Gift: Way Out West
FIRMCD 9 / Dec '96 / Firm

☐ CLUB VIBE
JAPECD 106
JAPEPX 106 / Feb '96 / Escapade

☐ CLUB X:PRESS
XPS 1CDU / May '95 / X-Press

☐ CLUB ZONE
Show me love: Robin S / Real vibration (I want your love): Express Of Sound / Celebrate the love: Zhivago / People hold on: Lisa & Tori / You're the one: AT Project / Jump up in the air: London Boy / If Madonna calls: Vasquez, Junior / Take me away: Respect / Get freaky: Bass Symphony / Blow job: Shocking Rose / Funk phenomenon: Van Helden, Armand / You make me feel: Real DJ / It must be love: Club Freaks / Fill me up: Libra
DC 881322 / Jul '97 / Disky

☐ CLUBBED OUT IN IBIZA (2CD Set)
Voyager: Mr. Spring / Superstar: Novy & Eniac / Beat goes on: All Seeing I / Feels so right: Almonds solution / Desire: BBE / Testify: Stingily, Byron / Ghetto girl: Mighty Dub Katz / Sugar: Mr. Pink / Deeper: Serious Danger / Bad girls: Burger Queen / Somethings going on: Terry, Todd / Can U feel it: CLS / Feel it: Tamperer / On da run: Da Boss / Burning: Baby Bumps / Disco rouge: Disco Rouge / Give a little love: Invisible Man / Energy: Disco Droids / Touch me: Full Frequency / Can U feel it: QED / Kick the party: Ruff Da Menace / Freak da funk: Freak Da Funk / Jupiter: Karma / Get with it: Quench / Espiritu de Ibiza: Miguel & Marco / House it up: D'Menace / I believe: Dance Federation / Space mac: Space Mac / Hooligan: Da Hooloigan / It's not over: James & Ryder
MMCCD 010 / 3 Aug '98 / Massive

☐ CLUBBED TO DEATH
RDCD 001 / Feb '95 / RDR

☐ CLUBBIN' (Dance For A Generation - 2CD Set)
Turn it up: Busta Rhymes / Remember: BT / Kung FU: 187 Lockdown / Rude boy rock: Lionrock / Superstar: Novy, Tom & Eniac / Move on up: Trickster / Hideaway: DeLacy / So good: Roberts, Juliet / Can you feel it: CLS / RU Sleeping: Indo / Ain't going to Goa: Alabama 3 / Nobody better: Moore, Tina / Theme: Dreem Teem / Heaven: Kinane / This is it: State Of Mind / Never ever: All Saints / Push it: Garbage / Breathe: Minogue, Kylie / Bamboogie: Bamboo / Belo horizonte: Heartists / Thank you: Winans, Bebe / Want love: Hysteric Ego / Ghetto heaven: Family Stand / It's like that: Run DMC / Renegade master: Wildchild / Fun: Da Mob & Jocelyn Brown / Shout to the top: Fire Island & Loleatta Holloway / Much love: Ama, Shola / Nobody's business: Peace By Piece / Life ain't easy: Cleopatra / Brimful of Asha: Cornershop / Sunchyme: Dario G / Troubled girl: Dario G / Spin spin sugar: Sneaker Pimps / Whine and grine: Prince Buster / You make me feel: Stingily, Byron / No no no: Destiny's Child / Uh la la la: Alexia / Naked and sacred: Nayler, Maria / Meet her at the love parade: Da Hool / Free: Ultra Nate / Boogie: Dive / Casual sub: ETA / Carneval de Paris: Dario G / Rock the funky beat: Natural Born Chillers
9548364262 / 4 May '98 / Warner ESP

☐ CLUBLAND (2CD Set)
You're not alone: Olive / Closer than close: Gaines, Rosie / Ecuador: Sash & Rodriguez / Flylife: Basement Jaxx / Make the world go round: Sandy B / Way: Funky Green Dogs / I love you...stop: Red 5 / Guidance: Kamillion / Oye como va: Puente, Tito & His Latin Ensemble / 6 underground: Sneaker Pimps / Help me make it: Huff & Puff / Scared: Slacker / Sound Of Eden: Casino / Woamnchild: Duke / I'll be your friend: Owens, Robert / What would we do: Sol Brothers / Morning light: Team Deep / I have peace: Strike / Shine: Space Brothers / Grooverbird: Natural Born Groovers / Flash: BBE / Armed and extremely dangerous: BBE / Encore une fois: Sash / Dance with me: Tin Tin Out / People hold on: Stansfield, Lisa & Dirty Rotten Scoundrels / Let's groove: Phat & Funky / Ready or not: Course / You got the love: Source & Candi Staton / My love is deeper: Parker, Sara / Out of my head 97: Marradonna / Harmonica track: Soul Boy / Flowtation: De Moor, Vincent / Footprint: Disco Citizens / Walkin' on up: DJ Prof X Or
TCD 2912 / Jun '97 / Telstar

☐ CLUBLAND VOL.2 (2CD Set)
Plastic dreams: *Jaydee* / Stay: *Sash* / Staxx: *Staxx* / Just gets better: *TJR* / Sandman: *Blueboy* / Freed from desire: *Gala* / Post modern sleaze: *Sneaker Pimps* / Gypsy boy gypsy girl: *Sharada House Gang* / Feel what you want: *Kristine W* / Magic carpet ride: *Mighty Dub Katz* / Anytime: *Nu Birth* / London thing: *Garcia, Scott* / Moment of my life: *D'Ambrosio, Bobby* / Hold your head up: *Problem Kids* / Clouds: *Problem Kids* / Flame: *Crustation* / Offshore: *Chicane* / Flaming June: *BT* / Cloudburst: *Niagra* / Your face: *Slacker* / Someone: *Ascension* / Home: *Chakra* / Rock the bells: *Kadoc* / Witch doktor: *Van Helden, Armand* / Be my baby: *Cappella* / Deep in you: *Livin' Joy* / No stoppin': *Big Band Experience* / Bit goes on: *Snakebite* / Playmate puzzle: *Discotecs* / Loverwoman: *Groove Kittens* / Put your faith in me: *Limerick, Alison* / Hypnotize: *D-Influence*
TTVCD 2928 / 15 Sep '97 / Telstar TV

☐ CLUBLIFE (2CD Set)
Renegade master: *Wildchild* / Make the world go round: *Sandy B* / So good: *Roberts, Juliet* / Spin spin sugar: *Sneaker Pimps* / B boy stance: *Freestylers* / Je regarde le DJ: *Encore* / Keep on pushin': *Z-Factor* / Saturday: *East 57th Street* / Good enough: *Milk Inc.* / Choose life: *PF Project* / Hideaway: *DeLacy* / Give me rhythm: *Black Connection* / So in love with you: *Duke* / I refuse (what you want): *Somore* / Dreams: *Smokin' Beats* / Mother's pride: *Floribunda Rose* / Yim: *Jez & Choopy* / Vamp: *Outlander* / Free: *Ultra Nate* / Love love love: *Rollo Goes Mystic* / Never let you go: *Moore, Tina* / Telefunkin': *N-Tyce* / Gunman: *187 Lockdown* / Don't stop: *Ruff Driverz* / Belo horizonti: *Heartists* / Beachball: *Nalin & Kane* / Twister: *Viper* / Magnificent: *Agent 00* / I feel divine: *SJ* / Dreem Teem theme: *Dreem Teem* / Stay: *Sash* / Get higher: *Black Grape* / I thought it was you: *Sex-O-Sonique* / Mighty high: *Revival 3000* / Missing you: *Blige, Mary J.* / Horns of Jericho: *DJ Supreme* / Open your mind '97: *Usura* / Lift me up: *Red 5* / Let a boy cry: *Gala* / That's the way: *Clock*
TTVCD 2946 / 23 Feb '98 / Telstar TV

☐ CLUBLIFE VOL.2 (2CD Set)
Mysterious times: *Sash* / Spank: *D'Menace* / El nino: *Agnelli & Nelson* / Real good time: *Alda* / Burnin': *Baby Bumps* / Feel it: *Tamperer* / Bounce with the massive: *Tzant* / Freaks come out: *Fisher, Cevin* / Cafe del mar: *Energy 52* / Music is the answer: *Tenaglia, Danny* / Never ever: *All Saints* / Deeper love: *Ruff Driverz* / Catch the light: *Wash, Martha* / Busiest rhymes: *Porn Kings & Young MC* / Kung fu: *187 Lockdown* / Found a cure: *Ultra Nate* / Heaven: *Kinane* / Treat infamy: *Rest Assured* / Let me show you: *Camisra* / To the world: *Organ* / Lover: *McFarlane, Rachel* / Take control: *State of mind* / Superstar: *Novy & Eniac* / Been a long time: *Fog* / Move on up: *Trickster* / Real good: *Double Six* / Anytime: *Nu Birth* / London Town: *JDS* / Masquerade: *Gerideau* / You are somebody: *Full Intention* / East west: *East West Connection* / All my life: *K-Ci & Jo Jo* / Fight for your right to party: *NYCC* / Nobody better: *Moore, Tina* / Turn back time: *Aqua* / Travelling man: *Studio 2* / Say the word: *Voices Of Life* / Carnaval de Paris: *Dario G*
TTVCD 2960 / 10 Aug '98 / Telstar TV

☐ CMP STORY VOL.1 (Breaking The Barriers Of Jazz/2CD Set)
CMPCD 2102 / 6 Apr '98 / CMP

☐ CMP STORY VOL.2 (Breaking The Barriers Of World Music/2CD Set)
CMPCD 2101 / 6 Apr '98 / CMP

☐ CMP STORY VOL.3 (Breaking The Barriers Of Rock/2CD Set)
CMPCD 2103 / 6 Apr '98 / CMP

☐ CMPLER VOL.1
CMPCD 5001 / 30 Mar '98 / CMP

☐ CMPLER VOL.2
CMPCD 5002 / 30 Mar '98 / CMP

☐ COAST TO COAST
Voice of America: *Dark Star* / American fool: *Green, Jack* / Better late than never: *XS* / How far Jerusalem: *Magnum* / Call of the wild: *Sabu* / Hold back the night: *Multi-Story* / Stand me up: *Statetrooper* / Dancin' on midnight: *White Sister* / Shoot for the heart: *Lawrence, Karen* / Surrender: *Joshua*
WKFMXD 96 / Jul '87 / FM

☐ COASTAL BREAKS VOL.1 (2CD Set)
AVEXCD 46 / Nov '96 / Avex

☐ COASTAL BREAKS VOL.2 (Mixed By Adam Freeland - 2CD Set)
Return to the force: *Age* / Drunk as a monk: *Banco De Gaia* / Posessed: *R-Kidz* / My beat box: *DJ Punk Rok* / Storm 3000: *Leftfield* / Boof 'n' baff 'n' biff: *Black Uhuru* / I saw the future: *Sabotage* / Mercury uno: *A Terran Collective* / Madness: *Uptown Connection* / Down: *Street technique* / Funky as...: *High Prime* / Chief rocka: *Beber* / Capricorn: *9 Nickel* / Reverberation: *Southside Reverb* / She's breaking up: *Biting Back* / Phat phuzz: *Silicon Valley Def Stars* / Timebomb: *Atomic Dog* / Doctors dentists and architects: *Blake* / Trip to genetica: *Tonic* / Blockhead: *Single Cell Orchestra* / Miami breaks: *PSS* / Drop da boom: *Freestylers* / Let it play: *Matthew B* / About that time: *ILS* / Twister: *Tipper* / Nightshift: *Makesome Breaksome* / Timber: *Coldcut* / Leone: *Almighty Beatfreakz* / Dawn of the standing wave: *Tsunami One*
REACTCDX 125
REACTCD 125 / 1 Jun '98 / React

☐ COCKNEY CHRISTMAS, A
Hark the herald angels sing / O little town of Bethlehem / Once in Royal David's City / See amid the winter's snow / While shepherd's watched their flocks by night / O come all ye faithful (adeste fidelis) / Jingle bells / Good King Wenceslas / Ding dong merrily on high / God rest ye merry gentlemen / Deck the halls / White Christmas / Twelve days of Christmas / First Noel / Away in a manger / Holly and the ivy / Gloucestershire wassail / Santa Claus is coming to town / Frosty the snowman / Rudolf the red nosed reindeer / Sleigh ride / Winter wonderland / Merry Christmas everybody / All I want for Christmas is my two front teeth / Rockin' around the Christmas tree / Jingle bell rock / I wish it could be Christmas every day / Merry Christmas everybody (reprise) / Happy Christmas war is over / Mistletoe and wine / Silent night / We wish you a merry Christmas
XMAS 005 / Dec '96 / Tring

☐ COCKNEY KINGS OF THE MUSIC HALL
CDSDL 413 / Oct '95 / Saydisc

☐ COCKTAILS
HEMP 19CD / 25 May '98 / Hydrogen Dukebox

☐ CODE OF THE STREETS, THE (2CD Set)
TOVCD 01 / 27 Oct '97 / Trouble On Vinyl

☐ COEUR DE FRANCE
La chavannee: *La Chavanee* / Polka du lac: *Blanchard, Jean & Eric Montbel* / Au point du jour: *Les Ecoliers De Saint Genest* / La marotte / Bourrees de Gatignol et de Leonard de la Vedrenne: *La Concorde Des Temps* / Valse a Dede: *Les Brayauds* / Le crab noir: *La Grande Bande Des Cornemuses* / Suite de bourrees: *Melusine* / Michel / Pause cafe / Grand frise: *Trio Cornemuse* / Le retour de la veillee / La polka des Coustouby: *Cafe Charbons* / Frere Nicolas: *Cafe Charbons* / Ego sum pauper/Valse a Bouffard: *Vielleux Du Bourbonnais*
B 6848 / May '97 / Auvidis/Ethnic

☐ COFFEE TABLE MUSIC (Sounds And Sountracks Mixed By Grantby)
How we used to live: *Brown Susan* / High over Glenelg: *Narcoleptics* / Chase scene 3: *Brothers Grimm* / Large block of flats: *Jobclub Music Workshop* / Glass shards: *Picturebox* / Timebooth: *Grantby* / Don't trust the brains trust: *Kaysound Fashion* / Vamos a la playa: *Emiliano* / R53: *Albert Hall* / Dementia pugilistica: *Lake, Kirk*
COTCD 018 / 22 Jun '98 / Cup Of Tea

☐ COLDKRUSHCUTS
Groover: *Funki Porcini* / Global chaos: *KT & Hex* / Sometimes: *2 Player & The Herbaliser* / Breaks: *DJ Vadim & Mark B* / Real kilter part 2: *Herbaliser* / Get your head down: *Vibert, Luke* / Goodbye cruel world: *London Funk Allstars* / Naked leaves: *Coldcut* / Spiral dub: *DJ Food* / Harmonic: *Hex* / Mod you: *Cabbageboy* / Readybrek: *DJ Toolz* / Creatures: *Amon Tobin* / Nightrous: *Peezee* / An unmarked grave: *Up Bustle & Out* / Revolutionary woman of the windmill: *Up Bustle & Out* / Mr. Chombee has the flaw: *Herbaliser* / Breaks of wrath: *DJ Food* / Alice Effekt: *DJ Food* / Glass: *Gideon* / Sunvibes: *DJ Food* / Oddly Godly: *EVA* / Going down: *Funki Porcini* / Forty winks: *Herbaliser* / B Boy: *DJ Vadim* / Headz still ain't ready: *DJ Vadim* / Aural prostitution: *DJ Vadim* / Electric lazyland: *9 Lazy 9* / Give it to me raw: *London Funk Allstars* / Broadcasting live from planet Blapps: *London Funk Allstars* / Today London, tomorrow the world: *London Funk Allstars* / Junkies bad trip: *London Funk Allstars* / Knee deep in the beats part 1: *London Funk Allstars* / Sign: *Coldcut* / Call me: *DJ Vadim* / Bass city roller: *DJ Food* / Mother: *Herbaliser* / Aural prostitution: *DJ Vadim* / Morning prayer: *DJ Vadim* / Dark lady: *DJ Food* / Lounge shiznitz: *DJ Vadim* / Love is what you need: *London Funk Allstars*
ZENCD 026LTD
ZENCD 026 / Feb '97 / Ninja Tune

☐ COLEURS SUD (Music From Southern France)
Nove dai corporacions: *Tesi, Riccardo & Patrick Vaillant* / Bruna de laguna: *Carlotti, Jean-Marie & Daniele Craighead/Riccardo Tesi* / Brouillard epais: *Une Anche Passe* / Tossa bonica: *Cobles* / Aquela des adrets: *Zephirin Castellon* / Revolunuit sia l'amour: *Jurie, Renat* / Gaztetasunak bainerabila: *Achiary, Benat* / Banbulak dantza: *Folc, Perlinpinpin* / Per non languir: *Carlotti, Jean-Marie* / Vivem totjorn en montanha: *Zephirin Castellon* / Sardana curta: *Cobles* / La mare de deu: *Achiary, Benat* / Lili purpurea: *Achiary, Benat* / La batalha d'Achos: *Folc, Perlinpinpin* / Lundi: *Jurie, Renat* / Un joen pastor quitava: *Jurie, Renat* / Ba nin adixkide bat: *Achiary, Benat* / Marche de la Saint Blaise: *Une Anche Passe*
B 6851 / Aug '97 / Auvidis/Ethnic

☐ COLLECTED SOUNDS, THE
SLIPCD 45 / Jun '96 / Slip 'n' Slide

☐ COLLECTED VOL.2
TLCCOLCD 2 / 27 Jul '98 / True Love Electronic

☐ COLLECTED WORKS - 15 YEARS OF MUSIC
SP 116CD / Oct '93 / Stony Plain

☐ COLLECTION FEDERICO GARCIA LORCA VOL.2
20106CD / Aug '97 / Sonifolk

☐ COLLECTION OF MODERN SOUL CLASSICS, A
Just loving you: *Andrews, Ruby* / Come back baby: *Justice Department* / I'm so glad you're mine: *Perkins, George* / Lonely girl: *Side Show* / Talkin': *Vee Gees* / Making new friends: *Tracy, Jeanie* / Girl, you're my kind of wonderful: *Relf, Bobby* / Girl I've been trying to tell you: *Ultimates* / Lightin' up: *Karim, Ty* / Teasin you again: *Tee, Willie* / Let's go fishing: *Turner Bros* / Dream: *Creations* / I need your love: *Woods, Ella* / Here stands a man who needs you: *Wilson, George* / Given up on love: *Thompson, Johnny* / If it's not love don't waste my time: *Johnson, Dorothy* / Have I really loved you: *Smoke* / Footsteps across your mind: *Shock* / Girl I love you: *Fisher, Shelley* / You're gone: *Hardin, Celest* / Better to bend than break: *Simmons, Cissie* / Colour him father: *Winstons* / Wash and wear love: *Vernado, Lynne*
GSCD 009 / Jan '93 / Goldmine

☐ COLLECTION, THE
APR 009CD / 3 Nov '97 / April

☐ COLLECTOR'S CHOICE VOL.1
JASCD 17 / 8 Jun '98 / Sarge

☐ COLORES DE CUBA
74321283392 / May '96 / Milan

☐ COLORS OF ZOTH OMMOG, THE
CDZOT 121 / Nov '94 / Zoth Ommog

☐ COLOURS - THE FULL SPECTRUM (2CD Set)
Hold on: *Nesby, Ann* / Heaven is calling: *Watford, Michael* / Send me love: *Da Mooch* / Come on: *Sabrynaah* / Touch of magic: *Tim Deluxe* / I like it: *Moraes, Angel* / Dancing in outer space: *Atmosfear* / It's you: *Chandler, Kerri* / L'ombelico del mondo: *Jovanotti* / Not much heaven: *Uptown Express* / Groove on: *Yo Yo Honey* / Way that you feel: *Adeva* / Harvest for the world: *Hunter, Terry* / Nobody's business: *H2O & Billie* / Ecravos de jo: *Chandler, Kerri* / Ncameu: *USG* / Do you really wanna love: *Deep Swing* / Club Lonely: *Cabrini, Greens & Cornbread* / Tick tock: *Chia Pet* / Somebody: *Green Flame & Mr. G* / Rollerblade: *Movin' Melodies* / Rain: *Wet Dreams* / Atom bomb: *DJ Pierre* / Can't fight the feeling: *Problem Kids* / No one loves you more than me: *Jones, Hannah* / Prayer: *Jephtecuerame*
LIMB 76CD / 27 Oct '97 / Limbo

☐ COLOURS OF THE WORLD
Mama yo / Charquia walla / Simera / Fire dance / Araguaney / Roga pa Sabta Barba / Drissa barani / Fan karaibo / Vanne ca maille la / Nihon minyo kumikyoku dai ichi-ban / Friarhalling / Dansa / 'Lfraj rabby / Jeu de harpe / Chant of the port keats men / Jansa
PS 66008 / Jun '97 / PlayaSound

☐ COLUMBIA - PRINCETOWN ELECTRONIC MUSIC CENTRE
805212 / Jun '98 / New World

☐ COLUMBIA GOSPEL 1938
DOCD 5487 / Nov '96 / Document

☐ COMBO VOCAL GROUPS VOL.1
Just once more: *Paramounts* / First day of school: *Ko-Kos* / I've got a feeling: *Native Boys* / Take my hand: *Echoes* / Fine fine baby: *Porter, Jake & The Laurels* / I love you: *Brother Woodman & The Chanters* / At midnite: *Nutones* / Where are you tonight: *Squires* / Let's give love a try: *Squires* / Watts: *Brother Woodman & The Chanters* / Darline: *Frazier, Ray & The Blenders* / Strange love: *Native Boys* / Oh dear beloved: *Ko-Kos* / Tears: *Native Boys* / On little blessing: *Belvin, Jesse* / (Why can't we be) as other lovers are: *Debonairs* / Honey babe: *Sharps* / Sunshine: *Ell, Carl* / Sweet Sue: *Starliters* / It all comes back to you: *Mason, Bill* / Darling stay with me: *Savoys* / Reap what you sow: *Moore, Gene & The Chimes* / Am I a fool: *Wilburn, Delmar* / Emmy Lou: *Frazier, Ray & The Blenders* / I'm such a lovin' man: *Sharps* / Oh darling: *Squires*
CDCHD 599 / 29 Jun '98 / Ace

☐ COMBUSTION EP
DDRAGCD 019 / 25 May '98 / Dope Dragon

☐ COME AGAIN (2CD Set)
Ode to Billy Joe: *Butler, John* / Submission: *Carlisle, Belinda & Radiator* / When you're in love with a beautiful woman: *Cecil* / Jealousy: *Dubstar* / Air that I breathe: *Feline* / Baker Street: *Foo Fighters* / We have all the time in the world: *Fun Lovin' Criminals* / Where did our love go: *Gluebound* / Go buddy go: *Jesus Jones* / It started with a kiss: *Kenickie* / Duchess: *My Life Story* / Starman: *Octopus* / Why should I love you: *Scott, Mike* / Wish you were here: *Sparklehorse & Thom Yorke* / You're my best friend: *Supernaturals* / For ever and ever: *Terrorvision* / Ziggy Stardust: *White Buffalo* / Rhinestone cowboy: *White Town* / Ev'ry time we say goodbye: *Williams, Robbie* / See Emily play: *Wireless* / Martha my dear: *World Party* / Do wah diddy diddy: *Lachlan Young, Murray*
CDCOMAG 001 / 8 Sep '97 / EMI

☐ COME BACK TO ERIN
Come back to Erin: *O'Hara, Maureen* / Do you remember that night, love: *O'Hara, Maureen* / Next market day: *O'Hara, Maureen* / Nora Lee/I once loved a boy: *O'Hara, Maureen* / I'll take you home again Kathleen: *Parker, Frank* / Galway Bay: *Parker, Frank* / Danny Boy: *Parker, Frank* / Peggy: *Harrington, Pat* / Donnaree: *Quinn, Carmel* / Spinning wheel: *Quinn, Carmel* / If I were a blackbird: *Quinn, Carmel* / Irishmeela: *Quinn, Carmel* / Give him to me: *O'Hara, Maureen* / He moved through the fair: *O'Hara, Maureen* / Come to me, bend to me: *Parker, Frank* / Rose of Tralee: *Downey, Morton*
CK 53630 / Mar '97 / Columbia
4896832 / 2 Mar '98 / Columbia

☐ COME DANCING FAVOURITES
Let's face the music and dance / Carousel waltz / Hernando's hideaway / Lambada de amor / Gito / Tales from the Vienna woods / Mambo paradiso / Lambada / Tie a yellow ribbon round the old oak tree / Swingin' safari / Hello Dolly / Americana / Johnny's mambo / El Beso / Tea for two / Tango Verano / 1001 nights / Blue tango
308172 / 13 Oct '97 / Hallmark

☐ COME DANCING QUICKSTEP
When you wish upon a star / It's a hap hap happy day / Moonlight avenue / Give a little whistle / You're dancing in my heart / In the middle of a dream / Where or when / Chicago / Apple for the teacher / Begin the beguine / In the still of the night / Walk in the black forest / L A international airport / Don't say goodbye / There will never be another you
306112 / Jan '97 / Hallmark

☐ COME DANCING SALSA
Taka taka-ta / Cogo el camaron / Pare cochero / Lo que me paso en la / Mi chiquita / El coco / Eso que anda / Se muere la tia / Yo no quiero que seas celosa / El bobo de la yuca / La protesta de los chivos / Santa Barbara / Longina / Los sitios entero
306102 / Jan '97 / Hallmark

☐ COME GO WITH US (25 Classic Northern Soul Tracks From The Vaults Of EMI)
Pretty little girl: *Smith, George* / I hurt on the other side: *Cook, Jerry* / With all that's in me: *Johnson, Marv* / You've got to look up: *Drapers* / You've got the love: *Little, Rosie* / What's gonna happen to me: *Hodges, Charles* / I can't help loving you: *Breedlove, Jimmy* / She blew a good thing: *Height, Donald* / Don't cry at the party: *Mad Lads* / Baby I need you: *Williams, T.J.* / No more dreams: *Patton, Alexander* / Time will change: *Inverts* / I'm not the one: *Thieves* / Can't take no more: *Turnarounds* / No explanation needed: *Themes* / River of tears: *Banks, Barbara* / You lied, I cried, love died: *Mosley, Tommy* / One day love: *Dodson, Tommy* / Watch yourself: *Nature Boys* / Sweet sweet love: *Sheen, Bobby* / Turn around baby: *Lena & The Deltanettes* / You're a puzzle: *Jive Five* / Come go with me: *Jones, Gloria* / Queen is on her knees: *Tynes, Maria* / Wrong girl: *Showmen* / Cover girl: *Spencer, Carl*
GSCD 084 / Sep '96 / Goldmine

☐ COME ON PEEL THE NOISE
TANGCD 11 / Jul '95 / Tangerine

☐ COMEDIENS 1930-1939 (2CD Set)
982742 / Jun '93 / EPM

☐ COMEDIES/OPERAS FROM SRI LANKA
CMT 2741006CD / Jul '95 / La Chant Du Monde

☐ COMIN' HOME TO THE BLUES VOL.1
She's into something: *Cray, Robert* / You can't judge a book by the cover: *Buchanan, Roy* / Two fisted mama: *Webster, Katie* / Blues overtook me: *Musselwhite, Charley* / Don't you call that boogie: *Hopkins, Lightnin'* / That woman is poison: *Thomas, Rufus* / Everyday I have the blues: *Memphis Slim* / Sonny's whoopin' the doop: *Terry, Sonny* / I think I got the blues: *Dixon, Willie* / What am I living for: *Brown, Clarence 'Gatemouth'* / Don't take advantage of me: *Winter, Johnny* / Who's lovin' you tonite: *Eaglin, Snooks* / Moon is full: *Collins, Albert* / Jump for joy: *Taylor, Koko* / Whole lotta lovin': *Professor Longhair* / Drinkin' wine spo-dee-o-dee: *Otis, Johnny*
MCCD 016 / Feb '91 / Music Club

☐ COMIN' HOME TO THE BLUES VOL.1-3 (3CD Set)
MCBX 002 / Jan '93 / Music Club

☐ COMIN' HOME TO THE BLUES VOL.2
Little red rooster: *Howlin' Wolf* / I'm a man: *Diddley, Bo* / Your funeral and my trial: *Williamson, Sonny Boy* / Wee wee hours: *Berry, Chuck* / First time I met the blues: *Guy, Buddy* / Mannish boy: *Waters, Muddy* / Dust my broom: *James, Elmore* / Juke: *Little Walter* / So many roads, so many trains: *Rush, Otis* / Tell mama: *James, Etta* / Walking the blues: *Dixon, Willie* / Sugar mama: *Hooker, John Lee* / I asked for water (she gave me gasoline): *Howlin' Wolf* / Bring it to Jerome: *Diddley, Bo* / Worried life blues: *Berry, Chuck* / Got my mojo working: *Waters, Muddy* / Don't start me talkin': *Williamson, Sonny Boy* / In the mood: *Hooker, John Lee* / Chicago bound: *Rogers, Jimmy* / Wang dang doodle: *Taylor, Koko* / I'd rather go blind: *James, Etta* / Diggin' my potatoes: *Washboard Sam* / Reconsider baby: *Fulson, Lowell* / My baby: *Little Walter*
MCCD 026 / May '91 / Music Club

☐ COMIN' HOME TO THE BLUES VOL.3
When you see the tears from my eyes: *Guy, Buddy* / Goin' mad blues: *Hooker, John Lee* / All my love in vain: *Williamson, Sonny Boy* / Standing at the burial ground: *McDowell, 'Mississippi' Fred* / Hi-heel sneakers: *Tucker, Tommy* / She's 19 years old: *Waters, Muddy* / How blue can you get: *Collins, Albert* / Hoodoo man: *Wells, Junior* / No friend around: *Hooker, John Lee* / Don't know where I've been: *Diddley, Bo* / Christo redemptor: *Musselwhite, Charley* / Blue and lonesome: *McPhee, Tony & Billy Boy Arnold* / Hoochie coochie man: *Waters, Muddy* / Baptize me in wine: *Hawkins, Screamin' Jay* / Sad hours: *Little Walter* / One room country shack: *Butterfield, Paul*
MCCD 044 / Sep '91 / Music Club

☐ COMING DOWN
CRECD 135 / Feb '95 / Creation

☐ COMING ON STRONG (2CD Set)
NSCD 004 / Feb '95 / Newsound

☐ COMING ROUND AT CALUM'S
OCH 3CD / 3 Nov '97 / Ochre

☐ COMMITTED TO JUNGLE
VZS 16CD / Apr '95 / Vizion Sound

☐ COMMON GROUND - CELTIC VOICE
'O bhean a 'ti: *Brennan, Maire* / Mary of the south seas: *Finn, Tim & Neil* / Tomorrow: *Bono & Adam Clayton* / Cavan potholes: *Shannon, Sharon* / Help me to believe: *Brady, Paul* / On Raglan Road: *O'Connor, Sinead* / As I roved out: *Kennedy, Brian* / Night before Larry was stretched: *Costello, Elvis* / Mna na h'eireann: *Bush, Kate* / Whistling low/Errigal: *Spillane, Davy & Donal Lunny* / My heart's tonight in Ireland: *Irvine, Andy* / Cathain: *O'Maonlai, Liam* / Bogie's bonnie belle: *Moore, Christy*
PRMTVCD 1 / May '96 / Premier/EMI

☐ COMPACT D'AFRIQUE
Adjani Muana Kini: *Mabele, Aurlus* / Iyole: *Kanda Bongo Man* / Masquereau: *Les Quatre Etoiles* / Sane-mamadou: *Tchico & Les Officers Of African Music* / Lascar Pa Kapi: *Choc Stars* / Izia: *Papa Wemba Et Mavuela* / Le bon samaritain: *Sukami, Teddy*
CDORB 907 / Aug '86 / Globestyle

☐ COMPAGNU TI MANNU
TA 012CD / Apr '95 / Robi Droli

☐ COMPATED CATS
CLCD 4444 / 31 Jul '98 / Collector/ White Label

☐ COMPETING HIGHLAND DANCER, THE (Highland & National Dances From Beginners To Open Dancers)

Pas de basque / Pas de basque and highcut / Highland fling 4 steps / Highland fling 6 steps / Sword dance 2\1 / Sword dance 3\1 / Sword dance 2\2 / Seann triubhas 3\1 / Seann triubhas 4\2 / Hullachan 1\2 / Hullachan full / Strathspey and reel of tulloch / Strathspey and highland reel / Broadswords 3\1 / Flora macdonald 4 steps / Scottish lilt 4 steps / Scottish lilt 6 steps / Village maid 4 steps / Hielan laddie 4 steps / Barracks johnnie 4 steps / Sailors hornpipe 4 steps / Sailors hornpipe 5 steps / Irish jig 4 steps / Irish jig 5 steps / Shepherd's crook

CDITV 516 / Jul '90 / Scotdisc

☐ COMPILATION OF DELETED DIALOGUE VOL.1, A (2CD Set)

MORTCD 070 / 27 Oct '97 / Mortarhate

☐ COMPILATION OF WARPED MUSIC

SD 1207CD / 3 Aug '98 / Side One

☐ COMPILATIONS

NATCD 50 / Feb '95 / Nation

☐ COMPLETE 'D' SINGLES COLLECTION VOL.1, THE (4CD Set)

Can't play hookey: Noack, Eddie / My steady dream: Noack, Eddie / Mom and Dad I love you too: Travis, Al / He brough us together: Travis, Al / Cotton picker: Watts, Wortham / Lonesome: Watts, Wortham / Never meant for me: Carl, Utah / Treasured memories: Carl, Utah / I can't find the doorknob: Jimmy & Johnny / Keep telling me: Jimmy & Johnny / Baby, when the sun goes down: Douglas, Tony / World in my arms: Douglas, Tony / Talk to me lonesome heart: O'Gwynn, James / Changeable: O'Gwynn, James / I want to be where you're gonna be: Singleton, Margie / Shattered kingdom: Singleton, Margie / Chantilly lace: Big Bopper / Purple people eater meets the witch doctor: Big Bopper / Gonna pack up my toubles: Hall, Sonny & The Echoes / My big fat baby: Hall, Sonny & The Echoes / Walking away: Dollar, Johnny / No memories: Dollar, Johnny / Texas Alaska: Jackson, Ray / Alaska: Jackson, Ray / I played the fool: Four B's / Love eternal: Four B's / Don't hold me to a vow: Moncrief, Bobby / Here is my heart: Moncrief, Bobby / Dreaming in vain: Sheets, Sonny / Wheels: Terry & The Pirates / Blues got me: Bond, Eddie / Standing in your window: Bond, Eddie / Same old fool: Barber, Glen / Tomorrow: Barber, Glen / Hello sadness: Barber, Glen / Daydreaming again: Bragg, Doug / If I find my dreamgirl: Bragg, Doug / Have blues, will travel: Noack, Eddie / Price of love: Noack, Eddie / Ohh wow: Dee & Patty / Sweet lovin' baby: Dee & Patty / Understand: Forrer, Johnnie / Fools paradise: Forrer, Johnnie / Blue memories: O'Gwynn, James / You don't want to hold me: O'Gwynn, James / Draggin' the fiddle: Choates, Harry / Allons a lafayette: Choates, Harry / Jole Blon: Choates, Harry / Corpus Christie waltz: Choates, Harry / Echo mountain: Jackson, Ray / Tears of tomorrow: Jackson, Ray / Lookin: Porter, Royce / I still belong to you: Porter, Royce / Lonely night: Mathis, James / I've been known to cry: Mathis, James / Stealin' sugar: Lindsay, Merle / Hoy rag: Lindsay, Merle / I'm all wrapped up: Doyle, Ted / He made you mine: Doyle, Ted / Mean autry: Thibodeaux, Rufus / Cameron memorial waltz: Thibodeaux, Rufus / True affection: Johnson, Byron / You were only fooling: Johnson, Byron / I need someone: Mac, Johnny / That's all I can do: Mac, Johnny / Step aside old heart: Timmons, Patsy / I understand him: Timmons, Patsy / Won't you tell me: Stanford, Doug / Sady: Stanford, Doug / Men do cry: Hall, Sonny / Day you walked away: Hall, Sonny / I kept it a secret: Edge, Dave / I didn't think of you: Edge, Dave / I don't live there any more: Noack, Eddie / Walk' em off: Noack, Eddie / Reprieve of Tom Dooley: Johnson, Rick / Barbara Allen: Johnson, Rick / Maple sugar: Allen, Ward / Back up and push: Allen, Ward / Bugger burns: Lynn, Jerry / Queen of the moon: Lynn, Jerry / It'll be my first time: Kilgore, Merle / I take a trip to the moon: Kilgore, Merle / Opelousas waltz: Choates, Harry / Poor Hobo: Choates, Harry / Honky tonk boogie: Choates, Harry / Port arthur waltz: Choates, Harry / I'm all alone: Bragg, Doug / Calling me back: Bragg, Doug / Whirlwind: Bragg, Doug / Man I met: Campi, Ray / Ballad of Donna and Peggy Sue: Campi, Ray / Dottie: McCoy, Doyle / Some how I don't mind: McCoy, Doyle / Justice of love: Bowman, Cecil / Man awaitin': Bowman, Cecil / Penalty of love: Velvetones / Come back: Velvetones / Born to love you: Heap, Jimmy / Some one else is filling my shoes: Heap, Jimmy / I love only you: Heap, Jimmy / I Like it: Heap, Jimmy / Gold records in the snow: Heap, Jimmy / Happy little bluebird: Barnes, Benny / Chantilly lace cha cha: Kimbrough, Bill / Egg head: Kimbrough, Bill / From a kiss to the blues: Mathis, Johnny / Since I said goodbye to love: Mathis, Johnny / What makes you cry: Jackson, Ray / Tea leaves don't cry: Jackson, Ray / Trumpets and clarinets: Kucera, Ernie / Annie waltz: Kucera, Ernie / One more heartache: Doyle, Ted / Just for the thrill: Doyle, Ted / It's wrong for me to love you: Johnson, Byron / Our love is not worth living for: Johnson, Byron / Letter overdue: Gray, Claude / I'm not supposed: Gray, Claude / Don't look behind: Noack, Eddie / Thinking man's woman: Noack, Eddie / Baby don't go: Charles, Andy & The Blues Kings / Love come back: Charles, Andy & The Blues Kings

BCD 15832 / Nov '95 / Bear Family

☐ COMPLETE IRISH DANCING SET (2CD Set)

CDH 1050CD / Jul '95 / Outlet

☐ COMPLETE IRISH NATIONAL ANTHEM, THE

IRBCD 1937 / Jul '94 / Outlet

☐ COMPLETE NOCTURNE VOL.1, THE (3CD Set)

NR 101 / 1 Jun '98 / Nocturne

☐ COMPLETE STAX/VOLT SINGLES 1959-1968, THE (9CD Set)

Fool in love: Veltones / Because I love you: Carla & Rufus / Gee whiz: Thomas, Carla / You make me feel so good: Chips / Love of my own: Thomas, Carla / Last night: Mar-Keys / I didn't believe: Rufus & Friend / I'm going home: Prince Conley / (Mama, mama) Wish me good luck: Thomas, Carla / Morning after: Mar-Keys / Life I live: Stephens, Barbara / About noon: Mar-Keys / Burnt biscuits: Triumphs / I kinda think he does: Thomas, Carla / Foxy: Mar-Keys / You don't miss your water/Formula of love: Bell, William / Goofin' off: Skipper, Macy / Wait a minute: Stephens, Barbara / Sunday jealous: Charles, Nick / That's the way it is with me: Stephens, Barbara / Pop-eye stroll: Mar-Keys / Three dogwoods: Charles, Nick / No tears: Tonettes / Why should I suffer: Canes / What's happenin': Mar-Keys / Just across the street/There's a love: Del-Rios / Can't ever let go: Thomas, Rufus / Green onions/Behave yourself: Booker T & The MG's / Any other way: Bell, William / I'll bring it home to you: Thomas, Carla / Sack o' woe: Mar-Keys / These arms of mine: Redding, Otis / Teardrop sea: Tonettes / Dog: Thomas, Rufus / Jelly bread: Booker T & The MG's / I told you so: Bell, William / Bo-time: Mar-Keys / Home grown: Booker T & The MG's / My imaginary guy: Parker, Deanie / Just as I thought: Bell, William / What a fool I've been: Thomas, Carla / Hawg: Kirk, Eddie / Don't be afraid of love: Mack, Oscar / That's my guy: Johnson, Cheryl & Pam / Chinese checkers: Booker T & The MG's / Somebody mentioned your name: Bell, William / What can I do: Marchan, Bobby / That's what my heart needs: Redding, Otis / What can it be: Astors / Bango: Billy & The King Bees / Them bones: Kirk, Eddie / Walking the dog: Thomas, Rufus / I'll show you: Bell, William / Pain in my heart: Redding, Otis / Gee whiz it's Christmas: Thomas, Carla / Mo' onions: Booker T & The MG's / Frog stomp: Newman, Floyd / Can your monkey do the dog: Thomas, Rufus / You won't do right: Marchan, Bobby / Wondering: Drapels / Each step I take: Parker, Deanie / Honeydripper: Van-Dells / Who will it be tomorrow: Bell, William / Come to me/Don't leave me this way: Redding, Otis / I don't want you anymore: Jefferson, Eddie / Restless: Cobras / Somebody stole my dog: Thomas, Rufus / Big party: Barbara & The Browns / That's really some good/ Night time is the right time: Rufus / Security: Redding, Otis / Dream girl: Mack, Oscar / Closer to my baby: Williams, Dorothy / I've got no time to lose: Thomas, Carla / Young man: Drapels / Soul dressing: Booker T & The MG's / After laughter (comes tears): Rene, Wendy / Can't explain how it happened: Hunter, Ivory Joe / Bush bash: Mar-Keys / Please return to me: Fleets / Jump back: Thomas, Rufus / Chained and bound: Redding, Otis / In my heart: Barbara & The Browns / Spunky: Jenkins, Johnny / Bar B Q: Rene, Wendy / Sidewalk surf: Mad Lads / Can't be still: Booker T & The MG's / Woman's love: Thomas, Carla / Yank me (doodle): Baracudas / That's how strong my love is/Mr. Pitiful: Redding, Otis / Don't let her be your baby: Del-Rays / Can't see you when I want you: Porter, David / My lover: Barbara & The Browns / Got you on my mind: Barbara & The Browns / How do you quit (someone you love): Thomas, Carla / Biggest fool in town: Gorgeous George / Banana juice: Mar-Keys / Little Sally Walker: Thomas, Rufus / Goodnight baby: Sam & Dave / Boot-leg/Outrage: Booker T & The MG's / I've been loving you too long: Redding, Otis / Candy: Astors / Give you what I got/Reap what you sow: Rene, Wendy / Stop look what you're doin': Thomas, Carla / Willy willy: Thomas, Rufus / Don't have to shop around: Mad Lads / Crying all by myself: Bell, William / I take what I want: Sam & Dave / When you move you lose: Thomas, Rufus & Carla / Respect: Redding, Otis / Make it me: Premiers / World is round: Thomas, Rufus / In the twilight zone: Astors / Blue groove: Sir Isaac & The Dodads / You don't know like I know: Sam & Dave / Grab this thing: Mar-Keys / Be my lady: Booker T & The MG's / Comfort me: Thomas, Carla / I can't turn you loose/Just one more day: Redding, Otis / I want someone: Mad Lads / Birds and the bees: Thomas, Rufus & Carla / Philly dog: Mar-Keys / I had a dream: Taylor, Johnnie / Satisfaction: Redding, Otis / Things get better: Floyd, Eddie / I'll run your hurt away: Johnson, Ruby / Hot dog: Four Shells / Let me be good to you: Thomas, Carla / Hold on I'm comin': Sam & Dave / Laundromat blues: King, Albert / Sugar sugar: Mad Lads / Share what you got/Marching off to war: Bell, William / My lover's prayer: Redding, Otis / Your good thing is about to end: John, Mable / I got to love somebody's baby: Taylor, Johnnie / What will love tend to make: Mad Lads / Knock on wood: Floyd, Eddie / B-A-B-Y: Thomas, Carla / My sweet potato/ Booker-loo: Booker T & The MG's / Oh pretty woman: King, Albert / Said I wasn't gonna tell nobody: Sam & Dave / Never like this before: Bell, William / Fa fa fa fa fa (Sad song): Redding, Otis / Patch my heart: Mad Lads / Sister's got a boyfriend: Thomas, Rufus / Come to me my darling/When love comes down: Johnson, Ruby / Try a little tenderness: Redding, Otis / Crosscut saw: King, Albert / Little bluebird/Toe hold: Taylor, Johnnie / Jingle bells: Booker T & The MG's / You got me hummin': Sam & Dave / You're taking up another: John, Mable / All I want for Christmas is you: Thomas, Carla / Please uncle Sam: Charmels / Something good: Thomas, Carla / Raise your head: Floyd, Eddie / Ain't that lovin' you: Taylor, Johnnie / I don't want to lose: Mad Lads / When something is wrong: Sam & Dave / Let me down slow: Wilson, Bobby / Hip hug-her: Booker T & The MG's / Everybody loves a winner: Bell, William / Minnie skirt Minnie: Rice, Sir Mack / When tomorrow comes: Thomas, Carla / Spoiler: Purrell, Eddie / I love you more than words can say: Redding, Otis / If ever I needed love: Johnson, Ruby / Same time, same place: John, Mable / Tramp: Redding, Otis & Carla Thomas / Soul finger/Knucklehead: Bar-Kays / Shake: Redding, Otis / Born under a bad sign: King, Albert / Soothe me/I can't stand up: Sam & Dave / Don't rock the boat: Floyd, Eddie / My inspiration: Mad Lads / Love sickness: Rice, Sir Mack / How can you: Jeanne & The Darlings / Sophisticated Cissy: Thomas, Rufus / I'll always have faith in you: Thomas, Carla / Love is a doggone good thing: Floyd, Eddie / Groovin'/Slim Jenkins place: Booker T & The MG's / Glory of love: Redding, Otis / I'm a big girl now/Wait you dog: John, Mable / You can't get away from it: Taylor, Johnnie / Eloise: Bell, William / Knock on wood: Redding, Otis & Carla Thomas / I'm glad to do it: Blast, C.L. / You can't run away from your heart: Clay, Judy / I'll gladly take you back: Charmels / Soul man: Sam & Dave / Daddy didn't tell me: Astors / Give everybody some: Bar-Kays / On a Saturday night: Floyd, Eddie / Don't hit me no more: John, Mable / Somebody's sleeping: Taylor, Johnnie / Winter snow: Booker T & The MG's / Every day: Bell, William / What I'll do for satisfaction: Daye, Johnny / Pick up the pieces: Thomas, Carla / Down ta my house: Thomas, Rufus / As long as I've got you: Charmels / Soul girl: Jeanne & The Darlings / Cold feet: King, Albert / I thank you/Wrap it up: Sam & Dave / (Sittin' on the) dock of the bay: Redding, Otis / Don't pass your judgement: Memphis Nomads / Lovey dovey: Redding, Otis & Carla Thomas / I got a sure thing: Nightingales / Big bird: Floyd, Eddie / Hard day's night: Bar-Kays / Next time: Taylor, Johnnie / Tribute to a king/Every man: Bell, William / Able mable: John, Mable / Memphis train/I think I made a boo boo: Thomas, Rufus / What will later on be like/Hang me now: Jeanne & The Darlings / Soul power: Martin, Derek / Bring your love back to me: Lyndell, Linda / Dime a dozen: Thomas, Carla / Whatever hurts you: Mad Lads / Happy song: Redding, Otis / Lucy: King, Albert / I ain't particular: Taylor, Johnnie

7822182 / 30 Mar '98 / Stax

☐ COMPLETE STAX/VOLT SOUL SINGLES VOL.2, THE (1968-1971/9CD Set)

I was born to love you: Walton, Shirley / Precious, precious: Hayes, Isaac / Send peace and harmony home: Walton, Shirley / Soul limbo: Booker T & The MG's / I've never found a girl: Floyd, Eddie / It's been a long time coming: Delaney & Bonnie / What a man: Lyndell, Linda / I like everything about you: Hughes, Jimmy / Stay baby stay: Daye, Johnny / Private number: Clay, Judy & William Bell / So nice: Mad Lads / Long walk to DC: Staple Singers / Give 'em love: Soul Children / Funky Mississippi: Thomas, Rufus / Lovin' feeling: Charmels / Where do I go: Thomas, Carla / Bed of roses: Clay, Judy / Bring it on home to me: Floyd, Eddie / It's unbelievable (how you control my soul): Jeanne & The Darlings / Who's making love: Taylor, Johnnie / Mighty cold Winter: Dino & Doc / Hang 'em high: Booker T & The MG's / You're leaving me: Ollie & The Nightingales / Copy kat: Bar-Kays / I forgot to be your lover: Bell, William / Running out: John, Mable / My baby specializes: Bell, William & Judy Clay / I'll understand: Soul Children / Ghetto: Staple Singers / Blues power: King, Albert / Echo: Epsilons / Funky way: Thomas, Rufus / Take care of your homework: Taylor, Johnnie / I like what you're doing (to me): Thomas, Carla / I've got to have your love: Floyd, Eddie / Let 'em down baby: Hughes, Jimmy / Love is here today and gone tomorrow: Mad Lads / It ain't long enough: Clay, Judy / Mellow way you treat your man: Ollie & The Nightingales / Private number: Stitt, Sonny / Time is tight: Booker T & The MG's / Double or nothing: Mar-Keys / (Sittin' on the) dock of the bay: Staple Singers / So I can love you: Emotions / Don't stop dancing (to the music): Bar-Kays / One more chance: Joseph, Margie / I wanna be good (to you): Dotson, Jimmy / Finger lickin' good: Miller, Art Jerry / Tighten up my thang: Soul Children / Whole world is falling down: Bell, William / Testify (I wonna): Taylor, Johnnie / Drowning on dry land: King, Albert / Do the cissy: Stingers / Don't tell your mama: Floyd, Eddie / Mrs. Robinson: Booker T & The MG's / Love's sweet sensation: Bell, William & Mavis Staples / Just because your love has gone: Banks, Darrell / Chains of love: Hughes, Jimmy / Happy: Bell, William / Challenge: Staple Singers / Soul-a-lujah: Taylor, Johnnie/Eddie Floyd/William Bell / Never, never let you go: Floyd, Eddie & Mavis Staples / Just keep on loving me: Taylor, Johnnie & Carla Thomas / I need you woman: Bell, William & Carla Thomas / I've got a feeling: Ollie & The Nightingales / It's time to pay for the fun (we've had): Jeanne & The Darlings / I could never be president: Taylor, Johnnie / By the time I get to Phoenix: Mad Lads / Long and lonely world: Kelly, Colette / Midnight cowboy: Bar-Kays / I've fallen in love (with you): Thomas, Carla / Slum baby: Booker T & The MG's / Best part of a love affair: Emotions / By the time I get to Phoenix: Hayes, Isaac / Walk on by: Hayes, Isaac / Tupelo Part 1: Staples, Pops/ Steve Cropper/ Albert King / Water: Staples, Pops/ Steve Cropper/ Albert King / Sweeter he is: Soul Children / You're driving me (To the arms of a stranger): Staples, Mavis / Open up your heart: Newcomers / Why is the wine sweeter (on the other side): Floyd, Eddie / When will we be paid: Staple Singers / Grinder man: Hooker, John Lee / Born under a bad sign: Bell, William / What you gonna do: Joseph, Margie / I'm so glad: Hughes, Jimmy / Beautiful feelings: Banks, Darrell / Your love was strange: Dramatics / Love bones: Taylor, Johnnie / Hard to say goodbye: Delaney & Bonnie / Got to get rid of you: Barnes, J.J. / Habit forming love: Milner, Reggie / My thing is a moving thing: TSU Tornadoes / Stealing love: Emotions / Wrapped up in love again: King, Albert / Do the funky chicken: Thomas, Rufus / California girl: Floyd, Eddie / Tribute to a blackwoman, Part 1: Hayes, Bernie / Song and dance: Bar-Kays / Hold on I'm comin': Soul Children / Love's gonna tear your playhouse down Part 1: Brooks, Chuck / Help me put out the flame (in my heart): Hines, Ernie / Black boy: Staples, Pops / Bracing myself for a fall: Ollie & The Nightingales / All I have to do is dream: Bell, William & Carla Thomas / Singing about love: Jeanne & The Darlings / Goodies: Chris & Shack / Just the way you are today: Lewis, Barbara / Creeper returns: Little Sonny / Guide me well: Thomas, Carla / Give a damn: Staple Singers / Steal away: Taylor, Johnnie / Your sweet lovin': Joseph, Margie / I forgot to remember: Jones & Blumenburg / Can't see you when I want you: Porter, David / Never be true: Thomas, Carla / Can't you see what you're doing to me: King, Albert / Sixty minute man: Thomas, Rufus / Preacher and the bear: Thomas, Rufus / Something: Booker T & The MG's / Seeing is believing: Mad Lads / You're my only temptation: Ryan, Roz / What I don't know won't hurt me: Thompson, Paul / Right, tight and out of sight: Branding Iron / (What's under) The natural do: Kasandra, John / My girl: Floyd, Eddie / I have learned to do without you: Staples, Mavis / Play the music tornadoes: TSU Tornadoes / Lonely soldier: Bell, William / Heart association: Emotions / I stand accused: Hayes, Isaac / Brand new day: Staple Singers / Sweeter tomorrow: Joseph, Margie / Cool strut: Hayes, Bernie / You put the sunshine back in my world: Newcomers / Montego Bay: Bar-Kays / Got it together parts I and II: Robinson, Rudy & The Hungry Five / Wade in the water: Little Sonny / You're movin' much too fast: Nightingales / Best year of my life: Floyd, Eddie / I am somebody: Taylor, Johnnie / I loved you like I love my very life: Thomas, Carla / Soul machine: Milner, Reggie / (Follow her) Rules and regulations: Temprees / Do the Push and pull (part 1): Thomas, Rufus / Love changes: Charlene & The Soul Serenaders / Put your world in my world (Best of two worlds): Soul Children / Love is plentiful: Staple Singers / Heavy makes you happy: Staple Singers / Who took the merry out of christmas: Staple Singers / Too many lovers: Shack / Black christmas: Emotions / Mistletoe and me: Hayes, Isaac / Ask the lonely: Lewis, Barbara / Jody's got your girl and gone: Taylor, Johnnie / Finish me off: Soul Children / Oh how it rained: Floyd, Eddie / Look of love: Hayes, Isaac / Electrified love: Hines, Ernie / Melting pot: Booker T & The MG's / That's the way I like it (I like it that way): Lewis, Barbara / Mr. Big Stuff: Knight, Jean / You make me want to love you: Emotions / Stop, In the name of love: Joseph, Margie / I don't wanna lose you: Taylor, Johnnie / Girl I love you: Temprees / World is round: Thomas, Rufus / Penny for your thoughts: Bell, William / Never can say goodbye: Hayes, Isaac / I don't want to be like my daddy: Nightingales / You've got to earn it: Staple Singers / Hold on to it: Limitations / What'cha see is what'cha get: Dramatics / Born too late: Branding Iron / Just ain't as strong as I used to be: Hughes, Jimmy / That other woman got my man and gone: Joseph, Margie / If you think it (You may as well do it): Emotions / Shame on the family name: Scott, Calvin / Blood is thicker than water: Floyd, Eddie / Hijackin' love: Taylor, Johnnie / Sweetback's theme: Van Peebles, Melvin / Breakdown (part 1): Thomas, Rufus / Pin the tail on the donkey: Newcomers / Them hot pants: Sain, Lee / If that ain't a reason (for your woman to leave you): Little Milton / It's good to be careful (But it's better to be loved): Shack / Where would you be today: Ilana / Everybody wants to go to heaven: King, Albert / Got to get away from it all: Soul Children / Love's creepin' up on me: United Image / Show me how: Emotions / If I give it up, I want it back: Porter, David / Woman named trouble: Little Sonny / Losing boy: Giles, Eddie / Respect yourself: Staple Singers / I'll kill a brick (About my man): Hot Sauce / You think you're hot stuff: Knight, Jean / All for the love of a woman: Bell, William / Shaft: Hayes, Isaac / Jamaica this morning: MG's / Promises of yesterday: Mad Lads / Girl, come on home: Major Lance / (Let hurt put you in the) Loser's seat: Wilson, Joni / My baby love: Temprees / How do you move a mountain: Leaders / Black nasty boogie: Black Nasty / Do the funky penguin (part 1): Thomas, Rufus / You've got a cushion to fall on: Thomas, Carla / Get up and get down: Dramatics / Son of Shaft: Bar-Kays / Don't you mess with my money, my honey or my woman: Johnson, L.V. / I can smell that funky music: Mercury, Eric / Sadness for things: Scott, Calvin / That's what love will make you do: Little Milton / Standing in for Jody: Taylor, Johnnie

9SCD 4411 / Sep '93 / Stax

☐ COMPLETE STAX/VOLT SOUL SINGLES VOL.3, THE (1972-1975/ 10CD Set)

Yum yum yum (I want some): Floyd, Eddie / Carry on: Knight, Jean / Do your thing: Hayes, Isaac / I've been lonely for so long: Knight, Frederick / Nothing is everlasting: Thomas, Annette / Hearsay: Soul Children / Angel of mercy: King, Albert / In the rain: Dramatics / She's my old lady too: Sain, Lee / Explain it to her Mama: Temprees / Right on: Sons Of Slum / Doing my own thing: Taylor, Johnnie / My honey and me: Emotions / Let's stay together: Hayes, Isaac / Bring it home (amd give it to me): Hot Sauce / Look around you: Black Society / Don't do it: Nightingales / I'm with you: Nightingales / I'll take you there: Staple Singers / Which way: Leaders / Living a life without you: Brown, Veda / What's good for you (don't have to be good to you): Scales, Harvey / Let me repair your heart: Mad Lads / What's usual seems natur'l: Mercury, Eric / I wanna make up (before we break up): Major Lance / Ain't that lovin' you: Hayes, Isaac & David Porter / Walking the back streets and crying: Little Milton / Save us: Bell, William / 6-3-8 (that's the number to play): Thomas, Rufus / Starting all over again: Mel & Tim / Keep on loving me: Stefan / (I'm afraid) the masquerade is over: Porter, David / Going down slow (parts 1 and 2): Little Sonny / I could never be happy: Emotions / Don't take my kindness for weakness: Soul Children / I'll play the blues for you: King, Albert / I dedicate my life for you: Hatcher, Roger / Do the sweetback: March Wind / Getting funky round here: Black Nasty / When the chips are down: Porter, David / Sugar: Thomas, Carla / You're good enough (to be my baby): Floyd, Eddie / This world: Staple Singers / Helping man: Knight, Jean / Ain't I good: Kasandra, John / Dance, dance, dance: Bar-Kays / Dedicated to the one I love: Temprees / Toast to the fool: Dramatics / Stop doggin' me: Taylor, Johnnie / Trouble: Knight, Frederick / I'm gonna cry a river: Little Milton / Itch and scratch (part 1): Thomas, Rufus / What would I do: Hines, Ernie / I know It's not right (to be in love with a married man): Brown, Veda / Holy cow: Stefan / What goes around (must come around): Sons Of Slum / Men: Hayes, Isaac / Endlessly: Staples, Mavis / You hurt me for the last time: Foxx, Inez / My sweet Lord: Williams, John Gary / Breaking up somebody's home: King, Albert / How can you mistreat the one you love: Love, Katie / From toys to boys: Emotions / Dryer: Johnson, Roy Lee & The Villagers / I may not be all you want (but I'm all you got): Thomas, Carla / Ain't no sweat: Major Lance / Do me: Knight, Jean / Rainy day: Little Milton / It ain't always what you do (it's who you let see you do it): Soul Children / I may not be what you want: Mel & Tim / Funky robot (part 1): Thomas, Rufus / Don't you fool with my soul (part 1): Taylor, Johnnie / Oh la de da: Staple Singers / What do you see in her: Hot Sauce / Thousand miles away: Temprees / Hey you get off my mountain: Dramatics / Rolling down a mountainside: Hayes, Isaac / You're still my brother: Bar-Kays / Stop half loving these women: Lewis, Jimmy / Lovin' on borrowed time: Bell, William / Lay your loving on me: Floyd, Eddie / Time: Foxx, Inez / Heaven knows: Mel & Tim / I believe in you (you believe in me): Taylor, Johnnie / Short stopping: Brown, Veda / Be what you are: Staple Singers / I've got to love somebody's baby: Stefan / Playing on me: King, Albert / Long as you're the one somebody in the world: Porter, David / This is my song of love to you: Knight, Frederick / Sugarcane: MG's / Love is a hurtin' thing: Soul Children / Baby, lay your head down: Floyd, Eddie / Check me out: Floyd, Eddie / Running (back and forth): Emotions / Crossing over the bridge: Foxx, Inez / Love's maze: Temprees / It ain't easy: Bar-Kays / Love among people: Thomas, Carla / What is it: Little Milton / I've got to go without you: Bell, William / Love is taking over: Mercury, Eric / Ruby Dean: Hicks, Joe / I'm so glad I fell in love with you: Mad Lads / Fell for you: Dramatics / Cheaper to keep her: Taylor, Johnnie / I know you don't want me no more: Thomas, Rufus / If you're ready (come go with me): Staple Singers / Slipped and tripped: Sweet Inspirations / Peace, be still: Emotions / I'll be the other woman: Soul Children / Martin hop: Newcomers / I had a talk with my man: Foxx, Inez / At last: Temprees / Joy: Hayes, Isaac / Good woman turning bad: Hot Sauce / Mose (part 3): Kasandra, John / I'll be your Santa baby: Thomas, Rufus / I wanna do things for you: Floyd, Eddie / That's what the blues is all about: King, Albert / One way love affair: Hurley, Carolyn / Tin pan alley: Little Milton / Funky bird: Thomas, Rufus / We're getting careless with our love: Taylor, Johnnie / What do the lonely get at Christmas: Emotions / Season's greetings: Cix Bits / Don't lose faith in me Lord: Mercury, Eric / Don't start lovin' me (If you're gonna stop): Brown, Veda / Touch a hand, make a friend: Staple Singers / I panicked: Dramatics / Change it all: Flemming, Joy / Gettin' what you want (losin' what you get): Bell, William / He's mine: Verdell, Jackie / My woman is good to me: Little Sonny / I got you and I'm glad: Porter, David / Put a little love away: Emotions / Suzy: Knight, Frederick / Same folks: Mel & Tim / You make the sunshine: Temprees / Whole damn world is going crazy: Williams, John Gary / Circuits overloaded: Foxx, Inez / Wonderful: Hayes, Isaac / Behind closed doors: Little Milton / Guess who: Floyd, Eddie / Sweet inspiration: Dirty Tricks / Which way did it go: Pop Staples / Talking to the people: Black Nasty / I've been born again: Taylor, Johnnie / Neckbone: MG's / Wounded woman: Wright,

Sandra / Stop dogging me: *Hot Sauce* / Goodness gracious: *Weston, Kim* / City in the sky: *Staple Singers* / Title theme: *Hayes, Isaac* / Soul street: *Floyd, Eddie* / Flat tire: *King, Albert* / Love makes it right: *Soul Children* / Mr. Cool that ain't cool: *Temprees* / Boogie ain't nuttin' (but gettin' down): *Thomas, Rufus* / Highway to heaven: *Banks, Ron & The Dramatics* / Get it while it's hot: *Bell, William* / Passing thru: *Knight, Frederick* / Keep an eye on your close friends: *Newcomers* / My main man: *Staple Singers* / There is a God: *Staple Singers* / That's the way I want to live my life: *Mel & Tim* / Forever and a day: *Mel & Tim* / Baby, I'm through: *Emotions* / It's September: *Taylor, Johnnie* / Woman to woman: *Brown, Shirley* / Did you hear yourself: *Brown, Randy* / You need a friend like mine: *Thomas, Annette* / I love, I love: *Temprees* / Let me back in: *Little Milton* / Crosscut saw: *King, Albert* / Coldblooded: *Bar-Kays* / Bump meat: *Rice, Sir Mack* / (Too little in common to be lovers) Too much going to say go: *Newcomers* / Bump and boogie (part 1): *Wrecking Crew* / What's happening baby (part 1): *Soul Children* / Who made the man: *Staple Singers* / I keep thinking to myself: *Benton, Brook* / I got a reason to smile (cause I got you): *Floyd, Eddie* / Try to leave me if you can (i bet you can't do it): *Banks, Bessie* / Burning on both ends: *Singleton, Willie* / There are more questions than answers: *Emotions* / Santa Claus wants some lovin': *King, Albert* / I can't let you go: *Hot Sauce* / I betcha didn't know that: *Knight, Frederick* / Lovin' you, lovin' me: *Wright, Sandra* / Do the double bump: *Thomas, Rufus* / Come and get your love: *Temprees* / Dark skin woman: *Rice, Sir Mack* / It ain't no fun: *Brown, Shirley* / If you talk in your sleep: *Little Milton* / Talk to the man: *Floyd, Eddie* / You're astounding: *Barbara & Joe* / Dy-no-mite (Did you say my love): *Green Brothers* / Boom-a-rang: *Dynamic Soul Machine* / Come what may: *Williams, John Gary* / Try me tonight: *Taylor, Johnnie* / Groovin' on my baby's love: *Waters, Freddie* / I can't shake your love (can't shake you lose): *Fiestas* / I wanna play with you: *Knight, Frederick* / I'm doing fine: *King, Albert* / No way: *Davis, Theresa* / Back road into town: *Staple Singers* / I'm so glad I met you: *Floyd, Eddie* / Packed up and took my mind: *Little Milton* / Just keep on loving me: *Taylor, Johnnie* / How can I be a witness: *Hudmon, R.B.* / Jump back '75 (part 1): *Thomas, Rufus* / I got to be myself: *Staple Singers* / It's worth a whipping: *Brown, Shirley* / Holy ghost: *Bar-Kays*

10SCD 4415 / Oct '94 / Stax

☐ **COMPLI MALI**

381482 / 24 Feb '98 / Melodie

☐ **COMPOSE DISCOMPOSE**

COMPOSE 0128 / 6 Apr '98 / Compose

☐ **COMPTINES & CHANSONS - ENFANTS**

983262 / Oct '96 / EPM

☐ **COMPUTER MUSIC CURRENTS 12**

WER 2032 / Feb '96 / Wergo

☐ **CONCEPTION**

OJCCD 172 / Feb '93 / Original Jazz Classics

☐ **CONCORD JAZZ CHRISTMAS, A**

Christmas time is here: *Clooney, Rosemary* / Have yourself a merry little Christmas: *Peplowski, Ken* / I'll be home for Christmas: *Harris, Gene* / Apple, an orange and a little stick doll: *Cheatham, Jeannie & Jimmy* / Angels we have heard on high: *Scaggiari Trio* / Carol of the bells: *Byrd, Charlie* / Secret of Christmas: *McCorkle, Susannah* / God rest ye merry gentlemen: *McPartland, Marian* / Jingle bells: *Vignola, Frank* / Coventry carol: *Allyson, Karrin* / Christmas love song: *Hamilton, Scott* / Santa Claus is coming to town: *Bruno, Jimmy* / Christmas waltz: *McConnell, Rob* / Let it snow, let it snow, let it snow: *Atwood, Eden* / Little town of Bethlehem: *McKenna, Dave* / Winter wonderland: *Alden, Howard & Ken Peplowski* / What are you doing New Year's Eve: *Sloane, Carol*

CCD 4613 / Oct '94 / Concord Jazz

☐ **CONCORD JAZZ COLLECTOR'S SERIES SAMPLER**

Sweetback / Benny's bugle / Spring is here / I'm on my way / Look for the silver lining / Summertime, bidin' my time / After you've gone / Seven come eleven / Soft shoe / Carioca hills / Embraceable you / Smooth one / I wish I were in love again / I've found a new baby

CCD 6013 / Nov '93 / Concord Jazz

☐ **CONCORD JAZZ GUITAR COLLECTION VOL.1 & 2**

La petite mambo / Isn't this a lovely place / Dolphin dance / Zigeuner / Prelude to a kiss / I'm on my way / I can't get started (with you) / Side track / Georgia on my mind / You don't know what love is / Claire de Lune / Seven come eleven / When Sunny gets blue / Orange, brown and green / Don't cry for me Argentina

CCD 4160 / Mar '90 / Concord Jazz

☐ **CONCORD JAZZ GUITAR COLLECTION VOL.3**

Band call / Ecaroh / Joy spring / Avalon / Count down / Ain't misbehavin' / Too marvellous for words / East to West / Beija fior / There will never be another you / Song is you / Reflections in d / Skye boat song

CCD 4507 / May '92 / Concord Jazz

☐ **CONCRETE PRESENTS STRUCTURALLY SOUND**

HARD 21LPCD / Jun '97 / Concrete

☐ **CONFEDERATE TALES (White Mansions/Jesse James - 2CD Set)**

5407912 / 22 Sep '97 / A&M

☐ **CONFERENCE OF THE BIRDS - LIVE AT WILLISAU**

Meet you there / Fortune cookie / Ooyah / Hello / Conference of the birds / I'm nobody / Prelude

ITM 970070 / Sep '92 / ITM

☐ **CONFESSIN' THE BLUES**

IGOCD 2020 / Jun '95 / Indigo

☐ **CONGO DRUMS**

PS 65164 / May '96 / PlayaSound

☐ **CONGOLESE MASS**

087262 / Mar '96 / Melodie

☐ **CONGRATULATIONS**

I 3896042 / Oct '96 / Galaxy

☐ **CONJUNTO VOL.1 (Tex Mex Border Music)**

ROUCD 6023 / '88 / Rounder

☐ **CONJUNTO VOL.2**

ROUCD 6024 / '88 / Rounder

☐ **CONJUNTO VOL.3**

ROUCD 6030 / ' / Rounder

☐ **CONJUNTO VOL.4**

ROUCD 6034 / ' / Rounder

☐ **CONJUNTO VOL.5 (Polkas De Oro)**

ROUCD 6051 / Feb '94 / Rounder

☐ **CONJUNTO VOL.6 (Contrabando)**

ROUCD 6052 / Apr '94 / Rounder

☐ **CONNECTED (2CD Set)**

Brimful of Asha: *Cornershop* / It's like that: *Run DMC & Jason Nevins* / My star: *Brown, Ian* / Ballad of Tom Jones: *Space* / This is hardcore: *Pulp* / Stay: *Butler, Bernard* / Closed for business: *Mansun* / Rude boy rock: *Lionrock* / Renegade master: *Wildchild* / Smack my bitch up: *Prodigy* / Marbles: *Black Grape* / That's why we lose control: *Young Offenders* / Tourniquet: *Headswim* / Never never: *Warm Jets* / I will be your girlfriend: *Dubstar* / Summertime: *Sundays* / Nothing lasts forever: *Echo & The Bunnymen* / Untouchable: *Rialto* / It's great when we're together: *Quaye, Finley* / Mulder and Scully: *Catatonia* / She left me on a Friday: *Shed Seven* / All around the world: *Oasis* / El President: *Drugstore* / It's a beautiful thing: *Drugstore* / Local boy in the photograph: *Stereophonics* / Destiny calling: *James* / Nanny in Manhattan: *Lilys* / Legend of a cowgirl: *Coppola, Imani* / Gunman: *187 Lockdown* / Bentley's gonna sort you out: *Bentley Rhythm Ace* / Step into my world: *Hurricane No.1* / If you can't do it when you're young: *Theaudience* / Mermaids: *Weller, Paul* / I'm so lonely: *Cast* / Suffocate: *Feeder* / James Bond theme: *Moby* / Digital: *Goldie & KRS1*

5555952 / 20 Apr '98 / PolyGram TV

☐ **CONNECTED**

Touch the stars: *Blackalicious* / Ducking lessons: *Sha Key & Priest* / Red Rum: *Angel & Cokni O'Dire* / Otha side of midnight: *Angel & Cokni O'Dire* / Don't stop the reggae music: *Tarantula Crew* / It's all the way live: *Ultramagnetic MC's* / WROK: *Ayce International* / ZIKR: *Badawi* / Wreckoning: *Lateef, Yusef* / Gimme a breaks: *Dubmarine* / Dubmeter: *Templeroy* / Soundtrack dub: *Fresh, Doug E* / Get down: *Labtekwon* / Right on: *Datbu* / Alchemist: *Jahred Jedeye* / CB stories: *Ticklah*

T21CD 1000 / 27 Apr '98 / 3-2-1

☐ **CONSCIOUS RAGGA VOL.1**

GRELCD 220 / Oct '95 / Greensleeves

☐ **CONSCIOUS RAGGA VOL.2**

GRELCD 225 / Jun '96 / Greensleeves

☐ **CONSPIRACAO BAIANA**

68970 / Jul '97 / Tropical

☐ **CONTEMPORARY FLUTE**

BVHAASTCD 9211 / Dec '91 / Bvhaast

☐ **CONTEMPORARY TRADITIONAL SONGS FROM ITALY**

926872 / 24 Apr '98 / BUDA

☐ **CONTROVERSY OF PIPERS, A**

COMD 1008 / Apr '95 / Temple

☐ **COOKING VINYL SAMPLER VOL.4**

Ontario, quebec and me: *Bragg, Billy* / Levens lament: *Leven, Jackie* / Jam tomorrow: *Oyster Band* / Memphis: *Pere Ubu* / Summer heat: *Jansch, Bert* / Cachapaya shuffle: *Incantation* / All our trades: *Tabor, June* / How can you keep on moving: *McLeod, Rory* / Roll on forever: *Rockingbirds* / Let it go: *Goats Don't Shave* / No dancing: *Immaculate Fools* / You gotta survive: *TRB* / Persons unknown: *Poison Girls* / Liberty: *Barely Works* / Blackberry blossom: *Barely Works* / Cuckoo's nest: *Barely Works* / Rumbidzai: *Four Brothers*

GRILLCD 008 / Aug '95 / Cooking Vinyl

☐ **COOKING VINYL SAMPLER VOL.5**

GRILLCD 009 / Sep '96 / Cooking Vinyl

☐ **COOKING VINYL SAMPLER VOL.6 - 1997 (2CD Set)**

Not like Jordan: *Oyster Band* / Homemade blood: *Prophet, Chuck* / Mari mac: *Great Big Sea* / Bonny besses: *Rev Hammers Freeborn John* / In or out: *Di Franco, Ani* / Extremely violent man: *Leven, Jackie* / Sugardaddy: *Bragg, Billy* / Negative equity: *Carter* / Snake eyes: *Wedding Present* / Hand in my pocket: *White, Andy* / Hurry back: *Thomas, David* / Promises: *Wired To The Moon* / By my rambling woman: *McLeod, Rory* / Holding on: *Di Franco, Ani* / Dawn: *Stevenson, Savourna & Danny Thompson* / Kachembere: *Bhundu Boys* / Codex: *Pere Ubu* / Makorokoto: *Four Brothers* / Bjorn again polka: *Edward II & The Red Hot Polkas* / Catchapaya shuffle: *Incantation* / Raining (my eyes are filled with clouds): *Ancient Beatbox* / Who cares: *Shocked, Michelle* / Back home: *Jansch, Bert* / Big river: *Barely Works* / Windy city: *Tabor, June* / Breaths: *Sweet Honey In The Rock* / Dirty old town: *MacColl, Ewan* / Rumours of glory: *Cockburn, Bruce* / Las Vegas (in the hills of Donegal): *Goats Don't Shave* / We had it all: *Rockingbirds* / Spivaye solovey: *Ukrainians* / Ready for me: *Immaculate Fools* / Loved: *Robinson, Tom* / Old tarts song: *Poison Girls*

GRILLCD 010 / Jul '97 / Cooking Vinyl

☐ **COOL & CRAZY**

Kool kat: *Sherrell, Bill* / Rock on baby: *Sherrell, Bill* / Rock 'n' roll teenager: *Sherrell, Bill* / Yes, no, or maybe: *Sherrell, Bill* / Rock crazy baby: *Adams, Art* / Dancing doll: *Adams, Art* / Imogene: *Ray, Don* / Those rock 'n' roll blues: *Ray, Don* / Cool cat: *Montgomery, Joe* / Woodpecker rock: *Couty, Nat* / Won't you come along with me: *Couty, Nat* / Bon bon baby: *Coulston, Jerry* / Little rocker: *Stuart, Scottie* / Marlene: *Sonics* / Minus one: *Sonics* / Blast off: *Sonics* / Cool cool baby: *Yarborough, Lafayette* / Living doll: *Yarborough, Lafayette* / Rock 'n' roll fever: *Graham B* / Cool baby: *Cole, Lee* / Short fat Ben: *Barclay, Phil* / I love me all: *Barclay, Phil* / Come along with me: *Parker, Malcom* / Servant of love: *Van Bros* / Cool cats: *Huften, Jim* / Get hot or go home: *Kerby, John* / Pizza pie: *Irwin, Phil* / Little bitty boy: *Hulin, T.K.* / Cool baby cool: *Hulin, T.K.* / Ricky Tic: *Davis, Al* / She's cool: *Vikings*

CDBB 55006 / Apr '94 / Buffalo Bop

☐ **COOL - TALKIN' VERVE**

5332462 / May '97 / Verve

☐ **COOL BEAT**

RENCD 101 / Jul '95 / Castle

☐ **COOL CHRISTMAS**

Please come home for Christmas: *Eagles* / Blanche comme la neige: *McGarrigle, Kate & Anna* / Lights of the stable: *Harris, Emmylou* / Soon after Christmas: *Nordenstam, Stina* / White Christmas: *Redding, Otis* / Winter: *Amos, Tori* / Fairytale of New York: *Pogues* / Silent night: *Enya* / Coventry carol: *Paige, Elaine* / 2000 miles: *Pretenders* / Driving home for Christmas: *Rea, Chris* / Power of love: *Frankie Goes To Hollywood* / Walk out to winter: *Aztec Camera* / Winter wonderland: *Booker T & The MG's* / Christmas in February: *Reed, Lou* / Santa's beard: *They Might Be Giants* / Little boy that Santa Claus forgot: *Associates* / Christmas card from a hooker in Minneapolis: *Waits, Tom*

9548324852 / Dec '93 / WEA

☐ **COOL GROOVES (2CD Set)**

5651622 / 24 Aug '98 / PolyGram TV

☐ **COOL RAGGA MIX**

VPCD 1477 / Oct '96 / VP

☐ **COOL SOUNDS FOR WARM NIGHT**

MCCD 195 / Mar '95 / Music Club

☐ **COOL STRUTTIN'**

99 2120 / Jul '96 / Ninetynine

☐ **COOL WORLD (41 Australian Rock Singles 1976-1986/2CD Set)**

Deep water: *Clapton, Richard* / (Boys) what did the detective say: *Sports* / So young: *Zep, Jo Jo & The Falcons* / Beautiful people: *Australian Crawl* / Nips are getting bigger: *Mental As Anything* / Can't help myself: *Flowers* / Stay young: *INXS* / Unguarded moment: *Church* / They won't let my girlfriend talk to me: *Jimmy & The Boys* / Quasimodo's dream: *Reels* / No secrets: *Angels* / Happy man: *Sunnyboys* / Smith and Wesson blues: *Radio Birdman* / Know your product: *Saints* / Who can it be now: *Men At Work* / Cool world: *Mondo Rock* / Never gonna die: *Choirboys* / Breakfast at sweethearts: *Cold Chisel* / I hear motion: *Models* / Great Southern land: *Icehouse* / Boys in town: *Divinyls* / Solid rock: *Goanna* / Rain: *Dragon* / Six months in a leaky boat: *Split Enz* / Gimme some lovin': *GANGgajang* / Throw your arms around me: *Hunters & Collectors* / Cattle and cane: *Go-Betweens* / No say in it: *Machinations* / Big girls: *Electric Pandas* / Send me an angel: *Real Life* / We will together: *Eurogliders* / Girl on the wall: *Clifton, Jane* / No lies: *Noiseworks* / Great wall: *Boom Crash Opera* / Man overboard: *Do Re Mi* / Wide open road: *Triffids* / I want you back: *Hoodoo Gurus* / Weirdo libido: *Lime Spiders* / Sad girl: *Stems* / Daughters of glory: *Black Sorrows* / Before too long: *Kelly, Paul & The Coloured Girls*

RVCD 55 / Feb '97 / Raven

☐ **COOLER SHAKERS (30 Northern Soul Floorstompers)**

Lonely for you baby: *Dees, Sam* / Nothing can stop me: *Chandler, Gene* / Getting mighty crowded: *Everett, Betty* / Breakaway: *Valentines* / Come on train: *Thomas, Don* / Nothing worse than being alone: *Ad Libs* / I hurt on the other side: *Barnes, Sidney* / Just another heartache: *Little Ritchie* / Don't let me down: *Hughes, Freddie* / Touch me hold me kiss me: *Inspirations* / That's enough: *Robinson, Roscoe* / You've been gone too long: *Sexton, Ann* / Sweet and easy: *McCoy, Van* / I'm a fool I must love you: *Falcons* / I'd think it over twice: *Fletcher, Sam* / Dearly beloved: *Montgomery, Jack* / That's no way to treat a girl: *Knight, Marie* / Please stay: *Ivorys* / You hit me like TNT: *Jones, Linda* / Get it baby: *Mitchell, Stanley* / Love slipped through my fingers: *Ohio Players* / Stop and get a hold: *Knight, Gladys & The Pips* / Wrong girl: *Showmen* / One in a million: *Brown, Maxine* / Black eyed girl: *Thompson, Billy* / That's my girl: *Clark, Dee* / Do you love me baby: *Masqueraders* / That girl: *Porgy & The Monarchs* / I'm stepping out of the picture: *Maestro, Johnny* / Long after tonight is all over: *Radcliffe, Jimmy*

MCCD 319 / 6 Oct '97 / Music Club

☐ **COOLIN', THE (Classic Irish Slow-Airs & Laments)**

Roisin dubh: *Conlan, Festy* / Spailpin a ruin: *Clancy, Willie* / Nil se na la/The hunours of Winnington: *McConnell, Cathal & Robin Morton* / Paddy rambles through the park: *Doherty, John* / Coolin': *Doran, Felix* / Lark in the clear air: *Pepper, Noel* / Willy Reilly: *Daly, Jackie* / An cailin rua: *McDermott, Josie* / Boolavogue/The old bog road: *Rowsome, Leo* / Air from Thomas Moore: *Solus Lillis* / Se bheath mo bhfuartha: *Griffin, Vincent* / Molly O'Malone: *Ennis, Seamus* / An Eirinn no n'eosfhainn ce h'i: *Droney, Chris* / Red haired boy: *Clifford, Julia* / Lord Mayo: *Mitchell, Pat* / Blackbird: *Kelly, John* / Faithful brown cow: *Walsh, Liam* / Old caubeen: *Kelly, Gene* / Old man rocking the cradle: *O'Keeffe, Padraig* / Fairy child: *Mac Aogain, Michael* / Spalpeen's lament: *Doonan, John* / Bean dubh an ghleanna: *McMahon, Tony* / Blind Mary: *McAloon, Sean* / Melodious little fort of Bruff: *Bailie, Brian* / Lament of Aughrim: *McPeake Family Trio*

CDORBD 093 / Oct '96 / Globestyle

☐ **COP**

Sun: *Under The Noise* / Eclipse: *Fishtank* / Open your eyes: *DLI* / Ne plus ultra: *Index* / Transit: *Battery* / Victim (sanction of the victim): *Heavy Water Factory* / Orchid: *Osas* / Stuck: *Slave Unit* / Cutting thin blue lines: *DLI* / Christine: *Battery* / Halcyon ghetto: *Index* / Manna: *Under The Noise* / Angela: *Razor Skyline*

COPCD 026 / Dec '96 / Cop International

☐ **COPULATIN' BLUES**

JCD 1 / Oct '91 / Jass

☐ **COPULATIN' COLLECTION VOL.1**

VN 168 / Aug '95 / Viper's Nest

☐ **CORASON CALIENTE COLLECTION**

Legba mia mia: *Les Grandes Vissages De Cyvadier* / El sombrerito (el enfermo y el doctor iii): *Los Camperos De Valles* / Harina de maiz: *Septeto Tipico Oriental* / La vieja: *La Negra Graciana* / Oyelos de nuevo: *Los Munequitos De Matanzas* / Canero no.15: *Los Guanches* / Laos, Cambodia y Vietnam: *Grupo Changui De Guantanamo* / Baile en la calle: *Cachucha Y Su Conjunto* / Los perros del curo: *Cachucha Y Su Conjunto* / Las abajenas: *Mariachi Reyes Del Aserradero* / La tortolita: *Reynoso, Juan* / Amarrao con P: *Cuarteto Patria* / Male amalita: *Dueto De Comachuen* / El canelo: *Conjunto Cosamaloapan* / Mayeye: *Canambu* / El principe de los Bongoceros: *Septeto Habanero* / Camino a Mayaguez: *Guateque* / Go mango walk: *Mini-Musical Female Duet* / Contigo en la distancia: *Garzon, Armando & Quinteto Oriente*

CRSCD 801 / Feb '97 / CRS

☐ **CORES DO BRASIL VOL.1 (Vozes)**

Para-raio: *Djavan* / Ole ola: *Buarque, Chico* / Cavalgada: *De Belem, Fafa* / Mariano: *Camargo, Cesar* / Bodas de prata: *Regina, Elis* / Outubro: *Nascimento, Milton* / Denise rei: *Ben, Jorge* / Viramundo: *Bethania, Maria* / Maravilha: *Hime, Francis & Chico Buarque* / Abre alas: *Lins, Ivan* / Ive brussel: *Ben, Jorge & Caetano Veloso* / Toada: *Lobo, Edu* / Doce maggia: *De Belem, Fafa* / Ate segunda feira: *Buarque, Chico* / Curumin chama cunhata que eu vou contar: *Ben, Jorge* / Travessia: *Nascimento, Milton* / Preta pretinha: *Baianos, Novos* / Coisas cristalinas: *Wando* / Ventos do norte: *Djavan* / Faz parte do meu show: *Creuza, Maria*

NSCD 001 / Jul '91 / Nascente

☐ **CORES DO BRASIL VOL.2 (Samba)**

Bizantina bizancia: *Ben, Jorge* / La vem o Brasil descendo a ladeira: *Moreira, Moraes* / Prata da noite: *De Sa, Estacio* / O bebado e o equilibrista: *Bosca, Joao* / Moenda: *Machado, Elaine* / Swing de campo grande: *Balonos, Novos* / Flor de lis: *Djavan* / Fruta mulher: *Moreira, Moraes* / Acorda que eu quero ver: *Caymmi, Nana* / O dia que o sol declarou o seu amor pela terra: *Ben, Jorge* / Quem te viu, quem te ve: *Buarque, Chico* / Brasil pandeiro: *Balonos, Novos* / A rita: *Buarque, Chico* / No reino encantado do amor: *Ben, Jorge* / Maria vai com as outras: *Creuza, Maria* / Tem que se tirar da cabeca: *Do Salgeuiro, Academicos* / Quilombo do dumba: *De Jesus, Clementina* / Roda viva: *Buarque, Chico* / O dia se zangou: *Negra, Jovelina Perola* / Era umas ves 13 pontos: *Ben, Jorge* / Contraste: *Macale, Jards* / Que maravilha: *Ben, Jorge & Toquinho*

NSCD 002 / Jul '91 / Nascente

☐ **CORES DO BRASIL VOL.3 (Bossa Nova)**

Embola a bola: *Djavan* / Samba de bencao: *De Moraes, Vincius* / Chega de saudade: *Creuza, Maria* / Mais um adeus: *Toquinho & Marilia Medalha* / A felicidade: *Dos Santos, Agostinho* / Para viver um grande amor: *De Moraes, Vincius* / Para que digladiar: *Ben, Jorge* / Desencontro: *Buarque, Chico & Toquinho* / Samba de veloso: *Zimbo Trio* / Sao demals os perigos desta vida: *Vinicius & Toquinho* / Apelo: *Bethania, Maria & Vinicius* / Canto de ossanha: *Creuza, Maria & Vinicius & Toquinho* / Na boca de beco: *Djavan* / Voce abusu: *Creuza, Maria* / Carolina: *Buarque, Chico* / Girl from Ipanema: *De Moraes, Vincius* / Corcovado: *Creuza, Maria* / Morena de flor: *De Moraes, Vincius* / Marina: *Creuza, Maria* / Paiol de polvora: *De Moraes, Vincius* / Trocando em miudo: *Hime, Francis* / Katarina, Katarina: *Ben, Jorge*

NSCD 003 / Jul '91 / Nascente

☐ **CORES DO BRASIL VOL.4 (Samba Com Jazz)**

Milagre: *Quarteto Em Cy* / Agua de beber: *Zimbo Trio* / Tres pontas: *Nascimento, Milton* / Samba do aviao: *Jobim, Antonio Carlos & Miucha* / Reza: *Zimbo Trio* / Mas que nada: *Creuza, Maria* / Samba sem voce: *Passos, Rosa & Emilio Santiago* / Bon tempo: *Buarque, Chico* / Muito obrigado: *Djavan* / Como diza o poeta: *Vinicius & Toquinho* / Noite dos mascarados: *Buarque, Chico* / Consolacao: *Zimbo Trio* / O morro nao engana: *Melodia, Luiz* / Cancao de busios: *Sa, Sandra* / Samba de verao: *Valle, Marcus* / Bem bem: *Costa, Gal* / Pra fazer o sol nascer: *Gil, Gilberto* / Madalena ful pro mar: *Buarque, Chico* / Requebra que eu dou um doce: *Hime, Olivia & Dory Caymmi* / Um vestido de bolero: *Hime, Olivia & Dory Caymmi* / Onde e que voce esteva: *Buarque, Chico* / Gira giro: *Nascimento, Milton* / Arrastao: *Zimbo Trio* / Espelho christalino: *Valenca, Alceu*

NSCD 004 / Jul '91 / Nascente

☐ **CORES DO BRASIL VOL.5 (Saudade)**

No dia em que eu vim embora: *Regina, Elis* / Boca da noite: *Toquinho* / Cavaleiro: *Veloso, Caetano* / Primavera: *Joyce* / Uma vez um caso: *Lobo, Edu & Joyce* / Corsario: *Regina, Elis* / Gongaba: *Hime, Olivia & Edu Lobo* / Dindi: *Creuza, Maria* / Dreamer: *Wanda* / Sem fantasia: *Buarque, Chico* / Ultimo desejo: *Bethania, Maria* / Umas e outras: *Buarque, Chico* / Eu sel que vou te amar: *Creuza, Maria & Vinicius & Toquinho* / Pra nao mais voltar: *De Belem, Fafa* / Irmao de fe: *Nascimento, Milton* / How insensitive: *Creuza, Maria* / Sabia: *Buarque, Chico* / Da cor do pecado: *Creuza, Maria* / Acabou chorare: *Baianos, Novos* / Rosa flor: *Vandre, Geraldo* / Apelo: *Toquinho & Vincius De Moraes*

NSCD 005 / Jul '91 / Nascente

☐ **CORES DO BRASIL VOL.6 (Danca)**

Roda: *Gil, Gilberto* / Besta e tu: *Baianos, Novos* / Fato consumado: *Djavan* / Te futuco: *Guerreiro, Cid* / Taj Mahal/Filhomaravilha/Pais Tropical: *Ben, Jorge* / A tongo da mironga do kabulete: *Toquinho & Vinicius* / Rei no bagaco coisas do vida: *De Belem, Fafa* / Salve simpatia: *Ben, Jorge* / Tiro de

CORES DO BRASIL VOL.6

misericordia: Bosco, Joao & Chico Batera / Adelita: Ben, Jorge / A banda do ze pretinho: Ben, Jorge / Nem ouro nem prata: Maurity, Ruy / Ague negra da lagoa: Toquinho / Africaner brother bound: Shock, Obina & Gilberto Gil / Gabriel Guerreiro galactico: Ben, Jorge / Mambembe: De Belem, Fafa / Perfume de cebola (Fragance of onion): Filo / Da cor do pecado: Creuza, Maria / Em matogrosso fronteira com: Ben, Jorge

NSCD 006 / Jul '91 / Nascente

☐ **CORNEMUSE ECOSSAISE**
Massed pipes and drums / Country dance / Grand march / Set dance / Pipe major march / Quick march / Piper dance / Pipes and drums in Kathmandup / Scottish dance / Royal Scots polka / Drummer's call / Hills of Glenorchy / Greenwood side / Slow march / Banks of Allan / Amazing grace / Auld Lang Syne / Military fanfare / Black bear / Fanfare Drawbridge

ARN 64030 / '87 / Arion

☐ **CORNERS OF THE MOUTH, THE**
EFA 805142 / 3 Nov '97 / Bubblecore

☐ **CORNERSTONE CONNECTION**
SONCD 0069 / Oct '94 / Sonic Sounds

☐ **CORONATION STREET (25th Anniversary Album)**
Coronation street theme / Beatles medley / You needed me / This old heart of mine / Never can say goodbye / To all the men I've loved before / Unchained melody / Pop party medley / These boots are made for walkin' / Street medley / All of me / George Formby medley / You make me feel so young / Street like ours / Old time sing-a-long medley

ECD 3115 / Jan '95 / K-Tel

☐ **CORPORATE ROCK WARS**
Strike it: Dub War / My mind still speaks: Misery Loves Company / Lighter form of killing: Pitch Shifter / Exodus: Scorn / Joy of irony: Fudge Tunnel / Freak wow: Old / Crush my soul: Godflesh / North Korea goes bang: Violent, Johnny / Honour code loyalty: Misery Loves Company / Mental: Dub War / NCM: Pitch Shifter / Sex mammoth: Fudge Tunnel / Glitch: Old / Electric chair: Ultraviolence / New spite: Godflesh / End: Scorn

MOSH 136CD / May '95 / Earache

☐ **CORPUS OF DESTRUCTION**
TZ 100012 / Feb '98 / Terrazone

☐ **CORRIB FOLK, THE**
CDBALLAD 006 / Jan '95 / Outlet

☐ **CORRIDINHOS**
PS 65093 / Aug '92 / PlayaSound

☐ **COSMIC CONSPIRACY**
IBIZAMUSIC 003 / Mar '97 / Ibiza

☐ **COSMIC CUBES VOL.1 (2CD Set)**
SPV 08938252 / Feb '95 / SPV

☐ **COSMIC CUBES VOL.2 (2CD Set)**
SPV 08938342 / Jun '95 / SPV

☐ **COSMIC CUBES VOL.3 (2CD Set)**
K People: Nailin & Kane / Dawn goddess: Quatermass / Sweet gravity: LSG / Hovercab: Spacebuggy / Don't cry my love: Love Religion / Chemical trance: Ethnica / Gobi desert: 100 Monkeys & Tristan / Bombay: Caunos / Intimate encounter: New Balance Crossover / Flow: Model 500 / Visual imagination: Hyber Nation / One of the frightened: Angeldust / Polterguys: Kashmir / Positive education: SLAM / Rising rasoli: Ru-Rapente / Blue dream chapter 2: Plasma / Dirty life: Illegal District / Synasthasia: Source Experience / Neria fetisch: L'Auberge / How to bluff your way in techno music: Max 404

SPV 08938662 / May '96 / SPV

☐ **COSMIC CUBES VOL.4 (2CD Set)**
Party spirit: Deep Sound / Wired: 10th Chapter / All because of you: Universal State Of Mind / Sundae 6 am: Van Dyke, Paul / Train of thought: Matipo Pyramid / 03: O-Lab / Subconsciousness: Elysium / Afterlife: Astralasia / T 96: A.M.D / Tommy: Terra C / Cat and the canary: Miherobenics / Nautilus: Scan Carriers / Caunos: Caunos / Mission: Watchman / Indian fate: Haramatix / Cosmic wave: DJ Warlock / Vallhalla: Hmetico / Answer: NDMA

SPV 08947342 / Apr '97 / SPV

☐ **COSMIC CUBES VOL.5 (2CD Set)**
Enigma: Canyon / Far beyond: EDT / My definition of trance: Flex / Plonk: Intensity / East: Humate & Rabbit In The Moon / Netherworld: LSG / Haleidoscope: Art Of Trance / Air: Abion / Blue fear: Armin / La paloma: Dove Beat / Bells of Brixton: Friends Lovers & Family / Straight: Caunos / Prosac: DJ Tonicraft / Magnetic fields: Magnetic Fields / Screwdriver: Planet Ben / Deep space 50: Dimension 5 / Universe: Killer Eyes / Red signal: Citizen X / Status X: Framic / Sweet music: Trancelate

SPV 08947562 / Sep '97 / SPV

☐ **COSMIC CUBES VOL.6 (2CD Set)**
SPV 08947842 / 2 Feb '98 / SPV

☐ **COSMIC DISCO, THE**
Prayer: Guillaume, Jephte / Big knockers: Jedi Knights / Chord symbolis: Glitch City / 2 Stratup gods: Trouble / Republic Earthshaker EP: Earthshaker / Turntable brothers Mk II EP: Get Ready / Gimme some horns: Essentials / You can't hide from your bud: DJ Sneak / Visions of the future: Farris, Geke / Only 4 U: Cajmere / Land of the lost: Green Velvet / Bozz eyes: Fandango Wideowheels & Huggy Bear / Answering machine: Green Velvet / Groovin': House 'N' Control / Life is changing: Castelli, Cricco / Get down: X-OR / Hot music: Soho / Action 78: DJ 78

MMLCD 023 / May '97 / Mixmag Live

☐ **COSMIC ENERGY VOL.1 (2CD Set)**
IR 002CD / Jan '96 / Independence

☐ **COSMIC KURUSHI MONSTERS (Tokyo Invasion Vol.1) (2CD Set)**
TOKYO 1 / Jul '96 / Virgin

☐ **COSMIC TANTRA (Ambient Music For Relaxation)**
Moonraga / Shiva's flute / Palace of the winds / Return / Cosmic light / Elevation / Rajastan flower / Krishna's raga / Lotus blossom

21145 / Nov '97 / Laserlight

☐ **COSMIC TRANCE**
DI 242 / Dec '95 / Distance

☐ **COSMIC TRANCE VOL.1 (2CD Set)**
560062 / Mar '97 / Westcom

☐ **COSMIC TRANCE VOL.2**
SUB 48382 / Apr '97 / Distance

☐ **COSMIC TRANCE VOL.2 (2CD Set)**
Whale island: Judicial Weight / Fragile: LSG / Halfmoon AM: Hip'ee / Vision: Yum Yum / This: Stigma / Don't you want my love: DJ Marcelo / Alien love song: Astralasia / Fiddler: Inder Tracks / Vampire state building: Kaylyn / Mindflow: Planet Ben / Forbidden channel: Canyon / Futura: Amethyst / Discorder: Havana / Seadog: Clanger / 97 Stars: Quazar / Back to nature: Magnetic Slides / Turban kaos: Drop & Dash / Train: Materia Magica

560202 / 23 Feb '98 / Nova Tekk

☐ **COSMIC TRAVELLERS**
Right stuff: Pressurehead / Between worlds: Underground Zero / We do it: Hawkwind / Grid coordinate-vorp one: Anubian Lights / Time of: Hawklords / Venusian skyline: Melting Euphoria / Master: Helios Creed / Trip to G9: Spiral Realms / Seeing strange nights: Dark Matter / Pre-cambrian shuffle: Brain / Space does not care: Zero Gravity

CDMGRAM 105 / Apr '96 / Anagram

☐ **COSMOSOUND (The Art Of Drum 'n' Bass & Trip Hop)**
CLP 9992 / Jun '97 / Cleopatra

☐ **COTTON CLUB**
15707 / Apr '94 / Laserlight

☐ **COTTON CLUB 1924-1936**
FA 074 / 24 Feb '98 / Fremeaux

☐ **COTTON CLUB, THE**
Cotton Club stomp: Ellington, Duke Cotton Club Orchestra / Just a crazy song: Robinson, Bill 'Bojangles' / Am I blue: Waters, Ethel / Heebie jeebies: Webb, Chick & His Orchestra / I must have that man: Hall, Adelaide / Stormy weather: Arlen, Harold / When you're smiling: Armstrong, Louis Orchestra / Lazybones: Williams, Midge / Old yazoo: Calloway, Cab Orchestra / Honey just for you: Kirk, Andy & His Twelve Clouds of Joy / Between the Devil and the deep blue sea: Armstrong, Louis Orchestra / Sweet rhythm: Lunceford, Jimmie & his Chickasaw Syncopators / Blues I love to sing: Hall, Adelaide / Kicking the gong around: Calloway, Cab Orchestra / Serenade to a wealthy widow: Foresythe, Reginald / Jubilee stomp: Ellington, Duke Cotton Club Orchestra / I can't give you anything but love: Waters, Ethel / Doin' the new low down: Mills, Irving

CDAJA 5031 / Oct '88 / Living Era

☐ **COTTON PICKERS 1922-1925, THE**
Hot lips / Loose feet / Way down yonder in New Orleans / Snakes hips / Rampart Street blues / Back o' town blues / Shufflin' Mose / Do yo' dooty Daddy / Blue rose / Jimtown blues / Mishawaka blues / Down and out blues

CBC 1029 / 29 Jun '98 / Timeless Historical

☐ **COTTON PICKIN' BLUES**
Southern can is mine: McTell, 'Blind' Willie / Lay down St Louis blues: Johnson, Lonnie / Milkcow's calf blues: Johnson, Robert / I ain't no telling: Hurt, 'Mississippi' John / Pigmeat is what I crave: Carter, Bo / Fixing to die blues: White, Bukka / Lord, I just can't keep from crying: Johnson, 'Blind' Willie / Stormy night blues: Carr, Leroy / Spreadin' snakes blue: Broonzy, 'Big' Bill / Fort Worth and Dallas blues: Leadbelly / Baby won't you please come home: Smith, Bessie / Sweet home blues: Wheatstraw, Peetie / Truckin' my blues away: Fuller, Blind Boy / Nothing in particular: Memphis Minnie / Reverence man blues: Patton, Charlie / Matchbox blues: Jefferson, Blind Lemon

305682 / Apr '98 / Hallmark

☐ **COUNTDOWN COMPILATION**
Only time will tell: Makin' Time / Dreams come true: Combine / Guilty: Alljacks / Not ready for love: Co-Stars / Stuck on the edge of a blade: Kick / Bend don't break: Stupidity / Whatever happened to Thames beat: Stupidity / Faker: Gents / Sticks and stones: Moment / Inside out: Scene / I don't need no doctor: Fast Eddie / Wednesday girl: Jetset / I can't let go: Kick / Armchair politician: Kick / My babe: Fast Eddie / Help me: Fast Eddie / Sweet sensation: Fast Eddie

MODSKACD 006 / 3 Nov '97 / Captain Mod

☐ **COUNTER CULTURE**
Strings: Astrm Farm / Love is what we need: 99 All Stars / Calling: Solar Stone / Help me make it: Huff & Puff / Walk with me: Heliotropic / Disco screw: Protein Boy / Atomic life: Atom Heart / Snow: ORN / Small town boy: Legato / Spin spin sugar: Sneaker Pimps / Cafe del mar: Energy 52 / Dark and loud: Underworld / Galaxia: Moonman / May go wild: Grooveyard

KICKCD 52 / Jun '97 / Kickin'

☐ **COUNTER CULTURE VOL.2**
KICKCD 64 / 17 Nov '97 / Kickin'

☐ **CAT'N AROUND**
KKCD 07 / Feb '93 / Krazy Kat

☐ **COUNTRY**
Turn me loose and let me swing: Nelson, Willie & Curtis Potter / Brand new ways: McCallister, Don Jr & His COWboy Jazz Revue / Black rose: Whitfield, Barrence & Tom Russell / Midnight ride: Roy, Jimmy 5 Star Hillbillies / She makes the angels cry: Broussard, Rick / Undying love: Swan, Billy & Van Duren / Just to hear your voice: Price, Toni / Yeah, yeah, yeah: Blazers / It's over: Flores, Rosie / Corazon viajero: Hinojosa, Tish / Monterrey: McGhee, Wes / Border radio: Alvin, Dave / Prairie blues: Bennett, Pinto & The Motel Cowboys / Friends: Lost Gonzo Band / I gotta have my baby back: Rattlesnake Annie / Walkin' on the moon: Moffatt, Katy / No place to fall: Van Zandt, Townes / Factory town: Donovan, Barb / Ain't licked yet: Hamilton, Dirk / I don't feel that way anymore: Robinson, Charlie / Fool: Pickett's / Fool such as I: Chiavola, Kathy / Door number one: Frazisco, George / Jack / O holy night: Butler, Jerry / If we make it through December: Butler, Jerry / Rockin' around

5542422 / Oct '97 / Spectrum

☐ **COUNTRY CHRISTMAS VOL.1 (Christmas For Cowboys)**
Little drummer boy: Campbell, Glen / White Christmas: Walker, Billy / What child is this: Carnes, Kim / O come all ye faithful (adeste fidelis): Lee, Brenda / Christmas for Cowboys: Denver, John / We wish you a merry Christmas: Nelson, Willie / Twelve days of Christmas: Greenwood, Lee / Jolly old St. Nicholas: Greenwood, Lee / All I want for Christmas: Mandrell, Louise / I'll be home for Christmas: Greene, Jack / O holy night: Butler, Jerry / If we make it through December: Butler, Jerry / Rockin' around the Christmas tree: Fargo, Donna / We three kings: Lettermen / Pretty paper: Nelson, Willie

120082 / Oct '97 / Jingle

☐ **COUNTRY CHRISTMAS VOL.2 (O Christmas Tree)**
O Christmas tree: Hall, Tom T. / Deck the halls: Nelson, Willie / First Noel: Thomas, B.J. / Have yourself a merry little Christmas: Raven, Eddy / O little town of Bethlehem: Carnes, Kim / God rest ye merry gentlemen: Clark, Roy / My favourite things: Todd, Paul / Joy to the world: Pride, Charley / Silver bells: Riley, Jeannie C. / Up on the housetop: Boxcar Willie / I heard the bells on Christmas day: Gatlin, Larry / Rudolph the red-nosed reindeer: Davis, Skeeter / Blue Christmas: Sherman, Bobby / Please come home for Christmas: Stampley, Joe / O holy night: Lettermen

120092 / Oct '97 / Jingle

☐ **COUNTRY CHRISTMAS VOL.3 (Jingle Bells)**
Silent night: Lee, Brenda / Carol medley: Campbell, Glen / Christmas song: Walker, Billy / It came upon a midnight clear: Anderson, Bill / Jingle bells: Wagoner, Porter / Santa Claus and popcorn: Haggard, Merle / Hark the herald angels sing: Montgomery, Melba / Away in a manger: Jennings, Waylon / Jingle bell rock: Stampley, Joe / Hallelujah: Gayle, Crystal / Carol of the bells: Todd, Paul / Santa Claus is coming to town: Davis, Skeeter / Here comes Santa Claus: Davis, Skeeter / Don't it make you want to be a kid again: Boxcar Willie / Go tell it on the mountain: Lettermen

120102 / Oct '97 / Jingle

☐ **COUNTRY CHRISTMAS, A (3CD Set)**
Little drummer boy: Campbell, Glen / White Christmas: Walker, Billy / What child is this: Carnes, Kim / O come all ye faithful (adeste fidelis): Lee, Brenda / Christmas for Cowboys: Denver, John / We wish you a merry Christmas: Nelson, Willie / Twelve days of Christmas: Greenwood, Lee / Goin' home: Sherman, Bobby / All I want for Christmas (dear is you): Mandrell, Louise / I'll be home for Christmas: Greene, Jack / O holy night: Butler, Jerry / Rockin' it through December: Haggard, Merle / Rockin' around the Christmas tree: Fargo, Donna / Christmas at Excelsior bay: Todd, Paul / Pretty kiss: Nelson, Willie / Christmas is coming to town: Raven, Eddy / O little town of Bethlehem: Carnes, Kim / God rest ye merry gentlemen: Clark, Roy / My favourite things: Todd, Paul / Silent night: Lee, Brenda / Carol medley: Campbell, Glen / Christmas song: Walker, Billy / It came upon a midnight clear: Anderson, Bill / Jingle bells: Wagoner, Porter / If I was a merry little Christmas: Thomas, Raven, Eddy / O little town of Bethlehem: Carnes, Kim / God rest ye merry gentlemen: Clark, Roy / My favourite things: Todd, Paul / Hark the herald angels sing: Montgomery, Melba / Away in a manger: Jennings, Waylon / Jingle bell rock: Stampley, Joe / Hallelujah: Gayle, Crystal / Carol of the bells: Todd, Paul / Santa Claus is coming to town: Davis, Skeeter / Blue Christmas: Sherman, Bobby / Please come home for Christmas: Stampley, Joe / holy night: Lettermen / Silent night: Lee, Brenda / Carol medley: Campbell, Glen / Christmas song: Walker, Billy / It came upon a midnight clear: Anderson, Bill / Jingle bells: Wagoner, Porter / Santa Claus and popcorn: Haggard, Merle / We wish you a merry Christmas: Lettermen

120072 / Oct '97 / Jingle

☐ **COUNTRY CLASSICS**
Rose garden: Anderson, Lynn / Big bad John: Dean, Jimmy / No charge: Montgomery, Melba / Harper Valley PTA: Riley, Jeannie C. / Four in the morning: Young, Faron / Achey breaky heart: Please help me, I'm falling: Locklin, Hank / Wolverton mountain: King, Claude / From a jack to a king: Miller, Ned / One day at a time: Seely, Jeannie / Mr. Walker, it's all over: Spears, Billie Jo / Country Bumpkin: Smith, Cal / You're my best friend: Williams, Don / Crazy: Cline, Patsy / Satin sheets: Pruett, Jeanne / Meet me in Montana: Osmond, Marie & Dan Seals / Ode to Billie Joe: Gentry, Bobbie / Harper Valley PTA: Riley, Jeannie C. / I walk the line: Cash, Johnny

ECD 3057 / Jan '95 / K-Tel

☐ **COUNTRY CLASSICS (2CD Set)**
Hello walls: Young, Faron / Okie from Muskogee: Haggard, Merle / Happiest girl in the whole USA: Fargo, Donna / Before the next teardrop falls: Fender, Freddy / Country bumpkin: Smith, Cal / You're my best friend: Williams, Don / Crazy: Cline, Patsy / Satin sheets: Pruett, Jeanne / Meet me in Montana: Osmond, Marie & Dan Seals / Ode to Billie Joe: Gentry, Bobbie / Harper Valley PTA: Riley, Jeannie C. / I walk the line: Cash, Johnny / LA international airport: Raye, Susan / Baby's got her blue jeans on: McDaniel, Mel / Let it be me: Campbell, Glen & Bobbie Gentry / In the middle of a heartache: Jackson, Wanda / Easy lovin': Hart, Freddie / Heaven in the evening: Overstreet, Tommy

DOU 882582 / 2 Feb '98 / Disky

☐ **COUNTRY 'N' IRISH ACCORDION**
Country roads medley / Botany bay medley / When Irish eyes are smiling medley / These are my mountains medley / I'll take you home again Kathleen / Tom Dooley medley / All for me grog / Walkin' after midnight / Isle of Innisfree medley / When your old wedding ring was new medley / Maggie medley / Leaving of Liverpool

CD 6081 / Jun '97 / Music

☐ **COUNTRY AND WESTERN FAVOURITES (4CD Set)**
MBSCD 410 / Jan '95 / Castle

☐ **COUNTRY AND WESTERN GREATS (Sea Of Heartbreak)**
I can't stop loving you: Gibson, Don / Almost persuaded: Jones, George / Ruby, don't take your love to town: Rogers, Kenny / Where do I go from here: Williams, Don / Shelter of my arms: Nelson, Willie / For the good times: Husky, Ferlin / Four in the morning: Young, Faron / But I do: Fender, Freddy / Glen Christmas song: Murray, Billie / It came upon a midnight clear: Anderson, Bill / Jingle bells: Russell, Johnny / Love's gone away here: Jennings, Waylon / There goes everything: Greene, Jack / Things to talk about: Jackson, Stonewall / Send me the pillow that you dream on: Locklin, Hank / Son of Hickory Holler's tramp: Darrell, Johnny / Sea of heartbreak: Gibson, Don / Talk back trembling lips: Jones, George / Rueben James: Rogers, Kenny / Tears: Williams, Don / Broken promises: Nelson, Willie

MUCD 9013 / Apr '95 / Musketeer

☐ **COUNTRY BLUES COLLECTORS ITEMS 1924-1928**
DOCD 5169 / May '93 / Document

☐ **COUNTRY BLUES COLLECTORS ITEMS VOL.2**
SOB 035402 / Apr '93 / Story Of The Blues

☐ **COUNTRY BLUES GUITAR**
Done left here: McDowell, 'Mississippi' Fred / Walkin' blues: Block, Rory / Honeymoon blues: Hammond, John / Blues for Tampa Red: Mitchell, Paul & Annie Raines / Broke down engine: Geremia, Paul / Going to the river: Shines, Johnny / Mean old blues: Frisco: Hovington, Frank / Long tall Mama: Broomberg, David / John Henry: Olsen, Kristina / Reno factory: Cephas, John / Bowling Green' & Phil Wiggins / Mississippi blues: Bookbinder, Roy / One dime blues: Baker, Etta

EDCD 7051 / Sep '97 / Easydisc

☐ **COUNTRY BLUES HARD HITTERS (How You Want It Done)**
How you want it done: Broonzy, 'Big' Bill / Walk right in: Cannon, Gus & His Jug Stompers / Back to the woods: Arnold, Kokomo / Voice throwing blues: Hawkins, Walter 'Buddy Boy' / Two white horses in a line: Evans, Joe & Arthur McClain / Dark angel: Moore, Alice / Statesboro blues: McTell, 'Blind' Willie / Believe I'll go back home: Kelly, Jack & His South Memphis Jug Band / Devil and my brown: Jackson, Bo Weevil / Rolling log blues: Beaman, Lottie / Don't hang my clothes on no barbed wire line: Wheatstraw, Peetie / Denomination blues: Phillips, Washington / Teasin' brown blues: Lasky, Louie / Bottle wash diddie: Blake, Arthur 'Blind' / Wild cow blues: Williams, 'Big' Joe / Big chief blues: Lewis, Furry / Whiskey and women: Black Ace / Dope head blues: Spivey, Victoria / Girl I love she got long curly hair: Estes, Sleepy' John / See that my grave is kept clean: Jefferson, Blind Lemon / Chickasaw train blues: Memphis Minnie / Little green slippers: Memphis Jug Band / Right now blues: Reece, Bill / I'm so glad: James, Skip

PM 002 / Sep '96 / Pigmeat

☐ **COUNTRY BOX (3CD Set)**
TBXD 505 / Jan '96 / TrueTrax

☐ **COUNTRY BOX (2CD Set)**
PBXCD 505 / Nov '96 / Pulse

☐ **COUNTRY CHARTBUSTERS VOL.1**
Devil went down to Georgia: Daniels, Charlie Band / Rose garden: Anderson, Lynn / Stand by your man: Wynette, Tammy / Always on my mind: Nelson, Willie / El Paso: Robbins, Marty / Me and Bobby McGee: Kristofferson, Kris / Rhinestone cowboy: Campbell, Glen / Teddy bear: Pride, Charley / Would you lay with me: Tucker, Tanya

4771202 / 27 Jul '98 / Embassy

☐ **COUNTRY CHRISTMAS**
DCD 5353 / Dec '93 / Disky

☐ **COUNTRY CHRISTMAS**
Winter wonderland: Francis, Connie / Jingle bells: Statler Brothers / Santa Claus is coming to town: Page, Patti / Santa Claus' daughter: Rich, Charlie / Please come home for Christmas: Kershaw, Sammy / White Christmas: I've got my love to keep me warm: Mathis, Johnny / Calling / Christmas is: Oslin, K.D. / There's a new kid in town: Mattea, Kathy / Calling you: Williams, Hank / Christmas to Christmas: Nash, Toby / Me and Jesus: Hall, Tom T. / I saw the light:

DOU 882582 / 2 Feb '98 / Disky

☐ COUNTRY COLLECTION (Ruby Don't Take Your Love To Town)
Ruby, don't take your love to town: *Rogers, Kenny* / Six days on the road: *Dudley, Dave* / I've been everywhere: *Anderson, Lynn* / (There's) always something there to remind me: *Williams, Don* / Walk on by: *Van Dyke, Leroy* / 9,999,999 tears: *Baily, Razzy* / I gave my love to a railroad man: *Mandrell, Barbara* / Almost persuaded: *Houston, David* / It's all over: *Murray, Anne* / I washed my hands in muddy water: *Jackson, Stonewall* / I'm so lonesome I could cry: *Thomas, B.J.* / Release me: *Parton, Dolly* / Honeysuckle: *Owens, Buck* / Teddy Bear song: *Fairchild, Barbara* / Satin sheets: *Pruett, Jeanne* / Tender years: *Jones, George*
100962 / May '97 / A-Play Collection

☐ COUNTRY COLLECTION (Crazy)
Denver: *Milsap, Ronnie* / Redneck: *Perkins, Carl* / Kawliga: *Mandrell, Barbara* / Crying: *Anderson, Lynn* / I want to be with you tonight: *Alabama* / It makes no difference now: *Spears, Billie Jo* / Crazy: *Lynn, Loretta* / Don't think twice: *Jennings, Waylon* / Right after the dance: *Owens, Buck* / Something's burning: *Rogers, Kenny* / Things have gone to pieces: *Jones, George* / Mistakes by the number: *Kershaw, Doug* / There's never been a time: *Williams, Don* / I can't help it: *Shannon, Del* / Because of you: *Posey, Sandy* / One step beyond: *Nelson, Willie*
100982 / May '97 / A-Play Collection

☐ COUNTRY COLLECTION (Rose Garden)
Rose Garden: *Anderson, Lynn* / Patches: *Alabama* / Jambalaya: *Jones, George* / Green green grass of home: *Ives, Burl* / Abilene: *Jennings, Waylon* / Wayward wind: *Mandrell, Barbara* / For the good times: *Rogers, Kenny* / Look what they've done to my song: *Spears, Billie Jo* / Road that I walk: *Twitty, Conway* / Puppy love: *Parton, Dolly* / We did in '54: *Perkins, Carl* / Sunday morning coming down: *Smith, Sammi* / I just can't help believing: *Thomas, B.J.* / Boys ain't supposed to cry: *Davis, Mac* / Take my hand: *Williams, Don* / Dreamin': *Gibbs, Terry*
100972 / May '97 / A-Play Collection

☐ COUNTRY COLLECTION (3CD Set)
Ruby, don't take your love to town: *Rogers, Kenny & The First Edition* / Six days on the road: *Dudley, Dave* / I've been everywhere: *Anderson, Lynn* / (There's) always something there to remind me: *Williams, Don* / Walk on by: *Van Dyke, Leroy* / 9999999 tears: *Baily, Razzy* / I gave my love to a railroad man: *Mandrell, Barbara* / Almost persuade: *Houston, David* / It's all over: *Murray, Anne* / I washed my hands in muddy water: *Jackson, Stonewall* / I'm so lonesome I could cry: *Thomas, B.J.* / Release me: *Parton, Dolly* / Honeysuckle: *Owens, Buck* / Teddy bear song: *Fairchild, Barbara* / Satin sheets: *Pruett, Jeanne* / Your tender years: *Jones, George* / Rose garden: *Anderson, Lynn* / Patches: *Alabama* / Jambalaya: *Jones, George* / Green green grass of home: *Ives, Burl* / Abilene: *Jennings, Waylon* / Wayward wind: *Mandrell, Barbara* / For the good times: *Rogers, Kenny & The First Edition* / Look what they've done to my song: *Spears, Billie Jo* / Road that I walk: *Twitty, Conway* / Puppy love: *Parton, Dolly* / We did in '54: *Perkins, Carl* / Sunday morning coming down: *Smith, Sammi* / I just can't help believing: *Thomas, B.J.* / Boys ain't suppose to cry: *Davis, Mac* / Take my hand: *Williams, Don* / Dreamin': *Gibbs, Terry* / Denver: *Milsap, Ronnie* / Redneck: *Perkins, Carl* / Kawliga: *Mandrell, Barbara* / Crying: *Anderson, Lynn* / I want to be with you tonight: *Alabama* / It makes no difference now: *Spears, Billie Jo* / Crazy: *Lynn, Loretta* / Don't think twice: *Jennings, Waylon* / Right after the dance: *Owens, Buck* / Something's burning: *Rogers, Kenny & The First Edition* / Things have gone to pieces: *Jones, George* / Mistakes by the number: *Kershaw, Doug* / There's never been a time: *Williams, Don* / I can't help it: *Shannon, Del* / Because of you: *Posey, Sandy* / One step beyond: *Nelson, Willie*
100952 / May '97 / A-Play Collection

☐ COUNTRY COLLECTION (3CD Set)
Ruby, don't take your love to town: *Rogers, Kenny & The First Edition* / Most beautiful girl: *Rich, Charlie* / Listen to a country song: *Anderson, Lynn* / (There's) always something there to remind me: *Williams, Don* / U.S. of America: *Fargo, Donna* / End of the world: *Davis, Skeeter* / These boots are made for walking: *Jackson, Latoya* / Almost persuaded: *Houston, David* / It's only make believe: *Jordanaires* / Teddy bear song: *Fairchild, Barbara* / Home is where you're happy: *Nelson, Willie* / Hey Loretta: *Lynn, Loretta* / Before the next teardrop falls: *Fender, Freddy* / Southern comfort: *McCoy, Charlie* / Rose garden: *Anderson, Lynn* / Behind closed doors: *Rich, Charlie* / Funny face: *Fargo, Donna* / Coal miner's daughter: *Lynn, Loretta* / Abilene: *Jennings, Waylon* / Wolverton mountain: *King, Claude* / For the good times: *Rogers, Kenny & The First Edition* / Please helpme I'm falling: *Locklin, Hank* / (Hey won't you play) Another somebody done somebody wrong so: *Jordanaires* / Abilene: *Hamilton, George IV* / What you don't say: *Jackson, Latoya* / You were always on my mind: *McCoy, Charlie* / Take my hand for a while: *Williams, Don* / I let my mind wonder: *Nelson, Willie* / Happiest girl in the whole U.S.A.: *Fargo, Donna* / There won't be anymore: *Rich, Charlie* / Top of the world: *Anderson, Lynn* / Wasted days and wasted nights: *Fender, Freddy* / Sweet dreams: *Jordanaires* / Crazy: *Lynn, Loretta* / Don't think twice: *Jennings, Waylon* / Something's burning: *Rogers, Kenny & The First Edition* / Oh lonesome me: *Gibson, Don* / There's never been a time: *Williams, Don* / Orange blossom special: *McCoy, Charlie* / Gonna get along without you now: *Davis, Skeeter* / One step beyond: *Nelson, Willie* / Burnin' love: *Jackson, Latoya*
101452 / May '97 / A-Play Collection

☐ COUNTRY COLLECTION (4CD Set)
SUMBX 4004 / Jan '98 / Summit

☐ COUNTRY COLLECTION VOL.1 (Ruby Don't Take Your Love To Town)
Ruby don't take your love into town: *Rogers, Kenny & The First Edition* / Most beautiful girl in the world: *Rich, Charlie* / Listen to a country song: *Anderson, Lynn* / Always something there to remind me: *Williams, Don* / US of America: *Fargo, Donna* / End of the world: *Davis, Skeeter* / These boots are made for walking: *Jackson, Latoya* / Almost persuaded: *Houston, David* / It's only make believe: *Jordanaires* / Teddy bear song: *Fairchild, Barbara* / Home is where you're happy: *Nelson, Willie* / Hey Loretta: *Lynn, Loretta* / Before the next teardrop falls: *Fender, Freddy* / Southern comfort: *McCoy, Charlie*
101462 / May '97 / A-Play Collection

☐ COUNTRY COLLECTION VOL.2 (Rose garden)
Rose garden: *Anderson, Lynn* / Behind closed doors: *Rich, Charlie* / Funny face: *Fargo, Donna* / Coal miners daughter: *Lynn, Loretta* / Abilene: *Jennings, Waylon* / Wolverton mountain: *King, Claude* / For the good times: *Rogers, Kenny & The First Edition* / Please help me I'm falling: *Locklin, Hank* / Another somebody done somebody wrong song: *Jackson, Latoya* / You were always on my mind: *McCoy, Charlie* / Take my hand for a while: *Williams, Don* / I let my mind wonder: *Nelson, Willie*
101472 / May '97 / A-Play Collection

☐ COUNTRY COLLECTION VOL.3 (Crazy)
Happiest girl in the whole USA: *Fargo, Donna* / There won't be anymore: *Rich, Charlie* / Top of the world: *Anderson, Lynn* / Wasted days and wasted nights: *Fender, Freddy* / Sweet dreams: *Jordanaires* / Crazy: *Lynn, Loretta* / Don't think twice: *Jennings, Waylon* / Something's burning: *Rogers, Kenny & The First Edition* / Oh lonesome me: *Gibson, Don* / There's never been a time: *Williams, Don* / Orange blossom special: *McCoy, Charlie* / Gonna get along without you now: *Davis, Skeeter* / One step beyond: *Nelson, Willie* / Burnin' love: *Jackson, Latoya*
101482 / May '97 / A-Play Collection

☐ COUNTRY COLOURS (A Magical Blend Of Music And The Sounds Of Nature)
57522 / May '97 / Nature's Harmony

☐ COUNTRY CREAM VOL.1 (2CD Set)
CDSGP 0100 / Aug '94 / Prestige

☐ COUNTRY DUETS
Something up my sleeve: *Bogguss, Suzy & Billy Dean* / We fell in love anyway: *Francis, Cleve & Patti Austin* / We're both to blame: *Greenwood, Lee & Tanya Tucker* / Bye bye love: *Dalton, Lacy J. & Eddie Rabbitt* / Angels love bad men: *Mandrell, Barbara & Waylon Jennings* / What'cha gonna do with a cowboy: *LeDoux, Chris & Garth Brooks* / Don't underestimate love: *Nitty Gritty Dirt Band* / Cowboys like a little rock 'n' roll: *LeDoux, Chris & Charlie Daniels* / Hopelessly yours: *Greenwood, Lee & Suzy Bogguss* / Don't go out: *Tucker, Tanya & T. Graham Brown* / You've lost that lovin' feeling: *Rogers, Kenny & Dottie West* / All I have to do is dream: *Campbell, Glen & Bobby Gentry* / Willingly: *Nelson, Willie & Shirley Collie* / Let your love flow: *Reeves, Del & Billie Jo Spears* / Something 'bout you baby I like: *Campbell, Glen & Rita Coolidge*
CDMFP 6331 / Apr '97 / Music For Pleasure

☐ COUNTRY DUETS
Wild side of life / Slowly / Let's get together / Dear John letter / Good hearted woman / Making plans / Rings of gold / Till a tear becomes a rose / Jeanie's afraid of the dark / Under the spell again / You don't bring me flowers / Just to satisfy you / Our love / Sweet memories / I love you / Have I told you lately that I love you / Don't let me cross over / Mocking bird hill / Storms never last / Love is no excuse
74321378422 / Apr '97 / Camden

☐ COUNTRY DUETS (2CD Set)
DC 886052 / 2 Feb '98 / Disky

☐ COUNTRY DYNASTY
Sylvia's mother: *Dr. Hook* / Me and Bobby McGee: *Kristofferson, Kris* / Crying: *Orbison, Roy* / Walkin' after midnight: *Cline, Patsy* / Golden ring: *Jones, George & Tammy Wynette* / Jackson: *Cash, Johnny & June Carter* / Thing called love: *Cash, Johnny* / Help me make it through the night: *Kristofferson, Kris & Brenda Lee* / What will baby be: *Parton, Dolly* / Always on my mind: *Nelson, Willie* / To all the girls I've loved before: *Haggard, Merle* / Behind closed doors: *Rich, Charlie* / Seven year ache: *Cash, Johnny* / Downtown train: *Carpenter, Mary-Chapin* / You're gonna love yourself in the morning: *Nelson, Willie & Brenda Lee* / Honey come back: *Anderson, Lynn* / There goes my everything: *Wynette, Tammy*
4747912 / Nov '93 / Columbia

☐ COUNTRY FAVOURITES (4CD Set)
HADCDMS 6 / Oct '96 / Javelin

☐ COUNTRY FAVOURITES
Where do we go from here: *Williams, Don* / World's worst loser: *Jones, George* / Love hurts: *Parsons, Gram & Emmylou Harris* / Hello walls: *Young, Faron* / Fly like an eagle: *Fat Cat Band* / All that's keeping me alive: *Fat Cat Band* / How do I hide from a memory: *Pillow, Ray* / It's so easy: *Jennings, Waylon* / By the time I get to Phoenix: *Nashville West* / You still want to go: *Henderson, Kelvin* / Release me: *Parton, Dolly* / Lighthouse bar: *Blackwater Band* / Is there something on your mind: *Nelson, Willie* / Way out there: *Parsons, Gene* / Wing of a dove: *Husky, Ferlin* / What she deserves: *Powers, Laura* / Let the sunshine on the people: *Jackson, Stonewall* / Silver wings: *Fender, Freddy* / You'll never walk alone: *Twitty, Conway*
306082 / Jan '97 / Hallmark

☐ COUNTRY FAVOURITES (4CD Set)
PBXCD 414 / 20 Apr '98 / Pulse

☐ COUNTRY FIT FOR HEROES VOL.1 & 2, A
Future must be ours: *Blitzkrieg* / Die with dignity: *Violators* / Goverment stinks: *Violators* / Fight back: *Hostile Youth* / Government downfall: *Samples* / Jerusalem: *One Way System* / Blue patrol: *Attak* / Orders: *Protest* / CLA: *Crux* / Action man: *Distortion* / Power schemes: *Pseudo Sadists* / Whose bomb: *Chaotic Youth* / Unknown soldiers: *Patrol* / Blood money: *Mania* / Did he or didn't he: *Government Lies* / Country boy rocker: *ABH* / Wanna riot: *ABH* / Snow blindness: *Cadaverous Clan* / Storm trooper tactics: *Impact* / Ghost time: *Intensive Care*
AHOYCD 015 / 3 Nov '97 / Captain Oi

☐ COUNTRY GENTLEMEN
Lonesome number one: *Gibson, Don* / I love you because: *Jackson, Stonewall* / Please help me, I'm falling: *Locklin, Hank* / There goes my everything: *Greene, Jack* / Convoy: *Husky, Ferlin* / Take this job and shove it: *Paycheck, Johnny* / Misery loves company: *Wagoner, Porter* / Jambalaya: *Russell, Johnny* / Alone with you: *Young, Faron* / Never ending song of love: *Lee, Dickey* / You can have her: *Brown, Jim Ed* / Little black book: *Dean, Jimmy* / Almost persuaded: *Houston, David* / Hitchin' a ride: *Reno, Jack* / Pick me up on your way down: *Walker, Charlie* / Juanita Jones: *Phillips, Stu* / Take a letter Miss Gray: *Tubb, Justin* / Country bumpkin: *Smith, Cal*
ECD 3068 / Dec '96 / K-Tel

☐ COUNTRY GIANTS VOL.1
Reuben James: *Rogers, Kenny* / Honky tonk angels: *Rogers, Kenny* / Sweet dreams: *Young, Faron* / Then you'll know: *Young, Faron* / I'm so lonesome I could cry: *Spears, Billie Jo* / I can't find the time: *Nelson, Willie* / Ruby, don't take your love to town: *Rogers, Kenny* / Things to talk about: *Jackson, Stonewall* / Talk about me: *Paycheck, Johnny* / I didn't sleep a wink: *Nelson, Willie* / From a Jack to a King: *Miller, Ned* / White lightning: *Jennings, Waylon* / Look what they've done to my song ma: *Spears, Billie Jo* / Making believe: *Parton, Dolly* / Home is where you're happy: *Nelson, Willie* / Wings of a dove: *Husky, Ferlin* / Shine on Ruby mountain: *Rogers, Kenny* / Sticks and stones: *Fargo, Donna* / Rose garden: *Anderson, Lynn* / Turn the cards slowly: *Cline, Patsy* / Ramblin' rose: *Lee, Johnny* / Country girl: *Young, Faron* / Dear heart: *Miller, Roger* / Heart you break may be your own: *Cline, Patsy* / Little green apples: *Miller, Roger*
CDGFR 003 / Jun '92 / Tring

☐ COUNTRY GIANTS VOL.1
Reuben James: *Rogers, Kenny* / Walkin' after midnight: *Cline, Patsy* / Country girl: *Young, Faron* / Face of a fighter: *Nelson, Willie* / Sweet evening breeze (bring my baby back to me): *Reeves, Jim* / Shake 'em up, roll 'em: *Jackson, Stonewall* / Making believe: *Parton, Dolly* / Six days on the road: *Boxcar Willie* / Wings of a dove: *Husky, Ferlin* / Sticks and stones: *Fargo, Donna* / 9,999,999 tears: *Bailey, Razzy* / Sally was a good old girl: *Jennings, Waylon* / Luckenbach Texas: *Drusky, Roy* / Kaw-Liga: *Mandrell, Barbara* / I'll repossess my heart: *Wells, Kitty* / That girl who waits on tables: *Fender, Freddy* / Fraulein: *Gilley, Mickey* / Jambalaya: *Jones, George* / Elvira: *Rogers, Kenny* / North to Alaska: *Boxcar Willie*
QED 003 / Nov '96 / Tring

☐ COUNTRY GIANTS VOL.2
Is there something on your mind: *Nelson, Willie* / Rhythm 'n' booze: *Owens, Buck* / Candy store: *Lee, Johnny* / Stop, look and listen: *Cline, Patsy* / Four in the morning: *Young, Faron* / Hello walls: *Young, Faron* / Wishful thinking: *Fargo, Donna* / Reuben James: *Rogers, Kenny* / Both sides now: *Murray, Anne* / Billy Jack Washburn: *Paycheck, Johnny* / Shelter of my arms: *Nelson, Willie* / This ole house: *Perkins, Carl* / Then you'll know: *Cline, Patsy* / Letter to heaven: *Parton, Dolly* / Ol' blue: *Jackson, Stonewall* / Sally was a good old girl: *Jennings, Waylon* / Honky tonk merry go round: *Laine, Frankie* / Moonlight gambler: *Laine, Frankie* / Wine me up: *Young, Faron* / Send me the pillow that you dream on: *Locklin, Hank* / Building heartaches: *Nelson, Willie* / Ease the want in me: *Spears, Billie Jo* / Sad and lonely days: *Dudley, Dave* / Heartaches by the number: *Mitchell, Guy* / Blue is the way I feel: *Twitty, Conway*
CDGFR 004 / Jun '92 / Tring

☐ COUNTRY GIANTS VOL.2
I'm so lonesome I could cry: *Spears, Billie Jo* / Ruby don't take your love to town: *Rogers, Kenny* / Then you'll know: *Cline, Patsy* / Crying: *Jennings, Waylon* / Convoy: *Boxcar Willie* / Home: *Reeves, Jim* / Little blossom: *Parton, Dolly* / Ol' blue: *Jackson, Stonewall* / If you ain't lovin': *Young, Faron* / Daddy: *Fargo, Donna* / That heart belongs to me: *Gilley, Mickey* / Take this job and shove it: *Paycheck, Johnny* / Sweeter than candy: *Perkins, Carl* / What have they done to my song Ma: *Spears, Billie Jo* / Shine on Ruby mountain: *Rogers, Kenny* / Pick me up on your way down: *Cline, Patsy* / Roly poly: *Reeves, Jim* / Keep off the grass: *Jackson, Stonewall* / Green green grass of home: *Paycheck, Johnny* / Truck driving man: *Boxcar Willie*
QED 179 / Nov '96 / Tring

☐ COUNTRY GIRL
11814 / Feb '96 / Music

☐ COUNTRY GIRLS
Wrong road again: *Gayle, Crystal* / Somebody loves you: *Gayle, Crystal* / What I've got in mind: *Spears, Billie Jo* / '57 Chevrolet: *Spears, Billie Jo* / Daddy and home: *Tucker, Tanya* / Strong enough to bend: *Tucker, Tanya* / All I have to do is dream: *Newton, Juice* / Sweetest thing (I've ever known): *Newton, Juice* / I wish that I could fall in love today: *Mandrell, Barbara* / It all came true: *Mandrell, Barbara* / Pinkertons flowers: *Montgomery, Melba* / Hey Mr. Dream Maker: *West, Dottie* / Still crazy after all these years: *Dalton, Lacy J.* / Reuben James: *Jackson, Wanda* / Mississippi delta: *Gentry, Bobbie* / Under the sun: *Bogguss, Suzy* / Slippin' away: *Shepard, Jean* / Coat of many colours: *Peppers, Nancy* / It's morning (and I still love you): *Colter, Jessi* / Simple little words: *Lane, Christy*
CDMFP 5911 / Apr '91 / Music For Pleasure

☐ COUNTRY GIRLS
MACCD 114 / Aug '96 / Autograph

☐ COUNTRY GIRLS
DC 886032 / 2 Feb '98 / Disky

☐ COUNTRY GOLD (It's Only Make Believe)
MU 5055CD / Oct '92 / Musketeer

☐ COUNTRY GOLD (2CD Set)
Guitar man: *Presley, Elvis* / Rhinestone cowboy: *Campbell, Glen* / Crazy: *Cline, Patsy* / Blue bayou: *Orbison, Roy* / Jolene: *Parton, Dolly* / Ring of fire: *Cash, Johnny* / Stand by your man: *Wynette, Tammy* / Behind closed doors: *Rich, Charlie* / Rose garden: *Anderson, Lynn* / Lucille: *Rogers, Kenny* / I can help: *Swan, Billy* / Don't it make my brown eyes blue: *Gayle, Crystal* / I love you because: *Reeves, Jim* / '57 Chevrolet: *Spears, Billie Jo* / Funny how time slips away: *Nelson, Willie* / Coal miner's daughter: *Lynn, Loretta* / Four in the morning: *Young, Faron* / I'm sorry: *Lee, Brenda* / Sea of heartbreak: *Gibson, Don* / I will always love you: *Parton, Dolly* / Achy breaky heart: *Cyrus, Billy Ray* / When you're in love with a beautiful woman: *Dr. Hook* / Let your love flow: *Bellamy Brothers* / Country road: *Taylor, James* / Banks of the Ohio: *Newton-John, Olivia* / Wind beneath my wings: *Greenwood, Lee* / Crystal chandeliers: *Pride, Charley* / Sweet dreams: *Cline, Patsy* / All I have to do is dream: *Everly Brothers* / He'll have to go: *Reeves, Jim* / Theme from the dukes of hazard (good ol'boys): *Jennings, Waylon* / Honky tonk man: *Yoakam, Dwight* / Have mercy: *Judds* / Lone star state of mind: *Williams, Don* / Return of the grievous angel: *Parsons, Gram* / Together again: *Harris, Emmylou* / From a distance: *Griffith, Nanci* / Mr. Tambourine man: *Byrds* / End of the world: *Davis, Skeeter* / Love me tender: *Presley, Elvis*
RADCD 25 / Mar '96 / Global TV

☐ COUNTRY GOLD
MACCD 112 / Aug '96 / Autograph

☐ COUNTRY GOLD VOL.1
Sweet dreams: *Cline, Patsy* / You're my best friend: *Williams, Don* / Dream lover: *Campbell, Glen & Tanya Tucker* / I've cried the blue right out of my eyes: *Gayle, Crystal* / Coal miner's daughter: *Lynn, Loretta* / Ramblin' fever: *Haggard, Merle* / Big four poster bed: *Lee, Brenda* / Sail away: *Oak Ridge Boys* / You've never been this far before: *Twitty, Conway* / Hand that rocks the cradle: *Campbell, Glen* / Texas (When I die): *Tucker, Tanya* / I was country when country wasn't cool: *Mandrell, Barbara* / Somebody's knockin': *Gibbs, Terri* / There goes my everything: *Greene, Jack* / Satin sheets: *Pruett, Jeanne* / Still: *Anderson, Bill* / Busted: *Conlee, John* / Country bumpkin: *Smith, Carl* / My special angel: *Helms, Bobby* / Hello darlin': *Twitty, Conway*
MCCD 080 / Jun '92 / Music Club

☐ COUNTRY GOLD VOL.2
MCCD 053 / '93 / Music Club

☐ COUNTRY GOLD VOL.2 (2CD Set)
King of the road: *Miller, Roger* / Danny boy: *Twitty, Conway* / Fightin' side of me: *Haggard, Merle* / Marie Laveau: *Bare, Bobby* / Devoted to you: *Everly Brothers* / Crying time: *Kendalls* / 500 miles away from home: *Bare, Bobby* / Hey good lookin': *Boxcar Willie* / Are you lonesome tonight: *Jordanaires* / I wish that I could hurt that way again: *Brown, T. Graham* / Stand up: *McDaniel, Mel* / Ring on her finger, time on her hands: *Greenwood, Lee* / No charge: *Barrie, J.J.* / Life's railway to heaven: *Cline, Patsy* / Hello darlin': *Twitty, Conway* / Mama tried: *Haggard, Merle* / God bless the USA: *Greenwood, Lee* / Blanket on the ground: *Spears, Billie Jo* / Hell and high water: *Brown, T. Graham* / Wear my ring around your neck: *Jordanaires* / Engine no.9: *Miller, Roger* / Heartaches by the number: *Kendalls* / Wreck of the old '97: *Boxcar Willie* / This little girl of mine: *Everly Brothers* / Misty: *Stevens, Ray* / Three cigarettes in an ashtray: *Cline, Patsy* / It's only make believe: *Twitty, Conway* / Somebody's gonna love you: *Greenwood, Lee*
SD 885422 / 2 Feb '98 / Disky

☐ COUNTRY GOLD VOL.3
MCCD 132 / Sep '93 / Music Club

☐ COUNTRY GOLDEN HITS
DCD 5309 / Dec '93 / Disky

☐ COUNTRY GOSPEL
Hellelujah special: *Perkins, Carl* / Old time religion: *Reeves, Jim* / Pictures from life's other side: *Lewis, Jerry Lee* / Wreck on the highway: *Pitney, Gene & George Jones* / He'll do for you: *Cline, Patsy* / Family bible: *Jones, George* / When god dips his love in my heart: *Reeves, Jim* / Why me lord: *Cash, Johnny* / He means all the world to me: *Oak Ridge Boys* / I saw the light: *Phillips, Bill* / Without god: *Oak Ridge Boys* / Daddy sang bass: *Perkins, Carl* / Reuben James: *Rogers, Kenny* / Hobo heaven: *Boxcar Willie* / Peace in the valley: *Cash, Johnny* / Old country church: *Oak Ridge Boys* / Life's railway to heaven: *Cline, Patsy* / Softly and tenderly: *Reeves, Jim* / Old brush arbors: *Jones, George* / Let me live in the light of his love: *Pride, Charley*
300902 / Jul '96 / Hallmark

☐ COUNTRY GOSPEL 1929-1946
Motherless children: *Carter Family* / Presentjoys: *Alabama Sacred Heart Singers* / Rocky road: *Alabama Sacred Heart Singers* / There's evil in ye children: *Davis, Jimmie* / You'll never miss your mother: *Grayson & Whitter* / On the rock where Moses stood: *Carter Family* / I'll lead a Christian life: *Carter Family* / Dry bones: *Lunsford, Bascom Lamar* / We shall all be reunited: *Karnes, Alfred G.* / Old time religion: *Phipps, Ernest & Holiness Quartet* / No telephone in heaven: *Carter Family* / Mother came to get her boy from jail: *Mainer, Wade* / What would you give in exchange for your soul: *Mainer, Wade* / God holds the future in his hands: *Mainer, Wade* / Saints go marching in: *Monroe Brothers* / Shining city over the river: *Dixon Brothers* / In the vine covered chapel: *Delmore Brothers* / Heavenly light is shining on me: *Delmore Brothers* / Will the circle be unbroken: *Monroe Brothers* / Open up them pearly gates: *Robinson, Carson* / Just inside the pearly gates: *Anglin Twins* / When the golden train comes down: *Sons Of The Pioneers* / You must come in at the door: *Sons Of The Pioneers* / It won't be long: *Acuff, Roy* / Prodigal son: *Acuff, Roy* / Precious memories: *Shelton Brothers* / Address from heaven: *Armstrong Twins* / Calling you: *Williams, Hank* / Wealth won't save your soul: *Williams, Hank* / Speak to me little darling: *Blue Sky Boys* / My Lord keeps a record: *Story, Carl* / Are you afraid to die: *Story, Carl* / Echose from the burning bush: *Story, Carl* / Wicked path of sin: *Monroe, Bill* / Drunken driver: *O'Day, Molly* / Tramp on the street: *O'Day, Molly*
FA 055 / Apr '97 / Fremeaux

☐ COUNTRY GOSPEL 1946-1953
DOCD 5221 / Apr '94 / Document

☐ COUNTRY GREATS (4CD Set)
MBSCD 429 / Sep '94 / Castle

☐ COUNTRY GREATS
CPMV 023 / Sep '94 / Cromwell

☐ COUNTRY GREATS
MACCD 115 / Aug '96 / Autograph

☐ COUNTRY GREATS (4CD Set)
Reuben James: *Rogers, Kenny & The First Edition* / Walkin' after midnight: *Cline, Patsy* / Country girl: *Young, Faron* / Face of a fighter: *Nelson, Willie* / Sweet evening breeze bring my baby back to me: *Reeves, Jim* / Shake 'em up roll'em: *Jackson, Stonewall* / Making believe: *Parton, Dolly* / Six days on the road: *Boxcar Willie* / Wings of a dove: *Husky, Ferlin* / Luckenbach Texas: *Drusky, Roy* / Kaw-liga:

COUNTRY GREATS COMPILATIONS R.E.D. CD CATALOGUE

Mandrell, Barbara / I'll reposses my heart: Wells, Kitty / That girl who waits on tables: Fender, Freddy / Fraulein: Gilley, Mickey / Jambalaya: Jones, George / Elvira: Rogers, Kenny / North to Alaska: Boxcar Willie / I'm so lonesome I could cry: Spears, Billie Jo / Ruby don't take your love to town: Rogers, Kenny & The First Edition / Then you'll know: Cline, Patsy / Crying: Jennings, Waylon / Convoy: Boxcar Willie / Home: Reeves, Jim / Little blossom: Parton, Dolly / Ol' blue: Jackson, Stonewall / If you ain't lovin': Young, Faron / Daddy: Fargo, Donna / That heart belongs to me: Gilley, Mickey / Take this job and shove it: Paycheck, Johnny / Sweeter than candy: Perkins, Carl / What have they done to my song ma: Spears, Billie Jo / Shine on ruby mountain: Rogers, Kenny & The First Edition / Pick me up on your way down: Cline, Patsy / Roly poly: Reeves, Jim / Keep off the grass: Jackson, Stonewall / Green green grass of home: Paycheck, Johnny / Truck driving man: Boxcar Willie / Sweet dreams: Young, Faron / I've loved and lost again: Cline, Patsy / Don't think twice: Jennings, Waylon / I can't find the time: Nelson, Willie / I never promised you a rose garden: Anderson, Lynn / Always leaving always gone: Rogers, Kenny & The First Edition / Hello walls: Drusky, Roy / Wishful thinking: Fargo, Donna / I can't get enough of you: Jackson, Stonewall / Before the next teardrop falls: Fender, Freddy / Release me: Mandrell, Barbara / Have I told you lately that I love you: Reeves, Jim / Lonely wine: Gilley, Mickey / Makin' believe: Wells, Kitty / Four in the morning: Young, Faron / Your tender years: Jones, George / Hungry for love: Cline, Patsy / She even woke me up to say goodbye: Rogers, Kenny & The First Edition / Last letter: Drusky, Roy / I don't know why I love you but I do: Fender, Freddy / Blue eyes cryin' in the rain: Drusky, Roy / Ease the want in me: Spears, Billie Jo / Almost persuaded: Paycheck, Johnny / Something's burning: Rogers, Kenny & The First Edition / Just out of reach: Cline, Patsy / He'll have to go: Reeves, Jim / Apartment no.9: Young, Faron / Dream baby: Jennings, Waylon / Dixie: Boxcar Willie / Old kentucky home: Boxcar Willie / Baby I want to love you: Fender, Freddy / Things have gone to pieces: Jones, George / Should I go home: Jackson, Stonewall / Someone to give my love to: Paycheck, Johnny / Shelter of your arms: Nelson, Willie / Night after night: Gilley, Mickey / Once a day: Young, Faron / Never no more: Cline, Patsy / Going out with the tide: Fender, Freddy / Am I losing you: Reeves, Jim / Sticks and stones: Fargo, Donna / 9,999,999 tears: Bailey, Razzy / Sally was a good old girl: Jennings, Waylon

QUAD 003 / Nov '96 / Tring

☐ **COUNTRY GREATS (Blue Eyes Cryin' In The Rain)**

Blue eyes cryin' in the rain: Drusky, Roy / Ease the want in me: Spears, Billie Jo / Almost persuaded: Paycheck, Johnny / Something's burning: Rogers, Kenny & The First Edition / Just out of reach: Cline, Patsy / He'll have to go: Reeves, Jim / Apartment 9: Young, Faron / Dream baby: Jennings, Waylon / Dixie: Boxcar Willie / Baby I want to love you: Fender, Freddy / Things have gone to pieces: Jones, George / Should I go home: Jackson, Stonewall / Someone to give my love to: Paycheck, Johnny / Shelter of your arms: Nelson, Willie / Night after night: Gilley, Mickey / Once a day: Young, Faron / Never no more: Cline, Patsy / Going out with the tide: Fender, Freddy / Am I losing you: Reeves, Jim / Old Kentucky home: Boxcar Willie

QED 049 / Nov '96 / Tring

☐ **COUNTRY GREATS**

She's just a girl I used to know: Jones, George / Will you remember mine: Nelson, Willie / I fall to pieces: Young, Faron / Treat me mean treat me cruel: Twitty, Conway / Daddy sang bass: Perkins, Carl / Livin' in the sunshine of your love: Pillow, Ray / Airport song: Blackwater Band / Georgia in a jug: Paycheck, Johnny / I don't need to know that right now: Paycheck, Johnny / Your cheatin' heart: Young, Faron / Can't change overnight: Jones, George / And so will you my love: Nelson, Willie / What am I living for: Perkins, Carl / Lighthouse bar: Blackwater Band / Where I stand: Twitty, Conway / We're together again: Pillow, Ray

300482 / Jul '96 / Hallmark

☐ **COUNTRY GREATS (2CD Set)**

Single girl: Posey, Sandy / Wasted days wasted nights: Fender, Freddy / From a jack to a king: Miller, Ned / Rose garden: Anderson, Lynn / Wings of a dove: Husky, Ferlin / Raindrops keep falling on my head: Thomas, B.J. / Kiss an angel good morning: Pride, Charley / Take this job and shove it: Paycheck, Johnny / Coalminer's daughter: Lynn, Loretta / End of the world: Lee, Brenda / Ruby don't you take your love to town: Rogers, Kenny / Crystal candeliers: Spears, Billie Jo / Singing the blues: Mitchell, Guy / King of the road: Miller, Roger / Rainy night in Georgia: Benton, Brook / Hello walls: Young, Faron / Please help me I'm falling: Locklin, Hank / These boots are made for walking: Hazelwood, Lee / In the misty moonlight: Wallace, Jerry / I'll just stay here and drink: Haggard, Merle / Crazy love: Fairchild, Barbara / Ol' blue: Jackson, Stonewall / Memory trainAllen, rex junior: Allen, Rex Jr. / ABilene: Jennings, Waylon / How do I hide from a memory: Pillow, Ray / Honky tonkitis: Walker, Billy / Take these chains from your heart: Gibson, Don / Fall to pieces: Houston, David / I fall to pieces: Houston, David / Most beautiful girl in the world: Clark, Roy / Beautiful lady: Green, Jack / Jambalaya: Russell, Johnny / On her way to being a woman: Williams, Don / Good year for the roses: Jones, George / Detroit city: Bare, Bobby / Sweet dreams: Gibson, Don / Recall a gypsy woman: Thompson, Hank / It's only make believe: Twitty, Conway / Green green grass of home: Wagoner, Porter / End of understanding: Nelson, Willie / Bridge washed out: Mack, Warner

PC 608 / 10 Nov '97 / Platinum Collection

☐ **COUNTRY GREATS VOL.1**

TRTCD 174 / Jun '95 / TrueTrax

☐ **COUNTRY GREATS VOL.2**

TRTCD 189 / Feb '96 / TrueTrax

☐ **COUNTRY HEARTBREAKERS**

Heartaches: Cline, Patsy / She's got you: Cline, Patsy / It hurts so much: Reeves, Jim / When two worlds collide: Reeves, Jim / I will always love you: Parton, Dolly / Daddy come and get me: Parton, Dolly / Don't fall in love with a dreamer: Rogers, Kenny / Till I can make it on my own: Rogers, Kenny / Cry me a river: Gayle, Crystal / I still miss someone: Gayle, Crystal / Your cheatin' heart: Lynn, Loretta / Paper roses: Lynn, Loretta / Please Mr. Please: Newton-John, Olivia / I honestly love you: Newton-John, Olivia / Honey come back: Campbell, Glen / Hey won't you play another somebody done somebody wrong song: Spears, Billie Jo / Misty blue: Spears, Billie Jo / I'll never fall in love again: Gentry, Bobbie / There'll be no teardrops tonight: Nelson, Willie / It keeps right on a-hurtin': Shepard, Jean

CDMFP 6116 / Mar '94 / Music For Pleasure

☐ **COUNTRY HEROES**

DC 886042 / 2 Feb '98 / Disky

☐ **COUNTRY HICKS VOL.1**

BARKLOG 1CD / Sep '95 / No Hit

☐ **COUNTRY LADIES**

Gonna get along without you now: Davis, Skeeter / I can't stop loving you: Wells, Kitty / Crazy: Jackson, Wanda / Satin sheets: Pruett, Jeannie / How can I unlove you: Anderson, Lynn / Misty blue: Burgess, Wilma / Let's go all the way: Jean, Norma / I'll love you more: Seely, Jeannie / Mr. Walker it's all over: Spears, Billie Jo / There never was a time: Riley, Jeannie C. / Ain't had no lovin': Smith, Connie / Superman: Fargo, Donna / Send me the pillow you dream on: Smith, Sammi / Pitty pitty patter: Raye, Susan / It only hurts for a while: Smith, Margo / Shake me I rattle: Worth, Marion / Kid stuff: Fairchild, Barbara / Satisfied mind: Shepard, Jean

ECD 3067 / Dec '96 / K-Tel

☐ **COUNTRY LADIES (2CD Set)**

MCD 211611 / Mar '97 / MCA

☐ **COUNTRY LEGENDS**

Talking in your sleep: Gayle, Crystal / By the time I get to Phoenix: Campbell, Glen / Better love next time: Dr. Hook / Queen of the house: Miller, Jody / Funny how time slips away: Nelson, Willie / If you could read my mind: Newton-John, Olivia / Wichita lineman: Campbell, Glen / I love you because: Spears, Billie Jo / Gambler: Rogers, Kenny / Give me your word: Ford, Tennessee Ernie / Hey Mr. Dream maker: West, Dottie / All I have to do is dream: Campbell, Glen & Bobbie Gentry / Don't it make my brown eyes blue: Gayle, Crystal / Games people play: South, Joe / When you're in love with a beautiful woman: Dr. Hook / She believes in me: Rogers, Kenny / Ode to Billie Joe: Gentry, Bobbie / Crazy: Nelson, Willie / I honestly love you: Newton-John, Olivia / '57 Chevrolet: Spears, Billie Jo

CDSL 8259 / Jul '95 / EMI

☐ **COUNTRY LEGENDS**

Crazy: Cline, Patsy / Coward of the county: Rogers, Kenny / From a distance: Griffith, Nanci / You're my best friend: Williams, Don / DIVORCE: Parton, Dolly / Last one to know: McEntire, Reba / Boy named Sue: Cash, Johnny / Blanket on the ground: Spears, Billie Jo / Don't let your babies grow up to be cowboys: Nelson, Willie / Most beautiful girl in the world: Rich, Charlie / Help me make it through the night: Kristofferson, Kris / She's in love with the boy: Yearwood, Trisha / Talking in your sleep: Gayle, Crystal / Wind beneath my wings: Greenwood, Lee / El Paso: Robbins, Marty / Brand new heartache: Everly Brothers / Cola miner's daughter: Lynn, Loretta / It's only make believe: Campbell, Glen

MACCD 110 / Aug '96 / Autograph

☐ **COUNTRY LEGENDS**

PDSCD 501 / 1 Sep '97 / Pulse

☐ **COUNTRY LINE DANCING**

Boys and me / Girls with guitars / Talk dirty to me / Don't step out of line / That's what I get for losin' you / Cowboy reggae / Swamp thing / Back on the streets / Soft touch / XXX's and OOO's (An American girl) / Cotton Eye Joe / Deadwood stage / Line King / Nobody wins / Angel of the night / Any man of mine / Fast Fingers Freddie / Meet me on the corner / Wrong train, wrong line / Time won't let me slow down / When you walk in the room / Duelling banjos

QED 032 / Nov '96 / Tring

☐ **COUNTRY LINE DANCING VOL.1**

Achy breaky heart / Boot scootin' boogie / Down at St. Domas Walkers / Wink / Livin' on love / God bless Texas / Fast as you / Kick a lttle / Love bug / Ain't going down til the sun comes up / American honky tonk bar association / Holdin' heaven / I feel lucky / Down on the farm / Baby likes to rock it / Xxx's and Ooo's / Honky tonk blues

CDMFP 6280 / Nov '96 / Music For Pleasure

☐ **COUNTRY LINE DANCING VOL.2**

Cadillac ranch / Hillbilly rock / Chattahoochee / Rock my world (little country girl) / If bubba can dance (I can too) / Whiskey ain't workin' / Mercury blues / He thinks he'll keep her / Why haven't I heard from you lately / Neon moon / What the cowgirls do / Summertime blues / Gone country / Goin' through the big D / Little miss honky tonk / Third rate romance / Big one / Any man of mine

CDMFP 6343 / Apr '97 / Music For Pleasure

☐ **COUNTRY LOVE**

MACCD 258 / Aug '96 / Autograph

☐ **COUNTRY LOVE (16 Country Classics)**

Send me the pillow you dream on: Locklin, Hank / Help me make it through the night: Bare, Bobby / Dreams of the everyday housewife: Campbell, Glen / Three cigarettes in an ashtry: Cline, Patsy / Sweet dreams: Jones, George / Across the wide Missouri: McCall, Cash / You're my man: Spears, Billie Jo / Alone with you: Young, Faron / By the time I get to Phoenix: Campbell, Glen / You're eyes don't lie to me: Anderson, Bill / Box of memories: Riley, Jeannie C. / Little green apples: Miller, Roger / Simple thing as love: Clark, Roy / Love's gonna live here: Jennings, Waylon / Touch of my woman: Walker, Billy / I've loved and lost again: Cline, Patsy / There's a way: Yuro, Timi & Willie Nelson / My elusive dreams: Miller, Roger / From a jack to a king: Miller, Roger / Love me tender: Stevens, Stu / Take these chains from my heart: Drusky, Roy / Shelter of your arms: Nelson, Willie / Single girl: Posey, Sandy / Half as much: Whitman, Slim / You don't know me: Rich, Charlie

SUMCD 4050 / Nov '96 / Summit

☐ **COUNTRY LOVE (3CD Set)**

Don't it make you brown eyes blue: Gayle, Crystal / Most beautiful girl: Rich, Charlie / Good year for the roses: Jones, George / Rose garden: Anderson, Lynn / Anytime: Whitman, Slim / I fall to pieces: Jackson, Wanda / Please help me I'm falling: Locklin, Hank / I'm so lonesome: Tillotson, Johnny / Crazy: Spears, Billie Jo / It's only make believe: Twitty, Conway / Heaven's just a sin away: Kendalls / Little green apples: Miller, Roger / Lonesome number one: Gibson, Don / Last thing on my mind: Murray, Anne / Am I losing you: Reeves, Jim / Did I ever love you: Yuro, Timi & Willie Nelson / Release me: Whitman, Slim / My last date with you: Davis, Skeeter / Ribbon of darkness: Jordanaires / Walkin' after midnight: Cline, Patsy / For the good times: Rogers, Kenny / In the misty moonlight: Wallace, Jerry / Love hurts: Parsons, Gram & Emmylou Harris / Have you ever been lonely: Whitman, Slim / Born a woman: Posey, Sandy / Lookin' for love: Lee, Johnny / Love's gonna live here: Jennings, Waylon / Blanket on the ground: Spears, Billie Jo / Behind closed doors: Rich, Charlie / Talk back trembling lips: Jones, George / That's how I got to Memphis: Bare, Bobby / Ready for the times to get better: Gayle, Crystal / Hello walls: Young, Faron / What I've got in mind: Spears, Billie Jo / Follow me back to Louisville: Williams, Don / Baby I want to love you: Fender, Freddy / My special angel: Helms, Bobby / Making believe: Wells, Kitty / Blue blue day: Kendalls / You win again: Cash, Johnny / Stand by your man: Anderson, Lynn / 'Til I waltz again with you: Whitman, Slim / Have I told you lately that I love you: Miki & Griff / Once a day: Jones, George / Rain and tears: Price, Ray / Misty blue: Spears, Billie Jo / Mary Ann regrets: Clark, Roy / I've loved and lost again: Cline, Patsy / Walking the floor over you: Tubb, Justin / Crying time: Kendalls / Send me the pillow that you dream on: Tillotson, Johnny

PBXCD 321 / 3 Aug '98 / Pulse

☐ **COUNTRY LOVE CLASSICS**

SELCD 518 / 27 Jun '98 / Castle Select

☐ **COUNTRY LOVE SONGS**

I can't stop loving you: Gibson, Don / Lovesick blues: Williams, Hank / It's only make believe: Jackson, Wanda / I've loved and lost again: Cline, Patsy / I believe in you: Williams, Don / Help me make it through the night: Pride, Charley / Please release me: Parton, Dolly / Rose marie: Whitman, Slim / I fall to pieces: Jackson, Wanda / Sweet dreams: Gibson, Don / You're my best friend: Williams, Don / Today I started loving you again: Haggard, Merle / I cried all the way to the altar: Cline, Patsy / Have I told you lately that I love you: Reeves, Jim / Heartbreak USA: Wells, Kitty / Cold cold heart: Jones, George / I believe: Laine, Frankie / Stranger in my arms: Cline, Patsy / I'm so lonesome I could cry: Williams, Hank / Kiss an angel good morning: Pride, Charley

CD 6095 / 29 Sep '97 / Music

☐ **COUNTRY LOVE SONGS**

On a bus to St. Cloud: Yearwood, Trisha / I still believe in you: Grill, Vince / I give my heart: Berry, John / Letting go: Bogguss, Suzy / Wind beneath my wings: Greenwood, Lee / For the good times: Rogers, Kenny / You're my best friend: Williams, Don / Addicted: Seals, Dan / Sweetest thing: Newton, Juice / I didn't (every chance I had): Rodriguez, Johnny / I'm not Lisa: Colter, Jessi / Bluest heartache of the year: Dale, Kenny / I won't take less than your love: Tucker, Tanya / Talkin' in your sleep: Gayle, Crystal / It's only make believe: Twitty, Conway / Sweet dreams (of you): Cline, Patsy

DC 886502 / 2 Feb '98 / Disky

☐ **COUNTRY LOVE SONGS**

EABCD 104 / 30 Mar '98 / Eagle

☐ **COUNTRY MOODS**

MACCD 218 / Aug '96 / Autograph

☐ **COUNTRY MUSIC VOL.1**

3003662 / Jan '97 / IMP

☐ **COUNTRY MUSIC VOL.2**

3003652 / Jan '97 / IMP

☐ **COUNTRY NEGRO JAM SESSIONS**

ARHCD 372 / Apr '95 / Arhoolie

☐ **COUNTRY NIGHTS**

MACCD 113 / Aug '96 / Autograph

☐ **COUNTRY OF SONGS 1958-1995 (Music From Lithuania)**

C 600005 / May '97 / Ocora

☐ **COUNTRY ORIGINALS VOL.1**

I will always love you: Parton, Dolly / Love of the common people: Jennings, Waylon / Guitar man: Reed, Jerry / I can't stop loving you: Gibson, Don / Tobacco road: Loudermilk, John D. / Gentle on my mind: Harford, John / Green green grass of home: Wagoner, Porter / In the ghetto: Davis, Mac / Help me make it through the night: Kristofferson, Kris / Singin' the blues: Robbins, Marty / For the good times: Price, Ray / Crazy: Nelson, Willie / Everybody's talkin': Neil, Fred / Rose garden: South, Joe / Sweet dreams: Young, Faron / Good year for the roses: Jones, George / Always on my mind: Lee, Brenda / From a distance: Griffith, Nanci / Wind beneath my wings: Greenwood, Lee / Misty blue: Burgess, Wilma

VSOPCD 204 / Nov '95 / Connoisseur Collection

☐ **COUNTRY ORIGINALS VOL.2**

Leaving on a jet plane: Denver, John / Love is like a butterfly: Parton, Dolly / Oh lonesome me: Gibson, Don / Bring me sunshine: Nelson, Willie / End of the world: Davis, Skeeter / Ruby: Darrell, Johnny / Minute you're gone: James, Sonny / Change the world: Wynonna / What made Milwaukee famous (has made a loser out of me): Lewis, Jerry Lee / Rhinestone cowboy: Weiss, Larry / Most beautiful girl: Wilson, Norro / Crying: Orbison, Roy / Me and Bobby McGhee: Kristofferson, Kris / Release me: Price, Ray / American trilogy: Newbury, Mickey / Burning love: Linde, Dennis / No charge: Montgomery, Melba / Rainy night in Georgia: White, Tony Joe / I fought the law: Curtis, Sonny / Love will build a bridge: Judds

VSOPCD 242 / 17 Nov '97 / Connoisseur Collection

☐ **COUNTRY RADIO SHOWS VOL.1**

OTA 101908 / Mar '96 / On The Air

☐ **COUNTRY RADIO SHOWS VOL.2**

Crazy: Cline, Patsy / Walkin' after midnight: Cline, Patsy / San Antonio rose: Cline, Patsy / I love you so much it hurts: Cline, Patsy / I fall to pieces: Cline, Patsy / Lovin' in vain: Cline, Patsy / Marine's hymn: Cline, Patsy / I love you more: Reeves, Jim / Home: Reeves, Jim / I'm beginning to forget you: Reeves, Jim / Have I told you lately that I love you: Reeves, Jim / Just call me lonesome: Reeves, Jim / How's the world treating you: Reeves, Jim / If heartaches are the fashion: Reeves, Jim / Till the end of the world: Reeves, Jim / Making believe: Reeves, Jim / Oklahoma Hills: Reeves, Jim / Highway to nowhere: Reeves, Jim / I've lived a lot in my time: Reeves, Jim / Tips of my fingers: Young, Faron / King of the road: Young, Faron / Almost persuaded: Young, Faron / Live fast, love hard, die young: Young, Faron / Apartment: Young, Faron / Crying time: Young, Faron / Together again: Young, Faron / Yonder comes a sucker: Young, Faron / Invitation to the blues: Young, Faron

OTA 101909 / Mar '96 / On The Air

☐ **COUNTRY ROADS (2CD Set)**

Don't it make my brown eyes blue: Gayle, Crystal / Mountain music: Alabama / Ruby don't take your love to town: Rogers, Kenny & The First Edition / Jolene: Parton, Dolly / Ladies love outlaws: Jennings, Waylon / Behind closed doors: Rich, Charlie / Blanket on the ground: Spears, Billie Jo / I walk the line: Cash, Johnny / Crystal chandeliers: Pride, Charley / Are you sure Hank done it this way: Jennings, Waylon / Crazy arms: Nelson, Willie / I fall to pieces: Cline, Patsy / Rhinestone cowboy: Campbell, Glen / Bargain store: Parton, Dolly / Mason Dixie lines: Jennings, Waylon / Fire and rain: Nelson, Willie / He'll have to go: Reeves, Jim / Ring of fire: Cash, Johnny / Orange blossom special: Monroe, Bill & His Bluegrass Boys / Walking after midnight: Cline, Patsy / Lonesome on'ry and mean: Jennings, Waylon / Me and Paul: Nelson, Willie / Harper Valley PTA: Parton, Dolly / Reuben James: Rogers, Kenny / Misty blue: Spears, Billie Jo / Most beautiful girl in the world: Rich, Charlie / I know one: Reeves, Jim / Me and Bobby McGee: Pride, Charley / Heartbreaker: Parton, Dolly / My home is in Alabama: Alabama / Whitchita lineman: Campbell, Glen / Gentle on my mind: Hartford, John / Take me home country roads: Davis, Skeeter / Shadows of my mind: Everette, Leon / Talking in your sleep: Gayle, Crystal / Distant drums: Reeves, Jim / Honky tonk blues: Pride, Charley / In my Tennessee mountain home: Parton, Dolly

RCACD 204 / Jul '97 / RCA

☐ **COUNTRY ROCKERS LIVE**

15403 / Mar '95 / Laserlight

☐ **COUNTRY SALOON (20 Drinkin' Country Classics)**

Little ole wine drinker me: Haggard, Merle / Girl don't have to drink to have fun: Jackson, Wanda / Never did like Whiskey: Spears, Billie Jo / Bubbles in my beer: Jones, George / Honky tonk habits: Emilio / Misery and gin: Dean, Billy / Drink up and be somebody: Haggard, Merle / Hangover tavern: Thompson, Hank / Warm red wine: Thompson, Hank / Tears will be the chaser for your wine: Jackson, Wanda / Paintin' this old town blue: Gayle, Crystal / Wishful drinkin': Pfeifer, Diane / Your good girls gonna go bad: Spears, Billie Jo / Honky tonk heaven: Edwards, Stoney / Wake up and smell the whiskey: Miller, Dean / Six pack to go: Thompson, Hank / Alcohol and tears: Adams, Kay / Letter that Johnny Walker read: Asleep At The Wheel / There's a tear in my beer: Lister, Big Bill

4949172 / 1 Jun '98 / EMI Gold

☐ **COUNTRY SELECTION, THE (2CD Set)**

Walkin' after midnight: Cline, Patsy / He'll have to go: Reeves, Jim / Crystal candeliers: Pride, Charley / White lightning: Jennings, Waylon / Take this job and shove it: Paycheck, Johnny / Cold cold heart: Jones, George / Stranger in my arms: Cline, Patsy / Kiss an angel good morning: Cline, Patsy / I fall to pieces: Jackson, Wanda / Have I told you lately that I love you: Reeves, Jim / Pease help me I'm falling: Looklin, Hank / I'm the only hell mama ever raised: Paycheck, Johnny / Love of the common people: Jennings, Waylon / Worlds' worst lover: Jones, George / Four walls: Reeves, Jim / Night life: Nelson, Willie / Church, a courtroom, then goodbye: Cline, Patsy / Help me make it through the night: Cline, Patsy / It wasn't God who made honky tonk angels: Wells, Kitty / Ruby don't take your love to town: Rogers, Kenny / Baby on my mind: Spears, Billie Jo / Rose garden: Anderson, Lynn / Harper valley PTA: Riley, Jeannie C. / No tomorrow in sight: Nelson, Willie / Jackson: Lewis, Jerry Lee & Linda Gail / Big town: Twitty, Conway / Lonely women make good lovers: Luman, Bob / Music city USA: Bare, Bobby / Wild side of life: Thompson, Hank / Rhinestone cowboy: Campbell, Glen / Satisfied mind: Wagoner, Porter / Rock island line: Cash, Johnny / King of the road: Miller, Roger / Big bad john: Dean, Jimmy / Take me home: Boxcar Willie / Four in the morning: Young, Faron

DCD 3010 / Jun '97 / Music

☐ **COUNTRY STAR COLLECTION (2CD Set)**

Six days on the road: Dudley, Dave / Fraulein: Gilley, Mickey / Half a man: Nelson, Willie / Listen to a country song: Anderson, Lynn / Rawhide: Laine, Frankie / Don't think twice: Jennings, Waylon / It's all over: Murray, Anne / Home is where you're happy: Nelson, Willie / Wings of a dove: Husky, Ferlin / Devil went down to Georgia: Anderson, Lynn / Broken promises: Nelson, Willie / Paths of victory: Murray, Anne / Burning memories: Jennings, Waylon / Cheatin' kind: Spears, Billie Jo / Three hearts in a tangle: Drusky, Roy / Both sides now: Murray, Anne / Answer me: Laine, Frankie / Rose garden: Anderson, Lynn / Things to remember: Nelson, Willie / 16 tons: Travis, Merle / Little bitty tear: Ives, Burl / You can't put the city in a country girl: Fairchild, Barbara / Moonlight gambler: Laine, Frankie / Got a lot of rhythm in my soul: Cline, Patsy / Have I stayed away too long: Ritter, Tex / Making believe: Parton, Dolly / Dallas: Spears, Billie Jo / In the shelter of his arms: Oak Ridge Boys / Funny way of laughing: Ives, Burl / Lovesick blues: Cline, Patsy / Hillbilly heaven: Ritter, Tex / Gone: Husky, Ferlin / Cheating is: Fairchild, Barbara / High noon: Laine, Frankie

330282 / Mar '97 / Hallmark

☐ COUNTRY STARS OF THE 80'S - LIVE
15405 / Aug '91 / Laserlight

☐ COUNTRY SUNRISE
DC 879492 / Oct '97 / Disky

☐ COUNTRY SUNSET
DC 879632 / Oct '97 / Disky

☐ COUNTRY SUPERSTARS (CD/CD Rom Set)
WWCDR 007 / Apr '97 / Weton-Wesgram

☐ COUNTRY WOMAN (2CD Set)
Rose garden: Anderson, Lynn / Misty blue: Spears, Billie Jo / Just out of reach: Cline, Patsy / Crazy: Jackson, Wanda / Both sides now: Murray, Anne / Harper Valley PTA: Riley, Jeannie C. / End of the world: Davis, Skeeter / DIVORCE: West, Dottie / Coalminer's daughter: Lynn, Loretta / Jamestown ferry: Tucker, Tanya / Release me: Mandrell, Barbara / No charge: Montgomery, Melba / I wish I could fall in love again: Howard, Jan / Wishful thinking: Fargo, Donna / Single girl: Posey, Sandy / Crazy love: Fairchild, Barbara / Comin' on strong: Lee, Brenda / Makin' believe: Wells, Kitty / Danger of a stranger: Parton, Stella / Talkin' in your sleep: Gayle, Crystal / (It wasn't God who made) Honky tonk angels: Parton, Dolly / Blue bayou: Anderson, Lynn / It's only make believe: Jackson, Wanda / Man that turned my mama on: Tucker, Tanya / Tennessee waltz: Page, Patti / I've loved and lost again: Cline, Patsy / Let your love flow: Lynn, Loretta / Crystal chandeliers: Spears, Billie Jo / Girl left alone: Parton, Dolly / Heartaches by the number: Kendalls / Born a woman: Posey, Sandy / Kaw liga: Mandrell, Barbara / When I Dream: Gayle, Crystal / Words that go unspoken: Peppers, Nancy / I'm sorry: Lee, Brenda / Blanket on the ground: Spears, Billie Jo / Little blossoms: Parton, Dolly / Stop the world: Cline, Patsy / It ain't easy being easy: Frickie, Janie / Help me make it through the night: Smith, Sammi
PC 623 / 1 Jun '98 / Platinum Collection

☐ COUNTRY'S MOST WANTED (20 Classic Country Hits)
No love have I: Pierce, Webb / Crazy: Cline, Patsy / Little bitty tear: Ives, Burl / Bridge washed out: Mack, Warner / Misty blue: Burgess, Wilma / Statue of a fool: Greene, Jack / Fifteen years ago: Twitty, Conway / One's on the way: Lynn, Loretta / Don't she look good: Anderson, Bill / Funny face: Fargo, Donna / Heaven is my woman's love: Overstreet, Tommy / This much a man: Robbins, Marty / Wasted days and wasted nights: Fender, Freddy / You rubbed it in all wrong: Craddock, Billy / Some broken hearts never mend: Williams, Don / Last cowboy song: Bruce, Ed & Willie Nelson / Elvira: Oak Ridge Boys / Ring on her finger time on her hands: Greenwood, Lee / Guitar town: Earle, Steve / Rough and rowdy days: Jennings, Waylon
MCCD 301 / Jun '97 / Music Club

☐ COVER ME (12 Klone Classics)
CDKOPY 106 / Mar '97 / Klone

☐ COVERED
RR 87982 / 10 Nov '97 / Roadrunner

☐ COVERED IN REGGAE
EMPRCD 704 / Mar '97 / Emporio

☐ COVERSATIONS WITH THE FRENCH CONNECTION
YP 005CD / Jul '96 / Yellow

☐ COVERT OPERATIONS
PRRUKCD 004 / 20 Jul '98 / Planet Rhythm UK

☐ COW COW BOOGIE 1943
PHONTCD 7671 / Apr '94 / Phontastic

☐ COWBOY COUNTRY VOL.1 (20 Country Classics)
Rawhide: Laine, Frankie / Wichita lineman: Campbell, Glen / Galveston: Campbell, Glen / Don't think twice it's alright: Jennings, Waylon / Country girl: Young, Faron / You're still mine: Young, Faron / Send me the pillow you dream on: Locklin, Hank / These arms you push away: Locklin, Hank / I wonder if God likes country music: Anderson, Bill / Deck of cards: Anderson, Bill / Poppin' Johnny: Miller, Frankie / Big talk of the town: Miller, Frankie / Tender years: Jones, George / My favourite lies: Jones, George / That's how I got to Memphis: Bare, Bobby / Me and Bobby McGee: Bare, Bobby / Twilight on the trail: McCall, Cash / Red river valley: McCall, Cash / Thousand miles of ocean: Copas, Cowboy / I dreamed of a hillbilly heaven: Copas, Cowboy
SUMCD 4038 / Nov '96 / Summit

☐ COWBOY COUNTRY VOL.2 (20 Country Classics)
Southern nights: Campbell, Glen / By the time I get to Phoenix: Campbell, Glen / I walk the line: Cash, Johnny / Folsom Prison blues: Cash, Johnny / Daddy don't you walk so fast: Clark, Roy / Most beautiful girl in the world: Clark, Roy / You're my man: Spears, Billie Jo / Dallas: Spears, Billie Jo / Love on borrowed time: Steele, Jo Ann / Beginning of goodbye: Steele, Jo Ann / Girl most likely: Riley, Jeannie C. / Cotton patch: Riley, Jeannie C. / Walkin' after midnight: Cline, Patsy / Stop, look and listen: Cline, Patsy / Willow tree: Sovine, Red / Wound time can't erase: Sovine, Red / San Antonio Rose: Autry, Gene / Dixie cannonball: Autry, Gene / Little green apples: Miller, Roger / King of the road: Miller, Roger
SUMCD 4068 / Nov '96 / Summit

☐ COWBOY RECORDS COMPILATION VOL.2
2 Damned free: Perks Of Living Society / I want you: Secret Life / Timetravellers: Lovechild & Rolfe / All over me: Carr, Suzi / Peace, love, harmony: Re-Joice / How sweet the sound: Forthright / Why why why: Deja Vu / Only you: Talizman / Trippin' on sunshine: Pizzaman / Rock the discotheque: Ramp / If this is love: Tracey, Jeanie / All I do: Voodoo Blue
RODEO 2CD / Nov '94 / Cowboy

☐ COWBOY RHYTHMS
ECD 3379 / 18 Aug '97 / K-Tel

☐ COWBOYS SONGS ON FOLKWAYS
CDSF 40043 / Aug '94 / Smithsonian Folkways

☐ CRAZY 'BOUT LINE DANCING
Mexico / One more ride / Black velevtAll I wanna do / Lose again / One of these nights / Nine to five / Way down / Road goes on forever / Every day is a winding road / Get back / Always on my mind / Take it easy / Constant craving / Burning love / Wonderful tonight / Islands in the street / Rhinestone cowboy / Copperhead ro / Achy breaky heart / By the rio grande / I'll stay around / My baby loves me / Whenever kindness fails / Money in the bank / Li8fe's a dance / Funky hcowboy / New Delhi freight train / Adalida / 1-800 used to be / Walk of life / Sweet home Alabama / Romeo / Line king / I feel lucky / Honky tonky man / Chattahoochee / Bootscoootin' boogie / Baby likes to rock it / Honky tonk attitude / Let's rock
CDVDB 3 / 4 Aug '97 / Virgin

☐ CREAM - ANTHEMS
Bomb: Bucketheads / Let me show you how: K-Klass / Get your hands off my man: Vasquez, Junior / Caught in the middle: Roberts, Juliet / Love and happiness: India / Love: Roberts, Joe / Saturday night, Sunday morning: T-Empo / Lemon: U2 / Girls and boys: Hed Boys / Hideaway: De'Lacy / Where love lies: Limerick, Alison / Musik: X-Press 2 / Bells of NY: Slo Moshun / Plastic dreams: Jaydee / Question: Seven Grand Housing Authority / Is there anybody out there: Bassheads / Eighteen strings: Tin Man / Yeke yeke: Kante, Mory / Chemical beats: Chemical Brothers / My mercury mouth: Chemical Brothers / On ya way: Helicopter / Funkaterium: Jump / All funked up: Mother / Passion: Gat Decor / One: Mindwarp / Acperience: Hardfloor / Waterfall: Atlantic Ocean / Positive education: Soma / In the dark we live: Aphrohead / Into your heart: Rozzo
74321326152 / Oct '95 / De-Construction

☐ CREAM ANTHEMS 1997 (2CD Set)
You're not alone: Olive / Flash: BBE / Plastic dreams: Jaydee / Remember: BT / Prophet: Bolland, C.J. / Schoenberg: Marmion / X-ray: Spacefrog / Nightmare: Brainbug / Home: Chakra / Reflect: 3 In 1 / Cafe del mar: Energy 52 / Mystery land: Y-Traxx / Prophase: Transa / Rendezvous: Tilt / Y: DJ Scot Project / Breathe: Prodigy / Block rocking beats: Prodigy / Cowgirl: Underworld / Free: Ultra Nate / Belo horizontal: Heartists / Get up go insane: Stretch n' Vern / Offshore: Chicane / Your face: Slacker / Ajare: Way Out West / Nine ways: JDS / Don't be afraid: Moonman / Gunman: 187 Lockdown / Plannet funk 2: Neri, Alex / Sunchyme: Dario G / Everytime: Lustral
74321529622 / 1 Nov '97 / De-Construction

☐ CREAM LIVE VOL.1 (DJs Paul Oakenfold/Pete Tong/Justin Robertson/Graeme Park)
Club lonely: Ellis, Sam / Keeping the jam going: Ill Disco / Feel it: Bailey, Carol / Sexual: Rowe, Maria / Love's got me (on a trip so high): Clark, Loni / Drunk on love (roger's ultimate anthem): Basia / True faith: New Order / Train of thought: Excrima / Sight for sore eyes: M-People / Always: Tin Tin Out / Only me: Hyper Logic / Sound of Eden: Shades Of Rhythm / Things can only get better: D:Ream / Witch doktor: Van Helden, Armand / Witch doktor (remix): Van Helden, Armand / Boys revenge: Original Creators / Wild pitch: Music Freaks / Yes it is: Lady B / Voodoo Ray: Guy Called Gerald / Let's get ready to rhumble: DJ Fiovanni / So get up: Underground Sound Of Lisbon / I luv you baby: DJ Pipi / Ajare: Way Out West / Your loving arms: Martin, Billie Ray / Save the day: Disscuss / Odyssey to Anyoona: Jam & Spoon / Let me be your fantasy: Baby D / Le voie: Subliminal Cuts / Vernon's wonderland: Vernon / How can I love you more: M-People / Kut it: Reo Eye
74321272192 / Apr '95 / De-Construction

☐ CREAM OF AMBIENT VISIONS, THE
Chase the Manhattan: Black Dog / Dark and long: Underworld / My beautiful blue sky: Moby / Dr. Peter: Rejuvination / Wilmot: Sabres Of Paradise / Dolce vita: Optica / Lost continent: Inner Circle / Wave form: Mono Now / Mission impossible: Naturists / Dream: Evolve Now / Total toxic tranquillity: Holmes & McMillan
KOLDCD 008 / Apr '95 / Arctic

☐ CREAM OF IRELAND, THE
When you and I were young Maggie: Doonican, Val / When you were sweet sixteen: Furey Brothers & Davy Arthur / When I leave the world behind: Rose Marie / Grace: McCann, Jim / My lovely rose of Clare: Reilly, Paddy / Pal of my cradle days: Breen, Ann / Leaving nancy: Dubliners / Don't forget to remember: O'Donnell, Daniel / Veil of white lace: O'Brien, Michael / Wedding song: Duncan, Hugo / Daddy's hands: Duff, Mary / I know that you know (that I love you): Hogan, John / Gentle mother: Big Tom & The Mainliners / Village of Asdee: McCann, Susan
SUMCD 4145 / Sep '97 / Summit

☐ CREAM OF IRISH FOLK
CHCD 1040 / May '95 / Chyme

☐ CREAM OF JAZZ HOUSE, THE
CDHIGH 7 / 1 Sep '97 / High On Rhythm

☐ CREAM OF NEW COUNTRY, THE
Long time gone: Starling, John & Lowell George / Amarillo highway: Allen, Terry / Smokin' in the rain: Hancock, Butch & Jimmie Dale Gilmour / Meadow green: Rowan, Peter & Maura O'Connell / Road goes on forever: Keen, Robert Earl / Time to learn: O'Brien, Tim & Mary Chapin Carpenter / Loose again: Krauss, Alison & Union Station / I'll stay around: Skaggs, Ricky & Emmylou Harris / One more ride: Stuart, Marty & Johnny Cash/Doc Watson/Jerry Douglas / Talk about sufferin': Skaggs, Ricky / Playin' fool: Moffatt, Katy / Whenever kindness fails: Keen, Robert Earl / By the Rio Grande: Hinojosa, Tish / New day medley: Douglas, Jerry / Hickory wind: Hillman, Chris / New Delhi freight train: Allen, Terry
MCCD 137 / Jan '94 / Music Club

☐ CREAM OF TRIP HOP VOL.1, THE
Cosmic trigger happy: Glamorous Hooligan / Small world: Small World / Shaolin Buddha finger: Depth Charge / Electric lazyland: 9 Lazy 9 / Move ya: Rising High Collective & Plavka / Santa Cruz: Fatboy Slim / Know kname (Down): Juryman / Anafey: Hip Optimist / Showdown at Voodoo Creek: Deep Freeze Productions / Onamission: Coldcut / Shadiest breeds: Dark Globe
KOLDCD 009 / Jun '95 / Arctic

☐ CREAM OF TRIP HOP VOL.2, THE
KOLDCD 011 / Sep '95 / Arctic

☐ CREAM OF TRIP HOP VOL.3, THE
KOLDCD 012 / Feb '96 / Arctic

☐ CREAM OF TRIP HOP VOL.4, THE
KOLDCD 014 / Jun '96 / Arctic

☐ CREAM OF TRIP HOP VOL.5, THE
KOLDCD 016 / Sep '96 / Arctic

☐ CREAM OF UNDERGROUND HOUSE VOL.1, THE
De Niro: Disco Evangelists / Ethnic Prayer: Havanna / Percussion obsession: Okatu / Devo: Crunch / Buruchacca: Mukka / Slumberland: Solitaire Gee / Skelph: Harri / Givin' you no rest: E-Lustrious / Le Noir: Diceman / Two fatt Guitars: Direckt / Jump to my beat: Wildchild Experience / Te Quiero: La Camorra
KOLDCD 001 / Mar '96 / Arctic

☐ CREAM OF UNDERGROUND HOUSE VOL.2, THE
Skinnybumblebee: Gipsy / London x-press (the journey continues): Xpress 2 / Tonight (dub mix): 108 Grand / Requiem part 1: Rejuvination / I've got it: Rollin' Gear / Journey: Rollin' Gear / Rez: Underworld / Positive education: Slam / Babyloop: Pizzaman / Funk and drive: K&M Project / Trumpet release (no mercy mix): Funky Punch
KOLDCD 003 / Mar '96 / Arctic

☐ CREAM OF UNDERGROUND HOUSE VOL.3, THE
Open up: Leftfield & John Lydon / Texas cowboys: Grid / Say what: X-Press 2 / Good time: Luvdup / Saturday night party: Alex Party / Back stab: Direct 2 Disc / Theme from outrage: Outrage / Trancespotter: Vinyl Blair / Dubious kettle: Channel / Musik: Technicality / Mandala: Monumental
KOLDCD 004 / Mar '96 / Arctic

☐ CREAM OF UNDERGROUND HOUSE VOL.4, THE
On ya way: Helicopter / Who runs the show: Question / In your dance: E-Lustrious / It's gonna be alright: Ill Disco / Make it funky: Rebound / Feeling: Tin Tin Out / Echo drop: Taiko / Choir boys and kinky girls: Social Outrage Choir / Psychotherapy: Rejuvination / Dope: Vinyl Blair / Blinder: Mukkaa
KOLDCD 005 / Mar '96 / Arctic

☐ CREAM OF UNDERGROUND HOUSE VOL.5, THE
You and me: Rhyme Time Productions / Do what U like: Goodfellos / Partners: Move Inc. / No pain: Dark Star / 4 you: 4th Measure Men / Beat beat: Nostalgia Freaks / Keep the jam going: Ill Disco / Cognoman: Clubland Refugees / So damn tuff: Boomerang / Retro Euro vibe piece: Woomera / Spirit: Eskubar
KOLDCD 006 / Mar '96 / Arctic

☐ CREAM OF UNDERGROUND HOUSE VOL.7, THE
KOLDCD 010 / Mar '96 / Arctic

☐ CREAM OF UNDERGROUND HOUSE, THE (La Creme De La Creme Vol.1 - 3CD Set)
KOLDCD 013 / Mar '96 / Arctic

☐ CREAM OF UNDERGROUND HOUSE, THE (La Creme De La Creme Vol.2 - 3CD Set)
KOLDCD 015 / Aug '96 / Arctic

☐ CREAM SEPARATES (The Collection/ 3CD Set)
Never tell you: Rhythm & Sound/Tikiman / Rise: Rivera, Sandy & Kings Of Tomorrow Presents / Flirt: Horn / Glide by shooting: Two Lone Swordsmen / Fade II black: Kot / Love revolution: Mysterious People / Fly life: Basement Jaxx / Untitled: Listenin' Parlour / Gosp: LWS / Summer madness: Daemyon, Jerald / Twenty minutes of disco glory: DJ Garth & ETI / Tick tock: Chia Pet / Don't ever stop: Dubbing Double / Theme from the Blue Cucaracha: Innocent / Samba magic: Summer Daze / In your soul: Latino Circus / Seawall: Envoy / Modus vivendi: Modus Vivendi / Paper moon: 51 Days / Indulge: Howard, Neal / In a vision: Virgo Four / Unicorn: Blue Maxx / Warior: Oniero / Airport martini: Curtin, Dan / Party: Willpower / Sugar: Nimbus Quartet / Sueno latino: Sueno Latino / Song for Olivia: Cliff Hanger / Art Lukm: Holy Ghost Inc. / Confusion the waitress: Underworld / Illegal gunshot: Ragga Twins / Gettin' stupid: Dirty Beatniks / We wanna go back: Word Up / There's gonna be a riot: Dub Pistols / Trickshot: Ceasefire / Karaoke with Buddah: Eboman / King of the beats: Mantronix / Loose caboose: Electroliners / Wrecktify: Laidback / Scared: Slacker / Psychic bounty killaz: DJ Sneak & Armand Van Helden / Jack another day: Innocent / Fat cow: Fiasco / Body music: Wulf n' Bear / Theme from OP Art: As One
74321463782 / Mar '97 / De-Construction

☐ CREATION REBEL
LG 21110 / Jul '95 / Lagoon

☐ CREATION ROCKERS VOL.1 & 2
Guns fever: Brooks, Baba / Message from a black man: Harriott, Derrick / I've got soul: Carlton & His Shoes / Flashing my whip: U-Roy / Blood and fire: Niney The Observer / Little way different: Dunkley, Errol / Reggae phenomenom: Big Youth / Finanacial endorsement: Isaacs, Gregory / Enter into his gates with praise: Clarke, Johnny / Big rip off: Pablo, Augustus / Man hungry: Minott, Sugar / I and I are the chosen one: Prince Far-I / Dance crasher: Ellis, Alton / My conversation: Smith, Slim / Caution: Wailers / My satisfaction: Holt, John / Feeling soul: Andy, Bob / More music: McCook, Tommy / Brand new second hand: Tosh, Peter / Glitter not gold: Big Joe / Pretty girl: Wilson, Delroy / Conquerer: Brown, Dennis / Step by step: Mikey Dread / You're no good: Boothe, Ken
CDTRL 180 / Jun '94 / Trojan

☐ CREATION SOUP VOL.1
CRECD 101 / May '94 / Creation

☐ CREATION SOUP VOL.5
CRECD 105 / May '94 / Creation

☐ CREATION'S JOURNEY (Native American Music)
SFWCD 40410 / May '95 / Smithsonian Folkways

☐ CREATIVE DRUM 'N' BASS (Dr. S. Gachet/DJ SS - 2CD Set)
Forbidden agenda: Dr. S. Gachet / Phuturistic joint: C4 / Sea breeze: Matrix / Can't go wrong: Subject To Reason / Underwater communications: Jonny L / Flight: Wallace, Dave / Blue nights: Zed / 3 days: Eugenix / Horn section: Rogue Unit / Mystical people: Nookie & Larry Heard / Mutant jazz: T-Power / Helicopter '96: Deep Blue / Message: Shy FX / Twister: Mental Power / Sights beyond: John B / Future: $ Man / Cooper: ICI / Times Square: Decoder / Urban jazz: Zed / After dark: A-Sides & DJ Flex
ZIPCD 003 / Mar '97 / Club Masters

☐ CREATIVE GARAGE (Paul 'Trouble' Anderson/Noel Watson - 2CD Set)
Cape fear: KMA Productions / Dreams: Smokin' Beats / Feel it: Electric Circus / French girls: Mantronik, Curtis / Happy days: Hope, Alexander / I need you now: Sinnamon / 10 Minute high: Kings Of Tomorrow & Michelle Weeks / Your heaven: Urban Blues Project / All the ladies: Blackjack Collective / Won't somebody take you home: N V-US / Together forever: Raven Maize / Times are changing: Smokin' Beats / Gentle touch: Da Players / Sunny muzik: Roberts, Andy / Higher and higher: Oval Emotion / River of love: Splice Of Life & Shawn Benson / Do you feel me: Simonelli, Victor / So in love: Wild Pursuit & Gerideau / Over U (big splash): Baffled 2 / Free love: Soul Source
ZIPCD 002 / Oct '96 / Club Masters

☐ CREATIVE HOUSE (Graham Gold/ Ramp - 2CD Set)
I wanna know: Supernature / Up to no good: Porn Kings / Born workin': Grand Larceny / Future trance: Sider, Jones / Calling angels: Ling, Andy / First picture of you: Beautiful Imbalance / Rise: Modifiers / Systematic: De Moor, Vincent / Sensations: Imperial / Chevignon: Shadowman 2 / Old skool: DJ Tonka / Use your ears: DJ Tonka / Never give it up: Serena / Lay love: D-Crew / Gotta keep pushin': Z-Factor / Bar-B-Q: DJ Linus / Disco fever: Extra Lights / New world, old ways: Planet Heaven / Brothers and sisters: 2 Funky 2 / Gotta get on: Earl Grey
ZIPCD 001 / Oct '96 / Club Masters

☐ CREATIVE TECHNO
ZIPCD 006 / 13 Oct '97 / Club Masters

☐ CREATIVE TRANCE
ZIPCD 005 / 13 Oct '97 / Club Masters

☐ CREATIVE TRIP HOP (Mixed By Pressure Drop & Dave Tipper)
Weekend starts here: Fatboy Slim / Blood: Juryman / Get a grip: Bass Kittens / Finders Kreepers: Run-a-ways / Dusk: Pressure Drop / Mondo Scurro: Dark Globe / Mektob: Les Gazons Lumieres / Depth charge: Depth Charge / Train stop: Cujo / Revolutionary woman: Up Bustle & Out / 5 o'clock charlie: DJ 10 Plate / Bentley's gonna sort you out: Bentley Rhythm Ace / Jay relf: Tokya Too / Peter the wolf: It Spy / Phantom (nya bingt): Zebulon / Hot and bothered: Headrillaz / Six pak: Tipper / Funky shit: 611 / Long time coming: Kolonel Kurtz / Blinky blue eyed sunrise: Metaluna Mutant / Anchored in acid: Tipper, Dave / Bassgunner: Tipper, Dave / Hot tuna: Pelirocco
ZIPCD 004 / Mar '97 / Club Masters

☐ CREATIVE WAX REVIEWS
Silent voices: DJ Pulse & Wax Doctor / Taken over: Fallen Angels / Body and soul: Rising Sons / Revelations: Tango & Fallout / Untitled: Unit One / Final conflict: Committee / Killa instinct: Bounty Killaz / 2 faced: Digital / Groove: Reece, Alex / Love me: Unit One
CWCD 002 / 1 Dec '97 / Creative Wax

☐ CREEPY CRAWL LIVE
AP 6007CD / May '97 / Another Planet

☐ CREMA
Valid: Breach / Everything sux: Descendents / Lost: Satanic Surfers / One shot: Pulley / Girls I had: Liberator / Harrison Bergeron: Snapcase / Waiting: Strife / Diseased prey within casing: Integrity / Los hombres Nollurah: Voodoo Glowskulls / Ume hilak: Negu Gorriak / Se que no/Requebra: Todos Tus Muertos / Where eagles dare: Nofunatall / Red sea: Mad Juana / I can't stand it anymore: Union 13 / My pathetic past: SNFU / Twenty two: Millencolin / Broken: Pennywise / What would you do: Chickenpox / No easy way out: Kramer, Wayne / Alice Mae: Burnside, R.L. / Dukes of Hazzard: Loosegoats
SPI 51CD / 23 Mar '98 / Spinefarm

☐ CREOLE KINGS OF NEW ORLEANS VOL.1
Going back to New Orleans: Liggins, Joe & His Honey Drippers / Louisiana: Mayfield, Percy / River's invitation: Mayfield, Percy / Lawdy Miss Clawdy: Price, Lloyd / Where you at: Price, Lloyd / Frog legs: Price, Lloyd / Teachin' and preachin': Royal Kings / Things that I used to do: Guitar Slim / Till I say well done: Kings / Ay tete fee: Chenier, Clifton / Oh how I need your love: Hall, Alberta / Send me some lovin': Price, Leontyne / Do baby do: Kador, Ernest / Who's been foolin' you: Myles, Big Boy & Sha-Weez / Rich woman: Millet, Lil / Whistlin' Joe: Lambert, Lloyd / No buts, no maybes: Professor Longhair / Baby, let me hold your hand: Professor Longhair / Everytime I hear that mellow saxophone: Montrell, Roy / Bop

sitin blues: Blanchard, Edgar / Just to hold my hand: Myles, Big Boy / Lights out: Byrne, Jerry / Cha dooky-doo: Neville, Art / I'm a fool to care: Neville, Art / Jockomo: Williams, Larry / Bad boy: Williams, Larry
CDCHD 393 / Mar '92 / Ace

☐ **CREOLE KINGS OF NEW ORLEANS VOL.2**
Bouncin' the boogie: Royal Kings / Got a brand new baby: Little Mr. Midnight & Paul Gayten Band / Four o'clock blues: Little Mr. Midnight & Paul Gayten Band / Restless heart: Price, Lloyd / Ain't it a shame: Price, Lloyd / Say baby: Johnson, Willie / That night: Johnson, Willie / Eating and sleeping: King, Earl / Heavy sugar: Lambert, Lloyd / Think it over: Guitar Slim / So glad you're mine: Kador, Ernest / That girl I married: Myles, Big Boy & Sha-Weez / Squeeze box boogie: Chenier, Clifton / Good golly Miss Molly: Blackwell, Bumps / Oooh wow: Montrell, Roy / Stepping high: Blanchard, Edgar / All around the world: Millet, Lil / Oooh-wee baby: Neville, Art / Just because: Williams, Larry / Cry pretty baby: Professor Longhair / Look what you're doing to me: Professor Longhair / Misery: Professor Longhair / Look no hair: Professor Longhair / Rock 'n' roll fever: Monitors / Carry on: Byrne, Jerry
CDCHD 477 / Jun '93 / Ace

☐ **CREOLE MUSIC OF PERU**
X 55520 / Sep '95 / Aspic

☐ **CRESCENT CITY SOUL (The Sound Of New Orleans 1947-1974/4CD Set)**
Mardi Gras in New Orleans: Professor Longhair / Fat man: Domino, Fats / Mighty mighty man: Brown, Roy / Lawdy Miss Clawdy: Price, Lloyd / Things that I used to do: Guitar Slim / I didn't want to do it: Spiders / Jock-a-mo: Crawford, Sugar Boy / I hear you knocking: Lewis, Smiley / Tutti frutti: Little Richard / Ain't that a shame: Domino, Fats / Let the good times roll: Shirley & Lee / Ain't got no home: Henry, Clarence 'Frogman' / Let the four winds blow: Brown, Roy / Monkey: Bartholomew, Dave / Don't you just know it: Smith, Huey 'Piano' / Ooh poo pah doo: Hill, Jessie / Walking to New Orleans: Domino, Fats / Mother in law: K-Doe, Ernie / She put the hurt on me: Prince La La / It will stand: Showmen / I know (you don't love me no more): George, Barbara / It's raining: Thomas, Irma / Working in a coal mine: Dorsey, Lee / Tell it like it is: Neville, Aaron / Cissy strut: Meters / Lady marmalade: Labelle / Boogie woogie Mama: Ridgley, Tommy / Detroit city blues: Domino, Fats / 3x7=21: Jewel King / That's how you got killed before: Bartholomew, Dave / Tee-nah-nah: Lewis, Smiley / Stack-a-Lee: Archibald / Poppa Stoppa theme song: Bartholomew, Dave / Jumpin' tonight: Turner, Joe / Ain't gonna do it: Bartholomew, Dave / Every night about this time: Domino, Fats / Shake shake baby: Archibald / Good jax boogie: Bartholomew, Dave / I'm gone: Shirley & Lee / Looped: Ridgley, Tommy / Bells are ringing: Lewis, Smiley / Who drank my beer while I was in the rear: Bartholomew, Dave / Goin' home: Domino, Fats / Lillie Mae: Lewis, Smiley / Great big eyes (those little reds): Archibald / Little girl sing ding a ling: Bartholomew, Dave / Bon Ton Roulet: Garlow, Clarence / You've gotta reap: Fulson, Lowell / Going to the river: Domino, Fats / Baby's gone: Toppers / Blue Monday: Lewis, Smiley / You're the one: Spiders / Sittin' and wonderin': Allen, Jesse / ABC's (part 1): Smilin' Joe / ABC's (part 2): Smilin' Joe / Toy bell: Bees / I'm slippin' in: Spiders / Single life: Tate, Blind Billy / Runnin' wild: Crayton, Pee Wee / Four winds: Bartholomew, Dave / Feels so good: Shirley & Lee / Travellin' mood: Wayne, Wee Willie / Would you: Bartholomew, Dave / Witchcraft: Spiders / I'm in love again: Domino, Fats / One night: Lewis, Smiley / Try rock 'n' roll: Mitchell, Bobby / I feel good: Shirley & Lee / Someday: Lewis, Smiley / Rockin' at Cosmo's: Allen, Lee / Chicken Shack boogie: Milburn, Amos / Please believe me: Brown, Charles / Shame shame shame: Lewis, Smiley / Sick and tired: Kenner, Chris / Sister Jenny: Fuller, Johnny / I'll be the bee: Ruth & Al / I'm walkin': Domino, Fats / Keeper of my heart: Adams, Faye / I'm gonna be a wheel someday: Mitchell, Bobby / I want to walk you home: Domino, Fats / Ooh poo pah doo: Hill, Jessie / Tiddle winks: Allen & Allen / Over you: Neville, Aaron / Whip it on me: Hill, Jessie / Hello my lover: K-Doe, Ernie / I just want you: Charles, Bobby / It keeps raining: Domino, Fats / Tain't that the truth: K-Doe, Ernie / Come on: King, Earl / Heavenly baby: Allen & Allen / True love never dies: Orange, Allen / New Orleans twist: Blazer Boy / Cry on: Thomas, Irma / It won't be me: Diamond, Lee / Let's live: Neville, Aaron / Grumblin' fussin' nag nag: Del-Royals / I cried my last tear: K-Doe, Ernie / Country fool: Showmen / Te ta te ta ta: K-Doe, Ernie / I done got over it: Thomas, Irma / Oogsey moo: Hill, Jessie / Certain girl: K-Doe, Ernie / Fate planned it this way: Showmen / I want somebody: Taylor, Tommy / Searching for the olive oil: Senors / Help yourself: Diamond, Lee / Blues: Robinson, Al / Always a first time: King, Earl / Fortune teller: Spellman, Benny / Valley of my tears: Lee, Calvin / Trick bag: King, Earl / Every now and then: Spellman, Benny / Never again: Reeder, Eskew / Lipstick traces: Spellman, Benny / Ruler of my heart: Thomas, Irma / 39-21-40: Showmen / Take a look: Thomas, Irma
CRESCENT 1 / May '97 / EMI

☐ **CRIMINAL JUSTICE**
Banana co: Radiohead / 911 is a joke: Duran Duran / Ground level: Stereo MC's / Impact: Orbital / Kids: Jamiroquai / Lay my troubles down: Aswad / Moment in darkness: Shamen / Perfect day: EMF / Revolution: Dodgy / Practice what you preach: Corduroy / Paranoid: Inspiral Carpets
CDCRIM 001 / Jul '95 / Ultimate

☐ **CRIPPLED CHAMPION**
EFA 044002 / 2 Mar '98 / Crippled Dick Hot Wax

☐ **CROON TUNES AND KITSCHERAMA (Swingin' Cheese)**
4886892 / 16 Sep '97 / Irma

☐ **CROONERS**
MCCD 104 / May '93 / Music Club

☐ **CROONERS (3CD Set)**
MCBX 010 / Apr '94 / Music Club

☐ **CROONING ON VENUS**
Rangers in the night: Wyatt, Robert / Time: Sly & The Family Stone / Yet so beautiful: MacDonald, Laurel / Cais: Nascimento, Milton / I still love Albert Einstein: Earthling / Mercury: Royal Trux / See through love: Russell, Arthur / My ideal: Baker, Chet / I see you again: Nordenstam, Stina / Take me as I am: Hooker, John Lee / Starsailor: Buckley, Tim / Rain: Tenko / Taity Inty: YMA Sumac / Dealer: Walker, Scott / White jam: Captain Beefheart / Young and supernatural: Lilacs / Falling: Cruise, Julee / Death of Polly: Bates, Martyn / Autumn leaves: Coldcut / Prtelude/Lawns of Dawns: Mico / Protection: Massive Attack / Diabaram: Sakamoto, Ryuichi / Wind chimes: Beach Boys / Honey moon: Hosono, Haruomi / You will be loved again: O'Hara, Mary Margaret / Twilight zone: Dr. John / Higher than the sun: Primal Scream / Brilliant trees: Sylvian, David / Small hours: Martyn, John / Ever so lonely/Eyes/ Ocean: Chandra, Sheila / Lifeforms: Future Sound Of London
AMBT 13 / May '96 / Virgin

☐ **CROSS COUNTRY**
Okie from Muskogee: Haggard, Merle / Rhinestone cowboy: Campbell, Glen / Blanket on the ground: Spears, Billie Jo / Coward of the county: Rogers, Kenny / Crazy: Nelson, Willie / Don't it make my brown eyes blue: Gayle, Crystal / Rose Marie: Whitman, Slim / Rawhide: Laine, Frankie / Love me like you used to do: Tucker, Tanya / Harper valley PTA: Riley, Jeannie C. / Give me your word: Ford, Tennessee Ernie / We've got tonight: Rogers, Kenny & Sheena Easton / Son of a preacher man: Gentry, Bobbie / Angel of the morning: Newton, Juice / Honey: Goldsboro, Bobby / Hello walls: Young, Faron / Country girl: Newton-John, Olivia
KS 875092 / Jul '97 / Disky

☐ **CROSSING BORDERS**
CBM 010CD / Mar '94 / Cross Border Media

☐ **CROSSING CULTURES**
39840712 / 21 Aug '97 / Blue Flame

☐ **CROSSROADS**
BN 043 / Apr '98 / Blue Nite

☐ **CROSSROADS - SOUTHERN ROUTES (The Music Of The American South - CD/CD-Rom Set)**
Rising sun: McGhee, Brownie & Sonny Terry / Statesboro blues: Allman Brothers / Blue Monk: Dirty Dozen Brass Band / 15 ans: Les Quatre Vieux Garcons / Woke up this mornin': SNCC Freedom Singers / Brother John: Neville Brothers / Blue suede shoes: Perkins, Carl / Anque me odies: Mendoza, Lydia / Apartment: Wynette, Tammy / Too many hungry mouths: LaSalle, Denise / Southbound: Watson, Doc / There is none like him: Mississippi Mass Choir / Travellin' shoes: Hall-Ward, Vera / Mice and the bad angel: Jumper, Betty Mae / Turtle's song to the wolf: Jumper, Betty Mae / Iko iko: Neville Brothers / White House blues: Monroe, Bill / I'd rather be an old time Christian: Watson, Merle
SFWCD 40080 / Sep '96 / Smithsonian Folkways

☐ **CROSSROADS CEILI**
CHCD 015 / Oct '96 / Chart

☐ **CRUCIAL REGGAE (18 Red Hot Reggae Tunes)**
OK Fred: Dunkley, Errol / Starvation: Pioneers / Stick by me: Holt, John / Three ring circus: Biggs, Barry / Back a yard: In Crowd / Love again: George, Sophia / Baby my love: Calendar, Phil / Eighteen yellow roses: Gardiner, Boris / Everybody join hands: Dekker, Desmond / Night like this: Biggs, Barry / I think I love you: Donaldson, Eric / Uptown sharon: Isaacs, Gregory / Maga dawg: George, Sophia / You are my destiny: Gardiner, Boris / Please don't make me cry: Winston Groovy / You are everything to me: Holt, John / One big happy family: Ruffin, Bruce / Elizabethan reggae: Gardiner, Boris
SUMCD 4143 / Sep '97 / Summit

☐ **CRUISIN'**
Boom boom: Hooker, John Lee / No particular place to go: Berry, Chuck / Got my mojo working: Waters, Muddy / Working in the coalmine: Dorsey, Lee / Barefootin': Parker, Robert / Reet petite: Parker, Robert / It's in his kiss (The shoop shoop song): Everett, Betty / Wonderful world: Cooke, Sam / When a man loves a woman: Sledge, Percy / Will you still love me tomorrow: Shirelles / Twenty four hours from Tulsa: Pitney, Gene / Leader of the pack: Shangri-Las / You can't judge a book by the cover: Diddley, Bo / But I do: Henry, Clarence / Chapel of love: Dixie Cups / Oh what a night: Dells / Harlem shuffle: Bob & Earl / Smokestack lightnin': Howlin' Wolf / Walking through the park: Waters, Muddy / You can't catch me: Berry, Chuck
CPCD 8056 / Feb '95 / Charly

☐ **CRUISIN' - CRUISIN' WITH THE BLUES**
CPCD 8110 / Apr '96 / Charly

☐ **CRUISIN' - SOUL CRUISIN'**
CPCD 8111 / Apr '96 / Charly

☐ **CRUISIN' 1955 ('Jumpin' George Oxford/KSAN San Francisco)**
Rock 'n' roll: Morrow, Buddy / I got a woman: Charles, Ray / Sincerely: Moonglows / My babe: Little Walter / Earth angel: Penguins / Maybellene: Berry, Chuck / Only you: Platters / Ain't that a shame: Domino, Fats / Story untold: Nutmegs / Bo Diddley: Diddley, Bo / Pledging my love: Ace, Johnny
INCD 1955 / Jul '96 / Increase

☐ **CRUISIN' 1956 (Robin Seymour/WKMH Dearborn)**
Robin Seymour theme: Four Lads / Roll over Beethoven: Berry, Chuck / Eddie my love: Teen Queens / Ooby dooby: Orbison, Roy / Tonite tonite: Mello Kings / Great pretender: Platters / Tutti frutti: Little Richard / Stranded in the jungle: Cadets / Oh what a night: Dells / In the still of the nite: Five Satins / Blue suede shoes: Perkins, Carl
INCD 1956 / Jul '96 / Increase

☐ **CRUISIN' 1957 (Joe Niagra/WIBG Philadelphia)**
Suzie Q: Hawkins, Dale / Happy, happy birthday baby: Tune Weavers / School days: Berry, Chuck / Goodnight sweetheart: Spaniels / Little darlin': Diamonds / Over the mountain across the sea: Johnny & Joe / Bony Moronie: Williams, Larry / To the aisle: Five Satins / Whole lotta shakin' goin' on: Lewis, Jerry Lee / Long lonely nights: Andrews, Lee & The Hearts
INCD 1957 / Jul '96 / Increase

☐ **CRUISIN' 1958 (Jack Carney/WIL St. Louis)**
At the hop: Danny & The Juniors / Tequila: Champs / Book of love: Monotones / Rock 'n' roll music: Berry, Chuck / Short shorts: Royal Teens / Chantilly lace: Big Bopper / Rockin' Robin: Day, Bobby / Get a job: Silhouettes / Ten commandments of love: Harvey & The Moonglows / Rebel rouser: Eddy, Duane
INCD 1958 / Jul '96 / Increase

☐ **CRUISIN' 1959 (Hunter Hancock/KGFJ Los Angeles)**
Baby hully gully: Olympics / There is something on your mind: Big Jay McNeely / Almost grown: Berry, Chuck / What a difference a day makes: Washington, Dinah / Say man: Diddley, Bo / Sixteen candles: Crests / Personality: Price, Lloyd / It's just a matter of time: Benton, Brook / Sea of love: Phillips, Phil / Kansas City: Harrison, Wilbert
INCD 1959 / Jul '96 / Increase

☐ **CRUISIN' 1960 (Dick Biondi/WKBW Buffalo)**
Big boy Pete: Olympics / Baby (you've got what it takes): Benton, Brook & Dinah Washington / What in the world's come over you: Scott, Jack / Angel baby: Rosie & The Originals / Alley oop: Hollywood Argyles / Stay: Williams, Maurice & The Zodiacs / Running bear: Preston, Johnny / Big hurt: Fisher, Toni / Because they're young: Eddy, Duane / Fannie Mae: Brown, Buster
INCD 1960 / Jul '96 / Increase

☐ **CRUISIN' 1961 (Arnie 'Woo Woo' Ginsburg/WMEX Boston)**
Arnie Ginsburg theme: 3D's / My true story: Jive Five / Nadine: Berry, Chuck / But I do: Henry, Clarence 'Frogman' / Those oldies but goodies: Little Caesar & The Romans / Tossin' and Turnin': Lewis, Bobby / Daddy's home: Shep & The Limelites / Runaway: Shannon, Del / Ya ya: Dorsey, Lee / Peanut butter: Marathons / Wooden heart: Dowell, Joe
INCD 1961 / Jul '96 / Increase

☐ **CRUISIN' 1962 (Russ 'Weard Beard' Knight/KLIF Dallas)**
Soldier boy: Shirelles / I need your lovin': Gardner, Don & Dee Dee Ford / Hey baby: Channel, Bruce / Duke of Earl: Chandler, Gene / You'll lose a good thing: Lynn, Barbara / Let me in: Sensations / What's your name: Don & Juan / Wanderer: Dion / Sealed with a kiss: Hyland, Brian / I know you don't love me no more: George, Barbara
INCD 1962 / Jul '96 / Increase

☐ **CRUISIN' 1963 (B. Mitchell Read/ WMCA New York)**
Hand clappin': Prysock, Red / Sally go round the roses: Jaynettes / He's so fine: Chiffons / Twist and shout: Isley Brothers / Baby it's you: Shirelles / It's my party: Gore, Lesley / Walk right in: Rooftop Singers / Denise: Randy & The Rainbows / Mama didn't lie: Bradley, Jan / Hey Paula: Paul & Paula / Louie Louie: Kingsmen
INCD 1963 / Jul '96 / Increase

☐ **CRUISIN' 1964 (Johnny Holliday/WHK Cleveland)**
Harlem shuffle: Bob & Earl / Nitty gritty: Ellis, Shirley / Dang me: Miller, Roger / Chapel of love: Dixie Cups / Since I fell for you: Welch, Lenny / Girl from Ipanema: Getz, Stan & Astrud Gilberto / It's in his kiss (The shoop shoop song): Everett, Betty / Talk back tremblin' lips: Tillotson, Johnny / It's alright: Impressions / Funny: Hinton, Joe / Remember (walkin' in the sand): Shangri-Las / Suspicion: Stafford, Terry
INCD 1964 / Jul '96 / Increase

☐ **CRUISIN' 1965 (Robert W. Morgan/KHJ Los Angeles)**
Wooly bully: Sam The Sham & The Pharaohs / You've lost that lovin' feelin': Righteous Brothers / Birds and the bees: Akens, Jewel / King of the road: Miller, Roger / Sweet little sixteen: Berry, Chuck / Name game: Ellis, Shirley / In crowd: Lewis, Ramsey / It ain't me babe: Turtles / Yes I'm ready: Mason, Barbara / Eve of destruction: McGuire, Barry
INCD 1965 / Jul '96 / Increase

☐ **CRUISIN' 1966 (Pat O'Day/KJR Seattle)**
Sunny: Hebb, Bobby / Wipeout: Surfaris / Soul and inspiration: Righteous Brothers / Psychotic reaction: Count Five / Born a woman: Posey, Sandy / Pushin' too hard: Seeds / Walk away Renee: Left Banke / Li'l Red Riding Hood: Sam The Sham & The Pharaohs / California dreamin': Mamas & The Papas / Sweet pea: Roe, Tommy
INCD 1966 / Jul '96 / Increase

☐ **CRUISIN' 1967 (Dr. Don Rose/WQXI Atlanta)**
Judy in disguise: John Fred & Playboy Band / Apples, peaches and pumpkin pie: Jay & The Techniques / Happy together: Turtles / Gimme little sign: Wood, Brenton / (We ain't got) nothin' yet: Blue Magoos / Snoopy Vs. the Red Baron: Royal Guardsmen / 98.6: Keith / Little bit of soul: Music Explosion / Rain the park and other things: Cowsills / Incense and peppermints: Strawberry Alarm Clock
INCD 1967 / Jul '96 / Increase

☐ **CRUISIN' 1968 (Johnny Dark/WCAO Baltimore)**
Magic carpet ride: Steppenwolf / I wish it would rain: Temptations / Spooky: Classics IV / Cry like a baby: Box Tops / Honey: Goldsboro, Bobby / Angel of the morning: Rush, Merrilee / Girl watcher: O'Kaysions / Midnight confession: Grass Roots / Love child: Supremes / I heard it through the grapevine: Gaye, Marvin
INCD 1968 / Jul '96 / Increase

☐ **CRUISIN' 1969 (Harv Moore/WPGC Washington DC)**
Lover please: McPhatter, Clyde / He will break your heart: Groovers / Tequila: Champs / Working on a groovy thing: 5th Dimension / Talk to me: Sunny & The Sunglows / Abraham, Martin and John: Robinson, Smokey & The Miracles / My boyfriend's back: Angels / Israelites: Dekker, Desmond / Pushin' too hard: Seeds / My cherie amour: Wonder, Stevie
INCD 1969 / Jul '96 / Increase

☐ **CRUISIN' 1970 (Kris Erik Stevens/WLS Chicago)**
Spirit in the sky: Greenbaum, Norman / Drowning in the sea of love: Simon, Joe / Green-eyed lady: Sugar Loaf / Gypsy woman: Hyland, Brian / Commercial vehicle: Ides Of March / One less bell to answer: 5th Dimension / Don't let the green grass fool you: Pickett, Wilson / Will you love me tomorrow: Shirelles / Sunshine: Edwards, Jonathan / Celebrate: Three Dog Night / New world coming: Mama Cass
INCD 1970 / Jul '96 / Increase

☐ **CRUISIN' CLASSICS (2CD Set)**
Knock on wood: Floyd, Eddie / Roses are red: Carroll, Ronnie / Kiddio: Benton, Brook / Charlie Brown: Coasters / Smoke gets in your eyes: Platters / Twenty five miles: Starr, Edwin / Wimoweh: Denver, Karl / Save the last dance for me: Drifters / When you're young and in love: Marvelettes / Soul man: Sam & Dave / Dizzy: Roe, Tommy / Baby love: Supremes / Good timin': Jones, Jimmy / Maybelline: Berry, Chuck / Tell me when: Applejacks / When a man loves a woman: Sledge, Percy / Personality: Price, Lloyd / Juliet: Four Pennies / Walking back to happiness: Shapiro, Helen / Patches: Carter, Clarence / California girl: Floyd, Eddie / My heart's a symphony: Lewis, Gary & The Playboys / Moon river: Williams, Danny / Nadine: Berry, Chuck / Bring it on home to me: Sledge, Percy / Boll weevil song: Benton, Brook / You were on my mind: St. Peters, Crispian / Sheila: Roe, Tommy / Going to a go go: Monitors / Yakety yak: Coasters / Don't mess with Bill: Marvelettes / Stagger Lee: Price, Lloyd / Only you: Platters / I'll pick a rose for my rose: Johnson, Marv / I believe: Laine, Frankie
330322 / Mar '97 / Hallmark

☐ **CRUISIN' GREATS VOL.1**
He's so fine: Chiffons / Runaway: Shannon, Del / Stagger Lee: Price, Lloyd / Duke of Earl: Chandler, Gene / Night has a thousand eyes: Vee, Bobby / Under the moon of love: Lee, Curtis / Under the boardwalk: Drifters / Tequila: Champs / Leader of the pack: Shangri-Las / Little darlin': Diamonds / Slippin' and slidin': Little Richard / Barefootin': Parker, Robert / Chapel of Love: Dixie Cups / 24 hours from Tulsa: Pitney, Gene / Little town flirt: Shannon, Del / Rebel rouser: Eddy, Duane / Great pretender: Platters / Save the last dance for me: Drifters / Will you love me tomorrow: Shirelles / Surfin' safari: Beach Boys
QED 178 / Nov '96 / Tring

☐ **CRUISIN' YEARS, THE (A History Of Rock & Roll Radio)**
I got a woman: Charles, Ray / Roll over Beethoven: Berry, Chuck / Suzie Q: Hawkins, Dale / At the hop: Danny & The Juniors / Hully gully: Olympics / Teen angel: Dinning, Mark / Blue moon: Marcels / My true story: Jive Five / Sally go round the roses: Jaynettes
INCD 1000 / Jul '96 / Increase

☐ **CRUSADE FROM THE NORTH (2CD Set) (Enslaved/Darkthrone/Storm/ Satyricon/Immortal/Isengard)**
FOG 010CD / Feb '96 / Moonfog

☐ **CRUSH (2CD Set)**
Saturday night: Suede / Candy girl: Baby Bird / I am, I feel: Alisha's Attic / If you're thinking of me: Dodgy / You do something to me: Weller, Paul / Oh yeah: Ash / Find the river: REM / Chasing rainbows: Shed Seven / Something changed: Pulp / On and on: Longpigs / High and dry: Radiohead / Lovefool: Cardigans / 500 (Shake baby shake): Lush / Female of the species: Space / You and me song: Wannadies / Frog Princess: Divine Comedy / Huckleberry grove: Ocean Colour Scene / From the bench at Belvidere: Boo Radleys / Champagne supernova: Oasis / Walkaway: Cast / Being brave: Menswear / For the dead: Gene / (I'm gonna) cry myself blind: Primal Scream / Stay together: Suede / Little arithmetics: dEUS / Milk: Garbage & Tricky / Dark therapy: Echobelly / Stars: Dubstar / Missing: Everything But The Girl / Only love can break your heart: St. Etienne / Love will tear us apart '95: Joy Division / Come home: James / After all: Frank & Walters / There she goes: La's / It's about time: Lemonheads / Julie: Levellers / Mellow doubt: Teenage Fanclub / No rain: Blind Melon / To sir, with love: Trash Can Sinatras / Love song: Cure
5532952 / Feb '97 / PolyGram TV

☐ **CRY NOW CRY LATER VOL.1 & 2**
PESS 25CD / 8 Jun '98 / Pessimiser

☐ **CRY NOW CRY LATER VOL.3 & 4**
PESS 26 / 13 Jul '98 / Pessimiser

☐ **CRY OF THE BLUES, THE**
Don't start me talkin': Cotton, James / Georgina: Dupree, 'Champion' Jack / Kidney stew blues: Vinson, Eddie 'Cleanhead' / Sweet home Chicago: Baker, Mickey / Long John Blues: Washington, Dinah / How long blues: Memphis Slim / You got good business: Jones, Curtis / Every dog's got his day: Copeland, Johnny / Eagle rock: Memphis Slim / I'm in love: Walker, T-Bone / Saint Lewis blues: Lewis, Furry / Who she do: Williams, Joe / They call me Doctor Professor Longhair: Professor Longhair / Married man blues: Humes, Helen / Just out of Louisiana: Hopkins, Lightnin' / Backwater blues: Broonzy, 'Big' Bill / Long way home: Brown, Clarence 'Gatemouth'
5526382 / Mar '97 / Spectrum

☐ **CRYIN' LYIN' LOVIN' AND LEAVIN'**
1509595292 / 31 Mar '98 / Intersound

☐ **CRYING SCENE**
NSCD 017 / May '95 / Newsound

☐ **CRYPT CHEAPO SAMPLER**
EFA 115672 / Apr '94 / Crypt

☐ **CRYPT CHEAPO SAMPLER VOL.1**
EFACD 12885 / 26 Sep '97 / Crypt

☐ **CRYPT CHEAPO SAMPLER VOL.2**
EFACD 12886 / Jun '97 / Crypt

☐ **CRYSTAL BALL RECORDS VOL.1 (The 45rpm Days)**
Arlene: *Four Winds* / Little Miss Muffet: *Colonials* / 1-2-3: *Fascinations* / I got a girl: *Sinceres* / Better him than me: *Royal Knights* / Close the door: *Byron, Donald & The Montclairs* / Valentine: *Statens* / Hope prayer and dream: *Del-Fi's* / Where there is a will: *Riffs* / Declaration of love: *Envoys* / Unchained melody: *Five Discs* / Lonesome weekend: *Elegants* / So very wrong: *Four Deans* / Let me make you smile again: *Doreen & Tammy* / Come on baby: *Four Wheels* / Mexico: *Vinny & The Visuals* / Please tell me baby: *Lenny & The Castels* / Go ahead and cry: *Felix & The Ideals* / Don't cry little girl: *Demolyrs* / Goodnight: *Exotics* / Gloria: *Gems* / I need your love: *Little Willie & The Rhythm Cadets* / Moonlight angel: *Revlons* / Your initials: *Four Graduates* / Tell me why: *Allumes* / Mr. Fortune Teller: *Frankie & The Darvels*
CDBB 55056 / Mar '98 / Buffalo Bop

☐ **CRYSTAL BALL RECORDS VOL.2 (The 45rpm Days)**
Dear Judy: *Four Winds* / My darling: *Del-Fi's* / Springtime: *Envoys* / Wendy you're mine: *Emanons* / Portrait of love: *Stevens, Mark & The Charmers* / Where was I: *Statens* / My heart belongs to only you: *Exotics* / Don't take the stars: *Knee, Bonnie Group* / My girl Pearl: *Premonitions* / She's gone: *Jordan & The Fascinations* / Storm: *Riffs* / Rain: *Demolyrs* / She's my angel: *Dahills* / Winner take all: *Allumes* / I dreamed: *Tommy Tomorrow & The Yesterdays* / Caught in a lie: *Four Graduates* / Rosemarie: *Nicky & The Del-Fives* / It's just a matter of time: *Elegants* / Linda: *Nick & The Nacks* / Goodnight: *Jordan & The Fascinations* / Last goodbye: *Frankie & The Darvels* / Elanor: *Little Willie & The Rhythm Cadets* / School house love: *Jimmy & The Teen Chordials* / May I have this dance: *Four Graduates* / Once in love: *Carol & The Teens* / Mr. Fortune Teller: *Frankie & The Darvels*
CDBB 55057 / Mar '98 / Buffalo Bop

☐ **CRYSTAL BALL RECORDS VOL.3 (From The Vaults)**
Stormy weather: *Vinny & The Visuals* / Dream angel: *Dreamairs* / Cameo: *Interludes* / You can't judge a book by its cover: *Tommy Tomorrow & The Yesterdays* / Please be mine: *Byron, Donald & The Montclairs* / You: *Felix & The Diamonds* / Possibility: *Danny & The Diamonds* / Three charms: *Lenny & The Castels* / Dreamland: *Exotics* / That's my desire: *Sherwoods* / Not too young: *Joey & The Satilites* / Tomorrow: *Nicky & The Del-Fives* / Those precious words: *Interludes* / I got a girl: *Di Martino, Vinnie & The Clouds* / Nothin' went right: *Regina & The Redheads* / I'm ready to go steady: *Little Eddie & The Excellents* / Two hearts in love: *Velvetones* / Everybody's somebody's fool: *Eddie & The Embers* / Canadian sunset: *Emanons* / Introduction to romance: *Royal Knights* / Can't believe you're mine tonight: *Del-Larks* / Search: *Sherwoods* / Wonderful love: *Eddie & The Embers* / Sunday kind of love: *Del-Chateaus* / Carol: *Deans* / Those wonderful moments: *Shepherds* / Dry your eyes: *Revlons* / Mr. Fortune Teller: *Frankie & The Darvels*
CDBB 55062 / Mar '98 / Buffalo Bop

☐ **CRYSTALIZE YOUR MIND (Nuggets From The Golden State)**
Crystalize your mind: *Living Children* / Now it's over: *Living Children* / I'll be around: *Poor Souls* / Shadows: *Vejtables* / Feel the music: *Vejtables* / Excitation: *Rear Exit* / Miles beyond: *Rear Exit* / Train: *Transatlantic Train* / You're bringing me down: *Transatlantic Train* / She was a lady: *Transatlantic Train* / I'm going: *Flying Circus* / Midnight highway: *Flying Circus* / Green eyes green world: *Flying Circus* / Swallow the sun (dark on you now): *Love Exchange* / Light switch: *Mourning Reign* / Cut back: *Mourning Reign* / Kissy face: *Maze* / Dejected soul: *Maze* / Napoleon: *Staff* / Would you take me for a ride: *Staff* / Morning: *Afterglow* / Susie's gone: *Afterglow*
CDWIKD 131 / Aug '94 / Big Beat

☐ **CUBA**
Mi corazon hace tic-tac: *Gonzalez* / El muneco: *Mandingo, Felipe* / Lo que me gusta de ti: *America, Ima* / Nuevo horizonte: *Valdez, Marco* / Volveras: *Oliveira, Valdeci* / Abomey: *Mivekannin, Renaud* / Guantanamera: *America, Ima* / Vuela: *Moreno, Jorge* / Pandara: *Oliveira, Valdeci* / Casual encuentro: *Garcia, Franco* / Hoy mi voz: *Collantes, Posi* / Si senor: *Valdez, Marco* / La Llegada: *Garcia, Franco* / Bacuranao: *Collantes, Posi*
12603 / Aug '96 / Laserlight

☐ **CUBA - I AM TIME (4CD/Book Set)**
El sinsonte: *Quinto, Pancho & Anag 7* / Obatala: *Valdes, Merceditas* / La voz del congo: *Clave & Guaguanco* / Chacho: *Los Munequitos De Matanzas* / Yemaya: *Conjunto Folklorico Nacional De Cuba* / Pappa Aggun: *Mendoza, Celeste & Los Papines* / Santa Barbara: *Gonzalez, Celina* / Son cu pin pin: *Comparsa San Agustin* / Bata rhythm / Osain: *Valdes, Merceditas* / Chivo que rompe tambo: *Bola De Nieve* / Soy todo: *Formell, Juan Y Los Van Van* / Assokere: *Sintesis* / Arrolla Cubano: *Vera, Maria Teresa* / Mamita cambia: *Valdes, Miguelito* / Saoco: *Mendoza, Celeste* / Yo si tumbo cana: *Cuarteto D'Aida* / Guajira Guantanamera: *Fernandez, Joseito* / Son de la loma: *Trio Matamoros* / Maria Cristina: *Saquito, Nico* / El derdulero: *Alvarez, Paulina* / El diablo tun tun: *Cuni, Miguelito* / Ritmo pilon: *Alonso, Pacho* / Y manana me caso contigo: *Faz, Roberto Y Su Conjunto* / Drume negrita: *Valdes, Merceditas* / Yayabo: *Gomez, Tito* / Sabanas biancas: *Alfonso, Gerado* / Mariposa: *Ferrer, Pedro Luis* / Identidad: *Milanes, Pablo* / A Bayamo en coche: *Alvarez, Adalberto & Su Son* / Pa que te salves: *Delgado, Isaac Y Su Orquesta* / Que bueno baila usted: *More, Benny* / Rumba caliente: *Reve Y Su Charangon* / Lliana quiere chocolate: *Pello Afrokan* / Echale salista: *Pineiro, Ignacio Septeto Nacional* / Tres lindas Cubanas: *Sexteto Habanero* / Pare cochero: *Orchestra Aragon* / Sociedad Antonio Maceo: *Lopez, Israel 'Cachao'* / Mulatica revoltosa: *Arcano Y Sus Maravillas* / Adivinalo: *Rodriguez, Arsenio* / Oye el corborero: *Cuni, Miguelito* / Que sorpresa: *Formell, Juan Y Los Van Van* / Recordando al sonero: *Alvarez, Adalberto & Su Son* / La bruja camara: *Cortes, Jose Luis Y Ng La Banda* / La bola: *Mandolin El Medico De La Salsa* / Se te fue la mano: *Delgado, Isaac Y Su Orquesta* / Mambo: *Bauza, Mario* / Descarga numero dos: *O'Farrell, Chico* / Juana: *Irakere* / Nueva vision: *Salvador, Emilio* / Bemba'e cuchara: *Cachao* / Tumbao de coqueta: *Alemany, Jesus* / Sobre un canto a eleggua: *Grupo Afro-Cuba* / Parraga: *Valle, Orlando 'Maraca'* / El noticiero: *Los Terry* / Woody 'n' you: *Rubalcaba, Gonzala* / Monturo: *Coleman, Steve Mystic Rhythm Society & Afro Cuba De Matanzas*
BJAC 50102 / Aug '97 / Blue Jackel

☐ **CUBA FESTIVAL DE VOCES**
9944132382 / 27 Apr '98 / Orfeon

☐ **CUBA IN WASHINGTON (Recorded Live At 1989 Festival Of American Folklife)**
SFWCD 40461 / Aug '97 / Smithsonian Folkways

☐ **CUBA LIBRE VOL.1 (Afro-Cuba)**
Cuban lullaby: *Bauza, Mario* / Mambo: *Bauza, Mario* / Yo siempre oddara: *Bunnett, Jane* / Despojo: *D'Rivera, Paquito* / Relax: *Sandoval, Arturo* / El montuno de patatp: *Patato* / Guaguanjira: *D'Rivera, Paquito* / La comparsa: *D'Rivera, Paquito* / Come fue: *D'Rivera, Paquito* / El mansiero: *Bauza, Mario* / Comelon: *Patato* / Adios pampa mia: *Patato* / GMS: *Bunnett, Jane*
NSCD 007 / Oct '95 / Nascente

☐ **CUBA LIBRE VOL.2 (Latin Jazz)**
Tanga: *D'Rivera, Paquito* / Snow samba: *D'Rivera, Paquito* / Lorenzo's wings: *D'Rivera, Paquito* / Bahia san juan: *Hidalgo, Giovanni* / Jazz sabor: *Seis Del Solar* / Zambia: *Bauza, Mario* / Night in Tunisia: *Bauza, Mario* / Azulito: *Bauza, Mario*
NSCD 008 / Oct '95 / Nascente

☐ **CUBA LIBRE VOL.3 (Made In Heaven)**
NSCD 012 / Nov '96 / Nascente

☐ **CUBAN ALLSTARS (4CD Set)**
TMGBOX 1 / 29 Jun '98 / Tumi

☐ **CUBAN BOX SET (4CD Set)**
320302 / Jan '96 / Milan

☐ **CUBAN CLASSICS**
Taka taka-ta: *Irakere* / El coco: *Irakere* / Locas por el mambo: *More, Benny* / Mi chiquita: *More, Benny* / El bobo de la yuca: *More, Benny* / Lo que me paso en la guagua: *Alvarez, Alberto* / Longina: *Burke, Malena* / Santa Barbara: *Gonzalez, Celina* / Pare cochero: *Orquesta Aragon* / Yo no quiero que seas celosa: *Reve Y Su Charangon* / Los sitios entero: *Ng La Banda* / La protesta de los chivos: *Ng La Banda* / Coge el Camaron: *Origina De Manzanillo* / Se muere la tia: *Los Van Van* / Eso que anda: *Los Van Van*
HADCD 169 / May '94 / Javelin

☐ **CUBAN DANZONERAS 1932-1946**
Tuya es me vida: *Sigler, Vincent* / La montunita oriental: *Bryon, Enrique* / De tamarindo fresca: *Bryon, Enrique* / Bella cubana: *Belen, Che* / La cachimba de San Juan: *Belen, Che* / Canta contrabajo canta: *Maravillas De Arcano* / Quien pudiera: *Maravillas De Arcano* / Rarezas: *Maravillas De Arcano* / Cuentame algo: *Maravillas De Arcano* / Coconay: *Contreras, Hermanos* / Botamos la pelota: *Contreras, Hermanos* / Ano 40: *Lopez, Belisario* / Desde que te conoci: *Lopez, Belisario* / Siga la flecha: *Lopez, Belisario* / La calandria: *Lopez, Belisario* / Matagua: *Romeu, Antonio* / El genio alegre: *Romeu, Antonio* / Salvaje: *Alvarez, Paulina* / Honda pena: *Alvarez, Paulina* / Mi acoiris: *Almendra*
HQCD 65 / 15 Jun '98 / Harlequin

☐ **CUBAN EXPRESS**
CDHOT 641 / 29 Jun '98 / Charly

☐ **CUBAN FANTASY**
CD 62023 / Apr '94 / Saludos Amigos

☐ **CUBAN RHYTHMS**
CCD 504 / Nov '95 / Caney

☐ **CUBAN ROMANCE**
CDHOT 632 / Dec '97 / Charly

☐ **CUBAN SANTERIA**
SFWCD 40419 / Oct '95 / Smithsonian Folkways

☐ **CUBAN SEXTETOS/CONJUNTOS**
HQCD 64 / Jun '96 / Harlequin

☐ **CUBANS IN EUROPE VOL.1 1929-1932**
Arriba guajiro: *Septeto Nacional* / Asturias partia: *Septeto Nacional* / El que siembra su maiz: *Septeto Nacional* / Bururu barara: *Septeto Nacional* / A la loma de Belen: *Septeto Nacional* / Aurora: *Septeto Nacional* / Maroxina: *Septeto Nacional* / Duo punto Cubano: *De La Cruz, Juan & Bienvenido Leon* / Bruno Zayas: *Castellanos* / Cuba en Paris: *Castellanos* / Mi tumbao: *Castellanos* / Les trois coups: *Rico* / Melody's bar: *Barreto, Don* / Negro bembon: *Grenet, Eliseo* / Merse: *Grenet, Eliseo* / Songoro cosongo: *Grenet, Eliseo* / Lamento Cubano: *Grenet, Eliseo* / Recuerdos tu: *Los Siboneyes Orquesta* / Por es yo te vanto ati: *Los Siboneyes Orquesta* / Digen que no me quieres: *Los Siboneyes Orquesta* / Caminando: *Azpiazu, Don*
HQCD 37 / Oct '96 / Harlequin

☐ **CUBANS IN EUROPE VOL.2**
Voodoo: *Azpiazu, Don* / Mulata sandunguera: *De La Cruz, Juan & Bienvenido Leon* / Mujer de fuego: *De La Cruz, Juan & Bienvenido Leon* / La negrilla: *Grenet, Eliseo* / Tanto tren: *Grenet, Eliseo* / Yo no tumbo cana: *Grenet, Eliseo* / Mueveme tu cintura: *Grenet, Eliseo* / Invitacion a la rumba: *Castellanos* / Green eyes: *Castellanos* / Chivo que rompe tambo: *Cueva, Julio* / Buscando millionarias: *Cueva, Julio* / Flan y merengue: *Cueva, Julio* / Maria la o: *Cueva, Julio* / Rico son: *Cueva, Julio* / Una cabana y una Inglesa: *Cueva, Julio* / Invitacion a la rumba: *Orchestre Cubain*
HQCD 56 / Jan '97 / Harlequin

☐ **CUBANS IN EUROPE VOL.3 1934-1954**
La conga / La comparsa de los congos / Trinitaria / Maria Antonia / Lady in red / Negro bembom / Alma de mujur / Loca rumba / Conga de la Havana / Son retozon / Viva la conga / Cachumbambe / Priquitin pim pom / Con picante y sin picante / A gozar / Marinita de mi amor / La sultana / Nuits de Paris / Tristeza / Conga mi Rosa / Bailando la guaracha / Damelo / La morita / Bim bam bum / Tin tan mambo / El manisero
HQCD 109 / Apr '98 / Harlequin

☐ **CUE THE MAMBO**
CDHOT 604 / Jun '96 / Charly

☐ **CULT AGE**
CDACV 2009 / Jun '96 / ACV

☐ **CULT VOL.2 (A Miracle Summer Breeze/The Psychedelic Trance Compilation)**
Next stop oblivion: *Z To A* / Free lemonade: *Total Eclipse* / Gilis voyage: *Etnica* / Probe: *Tufaan* / Forbidden: *Disco Volante* / Mouli karaki: *Joking Sphinx* / Ushuala: *Ushuala* / Yes: *Axelerator* / Vacant vacation: *Synchro*
SPV 08538742 / Sep '96 / SPV

☐ **CULTURAL FASHION**
FADCD 035 / Sep '97 / Fashion

☐ **CULTURE CENTRE VOL.2**
PHCD 2050 / Jan '97 / Penthouse

☐ **CULTURE MIX VOL.1**
BWD 0001 / May '97 / Brickwall

☐ **CULTURE TRAIN VOL.2**
SBCD 011 / 5 May '98 / Soul Beat

☐ **CUMBIA CUMBIA VOL.2**
WCD 033 / Apr '93 / World Circuit

☐ **CUMBIA MIX**
8867220492 / 24 Mar '98 / Max Music

☐ **CUMBIAS, BABUCOS & PASILOS**
PS 65123 / Apr '94 / PlayaSound

☐ **CUP OF TEA RECORDS VOL.1**
Love anybody: *Barcode* / Up in the air: *Static Sound System* / Revolutionary pilot: *Static Sound System* / Secret love: *Static Sound System* / Doge of Venice: *Dedamo* / Crimes: *Spaceways* / I water my plants: *Monk & Canatella* / Rough head: *Monk & Canatella* / Squeeler: *Red* / Timber: *Grantby* / This time it's different: *Monk & Canatella* / Passion: *Purple Penguin* / Japanese flute: *Spaceways* / Float: *Oska*
COTCD 001 / Jul '96 / Cup Of Tea

☐ **CUP OF TEA RECORDS VOL.2**
Drifter: *Fruit Loop* / Oil oil oil: *Invisible Pair Of Hands* / Hilary: *Slick 60* / Charlie X: *Spaceways* / Recliner classic: *Slick 60* / Picnics: *Monk & Canatella* / Apology: *Monk & Canatella* / O driscolls curse: *Monk & Canatella* / Outsider now: *Statik Sound System* / Discendent: *Purple Penguin* / Amazed by you: *Statik Sound System* / Mouse at the organ: *Mr. Scruff* / What da fuck: *Receiver* / Trois: *Sly* / Socrates dream: *OST*
COTCD 012 / 20 Oct '97 / Cup Of Tea

☐ **CURRENT ARTISTS AT STUDIO ONE VOL.1**
SOCD 50148 / Oct '96 / Studio One

☐ **CURRENT ARTISTS AT STUDIO ONE VOL.2**
SOCD 50150 / Oct '96 / Studio One

☐ **CURTOM SOUL TRIPPIN'**
Nothing on me (cocaine song): *Mayfield, Curtis* / Sooner or later: *Impressions* / What's happening here: *Natural Four* / Make me twice the man: *Notations* / Mix it up: *Stridells* / Where did love go: *Hutson, Leroy* / Never gonna stop: *Clifford, Linda* / Fill you up: *Mystique* / How have you been: *Natural Four* / We'll always be together: *Christopher, Gavin* / Impossible decision: *Dewi, Cheetum & Howe* / I can't let this good thing get away: *Clifford, Linda* / Play my music: *Butler, Billy* / I turn to you: *Jones Girls*
CDNEW 115 / Nov '97 / Curtom

☐ **CURTOM STORY, THE (1966-1980/ 2CD Set)**
CDLAB 107 / Jan '96 / Charly

☐ **CURTOM SUPERPEOPLE VOL.1**
CDNEW 110 / Jul '97 / Charly

☐ **CURTOM SUPERPEOPLE VOL.2**
CDNEW 125 / 1 Jun '98 / Charly

☐ **CUTTING EDGE METAL**
HNF 043CD / 29 Jun '98 / Head Not Found

☐ **CUTTING IT TO THE X-TREME**
XTR 11CD / Jun '94 / Cutting

☐ **CYBERLAB (2CD Set)**
Stray bullet: *KMFDM* / Kill: *Birmingham 6* / Overflow: *Razed In Black* / Turn: *Hexedene* / Thermal noise: *Statemachine* / Believe: *Cleen* / Metamorphosis: *(In)ternal* / Tullaby: *Dust Of Basement* / Pleiadian agenda: *Hanzel & Gretyl* / I don't think they know: *Mesh* / Time for me: *Fiction 8* / Changes: *Girls Under Glass* / Embodied: *Spahn Ranch* / Slowly mutating: *Implant* / Rain of blood: *Die Form* / Columbian necktie: *Frontline Assembly* / Words of power: *Funker Vogt* / Kim: *Pierrepoint* / Dark room: *Dive* / Still alive: *Blind Passengers* / Mind energy: *Inertia* / Lucifer's garden: *Evil's Toy* / Les amants: *Hyperdex-I-Sect* / Space divider: *Neuroactive* / Under my control: *Leaether Strip* / City of lies: *Plastic Noise Experience* / Turn of the tide: *X Marks The Pedwalk* / Wirklichkeit: *Regenerator*
NB 3132 / 6 Jul '98 / Nuclear Blast

☐ **CYCLOPS SAMPLER VOL.3**
CYCL 046 / Jan '97 / Cyclops

☐ **CYLINDER JAZZ 1913-1927**
Hungarian rag / Clarinet squawk: *Louisiana Five* / Dardanella: *Raderman, Harry's Jazz Orchestra* / Meadow lark: *Yellman, Duke & his orchestra* / Where's my sweetie hiding: *Merry Sparklers* / Blue eyed sally / Ain't she sweet / She's a cornfed Indiana gal: *Oliver, Earl's Jazz Babies* / Make that trombone laugh: *Raderman, Harry's Jazz Orchestra* / Night time in Little Italy: *Frisco Jazz Band* / I'm going to park myself in your arms: *Yellman, Duke & his orchestra* / That certain feeling: *Tennessee Happy Boys* / Do it again / Louisville Lou
CDSDL 334 / Mar '94 / Saydisc

D

☐ **D MAD BULL CREW VOL.1**
MBM 001 / Mar '98 / Mad Bull

☐ **D&D PROJECT, THE**
One-two pass it: *D&D All Stars* / Look alive: *Big C* / Act up: *Ill Breed* / Da good die young: *N-Tense* / Stone to the bone: *Big Jaz* / From within out: *Fabidden Frut* / Get up: *Maniac Mob* / Just a little flava: *Il Unorthodox* / Blowin' up the spot: *Ill Will* / Rude boy: *Night Dwellers* / Nine inches hard: *Juice* / Mental illness: *2 Mental*
07822187802 / Jun '95 / Arista

☐ **D-DAY 50TH ANNIVERSARY: A MUSICAL TRIBUTE**
DDAY 50 / Feb '97 / Start

☐ **DA MINIMAL (2CD Set)**
EFA 626242 / 20 Apr '98 / Raw Elements

☐ **DA MINIMAL FUNK**
EFA 626152 / Apr '97 / Raw Elements

☐ **DADDIES SING GOOD NIGHT (A Collection Of Sleepytime Songs)**
SHCD 3821 / Mar '94 / Sugar Hill

☐ **DAFFAN SINGLES (2CD Set)**
These hands: *Jericho, Jerry* / Walk my way: *Jericho, Jerry* / Tangled mind: *Irby, Jerry* / Bottom of the list: *Irby, Jerry* / Heartaches for gold: *Tillman, Floyd* / Running away: *Tillman, Floyd* / Always lend a helping hand: *Jericho, Jerry* / I'm getting more than my share: *Jericho, Jerry* / Our daily bread: *McBride, Dickie* / Silent partners: *McBride, Dickie* / Call for me Darling: *Irby, Jerry* / It's time you started looking: *Irby, Jerry* / How foolish can woman be: *McBride, Laura Lee* / I want my man: *McBride, Laura Lee* / Clickety clack: *Irby, Jerry* / Man is a slave: *Irby, Jerry* / Rich and the poor: *Jericho, Jerry* / Which way are you going: *Jericho, Jerry* / Be kind to a man: *Jericho, Jerry* / So ashamed: *Jericho, Jerry* / That's too bad: *Irby, Jerry* / I'd give you anything in this world: *Irby, Jerry* / Waltz you saved for me: *Jericho, Jerry* / Floyd's song: *Tillman, Floyd* / Cold, cold beer: *Tillman, Floyd* / Hopeless: *Fidlo* / Triflin' heart: *Fidlo* / Who's getting your love: *Lee, Ted* / Blues that way: *Lee, Ted* / Dig that crazy driver: *Pennix, William* / How old do you get: *Pennix, William* / Teach 'em how to swim: *Pennix, William* / Them old blues got me: *Pennix, William* / Ride the waves of love: *Elliott, Margaret* / Last call: *Elliott, Margaret* / Strange love: *Bundrick, John 'Rabbit'* / Made in Japan: *Bundrick, John 'Rabbit'* / This wallflower's gonna bloom: *Elliott, Margaret* / What's her name: *Elliott, Margaret* / Cold grey walls of yesterday: *Pickering Bros* / Please (come back to me): *Pickering Bros* / Surviving half of a love affair: *Pickering Bros* / Lady luck my love: *Pickering Bros* / Letter from nashville: *Pickering Bros*
BCD 15878 / Jun '95 / Bear Family

☐ **DAIGAN**
TRADD 183CD / May '97 / Fflach

☐ **DAKAR SOUND VOL.3**
2002853 / Jan '97 / Dakar Sound

☐ **DAKAR SOUND VOL.4**
2002852 / Jan '97 / Dakar Sound

☐ **DALGAS 1928-1933**
HTCD 34 / Jan '97 / Heritage

☐ **DAMAGED GOODS CHEEP SAMPLER**
Virtually happy: *Holly Golightly* / We love you: *Helen Love* / Tickle me: *Budget Girls* / We hate the fuckin' NME: *Thee Headcoats* / Endless summer: *Honeyrider* / Young mother: *J-Church* / Davey Crocket: *Thee Headcoats* / New art riot: *Manic Street Preachers* / Sunflower: *Lovesick* / Sorry to embarrass you: *Television Personalities* / She says: *Anorak Girl* / Danny Edwards: *Sexton Ming* / Et moi, et moi, et moi: *Dutronc* / It's a dog's life: *Twister* / Baby oil: *Hopper* / Love me for a reason: *Oizone* / Endless song: *Cuckooland* / Ghost boy: *Phantom Pregnancies* / Nothing at all: *Toast* / Questions I can't answer: *Bristols* / Sent apart: *Dustball* / Jack the ripper: *Revillos* / Justify your book: *Wat Tyler* / Harbour master: *Cee Bee Beaumont* / Heroes: *Period Pains* / Stem the slide: *Reverse* / Feed my ego: *Bette Davis & The Balconettes* / Shirts off: *Armitage Shanks* / Retard: *Dweeb* / On the move: *Adventures Of Parsley*
DAMGOOD 144CD / 1 Jun '98 / Damaged Goods

☐ **DAN MASKS**
C 580048 / Nov '93 / Ocora

☐ **DANCE 50 (The Independence Trance Revival)**
21102 / 27 Jul '98 / Phonokol

☐ DANCE '95
Cotton eye Joe: *Rednex* / Set you free: *N-Trance* / Total eclipse of the heart: *French, Nicki* / Another night: *MC Sar & The Real McCoy* / Saturday night: *Whigfield* / Let me be your fantasy: *Baby D* / Sweet love: *M-Beat & Nazlyn* / Can you feel it: *Reel 2 Real* / Baby come back: *Pato Banton* / Baby, I love your way: *Big Mountain* / Love so strong: *Secret Life* / Don't leave me this way: *Houston, Thelma* / Apparently nothin': *Anderson, Carleen* / Sweetness: *Gayle, Michelle* / Midnight at the oasis: *Brand New Heavies* / Welcome to tomorrow (are you ready): *Snap* / Texas cowboys: *Grid* / Eighteen strings: *Tinman* / What's up: *DJ Miko* / Sign: *Ace Of Base*
VTCD 43 / Feb '95 / Virgin

☐ DANCE ANTHEMS
I luv you baby: *Original* / Professional widow: *Amos, Tori* / Son of a gun: *JX* / Don't stop movin': *Livin' Joy* / Groove is in the heart: *Deee-Lite* / Children: *Miles, Robert* / Things can only get better: *D:Ream* / Free: *Ultra Nate* / Everybody's free to feel good: *Rozalla* / Sunshine: *Umboza* / Show me love: *Robin S* / Rhythm of the night: *Corona* / Anthem: *N-Joi* / Show me your love: *Alex Party* / Such a good feeling: *Brothers In Rhythm* / Shine on: *Degrees Of Motion* / Gonna make you sweat: *C&C Music Factory* / Where love lives: *Limerick, Alison* / Insanity: *Oceanic* / Missing: *Everything But The Girl* / Don't you want me: *Felix* / Real thing: *Di Bart, Tony* / I believe: *Happy Clappers* / Fired up: *Funky Green Dogs* / Set you free: *N-Trance* / Encore une fois: *Sash* / Sugar is sweeter: *Bolland, C.J.* / You got the love: *Source & Candi Staton*
ANTHCD 1 / 13 Oct '97 / Beechwood

☐ DANCE ATTACK
ZYX 550732 / Feb '97 / ZYX

☐ DANCE BAND HITS OF THE BLITZ (2CD Set)
It can't be wrong: *Geraldo & His Orchestra* / Long ago and far away: *Geraldo & His Orchestra* / Humpty Dumpty heart: *Geraldo & His Orchestra* / Every night about this time: *Geraldo & His Orchestra* / I don't want to set the world on fire: *Geraldo & His Orchestra* / Anywhere on earth is heaven: *Geraldo & His Orchestra* / I'm nobody's baby: *Gonella, Nat & His New Georgians* / Aurora: *Gonella, Nat & His New Georgians* / I can't get Indiana off my mind: *Gonella, Nat & His New Georgians* / Be careful it's my heart: *Roy, Harry & His Band* / Daddy: *Roy, Harry & His Band* / Sand in my shoes: *Roy, Harry & His Band* / Pennsylvania polka: *Roy, Harry & His Band* / That lovely weekend: *Roy, Harry & His Band* / Five o'clock whistle: *Roy, Harry & His Band* / White Christmas: *Roy, Harry & His Band* / Down Forget-Me-Not Lane: *Loss, Joe & His Orchestra* / I'll never smile again: *Loss, Joe & His Orchestra* / You made me care: *Loss, Joe & His Orchestra* / How sweet you are: *Benson, Ivy & Her Girls Band* / If I had my way: *Benson, Ivy & Her Girls Band* / I'm sending my blessing: *Benson, Ivy & Her Girls Band* / Home coming waltz: *Benson, Ivy & Her Girls Band* / Does she love me: *Leader, Harry & His Band*
CDDL 1185 / Aug '93 / Music For Pleasure

☐ DANCE BANDS OF THE 1940'S (A Dream World Is Waiting)
Dream world is waiting: *Geraldo & His Orchestra* / Sentimental interlude: *Gonella, Nat & His New Georgians* / Night flight: *Winstone, Eric* / Let him go let him tarry: *Geraldo & His Orchestra* / Roundabout goes round: *Roy, Harry & His Band* / Hot dogs: *Gonella, Nat & His New Georgians* / Is you is or is you ain't my baby: *Barriteau, Carl Orchestra* / I'm looking for a melody: *Roy, Harry & His Orchestra* / Promenade: *Winstone, Eric & His Band* / And then you kissed me: *Geraldo & His Orchestra* / I'll always be with you: *Loss, Joe & His Orchestra* / Ol' Man Mose: *Barriteau, Carl Orchestra* / Yankee doodle came to London town: *Roy, Harry & His Band* / There I've said it again: *Geraldo & His Orchestra* / Tanks for the boogie ride: *Gonella, Nat & His New Georgians* / Blue note paper: *Gibbons, Carroll & Savoy Hotel Orpheans* / I want my Mama: *Roy, Harry & His Band* / I'll get by: *Barriteau, Carl Orchestra* / Ferry boat serenade: *Gibbons, Carroll & Savoy Hotel Orpheans* / Gotta be this or that: *Geraldo & His Orchestra* / No need for words: *Loss, Joe & His Orchestra* / It's always you: *Roy, Harry & His Band*
PLCD 543 / Jun '96 / President

☐ DANCE BANDS OF THE 30'S AND 40'S
You try someone else / Leave the rest to nature / Outside of you / You started me dreaming / I can't get Mississippi off my mind / She's my secret passion / Linda / My old dog / Until we meet again / Bitin' the dust / Little things that mean so much / I'm in love for the last time / It's the bluest kind of blues my baby sings / Talk to me / Ain't nobody here but us chickens / Goodnight my beautiful / Seven day's leave / We speak of you often / Don't dilly dally on the way / Bow bells / Leicester Square rag / Old music master / Shoemaker's serenade / Give me my ranch / Far away place
CDMFP 6362 / Jun '97 / Music For Pleasure

☐ DANCE BUZZ
Guaglione: *Prado, Perez* / Surrender your love: *Nightcrawlers* / Your loving arms: *Martin, Billie Ray* / Scatman: *Scatman John* / Freedom: *Gayle, Michelle* / Dreamer: *Livin' Joy* / Love city groove: *Love City Groove* / Baby baby: *Corona* / Not over yet: *Grace* / Don't stop (wiggle wiggle): *Outhere Brothers* / Love and devotion: *Real McCoy* / Two can play that game: *Brown, Bobby* / Turn on tune in cop out: *Freakpower* / Open your heart: *M-People* / Max don't have sex with your ex: *Erotic* / Buring: *MK* / Call it love: *Deuce* / Steam: *East 17* / Move your body: *Eurogroove* / Sex on the streets: *Pizzaman*
RADCD 17 / Jun '95 / Global TV

☐ DANCE CLASSICS
DSPCD 106 / Sep '93 / Disky

☐ DANCE COLLECTION (3CD Set)
TBXCD 504 / Jan '96 / TrueTrax

☐ DANCE COLLECTION (3CD Set)
Get dancin': *Disco Tex & The Sexolettes* / This is it: *Moore, Melba* / (7,6,5,4,3,2,1) blow your whistle: *Rimshots* / Disco stomp: *Bohannon, Hamilton* / Sunshine day: *Osibisa* / Boogie on down (get funky now): *Real Thing* / Come on dance, dance: *Saturday Night Band* / What's your name, what's your number: *True, Andrea Connection* / Take that to the bank: *Shalamar* / Shame shame shame: *Shirley & Company* / White lines (don't do it): *Grandmaster Flash* / Rapper's delight: *Sugarhill Gang* / Last night a DJ saved my life: *Indeep* / Disappearing act: *Shalamar* / Get up (before the night is over): *Technotronic* / Somebody else's guy: *Brown, Jocelyn* / Can you handle it: *Redd, Sharon* / Hip hop, be bop (don't stop): *Man Parrish* / Just let me do my thing: *Sine* / Let the music play: *Shannon* / You're the one for me: *D-Train* / Foot stompin' music: *Bohannon, Hamilton* / Can you feel the force: *Real Thing* / Night to remember: *Shalamar* / Feels like I'm in love: *Marie, Kelly* / Body music: *Strikers* / Step off: *Grandmaster Flash* / Pump up the jam: *Technotronic* / What I got is what you need: *Unique* / Dancing the night away: *Voggue* / Menergy: *Cowley, Patrick* / Midas touch: *Midnight Star* / Over and over: *Shalamar* / More, more, more: *True, Andrea Connection* / Never give you up: *Redd, Sharon* / Rock steady: *Whispers* / It's not what you got (it's how you use it): *Lucas, Carrie* / When boys talk: *Indeep* / Hot love: *Marie, Kelly* / I wish you would: *Brown, Jocelyn* / Go deh yaka (go to the top): *Monyaka* / Sending out an SOS: *Young, Retta* / This beat is technotronic: *Technotronic* / Music: *D-Train* / I don't want to be a freak: *Dynasty* / Message: *Grandmaster Flash*
PBXCD 504 / Nov '96 / Pulse

☐ DANCE CRASHER (Ska To Rock Steady)
Big bamboo: *Lord Creator* / Latin goes ska: *Skatalites* / Garden of love: *Drummond, Don* / Rough and tough: *Cole, Stranger* / Beardman ska: *Skatalites* / Shame and scandal: *Tosh, Peter & The Wailers* / Street corner: *Skatalites* / Bonanza ska: *Malcolm, Carlos & Afro Caribs* / Dance crasher: *Ellis, Alton & The Flames* / Let George do it: *Drummond, Don* / Rudie bam bam: *Clarendonians* / Dr. Dick: *Perry, Lee 'Scratch' & The Soulettes* / Ball o' fire: *Skatalites* / Independence ska: *Brooks, Baba & Band* / Don't be a rude boy: *Rulers* / Ska jam: *McCook, Tommy & The Soulettes* / Hallelujah: *Toots & The Maytals* / Owe me no pay me: *Ethiopians*
CDTRL 260 / Mar '94 / Trojan

☐ DANCE CRAZY (From The Charleston To The Jive)
Charleston: *Savoy Orpheans* / Blue room: *Savoy Orpheans* / Black bottom: *Johnny Hamp's Kentucky Serenaders* / That's you, baby: *Hylton, Jack* / Walking with Susie: *Hylton, Jack* / Happy feet: *Whiteman, Paul* / Rockin' in rhythm: *Ellington, Duke* / Put on your old grey bonnet: *Casa Loma Orchestra* / Boogie woogie man: *Casa Loma Orchestra* / Man from Harlem: *Calloway, Cab* / Tiger rag: *Payne, Jack* / Tailspin: *Dorsey Brothers* / Clap hands, here comes Charlie: *Webb, Chick* / For dancers only: *Lunceford, Jimmie* / Just you, just me: *Norvo, Red* / At the swing cats' ball: *Jordan, Louis* / Deep night: *Dorsey, Tommy* / Boulder buff: *Miller, Glenn* / Jitney man: *Hines, Earl 'Fatha'* / King Porter stomp: *Crosby, Bob* / Hep hep - the jumpin' jive: *Gonella, Nat*
PPCD 78104 / Feb '95 / Past Perfect

☐ DANCE FLOOR HEAVEN VOL.1
Do you wanna funk: *Sylvester* / Menergy: *Cowley, Patrick* / Somebody else's guy: *Brown, Jocelyn* / You think you're a man: *Divine* / Last night a DJ saved my life: *Indeep* / Feels like I'm in love: *Marie, Kelly* / Downtown: *Clark, Petula* / Let the music play: *Shannon* / Can you feel the force: *Real Thing* / Can you handle it: *Redd, Sharon* / Night to remember: *Shalamar* / What's your name what's your number: *True, Andrea Connection* / Pump up the jam: *Technotronic* / Hip hop be bop (Don't stop): *Man Parrish* / Foot on the rock: *Cherry, Neneh & GMC*
TRTCD 119 / 20 Apr '98 / TrueTrax

☐ DANCE GALA VOL.1
340052 / Jul '97 / Koch International

☐ DANCE GALA VOL.2
340192 / Jul '97 / Koch International

☐ DANCE GALA VOL.3
340202 / Jul '97 / Koch International

☐ DANCE GALA VOL.4
340212 / Jul '97 / Koch International

☐ DANCEHALL RAWKUS
RWK 11072 / Mar '97 / Rawkus

☐ DANCEHALL REGGAE
MCCD 288 / Mar '97 / Music Club

☐ DANCE HEAT '95
Scatman: *Scatman John* / Dreamer: *Livin' Joy* / Your loving arms: *Martin, Billie Ray* / Don't make me wait: *Loveland* / Not over yet: *Grace* / Don't stop (wiggle wiggle): *Outhere Brothers* / Reach up: *Perfecto All Stars* / Guaglione: *Prado, Perez 'Prez'* / Bubbling hot: *Pato Banton & Ranking Roger* / Love city groove: *Love City Groove* / Crazy: *Morrison, Mark* / Two can play that game: *Brown, Bobby* / U sure do: *Strike* / Axel F: *Clock* / Max don't have sex with your ex: *E-Rotic* / Baby baby: *Corona* / Conway: *Reel 2 Real* / Always something there to remind me: *Tin Tin Out & Espiritu* / Take you there: *Simon, Ronni* / Too many fish: *Knuckles, Frankie* / I believe: *Happy Clappers* / Sex on the streets: *Pizzaman*
VTCD 50 / May '95 / Virgin

☐ DANCE HEAVEN
They say it's gonna rain: *Dean, Hazell* / On my radio: *Selecter* / Car wash: *Royce, Rose* / Close to perfection: *Brown, Miquel* / French kiss: *Big Louie* / Italio house mix: *Rococo* / Saddle up: *Christie, David* / Fan the flame: *Pennington, Barbara* / Heaven must be missing an angel: *Tavares* / Swing the mood: *Jive Bunny* / Going back to my roots: *Odyssey* / High energy: *Thomas, Evelyn* / Feels like I'm in love: *Marie, Kelly* / Jack mix 4: *Mirage* / Special brew: *Bad Manners* / Bass (how low can you go): *Harris, Simon* / Frankie: *Sister Sledge* / Hands off she's mine: *Beat*
305622 / Oct '96 / Hallmark

☐ DANCE HITS OF THE 80'S
Let's groove: *Earth, Wind & Fire* / Ooh la la: *Marie, Teena* / Jump: *Pointer Sisters* / She wants to dance with me: *Astley, Rick* / Alice, I want you just for me: *Full Force* / Rockit: *Hancock, Herbie* / My love is so raw: *Williams, Alyson* / I'm that type of guy: *LL Cool J* / Going back to my roots: *Odyssey* / Encore: *Lynn, Cheryl* / I wonder if I take you home: *Lisa Lisa & Cult Jam/Full Force* / Roses: *Haywoode* / Love come down: *King, Evelyn* / System addict: *Five Star* / Call me: *Spagna* / My toot toot: *LaSalle, Denise*
PWKS 4199 / Aug '94 / Carlton

☐ DANCE HITS OF THE 80'S
High energy: *Thomas, Evelyn* / Fan the flame: *Pennington, Barbara* / So many men, so little time: *Brown, Miquel* / Who knows what evil: *Man To Man* / Great minds think alike: *Wells, James* / Animal magnetism: *Pandy, Darryl* / Standing in line: *Mancha, Steve* / Take one step forward: *Wills, Viola & Noel McCalla* / Chalk it up to experience: *Thomas, Evelyn* / Close to perfection: *Brown, Miquel* / Hands off: *Pallas, Laura* / Ain't no mountain high enough: *Powell, Shezwae* / Love's gone mad: *Seventh Avenue*
QED 140 / Nov '96 / Tring
100092 / May '97 / A-Play Collection

☐ DANCE INFERNO (16 Explosive Hits Of The 1990's)
Be my lover / Welcome to tomorrow / Mr. Vain / What is love / Run away / Baby baby / I luv u baby / Don't give me your life / I like to move it / Surrender your love / Hideaway / Short short man / Move on baby / Human nature / Real thing / I'm gonna get you
SUMCD 4056 / Nov '96 / Summit

☐ DANCE INFERNO (Explosive Dance Collection/4CD Set)
SUMBX 4010 / Jan '98 / Summit

☐ DANCE LATINO
Tributo a Los Admirables: *Los Admirables* / La sopa en botella: *Cruz, Celia & La Sonora Matancera* / Compadre Pedro Juan: *Damiron Y Capuseaux* / Quiero Amanecer: *Lopez, Anardy* / A mayaguez: *Valle, Joe* / Que me digan feo: *Estrellas Cubanos* / Colombina: *Conjunto Tipico Cibaeno* / Maria Morena: *Beltran, Alberto & Willie Rosario Orchestra* / Mujer celosa: *Pinedo, Nelson & La Sonora Matancera* / A Puerto Rico: *Hernandez, Mario Y Sus Diablos Del Caribe* / Pa' chismoso tu: *Morel, Manolin* / Coda tierra con su ritmo: *Kalaff, Luis* / El yerbero moderno: *Cruz, Celia* / La cruz: *Damiron Y Capuseaux* / Donde vives: *Lopez, Anardy* / La lapa: *Cuba, Joe Sextet* / No hay mal que por bien no venga: *Rodriguez, Johnny* / Galletana: *America Del 55* / Potaje: *Faz, Roberto Y Su Conjunto* / Pa' despues venir llorando: *Kalaff, Luis*
CDHOT 621 / Apr '97 / Charly

☐ DANCE MIX '96 (16 Hypnotic Movers)
Feel the pulse: *Euripides* / Real beat: *Cuban Heart* / In the mix (nu disco): *Koka* / Free stylin': *Koka* / Blown away: *Beat Fantastic* / Eastern promise: *Euripides* / Hot baby: *Rap Noise* / House of scratch: *Koka* / Unstoppable: *Beat Fantastic* / Enigmatic: *Tone Poets* / Shake your move: *Euripides* / Hypnotic: *Tone Poets* / Scat new jack: *Koka* / Down on the upbeat: *Beat Fantastic* / Techno jam: *Koka* / Dance crazy: *Mister M*
305612 / Oct '96 / Hallmark

☐ DANCE MIX OF THE YEAR
085703252 / 9 Feb '98 / House Nation

☐ DANCE MIX UK VOL.1 (2CD Set)
Children: *Miles, Robert* / Night train: *Kadoc* / Don't you want me: *Felix* / Passion: *Gat Decor* / Missing: *Everything But The Girl* / Search for the hero: *M-People* / Just a step from heaven: *Eternal* / Whatta man: *Salt n' Pepa & En Vogue* / Gangsta's paradise: *Coolio & LV* / This is how we do it: *Jordan, Montell* / I've got a little something for you: *MN8* / I like to move it: *Reel 2 Real* / Connected: *Stereo MC's* / Here comes the hotstepper: *Kamoze, Ini* / Twist and shout: *Chaka Demus & Pliers* / Mr. Loverman: *Shabba Ranks* / Baby come back: *Pato Banton* / Baby I love your way: *Big Mountain* / Searching: *China Black* / All that she wants: *Ace Of Base* / Things can only get better: *D:Ream* / Dreamer: *Livin' Joy* / Saturday night: *Whigfield* / Sunshine after the rain: *Berri* / Swamp thing: *Grid* / Axel F: *Clock* / U sure do: *Strike* / Try me out: *Corona* / I luv you baby: *Original* / Son of a gun: *JX* / Real thing: *Di Bart, Tony* / Right in the night: *Jam & Spoon* / Move your body: *Xpansions* / Stayin' alive: *N-Trance* / Bomb: *Bucketheads* / Hideaway: *De'Lacy* / Show me love: *Robin S* / We are family: *Sister Sledge* / Gonna to make you sweat: *C&C Music Factory* / Groove is in the heart: *Deee-Lite*
RADCD 37 / Apr '96 / Global TV

☐ DANCE MIX UK VOL.2 (2CD Set)
Flava: *Andre, Peter* / We've got it goin' on: *Backstreet Boys* / Macarena: *Los Del Rio* / There's nothin I won't do: *JX* / Don't stop movin': *Livin' Joy* / Keep on jumpin': *Lisa Marie Experience* / Disco's revenge: *Gusto* / I need a lover tonight: *Kendoh* / Don't give me your life: *Alex Party* / Fable: *Miles, Robert* / X-Files: *DJ Dado* / Theme from s'express: *S'Express* / Where love lives: *Limerick, Alison* / Jazz it up: *Reel 2 Real* / One night in heaven: *M-People* / U r the best thing: *D:Ream* / I'm gonna get you: *Bizarre Inc.* / Everybody's free: *Rozalla* / Key the secret: *Urban Cookie Collective* / Ain't no love (ain't no use): *Sub Sub & Melanie Williams* / Run to you: *Rage* / Blue monday: *New Order* / Ooh ahh, just a little bit: *Gina G* / I need your loving (everybody's gotta learn sometimes): *Baby D* / Stay another day: *East 17* / Relight my fire: *Take That* / Finally: *Peniston, Ce Ce* / Two can play that game: *Brown, Bobby* / Luv 4 luv: *Robin S* / Now that we've found love: *Heavy D & The Boyz* / Let's talk about sex: *Salt n' Pepa* / Boom, shake the room: *DJ Jazzy Jeff & The Fresh Prince* / Boom boom boom: *Outhere Brothers* / Rhythm of the night: *Corona* / Whooph (there it is): *Corona* / Return of the mack: *Morrison, Mark* / I got 5 on it: *Luniz* / Creep: *TLC* / Dreams: *Gabrielle* / Sweetness: *Gayle, Michelle* / She's got that vibe: *R Kelly* / Sweets for my sweet: *Lewis, C.J.* / Shine: *Aswad* / Oh carolina: *Shaggy*
RADCD 42 / Aug '96 / Global TV

☐ DANCE MUSIC
CDLBP 2024 / Jul '96 / Lochshore

☐ DANCE MUSIC OF IRELAND: JIGS AND REELS
Maudabawn Chapel/Wild Irishman/Moher reel: *Burke, Kevin & Michael O'Dohmhaill* / Paddy O'Brien's/Scatter the mud/Arthur Daley's: *Trimble, Gerald* / Stone in the field/Steeplechase/Culfodda reel: *Keane, James* / Dillon's fancy/Maids in the meadow/Toss the feathers: *Crawford, Kevin* / Paddy Fahy's jig/Sean Ryan's jig: *Hayes, Martin* / Robbie Hannan's jigs: *O'Sullivan, Jerry* / Johnny Doherty's/Sean sa cheo/Lady Gordon: *Madden, Joanie* / Congress reel/Down the broom/Star of Munster: *Irish Tradition* / Humours of Ballyloughlin/Knocknagow: *Ivers, Eileen* / Green field of Woodford/Cat's rambles: *Coen, Jack* / Bucks of Oranmore/Wind that shakes the barley: *Burke, Joe & Charlie Lennon* / Cul aodh jig/Blue angel: *Buttons & Bows* / Dunmore lassies/McFadden's handsome daughter: *Moloney, Mick* / Sculley Casey's/The tidy woman: *Williams, John*
CELT 9001 / May '97 / Celtophile

☐ DANCE NATION VOL.1 (2CD Set)
DNCD 96 / Apr '96 / Ministry Of Sound

☐ DANCE NATION VOL.2 (2CD Set)
DNCD 962 / Jul '96 / Ministry Of Sound

☐ DANCE NATION VOL.3 (Mixed By Pete Tong & Judge Jules/2CD Set)
Remember me: *Blueboy* / You got the love: *Source & Candi Staton* / Take California: *Propellerheads* / Get up: *Stingily, Byron* / Take me by the hand: *Submerge* / Soothe: *Furry Phreaks* / Let me tell you something: *2 Guys On Warwick* / Lost without you: *Hanna, Jayn* / Zoe: *Paganini Traxx* / Barrel of a gun: *Depeche Mode* / Closer to your heart: *JX* / Encore une fois: *Sash* / Nightmare: *Brainbug* / Breathe: *Prodigy* / Ain't talkin' 'bout dub: *Apollo 440* / She drives me crazy: *Fine Young Cannibals* / Body music intersection: *Friday Night Traffik* / I believe: *Absolute* / Gotta love for you: *Serial Diva* / Jump: *Funkatarium* / Can you feel the heat: *Carle Younge Project* / Walk with me: *Heliotropic* / Cafe Del Mar: *Energy 52* / Tempest: *Amethyst* / Offshore: *Chicane* / Take me there: *Maximum* / Sugar is sweeter: *Bolland, C.J.* / Inferno: *Souvlaki*
DNCD 3 / Mar '97 / Ministry Of Sound

☐ DANCE NATION VOL.4 (Mixed By Boy George & Pete Tong - 2CD Set)
DNCD 4 / 1 Sep '97 / Ministry Of Sound

☐ DANCE NATION VOL.5 (2CD Set)
DNCD 5 / 16 Mar '98 / Ministry Of Sound

☐ DANCE NRG
FARECD 101 / Oct '92 / Fanfare

☐ DANCE OF HEAVEN'S GHOSTS (Music From Greece)
Les ke kratages maheria: *Vitali, Eleni* / Halali ine o erotas: *Mazaraki, Nikoletta* / I mangues then iparhoun pla: *Alexiou, Haris* / To ponemeno stithos mou: *Parios, Yannis* / To hioni: *Papadopoulou, Katerina* / Mirodia kalokeriou: *Leonardou, Sotiria* / Mia ine I oussia: *Alexiou, Haris* / O Amerikanos: *Zervoudakis, Dimitris* / Ba mazi mou: *Diamandi, Litsa* / Trikimia: *Morali, Athina* / Mia gyneka bori: *Vitali, Eleni* / Eho mia dipsa: *Patrios, Yannis* / Edo sto pezodromia: *Koumbaroulis, Andreas* / Oil me len tragoudisse: *Aidonidis, Hronis*
HEMICD 24 / Feb '97 / Hemisphere

☐ DANCE OF THE CELTS
5 Pound flute: *Old Blind Dogs* / An drochaid chluiteach: *Mhoireach, Anna* / Cregg's pipe set: *Tabache* / Inisheer: *Buttons & Bows* / Christy Barry's set: *Crawford, Kevin* / Trip to sligo set: *Dervish* / Trip to Skye: *Whelan, John* / Boy in the gap: *Kilbride, Pat* / Gavotten ar menez: *Kornog* / Andy de Jarlis: *Altan* / Gartrai na bhfeileoig: *Bergin, Mary* / Flight of the termite: *Deanta* / Finn MacCool's reel: *Kirtley, Pat* / Shetland jumper: *McGann, John* / Leis lacha: *Masterson, Declan* / Cail'n an t'mh-ir: *Masterson, Declan*
ND 63932 / May '97 / Narada
VNDCD 7 / 25 May '98 / Virgin

☐ DANCE OPERA VOL.3
PIAS 094047720 / Apr '97 / Dance Opera

☐ DANCE OPERA VOL.6 (2CD Set)
PIAS 094045523 / Jun '96 / Dance Opera

☐ DANCE PARTY
BLS 1015 CD / Jul '92 / BLS

☐ DANCE PARTY
Choice: *Blow Monkeys* / Never gonna give you up: *Astley, Rick* / Indestructible: *Four Tops* / Love take over: *Five Star* / I'm so excited: *Pointer Sisters* / Flashback: *Imagination* / Going back to my roots: *Odyssey* / Love come down: *King, Evelyn* / Runner: *Three Degrees* / Gonna get along without you know: *Wills, Viola* / Armed and extremely dangerous: *First Choice* / (We've got a) Good thing going: *Minott, Sugar*
74321339232 / Jan '96 / Camden

☐ DANCE PLANET
MNF 05432 / 30 Mar '98 / Manifold

☐ DANCE PLANET - SOUNDS OF THE DETONATOR
DPRCD 1 / Sep '95 / Dance Planet

☐ DANCE PLANET - THE RETRO MIXES VOL.1 (2CD Set/Mixed By Jim 'Shaft' Ryan & DJ Sy/Iks)
Sweet harmony: *Liquid* / Every time I see her: *Shades Of Rhythm* / Get down: *M-D Emm* / Lock up: *Zero B* / Everybody in the place: *Prodigy* / Blame: *Blame* / Dance with power: *Bass Construction* / We are ie: *Reel 2 Real* / We are hardcore: *House Crew* / This sound is for the underground: *Krome & Time* / On a ragga tip: *SL2* / Innersence: *Liquid Crystal* / Hurt you so: *Jonny L* / Fires burning: *Run Tings* / My own: *Seduction* / Far out: *Sonz Of A Loop Da Loop Era* / Rhythm for reasons: *Rhythm For Reasons* / Edge 1: *Edge 1* / Blow out: *Bass Selective* / Baptised by dub: *Criminal Minds* / Keep the fires burning: *House Crew* / Peace and loveism: *Sonz Of A Loop Da Loop Era* / Really livin': *Really Livin'* / Livin' in darkness: *Top Buzz* / EQ: *EQ* / Feel real good: *Manix* / Your love: *Prodigy* / Give it to me baby: *Love Revolution* / Can you feel it: *Elevation* / Don't go: *Awesome 3*
IKSCD 1 / Feb '97 / Dance Planet

R.E.D. CD CATALOGUE

COMPILATIONS

DANZA LATINA

☐ **DANCE POWER VOL.3**
MNF 05272 / Jun '97 / Manifold

☐ **DANCE POWER VOL.4**
MNF 05322 / 29 Sep '97 / Manifold

☐ **DANCE POWER VOL.5**
MNF 05372 / 2 Feb '98 / Manifold

☐ **DANCE POWER VOL.6**
MNF 05392 / 29 Jun '98 / Manifold

☐ **DANCE SOUNDS OF DETROIT (2CD Set)**
Memories and souveniers: *Payne, Freda* / I want to be loved: *Supremes* / Fear: *Starr, Edwin* / Two way street: *Jacas, Jake* / Don't wait around: *Elgins* / Sitting in the park: *Lovetones* / Right direction: *Littles, Hattie* / Fresh out of tears: *Laurence, Lynda* / One shot at happiness: *Demps, Louvain* / Wake me up when it's over: *Ruffin, Jimmy* / Which way do I turn: *Crawford, Carolyn* / Send some love: *Barnes, Ortheia* / Lost: *Randolph, Barbara* / I'm dedicating my love: *McNeir, Ronnie* / Weak hearted: *Taylor, Sherri* / Hotter than the summer days: *Edwards, Sandra* / See this man in love: *Wylie, Richard 'Popcorn'* / Look into the future: *Leverette, Chico* / Look into the eyes of a fool: *Bristol, Johnny* / Better love next time: *Johnson, Marv* / City lights: *Lewis, Pat* / Grazing in the grass: *Monitors* / Timeless: *Crawford, Carolyn* / I've fallen and can't get up: *Fantastic Four* / Come back and start again: *Nero, Frances* / Six by six: *Van Dyke, Earl* / Sister Lee: *Ward, Sammy* / Fire alarm: *Lovetones* / One and one makes two: *Starr, Edwin* / That girl is dangerous: *Jacas, Jake* / Lovestruck: *Edwards, Sandra* / All around the motorcity: *Andantes* / Just us: *Royster, Vermettya* / Half hearted: *Gordon, Billy* / Bad case of nerves: *Marvelettes* / Breaking into my heart: *Randolph, Barbara*
3035990077 / Oct '95 / Old Gold

☐ **DANCE SOUNDS OF THE 70'S**
JHD 105 / Aug '93 / Tring

☐ **DANCE TIP (2CD Set)**
RADCD 86 / 1 Dec '97 / Global TV

☐ **DANCE TIP 2000 (2CD Set)**
Breathe: *Prodigy* / Born slippy: *Underworld* / One to one: *Miles, Robert* / Seven days and one week: *BBE* / X-files: *DJ Dado* / Wrong: *Everything But The Girl* / Offshore: *Chicane* / Higher state of consciousness: *Wink, Josh* / Klubbhopping: *Klubb Heads* / I need a lover tonight: *Kendoh* / Nighttrain: *Kadoc* / Disco's revenge: *Gusto* / Stamp: *Healy, Jeremy & Amos* / Don't you want me: *Felix* / That look: *De'Lacy* / Naughty north and the sexy south: *E-Motion* / Loving you more: *BT & Vincent Covello* / Gift: *Way Out West* / One night stand: *Aloof* / I wanna be a hippy: *Technohead* / Ooh ahh...just a little bit: *Gina G* / Flava: *Andre, Peter* / You're makin' me high: *Braxton, Toni* / Children: *Miles, Robert* / Megamix: *Corona* / Don't stop movin': *Livin' Joy* / Return of the mack: *Morrison, Mark* / Keep on jumpin': *Lisa Marie Experience* / Megamix: *Outhere Brothers* / Get down: *Backstreet Boys* / Oh what a night: *Clock* / Jazz it up: *Reel 2 Real* / I belong to you: *Gina G* / Where love lives: *Limerick, Alison* / Driving: *Everything But The Girl* / Sunshine: *Umboza* / Cuba: *El Mariachi* / Creep: *TLC* / Golden brown: *Kaleef* / Search for the hero: *M-People*
RADCD 50 / Dec '96 / Global TV

☐ **DANCE TRAX (18 Original Hits/3CD Set)**
Love is all around: *DJ Bobo* / What is love: *Haddaway* / Shimmy shake: *740 Boyz* / Whammer slammer: *Warp 9* / Music instructor: *Hymn* / Got to move your body: *Lick & Kentucky Martha* / Jump for joy: *2 Unlimited* / Time is up: *Milton, C.B.* / Flying high: *Captain Hollywood* / I wish: *Skee Lo* / Feel my riddim: *Skibby* / Don't give me your life: *Alex Party* / Spontaneous: *Spymaster & Eric Nouhan* / Mercedes Benz: *T-Spoon & Jean Shy* / Don't stop (wiggle wiggle): *Outhere Brothers* / Try me out: *Corona* / In spirit: *Dilemma* / Total eclipse of the heart: *French, Nicki*
LAD 873822 / Nov '96 / Disky

☐ **DANCE TRIP FROM NY TO LA**
4888452 / 16 Oct '97 / Irma

☐ **DANCE WITH ME - THE AUTUMN TEEN SOUND**
Dance with me: *Mojo Men* / She goes with me: *Mojo Men* / Off the hook: *Mojo Men* / Draggin' the main: *Upsetters* / Little one: *Spearmints* / Anything: *Vejtables* / I still love you: *Vejtables* / Where did I fail: *Knight Riders* / I: *Knight Riders* / Torture and pain: *Knight Riders* / Won't you be my baby: *Knight Riders* / I should be glad: *Gear One* / Hello little girl: *Gear One* / I think it's time: *Chosen Few* / Nobody but me: *Chosen Few* / Pay attention to me: *Tikis* / I'll never forget about you: *Tikis* / Darkest night of the year: *Tikis* / Blue eyes: *Tikis* / Just me: *Us* / How can I tell her: *Us* / Mark my words: *Bundles* / Watch me girl: *Bundles* / Something bad: *Mojo Men* / My woman's head: *Mojo Men* / Can't you see that she's mine: *Mojo Men* / Why: *Mojo Men* / As I get older: *Mojo Men* / All over town: *Au Go Go's* / I still love you (version): *Vejtables*
CDWIKD 128 / Mar '94 / Big Beat

☐ **DANCE ZONE '95 (2CD Set)**
5350452 / Oct '95 / PolyGram TV

☐ **DANCE ZONE MEGAMIX VOL.1**
Roffo's theme V - the hitman / Termination party / I breathe you / Blue Monday / Love is a stranger / Passion / I feel love / Cocoon / Energize / Knock on wood
QED 074 / Nov '96 / Tring

☐ **DANCE ZONE VOL.5**
I need your loving (everybody's gotta learn sometime): *Baby D* / Scatman: *Scatman John* / Boom boom boom: *Outhere Brothers* / Your loving arms: *Martin, Billie Ray* / Hold my body tight: *East 17* / Dreamer: *Livin' Joy* / Love and devotion: *Real McCoy* / Not anyone: *Black Box* / Eternity: *Snap* / I need you: *Deuce* / Two can play that game: *Brown, Bobby* / Not over yet: *Grace* / Raise your hands: *Reel 2 Real* / Respect: *Cheeks, Judy* / Open your heart: *M-People* / Love city groove: *Love City Groove* / Swing low, sweet chariot: *Ladysmith Black Mambazo & China Black* / Turn on tune in cop out: *Freakpower* / Let it rain: *East 17* / Tears don't lie: *Mark Oh* / Guaglione: *Prado, Perez 'Prez'* / Think of you: *Whigfield* / Sex on the streets: *Pizzaman* / I believe: *Happy Clappers* / JJ tribute: *ASHA* / Direct me: *Reese Project* / Take you there: *Simon, Ronni* / Work it out: *Shiva* / Everybody in the world: *Ashah* / Access: *DJ Misjah* / Move your body: *Eurogroove* / High as a kite: *One Tribe* / Love love love: *Rollo Goes Mystic* / Always something there to remind me: *Tin Tin Out & Espiritu* / Wizards of the sonic: *Westbam* / Invader: *Koolworld Productions* / Gudvibe: *Tinman* / Spirit inside: *Spirits* / Bomb (These sounds fall into my mind): *Bucketheads* / Lifting me higher: *Gems For Jem*
5256332 / Jul '95 / PolyGram TV

☐ **DANCE ZONE VOL.7**
Keep on jumpin': *Lisa Marie Experience* / Nakasaki (I need a lover tonight): *Kendoh* / State of independence: *Summer, Donna* / Stars: *Dubstar* / Disco 2000: *Pulp* / Klubbhopping: *Klubb Heads* / Nightrain: *Kadoc* / Over and over: *Plux & Georgia Jones* / Passion: *Gat Decor* / So pure: *Baby D* / My life is in your hands: *Meltdown* / Be as one: *Sasha & Maria* / Give me a little more time: *Gabrielle* / Do U still: *East 17* / Lifted: *Lighthouse Family* / 1,2,3,4 (sumpin' new): *Coolio* / Itychoo park: *M-People* / Everyday: *Incognito* / Are you gonna be there: *Up Yer Ronson* / I wanna be a hippy: *Technohead* / Are you out there: *Crescendo* / Give me luv: *Alcatraz* / Disco's revenge: *Gusto* / America (I love America): *Full Intention* / I got the vibration: *Black Box* / Got myself together: *Bucketheads* / Ultra flava: *Heller & Farley Project* / Skin on skin: *Grace* / Loving you more: *BT* / In spirit: *Dilemmas* / Hide-a-way: *Nu Soul & Kelli Rich* / On ya way: *Helicopter* / And I'm telling you I'm not going: *Giles, Donna* / Naughty north and the sexy south: *E-Motion* / Geve me strength: *Jon Of The Pleased Wimmin* / I'll be there: *99th Floor Elevators* / Wham bam: *Candy Girls & Sweet Pussy Pauline* / To the beat of the drum (la luna): *Ethics* / Forever young: *Interactive* / Access: *DJ Misjah & Tim*
5354272 / Apr '96 / PolyGram TV

☐ **DANCE ZONE VOL.8 (2CD Set)**
I'm alive: *Stretch n' Vern & Maddog* / Let's all chant: *Gusto* / Ain't nobody's business if I do: *H2O & Billie* / We've got it goin' on: *Backstreet Boys* / Hello Honky Tonks (Rock your body): *Pizzaman* / Don't stop movin': *Livin' Joy* / There's nothing I won't do: *JX* / Ooh aah...just a little bit: *Gina G* / Everybody's free: *Rozalla* / That look: *De'Lacy* / Read my lips: *Alex Party* / Oh what a night: *Clock* / Flava: *Andre, Peter* / Groovin': *Pato Banton & The Reggae Revolution* / Return of the Mack: *Morrison, Mark* / Krupa: *Apollo 440* / Take me to heaven: *Baby D* / You're not alone: *Olive* / Sunshine: *Umboza* / Macarena: *Los Del Mar* / Keep on jumpin': *Terry, Todd & Martha Wash/ Jocelyn Brown* / Tha wildstyle: *DJ Supreme* / Higher state of consciousness: *Wink, Josh* / Do that to me: *Lisa Marie Experience* / Where love lives: *Limerick, Alison* / In de ghetto: *Morales, David & The Bad Yard Club/Crystal Waters/Delta* / Move your body: *Ruffneck & Yavahn* / Wrong: *Everything But The Girl* / Stand up: *Lovetribe* / Jazz it up: *Reel 2 Real* / Klubbhopping: *Klubb Heads* / If Madonna calls: *Vasquez, Junior* / Rays of the rising sun: *Mozaic* / It's just another groove: *Mighty Dub Katz* / Jus come: *Cool Jack* / Vicious circle: *Poltergeist* / Arms of Loren: *E'voke* / One day I'll fly away: *Llorena, Kelly* / Down to earth: *Grace* / Fable: *Miles, Robert*
5359032 / Sep '96 / PolyGram TV

☐ **DANCE ZONE VOL.9 (2CD Set)**
Shine: *Space Brothers* / Prophet: *Bolland, C.J.* / I love you...stop: *Red Five* / Reday or not: *Course* / Encore une fois: *Sash* / Lovefool: *Cardigans* / Saint: *Orbital* / Sometimes: *Brand New Heavies* / It's alright, I feel it: *Nu Yorican Soul* / Underwater love: *Smoke City* / Fired up: *Funky Green Dogs* / Sound of eden: *Casino* / People hold on: *Dirty Rotten Scoundrels & Lisa Stansfield* / My love is deep: *Parker, Sara* / Do you know: *Gayle, Michelle* / Scared: *Slacker* / Hand in hand: *Grace* / Tha wildstyle: *DJ Supreme* / Where can I find love: *Livin' Joy* / I belong to you: *Gina G* / One and one: *Miles, Robert & Maria Naylor*
5377162 / May '97 / PolyGram TV

☐ **DANCEFLOOR FEVER (20 Essential Grooves)**
I'm doin' fine now: *New York City* / Hold back the night: *Trammps* / More more more: *True, Andrea Connection* / Shame shame shame: *Shirley & Company* / Swing your Daddy: *Gilstrap, Jim* / Dolly my love: *Moments* / Dial L for the love squad: *Carr, Linda* / Ride a wild horse: *Clark, Dee* / Get dancing: *Disco Tex & The Sexolettes* / This is it: *Moore, Melba* / Now is the time: *James, Jimmy & The Vagabonds* / Baby don't change your mind: *Knight, Gladys & The Pips* / Take that to the bank: *Shalamar* / Galaxy of love: *Crown Heights Affair* / I gotta keep dancin': *Lucas, Carrie* / In the bush: *Musique* / I don't want to be a freak (but I can't help myself): *Dynasty* / We got the funk: *Positive Force* / Check out the groove: *Thurston, Bobby* / Can you handle it: *Redd, Sharon*
SUMCD 4102 / Nov '96 / Summit

☐ **DANCEFLOOR JAZZ VOL.6**
5535771CD / 16 Jul '97 / Motor

☐ **DANCEHALL '63**
SOL 03193 / 15 Jun '98 / Studio One

☐ **DANCEHALL 1998**
PHLP 2074 / 6 Apr '98 / Penthouse

☐ **DANCEHALL CONNECTION VOL.1 & 2**
MFCD 006 / Dec '92 / Mafia/Fluxy

☐ **DANCEHALL DAYS**
FILECD 458 / Jan '95 / Profile

☐ **DANCEHALL EXTRAVAGANZA**
JFCD 3000 / 26 Jan '98 / VP

☐ **DANCEHALL HITS VOL.1**
VPCD 1335 / Oct '93 / Digital B

☐ **DANCEHALL HITS VOL.1**
PHCD 2001 / Aug '93 / Penthouse

☐ **DANCEHALL HITS VOL.2**
PHCD 2003 / Aug '93 / Penthouse

☐ **DANCEHALL HITS VOL.2**
VPCD 1321 / Sep '93 / Digital B

☐ **DANCEHALL HITS VOL.3**
PHCD 2004 / Aug '93 / Penthouse

☐ **DANCEHALL HITS VOL.3**
VPCD 1344 / Dec '93 / VP

☐ **DANCEHALL HITS VOL.4**
PHCD 2015 / Aug '94 / Penthouse

☐ **DANCEHALL KILLERS**
792092 / Jun '93 / Jammy's

☐ **DANCEHALL KILLERS VOL.3**
SHCD 45018 / Dec '94 / Shanachie

☐ **DANCEHALL KINGS**
SONCD 0083 / Apr '96 / Sonic Sounds

☐ **DANCEHALL LOVERS**
RN 7042 / 25 May '98 / Rhino

☐ **DANCEHALL ROUGHNECK**
HBCD 148 / Aug '93 / Greensleeves

☐ **DANCEHALL SLAM**
SHCD 45025 / Mar '96 / Shanachie

☐ **DANCEHALL STYLEE VOL.2**
Here I come (Broader than Broadway): *Levy, Barrington* / Burrup: *Nardo Ranks* / Murder dem: *Ninjaman* / Ring the alarm: *Tenor Saw* / Drum pan sound: *Reggie Stepper* / Stop loving you: *McGregor, Freddie* / Roots and culture: *Shabba Ranks* / Cabin stabbin': *Super Cat & Nico Demus/Junior Demus* / Wicked in bed: *Shabba Ranks* / DJ in my country: *Clement Irie* / Proud to be black: *Crucial Robbie* / Golden touch: *Brown, Rula & Commander Shad*
FILECD 291 / Feb '91 / Profile

☐ **DANCEHALL SYMPHONY**
JDCD 0006 / 27 Apr '98 / JD

☐ **DANCEHALL VIBES**
PHCD 2073 / 26 Jan '98 / Penthouse

☐ **DANCEPOWER VOL.2**
MNF 05232 / Jan '97 / Manifold

☐ **DANCES OF THE GODS**
C 559 051 / Apr '89 / Ocora

☐ **DANCES OF THE WORLD (Music From Elektra Nonesuch 'Explorer' Series)**
7559791672 / Jan '95 / Nonesuch

☐ **DANCIN' IN D-TOWN**
Cracked up over you: *Rogers, Lee* / All the way home: *Edwards, Dee* / Mr. Blue: *Black, Cody* / Love of my life: *Fabulous Peps* / Words won't come: *Van Dyke, Connie* / Love's hideaway: *Heart, Don* / Save your love: *Lamp, Buddy* / How can I forget you: *Magictones* / Find a quiet place: *Davis, Melvin* / Everybody's going wild: *International Kansas City Playboys* / Sock some love power to me: *Rogers, Lee* / (I've got a) shield round my heart: *Dupree, Lillian* / My love looks good on you: *Fabulous Peps* / Pizza pie man: *Grier, Roosevelt* / Save your love for me: *Butler, Freddy* / I wanna tell you about my baby: *Precisions* / Don't do nothing I wouldn't do: *Van Dyke, Connie* / Love can really hurt you deep: *Rogers, Lee* / You must be in love: *Black, Cody* / Gypsy woman: *Fabulous Peps* / Just a little bit of lovin': *Lamp, Buddy* / I'm coming in: *Rand, Romeo* / Hide and seek: *Dupree, Lillian* / With those eyes: *Fabulous Peps* / How are you fixed for love: *Rogers, Lee* / You say you love me: *Edwards, Dee* / Speak your peace: *Fabulous Peps* / I wanna go home: *Lamp, Buddy* / Quittin' time: *International Kansas City Playboys* / I've got heartaches: *Lil' Soul Brothers*
GSCD 131 / 27 Apr '98 / Goldmine

☐ **DANCING 'TIL DAWN**
Last minute miracle: *Shirelles* / Help me: *Wilson, Al* / This man / Woman lover thief: *Stemmons Express* / One in a million / Come back baby: *Dodds, Nella* / Everything is everything / Marching / Out on the street again: *Candy & The Kisses* / Love it's getting better / Get on up / Desiree / Do you believe it / I'm your yes man: *Reid, Clarence* / Work song / These chains of love (Are breaking me down): *Jackson, Chuck* / Ain't that peculiar: *Tindley, George* / Stop sign / Ain't no soul / Name it and claim it: *Stewart, Darryl* / Tightrope / You busted my mind: *Clay, Judy* / Love is a good foundation / There comes a time / I don't have a mind of my own / Lost love: *Irma & The Fascinations* / Please stay: *Ivorys* / Show me a man: *Bradshaw, Bobby* / Livin' the nightlife: *Charts* / Let me give you my lovin': *Brown, Maxine* / Black eyed girl: *Thompson, Billy*
CDKEND 106 / Feb '94 / Kent

☐ **DANCING AT THE PALAIS (Recollections From The Palais Days)**
I'm so alone: *Preager, Lou & His Orchestra* / I want my Mama: *Roy, Harry & His Band* / When the Rose Of Tralee met Danny Boy: *White, Jack & His Band* / Chatanooga choo choo: *Loss, Joe & His Orchestra* / Mean to me: *Gonella, Nat & His New Georgians* / You're breaking my heart all over again: *White, Jack & His Band* / Ashby De La Zooch: *Preager, Lou & His Orchestra* / Carolina: *Preager, Lou & His Orchestra* / Russian serenade: *Roy, Harry & His Band* / Jee bie hop: *Leader, Harry & His Orchestra* / Let him go, let him tarry: *Geraldo & His Orchestra* / Down in New Mexico: *Gonella, Nat & His New Georgians* / Sally Water: *Munn, Billy & His Orchestra* / I'm nobody's baby: *White, Jack & His Band* / Woe is me: *Rabin, Oscar & His Band* / Little smile: *Leader, Harry & His Orchestra* / Good, good, good: *Preager, Lou & His Orchestra* / For all that I care: *White, Jack & His Band* / It only takes a small cloud: *White, Jack & His Band* / I'm beginning to see the light: *Geraldo & His Orchestra* / It had to be you: *Roy, Harry & His Band* / I'll always be with you: *Preager, Lou & His Orchestra*
RAJCD 879 / Apr '97 / Empress

☐ **DANCING BRAZIL**
15343 / May '94 / Laserlight

☐ **DANCING IN THE STREET (2CD Set)**
Standing at the crossroads: *James, Elmore* / Good Holly Miss Molly: *Little Richard* / Blueberry hill: *Domino, Fats* / That's alright Mama: *Crudup, Arthur 'Big Boy'* / Surfin' USA: *Beach Boys* / Stand by me: *King, Ben E.* / You've lost that loving feeling: *Righteous Brothers* / Mr. Tambourine man: *Byrds* / What I'd say: *Charles, Ray* / Respect: *Franklin, Aretha* / In the midnight hour: *Pickett, Wilson* / Boom boom: *Hooker, John Lee* / House of the rising sun: *Animals* / Sunshine of your love: *Cream* / Somebody to love: *Jefferson Airplane* / Ball and chain: *Big Brother & The Holding Company* / I'm waiting for the man: *Velvet Underground* / I'm eighteen: *Cooper, Alice* / Walk on the wild side: *Reed, Lou* / What do I get: *Buzzcocks* / Roadrunner: *Richman, Jonathan* / Heart of glass: *Blondie* / Please, please, please: *Brown, James* / Dance to the music: *Sly & The Family Stone* / If you don't know me by now: *Melvin, Harold* / Message: *Grandmaster Flash* / What's going on: *Gaye, Marvin* / Purple haze: *Hendrix, Jimi* / Dancing in the street: *Reeves, Martha & The Vandellas* / Rock Island line: *Donegan, Lonnie* / Da doo ron ron: *Crystals* / Holidays in the sun: *Sex Pistols* / Baby please don't go: *Them*
3036400162 / Jul '96 / Carlton

☐ **DANCING STRINGS OF SCOTLAND**
Reel of the 51st division / Linton ploughman / Scottish waltz / Hamilton house / Dashing white sergeant / Duke of Perth / Strip the willow / Gay Gordons / Petronella / Highland Schottische / Circassian circle
LCOM 5175 / Nov '96 / Lismor

☐ **DANCING TO THE FLUTE (Music & Dance In Indian Art)**
131352 / Jul '97 / Celestial Harmonies

☐ **DANDELION SAMPLER 1969-1972, THE**
Coathanger: *Ward, Clifford T.* / Nice: *St. John, Bridget* / Pictures in the sky: *Medicine Head* / Strange locomotion: *Siren* / Ruby baby: *Vincent, Gene* / Ravenscroft 13 bar boogie: *Tractor* / Missed my times: *Occasional Word* / Asmoto Running Band: *Principal Edwards Magic Theatre* / Please bring back the birch for the milkman: *Hart, Mike* / Little triple one shot: *Coxhill, Lol* / Roadrunner: *Stackwaddy*
SFMD 96 / Sep '96 / See For Miles

☐ **DANGER URBAN ELECTRONIC DISORDER**
Biohazard: *Dazzle T & Buzz K* / Southgates remorse: *BLIM* / Projects: *Two Plus One* / Anger: *Footloose* / Planet: *Elementz Of Noize* / Mutant revisited: *DJ Trace* / Onza: *BLIM* / Implants: *Genetix* / Jeamland '96: *DJ Trace* / Renegade fazed: *Tonic* / Vision: Rescale / Shadow: *Frey Nasty*
EMFCDLP 002 / Jan '97 / Emotif

☐ **DANGER ZONE (2CD Set)**
Song 2: *Blur* / Richard III: *Supergrass* / Bruise pristine: *Placebo* / Hey dude: *Kula Shaker* / 100 Mile high city: *Ocean Colour Scene* / Nuclear holiday: *3 Colours Red* / Faster: *Manic Street Preachers* / Punka: *Kenickie* / Hit: *Wannadies* / Just another Illusion: *Hurricane No.1* / What's in the box: *Boo Radleys* / Take it easy chicken: *Mansun* / Getting better: *Shed Seven* / Place your hands: *Reef* / Talk to me: *60ft Dolls* / Mouse in a hole: *60ft Dolls* / Sitting at home: *Honeycrack* / Kowalski: *Primal Scream* / I feel you: *Depeche Mode* / Ashes to ashes: *Faith No More* / Perseverence: *Terrorvision* / I can dream: *Skunk Anansie* / Sugar cane: *Sonic Youth* / Out there: *Dinosaur Jr.* / Word up: *Gun* / Lump: *Presidents Of The USA* / Ready or not: *Manbreak* / Strictly hardcore: *Goldblade* / Monster: *L7* / Mexican wave: *Kerbdog* / Hobo humpin' slobo babe: *Whale* / I want to touch you: *Catherine Wheel* / Whole lotta love: *Goldbug* / No fronts: *Dog Eat Dog* / Anthem: *Wildhearts* / Ain't talkin' 'bout dub: *Apollo 440*
5538702 / 18 Aug '97 / PolyGram TV

☐ **DANIEL POOLE - WORLD SOUND SYSTEMS**
TLCDPCD 001 / Jan '96 / TLC

☐ **DANISH DRIVE (The Finest Collection Of Danish Jazz)**
MECCACD 2020 / Jan '98 / Music Mecca

☐ **DANISH TRAD JAZZ VOL.1**
MECCACD 1006 / Aug '90 / Music Mecca

☐ **DANISH TRAD JAZZ VOL.2**
MECCACD 1031 / Nov '94 / Music Mecca

☐ **DANISH TRAD JAZZ VOL.3**
MECCACD 1099 / May '97 / Music Mecca

☐ **DANSE MACABRE SAMPLER**
EFA 11213 / Apr '93 / Danse Macabre

☐ **DANSKE JAZZ '95**
MECCACD 1069 / May '97 / Music Mecca

☐ **DANSKE JAZZ '96**
MECCACD 2009 / May '97 / Music Mecca

☐ **DANZA LATINA**
Todo paol no se pica: *Manaure* / El tamalito: *Hermanos Santa Cruz* / Contigo mi vida: *Selva* / Me he de guardar: *Saravia, Patricia* / Mama no deja: *Rego, Elisa* / Yo no say pilon de machacar: *Rodriguez, Lalo* / Entre rejas: *Orquesta Bamba* / Caramelos: *Los Amaya* / Contratiempos: *Navajita Platea* / Buleria del solitaire: *Arebato* / Saca los manos: *Freundt, Julie* / Ciega: *Jailene* / Tambito: *Son, Caribe Gaita Y* / Borrando fronteras: *Carabajal, Peteco* / Gitanos y morenos: *Perez, Gato* / Hablame: *Garcia, Carangano Y Jose Luis* / He vuelto para andar: *Laugart, Ziomara*
HEMICD 25 / Feb '97 / Hemisphere

☐ DARGASON MUSIC SAMPLER
DM 118CD / Nov '96 / Dargason Music

☐ DARK EMPIRE STRIKES BACK
DARK 0052 / Apr '94 / Dark Empire

☐ DARK PASSAGES VOL.2
RISE 012CD / Jul '96 / Rise Above

☐ DARK PROGRESSIVE SOUND VOL.1
EFACD 91011 / Jul '96 / Zillo

☐ DARK SONICS
CD 8419732 / Apr '96 / SPV

☐ DARK ZONE
MILL 060CD / 30 Mar '98 / Millenium

☐ DARKEND GOTHIC ROCK COMPILATION
DARK 001CD / Feb '97 / Darkend

☐ DARKEST HOUR, THE
CLP 0029 / Aug '97 / Hypnotic

☐ DARN IT - POEMS BY PAUL HAINES/ MUSIC BY MANY
AMCL 1014 / May '94 / Normal

☐ DARQUE FONQUE
MIDDLE 9CD / 3 Nov '97 / Middle Earth

☐ DAS MACH ICH MIT MUSIK
Das mach ich mit musik: Johns, Bibi / Die gipsy band: Johns, Bibi / Bimbo: Johns, Bibi / Billy boy: Sauer, Wolfgang & Angele Durand / Das klavier uber mir: Kuhn, Paul / Swing hei: Kuhn, Paul / Federball: Kuhn, Paul / Chanson d'amour: Durand, Angele / Sailor's boogie: Durand, Angele / Warum strahlen heut' nacht di sterne so hell: Sauer, Wolfgang / Liebe im April: Sauer, Wolfgang / Little rock: Durand, Angele & Bibi Johns / Bye bye baby: Durand, Angele & Bibi Johns / Ich mocht auf deiner hochzeit tanzen: Kuhn, Paul & Bibi Johns / Lillie boogie: Serrano, Rosita / Mitternachts blues: Schachtner, Heinz / Dein herz aus stein: De Vale, Mariette / Willy lilly rock a billy: Boswell, Eve / Paris dixie: Cordy, Annie / Ma belle mademoiselle: Constantine, Eddie
BCD 15413 / Dec '87 / Bear Family

☐ DATAFILE
REXDF 001 / Oct '96 / Ruffex

☐ DAUGHTERS OF TEXAS
Young and dumb / Breaking up somebody's home / In the mood / Say the wrong thing / Rock 'n' roll fever / Horny old buzzard, dirty old man / Your magic touch (quit working on me) / Nobody knows you (when you're down and out) / Walk rightin / I can tell I'm losing you / Stepping up in class / Breaking mama's rule / Ain't nobody gonna take my man
CDTB 080 / Jan '92 / Thunderbolt

☐ DAVE GODIN'S DEEP SOUL TREASURES (Taken From The Vaults)
I'm never gonna live it down: Knight Brothers / Easy as saying 1-2-3: Willis, Timmy / Lights out: Hicks, Zerben R. & The Dynamics / Anybody who knows what love is (will understand): Thomas, Irma / Have a little mercy: Wells, Jean / Try love: Grayson, Dori / I can't make it without him: Davis, Brendetta / Showdown: Carter, Kenny / I'm not the one: Banks, Larry / Turning point: Holiday, Jimmy / Standing here crying: Incredibles / She broke his heart: Just Brothers / You're on top: Untouchables / It's not that easy: Bell, Reuben & The Casanovas / Cry baby cry: Van & Titus / I still love you: Stanback, Jean / Try to leave me if you can (I bet you can't do it): Banks, Bessie / Songs to sing: Raw Spitt / How much longer (must I wait): Moses, Lee / Nothing's too much (nothing's too good): Young, Billy / I feel like cryin': Sam & Bill / I'm goin' for myself: Eddie & Ernie / Tried so hard to please her: Knight Brothers / Love of my man: Gray, Pearlean & The Passengers / You got me: Jaibi
CDKEND 143 / Apr '97 / Kent

☐ DAVE HAMILTON'S DETROIT DANCERS (The Soul Providers)
What should I do: Little Annie / Happiness is here: Lark, Tobi / You did: Page, Priscilla & Ronny Darrell / My sweet baby: JT Rhythm / I'm shooting high (I reach for the sky): Tolbert, OC / Love friends and money: Lately, James / (Marriage is only) a state of mind: Carpenter, James / That's all she wrote: Billingsley, Gil / Deacons: Hamilton, David / You won't miss the water: Chico & Buddy / I'll take my flowers out right now: Barrino Brothers / Just a mistake: Barrino Brothers / Shoop doop: Hamilton, David / Sweep it out in the shed: Lark, Tobi / Lean lanky Daddy: Little Annie / Your love is what I want: Ravins / Who are you trying to fool: Hamilton, David orchestra / Talkin' 'bout I love: Lark, Tobi / I'm pretending: Page, Priscilla / Nothing in this world: Dottie & Millie / All I want is you: Tolbert, OC / Deep shadows: Little Annie / Heavenly thing: Mar-Keys / Blue funk: Hamilton, David
CDKEND 154 / 23 Mar '98 / Kent

☐ DAVE PIERCE PRESENTS... (2CD Set)
0091382W2R / 20 Oct '97 / Deep Distraxion/Profile

☐ DAVID HAMILTON'S FAVOURITE MELODIES (Relaxing Moods)
Deep purple: Temple, nino & April stevens / Rhythm of the rain: Cascades / Here it comes again: Fortunes / You were on my mind: St. Peters, Crispian / It hurts to be in love: Pitney, Gene / Maria: Proby, P.J. / He's so fine: Chiffons / Breaking up is hard to do: Sedaka, Neil / Venus: Avalon, Frankie / Cupid: Drifters / Warm and tender love: Sledge, Percy / Groovy kind of love: Fontana, Wayne / Here comes that rainy day feeling: Fortunes / Reflections of my life: Marmalade / Town without pity: Pitney, Gene / Remember(walkin' in the sand): Shangri-Las / Stranger on the shore: Bilk, Acker
ANT 018 / Nov '96 / Tring

☐ DAVID HAMILTON'S FAVOURITE MELODIES (Sixties Hits)
Sugar sugar: Archies / Ruby don't take your love to town: Rogers, Kenny / If I had a hammer: Lopez, Trini / Sweet talkin guy: Chiffons / Sha la la la lee: Small Faces / Letter: Box Tops / Little town flirt: Shannon, Del / It hurts to be in love: Pitney, Gene / Rockin' robin: Day, Bobby / Barefootin: Parker, Robert / Duke of earl: Chandler, Gene / It's in his kiss (the shoop shoop song): Everett, Betty / I'm into something good: Herman's Hermits / One fine day: Chiffons / Backstage (I'm lonely): Pitney, Gene / Poetry in motion: Tillotson, Johnny / Louie louie: Kingsmen / Hit's of the 70's (David Hamilton's favourite melodies)
ANT 019 / Nov '96 / Tring

☐ DAVID HAMILTON'S FAVOURITE MELODIES (Hits Of The 70's)
Lady rose: Mungo Jerry / Hitchin' a ride: Vanity Fare / Now is the time: James, Jimmy & The Vagabonds / Lets get together again: Glitter Band / Run back: Douglas, Carl / Black and white: Greyhound / I'm doin fine now: New York City / Girls: Moments / Freedom come freedom go: Fortunes / I only want to be with you: Bay City Rollers / Love will keep us together: Sedaka, Neil / Up in a puff of smoke: Brown, Polly / Sugar baby love: Rubettes / You can get it if you really want: Decker, Desmond & the Aces / Yellow river: Christie / I get a little sentimental over you: New Seekers / Shang a lang: Bay City Rollers / People like you and people like me: Glitter Band
ANT 020 / Nov '96 / Tring

☐ DAVID HAMILTON'S FAVOURITE MELODIES (Disco Party Mix)
I'll go where your music takes me: James, Jimmy & The Vagabonds / I love to love: Charles, Tina / I will survive: Gaynor, Gloria / Hold back the night: Trammps / Band of Gold: Payne, Freda / Get dancin': Disco Tex & The Sexolettes / Saddle up: Christie, David / Twist: Checker, Chubby / Do the funky chicken: Thomas, Rufus / You little trustmaker: Thymes / Dance little lady dance: Charles, Tina / I wanna dance wit choo: Disco Tex & The Sexolettes / Don't take away the music: Tavares / High energy: Thomas, Evelyn / Feel like I'm in love: Marie, Kelly
ANT 021 / Nov '96 / Tring

☐ DAVID HAMILTON'S FAVOURITE MELODIES (Lover's Fireside)
Night has a thousand eyes: Vee, Bobby / My special prayer: Sledge, Percy / Chapel of love: Dixie Cups / Something's gotten hold of my heart: Pitney, Gene / Everything I own: Boothe, Ken / Somewhere: Proby, P.J. / Every beat of my heart: Knight, Gladys & The Pips / Single Girl: Posey, Sandy / 24 hours from Tulsa: Pitney, Gene / Love is all around: Troggs / So many ways: Benton, Brook / Sixteen candles: Crests / Hurt: Yuro, Tumi / Will you love me tomorrow: Shirelles / Like it is: Neville, Aaron / Letter full of tears: Knight, Gladys & The Pips / You'll never walk alone: Gerry & The Pacemakers
ANT 022 / Nov '96 / Tring

☐ DAWNING OF PURE EVIL (Necropolis Sampler)
NRPR 002CD / 20 Jul '98 / Necropolis

☐ DAY MY FAVOURITE INSECT DIED, THE
KS 14CD / Feb '97 / Kollaps

☐ DAY TRIP TO BRISCO
FABRISCOCD / 29 Jun '98 / Fused & Bruised

☐ DAY TRIPPER
Magic bus: Swervedriver / Mysteries: Happy Campers / Fun for me: Moloko / In a room: Dodgy / Simple life: Chamberlain / 36 degrees: Placebo / Tattva: Kula Shaker / Midnight in a perfect world: DJ Shadow / What now: Pressure Drop / Sunrise shakers: Reef / Straight line: Tribute To Nothing / Love spreads: Stone Roses / Worst case scenario: Stanford Prison Experiment / Descend: Feeder / Insects are all around us: Money Mark / Stereo: Spooky / Airhead: Millencolin / Untitled: DJ Shadow
5406772 / Feb '97 / A&M

☐ DAYTRIPPERS (3CD Set)
DTKBOX 52 / 1 Jun '98 / Dressed To Kill

☐ DE NEDERLANDSCHE UNDERGROUND
PRIME 052CD / Oct '96 / Prime

☐ DE NOVA DA CAPO COMPILATION
DNDC 007CD / Oct '96 / De Nova Da Capo

☐ DEAR OLD ERIN'S ISLE
NI 5350 / Sep '94 / Nimbus

☐ DEATH IS JUST THE BEGINNING VOL.3
NB 111CD / 9 Mar '98 / Nuclear Blast

☐ DECADE OF CALLIGRAPH, A
Lady Jekyll and Mistress Hyde: Lyttelton, Humphrey / Black butterfly: Lyttelton, Humphrey / Caribana Queen: Lyttelton, Humphrey / Strange Mr Peter Charles: Lyttelton, Humphrey / My funny valentine: Lyttelton, Humphrey / Bad penny blues: Lyttelton, Humphrey / Happy go lucky local: Lyttelton, Humphrey / Jack the bear: Lyttelton, Humphrey / Madly: Lyttelton, Humphrey / Drop me off in Harlem: Shapiro, Helen / When a woman loves a man: Shapiro, Helen / Turner minor: Turner, Bruce / Buddy Tate from Texas State: Lyttelton, Humphrey & Buddy Tate / I got a pocket of dreams: Daniels, Maxine & Brian Lemon / Fascinating rhythm: Barnes, Johnny / Down in honky tonk town: Lyttelton, Humphrey & Lillian Boutte / My Mama socks me: Davern, Kenny / Summertime: Lyttelton, Humphrey & Acker Bilk
CLGCD 031 / Oct '95 / Calligraph

☐ DECADE OF GAME
Intro: Ruthless / 24 hours to live: Ruthless / Dopeman: NWA / Untouchable: Above The Law / Same ole shit: MC Ren / Greatz tatze: HWA / It's funky enough: DOC / Always into somethin': NWA / Fuck what ya heard: MC Ren / I ain't no lady: HWA / Murder rap: Above The Law / Real muthapuckkin' G's: Eazy E / Black nigga killa: Eazy E / 8 ball: NWA / Final frontier: MC Ren / Formula: DOC / Black superman: Above The Law / Supersonic: JJ Fad / Boyz-n-hood: Eazy E / Something in my heart: Michel'le / Nicety: Michel'le / Grand finale: DOC / Outro: DOC
4890012 / 23 Mar '98 / Ruthless

☐ DECADE OF IBIZA, A (2CD Set)
TCD 2902
XTCD 2902 / Jun '97 / Telstar

☐ DECAY
ASH 39 / 8 Dec '97 / Ash International

☐ DECAY PRODUCT
EFA 503032 / 22 Sep '97 / Chain Reaction

☐ DECEPTIVE 50
Thundersley invacar: Collapsed Lung / Stutter: Elastica / Alkaline: Scarfo / Come and gone: Snuff / I see red: Unun / Give me daughters: Jonathan Fire Eater / Annihilate now: Idlewild / Drowning by numbers: Placebo / Be my light be my guide: Gene / That good one: Meices / Teenage girl crush: Angelica / Mea culpa blues (It's my fault): Colouring Lesson / Smile it's sugar: Spare Snare / Shine on me: Prisoners / On me not in me: Earl Brutus & Alan Vega / Bar bar bar: Elastica / Whatever happened to the likely lads: Snuff / I want you: Scarfo / Connection: Collapsed Lung
BLUFF 050CD / 5 Jan '98 / Deceptive

☐ DECK THE HALLS
15304 / Nov '95 / Laserlight

☐ DECLARATION OF INDEPENDENCE
LF 308CD / 6 Jul '98 / Lost & Found

☐ DECONSTRUCTION CLASSICS
Ride on time: Black Box / Rhythm is a mystery: K-Klass / Anthem: N-Joi / Dream 17: Annette B / Higher ground: Sasha / Confide in me: Minogue, Kylie / Sight for sore eyes: M-People / Don't you want me: Felix / Open your mind: Usura / Texas cowboys: Grid / High: Hyper Go Go / Carino: T-Coy / Movin' on up: M-People / Infinity: Guru Josh / How can I love you more: M-People / Packet of peace: Lion Rock / Love thing: Evolution / I'm in love: Sha-Lor / Everybody everybody: Black Box / Don't come to stay: Hot House / Sly one: Van-Rooy, Marina / Is there anybody out there: Bassheads / Future FJP: Liaison D / Ajare: Way Out West / Girls and boys: Hed Boys / Swamp thing: Grid
74321299002 / Aug '95 / De-Construction

☐ DEDICATED TO THE ONE I LOVE
MCCD 087 / Dec '92 / Music Club

☐ DEDICATED TO THE ONE I LOVE
Little darling: Diamonds / Earth angel: Penguins / Chapel of love: Dixie Cups / Fools rush in: Benton, Brook / Uptown: Crystals / Pillow you dream on: Locklin, Hank / Embraceable you: Day, Doris / Up on the roof: Drifters / Night has a thousand eyes: Vee, Bobby / So many ways: Benton, Brook / Runaway: Shannon, Del / Because you're mine: Day, Doris / I loved and lost again: Cline, Patsy / Single girl: Posey, Sandy / Love walked in: Benson, George / Just the two of us: Jones, Jack / Portrait of my love: Clark, Dee / Give him a great big kiss: Shangri-Las / One who really loves you: Wells, Mary / Why do fools fall in love: Diamonds / Let your love flow: Burke, Solomon / Singin' the blues: Mitchell, Guy / While I dream: Sedaka, Neil / Crying my heart out for you: Day, Doris / Tell Laura I love her: Peterson, Ray
GRF 131 / Apr '93 / Tring

☐ DEDICATED TO YOU (18 More Songs From The Heart)
Coward of the county: Rogers, Kenny / I will always love you: Parton, Dolly / Have I told you lately that I love you: Reeves, Jim / Roses are red: O'Donnell, Daniel / Who's sorry now: Francis, Connie / Years from now / I don't know why I love you: Rose Marie / Blanket on the ground: Spears, Billie Jo / Honey: Goldsboro, Bobby / Crystal chandeliers: Pride, Charley / Sunshine of your smile: Berry, Mike / You are my sunshine: Boxcar Willie / Love is like a butterfly: Parton, Dolly / I need you: O'Donnell, Daniel / Anniversary waltz: Rose Marie / Little green apples: Miller, Roger / Single girl: Posey, Sandy / Last farewell: Whittaker, Roger
PLATCD 3901 / Oct '88 / Platinum

☐ DEE JAYS RULE (2CD Set)
AVEXCD 52 / Jan '97 / Avex

☐ DEEP BLUE (Rounder 25th Anniversary Blues Anthology)
ROUCDAN 20 / Nov '95 / Rounder

☐ DEEP BLUES
Jumper on the line: Burnside, R.L. / Jr Blues: Kimbrough, Junior / Catfish blues: Johnson, 'Big' Jack / Daddy, when is Momma coming home: Johnson, 'Big' Jack / Big boy now: Johnson, 'Big' Jack / Midnight prowler: Frost, Frank / You can talk about me: Hemphill, Jessie Mae / Shame on you: Hemphill, Jessie Mae / Long haired doney: Burnside, R.L. / Heartbroken man: Barnes, Roosevelt 'Booba' / Ain't gonna worry about tomorrow: Barnes, Roosevelt 'Booba' / Love like I wanna: Barnes, Roosevelt 'Booba' / Terraplane blues: Pitchford, Lonnie / If I had possession over judgement day: Pitchford, Lonnie / Devil blues: Owens, Jack & Bud Spires
4509919812 / Mar '93 / WEA

☐ DEEP CONCENTRATION (2CD Set)
Lesson six: Cut Chemist / DJ Price Paul vs the world: Prince Paul / Radar frees Tibet: Radar Bros. / Strange times: Angel & Cokni O'Dire / Poesis: Def, Eddie / Centaurus space bass: DJ Swingsett & DJ Wally / Turntable experience: X-Men / Say that: Lyrik Born Clique / They don't fall down: Peanutbutter Wolf / On wax: Beyond There / Mountains of madness: DJ Mumbles / Book of changes: Q-Burns Abstract Message
OM 006CD / May '97 / OM

☐ DEEP DISTRAXION
Geera: Monumental / Not gonna do it: S1000 / Do one more: Spoonio / Mandala: Monumental / Stoneage: Floorjam / Who's in the house: S1000 / Viewfinder: Back II Front / Deep distraxion: Floorjam / I'm gonna get you: Hook Line & Sinker / Ibiza: Back II Front / By dawn's early light: Thee Madkatt Courtship / Lego beat: Happy Larry
SLIKCD 002 / Jul '94 / Deep Distraxion/ Profile

☐ DEEP DOWN IN FLORIDA (TK Deep Soul)
All because of your love: Clay, Otis / Honey honey: Hudson, David / Sometimes: Facts Of Life / If he hadn't slipped up and got caught: Patterson, Bobby / Sweet woman's love: Clay, Otis / God blessed our love: Allen, Charles / All I need is you: Clay, Otis / I've tried it all: Meadows Bros. / Baby I cried cried cried: Johnson, Charles / Today my whole world fell: Clay, Otis / It's never too late: Willie & Anthony / Let me in: Clay, Otis / Love on the phone: Mitchell, John / Caught in the act: Facts Of Life / Love you save: Williams, Lee Shot / When I'm loving you: Hudson, David / Special kind of love: Clay, Otis
NEMCD 721 / Mar '95 / Sequel

☐ DEEP DOWN SOUTH
CDRB 29 / Nov '95 / Charly

☐ DEEP GREEN
Save a place for me / Deep green / Carlin how / Old man of the ocean / Skinningrove bay / North country girl / Kilten castle / Abbess St. Hilda
FG 2803 / Apr '96 / Frog

☐ DEEP HARMONICA BLUES
Courtin' in a cadillac: McCain, Jerry / That's what they want: McCain, Jerry / Calling all cows: Blues Rockers / Johnny Mae: Blues Rockers / Not welcome anymore (Sanafee): Warren, Baby Boy & Sonny Boy Williamson / Chuc-a-luck chicken: Warren, Baby Boy & Sonny Boy Williamson / Love shock: Little Sonny / I'll love you baby (until the day I die): Little Sonny / Bring me my machine gun: Warren, Baby Boy & Sonny Boy Williamson / Hello stranger: Warren, Baby Boy & Sonny Boy Williamson / You better change: Ole Sonny Boy / Blues and misery: Ole Sonny Boy / You don't love me no more: McCain, Jerry / Things ain't right: McCain, Jerry / Goin' home: Lightnin' Slim / I'm grown: Lightnin' Slim / Wonderin' and worryin': Harpo, Slim / They call me Lazy: Lazy Lester / Harmonica twist: Smith, Whispering / Please give me one more twist: Smith, Whispering / Shut your mouth: Anderson, Jimmy / Rats and roaches on your mind: Anderson, Jimmy / When I met you baby: Jolly George / She's got me: Jolly George
CDCHD 604 / Nov '96 / Ace

☐ DEEP HOUSE VOL.1 (The Sound Of The UK Underground)
CDTOT 43 / Jul '96 / Jumpin' & Pumpin'

☐ DEEP IN A DREAM (20 Dreamy Mood Grooves)
Dream: Pied Pipers / I dream of you: Sinatra, Frank / My dreams are getting better: Day, Doris / Meet me tonight in dreamland: Mills Brothers / Have a little dream on me: Waller, Fats / Dream lullaby: Carter, Benny & His Orchestra / Someone's rocking my dreamboat: Ink Spots / When or where: Horne, Lena / I've got a pocketful of dreams: Ambrose & His Orchestra / If dreams come true: Goodman, Benny Orchestra / I've got a date with my dream: Holiday, Billie / Dreaming a dream: Bowlly, Al / Laura: Herman, Woody & His Orchestra / I had the craziest dream: Forrest, Helen / Day dream: Hodges, Johnny Orchestra / Did you ever see a dream walking: Crosby, Bing / Yesterday's dreams: Hutchinson, Leslie 'Hutch' / Wrap your troubles in dreams: Cole, Cozy Orchestra & Coleman Hawkins / I'm always chasing rainbows: Garland, Judy / Put your dreams away: Sinatra, Frank
305542 / Oct '96 / Hallmark

☐ DEEP IN THE HEART OF TEXAS
Deep in the heart of Texas: Kevin & The Blacktears / Let somebody else drive: Kevin & The Blacktears / Will you love me manana: Saldana, Sir Doug / Whiter shade of pale: Saldana, Sir Doug / Black cat: Beall, Charlie / Take a walk in the rain: Kosub, Kevin / Loco vaquero: Jimenez, Flaco / Joint is jumpin': Meyers, Augie / I don't get the blues when I'm stoned: Dogman & The Shepherds / Mexico: Torres, Toby / I got it: Mike The Leadsinger
CDZ 2016 / Apr '94 / Zu Zazz

☐ DEEP IN THE HEART OF TUVA
ELLICD 4080 / May '97 / Ellipsis Arts

☐ DEEP IN THE PHILLY GROOVE
La la means I love you / I need your love so bad / So long, goodbye, it's over / When times are bad / Goodbye pain / Face the future / Didn't I / One and one is five / When the bottom falls out / Follow the lamb / Not goin' to let you (Talk to me that way) / Didn't we make it / Puff puff, you're gone / Ruby Lee / You are my sun sign part 1 / Handle with care / I want to be your lover / Player / Armed and extremely dangerous / Smarty pants / Delfonics theme / Can't go on living
CDKEND 115 / May '94 / Kent

☐ DEEP LANCASHIRE (Songs & Ballads Of The Industrial North West)
Hand loom weaver's lament / Hop hop hop / Beg your leave / Ale is physic for me / Gettin' wed / Clogs / Merry little doffer / Rawtenstall annual fair / Coqlouse medley / Cob a coalin' / Seaur pies / Bury new loom / Ten per cent / Man like thee / Lancashire liar
TSCD 485 / Jul '97 / Topic

Column 1

☐ DEEP ORIENT VOL.1 (Musiques De Jour)
325102 / 21 Aug '97 / Melodie

☐ DEEP ORIENT VOL.2 (Musiques De Nuit)
325112 / 21 Aug '97 / Melodie

☐ DEEP POLKA (Dance Music From The Midwest)
SFW 40088 / 29 Jun '98 / Smithsonian Folkways

☐ DEEP SOUND OF IBIZA, THE
SPV 08547882 / Nov '97 / SPV

☐ DEEP SOUTH BLUES PIANO 1935-1937
DOCD 5233 / May '94 / Document

☐ DEEPER SHADES
Pissed apache: Disscuss / Cafe del mar: Energy 52 / Calling: Solar Stone / Beachball: Nalin & Kane / Netherworld: LSG / Angel: Lost Tribe / Gamesmaster: Lost Tribe / Schoneberg: Marmion / Day by day: Solar Stone / Fragile: LSG / Everytime: Lustral
HOOJCD 004 / 15 Dec '97 / Hooj Choons

☐ DEEPEST SHADE OF TECHNO VOL.1
REFCD 001 / Apr '94 / Reflective

☐ DEEPEST SOUL VOL.1
I'm lonely: Sanders, Nelson / You got me on a string: Freeman Brothers / You should have told me: New Yorkers / I'll be gone: Turner, Tommy / Just a little more love: Soul Commanders / Love as true as mine: Roc-kays Band / I've learned my lesson: Richardson, Donald Lee / Don't waste my time: Sinceres / Ain't gonna do you no good: Willis, Betty / These feelings: Phil & Del / Helpless girl: Staten, Little Mary / Whole lot of tears: Stuart, Jeb / Pick yourself up: Taylor, E.G. & The Sound of Soul / I'm hurt: Little Tom / Human: Ad Libs / I worship the ground you walk on: Ad Libs / Teach me to love again: Scott, Kurtis / It won't hurt: Bogen, Richard / I'll be there: Tenderonies / Please come back: Tate, Jimmy / Make the best of what you've got: Patton, Alexander / I'm beggin' you baby: Vibra-Tones & George Johnson / Never let me go: Vibra-Tones & George Johnson
GSCD 016 / Jul '93 / Goldmine

☐ DEEPEST SOUL VOL.2
This beautiful day: Jackson, Levi / Serving a sentence of life: Douglas, Carl / Beautiful night: Thomas, Jimmy / What love brings: Bernard, Kenny / I'll hold you: Frankie & Johnny / Don't pity me: Lynn, Sue / Lost summer love: Silva, Lorraine / Our love is getting stronger: Night, Jason / Love is wonderful: Parfit, Paula / Stop and you'll become aware: Shapiro, Helen / Nobody knows: St. John, Tammy / Everything's gonna be alright: Arnold, P.P. / Invitation: Band Of Angels / If you knew me: Keyes, Ebony / Number one in your heart: Goins, Herbie / Need your love: Notations / Movin away: Lynch, Kenny / Baby I don't need your love: Chants / Stand accused: Colton, Tony / Never ever: Clements, Soul Joe / Tears of joy: Merrell, Ray
GSCD 041 / Jun '93 / Goldmine

☐ DEF JAM 10TH ANNIVERSARY BOX SET (4CD Set)
5238482 / Nov '95 / Def Jam

☐ DEFENDERS OF THE OPPRESSED BREED (2CD Set)
VEG 001CD / Mar '97 / Dolores

☐ DEFINITELY GARAGE (3CD Set)
Give yourself: Sima / Stand up: House Vibe & Loleatta Holloway / Your Higher State / I'll be a freak for you '96: Royal Delite / Spell: Johan S / Come together: Johan S / Hold me: Rhythm Alive / Where is the love: SDA & Gary Des'Etages / Disoco love: Uncut Grooves / Don't give up: Anorak Trax / Paradise: Malone & Mollison / Show ya love: Soft Butter Productions / Da mental groove: Johan S & Dynamic Kutz / From my mind: Rhythm Alive / Fix: Soft Butter Productions / Music: Rhythm Alive / Da mental groove: Johan S & Dynamic Kutz / There it goes again: Nova / Da mental g: Johan S & Dynamic Kutz / Hot enuff: Tuff & Jam / Vybes in house: Johan S & Dynamic Kutz / I need love: Symbiose / Tell the world: Rhythm Inc & Nevada / Forever: Key To Life / Amazone: Symbiose / Better way: Circle Line / Mass confusion: Freestyle Orchestra / Funky groove: Windross, Norris 'The Boss' / Anorak trax: Anorak Trax / Keep on pushing: Big Noise / Spirit: Johan S & Integrated Society / Find a way: Key To Life
ECD 3409 / 3 Nov '97 / Definitely Dance

☐ DEFINITELY HOUSE (3CD Set)
Pianospilifico: Santini / Make it right: Anorak Trax / Ibiza: Delira / Elevation: Diddy Di Doe / Luv it up: Jump / Reachin' for your love: Tantrum Twins / Surrender: Love Deluxe / Don't go away: Mauritio / Work it: Anorak Trax / Wanna be free: 2 High / Your love: BB Club / It's comin' on: Anorak Trax / Annihalting rhythm: Bass Shakers / Push the tempo: Bass Funktion / Let's go round again: 5 Minutes Of Funk / Party time: Bass Shakers / Catch the beat: Marradonna / To the limit: Bass Shakers / 2high's groove: 2 High / Marrucial: Malone, Richie / Scat: Marradonna / Fundamental: Bass Funktion / Strings 'n' tings: Malone, Richie / MUSIC: 2 High / Based on acid: DJ Ablaze / Concept of roundness and neurocumbical energy: Choci & Freedom Of Sound / Tunnel vision: Relative Progress / Breakdown: Incisions / What is going on: Dax / Energy flash: Incisions / Panic: Relative Progress / Bring it back: 5 Minutes Of Funk / Bouncy castle: Talisman / E's theory: Relative Progress / Techno going: Incisions / Trancition: Choci & Freedom Of Sound
ECD 3407 / 3 Nov '97 / Definitely Dance

☐ DEFINITELY IBIZA (3CD Set)
Let there be love: Deluxtra / Meaning: Sound Gathering / Feel the rhythm: Terrorize / Fishead: Fishead / Til da break: Freestyle Orchestra / No rich fat daddy: Jump / Blackout: Keep WKW Right before my eyes: Bolton, Jennifer / Fever of love: Energiser / Solid sin: Chalk 'n' Cheez / All the bitches: Go-Zo / Go-go: Bomb Squad / Sso groove: Freestyle

Column 2

Orchestra / Feel like movin': Anorak Trax / Invader: Koolworld Productions / Swallow the light: Method Man & Becks / Sunrise: Adagio / Fall into you: AMD / Take me away: Beserker / Power: Deep Wave / Here somes the night: Bus Stop / Hey everybody: Maltese Massive / Pleasure and pain: Axel / LSD: Axel / Solid sin: Chalk 'n' Cheez / Sso groove: Freestyle Orchestra / Meaning: Sound Gathering / Til da break: Freestyle Orchestra / All the bitches: Go-Zo / Let there be love: Deluxtra / Right before my eyes: Bolton, Jennifer / Power: Deep Wave / Lsd: Axel / Hey everybody: Maltese Massive / Darkbag: KWP / Invader: Koolworld Productions / Swallow the light: Menthol Man & Becks / Pressure and pain: Axel
ECD 3410 / 3 Nov '97 / Definitely Dance

☐ DEFINITELY TECHNO (3CD Set)
Pump 1: Beyer, Adam / Violent storms: Nu-Era / Incessant sound: Melrob / Slammin': Pandemic / Filtermulie: Throb / Grasshopper: Headspace / Aux 5: Citadel Of Kaos / Loose control: Celtic Sons / Lift me up: Bishop / In the heat of the night: Overhead Noise / Frozen love: Minouche / East of Eden: Minouche / Moment: Faces / On a journey: Secret Society / Forcefield: Space Debris / Shofou: Tyoussi / So addicted: Bishop, Rodney / Free as a journey: Berserker / London's on acid: Cabbage Patch / Spectrum: DAC / Future: DAC / Spiritual blessings: Tekno Dred & Ad Man / Here I come: Nu-Era / Pump 1: Beyer, Adam / Grasshopper: Headspace / Filtermulie: Throb / Lenks 808: Mould Impression / Incessant sound: Melrob / London's on acid: Cabbage Patch / In the heat of the night: Overhead Noise / Loose control: Celtic Sons / Violent storms: Nu-Era / Frozen luv: Minouche / East of Eden: Minouche / Lift me up: Bishop / So addicted: Bishop / Spiritual blessings: Tekno Dred & The Adman
ECD 3408 / 3 Nov '97 / Definitely Dance

☐ DEFINITION OF HARDCORE
RIVETCD 3 / Sep '93 / Reinforced

☐ DEFINITIVE BLUES
Boom boom: Hooker, John Lee / Whisky and wimmen: Hooker, John Lee / Time is marchin': Hooker, John Lee / Don't you remember me: Hooker, John Lee / Ain't nobody's business: Witherspoon, Jimmy / New Orleans woman: Witherspoon, Jimmy / No rolling blues: Witherspoon, Jimmy / Sweet lovin' baby: Witherspoon, Jimmy / Blowin' the fuse: Hopkins, Lightnin' / Don't need no job: Hopkins, Lightnin' / Chain gang blues: Hopkins, Lightnin' / Everybody's blue: Hopkins, Lightnin' / CC rider: Leadbelly / Baby don't you love me no more: Leadbelly / Matchbox blues: Leadbelly / Bourgeois blues: Leadbelly / Highway 49: Howlin' Wolf / Poor baby: Howlin' Wolf / Little red rooster: Howlin' Wolf / Wang dang doodle: Howlin' Wolf
SUMCD 4046 / Nov '96 / Summit

☐ DEFINITIVE COLLECTION OF IRISH BALLADS VOL.1, A (2CD Set)
BALLAD 001CD / Aug '94 / Outlet

☐ DEFINITIVE COLLECTION OF IRISH BALLADS VOL.2, A (2CD Set)
BALLAD 002CD / Aug '94 / Outlet

☐ DEFINITIVE HOUSE FOR ALL
XTR 16CD / Jul '95 / X-Treme

☐ DEFINITIVE NRG (4CD Set)
CDBDHN 1 / 20 Apr '98 / Passion

☐ DEL-FI AND DONNA STORY VOL.1, THE
Hippy hippy shake: Romero, Chan / I don't care now: Romero, Chan / I want some more: Romero, Chan / My little Ruby: Romero, Chan / That's my little Suzie: Valens, Ritchie / La Bamba: Valens, Ritchie / My babe: Holden, Ron / Love you so: Holden, Ron / Jungle fever: Shadows / Under stars of love: Shadows / Rumours: Crawford, Johnny / Proud: Crawford, Johnny / Little cupid: Carlos Brothers / Gonna see my baby: Addrisi Brothers / Cherrystone: Addrisi Brothers / Back to the old salt mine: Addrisi Brothers / Marie: Dale, Dick / Untouchables: Hall, Rene / Fast freight: Valens, Ritchie / Blabbermouth: Fantastics / Is it a dream: Flamingo, Johnny / When I do the mashed potato: Bright, Larry / Little more wine my dear: Hawks / To be loved (forever): Pentagons / Everything's gonna be alright: Holden, Ron / Please please dream: Flamingo / Lively ones: Casuals / Misirlou: Lively Ones / Big surf: Sentinals / Okie surfer: Gates, David / Original surferstomp: Johnstone, Bruce / Kilica angle: Surfettes
CDCHD 313 / Jul '91 / Ace

☐ DEL-FI AND DONNA STORY VOL.2, THE
Intro / Come on let's go: Valens, Ritchie / Alone and cryin': Addrisi Brothers / Wild twist: Roller Coasters / You can't fool around: Roller Coasters / For your love: Romero, Chan / She don't wanna dance (no more): Little Caesar & The Romans / Quiet as it's kept: Nelson, Chip / You're mine: Flamingo, Chan / Fuzzy: Hawks / Big toe: Nitehawks / Dancing in the sand: Hollers, Wayne / Watusi bongos: Epps, Preston / Seeing double: Holden, Ron / If I had my way: Romero, Chan / Sugar baby: Romero, Chan / Addrisi Brothers: Romero, Chan / Terror: Addrisi Brothers / Matilda: Swags / Summertime blues: Valens, Ritchie / Hippy hippy shake: Romero, Chan / Rock house wine my dear: Hawks / Donna: Valens, Ritchie / Bamba: Romero, Chan / My little Ruby: Romero, Chan / Slaucson sax: Romancers / Tell me: Langford, Gerry / Blowin' the blues: Swags / Betty Jean: Little Caesar & The Romans / True love can be: Holden, Ron / Walking alone: Pentagons / I want some more: Romero, Chan
CDCHD 489 / Apr '94 / Ace

☐ DELAYED ACTION MINE
HOTROD 01 / Apr '98 / Hotrod

☐ DELETIONS VOL.1
Surface noise: Planetary Assault Systems / Gruve: Planetary Assault Systems / Funk electric: Planetary Assault Systems / CVO trance: Glenn Underground / Assault Systems / CVO trance: Glenn Underground / Seaquest: Glenn Underground / Cat NA thru trap: Glenn Underground / Summer funk: Purveyors Of Fine Funk / No road: Purveyors Of Fine Funk / Hot: Purveyors Of Fine Funk / Ashes smashing red: Purveyors Of Fine Funk
PFEC 01 / Jun '97 / Peacefrog

Column 3

☐ DELETIONS VOL.2
Shake: Shakir, Anthony / Mind you don't trip: Neuropolitique / Surkit: Reel By Reel / Sunlight: Infiniti / Takks: Landstrumm, Neal / Disfunction: Landstrumm, Neal / Field preaching: Landstrumm, Neal / Telex: Landstrumm, Neal / Superfreak: DBX / Spacetalk: DBX / Signal zero: DBX / City on the edge of forever: DBX
PFEC 002CD / 13 Oct '97 / Peacefrog

☐ DELETIONS VOL.3
Planetary funk vol.1: Planetary Assault Systems / DBX: DBX / Come of age: St. Vitus Dance
PFEC 003CD / 25 May '98 / Peacefrog

☐ DELICIOUS (2CD Set)
DOMECD 12 / 11 May '98 / Dome

☐ DELIRIUM PRESENTS AFTER 6AM
DELACD 02 / Jan '94 / Delirium

☐ DELIRIUM PRESENTS AFTER 6AM VOL.2
DELACD 03 / May '95 / Delirium

☐ DELMARK 40TH ANNIVERSARY - BLUES
DXCD 2 / Aug '93 / Delmark

☐ DEMAGNETIZED
MAGNETCD 13 / Nov '95 / Magnetic North

☐ DEMENTERTAINMENT
TWSCD 2 / 25 May '98 / Twisted

☐ DENZ DA DENZ VOL.2
NL 609022 / Jun '97 / Basic Beat

☐ DER KLANG DER FAMILLE
NOMU 4CD / Jul '92 / Nova Mute

☐ DESCENDENTS OF THE ITINERANT GYPSIES (Melodies Of Sorrow And Joy/Hungary & Romania)
Khelimaski dyili / Meselaki dyili / Csardas / Funeral piece / Men's dance / Keserves / Dance piece / Wedding march / Flirtation dance for men and women
MCM 3010 / May '97 / Multicultural Media

☐ DESERT OF SPIRITS (Musical Moods & Chants Of Native Africa)
Dawn on the plain / Asumbele / Song of the wild (Uma Uma) / Journey home / Kikuyu dance / Sacred chant (Sinarah part 1) / Sacred chant (Sinarah part 2) / Dusk on the plain / Night melody / Contemplation / From the horizon / Broken reed
DC 881542 / 29 Aug '97 / Disky

☐ DESERT SESSIONS VOL.1 & 2, THE
MR 093 / 23 Feb '98 / Man's Ruin

☐ DESIGNER COLLECTION (2CD Set)
UMCD 001 / Oct '96 / United Dance

☐ DESPERATE DALLAS DEMOS (1950's Texas Rock & Roll)
NOHITCD 003 / Feb '97 / No Hit

☐ DESPERATE ROCK 'N' ROLL VOL.1
FLAMECD 001 / Jul '95 / Flame

☐ DESPERATE ROCK 'N' ROLL VOL.2
Woman love: Johnson, Jimmy / I love you: Kirkland, Eddie / I don't need you no more: Rumblers / Ice water: Barber, Glen / Rockin' out the blue: Rascal / Lynn Twins / Cruisin': Bucky & Premiers / Is it just a game: Buddy & The Cats / Long legged Linda: Kids From Texas / Not like now: Robinson, Freddie / Live it up: Sundowners / There ain't nothin' true about you: Nelson, Bobby / Hey Bo Diddley: Genova, Tommy / Rock on: Rebb, Johnny / Chocolate fizz: Sax Cari / I want some of that: Rai, Kai / She's my kid: Tyler, Kip / Jealous of you baby: Tyler, Kip / Rollin' dynamite: McKay, Scotty / Steamer: Bellemo, Johnny / Rockin' in rollin': Horning, W.L. / Think it over baby: Cleary, Eddie / Dirty dirty feelin': Debs, Denny / I'm hurt: Rick & The Rockers / Big time mama: Symuon, Jimmy / Granny tops 'em at the hop: Grady, Bob / Function at the junction: Whitfield, Charles / Indian summer: Reeves, Glenn / Beat up tennis shoe: Dresser, Lee / I can't wait: Stanley, Ray / You ain't no good for me: Lee, Jimmy
FLAMECD 002 / Jul '95 / Flame

☐ DESPERATE ROCK 'N' ROLL VOL.3
FLAMECD 003 / Jul '95 / Flame

☐ DESPERATE ROCK 'N' ROLL VOL.4
FLAMECD 004 / Jul '95 / Flame

☐ DESPERATE ROCK 'N' ROLL VOL.5
FLAMECD 005 / Sep '95 / Flame

☐ DESTINATION BOMP BOMP (2CD Set)
BCD 4048/2 / Jul '96 / Bomp/Blue Rose

☐ DESTINATION FRANTIC (US Garage Greats)
Z66 R1001 / 5 Jan '98 / Zonw 66

☐ DESTRUCTIVE URGES
BENT 0020CD / May '96 / Creeping Bent

☐ DETROIT 313
EFA 017922 / Apr '96 / Tresor

☐ DETROIT SOUL FROM THE VAULTS VOL.1
Soul sloopy: Dynamics / Yes I love you baby: Dynamics / Head and shoulders: Young, Patti / Love what's wrong with your love (#1): Metros / We still have time: Metros / Cardie: Burdick, Doni / What'cha gonna do: Burdick, Doni / Make a change (inst): Rogers, Johnny / Soul food: Rogers, Johnny / If you walk out of my life: Burdick, Doni / Bari track: Burdick, Doni / Marry go round: Frontera, Tommy / Fascinating girl: Lemons, George / We go to pieces: Hairston, Forest / Whenever I'm without you: Dynamics / Nobody likes me: White, Willie / Go down: Highlights / Lookin' for a woman: Brooks Brothers / I'll be on my way: Bob & Fred
GSCD 117 / 22 Jun '98 / Goldmine

Column 4 (far right)

love: Metros / It's real: Sanders, Nelson / Music in my soul: Milner, Reggie / Make a change: Rogers, Johnny / Soul food: Rogers, Johnny / Open the door to your heart: Burdick, Doni / Have faith in you: Burdick, Doni / Give my heart a break: Turner, Sammy / Fascinating girl: Lemons, George / We go to pieces: Hairston, Forest / Love to a guy: Dynamics / Keep a hold on me: Lewis, Diane / Hangaroo dance: Williams, Lloyd & Highlights / Opposites attract: Swingers / I'll be on my way: Bob & Fred
GSCD 019 / Aug '93 / Goldmine

☐ DETROIT SOUL FROM THE VAULTS VOL.2
Yes I love you baby: Dynamics / Head and shoulders: Young, Patti / I've got that feelin': Garcia, Frankie / Lovin' touch: Satin Dolls / First degree love: Vaughan, Lafayette / Arabia: Royal Playboys / What's wrong with your love (#1): Metros / We still have time: Metros / Cardie: Burdick, Doni / What'cha gonna do: Burdick, Doni / Make a change (inst): Rogers, Johnny / Soul food: Rogers, Johnny / If you walk out of my life: Burdick, Doni / Bari track: Burdick, Doni / Marry go round: Frontera, Tommy / Fascinating girl: Lemons, George / We go to pieces: Hairston, Forest / Whenever I'm without you: Dynamics / Nobody likes me: White, Willie / Go down: Highlights / Lookin' for a woman: Brooks Brothers / I'll be on my way: Bob & Fred
GSCD 020 / Aug '93 / Goldmine

☐ DETROIT UNDERCOVER
(You're my) leading lady: Frontera, Tommy / One alone: Fabulous Apollas / Magic corner: Woods, Belita / Mighty lover: Ideals / Easy livin': Holidays / She keeps driving me wild: Mighty Lovers / Picture me and you: Michaels, Tony / Hey: Mercer, Barbara / Undercover: Bongalis / Party over yonder: Hatcher, Roger / I'll make her mine: Valiant Trio / You're welcome back: Felton, Terry / If only I knew them: New Holidays / Such a nasty boy: Third Party / Devil's gotten hold of my baby: Devotians / No more heartaches: Posey, Art / Wait for me: Brown Bombers & Soul Partners / Giving up you love is like (giving up the world): Twenty Grands / Under the moon: Wonder, Rufus / It's been a long time: Yates, Ruby & The Sounding Rocks / (I'm not gonna be worried: Joe L. / Find a love: Gambrells / Jive talk: Gambrells / I love you only: Carlton, Carl / Don't you think I ought to know: James, Billy / (Somebody) stop that girl: Clarke, Jimmy Soul / With a lonely heart: 4 Voices / Spellbound: Boo, Betty / You're too good (to me baby): Hargreaves, Silky
GSCD 117 / 22 Jun '98 / Goldmine

☐ DETROIT: BEYOND THE THIRD WAVE
Impolite to refuse: Young, Claude / Frozen: Deason, Sean / 8th wonder: Kosmic Messenger / Come on now baby: K-Hand / Sandblaster: Shake / Insert another data disk: Ectomorph / Life on teb: Web, Will / Solid signal: DJ T1000 / Midnight hours: Dixon, Terence / Last trip: Mode Selector
ASW 6170 / May '96 / Astralwerks

☐ DEUTSCHES JAZZ FESTIVAL 1954-1955 (8CD Set)
Jennie's ball: 2 Beat Stompers / Flamingo: Strasser, Hugo / Fine and dandy: Koller, Hans New Jazz Stars / Just you, just me: Edelhagen All Stars / Is you is or is you ain't my baby: Valente, Caterina / I never knew: Hipp, Jutta Combo / Creole love call: Bunge, Fred Star Band / September song: Kuhn, Rolf All Stars / Jazz time ref: Edelhagen, Kurt / Paul's festival ref: Edelhagen, Kurt / Lullaby of Birdland: Redske, Johannes Quintet / Aglojta: Schonberger, Heinz / Festival jump: Valente, Caterina / Get out of here: Spree City Stompers / Just a blues: Spree City Stompers / Just a closer walk with thee: Spree City Stompers / St. James infirmary: Spree City Stompers / That da da strain: Spree City Stompers / Mississippi mud: 2 Beat Stompers / Got no blues: 2 Beat Stompers / Panama: 2 Beat Stompers / Black bottom blues: 2 Beat Stompers / I'm confessin' that I love you: 2 Beat Stompers / Music goes 'round and around: 2 Beat Stompers / Manuskript blues: Haensch, Delle Jump Combo / Blue moon: Haensch, Delle Jump Combo / There's no one but you: Haensch, Delle Jump Combo / Hey good lookin': Haensch, Delle Jump Combo / Flamingo special: Haensch, Delle Jump Combo / Plaza de toros: Edelhagen, Kurt / Big John special: Edelhagen, Kurt / You go to my head: Edelhagen, Kurt / Jazz 55: Edelhagen, Kurt / Nancy and the colonel: Edelhagen, Kurt / Night and day: Edelhagen, Kurt / Stuff lover: Edelhagen, Kurt / Flying home: Edelhagen, Kurt / My funny valentine: Edelhagen, Kurt / Don't blame me: Edelhagen, Kurt / Teach me tonight: Edelhagen, Kurt / Purple hyazinth: Edelhagen, Kurt / All the things you are: Francesco, Silvio Quartet / Long journey: Francesco, Silvio Quartet / Ain't misbehavin': Francesco, Silvio Quartet / Rio: Francesco, Silvio Quartet / All of me: Buschmann, Glen Quartet / Farewell blues: Buschmann, Glen Quartet / St. Louis blues: Buschmann, Glen Quartet / Blue prelude: Buschmann, Glen Quartet / For you my love: Buschmann, Glen Quartet / Just one of those things: Buschmann, Glen Quartet / Shine: Buschmann, Glen Quartet / Bei mir bist du schon: Buschmann, Glen Quartet / Too marvellous for words: Kuhn, Rolf Quintet / Frankfurt blues (now's the time): Kuhn, Rolf Quintet / Hipp noses: Hipp, Jutta Quartet / Song is you: Hipp, Jutta Quartet / Indian summer: Hipp, Jutta Quartet / Good talk: Hipp, Jutta Quartet / These foolish things: Hipp, Jutta Quartet / Gone with the wind: Hipp, Jutta Quartet / Jutta: Koller, Hans New Jazz Stars / Iris: Koller, Hans New Jazz Stars / When your love hath gone: Koller, Hans New Jazz Stars / Porsche: Koller, Hans New Jazz Stars / Summer set: Koller, Hans New Jazz Stars / Brandt, Helmut Combo / Breeze and I: Brandt, Helmut Combo / Brandt, Helmut Combo / Out of nowhere: Wenig, Erhard Quartet / Tenor jump: Wenig, Erhard Quartet / September mfl: Wenig, Erhard Quartet / I believe that you're in love with me: Brandt, Helmut Combo / Out of nowhere: Wenig, Erhard Quartet / Tenor jump: Wenig, Erhard Quartet / Cave souvenir: Lauth, Wolfgang Quartet / Jumpin' with Symphony Sid: Lehn, Erwin / Blues intermezzo: Lehn, Erwin / Gerry walks: Lehn, Erwin / Old man river: Lehn, Erwin / Autumn nocturne: Lauth, Wolfgang Quartet / Conference mit mosch: Lehn, Erwin / What is this thing called love: Lehn, Erwin / Blues for Tenorsaxophon: Lehn, Erwin / Tema con variaziones: Lehn, Erwin / Intermezzo: Lehn, Erwin / Moon over Miami: Banter, Harald Ensemble / Autumn in New York: Banter, Harald

Ensemble / Tabu jump: *Banter, Harald Ensemble* / Polyphona: *Banter, Harald Ensemble* / Nature boy: *Banter, Harald Ensemble* / Happy days are here again: *Banter, Harald Ensemble* / To dance or not to dance: *New Jazz Group Hannover* / I only have eyes for you: *New Jazz Group Hannover* / Lover man: *New Jazz Group Hannover* / Continuation: *New Jazz Group Hannover* / Cloe: *Rediske, Johannes Quintet* / Boptical illusion: *Rediske, Johannes Quintet* / Sweet Georgia Brown: *Rediske, Johannes Quintet* / Thou swell: *Kuhn, Paul Quintet* / Dancing in the dark: *Kuhn, Paul Quintet* / Delaunay's dilemma: *Rediske, Johannes Quintet* / Jumpin' at the rosengarten: *Rediske, Johannes Quintet* / Flip: *Rediske, Johannes Quintet* / I don't stand a ghost of a chance with you: *Rediske, Johannes Quintet* / Crazy rhythm: *Rediske, Johannes Quintet*

BCD 15430 / Oct '90 / Bear Family

☐ DEVOTED TO YOU (16 Songs From The Heart)

Crazy: *Cline, Patsy* / Some broken hearts never mend: *Williams, Don* / Happy anniversary: *Whitman, Slim* / Wheel of fortune: *Rose Marie* / She wears my ring: *King, Solomon* / Hurt: *Yuro, Timi* / With pen in hand: *Carr, Vikki* / Devoted to you: *Everly Brothers* / Sing me an old fashioned song: *Spears, Billie Jo* / Have I got some blues for you: *Pride, Charley* / I will love you all my life: *Foster & Allen* / Pal of my cradle days: *Breen, Ann* / When I leave the world behind: *Rose Marie* / I fall to pieces: *Cline, Patsy* / All I'm missing is you: *Williams, Don* / So sad (to watch good love go bad): *Everly Brothers* / Ebony eyes: *Everly Brothers* / Love hurts: *Everly Brothers*

PLATCD 21 / Apr '88 / Platinum

☐ DEWAR'S BAGPIPE FESTIVAL

KFWCD 133 / Nov '94 / Knitting Factory

☐ DIAL M FOR MERTHYR

NONG 02CD / 2 Mar '98 / Fierce Panda

☐ DIALOGUES

Frissell frazzle / Calypso Joe / Uncle Ed / Snowbound / Dream steps / Bon Ami / Stern stuff / Skylark / Simple things / Dialogue

CD 83369 / Nov '95 / Telarc

☐ DIAMOND HIDDEN IN THE MOUTH OF A CORPSE, A

Won't change: *Husker Du* / Johnsonius: *Johansen, David* / Scum and slime: *Giorno, John Band* / President, Colonel Bradford, every man a god: *Burroughs, William S.* / Halloween: *Sonic Youth* / Dead man's shoes: *Cabaret Voltaire* / Eyes without blood: *Galas, Diamanda* / Neither his nor yours: *Coil* / Game: *Gira, Michael* / Out of the frying pan: *Van Tieghem, David* / Tenement lover: *Hagedorn, Jessica & The Gangster Choir*

VICD 011 / Apr '97 / Visionary/ Jettisoundz

☐ DIAMOND JUBILEE PIPE BAND CHAMPIONSHIPS

CDMON 809 / Sep '90 / Monarch

☐ DIANA TRIBUTE ALBUM (2CD Set)

Who wants to live forever: *Queen* / You have been loved: *Michael, George* / Angel: *Lennox, Annie* / Make me a channel of your peace: *O'Connor, Sinead* / Miss Sarajevo: *U2 & Luciano Pavarotti* / Sonnet no.18: *Ferry, Bryan* / Little willow: *McCartney, Paul* / Tears in Heaven: *Clapton, Eric* / Everybody hurts: *REM* / Streets of Philadelphia: *Springsteen, Bruce* / Don't dream it's over: *Finn, Neil* / Hymn to her: *Pretenders* / Love minus zero/No limit: *Stewart, Rod* / In the sun: *Gabriel, Peter* / Watermark: *Enya* / Evergreen: *Streisand, Barbra* / Every nation: *Red Hot All Stars* / I'll fly away: *Franklin, Aretha* / I'll be missing you: *Puff Daddy* / Because you loved me: *Dion, Celine* / Gone too soon: *Jackson, Michael* / You were loved: *Houston, Whitney* / You've gotta be: *Des'ree* / Hero: *Carey, Mariah* / Prayer for the dying: *Seal* / Missing you: *Ross, Diana* / Wish you were here: *Bee Gees* / Angel: *Braxton, Toni* / Love is a beautiful thing: *Turner, Tina* / All that matters: *Richard, Cliff* / Mama: *Spice Girls* / Don't want to lose you: *Estefan, Gloria* / Stars: *Simply Red* / Ave Maria: *Domingo, Placido & Michael Bolton* / Pavane: *Garrett, Lesley* / I'm in love with the world: *Chicken Shed Theatre Company*

VVR 1001052 / 1 Dec '97 / Princess Diana Trust

☐ DIATONIC ACCORDION SHORT STORY, A

178002 / 24 Apr '98 / Musidisc

☐ DIDJERIDOO AND AFRICAN PERCUSSION

PS 65200 / May '98 / PlayaSound

☐ DIE HART (2CD Set)

ZYX 811202 / 6 Oct '97 / ZYX

☐ DIEHARD SAMPLER

PCD 24 / Nov '96 / Die Hard/Progress

☐ DIFFERENT COLOURS OF DRUM 'N' BASS VOL.1 (2CD Set)

Razorback: *Deason, Sean* / Future reality: *Deason, Sean* / Mood swing: *Dead Calm* / Sphing: *Dead Calm* / Nine miles deep: *Ronnie & Clyde* / Soul of darkness: *Omni Trio* / Mr. Bond: *Nicky Blackmarket & D-Lux* / Turn it up: *S-Man* / Wave: *Wallace, Dave* / Port Rhombus: *Squarepusher* / Tian Craxx: *Plastik & Feedback* / Rhode tune: *Flytronix* / Manifest: *D-Lux* / King of the beats: *Amazon II* / Mash up yer know: *Aladdin* / What the time dred: *Dred Bass* / Dub plate circles: *Undercover Agent* / Jungle makes me: *Green Piece* / U down: *DJ Pulse & The Jazz Cartel* / Drop top: *Aphrodite & Mickey Finn*

560142 / 23 Feb '98 / Nova Tekk

☐ DIFFERENT COLOURS OF DRUM 'N' BASS VOL.2 (2CD Set)

Side effect: *Bassociation* / On line: *Periferico* / Fever: *E-Z Rollers* / Love hurts: *Paris Red* / Piano a go go: *Plastik & Feedback* / Bien agiter: *Bo Qus* / Straight Beat Fluidoscope: *Cosmorama* / Waves of the world: *Four Ears* / Expressions: *Wallace, Dave* / Partenza: *Gah Sato* / Jam: *Electric Lady* / Hot flush: *Red Snapper* / Polarized again: *Polpolar* / People of the planet Alderaan: *Poke* / East coast fusion: *Kudos* / Macro scopic: *Ronnie & Clyde* / Uforide: *Third Coming* / Nostro: *Eigenaat* / Space odyssey: *Cosmorama*

560192 / 23 Feb '98 / Nova Tekk

☐ DIFFERENT GIRLS

OCD 013 / 6 Apr '98 / Ocean Deep

☐ DIG THE NU BREED

Contraflow: *Synchromesh* / Rattlesnake: *Scare-Electric* / Drifter: *Fruit Loop* / Who da fuck: *Semi-Detached Production* / Touching bass: *Tiny Stars* / Vanishin' point: *Tipper* / Sub zero: *Red Myers* / Daylight robbery: *Wide Receiver* / Big rock: *Barillo, Sloop John* / Dalai beats: *Mr. Natural*

WALLCD 012 / Mar '97 / Wall Of Sound

☐ DIGGIN' DEEPER

Great ocean road: *Coco Steel & Lovebomb* / Encounter in Bahia: *Thievery Corporation* / Eighteen Months: *World Of Apples* / Departure lounge - smoking area: *Hightower Set* / Cuica laranja azeda: *Azymuth* / Emerald alley: *Up Bustle & Out* / Comfy club: *Pnu Riff* / Got sunshine in my eyes: *Bix* / Rhythm inferno: *Suburban Ghetto* / Le cauchemnar de James: *Money Penny Project* / Dawn man introducung NYC Dharma: *Reminiscent Drive*

SPECCD 504 / 12 Jan '98 / Dust II Dust

☐ DIGGIN' DEEPER VOL.1 (2CD Set)

Pastime paradise: *Barretto, Ray* / Am I black enough for you: *Paul, Billy* / Cloud nine: *Santamaria, Mongo* / Also sprach zarathustra: *Deodato, Eumir* / Kissing my love: *Withers, Bill* / Home is where the hatred is: *Phillips, Esther* / So what: *Benson, George* / Right down here: *Puthli, Asha* / Love for a day: *Lewis, Ramsey* / Latin America: *Walton, Cedar* / In the park: *Smith, Lonnie Liston* / Consolacao: *Os Ipanemas* / Brazil: *Jobim, Antonio Carlos* / On the path: *Franklin, Rodney*

4838992 / Jul '96 / Sony Jazz

☐ DIGGIN' DEEPER VOL.2

Superstrut: *Deodato, Eumir* / Sideman: *Smith, Lonnie* / Use me: *Phillips, Esther* / Living for the city: *Lewis, Ramsey* / I remember Wes: *Benson, George* / Lookin' good: *Gale, Eric* / Midnight at the oasis: *Hubbard, Freddie* / Ricky tick: *Santamaria, Mongo* / Berimbau: *Os Ipanemas* / Old castle: *Barretto, Ray* / Nunya: *Scott, Tom* / Sugar Loaf Mountain: *Duke, George* / Just around the corner: *Hancock, Herbie*

4874782 / Jun '97 / Sony Jazz

☐ DIGGIN' DEEPER VOL.3

Jaws: *Schifrin, Lalo* / Return of the prodigal son: *Benson, George* / Storm: *Turrentine, Stanley* / Take inventory: *Isley Brothers* / Skyscrapers: *Deodato, Eumir* / Little baby: *Austin, Patti* / Always there: *Bobo, Willie* / El bobo: *Lewis, Webster* / Cubano chant: *Blakey, Art* / Besame mucho: *Pike, Dave* / Sneakin' in the back: *Scott, Tom* / Fly: *Ferguson, Maynard* / Sugar free: *Crawford, Hank* / Gentle thoughts: *Hancock, Herbie*

4892592 / 4 May '98 / Sony Jazz

☐ DIGGIN' FOR GOLD VOL.1

MMCD 6071 / Sep '97 / Music Maniac

☐ DIGGIN' FOR GOLD VOL.2

MMCD 66072 / Dec '97 / Music Maniac

☐ DIGGIN' IN THE CRATES (Profile Rap Classics Vol.1)

Sucker MC's (Krush-groove 1): *Run DMC* / King Kut: *Word Of Mouth & DJ Cheese* / Genius rap: *Dr. Jekyll & Mr. Hyde* / Drag rap: *Showboys* / Fly guy: *Pebblee-Poo* / I can't wait (To rock the mike): *Spyder D & DJ Doc* / Beat bop: *Rammelzee & K-Rob* / Here comes that beat: *Pumpkin & The Profile All Stars* / Rock box: *Run DMC* / Lifestyles Of The Fresh And Fly: *MC Dollar Bill* / Fresh: *Fresh 3 MC's* / Nightmares: *Dane, Dana*

FILERCD 449 / Jun '94 / Profile

☐ DIGGIN' TEXAS SWING 1946-1955

12th Street rag: *Texas Tophands* / Quit rockin' the boat: *Texas Tophands* / Sweet Lucy: *Johnston, Wayne* / Shanty town: *Millers Brothers Orchestra* / Miller's boogie: *Millers Brothers Orchestra* / Steel guitar bounce: *Lonestar playboys* / XIT songs: *Briggs, Billy* / How long must I wait: *Thompson, Cotton* / West wind: *Whitley, Smiley* / Operation blues: *Clemons, Homer* / Live and let live: *Prince, Jimmy* / Big beaver: *Roberts, Buck* / Texas blues: *Coats, Ray* / Truck stop Lucy: *Crabb, Gene* / Prairie dog ramble: *Schroder, Andy* / Cowboy boogie: *Woodward, Red* / I don't get no lovin': *McBride, Dickie* / Right key: *Thomason, Jimmy* / Don't check out on me: *Thomason, Jimmy* / Whistlin' blues: *Dyson, Dick* / You waited too long blues: *Dyson, Dick* / Rag mop: *James, Jesse* / Adam's apple: *Prine, Richard* / Texas cowboy rag: *Christian, Ben* / Texas swing: *Davis, Link* / Diggin': *Jones, Dickie* / Seperate ration blues: *Freeman, Bill*

KKCD 24 / Sep '98 / Krazy Kat

☐ DIGIDOGHEADLOCK

Ich bin Auslander: *Pop Will Eat Itself* / Naked and ashamed: *Dylan Rhymes* / Adultury: *Ultraviolence* / Jahazralah: *Sensorium* / Crash pow: *Mad Capsule Markets* / Message: *Breed '77* / Bad faith: *Cassandra Complex* / Ah ah: *Moby* / Happy happy joy joy: *Disaster Area* / God is God: *Juno Reactor* / Chaos: *Nervosa* / Hiss: *London After Midnight* / Reviver gene: *Foil* / Shout: *Dominion* / Tarot: *Alien Sex Fiend* / Caged: *Randrere, Si*

JVC 90362 / 27 Jul '98 / JVC

☐ DIGITAL MENU

GAT 101 / 1 Sep '97 / Groove-A-Thon

☐ DIGITAL MILLENNIUM (2CD Set)

GPRDCD 18 / 13 Oct '97 / GPR

☐ DIGITAL SCIENCE

Quadrant 6: *Dom & Optical* / Circuit breaker: *Decoder* / Springbox: *Matrix & Dilemma* / Piper: *Jonny L* / Mutation: *Shimon & Andy C* / System: *DJ Kane* / Triton: *Future Force* / Time: *Vagrant* / Rest in space: *Mission Control* / Clockwork: *Spirit* / Vibrations: *Embee*

KICKCD 78 / 20 Apr '98 / Kickin'

☐ DIGNITY OF HUMAN BEING IS VULNERABLE

AWA 1993CD / May '93 / Konkurrel

☐ DILLINQUENTS GREEN, THE

DILL 1902/03 / 2 Mar '98 / Dill

☐ DILLINQUENTS RED, THE

DILL 020 / 2 Mar '98 / Dill

☐ DIM VIEW OF THE FUTURE

Hemza/Hotel d'amore: *Symphony of terror* / Cain or an opera vein: *Apocalypse Theatre* / Forever came today: *Shadow Project* / 3 peat: *Skull flux* / Hymn: *Filmstrip* / Underworld: *Nocturne* / What seeks the land: *Confession of Faith* / Anastasia: *Near Death experience* / Rajababa: *Needulhed* / Violence: *Diochotomy* / Assembalage of the desolate: *Hexenhaus* / ESP: *Morgana Athena* / Devout: *Funeral in Berlin*

TX 60005CD / 17 Aug '98 / Triple XXX

☐ DIMENSION VOL.2

EFA 200872 / Jul '95 / Trip Trap

☐ DIMENSIONE JAZZ

RTCL 810CD / Jul '96 / Right Tempo

☐ DINER (20 Rock 'n' Roll Classics)

Johnny B Goode: *Berry, Chuck* / See you later alligator: *Haley, Bill & The Comets* / Rock 'n' roll is here to stay: *Danny & The Juniors* / That'll be the day: *Holly, Buddy & The Crickets* / Bony moronie: *Williams, Larry* / Rave on: *Holly, Buddy* / Come go with me: *Del-Vikings* / Wonderful time up there: *Boone, Pat* / Seventeen: *Fontane Sisters* / Short shorts: *Royal Teens* / Shake rattle and roll: *Haley, Bill & The Comets* / Book of love: *Monotones* / Good golly Miss Molly: *Little Richard* / Stagger lee: *Price, Lloyd* / Ain't that a shame: *Boone, Pat* / Roll over Beethoven: *Berry, Chuck* / Black slack: *Bennett, Joe & The Sparkletones* / When: *Kalin Twins* / Rock rock rock: *Cavello, Jimmy & the House Rockers* / At the hop: *Danny & The Juniors*

ASTCD 4004 / Oct '97 / Go On Deluxe

☐ DINNER AT EIGHT (The Great London Dance Bands)

Dancing in the dark / Without rhythm / This'll make you whistle / Honey coloured moon / Star fell out of heaven / You turned the tables on me / You / I won't dance / It's easy to remember / Dinner at eight / My romance / Zing, went the strings of my heart / One, two, button your shoe / Toy trumpet / Soft lights and sweet music / Alone / Nice work if you can get it / When you've got a little springtime in your heart / Tinkle, tinkle, tinkle / Over my shoulder / Not bad / Here's to the next time / Auf wiedersehen, my dear / Smoke gets in your eyes / Keep a twinkle in your eye

PLCD 539 / Oct '95 / President

☐ DINNER JAZZ

MUSCD 024 / Nov '94 / MCI Music

☐ DINNER JAZZ AMERICAN CLASSICS

JAZZFMCD 1 / Oct '96 / Jazz FM

☐ DINNER JAZZ LOVE SONGS

My romance: *Tuck & Patti* / Don't explain: *Gordon, Dexter* / What is there to say: *Cole, Nat 'King'* / Certain smile: *Taylor, Martin* / But beautiful: *Alexandria, Lorez* / Falling in love again: *Ambrosetti, Franco* / Don't go to strangers: *Jones, Etta* / All the things you are: *Webster, Ben & Art Tatum* / Nearness of you: *Wilson, Nancy & George Shearing* / Close enough for love: *Dunlap, Bruce* / And I love you: *Krall, Diana* / When morning comes: *Reeves, Dianne*

JAZZFMCD 5 / 6 Oct '97 / Jazz FM

☐ DIRE TEMPO

RTCL 803CD / Jul '96 / Right Tempo

☐ DIRECT HITS FROM BULLSEYE

BB 9001CD / May '93 / Bullseye Blues

☐ DIRECTION

POLYVINYL 5CD / Nov '96 / Polyvinyl

☐ DIRECTION AFRICA (A Collection Of African Grooves From Celluloid)

CDNEW 106 / Apr '97 / Charly

☐ DIRTY HOUSE VOL.1

Indoctrinate: *Castle Trancelot* / Don't stop my beat: *Trigger* / Disco's revenge: *Gusto Love* / Danger zone: *Dangerous Society* / Rhythm graffitt: *Crime* / Things I like: *Aaliyah* / Driftwood: *Foot Club* / Shake your booty: *Ill Disco* / Rollerskate disco: *Pooley, Ian* / I just can't go: *Space Warlock* / Turn me on: *Brown, Kathy* / Never be the same: *Northbound* / I think about you: *King, Evelyn 'Champagne'*

CDHIGH 2 / Nov '95 / High On Rhythm

☐ DIRTY HOUSE VOL.2 (14 Tough Euro/ US/UK House Anthems - Mixed By DJ Bambach)

All of me: *Brunson, Tyrone & Chanelle* / On my knees: *Skiffle* / Satisfied: *H2O & Billie* / America: *Full Intention* / Work it out: *RIP Productions* / Screamer: *Yosh & Lovedeejay Akemi* / Feel good: *B-Code* / Jump for joy: *2 Unlimited* / Drop: *Mr. Whippy* / Wanna drop a house (on that bitch): *Urban Discharge & She* / I get high: *Upstate* / Remember me: *Jubb, Phil* / VII: *XVX* / Up and down: *D&T*

CDHIGH 3 / Jun '96 / High On Rhythm

☐ DIRTY ROCK VOL.1

KNEWCD 736 / Apr '94 / Kenwest

☐ DIRTY ROCK VOL.2

KNEWCD 737 / Apr '94 / Kenwest

☐ DISAGREEMENT OF THE PEOPLE, THE

Ain't but just one way: *Cope, Julian* / Justice/ Injustice: *Chumbawamba* / Guildford Four: *White, Andy* / Won't get fooled away: *McNabb, Ian* / Birmingham six: *Pogues* / All our trades: *Tabor, June* / How can you keep moving on: *McLeod, Rory* / Electro Ray's: *Back To The Planet* / Hobo: *Reservoir Frogs* / Men of England: *New Model Army & Joolz* / One green hill: *Oyster Band* / Babylon: *Det-Ri-Mental* / Clay jugg: *Leven, Jackie & Mike Scott* / Stonehenge: *Poison Girls* / Pastor Niemoler's lament (Never Again): *Kitchens Of Distinction* / Come dancing: *Credit To The Nation* / This land: *Bragg, Billy*

COOKCD 088 / Jun '95 / Cooking Vinyl

☐ DISAPPEARING WORLD, THE

CDSDL 376 / Mar '94 / Saydisc

☐ DISCO 2000 (The Last Hours Of 1999)

Sphere: *Blame* / High on the vine: *Plug* / Metal beatbox: *Witchman* / Atomic moog 2000: *Coldcut* / Millenium hand and shrimp: *u-Ziq* / Fuck the millenium: *2K* / Year of the apocalypse: *Tenor, Jimi* / Disco heist: *Glamorous Hooligan* / I'm a policeman: *Diskohead Kollective* / Let there be flutes: *Bentley Rhythm Ace* / Dust covered discotheque: *Conemelt* / Actio surrealisimo: *Ishii, Ken* / Disco 2029: *Alabama 3*

BOKA 002CD / Jun '98 / Abokadisc

☐ DISCO BISCUITS

HF 52CD / Mar '97 / PWL

☐ DISCO CLASSICS (2CD Set)

Going back to my roots: *Odyssey* / Shake your body: *Jacksons* / Funkytown: *Lipps Inc.* / Family affair: *Sly & The Family Stone* / September: *Earth, Wind & Fire* / Boogie nights: *Heatwave* / Never can say goodbye: *Gaynor, Gloria* / Lady Marmalade: *Labelle* / Jump to it: *Franklin, Aretha* / Night to remember: *Shalamar* / Love come down: *King, Evelyn 'Champagne'* / You make me feel (mighty real): *Sylvester* / I can't stand the rain: *Eruption* / Can you feel the force: *Real Thing* / System addict: *Five Star* / Automatic: *Pointer Sisters* / Shame: *King, Evelyn 'Champagne'* / Shaft: *Hayes, Isaac* / You're the first, my last, my everything: *White, Barry* / Disco nights: *GQ* / Low rider: *War* / I can make you feel good: *Shalamar* / Sing a simple song: *Sly & The Family Stone* / Dare me: *Pointer Sisters* / And the beat goes on: *Whispers* / Use it up, wear it up: *Odyssey* / Love really hurts without you: *Ocean, Billy* / Contact: *Starr, Edwin* / Ms. grace: *Tymes* / Giving up, giving in: *Three Degrees* / Is this a love thing: *Raydio* / Morning dance: *Spyro Gyra* / Rivers of Babylon: *Boney M* / You're more than a number in my little red book: *Drifters* / Rock the boat: *Hues Corporation* / Yes sir I can boogie: *Baccara*

RCACD 206 / Jul '97 / RCA

☐ DISCO COLLECTION, VOL.1 (I Will Survive)

I will survive: *Gaynor, Gloria* / Go west: *Village People* / Saddle up: *Christie, David* / Don't let me be misunderstood: *Gomez, Leroy Of Santa Esmeralda* / In Zaire: *Wakelin, Johnny* / What's your name what's your number: *True, Andrea* / Get ready: *Temptations* / I'm in the mood for dancing: *Nolans* / On the run (the battle is over): *Ocean, Billy* / Dancing in the street: *Reeves, Martha* / Feels like I'm in love: *Marie, Kelly* / Singing in the rain: *Taco* / It's been so long: *McCrae, George* / I wanna get next to you: *Royce, Rose*

101422 / May '97 / A-Play Collection

☐ DISCO COLLECTION, VOL.2 (Dance Little Lady Dance)

Dance little lady dance: *Charles, Tina* / Black superman (Muhammed Ali): *Wakelin, Johnny* / I wish it would rain: *Temptations* / Wishing on a star: *Royce, Rose* / Jimmy mack: *Reeves, Martha* / Macho man: *Village People* / Living it up: *Christie, David* / Never can say goodbye: *Gaynor, Gloria* / Puttin' on the ritz: *Taco* / Clapping song: *Humphries, Les Singers* / Get dancin': *Disco Tex & The Sexolettes* / Don't take away the music: *Tavares* / Whose little girl is you: *Ocean, Billy* / Disco kid: *First Class*

101432 / May '97 / A-Play Collection

☐ DISCO COLLECTION, VOL.3 (In The Navy)

In the navy: *Village People* / More more more: *True, Andrea* / Knock on wood: *Floyd, Eddie* / Attention to me: *Nolans* / Rock your baby: *McCrae, George* / Oh what a night: *Dells* / Reach out I'll be there: *Gaynor, Gloria* / Dance dance dance: *Humphries, Les Singers* / I love to love: *Charles, Tina* / Wake up everybody: *Melvin, Harold & The Bluenotes* / Car wash: *Royce, Rose* / Heatwave: *Reeves, Martha* / It only takes a minute: *Tavares* / Be my baby: *Svenne & Lotta*

101442 / May '97 / A-Play Collection

☐ DISCO CONNECTION VOL.1

Got a feeling: *Jungle Jive* / Can't get high without you: *Joey Negro & Taka Boom* / Kinky kut: *S&M* / Gotta get up: *Flashback Of A Genius* / Bamboogie: *Bamboo* / Two tons of Doug: *Willis, Doug* / Dancing in outer space: *Atmosfear* / When u touch me: *Big Bang Theory & Carolyn Harding* / Motion picture: *Aquarius Recordings* / Disco dance: *Maceo & Matos* / French boy: *Garcons* / Smokin' daughter: *Jeep Grrlz* / Something I feel: *Mateo & Matos* / Breakin' the 90's: *Krieg, Marcel* / Get on down: *Boogie Man* / Cosmic funk: *Ducane, Joey & Arthur Baker* / After hours: *Plain Lazy*

SUB 48672 / 9 Feb '98 / Polyester

☐ DISCO DIVAS

I will survive: *Gaynor, Gloria* / Ring my bell: *Ward, Anita* / High energy: *Thomas, Evelyn* / Givin' up givin' in: *True, Andrea* / Stoned love: *Supremes* / Band of gold: *Payne, Freda* / Don't get mad get even: *Wilson, Mary* / So many men so little time: *Brown, Miquel* / Feels like I'm in love: *Marie, Kelly* / Who's crying now: *Sims, Joyce* / Somebody else's guy: *Brown, Jocelyn* / Hit 'n' run lover: *Jiani, Carol* / They say it's gonna rain: *Dean, Hazell* / I can't dance to that music you're playin': *Syreeta* / Loving just for fun: *Marie, Kelly* / I wanna make it on my own: *Thomas, Evelyn* / I am what I am: *Gaynor, Gloria*

ECD 3405 / Feb '98 / K-Tel

☐ DISCO EXPLOSION

GRF 211 / Apr '93 / Tring

☐ DISCO FEVER (4CD Set)

Feels like I'm in love: *Marie, Kelly* / Dance little lady dance: *Charles, Tina* / Rock your baby: *McCrae, George* / Kung fu fighting: *Douglas, Carl* / Cuba: *Gibson Brothers* / I wanna dance wit choo: *Disco Tex & The Sexolettes* / Boys: *Sabrina* / Summer of '42: *Biddu Orchestra* / High energy: *Thomas, Evelyn* / Love I lost: *Melvin, Harold & The Bluenotes* / More more more: *True, Andrea* / Hey there, lonely girl: *Holman, Eddie* / Reach out I'll be there: *Gaynor, Gloria* / Now is the time: *James, Jimmy & The*

Vagabonds / Hands up: Ottawan / You little trustmaker: Tymes / So many men, so little time: Brown, Miquel / Runner: Three Degrees / My hearts beating wild (tic tac tic tac): Gibson Brothers / Hold back the night: Trammps / DISCO: Ottawan / I'm on fire: 5000 Volts / Boogie nights: Heatwave / On a crowded street: Pennington, Barbara / I will survive: Gaynor, Gloria / It's been so long: McCrae, George / Ooh what a life: Gibson Brothers / All of me: Sabrina / Rain forest: Biddu Orchestra / He's a saint, he's a sinner: Brown, Miquel / Hey girl don't bother me: Tams / Disco fever: James, Jimmy & The Vagabonds / Look back over your shoulder: Bell, Archie & The Drells / Love's gone mad: Seventh Avenue / Wake up everybody: Melvin, Harold & The Bluenotes / My simple heart: Three Degrees / If you want it (do it yourself): Gaynor, Gloria / Fairytales: Charles, Tina / Latin america: Gibson Brothers / Dance the kung fu: Douglas, Carl / I love to love: Charles, Tina / Better do it salsa: Gibson Brothers / Saddle up: Christie, David / I am what I am: Gaynor, Gloria / Get dancin': Disco Tex & The Sexolettes / Fan the flame: Pennington, Barbara / Always and forever: Heatwave / You're ok: Ottawan / Run back: Douglas, Carl / Close to perfection: Brown, Miquel / I can't leave you alone: McCrae, George / Love really hurts without you: Ocean, Billy / Satisfaction guaranteed: Melvin, Harold & The Bluenotes / Don't stop till you get enough: Ashaye / You to me are everything: Real Thing / My claim to fame: Wells, James / Treat her like a lady: Cornelius Brothers / Masquerade: Thomas, Evelyn / Trippin' on a soul cloud: Biddu Orchestra / Dancin' on a Saturday night: Blue, Barry / Ring my bell: Ward, Anita / Que sera mi vida: Gibson Brothers / Love train: Three Degrees & Harold Melvin / Stress: Christie, David / Can't take my eyes off you: Gaynor, Gloria / Do it any way you wanna: People's Choice / Metropolis: Gibson Brothers / Heartless: Thomas, Evelyn / If you don't know me by now: Melvin, Harold & The Bluenotes / Help me get some help: Ottawan / Hey girl: James, Jimmy & The Vagabonds / Reaching for the best: Exciters / Twenty four hours a day: Pennington, Barbara / Mariana: Gibson Brothers / Reflections: Thomas, Evelyn / Doctor's orders: Sabrina / Love I lost: Seventh Avenue / When will I see you again: Three Degrees / I'll go where the music takes me: James, Jimmy & The Vagabonds / Never can say goodbye: Gaynor, Gloria
TFP 031 / Jan '95 / Tring

☐ DISCO FEVER (18 All-Time Dancefloor Favourites)
Feels like I'm in love: Marie, Kelly / Hang on in there baby: Bristol, Johnny / I will survive: Gaynor, Gloria / Feel the need in me: Detroit Emeralds / Band of gold: Payne, Freda / Rock your baby: McCrae, George / You little trustmaker: Tymes / Heaven must have sent you: Elgins / Harlem shuffle: Bob & Earl / High energy: Thomas, Evelyn / Nathan Jones: Supremes / Going back to my roots: Odyssey / More, more, more: True, Andrea / Hey girl don't bother me: Tams / Knock on wood: Floyd, Eddie / Ring my bell: Ward, Anita / Heaven must be missing an angel: Tavares / Frankie: Sister Sledge
ECD 3257 / Feb '97 / K-Tel

☐ DISCO FEVER (2CD Set)
Ain't no stopping us now: McFadden & Whitehead / Lady love: Rawls, Lou / Don't let me be misunderstood: Santa Esmeralda / You sexy thing: Hot Chocolate / If you can't give me love: Quatro, Suzi / When you're in love with a beautiful woman: Dr. Hook / Movie star: Harpo / Heaven must be missing an angel: Tavares / One for you one for me: La Bionda / Some girls: Racey / Gonna get along without you now: Wills, Viola / Baker Street: Rafferty, Gerry / That's the way I like it: KC & The Sunshine Band / Pick up the pieces: Average White Band / Where is the love: Delegation / You and me: Spargo / Feels like I'm in love: Marie, Kelly / Sexy eyes: Dr. Hook / Everyone's a winner: Hot Chocolate / Girls: Moments & Whatnauts / Rapper's delight: Sugar Hill Gang / You to me are everything: Real Thing / Rock your baby: McCrae, George / Dancing in the city: Hain, Marshall / Please don't go: KC & The Sunshine Band / Kung fu fighting: Douglas, Carl / Hold back the night: Trammps / You make me feel like dancing: Sayer, Leo / If you could read my mind: Wills, Viola / Darlin': Miller, Frankie
DOU 878242 / 2 Feb '98 / Disky

☐ DISCO FOX VOL.4
ZYX 810912 / Feb '97 / ZYX

☐ DISCO GENERATION (2CD Set)
Don't let me be misunderstood: Santa Esmeralda / Move your feet: Hithouse / Motorcity mix: Beatsamatic / Living on video: Trans X / Let's all chant: Zager, Michael / Walk in the park: Straker, Nick / Let your love flow: Bellamy Brothers / Love is in the air: Young, John Paul / Knock on wood: Stewart, Amii / I'm on fire: 5000 Volts / Dreams are ten a penny: Kincaid / Under the moon of love: Showaddywaddy / I'm the leader of the gang: Glitter, Gary / Kung fu fighting: Douglas, Carl / Typically tropical: Barbados / Two man sound: Brown, Charlie / Paloma blanca: Baker, George Selection / Bino: Mama Leone / Live is life: Opus / Rain in May: Werner, Max / Jeans on: Dundas, David / Get down: O'Sullivan, Gilbert / Substitute: Clout / Standing in the rain: Young, John Paul / Love me like a lover: Charles, Tina / Disco stomp: Bohannon / Miss Broadway: Belle Epoque / Fire in the night: Hotshots / Dance all night: Block / Yes sir I can boogie: Baccara / Ooh, yes I do: Luv / Sun of Jamaica: Goombay Dance Band / It's a heartache: Tyler, Bonnie / More than I can say: Sayer, Leo / Train to yesterday: Christie, Tony / Tried so hard: Outsiders
24345 / Feb '97 / Laserlight

☐ DISCO INFERNO
I wanna dance wit' choo: Disco Tex & The Sexolettes / Ring my bell: Ward, Anita / I will survive: Gaynor, Gloria / Kung fu fighting: Douglas, Carl / Dance little lady dance: Charles, Tina / Rain forest: Biddu Orchestra / I'll go where your music takes me: James, Jimmy & The Vagabonds / Hold back the night: Trammps / Reaching for the best: Exciters / (Dancing) on a Saturday night: Blue, Barry / Saddle up: Christie, David / Band of gold: Payne, Freda / Run back: Douglas, Carl / I love to love (but my baby just loves to dance): Charles, Tina / Love really hurts without you: Ocean, Billy / Boogie nights: Heatwave
QED 048 / Nov '96 / Tring

☐ DISCO INFERNO VOL.1
Lost in music: Sister Sledge / Le Freak: Chic / You make me feel (Mighty real): Sylvester / I'm every woman: Khan, Chaka / Young hearts run free: Staton, Candi / Is it love you're after: Rose Royce / Jump to the beat: Lattisaw, Stacy / Working my way back to you: Detroit Spinners / Here I go again: Bell, Archie / Supernature: Cerrone / Disco Inferno: Trammps / Dance, dance, dance: Chic / Nights on Broadway: Staton, Candi / Lover's holiday: Change / I shoulda loved ya: Walden, Narada Michael / Then came you: Warwick, Dionne & The Detroit Spinners / Spacer: Sheila B. Devotion / Searching: Change / We are family: Sister Sledge / Shaft: Hayes, Isaac
9548319632 / Jul '95 / East West

☐ DISCO INFERNO VOL.2
Shame: King, Evelyn 'Champagne' / Funkin' for Jamaica: Browne, Tom / Thinking of you: Sister Sledge / Native New Yorker: Odyssey / I'll be around: Detroit Spinners / Keep the fire burning: McCrae, Gwen / Love has come around: Byrd, Donald / You're a star: Aquarian Dream / Southern Freeez: Freeez / He's the greatest dancer: Sister Sledge / Everybody dance: Chic / It makes you feel like dancin': Rose Royce / Just a touch of love: Slave / Glow of love: Change / Ghetto child: Detroit Spinners / Funky nassau: Beginning Of The End / Get up and boogie: Silver Convention / Funky sensation: McCrae, Gwen / Forget me nots: Rushen, Patrice
9548324232 / Dec '93 / East West

☐ DISCO JUICE (2CD Set)
CDNEW 1092 / Aug '97 / Charly

☐ DISCO MIX '96 (2CD Set)
Lady marmalade / Going back to my roots / Hustle / Young hearts run free / Disco inferno / Rasputin / If I can't have you / Blame it on the boogie / Ring my bell / Working my way back to you forgive me girl / I feel love / Boogie nights / Theme from shaft / I o u / Ain't nobody / Forget me nots / Play that funky music / You make me feel (mighty real) / Let's groove / Use it up and wear it out / Heaven must be missing an angel / You to me are everything / That's the way (i like it) / Funkytown / And the beat goes on / I will survive / Boogie wonderland / Boogie oogie oogie / Yes sir I can boogie / Celebration / Best of my love / Night to remember / Jump to the beat / Hang on in there baby / Is it love you're after / Good times / We are family / Lost in music / Le freak / I'm every woman
9548348072 / Oct '96 / Warner Bros.

☐ DISCO MIXES
JHD 087 / Mar '93 / Tring

☐ DISCO MOONLIGHT
Fyonk: Freeform / Pink beanie: Dunderhead / Nomad: Farmer's Manual / Stealth: Survivors / Blue haze: Plasma Lamp / Toilet seat: Milky Boy / Stochast: Valard, Rook / Departure: Baraki / Steps: Asphere / Celesta: Kristian, David
WI 011 / 3 Nov '97 / Worm Interface

☐ DISCO NIGHTS
Disco nights: GQ / Car wash: Rose Royce / Boogie wonderland: Earth, Wind & Fire / Rock the boat: Hues Corporation / Use it up wear it out: Odyssey / Turn the beat around: Robinson, Vickie Sue / Ms. Grace: Tymes / Which way is up: Starguard / Shame: King, Evelyn / Instant replay: Hartman, Dan / Hi fidelity: Kids from Fame / Daddy cool: Boney M / One way ticket: Eruption / Givin' up givin' in: Three Degrees / You're more than a number in my little red book: Drifters / Disco lady: Taylor, Johnny / Everybody up: Ohio Players / YMCA: Village People
74321290382 / Feb '97 / Ariola

☐ DISCO NIGHTS
Going back to my roots: Odyssey / Celebration: Kool & The Gang / High energy: Thomas, Evelyn / Feels like I'm in love: Marie, Kelly / Get dancin': Bombers / Don't stop the music: Carroll, Dina / Something old, something new: Fantastics / So many men, so little time: Brown, Miquel / He's the greatest dancer: Sister Sledge / Armed and extremely dangerous: M-Brace / Don't stop till you get enough: Ashaye / Is it love you're after: Rose Royce / Footsteps following me: Nero, Frances / Love machine: Miracles / Ladies night: Kool & The Gang / Get down on it: Kool & The Gang / Heaven must have sent you: Elgins / We are family: Sister Sledge
CD 6086 / Aug '97 / Music

☐ DISCO PARTY
That's the way I like it: KC & The Sunshine Band / Dance across the floor: Horne, Jimmy 'Bo' / One for you one for me: La Bionda / Heaven must be missing an angel: Tavares / This is my life: Bassey, Shirley / Get off: Foxy / Hot shot: Young, Karen / Ring my bell: Ward, Anita / Follow me: Lear, Amanda / Saddle up: Christie, David / Gonna get along without you now: Wills, Viola / Can you feel the force: Real Thing / Let's all chant: Zager, Michael Band / Feels like I'm in love: Marie, Kelly / Do it: BT Express / Swing your daddy: Gilstrap, Jim
DC 880272 / Jul '97 / Disky

☐ DISCO PLATES VOL.1
ONUCD 12 / 9 Feb '98 / On-U Sound

☐ DISCO SEXY (2CD Set)
I can make you feel good: Shalamar / Shame shame shame: Shirley & Company / Red light spells danger: Ocean, Billy / Think I'm gonna fall in love with you: Dooleys / Smarty pants: First Choice / Contact: Starr, Edwin / Hold on to my love: Ruffin, Jimmy / Mr. Tamborine man: Johnson, Johnny & Bandwagon / Love I lost: Melvin, Harold & The Bluenotes / Yes sir I can boogie: Baccara / I'm gonna run away from you: Lynn, Tammi / Everybody plays the fool: Main Ingredient / Spacer: Sheila B. Devotion / Sound of Philadelphia: MFSB / More, more, more: True, Andrea Connection / Everything's Tuesday: Chairmen Of The Board / New York, New York: Kenny, Gerard / Jump to the beat: Lattisaw, Stacy / Let's go round again: Average White Band / Hallelujah freedom: Campbell, Junior / Funkytown: Lipps Inc. / Hustle: McCoy, Van / Nights on Broadway: Staton, Candi / Queen of the rapping scene: Modern Romance / Pillow talk: Sylvia / Lincoln county: Love Affair / La la means I love you: Delfonics / You're more than a number in my little red book: Drifters / Baby blue: Springfield, Dusty / Jack and Jill: Raydio / I love to love (but my baby just loves to dance): Charles, Tina / All I have to do is dream: Matthews, Al / It's up to you Petula: Edison Lighthouse / Feel the need in me: Detroit Emeralds / Candida: Dawn / Come back and shake me: Rodgers, Clodagh / Galaxy of love: Crown Heights Affair / Mind blowing decisions: Heatwave / Intuition: Linx / Jack in the box: Moments
3036400292 / Mar '97 / Carlton

☐ DISCO SUBVERSION VOL.1 (2CD Set)
FIM 1020 / May '96 / Force Inc.

☐ DISCO SUBVERSION VOL.2
EFA 044282 / 15 Jun '98 / Force Inc.

☐ DISCO SUCKS
CHE 60CD / Jul '96 / Che

☐ DISCO TECH
Papillon: Vandross, Luther & Cissy Houston / More more more: Vandross, Luther & Cissy Houston / Paradise: Vandross, Luther & Cissy Houston / Chains: Vandross, Luther & Cissy Houston / Cream always rises to the top: Vandross, Luther & Cissy Houston / More more more: True, Andrea Connection & Samantha Fox / Hot butterfly: Khan, Chaka / Risky changes: Bionic Boogie Band / Starcruiser: Starcruiser Band / Fancy dancer: Starcruiser Band / Tiger tiger: Vandross, Luther & Cissy Houston / Crazy lady luck: Vandross, Luther / Most of all: Gaynor, Gloria / More more more: Bananarama
CDPS 001 / 27 Mar '98 / Pulsar

☐ DISCO-VERED
ALMYCD 21 / 1 Sep '97 / Almighty

☐ DISCOTECA COLLECTION, THE (Missao De Pesquisas Folcloricas)
RCD 10403 / 22 Sep '97 / Rykodisc

☐ DISCOVER NARADA
From the forge to the field: Arkenstone, David & Kostia/David Lanz / Day by day by day: Mann, Brian / Americana: Rubaja, Bernardo / Behind the waterfall/ Desert rain: Lanz, David / Rug merchant: Arkenstone, David / Millennium theme: Zimmer, Hans / Seven days: Kolbe, Martin / Parterre: Tingstad, Eric & Nancy Rumbel / Simple joys: Souther, Richard / Overture: Mirowitz, Sheldon / Lament for Hetch Hetchy: Fraser, Alasdair / New Amazon: Junior Homrich / Stand and water: Kostia / Nebraska: Buffett, Peter / Hawk: Trapezoid / Endings: Jones, Michael
CD 9002 / Jun '92 / Narada

☐ DISCOVER NARADA VOL.2
ND 69008 / Nov '93 / Narada

☐ DISCOVER SCOTLAND VOL.1
Original: Carmichael, John & His Band / Kathleen's reel: Carmichael, John & His Band / Bauaria: Carmichael, John & His Band / Dixie: Carmichael, John & His Band / Do you think you could love me again: MacLeod, Jim & His Band / Skye boat song: Scott, Tommy Strings of Scot / Richmora: Oakbank Sound / Pomander jig: Oakbank Sound / Wee sergeant: Oakbank Sound / Rab Smillies JG: Oakbank Sound / Maggie: Gillies, Alasdair / Silver darlin': Marlettes / Marie's wedding: Garden, Bill & His Highland Fiddle Orchestra / Vist tramping songs: Garden, Bill & His Highland Fiddle Orchestra / Marquis of Huntly: Garden, Bill & His Highland Fiddle Orchestra / Roxburgh Castle: Garden, Bill & His Highland Fiddle Orchestra / Scotland the brave: Garden, Bill & His Highland Fiddle Orchestra / From Scotland with love: Scott, Tommy Strings of Scot / Wild mountain thyme: Marlettes / Marching through the heather: Frazer, Grant / Johnny lad: Frazer, Grant / Flower of Scotland: Frazer, Grant / Jig time: Garden, Bill & His Highland Fiddle Orchestra / McFlannels: Garden, Bill & His Highland Fiddle Orchestra / Para Handy: Garden, Bill & His Highland Fiddle Orchestra / Man's a man for a' that: Harper, Addie & The Wick Trio / Scots wha hae: Harper, Addie & The Wick Trio / Auld lang syne: Harper, Addie & The Wick Trio / I love a lassie: Anderson, Stuart / Roamin' in the gloamin': Anderson, Stuart / Wee Deoch an' Doris: Anderson, Stuart / Stop your ticklin' Jock: Anderson, Stuart / Keep right on to the end of the road: Anderson, Stuart / Denny and Dunipace Pipe Band: Denny & Dunipace Pipe Band / Major Bobby: Denny & Dunipace Pipe Band / Muckin' o' Geordie's byre: Denny & Dunipace Pipe Band / Glendaurel highlanders: Denny & Dunipace Pipe Band / Bonnie Dundee: Denny & Dunipace Pipe Band
CDITV 428 / Aug '88 / Scotdisc

☐ DISCOVERED
ALMYCD 24 / 13 Apr '98 / Almighty

☐ DISCOVERED '97
SUGA 14CD / May '97 / Sugar

☐ DISCOVERING FRANCE (4CD Set)
B 6852 / Dec '97 / Auvidis/Ethnic

☐ DISKO KUGEL DORTMUND (2CD Set)
DRAFTCD 001 / 9 Mar '98 / Draft

☐ DISRAELI YEARS (5CD Set)
DTKBOX 69 / 1 Jun '98 / Dressed To Kill

☐ DISTANCE TO ACID TRANCE VOL.1
DI 192 / Dec '95 / Distance

☐ DISTANCE TO ACID TRANCE VOL.2
SUB 48102 / Jul '96 / Distance

☐ DISTANCE TO GOA VOL.1
DI 152 / Dec '95 / Distance

☐ DISTANCE TO GOA VOL.2
DI 172 / Dec '95 / Distance

☐ DISTANCE TO GOA VOL.3 (2CD Set)
SUB 48022 / Mar '96 / Distance

☐ DISTANCE TO GOA VOL.4
SUB 48169 / Jul '96 / Distance

☐ DISTANCE TO GOA VOL.5 (2CD Set)
Deranger: Hallucinogen / Stardiver: Electric Universe / Phenomena: Miranda / Wizard: Deedrah / Lepton Head: Shakta / Land of freedom: Transwave / Dreampod: Psychopod / Hybrid: Eat Static / Walk on the moon: Antidote / Spiral spit trick: Katayama / Chitty bang: Ololluqut / Liquid: Orion / Free return: Alienated / Simplicity: Project System / I wanna expand: Cwithe / Radio SPACE: Electric Universe / Malaka dance: Transwave / Alien pets: Prana / SPQR: Shiva Chandra / Reefer madness: Lunar Asylum
SUB 48352 / Apr '97 / Distance

☐ DISTANCE TO HAPPY TRANCE - THE ENERGISER
DI 232 / Dec '95 / Distance

☐ DISTANCE TO TECHNOLAND (2CD Set)
SUB 48179 / Nov '96 / Distance

☐ DISTORTION TO HELL
DISTCD 5 / Oct '94 / Distortion

☐ DISTORTION TO HELL AGAIN
DISTCD 16 / Feb '96 / Distortion

☐ DISTURB MY SOUL (Gospel From Stax Records' Chalice Label)
Assassination: Dixie Nightingales / Nail print: Dixie Nightingales / Hush hush: Dixie Nightingales / He's a friend of mine: Jubilee Hummingbirds / Our freedom song: Jubilee Hummingbirds / All I need is some sunshine in my life: Dixie Nightingales / I don't know: Dixie Nightingales / All these things to me: Stars Of Virginia / Wade in the water: Stars Of Virginia / God's promise: Pattersonaires / I learned to pray: Pattersonaires / Stop laughing at your fellow man: Jubilee Hummingbirds / Jesus will fix it: Jubilee Hummingbirds / This is our prayer: Dixie Nightingales / It comes at the end of the race: Dixie Nightingales / He's worthy: Pattersonaires / Child of God: Pattersonaires / Till Jesus comes: Pattersonaires / Give me one more chance: Jubilee Hummingbirds / Press my dying pillow: Jubilee Hummingbirds / There's not a friend: Dixie Nightingales / Forgive these fools: Dixie Nightingales / Son of God: Stars Of Virginia / Even me: Stars Of Virginia
CDSXD 086 / Feb '94 / Stax

☐ DIVA
Fever: Lee, Peggy / Wild is the wind: Simone, Nina / Crazy: Starr, Kay / Stormy weather: Vaughan, Sarah / Cry me a river: London, Julie / It had to be you: Shore, Dinah / Fifty ways to leave ways: Clooney, Rosemary / I get along without you very well: Clooney, Rosemary / Too close for comfort: Kitt, Eartha / I'm a woman: Lee, Peggy / Big spender: Bassey, Shirley / Bell bottom blues: Cogan, Alma / Fly me to the moon: Vaughan, Sarah / Heatwave: Boswell, Eve / Is you is or is you ain't my baby: Washington, Dinah / My funny valentine: Shore, Dinah
4935842 / 16 Feb '98 / EMI Gold

☐ DIVA X MACHINA
COPCD 027 / May '97 / Cop International

☐ DIVANA (Music Of Rajasthan Vol.2)
3018632 / Feb '97 / Long Distance

☐ DIVAS
MOTCCD 67 / Oct '92 / Motor City

☐ DIVAS EN ROOTS
ARICD 089 / Jul '96 / Ariwa Sounds

☐ DIVAS OF JAZZ SING (20 Classics)
CWNCD 2027 / Jul '96 / Javelin

☐ DIVAS OF MALI (Great Vocal Performances From A Fabled Land)
Sekou semega: Damba, Fanta / Banga diabate: Kouyate, Tata Bambo / Kotuba: Koita, Ami / Djina Moussou: Doumbia, Nahawa / Youcoba sylla: Sidibe, Sali / Jakha: Kouyate, Kandia / Karamoko: Kouyate, Sanougoue
SH 64078 / Dec '96 / Shanachie

☐ DIVINE DIVAS (3CD Set)
Tierradentro: Gomez, Claudia / La sombra negra: La Mompasina, Toto / Rain song: Burch, Sharon / Femmes d'Afrique: Bell, Nayanka & Tshala Muana/ Djanka Diabate / Comment te dire adieu: Hardy, Francoise / Dejame llorar: Hinojosa, Tish / Canto di Hecate: Belloni, Alessandra / Your scarf will not hold your hair: Leskaj, Zana & Luljeta Hia / Mai kai no kauai: Moe, Rose / Emo neuvoi: MeNaiset / Amazing grace: Di Franco, Ani / Foggy dew: O'Sullivan, Cathie / Dejate amar: India / Laban Ko: Doumbia, Nahawa / Receita de samba: Joyce / Jheel mai chand: Najma / Maria Lando: Baca, Susana / Ya habibi: Maideh, Malouma Mint / Wayala: Fadela, Cheb & Cheb Sahraoui / Baby, now that I've found you: Krauss, Alison / Thugamar fein an samradh linn: Ni Riain, Noirin / Sorban palid: Kurnia, Detty / Lamara: Bel, M'Bilia / Stepping out of babylon: Griffiths, Marcia / Illoqarfik: Marina / Durme hermoza donzella: Frankel, Judy / Come on in my kitchen: Wilson, Cassandra / Sekusile: Dark City Sisters / La Guyanaise: Cedia, Sylviane / Mango mangue: Valdes, Merceditas / Mal' de amor: Saozinha / Prisoner's song: Molnar, Eva & Vasmalom / Moritat: Krause, Dagmar / Sudden waves: Tabor, June / Viento Pasajero: Junaro, Emma / Navai: Deyhim, Sussan / Souffle van: Bissainthe, Toto
ROUCD 507123 / Mar '97 / Rounder

☐ DIVINE INSPIRATION
Witness: Mindjuice / Guardian angel: J-Faktor / Memories: GNA / Saviour: Peaches / Star: Stroppy / Free again: Shin / Space I'm in: Explain / You be you: Ratfink / Sweet and sour: Cloud / Stine: Bellatrix / Out of reach: Crimson / Atom bomb: Know It Alls
SEMACD 001 / 28 Jul '98 / SEM

☐ DIWAN OF BISKRA, THE (Music From Algeria)
C 5560088 / Jan '97 / Ocora

☐ DIX IMPROVISATIONS - VICTORIAVILLE 1989
VICTOCD 09 / Nov '94 / Victo

☐ DIXIELAND
490311 / Jul '95 / RCA

☐ **DIXIELAND**
Dixieland jazz band one-step: *Original Dixieland Jazz Band* / Maple leaf rag: *Bechet, Sidney* / Weary blues: *Spanier, Muggsy & His Ragtimers* / Ostrich walk: *Original Dixieland Jazz Band* / High society: *Spanier, Muggsy & His Ragtimers* / Big butter and egg man: *Spanier, Muggsy & His Ragtimers* / Tiger rag: *Original Dixieland Jazz Band* / Indian summer: *Bechet, Sidney* / Sensation rag: *Original Dixieland Jazz Band* / At the Jazz Band hall: *Bechet, Sidney* / Margie: *Original Dixieland Jazz Band* / Muskrat ramble: *Spanier, Muggsy & His Ragtimers* / Broadway rose: *Original Dixieland Jazz Band* / Jazz me blues: *Original Dixieland Jazz Band* / (What did I do to be so) Black and blue: *Spanier, Muggsy & His Ragtimers* / St. Louis blues: *Original Dixieland Jazz Band* / Twelfth Street rag: *Bechet, Sidney*
74321584822 / Jun '98 / RCA Victor

☐ **DIXIELAND FAVOURITES**
Muskrat ramble / Canal street blues / When you're smiling / Doctor Jazz / Tishomingo blues / Black and blues / I want a big butter and egg man / Memphis blues / At the jazz band ball / Do you know what it means to miss New Orleans / Just a closer walk with thee / High society / Maple leaf rag / When you wore a tulip (and I wore a big red rose)
EMPRCD 521 / Oct '94 / Emporio

☐ **DIXIELAND FAVOURITES**
Make up my mind: *Teagarden, Jack* / Prelude in C minor: *Teagarden, Jack* / Original Dixieland one step: *Teagarden, Jack* / High society: *Teagarden, Jack* / Shine: *Teagarden, Jack* / Down by the riverside: *Jones, Jonah* / Beale street blues: *Jones, Jonah* / Sheik of Araby: *Jones, Jonah* / California here I come: *Russell, Pee Wee* / Love is here to stay: *Russell, Pee Wee* / Coquette: *Russell, Pee Wee* / Royal garden blues: *Hunt, Pee Wee* / After you've gone: *Hunt, Pee Wee* / Basin street blues: *Hunt, Pee Wee* / Creole love call: *Ory, Kid* / Muskrat rumble: *Ory, Kid* / That's a plenty: *Ory, Kid* / At the Jazz Band Ball: *Spanier, Muggsy* / Sugar foot stomp: *Spanier, Muggsy* / Dinah: *Spanier, Muggsy*
SUMCD 4107 / Mar '97 / Summit

☐ **DIXIELAND JAZZ - THE COLLECTION**
Tiger rag: *Original Dixieland Jazz Band* / Look at 'em doing it now: *Original Dixieland Jazz Band* / Copenhagen: *Wolverine Orchestra* / Careless love: *Original Tuxedo Jazz Orchestra* / She's crying for me: *Original New Orleans Rhythm Kings* / That's no bargain: *Nichols, Red & His Five Pennies* / Way down yonder in New Orleans: *Trumbauer, Frank & His Orchestra* / I'm more than satisfied: *Chicago Loopers* / Royal goden blues: *Beiderbecke, Bix & His Gang* / Nobody's sweetheart: *McKenzie & Condon's Chicagoans* / Coquette: *Whiteman, Paul & His Orchestra* / I found a new baby: *Chicago Rhythm Kings* / There'll be some changes made: *Chicago Rhythm Kings* / Shake your can: *Dodds, Johnny* / Moanin' low: *Mole, Miff Molers* / Strut Miss Lizzie: *Mills, Irving & His Hotsy Totsy Gang* / Georgia on my mind: *Carmichael, Hoagy Orchestra* / After you've gone: *Venuti-Lang All Stars* / Spider crawl: *Banks, Billy & His Orchestra* / Eel: *Condon, Eddie & His Orchestra* / When the saints go marching in: *Armstrong, Louis* / At the jazz band ball: *Rhythm Cats* / Relaxin' at the touro: *Spanier, Muggsy* / Muskrat ramble: *Armstrong, Louis*
QED 101 / Nov '96 / Tring

☐ **DIXIELAND JUBILEE (2CD Set)**
DBG 53030 / Jan '94 / Double Gold

☐ **DIXIELAND TO SWING GOLD (2CD Set)**
R2CD 4009 / 13 Apr '98 / Deja Vu

☐ **DIXIELAND VOL.1**
Joshua fit de battle of Jericho: *Original Dixieland Stompers* / When the saints: *Original Dixieland Stompers* / Buddy Bolden blues: *Original Dixieland Stompers* / Sweet Georgia Brown: *Brixie Dixie Jazz Band* / When you're smiling: *Brixie Dixie Jazz Band* / Honeysuckle rose: *Brixie Dixie Jazz Band* / Down by the riverside: *Original Dixieland Stompers* / Go tell it to the mountains: *Original Dixieland Stompers* / Lizzy's rag: *Original Dixieland Stompers* / I want a little girl: *Brixie Dixie Jazz Band* / When my sugar walks down the street: *Brixie Dixie Jazz Band* / Georgia: *Dutch Swing College Band* / Bad, bad Leroy Brown: *Dutch Swing College Band* / Play it to me: *Original Dixieland Stompers* / Champs Elysses: *Dutch Swing College Band* / Ice cream: *Brixie Dixie Jazz Band*
12460 / Nov '95 / Laserlight

☐ **DIXIELAND VOL.2**
Midnight in Moscow: *Ball, Kenny* / Riverboat shuffle: *Dukes Of Dixieland* / Winin' boy blues: *Dukes Of Dixieland & Danny Barker* / Eh, la bas: *Original Dixieland Stompers* / My bonnie is over the ocean: *Original Dixieland Stompers* / Black roses blues: *Original Dixieland Stompers* / It's a plenty: *Brixie Dixie Jazz Band* / Somebody loves me: *Brixie Dixie Jazz Band* / March of the Siamese children: *Ball, Kenny* / Alexander's ragtime band: *Dukes Of Dixieland* / Bugle call blues: *Original Dixieland Stompers* / CC rider: *Original Dixieland Stompers* / Basin Street blues: *Brixie Dixie Jazz Band* / Raggie time: *Original Dixieland Stompers* / Casey Jones: *Station Hall Jazz Band* / Over in the Gloryland: *Original Dixieland Stompers*
12461 / Nov '95 / Laserlight

☐ **DJ BOX VOL.1, THE (40 Drum & Bass Anthems) (3CD Set)**
BDRCD 12 / Apr '96 / Breakdown

☐ **DJ BOX VOL.2, THE (40 Drum 'n' Bass Anthems/3CD Set)**
BDRCD 18 / Nov '96 / Breakdown

☐ **DJ CULTURE VOL.1 (Vintage Mixes 1992-1994/Sasha/Seaman/Digweed/ 2CD Set))**
STRMIX 1CD / Sep '96 / Stress

☐ **DJ CULTURE VOL.2 (Mixed By Seaman/Whitehead/Warren) (3CD Set)**
STRMIX 2CD / Sep '96 / Stress

☐ **DJ CULTURE VOL.3 (Mixed By Kaye/ Bouthier/Pappa/3CD Set)**
Orange sunshine: *Superstars Of Rock* / Coming home: *Visions & Dianne Lynne* / When you love someone: *Daphne* / Don't fail: *Johnny Fiasco* / LA nights: *Prince Of Bel Air* / Journey: *Spastik Plastik* / Planet funk: *Neri, Alex* / Final: *Hustlers Convention* / Watcha gonna do: *Joy For Life* / I found it: *Daphne* / Last rhythm: *Last Rhythm* / Everything is gonna change: *Rusty* / Warm it up: *Joy For Life* / Watcha gonna do (master mix): *Joy For Life* / Release the tension: *Greed* / Get down: *Hustlers Convention* / Uptown downtown: *Full Intention* / Return to the rare groove republic: *Route 66* / Spirits dancing: *Coyote* / Last rhythm (Way Out West mix): *Last Rhythm* / Tune in: *Chris & James* / Decadence: *Reefa* / America (I love America): *Full Intention* / Everything is gonna change (Sasha's dub): *Rusty* / Love me tonight: *White, Anthony* / Dub up the volume: *Greed* / Planet funk (Moonchild mix): *Neri, Alex* / Wildstyle groove: *Paninaro* / Gimme your love: *Sharon S* / Coming home (Freefall remix): *Visions & Dianne Lynne* / For what you dream of: *Bedrock & KYO* / Spirits dancing (mix): *Coyote* / Last rhythm (Way Out West remix): *Last Rhythm* / Send your drummage: *Reefa* / Send your spirit: *Reefa* / On my way: *Reefa* / Healing dream: *Sunday Club* / Coming home (Sunday Club remix): *Visions & Dianne Lynne* / Way it is: *Chameleon*
STRMIX 3CD / Sep '96 / Stress

☐ **DJ JUNGLE FEVER UK**
RSNCD 35 / Jun '95 / Rising High

☐ **DJ MIX - 25 YEARS OF DANCE (2CD Set)**
8255154162 / 27 Apr '98 / Beast

☐ **DJ MORPHEUS PRESENTS LYSERGI**
Jeune amour: *Uriel* / Butterfly: *Craig, Carl* / No 100 flow: *Cambio* / Whispers special: *Sluta Leta* / Breakers special 93: *Zeb-Roc-Ski & Stieber Twins* / Yoshi: *Dunderhead* / Chart flow: *Eight Miles High* / Norton midgate: *Eight Miles High* / Rather be here: *Random House* / Why things change: *Spank Da Monkey* / Sykodelic: *Spank Da Monkey*
SSR 178 / Mar '97 / SSR

☐ **DJ POOL VOL.3**
085703412 / 30 Mar '98 / House Nation

☐ **DJ POOL VOL.4**
085703702 / 1 Jun '98 / House Nation

☐ **DJ POWER VOL.1**
POWCD 1 / Aug '94 / Escapade

☐ **DJ POWER VOL.2**
POWCD 2 / Nov '94 / Escapade

☐ **DJ REMIX CULTURE**
STRSCD 5 / Nov '94 / Stress

☐ **DJ SELECTIONS VOL.1**
ZZCD 022 / Sep '96 / Zola & Zola

☐ **DJ SY**
SDIMCD 2 / Jun '95 / Sound Dimension

☐ **DJEM ALEVI CEREMONY, THE**
C 560125 / May '98 / Ocora

☐ **DJ'S DEELITE**
504582 / Nov '95 / Declic

☐ **DJ'S DELITE - THE GOLD COLLECTION (3CD Set)**
Vol.4: SMD / Feel free: *Dougal & Vibes* / Vol.1: Norty Norty / Vol.1: *Ravers Choice* / Six days: *Jay, Jimmy & Cru-L-T* / Da vibes: *Remarc* / Zurich: *Dougal* / Perfect dreams: *DJ Force & Evolution* / Crowd control: *Ramos & Supreme* / Vol.2: *DJ Anthems* / You are the one: *DJ Red Alert & Mike Slammer* / Vol.3: SMD / Vol.2: *Crowd Pleasers* / Sky high: *Dougal* / Sweetest love: *Vibes & Wishdokta* / Take me away: *Jay, Jimmy & Cru-L-T* / We got it: *Substate* / Feel good: *Vibes & Wishdokta* / 95 Rampage: *In Between The Lines* / Hello lover: *Hello Lover* / Rollige: *DJ SS* / We enter: *Alladin* / Really love: *Ascend & Ultravibe* / Lighter: *Sound Of The Future* / Dubwars: *Badman* / Mood of music: *Tekniq* / Hearing is believing: *MA2* / DJ SS: *Tarzan* / Easy men: *Easy Men* / Half step: *International Rude* / Black: *Black* / Hot flames: *Dextrous & H Pee* / Reality: *Phaze 3 & Klass A* / White: *White* / Jungle: *Smith, Simon 'Bassline'* / Badman tings: *Terrible Tings* / Lazy bones: *Smith, Simon 'Bassline'* / Systematic: *Brown, Scott* / Faze 1: *Forbes & Cyclone* / Do what you like: *Brown, Scott* / Higher: *Kinetic Pleasure* / Rock this place: *DJ Chewy* / Around the world: *Sense Of Summer* / Let yourself go: *DJ Ham* / Samplemania: *DJ Seduction* / No more tears: *Vibes & Wishdokta* / Take me up: *Substate* / Bust the new jam: *Seduction & Eruption* / Ultimate seduction: *DJ Hixxy* / Come together: *Storm Syndicut* / Party pumper: *DJ Brisk & Rebel Alliance* / Groovy dimensions: *WE-3* / Give yourself to me: *Icon* / Home: *Alk E-D* / Misunderstanding: *DJ Slam* / Another day: *Substate*
DBM 2204 / Jan '97 / Death Becomes Me

☐ **DJ'S DELITE VOL.1**
TROOPCD 6 / Jan '95 / Rogue Trooper

☐ **DJ'S DELITE VOL.2**
DBMTROOPCD 9 / Jun '95 / Rogue Trooper

☐ **DJ'S DELITE VOL.3**
DBMTRCD 22 / Nov '95 / Rogue Trooper

☐ **DJ'S DELITE VOL.4 (Mixed By Marc Smith)**
DBM 2011 / Sep '96 / DJ's Delite

☐ **DJ'S IN A BOX VOL.4 (Mixed By Phil Jubb)**
UCCD 004 / Jun '96 / Urban Collective

☐ **DJ'S IN A BOX VOL.6 (Mixed By Anthony Papa)**
UCCD 006 / Aug '96 / Urban Collective

☐ **DJ'S IN A BOX VOL.7**
UCCD 007 / Sep '96 / Urban Collective

☐ **DJ'S IN THE HOUSE**
MACCD 160 / Aug '96 / Autograph

☐ **DJ'S MEET THE SINGERS VOL.2**
SONCD 0049 / Jul '93 / Sonic Sounds

☐ **DJ'S TAKE CONTROL (All Mixed Up - Mixed By Sanchez/Deep Dish/Colon/ 3CD Set)**
ORCD 032 / 25 Aug '97 / One

☐ **DJ'S TAKE CONTROL - THE COLLECTION (3CD Set)**
ORCD 030 / Apr '97 / One

☐ **DJ'S UNITE - THE COMPLETE SERIES (3CD Set)**
Hypnosis: *Smith, Simon 'Bassline'* / Twisted girl: *Ruff With The Smooth & Donovan 'Bad Boy' Smith* / Engineers without fears: *DJ Rap* / Life began changing: *Van Cleef* / Natural high: *Chaos & Julia Set* / I feel free: *DJ Phantasy & Gemini* / You take me up: *DJ Aphrodite* / Dream on: *Phantasy & Smooth* / Ruffer: *DJ Force & Evolution* / Hear me: *Slipmatt* / Summer Breeze: *Bonnie The Highlander* / Above the clouds: *Sunshine Productions* / Cops: *DJ Hype* / Take your soul: *NC & Asend* / Big boo yaa: *Aphrodite & Tony B* / Rollin' voodoo: *DJ Spatts* / Hitman: *Marvellous Caine* / You as one: *Ryder, Ned* / Atmosphere: *DJ Phantasy* / Long time coming: *Danny Breaks* / Dubwars: *Badman* / Rollers convention part 3: *DJ SS* / Out in the streets: *Rude Bwoy Monty* / Use of weapons: *Chaos & Julia Set* / Tuneful: *Nut-E-1 & Technarchy* / Passion: *DJ Vibes & Wishdokta* / Party pumper: *DJ Brisk & Rebel Alliance* / Kick some ass: *DJ Druid & Rebel Alliance* / Rhythm: *Just Another Artist* / Cheddar 3: *DJ Sy* / Carousel: *Dougal & Micky Skeedale* / World war part 1: *DJ Hixxy* / Influence: *DJ Slam* / Perfect dreams: *DJ Force & Evolution* / Let yourself go: *DJ Ham* / Disco hardcore: *DJ Seduction* / I need you: *Sub-State & DJ Jack B*
DBM 2516 / Jan '97 / Death Becomes Me

☐ **DJ'S UNITE VOL.1**
TROOPCD 2 / Oct '94 / Rogue Trooper

☐ **DJ'S UNITE VOL.2**
TROOPCD 10 / May '95 / Rogue Trooper

☐ **DJ'S UNITE VOL.3**
DBMTRCD 20 / Oct '95 / Rogue Trooper

☐ **DJ'S UNITE VOL.4 (2CD Set)**
Let yourself go: *El Bruto* / Your love (get down): *Force & Styles/Jenna* / I got something: *DJ Reno & Eatsum & The Kidz* / Rock dis place: *DJ Elevation* / Touch of klass: *DJ Happy Raver & The Smile-E* / Giving all my love: *Forbes, Davie* / Givin' all I got: *DJ Vibes & Wishdokta* / Everybody here tonight: *Jack Speed* / It's gonna be: *DJ Poosie* / Raw: *Alk E-D* / Let's go: *Jimmy J & Cru-L-T* / It would be: *DJ Ham* / You're gonna love me: *DJ Pleasure* / Smile, fuck up: *DJ Psycangle*
DBM 2521 / Jan '97 / Death Becomes Me

☐ **DO BRAZIL (2CD Set)**
R2CD 4051 / 13 Apr '98 / Deja Vu

☐ **DO IT AGAIN VOL.5 (2CD Set)**
ZYX 811482 / 27 Apr '98 / ZYX

☐ **DO IT FLUID/B&G PARTY (14 Rare Grooves)**
Fantasy: *Smith, Johnny 'Hammond'* / Shifting gears: *Smith, Johnny 'Hammond'* / Joyous: *Pleasure* / Hump: *Rushen, Patrice* / Always there: *Side Effect* / Keep that same old feeling: *Side Effect* / Do it fluid: *Blackbyrds* / Rock creek park: *Blackbyrds* / Concrete jungle: *Three Pieces* / Glide: *Pleasure* / Ghettos of the mind: *Pleasure* / Straight to the bank: *Summers, Bill* / I've learned from my burns: *Spyder's Webb* / Sister Jane: *Funk Inc.*
CDBGPD 035 / Apr '92 / Beat Goes Public

☐ **DO NOT ADJUST YOUR SET**
Burnin' down: *Strange Brew* / Angel: *Friday, Gavin* / Watch me now: *Grooveyard* / Freak of the week: *Freakpower* / Too far gone: *13th Sign* / Release one: *Leftfield* / Dubiliscious demo groove: *Crystal Method* / Rematerialized: *Death In Vegas* / Yimpop: *Hardfloor* / Fuck dub: *Tosca* / Weekend starts here: *Fatboy Slim* / Keep on: *Wiseguys* / Six underground: *Sneaker Pimps* / Ticket: *11-59* / Heidi: *Ruby*
IMPCD 003 / Feb '97 / More Protein

☐ **DO THE CROSSOVER BABY**
I'll never stop loving you: *Thomas, Carla* / I got the vibes: *Armstead, Jo* / Stars: *Lewis, Barbara* / I'm the one who loves you: *Banks, Darrell* / I may not be what you want: *Mel & Tim* / Whole damned world gone crazy: *Williams, John Gary* / Be my lady: *Astors* / Since I lost my baby's love: *Major Lance* / Bark at the moon: *Floyd, Eddie* / Catch that man: *Johm, Mable* / Little by little and bit by bit: *Weston, Kim* / You're my only temptation: *Ryan, Roz* / Whole world's a picture show: *Newcomers* / Special kind of woman: *Thompson, Paul* / I play for keeps: *Thomas, Carla* / Sweet sherry: *Barnes, J.J.* / Sacrifice: *Bell, William* / Loving by the pound: *Redding, Otis* / Just keep on loving me: *Mancha, Steve* / Man in the street: *Bell, William* / Trippin' on your love: *Staple Singers* / Did my baby call: *Mad Lads* / Where would you be today: *Ilana* / One more chance: *Joseph, Margie*
CDKEND 105 / Aug '93 / Kent

☐ **DO THE NUCLEAR TESTS IN PARIS AND BEIJING**
Queenie: *Pimlico* / 911 KGGI: *Citrus* / Face on the bar room floor: *Flaming Stars* / Spineless little shit: *Thee Headcoatees* / GLC: *Armitage Shanks* / I'm afraid they're all talking about me: *Mickey & Ludella* / Shit parade: *Tokyo Skunx* / Jet tone boogie: *Rockings* / I wanna go to Coney Island: *Jet Boys* / Hello there: *Gigantor* / Scuba scuba: *Revillos* / Little terrors: *Revolta* / Hangover head: *Diaboliks* / He used to paint in colours: *TV Personalities* / Mud: *Grape* / My boy and his motorbike: *Carousel* / Nostalgia: *Weekend* / New crush: *Bugbear* / Winona, I'll be up my Nan's: *Parker, Pop* / Clearly: *McTells* / Open to persuasion: *Chesterfields* / I wanna bang on the drum: *Dee, Johnny* / Cars in the grass: *Moxham, Stuart & The Original Artists* / Good enough: *Holly Golightly* / Cheat: *Earls Of Suave*
MASKCD 058 / Feb '96 / Vinyl Japan

☐ **DO THE OOBY DOOBY**
Good rockin' tonight: *Wray, Link* / Cat all nite: *Flynn, Lee* / Rockin' Robin: *Henchmen* / Big bounce: *Caddell, Shirley* / Shake: *Fleming, George* / Paul Jones rock: *Ginger & Johnny* / Rock a square dance: *Reilly, Tommy & The QC Boys* / Ooby dooby: *Teen Kings* / Wild wild party: *Dickie Doo & The Don'ts* / Wash machine boogie: *Echo Valley Boys* / Buck dancin': *Kennedy, Ace* / Birmingham bounce: *Gunter, Hardrock* / Georgia slop: *Downing, 'Big' Al* / Rock rock: *Powers, Johnny*
305242 / Jun '97 / Hallmark

☐ **DO YOU BELIEVE IN LOVE**
CRECD 063 / May '94 / Creation

☐ **DO YOU BELIEVE IN LOVE (2CD Set)**
NSCD 007 / Feb '95 / Newsound

☐ **DO YOU WANNA DANCE (Hits Of The 70's)**
Flight tonight: *Nazareth* / Brand new key: *Melanie* / Baby jump: *Mungo Jerry* / That same old feeling: *Pickettywitch* / In my chair: *Status Quo* / Part time love: *Knight, Gladys & The Pips* / Do you wanna dance: *Blue, Barry* / After the goldrush: *Prelude* / Bad, Bad Leroy Brown: *Croce, Jim* / Lola: *Kinks* / Kung fu fighting: *Douglas, Carl* / Sad sweet dreamer: *Sweet Sensation* / What have they done to my song Ma: *Melanie* / Medley: *Knight, Gladys & The Pips* / Alright alright alright: *Mungo Jerry* / Black superman (Muhammed Ali): *Wakelin, Johnny* / Time in a bottle: *Croce, Jim* / Shame shame shame: *Shirley & Company* / Swing your daddy: *Gilstrap, Jim* / Have you seen her: *Chi-Lites*
TRTCD 108 / 2 Feb '98 / TrueTrax

☐ **DO YOUR DUTY**
IMP 940 / Jul '95 / Iris Music

☐ **DOCTOR JAZZ SAMPLER**
STCD 6040 / Aug '94 / Storyville

☐ **DOES THE WORD 'DUH' MEAN ANYTHING TO YOU**
CHE 40CD / Sep '95 / Che

☐ **DOGS 4 LIFE**
GOGZ 4CD1 / May '97 / Rude & Deadly

☐ **DOING GOD'S WORK (A Creation Compilation)**
Ten miles: *Wilson, Phil* / In a mourning town: *Biff Bang Pow* / Murderers, the hope of women: *Momus* / Shine on: *House Of Love* / Cut me deep: *Jasmine Minks* / Word around town: *Westlake* / Kiss at dawn: *Sudden, Nikki* / Catch me: *Blow Up*
CRECD 024 / May '94 / Creation

☐ **DOING IT FOR THE KIDS**
Cut me deep: *Jasmine Minks* / Ballad of the band: *Felt* / Christine: *House Of Love* / Well done sonny: *Weather Prophets* / All fall down: *Primal Scream* / She paints: *Biff Bang Pow* / Loft 49: *Jazz Butcher* / North shore train: *Berry, Heidi* / Death is hanging over me: *Sudden, Nikki* / Cigarette in my bed: *My Bloody Valentine* / Jetstream: *Pacific* / Godevil: *Times* / Complete history of sexual jealousy Parts 17 - 24: *Momus* / Reflects of rye: *Emily* / Brighter now: *Razorcuts*
CRECD 037 / Aug '88 / Creation

☐ **DOING IT RIGHT**
ZNIP 502 / 6 Apr '98 / Zippo

☐ **DOMINO RECORDS STORY, THE**
I got my mojo working: *Harris, Joyce & The Daylighters* / Your kind of woman: *Harris, Joyce & The Daylighters* / No way out: *Harris, Joyce* / Dreamer: *Harris, Joyce* / I'll never let you go: *Daylighters* / Something is wrong: *Daylighters* / Baby: *Spades* / You mean everything to me: *Spades* / Waddle: *Slades* / You cheated: *Slades* / Right here: *Webb, Joyce & The Slades* / After you've gone: *Webb, Joyce & The Slades* / I don't care: *Webb, Joyce* / No time: *Slades* / You gambled: *Slades* / My screamin' screamin' mini: *Campi, Ray* / With you: *Campi, Ray* / I cheated: *Harris, Joyce & The Slades* / Just you: *Slades* / It's better to love: *Slades* / Summertime: *Slades* / You must try: *Slades* / It's your turn: *Slades* / Take my heart: *Slades* / So tough: *Slades* / Little star: *Slades* / I've had it: *Slades* / In the still of the night: *Slades* / Ling ting tong: *Slades* / Gee whiz: *Slades*
CDCHD 506 / 30 Mar '98 / Ace

☐ **DONE STILL GOT THE BLUES**
MACCD 200 / Aug '96 / Autograph

☐ **DONEGAL FIDDLE, THE**
RTE 196CD / Nov '96 / RTE/Europe 1

☐ **DON'S PARTY**
DHP 0082 / 6 Apr '98 / Don's Music

☐ **DON'T ASK FOR THE MOON, WE HAVE THE STARS**
Way you look tonight: *Astaire, Fred* / Let there be love: *Hutchinson, Leslie 'Hutch'* / Boy next door: *Garland, Judy* / September song: *Huston, Walter* / She's funny that way: *Sinatra, Frank* / You're a sweetheart: *Bowlly, Al* / I'm making believe: *Ink Spots & Ella Fitzgerald* / Amor amor: *Rey, Monte* / I'm knee deep in daisies: *Smith, Whispering* / How do I

know it's real: *Sullivan, Maxine* / That old feeling: *Lee, Peggy & Capitol Jazzmen* / Too marvellous for words: *Stafford, Jo* / That old black magic: *Whiting, Margaret & Freddie Slack* / Sweet Lorraine: *Cole, Nat 'King' Trio* / It can't be wrong: *Carless, Dorothy* / Let's do it: *Martin, Mary* / Never took a lesson in my life: *Carlisle, Elsie* / Let's get away from it all: *Lane, Muriel & Woody Herman* / Long ago and far away: *Forrest, Helen & Dick Haymes* / Only forever: *Crosby, Bing* / Dinah: *Cantor, Eddie* / I've got a heart filled with love: *Desmond, Johnny & Glenn Miller* / Very thought of you: *Holiday, Billie* / Boy what love has done to me: *Froman, Jane* / I remember you: *Forrest, Helen & Harry James* / Now voyager: *Davis, Bette & Paul Henried*

UCD 400 / Feb '97 / Happy Days

☐ DON'T CALL ME SKA FACE (3CD Set)

DTKBOX 56 / 1 Jun '98 / Dressed To Kill

☐ DON'T CRY FOR ME ARGENTINA

MACCD 307 / Aug '96 / Autograph

☐ DON'T FENCE ME IN (Western Music)

ROUCD 1102 / Mar '96 / Rounder

☐ DON'T FORGET TO BREATHE

E 802042 / Mar '97 / Crank

CRC 11CD / 23 Feb '98 / Crank

☐ DON'T MESS WITH THE BLUES

MACCD 197 / Aug '96 / Autograph

☐ DON'T STOP THE MUSIC (Dance Favourites From The 1970's-1990's/ 2CD Set)

Rock your baby: *McCrae, George* / Feels like I'm in love: *Marie, Kelly* / Fan the flame: *Pennington, Barbara* / So many men so little time: *Brown, Miquel* / High energy: *Thomas, Evelyn* / After dark: *Brookes, Patti* / He's number one: *Fantasy* / Something old, something new: *Fantastics* / Feel the need in me: *Detroit Emeralds* / Love and desire: *Arpeggio* / Frankie: *Sister Sledge* / Queen of fools: *Williams, Jessica* / I'm in the mood for dancing: *Nolans* / Saddle up: *Nolans* / Love machine: *Miracles* / Satellites: *Warren, Ellie* / Heaven must be missing an angel: *Tavares* / Going back to my roots: *Odyssey* / Love in the night: *VHF* / It's too late: *Core & Louise* / That's when we'll be free: *State Of Grace* / Heart of glass: *Desiderata* / Car wash: *Rose Royce* / Medley: *Gaynor, Gloria* / Footsteps following me: *Nero, Frances* / Haven't stopped dancing yet: *Faces* / Ain't nothing but a house party: *Contours* / Get dancin': *Bombers* / Don't stop the music: *Carroll, Dina* / Love I lost: *Seventh Avenue* / Another man: *Mason, Barbara*

330302 / Mar '97 / Hallmark

☐ DON'T TALK JUST KISS

UPCD 05 / Sep '95 / Nitro

☐ DON'T TOUCH THAT DIAL VOL.1 (Johnnie Walker On Radio Caroline 1968)

Because they're young: *Eddy, Duane* / Judy in disguise: *Fred, John & His Playboy Band* / Rescue me: *Bass, Fontella* / She'd rather be with me: *Turtles* / Spooky: *Classics IV* / Days of Pearly Spencer: *McWilliams, David* / Harlem shuffle: *Bob & Earl* / B-A-B-Y: *Thomas, Carla* / Soul man: *Sam & Dave* / Knock on wood: *Floyd, Eddie* / Stand by me: *King, Ben E.* / All my loving: *Martin, George* / Warm and tender love: *Sledge, Percy* / For your love: *Yardbirds* / Livin' above your head: *Jay & The Americans*

TJLCD 1968A / Jul '96 / Jumbo

☐ DON'T TOUCH THAT DIAL VOL.2 (Bob Stewart On Radio Caroline 1966)

Shapes of things: *Yardbirds* / What'd I say: *Lewis, Jerry Lee* / Sha la la la lee: *Small Faces* / You send me: *Cooke, Sam* / Oh no not my baby: *Brown, Maxine* / My babe: *Little Walter* / Backstage: *Pitney, Gene* / Hard day's night: *Lewis, Ramsey Trio* / Love letters: *Lester, Ketty* / It's in his kiss (the shoop shoop song): *Everett, Betty*

TJLCD 1966 / Jul '96 / Jumbo

☐ DON'T WORRY SING THE BLUES

Pocket of money: *Murphy, Willie* / Play the blues: *Cranston, lamont* / It ain't easy bein' me: *Hoopsnakes* / See that my grave is kept clean: *Solberg, James Band* / Tried to call you: *Lynwood Slim* / Do you call that a buddy: *Lynwood Slim* / SLick chick: *Rogers, Jimmy* / Feed me: *Sumlin, Hubert* / She's murder: *Mischo, R.J. & Teddy Morgan Band* / I refuse: *Lynwood Slim* / First man: *Hoopsnakes* / Cold winds: *Cranston, lamont* / Rock me: *Rapone, Al* / I ain't drunk: *Butanes Soul Revue*

ATM 1131 / Feb '98 / Atomic Theory

☐ DON'T YOU FEEL MY LEG

Buy me some juice: *Barker, 'Blue' Lu* / Where's Joe: *Barker, 'Blue' Lu* / Lyin' in jail: *Barker, 'Blue' Lu* / Easy riding blues: *Booze, Wee Bea* / I just ain't feelin' right: *Booze, Wee Bea* / Feel it: *Dee, Baby* / I want to see my Daddy: *Dee, Baby* / Don't you feel my leg: *Barker, 'Blue' Lu* / That made him mad: *Barker, 'Blue' Lu* / I feel like laying in another woman's husband's arms: *Barker, 'Blue' Lu* / Don't tell me nothin' 'bout my man: *Booze, Wee Bea* / I'm gonna put you down: *Booze, Wee Bea* / I just ain't feelin' right: *Booze, Wee Bea* / Look what baby's got for you: *Dee, Baby* / Baby Dee blues: *Dee, Baby* / Buy me some juice: *Barker, 'Blue' Lu* / You gotta show it to me baby: *Barker, 'Blue' Lu* / There was a I'il mouse: *Barker, 'Blue' Lu*

DE 684 / Nov '96 / Delmark

☐ DONUTS VOL.1 (Slam Dunkin' Good Tunes)

BLSCD 1 / Feb '97 / Bolshi

☐ DONUTS VOL.2

Fried eggs and salad: *Plastic Surgeons* / Afro: *Rasmus* / Bad magic: *IHB* / Beast from the east: *Westway* / Rabid punk: *Freewheelers* / Good christian beats: *Rasmus* / International: *Laidback* / Madness: *Filthy Lucre* / Bad magic: *IHB* / Waiting for a beach: *Beachcomas* / Coldrock: *Laidback* / Mass hysteria: *Rasmus*

BLSCD 3 / 1 Dec '97 / Bolshi

☐ DOO BOP JIVERS VOL.9

WOP 009 / 10 Nov '97 / Sabam

☐ DOO WOP - UNDER THE COVERS

Why do fools fall in love: *Essex* / Out of sight, out of mind: *Essex* / Gee whizz (look at his eyes): *Essex* / We belong together: *Essex* / Creation of love: *Essex* / Thousand miles away: *Anthony, Wayne* / Silhouettes: *Lymon, Frankie* / Buzz buzz buzz: *Lymon, Frankie* / I cover the waterfront: *Little Anthony & The Imperials* / Please say you want me: *Little Anthony & The Imperials* / Over the rainbow: *Little Anthony & The Imperials* / When you wish upon a star: *Little Anthony & The Imperials* / Earth angel: *Cleftones* / Glory of love: *Cleftones* / Hundred pounds of clay: *Cleftones* / Red sails in the sunset: *Cleftones* / Heavenly father: *Span, Patricia & The Cleftones* / Tonight's the night: *Teenagers* / Diamonds and pearls: *Turbans* / I'm confessin': *Uniques* / Beside you: *Flamingos* / Gee: *Harmony Grits* / Come softly to me: *Barrett, Richard & The Sevilles* / Blue velvet: *Page, Joey* / Glory of love: *Angels* / (I love you) for sentimental reasons: *Devotions*

NEMCD 917 / Jul '97 / Sequel

☐ DOO WOP ALBUM, THE

For your precious love: *Impressions* / Red sails in the sunset: *Spaniels* / I only have eyes for you: *Flamingos* / Zoom zoom zoom: *Collegians* / In the still of the night: *Five Satins* / Could this be magic: *Dubs* / Maybe: *Chantels* / Bim bam bam: *El Dorados* / I just got lucky: *Orioles* / I understand: *G-Clefs* / Speedo: *Cadillacs* / Don't do that: *Five Tinos* / Real gone Mama: *Moonglows* / Lover's prayer: *Delltones* / Heart and soul: *Cleftones*

SUMCD 4118 / May '97 / Summit

☐ DOO WOP CLASSICS

Book of love: *Monotones* / Over and over again: *Harvey & The Moonglows* / Please come back come: *Flamingos* / Heart and soul: *Cleftones* / Baby, please don't go: *Orioles* / Tell it to the judge: *Monotones* / Real gone Mama: *Harvey & The Moonglows* / Chica boom (that's my baby): *Flamingos* / Little girl of mine: *Cleftones* / Crying in the chapel: *Orioles* / Look in my eyes: *Chantels* / Secret love: *Harvey & The Moonglows* / I found a new baby: *Flamingos* / Maybe: *Chantels* / Sixteen candles: *Crests* / Blue moon: *Marcels* / Just for a trick: *Flamingos* / Blue velvet: *Harvey & The Moonglows* / Legend of sleepy hollow: *Monotones*

GRF 196 / Jan '93 / Tring

☐ DOO WOP FROM DOLPHIN'S OF HOLLYWOOD VOL.1

Goose is gone aka the nest is warm: *Turbans* / Tick tock a woo: *Turbans* / No no cherry: *Turbans* / When I return: *Turbans* / Two things I love: *Voices* / Why: *Voices* / Crazy: *Voices* / Takes two to make a home: *Voices* / Hunter Hancock radio ad: *Voices* / My aching feet: *Gassers* / Why did you leave me: *Gassers* / Tell me: *Gassers* / Beloved: *Gassers* / Hum-de-hum: *Gassers* / Untitled blues: *Relf, Bobby & The Laurels* / Our love: *Relf, Bobby & The Laurels* / Honey bun: *Turks* / It can't be true: *Turks* / How to be a lover: *Hodge, Gaynell & The Blue Aires* / Love you right: *Hodge, Gaynell & The Blue Aires* / One time is enough: *Byrd, Bobby* / Hold me baby: *Byrd, Bobby* / Girl named Joe: *Miracles* / My angel: *Miracles* / Nine Boogie: *Miracles* / Let us be as one (aka Sweet thing): *Miracles*

CDCHD 364 / Jan '92 / Ace

☐ DOO WOP GROUPS & CROONERS

CWNCD 2019 / Jul '96 / Javelin

☐ DOO WOP VOL.1 (To Be Loved Forever)

DLF 71256 / 23 Mar '98 / Del-Fi

☐ DOO WOP VOL.2 (One Teardrop Too Late)

DLF 71257 / 23 Mar '98 / Del-Fi

☐ DOO WOP VOL.3 (Honey For Sale)

DLF 71258 / 23 Mar '98 / Del-Fi

☐ DOOTONE STORY VOL.1, THE

Ding a ling: *Crescendos* / Baby doll: *Crescendos* / I can't go on: *Milton, Roy & his Orchestra* / You got me reelin' and rockin': *Milton, Roy & his Orchestra* / My girl: *McCullough, Charles & the Silks* / I got tore up: *Julian, Don & The Meadowlarks* / This must be paradise: *Julian, Don & The Meadowlarks* / Please Mr. Jordan: *Duncan, Cleve & the Penguins* / Flee oo wee: *Calvanes* / Wet back hop: *Higgins, Chuck* / Don't you know I love you: *Higgins, Chuck* / Boogie woogie teenage: *Meadowlarks* / Be fair: *Pipes* / Buick '59: *Green, Vernon & the Medallions* / Magic mountain: *Green, Vernon & the Medallions* / Jump and hop: *Romancers*

CDCHD 579 / Jan '96 / Ace

☐ DOOTONE STORY VOL.2, THE

Crazy over you: *Calvanes* / Heaven and paradise: *Julian, Don & The Meadowlarks* / I wonder why: *Fascinators* / I still remember: *Romancers* / Honey gee: *Saigons* / Lawful wedding: *Cuff Links* / Ay si si (mambo): *Dootones* / Baby come on come: *Calvanes* / Jump and hop: *Romancers* / I ain't gonna cry no more: *Penguins* / Did I do wrong: *Cuff Links* / Tell me baby: *Collins, Lee* / Sailor boy: *Dootones* / Speedin': *Medallions* / You're heavenly: *Saigons* / My heart: *Cuff Links* / I'm betting my heart (on you): *Duncan, Cleve & The Radiants* / You're an angel: *Pipes* / House cat: *Romancers* / If you were my darling: *Dootones* / One more kiss: *Calvanes* / That'll make it nice: *Eli & The Manhattans* / I'll never love again: *Johnny Twovoice & The Medallions* / Two crazy scientists: *Collins, Lee* / May we be on better terms: *Debonaires* / So long Daddy: *Souvenirs* / Ding a ling: *Maye, Arthur Lee* / This is goodbye: *Romancers*

CDCHD 588 / Feb '97 / Ace

☐ DOOTONE STORY VOL.3, THE

Be fair: *Pipes* / Trick knees: *Cuff Links* / My big dream: *Eli & The Manhattans* / Shivers and shakes: *Fascinators* / Going away baby: *Fascinators* / Chancing my love: *Cuff Links* / Strange love affair: *Dootones* / Look at a fool: *Souvenirs* / Baby let's make some love: *Penguins* / I've had you: *Creators* / So tough: *Cuff Links* / Edna: *Medallions* / Please don't stop: *Dootones* / I cried all night: *McCullough, Charles & the Silks* / Hard time lover: *Cuff Links* / Teardrop eyes: *Fascinators* / Baby drop top: *Fabulous Pearls* / Teller of fortune: *Dootones* / I don't want nobody: *Cuff Links* / Darling be mine: *Doowhoppers* / I love the life I live: *Pipes* / Cause of a bad romance: *Pipes* / My love is with you: *Pipes* / I found someone: *Pipes* / Back home again: *Pipes* / Baby doll: *Pipes* / Zorro: *Pipes* / Fool's fortune: *Cuff Links*

CDCHD 676 / 26 Jan '98 / Ace

☐ DOPE CLASSICS (2CD Set)

Mother fuckin' remix: *East Side Hoods* / DJ talk: *Kicks Like A Mule* / Depth charge: *Depth Charge* / Wede man: *Selectah* / Zulu war chant: *Bambaataa, Afrika & Time Zone* / Theme from funky killer: *S'Express* / Knife and a fork: *Think Tank* / Ride the pressure: *Coldcut* / Alarm clock: *Westbam* / Untitled: *Hardnoise* / Ozone breakdown: *Renegade Soundwave* / Intoxication: *React 2 Rhythm* / Who's the bad man: *Patten, Dee* / Poor man's glory: *LS Diezel & Launch Dat* / Not forgotten: *Leftfield* / Dance: *Rhythm Is Rhythim* / Rush: *Rhythm Masters* / You won't get away: *Pirates Of The Carribean* / Walk on: *Smith & Mighty* / DJ premier in deep concentration: *Gang Starr* / 20 seconds to comply: *Silver Bullet* / Keep it up: *YBU* / Hey hey can u relate: *DJ Mink* / Sleng teng: *Smith, Wayne*

REACTCD 104 / 22 Sep '97 / React

☐ DOPE GUNS 'N' FUCKING IN THE STREETS VOL.8-11

ARRCD 80023 / Apr '97 / Amphetamine Reptile

☐ DOPE ON PLASTIC VOL.1

Ode to a blunt: *Men With Sticks* / Dubble agent (Spying On-u): *Strange Brew* / Is it a wizard or a blizzard: *Mighty Truth* / Reefer man cometh: *Woodshed* / Conversations with Julian Dexter: *Grassy Knoll* / Snapper: *Red Snapper* / Cities: *APE* / Steppin': *Box Saga* / Inner spaces: *Digi Alliance* / Black jesus: *9 Lazy 9* / Tempest dub: *Edge Test 2* / Seashell: *Skylab*

REACTCD 055 / Jan '95 / React

☐ DOPE ON PLASTIC VOL.2

Radio Woodshed: *Woodshed* / Jailbird: *Primal Scream* / Spirit: *Kitachi* / To the hip: *Bootman* / Striplight: *APE* / Tribhuwan: *Purple Penguin* / Sinsemilia: *Dillingers Massive Dub Beats* / Wildfire: *Disciples* / Now or never: *Crustation* / Acoustic blues: *Cool Breeze* / It's not a man's world: *Strata 3*

REACTCD 065 / Jul '95 / React

☐ DOPE ON PLASTIC VOL.3

Worlds: *Midfield General* / Go off (cut le roc goes off): *Midfield General* / Mountain: *Purple Penguin* / DD Luxe: *Clutch Deluxe* / Livin free: *Small World* / GBH Dub: *Death In Vegas* / Scratch: *Kitachi* / Wallop: *DJ Food* / Just a lil dope: *Masters At Work* / 29: *Turntable TEchnova* / Bobimore dub: *Henry & Louis* / We wanna go back: *Word Up* / Images: *Aquasky* / 89: *Funky Fresh News* / Shine the light: *Wood, Matt* / Bean to the world: *Cabbage Boy*

REACTCD 073

REACTCDX 073 / Feb '96 / React

☐ DOPE ON PLASTIC VOL.4 (2CD Set)

Indian summer: *Saber, Danny* / Insomniac: *Killer Moses* / Herb: *Hidden Chipsters* / Angel dust: *Dragonfly* / Let me clear my throat: *DJ Kool* / Ride on: *Little Axe* / Work mi' body: *Monkey Mafia* / Time out: *Kitachi* / Confusion: *Dubdog* / Mo' bounce: *Love Lee* / For those who like to groove: *Scope* / Third eye: *Finger* / Return of the rebel: *Raw Deal* / Remember me: *Blueboy* / Phat 'n' fresh: *Gee, Tommy* / Apache rock: *Roxy Breaks* / Watch me rollin': *Cut & Paste* / Ahooga: *Awesome 2* / Dedication: *DJ Eclipse* / Shoplifter: *Red Myers* / Bouncy lady: *Danny Hibrid* / Tee meenie: *Tee Noize* / My mate Paul: *Holmes, David* / Goodbye cruel world: *London Funk Allstars*

REACTCDX 097

REACTCD 097 / Jan '97 / React

☐ DOPE ON PLASTIC VOL.5 (2CD Set)

Trainspotter: *Romin & Joe Schmoe* / Know your enemy: *Indian Rope Man* / Strange skies: *Mr. Dan* / Macro scope: *Cyclops 4000* / B-boy stance: *Freestylers & Tenor Fly* / DJ for Prez: *Steady G* / New York joint: *Smoke & Mirrors* / And you don't stop: *45 King* / Taking of the underground 1 2 3: *Il Tone Committee* / Flicker: *Lhooq* / Pig Lick: *Capoeira Twins* / 12345678: *Prince Abooboo* / Breakout: *Laidback* / 1972: *Freddie Fresh* / Between the fro: *Bassbin Twins* / Racerbill: *Mushroomers* / King of the funk: *Way Out West* / Magic sponge: *Wide Receiver* / Wiggin': *DJ Wally & Swingsett* / Beatnik mack: *Deeds Plus Thoughts* / Poetic justice: *Eurisco* / Man: *Khao*

REACTCDX 118

REACTCD 118 / 23 Feb '98 / React

☐ DOPPLER ACT - ELECTRIC MIX SESSION (Lady Aida Presents)

PIAS 213003820 / 20 Oct '97 / Play It Again Sam

☐ DORADO - FINE GOLD

DOR 48CD / Feb '96 / Dorado

☐ DORADO COMPILATION VOL.1

Scheme of things: *D-Note* / Impressions: *Giant Steps NYC* / Sally's knocking: *Jhelisa* / Thirteenth key: *Sunship* / Rain: *D-Note* / Ain't no fun: *Monkey Business* / Circle of cruelty: *Circle in the sand*

DOR 8 / Sep '92 / Dorado

☐ DORKCRUSHER

TUPEPCD 031 / Jul '91 / Tupelo

☐ DOT ROCK 'N' ROLL

Fool: *Clark, Sanford* / Chicken shack: *Van Dyke, Leroy* / Set it up and go: *Wiseman, Mac* / You're late Miss Kate: *Dee, Jimmy & The Offbeats* / Transfusion: *Nervous Norvous* / It ain't me: *Campi, Ray* / Playboy: *Denton, Bob* / Ballroom baby: *Lory, Dick* / I like this kind of music: *Ringo, Jimmy* / Pucker paint: *Wolfe, Danny* / Big door: *Brown, Gene* / Trapped love: *Courvale, Keith* / Johnny Johnny Johnny: *Jones, Kay Cee* / It's all over: *Sullivan, Niki* / Oh my baby's gone: *Sharpe, Ray* / Let's flat git it: *Wolfe, Danny* / Stop let me off the bus: *Lanson, Snooky* / Oh yeah: *Danton, Tommy* / Baby you've had it: *Paul, Joyce* / Skinnie Minnie: *Denton, Bob* / Call me Shorty: *Gilley, Mickey* / That's the way I feel: *Sharpe, Ray* / Carry on: *Newman, Jimmy C.* / Jitterbuggin': *Five Bops* / Modern romance: *Clark, Sanford* / You heard me knocking: *Adams, Billy* / Henrietta: *Dee, Jimmy & The Offbeats*

CDCHD 592 / Oct '96 / Ace

☐ DOT'S COVER TO COVER (Hit Upon Hit)

Hearts of stone: *Fontane Sisters* / Two hearts: *Boone, Pat* / Maybellene: *Lowe, Jim* / Why don't you write me: *Lanson, Snooky* / Ain't that a shame: *Boone, Pat* / Only you (and you alone): *Hilltoppers* / Rollin' stone: *Fontane Sisters* / At my front door: *Boone, Pat* / Blue suede shoes: *Lowe, Jim* / Eddie my love: *Fontane Sisters* / Ka-ding-dong: *Hilltoppers* / I hear you knocking: *Storm, Gale* / Seventeen: *Fontane Sisters* / I'll be home: *Boone, Pat* / Why do fools fall in love: *Storm, Gale* / Seven days: *Lanson, Snooky* / Long tall Sally: *Boone, Pat* / Ivory tower: *Storm, Gale* / I'm in love again: *Fontane Sisters* / I almost lost my mind: *Boone, Pat* / Please don't leave me: *Fontane Sisters* / Chains of love: *Boone, Pat* / Lucky lips: *Storm, Gale* / Young love: *Hunter, Tab* / Marianne: *Hilltoppers* / Plaything: *Todd, Nick* / Raunchy: *Vaughn, Billy* / Get a job: *Mills Brothers* / Joker: *Hilltoppers* / At the hop: *Todd, Nick*

CDCHD 609 / May '95 / Ace

☐ DOUBLE AGENT 1980

AGENT 1980 / Feb '97 / Double Agent

☐ DOUBLE ARTICULATION (Folds And Rhizomes Remixed)

SR 110 / Feb '97 / Sub Rosa

☐ DOUBLE D'OR - ITALIE (2CD Set)

3030822 / Jun '97 / Arcade

☐ DOUBLE D'OR ANTILLES (2CD Set)

3026672 / 5 Jan '98 / Arcade

☐ DOUBLE D'OR MUSETTE (2CD Set)

3026652 / Jan '98 / Arcade

☐ DOUBLE ECLIPSE - TRIBUTE TO NEDLY ELSTAK

BVHAASTCD 9210 / Dec '89 / Bvhaast

☐ DOUBLE UP VOL.2

BW 007 / 26 Jan '98 / Brickwall

☐ DOWN AND OUT BLUES (4CD Set)

MBSCD 434 / Nov '95 / Castle

☐ DOWN MEMORY LANE

Fine romance: *Dieval, Jack* / Cheek to cheek: *Osborne, Tony* / By the light of the silvery moon/On Moonlight Bay: *John, Michael Singers* / I'm beginning to see the light: *Moorhouse, Alan* / Yours: *Ternent, Billy* / I won't dance: *Dieval, Jack* / Quando, quando: *Tait, Basil* / I've got my love to keep me warm: *Osborne, Tony* / Way you look tonight: *Dieval, Jack* / Five foot two, eyes of blue: *Ternent, Billy* / Three o'clock in the morning: *Moorhouse, Alan* / Broken doll: *John, Michael Singers* / Anything goes: *Britannia Band* / You were meant for me: *Ternent, Billy* / I only have eyes for you: *Evans, Tony* / Fascination: *Sherwood Foresters* / Stars fell on Alabama: *Ternent, Billy* / Is it true what they say about Dixie: *John, Michael Singers* / Goodnight sweetheart/I'll see you in my dreams: *John, Michael Singers*

305182 / Jul '97 / Hallmark

☐ DOWN TO MARGATE

Oh Margate: *Judge Dread & Buster Bloodvessel* / Best of the non league heroes: *Kay, Arthur Originals* / Bonanza ska: *Bad Manners* / Hurry up bugsy: *Filth FC* / Never say never: *Business* / Down to Margate: *Buster Bloodvessel* / Can can: *Bad Manners* / MARGATE: *Filth FC* / Oh Margate: *Judge Dread & Buster Bloodvessel* / Psycho: *Exploited* / Do ya wanna be in Margate: *Backseat Warriors* / Margate madness: *Margate Marauders*

MOGCD 100 / 17 Nov '97 / Mog

☐ DOWN TO THE ROACH (New Trip Hop - The Ultimate In Tripped Out Beats)

Theme from Lounge: *Lounge* / Freshness: *Hookian Mindz* / Talking drum: *APE* / Desire: *69* / Tow truck: *Sabres Of Paradise* / Essential philosophy: *Fire & Theft* / Sisterettes and Brotherettes: *8 Up* / Temple trax 003: *4E* / Freedom: *DJ Food* / Fourth way: *Daddy Longlegs* / Natural high: *Warp 69*

CDTEP 9 / Sep '95 / Step 2

☐ DOWNEY BLUES

HMG 5504 / Dec '97 / Hightone

☐ DOWNLOW HIP HOP (The Hip Hop Underground)

Die young: *Intro* / I was forgotten: *Godfather Don* / Frankenstein's pain: *Frankenstein* / Do yo' thing: *Tariq, Al* / Next type of motion: *Roots Manuva* / Let me know something: *Chill Rob G* / Mysteries of life: *Parker, Lewis* / Tried by 12: *East Flatbush Project* / Real estate: *Blak Twang* / Braggin writes: *J-Live* / You made me: *Prince Paul* / TCB: *Outro*

SOUNDSCD 10 / Oct '96 / Street Sounds

☐ DR. BOB JONES PRESENTS THE FUNK CONNECTION

PAZ 802CD / Sep '97 / La Plaza

☐ DRACULA KING OF VAMPIRES

CLP 0129 / 2 Feb '98 / Cleopatra

☐ DRAG ADDICT

Work to do: *Roach Motel* / Diva (Diva's talk): *Club 69* / Sugar pie guy (the absolute high): *Club 69* / Ku koo for cocoanuts: *One Groovy Cocoanut* / Oh Daddy shit (big Daddy remix): *That Kid Chris* / Men adore (12 inches just the right size): *Fierce Child* / Give it to Mama: *Yvette* / Accident: *Ride Committee* / Officer where's your brother (get her): *Morel's Grooves* / Wham bam (Sharon's supa-sonic mix): *Candy Girls* / Down to the waistline (honey): *Morel's Grooves* / Radikal bitch (London fierce pussy mix): *Armando* /

Get your hands off my man (a dub 4 junior): *Junior* / X-Xuses (Acapella): *Blacktivity* / Filthy hetro (nu industrial mix): *Tracy & Sharon* / Love to do it: *Ride* / Boyfriend (sweet machine mix): *Love & Sex* / Get to know me: *Tracy & Sharon*
CDHUT 34 / Feb '96 / Hut

☐ **DRAG CITY HOUR**
SN 2 / Dec '96 / Sea Note

☐ **DRAUMKVEDET**
HCD 7098CD / Apr '95 / Musikk Distribujson

☐ **DREAD BEAT & RIDDIMS VOL.2**
CRSCD 902 / Aug '96 / CRS

☐ **DREAD POETS SOCIETY**
EFA 11665CD / Apr '93 / T'Bwana

☐ **DREAM EDITION VOL.2 (Rave Mission/ 2CD Set)**
Floating: *Terra Ferma* / Lost in trance: *Jet Set & Plastic Angel* / Flaming star: *Little Jam* / In my dream: *Scoopex* / Tears: *Solid Sleep* / Interlude: *Paraphobia* / La: *Marc Et Claude* / Meganomic: *Vector Mode* / It's a dreamsong: *DJ Hooligan* / Share of bitterness: *Paragliders* / Future: *Velocity* / Papua New Guinea: *Future Sound Of London* / Go: *Moby* / Awakening: *POB & Xavia* / Birds: *Ventura* / Forbidden fruit: *Van Dyke, Paul* / Excalibar's revenge: *Blue Planet* / Silencer: *DJ The Crow* / Feel the love: *E&B Project* / Wake up little child: *M-Traxx* / World of aqua: *Aqua* / Unison: *Unison* / Space trumpets: *Trance Motion* / Touch me: *En Garde* / Bagdad: *Paragliders* / Chrysler: *Dread*
SPV 09247792 / 6 Apr '98 / SPV

☐ **DREAM IN COLOUR**
NTHEN 009CD / Sep '95 / Now & Then

☐ **DREAM INJECTION VOL.2 (2CD Set)**
Bass cadet: *Autechre* / Oil zone: *Speedy J* / Welcome home: *Kosmik Kommando* / Malmo: *Capslock* / First mechanical: *Red Sector A* / Chemical: *Tapeworm* / Dark: *Finitribe* / Windscreen wiper: *Shaolin Wooden Men* / Herbstwald: *Time Modem* / Ereximus: *Xyphax* / Start as you mean to go on: *Aphex Twin* / Ballad of Nicky McGuire: *Sabres Of Paradise* / Java: *Larkin, Kenny* / Envelope: *Immersion* / Credo: *Pentatonik* / Manifestation: *Haujobb* / Open mind: *Orbital* / Luxor: *Code* / Sudafelm: *Beaumont Hannant* / Nutrient: *Brain Pilot* / Attalal: *Download* / Swan Vesta: *u-Ziq*
08938692 / Apr '96 / Westcom

☐ **DREAM INJECTION VOL.3 (Trance & Ambience/2CD Set)**
Deep blue sea: *Scuba* / Halcyon and on and on: *Orbital* / Blueprints: *Price, Darren* / Affective: *Lobe* / Con spirito: *C.J. Bolland* / Casablanca: *Ambush* / Stardancer: *Morley, David* / Psi-onyx (mmm): *Beaumont Hannant* / Low-key sonics: *Zero Men* / TN-forces: *Xyphax* / Union of ilk: *Nuw Idol* / Atlantis: *Red Sector A* / Traume: *Cosmic Baby* / Surrender: *Interloper* / Dynamic solution: *Plastic System* / Dark side: *Resistance D* / No future: *Klange* / Corporate anthem: *Soma* / Muta 3: *Anibaldi, Leo* / On: *Aphex Twin* / Love song: *Influx* / Dream injection: *It*
SPV 08947432 / Feb '97 / Westcom

☐ **DREAM INJECTION VOL.4 (2CD Set)**
DCD 08947522 / May '97 / Westcom

☐ **DREAM INJECTION VOL.5 (3CD Set)**
Beneath: *SLAM* / Stormwatch: *Morph* / Form feminique: *Friends, Lovers & Family* / Placebo: *Lobe* / Dialogue: *Hurosawa, Takeshi* / Epilion: *B12* / ISM: *Cherry Bomb* / All that I need is to be loved: *Moby* / Nec plus ultra: *Bolland, C.J.* / Poke in the dark: *Vostok* / T-Raenon: *Photek* / Razorback: *Deason, Sean* / Guiding star: *Unitone Hi-Fi* / Light: *Namlook, Pete* / Trouble and desire: *Effective Force* / Nod to N20: *Rainer* / Exit 101: *Swandive* / Stygian vista: *Soma* / Molten: *Beaumont Hannant* / Above your eyes: *Scanner* / Chatter: *Autechre* / Pure energy: *Speedy J* / Gumpie: *Jeyenne* / Trance: *Beltram, Joey* / Lost: *Max 404* / For Max: *Garnier, Laurent* / Clan (Mongol hordes): *Black Dog* / Soul man: *Larkin, Kenny* / Flow: *Dimension 5* / Good morning riot: *Dimension 5* / Eclectic: *Dark Comedy* / Solitude: *Brown, Stephen*
09247772 / 8 Dec '97 / Westcom

☐ **DREAM MIX VOL.3**
DST 055702823 / Nov '97 / SPV

☐ **DREAM TEAM IN THE MIX (The London Dream Team In Session)**
Closer than close: *Gaines, Rosie* / Love can't turn around: *Farley Jackmaster Funk* / Keep on moving: *DJ Disciple* / Find the path: *New Horizon* / Special: *Colour Girl* / Freaky: *Timmi Magic* / Wanna spend the night: *Lewis, Danny J.* / Things are never: *Operator & Baffled* / Deliver me: *Urban Blues Project* / Dreams: *Smokin' Beats* / Bad boys: *Baffled Republic* / Release the pressure: *Foster, Danny* / Lift me up: *Vasquez, Junior* / One more time: *King, Evelyn 'Champagne'*
LIBTCD 002 / Jun '97 / 4 Liberty

☐ **DREAM TIME (Spiritual Music Of The Australian Aborigine)**
Spirit of Uluru / Noorooma - Myths and magic / Ilingka - the dreamtime / Bieningana - eternal sunrise / Sacred river / Kiparra - awakenings
DC 881552 / 29 Aug '97 / Disky

☐ **DREAM TOPPING**
Tidal wave: *Apples* / Camera loves me: *Would-Be-Goods* / Sit down I think I love you: *Fisher-Turner, Simon* / Discoteheque: *Bad Dream Fancy Dress* / Angel delight: *Mr. Martini* / Hot cherry love bombs: *Magnificent Andersons* / Toffee spot: *Magnificent Andersons* / Oh Constance: *Marden Hill* / Jacky Onassis: *Milky* / Complicated: *Momus* / Mating game: *Monochrome Set* / Smash hit wonder: *King Of Luxembourg* / Trouble in teen town: *Darlene Fanclub* / Dirty: *Butterfingers* / Run for your life: *Would-Be-Goods* / 6AM: *Daily Planet* / Martine: *Philippe, Louis* / Ulysses: *Adverse, Anthony* / Hanover square: *Mr. Wright* / Gary Lineker-A young girls dream: *Romaine* / Pure: *Pulling Jessica's Hair* / Grant me the day: *Marbles*
MONDE 21CD / 9 Mar '98 / Richmond

☐ **DREAMBOAT**
CASS 006 / Sep '97 / Cassiel

☐ **DREAMHOUSE VOL.1 (Le Voyage)**
Fly: *D'Agostino Planet* / Jack of the green: *Land Of Oz* / Bakerloo symphony: *Picotto, Mauro* / Giallone remix: *D'Agostino, Gigi* / Happily: *D'Agostino, Gigi* / Hit the bang: *Groove Park* / Children: *Miles, Robert* / Noise maker theme: *D'Agostino, Gigi* / My house: *Picotto, Mauro* / Halleluja: *Picotto, Mauro* / Harmonic: *D'Agostino, Gigi* / Marimba: *D'Agostino Planet* / Melody voyager: *D'Agostino Planet* / Android: *2 Culture In A Room* / For love: *D'Agostino Planet* / Groovebird: *Natural Born Groovers*
MCD 60015 / Jul '96 / MCA

☐ **DREAMMACHINE, THE (2CD Set)**
DREAM 0012 / 15 Jun '98 / Dream

☐ **DREAMS AND THEMES (20 Synth Classics)**
Chase / Magic fly / Axel F / Moments in love / I hear you now / Second time / Equinoxe / Chariots of fire / Eve of the war / Dune / Oxygene / Theme from Rainman / Take my breath away / Falling / Tao of love / Crockett's theme / Lily was here / Another day in paradise / Eternal flame
SUMCD 4011 / Nov '96 / Summit

☐ **DREAMS AND THEMES (4CD Set)**
SUMBX 4020 / Jan '98 / Summit

☐ **DREAMS IN THE WITCHOUSE**
FETISH 666CD / May '96 / Grave News

☐ **DREAMS OF ANGELS (A Magical Blend Of Music And The Sounds Of Nature)**
57672 / May '97 / Nature's Harmony

☐ **DREAMS OF FLYING - ASTRAL JAZZ**
WCL 11014 / Feb '96 / White Cloud

☐ **DREAMSCAPE VOL.2 (3CD Set)**
DSRCD 002 / 8 Nov '97 / Dreamscape

☐ **DRIFTWORKS (4CD Set)**
ABB 1000CD / 13 Oct '97 / Big Cat

☐ **DRINK ME SAMPLER '96**
DRINK 1 / Jan '96 / Echo

☐ **DRINKING AND LOVE SONGS OF SOUTH WEST CHINA**
ARN 64363 / Sep '96 / Arion

☐ **DRIVE ON (2CD Set)**
Riverboat song: *Ocean Colour Scene* / Are you gonna go my way: *Kravitz, Lenny* / Losing my religion: *REM* / Everything must go: *Manic Street Preachers* / Sandstorm: *Cast* / Passenger: *Iggy Pop* / Road to nowhere: *Talking Heads* / Alright: *Supergrass* / Mmm mmm mmm mmm: *Crash Test Dummies* / Girl like you: *Collins, Edwyn* / How soon is now: *Smiths* / Made of stone: *Stone Roses* / Star: *Primal Scream* / Inside: *Stiltskin* / 20th Century boy: *T-Rex* / Don't you (forget about me): *Simple Minds* / Thorn in my side: *Eurythmics* / Don't get me wrong: *Pretenders* / Walk on the wild side: *Reed, Lou* / Sweet child of mine: *Guns n' Roses* / Legs: *ZZ Top* / Two princes: *Spin Doctors* / Bad love: *Clapton, Eric* / Long train runnin': *Doobie Brothers* / School's out: *Cooper, Alice* / Everything about you: *Ugly Kid Joe* / Word up: *Gun* / We care a lot: *Faith No More* / She sells: *Cult* / Just like paradise: *Roth, David Lee* / Don't fear: *Blue Oyster Cult* / Modern girl: *Meat Loaf* / Hazard: *Marx, Richard* / These dreams: *Marx, Richard* / Is this love: *Whitesnake* / Free bird: *Lynyrd Skynyrd*
RADCD 55 / 18 Aug '97 / Global TV

☐ **DRIVEN TO DEATH**
CLAYCD 105 / Apr '93 / Clay

☐ **DRIVIN' COUNTRY**
Rhinestone cowboy: *Campbell, Glen* / Talking in your sleep: *Gayle, Crystal* / Blanket on the ground: *Spears, Billie Jo* / Rose Marie: *Whitman, Slim* / Have I told you lately that I love you: *Nelson, Willie* / Another place another time: *Williams, Don* / Sweet dreams: *Young, Faron* / I'll never fall in love again: *Gentry, Bobbie* / Stand by your man: *Jackson, Wanda* / All I have to do is dream: *Newton, Juice* / Wings of a dove: *Husky, Ferlin* / King of the road: *Ford, Tennessee Ernie* / When you're in love with a beautiful woman: *Dr. Hook* / I honestly love you: *Newton-John, Olivia* / Games people play: *South, Joe* / I just had you on my mind: *Caddock, Billy 'Crash'* / Crazy: *Nelson, Willie* / Still crazy after all these years: *Dalton, Lacy J.*
CDMFP 6228 / Aug '96 / Music For Pleasure

☐ **DRIVIN' EASY**
Fever: *Lee, Peggy* / Memories are made of this: *Martin, Dean* / Let there be love: *Cole, Nat 'King'* / Cry me a river: *London, Julie* / Angie baby: *Reddy, Helen* / Portrait of my love: *Monro, Matt* / Volare: *Martino, Al* / And I love you so: *Bassey, Shirley* / Don't it make my brown eyes blue: *Gayle, Crystal* / Galveston: *Campbell, Glen* / If not you: *Dr. Hook* / Crying: *McLean, Don* / Wind beneath my wings: *Keel, Howard* / On the street where you live: *Damone, Vic* / Moon river: *Williams, Danny* / You belong to me: *Stafford, Jo* / I'll never find another you: *Seekers* / He ain't heavy, he's my brother: *Hollies*
CDMFP 6238 / Aug '96 / Music For Pleasure

☐ **DRIVIN' HITS**
Simply irresistable: *Palmer, Robert* / Nutbush City limits: *Turner, Ike & Tina* / My Sharona: *Knack* / Call me: *Blondie* / Bang bang (my baby shot me down): *Cher* / Missing you: *Waite, John* / Bette Davies eyes: *Carnes, Kim* / Vienna: *Ultravox* / True: *Spandau Ballet* / Golden brown: *Stranglers* / Running up that hill: *Bush, Kate* / Here comes the sun: *Harley, Steve & Cockney Rebel* / Walking on sunshine: *Katrina & The Waves* / Geno: *Dexy's Midnight Runners* / Call me: *Go West* / Baker St.: *Rafferty, Gerry* / Roll over Beethoven: *ELO* / Hi ho silver lining: *Beck, Jeff*
CDMFP 6227 / Aug '96 / Music For Pleasure

☐ **DRIVIN' ROCK 'N' ROLL**
Blueberry Hill: *Domino, Fats* / Take good care of my baby: *Vee, Bobby* / Walk don't run: *Ventures* / Be bop a lula: *Vincent, Gene* / Somethin' else: *Cochran, Eddie* / I'm walkin': *Domino, Fats* / Why do fools fall in love: *Lymon, Frankie & The Teenagers* / Rubber ball: *Vee, Bobby* / Summertime blues: *Cochran, Eddie* / Willie and the hand jive: *Otis, Johnny Show* / Dreaming: *Burnette, Johnny* / Blue Jean bop: *Vincent, Gene* / I'm not a juvenile delinquent: *Lymon, Frankie & The Teenagers* / Shakin' all over: *Kidd, Johnny & The Pirates* / Only sixteen: *Douglas, Craig* / Blue moon: *Marcels* / Love potion no.9: *Clovers* / Tell Laura I love her: *Valence, Ricky* / You've got what it takes: *Johnson, Mary* / Party doll: *Knox, Buddy* / You're sixteen: *Burnette, Johnny* / Saturday night at the Duck Pond: *Cougars*
CDMFP 6229 / Aug '96 / Music For Pleasure

☐ **DRIVIN' ROCK VOL.1**
KNEWCD 729 / Feb '94 / Kenwest

☐ **DRIVIN' ROCK VOL.2**
KNEWCD 730 / Feb '94 / Kenwest

☐ **DRIVIN' ROCK VOL.3**
KNEWCD 731 / Feb '94 / Kenwest

☐ **DRIVIN' ROCK VOL.4**
KNEWCD 732 / Feb '94 / Kenwest

☐ **DRIVING ROCK (2CD Set)**
Radio ga ga: *Queen* / Here I go again: *Whitesnake* / Legs: *ZZ Top* / Rhiannon: *Fleetwood Mac* / Long train runnin': *Doobie Brothers* / Rock 'n' me: *Miller, Steve Band* / Two princes: *Spin Doctors* / Mm mm mm mm: *Crash Test Dummies* / Inside: *Stiltskin* / Lil' devil: *Cult* / Can't get enough: *Bad Company* / Black velvet: *Myles, Alannah* / You can go your own way: *Rea, Chris* / Rocky mountain way: *Walsh, Joe* / Well all right: *Santana* / Dead ringer for love: *Meat Loaf* / If I could turn back time: *Cher* / Voodoo chile: *Hendrix, Jimi* / Drive: *Cars* / Hazard: *Marx, Richard* / To be with you: *Mr. Big* / Show me heaven: *McKee, Maria* / Abracadabra: *Miller, Steve Band* / Stop draggin my heart around: *Nicks, Stevie* / Because the night: *Smith, Patti* / Sweet home Alabama: *Lynyrd Skynyrd* / There goes another love song: *Outlaws* / More than a feeling: *Boston* / Hold the line: *Toto* / Love is the drug: *Roxy Music* / China in your hand: *T'Pau* / Life's been good: *Walsh, Joe* / I can't go for that (no can do): *Hall & Oates* / Nothing's gonna stop us now: *Starship* / Broken wings: *Mr. Mister* / Time after time: *Lauper, Cyndi* / Black betty: *Ram Jam* / I want to know what love is: *Foreigner*
GLOCD 3 / Jul '97 / Global TV

☐ **DRONES AND THE CHANTERS, THE**
CC 61CD / Mar '95 / Claddagh

☐ **DROP ACID AND LISTEN TO THIS**
She's everything Mr.H: *Kramer* / Huge: *Kramer* / These diamonds are very: *Lo Galluccio* / Beingvised: *Lo Galluccio* / Miranda screaming: *Lo Galluccio* / Necropolis: *DJ Spooky* / If 6 were 9: *Spanish Fly* / From rags to britches: *Spanish Fly* / Talking drums: *Roots* / Happens like that: *Zony Mash* / Cold spell: *Zony Mash* / Used 60-60: *Umezu, Kazutoki* / First deserter: *Umezu, Kazutoki* / Apocalyptica/Weeds: *Liminal* / Nosferatu: *Liminal* / Band of weeds: *Revolution 9* / Downtown does the Beatles: *Revolution 9* / Flow: *Hooker, William* / Mindfulness: *Hooker, William* / Something to be desired: *Wisdom Tooth* / Mental floss: *Wisdom Tooth* / Abstract concrete: *Wisdom Tooth* / Preset no.1: *Liminal Lounge* / Preset: *Liminal Lounge* / September 1st: *Umezu, Kazutoki*
KFWCD 218 / 20 Apr '98 / Knitting Factory

☐ **DROP DEAD GORGEOUS VOL.1 (40 Of The Coolest Sexiest Chart Hits - 2CD Set)**
Torn: *Imbruglia, Natalie* / Old before I die: *Williams, Robbie* / Angel of mine: *Eternal* / As long as you love me: *Backstreet Boys* / Different beat: *Boyzone* / Arms around the world: *Louise* / All night all right: *Andre, Peter & Warren G* / Tubthumping: *Chumbawamba* / I'll be there for you: *Solid Harmonie* / Open road: *Barlow, Gary* / Slam dunk da funk: *Five* / Stay another day: *East 17* / Ain't that just the way: *McNeal, Lutricia* / Clementine: *Owen, Mark* / Did it again: *Minogue, Kylie* / Crazy little party girl: *Carter, Aaron* / All I wanna do: *Minogue, Dannii* / Do ya think I'm sexy: *N-Trance & Rod Stewart* / You sexy thing: *Hot Chocolate* / 5678: *Steps* / Drop dead gorgeous: *Republica* / Wonderwall: *Oasis* / Avenging angels: *Space* / Lovefool: *Cardigans* / You're gorgeous: *Baby Bird* / Perfect day: *Reed, Lou* / Six underground: *Sneaker Pimps* / You're not alone: *Olive* / Never let you go: *Moore, Tina* / Sunchyme: *Dario G* / One and one: *Miles, Robert* / Feels so good: *Mase* / Do you know: *Gayle, Michelle* / That's the way (I like it): *Clock* / Just a little bit: *Gina G* / Where do you go: *No Mercy* / We come to party: *N-Tyce* / Don't leave me: *Blackstreet* / Wind beneath my wings: *Houghton, Steven* / I believe I can fly: *R Kelly*
RADCD 73 / 9 Feb '98 / Global TV

☐ **DROP DEAD GORGEOUS VOL.2 (2CD Set)**
RADCD 94 / 18 May '98 / Global TV

☐ **DROP OF THE IRISH, A**
PASTCD 9799 / Sep '92 / Flapper

☐ **DROP THE BOX**
CDLDL 1234 / Oct '95 / Lochshore

☐ **DROS BIANT Y BYD**
SCD 2113 / Aug '95 / Sain

☐ **DRUG TEST VOL.1**
INV 081CD / May '97 / Invisible

☐ **DRUG TEST VOL.3**
INV 109CD / 13 Oct '97 / Invisible

☐ **DRUM, CHANT & INSTRUMENTAL MUSIC OF NIGER, MALI & UPPER VOLT**
7559720732 / Jan '95 / Nonesuch

☐ **DRUM CRAZY VOL.1**
DCCD 001 / Jul '96 / Drum Crazy

☐ **DRUM CRAZY VOL.2**
DCCD 002 / Jul '96 / Drum Crazy

☐ **DRUM CRAZY VOL.3**
DCCD 003 / Jul '96 / Drum Crazy

☐ **DRUM CRAZY VOL.4**
DCCD 004 / Jul '96 / Drum Crazy

☐ **DRUM CRAZY VOL.5**
DCCD 005 / Jul '96 / Drum Crazy

☐ **DRUMFUNK HOOLIGANS**
ASHADOW 14C / 1 Sep '98 / Moving Shadow

☐ **DRUM 'N' BASS (3CD Set)**
DTKBOX 65 / Nov '97 / Dressed To Kill

☐ **DRUM 'N' BASS (Underground & Loud)**
You rang: *Mask* / Square waves: *Genotype* / Bibo: *More Rockers* / One: *Brass Wolf* / Drum: *D'Cruze* / Drivin' south: *Grasscutter* / Stalking moon: *Kinetix* / Pimp: *Flynn & Flora* / Amen sister: *Extra Breaks* / Doin' fine: *Mental Power* / Solarize: *Fellowship* / Nyquest: *Ambisonics*
JCRACD 009 / 31 Aug '98 / Just Create

☐ **DRUM 'N' BASS COLLECTION VOL.1 (Drum 'n' Bass Selection Vol.1 & 2/4CD Set)**
BDRBOX 1 / Nov '95 / Breakdown

☐ **DRUM 'N' BASS COLLECTION VOL.2 (Drum 'n' Bass Selection Vol.3 & 4/ Telepathy/5CD Set)**
BDRBOX 2 / Nov '95 / Breakdown

☐ **DRUM 'N' BASS EXPLOSION**
Solar weightlessness: *Conduit* / Flick knife reality: *Tacye* / All tooled up: *Resistance Quad* / My generation: *Birch, Mark & Wicked Wayne* / Sclerotic coat: *Taskmasters* / Wronged by righteousness: *Ashbone* / Insectiside: *PLATE* / Treatment room 127: *DJ Tyrone* / Legacy: *Fowley, Kim* / Alien menagerie: *Screen* / Domino effect: *Domino Effect* / Asteroid: *Screen* / Dub contract killing: *Silver-E* / Gingivitus dance: *Drum 'n' Bass Brothers* / Lunar weightlessness: *Conduit*
TOYCD 1005 / 24 Nov '97 / Intrinsic

☐ **DRUM 'N' BASS FEVER**
TOYCD 1002 / Nov '96 / Intrinsic

☐ **DRUM 'N' BASS FRENZY (The Ultimate Junglist Experience/2CD Set)**
Alien incision: *PLATE* / Element: *Conduit* / Funkster dub: *DJ Tyrone* / New world penetration: *Feist* / Simba: *Resistance Quad* / First discovery: *Screen* / Hostage: *Tacye* / Crackdown: *Vibe Posse* / Crook the thief and the liar: *Jungra Boyz* / Ice maiden: *Drum 'n' Bass Brothers* / Predator/Ether people: *Philips, Mark & Conduit* / Juggler of deceit: *Davenport, Mikey* / Free the wicker man: *Taskmasters* / Equestrian delirium: *D-Teaze* / Did Harry send ya: *Hyperblade* / Cosmos psychosis symplex: *Microcosm* / Power struggle: *On A Roll* / 7th apparition: *Vibe Posse* / Return to Jupiter: *Screen* / Eye: *Tacye* / City Road: *Sisterhood* / State interceptor: *PLATE* / Laughing boy: *Resistance Quad* / Ancient art of astral projection: *D-Teaze* / Ploy: *Hiding In The Tall Grass* / Vhujon dub splendor: *Microcosm* / Katpod: *Conduit* / Towerblock runners: *Taskmasters* / Wolverine: *PLATE & Tacye* / Imploding for effect: *Caroline*
DEMPCD 025 / Sep '97 / Emporio

☐ **DRUM 'N' BASS MANIA**
EMPRCD 702 / Mar '97 / Emporio

☐ **DRUM 'N' BASS MIX 1997 (2CD Set)**
Ain't talkin' 'bout dub: *Apollo 440* / Sweet love: *M-Beat & Nazlyn* / Inner city life: *Goldie* / Feel the sunshine: *Reece, Alex* / Sea: *St. Etienne* / One day I'll fly away: *Llorena, Kelly* / Far away: *Doc Scott* / Wetern tune: *PFM* / To give but not forget: *Outside* / It's a jazz thing: *Roni Size* / Impact: *City Connection* / Psychosis: *Peshay* / Horn section: *Rogue Unit* / Mindz: *Mind 21* / Rhode tune: *Flytronix* / Take me to heaven: *Baby D* / Do U know: *M-Beat & Jamiroquai* / Greater love: *Soundman & Don Lloydie/Elizabeth Troy* / Morning will come: *M-Beat & Junior Giscombe* / Smooth note: *Mouse, Jason* / Piano tune: *Peshay* / Rays of sun: *Acetate* / Bubblegum: *One True Parker* / Wishing on a star: *88.3 & Lisa May* / Renegade snares: *Omni Trio* / So many dreams: *Guy Called Gerald* / Moments in space: *Nookie* / Urban blues: *Gurley, S.* / Spectrum: *Wax Doctor* / Play the game: *Freestyles* / Feenin': *Jodeci* / F-Jam: *Adam F* / Walking wounded: *Everything But The Girl* / Can't knock the hustle: *Jay-Z & Mary J. Blige* / Cotton wool: *Lamb*
5533952 / Mar '97 / PolyGram TV

☐ **DRUM 'N' BASS SELECTION VOL.2 (2CD Set)**
Rrroll da bbeats: *DJ Hype* / Maximum style: *Tom & Jerry* / Hello lover: *Fallen Angel* / Sweet vibrations: *DMS & Boneman X* / Maniac music: *Lick Back Organisation* / Johnny 94: *Johnny Jungle* / It's a jazz thing: *Roni Size* / Mo musik: *DJ Ron* / Stand easy: *JB* / Callin' all the people: *A-Zone* / Terrorist: *Renegade* / You must think first: *Dope Style* / Predator: *Shimon* / Ruff revival: *Run Tings* / Droppin' science vol.1: *Droppin' Science* / Screw face: *Brain Killers* / Time to move: *DJ Dextrous* / Kall da kops: *Sacred* / What kind of world: *Send* / Burial: *Leviticus*
BDRCD 3 / Sep '94 / Breakdown

☐ **DRUM 'N' BASS SELECTION VOL.3 (2CD Set)**
Cool down: *Andy C* / Lionheart: *Bert & Dillinger* / King of the jungle: *King Of The Jungle* / Feel the magic: *Sophisticated Bad Boyz* / War in '94: *Badman* / Dead bass: *Dead Dred* / Air freshener: *Tom & Jerry Vol 9* / Booyaaa: *Amazon II* / Rude boy: *Flex* / Hitman: *Marvellous Caine* / Ganja man: *Krome & Time* / Little roller Vol 1: *L-Double* / Sound murderer: *Remarc* /

Heavenly body: DJ Dextrous / Firing line: Droppin' Science / Mash up da place: Ganga Vol 4 / Ali Baba: Hopa & Bones / Yeah man: Dream Team / Alive and kicking (origin unknown mix): Red One / Selectors roll: Rus De Tox & Teebone
BDRCD 5 / Nov '94 / Breakdown

☐ **DRUM 'N' BASS SELECTION VOL.4 (2CD Set)**
BDRCD 6 / Apr '95 / Breakdown

☐ **DRUM 'N' BASS SELECTION VOL.5 (2CD Set)**
BDRCD 9 / Sep '95 / Breakdown

☐ **DRUM 'N' BASS VOL.1 (2CD Set)**
ZYX 811222 / 29 Sep '97 / ZYX

☐ **DRUM 'N' BASS VOL.2**
ZYX 811332 / 9 Feb '98 / ZYX

☐ **DRUM SONG (Mighty Mike's Continuous Mix)**
RN 0047 / Feb '97 / Rhino

☐ **DRUMMERS FANFARE**
Drum fanfare: Shotts & Dykehead Caledonia Pipe Band / Selection: Cook, Arthur / March, strathspey and reel: Kilpatrick, Jim / Selection: Ward, Eric
LCOM 5174 / Feb '97 / Lismor

☐ **DRUMS OF DEATH (Ghana)**
AVAN 062 / Mar '98 / Avant

☐ **DRUMS OF SOUTH AMERICA (Guadeloupe/Venezuela/Cuba/3CD Set)**
C 570302 / Mar '97 / Ocora

☐ **DRUMS OF THE EARTH VOL.1**
AUB 6773 / Mar '93 / Auvidis/Ethnic

☐ **DRUMS OF THE EARTH VOL.2 (Asia)**
AUB 6774 / Apr '93 / Auvidis/Ethnic

☐ **DRUMS PARADE 1937-1945**
158692 / Jan '97 / Jazz Archives

☐ **DUB BACKUPS**
E 11010 / 2 Feb '98 / Electrolux

☐ **DUB EXPLOSION**
CDTRL 366 / Jan '96 / Trojan

☐ **DUB FROM JAMAICA ROOTS**
OMCD 034 / Sep '96 / Original Music

☐ **DUB GENERALS**
WRCD 2191 / 12 Jan '98 / Wackies

☐ **DUB HOUSE DISCO VOL.1**
GRCD 004 / Aug '92 / Guerilla

☐ **DUB HOUSE DISCO VOL.2 (2000)**
Land of Oz: Spooky / I still want ya: Outer Mind / Feel: Chameleon Project / Schudelfloss: Dr. Atomic / Product: 10th Chapter / Alchemy: Drum Club / Oh yeah: DOP / Dub house disco: 2 Shiny Heads / Feeling warm: Eagles Prey / Supereal: One Nation / Intoxication: React 2 Rhythm / Schmoo: Spooky
GRCD 007 / Jul '94 / Guerilla

☐ **DUB HOUSE DISCO VOL.3 (The Third)**
Little bullet: Spooky / Here I go: DOP / Underground: Matter / Aquamarine: Lemon Sol / Blue beyond: Supereal / Persuasion: Martin, Billie Ray & Spooky / Come into my life: Abfahrt / Higher: Code MD / Columbia: Chameleon Project / Prologue: 10th Chapter / Solar: Shape Navigator / Persuasion (mix): Martin, Billie Ray & Spooky
GRCD 012 / Jul '94 / Guerilla

☐ **DUB OR DIE VOL.1**
RE 099CD / Jul '97 / ROIR

☐ **DUB OR DIE VOL.2**
RE 098CD / Jul '97 / ROIR

☐ **DUB OVER DUB**
CDHB 202203 / Feb '96 / Heartbeat

☐ **DUB PLATE SELECTION**
STHCCD 15 / Sep '95 / Strictly Hardcore

☐ **DUB REVOLUTION**
RUSCD 8207 / Jul '95 / ROIR

☐ **DUB TRILOGY (3CD Set)**
RN 7053 / 8 Jun '98 / Rhino

☐ **DUB, TRIP AND HOP**
FRCD 5 / Jun '95 / Flex

☐ **DUBBED ON PLANET SKUNK**
CDDUBM 002 / 3 Nov '97 / Dubmission

☐ **DUBBED OUT IN DC (Tripped Out Grooves From The Capital Of US Of Kiss My Ass)**
Transcendence: Thievery Corporation / Hijack: Thunderball / Collector: Liftoff / Far East coast: Exodus Quartet / Summer down: England, Kevin / Foundation: Thievery Corporation / Angel headed hipsters: Liftoff / As red as my eyes get: Peace Bureau / Ultra thin: Thunderball / So vast as the sky: Thievery Corporation / Maenad: England, Kevin
ESL 006 / Sep '97 / 18th Street Lounge

☐ **DUBBLE ATTACK (Dee-Jay Collection 1972-1974)**
No. 1 in the world: U-Roy / Opportunity rock: Big Youth / Meaning of one: Prince Jazzbo / Rasta on a Sunday: I-Roy / Father's call: Beckford, Dean / This is a year for rebels: Godsons / Spider to the fly: Big Youth / Brother Toby is a movie from London: I-Roy / Mr. Harry Skank: Prince Jazzbo / Dubble attack: Big Youth / Whole lot of sugar: Prince Hammer / Festive season: I-Roy / Mr. Want All: Prince Jazzbo / Butter bread: Young, Lloyd
GRELCD 601 / May '90 / Greensleeves

☐ **DUBHEAD - THE 90'S DUB SAMPLER VOL.1**
IVECD 2 / Oct '95 / Shiver

☐ **DUBHEAD - THE 90'S DUB SAMPLER VOL.2**
IVECD 4 / Mar '96 / Shiver

☐ **DUBHEAD - THE 90'S DUB SAMPLER VOL.3**
IVE 005CD / Jul '97 / Shiver

☐ **DUBHEAD - THE 90'S DUB SAMPLER VOL.4**
IVECD 6 / 27 Jul '98 / Shiver

☐ **DUBITAMIN**
Repetitive beats: Retribution / No dog bark: Dub Syndicate / Earth rocker: Bush Chemists / I wah 4000: Mixman / Zion ring: Zion Train / Splash say the fishes in the sea: Wimbish, Doug / Tabla school: Suns Of Arqa / High speed dubbing: Bush Chemists & Culture Freeman / Rightway: Power Steppers / Mastermonk: Electric Source / Outer space: Tassilli Players / Circle line: Blue / Sunshine dub: Vibe Tribe Soundsystem & Don Abi
EFA 063512 / Jan '97 / Roundtrip

☐ **DUBLIN ONE RECORDINGS VOL.1**
DONECD 1 / 13 Oct '97 / Dublin One

☐ **DUBLIN SONGS**
Molly Malone: Band Of Dubs / Rocky road to Dublin: Dubliners / Spanish lady: Reilly, Paddy / Biddy Mulligan: Grace, Brendan / Rare ould times: Dubliners / St. Laurence O'Toole: Fureys & Davey Arthur / Dublin, my Dublin: Reilly, Paddy / Ringsend rose: Grace, Brendan / Raglan Road: McCann, Jim / Dublin saunter: Reilly, Paddy / Night ferry: Fureys & Davey Arthur / Dublin town: Grace, Brendan / Foggy dew: McCann, Jim / Auld triangle: Dubliners / Summer in Dublin: McCann, Jim / Anna Liffey: Dubliners / Dublin in my tears: Fureys & Davey Arthur / Jem: Drew, Ronnie / Dublin - take me: Fureys & Davey Arthur
MCCD 042 / Sep '91 / Music Club

☐ **DUBMISSION VOL.1**
Destination unknown: Sly & Robbie / Demolition city: Sly & Robbie / Ion storm: Black Uhuru / Boof n' baff n' biff: Black Uhuru / Flikaflame: Aswad / Tuffist: Aswad / I and I survive: Burning Spear / Reality: Johnson, Linton Kwesi / Shocking: Johnson, Linton Kwesi / Night nurse: Isaacs, Gregory
5242942 / 25 Aug '97 / Quango

☐ **DUBMISSION VOL.2 (The Remixes)**
Night nurse: Isaacs, Gregory / Boof n' baff n' biff: Black Uhuru / Destination unknown: Sly & Robbie / I and I survive: Burning Spear / Boof n' baff n' biff: Black Uhuru / Demolition city: Sly & Robbie / Demolition city: Sly & Robbie / Ion storm: Black Uhuru / Boof n' baff n' biff: Black Uhuru / Night nurse: Isaacs, Gregory
5244212 / 24 Nov '97 / Quango

☐ **DUBNOLOGY VOL.1**
MIDDL 4CD / Nov '95 / Middle Earth

☐ **DUBNOLOGY VOL.2 (Lost In Bass) (2CD Set)**
MIDDLE 7CD / Oct '96 / Middle Earth

☐ **DUBS FOR DAZE VOL.1 (Jim Fox Dubs Up The Ras Tapes/2CD Set)**
Knock knock dub: Don Carlos / Rastafari dub: Broggs, Peter / Got to be dub: Broggs, Peter / Dub rider: Don Carlos / Leaving dub: Don Carlos / Jah a de dub: McGregor, Freddie / Cool dub: Don Carlos / Dub sheriff: Broggs, Peter / Sunshine dub: Don Carlos / Nice to be dub: Roots Radics / General dub: Charlie Chaplin / Always dub: Brown, Foxy / Dub farmer: Broggs, Peter / Hungry dub: McGregor, Freddie / Coming home dub: Broggs, Peter / Live as dub: Brown, Foxy / Lyrics of dub: Brigadier Jerry / Dub divorce: Sanchez / Mandela dub: Brigadier Jerry / Dub we land: Roots Radics / Crucial dub: Lazo / Don't you dub: Lazo / Game called dub: Isaacs, Gregory / Whole world dub: Ras Pidow / Dub overdue: Ras Pidow / Afrika dub: Ras Pidow / Real dub: Lazo / Give a little dub: Isaacs, Gregory / Dub and go: Isaacs, Gregory / Broken dub: Pardon Me / Roots dub: Ras Pidow / Peace and dub: Lazo / Dreamer dub: Lazo / Shabada dub: Lazo / House of rising dub: Isaacs, Gregory
RAS 3504 / May '97 / Ras

☐ **DUBS FOR DAZE VOL.2 (Scientist Dubs Up The Ras Tapes/2CD Set)**
Goon a dub: Eek-A-Mouse / Ready for dub: Yellow Man / Praising dub: Broggs, Peter / Dub belly: McGregor, Freddie / Wild wild dub: Yellow Man / Aids man: Yellow Man / Bossman dub: Smith, Wayne / Mess with dub: Broggs, Peter / Me oh my oh dub: Eek-A-Mouse / Mama mama dub: McGregor, Freddie / Lying dub: Eek-A-Mouse / Dub gone dub: Broggs, Peter / Virgin dub: Yellow Man / Merry dub / Jingle bells / Do dub: Eek-A-Mouse / Pass the dub: Michigan & Smiley / International dub: Broggs, Peter / Damn dub: Smith, Wayne / Ease up dub: Yellow Man / Ethiopia dub: Broggs, Peter / Dubbing home: McGregor, Freddie / Golden dub: Broggs, Peter / Girlish dub: Eek-A-Mouse / Too hot dub: Yellow Man / Party dub: Yellow Man / Boys want dub: Yellow Man / Here we dub: Michigan & Smiley / Loving dub: Yellow Man / Freaky dub: Eek-A-Mouse
RAS 3505 / May '97 / Ras

☐ **DUBWISE AND OTHERWISE (Blood & Fire Audio Catalogue)**
In the ghetto: Big Joe / Wreck up a version: Prince Jammy & The Aggrovators / Michael Talbot affair: Hudson, Keith / Institution: Burning Spear / Jah love dub: Yabby You & King Tubby / Government land: Andy, Horace / Dub MPLA: Tappa Zukie / Children crying: Congos / African people: Jah Stitch / Ethiopian version: King Tubby & The Soul Syndicate / One man dub: Scientist / King Tubby's in fine style: King Tubby / Assack lawn number one dub: Brown, Glen & King Tubby / Look a boom: I-Roy / Concord: Morwell Unlimited & King Tubby / Good vibes: Andy, Horace
BFCDS 903 / 17 Nov '97 / Blood & Fire

☐ **DUBWISE VOL.1 & 2**
PRFCD 45 / Aug '97 / Phase One

☐ **DUCK AND COVER**
SST 263CD / Aug '90 / SST

☐ **DUENDE**
ELLICD 3350 / Oct '94 / Ellipsis Arts

☐ **DUETS**
CWNCD 2004 / Jun '95 / Javelin

☐ **DUETS (2CD Set)**
Ebony and ivory: McCartney, Paul & Stevie Wonder / Don't know much: Ronstadt, Linda & Aaron Neville / Waltz away dreaming: Rourke, Toby & George Michael / If you ever: East 17 & Gabrielle / Senza una donna: Zucchero & Paul Young / Delicate: D'Arby, Terence Trent & Des'ree / With you I'm born again: Preston, Billy & Syreeta / Would I lie to you: Charles & Eddie / You're all I need to get by: Gaye, Marvin & Tammi Terrell / Somethings gotten hold of my heart: Almond, Marc & Gene Pitney / Too much too little too late: Mathis, Johnny & Deniece Williams / All I have to do is dream: Gentry, Bobbie & Glen Campbell / Sometimes love just ain't enough: Smyth, Patty & Don Henley / Passing strangers: Vaughan, Sarah & Billy Eckstine / Something stupid: Sinatra, Frank & Nancy / Baby come to me: Austin, Patti & James Ingram / All I ask for you: Crawford, Michael & Barbara Bonney / Je T'aime...moi non plus: Birkin, Jane & Serge Gainsbourg / Up on the roof: Robson & Jerome / Up where we belong: Cocker, Joe & Jennifer Warnes / Love wars: Womack & Womack / Yah mo b there: Ingram, James & Michael McDonald / Sisters are doin' it from themselves: Eurythmics & Aretha Franklin / Solid: Ashford & Simpson / Reunited: Peaches & Herb / It takes two: Gaye, Marvin & Kim Weston / I got you babe: Sonny & Cher / Could it be I'm falling in love: Grant, David & Jaki Graham / You are everything: Roberts, Joe & Melanie Williams / We've got tonight: Easton, Sheena & Kenny Rogers / Dream a little dream: Armstrong, Louis & Ella Fitzgerald / Lily was here: Stewart, Dave & Cindy Duffer / I can't go for that: Hall & Oates / In a life time: Clannad & Bono / I know him so well: Paige, Elaine & Barbara Dickson / Little drummer boy: Bowie, David & Bing Crosby
TTVCD 2927 / 17 Nov '97 / Telstar TV

☐ **DULCE & FORTISSIMAE**
NT 6733CD / Apr '95 / Robi Droli

☐ **DUNGEON OF DELIGHT (2CD Set)**
NZ 010CD / Jun '94 / Nova Zembla

☐ **DUOLOGUE**
LYRCD 7430 / Nov '97 / Lyrichord

☐ **DUST OFF RIDDIM**
VPCD 2075 / 8 Jun '98 / VP

☐ **DUSTY AND FORGOTTEN (1950's Vocal Groups)**
FLYCD 54 / Feb '94 / Flyright

☐ **DUTCH HARBOR**
ALP 85CD / Apr '97 / Atavistic

☐ **DYNAMO OPEN AIR 10TH ANNIVERSARY**
Self-bias resistor: Fear Factory / Once solemn: Paradise Lost / Blood and fire: Type O Negative / Ball of destruction: Madball / Gorrit: Dub War / No fronts: Dog Eat Dog / Paint it black: Grip Inc. / Old: Machine Head / Till the end of time: Trouble / Proof: Eleven Pictures / Still pounds: Mental Hippie Blood / Systems failing: Nevermore / On the toad again: Motorpsycho / Pump it up: Warrior Soul / Liefe: Waving Corn / Whatever that hurts: Tiamat / Body cry: Downset / Falling: Biohazard
RR 89272 / Sep '96 / Roadrunner

E

☐ **EAR PIERCING PUNK**
AIPCD 1056 / Jan '97 / Archive

☐ **EARLY AMERICAN RURAL MUSIC VOL.1 (Times Ain't Like They Used To Be - 1920's/1930's)**
YAZ2030 / May '97 / Yazoo

☐ **EARLY AMERICAN RURAL MUSIC VOL.2 (Times Ain't Like They Used To Be - 1920's/1930's)**
YAZ 2031 / May '97 / Yazoo

☐ **EARLY B ANTHOLOGY, THE**
MRCD 6 / 22 Jun '98 / Midnight Rock

☐ **EARLY CANADIAN ROCKERS VOL.3**
CLCD 4432 / Sep '96 / Collector/White Label

☐ **EARLY CANTE FLAMENCO VOL.1 (The Early 1930's)**
ARHCD 326 / Apr '95 / Arhoolie

☐ **EARLY DAWN (2CD Set)**
DSRCD 004 / 27 Jul '98 / Dreamscape

☐ **EARLY GIRLS VOL.1 (Popsicles & Icicles)**
Doo wah diddy: Exciters / You're no good: Everett, Betty / Name game: Ellis, Shirley / Chains: Cookies / It might as well rain until September: King, Carole / I'm into something good: Earl Jean / I can't stay mad at you: Davis, Skeeter / I wish I were a princess: March, 'Little' Peggy / I told every little star: Scott, Linda / Triangle: Grant, Janie / West of the wall: Fisher, Toni / Pink shoelaces: Stevens, Dodie / Music music music: Sensations / Dear Abby: Hearts / Whenever a teenager cries: Reparata & The Delrons / Popsicles and icicles: Murmaids / Wonderful summer: Ward, Robin & The Rainbows / I love how you love me: Paris Sisters / Dark moon: Guitar, Bonnie / You: Aquatones / Till: Angels / Great pretender: Young, Kathy / Angel baby: Rosie & The Originals / Eddie my love: Teen Queens / He's gone: Chantels / Dedicated to the one I love: Shirelles / Son in law: Blossoms / Easier said than done: Essex
CDCHD 608 / Sep '95 / Ace

☐ **EARLY GIRLS VOL.2**
My boy lollipop: Gaye, Barbie / Tell him: Exciters / Our day will come: Ruby & The Romantics / Boy next door: Secrets / Every beat of my heart: Knight, Gladys / Cry baby: Bonnie Sisters / You don't own me: Gore, Lesley / Street: Terry & The Tunisians / Bobby's girl: Blane, Marcie / Sugartime: McGuire Sisters / Tonight you belong to me: Patience & Prudence / Kind of boy you can't forget: Raindrops / Fever: Lee, Peggy / September in the rain: Washington, Dinah / I'll save the last dance for you: Jo, Damita / Teach me tiger: Stevens, April / I just don't understand: Ann-Margaret / I met him on a Sunday: Shirelles / Lonely blue nights: Rosie & The Originals / Forgive me (for giving you such a bad time): Tino, Babs / Thousand stars: Young, Kathy / Let me in: Sensations / Well, I told you: Chantels / Lonely nights: Hearts / Duchess of earl: Pearlettes / Move on: Blossoms / Letter full of tears: Knight, Gladys & The Pips / What's a matter baby (is it hurting you): Yuro, Timi
CDCHD 657 / Jun '97 / Ace

☐ **EARLY MUSIC OF THE NORTH CARIBBEAN 1916-1920**
HQCD 67 / May '96 / Harlequin

☐ **EARLY NEGRO VOCAL GROUPS VOL.2 1893-1923**
DOCD 5288 / Dec '94 / Document

☐ **EARLY NEGRO VOCAL GROUPS VOL.3 1921-1924**
DOCD 5355 / Jun '95 / Document

☐ **EARLY NEGRO VOCAL GROUPS VOL.4 1921-1924**
DOCD 5531 / Apr '97 / Document

☐ **EARLY RHYTHM 'N' BLUES 1943-1953**
Five guys named moe: Jordan, Louis / Marry a woman uglier than you: Duke Of Iron / Whitman platter: Whitman, Ernest 'Bubbles' / Honky tonk train blues: Lewis, Meade 'Lux' / I'm gonna move to the outskirts of town: Jordan, Louis / Infantry blues: Jordan, Louis / In the mood: Morris, Ernie / Comedy routine: McQueen, Butterfly & Ernest 'Bubbles' Whitman / This train: Tharpe, Sister Rosetta / Knock me a kiss: Jordan, Louis / Pink champagne: Liggins, Joe 'Honeydripper' / Harlem nocturne: Otis, Johnny Band / Goof: McNeely, 'Big' Jay Band / Serenade in blue: McNeely, 'Big' Jay Band / Deacon's parade: McNeely, 'Big' Jay Band / Boogie in the front: McNeely, 'Big' Jay Band / Body and soul: McNeely, 'Big' Jay Band / Deacon's hop: McNeely, 'Big' Jay Band / I'm just a fool in love: Milburn, Amos / Charmaine: Vinson, Eddie 'Cleanhead' / Didn't it rain children: Tharpe, Sister Rosetta / Time alone will tell: Jackson, Bull Moose / Let's ball tonight
CDMOJO 307 / Nov '96 / Mojo

☐ **EARLY SHAKER SPIRITUALS**
ROUCD 0078 / Aug '96 / Rounder

☐ **EARLY WAR YEARS, THE**
We're gonna hang out the washing: Flanagan & Allen / Yours: Lynn, Vera / Nearness of you: Hutch / I'm stepping out with a memory: Mesene, Jimmy & Al Bowlly / Wings over the navy: Stone, Lew & Sam Browne / I haven't time to be a millionaire: Mesene, Jimmy & Al Bowlly / Our sergeant major: Formby, George / American patrol: Miller, Glenn / It's a hap-hap-happy day: Roy, Harry & Ray Ellington / Run rabbit run: Flanagan & Allen / It's a pair of wings for me: Gonella, Nat & His New Georgians / Bless 'em all: Cotton, Billy & Allan Breeze / Turn the money in your pocket: Mesene, Jimmy & Al Bowlly / I'll never smile again: Mesene, Jimmy & Al Bowlly / We'll go smiling along: Mesene, Jimmy & Al Bowlly / We must all stick together: Geraldo & Cyril Grantham / White cliffs of Dover: Lynn, Vera / My prayer: Henderson, Chick & Joe Loss Orchestra / Oh buddy I'm in love: Gonella, Nat / Oh Johnny oh: Roy, Harry & His Tiger Ragamuffins / Kiss me goodnight sergeant major: Cotton, Billy & Allan Breeze / Juke box saturday night: Miller, Glenn / All over the place: Thorburn, Billy & His Dance Band / Moonlight serenade: Miller, Glenn / Wish me luck as you wave me goodbye: Fields, Gracie
PASTCD 7017 / Mar '97 / Flapper

☐ **EARLY YEARS VOL.2**
WBRCD 802 / Nov '92 / Business

☐ **EARLY YEARS VOL.3**
WBRCD 803 / Mar '94 / Business

☐ **EARPLUGGED VOL.1**
MOSH 115CD / Sep '94 / Earache

☐ **EARPLUGGED VOL.2**
Breed to breathe: *Napalm Death* / Stained glass horizon: *Cathedral* / Keep on rotting in the free world: *Carcass* / Blinded by fear: *At The Gates* / Circle of shit: *Godflesh* / Strike it: *Dub War* / Hippy fascist: *Pulkas* / Million lies: *Misery Loves Company* / Strangled: *Ultraviolence* / Undead: *Haunted* / Big loader: *Iron Monkey* / Underachiever: *Pitch Shifter* / Stranger aeons: *Entombed* / Technology's Gay: *AC/Damage* 381: *Extreme Noise Terror*
MOSH 187CD / 1 Sep '97 / Earache

☐ **EARTH BEAT**
Mental cube-Q: *Mental Cube* / Quazi: *Yage* / You took my love: *Candese* / Papua New Guinea: *Future Sound Of London* / So this is love: *Mental Cube* / Child of the bass generation: *Mental Cube* / Tingler: *Smart Systems* / Coda coma: *Yage* / Owl: *Indo Tribe* / People livin' for today: *Semi Real* / Theme from Hot Burst: *Yage* / Shrink: *Indo Tribe* / Stakker humanoid: *Humanoid* / In the mind of a child: *Indo Tribe* / Creator: *Smart Systems* / Bite the bullet baby: *Indo Tribe*
CDTOT 7 / Nov '91 / Jumpin' & Pumpin'

☐ **EARTH RITUAL (A Journey Into Drum 'n' Bass)**
CLP 0105 / 6 Oct '97 / Hypnotic

☐ **EARTH SONGS (12 Original Songs Honouring The Earth)**
My heart soars: *Friedmann* / Out of the earth: *Wynberg, Simon* / Desert song: *Stein, Ira* / Thousand small gold bells: *Arkenstone, David* / Earth cry mercy: *Gettel, Michael* / In return: *Tingstad, Eric & Nancy Rumbel* / Calling: *Jones, Michael* / Universal garden: *Kostia* / Remember remember: *Mirowitz, Sheldon* / Forgotten places: *Illenberger, Ralf* / Which is yes: *Brewer, Spencer* / Earth tribe: *Lauria, Nando*
ND 63913 / Oct '93 / Narada

☐ **EARTHDANCE (2CD Set)**
TRANR 617CD / 8 Jun '98 / Transient

☐ **EARTHQUAKE ALBUM, THE**
Smoke on the water: *Rock Aid Armenia* / All right now: *Free* / Since you've been gone: *Rainbow* / Headless cross: *Black Sabbath* / Turn it on again: *Genesis* / Fool for your loving: *Whitesnake* / Heat of the moment: *Asia* / We built this city: *Starship* / Run to the hills: *Iron Maiden* / Silent running: *Mike & The Mechanics* / Amanda: *Boston*
ANT 010 / Nov '96 / Tring

☐ **EARTHRISE SHADOW VOL.3**
Azulee: *Shantel* / Maxwell's demon: *Taran* / Lo: *Megashira* / Blind television: *Jammin' Unit* / Mosaik: *Kosma* / Splendid: *Marschmellows* / Sighting: *Cujo* / Charlie X: *Spaceways* / On the loose: *Slowly* / Le funkster: *Le Gooster* / Blow jam: *Mr. Electric Triangle* / Free radicals: *Futique* / Blind man's bluff: *Spectral Assignment*
SDW 0262 / Jun '97 / Shadow

☐ **EASIN' IN (Essential Texas Blues)**
Cottonfield blues: *Thomas, Henry* / Bull-doze blues: *Thomas, Henry* / Fishing blues: *Thomas, Henry* / Dallas rag: *Dallas String Band* / Got the blues: *Jefferson, Blind Lemon* / Long lonesome blues: *Jefferson, Blind Lemon* / Bad luck blues: *Jefferson, Blind Lemon* / Matchbox blues: *Jefferson, Blind Lemon* / See that my grave's kept clean: *Jefferson, Blind Lemon* / Doggone my good luck soul: *Hudson, Hattie* / Double crossing blues: *Alexander, Texas* / Hungry wolf blues: *Smith, J.T. 'Funny Paper'* / Ground hog blues: *Ramblin' Thomas* / Easin' in: *Cadillac, Bobbie* / Elm Street blues: *Day, Texas Bill* / Thieving blues: *Ranger, Jack* / Hurry blues: *Jones, Little Hat* / Blue goose blues: *Thomas, Jesse* / Black gal what makes your head so hard: *Pullum, Joe* / Ninth Street stomp: *Edwards, Bernice* / Bull cow blues: *Moore, Alex* / Trifling woman: *Black Ace* / You gonna need my help some day: *Black Ace* / Got a break baby: *Walker, T-Bone*
IGOCD 2043 / Nov '96 / Indigo

☐ **EAST COAST ASSAULT VOL.1**
TOODAMNHY 22 / May '97 / Too Damn Hype

☐ **EAST COAST ASSAULT VOL.2 (2CD Set)**
TDH 020 / Feb '97 / Too Damn Hype

☐ **EAST COAST BLUES**
FLYCD 45 / Nov '92 / Flyright

☐ **EAST COAST BLUES**
Crow Jane blues: *Daniels, Julius* / You gonna quit me blues: *Blake, Arthur 'Blind'* / Church bells blues: *Jordan, Louis* / Pick poor Robin clean: *Jordan, Louis* / Cocaine blues: *Jordan, Louis* / Barbershop rag: *Moore, William* / Old country rock: *Moore, William* / Raggin' the blues: *Moore, William* / Every day in the week blues: *Anderson, Pink & Simmie Dooley* / Brownie blues: *Tarter & Gay* / Unknown blues: *Tarter & Gay* / Dupree blues: *Walker, Willie* / South Carolina rag: *Walker, Willie* / Good gal: *White, Joshua* / Low cotton: *White, Joshua* / Blood red river: *White, Joshua* / I'm throwin' up my hands: *Davis, 'Blind' Gary* / Cross and evil woman blues: *Davis, 'Blind' Gary* / Farewell to you baby: *Martin, Carl* / Badly mistreated man: *Martin, Carl* / Crow Jane: *Martin, Carl* / Old time blues: *Martin, Carl* / Picking my tomatoes: *McGhee, Brownie* / Dealing with the devil: *McGhee, Brownie*
IGOCD 2044 / Mar '97 / Indigo

☐ **EAST COAST BLUES IN THE THIRTIES**
SOB 035282 / Feb '93 / Story Of The Blues

☐ **EAST COAST JIVE (Apollo Theatre Recordings)**
Everything's cool: *Gonzales, Babs* / 1280 special: *Gonzales, Babs* / Phipps' deep: *Gonzales, Babs* / It takes a long, tall, brown skin gal: *Four Blues* / Re bop de boom: *Four Blues* / It ain't what you had: *Four Blues* / Call the police: *Simms, Artie* / Take it easy baby: *Simms, Artie* / Darktown strutters ball: *Morgan, Loumell* / Bow tie Jim: *Morgan, Loumell* / Blackstick boogie: *Smith, Ben* / Travelin' Papa: *Smith, Ben* / No lovin' woman: *Smith, Ben* / Roy's groove: *Gonzales, Babs* / Phipps' deep: *Gonzales, Babs* / Blues in the night: *Morgan, Loumell* / Old man river: *Morgan, Loumell* / Whistlin' at the chicks: *Wallace, Babe* / Ain't gonna worry 'bout nothin': *Wallace, Babe* / I'd rather have you fat and happy: *Four Blues* / Vegetable song: *Four Blues*
DE 669 / Mar '97 / Delmark

☐ **EAST COAST VOL.1**
ECCD 0001 / May '96 / East Coast

☐ **EAST COAST VOL.2**
ECCD 00022 / Jul '97 / East Coast

☐ **EAST ST. LOUIS**
Hey hey: *Renrut, Icky* / Tell me why: *Renrut, Icky* / Jack rabbit: *Renrut, Icky* / Ho ho: *Renrut, Icky* / In your eyes baby: *Renrut, Icky* / Star above: *Foster, Bobby* / Pracin': *Renrut, Icky* / Angel of love: *Foster, Bobby* / I do love you: *Foster, Bobby* / Hey hey: *Renrut, Icky* / You're the only one: *Foster, Bobby* / Lovin' man: *Cooper, Timothy* / Look at that chick: *Wright, Johnny* / Gotta have you for myself: *Wright, Johnny* / Shirley can't you see: *Little Bobby Foster* / I woke up one morning: *Little Bobby Foster* / I don't want to lose your love: *Grimes, Sammy Band* / Bad pipe special: *Grimes, Sammy Band* / Moving slow: *Little Cooper & the Drifters* / Evening train: *Little Cooper & the Drifters* / East St.Louis rock: *Cooper, Timothy* / Lovin' man: *Cooper, Timothy* / Leaving Kansas city: *Cooper, Timothy*
NEMCD 940 / 29 Sep '97 / Sequel

☐ **EAST-WESTERCISM (2CD Set)**
LAANGE 2CD / May '97 / Law & Auder/ Blue Angel

☐ **EASTERN PENNSYLVANIA ROCK VOL.1**
AA 069 / 27 Apr '98 / Arf Arf

☐ **EASTERN PENNSYLVANIA ROCK VOL.2**
AA 070 / 27 Apr '98 / Arf Arf

☐ **EASTERN UPRISING (2CD Set)**
Goddess: *Joi* / Core: *Cocoon* / Sitar funk: *Earthtribe* / Harmon dub: *Black Star Liner* / Dum maro dum: *Safri Goes To Bollywood* / Return of the shankar: *Krome Assassins* / Temple of doom: *Tango Padre* / Ruffistahn: *Bedouin Ascent* / RAFI: *Asian Dub Foundation Sound System* / Loaded mantra: *Masters Of Sound* / Earthtribe: *Earthtribe* / Om: *Patrina*
4872162 / Apr '97 / Higherground

☐ **EASTSIDE SOUND, THE**
BA 08CD / Apr '96 / Bacchus Archives

☐ **EASTWOOD AFTER HOURS (Live At Carnegie Hall/2CD Set)**
Misty / First time ever I saw your face / This time the dream's on me / Hootie's blues / San antonio rose / Satin doll / After hours (suite) / Straight No Chaser / Round midnight / I see your face / Cherokee / Laura / I didn't know what time it was / Parker's mood / Thsese foolish things / Lester leaps in / After hours/ C.E. blues
9362465462 / 24 Nov '97 / Warner Bros.

☐ **EASY AND SLOW**
HCD 127 / Apr '95 / GTD

☐ **EASY LISTENING (2CD Set)**
Il senzio: *Rosso, Nini* / Wonderland by night: *Strings Of Paris* / Brazil: *Papetti, Fausto* / Stranger on the shore: *Bilk, Acker* / Red roses for a blue lady: *Dana, Vic* / Guitar tango: *Vandyke, Lex* / Tequila: *Prado, Perez* / Midnight cowboy: *Strings Of Paris* / You're nobody till somebody loves you: *Martin, Dean* / Girl from Ipanema: *Ipanema Beach Orchestra* / More I see you: *Humperdinck, Engelbert* / Besame mucho: *Vandyke, Lex* / Fool on the hill: *Ipanema Beach Orchestra* / MacArthur Park: *Ipanema Beach Orchestra* / One note samba: *Ipanema Beach Orchestra* / Somethin stupid: *Ipanema Beach Orchestra* / Aqua de beber: *Ipanema Beach Orchestra* / Malaguena: *Trio Trakitan* / Quizas quizas quizas: *Trio Trakitan* / Shadow of your smile: *Papetti, Fausto* / My way: *Papetti, Fausto* / Raindrops keep falling on my head: *Thomas, B.J.* / Hooked on a feeling: *Thomas, B.J.* / Hawaiian wedding song: *Waikiki Minstrels* / Moon river: *Valentino, Serge* / I say a little prayer: *Warwick, Dionne* / Do you know the way to San Jose: *Warwick, Dionne* / El condor pasa: *Bomha, Dinu* / La montanara: *Rosso, Nini* / Petite fleur: *Kaper, Bob* / Amor, amor, amor: *Vandyke, Lex* / La comparsa: *Vandyke, Lex* / Et maintenant: *Strings Of Paris* / Man and a woman: *Strings Of Paris* / Send in the flowers: *Gorme, Eydie* / You'll always be the one I love: *Martin, Dean* / Patricia: *Prado, Perez* / Once upon a time in the west: *Soho Strings* / Sleepwalk: *Santo & Johnny* / Deep purple: *Tempo, Nino & April Stevens* / Georgia on my mind: *Kaper, Bob* / In crowd: *Lewis, Ramsey Trio*
DBG 53053 / Jul '96 / Double Gold

☐ **EASY LISTENING**
I just called to say I love you: *Strasser, Hugo & Sein Tanzorchester* / They can't take that away from me/ C'est si bon: *Wunderlich, Klaus* / Moonlight serenade: *Manuel & The Music Of The Mountains* / Vaya con dios: *Love, Geoff & His Orchestra* / Cherry pink and apple blossom white: *Calvert, Eddie* / Breeze and I/More/I could have danced all night: *Wunderlich, Klaus* / Rivers of Babylon: *Loss, Joe* / Mr. Sandman: *Silvester, Victor & His Ballroom Orchestra* / Ella: *Moss, Andre* / Du schwarzer Zigeuner: *Orchestre Grand Cafe* / Sleepy shores: *Pearson, Johnny*
KS 875102 / Jul '97 / Disky

☐ **EASY LISTENING COLLECTION, THE (Moonlight Serenade/Alley Cat/Sail Along Silvery Moon/3CDSet)**
Moonlight serenade: *Miller, Glenn Orchestra UK* / Solitaire: *Vaughn, Billy Orchestra* / Raindrops keep falling on my head: *Winterhalter, Hugo* / Sandy roads: *Bent Fabric* / Glutrote rosen: *Ingmann, Jorgen* / Love story: *Vaughn, Billy Orchestra* / How deep is your love: *Erling, Ole* / Never my love: *Winterhalter, Hugo* / Red roses for a blue lady: *Vaughn, Billy Orchestra* / Stranger, where are you now: *Bent Fabric* / Blue eyes crying in the rain: *Hirt, Al* / Fernando: *Erling, Ole* / Rose from Santa Monica: *Ingmann, Jorgen* / Spanish eyes: *Vaughn, Billy Orchestra* / Taste of honey: *Winterhalter, Hugo* / Wonderland by night: *Hirt, Al* / Alley cat: *Bent Fabric* / Theme from 'A Summer Place': *Vaughn, Billy Orchestra* / Faded love: *Hirt, Al* / California dreaming: *Winterhalter, Hugo* / From now on: *Bent Fabric* / Killing me softly with his song: *Erling, Ole* / Sentimental journey: *Miller, Glenn Orchestra UK* / Strangers in the night: *Vaughn, Billy Orchestra* / This guy's in love with you: *Ingmann, Jorgen* / Born free: *Winterhalter, Hugo* / Yesterday: *Erling, Ole* / Norwegian sunset: *Bent Fabric* / Greensleeves: *Vaughn, Billy Orchestra* / La la la: *Ingmann, Jorgen* / Not a bit in love: *Bent Fabric* / Is blue: *Vaughn, Billy Orchestra* / Sail along silvery moon: *Vaughn, Billy Orchestra* / Theme from 'Love Story': *Winterhalter, Hugo* / Oh my papa (Oh mein papa): *Hirt, Al* / Matador: *Bent Fabric* / Long and winding road: *Winterhalter, Hugo* / Wishing and hoping: *Ingmann, Jorgen* / Matrimony: *Erling, Ole* / Java: *Hirt, Al* / Stranger on the shore: *Vaughn, Billy Orchestra* / When shadows fall: *Bent Fabric* / Rhapsody in blue: *Hirt, Al* / La mer: *Ingmann, Jorgen* / Love is a riddle: *Bent Fabric* / Love theme from 'Romeo and Juliet': *Winterhalter, Hugo* / Tie a yellow ribbon round the old oak tree: *Erling, Ole* / Only yesterday: *Vaughn, Billy Orchestra*
101112 / May '97 / A-Play Collection

☐ **EASY LISTENING MOODS**
5404142 / Sep '95 / A&M

☐ **EASY LISTENING VOL.1 (Moonlight Serenade)**
Moonlight serenade: *Miller, Glenn & His Orchestra* / Solitaire: *Vaughn, Billy Orchestra* / Raindrops keep falling on my head: *Winterhalter, Hugo* / Sandy roads: *Bent Fabric* / Glutrote rosen: *Ingmann, Jorgen* / Rose from Santa Monica: *Ingmann, Jorgen* / Love story: *Vaughn, Billy Orchestra* / Red roses for a blue lady: *Vaughn, Billy Orchestra* / Spanish eyes: *Vaughn, Billy Orchestra* / How deep is your love: *Erling, Ole* / Fernando: *Erling, Ole* / Never my love: *Winterhalter, Hugo* / Taste of honey: *Winterhalter, Hugo* / Stranger where are you now: *Bent Fabric* / Blue eyes crying in the rain: *Hirt, Al* / Wonderland by night: *Hirt, Al*
101122 / May '97 / A-Play Collection

☐ **EASY LISTENING VOL.2 (Alley Cat)**
Alley cat: *Bent Fabric* / From now on: *Bent Fabric* / Norwegian sunset: *Bent Fabric* / Not a bit in love: *Bent Fabric* / Theme from 'A summer place': *Vaughn, Billy Orchestra* / Strangers in the night: *Vaughn, Billy Orchestra* / Greensleeves: *Vaughn, Billy Orchestra* / Blue: *Vaughn, Billy Orchestra* / Faded love: *Hirt, Al* / California dreaming: *Winterhalter, Hugo* / Born free: *Winterhalter, Hugo* / Killing me softly with his song: *Erling, Ole* / Yesterday: *Erling, Ole* / Sentimental journey: *Miller, Glenn & His Orchestra* / This guy's in love with you: *Ingmann, Jorgen* / La la la: *Ingmann, Jorgen*
101132 / May '97 / A-Play Collection

☐ **EASY LISTENING VOL.3**
Sail along silvery moon: *Vaughn, Billy Orchestra* / Stranger on the shore: *Vaughn, Billy Orchestra* / Only yesterday: *Vaughn, Billy Orchestra* / Love story: *Winterhalter, Hugo* / Long and winding road: *Winterhalter, Hugo* / Romeo and Juliet: *Winterhalter, Hugo* / Oh my Papa: *Hirt, Al* / Rhapsody in blue: *Hirt, Al* / Matador: *Bent Fabric* / When shadows fall: *Bent Fabric* / Love is a riddle: *Bent Fabric* / Java: *Hirt, Al* / Matrimony: *Erling, Ole* / Tie a yellow ribbon round the old oak tree: *Erling, Ole* / Wishing and hoping: *Ingmann, Jorgen* / La Mer: *Ingmann, Jorgen*
101142 / May '97 / A-Play Collection

☐ **EASY LISTENING VOLUME.3**
NORMAL 192CD / Aug '95 / Normal

☐ **EASY PROJECT VOL.1, THE (20 Lounge Favourites)**
Shake: *Johnston, Laurie Orchestra* / Kinda kinky: *McVay, Ray Orchestra* / Mas que nada: *Sounds Orchestral* / Lunar walk: *Hawksworth, Johnny Orchestra* / Walk on the wild side: *Tew, Alan Orchestra* / It's murder: *Hawksworth, Johnny Orchestra* / Theme from San Benedict: *Keating, Johnny Orchestra* / House of the rising sun: *Synthesonic Sound* / Blue 'n' groovy: *Paraffin Jack Flash Ltd* / Clown: *Keating, Johnny Orchestra* / Echo four two: *Johnson, Laurie Orchestra* / Mucho Mexico Seven-O: *Shakespeare, John Orchestra* / High society: *Reed, Les Piano* / Staccato: *Eliminators* / Ironside: *Tew, Alan Orchestra* / Getaway: *Keating, Johnny & The Z Men* / Superfly: *Synthesonic Sound* / Revenge: *McVay, Ray Orchestra* / But she ran the other way: *Schroeder, John Orchestra* / Spiral: *Roache, Harry Constellation*
NEMCD 772 / Oct '95 / Sequel

☐ **EASY PROJECT VOL.2, THE (Welcome To The House Of Lounge)**
Fear is the key: *Budd, Roy Orchestra* / Out of this world: *Hatch, Tony* / Funko: *Saint Orchestra* / West End: *Saint Orchestra* / Mr. Rose: *Budd, Roy* / Sportsnight: *Hatch, Tony Orchestra* / Pinball wizard: *Roche, Harry Constellation* / Wana nana wana nana: *Schroeder, John Orchestra* / Turnpike Lane: *Moore, Pete Orchestra/Chorus* / Love today, cry tomorrow: *Stapleton, Cyril* / Man alive: *Hatch, Tony Sound* / Blue streak: *Allen, Jerry Trio* / Sleep walk: *Killer Watts* / Virgin soldiers march: *Schroeder, John Orchestra* / Le blon: *City Of Westminster String Band* / Colditz march: *Ainsworth, Alyn Orchestra* / Peter Popgunn: *Schroeder, John Orchestra* / Limehouse: *Johnson, Laurie Orchestra* / London life: *Harris, Anita* / Bird has flown: *Schroeder, John Orchestra* / Car chase: *Budd, Roy Orchestra* / We can work it out/Hey Jude: *Killer Watts*
NEMCD 842 / Jun '96 / Sequel

☐ **EASY PROJECT VOL.7, THE (Sounds Chartbound)**
NEMCD 938 / 30 Mar '98 / Sequel

☐ **EASY TEMPO VOL.3 (A Further Cinematic Easy Listening Experience)**
Saudade / Nago / I cavalli / Bob E Hellen / North Pole penguin / Frenesia / La bikinia / Il Libanese / Lady Magnolia / Diamond bossa nova / Amanda's train / Beryl's tune / La seduzione / Easy lovers / Flute sequence / Beryl's tune / Soul samba / Casa di moda / Honey, rhythm and butter / Danza citar free / Esquetando os tambourinos e cuica
ET 904CD / Oct '97 / Easy Tempo

☐ **EASY TEMPO VOL.5**
Nanaue: *Martelli, Augusto* / Auke nuraught: *Euriquez, Luis* / L'Areangelo: *Umiliani, Piero* / Runnung fast: *Torossi, Stefano* / Blazing magnum: *Trovajoli, Armando* / Trops: *Baldan-Bembo, Alberto* / Loco love motor: *Martelli, Augusto* / Vuca: *Mimms, Tony* / Chicken: *Oliver, Dick* / La rai si presenta: *Piccioni, Piero* / Bagilore: *Lesiman* / Apollo beat: *Migliori, Jay* / Adonal: *Morricone, Ennio* / Montreal non stop: *Bacalav, Luis Enriquez* / Frog: *Martelli, Augusto* / Upa neguino: *Martelli, Augusto*
ET 911 / Apr '98 / Easy Tempo

☐ **EAT RAW INTERNATIONALISTS**
EAT 013 / 11 May '98 / Eat Raw

☐ **EAT YOUR HEAD**
ANDA 225CD / Nov '97 / Au-Go-Go

☐ **EBB STORY VOL.1, THE**
I've got a feeling / What is life without a home / If you please / Time brings about a change / Look what you're doing to me / True lips / Buzz buzz buzz / Way you carry on / Love like a fool / Look no hair / I wanna know / Darkness / Keep walkin' on / Good mornin' baby / Sure nuff / You fascinate me / Mine all mine / Voodoo love / Never let me go / Wrapped up in a dream / She's my witch / Oh Linda / Lucky Johnny / Need your lovin' / Much too much / Come on / My silent prayer / Run run run / Kiss me squeeze me / Hali-lou
CDCHD 524 / Feb '95 / Ace

☐ **EBB STORY VOL.2, THE**
Everywhere I go: *Taylor, Ted* / Live like a king: *Twilighters* / Days are dark: *Taylor, Ted* / Very truly yours: *Taylor, Ted* / If I don't see you again: *Taylor, Ted* / Hold on (I've got the chills): *Taylor, Ted* / Picadilly: *Jaguars* / Hold me tight: *Jaguars* / Trinidad woman: *Ebb Tones* / Beautiful city: *Zion Travellers* / Believe in me: *Zion Travellers* / When I get you back: *Harris, Tony* / Give me back my heart: *Hollywood Flames* / Two little bees: *Hollywood Flames* / There is something on your mind: *Hollywood Flames* / Just for you: *Hollywood Flames* / Close to you: *Fabulous Tones* / Burning desire: *Tempo-Mentals* / Weathers stormy: *Lampkin, Tony* / True confession: *Ruffin, Riff* / Look up: *Erkard, Tommy* / Bump de bump: *Souvenirs* / When the deal goes down: *Agee, Ray* / Why in the world: *Allen, Tony* / Heavenly escort: *5 Orleans* / Baby let me hold your hand: *Professor Longhair* / Misery: *Professor Longhair* / Harlem nocturne: *Jones, JJ*
CDCHD 603 / Jun '97 / Ace

☐ **EBONY ELEMENTS VOL.1**
NL 703024 / Jun '97 / Essential Dance Music

☐ **EBONY ELEMENTS VOL.2**
NR 70303031 / 30 Mar '98 / Urban Essentials

☐ **ECHO BEACH (Far Away In Time)**
EB 016 / 9 Feb '98 / Echo Beach

☐ **ECHOES IN TIME VOL.1 & 2**
SOLAR 23 / Nov '97 / Solar

☐ **ECHOES OF MADISON COUNTY**
2148 / Aug '96 / NorthSound

☐ **ECHOES OF THE ANDES (A Magical Blend Of Music And The Sounds Of Nature)**
50532 / May '97 / Nature's Harmony

☐ **ECHOES OF THE NILE (Aspects Of Egyptian Music)**
Bell announcing Sunday morning mass / Paean from mass for day of fasting / Sample performances of small cymbals / Church bell/Coptic bible recitation / Coptic wedding reception/Song and dance / Qu'ran recitation and azan / Muhammad festival / Ud improvisation / Bashraf / Ruins / Rhythm patterns / Rhythmic improvisation / Sounds of the Mizmar / Farewell beloved / Get our old stuff / Nubian girl
MCM 3005 / May '97 / Multicultural Media

☐ **ECHOES OF THE OZARKS VOL.1**
COCD 3506 / May '96 / County

☐ **ECHOES OF THE OZARKS VOL.2**
COCD 3507 / May '96 / County

☐ **ECLECTRO (2CD Set)**
Return of the rebel: *Raw Deal* / Duden: *Atlas, Natacha* / Somatime: *Click & Cycle* / Moody pan pipes: *Zone 12* / Kush: *Zone 12* / Deep blue "C": *Alien 3* / Raw uncut: *Roots Manuva* / Positive polarity: *T-Power* / Hell bent: *BLIM* / Machines: *Doc Scott* / Mutant revisited: *DJ Trace* / One man dead: *Native Bass* / Dawn breaker: *Jazzed Up* / Blown it: *Infinite Wheel* / Global game: *Interference*
ANTICDLP 001 / Oct '96 / Anti-Static

☐ **ECLIPSE**
TWSCD 3 / 27 Jul '98 / Twisted

☐ **ECLIPSE PRESENTS (NORTH)**
Go: *Moby* / Activ 8: *Altern 8* / Hardcore heaven: *DJ Seduction* / Hardcore uproar: *Together* / Lock up: *Zero B* / Peace and harmony: *Brothers In Rhythm* / Total confusion: *Homeboy, A Hippy & A Funki-Dred* / Way in my brain: *SL2* / Feel so real: *Dream Frequency & Debbie Sharp* / Injected with a poison: *Khan, Praga* / Some justice '96: *Urban Shakedown* / Dominator: *Human Resource* / Playing with knives: *Bizarre Inc.* / I want you (forever): *Cox, Carl* / Is anybody out there: *Bassheads* / Rhythm is a mystery: *K-Klass* / Not forgotten: *Leftfield* / Gonna make you sweat (Everybody dance now): *C&C Music Factory* / Theme (unique radio edit): *Unique 3* / Is there anybody out there: *Bassheads* / Free (c'mon): *Catch* / Let me see ya move: *Visa* / Hurt you so: *Jonny L* / On a ragga tip: *SL2* / Far out: *Sonz Of A Loop Da Loop Era*
VTDCDN 73 / Mar '96 / Virgin

☐ ECLIPSE PRESENTS (SOUTH)
Go (woodtick mix): *Moby* / Activ 8: *Altern 8* / Hardcore heaven: *DJ Seduction* / Hardcore uproar: *Together* / Lock up: *Zero B* / Peace and harmony: *Brothers In Rhythm* / Total confusion: *Homeboy, A Hippy & A Funki-Dred* / Way in my brain: *SL2* / Feel so real (edit): *Dream Frequency & Debbie Sharp* / Injected with a poison: *Khan, Praga* / Some justice '95: *Urban Shakedown* / Dominator: *Human Resource* / Playing with knives: *Bizarre Inc.* / I want you (forever): *Cox, Carl* / Is there anybody out there: *Bassheads* / Rhythm is a mystery: *K-Klass* / Not forgotten: *Leftfield* / Gonna make you sweat (everybody dance now): *C&C Music Factory* / Theme (unique radio edit): *Unique 3* / Go: *Moby* / DJ'S take control: *SL2* / Insomniak: *DJ PC* / Anathasia: *T-99* / Feel so real: *Dream Frequency & Debbie Sharp* / Night in motion: *Cubic 22* / Nightbird: *Convert* / It's just a feeling: *Terrorize* / Far out: *Sonz Of A Loop Da Loop Era* / Some jsutice '95: *Urban Shakedown* / Feel real good: *Manix* / Don't go: *Awesome 3* / On a ragga tip: *SL2*
VTDCDS 73 / Mar '96 / Virgin

☐ ECLIPTIC
MPCD 15 / Jun '98 / Matsuri

☐ ECSTATIC VOL.1 (2CD Set)
PACT 1CD / Sep '96 / Impact

☐ ECSTATIC VOL.2 (2CD Set)
Hallelujah: *DJ Seduction* / Hop on the dancefloor: *Bunter & Seduction* / Let the bass kick: *DJ Sy & Unknown* / Higher now: *DJ Seduction* / Sensation: *Vibes & Wishdokta* / Come down: *Rise & Shine* / Show me your love: *Euphoria* / Touch the magic: *Stripey J* / DJ's mixing: *Edit V* / Bust the new jam: *Seduction & Eruption* / Imagination: *DJ Seduction* / Got to believe: *DJ DNA* / Go with the flow: *DJ Unknown* / Live for the future: *DJ Pooch* / Down to Love: *Force & Styles* / It's not over: *Dougal & Seduction* / Want to be free: *Sedders*
PACT 2CD / Feb '97 / Impact

☐ EDINBURGH MILITARY TATTOO 1996
EMTCD 113 / Jul '96 / Tattoo

☐ EDINBURGH MILITARY TATTOO 1997
EMTCD 114 / Aug '97 / Tattoo

☐ EGG FILES, THE
Whatever we do: *Ruts DC* / Reggae music: *Mad Professor* / Blackout: *Marineville* / Pincers: *ISM* / Dub one another: *Jah Free* / Awakening: *Vibronics* / Sweetdust: *Sounds From The Ground* / Moonwalking: *Tassilli Players* / Cuttlefish: *Zion Train* / Vibes 23: *Bong Messages* / Panatonic Analogic: *Penumbrah* / Gamma: *Extremadura* / Byte sized: *Power Steppers* / Powermix tabla: *Captain Black* / Haven brow: *Charlesworth, Bob*
WWCD 23 / 15 Sep '97 / Universal Egg

☐ EIGHT BALL - THE SOUND OF NEW YORK
XTR 13CD / Sep '94 / X-Treme

☐ EIGHT OVER THE EIGHT BALL
EBALL 2CD / Feb '95 / Produce

☐ EIGHTBALL RECORDS COMPILATION VOL.1
EBCD 1 / Jan '95 / Eightball

☐ EIGHTBALL RECORDS COMPILATION VOL.2
EBCD 3 / Jan '96 / Eightball

☐ EIGHTBALL RECORDS COMPILATION VOL.3 (Mixed By Bill Coleman/Live From The Peace Bisquit Lounge)
Intoxication: *Aaron, Robert & Edwige* / Boom: *Peace Bureau* / Tell me what's on your mind: *La Desirade* / Struck by luv: *Lectroluv & Alvaughn Jackson* / Thoughts of you: *Wave* / Hands of a raindrop: *Tiny Bubbles* / Hallelujah: *Funky Fusion Band* / Rejoice: *250lbs Of Blue & Elizabeth Mordaunt* / On the sand: *Groove Thing* / Try my lovin': *Bluejean* / Black thoughts: *African Dream* / I can't let you go: *Mack Vibe & Jacqueline* / Risin' to the top: *250lbs Of Blue & Storm* / Trouble: *Cardwell, Joi* / Real thing: *Screamin' Rachel*
EBCD 52 / Jan '95 / Eightball

☐ EIGHTH DIMENSION SELECTED MATERIAL
Because blonde wore red: *Pimp Daddy Nash* / Sound in the round: *DJ BMF* / Shelter: *Lickerish Quartet* / Check it out: *Dynagrooves* / Total maza: *Q-Burns Abstract Message* / Illadin: *DJ BMF & Q Burns Abstract Message* / Joe dropped the swing: *Pimp Daddy Nash* / Lovin' dub: *Dubmarine* / Listening (I promise): *Lickerish Quartet* / Brain wormed: *Q-Burns Abstract Message*
ASW 6205 / 22 Sep '97 / Astralwerks

☐ EIN SCHIFFWIRD KOMMEN
Komm wi machen eine kleine reise: *Lind, Gitta & Christa Williams* / Vaya con dios: *Lind, Gitta & Christa Williams* / Kein auto: *Lind, Gitta & Christa Williams* / Denn sic fahren hinaus auf das meer: *Brown, Peggy* / Musik von zuckerhut: *Club Jamaika* / Augen has du wie kakao: *Club Jamaika* / Adieu lebewohl goodbye (Tonight is so right for love): *Bottcher, Gerd* / Ich komme wieder: *Bottcher, Gerd* / Abends in Athen: *Andersen, Lale* / Ein schiff wird kommen: *Andersen, Lale* / Ein fremder mann: *Andersen, Lale* / Bahama melodie: *Bertelmann, Fred* / Das blaue meer und du: *Bertelmann, Fred* / Einen ring it zwei blutroten steinen: *Valente, Caterina* / Wos ist das land: *Valente, Caterina* / Schick mir einen gruss: *Valente, Caterina* / Weisse mowe flieg in die ferm: *Valente, Caterina* / Wenn die sonne scheint in Portugal: *Assia, Lys* / Zeig mir bei nacht die sterne: *Engel, Detlef* / Mr. Blue: *Engel, Detlef* / Komm zu mir wenn du einsam bist: *Torriani, Vico* / Sweet Hawaii: *Gitte & Rex Gildo* / Fern von de Heimat: *Lind, Gitta* / Wo die sonne in das meer versinkt: *Durand, Angele* / Heim, heim mocht ich zienn: *Bottcher, Gerd & Detlef Engel*
BCD 15414 / Dec '87 / Bear Family

☐ EITHER SIDE OF MIDNIGHT (30 Cool Jazz Classics/2CD Set)
I'm a fool to want you: *Morgan, Lee* / All blues: *Bridgewater, Dee Dee* / But not for me: *Jamal, Ahmad* / I don't know what time it was: *Shorter, Wayne* / Willow weep for me: *Edison, Harry* / Here's the rainy day: *Bridgewater, Dee Dee* / Make the man love me: *Kelly, Wynton* / I got it bad and that ain't good: *Webster, Ben* / Lover man: *McRae, Carmen* / 'Round midnight: *Ellington, Duke* / Little girl blue: *Simone, Nina* / Tenderly: *Byas, Don* / I loves you porgy: *Simone, Nina* / My one and only love: *Grappelli, Stephane* / Mellow mood: *Marmarosa, Dodo* / Star eyes: *Kral, Irene* / Pleasingly plump: *Basie, Count* / Turn out the stars: *Evans, Bill* / Blue gardenia: *Washington, Dinah* / Come rain or come shine: *Kelly, Wynton* / Why try to change me now: *Foster, Frank* / What are you doing the rest of your life: *Evans, Bill* / Indian summer: *Hawkins, Coleman* / Darn that dream: *Washington, Dinah* / Mr. Lucky: *Byrd, Donald* / Moonlight in Vermont: *McRae, Carmen* / Waltz Latino: *Feldman, Victor* / In a sentimental mood: *Stitt, Sonny*
CPCD 82302 / Oct '96 / Charly

☐ EITHER SIDE OF MIDNIGHT VOL.2 (2CD Set)
Blue room: *Sims, Zoot* / More I see you: *Vaughan, Sarah* / Detour ahead: *Evans, Bill* / Just in time: *Morgan, Lee* / Girl talk: *Burrell, Kenny* / Misty: *Bridgewater, Dee Dee* / All or nothing at all: *Shorter, Wayne* / Everything happens to me: *Marmarosa, Dodo* / Crazy he calls me: *Washington, Dinah* / In a mellow tone: *Ellington, Duke* / Lonely melody: *Ashby, Dorothy* / My funny Valentine: *Farmer, Art* / Lullaby of Birdland: *Torme, Mel* / You've changed: *Weller, Don* / Theodora: *Taylor, Billy* / Playtime: *Rich, Buddy* / I could write a book: *McRae, Carmen* / In a sentimental mood: *Webster, Ben* / 'S wonderful: *Braff, Ruby* / All the things you are: *Jamal, Ahmad* / Lulu's back in town: *Torme, Mel* / Here's that rainy day: *Montgomery, Wes* / Prelude to a kiss: *Stitt, Sonny* / Autumn leaves: *Kelly, Wynton* / How long has this been going on: *Connor, Chris* / Confessin': *Norvo, Red* / Hey there: *Gray, Wardell* / When the world was young: *Bryant, Ray* / Love me or leave me: *Simone, Nina*
CDPCD 81402 / Oct '95 / Charly

☐ EL BOLERO MEXICANO 1931-1945
KAR 078 / Nov '97 / IMP

☐ EL CAIMAN
CORA 129 / Aug '96 / Corason

☐ EL CHA CHA CHA DE CU
283382 / Jan '96 / Total

☐ EL CHE VIVE
3018342 / Feb '97 / Arcade

☐ EL CONDOR PASA (South American Indian Harp & Flute Music)
15163 / May '94 / Laserlight

☐ EL CONDOR PASA
CD 62042 / Nov '93 / Saludos Amigos

☐ EL CONDOR PASA (Traditional Pan Pipes - 2CD Set)
Mon amour: *Thore, Francke* / Pipe dreams: *Thore, Francke* / Greensleeves: *Thore, Francke* / Blue rondo a la turk: *Thore, Francke* / Meditation: *Thore, Francke* / Carillon: *Thore, Francke* / Spain: *Thore, Francke* / Solvejg's song: *Thore, Francke* / Entre des aguas: *Barreros, Paco* / Manha de carnaval: *Barreros, Paco* / New Year: *Barreros, Paco* / Papel de plata: *Barreros, Paco* / Lotus feet: *Barreros, Paco* / Alturas: *Barreros, Paco* / Dentro de tu alma: *Barreros, Paco* / Toki Doki: *Barreros, Paco* / Rio Ancho: *Barreros, Paco* / Moyobamaba: *Los Indios De Cuzco* / El indio del Altiplano: *Los Indios De Cuzco* / Pa'ti cholita: *Patoruzu Y Su Conjunto* / El pajaron: *Patoruzu Y Su Conjunto* / El zaino: *Patoruzu Y Su Conjunto* / Pajaritos: *Patoruzu Y Su Conjunto* / Diecenueve de enero: *Patoruzu Y Su Conjunto* / Kena misky: *Patoruzu Y Su Conjunto* / Francisca Teresa Luisa: *Patoruzu Y Su Conjunto* / Huayno di Juanico: *Patoruzu Y Su Conjunto* / Naco del carnaval: *Patoruzu Y Su Conjunto* / La piojosa: *Patoruzu Y Su Conjunto* / Chasquinanes: *Patoruzu Y Su Conjunto* / Sentimientos: *Patoruzu Y Su Conjunto* / Yaravi de San Lorenzo: *Patoruzu Y Su Conjunto* / La feria de los flores: *Santiago Conjunto Viracocha* / Vicunitas: *Santiago Conjunto Viracocha* / Misteru: *Los Indios De Cuzco*
RCACD 209 / Jul '97 / RCA

☐ EL CONDOR PASA
MACCD 306 / Aug '96 / Autograph

☐ EL MANISERO
TCD 801 / 24 Apr '98 / Tumbao

☐ EL PASO (Und Andere Wahre Geschichten Aus Dem Wilden Westen)
El Paso: *Western Trio* / Texas ranger melody: *Oklahoma Boys* / Texas cowboy und Mexico girl: *Sondock, Mal* / Halbblut: *Dooley, Tom Trio* / Mein pony und ich: *Herwig, Claus* / Geh' nicht zu den indios: *Wiklund, Gunnar* / Tom Dooley: *Nilsen Bros* / Zehntausend meilen weit (hey Jackie): *Herwig, Claus* / Endlos weit (Nebraska melodie): *Braun, Pinkas* / Wenn die prarielilien bluhn: *Olsen, Frankie* / Tim und Tom: *Bennett, Peter* / Cowboy bonny: *Country Singers* / Jim ich trug ein weisses hemd: *Felgen, Camillo* / Das navajo kind: *Paulsen, Ralf* / Der letzte mohikaner: *Yellowstone Trio* / Am fuss der blauen berge: *Silbersee trio* / Die story vom tapferen cowboy: *Wilson, Eddie* / Roter mann vom Yellow River: *Silbersee trio* / Hab ein haus auf der prarie: *Olsen, Frankie* / Fury: *Paulsen, Ralf* / Mein braves pferd: *Namenlosen* / Mohikana: *Bendix, Ralf* / Tennessee melodie: *Yellowstone Trio* / Einsamer cowboy: *Kuhn, Paul* / Das lied vom Tod: *Lukschy, Wolfgang*
BCD 16174 / Aug '97 / Bear Family

☐ EL PRIMITIVO (American Rock 'n' Roll & Rockabilly)
Save it: *Robbins, Mel* / Oh yeah: *Jeffrey, Wally* / I wanna dance all night: *Wiley, Chuck* / It's love: *Wiley, Chuck* / Bandstand: *Nash, Cliff* / Times is tough: *Wiley, Chuck* / Are you with me: *Robbins, Mel* / I wanna shake it: *Hobock, Curtis* / I love you dearly: *Hurt, Jimmy & the Del Rio's* / Thump: *Embers* / Baby moon: *Smith, Herbie* / Best dressed beggar in town: *Turner, Buck* / Door to door: *Wiley, Chuck* / Uh oh: *Imps* / I walked all night: *Embers* / Explosion: *Nash, Cliff* / Out of gas: *Howard, Chuck* / Tell me baby: *Nash, Cliff* / Why worry about me: *Wiley, Chuck* / That'll get it: *Imps* / No time for sister: *Nash, Cliff* / I love you so much: *Wiley, Chuck* / Jenny Lou: *Nash, Cliff*
CDCHD 473 / Aug '93 / Ace

☐ EL RITMO LATINO VOL.1 (18 Classic Latin Grooves)
Hit the bongo: *Puente, Tito* / Muneca: *Palmieri, Eddie* / El escencia del guaguanco: *Pacheco, Johnny* / Senor Serano: *Miranda, Ismael* / Jive samba: *Constanzo, Jack & Gerry Woo* / La verdad: *Palmieri, Eddie* / El malecon: *Orchestra Harlow* / Manteca: *Alegre All Stars* / Aguzate: *Ray, Ricardo* / Mambo tipico: *Puente, Tito & His Orchestra* / Fever: *La Lupe* / Wipeout: *Barretto, Ray* / La jicota: *Ruiz, Rosendo Jr.* / Work song: *Puente, Tito* / Mambo Manila: *Rodriguez, Tito & His Orchestra* / Carmelina: *Valdes, Alfredito* / Song for my Father: *Valentin, Bobby* / Arsenio: *Harlow, Larry*
MCCD 025 / May '91 / Music Club

☐ EL RITMO LATINO VOL.2
MCCD 232 / Mar '96 / Music Club

☐ EL SALAO
TUMICD 023 / '92 / Tumi

☐ EL SONIDO DE FLAMENCO
Menos faltarlea mi mare: *Pinto, Pepe* / Mi trigo limpio: *Pinto, Pepe* / Melon sabroso: *Marchena, Pepe* / Los Cuatro Muleros: *Marchena, Pepe* / Los Campanilleros: *De La Puebla, Nina* / Quien critica a una mujer: *Perlita De Huelva* / El cantaor: *Valderrama, Juanito* / Cualro punlales: *Valderrama, Juanito* / Belingonero Flamenco: *Canalejas De Puerto Real* / Libre quiero ser: *Fosforito* / El que quiera a la Malena: *Porrina De Badajoz* / Mi Corcel: *Penuela, Antonita* / Maralo la moro: *Naranjito De Triana* / Yo canto a huelva: *Perlita De Huelva* / Mi ruisenor: *Maravilla, Juanito* / Romance de Juan De Osuna: *La Paquera De Jerez*
NSCD 031 / 11 May '98 / Nascente

☐ ELECTRIC BALLROOM (Synthetic Pop from the 1980's/1990's/2CD Set)
True faith: *New Order* / Temptation: *Heaven 17* / My soul unwraps tonight: *Savage Progress* / Waves: *Blancmange* / Golden brown: *Stranglers* / Hymn: *Ultravox* / Bird song: *Lovich, Lena* / It's my party: *Stewart, Dave & Barbara Gaskin* / Hey little girl: *Icehouse* / Are friends electric: *Numan, Gary & Tubeway Army* / (I want to live) In harmony: *Boytronic* / This city: *Foxx, John* / Kitchen at parties: *Lewie, Jona* / Thank God it's friday: *Automatic* / In a manner of speaking: *Tuxedo Moon* / Fall: *Endzeit* / Africa: *Twice A Man* / Blue moon: *De/Vision* / Moonlight lovesong: *Second Decay* / Good bye horses: *Psyche* / Boat on the river: *Blind Passengers* / Stranged: *SPOCK* / Save me: *Elegant Machinery* / Lost little robot: *Beborn Beton* / Imagination: *Daily Planet* / Over my home: *Northern Territories* / Morning light: *Silent Gift* / Just in case: *Philtron* / Midnight: *Chateau De Joie* / Space's embrace: *Rame* / Holegrain: *Statemachine* / Pictures: *X-Act* / In your heart: *Infame* / Rosen: *Spell Inside*
SPV 08847242 / Apr '97 / SPV

☐ ELECTRIC DREAMS
Blue Monday: *New Order* / Love is a stranger: *Eurythmics* / Mirror man: *Human League* / Tainted love: *Soft Cell* / Victim of love: *Erasure* / If I was: *Ure, Midge* / Heart of glass: *Blondie* / Mad world: *Tears For Fears* / Come live with me: *Heaven 17* / Wood beez (pray like Aretha Franklin): *Scritti Politti* / Living on the ceiling: *Blancmange* / Situation: *Yazoo* / Careless memories: *Duran Duran* / Quiet life: *Japan* / All stood still: *Ultravox* / Chant no.1 (I don't need this pressure on): *Spandau Ballet* / Talk Talk: *Talk Talk* / We close our eyes: *Go West* / Politics of dancing: *Re-Flex* / Together in electric dreams: *Moroder, Giorgio & Philip Oakey* / Enola Gay: *OMD* / Change: *Tears For Fears* / Fade to grey: *Visage* / Never never: *Assembly* / Are friends electric: *Tubeway Army* / Wishing (If I had a photograph of you): *Flock Of Seagulls* / Wishful thinking: *China Crisis* / I'm in love with a German film star: *Passions* / Don't go: *Yazoo* / Torch: *Soft Cell* / Is it a dream: *Classix Nouveaux* / Treason: *Teardrop Explodes* / Love on your side: *Thompson Twins* / Change your mind: *Sharpe & Numan* / Sgt. Rock (Is going to help me): *XTC* / Wouldn't it be good: *Kershaw, Nik* / Love shadow: *Fashion* / Vienna: *Ultravox*
5254352 / Feb '95 / PolyGram TV

☐ ELECTRIC GUITAR STORY 1935-1945, THE
158522 / Jul '96 / Jazz Archives

☐ ELECTRIC LADYLAND VOL.1
EFA 006692 / Nov '95 / Mille Plateau

☐ ELECTRIC LADYLAND VOL.2
EFA 006742 / Apr '96 / Mille Plateau

☐ ELECTRIC LADYLAND VOL.3
EFA 006792 / Oct '96 / Mille Plateau

☐ ELECTRIC LADYLAND VOL.4
EFA 006892 / May '97 / Mille Plateau

☐ ELECTRIC LADYLAND VOL.5 (2CD Set)
EFA 006982 / 23 Mar '98 / Mille Plateau

☐ ELECTRIC PSYCHEDELIC SITAR HEADSWIRLERS
PL 003CD / 30 Mar '98 / Purple Lantern

☐ ELECTRIC RADIO SAMPLER MUSIC TEST
TEST 001CD / Sep '93 / Haven

☐ ELECTRIC SUGAR CUBE FLASHBACKS
AIPCD 1054 / 16 Mar '98 / Archive

☐ ELECTRICITY (18 Synth Pop Hits)
MUSCD 008 / Sep '93 / MCI Music

☐ ELECTRICK LOSERS
BK 7933 / Sep '97 / Germanofon

☐ ELECTRO BEATS
Cuts it up: *Grandmixer DST* / Home of hip hop: *Grandmixer DST* / Megamix: *Grandmixer DST* / Mean machine: *Grandmixer DST & Jalal* / Change the beat: *Fab Five Freddy* / Escapades of Futura 2000: *Futura 2000 & The Clash* / Wild style: *Time Zone* / World destruction: *Time Zone*
CDNEW 103 / Jan '97 / Charly

☐ ELECTRO BEATZ VOL.4
8402310192 / 24 Mar '98 / Street Beat

☐ ELECTRO CUT VOL.1
WLCD 4001 / 10 Nov '97 / White Label

☐ ELECTRO FORCE VOL.1
MNF 05632 / 8 Jun '98 / Manifold

☐ ELECTRO JEWELS
IG 0082 / 6 Jul '98 / Progressive Nation

☐ ELECTRO JUICE
SABO 12CD / Nov '96 / Sabotage

☐ ELECTROCITY VOL.4
EFA 063212 / Dec '93 / Ausfahrt

☐ ELECTROCITY VOL.5
EFA 053232 / Aug '94 / Ausfahrt

☐ ELECTROCITY VOL.6
EFA 063262 / Apr '95 / Ausfahrt

☐ ELECTROCITY VOL.7
EFA 063292 / Feb '96 / Ausfahrt

☐ ELECTROCITY VOL.8
EFA 063322 / Apr '97 / Dossier

☐ ELECTROFIELDS
DENSCD 0012 / 15 Jun '98 / Density

☐ ELECTRON X
ZYX 551112 / 8 Jun '98 / ZYX

☐ ELECTRONIC DREAMS
Etoile polaire: *North Star* / Kiew mission: *Tangerine Dream* / Airlight: *Schulze, Klaus* / Ocean of tenderness: *Ashra* / Phase be phase: *Baumann, Peter* / Specific gravity of smile: *Froese, Edgar* / Black garden view: *Franke, Christopher* / King Aelous: *Bedford, David* / Taurus 1: *Oldfield, Mike*
CDOVD 496 / 29 Sep '97 / Virgin

☐ ELECTRONIC FRANKFURT (2CD Set)
PODDCD 023 / Sep '94 / Pod

☐ ELECTRONIC SPECIES
EFA 120952 / May '96 / Estontrager

☐ ELECTRONIC TOYS
QDKCD 013 / Aug '96 / QDK Media

☐ ELECTRONIC WARFARE (Mixed By Mr. C)
Versuvius: *Stranger* / Two: *Morohas, Hiroshi* / Fog of the unknown: *God Of The Machine* / Plutobeat: *Pluto* / Limbo of the vanished poss: *Tone Theory* / Sea 2 sea: *Kosmic Messenger* / Nude machinery: *God Of The Machine* / Rize: *Mantrac* / Scenic route: *Urban Groove* / Darkness: *Megalon* / MASP: *Insync & Invisible Force* / Incoming: *Urban Groove* / Niteflight: *Somnambulist* / Idax: *Megalon* / Waterwurld: *Underground Science* / Fax wars: *Innersound* / Motion: *Megalon* / Found object: *Else* / Reflex: *Underground Science*
PLKMCD 7 / 13 Oct '97 / Plink Plonk

☐ ELECTRONICA (Full-On Big Beats) (2CD Set)
Block rockin' beats: *Chemical Brothers* / Nightmare: *Brainbug* / Take California: *Propellerheads* / It's no good: *Depeche Mode* / Open up: *Leftfield & John Lydon* / Absurd: *Fluke* / We have explosive: *Future Sound Of London* / Naked and ashamed: *Dylan Rhymes* / Encore une fois: *Sash* / Groovebird: *Natural Born Groovers* / Satan: *Orbital* / Going out of my head: *Fatboy Slim* / Rollercoaster: *Grid* / For what you dream of: *Bedrock & KYO* / Bullet (bitten): *Fluke* / Scared: *Slacker* / Ain't talkin' about dub: *Apollo 440* / Children: *Miles, Robert* / Seven days and one week: *BBE* / Born slippy: *Underworld* / Breathe: *Prodigy* / Life is sweet: *Chemical Brothers & Tim Burgess* / Come with me: *Qattara* / Extremis: *Hal & Gillian Anderson* / Earth angel: *Dreadzone* / Valley of the shadows: *Origin Unknown* / Spin spin sugar: *Sneaker Pimps* / Wilmot: *Sabres Of Paradise* / Zoe: *Paganini Traxx* / You're not alone: *Olive* / Inner City Life: *Goldie* / Walking wounded: *Everything But The Girl* / Protection: *Massive Attack*
VTDCD 131 / Jun '97 / Virgin

☐ ELEMENTAL FORCE OF PHUNKEE NOIZE VOL.2
RSNCD 44 / Jul '96 / Rising High

☐ ELEMENTS
Stratus: *Cobham, Billy* / Back together again: *Mouzon, Alphonse & Larry Coryell* / Oceanliner: *Passport* / Black market: *Weather Report* / Birds of fire: *Mahavishnu Orchestra* / Hello Jeff: *Clarke, Stanley* / Dinner music of the gods: *Di Meola, Al* / Romantic warrior: *Corea, Chick & Return To Forever* / Nuclear burn: *Brand X* / War dance: *Colosseum II*
VSOPCD 218 / Aug '95 / Connoisseur Collection

☐ ELEMENTS OF JAZZ
KICKCD 41 / Sep '96 / Kickin'

☐ **ELEMENTS OF JAZZ VOL.2**
Mercy no mercy: Caron, David / Morning session: Martin, Alex Ensemble / Transparent: Reflection / Silicon jazz: Wavescape / Piano: Read, Jaime / Soul searcher dub: Underground Evolution / Destination other: As One / Dayride: O'Brian, Ian / Snooky's spirit: Black Jazz Chronicles / Scuba: Scuba / Astralwerks: Model 500
KICKCD 54 / 1 Sep '97 / Kickin'

☐ **ELEVATION**
79632778012 / 14 Jul '98 / ETO

☐ **ELEVEN YEARS FROM YESTERDAY**
FMRCD 02 / Feb '88 / Future

☐ **EMERALD FAVOURITES (24 Best Irish Songs)**
Irish harvest day / Danny Boy / Galway shawl / Dirty old town / Castle of Dromore / Golden jubilee / Holy ground / Courtin' in the kitchen / Let him go let him tarry / Good ole mountain dew / Donegal shore / Red rose cafe / Town I love so well / Boys from Killybegs / Mountains of Mourne / Green Glens of Antrim / Mary from Dungloe / Forty shades of green / McAlpines fusiliers / Black velvet band / Fields of Athenry / Three leaf Shamrock / Sweet sixteen
RBCD 521 / Jun '97 / Sharpe

☐ **EMERALD GEMS**
Mason's apron: Gallowglass Ceili Band / Connemara rose: O'Brien, Dermot / My Eileen: Rock, Dickie / Shaskeen: Shaskeen / West of the old river Shannon: Rosie, Margo & Sean Dunphy / Anything's better than nothing: Lynham, Ray & Philomena Begley / Paddy McGinty's goat: Dunphy, Sean / Old Fenian gun: Cunningham, Larry / Red is the rose: Margo / Till: Rock, Dickie / I've been everywhere: Hegarty, Dermot / Mr. and Mrs. used to be: Lynham, Ray & Philomena Begley / Jimmy Brown the newsboy: Hegarty, Dermot
302912 / Feb '98 / Hallmark

☐ **EMERALD ISLE DREAMS**
57572 / May '97 / Nature's Harmony

☐ **EMERALD MOODS (Pan Pipes Collection/25 Timeless Irish Evergreens)**
When Irish eyes are smiling/Mountains of Mourne / Bunch of thyme/Fields of Athenry / How can you buy Killarney/Mother MacRee/Tooraloora loora / Danny boy / Will you go lassie go/Spinning wheel / Carrickfergus / Forty shades of green/Sweet sixteen / Galway Bay/Isle of Innisfree / Mary from Dungloe/ Magpie / Cockles and mussels/Black velvet band/ The wild rover / I'll take you home again Kathleen / Cliffs of Dooneen/Rose of Tralee / On the banks of my own lovely Lee / I'll tell my Ma/Courtin' in the kitchen
COMCD 08 / 2 Feb '98 / Commercial

☐ **EMERALD ROCK**
Where the streets have no name: U2 / Linger: Cranberries / Whole of the moon: Waterboys / Small bit of love: Saw Doctors / Real real gone: Morrison, Van / I don't like Mondays: Boomtown Rats / Dancin' in the moonlight: Thin Lizzy / Nowhere: Therapy / Teenage kicks: Undertones / Somebody to love: In Tua Nua / Don't go: Hothouse Flowers / Mandinka: O'Connor, Sinead / Nobody knows: Brady, Paul / Parisienne walkways: Moore, Gary & Phil Lynott / Good heart: Sharkey, Feargal / After all: Frank & Walters / In the midnight hour: Commitments / She's the one that I adore: Energy Orchard / Big decision: That Petrol Emotion / In the name of the Father: Bono & Gavin Friday
5149442 / Mar '95 / Polydor

☐ **EMIT 1197**
Vox 25: Bone, Richard / What's in the box: Bad Data / Unc: 8M2 Stereo / Giant stroke: Woob / Oxygen: Gas / Imagination satellite: International People's Gang / Waterpump: Simpson, Dallas / Dead eye: Miasma / Apus apus: Davies, Hywel
EMIT 1197 / Jun '97 / Emit

☐ **EMIT 2296**
EMIT 2296 / Dec '96 / Time Recordings

☐ **EMO DIARIES VOL.1 (What's Mine Is Yours)**
DER 362CD / 6 Jul '98 / Deep Elm

☐ **EMO DIARIES VOL.2 (A Million Miles Away)**
DER 367CD / 6 Jul '98 / Deep Elm

☐ **EMOTIONS FOR THE WEISHUI RIVER**
PAN 149CD / Aug '94 / Pan

☐ **EMPIRE STATE RECORDS DJ MASTERMIX**
EBCD 9 / Jan '95 / Eightball

☐ **EMPTY BED BLUES**
PLSCD 115 / Apr '96 / Pulse

☐ **EMPTY SAMPLER VOL.1**
MTR 273CD / Jun '94 / Empty

☐ **EMPTY SAMPLER VOL.2**
MTR 353CD / May '97 / Empty

☐ **EN ATTENDANT LE TOUR**
DEM 015 / Feb '96 / IMP

☐ **EN VISITANT L'EXPO**
DEM 014 / Feb '96 / IMP

☐ **ENCHANTED CAROLS**
Church bells: Townsend, Dave & Nick Hooper / Hark the herald angels sing / Virgin most pure: Dartington Handbell Choir / Jingle bells: Penny piano / Star of Bethlehem / Angels from the realms of glory: Grosmont Handbell Ringers / Away in a manger: Grosmont Handbell Ringers / O little town of Bethlehem: Grosmont Handbell Ringers / First Noel: Grosmont Handbell Ringers / As, with gladness, men of old: Sun Life Stanshawe Band / Glory to God in the highest: Sun Life Stanshawe Band / See amid the winter's snow: Sun Life Stanshawe Band / O come all ye faithful (Adeste Fidelis) / Silent night / Down in yon forest: Dartington Handbell Choir / Good King Wenceslas / Little Jesus sweetly sleep: Launton Handbell Ringers / Little drummer boy: Launton Handbell Ringers / Deck the halls with boughs of holly: Launton Handbell Ringers / Little donkey: Launton Handbell Ringers / While shepherds watched their flocks by night: Barrel Organ / Auld lang syne
CDSDL 327 / '85 / Saydisc

☐ **ENCHANTED MOODS (3CD Set)**
EMTBX 310 / Aug '97 / Emporio

☐ **ENCHANTING MONGOLIA**
EFA 119492 / Feb '94 / Nebelhorn

☐ **ENCOUNTER**
EFA 11606CD / Apr '93 / EFA

☐ **END OF MUSIC**
DANCD 078 / Nov '94 / Danceteria

☐ **END OF THE BEGINNING, THE (2CD Set)**
Golden Gate: Strange Attractor / Love the DJ: Herbert / Non-stop: Herbert / Shuffler: Herbert / UK spring: Herbert / Our love: Herbert / Journey through happiness: Herbert / I am an instrument: Herbert / Game of two halves: Point Blank / Touched up: Max / Go with the beat: Herbert / Over and out: Herbert / UK spring: Herbert / Rog: Point Blank / Our love: Herbert / Journeys through sadness: Freaks / Ether's whisper: Deep Dish / People that make the music: Herbert / Frug: Point Blank / Jazz journey: DJ Assassin / Shrunken head: Freaks / Game of two halves: Point Blank / Mindless funk: Freaks / Luxor: Strange Attractor / Sensory elements: Herbert
PHONOCD 004 / 17 Nov '97 / Phonography

☐ **END OF UTOPIA, THE**
SR 132 / 29 Jun '98 / Sub Rosa

☐ **ENDLESS JOURNEY VOL.2**
FARCD 405 / Jul '96 / Family Affair

☐ **ENDLESS LOVE (2CD Set)**
One last love song: Beautiful South / Bump 'n' grind: R Kelly / Crazy for you: Let Loose / Around the world: East 17 / I'll stand by you: Pretenders / Crash boom bang: Roxette / Kiss from a rose: Seal / Stay: Eternal Basement / Stars: China Black / Don't be a stranger: Carroll, Dina / Can't stay away from you: Estefan, Gloria / Love ain't here anymore: Take That / Now and forever: Marx, Richard / I'll never fall in love again: Deacon Blue / When love breaks down: Prefab Sprout / Ordinary world: Duran Duran / La la (means I love you): Swing Out Sister / Nothing compares 2 U: O'Connor, Sinead / Love me for a reason: As We Speak / Endless love: Ross, Diana & Lionel Richie / Love don't live here anymore: Nail, Jimmy / Jealous guy: Roxy Music / Every breath you take: Police / I don't want to talk about it: Everything But The Girl / Don't let the sun go down on me: John, Elton / Unchained melody: Righteous Brothers / Without you: Nilsson, Harry / If you leave me now: Chicago / My love: McCartney, Paul / Man with the child in his eyes: Bush, Kate / On the wings of love: Osborne, Jeffrey / Secret lovers: Atlantic Starr / Love and affection: Armatrading, Joan / Babe: Styx / I wanna stay with you: Gallagher & Lyle / Love is all around: Troggs / Nights in white satin: Moody Blues / I'm not in love: 10cc
5253412 / Jan '95 / Polydor

☐ **ENDLESS LOVE (18 Instrumental Love Songs)**
Still / Hello / Lady / Endless love / Touch me in the morning / I don't wanna lose you / When you tell me that you love me / One more night / Against all odds / Sorry seems to be the hardest word / Where do broken hearts go / Didn't we almost have it all / I'm still waiting / One day in your life / Blue eyes / Lately / My cherie amor / You are the sunshine of my life
SUMCD 4063 / Nov '96 / Summit

☐ **ENDLESSNESSISM (2CD Set)**
DOTCD 04 / 18 May '98 / Dot

☐ **ENERGY 1994 & STREET PARADE**
Milky way: Borealis, Aurora / Bagdad: Paragliders / Spoken word is weak: Mike Ink & Burger Industries / House of house: DJ Yves De Ruyther & DJ Franky / Orient: Luke Slaters 7th Pain / Ambulance two: Armani, Robert / Primitive passion: Dee, Alici & Ralphie / Boo ya: Jens / Symphony: Gangsta / We don't care: T-Bass & O. Kunze / Aural 721: Hood, Robert / Helix: Synetics / M 3 of canes venatici: Direct Force / Kneels before me: Agent Loft
SUPER 2022CD / Aug '94 / Superstition

☐ **ENERGY 1996**
CDACV 2010 / Feb '97 / ACV

☐ **ENERGY BOX VOL.2 (2CD Set)**
ZYX 811362 / Feb '98 / ZYX

☐ **ENERGY RAVE VOL.5 (2CD Set)**
9010722 / Mar '97 / Immediate

☐ **ENERGY RAVE VOL.6 (2CD Set)**
9010762 / Mar '97 / Immediate

☐ **ENERGY TRANCE (The Ultimate Trance Collection)**
341642 / Dec '94 / Koch

☐ **ENEZ EUSA OUESSANT**
861CD / Nov '96 / Escalibur

☐ **ENFORCERS (Beginning Of The End)**
RIVETCD 9
RIVETCD 9M / 3 Nov '97 / Reinforced

☐ **ENFORCERS - ABOVE THE LAW (2CD Set)**
RIVETCD 7 / Oct '96 / Reinforced

☐ **ENFORCERS VOL.4**
RIVETCD 49 / Sep '93 / Reinforced

☐ **ENFORCERS VOL.5**
RIVETCD 52 / Oct '93 / Reinforced

☐ **ENGLISH & SCOTTISH FOLK BALLADS**
Henry Martin: Lloyd, A.L. / Baron of Brackley: MacColl, Ewan / Reynardine: Briggs, Anne / Bramble briar: Killen, Louis / Jack Orion: Lloyd, A.L. / Cruel ships carpenter: Waterson, Mike / Cruel mother: Lloyd, A.L. / Lord Randal: MacColl, Ewan / Bitter withy: Lloyd, A.L. / Forester: Kennedy, Norman / Willie O'Winsbury: Briggs, Anne / Sweet Kumadie: MacColl, Ewan / Demon lover: Lloyd, A.L. / Young Edwin in the Lowlands: Lloyd, A.L. / Hughie The Graeme: MacColl, Ewan / Drumdelgie: Kennedy, Norman / Prickly bush: Lloyd, A.L. / Beggar man: MacColl, Ewan
TSCD 480 / Jun '96 / Topic

☐ **ENGLISH CUSTOMS AND TRADITIONS**
Helston furry and hal-an-tow / Padstow hobby horse / Castleton garland day / Bampton morris / Headington morris / Abbots Bromley horn dance / Antrobus soulcakers / St Clements day song / Singing of the travels / As I sat on a sunny bank / Cherry tree carol / Bitter withy / Lazurus / West country wassailers / John barleycorn / Shrove tuesday / Gower wassail
CDSDL 425 / Nov '97 / Saydisc

☐ **ENGLISH FOLK SONGS (A Selection From The Penguin Book Of English Folk Songs)**
When I was young / Gaol song / Whale catchers / Young and single sailor / False bride / Ratcliffe highway / Grey cock / Basket of eggs / One night as I lay on my bed / Banks of Green Willow / All things are quite silent / Banks of Newfoundland
FE 047CD / Nov '95 / Fellside

☐ **ENGLISH FREAKBEAT VOL.1**
AIPCD 1039 / May '95 / Archive

☐ **ENGLISH FREAKBEAT VOL.2**
AIPCD 1047 / Feb '96 / Archive

☐ **ENGLISH FREAKBEAT VOL.3**
AIPCD 1048 / 29 Sep '97 / AIP

☐ **ENGLISH FREAKBEAT VOL.4**
AIPCD 1051 / 29 Sep '97 / AIP

☐ **ENGLISH FREAKBEAT VOL.5**
AIPCD 1049 / Mar '93 / Archive

☐ **ENGLISH FREAKBEAT VOL.6**
AIPCD 1055 / Oct '96 / Archive

☐ **ENJA - 20TH ANNIVERSARY**
Dance Benita dance: Blythe, Arthur / Maybe September: Flanagan, Tommy / Sossity; you're a woman: Krantz, Wayne / Wow: Dennerlein, Barbara / Green chimneys: Reedus, Tony / Time until: Degen, Bob / Storyteller: Abou-Khalil, Rabih / Giant steps: Tyner, McCoy / Phantoms: Barron, Kenny / You and I: Lincoln, Abbey / Lakutshon ilanga: Ibrahim, Abdullah / Straight no chaser: Wallace, Bennie / Yawn: Scofield, John / Ballad to Mahalia: Tsilis, Gust William / Edge to edge: Formanek, Michael / My funny valentine: Baker, Chet
ENJACD 80602 / Jun '94 / Enja

☐ **ENLIGHTENMENT**
KRCD 006 / 30 Mar '98 / Koyote

☐ **ENRAPTURED GIG ALBUM**
RAPTCD 15 / 11 May '98 / Enraptured

☐ **ENTER THE CYBER LOUNGE (The Best In Trip Hop & Psychedelic Rhythms)**
Can't deal with this: Cool Breeze / Atlas Earth: Spacer / Aqualibra: Cold Blue / Cap Colombie: Arteq / Fast and loose: Bliss 'n' Tumble / Who are you: Larceny / At Least the American Indian people know exactly how...: Fire This Time / Spirit: Kitachi / Definition: Dom & Roland / No inference: Fire & Theft / Satellite: Ryder, Mark / Dust bucket: Freddie Fresh
CDTOT 42 / Jul '96 / Jumpin' & Pumpin'

☐ **ENTER THE HARDBAG**
Fee fi fo fum: Candy Girls & Sweet Pussy Pauline / Something about you: Mr. Roy / Move your body: Xpansions / Son of a gun: JX / It's what's upfront that counts: Yosh / Diablo: Grid / Conway: Reel 2 Real / I'm rushin': Bump / Bullet: Fluke / Deeper: Funky See Funky Do / Happiness (is just around the bend): Brooklyn's Poor & Needy / Joanna: Mrs. Wood / Sweet harmony: Liquid / Don't you want me: Felix / Blue Monday: New Order / Club America: Club America / All night: Tocayo / Housework: Rizzo / Burning up: De Vit, Tony / Magic: Blu Peter / Hooked: 99th Floor Elevators / Only me: Hyperlogic / I need a man: Li Kwan / Stomp: Ramp / Let the rhythm flow: Diva Rhythms / Want me love me: Justine
5404572 / Dec '95 / A&M

☐ **EP COLLECTION SAMPLER, THE**
I'll keep you satisfied: Kramer, Billy J. / I go to pieces: Peter & Gordon / Jennifer Juniper: Donovan / Perfidia: Shadows / Rocky road blues: Vincent, Gene / Look through any window: Hollies / Do wah diddy: Manfred Mann / I'm into something good: Herman's Hermits / Pipeline: Ventures / I like it: Gerry & The Pacemakers / Little devil: Shapiro, Helen / I'm telling you now: Freddie & The Dreamers / Take good care of my baby: Vee, Bobby / Summertime blues: Cochran, Eddie / Ain't that a shame: Domino, Fats / Good things are coming my way: Proby, P.J.
SFMEP 101 / Oct '96 / See For Miles

☐ **EPIC HOUSE EXPERIENCE**
TRIPCD 5 / Jun '96 / Rumour

☐ **EPIDEMIC**
SABOTAGE 01CD / May '95 / Sabotage

☐ **EPITONE**
BTR 002CD / Nov '95 / Bad Taste

☐ **ERA UMA VEZ NACIONAL**
21772 / 12 May '98 / Som Livre

☐ **ERNIE'S RECORD MART**
John R theme: John R / Miss you so: Offitt, Lillian / It's love baby (24 hours a day): Brooks, Louis & His Hi-Toppers / Pork and beans: Solotones / Front page news: Solotones / Now listen baby: Kid King / Love love love: Jarrett, Ted / Pleadin' for love: Birdsong, Larry / My mumblin' baby: Green, Rudy / Cool lovin' Mama: Green, Rudy / Hear my plea baby: Gunter, Arthur / Hot potato: Guitar Red / I'll be good: Sugar & Sweet / My next door neighbour: McCain, Jerry / We're gonna shake: Gunter, Arthur / Slim Lizard: Harris, Ralph & Skippy Brooks / Oh how I tried: Birdsong, Larry / Out of darkness: Brown, Chuck / You must be crazy: Garner, Al / Have you ever: Williams, Eddie / Got plenty troubles: Brown, Lattimore / It hurts me so: Brown, Lattimore / Gonna stop my drinkin': Garner, Al / Somebody's gonna miss me: Brown, Lattimore
CDCHD 684 / Jun '98 / Ace

☐ **ESCAPE FROM SAMSARA**
SETCD 1 / 24 Nov '97 / Secret

☐ **ESCAPE TO TRANSCYBERIA**
K7 036CD / Oct '96 / Studio K7

☐ **ESPECIAL CANCOES ROMANTICAS**
V 20282 / 12 May '98 / Eldorado

☐ **ESQUIRE ALL AMERICAN JAZZ CONCERT 1944**
158262 / Jan '95 / Jazz Archives

☐ **ESQUIRE JAZZ CONCERT, METROPOLITAN OPERA HOUSE**
CD 53035 / Jan '89 / Giants Of Jazz

☐ **ESQUIRE SKIFFLE SESSIONS 1957, THE**
This little light: 2.19 Skiffle Group / Texas lady: 2.19 Skiffle Group / Freight train blues: 2.19 Skiffle Group / Union maid: 2.19 Skiffle Group / Tom Dooley: 2.19 Skiffle Group / Hugged my honey: Station Skiffle Group / Don't you rock me daddy-o: Station Skiffle Group / Titanic: Station Skiffle Group / Steam boat Bill: Station Skiffle Group / Skip to my Lou: Delta Skiffle Group / John Brown's body: Delta Skiffle Group / KC Moan: Delta Skiffle Group / Pick a bale of cotton: Delta Skiffle Group / Streamline train: Lea Valley Skiffle Group / Railroad Bill: Lea Valley Skiffle Group / I'm gonna walk and talk with Jesus: Lea Valley Skiffle Group / Oh Mary don't you weep: Lea Valley Skiffle Group / Mr and Mrs Mississippi: Christmas, Johnny & The Sunspots / Don't rock me daddy-o: Station Skiffle Group / Titantic: Station Skiffle Group
LACD 90 / 9 Mar '98 / Lake

☐ **ESSENCE OF AMBIENCE (4CD Set)**
CDBTOT 5 / 23 Feb '98 / Jumpin' & Pumpin'

☐ **ESSENCE OF FUNK**
Cornbread / Loose change / Slow drag / Eternal flame / Freedom jazz dance / Jive samba / Comin' home baby
HIBD 8007 / Oct '95 / Hip Bop

☐ **ESSENCE OF JUNGLE**
NURCD 1 / Jun '96 / Nur Ents

☐ **ESSENCE OF THE BLUES, THE (3CD Set)**
MCBX 015 / Dec '94 / Music Club

☐ **ESSENTIAL ACID JAZZ (2CD Set)**
Dream come true: Brand New Heavies / Always there: Incognito / Work it out: Stetsa / Turn on tune in cop out: Freakpower / You make me feel: Honey / Apparently nothin': Young Disciples / On my mind: All Stars / Meateater: Meateaters / Chilling: Moist, Lionel Sextet / Bee hop: Nuff Kilo / Feel it: Ultra Revival / Feels like: Ebony / Shine: Chuff Nuts / I surrender: JC / Upstairs at train trax: Tomb Raiders / I'm gonna love you: Big Cheese All Stars / Space Jam: Brown Starr / Herron: Dr. Villock / In the thick of it: Meateaters / Your love: Shan
ESSECD 6 / 22 Jun '98 / Beechwood

☐ **ESSENTIAL AMBIENT**
Celestial dawn: United Trance Foundation / Deliverance: Zodiac 649 / Pulse: Amorphic Field / Isle of dreams: Tacye / Trance visionary: Wishbone Ash / Domino effect: Domino Effect / Electro mantra: Microcosm / Conspiracy: Fowley, Kim & Norman Blake / Aqualluna dub: Venusian / 5TH dimension: Soundscape UK / Angelic: United Trance Foundation / How pure: Tacye / Hiding in the tall grass: Elixion / Starlight dove: Future Pilot AKA & Brix Smith / Eternity's slave: Soundscape UK
TOYCD 1003 / 26 Aug '97 / Intrinsic

☐ **ESSENTIAL BIG BANDS**
4671502 / Jan '95 / Sony Jazz

☐ **ESSENTIAL BLUES**
Cry before I go: Reed, Jimmy / Hard walking Hanna: Reed, Jimmy / Hi heel sneakers: Tucker, Tommy / Drunk: Tucker, Tommy / House rent boogie: Hooker, John Lee / Stomp boogie: Hooker, John Lee / Dust my broom: James, Elmore / Coming home: James, Elmore / Little red rooster: Howlin' Wolf / I ain't superstitious: Howlin' Wolf / Lonesome: Memphis Slim / Let the good times roll creole: Memphis Slim / 40 days and 40 nights: Waters, Muddy / Rollin' and tumblin': Waters, Muddy / Don't stay out all night: Arnold, Billy Boy & Tony McPhee / I wish you would: Arnold, Billy Boy & Tony McPhee
ECD 3106 / Jan '95 / K-Tel

☐ **ESSENTIAL BLUES PIANO HARMONICA AND SLIDE GUITAR (3CD Set)**
Pinetop's boogie woogie: Smith, Pine Top / Cow cow blues: Davenport, Cow Cow / Heifer dust: Ezell, Will / Detroit rocks: Taylor, Montana / Soon this morning blues: Spand, Charlie / 44 blues: Sykes, Roosevelt / Head rag hop: Nelson, Romeo / Wilkins' street stomp: Speckled Red / No.29: Wallace, Wesley / Blue bloomer blues: Moore, 'Whistlin' Alex /

Vicksburg blues: Little Brother Montgomery / If you haven't any hay: James, Skip / Fives: Parrish, Turner / Blues before sunrise: Carr, Leroy / Every morning blues: Roland, Walter / Strut that thing: Loften, Cripple Clarence / Honky tonk train blues: Meade Lux Lewis / Boogie woogie blues: Ammons, Albert / Junker blues: Dupree, 'Champion' Jack / Death day boogie: Johnson, Pete / Worried life blues: Big Maceo / Yancey special: Yancey, Jimmy / Pan American blues: Bailey, Deford / Up country blues: Bailey, Deford / Alcoholic blues: Bailey, Deford / McAbee's railroad piece: McAbee, Palmer / Escaped convict: Williams, George 'Bullet' / Touch me light mama: Williams, George 'Bullet' / Medley of blues: Stowers, Freeman / All out and down: Stowers, Freeman / Old time blues: Stowers, Freeman / Hog in the mountain: Stowers, Freeman / Need more blues: Cooksey, Robert / Man trouble blues: Jailbird Coleman / Jug band waltz: Shade, Will & Memphis Jug Band / Cow cow blues: Davenport, Cow Cow / Chickaswa special: Lewis, Noah / Devil in the woodpile: Lewis, Noah / Mean low blues: Blues Birdhead / Beale street breakdown: Davenport, Jed & Beale Street Jug Band / Coffee grinder blues: Jailbird Coleman / Friday moan blues: Lewis, Alfred / Drop down mama: Nixon, Hammie & Sleepy John Estes / Sarah Jane: Gillum, Bill 'Jazz' / Harmonica and Washboard blues harmonica stomp: Terry, Sonny / Good morning little school girl: Williamson, Sonny Boy / You can't keep no brown: Jackson, Bo Weevil / Jack o'diamonds blues: Jefferson, Blind Lemon / Guitar rag: Weaver, Sylvester / Falling down blues: Lewis, Furry / Mama 'tain't long fo' day: McTell, 'Blind' Willie / Dark was the night: Johnson, 'Blind' Willie / So lonesome: Ramblin' Thomas / Roll and tumble blues: Newbern, 'Hambone' Willie / Spoonful blues: Patton, Charlie / Walking blues: House, Son / Atlanta moan: Barbecue Bob / Whoopee blues: King Solomon / Packin' trunk: Leadbelly / Denver blues: Tampa Red / Old original Kokomo blues: Arnold, Kokomo / Lone wolf blues: Woods, Oscar 'Buddy' / You just as well let her go: Weldon, Casey Bill / Terraplane blues: Johnson, Robert / Black ace: Black Ace / I'm a stranger here: Fuller, Blind Boy / Bukka's jitterbug swing: White, Bukka / I be's troubled: Waters, Muddy

IGOBCD 002 / Dec '97 / Indigo

☐ ESSENTIAL CHRISTMAS GOSPEL (16 Celebratory Songs Of Joy & Happiness)

Silent night: Moore, Rev. James / Celebrating new life: Anointed Pace Sisters / Joy to the world: Hayes, Charles / Come let us adore him: Murrell, Carnell & Newark CC / Holy night: Wade, Rev. Melvin / Down home Christmas: Williams Brothers / Christmas season: Canton Spirituals / Prince of peace: Ward Singers / For Christmas: Williams Brothers / No room in the inn: Cleveland, Rev. James / When was Jesus born: Williams, Marion / Sending out love and peace: Williams Brothers / No room at the inn: Williams, Marion / Rock me to sleep: Gospel Clefs / I'm gonna trust in the Lord: Burke, Solomon / Roll on: Caesar, Shirley & The Caravans

MCCDX 018 / 6 Oct '97 / Music Club

☐ ESSENTIAL CHRISTMAS PARTY BOX, THE (3CD Set)

Rudolf the red nosed reindeer / Santa claus is coming to town / We wish you amerry christmas / Lonely this christmas / I wish it could be christmas / Everyday / Twelve days of christmas / Blue christmas / Silent night / Winter wonderland / Jingle bells / I have a dream / Another rock and roll christmas / Mary's boy child / Last christmas / Mistletoe and wine / Rockin' around the christmas tree / Pretty woman / Dancing in the street / Black is black / Bend me shape me / You really got me / All day and all of the night / Hippy hippy shake / Mony mony / Do wah diddy / Stay / Big girls don't cry / Proud Mary / Pretty woman (reprise) / In the mood / Rock around the clock / Rock a beatin' boogie / Tutti frutti / Wake up little Susie / C'mon everybody / Hound dog / Shake rattle and roll / All shook up / Jailhouse rock / At the hop / Jive bunny / Bump 1 / Fancy pants / Sugar baby love / I can do it / Tell him / New York groove / Glass of champange / (Dancing) on a Saturday night / Do you wanna dance / Glam rock allstars / Say you'll be there / Wannabe / Spice up your life / Who do you think you are / Two become one / Too much / Startrax club disco / More than a woman / Night fever / Tragedy / Love you inside out / Jive talkin' / Boogie child / Too much heaven / (Our love) don't throw it all away / You stepped into my life / If I can't have you / New York mining disaster 1941 / Stayin' alive / Nights on broadway / Massachusetts / How deep is your love / Reaching out / You should be dancing / Spirits (have flown) / Can't keep a good man down / I've got to get a message to Fanny / Love so right first of May / IOIO / Saved by the bell / Words / Ticket to ride / Hard day's night / Please please me / From me to you / I want to hold your hand / My sweet lord / Get back / No reply / I'll be back / Drive my car / Do you want to know a secret / We can work it out / Should have known better / Nowhere man / You're going to loose that girl / Daytripper / Eleanor rigby / Stars on 45 / Sherry / I've got you under my skin / Working my way back to you / Rag doll / Will you still love me tomorrow / Let's hang on / Gidea park / Hawaii Five-O / Let's twist again / Wipe out / Great balls of fire / Johnny B goode / Good golly Miss Molly / Twist / Summertime blues / Razzle dazzle / Runaround Sue / Chantiliy lace / California girls / Wouldn't it be nice / Help me Rhonda / Little girl I once knew / All summer long / Catch a wave / I get around / Little old lady from Pasadena / Fun fun fun / Sloop John B / Dance dance dance / Good vibrations / It takes two / This old heart of mine / I can't help myself / Just a little misunderstanding / Heaven must have sent you / My guy / He was really saying something / Heatwave / Stop her on sight (SOS) / Motorcity allstars / SOS / Bang a boomerang / Money money money / Knowing me knowing you / Fernando / Winner takes it all / Super trooper / Reggae for it now / Could you be loved / Cupid / Love of the common people / Message to you Rudy / Liquidator / Harder they come / Dreadlock holiday / Hold me tight / This Monday morning feeling / Montego bay / Barbados / Startrax / Hello hello I'm back again / I'm the leader of the gang (I am) / Glisten yeah / Rock and roll / Didn't know I loved you (till I saw you) / Do you wanna touch me / I love you love / King creole / I need your love tonight / Teddy bear / Don't be cruel / Good luck charm / She's not you / Return to sender / Let's have a party / Big hunk O' love / Rock a hula baby / Blue suede shoes / All the king's men / DISCO / Use it up and wear it out / That's the way (I like it) / Band of gold / All right now / Feels like I'm in love / Ladies night / Que sera mi vida / Love train~

390612 / 17 Aug '98 / Hallmark

☐ ESSENTIAL CLUBSCENE VOL.3

CSR 011 / Jan '97 / Clubscene

☐ ESSENTIAL COUNTRY COLLECTION, THE (3CD Set)

EMTBX 304 / Aug '97 / Emporio

☐ ESSENTIAL DANCEFLOOR LABELS CLASSICS VOL.2 (The Best Of Sutra)

So different: Kinky Foxx / Don'tcha go nowhere: Dee, Donald / Last night a DJ saved my life: Indeep / Keep on tryin': Sizzle / Bad times (I can't stand it): Captain Rapp / Thanks to you: Sinnamon / In motion: Payne, Freda / Every way but loose: Plunky & The Oneness Of Ju Ju / Ain't no stoppin' (ain't no way): McFadden & Whitehead / Rock the beat: Jamaica Girls / Happy feeling: Morgan, Denroy / Treat yourself to my love: Gonzales, Terri

DGPCD 797 / Jul '96 / Deep Beats

☐ ESSENTIAL DETROIT SOUL COLLECTION, THE

(I'll be your champion) I'll be your winner: Clark, Jimmy Soul / Not a chance in a million: Mitchell, Jock / Now: Masqueraders / Did my baby call: Mancha, Steve / I need my baby: Beavers, Jackie / Don't turn your back on me: Montgomery, Jack / Your love is getting stronger: Four Voices / I'm gonna cry a river: Ward, Robert & The Ohio Players / Crying over you: Browner, Duke / I am nothing: Williams, Al / Why weren't you there: Lindsay, Thelma / Keep loving me (like you do): Hargreaves, Silky / Ain't nothing you can do: Mathews, Joe / Nothing sweeter (than you girl): Hill, Eddie / Sweet sweet kisses: Wright, Larry / That's alright: Crook, Ed / That's why I love you: Proffessionals / Love that never grows cold: Beavers, Jackie / (They call me) A wrong man: Clarke, Tony / Pizza pie man: Grier, Roosevelt / No more heartaches: Posey, Art / You can lump it: Seminoles / That's the way he is: Perry, Ann

GSCD 003 / Mar '92 / Goldmine

☐ ESSENTIAL DRUM 'N' BASS

Bonus hop: Half Breed / Booya: Insolent Bo / Dark justice: Evil-Ed / Every posse: Shaper / Good old days: Fader / Chainsaw: Scan / Sizeable respect: Scan / Criminal: Half Breed / Need you: Redneck / Selecta: Rockers / Lazy Sunday: Roots / Icecold: Ken, Kenny & Cool Breeze / Live and direct: Facs / Beware: Facs / Stand bold: Universal Flava / Work dat sucker: Smokey Joe / Dogs on the set: Grimm, Ben / Crazy juice: Headman / Jazz creation: Universal Flava / Mistical journey: Elusive

ESSECD 1 / Jun '97 / Beechwood

☐ ESSENTIAL DRUM 'N' BASS VOL.1 (2CD Set)

DBMEM 1 / Dec '95 / Essential Dance

☐ ESSENTIAL DRUM 'N' BASS VOL.2 (2CD Set)

Witchcraft: Size, Roni & Krust / T'Raenon: Photek / Muzik: LTJ Bukem / Mr. Kirks nightmare: 4 Hero / Landcruiser: Raxmus / So many dreams: Guy Called Gerald / Sidestepper: Amorphouse / Trippin': Dealer / 2001: Era productions / First note: Conspiracy Theory / Chain reaction: Voyager Cru / Joy and pain: Eternity / Capability: CTX / Freedom: Force ID / Nightshade: Tyrone S / Phuture Phunk: Science Orchestra / Danger: Sub Sequence / Distance: By Pass / Subtrackt: Tiefenentzere / Sax lick: Intense

ESSECD 8 / 24 Aug '98 / Beechwood

☐ ESSENTIAL ELEMENTS VOL.8

NR 703029 / 17 Nov '97 / Essential Dance Music

☐ ESSENTIAL ELLA, BILLIE, SARAH, ARETHA, MAHALIA

4737332 / Jan '95 / Sony Jazz

☐ ESSENTIAL GARAGE DANCEFLOOR CLASSICS VOL.2

Music is the answer: Abrams, Colonel / You can't run from my love: Singleton, Maxine / Who's gonna ease the pressure: Thornhill, Mac / Touch me (love me tonight): Keith, Brian / I can't wait too long: Church, Joe / Music's got me: Visual / One hot night: Pure Energy & Lisa Stevens / Love itch: Flemming, Rochelle / You are the one: Pilot / I'd like to: Feel / I need you now: Sinnamon

DGPCD 739 / Nov '95 / Deep Beats

☐ ESSENTIAL GROOVE

This DJ: Warren G / Bump 'n' grind: R Kelly / Cry for you: Jodeci / Your love is a 187: Whitehead Brothers / Midnight at the oasis: Brand New Heavies / Everything's gonna be alright: Sounds Of Blackness / Blow your mind: Jamiroquai / Ease my mind: Arrested Development / Anything: SWV / True spirit: Anderson, Carleen / Looking through patient eyes: PM Dawn / Sly: Massive Attack / All about Eve: Marxman / Spiritual love: Urban Species / Twyford Down: Galliano / You know how we do it: Ice Cube / Outside: Omar / Love makes the world go round: Don-E / Get in touch: Freakpower / Don't you worry about a thing: Incognito

5254382 / Mar '95 / Polydor

☐ ESSENTIAL HAPPY HARDCORE VOL.1 (2CD Set)

74321574352 / 30 Mar '98 / Logic

☐ ESSENTIAL HAPPY HARDCORE VOL.2 (2CD Set)

74321591162 / 22 Jun '98 / Logic

☐ ESSENTIAL HARDCORE

Understand your destiny: Suzy Shoes / Ard corr: Well Ard / Parsley: DJ Splix / Blue skies: Because I Am / Dance with power: Bass Construction / Tingler: Smart Systems / Q: Mental Cube / Wonderful day: Flag / Quazi: Yage / Fire when ready: G Double / Can you feel me: Circa 91 / Heavy ride: China Boy / Owl: Indo Tribe / 550 state: Blood Brothers / 54321 carry on: AWOL / Braineater (I need my hardcore): Danse City

305102 / Jun '97 / Hallmark

☐ ESSENTIAL HOLLYWOOD JAZZ

4743732 / Jan '95 / Sony Jazz

☐ ESSENTIAL IBIZA (2CD Set)

Offshore: Chicane / You got the love: Source & Candi Staton / Soundscapes: Force ID / THC: Cloud City / Born slippy: Underworld / Ecstasy: Real / Hold your head: Problem Kids & Rose Windross / Raw concept: Raw Book / Comin' on strong: Supernature / Secret: Stimulate / Plastic dreams: Jaydee / Take me to a higher love: Mac, Keith Project / Feel good: BabySwankenstein / High in a groove: Spirit Of Eden / Dawn: Mystical / Free spirit: Tek 7 / Do what you wanna: Everyday People / I feel: Evolution / Transformations: Southside Productions / Gotta be strong: Uptown

ESSECD 5 / 22 Jun '98 / Beechwood

☐ ESSENTIAL IRISH COLLECTION, THE

Miss Mcleod's reel / Whiskey in the jar / I'll tell me Ma / Muirsheen Durkin / Lord of the dance / Gypsy rover / Boys of County Armagh / Black velvet band / Wild rover / Danny boy / Higgins hornpipe / Lanigans ball / Drowsy Maggie's / Leaving of Liverpool / Roddy McCauley / Irish rover / Patsy McCann / Far away in Australia / Spancil Hill / Molly Malone / Maggie / Red is the rose / After all these years / Irish washerwoman / Captain Pugwash / Fields of Athenry / Hills of Donegal / Holy ground / Mason's apron / Keel row / Scotland the brave / Minstrel boy / MacNamara's band / Peter Street

QED 136 / Nov '96 / Tring

☐ ESSENTIAL IRISH FOLK COLLECTION, THE (2CD Set)

DOL2CD 100 / Oct '96 / Dolphin

☐ ESSENTIAL ITALIAN HOUSE

DBMEM 3 / Sep '96 / Death Becomes Me

☐ ESSENTIAL JAZZ

Ain't misbehavin': Armstrong, Louis / I can't get started: Parker, Charlie / God bless the child: Holiday, Billie / Last night a miracle happened: Waller, Fats / Stormy weather: Garner, Erroll / High society: Morton, Jelly Roll / I got rhythm: Reinhardt, Django / Yardbird suite: Davis, Miles / C'est si bon: Armstrong, Louis / Honey hush: Waller, Fats / Stardust: Garner, Erroll / Lover man: Holiday, Billie / Ballin' the jack: Morton, Jelly Roll / Sweet Georgia Brown: Reinhardt, Django / I get a kick out of you: Parker, Charlie / Ornithology: Davis, Miles

ECD 3105 / Jan '95 / K-Tel

☐ ESSENTIAL JAZZ (18 Classic Jazz Tracks)

I wish I knew (how it would feel to be free): Taylor, Billy / Night in Tunisia: Parker, Charlie & Miles Davis / I got it bad and that ain't good: Ellington, Duke / Alfie's theme: Rollins, Sonny / It's only a paper moon: Fitzgerald, Ella / Nuages: Reinhardt, Django / 'Round midnight: Gordon, Dexter / Double-O: Basie, Count / Love for sale: Adderley, Cannonball & Miles Davis / My man: Holiday, Billie / My funny valentine: Baker, Chet & Gerry Mulligan Quartet / Midnight blue: Burrell, Kenny / So relax: Redbone, Leon / So it may secretly begin: Metheny, Pat Group / Morning dance: Spyro Gyra

MUSCD 30 / Jan '97 / MCI Music

☐ ESSENTIAL JAZZ CONCERTS

4685742 / Jan '95 / Sony Jazz

☐ ESSENTIAL JAZZ LEGENDS

4716842 / Jan '95 / Sony Jazz

☐ ESSENTIAL JAZZ PIANO

4685722 / Jan '95 / Sony Jazz

☐ ESSENTIAL JAZZ SAX

4741862 / Jan '95 / Sony Jazz

☐ ESSENTIAL JAZZ VOL.1

Take five: Brubeck, Dave / Girl from Ipanema: Getz, Stan & Astrud Gilberto / One note samba: Gillespie, Dizzy / I've got you under my skin: Washington, Dinah / Summertime: Vaughan, Sarah / Foggy day: Marsalis, Wynton / Take the 'A' train: Marsalis, Wynton / Love for sale: Davis, Miles / God bless the child: Holiday, Billie / Laird baird: Parker, Charlie / Polka dots and moonbeams: Peterson, Oscar / Autumn leaves: Evans, Bill / Goodbye Pork Pie Hat: Mingus, Charles / Soul eyes: Coltrane, John / Ain't misbehavin': Armstrong, Louis / I can't get started: Parker, Charlie

MUSCD 005 / Nov '92 / MCI Music

☐ ESSENTIAL JAZZ VOL.2 (15 Classic Jazz Tracks)

Take the 'A' train: Ellington, Duke / Straighten up and fly right: Cole, Nat 'King' / Sidewinder: Morgan, Lee / I guess I'll hang my tears out to dry: Gordon, Dexter / Laura: Parker, Charlie / Folks who live on the hill: Grappelli, Stephane & George Shearing / They can't that away from me: Gillespie, Dizzy / Lullaby of birdland: Jones, Quincy / April in Paris: Basie, Count / Fever: Lee, Peggy / Misty: Garner, Erroll / On green dolphin street: Peterson, Oscar / Nuit sur Les Champs Elysees: Davis, Miles / Watermelon man: Hancock, Herbie / More I see you: Mobley, Hank

MUSCD 031 / Jan '97 / MCI Music

☐ ESSENTIAL MELLOW GROOVE, THE

I've been trying: Chants / By my side: Pure Pleasure / While I'm Alone: Beverly, Frankie / That's love: Marshall Donovan Broomfield / Mellow me mellow me: Nelson, Jimmy / Wind: Sahara / Trying to make a wrong thing right: Wilson, Charles / Till I get home: Perfections / Wear your natural baby: Towanda & The Total Destruction / Trust me: Aged In Harmony / Try my love: Debbie S / AiAin't nothing but a love thang: Peace Love & Happiness / My conscience: Lovelites / Lucky fellow: Jackson, Maurice / Steppin' out: Andrews, Harvey / This love: Joytones / Crazy 'bout your love: Thomas, Robert / Give him up: Whatnauts

GSCD 005 / Sep '92 / Goldmine

☐ ESSENTIAL MERENGUE - STRIPPING THE PARROTS

CORACD 122 / Feb '95 / Corason

☐ ESSENTIAL MIX VOL.1 (Tong/Cox/Sasha/Oakenfold/2CD Set)

Hide-a-way: Rich, Kelli / Over and over: Plux & Georgia Jones / Nakasaki: Kendoh / Tempo fiesta: Itty Bitty Boozy Woozy / Dancing daffodils: Beat Syndicate / Are you out there: Crescendo / I need you: Pendulum / Access: DJ Misjah & Tim / Are you ready to fly: Dune / Neurodancer: Wippenberg / Harmonio groove: Garnier, Laurent / Outrage: DJ Powerout / Dance 2 the music: Men With Rhythm / Education: Pox And Cowell / Mantra to the Buddha: Hyperspace / Cut for life: Leftfield / Static: Markey / Step back: Slam / Thunder: Clarke, Dave / Lets turn it on: Doof / Paradise regime: Blue Amazon / Save me: Beat Foundation / Wired: 10th Chapter / Rays of the rising sun: Mozalo / Runaway: Evoke / Coma aroma: Inaura / Survive: Brothers Grimm / Skylined: Prodigy / Floor essence: Man With No Name / Down to earth: Grace / Star: Utah Saints / Sun: Virus

8287012 / Nov '95 / FFRR

☐ ESSENTIAL MIX VOL.2

Call on me: Johnny X / Lover that you are: Pulse / Heaven knows: Moraes, Angel / Keep on jumpin': Lisa Marie Experience / Cut the midrange: Watchman / Read my lips: Future Breeze / There's nothing I won't do: JX / Eugina: Salt Tank / Stand up: Love Tribe / What you want: Future Force / Day in the life: Terry, Todd / Edge of time: FK / What a sensation: Kenlou III / Everybody be somebody: Ruffneck / Pearl's girl: Underworld / Straight forward: Secret Cinema / Circuit maximus: Unknown Force / Side on: Space DJ's / Cantina tango: Dirty House Crew / Spacewreck: Manmade / Flash: Cosmic Messenger / Bite and scratch: Vogel, Christian

5354312

5354242 / Apr '96 / FFRR

☐ ESSENTIAL MIX VOL.3 (Tong/Seaman/Judge Jules/Carter) (Ltd Edition 2CD/Rom Set)

To be real: Fuzz / La tropicana: La Tropicana / It's just another groove: Mighty Dub Katz / Windows: SIL / Blue room: T-Empo / Mystery land: Y-Traxx / Born slippy: Underworld / Quattara: Quattara / Last rhythm: Last Rhythm / I am: Chakra / Coming home: Visions / Horn: Digidance / Ain't no way: Nemen / Always on my mind: Pink Noise / Outrageous: Stix 'N' Stoned / Kiss of life: Fanny Flow / Difference: Funny Walker / U (I got the feeling): Scot Project / Imagination: Time Zone / I'm alive: Stretch n' Vern / Jumpin': Terry, Todd / Life: Blair / Disco cubism: I-Cube / Carry on: Washington, Martha / Future: Armando / One for MAW: Jedi Knights / I think of you: Rednail Kidz / This is the house: Freaks / Shout and out: Lood / Feeling mm-pa-paa-paa: Dee

5358262

5358292 / Sep '96 / FFRR

☐ ESSENTIAL MIX VOL.4 (Pete Tong/Paul Oakenfold/Dave Carter - 2CD Set)

Pushing against the flow: Raw Stylus / Fired up: Funky Green Dogs / Fly life: Basement Jaxx / Flame: Fine Young Cannibals / She drives me crazy: Fine Young Cannibals / Ride a rocket: Li / Warning: Fah / Ice rain: Whitcombe, Alex & Big C / Offshore: Chicane / Run to you: Carroll, Dina / Closer to you: JX / Life's too short: Hole In One / Trommelaschine: Der Dritte Raum / Arkham asylum: Sasha / Places: Tilt / Mammal: Virtual Symmetry / Inner city life: Goldie / Say my name: Zee / Voices of KA: Van Leeuwen, Sjef / Blue skies: BT & Tori Amos / Off shore: Chicane / Eternally: Quadran / Anomaly: Libra / Words: Van Dyke, Paul / Pan fried: Light / Sensemilla: Dillingers Massive Dub Beats / Phantom: Trippatrazz / Zig it up: Ninjaman & Flourgan / Let me clear my throat: DJ Kool / Enter/Other: Q-Burns Abstract Message / Mad them: General Levy / Silence go boom: Sons Of Silence / Filthy: St. Etienne & Q-Tee / Trickshot: Ceasefire / Blow the whole joint up: Monkey Mafia / Just feel it (Live '92): Kix / Inspire me: Frontier Man / Killa: Smith & Mighty / Who da fuck: Semi-Detached Production / There's gonna be a riot: Dub Pistols / In da jungle: Playboy / Wickedest sound: Rebel MC / Breaking into a sweat: Interspin / Narramine: Genaside II / Killin': Ghostrider & Special K / Super sharp shooter: Ganja Kru / Neptune: Blame / Buddy bye bye: Osbourne, Johnny

5531532

5531672 / Nov '96 / FFRR

☐ ESSENTIAL NASHVILLE

74321367022 / Apr '96 / RCA

☐ ESSENTIAL NORTHERN SOUL COLLECTION, THE

No one can take your place: Inspirations / Wait till I get to know ya: Treetop, Bobby / Nothing can compare to you: Velvet Satins / (I love her so much) It hurts me: Majestics / If you ever walk out of my life: Barnes, Dena / She's wanted: Clinton, Larry / Since you left: Inticers / Strange change: Ward, Herb / I'll pay the price: Dillard, Moses & The Dynamic Showmen / Can't lose my head: Blackwell, George / I don't want to lose you: Bell Boys / I don't like to lose: Group & Cecil Washington / I'm not strong enough: Four Perfections / Because of my heart: Beverly, Frankie & The Butlers / Just like you did to me: Vernee, Yvonne / Sitting in my class: McNeir, Ronnie / World without sunshine: Phillips, Sandra / It rained 40 days and nights: Scott, Little Jimmy / Head and shoulders: Young, Patti / You don't love me: Epitome Of Sound / My world is on fire: Mack, Jimmy / Naughty boy: Day, Jackie / I'm gonna love you: Hamilton, Edward / Burning sensation: Lawson, Robby / Not my girl: Hampton, John

GSCD 001 / Sep '91 / Goldmine

☐ ESSENTIAL OLD SCHOOL HARDCORE (2CD Set)

DCID 004 / 16 Mar '98 / Dance Club International

☐ ESSENTIAL OLD SCHOOL RAP DANCEFLOOR CLASSICS VOL.1

Funky sound (Tear the roof off): Sequence / Do you want to rock (before I let go): Funky Four / King Heroin: Funky Four / Showdown: Furious Five & Sugarhill Gang / Pump me up: Trouble Funk / Birthday party: Grandmaster Flash & The Furious Five / Apache: Sugarhill Gang / Feel it (The Mexican): Funky Four / Eighth wonder: Sugarhill Gang / Ice cream dreams: Lady L / Mosquito: West Street Mob / Message: Grandmaster Flash & The Furious Five

DGPCD 708 / Mar '95 / Deep Beats

☐ ESSENTIAL OLD SCHOOL RAP DANCEFLOOR CLASSICS VOL.2
Adventures of Grand Master Flash on the wheels of steel: *Grandmaster Flash & The Furious Five* / Hey fellas: *Trouble Funk* / Sucker DJ: *Dimples D & Marley Marl* / Got it good: *Tricky Tee* / Success is the word: *12:41* / Fat boys: *Disco 3* / Ya mama: *Wuf Ticket* / Our picture of a man: *Playgirls* / It's good to be the queen: *Sylvia* / Monster jam: *Spoonie Gee & The Sequence*
DGPCD 741 / Nov '95 / Deep Beats

☐ ESSENTIAL PEBBLES (2CD Set)
AIPCD 1058 / 2 Feb '98 / AIP

☐ ESSENTIAL PEBBLES VOL.2 (2CD set)
AIPCD 1060 / 6 Jul '98 / AIP

☐ ESSENTIAL REGGAE (16 Reggae Hits)
Uptown top ranking: *Althia & Donna* / Hurt so good: *Cadogan, Susan* / Irie feelings: *Edwards, Rupie* / Red red wine: *Tribe, Tony* / Double barrel: *Barker, Dave & Ansell Collins* / Wonderful world, beautiful people: *Cliff, Jimmy* / Liquidator: *Harry J All Stars* / Black pearl: *Faith, Horace* / Some guys have all the luck: *Harriott, Derrick* / Money in my pocket: *Brown, Dennis* / You can get it if you really want it: *Dekker, Desmond* / Love of the common people: *Thomas, Nicky* / Help me make it through the night: *Holt, John* / Let your yeah be yeah: *Pioneers* / Black and white: *Greyhound* / Young, gifted and black: *Bob & Marcia*
CDGOLD 1056 / Oct '96 / EMI Gold

☐ ESSENTIAL ROCK
Dirty love: *Thunder* / All the young dudes: *Dickinson, Bruce* / Fireball: *Deep Purple* / Mean man: *WASP* / I've done everything for you: *Hagar, Sammy* / Your mamma don't dance: *Poison* / 747 (strangers in the night): *Saxon* / Silver machine: *Hawkwind* / Something better change: *Stranglers* / Ships in the night: *Be-Bop Deluxe* / Down at the doctors: *Dr. Feelgood* / Centrefold: *Geils, J. Band* / Let's work together: *Canned Heat* / Garden party: *Marillion* / Roll over Beethoven: *ELO* / Whole lotta love: *CCS*
CDGOLD 1037 / May '96 / EMI Gold

☐ ESSENTIAL SELECTION SUMMER '98 (2CD Set)
5560472
5560422 / 17 Aug '98 / London

☐ ESSENTIAL SELECTION VOL.1 (2CD Set)
5538862 / Aug '97 / PolyGram TV

☐ ESSENTIAL SELECTION VOL.2 (2CD Set)
5550932 / 3 Nov '97 / PolyGram TV

☐ ESSENTIAL SELECTION VOL.3 (2CD Set)
Rude boy rock: *Lionrock* / Beat goes on: *All Seeing I* / Brimful of Asha: *Cornershop* / Fixy jointy: *Psychedeliasmith* / Love bug: *Ramsey & Fen* / Believe: *Goldie* / Weekend: *Terry, Todd Project* / Funk phenomena: *Van Helden, Armand* / Never ever: *All Saints* / So good: *Roberts, Juliet* / Word is love (say the word): *Voices Of Life* / Movin' on: *Pender, Debbie* / Sincere: *Cole, MJ* / Beat that bitch: *Johnny Dangerous* / Give me rhythm: *Black Connection* / Gotta keep pushin': *Z-Factor* / Lady Marmalade: *All Saints* / It's like that: *Run DMC & Jason Nevins* / El Magnifico: *El Magnifico* / Renegade master: *Wildchild* / Smack my bitch up: *Prodigy* / I refuse: *Somore* / Coming back: *DJ Dado* / You make me feel (mighty real): *Stingily, Byron* / Where do we go: *Wamdue Project* / Disco dancing: *Plastika* / Here I go: *DOP* / Can U feel it: *CLS* / Let me show you: *Camisra* / Meet her at the love parade: *Da Hool* / Dark and long: *Underworld* / Treat infamy: *Rest Assured* / Angels landing: *Salt Tank*
5557862 / 6 Apr '98 / FFRR

☐ ESSENTIAL SLOW GROOVE DANCEFLOOR CLASSICS VOL.2
I'm the one for you: *Whispers* / Over and over: *Shalamar* / Show me where you're coming from: *Lucas, Carrie* / Window on a dream: *Wolfer, Bill* / Curious: *Midnight Star* / Winners and losers: *Collage* / Two occasions: *Deele* / Don't keep me waiting: *Whispers* / Hello stranger: *Lucas, Carrie* / Feels so good: *Midnight Star* / One girl: *Dynasty* / No pain, no gain: *Whispers* / This is for the lover in you: *Shalamar*
DGPCD 711 / Feb '95 / Deep Beats

☐ ESSENTIAL SOUL
Tainted love: *Jones, Gloria* / Right back where we started from: *Nightingale, Maxine* / Good time tonight: *Soul Sisters* / Looking for you: *Mimms, Garnet* / Lot of love: *Banks, Homer* / Everybody needs help: *Holiday, Jimmy* / Ready, willing and able: *Holiday, Jimmy & Clydie King* / Better use your head: *Little Anthony & The Imperials* / Dance, dance, dance: *Casualeers* / No.1 in your heart: *Goins, Herbie* / In the midnight hour: *Preston, Billy* / Who's that lady: *Isley Brothers* / Lipstick traces: *O'Jays* / You got what it takes: *Johnson, Marv* / Do wah diddy diddy: *Exciters* / Love potion no.9: *Clovers* / What's wrong with me baby: *Invitations* / Seven days too long: *Woods, Chuck* / I'm on my way: *Parrish, Dean* / Drifter: *Pollard, Ray*
CDGOLD 1031 / May '96 / EMI Gold

☐ ESSENTIAL SPEED GARAGE VOL.1 (2CD Set)
Closer than close: *Gaines, Rosie* / Fantastic voyage: *MC Spin* / It's a London thing: *Garcia, Scott & MC Styles* / Soul in motion: *Mixman* / Crazy beats: *Storm Posse* / Fat city: *DJ Vapour* / Spin spin sugar: *Sneaker Pimps* / Heroes: *MC Inferno* / Soul mine: *Plus 8* / Blackout: *Front Line* / Freestyle break: *Sonique* / End of the beginning: *Lock Bwoy* / Within these walls: *VIP* / Fourth wave: *Sky* / Killa b line: *Sam Force* / Take off: *Ground Zero* / Easy rider: *Good Bad & The Ugly* / Lost tribe: *DJ Blackout* / Automatic: *Underground Collective* / You looking at me: *Funkster*
ESSECD 3 / 16 Feb '98 / Beechwood

☐ ESSENTIAL SPEED GARAGE VOL.2 (2CD Set)
Lovebug: *Ramsey & Fen* / Love shy: *Blond, Kristine* / Redemption: *DJ FX* / Gabriel: *Davis, Roy Jr.* / On and on: *Seduction* / Extreme pressure: *Fono* / Freestylin': *Hustler, Alex* / Make the world go round: *Sandy B* / Freeze frame: *London Underground Collective* / Extra large: *Global* / Sweet monster dub: *Dub Monsters* / Tears: *Underground Solution* / Phantasy: *Fleece* / Duster: *Wise Guys & Dave Courtney* / Tears: *Freefall* / Don't give up: *Levi* / Shelter me: *Divine Intervention* / Bassline connection: *DC1* / Step to it: *Brown, Everton* / Out of time: *Speedy Gonzales*
ESSECD 4 / 1 Jun '98 / Beechwood

☐ ESSENTIAL SUN ROCKABILLIES VOL.1
Put your cat clothes on: *Perkins, Carl* / Red hot: *Riley, Billy Lee* / We wanna boogie: *Burgess, Sonny* / Tennessee zip: *Parchman, Kenny* / Rabbit action: *Haggett, Jimmy* / Come on little mama: *Harris, Ray* / Madman: *Wages, Jimmy* / Red cadillac and a black moustache: *Smith, Warren* / Mama mama mama: *Thompson, Hayden* / Flat foot Sam: *Blake, Tommy* / Crowdad hole: *Earls, Jack* / Goin' crazy: *Self, Mack* / Crazy woman: *Simmons, Gene* / Tough tough tough: *Anderson, Andy* / Huh babe: *McDanie, Luke* / Ten cats down: *Miller Sisters* / Rakin' and scrapin': *Beard, Dean* / Rockin' with my baby: *Yelvington, Malcolm* / Bottle to the baby: *Feathers, Charlie* / This ole heart of mine: *Bond, Eddie* / Milkshake mademoiselle: *Lewis, Jerry Lee* / Your lovin' man: *Taylor, Vernon* / Me and my rhythm guitar: *Powers, Johnny* / Just in time: *Jenkins, Harold* / Ooby dooby: *Orbison, Roy*
CPCD 8099 / Jun '95 / Charly

☐ ESSENTIAL SUN ROCKABILLIES VOL.2
CPCD 8118 / Aug '95 / Charly

☐ ESSENTIAL SUN ROCKABILLIES VOL.3
CPCD 8161 / Mar '96 / Charly

☐ ESSENTIAL SUN ROCKABILLIES VOL.4
Red headed woman: *Burgess, Sonny* / High high high: *McDaniel, Luke* / Lonely woman: *Harris, Ray* / I feel like rockin': *Parchman, Kenny* / You better believe it: *Blake, Tommy* / Don't lie to me: *Beard, Dean* / Pop and Mama: *Simmons, Gene* / Fairlane rock: *Thompson, Hayden* / Miss Pearl: *Wages, Jimmy* / Lovin' memories: *Self, Mack* / Blue day tomorrow: *Taylor, Vernon* / Drive in: *Vickery, Mack* / Oh yeah: *McVoy, Carl* / I need your lovin': *Jenkins, Howard* / My bonnie: *Hoback, Curtis* / Love is my business: *Greaves, Cliff* / Whole lotta shakin' goin' on: *Gilley, Mickey* / Cindy Lou: *Penner, Dick* / Donna Lee: *Rich, Charlie* / To be with you: *Dorman, Harold* / Thousand guitars: *Pendarvis, Tracy* / Honey bee: *Hinton, Don* / Heart throb: *Frost, Jack* / Watch that stuff: *Skipper, Macy* / My girl and his girl: *Hall, Roy* / Frankie and Johnny: *Feathers, Charlie* / Linda: *Chaffin, Ernie* / My babe: *Felts, Narvel*
CPCD 8236 / Nov '96 / Charly

☐ ESSENTIAL SUN ROCKABILLIES VOL.5
Green back dollar watch and chain: *Harris, Ray* / Take me: *Wages, Jimmy* / Rhythm called rock 'n' roll: *Haggett, Jimmy* / Get it off your mind: *Parchman, Kenny* / Lonesome feeling: *Felts, Narvel* / Money money money: *Simmons, Gene* / I need your love: *Beard, Dean* / Don't you worry: *Watson, Sid* / Red headed woman: *Burgess, Sonny* / Where'd you stay last night: *Harris, Ray* / Sweetie pie: *Blake, Tommy* / Doll baby: *Bruce, Edwin* / Lonely river: *Felts, Narvel* / Let 'em know: *Ruick, Tommy* / Hypnotised: *Pendarvis, Tracy* / Crazy dreams: *Jenkins, Harold* / Please don't cry over me: *Williams, Jimmy* / I lost my baby: *Hall, Roy* / Don't need your lovin' baby: *Penner, Dick* / Good lovin': *Lee, Dickey* / Bop bop baby: *Wade & Dick* / Mad at you: *Self, Mack* / Broke my guitar: *Bond, Eddie* / That's what I tell my heart: *McDaniel, Luke* / Laughin' and jokin': *Chaffin, Ernie* / Yakety yak: *Yelvington, Malcolm*
CPCD 8317 / Oct '97 / Charly

☐ ESSENTIAL SWEET SOUL SELECTION, THE
We're gonna be together: *Dynamics* / Hey foxy lady: *Natural Resources* / Why should I forgive you: *Clock* / Tricky dick: *Train Robbers* / Vibrations: *5 Farenheit* / What a lovely way to meet: *True Movement* / Don't ask me: *Norfolk* / Turned around over you: *Imperial Wonders* / I stand alone: *Malibus, Calif* / How do you say goodbye: *Heartbreakers* / Let me take care of your heart: *Smith Brothers* / I do love my lady: *Haze* / Stop to think it over: *God's Gift To Women* / Young hearts get lonely too: *New Young Hearts* / No one in this world: *Enchanting Enchanters* / Now I know: *Final Chapter* / Bet you didn't know: *Mind Readers* / Don't let go: *Sweet Berry* / You mean everything to me: *Four Tracks* / Never turn your back on the one you love: *Stone Luv* / I love you, baby: *Moovers*
GSCD 120 / Apr '97 / Goldmine

☐ ESSENTIAL SWING (2CD Set)
She's got that vibe: *R Kelly* / C u when you get there: *Coolio* / Sugar honey: *DJ Solar* / What's not yours: *Darkman* / Back and forth: *Aaliyah* / Stay: *Nelson, Evon* / Real thing: *Crush Crew* / Peace and free: *Xavier & IV Real* / Be mine tonight: *George, Jacqui* / Sweet soul: *Dana* / Close to you: *Treverson, George* / Ain't no doubt: *Williams, Nita* / Love to love: *Eternity* / Keep on giving me love: *Truce* / Just the way: *Ishmael, Jeff* / Giving me love: *MC Ace* / Downlow: *Prophet* / Uptown: *Rugged & Raw* / Take you home: *Frazer, Wayne* / Back to the lab: *Font La Roy & Darkman*
ESSECD 2 / 16 Feb '98 / Beechwood

☐ ESSENTIAL TECHNO (3CD Set)
DBMEM 2 / Jun '96 / Death Becomes Me

☐ ESSENTIAL TECHNO (2CD Set)
Breathe: *Prodigy* / Digeridoo: *Aphex Twin* / Dark and long: *Underworld* / Time zone: *Logic* / Tribal jedi: *Cox, Carl* / Source: *Phazer* / All that rises: *Pure* / Dominions complete: *Florence* / Tour: *De Force* / Below and above: *Trio* / Maximum impact: *X-Wing* / Fall out: *Cubase* / Mass observation: *Scanner* / We no longer understand: *As One* / On the brink: *Ultramarine* / Planet surfing: *Masquerade* / Progression: *Mantra* / Hypnotic state: *Fantasy Flight* / Plastic love: *Delta* / Astrofarm: *Digital Source*
ESSECD 7 / 24 Aug '98 / Beechwood

☐ ESSENTIAL TRANCE CLASSICS
DCID 006 / 20 Apr '98 / Dance Club International

☐ MODERN SOUL VOL.1
Trying to get next to you: *Blair, Arnold* / Anything I can do: *Collins, Will & Will Power* / Everything man: *Daybreak* / Good lovin': *Mason, Al* / Love is trying to get a hold on me: *Tavasco* / Dance your blues away: *Neville, Ivan* / My reaction to you: *Essex IV* / Heaven in the afternoon: *Kirton, Lew* / Don't send me away: *Fleming, Garfield* / Never had a love so good: *Johnson, Charles* / I did it again: *Cutchins, Bobby* / Streets got my lady: *Brandon, Bill* / (I can) deal with that: *Edwards, Dee* / Gettin' ready for the getdown: *ZZ & Co.* / I need love: *Daybreak* / My baby's got (ESP): *4 Below Zero*
GSCD 002 / Mar '93 / Goldmine

☐ MODERN SOUL VOL.3
For real: *Flowers* / Alone again: *Baker, Ernest* / Da da da da da (I love you): *Naturals* / I think I've got a good chance: *Barnes, J.J.* / Can this be real: *Perfections* / He's a better liar than me: *Lampkin, Tony* / I just want to do my own thing: *Reachers* / That's the way the world should be: *Up From The Bottom* / All work and no play: *Jordan, Vivalore* / Put your lovin' on me: *Fisher, Willie* / Since you said you'd be mine: *Ragland, Lou* / Can't nobody love me like you do: *Storm* / I gotta make you believe in me: *BJB* / I'll do anything for you: *McDonald, Lee* / Doin' it cause it feels good: *Strong, Chuck* / All of a sudden: *Moore, Melvin* / Ain't nothing like the love: *Simmons, John* / Hungry: *Sandy's Gang* / What does the future hold: *24 Karat Gold*
GSCD 040 / Jun '94 / Goldmine

☐ ETERNAL FLAME (Baltimore Jam)
STBCD 2504 / Sep '95 / Stash

☐ ETERNAL LOVE
WBRCD 1001 / Aug '94 / Business

☐ ETERNAL TRANCE
21032 / 27 Jul '98 / Trust In Trance/ Phonokol

☐ ETERNAL VOICES (2CD Set)
NAR 053 / May '94 / New Alliance

☐ ETERNALLY ALIVE VOL.2
MILL 017CD / Nov '95 / Millenium

☐ ETERNALLY ALIVE VOL.3
MILL 027CD / Sep '96 / Millenium

☐ ETERNALLY ALIVE VOL.4
MILL 064CD / 27 Jul '98 / Millenium

☐ E'THING YOU ALWAYS WANT...
AA 041 / Jul '97 / Arf Arf

☐ ETHIOPIQUES VOL.1 (Modern Ethiopian Music 1969-1975)
829512 / Nov '97 / BUDA

☐ ETHIOPIQUES VOL.2
829522 / 5 Jan '98 / BUDA

☐ ETHIOPIQUES VOL.3 1969-1975
829632 / 24 Apr '98 / BUDA

☐ ETHIOPIQUES VOL.4 1969-1974
829642 / 24 Apr '98 / BUDA

☐ ETHNO PUNK (Around The World With Attitude)
Children come and go: *Poliker, Yehuda* / Mireme miss: *Jardin, Ciudad* / Lena gia mena: *Pyx-Lax* / More and more: *Salt & Nails* / Det ar jag: *Den Fule* / Sid h'bidi: *Mano Negra* / Katami-bushi: *Parsha Club* / I tak warto zyc: *Raz Daw Trzy* / Make mana: *Mau Mau* / Rockin' the Bronx: *Black 47* / Nao me estrague o dia: *Os Paralamas Do Sucesso* / Wild on the snow: *Ciu Jian* / Waiting for Conrad: *Shooglenifty* / Aivoton: *Hadningarna* / Mamo feber: *Wilmer X*
CDEMC 3750 / May '96 / Premier/EMI

☐ EUPHORIA
CDRAID 516 / Mar '94 / Rumour

☐ EUPHORIA
SPV 08538892 / Jul '94 / SPV

☐ EUROBEAT 2000 - CLUB CLASSICS BOX SET (3CD Set)
KICKCD 65 / 15 Dec '97 / Kickin'

☐ EUROBEAT 2000 - CLUB CLASSICS VOL.1
KICKCD 13 / Oct '94 / Kickin'

☐ EUROBEAT 2000 - CLUB CLASSICS VOL.2
KICKCD 19 / Mar '95 / Kickin'

☐ EUROBEAT 2000 - CLUB CLASSICS VOL.3
KICKCD 32 / Jan '96 / Kickin'

☐ EUROBEAT 2000 - CLUB CLASSICS VOL.4
Prepare to jam: *Lindsay, Patrick* / Pain in my brain: *Outsider* / Circuit sex: *Blunted Boy Wonder* / Paroles: *Mike Ink* / Thunder: *Clarke, Dave* / Game form: *Beltram, Joey* / Bite and scratch: *Vogel, Christian* / Rabbits name was: *A&E Dept* / Der klang der familie: *3 Phase* / Strange funk: *Aura-Z* / Acid memory: *Dearborn, Mike* / Robot rebellion: *Sunrise Society*
KICKCD 48 / Jan '97 / Kickin'

☐ EUROCLUB VOL.1
Get up: *Technotronic* / Jack to the sound of the underground: *Hithouse* / Don't let me be misunderstood: *Santa Esmeralda* / James Brown in still alive: *Holy Noise* / Quadraphonia: *Quadrophonia* / Sonar system: *Meng Syndicate* / To piano: *Clarke, Rozline* / Dancing is like making love: *Mainx* / Can this be love: *Eden* / Make my day: *Grace Under Pressure* / Move: *Guaranteed Raw* / Fell the groove: *Cartouche* / I won't let you down: *Two Boys* / Nightlife: *TPFF* / Feel good: *Chique* / Keep the fire burning: *Bass X* / Let your love flow: *Melissa* / Down on the street: *Glow* / This beat is technotronic: *Technotronic*
EUROCD 1 / Jul '95 / Charly

☐ EUROCLUB VOL.2
Pump up the jam: *Technotronic* / Voices: *KC Flightt* / Good love: *Xaviera Gold* / Alice (who the fuck is Alice): *Steppers* / Wave of the future: *Quadrophonia* / Go with love: *Black Diamond* / I can handle it: *MSD* / 99 Luftballons: *Donn-Ah* / Fue amor: *Jazzy Mel* / Glow of love: *Grace Under Pressure* / Hot (wonderful world): *Reggie* / Touch the sky: *Cartouche* / Just the two of us: *2 Boy's* / Just a little pain: *Laurenz* / Rage: *Twins* / Night is mine (x-tra compact mix): *MC-X* / Give me your love: *Bobbylone* / Gonna move your body: *Voice Over*
EUROCD 2 / Jul '95 / Charly

☐ EUROPEAN BRASS BAND CHAMPIONSHIP 1992
Praise / Myfanwy / Danses Polovtsiennes / Five blooms in a Welsh garden / Third symphony / Blenheim flourishes / Rock music III / Year of the dragon / Speed your journey / Finale / Enigma variations
QPRL 051D / Oct '97 / Polyphonic

☐ EUROPEAN BRASS BAND CHAMPIONSHIP 1993
West Country fantasy / Sounds / I hear you calling me / Variations on an enigma / I got rhythm / Old chalet / Endearing young charms / Greensleeves / Cambridge variations
QPRL 059D / Oct '97 / Polyphonic

☐ EUROPEAN CLUB SHOES
Search: *Trancesetters* / Work it: *Liquid Groove* / Perception: *R-Factor* / Shine on: *Sirius 5* / You make me happy: *Danceorder 2* / Sides of iron: *Chaser* / First word: *Soundsurf* / Jack the beat: *Wicked Wipe* / Extra: *Ishii, Ken* / Needle damage: *Autorepeat* / Amazing space funk: *Silent Breed*
SPV 08768262 / Apr '96 / SPV

☐ EUROPEAN POLKA HITS
Trumpet echo / Cross polka / Polka from Tegernsee / Fast polka
15282 / '91 / Laserlight

☐ EUROPEAN TRUMPET SUMMIT
EFA 084282 / Apr '95 / Konnex

☐ EVE OF THE WAR (Synthesizer Hits)
MACCD 314 / Aug '96 / Autograph

☐ EVEN MORE ORIGINAL RAW SOUL
INS 371 / 20 Apr '98 / Instinct

☐ EVEN SANTA GETS THE BLUES
Christmas celebration: *King, B.B.* / I'll be coming home for Christmas: *Brooks, Hadda* / Merry Christmas baby: *Brown, Charles* / I want you with me at Christmas: *Belvin, Jesse* / White Christmas: *Brooks, Hadda* / La Christmas blue: *Brooks, Hadda* / Please come home for Christmas: *Winter, Johnny* / I wanna spend Christmas with you: *Fulson, Lowell* / Only if you were here: *Hayes, Isaac* / So glad you were born: *Hayes, Isaac*
VPBCD 28 / Nov '95 / Virgin

☐ EVENING CONCERTS - NEWPORT FOLK FESTIVAL 1963
VCD 77002 / Jan '96 / Vanguard

☐ EVENING IN THE COMPANY OF VESPERTINE, AN
VES 004 / 1 Dec '97 / Vespertine

☐ EVENING SESSION - PRIORITY TUNES (2CD Set)
Babies: *Pulp* / Changing man: *Weller, Paul* / Day we caught the train: *Ocean Colour Scene* / Something 4 the weekend: *Super Furry Animals* / Lump: *Presidents Of The USA* / Does your mother know: *Ash* / Fine time: *Cast* / Born slippy: *Underworld* / Firestarter: *Prodigy* / Valley of the shadows: *Origin Unknown* / Box: *Orbital* / Eurochild: *Massive Attack* / Street spirit: *Radiohead* / I believe: *Booth, Tim & Angelo Badalamenti* / Wrong: *Everything But The Girl* / Stars: *Dubstar* / What do I do now: *Sleeper* / Vow: *Garbage* / Drowners: *Suede* / Female of the species: *Space* / Champagne supernova: *Oasis* / Far: *Longpigs* / Connection: *Elastica* / Speakeasy: *Shed Seven* / Lose it: *Supergrass* / Weak: *Skunk Anansie* / Pig valentine: *60ft Dolls* / Rollercoaster: *Northern Uproar* / Ladykillers: *Lush* / Kandy pop: *Bis* / Take it easy chicken: *Mansun* / Just: *Radiohead* / Bank holiday: *Blur* / Penny royalty: *Manic Street Preachers* / Caught in session: *Snuff* / Born in '69: *Rocket From The Crypt* / Wuthering heights: *China Drum* / Come home: *Placebo* / Shining in the wood: *Tiger* / Chart rider space invader: *Dweeb* / Come out 2nite: *Kenickie*
VTDCD 88 / Aug '96 / Virgin

☐ EVERLASTING SAX
Everlasting love / You make me feel brand new / It's impossible / Clouds / Autumn leaves / Everything I own / With you I'm born again / Shadow of your smile / Strabnger on the shore / Three times a lady / As time goes by / Where is the love / Here's that rainy day / You're part of me / Laura / Walkin' my baby back home / Music of the niWay we were / Someone in your life / Crying / You light up my life
EMPRCD 603 / Nov '97 / Emporio

☐ EVERY BEAT YOU EAT
DQCD 01 / Aug '97 / Don Q

☐ EVERY DAY I HAVE THE BLUES
Crawling Kingsnake: *Hooker, John Lee* / Blues after hours: *Crayton, Pee Wee* / Straighten up baby: *Wilson, Smokey* / Lonesome dog blues: *Hopkins, Lightnin'* / TV Mama: *Turner, Joe* / Me and my chauffer: *Thornton, Willie Mae 'Big Mama'* / Shattered dreams: *Fulson, Lowell* / Every day I have the blues: *King, B.B.* / Sneakin' around: *King, B.B.* / House rockin' boogie: *Howlin' Wolf* / Too many drivers: *Fulson, Lowell* / Have mercy someone: *Hill,*

Z.Z. / Chains of love: Turner, Joe / Good morning little school girl: Hogg, Smokey / Telephone blues: Smith, Little George / Gone with the wind: Roosevelt Skyes / Jealous woman: Walker, T-Bone / Happy home: James, Elmore

306652 / Apr '98 / Hallmark

☐ EVERY DAY I HAVE THE BLUES

BN 046 / Apr '98 / Blue Nite

☐ EVERY SONG TELLS A STORY

Boxer: Simon & Garfunkel / Candle in the wind: John, Elton / Praying for time: Michael, George / Little time: Beautiful South / Alison: Costello, Elvis / Hazard: Marx, Richard / Romeo and Juliet: Dire Straits / Living years: Mike & The Mechanics / Dignity: Deacon Blue / Up the junction: Squeeze / You're so vain: Simon, Carly / WOLD: Chapin, Harry / Ode to Billy Joe: Gentry, Bobbie / Ruby, don't take your love to town: Rogers, Kenny / Babooshka: Bush, Kate / Vincent: McLean, Don / Uptown, uptempo woman: Edelman, Randy / Waterloo sunset: Kinks / Classic: Gurvitz, Adrian

5251702 / Apr '95 / PolyGram TV

☐ EVERY WOMAN'S BLUES

Gone woman blues: Block, Rory / Put your money where your mouth is: Foley, Sue / Ooh his love is so good: Lady Bianca / Livin' on lies: Davies, Debbie / Roll with me: Coleman, Deborah / Checks and love letters: Bogart, Deanna / Love me like a guitar: Alicia / Baby you busted: Hooker, Zakiya / Talk to the hand: Queen, B.B. / Devil's best disguise: Brown, Sarah / Look at me look at me: Greeson, Liz Mandville / When you're being nice: Connor, Joanna / Don't you tell me: Saffire / Going back home: Williams, Lucinda & Taj Mahal

SHANCD 9009 / Apr '98 / Shanachie

☐ EVERYBODY DANCE

RENCD 110 / Mar '96 / Renaissance Collector Series

☐ EVERYBODY DANCE

AMSC 632 / 27 Apr '98 / Avid

☐ EVERYBODY IS LINE DANCIN' (2CD Set)

KEG 101 / Jul '97 / Southbound

☐ EVERYBODY SALSA (The New UK Salsa Club Scene Compilation)

Everybody salsa: Que Barbara & Alfonso Jimenez / Te llamo: Hugo, Victor & La Banda / Chu chu chu: Pla, Roberto Latin Jazz Ensemble / There's nothing like this: Snowboy & The Latin Section / Dame mas tiempo: Que Barbara & Alfonso Jimenez / Baby I love your way: Casa Latina Allstars / Violin pachanguero: Charanga Del Norte / Sabrosa sabrosa: Lorza, Dorance Y Sexteto Cafe / Suavito: Casa Latina Allstars / 42nd and Broadway: Snowboy / Cumbia Dominique: Pla, Roberto Latin Jazz Ensemble / Santa Barbara bendita: Candela / No me cambies lo bailao: Pla, Roberto / Tarde no es: Hugo, Victor & La Banda

AVC 636 / Apr '98 / Avid

☐ EVERYBODY'S GOTTA LEARN SOMETIME (International Hostage Release album)

Give blood: Townshend, Pete / Architectural number: Holland, Jools / Almost seems (too late to turn): Clannad / Answers to nothing: Ure, Midge / If you really love me: Woore, Colin / Desert island: Harper, Roy / Nothing too serious: Icehouse / It's my life: Talk Talk / Candles: Rea, Chris / My nation underground: Cope, Julian / War baby: Robinson, Tom / Everybody's gotta learn sometime: Korgis / Driftwood: Moody Blues / Happy ending: Dorsey, Gail Ann / Hostage: Oldfield, Mike / Morning side: Winwood, Steve / Belfast child: Simple Minds / We don't need another hero: Turner, Tina / Never promise anyone forever: All About Eve / Man's too strong: Dire Straits / Don't give up: Gabriel, Peter & Kate Bush

WKFMXD 155 / Jan '91 / FM

☐ EVERYONE'S A WINNER

Everyone's a winner: Hot Chocolate / That's the way I like it: KC & The Sunshine Band / Gold: Spandau Ballet / Success: Duran Duran / Play to win: Heaven 17 / T'aint what you do (it's the way that you do it): Fun Boy Three & Bananarama / Win or lose: Grant, Eddy / Going for the big one: Living In A Box / Rise to the occasion: Jesus Jones / Success: Sigue Sigue Sputnik / Best in the world: Dr. Feelgood / I'm forever blowing bubbles: Cockney Rejects

4949462 / 1 Jun '98 / EMI Gold

☐ EVERYTHING OFF-BEAT

JUMP 927 / 22 Sep '97 / Jump Up

☐ EVERYTIME I FEEL THE SPIRIT

CPCD 8164 / Mar '96 / Charly

☐ EVIDENCE BLUES SAMPLER VOL.1

ECD 260002 / Jan '92 / Evidence

☐ EVIDENCE BLUES SAMPLER VOL.2

Johnnie's boogie: Johnson, Johnnie / Ramblin' on my mind: Lockwood, Robert Jr. / Worried about the blues: Fulson, Lowell / You say that you love me honey: Odom, Andrew / Giving up on love: Davis, Larry / Choo choo ch' boogie: Brown, Clarence 'Gatemouth' / Trouble in mind: Smith, Carrie / Blues is alright: Little Milton / Orange driver: Burns, Eddie Band / My baby and me: Shaw, Eddie / Talking to anna mae, part 1: Taylor, Melvin / Takes money: Young, 'Mighty' Joe / Special road: Robinson, Fenton / Young man young woman blues: Robinson, Fenton / That's your thing: Benton, Buster / All for business: Dawkins, Jimmy

ECD 260402 / Sep '93 / Evidence

☐ EVIDENCE BLUES SAMPLER VOL.3

House cat blues: Linkchain, Hip / Don't throw your love on me so strong: Campbell, Eddie C. / Boxcar shorty: Cousin Joe / Giving up on love: Davis, Larry / Little red rooster: Peterson, Lucky / Night life: Witherspoon, Jimmy / That's alright: Rogers, Jimmy / Cold cold feeling: Taylor, Melvin / You've got me running: Johnson, Luther 'Georgia Snake Boy' / Don't you lie to me: Edwards, David 'Honeyboy' / It hurts me too: Wells, Junior / You just a baby child: Dawkins, Jimmy / Broke and hungry: Sumlin, Hubert / I can't quit you baby: Rush, Otis

ECD 260482 / Mar '94 / Evidence

☐ EVITA'S TANGO (The Golden Age Of The Tango 1945-1952)

74321447932 / Feb '97 / Milan Sur

☐ EVOLUTION

LHCD 009 / Jul '96 / Luv n' Haight

☐ EVOLUTION OF SOUND VOL.2 (2CD Set)

HGCD 0092 / 2 Mar '98 / House Grooves

☐ EVOLUTION THE SOUND

H&GCD 0122 / 6 Jul '98 / H&G

☐ EVOLUTION'S CHRISTMAS

EVCD 3 / Dec '95 / Evolution

☐ EVOLVING TRADITION

Trip to Fowey/Indian Queen: Kings Of Calicut / Tom Clarke's trip to Russia: Henderson, Ingrid & Allan / Johnny 'Watt' Henry's/Aly Bain's: Daniels, Luke Trio / Flower of Magherallyo: Oige / Flatulent Friar of Frome/Lizzie Watling's jig: Plews, Dan & Cath James / Tamlin's reel/Bucks of Oranmore/Bunker Hill: Sherburn, Chris & Denny Bartley / Bonny Light Horseman/Michael Turner's waltz: Carthy, Eliza & Nancy Kerr / PJ Cunningham's old dance: Cythara / Doon hingin tie/Tammy Anderson: Shetland's Young Heritage / Recruited collier: Rusby, Kate & Kathryn Roberts / Raag kirvani/Tintaal: Sood, Rajan & Rakhi / Faroe rum/Andowin ida bow/Sleep soond ida moarnin/Lasses tru: MacDonald, Catriona & Ian Lowthian / Robin Hood/The tolling bell: Hedgerows / Left side jigs: Thoumire, Simon & Ian Carr / Jolie Bassette: Lewery, Gavin & Jock Tyldesley / Tralee gaol/The chanter: Van Eyken, Tim & Kerensa Wragg / Road to recovery/Humours of Galway/Farewell to the Shetland: Anglim, Carlene & Simon Howarth / Lord Gresham: Bohinta / Tom and Jerry: Wrigley, Jennifer & Hazel / Fairfield march/Pit stop/The rushing reel: Lakeman Brothers / Bransle du chien/ Bar room brawl: Chipolata 5

MCRCD 5991 / Apr '95 / Mrs. Casey

☐ EXCELLO HITS

Little darlin': Gladiolas / Raining in my heart: Harpo, Slim / Oh Julie: Crescendos / Prisoner's song: Storm, Warren / Rollin' stone: Marigolds / Pleadin' for love: Birdsong, Larry / Congo mombo: Guitar Gable / Hey baby: Ferrier, Al / Emmitt Lee: Fran, Carol / Shoop shoop: Gladiolas / I'm a mojo man: Lonesome Sundown / This should go on forever: King Karl / I'm a lover not a fighter: Lazy Lester / Now that she's gone: King Crooners / Doin' the horse: Brooks, Skippy / Rooster blues: Lightnin' Slim / Please think it over: Shelton, Roscoe / School daze: Little Rico & The King Crooners / Hello Mary Lee: Lightnin' Slim / You know baby: Meloaires / Baby scratch my back: Harpo, Slim / Snake out of the grass: Anderson, Roshell

CDCHD 400 / Jan '94 / Ace

☐ EXCELSIOR (A Compilation Of Dutch Guitar Pop)

SPART 61 / 6 Jul '98 / Spin Art

☐ EXCERPTS FROM THE DATA BASS

Geomantik: Prana / I think we can go the moon: Doof / Rezwalker: Transwave / Overture: Typhoon / Magic frequencies: Typhoon / Joy: Endora / X-1: Process / Scientific experiment: Manmademan

MPCD 9 / 22 Sep '97 / Matsuri

☐ EXCLUSIVE ALTERNATIVES

CLP 9948 / Jun '97 / Cleopatra

☐ EXCURSIONS (2CD Set)

Fantasy on a fantasy: Caron, David / Claire: 10 / Firescratch: Midnight Funk Association / Warrior: Stasis / Summer madness: DJ Solo & DJ Aura / Harry's law: Twig Bud / Twice the lips: Midnight Funk Association / Altares: Stasis / Night-side: Prunes / Libre: 10 / Take heed: DJ Solo & DJ Aura / Davoff: Twig Bud / Plot: Prunes / Mr. Jolly lives next door: Prunes / Hardcore hip hop: DJ Shadow / Night shade: Prunes / Last stop: DJ Shadow / Libro: 10 / Time in advance: Stasis / In from the cold: Stasis / Pressure: DJ Solo

MW 056CD / Dec '96 / Mo Wax

☐ EXIT DANCE

HHCD 011 / Mar '97 / Harthouse

☐ EXOTIC VOICES & RHYTHMS OF BLACK AFRICA

EUCD 1204 / Sep '93 / ARC

☐ EXOTIC VOICES & RHYTHMS OF THE SOUTH SEAS

EUCD 1254 / Mar '94 / ARC

☐ EXOTICA (World Music Divas)

Amaria: Mammas / Miro rom hin ternoro: Bila, Vera & Kale / Miss Perfumado: Evora, Cesaria / Cantigueiras: Nunez, Carlos & Xiradela / O boro braindi braindi: Minogue, Aine / Caravan: Shai No Shai / Como se: Venegas, Julieta / Tu me camelas: Pastori, Nina & Radio Tarifa / Free: Nin, Khadja / My Ethiopian boy: Haza, Ofra

09026689882 / Jul '98 / RCA Victor

☐ EXPANSION PHAT JAMS VOL.1

Just let me be close to you: Valentine Brothers / No more tears: Jeter, Genobia / Beverly: Jamariah / You know what it's like: Brooks, Calvin / Callin' up (Old memories): Haynes, Victor / Shoulda been you: Ware, Leon / Didn't mean to hurt you: Valentine, Billy / Starlite: Ballin, Chris / Victory: Baylor, Helen / Kissing in the dark: Rodni / Miss you: Fresh Air / Love hurts: Glaze / Show your love: Hutson, Leroy / I can't stand the pain: Lorenzo / If you don't want my love: Williams, Lewis

EXCDP 3 / Jun '94 / Expansion

☐ EXPANSION PHAT JAMS VOL.2

Morning glow: James, Josie / Any time, any place: Gary / I'll treat U rite: Perry, Trina / No one move me like you do: Gaines, Billy & Sarah / Whenever I'm lonely: Dawkins & Dawkins / I need your help: Austin, Dennis / Memory: King, James / This love: Baylor, Helen / We got something: Valentine, Billy / Share your love: Hutson, Leroy / Talk to me: Brooks, Calvin / I'll always love you: Robbins, Rockie / Another lonely night: Jous / You are my one and only love: Webb, Rick / Let's turn the lights down low: Jamariah

EXCDP 4 / Jul '95 / Expansion

☐ EXPANSION SOUL SAUCE VOL.1

My favourite thing: Brooks, Calvin & Hari Paris / Share your love: Hutson, Leroy / Oasis: Baylor, Helen / I found someone: Gaines, Billy & Sarah / Shine: Aja / Heartbeat: Ware, Leon / Win your love: James, Josie / Everybody's in a hurry: McNeir, Ronnie / Main squeeze: Crook, General / Hang on: Robbins, Rockie / Love is the magic: Blu, Peggi / We got one: Covington, Matt / Power to the people: Linsey / Friends or lovers: Burke, Keni / Promises: Glaze

CDEXP 1 / Jul '93 / Expansion

☐ EXPANSION SOUL SAUCE VOL.2

Late night hour: Waters, Kim / Surrender (my soul): Skinner, Belinda A. / Paradise: Tankard, Ben / Give me all your love: Ballin, Chris / You are my star: Reeves, Paulette / Forever: Felder, Wilton / I can only think of you: McCrae, Gwen / Fool for love: Warren, Tony / It's up to me: James, Josie / One step back for love: El Coco / Stay with me: Clear, Crystal / Shame on you: Lovesmith, Michael / Goodbye song: Vanesse & Carolyn / Look of love: Hutson, Leroy / After affect: Taylor, Gary

CDEXP 3 / May '93 / Expansion

☐ EXPANSION SOUL SAUCE VOL.3

Think about it: Webb, Rick / Ja miss me: Valentine, Billy / I don't know why: White, Lynn / One and only: Rodni / Take a little time: James, Josie / Days and nights: Haynes, Victor / Blind to it all: Taylor, Gary / Love's gonna bring you home: Rockmelons / All my love: Carmichael, James / This kind of love (so special): Valentine Brothers / I'd like to into you: Kelly, Denise & Fame / Get into your life: Beloyd / Losers weepers: Blackfoot, J. / If you don't want my love: Williams, Lewis

CDEXP 6 / Nov '93 / Expansion

☐ EXPANSION SOUL SAUCE VOL.4

Down low: Redd, Jeff / When ever you're ready: Purnell, Tiffany / Keep holdin' on: Tyronza / Deeper and deeper: Wilson, Pauline / Fly away: Wall, Jeremy / Rockin' you tonite: Gary / Any kind of love: Tankard, Ben / Miracle: Dawkins & Dawkins / Come share your love: Kymiztre / Heart is a house for love: Valentine, Billy / You got what I want: Jous / Love at first sight: Epps, James / If It was me: Sunday Tucker / I get high on your memory: Jacobs, Sheila

CDEXP 9 / Feb '95 / Expansion

☐ EXPANSION SOUL SAUCE VOL.5

So good: Bristol, Johnny / I need: Coleman, Margi / U should be with me: Bleu, Mikki / Can't miss: Jackson, Nicole / Don't keep me waiting: Wilde, Dee Dee / Solitaire: Davis, Michael / My joy (is you): Wanda / No one (can give the love you give): Simpson, Nate / All out of love: Morgan, Cozette / You're so good: Martinez, Nigel / Jive: Jive / Soap opera love affair: Clayton, Willie / Night like this in Georgia: Cameron, G.C. / I think I'm falling in love with you: Natural High

CDEXP 11 / Apr '96 / Expansion

☐ EXPLICIT BASS (2CD Set)

B2BCD 1 / Nov '96 / Back 2 Basics

☐ EXPLORATIONS VOL.1

URCD 006 / Jul '96 / Ubiquity

☐ EXPLORATIONS VOL.2

URCD 008 / Jul '96 / Ubiquity

☐ EXPLORATIONS VOL.3

URCD 013 / Jul '96 / Ubiquity

☐ EXPLORING THE FRONTIERS OF ROCK JAZZ AND WORLD MUSIC

Bestial cluster: Karn, Mick / Politician: Bruce, Jack / Sorcerer: Shrieve, Michael / Low flying doves: Summers, Andy / What was once...: Torn, David / Ships in the night: Bruce, Jack / Folksong: Bruce, Jack / Red sleep: Torn/Karn/Bozzio / Little les hope: Karn, Mick / Once I wished a tree upside down: Gurtu, Trilok / Living with the law: Shrieve, Michael / Other tune: Gurtu, Trilok / Triangles: Summers, Andy

CMPCD 5005 / 22 Sep '97 / CMP

☐ EXPLOSAO DO BRASIL

1918202 / Jul '97 / EPM

☐ EXPLOSIVE DOO WOP VOL.11

One minute more: Marx / Scribbling on the wall: Gallant, Billy & The Roulettes / School is over: Adrian, Lee / No: Spiedels / My love is just for you: Blendairs / Hey there: Irridescents / Please be fair: Maresca, Ernie / White cliffs of Dover: Robins / Hasten Jason: Singing Roulettes / Sing a song of sixpence: Corvairs / Can't believe that you've grown up: Squires / Dolores: Mood Makers / Now it's your turn: Blends / Rama lama ding dong: Edsels / Do you love her: Impressors / Happy teenager: Carr, Linda & The Impossibles / Teardrops follow me: Devotions / Zoom zoom zoom: Schaeffer, Freddy / Say that you love me: Del-Chords / Loving time: Hideaways / Never will forget: Royal Jesters / Dreaming of you: Five Shits / She's my baby: Five Playboys / Come on Oz: Emerald City Bandits / Sweet Juanita: Kappas / Gaudeamus: Escorts

BB 55058 / Aug '97 / Buffalo Bop

☐ EXPLOSIVE DOO WOP VOL.12

Sweet Lorraine: Allen, Ray & The Upbeats / Teresa: Treble Chords / Boy for me: Tassels / Dressing up: Elegants / Wishing time: Cari, Eddie / You guardian angel: Como, Nicky / Cathy: Four Temptations / Heartbeat: Whirlwinds / I remember: Suburbans / Without warning: Darrels / Love so sweet: Vines / Gee: Harmony Grits / While walking: Tony & The Raindrops / These foolish things: Companions / I believe: Arthur & The Corvets / I love you for sentimental reasons: Little Joe & The Thrillers / Tra-la-la: Bobby & The Counts / My guy and I: Tassels / Mr. Hard Luck: Orbits / Lovely love: King Bees / Lily Maybelle: Del-Rays / Why why why: Stevens, Scott & The Cavaliers / My baby's alright: Castaliers / This makes me mad: Charters / Secret world of tears: Vision / Carioca: Aqua Nites

BB 55059 / Aug '97 / Buffalo Bop

☐ EXPLOSIVE ROCKSTEADY/JACKPOT OF HITS

I'm moving on: Pioneers / Miss Tourist: Pioneers / Just like a river: Cole, Stranger & Gladstone Anderson / Uncle Sam's country: Walks, Dennis / Long shot kick de bucket: Pioneers / Train to soulsville: Cool Sticky / Love love everyday: Pioneers / Hold them: Shirley, Roy / Come brothers: Malcolm, Hugh / Give me a little loving: Pioneers / Push it in: Versatiles / Love brother love: Dunkley, Errol / Jackpot: Pioneers / Feel good: Mellotones / No dope me pony: Pioneers / Secret weapon: Collins, Ansell / El Casino Royale: Taitt, Lynn & The Jetts / What Moma no want she gets: Cole, Stranger / Catch the beat: Pioneers / Good time rock: Malcolm, Hugh / Hurry come up: Crashers / Just can't win: Versatiles / Seeing is knowing: Cole, Stranger & Gladstone Anderson / Holding out: Creations

CDTRL 377 / Mar '97 / Trojan

☐ EXPOSE YOURSELF

Day Squids gerbil died: Lunachicks / My favourite mistake: Weston / My danger: Shake Appeal / Not again: Mustard Plug / Wrecking ball: Bluebird / COI: Heckle / Watch it burn: Cast Iron Hike / Blister: Strife / Weirdo: Limp / Ye olde folke: Twatte / Take me back: Ataris / No time: Assorted Jelly Beans / Spoken words: Silent Majority / I wasn't going to call you anyway: Toasters / Idiot box: Aquabats / Feel like Morrissey: 30 Foot Fall / Gracias: Pezz / Bleed: Field Day / Groovie ghoulies: Groovie Ghoulies / Manipulate me: Groovie Ghoulies / Tune me out: MU330 / California: Facet / Squirtgun: Squirtgun / So sorry: 22 Jacks / Ten yard fight: Ten Yard Fight / Parliament of whores: Jughead's Revenge

GK 038 / 29 Jun '98 / Go-Kart

☐ EXPOSED

IYF 01CD / Sep '96 / In Yer Face

☐ EXPRESS YOURSELF (Charly's Funky Grooves)

It's a new day: Skull Snaps / Sissy walk: Jones, Sonny / Soul junction: Backyard Heavies / Express yourself: SOUL / We're doing it (thang): Bo, Eddie / Machine shop: Untouchable Machine Shop / Got to getcha: Maceo & All The King's Men / If it's good to you (it's good for you): Bo, Eddie / I've got reasons: Hooper, Mary Jane / Hey Pancho: Young-Holt Unlimited / Sissy walk: Jones, Sonny / You're losing me: Sexton, Ann / Just keep on truckin': Backyard Heavies / Loose Boodie: Pitts, Vic Cheaters / Burning spear: SOUL / We're doing it (thang): SOUL

CDNEW 114 / Oct '97 / Charly

☐ EXPRESSIONS (The Violin - Its Many Moods And Styles)

Partita / Autumn from 'The Four Seasons' / King of the fairies / Kalinka / Honeysuckle rose / Bobby's blues / Pie Jesu / Caprice Viennoise / Danny air / Bahr bela ma / Raving / Jigs and reels medley / Mrs. Hamilton of Pencaitland / Eriskay love lilt / Double violin concerto in A major / Age of glass

303732 / Jun '97 / Hallmark

☐ EXPRESSIONS (The Electric Guitar - It's Many Moods And Styles)

Maverick / Driving seat / Echo sixties / Country pickin' / Rollin' / Julie / Time and again / RADIO / Gambler / Interlude / Nevada / Holiday blues / Guy in a hole / Cat Billy / Woman in love / Groove / Cacoethes/Flip flap / Highway driver / Heading home

304542 / Jun '97 / Hallmark

☐ EXPRESSIONS OF WORSHIP (Purify My Heart)

Jesus we celebrate your victory / Be strong and take courage / Jesus is alive / No condemnation / Not by might / Not power / I love to be in your presence / Thy word / No eyes have seen / O Lord to you / Into your courts / Only by grace / Purify my heart

97122 / Apr '98 / Fairhope

☐ EXPRESSIONS OF WORSHIP VOL.1 (God Is Good)

Give thanks / Spirit of the Lord / We will come and save you / Shout to the Lord / Firm foundation / Lamb of God / You are glorious / God is able / Solid rock / God is good / Mighty is our god / Shine Jesus shine

97102 / Apr '98 / Fairhope

☐ EXPRESSIONS OF WORSHIP VOL.2 (On Bended Knee)

I worship you almighty God / Under the shadow / Lead me to the rock / Heaven is in my heart / Some may trust in chariots / We give you thanks / God will make a way / O Lord your tenderness / On bended knee / Pure in heart

97112 / Apr '98 / Fairhope

☐ EXTRA HOT VOL.10

DMUT 1306 / Mar '96 / Multitone

☐ EXTREME MUSIC FROM AFRICA

SLCD 016 / Feb '97 / Susan Lawley

☐ EXTREME POSSIBILITIES

LCD 01 / 9 Feb '98 / Lo Recordings

☐ EXTREME Q

DQCD 02 / 20 Apr '98 / Don Q

☐ EXTREME ROCK - A NEW AGE

M 7021CD / Sep '96 / Mascot

☐ EYE OF THE SUN (The Heart & Soul Of The Native Americans)

Night song / Crying rabbit / Eye of the sun / Caller / Flying eagle / Harvest dreams (part 1) / Harvest dreams (part 2) / Cry for rain (part 1) / Cry for rain (part 2) / Dancing squaws / War song / Like a snake / Spot song / Hungry dog

DC 881532 / 29 Aug '97 / Disky

☐ **EYE ON THE PRIZE**
Together forever: Exodus / Keep in touch: *Shades Of Love* / Heavy vibes: *Montana, Vince Jr.* / Get down: *Aleem & Leroy Burgess* / Long enough: *Last Poets* / Barely breaking even: *Universal Robot Band* / Weekend: *Class Action* / What happend to the music: *Trammps*
SURCD 02 / Jun '94 / Grapevine

☐ **EYE Q CLASSICS VOL.1**
EYECL 001 / 27 Apr '98 / Eye Q

F

☐ **FAB HITS OF THE 60'S**
Ob-la-di-ob-la-da: *Marmalade* / Girl don't come: *Shaw, Sandie* / Venus in blue jeans: *Wynter, Mark* / Poor man's son: *Rockin' Berries* / Picture of you: *Brown, Joe & The Bruvvers* / Don't sleep in the subway: *Clark, Petula* / Theme from Z cars: *Keating, Johnny & The Z Men* / Warpaint: *Brook Brothers* / Ice in the sun: *Status Quo* / (Call me) number one: *Tremeloes* / Tin soldier: *Small Faces* / Sugar and spice: *Searchers* / Twist and shout: *Isley Brothers* / Barefootin': *Parker, Robert* / In the bad old days before you loved me: *Foundations* / Make me an island: *Dolan, Joe* / Cast your fate to the wind: *Sounds Orchestral* / Colour of my love: *Jefferson* / Ain't nothing but a house party: *Showstoppers* / Natural born bugie: *Humble Pie*
MCCD 296 / May '97 / Music Club

☐ **FABULOUS 30'S, THE**
DCD 5335 / Dec '93 / Disky

☐ **FABULOUS FIFTIES HIT BOX (3CD Set)**
Oh oh I'm falling in love again: *Rodgers, Jimmie* / Just walkin' in the rain: *Ray, Johnnie* / Earth angel: *Crew Cuts* / Standing on the corner: *Four Lads* / Only you: *Hilltoppers* / Love letters in the sand: *Boone, Pat* / Freight train: *McDevitt, Chas* / High noon: *Laine, Frankie* / Singing the blues: *Mitchell, Guy* / Great Pretender: *Platters* / Tutti frutti: *Little Richard* / My special angel: *Helms, Bobby* / Little darlin': *Diamonds* / Rebel rouser: *Eddy, Duane* / Purple people eater: *Wooley, Sheb* / Petite fleur: *Barber, Chris* / Ivory tower: *Carr, Cathy* / Charlie Brown: *Coasters* / Changing partners: *Page, Patti* / I believe: *Laine, Frankie* / Sea of love: *Phillips, Phil* / Walkin' my baby back home: *Ray, Johnnie* / Hey there: *Clooney, Rosemary* / Sh-boom: *Crew Cuts* / Big man: *Four Preps* / I'll be home: *Boone, Pat* / Fool: *Clark, Sanford* / All American boy: *Parsons, Bill* / Rock-a-billy: *Mitchell, Guy* / Twilight time: *Platters* / Baby face: *Little Richard* / Honeycomb: *Rodgers, Jimmie* / Yakety yak: *Coasters* / Forty miles of bad road: *Eddy, Duane* / Big hurt: *Fisher, Toni* / Seven little girls: *Evans, Paul* / Do you wanna dance: *Freeman, Bobby* / Does your chewing gum lose it's flavour: *Donegan, Lonnie* / Band of gold: *Cherry, Don* / At the hop: *Danny & The Juniors* / Cry: *Ray, Johnnie* / Three coins in the fountain: *Four Aces* / Smoke gets in your eyes: *Platters* / Good golly miss molly: *Little Richard* / Little star: *Elegants* / Tom Dooley: *Kingston Trio* / Susie darlin': *Luke, Robin* / Venus: *Avalon, Frankie* / Sleep walk: *Santo & Johnny* / Personality: *Price, Lloyd* / Red river rock: *Johnny & The Hurricanes* / You got what it takes: *Johnson, Marv* / Tennesse waltz: *Page, Patti* / Hold my hand: *Cornell, Don* / Honky tonk: *Doggett, Bill* / Green door: *Lowe, Jim* / Rockin' robin: *Day, Bobby* / Wayward wind: *Grant, Gogi*
390522 / Aug '97 / Hallmark

☐ **FABULOUS FIFTIES ROCK 'N' ROLL**
Great balls of fire: *Lewis, Jerry Lee* / Shake, rattle and roll: *Haley, Bill & The Comets* / Bony moronie: *Williams, Larry* / Raunchy: *Justis, Bill* / Lucille: *Little Richard* / Tiger: *Fabian* / Claudette: *Everly Brothers* / Leroy: *Scott, Jack* / Rave on: *Holly, Buddy & The Crickets* / Johnny B Goode: *Berry, Chuck* / (We're gonna) Rock around the clock: *Haley, Bill & The Comets* / Blue suede shoes: *Perkins, Bill* / When: *Kalin Twins* / Tallahassie lassie: *Cannon, Freddy* / Good golly Miss Miss: *Little Richard* / Wake up little Susie: *Everly Brothers* / Lawdy Miss Clawdy: *Price, Lloyd* / Whole lotta shakin' goin' on: *Lewis, Jerry Lee*
PWKS 4180 / Oct '94 / Carlton

☐ **FABULOUS FLIPS VOL.1**
Slow down: *Williams, Larry* / Give me love: *Rosie & The Originals* / Leroy: *Scott, Jack* / I wonder if I care as much: *Everly Brothers* / Sweetheart please don't go: *Gladiolas* / Miss Ann: *Little Richard* / Crazy: *Hollywood Flames* / Train to nowhere: *Champs* / My little girl: *Crescendos* / What'cha gonna do: *Kuf Linx* / Did you cry: *Dicky Doo & Don'ts* / Can it be: *Titans* / Swag: *Wray, Link & His Raymen* / She's the one for me: *Aquatones* / Flippin': *Hall, Rene* / Gotta getta date: *Jan & Arnie* / Over and over: *Day, Bobby* / One night, one night: *Skyliners* / Beside you: *Crests* / Crazy baby: *Rockin' R's* / Rock 'n' roll cha cha: *Eternals* / Love me as I love you: *Cortez, Dave 'Baby'* / Taking care of business: *Turner, Titus* / Last night I dreamed: *Fiestas* / Sweet thing: *Bland, Billy* / My babe: *Holden, Ron*
CDCHD 444 / Oct '93 / Ace

☐ **FABULOUS FLIPS VOL.2**
Little Billy boy / Lonesome for a letter / Trouble, trouble / It's really you / Why / Well / Little Queenie / Ch-kow-ski / I can't hold out any longer / Don't start cryin' now / Cast iron arm / Bad boy / Gee how I wish you were here / Sail along sil'vry moon / Red sails in the sunset / Rubber dolly / Living's loving you / Sweet was the wine / Tight capris / Girl of my dreams / Love is a swingin' thing / Gunshot / Chicken necks / Havin' so much fun / Back shack track / Monster
CDCHD 560 / Apr '95 / Ace

☐ **FABULOUS FLIPS VOL.3**
I can't go on (Rosalie): *Dion & The Belmonts* / Wail: *Royaltones* / Dirty robber: *Wailers* / Fortune teller: *Spellman, Benny* / Am I asking to much: *String-A-Longs* / I am lonely: *Silhouettes* / That's the way it's gonna be: *Shields* / Red sails in the sunset: *Sharpe, Ray* / Smoke from your cigarette: *Belmonts* / Getting dizzy: *Elegants* / Stay awhile: *Clovers* / Mr. Dillon: *Delacardos* / Before I grow too old: *Domino, Fats* / Rockin' shoes: *Ames Brothers* / Come my little baby: *Chantels* / Goddess of angels: *Falcons* / Cincinnati fireball: *Falcons* / Big fat woman: *Freeman, Bobby* / Ooh la la: *Avalon, Frankie* / Waddle: *Slades* / High school dance: *Williams, Larry* / I ain't goin' for that: *Church, Eugene* / Country fool: *Showmen* / Beverly Jean: *Lee, Curtis* / Saccharin Sally: *Tu-Tones* / Down at the beach: *Pentagons*
CDCHD 645 / Feb '97 / Ace

☐ **FABULOUS LOW PRICE BLUES SAMPLER**
HMG 4003 / Dec '97 / Hightone

☐ **FACE OF THE FUTURE**
BDRCD 4 / Nov '94 / Breakdown

☐ **FACE THE CHALLENGE IN MUSIC VOL.1**
CHR 70020 / Sep '95 / Challenge

☐ **FACE THE CHALLENGE IN MUSIC VOL.3 (Today's Jazz Classics)**
Three for two: *Alter, Myriam* / Toda a gente que passa: *Bacan & Lilian Vieira* / 13 bar blues: *Margitza, Rick* / Kidney stew: *Davis, Spanky & Roy Eldridge* / Wheeling: *Baseline* / Ascot: *Van't Hof, Jasper* / Speak low: *Citroen, Soesja* / Take the 'A' train: *Houdinis* / Blue again: *McHugh, Jimmy & Dorothy Fields* / Elephant walk: *Vloeimans, Eric* / Los aretes de la luna: *Winanda Del Sur* / You took advantage of me: *Kellaway, Roger* / Grand slam: *De Graaf, Dick & Tony Lakatos Trio*
CHR 719970 / Jul '97 / Challenge

☐ **FACE THE MUSIC - TORVILL & DEAN**
Mack and Mabel / Summertime / Barnum / Bolero / Capriccio / Song of India / Venus / Love duet from Fire and Ice / Snow maiden - the Procession of the Tsar Berendey / Incantation / Oscar tango / Iceworks / Skaters' waltz / Let's face the music and dance / History of love / Medley
8450652 / Feb '94 / PolyGram TV

☐ **FACES OF THE HARP**
Austin's planxty: *Doyle, Dennis* / Tipsy elk: *Loefke, Thomas* / Dance of the lambs: *Robertson, Kim* / Saguaro: *Riley, L & M. MacBean* / Castlebay scrap/ Stuart's rant: *Sileas* / Dialogue with a brook: *Woods, Sylvia* / Bennachie sunrise/Willie trip to Toronto: *Sedrenn* / Waterdance/Gay feather: *Waldren, K.L. & C. Kreitlow* / Memories of that isle: *Bell, Derek* / Eclipse: *Williams, Ani* / Blessing way: *Haines, Julia* / Mushrooms of Fagernes: *Northern Lights* / Bas alastruim/McAlistrum's march: *Heymann, Ann & Alison Kinnaird* / Wedding of pysche and eros: *Pinter, Judith* / Spring: *Lee, R.*
ND 63934 / Jun '97 / Narada

☐ **FACING THE WRONG WAY**
FTWW 1 / Sep '95 / 4AD

☐ **FACTOR 20**
Karma chameleon: *Culture Club* / Tide is high: *Blondie* / Turn to gold: *Austin, David* / Love in our hearts: *Brown, Peter* / Night in New York: *Elbow Bones & Racketeers* / Everything I own: *Boy George* / Kiss me: *Duffy, Stephen* / On my way to LA: *Carmen, Phil* / Baby I need your lovin': *Turner, Ruby & The Four Tops* / Calyso crazy: *Ocean, Billy* / Place in the sun: *Winjama* / Don't go lose it baby: *Masekela, Hugh* / One cup of coffee: *Shaffer, Paul* / You can leave your hat on: *Chippendales* / Lion sleeps tonight: *Tight Fit* / Queen of clubs: *KC & The Sunshine Band* / Wonderful world beautiful people: *Amazulu* / Tena's song: *Foxy*
DC 880812 / May '97 / Disky

☐ **FADO 1926-1931 (2CD Set)**
FA 153 / 1 Jun '98 / Fremeaux

☐ **FADO DE LISBOA**
HTCD 14 / Jan '93 / Heritage

☐ **FAIKAVA: THE TONGAN KAVA CIRCLE**
PAN 2022CD / Oct '93 / Pan

☐ **FAITH**
TB 2077 / 27 Jul '98 / 2 Bad Productions

☐ **FAITH, A MESSAGE FROM THE SPIRITS**
Introduction, faith / Chango / Damaru drum/Chant for deity dharmaraja / Evangelist sheila / Djouba / Gaj jatra / Tsok choe / I specialize / Mravaldzanier / Torah recital/Yaashe shalom / Koran recital / Eleggua / Tsimindao upalo / Bells / Let god turn it around for you / Tsok choe
SJRCD 034 / Mar '97 / Soul Jazz

☐ **FAITH AND INSPIRATION**
MTVCD 1001 / 11 May '98 / Mobius

☐ **FAITH HOPE AND PSYCHEDELIA**
ASHACD 1 / 15 Dec '97 / Asha

☐ **FAKE FRUIT AND HORRIBLE SHOES (A Pure Plastic Compilation No.1)**
Funked up / Halcyon / Spring / Endless filters / 20ft scarf / Nine open / Slingshot / Room and air / Tropica
PPCDCOMP 1 / Jun '97 / Pure Plastic

☐ **FALLOUT PUNK SINGLES COLLECTION, THE**
Fallen hero: *Enemy* / Viva la revolution: *Adicts* / Suicide bag: *Action Pact* / Punks alive: *Enemy* / Jubilee: *Rabid* / New barbarians: *Urban Dogs* / People: *Action Pact* / Limo life: *Urban Dogs* / Last rites: *Enemy* / London bouncers: *Action Pact* / Another typical city: *UK Subs* / Question of choice: *Action Pact* / Decapitated: *Broken Bones* / Amphetamine blues: *Fallen Angels* / Private army: *UK Subs* / Cruxifix: *Broken Bones* / Yet another dole queue song: *Action Pact* / Inner planet love: *Fallen Angels* / Cocktail credibility: *Action Pact* / Seeing through my eyes: *Broken Bones* / This gun says: *UK Subs* / Champs Elysees: *Adicts* / Never say die: *Broken Bones* / Hey Santa: *UK Subs* / Jodie Foster: *UK Subs*
CDPUNK 30 / Mar '94 / Anagram

☐ **FAMILIA RMM EN VIVO**
Oiga, mire, vea: *Orquesta Guayacan* / Overture: *Orchestra RMM* / Apaga la luz: *Cartagena, Antonio* / Para que: *Pena, Miles* / Por eso esta conmigo: *Rivera, Johnny* / Mi primera rumba: *India* / Hasta que te conoci: *Anthony, Marc* / Aparentemente: *Vega, Tony* / Amores como tu: *Nieves, Tito* / Otra noche caliente: *De La Paz, Ray* / Disculpeme senora: *Alberto, Jose* / Azucar negra: *Cruz, Celia*
RMD 81454 / 24 Mar '98 / RMM

☐ **FAMILY AFFAIR VOL.2**
SUMO 007 / 23 Feb '98 / Supermodern

☐ **FAMILY CIRCLE FAMILY TREE**
Off with the old: *Chameleon Church* / In kindly way: *Chameleon Church* / Here's a song: *Chameleon Church* / Ready Eddie: *Chameleon Church* / Camellia is changing: *Chameleon Church* / Your golden love: *Chameleon Church* / Remembering's all I can do: *Chameleon Church* / Blueberry pie: *Chameleon Church* / Tompkins Square Park: *Chameleon Church* / Spring this year: *Chameleon Church* / Maybe more than you: *Lost* / Back door blues: *Lost* / I want to know: *Lost* / Here she comes: *Lost* / Everybody knows: *Lost* / Violet gown: *Lost* / Mystic: *Lost* / Kaleidoscope: *Lost* / Happiness child: *Ultimate Spinach* / Everybody knows: *Alexender, Willie & Bagatelle* / Everybody knows: *Alexender, Willie 'Loco' & The Boom Boom Band* / Back door blues: *Ultimate Spinach*
CDWIKD 146 / Jan '96 / Big Beat

☐ **FAMILY TREE INTERNATIONAL**
99 2146 / Jul '96 / Ninetynine

☐ **FAMOUS CHARISMA BOX, THE (4CD Set)**
Hoopoe's tales: *Stanshall, Vivian* / Sympathy: *Rare Bird* / Refugees: *Van Der Graaf Generator* / Lady Eleanor: *Lindisfarne* / Knife: *Genesis* / Indian summer: *Audience* / Witchi-tai-to: *Topo D Bil* / Terry keeps his clips on: *Stanshall, Vivian* / Hungarian peasant girl: *Billmuss, Trevor* / Regent street incident: *String Driven Thing* / Gaye: *Ward, Clifford T.* / Imperial zeppelin: *Hammill, Peter* / Painted ladies: *Moore, G T* / Money game: *Hull, Alan* / Ooh mother: *Unicorn* / Liar: *Brown, Capability* / Intermezzo from Karelia suite: *Nice* / Quark, strangeness and charm: *Hawkwind* / Solsbury Hill: *Gabriel, Peter* / Lucinda: *Werth, Howard* / Why can't I be satisfied: *Jack The Lad* / Doubting Thomas: *Heights, Jackson* / Fog on the Tyne: *Lindisfarne* / I get a kick out of you: *Shearston, Gary* / Ritt Mickley: *Refugee* / Disco suicide: *Brand X* / Working in line: *Rutherford, Mike* / Go placidly: *Every Which Way* / Robot man: *Wakeman, Rick* / And the wheels keep turning: *Banks, Tony* / Out in the sun: *Moraz, Patrick* / How can I: *Hackett, Steve* / Too many people: *Bell, Graham* / Happy the man: *Genesis* / She belongs to me: *Bell & Arc* / Window city: *Stanshall, Vivian* / Travel agent sketch (Live at Drury Lane): *Monty Python* / Cultural attache: *Humphries, Barry* / Talks turf: *O'Sullevan, Peter* / Three fold attunement: *Turner, Gordon* / Talks cricket: *Arlott, John* / One and tow: *Lang, R D* / Sir Henry at Rawlinson End: *Stanshall, Vivian* / Finland: *Monty Python* / Varsity students rag: *Betjeman, Sir John* / I bet you they won't play this song on the radio: *Monty Python* / Theme one: *Van Der Graaf Generator* / Window city (Fade): *Stanshall, Vivian* / Chasing sheep is best left to shepherds: *Nyman, Michael* / Front door: *Isaacs, Gregory* / Cloudy day: *Congo Ashanti Roy* / Put it out: *Prince Far-I* / Don't leave me this way: *Desperadoes* / Move it on up: *Moore, G T* / (Hey you) the Rocksteady crew: *Rocksteady Crew* / Hey DJ: *World's Famous Supreme Team* / Paperheart: *King, Robert* / Anticipation: *Delta 5* / All about you: *Scars* / Ten don't for honeymooners: *Monochrome Set* / Making time: *Creation* / Freedom dance jazz: *Emerson, Keith* / It's all over now baby blue: *Wray, Link* / Embezzler: *Werth, Howard & The Moonbeams* / Kittiwake: *Jansch, Bert* / Too late for goodbyes: *Lennon, Julian* / God rock: *Turner, Nik*
CASBOX 1 / Nov '93 / Charisma

☐ **FAMOUS MEXICAN SONGS**
995822 / Nov '97 / EPM

☐ **FAMOUS NEOPOLITAN SONGS**
995912 / 1 Jun '98 / EPM

☐ **FAMOUS RUSSIAN CHOIRS 1930-1940**
995852 / 5 Jan '98 / EPM

☐ **FAMOUS SPIRITUAL & GOSPEL FESTIVAL 1965**
Jesus said if you go / Lord send the rain / Travelling shoes / Preaching/Exodus, 3rd / Tell me how long the train been gone / It's a needed time / It's in my heart / What love / Good somewhere / John saw the number / O why / Lord you have been good to me
CDLR 44005 / Feb '92 / L&R

☐ **FAMOUS VIENNA WALTZES (5CD Set)**
On the beautiful blue Danube / Roses from the south / Be united millions / Where the lemon trees blossom / Artist's life / Treasure waltz / Voices of spring / Little Danube woman / Kiss waltz / Cagliostro waltz / Rathausball tanze / Pictures from the North sea / Tales from the Vienna woods / Vienna blood / At home / Accelerations / Sounds of the spheres / My life is love and pleasure / Village swallows from Austria / Wine women and song / Love songs / Emporer waltz / Morning papers / Loreley / Rhein klange / Court ball dances / Enjoy your life waltz / You and you / Vienna bon bons waltz / Deliriums / Sound of Mary / Espana / Sirenenzauber / Ice skater
15986 / Jan '98 / Laserlight

☐ **FANBAI (Hymns To The Three Jewels)**
C 560109 / Dec '97 / Ocora

☐ **FANITULLEN VOL.1 & 2**
GR 4098CD / Jun '96 / Grappa

☐ **FANTASTIC 40'S, THE**
DCD 5336 / Dec '93 / Disky

☐ **FANTASTIC 80'S VOL.1, THE (2CD Set)**
Wake me up before you go go: *Wham* / Reflex: *Duran Duran* / Take on me: *A-Ha* / Come on Eileen: *Dexy's Midnight Runners* / Karma chameleon: *Culture Club* / When the going gets tough: *Ocean, Billy* / Never gonna give you up: *Astley, Rick* / Girls just wanna have fun: *Lauper, Cyndi* / Breakout: *Swing Out Sister* / Good heart: *Sharkey, Feargal* / Fantastic day: *Haircut 100* / I'm still standing: *John, Elton* / If you let me stay: *D'Arby, Terence Trent* / I don't wanna dance: *Grant, Eddy* / Respectable: *Mel & Kim* / Down under: *Men At Work* / Imgination: *Belouis Some* / Where I lay my hat: *Young, Paul* / Hold on tight: *ELO* / Bette Davis eyes: *Carnes, Kim* / Two tribes: *Frankie Goes To Hollywood* / You spin me round: *Dead Or Alive* / Don't you want me: *Human League* / What is love: *Jones, Howard* / Hold me now: *Thompson Twins* / Sweet dreams: *Eurythmics* / Nobody's diary: *Yazoo* / Stand or deliver: *Adam & The Ants* / Love plus one: *Haircut 100* / Tempted: *Squeeze* / Going underground: *Jam* / I can't stand up for falling down: *Costello, Elvis* / Golden brown: *Stranglers* / Swords of 1000 men: *Tenpole Tudor* / Kids in America: *Wilde, Kim* / 99 red balloons: *Nena* / Mickey: *Basil, Toni* / Annie I'm not your daddy: *Kid Creole* / Too shy: *Kajagoogoo* / Vienna: *Ultravox*
SONYTV 37CD / 23 Feb '98 / Sony Music

☐ **FANTASTIC 80'S VOL.2, THE (2CD Set)**
Club tropicana: *Wham* / Sun always shines on TV: *A-Ha* / Wild boys: *Duran Duran* / There must be an angel: *Eurythmics* / Everybody wants to rule the world: *Tears For Fears* / Only way is up: *Yazz* / She drives me crazy: *Fine Young Cannibals* / Venus: *Bananarama* / Nineteen: *Hardcastle, Paul* / Pump up the volume: *MARRS* / I should be so lucky: *Minogue, Kylie* / When will I be famous: *Bros* / Showing out: *Mel & Kim* / Relax: *Frankie Goes To Hollywood* / Sometimes: *Erasure* / Perfect: *Fairground Attraction* / Church of the poisoned mind: *Culture Club* / I don't want to be a hero: *Johnny Hates Jazz* / Safety dance: *Men Without Hats* / I eat cannibals: *Toto Coelo* / Love action: *Human League* / New song: *Jones, Howard* / Nothing's gonna stop us now: *Starship* / Take my breath away: *Berlin* / Wonderful life: *Black* / Gold: *Spandau Ballet* / Love on your side: *Thompson Twins* / Loco in Acapulco: *Four Tops* / Come back and stay: *Young, Paul* / Love and pride: *King* / Somewhere in my heart: *Aztec Camera* / Story of the blues: *Mighty Wah* / (Feels like) Heaven: *Fiction Factory* / Echo beach: *Martha & The Muffins* / Final countdown: *Europe* / System addict: *Five Star* / Antmusic: *Adam & The Ants* / Land of make believe: *Bucks Fizz* / Japanese boy: *Aneka* / Video killed the radio star: *Buggles*
SONYTV 45CD / 11 May '98 / Sony TV

☐ **FANTASTIC FIFTIES, THE (2CD Set)**
Great pretender: *Platters* / Bernadine: *Boone, Pat* / Rock around the clock: *Haley, Bill & The Comets* / Personality: *Price, Lloyd* / Suzie Q: *Hawkins, Dale* / Yakety yak: *Coasters* / Lover's question: *McPhatter, Clyde* / Kansas City: *Harrison, Wilbert* / Donna: *Valens, Ritchie* / Stardust: *Cole, Nat 'King'* / Glow worm: *Mills Brothers* / Tom Dooley: *Kingston Trio* / Sleep walk: *Santo & Johnny* / One summer night: *Danleers* / Sea of love: *Phillips, Phil & The Twilights* / Answer me: *Laine, Frankie* / Somebody stole my gal: *Ray, Johnnie* / Do you wanna dance: *Freeman, Bobby* / Blue suede shoes: *Perkins, Carl* / Send me the pillow: *Locklin, Hank* / To be loved: *Wilson, Jackie* / Stagger Lee: *Price, Lloyd* / Tequila: *Champs* / Charlie Brown: *Coasters* / Smoke gets in your eyes: *Platters* / Tears on my pillow: *Little Anthony & The Imperials* / It's all in the game: *Edwards, Tommy* / Great balls of fire: *Lewis, Jerry Lee* / Come go with me: *Del-Vikings* / Reveille rock: *Johnny & The Hurricanes* / I believe: *Laine, Frankie* / Alone: *Shepherd Sisters* / Walkin' my baby back home: *Ray, Johnnie & Frankie Laine* / Be bop a lula: *Vincent, Gene* / Rockin' Robin: *Day, Bobby* / Alley oop: *Hollywood Argyles*
TNC 96227 / Aug '96 / Natural Collection

☐ **FANTASTIC HOUSE (2CD Set)**
MOODCD 58 / 17 Aug '98 / Sony TV

☐ **FANTASTIC ROCK 'N' ROLL**
CLCD 4402 / Nov '96 / Collector/White Label

☐ **FANTAZIA CLUB CLASSICS VOL.1 (3CD Set)**
FHCCC 1CDSL
FHCCC 1CD / Feb '96 / Fantazia

☐ **FANTAZIA CLUB CLASSICS VOL.2 (2CD Set)**
FHCCC 2CD
FHCCC 2CDL / Sep '96 / Fantazia

☐ **FANTAZIA CLUB CLASSICS VOL.3 (3CD Set)**
Think about: *DJ H & Steffy* / Let your body be free: *Volcano* / Where love lives (come on in): *Limerick, Alison* / 40 Miles: *Congress* / Perfect motion: *Sunscreem* / It's gonna be a lovely day: *SOUL System* / Plastic dreams: *Jaydee* / Out there: *Friends Of Matthew* / Everybody's free: *Rozalla* / Berry: *TC 1991* / Kenetic: *Golden Girls* / Degrees of passion: *Gat Decor* / Belfast: *Orbital* / Keep on jumpin': *Terry, Todd* / London X-Press: *X-Press 2* / Girls and boys: *Hed Boys* / Trippin' on sunshine: *Pizzaman* / Reach: *Lil' Mo' Yin Yang* / Everybody be somebody: *Ruffneck* / Give me luv: *Alcatraz* / And I'm telling you I'm not going: *Giles, Donna* / Been a long time: *Fog* / Who keeps changing your mind: *South Street Players* / Direct me: *Reece Project* / Caught in the middle: *Roberts, Juliet* / Saturday night Sunday morning: *T-Empo* / Let no man put asunder: *First Choice* / Runaway: *Nu Yorican Soul* / I get high: *Upstate* / So in love with you: *Duke* / Scared: *Slacker* / Life's too short: *Hole In One* / Flowtation: *De Moor, Vincent* / Cafe del mar: *Energy 52* / Walk with me: *Heliotropic* / Small town boy: *Legato* / Just come back to me: *Hypertrophy* / Come with me: *Qattara* / Offshore: *Chicane*
FHCCC 3CD / May '97 / Fantazia

☐ **FANTAZIA DJ COLLECTION VOL.1**
Deep in Milan: *Hyper Space Europa* / Sun dreams: *Wax* / Infanta-ci: *Baby Doc & The Dentist* / Midi function: *System* / In the dark we live: *Aphrohead Aka Felix Da Housecat* / Mania: *Rainforest* / Shivaratri: *Fsom* / Mr. Peacock goes to Boscaland: *White Label* / Moonflux: *Black & Brown* / Nervous distortion: *Judge Dread* / Second rebirth: *Jones & Stephenson* / Killer: *Buzz & Ace* / Odyhand trance:

Osysee / Ride: English Muffin / Do you wanna party: DJ Scott / Inflitrator: Technosis / Mad one: Smith, Marc / Varispeed: DJ Edge / On the groove: Interstate / Point break: Sulfurex / Storm: Jack Speed

FANTA 7CD / Oct '94 / Fantazia

☐ **FANTAZIA HOUSE COLLECTION VOL.1 (2CD Set)**

Lifting me higher: Gems For Jem / Sexy movemaker: Fifth Circuit / Anthem: Black Shells / Choose me: Cookie / Angel: Sub Sub / I'm in love: Summers, Kathy / Make my love: Christopher, Shawn / All over me: Carr, Suzi / Get down to love: Music Choir / You can't turn around: Bottom Dollar / Trouble: Cardwell, Joi / Time to stop: Sanchez, Roger / House luck: Jump Cutz / 2 Fatt guitars: Direckt / Le voie le soleil: Subliminal Cuts / Action: Alfredo / I've got the freedom: Tin Tin Out / Retro Euro vibe peace: Woomera / Callin': Callin / Foreplay EP: UK Movin / Ibiza go wild: Pedro & Raoul / Into your heart: Rozzo / Calm down: Chris & James / Voices inside my handbag: Patterson & Price / So damn tuff: Boomerand / Hot dog: Key Aura / Better with Gee: Thermo Statik / Time travellers: Love Child & Rolfe / Never gonna give you up: Turner, Ruby / Ay ninos: Amnesia / 2 Fatt guitars (mix): Direckt / Tripping on sunshine: Pizzaman / Echo drop: Taiko / You and me: Rhyme Time Productions / Testiment one: Chubby Chunks / Beatniks: Delorme / Shake your body: LWS / Better vibes: Funky Monkey / Acid folk: Perplexer

FHC 1CD / Nov '94 / Fantazia

☐ **FANTAZIA HOUSE COLLECTION VOL.2 (2CD Set)**

Useless man: Minty / House fever: Burger / G marks the spot: Sensoria / Throw: Paperclip People / Sweet attitude: Sophie's Boys / Easy does it: Sound Crowd / Throw reprise: Paperclip People / Liberation: Lippy You / Love Vs. Hate: League Of Sinners / Nu energy: Hard 2 Dance / Why are your feet stompin': Hard 2 Dance / Cod n' chips EP: Hard 2 Dance / Pitch 'n' drop: Cakebread, Lee / Where's the party: DJ Saab / It's alright: Sain II / Manhattan anthem: East Village Loft Society / Feel it: Creation / Submarine: Submarine / In T house: Johan S / You took my lovin': Total Control / Basement in sound: More & Groove / Feel the music: BBR Street Gang / Stomp: Shimmon / Funky thing: Indigo / Everybody is somebody: Flipped Out / Tall and handsome: Outrage / Hey man: Arityma / Son of Eilmot: Mighty Dub Katz / Strong: Phorce / Cry boy: Cosmopolitan / Krazy noise: Numerical Value / Driftwood: Tom Tom / Mooncat: Shaker / Good times: Funkydory / Hooked: 99th Floor Elevators / Bits and pieces: Artomesia / Burning up: De Vit, Tony / Gotta get: Must / Keep ya head on: Rizzo / Organgrinder: Deeper Cut / Rock express: Wizzard

FHC 2CD / Apr '95 / Fantazia

☐ **FANTAZIA HOUSE COLLECTION VOL.3 (2CD Set)**

FHC 3CD / Sep '95 / Fantazia

☐ **FANTAZIA HOUSE COLLECTION VOL.4 (2CD Set)**

FHC 4CD / Jun '96 / Fantazia

☐ **FANTAZIA HOUSE COLLECTION VOL.5 (2CD Set) (Whitehead, Alistair & Tall Paul)**

Isn't it time: Kuva / Keep hope alive: Serial Diva / Fired up: Funky Green Dogs / I'm still waiting: Angel Heart / Watcha gonna do: Joy For Life / I get high: Upstate / Jus' come: Cool Jack / Jumangi's house: RM Project / Keep pushin': Z-Factor / Feels so right: Solution / Don't lose the love: Hit The Boom / Do you feel me: NY's Finest / White love: One Dove / Sugar is sweeter: Bolland, C.J. / Bifter: Low Pressure / Phunkee muzeek: Shazzamm / Living in danger: Ace Of Base / Curse of Voodoo Ray: May, Lisa / Let the music hypnotize you: Blue Lagoon / 100%: Kiani, Mary / Forerunner: Natural Born Groovers / Love resurrection: Floor Federation / Antheum: Digital Blondes / This love: Red Sun / Feel the beat: Sunglasses Ron / Global fazes: Jon The Dentist

FHC 5CD / Mar '97 / Fantazia

☐ **FANTAZIA HOUSE COLLECTION VOL.6 (Mixed By Paul Oakenfold/Mike Cosford - 2CD Set)**

Milk: Garbage / No good: Depeche Mode / Your face: Slacker / Box: Orbital / Someone: Ascension / You're not alone: Olive / Down to earth: Grace / Flaming June: BT / Butterfly: Tilt / Home: Chakra / Sin city: Three 'n One / Hypnotised: Virus / Dark and long: Underworld / Love you more: Sunscreem / Gotta have hope: Blackout / When I lose control: Desire / Gypsy boy gypsy girl: Sharada House Gang / Mighty high: Revival 3000 / Jump around: House Of Pain / Move it up: Blue Adonis / Get up stand up: Phunky Phantom / Mission 2: Global Transmission / Somewhere out there are aliens: Kinky Toys / Everytime: Lustral / So good: Madagascar / Mind to mind: Music is my life / Pacific melody: Airscape

FHC 6CD / 22 Sep '97 / Fantazia

☐ **FANTAZIA PRESENTS BRITISH ANTHEMS (The Best Of British Clubbing - 2CD Set)**

Got funk: Funkjunkeez / Don't stop: Ruff Driverz / Deeper: Serious Danger / Over me: Whiplash / Ready or not: Course / Do you understand English: Afrowax / Ghetto girl: Mighty Dub Katz / Everybody loves a carnival: Fatboy Slim / Horn: DJ Dero / Hot shot: Young, Karen / Jumpin' and pumpin': Son / Nightmare: Brainbug / Turn me out (turn to sugar): Praxis & Kathy Brown / Schoneberg: Marmion / 20hz: Capricorn / Heartists: Belo Horizonti / Funk magic: Angel, Dave / Happy days: PJ / Spiller from Rio: Laguna / Raise your hands in the air: Trailer Parks / Why: Sybil / Music is pumping: People Underground & Sharon Williams / Our house: Nightmovers / Give me rhythm: Black Connection / Saturday: East 57th Street / Love commandments: Jackson, Gisele / Finally: Peniston, Ce Ce / Plastic dreams: Jaydee / As until the day: Knowledge / Bamboogie: Bamboo / Let the beat hit 'em: Shena & Byron Stingly / I thought it was you: Sex-O-Sonique

FBA 1CD / 9 Feb '98 / Fantazia

☐ **FAR OUT**

ASSCD 003 / Jul '96 / Funky Ass

☐ **FAREWELL TO LISSY CASEY**

OSS 79CD / Aug '95 / Ossian

☐ **FAREWELL TO THE ROXY**

Strange boy: Blitz / Smile and wave goodbye: Acme Sewage Co. / Relics from the past: Karloff, Billy / I live in a car: UK Subs / Get yourself killed: Tickets / Never wanna leave: Red Lights / Here comes the knife: Fireball XL5 / TV drink: Jets / Sniper: Streets / Tough on you: Plastix / Fun, fun, fun: Bears / Vertigo: Open Sore / Lullabies lie: Crabs

AHOYCD 086 / 13 Apr '98 / Captain Oi

☐ **FARMER'S WEDDING IN JOURE**

PAN 2004CD / Aug '94 / Pan

☐ **FASCINATION (2CD Set)**

24021 / Mar '95 / Delta Doubles

☐ **FASHION STATEMENT, A**

RASCD 3172 / Apr '96 / Ras

☐ **FAST FALLS THE RAIN (A Compilation Of Moravian Folk Music)**

LT 0014 / Nov '95 / Lotos

☐ **FAST FORWARD (Mixed By DJ Jesse)**

IDT 000557 / Nov '96 / ID&T

☐ **FAST FORWARD**

IC 03362 / 29 Jun '98 / Infracom

☐ **FAT FAT FAT (Now Even Fatter)**

BLUBBACD 484848 / Feb '97 / No Hit

☐ **FAT MUSIC FOR FAT PEOPLE**

Anti Manifesto: Propaghandi / Know it all: Lagwagon / In harm's way: Strung Out / Skin deep: Guns n' Wankers / 2 RAK 005: Bracket / Weave and unravel: Tilt / You got a problem: Face To Face / United cigar: Good Riddance / Just a feeling: Rancid / Mr. Coffee: Lagwagon / Homophobes are just pissed cause they can't get laid: Propaghandi / Kill all the white man: NOFX

FAT 520CD / 17 Aug '98 / Fatwreck Chords

☐ **FATHER'S FAVOURITES**

CDC 5388 / May '94 / Disky

☐ **FAULT IN THE NOTHING, A (2CD Set)**

ASH 26CD2 / Mar '96 / Ash International

☐ **FAVOURITE BRASS BANDS**

Floral dance: Brighouse & Rastrick Band / Colonel bogey on parade: Mortimer, Harry Band / There's no business like show business: Black Dyke Mills Band / Magnificent seven: Cory Band / Guns of Navarone: Cory Band / Battle of Britain: Brighouse & Rastrick Band / Sweet Georgia Brown: Grimethorpe Colliery Band / Danny boy: Grimethorpe Colliery Band / Amazing Grace: Brighouse & Rastrick Band / Summertime: Black Dyke Mills Band / Coronation Street theme: GUS Footwear Band / Macartur Park: Grimethorpe Colliery Band / Skye boat song: Wingates Temperance Band / Semper sousa: Men O' Brass / Can can: Mortimer, Harry Band / Great little army: Brighouse & Rastrick Band / Napoleon galop: GUS Footwear Band / Bold gendarmes: Scottish CWS Band / Gallop: Mortimer, Harry Band / William Tell overture: Grimethorpe Colliery Band

4943472 / 27 Apr '98 / Music For Pleasure

☐ **FAVOURITE CAPITOL CLASSICS**

I love you because: Martino, Al / Strangers in the night: Monro, Matt / Stardust: Anthony, Ray / Miss Otis regrets: Wilson, Nancy / Don't sit under the apple tree: Andrews Sisters / Memories are made of this: Martin, Dean / Around the world: Cole, Nat 'King' / Best things in life are free: Stafford, Jo / I had to be you: Hutton, Betty / Love of the common people: Four Preps / Blue moon: Torme, Mel / On the streets where you live: Lee, Peggy / I'm beginning to see the light: James, Harry / Mad about the boy: May, Billy / Route 66: Four Freshmen / Chicago: Garland, Judy / Hello dolly: Darin, Bobby / Let's do it (let's fall in love): Riddle, Nelson & Orchestra / More I see you: Haymes, Dick / I only had eyes for you: Shore, Dinah

4943502 / 27 Apr '98 / Music For Pleasure

☐ **FAVOURITE COUNTRY BLUES**

Sloppy drunk again: Davis, Walter / Don't sell it don't give it away: Woods, Buddy / Poker woman blues: Blind Blake / West side blues: Harris, William / Shook it this morning blues: Evans, Joe / Good gal: Spand, Charlie / New Orleans stop time: Bumble Bee Slim / Tired of being mistreated: Sykes, Roosevelt & Clifford Gibson / Poor coal passer: Springback James / Down in black bottom: Evans, Joe / Back to the woods blues: Spand, Charlie / Monkey man blues: Loften, Cripple Clarence / Sloppy drunk blues: Carr, Leroy / Blues is all wrong: Manning, Leola

YAZCD 1015 / Mar '98 / Yazoo

☐ **FAVOURITE EASY LISTENING**

Kiss: Martin, Dean / Folks who live on the hill: Lee, Peggy / Chicago: Bennett, Tony / Let's face the music and dance: Riddle, Nelson / Blossom fell: Cole, Nat 'King' / For all we know: Bassey, Shirley / Begin the beguine: Shaw, Artie / We've only just begun: Crosby, Bing / You're getting to be a habit with me: Torme, Mel / Fly me to the moon: Darin, Bobby / Strangers in the night: Freeman, Stan / Moon river: Williams, Danny / Man that got away: Garland, Judy / Way you look tonight: Haymes, Dick & Ian Bernard / I say a little prayer: Goodwin, Ron & His Orchestra / Softly as I leave you: Monro, Matt / It had to be you: Shore, Dinah / I don't know how to love him: Reddy, Helen / Man and a woman: Love, Geoff & His Orchestra / Love me tender: Hill, Vince

4943492 / 27 Apr '98 / Music For Pleasure

☐ **FAVOURITE FEMALE VOCALISTS**

Lady is a tramp: Lee, Peggy / Something: Bassey, Shirley / Man I love: Shore, Dinah & Andre Previn / Very thought of you: Wilson, Nancy / Ev'ry time we say goodbye: Vaughan, Sarah / Thats entertainment: Garland, Judy / Call me irresponsible: Washington, Dinah / Walk on by: Shapiro, Helen / It had to be you: Minnelli, Liza / Angie baby: Reddy, Helen / Down it make my brown eyes blue: Gayle, Crystal / Something tells me (something's gonna happen tonight): Black, Cilla / I'd rather take my time: Anthony, Billie / Raindrops keep falling on my head: Gentry, Bobbie / Anyone who had a heart: Carr, Vikki / Heartbeat: Murray, Ruby / What the world needs now is love: Horne, Lena / Crazy: Starr, Kay / Gypsy in my soul: Boswell, Eve / Why do fools fall in love: Cogan, Alma

4943462 / 27 Apr '98 / Music For Pleasure

☐ **FAVOURITE FIFTIES**

Comes along a love: Starr, Kay / Here in my heart: Martino, Al / Limelight: Goodwin, Ron & His Orchestra / Smile: Cole, Nat 'King' / Dreamboat: Cogan, Alma / Rose Marie: Whitman, Slim / Softly softly: Murray, Ruby / Cherry pink apple blossom white: Calvert, Eddie / Why do fools fall in love: Lymon, Frankie & The Teenagers / Sixteen tools: Ford, Tennessee Ernie / Memories are made of this: Martin, Dean / No other love: Hilton, Ronnie / White sport coat: King Brothers / Fever: Lee, Peggy / Big man: Four Preps / What do you want: Faith, Adam / Side saddle: Conway, Russ / Seven little girls sitting in the backseat: Conway, Russ / Only sixteen: Conway, Russ

4943432 / 27 Apr '98 / Music For Pleasure

☐ **FAVOURITE GREAT BRITISH GROUPS**

Dance on: Shadows / I'm telling you know: Freddie & The Dreamers / Do you want to know a secret: Kramer, Billy J. & The Dakotas / Hippy hippy shake: Kramer, Billy J. & The Dakotas / I like it: Gerry & The Pacemakers / House of the rising sun: Animals / 54321: Manfred Mann / Little loving: Fourmost / Got to get you into my mind: Bennett, Cliff & The Rebel Rousers / Bus stop: Hollies / Something is happening: Herman's Hermits / Freedom come freedom go: Fortunes / First time: Faith, Adam / You were made for me: Freddie & The Dreamers / Poison ivy: Paramounts / You're no good: Swinging Blue Jeans / Tobacco road: Nashville Teens / Do wah diddy: Manfred Mann / How do you do it: Gerry & The Pacemakers / Just one look: Hollies

4933512 / 27 Apr '98 / Music For Pleasure

☐ **FAVOURITE HYMNS**

Lord's prayer: Kentwood Choir / Guide me o thou great Jehovah: Caerphilly Male Voice Choir / Now the day is over: Northern Choir / Onward Christian soldiers: Choir Of St. Mary / How great thou art: Choir Of St. Mary / Lord is my shepherd: Choir Of St. Mary / Land of my fathers: Caerphilly Male Voice Choir / All things bright and beautiful: Choir Of St. Mary / I was glad: Atherstone Choral Society / Oh Virgin of the angel host: Caerphilly Male Voice Choir / Abide with me: Hussar Choir / Oh rejoice that the Lord has arisen: Kentwood Choir / For all the saints: Kentwood Choir / Praise my soul the king of heaven: Choir Of St. Mary

300562 / May '98 / Hallmark

☐ **FAVOURITE IRISH DRINKING SONGS**

If you're Irish / Bold O'Donaghue / I'll tell me ma / Courtin' in the kitchen / Wild Rover / Molly Malone / I belong to Glasgow / Loch Lomond / When Irish eyes are smiling / Irish rover / Brennan on the moor / Wild colonnial boy / Mursheen Durkin / Rose of Aranmore / Where the three counties meet / Danny boy / Galway bay rose of Tralee / Goodbye oh Johnny dear / Old bog road / Farewell to Galway / Whiskey in the jar / Waxies dargle / Dicey Riley / Whiskey you're the devil / Holy ground / It's a long way to Tipperary / Hello Patsy Fagan / Come down the mountain Katie Daly / When I was single / Love is teasing / Never wed an old man / Boys of Killybegs / Tim Kinnegan's wake / Old maid in a garret / Goodbye Mick / Dublin O'Shea / Moonshiner / Juice of the barley / Rosin' the bow / Maggie / Silver threads among the gold / Fiddlers green / Fiddler's green / Black velvet band / Boul'thady quill / Boys from the CoArmagh / Garden where the praties grow / Dan O'Hara / Home, boys, home / Tongs by the fire / Hannigan's hooley / Mcnamara's band / Humour is on me now / Westmead bachelor / Blackthorn stick

EMPRCD 520 / Jul '94 / Emporio

☐ **FAVOURITE IRISH SONGS**

Mountains of Mourne: McCann, Jim / Green fields 'round Ferbane: Far Tulla / Isle of Innisfree: Kerr, John / Fields of Athenry: Reilly, Paddy / Dingle Bay: Margo / Spancil Hill: Far Tulla / Green hills of Sligo: Murrihy, P.J. / Grace: Kenny, Tony / Rose of Mooncoin: McEvoy, Johnny / Rare oul times: Erin's Isle Singers / Shanagolden: Margo / Cliffs of Dooneen: Margo / Flight of earls: Kerr, John / Banks of the Lee/Come back Paddy Reilly: Erin's Isle Singers

CHCD 033 / Oct '96 / Chart

☐ **FAVOURITE MALE VOCALISTS**

Let there be love: Cole, Nat 'King' / Spanish eyes: Martino, Al / On the street where you live: Damone, Vic / I wonder who's kissing her now: Darin, Bobby / Heartbeat: Vee, Bobby / Anything goes: Bennett, Tony & Count Basie Orchestra / I'll never fall in love again: Crosby, Bing / Return to me: Martin, Dean / More I see you: Haymes, Dick / From Russia with love: Monro, Matt / So in love: Keel, Howard / Around the world: Hilton, Ronnie / Wind beneath my wings: Tarmey, Bill / Summertime: Rawls, Lou / Honey come back: Campbell, Glen / Look round and you find me there: Hill, Vince / Story of my life: Holliday, Michael / There must be a way: Vaughan, Frankie / Moon river: Williams, Danny / My special angel: Vaughan, Malcolm

4943452 / 27 Apr '98 / Music For Pleasure

☐ **FAVOURITE MILITARY BANDS**

Colonel Bogey: Grenadier Guards Band / Royal air force march past: Central Band of The Royal Air Force / Anchors aweigh: Band Of The HM Royal Marines / Men of harlech: Grenadier & Coldstream/ Scottish/Irish/Welsh Guards / Medley: Royal Scots Dragoon Guards / Amazing Grace: Royal Scots Dragoon Guards / Stars and stripes: Band Of The HM Royal Marines / Those magnificient men in the flying machines: Central Band of The Royal Air Force / 633 squadron: Central Band of The Royal Air Force / Dambusters: Central Band of The Royal Air Force / Rule Britannia: Band Of The HM Royal Marines / Satndard of St. George: Pipes & Drums Of The Gordon Highlanders / Washington Post: Band Of The HM Royal Marines / Mull of Kintyre: Regimental Band, Pipes & Drums of Royal Scots Dragoon Band / Golden spurs: Band Of The Scots Guards / Duke OF York: Grenadier Guards Band / Liberty bell: Grenadier Guards Band / Battle of Trafalgar: Band Of The HM Royal Marines / Auld lang syne: Argyll & Sutherland Highlanders

4943482 / 27 Apr '98 / Music For Pleasure

☐ **FAVOURITE SIXTIES**

Honey: Goldsboro, Bobby / Big spender: Bassey, Shirley / Help me Rhonda: Beach Boys / Step inside love: Black, Cilla / Wicita lineman: Campbell, Glen / It must be him: Carr, Vikki / Ramblin' rose: Cole, Nat 'King' / Tears: Dodd, Ken / Mellow yellow: Donovan / Kites: Dupree, Simon & The Big Sound / As you like it: Faith, Adam / I understand (just how you feel): Freddie & The Dreamers / I'll never fall in love again: Gentry, Bobbie / Ferry cross the Mersey: Gerry & The Pacemakers / There's a kind of hush: Herman's Hermits / He ain't heavy he's my brother: Hollies / Yesterday: Monro, Matt / True love ways: Peter & Gordon / World of our own: Durham, Judith & The Seekers / Moon river: Williams, Danny

4943442 / 27 Apr '98 / Music For Pleasure

☐ **FAX IT, CHARGE IT, DON'T ASK ME WHAT'S FOR DINNER**

SHCD 8018 / Oct '95 / Shanachie

☐ **FEAR OF A RUFF PLANET**

RUF 026 / 29 Apr '98 / Ruff Neck

☐ **FEAR OF SMELL**

VMFM 11CD / 26 Jan '98 / Vermiform

☐ **FEARLESS FLUSH SAMPLER, THE**

F 0272 / Jun '97 / Fearless

☐ **FEAST OF LIFE, THE (A Musical Of Hope From Christian Aid)**

Feast of life / We hear you cry Lord / World of difference / Dance on injustice / Walk the talk / That's why we're here / Living God / We need your mother love o' God / For a fairer world / Child is the future / Hands of Jesus / Pray for you sister / Time for jubilee / Chain of love

WMD 004 / May '98 / Word

☐ **FEASTS MUSIC FROM MEDITERRANEAN COUNTRIES**

926542 / Sep '96 / BUDA

☐ **FEASTS OF THE SAVANNA (A Musical Journey Through East & West Africa)**

Sock selue / Yentchable / Initiation dance / Kbunse / Nje / Ceremonial drums / Traditional doctor's cure / Drum session / Sansa / Dingidi song / Jopadhola malinda / Enanga / Werga / Children's song / Dogon children's flute / Dogon harp / Narrative/Kora accompaniment

MCM 3006 / May '97 / Multicultural Media

☐ **FEDERATION OF TECHNO HOUSE VOL.1 (2CD Set)**

LD 9455CD / Feb '95 / LD

☐ **FEED YOUR HEAD**

BARKCD 022 / Nov '96 / Planet Dog

☐ **FEEL LIKE MAKING LOVE**

AHLCD 25 / Feb '95 / Hit

☐ **FEEL THE FIRE DUETS**

12544 / May '95 / Laserlight

☐ **FEEL THE NOYZE**

Fugue: Soul Oddity / Omniman: Download / Teeth: Nuw Idol / Relentless mutoid monster epic: Germinating Seeds Of Doda / Itchy witches of androgenetico: Reflecta / Ka el mono: Deflo / Return of the borg: Kinetic A.T.O.M. / Whipbird: Kopuss Resonator / Ancient suns: Fluro Conspiracy / CD2 I did: Hardknox

MPCD 8 / 8 Sep '97 / Matsuri

☐ **FEELIN' BLUE**

BN 049 / Apr '98 / Blue Nite

☐ **FEELIN' GOOD**

LHCD 024 / Jul '96 / Luv n' Haight

☐ **FEELIN' GOOD - AMERICAN R&B HITS VOL.1**

CDRB 11 / Nov '94 / Charly

☐ **FEELING THE BLUES**

Poor boy blues: Atkins, Chet & Mark Knopfler / I'd rather go blind: Chicken Shack / Hoochie coochie man: Waters, Muddy / Ain't gone 'n' give up on love: Vaughan, Stevie Ray & Double Trouble / Cheap tequila: Winter, Johnny / Tabacco road: Winter, Edgar / Gamblers roll: Allman Brothers / Need your love tonight: Fleetwood Mac / Tuff enuff: Fabulous Thunderbirds / Season of the witch: Bloomfield, Mike & Al Kooper / Skyscraper blues: Derringer, Rick / Down in Mississippi: Omar & The Howlers / Boogie my way back home: Moore, Gary / Brothers: Vaughan Brothers / Schoolgirl: Argent / Killing floor: Electric Flag

4758282 / Oct '95 / Columbia

☐ **FEELINGS (Romantic Guitar)**

MACCD 326 / Aug '96 / Autograph

☐ **FEELINGS**

Love story (where do I begin) / Strangers in the night / Something / Bright eyes / Woman / You are the sunshine of my life / Michelle / Lara's theme / To all the girls I loved before / Spanish eyes / Don't it make my brown eyes blue / Tara's theme / Feelings / Annie's song / Love is blue / If you leave me now / Unchained melody / Memory / Nights in white satin / Song sung blue / Guantanamera / Don't cry for me

Argentina / Oh happy day / Fool on the hill / September wind / Bilitis / Last farewell / Sailing / Greensleeves / Eleanor Rigby / House of the rising sun / Banks of the Ohio / Cast your fate to the wind / Whiter shade of pale / My way
DCD 3008 / Jun '97 / Music

☐ FEELINGS NOT FREQUENCIES
ABCD 001 / Feb '95 / Holistic

☐ FEELINGS... (Beautiful Songs & Wonderful Performances/2CD Set)
Something to remember you by: *Dale, Syd & His Orchestra* / Misty: *Sentimental Sax* / I wish you love: *Emblow, Jack* / Love walked in: *Osborne, Tony Orchestra* / Sentimental journey: *Dale, Syd & His Orchestra* / No other love: *Osborne, Tony Orchestra* / Sounds of romance: *Master Strings* / Stay as sweet as you are: *Dale, Syd & His Orchestra* / Summertime: *Sentimental Sax* / Man and a woman: *Dale, Syd & His Orchestra* / It could happen to you: *London Theatre Orchestra* / Because of you: *Master Strings* / Body and soul: *Sentimental Sax* / Moonglow: *London Theatre Orchestra* / In a sentimental mood: *Sentimental Sax* / Woman in love: *Aprile, J.C. & His Orchestra* / Days of wine and roses: *London Theatre Orchestra* / Foggy day in London town: *Swift, Roger* / Nuances: *Master Strings* / Lady: *Dale, Syd & His Orchestra* / Gigi: *John, Michael Singers* / Party's over: *Dale, Syd & His Orchestra* / Feelings: *Aprile, J.C. & His Orchestra* / Once in a while: *London Theatre Orchestra* / Shadow of your smile: *Angelo, Michael & his Orchestra* / Wisteria: *Master Strings* / Almost there: *Dale, Syd & His Orchestra* / My ideal: *John, Michael Singers* / Yesterday: *London Theatre Orchestra* / Second time around: *Dale, Syd & His Orchestra* / Way we were: *Aprile, J.C. & His Orchestra* / All the love in the world: *Aprile, J.C. & His Orchestra* / How insensitive: *London Theatre Orchestra*
330452 / Mar '97 / Hallmark

☐ FELIDAE (A Benefit For Cedarhill Animal Sanctuary)
EXIT 1CD / May '97 / Last Exit

☐ FELIX HERNANDEZ'S RHYTHM REVUE (3CD Set)
40102 / Sep '97 / TVT

☐ FEMALE BLUES 1922-1927
JPCD 1526 / Jan '97 / Jazz Perspectives

☐ FEMALE BLUES SINGERS 1921-1928 (The Remaining Titles)
DOCD 1005 / Apr '97 / Document

☐ FEMALE BLUES SINGERS VOL.1 1924-1932
DOCD 5505 / Jan '97 / Document

☐ FEMALE BLUES SINGERS VOL.10 1923-1929
DOCD 5514 / Jan '97 / Document

☐ FEMALE BLUES SINGERS VOL.11 1921-1931
DOCD 5515 / Jan '97 / Document

☐ FEMALE BLUES SINGERS VOL.12 1922-1935
DOCD 5516 / Jan '97 / Document

☐ FEMALE BLUES SINGERS VOL.13 1921-1931
DOCD 5517 / Mar '97 / Document

☐ FEMALE BLUES SINGERS VOL.14 1923-1932
DOCD 5518 / Mar '97 / Document

☐ FEMALE BLUES SINGERS VOL.2 1922-1928
DOCD 5506 / Jan '97 / Document

☐ FEMALE BLUES SINGERS VOL.3 1923-1928
DOCD 5507 / Jan '97 / Document

☐ FEMALE BLUES SINGERS VOL.4 1921-1940
DOCD 5508 / Jan '97 / Document

☐ FEMALE BLUES SINGERS VOL.5 1921-1929
DOCD 5509 / Jan '97 / Document

☐ FEMALE BLUES SINGERS VOL.6 1922-1928
DOCD 5510 / Jan '97 / Document

☐ FEMALE BLUES SINGERS VOL.7 1922-1929
DOCD 5511 / Mar '97 / Document

☐ FEMALE BLUES SINGERS VOL.8 1923-1928
DOCD 5512 / Jan '97 / Document

☐ FEMALE BLUES SINGERS VOL.9 1923-1930
DOCD 5513 / Jan '97 / Document

☐ FEMALE BLUES VOL.2 1938-1949
JPCD 1528 / Dec '97 / Jazz Perspectives

☐ FEMALE COUNTRY BLUES VOL.1 (The Twenties)
SOB 035292 / Dec '92 / Story Of The Blues

☐ FEMME FATALE (3CD Set)
DTKBOX 64 / Jun '97 / Dressed To Kill

☐ FEMMES NOIRES
DECLI 17745 / 3 Mar '98 / Munich

☐ FEMO JAZZ FESTIVAL - 25TH ANNIVERSARY
MECCACD 1038 / Nov '94 / Music Mecca

☐ FERIA - THE BEST SEVILLANAS
Rociadora / Y las arenas / Desde el alma / Voy pal rocio / Mi medalla rociera / Acurela del rocio / Cuardo paso triana / Coria del rio / Cebolla, pimiento y colifior / La marisma se alborota / Mi devocion / Por las arenas / Y todos los años / Antes de nacer / Po "Poeso" / Tengo que volver / Stones rocleros / Noches del camino / Bambolero / Cantinero de cuba / Djobi, djoba / Se pasavan los pias / Me, va, me va / Mi guitarra / Color moreno / Ay peregrinal / Que sabre la gente / Salve rociera del ole, ole
EMO 93072 / Jun '96 / Emocion

☐ FERRY ACROSS THE MERSEY
Ferry Across the Mersey: *Gerry & The Pacemakers* / Sweets for my sweet: *Searchers* / Lily the pink: *Scaffold* / You're my world (il mio mondo): *Black, Cilla* / Hippy hippy shake: *Swinging Blue Jeans* / Hello little girl: *Fourmost* / Do you want to know a secret: *Kramer, Billy J. & The Dakotas* / Breakaway: *Marsden, Beryl* / I like it: *Gerry & The Pacemakers* / America: *Storm, Rory & The Hurricanes* / Little loving: *Fourmost* / Needles and pins: *Searchers* / Bad to me: *Kramer, Billy J. & The Dakotas* / You're no good: *Swinging Blue Jeans* / You'll never walk alone: *Gerry & The Pacemakers* / Thank u very much: *Scaffold*
DC 878872 / Jul '97 / Disky

☐ FEST DEIZ FEST NOZ
CD 443 / Aug '97 / Arfolk

☐ FEST NOZ DE KLEG
GLEG 001CD / Aug '95 / Diffusion Breizh

☐ FEST NOZ LIVE
KMCD 76 / Jun '97 / Keltia Musique

☐ FEST-DEIZ ACCORDEONS
CD 427 / Jul '94 / Diffusion Breizh

☐ FESTA DA MUSICA
21712 / 14 Apr '98 / Som Livre

☐ FESTIVAL DE MUSIQUES IRLANDAISES VOL.3
GRI 190812 / Sep '96 / Griffe

☐ FESTIVAL FLAMENCO
EUCD 1210 / Sep '93 / ARC

☐ FESTIVAL FLAMENCO GITANO VOL.3
CDLR 44015 / ' / L&R

☐ FESTIVAL INTERCELTIQUE DE L'ORIENT/CONCERT BINIOU BOMBARDE
ERO 057 / Nov '96 / Eromi

☐ FESTIVAL INTERNATIONAL DE TANGO GRANADA 1993
9304CD / 24 Apr '98 / Karonte

☐ FESTIVAL INTERNATIONAL DE TANGO GRANADA 1994
9427CD / 24 Apr '98 / Karonte

☐ FESTIVAL INTERNATIONAL DE TANGO GRANADA 1995 VOL.1
9539CD / 24 Apr '98 / Karonte

☐ FESTIVAL INTERNATIONAL DE TANGO GRANADA 1995 VOL.2
9644CD / 24 Apr '98 / Karonte

☐ FESTIVAL INTERNATIONAL DE TANGO GRANADA 1996
9767CD / 24 Apr '98 / Karonte

☐ FESTIVAL ITALIANO 1994
472072 / May '96 / Flarenasch

☐ FESTIVAL LATINO (20 Seeco Latin Hits)
Cachondea: *Feliciano, Jose 'Cheo'* / Besito de coco: *Rivera, Ismael* / Cuca la loca: *Bienvenido Granda* / Un mondo raro: *Flores, Lola* / Luna de miel en Puerto Rico: *Capo, Bobby* / Ave Maria Lola: *Argentino, Carlos* / Besame morenita: *Pinedo, Nelson* / Fina estampa: *Alfaro, Xiomara* / Desolacion: *Jaramillo, Julio* / Borracho no vale: *Santos, Daniel* / Ya no tengo amigos: *Feliciano, Jose 'Cheo'* / El chivo de la campana: *Rivera, Ismael* / Rico guaguanco: *Bienvenido Granda* / Tu rica boca: *Flores, Lola* / La coca leca: *Capo, Bobby* / Ay que rico amor: *Argentino, Carlos* / El vaquero: *Pinedo, Nelson* / Cuando ya no me quieras: *Alfaro, Xiomara* / Amor sin esperanza: *Jaramillo, Julio* / El cornetta: *Santos, Daniel*
CDHOT 614 / Dec '96 / Charly

☐ FESTIVAL MUSIC OF KERALA
VICG 53502 / Mar '96 / JVC World Library

☐ FESTIVAL OF BRASS, A
DOYCD 008 / Oct '92 / Doyen

☐ FESTIVAL OF CAROLS, A
Once in Royal David's City: *Guildford Cathedral Choir* / While shepherds watched their flocks by night: *Sunbury Junior Singers Of The Salvation Army* / Holly and the ivy: *St. Paul's Cathedral Choir* / God rest ye merry gentlemen: *Guildford Cathedral Choir* / Unto us is born a son: *Westminster Abbey Choir* / As with gladness men of old: *Guildford Cathedral Choir* / O little town of Bethlehem: *St. Paul's Cathedral Choir* / Hark the herald angels sing: *Guildford Cathedral Choir* / I saw three ships: *St. Paul's Cathedral Choir* / Silent night: *Sunbury Junior Singers Of The Salvation Army* / In dulci jubilo: *Westminster Abbey Choir* / First Noel: *Guildford Cathedral Choir* / In the bleak midwinter: *St. Paul's Cathedral Choir* / Good King Wenceslas: *Guildford Cathedral Choir* / Rocking: *Sunbury Junior Singers Of The Salvation Army* / Coventry carol: *St. Paul's Cathedral Choir* / It came upon a midnight clear: *Guildford Cathedral Choir* / Away in a manger: *Westminster Abbey Choir* / Ding dong merrily on high: *Sunbury Junior Singers Of The Salvation Army* / O come all ye faithful (Adeste Fidelis): *Guildford Cathedral Choir*
CDMFP 6080 / Dec '94 / Music For Pleasure

☐ FESTIVAL OF FOLK, A (2CD Set)
DEMPCD 002 / Mar '96 / Emporio

☐ FESTIVAL OF GOSPEL AND NEGRO SPIRITUAL, A (2CD Set)
FA 403 / Nov '95 / Fremeaux

☐ FESTIVAL OF GROUPS, A (New York Doo Wop 1958-1966)
Love bound: *Universals* / Dreaming: *Universals* / Kisses in my dreams: *Universals* / Ol' man river: *Ricks, Jimmy & the Ravens* / Daddy rollin' stone: *Ricks, Jimmy & the Ravens* / You've got just what I need: *Ricks, Jimmy & the Ravens* / Deep river: *Ricks, Jimmy & the Ravens* / Homesick: *Ricks, Jimmy & the Ravens* / Oh what a feeling: *Ricks, Jimmy & the Ravens* / Cecilia: *Ricks, Jimmy & the Ravens* / Umgowa twist: *Ricks, Jimmy & the Ravens* / Night and day: *Orioles* / So long: *Orioles* / Sincerely: *Orioles* / Some of this, some of that: *Orioles* / Poor baby: *Clovers* / He sure could hypnotise: *Clovers* / Do the zombie: *Symbols* / Snatchin' peaches: *Chanteclairs* / Invasion: *Dovers* / Sha-he-be: *Essentials* / Daddy can I go to the hop: *Cashmeres & Eddie Jones* / Sardines: *Magnetics* / (Down at) Ling Ting laundry: *Chanteclairs* / Earth cousins: *Middleton, Tony & Jack Hammer*
NEMCD 939 / Jul '97 / Sequel

☐ FESTIVAL OF IRISH FOLK MUSIC VOL.1, A (2CD Set)
Cliffs of Dooneen: *Dublin City Ramblers* / Slievenamon: *Dublin City Ramblers* / Finnegan's wake: *Dublin City Ramblers* / Town I loved so well: *Dublin City Ramblers* / Sea around us: *Dublin City Ramblers* / Four green fields: *Dublin City Ramblers* / My lovely rose of Clare: *Reilly, Paddy* / Snowy breasted pearl: *Reilly, Paddy* / Rose of Allendale: *Reilly, Paddy* / Come back Paddy Reilly: *Reilly, Paddy* / Down by the Sally gardens: *Reilly, Paddy* / Black velvet band: *Dubliners* / McAlpine's fusiliers: *Dubliners* / Fairmoye lasses/Sporting Paddy: *Dubliners* / Seven drunken nights: *Dubliners* / Home boys home: *Dubliners* / Blue mountain rag: *Dubliners* / Raglan road: *Reilly, Paddy* / Steal away: *Furey Brothers & Davy Arthur* / Now is the hour: *Furey Brothers & Davy Arthur* / Silver threads among the gold: *Furey Brothers & Davy Arthur* / When you were sweet sixteen: *Furey Brothers & Davy Arthur* / My love is like a red red rose: *Furey Brothers & Davy Arthur* / Song for Ireland: *Furey Brothers & Davy Arthur* / Dirty old town: *Dubliners* / Farewell to Carlingford: *Dubliners* / Foggy dew: *Dubliners* / Parcel o' rogues: *Dubliners* / Bunclody: *Dubliners* / Rare ould times: *Dubliners* / Man you don't meet every day: *Barleycorn* / Donegal Danny: *Barleycorn* / Only our river run free: *Barleycorn* / Lakes of Coolfin: *Barleycorn* / This land is your land: *Barleycorn* / Buachaill an Eirne: *Barleycorn*
CHCD 1013 / Oct '90 / Chyme

☐ FESTIVAL OF IRISH FOLK MUSIC VOL.2, A (2CD Set)
Butterfly: *Bothy Band* / Kesh jig: *Bothy Band* / Sixteen come next Sunday: *Bothy Band* / Rip the calico: *Bothy Band* / Strayaway child: *Bothy Band* / Death of Queen Jane: *Bothy Band* / Dheanainn sugradh: *Clannad* / By chance it was: *Clannad* / Rince Briotanach: *Clannad* / Dulaman: *Clannad* / Mo mhaire: *Clannad* / Cumha eoghain rue ui neill: *Clannad* / Teddy bears head: *Wolfetones* / Ode to Biddy Magee: *Wolfetones* / Foggy dew: *Wolfetones* / Tri-coloured ribbon: *Wolfetones* / Banks of the Ohio: *Wolfetones* / Black Ribbon Band: *Wolfetones* / Whiskey in the jar: *Dubliners* / Town I loved so well: *Dubliners* / Free the people: *Dubliners* / Lord of the dance: *Dubliners* / Musical priest/Blackthorn stick: *Dubliners* / Finnegan's wake: *Dubliners* / Green fields of France: *Furey Brothers & Davy Arthur* / Garrett Barry's jig: *Furey Brothers & Davy Arthur* / Reason I left Mullingar: *Furey Brothers & Davy Arthur* / Morning lies heavy: *Furey Brothers & Davy Arthur* / Ted Furey's selection: *Furey Brothers & Davy Arthur* / Lament: *Furey Brothers & Davy Arthur* / Ril gan ainm/Cinnte le dia/The union reel: *Bergin, Mary* / Garrai na bhfeileoig/Miss Galvin: *Bergin, Mary* / Step it out Mary: *Doyle, Danny* / Irish soldier laddie: *Doyle, Danny* / Red haired Mary: *Doyle, Danny* / Whiskey on a Sunday: *Doyle, Danny*
CHCD 1035 / Sep '93 / Outlet

☐ FESTIVAL OF IRISH FOLK VOL.1, A (2CD Set)
Seven drunken nights: *Dubliners* / Auld triangle: *Dubliners* / Finnegan's wake: *Dubliners* / Holy ground: *Dubliners* / Joe Hill: *Kelly, Luke* / Song for Ireland: *Kelly, Luke* / Tomorrow morning: *McGuire, Sean & Joe Burke* / Friendly visit: *McGuire, Sean & Joe Burke* / Farl O'Gara: *McGuire, Sean & Joe Burke* / Trim the velvet: *McGuire, Sean & Joe Burke* / Copperplate 1: *McGuire, Sean & Joe Burke* / Copperplate 2: *McGuire, Sean & Joe Burke* / Port padraig na cara: *Burke, Joe* / Frost is all over: *Burke, Joe* / Spike island lassies: *Burke, Joe* / Farewell to Leitrim: *Burke, Joe* / Return from Camden Town: *Burke, Joe* / Tom Moyland's frolic: *Burke, Joe* / Green fields of France: *Fureys & Davey Arthur* / Steal away: *Fureys & Davey Arthur* / Gallipoli: *Fureys & Davey Arthur* / Old bush: *Bealfeirste* / Bucks of Oranmore: *Bealfeirste* / Toss the feathers: *Bealfeirste* / Toss the feathers: *Bealfeirste* / Out in the ocean: *Bealfeirste* / Hag with the money: *Bealfeirste* / Galway races: *McCann, Jim* / Easy and slow: *McCann, Jim* / Irish ways and Irish laws: *Close, John* / Back home in Derby: *Close, John* / Botany bay: *McEvoy, Johnny* / Murshesen Durkin: *McEvoy, Johnny* / Coulin: *Innisfree Ceoil* / Roisin dubh: *Innisfree Ceoil* / Lonesome boatman: *Innisfree Ceoil* / King of the fairies: *Innisfree Ceoil* / Carrickfergus: *Innisfree Ceoil* / Dawning of the day: *Innisfree Ceoil* / Sam Hall: *Reilly, Paddy* / Spancil hill: *Reilly, Paddy* / Rocky road to Dublin: *Reilly, Paddy* / Sullivans: *Reilly, Paddy* / Rose of Allandale: *Reilly, Paddy*
PTICD 2001 / Mar '97 / Pure Traditional Irish

☐ FESTIVAL OF IRISH FOLK VOL.2, A (2CD Set)
On Raglan Road: *Kelly, Luke* / Foggy dew: *Kelly, Luke* / Wild rover: *Dubliners* / Dublin in the rare oul times: *Dubliners* / Molly Maguires: *Dubliners* / Musical priest: *Dubliners* / Blackthorn stick: *Dubliners* / Last night's fun: *Dubliners* / Congress reel: *Dubliners* / Four green fields: *Dubliners* / Black velvet band: *Dubliners* / Miss McNamara: *Na Fili* / Follow me down to Limerick: *Na Fili* / Boulavouge: *McHaile, Tom* / Gooseberry bush: *McHaile, Tom* / Maid behind the bar: *McHaile, Tom* / Coolies No.3: *McHaile, Tom* / Miss Monaghan's: *McKillop, Jim* / Spey in spate: *McKillop, Jim* / Mist in the glenn: *McKillop, Jim* / Knights of St. Patrick: *McKillop, Jim* / Nancy Spain: *Dublin City Ramblers* / John O'Dreams: *Dublin City Ramblers* / Ferryman: *Dublin City Ramblers* / Fields of Athenry: *Reilly, Paddy* / Carrickfergus: *Reilly, Paddy* / Town I loved so well: *Reilly, Paddy* / Fairy: *Tansey, Seamus* / Clougher: *Tansey, Seamus* / Round Kilavelle: *Tansey, Seamus* / Mail coach road to Silgo: *Tansey, Seamus* / Richards Dwyer's reel: *Burke, Joe* / Paddy Kelly's reel: *Burke, Joe* / Jackson's jig: *Burke, Joe* / Monaghan's jig: *Kelly, John & James* / Ceathru cavan: *Kelly, John & James* / Wild Irishman: *Kelly, John & James* / Irish rover: *Drew, Ronnie* / Song for Ireland: *Kelly, Luke* / Lord Inchquinn: *Dubliners* / Down the broom: *Ceannt, Eamonn Ceili Band* / Saint Ruth's brush: *Ceannt, Eamonn Ceili Band* / Preston's: *Ceannt, Eamonn Ceili Band* / Woeful widow: *Ceannt, Eamonn Ceili Band* / New York jig: *Ceannt, Eamonn Ceili Band* / Tie the bonnet: *Shaskeen* / Innisfree: *Innisfree Ceoil* / Give me your hand: *Innisfree Ceoil* / Women of Ireland: *Innisfree Ceoil*
PTICD 2002 / Mar '97 / Pure Traditional Irish

☐ FESTIVAL OF IRISH MUSIC VOL.1, A
EUCD 1323 / Nov '95 / ARC

☐ FESTIVAL OF IRISH MUSIC VOL.2, A
EUCD 1160 / '91 / ARC

☐ FESTIVAL OF IRISH MUSIC VOL.3, A
Summer in Ireland: *Oisin* / Mungo Kelly's: *Oisin* / Winds of change: *Oisin* / Blantyre explosion: *Dubliners* / Botany Bay: *McLoughlin, Noel* / Baloo baleerie: *Butler, Margie* / Kid on the mountain: *Pied Pipers* / Leithrim fancy: *Pied Pipers* / Cold blow and the rainy night: *McLoughlin, Noel* / Star of the county down: *Golden Bough* / Hare's paw and Jackie Coleman's No 2: *Golden Bough* / Carrickfergus: *McLoughlin, Noel* / Samhradh samradh: *Tara* / Chief O'Neill's favourite: *Pied Pipers* / Nine points of rougery: *Pied Pipers* / Faral O'Gara: *Pied Pipers* / Spancil hill: *McLoughlin, Noel* / Wake of the barrel: *Golden Bough* / Lea Rig: *Butler, Margie* / Kind Robin: *Butler, Margie* / Foggy dew: *Dubliners* / Jeannie C: *Oisin*
EUCD 1212 / Sep '93 / ARC

☐ FESTIVAL OF IRISH MUSIC, A
EUCD 1156 / Jun '91 / ARC

☐ FESTIVAL OF LIGHT, A
5310692 / 5 Jan '98 / Six Degrees

☐ FESTIVAL OF MALE CHOIRS, A (Massed Welsh Male Voice Choirs)
Bandit's chorus / Fair maid of Perth / Take me home / Sarah / Memory / By Babylon's wave / Ar yd y nos / Laudamus / Pilgrim's chorus / I'se weary of waitin' / Softly as I leave you / Arwelfa / Silver birch / Close thine eyes / Battle hymn of the republic
QPRZ 004D / Oct '97 / Polyphonic

☐ FESTIVAL OF MASSED MALE CHOIRS, A
Speed your journey / Dashenka / Non parti / Last words of David / Deus salutis / Pilgrim's chorus / Psalm 23 / Love could I only tell thee / Laudamus / William Williams / Arwelfa / My Lord what a morning / Comrades' song of hope / Cyfri'r Geifr / Cwm Rhondda / Nant y myndd / Myfanwy / Nidaros
SCD 4076 / Jun '98 / Sain

☐ FESTIVAL OF SAN MIGUEL TZINACAPAN MEXICO, A
C 560099 / Nov '96 / Ocora

☐ FESTIVAL OF SON 1986, A (All Star Soneros)
RMD 82244 / 21 Apr '98 / RMM

☐ FESTIVAL OF TRADITIONAL IRISH MUSIC, A (2CD Set)
CHCD 1037 / Aug '94 / Chyme

☐ FESTIVAL OF YORKSHIRE VOICES, A
March of the peers / Let there be peace on earth / Song of the jolly Roger / Valse / Funiculi, funicula / Softly as I leave you / Finlandia / On Ilkley moor baht'at / Lost chord / When the saints go marching in / Sound an alarm / Morte Criste / Gwahoddiad / Ouverture solenelle (1812) / Pomp and circumstance No.1
QPRZ 008D / Oct '97 / Polyphonic

☐ FESTIVAL TROPICAL
EUCD 1250 / Mar '94 / ARC

☐ FETISH SOUNDTRACKS VOL.2
Hate: *Die Form* / I feel the skin: *Call* / Justify my love: *Sleep Chamber* / Love me to death: *Sabotage* / Torture: *Call* / Slave: *Phallus Dei* / Aufgang: *Infox* / Wilde kinder: *Sabotage* / Graduation humour: *Fetish Park* / Akuma: *Die Form*
HYP 0850465CD / 13 Apr '98 / Hypnobeat

☐ FEVER IN THE JUNGLE VOL.1
F2FCD 1 / Oct '94 / Fist 2 Fist

☐ FEVER IN THE JUNGLE VOL.2
F2FCD 2 / Apr '95 / Fist 2 Fist

☐ FEVER PITCH
FADCD 028 / Aug '93 / Fashion

☐ FFIDIL (Traditional Welsh Fiddle Music)
TRADD 182CD / May '97 / Fflach

☐ FIAFIA (Dances From The South Pacific)
PAN 150CD / Dec '94 / Pan

☐ FIDDLE JAM SESSION
VOY 301CD / Mar '98 / Voyager

☐ FIDDLE MUSIC OF DONEGAL, THE
CNF 001CD / Nov '96 / CNF

☐ FIDDLE STICKS
NI 5320 / Sep '94 / Nimbus

☐ FIDDLERS OF EASTERN PRINCE EDWARD ISLAND, THE
Prince Edward Island wedding/Big John MacNeil / Fiddlin' Phil / Blue mountain hornpipe / Watermelon / Lord MacDonald's reel/Chaisson reel / Green fields of America / Pride of the ball/Drunken piper / Maid on the green/Kenmures awa / MacSwain's reel / North side tune / Souris breakwater / Medley / Stan's jig / Walk on water reel / Jay's reel / East newk of fife / Isle of my birth / Milltown cross fire / Tarbolton lodge/ Burnt leg / Liberty two-step / MacKinnon's rant/ Johnny Cope reel / Cock of the north/Uncle Jim / Johnny's reel / Miramichi fire / Haggis/Bird's nest / Rose in the garden / Paddy on the turnpike / Medley / Nelly Grey
ROUCD 7015 / Nov '97 / Rounder

☐ FIDDLERS OF WESTERN PRINCE EDWARD ISLAND, THE
Island boy / Acadian reel / Brae reel / Princess reel / Denny Pitre's reel / Draggers reel / Medley / Miramichi fire / Beautiful Sunday / Farmer's reel / Twin sisters (pigeon on the gatepost) / Herring reel / Sugar in the gourd / Heather's breakdown / House of MacDonald / Homeward bound/Jerome's farewell / Carlton county breakdown / Sidney Baglole's reel / Rippling water's jig / Money musk / Joe MacKinnon's reel / High level hornpipe / White river stomp / Latex jig / St. Anne's reel / Old timer's reel / Great George street waltz / Ottawa valley reel / Zella's harmonica reel / Tavern in the town / St. Anne's reel
ROUCD 7014 / Nov '97 / Rounder

☐ FIDELITY VOL.1
CON 0212 / 30 Mar '98 / Confused

☐ FIDJERI - SONGS OF THE PEARL DIVERS (Music from Bahrain)
AUD 08046 / Feb '93 / Auvidis/Ethnic

☐ FIELD RECORDINGS VOL.1 (Virginia 1936-1941)
DOCD 5575 / Dec '97 / Document

☐ FIELD RECORDINGS VOL.10 & 11 (1933-1941/2CD Set)
DOCD 5600 / 24 Mar '98 / Document

☐ FIELD RECORDINGS VOL.2 (North & South Carolina/Georgia/Tennessee/ Arkansas)
DOCD 5576 / Dec '97 / Document

☐ FIELD RECORDINGS VOL.3 (Mississippi 1936-1942)
DOCD 5577 / Dec '97 / Document

☐ FIELD RECORDINGS VOL.4 (Mississippi/Alabama 1934-1942)
DOCD 5578 / Dec '97 / Document

☐ FIELD RECORDINGS VOL.5 (Louisiana/ Texas/Bahamas 1933-1940)
DOCD 5579 / Dec '97 / Document

☐ FIELD RECORDINGS VOL.6 (Texas 1933-1958)
DOCD 5580 / Dec '97 / Document

☐ FIELD RECORDINGS VOL.7 (Florida)
DOCD 5587 / Dec '97 / Document

☐ FIELD RECORDINGS VOL.8 (Louisiana/ Alabama/Mississippi 1934-1947)
DOCD 5598 / 24 Mar '98 / Document

☐ FIELD RECORDINGS VOL.9 (Georgia/ South & North Carolina/Virginia/ Kentucky 1924-1939)
DOCD 5599 / 24 Mar '98 / Document

☐ FIELDS OF DREAMS
GFS 080 / Nov '97 / Going For A Song

☐ FIESTA COMES ALIVE
SAH 40CD / 15 Dec '97 / Slap A Ham

☐ FIESTA PICANTE (The Latin Jazz Party Collection/2CD Set)
Hey bud: Sanchez, Poncho / Ode to Cachao: Puente, Tito / Mother Jones: Santamaria, Mongo / Leyte: Escovedo, Pete / Watermelon man: Sanchez, Poncho & Mongo Santamaria / Killer Joe: Dalto, Jorge / Guachi guaro: Tjader, Cal / Oye como va: Puente, Tito / On a Sunday afternoon: Barretto, Ray / Day tripper: Santamaria, Mongo / Cinderella: Sanchez, Poncho / Things to come: Puente, Tito / La familia: Sanchez, Poncho / Cu-bop alert: Santamaria, Mongo / Ancestral messages: Barretto, Ray / Esta noche: Escovedo, Pete / Serengeti: Tjader, Cal / Greenhouse: Vega, Ray / Coco may may: Sanchez, Poncho / Descarga: Puente, Tito / Work song: Barretto, Ray / Mauteca: Santamaria, Mongo / Lambada timbales: Puente, Tito
CCD 247822 / 6 Oct '97 / Concord Picante

☐ FILL YOUR HEAD WITH PHANTASM VOL.1
PTM 131 / May '95 / Phantasm

☐ FILTERLESS COLLECTIVE VOL.1 & 2
12FKFCDLP / Jul '97 / Filterless

☐ FILTERLESS COLLECTIVE VOL.1, THE
5FKFCD / Jul '95 / Filterless

☐ FINAL NOTES
PLACCD 0102 / 17 Nov '97 / Plastic City UK

☐ FINE AS WINE
FLYCD 30 / Apr '91 / Flyright

☐ FINEST VINTAGE JAZZ (Greatest Jazz 1918-1940)
Savoy blues: Armstrong, Louis / When it's sleepy time down South: Armstrong, Louis / Jumpin' at the woodside: Basie, Count / Blues in thirds: Bechet, Sidney & Earl Hines / Singin' the blues: Beiderbecke, Bix / Symphony in riffs: Carter, Benny / Big noise from Winnetka: Crosby, Bob Orchestra / Marie: Dorsey, Tommy / East St. Louis toodle-oo: Ellington, Duke / Sing me a swing song: Fitzgerald, Ella / Roll 'em: Goodman, Benny / Creole love call: Hall, Adelaide / Running wild: Hampton, Lionel / Crazy rhythm: Hawkins, Coleman / Easy living: Wilson, Teddy & Billie Holiday / Walkin' and swingin': Kirk, Andy & His Twelve Clouds of Joy / Handful of riffs: Lang, Eddie & Lonnie Johnson / Honky tonk train blues: Lewis, Meade 'Lux' / Feelin' no pain: Nichols, Red & His Five Pennies / Livery stable blues: Original Dixieland Jazz Band / I got rhythm: Reinhardt, Django & Stephane Grappelli / St. Louis blues: Smith, Bessie & Louis Armstrong / Relaxin' at the Touro: Spanier, Muggsy / I gotta right to sing the blues: Teagarden, Jack & Benny Goodman / Honeysuckle rose: Waller, Fats
CDAJA 5117 / Oct '93 / Living Era

☐ FINGERPRINTS
02602 / May '95 / Glitterhouse

☐ FINNISH TECHNO COMPILATION
FU 502CD / Nov '96 / Function

☐ FIRE DOWN BELOW
Fire down below: Burning Spear / African skank: Prince Francis / Love and peace: Marshall, Larry / No happiness: Webber, Marlene / What does it take: Francis, Winston & Alton Ellis / Nite ride: 'Im & Dave / Up park camp: Jarrett, Winston / Reggae children: Richards, Roy / What is love: Brown, Errol / Midnight soul: 'Im & The Invaders / Sweet talking: Heptones / Love again: Jackie & The Invaders / Rainy night in Georgia: Parker, Ken / Mission impossible: Mittoo, Jackie
CDHB 81 / Sep '90 / Heartbeat

☐ FIRE/FURY STORY (2CD Set)
CDLAB 102 / Mar '96 / Charly

☐ FIRED
FI 001 / Oct '96 / Fire Island

☐ FIREPOINT
See me running: Cooper, Mike / I wouldn't mind: Moore, Gerald / No whiskey: Robinson, Tom / Here's to the future kid: Cooper, Mike / No more doggin': Kelly, Dave / City woman: Power, Duffy / Oh really: Cooper, Mike / Leaf without a tree: Mitchell, Sam / Big boss man: Robinson, Tom / Sunflower: Robinson, Tom / Halfway: Power, Duffy
C5CD 593 / Aug '96 / See For Miles

☐ FIRESTORM (2CD Set)
CM 77195CD / Oct '97 / Century Media

☐ FIRST CIRCLE SAMPLER, THE
CSCD 1 / Jan '97 / Circle

☐ FIRST CROONERS VOL.1 1920'S, THE
TT 411 / May '98 / Take Two

☐ FIRST CROONERS VOL.2 1930-1934, THE
TT 418 / May '98 / Take Two

☐ FIRST DECADE VOL.1 1987-1997, THE (2CD Set)
Trip to the moon: Acen / We are hardcore: House Crew / Let me be your fantasy: Baby D / Field of dreams: Brothers Grimm / Free: X-Static / Future of Latin: Nino / Exterminate: DMS / Close your eyes: Acen / Super hero: House Crew / Murderous style: X-Static / Reality: Nino / Darkage: DJ Solo / Rumble: DJ Nut Nut & Pure Science / Keep the fire burning: House Crew / SOS: DMS & Boneman X / Casanova: Baby D / Life and crimes of a ruffneck: Acen / Life can begin: Anti Chaos / All we wanna do is dance: House Crew / Daydreaming: Baby D
PNCCA 10 / Sep '97 / Production House

☐ FIRST FLIGHT
ARFCD 1 / Jun '96 / Flying Rhino

☐ FIRST IRISH FOLK FESTIVAL, THE
CMCD 038 / Dec '97 / Celtic Music

☐ FIRST LIGHT - PIANO SOLOS
Private thoughts: Paul, Glenn / Rainforest: Paul, Glenn / Eleanora's falcon: Paul, Glenn / Poetic justice: Larkin, Sheila / Cape clear: Larkin, Sheila / Provincetown set: Larkin, Sheila / Loving the unknown: Jang, Mia / Silent song: Jang, Mia / Waiting: Jang, Mia / Bridge: Dehaas, John B / San blas: Dehaas, John B / Healing: Dehaas, John B / Colour of love: Carr, Adrian / Rachel: Carr, Adrian / You don't know me: Carr, Adrian
ND 61059 / Dec '96 / Narada

☐ FIRST NOEL
Silent night: Thomas, B.J. / Deck the halls: Lynn, Loretta / O little town of Bethlehem: Pride, Charley / It came upon a midnight clear: Clark, Roy / O come all ye faithful (adeste fidelis): McCoo, Marilyn / O holy night: Thomas, B.J. / Jingle bells: McCoo, Marilyn & Billy Davis Junior / Away in a manger: Lynn, Loretta / What child is this: Greenwood, Lee / First Noel: Nelson, Willie / Jolly old St. Nicholas: Lettermen / Joy to the world: Gilley, Mickey / We wish you a merry Christmas: Wagoner, Porter
120322 / Oct '97 / Jingle

☐ FIRST R & B FESTIVAL IN ENGLAND, THE
14554 / 20 Apr '98 / Spalax

☐ FIRST REVOLUTION (A Capella Gospel Singers/2CD Set)
Down by the riverside / Oh freedom / Glory glory hallelujah / Family circle / At the cross / He's okay / Hey sinner / Please remember me / He really cares / Hymn book holy book and pocket book / I'm gonna serve the Lord / I made up my mind / It's gonna rain / Balm in giliead / I shall not be moved / Good Lord I have done / Jesus hits like the atom bomb / Lord I want to be a christian / Old time religion / I'll be somewhere listening for my name / Ezekiel saw the wheel / Deep river / People don't do like they used to do / Dry bones in the valley / Amazing Grace / Didn't it rain / Wade in the water / Wake Nicodemus / Woke up this morning / Back to the church / Straighten up and fly right / Sometimes I feel like a motherless child
24338 / Nov '97 / Laserlight

☐ FIRST TAKE IS THE DEEPEST, THE (Unissued Alternate Versions From The Vaults Of Ace)
I was wrong: Cook, Roland / Can't let you go I love you so: Scott, Albert / I'll never let you go: Marchan, Bobby / Nervous breakdown: King, Earl / Will you: Joe & Ann / Bugs in your head: Spears, Calvin / I know: Marchan, Bobby / Blessed are these tears: Tex, Joe / That's all I can say: Smith, Huey / What I learned about you: Hall, Gerri / Mr. Blues: Joe & Ann / It hurts me to my heart: Marchan, Bobby / Well-o well-o baby: Marchan, Bobby / Honey honey: Supremes / Teenage rock: Little Booker / Doin' the rock 'n' roll: Spears, Calvin / Chickee wah wah: Marchan, Bobby / Wherever you may be: Joe & Ann / Heaven came down: Joe & Ann / My love is strong: King, Earl / It's not as easy as that: Hall, Gerri / I'm not satisfied: Dixon, David / Gee baby: Joe & Ann / Yes I got you: Garbo, Chuck
WESA 811 / 20 Apr '98 / Westside

☐ FIRST TORCH SINGERS VOL.1 1920'S, THE
TT 407 / May '98 / Take Two

☐ FIRST TORCH SINGERS VOL.2 1930-1934, THE
TT 412 / May '98 / Take Two

☐ FISTFUL OF HARDCORE, A
GAIN 017CD / 20 Jul '98 / Gain Ground

☐ FISTFUL OF PUSSIES/FOR A FEW PUSSIES MORE, A
Repo man: Meteors / Mystery street: Batmobile / Alley cat king: Frantic Flintstones / Spy catcher: Guana Batz / Brand new Cadillac: Milkshakes / No dog: Turnpike Cruisers / Hangman's Caesars: Quakes / Cyclonic: Quakes / I knew sky: Golden Horde / My brain is in the cupboard: Alien Sex Fiend / Surf city: Meteors / I get so exited: Dexter, Levi & The Ripchords / Rumble in the jungle: Rochee & The Sarnos / Holy hack Jack: Demented Are Go / Thirteen lines: Wigs / Boneshaker baby: Alien Sex Fiend / She's gone: Riverside Trio / Thee holy jukebox: Raymen
CDMGRAM 36 / May '93 / Anagram

☐ FIT FOR KINGS
DFR 37 / 27 Jul '98 / Drunken Fish

☐ FIVE
SABO 20 / 3 Nov '97 / Sabotage

☐ FIVE STAR BOLEROS
RMD 82277 / 24 Mar '98 / RMM

☐ FLAMENCO (Masters Of The Flamenco Guitar)
Zapateado / Taranto camino de linares / Con un clavel / Salero gaditano / El albacin / Serrana juncal: Ricardo, Nino / Marisma de huelva: Ricardo, Nino / Gitana gaditana: Ricardo, Nino / Gitana gaditan: Ricardo, Nino / Liego el frutero: De Huelva, Manolo & The Singing Of Vallego / Yo no me hubiera perdido: De Huelva, Manolo & The Singing Of Vallego / Ese me gusto seria: De Huelva, Manolo & The Singing Of Vallego / Ni hermosa ni dinero: De Huelva, Manolo & The Singing Of Vallego / Bulerias: De Marchena, Melchor / Tranguillos de cadiz: De Marchena, Melchor / Sevillanes: De Marchena, Melchor / Petenras: De Marchena, Melchor / Serranas: De Marchena, Melchor / Solares: De Marchena, Melchor
HEMIMDCD 106 / 6 Oct '97 / Hemisphere

☐ FLAMENCO HIGHLIGHTS FROM SPAIN
15162 / '91 / Laserlight

☐ FLAMENCO RUMBA GITANA
EUCD 1208 / Sep '93 / ARC

☐ FLAMENCO VIVO - FIESTA
B 6870 / Jun '98 / Auvidis/Ethnic

☐ FLAMENCO VIVO COLLECTION (Gypsies & Flamenco - 2CD Set)
B 6824 / Feb '97 / Auvidis/Ethnic

☐ FLAMENCO, FIRE AND GRACE
Mori sonando: De La Bastide, Miguel / Callejon De Las Canteras: Tomatito / Crisol: Morente, Enrique / Buleriando: Moraito / Aguita clara: Riqueni, Rafael / Mi hijo jonato: El Viejin / Viajero: De La Bastide, Miguel / Chicuelina: Riqueni, Rafael / Voz de referencia: Carrasco, Diego / Caminillo viejo: Tomatito / Tangos de la plaza: Morente, Enrique / Into the dark: Cook, Jesse
ND 63924 / May '96 / Narada

☐ FLAMES OF HELL (Swamp Music Vol.1)
TRIKONT 0156 / Jan '95 / Trikont

☐ FLAMIN'
TX 51218CD / Mar '96 / Triple X

☐ FLAMING BURNOUT (An Estrus Benefit Compilation)
MR 089CD / 8 Sep '97 / Man's Ruin

☐ FLAPPER BOX, THE (5CD Set)
Begin the beguine: Shaw, Artie / Drum stomp: Hampton, Lionel / Bugle call rag: Roy, Harry / Georgia on my mind: Gonella, Nat / Stompin' at the Savoy: Goodman, Benny / Love is the sweetest thing: Bowlly, Al / Save it pretty Mama: Armstrong, Louis / World is waiting for the sunrise: Geraldo & His Orchestra / Continental: Stone, Lew / One o'clock jump: Basie, Count / On the air: Gibbons, Carroll / Say it with music: Payne, Jack / Whispering: Fox, Roy / Take the 'A' train: Ellington, Duke / Sweetest music this side of Heaven: Winnick, Maurice / Somebody stole my gal: Cotton, Billy / In the mood: Loss, Joe / Here's to the next time: Hall, Henry / At the woodchoppers' ball: Herman, Woody / I used to be colour blind: Hylton, Jack / Trumpet blues and cantabile: James, Harry / Hors d'oeuvres: Ambrose & His Orchestra / Donkey serenade: Jones, Allan / You've done something to my heart: Laye, Evelyn / Night and day: Astaire, Fred / Indian love call: Eddy, Nelson & Jeanette MacDonald / My heart belongs to Daddy: Martin, Mary / Louise: Chevalier, Maurice / Amapola: Durbin, Deanna / Goodnight Vienna: Buchanan, Jack / Let yourself go: Rogers, Ginger / One night of love: Moore, Grace / Little white room: Day, Frances & John Mills / Inka dinka doo: Durante, Jimmy / Lovely to look at: Dunn, Irene / I'll see you again: Coward, Sir Noel / Falling in love again: Dietrich, Marlene / I'll get by: Haymes, Dick / I can give you the starlight: Ellis, Mary / Experiment: Lawrence, Gertrude / Thanks for the memory: Hope, Bob & Shirley Ross / Dancing on the ceiling: Matthews, Jessie / I get a kick out of you: Merman, Ethel / We're gonna hang out the washing on the Siegfried line: Flanagan & Allen / Yours: Lynn, Vera / Nearness of you: Hutchinson, Leslie 'Hutch' / I'm stepping out with a memory tonight: Bowlly, Al & Jim Mesene / I haven't time to be a millionaire: Bowlly, Al & Jim Mesene / Wings over the Navy: Stone, Lew / Our Sergeant Major: Formby, George / American patrol: Miller, Glenn / It's a hap-hap-happy day: Roy, Harry / Run rabbit run: Flanagan & Allen / It's a pair of wings for me: Gonella, Nat / Bless 'em all: Cotton, Billy / Turn the money in your pocket: Bowlly, Al & Jim Mesene / I'll never smile again: Bowlly, Al & Jim Mesene / We'll go smiling along: Bowlly, Al & Jim Mesene / We must all stick together: Geraldo & Cyril Grantham / White cliffs of Dover: Lynn, Vera / My prayer: Henderson, Chick / Oh buddy I'm in love: Gonella, Nat / Oh Johnny oh: Roy, Harry & His Tiger Ragamuffins / Kiss me goodnight, Sergeant Major: Cotton, Billy / Jukebox Saturday night: Cotton, Billy / All over the place: Thorburn, Billy / Moonlight serenade: Miller, Glenn / Wish me luck as you wave me goodbye: Fields, Gracie / If you were the only girl in the world: Ziegler, Anne & Webster Booth / Be careful it's my heart: Sinatra, Frank / Bless you: Ink Spots / Little white gardenia: Brisson, Carl / Very thought of you: Bowlly, Al / J'Attendrai: Rossi, Tino / Stop beatin' around the mulberry bush: Merry Macs / What do you know Jo: Stafford, Jo & The Pied Pipers / Great mistake of my life: Henderson, Chick / Body and soul: Boswell, Connee / Sonny boy: Jolson, Al / Tisket-a-tasket: Fitzgerald, Ella / Without a song: Dennis, Denny / How about you: Carless, Dorothy / Where the blue of the night meets the gold of the day: Crosby, Bing / Trans-Atlantic lullaby: Hall, Adelaide / Last time I saw Paris: Martin, Tony / Fools rush in: Shelton, Anne / My very good friend the milkman: Waller, Fats / Pennsylvania 6-5000: Andrews Sisters / These foolish things: Layton, Turner / Someone to watch over me: Langford, Frances / Ma, I miss your apple pie: Ambrose & His Orchestra / There's a land of Begin Again: Loss, Joe / Don't sit under the apple tree: Andrews Sisters / I'll never smile again: Sinatra, Frank / You are my sunshine: Roy, Harry / I don't want to walk without you: Lipton, Celia / String of pearls: Miller, Glenn / When I see an elephant fly: Lea, Jimmy / That lovely weekend: Carless, Dorothy & Geraldo / Moonlight becomes you: Crosby, Bing / Someone's rocking my dreamboat: Crosby, Bing / Drummin' man: Squadronaires / Who wouldn't love you: Ink Spots / Elmer's tune: Miller, Glenn / Kiss the boys goodbye: Martin, Mary / My devotion: Winstone, Eric & His Band / Rancho pillow: Martin, Freddy / Beat me Daddy, eight to the bar: Shearing, George / Daybreak: Sinatra, Frank / I've got a gal in Kalamazoo: Andrews Sisters / Nightingale sang in Berkeley Square: Shelton, Anne / White Christmas: Crosby, Bing
PASTCDS 7010 / Jun '93 / Flapper

☐ FLASH OF '29, A (Portrait Of music In 1929)
Some of these days / If I had a talking picture of you / Mess-a-stomp / Louise / Dinah / Button up your overcoat / Honey / Won't you get up off it, please / Muskrat ramble / After you've gone / Black and blue / When you're smiling / Wang wang blues / I'm a dreamer (aren't we all) / Everybody loves my baby / Bashful baby
PHONTCD 7608 / '93 / Phontastic

☐ FLASHBACK
Flashback: Imagination / Let's groove: Earth, Wind & Fire / Celebration: Kool & The Gang / Contact: Starr, Edwin / Love come down: King, Evelyn 'Champagne' / Gangsters of the groove: Heatwave / Cuba: Gibson Brothers / Going back to my roots: Odyssey / Don't stop the music: Yarbrough & Peoples / Oops upside your head: Gap Band / Funky

town: Lipps Inc. / I will survive: Gaynor, Gloria / DISCO: Ottawan / YMCA: Village People / Car wash: Rose Royce / Hustle: McCoy, Van / I love to love (but my baby loves to dance): Charles, Tina / You're the first, the last, my everything: Charles, Tina
MUSCD 004 / Nov '92 / MCI Music

☐ FLAT PICKING GUITAR FESTIVAL
Medley: Watson, Doc / Paddy on the swingpipe: Lieberson, Richard / Medley: Crary, Dan / All of me: Solomon, Barry / Big sandy river: Fegy, Dick / El chicken real: Lieberson, Richard / Kitchen girl: Bromberg, David / Down yonder: Watson, Doc / Fire hose reel: Fegy, Dick / Alabama jubilee: Aumen, Michael / Irish reels: Thompson, Eric / Hippodrome real: Fegy, Dick / Back home in Indiana: Solomon, Barry / Indian killed a woodcock: Lieberson, Richard / Medley: Watson, Doc / Port ARthur blues: Thompson, Eric / Possum up a gum stump: Fegy, Dick / Beaumont rag: Aumen, Michael / Texas gals: Thompson, Eric / Drunken billy goat: Fegy, Dick / Soldier's joy: Aumen, Michael / Red haired boy: Fegy, Dick / Sheik of araby: Aumen, Michael
SH 98003 / Mar '98 / Shanachie

☐ FLATLINE
MGOUTCD 7 / Sep '96 / Granite

☐ FLAVAS
Tha crossroads / Gangsta's paradise / Diggin' on you / Waterfalls / I got 5 on it / Loungin' / Get money / Fu-gee-la / California love / Get on up / You're the one / Return of the mack / I wish / Too hot / Flava/ 1,2,3,4 sumpin' new
SUMCD 4108 / Feb '97 / Summit

☐ FLAVOUR OF INDIA, A
Raag darbari / Raag bhairvi / Raag des (Chanchal taal) / Raag jai jai wanti (Teen taal) / Raag mian ki todi
NSCD 027 / 16 Feb '98 / Nascente

☐ FLAVOURS OF JAZZ FUN
RENCD 112 / Mar '96 / Renaissance Collector Series

☐ FLAVOURS OF LATIN JAZZ
Be bop: Puente, Tito / Happy now: Sanchez, Poncho / Sangria: Maria, Tania / Samba da soho: Manfredo fest / Airegin: Puente, Tito / Roger's samba: Tjader, Cal / Keep the spirits singing: Trio Da Paz / Killer joe: Barretto, Ray & New World Spirit / Lost in Amazonia: Maria, Tania / All blues: Puente, Tito / Sun is out: Purim, Flora & Airto Moreira / Watermelon man: Sanchez, Poncho / Cookie: Santamaria, Mongo / Fascinating rhythm: Fest, Manfredo
RENCD 122 / 29 Sep '97 / Renaissance Collector Series

☐ FLEADH CEILI
CDC 007 / Feb '97 / Ceol

☐ FLEADH CEILI BANDS
Marches / Reels / Hornpipes / Jigs / Waltz / Reels / Set dances / Jigs / Reels / Hornpipes / Marches / Reels / Jigs / Hornpipes / Jigs / Marches
CD 21214 / Nov '97 / Laserlight

☐ FLESH EATERS (The Return Of The Undead/3CD Set)
DTKBOX 57 / 1 Jun '98 / Dressed To Kill

☐ FLESH, FANGS AND FILIGREE (3CD Set)
DTKBOX 60 / 1 Jun '98 / Dressed To Kill

☐ FLICKNIFE PUNK SINGLES COLLECTION
Shake some action / Total control / Shell shock / Waiting for the man / Teenage in love / Do the geek / Thatcher / Follow the leader / Fight to win / Let's get crazy / Werewolf / We don't care / Wanna world / No romance / No sign of life / Leaders of tomorrow / Respectable / Playing cards with dead men / Summertime now / Nicely does it
CDPUNK 42 / Feb '95 / Anagram

☐ FLIGHT OF THE GREEN LINNET
RCD 20075 / May '96 / Rykodisc

☐ FLOORPACKIN'
You should of held on: 7th Avenue Aviators / Tears: Roye, Lee / I'm where it's at: Jades / If that's what you wanted: Beverly, Frankie / Soul self satisfaction: Jackson, Earl / Little togetherness: Young Hearts / You didn't have to leave: Ellusions / Nothing can compare to you: Velvet Satins / I'm not strong enough: Four Perfections / Stick by me baby: Salvadors / That beatin' rhythm: Temple, Richard / Sliced tomatoes: Just Brothers / Double cookin': Checkerboard Squares / Try a little harder: Fi Dels / Countdown: Tempos / Per-so-nally: Paris, Bobby / Lend a hand: Hutton, Bobby / She'll come running back: Britt, Mel / Hung up on your love: Montclairs / You've been gone too long: Sexton, Ann / Dearly beloved: Montgomery, Jack / I'm comin' home: Pride, Lou / I'm not built that way: Hesitations / My sugar baby: Clarke, Connie / Put your arms around me: Sherrys / It's all over: Mann, Charles
SSCD 004 / Mar '97 / Goldmine

☐ FLOW: AN EXPERIENCE IN DRUM 'N' BASS
Alltitude: Architex / Airtight: Funki Technicians / Drifting: KMC / Coming on strong: Cold Mission / Inertia: Mouly & Lucinda / Sorrow: Future Bound / Liquid velvet: J-Majik / Sound ceased: Xedos / Can't you see: Technical Itch / Oceans: Subject 13 / Generations: Intensity
KUB 932 / Jun '97 / Kubin

☐ FLOWER POWER
HRCD 8041 / May '94 / Disky

☐ FLOWER POWER
TIN 861212 / Aug '96 / Disky

☐ FLOWER POWER DAZE VOL.1
DCD 5297 / Sep '93 / Disky

☐ FLOWER POWER DAZE VOL.2
DCD 5359 / Apr '94 / Disky

☐ FLOYD'S CAJUN FAIS DO DO
Wafus two step: Sundown Playboys / Valse de soleil coucher: Cormier, Lesa & The Sundown Playboys / Back home again in Louisiana: Cormier, Lesa & The Sundown Playboys / La valse san espoir: Cormier, Lesa & The Sundown Playboys / Step it fast: Bonsall, Joe / La pointe au pain: Hebert, Adam / I can't sleep at night: Hebert, Adam / Rosalie: Hebert, Adam / Valse de toute le monde: Prejean, Leeman / Teardrop special: Barro & The Teardrops / 73 special: Lejeune, Rodney / Flumes d'enfer: Pitre, Austin / Fee Fee can't dance: Cajun Trio + 1 / One step de duson: Cormier, Louis / Ville platte widow: Fontenot, Allen / Bachelor's life: Badeaux & The Louisiana Aces / Valse de meche: Barzas, Maurice & The Mamau Playboys / Rodare special: Thibodeaux, Eugene / Webb Pierce blues: Fontenot, Allen / Si tu m'aimes: Bruce, Vin / Bo Sparkle waltz: Broussard, August / Calcasieu rambler's special: Broussard, August
CDCH 304 / Oct '90 / Ace

☐ FLUTE & SITAR MUSIC OF INDIA
12178 / Aug '95 / Laserlight

☐ FLUTE AND GAMELAN MUSIC OF WEST JAVA
TSCD 913 / Apr '95 / Topic

☐ FLUTES OF THE MANDARA MOUNTAINS, THE (Music From Cameroon)
C 560110 / Jan '97 / Ocora

☐ FLUTES OF THE WORLD
PS 660077 / Oct '96 / PlayaSound

☐ FLY AFRICAN EAGLE (The Best Of African Reggae)
SH 45033 / Jul '97 / Shanachie

☐ FLY DE GATE
VPCD 1285 / May '93 / VP

☐ FLYIN' TRAPS
162064 / Sep '97 / Hollywood

☐ FLYING HIGH
Mooncat: Shaker / Euro friendly: Bootleg Boys / Toccata: Childs, Sky / Gotta get (Loose): Must / Keep your luv: Partisans / Krazy noise: Numerical Value / On ya way: Helicopter / Flagship: Blue Peter / Driver: Epik / Tree frog: Hope Experience / Check it out: Kinky Riba / Organ grinder: Deeper Cut
CDTOT 25 / Apr '95 / Jumpin' & Pumpin'

☐ FLYING TRANCE CLASSICS (2CD Set)
ZYX 811122 / Aug '97 / ZYX

☐ FM POWER (2CD Set)
I've been in love before: Cutting Crew / Kayleigh: Marillion / Bette Davis eyes: Carnes, Kim / True: Spandau Ballet / Love hurts: Nazareth / Every rose has it's thorn: Poison / Apache: Shadows / Save a prayer: Duran Duran / Dum dum girl: Talk Talk / Temptation: Heaven 17 / Dancing with tears in my eyes: Ultravox / Kids in America: Wilde, Kim / Golden brown: Stranglers / Centerfold: Geils, J. Band / Love is a battlefield: Benatar, Pat / Words: David, F.R. / Baker street: Rafferty, Gerry / Stuck with you: Lewis, Huey & The News / Heart and soul: T'Pau / Loud music in cars: Bremner, Billy / Heroes: Meat Loaf / Roll over Beethoven: ELO / Radar love: Golden Earring / Thunder in my heart: Sayer, Leo / Hot in the city: Idol, Billy / Some kinda wonderful: Grand Funk Railroad / Ride like the wind: Saxon / Spanish stroll: Mink Deville / Touch me (I want your body): Fox, Samantha / So long: Fischer Z
DC 880002 / 30 May '97 / Disky

☐ FOLDS AND RHIZOMES
SR 99 / Feb '96 / Sub Rosa

☐ FOLK & CEREMONIAL MUSIC FROM CAMBODIA
D 8068 / Feb '96 / Unesco

☐ FOLK AND SACRED SONGS FROM ITALY
926522 / Sep '96 / BUDA

☐ FOLK BOX (2CD Set)
TBXCD 513 / Jan '96 / TrueTrax

☐ FOLK BOX (2CD Set)
PBXCD 513 / Nov '96 / Pulse

☐ FOLK COLLECTION VOL.1, THE
Another Irish rover: Four Men & A Dog / Carthy's reel/ The return to Camden Town: Carthy, Martin & Dave Swarbrick / Almost every circumstance: Prior, Maddy & June Tabor / Oh I swear: Thompson, Richard / Company policy: Carthy, Martin / I specialise: Gregson & Collister / Party's over: Albion Band / Brighton camp/March past: Kirkpatrick, John / Good old way: Watersons / Johnny Cope: MacColl, Ewan / Battle of Falkirk Muir: Battlefield Band / Reaper: Tabor, June / Farewll to the gold: Jones, Nic / Reconciliation: Alias Ron Kavana / Walsh's polkas: Patrick Street / Lakes of ponchartrain: Simpson, Martin / Mariano: Keen, Robert Earl / Through moorfields: Cronshaw, Andrew / Now westlin' winds: Gaughan, Dick
TSCD 470 / Oct '93 / Topic

☐ FOLK COLLECTION VOL.2, THE
TSCD 481 / Oct '95 / Topic

☐ FOLK GUITAR
TRTCD 216 / Jul '96 / TrueTrax

☐ FOLK HEARTBEAT
Can't help falling in love: Lick The Tins / Bride 1945: Matthews, Iain / Choo choo ch'boogie: Chilli Willi & Red Hot Peppers / False knight on the road: Hart, Tim & Maddy Prior / Hal-an-tow: Collins, Shirley & The Albion Country Band / Belle of Belfast city: Lick The Tins / Female drummer: Steeleye Span / This train: Denny, Sandy / Ramblin' boy: Denny, Sandy / Blacksmith: Steeleye Span / Rave on: Steeleye Span / Dalesman litany: Hart, Tim & Maddy Prior / Midnight bus: Chilli Willi & Red Hot Peppers / Famous flower of serving men: Carthy, Martin / Marrowbones: Steeleye Span / Claudy banks: Collins, Shirley & The Albion Country Band
EMPRCD 595 / Jun '96 / Emporio

☐ FOLK HERITAGE VOL.1
Fiddle diddle: Chilli Willi & Red Hot Peppers / Dalesman's litany: Hart, Tim & Maddy Prior / Calling on song: Steeleye Span / Handsome Polly-O: Carthy, Martin / Copshawholme Fair: Steeleye Span / Sing me back home: Matthews, Iain / My ramblin' boy: Denny, Sandy / Fool like you: Moore, Tim / Famous flower of serving men: Carthy, Martin / Adieu sweet lovely Nancy: Hart, Tim & Maddy Prior / Blacksmith: Steeleye Span / Just as the tide was flowing: Collins, Shirley / Rock 'n' roll love letter: Moore, Tim / Last thing on my mind: Denny, Sandy / Lark in the morning: Steeleye Span / Wager a wager: Hart, Tim & Maddy Prior
MCCD 043 / Sep '91 / Music Club

☐ FOLK HERITAGE VOL.1-3 (3CD Set)
MCBX 004 / Jan '93 / Music Club

☐ FOLK HERITAGE VOL.2
Time to ring some changes: Thompson, Richard / Not a day passes: Gregson & Collister / Ramble away: Albion Band / Music for a found harmonium: Patrick Street / Song of the iron road: MacColl, Ewan / Band played waltzing Matilda: Tabor, June / Handsome Molly: Simpson, Martin / World turned upside down: Gaughan, Dick / Sovay: Carthy, Martin & Dave Swarbrick / All things are quite silent: Collins, Shirley / Spaghetti panic: Blowzabella / Hidden love/ Sheila Coyles: Four Men & A Dog / Fine horsemen: Silly Sisters / Lovely cottage/Gold ochra at Killarney point to points: Alias Ron Kavana / Canadee-I-O: Jones, Nic / Country life: Watersons
MCCD 049 / Mar '92 / Music Club

☐ FOLK HERITAGE VOL.3
Granite years: Oyster Band / Who cares: Shocked, Michelle / First time ever I saw your face: MacColl, Ewan / Mississippi summer: Tabor, June & The Oyster Band / Hush little baby: Horseflies / Breaths: Sweet Honey In The Rock / Hopak: Ukrainians / Silver wheels: Cockburn, Bruce / Byker hill: Barely Works / Angry love: McLeod, Rory / Six string street: White, Andy / Sea never dry: God's Little Monkeys / Turn things upside down: Happy End / That's entertainment: Colorblind James Experience / Free Mexican airforce: Jimenez, Flaco / Raining: Ancient Beatbox
MCCD 076 / Jun '92 / Music Club

☐ FOLK HEROES
RTECD 190 / Oct '97 / RTE/Europe 1

☐ FOLK LIVE FROM THE MOUNTAIN STAGE
It sure was better back then: Forbert, Steve / Fishin' in the dark: Nitty Gritty Dirt Band / Sweet is the melody: DeMent, Iris / Gentle on my mind: Hartford, John / Beat the retreat: Thompson, Richard / Driving home: Wheeler, Cheryl / Time passage: Stewart, Al / Take this hammer: Taj Mahal / Letter from heaven: Morrissey, Bill / Lives in the balance: Havens, Richie / John Wayne lives in Hoboken: Delevantes / Sun won't stop: Near Holly
BPM 310CD / May '97 / Blue Plate

☐ FOLK MASTERS
SF 40047CD / Dec '94 / Smithsonian Folkways

☐ FOLK MASTERS
CDAR 1017 / Oct '94 / Action Replay

☐ FOLK MUSIC FROM BELGIUM (2CD Set)
B 6844 / Feb '97 / Auvidis/Ethnic

☐ FOLK MUSIC FROM NORTHEN IRELAND
CDN 1101 / Apr '97 / Outlet

☐ FOLK MUSIC FROM NORTHERN SPAIN
CMT 2741003CD / Jul '95 / La Chant Du Monde

☐ FOLK MUSIC FROM SCOTLAND
12250 / Apr '94 / Laserlight

☐ FOLK MUSIC IN SWEDEN (Folk Music In Transition)
CAP 21548CD / Mar '98 / Caprice

☐ FOLK MUSIC IN SWEDEN VOL.11 (Fiddlers From Five Provinces)
CAP 21487CD / Aug '96 / Caprice

☐ FOLK MUSIC IN SWEDEN VOL.12 (The Songs Of The Tornedalen)
CAP 21485CD / Nov '96 / Caprice

☐ FOLK MUSIC IN SWEDEN VOL.13 (Nordic Folk Instruments)
CAP 21484CD / Aug '96 / Caprice

☐ FOLK MUSIC IN SWEDEN VOL.14 (Folk Tunes From Jamtland)
CAP 21489CD / Nov '96 / Caprice

☐ FOLK MUSIC IN SWEDEN VOL.15 (Songs Of Sailors & Navies)
CAP 21540CD / May '97 / Caprice

☐ FOLK MUSIC IN SWEDEN VOL.16 & 17 (Tunes From Rattvik, Boda & Binsjo/ 2CD Set)
CAP 22044CD / May '97 / Caprice

☐ FOLK MUSIC IN SWEDEN VOL.18 (Tunes From Dala Floda, Enviken & Ore)
CAP 21541CD / May '97 / Caprice

☐ FOLK MUSIC IN SWEDEN VOL.19 (Blood Corpses & Tears)
CAP 21542CD / Aug '97 / Caprice

☐ FOLK MUSIC IN SWEDEN VOL.20
CAP 21543CD / Dec '97 / Caprice

☐ FOLK MUSIC IN SWEDEN VOL.21-23 (3CD/Book Set)
CAP 21544CD / Mar '98 / Caprice

☐ FOLK MUSIC IN SWEDEN VOL.24
CAP 21547CD / Dec '97 / Caprice

☐ FOLK MUSIC IN SWEDEN VOL.5
CAP 21476CD / Nov '95 / Caprice

☐ FOLK MUSIC IN SWEDEN VOL.9 & 10
CAP 22043 / May '96 / Caprice

☐ FOLK MUSIC OF ALBANIA
TSCD 904 / Oct '94 / Topic

☐ FOLK MUSIC OF BULGARIA
TSCD 905 / Sep '94 / Topic

☐ FOLK MUSIC OF CUBA
D 8064 / Oct '95 / Unesco

☐ FOLK MUSIC OF GREECE
TSCD 907 / Sep '94 / Topic

☐ FOLK MUSIC OF NORTHERN SPAIN
CMT 2741003 / Apr '95 / La Chant Du Monde

☐ FOLK MUSIC OF TURKEY
TSCD 908 / Sep '94 / Topic

☐ FOLK MUSIC OF YUGOSLAVIA
TSCD 906 / Sep '94 / Topic

☐ FOLK MUSIC VOL.1
D8005 / Jun '89 / Auvidis/Ethnic

☐ FOLK MUSIC VOL.2
D8003 / Jun '89 / Auvidis/Ethnic

☐ FOLK 'N' HELL
Flick it up and catch it: Sutherland, Jim / Half way round/walking the line: Burach / If and when: Bongshang / Pipe tunes: Shooglenifty / Passing away: Mounsey, Paul / Sun fire majestic: Colour Of Memory / Jolly beggar/man in black: Coelbeg / Superwasp/Along the coast of Norway/Neckbuster: Seelyhoo / All together: MacLean, Dougie / By the right: MacKenzie, Fergus & Simon Thoumire / Beaujolais nouveau: Humpff Family / Grandmother's eyes: Rock Salt & Nails / Hoagies/Porshe: Poozies / Burning of Auchindoun/Turn again: Iron Horse / O ho na Ribeannan/Sean triubhas/Faca tu saor an T-Sabhaidh: Tannas / Bitter honey: Khartoum Heroes / Willie's aul' trews/Auld reel 1/Auld reel 2: Old Blind Dogs
PRMDCD 16 / Oct '96 / Hemisphere

☐ FOLK ROUTES
Siege of Yaddlethorpe: Amazing Blondel / Matty Groves: Fairport Convention / John Barleycorn: Traffic / Seven black roses: Martyn, John / It suits me well: Denny, Sandy / Road: Drake, Nick / When I get to the border: Thompson, Richard & Linda / Strangely strange but oddly normal: Dr. Strangely Strange / Black Jack David: Incredible String Band / Nutting girl: Hutchings, Ashley / She moved through the fair: Fairport Convention / I was a young man: Albion Country Band / Peace in the end: Fotheringay / Long odds/Mr. Cosgill's delight: Hutchings, Ashley & John Kirkpatrick / Audrey: Heron, Mike / Man of iron: Denny, Sandy / Girl in the month of May: Bunch / Hornpipe: Locke, John
IMCD 197 / Jul '94 / Island

☐ FOLK SCENE COLLECTION, THE
RHRCD 109 / May '98 / Red House

☐ FOLK SONGS OF NORTH EAST SCOTLAND
CDTRAX 5003 / Nov '95 / Greentrax

☐ FOLK SONGS VOL.1
VICG 50222 / Feb '96 / JVC World Library

☐ FOLK SONGS VOL.2
VICG 50232 / Feb '96 / JVC World Library

☐ FOLK THEATRE OF NORTH VIETNAM
ARN 64368 / Nov '96 / Arion

☐ FOLKLORE FROM VENEZUELA
EUCD 1237 / Nov '93 / ARC

☐ FOLKLORIC INSTRUMENTAL TRADITIONS OF KOREA VOL.1
VICG 50202 / Mar '96 / JVC World Library

☐ FOLKLORIC INSTRUMENTAL TRADITIONS OF KOREA VOL.2
VICG 50212 / Mar '96 / JVC World Library

☐ FOLKS LIVE
BPCD 1003 / Mar '96 / Blue Planet

☐ FOLKSONGS (Old Time Country Music 1926-1944) (2CD Set)
FA 047 / Apr '96 / Fremeaux

☐ **FOLKSONGS AND BALLADS**
Lincolnshire poacher: *Pears, Peter & Benjamin Britten* / Foggy foggy dew: *Pears, Peter & Benjamin Britten* / Sweet Polly Oliver: *Pears, Peter & Benjamin Britten* / Early one morning: *Pears, Peter & Benjamin Britten* / Last rose of summer: *Pears, Peter & Benjamin Britten* / Blow the wind southerly: *Ferrier, Kathleen & Phyllis Spurr* / Keel row: *Ferrier, Kathleen & Phyllis Spurr* / Drink to me only with thine eyes: *Ferrier, Kathleen & Phyllis Spurr* / Down by the Salley: *Ferrier, Kathleen & Phyllis Spurr* / Up from Somerset: *Luxon, Benjamin & David Willison* / Nearer my God to thee: *Luxon, Benjamin & David Willison* / Break the news to Mother: *Luxon, Benjamin & David Willison* / In an old fashioned town: *Palmer, Felicity & John Constable* / Bless this house: *Palmer, Felicity & John Constable* / Somewhere a voice is calling: *Palmer, Felicity & John Constable* / Home sweet home: *Palmer, Felicity & John Constable* / Linden lea: *Tear, Robert & Phillip Ledger* / Water mill: *Tear, Robert & Phillip Ledger* / Silent noon: *Tear, Robert & Phillip Ledger* / Lass of Richmond Hill: *Tear, Robert*
4500202 / 17 Aug '98 / Belart

☐ **FOLKSONGS OF THE LOUISIANA ARCADIANS VOL.1**
ARHCD 359 / Apr '95 / Arhoolie

☐ **FOLLOW THAT ROAD (2nd Annual Vineyard Retreat - 2CD Set)**
PH 1165/66CD / Sep '94 / Philo

☐ **FONG NAAM (Ancient Contemporary Music From Thailand)**
140982 / Oct '95 / Celestial Harmonies

☐ **FOOD FOR THOUGHT**
GFS 081 / Nov '97 / Going For A Song

☐ **FOOM FOOM**
BFCD 05 / Oct '93 / Bruce's Fingers

☐ **FOOTBALL (3CD Set)**
EMTBX 311 / 20 Apr '98 / Emporio

☐ **FOOTBALL CLASSICS (Classical Music That Celebrates The Great Game/2CD Set)**
8554410/11 / 8 May '98 / Naxos

☐ **FOOTBALL CRAZY**
Blue is the colour: *Chelsea FC* / Can we kick it (no we can't): *World Of Orange* / Wooly bully: *Jones, Vinnie* / You reds: *Resistance 77* / Andy Cole song: *Palmer, Harry* / Soccer fan: *Real Sounds Of Africa* / Roger Milla is my no.9 dream: *Rainbow Choir* / Do it cos you like it: *Rainbow Choir* / Arsenal rap: *A-Team* / Nice one Gazza: *New Cockney Chorus* / Cry Gazza cry: *Spittin' Image* / Ohh Gary Gary: *Her* / Milan Milan: *West, Keith* / Super Marco Van Basten: *Rainbow Choir* / Ryan Giggs we love you: *Rainbow Choir* / Glory glory Man Utd: *Stretford End Boys* / Canaries: *Norwich City* / Alouette: *Webb, David* / We will follow united: *Palmer, Harry* / You'll never walk alone: *Liverpool FC*
EMPRCD 626 / Jun '96 / Emporio

☐ **FOOTBALL FEVER (2CD Set)**
NSCDD 1998 / 18 May '98 / Nascente

☐ **FOOTBALL HEAVEN**
Match of the day / Grandstand / Aztec Gold / Tutti al mondo / You are the number one / We are the champions / To be the number one / Gloryland / World in motion / When the saints go maching in / Whatever will be will be (Que sera sera) / That's amore / Life of riley / Guantanamera / John Brown's Body / Champions league / You'll never walk alone / March of triumph / Ode to joy / Nessun dorma
ANT 011 / Nov '96 / Tring

☐ **FOR A FEW CRASH HELMETS MORE VOL.3**
RRCD 008 / 13 Apr '98 / Retch

☐ **FOR A LOVELY MOTHER**
DCD 5382LM / May '94 / Disky

☐ **FOR A LOVELY MOTHER (Instrumental)**
CNCD 5994LM / May '94 / Disky

☐ **FOR COLLECTORS ONLY (Kent/ Modern's Serious Shades Of Soul)**
You brought it all on yourself: *Hammond, Clay* / Burning out: *Garrett, Vernon* / Long as I've got my baby: *Day, Jackie* / I've been done wrong: *Holiday, Jimmy* / Nobody but me: *Other Brothers* / I'm coming home: *John, Bobby* / Remove my doubts: *Johnson, Stacey* / You make me feel like someone: *Gilliam, Johnny* / You are my sunshine: *Shane, Jackie* / Baby I'm sorry: *Hill, Z.Z.* / Them love blues: *Wright, Earl* / Beauty is just skin deep: *Sweethearts* / You are my first love: *Hunt, Pat* / I'm lonely for you: *Adams, Arthur* / All that shines isn't gold: *Windjammers* / One more chance: *Four Tees* / My love, she's gone: *Intentions* / I'm in love: *Sanders, Larry* / Would you like to love me: *Holiday, Jimmy* / Like it stands: *Ramsey, Robert* / You make me cry: *Adams, Arthur* / I was born to love you: *Copeland, Johnny* / I need money: *Davis, Ruth* / It's been a long time baby: *Other Brothers* / Think it over baby: *Love, Mary*
CDKEND 119 / Sep '95 / Kent

☐ **FOR DANCERS FOREVER (25 Storming 60's Soul Sounds)**
You turned my bitter into sweet: *Love, Mary* / Baby, without you: *Monday, Danny* / Before it's too late: *Day, Jackie* / Your love has made me a man: *Hutch, Willie* / You just cheat and lie: *Hill, Z.Z.* / This man wants you: *Cox, Wally* / Three lonely guys: *Brilliant Corners* / My baby needs me: *Baker, Yvonne* / I don't need: *Turner, Ike & Tina* / You better be good: *Woods, Peggy* / Lay this burden down: *Love, Mary* / If I could turn back the hands of time: *Garrett, Vernon* / Can it be me: *Williams, Mel* / Dancing fast, dancing slow: *Intentions* / My jealous girl: *Hammond, Clay* / My aching back: *Fulson, Lowell* / I can't believe what you say: *Turner, Ike & Tina* / This couldn't be me: *Sweethearts* / Love is gonna get you: *Woods, Peggy* / I can feel your love: *Taylor, Felice* / Oh what heartaches: *Day, Jackie* / No puppy love: *Copeland, Johnny* / What more: *Hill, Z.Z.* / I'm so thankful: *Ikettes* / I'm in your hands: *Love, Mary*
CDKEND 100 / Sep '92 / Kent

☐ **FOR MILLIONAIRES ONLY VOL.1**
Say something nice to me: *Kline, Bobby* / Heartaches I can't take: *Gaylettes* / I'll be back: *Wallace, Jimmy* / Girls are against me: *Utopias* / Go for yourself: *Antiques* / That's the kind of man I am: *Adams, Bobby* / Heart you're made of stone: *Magnetics* / My love gets stronger: *Ridgley, Tommy* / Bring your fine self home: *Soulettes* / I'm still young: *Summers, Johnny* / Soul step: *Dogs* / One way or the other: *Roberts, Tina* / Female ingenuity: *Ruby* / Lady lady: *Colt 45's* / Heartaches, Souvenirs: *Powell, Will* / Lonely girl: *Mercury, Eric* / I got the power: *Coarcy, Joanne* / What more do you want: *Toones, Gene* / I'm going over: *Honeycutt, Johnny* / I couldn't care less: *Fredreick, Carol*
GSCD 099 / Nov '96 / Goldmine

☐ **FOR MILLIONAIRES ONLY VOL.2**
All of my life: *Four Temples* / Lady in green: *Magnetics* / Johnny on the spot: *Edwards, Dennis* / It's better: *Alexander, Reggie* / Tough girl: *Arnell, Billy* / Dancin' a hole in the world: *Delphs, Jimmy* / You had me fooled: *Woods, Danny* / What about me: *Herman, Sonny* / Deceived: *Ruby* / Showstopper: *Cashmeres* / Don't leave me baby: *Limeliters* / What's my chances: *Flamingo, Chuck* / Nothing you can do: *Womack, Bobby* / I've got something of value: *Rey, Eddie* / Love's such a funny thing: *Wesley, John* / I check the mailbox: *Curtis, Debbie* / There's room for me: *Davis, Jesse* / Crazy: *Tee, John* / Love is a trap: *Robinson, Cleveland Jr.* / Image of a man: *Quintessants*
GSCD 101 / 27 Oct '97 / Goldmine

☐ **FOR MY VALENTINE**
WMCD 5677VT / Feb '94 / Disky

☐ **FOR ONE AND ALL**
9425742 / Jan '96 / Music For Little People

☐ **FOR SENTIMENTAL REASONS**
Mountain greenery: *Torme, Mel* / Blueberry Hill: *Armstrong, Louis* / Tammy: *Reynolds, Debbie* / Too close for comfort: *Gorme, Eydie* / (I love you) for sentimental reasons: *Fitzgerald, Ella* / Standing on a corner: *Mills Brothers* / True love ways: *Holly, Buddy* / Dream a little dream of me: *Mama Cass* / Friendly persuasion: *Boone, Pat* / Pretty blue eyes: *Lawrence, Steve* / Love me or leave me: *Davis, Sammy Jr.* / Unchained melody: *Hibbler, Al* / Lollipops and roses: *Jones, Jack* / Sweet old fashioned girl: *Brewer, Teresa* / Around the world: *Crosby, Bing* / Mr. Wonderful: *Lee, Peggy* / Love is a many splendoured thing: *Four Aces* / Moonglow and theme from picnic: *Stoloff, Morris*
3035900032 / Oct '95 / Carlton

☐ **FOR THE DEAD IN SPACE**
MES 12CD / 15 Sep '97 / Magick Eye Singles

☐ **FOR YOU WITH LOVE**
I 3896022 / Oct '96 / Galaxy

☐ **FOR YOUR PRECIOUS LOVE (2CD Set)**
DBG 53040 / Jun '95 / Double Gold

☐ **FORCE 1 - THE CLUB IS HERE**
343322 / Nov '95 / Koch Dance Force

☐ **FOREGANGARE**
MNW 240/2 / Jan '94 / MNW

☐ **FOREST OF GOLD TOPS IN THE LAND OF OZ, A**
GCD 1001 / 5 Jan '98 / Gift

☐ **FOREVER AND ALWAYS**
Father and son / Why / Someday / Love me for a reason / Because you loved me / I love you always forever / Killing me softly / Forever love / Spinning the wheel / Always be my baby / One sweet day / How deep is your love / You are not alone / Words / Count on me / Give me a little more time / I am blessed / Unbreak my heart
305962 / Jan '97 / Hallmark

☐ **FOREVER AND EVER (18 Songs From The Heart)**
Gambler: *Rogers, Kenny* / True love ways: *Holly, Buddy* / You're breaking my heart: *Rose Marie* / What a wonderful world: *Armstrong, Louis* / When your old wedding ring was new: *Longthorne, Joe* / Love letters: *Lester, Ketty* / Something's gotten hold of my heart: *Pitney, Gene* / It's only make believe: *Twitty, Conway* / Wind beneath my wings: *Greenwood, Lee* / Long arm of the law: *Rogers, Kenny* / Sweet dreams: *Cline, Patsy* / You're my best friend: *Williams, Don* / If I were you: *Judds* / Someone loves you honey: *Pride, Charley* / Jackson: *Sinatra, Nancy & Lee Hazelwood* / Just beyond the moon: *Ritter, Tex* / Dedicated to the one I love: *Mamas & The Papas* / Moonlight and roses: *Reeves, Jim*
PLATCD 3906 / Jun '89 / Platinum

☐ **FOREVER CELTIC**
Still in love with you: *Thin Lizzy* / Deep in your heart: *Brady, Paul* / Borderline: *De Burgh, Chris* / Ancient rain: *Coughlan, Mary* / Gone to Pablo: *Bloom, Luka* / Gort na saileán: *Tamalin* / Against the wind: *Brennan, Maire* / New grange: *Clannad* / You're in my love: *Lohan, Sinead* / Wonderful thing: *Dowdall, Leslie* / Song for Ireland: *Black, Mary* / Forever frozen: *Spillane, Davy* / Place among the stones: *Spillane, Davy* / Three babies: *O'Connor, Sinead* / Ansacht na nansacht: *Aoife* / Parisienne walkways: *Moore, Gary* / Lonesome boatman: *Fureys* / Wall of tears: *Black, Frances* / Weakness in me: *Goss, Kieran*
RENCD 116 / Jun '97 / Renaissance Collector Series

☐ **FOREVER DOO WOP VOL.1 (2CD Set)**
KNEWCD 738 / Apr '94 / Kenwest

☐ **FOREVER DOO WOP VOL.2 (2CD Set)**
KNEWCD 739 / Apr '94 / Kenwest

☐ **FOREVER IRELAND (20 Traditional Irish Pub Songs)**
Flight of the Earls / Grace / Ringsend rose / Fields of Athenry / Cliffs of Dooneen / Galway shawl / Carrickfergus / Mountains of Mourne / Spancil Hill / Town I loved so well / Auld triangle / Dublin in the rare oul' times / Johnson's motor car / Irish ways and Irish laws / Avondale / Farewell to my own native land / Rocky road to Dublin / Back home in Derry / Castle of Dromore / Whiskey in the jar
CDPUB 023 / Jun '98 / Outlet

☐ **FOREVER MELODIES**
4301121022 / 27 Apr '98 / ANS

☐ **FOREVER PSYCHEDELIC**
MPCD 14 / 14 Apr '98 / Matsuri

☐ **FORMATION 60**
JCR 0032 / 10 Aug '98 / Jazzanova

☐ **FORMULE TECHNO VOL.1 (2CD Set)**
7142615 / Dec '96 / Fairway

☐ **FORMULE TECHNO VOL.2 (2CD Set)**
7142628 / Apr '97 / Fairway

☐ **FORTIES DANCE BAND HITS**
There's a harbour of dreamboats / I'm gonna get lit up (when the lights go on in London) / Baby please stop and think about me / As time goes by / Coming in on a wing and a prayer / Why don't you fall in love with me / Ragtime cowboy Joe / I left my heart at the stage door canteen / Lady who didn't believe in love / Lover lullaby / Don't get around much anymore / It can't be wrong / Pistol packin' Mama / Sunday, Monday or always / Walkin' by the river / Mr. Five by five / If I had my way / In the blue of evening / Johnny Zero / What's the good word Mr Bluebird / Tell me the truth / Where's my love / So long Sarah Jane
RAJCD 818 / Sep '97 / Empress

☐ **FORTY SHADES OF GREEN**
PDSCD 519 / Sep '97 / Pulse

☐ **FORTY YEARS OF WOMEN IN JAZZ (2CD Set)**
JCD 09/10 / Oct '91 / Jass

☐ **FORWARD (Selection Of Top Greensleeves Singles 1977-1982)**
Another one bites the dust: *Clint Eastwood & General Saint* / Wa-do-dem: *Eek-A-Mouse* / Diseases: *Michigan & Smiley* / Gun man: *Prophet, Michael* / Fattie boom boom: *Ranking Dread* / Born for a purpose: *Dr. Alimantado* / Bathroom sex: *General Echo* / War: *Wailing Souls* / Yellowman get's married: *Yellowman* / Fat she fat: *Holt, John*
GRELCD 60 / Mar '94 / Greensleeves

☐ **FOUND IN THE FLURRY**
BEST 1073CD / Nov '95 / Acoustic Music

☐ **FOUR BITCHIN' BABES**
SH 8018CD / Nov '95 / Shanachie

☐ **FOUR DECADES OF POP (2CD Set)**
MBSCD 433 / Feb '95 / Castle

☐ **FOUR FRENCH HORNS**
Four men on a horn / Come rain or come shine / On the Alamo / Blues for Milt / Lobo nocho / Mood in motion / I want to be happy / Wilhemine Worthington Valley
SV 0214 / Oct '97 / Savoy Jazz

☐ **FOUR IN THE MORNING**
It wasn't God that made honky tonk angels: *Wells, Kitty* / Ruby, don't take your love to town: *Rogers, Kenny* / Rose garden: *Anderson, Lynn* / Harper Valley PTA: *Riley, Jeannie C.* / No tomorrow in sight: *Nelson, Willie* / Jackson: *Lewis, Jerry Lee* / Big town: *Twitty, Conway* / Lonely woman make good lovers: *Luman, Bob* / Music city USA: *Bare, Bobby* / Wild side of life: *Thompson, Hank* / Rhinestone cowboy: *Campbell, Glen* / Satisfied mind: *Wagoner, Porter* / Rock Island line: *Cash, Johnny* / King of the road: *Miller, Roger* / Big bad John: *Dean, Jimmy* / Take me home: *Boxcar Willie* / Four in the morning: *Young, Faron*
11977 / Feb '96 / Music

☐ **FOUR TRUMPET STARS: LOUIS, DIZZY, MILES & CHET**
4749242 / Jan '95 / Sony Jazz

☐ **FOUR WOMEN BLUES (The Victor/ Bluebird Recordings)**
I'm goin' back home: *Memphis Minnie* / Bumble bee blues: *Memphis Minnie* / I never told a lie: *Memphis Minnie* / Don't want no woman: *Memphis Minnie* / Georgia skin: *Memphis Minnie* / You wrecked my happy home: *Memphis Minnie* / I'm waiting on you: *Memphis Minnie* / Keep on goin': *Memphis Minnie* / When the sun goes down: *Memphis Minnie* / Hustlin' woman blues: *Memphis Minnie* / Selling my pork chops: *Memphis Minnie* / Doctor, doctor blues: *Memphis Minnie* / Hardworking woman blues: *Mississippi Matilda* / Happy home blues: *Mississippi Matilda* / Christmas mornin' blues: *Kansas City Kitty* / Double trouble blues: *Kansas City Kitty* / Leave my man alone: *Kansas City Kitty* / Mistreatin' easy rider: *Kansas City Kitty* / Staggering blues: *Moore, Miss Rosie Mae* / Ha ha blues: *Moore, Miss Rosie Mae* / School girl blues: *Moore, Miss Rosie Mae* / Stranger blues: *Moore, Miss Rosie Mae*
7863667192 / Feb '97 / RCA

☐ **FOXTROT**
In my head a crystal sphere of heavy fluid: *Christopherson, Peter* / Bone frequency: *Inflatable Sideshow* / Think jazz think punk attitude: *Nurse With Wound* / Spooky loop: *Nurse With Wound* / Blue rats: *Coil* / Heartworms: *Coil* / Dream of the inmost light: *Current 93*
GRAAL 1CD / Jan '98 / World Serpent

☐ **FRA SVARTLAMON WITH LOVE**
PRO 028 / 11 Aug '97 / Progress

☐ **FRAGMENTED COMPILATION VOL.1**
FMDCD 002 / 16 Feb '98 / Fragmented

☐ **FRANCISCAN POLYPHONY**
B 6855 / Feb '98 / Auvidis/Ethnic

☐ **FRANCOPHONIX**
CPCD 8132 / Oct '95 / Charly

☐ **FRANKFURT HARD TRANCE HISTORY (3CD Set)**
PIAS 556200825 / Dec '96 / DJ's Present

☐ **FRANKFURT TRANCE**
FRIE 0072 / 3 Aug '98 / Friends

☐ **FRANKLINTON MUSCATEL SOCIETY**
CDBM 091 / Apr '93 / Blue Moon

☐ **FRATERNITY OF HOUSE VOL.2**
Disco shopping: *Klubb Heads* / Brainstorm: *DJ George Dee & Dan Racoon* / I wanna make u: *Sequential One* / Runnin': *Bass Bumpers* / Da lower you go: *Striking Man* / Nowhere to run: *Chiara* / Housetime is anytime: *KK System* / Lost worlds: *White Moon* / Deeper love: *Love & Fate* / Lift me up: *Red 5* / Flexxible: *Toss & Turn* / Koma '97: *Interactive*
DST 085702592 / Sep '97 / Dance Street

☐ **FREAK OUT**
Blame it on the boogie: *Jacksons* / Boogie nights: *Heatwave* / Love really hurts without you: *Ocean, Billy* / Boogie weekend: *Earth, Wind & Fire* / Best of my love: *Emotions* / Lady marmalade: *Labelle* / Instant replay: *Hartman, Dan* / You bet your love: *Hancock, Herbie* / Love train: *O'Jays* / Give it up: *KC & The Sunshine Band* / Dance to the music: *Sly & The Family Stone* / Play that funky music: *Wild Cherry* / Ain't gonna bump no more: *Wild Cherry* / I love to love: *Charles, Tina* / Soul city walk: *Bell, Archie & The Drells* / It's disco night: *Isley Brothers* / Got to be real: *Lynn, Cheryl* / Do it any way you wanna: *People's Choice*
4850052 / 3 Aug '98 / Columbia

☐ **FREAKBEAT FREAKOUT**
Feels like a woman: *Troggs* / Baby I go for you: *Blue Rondos* / Let me in: *Sorrows* / (We ain't got) nothin' yet: *Spectres* / Leave my kitten alone: *First Gear* / I'm a lover not a fighter: *Brand* / Hungry: *5 AM Event* / Fortune teller: *Jackson, Tony & The Vibrations* / I wonder if she remembers me: *Raven, Simon* / It must be love: *Sheffields* / We didn't kiss, we didn't love, but now we do: *Clique* / You said: *Primitives* / That's alright: *Powell, Jimmy & The Dimensions* / It's all for you: *Meddyevils* / Scratch my back: *Panter, Jan* / Got the blame: *Worrying Kynde* / That's when happiness began: *Montanas* / Jump and dance: *Carnaby* / You've got what I want: *Sorrows* / Roses: *Craine, Don & The New Dowliners Sect* / Baby you've got it: *Truth* / Tell her: *Movement* / Help me: *Primitives* / Ma's place: *Meddyevils* / She ain't no good: *Clique* / Plenty of love: *Sheffields* / She's too way out: *Dangerfield, Tony & The Thrills* / Walk, baby walk: *Neal, Johnny & The Starliners*
NEMCD 952 / 24 Nov '97 / Sequel

☐ **FREAKTOWN**
EFA 12739CD / Mar '97 / Subterfuge

☐ **FREDDIE MCGREGOR PRESENTS THE BEST OF BIG SHIP**
RASCD 3162 / Dec '95 / Ras

☐ **FREE PARTY - LIVE AT AN UNDERGROUND VENUE (Mixed By Steve Johnson/2CD Set)**
Music maker: *MC MC & The Rush Hour* / Titanic: *DJ Iceberg* / Spiritual blessings: *Tekno Dred Alliance* / Netherworld: *LSG* / Nazca plains: *Crafty* / Sound: *Warlock* / Tune in: *Johnson, Steve* / Machine: *Lab 4* / Based on acid: *DJ Ablaze* / Easy access: *Pharmacy* / Powertrax 2.1: *Casseopaya* / Sanctus dominus: *Helix & Fury*
TRIPCD 14 / 20 Jul '98 / Rumour

☐ **FREE SPIRIT**
I want it all: *Queen* / If I could turn back time: *Cher* / Poison: *Cooper, Alice* / Talking to myself: *Terraplane* / It must have been love: *Roxette* / Need you tonight: *INXS* / Touch: *Noiseworks* / Best: *Tyler, Bonnie* / You took the words right out of my mouth: *Meat Loaf* / You give love a bad name: *Bon Jovi* / How can we be lovers: *Bolton, Michael* / I don't love you anymore: *Quireboys* / Carrie: *Europe* / Black velvet: *Myles, Alannah* / (I just) died in your arms: *Cutting Crew* / Flame: *Cheap Trick* / Living years: *Mike & The Mechanics*
MOODCD 16 / Apr '91 / Columbia

☐ **FREE THE FUNK VOL.1**
Philip Marlow: *Word Up* / Where I'm going: *Fried Funk Food* / Punks not dead: *Dadamo* / Sundown: *Koh Tao* / Step into Eden: *Balistic Brothers* / Dark jazz: *Daphreephunkateerz* / Drakes equation: *Spacer* / On da rocks: *Bangalter, Thomas* / Sportif: *Heights Of Abraham* / Hot flush: *Red Snapper* / Flow: *Model 500* / What I'm feelin' (good): *Nightmares On Wax*
RS 95085CD / Jan '96 / R&S

☐ **FREE THE FUNK VOL.2**
RS 96102CD / Jul '96 / R&S

☐ **FREEDOM TIME**
Do you believe: *Lewis, Webster* / Freedom time: *Tillery, Linda* / Times are gettin' hard: *Nunez, David* / It's you: *Cooling, Joyce* / In the name of love: *Rankin, Kenny* / Blues for hari: *MacKay, Dave* / Norweigan wood: *Checkfield* / Descharge yema ya: *Fischer, Clare* / Didn't I: *Dorando* / Wonderful world: *Montage Project* / Spirit: *Checkfield*
CRC 004 / 16 Oct '97 / Counterpoint

☐ **FREESTYLE CANDIES**
KLANGCD 2 / Dec '96 / Klang

☐ FREESTYLE FILES USA
Glass bead game: *Thievery Corporation* / Modus operandi: *Better Daze* / Kairo - Absolut black: *Spacetime Continuum* / Photon torpedo: *Sub Dub* / Cinnabar: *Tipsy* / Joe dropped the swing: *Pimp Daddy Nash* / Try to love me: *Myerson, Jamie* / Island of lost souls: *DJ Spooky* / Possi purple: *DJ Wally*
K 7062CD / 16 Feb '98 / Studio K7

☐ FREESTYLE FILES VOL.2 (2CD Set)
K7 053CD / Mar '97 / Studio K7

☐ FREESTYLE FILES VOL.3 (Nu Beat Science - 2CD Set)
Tokyo power: *Terranova* / Urban haze: *Basement Jaxx* / Catch the break: *J-Knights* / Tell the truth: *Aphrodite & Johnny Yout* / Atomic moog 2000: *Coldcut* / Civilised: *Sluts n' Strings & 909* / Vitamin C: *Can* / Me and Mr. Jones: *Plug* / Man: *Khao* / Naughty mouse mice at the organ: *Mr. Scruff* / Rule of the bone: *Ballistic Brothers* / Fuck dub: *Tosca* / Space invaders: *I-F* / Cool it vixen: *Depth Charge* / Spudink: *Plaid* / Transparent: *Reflection* / Marrakesh: *East Of Suez*
K7 063CD / 26 Jan '98 / Studio K7

☐ FREESTYLE FILES VOL.4 (Crackers Delight/2CD Set)
Groovin' with you: *Gentle People* / La danse electrique: *Drum Island* / Remembering dawn: *Max 404* / Byte the bullet: *Midnight Funk Association* / Anger/Rare force 2 mega mix: *Sakamoto, Ryuichi* / Get up man: *Gumix* / Tribute: *Soul Ascendants* / Happy hip hop: *5 Sterne Deluxe & DJ Koze* / Return of the rebel: *Raw Deal* / Tanzen: *Pole* / Miss excitement: *Tipsy* / Au-pair: *Kreidler* / Medal: *Panasonic & Alan Vega* / Angular art: *Parker, Andrea* / Wall of pressure: *Impulse* / Contact/DJ Kicks: *Terranova* / Disco airlines/Tet air mix: *Depth Charge* / Don't fall asleep: *Leila* / Play-ah hate-ah: *Parker, Terrence*
K7 069CD / 8 Jun '98 / Studio K7

☐ FREESTYLE VOL.4
Play your own risk: *Planet Patrol* / Promise me: *Lil Suzy* / I wanna be the one: *Stevie B* / Now I found you: *Garcia, Tony* / Don't go away: *Johnny O* / Bad of the heart: *Lamond, George* / Can I stop the love: *Naif* / I need you: *GT* / Someone to hold: *April* / If you were mine: *D'Lan, Lorenzo* / I believe: *April* / I can't live without you: *Garcia, Tony* / Up and down: *Chicco* / You are the only one: *Giant* / I'll be loving you: *Collage* / Holding on: *Torrez, Judy* / Shake your body: *Beat Production* / Limelight: *Dee, Gina*
ZYX 550772 / Apr '97 / ZYX

☐ FREEWAY
5259192 / Feb '96 / PolyGram TV

☐ FREEZONE VOL.1 (The Phenomenology Of Ambient - 2CD Set)
Cherchez la lumiere / New frontier / La couleur / Ocean view / Voyage 34-phase iv (instrumental extract) / Desert equations (for brion gysin) / Travelling without moving-trip 8 / Machu picchu / Preparationjoyeux regrets / Stars / Water dragon / Launchpad / Orphic mysteries / Hierophone / Sunrise / Flow motion / Om / Hovering glows / Save the whale / Myopia / Enoch arden-brandan / Riding the silver chord-sphinx-orval / Forest hymn
SSR 129 / May '94 / SSR

☐ FREEZONE VOL.3 (2CD Set)
SSR 167CD / May '96 / SSR

☐ FREEZONE VOL.4 (Dangerous Lullaby - 2CD Set)
Space pin: *Basement Jaxx* / One: *Thievery Corporation* / Offset acoustics: *Flytronix* / Never tell you: *Rhythm & Sound* / Columbus: *Four Ears* / Key: *Tosca* / Lust in space: *Dimitri From Paris* / Trip to nowhere: *Funki Porcini* / Enlightment: *Endemic Void* / Supersex: *Morphine* / Once around the moon: *Stasis* / Blowin' it: *Only Child* / I wnt to...: *Geist, Morgan* / Night of the living blenders: *Fields, Jordan* / It could be g: *Craig, Carl* / Through the surface: *Jimpster* / Turn and waist: *Treva Whateva* / Young at heart: *Herbert & Love From San Francisco* / Boneskin: *Crewmunity* / Starting block: *Stade* / RSI: *Juryman & Spacer* / 10: *Juryman & Spacer* / Zoned: *Niew*
SSR 187CD / Jun '97 / SSR

☐ FRENCH CAFE ACCORDIAN MUSIC
REWCD 351 / Feb '98 / Reactive

☐ FRENCH COLLECTION VOL.1, THE
CD 352070 / May '93 / Duchesse

☐ FRENCH COLLECTION VOL.1, THE (3CD Set)
CD 333503 / Nov '93 / Duchesse

☐ FRENCH COLLECTION VOL.1, THE
CDWNCD 2009 / Jun '95 / Javelin

☐ FRENCH COLLECTION VOL.2, THE
CD 352133 / Jul '93 / Duchesse

☐ FRENCH COLLECTION VOL.3, THE
CD 352134 / Jul '93 / Duchesse

☐ FRENCH CONNECTION
PIAS 453000120CD / 25 Aug '97 / Pronto

☐ FRENCH FRIED FUNK (2CD Set)
Dieu recconaitre les siens: *DJ Cam* / Chicago babe: *Trankilou* / Ecouter fumer: *La Chatte Rouge* / Le turbo personnel: *Alex Gopher* / Le patron est devenu fou: minos / Interplanetary dreams: *Playing For The City* / Live at the CBGB: *Blackstrobe* / Modular: *Air* / Sunshine: *Mozesli* / Pissed on Brooklyn Bridge: *Mozesli* / Don't fuck with my shit: *Dirty Jesus* / Free ton style: *Dimitri From Paris* / Super disco: *Alex Gopher* / Interplanetary dream: *Playin' 4 The City* / Higher and ailleurs: *Playin' 4 The City* / Deep toothbrush: *Magenta* / Dirty Larry: *Dimitri From Paris* / Get the cash and run: *Dimitri From Paris* / Orbit: *Playin' 4 The City* / Disco cubism: *I-Cube*
SLIPCD 63 / 1 Sep '97 / Slip 'n' Slide

☐ FRENCH FRIED FUNK VOL. 2
KICKCD 74 / 7 Sep '98 / Kickin'

☐ FRENCH SESSIONS VOL.1 (Mixed By Jerome Pacman)
Natural high: *Yost, Kevin* / Late night jam: *Sixteen Souls* / Feel the rhythm: *Mateo & Matos* / Groove box: *Huckaby, Mike* / Wanna sing: *DJ Sneak* / Players theme: *Wade, Rick* / Function: *Mood II Swing* / Persuader: *Dahlback, J.* / Freaked out: *Brown, Charly* / Another Saturday night: *Maas* / Hardgroove: *Paris & Geles* / Deep penetration: *Second Thought* / Phunk theory: *New Phunk Theory* / Driving deep south: *Future Homosapiens*
SUB 48612 / 30 Mar '98 / Distance

☐ FRENCH SESSIONS VOL.2 (Mixed By DJ Bertrand)
SUB 48629 / 27 Jul '98 / Distance

☐ FRENCH SESSIONS VOL.3
San Francisco nights: *DJ Rasoul* / Lifted fusion: *Reel Fusion Band* / Cassio's theme: *Deep* / Joint groove: *Alford, Tee* / Deep in love: *DJ Vice* / Egyptian jazz: *Men From The Nile* / Destination: *Ananda Project* / El Camino: *Shazz* / Baianihas: *Carinhoso Project* / Besos de Los Angeles: *Fresh & Low* / Eber's groove: *Bright Lights* / Directions: *Blaze* / Trust in me: *Digital Kid*
DI 0902 / 17 Aug '98 / Distance

☐ FRENCH-BELGIAN INDUSTRIES
MA 432 / Apr '94 / Machinery

☐ FRENCHY SCISSORHANDS (The True Story Of Flicknife Records)
CDMGRAM 59 / Jul '88 / Anagram

☐ FRENESI - 1940
Frenesi: *Shaw, Artie* / Koko: *Ellington, Duke* / Sweet Lorraine: *Cole, Nat 'King'* / Gilly: *Goodman, Benny* / Laughin': *Holiday, Billie* / Boo wah, boo wah: *Calloway, Cab* / Fats Waller's original E-flat blues: *Waller, Fats* / Swingtime up in Harlem: *Dorsey, Tommy* / When day is done: *Hawkins, Coleman* / Just like taking candy from a baby: *Astaire, Fred* / Boogie woogie on St. Louis blues: *Hines, Earl 'Fatha'* / Jack hits the road: *Freeman, Bud* / Louisiana: *Basie, Count* / I'll never smile again: *Dorsey, Tommy* / Boog it: *Miller, Glenn* / Singin' the blues: *Hackett, Bobby* / Okay for baby: *Lunceford, Jimmie* / 2.19 blues: *Armstrong, Louis* / Jazz me blues: *Bobcats* / King Porter stomp: *Metronome All Star Band*
PHONTCD 7668 / Apr '90 / Phontastic

☐ FRESH
MSS 0032 / 18 May '98 / Mutant Sound System

☐ FRESH BLUES
I've got the blues: *Blues Company* / Texas: *Connor, Joanna Band* / Broken hearted melody: *Webb, Stan & Chicken Shack* / Good morning love: *Allison, Luther* / Remembering love: *Cadillac Blues Band* / Red blood: *Blues Company* / Going down: *Allison, Bernard* / Roberta: *Electric Blues Duo* / It hurts me too: *Kelly, Dave Band* / Sky is crying: *Connor, Joanna Band* / Thrill is gone: *Farlowe, Chris & Peter York* / Don't you worry about a thing: *Webb, Stan & Chicken Shack* / Silent nite: *Blues Company*
INAK 19001CD / Jul '97 / In Akustik

☐ FRESH EMISSIONS (2CD Set)
Frust: *Being* / Try: *Being* / Anackrohn: *Vermin* / Afflicted: *Vermin* / Pedal bin liner boy melts the bag: *Bishop* / Charic roots: *Herb* / Splinter group: *Conemelt* / Hats off to tracksuit: *Conemelt* / Funky five minutes: *Panash* / Lemmy parts 1 and 2: *Panash* / Space is forever: *Uriel* / Andromeda session: *Uriel* / Through mist at one hundred: *Two Lone Swordsman* / Midnight automatic: *Day, Deanne* / No-fi: *Corridor* / 1: *Bios* / 2: *Bios*
SOP 005CD / Nov '95 / Emissions

☐ FRESH FLAVOUR
My prerogative: *Brown, Bobby* / I just can't handle it: *Hi-Five* / Judy had a boyfriend: *Riff* / Here we go again: *Portrait* / Down for the one: *Knight, Beverley* / Stone cold gentlemen: *Tresvant, Ralph* / Real love: *Blige, Mary J.* / Back and forth: *Aaliyah* / In my nature: *Nuttin' Nyce* / Ain't no stoppin' us now: *Davis, Mike* / Every little thing u do: *Williams, Christopher* / Make up your mind: *One Li 3* / Is it good to you: *Riley, Teddy & Tammy Lucus* / DOG me out: *Guy* / Rump shaker: *Wreckx n' Effect*
RB 881702 / 2 Feb '98 / Disky

☐ FRESH HITS '98 (2CD Set)
C'est la vie: *B-Witched* / Got the feelin': *Five* / Feel it: *Tamperer* / My heart will go on (love theme from Titanic): *Dion, Celine* / Gone till November: *Wyclef Jean* / Turn it up/fire it up: *Busta Rhymes* / Carnival de Paris: *Dario G* / Last thing on my mind: *Steps* / Life ain't easy: *Cleopatra* / Doctor Jones: *Aqua* / Stranded: *McNeal, Lutricia* / Found a cure: *Ultra Nate* / Gimme love: *Alexia* / Say it once: *Ultra* / Kung fu fighting: *Bus Stop* / Diva: *Dana International* / Nobody better: *Moore, Tina* / Do you really want me: *Robyn* / No matter what I do: *Mellor, Will* / Three lions 1998: *Baddiel & Skinner & Lightning Seeds* / Let me entertain you: *Williams, Robbie* / Wishing I was there: *Umbruglia, Natalie* / Road rage: *Catatonia* / Sound of drums: *Kula Shaker* / Here's where the story ends: *Tin Tin Out* / Say you love me: *Simply Red* / Dreams: *Corrs* / Ooh la la: *Stewart, Rod* / Kiss the rain: *Myers, Billie* / High: *Lighthouse Family* / Never ever: *All Saints* / Ice hockey hair: *Super Furry Animals* / No way: *Freakpower* / Sounds of wickedness: *Tzant* / Beep me 911: *Elliott, Missy* / Rose is still a rose: *Franklin, Aretha*
MOODCD 59 / 22 Jun '98 / Columbia

☐ FRESH HITS 1996
Killing me softly: *Fugees* / Macarena: *Los Del Rio* / Crazy: *Morrison, Mark* / Mysterious girl: *Andre, Peter* / Better watch out: *Ant & Dec* / Nobody knows: *Rich, Tony Project* / You're making me high: *Braxton, Toni* / Because you loved me: *Dion, Celine* / We're in this together: *Simply Red* / Three lions: *Lightning Seeds & David Baddiel/Frank Skinner* / We've got it goin' on: *Backstreet Boys* / Naked: *Louise* / Freedom 90: *Michael, George* / Walking wounded: *Everything But The Girl* / Don't stop movin': *Livin' Joy* / Good thing: *Eternal* / Fable: *Miles, Robert* / X files: *DJ Dado* / That look: *De'Lacy* / Where love lives: *Limerick, Alison* / Krupa: *Apollo 440* / Born Slippy: *Underworld* / Design for life: *Manic Street Preachers* / Oh yeah: *Ash* / Tattva: *Kula Shaker* / Trash: *Suede* / Day we caught the train: *Ocean Colour Scene* / Sale of the century: *Sleeper* / Champagne supernova: *Oasis* / Peaches: *Presidents Of The USA* / 500 (Shake baby shake): *Lush* / Female of the species: *Space* / 24/7: *3T* / Lifted: *Lighthouse Family* / Do you know where you're coming from: *M-Beat & Jamiroquai* / Woo hah got you all in check: *Busta Rhymes* / Tha crossroads: *Bone Thugs n' Harmony* / You're the one: *SMV* / I can't sleep baby (If I): *R Kelly* / Something for the weekend: *Divine Comedy* / Daydream believer: *Robson & Jerome*
MOODCD 46 / Aug '96 / Sony Music

☐ FRESH HITS 1997 (2CD Set)
RADCD 70 / Aug '97 / Global TV

☐ FRESH RECORDS PUNK SINGLES COLLECTION
My friends: *Dark* / John Wayne: *Dark* / Einstein's brain: *Dark* / On the wires: *Dark* / Masque: *Dark* / Punk rock stars: *Art Attacks* / Rat city: *Art Attacks* / Madman: *Cuddly Toys* / Astral Joe: *Cuddly Toys* / Someone's crying: *Cuddly Toys* / It's a shame: *Cuddly Toys* / Hawaii Five-O: *Dark* / Young one's: *Menace* / Debbie Harry: *Family Fodder* / I've had the time of my life: *Manufactured Romance* / Hobby for a day: *Wall* / Earbending: *JC's Mainmen* / Poison takes hold: *Play Dead* / Rebecca's room: *Wasted Youth* / Puppets of war: *Chron Gen* / TV eye: *Play Dead*
CDPUNK 32 / May '94 / Anagram

☐ FRESHEN UP VOL.1
U sure do: *Strike* / Love come rescue me: *Lovestation* / Saved: *Mr. Roy* / Feel the spirit: *Giant City* / Do U feel 4 me: *Eden* / Open sesame: *Jinx* / Love (A wonderful thing): *Karess* / Shine on me: *Lovestation* / Formula 1: *Strike* / Something about U: *Mr. Roy* / Best of my love: *Lovestation* / Control: *Time Of The Mumph*
FRSHCD 1 / May '95 / Fresh

☐ FRESHNESS ON WAX - PHUNK NOT PUNK (Further Adventures In Quality Dope Beats)
DBMFLAGCD 113 / Jun '96 / Flagbearer

☐ FRESKA VOL.2
Dreamer: *Livin' Joy* / Don't wait for me: *Loveland* / I believe: *Happy Clappers* / Taking me higher: *Gems For Jem* / Invader: *Kool World* / Horny as funk: *Soapy* / Love and sex: *Boyfriend* / Ooh baby: *Raw Tunes* / Hot: *Majick Village* / It's alright: *SAIN* / Dance MF: *Nelson, Grant* / Latinos on parade: *Franco, Chinco* / Let the rhythm flow: *Diva Rhythms* / You can have it: *Casanova, Charlie* / Fe fi fo fum: *Raw* / Do you wanna party: *Wand & Storm HQ* / Sex on the streets: *Pizzaman* / Krazy noise: *Numerical Value*
REACTCDX 061
REACTCD 061 / Jun '95 / React

☐ FRIDAY NIGHT FEVER (2CD Set)
5557332 / 13 Apr '98 / PolyGram TV

☐ FRIED TO PERFECTION BY EXPERTS
Mary Queen of Scots: *Eugenius* / Pillow fight: *18 Wheeler* / Wet dream: *18 Wheeler* / Butterfly boy: *Shonen Knife* / Get the wow: *Shonen Knife* / Apple: *Boyfriend* / Summer thing: *Boyfriend* / Don't get 2 close 2 my fantasy: *Ween* / Sarah: *Ween* / She must be Spanish: *Autohaze* / Here tonight: *Autohaze* / Plant me: *Suddenly Tammy*
RUST 011CD / Sep '93 / August

☐ FRIENDS IN HIGH PLACES VOL.1 (14 Urban Contemporary Gospel & Inspired Soul Performances)
More than a friend: *Baylor, Helen* / Out front: *Angel* / You changed my life: *Marquis Ubu* / Thank you Jesus: *Jasper, Chris* / Call me: *Smith, Kenny* / Step by step: *Hammond, Fred* / One love one people: *Taylor, Gary* / I'll shine for you: *Austin, Dennis* / Empty promises: *Futrel* / God in you: *Dawkins & Dawkins* / Will you be ready: *Redeemed* / It's only natural: *Thomas, Keith* / Be for real: *Mitchell, Vernessa* / Love's the key: *Gaines, Billy & Sarah*
CDEXP 5 / Dec '93 / Expansion

☐ FRIENDS IN HIGH PLACES VOL.2 (14 Urban Contemporary Gospel & Inspired Soul Performances)
Any way: *Garmon, Terry* / Every time: *Winans, Cece* / My treasure: *Baker, Sam* / If I ever fall: *Winans* / Don't be afraid: *Kingdom* / Turn to Jesus: *Moss, J.* / Heaven is mine: *Futch Brothers* / Thank you Lord: *Disciples Of Christ* / Miracle: *Clarke Sisters* / Never alone: *Williams, Kelli* / Call on me: *Staten, Keith* / Over and over again: *Sapp, Marvin* / Whatever it takes: *Sign Of The Times* / Call his name: *Hewett, Howard*
CDEXP 10 / Jun '96 / Expansion

☐ FRIFOT
CAP 2138CD / Nov '95 / Caprice

☐ FRISCO RECORDS STORY, THE (New Orleans R&B To Early Soul)
Kiss tomorrow goodbye: *White, Danny* / Baby it's love: *Adams, Al* / You told me: *West, Willie* / Men of war: *Rouzan Sisters* / Little bitty things: *White, Danny* / My heavy load: *Royal Dukes Of Rhythm* / Say yeah: *Porgy & The Polka Dots* / Too many heartaches: *Adams, Al* / I'm back again: *West, Willie* / Lost love: *West, Willie* / Never tell your friend: *White, Danny* / Why must I be blue: *White, Danny* / Twitch: *White, Danny* / I need your love (baby): *West, Willie* / One little lie: *White, Danny* / Love me a handkerchief: *White, Danny* / Don't be ashamed to cry: *West, Willie* / Am I the fool: *West, Willie* / Flirt: *Royal Dukes Of Rhythm* / Dance every dance: *Rouzan Sisters* / Long time no see: *Rouzan, Wanda* / Would you love me: *Rouzan, Wanda* / Can't do nothing without you: *White, Danny* / My living doll: *White, Danny* / Kiss tomorrow goodbye: *White, Danny*
CDCHD 679 / 30 Mar '98 / Ace

☐ FROLIC DINER
UXOX 092 / 15 Dec '97 / Romulan

☐ FROM ACOUSTIC TO ELECTRIC BLUES
D2CD 08 / Dec '92 / Deja Vu

☐ FROM BAM BAM TO CHERRY OH BABY
Bam bam: *Toots & The Maytals* / Ba ba boom: *Jamaicans* / Intensified: *Dekker, Desmond* / Sweet and dandy: *Toots & The Maytals* / Boom shacka lacka: *Lewis, Hopeton* / Unity is love: *Dice, Billy* / Da da: *Byles, Junior* / Pomp and pride: *Toots & The Maytals* / Festival 10: *Morgan, Derrick* / Cherry oh baby: *Donaldson, Eric*
JMC 200101 / Nov '92 / Jamaican Gold

☐ FROM BRUSSELS WITH LOVE
TWI 0072 / Mar '96 / Les Disques Du Crepuscule

☐ FROM CAKEWALK TO RAGTIME (2CD Set)
Eli green cake walk / Cake walk / Smoky mokes / Whistling Rufus / Cake walk in the sky / Saint Louis tickle / Dixie girl / Le vrai cake walk / Bunch of rags / Buffalo rag / Alexander's ragtime band / Slippery place rag / Black diamond rag / Stomp dance / Mysterious rag / Grizzly bear / Dill pickles / Hot stuff / Ragtime frolics / I'll dance till de sun breaks breaks through / Oh that yankiana rag / Bachhannal rag / Too much mustard / Down home rag / You're here and I'm here / Castle walk / Notoreity rag / That moaning saxophone rag / Operatic rag / Raggin' the scale / Two key rag
FA 067 / Nov '97 / Fremeaux

☐ FROM DIXIELAND TO SWING
D2CD 09 / Dec '92 / Deja Vu

☐ FROM GALWAY TO DUBLIN
ROUCD 1087 / Feb '93 / Rounder

☐ FROM HERE TO TRANQUILITY VOL.1
PS 9336 / Nov '93 / Silent

☐ FROM HERE TO TRANQUILITY VOL.2
SR 9343 / May '94 / Silent

☐ FROM HERE TO TRANQUILITY VOL.3
SR 9460 / Feb '95 / Silent

☐ FROM HORSE TO TANK
Boots and saddles: *Queen's Royal Hussars* / Royal Tank Regiment: *Royal Tank Regiment Bands* / Light Cavalry Overture: *9/12 Royal Lancers* / Fear naught: *Royal Tank Regiment Bands* / With sword and lance: *16th/5th Queen's Royal Lancers* / Vimy ridge: *Royal Tank Regiment Bands* / Old grey mare: *16th/5th Queen's Royal Lancers* / Blue flash: *Royal Tank Regiment Bands* / Final charge: *Queen's Dragoon Guards* / Scarlet and green: *16th/5th Queen's Royal Lancers* / Fifth Royal Tank Regiment: *Royal Tank Regiment Bands* / St. Cecilia: *9th/12th Royal Lancers* / Evening hymm and cavalry last post: *9th/12th Royal Lancers* / Tank town: *Royal Tank Regiment Bands* / Thin red line: *16th/5th Queen's Royal Lancers* / March past: *Royal Tank Regiment Bands*
305192 / Jun '97 / Hallmark

☐ FROM MINSTREL TO MOJO 1893-1946 (9CD Set)
WH 1017 / Jun '98 / Music & Arts

☐ FROM MONK TO BACH
9100102 / Oct '97 / Winter & Winter

☐ FROM MOUNTAIN AND VALLEY
QPRZ 006D / Jun '91 / Polyphonic

☐ FROM NASHVILLE WITH LOVE
CURCD 035 / Apr '97 / Curb

☐ FROM OUT OF NOWHERE VOL.1
Shove: *Cosmic Psychos* / Modern girl: *Dubrovniks* / Heading right back to you: *Dubrovniks* / Build it up: *Nursery Crimes* / Eleanor Rigby: *Nursery Crimes* / Fatal fascination: *Screaming Tribesmen* / Bugging: *Screemfeeder* / End of this day: *Screemfeeder* / Dreaming: *Chevelles* / Run and hide: *Chevelles* / Degenerate boy: *Bored* / Rain: *Bored* / Shame: *You Am I* / Snake tide: *You Am I* / Cheers: *Front & Loader* / Me to know: *Front & Loader* / Chrysalidz: *Mass Appeal*
SUR 525CD / Jun '93 / Survival

☐ FROM REELS TO RAGA (A Musical Journey Around The World) (2CD Set)
Lodge road/From night till morn / Scotland the brave / Road to Sligo/Tripping up the stairs / All through the night / Le village Francais / La vino chianti / Refleo del agua / Cantares do emigrante / Eine kleine biermusik / Alpenzauber / Szomoru vasarnap / Danse Roumaine / Svietit Miessiatz / Nasza muzyka / Enzeli / Night in Plaka / Loukoum / Sh' dematy / Bedouin music and dance / Ras el hanout / Banani / Ewondo / Benguela / Upendo wa bwana / Tugela kwela / Raga bhairava / Tarian Asyek / Tchang fou / Tchango-tchoum / Summer / Umeke ohana / Milongueo del ayer / Rin del angelito / Huayno de la roca / Las calenas / Samba carnaval / Antigua / Mambo y cha cha cha / La cucaracha / Tender hearted cowboys
330172 / Jul '96 / Hallmark

☐ FROM SWEDEN TO AMERICA
CAP 21552CD / Aug '96 / Caprice

☐ FROM THE CORNERS OF THE WORLD
CAP 21468CD / May '97 / Caprice

☐ FROM THE DANUBE TO THE BALKAN (Music From Bulgaria)
CMT 274981 / Dec '95 / La Chant Du Monde

☐ FROM THE DERWENT TO THE GARONNE
ALIENCD 6 / May '97 / Alienor

☐ FROM THE HEART (Corason Sampler)
CORACD 701 / Feb '95 / Corason

☐ FROM THE HEART OF STUDIO A (The Folkscene Collection)
3365101092 / 21 Apr '98 / RDH

☐ FROM THE IRISH TRADITION VOL.3
CDTCD 003 / Dec '94 / Gael Linn

☐ FROM THE MOUNTAINS TO THE SEA (The Music Of Peru/The 1960's)
El contrapunto: *Los Mensajeros De La Libertad* / El inmenso altiplano: *Los Kcollas* / El penado: *Barssy, Jorge Y Su Conjunto* / Separacion: *Los Tupas* / Soy trujillanita: *Banda Sinfonica Sunicancha* / Manana me voy: *Solitaria Andajina* / Ayhuala: *Banda Filarmonica Andajina* / Te quiero porque me queres: *Boachet, Beto* / Mi china Lola: *Conjunto Cachicadan* / El pelicano: *Coronado, Blackie* / El serranito: *Los Ases Del Ande* / El Alcatraz: *Coronado, Blackie* / Que viva el Santo: *Conjunto Los Chiroques* / Cachirpunta: *Conjunto Virgen De Natividad De Cajamarquilla* / Ingrata huancay bambina: *Los Canarios Del Peru* / El proletario: *Conjunto Los Condores De Parinacocha* / Pretenciosa huancaynita: *Trio Los Andes* / Gorrioncito: *Picaflor De Los Andes* / Vicunita de ancahuasi: *Conjunto Costumbrista* / Ardorosa pasion: *Juajina, Alam Conjunto* / Ayacuchana: *Conjunto Lira Folklorica Del Peru* / Vicunitas de atlas punas: *Conjunto San Cristobel De Bishongo* / La ultima copa: *Jara, Alberto* / 039: *Avila, Tito Y Sus Costenos* / El consuelo de llorar: *Los Yungas* / Los pampa y la puna: *Los Dandys Y Su Conjunto* / Soy criollo: *Los Monarcos*
ARHCD 400 / Nov '96 / Arhoolie

☐ FROM YOURS TO YOU...A VALENTINE BOUQUET (20 Sweet & Sentimental Love Songs)
My melancholy baby: *Crosby, Bing* / Begin the beguine: *Andrews Sisters* / I should care: *Winstone, Eric & His Orchestra* / In a shady nook by a babbling brook: *Peers, Donald* / Very thought of you: *Holiday, Billie* / All I do is dream of you: *Miller, Glenn Orchestra* / That's my home: *Gonella, Nat & His New Georgians* / Laura: *Shelton, Anne* / Kiss me again: *Sinatra, Frank* / I remember you: *Dorsey, Jimmy & His Orchestra* / I'll close my eyes: *Squires, Dorothy* / I had the craziest dream: *Lynn, Vera* / No one else will do: *Preager, Lou & His Orchestra* / It can't be wrong: *Carless, Dorothy* / Way you look tonight: *Astaire, Fred* / Masquerade is over: *Daniels, Bebe* / Nearness of you: *Lombardo, Guy & His Royal Canadians* / Night and day: *Bowlly, Al* / At last: *Geraldo & His Orchestra* / Embraceable you: *Garland, Judy*
EMPUCD 1 / Jan '97 / Empress

☐ FRONTLINE REGGAE
CONQ 998CD / May '95 / Conqueror

☐ FROZEN BRASS: AFRICA & LATIN AMERICA
PAN 2026CD / Oct '93 / Pan

☐ FRUIT OF THE ORIGINAL SIN
TWI 0352 / Mar '96 / Les Disques Du Crepuscule

☐ FRUITED OTHER SURFACES
VMFM 039CD / 23 Feb '98 / Vermiform

☐ FRYING THE FAT
Jazz hypnosis: *First Priority* / Concentrate: *Aim* / In Rhodes: *Rae & Christian* / Dirty dog: *Tony D* / Diggin' Dizzy: *Aim* / Free rolling: *Rae* / I thought I'd find you here: *Howie, Alex* / Still blowin' free: *Funky Fresh Few* / Ways of the underground: *Funky Fresh Few* / Pure arithmetic: *First Priority* / Let the funk ride: *Aim* / Bang bang: *Howie, Alex* / Fat slug: *Mr. Scruff* / First cut is the deepest: *First Priority* / Central J Parlay: *Tony D*
GCCD 100 / Jun '96 / Grand Central

☐ FUBAR CLUB, THE (2CD Set)
FARCD 1 / Jul '96 / Inner Rhythm

☐ FUCKING HARDCORE VOL.3
Fucking hardcore: *Chosen Few* / I wanna be a hippy: *Technohead* / Freak tonight: *Speedfreak* / Edge of panic: *Cyanide* / Realm of darkness: *Annihilator* / Abba gabba: *Riot Nation* / Toxic waste 396: *High Energy* / Headsex: *Technohead* / Don't fuck with me: *Original Gabber* / To da rhythm: *Dee, Lenny* / Voodoo vibe: *Tellurian* / Happ-e-people: *Search & Destroy* / We keep going on: *Riot Nation* / This is not the end: *One, Walter* / Energy boost: *DJ Dano & Liza N. Eliaz*
DB 47932 / Jul '95 / Deep Blue

☐ FUCKING HARDCORE VOL.4
DB 47882 / Apr '96 / Deep Blue

☐ FUCKING HARDCORE VOL.5
DB 47842 / Nov '96 / Deep Blue

☐ FUCKING HARDCORE VOL.6
Fucking hardcore no.6: *Chosen Few* / Sound of the underground: *Tellurian* / Hardcore headz: *Outside Agency* / T-1000: *Fear Factory* / Thermal fuse: *Demolition Team* / Big time noise: *DJ Dano* / Stormfront: *Painkiller* / Live in hell: *Walter One* / Zlam (here it comez): *Chosen Few* / Speaker blow: *Ceasefire* / Name of the DJ: *Chosen Few* / I won't stop rocking: *Tellurian* / Narcoterror: *Elvis Jackson* / Touch the darkness: *Outside Agency* / Trip 2 pussyland: *Search & Destroy* / Speedjack: *Walter One* / Starcore: *Aggroman*
DB 47822 / Jul '97 / Mokum

☐ FUCKING HARDCORE VOL.7
DB 47792 / 1 Dec '97 / Deep Blue

☐ FUCKING HARDFLOOR VOL.1 & 2 (2CD Set)
ATOM 005DCD / Oct '95 / Atomic Fate Inc

☐ FULL ENERGY VOL.1
ZEN 007CD / Feb '96 / Indochina

☐ FULL ENGLISH BREAKFAST
TLCD 299 / 13 Apr '98 / Tea Leaf

☐ FULL MONTY, THE (The Best Of Brass, Military & Pipe Bands/4CD Set)
SUMBX 4022 / Jan '98 / Summit

☐ FULL ON
HMCD 1 / 27 Jul '98 / Hom-Mega

☐ FULL ON DRUM 'N' BASS (4CD Set)
Quest: *Shimmon & Andy C* / Slightly sinister: *Bliss 'n' Tumble* / Dred bass: *Dead Dred* / Lethal dosage: *Procedure 769* / Midnight picture: *Enhanced Blood* / Jungle warriors: *Bay B Kane* / One for the ladies: *Ellis D* / Always something about you: *Qube* / Soothe my soul: *Justice* / Darkage: *DJ Solo* / Thunder: *Rood Project* / Funkin' dem up: *Shy FX* / Ya don't stop: *Stakka & K-Tee* / Drummin' space: *Sub Sequence* / Space traveller: *New London Jazz Connection* / Genetix: *Shimmon & Andy C* / Realism: *Alpha Omega* / Shadowlandz: *Flytronix* / Squelch: *Finitribe* / Smokin' a blunt: *Chuck E* / Super hero: *House Crew* / Spin value: *Emotionally* / Distant hopes: *Eko* / Wind changes: *Mission Control* / Valley of the shadows: *Origin Unknown* / Drum 'n' bass wise: *Remarc* / Garden: *MLO* / Life is a circle: *DMS & Boneman X* / Crashing dream: *Seiji* / Open your mind: *Future Passed* / Ooh boy: *Ellis D* / Calling the people: *A-Zone* / Dream station: *Duster* / After dark: *A-Sides & Cool Hand Flex* / Sound murderer: *Remarc* / Mind elevation: *New London Jazz Connection*
DCBX 102 / 6 Oct '97 / Dance Club International

☐ FULL ON HOUSE (4CD Set)
Move your body: *Jefferson, Marshall* / Pulse: *Beltram, Joey* / (I wanna give you) devotion: *Nomad* / I can't forget: *Mr. Lee* / Yor love: *Knuckles, Frankie* / Last night a DJ saved my life: *Dubgate & Tasha* / Real thing: *Screamin' Rachael* / Pulling the strings: *Sharp, Kasie* / Push the tempo: *Bass Funktion* / Acid tension: *Corola, Marco* / Sound of eden: *Casino* / 2 high's groove: *2 High* / House nation: *House Master Boyz* / You used to hold me: *Rosario, Ralphi* / No way back: *Adonis* / Stayin' alive: *N-Trance* / Rok da house: *Beatmasters & Cookie Crew* / Theme from s-express: *S'Express* / Give it up: *French, Nicki* / Face it: *Master C & J* / Nothing is forever: *Ultracynic* / Jump: *Wildman* / Saunders, *JessieOn* and on: *Wildman* / Luv it up: *Jump* / Runaway: *Salsoul Orchestra* / Baby wants to ride: *Knuckles, Frankie* / Love can't turn around: *Farley Jackmaster Funk* / Let's get brutal: *Nitro Deluxe* / Doin' the do: *Boo, Betty* / Ain't no love: *Sub Sub & Melanie Williams* / Ruff kutz: *Chemist* / I wanna know: *French, Nicki* / Party people: *Bass Shakers* / Open up: *Leftfield & John Lydon* / Turn the music up: *Johan S* / Let no man put asunder: *Separate Reality* / Let's get brutal: *Nitro Deluxe* / Baby just wants to ride: *Knuckles, Frankie* / No way back: *Adonis* / You used to hold me: *Rosario, Ralphi* / Move your body: *Jefferson, Marshall* / (I wanna give you) devotion: *Nomad* / Luv it up: *Jump* / Ain't no love: *Sub Sub & Melanie Williams* / Pulling the strings: *Sharp, Kasie*
DCBX 104 / 6 Oct '97 / Dance Club International

☐ FULL ON IBIZA (4CD Set)
High energy: *Maltese Massive* / I just can't wait: *Smith, Mandy* / Bits and pieces: *Artemesia* / Karnival: *Malone, Richie* / Gotta get loose: *Mr. & Mrs. Smith* / Mambo white: *Nox Alba* / Koolectro: *DA & JMV* / Lift me up: *Bishop, Rodney* / Waterfall: *Atlantic Ocean* / Warm it up: *Joy For Life* / High's theme: *2 High* / Calling: *Solar Stone* / I believe: *Happy Clappers* / Disco frenzy: *Divine Intervention* / Schonberg: *Marmion* / Release your mind: *Naughty But Nice* / Cafe del mar: *Energy 52* / Lust not love: *Ya Programme* / Second coming: *Libido* / Philadelphia: *Brooklyn Friends* / Gotta get (loose): *Must* / Bass power: *Shakavara* / Your love: *BB Club* / Thunderdome: *Thursday Club* / Up to no good: *Porn Kings* / Don't make me wait: *Loveland & Rachel McFarlane* / Invader: *Koolworld Productions* / Utopia: *Bolton, Jennifer* / So addicted: *Bishop, Rodney* / Il nostra tempo del la vita: *Torfinn* / New generation: *MLO* / Remember me: *Jubb, Phil* / Want you now: *Must* / Bring it back: *5 Minutes Of Funk* / Take me away: *Bolton, Jennifer* / Pianomania: *Pianomania* / Mambo white: *Nox Alba* / Il nostra tempo del la vita: *Torfinn* / 2 high's theme: *2 High* / High energy: *2 High* / Remember me: *Jubb, Phil* / Second coming: *Libido* / Cafe del mar: *Energy 52* / Bass power: *Shakavara* / Invader: *Koolworld Productions* / Calling: *Solar Stone* / Schonberg: *Marmion*
DCBX 101 / 6 Oct '97 / Dance Club International

☐ FULL ON TECHNO (4CD Set)
Girl/boy: *Aphex Twin* / Psycho: *Tekno 2* / Barn: *Squarepusher* / Sleeping with an angel: *Transformer 2 & Adamski* / Humaniser: *Humaniser* / Cookin' up ya brain: *4 Hero* / Liftin' me: *Techno High* / Quarter pounder: *Angel, Dave* / Funkatarium: *Jump* / Beyond motion: *Incisions* / Joyrider: *Criminal Minds* / Move any mountain: *Shamen* / Music makes you: *Blame* / It's just a feeling: *Terrorize* / Injected with a poison: *Praga Khan* / Hold it down: *2 Bad Mice* / Rockin' it: *Porker, Mindy* / Shofou: *Tyoussi* / Got the bug: *Phuture* / Ebeneezer goode: *Shamen* / 17 days of acid rain: *Nouveau Nation* / Mr Kirk's nightmare: *4 Hero* / Activ 8: *Altern 8* / In the heat of the night: *Overhead Noise* / I wanna be a hippy: *Technohead* / Tricky disco: *Tricky Disco* / Brutal-8-e: *Altern 8* / Spank spank: *Phuture Fantasy Club* / Jet star: *Tekno 2* / Thunderdome: *Thursday Club* / Journey from the light: *4 Hero* / I'm gonna get you: *Bizarre Inc. & Angie Brown* / Take me away: *Beserker* / Work it out: *FOAD* / Sesame's treet: *Smart E's* / Original man: *Angel, Dave* / Girl/Boy: *Aphex Twin* / Barn: *Squarepusher* / Quarter pounder: *Angel, Dave* / Brutal-8-e: *Altern 8* / Tricky disco: *Tricky Disco* / Move any mountain: *Shamen* / Sleeping with an angel: *Transformer 2 & Adamski* / Fumnkatarium: *Jump* / I'm gonna get you: *Bizarre Inc. & Angie Brown*
DCBX 103 / 6 Oct '97 / Dance Club International

☐ FULL TILT - PAST PRESENT AND FUTURE
Need another one: *Misery Loves Company* / Martyr: *Fear Factory* / Oxyacetylene: *Cubanate* / Dreamworld: *Girls Under Glass* / Atoms: *Zodiac Youth* / It's alive: *Stimulator* / Barrel of a gun: *Depeche Mode* / Self pity: *Global Noise Attack* / Soap opera: *Inaura* / Burn: *Seven* / My girlfriend's girlfriend: *Type O Negative* / Give it up: *Enrapture* / Shift IV: *C-Tec* / Democracy: *Killing Joke* / E headz must die: *Johnny Violent*
JVC 90292 / 17 Nov '97 / JVC

☐ FULL TILT VOL.2
Crash pow / Systematic / What / Water / Have no fear / Sickly bug / JMP / 3.31 / Asphalt beach / Lose it / Freak is born / Do justice to yourself / Creature / Systematic / Crash pow / Creature
JVC 90352 / 27 Jul '98 / JVC

☐ FULL VELOCITY (Progressive Drum 'n' Bass)
RZ 012CD / May '97 / Runningz

☐ FULL-E RECORDS VOL.1
FUE C1 / Nov '95 / Full-E

☐ FULSOM PRISON BLUES
MACCD 215 / Aug '96 / Autograph

☐ FUN OF THE FAIR
Cabaret / Me and my shadow / Ciribiribin / Stripper / Can can / My blue heaven / Viva Espana / Twelfth street rag / I do like to be beside the seaside / At the Darktown strutter's ball / King cotton / Waiting for the Robert E Lee / Carolina in the morning / Pretty baby / Toot toot tootsie goodbye / I'm sitting on top of the world / I'm looking over a four leaf clover / Chinatown, my Chinatown / Baby face / California here I come / Avalon / Little boogie / Skokiaan / Annen polka / Day trip to Bangor / Roses from the South / Eleanor waltz / Dinah / Alexander's ragtime band
SOV 007CD / Jun '92 / Sovereign

☐ FUN WITH MUSHROOMS
Toadstool soup (slight send slight return): *Boris & His Bolshie Balalaika* / Night descent: *Bazaar, Saddar* / Electric sensation: *Praise Space Electric* / Yuppi deadhead party: *14th Wray* / Government surplus 3am: *Carter, Dean & The High Commission* / Awakened: *Omnia Opera* / Who's my name: *Inn* / Uncle Sam: *Juana, Harold* / Chocolate staircase: *Dead Flowers* / Half moon flower: *Tangle Edge* / Did you feed the fish: *Watch children* / Thoughts of the sky: *Wobble jaggle jiggle* / Thought dial: *Mooseheart Faith* / Ritual people: *Cosmic kangaroos* / Mr. and Mrs. Creature: *Reefus moons* / Thirteen ghosts: *Marshmallow Overcoat* / Freakbeat: *Dr. Brown* / River: *Jasmine Love Bomb*
DELECCD 009 / Jun '93 / Delerium

☐ FUNK 21 - THE ALBUM (2CD Set)
Blush response: *Tunduska* / Wolf: *Tertius & Professor Smalls* / Ain't who va no-watch a no: *Selim & Steel* / Space walkin': *Organic Synthetic* / Outpost: *Seeka* / Trancer: *Pariah* / Dialogue: *Seeka* / 9th episode: *Tertius & Professor Smalls* / For real: *Pariah* / Cosmos: *Organic Synthetic* / Steel's theme: *Selim & Steel* / Outpost: *Seeka* / Side fx: *Justice & Lab Rats* / Comet theory: *Tunduska*
PARTFKC 601 / 3 Aug '98 / Partisan

☐ FUNK ELECTRIC
DUKE 043CD / 4 May '98 / Hydrogen Dukebox

☐ FUNK ESSENTIALS
CDNEW 122 / 30 Mar '98 / Charly

☐ FUNK OFF THE LIGHTS
FR 368CD / 31 Aug '98 / Big Cheese

☐ FUNKADELIKK DUB
CLP 0190 / 23 Mar '98 / Hypnotic

☐ FUNKIEST LINE DANCE ALBUM IN THE WORLD, THE
Why'da pick on me: *Swamp Honkys* / Fool and his money: *Hawks, Chip* / What a man's gotta do: *Shot To Pieces* / Thinkin' 'bout you: *Capricorn* / I don't do sad anymore: *Richmond, Simon* / No money: *Payne, Les* / Honky tonk ballroom: *Richmond, Simon* / Freeze: *Caffrey, Phil* / Arlene: *Capricorn* / Outta my head: *Swamp Honkys* / Bullet proof vest: *Shot To Pieces* / Picture frame: *Capricorn* / R 'n' R time capsule: *Weller, Freddy* / I must be stupid: *Swamp Honkys* / Don't let go: *Shot To Pieces* / Whatever it takes: *Richmond, Simon* / Born in Britain: *Corridor 38* / Goodbye love (hello heartache): *Richmond, Simon* / Hand clappin', foot tappin', good lookin' girl: *Capricorn* / Caroline: *Richmond, Simon*
ECD 3374 / Jun '97 / K-Tel

☐ FUNKMASTER MIX (2CD Set)
Word up: *Cameo* / Oops up side your head: *Gap Band* / Movin': *Brass Construction* / Funky Nassau: *Beginning Of The End* / Brick house: *Commodores* / (Are you ready) Do the bus stop: *Fatback Band* / Papa's got a brand new pigbag: *Pigbag* / Get up offa that thing: *Brown, James* / Funkin' for Jamaica: *Browne, Tom* / Stomp: *Brothers Johnson* / Tell me something good: *Rufus* / War: *Starr, Edwin* / Shaft: *Hayes, Isaac* / Cuba: *Gibson Brothers* / Shoorah shoorah: *Wright, Betty* / Funky weekend: *Stylistics* / That lady: *Isley Brothers* / Sound that funky horn: *KC & The Sunshine Band* / Play that funky music: *Wild Cherry* / Hang on in there baby: *Bristol, Johnny* / Le freak: *Chic* / Lady Marmalade: *Labelle* / Get down on it: *Kool & The Gang* / Let's groove: *Earth, Wind & Fire* / Shake your body: *Jacksons* / Rock the boat: *Hues Corporation* / Move on up: *Mayfield, Curtis* / Strut your funky stuff: *Frantique* / Car wash: *Rose Royce* / Shame: *King, Evelyn 'Champagne'* / Ain't no stoppin' us: *McFadden & Whitehead* / Family affair: *Sly & The Family Stone* / If you're ready (come go with me): *Staple Singers* / Behind the groove: *Marie, Teena* / Forget me nots: *Rushen, Patrice* / Use it up and wear it out: *Odyssey* / Boogie nights: *Heatwave* / Pick up the pieces: *Average White Band* / Rock it: *Hancock, Herbie* / Green onions: *Booker T & The MG's*
5355762 / May '96 / PolyGram TV

☐ FUNKY ALTERNATIVES (The Best Of Funky Alternatives)
INDIGO 41412 / May '97 / Echo Beach

☐ FUNKY ALTERNATIVES VOL.7
CPRODCD 021 / Feb '94 / Concrete Productions

☐ FUNKY ALTERNATIVES VOL.8
Menofearthe reaper: *Pop Will Eat Itself* / Pure spite: *Godflesh* / Crackin' up: *Revolting Cocks* / You coma: *Optimum Wound Profile* / Bombs in my head: *Ultraviolence* / Momentous lamentous: *Pig* / Mind razor: *Gunshot* / Untitled: *Surfers for Satan* / Obsession: *Shining* / We know who you are: *Judda* / Compassion: *Mussolini Headkick*
CPRODCD 026 / Mar '95 / Concrete Productions

☐ FUNKY CHICKEN
CDTBL 137 / Aug '96 / Trojan

☐ FUNKY DIVAS (2CD Set)
RADCD 77 / 1 Dec '97 / Global TV

☐ FUNKY GUITAR BEATS
Fire eater: *Bryant, Rusty* / Odds on: *Kynard, Charles* / Dirty apple: *Smith, Johnny 'Hammond'* / Thank you: *Sparks, Melvin* / Sweet Georgia Brown: *Butler, Billy* / We'll be together: *Jones, Ivan 'Boogaloo Joe'* / Shadow dancers: *Benson, George* / Swivel hips: *Jackson, Willis* / Thrill is gone: *Funk Inc.* / Billie Jean: *Ponder, Jimmy*
PRCD 24162 / Jun '96 / Prestige

☐ FUNKY JAMS VOL.1
Space funk: *Manzel* / Did you mean it: *Bell, Arlene* / Family tree: *Family Tree* / Give the drummer some more: *Little Hooks & Ray Nato/The Kings* / Searching for the soul: *Wade, Jake & The Soul Searchers* / Watermelon man: *Smith, Miss Elsie* / Sorry 'bout that: *Poole, Benny* / For your love: *1619 Bab* / Lunar funk: *Fabulous Counts* / Superpeople: *Notations* / Cold bear: *Gaturs* / Skin it back: *Bush, Tommy*
HUBCD 1 / Aug '95 / Hubbub

☐ FUNKY JAMS VOL.2
Whatcha want us to do: *Dynamic Concepts* / Sweet Peter: *Nichols, Frieda & Homer Brown Group* / Chocolate sugar: *Berry Street Station* / D minor vamp: *Yesterday, Today & Tomorrow* / Honey trippin': *Mystic Moods* / Let's keep on jukin': *King Tutt & The Untouchables* / Wastin' no time: *New Editions* / Nabbit juice: *Eastwind* / Do what you want to do: *Chapter II* / Whole thing: *Big Barney* / Impeach the president: *Honey Drippers*
HUBCD 2 / Sep '95 / Hubbub

☐ FUNKY JAMS VOL.3
Cornbread and beans: *Brodie, Hugh* / Can you feel it: *SOUL* / Stand up and be counted: *Getto Kitty* / Machine shop: *Untouchable Machine Shop* / My friend: *Marrero, Ricardo & The Group* / Freakin' time: *Asphalt Jungle* / Ain't it good enough: *Nu Sound Express Ltd* / Funky key: *Dynamics* / Funky four corners: *Marks, Richard* / She's a love maker: *Fields, Lee* / Time to love: *Candy Coated People* / Boot's groove: *Soul Tornadoes*
HUBCD 4 / Nov '95 / Hubbub

☐ FUNKY JAMS VOL.4
Swivel your hips: *Gaturs* / Fatbackin': *Fatback Band* / Reborn: *Barbarin, Marilyn* / Crackerjack: *Mickey & His Mice* / Hey Ruby (shut your mouth): *Ruby & The Party Gang* / Stories: *Chakchas* / Cookies: *Brother Soul* / Earthquake: *Brand New* / World: *1619 Bab* / Don't push your luck: *Peacemakers* / Soul Makossa: *Kenyatta, Simon Troup* / Catch a groove: *Juice*
HUBCD 6 / Mar '96 / Hubbub

☐ FUNKY JAMS VOL.5
Get down people: *Fabulous Counts* / Freakish love: *Rhythm Machine* / Gettin' down: *Blackwell, Eugene* / East side: *Jacobs, Hank* / Dipstick: *Perfect Circle* / Get into funky music: *Funkhouse Express* / Hot pants: *Carbo, Hank* / It's your thing: *Semper, George* / Picses pace: *Hamilton, Dave* / Living in a world of trouble: *Samson & Delilah* / Upstairs on Boston Road: *Gordon, Sammy & The Hiphuggers* / Pearl baby pearl: *Poole, Benny*
HUBCD 7 / May '96 / Hubbub

☐ FUNKY JAMS VOL.6
HUBCD 10 / Sep '96 / Hubbub

☐ FUNKY JAMS VOL.7
If it don't fit don't force it: *Patterson, Kellee* / Funky jam: *Funk Proof* / It's insane: *In One Piece* / There she blows: *Wee Willie & B. Clark* / Don't let the pusher push you: *McKay, Murray* / Hector: *Village Callers* / For your funkification: *Perfect Circle* / Built for speed: *Murray, Juggy* / You're barking up the wrong tree: *Anderson, Sister Gail* / Cissy strut: *Funky Brothers Inc.* / Hip drop: *Explosions* / Tijuana: *Semper, George & His Kingsmen*
HUBCD 15 / Feb '97 / Hubbub

☐ FUNKY JAMS VOL.8
I'm a carpenter: *Robinson, David* / Down the line: *Chocolate Fudge Express* / I've got reasons: *Hooper, Mary Jane* / Live it up: *James K Nine* / In one piece: *In One Piece* / Funk time: *Funk Proof* / Can I be your squeeze: *Garbo, Chuck* / Spread the news: *Perfect Circle* / Beaver shot: *Atlantics* / Inside America: *Murray, Juggy* / Kickin' the habit: *Johnson, Jesse* / Kiss by kiss: *Johnson, Syl*
HUBCD 18 / Mar '97 / Hubbub

☐ FUNKY MILESTONES (2CD Set)
ZYX 811072 / 1 Sep '97 / ZYX

☐ FUNKY NIGHTS (2CD Set)
Heaven must be missing an angel: *Tavares* / Car wash: *Rose Royce* / We are family: *Sister Sledge* / More than woman: *Tavares* / He's the greatest dancer: *Sister Sledge* / Wishing on a star: *Rose Royce* / Medley 1: *Tavares* / I wanna get next to you: *Rose Royce* / True love: *Sister Sledge* / Motown Philly: *Tavares* / Brother brother stop: *Sister Sledge* / Frankie: *Sister Sledge* / Bad times: *Tavares* / Is it love you're after: *Rose Royce* / Never had love like this before: *Tavares* / Medley 2: *Sister Sledge* / Do your dance: *Rose Royce* / Turn your love around: *Tavares* / I'm in love (and I love the feeling): *Rose Royce* / Everybody dance: *Sister Sledge* / Can't take the blame for losing you: *Tavares* / Love of the Lord: *Sister Sledge* / You are the words: *Tavares*
TNC 96212 / Aug '96 / Natural Collection

☐ **FUNKY TALES (Southern Fried Funk From Excello, A-Bet & Mankind Records)**
Little Royal freeze: *Little Royal* / Daddy don't know about Sugar Bear: *Whitney, Marva* / Baby don't do it to me: *Washington, Jerry* / Funky tale to tell: *Maceo & All The King's Men* / I ain't gonna tell (nobody): *Brown, Shirley* / Maybe your baby: *Nazty* / I got my finger on your trigger: *Harpo, Slim* / Chain of fools: *Brown, Jimmy* / Boogaloo investigator: *Exotics* / Music for the brothers: *Solicitors* / Bus stop: *Sain, Oliver* / Shaky pudding: *Morrison, Jesse* / Precious woman: *Dynamic Corvettes* / Keep on loving: *Little Royal* / Love to hate: *North, Freddie* / Your good good loving: *Powell, Bobby* / Ain't nothing in the streets: *Stanback, Jean* / I'd do it all over you: *Duke, Doris* / Do your thing: *Whitney, Marva* / I got to move: *Nazty* / Let our music make love to you: *Ureaus* / Party hearty: *Sain, Oliver* / Born to wander: *Maceo & All The King's Men* / We need more (but somebody gotta sacrifice): *Marva & Ellis*
CDSEWD 111 / Jun '96 / Southbound

☐ **FURRY LOGIC VOL.1**
Microgravity: *Heard, Larry* / Obrigado: *Fila Brazillia* / Donau experience: *Count Basic* / Orbit 1: *Playing For The City* / Sugarplums: *Marden Hill* / Wild strawberry: *Dub Alchemist* / Frozen hands: *Neotropic* / I see: *Ozman* / Post-sunset misunderstanding: *Fauna Flash* / Finley's rainbow: *Guy Called Gerald* / Bengali song: *Sawhney, Nitin* / One day in paradise: *Padilla, Jose*
FLCD 001 / Jul '97 / Furry Logic

☐ **FURTHER ADVANCES IN TECHNO SOUL**
At les: *Craig, Carl* / Don't electric shock me: *Torske, Bjorn* / Express: *Stasis* / Around the corner: *Rue East* / Blue ink: *Aubrey* / Rudder: *4th Wave* / Sirius at the pier: *Brennan, Max* / Longest night: *Curtin, Dan* / Estamos perdidos: *Invisibles* / Rudiment sketch: *Idiot Savant* / Cube of the blues: *Fusion*
FERCD 004 / 17 Apr '98 / Ferox

☐ **FURTHER EAST**
SPCD 07 / Mar '97 / Superpower

☐ **FURTHER EAST WESTERCISMS**
LA 4CD / 6 Apr '98 / Law & Auder

☐ **FURTHER MUTATIONS**
Feelin' brown: *Twisted Science* / Pooo: *Kraut, Peter* / Spiegels: *Vibert, Luke* / Blasted wook: *Vibert, Luke* / See sawing sea: *Kristian, David* / Clockwork: *Cujo* / Time T-bone: *Sycophants* / We can't play from shit E: *Wormhole* / DMN 97: *Burzootie* / Wooden league: *Voafose* / Feelin' brown: *Twisted Science* / Lo-band-width: *Hood* / My name is sugar cane: *Barbed* / Space notes: *Mellowtrons* / Cry from the city: *Fish Out Of Water* / Cloaking device: *Underdog* / Scratch: *Ganger* / An itch you can't fucking scratch: *Thomas, Richard* / Epicycle: *Chasm* / Eternal boy: *Bedouin Ascent* / I'm going to hit the ground running: *Thomas, Richard* / Careful with that rake Eugene: *Moore, Thurston & Eugene Chadbourne* / 2player: *2 Player & DJ Vadim* / Demo: *Freezer*
LCD 05 / 9 Feb '98 / Lo Recordings

☐ **FURTHER SELF EVIDENT TRUTHS VOL.3**
RSNCD 43 / Apr '96 / Rising High

☐ **FURTHUR MORE**
HY 20003 / Jul '97 / Hybrid

☐ **FURY, THE**
DBM 2053 / Jul '97 / Death Becomes Me

☐ **FURY-MENTAL**
Surfin' gorilla: *Surfin' Gorillas* / Friction: *Arousers* / Rhythm riot: *Potter, Jeff* / Mooncrest: *Muskrats* / Fury: *Razorbacks* / Warpath: *Rough Diamonds* / Bronco loco: *Condo, Ray* / Strollin' guitar: *Higham, Darrel* / Mohawk twist: *Jackals* / Green Jeans: *Rapiers* / Stampede: *Bopshack Stompers* / Stiletto: *Blue Devils* / Dinosaur: *Hot Boogie Chillun* / Lockjaw: *Roadrunners* / Rattlesnake: *Haywire* / Roswell crash: *Atomic Spuds* / Gypsy beat: *Flames* / Invitation to death: *Playboys* / Haunted highway: *Terry, Iain* / Run chicken run: *School House Rock*
FCD 3051 / May '97 / Fury

☐ **FUSE VOL.1 & 2**
NATCD 35 / Jul '94 / Nation

☐ **FUSE VOL.3 (Global Chaos)**
NRCD 1063 / May '96 / Nation

☐ **FUSED (35 New Directions In Indie-Dance - 2CD Set)**
Saint: *Orbital* / It's no good: *Depeche Mode* / Scared: *Slacker* / Prophet: *Bolland, C.J.* / Firestarter: *Prodigy* / Ain't talkin' 'bout dub: *Apollo 440* / 9 acre dust: *Charlatans* / Open up: *Leftfield & John Lydon* / Ready to go: *Republica* / Lopez: *808 State* / Diablo: *Grid* / World: *New Order* / Skin on skin: *Grace* / Children: *Miles, Robert* / Ride a rocket: *Lithium & Sonya Madan* / Naked and ashamed: *Dylan Rhymes* / Higher state of consciousness: *Wink, Josh* / Asylum: *Orb* / Underwater love: *Smoke City* / Sour times: *Portishead* / Goreki: *Lamb* / Dark and long: *Underworld* / Box: *Orbital* / Trigger hippie: *Morcheeba* / Spin spin sugar: *Sneaker Pimps* / Hyperballad: *Bjork* / Wild wood: *Weller, Paul* / Wish you were here: *Aloof* / Original: *Leftfield & Toni Halliday* / Stay: *18 Wheeler* / Papua New Guinea: *Future Sound Of London* / So many dreams: *Guy Called Gerald* / Angel: *Goldie* / Feel the sunshine: *Reece, Alex & Deborah Anderson* / Darkheart: *Bomb The Bass*
5534822 / May '97 / PolyGram TV

☐ **FUSION OF CLASSICAL AND POP STYLES VOL.2, A**
SPOTS 14 / Oct '91 / Intersound

☐ **FUSION OF CLASSICAL AND POP STYLES, A**
SPOTS 13 / Oct '91 / Intersound

☐ **FUSION PHEW VOL.1**
Sudden samba: *Larson, Neil* / Latin America: *Walton, Cedar* / Hip skip: *Williams, Tony* / El bobo: *Lewis, Webster* / Hump: *Rushen, Patrice* / Rio: *Glenn, Roger* / Caveman boogie: *Wilson, Lesette* / Harlem boys: *Rollins, Sonny* / Walk tall: *Soskin, Mark* / Do it to it: *Owens, Jimmy* / Little sunflower: *Hubbard, Freddie* / On the path: *Franklin, Rodney*
CDELV 10 / Dec '93 / Elevate

☐ **FUSION PHEW VOL.2**
Ju ju: *McDuff, Jack* / He loves you: *Seawind* / Goldenwings: *OPA* / Bittersweet: *Escovedo, Pete* / Sugar loaf mountain: *Duke, George* / Happy song: *Foster, Ronnie* / Baby don't you know: *Humphrey, Bobbi* / I'm staying forever: *Henderson, Wayne* / Life is like a samba: *Benoit, David* / There are many stops along the way: *Sample, Joe* / Scapegoat: *Johnson, Al* / Slick Eddie: *Stitt, Sonny*
CDELV 15 / Jun '94 / Elevate

☐ **FUTURAPOCALYPTIC DUB (Rootsman Presents)**
LRCD 007 / 1 Jun '98 / Lush

☐ **FUTURE (A Journey Through The Electronic Underground)**
Extremis: *Hal & Gillian Anderson* / Atom bomb: *Fluke* / KJZ: *Photek* / Smokin' Japanese babe: *Future Sound Of London* / Karmacoma: *Massive Attack* / Winter ceremony: *Sacred Spirit* / Loops of fury: *Chemical Brothers* / Snake hips: *Future Sound Of London* / Extremis: *Hal & Gillian Anderson* / Absurd: *Fluke* / Salsa with mesquite: *u-Ziq* / Ostiak: *Hal* / Water from a vine leaf: *Orbit, William* / Smokebelch II: *Sabres Of Paradise* / Crystal clear: *Grid* / Space diary 1: *Jah Wobble & Brian Eno* / Sleep 2: *Schutze, Paul* / Spiritual invocation: *Air* / Lizard point: *Eno, Brian* / Mr. lullaby should have rocked you: *Toop, David* / Their memories: *Budd, Harold & Brian Eno* / Home: *Sylvian, David*
VTDCD 118 / Jun '97 / Virgin

☐ **FUTURE COOL (Drum 'n' Bass Jazz Space)**
CKR 002CD / Jun '97 / Cooker

☐ **FUTURE FORCES**
What you want: *Future Force* / Heaven: *Washington, Sarah* / Pleasure principle: *Jackson, Janet* / Klubbhopping: *Klubb Heads* / Stand up: *Love Tribe* / Bring me love: *Mendez, Andrea* / Girls and boys: *Morel's Grooves*
FFCD 2 / May '96 / AM:PM

☐ **FUTURE FUNK**
325032 / 24 Feb '98 / Melodie

☐ **FUTURE FUNK 4U VOL.1**
325092 / 21 Aug '97 / Melodie

☐ **FUTURE FUNK 4U VOL.2**
325052 / 21 Aug '97 / Melodie

☐ **FUTURE FUNK 4U VOL.5**
325122 / Jan '98 / Melodie

☐ **FUTURE FUNK VOL.1 (2CD Set)**
Inner city life: *Goldie & The Metalheadz* / Inspection: *Leftfield* / Leave home: *Chemical Brothers* / Clank: *Spooky* / Salt water fish: *Ruby* / Born slippy: *Underworld* / Cool kids of death: *St. Etienne* / Bump: *Angel, Dave* / Mutant jazz: *T-Power* / I'll fly away: *Ballistic Brothers* / Peace: *DJ Food* / Barbola work: *Black Dog* / Space junk: *Burning Bush* / Karmacoma: *Massive Attack* / One to one religion: *Bomb The Bass* / Journeyman part 2: *Outside* / Isobel: *Bjork* / Killing: *Olive* / Friendly pressure: *Jhelisa* / Only the strong survive: *DJ Krush* / Fallen: *APE* / Tosh: *Fluke* / Drum head: *Stoppa* / Clubbed to death: *Rob D* / Nights introlude: *Nightmares On Wax* / Garden of earthly delights: *D-Note*
5404952 / Feb '96 / A&M

☐ **FUTURE FUNK VOL.3**
325072 / 24 Feb '98 / Melodie

☐ **FUTURE PERFECT**
Domus in nebulae: *Eno, Roger* / Saint columbas walk: *Eno, Roger* / Western island of apples: *Partridge, Andy* / Bruegel: *Partridge, Andy* / Stravinsky: *Eno, Brian* / Distant hill: *Eno, Brian* / Radiothesia III: *Eno, Brian* / Testify: *Channel Light Vessel* / Faint aroma of snow: *Channel Light Vessel* / For the love of you: *St. John, Kate* / Your promised land: *St. John, Kate* / Big noise in Twangtown: *Nelson, Bill* / Her presence in flowers: *Nelson, Bill*
ASCD 024 / Mar '95 / All Saints

☐ **FUTURE SOUL**
5243332 / Jan '97 / Quango

☐ **FUTURE SOUND OF CHICAGO**
SOMCD 5 / Jun '96 / Ministry Of Sound

☐ **FUTURE SOUND OF HARDCORE, THE**
KFCD 002 / Jan '96 / Kniteforce

☐ **FUTURE SOUND OF JAZZ VOL.1, THE**
COMP 010CD / 23 Feb '98 / Compost

☐ **FUTURE SOUND OF JAZZ VOL.2, THE**
COMP 017CD / 23 Feb '98 / Compost

☐ **FUTURE SOUND OF JAZZ VOL.3, THE (2CD Set)**
COMP 030CD / 23 Feb '98 / Compost

☐ **FUTURE SOUND OF JAZZ VOL.4, THE (2CD Set)**
COMP 039CD / 1 Dec '97 / Compost

☐ **FUTURE SOUND OF PARIS VOL.1**
Away: *Nature* / Bad vibes: *Motorbass* / Psycho phunk reaction: *Daphreephunkateerz* / Bill collector: *Trankilou* / Just about right: *Dimitri From Paris* / Free Jah: *Zend Avesta* / Rock it tonight: *Seven Dub* / Earth whispers: *Aphrodisiac* / Solar sequences experience: *Solar Side's Experience* / Make it freaky: *Malca, Stephane* / Disco 2000 selector: *Space Funk Project* / She's a model: *Magenta* / Feet Food's theme: *Dirty Jesus* / Soul experience: *Dax Riders*
5337382 / Feb '97 / London

☐ **FUTURE SOUND OF PARIS VOL.2 (The City Returns)**
5378902 / 2 Mar '98 / London

☐ **FUTURE SOUND OF THE UK VOL.2 (2CD Set)**
FSUKCD 2 / 25 May '98 / FSUK

☐ **FUTURE SOUNDS (4CD Set)**
DTKBOX 88 / 1 Jun '98 / Dressed To Kill

☐ **FUTURE WAVE**
CLP 199 / 20 Apr '98 / Cleopatra

☐ **FUTURSONICS (2CD Set)**
PIAS 26000223 / Jun '96 / Elypsia

☐ **FX FILES (5CD Set)**
DTKBOX 67 / 1 Sep '97 / Doppelganger

G

☐ **G-SPOT VOL.1 (Club Classics)**
GSPOTCD 1 / Mar '97 / Beechwood

☐ **G-SPOT VOL.2 (Swing)**
You might need somebody: *Ama, Shola* / Can we: *SWV* / Can I get you home: *Brown, Foxy* / Everytime I close my eyes: *Babyface* / I shot the sheriff: *Warren G* / Can't knock the hustle: *Jay Z & Mary J. Blige* / For you I will: *Monica* / Sometime: *Brand New Heavies* / Don't you love me: *Eternal* / Moan and groan: *Morrison, Mark* / Hold on: *En Vogue* / Doin' it: *LL Cool J* / I believe I can fly: *R Kelly* / Tha crossroads: *Bone Thugs n' Harmony* / Cold rock the party: *MC Lyte* / Sumthin' sumthin': *Maxwell* / Love guarenteed: *Damage* / One in a million: *Aaliyah* / Give me the night: *Crawford, Randy* / Crush on you: *Lil' Kim* / 5 miles to empty: *Brownstone* / Request line: *Zhane*
GSPOTCD 2 / Jun '97 / Beechwood

☐ **G.S. MACLENNAN MEMORIAL INVITATIONAL PIPING COMPETITION VOL.**
GSM 1996/2 / Dec '97 / Bydand Forever

☐ **G.S. MCLENNAN MEMORIAL INVITATIONAL PIPING COMPETITION VOL.1**
GSM 1996/1 / Dec '97 / Bydand Forever

☐ **G.S. MCLENNAN PIPING COMPETITION 1997 (2CD Set)**
GSM 1997 / Feb '98 / Bydand Forever

☐ **GABBA 4 LIFE**
Overload: *X-Buzz* / Resurrection: *DJ Paranoide* / ANNEKE: *Darkcreator* / Crimson and timo: *DJ Acesone* / Backstage: *SPDK* / Tales of your life: *Dreamers* / Let the beat control your body: *X-Masters* / Home of da sick: *DJ Smurf* / Evil death: *DJ Paranoide & The Outsider* / Get out of the way: *Angels Of Thunder* / Tina: *DJ Acesone* / Drop the beat: *X-Treme DJ Team* / Let no fear: *Dorpzicht* / Gabba bonus beats: *DJ Petrov & House Federation*
OVERKILL 004 / Sep '97 / Overkill

☐ **GAEL FORCE**
RTECD 210 / Nov '97 / RTE/Europe 1

☐ **GAGAKU**
LYRCD 7126 / Aug '94 / Lyrichord

☐ **GAGAKU**
VICG 53542 / Mar '96 / JVC World Library

☐ **GAL YU GOOD**
VPCD 1123 / Oct '90 / VP

☐ **GALAKTIC SOUND LAB VOL.1**
GSL 003CD / 6 Apr '98 / Galaktic Sound Lab

☐ **GALAXY OF SOUND, A (2CD Set)**
Go: *Moby* / Stellar supreme: *Cosmic Baby* / How much can you take: *Visions Of Shiva* / Hello San Francisco: *Dance 2 Trance* / Environ-mentally: *Microglobe* / Energy flow eternal: *Lissat, Jens* / Loops and things: *Jens* / Backfired: *Robotnico* / LSI: *Shamen* / All I need is love: *De'Lacy* / Epidemic: *Exit EEE* / Who is Elvis: *Interactive* / Quadrophonia: *Quadrophonia* / Calling earth: *Deruyter, Yves* / Pacific dance: *State Of House* / 20 Hz: *Capricorn* / Loop fuse: *LFO & Fuse* / Mantra: *Bolland, C.J.* / No fate: *Zyon* / Feel what you want: *Kristine W* / Plastic dreams: *Jaydee* / Wonderer: *Vernon* / Cafe del mar: *Energy 52* / Love stimulation: *Humate* / Schoneberg: *Marmion* / Let's groove: *Morel, George* / Face it: *Vath, Sven* / Loops of infinity: *Cosmic Baby* / Age of love: *Age Of Love*
STATION 02 / 1 Sep '98 / Station 1

☐ **GALAXY TRIBE (A Drum 'n' Bass Odyssey)**
MEYCD 20 / Aug '97 / Magick Eye

☐ **GALLERY MODERN MASTERS VOL.1, THE (2CD Set)**
Insomnia: *Faithless* / Let the madness begin: *Motif* / Scream: *Invisible* / One way: *Three 'n One* / Keep on dancin (let's go): *Perpetual Motion* / Sounds of the wickedness: *Tzant* / I'm a disco dancer (and a sweet romancer): *Just, Christopher* / Phunkee muzeek: *Shazzam* / Furious angels: *Dougan, Rob* / Velvet pants: *Propellerheads* / Give a little love: *Invisible Man* / Rhyme: *Strike Boys* / Bad boy: *Wildchild* / Delirious: *DJQ* / Aftermath: *Nightmares On Wax* / Windows: *SIL* / Ultimate: *Funky Choad & Nick Skitz* / Intensify: *Faithless allstars* / Dreamin': *Les Rhythmes Digitales* / Here's where the story ends: *Tin Tin Out* / Subenos juntos (we rise together): *Recall 22* / Flaming June: *BT* / At the river: *Groove Armada* / Confusing the sun: *Quazar* / I've been waiting: *Kinky Plants* / Badman: *Sister Bliss* / Ya yae ya yo yo yo: *Voices Of Kwahn AD* / Been a long time: *Fog* / Boglektro: *Urban DK* / Just let go: *Petra & Co* / Uprising: *Ecomo, Silvio* / Let me show you: *Camisra* / Stomping system: *JS 16* / Disco to disco: *Whirlpool Productions* / Ooh la la: *Wiseguys* / Drop the break: *Cirrus* / Floribunda: *Mothers Pride* / Tribute to Jazzy Jay: *Bronx Dogs* / Stump juice: *Capoeira Twins* / LA: *Marc Et Claude*
VTDCD 188 / 4 May '98 / Virgin

☐ **GAMELAN ENSEMBLE OF BATUR**
C559 002 / '88 / Ocora

☐ **GAMELAN GONG GEDE**
VICG 52162 / Mar '96 / JVC World Library

☐ **GAMELAN GONG KEBYAR VOL.1**
VICG 52152 / Mar '96 / JVC World Library

☐ **GAMELAN GONG KEBYAR VOL.2**
VICG 52652 / Mar '96 / JVC World Library

☐ **GAMELAN MUSIC OF BALI**
LYRCD 7179 / Nov '97 / Lyrichord

☐ **GAMELAN OF SURAKARTA**
VICG 52632 / Mar '96 / JVC World Library

☐ **GAMELAN SEMAR PAGULINGAN FROM BESANG ABABI (Music From Bali)**
SM 1609 / Oct '96 / Wergo

☐ **GAMES AND RITES OF THE LOBI PEOPLE (Music From Burkina Faso/ Ivory Coast/Ghana)**
ARN 64341 / Apr '96 / Arion

☐ **GARAGE (4CD Set)**
DCBX 106 / 16 Mar '98 / Dance Club International

☐ **GARAGE NATION (2CD Set)**
Give you myself: *Sima* / Over you: *M-Dubs* / R u sleeping: *Indo* / Deep: *JK Size* / Desire: *Ramsey & Fen* / Weakness: *Stainer, Greg* / Sing it: *Slip'd By* / Don't stop: *Ruff Driverz* / Style: *Ramsey & Fen* / We can make it happen: *Craig, Robbie* / Unreleased project vol.1: *Tuff Productions* / Never forget: *Pisces* / Let me show you love: *Romanthony* / Touch me: *Sixty Brown* / Unreleased project: *Akh & Jay Dee* / I saw the future: *Strike* / Ganjaman: *Hypercrew* / Deeper: *Serious Danger* / Love is forever: *Serious Danger* / Don't stop: *Ruff Driverz* / I believe in you: *Baffled & Colour Girl* / Say what: *Paulo & Rodriguez* / Bizzi's party: *Bizzi* / Dark: *Glass* / Dubtrain: *DB Selective* / Dangerous: *Same People* / Hold your head up high: *Dlugosch, Boris* / Feel free: *Livin' Large* / Do me baby: *New Horizon* / Give me joy: *Wood, Kathy* / Keep on: *M&S* / Breathless: *Rocksteady* / Spend the night: *Lewis, Danny J.* / Keep your love: *Ordinary People* / Straight from the heart: *24 Hour Experience* / I need your loving: *E-Merge*
GNCD 001 / 6 Apr '98 / Garage Nation Music

☐ **GARAGE PUNK UNKNOWNS VOL.1**
EFACD 11572 / 16 Mar '98 / Crypt

☐ **GARAGE PUNK UNKNOWNS VOL.2**
EFA 11580 / 16 Mar '98 / Crypt

☐ **GARAGE SOUNDS VOL.4**
CDRAID 531 / Jul '96 / Rumour

☐ **GARNI: ARMENIAN DANCES**
VANGEEL 9404 / Aug '95 / Van Geel

☐ **GARO OF THE MUDHUPAR FOREST, THE**
C 580054 / May '94 / Ocora

☐ **GARVEY TO THE RESCUE**
SPCD 0130 / 17 Nov '97 / Superpower

☐ **GARY D PRESENTS D TRANCE VOL.6 (3CD Set)**
PIAS 556201725CD / 25 Aug '97 / Play It Again Sam

☐ **GATHERING OF THE ELDERS, THE**
WLAAS 25CD / Nov '95 / Waterlily Acoustics

☐ **GATHERING, THE**
Lay dee at de / Spence's reel / Faery reel / Mrs. Hamilton of Pitcaithland / Untitled / Lord MacDonald's reel / Horseshoe harbour / Christy Barry's / Mrs. Heidi Hendy / Sandymount / Untitled / Lucy Campbell's / Fermoy lasses / Last chance / Venus jig / Reel du pendu (hangman's reel) / Kildare fancy / Golden eagle / Sweep's hornpipe / Lafferty's / Grogans / Star of Munster / L'air du menuisier / Kola

stala vlajna / Valse clog / Green brechans of Branton / Peacock's march / I saw my love come passing me by / Rathlin island / Braes of Mar / Jenny Dang the weaver / Miss Girdle / Tail toddle / Canto de afiador / Hurlondo / Jig jazz

CDRW 62 / Apr '97 / Realworld

☐ **GAY 90'S, THE (Musical Boxes/ Pianolas)**
Runaway girl / Robin Hood / Florodora / Belle of New York / Geisha / Greek slave and San toy / Dozen discs / Canary and nightingale warble / Evergreens / Stephen Foster favourites / Gay 90's favourites / Miscellany

CDSDL 312 / Jun '92 / Saydisc

☐ **GAY ANTHEMS VOL.1**

ALMYCD 11 / Feb '98 / Almighty

☐ **GAY ANTHEMS VOL.2**
Love I lost: West End & Sybil / Where love lies: Limerick, Alison / How could he do this to me: Gordon, Lonnie / Loving game: Obmana, Vidna & Steve Reich / Save your love for me: Destination / And I'm telling you I'm not going: Giles, Donna / Love eviction: Quartz Lock / Armed and extremely dangerous: Respect & Shirley Lewis / Visitors: Abbacadabra / Losing my religion: Abigail / Without your love: Cut Glass / Sky high: Newton / No more tears: Brown, Jocelyn & Kym Mazelle / Careless whisper: Washington, Sarah

ALMYCD 16 / Feb '98 / Almighty

☐ **GAY ANTHEMS VOL.3**
I feel love: Summer, Donna / To deserve you: Deja Vu & Tasmin / You were mean't for me: Barby Q / Because you loved me: Rye, Suzanne / Young hearts run free: Respect & Hannah Jones / Shine: Obsession / Bailando con lobos: Cabana / All by myself: So Emotional / Reach: Cheeks, Judy / Say what you want: Lipstick / Bette Davis eyes: Carnes, Kim / Lay all your love on me: Abbacadabra / Bitch: Jackie O / There's nothing I won't do: Jackie O

BLSTCD 06 / Feb '98 / Blast

☐ **GAY CLASSICS VOL.1 (Over The Rainbow)**

BLSTCD 01 / Aug '95 / Blast

☐ **GAY CLASSICS VOL.1 (Ridin' The Rainbow)**

HTCD 3399 / 20 Apr '98 / Hot Productions

☐ **GAY CLASSICS VOL.2 (Over The Rainbow)**

BLSTCD 02 / Mar '96 / Blast

☐ **GAY CLASSICS VOL.2 (Outstanding)**

HTCD 33100 / 20 Apr '98 / Hot Productions

☐ **GAY CLASSICS VOL.3 (Over The Rainbow)**
Step back in time: Minogue, Kylie / Jack and Jill: Essence / Young hearts run free: Respect & Hannah Jones / Don't take away the music: Tavares / Vertigo/Relight my fire: Hartman, Dan / Body rock: Vidal, Maria / Losing my religion: Abigail / In private: Springfield, Dusty / Evergreen: Myles, Paula / Hypnotic tango: Blanca / Suspicious minds: Obsession / It's raining men: Weather Girls

BLSTCD 04 / Feb '98 / Blast

☐ **GAY CLASSICS VOL.3 (Out Loud Proud)**

HTCD 331022 / 27 Apr '98 / Hot Productions

☐ **GAY CLASSICS VOL.4 (Outrageous)**

HTCD 331032 / 20 Apr '98 / Hot Productions

☐ **GAY DANCING (2CD Set)**

ZYX 811112 / Aug '97 / ZYX

☐ **GAY, FREE & HAPPY**
This wheels on fire: Suns Of Shiva / Give it to me good: Freaky Baby / Pardon me: Kon Kan / Fantasia 2: Suns Of Shiva / Here and now: Kater / In from wan' it: New York Connection / Entangled: Human, Wayne / Back again: General Base / I will stand by you: Petroleum Jell / Who's gonna cry: Taylor, Ann Marie / You could have been with me last night: Primitive Fire / Strong to survive: Shaker / Poison: General Base / Breathless: Gold, Angie

ST 9601 / Jun '96 / Stonewall

☐ **GAY HAPPENING VOL.1 (2CD Set)**
Love in the first degree: Bananarama / Happenin' all over again: Gordon, Lonnie / I am what I am: Gaynor, Gloria / Somebody else's guy: Brown, Jocelyn / Can't shake the feeling: Big Fun / Can you handle it: Redd, Sharon / Male strippers: Man 2 Man/Man Parrish / E: Man 2 Man/Man Parrish / Dangerous: Logical beat / You spin me around: Dead Or Alive / It's raining men: Weather Girls / It's feels like I'm in love: Marie, Kelly / Follow me: Lear, Amanda / One moment in time: Grant, Natalie / Fur mich soll's rote rosen regnen: Knef, Hildegard / Jacky: Almond, Marc / Don't leave me this way: Communards / Bow down mister: Boy George / Lost in music: Sister Sledge / Megamix: Boney M / It's my party: Rhonda & Physical Motion / Tainted love: Soft Cell / Megamix: Village People / To the top: Beverly / Er gehort zu mir: Rosenberg, Marianne / Take me: Souler & Kim Davis / Love stinks: Soft Cell / Megamix: Life / I've lost: West End & Sybil / Gonna get along without you now: Wills, Viola / Power of love: Beverly / Doop: Doop / I will always love you: Washington, Sarah / Band of gold: Payne, Freda / Professional Widow's Beat / Ain't nobody: PLP Enterprise / I will survive: Gaynor, Gloria / Greatest love of all: Grant, Natalie / When will I see you again: Dream Girls / Without you: Next Generation / Give it up: Goodmen

DST 08542582 / Sep '97 / Dance Street

☐ **GAY HAPPENING VOL.2**
Where is my man: Kitt, Eartha / Can u feel it: Weather Girls / Let the water in: McKane, Lorraine / Love I've lost: West End & Sybil / Gonna get along without you now: Wills, Viola / Power of love: Beverly / Doop: Doop / I will always love you: Washington, Sarah / Band of gold: Payne, Freda / Professional Widow's Beat / Ain't nobody: PLP Enterprise / I will survive: Gaynor, Gloria / Greatest love of all: Grant, Natalie / When will I see you again: Dream Girls / Without you: Next Generation / Give it up: Goodmen

DST 08542582 / Sep '97 / Dance Street

☐ **GAY HAPPENING VOL.3**
Endless love: Love Construction / So many men so little time: Touchez / Finally: Ce Ce Peniston / Pompoos part.1: Pompoos / Can you feel the love tonight: Harakuku / We shall all be free: Weather Girls / No more tears: Mazelle, Kym & Jocelyn Brown / I was tired of being alone: Klodya / If I can't have you: Obsession / I'll do my best: Ritchie Family / Free gay and happy: Connical Out Krew / Total eclipse of the heart: French, Nicki / Hot stuff: DJ Miko / 100% pure love: Waters, Crystal / Legendary children: Johnson, Holly / Bob's adventure: Flip Da Scrip

DST 08542592 / Sep '97 / Dance Street

☐ **GAY HAPPENING VOL.4**
Young hearts run free: Respect & Hannah Jones / Knock me out: Kymelle / I love the nightlife: Bridges, Alicia / Your loving arms: Eurotribe / Can't stop the boogie: B-One / I love you baby: Original / Give it to you: Wash, Martha / Shut up (and sleep with me): Sin With Sebastian / You'll never love the same way: Rozalla / Let no man put assunder: First choice & Michelle Fleming / Who's gonna kiss that man: Turner, Marissa / Let's go all the way: One Way Street / Tonight it's party time: Outta control / Going back to my roots: Movement club / Armed and extremely dangerous: M-Brace & Angie / Don't you wanna be mine: Real Deal & Anette Taylor / Treat me right: Temple Of The Groove

DST 08542602 / Sep '97 / Dance Street

☐ **GAY JAMAICA INDEPENDENCE TIME**

444162 / 22 Jun '98 / Jet Set

☐ **GAZEL (Classical Music Of The Ottoman Empire)**

CMPCD 3012 / 30 Mar '98 / CMP

☐ **GEARHEAD PRESENTS ALL PUNK RODS**

LK 193CD / 23 Mar '98 / Lookout

☐ **GEMS OF THE MUSIC HALL**
I love a lassie: Lauder, Harry / Every little movement: Lloyd, Marie / Lily of Laguna: Stratton, Eugene / Gas inspector: Little Tich / I can't take a rise out of oh: Chevalier, Albert / Put on your slippers: Lloyd, Marie / Burlington Bertie from Bow: Shields, Ella / Little idea of my own: Robey, George / Little Dolly daydream: Elliott, G.H. / When I took my morning parade: Lloyd, Marie / Has anyone here seen Kelly: Forde, Florrie / Whistling bowery boy: Whelan, Albert / Same as his father did before him: Lauder, Harry / Archibald certainly not: Robey, George / Going to the races: Leno, Dan / When father papered the parlour: Williams, Billy / Old bull and bush: Forde, Florrie / Preacher and the bear: Whelan, Albert / Hold your hand out, naughty boy: Forde, Florrie / Fill 'Em Up: King, Hetty / 'E dunno where 'E are: Elen, Gus / Three trees: Whelan, Albert

PASTCD 7005 / Mar '93 / Flapper

☐ **GENERAL MEETS THREE BLIND MICE**

790092 / Jun '93 / King Dragon

☐ **GENERATION MEDIA TROPICAL**

3013512 / Jan '97 / Flarenasch

☐ **GENETIC DRIFT (2CD Set)**

PKPWS 5 / Oct '96 / Fax

☐ **GENIOS DE LA GUITARRA FLAMENCA VOL.1**
Alegrias: Sabicas / Sevillanas: Sabicas / Bulerias: Martinez, Pepe / Fandangos: Martinez, Pepe / Malaguena: De Lucia, Paco / Granadinas: Sabicas / Bulerias: Sabicas / Zapateado: De Sanlucar, Esteban / Farruca: De Sanlucar, Esteban / Molienda Cafe: De Lucia, Paco / Maria de la O: De Lucia, Paco

CD 62095 / Mar '97 / Saludos Amigos

☐ **GENIOS DE LA GUITTARA FLAMENCA VOL.2**
Fantasia Salinera: Ricardo, Nino / Nostalgia Granadina: Ricardo, Nino / Soleares: Simon, Paquito / Aires de Cadiz: Simon, Paquito / Zapateado: Albaicin, Antonio / Tientos: Albaicin, Antonio / Granadinas Holaigas: Serrano, Paquito / Soleares: Serrano, Juanito / Jaleos Cale: Serrano, Juanito / Temas farrucos: Ricardo, Nino / Soleares #2: Ricardo, Nino / Fiesta en la Muralla: Serrano, Juanito / Seguiriyas: Serrano, Juanito / Verdiales: Simon, Paquito / Danza Mora: Simon, Paquito / Mantecas lo Mudalie: De Lucia, Paco / De Puerta a Puerta: De Lucia, Paco

CD 62099 / Mar '97 / Saludos Amigos

☐ **GENIUS OF BOOGIE-WOOGIE**

CD 53053 / Mar '90 / Giants Of Jazz

☐ **GENTLE BREEZE**

CELT 9016 / Jul '98 / Celtophile

☐ **GENTLE MOODS**
Chi mai / Bilitis / Holding back the years / Feelings / Sadness / Evergreen / Mahogany / Here comes the sun / Tubular bells / Long and winding road / Emotions / Change on the shore / Sailing / Talking in your sleep / Woman no cry / No woman no I made it through the rain / Something / Chariots of fire / Yesterday / Last farewell

GRF 313 / Apr '98 / Tring

☐ **GENTLE MOODS (4CD Set)**
Holding back the years: Intimate Orchestra / Sailing: Intimate Orchestra / Stranger on the shore: Intimate Orchestra / Twin Peaks theme: Intimate Orchestra / Do you know where you're going to: Intimate Orchestra / Unchained melody: Intimate Orchestra / Love's theme: Intimate Orchestra / Rose: Intimate Orchestra / Chariots of fire: Intimate Orchestra / Way we were:

Intimate Orchestra / Theme from the Godfather: Intimate Orchestra / One day in your life: Intimate Orchestra / Sacrifice: Intimate Orchestra / Oxygene: Intimate Orchestra / Ebony and ivory: Intimate Orchestra / That's what friends are for: Intimate Orchestra / Hopelessly devoted to you: Intimate Orchestra / Send in the clowns: Intimate Orchestra / Let it be: Intimate Orchestra / To all the girls I've loved before: Intimate Orchestra / Chi mai: Intimate Orchestra / Do that to me one more time: Intimate Orchestra / Strangers in the night: Intimate Orchestra / There'll be sad songs: Intimate Orchestra / Lady: Intimate Orchestra / Lost without your love: Intimate Orchestra / Aranjuez: Intimate Orchestra / Mon amour: Intimate Orchestra / Sealed with a kiss: Intimate Orchestra / Toccata: Intimate Orchestra / Heartbreaker: Intimate Orchestra / Something: Intimate Orchestra / You don't bring me flowers: Intimate Orchestra / Sittin' on the) dock of the bay: Intimate Orchestra / We have no money: Intimate Orchestra / Cavatina: Intimate Orchestra / Bilitis: Intimate Orchestra / Almaz: Intimate Orchestra / La vie en rose: Intimate Orchestra / Woman in love: Intimate Orchestra / Maid of New Orleans: Intimate Orchestra / I guess that's why they call it the blues: Intimate Orchestra / Out of Africa: Intimate Orchestra / Man and a woman: Intimate Orchestra / Moon river: Intimate Orchestra / Bridge over troubled water: Intimate Orchestra / Amazing Grace: Intimate Orchestra / Your song: Intimate Orchestra / Don't cry for me Argentina: Intimate Orchestra / Help me make it through the night: Intimate Orchestra / Magnetic fields part 2: Intimate Orchestra / Do that to me one more time: Intimate Orchestra / Midnight: Intimate Orchestra / Song for Guy: Intimate Orchestra

TFP 047 / Apr '95 / Tring

☐ **GENTLE RAIN (A Magical Blend Of Music And The Sounds Of Nature)**

57722 / May '97 / Nature's Harmony

☐ **GENTLEMEN OF SONG (2CD Set)**
All the way: Sinatra, Frank / Blue skies: Como, Perry / You're a sweet little headache: Crosby, Bing / Lazy: Haymes, Dick / Darling, Je vous aime beaucoup: Cole, Nat 'King' / My Mammy: Jolson, Al / My everlasting love: Jolson, Al / I'm confessin': Sinatra, Frank / I love you: Como, Perry / Apple for the teacher: Crosby, Bing / Thinking of you: Haymes, Dick / It's crazy but I'm in love: Cole, Nat 'King' / There's a rainbow round my shoulder: Jolson, Al / Side by side: Mitchell, Guy / Jeepers creepers: Bennett, Tony / I believe: Laine, Frankie / Think twice: Benton, Brook / On the road to Mandalay: Sinatra, Frank / Goodbye Sue: Como, Perry / April played the fiddle: Crosby, Bing / Nevertheless: Haymes, Dick / Once upon a time: Cole, Nat 'King' / Sonny boy: Jolson, Al / Call Rosie on the phone: Mitchell, Guy / With plenty of money and you: Bennett, Tony / There must be a reason: Laine, Frankie / Lie to me: Benton, Brook / I've got the world to keep me warm: Sinatra, Frank / All through the day: Como, Perry / I have eyes: Crosby, Bing / That lucky old sun: Haymes, Dick / You stepped out of a dream: Cole, Nat 'King' / Let me sing and I'm happy: Jolson, Al / Music, music, music: Mitchell, Guy / Chicago: Bennett, Tony / Wheel of fortune: Laine, Frankie / Revenge: Benton, Brook

MUCD 9512 / May '96 / Musketeer

☐ **GENTLEMEN OF THE COUNTRY**

HADCD 177 / Nov '95 / Javelin

☐ **GENTLEMEN PIPERS, THE (Classic Recordings Of Irish Traditional Piping)**
Banks of the Suir: Walsh, Liam / Portlaw reel: Walsh, Liam / Ask my father/The mountain lark: Andrews, William / May day/The Cuckoo's nest: Andrews, William / Top of the Cork road/The Irish washerwoman: Rowsome, Leo / Kiss the maid behind the barrel/Touch me if you dare: Rowsome, Leo / Snowy breasted pearl: Rowsome, Leo / Langstern pony: Clancy, Willie / Boys of Bluehill/Dunphy's hornpipe: Ennis, Seamus / Queen of Dublin/Wind that shakes the barley: Ennis, Seamus / Wandering minstrel/Jackson's morning brush: Ennis, Seamus / Blackbird: Ennis, Seamus / First house in Connaught/The copperplate: McAloon, Sean & John / An buachaill caol dubh/ Drops of brandy: McAloon, Sean / Aah (plain): Felix / Lark in the morning: Doran, Felix / Mary of Murroe/The green gates: Doran, Felix / Mary of Dingle: Doran, Felix / Frieze breeches: Mitchell, Pat / Mairseail alasdruim: Mitchell, Pat / Garrett Barry's/ The Virginia reel: Mitchell, Pat / Ballyoran: O'Brien, Michael / Rakish Paddy/Castle Kelly: O'Brien, Michael

CDORBD 084 / Mar '94 / Globestyle

☐ **GENUINE EXCELLO R&B**
Go on pretty baby: Hogan, Silas / I'm a king bee: Anderson, Jimmy / Roll on ole mule: Thomas, Tabby / Don't leave me baby: Smith, Whispering / Frankie and Johnny: Anderson, Jimmy / Stranger in town: Lightnin' Slim / Courtroom blues: Lazy Lester / Hound dog twist: Smith, Whispering / Please be on that: Lonesome Sundown / Dirty woman blues: Johnson, Joe / We gonna rub: Johnson, Joe / I'm hoping someday: Lazy Lester / Bad luck blues: Lonesome Sundown / Sitting in with the blues: Lazy Lester / Be kind: Washington, Leroy / Hello my worry: Lonesome Sundown / Bow legged knock kneed and big eyed: Washington, Leroy / Sitting on another man's knee: Washington, Leroy / Hello stranger: Washington, Leroy / One day baby: Lazy Lester / Rainin' in my heart: Harpo, Slim / Don't ever wanna man like me: Nelson, Jay & His Jumpers

CDCHD 678 / 23 Feb '98 / Ace

☐ **GENUINE HOUSEROCKIN' VOL.1**

ALCD 101 / Oct '93 / Alligator

☐ **GENUINE HOUSEROCKIN' VOL.2**

ALCD 102 / Oct '93 / Alligator

☐ **GENUINE HOUSEROCKIN' VOL.3**

ALCD 103 / Oct '93 / Alligator

☐ **GENUINE HOUSEROCKIN' VOL.4**

ALCD 104 / Oct '93 / Alligator

☐ **GENUINE HOUSEROCKIN' VOL.5**

ALCD 109 / Nov '93 / Alligator

☐ **GEORGE PHANG PRESENTS POWERHOUSE VOL.1**

SONCD 0007 / Feb '91 / Sonic Sounds

☐ **GEORGIA BLUES**

IGOCD 2045 / Jun '96 / Indigo

☐ **GEORGIA BLUES & GOSPEL 1927- 1931**

DOCD 5160 / May '93 / Document

☐ **GEORGIA SEA ISLAND SONGS**
Moses: Davis, John / Kneebone: Armstrong, Joe / Sheep, sheep, don't you know the road: Davis, Bessie / Live humble: Davis, John / Daniel: Proctor, Willis / O Death: Jones, Bessie / Read 'em John: Davis, John / Beulah land: Davis, John / Buzzard lope: Jones, Bessie / Raggy Levi: Davis, John / Ain't I right: Morrison, Henry / See Aunt Dinah: Jones, Bessie / Walk, Billy Abbot: Proctor, Willis / Reg'lar reg'lar rollin' under: Jones, Bessie / Pay me: Armstrong, Joe / Carrie Belle: Davis, John / Laz'rus: Morrison, Henry / Titanic: Jones, Bessie

802782 / Mar '96 / New World

☐ **GEORGIA STRING BANDS 1928-1930**

SOB 035162 / Feb '93 / Story Of The Blues

☐ **GEORGIA STRING BANDS VOL.1 1927- 1930**

DOCD 8021 / 20 Apr '98 / Document

☐ **GEORGIAN POLYPHONY**

VICG 50032 / Mar '96 / JVC World Library

☐ **GEORGIE - THE BEST ALBUM**

PELE 13CD / Mar '97 / Exotica

☐ **GERMAN BIERFEST FAVOURITES**
O du lieber Augustin: Bavarian Oompah Band / Du kannst nicht treu sein: Bavarian Oompah Band / Bierwalzer: Bavarian Oompah Band / Oompah polka: Bavarian Oompah Band / Auf lustiger fahrt: Big Bavarian Band / Mariandi: Bavarian Oompah Band / Mama mia Lisesi: Bavarian Oompah Band / In munchen steht ein hofbrauhaus: Bavarian Oompah Band / Hoch die tassen: Big Bavarian Band / Trudies tanz: Bavarian Oompah Band / Phyllis und die mutter: Bavarian Oompah Band / Urtummelied: Bavarian Oompah Band / Die lorelei: Bavarian Oompah Band / In Munchen steht ein hofbrauhaus: Bavarian Oompah Band / Muss I denn, muss I denn zum stadtele 'raus: Bavarian Oompah Band / Del mai ist gekommen: Bavarian Oompah Band / Auf wiedersehn: Bavarian Oompah Band / Lieb heimatland ade: Bavarian Oompah Band / Rose: Bavarian Oompah Band / Es zogen drei buschen wohl uber den Rhein: Bavarian Oompah Band / In schwarzen walfisch: Bavarian Oompah Band / Das war der herr von Rodenstein: Bavarian Oompah Band / Trumpeten echo: Big Bavarian Band

300572 / Jul '96 / Hallmark

☐ **GERMAN DJ PLAYLIST**

OXA 20012 / 27 Apr '98 / OXA

☐ **GERMAN DRINKING SONGS**

MCD 71419 / Jun '93 / Monitor

☐ **GERMAN MYSTIC SOUND SAMPLER**

EFA 910102 / Dec '95 / Zillo

☐ **GET A BOARD**

SRD 1007 / 6 Apr '98 / Satan

☐ **GET DANCIN' (16 Original Soul Hits)**

12214 / Jan '94 / Laserlight

☐ **GET DANCING**

MU 5044 / Oct '92 / Musketeer

☐ **GET DANCING**

PDSCD 513 / Sep '97 / Pulse

☐ **GET DOWN TONIGHT**

PLSCD 143 / Apr '96 / Pulse

☐ **GET EASY VOL.3 (French Pops Collection)**

5537392CD / 16 Oct '97 / Motor

☐ **GET EASY VOL.4**

5535982CD / 16 Oct '97 / Motor

☐ **GET HOT OR GO HOME (Vintage RCA Rockabillies 1956-1959 - 2CD Set)**
Duck tail: Clay, Joe / Sixteen chicks: Clay, Joe / Doggone it: Clay, Joe / Goodbye goodbye: Clay, Joe / Slipping out and sneaking in: Clay, Joe / Get on the right track baby: Clay, Joe / You look that good to me: Clay, Joe / Crackerjack: Clay, Joe / Did you mean jelly bean (what you said cabbage head): Clay, Joe / Only the rhythm rebels / Ac'cent the positive: Clay, Joe / I wancha to know: Cartey, Ric / Mellow down easy: Cartey, Ric / My babe: Cartey, Ric / Two tone shoes: Homer & Jethro / Catty Town: King, Pee Wee / Sugar sweet: Houston, David / Honky tonk mind: Blake, Tommy & the rhythm rebels / Lordy hoody: Blake, Tommy & the rhythm rebels / Now stop: Carson, Martha / Love me to pieces: Martin, Janis / Two long years: Martin, Janis / All right baby: Martin, Janis / Chicken house: Rich, Dave / Teen Billy Baby: Sprouts / Don't bug me baby: Allen, Milt / Rainbow Doll: Delli, Jimmy / It ain't right: Terry, Gordon / Let's get goin': Morgan Twins / Almost eighteen: Orbison, Roy / Little boy blue: Johnson, Hoyt

CMFCD 014 / Jan '93 / Country Music Foundation

☐ GET INLINE
Funk phenomenon: Van Helden, Armand / Got myself together: Bucketheads / Spontaneous: Spymaster & Eric Nouhan / Let yourself go: DJ Jean & Peran / Da beat goes on: Red 5 / Up to no good: Porn Kings / Jump up in the air: London Boy / Mental atmosphere: Klubber's Revenge / Fever: Jaimin & Djaybee / Real vibration (I want love): Express Of Sound / You're the one: AT Project / Take me away: Respect / People hold on: Lisa & Tori / Get freaky: Bass Symphony
DC 881394 / Jul '97 / Disky

☐ GET INTO THE GROOVE
Keep that same old feeling: Side Effect / Jazz carnival: Azymuth / Rock Creek Park: Blackbyrds / Do it fluid: Blackbyrds / Walking in rhythm: Blackbyrds / Joyous: Pleasure / Beale Street: Adams, Arthur / Dancin': McWilliams, Paulette / Midnight and you: Turrentine, Stanley / Giving it back: Hurtt, Phil / I don't know what's on your mind: Spider's Webb / Will they miss me: Simmons, David / Ghettos of the mind: Pleasure / Space bass: Slick / I don't want to be alone ranger: Watson, Johnny 'Guitar' / Sweet Dan: Everett, Betty / Let your heart be free: Rushen, Patrice
CDSEWD 034 / Jan '91 / Southbound

☐ GET LOST (2CD Set)
MPCD 02 / Nov '96 / Multiplex

☐ GET ME JESUS ON THE LINE
Good news: Staple Singers / He has a way: Greatest Harvest Choir / See how he kept me: Argo Singers / It's Jesus in me: Caravans / This may be the last time: Staple Singers / Will the circle be unbroken: Staple Singers / Working on the building: Highway QC's / I'm going through: Caravans / Please hear my call: Bells Of Joy / One talk with Jesus: Five Blind Boys Of Mississippi / Where there's a will: Five Blind Boys Of Mississippi / Father I stretch my hand to thee: Harmonizing Four / I can see everybody's Mother: Five Blind Boys Of Alabama / He saved my soul: Swan Silvertones / Oh Mary don't you weep: Swan Silvertones / Get your soul right: Swan Silvertones / What about you: Swan Silvertones / God is standing by: Soul Stirrers / Wade in the water: Harmonizing Four
REMCD 519 / Feb '98 / Reactive

☐ GET ON BOARD LITTLE CHILDREN
Get on board little children / Climbing Jacob's ladder / Go devil / Satisfied / Steal away to Jesus / Brother Noah / Charge to keep I have / Just a little talk with Jesus / Why should I worry / Jesus said if you go / In my saviour's care / Heavenly highway / Those chiming bells / Sun will never go down / Dig a little deeper / I took my master's hand / God rode into the windstorm / Take your burdens to the Lord / I John Saw / King Jesus is listening / I wanna see Jesus / Daniel / I'll rest after a while / Lord remember me / On the battlefield for the Lord / Father I Stretch my arms to thee / On my way (got my travellin' shoes)
CDCHD 537 / Feb '95 / Ace

☐ GET RHYTHM
RAUCD 031 / 27 Apr '98 / Raucous

☐ GET RIGHT WITH GOD VOL.1 (Hot Gospel 1947-1953)
Tree of life: Powers, Prophet / Blood done signed my name: Radio Four / I got good religion: National Independent Gospel Singers / Tell me why you like Roosevelt: Jackson, Otis
HTCD 01 / Jan '89 / Heritage

☐ GET SMASHED (2CD Set)
Magic touch: Audio Assault / Hardcore vibes: DJ Sy & Unknown Artist / Cloudy daze: Bang / Live at Liverpool: DJ Brisk & DJ Ham / Licence: DJ Demo / Power jam: Vinylgroover / Sailaway: Bang / Renegade master: DJ Demo / Check it out: Frantic / Rush me: DJ Sy & Unknown Artist / Let me play: DJ Brisk / You belong to me: Kingsize & Eternity / Perfect harmony: DJ Demo / Break of dawn: Bang / Muzik: Happy Rollers / Your mine: DJ Demo / Command your soul: DJ Sy & Unknown Artist / Sub dub: Seduction / Finest: DJ Demo & DJ Ham / Something like dis: Slippery Project / 14th dream: DJ Hixxy
DSRCD 005 / 20 Jul '98 / Dreamscape

☐ GET THE PARTY MOVIN'
Funkin' for Jamaica: Browne, Tom / Love come down: King, Evelyn 'Champagne' / Going back to my roots: Odyssey / Turn the beat around: Odyssey / Caribbean queen: Ocean, Billy / Flashback: Imagination / Get down Saturday night: Cheatham, Oliver / Make that move: Shalamar / Automatic: Pointer Sisters / Rock the boat: Hues Corporation / Blame it on the boogie: Big Fun / You make me feel: Sylvester / Can you feel the force: Real Thing / Shout: Isley Brothers / Rescue me: Bass, Fontella / Shaft: Hayes, Isaac / Wade in the water: Lewis, Ramsey
ASTCD 4003 / Oct '97 / Go On Deluxe

☐ GET THE RHYTHM (2CD Set)
24302 / May '94 / Delta Doubles

☐ GET WEAVING VOL.1
GWCD 001 / Jun '92 / Weaving

☐ GET WEAVING VOL.2 (The Cajun/ Zydeco Collection)
GWD 02CD / Aug '93 / Weaving

☐ GET WEAVING VOL.3 (Country & Americana)
GWCD 006 / Mar '96 / Weaving

☐ GET WITH THE BEAT - THE MAR-VEL MASTERS (A Lost Decade of American Rock & Roll)
Get with the beat: Nix, Billy / Honky tonkin' rhythm: Sisco, Bobby / Come on let's go: Dallis, Chuck / Jump baby jump: Carter, Harry / My friend: Dallis, Chuck / Seven lonely days: Carter, Ginny / Out of the picture: Bradshaw, Jack / I'm settin' you free: Allen, Harold & J T Watts / I need some lovin': Allen, Harold / Heartsick and blue: Wall, Rem / Count down: Smith, Lorenzo / Hot lips baby: Duncan, Herbie / Ha ha hey hey: Kimbrough, Mel / Would it matter at all: Gatlin, Jim / Boogie woogie baby of mine: Burton, Bob / I don't want you: Carter, Harry / Basil Smith stomp: Smith, Basil / Way you're treating me: Gatlin, Jim / Forty acres of my heart: Burton, Bob / Panhandle rag: Durbin, Ronnie / A-sleepin' at the foot: Ashford, Shorty / Let me love you: Hall, Billy / Ronnie's boogie: Durbin, Ronnie / Tired of rocking: Burton, Bob / Itchy feet: Jennings, Rex / Sweet Lucy: Ashford, Shorty
RCD 20126 / Feb '93 / Rykodisc

☐ GET YOUR KICKS ON ROUTE 66 (2CD Set)
Highway star: Deep Purple / Saturday Night Special: Lynyrd Skynyrd / River deep mountain high: Turner, Ike & Tina / Locomotion: Grand Funk Railroad / Goin' up country: Canned Heat / Mama told me not to come: Three Dog Night / Carlifornia dreaming: Mamas & The Papas / God only knows: Beach Boys / Let's live for today: Grass Roots / Jenny take a rie: Grass Roots / Viva tirado: El Chicano / House of the rising sun: Animals / Tobacco road: Nashville Teens / Roll over Beethoven: ELO / Blowin' free: Wishbone Ash / (Get your kicks on) Route 66: Dr. Feelgood / Hush: Deep Purple / Gimme purple: Grand Funk Railroad / What's your name: Lynyrd Skynyrd / I'd love to change the world: Ten Years After / Midnight Confessions: Grass Roots / Woodstock: Matthew's Southern Comfort / Dizzy: Roe, Tommy / I saw her again last night: Mamas & The Papas / We've gotta get out of this place: Animals / Day that curly Billy shot crazy Sam McGee: Hollies / If you gotta go go now: Manfred Mann / It's a long way there: Little River Band / Give up your guns: Buoys / Polk Salad Annie: White, Tony Joe
DOU 886712 / 2 Feb '98 / Disky

☐ GETTIN' IT OFF - WESTBOUND FUNK
Gettin' it off (Instrumental): Haskins, Fuzzy / Just us: Crowd Pleasers / Thinking single: Counts / Funk it down: Frazier, Ceasar / Super funk: Erasmus Hall / In the pocket: Boots & His Buddies / Walt's first trip: Ohio Players / Funky world part 1 and 2: Silky Vincent / Get down with the get down: Sparks, Melvin / Super J: Morrison, Junie / Which way do I disco: Haskins, Fuzzy / Be what you is: US Music & Funkadelic / Funky Beethoven: Anderson, Gene / Crazy legs: Austin, Donald / What's up front that counts: Counts / Loose booty: Funkadelic / Satan's boogie: Ohio Players / Sweet thing: Houston Outlaws / Hit it and quit it: Bobby Franklin's insanity / Hicky Burr: Frazier, Ceasar
CDSEWD 061 / Apr '93 / Westbound

☐ GHAFRAN
MFTEQ 931 / Jun '93 / NMC

☐ GHANA - ANCIENT CEREMONIES/ DANCE MUSIC & SONGS
7559720822 / Jan '95 / Nonesuch

☐ GHANA - THE NORTHERN TRIBES
LYRCD 7321 / '91 / Lyrichord

☐ GHETTO BLASTER VOL.1
KTR 100022 / Dec '96 / K-Town

☐ GHETTO BLASTER VOL.2
KTR 100032 / 13 Oct '97 / K-Town

☐ GHETTO CELEBRITY
BB 2811 / Apr '95 / Blue Beat

☐ GHETTO FEEL
Part time lover: Yinka / Bustin' outta play pen: Da Bigg Kidz / Get with you tonight: Montage / Friend not a lover: Serenade / You make me feel: Rhythm Within / Don't lead me on: Serenade / Blast from the past: Da Bigg Kidz / Come correct: Yinka / Tell me: Da Fellas / You're the one for me: Montage
CDMISH 1 / Dec '93 / Mission

☐ GHOSTS OF CHRISTMAS PAST
TWI 0582 / Jan '91 / Les Disques Du Crepuscule

☐ GI JIVE
GI jive: Miller, Glenn / At last: Miller, Glenn / My blue heaven: Miller, Glenn / Money is the root of all evil: Andrews Sisters / Rumours are flying: Andrews Sisters / Coax me a little: Andrews Sisters / Shoo shoo baby: Andrews Sisters / One meat ball: Andrews Sisters / Who's sorry now: Miller, Glenn / Put the blame on Mame: Herth, Milt Trio / Who told you that lie: Boswell, Connee & The Paulette Sisters / Come to baby do: Dorsey, Jimmy Orchestra / You always hurt the one you love: Barnet, Charlie Orchestra / Little John Ordinary: Barnet, Charlie Orchestra / Serenade in blue: Langford, Frances / Jumpin' jive: Hampton, Lionel & His Orchestra / Into each life some rain must fall: Barnet, Charlie Orchestra / Yes indeed: Dorsey, Tommy & His Orchestra / I'm gonna see my baby: Moore, Phil Four / Together: Moore, Phil Four / I'm beginning to see the light: Fitzgerald, Ella & The Ink Spots
RAJCD 888 / Nov '97 / Empress

☐ GI JUKEBOX (100 Original Hits From The Swing Era 1936-46 - 5CD Set)
H5CD 3345 / Sep '93 / Hindsight

☐ GI JUKEBOX VOL.2
HCD 2002 / Sep '93 / Hindsight

☐ GI JUKEBOX VOL.4
HCD 2004 / Sep '93 / Hindsight

☐ GI JUKEBOX VOL.5
HCD 2005 / Sep '93 / Hindsight

☐ GIANT JINGLES - 60 OF THE BEST FROM THE 70'S
GJ 001CD / Nov '93 / Giant Jingles

☐ GIANT JINGLES - 99 ORIGINAL CUTS
GJ 003CD / Nov '93 / Giant Jingles

☐ GIANTS OF COUNTRY (4CD Set)
HADCDMS 4 / Oct '96 / Javelin

☐ GIANTS OF JAZZ COLLECTION, THE (2CD Set)
CDB 912 / Jan '93 / Giants Of Jazz

☐ GIANTS OF ROCK
MACCD 119 / Aug '96 / Autograph

☐ GIANTS OF ROCK 'N' ROLL VOL.1
11819 / Feb '96 / Music

☐ GIANTS OF ROCK 'N' ROLL VOL.2
11820 / Feb '96 / Music

☐ GIANTS OF ROCK 'N' ROLL VOL.3
11821 / Feb '96 / Music

☐ GIANTS OF ROCK 'N' ROLL, THE (4CD Set)
SUMBX 4003 / Jan '98 / Summit

☐ GIANTS OF TRADITIONAL JAZZ
Shim-me-sha-wabble / Slow drivin' (part one) / Slow drivin' (part two) / Ostrich walk / Cake walking babies / Joplin's sensation / Chrysanthemum / Entertainer / Fidgety feet / Indiana / Some of these days / Black and blue / Who's sorry now / When it's sleepy time down South / I told you once, I told you twice / Georgia on my mind / Clarinet marmalade / Joe's blues / Village blues / Tiger rag / Memphis blues / Squeeze me / Mighty like a rose / Careless love / Please don't talk about me when I'm gone / Bugie call rag / When a woman loves a man / You made me love you / My ideal / Lime house blues
SV 0277 / Oct '97 / Savoy Jazz

☐ GIFT OF IRISH MUSIC, A (3CD Set)
TDCD 301 / 16 Mar '98 / Dara

☐ GIMME A BREAK VOL.1 (Floor Rocking Big Beats - Mixed By Danmass)
Saint: Spaghetti Surfers / Bomb: Mr. Dan / Racerbil: Mushroomers / Chinese friend: Stuntmen / Moog attacks: Moog / Gotta learn: Danmass / B-boy stance: Freestylers & Tenor Fly / 4 tha ho's: Jeep Beat Collective / Dust2rust: Koku / Bad magic: LHB / Duck on a bike: Pendulum / Cause and effect: Terminal Head / Fruit: Scope / Rockit: Emperor Sly / International: Laidback / Black box: Danmass
KOFCD 201 / 9 Mar '98 / Kettle Of Fish

☐ GIMME SHELTER
EINCD 1 / 9 Mar '98 / Einnor

☐ GIN HOUSE BLUES
What have you done to make me feel this way: Smith, Mamie / Graysom Street blues: Johnson, Margaret / Gin house blues: Smith, Bessie / Sweet Virginia blues: Smith, Mamie / Low down dirty: McGraw, Lether / When a 'gator hollers, folk say its a sign of rain: Johnson, Margaret / After you've gone: Smith, Bessie / Way after one and my daddy ain't come home yet: Winston, Edna / Rent man blues: Winston, Edna / Goin' crazy with the blues: Smith, Mamie / Hard driving papa: Smith, Bessie / If you're a viper: Howard, Rosetta / Do your duty: McGraw, Lether / My daddy rocks me (Parts 1 and 2): Smith, Trixie / I've lost my head over you: Hines, Babe / I'm tired of fattenin' frogs for snakes: Crawford, Rosetta / Young woman's blues: Smith, Bessie / Double crossin' papa: Crawford, Rosetta / This is the end: Hines, Babe / What's the matter now: Smith, Bessie
PASTCD 9788 / Jun '92 / Flapper

☐ GIRL FROM IPANEMA, THE (Samba & Bossa Nova)
CD 56046 / Nov '94 / Jazz Roots

☐ GIRL FROM IPANEMA, THE
CD 62022 / Jan '93 / Saludos Amigos

☐ GIRL POWER (2CD Set)
RADCD 56 / Feb '97 / Global TV

☐ GIRL POWER (4CD Set)
ECD 3445 / 3 Aug '98 / K-Tel

☐ GIRL TALK
Marie Celeste: Adverse, Anthony / Lemon tarts: Bad Dream Fancy Dress / Marvellous boy: Would-Be-Goods / Libera me: Cagliostra / Oh Constance: Marden Hill / Man of mine: Florentines / Perfect dear: Would-Be-Goods / Rave up: Bad Dream Fancy Dress / Curtain: Marden Hill / Camera loves me: Would-Be-Goods / Goodbye again: Adverse, Anthony
ACME 20CD / 15 Jun '98 / El

☐ GIRLS AND GUITARS VOL.1
Stay I missed you: Loeb, Lisa / Show me heaven: McKee, Maria / Constant craving: Lang, k.d. / Rooms on fire: Nicks, Stevie / Hazy shade of winter: Bangles / Love and affection: Armatrading, Joan / I believe: Detroit, Marcella / Hold on: Wilson Phillips / Chuck e's in love: Jones, Rickie Lee / Blue: Mitchell, Joni / You've placed a chill in my heart: Eurythmics / You're so vain: Simon, Carly / Luka: Vega, Suzanne / At 17: Ian, Janis / Good tradition: Tikaram, Tanita / Good times: Brickell, Edie / Anchorage: Shocked, Michelle / From a distance: Griffith, Nanci / Passionate kisses: Carpenter, Mary-Chapin / Girls and guitars: Judd, Wynonna
RADCD 06 / Feb '95 / Global TV

☐ GIRLS FROM IPANEMA, THE (The Best Of Bossa Nova/2CD Set)
8413962 / Jan '90 / Verve

☐ GIRLS GIRLS GIRLS
TMPCD 009 / Jan '95 / Temple

☐ GIRLS GIRLS GIRLS
12522 / May '95 / Laserlight

☐ GIRLS GIRLS GIRLS
RNCD 2112 / Jul '95 / Rhino

☐ GIRLS GIRLS GIRLS
I heard it through the grapevine: Reeves, Martha / Rescue me: Bass, Fontella / My guy: Wells, Mary / Gee whiz: Thomas, Carla / Baby it's you: Shirelles / Love makes a woman: Acklin, Barbara / He's a rebel: Crystals / Midnight at the oasis: Muldaur, Maria / I will: Winters, Ruby / Just one look: Troy, Doris / It's in his kiss (the shoop shoop song): Everett, Betty / Heatwave: Reeves, Martha / BABY: Thomas, Carla / I'm a woman: Muldaur, Maria / There's no other: Crystals / I know (you don't love me no more): George, Barbara / Two lovers: Wells, Mary / Will you still love me tomorrow: Shirelles
ECD 3125 / Jan '95 / K-Tel

☐ GIRLS GIRLS GIRLS
10532 / Jun '97 / A-Play Collection

☐ GIRLS GIRLS GIRLS
Kids in America: Wilde, Kim / China in your hands: T'Pau / Walking on sunshine: Katrina & The Waves / Sunglasses: Ullman, Tracey / Love is a battlefield: Benatar, Pat / French kissin' in the USA: Harry, Deborah / Nutbush city limits: Turner, Ike & Tina / I touch myself: Divinyls / All I wanna do is make love to you: Heart / Let's spend the night together: Turner, Tina / In the heat of the night: Sandra / Hold on: Wilson Phillips / Denis: Blondie / If you can't give me love: Quatro, Suzi / Bette Davis eyes: Carnes, Kim / Morning train (nine to five): Easton, Sheena
DC 886552 / 2 Feb '98 / Disky

☐ GIRLS GIRLS GIRLS
Will you love me tomorrow: Shirelles / Remember (walking in the sand): Shangri-Las / I wanna love him so bad: Jelly beans / Down the aisle: Labelle, Patti & The Bluebells / Iko iko: Dixie Cups / I wonder: Butterflies / Foolish little girl: Shirelles / You don't have to be a baby to cry: Caravelles / Baby be mine: Jelly beans / Leader of the pack: Shangri-Las / I sold my heart to the junkman: Labelle, Patti & The Bluebells / Welcome to my heart: Bouquets / Chapel of love: Dixie Cups / You should have seen the way he looked at me: Jelly beans / Chains: Cookies / Give him a great big kiss: Shangri-Las / People say: Dixie Cups / Goodnight baby: Butterflies
308632 / Jun '98 / Hallmark

☐ GIRLS GO SKA
SD 002CD / 1 Sep '97 / Simmerdown Productions

☐ GIRLS IN GARAGE VOL.2
UFOX 122 / Jul '97 / Romulan

☐ GIRLS OF REGGAE
Girlie girlie: George, Sophia / First cut is the deepest: Penn, Dawn / Rock my soul: Griffiths, Marcia / Angel of the morning: Jones, Barbara / Own true love: Davis, Maureen / Love me for a reason: Miller, Maxine / O mama: Dean, Nora / Cry me a river: Davis, Carlene / Dynamic: Paula / Baby lay down: Schaffer, Doreen / All the way in or all the way out: Schloss, Cynthia / Just for a night: Sterling, Yvonne / Ba bo ba: Griffiths, Marcia / Love again: George, Sophia / Come to me softly: Davis, Carlene / Heroes: Ford, Charmaine / Happy anniversary: Schloss, Cynthia / Could I have this dance: Schaffer, Doreen
ECD 3317 / Jun '97 / K-Tel

☐ GIRLS' SOUND 1957-1966, THE (2CD Set)
DBG 53032 / Jun '94 / Double Gold

☐ GIROTONDO (3CD Set)
EVECD 98002 / 6 Jul '98 / Eve

☐ GIVE 'EM ENOUGH BEATS
WALLCD 4 / May '95 / Wall Of Sound

☐ GIVE 'EM ENOUGH DOPE VOL.1
WALLCD 001 / Feb '95 / Wall Of Sound

☐ GIVE 'EM ENOUGH DOPE VOL.3
WALLCD 010 / Sep '96 / Wall Of Sound

☐ GIVE 'EM THE BOOT
Brothels: Rancid / Watch this: Slacker / Can't wait: Hepcat / New breed: Pietasters / Spirit of the streets: Business / Los hombres no lloran: Voodoo Glowskulls / Barroom hereos: Dropkick Murphys / SkDoes he love you: Skinner Box / 17 at 17: Upbeat / OPen season: Upbeat / Beautiful girl: Gadjits / Roots radical: Union 13 / Jaks: US Bombs / Fifteenth and T: Swinging Utters / Latin goes ska: Skatalites / Policeman: Silencers / Heart like a lion: Pressure Point / Infested: Choking Victim / No time: F-Minus / Playtime: Hillyard, Dave Rocksteady 7
04022 / Jul '97 / Epitaph

☐ GIVE ME A HOME AMONG THE GUM TREES
LARRCD 232 / Nov '94 / Larrikin

☐ GLAD I'M A GIRL
EFA 061942 / Aug '95 / House In Motion

☐ GLAD TO BE GAY VOL.1
Don't leave me this way: Communards / You make me feel: Sylvester / Smalltown boy: Bronski Beat / Tainted love: Soft Cell / Shoot your shot: Divine / High energy: Thomas, Evelyn / I am what I am: Gaynor, Gloria / Crucified: Army Of Lovers / Do you really want to hurt me: Culture Club / I love men: Kitt, Eartha / Heaven in pain: Our Heaven & Darrian Huss / Where is my man: Kitt, Eartha / I'm too sexy: Right Said Fred / You think you're a man: Divine / Boogie woogie dancing shoes: Barry, Claudja / Persuasion: Martin, Billie Ray & Spooky
SPV 08493982 / Dec '96 / SPV

☐ GLAD TO BE GAY VOL.2
Why: Bronski Beat / Can't take my eyes off you: Boystown Gang / West End Girls: Pet Shop Boys / I'm on fire: Salico / Power of love: Texture / Somebody else's guy: Brown, Jocelyn / Wind beneath my wings: New York City Gay Men's Chorus / Angel lies sleeping: Psyche / Fly to me: Aleph / Knock on wood: Hot Stuff
SPV 08496232 / Dec '96 / SPV

☐ GLAD TO BE GAY VOL.3
Heartbeat: Somerville, Jimmy / I believe: Roland, Calvin / Hand up lovers: Right Said Fred / It's raining men: Weather Girls / Blame it on the boogie: Big Fun / Let me be your underwear: Club 69 / Sex Dwarf: Soft Cell / I'm so beautiful: Divine / In the navy: Village People / Legendary children (all of them

queer): Johnson, Holly / Free gay and happy (coming out anthem): *Coming Out Krew* / Lover come back to me: *Dead Or Alive* / She drives me crazy: *Fine Young Cannibals* / Walk on the wide side: *No Soul* / Rumpelstilzchen: *Golden Shower*
CD 08589912 / Dec '96 / SPV

☐ **GLAM PARTY SUPERMIX (The Glam Rock All-Stars)**
Hello hello I'm back again / I'm the leader of the gang I am / Glisten yeah / Rock 'n' roll part 1 / I didn't know I loved you (till I saw you rock'n'roll) / Do you wanna touch me (Oh yeah) / I love you love me love / Blockbuster / Teenage rampage / Wig-wam bam / Ballroom blitz / Hell raiser / Fox on the run / Daytona demon / Can the can / Devilgate Drive / 48 Crash / You you you / Red dress / My coo ca choo / Jealous mind / Hot love / Metal guru / Get it on / 20th century boy / Shang-a-lang / All of me loves all of you / Remember (sha-la-la) / Bye bye baby / Skweeze me pleeze me / Cum on feel the noize / Mama weer all crazee now / Gudbuy t'Jane / Tears I cried / Let's get together again / Angelface / Goodbye my love / Waterloo / Mamma Mia / SOS / Dynamite / Crazy / L-L-Lucy / Tiger feet / Rebel rebel / Diamond dogs / Jean Genie / John I'm only dancing / Bump / Fancy pants / Sugar baby love / I can do it / Tell him / New York groove / Glass of champagne / (Dancing) On a Saturday night
3036000762 / Feb '97 / Carlton

☐ **GLAM ROCK SPECIAL**
12539 / May '95 / Laserlight

☐ **GLAMTASTIC 70'S MEGA MIX**
Yeah glisten / Rock 'n' roll / Do you wanna touch me / Can the can / Devil gate drive / 48 crash / My coo ca choo / Jealous mind / Blockbuster / Hot love / Metal guru / Get it on / Sugar baby love / Dynamite / Angel face / Goodbye my love / Cum on feel the noize / Mama weer all crazee now / Gudbuy t'Jane / Son of my father / Jean Genie / Waterloo / Mama mia / SOS / Glass of champagne / On a Saturday night / Do you wanna dance / Summer love sensation / Bye bye baby / All the way from Memphis / Roll away the stone / Honaloochie boogie / School's out / Elected / This town ain't big enough for the both of us / Amateur hour / Virginia plain / Angel fingers / See my baby jive / Touch too much / Saturday night alright / Crocodile rock / Tiger feet / John I'm only dancing / Ballroom blitz / Hell raiser / Fox on the run / I can do it / Tell him / Hello hello I'm back agin / I'm the leader of the gang / Yeah glisten
EMPRCD 753 / 6 Oct '97 / Emporio

☐ **GLASGOW UNDERGROUND VOL.1**
Just a mood: *Studio Blue* / Two fisted smoke: *Preston, Rick* / Keep on dancin': *Mateo & Matos* / Freak vibrations: *Carrick, Andy* / Baby love: *Cassio* / Black America: *Muzique Tropique* / Original porn king: *DJ Q* / Late night jam: *Sixteen Souls* / Do you think you can love me: *Romanthony & Naida*
GUCD 003 / 1 Jun '98 / Glasgow Underground

☐ **GLASS OF CHAMPAGNE**
10452 / Jun '97 / A-Play Collection

☐ **GLASTONBURY LIVE '97 (Mud For It)**
VTCD 153 / 25 Aug '97 / Virgin

☐ **GLEN OF TRANQUILLITY**
Rosebud / Annie Laurie / Glen of tranquillity / Morning has broken / My heart is in the highlands / Rowan tree / Flow gently sweet Afton / Mother nature's son / Rest thy weary head / Come oe'r the stream Charlie / Wee highland glen / Land o' the Leel / Ye banks and braes
RECD 512 / Dec '97 / REL

☐ **GLENFIDDICH PIPING CHAMPIONSHIP (Ceol Mor Piobaireachd)**
CDMON 811 / Jul '94 / Monarch

☐ **GLENFIDDICH PIPING CHAMPIONSHIP (Ceol Beag - March, Strathspey & Reel)**
CDMON 812 / Jul '94 / Monarch

☐ **GLITTERS IS GOLD**
Tyger tyger: *Jah Wobble* / Songs of innocence: *Jah Wobble* / Whole wide world: *Eno, Roger* / In water: *Eno, Roger* / Sidelong glance from my round Nefertiti: *Budd, Harold* / Feral: *Budd, Harold* / Swanky: *Eno, Brian* / Blissed: *Eno, Brian* / Coventry carol: *St. John, Kate* / Notti senza amore: *St. John, Kate* / Sphere of no form: *Biosphere* / Kobresia: *Biosphere*
ASCD 031 / May '97 / All Saints

☐ **GLOBAL BRAZILIANS**
EFA 064622 / Aug '95 / Metalimbo

☐ **GLOBAL CELEBRATION (4CD Set)**
ELLICD 3230 / Apr '94 / Ellipsis Arts

☐ **GLOBAL CUTS VOL.1**
Piano power: *Remy & Sven* / 20 Hz: *Capricorn* / Hectic boogie: *X-Tatic* / Hammond groove: *Mr. Marvin* / Monkey forest: *X-Tatic* / Cool lemon: *Cool Lemon* / Tsjika boem tsjak: *Remy & Sven* / Ride the wave: *Manpower* / Warwick: *Fowlkes, Eddie 'Flashin'* / LFOhhhh: *Remy & Sven* / Tribal zone: *OHM* / Crystal clear: *Soul Searchers*
RSGC 012CD / Jul '93 / Global Cuts

☐ **GLOBAL CUTS VOL.2**
In thee garden: *Aphrohead* / Soul glow: *Soap Factory* / Planet jupiter 6: *Van Hees, Sven* / Saints go marching on: *K-Hand* / Smoke: *Dynetic* / Inside your mind: *God* / One dance: *Fowlkes, Eddie 'Flashin'* / Psychedelic bellydance: *Van Hees, Sven* / Harder: *FRS* / Drop (take off): *Symmetrics* / Lush: *Orbital* / Dynetic: *Smoke*
RSGC 026CD / Nov '95 / Global Cuts

☐ **GLOBAL DIVAS (3CD Set)**
ROUCD 5062/3/4 / Dec '95 / Rounder

☐ **GLOBAL EXPLORER**
ZD 17CD / 10 Nov '97 / Zip Dog

☐ **GLOBAL HOUSE GROOVES VOL.1**
BDRCD 2 / Jul '94 / Breakdown

☐ **GLOBAL HOUSE GROOVES VOL.2**
BDRCD 7 / Apr '95 / Breakdown

☐ **GLOBAL HOUSE VOL.1**
SUN 49892 / Nov '95 / Mokum

☐ **GLOBAL HOUSE VOL.2**
SUN 49882 / May '96 / Mokum

☐ **GLOBAL MEDITATION (4CD Set)**
ELL 3210 / Oct '93 / Ellipsis Arts

☐ **GLOBAL NITE LIFE VOL.1 (4CD Set)**
Disco love: *Uncut Grooves* / Will there be: *Anorak Trax* / Surrender: *Love De Luxe* / Work: *Dynamic Kutz* / Funky groove: *Windross, Norris* / What is going on: *Dex* / Cookie crumbs: *Bash Street Kids* / Falling like dominoes: *Jazzheads* / Don't go away: *Mauritio* / Native love: *Wild Women Of Wonga* / So addicted: *XXX & Eliza* / Can't fight this feeling: *Hyper Rhythm* / Chant: *Gangster Hood Corp* / Nature: *Nature* / Luv it up: *Jump* / Trance dance: *Njoko* / Thank you: *Wild Women Of Wonga* / Gotta get loose: *Must* / No rich fat Daddy: *Jump* / Samarkand: *MLO* / Way down inside: *Fat Tulips* / Perfect chaos: *Justice* / Place called acid: *Thursday Club* / Ooh boy: *Ellis D* / My generation: *Peter Piper* / Space traveller: *New London Jazz Connection* / Squelch: *Finitribe* / On T go: *RAW* / Give me a wink: *Fingers Project* / Ska kore: *Mass Energy* / Beyond motion: *Incisions* / London's on acid: *Cabbage Patch* / Calling the people: *A-Zone* / In the heart of the night: *Overhead Noise* / Ibiza: *Denia* / To amora: *Mamba*
GLNCD 001 / Jul '97 / Global Nite Life

☐ **GLOBAL PARTNERSHIP VOL.2**
RGNET 1003CD / Oct '95 / World Music Network

☐ **GLOBAL PSYCHEDELIC TRANCE COMPILATION VOL.1**
Zoa: *Kuro* / Solar energy: *Electric Universe* / Telepathy: *Infinity Project* / Seventh L: *Crossbreed* / Harddome 140: *Adrenalin Drum* / Neutron dance: *Electric Universe* / Binary neuronaut: *Infinity Project* / Hypnotiser: *Adrenalin Drum* / Brix: *Crossbreed*
SPIRIT 4006 / May '95 / Spiritzone

☐ **GLOBAL RHYTHM VOL.2 (4CD Set)**
GNLCD 002 / 8 Dec '97 / Global Nite Life

☐ **GLOBAL UNDERGROUND SAMPLER**
Air: *Albion* / Beachball: *Nalin & Kane* / Summersault: *Taste Xperience* / Down the river: *Hong Kong Trash* / Lose it: *Desert* / Submissions: *Freak & Mac Zimms* / Tranceilliusion: *VFR* / Waters: *Taucher* / Axiational: *EJ Doubell* / Delicious: *Bush Babies* / Reality detatched: *Forth* / Stargazer: *Deepsky* / Breathe in me: *Tekara* / Sex drive: *Private Productions* / Cafe del mar: *Energy 52* / 3 drives on vinyl: *Greece 2000* / Indica: *Pink Bomb*
GUSAM 1CD / 7 Sep '98 / Global Underground

☐ **GLOBESTYLE WORLDWIDE - YOUR GUIDE**
Saludando / Yachilvi veyachail / Kesetse Mahiomolenu / Chorepste / Raha manina / Sirvientas / El anillo / Le Brijano / Iyole / El Beso / Ah laa jarah / Knowale / Chedh Hime Dh'Loumayere / Fuego Lento / Les Dorlanes / Feam Baliha
CDORB 018 / Mar '88 / Globestyle

☐ **GLOBUS HOUSE MIX VOL.2**
Intro: *Baxter, Blake* / One more time: *Baxter, Blake* / I've got something: *Disco Freaks* / Smooth: *Basic Bastard* / Drum major: *Baxter, Blake* / Touch me/X press 2: *Baxter, Blake* / Bounce: *Markey* / These sounds lead the way: *K-Hand* / Go Miss Thing: *Jack & Jill* / Sexuality: *Baxter, Blake* / Get your hands of my man: *Vasquez, Junior* / Brother gonna work it out: *Baxter, Blake* / Disko: *Baxter, Blake* / From the ghetto funk: *Fix* / Visions of you: *Rockcliffe, Trevor & Blake Baxter* / When we used to play: *Baxter, Blake* / Outro: *Baxter, Blake*
EFA 292982 / 24 Aug '98 / Tresor

☐ **GLOBUS MIX VOL.1 (Mixed By Mitja Prinz)**
EFA 292932 / 2 Mar '98 / Tresor

☐ **GLORIOUS SUNRISE (A Magical Blend Of Music And The Sounds Of Nature)**
57612 / May '97 / Nature's Harmony

☐ **GLORY OF CHRISTMAS, THE (4CD Set)**
O come all ye faithful (adeste fidelis) / God rest ye merry gentlemen / Holly and the ivy / Unto us is born a son / Once in Royal David's city / Silent night / Away in a manger / It came upon a midnight clear / I saw three ships / O little town of Bethlehem / Ding dong merrily on high / Hark the herald angels sing / First Noel / Deck the halls / Coventry carol / While shepherd's watch / Good King Wenceslas / In the bleak mid winter / Infant holy, infant lowly / We wish you a merry Christmas / O little town of Bethlehem / O come all ye faithful (adeste fidelis) / God rest ye merry gentlemen / Silent night / Hark the herald angels sing / While shepherds watched their flocks / Good King Wenceslas / We wish you a merry Christmas / Twelve days of Christmas / Torches / Christmas is coming / Of the father's heart begotten / Personent hodie / O come, O coem Emmanuel / Holly and the ivy / As with gladness men of old / We three Kings / Personent hodie / Infant King / Quiem pastores laudavere / In dulci jubilo / Sussex carol / Adam lay y bounden / Whence is that goodly fragrance / Of the Father's heart begotten / In the bleak mid winter / Cherry tree carol / Tomorrow shall be my dancing day / Virgin most pure / O come, O come Emmanuel / Joys seven / Twelve days of Christmas / See amid the winter's snow / Past three o'clock / Jingle bells / King Jesus hath a garden / Shepherd's pipe carol / Christmas is coming / Sans day carol / Torches / Great and mighty wonder / Angels from the realms of glory / Jesus Christ the apple tree / O little town of Bethlehem / Infant holy, infant lowly / Candlelight carol / Once in Royal David's City / Star carol / In the winter darkness / Carol of the children / Here comes Christmas / Silver sleigh / Christmas cheer / Away in a manger / Nativity carol / I saw three ships / In the bleak mid winter / Mary had a baby / Sussex carol / Little Jesus sweetly slept / While shepherds watched their flocks / Child in the manger / Unto us is born a son / Cowboy carol
QUAD 019 / Nov '96 / Tring

☐ **GLORY OF GOSPEL (2CD Set)**
DEMPCD 003 / Mar '96 / Emporio

☐ **GLORY OF ITALY**
CDMOIR 420 / May '93 / Memoir

☐ **GLORY OF LOVE**
12204 / Dec '94 / Laserlight

☐ **GLORY OF SPAIN**
CDMOIR 416 / Oct '92 / Memoir

☐ **GLORY OF THE MUSIC HALL VOL.1, THE**
Let's have a song upon the gramophone: *Williams, Billy* / Seaside holiday at home: *Campbell, Herbert* / Man who broke the bank at Monte Carlo: *Coborn, Charles* / Two lovely black eyes: *Coborn, Charles* / Topsy turvy: *Roberts, Arthur* / Fishing club: *Anderson, Harry* / I wouldn't leave my little wooden hut for you: *Shepard, Burt* / Something tickled her fancy: *Randall, Harry* / Our little nipper: *Chevalier, Albert* / Adam missed it: *Knowles, R.G.* / Girl, the woman and the widow: *Knowles, R.G.* / Little Dolly Daydream: *Stratton, Eugene* / Wait 'til I'm his father: *Leno, Dan* / Wait 'til the work comes round: *Elen, Gus* / Never introduce yer Donah to a pal: *Elen, Gus* / There's another fellow looks like me: *Lashwood, George* / Piccaninny: *Hurley, Alec* / What a nut: *Tilley, Vesta* / There's a good time coming for the ladies: *Tilley, Vesta* / You can't help laughing can yer: *Champion, Harry* / Wotcher, my old brown son: *Champion, Harry* / Paperbag cookery: *Fragson, Harry* / Goodbye Dolly Gray: *Stormont, Leo* / Belgium put the kibosh on the Kaiser: *Sheridan, Mark* / Here we are again: *Sheridan, Mark*
GEMMCD 9475 / Feb '91 / Pearl

☐ **GLORY OF THE MUSIC HALL VOL.2, THE**
Poor, proud and particular: *Ford, Harry* / Tally ho: *Little Tich* / Best man: *Little Tich* / Editress: *Robey, George* / Servants' registry office: *Robey, George* / Something on his mind: *Lloyd, Marie* / Wee Jean McGregor: *Lauder, Harry* / Rob Roy-Tam-O-Chanter O'Brian: *Lauder, Harry* / Cuckoo: *Wallace, Nellie* / Mother's pie crust: *Wallace, Nellie* / Honeysuckle and the bee: *Davies, Belle* / While you wait: *Albert, Ben* / I'll be your sweetheart: *Hawthorne, Lil* / Fishing: *Tate, Harry* / I was having my breakfast in bed: *Mayo, Sam* / Put that gramophone record on again: *Mayo, Sam* / I shall sulk: *Pleasants, Jack* / I'm shy, Mary Ellen, I'm shy: *Pleasants, Jack* / Give it a smile: *Whelan, Albert* / Everybody loves me: *Terriss, Ellaline* / I can say 'truly rural': *Bard, Wilkie* / It's nice to have a friend: *Forde, Florrie* / Old Bull and Bush: *Forde, Florrie* / Come into the garden John: *Williams, Billy* / Here we go again: *Williams, Billy*
GEMMCD 9476 / Feb '91 / Pearl

☐ **GLORY OF THE MUSIC HALL VOL.3, THE**
If you knew Susie like I know Susie: *Shields, Ella* / Ours is a nice 'ouse, ours is: *Lester, Alfred* / Germs: *Lester, Alfred* / Odds and ends, or Sunday mornings: *Formby, George* / I kept on waving my flag: *Formby, George* / If the wind had only blown the other way: *Scott, Maidie* / Spaniard who blighted my life: *Merson, Billy* / I've had my future told: *Elliott, G.H.* / I can't do my bally bottom button up: *Mayne, Ernie* / Moonlight bay: *Connolly, Dolly* / Agatha Green: *Cooper, Margaret* / So long Sally: *Weldon, Harry* / What do you want to make (parody): *Weldon, Harry* / Gretchen: *Moore Duprez, May* / And it was: *Laurier, Jay* / Anna Gray: *Gitana, Gertie* / Never mind: *Gitana, Gertie* / Rickety stairs: *Latona, Jen* / Come over the garden wall: *Mayne, Clarice & That* / Mr. and Mrs. Smith: *Mayne, Clarice & That* / Don't have any more, Mrs. Moore: *Morris, Lily* / I want a girl - just like the girl that married dear old Dad: *Ward, Dorothy* / Oh Mr. Porter: *Blaney, Norah* / 'E can't take a roise out of oi: *Chevalier, Albert*
GEMMCD 9477 / Feb '91 / Pearl

☐ **GLUCKLICH VOL.2**
COMP 021CD / Jun '96 / Compost

☐ **GNAWA FROM MARRAKECH (Songs For Sidi Mimoun)**
RDC 5035CD / May '97 / Robi Droli

☐ **GO AHEAD PUNK MAKE MY DAY**
158092 / Nov '96 / Nitro

☐ **GO AHEAD VOL.3 (2CD Set)**
H&GCD 004 / Jun '97 / H&G

☐ **GO AHEAD VOL.4 (2CD Set)**
HGCD 0072 / 17 Nov '97 / Go Ahead

☐ **GO GLOBAL (Blue Flame Sampler)**
39840932 / 24 Feb '98 / Blue Flame

☐ **GO GO POWER**
Go go power: *Desanto, Sugar Pie* / Let's wade in the water: *Shaw, Marlena* / Jerk and twine: *Ross, Jackie* / Love ain't nothin': *Nash, Johnny* / Secret love: *Stewart, Billy* / In the basement: *Desanto, Sugar Pie & Etta James* / Mellow fellow: *James, Etta* / Grits ain't groceries: *Little Milton* / Ain't love good, ain't love proud: *Clarke, Tony* / Look at me now: *Callier, Terry* / Peak of love: *McClure, Bobby* / Do I make myself clear: *Desanto, Sugar Pie & Etta James* / Seven day fool: *James, Etta* / That'll get it: *Knight Brothers* / I don't wanna fuss: *Desanto, Sugar Pie* / Strange feeling: *Nash, Johnny* / Take me for a little while: *Ross, Jackie* / Love is a five letter word: *Phelps, James* / Ain't no big deal: *Little Milton*
CDARC 512 / Jan '93 / Charly

☐ **GO SKA GO**
CDHB 199 / Nov '95 / Heartbeat

☐ **GO WILD WITH THE PARTY ANIMAL (2CD Set)**
Sunchyme: *Dario G* / Everybody: *Backstreet Boys* / Where do you go: *No Mercy* / Freed from desire: *Gala* / Encore une fois: *Sash* / One and one: *Miles, Robert* / Never gonna let you down: *Moore, Tina* / Closer than close: *Gaines, Rosie* / Ready or not: *Course* / Son of a gun: *JX* / One night in heaven: *M-People* / People hold on: *Stansfield, Lisa* / Remember me: *Blueboy* / She's got that vibe: *R Kelly* / Finally: *Ce Ce Peniston* / Gonna make you sweat: *C&C Music Factory* / Do ya think I'm sexy: *N-Trance & Rod Stewart* / S express: *S'Express* / Boom boom boom: *Outhere Brothers* / Ready to go: *Republica* / Disco 2000: *Pulp* / Macarena: *Los Del Rio* / I've got a little something for you: *MN8* / House of love: *East 17* / Girls just want to have fun: *Lauper, Cyndi* / Mama weer all crazee now: *Slade* / Black betty: *Ram Jam* / Shoop shoop song: *Cher* / Jailhouse rock: *Presley, Elvis* / Rock around the clock: *Haley, Bill* / This ole house: *Stevens, Shakin'* / Reet petite: *Wilson, Jackie* / Venus: *Bananarama* / Don't go breaking my heart: *John, Elton & Kiki Dee* / Achy breaky heart: *Cyrus, Billy Ray* / Hillbilly rock hillbilly roll: *Woolpackers* / 5678: *Steps* / Ghostbusters: *Parker, Ray Jr.* / When the going gets tough: *Ocean, Billy* / Le freak: *Chic* / Give it up: *KC & The Sunshine Band* / Blame it on the boogie: *Jacksons* / Get down on it: *Kool & The Gang* / Pump up the jam: *Technotronic*
RADCD 82 / 15 Nov '97 / Global TV

☐ **GO WITH THE FLOW**
Dream on dreamer: *Brand New Heavies* / Always there: *Incognito & Jocelyn Brown* / Space cowboy: *Jamiroquai* / Apparently nothin': *Young Disciples* / Long time gone: *Galliano* / Dream's a dream: *Soul II Soul* / Everthing is going to be alright: *Sounds Of Blackness* / Real love: *Driza Bone* / Mama said: *Anderson, Carleen* / Pushing against the flow: *Raw Stylus* / Turn in turn on cop out: *Raw Stylus* / Everyday: *Incognito* / Midnight at the oasis: *Brand New Heavies* / Moving on up: *M-People* / Masterplan: *Brown, Diana & Barrie K Sharpe* / Love the life: *Taylor, James Quartet* / Won't talk about it: *Beats International* / People in tha middle: *Spearhead* / Everybody's got summer: *Atlantic Starr* / Cantaloop: *US 3*
5352412 / Feb '96 / PolyGram TV

☐ **GO-KART VS. THE CORPORATE GIANT**
GKCD 021 / Mar '97 / Go-Kart

☐ **GOA HEAD VOL.1**
560002 / Oct '96 / Westcom

☐ **GOA HEAD VOL.2 (2CD Set)**
560072 / Mar '97 / Westcom

☐ **GOA HEAD VOL.3 (2CD Set)**
Ionised: *Astral Projection* / Astral voyage: *Electric Universe* / UX: *Dominion* / Taiyo: *Prana* / *SecrPagan* dance: *Secret* / Audio engine: *Multiplex* / Neuromancer: *Shakta* / Million miles an hour: *Beach Buddha* / MiGreen man: *Miranda* / Jungle storm: *Talamasca* / Ancient forest: *Sundog* / Sunset skyline: *Electric Universe* / Zero: *Astral Projection & Dedrah* / Overwind: *Infinity Project* / Two vindaloos and an onion bhagee: *Green Nuns Of The Revolution* / Tribalistic: *Ominus* / Deep space 5d: *Dimension 5* / To eternity: *MFG* / Answer: *NDMA* / AlphaNew shoes: *Alphanaut*
560172 / Aug '97 / Nova Tekk

☐ **GOA HEAD VOL.4 (2CD Set)**
560162 / 9 Feb '98 / Nova Tekk

☐ **GOA PSYCHEDELIC (New Trips In Acid Trance)**
High energy: *Mekhala* / Chant of the sun: *Pot Heads* / Freak out: *Shamanic Tribes On Acid* / Pranayama: *Mantra* / Acidity level increase: *Acid Trip* / Mindwarper: *Dr. Psychedelic* / Psychohead: *Psychoheads* / Stoned again: *Curly Whirly Spirits* / Psychedelic temple of breakbeats: *Super Skunk* / Deep space mission: *Alien Mutation*
TRIPCD 13 / 16 Mar '98 / Rumour

☐ **GOA RAUME VOL.1 (A Journey Into Psychedelic Trance/2CD Set)**
Trommelmaschine: *Der Dritte Raum* / Braindance: *Kaaya* / Stratosfearless: *Koxbox* / UX: *Disco Volante* / Padomania: *Charm* / Zeta reticuli: *Pleindians* / Viral spiral: *Deviant Electronics* / Enter the 2nd earth: *Schuldt, Tim* / Great sin: *Spacetribe* / Psycho activity: *X-Dream* / Liquid troll: *Chakra & Edi Mis* / Satellite: *Moon & The Sun* / Step to the star: *Miranda* / Close zen counters: *Tristan* / Online information: *Electric Universe* / Pile: *Semsis* / Smell's electronic: *Metal Spark*
SPV 08992562 / Mar '97 / SPV

☐ **GOA SPIRIT VOL.2 (Hard Psychedelic Trance/2CD Set)**
3021322 / 27 Apr '98 / Techno Import

☐ **GOA TRANCE VOL.1**
TRIPCD 2 / Oct '95 / Rumour

☐ **GOA TRANCE VOL.2**
TRIPCD 3 / Jan '96 / Rumour

☐ **GOA TRANCE VOL.3**
TRIPCD 4 / May '96 / Rumour

☐ **GOA TRANCE VOL.4**
TRIPCD 6 / Aug '96 / Rumour

☐ **GOA TRANCE VOL.5**
TRIPCD 09 / Jan '97 / Rumour

☐ **GOA TRANCE VOL.6**
Project Oblivion: *Conspiracy Theory* / Spirit: *Sourmash* / Drama: *Manmademan* / Alien hitmen: *Slide* / Starkissed: *Secret* / Crowd nine: *Eco* / Abraxis: *Shining Path* / Omnifarious Splifferous: *Shamanic Tribes On Acid* / Planet Bliss: *Super Skunk* / Spectre: *Blue Book*
TRIPCD 11 / Jun '97 / Rumour

☐ **GOA TRANCE VOL.7 (2CD Set)**
TRIPCD 12 / 24 Nov '97 / Rumour

GOA TRANCENDENTAL VOL.1
TRIPCD 8 / Nov '96 / Rumour

GOA TRANCENDENTAL VOL.2
TRIPCD 10 / Mar '97 / Rumour

GOA VIBES VOL.3
20422 / 23 Mar '98 / Trust In Trance/
Phonokol

GOD IS THE OWNER OF THEE WORLD
ALCHECD 001 / Feb '94 / Spinefarm

GOD LESS AMERICA
EFACD 11595 / 29 Sep '97 / Crypt

GOD SAVE THE PUNKS (2CD Set)
Pretty vacant: Sex Pistols / Denis: Blondie / Valley of
the dolls: Generation X / Little girl: Banned / Danger
signs: Penetration / Death disco: Public Image Ltd. /
Decontrol: Discharge / Substitute: Ramones /
Peaches: Stranglers / Born to lose: Vicious, Sid /
Limbo: Fischer Z / Saints are coming: Skids /
Hanging on the telephone: Blondie / Public image:
Public Image Ltd. / Oh bondage up yours: X-Ray
Spex / Banned in DC: Bad Brains / No survivors:
GBH / Never again: Discharge / Surf city: Ramones /
Get a grip on yourself: Stranglers / Millionaires
against hunger: Red Hot Chili Peppers / Emergency:
999 / This perfect day: Saints / Everybody's happy
nowadays: Buzzcocks / No one is innocent: Sex
Pistols
DOU 882552 / 2 Feb '98 / Disky

**GOD SAVE THE QUEEN (20 Years Of
Punk - 3CD Set)**
KITOFF 50 / Apr '97 / Dressed To Kill

GODFATHERS OF BRITPOP, THE
5352572 / Jan '96 / PolyGram TV

**GODFATHERS OF GERMAN GOTH
VOL.2**
SPV 08438372 / Jul '95 / SPV

GODS OF DARKNESS
NB 285CD / 24 Nov '97 / Nuclear Blast

**GOIN' COUNTRY (The Definitive Line
Dancing Album)**
Goin' country: Watermelon Henry / There you go:
White, Martin / EJ's bar: Richmond, Simon / Country
married rock 'n' roll: Aaron & The Buzz Band / Line
dancin' days: Capricorn / Country music hall of
fame: McCall, T.J. / This don't feel like dancin': Lee,
Bobby / No honky tonks in Heaven: Hollywood
Hillbillies / Too easy: Shot To Pieces / Good times
come around: Richmond, Simon / Love my car:
Watermelon Henry / Love kept it's hold on me: Harton, Quinton
Sayer, Chris / I learnt a thing or two: Horton, Quinton
/ Ain't life wonderful: Shot To Pieces / Saddle up
country style: Christie, David / Louisiana:
Watermelon Henry / Daddy's got his blue jeans on:
Richmond, Simon / Cheap Seats / Three lime loser: Hollywood Hillbillies / Here, there
and everywhere: Cheap Seats / Situation vacant:
Northern Lights / Burnin' fire: Watermelon Henry /
Let's hear it for the ladies: Richmond, Simon
5526492 / Jan '97 / Spectrum

GOING BACK IN TIME
KWCD 807 / Jul '94 / Kenwest

**GOLDEN AGE OF AMERICAN ROCK 'N'
ROLL VOL.1, THE (Hard-To-Get Hot
100 Hits From 1954-1963)**
Denise: Randy & The Rainbows / Sally go round the
roses: Jaynetts / Mule skinner blues: Fendermen /
Sixteen candles: Crests / Pretty little angel eyes:
Lee, Curtis / Love how you love me: Paris Sisters /
Big hurt: Fisher, Miss Toni / Thousand stars: Young,
Kathy / Rockin' robin: Day, Bobby / Earth angel:
Penguins / Bongo rock: Epps, Preston / Tossin' and
turnin': Lewis, Bobby / My true story: Jive Five /
Stranded in the jungle: Cadets / Angel baby: Rosie &
The Originals / Party lights: Clark, Claudine / When
we get married: Dreamlovers / Cindy's birthday:
Crawford, Johnny / Let's dance: Montez, Chris /
Who's that knocking: Genies / Love you so: Holden,
Ron / Cherry pie: Skip & Fly / Since I don't have you:
Skyliners / Louie Louie: Kingsmen / Since I fell for
you: Welch, Lenny / Image of a girl: Safaris / Smoky
places: Corsairs / Gee whiz: Innocents / Little bit of
soap: Jarmels / Eddie my love: Teen Queens
CDCHD 289 / Oct '91 / Ace

**GOLDEN AGE OF AMERICAN ROCK 'N'
ROLL VOL.2, THE (Hot 100 Hits From
1954-1963)**
Memphis: Mack, Lonnie / I sold my heart to the
junkman: Blue Belles / You belong to me: Duprees /
Your Ma said you cried in your sleep last night: Dino,
Kenny / Million to one: Charles, Jimmy / Rockin' in
the jungle: Eternals / Wild weekend: Rockin' Rebels /
Stay: Williams, Maurice & The Zodiacs / Down the
aisle of love: Quintones / Mountain of love: Dorman,
Harold / Nag: Halos / Let the little girl dance: Bland,
Billy / There's a moon out tonight: Capris / Get a job:
Silhouettes / You: Aquatones / Buzz buzz buzz:
Hollywood Flames / I've had it: Bell Notes / I know
(you don't love me no more): George, Barbara / Mr.
Lonely: Videls / In the still of the nite: Five Satins /
Church bells may ring: Willows / That's life (that's
tough): Gabriel & the angels / Rumble: Wray, Link /
Let's stomp: Comstock, Bobby / Oh Julie:
Crescendos / Little darlin': Gladiolas / Teen beat:
Nelson, Sandy / Diamonds and pearls: Paradons /
Alley oop: Hollywood Argyles / California sun:
Rivieras
CDCHD 445 / May '93 / Ace

**GOLDEN AGE OF AMERICAN ROCK 'N'
ROLL VOL.3, THE (Hot 100 Hits From
1954-1963)**
All American boy: Parsons, Bill / Kansas City:
Harrison, Wilbert / My true love: Scott, Jack / Jennie
Lee: Jan & Arnie / Joker: Myles, Billy / Beat: Rockin
R's / To know him is to love him: Teddy Bears / When
you dance: Turbans / Love letters: Lester, Ketty / La dee
dah: Billie & Lillie / Endless sleep: Reynolds, Jody /

Chicken baby chicken: Harris, Tony / Lover's island:
Blue Jays / No chemise please: Granahan, Gerry / It
was I: Skip & Flip / Tonight I fell in love: Tokens /
Happy birthday blues: Young, Karen & The
Innocents / Rockin' little angel: Smith, Ray / Tonite
tonite: Mello Kings / Cha hua hua: Pets / Western
movies: Olympics / Girl in my dreams: Cliques /
Sugar shack: Fireballs / There is something on your
mind: McNeely, 'Big' Jay / Womans a mans best
friend: Teddy & The Twilights / Sacred: Castells /
Freeze: Tony & Joe / Click clack: Dicky Doo & Don'ts
CDCHD 497 / Jan '94 / Ace

**GOLDEN AGE OF AMERICAN ROCK 'N'
ROLL VOL.4, THE (Hot 100 Hits From
1954-1963)**
Linda Lou: Sharpe, Ray / Little by little: Brown,
Nappy / Rama lama ding dong: Edsels / Flamingo
express: Royaltones / New Orleans: Bonds / Maybe:
Chantels / Drip drop: Dion / Start movin' (in my
direction): Mined, Sal / Lonely Saturday night:
French, Don / Don't let go: Hamilton, Roy / Pop pop
pop-pie: Sherrys / Life's too short: Harris, Lafayette
Jr. / High school USA: Facenda, Tommy / Glory of
love: Roomates / Peanuts: Little Joe & The Thrillers /
Need you: Owens, Donnie / Party doll: Knox, Buddy /
Could this be magic: Dubs / Killer Joe: Rocky Fellers
/ Barbara: Temptations / Peek-a-boo: Cadillacs /
You'll lose a good thing: Lynn, Barbara / Lucky
ladybug: Billie & Lillie / Tears on my pillow: Imperials /
Baby talk: Jan & Dean / Here I stand: Rip Chords / Do
the mashed potato: Kendrick, Nat / Why don't you
write me: Jacks / Barbara Ann: Regents / Those
oldies but goodies (remind me of you): Little Caesar
& The Romans
CDCHD 500 / Oct '94 / Ace

**GOLDEN AGE OF AMERICAN ROCK 'N'
ROLL VOL.5, THE (Hot 100 Hits From
1954-1963)**
Wiggle wiggle: Accents / Love potion no. 9: Clovers /
I'm leaving it up to you: Dale & Grace / You cheated:
Shields / It will stand: Showmen / Sleepwalk: Santo &
Johnny / Nothin' shakin': Fontaine, Eddie / Happy,
happy birthday baby: Tune Weavers / Heart and
soul: Jan & Dean / What's your name: Don & Juan /
Little bitty pretty one: Harris, Thurston & The Sharps
/ Darling Lorraine: Knockouts / Tallahassee lassie:
Cannon, Freddy / Tell me why: Belmonts / Over the
mountain, across the sea: Johnnie & Joe / Ka-ding
dong: G-Clefs / Underwater: Frogmen / She cried:
Jay & The Americans / Just a little bit: Gordon, Roscoe
/ Sometime: Thomas, Gene / Ain't gonna kiss ya:
Ribbons / Midnight stroll: Revels / Walk: McCracklin,
Jimmy / Hey little girl: Clark, Dee / This is the night:
Valiants / Tell him no: Travis & Bob / Bad boy: Jive
Bombers / Stranded in the jungle: Jayhawks / Duke
of Earl: Chandler, Gene / Goodnight sweetheart
goodnight: Spaniels
CDCHD 600 / Sep '95 / Ace

**GOLDEN AGE OF AMERICAN ROCK 'N'
ROLL VOL.6, THE (Hot 100 Hits From
1954-1963)**
Shirley: Fred, John / Come go with me: Del-Vikings /
Black slacks: Bennett, Joe & The Sparkletones /
Lollipop: Ronald & Ruby / Ten commandments of
love: Harvey & The Moonglows / Love bug crawl:
Edwards, Jimmy / Do you want to dance: Freeman,
Bobby / Hard times (the slop): Watts, Noble 'Thin
Man' / Imagination: Quotations / I wonder (if your
love will ever belong to me): Platters, Johnny / From the
door: El Dorados / You're so fine: Falcons / Tall cool
one: Wailers / Shape I'm in: Restivo, Johnny / Little
star: Elegants / Lover please: McPhatter, Clyde /
Charlena: Sevilles / Pledging my love: Ace, Johnny /
Itchy twitchy feeling: Hendricks, Bobby / Priscilla:
Cooley, Eddie & The Dimples / Hold back the tears:
Delacardos / You can make it it you try: Allison, Gene
/ Real wild child: Ivan / Quarter to three: Bonds /
Stompers / Don't you just know it: Smith, Huey /
'Piano' & The Clowns / I'm walkin': Nelson, Rick / I
love an angel: Little Bill & The Bluenotes / Short
shorts: Royal Teens / Hide and go seek: Hill, Bunker /
Papa-oom-mow-mow: Rivingtons
CDCHD 650 / Jan '97 / Ace

GOLDEN AGE OF BEGUINE, THE
995672 / Jul '96 / EPM

**GOLDEN AGE OF BLACK MUSIC
VOL.1, THE**
Don't play that song: Franklin, Aretha / Day
dreaming: Franklin, Aretha / Until you come back to
me (That's what I'm gonna do): Franklin, Aretha /
Groove me: Floyd, King / Precious, precious: Moore,
Jackie / Don't let the green grass fool you: Paul,
Wilson / Don't knock my love (part 1): Pickett, Wilson
/ First time I ever saw your face: Flack, Roberta /
Killing me softly: Flack, Roberta / Feel like makin'
love: Flack, Roberta / Could it be I'm falling in love:
Spinners / Then came you: Warwick, Dionne & The
Detroit Spinners / Sideshow: Blue Magic / They just
can't stop it (games people play: Blue Magic
7567819122 / Jan '97 / Atlantic

**GOLDEN AGE OF BLACK MUSIC
VOL.2, THE**
Dance dance dance: Chic / Le freak: Chic / Closer I
get to you: Flack, Roberta & Donny Hathaway / We
are family: Sister Sledge / Good times: Chic / You are
in the system: System / Don't disturb this groove:
System / (Pop, pop, pop) Goes my mind: Levert /
Casanova: Levert / Miki Howard come share my
love: Levert / So amazing: Albright, Gerald
7567819132 / Jan '97 / Atlantic

GOLDEN AGE OF BOLERO, THE
995662 / May '96 / EPM

**GOLDEN AGE OF SWING VOL.1 1929-
1939, THE (Big Band Legends)**
158462 / Nov '95 / Jazz Archives

**GOLDEN AGE OF SWING VOL.1, THE
(20 Greatest Hits)**
Eager beaver: Kenton, Stan / Yes indeed: Dorsey,
Tommy & Jo Stafford/Sy Oliver / Perdido: Ellington,
Duke / Let me off uptown: Krupa, Gene & Anita
O'Day/Roy Eldridge / One for the trail: Lunceford,
Jimmie & Dan Grissom / Blues in the night:
Goodman, Benny / Woodchoppers ball: Herman,
Woody / Chatanooga choo choo: Miller, Glenn & Tex
Beneke/Dorothy Dandridge / Concerto for clarinet:
Shaw, Artie / Tangerine: Dorsey, Jimmy & Bob
Eberly/Helen O'Connell / South Rampart Street
Parade: Crosby, Bob / Any old time: Shaw, Artie &
Billie Holiday / And the angels sing: Elman, Ziggy /

Why don't you do right: Goodman, Benny & Peggy
Lee / Cherokee: Barnet, Charlie / Mr. Paganini:
Webb, Chick & Ella Fitzgerald / One o'clock jump:
Basie, Count / Two o'clock jump: James, Harry /
Sing sing sing: Henderson, Fletcher & Georgia Boy
Simpkins / Swing home: Hampton, Lionel
DBMCD 3001 / Nov '96 / Horatio Nelson

**GOLDEN AGE OF SWING VOL.2 (Big
Band Legends)**
158462 / Jul '96 / Jazz Archives

**GOLDEN AGE OF SWING VOL.3 (1929-
1945)**
158882 / Jun '97 / Jazz Archives

**GOLDEN COLLECTION OF IRISH
MUSIC (2CD Set)**
DCDP 3 / Sep '96 / Dolphin

**GOLDEN COUNTRY VOL.1 (Let Your
Love Flow)**
MU 5029 / Oct '92 / Musketeer

**GOLDEN COUNTRY VOL.2 (From A
Jack To A King)**
MU 5030 / Oct '92 / Musketeer

GOLDEN COUNTRY VOL.3 (Love Hurts)
MU 5031 / Oct '92 / Musketeer

**GOLDEN COUNTRY VOL.4 (Love Me
Tender)**
MU 5032 / Oct '92 / Musketeer

**GOLDEN COUNTRY VOL.5 (Games
People Play)**
MU 5033 / Oct '92 / Musketeer

GOLDEN DAYS, THE
Route 66: Cole, Nat 'King' / You're the cream in my
coffee: Cole, Nat 'King' / Too marvellous for words:
Cole, Nat 'King' / When you're smiling (The whole
world smiles with you): Cole, Nat 'King' / I miss you so:
Cole, Nat 'King' / Mona Lisa: Cole, Nat 'King' / For all
the moon: Miller, Glenn / Friendship: Garland,
Judy & Johnny Mercer / Opus No.1: Dorsey, Tommy
/ Shine: Crosby, Bing & The Mills Brothers /
MacPherson is rehearsin' (To swing): Fitzgerald, Ella
/ Take the "A" train: Ellington, Duke / In a moment of
weakness: Powell, Dick / Somebody loves you: Laine,
Sinatra, Frank / Enjoy a little song: Crosby, Bing &
Jane Wyman / Taking a chance on love: Fitzgerald,
Ella / Chattanooga choo choo: Miller, Glenn / Ida
sweet as apple cider: Mills Brothers / How about
you: Sinatra, Frank / Civilization (bongo, bongo,
bongo): Andrews Sisters & Danny Kaye / Little Miss
Broadway: Temple, Shirley & George Murphy /
Darktown strutter's ball: Fitzgerald, Ella / You were
never lovelier: Astaire, Fred / Connecticut: Garland,
Judy & Bing Crosby / I'll be seeing you: Sinatra,
Frank
ECD 3328 / Mar '97 / K-Tel

GOLDEN FLUTE
GRF 238 / Aug '93 / Tring

GOLDEN GIRLS OF THE 60'S
PLATCD 344 / Oct '90 / Platinum

GOLDEN GROUPS
Tears on my pillow: Chimes / I'll find her: Dukes /
Don't you know (I love you so): Maye, Arthur Lee &
The Crowns / New: Allen, Tony & The Champs /
Love you so: Crystals / Chimes ring out: Chimes /
Foolish fool: Zappa, Ben Joe & The Zephyrs / So long
love: Dukes / Cool loving: Maye, Arthur Lee & The
Crowns / She's gone: Robertson /
Tropicals / My little girl: Pharaohs / It's true:
Twilighters / Chop chop: Chimes / Gloria: Maye,
Arthur Lee & The Crowns / I want cha baby: Gipson,
Byron 'Slick' & The Sliders / Our romance: King,
Clyde / Over the rainbow: Echoes / It's spring again:
Pentagons / Silly dilly: Pentagons / Arlene: Titans /
What have I done: Titans / Our deepest dreams: Monitors
/ Closer to heaven: Monitors / Miracle: Five Knights
CDCHD 515 / Jan '94 / Ace

GOLDEN HITS OF SOCA CALYPSO
CR 002 / 13 Oct '97 / Charlie's

GOLDEN IRISH FAVOURITES
MACCD 311 / Aug '96 / Autograph

GOLDEN MEMORIES
Happy years / It's our anniversary / Old flames / With
this ring / Eighteen yellow roses / Absent friends /
Daddy's hands / Old love letters / After all these
years / When you were sweet sixteen / When your old
wedding ring was new / Just for old time's sake /
Yellow roses / Waltzing with you tonight / Walking on
my memories / Gold and silver days / Wedding song /
Turn back the years / Golden years / Bless this house
RZRCD 567 / 10 Nov '97 / Ritz

GOLDEN MILES 1969-1974 (2CD Set)
RVCD 39 / Dec '94 / Raven

GOLDEN ORGAN FAVOURITES
So what's new/Tie a yellow ribbon/Try a little
kindness / Fireworks/ Born from Ipanema/In a little
Spanish town/Elizabeth / We've only just begun/
Strangers in the night/If / Anna/Amorada/Tico tico /
Waterloo/Ring ring/Money money money / Swingin'
shepherd blues / For the good times/Don't it make
my brown eyes blue/After th / Beautiful Sunday/
Knock three times/Yellow river / Breeze and I/The
shadow of your smile/Perfidia/In the mood / Hi lili hi
lo / Everybody loves me baby/The last waltz / Rivers of
Babylon/Love is in the air/Feelings / Trumpet
voluntary
QED 142 / Nov '96 / Tring

GOLDEN PIANO FAVOURITES
Almaz / When I fall in love / One more night / Song for
guy / I just called to say I love you / When a man love
a woman / Careless whisper / Lady in red / Feelings /
Cavatina / Endless love / How do you keep the rainbow /
Lucy in the
story / Softly as I leave you / Way we were / Don't cry
for me Argentina / As time goes by / Everything I do) I
do it for
QED 069 / Nov '96 / Tring

GOLDEN SAXOPHONE
GRF 239 / Aug '93 / Tring

GOLDEN SHOWER OF 73 HITS
LF 200DCD / Aug '95 / Lost & Found

GOLDEN SOUNDS OF HOME
321062 / Sep '92 / Koch

**GOLDEN SWING BANDS OF THE
FORTIES**
Blue Lou / Blues / Livery stable blues / At the jazz
band Ball / Big butter and egg man / Dippermouth
blues / Bach goes to town / Farewell blues / One
o'clock jump / Bugle call rag / I wish I could shimmy
like my sister Kate / Eccentric / Uptown blues / Liza
(all the clouds roll away) / Cheatin' on me / 'Taint
what you do (it's the way that you do it) / Four or five
times / I've found a new baby / Honeysuckle rose
QED 141 / Nov '96 / Tring

GOLDEN TORCH STORY VOL.1, THE
Just like the weather: Chance, Nolan / I've got
something: Sam & Kitty / Sliced tomatoes: Just
Brothers / Sweet darlin': Clarke, Jimmy 'Soul' / Our
love: Barnes, J.J. / Honey bee: Johnson, Johnny / I
can't get away: Garrett, Bobby / I still love you:
Superlatives / Crackin' up over you: Hamilton, Roy /
Love you baby: Parker, Eddie / Personally: Paris,
Bobby / One in a million: Brown, Maxine / Thumb a
ride: Wright, Earl / I'm talking: Lundy, Rufus / I feel
an urge: Armstead, Jo / I don't want to cry: Gray,
Pearlean & The Passengers / Exus trek: Ingram,
Luther / Keep on keeping on: Porter, N.F. / I'm so
glad: Johnson, Herb / Quick change artist: Soul
Twins / One wonderful moment: Shakers / Hit and
run: Shakers / Soul self satisfaction: Jackson, Earl /
That's alright: Crook, Ed / Compared to what: Mr.
Floods Party / Blowing up my mind: Exciters / Please
let me in: Barnes, J.J. / I love you baby: Scott, Cindy /
Queen of the Go-Go: Garvin, Rex / Angel baby:
Banks, Darrell
GSCD 061 / May '95 / Goldmine

**GOLDEN TORCH STORY VOL.2, THE
(Revisited)**
Just ask me: Guess, Lenis / Surprise party: Vibratin'
Vibrations / What kind of lady: Sharp, Dee Dee / Free
for all: Mitchell, Phillip / It ain't necessary: Galore,
Mamie / I got the fever: Prophets / Breakaway:
Valentines / Suzy's serenade: Wilson, Bob / Inky
dinky wang dang doo: Dramatics / What would I do:
Superiors / Unsatisfied: Johnson, Lou / Running for
my life: Shelton, Roscoe / What would I do: Tranes /
Grace be over: Sequins / Love game A-Z: Royal Jokers
/ Too much: Conwell, Jimmy / They say: Ovations / If
it's all the same to you babe: Ingram, Luther / Music:
White, Jeanette / Bingo: Dynamics / Frantic escape:
Innocent: Bystanders / Don't be sore at me:
Parliaments / Prove yourself a lady: Bounty, James /
Number one: Exciters / I love the life I live: Michaels,
Tony
GSCD 092 / May '97 / Goldmine

**GOLDEN TREASURY OF
ELIZABETHAN MUSIC**
Sellengers round: Broadside Band / This is the
record of John: Read By & The Rose Consort Of
Viols / Bergamasca: Broadside Band / In nomine a 5:
Fretwork Consort Of Viols / Coventry carol: Sneak's
Noyse / Passamezzo pavan: Weigand, George / Sing
unto God: Red Byrd & The Rose Consort Of Viols /
Spanish pavan/Galliard la gamba: York Waites / Go
cristall tears: Trevor, Carolina & The Rose Consort Of
Viols / A toye: Burnett, Richard / La doune cella: York
Viols / A rose: Broadside Band / Pavana the
Broadside Band / Crimson velvet: York Waites /
There dwelt a man in Babylon: Roberts, Deborah &
The Broadside Band / I am a little nut tree: York
Waites / Come live with me: Potter, John & The
Broadside Band / Bonny sweet Robin: Weigand,
George / Pavan - Heigh ho Holyday: York Waites /
Sweet was the song the virgin sung: Red Byrd & The
Rose Consort Of Viols / Staines Morris: York Waites /
Libera nos - salva nos a 5: Fretwork Consort Of Viols
/ Fortune my foe: Roberts, Deborah & The Broadside
Band / Dulcina/All you that love good fellowes: York
Waites / Poor soul sat sighing: Roberts, Deborah &
The Broadside Band / Fantasy a 5: Browning: Rose
Consort Of Viols / Pavan - The cradle: York Waites /
Farewell dear love: Potter, John & The Broadside
Band / La bounette: York Waites
CDSAR 62 / Feb '96 / Amon Ra

GOLDEN TRUMPET GREATS
Somewhere / Groovy kind of love / I don't know how
to love him / If / What a wonderful world / All I ask of
you / From a distance / Wind beneath my wings / It
had to be you / Somewhere out there / Unchained
melody / Everything I do) I do it for you / Saltwater /
Music of the night / That's what friends are for /
Unforgettable
QED 119 / Nov '96 / Tring

GOLDEN YEARS OF JAZZ VOL.1, THE
Muskrat ramble: Armstrong, Louis / St. Louis blues:
Tatum, Art / Saving myself for you: Fitzgerald, Ella /
Blue skies: Teagarden, Jack / Lady is a
tramp: Horne, Lena / I got rhythm: Reinhardt, Django
/ Swing low, sweet clarinet: Herman, Woody & His
Thundering Herd / Relaxin' at the Touro: Guttering,
Muggsy / Original Jelly Roll blues: Morton, Jelly Roll
& His Red Hot Peppers / Tenor king: Young, Lester /
Stompin' at the Savoy: Wilson, Teddy / Body and
soul: Goodman, Benny & Quartet / Doggin' that thing:
Allen, Henry 'Red' / Sophisticated lady: Ellington,
Duke Orchestra / Harlem lament: Hines, Earl 'Fatha'
/ Loverman: Holiday, Billie
CDSGPBJZ 31 / 16 Mar '98 / Prestige

GOLDEN YEARS OF JAZZ VOL.10, THE
Do nothin' 'til you hear from me: Ellington, Duke
Orchestra / Avalon: Hawkins, Coleman / First time I
saw you: Lunceford, Jimmie / Tiger rag: Armstrong,
Louis / Sheik of Araby: Tatum, Art / Nobody knows
the trouble I've seen: Horne, Lena / Just wild about
Harry: Hechet, Sidney / In the mood: Miller, Glenn /
Easy money: Henderson, Fletcher / China boy:
Wilson, Teddy / Livery stable blues: Spanier,
Muggsy / Lullaby of Birdland: Fitzgerald, Ella / Take
your tomorrow: Beiderbecke, Bix / Boogie woogie:
Dorsey, Tommy Orchestra / Someday sweetheart:
Morton, Jelly Roll & His Red Hot Peppers / Sax a
plenty: Young, Lester
CDSGPBJZ 40 / 16 Mar '98 / Prestige

☐ GOLDEN YEARS OF JAZZ VOL.2, THE
Someday sweetheart: *Spanier, Muggsy* / Diminuendo and crescendo in blue: *Ellington, Duke Orchestra* / Strange fruit: *Holiday, Billie* / Honky tonk train blues: *Lewis, Meade 'Lux'* / Stardust: *Hawkins, Coleman* / It's a sin to tell a lie: *Waller, Fats & His Rhythm* / Stardust: *Morton, Jelly Roll & His Red Hot Peppers* / Doctor Jazz stomp: *Fitzgerald, Ella* / We can't go on this way: *Fitzgerald, Ella* / Flat hat blues: *Young, Lester* / Blue and sentimental: *Basie, Count Orchestra* / Bugle call rag: *Goodman, Benny Orchestra* / Coquette: *Wilson, Teddy & His Piano Orchestra* / St. James Infirmary: *Armstrong, Louis* / Sweet Lorraine: *Tatum, Art* / Masquerade is over: *McRae, Carmen*
CDSGPBJZ 32 / 16 Mar '98 / Prestige

☐ GOLDEN YEARS OF JAZZ VOL.3, THE
Time on my hands: *Goodman, Benny Quartet* / Honeysuckle rose: *Waller, Fats & His Rhythm* / Moonglow: *Garner, Erroll* / Chicago flyer: *Lewis, Meade 'Lux'* / Moonlight serenade: *Miller, Glenn Orchestra* / My melancholy baby: *Teagarden, Jack* / It's only a paper moon: *Young, Lester* / Fine romance: *Horne, Lena* / Henderson stomp: *Henderson, Fletcher* / Freight train blues: *Bechet, Sidney* / My melancholy baby: *Lunceford, Jimmie* / Jeepers creepers: *Reinhardt, Django* / Oh lady be good: *Hawkins, Coleman* / Chicago rhythm: *Hines, Earl 'Fatha'* / All of me: *Holiday, Billie* / Deep purple: *Tatum, Art*
CDSGPBJZ 33 / 16 Mar '98 / Prestige

☐ GOLDEN YEARS OF JAZZ VOL.4, THE
You look good to me: *Waller, Fats & His Rhythm* / Basin Street blues: *Fitzgerald, Ella* / Begin the beguine: *Shaw, Artie Orchestra* / Chimes blues: *Armstrong, Louis* / Black bottom stomp: *Morton, Jelly Roll & His Red Hot Peppers* / Lullaby of the leaves: *Tatum, Art* / One o'clock jump: *Basie, Count Orchestra* / Best years of my life: *Christy, June* / Got a penny: *Cole, Nat 'King' Trio* / Characteristic blues: *Bechet, Sidney* / Sweet Georgia Brown: *Reinhardt, Django* / Take the 'A' train: *Ellington, Duke Orchestra* / Love me or leave me: *Horne, Lena* / Chimes in blues: *Hines, Earl 'Fatha'* / Mad house: *Goodman, Benny Orchestra* / That sugar baby o' mine: *Holiday, Billie*
CDSGPBJZ 34 / 16 Mar '98 / Prestige

☐ GOLDEN YEARS OF JAZZ VOL.5, THE
Dippermouth blues: *Spanier, Muggsy* / April in Paris: *Parker, Charlie* / So many times: *Teagarden, Jack* / Carnival of Venice: *James, Harry Orchestra* / Moonlight in Vermont: *Fitzgerald, Ella* / Prisoner of love: *Wilson, Teddy* / Closing hour blues: *Lewis, Meade 'Lux'* / Solitude: *Ellington, Duke Orchestra* / Rhythm club stomp: *Oliver, Joe 'King'* / St. Louis shuffle: *Henderson, Fletcher* / Doggin' around: *Basie, Count Orchestra* / Out of nowhere: *Hawkins, Coleman* / Sad eyes: *Young, Lester* / Whose honey are you: *Waller, Fats & His Rhythm* / Indian summer: *Bechet, Sidney* / Stormy weather: *Tatum, Art*
CDSGPBJZ 35 / 16 Mar '98 / Prestige

☐ GOLDEN YEARS OF JAZZ VOL.6, THE
Stompology: *Hampton, Lionel Orchestra* / Alligator crawl: *Waller, Fats & His Rhythm* / Nice work if you can get it: *Goodman, Benny Quartet* / Jelly roll blues: *Armstrong, Louis* / I'll remember: *Teagarden, Jack* / Now will you be good: *Basie, Count Orchestra* / Georgia on my mind: *Holiday, Billie* / Piano man: *Hines, Earl 'Fatha'* / Skyliner: *Barnet, Charlie Orchestra* / Wild man blues: *Morton, Jelly Roll & His Red Hot Peppers* / Honey keep your mind on me: *Lunceford, Jimmie* / Don't you think I love you: *Oliver, Joe 'King'* / Black and tan fantasy: *Ellington, Duke Orchestra* / Loverman: *Horne, Lena* / Polka dot rag: *Bechet, Sidney Orchestra* / April in Paris: *Fitzgerald, Ella*
CDSGPBJZ 36 / 16 Mar '98 / Prestige

☐ GOLDEN YEARS OF JAZZ VOL.7, THE
I only have eyes for you: *Holiday, Billie* / Dippermouth blues: *Armstrong, Louis* / Dinah: *Waller, Fats & His Rhythm* / Down home jump: *Hampton, Lionel Orchestra* / Flying home: *Fitzgerald, Ella* / Vom vim veedle: *Cole, Nat 'King' Trio* / I'll keep remembering: *Basie, Count Orchestra* / Muddy river blues: *Teagarden, Jack* / All or nothing at all: *James, Harry Orchestra* / One o'clock jump: *Ellington, Duke Orchestra* / Hyena stomp: *Morton, Jelly Roll & His Red Hot Peppers* / Crazy rhythm: *Reinhardt, Django* / Pennsylvania 6-5000: *Miller, Glenn Orchestra* / Bugle call rag: *Wilson, Teddy* / My honey's lovin' arms: *Goodman, Benny Orchestra* / Takin' a chance on love: *Young, Lester*
CDSGPBJZ 37 / 16 Mar '98 / Prestige

☐ GOLDEN YEARS OF JAZZ VOL.8, THE
Memories of you: *Wilson, Teddy* / King Porter stomp: *Henderson, Fletcher* / My man: *Holiday, Billie* / Crying all day: *Beiderbecke, Bix* / Fly me to the moon: *Elgart, Les & His Orchestra* / Chinatown, my chinatown: *Dorsey, Tommy Orchestra* / Serenade in blue: *Miller, Glenn Orchestra* / Love me or leave me: *Young, Lester* / My old flame: *Clayton, Buck Orchestra & Frankie Laine* / Jamaica shout: *Hawkins, Coleman* / Loverman: *Parker, Charlie* / C jam blues: *Ellington, Duke Orchestra* / Smoke house blues: *Morton, Jelly Roll & His Red Hot Peppers* / Flight of the bumble bee: *James, Harry Orchestra* / Royal Garden blues: *Armstrong, Louis* / Roseland shuffle: *Basie, Count Orchestra*
CDSGPBJZ 38 / 16 Mar '98 / Prestige

☐ GOLDEN YEARS OF JAZZ VOL.9, THE
Don't you miss your baby: *Basie, Count Orchestra* / Wolverine blues: *Morton, Jelly Roll & His Red Hot Peppers* / Oh lady be good: *Fitzgerald, Ella* / Black snake blues: *Oliver, Joe 'King'* / I'm crazy 'bout my baby: *Spanier, Muggsy* / Summertime: *Bechet, Sidney* / Table in a corner: *Teagarden, Jack* / Creole rhapsody: *Ellington, Duke Orchestra* / Stormy weather: *Holiday, Billie* / Patrol wagon blues: *Allen, Henry 'Red'* / Somebody loves me: *Hawkins, Coleman* / I surrender dear: *Wilson, Teddy* / Stardust: *Garner, Erroll* / Moonglow: *Goodman, Benny Quartet* / Honeysuckle rose: *Reinhardt, Django* / Ain't misbehavin': *Armstrong, Louis*
CDSGPBJZ 39 / 16 Mar '98 / Prestige

☐ GOLDEN YEARS OF MUSIC HALL, THE
CDSDL 380 / Mar '94 / Saydisc

☐ GONE SURFIN'
74321500272 / Jun '97 / Camden

☐ GOOD BLUES TONIGHT
Church bell blues: *Jordan, Luke* / Mr. McTell got the blues: *McTell, 'Blind' Willie* / She stays out all night long: *Memphis Jug Band* / Suzie Q: *Williamson, Sonny Boy* / Good morning blues: *Leadbelly* / Roberta: *Leadbelly* / 32-20 blues: *Johnson, Robert* / Terraplane blues: *Johnson, Robert* / Stompin' 'em along slow: *Johnson, Lonnie* / Southern Casey Jones blues: *James, Jesse* / Lonesome day blues: *James, Jesse* / State Street blues: *Theard, Sam* / Macon blues: *Everetts, Dorothy* / Fat mouth blues: *Everetts, Dorothy* / Tight in Chicago: *Anderson, Mozelle* / Sadie's servant room blues: *Burleson, Hattie* / Superstitious blues: *Burleson, Hattie* / Heavenly sunshine: *Henton, Laura* / Dirty TB blues: *Spivey, Victoria* / Chicago stomp: *Blythe, Jimmy* / Armour Avenue struggle: *Blythe, Jimmy* / Big Bill blues: *Broonzy, 'Big' Bill* / Truckin' little woman: *Broonzy, 'Big' Bill* / Southern flood blues: *Broonzy, 'Big' Bill* / Good old cabbage greens: *Washboard Sam*
CDMOIR 503 / Aug '93 / Memoir

☐ GOOD GROOVIN'
Last night a DJ saved my life / Never knew love like this before / Rock the boat / Ooh what a life / Gloria / Car Wash / Walking on sunshine / Don't take away the music / Black is black / Rescue me / Strut your funky stuff / Feels like I'm in love
ECD 3202 / Mar '95 / K-Tel

☐ GOOD HOUSEKEEPING PRESENTS A MUSICAL CHRISTMAS
GHCD 941 / 10 Nov '97 / RCA Victor

☐ GOOD LIFE VOL.2
ED 022CD / 23 Mar '98 / Good Life

☐ GOOD MORNIN' BLUES
Went out on the mountain: *Leadbelly* / Whoa back: *Leadbelly* / Worried blues: *Leadbelly* / Good morning blues: *Leadbelly* / You can't lose me Charlie: *Leadbelly* / Boll weevil song: *Leadbelly* / Babylon is falling down: *Smith, Dan* / Where shall I be: *Smith, Dan* / Lining the track: *Smith, Dan* / Cotton needs pickin': *Smith, Dan* / Candy man: *Davis, Rev. Gary* / Hesitation blues: *Davis, Rev. Gary* / Whistlin' blues: *Davis, Rev. Gary* / How happy I am: *Davis, Rev. Gary* / Soon my work will all be done: *Davis, Rev. Gary*
BCD 113 / Jul '91 / Biograph

☐ GOOD MORNING BLUES (4CD Set)
CDDIG 18 / Jun '95 / Charly

☐ GOOD MORNING VIETNAM (3CD Set)
Somebody to love: *Jefferson Airplane* / California dreamin': *Mamas & The Papas* / On the road again: *Canned Heat* / Magic carpet ride: *Steppenwolf* / Games people play: *South, Joe* / Time of the season: *Zombies* / Mellow yellow: *Donovan* / Aquarius: *5th Dimension* / Let the sunshine in: *5th Dimension* / Happy together: *Turtles* / He ain't heavy, he's my brother: *Hollies* / Letter: *Box Tops* / River deep, mountain high: *Turner, Ike & Tina* / In the year 2525: *Zager & Evans* / Tell it like it is: *Neville, Aaron* / Drift away: *Gray, Dobie* / Time in a bottle: *Croce, Jim* / Five o'clock world: *Vogues* / Bring it on home to me: *Animals* / God only knows: *Beach Boys* / Give up your guns: *Buoys* / White rabbit: *Jefferson Airplane* / Monday Monday: *Mamas & The Papas* / Friday on my mind: *Easybeats* / Born to be wild: *Steppenwolf* / Let's go to San Francisco: *Flowerpot Men* / She's not there: *Eve Of Destruction* / Weight: *Band* / Judy in disguise: *Fred, John & The Playboys* / Spirit in the sky: *Greenbaum, Norman* / Universal soldier: *Donovan* / Without you: *Nilsson, Harry* / Bad bad Leroy Brown: *Croce, Jim* / Hereos and villains: *Beach Boys* / Tossin' and turnin': *Ivy League* / I fought the law: *Bobby Fuller Four* / Incense and peppermints: *Strawberry Alarm Clock* / Sunny afternoon: *Kinks* / Sympathy: *Rowland, Steve & Family Dog* / I'm the urban spaceman: *Bonzo Dog Band* / Ball of confusion (that's what the world is today): *Temptations* / Going up the country: *Canned Heat* / (Don't fear) the reaper: *Blue Oyster Cult* / I get around: *Beach Boys* / Spooky: *Classics IV* / Brother Louie: *Stories* / Honky tonk woman: *Turner, Ike & Tina* / Fireball: *Deep Purple* / Up on cripple creek: *Band* / Elenore: *Turtles* / Soldier boy: *Shirelles* / San Franciscan nights: *Burdon, Eric* / Jenny take a ride: *Ryder, Mitch & The Detroit Wheels* / It's a long way there: *Little River Band* / Paranoid: *Black Sabbath* / Hooked on a feeling: *Thomas, B.J.* / Long tall glasses (I can dance): *Sayer, Leo* / Showdown: *ELO* / Who do you love: *Quicksilver Messenger Service* / Louie Louie: *Kingsmen*
HR 863812 / Sep '96 / Disky

☐ GOOD MORNING VIETNAM VOL.1
Somebody to love: *Jefferson Airplane* / California dreamin': *Mamas & The Papas* / On the road again: *Canned Heat* / Magic carpet ride: *Steppenwolf* / Games people play: *South, Joe* / Time of the season: *Zombies* / Mellow yellow: *Donovan* / Aquarius: *5th Dimension* / Let the sunshine in: *5th Dimension* / Happy together: *Turtles* / He ain't heavy, he's my brother: *Hollies* / Letter: *Box Tops* / River deep mountain high: *Turner, Ike & Tina* / In the year 2525: *Zager & Evans* / Tell it like it is: *Neville, Aaron* / Drift away: *Gray, Dobie* / Time in a bottle: *Croce, Jim* / Five o'clock world: *Vogues* / Bring it on home to me: *Animals* / God only knows: *Beach Boys* / Give up your guns: *Buoys*
LB 8049 / Nov '96 / Disky

☐ GOOD MORNING VIETNAM VOL.2
White rabbit: *Jefferson Airplane* / Monday monday: *Mamas & The Papas* / Friday on my mind: *Easybeats* / Born to be wild: *Steppenwolf* / Lets go to San Francisco: *Flowerpot Men* / She's not there: *Zombies* / Eve of destruction: *MacGuire, Barry* / Weight: *Band* / Judy in disguise: *Fred, John & The Playboys* / Spirit in the sky: *Greenbaum, Norman* / Universal soldier: *Donovan* / Without you: *Nilsson, Harry* / Bad bad Leroy Brown: *Croce, Jim* / Heroes and villains: *Beach Boys* / Tossin' and turnin': *Ivy League* / I fought the law: *Bobby Fuller Four* / Incense and peppermints: *Strawberry Alarm Clock* / Sunny afternoon: *Kinks* / Sympathy: *Rowland, Steve & Family Dog* / I'm the urban spaceman: *Bonzo Dog Band*
DCA 863832 / Nov '96 / Disky

☐ GOOD MORNING VIETNAM VOL.3
Ball of confusion: *Temptations* / Going up the country: *Canned Heat* / (Don't fear) the reaper: *Blue Oyster Cult* / I get around: *Beach Boys* / Spooky: *Classics IV* / Brother Louie: *Stories* / Honky tonk woman: *Turner, Ike & Tina* / Fireball: *Deep Purple* / Up on cripple creek: *Band* / Elenore: *Turtles* / Soldier boy: *Shirelles* / San Franciscan nights: *Burdon, Eric* / Jenny take a ride: *Ryder, Mitch & The Detroit Wheels* / It's a long way there: *Little River Band* / Paranoid: *Black Sabbath* / Hooked on a feeling: *Thomas, B.J.* / Long tall glasses: *Sayer, Leo* / Showdown: *ELO* / Who do you love: *Quicksilver Messenger Service* / Louie louie: *Kingsmen*
DCA 863842 / Nov '96 / Disky

☐ GOOD NEWS (22 Gospel Greats)
I'm going through: *Caravan* / It's Jesus in me: *Caravan* / I'm a rollin': *Five Blind Boys Of Mississippi* / Where there's a will: *Five Blind Boys Of Mississippi* / Wade in the water: *Harmonizing Four* / Father I stretch my arms to thee: *Harmonizing Four* / Nobody knows: *Highway QC's* / Working on the building: *Highway QC's* / Uncloudy day: *Staple Singers* / This may be the last time: *Staple Singers* / Going away: *Staple Singers* / Good news: *Staple Singers* / Don't drive me away: *Staple Singers* / Will the circle be unbroken: *Staple Singers* / Too close: *Staple Singers* / Great day in December: *Swan Silvertones* / Oh Mary don't you weep: *Swan Silvertones* / How I got over: *Swan Silvertones* / What about you: *Swan Silvertones* / Brighter day ahead: *Swan Silvertones* / Seek, seek: *Swan Silvertones* / I'll search heaven: *Swan Silvertones*
CPCD 8215 / Feb '97 / Charly

☐ GOOD RECORDS
Diskoking: *Hacienda* / Ycool: *Ceiver, Jiri & Jinks* / Drums in a grip: *De Wulf, Frank* / 10" of funk: *Bill & Ben* / Monster: *Planet Jazz* / Chupacabbra: *Freddie Fresh* / Phat jive: *Lindsey, Patrick* / Wait for a day: *Yokota* / Evil needle: *Alter Ego & David Holmes* / Beavis at bat: *Hardfloor* / One way: *Yokota* / Peterson session: *Braincell*
HHUKCD 003 / Jun '97 / Harthouse

☐ GOOD ROCKIN' TONIGHT (The Birth Of Rock 'N' Roll Vol.3/2CD Set)
CPCD 83262 / 16 Mar '98 / Charly

☐ GOOD ROCKIN' TONIGHT
Blue suede shoes: *Cochran, Eddie* / Whole lotta shakin' goin' on: *Nelson, Ricky* / Don't be cruel: *Jordanaires* / Rip it up: *Vincent, Gene* / Hard headed woman: *Jackson, Wanda* / Girl of my best friend: *Burnette, Johnny* / Johnny B Goode: *Freddie & The Dreamers* / Jailhouse rock: *Craddock, Billy* / One night: *Lewis, Smiley* / Blue moon: *Marcels* / Lawdy Miss Clawdy: *Swinging Blue Jeans* / Got a lot of livin' to do: *Horton, Stephen Wayne* / Hound dogs: *Easybeats* / Heatbreak hotel: *Faith, Adam* / Let's have a party: *Jackson, Wanda* / Runaway: *Shannon, Del* / What I'd say: *Crickets* / Such a night: *Sands, Tommy* / There's good rockin' tonight: *Nelson, Ricky* / I gotta know: *Vee, Bobby* / Long tall Sally: *Cochran, Eddie* / Blueberry Hill: *Domino, Fats* / Maybelline: *Vincent, Gene* / Fool: *Burnette, Johnny* / Shake rattle and roll: *Swinging Blue Jeans*
4954732 / 6 Jul '98 / EMI Gold

☐ GOOD SAX GUIDE, THE
Hold 'em Joe: *Rollins, Sonny* / Man I love: *Sims, Zoot* / I remember Clifford: *Moody, James* / Someone to watch over me: *Webster, Ben* / Quando vuelva a tu lado: *Barbieri, Gato* / One to love: *Avery, Teodross* / Ode to the doo da day: *Brecker, Michael* / Feeling of jazz: *Turrentine, Stanley* / Brazilian dream: *Marienthal, Eric* / Fool on the hill: *Scott, Tom* / Desafinado: *Hawkins, Coleman* / Soul station: *Hawkins, Coleman* / CarterBody and soul: *Carter, Benny* / Let it be: *Rangell, Nelson*
GRLD 19368 / 6 Apr '98 / Geffen

☐ GOOD THINGS ARE HAPPENING (Nuggets From The Golden State)
Hide yourself: *Vejtables* / Better rearrange: *Vejtables* / Good things are happening: *Vejtables* / Good times: *Vejtables* / Time and place: *Vejtables* / I can't do it: *E-Type* / Long before: *E-Type* / I'm over you: *Shillings* / Part time man: *Shillings* / Going home: *Engle, Butch & The Styx* / Hey I'm lost: *Engle, Butch & The Styx* / If you believe: *Engle, Butch & The Styx* / I call her name: *Engle, Butch & The Styx* / I can't hide: *Soul Owners* / I'll cry: *Soul Owners* / In my way: *Dutch Masters* / Revenge: *Others* / I'm in need: *Others* / Satisfaction guaranteed: *Mourning Reign* / Our fate: *Mourning Reign* / I'm a lover not a fighter: *Pullice* / Little girl: *Pullice* / Tomorrow is another day: *Navarros* / Sad man: *Navarros* / My chance will come: *Origiani Wild Oats* / I'll get my way: *Chimney Sweeps* / Knock knock: *Innocents*
CDWIKD 133 / Oct '94 / Big Beat

☐ GOOD TIME JAZZ STORY, THE (4CD Set)
Honky tonk music: *Morton, Jelly Roll* / Winin' boy blues: *Morton, Jelly Roll* / Finger buster: *Morton, Jelly Roll* / Creepy feeling: *Morton, Jelly Roll* / Temptation rag: *Bales, Burt* / New Orleans joys: *Bales, Burt* / Black bottom stomp: *Lingle, Paul* / Yellow dog blues: *Lingle, Paul* / Nothin': *Roberts, Luckey* / Railroad blues: *Roberts, Luckey* / Relaxin': *Smith, Willie 'The Lion'* / Between the devil and the deep blue sea: *Smith, Willie 'The Lion'* / Black and white rag: *Rose, Wally* / Pearls: *Rose, Wally* / Harlem rag: *Rose, Wally* / I wonder who's kissing her now: *Banjo Kings* / By the light of the silvery moon: *Banjo Kings* / Bill Bailey: *Banjo Kings* / Take this hammer: *Fuller, Jesse* / Leavin' Memphis: *Fuller, Jesse* / Frisco bound: *Fuller, Jesse* / San Francisco bay blues: *Fuller, Jesse* / John Henry: *Fuller, Jesse* / Storyville blues: *Johnson, Bunk* / Moose march: *Johnson, Bunk* / Careless love: *Johnson, Bunk* / Down by the riverside: *Johnson, Bunk* / Blues for Jimmie Noone: *Ory, Kid Creole Jazz Band* / Do what Ory say: *Ory, Kid Creole Jazz Band* / 1919 rag: *Ory, Kid Creole Jazz Band* / Burgundy Street blues: *Lewis, George* / Mama don't allow: *Lewis, George* / Walk through the streets of the city: *Lewis, George* / Gallatin Street grind: *Wiggs, Johnny* / Everybody loves my baby: *Wiggs, Johnny* / Gettysburg march: *Pierson, Eddie Band* / Alabamy bound: *Pecora, Santo & The Tailgators* / My old time sweetheart: *Hug, Armand Trio* / Look what you've missed: *Bonano, Sharkey* / Too late: *Barbarin, Paul* / Maryland, my Maryland: *Matthews, Bill* / Doctor Jazz: *Girard, George* / Congo Square: *Silver Leaf Jazz Band* / Jelly roll blues: *Silver Leaf Jazz Band* / Snake rag: *Hot Horns* / Muskrat ramble: *Watters, Lu & The Yerba Buena Jazz Band* / Riverside blues: *Watters, Lu & The Yerba Buena Jazz Band* / Friendless blues: *Watters, Lu & The Yerba Buena Jazz Band* / Annie Street rock: *Watters, Lu & The Yerba Buena Jazz Band* / That's a plenty: *Watters, Lu & The Yerba Buena Jazz Band* / Kansas City stomp: *Strickler, Benny* / Brother lowdown: *Murphy, Turk Jazz Band* / Chimes blues: *Murphy, Turk Jazz Band* / Trombone rag: *Murphy, Turk Jazz Band* / St. James infirmary: *Murphy, Turk Jazz Band* / Minstrel of Annie Street: *Murphy, Turk Jazz Band* / Bay city: *Murphy, Turk Jazz Band* / Oh Daddy: *Murphy, Turk Jazz Band & Claire Austin* / Dippermouth blues: *Scobey, Bob Frisco Band* / Wolverine blues: *Scobey, Bob Frisco Band* / Ace in the hole: *Scobey, Bob Frisco Band* / Silver dollar: *Scobey, Bob Frisco Band* / Angry: *Scobey, Bob Frisco Band* / Battle hymn of the republic: *Scobey, Bob Frisco Band* / Indiana: *Scobey, Bob Frisco Band* / Arab strut: *Bay City Jazz Band* / New Orleans stomp: *Bay City Jazz Band* / Monday date: *Ewell, Don* / Blues my naughty sweetie gives to me: *Ewell, Don* / Honeysuckle rose: *Hayes, Clancy* / Ain't she sweet: *Hayes, Clancy* / Clarinet marmalade: *Daily, Pete Rhythm Kings* / Jazz man strut: *Daily, Pete Rhythm Kings* / St. Louis blues: *Ory, Kid Creole Jazz Band* / South Rampart Street Parade: *Ory, Kid Creole Jazz Band* / Down hearted blues: *Ory, Kid Creole Jazz Band & Claire Austin* / Indiana: *Ory, Kid Creole Jazz Band* / Oh didn't he ramble: *Ory, Kid Creole Jazz Band* / Creole song: *Ory, Kid Creole Jazz Band* / Torch: *Castle Jazz Band* / Careless love: *Castle Jazz Band* / Five pennies: *Castle Jazz Band* / When the saints go marching in: *Castle Jazz Band* / Firehouse stomp: *Firehouse Five Plus Two* / Mississippi rag: *Firehouse Five Plus Two* / At a Georgia camp meeting: *Firehouse Five Plus Two* / Tishomingo blues: *Firehouse Five Plus Two* / Hindustan: *Firehouse Five Plus Two* / Isle of Capri: *Firehouse Five Plus Two* / Storyville blues: *Firehouse Five Plus Two* / Smokey mokes: *Firehouse Five Plus Two* / High society: *Firehouse Five Plus Two*
4GTJCD 4416 / Nov '96 / Good Time Jazz

☐ GOOD VIBRATIONS
Good vibrations: *Beach Boys* / Dancing in the street: *Reeves, Martha & The Vandellas* / Yeh yeh: *Fame, Georgie* / Pretty flamingo: *Manfred Mann* / Leader of the pack: *Shangri-Las* / Son of a preacher man: *Springfield, Dusty* / River deep mountain high: *Turner, Ike & Tina* / Somebody help me: *Davis, Spencer Group* / Sunshine superman: *Donovan* / King of the road: *Miller, Rodger* / Guanatanamera: *Sand Pipers* / Surf city: *Jan & Dean* / Got to get you into my life: *Bennett, Cliff & The Rebel Rousers* / Don't let the sun catch you cryin': *Gerry & The Pacemakers* / High time: *Jones, Paul* / Bus stop: *Hollies* / All or nothing: *Small Faces* / Here it comes again: *Fortunes* / Morningtown Ride: *Seekers* / Bend it: *Dave Dee, Dozy, Beaky, Mick & Tich*
5529062 / Oct '97 / Spectrum

☐ GOOD VIBRATIONS
TSS 116 / 11 May '98 / BMG

☐ GOOD VIBRATIONS PUNK
Big time / Strange things by night / Love is for sops / Emergency cases / Dance away love / Don't ring me up / Listening in / Parents / Dancing in the street / Cops are comin' / Overcome by fumes / Cross the line / Love affair / Ya don't do ya / I spy / Airline disaster / Self concious over you / Love you for never / On my mind / Decisions / Original terminal / Belfast telegraph / I don't want you / Bondage in Belfast / Laugh at me
CDPUNK 36 / Sep '94 / Anagram

☐ GOOD WHISKEY BLUES VOL.1 (Collection Of Contemporary Blues Songs From Tennessee)
TX 1004CD / Jan '94 / Taxim

☐ GOOD WHISKEY BLUES VOL.2 (Collection Of Contemporary Blues Songs From Tennessee)
TX 1010CD / Jan '94 / Taxim

☐ GOODNIGHT SAIGON (3CD Set)
Nutbush city limits: *Turner, Ike & Tina* / Vietnam: *Cliff, Jimmy* / War drags on: *Donovan* / Brother Louie: *Hot Chocolate* / Proud Mary: *Turner, Ike & Tina* / Melting pot: *Blue Mink* / Why can't we live together: *Thomas, Timmy* / Baby I need your loving: *Rivers, Johnny* / Rubber bullets: *10cc* / We've gotta get out of this place: *Animals* / Love potion no.9: *Searchers* / House of the rising sun: *Animals* / Air that I breathe: *Hollies* / Ain't got no home: *Band* / I put a spell: *Price, Alan* / Black night: *Deep Purple* / You're the one: *Vogues* / Let's work together: *Canned Heat* / Roll over Beethoven: *ELO* / 10538 overture: *ELO* / Baby Jane (Mo-Mo Jane): *Ryder, Mitch & The Detroit Wheels* / Some kind of wonderful: *Grand Funk Railroad* / Silver machine: *Hawkwind* / Who do you love: *Juicy Lucy* / Gimme shelter: *Grand Funk Railroad* / Green tambourine: *Lemon Pipers* / Don't let me be misunderstood: *Animals* / I'm coming on: *Ten Years After* / American dream: *Dirt Band* / Summer in the city: *Lovin' Spoonful* / When I'm dead and gone: *McGuinness Flint* / Little green bag: *Ten Years After* / Sister golden hair: *America* / You don't mess around with Jim: *Croce, Jim* / She'd rather be with me: *Turtles* / Darlin' be home soon: *Lovin' Spoonful* / Lay down candles in the rain: *Melanie* / Mr. Bojangles: *Nitty Gritty Dirt Band* / Timothy: *Buoys* / Where peaceful waters flow: *Knight, Gladys & The Pips* / Soldier: *Groundhogs* / I'd love to change the world: *Ten Years After* / Do wah diddy diddy: *Manfred Mann* / Cotton fields: *Beach Boys* / Lucky man: *Emerson, Lake & Palmer* / Where's the playground, Susie: *Campbell, Glen* / Hi-ho silver lining: *Beck, Jeff & Rod Stewart* / American pie: *McLean, Don* / Horse with no name: *America* / I can hear music: *Beach Boys* / Light my fire: *Thomas, B.J.* / Feeling alright: *Grand Funk Railroad* / Good vibrations: *Beach Boys* / Stagger Lee and Billy: *Turner, Ike & Tina* / Clap for the wolfman: *Guess Who* / Midnight train to Georgia: *Knight, Gladys & The Pips* / Blowin' in the wind: *James, Etta* / Good morning freedom: *Blue Mink* / Peace will come: *Melanie* / Smoke on the water: *Deep Purple*
HR 864252 / Oct '96 / Disky

☐ GORAU GWERIN CYFROL (The Best of Welsh Folk Music)
Torth of fara / Y gwr a'i farch / Mi gysgi di' maban / Cerrig yr afon / Mor o gariad / Mae 'ngharied i'n fenws / Llancesau trefaldwyn / Bachgen bach o dincer / Y g'lomen / Ymryson canu / Ar gyfer heddiw'r bore / Clychau Aberdyfi / Ymdaith milwr mwnc / Cyfri'r geifr / Machynlleth / Cwm rhymni / Ffidl ffadl / Ffarwel i ddociau lerpwl / Wyres Megan / Gwrachod Llanddona / Mil harddach wyt / Yma o hyd
SCD 2006 / Oct '88 / Sain

☐ GORGEOUS (37 Irresistible Songs)
You're gorgeous: *Baby Bird* / 2 Become 1: *Spice Girls* / Nobody knows: *Rich, Tony Project* / Kiss from a rose: *Seal* / If you ever: *Gabrielle & East 17* / Goodbye heartbreak: *Lighthouse Family* / Thrill me: *Simply Red* / Cosmic girl: *Jamiroquai* / I can make you feel good: *Kavana* / Quit playing games: *Backstreet Boys* / Day we find love: *911* / If you love me: *Brownstone* / My lovin': *En Vogue* / Trippin': *Morrison, Mark* / I feel you: *Andre, Peter* / Forever: *Damage* / Searching: *China Black* / Bill: *Scott-Adams, Peggy* / Natural: *Andre, Peter* / Undivided love: *Louise* / Don't make me wait: *911* / When I fall in love: *Ant & Dec* / Crazy for you: *Let Loose* / Love me for a reason: *Boyzone* / I just wanna make love to you: *James, Etta* / Girl like you: *Collins, Edwyn* / Best: *Turner, Tina* / Heaven is a place on earth: *Carlisle, Belinda* / Cecilia: *Suggs* / Dark clouds: *Space* / Oh yeah: *Ash* / Saturday night: *Suede* / Missing: *Everything But The Girl* / Don't dream it's over: *Crowded House* / Chains: *Arena, Tina* / Child: *Owen, Mark* / Sometimes when we touch: *Newton*
VTDCD 121 / Apr '97 / Virgin

☐ GOSPEL (3CD Set)
EMTBX 308 / Aug '97 / Emporio

☐ GOSPEL
Oh glory hallelujah: *Griffin, Bessie* / Joshua fit the battle of Jericho: *Golden Gate Quartet* / Great big god: *Williams, Marion* / Sometimes I feel like a motherless child: *Jackson, Mahalia* / Why am I treated so bad: *Staple Singers* / Amazing grace: *Hawkins, Tramaine* / How I got over: *Williams, Marion* / Moses smote the water: *Golden Gate Quartet* / I love the lord: *Jackson, Mahalia* / Take them and leave them: *Abyssinian Baptist Choir* / Lord will make a way: *Abyssinian Baptist Choir* / One day: *Angelic Gospel Singers & The Dixie Hummingbirds* / I'll live again: *Dixie Hummingbirds*
48781402 / 29 Sep '97 / Sony Jazz

☐ GOSPEL & NEGRO SPIRITUAL FESTIVAL (2CD Set)
FA 412 / Oct '96 / Fremeaux

☐ GOSPEL AT NEWPORT 1959 & 1963-1966
VCD 77014 / Jan '96 / Vanguard

☐ GOSPEL CHRISTMAS
Hark the herald angels sing: *Hutchins, Norman* / O holy night: *Smallwood, Richard* / Away in a manger/ Silent night: *West Angeles COGIC Angelic & Mass Choir* / Angels we have heard on high: *Crouch, Sandra* / Joy to the world: *West Angeles COGIC Angelic & Mass Choir* / First Noel: *Grundy, Rickey Chorale* / Go tell it on the mountain: *Winans, Mom & Pop* / O come, o come: *Coley, Daryl* / Hallelujah chorus: *Alford, Pastor Donald & The Progressive Radio Chorus*
CDMFP 6196 / Oct '96 / Music For Pleasure

☐ GOSPEL CLASSICS
DOCD 5190 / Mar '95 / Document

☐ GOSPEL CLASSICS 1950-1958
DOCD 5464 / Jun '96 / Document

☐ GOSPEL CLASSICS VOL.2 1927-1935
DOCD 5313 / Dec '94 / Document

☐ GOSPEL CLASSICS VOL.3
DOCD 5350 / May '95 / Document

☐ GOSPEL COLLECTION, THE
DCD 5271 / Aug '92 / Disky

☐ GOSPEL COUNTRY
DCD 5314 / Nov '93 / Disky

☐ GOSPEL EVANGELISTS
HTCD 09 / '92 / Heritage

☐ GOSPEL LIVE FROM MOUNTAIN STAGE
This little light of mine: *Bass, Fontella* / Brother Moses: *Five Blind Boys Of Alabama* / Dig a little deeper: *Fairfield Four* / I want Jesus to walk with me: *Holmes Brothers* / Ring them golden bells: *Gospel Christian Singers* / Up above my head: *Austin, Ethel Caffie* / Beatitudes/Peace: *Sweet Honey In The Rock* / Fix it Jesus: *Sounds Of Heaven* / Why am I treated so bad: *Staples, Pops* / Standing in the safety zone: *Fairfield Four* / Leaning on the everlasting arms: *Bass, Fontella*
BPM 309CD / May '97 / Blue Plate

☐ GOSPEL SHIP, THE
802942 / Oct '94 / New World

☐ GOSPEL SINGERS AND CHOIRS
TPZ 1011 / Jun '95 / Topaz Jazz

☐ GOSPEL SOUND OF CHICAGO
SHAN 6008CD / Dec '93 / Shanachie

☐ GOSPEL TRAIN
Lift up your hands / Constant love / Potter's house / Somebody somewhere / It's mighty nice to be on the Lord's side / He's got up / What shall I do / Give me Jesus / Want to get to know you / Holy is your name / Lord's prayer / Joyful, joyful
ALD 027 / Jan '96 / Alliance Music

☐ GOSPEL TRAIN IS LEAVING, THE
IMP 939 / 21 Aug '97 / IMP

☐ GOSPEL VOL.3 1927-1944 (2CD Set)
FA 044 / Nov '95 / Fremeaux

☐ GOSPEL WARRIORS
Just a closer walk with me: *Tharpe, Sister Rosetta* / Savior don't pass me by: *Tharpe, Sister Rosetta* / Lordy won't you come by here: *Georgia Peach* / Lord have mercy: *Georgia Peach* / I'll wait on the Lord: *Johnson-Davis, Mary* / He satisfies: *Johnson-Davis, Mary* / At the cross: *Ward, Clara* / Precious Lord: *Ward, Clara* / Storm is passing over: *Williams, Marion* / It's getting late in the evening: *Williams, Marion* / I want to rest: *Griffin, Bessie* / Well well well: *Griffin, Bessie* / I'll be satisfied then: *Renfro, Sister Jessie Mae* / I've had my chance: *Renfro, Sister Jessie Mae* / Moan Frances: *Steadman, Frances* / Dry bones: *Steadman, Frances*
SFCD 1003 / Mar '98 / Spirit Feel

☐ GOSPELLING TO THE BEAT VOL.2 (2CD Set)
5033599000095 / Aug '98 / Scripture Union

☐ GOSPELS AND SPIRITUALS (2CD Set)
R2CD 4025 / 13 Apr '98 / Deja Vu

☐ GOSPELS AND SPIRITUALS GOLD (2CD Set)
R2CD 4026 / 13 Apr '98 / Deja Vu

☐ GOT A GOOD THING GOING (25 R&B Radio Hits Of The 1960's)
You're no good: *Warwick, Dee Dee* / Cry to me: *Harris, Betty* / Hey girl: *Scott, Freddie* / I'll find you: *Valerie & Nick* / You better go: *Martin, Derek* / Bitter with the sweet: *Gardner, Don* / But it's all right: *Jackson, J.J.* / It's all in the game: *Ricks, Jimmy* / Say you'll never (never leave me): *Clark, Alice* / Forget it: *Sandpebbles* / Lookin' for a home: *Little Buster* / Baby, you're my everything: *Williams, Jerry* / I'm gonna change my life for you: *Love, Jimmy* / Something I want to tell you: *Johnny & The Expressions* / Brand new world: *Scott, Freddie* / Doctor: *Wells, Mary* / Tired of being nobody: *Valentinos* / Don't let me down: *Height, Donald* / People sure act funny (when they've got a little money): *Turner, Titus* / Hymn no.5: *Mighty Hannibal* / Snap your fingers: *Ricks, Jimmy* / Little blue girl: *Gardner, Don* / I've got a good thing going: *Little Buster* / You got a deal: *Clark, Alice* / Your Daddy wants his baby back: *Martin, Derek*
NEMCD 785 / Apr '96 / Sequel

☐ GOT HARP IF YOU WANT IT
CCD 11030 / '92 / Crosscut

☐ GOT TO GET YOUR OWN (Some Rare Grooves, Vol 1)
Got to get your own: *Wilson, Reuben* / Black water gold: *African Music Machine* / Goo bah: *Continental Showstoppers* / Funky song: *Ripple* / Moon walk: *Ellis, Pee Wee* / Tropical: *African Music Machine* / You're losing me: *Sexton, Ann* / I don't know what it is but it sure is funky: *Ripple* / (I've got) so much trouble in my mind: *Quatermain, Joe* / That thang: *Ellis, Pee Wee* / Dapp: *African Music Machine* / I don't dig no phony, part 2: *Scott, Moody* / Brother man, sister Ann: *Smith, Clemon*
CDINS 5050 / Sep '91 / Charly

☐ GOTH BOX, THE (4CD Set)
CLP 9798 / Oct '96 / Cleopatra

☐ GOTHAM BEAT
HCD 258 / Aug '95 / Hindsight

☐ GOTHIC COLLECTION VOL.6
GOTHN 026CD / 29 Sep '97 / AM Music

☐ GOTHIC ROCK VOL.3 (Black Is Black)
FREUDCD 59 / 18 May '98 / Jungle

☐ GOTHIC SOUND OF NIGHTBREED, THE
NIGHTCD 010 / Jul '96 / Nightbreed

☐ GOTHIC SOUNDS OF NIGHTBREED VOL.1&2, THE
CLP 240 / 5 May '98 / Cleopatra

☐ GOTHIC SOUNDS OF NIGHTBREED VOL.2
NIGHTCD 016 / 27 Oct '97 / Nightbreed

☐ GOTHIC SPIRIT VOL.1
SPV 07625242 / Oct '94 / SPV

☐ GOTH'S UNDEAD (3CD Set)
CLP 0038 / Aug '97 / Cleopatra

☐ GOTHSPOTTING
CLEO 224 / 20 Apr '98 / Cleopatra

☐ GOURD MUSIC SAMPLER, THE
BMCD 526 / 5 Jan '98 / Blue Moon

☐ GRAMAVISION'S 10TH ANNIVERSARY
GV 794612 / Dec '90 / Gramavision

☐ GRAMMY LYRICS VOL.2
VPRL 1170 / May '97 / VP

☐ GRAMMY NOMINEE ALBUM, THE
5332922 / Feb '97 / Polydor

☐ GRAMMY NOMINEES 1998
MCD 11752 / 9 Feb '98 / MCA

☐ GRAMMY'S GREATEST MOMENTS (2CD Set)
What's love got to do with it: *Turner, Tina* / Sweet dreams: *Eurythmics* / She works hard for the money: *Summer, Donna* / Thing called love: *Raitt, Bonnie* / Don't wanna lose you: *Estefan, Gloria* / Another day in paradise: *Collins, Phil* / Unforgettable: *Cole, Natalie & Nat 'King' Cole* / Cradle of love: *Idol, Billy* / Sexual healing: *Gaye, Marvin* / Russians: *Sting* / You don't bring me flowers: *Streisand, Barbra & Neil Diamond* / We didn't start the fire: *Joel, Billy* / Heart of rock 'n' roll: *Lewis, Huey & The News* / Come together: *Aerosmith* / Vision of love: *Carey, Mariah* / What a fool believes: *Doobie Brothers* / Save the best for last: *Williams, Vanessa* / Respect: *Franklin, Aretha* / How am I supposed to live without you: *Bolton, Michael & Kenny G* / If you let me stay: *D'Arby, Terence Trent* / Constant craving: *Lang, k.d.* / One moment in time: *Houston, Whitney* / Tears in heaven: *Clapton, Eric*
7567805822 / Apr '94 / Atlantic

☐ GRAN TURISMO (Playstation Soundtrack)
4950632 / 8 Jun '98 / EMI

☐ GRAND AIRS OF CONNEMARA (Various Traditional Irish Songs)
Mainistir na buille: *MacDonnchadha, Sean* / An Caisdeach ban: *O'Cathain, Padraic* / Piopa Andy mhoir: *O'Neachtain, Tomas* / Una bhan: *O'Connluain, Feichin* / Bean on fhir rua: *O'Cathain, Padraic* / Stor mo chroi: *MacDonnchadha, Sean* / Noirin mo mhian: *MacDonnchadha, Sean* / Cailin schoth na luachra: *O'Cathain, Padraic* / Peigi Misteal: *O'Neachtain, Tomas* / An goirtin eornan: *O'Connluain, Feichin* / Cuaichin Ghleann Neifin: *O'Cathain, Padraic* / An spailpin fanach: *MacDonnchadha, Sean*
OSS 28CD / Dec '93 / Ossian

☐ GRAND CONCERT OF SCOTS PIPING
TRAXCD 110 / May '96 / Greentrax

☐ GRAND HIT PACK, THE
HRCD 8044 / Jul '94 / Disky

☐ GRANDES ORCHESTRES MUSIC HALL VOL.1
984042 / Jun '97 / EPM

☐ GRANDES ORCHESTRES MUSIC HALL VOL.2
984052 / Jun '97 / EPM

☐ GRANDES ORQUESTAS LATINAS
CCD 903 / Jul '97 / Caney

☐ GRANDES VALSES POPULAIRES 1900-1920
983962 / Apr '97 / EPM

☐ GRANDS AUTEURS DU XIX SIECLE
983272 / Oct '96 / EPM

☐ GRAPEVINE 1997 (May Our Worship)
SPND 010 / Oct '97 / Spirit Of Praise

☐ GREAT 1955 SHRINE CONCERT, THE
Spoken introduction: *Pilgrim Travellers* / All the way: *Pilgrim Travellers* / Straight Street: *Pilgrim Travellers* / Since I met Jesus: *Caravans* / What kind of man is this: *Caravans* / It's a long, long way: *May, Brother Joe* / I'm happy working for the Lord: *May, Brother Joe* / Consider me: *May, Annette* / I have a friend above all others: *Soul Stirrers* / Be with me, Jesus: *Soul Stirrers* / Nearer to thee: *Soul Stirrers* / My troubles are so hard to bear: *Davenport, Ethel* / Medley: *Love Coates, Dorothy*
CDCHD 483 / Jul '93 / Ace

☐ GREAT ACOUSTICS
CIC 067CD / Nov '93 / Clo Iar-Chonnachta

☐ GREAT AMERICAN BIG BANDS
Sent for you yesterday: *Basie, Count* / Chicks is wonderful: *Teagarden, Jack* / These foolish things: *Carter, Benny* / When I get low I get high: *Webb, Chick* / Christopher Columbus: *Goodman, Benny* / I never knew: *Armstrong, Louis* / Flop: *Venuti, Joe* / Take the 'A' train: *Ellington, Duke* / Strictly instrumental: *James, Harry* / All of me: *Dorsey, Jimmy* / Prisoner's song: *Berigan, Bunny* / Barrelhouse Bessie from Basin Street: *Crosby, Bob* / My blue heaven: *Lunceford, Jimmie* / String of pearls: *Miller, Glenn* / Run little rabbit: *Calloway, Cab* / Twin City blues: *Herman, Woody* / I wonder who's kissing her now: *Weems, Ted* / Stop, look and listen: *Dorsey, Tommy* / I hope Gabriel likes my music: *Trumbauer, Frankie* / Study in brown: *Casa Loma Orchestra* / Deep purple: *Shaw, Artie* / Drummin' man: *Krupa, Gene* / Nola: *Hampton, Lionel*
PPCD 78101 / Feb '95 / Past Perfect

☐ GREAT AMERICAN COMPOSERS
CD 112 / Jul '94 / New Note

☐ GREAT AMERICAN SONGWRITERS, THE (5CD Set)
15991 / Oct '95 / Laserlight

☐ GREAT BANDS OF TANGO'S GOLDEN AGE 1936-1947
HQCD 89 / Apr '97 / Harlequin

☐ GREAT BANDS, THE
Begin the beguin: *Shaw, Artie Orchestra* / Drum stomp: *Hampton, Lionel & His Orchestra* / Bugle call rag: *Roy, Harry & His Orchestra* / Georgia on my mind: *Gonella, Nat & His Georgians* / Stompin' at the Savoy: *Goodman, Benny Orchestra* / Love is the sweetest thing: *Bowlly, Al & Ray Noble* / Save it pretty mama: *Armstrong, Louis Orchestra* / World is waiting for the sunrise: *Geraldo & His Orchestra* / Continental: *Stone, Lew & His Band* / One o'clock jump: *Basie, Count & His Orchestra* / On the air: *Gibbons, Carroll & The Savoy Hotel Orpheans* / Say it with music: *Payne, Jack & His Band* / Whispering: *Fox, Roy & His Band* / Take the 'A' train: *Ellington, Duke Orchestra* / Sweetest music this side of heaven: *Winnick, Maurice & his Orchestra* / Somebody stole my gal: *Cotton, Billy & His Band* / In the mood: *Loss, Joe & His Orchestra* / Here's to the next time: *Hall, Henry & His Orchestra* / At the woodchopper's ball: *Herman, Woody & His Orchestra* / I used to be colour blind: *Hilton, Jack & His Orchestra* / Trumpet blues and cantabile: *James, Harry & His Band* / Hors d'Oeuvres: *Ambrose & His Orchestra*
PASTCD 7015 / Mar '97 / Flapper

☐ GREAT BANDS, THE
Black bottom stomp / Potato head blues / West end blues / Gee baby ain't I good to you / Panama / After you've gone / Moten swing / Symphony in riffs / Bubbling over / Down South camp meeting / Don't be that way / Rhythm is our business / King Porter stomp / Song of India / One o'clock jump / Begin the beguine / Floyd's guitar blues / At the woodchopper's ball / Chant of the weed / Ko ko / Flying home / Sepian bounce / Skyliner
TPZ 1031 / Nov '97 / Topaz Jazz

☐ GREAT BERLIN BAND SHOW, THE
National anthems / Fanfare - Union Jack / Jupiter / Posthorn galop / Crown of state / Per mare per terram / Globe and lauret / Rule Britannia / Pipes and drums / Glendaurel highlanders / Skye boat song / Caledonian canal / Lexy border / Bugler's delight / Light infantry / Londonderry air / St. Patrick's Day / Caubeen trimmed with blue / Irish washerwoman / Flight of the bumble bee / Brandenburg concerto / David of the White Rock / Men of Harlech / All through the night / God bless the Prince of Wales / Radetzky march / Prussia's glory / Drum display / British Grenadiers / Yorkshire march / Muss I dehn / Royal standard / Zadok the priest / Water music / Music from the Royal fireworks / Lament / Salute to Berlin / Berliner luft / Auld lang syne
BNA 5047 / '91 / Bandleader

☐ GREAT BIG BAND SINGERS
HCD 326 / Jun '95 / Hindsight

☐ GREAT BIG BAND THEMES
HCD 321 / Mar '95 / Hindsight

☐ GREAT BIG BANDS OF THE '50S
Fanfare boogie: *Winstone, Eric* / Drum crazy: *Johnson, Laurie* / Rhythm and blues: *Winstone, Eric* / Anticipation: *Winstone, Eric* / Nexy train out of town: *Miller, Betty* / Cobbler's song: *Winstone, Eric* / Heatwave: *Johnson, Laurie* / In a Persian market: *Johnson, Laurie* / Fascinating rhythm: *Clark, Petula* / Hallelujah: *Johnson, Laurie* / Frustration: *Winstone, Eric* / Treasure of love: *Shepherd, Pauline* / Jamboree: *Johnson, Laurie* / Slow train blues: *Winstone, Eric* / Cat walk: *Winstone, Eric* / Georgia's got a moon: *Miller, Betty* / Opus one mambo: *Winstone, Eric* / Heartbreak: *Winstone, Eric* / It might as well be spring: *Johnson, Laurie* / Robber's march: *Winstone, Eric* / Majorca: *Clark, Petula* / Stick or twist: *Johnson, Laurie* / Things we did last summer: *Johnson, Laurie*
C5LCD 601 / May '94 / See For Miles

☐ GREAT BLACK GOSPEL MUSIC (2CD Set)
Oh happy day: *Hawkins, Edwin Singers* / Goodness of Jesus: *Smith, Charles* / Stand the storm: *Caesar, Shirley* / Baptized believer: *Voices Of White Rock* / Oh to kept by Jesus: *Cleveland, Rev. James* / I love him: *Christ Tabernacle Choir* / Journey: *Robinson, Rev. Billy* / Old ship of Zion: *Brunson, Milton* / Rapture: *Caesar, Shirley* / Happy on my way: *Cleveland, Rev. James* / He will fix it: *Walker, Albertina* / Close to thee: *Brunson, Milton* / I've got a long way to go: *Caesar, Shirley* / Never let go: *Austin, James* / I believe: *Walker, Albertina* / Think about it: *Walker, Albertina* / Christ is coming back again: *Cleveland, Rev. James* / Living for Jesus: *Five Blind Boys Of Alabama* / Peace in the valley: *Raspberry Singers* / You brought me from a long way: *Caesar, Shirley* / Something got a hold of me: *Cleveland, Rev. James* / Jesus hold my hand: *Royal Travellers* / Getting up morning: *New Hope Baptist Choir* / God almighty: *Brunson, Milton* / No secret: *Swan Silvertones* / Why me lord: *Caesar, Shirley* / I walk with God: *Cleveland, Rev. James* / Bye and bye: *Five Blind Boys Of Alabama* / Sit down servant: *Gospel Singers Ensemble* / I won't be troubled no more: *Caesar, Shirley* / He didn't have to answer my prayer: *Bell, Maggie* / How I got over: *Walker, Albertina* / Glory halleluja amen: *Cleveland, Rev. James*
SD 886202 / 2 Feb '98 / Disky

☐ GREAT BLUES GUITAR LEGENDS, THE (4CD Set)
HRCD 8030 / May '93 / Disky

☐ GREAT BLUES SESSIONS
CWNCD 2035 / Jun '97 / Crown

☐ GREAT BRITISH BANDS (4CD Set)
HRCD 8026 / May '93 / Disky

☐ GREAT BRITISH DANCE BANDS, THE
Did you mean it: *Hylton, Jack* / I guess I'll have to change my plan: *Ambrose* / Got to dance my way to heaven: *Hall, Henry* / You go to my head: *Loss, Joe* / One in a million: *Lawrence, Brian* / I've got beginner's luck: *Fox, Roy* / From the top of your head: *Gibbons, Carroll* / Eyes of the world are on you: *Levy, Louis* / My heart belongs to Daddy: *Cotton, Billy* / Just as long as the world goes round and around: *Wilbur, Jay* / Mr. Rhythm Man: *Gonella, Nat* / You turned your head: *Jackson, Jack* / Let's fall in love for the last time: *Mantovani* / Temptation rag: *Roy, Harry* / Walkin' by the river: *Geraldo* / Crazy rhythm: *Silvester, Victor* / Organ grinder swing: *Payne, Jack* / Plain Mary Jane: *Hylton, Mrs Jack* / Stars fell on Alabama: *Stone, Lew* / My pet: *Firman, Bert* / Palais de Danse: *Phillips, Sid* / Shout for happiness: *Noble, Ray*
PPCD 78112 / Feb '95 / Past Perfect

☐ GREAT BRITISH JAZZ BANDS
Jazz ma blues / Someday sweetheart / Imagination / Petite fleur / Original dixieland one step / Prelude to a kiss / Idaho / Very thought of you / K.C. BLUES / Nightingale sang in Berkeley Square / Gypsy / Limehouse blues
EMPRCD 709 / Apr '97 / Emporio

☐ GREAT BRITISH PUNK ROCK EXPLOSION VOL.1, THE
Anarchy in the UK: *Sex Pistols* / No time to be 21: *Adverts* / First time: *Boys* / New rose: *Damned* / I hate people: *Anti Nowhere League* / Homicide: *999* / I live in a car: *UK Subs* / Blind ambition: *Partisans* / Dogs of war: *Exploited* / Flares and slippers: *Cockney Rejects* / Murder of liddle towers: *Angelic Upstarts* / Harry May: *Business* / I wanna be me: *Sex Pistols* / Let's break the law: *Anti Nowhere League* / Disco man: *Damned* / One chord wonders: *Adverts* / Ain't got a clue (Live): *Lurkers* / Tin soldier: *Stiff Little Fingers* / Borstal breakout: *Sham 69* / CID: *UK Subs* / Baby baby: *Vibrators*
DOJOCD 122 / Feb '94 / Dojo

☐ GREAT BRITISH PUNK ROCK EXPLOSION VOL.2, THE
Safety in numbers: *Adverts* / Woman in disguise: *Angelic Upstarts* / Pretty vacant: *Sex Pistols* / Brickfield nights: *Sex Pistols* / Everybody's happy nowadays: *Buzzcocks* / BIC: *UK Subs* / Nobody's heroes: *Stiff Little Fingers* / Feelin' alright with the crew: *999* / Ignite: *Damned* / Streets of London: *Anti Nowhere League* / Bored teenagers: *Adverts* / I don't need to tell her: *Lurkers* / National insurance blacklist: *Business* / Viv la revolution: *Adicts* / Punk's

not dead: *Exploited* / You'll never know: *Vice Squad* / Judy says: *Vibrators* / Warriors: *Blitz* / Something that I said: *Ruts* / I think I'm wonderful: *Damned* / For you: *Anti Nowhere League* / Jinx: *Peter & The Test Tube Babies* / Alternative: *Exploited* / Angels with dirty faces: *Sham 69*

DOJOCD 131 / May '93 / Dojo

☐ GREAT CLASSIC BLUES SINGERS

158092 / Oct '93 / Blues Collection

☐ GREAT COUNTRY LEGENDS

Walkin' after midnight: *Cline, Patsy* / Walk on by: *Van Dyke, Leroy* / Rose garden: *Anderson, Lynn* / What a way to live: *Nelson, Willie* / If I needed you: *Van Zandt, Townes* / Alligator man: *Newman, Jimmy C.* / Girl most likely: *Riley, Jeannie C.* / There you go: *Cash, Johnny* / In the jailhouse now: *Pierce, Webb* / You win again: *Lewis, Jerry Lee* / King of the road: *Miller, Roger* / Tennessee waltz: *Page, Patti* / Abilene: *Jennings, Waylon* / Stand by your man: *Spears, Billie Jo* / From a jack to a king: *Miller, Ned* / CB savage: *Hart, Rod* / I can't help you (I'm fallin' too): *Davis, Skeeter* / Me and my old CB: *Dudley, Dave* / Walk through this world with me: *Jones, George* / Send me the pillow you dream on: *Locklin, Hank*

306842 / Jun '97 / Hallmark

☐ GREAT CROONERS, THE

Anything goes: *Bennett, Tony* / Granada: *Laine, Frankie* / Love letters: *Como, Perry* / Blue skies: *Haymes, Dick* / Swanee: *Jolson, Al* / Come fly with me: *Sinatra, Frank* / My heart is taking lessons: *Crosby, Bing* / Mona Lisa: *Cole, Nat 'King'* / Cry: *Ray, Johnnie* / Life is a song: *Bennett, Tony* / Woman in love: *Laine, Frankie* / Song of songs: *Como, Perry* / Night and day: *Haymes, Dick* / You made me love you: *Jolson, Al* / East side of heaven: *Crosby, Bing* / Hernando's hideaway: *Ray, Johnnie* / Unforgettable: *Cole, Nat 'King'* / I've got you under my skin: *Sinatra, Frank*

SUMCD 4165 / 26 Jan '98 / Summit

☐ GREAT DANCE FAVOURITES

HCD 328 / Jun '95 / Hindsight

☐ GREAT DAYS OF MUSIC HALL

Jolly good luck to the girl who loves a soldier: *Tilley, Vesta* / When father papered the parlour: *Williams, Billy* / Gas Inspector: *Little Tich* / I may be crazy: *Stratton, Eugene* / Has anybody here seen Kelly: *Forde, Florrie* / Archibald certainly not: *Robey, George* / Burlington Bertie from Bow: *Shields, Ella* / Lily of Laguna: *Stratton, Eugene* / Every little movement: *Lloyd, Marie* / My old Dutch: *Chevalier, Albert* / Naughty Victorian days: *Byng, Douglas* / Mocking bird: *Leno, Dan* / It's a big shame: *Elen, Gus* / 'Arf a pint of ale: *Elen, Gus* / Three trees: *Whelan, Albert* / Preacher and the bear: *Whelan, Albert* / Don't send my boy to prison: *Williams, Billy* / Music Hall medley: *Retford, Ella* / PC 49: *Fay, Harry* / Two lovely black eyes: *Coburn, Charles* / Three times a day: *Wallace, Nellie*

RAJCD 834 / Feb '98 / Empress

☐ GREAT DAYS OF THE ACCORDION BANDS

Old timer: *Geraldo & His Orchestra* / Sleepy time in sleepy hollow: *Geraldo & His Orchestra* / Marching along together: *Geraldo & His Orchestra* / At eventide: *Geraldo & His Orchestra* / Song of the bells: *Geraldo & His Orchestra* / Silver hair and heart of gold: *Geraldo & His Orchestra* / Sing a new song: *Geraldo & His Orchestra* / Clouds will soon roll by: *Geraldo & His Orchestra* / Marta: *Geraldo & His Orchestra* / Sweetest song in the world: *Reid, Billy & His Orchestra* / First time I saw you: *Reid, Billy & His Orchestra* / Blossoms on broadway: *Reid, Billy & His Orchestra* / Remember me: *Reid, Billy & His Orchestra* / Little drummer boy: *Reid, Billy & His Orchestra* / Moonlight on the waterfall: *Reid, Billy & His Orchestra* / So many memories: *Reid, Billy & His Orchestra* / Sweetest sweetheart: *Reid, Billy & His Orchestra* / My heaven in the pines: *Reid, Billy & His Orchestra* / Are you sincere: *Reid, Billy & His Orchestra* / Rose covered shack: *Reid, Billy & His Orchestra* / Chocolate soldier's daughter: *Reid, Billy & His Orchestra* / Apple blossom time: *London Piano Accordion Band* / South of the border (Down Mexico way): *London Piano Accordion Band* / All alone with my shadow: *London Piano Accordion Band* / Whose little what's it are you: *London Piano Accordion Band* / For all that I care: *Scala, Primo Accordion Band* / Down forget-me-not lane: *Scala, Primo Accordion Band* / I yi yi yi yi (I like you very much): *Scala, Primo Accordion Band* / There goes that song again: *Scala, Primo Accordion Band* / Hey little hen: *Scala, Primo Accordion Band*

RAJCD 828 / Jul '97 / Empress

☐ GREAT DOBRO SESSIONS, THE

SHCD 2206 / Oct '94 / Sugar Hill

☐ GREAT FEMALE JAZZ SINGERS

VN 164 / Mar '96 / Viper's Nest

☐ GREAT FIGURES OF FLAMENCO VOL.1-4 (4CD Set)

CMX 2741057-60 / May '97 / Le Chant Du Monde

☐ GREAT FIGURES OF FLAMENCO VOL.13-16 (4CD Set)

CMX 2741069-72 / May '97 / Le Chant Du Monde

☐ GREAT FIGURES OF FLAMENCO VOL.17-20 (4CD Set)

CMX 2741073-76 / May '97 / Le Chant Du Monde

☐ GREAT FIGURES OF FLAMENCO VOL.5-8 (4CD Set)

CMX 2741061-64 / May '97 / Le Chant Du Monde

☐ GREAT FIGURES OF FLAMENCO VOL.9-12 (4CD Set)

CMX 2741065-68 / May '97 / Le Chant Du Monde

☐ GREAT GIRL SINGERS

It's been so long: *Forrest, Helen* / If that's the way you want it baby: *Forrest, Helen* / I couldn't sleep a wink last night: *Forrest, Helen* / At least you could say hello: *O'Connell, Helen* / I'm steppin' out with a memory tonight: *O'Connell, Helen* / Just for a thrill: *O'Connell, Helen* / Them there eyes: *Starr, Kay* / It's a good day: *Starr, Kay* / I only have eyes for you: *Starr, Kay* / I'll never forget you: *Clooney, Rosemary* / You make me feel so young: *Clooney, Rosemary* / Don't worry 'bout me: *Clooney, Rosemary*

HCD 320 / Apr '95 / Hindsight

☐ GREAT GIRL SINGERS

HCD 414 / Sep '92 / Hindsight

☐ GREAT GOOGA MOOGA VOL.1 (Rhythm 'n' Bluesin' With King/ Federal/Deluxe Vocal Groups)

Bo peep: *Lamplighters* / No other one: *Tenderfoots* / I wasn't thinkin', I was drinkin': *Checkers* / Baby let's play house: *Thunderbirds* / Good googa mooga: *Magic Tones* / Midnight hours: *Drivers* / So fine: *Sheiks* / That's your mistake: *Williams, Otis New Group* / All night long: *Orchids* / One moment with you: *Ward, Billy & The Dominoes* / Chicken backs: *Carpets* / Hug a little, kiss a little: *Lamplighters* / Oh Miss Nellie: *Drivers* / Cool cool baby: *Magic Tones* / Only you: *Platters* / La verne: *Tenderfoots* / Mama's daughter: *Checkers* / And I need you: *Pyramids* / Goodbye baby: *Four Jacks* / Be bop wino: *Lamplighters*

NEMCD 907 / Jan '97 / Sequel

☐ GREAT GOSPEL CHOIRS

HRCD 8054 / Apr '94 / Disky

☐ GREAT GOSPEL MEN

SHAN 06005CD / Aug '93 / Shanachie

☐ GREAT GOSPEL SONGS (2CD Set)

Oh happy day: *Hawkins, Edwin Singers* / Amen: *Impressions* / Hallelujah: *Gayle, Crystal* / Lord's prayer: *Adams, Johnny* / I don't know how to love him: *Phillips, Ann* / Farewell: *Belafonte, Harry* / Lay down (candles in the rain): *Melanie & The Edwin Hawkin Singers* / Swing down chariot: *Staple Singers* / God bless the child: *Cooke, Sam* / Down by the riverside: *Jericho Group* / Just a closer walk with thee: *Abend, Joe Singers* / Army of the Lord: *King, B.B.* / Joy to the world: *Wilson, Jackie* / It's me oh Lord: *Jericho Group* / Sundays are the sun days for my Lord: *Perkins, Carl* / Jesus loves me (this I know): *Abend, Joe Singers* / I know I've got religion: *Staple Singers* / Read your bible: *Jericho Group* / He's got the whole world in his hands: *Simone, Nina* / Amazing Grace: *Phillips, Ann* / When the saints go marchin' in: *Lewis, Jerry Lee* / Ave Maria: *Stuarti, Enzo* / Michael row the boat ashore: *Lopez, Trini* / My true confession: *Benton, Brook* / Joshua fit de battle of Jericho: *Jericho Group* / God's wonderful love: *Staple Singers* / Save a seat for me: *King, B.B.* / Hallelujah special: *Perkins, Carl* / Ol' man river: *Cooke, Sam* / Old time religion: *Jericho Group* / What child is this: *Jackson, Mahalia* / All God's lonely children: *Rogers, Kenny* / Something's got a hold on me: *James, Etta* / Go tell it on the mountain: *Abend, Joe Singers* / Go down Moses: *Jericho Group* / I got a jump: *Belafonte, Harry*

TNC 96238 / Aug '96 / Natural Collection

☐ GREAT GOSPEL WOMEN VOL.1

SHAN 06004CD / Aug '93 / Shanachie

☐ GREAT GOSPEL WOMEN VOL.2

SHCD 6017 / Mar '96 / Shanachie

☐ GREAT GUITARS

CCD 6004 / Jul '88 / Concord Jazz

☐ GREAT HARP PLAYERS

DOCD 5100 / Nov '92 / Document

☐ GREAT HYMNS OF WALES, THE

SCD 2116 / Feb '96 / Sain

☐ GREAT INSTRUMENTAL FAVOURITES

HCD 325 / May '95 / Hindsight

☐ GREAT JAZZ BANDS

Rock-a-bye Basie: *Basie, Count* / Baby, won't you please come home: *Basie, Count* / Jumpin' at the woodside: *Basie, Count* / Someone: *Ellington, Duke* / Suddenly it jumped: *Ellington, Duke* / Perdido: *Ellington, Duke* / Jeep is jumpin': *Ellington, Duke* / Together: *Kirk, Andy* / 9.20 Special: *Kirk, Andy* / For dancers only: *Lunceford, Jimmie* / Holiday for strings: *Lunceford, Jimmie* / Wham: *Lunceford, Jimmie*

HCD 413 / Sep '92 / Hindsight

☐ GREAT JAZZ BANDS

Rock-a-bye basie / Someone / Together / For dancers only / Baby won't you please come home (vocal jimmie lunceford) / Suddenly it jumped / Holiday for strings / Jumpin' a the woodside / Peridido / 920 special / Wham / Jeep is jumpin'

HCD 323 / Apr '95 / Hindsight

☐ GREAT JAZZ PIANISTS, THE

Carolina shout: *Waller, Fats* / Ain't misbehavin': *Waller, Fats* / Fifty seven varieties: *Hines, Earl 'Fatha'* / My melancholy baby: *Hines, Earl 'Fatha'* / Snowy morning blues: *Johnson, James P.* / You've got to be modernistic: *Johnson, James P.* / King Porter stomp: *Morton, Jelly Roll* / Original rags: *Morton, Jelly Roll* / Swampy river: *Ellington, Duke* / Passionette: *Smith, Willie 'The Lion'* / Morning air: *Smith, Willie 'The Lion'* / Humoresque: *Tatum, Art* / Begin the beguine: *Tatum, Art* / Tiger rag: *Wilson, Teddy* / When you and I were young: *Wilson, Teddy* / Maggie: *Wilson, Teddy* / Finishing up a date: *Kyle, Billy* / My blue heaven: *Weatherford, Teddy* / Pilgrim's chorus: *Lambert, Donald* / Rockin' chair: *Wilson, Garland* / Swingin' for joy: *Williams, Mary Lou* / Ladder: *Turner, 'Big' Joe* / Little Rock getaway: *Sullivan, Joe*

PPCD 78107 / Feb '95 / Past Perfect

☐ GREAT JAZZ VOCALISTS, THE

Now you has jazz: *Crosby, Bing & Louis Armstrong* / Late late show: *Staton, Dakota* / Pete Kelly's blues: *Fitzgerald, Ella* / I know that you know: *Cole, Nat 'King'* / Midnight sun: *Christy, June* / Satin doll: *Wilson, Nancy* / Dinah: *Williams, Joe* / Call me irresponsible: *Washington, Dinah* / Honeysuckle rose: *Dankworth, John Seven & Cleo Laine* / Lulu's back in town: *Hi-Lo's* / I got rhythm: *Vaughan, Sarah* / Star eyes: *McRae, Carmen & Dave Brubeck* / Got the gate on the golden gate: *Torme, Mel* / Things are swinging: *Lee, Peggy* / Her tears flowed like wine: *O'Day, Anita* / Love is just around the corner: *Four Freshmen* / Walk in the Black Forest: *Jones, Salena* / Lil' darlin: *Lambert, Hendricks & Ross* / Jon Hendricks: *Four Brothers* / God bless the child: *Holiday, Billie*

CDMFP 6162 / May '95 / Music For Pleasure

☐ GREAT LADIES OF SONG (2CD Set)

Lover man: *Horne, Lena* / Too young: *Lee, Peggy* / Taking a chance on love: *Fitzgerald, Ella* / Them there eyes: *Starr, Kay* / Moon river: *Garland, Judy* / My blue Heaven: *Day, Doris* / St. Louis blues: *Holiday, Billie* / More I see you: *Vaughan, Sarah* / Manhattan serenade: *Shore, Dinah* / South American way: *Andrews Sisters* / I've got my love to keep me warm: *Starr, Kay* / September in the rain: *Day, Doris* / Yes my darling daughter: *Shore, Dinah* / I've got the world on a string: *Vaughan, Sarah* / Honeysuckle rose: *Horne, Lena* / As long as he needs me: *Garland, Judy* / Just one more chance: *Lee, Peggy* / All of me: *Holiday, Billie* / Imagination: *Fitzgerald, Ella* / Boogie woogie bugle boy: *Andrews Sisters* / Lady is a tramp: *Lee, Peggy* / I'm nobody's baby: *Garland, Judy* / Blue skies: *Day, Doris* / Pretty baby: *Starr, Kay* / Oh Johnny, oh Johnny oh: *Andrews Sisters* / I hear a rhapsody: *Shore, Dinah* / Love can change the stars: *Horne, Lena* / Three little words: *Fitzgerald, Ella* / I'll be seeing you: *Vaughan, Sarah* / God bless the child: *Holiday, Billie* / These foolish things: *Lee, Peggy* / I got it bad and that ain't good: *Fitzgerald, Ella* / Am I blue: *Holiday, Billie* / Are you certain: *Vaughan, Sarah* / You and I: *Shore, Dinah* / Fly me to the moon: *Garland, Judy* / 'S wonderful: *Day, Doris* / My man: *Fitzgerald, Ella* / You've got to see Mama every night: *Starr, Kay* / Bei mir bist du schon: *Andrews Sisters*

MUCD 9514 / May '96 / Musketeer

☐ GREAT MALE JAZZ SINGERS

VN 166 / Mar '96 / Viper's Nest

☐ GREAT MARCHES VOL.1, THE

Colonel Bogey / Blaze away / On the quarterdeck / Liberty bell / Washington greys / Army of the Nile / Berliner luft / Great little army / Radetzky march / With sword and lance / National emblem / Holyrood / Semper fidelis / Boots and saddles / La reve passe / Scarlet and gold / Thunderer / Fehrbelliner reitermarsch / Thin red line / Anchors aweigh / Old comrades / Standard of St. George

BNA 5006 / Apr '87 / Bandleader

☐ GREAT MARCHES VOL.3, THE

Voice of the guns / Golden spurs / Wings / Royal Air Force march past / Black horse troop / Gunners / Barvada / Officer of the day / Mad major / Red cloak / Down the Mall / Iron regiment / Trombone king / Cavalry of the clouds / Imperial Life Guards / Trumpet major / Grid iron club / My congratulations / Royal standard / Purple pageant / Marche des parachutistes belges / Chief of staff / Inkerman / Pentland hills / Imperial march

BNA 5029 / Aug '89 / Bandleader

☐ GREAT MARCHES VOL.5, THE

Contemptibles / On the square / Aces high / King's guard / Hoch und deutschmeister / Vedette / Cavalry walk / Carmen march / H M Jollies / Alma / Sounding brass / BB and CF / March of the Royal British Legion / British Eighth / Barnum and Bailey's favourite / Guard's parade / Old gray mare / Grandioso / Flying eagle / Cavalry of the steppes / Through night to light / Blue devils / Marche Americaine / My regiment

BNA 5060 / Apr '92 / Bandleader

☐ GREAT MARCHES VOL.7, THE

Stars and stripes forever / Imperial echoes / Army and marine / Father Rhine / Wait for the wagon / Sarie Marais / Grenadier Mars / Gladiator's farewell / Thundering guns / Quality plus / Under freedom's banner / Royal buglers

BNA 5112 / Nov '94 / Bandleader

☐ GREAT MARCHES VOL.8, THE

Bond of friendship / 3 DG's / Washington Post / Fortune favours the bold / Chimes of liberty / Salamanca / Queen's division / Rifle Regiment / Quickest and best / Battleaxe company / El Capitan / Cockney cockney / Viscount Nelson U / Red Square review / Regimentsgruss / Swift and sure / Under the Allied banner / Blow away the morning's dew / Marche vanier / Ship to shore / All American soldier / Agrippa / First post / Pride of lions / St. Louis blues march

BNA 5128 / Dec '96 / Bandleader

☐ GREAT MARCHES VOL.9, THE

BNA 5140 / 13 Apr '98 / Bandleader

☐ GREAT MUSICAL MEMORIES

HCD 322 / Jul '95 / Hindsight

☐ GREAT NEW YORK SINGLES

RE 116CD / Nov '94 / ROIR

☐ GREAT PRESTIGE JAZZ COLLECTION VOL.1, THE

120101 / 11 May '98 / Prestige

☐ GREAT PRESTIGE JAZZ COLLECTION VOL.2, THE

120102 / 11 May '98 / Prestige

☐ GREAT RADIO STARS OF THE 30'S VOL.1

It's that man again: *Handley, Tommy* / Mermaid: *Fletcher, Cyril* / Down upon the farm: *Sarony, Leslie & Leslie Holmes* / On the telephone: *Mrs. Feather* / Goes naughty: *Oliver, Vic* / Gert, Daisy and a piano: *Waters, Elsie & Doris* / Play the game, you cads: *Western Brothers* / Police station: *Wilton, Robb* / Kiss me goodnight, Sergeant Major: *Carlisle, Elsie* / Last year's calendar: *Stainless Stephen* / Bugginses at the seaside: *Constandurous, Mabel/Michael Hogan & Company* / We must all stick together: *Murgatroyd & Winterbottom* / Tomsky, the great counter-spy: *Handley, Tommy* / It's an over-rated pastime: *Frankau, Ronald* / I taught her to play br-oop, br-oop: *Fields, Gracie* / Joe Ramsbottom at the dentist: *Evans, Norman* / Woodland romance: *Gourley, Ronald* / Play up and pay the dame: *Wakefield, Oliver* / Why should the dustman get it all: *Miller, Max* / Good old General Guiness: *Handley, Tommy*

PASTCD 9721 / '90 / Flapper

☐ GREAT RADIO STARS VOL.2

Bee song / I didn't orter a'ett it: *Warner, Jack* / Laughing bachelor: *Penrose, Charles* / Trains: *Gardiner, Reginald* / Rachmaninov's prelude: *Henson, Leslie* / Annual dinner of the slate club secretaries: *Johnson, Cecil* / Chin chin cheerio: *Frankau, Ronald* / Stanelli and his hornchestra: *Stanelli* / Much ado about little or nothing: *Wakefield, Oliver* / More chestnut corner: *Askey/Murdoch* / Pussy cat news: *Flotsam & Jetsam* / Splitting up: *Flanagan & Allen* / Teasing tongue twisters: *Comber, Bobbie* / Fiddling and fooling: *Ray, Ted* / I must have one of those: *Henry, Leonard* / Lion and ALbert: *Holloway, Stanley* / Jolly old ma, jolly old Pa: *Sarony, Leslie* / Truth about society: *Potter, Gillie*

PASTCD 9728 / '90 / Flapper

☐ GREAT SEX

Bump 'n' grind: *Kelly, R* / Sexual healing: *Gaye, Marvin* / Move closer: *Nelson, Phyllis* / Between the sheets: *Isley Brothers* / Slow hand: *Pointer Sisters* / Get up, I feel like being a sex machine: *Brown, James* / I want to sex you up: *Color Me Badd* / Body talk: *Imagination* / All night long: *Mary Jane Girls* / If only for one night: *Vandross, Luther* / Touch me in the morning: *Ross, Diana* / I'm gonna love you just a little more babe: *White, Barry* / Your body's calling: *Kelly, R* / Let's get it on: *Jade* / Stroke you up: *Changing Faces* / I'm goin' down: *Blige, Mary J.* / G-spot: *Marshall, Wayne* / Slow tongue: *Jackson, Millie* / Love won't let me wait: *Harris, Major* / Je t'aime, moi non plus: *Sweet Sex Symphony*

RADCD 16 / Jun '95 / Global TV

☐ GREAT SOUND OF COUNTRY VOL.1, THE

EMPRCD 541 / Sep '94 / Emporio

☐ GREAT SOUND OF COUNTRY VOL.2, THE

Five minutes of the latest blues: *Tubb, Justin* / Down the street to 301: *Cash, Johnny* / He made a women out of me: *Riley, Jeannie C.* / Down on the corner of love: *Owens, Buck* / I think I'll just stay here and drink: *Haggard, Merle* / Single girl: *Posey, Sandy* / Up against the wall, redneck cowboy: *Hubbard, Ray Wylie* / How the time flies: *Wallace, Jerry* / Yellow rose: *Lee, Johnny* / Comin' on strong: *Lee, Brenda* / Whispering pines: *Anderson, Bill* / Yesterday when I was young: *Clarke, Roy* / Most beautiful girl in the world: *Stampley, Joe* / Best years of my life: *Red Sovine* / Midnight driver: *Weller, Freddy* / I wished a thousand times: *Husky, Ferlin* / That's the way I feel: *Jones, George*

EMPRCD 542 / Sep '94 / Emporio

☐ GREAT SOUND OF COUNTRY VOL.3, THE

I saw your face in the moon: *Pierce, Webb* / One is a lonely number: *Jones, George* / I heard the jukebox playing: *Young, Faron* / There you go: *Cash, Johnny* / Seasons of my heart: *Jones, George* / Help me make it through the night: *Pride, Charley* / Hello walls: *Young, Faron* / Hooked on a feeling: *Thomas, B.J.* / I've loved and lost again: *Cline, Patsy* / What am I doing in your world: *Sealey, Jeannie*

EMPRCD 543 / Nov '94 / Emporio

☐ GREAT SOUND OF COUNTRY VOL.4, THE

Sweethearts in heaven: *Owens, Buck* / Ruebens train: *Dillards* / Just out of reach: *Cline, Patsy* / Coalminer's daughter: *Lynn, Loretta* / Garden party: *Nelson, Rick* / Lovesick blues: *Cline, Patsy* / Sticks and stones: *Fargo, Donna* / Mama tried: *Haggard, Merle* / Kiss an angel good morning: *Pride, Charley* / She's a lady: *Stampley, Joe* / Wait a little longer baby: *Thompson, Hank* / Freight train blues: *Dean, Jimmy* / Too much: *Red Sovine* / Boll weevil: *Glazer, Jim* / King of the road: *Miller, Roger* / I love you because: *Jones, George* / Done rovin': *Harton, Johnny*

EMPRCD 544 / Nov '94 / Emporio

☐ GREAT SOUND OF COUNTRY, THE (4CD Set)

EMPRBX 006 / Sep '94 / Emporio

☐ GREAT SWEET BANDS

HCD 324 / Jul '95 / Hindsight

☐ GREAT SWING JAM SESSIONS 1938-1939

Keep smilin' at trouble / Just the blues / China boy / Someday sweetheart / Sugar / St. Louis blues / You took advantage of me / Someday sweetheart / Basin Street blues / Honeysuckle rose / (I would do) anything for you / Boogie woogie blues / I'm coming Virginia

JUCD 2029 / Mar '95 / Storyville

☐ GREAT TENORS OF WALES, THE

SCD 2129 / Nov '96 / Sain

☐ GREAT VOCALISTS, THE

If you were the only girl in the world: *Ziegler, Anne & Webster Booth* / Be careful, it's my heart: *Sinatra, Frank & Tommy Dorsey Orchestra* / Bless you: *Ink Spots* / Little white gardenia: *Brisson, Carl* / Very thought of you: *Bowlly, Al* / J'attendrai: *Rossi, Tino* / Stop beating around the mulberry bush: *Merry Macs* / What do you know Jo: *Stafford, Jo & The Pied Pipers* / Great mistake of my life: *Henderson, Chick* / Body and soul: *Boswell, Connee* / Sonny boy: *Jolson, Al* / Tisket a tasket: *Fitzgerald, Ella* / Without a song: *Dennis, Denny* / How about you: *Carless, Dorothy* / Where the blue of the night: *Crosby, Bing* / Transatlantic lullaby: *Hall, Adelaide* / Last time I saw Paris: *Martin, Tony* / Fools rush in: *Shelton, Anne* / My good friend the milkman: *Waller, Fats* / Pennsylvania 6-5000: *Andrews Sisters* / These foolish things: *Layton, Turner* / Someone to watch over me: *Langford, Frances*

PASTCD 7018 / Mar '97 / Flapper

☐ GREAT VOCALISTS, THE

Baby doll / Creole love call / I'm crazy 'bout my baby / St. Louis blues / That's my home / I gotta right to sing the blues / Sing me a swing song (and let me dance) / Smoke dreams / Good morning blues / It's funny that way / T'ain't what you do (it's the way that you do it) / Blame it on my last affair / Stormy weather / Let's fly away / Piney brown blues / Sweet Lorraine / St. James Infirmary / Stormy Monday / Knock me a kiss / Murder he says / Five guys named Moe / Cherry red blues

TPZ 1033 / Nov '97 / Topaz Jazz

☐ GREAT VOICES OF BULGARIA

Little bird is singing / Little flute is playing / Our father / Oh Lord many long years / First part of the high mass / We sing for you lord / Good thief / Song of Macedonia / Oh Lord / Our father / Oh Lord save my people / Praise to the virgin / Lord bless our souls / Joyful song from the town of Tran / In the country there was a birch tree / Sunny land

B 6859 / Mar '98 / Auvidis/Ethnic

☐ GREAT VOICES OF SOUL, THE (3CD Set)

DTKBOX 79 / 26 May '98 / Dressed To Kill

☐ GREAT WAR THEMES

Dam busters march: Band Of The RAF / Longest day: Central Band Of Royal British Legion / Bridge too far: Band Of The Parachute Regiment / Colditz march: Band Of The Queen's Lancashire Regiment / High on a hill: Band Of The Blues And Royals / Colonel Bogey: Central Band Of Royal British Legion / Top Gun: Band Of The Duke Of Edinburgh's Royal Regiment / Aces high: Royal Marines / Great escape: Royal Anglian Regiment / Lawrence of Arabia: Royal Marines / Cockleshell heroes: Royal Marines / MASH: Band Of The Duke Of Edinburgh's Royal Regiment / Road to Vitez: Band Of The Cheshire Regiment / Raiders march/Imperial march: Royal Marines / Cavalry of the clouds: Band Of The Royal Air Force College Cranwell / Cavatina: Band Of The Light Infantry / Berliner luft: Band Of The Duke Of Edinburgh's Royal Regiment / 633 squadron: Band Of The RAF / Battle of Britain march: Western Band Of The RAF

309222 / 13 Jul '98 / Hallmark

☐ GREATEST ALL-TIME NEW COUNTRY LINE DANCE

MCCD 284 / Dec '96 / Music Club

☐ GREATEST BALLADS

Would I lie to you: Charles & Eddie / Release me: Wilson Phillips / Cambodia: Wilde, Kim / Orchard road: Sayer, Leo / Mated: Grant, David & Jaki Graham / Suddenly last summer: Motels / Whenever you need me: T'Pau / I've been in love before: Cutting Crew / Harder I try: Brother Beyond / Sweet sixteen: Idol, Billy / Missing you: Waite, John / For your blue eyes only: Hadley, Tony / Home on Monday: Little River Band / What other reason: Johnny Hates Jazz / Something's gotten hold of my heart: Almond, Marc & Gene Pitney / Caravan of love: Housemartins

BXB 877442 / Jul '97 / Disky

☐ GREATEST COUNTRY SHOW, THE

HRCD 8020 / Jul '93 / Disky

☐ GREATEST EVER CHRISTMAS PARTY MEGAMIX, THE

Merry Christmas everybody / I wish it could be Christmas every day / Winter wonderland / All I want for Christmas is my two front teeth / Rockin' around the Christmas tree / Jingle bell rock / Santa Claus is coming to town / Silver bells / Gloucestershire wassail / Mistletoe and wine / Silent night / We wish you a merry Christmas / Happy Christmas war is over / When a child is born / Christmas song / Winter wonderland / Here comes Santa Claus / Santa Claus is coming to town / Frosty the snowman / Rudolph the red nosed reindeer / Sleigh ride / Blue Christmas / Mary's boy child / Good King Wenceslas / Ding dong merrily on high / God rest ye merry gentlemen / Deck the halls / I believe in Father Christmas / Do they know it's Christmas / Auld lang syne

XMAS 006 / Nov '96 / Tring

☐ GREATEST EVER JUNIOR PARTY MIX, THE

Ghostbusters / Doin' the doo / Holiday / You got it (the right stuff) / Chicken song / Lambada / Got to get it / Birdie song / Hound dog / Look / Oops upside your head / Turtle power / Brown girl in the ring / Angel face / Ain't nothin' but a house party / Locomotion / Hand on your heart / Happenin' all over again / All shook up / Great balls of fire / Don't be cruel / See you later alligator / Let's twist again / Rock around the clock / Hound dog (reprise) / When the going gets tough / Agadoo / Too many broken hearts / Simple Simon / Itsy bitsy teeny weeny / Bat dance / Baggy trousers / Star treckin' / Ghostbusters (reprise)

XMAS 008 / Nov '96 / Tring

☐ GREATEST GOSPEL GEMS VOL.1 & 2

Last mile of the way: Cooke, Sam & The Soul Stirrers / Touch the hem of his garment: Cooke, Sam & The Soul Stirrers / Search me, Lord: May, Brother Joe / Do you know him: May, Brother Joe / Mother bowed: Pilgrim Travellers / Straight street: Pilgrim Travellers / Jesus met the woman at the well: Pilgrim Travellers / Oh Lord, stand by me: Five Blind Boys Of Alabama / I'll fly away: Five Blind Boys Of Alabama / Too close to heaven: Bradford, Alex / Lord, Lord, Lord: Bradford, Alex / Get away Jordan: Love Coates, Dorothy / He's calling me: Love Coates, Dorothy / I'm sealed: Love Coates, Dorothy / Swan Silvertones / Jesus is a friend: Swan Silvertones / Let god abide: Anderson, Robert / Prayer for the doomed: Chosen Gospel Singers / Ball game: Carr, Sister Wynona / By and by: Soul Stirrers / Love of god: Taylor, Johnnie / I'm determined to run this race: Meditation Singers / Lead me, guide me: May, Brother Joe / How the day is over: Cleveland, Rev. James

CDCHD 344 / May '91 / Ace

☐ GREATEST GOSPELS, THE

ZYX 550912 / Nov '97 / ZYX

☐ GREATEST HITS OF 1997, THE (2CD Set)

Who do you think you are: Spice Girls / Barbie girl: Aqua / Don't speak: No Doubt / D'you know what I mean: Oasis / As long as you love me: Backstreet Boys / Star people: Michael, George / Isn't it a wonder: Boyzone / I believe I can fly: Kelly, R / You're not alone: Olive / Encore une fois: Sash / Professional widow: Amos, Tori / Freed from desire: Gala / Closer than close: Gaines, Rosie / Remember me: Blueboy / C U when I get there: Coolio / Everything: Blige, Mary J. / If you ever: East 17 & Gabrielle / Love won't wait: Barlow, Gary / Where do you go: No Mercy / U sexy thing: Clock / Do ya think I'm sexy: N-Trance & Rod Stewart / Stay: Sash / Breathe: Prodigy / Old before I die: Williams, Robbie / Beetlebum: Blur / Your woman: Whiteman / Underwater love: Smoke City / Paranoid Android: Radiohead / Life less ordinary: Ash / Traveller's tune: Ocean Colour Scene / Richard III: Supergrass / North country boy: Charlatans / Susan's house: Eels / Sunday shining: Quaye, Finley / Earthbound: Reeves, Conner / Shout: Ant & Dec / Wonderful tonight: Damage / Smokin' me out: Warren G / Don't leave me: Blackstreet / On and on: Badu, Erykah / Virginia Plain: Roxy Music

TTVCD 2938 / 3 Nov '97 / Telstar TV

☐ GREATEST HITS OF THE 60'S/70'S

HRCD 8046 / Dec '93 / Disky

☐ GREATEST HITS OF THE 70'S

MACCD 122 / Aug '96 / Autograph

☐ GREATEST HITS OF THE 70'S (3CD Set)

Some girls: Racey / Mama loo: Humphries, Les Singers / Under the moon of love: Showaddywaddy / Lost in your love: Young, John Paul / Devil gate drive: Quatro, Suzi / Oh Carol: Smokie / When you're in love with a beautiful woman: Dr. Hook & Ray Sawyer / She believes in me: Rogers, Kenny / Falling apart at the seams: Marmalade / Jealous minds: Stardust, Alvin / Love bug: Charles, Tina / Chirpy chirpy cheep cheep: Middle Of The Road / Remember (sha la la la): Bay City Rollers / Let your love flow: Bellamy Brothers / Substitute: Clout / Baby jump: Mungo Jerry / I will survive: Gaynor, Gloria / You ain't seen nothing yet: Bachman-Turner Overdrive / Bang-a-boomerang: Svenne & Lotta / Dancin' party: Showaddywaddy / Something's been making me blue: Smokie / Love is in the air: Young, John Paul / Bye bye baby (baby goodbye): Bay City Rollers / Beach baby: First Class / Don't play your rock 'n roll to me: Smokie / In the summertime: Mungo Jerry / Little bit more: Dr. Hook & Ray Sawyer / Three steps to heaven: Showaddywaddy / Lay your love on me: Racey / Four letter word: Quatro, Suzi / Some girls: Racey / Be my baby: Svenne & Lotta / Mexico: Humphries, Les Singers / Save me: Clout / Stop in the name of love: Gaynor, Gloria / Yellow river: Christie / Radancer: Marmalade / Such a night (to have a party): Racey / Roll on down the highway: Bachman-Turner Overdrive / She's in love with you: Quatro, Suzi / Red dress: Stardust, Alvin

10742 / Oct '97 / Go On Deluxe

☐ GREATEST HITS OF THE 70'S, VOL.1 (In The Summertime)

In the summertime: Mungo Jerry / I'll go where the music takes me: Charles, Tina / Mama loo: Humphries, Les Singers / Beach baby: First Class / Beg steal or borrow: New Seekers / Back on the road again: Marmalade / Love really hurts without you: Ocean, Billy / Sugar baby love: Rubettes / Do you wanna dance: Svenne & Lotta / Hi ho silver lining: Black Lace / Night Chicago died: Paper Lace / I only wanna be with you: Bay City Rollers / Rock your baby: McCrae, George / Don't make waves: Nolans

101782 / May '97 / A-Play Collection

☐ GREATEST HITS OF THE 70'S, VOL.1 (Some Girls)

Some girls: Racey / Mama loo: Humphries, Les Singers / Under the moon of love: Showaddywaddy / Lost in your love: Young, John Paul / Devil gate drive: Quatro, Suzi / Oh Carol: Smokie / When you're in love with a beautiful woman: Dr. Hook & Ray Sawyer / She believes in me: Rogers, Kenny / Falling apart at the seams: Marmalade / Jealous minds: Stardust, Alvin / Love bug: Charles, Tina / Chirpy chirpy cheep cheep: Middle Of The Road / Remember (sha la la la): Bay City Rollers / Let your love flow: Bellamy Brothers / Substitute: Clout / Baby jump: Mungo Jerry / I will survive: Gaynor, Gloria / You ain't seen nothing yet: Bachman-Turner Overdrive / Bang-a-boomerang: Svenne & Lotta / Dancin' party: Showaddywaddy / Something's been making me blue: Smokie

10752 / Oct '97 / Go On Deluxe

☐ GREATEST HITS OF THE 70'S, VOL.1 (Garden Party)

Garden party: Nelson, Rick / Never ending song of love: New Seekers / Soley soley: Middle Of The Road / Yellow river: Christie / Foe-de-o-die: Marmalade / Rainbow: Marmalade / I can't leave you alone: McCrae, George / Ready for the 80's: Village People / Bobby dazzler: First Class / Roll away the stone: Mott The Hoople / Billy, don't be a hero: Paper Lace / If you don't know me by now: Melvin, Harold & The Bluenotes / Will you still love me tomorrow: Vanity Fair / Last farewell: Whittaker, Roger

101792 / May '97 / A-Play Collection

☐ GREATEST HITS OF THE 70'S, VOL.2 (Save Me)

Love is in the air: Young, John Paul / Bye bye baby (baby goodbye): Bay City Rollers / Beach baby: First Class / Don't play your rock 'n roll to me: Smokie / In the summertime: Mungo Jerry / Little bit more: Dr. McGowan, Shane / Feel too good: Beggar & Co / Rock n roll kids: Harrington, Paul / Lonesome road: McGowan, Shane / Feel too good: Beggar & Co / My hero: Rogers, Kenny / Three steps to heaven: Showaddywaddy / Lay your love on me: Racey / Four letter word: Quatro, Suzi / I love to love: Charles, Tina

/ Be my baby: Svenne & Lotta / Mexico: Humphries, Les Singers / Save me: Clout / Stop in the name of love: Gaynor, Gloria / Yellow river: Christie / Radancer: Marmalade / Such a night (to have a party): Racey / Roll on down the highway: Bachman-Turner Overdrive / She's in love with you: Quatro, Suzi / Red dress: Stardust, Alvin

10762 / Oct '97 / Go On Deluxe

☐ GREATEST HITS OF THE 70'S, VOL.3 (Y.M.C.A.)

Y.M.C.A.: Village People / Bye bye baby: Bay City Rollers / Juke box jive: Rubettes / Heaven must be missing an angel: Tavares / I love to love: Charles, Tina / San bernadino: Christie / Wigwam bam: Black Lace / Mexico: Humphries, Les Singers / Car wash: Royce, Rose / Freedom come freedom go: Fortunes / Bang-a-boomerang: Svenne & Lotta / Radancer: Marmalade / Dragonfly: Nolans / Feels like I'm in love: Marie, Kelly

101802 / Jun '97 / A-Play Collection

☐ GREATEST HITS OF THE 70'S, VOL.3 (Glass Of Champagne)

Living next door to Alice: Smokie / My coo-ca-choo: Stardust, Alvin / Glass of champagne: Sailor / Little bit of soap: Showaddywaddy / Under fire: Clout / San Bernadino: Christie / Cars the can: Quatro, Suzi / Sacramento: Middle Of The Road / Sylvia's mother: Dr. Hook & Ray Sawyer / Boy oh boy: Racey / Dance (while the music still goes on): Svenne & Lotta / Walk in the park: Straker, Nick Band / Dance little lady: Charles, Tina / To my fathers house: Humphries, Les Singers / Race is on: Quatro, Suzi / All because of you: Geordie & Brian Johnson / Shang-a-lang: Bay City Rollers / She believes in me: Rogers, Kenny / Dreams are ten a penny: First Class / Lay back in the arms of someone: Smokie / Hey rock 'n' roll: Showaddywaddy

10772 / Oct '97 / Go On Deluxe

☐ GREATEST HITS OF THE SEVENTIES (3CD Set)

In the summertime: Mungo Jerry / I'll go where the music takes me: Charles, Tina / Don't make waves: Nolans / Mama Loo: Humphries, Les Singers / Beach baby: First Class / You can get it if you really want: Dekker, Desmond / Love really hurts without you: Ocean, Billy / Popcorn: Hot Butter / Sandy: Travolta, John / Speak to the sky: Springfield, Rick / Do you wanna dance: Svenne & Lotta / Achy breaky heart: Black Lace / I just can't help believin': Thomas, B.J. / I only wanna be with you: Bay City Rollers / Laughter in the rain: Sedaka, Neil / Even the bad times are good: Tremeloes / Garden party: Nelson, Rick / Crying in the rain: Everly Brothers / My baby left me: Presley, Elvis / Jilted: McGregor, Mary / Dedicated to the one I love: Mamas & The Papas / beautil sunday: Boone, Pat / Montego bay: Bloom, Bobby / Jeans on: Dundas, David / This diamond ring: Lewis, Gary & The Playboys / Heaven must be missing an angel: Tavares / Israelites: Dekker, Desmond / Mexico: Humphries, Les Singers / Angel face: Glitter Band / I love to love: Charles, Tina / Car wash: Rose Royce / Freedom come, freedom go: Fortunes / Feels like I'm in love: Marie, Kelly / Julie, do ya love me: Osmond, Donny / Black is black: La Belle Epoque / Funky Moped: Dury, Ian / Rose garden: Anderson, Lynn

100832 / May '97 / A-Play Collection

☐ GREATEST HITS OF THE SEVENTIES VOL.3 (Bye Bye Baby)

Bye bye baby: Bay City Rollers / December '63 (oh what a night): Four Seasons / This diamond ring: Lewis, Gary & The Playboys / Heaven must be missing an angel: Tavares / Israelites: Dekker, Desmond / Mexico: Humphries, Les Singers / Angel face: Glitter Band / I love to love: Charles, Tina / Car wash: Royce, Rose / Freedom come, freedom go: Fortunes / Feels like I'm in love: Marie, Kelly / Julio do ya love me: Osmond, Donny & The Playboys / Mandy / Jeans on: Dundas, David / Julie, do ya love me: Osmond, Donny

100862 / May '97 / A-Play Collection

☐ GREATEST IN COUNTRY BLUES VOL.1, THE

SOB 35212 / Dec '92 / Story Of The Blues

☐ GREATEST IN COUNTRY BLUES VOL.2, THE

SOB 35222 / Dec '92 / Story Of The Blues

☐ GREATEST IN COUNTRY BLUES VOL.3, THE

SOB 35232 / Dec '92 / Story Of The Blues

☐ GREATEST IRISH ALBUM EVER MADE, THE (2CD Set)

Ride on: Moore, Christy / Three babies: O'Connor, Sinead / Harry's Game: Clannad / Love me: Black, Frances / Isle of Innisfree: O'Donnell, Daniel / Only a woman's heart: McEvoy, Eleanor / Care to here: Griffiths, Nanci / Better man: Kennedy, Brian / What's another year: Logan, Johnny / Town I loved so well: Coulter, Phil / All kinds of everything: Dana / Christmas / Bunch of thyme: Foster & Allen / Mountains to the sea: Moore, Christy & Sinead O'Connor / Maggie: Foster & Allen / Danny boy: O'Donnell, Daniel / Town I loved so well: Dubliners / Brown eyed girl: Morrison, Van / Whiskey in the jar: Thin Lizzy / Don't go: Hothouse Flowers / World is what you make it: Brady, Paul / Rhythm and breaks: Orch, John Anderson / Rock n roll kids: Harrington, Paul / Lonesome road: McGowan, Shane / Irish molly O: Dannan, & De Maura O'Connell / Old

10752 / Oct '97 / Go On Deluxe

Right column (R.E.D. CD CATALOGUE)

/ Be my baby: Svenne & Lotta / Mexico: Humphries, Les Singers / Save me: Clout / Stop in the name of love: Gaynor, Gloria / Yellow river: Christie / Radancer: Marmalade / Such a night (to have a party): Racey / Roll on down the highway: Bachman-Turner Overdrive / She's in love with you: Quatro, Suzi / Red dress: Stardust, Alvin

TTVCD 2939 / 24 Nov '97 / Telstar TV

☐ GREATEST JAMAICAN BEAT

444152 / 22 Jun '98 / Rhino

☐ GREATEST JAZZ, BLUES AND RAGTIME OF THE CENTURY

Squeeze me: Waller, Fats / I'm crazy 'bout my baby: Waller, Fats / Ivy: Johnson, James P. & J. Russell Robinson / Charleston: Johnson, James P. / Daddy blues: Jones, Clarence / Doggone blues: Jones, Clarence / Fast stuff blues: Blythe, Jimmy / Alley rat blues: Blythe, Jimmy / Charleston blues: Blake, Eubie / Maple leaf rag: Joplin, Scott / Gin mill blues: Fowler, Lemuel / Fowler's hot stuff: Fowler, Lemuel / King Porter stomp: Morton, Jelly Roll / Bucksnort stomp: Tichenor, Trebor

BCD 116 / Jul '91 / Biograph

☐ GREATEST JUKE BOX COLLECTION EVER

HADCD 209 / Jul '96 / Javelin

☐ GREATEST LAUNCHES VOL.1 (2CD Set)

MISSILECD 1 / 6 Oct '97 / Missile

☐ GREATEST LOVE SONGS

Honey: Goldsboro, Bobby / Seasons in the sun: Jacks, Terry / Without you: Nilsson, Harry / Torn between two lovers: McGregor, Mary / Dedicated to the one I love: Mamas & The Papas / beautil sunday: Boone, Pat / Montego bay: Bloom, Bobby / Jeans on: Dundas, David / This diamond ring: Lewis, Gary & The Playboys / Heaven must be missing an angel: Tavares / Israelites: Dekker, Desmond / Mexico: Humphries, Les Singers / Angel face: Glitter Band / I love to love: Charles, Tina / Car wash: Rose Royce

TMPCD 004 / Jan '95 / Temple

☐ GREATEST LOVE VOL.1

TMPCD 004 / Jan '95 / Temple

☐ GREATEST LOVE VOL.2

TMPCD 005 / Jan '95 / Temple

☐ GREATEST LOVE VOL.3

TMPCD 006 / Jan '95 / Temple

☐ GREATEST LOVE, THE

MACCD 102 / Aug '96 / Autograph

☐ GREATEST LOVE, THE

PDSCD 502 / Sep '97 / Pulse

☐ GREATEST PARTY BOX, THE (4CD Set)

Happy birthday to you / 21 today / Celebration / Congratulations / Happy birthday / Birthday medley / Wedding march / Wedding march / Conga / Knees up Mother Brown / Hokey cokey / Charleston / Glenn Miller / Essential waltz / Last waltz / Agadoo / Can can / Birdie song / Simple Simon says / Big Ben strikes / Auld lang syne / National Anthem / Merry Christmas everybody / I wish it could be Christmas everyday / Winter wonderland / All I want for Christmas is my two front teeth / Rockin' around the Christmas tree / Jingle bell rock / Santa Claus is coming to town / Silver bells / Gloucestershire Wassail / Mistletoe and wine / Christmas (war is over) / When a child is born / Christmas song / Winter wonderland / Here comes Santa Claus / Santa Claus is coming to town / Frosty the snowman / Santa Claus is coming to town / Rudolph the red nosed reindeer / Sleigh ride / Blue Christmas / Mary's boy child / Good King Wenceslas / Ding dong merrily on high / God rest ye merry gentlemen / Deck the halls / I believe in Father Christmas / Do they know it's Christmas / Auld lang syne / Ghostbusters / Doin' the doo / Holiday / You got it (the right stuff) / Chicken song / Lambada / Got to get it / Hound dog / Oops upside your head / Turtle power / Brown girl in the ring / Angel face / Ain't nothin' but a house party / Locomotion / Hand on your heart / Happenin' all over again / All shook up / Great balls of fire / Don't be cruel / See you later alligator / Let's twist again / Rock around the clock / Hound dog (reprise) / When the going gets tough / Agadoo / Too many broken hearts / Simple Simon says / Itsy bitsy teeny weeny / Bat dance / Baggy trousers / Star treckin' / Ghostbusters (reprise) / Rudolph the red nosed

1034

reindeer: *Dixie Cups* / White Christmas: *Ford, Frankie* / Frosty the snowman: *Coasters* / Christmas song: *Drifters* / Deck the halls: *Crickets* / Sleigh ride: *Diamonds* / If I could spend Christmas with you: *Roe, Tommy* / Little drummer boy: *Tokens* / Silent night: *Shirelles* / New baby for Christmas: *Preston, Johnny* / Winter wonderland: *Rockin' Robin* / Rockin' around the Christmas tree: *Jones, Davy*

QUAD 020 / Nov '96 / Tring

□ GREATEST POP BALLADS (3CD Set)

Rush rush: *Abdul, Paula* / Eyes without a face: *Idol, Billy* / Dum dum girl: *Talk Talk* / I touch myself: *Divinyls* / Love is love: *Culture Club* / Kayleigh: *Marillion* / Move closer: *Nelson, Phyllis* / True: *Spandau Ballet* / Room in your heart: *Living In A Box* / Looking for Linda: *Hue & Cry* / Stay: *Thomas, Kenny* / Turn back the clock: *Johnny Hates Jazz* / Mary's prayer: *Danny Wilson* / Tracks of my tears: *Go West* / Love don't live here anymore: *Nail, Jimmy* / Closest thing to heaven: *Kane Gang* / Save a prayer: *Duran Duran* / Picture postcards from LA: *Kadison, Joshua* / So long: *Fischer Z* / Everything I own: *Boy George* / Walking on ice: *River City People* / This must be the night: *Mink Deville* / Good heart: *Sharkey, Feargal* / She makes my day: *Palmer, Robert* / I'll never fall in love: *Harry, Deborah* / True love: *Benatar, Pat* / You could have been with me: *Easton, Sheena* / Love disappears: *Gaines, Jeffrey* / Don't turn away: *Go For It* / Lover spurned: *Almond, Marc* / Heaven is a secret: *Spandau Ballet* / When you walk in the room: *Carrack, Paul* / Would I lie to you: *Charles & Eddie* / Release me: *Wilson Phillips* / Cambodia: *Wilde, Kim* / Orchard Road: *Sayer, Leo* / Mated: *Grant, David & Jaki Graham* / Suddenly last summer: *Motels* / Whenever you need me: *T'Pau* / I've been in love before: *Cutting Crew* / Harder I try: *Brother Beyond* / Sweet sixteen: *Idol, Billy* / Missing you: *Waite, John* / For your blue eyes only: *Hadley, Tony* / Home on Monday: *Little River Band* / What other reason: *Johnny Hates Jazz* / Something's gotten hold of my heart: *Almond, Marc & Gene Pitney* / Caravan of love: *Housemartins*

HR 877412 / Mar '97 / Disky

□ GREATEST POP BALLADS VOL.1

Rush rush: *Abdul, Paula* / Eyes without a face: *Idol, Billy* / Dum dum girl: *Talk Talk* / I touch myself: *Divinyls* / Love is love: *Culture Club* / Kayleigh: *Marillion* / Move closer: *Nelson, Phyllis* / True: *Spandau Ballet* / Room in your heart: *Living In A Box* / Looking for Linda: *Hue & Cry* / Stay: *Thomas, Kenny* / Turn back the clock: *Johnny Hates Jazz* / Mary's prayer: *Danny Wilson* / Tracks of my tears: *Go West* / Love don't live here anymore: *Nail, Jimmy* / Closest thing to heaven: *Kane Gang*

BXA 877422 / May '97 / Disky

□ GREATEST POP BALLADS VOL.2

Save a prayer: *Duran Duran* / Picture postcards from LA: *Kadison, Joshua* / So long: *Fischer Z* / Everything I own: *Boy George* / Walking on ice: *River City People* / This must be the night: *Mink Deville* / Good heart: *Sharkey, Feargal* / She makes my day: *Palmer, Robert* / I'll never fall in love: *Harry, Deborah* / True love: *Benatar, Pat* / You could have been with me: *Easton, Sheena* / Love dissapears: *Gaines, Jeffrey* / Don't turn away: *Go For It* / Lover spurned: *Almond, Marc* / Heaven is a secret: *Spandau Ballet* / When you walk in the room: *Carrack, Paul*

BXA 877432 / May '97 / Disky

□ GREATEST POP BALLADS VOL.3

Would I lie to you: *Charles & Eddie* / Release me: *Wilson Phillips* / Cambodia: *Wilde, Kim* / Orchard road: *Sayer, Leo* / Mated: *Grant, David & Jaki Graham* / Suddenly last summer: *Motels* / Whenever you need me: *T'Pau* / I've been in love before: *Cutting Crew* / Harder I try: *Brother Beyond* / Sweet sixteen: *Idol, Billy* / Missing you: *Waite, John* / For your blue eyes only: *Hadley, Tony* / Home on Monday: *Little River Band* / What other reason: *Johnny Hates Jazz* / Something's gotten hold of my heart: *Almond, Marc & Gene Pitney* / Caravan of love: *Housemartins*

BXA 877442 / May '97 / Disky

□ GREATEST RAGTIME OF THE CENTURY

Shreveport stomp: *Morton, Jelly Roll* / Sweet man: *Morton, Jelly Roll* / Tom cat blues: *Morton, Jelly Roll* / New kind of man: *Waller, Fats* / Nobody but my baby: *Waller, Fats* / Got to cool my doggies now: *Waller, Fats* / Maple leaf rag: *Joplin, Scott* / Weeping willow rag: *Joplin, Scott* / Something doing: *Joplin, Scott* / Steeplechase rag: *Johnson, James P.* / Twilight rag: *Johnson, James P.* / Charleston rag: *Blake, Eubie* / It's right here for you: *Blake, Eubie* / Fare thee honey blues: *Blake, Eubie* / Mr. Freddie blues: *Blythe, Jimmy* / Regal stomp: *Blythe, Jimmy*

BCD 103 / Jul '91 / Biograph

□ GREATEST REGGAE (2CD Set)

DTKBOX 87 / 8 Jun '98 / Dressed To Kill

□ GREATEST ROCK 'N' ROLL PARTY EVER

Blue suede shoes: *Perkins, Carl* / Be bop a lula: *Vincent, Gene* / Peggy sue: *Holly, Buddy* / Three steps to heaven: *Cochran, Eddie* / Razzle dazzle: *Haley, Bill & The Comets* / Good golly Miss Molly: *Little Richard* / Roll over Beethoven: *Berry, Chuck* / Rockin' Robin: *Day, Bobby* / Tiger: *Fabian* / Runaround Sue: *Dion* / Why do fools fall in love: *Lymon, Frankie & The Teenagers* / Hello Mary Lou: *Nelson, Ricky* / Bye bye love: *Everly Brothers* / There goes my heart again: *Domino, Fats* / Not fade away: *Crickets* / Party doll: *Knox, Buddy* / Great balls of fire: *Lewis, Jerry Lee* / Red hot: *Riley, Billy Lee*

DC 880212 / Jul '97 / Disky

□ GREATEST ROCK 'N' ROLL SHOW

HRCD 8021 / Jul '93 / Disky

□ GREATEST SINGERS GREATEST SONGS (3CD Set)

Over the rainbow: *Garland, Judy* / Zing went the strings of my heart: *Garland, Judy* / Little children: *Kramer, Billy J. & The Dakotas* / Dance, ballerina, dance: *Cole, Nat 'King'* / Smile: *Cole, Nat 'King'* / Let there be love: *Cole, Nat 'King'* / It must be him: *Carr, Vikki* / When you're in love with a beautiful woman: *Dr. Hook* / Climb every mountain: *Bassey, Shirley* / On the street where you live: *Damone, Vic* / Dreamboat: *Cogan, Alma* / Lady: *Rogers, Kenny* / Lucille: *Rogers, Kenny* / Shrimp boats: *Stafford, Jo* / Portrait of my love: *Monro, Matt* / Softly as I leave you: *Monro, Matt* / Walk away: *Monro, Matt* / Folks who live on the hill: *Lee, Peggy* / Story of my life: *Holliday, Michael* / Starry eyed: *Holliday, Michael* / Talking in your sleep: *Gayle, Crystal* / Don't it make my brown eyes blue: *Gayle, Crystal* / Volare: *Martin, Dean* / Memories are made of this: *Martin, Dean* / That's amore (That's love): *Martin, Dean* / Come along a love: *Starr, Kay* / Still: *Dodd, Ken & Geoff Love Orchestra* / He was beautiful: *Williams, Iris* / Honey: *Goldsboro, Bobby* / Air that I breathe: *Hollies* / Cry me a river: *London, Julie* / Dreams of an everyday housewife: *Campbell, Glen* / To sir with love: *Lulu* / Sing me an old fashioned song: *Spears, Billie Jo* / What I've got in mind: *Spears, Billie Jo* / O what a beautiful morning: *Keel, Howard* / Walkin' back to happiness: *Shapiro, Helen* / And I love you so: *Reddy, Helen* / And I love you so: *McLean, Don* / Loving you: *Riperton, Minnie* / Spanish eyes: *Martino, Al* / Carnival is over: *Seekers* / Call me irresponsible: *Washington, Dinah* / Edelweiss: *Hill, Vince* / Good vibrations: *Beach Boys*

CDTRBOX 320 / 6 Oct '97 / EMI Gold

□ GREATEST TRANCE TRACKS

IG 0042 / Jun '97 / Intergroove

□ GREATEST VALLENATOS CLASSICS OF COLOMBIA

76754213032 / 12 May '98 / Vedisco

□ GREATEST VOICES OF OUR TIME VOL.1

GCMD 504 / Jun '97 / GCM

□ GREECE - BYZANTINE MUSIC

LDX 274971 / Apr '94 / La Chant Du Monde

□ GREEK FOLK DANCES AND SONGS

MM 207 / 11 May '98 / Musurgia Graeca

□ GREEK POPULAR SONGS OF THE 1930/1940S

995862 / 24 Feb '98 / EPM

□ GREEN CRYSTAL TIES VOL.1

COLCD 0721 / 8 Jun '98 / Collectables

□ GREEN CRYSTAL TIES VOL.10

COLCD 0730 / 8 Jun '98 / Collectables

□ GREEN CRYSTAL TIES VOL.2

COLCD 0722 / 8 Jun '98 / Collectables

□ GREEN CRYSTAL TIES VOL.3

COLCD 0723 / 8 Jun '98 / Collectables

□ GREEN CRYSTAL TIES VOL.4

COLCD 0724 / 8 Jun '98 / Collectables

□ GREEN CRYSTAL TIES VOL.5

COLCD 0725 / 8 Jun '98 / Collectables

□ GREEN CRYSTAL TIES VOL.6

COLCD 0726 / 8 Jun '98 / Collectables

□ GREEN CRYSTAL TIES VOL.7

COLCD 0727 / 8 Jun '98 / Collectables

□ GREEN CRYSTAL TIES VOL.8

COLCD 0728 / 8 Jun '98 / Collectables

□ GREEN CRYSTAL TIES VOL.9

COLCD 0729 / 8 Jun '98 / Collectables

□ GREEN LINNET 20TH ANNIVERSARY COLLECTION (2CD Set)

GLCD 106 / Aug '96 / Green Linnet

□ GREEN VELVET (4CD Set)

MBSCD 436 / Nov '95 / Castle

□ GREENBELT FRINGE '95

Defiled: *Fresh Claim* / Magnum mysterium: *Eve & The Garden* / Paper chain: *3rd Day* / Who you really are: *Before & Beyond* / Take me: *Rumours Are True* / Wake me when the madness ends: *Full Circle* / Isn't he: *Catley, Marc* / Thank God for car stockers: *Catley, Marc* / Set the moose loose: *Moose Machine* / Bold love: *Red Delivery Animal* / It's like everything else: *Worner-Phillips, Nigel* / Never mind: *Bernards's Dog* / Calling: *Skellig* / Watching the war: *Ryder, Pete* / Children: *Mudhead's Monkey* / Really me: *Obviously 5 Believers* / Flawed: *Days, Jonathan Earthhouse* / Just one minute: *Bickley, Jon & Angel Train* / Rain people: *Hunt* / Art of the artsong song: *Paley's Watch* / Dreamscape: *Asylum*

PCDN 147 / Nov '95 / Plankton

□ GREENLAND CALLING VOL.1

ULO 75 / May '96 / Ulo

□ GREENLAND CALLING VOL.2

ULO 76 / May '96 / Ulo

□ GREENSLEEVES SAMPLER VOL.1

Crazy list: *Brown, Dennis* / Feel the rydim: *Minott, Sugar* / Zungguzungguguzungguzeng: *Yellowman* / Pass the Tu-Sheng-Peng: *Paul, Frankie* / Let off supm: *Isaacs, Gregory* / Africa must be free by 1983: *Mundell, Hugh* / I love King Selassie: *Black Uhuru* / They don't know Jah: *Wailing Souls* / Dematerialise: *Scientist* / Ganja smuggling: *Eek-A-Mouse* / Stop that train: *Eastwood & Saint* / We are going: *Burning Spear* / Winnie Mandela: *Davis, Carlene* / Real enemy: *Mighty Diamonds*

GREZCD 1 / Jun '87 / Greensleeves

□ GREENSLEEVES SAMPLER VOL.10

Under mi sensi: *Levy, Barrington & Beenie Man* / Gangster: *Lieutenant Stitchie* / No no no (World a respect mix): *Penn, Dawn* / Can't stop the dance: *Yardcore Collective* / Down in the ghetto: *Bounty Killer* / Bumptious girl: *Sanchez & Stingerman* / Press button (Remix): *Beenie Man* / Fowl affair: *Silver Cat* / All over you: *Roach, Colin* / Shoo-be-doo: *Papa San* / Reminiscing: *Redrose & Spragga Benz* / One love: *Cocoa T & Shaka Shamba* / Bad publicity: *Ninjaman* / One good turn: *Isaacs, Gregory & Beres Hammond* / Runaround girl: *Bounty Killer & Chuck Turner* / You don't love me (no no no): *Penn, Dawn*

GREZCD 10 / Sep '94 / Greensleeves

□ GREENSLEEVES SAMPLER VOL.13

GREZCD 13 / Mar '96 / Greensleeves

□ GREENSLEEVES SAMPLER VOL.14

GREZCD 14 / Aug '96 / Greensleeves

□ GREENSLEEVES SAMPLER VOL.15

Man tief sonata: *Buccaneer* / Rumours: *McGregor, Freddie* / Shelly Ann: *Red Rat* / This is the time: *Luciano* / Healing: *Lady Saw & Beenie Man* / Living dangerously: *Levy, Barrington* / Slop dem: *Stephens, Richie* / Rude boy life: *Bushman* / Bounce along: *Wayne Wonder & Spragga Benz* / Time is slipping away: *Redd, Jeff* / Mr. Hardcore: *Mad Cobra* / Girls galore: *Stephens, Richie & General Degree* / Nuff gal: *Beenie Man* / So many girls: *Merciless* / Rub a dubit: *Reid, Junior & Outlaw Candy* / Tears: *Papa San*

GREZCD 15 / May '97 / Greensleeves

□ GREENSLEEVES SAMPLER VOL.16

Rocking chair: *Merciless & Queen Yemisi* / Big man little yute: *Red Rat & Goofy* / Love don't live here anymore: *Robyn & Bounty Killer* / One bingi man: *Morgan Heritage* / Can't stop now: *Campbell, Al* / Herb fi bun: *Daddy Rings & Cocoa T* / Dwayne: *Red Rat* / Black woman and child: *Sizzla* / Plenty more gal: *Buccaneer* / You give me your love: *Gold, Brian & Tony/Shaggy* / Reggae ska: *McGregor, Freddie* / Big ninja bike: *Stephens, Tanya* / Nyah man chant: *Bushman* / My gal dem: *Beenie Man* / Baby to enjoy: *Merciless & Lady Saw* / Build a better world: *Luciano & Sizzla*

GREZCD 16 / 27 Oct '97 / Greensleeves

□ GREENSLEEVES SAMPLER VOL.17

GREZCD 17 / 30 Mar '98 / Greensleeves

□ GREENSLEEVES SAMPLER VOL.18

GREZCD 18 / 27 Jul '98 / Greensleeves

□ GREENSLEEVES SAMPLER VOL.2

Telephone love: *Lodge, J.C.* / She loves me now: *Hammond, Beres* / Rock me: *Mowatt, Judy* / Man is a man: *Boothe, Ken* / Knight in shining armour: *Glasgow, Deborahe* / Fly me to the moon: *Burning Spear* / Rumours: *Isaacs, Gregory* / Tonight I'm going to take it easy: *Mighty Diamonds* / Girl E: *Kamoze, Ini* / Magnet and steel: *Fraser, Dean* / Miserable woman: *McGregor, Freddie* / Blueberry Hill: *Yellowman* / More them chat: *Cocoa T & Krystal* / Golden touch: *Shabba Ranks*

GREZCD 2 / Sep '88 / Greensleeves

□ GREENSLEEVES SAMPLER VOL.3

GREZCD 3 / Oct '89 / Greensleeves

□ GREENSLEEVES SAMPLER VOL.4

Twice my age: *Shabba Ranks & Krystal* / Report to me: *Isaacs, Gregory* / Love me baby: *Tiger* / Pirate's anthem: *Home T & Cocoa T/Shabba Ranks* / No more walls: *Brown, Dennis* / Wicked and wild: *Little Lenny* / Mr. Loverman: *Glasgow, Deborahe & Shabba Ranks* / Blinking something: *Pinchers* / Round table talk: *Papa San* / Why turn down the sound: *Cocoa T* / Make up your mind: *Brown, Dennis & Tiger* / Tell me which one: *Admiral Tibet*

GREZCD 4 / Apr '90 / Greensleeves

□ GREENSLEEVES SAMPLER VOL.5

Your body's here with me: *Home T & Cocoa T/ Shabba Ranks* / It's not enough: *Papa San & Fabian* / Ruling cowboy: *Cocoa T* / Home boy: *Brown, Dennis* / Gun talk: *Redrose & Tony Rebel* / Roughneck sound: *Robinson, Ed 'Roughneck'* / Going is rough: *Home T & Cocoa T/Shabba Ranks* / Monday morning blues: *Mikey Melody* / Shepherd be careful: *Cocoa T & Dennis Brown* / Guilty: *Mowatt, Judy* / More them chat: *Cocoa T & Krystal* / Golden touch: *Shabba Ranks*

GREZCD 5 / Nov '90 / Greensleeves

□ GREENSLEEVES SAMPLER VOL.6

Fanciness: *Shabba Ranks & Lady G* / One way woman: *Cocoa T* / John Law: *Isaacs, Gregory & Freddie McGregor/Ninjaman* / Mr. Bodyguard: *Mighty Diamonds* / Something in my heart: *Levy, Barrington & Reggie Stepper* / Mixed feelings: *Brown, Dennis & Fabiana* / Another one for the road: *Home T & Cocoa T/Shabba Ranks* / Midnight Lover: *McGregor, Freddie* / Looking for love: *Cutty Ranks & Barrington Levy* / Fancy girl: *Fabiana & Shabba Ranks* / I'm your man: *Brown, Dennis & Reggie Stepper* / Stallion: *Chaka Demus*

GREZCD 6 / Apr '92 / Greensleeves

□ GREENSLEEVES SAMPLER VOL.7

Oh Carolina: *Shaggy* / Bed work sensation: *Bajja Jedd* / I Spy: *General TK* / Getting closer: *Cocoa T* / Yardie: *Buju Banton* / Don man girl: *Isaacs, Gregory* / Ting a ling a ling a school pickney sing ting: *Ninjaman* / Tender loving: *Cocoa T & Shaka Shamba* / Wealth: *Cutty Ranks* / Playing hard to get: *McGregor, Freddie* / After dark: *Capleton* / I need a roof: *Mighty Diamonds* / Screwface: *General TK* / Bedroom eyes: *Yellowman* / Certain friends: *Lady G* / Dance hall queen: *Lloyd, Peter*

GREZCD 7 / May '93 / Greensleeves

□ GREENSLEEVES SAMPLER VOL.8

GREZCD 8 / Nov '93 / Greensleeves

□ GREENSLEEVES SAMPLER VOL.9

Two sounds: *Levy, Barrington & Beenie Man* / Gimme little sign: *Harvey, Maxine* / Tune in: *Cocoa T* / Statement: *Bounty Killer* / One way ticket: *Luciano* / I will forever love you: *Sanchez* / More than loving: *Capleton & Nadine Sutherland* / Love and devotion: *Hammond, Beres* / One jamaican: *Osbourne, Johnny* / Nice and lovely: *Shaggy & Rayvon* / Not because I smile: *Isaacs, Gregory* / He will see you through: *Griffiths, Marcia* / Inna de dance: *Reid, Junior* / More love: *French, Robert & Heavy D* / Rude boys ride again: *Cutty Ranks* / There's nothing like this: *Brown, Dennis*

GREZCD 9 / Apr '94 / Greensleeves

□ GREETINGS FROM GOA (2CD Set)

560102 / Apr '97 / Nova Tekk

□ GREETINGS FROM HAWAII

15184 / '91 / Laserlight

□ GRIOTS - TRADITIONAL MUSIC, THE

AAA 162 / May '98 / Club Du Disque Arabe

□ GROOVE IS IN THE HEART (Sample Of Dance Classics)

Every little thing I do: *Soul For Real* / Love supreme: *Downing, Will* / Say no go: *De La Soul* / Set adrift on memory bliss: *PM Dawn* / Downtown: *SWV* / Thinking of you: *Usher* / My definition of a boombastic: *Dream Warriors* / Believe in me: *Utah Saints* / Shout: *Louchie Lou & Michie One* / Can you handle it: *DNA & Sharon Redd* / Ice ice baby: *Vanilla Ice* / People everyday: *Arrested Development* / Can I kick it: *Tribe Called Quest* / Down for whateva: *Nuttin' Nyce* / Summertime: *DJ Jazzy Jeff & The Fresh Prince* / Boom shake the room: *DJ Jazzy Jeff & The Fresh Prince* / Rappers delight: *Sugarhill Gang*

RENCD 120 / Mar '97 / Renaissance Collector Series

□ GROOVE THE COMPILATION VOL.3 (2CD Set)

EFA 114002 / 24 Nov '97 / Groove

□ GROOVEADELIC (2CD Set)

Psychic bounty killaz: *DJ Sneak & Armand Van Helden* / Happy days: *Happy Days* / Maw War (Gotta get that groove thang): *Kenlou* / I like it: *Tyree* / Heart but house: *De Borah, Nathalie* / Emancipation of my soul: *Parker, Terrence* / Lift me up: *MK & Claire Rivers* / Hear the music: *Johnson, Paul* / Alabama blues: *St. Germain* / Don't stop the feelin': *Gu & Terence FM* / In de ghetto: *Morales, David & The Bad Yard Club* / Dancer: *Moodyman* / Handbag: *Eric KJ Project* / We are one: *DJ Q* / Da lost trip: *Clubheroes* / It's so hard: *Moraes, Angel* / Morel s sax groove: *Morel Inc* / Only 4 U: *Cajmere* / I need you know: *Sinnamon* / Make the world go round: *Sandy B*

SPVDCD 08947312 / Mar '97 / SPV

□ GROOVEBOX EXPERIENCE

SUB 48552 / 15 Dec '97 / Distance

□ GROOVES - 80'S DANCE

PDSCD 539 / Aug '96 / Pulse

□ GROOVESSENTIALS

Thing to do: *Lewis, Glenn* / Rock with you: *Mischke* / Making me feel: *Sparks, Jamie* / Nasty: *West, Daryl* / Baby c'mon: *Morgan, Carlos* / How may I do U: *Unique* / Tonight: *Denosh* / Give me the chance: *Brown, Wade O.* / Feelin': *Just* / Forever indebted: *Kuya* / Don't leave me hangin': *Douglas, Camille* / To tha break a dawn: *Levant's Crew* / Rock with you: *Mischke* / Tonight: *Mischke* / I just want to be your everything: *McAuley Boys*

CDRHYTHM 5 / 8 Sep '97 / Parlophone

□ GROOVESVILLE REVIEW VOL.2, THE

Recipe: *Johnson, L.V.* / Don't let me lose it: *Gilford, Jimmy & Jimmy Scruggs* / Girl crazy: *Soul, Sharon* / Love on a lease plan: *Taylor, Johnny* / I will fear no evil: *Ward, Robert* / Dance time: *Griffin, Herman* / Genie: *Bryant, Terri* / Baby I cried: *Hill, Eddie* / Pick up the pieces: *Jones, Willi* / Baby please come back home: *Barnes, J.J.* / Somebody somewhere needs you: *Banks, Darrell* / Got to get rid: *Johnson, L.V.* / Your love got sweeter: *Mancha, Steve* / I'm in love again: *Debonaires* / Hey senorita: *Tokays* / You brought love to my life: *Johnson, L.V. & J.J. Barnes* / Pigfeet (deeper in love): *Mancha, Steve* / Harder you love: *Barnes, J.J.* / Hit and run: *Lewis, Pat* / I'm the one who loves you: *Davis, Melvin* / Snowflakes: *Johnson, L.V.* / I won't hurt you anymore: *Kingfish, Joey & Eddie Anderson* / I need my baby: *Davis, Melvin & Steve Mancha* / Souvenirs: *Mancha, Steve* / You're still in my heart: *Davis, Melvin*

GSCD 087 / 10 Nov '97 / Goldmine

□ GROOVIN'

Peaceful easy feeling: *Alexander, Rob* / Money runner: *Jones, Quincy* / Funky sensation: *McCrae, Gwen* / World is a ghetto: *War* / Viva tirado: *El Chicano* / Mama said: *Anderson, Carleen* / Mr. Magic: *Washington, Grover Jr.* / All for you: *Van Dyke, Earl* / When the world turns blue: *Clayton, Merry* / Holy ghost: *Bar-Kays* / Billy's bag: *Preston, Billy* / You've got it bad girl: *Jones, Ivan 'Boogaloo Joe'*

JAZZFMCD 3 / Mar '97 / Jazz FM

□ GROOVIN' AT THE GO-GO

Not only the girl knows: *Victors* / Hurt: *Victors* / Stay mine for heaven's sake: *Holman, Eddie* / Eddie's my name: *Holman, Eddie* / I'll cry 1000 tears: *Holman, Eddie* / I can't break the habit: *Garrett, Lee* / One more year: *United 4* / It's gonna be a false alarm: *Volcanos* / Deeper than that: *Preludes* / Shiggy diggy: *Preludes* / Groovin' at the Go-Go: *Four Larks* / She's puttin' you on: *United 4* / I still love you: *Four Larks* / Another chance: *Four Larks* / Without you baby: *Larks* / For the love of money: *Larks* / I surrender: *Holman, Eddie* / Where I'm not wanted: *Holman, Eddie* / Hurt: *Holman, Eddie* / She's wanted: *Clinton, Larry* / Focused on you: *Williams, B.* / It's needless to say: *Williams, B.*

GSCD 026 / Nov '93 / Goldmine

□ GROOVIN' HIGH (The Age Of Modern Jazz Begins)

Groovin' high: *Gillespie, Dizzy & Charlie Parker* / All the things you are: *Gillespie, Dizzy & Charlie Parker* / Salt peanuts: *Gillespie, Dizzy & Charlie Parker* / Hallelujah: *Norvo, Red & Dizzy Gillespie/Charlie Parker* / Lonesome lover blues: *Eckstine, Billy* / Disorder at the border: *Hawkins, Coleman* / Bu-de-dah: *Hawkins, Coleman* / Jumpin' blues: *McShann, Jay* / Co pilot: *Auld, Georgie* / I'll wait and pray: *Vaughan, Sarah* / Street beat: *Vaughan, Sarah* / Night in Tunisia: *Raeburn, Boyd & Dizzy Gillespie* / I can't get started: *Gillespie, Dizzy* / Apple honey: *Herman, Woody* / Buster's last stand: *Thornhill, Claude* / Blue 'n' boogie: *Gillespie, Dizzy & Dexter Gordon* / Now's the time: *Parker, Charlie* / Red cross: *Grimes, Tiny* / Koko: *Parker, Charlie*

306322 / Jan '97 / Hallmark

□ GROOVSVILLE REVIEW, THE

Has it happened to you yet: *Starr, Edwin* / Let's party: *Mancha, Steve* / Happiness is here: *Mercer, Barbara* / Heart trouble: *Parliaments* / I miss my baby / That's why I love you: *Professionals* / Searching: *Hatcher, Willie* / I need my baby: *Davis, Melvin & Steve Mancha* / Trying to forget you: *Turner, Spyder* / Good understanding: *Mancha, Steve* / You're gonna be sorry / Solid as a rock: *Vincent, Joyce* / You're my

mellow: *Starr, Edwin* / Chains of love: *Davis, Melvin* / He stole the love that was mine: *Davis, Melvin* / Time fades away: *Henry, Andrea* / Need to be needed: *Mancha, Steve* / Pigfeet (deeper in love): *Ward, Robert* / I'm the one who loves you: *Banks, Darrell* / Goings on: *Barnes, J.J.* / Unyielding: *Mancha, Steve* / Everloving / You're still in my heart: *Ruffin, David*
GSCD 121 / Apr '97 / Goldmine

☐ **GROOVY KIND OF SAX, A**
We've only just begun / All the things you are / If / Saving all my love for you / Just the way you are / Moon river / I love you because / Just for you / Love me tender / Always / Sometimes when we touch / Rose / Very thought of you / Beautiful friendship / Chanson d'amour / Killing me softly / Groovy kind of love / Arthur's theme / Misty / My cherie amour
EMPRCD 601 / Jun '96 / Emporio

☐ **GROOVY REGGAE STARS (2CD Set)**
24314 / Oct '95 / Delta Doubles

☐ **GROOVY VOL.3**
Sung sung lord: *Bley, Carla* / Black eyed blues: *Phillips, Esther* / Aht uh mi hed: *Otis, Shuggie* / My woman's gone now: *Emergency* / Clear day: *Paul, Billy* / Hello Quincey: *Enriquez, Luis* / Mambero: *Tjader, Cal* / About love: *Sidran, Ben* / Give peace a chance: *Smith, Lonnie Liston* / Aglio: *Rocchi, Oscar* / Watch a dog: *Winley, Anne* / Girl I like the way you move: *Stone*
IRMA 491203CD / 26 May '98 / Irma

☐ **GROUPS OF WRATH, THE (Songs Of The Naked City)**
DANCD 080 / Feb '95 / Danceteria

☐ **GROWIN' UP TOO FAST (The Girl Groups Anthology)**
My boyfriend's back: *Angels* / Remember (walkin' in the sand): *Shangri-Las* / My best friend Barbara: *Francis, Connie* / Navy blue: *Renay, Diane* / She don't deserve you: *Honey Bees* / Please don't talk to the lifeguard: *Ray, Diane* / It comes and goes: *Sadina* / Maybe I know: *Gore, Lesley* / It's gonna take a miracle: *Royalettes* / Boy next door: *Secrets* / I wish I knew what dress to wear: *Arnell, Ginny* / 442 Glenwood Avenue: *Pixies Three* / Johnny's back in town: *D'Andrea, Ann* / Stay awhile: *Springfield, Dusty* / So soft, so warm: *Nu Luvs* / Look of love: *Gore, Lesley* / Beatles, please come back: *Parker, Gigi & The Lonelies* / Summertime USA: *Pixies Three* / Can't the take a hint: *Woods, Kenni* / Wow wow wee (he's the boy for me): *Angels* / Always waitin': *Paris Sisters* / Watch out Sally: *Renay, Diane* / Wonder boy: *Gore, Lesley* / Hey big boy: *Secrets* / Sweet sounds of summer: *Shangri-Las*
5281712 / Nov '96 / Mercury

☐ **GS I LOVE YOU (Japanese Garage Bands Of The 1960's)**
You gat a call me: *Out Cast* / Everything's alright: *Out Cast* / Dynamite: *Spiders* / Monkey dance: *Spiders* / One more please: *Blue Jeans* / Stop dance: *Terrys* / Shevidevi de Yuko: *Playboy* / Kaette okure: *Playboy* / Kokoro no tokimeki (ajoen ajoen): *Swing West* / Let's go Rangers: *Rangers* / Koi O Kesunda: *Napoleon* / Aphrodite: *Cougars* / Suki Nanda: *Cougars* / Wipeout: *Spiders* / Furi furi: *Spiders* / I saw her standing there: *Burns* / Bara O Anokoni: *Days & Nights* / Let's go on the beach: *Out Cast* / Bokuno Sobakara: *Out Cast* / Hold on I'm comin': *Voltage* / J and A: *Cougars* / Seishun a go go: *Spiders* / Hey girl: *Van Dogs* / Omiyasan: *Toys* / Long tall Sally: *Out Cast* / Kimamana Shelly: *Out Cast* / Jane Jane: *Out Cast* / Fire: *Swing West*
CDWIKD 159 / Jun '96 / Big Beat

☐ **GUADELOUPE VOL.1**
C 560030 / Jan '93 / Ocora

☐ **GUADELOUPE VOL.2**
C 560031 / Jan '93 / Ocora

☐ **GUANTANAMERA (Latin Dance Party)**
ML 51025 / 14 Apr '98 / Musica Latina

☐ **GUANTANAMERA - SON DE CUBA**
3015992 / Feb '97 / Flarenasch

☐ **GUARANTEED PURE HEAVY FUNK VOL.1**
CS 85362 / 24 Nov '97 / C&S/Pure

☐ **GUERILLA BEATS (2CD Set)**
CLP 196 / 14 Apr '98 / Hypnotic

☐ **GUERILLA IN DUB**
Rhythm is life: *Lemon Sol* / Schmooo/aqualung: *Spooky* / Alchemy: *Drum Club* / Oh no: *DOP* / Dub house disco: *2 Shiny Heads* / Intoxication: *React 2 Rhythm* / Schudelfloss: *Dr. Atomic* / Higher: *Code MD* / Dub house disco (reprise): *2 Shiny Heads*
GRCD 011 / Jul '94 / Guerilla
PWD 7450 / May '94 / Pow Wow

☐ **GUIDE FOR THE PERPLEXED, A**
KFWCD 216 / Apr '98 / Jewish Alternative Movement

☐ **GUINEA: RECITS ET EPOPEES**
C 560009 / Nov '92 / Ocora

☐ **GUITAR BLUES**
12336 / May '94 / Laserlight

☐ **GUITAR EVANGELIST**
DOCD 5101 / Nov '92 / Document

☐ **GUITAR EXPLORATION**
WKFMXXD 169 / Apr '91 / FM

☐ **GUITAR FINGERSTYLE**
Little Martha: *Farrell, Tim* / Crow: *Gerbard, Edward* / South by winterwest: *McLaughlin, Billy* / Daisy goes a dancing: *Kirtley, Pat* / That'll be the phone: *Ross, Don* / Soul discovery: *Woolman, Benjamin* / Lunar eclipse: *Juber, Laurence* / To B or not To B: *Anderson, Muriel* / Peristroika: *Bennett, Stephen* / If I only had wings: *Auten, D.R.* / First ride: *Ross, Don* / It never gets easier: *Anderson, Muriel* / Helms place: *McLaughlin, Billy* / Only my heart: *Jones, Tommy* / Angela: *Auten, D.R.* / Grandpa's lullaby: *Kirtley, Pat*
ND 61056 / Aug '96 / Narada

☐ **GUITAR HEROES**
KBOX 350 / Oct '95 / Collection

☐ **GUITAR HEROES**
Apache: *Shadows* / Hawaii Five-O: *Ventures* / Guitar boogie shuffle: *Weedon, Bert* / Telstar: *Tornados* / Raunchy: *Justis, Bill* / Cruel sea: *Dakotas* / Pipeline: *Chantays* / Rumble: *Wray, Link* / Sleepwalk: *Santo & Johnny* / Mexican: *Fentones* / Wipe out: *Surfaris* / Memphis: *Mack, Lonnie* / Tico tico: *Paul, Les* / Walk don't run: *Ventures* / FBI: *Shadow Talk* / Fireball XL5: *Flee Rekkers*
DC 880192 / Jul '97 / Disky

☐ **GUITAR HEROES**
Dimples: *Hooker, John Lee* / Red house: *Hendrix, Jimi* / Good morning little school girl: *Yardbirds* / Matchbox: *Perkins, Carl* / I see a man downstairs: *Page, Jimmy* / Want to come home: *Hopkins, Lightnin'* / Gangster of love: *Winter, Johnny* / Big boss man: *Reed, Jimmy* / Under the table: *Hendrix, Jimi* / Crawling king snake: *Hooker, John Lee* / Score: *Cray, Robert* / Soul sacrifice: *Santana* / Sky is crying: *James, Elmore* / I got a break baby: *Walker, T-Bone* / Shapes of things: *Yardbirds* / Dust my broom: *James, Elmore* / Five long years: *Yardbirds* / Jeff's blues: *Beck, Jeff* / Everybody's trying to be my baby: *Perkins, Carl* / Big man: *Mayall, John*
308102 / 13 Oct '97 / Hallmark

☐ **GUITAR HEROES VOL.1 (Neo-Classical)**
RR 87822 / 20 Oct '97 / Roadrunner

☐ **GUITAR HEROES VOL.2**
RR 87812 / 20 Oct '97 / Roadrunner

☐ **GUITAR HEROES VOL.3 (Ballads)**
RR 87802 / 20 Oct '97 / Roadrunner

☐ **GUITAR MAN**
NSCD 022 / May '95 / Newsound

☐ **GUITAR MOODS**
MACCD 325 / Aug '96 / Autograph

☐ **GUITAR MOODS (16 Acoustic Classics)**
If you leave me now / Endless love / Come back to me / Wind beneath my wings / Piano in the dark / Almaz / Let's wait a while / Jesus to a child / It's too late / Fields of gold / Kiss from a rose / Massachusetts / All by myself / If / Here we are / All out of love
SUMCD 4204 / 11 May '98 / Summit

☐ **GUITAR WORKS**
Monogahela: *Tingstad, Eric* / Barcelona: *White, Andy* / Hexagram of the heavens: *Kolbe, Martin* / Light a candle: *Ellwood, William* / Inner movement: *Illenberger, Ralf* / Leaving home: *Mirowitz, Sheldon* / Nocturne: *Wynberg, Simon* / Maria's watermill: *Wynberg, Simon* / Sonho (Dream): *Lauria, Nando* / Since you asked: *Mirowitz, Sheldon* / Amber: *Montfort, Matthew* / Remembering greensleeves: *Doan, John* / By bye lullaby: *Kolbe, Martin*
ND 31032 / Nov '92 / Narada

☐ **GUITAR WORKSHOP IN LA**
Take it all / Bawls / Donna / Bull funk / Blues for Ronnie / Skunk blues / Hyper stork / Vicky's song / Beverly Hill / Roppongi
JD 3314 / May '89 / JVC

☐ **GUITAR WORKSHOP VOL.1**
Trout joins the cavalry: *Boswell, Simon* / Nefarious doings: *Hardy, Chris* / Black scrag: *Lee, Philip John* / One blue guitar: *Berryman, Peter* / Loneliness of the long distance acoustic guitarist: *Barrett, Willy* / Ferdinand the spider: *Murrell, Davey* / Rock salmon suite: *Tilston, Steve* / South Devon atmospheric: *Rogers, Mike* / Mica: *Hardy, Chris* / Trout sundae: *Boswell, Simon* / Stalks and seeds: *Lee, Philip John* / Entertainer: *Rogers, John* / Kenneth's riverbank song: *Murrell, Davey* / Hair accross the frets: *Barrett, Willy* / Brother nature: *Rogers, John & Mike*
ESMCD 495 / Apr '97 / Essential

☐ **GUITAR WORKSHOP VOL.2**
Fingerlude: *Guillory, Isaac* / Quasimodo: *Guillory, Isaac* / Northside 33: *Foster, Bob* / Annie Lou: *Foster, Bob* / Modulations: *Legg, Adrian* / Hackney picker: *Legg, Adrian* / Valse: *Holland, Bernie* / Autumn song: *Holland, Bernie* / Minda: *Willsher, Pete* / Stealin' and dealin': *Willsher, Pete* / Dancing angel: *Banks, Peter* / Warning: Rumble strips: *Banks, Peter* / Lucifer's cage: *Giltrap, Gordon* / Confusion: *Giltrap, Gordon* / Marigold chrome: *Rogers, Mike* / And the dog was sleeping in the corner: *James, John* / Two fifteen string guitars for nice people: *Geesin, Ron*
ESMCD 496 / Jul '97 / Essential

☐ **GUITAR ZONE**
CMPCD 5006 / 1 Sep '98 / CMP

☐ **GUITARES CELTIQUES**
GR 1190602 / Nov '95 / Griffe

☐ **GUITARES DE PARIS**
995612 / Mar '96 / EPM

☐ **GUITARES DU BRASIL**
3001808 / 24 Apr '98 / IMP

☐ **GUITARISMA**
Across the water: *Eko* / Send me an angel: *Schon, Neil* / Villa de martin: *Emmanuel, Tommy* / Acoustic planet: *Chaquico, Craig* / Surrender 2 love: *Liebert, Ottmar* / Soul fruit: *Hughes, Brian* / Exotico: *Lara & Reyes* / Castles in the air: *Blonker* / Ras lila: *BecVar, Bruce* / Through your eyes: *Shanin & Sepehr* / Ring of gold: *Camozzi, Chris*
VHOCD 3 / Jul '98 / Virgin

☐ **GUITARS ON MARS**
It's karate time: *Wammack, Travis* / Come una sentenza: *Morricone, Ennio* / Flavour bud lining: *Captain Beefheart & His Magic Band* / Gulch: *Small Good Thing* / Ode to perfume: *Czukay, Holger* / Upper Clapton nocturne: *Bailey, Derek* / Magnetic field: *Meek, Joe & The Blue Men* / Audio bongo: *Norman, Monty* / New groove loop: *Renaldo, Lee* / Stained angel morning: *Russell, Ray* / Human jungle: *Barry, John & Studio Orchestra* / Sleepwalker: *Cooper, Mike* / Man from nowhere: *Harris, Jet & Tony Meehan* / VentBat: *Ventures* / Starship: *MC5* / Smashing of the amps: *Hendrix, Jimi* / Rumble: *Wray, Link* / Missing link: *Allan, Davie & The Arrows* / Foldback time: *Grateful Dead* / Nine types of industrial pollution: *Zappa, Frank* / Angel wings: *Love Cry Want* / I hear voices too: *MacCol, Neil & David Toop* / Sombre reptiles: *Eno, Brian* / Pet sounds: *Beach Boys* / Terror by night: *Death Cube K* / Misbelieving baby: *Hooker, John Lee* / Dayton: *Little Axe* / Munk: *Koh Tao* / Sandpaper blues: *Cole, B.J.* / Evening bell: *Captain Beefheart & His Magic Band* / Eat beat eat: *Merzbow*
AMBT 24 / 22 Sep '97 / Virgin

☐ **GUITARS UNLIMITED (2CD Set)**
BB 895 / Jun '97 / Black & Blue

☐ **GULF COAST BLUES**
Everyday is not the same / Emmitt Lee / Miss too fine / Apron strings / Lonesome saxophone part I / Lonesome saxophone part II / Young girl's got a lot of patience / I work five days a week / I don't want your money / Texas son
BT 1055CD / Sep '94 / Black Top

☐ **GULF COAST GREASE: THE SANDY STORY VOL.1**
Rockin' in the graveyard: *Morningstar, Jackie* / No date tonight: *Morningstar, Jackie* / Sugar baby: *Bozeman, Helen* / Because I love you: *Vincent, Darryl* / Wild wild party: *Vincent, Darryl* / I saw a dream walking: *Clark, Billy* / I know why: *Clark, Billy* / Juke box rock: *Wainwright, Happy* / Brand new baby: *Whitehurst, Floyd* / Juke box Queen: *Keenan, Ronny* / Stpo sign on your heart: *Keenan, Ronny* / Stop sign on your heart: *Keenan, Ronny* / Rockin' satellite: *Sawyer, Roy* / Walking and talking: *Wainwright, Happy* / Shenandoah waltz: *Simmons, Morris* / Trackdown: *Bozeman, Ken* / Close to you: *Richardson, George* / I'm gonna leave: *Sawyer, Roy* / Daddy's goin' batty: *Vincent, Darryl* / Woke up this morning: *Spivey, Kenny* / My baby don't love me no more: *Wainwright, Happy* / Jungle rock: *Bo & Jo* / Knocking at your door: *Bunyard, Curtis* / Mercy me: *Vincent, Darryl*
CDCHD 595 / Nov '96 / Ace

☐ **GUMBO STEW VOL.1 (New Orleans R&B)**
Olde wine: *Afo executives* / I know (You don't love me no more): *George, Barbara* / Mojo hanna: *Lynn, Tammi* / Things have changed: *Prince La La* / Tee na na na na: *Bo, Eddie* / My key don't fit: *Dr. John & Ronnie Barron* / Mary: *Tick tocks* / All for one: *Tee, Willie* / Private eye: *Johnson, Wallace* / Pot: *Dr. John* / Keep on lovin' you: *Pistol* / Time has expired: *Carson, Charles* / I'll make a bet: *Nookie boy* / True love: *Lee, Robbie* / I found out (You are my cousin): *Tee, Willie* / Is it too late: *Tick tocks* / Tell me the truth: *Turquinettes* / Tuned in, turned on: *Robinson, Alvin* / Give her up: *Robinson, Alvin* / Ignat: *Lastie, Melvin & Harold Battiste/Cornell Dupree* / Empty talk: *Robinson, Alvin* / I shall not be moved: *Pastor*
CDCHD 450 / Apr '93 / Ace

☐ **GUMBO STEW VOL.2**
Ya ya: *Dorsey, Lee* / Clap your hands: *Johnson, Wallace* / Always accused: *Tee, Willie* / Need you: *Prince La La* / You better check: *Bo, Eddie* / Talk that talk: *Dr. John & Ronnie Barron* / World of dreams: *Lynn, Tammi* / Gonna get you yet: *Tick tocks* / Peace of mind: *Johnson, Wallace* / Two weeks three days: *Duvall, Joan* / Fix (One naughty flat): *Dr. John* / Try me: *George, Barbara* / Make her you wife: *Pistol* / It was you: *Tee, Willie* / Wyld: *Afo executives* / Let me know: *Lee, Robbie* / Better be cool: *Robinson, Alvin* / I've never been in love: *Robinson, Alvin* / Light my fire: *Lynn, Tammi* / Johnny A's blues: *Adams, Johnny*
CDCHD 462 / Sep '93 / Ace

☐ **GUN COURT DUB VOL.1**
SBCD 002 / Aug '94 / Soul Beat

☐ **GUN COURT DUB VOL.2**
SBCD 008 / May '95 / Soul Beat

☐ **GUN COURT DUB VOL.3**
SBCD 010 / Aug '96 / Soul Beat

☐ **GUN SHOT LICKS**
RNCD 2069 / Jul '94 / Rhino

☐ **GUNS OF NAVARONE/RIDE YOUR DONKEY**
Guns of Navarone: *Skatalites* / River bank: *Brooks, Baba* / Illya Kuryakin: *Bennett, Ike & The Crystalites* / Saboo: *McCook, Tommy & The Supersonics* / Bonanza ska: *Malcolm, Carlos & His Jamaican Rhythms* / Vitamin A: *Brooks, Baba* / Something stupid: *Taitt, Lynn & The Jetts* / Copy me donkey: *Tennors* / El pussy cat ska: *Alphonso, Roland* / Penny reel: *Morris, Eric* / Sound pressure: *Soul Brothers* / Napoleon solo: *Taitt, Lynn & The Jetts* / Guns fever: *Brooks, Baba* / Ride your donkey: *Tennors* / Save a bread: *Hinds, Justin & The Dominoes* / Rude boy gone jail: *Clarendonians* / Combination: *Beckford, Kelynne* / One Scotch one bourbon one beer: *Brown, Alfred* / Rub and squeeze: *Perry, Lee 'Scratch' & The Soulettes* / Hold your jack: *Morgan, Derrick* / Dr. Dick: *Perry, Lee 'Scratch'* / Silent river runs deep: *Gaylettes* / Congo war: *Lord Brynner* / Dance all night: *Tartans* / I'm in a dancing mood: *Wilson, Delroy* / I like your world: *Gaylettes* / Penny for your song: *Federals*
CDTRL 384 / Jul '97 / Trojan

☐ **GWLAD I MI VOL.2 (The Best Of Welsh Country Music)**
Disgwyl: *John Ac Alun* / Clywed swn: *Iwcs a Doyle* / Weithiau bydd y fflam: *Iwan, Dafydd* / Eiddo i arall: *Parry, Dylan & Neil* / Yr uffern hon: *Cajuns Denbo* / Milltiroedd: *Iona Ac Andy* / Rho i mi dy galon: *Broc Mor* / Beth yw lliw y Gwynt: *Iona Ac Andy* / Hen wlad llyn: *Parry, Dylan & Neil* / Os na ddaw yfory: *John Ac Alun* / Elen: *Cajuns Denbo* / Celwydd yn dy lygaid: *Broc Mor* / Ffydd y crydd: *Iwcs a Doyle* / I'r gad: *Iwan, Dafydd*
SCD 2166 / May '97 / Sain

☐ **GYPSY JAZZ**
JHR 73588 / Oct '95 / Jazz Hour

☐ **GYPSY MUSIC FROM MACEDONIA**
TSCD 514 / Aug '96 / Topic

☐ **GYPSY NIGHTS**
Una aventura / El ventilador / Quiero ser Feliz / Macumba / Kalimba de luna / Borriquito / Perdidio amor / La botella / Mi desengano / Dime Carmen / Volare / La vida en rosa / Amor de mis amores / La colegiala
12278 / 22 Sep '97 / Laserlight

☐ **GYPSY PASSION**
Lucia: *Lopez, Oscar* / Gipsy: *Cook, Jesse* / Gypsy flame: *Armik* / Dulce libertad: *Lara & Reyes* / 2 In the night: *Liebert, Ottmar* / Bola: *Strunz & Farah* / Danza Mora: *Tingstad, Eric* / Rumba rumba gitanita: *Romero, Ruben & Lydia Torea* / Torero: *Govi* / Istanbul: *BecVar, Bruce* / Torrecillo del leal: *De La Bastide, Miguel* / Rockin' gypsies: *Willie & Lobo*
VNDCD 8 / 11 May '98 / Virgin

☐ **GYPSY PASSIONS: THE FLAMENCO GUITAR**
LYRCD 7399 / '91 / Lyrichord

☐ **GYPSY SONGS**
PS 65203 / Aug '98 / PlayaSound

☐ **GYPSY SONGS AND MUSIC**
CDCH 295 / Feb '91 / Milan

☐ **GYPSY SOUL**
Fire and fury: *Lopez, Oscar* / Ritmos de valarta: *Benedetti & Svoboda* / Duende: *Stevens, Bozzio Levin* / Mi carmen: *Bastide, Miguel de la* / Rattle and burn: *Cook, Jesse* / Malguena: *Romero, Ruben* / Mi amor: *Armik* / Driving 2 Madrid: *Liebert, Ottmar* / Luna de fiesta: *Encinas, Jose Luis* / Gloria Bendita: *Chuscales* / Heat of the sun: *Strunz, Jorge* / Obsession confession: *Slash*
2438455062 / 24 Mar '98 / Narada
VNDCD 10 / 11 May '98 / Virgin

H

☐ **HADRA OF THE GNAWA OF ESSAOUIRA**
C 560006 / Mar '93 / Ocora

☐ **HAIL ROCK 'N' ROLL (3CD Set)**
KBOX 375 / Aug '97 / Collection

☐ **HAIL VARIETY**
At the Holborn Empire: *Miller, Max* / Come into the garden Maud: *Nash, Heddle* / Boiled beef and carrots: *Champion, Harry* / Burlington Bertie from Bow: *Shields, Ella* / When father papered the parlour: *Williams, Billy* / Little of what you fancy: *Lloyd, Marie* / Tower of London: *Leno, Dan* / To suffer for the likes of him: *Elen, Gus* / Don't have any more Mrs. Moore: *Morris, Lily* / My old Dutch: *Chevalier, Albert* / Goodbye Johnny I must leave you / Sons of the sea: *Reece, Arthur* / If you were the only girl in the world: *Robey, George & Violet Loraine* / I'm one of the boys of the Old Brigade: *Little Tich* / Nellie Dean: *Gitana, Gertie* / Roamin' in the gloamin': *Lauder, Harry* / PC Parker: *Austin, Charles* / In his new motor car: *Tait, Harry* / Magna Carta: *Hay, Will & his Scholars* / Lily of Laguna: *Stratton, Eugene* / Down at the old Bull and Bush: *Forde, Florrie* / Jolly brothers: *Whelan, Albert* / Man who broke the bank at Monte Carlo: *Coburn, Charles* / Love will find a way: *Collins, Jose* / And her mother comes too: *Buchanan, Jack* / He never said he loved me: *Lawrence, Gertrude* / I'll see you again: *Laye, Evelyn* / She's my lovely: *Howes, Bobby* / Mad dogs and Englishmen: *Coward, Sir Noel* / When day's done: *Ambrose & His Orchestra* / Say it with music: *Payne, Jack & His Orchestra* / Here's to the next time: *Hall, Henry* / Coal black Mammy: *Hylton, Jack* / Sally: *Fields, Gracie* / Underneath the arches: *Flanagan & Allen* / Navy sketch: *Handley, Tommy* / Bee: *Askey, Arthur* / Auf wiederseh'n sweetheart: *Lynn, Vera* / Tulips from Amsterdam: *Bygraves, Max* / Don't laugh at me: *Wisdom, Norman* / Charmaine: *Mantovani* / Garden of Eden: *Vaughan, Frankie* / With all my heart: *Clark, Petula* / Cumberland gap: *Donegan, Lonnie* / Lay down your arms: *Shelton, Anne* / We will make love: *Hamilton, Russ* / Cara Mia: *Whitfield, David* / Rock with the caveman: *Steele, Tommy*
LCOM 5249 / Feb '96 / Lismor

☐ **HAILE SELASSIE CENTENARY VOL.2**
SZCD 4 / May '96 / Surr Zema Musik

☐ **HAILE SELLASSIE CENTENARY DUB VOL.2**
S 200002 / Apr '94 / Surr Zema Musik

☐ **HAITI RAP & RAGGA**
3192 / Apr '95 / Declic

☐ **HAKKEUH (HARDCORE) (2CD Set)**
IDT 001505 / Mar '97 / ID&T

☐ HALBSTARKE
Nimm das madchen: *Kane, Eden* / Geraldine: *Renk, Bobby* / Du liebst nicht heisse rhythmen: *Bennett, Robert* / Ich brauche dich dazu: *Kent, Tommy* / King creole: *Brandes, Will* / Jakety jak: *Sanders, Billy* / Weit im suden von New Orleans: *Wurges, Paul* / In unserem stadtchen: *Berger, Boy* / Und dann nehm ich die guitar: *Hoop, Wyn* / Und dann kam Jimmy Jones: *Blum, Hans* / Lonely man: *Koller, Eddie* / Bim bam: *Wust, Hannes* / Ich brauche keinen ring: *Herold, Ted* / Babbalina: *Ellery, dan* / Ohne ein bestimmtes ziel: *Spier, Bernd* / Hey little Lucy: *Herwig, Claus* / Mona wie keine andere: *Carell, Freddy* / Mach dich schon: *Kraus, Peter* / Schaut schaut das ist meine braut: *Brock, Fredy* / Hipp hipp: *Twen, Ronny* / Mondschein rock: *Schmid, Geschwister* / Tinga-tanga rock: *Hinnen, Peterli* / Whoo hoo: *Muller, Werner & Die Woo Hoos* / Rock baby rock: *Quick, Conny* / Warenhaus rock: *Haensch, Della & Die Rockies*
BCD 15986 / Aug '97 / Bear Family

☐ HALLELUJAH (18 Uplifting Gospel Songs Of Faith & Inspiration)
In the hands of the Lord: *Five Blind Boys Of Mississippi* / Canaan: *Ward, Clara & The Ward Sisters* / Ways of the Lord: *Ward, Clara & The Ward Sisters* / Bedside of a neighbour: *Ward, Clara & The Ward Sisters* / Motherless children: *Gospelaires* / You're gonna need somebody: *Andrews, Inez* / If it's alright: *Jackson Southernaires* / Friend in Jesus: *Mighty Clouds Of Joy* / Old ship of Zion: *Pilgrim Jubilee Singers* / Burying ground: *Sensational Nightingales* / Spirit of Memphis: *Spirit Of Memphis Quartet* / Oh Jesus programme: *Sunset Travellers* / He's my saviour: *Williams Bros. & Ida Lee Brown*
MCCD 298 / May '97 / Music Club

☐ HAMBURG STRIKES BACK
HYCD 21034 / Nov '92 / Hypertension

☐ HAMMOND STYLE SINGALONG
SWBCD 206 / Oct '95 / Sound Waves

☐ HAND PICKED (25 Years Of Rounder Bluegrass)
ROUCDAN 22 / Nov '95 / Rounder

☐ HAND THAT HOLDS THE BREAD, THE (Songs Of Progress & Protest In The Gilded Age)
802672 / Aug '97 / New World

☐ HANDFUL OF KEYS (13 Great Jazz Pianists)
Monday date: *Hines, Earl 'Fatha'* / I ain't got nobody: *Hines, Earl 'Fatha'* / Black beauty: *Ellington, Duke* / Swampy river: *Ellington, Duke* / Don't blame me: *Wilson, Teddy* / Every now and then: *Wilson, Teddy* / Honky tonk train blues: *Lewis, Meade 'Lux'* / Shout for joy: *Ammons, Albert* / How long blues: *Basie, Count* / Dirty dozens: *Basie, Count* / Between sets: *Kyle, Billy* / Finishing up a date: *Kyle, Billy* / Handful of keys: *Waller, Fats* / Numb fumblin': *Waller, Fats* / Overland: *Williams, Mary Lou* / Pearls: *Williams, Mary Lou* / Gin mill blues: *Sullivan, Joe* / Onyx bringdown: *Sullivan, Joe* / In a mist: *Beiderbecke, Bix* / In the dark: *Stacy, Jess* / Flashes barrelhouse: *Stacy, Jess* / World is waiting for the sunrise: *Stacy, Jess* / Gone with the wind: *Tatum, Art* / Stormy weather: *Tatum, Art*
CDAJA 5073 / Sep '90 / Living Era

☐ HANDLE WITH CARE
SAB 05CD / Mar '96 / Sabotage

☐ HANG ELEVEN (MUTANT SURF PUNKS)
I want my woody back: *Barracudas* / Who stole the summer: *Surfin' Lungs* / 308: *Malibooz* / Herman's new woody: *Palominos* / Fun at the beach: *B-Girls* / Gas money: *Lloyd, Bobby & The Windfall Prophets* / Pipeline: *Agent Orange* / Tuff little surfer boy: *Truth & Beauty* / Girls cars girls sun girls surf girls fun girls: *Corvettes* / Automobile: *Stickshifts* / Day they raised the Thames barrier: *Beach Bums* / Shotgun: *Beach Coma* / Surfin' CIA: *Buzz & The B-Days* / Mighty morris ten: *Episode Six* / Depth charge: *Jon & The Nightriders*
CDGRAM 23 / May '95 / Cherry Red

☐ HANG IT OUT TO DRY
1008 / May '97 / Satan

☐ HANG ON (Vintage Jazz At The Hayes Country Club 1996)
PKCD 066 / Mar '97 / PEK

☐ HAPPY ALBUM VOL.2
Stomp it up: *JDS* / Kaos: *Q-Tex* / Looking for love: *New Motion* / Paradise lost: *Citadel Of Kaos* / Dancing thru the knite: *DJ Brisk* / Horny raver: *D-Zyne Fury* / Metamorphisis: *Ramos & Supreme/ Sunset Regime* / Deep in the underground: *Lock Jaw* / Now is the time: *Brown, Scott* / Going crazy: *Rave Nation* / As cold as ice: *Stingray* / Raging desire: *Happy Tunes*
CDTOT 34 / Oct '95 / Jumpin' & Pumpin'

☐ HAPPY ANTHEMS VOL.1
CDRAID 520 / Oct '94 / Rumour

☐ HAPPY ANTHEMS VOL.2
CDRAID 522 / Mar '95 / Rumour

☐ HAPPY ANTHEMS VOL.3
CDRAID 526 / Oct '95 / Rumour

☐ HAPPY ANTHEMS VOL.4
CDRAID 528 / Feb '96 / Rumour

☐ HAPPY BIRTHDAY BABY JESUS (2CD Set)
SFTRI 1396CD / Nov '95 / Sympathy For The Record Industry

☐ HAPPY BIRTHDAY/AULD LANG SYNE/ FOR HE'S A JOLLY GOOD FELLOW..
PARCD 001 / Mar '96 / Image

☐ HAPPY DAYS
DSPCD 112 / Sep '94 / Disky

☐ HAPPY DAZE
Died in your arms tonight: *Go Mental* / Your my life: *DJ Synergy* / My love: *DJ Codeine* / Raise your hands: *H-Men* / Rushing: *DJ Mixmatt & Rebel Alliance* / Life force generator: *Ramos & Supreme/ Sunset Regime* / Party pumper: *DJ Brisk* / Flashdance (What a feeling): *Magika* / Check dis out: *Serious* / Let the music: *Eruption* / Harmony: *Force & Styles* / Positive energy: *Happy Tunes*
CDELIC 1 / Jun '96 / Passion

☐ HAPPY HARDCORE ANTHEMS (4CD Set)
DAM 004 / Dec '96 / Tring

☐ HAPPY HARDCORE FEVER VOL.1
TROOPHTCD 16 / Jul '95 / Happy Trax

☐ HAPPY HARDCORE FEVER VOL.2 (Mixed By D.J. Vibes)
DBMPCHCD 1A
DBMPCHCD 1 / May '96 / Punch

☐ HAPPY HARDCORE FEVER VOL.4 (Includes Bonus Megamix CD/2CD Set)
Runaway: *Jimmy J & Cru-L-T* / Higher: *DJ Ham* / Survival: *Tailbone* / Yee-haaa: *Forbes, Davie* / Flava: *DJ Happy Raver* / Motorway madness: *DJ Vibes & Wishdokta* / Heaven: *El Bruto* / Piano obsession: *Luna-C* / Gimme the world: *T3* / Gimme the world: *DJ Pleasure* / Love is: *DJ Brian* / Airhead: *DJ Brisk* / Inner access: *DJ Demo* / Simply electric: *DJ Force & Evolution* / Lift me up: *Future Primitive*
DBM 2738 / Feb '97 / Death Becomes Me

☐ HAPPY HARDCORE HYSTERIA (4CD Set)
CDBTOT 3 / 26 Jan '98 / Jumpin' & Pumpin'

☐ HAPPY HARDCORE VOL.1
Breakin' free: *Slipmatt* / Visions of light: *Higher Level* / Don't beg 4 love: *Jack 'n' Phil* / Ronnie's revenge (remix): *Citadel Of Kaos* / Kounter attack: *Druid & Vinyl Groover* / Rhythm: *Just Another Artist* / Drop the bass: *DJ Seduction* / Positive: *Love Nation* / Piano progression (mix): *Luna-C* / In complete darkness: *Fat Controller* / Take me away: *Jimmy J & Cru-L-T* / Let's do it: *DJ Red Alert & Mike Slammer*
CDTOT 18 / Oct '94 / Jumpin' & Pumpin'

☐ HAPPY HARDCORE VOL.2
Make it ruff: *DJ Brisk* / Play the theme: *DJ Sy & Unknown* / Feel so real: *DJ Red Alert & Mike Slammer* / Better day: *DJ Seduction & Dougal* / Hold me in your arms: *Storm Syndicut* / Feels good: *Vibes & Wishdokta* / Movin': *Justin Time* / Burn baby burn: *Sensitize* / Summer vibe: *DEA* / Lust: *Just Another Artist* / Slave to the rave: *Love Nation* / Lift me up: *Future Primitive*
CDTOT 22 / Jan '95 / Jumpin' & Pumpin'

☐ HAPPY HARDCORE VOL.3
Hardcore business: *Vibes & Wishdokta* / Take me to the top: *Sunshine Productions* / I just can't stop: *DJ Brisk* / Ultimate seduction: *DJ Hixxy* / Drop the bass: *DJ Seduction* / Teknomancer: *Sunset Regime* / I need somebody: *Eruption* / JT Goes north: *Justin Time* / Looking into the night: *DJ Slam* / Groove control: *Midas* / Detrimental: *DJ Demand* / Warped: *Citadel Of Kaos*
CDTOT 30 / Jun '95 / Jumpin' & Pumpin'

☐ HAPPY HARDCORE VOL.4
Ride like the wind: *Bunter, Billy & D'Zyne/JDS* / Luv you more: *Elstak, Paul* / Higher love: *JDS* / Just like that: *Terrible twins* / Let the music: *Eruption* / Help me: *Justin Time* / It's gonna be: *DJ Poosie* / Shout now: *Time Span & Bertie* / Looking for love: *New Motion* / Woo woo wanting you: *Icon* / Take me up: *Sub State* / Red alert: *Red Alert*
CDTOT 37 / Mar '96 / Jumpin' & Pumpin'

☐ HAPPY HARDCORE VOL.5
Better day: *GBT Inc. & Joanne Robertson* / Freedom: *DJ Unity* / Died in your arms: *Go Mental* / Giving it all I've got: *Vibes & Wishdokta* / Simply electric: *Force & Evolution* / Is there anybody out there: *DJ Ham* / Lift me up: *DJ Demo* / Go insane: *DJ DNA* / Get down: *M-D Emm* / Life force generator: *Ramos & Supreme* / Burning love: *Critical Mass* / Keep on loving: *Grassie, Donna*
CDTOT 44 / Aug '96 / Jumpin' & Pumpin'

☐ HAPPY MAIO FAMILY, A (Dance & Song From SW China)
PANCD 2023 / Aug '94 / Pan

☐ HAPPY MEALS
MYRECORDS 001CD / Mar '96 / My Records

☐ HAPPY TO MEET (Classic Recordings Of Traditional Irish Dance Music)
Bridie Morley/Duigan's favourite: *Duigan, Packie* / Knights of St. Patrick: *Doherty, John & Tommy McMahon* / I have a bonnet trimmed with blue/The rakes of Mallow: *O'Sullivan, Bernard & Tommy McMahon* / Peg McGrath/Ganley's reel: *McDermott, Josie* / Pipe on the hob: *Clancy, Willie* / Boil the breakfast early: *Tansey, Seamus & Eddie Corcoran* / Mountain hornpipe/Kingston hornpipe: *Rea, John* / Tommy Glenny's reel: *Russell, Micko & Packie* / Gillian's apples: *Doonan, John & John Wright* / St. Anne's reel: *Pepper, Noel* / Kerry Mills: *Teahan, Terry* / Two Woodford flings: *Coen, Jack & Charlie* / Night in Ennis/The maid behind the bar: *Griffin, Vincent* / Port Liadroma/Sean Tiobraidd Arann: *Mitchell, Pat* / Duke of Leinster: *Duigan, Packie & Seamus Horan* / Cuckoo hornpipe: *Droney, Chris* / Bonny Kate/Jenny's chickens: *Tansey, Seamus & Eddie Corcoran* / Untitled mazurka: *Doherty, John* / Tatter Jack Walsh: *Russell, Micko & Gussie* / Teetotaller/Bunch of keys: *Murphy, Rose* / Ashplant/ Maid of Mont Cisco: *O'Sullivan, Bernard* / Boys of the town/Dwyer's jig: *McDermott, Josie* / George White's favourite/Ivy leaf: *Doran, Felix* / We were drinking and kissing the ladies/Old Tipperary: *Kelly, John* / Barn dance: *O'Dwyer, Ellen* / Kitty's fancy/ Lady Anne Hope: *Rea, John* / Sean Hayes/If there weren't any women in the world: *Kelly, Gene* / Irish washerwoman/Father O'Flynn/Lilting fisherman: *Doonan, John* / Happy to meet, sorry to part: *Ennis, Seamus* / Foxhunter's jig: *Neylan, Paddy*
CDORBD 092 / Oct '96 / Globestyle

☐ HAPPY TOGETHER
Happy together: *Turtles* / Somebody else's guy: *Brown, Jocelyn* / I'll have to say I love you in a song: *Croce, Jim* / Baby I'm yours: *Lewis, Barbara* / Where did our love go: *Elbert, Donnie* / Love's gotta hold on me: *Dollar* / It's a love thing: *Whispers* / Making up again: *Goldie* / More than a lover: *Tyler, Bonnie* / You'll never know: *Hi-Gloss* / Waterloo sunset: *Kinks* / (You're love keeps lifting me) higher and higher: *Wilson, Jackie* / Best thing that ever happened to me: *Knight, Gladys* / Feels like I'm in love: *Marie, Kelly* / Sad sweet dreamer: *Sweet Sensation* / Jack in the box: *Moments* / This is it: *Moore, Melba* / You to me are everything: *Real Thing* / I can make you feel good: *Shalamar* / Say you don't mind: *Blunstone, Colin*
TRTCD 158 / 16 Feb '98 / TrueTrax

☐ HARD AS HELL VOL.3
MODEF 3CD / May '88 / Music Of Life

☐ HARD AS HELL VOL.4
MODEF 4CD / Dec '90 / Music Of Life

☐ HARD BEAT VOL.1
PSNC 0078 / 3 Nov '97 / Nukleuz

☐ HARD CELL
MAUCD 622 / Aug '92 / Mau Mau

☐ HARD EDUCATION
Untitled 1: *Surgeon* / Untitled 2: *Surgeon* / Untitled 1: *Regis* / Untitled 2: *Regis* / Untitled 1: *Female* / Untitled 2: *Female* / Untitled 1: *Portion Reform* / Untitled 2: *Portion Reform*
DNCD 003 / Jun '97 / Downwards

☐ HARD HOUSE (4CD Set)
DCBX 105 / 16 Mar '98 / Dance Club International

☐ HARD LEADERS (The History Of Drum & Bass/4CD Set)
KICKCD 35 / Feb '96 / Kickin'

☐ HARD LEADERS VOL.3
KICKCD 7 / Oct '93 / Kickin'

☐ HARD LEADERS VOL.4
KICKCD 8 / Apr '94 / Kickin'

☐ HARD LEADERS VOL.7
KICKCD 23 / May '95 / Kickin'

☐ HARD NIGHTS DAY, A (The Best Of Stiff Records - 2CD Set)
MCD 60047 / 22 Sep '97 / MCA

☐ HARD ROCK COLLECTION
PDSCD 506 / Sep '97 / Pulse

☐ HARD TECHNO
7142616 / Dec '96 / Fairway

☐ HARD TECHNO CLASSICS (The Complete Series)
DBM 2460 / May '97 / Death Becomes Me

☐ HARD TECHNO CLASSICS FROM DEEPEST GERMANY VOL.2
UNDLAB 24CD / May '95 / Labworks

☐ HARD TECHNO CLASSICS FROM DEEPEST GERMANY VOL.3
DBLABCD 13 / Apr '96 / Labworks

☐ HARD TIMES AND HEARTACHES
Preachin' blues: *Johnson, Robert* / Long tall Mama: *Broonzy, 'Big' Bill* / Ain't it a cryin' shame: *Fuller, Blind Boy* / Packin' trunk: *Leadbelly* / Dark was the night: *Johnson, 'Blind' Willie* / Denver blues: *Tampa Red* / Bukka's jitterbug swing: *White, Bukka* / Southern can is mine: *McTell, 'Blind' Willie* / Steppin' on the blues: *Johnson, Lonnie* / Goodbye now: *McGhee, Brownie* / St. Louis blues: *Smith, Bessie* / Hurry down sunshine: *Dupree, 'Champion' Jack* / Death letter: *House, Son* / I can't be satisfied: *Waters, Muddy* / Dust my broom: *Taj Mahal* / Stateboro blues: *Rising Sons*
4766832 / May '94 / Columbia

☐ HARD TRANCE AND PSYCHEDELIC TECHNO VOL.1
PTM 129 / Feb '95 / Phantasm

☐ HARD TRANCE AND PSYCHEDELIC TECHNO VOL.2
PTM 130CD / Feb '95 / Phantasm

☐ HARD TRANCE CLASSICS - THE COMPLETE SERIES (3CD Set)
D-9-5: *Colone* / This ain't no 303: *SDL* / Kayht: *Sabotage* / Science: *Spectral Emotions* / Feel: *Icons* / Elevator regained: *Colone* / Time mode: *Intergrated Circuits* / Ascend from the mind: *SDL* / Chiswick days: *Spectral Emotions* / Mission: *SDL* / Beets: *4D* / Milchglas: *Josef & His Cousin* / Accelerator: *Syntax Morph* / Centrifugal force: *SDL* / Patience: *Intergrated Circuits* / Dro-gen: *Elin* / Trip to Africa: *MG-3* / Plastic sex: *Nervous Project* / Drop: *Church Windows* / Oceanic: *Trax Beyond Subconscious* / Alfa test: *Pagan Acid* / Mirror of J: *Integrated Circuits* / Atom V20: *Syntax Morph* / Sauna: *Pleasure* / Nightrocker: *Just, Christopher* / Attractor V20: *Syntax Morph* / Head is not longer than the body: *4D* / Before the day: *Hemisphear* / Audition Colouree: *Pagan Acid* / Rattlesnake: *Integrated Circuits* / Transabotage: *Sabotage* / Alex the sugar daddy: *4D* / Danger: *Radiation* / Lock 2: *Doorkeeper* / Darkside: *Colone* / Incline: *Integrated Circuits* / Screw loose: *Doorkeeper* / Hard trance: *Doorkeeper*
DBM 2459 / Jan '97 / Death Becomes Me

☐ HARD TRANCE CLASSICS FROM DEEPEST GERMANY VOL.3
DBMLABCD 12 / Dec '95 / Labworks

☐ HARDBEATS AND SOFT DRINKS
OZONCD 25 / Apr '92 / Ozone

☐ HARDCLUBBING VOL.3
SUB 48522 / Jul '97 / Dunkla

☐ HARDCLUBBING VOL.4
SUB 48712 / 3 Nov '97 / Distance

☐ HARDCORE
AUM 004116 / Nov '96 / 80 AUM

☐ HARDCORE - LEADERS OF THE NEW SCHOOL VOL.1
KICKCD 3 / Nov '92 / Kickin'

☐ HARDCORE - LEADERS OF THE NEW SCHOOL VOL.2
KICKCD 5 / Mar '93 / Kickin'

☐ HARDCORE - LEADERS OF THE NEW SCHOOL VOL.5 (Jungle Dub)
KICKCD 12 / Aug '94 / Kickin'

☐ HARDCORE BLAST
Name of the DJ: *Chosen Few* / Cocaine: *Technohead* / Hardcore motherfuckers: *Tellurian* / Mad creator: *Santana, Omar* / Out of focus: *Brown, Scott* / Der computer ist tot: *Narcanosis* / Brainwaves: *Outside Agency* / Slapback: *Titanium Steel* / Fukem all: *DJ Dano* / Chosen paradize: *Chosen Few* / Ye shall die: *Brown, Scott* / Misadventures of the spiegel man pt 1: *Party Animals* / Abba gabba: *Riot Nation* / Hardcore suckers: *One, Walter* / Come with me (into the stars): *Narcanosis* / Put it on the table: *DJ Dano*
DB 47832 / Apr '97 / Mokum

☐ HARDCORE CHEDDAR VOL.1 (Dutch Masters)
CDRAID 527 / Oct '95 / Rumour

☐ HARDCORE CHEDDAR VOL.2 (Dutch Masters)
CDRAID 530 / Jun '96 / Rumour

☐ HARDCORE CHEDDAR VOL.4
CDRAID 533 / Nov '96 / Rumour

☐ HARDCORE DOO-WOP (In The Hallway - Under The Street Lamp)
Wheel of fortune: *Four Flames* / Dream girl: *Jesse & Marvin* / Nite owl: *Allen, Tony & The Champs* / Oooh-Rooba-Lee: *Maye, Arthur Lee & The Crowns* / Where's my girl: *Belvin, Jesse* / I: *Allen, Tony & The Champs* / Sweet breeze: *Green, Vernon & The Phantoms* / Check yourself baby: *Allen, Tony & The Chimes* / Foot loose and fancy free: *Gipson, Byron 'Slick' & The Sliders* / Gloria: *Maye, Arthur Lee & The Crowns* / Especially: *Allen, Tony & The Chimes* / Baby need (ting-a-ling): *Zeppa, Ben Joe & The Zephyrs* / Old willow tree: *Green, Vernon & The Phantoms* / Cool loving: *Maye, Arthur Lee & The Crowns* / Pretty little girl: *Chimes* / How long: *Church, Eugene* / Malinda: *Mandolph, Bobby* / Hold me tight: *Jaguars* / Don't you know: *Maye, Arthur Lee & The Crowns* / Never let you go: *Ambers & Ralph Mathis* / Open up your heart: *Church, Eugene* / Mine all mine: *Jaguars* / Guardian angel: *Selections* / Soft and sweet: *Selections*
CDCHD 514 / Jan '94 / Ace

☐ HARDCORE EXPOSURE (Mixed By Spinback & Bunjy)
KICKCD 57 / 22 Sep '97 / Kickin'

☐ HARDCORE FUTURE VOL.5
Listen carefully: *Wagner, Robert* / Hardcore power: *Brown, Scott* / Centre of the earth: *Zelator* / We'll tear your soul apart: *Leviathan* / CryRise and shine: *Crypt 1* / At war: *Syphax* / Whiteline: *Trickster* / Don't fuck with me: *Dark Destination* / Stab ya brain: *Too Hostile* / Suffer: *DJ Fuckface & DJ Crizz*
CDRAID 536 / Aug '97 / Rumour

☐ HARDCORE HAPPINESS VOL.1
J4U 001CD / Mar '95 / Just 4 U

☐ HARDCORE HAPPINESS VOL.3 (2CD Set/Mix Tape By Slipmat)
J4U 003CD / Apr '96 / Just 4 U

☐ HARDCORE HEAVEN VOL.2 (2CD Set)
HMLCD 102 / Jul '97 / Heaven

☐ HARDCORE HEAVEN VOL.3
HMLCD 103 / 2 Feb '98 / Heaven

☐ HARDCORE HEAVEN VOL.4 (2CD Set)
HMLCD 104 / 27 Jul '98 / Heaven

☐ HARDCORE HOLIDAY
420172 / Nov '96 / Frantic

☐ HARDCORE HURRICANE
Second coming: *DJ Rob* / Original: *SPC Hardcore* / Cool please brother: *Brown, Scott* / Sarin: *DJ Jordens* / Jaxx eargasm: *DJ Fuckface* / Tell me what your find: *Wasting Program* / Destronation: *Dark Destination* / Slow as fuck: *DJ Attik & DJ Stylzz* / Enjoy the pain: *DJ Epitaph* / Rob's 20 seconds: *DJ Rob* / Don't ever stop: *Brown, Scott* / We like da music: *DJ Perpetrator* / Mother fuckin' motherfucker: *Stunned Guys* / Outro: *Rave Creators* / Drifting: *DNM*
DC 878852 / May '97 / Disky

☐ **HARDCORE JUNGLIST FEVER VOL.1**
STHCCD 6 / Aug '94 / Strictly Underground

☐ **HARDCORE JUNGLIST FEVER VOL.2**
STHCCD 7 / '94 / Strictly Underground

☐ **HARDCORE MASSIVE VOL.1**
TROOPCD 14 / Jul '95 / Rogue Trooper

☐ **HARDCORE MISSION (3CD Set)**
Genesis: *Johnson, Steve* / Enervate: *Transa* / E spot: *Harding, Paul & Liberator* / Give it to me: *EC1 & Choci* / Deep in thought: *Sharp, Kenny* / Feel my desire: *Code 28* / Mackerel Lord of remix: *Chris C & M-Zone* / Grand hall: *Senza Volto* / Reformation: *Lab 4* / Cuba: *Cortex* / Tripswitch: *Tic Tac* / Tekno creche: *Ramos & UFO* / Echo plex: *Smith, Mark* / Phuture phunk: *SLAM* / Promised land: *Tekno Dred Alliance* / Digital havoc: *D-Zyne* / Gates of oblivion: *Vanden, Rob* / Lost in space: *Citadel Of Kaos* / Hyperhydosis: *D-Zyne & DJ Fury* / Life death and chocolate: *Helix* / Tardis to Brooklyn: *Bang The Future* / Energy: *DJ Tibby* / Anti clockwise: *DJ Energy* / Synergy: *UFO*
HMISCD 1 / 6 Oct '97 / Beechwood

☐ **HARDCORE RAGGAMUFFIN**
GRELCD 151 / Nov '90 / Greensleeves

☐ **HARDCORE SLAM (32 Happy Gabba Monsters/2CD Set)**
560032 / Apr '97 / Nova Tekk

☐ **HARDCORE SLAM VOL.2 (2CD Set)**
Good to go: *MC Remsey* / One to two: *Forze DJ Team* / Your local DJ: *DJ Delirium* / Feel the rhythm: *Prezioso* / Like a dream: *Bass D and King Matthew feat XD* / Slaves to the raves: *Inferno Brothers* / With u: *Fuzz* / Ouzo: *Goliath* / Beast time: *DJ Waxweazle* / On a posse: *Old School Terrorists* / Used and abused: *Party Animals* / Fatal morgana: *Fuzz* / I am the future: *Angel* / Da bat device: *Dr. Z-Vago* / Get this motherfucker: *Guys* / You're dealin' with...: *Corps* / Hardcore to da bone: *Masters Of Ceremony* / 909 Trauma: *Forze DJ Team* / Jungle sickness: *Miss Groovey* / Unfucking believable: *DJ Waxweazle* / Out of order: *Physical Force* / Work that body: *Guys* / Superior: *Dr. Z-Vago* / Da east: *Bruyaa & Ozonic* / No happy shit: *Corps* / Message from hell: *Euromasters*
560152 / Aug '97 / Nova Tekk

☐ **HARDCORE WARRIORS VOL.1**
AUM 004079 / Nov '96 / 80 AUM

☐ **HARDCORE WARRIORS VOL.2 (2CD Set)**
AUM 975004 / 1 Sep '97 / ZYX

☐ **HARDCORE XPERIENCE VOL.1**
I 2884362 / Jul '97 / Galaxy

☐ **HARDCORE XPERIENCE VOL.2**
I 3884372 / Jul '97 / Galaxy

☐ **HARDCORE XPERIENCE VOL.3**
I 3884382 / Jul '97 / Galaxy

☐ **HARDCORE XPLOSION VOL.2 (2CD Set/Mixed By Billy 'Daniel' Bunter & Slipmatt)**
Let the music: *Eruption* / Body slam: *Bang The Future* / One style: *Vinyl Junkie & Elation* / All on you: *Bang The Future* / Hyde Smithy: *Oxidiser* / Calling: *Bang The Future* / Electec: *Bang The Future* / Deal with the pain: *Bang The Future* / Look for the truth: *Future Collective* / Acid sunshine: *Trance Masters* / Begining of a new era: *Tailbone* / Real world: *Bang The Future* / Atomic lullaby: *Bang The Future* / Excession: *Fury & Dzyne* / It's my thing: *Bang The Future* / You belong to me: *Kingsize & Eternity* / Rock a jam: *Kingsize & Eternity*
SUMCD 226 / 1 Sep '97 / Supreme Underground

☐ **HARDER THAN THE REST**
Signe says: *Killout Trash* / Deutschland: *Atari Teenage Riot* / We need a chance: *EC8OR* / Suicide: *Alec Empire* / Sweat shizuo: *Shizuo* / Turntable terrorist: *Sonic Subjunkies* / Nizza: *Hanin* / Deaf dumb and blind: *DJ Bleed* / Into the death: *Atari Teenage Riot* / Straight outa Berlin: *Killout Trash* / Discriminate: *ES8TOR* / Central industrial: *Sonic Subjunkies* / Smash him to ground: *EC8TOR & Moonraker* / Anarchy: *Shizuo* / Destroyer: *Alec Empire*
DHRCD 002 / Oct '95 / Digital Hardcore

☐ **HARDTRANCE CLASSICS VOL.1 (2CD Set)**
Wake up: *Garnier, Laurent* / Skyline: *Resistance D* / Fragile: *LSG* / Love stimulation: *Humate* / Trancescript: *Hardfloor* / Una musica senza ritmo: *Degeneration* / Unknown track: *Unknown Artist* / Trancesylvania x-press: *X-Dream* / Little fluffy clouds: *Orb* / Two full moons and a trout: *Union Jack* / Mantra: *Bolland, C.J.* / Spectrum: *Metal Master* / How much can you take: *Visions Of Shiva* / Eternal spirit: *4-Voice* / Paraglide: *Paragliders* / With a medium into trance: *Hearts Of Space* / Contrex ville: *Redeye* / Beat just goes straight on and on: *Perry & Rhodan* / Acid Eiffel: *Choice* / Alcatraz: *Peyote*
SPV 08539092 / Aug '98 / SPV

☐ **HARDTRANCE CLASSICS VOL.2 (2CD Set)**
Hymn (this is my dream): *Moby* / Stars (what is space): *Microglobe* / X-plain the un-x-plained: *Arpeggiators* / Transformation: *Transform* / Samurai: *Juno Reactor* / Gloria: *Art Of Trance* / Papua New Guinea: *Future Sound Of London* / Dark and long: *Underworld* / Alice in wonderland: *Cybordelics* / Planet sex: *Garnier, Laurent* / Trancition: *Choci & Freedom Of Sound* / Sundown: *Overlords* / Cosmic evolution: *Microbots* / Lubianata: *Blue Planet Co-operation* / Catching the scent of mystery: *4-Voice* / Moments in noise: *Sequencer* / We came in peace: *Dance 2 Trance* / Lollipop man: *Union Jack* / Love letter: *Van Dyke, Paul* / Into my dream: *Krid Snero* / Be yourself: *Rototype* / Meltdown: *Lunatic Asylum*
SPV 08539102 / Aug '98 / SPV

☐ **HARDTRANCE CLASSICS VOL.3 (2CD Set)**
Mahadeva: *Astral Projection* / Floor essence: *Man With No Name* / LSD: *Hallucinogen* / High energy protons: *Juno Reactor* / Aliens: *Total Eclipse* / Uforica: *Infinity Project* / Scarab: *Prana* / Insect: Koxbox / Bony incus: *Eat Static* / Near to the divine: *Kode IV* / Generator: *Blue Planet Co-operation* / Shiva: *Indoor* / Elektron bender: *Technossomy* / Lunar juice: *Slinky Wizard* / Moonraker: *Disco Volante* / Robostyx: *Transwave* / Morphic resonance: *Third Eye* / Two vindaloos and an onion bhagee: *Green Nuns Of The Revolution* / Deliverance: *Butler & Wilson* / Gas: *Voov* / Next stop oblivion: *Z To A* / Octopus: *Art Of Trance*
SPV 08539142 / Aug '98 / SPV

☐ **HARDTRANCE CLASSICS VOL.4 (2CD Set)**
Hello San Francisco: *Dance 2 Trance* / Spanish fly: *Delorme* / Perfect day: *Visions Of Shiva* / Hold me now: *Solace* / Blueprint: *LSG* / Play with the voice: *Vanelli, Joe T.* / Melody: *Beltram, Joey* / Brainticket: *Ramin* / Fifth dimension: *X-Dream & Planet BEN* / Musical science: *Musical Science* / Only with you: *Captain Hollywood* / Tantrum: *Technova* / Move: *Pulse* / Seven stars: *Quazar* / Bjango: *Lucky Monkeys* / Sun arise: *Unitone Rockers* / Agent O: *Aloof* / East: *Humate & Rabbit In The Moon* / Starburst: *Mystic Force* / Orbital 3: *Alcatraz*
SPV 08539232 / Aug '98 / SPV

☐ **HARDTRANCE MANIA VOL.1**
H&GCD 0112 / 15 Jun '98 / H&G

☐ **HARDTRANCE MANIA VOL.2**
H&GCD 0142 / 3 Aug '98 / H&G

☐ **HARDVIBE '96 (4CD Set)**
CDB 140 / Aug '96 / Michelle

☐ **HARJEDALSPIPAN**
DR 08CD / Aug '96 / Drone

☐ **HARLEM BIG BANDS 1925-1931**
Don't forget you'll regret day by day: *Johnson, Charlie & His Paradise Orchestra* / Meddlin' with the blues: *Johnson, Charlie & His Paradise Orchestra* / Paradise wobble: *Johnson, Charlie Paradise Ten* / Birmingham black bottom: *Johnson, Charlie Paradise Ten* / Don't leave me here: *Johnson, Charlie Paradise Ten* / You ain't the one: *Johnson, Charlie Paradise Ten* / Charleston is the best dance of all: *Johnson, Charlie Paradise Ten* / Hot tempered blues: *Johnson, Charlie Paradise Ten* / Boy in the boat: *Johnson, Charlie Paradise Ten* / Walk that thing: *Johnson, Charlie Paradise Ten* / Harlem drag: *Johnson, Charlie & His Paradise Orchestra* / Hot bones and rice: *Johnson, Charlie & His Paradise Orchestra* / Harlem shuffle: *Scott, Lloyd & his orchestra* / Symphonic scronch: *Scott, Lloyd & his orchestra* / Happy hour blues: *Scott, Lloyd & his orchestra* / Lawd, lawd: *Scott, Cecil & his Bright Boys* / In a corner: *Scott, Cecil & his Bright Boys* / Bright boy blues: *Scott, Cecil & his Bright Boys* / Springfield stomp: *Scott, Cecil & his Bright Boys* / (I'll be glad when you're dead) you rascal you: *Russell, Luis & His Orchestra* / Goin' to town: *Russell, Luis & His Orchestra* / Say the word: *Russell, Luis & His Orchestra* / Freakish blues: *Russell, Luis & His Orchestra* / I've found a new baby: *Preer, Andy & The Cotton Club Orchestra*
CBC 1010 / Aug '94 / Timeless Historical

☐ **HARLEM COMES TO LONDON**
Silver rose: *Plantation Orchestra* / Arabella's wedding day: *Plantation Orchestra* / Smilin' Joe: *Plantation Orchestra* / For baby and me: *Plantation Orchestra* / Camp meeting day: *Sissle, Noble Orchestra* / Sophisticated lady: *Ellington, Duke Orchestra* / Ike: *Ellington, Duke Orchestra* / Dinah: *Hatch & his Harlem Stompers* / Some of these days: *Hatch & his Harlem Stompers* / I can't dance / I must have that man: *Valaida* / Keep a twinkle in your eye: *Nicholas Brothers* / Your heart and mine: *Nicholas Brothers* / Dixie isn't Dixie any more: *Carter, Lavaida* / Jo Jo the cannibal kid: *Carter, Lavaida* / Breakfast in Harlem: *Buck & Bubbles* / I ain't got nobody: *Buck & Bubbles* / Sweet Georgia Brown: *Buck & Bubbles* / Harlem in my heart: *Welch, Elisabeth* / Ain't misbehavin': *Waller, Fats & His Continental Rhythm* / I can't give you anything but love
DRGCD 8444 / Sep '93 / DRG

☐ **HARLEM JOYS**
Riffs: *Johnson, James P.* / Handful of keys: *Waller, Fats* / Ain't misbehavin': *Armstrong, Louis* / New call of the freaks: *Russell, Luis* / Horse feathers: *Jackson, Cliff* / Jungle nights in Harlem: *Ellington, Duke* / Stop crying: *Oliver, Joe 'King'* / Sugarfoot stomp: *Henderson, Fletcher* / Trickeration: *Calloway, Cab* / Hot and anxious: *Redman, Don* / Strange as it seems: *Hall, Adelaide* / Swing it: *Carter, Benny* / Harlem joys: *Smith, Willie 'The Lion'* / I cried for you: *Holiday, Billie* / Brittwood stomp: *Newton, Frankie* / Church street sobbin' blues: *Hopkins, Claude* / King Porter stomp: *Hill, Teddy* / Jammin' for the jackpot: *Milinder, Lucky & Mills Blue Rhythm Band* / Time out: *Basie, Count* / Harlem congo: *Webb, Chick* / In the mood: *Hayes, Edgar* / Miss Annabella Brown: *Hawkins, Erskine* / Honey in the bee ball: *Jordan, Louis* / Tea for two: *Profit, Clarence* / Uptown blues: *Lunceford, Jimmie*
CDMOIR 507 / Apr '94 / Memoir

☐ **HARLEM SHUFFLE (Charly R&B Masters Vol.18)**
Gimme little sign: *Wood, Brenton* / Dancin' holiday: *Olympics* / Love makes the world go round: *Jackson, Deon* / Spring: *Birdlegs & Pauline* / Expressway to your heart: *Soul Survivors* / Ooh wee baby: *Hughes, Freddie* / Baby, I'm yours: *Lewis, Barbara* / Cool jerk: *Capitols* / Get on up: *Esquires* / And get away: *Esquires* / Duck: *Lee, Jackie* / I know: *George, Barbara* / Snake: *Wilson, Al* / Harlem shuffle: *Bob & Earl* / Hello stranger: *Lewis, Barbara* / Oh how happy: *Shades Of Blue* / Oogum boogum song: *Wood, Brenton* / Bounce: *Olympics* / Backfield in motion: *Mel & Tim* / Make me your baby / You can make it if you try
CDRB 18 / Mar '95 / Charly

☐ **HARLEM SHUFFLE (The Sound Of Blaxploitation)**
PLRCD 002 / Jun '97 / Plastic

☐ **HARMONICA BLUES 1927-1941 (2CD Set)**
FA 040 / Nov '95 / Fremeaux

☐ **HARMONICA BLUES 1929-1940**
WSECD 106 / Jul '96 / Wolf

☐ **HARMONICA BLUES OF THE 1920S AND 1930S**
YAZCD 1053 / Apr '91 / Yazoo

☐ **HARMONICA HITS**
We've only just begun / Never been in love this way before / Man and a woman / Greatest love of all / You've got a friend / Summer knows / Yesterday's love / Summertime / La vie en rose / Blues for Monica / Charade / Woman in love / I can see clearly now / Moon river / Love story / Smoke gets in your eyes / Reunited / Misty
CD 6125 / Jul '98 / Music

☐ **HARMONICA MASTERS**
YAZCD 2019 / May '96 / Yazoo

☐ **HARMONY AND INTERPLAY**
ELL 3210B / Oct '93 / Ellipsis Arts

☐ **HARP BEAT OF THE SWAMP**
Sugar coated love: *Lazy Lester* / Back to Bogalusa: *Nelson, Bob* / I have eyes for you: *Neal, Raful* / Hoodoo woman blues: *Smokehouse* / Don't cry baby: *Sonsone, Johnny* / Why you wanna do me like that: *Coleman, Tony* / Hurricane blues: *Wharton, Bill* / Your love is a lie: *Moreland, Ace* / Luberta: *Midnight Creepers* / Came home this morning: *Nelson, Bob* / Sticking to my guns: *Guerin, Erica* / Starlight diamond: *Neal, Raful* / Low down rider: *Smokehouse* / Midnight 'til morning: *Sonsone, Johnny* / Harder than I figured: *Midnight Creepers* / Head in the bottle: *Moreland, Ace* / Same thing could happen to you: *Lazy Lester* / Straight line: *Hodgson, Mark*
KS 033 / May '98 / King Snake

☐ **HARP BLOWERS 1926-1929**
DOCD 5164 / May '93 / Document

☐ **HARP MOODS**
Candle in the wind / Windmills of your mind / We've only just begun / Vincent / Shadow of your smile / Close to you / Hey Jude / You are the sunshine of my life / Daniel / Imagine / Love story / First time I ever saw your face / Over the rainbow / Leaving on a jetplane / Annie's song / Nights in white satin
MCCD 346 / 15 Jun '98 / MCI Music

☐ **HARP OF APOLLO, THE**
VICG 50132 / Mar '96 / JVC World Library

☐ **HARPBEAT OF THE SWAMP (Kingsnake Harp Classics)**
KS 033CD / Jul '97 / King Snake

☐ **HARPS OF THE WORLD**
PS 66004CD / Jul '95 / PlayaSound

☐ **HARRY SMITH CONNECTION, THE (A Live Tribute To The Anthology Of American Folk Music)**
SFW 40085 / 1 Sep '98 / Smithsonian Folkways

☐ **HARTHOUSE VOL.2 (Dedicated To The Omen)**
Clapconfusion: *Zaffarano, Marco* / Spirit of fear: *Spicelab* / Astralis: *Frankfurt/Tokyo Connection* / Adventure of dama: *Cybordelics* / Mikado: *Pulse* / X-plain the un-x-plained: *Arpeggiators* / Human: *Resistance D* / Mecon: *Aurin* / Multiplex: *Aurin* / Secrets of love: *Progressive Attack* / Schneller pfeil: *Curare*
4509942612 / Dec '96 / Harthouse

☐ **HARTHOUSE VOL.8 (2CD Set)**
HHSP 12CD / Nov '96 / Harthouse

☐ **HARVEST IN TECHNICOLOUR**
Homicidal diary: *Air Liquide* / Wild horse Annie as herself: *Bionaut* / Bring trance back: *Burger Ink* / Data girl: *Modernist* / Now is the time: *Hearnow* / Wunschmaschinenpark: *Bionaut* / Dankeschon klass: *Trinkwasser* / Never been on E: *Oral Experience* / Tausend und eine nacht: *Kron* / Fackeln im sturm: *Dom* / Turn me out: *Hearnow* / Ox: *UMO* / Empire state building: *Khan & Walker* / Das funfte Tal: *Tal*
HAR 8215392 / 24 Nov '97 / Harvest

☐ **HARVEST STORM**
TUT 727493 / Jan '94 / Wundertute

☐ **HASCISCH PARTY, THE**
DJM 001CD / 16 Sep '97 / DJ Mix

☐ **HAUNTED HOUSE PARTY**
JCD 623 / Dec '87 / Jass

☐ **HAUSFLO VOL.7 (2CD Set)**
UCACD 0142 / 15 Jun '98 / UCA

☐ **HAUSFLOOR VOL.4**
UCACD 009 / Jun '97 / UCA

☐ **HAUSMUSIK: FESTPLATTE**
HM 21CD / Dec '96 / Hausmusik

☐ **HAVANA CLUB**
74321378102 / Jul '96 / Milan

☐ **HAVANA CUBA BOYS VOL.1**
HQCD 48 / Jan '95 / Harlequin

☐ **HAVANA FLUTE SUMMIT**
860052 / Jun '97 / Naxos Jazz

☐ **HAVE A WONDERFUL CHRISTMAS**
CNCD 5955 / Dec '93 / Disky

☐ **HAVE I TOLD YOU LATELY THAT I LOVE YOU**
295732 / May '92 / Ariola Express

☐ **HAVE ONE**
GRCD 425 / 23 Feb '98 / Glitterhouse

☐ **HAVE YOURSELF A SOULFUL CHRISTMAS**
CPCD 8145 / Nov '95 / Charly

☐ **HAVE YOURSELF AN EASY LISTENING CHRISTMAS**
Christmas is here to stay: *Crosby, Bing* / Baby's first Christmas: *Francis, Connie* / White Christmas: *Platters* / Little drummer boy: *Simeone, Harry Chorale* / Winter's tale: *Essex, David* / Sleigh ride: *Simeone, Harry Chorale* / Little shepherd: *Whittaker, Roger* / I believe in Father Christmas: *Swingles* / Christmas song: *St. Clair, Isla* / Holly and the ivy: *Gregory, John Strings & Voices* / Mary's boy child: *Peters & Lee* / And Kings came a calling: *Beverley Sisters* / Must be Santa: *Steele, Tommy* / First Noel: *Kerr, Anita Singers* / Bambino: *Springfields* / Christmas Eve: *Statler Brothers* / Musical Christmas card: *Sweet Substitute* / Christmas Day is coming: *Blue Diamonds* / Greensleeves: *Martin, Sari* / Rudolph the red nosed reindeer: *New Jordal Singers*
5521102 / Nov '96 / Spectrum

☐ **HAVEN'T STOPPED DANCING YET**
I will survive: *Gaynor, Gloria* / Upside down: *Ross, Diana* / Celebration: *Kool & The Gang* / MacArthur Park: *Summer, Donna* / Funky town: *Lipps Inc.* / Please don't go: *KC & The Sunshine Band* / More than a woman: *Tavares* / Haven't stopped dancing yet: *Gonzalez* / Boogie oogie oogie: *Taste Of Honey* / British hustle: *Hi-Tension* / I was made for dancin': *Garrett, Leif* / Rock me gently: *Kim, Andy* / Never knew love like this: *Mills, Stephanie* / Dancing in the city: *Hain, Marshall* / Don't push it, don't force it: *Haywood, Leon* / Oops upside your head: *Gap Band* / Behind the groove: *Marie, Teena* / Mama used to say: *Junior* / Ladies night: *Kool & The Gang* / So you win again: *Hot Chocolate*
5529162 / Oct '97 / Spectrum

☐ **HAVIN' IT IN THE UK VOL.2**
Havin' it anthem: *Stonedrive & Dee & Wee* / 2 For joy: *Bliss* / Flight high: *Classwork* / Voices inside my head: *Police* / Reach me: *Anita K* / Take you there: *Simon, Ronni* / Deliver me: *Hawkshaw, Geoffrey* / Music takes you: *Carpe Diem 7* / Get your hands off my man: *Vasquez, Junior* / Love it: *Gorgeous Darling* / Yeow: *Buckle & Fogey* / Prayer to the music: *Polo, Marco* / Direct me: *Reese Project* / Invader: *Kool World*
HAVINCD 005 / Sep '95 / 21st Century Opera

☐ **HAVIN' IT STATESIDE VOL.1**
Forever: *Key To Life* / Love is what we need: *Dream Team* / Satisfied: *H2O & Billie* / Gotta new love: *Blakely, Donna* / Body to body: *Shades Of Love* / Keep on luvin': *Myles, Maddie* / Feel it: *Workin' Happily* / Murder track: *Delgado, Mike* / Sex with him: *Rosario, Ralphi* / I know a place: *Sound Of One* / Premonition of lost love: *Heard, Larry* / I've got something for you: *Federal Hill* / Souffles H: *Mondo Grosso* / Huh I gotta: *Shoot Tha' Juice*
HAVINCD 004 / Jun '95 / 21st Century Opera

☐ **HAWAIIAN CHRISTMAS, A**
White Christmas / Silent night / Rudolph the red nosed reindeer / I'll be home for Christmas / I saw Mommy kissing Santa Claus / Peace Carol / It came upon a midnight clear / Snowy white snow and jingle bells / Jingle bells / Silver bells / Have yourself a merry little Christmas / Winter wonderland / Sleigh ride / We wish you a merry Christmas / We three kings / Away in a manger / Holly and the ivy / We wish you a merry Christmas (reprise)
CDVIP 140 / Nov '96 / Virgin VIP

☐ **HAWAIIAN DREAMS (2CD Set)**
24025 / Jun '96 / Delta Doubles

☐ **HAWAIIAN DREAMS**
Moonlight and roses / Sweet Hawaiian chimes / Hawaiian gems / Toger shark / Song of the islands / Tropical love / Nobody's sweetheart / Hilo March / Hawaiian happiness / Chez moi / Hawaiian gems / Honolulu moon / Dinah / Little grass shack in Kealakekua / Hawaiian happiness / Wabash blues / Roses of picardy / Say the word and it's yours / Farewell to thee / When the leaves bid the trees goodbye / My old hawaiian home / Hawaiian war chant
PASTCD 7817 / 23 Feb '98 / Flapper

☐ **HAWAIIAN DRUM DANCE CHANTS (Sounds Of Power In Time)**
SFWCD 40015 / May '95 / Smithsonian Folkways

☐ **HAWAIIAN SLACK KEY GUITAR**
DCT 38032CD / Mar '96 / Dancing Cat

☐ **HAWAIIANS IN PARIS 1916-1926**
Echos hawaiens / Kilima waltz / Hawaiian hula medley / Yaaka hula hickey dula / Glow worm / Hawaiian dreams / Alabama moon: *Ferera, Frank & Mme Lousie* / Isle of paradise: *Ferera, Frank & Anthony Francini* / In my tippy canoe: *Ferera, Frank & Anthony Francini* / Dream kiss: *Ferera, Frank & Anthony Francini* / Moana chimes: *Ferera, Frank & Anthony Francini* / Under the south sea palms: *Ferera, Frank & Anthony Francini* / Ciribiribin: *Ferera, Frank & Mme Lousie* / My land of memory: *Ferera, Frank & Anthony Francini* / Dreamy Hawaii: *Ferera, Frank & Anthony Francini* / Hawaiian butterfly: *Ferera, Frank & Mme Lousie* / Runnin' wild: *Orchestre Hawaiien* / Tea for two: *Orchestre Hawaiien*
FA 066 / Nov '97 / Fremeaux

☐ **HAWZI (Music From Algeria)**
AAA 149 / Mar '97 / Club Du Disque Arabe

R.E.D. CD CATALOGUE | COMPILATIONS | HEARTBREAKERS

☐ HEADER VOL.2
HEADER 2 / 9 Mar '98 / Header

☐ HEADING BACK TO HOUSTON (Texas Country & Western 1950-1951)
KKCD 12 / Apr '97 / Krazy Kat

☐ HEADING IN THE RIGHT DIRECTION
LHCD 023 / Jul '96 / Luv n' Haight

☐ HEADPHONE HOUSE
SLIPCD 46 / Jul '96 / Slip 'n' Slide

☐ HEADQUARTERS
EFA 292946 / 23 Mar '98 / Tresor

☐ HEADZ VOL.1 (2CD Set)
Freedom now: Patterson / Contemplating jazz: Attica Blues / Symmetrical jazz: Awunsound / Stars: Nightmares On Wax / Ravers suck our sound: La Funk Mob / Miles out of time: MF Outa National / Inside: RPM / Lowride: Autechre / Wildstyle - The krush handshake: Oldie Scottish / Lost and found (SFL): DJ Shadow / Destroy all monsters: Skull / Don't fake it: Sallahr, Deflon / 2000: RPM / Slipper suite: Palm Skin Productions / Time has come: UNKLE & The Major Force Orchestra / Head west - gun fight at the OK Corrall: Howie B / They came in peace: Tranquility Bass / In flux: DJ Shadow
MW 026CD / May '96 / Mo Wax

☐ HEADZ VOL.2B (2CD Set)
Spectral arc: Luminis / Sharp AZ: Vibert, Luke / World lesson II: Money Mark / Swiss air: Twig Bud / Time has come: UNKLE / It's coming: Grantby / Wirecutter: Donut Productions / Intermission part 3: Prunes / Groomsman: Dust Brothers / Crash: Skull / Flute loop: Beastie Boys / Maze: DJ Krush / Sketch: Attica Blues / Ultimatum: Jungle Brothers / Science Fu beats: Danny Breaks / Future tense: Force / Beast: Palmskin Productions / Real thing: Peshay / In the mood: Dillinja / Tribetoon: Roni Size & DJ Krush / Silent witness: Source Direct / Counterpoint: As One / Bug in the bassbin: Inner Zone Orchestra / Object Orient: Black Dog / Trilogy: Special Forces / Quiddity: Max 404 / Shadow's legitimate mix: Zimbabwe Legit / Intermission parts 1 and 2: Prunes / Intermission parts 4-8: Prunes
MW 062CD / Oct '96 / Mo Wax

☐ HEART AND SOUL (2CD Set)
Midnight train to Georgia: Knight, Gladys / Summer breeze: Isley Brothers / Love train: O'Jays / That's what friends are for: Williams, Deniece / Sexual healing: Gaye, Marvin / Show me the way: Belle, Regina / Heaven must be missing an angel: Tavares / Night to remember: Shalamar / Tonight I celebrate my love: Flack, Roberta & Peabo Bryson / Mighty love: Stansfield, Lisa / Lean on me: Withers, Bill / It's a love thing: Whispers / I'll take you there: Staple Singers / When something is wrong with my baby: Purify, James & Bobby / Private number: Clay, Judy & William Bell / Angel of the morning: Rush, Merilee / To love somebody: Simone, Nina / Didn't I (blow your mind this time): Delfonics / I have learned to respect the power of love: Mills, Stephanie / That lady: Isley Brothers / Just don't want to be lonely: Main Ingredient / Love I lost: Melvin, Harold & The Bluenotes / Best thing that ever happened to me: Knight, Gladys / First cut is the deepest: Arnold, P.P. / Rescue me: Bass, Fontella / Mockingbird: Foxx, Inez & Charlie / Rock your baby: McCrae, George / I'm your puppet: Purify, James & Bobby / Kissin' in the back row of the movies: Drifters / Spooky: Classics IV / Ride your pony: Dorsey, Lee / Shoorah shoorah: Wright, Betty / Nothin' but a house party: Showstoppers / Walkin' in rhythm: Blackbyrds / Respect yourself: Staple Singers / Didn't it rain: Jackson, Mahalia / Ain't got no...I got life: Simone, Nina
RCACD 207 / Jul '97 / RCA

☐ HEART AND SOUL
Three steps from true love: Reflections / Love is the key: Maze / Everything is cool: T-Connection / Bad times: Tavares / I'd give it to you: Tee, Willie / Before you break my heart: Dunlap, Gene & The Ridgeways / LOVE: Green, Al / Falling: Moore, Melba / Memory lane: Riperton, Minnie / Help (somebody please): O'Jays / Round and around: Graham, Jaki / LOVE U: Brass Construction / Heaven in your arms: RJ's Latest Arrival / Medley: Mooney, Bobby
CDTMCD 317 / May '97 / EMI

☐ HEART AND SOUL (2CD Set)
Raincloud: Lighthouse Family / I need you: 3T / Trippin': Morrison, Mark / Walk on by: Gabrielle / One day I'll fly away: Crawford, Randy / I say a little prayer: Franklin, Aretha / You are everything: Ross, Diana & Marvin Gaye / Tracks of my tears: Robinson, Smokey & The Miracles / Delicate: D'Arby, Terence Trent / My one temptation: Paris, Mica / Everything: Blige, Mary J. / My father's son: Reeves, Conner / Five miles to empty: Brownstone / Keep on movin': Brownstone / There's nothing like this: Omar / Look of love: Knight, Gladys & The Pips / My cherie amour: Wonder, Stevie / Have you seen her: Chi-Lites / WIshing on a star: Rose Royce / I belive I can fly: R Kelly / Greatest love of all: Benson, George / Let's get it on: Gaye, Marvin / Got to be there: Jackson, Michael / Touch me in the morning: Ross, Diana / Tired of being alone: Green, Al / Hey lover: LL Cool J & Boyz II Men / Don't leave me: Blackstreet / Let's stay together: Turner, Tina / Me and Mrs Jones: Turner, Tina / Three times a lady: Commodores / Baby come to me: Austin, Patti & James Ingram / Always and forever: Vandross, Luther / Where is the love: Paris, Mica & Will Downing / Piano in the dark: Russell, Brenda / Be thankful for what you got: De Vaughn, William / What becomes of the broken hearted: Ruffin, Jimmy / Hey there lonely girl: Holman, Eddie / Move closer: Nelson, Phyllis / Hello: Richie, Lionel / Search for a hero: M-People
5550632 / 27 Oct '97 / PolyGram TV

☐ HEART AND SOUL OF PHILADELPHIA
Close the door: Pendergrass, Teddy / Brandy: O'Jays / Do you get enough love: Jones, Shirley / Lady love: Rawls, Lou / You're my sweetness: Paul, Billy / Trying to get the feeling again: Sharp, Dee Dee / Love TKO: Pendergrass, Teddy / Last night I needed somebody: Jones, Shirley / Slow Dancin': Hyman, Phyllis / If only you knew: Labelle, Patti / Without you: Paul, Billy / Best love I ever had: Butler, Jerry / Don't let it go to your head: Carn, Jean / I have you, you have me: Stylistics / Reach out for me: Butler, Jerry / We got some catching up to do: Carn, Jean / Lovin' you: O'Jays
MCCD 354 / 20 Jul '98 / Music Club

☐ HEART AND SOUL OF..., THE (Gladys Knight/The Supremes/The Marvelettes/Martha Reeves)
Every beat of my heart: Knight, Gladys / Letter full of tears: Knight, Gladys / Operator: Knight, Gladys / Come see about me: Knight, Gladys / Baby love: Supremes / Stop in the name of love: Supremes / Stoned love: Supremes / Love child: Supremes / When you're young and in love: Marvelettes / Don't mess with Bill: Marvelettes / Secret love affair: Marvelettes / Too many fish in the sea: Marvelettes / Dancing in the street: Martha & The Vandellas / Heatwave: Martha & The Vandellas / Jimmy Mack: Martha & The Vandellas / Nowhere to run: Martha & The Vandellas
PLATCD 212 / Feb '97 / Platinum

☐ HEART AND SOUL OF..., THE (Gloria Gaynor/Kool & The Gang/Rose Royce/ Tavares)
Celebration: Kool & The Gang / Ladies night: Kool & The Gang / Get down on it: Kool & The Gang / Cherish: Kool & The Gang / I will survive: Gaynor, Gloria / Every time you go away: Gaynor, Gloria / What a wonderful world: Gaynor, Gloria / Every breath you take: Gaynor, Gloria / Car wash: Rose Royce / Wishing on a star: Rose Royce / Love don't live here anymore: Rose Royce / Is it love you're after: Rose Royce / Heaven must be missing an angel: Tavares / More than a woman: Tavares / Don't take away the music: Tavares / She's gone: Tavares / Whodunnit: Tavares / Check it out: Tavares / It only takes a minute girl: Tavares / Remember what I told you to forget: Tavares
PLATCD 213 / Feb '97 / Platinum

☐ HEART AND SOUL OF..., THE (Edwin Starr/Percy Sledge/Chi-Lites/Brook Benton)
25 miles: Starr, Edwin / Stop her on sight (SOS): Starr, Edwin / Where is the sound: Starr, Edwin / Just another fool in love: Starr, Edwin / Warm and tender love: Sledge, Percy / When a man loves a woman: Sledge, Percy / Tell it like it is: Sledge, Percy / Take time to know her: Sledge, Percy / Have you seen her: Chi-Lites / You and I: Chi-Lites / I want to pay you back: Chi-Lites / Toby: Chi-Lites / Rainy night in Georgia: Benton, Brook / Endlessly: Benton, Brook / It's just a matter of time: Benton, Brook / Kiddio: Benton, Brook
PLATCD 214 / Feb '97 / Platinum

☐ HEART AND SOUL OF..., THE (Sister Sledge/Eddie Floyd/Detroit Emeralds/ Sam & Dave)
Soul man: Sam & Dave / Soul sister, brown sugar: Sam & Dave / Hold on I'm comin': Sam & Dave / Soothe me: Sam & Dave / We are family: Sister Sledge / Frankie: Sister Sledge / Thinking of you: Sister Sledge / Lost in music: Sister Sledge / Knock on wood: Floyd, Eddie / Bring it on home to me: Floyd, Eddie / Things get better: Floyd, Eddie / Raise your hand: Floyd, Eddie / Feel the need in me: Detroit Emeralds / You want it you got it: Detroit Emeralds / Dance school: Detroit Emeralds / Cutting the groove: Detroit Emeralds
PLATCD 215 / Feb '97 / Platinum

☐ HEART FULL OF SOUL (2CD Set)
RADCD 99 / 27 Jul '98 / Global TV

☐ HEART OF AMERICA
RENCD 105 / Jul '95 / Castle

☐ HEART OF ARGENTINIAN TANGO, THE
Taquito militar / Romance de barrio / Los mareados / El dia que me quieras / Corralera / Caseron de tejas / Niebla de reachuelo / Fuimos / Elegie / El portenito / La cumparsita
PV 795052 / Jul '95 / Disques Pierre Verany

☐ HEART OF DARKNESS
MEZCD 2 / Aug '96 / China

☐ HEART OF IRELAND
Whiskey in the jar / Four country roads / Green fields of France / Irish rover / When you were sweet sixteen / Boys from Killybegs / You seldom come to see me anymore / Boston burglar / After all these years / Isle of Innisfree / Black velvet band / Our house is not a home / Old bog road / Town I love so well / I'll take you home again Kathleen / Any Tipperary town / Hills of Kerry / Mountains of Mourne / Maggie / Rose of Tralee
CD 6020 / Apr '96 / Music

☐ HEART OF SOUTHERN SOUL VOL.1, THE
Falling in love again: Kelly Brothers / You're that great big feelin': Kelly Brothers / That's all I can do: Anderson, Kip / Snake out of the grass (part 1): Anderson, Roshell / Snake out of the grass (part 2): Anderson, Roshell / Soldier's sad story: Watkins, Tiny / Pretty little thing: Interpreters / Your love is worth the pain: Truitt, Johnny / Talk to me: Avons / Your love's so good: Webber, Lee / Somewhere out there: Matthis, Lucille / Mr. Fortune teller: Dee & Don / Midnight tears: Watkins, Tiny / Woman in me: Mariann / Steppin' stone: Wallace Brothers / Gonna need somebody: Lane, Stacy / I went off and cried: Anderson, Kip / You'll never know: Brown, Shirley / CC rider: Powell, Bobby / Price is too high: Harpo, Slim / There goes a girl: Truitt, Johnny / Do your thing: Whitney, Marva / Power is gone: Kemp, Eugene
CDCHD 568 / Sep '94 / Ace

☐ HEART OF SOUTHERN SOUL VOL.2, THE (No Brags - Just Facts)
Letter from my darling: Anderson, Kip / My love grows stronger: Kelly Brothers / I can't stand it: Dee & Don / (Those) Precious words: Wallace Brothers / You'll lose a good thing: Anderson, Kip / Way cross town: Watkins, Tiny / Here I am: Whitney, Marva / Don't let me be a cryin' man: Truitt, Johnny / I will: Brown, Lattimore / Seventh son: Webber, Lee / Look what I've done: Wiggins, Percy / Let me be a part of you: Exotics / Am I asking too much: Mathis, Lucille / Lifetime of a man: Lane, Stacy / Watch you work it out: Anderson, Kip / Forbidden fruit: Watkins, Tiny / Right here is where you belong: Washington, Jerry / Let's try to build a love affair: Exotics / Funky little train: Lane, Stacy / Let's walk down the street together: Chuck & Mariann / I don't want to go through life (being a fool): Mathis, Lucille / I'm through with you: Truitt, Johnny / No pity in the city: Kemp, Eugene / No brags just facts: Lane, Stacy
CDCHD 601 / Jun '96 / Ace

☐ HEART OF SOUTHERN SOUL VOL.3, THE (The Flame Burns On)
She's all I got: North, Freddie / It sure was fun: Duke, Doris / Kiss tomorrow goodbye: Davis, Rose / Ten carat fool: Jules, Jimmy / Tears (I shed for you): Big T & The Pacemakers / Next man: Stanback, Jean / Daddy's home: 5 Farenheit / I'm going to try you one more time: Powell, Bobby / You're killing me slowly but surely: North, Freddie / He's everything I need: Duke, Doris / For the good times: Seventh Wonder / Big bad rain: 5 Farenheit / This is my career: Gentry, Art / Bad water: Duke, Doris / My world tumbles down: Jules, Jimmy / Sun comes up: North, Freddie / I'm going to win her love: Powell, Bobby / Since I fell for you: Duke, Doris / Got to travel on: O'Dell, Brooks / Lovin' on back streets: North, Freddie / If she's your wife (who am I): Duke, Doris / I won't leave you hanging: Washington, Jerry
CDCHD 660 / 27 Oct '97 / Ace

☐ HEART OF THE CELTS (Songs Of Love)
When you return: Matheson, Karen / Mi le M'uillin air mo ghluin: Matheson, Karen / Ansacht na ansacht: Ni Fhearraigh, Aoife / Somebody: Dover, Connie / Fear an bhata: Dover, Connie / An clar bog deal: Ni Dhomhnaill, Maighread / Is Fada Liom Uaim L: Ni Dhomhnaill, Maighread / Martha, the flower of sweet Strabane: Ni Dhomhnaill, Maighread / Caitlin Triall: Ni Fhearraigh, Aoife / Cailin na gruaige baine: Ni Fhearraigh, Aoife / Laddie, lie near me: Dover, Connie / Ned of the hill: Dover, Connie / Rithill Aill: Matheson, Karen
ND 63936 / 17 Nov '97 / Narada

☐ HEART OF THE COUNTRY (4CD Set)
Rose garden: Anderson, Lynn / Wasted days and wasted nights: Fender, Freddy / For the good times: Price, Ray / Wings of a dove: Husky, Ferlin / Talk back trembling lips: Ashworth, Ernest / Please help me I'm falling: Locklin, Hank / (I can't help you) I'm falling too: Davis, Skeeter / Most beautiful girl in the world: Rich, Charlie / Three hearts in a tangle: Drusky, Roy / Act naturally: Russel, Johnny / Happiest girl in the whole USA: Fargo, Donna / Sea of heartbreak: Gibson, Don / Somebody's gonna love you: Greenwood, Lee / Jacqueline: Helms, Bobby / Don't touch me: Seely, Jeannie / I washed my hands in muddy water: Jackson, Stonewall / Deck of cards: Martindale, Wink / Good year for the roses: Paycheck, Johnny / I've got a happy heart: Raye, Susan / Green green grass of home: Wagoner, Porter / It wasn't God who made honky tonk angels: Wells, Kitty / All the time: Greene, Jack / Almost persuaded: Houston, David / No charge: Montgomery, Melba / Take this job and shove it: Paycheck, Johnny / You're my man: Anderson, Lynn / I wish I didn't have to miss you: Greene, Jack & Jeannie Seely / Pop a top: Brown, Jim Ed / Baby's got her blue jeans on: McDaniel, Mel / Once a day: Smith, Connie / May the bird of paradise fly up your nose: Dickens, 'Little' Jimmy / Satisfied mind: Wagoner, Porter / Country bumpkin: Smith, Cal / Single girl: Posey, Sandy / Funny how time slips away: Felts, Narvel / Blue blue day: Gibson, Don / Don't underestimate my love for you: Greenwood, Lee / My special angel: Helms, Bobby / With one exception: Houston, David / Let me be the one: Locklin, Hank / From a jack to a king: Miller, Ned / Jambalaya: Raven, Eddy & Jo El Sonnier / Teddy bear song: Fairchild, Barbara / Live fast love hard die young: Young, Faron / Welfare Cadillac: Drake, Guy / You ain't goin' nowhere: Byrds / Honky tonkin': Cannon, Ace / End of the world: Davis, Skeeter / Abilene: Hamilton, George IV / Before the next teardrop falls: Fender, Freddy / Mr. Walker it's all over: Spears, Billie Jo / Crazy arms: Price, Ray / Am I that easy to forget: Bellew, Carl / My last date: Davis, Skeeter / Oh lonesome me: Gibson, Don / I'll just have a cup of coffee: Gray, Claude / King of the road: Russel, Johnny / Queen of the house: Miller, Jody / You were always on my mind: Hirt, Al & Ace Cannon / Going going gone: Greenwood, Lee / (I'd be) A legend in my time: Husky, Ferlin / Crazy: Jackson, Wanda / I don't believe you've met my baby: Louvin Brothers / Good time Charlie's got the blues: Rich, Charlie / Harper valley PTA: Riley, Jeannie C. / It's four in the morning: Young, Faron / Until I met you Rodman, Judy: Young, Faron / He was a friend of mine: Byrds / Funny face: Fargo, Donna / Just a closer walk with thee: Gatlin Brothers / Satin sheets: Pruett, Jeanne / Slide off your satin sheets: Paycheck, Johnny / Gonna find me a bluebird: Rainwater, Marvin / Behind closed doors: Rich, Charlie / Six days on the road: Dudley, Dave / Big bad John: Dean, Jimmy / Kid stuff: Fairchild, Barbara / Just one time: Gibson, Don / There goes my everything: Greene, Jack / Waterloo: Jackson, Stonewall / Don't let me cross over: Butler, Carl & Pearl / Right or wrong: Jackson, Wanda / Love has made you beautiful: Kilgore, Merle / Hearts aren't made to break: Greenwood, Lee / Wolverton mountain: King, Claude / You were always there: Fargo, Donna / Send me the pillow you dream on: Locklin, Hank / Do what you do do well: Miller, Ned / Born a woman: Posey, Sandy / Frauline: Helms, Bobby / Gone: Husky, Ferlin / Make the world go away: Price, Ray / On my knees: Rich, Charlie & Janie Frickie / Heartbreak USA: Wells, Kitty / (My) Elusive dreams: Houston, David / Help me make it through the night: Smith, Sammi / Bridge washed out: Mack, Warner / Amazing grace: Gatlin Brothers
391312 / Aug '97 / Hallmark

☐ HEART OF THE GAELS
GLCD 0105 / Jun '88 / Green Linnet

☐ HEART OF THE LION
IR 022CD / Mar '94 / Iona

☐ HEARTACHES (20 Songs Of Love)
No more the fool: Brooks, Elkie / Let the heartaches begin: Baldry, Long John / I don't believe in miracles: Blunstone, Colin / Angel of the morning: Arnold, P.P. / Red red wine: James, Jimmy / It's a heartache: Tyler, Bonnie / You to me are everything: Real Thing / I'll have to say I love you in a song: Croce, Jim / Mirrors: Oldfield, Sally / Just one smile: Pitney, Gene / Sorry doesn't always make it right: Knight, Gladys & The Pips / Handbags and gladrags: Farlowe, Chris / Ruby Tuesday: Melanie / Darling be home soon: Lovin' Spoonful / Man of the world: Fleetwood Mac / Kiss me for the last time: Brooks, Elkie / Love's gotta hold on me: Dollar / Oh girl: Chi-Lites / Days: Kinks / One less set of footsteps: Croce, Jim
TRTCD 113 / Feb '96 / TrueTrax

☐ HEARTBEAT (Love Me Tender/2CD Set)
Always on my mind: Presley, Elvis / True love ways: Holly, Buddy / You're all I need to get by: Gaye, Marvin & Tammi Terrell / I say a little prayer: Franklin, Aretha / Can't take my eyes off you: Williams, Andy / Love letters: Lester, Ketty / Only the lonely: Orbison, Roy / Then I kissed her: Beach Boys / Will you still love me tomorrow: Shirelles / ('Till) I kissed you: Everly Brothers / Don't throw your love away: Searchers / First cut is the deepest: Arnold, P.P. / (Take a little) Piece of my heart: Franklin, Erma / Stand by me: King, Ben E. / I second that emotion: Supremes & Temptations / I just want to make love to you: James, Etta / My girl: Redding, Otis / Make it with you: Bread / Walk on by: Warwick, Dionne / I believe: Bachelors / More than I can say: Vee, Bobby / It's a man's man's man's world: Brown, James / Love me tender: Presley, Elvis / Chapel of love: Dixie Cups / Band of gold: Payne, Freda / Third finger left hand: Reeves, Martha & The Vandellas / There's a kind of rush: Herman's Hermits / Just like a woman: Manfred Mann / Waterloo sunset: Kinks / Lay lady lay: Dylan, Bob / Private number: Clay, Judy & William Bell / She's not there: Zombies / Everybody's talkin': Nilsson, Harry / Look of love: Springfield, Dusty / Smoke gets in your eyes: Platters / Rhythm of the rain: Cascades / I love you because: Reeves, Jim / Stranger on the shore: Bilk, Acker / Mad about the boy: Washington, Dinah / (I left my heart in) San Francisco: Bennett, Tony / I guess I'll always love you: Isley Brothers / Come see about me: Ross, Diana & The Supremes / (If paradise is) half as nice: Amen Corner / Everyone's gone to the moon: King, Jonathan / Hey Jude: Pickett, Wilson / Man of the world: Fleetwood Mac / Twelfth of never: Richard, Cliff
RADCD 72 / Nov '97 / Global TV

☐ HEARTBEAT
If I said that you had a beautiful body: Bellamy Brothers / Will you still love me tomorrow: Smokie / Heartbeat: Showaddywaddy / Thousand pieces: Goombay Dance Band / Only sixteen: Dr. Hook & Ray Sawyer / If you can't give me love: Quatro, Suzi / Time for a change of heart: Charles, Tina / Always and forever: Rogers, Kenny / Let it grow: Clout / Feel it all over: Andrews, Chris / Day that my heart caught fire: Young, John Paul / I feel love: Smokie / Suddenly: Stardust, Alvin / Funny how love can be: First Class / All I have to do is dream: Svenne & Lotta / Girl like you: Mungo Jerry / Rainbow: Marmalade / Adios auf wiedersehen: Humphries, Les Singers / Missing you takes up most of my time: Dr. Hook & Ray Sawyer
10872 / Oct '97 / Go On Deluxe

☐ HEARTBEAT OF SOWETO
Nwana wamina: Chauke, Thomas / Thathezakho: Mlokothwa / Jabula mfana: Emvelo, Amaswazi / Nsati wa wina: Shirinda, M.D. & Family / Siyoklishaya kusasa: Elimnyama, Kati / Waqala Ngowendlala: Usuthu / Mashama: ChiJumane, Arando Bila / Xumaxilovile: Chauke, Thomas & Shinyori / Yithinamhlaje: Mlokothwa / Bumnandi utshwala bakho: Elimnyama, Kati / Kamakhalawana: ChiJumane, Arando Bila / Ndzi Hkensa: Shirinda, M.D. & Family
SHANCD 43051 / Mar '89 / Shanachie

☐ HEARTBEAT REGGAE NOW
HBCDAN 9 / Jun '93 / Greensleeves

☐ HEARTBEAT VOL.2 (More Voices Of First Nations Women)
SFW 40455 / 29 Jun '98 / Smithsonian Folkways

☐ HEARTBEATS (2CD Set)
I've been in love before: Cutting Crew / Kayleigh: Marillion / Missing you: Waite, John / Bette Davis eyes: Carnes, Kim / We belong: Benatar, Pat / Love changes everything: Climie Fisher / True: Spandau Ballet / Love don't live here anymore: Nail, Jimmy / It started with a kiss: Hot Chocolate / Don't give up on us: Soul, David / Never ending story: Limahl / Cambodia: Wilde, Kim / Orchard Road: Sayer, Leo / Keep on moving: Soul II Soul & Caron Wheeler / You to me are everything: Real Thing / Good heart: Sharkey, Feargal / China in your hand: T'Pau / If I was: Ure, Midge / No doubt about it: Hot Chocolate / He ain't heavy he's my brother: Hollies / Love hurts: Nazareth / Every rose has its thorn: Poison / Killing me softly with his song: Bassey, Shirley / Apache: Shadows / Could it be I'm falling in love: Grant, David & Jaki Graham / More you live more you love: Flock Of Seagulls / Unforgettable: Cole, Nat 'King' / When I need you: Sayer, Leo / Save a prayer: Duran Duran / Dum dum girl: Talk Talk
DOU 878262 / 2 Feb '98 / Disky

☐ HEARTBREAK USA
Hertbreak USA: Wells, Kitty / Please release me: Parton, Dolly / Let's think about living: Luman, Bob / Me and Bobby McGee: Rogers, Kenny / Race is on: Jones, George / Dang me: Miller, Roger / Indiana wants me: Taylor, R. Dean / Tom Dooley: Kingston Trio / El paso: Robbins, Marty / Settin' the woods on fire: Williams, Hank / Sally was a good old girl: Jennings, Waylon / Thanks a lot: Tubb, Ernest / These boots are made for walking: Hazelwood, Lee / Next in line: Cash, Johnny / Truck drivin' outlaw: Olsen, Dennis / Rose Marie: Whitman, Slim / North to Alaska: Horton, Johnny / Oh, lonesome me: Gibson, Don
11978 / Feb '96 / Music

☐ HEARTBREAKER HITS (2CD Set)
R2CD 4042 / 13 Apr '98 / Deja Vu

☐ HEARTBREAKERS
Power of love: Rush, Jennifer / Afer the love has gone: Earth, Wind & Fire / I love you too much: Santana / Do I love you too much: Lake / Do I love you: Blunstone, Colin / Me and Mrs Jones: Paul, Billy / Kiss and say goodbye: Manhattans / In my dreams: REO Speedwagon / Most beautiful girl in the world: Rich, Charlie / You made me so very happy: Blood, Sweat & Tears / When your heart is weak: Cock Robin / Longer: Fogelberg, Dan / Something's gotten hold of my heart: Window Speaks / Long distance love: Bailey, Philip / Only one woman: Belcanto / How 'bout us: Champaign
4804442 / Oct '95 / Columbia

☐ HEARTBREAKERS
MACCD 147 / Aug '96 / Autograph

☐ HEARTBREAKERS (18 Classic Tear Jerkers)
Don't play that song (you lied): King, Ben E. / Goin' out of my head: Little Anthony & The Imperials / I will: Fury, Billy / What's a matter baby (is it hurting you): Yuro, Timi / It's just a matter of time: Benton, Brook / Since I don't have you: Skyliners / Behind closed doors: Sledge, Percy / Never my love: Association / Harbor lights: Platters / If loving you is wrong (I don't want to be right): Drifters / For the good times: Price, Ray / You'll lose a good thing: Lynn, Barbara / What in the world's come over you: Scott, Jack / Teen angel: Dinning, Mark / Then you can tell me goodbye: Casinos / Born a woman: Posey, Sandy / I can't help it (if I'm still in love with you): Thomas, B.J. / Going, going, gone: Greenwood, Lee
ECD 3213 / Mar '95 / K-Tel

☐ HEARTS DESIRE
RENCD 103 / Jul '95 / Castle

☐ HEAT
FADCD 026 / Nov '92 / Fashion

☐ HEAT IS ON, THE (2CD Set)
NSCD 002 / Feb '95 / Newsound

☐ HEAT IS ON, THE
Blood sun: Brown, Dennis / Gun man: Prophet, Michael / Don't get jumpy: Stewart, Roman / Blow wind blow: McKay, Freddie / Crying in the ghetto: Hell & Fire/Trinity / Pomp and pride: Toots & The Maytals / Selah: Ethiopians / One way: Maytones / Consolation: George, Earl / Grooving out on life: Lewis, Hopeton / Never will conquer me: Wilson, Delroy / My guiding star and pleated skirt: Brooks, Mike & Trinity / Follow instructions: Campbell, Cornell / How can I: McKay, Freddie / I am not a King: Smart, Leroy / Bam bam: Toots & The Maytals / Show us the way: Maytones / Unity is love: Dice, Billy
CDGR 210 / 2 Feb '98 / Charly

☐ HEATHEN CHANT, THE
RN 004 / Jun '96 / Runn

☐ HEATWAVE
Heatwave: Reeves, Martha / Birds and the bees: Akens, Jewel / Girlie girlie: George, Sophia / In the summertime: Mungo Jerry / Whiter shade of pale: Kelly, Pat / OK Fred: Dunkley, Errol / Red red wine: Boothe, Ken / Sideshow: Biggs, Barry / Wooly bully: Sam The Sham & The Pharaohs / Sunshine for me: Isaacs, Gregory / Tide is high: Holt, John / Tequila: Cannon, Ace / No woman no cry: Clarke, Johnny / Last farewell: Edwards, Jackie / Kingston town: Boothe, Ken / We play reggae: In Crowd / Jammin': Spence, Michael / Three ring circus: Biggs, Barry / Ain't no sunshine: Andy, Horace / Money in my pocket: Edwards, Jackie / Nice time: Dunkley, Errol / Rock my soul: Griffiths, Marcia / Everyday is just a holiday: Thomas, Ruddy / Sunshine people: Hammond, Beres & Mikey Zappow / I want to wake up with you: Holt, John
ECD 3433 / Aug '98 / K-Tel

☐ HEAVENLY GROOVES VOL.1
39101612 / Jan '97 / Hyperium

☐ HEAVENLY GROOVES VOL.2
Mine: Mine / Love of an alien: Faust IV / Purple: Crustation / Mask: Waldeck / Good boy: De Phazz / Ladybird: Baby Fox / Nutopian days: Swandive / Desire: Voyager / Moby: First Cool Hive / Opera: Lucky Loop / Boxy rhodes: Czech / Blind: Sabotage / Confession number 4: Little Aida / Folie: Locust
HYP 3910186CD / 25 May '98 / Hyperium

☐ HEAVENLY VOICES VOL.4
HYP 39101792CD / 13 Apr '98 / Hyperium

☐ HEAVY CHRISTMAS
SBCD 043 / 26 Jan '98 / Second Battle

☐ HEAVY GUITAR (2CD Set)
24079 / Mar '95 / Delta Doubles

☐ HEAVY METAL HEROES VOL.1 & 2
I won't surrender: Twisted Ace / Reaper: Grim Reaper / Stormchild: Jaguar / Storm of steel: Soldier / Strangers on the shore: Bitches Sin / Hard life: Metal Mirror / Cold as night: Buffalo / Rock Japan: Expozer / Running wild: Split Beaver / Do it: Dragster / Rabies: Witchfinder General / Lionheart: Lionheart / What the hells going on: Mendes Prey / Ice cold diamond: Mantle Swallow Palmer / Out of my head: Overkill / Devil's triangle: Cox, Jess / This fire inside: Twisted Ace / Free country: Witchfinder General / Oh well: No Faith / Calling for you: Persian Risk / Power and the key: No Quater
CDMETAL 9 / Feb '97 / Anagram

☐ HEAVY METAL HEROES VOL.3
HMRXD 153 / Aug '90 / Heavy Metal

☐ HEAVY METAL RECORDS COMPILATION
HMRXD 143 / Jul '90 / Heavy Metal

☐ HEAVY METAL SINGLES COLLECTION
CDMETAL 003 / Feb '97 / British Steel

☐ HEAVY OVERDOSE OF LYTE PSYCH
AA 062 / 16 Mar '98 / Arf Arf

☐ HEAVYAURAL...LIGHT FINANCIAL (21st Century Media Blitz)
CM 77193CD / 6 Oct '97 / Century Media

☐ HEAVYWEIGHT SOUND VOL.1 (A Blood & Fire Sampler)
Real gone crazy dub: King Tubby & The Aggrovators / Jah is I guiding star: Tappa Zukie & The Aggrovators / Falling dub: Prince Philip & The Musical Intimidators / Marcus children suffer: Burning Spear & The Black Disciples / Black heart: Hudson, Keith & The Soul Syndicate / Problems: Andy, Horace / Problems dub: Andy, Horace & Prince Jammy / Rock vibration: Yabby You & King Tubby / War and friction: I-Roy & The Aggrovators / Living style: Yabby You & King Tubby / Black right: Hudson, Keith & The Soul Syndicate / Judgement dub: Prince Philip & The Musical Intimidators / Marcus say Jah no dead: Burning Spear & The Black Disciples / Dub fi gwan: King Tubby & The Aggrovators
BAFCD 7 / Mar '96 / Blood & Fire

☐ HEAVYWEIGHT SOUND VOL.2 (Another Blood & Fire Sampler)
Late hour: I-Roy / World dub - away with the bad: Brown, Glen & King Tubby / Ragga muffin style: Jah Stitch / La la bam bam: Congos / Shooter dub: King Tubby & Santic Allstars / You're no good: Fraser, Philip / Wrong time: Congos / Only love can conquer: Prince Alla / Jah help the dread: Jah Stitch / Dub bible: Scientist & The Soul Syndicate / Higher ranking: King Tubby & The Aggrovators / Black rose: Prince Alla & Philip Fraser / Great stone: King Tubby & The Soul Syndicate / Version 78 style: Brown, Glen & King Tubby / Superfly: I-Roy / Drums of Africa: Prince Jammy & The Aggrovators
BAFCD 17 / Feb '97 / Blood & Fire

☐ HECTIC - CHAPTER ONE
HECTCD 001 / Oct '95 / Hectic

☐ HEIDI SEZ LOOKOUT
LOOKOUT 169CD / Oct '96 / Lookout

☐ HEIVA I TAHITI - FESTIVAL OF LIFE
EUCD 1238 / Nov '93 / ARC

☐ HELENA BLUES LEGACY, THE
BLUESUN 2000 / May '97 / Blue Sun

☐ HELLS BENT ON ROCKIN'
NERCD 017 / Nov '91 / Nervous

☐ HELL'S KITCHEN
DIW 405 / Mar '97 / DIW

☐ HELLSOUND VOL.5 (Blessed Are The Sick)
HSCOMP 005 / Apr '97 / ID&T

☐ HELLSPAWN
Day of suffering: Morbid Angel & Beserker / Breed to breathe: Naplam Death & Delta 9 / Strike: Dub War & Panacea / Strangled: Ultraviolence & Hellsau / Regression progression: Brutal Truth & Freak / Control: Pulkas & Shitspitter / Wake: Godflesh & Justin Broadrick / Abominations: Morbid Angel & Berzerker / Kiss your boots: Misery Loves Co & Pitchshifter
MOSH 199CD / 6 Jul '98 / Earache

☐ HELP
Fade away: Oasis / Oh brother: Boo Radleys / Love spreads: Stone Roses / Lucky: Radiohead / Adnan: Orbital / Mourning air (war child): Portishead / Fake the aroma: Massive Attack / Shipbuilding: Suede / Time for loving: Charlatans & The Chemical Brothers / Sweetest truth: Stereo MC's / Ode to Billy Joe: O'Connor, Sinead / Search light: Levellers / Raindrops keep falling on my head: Manic Street Preachers / Tom Petty loves Veruca Salt: Terrorvision / Magnificent: One World Orchestra / Message to crommie: Planet 4 Folk Quartet / Dream a little dream: Hall, Terry & Salad / 1,2,3,4,5: Cherry, Neneh & Trout / Eine kleine lift muzik: Blur / Come together: Smokin' Mojo Filters
8286822 / Sep '95 / Go Discs

☐ HELPING YOU BACK TO WORK VOL.1
LJCD 03 / Jul '97 / Lockjaw

☐ HELPING YOU BACK TO WORK VOL.2
Sick: Unsane / Make up: Everfresh / Won't be denied: Stampin' Ground / Backdown: Tribute To Nothing / She's radar: Zen Guerrilla / CLA: Shallow / Recess: Tiananmen / Flex: Turtlehead / Liar: Mindcore / Dirty bucks: JR / Mondo cain: Snub / Hype that feeling: Fat Babe / Come what may: Lever / 10 below: Monkey Boy / Yours: Stubborn / Black acid rape: Charger / House of Ruth: Sampson
LJCD 008 / 18 May '98 / Lockjaw

☐ HELTER SHELTER BOX (Elastica/Gene/Supergrass/S*M*A*S*H)
SP 1776 / Jul '95 / Sub Pop

☐ HELTER SKELTER (The Masters/3CD Set)
CDHSR 004 / 18 May '98 / Helter Skelter

☐ HELVETIC ART
HOS 7311CD / 27 Apr '98 / Hall Of Sermon

☐ HEMISPHERE NO MORE (A Listener Friendly Guide To Music Of The World)
Sango ya mawa: Dabany, Patience / La Cosecha De Mujeres: Tribu Band / Nereci (A name): Djavan / Konifale: Tangara, Kadja / Cortina: Vasconcelos, Nana / Midnight walker: Spillane, Davy / Khafet dhamon: Fouad, Mohamed / Sweet reggae: Harley & The Rasta Family / Yele congo: Ketu, Ara / Africa: Depeu, Dave / Madambadamba: Tshola, Tsepo / Koufenko: Manfila, Kante / E dai (A queda): Nascimento, Milton / Huajra: Inti-Illimani / Rag Pahadi: Sharma, Shivkumar
CDHEMI 2 / Jun '95 / Hemisphere

☐ HEMPILATION
5325512 / Sep '96 / Mercury

☐ HEN'S TEETH VOL.1
HEN 01CD / Oct '97 / Hen's Teeth

☐ HEN'S TEETH VOL.2
HEN 02CD / Oct '97 / Hen's Teeth

☐ HENT SANT JAKEZ
SHAM 1018CD / Aug '93 / Shamrock

☐ HEP CATS FROM BIG SPRING
Move mama: Hall, Ben / Be bop ball: Hall, Ben / Blue days black nights: Hall, Ben / Honey you talk too much: Fox, Orville & The Harmony Masters / Silly Sally: Lara, Sammy / Tell me: Regals / Waitin' (on the steps at school): Regals / Lover's regret: Classics / Hep cat: Teen Kings / Some day sweet day: Box, David & The Ravens / That's all I want from you: Box, David & The Ravens / I do the best I can: Box, David & The Ravens / Waitin' (don't wait too long): Box, David & The Ravens / Guitar hop: Welborn, Larry / It's gonna happpen: Osburn, Bob / Heart theif: Osburn, Bob / Goin' back to Louisiana: Osburn, Bob / Too young to love to old to cry: Nicholas, Don & The Four Teens / Bark like a dog: Allison, Bobby
RCCD 3003 / Oct '91 / Rollercoaster

☐ HER INFINITE VARIETY (Celtic Women In Music & Song/2CD Set)
GLCD 107 / Jan '98 / Green Linnet

☐ HER SONG (Exotic Voices of Women From Around the World)
Great Grampah's banjo: Pura Fe / Yola: Irena / Apne Hathon: Najma / Kirya: Haza, Ofra / Jiva mukti: Shakti, Nada / 'S Muldach mi's air: MacKenzie, Talitha / Return home: Solas & Karan Casey / Compassion: Flesh & Bone / Messenger: Shanandoa, Joanne / In your dark eyes: Ankri, Etti
SH 64077 / Dec '96 / Shanachie

☐ HERE COME THE BOYS VOL.1
Make up or break up: Leslie, Michael / Save your love: Rich, Tony / Stage door: Jackson, Tony / Can I get to know you better: Wynter, Mark / I could write a book: Chants / Bu-bop-a-lu-bop-a-lie: Storme, Robb & Whispers / Just as long as (you belong to me): Hill, Vince / Ecstasy: Reed, Oliver / Please don't cry: Newman, Brad / I don't care: Chants / That's the way love goes: Dickens, Charles / Don't fool yourself: Sumers, John / Lookin' for love: Watson, John L / Big black smoke: Mick & Malcolm / Seven lonely days: Migil 5 / Everything: Darrell, Guy / Leave a little love: Anton, Terry / Comes the dawn: Galt, James / That man's got no luck: Benson, Gary / My world fell down: Ivy League / Looking back: West Coast Consortium / One day: Sands Of Time / Only heartbreaks for me: Justice, Jimmy / Leave it to me: Band Of Angels
NEMCD 844 / Jul '97 / Sequel

☐ HERE COME THE DRUMS - HIP HOP DRUM 'N' BASS
CAI 2012 / 25 May '98 / Caipirinha

☐ HERE COME THE GIRLS VOL.1 (British Girl Singers Of The Sixties)
That's how it goes: Breakaways / We were lovers (when the party began): Barry, Sandra / There he goes (the boy I love): Antoinette / He knows I love him too much: Macari, Glo / As long as you're happy baby: Shaw, Sandie / Song without end: Ruskin, Barbara / Tell me what to do: Jackson, Simone / Put yourself in my place: Panter, Jan / It's hard to believe it: Collins, Glenda / So much in love: Brown, Polly / Very first day I met you: Cannon, Judy / How can I hide from my heart: Darren, Maxine / No other baby: Davis, Billie / Listen people: Lane, Sarah / Come to me: Grant, Julie / Dark shadows and empty hallways: St. John, Tammy / Happy faces: Silver, Lorraine / Something must be done: Harris, Anita / You'd better come home: Clark, Petula / When my baby cries: Prenosilova, Yvonne / Something I've got to tell you: Honeycombs / I want you: Jeannie & The Big Guys / I can't believe what you say: McKenna, Val / If you love me (really love me): Trent, Jackie
NEXCD 111 / Mar '90 / Sequel

☐ HERE COME THE GIRLS VOL.3 (Run Mascara)
Easier said than done: Essex / Walkin' miracle: Essex / She's got everything: Essex / Run mascara: Exciters / I want you to be my boy: Exciters / There they go: Exciters / Kind of boy you can't forget: Raindrops / What a guy: Raindrops / That boy is messing up my mind: Raindrops / My one and only Jimmy boy: Girlfriends / For my sake: Girlfriends / Lover's concerto: Toys / What's wrong with me baby: Toys / Can't stop lovin' the boy: Carolines / Evening time: Elena / Girl is not a girl: Wine, Toni / Johnny Angel: Fabares, Shelly / He don't love me: Fabares, Shelly / I'm into something good: Earl Jean
NEXCD 193 / Mar '92 / Sequel

☐ HERE COME THE GIRLS VOL.4 (You Can Be Wrong About Boys)
He doesn't love me: Breakaways / I've found love: Tandy, Sharon / Pay you back with interest: Gillespie, Dana / Thank goodness for the rain: Peanut / It's so fine: King, Dee / Where am I going: Clark, Petula / You can be wrong about boys: Page, Mally / He's the one for me: St. John, Tammy / Don't you know: Darren, Maxine / Thinking of you: West, Dodie / Well how does it feel: Ruskin, Barbara / You can't take it away: Reed, Tawney / When love slips away: Margo & The Marvettes / There he goes: Pickettywitch / London life: Harris, Anita / As I watch you walk away: Smith, Martha / Lonely without you: Grant, Julie / You really have started something: Britt / Someone has to cry (Why must I): Kay, Barbara / My life (is in your hands): Paper Dolls / Untrue unfaithful (That was you): Rossi, Nita / Scratch my back: Panter, Jan / Love ya Illya: Angela & The Fans
NEXCD 238 / Jun '93 / Sequel

☐ HERE COME THE GIRLS VOL.5 (Sisters From The City)
NEMCD 675 / Sep '94 / Sequel

☐ HERE COME THE GIRLS VOL.6
Question: Barry, Sandra / I'm tired just lookin' at you: St. John, Tammy / Life and soul of the party: St. John, Tammy / Take me away: Trent, Jackie / Reach out, I'll be there: Clark, Petula / Thank you for loving me: Antoinette / Here she comes: Breakaways / Donna Star: Douglas, Donna / Love is a many splendoured thing: Saxone, Linda / Please don't talk about me when I'm gone: Stern, Nina / Halfway to paradise: Ruskin, Barbara / Come on baby: Kim D / He don't want your love anymore: Doll, Linda & the Sundowners / Something I've got to tell you: Collins, Glenda / Da-di-da-da: Satin Bells / So goes love: Abicair, Shirley / Thank you boy: Gillespie, Dana / I know you'll be there: Silver, Lorraine / I know you: Angela & The Fans / He's no good: Baker Twins / Heaven is being with you: Brook, Patti / Long after tonight is all over: Rogers, Julie / In the deep of the night: West, Dodie / You make my head spin: Lee, Jacky
NEMCD 718 / Feb '95 / Sequel

☐ HERE COME THE GIRLS VOL.7 (The Trouble With Boys)
Baby baby (I still love you): Cinderellas / Please don't wake me: Cinderellas / Baby toys: Toys / See how they run: Toys / May my heart be cast in stone: Toys / Curfew lover: Essex / What did I do: Essex / Are you going my way: Essex / Moon of love: Bobbettes / Will you love me in heaven: Del-Vetts / Send him to me: Uniques / Breaking up is hard to do: Fabares, Shelly / Toom Toom (is a little boy): Applebee, Marie / Down by the sea (end of summer): Applebee, Marie / Hey lover: Dovale, Debbie / Opportunity: Jewels / I never wonder where my baby goes: Elaine / There's danger ahead: Elaine / It should'a been me (instead of company): Elaine / Get him: Little Eva / Trouble with boys: Little Eva
NEMCD 752 / Aug '95 / Sequel

☐ HERE COME THE GIRLS VOL.8
Fancy dancin' man: Clark, Petula / Love is a gamble: Lee, Jacky / Other side of love: Caravelles / Mixed up, shook up girl: McKenna, Val / Lost summer love: Silver, Lorraine / You can't blame a girl for trying: Ruskin, Barbara / All the time in the world: Paper Dolls / Dream world: Pickettywitch / My heart didn't lie: Collins, Glenda / That boy of mine: Breakaways / Can you keep a secret: Sparling, Candy / Just wait till spring is here: Moray, Moya / I love you, I need you: Brook, Patti / Home of the brave: Peanut / We'll start the party again: Young, Karen / (Walk tall) like a man: New Faces / Burning in the background of my mind: Tott, Tina / Here before the sun: Balmer, Lori / I've got to get a grip of myself: Dulittle, Liza / That's what angels are for: Kay, Barbara / Trains and boats and planes: Harris, Anita / Take it from me (little girl): Stern, Nina / I'm for you: Antoinette / Either way I lose: Trent, Jackie
NEMCD 845 / Jul '97 / Sequel

☐ HERE COME THE GIRLS VOL.9
NEMCD 950 / 30 Mar '98 / Sequel

☐ HERE COMES MY BABY (Hits Of The Swinging Sixties)
PLSCD 189 / Apr '97 / Pulse

☐ HERE COMES THE SUMMER
Hooray hooray it's a holi-holiday: Boney M / Summer love sensation: Bay City Rollers / Down on the beach tonight: Drifters / Farewell my summer love: Kaos / Everybody's got summer: Atlantic Starr / Gimme the sunshine: Curiosity / Loco in Acapulco: Four Tops / Fantastic day: Haircut 100 / Surfin' USA: Astronauts / Surfin' in the summertime: Ronny & The Daytonas / Summer (the first time): Goldsboro, Bobby / Aquarius (let the sunshine in): 5th Dimension / Seasons in the sun: Jacks, Terry / Good thing going: Minott, Sugar / Montego bay: Sugar Cane / Sunshine reggae: Laidback / Sun will shine: Feliciano, Jose / Island in the sun: Belafonte, Harry / Santa Monica sunshine: Sweet / Current of love: Hasselhoff, David
74321286102 / May '95 / Ariola

☐ HERE ME TALKIN'
Young woman's blues: Smith, Bessie / Easy rider blues: Jefferson, Blind Lemon / Bye bye blues: Johnson, Tommy / Hear me talking to you: Rainey, Gertrude 'Ma' / Dark night blues: McTell, 'Blind' Willie / Slippery rag: Blind Blake / Black hearted blues: Tampa Red / New bumble bee: Memphis Minnie / Ice and snow blues: Wheatstraw, Peetie / B and O blues: Bumble Bee Slim / Highway 61 blues: Sykes, Roosevelt / Hang it on the wall: Patton, Charlie / Sweet sixteen: Davis, Walter / Ain't it a shame: Carr, Leroy / Deep South blues: Estes, 'Sleepy' John / L and Y blues: Gaither, Bill / Stop breakin' down blues: Johnson, Robert / Shaggy like a bear: Fuller, Blind Boy / Jersey belle blues: Johnson, Lonnie / Plow hand blues: Broonzy, 'Big' Bill / She fooled me: Washboard Sam / You got to step back: Williamson, Sonny Boy
IGOCD 2076 / Jul '98 / Indigo

☐ HERE'S TO THE HIGHLANDS
CELT 9015 / Jul '98 / Celtophile

☐ HERITAGE
5244342 / 24 Feb '98 / Six Degrees

☐ HERITAGE 14-HIP HOP
We got our own thing: Heavy D & The Boyz / Hip hop junkies: Nice 'n Smoothe / Mama said knock you out: LL Cool J / I come off: Young MC / It takes two: Rob Base & DJ E-Z Rock / Make it happen: Ultramagnetic MC's / Flavor of the month: Black Sheep / OPP: Naughty By Nature / Jump: Kriss Kross / Express yourself: NWA / Fuck Compton: Dog, Tim / I'm ready: Caveman
CDELV 08 / Jul '93 / Elevate

☐ HERITAGE OF SCOTLAND
302692 / Jan '97 / Hallmark

☐ HERITAGE OF THE CELTS
302732 / Jan '97 / Hallmark

☐ HERITAGE-COLOSSUS STORY, THE
When we get married: Dreamlovers / Ain't nothing but a house party: Showstoppers / May I: Deal, Bill & The Rhondells / And suddenly: Cherry People / Ma belle Amie: Tee Set / Venus: Shocking Blue / Check yourself: Italian Asphalt & Paving Co / Little green bag: Baker, George Selection / Sooner I get to you: Biddu / Carolina on my mind: Crystal Mansion / Don't hang me up girl: Cherry People / I've been hurt: Deal, Bill & The Rhondells / Everything is beautiful: Ross, Jerry / You're gonna make it: Festivals / Give it to me: Mob / Venus: Ross, Jerry / Pick up my toys: Devonnes / What kind of fool do you think I am: Deal, Bill & The Rhondells / I dig everything about you: Mob / Goodnight my love: Duprees
NEMCD 677 / Nov '94 / Sequel

☐ HEROES OF POP MUSIC, THE (2CD Set)
24004 / Jun '96 / Delta Doubles

☐ HEROES OF ROCK 'N' ROLL (4CD Set)

Heartbreak hotel: Presley, Elvis / Long tall Sally: Presley, Elvis / I was the one: Presley, Elvis / Money Honey: Presley, Elvis / I got a woman: Presley, Elvis / Blue suede shoes: Presley, Elvis / Hound dog: Presley, Elvis / Baby let's play house: Presley, Elvis / Maybelline: Presley, Elvis / That's alright Mama: Presley, Elvis / Blue moon of Kentucky: Presley, Elvis / Good rockin' tonight: Presley, Elvis / Great balls of fire: Lewis, Jerry Lee / What'd I say: Lewis, Jerry Lee / Lucille: Lewis, Jerry Lee / Brown eyed handsome man: Lewis, Jerry Lee / Hey good lookin': Lewis, Jerry Lee / Roll over Beethoven: Lewis, Jerry Lee / Chantilly lace: Lewis, Jerry Lee / Little queenie: Lewis, Jerry Lee / Johnny B Goode: Lewis, Jerry Lee / No headstone on my grave: Lewis, Jerry Lee / Mexicali rose: Lewis, Jerry Lee / I'll find it where I can: Lewis, Jerry Lee / High school confidential: Lewis, Jerry Lee / Boogie woogie country man: Lewis, Jerry Lee / You are my sunshine: Lewis, Jerry Lee / Meat man: Lewis, Jerry Lee / Big legged woman: Lewis, Jerry Lee / Rockin' my life away: Lewis, Jerry Lee / Who's gonna play this old piano: Lewis, Jerry Lee / Whole lotta shakin' goin' on: Lewis, Jerry Lee / Blueberry hill: Domino, Fats / I'm ready: Domino, Fats / Ain't that a shame: Domino, Fats / My girl Josephine (hello Josephine): Domino, Fats / Blue monday: Domino, Fats / Jambalaya: Domino, Fats / What a price: Domino, Fats / I'm in the mood for love: Domino, Fats / Let the four winds blow: Domino, Fats / I want to walk you home: Domino, Fats / I'm gonna be a wheel someday: Domino, Fats / Whole lotta lovin': Domino, Fats / Dance with Mr. Domino: Domino, Fats / Fat man: Domino, Fats / Please don't leave me: Domino, Fats / I'm in love again: Domino, Fats / Be my guest: Domino, Fats / Red sails in the sunset: Domino, Fats / Goin' home: Domino, Fats / Lucille: Little Richard / Long tall Sally: Little Richard / Whole lotta shakin' goin' on: Little Richard / Good golly miss molly: Little Richard / Tutti frutti: Little Richard / Rip it up: Little Richard / Keep a knockin': Little Richard / Jenny jenny: Little Richard / Girl can't help it: Little Richard / Slippin' and slidin': Little Richard / She's got it: Little Richard / Money honey: Little Richard / Groovy little Suzy: Little Richard / Talking 'bout soul: Little Richard / Baby face: Little Richard / Blueberry hill: Little Richard / Hound dog: Little Richard / Send me some lovin': Little Richard

QUAD 016 / Nov '96 / Tring

☐ HET DAGHET INDEN OOSTEN (Bagpipes Of The Low Countries)

PANCD 2025 / May '97 / Pan

☐ HEX FILES VOL.1 (The Goth Bible - Compiled By Mick Mercer/2CD Set)

9040124 / Apr '97 / Nova Tekk

☐ HEX FILES VOL.2 (2CD Set)

Pantomime Clown: Damien Youth / Souvenirs: Life in Sodom / Descend: Falling Janus / This is the only name: Evidence / Autumn song: Darkside cowboys / Suenos: Nubis / This empty ocean: Love Like Blood / Swollen head: Gotterdammerung / Glitter: Suspiria / Velvet fuck: Trance To The Sun / Lost inside: Machine In The Garden / New dress: Cat fud / Yesterday's gone: Vendemian / Aglon: Rosa crux / New Christ: Gothic sex / I'd like to feel: Gothic sex / Return: Engelsstaud / Breath of de Sade: Cruciform / Magnet and the power: Black Tape For A Blue Girl / Nothing is real: Veil Of Thorns / Blind: Messiah of pain / Let me hold on: Shroud / Eyelid backspace poem: Catastrophe ballet / Final day: Meridian / Lucrezia: Artica / Your soul is not enough: Lux solemnis / Eden: Sofia run / Zennor: Mothburner / Oduarpa: Ataraixa / Wedding day: Damien Youth

9040324 / Aug '97 / Nova Tekk

☐ HEXENTEXT

CODE 1 / Oct '94 / Overground

☐ HEY BABY (The Rockin' South/30 Rockabilly Gems From Excello/Nasco)

Hey baby: Ferrier, Al / I'm the man: Ferrier, Al / Kiss a me quick: Toombs, Jackson / Big hearted Joe: Lindsey Brothers / Let's get down to business: Lindsey Brothers / Stealin' sugar: Batts, Ray / Somebody clipped your wings: Haggard, Don & The Sunset Drifters / Havin' a whole lot of fun: Jano, Johnny / I'd make a good man for you: Jano, Johnny / Trapped: Fortune, Billy / Bobby sox baby: Harpo, Slim / My baby's gone: Jenkins, Bobby / I'm out: Surf Riders / Little Andy: Trent, Jackie / Spellbound: McGuire, Lowell / Leave my girlie alone: McGuire, Lowell / Mama Mama Mama (look what your little boy's done): Storm, Warren / Swamp gal: Bell, Tommy / Little baby: Facenda, Tommy / It's love baby: Monorays / Werewolf: Warren, Gary / Shorty shorty: Bob & Ray / Troubles troubles: Storm, Warren / So long so long (goodbye goodbye): Storm, Warren / Honey bee (I love you): Angel, Tommy / Mama doll: Teo, Roy / Tell me: Trends / I'm a little boy (looking for love): Storm, Warren

CDCHD 641 / Apr '97 / Ace

☐ HEY BROTHER CAN YOU SPARE SKA VOL.3

VGR 007CD / 11 May '98 / Vegas

☐ HEY BROTHER CAN YOU SPARE SOME SKA VOL.2

VGR 004CD / 1 Dec '97 / Revelation

☐ HEY DRAG CITY

WIGCD 16 / Oct '94 / Domino

☐ HEY MARDI GRAS

EDCD 7015 / Feb '97 / Easydisc

☐ HEY MOM, THE GARAGE IS ON MY FOOT

DAMGOOD 102CD / Nov '96 / Damaged Goods

☐ HI FASHION JUST LIKE A RIVER VOL.1

2098730222 / 22 Dec '97 / Joe Gibbs

☐ HI RECORDS STORY, THE

HIUKCD 101 / Jul '89 / Hi

☐ HI RECORDS: THE EARLY YEARS VOL.2

My girl Josephine: Jayes, Jerry / Five miles from home: Jayes, Jerry / Middle of nowhere: Jayes, Jerry / Long black veil: Jayes, Jerry / Sugar bee: Jayes, Jerry / I'm in love again: Jayes, Jerry / I washed my hands in muddy water: Jayes, Jerry / Shackles and chains: Tucker, Tommy / I'm in love with a shadow: Tucker, Tommy / Wild side of life: Tucker, Tommy / Since I met you baby: Felts, Narvel / Dee Dee: Felts, Narvel / Eighty six miles: Felts, Narvel / Little bit of soap: Felts, Narvel / Dark shaded glasses: Eldred, Charles / Long tall texan: Kellum, Murray & Rhythm Four / I gotta leave this town: Sutton, Glenn / Shame shame shame: Tucker, Tommy / Listen to me lie: Simmons, Gene / Wedding bells: Simmons, Gene / Invitation to the blues: Simmons, Gene / Time is right: Lloyd, Jay B. / Honey babe: Arnold, Jerry / Son of Smokie: Black, Bill Combo / Crank case: Black, Bill Combo / TD's boogie woogie: Black, Bill Combo / Deep elem blues: Cannon, Ace & Bill Black's combo / Sittin' tight: Cannon, Ace

HIUKCD 128 / Apr '92 / Hi

☐ HI-BIAS EXPERIENCE, THE

CTR 20CDM / Mar '96 / X-Treme

☐ HI-BOP SKA

45019 / Dec '94 / Shanachie

☐ HI-FI ROCK 'N' ROLL PARTY

Lights out: Byrne, Jerry / Roll hot rod roll: McLollie, Oscar / Runaround sue: Dion / Sea cruise: Ford, Frankie / Little bit of soap: Jarmels / Thinking of you: Beasley, Jimmy / Maybellene: Walton, Mercy Dee / Poetry in motion: Tillotson, Johnny / Tutti frutti: Little Richard / Wake up little Susie: Everly Brothers / Peanut butter: Marathons / Promised land: Allan, Johnnie / Wanderer: Dion / Deuces wild: Wray, Link / Hush-a-bye: Mystics / Teenager in love: Dion & The Belmonts / Lollipop: Chordettes / My true story: Jive Five / Goodnight my love: Belvin, Jesse / He's so fine: Chiffons / Way I like it: Gunter, Shirley / Reet petite: Wilson, Jackie

CDCH 904 / May '86 / Ace

☐ HI-NRG HEAVEN (The Cream Of Hi-NRG)

Hi-energy: Thomas, Evelyn / So many men so little time: Brown, Miquel / Love I lost: Seventh Avenue / Sky high: Jigsaw / Emergency: Pallas, Laura / Catch me I'm falling in love: Raven, Marsha / I'm living my own life: Raven, Marsha / Visitors: Moonstone / Hit and run lover: Jiani, Carol / Frantic love: Eastbound Expressway / He's a saint, he's a sinner: Brown, Miquel / Action: Pearly Gates / Who knows what evil: Man To Man / Earthquake: Benson, Vicki / On a crowded street: Pennington, Barbara / Do you know the way to San Jose: Croisette / Masquerade: Thomas, Evelyn / Wanted for murder boys: Boystown Gang / This old heart of mine: Morris, Gee / Satisfy my desire: Havana

SUMCD 4112 / Mar '97 / Summit

☐ HI-NRG VOL.3 (4CD Set)

CDBPX 3 / 18 May '98 / Passion

☐ HIDDEN BEAUTY

Sunshower: Friedemann / Baghdad: Cook, Jesse / Tree of life: Rumbel, Nancy / Magic forest: Arkenstone, David / Ancient legend: Arkenstone, David / Shape of her face: Whalen, Michael / Through the parched land: Whalen, Michael / Ancestor: Roos, Randy / Heartsounds: Lanz, David / Leaving home: Mirowitz, Sheldon / L'Accordion: Mann, Brian / Mil amores: Cameron, Doug / Long riders: Souther, Richard

ND 63922 / Mar '96 / Narada

☐ HIDDEN ENGLISH

TSCD 600 / Oct '94 / Topic

☐ HIDDEN ROOMS

Jump MkII: Studio Pressure / Relics: Studio Pressure / Workout: Klute / Hidden rooms: Sounds Of Life / Currents: Sounds Of Life / Spice of jazz: Sounds Of Life / Wise movements: Motive One / FPOP: Klute / Right or wrong: Klute / Relics: Studio Pressure / Release the bells: Sounds Of Life / Presha III: Sounds Of Life / Funk 78 remix: Motive One / Technical wizardry: Motive One

CERT18CD 001 / Mar '97 / Certificate 18

☐ HIGH ATMOSPHERE

ROUCD 0028 / Apr '95 / Rounder

☐ HIGH ENERGY

JHD 042 / Jun '92 / Tring

☐ HIGH GEAR

VPCD 2059 / May '97 / Steely & Cleevie

☐ HIGH IN A BASEMENT

Full length: Idjut Boys & LAJ / Original disco motion: Faze Action / Downtime: Paper music issue one / Que tal America: Man Called Adam / Feel the warmth: Reel Howze / Chrystal wave: Century Falls / Rump funk: DIY / My sisters daughter: House Of Wacks / Zombie dawn: Tranquil Elephantizer / Jazz the sea turtle: 4AM / Jihad: Man Called Adam / Big C: Dawn / Jazz fuk: Idjut Boys & LAJ / In the trees: Faze Action

HVNLP 14CD / Aug '96 / Heavenly

☐ HIGH OCTANE FUNK (2CD Set)

DCID 003 / 16 Mar '98 / Dance Club International

☐ HIGH ON RHYTHM (4CD Set)

Lifting me higher: Gems For Jem / On my knees: Jonah, Julian / Race of survival: Sonz Of Soul / Cold stone lover: Chunky Mother / Never gonna be the same: Northbound / In the name of love: Massai / Spirit: Minds Of Faith / In my time of need: Shamir, Inca / I was tired of being alone: Klodya / Lovin' you: Trilogy / Looking for romance: Laws Of Rhythm / Rollercoaster: Ground Control / People living today: Semi Real / You took my love: Candese / Do that to me: Holloway, Loleatta / Satisfaction: Kadance / Can you feel me: Circa 91 / I'm coming up: Love Boutique / We can make it: Orr-Some / I'll be a freak for you: Layton, Lindy / 1000: Kings of Peace / I think about you: King, Evelyn 'Champagne' / Jump to it: Tough Two / Dream: 2 4 The Future / Dance with power: Bass Construction / One step ahead: Boneshakers / Dip: Ground Control / Yer: Diamond Cut / Hold On: 2 4 The Future / Groove me: Gems For Jem / Turn your love: Clockhouse Hours / Get on the move: Bass Construction / Love bizarre: Fratelli / Baby come on lets: Laws Of Rhythm / You keep me smilin': Circa 91 / Friend not a lover: Serenade / Shame: King, Evelyn 'Champagne' / Promises: Leon, Andre / I don't want to be part of you: Resistance / Moving on: Ipso Facto / Inspiration: Gems For Jem / Adrenalin: Jargon / Be my lady: Robbins, Rockie / Love is life: Candy Flip / Inside your love: TRIP / E-Go: Real Masters / Check how we jam: Bass Construction / Dreams bcum reality: Men From Del Bosca / Dub affair: Shakatak / Hey how ya doin': Father MC

CDBHOR 1 / 6 Oct '97 / High On Rhythm

☐ HIGH PERFORMANCE

MB 60082 / May '97 / Instinct Electronica

☐ HIGH PLATEAUX SONGS (Music From Madagascar)

PS 65096 / Oct '92 / PlayaSound

☐ HIGH STREET

Different world: DJ Stix / Forbidden territories: Avenue A / Adelphi's ladder: Adelphi / Jah weybridge: Adelphi / Imprint: Blindside / Mellow bug thunk: Plastic Digger / Greed: Avenue A / Boned: Meat Katie / Infix: P-Method / Silent partner: Red Myers / Weightless: P-Method / Palnet circus: DJ Stix

KSRCD 1 / Jun '97 / Kingsize

☐ HIGH VOLTAGE BLUES

Nervous: Dixon, Willie / Tramp: Fulson, Lowell / Things that I used to do: Guitar Slim / Baby let's play house: Gunter, Arthur / Baby scratch my back: Harpo, Slim / I'm a King Bee: Harpo, Slim / I'm gonna quit you pretty baby: Hogan, Silas / Boogie chillen: Hooker, John Lee / I'm in the mood: Hooker, John Lee / Little boy blue: Horton, Walter / Riding in the moonlight: Howlin' Wolf / House rockin' boogie: Howlin' Wolf / Dust my blues: James, Elmore / Homesick James: Homesick James / Crosscut saw: King, Albert / Sweet little angel: King, B.B. / Rock me baby: King, B.B. / I'm a lover not a fighter: Lazy Lester / Rooster blues: Lightnin' Slim / I'm a mojo man: Lonesome Sundown / Little Johnny Taylor: Taylor, Little Johnny / Those lonely, lonely nights: Watson, Johnny 'Guitar'

3035900182 / Jul '96 / Essential Gold

☐ HIGH VOLTAGE VOL.1

RNCD 2091 / Mar '95 / Rhino

☐ HIGHLIFE (2CD Set)

NDCD 025 / Jan '97 / Night & Day

☐ HIGHLIGHTS FROM EDINBURGH TATTOO 1965-1979 (2CD Set)

Fanfare: Royal Marines School Of Music / My love she's but a lassie yet: Massed Pipes & Drums / Haughs o' Cromdale: Massed Pipes & Drums / Mrs. MacDougall: Massed Pipes & Drums / Angus McKinnon: Massed Pipes & Drums / Thunderbirds: Massed Military Bands / 633 squadron: Massed Military Bands / Burns on the march: Massed Military Bands / Scotland the brave: Massed Military Bands / Athol Highlanders: Brigade Of Gurkhas / Dear old donegal: Brigade Of Gurkhas / Lutzow's wild hunt: Brigade Of Gurkhas / Sirmoor rifles: Brigade Of Gurkhas / Barren rocks Aden: Brigade Of Gurkhas / Dundee city: Brigade Of Gurkhas / Get me to the church on time: Corps Of Drums / Wonderful Copenhagen: Corps Of Drums / Cock o' the North: Massed Military Bands / British Grenadiers: Massed Military Bands / Soldiers in the park: Massed Military Bands / Dovecote park: Scots College Sydney / Road to the Isles: Scots College Sydney / Meetings of the waters: Scots College Sydney / Old rustic bridge: Scots College Sydney / Highland cradle song: Scots College Sydney / Whistle o'er the lave o't: Scots College Sydney / Earl of Mansfield: Scots College Sydney / HM Jollies: Massed Bands Of The Royal Marines / Blaze of brass: Massed Bands Of The Royal Marines / Edinburgh castle: Massed Bands Of The Royal Marines / Life on the ocean wave: Massed Bands Of The Royal Marines / Prinz Carlmarsch: Massed Pipes, Drums & Military Bands / Caubeen trimmed with blue: Massed Pipes, Drums & Military Bands / Heart of oak: Massed Pipes, Drums & Military Bands / Royal artilary slow march: Massed Pipes, Drums & Military Bands / Abide with me: Massed Pipes, Drums & Military Bands / Royal artillery slow match: Massed Pipes, Drums & Military Bands / Royal artillery last post: Massed Pipes, Drums & Military Bands / Lament for Red Hector of the Battles lone piper: Massed Pipes, Drums & Military Bands / Zum staedtli hinavs: Massed Pipes, Drums & Military Bands / We're no awa' tae bide awa': Massed Pipes, Drums & Military Bands / Loch Lomond: Massed Pipes, Drums & Military Bands

CDMFP 5993 / Jun '93 / Music For Pleasure

☐ HIGHLIGHTS FROM THE EUROPEAN CHAMPIONSHIPS 1997 (2CD Set)

Champions / Salamander / Freedom / Trittico / Pageantry / Waltonian / Fantaise op.94 / An epic symphony / Cry of the Celts / Introduction / Suil a ruin / Breakout / Lament / Finale - Lord of the dance

DOYCD 062 / Sep '97 / Doyen

☐ HIGHLY RECOMMENDED

FORMCD 3 / Nov '95 / Formation

☐ HIGHTONE RECORDS FIRST TEN YEARS SAMPLER, THE

HCD 2002 / Jul '94 / Hightone

☐ HIGHWAY AND LANDSCAPE (Chill Out Classics & Ethereal Anthems/2CD Set)

Qualia: Sun Electric / Curiosity (what is it): Molasses / Ultraviolet: International People's Gang / Joy to the world: T-Tauri / Out of body experience: Rabbit In The Moon / Eric: Amalgamation Of Soundz / Teleport to origin: Valleyman / Emotive: SLAM / Funkyar: Spacetime Continuum / Fallen destiny: Angel, Dave / Sueno Plutino: Pluto & Manuel Gottsching / Earthshake: Gas / Pickyparkdickbods: Solid Doctor / On a rowing trip: Valleyman / V-chip: Sie / Transmit liberation: Single Cell Orchestra / Amazing discoveries: Move D / Collage of dreams: Beltran, John / Toast: Q-Burns Abstract Message

SUB 48342 / Jun '97 / Distance

☐ HILLBILLY BLUES 1928-1946 (2CD Set)

Blue yodel: Rodgers, Jimmie / Heavy hearted blues: Darby & Tarlton / Freight train rumble: Darby & Tarlton / Arabella blues: Davis, Jimmie / Sewing machine blues: Davis, Jimmie / Lonesome jailhouse blues: Delmore Brothers / Chain gang blues: Puckett, Riley / Easy rider blues: Davis, Jimmie / New deal blues: Allen Brothers / Somebody's been using that thing: Brown, Milton / Texas hambone blues: Brown, Milton / No huggin' or kissin': Hartman's Earth Breakers / Grandpa and grandma: Hartman's Earth Breakers / Swing beats: Wills, Bob / Mean old lonesome blues: Jones, Buddy / Married man blues: Hunt, Helen / I'll keep my old guitar: Hofner, Adolph / Gettin' tired: Rambling Ramblers / Worried man's blues: Sunshine Boys / Honey what you gonna do: Wills, Bob / Mean Mama blues: Tubb, Ernest / What's the matter with the deep elm: Sunshine Boys / Lay me down beside my darling: Mullican, Moon / Midnight special: Paul, Les / Milk cow blues: Wills, Johnny Lee / Fort Worth jail: Tubb, Ernest / That's all: Travis, Merle / Texas' blues: Travis, Merle / Driftin' Texas sand: Coward, Buster / Going back to the blue ridge mountain: Delmore Brothers / Clouds rained trouble down: Guthrie, Jack / Guitar blues: Guthrie, Jack / Blue yodel no.4: Monroe, Bill / Kansas City blues: Sullivan, Gene / You better do it now: Cooley, Spade

FA 065 / Nov '97 / Fremeaux

☐ HILLBILLY FILLIES AND ROCKIN' CHICKS

Ten cats down: Miller Sisters / Welcome to the club: Chapel, Jean / I need a man: Pittman, Barbara / I wanna rock: Holcolm, Patsy / I won't be rockin' tonight: Chapel, Jean / You can't break the chains of love: Miller Sisters / Sentimental fool: Pittman, Barbara / Ain't got a worry: Ballman, Wanda / Heartbreak girl: Ballman, Wanda / Ooh that's good: Holcolm, Patsy / I can't show how I feel: Wood, Anita / Red velvet: Kirby Sisters / (I get the) Craziest feeling: Kirby Sisters / Two young fools in love: Pittman, Barbara / Memories of you: Priesman, Magel / Rock 'n' roll cinnamon tree: Wimberly, Maggie Sue / Jumpin' Jack: Thomas, Cliff & Ed/ Barbara / Everlasting love: Pittman, Barbara / Voice of a fool: Pittman, Barbara / Just one day: Pittman, Barbara / No matter who's to blame: Pittman, Barbara / Call me anything but call me: Wimberly, Maggie Sue / Someday you will pay: Miller Sisters / There's no right way to do me wrong: Miller Sisters / Love is a stranger: Sunrays / Got you on my mind: Miller Sisters / I know I can't forget you but I'll try: Miller Sisters / You can tell me: Miller Sisters / How long can it be: Wimberly, Maggie Sue

CPCD 8182 / Jun '96 / Charly

☐ HILLBILLY JAMBOREE

Mississippi sawyers: Mainer, J.E. Mountaineers / Ramshackle shack: Mainer, J.E. Mountaineers / Milk cow blues: Patterson, Uncle John / Plains Georgia rock: Patterson, Uncle John / Eight thirty blues: Armstrong Twins / Greenback dollar: Armstrong Twins / Leaves are falling: Hodges Brothers / Millers reel: Sherrill, Pappy / Boggy road to Texas: Sherrill, Pappy / Railroad blues: McGee, Sam / Wheels: McGee, Sam / Ching chong: McGee, Sam / Sun setting time in your life: Neely, Bill / Roll in my sweet baby's arms: McCoury, Del / Dreams: McCoury, Del / Dear companion: Any Old Time String Band / Hello stranger: Any Old Time String Band / Philadelphia lawyer: Maddox, Rose / Sally let your bangs hang down: Maddox, Rose / Turn your radio on: Maddox, Rose / Hen cackle: Patterson, Uncle John / Gathering flowers on the hillside: Hodges Brothers / Intro theme/I wonder how the old folks are at home: Carter Family / Run mountain: Mainer, J.E. Mountaineers

CDCHD 643 / 27 Jul '98 / Ace

☐ HILLBILLY ROCK

Watchdog / Everybody's rockin' but me / Oh yeah / Roughneck blues / Red hen bogie / Too many / Get me on your mind / Hey, honey / Started out a walkin' hey Mae / Good deal Lucille / Looking for love / What's the use (I still love you) / I ain't gonna waste my time / Billy goat boogie / I've got a brand new baby / Start all over / Lonesome journey / Hey you there / No help wanted

CDMF 034 / '91 / Magnum Force

☐ HILLS OF HOME: 25 YEARS OF FOLK MUSIC ON ROUNDER (2CD Set)

ROUCDAN 16/17 / Jul '95 / Rounder

☐ HIM DUB VOL.1

SZCD 002 / Mar '94 / Surr Zema Musik

☐ HIMENE (Polynesian Polyphonies)

926892 / Nov '97 / BUDA

☐ HINDU CEREMONY AT MINAKSI-SUNDARESVARA TEMPLE, A

VICG 53482 / Mar '96 / JVC World Library

☐ HIP CITY

LHCD 016 / Jul '96 / Luv n' Haight

☐ HIP HOP AND MORE

12610 / Oct '95 / Laserlight

☐ HIP HOP HURRAY

People every day: Arrested Development / Got to have your love: Mantronix / Mass appeal: Gang Starr / Moira Jane's Cafe: Definition Of Sound / Sugar hill: AZ / Back for more: Cash Crew / Georgia: Klio / Oregano flow: Digital Underground / Bonita applebum: Tribe Called Quest / Turn this mutha out: MC Hammer / PYT (playin young thugs): Smooth & 2Pac / I wish: Skee Lo / Nice and slow: Redhead Kingpin / '93 'til infinity: Souls Of Mischief / Monie in the middle: Monie Love / In my nature: Nuttin' Nyce

DC 881362 / Jul '97 / Disky

☐ HIP HOP PARADISE

XPS 4CD / Feb '97 / X-Treme

☐ HIP HOP PLANETE

Reality: *Third Eye* / Stressed out: *Tribe Called Quest* / Live on live long: *Capone* / Eye for an eye: *Mobb Deep & Nas/Raekwon* / Brooklyn's finest: *Jay-Z & Notorious BIG* / Step into a world: *KRS 1* / Gonna get mine: *MC Breed & Tupac* / Black nostaljack: *Camp Lo* / Wake up: *Killarmy* / On tha real: *Kamikaze & Nas/Cormega* / Street paraboles: *Shabazz & Lord Jamar* / Anthem: *Remedy & Killarmy* / Dangerous minds: *Gravediggaz* / Come on thru: *Brooklyn Zoo*

8454352 / 4 May '98 / Declic

☐ HIP HOP ROTATION

ZYX 551012 / 30 Mar '98 / ZYX

☐ HIP HOP UNLIMITED

ZYX 550712 / Jan '97 / ZYX

☐ HIP HOUSE (40 Funky Rap & House Tracks - 2CD Set)

Fight for your right: *NYCC* / It's like that: *Run DMC & Jason Nevins* / Mama said knock you out: *LL Cool J* / Jungle brother: *Jungle Brothers* / Sounds of the wickedness: *Tzant* / Deeper love: *Ruff Driverz* / Jumpin': *Terry, Todd* / Renegade master: *Wildchild* / Who's in the house: *Beatmasters & Merlin* / B-Boy stance: *Freestylers* / Hear the drummer get wicked: *Jackson, Chad* / I know you got soul: *Eric B & Rakim* / Jump around: *House Of Pain* / Sound of da police: *KRS 1* / Know how: *Young MC* / Talkin' all that jazz: *Stetsasonic* / Can I kick it: *Tribe Called Quest* / Say no go: *De La Soul* / Power: *Snap* / I'm alive: *Stretch n' Vern* / It's tricky: *Run DMC* / It takes two: *Rob Base & DJ E-Z Rock* / Bring the noise: *Public Enemy* / Flylife: *Basement Jaxx* / Street tuff: *Rebel MC & Double Trouble* / Turn up the bass: *Tyree* / Pump up the volume: *MARRS* / Love can't turn around: *Farley Jackmaster Funk* / Mr. Wendal: *Arrested Development* / King of the beats: *Mantronix* / It's a shame (my sister): *Monie Love* / Push it: *Salt n' Pepa* / I'm ready: *Caveman* / Back by dope demand: *King Bee* / Doo wutchyalike: *Digital Underground* / OPP: *Naughty By Nature* / Funky cold medina: *Tone Loc* / Get busy: *Mr. Lee* / My definition of a boombastic jazz style: *Dream Warriors* / Now that we've found love: *Heavy D & The Boyz*

TTVMC 2959

TTVCD 2959 / 25 May '98 / Telstar TV

☐ HIP IS HERE (A Hemisphere Sampler)

Yo no soy pilon de Machucar: *Rodriguez, Lalo* / De noite na cama: *Monteiro, Doris* / Verano porte am: *Garello, Raul* / Mirodia Kalokeriou: *Leonardou, Sotiria & Babis Stokis* / Orchestra replies: *Yosefa* / En el estribo: *Moreno, Gabriel* / Serevende: *Mapfumo, Thomas* / Rosa enjeitada: *De Noronha, Marie Teresa* / Ijex: *Nunes, Clara & Gilberto Gil* / Children come and go: *Poliker, Yehuda* / L'ombra della luce: *Battiato, Franco*

HEMISCD 3 / Jun '97 / Hemisphere

☐ HIPPY HIPPY SHAKE

Hippy hippy shake: *Swinging Blue Jeans* / Do you love me: *Poole, Brian & The Tremeloes* / I get around: *Beach Boys* / I'm into something good: *Herman's Hermits* / Remember (walking in the sand): *Shangri-Las* / I only want to be with you: *Springfield, Dusty* / House of the rising sun: *Animals* / It's my party: *Gore, Lesley* / Just one look: *Hollies* / I like it: *Gerry & The Pacemakers* / I'm telling you now: *Freddie & The Dreamers* / Juliet: *Four Pennies* / I'll never get over you: *Kidd, Johnny & The Pirates* / Little children: *Kramer, Billy J. & The Dakotas* / World without love: *Peter & Gordon* / Diamonds: *Harris, Jet & Tony Meehan* / Little lovin': *Fourmost* / Poison ivy: *Paramounts* / Shout: *Lulu* / 54321: *Manfred Mann*

5529042 / Oct '97 / Spectrum

☐ HIPPY HOUSE AND HAPPY HOP VOL.2

To the rhythm: *Dayglo, Johnny* / Manifesto: *Extasis* / Mainstream: *Sons of be-bop* / Aftertouch: *Prophet Five* / Let the good times roll: *Quiet Boys & Galliano* / Drop it: *MC Sleaze & Solid Gone* / Jack to this: *Silent Way*

JAZIDCD 054 / Oct '92 / Acid Jazz

☐ HIPPYDIP (2CD Set)

Gimme dat harp boy: *Captain Beefheart* / My dark hour: *Miller, Steve* / It takes a lot to laugh it takes a train to cry: *Russell, Leon* / Rag mamma rag: *Band* / Down in Texas: *Hourglass* / I got love if you want it: *Winter, Johnny* / Little games: *Yardbirds* / Shape of things: *Beck, Jeff Group* / Happy birthday: *Idle Race* / Walking down their outlook: *High Tide* / 10538: *ELO* / Speed king: *Deep Purple* / Machines: *Lothar & The Hand People* / Out demons out: *Broughton, Edgar Band* / Songs from the bottom of a well: *Ayers, Kevin* / Octopus: *Barrett, Syd* / Mona: *Quicksilver Messenger Service* / I'm going home: *Ten Years After* / Shake some action: *Flamin' Groovies* / Clifton in the rain: *Stewart, Al* / Superlungs my supergirl: *Reid, Terry* / Trip: *Donovan* / Mockingbird: *Harvest, James* / Leaving my home: *TIME* / Cherry red: *Groundhogs* / Evil woman: *Canned Heat* / Can blue men sing the whites: *Bonzo Dog Band* / Country girl: *Brinsley Schwarz* / Mythical kings and iguanas: *Previn, Dory* / Wall: *Haphash & The Coloured Coat* / Hang on to a dream: *Gandalf* / Living in the past: *Jethro Tull* / Daughter of the fireplace: *Man* / Seven by seven: *Hawkwind* / Do ya: *Move* / Sylvia: *Focus*

CDEM 1623 / Jul '97 / EMI

☐ HISTORIA DEL ROCKABILLY NACIONAL

OEMB 04 / 25 Mar '98 / Burning G

☐ HISTORICAL CD OF DIGITAL SOUND SYNTHESIS 1957-1966

WER 2033 / Feb '96 / Wergo

☐ HISTORY OF BRITISH POP, THE (2CD Set)

Do wah diddy diddy: *Manfred Mann* / I like it: *Gerry & The Pacemakers* / I'm telling you now: *Freddie & The Dreamers* / Bad to me: *Kramer, Billy J. & The Dakotas* / I'm the urban spaceman: *Bonzo Dog Band* / Got to get you into my life: *Bennett, Cliff & The Rebel Rousers* / Don't let me be misunderstood: *Animals* / Tobacco Road: *Nashville Teens* / Shakin' all over: *Kidd, Johnny & The Pirates* / Hippy hippy shake: *Swinging Blue Jeans* / Dandy: *Herman's Hermits* / Stop stop stop: *Hollies* / Bus stop: *Hollies* / Pretty flamingo: *Manfred Mann* / World without love: *Peter & Gordon* / Boat that I row: *Lulu* / Do you want to know a secret: *Kramer, Billy J. & The Dakotas* / Good golly Miss Molly: *Swinging Blue Jeans* / Super girl: *Bonney, Graham* / You were made for me: *Freddie & The Dreamers* / I'm into something good: *Herman's Hermits* / Walkin' back to happiness: *Shapiro, Helen* / You'll never walk alone: *Gerry & The Pacemakers* / Bring it on home to me: *Animals*

24349 / Mar '97 / Laserlight

☐ HISTORY OF CANADIAN 80'S GARAGE PUNK AND SURF

STOMP 008 / Jan '97 / Stomp

☐ HISTORY OF CHESS JAZZ, THE (2CD Set)

Poinciana: *Jamal, Ahmad* / My main man: *Stitt, Sonny & Benny Green* / Shaw' nuff: *Rodney, Red* / Killer Joe: *Jazztet* / Man I love: *Sims, Zoot* / Soul station: *Kirk, Rahsaan Roland* / Parker's mood: *Moody, James* / Keep on keepin' on: *Herman, Woody* / Gotta travel on: *Bryant, Ray* / Benny rides again: *Goodman, Benny* / My love has butterfly wings: *Klemmer, John* / At last: *James, Etta* / In crowd: *Lewis, Ramsey* / Ornithology: *Harris, Barry* / Last train from Overbrook: *Moody, James* / My foolish heart: *Ammons, Gene* / Baltimore oriole: *Alexandria, Lorez* / Bientot: *Nelson, Oliver* / Morning (excerpt): *Lateef, Yusef* / Mellow yello: *Brown, Odell & The Organizers* / Tonk: *Farmer, Art* / You're my thrill: *Jacquet, Illinois* / House warmin': *McGhee, Howard* / Tiny's blues: *Jackson, Chubby* / Candy: *Terry, Clark* / Touch: *Golson, Benny* / Silent night: *Burrell, Kenny*

GRP 2812 / Feb '96 / GRP

☐ HISTORY OF COUNTRY MUSIC - THE 1940S VOL.1 (2CD Set)

Bouquet of roses: *Arnold, Eddy* / When it's lamplighting time in the valley: *Ritter, Tex* / Guitar polka: *Dexter, Al* / Smoke on the water: *Foley, Red* / I'm biting my fingernails and thinking of you: *Tubb, Ernest & Andrews Sisters* / At mail call today: *Autry, Gene* / Detour: *Willing, Foy* / Prodigal son: *Acuff, Roy* / Lovesick blues: *Williams, Hank* / No letter today: *Daffan, Ted & The Texans* / Each night at nine: *Tillman, Floyd* / I'll hold you in my heart: *Arnold, Eddy* / I want to be a cowboy's sweetheart: *Allen, Rosalie* / Soldier's last letter: *Tubb, Ernest* / Shame on you: *Cooley, Spade* / Pistol packin' mama: *Dexter, Al* / New Spanish two-step: *Wills, Bob & His Texas Playboys* / Riders in the sky: *Monroe, Vaughan* / New San Antonio rose: *Wills, Bob & His Texas Playboys* / It's been so long Darling: *Tubb, Ernest* / Waltz of the wind: *Acuff, Roy* / It's a sin: *Arnold, Eddy* / Cool water: *Sons Of The Pioneers* / They took the stars out of heaven: *Tillman, Floyd* / New Jole blonde: *Foley, Red* / There's a new moon over my shoulder: *Davis, Jimmie* / Someday you'll want me to want you: *Britt, Elton* / Candy kisses: *Morgan, George* / I'll forgive you, but I can't forget: *Acuff, Roy* / Sugar moon: *Wills, Bob & His Texas Playboys* / Rainbow at midnight: *Tubb, Ernest* / Deep in the heart of Texas: *Autry, Gene* / Wedding bells: *Williams, Hank* / Tennessee saturday night: *Foley, Red* / Don't rob another man's castle: *Arnold, Eddy* / Pistol packin' mama: *Crosby, Bing & The Andrews Sisters*

KNEWCD 715 / Mar '93 / Kenwest

☐ HISTORY OF COUNTRY MUSIC - THE 1940S VOL.2 (2CD Set)

KNEWCD 716 / Jan '93 / Kenwest

☐ HISTORY OF COUNTRY MUSIC - THE 1950S VOL.1 (2CD Set)

Crazy arms: *Price, Ray* / Rumba boogie: *Snow, Hank* / Let old mother nature have her way: *Smith, Carl* / Jambalaya: *Williams, Hank* / Always late: *Frizzell, Lefty* / Gambler's guitar: *Draper, Rusty* / Chattanooga shoe shine boy: *Foley, Red* / I take the chance: *Browns* / In the jailhouse now: *Pierce, Webb* / Cattle call: *Arnold, Eddy* / White lightning: *Jones, George* / It wasn't God who made honky tonk angels: *Wells, Kitty* / Slow poke: *King, Pee Wee* / Mexican Joe: *Reeves, Jim* / So many times: *Acuff, Roy* / Singin' the blues: *Robbins, Marty* / Golden rocket: *Snow, Hank* / Blue suede shoes: *Perkins, Carl* / Story of my life: *Robbins, Marty* / I let the stars get in my eyes: *Hill, Goldie* / Let me go, lover: *Snow, Hank* / Four walls: *Reeves, Jim* / I wanna play house with you: *Arnold, Eddy* / Don't just stand there: *Smith, Carl* / I want to be with you always: *Frizzell, Lefty* / Birmingham bounce: *Foley, Red* / I forgot more than you'll ever know: *Davis Sisters* / There you go: *Cash, Johnny* / Hey Sheriff: *Rusty & Doug* / Your cheatin' heart: *Williams, Hank* / When it's springtime in Alaska: *Horton, Johnny* / City light: *Price, Ray* / Why baby why: *Pierce, Webb & Red Sovine* / Blue blue day: *Gibson, Don* / I walk the line: *Cash, Johnny* / One by one: *Wells, Kitty & Red Foley*

KNEWCD 717 / Mar '93 / Kenwest

☐ HISTORY OF COUNTRY MUSIC - THE 1950S VOL.2 (2CD Set)

KNEWCD 718 / Jan '93 / Kenwest

☐ HISTORY OF COUNTRY MUSIC - THE 1960S VOL.1 (2CD Set)

KNEWCD 719 / Mar '93 / Kenwest

☐ HISTORY OF COUNTRY MUSIC - THE 1960S VOL.2 (2CD Set)

KNEWCD 720 / Jan '93 / Kenwest

☐ HISTORY OF COUNTRY MUSIC - THE 1970S VOL.1 (2CD Set)

Kiss an angel good morning: *Pride, Charley* / Hello darlin': *Twitty, Conway* / I ain't never: *Tillis, Mel* / Happiest girl in the whole USA: *Fargo, Donna* / All for the love of sunshine: *Williams, Hank Jr.* / Chantilly lace: *Lewis, Jerry Lee* / Country bumpkin: *Smith, Carl* / Wasted days and wasted nights: *Fender, Freddy* / Riding my thumb to Mexico: *Rodriguez, Johnny* / Year that Clayton Delaney died: *Hall, Tom T.* / Only one love in my life: *Milsap, Ronnie* / On my knees: *Rich, Charlie & Janie Frickie* / Luckenbach, Texas (Back to the basics of love): *Jennings, Waylon* / Lizzie and the rainman: *Tucker, Tanya* / She never knew me: *Williams, Don* / Hey won't you play another somebody done somebody wrong song: *Thomas, B.J.* / Georgia on my mind: *Nelson, Willie* / Here you come again: *Parton, Dolly* / Rose garden: *Anderson, Lynn* / Watermelon wine: *Hall, Tom T.* / Linda on my mind: *Twitty, Conway* / There must be more to love than this: *Lewis, Jerry Lee* / Most beautiful girls: *Rich, Charlie* / Coca cola cowboy: *Tillis, Mel* / Teddy bear song: *Fairchild, Barbara* / I'm a ramblin' man: *Jennings, Waylon* / Eleven roses: *Williams, Hank Jr.* / Rub it in: *Craddock, Billy* / Golden tears: *Dave & Sugar* / You're my best friend: *Williams, Don* / Sunday morning coming down: *Cash, Johnny* / El paso city: *Robbins, Marty* / Coal miner's daughter: *Lynn, Loretta* / Blue eyes cryin' in the rain: *Nelson, Willie* / You can't be a beacon (If your lights don't shine): *Fargo, Donna* / Secret love: *Fender, Freddy*

KNEWCD 721 / Mar '93 / Kenwest

☐ HISTORY OF COUNTRY MUSIC - THE 1970S VOL.2 (2CD Set)

Tulsa time: *Williams, Don* / I can help: *Swan, Billy* / You've never been this far before: *Twitty, Conway* / Satin sheets: *Pruett, Jeanne* / Jolene: *Parton, Dolly* / Soul song: *Stampley, Joe* / Grand tour: *Jones, George* / Funny face: *Fargo, Donna* / Why me: *Kristofferson, Kris* / Are you sure Hank done it this way: *Jennings, Waylon* / Would you lay with me: *Tucker, Tanya* / Before the next teardrop falls: *Fender, Freddy* / Blue skies: *Nelson, Willie* / How can I unlove you: *Anderson, Lynn* / Good woman blues: *Tillis, Mel* / It was almost like a song: *Milsap, Ronnie* / Behind closed doors: *Rich, Charlie* / Take this job and shove it: *Paycheck, Johnny* / PS I love you: *Hall, Tom T.* / It's gonna take a little bit longer: *Pride, Charley* / I will always love you: *Parton, Dolly* / Paper roses: *Osmond, Marie* / Fifteen years ago: *Twitty, Conway* / Some broken hearts never mend: *Williams, Don* / I won't mention it again: *Price, Ray* / Bedtime story: *Wynette, Tammy* / Amanda: *Jennings, Waylon* / One piece at a time: *Cash, Johnny* / Ruby baby: *Craddock, Billy* / When the snow is on the roses: *James, Sonny* / I'm just me: *Pride, Charley* / You'll lose a good thing: *Fender, Freddy* / When you're hot, you're hot: *Reed, Jerry* / Door is always open: *Dave & Sugar* / Do you know you are my sunshine: *Statler Brothers* / You always come back: *Rodriguez, Johnny*

KNEWCD 722 / Jan '93 / Kenwest

☐ HISTORY OF COUNTRY MUSIC - THE 1980S VOL.1 (2CD Set)

Nine to Five: *Parton, Dolly* / City of New Orleans: *Nelson, Willie* / Love in the first degree: *Alabama* / Dukes of Hazzard: *Jennings, Waylon* / Thank god for the radio: *Kendalls* / My heart: *Milsap, Ronnie* / She got the goldmine (I got the shaft): *Reed, Jerry* / True love ways: *Gilley, Mickey* / Seven year ache: *Cash, Rosanne* / I believe in you: *Williams, Don* / Give me wings: *Johnson, Michael* / You look so good in love: *Strait, George* / He's back and I'm blue: *Desert Rose Band* / Goin' gone: *Mattea, Kathy* / Whatever happened to old fashioned love: *Thomas, B.J.* / Fire I can't put out: *Strait, George* / I wouldn't change you if I could: *Skaggs, Ricky* / Can't stop my heart from loving you: *O'Kanes* / Have mercy: *Judds* / Lost in the fifties tonight: *Milsap, Ronnie* / My heroes have always been cowboys: *Nelson, Willie* / Somebody lied: *Shelton, Ricky Van* / Cajun moon: *Skaggs, Ricky* / He stopped loving her today: *Jones, George* / Bobbie Sue: *Oak Ridge Boys* / Fourteen carat mind: *Watson, Gene* / Never been so loved (In all my life): *Pride, Charley* / Older women: *McDowell, Ronnie* / Drifter: *Sylvia* / Wanderer: *Rabbitt, Eddie* / I'll still be loving you: *Restless Heart* / I think I'll just stay here and drink: *Haggard, Merle* / Radio heart: *McClain, Charly* / Common man: *Conlee, John* / Take me down: *Alabama* / Elizabeth: *Statler Brothers*

KNEWCD 723 / Mar '93 / Kenwest

☐ HISTORY OF COUNTRY MUSIC - THE 1980S VOL.2 (2CD Set)

KNEWCD 724 / Jan '93 / Kenwest

☐ HISTORY OF DANCE VOL.1, A (1978)

Keep on jumpin': *Musique* / Boogie oogie oogie: *Taste Of Honey* / Galaxy: *War* / British hustle: *Hi-Tension* / You make me feel (mighty real): *Sylvester* / Now that we've found love: *Third World* / Galaxy of love: *Crown Heights Affair* / Eve of the war: *Wayne, Jeff* / Disco nights (rock freak): *GQ* / Instant replay: *Hartman, Dan* / Hit me with yor rhythm stick: *Dury, Ian & The Blockheads* / I thought it was you: *Hancock, Herbie*

CDOVD 474 / Jun '97 / Virgin

☐ HISTORY OF DANCE VOL.2, A (1979)

Ladies night: *Kool & The Gang* / Looking for love tonight: *Fat Larry's Band* / Contact: *Starr, Edwin* / Get down: *Chandler, Gene* / Heart of glass: *Blondie* / I will survive: *Gaynor, Gloria* / All this love I'm giving: *McCrae, Gwen* / Stomp: *Brothers Johnson* / Rapper's delight: *Sugarhill Gang* / Boogie wonderland: *Earth, Wind & Fire* / This time baby: *Moore, Jackie* / It's a disco night: *Isley Brothers*

CDOVD 475 / Jun '97 / Virgin

☐ HISTORY OF DANCE VOL.3, A (1980)

Just a touch of love: *Slave* / Let's go round again: *Average White Band* / And the beat goes on: *Whispers* / I shoulda loved ya: *Walden, Myron* / Celebration: *Kool & The Gang* / I owe you one: *Shalamar* / Don't stop the music: *Yarbrough & Peoples* / OOps upside your head: *Gap Band* / Taste of bitter love: *Knight, Gladys* / Walk in the park: *Straker, Nick Band* / Breaks: *Blow, Kurtis*

CDOVD 476 / Jun '97 / Virgin

☐ HISTORY OF DANCE VOL.4, A (1981)

I'm in love: *King, Evelyn 'Champagne'* / Girls on film: *Duran Duran* / Rapture: *Blondie* / Chant no.1 (I don't need this pressure on): *Spandau Ballet* / Tears are not enough: *ABC* / Favourite shirts (boys meets girl): *Spandau Ballet* / Love action (I believe in love): *Human League* / Going back to my roots: *Odyssey* / Pull up to the bumper: *Jones, Grace* / Body talk: *Imagination* / Let's groove: *Earth, Wind & Fire* / Never too much: *Vandross, Luther*

CDOVD 477 / Jun '97 / Virgin

☐ HISTORY OF DUB: THE GOLDEN AGE

MRMCD 10 / Jul '96 / Munich

☐ HISTORY OF HARDCORE, A

JOINT 3CD / Nov '95 / Suburban Base/ Moving Shadow

☐ HISTORY OF JAMAICAN VOCAL HARMONY, A

MRMCD 11 / Jul '96 / Munich

☐ HISTORY OF JAZZ, A (2CD Set)

NI 65160 / Jun '98 / Music Masters

☐ HISTORY OF POP 1958-1965 (2CD Set)

MBSCD 424 / Nov '93 / Castle

☐ HISTORY OF POP 1966-1973 (2CD Set)

MBSCD 425 / Nov '93 / Castle

☐ HISTORY OF POP 1974-1982 (2CD Set)

MBSCD 426 / Nov '93 / Castle

☐ HISTORY OF POP MUSIC

HRCD 8019 / Mar '93 / Disky

☐ HISTORY OF PUNK VOL.1, A

God save the Queen: *Sex Pistols* / Sex and drugs and rock 'n' roll: *Dury, Ian* / King Rocker: *Generation X* / Shot by both sides: *Magazine* / Day the world turned day glo: *X-Ray Spex* / Rich Kids: *Rich Kids* / Love song: *Damned* / Don't dictate: *Penetration* / Into the valley: *Skids* / Automatic lover: *Vibrators* / Peaches: *Stranglers* / Babylon's burning: *Ruts* / Satisfaction (I can't get me no): *Devo* / Typical girls: *Slits* / Ever fallen in love: *Buzzcocks* / Kill the poor: *Dead Kennedys* / Jilted John: *Jilted John* / Hersham boys: *Sham 69* / Do anything you wanna do: *Eddie & The Hot Rods* / Eton rifles: *Jam*

CDOVD 486 / Jun '97 / Virgin

☐ HISTORY OF PUNK VOL.2, A

Deutscher girls: *Adam & The Ants* / Sound of the suburbs: *Members* / Take me I'm yours: *Squeeze* / Public Image: *Public Image Ltd.* / At the edge: *Stiff Little Fingers* / All around the world: *Jam* / I just can't be happy today: *Damned* / I'm in love with a German film star: *Passions* / Life in a day: *Simple Minds* / Controversial subject: *The The* / Mannequin: *Wire* / Baby let's play house: *Sweet, Rachel* / Nellie the elephant: *Sweet, Rachel* / Banana splits: *Dickies* / Lucky number: *Lovich, Lena* / Dead cities: *Exploited* / Cruisers creek: *Fall* / Money: *Flying Lizards* / Airport: *Motors* / Science friction: *XTC*

CDOVD 487 / Jun '97 / Virgin

☐ HISTORY OF PUNK, A (2CD Set)

RDPCD 011 / 8 Jun '98 / Receiver

☐ HISTORY OF SKA (3CD Set)

CLP 9986 / Jun '97 / Cleopatra

☐ HISTORY OF SKA VOL.1, THE

LG 1063CD / Mar '93 / Lagoon

☐ HISTORY OF SKA VOL.2, THE

LG 21097 / May '94 / Lagoon

☐ HISTORY OF TECHNO VOL.1, THE (4CD Set)

ZYX 740042 / Nov '96 / ZYX

☐ HISTORY OF TECHNO VOL.2, THE (2CD Set)

ZYX 811212 / 13 Oct '97 / ZYX

☐ HISTORY OF THE BLUES (2CD Set)

Boogie chillun: *Hooker, John Lee* / Dimples: *Hooker, John Lee* / Little rain: *Reed, Jimmy* / Where can you be: *Reed, Jimmy* / Diggin' my potatoes: *Memphis Slim* / Boll weevil blues: *Leadbelly* / In New Orleans: *Leadbelly* / Sometimes she will: *Hopkins, Lightnin'* / It's my own fault baby: *King, B.B.* / How many more times you gonna dog me around: *Brookes, Robert C. & The Dan Band* / Hey now: *Charles, Ray* / I'm wonderin' I'm wonderin': *Charles, Ray* / On the road again: *Brookes, Robert C. & The Dan Band* / Send me to the 'lectric chair: *Smith, Bessie* / Careless love: *Smith, Bessie* / Fine and mellow: *Holiday, Billie* / Georgia on my mind: *Holiday, Billie* / Ain't nobody's business if I do: *Brookes, Robert C. & The Dan Band* / Terraplane blues: *Brookes, Robert C. & The Dan Band* / Dust my broom: *James, Elmore* / I believe: *James, Elmore* / Glory be: *Hopkins, Lightnin'* / Iodine in my coffee: *Waters, Muddy* / I'm glad I'm living: *Waters, Muddy* / I can't call her sugar: *Waters, Muddy* / Commit a crime: *Howlin' Wolf* / My mind is ramblin': *Howlin' Wolf* / Hold onto your money: *Howlin' Wolf* / Rollin' and tumblin': *Waters, Muddy* / I can't be satisfied: *Waters, Muddy* / Sadie: *Brookes, Robert C. & The Dan Band* / Letter: *King, B.B.* / Evil child: *King, B.B.* / Everybody has their turn: *Moore, Arnold 'Gatemouth'* / Boogie woogie Papa: *Moore, Arnold 'Gatemouth'* / Boom boom: *Hooker, John Lee* / Whisky and women: *Hooker, John Lee* / Shake that thing: *Hopkins, Lightnin'* / Rock me: *Waters, Muddy* / Union Hall jump: *Brookes, Robert C. & The Dan Band*

SAV 002 / Apr '96 / Tring

☐ HISTORY OF THE TANGO

10498 / May '95 / Laserlight

☐ HISTORY OF TRANCE VOL.1 1991-1996, THE (2CD Set)

Wake up: *Garnier, Laurent* / Skyline: *Resistance D* / Fragile: *LSG* / Love stimulation: *Humate* / Trancescript: *Hardfloor* / Una musica senza ritmo: *Degeneration* / Unknown track: *Unknown Artist* / Tranceslyvania x-press: *X-Dream* / Little fluffy clouds: *Orb* / Two full moons and a troat: *Union Jack* / Mantra: *Bolland, C.J.* / Spectrum: *Metal Master* / How much can you take: *Visions Of Shiva* / Eternal spirit: *4 Voice 4* / Paraglide: *Paragliders* / With a medium into trance: *Hearts Of Space* / Contrex ville: *Redeye* / Beat just goes on and on: *Perry & Rhodan* / Acid Eiffel: *Choice* / Alcatraz: *Peyote*

SPV 08947062 / Sep '96 / SPV

☐ HISTORY OF TRANCE VOL.2, THE (2CD Set)

Hymn: *Moby* / Stars: *Microglobe* / X-Plain: *Arpeggiators* / Transformation: *Transform* / Samurai: *Juno Reactor* / Gloria: *Art Of Trance* / Papua New Guinea: *Future Sound Of London* / Dark and long: *Underworld* / Alice in wonderland: *Cybordelics* / Planet sex: *Garnier, Laurent* / Trancition: *Choci & Freedom Of Sound* / Sundown: *Overlords* / Cosmic evolution: *Microbots* / Lubiantia: *Blue Planet Co-operation* / Catching the scent of mystery: *4 Voices* / Moments in noise: *Sequencer* / We came in peace: *Dance 2 Trance* / Lollipop man: *Union Jack* / Love letter: *Van Dyke, Paul* / Into my dream: *Krid Snero* / Be yourself: *Rototype* / Meltdown: *Lunatic Asylum*

SPV 08947412 / Apr '97 / SPV

☐ HISTORY OF TRANCE VOL.3, THE (The Psychedelic Movement/2CD Set)

Mahadeva: *Astral Projection* / Floor essence: *Man With No Name* / LSD: *Hallucinogen* / High energy protons: *Juno Reactor* / Scarab: *Phana* / Insect: *Hoxbox* / Bony Incus: *Eat Static* / Hear to the divine: *Hode IV* / Generator: *Blue Planet Co-operation* / Shiva: *Indooa* / Electron: *Technossomy* / Luna juice: *Slinky Wizard* / Two vindaloos and an onion bhajee: *Green Nuns Of The Revolution* / Moonraker: *Disco Volante* / Robostyx: *Transwave* / Morphic resonance: *Third Eye* / Deliverance: *Butler & Wilson* / GAS: *Voov* / Next stop oblivion: *2 To A* / Octopus: *Art Of Trance* / Aliens: *Total Eclipse* / Ulnica: *Infinity Project*

SPV 08947682 / Aug '97 / SPV

☐ HISTORY OF TRANCE VOL.5, THE (Technological Anthems/2CD Set)

Alienated: *Earth Nation* / Healing dream: *Sunday Club* / Dreams: *Quench* / Timeless land: *Yothu Yindi* / Alone in a dark room: *Silicium* / Spring yard: *Bolland, C.J.* / Teleport: *Man With No Name* / Solar cycle: *Third Man* / Nightflight: *Up* / Status X: *Framic* / Acid air raid: *Solar Quest* / Kinetic: *Golden Girls* / Pepper: *Speedy J* / Yab yum: *Uzma* / Snake in the system: *Crawlin' King Snake* / Digeridoo: *Aphex Twin* / Smokebelch II: *Sabres Of Paradise* / Mission: *Barbarella* / Blanche: *Purple Plejade* / Doodadoo: *Robotman*

DCD 08939112 / 1 Jun '98 / SPV

☐ HISTORY OF TROJAN RECORDS VOL.1 (1968-1971 - 2CD Set)

Jezebel: *Gray, Owen* / Miss Jamaica: *Cliff, Jimmy* / Silver dollar: *McCook, Tommy & The Skatalites* / New boss: *Smith, Slim* / Train to Skaville: *Ethiopians* / Tide is high: *Paragons* / ABC rock steady: *Gaylads* / Israelites: *Dekker, Desmond & The Aces* / Say I'm back: *Morris, Eric* / It mek: *Dekker, Desmond & The Aces* / If you can't beat them join them: *Conquerors* / Red red wine: *Tribe, Tony* / Fire corner: *King Stitt* / Long shot kick de bucket: *Pioneers* / Burial of Long Shot: *Prince Of Darkness* / Reggae in your jeggae: *Dandy* / Build my whole world around you: *Barker, Dave & The Upsetters* / Weep: *Andy, Bob* / Sun is shining: *Marley, Bob & The Wailers* / Return of Django: *Upsetters* / Wonderful world beautiful people: *Cliff, Jimmy* / Each day: *Isaacs, Gregory* / Rain: *Ruffin, Bruce* / Black and white: *Greyhound* / Shocks of mighty: *Barker, Dave & The Upsetters* / Montego Bay: *Notes, Freddie & The Rudies* / Monkey spanner: *Barker, Dave & Ansell Collins* / Let your yeah be yeah: *Pioneers* / Foolish plan: *Osbourne, Johnny & The Sensations* / Rivers of Babylon: *Melodians* / Liquidator: *Harry J All Stars* / Everybody loves a winner: *Dandy* / Pickney girl: *Dekker, Desmond* / Barbwire: *Dean, Nora* / Kaya: *Marley, Bob & The Wailers* / I can't hide: *Parker, Ken* / Skinhead girl: *Symarip* / You can get it if you really want: *Dekker, Desmond* / Little love: *London, Jimmy* / Young gifted and black: *Bob & Marcia* / Birth control: *Lloydie & The Lowbites* / African Herbsman: *Marley, Bob & The Wailers* / Ride your donkey: *Tennors* / Copy me donkey: *Tennors* / Double barrel: *Barker, Dave & Ansell Collins* / Pop a top: *Andy Capp* / Musical fever: *Enforcers* / Black pearl: *Faith, Horace* / My sweet Lord: *Rudies* / Crying every night: *Cole, Stranger* / Tom Drunk: *U-Roy* / Singer man: *Kingstonians* / My woman's love: *Uniques* / Love of the common people: *Thomas, Nicky* / Boom shacka lacka: *Lewis, Hopeton* / Niyah man: *Rico* / Pied piper: *Bob & Marcia* / Warrior: *Osbourne, Johnny & The Sensations* / Give and take: *Pioneers* / Moon river: *Greyhound*

CDTAL 700 / Feb '95 / Trojan

☐ HISTORY OF TROJAN RECORDS VOL.2 (1972-1995 - 2CD Set)

Them a fe get a beatin': *Tosh, Peter* / This beautiful land: *Melodians* / Addisababa: *Wilson, Delroy* / Festival da da: *Byles, Junior* / Merry up: *Godsons* / Keep on moving: *Marley, Bob & The Wailers* / All that we need is love: *Ellis, Alton* / S90 skank: *Big Youth* / Time has come: *Smith, Slim* / Yim mas gan: *Abyssinians* / Lorna banana: *Alcapone, Dennis & Prince Jazzbo* / Money in my pocket: *Brown, Dennis* / Salvation train: *Scotty* / Loving pauper: *Isaacs, Gregory* / Pauper and the King: *I-Roy* / African Queen: *Pablo, Augustus* / Words of my mouth: *Gatherers* / Purify your heart: *Osbourne, Johnny* / Higher the mountain: *U-Roy* / Stranger on the shore: *Isaacs, David* / John devour: *Dillinger* / Have I sinned: *Charmers, Lloyd* / Hail rasta brother hail: *Ethiopians* / Everything I own: *Boothe, Ken* / Help me make it through the night: *Holt, John* / Fire burning: *Andy, Bob* / Sweet bitter love: *Griffiths, Marcia* / Stalag 17: *Collins, Ansell* / Here I am baby: *Brown, Al* / None shall escape the judgement: *Clarke, Johnny* / Ire feelings: *Edwards, Rupie* / Play de music: *Stewart, Tinga* / Forward jah jah children: *Inner Circle* / Jah Jah bless the Dreadlocks: *Mighty Diamonds* / Hurt so good: *Cadogan, Susan* / Duke Of Earl: *Campbell, Cornell* / Duke Of Earl dub: *McCook, Tommy & The Aggrovators* / Soldering: *Starlights* / Keep cool Babylon: *Ras Michael & The Sons Of Negus* / Baby hang up the phone: *Parks, Lloyd* / Dreadlocks: *Heptones* / Ram goat liver: *Shervington, Pluto* / Heavy manners: *Prince Far-I* / Key of keys: *Rose, Michael* / People got to know: *Minott, Sugar* / Love the dread: *Mikey Dread* / I am a madman: *Perry, Lee 'Scratch'* / You are the sun: *Paul, Frankie*

CDTAL 900 / Feb '96 / Trojan

☐ HIT BOUND (The Revolutionary Sound Of Studio 1)

CDHB 43 / Jan '91 / Heartbeat

☐ HIT LOVE SONGS (CD/CD Rom Set)

WWCDR 009 / Apr '97 / Weton-Wesgram

☐ HIT ME WITH A FLOWER (The New Sounds Of San Francisco)

SPEXCD 5901 / Mar '94 / Normal

☐ HIT MIX '97 (2CD Set)

ZYX 810892 / Jan '97 / ZYX

☐ HIT MIX '98 (2CD Set)

ZYX 811302 / Jan '98 / ZYX

☐ HIT SOUND OF NEW ORLEANS

CDRB 24 / Aug '95 / Charly

☐ HIT THE DECKS VOL.2

QTVCD 008 / Jul '92 / Quality

☐ HIT THE DECKS VOL.3

Ultimation: *Megabass* / Learn to love: *Marveline* / Sesame's treet: *Smart E's* / Rumblism: *Serotonin* / Protein: *Sonic Experience 3* / Come on: *DJ Seduction* / Manic stampede: *Krome & Time* / Voice of Buddha: *Aurora* / On a ragga tip: *SL2* / Sound is for the underground: *Krome & Time* / Trip II the moon: *Acen* / Bad boy: *Bad Boy* / Hypnosis: *Psychotropic* / DJ's unite: *DJ's Unite* / Does it feel good to you: *Cox, Carl* / Temple of dreams: *Messiah* / Feel the rhythm: *Terrorize* / Peace and loveism: *Sonz Of A Loop Da Loop Era* / Keep you movin': *Nu Matic* / Bass shake: *Urban Shakedown* / Eliminator: *Radioactive* / Mother Dawn: *Blue Pearl* / Moog eruption: *Digital Orgasm* / 2 B Reel: *Zone Ranger* / Mind on the beat: *Groove Technology* / Jimi Hendrix was deaf: *Two Little Boys* / Revelations: *HHFD* / Million colours: *Channel X* / Sunshine: *Aurora* / Spectral bass: *Aurora* / Obumbratta: *Apotheosis* / Rave alert: *Khan, Praga* / Can we do it: *General Max*

QTVCD 017 / Oct '92 / Quality

☐ HIT THE FLOOR VOL.1

CDMUT 1123 / Apr '90 / Multitone

☐ HIT THE FLOOR VOL.2

CDMUT 1124 / Apr '90 / Multitone

☐ HIT ZONE - THE BEST OF '97 (2CD Set)

Who do you think you are: *Spice Girls* / I know where it's at: *All Saints* / Where's the love: *Hanson* / Lonely: *Andre, Peter* / Picture of you: *Boyzone* / Best love: *Course* / Free: *Ultra Nate* / Something goin' on: *Terry, Todd* / U sexy thing: *Clock* / Ecuador: *Sash* / Freed from desire: *Gala* / Saturday: *East 57th Street & Donna Allen* / Mighty high: *Revival 3000* / Old before I die: *Williams, Robbie* / What do you want from me: *Monaco* / Clementine: *Owen, Mark* / Love won't wait: *Barlow, Gary* / Finally: *Peniston, Ce Ce* / Waterloo sunset: *Dennis, Cathy* / Indestructible: *Alisha's Attic* / Black eyed boy: *Texas* / Midnight in Chelsea: *Bon Jovi, Jon* / Raincloud: *Lighthouse Family* / Do ya think I'm sexy: *N-Trance & Rod Stewart* / As long as you love me: *Backstreet Boys* / Sometimes: *Brand New Heavies* / Ooh la la: *Coolio* / I shot the sheriff: *Warren G* / I believe I can fly: *R Kelly* / Walk on by: *Gabrielle* / Hey child: *East 17* / Make it with you: *Universal* / Alone: *Bee Gees* / If I never see you again: *Wet Wet Wet* / Lovefool: *Cardigans* / North country boy: *Charlatans* / She's a star: *James* / Free me: *Cast* / Traveller's tune: *Ocean Colour Scene* / Nothing lasts forever: *Echo & The Bunnymen*

5550702 / 3 Nov '97 / PolyGram TV

☐ HIT ZONE SUMMER '97 (2CD Set)

Mmmbop: *Hanson* / Picture of you: *Boyzone* / All about us: *Andre, Peter* / Everybody (backstreet's back): *Backstreet Boys* / Rock me good: *Universal* / Ecuador: *Sash* / Freed from desire: *Gala* / Free: *Ultra Nate* / Something goin' on: *Terry, Todd* / Get up go insane: *Stretch n' Vern* / Discohopping: *Klubb Heads* / I love you stop: *Red Five* / I have peace: *Strike* / Bellisima: *DJ Quicksilver* / Magic carpet ride: *Mighty Dub Katz* / Ain't nobody: *Course* / Smokin' me out: *Warren G* / I'll be: *Brown, Foxy* / Love is all we need: *Blige, Mary J.* / Wonderful tonight: *Damage* / I believe I can fly: *R Kelly* / If I never see you again: *Wet Wet Wet* / Staring at the sun: *U2* / Halo: *Texas* / Waltzing along: *James* / Guiding star: *Cast* / How high: *Charlatans* / Come back brighter: *Reef* / Lovefool: *Cardigans* / Toxygene: *Orb* / Saint: *Orbital* / Air we breath: *Alisha's Attic* / Brazen (weep): *Skunk Anansie* / Susan's house: *Eels* / Star: *Primal Scream* / What do you wan't from me: *Monaco* / Staying out for the summer: *Dodgy* / Good intentions: *Livingstone* / Not where it's at: *Del Amitri* / Elegantly wasted: *INXS*

5538262 / 18 Aug '97 / PolyGram TV

☐ HITALIA VOL.4

472362 / Jul '96 / Flarenasch

☐ HITS '96

I believe: *Robson & Jerome* / Anywhere is: *Enya* / Missing: *Everything But The Girl* / Fairground: *Simply Red* / Waterfalls: *TLC* / I don't wanna be a star: *Corona* / Stayin' alive: *N-Trance* / Sunshine after the rain: *Berri* / I luv u baby: *Original* / What's that tune: *Dorothy* / Never forget: *Take That* / Eye of the tiger: *Bruno, Frank* / Hideaway: *DeLacy* / Happy just to be with you: *Gayle, Michelle* / Something about u (can't be beat): *Mr. Roy* / If you wanna party: *Molella & The Outhere Brothers* / Searching for the golden eye: *Motiv 8 & Kym Mazelle* / Guaglione: *Prado, Perez* / Living next door to Alice (who the fuck is Alice): *Smokie & Roy Chubby Brown* / Wonderwall: *Oasis* / Common people: *Pulp* / Alright: *Supergrass* / It's so quiet: *Bjork* / Queer: *Garbage* / King of the kerb: *Echobelly* / Girl like you: *Collins, Edwyn* / Fingers and thumbs: *Erasure* / He's on the phone: *St. Etienne* / What do I do know: *Sleeper* / Walkin' in memphis: *Cher* / Waiting in vain: *Lennox, Annie* / Prayer for the dying: *Seal* / I'm only sleeping: *Suggs* / Love rendezvous: *M-People* / (You make me feel like a) natural woman: *Blige, Mary J.* / Yah mo be there: *Seville, Louise* / You remind me of something: *R Kelly* / Boom, shake the room: *DJ Jazzy Jeff & The Fresh Prince*

RADCD 30 / Dec '95 / Global TV

☐ HITS '97

MOODCD 49 / Dec '96 / Sony Music

☐ HITS FROM THE 50'S (3CD Set)

Twenty tiny fingers: *Cogan, Alma* / Wake up little Susie: *King Brothers* / Stairway to heaven: *Holliday, Michael* / Treasure of love: *Anthony, Billie* / Tammy: *Lotis, Dennis* / Idle gossip: *Campbell, Jean* / Istanbul: *Vaughan, Frankie* / Slow coach: *Radio Revellers* / Wake the town and tell the people: *Brennan, Rose* / Heartbeat: *Murray, Ruby* / Mule train: *Tennessee Ernie Ford* / At last at last: *Hughes, David* / Mangos: *Day, Jill* / Day that the rains came: *Jones Boys* / I saw Esau: *Holliday, Michael* / Love and marriage: *Cogan, Alma* / In the middle of the island: *King Brothers* / Happiness street: *Day, Jill* / Somewhere along the way: *Cole, Nat 'King'* / If I give my heart to you: *Shelton, Anne* / Story of Tina: *Harris, Ronnie* / Softly softly: *Murray, Ruby* / Man from Laramie: *Hockridge, Edmund* / This ole house: *Anthony, Billie* / Have I told you lately that I love you: *Tanners Sisters* / Mona Lisa: *Cole, Nat 'King'* / Bewitched: *Boswell, Eve* / Hey there: *Hockridge, Edmund* / I'd love to fall asleep: *Nichols, Penny* / Orange coloured sky: *Cole, Nat 'King'* / You belong to me: *Cogan, Alma* / My foolish heart: *Conway, Steve* / Mr wonderful: *Yana* / Suddenly there's a valley: *Lawrence, Lee* / My house is your house: *Holliday, Michael* / I talk to the trees: *Nicholls, Joy* / Look at that girl: *Vaughan, Frankie* / Ricochet: *Cogan, Alma* / Green door: *Ellington, Ray* / Answer me: *Campbell, Jean* / Rock the clock: *Deep River Boys* / Sincerely: *Day, Jill* / Wanted: *Brent, Tony* / Wheel of fortune: *Starr, Kay*

CDTRBOX 304 / 6 Oct '97 / EMI Gold

☐ HITS FROM THE 60'S (3CD Set)

Surfin' USA: *Beach Boys* / Without you: *Monro, Matt* / Let true love begin: *Cole, Nat 'King'* / Pasadena: *Temperance Seven* / Just one look: *Hollies* / From a window: *Kramer, Billy J.* / Who could be bluer: *Lordan, Jerry* / Rubber ball: *Avons* / Pistol packin' mama: *Vincent, Gene* / She wears my ring: *King, Solomon* / Little lovin': *Fourmost* / Thank U very much: *Scaffold* / Lucky five: *Conway, Russ* / As you like it: *Faith, Adam* / Games people play: *South, Joe* / Goldfinger: *Bassey, Shirley* / Don't let me be misunderstood: *Animals* / I'm a tiger: *Lulu* / Happiness: *Dodd, Ken* / It's all in the game: *Richard, Cliff* / Don't let the sun catch you crying: *Gerry & The Pacemakers* / Hanky panky: *James, Tommy & The Shondells* / Got to get you into my life: *Bennett, Cliff* / Wild cat: *Vincent, Gene* / Fever: *Shapiro, Helen* / Lucky devil: *Ifield, Frank* / Hippy hippy shake: *Swinging Blue Jeans* / One fine day: *Chiffons* / Moon river: *Williams, Danny* / Way you look tonight: *Lettermen* / Poison ivy: *Paramounts* / 5-4-3-2-1: *Manfred Mann* / Bang bang (my baby shot me down): *Cher* / Oh no not my baby: *Manfred Mann* / James Bond: *Barry, John* / Apache: *Shadows* / Seventy six trombones: *King Brothers* / Tell Laura I love her: *Valance, Ricky* / Royal event: *Conway, Russ* / There's a kind of hush: *Herman's Hermits* / Do you want to know a secret: *Kramer, Billy J. & The Dakotas* / I'm crying: *Animals* / It must be him: *Carr, Vikki* / Morningtown ride: *Seekers* / Poor me: *Faith, Adam* / I'm telling you now: *Freddie & The Dreamers* / Sabre dance: *Love Sculpture* / Bus stop: *Hollies*

CDTRBOX 308 / 6 Oct '97 / EMI Gold

☐ HITS FROM THE 70'S (3CD Set)

48 crash: *Quatro, Suzi* / If you can't give me love: *Quatro, Suzi* / It's the same old song: *KC & The Sunshine Band* / How much love: *Sayer, Leo* / Let's work together: *Canned Heat* / Dynamite: *Mud* / I don't wanna lose you: *Kandidate* / Magic: *Pilot* / Down at the doctors: *Dr. Feelgood* / Spanish stroll: *Mink Deville* / Heart of stone: *Kenny* / Fancy pants: *Kenny* / Touch too much: *Arrows* / Judy Teen: *Harley, Steve & Cockney Rebel* / Here comes the sun: *Harley, Steve & Cockney Rebel* / Ships in the night: *Be-Bop Deluxe* / Ranking full stop: *Beat* / Heaven is in the back seat of my cadillac: *Hot Chocolate* / Every one's a winner: *Hot Chocolate* / On my radio: *Selecter* / Cotton fields: *Beach Boys* / Gertcha: *Chas & Dave* / Freedom come freedom go: *Fortunes* / Better use your head: *Imperials* / 10538 overture: *ELO* / My Sharona: *Knack* / Malt and barley blues: *McGuinness Flint* / Journey: *Browne, Duncan* / Rich kids: *Rich Kids* / Right back where we started from: *Nightingale, Maxine* / Rag mama rag: *Band* / Tonight: *Move* / You're my everything: *Garrett, Lee* / Peaches: *Stranglers* / Darlin': *Miller, Frankie* / Ball park incident: *Wizzard* / Movin': *Brass Construction* / This will be: *Cole, Natalie* / Softly whispering I love you: *Congregation* / Oh you pretty thing: *Noone, Peter* / Whole lot of love: *CCS* / Dancing in the city: *Marshall Hain* / Na na na: *Powell, Cozy* / Motor bikin': *Spedding, Chris* / Boogie oogie oogie: *Taste Of Honey* / Crazy: *Mud* / More like the movies: *Dr. Hook* / Prince: *Madness*

CDTRBOX 312 / 6 Oct '97 / EMI Gold

☐ HITS FROM THE 80'S (3CD Set)

Freeze: *Spandau Ballet* / Wizard: *Hardcastle, Paul* / Classic: *Gurvitz, Adrian* / What's wrong with dreaming: *River City People* / Mony mony: *Amazulu* / Lawn chairs: *Our Daughters Wedding* / People do rock steady: *Bodysnatchers* / Modern girl: *Easton, Sheena* / Missing you: *Waite, John* / It started with a kiss: *Hot Chocolate* / You're lying: *Linx* / Plan B: *Dexy's Midnight Runners* / This little girl: *Bonds, Gary 'US'* / View from a bridge: *Wilde, Kim* / Respect: *Adeva* / Girl crazy: *Hot Chocolate* / Talk talk: *Talk Talk* / Bette Davis eyes: *Carnes, Kim* / Tarzan boy: *Baltimore* / Crying: *McLean, Don* / Searchin' (I gotta find a man): *Dean, Hazell* / Missing words: *Selecter* / Sleep walk: *Ultravox* / Politics of dancing: *Re-Flex* / C30 C60 C90 Go: *Bow Wow Wow* / Summertime: *Fun Boy Three* / Oh well: *Oh Well* / I could be so good for you: *Waterman, Dennis* / Goodbye girl: *Go West* / Can you keep a secret: *Brother Beyond* / Rise to the occasion: *Climie Fisher* / Strange little girl: *Stranglers* / There there my dear: *Dexy's Midnight Runners* / Comin' on strong: *Broken English* / C'est la vie: *Nevil, Robbie* / I'm forever blowing bubbles: *Cockney Rejects* / Somebody let me out: *Beggar & Co* / Freeze frame: *Geils, J. Band* / That certain smile: *Ure, Midge* / Summer fun: *Barracudas* / Dancing with myself: *Generation X* / Round and round: *Graham, Jaki* / Turning Japanese: *Vapors* / I shot the sheriff: *Light Of The World* / Love missile F1-11: *Sigue Sigue Sputnik* / Big apple: *Kajagoogoo* / Is it a dream: *Classix Nouveaux*

CDTRBOX 316 / 6 Oct '97 / EMI Gold

☐ HITS, HITS AND MORE DANCE HITS (2CD Set)

Another night: *Real McCoy* / Let me be your fantasy: *Baby D* / Welcome to tomorrow: *Snap* / Sweetness: *Gayle, Michelle* / She's got that vibe: *R Kelly* / Rhythm of the night: *Corona* / Special kind of love: *Carroll, Dina* / Movin' on up: *M-People* / Get away: *Maxx* / Swamp thing: *Grid* / Boom shake the room: *DJ Jazzy Jeff & The Fresh Prince* / Things can only get better: *D:Ream* / Ain't no love, ain't no use: *Sub Sub* / Show me love: *Robin S* / We are family: *Sister Sledge* / Now that we've found love: *Heavy D & The Boyz* / Mr. Vain: *Culture Beat* / It's my life: *Dr. Alban* / What is love: *Haddaway* / Let the beat control your body: *2 Unlimited* / Baby I love your way: *Big Mountain* / Searching: *China Black* / Compliments on your kiss: *Red Dragon* / Mr. Loverman: *Shabba Ranks* / Best of my love: *Lewis, C.J.* / Things that make you go hmmm: *C&C Music Factory* / Love I lost: *West End* / Don't you want me: *Felix* / Open your mind: *Usura* / Long train running: *Doobie Brothers* / Right here: *SWV* / My lovin': *En Vogue* / Push it: *Salt n' Pepa* / Finally: *Peniston, Ce Ce* / Key the secret: *Urban Cookie Collective* / Fantasy: *Black Box* / Run to you: *Rage* / Deep: *East 17* / Confide in me: *Minogue, Kylie* / Re-light my fire: *Take That & Lulu*

RADCD 02 / Nov '94 / Global TV

☐ HITS IN THE FIRST DEGREE (2CD Set)

NSCD 013 / Feb '95 / Newsound

☐ HITS OF 1930

Happy days are here again: *Hylton, Jack & His Orchestra* / With a song in my heart: *Hutch* / Puttin' on the rinse: *Astaire, Fred & Debroy Somers Band* / Little white lies: *Hanshaw, Annette & Her Sizzling Syncopators* / Falling in love again: *Dietrich, Marlene & Friedrich Hollander Orchestra* / Happy feet: *Whiteman, Paul & His Orchestra* / Georgia on my mind: *Carmichael, Hoagy & Orchestra* / When you're smiling: *Armstrong, Louis Orchestra* / Dancing with tears in my eyes: *Layton & Johnstone* / You brought a new kind of love to me: *Chevalier, Maurice* / Exactly like you: *Carlisle, Elsie* / It happened in Monterey: *Boles, John* / Ten cents a dance: *Etting, Ruth* / Let me sing and I'm happy: *Jolson, Al & Brunswick Studio Orchestra* / Three little words: *Rhythm boys & Duke Ellington Orchestra* / Beyond the blue horizon: *MacDonald, Jeanette* / I'm confessin' that I love you: *Lombardo, Guy & His Royal Canadians* / My baby just cares for me: *Payne, Jack & His Band* / If I had a talking picture of you: *Hylton, Jack & His Orchestra* / Oh, Donna Clara: *Metaxa, George & The New Mayfair Orchestra* / You're driving me crazy: *Vallee, Rudy & His Connecticut Yankees* / Without a song: *Tibbett, Lawrence & Nat Shilkret Orchestra* / Body and soul: *Hanshaw, Annette*

CDAJA 5195 / Jun '97 / Living Era

☐ HITS OF 1931

Stardust: *Crosby, Bing & Victor Young Orchestra* / Please don't talk about me when I'm gone: *Austin, Gene & trio* / Between the devil and the deep blue sea: *Calloway, Cab Orchestra* / Rockin' chair: *Robeson, Paul & Ray Noble New Mayfair Orchestra* / Peanut vendor: *Ambrose & His Orchestra* / Nevertheless: *Etting, ruth & orchestra* / Life is just a bowl of cherries: *Hutchinson, Leslie 'Hutch'* / When I take my sugar to tea: *Boswell Sisters & Dorsey Brothers Orchestra* / Cuban love song: *Tibbett, Lawrence & Stewart Wille* / Just one more chance: *Crosby, Bing & Victor Young Orchestra* / Lady of Spain: *Folgar, Tino* / Marta: *Tracy, Arthur* / Walkin' my baby back home: *Chevalier, Maurice* / Would you like to take a walk: *Hanshaw, Annette* / I don't know why, I just do: *Layton & Johnstone* / Prisoner of love: *Columbo, Russ & Nat Shilkret orchestra* / Dancing in the dark: *Revellers* / Sweet and lovely: *Bowlly, Al & Savoy Orpheans* / Lazy river: *Armstrong, Louis* / River stay 'way from my door: *Robeson, Paul & Ray Noble orchestra* / Sally: *Fields, Gracie & Jay Wilbur orchestra* / Dream a little dream of me: *Nelson, Ozzie* / Wrap your troubles in dreams: *Crosby, Bing & Gus Arnheim orchestra* / Goodnight, sweetheart: *Metaxa, George & Ray Noble & the New Mayfair Dance orchestra*

CDAJA 5190 / Dec '96 / Living Era

☐ HITS OF 1932

As time goes by: *Hale, Binnie* / Sun has got his hat on: *Ambrose & His Orchestra* / Clouds will soon roll by: *Ambrose & His Orchestra* / Please: *Crosby, Bing* / It don't mean a thing if it ain't got that swing: *Ellington, Duke* / Love is the sweetest thing: *Bowlly, Al* / Goodbye blues: *Mills Brothers* / I'll never be the same: *Malneck, Matty & His Orchestra* / Mad dogs and Englishmen: *Coward, Sir Noel* / Mad about the boy: *Lawrence, Gertrude* / I don't stand a ghost of a chance with you: *Austin, Gene* / Happy-go-lucky you and broken-heart me: *Lipton, Sydney & His Grosvenor House Orchestra* / Underneath the arches: *Flanagan & Allen* / By the fireside: *Noble, Ray* / Gipsy moon: *Crooks, Richard* / Isn't it romantic: *MacDonald, Jeanette* / Song is you: *Tibbett, Lawrence* / I've told ev'ry little star: *Ellis, Mary* / When we're alone: *Fox, Roy* / Say it isn't so: *Keller, Greta* / Paradise: *Crosby, Bing* / Sleepy-time down South: *Robeson, Paul* / Auf wiederseh'n, my dear: *Robeson, Paul* / Let's put out the lights and go to sleep: *Vallee, Rudy & His Connecticut Yankees*

CDAJA 5182 / Oct '96 / Living Era

☐ HITS OF 1933

Did you ever see a dream walking: *Crosby, Bing & Lennie Hayton Orchestra* / Butterflies in the rain: *Browne, Sam & Ambrose & His Orchestra* / Lover: *Fulton, Jack & Paul Whiteman Orchestra* / My song goes round the world: *Schmidt, Joseph & George Walter Orchestra* / It's the talk of the town: *Boswell, Connee & Victor Young Orchestra* / I'm getting sentimental over you: *Layton & Johnstone* / There's a cabin in the pines: *Armstrong, Louis Orchestra* / Try a little tenderness: *Crosby, Bing & Lennie Hayton Orchestra* / Lazybones: *Mills Brothers* / Dinner at eight: *Rowland, Helen & Ben Selvin Orchestra* / Night and day: *Astaire, Fred* / Sophisticated lady: *Ellington, Duke Orchestra* / Stormy weather: *Arlen, Harold & Leo Reisman Orchestra* / Blue prelude: *Robeson, Paul & Ray Noble New Mayfair Orchestra* / I cover the waterfront: *Fox, Roy Band* / Brother can you spare a dime: *Crosby, Bing & Lennie Hayton Orchestra* / Close your eyes: *Bowlly, Al & Ray Noble Orchestra* / By a waterfall: *Powell, Dick & Victor Young Orchestra* / Don't blame me: *Hutchinson, Leslie 'Hutch'* / Shadow waltz: *Burke, Marie & Albert Sandler Orchestra* / I gotta right to sing the blues: *Teagarden, Jack & Benny Goodman Orchestra* / How deep is the ocean: *Browne, Sam & Ambrose* / Temptation: *Crosby, Bing & Lennie Hayton Orchestra* / Last round-up: *Autry, Gene*

CDAJA 5183 / Aug '96 / Living Era

☐ HITS OF 1934

Love in bloom: *Crosby, Bing* / April in Paris: *Hall, Henry* / My old flame: *Anderson, Ivie* / Smoke gets in your eyes: *Dunne, Irene* / Miss Otis regrets: *Byng, Douglas* / Everything I have is yours: *Austin, Gene* / Very thought of you: *Bowlly, Al* / I'll be thinking of you: *Ferdinando, Angelo* / Stay as sweet as you are: *Browne, Sam* / Carioca: *Boswell, Connee* / Let's fall in love: *Tracy, Arthur* / Isle of Capri: *Fields, Gracie* / Continental: *Browne, Sam* / Dancing on the ceiling: *Matthews, Jessie* / I'll string along with you: *Powell, Dick* / For all we know: *Hutchinson, Leslie 'Hutch'* / One night of love: *Moore, Grace* / It's only a paper moon: *Edwards, Cliff* / Moonglow: *Waters, Ethel* / What a difference a day made: *Roy, Harry & His Orchestra* / Two cigarettes in the dark: *Crosby, Bing* / Honeysuckle rose: *Waller, Fats* / Tiger rag: *Mills Brothers* / Stars fell on Alabama: *Teagarden, Jack* / Little man you've had a busy day: *Robeson, Paul*

CDAJA 5184 / Jun '96 / Living Era

☐ HITS OF 1935

Top hat, white tie and tails: *Astaire, Fred* / Cheek to cheek: *Astaire, Fred* / La Cucaracha: *Roy, Harry* / Anything goes: *Aubert, Jeanne* / I get a kick out of you: *Merman, Ethel* / Easter Parade: *Hall, Henry* / Everything stops for tea: *Buchanan, Jack* / Lovely to look at: *Dunne, Irene* / What a difference a day made: *Dennis, Denny & Roy Fox* / I'm gonna sit right down and write myself a letter: *Waller, Fats* / Alone: *Dorsey, Tommy* / Top of your head: *Crosby, Bing & the Dorsey Brothers Orchestra* / Your feet's too big:

Ink Spots / I'm in the mood for love: Langford, Frances / Canoe song: Robeson, Paul / Bess you is my woman now: Tibbett, Lawrence & Helen Jepson / My very good friend, the milkman: Waller, Fats / Darling, je vous aime beaucoup: Hildegarde / East of the Sun and West of the moon: Tracy, Arthur / Red sails in the sunset: Fields, Gracie / Blue moon: Trumbauer, Frankie / I wished on the moon: Holiday, Billie & Teddy Wilson / Lullaby of Broadway: Powell, Dick

CDAJA 5185 / Apr '96 / Living Era

☐ HITS OF 1937

Bei mir bist du schon: Andrews Sisters / On the sunny side of the street: Armstrong, Louis / Rockin' chair: Bailey, Mildred / That old feeling: Boswell, Connee / Will you remember: Costa, Sam / Bob White: Crosby, Bing & Connie Boswell / Moon got in my eyes: Crosby, Bing / Sweet Leilani: Crosby, Bing / I've got you under my skin: Day, Frances / Marie: Dorsey, Tommy / Moon at sea: Fields, Shep / Leaning on a lamp-post: Formby, George / All God's chillun got rhythm: Garland, Judy / To Mary with love: Geraldo / Oh they're tough, mighty tough in the West: Gonella, Nat / Pennies from heaven: Gonella, Nat / Nice work if you can get it: Holiday, Billie / Slap that bass: Ink Spots / Was it rain: Langford, Frances / Greatest mistake of my life: Mesene, Jimmy / I've got my love to keep me warm: Powell, Dick / Broken hearted clown: Roy, Harry / Can I forget you: Sablon, Jean / September in the rain: Tracy, Arthur / Where is the sun: Valaida

CDAJA 5116 / Nov '93 / Living Era

☐ HITS OF 1938

Oh ma-ma: Andrews Sisters / Ti-pi-tin: Andrews Sisters / Change partners: Astaire, Fred / I used to be colour blind: Astaire, Fred / Nice work if you can get it: Astaire, Fred / Bei mir bist du schon: Bowlly, Al / You couldn't be cuter: Bowlly, Al / Somebody's thinking of you tonight: Browne, Sam / Me and my girl: Cooper, Jack / Big noise from Winnetka: Crosby, Bob / My heart is taking lessons in love: Crosby, Bing / On the sentimental side: Crosby, Bing / Boogie woogie: Dorsey, Tommy / Donkey serenade: Fields, Gracie / Whistle while you work: Fields, Shep / Tisket-a-tasket: Fitzgerald, Ella / Just let me look at you: Geraldo / Dipsy doodle: Gonella, Nat / Flat foot floogie: Gonella, Nat / Two sleepy people: Lynn, Vera & Denny Dennis / I hadn't anyone till you: Martin, Tony / Down and out blues: Mesene, Jimmy / Begin the beguine: Shaw, Artie / Music maestro please: Waller, Fats

CDAJA 5104 / May '93 / Living Era

☐ HITS OF 1939

Small town: Bowlly, Al / What do you know about love: Bowlly, Al / Oh you crazy moon: Clare, Wendy / I cried for you: Crosby, Bing / My melancholy baby: Crosby, Bing / I'm falling in love with someone: Crosby, Bing & Frances Langford / On the outside looking in: Currie, Bill / (I'm afraid) the masquerade is over: Dennis, Denny / FDR Jones: Fitzgerald, Ella / Over the rainbow: Garland, Judy / Blue orchids: Grantham, Cyril / Wish me luck as you wave me goodbye: Grantham, Cyril / I get along without you very well: Hall, Adelaide / Transatlantic lullaby: Hall, Adelaide / At the woodchoppers' ball: Herman, Woody / My prayer: Ink Spots / Deep purple: Layton, Turner / And the angels sing: Lenner, Anne / We'll meet again: Lynn, Vera / Wishing: Lynn, Vera / They say: Melachrino, George / In the mood: Miller, Glenn / Goodnight children everywhere: Roy, Harry / Indian summer: Simms, Ginny

CDAJA 5086 / Mar '92 / Living Era

☐ HITS OF 1940

Beat me Daddy, eight to the bar: Andrews Sisters / Woodpecker song: Andrews Sisters / If I had my way: Crosby, Bing / I haven't time to be a millionaire: Crosby, Bing / Only forever: Crosby, Bing / I can't love you anymore: Daniels, Bebe / Amapola: Durbin, Deanna / Love is all: Durbin, Deanna / Shake down the stars: Hall, Adelaide / Begin the beguine: Henderson, Chick & Joe Loss / Maybe: Ink Spots / Whispering grass: Ink Spots / It's a hap-hap-happy day: Lipton, Celia / Faithful forever: Carmen & Guy Lombardo / I'm in love for the last time: Lynn, Vera / It's a lovely day tomorrow: Lynn, Vera / Nearness of you: Miller, Glenn / Pennsylvania 6-5000: Miller, Glenn / Tuxedo junction: Miller, Glenn / Comes love: O'Connell, Helen & Jimmy Dorsey / Vagabond song: O'Connor, Cavan / I'm stepping out with a memory tonight: Shelton, Anne & Ambrose / Fools rush in: Sinatra, Frank & Tommy Dorsey / I'll never smile again: Sinatra, Frank & Tommy Dorsey

CDAJA 5087 / Oct '92 / Living Era

☐ HITS OF 1941

When that man is dead and gone: Bowlly, Al / I'd know you anywhere: Crosby, Bing / San Antonio rose: Crosby, Bing / You are my sunshine: Crosby, Bing / Six lessons from Madame La Zonga: Dorsey, Jimmy / Beneath the lights of home: Durbin, Deanna / It's foolish but it's fun: Durbin, Deanna / Down Forget-Me-Not Lane: Flanagan & Allen / Daddy: Geraldo / Hey little hen: Gonella, Nat / Oh buddy I'm in love: Gonella, Nat / Five o'clock whistle: Herman, Woody / Yesterday's dreams: Hutchinson, Leslie 'Hutch' / Ring, telephone, ring: Ink Spots / We three: Ink Spots / Amapola: Loss, Joe / Yours: Lynn, Vera / Last time I saw Paris: Martin, Tony / Johnson rag: Miller, Glenn / Yes my darling daughter: Miller, Glenn / Frenesi: Shaw, Artie / There goes that song again: Shelton, Anne

CDAJA 5100 / Feb '93 / Living Era

☐ HITS OF 1942

Don't sit under the apple tree: Andrews Sisters / Pennsylvania polka: Andrews Sisters / Green eyes: Barreto, Don / Deep in the heart of Texas: Crosby, Bing & Woody Herman / Moonlight becomes you: Crosby, Bing / White Christmas: Crosby, Bing / Zoot suit: Crosby, Bob / Skylark: Eckstine, Billy & Earl Hines / Always in my heart: Geraldo / Lamplighter's serenade: Geraldo / Jingle jangle jingle: Gonella, Nat / That lovely weekend: Henderson, Chick & Joe Loss / Anywhere on Earth is heaven: Hutchinson, Leslie 'Hutch' / Who wouldn't love you: Ink Spots / You made me love you: James, Harry / Where in the world: Martin, Tony / Chattanooga choo choo: Miller, Glenn / I know why: Miller, Glenn / Miss you: Roy, Harry / Sailor with the navy blue eyes: Roy, Harry / Three little sisters: Shore, Dinah / How about you: Sinatra, Frank & Tommy Dorsey / Without a song: Sinatra, Frank & Tommy Dorsey / Someone's rocking my dreamboat: Winstone, Eric

CDAJA 5103 / Mar '93 / Living Era

☐ HITS OF 1943

He's my guy: Fitzgerald, Ella / I'm thinking tonight of my blue eyes: Crosby, Bing / I left my heart at the stage door canteen: Winstone, Eric / Johnny Zero: Song Spinners / Murder he says: Dorsey, Jimmy / What's the good word Mr. Bluebird: Roy, Harry / Mr. Five by five: Andrews Sisters / Dearly beloved: Astaire, Fred / Every night about this time: Geraldo / G'bye now: Tilton, Martha / Let's get lost: Winstone, Eric / Coming in on a wing and a prayer: Song Spinners / That old black magic: Barnet, Charlie / Ain't got a dime to my name: Crosby, Bing / In the blue of evening: Geraldo / I'm gonna get lit up (when the lights go on in London): Loss, Joe / When Johnny comes marching home: Miller, Glenn / Don't get around much anymore: Ink Spots / Hit the road to dreamland: Roy, Harry / I had the craziest dream: Lynn, Vera / Better not roll those blye blue eyes: Ambrose / Be honest with me: Heist, Horace / Really and truly: Lynn, Vera

RAJCD 829 / Jan '97 / Empress

☐ HITS OF 1945

One meat ball: Andrews Sisters / More I see you: Cavallaro, Carmen / Tampico: Christy, June & Stan Kenton / Temptation: Como, Perry / Till the end of time: Como, Perry / Nina: Coward, Sir Noel / Accentuate the positive: Crosby, Bing / Baia: Crosby, Bing / I can't begin to tell you: Crosby, Bing / Sentimental journey: Day, Doris & Les Brown / Opus No.1: Dorsey, Tommy / There's no you: Dorsey, Tommy / I'm beginning to see the light: Fitzgerald, Ella & Ink Spots / Together: Haymes, Dick & Helen Forrest / Laura: Herman, Woody / Estrellita: James, Harry / Cocktails for two: Jones, Spike / Caldonia: Jordan, Louis / Little on the lonely side: Lombardo, Guy / Juke box Saturday night: Miller, Glenn / Cool water: Monroe, Vaughan / Cow cow boogie: Morse, Ella Mae / Conversation while dancing: Stafford, Jo & Johny Mercer / We'll gather lilacs: Tauber, Richard / Moonlight in Vermont: Whiting, Margaret

CDAJA 5186 / Jan '96 / Living Era

☐ HITS OF 1946

On the Atchison, Topeka and the Santa Fe: Garland, Judy / It might as well be Spring: Haymes, Dick / McNamara's band: Crosby, Bing / Prisoner of love: Como, Perry / To each his own: Ink Spots / Green cockatoo: Inglez, Roberto Orchestra / I fall in love too easily: Sinatra, Frank / All through the day: Haymes, Dick & Helen Forrest / Route 66: Cole, Nat 'King' / Laughing on the outside: Shore, Dinah / South America, take it away: Crosby, Bing & The Andrews Sisters / Humoresque: Lombardo, Guy / You make me feel so young: Haymes, Dick / Ole buttermilk sky: Carmichael, Hoagy / You keep coming back like a song: Hutch / They say it's wonderful: Como, Perry / Choo choo ch'boogie: Jordan, Louis / Gypsy: Ink Spots / Aren't you glad you're you: Crosby, Bing / Nancy with the laughing face: Sinatra, Frank / Rockabye your baby with a dixie melody: Jolson, Al / I'll buy that dream: Haymes, Dick & Helen Forrest / Come closer to me: Ros, Edmundo / September song: Huston, Walter / It's a pity to say goodnight: Fitzgerald, Ella

CDAJA 5246 / Feb '97 / Living Era

☐ HITS OF 1947

Five minutes more: Sinatra, Frank & Axel Stordahl Orchestra / Rumours are flying: Carle, Frankie Orchestra & Marjorie Hughes / Huggin' and chalkin': Carmichael, Hoagy & The Chickadees/Vic Schoen Orchestra / For sentimental reasons: Cole, Nat 'King' Trio / Zip-a-de-doo-dah: Mercer, Johnny & The Pied Pipers/Paul Weston Orchestra / La mer: Trenet, Charles Orchestra / Gal in Calico: Crosby, Bing & The Calico Kids/John Scott Trotter Orchestra / Linda: Clark, Buddy & Anita Gordon/Ray Noble Orchestra / Anniversary song: Jolson, Al / Heartaches: Weems, Ted Orchestra & Elmo Tanner / That's my desire: Laine, Frankie / How are things in Glocca Morra: Haymes, Dick & Gordon Jenkins Orchestra / Peg o' my heart: Harmonicats / Across the alley from the Alamo: Mills Brothers / Mam'selle: Sinatra, Frank & Axel Stordahl Orchestra / Alexander's ragtime band: Crosby, Bing & Al Jolson / When you were sweet sixteen: Como, Perry & The Satisfiers/Lloyd Schaffer Orchestra / Near you: Craig, Francis & Bob Lamm / You do: Shore, Dinah & Sonny Burke Orchestra / Ballerina: Monroe, Vaughan Orchestra / This is my lovely day: Guertary, Georges & Lizbeth Webb / Whiffenpoof song: Crosby, Bing & Fred Waring Glee Club / Chi-baba chi-baba my bambino go to sleep: Como, Perry & The Satisfiers/Lloyd Schaffer Orchestra / Now is the hour: Fields, Gracie & Phil Green Orchestra

CDAJA 5258 / Feb '98 / Living Era

☐ HITS OF 1960-1964

How do you do it: Gerry & The Pacemakers / Love of the loved: Black, Cilla / Nobody I know: Peter & Gordon / Somewhere: Proby, P.J. / How about that: Faith, Adam / Tell me what he said: Shapiro, Helen / Time: Douglas, Craig / Sun arise: Harris, Rolf / Little children: Kramer, Billy J. & The Dakotas / Little loving: Fourmost / Hungry for love: Kidd, Johnny & The Pirates / Wonderful world of the young: Williams, Danny / Legion's Last Patrol: Thorne, Ken / You can never stop me loving you: Lynch, Kenny / Sharing you: Vee, Bobby / You're no good: Swinging Blue Jeans / I understand: Freddie & The Dreamers / From a Jack to a King: Miller, Ned / Beatnik fly: Johnny & The Hurricanes / Unchained melody: Young, Jimmy

CDSL 8270 / Sep '95 / Music For Pleasure

☐ HITS OF 1965-1969

Sloop John B: Beach Boys / Jennifer Juniper: Donovan / Supergirl: Bonney, Graham / I've been wrong before: Black, Cilla / Elusive butterfly: Doonican, Val / Lover's concerto: Toys / Trains and boats and planes: Kramer, Billy J. / Ode to Billy Joe: Gentry, Bobbie / Come tomorrow: Manfred Mann / Got to get you into my life: Bennett, Cliff / On the road again: Canned Heat / Sunny: Hebb, Bobby / Kites: Dupree, Simon & The Big Sound / Wichita lineman: Campbell, Glen / Me the peaceful heart: Lulu / Mockingbird: Foxx, Inez & Charlie / Georgy girl: Seekers / Rudi's in love: Locomotive / We gotta get out of this place: Animals / He ain't heavy, he's my brother: Hollies

CDSL 8271 / Sep '95 / Music For Pleasure

☐ HITS OF 1993

PHCD 001 / Apr '94 / Penthouse

☐ HITS OF INVICTUS & HOT WAX, THE

You've got me: Chairmen Of The Board / Crumbs off the table: Glass House / Give me just a little more time: Chairmen Of The Board / Somebody's been sleeping in my bed: 100 Proof (Aged In Soul) / Band of gold: Payne, Freda / She's not just another: Eighth Wonder / Finders keepers: Chairmen Of The Board / While you're out: Honey Cone / Westbound no.9: Flaming Ember / Chairman of the board: Chairmen Of The Board / One monkey: Chairmen Of The Board / Want ads: Honey Cone / Stick up: Honey Cone / Girls it ain't easy: Honey Cone / Everything's Tuesday: Chairmen Of The Board / Women's love rights: Lee, Laura / If you can beat me rockin': Lee, Laura / Mind, body and soul: Flaming Ember / Bring the boys home: Payne, Freda / Deeper and deeper: Payne, Freda / I'm on my way: Chairmen Of The Board

HDH CD 501 / Jul '89 / HDH

☐ HITS OF THE 1930'S AND 1940'S, THE

GALE 430 / 20 Apr '98 / Gallerie

☐ HITS OF THE 50'S

Good golly miss molly: Little Richard / At the hop: Danny & The Juniors / Rockin' robin: Day, Bobby / Waterloo: Jackson, Stonewall / Rebel rouser: Eddy, Duane / I'm walkin': Nelson, Ricky / Rock a billy: Mitchell, Guy / Yakety yak: Coasters / Personality: Price, Lloyd / Seven little girls sitting in the back seat: Evans, Paul / That's all you gotta do: Evans, Paul / Love potion no.9: Clovers / Reveille rock: Johnny & The Hurricanes / Teen beat: Nelson, Sandy

101532 / Jun '97 / A-Play Collection

☐ HITS OF THE 50'S VOL.1

Singin' the blues: Mitchell, Guy / Smoke gets in your eyes: Platters / All my love: Page, Patti / At the top: Danny & The Juniors / Love letters in the sand: Boone, Pat / Cry: Ray, Johnnie / Mr. Blue: Fleetwoods / Three coins in the fountain: Four Aces / This ole house: Clooney, Rosemary / Ain't that a shame: Boone, Pat / Tom Dooley: Kingston Trio / Answer me: Lane, Frankie / Great balls of fire: Lewis, Jerry Lee / Tequila: Champs / Heartache by the number: Mitchell, Guy / My prayer: Platters / (How much is that) doggie in the window: Page, Patti

MUCD 9005 / Apr '95 / Musketeer

☐ HITS OF THE 50'S VOL.2

(We're gonna) Rock around the clock: Haley, Bill & The Comets / April love: Boone, Pat / Great pretender: Platters / Sleep walk: Santo & Johnny / Rockabilly: Mitchell, Guy / Half as much: Clooney, Rosemary / Sh-boom: Crew Cuts / I believe: Laine, Frankie / It's only make believe: Twitty, Conway / Stagger Lee: Price, Lloyd / Tennese waltz: Page, Patti / Party doll: Knox, Buddy / Love is a many splendoured thing: Four Aces / Just walking in the rain: Ray, Johnnie / Twilight time: Platters / Come softly to me: Fleetwoods / I'll be home: Boone, Pat / I went to your wedding: Page, Patti

MUCD 9006 / Apr '95 / Musketeer

☐ HITS OF THE 50'S VOL.2

Only you: Platters / Love letters in the sand: Boone, Pat / Lonesome town: Nelson, Ricky / I can't stop loving you: Gibson, Don / Sleepwalk: Santo & Johnny / Just a dream: Clanton, Jimmy / Lavender blue: Turner, Sammy / Jamaican farewell: Nina & Frederick / Love is a many splendoured thing: Four Aces / Send me the pillow you dream on: Mitchell, Guy / Just walking in the rain: Ray, Johnnie / Come softly to me: Fleetwoods / There goes my baby: Drifters

101522 / May '97 / A-Play Collection

☐ HITS OF THE 60'S

Needles and pins / Always something there to remind me / Have I the right / Downtown / Catch the wind / Tossing and turning / Hang on Sloopy / Michelle / Out of time / Sunny afternoon / Summer in the city / Itchycoo Park / Let the heartaches begin / Silence is golden / First cut is the deepest / Build me up buttercup / Pictures of matchstick men / (If paradise is) Half as nice

MCCD 028 / Sep '91 / Music Club

☐ HITS OF THE 60'S (2CD Set)

Sunny afternoon: Kinks / Do wah diddy diddy: Manfred Mann / Daydream: Lovin' Spoonful / Lazy Sunday: Small Faces / Pictures of matchstick men: Status Quo / Flowers in the rain: Move / Man of the world: Fleetwood Mac / Out of time: Farlowe, Chris / Everlasting love: Love Affair / Go now: Moody Blues / Waterloo sunset: Kinks / Natural born boogie: Humble Pie / Light my fire: Feliciano, Jose / Death of a clown: Davies, Ray / Pretty flamingo: Manfred Mann / First cut is the deepest: Arnold, P.P. / Stop stop stop: Hollies / Hurdy gurdy man: Donovan / Albatross: Fleetwood Mac / Itchycoo park: Small Faces / Dedicated follower of fashion: Kinks / Sabre dance: Love Sculpture / Let's go to San Francisco: Flowerpot Men / In the year 2525: Zager & Evans / (If you're going to): McKenzie, Scott / Mr. Tambourine man: Byrds / Something's gotten hold of my heart: Pitney, Gene / Carrie Anne: Hollies / House of the rising sun: Animals / Bang bang: Cher / Get out my life woman: Dorsey, Lee / Ain't got no I got life: Simone, Nina / Ob-la-di ob-la-da: Marmalade / Tired of waiting for you: Kinks / Silence is golden: Tremeloes / Working in a coalmine: Dorsey, Lee / Aquarius/Let the sun shine in: Fifth Dimension / Colours: Donovan / Oh happy day: Hawkins, Edwin Singers

RCACD 201 / Jul '97 / RCA

☐ HITS OF THE 60'S

Let's have a party: Jackson, Wanda / My boyfriend's back: Angels / Tobacco road: Nashville Teens / With a girl like you: Troggs / Hats off to Larry: Shannon, Del / Ferry cross the Mersey: Gerry & The Pacemakers / Coming on strong: Lee, Brenda / Ob-la-di ob-la-da: Marmalade / Viva Bobby Joe: Equals / Then he kissed me: Crystals / He's so fine: Chiffons / Hippy hippy shake: Swinging Blue Jeans / Swiss maid: Shannon, Del / If I were a carpenter: Darin, Bobby / (Dance with) the guitar man: Eddy, Duane / Sea of heartbreak: Gibson, Don / Love is all around: Troggs / Only sixteen: Cooke, Sam / I heard it through the grapevine: Gaye, Marvin / Leader of the pack: Shangri-Las

CD 6078 / Jun '97 / Music

☐ HITS OF THE 60'S (4CD Set)

PBXCD 416 / 20 Apr '98 / Pulse

☐ HITS OF THE 60'S VOL.1 (4CD Set)

MBSCD 401 / Nov '95 / Castle

☐ HITS OF THE 60'S VOL.1

Chapel of love: Dixie Cups / Will you still love me tomorrow: Shirelles / I'm into something good: Herman's Hermits / I'm telling you now: Freddie & The Dreamers / Nut rocker: B-Bumble & The Stingers / Young girl: Puckett, Gary / King of the road: Miller, Roger / Sheila: Roe, Tommy / Hey Paula: Paul & Paula / Save the last dance for me: Drifters / I'm sorry: Lee, Brenda / My old man's a dustman: Donegan, Lonnie / Little children: Kramer, Billy J. / Harper Valley PTA: Riley, Jeannie C. / Everlasting love: Love Affair / Baby come back: Equals / Sugar sugar: Archies / You'll never walk alone: Gerry & The Pacemakers

MUCD 9007 / Apr '95 / Musketeer

☐ HITS OF THE 60'S VOL.1

PLSCD 137 / Apr '96 / Pulse

☐ HITS OF THE 60'S VOL.1 (It's In His Kiss)

It's in his kiss: Everett, Betty / Telstar: Tornados / Blue moon: Marcels / Let's twist again: Checker, Chubby / Lovin' things: Marmalade / Winchester cathedral: New Vaudeville Band / Shelia: Roe, Tommy / How do you do it: Gerry & The Pacemakers / I remember you: Ifield, Frank / Speedy gonzales: Boone, Pat / Fools rush in: Nelson, Rick / Hippy hippy shake: Swinging Blue Jeans / Let's go to San Francisco: Flowerpot Men / Apache: Ingmann, Jorgen

101732 / May '97 / A-Play Collection

☐ HITS OF THE 60'S VOL.2 (4CD Set)

MBSCD 427 / Nov '93 / Castle

☐ HITS OF THE 60'S VOL.2

MCCD 193 / Mar '95 / Music Club

☐ HITS OF THE 60'S VOL.2

Runaway: Shannon, Del / Bachelors: Diane / Bad to me: Kramer, Billy J. / Ob-la-di ob-la-da: Marmalade / It's my party: Gore, Lesley / Do you love me: Poole, Brian / I like it: Gerry & The Pacemakers / Leader of the pack: Shangri-Las / Telstar: Tornados / When a man loves a woman: Sledge, Percy / Baby, now that I've found you: Foundations / Moody river: Boone, Pat / Alley oop: Hollywood Argyles / Big bad John: Dean, Jimmy / Deep purple: Tempo, Nino & April Stevens / Stranger on the shore: Bilk, Acker / Blue moon: Marcels / Those were the days: Hopkin, Mary

MUCD 9008 / Apr '95 / Musketeer

☐ HITS OF THE 60'S VOL.2

PLSCD 138 / Apr '96 / Pulse

☐ HITS OF THE 60'S VOL.2

Sweets for my sweet: Drifters / House of the rising sun: Animals / Mr.Tambourine man: Byrds / Letter: Box Tips / Elenore: Turtles / Wooly bully: Sam The Sham / Baby now that I've found you: Foundations / Travelin' man: Nelson, Rick / Pepe: Ingmann, Jorgen / Love grows: Edison Lighthouse / I live for the sun: Vanity Fare / Wait for me marianne: Vanity Fare / Allet cat: Bent Fabric

101742 / May '97 / A-Play Collection

☐ HITS OF THE 60'S VOL.3

PLSCD 139 / Apr '96 / Pulse

☐ HITS OF THE 60'S VOL.3 (You'll never walk alone)

You'll never walk alone: Gerry & The Pacemakers / When a man loves a woman: Sledge, Percy / Young girl: Puckett, Gary & The Union Gap / Stand by me: King, Ben E. / Silence is golden: King, Ben E. / Jesamine: Casuals / Venus in blue jeans: Clanton, Jimmy / End of the world: Davis, Skeeter / A single girl: Posey, Sandy / Hello mary lou: Nelson, Rick / More than I can say: Vee, Bobby / My girl: Temptations / All alone am I: Lee, Brenda / Can't help falling in love: Jordanaires

101752 / May '97 / A-Play Collection

☐ HITS OF THE 60'S VOL.3, THE (You'll Never Walk Alone)

You'll never walk alone: Gerry & The Pacemakers / When a man loves a woman: Sledge, Percy / My girl: Temptations / Stand by me: King, Ben E. / Teenage idol: Nelson, Rick / Strangers in the night: Martino, Al / Venus in blue jeans: Clanton, Jimmy / My love: Clark, Petula / Where have all the flowers gone: Kingston Trio / Love is all around: Troggs / Do you want to know a secret: Kramer, Billy J. / Silence is golden: Tremeloes / To know him is to love him: Shirelles / Que sera: Feliciano, Jose / With this ring: Platters / Someone, someone: Poole, Brian

100822 / May '97 / A-Play Collection

☐ HITS OF THE 60'S VOL.4

PLSCD 140 / Apr '96 / Pulse

☐ HITS OF THE 60'S, THE

Longshot kick de bucket: Pioneers / That's nice: Christian, Neil / Tribute to Buddy Holly: Berry, Mike / 007: Dekker, Desmond / Wonderful world, beautiful people: Cliff, Jimmy / Lonely city: Leyton, Johnny / Red red wine: Tribe, Tony / Train to skaville: Ethiopians / My friend Jack: Smoke / Return of Django: Upsetters / Take a heart: Sorrows / Melting pot: Blue Mink / I put a spell on you: Price, Alan / Liquidator: Harry J All Stars / Shame: Price, Alan / Lone rider: Leyton, Johnny

EMPRCD 574 / Jul '95 / Emporio

☐ HITS OF THE 60'S, THE

PDSCD 540 / Aug '96 / Pulse

☐ HITS OF THE 70'S (2CD Set)

Denis: Blondie / Peaches: Stranglers / Mr. Blue sky: ELO / Daniel: John, Elton / Roadrunner: Richman, Jonathan & Modern Lovers / Apeman: Kinks / Cars: Numan, Gary / Baker Street: Rafferty, Gerry / Walk on the wildside: Reed, Lou / All the young dudes: Mott The Hoople / Love train: O'Jays / Heart of glass: Blondie / Show you the way to go: Jacksons / Vincent: McLean, Don / Native New Yorker: Odyssey / Make me smile: Harley, Steve & Cockney Rebel / Without you: Nilsson, Harry / Sylvia's mother: Dr. Hook & The Medicine Show / September: Earth, Wind & Fire / Lean on me: Withers, Bill / Egyptian reggae: Richman, Jonathan & Modern Lovers / All right now: Free / In the summertime: Mungo Jerry / Down down: Status Quo / Rasputin: Boney M / That lady: Isley Brothers / Rock your baby: McCrae, George / Love grows where my Rosemary goes:

Edison Lighthouse / See my baby jive: Wizzard / Blockbuster: Sweet / I'm the leader of the gang: Glitter, Gary / Who do you love: Juicy Lucy / Seasons in the sun: Jacks, Terry / Knock three times: Dawn / Best of my love: Emotions / Like sister and brother: Drifters / Lost in France: Tyler, Bonnie

RCACD 202 / Jul '97 / RCA

☐ HITS OF THE 70'S (18 Original Hits By The Original Stars)

Banner man: Blue Mink / (To be) young gifted and black: Bob & Marcia / If I had you: Korgis / Clog dance: Violinski / Oohh I do: De Paul, Lynsey / Nice one Cyril: Cockerel Chorus / Tomorrow night: Atomic Rooster / Love of the common people: Thomas, Nicky / Moon river: Greyhound / Suzanne beware of the devil: Livingstone, Dandy / Desperate Dan: Lieutenant Pigeon / Brandy scott: English, Scott / Snoopy vs the red dragon: Hotshots / 7 Teen: Regents / Chirpy chirpy cheep cheep: Kissoon, Mac & Katie / Hotshot: Blue, Barry

EMPRCD 583 / Oct '95 / Emporio

☐ HITS OF THE 70'S, THE

PDSCD 525 / Aug '96 / Pulse

☐ HITS OF THE 80'S

Centrefold: Geils, J. Band / Road to nowhere: Talking Heads / French kissin' in the USA: Harry, Deborah / Nineteen: Hardcastle, Paul / Wishful thinking: China Crisis / Running up that hill: Bush, Kate / If I was: Ure, Midge / She makes my day: Palmer, Robert / Heart and soul: T'Pau / True: Spandau Ballet / Cushed by the wheels of industry: Heaven 17 / Dancing with tears in my eyes: Ultravox / Don't worry, be happy: McFerrin, Bobby / We close our eyes: Go West / Letter from America: Proclaimers / More than I can say: Sayer, Leo

CDMFP 6136 / Feb '95 / Music For Pleasure

☐ HITS OF THE 80'S (2CD Set)

This is the right time: Stansfield, Lisa / True: Spandau Ballet / Don't stop the dance: Ferry, Bryan / Harry's Game: Clannad / Simply irresistable: Palmer, Robert / Call me: Blondie / I scare myself: Dolby, Thomas / Would I lie to you: Eurythmics / Chain reaction: Ross, Diana / Sometimes: Erasure / Walk like an Egyptian: Bangles / Only you: Yazoo / It doesn't have to be this way: Blow Monkeys / Do you really want to hurt me: Culture Club / Power of love: Rush, Jennifer / Ghostbusters: Parker, Ray Jr. / It ain't what you do: Fun Boy Three & Bananarama / Wherever I lay my hat: Young, Paul / White wedding: Idol, Billy / Walking on sunshine: Katrina & The Waves / Band of gold: Sylvester / Atmospherics: Robinson, Tom / I can't go for that (no can do): Hall & Oates / Love is a battlefield: Benatar, Pat / No more the fool: Brooks, Elkie / We built this city: Starship / Favourite shirts (Boy meets girl): Haircut 100 / Modern girl: Meat Loaf / System addict: Five Star / Loco in Acapulco: Four Tops / Who's zoomin' who: Franklin, Aretha / 19: Hardcastle, Paul / I'm so excited: Pointer Sisters / Ghost town: Specials / Perfect: Fairground Attraction / Friends: Stewart, Amii

RCACD 212 / Jul '97 / RCA

☐ HITS OF THE 80'S VOL.1

Love action (I believe in love): Human League / Church of the poison mind: Culture Club / Temptation: Heaven 17 / Echo beach: Martha & The Muffins / Black Man Ray: China Crisis / Love don't live here anymore: Nail, Jimmy / You little thief: Sharkey, Feargal / Driving away from home: It's Immaterial / We don't have to take our clothes off: Stewart, Jermaine / (I just) died in your arms: Cutting Crew / Shattered dreams: Johnny Hates Jazz / China in your hand: T'Pau / Sinful: Wylie, Pete / Dream kitchen: Frazier Chorus / Straight up: Abdul, Paula / Mary's prayer: Danny Wilson / If only I could: Youngblood, Sydney

CDVIP 126 / Jul '94 / Virgin

☐ HITS OF THE 80'S VOL.1

Love is a stranger: Eurythmics / Who's zoomin' who: Franklin, Aretha / Never gonna give you up: Astley, Rick / Perfect: Fairground Attraction / Slow hand: Pointer Sisters / Funkin' for Jamaica: Browne, Sandra / Ride on time: Black Box / I can't go for that (no can do): Hall & Oates / Runaway boys: Stray Cats / Broken wings: Mr. Mister / Every day hurts: Sad Cafe / Love plus one: Haircut 100

74321446882 / Feb '97 / Camden

☐ HITS OF THE 80'S VOL.1, THE

West End girls: Pet Shop Boys / Mickey: Basil, Toni / Special brew: Bad Manners / Feels like I'm in love: Marie, Kelly / Swing the mood: Jive Bunny / High energy: Thomas, Evelyn / Move closer: Jones, Tom / Transfer affection: Flock Of Seagulls / Bass (how low can you go): Harris, Simon / Touch me (I want your body): Fox, Samantha / Can't shake that feeling: Big Fun / You think you're a man: Divine / Fantasy Island: Tight Fit / Hands off she's mine: Beat / Jack mix IV: Mirage / On a crowded street: Pennington, Barbara

100102 / May '97 / A-Play Collection

☐ HITS OF THE 80'S VOL.2

Days: MacColl, Kirsty / Do you really want to hurt me: Culture Club / Christian: China Crisis / Life's what you make it: Talk Talk / Looking for Linda: Hue & Cry / Turning Japanese: Vapors / This is not a love song: Public Image Ltd. / Sit and wait: Youngblood, Sydney / Come live with me: Heaven 17 / Calling all the heroes: It Bites / Big fun: Inner City / Wild world: Priest, Maxi / Night boat to Cairo: Madness / Moonlight shadow: Oldfield, Mike / Too late for goodbyes: Lennon, Julian / Turn back the clock: Johnny Hates Jazz / Heart and soul: T'Pau / Bette Davis eyes: Carnes, Kim / Enola Gay: OMD

CDVIP 136 / Sep '95 / Virgin

☐ HITS OF THE 80'S VOL.2

Who's that girl: Eurythmics / Japanese boy: Aneka / Kyrie: Mr. Mister / Man eater: Hall & Oates / You're the voice: Farnham, John / Radio Africa: Latin Quarter / No memory: Scarlet Fantastic / Star: Dee, Kiki / Funkin' for Jamaica: Browne, Tom / Loco in Acapulco: Browne, Tom / Favourite shirts: Haircut 100 / Einstein a go go: Landscape / First picture of you: Lotus Eaters / Automatic: Pointer Sisters / Doctor doctor: Thompson Twins / Crash: Primitives / Nothing's gonna stop us now: Starship / All out of love: Air Supply

74321500262 / Jun '97 / Camden

☐ HITS OF THE 80'S VOL.2, THE

Kiss: Jones, Tom & Art Of Noise / Blame it on the boogie: Big Fun / That's what I like: Jive Bunny / Wishing (if I had a photograph of you): Flock Of Seagulls / Can can: Bad Manners / Lion sleeps tonight: Tight Fit / If you're ready (come go with me): Turner, Ruby & Jonathan Butler / Nothing's gonna stop me now: Fox, Samantha / Jack mix II: Mirage / Close to perfection: Brown, Miquel / Mirror in the bathroom: Beat / Fan the flame: Pennington, Barbara / I eat cannibal: Toto Coelo / Wee rule: Wee Papa Girl Rappers / Walk like a man: Divine / Saddle up: Christie, David / Here comes that sound: Harris, Simon

100112 / May '97 / A-Play Collection

☐ HITS OF THE 80'S, THE (3CD Set)

High energy: Thomas, Evelyn / Fan the flame: Pennington, Barbara / So many men, so little time: Brown, Miquel / Who knows the devil: Man To Man / Great minds think alike: Wells, James / Animal magnetism: Pandy, Darryl / Standing in line: Mancha, Steve / Take one step forward: Wills, Viola & Noel McCalla / Chalk it up to experience: Thomas, Evelyn / Close to perfection: Brown, Miquel / Hands off: Pallas, Laura / Ain't no mountain high enough: Powell, Shezwae / Love's gone mad: Seventh Avenue / West End girls: Pet Shop Boys / Mickey: Basil, Toni / Special brew: Bad Manners / Feels like I'm in love: Marie, Kelly / Swing the mood: Jive Bunny / High energy: Thomas, Evelyn / Move closer: Jones, Tom / Transfer affection: Flock Of Seagulls / Bass (how low can you go): Harris, Simon / Touch me (I want your body): Fox, Samantha / Can't shake that feeling: Big Fun / You think you're a man: Divine / Fantasy Island: Tight Fit / Hands off she's mine: Beat / Jack mix IV: Mirage / On a crowded street: Pennington, Barbara / Kiss: Jones, Tom & Art Of Noise / Blame it on the boogie: Big Fun / That's what I like: Jive Bunny / Wishing (if I had a photograph of you): Flock Of Seagulls / Can can: Bad Manners / Lion sleeps tonight: Tight Fit / If you're ready (come go with me): Butler, Jonathan / Nothing's gonna stop me now: Fox, Samantha / Jack mix II: Mirage / Close to perfection: Brown, Miquel / Mirror in the bathroom: Beat / Fan the flame: Pennington, Barbara / I eat cannibal: Toto Coelo / Wee rule: Wee Papa Girl Rappers / Walk like a man: Divine / Saddle up: Christie, David / Here comes that sound: Harris, Simon

101212 / May '97 / A-Play Collection

☐ HITS OF THE 90'S

Whole of the moon: Waterboys / Thinking about your love: Thomas, Kenny / King of the road: Proclaimers / Ring my bell: Adeva & Monie Love / Is it like today: World Party / Got to have your love: Mantronix / Love and anger: Bush, Kate / Hold on: Wilson Phillips / I believe: EMF / Faithful: Go West / One and only: Hawkes, Chesney / Don't worry: Appleby, Kim / U can't touch this: MC Hammer / Ice ice baby: Vanilla Ice / Turtle power: Partners In Kryme / Counting every minute: Sonia

CDMFP 6139 / Feb '95 / Music For Pleasure

☐ HITS OF THE 90'S

GFS 087 / Nov '97 / Going For A Song

☐ HITS OF THE BLITZ

If a grey-haired lady says How's yer father: Wilbur, Jay & his band / We'll meet again: Petersen, Joe / It's a hap-hap-happy day: Roy, Harry & His Orchestra / We must all stick together: Geraldo & His Orchestra / Mem'ry of a rose: Loss, Joe Band / Man who comes around: Connelly, Campbell & Co. Ltd / Oh Johnny oh Johnny: Young, Arthur / Run rabbit run: Ambrose & His Orchestra / Careless: White, Jack & His Collegians / Memories live longer than dreams: Dash, Irwin & Monte Ray / I haven't time to be a millionaire: Gonella, Nat & His New Georgians / It's a lovely day tomorrow: Hutchinson, Leslie 'Hutch' / Nightingale sang in berkeley square: Layton, Turner / I hear bluebirds: Organ Dance Band & Me / Tiggerty boo: Geraldo & His Orchestra / (We're gonna hang out the) washing on the Siegfried Line: Ambrose & His Orchestra / Make believe island: Bowlly, Al & Jim Mesene / I shall be waiting: Lipton, Sydney & His Grosvenor House Orchestra / Arm in arm: Lipton, Sydney & His Grosvenor House Orchestra / FDR Jones: Askey, Arthur & Jack Hylton / Crash bang I want to go home: Robins, Phyllis / In the mood: Philips, Sid Trio

PASTCD 9754 / Mar '92 / Flapper

☐ HITS OF THE PAST VOL.2

ANGCD 017 / Jul '96 / Angela

☐ HITS OF THE SEVENTIES

Band of gold: Payne, Freda / Feel the need in me: Detroit Emeralds / Ms. Grace: Tymes / Native New Yorker: Odyssey / Yellow river: Christie / Son of my father: Chicory Tip / Lost in music: Sister Sledge / Love really hurts without you: Ocean, Billy / Don't let it die: Hurricane smith / Patches: Carter, Clarence / Car wash: Royce, Rose / Heaven must be missing an angel: Tavares / Hang on in there baby: Bristol, Johnny / Love grows: Edison Lighthouse / I'm in the mood for dancing: Nolans / Ring my bell: Ward, Anita / Stoned love: Supremes / That same old feeling: Pickettywitch

CD 6085 / 29 Sep '97 / Music

☐ HITS OF THE WAR YEARS

CWNCD 2003 / Jun '95 / Javelin

☐ HITS REVIVAL

It's in his kiss (the shoop shoop song): Everett, Betty / Love on a mountain top: Knight, Robert / Dancing in the street: Reeves, Martha / Dizzy: Roe, Tommy / Happy together: Turtles / She's not there: Zombies / Harlem shuffle: Bob & Earl / Under the boardwalk: Drifters / Rock your baby: McCrae, George / In crowd: Gray, Dobie / It's my party: Gore, Lesley / What becomes of the broken hearted: Ruffin, Jimmy / If you don't know me by now: Melvin, Harold & The Bluenotes / Great pretender: Platters / Groovy kind of love: Fontana, Wayne / When a man loves a woman: Sledge, Percy / End of the world: Davis, Skeeter / Sorrow: Merseys

ECD 3050 / Jan '95 / K-Tel

☐ HITS THAT LIVE FOREVER - 1950'S (2CD Set)

When I fall in love: Cole, Nat 'King' / Blueberry Hill: Domino, Fats / Seven little girls sitting on the back seat: Avons / Why do fools fall in love: Lymon, Frankie & The Teenagers / Sixteen tons: Ford, Tennessee Ernie / This ole house: Anthony, Billie / Oh mein Papa: Calvert, Eddie / Dreamboat: Cogan, Alma / C'mon everybody: Cochran, Eddie / Side saddle: Conway, Russ / Cry me a river: London, Julie / No other love: Hilton, Ronnie / True love: Crosby, Bing & Grace Kelly / Comes-a-long-alove: Starr, Kay / That's amore: Martin, Dean / Lollipop: Mudlarks / Softly softly: Murray, Ruby / Stairway of love: Holiday, Michael / Kisses sweeter than wine: Rodgers, Jimmie / He's got the whole world in his hands: London, Laurie / Witch Doctor: Lang, Don / Be my girl: Dale, Jim / Come softly to me: Fleetwoods / Great pretender: Parkinson, Jimmy / Indian love call: Whitman, Slim / Fever: Lee, Peggy / Only sixteen: Douglas, Craig / Story of my life: Holiday, Michael / Pickin' a chicken: Boswell, Eve / Unchained melody: Baxter, Les / Memories are made of this: Martin, Dean / White sports coat: King Brothers / Ain't that a shame: Domino, Fats / Dragnet: Anthony, Ray / Zambesi: Busch, Lou / Ma he's making eyes at me: Otis, Johnny / Ragtime Cowboy Joe: Chipmunks / Here in my heart: Martino, Al / Tom Dooley: Kingston Trio / Be bop a lula: Vincent, Gene / St. Therese of the roses: Vaughan, Malcolm / Ballad of Davy Crocket: Ford, Tennessee Ernie / Don't laugh at me: Wisdom, Norman / Mad passionate love: Bresslaw, Bernard / Rose Marie: Whitman, Slim / Pretend: Cole, Nat 'King' / Cherry pink and apple blossom white: Calvert, Eddie / Big man: Four Preps / Teenager in love: Douglas, Craig / Bell bottom blues: Cogan, Alma

CDDL 1308 / Jun '96 / Music For Pleasure

☐ HITS THAT LIVE FOREVER - 1960'S (2CD Set)

House of the rising sun: Animals / God only knows: Beach Boys / Here I go again: Hollies / I'm telling you now: Freddie & The Dreamers / Hi Ho silver lining: Beck, Jeff / Do wha diddy diddy: Manfred Mann / Carnival is over: Seekers / Yesterday: Monro, Matt / Three steps to heaven: Cochran, Eddie / Walkin' back to happiness: Shapiro, Helen / How do you do it: Gerry & The Pacemakers / Poor me: Faith, Adam / What now my love: Bassey, Shirley / Shakin' all over: Kidd, Johnny & The Pirates / She wears my ring: King, Solomon / Little children: Kramer, Billy J. & The Dakotas / True love ways: Peter & Gordon / Wonderful land: Shadows / Standing on the corner: King Brothers / High time: Jones, Paul / Little loving: Fourmost / He ain't heavy, he's my brother: Hollies / There's a kind of hush: Herman's Hermits / You're sixteen: Burnette, Johnny / Boom bang-a-bang: Lulu / Good vibrations: Beach Boys / Anyone who had a heart: Black, Cilla / Pasadena: Temperance Seven / Where do you go to my lovely: Sarstedt, Peter / Mony Mony: James, Tommy & The Shondells / Michael: Highwaymen / World of our own: Seekers / I remember you: Ifield, Frank / Somewhere: Proby, P.J. / Lily the pink: Scaffold / Pretty flamingo: Manfred Mann / Hippy hippy shake: Swinging Blue Jeans / Rubber ball: Vee, Bobby / I'm the urban spaceman: Bonzo Dog Band / Up on the roof: Lynch, Kenny / Blue moon: Marcels / All I have to do is dream: Campbell, Glen & Bobbie Gentry

CDDL 1311 / Jun '96 / Music For Pleasure

☐ HITS THAT LIVE FOREVER - 1970'S (2CD Set)

Heart of glass: Blondie / Air that I breathe: Hollies / Make me smile (Come up and see me sometime): Harley, Steve & Cockney Rebel / Wow: Bush, Kate / Tap turns on the water: CCS / Baker Street: Rafferty, Gerry / Let's work together: Canned Heat / See my baby jive: Wizzard / American Pie: McLean, Don / I hear you knocking: Edmunds, Dave / So you win again: Hot Chocolate / Oh boy: Mud / Motor Bikin': Spedding, Chris / Summer(The First Time): Goldsboro, Bobby / Can the Can: Quatro, Suzi / Roll over Beethoven: ELO / Some girls: Racey / Don't let it die: Smith, Hurricane / January: Pilot / Tears of a Clown: Beat / You sexy thing: Hot Chocolate / Nutbush City Limits: Turner, Tina / Tiger Feet: Mud / Judy Teen: Harley, Steve & Cockney Rebel / Denis: Blondie / Little bit more: Dr. Hook / Devil Gate Drive: Quatro, Suzi / Queen of Clubs: KC & The Sunshine Band / Vincent: McLean, Don / 2-4-6-8 Motorway: Robinson, Tom / Sylvia: Focus / If I only had words: Fitzgerald, Scott & Yvonne Keeley / Living on the Frontline: Grant, Eddy / Where is the love: Wright, Betty / Dancing easy: Williams, Danny / Fancy pants: Kenny / Dance with the Devil: Powell, Cozy / Rock your baby: McCrae, George / Right back where we started from: Nightingale, Maxine / Dancing in the City: Hain, Marshall

CDDL 1314 / Jun '96 / Music For Pleasure

☐ HITZ BLITZ

Never forget: Take That / Search for a hero: M-People / Girl like you: Collins, Edwyn / Whiter shade of pale: Lennox, Annie / Boom boom boom: Outhere Brothers / Love rules: West End / Stuck on you: PJ & Duncan / Where is the feeling: Minogue, Kylie / Bomb: Bucketheads / Try me out: Corona / Surrender your love: Nightcrawlers / Shoot me with your love: D:Ream / Keep warm: Jinny / Right in the night (fall in love with the music): Jam & Spoon / Sing it: Mozaic / Humpin' around: Brown, Bobby / Freek n' you: Jodeci / Your loving arms: Martin, Billie Ray / Whoomph (there it is): Clock / Freedom: Gayle, Michelle / Hands up, hands up: Zig & Zag / Unchained melody: Robson & Jerome

RADCD 23 / Aug '95 / Global TV

☐ HITZ BLITZ

Ooh ah, just a little bit / We've got it going on / Macarena / Wannabe / Keep on jumpin' / X-files / Children / So pure / I don't wanna be a star / Missing / Born slippy / Mysterious girl / How bizarre / Return of the mack / 1,2,3,4,(sumpin' new) / Spaceman / How deep is your love / Breakfast at Tiffany's

SUMCD 4085 / Nov '96 / Summit

☐ HITZONE '97 (2CD Set)

If you ever: East 17 & Gabrielle / I'll never break your heart: Backstreet Boys / Father and son: Boyzone / Lifted: Lighthouse Family / Flame: Fine Young Cannibals / Make it with you: Let Loose / How bizarre: OMC / Flava: Andre, Peter / Do you still: East 17 / When I fall in love: Ant & Dec / Breathe: Prodigy / Born slippy: Underworld / Wrong: Everything But The Girl / Hyperballad: Bjork / Sugar is sweeter: C.J. Bolland / So pure: Baby D / I'm alive: Stretch n' Vern & Maddog / There's nothing I won't do: JX / Follow the rules: Livin' Joy / Blurred: Pianoman / Peacock suit: Weller, Paul / One to another: Charlatans / Twisted: Skunk Anansie / Getting better: Shed Seven / Sandstorm: Cast / Good enough: Dodgy / Goldfinger: Ash / Trash: Suede / You're gorgeous: Baby Bird / Day we caught the train: Ocean Colour Scene / Breakfast at Tiffany's: Deep Blue Something / She said: Longpigs / You and me versus the world: Space / One of us: Osbourne, Joan / So in love with you: Duke / Stressed out: Tribe Called Quest & Faith Evans / Golden brown: Kaleef / California love: 2Pac & Dr Dre / Whole lotta love: Goldbug / Theme from Mission: Impossible: Mullen, Larry & Adam Clayton

5331872 / Dec '96 / PolyGram TV

☐ HOBO BOP

Hobo bop: Nelson, Tommy / That long black train: Franklin, Stewart / Hey Mr. Porter: Pruitt, Ralph / I'm so lonely: Flagg, Bill / Goodbye train: Foley, Jim / Mystery train: Taylor, Vernon / Ho bo: Money, Curley / Midnight line: Riley, Bob / Long gone night train: Norman, Gene / One way track: Davis, Hank / Boxcar blues: Spurling, Hank / I'm a hobo: Reevers, Danny / Loco choo choo: Miller Bros. / Ride that train: James, Leon / Midnite express: Tremaines / Going back to Dixie: Busbice, Wayne / Big black train: Johnston, Stan / Midnight train: Newman, Wayne / Train wistle boogie: Dean, Charles / Big train: Law, Art / Lonely lonely train: Anderson, Sonny / Folsom Prison blues: Tidwell, Billy / Train: Runabouts / Haunted train: Millionaires / Woman train: Davis, Hank / Miami road: Phillipson, Larry Lee / Kansas city train: Lowery, Frankie / Long black train: Farmer, Larry / Train rock: Boni, Johnny

CDBB 55012 / Apr '94 / Buffalo Bop

☐ HOKUM BLUES 1924-1929

DOCD 5370 / Jul '95 / Document

☐ HOLD THAT DREAM

NTHEN 026CD / Mar '96 / Now & Then

☐ HOLD TIGHT - IT'S THE 60'S (2CD Set)

PBXCD 401 / Nov '96 / Pulse

☐ HOLDING ON

SHCD 6015 / Oct '95 / Shanachie

☐ HOLDING UP HALF THE SKY (Roots Daughters - Women In Reggae)

SH 45027 / Oct '96 / Shanachie

☐ HOLDING UP HALF THE SKY (Voices Of African Women)

SHCD 64073 / Apr '97 / Shanachie

☐ HOLDING UP HALF THE SKY (Voices Of Celtic Women)

Rosie my love: Clannad / Tinkerman daughter: Fisher, Cilla / Streets of Derry: Bothy Band / Rambling Irishman: Voice Squad / Water is wide: Woods, Gay & Steeleye Span / Fill iu o: MacKenzie, Talitha / ISle of St. Helena: Black, Mary & General Humbert / Storm in my heart: Keane, Dolores / She is like the swallow: Casey, Karan / Maggie: O'Connell, Maura / 12th of July: Ryan, Cathie / Green wood ladie: Ni Dhomhnaill, Maighread / Little pet: Ni Dhomhnaill, Maighread / Wild roving no more: Barnes, Sylvia & Kentigern

SHANCD 78011 / 9 Mar '98 / Shanachie

☐ HOLDING UP HALF THE SKY (Women's Voices From Around The World/4CD Set)

SH 6100 / Oct '97 / Shanachie

☐ HOLIDAY HIT MIX '97 (2CD Set)

ZYX 811192 / 29 Sep '97 / ZYX

☐ HOLIDAY IN GREECE (2CD Set)

Zorba the Greek / Thekos din karthoula sou / Doxa te theo / Lemaishani / Meray / To bouzouki echi kefia / Fantasia / Adzenta / State of angels / Medelinyia / Poune ta kronia / To yelasto pedi / Horos tou sakena / Aprillis / I kambanes / Oli nichta / Siko horepse sirtaki / Kai mis e dris ston kafenai / Lefteris / Sinchoriste to apopse to pedi / To ena ftero mou ekopses / Mikhalis / Epifania / Psilli sta ftiamo / Traditional bouzouki solo / Srata te strata / Kaymos / Palanta tou antrikou / Vraho vraho / Ekeine / O delefdaos mou stathmos / Thello varya thiblo benya

330192 / Jul '96 / Hallmark

☐ HOLIDAY TRAILS FROM ROUMANIA

CNCD 5983 / Apr '94 / Disky

☐ HOLIDAYS IN THE SUN VOL.1

HITS 01 / Jun '97 / Visionary/ Jettisoundz

☐ HOLIDAYS IN THE SUN VOL.2

HITS 02 / Jun '97 / Visionary/ Jettisoundz

☐ HOLLAND SUCKS

BC 1713CD / 29 Jun '98 / Bitzcore

☐ HOLLERIN'

ROUCD 0071 / Jul '95 / Rounder

☐ HOLLY AND THE IVY, THE (Early Christmas Music)

God rest ye merry gentlemen / In dulci jubilo / Holly and the Ivy / Ding dong merrily on high / Es ist ein rose / Personet hodie / Coventry carol / Puer natus / All ye who are to mirth inclined / Wexford Carol / Gabriel's message / Tomorrow shall be my day / Boar's head Carol / This truth sent from above / Blessed be Maid Marie / Joseph and Mary / Nuns of Chester

3036001202 / 15 Sep '97 / Carlton

☐ HOLLYWOOD ROCK 'N' ROLL VOL.1 (12 Rare Rockabilly Tracks)

Blue jeans: Glenn, Glen / Everybody's movin': Glenn, Glen / Would you: Rock 'n' Roll / Goofin' around: Glenn, Glen / I'm glad my baby's gone away: Glenn, Glen / One cup of coffee: Glenn, Glen / Don't push: Deal, Don / Topsy turvy: Zeppa, Ben Joe / Great shakin' fever: Burnette, Dorsey / Ezactly: Busch, Dick / Hollywood party: Busch, Dick / He will come back to me: Leslie, Alis

CDCHM 1 / Oct '89 / Ace

☐ **HOLLYWOOD ROCK 'N' ROLL VOL.2**

She just tears me up: *Stewart, Wynn* / Down on the farm: *Downing, 'Big' Al* / So tough: *Kuf Linx* / Three months to kill: *Duvall, Huelyn* / Kee-ro-ryin': *Johnny & Jonie* / Jungle hop: *Tyler, Kip* / Gotta lot of rhythm in my soul: *Cline, Patsy* / Shiver: *Burgess, Dave* / Uncle Tom got caught: *Stewart, Wynn* / Oh babe: *Downing, 'Big' Al* / Come on: *Stewart, Wynn* / Go little go cat: *Four Teens* / Spark plug: *Four Teens* / Didn't it rock: *Jim 'n' Rod* / Bad Dad: *Davis, Gene* / Great day in the morning: *Four Teens* / Life begins at four o'clock: *Milano, Bobby* / Shiverin' and shakin': *Beard, Dean* / Egad, Charlie Brown: *Beard, Dean* / Eyeballin': *Kuf Linx* / You can say that again: *Four Teens* / Double talkin' baby: *Milano, Bobby* / Machine gun: *Rip Tides* / Hey little car hop: *Weston, George* / Sneakin': *Weston, George* / Boo-be-ah-bee: *Coburn, Kimball* / Annie's not an orphan anymore: *Rochell & The Candles* / Rock roma rock it: *Crothers, Scat Man*

CDCHD 494 / Mar '94 / Ace

☐ **HOLLYWOOD SINGS - THE GIRLS**

It's foolish but it's fun: *Durbin, Deanna* / Body and soul: *Langford, Frances* / Lovely to look at: *Dunne, Irene* / Waltzing in the clouds: *Durbin, Deanna* / Jitterbug: *Garland, Judy* / Mister Five By Five: *Andrews Sisters* / Kiss the boys goodbye: *Martin, Mary* / When the roses bloom again: *Durbin, Deanna* / Man with the lollipop song: *Miranda, Carmen* / Someone to watch over me: *Langford, Frances* / One I love: *Fitzgerald, Ella* / Ferryboat serenade: *Andrews Sisters* / Falling in love again: *Dietrich, Marlene* / Over the rainbow: *Garland, Judy* / Say 'si si': *Andrews Sisters* / It never rains but it pours: *Garland, Judy* / Moon song: *Smith, Kate* / Cock eyed Major of Kaunakakai: *Andrews Sisters* / Katie went to Haiti: *Martin, Mary* / I've got you under my skin: *Langford, Frances*

304112 / Jun '97 / Hallmark

☐ **HOLLYWOOD SINGS - THE GUYS**

Moonlight becomes you: *Crosby, Bing* / Always in my heart: *Baker, Kenny* / Farming: *Kaye, Danny* / I'm thinking tonight of my blue eyes: *Crosby, Bing* / Rock-a-bye your baby with a Dixie melody: *Jolson, Al* / Fairy pipers: *Kaye, Danny* / Tchaikovsky (and other Russians): *Kaye, Danny* / There are two rivers to cross: *Baker, Kenny* / Stein song: *Powell, Dick* / 'Tis autumn: *Martin, Tony* / April showers: *Jolson, Al* / I have eyes: *Crosby, Bing* / Love walked in: *Baker, Kenny* / Blue Tahitian moon: *Baker, Kenny* / Moon and the willow tree: *Crosby, Bing* / I haven't time to be a millionaire: *Crosby, Bing* / Cancel the flowers: *Martin, Tony* / Indian summer: *Martin, Tony* / In a moment of weakness: *Powell, Dick* / Anatole of Paris: *Kaye, Danny*

304102 / Jun '97 / Hallmark

☐ **HOLY BIBLE, THE**

HOLY 019CD / Jul '96 / Holy

☐ **HOLY CHURCH OF PHARMA, THE**

EFA 089172 / 19 Jan '98 / Pharma

☐ **HOME AND AWAY**

STW 19CD / 24 Nov '97 / Scotland The What

☐ **HOME COOKIN'**

URCD 001 / Jul '96 / Ubiquity

☐ **HOME ON THE RANGE**

No one to call me darling: *Autry, Gene* / When the moon hangs high: *Hillbillies* / Any old time: *Rodgers, Jimmie* / Old trail: *Autry, Gene* / Why there's a tear in my eye: *Rodgers, Jimmie & Sara Carter* / Sunset trail: *Hillbillies* / Dusk: *Autry, Gene* / I've only loved three women: *Rodgers, Jimmie* / Home on the range: *Hillbillies* / Wonderful city: *Rodgers, Jimmie & Sara Carter* / Yodelling hobo: *Hillbillies* / Dying cowboy: *Hillbillies* / Round up time out west: *Rodgers, Jimmie* / Blue yodel No. 5: *Autry, Gene* / Colorado sunset: *Rogers, Roy* / There's a bridle hangin' on the wall: *Robison, Carson & His Pioneers* / I've got the jailhouse blues: *Autry, Gene* / Whisper your mother's name: *Autry, Gene* / There's a ranch in the rockies: *Rogers, Roy* / Pistol packin' papa: *Autry, Gene* / Blue river train: *Robison, Carson & His Pioneers* / I'll always be a rambler: *Autry, Gene*

PASTCD 7028 / Jan '94 / Flapper

☐ **HOME TO IRELAND**

Ramblin' Irishman / Rising of the moon / Road to Sligo/Tripping up the stairs / Ashplant / 10 franc pieces/St. Anne's reel/The scolair / O'Carolan's dream / White, orange and green / High road to Linton/Mrs. McLeod's reel / Foxhunters / Fiddler's green / Rocky road to Dublin / Arthur McBride / Cherish the ladies/Paddy Clancey's jig/Gillan's apples/Fathe / Gravelwalk / Couragie

CD 6044 / Sep '96 / Music

☐ **HOMEGROWN (18 Folk Tracks)**

Lady Eleanor: *Lindisfarne* / Sophisticated beggar: *Harper, Roy* / Bride 1945: *Matthews, Iain* / Blues run the game: *Frank, Jackson C.* / In the land of grey and pink: *Caravan* / Home grown: *Roberts, Andy* / Can't help falling in love: *Lick The Tins* / Famous flower of serving men: *Carthy, Martin* / False knight of the road: *Hart, Tim & Maddy Prior* / You never wanted me: *Hart, Tim & Maddy Prior* / Blacksmith: *Steeleye Span* / Claudy banks: *Collins, Shirley & The Albion Country Band* / Fool like you: *Moore, Tim* / Last time on my mind: *Denny, Sandy* / Red and gold: *Fairport Convention* / All fall down: *Hull, Alan* / Along the pilgrims way: *Albion Band* / After the goldrush: *Prelude*

CRESTSCD 500 / May '98 / Mooncrest

☐ **HOMELAND (Collection of Black South African Music)**

Ngayishela / Ea nyoloha khanyapa / Maraba start 500 / Ntlela a tingangeni / Nginbonile ubaba / Sayishayinduku / Khutsana / Umuntu / Mti wa ngwenda / Ntate bereng / Yashimizi / Nayintombi ibaleka

GRELCD 2002 / Jun '88 / Greensleeves

☐ **HOMMAGE A ALFRED MONTMARQUETTE**

TR 9501CD / Apr '96 / Transit

☐ **HONEST DON'S GREATEST SHITS**

Sleepy Soliloquy: *Diesel Boy* / When I hear your name: *Diesel Boy* / Monkeys: *Mad Caddies* / Bag lunch: *Limp* / Tearing everything down: *Anti Flag* / Something's wrong: *Fluf* / My restaurant: *Chixdiggit* / 100% woman: *Hagfish* / Nuisance: *Dance Hall Crashers* / Undisputed king of nothing: *J-Church* / Cup o' tea: *Mad Caddies* / I don't want to go to the party: *Riverdales* / 3's and 4's: *Diesel Boy* / Critic: *Limp*

DON 018CD / 3 Aug '98 / Honest Don's

☐ **HONEY FOR SALE VOL.3**

DFCD 71258 / 6 Jul '98 / Del-Fi

☐ **HONEYSUCKLE ROSE**

Honeysuckle rose: *Waller, Fats* / Concentratin' on you: *Boswell, Connee* / You're my ideal: *Hampton, Lionel & His Orchestra* / Apealin' apples: *Henderson, Fletcher Orchestra* / My fate is in your hands: *Baker, Josephine* / My gal is good for nothing but love: *Ellington, Duke Orchestra* / Keep a song in your heart: *Ellington, Duke Orchestra* / Handful of keys: *Waller, Fats* / I'm more than satisfied: *Robinson, Willard* / Angeline: *Calloway, Cab Orchestra* / Keepin' out of mischief: *Dorsey, Tommy Orchestra* / Willie tree: *Bailey, Mildred* / Blue turning grey over you: *Armstrong, Louis Orchestra* / Zonkey: *McKinney's Cotton Pickers* / Alligator crawl: *Waller, Fats* / Ain't cha glad: *Mole, Miff Molers* / I've got a feeling I'm falling: *Goodman, Benny Orchestra* / That rhythm man: *Webb, Chick* / Squeeze me: *Bechet, Sidney* / Ridin' but walkin': *Waller, Fats* / Whiteman stomp: *Whiteman, Paul & His Orchestra* / I can see you all over the place: *Smith, Willie 'The Lion' & His Cubs* / Oh you sweet thing: *Hines, Earl 'Fatha' Orchestra* / Black and blue: *Spanier, Muggsy Ragtime Band* / Jitterbug waltz: *Waller, Fats*

CECD 5 / 24 Aug '98 / Collector's Edition

☐ **HONEYWIND (Sounds From A Santal Village, India)**

SM 16122 / Jul '97 / Wergo

☐ **HONKERS AND BAR WALKERS VOL.2**

Pee wee (call of the Gators): *Jackson, Willis* / Return of BO plenty: *Lane, Morris & His Orchestra* / Gitchie gitchie-goomba: *Lane, Morris & His Orchestra* / Joe's beat: *Lane, Morris & His Orchestra* / Blue jeans: *Lane, Morris & His Orchestra* / Benson bounce: *Francis, Panama* / Darkness of the Delta: *Francis, Panama* / Bess's blues: *Francis, Panama* / 12:00 jump: *Francis, Panama* / I love her: *Harvey, Bill & His Orchestra* / Walk right in: *Harvey, Bill & His Orchestra* / Doll baby: *Ferguson, Charlie & His Orchestra* / Bean head: *Ferguson, Charlie & His Orchestra* / Hard times: *Ferguson, Charlie & His Orchestra* / Big G: *Ferguson, Charlie & His Orchestra* / That's for sure: *Smith, Bobby* / That's it: *Ferguson, Charlie & His Orchestra* / Low lights: *Ferguson, Charlie & His Orchestra* / Hi beam: *Ferguson, Charlie & His Orchestra* / I got it bad: *Ferguson, Charlie & His Orchestra* / Rush hour: *King Curtis* / Dynamite at midnite: *King Curtis*

DD 452 / Mar '97 / Delmark

☐ **HONKY TONK FAVOURITES**

SWBCD 205 / Sep '94 / Sound Waves

☐ **HONKY TONK JUMP PARTY**

Honky tonk / Jump children (vooit vooit) / House party / Strato cruiser / Breaking up the house / Good morning judge / Special delivery stomp / Club Savoy / Hucklebuck with Jimmy / Flying home / Joe Joe jump / Mighty mighty man / Deacon moves in / I want you to be my baby / Joops jump / Train kept a rollin' / Have mercy baby / Harlem nocturne / Kidney stew / Bloodshot eyes / Love don't love nobody

CDCHARLY 22 / Aug '86 / Charly

☐ **HONKY TONK ROCKABILLIES VOL.1**

CTJCD 3 / 24 Oct '97 / Goofin'

☐ **HONKY TONK ROCKABILLIES VOL.2**

CTJCD 4 / 24 Oct '97 / Goofin'

☐ **HONOUR (A Benefit For The Honour The Earth Campaign/2CD Set)**

All my relations: *Ulali* / Crazy life: *Toad The Wet Sprocket* / Wise users: *Cockburn, Bruce* / Future is war: *Cervenka, Exene* / Things we do: *Indigenous* / Bury my heart at wounded knee: *Bloom, Luka* / My mother is not the white dove: *Siberry, Jane* / Scattered: *Rusted Root* / Wounded knee: *Reversing Hour* / Home: *Raitt, Bonnie & Dave Grisman* / Out of the blues: *Trudell, John* / 21st century boy: *Williams, Victoria* / Wake up dolores: *Latin Playboys* / Motel notell: *Soul Asylum* / Small world: *Boyd, Jimmy* / One knee gospel: *Hyde, Frank & Mike Jones* / Blood quantum: *Indigo Girls* / Day in the life of a tree: *Sweet, Matthew* / Oil arms and drugs: *Ulali*

NORMAL 213CD / 1 Dec '97 / Normal

☐ **HOOK COLLECTION VOL.2 (2CD Set)**

HKCDXY 02 / 27 Oct '97 / Hook

☐ **HOOKED ON BIG BANDS**

Don't sit under the apple tree / Mack the knife / Boogie woogie bugle boy / Lady is a tramp / Chattanooga choo choo / Take the 'A' train / Boogie blues / Night train / Tommy's boogie woogie / Pennsylvania 6-5000 / Le vie en rose / I got you under my skin / St. Louis blues / C'est magnifique / Begin the beguine / It had to be you / You're nobody / I just called to say I love you / Sunny side of the street / C'est si bon / American patrol / C Jam blues / Little brown jug / Goody goody / Woodchoppers ball / Tie a yellow ribbon round the old oak tree / Song of India / It happened in Monterey / Perido / Lullaby of birdland / Frankie and Johnny / In the mood / How high the moon

EMPRCD 540 / Sep '94 / Emporio

☐ **HOOKED ON COUNTRY (3CD Set)**

TREB 3011 / Mar '95 / Scratch

☐ **HOOKED ON DISCO (45 Non-Stop Disco Classics)**

Fifth of Beethoven / Disco inferno / Salsation / Manhattan skyline / Calypso breakdown / K-Lee / More than a woman / Boogie shoes / Open sesame / Turn the beat around / Hustle / Dance, dance, dance (yowsah, yowsah, yowsah) / TSOP (The sound of Philadelphia) / Dance with me / Don't leave me this way / Shame / He's the greatest dancer / Rock the boat / I love music / Can't get enough of your love babe / Disco lady / Ring my bell / Rock your baby / I want your love / Reunited / You'll never find another love like mine / When will I see you again / Don't let me be misunderstood / Shake your groove thing / Heart of glass / Good times / Boogie fever / Never can say goodbye / Funkytown / Boogie oogie oogie / We are family / Disco nights (rock freak) / Le freak / In the navy / Get off / I will survive / That's the way (I like it) / That's where the happy people go / Love I lost

ECD 3343 / May '97 / K-Tel

☐ **HOOKED ON DIXIE**

Bugle call rag medley / Ja-da medley / Struttin' with some barbecue medley / Sweet gypsy rose medley / Piano roll blues medley / Sleepytime down south medley / Royal garden blues medley

EMPRCD 517 / Jul '94 / Emporio

☐ **HOOKED ON GLAM (The Glam Rock Allstars/2CD Set)**

Yeah glisten / Rock and roll part one / Do you wanna touch me / Can the can / Devil gate drive / 48 crash / My coo ca choo / Jealous mind / Blockbuster / Hot love / Metal guru / Get it on / Sugar baby love / Dynamite / Angel face / Goodbye my love / Cum on feel the noise / Gudbuy T'Jane / Son of my father / Jean genie / Waterloo / Mamma mia / SOS / Glass of champagne / (Dancing) / Do you wanna dance / Summerlove sensation / Bye bye baby / All the way from Memphis / Roll away the stone / Honaloochie boogie / School's out / Elected / This town ain't big enough for the both of us / AMateur hour / Virginia plain / Angel fingers / See my baby jive / Touch too much / Saturday night alright / Crocodile rock / Tiger feet / John I'm only dancing / Ballroom blitz / Hell raiser / Fox on the run / I can do it / Tell him / Heelo hello I'm back again / I'm the leader of the gang

ECD 3399 / 3 Nov '97 / K-Tel

☐ **HOOKED ON MELODIES AND MEMORIES (Hooked On 40's/Dixie/Big Bands/Switched On Swing - 4CD Set)**

EMPRBX 001 / Sep '94 / Emporio

☐ **HOOKED ON THE 60'S**

Hooked on surfin' / Dance medley / Break up medley / Hooked on love / Party medley / Hooked on a slow dance / Hooked on the radio

ECD 3228 / Jun '97 / K-Tel

☐ **HOOMII AND URTIN DUU**

VICG 52112 / Feb '96 / JVC World Library

☐ **HOOTENANNY**

Raining: *Ancient Beatbox* / Just as the ...: *Edward II & The Red Hot Polkas* / Valentine's: *Tabor, June & The Oyster Band* / Wind and the ...: *Weddings, Parties & Anything* / Vimbayi: *Four Brothers* / Frontera del ensueno: *Rey De Copas* / See how I miss you: *Cockburn, Bruce* / Liberty: *Barely Works* / Polka girl: *Colorblind James Experience* / Gastown: *God's Little Monkeys* / Travelling circus: *White, Andy* / Pigeon on the gate: *Spillane, Davy* / Tape decks all over hell: *Boiled In Lead* / Rumba for Nicaragua: *Happy End* / Collectorman: *McLeod, Rory* / Back to back: *Jolly Boys*

GRILLCD 003 / May '90 / Cooking Vinyl

☐ **HOOTENANNY**

653040 / 14 Jul '98 / Foil

☐ **HOPELESSLY DEVOTED TO YOU VOL.1**

HR 6142 / Jan '97 / Hopeless

☐ **HOPELESSLY DEVOTED TO YOU VOL.2**

HR 6322 / 18 May '98 / Hopeless

☐ **HORIZONS**

Children: *Miles, Robert* / Eugina: *Salt Tank* / X files: *DJ Dado* / Superstring: *Cygnus X* / Floating: *Terra Ferma* / Are you out there: *Crescendo* / Age of love: *Age Of Love* / Vernon's wonderland: *Vernon's Wonderland* / Magic fly: *Space Blaster* / Odyssey to Anyoona: *Jam & Spoon* / Alegrya: *Extasia* / Smokebelch II: *Sabres Of Paradise*

8287932 / Jun '96 / PolyGram TV

☐ **HORN, THE (The Tenor Sax In Jazz)**

Bird of Prey blues: *Hawkins, Coleman* / Newport news: *Freeman, Bud* / Prelude to a kiss: *Webster, Ben* / Neenah / No dues: *Cobb, Arnett* / You are too beautiful: *Davis, Eddie 'Lockjaw'* / Hey there: *Gray, Wardell* / Darn that dream: *Gordon, Dexter* / Going South: *Ammons, Gene* / Jive at five / Chase is on: *Rouse/Quinchette* / Way you look tonight: *Stitt/Holloway* / A la carte / I didn't know what time it was: *Shorter, Wayne* / I want to talk about you: *Coltrane, John* / Big George: *Coleman, George*

CDCHARLY 114 / Apr '88 / Charly

☐ **HOSPITAL**

Ultrasound: *London Electricity* / Fight the vulture: *Nice, Peter Trio* / Brother ignoramus: *London Electricity* / Sister stalking: *London Electricity* / Flight of the vulture: *Nice, Peter Trio* / Harp of gold: *Nice, Peter Trio* / Last supper: *Nice, Peter Trio* / Fear and loathing: *Dwarf Electro* / Agent orange: *Dwarf Electro* / Scrutiny: *E.S.T.* / Zed between the eyes: *Izit*

NHS 4CD / Apr '97 / NHS

☐ **HOT AIRE (American Hot Bands Of The Twenties)**

Hot aire: *Olsen, George & His Music* / If I had a girl like you: *Seattle Harmony Kings* / Darktown shuffle: *Seattle Harmony Kings* / I'm goin' out if Lizzie comes in: *Romano, Phil & His Orchestra* / Keep on croonin' a tune: *Romano, Phil & His Orchestra* / Melancholy Lou: *Lanin, Howard & His Ben Franklin Dance Orchestra* / Don't wake me up, let me dream: *Lanin, Howard & His Ben Franklin Dance Orchestra* / Paddlin' Madelin' home: *White Kaufman & His Orchestra* / Breezin' along with the breeze: *Seattle Harmony Kings* / How many times: *Seattle Harmony Kings* / Tiger rag: *Dornberger, Charles & His Orchestra* / Does she love me - positively, absolutely: *Garber, Jan & His Orchestra* / What do I care what somebody said: *Garber, Jan & His Orchestra* / You don't like it, not much: *Garber, Jan & His Orchestra* / Swanee shore: *Crawford, Jack & His Orchestra* / Sugar babe I'm leavin': *Blue Steele & His Orchestra* / When the Morning Glories wake up in the morning: *Renard, Jacques & His Cocoanut Grove Orchestra* / Baltimore: *Crawford, Jack & His Ochestra*

DHAL 16 / Sep '93 / Halcyon

☐ **HOT AND SPICY CHUTNEY**

Fan meh Paolourine: *Homefront* / Dottish boy: *Popo, Sundar* / Lotayla: *Edwards, Sally* / Butterfly: *Boyie Basdeo* / Ragga Dulahin: *Double D* / Dam maaro dam: *Samaroo, Celia* / Scorpion gyal: *Popo, Sundar* / Chutney rampage: *Ajala* / Chutney genie: *Ramdas, Madain* / Doo doo darling Dhulanie: *Maraj, Ramdeen* / Ta ra ra: *Singh, Ian* / Khirk na din: *Fonrose, Cecil* / Caura river: *Yankaran, Anand* / Trinidad kay babujee: *Yankaran, Anand*

NSCD 032 / 11 May '98 / Nascente

☐ **HOT AND SWEATY**

Feel my riddim: *Skibby* / Oh Carolina: *Shaggy* / Dedicated to the one I love: *McLean, Bitty* / Everything I own: *Boy George* / You sexy thing: *Stanfield & Brown* / La bamba: *Jungle Twins* / Tracks of my tears: *Anbessa* / Lay down: *Invaders & George Hughes* / Buk-in-ham palace: *Tosh, Peter* / I want to break free: *Los Angels* / Summertime: *La Danz & Van B King* / Somebody loves you honey: *T-Spoon* / It keeps rainin' (tears from my eyes): *McLean, Bitty* / Get up: *Inner Soul Expression* / I started a joke: *Skibby* / Fat bottomed girls: *Marga Dredd* / Sweets for my sweet: *Lewis, C.J.*

DC 880852 / May '97 / Disky

☐ **HOT BRITISH DANCE BANDS 1925-1937**

Riverboat shuffle: *Kit Kat Band* / Sugarfoot stomp: *Devonshire Restaurant Dance Band* / Stomp your feet: *Elizalde, Fred* / Buffalo rhythm: *Piccadilly Revels Band* / That's a plenty: *Rhythm Maniacs* / Tiger rag: *Hylton, Jack* / 11.30 Saturday night: *Arcadian Dance Orchestra* / Kalua: *Hughes, Spike* / Choo choo: *Payne, Jack* / Bessie couldn't help it: *Cotton, Billy* / Stomping: *Wornell, Jimmy Hot Blue-Bottles* / Nobody's sweetheart: *Fox, Roy* / White jazz: *Stone, Lew* / Sentimental gentleman from Georgia: *Loss, Joe* / Rockin' in rhythm: *Madame Tussaud's Dance Orchestra* / Your mother's son-in-law: *Six Swingers* / Shine: *Lawrence, Brian* / China boy: *Bond Street Swingers* / Milenberg joys: *Roy, Harry* / Cotton pickers' congregation: *Ambrose* / What a perfect combination: *Noble, Ray*

CBC 1005 / Jan '92 / Timeless Historical

☐ **HOT CURLY WEENIE**

RECESS 39 / Feb '97 / Roo Art

☐ **HOT DANCE TRACKS**

Captain Jack: *Captain Jack* / Allright: *Double Vision* / Got myself together: *Bucketheads* / Read my lips: *Alex Party* / Turn it up and down: *Capella* / I'm a raver: *Lipstick* / Smiling: *T-Spoon* / Hymn: *Music Instructor* / Spread your love: *2 Unlimited* / Deep in you: *Louise, Tania* / Spontaneous: *Spymaster & Eric Nouhan* / Let me be free: *Fox, Samantha* / Because you loved me: *Lost & Hally* / Higher state of consciousness: *Wink, Josh*

DC 879182 / Aug '97 / Disky

☐ **HOT GYPSY SUMMER**

HRCD 8058 / Jul '94 / Disky

☐ **HOT HATS INCLUDING FATS**

NCD 8812 / Dec '94 / Phontastic

☐ **HOT HOT REGGAE VOL.1 & 2**

840602 / '91 / FM

☐ **HOT HOT SOCA**

RRTGCD 7706 / '88 / Rohit

☐ **HOT JAZZ 1928-1930**

HRM 6004 / Jan '89 / Hermes

☐ **HOT JAZZ BISCUITS**

Who do you love: *White, Lenny* / Hot jazz biscuits: *Urbanator* / Bluesanova: *Browne, Tom* / Luny tune: *Essence All-Stars* / Funk in a deep freeze: *Bop City* / Jam for real: *Browne, Tom* / Up jumped Spring: *Essence All-Stars* / Late one night: *Meeting* / Dr. Jackle: *Essence All-Stars* / Cubano chant: *Essence All-Stars* / Magic: *Urbanator* / Savant: *White, Lenny* / Bass blues: *Essence All-Stars* / Freedom jazz dance: *Essence All-Stars*

HIBD 8801 / Dec '97 / Hip Bop

☐ **HOT JAZZ FROM NEW ORLEANS (20 Dixieland Stompers)**

Tiger rag: *Original Dixieland Jazz Band* / Stockyard strut: *Keppard, Freddie* / Squeeze me: *Miller, Punch* / Ory's creole trombone: *Ory, Kid* / Careless love: *Original Tuxedo Jazz Orchestra* / Tar paper stomp: *Manone, Wingy* / Sobbin' blues: *New Orleans Rhythm Kings* / Someday sweetheart: *Condon, Eddie Orchestra* / 6th Street: *Armstrong, Lil Dixielanders* / Dinah: *Russell, Pee Wee Rhythmakers* / Dippermouth blues: *Oliver, Joe 'King' & His Creole Jazz Band* / Black bottom stomp: *Red Miff's Stompers* / Really the blues: *Ladnier, Tommy* / Eel: *Freeman, Bud Summa Cum Laude Orchestra* / Sweet and lowdown: *Smith, Jabbo & His Rhythm Aces* / Down by the riverside: *Johnson, Bunk* / All the jazz band ball: *Beiderbecke, Bix & His Gang* / Roof blues: *Crosby, Bob & His Bobcats* / Harlem joys: *Smith, Willie 'The Lion' & His Cubs*

306702 / Jul '97 / Hallmark

☐ **HOT JAZZ ON BLUE NOTE (4CD Set)**

Blues whistle: *Lewis, Meade 'Lux'* / Careless love: *White, Josh Trio* / Profoundly blue no.2: *Hall, Edmond Quartet* / Gettysburg march: *Lewis, George & His New Orleans Stompers* / Burgundy street blues: *Lewis, George & His New Orleans Stompers* / Over the waves: *Lewis, George & His New Orleans Stompers* / When you wore a tulip: *Lewis, George & His New Orleans Stompers* / Days beyond recall: *Jones, Bunk & Sidney Bechet* / High society: *Bechet, Sidney & His Blue Note Jazzmen* / Mr. Jelly lord: *Hodes, Art Hot Seven* / Wolverine blues: *Hodes, Art Hot Seven* / Winin' boy blues: *Dodds, Baby Jazz Four* / Doctor jazz: *Hodes, Art & His Chicagoans* / Shoe shiners dinner: *Hodes, Art & His Chicagoans* / Blame it on the blues: *Bechet-Nicholas Blue Five* / Weary way blues: *Bechet-Nicholas Blue Five* / Moose march: *De Paris, Sidney & His Blue Note Stompers* / Careless love: *Dodds, Baby Jazz Four* / Memphis blues: *Hodes, Art Hot Five* / St. Louis

blues: *Bechet, Sidney & His Blue Note Stompers* / Yellow dog blues: *Hodes, Art & His Chicagoans* / Weary blues: *Bechet, Sidney & His Blue Note Stompers* / Tiger rag: *Bechet, Sidney & His Blue Note Stompers* / Original dixieland one step: *Bechet, Sidney & His Hot Six* / Dark strutters ball: *Hodes, Art Hot Five* / Fidgety feet: *Bechet, Sidney & His Blue Note Jazzmen* / At the jazz band ball: *Bechet, Sidney & His Blue Note Jazzmen* / That eccentric rag: *Hodes, Art Trio* / Royal garden blues: *Hall, Edmond & His Blue Note Jazzmen* / Sugar foot stomp: *Hodes, Art Blue Note Jazzmen* / Bugle call rag: *Bechet, Sidney & His Blue Note Jazzmen* / Roof blues: *Bechet, Sidney & His Blue Note Jazzmen* / Toshomingo blues: *Bechet, Sidney & His Blue Note Jazzmen* / That's a plenty: *Bechet, Sidney & His Hot Six* / Low down blues: *Hodes, Art Back Room Boys* / Cake walking babies from home: *Bechet, Sidney & His Blue Note Jazzmen* / Everybody loves my baby: *De Paris, Sidney & His Blue Note Stompers* / Mandy make up your mind: *Bechet, Sidney & His Blue Note Jazzmen* / Squeeze me: *Hodes, Art Blue Note Jazzmen* / Runnin' wild: *Bechet, Sidney & His Blue Note Jazzmen* / Clark and Randolph: *Hodes, Art & His Chicagoans* / Muskat ramble: *Bechet, Sidney & His Blue Note Jazzmen* / Apex blues: *Hodes, Art Blue Five* / Blues my naughty sweetie gives to me: *Bechet, Sidney & His Hot Six* / Nobody's sweetheart: *Hodes, Art Blue Five* / Please don't talk about me when I am gone: *De Paris, Sidney & His Blue Note Stompers* / Save it pretty mama: *Hodes, Art Hot Five* / There'll be some changes made: *Bechet, Sidney & His Hot Six* / Jug head boogie: *Hodes, Art Back Room Boys* / Jazz me blues: *Bechet, Sidney & His Blue Note Jazzmen* / Night shift blues: *Hall, Edmond & His Blue Note Jazzmen* / China boy: *Bechet, Sidney & His Blue Note Jazzmen* / Nobody knows when you are down and out: *Bechet, Sidney & His Blue Note Jazzmen* / Walkin' the dog: *Johnson, James P. Blue Note Jazzmen* / Blues at the blue note: *Hall, Edmond & His Blue Note Jazzmen* / Ballin' the jack: *Paris, Sidney de Blue Note Jazzmen* / Shine: *Hodes, Art Hot Five* / KMH Drag: *Hodes, Art Hot Five* / At the ball: *Johnson, James P. Blue Note Jazzmen* / Slow em down blues: *Hodes, Art & His Chicagoans* / Shim me sha wobble: *Hodes, Art & His Chicagoans* / Easy rider: *Johnson, James P. Blue Note Jazzmen* / Jammin' in four: *Hall, Edmond Celeste Quartet* / Avalon: *Bechet, Sidney & His Hot Six* / Feelin' at ease: *Dodds, Baby Jazz Four* / Who's sorry now: *Paris, Sidney de Blue Note Jazzmen* / Call of the blues: *Paris, Sidney de Blue Note Jazzmen* / SCH Blues: *Hodes, Art Back Room Boys* / Sweet georgia brown: *Hodes, Art Blue Note Jazzmen* / Blue Horizon: *Bechet, Sidney & His Blue Note Jazzmen*

CDP 8358112 / Dec '96 / Blue Note

☐ HOT MUSIC FROM CUBA 1907-1936

HQCD 23 / Oct '93 / Harlequin

☐ HOT NEWS

HARLCD 001 / 5 Feb '98 / Blue Harlem

☐ HOT NIGHTS IN THE CITY

WKFMXD 134 / Nov '89 / FM

☐ HOT NOTES

DGF 8 / Jul '96 / Frog

☐ HOT REGGAE FEVER

12232 / Sep '93 / Laserlight

☐ HOT RHYTHM AND COOL BLUES - TEXAS STYLE

IMP 702 / Jul '95 / Iris Music

☐ HOT ROCK HITS (2CD Set)

Baker street: *Rafferty, Gerry* / Bette Davis eyes: *Carnes, Kim* / Stuck with you: *Lewis, Huey & The News* / Love is a battlefield: *Benatar, Pat* / Freeze frame: *Geils, J. Band* / Heart and soul: *T'Pau* / Kids in America: *Wilde, Kim* / Missing you: *Waite, John* / Baby it's you: *Promises* / Loud music in cars: *Bremner, Billy* / Silver machine: *Hawkwind* / Hereos: *Meat Loaf* / Roll over Beethoven: *ELO* / Radar love: *Golden Earring* / Thunder in my heart: *Sayer, Leo* / Hot in the city: *Idol, Billy* / Some kinda wonderful: *Grand Funk Railroad* / Walking on sunshine: *Katrina & The Waves* / Ride like the wind: *Saxon* / We close our eyes: *Go West* / Rise to the occasion: *Fisher, Climie* / Unbelievable: *EMF* / Somelike it hot: *Power Station* / All together now: *Farm* / Loverboy: *Ocean, Billy* / Spanish stroll: *Mink Deville* / Every one's a winner: *Hot Chocolate* / Touch me: *Fox, Samantha* / So long: *Fox, Samantha* / Orchard road: *Sayer, Leo*

DOU 878302 / 2 Feb '98 / Disky

☐ HOT ROCKIN' INSTRUMENTALS

CLCD 4430 / Sep '96 / Collector/White Label

☐ HOT ROCKIN' INSTRUMENTALS

CLCD 4436 / Mar '97 / Collector's Edition

☐ HOT ROD GANG

Big wheel: *Benton, Walt* / This old bomb of mine: *Stange, Howie* / Hot rod: *Berry Brothers* / Spinning my wheels: *Brooks, Chuck* / Spinner hub caps: *Davis, Pat* / Full racing cam: *Ringo, Eddie* / Girl and a hot rod: *Deram, Richie* / Big green car: *Carroll, Jimmy* / Gas money: *Carroll, Jimmy* / Hot rod baby: *Davis, Rocky* / Long John's flagpole rock: *Roller, Long John* / Hot rod boogie: *Brady, Howard W* / Robin Hood and his '56 Ford: *Ball, Woody* / Shot rod: *Conny & Bellhops* / Ford and shaker: *Gallagher, James* / Hot-rodders dream: *Burden, Ray* / Hot rod race: *Williams, Rob* / Daddy Joe: *Ciolino, Pete* / Sidewalk rock 'n' roll: *Warden, J.W.* / I'll be leavin' you: *Moore, Turner* / Brake Jake: *Fern, Mike* / Cruisin': *Bucky & Premiers* / Red hot car: *Verne, Bobby* / Lorene: *Lemons, Bill* / Speedway rock: *Woodard, Jerry* / Stop jivin' start drivin': *Keyes, Burt* / Dig that crazy driver: *Penix, William* / Car hop: *Export* / High way robbery: *Fry, Bobby* / Cop car: *West, Rick*

CBBB 55005 / Apr '94 / Buffalo Bop

☐ HOT ROD HITS

Double a fueler: *Deuce Coupes* / Nite prowler: *Deuce Coupes* / Road rattler: *Deuce Coupes* / Tijuana gasser: *Deuce Coupes* / Gear masher: *Deuce Coupes* / Candy apple blues: *Deuce Coupes* / Satan's chariot: *Deuce Coupes* / Monkey see: *Deuce Coupes* / Nite surfer: *Deuce Coupes* / Dawn patrol: *Deuce Coupes* / Smooth stick: *Deuce Coupes* / Top eliminator: *Darts* / Street machine: *Darts* / Corn pone: *Darts* / Hollywood drag: *Darts* / Alky burner: *Darts* / Slauson and soto: *Darts* / Detroit iron: *Darts* / Cruisin': *Darts* / Four banger: *De-Fenders* / Deuces wild: *De-Fenders* / Taco wagon: *De-Fenders* / Movin' and groovin': *De-Fenders* / Skin diver: *De-Fenders* / Loose nuts: *De-Fenders* / Little Deuce Coupe: *De-Fenders* / Drag beat: *De-Fenders* / Wheelin' home: *De-Fenders* / Tequila Joe: *De-Fenders* / Rum runner: *De-Fenders* / Roadrunner: *De-Fenders*

CDCHD 303 / Feb '91 / Ace

☐ HOT RODS FROM HELL VOL.1

BREPD 5001 / Aug '96 / Blood Red Discs

☐ HOT RODS FROM HELL VOL.2

BRCD 5004 / 1 Jun '98 / Blood Red Discs

☐ HOT SUMMER NIGHTS

Sea and sky: *Springfield, Dusty & Michelle Grand* / Where do you go to (my lovely): *Sarstedt, Peter* / Use it up and wear it out: *Odyssey* / Midnight at the oasis: *Muldaur, Maria* / Who were you with in the moonlight: *Dollar* / Dancing in the street: *Reeves, Martha* / Spanish harlem: *King, Ben E.* / Summer of '42: *Legrand, Michel* / So much in love: *Tymes* / Greased lightnin': *Travolta, John* / Moon river: *Butler, Jerry* / Stranger on the shore: *Bilk, Acker* / You belong to me: *Duprees* / Halfway to paradise: *Fury, Billy* / Twilight time: *Platters* / Chapel of love: *Dixie Cups* / Good timin': *Jones, Jimmy* / This land is your land: *Lopez, Trini* / Night has a thousand eyes: *Vee, Bobby* / You've got what it takes: *Johnson, Marv* / Party doll: *Knox, Buddy* / (I don't know why) but I do: *Henry, Clarence 'Frogman'* / Lavender blue: *Turner, Sammy* / Sea of love: *Phillips, Phil* / On the sunny side of the street: *Bruce, Tommy*

ECD 3434 / Aug '98 / K-Tel

☐ HOT TRUMPETS (25 Great Jazz Trumpeters)

West End blues: *Armstrong, Louis Hot Five* / Swing out: *Allen, Red* / Singin' the blues: *Beiderbecke, Bix* / I can't get started: *Berigan, Bunny* / I'm free: *Butterfield, Billy* / Fiesta in blue: *Clayton, Buck* / What's the reason: *Coleman, Bill* / Heckler' shop: *Eldridge, Roy* / Swing high: *Elman, Ziggy* / Just a mood: *James, Harry* / If you see me comin': *Ladnier, Tommy* / Five point blues: *Lawson, Yank* / Swingin' at the Hickory House: *Manone, Wingy* / Black and tan fantasy: *Miley, Bubber* / Parkway stomp: *Miller, Punch* / Take the 'A' train: *Nance, Ray* / Panic is on: *Newton, Frankie* / That's no bargain: *Nichols, Red* / Dippermouth blues: *Oliver, Joe 'King'* / At the fat man's: *Shavers, Charlie* / Jazz battle: *Smith, Jabbo* / Baby doll: *Smith, Joe* / Relaxin' at the Touro: *Spanier, Muggsy* / Menelik - The Lion of Judah: *Stewart, Rex* / Cootie's concerto (Echoes of Harlem): *Williams, Cootie*

CDAJA 5208 / Jun '96 / Living Era

☐ HOT VIOLINS

Daphne / Dinah / Wild cat / After you've gone / Ain't misbehavin' / Sweet Georgia Brown / My syncopated melody man / Stompin' at the Savoy / Onyx club spree / I can't believe that you're in love with me / Sweet Sue / Somebody loves me / Fiddle blues / Bill Street blues / I got rhythm / Honeysuckle rose / Lady be good / Limehouse blues / Calling all keys / I've found a new baby / Parts 1 and 2

CD 53173 / Apr '98 / Giants Of Jazz

☐ HOT WAX EXCURSION

VPCD 2041 / Apr '96 / VP

☐ HOT WIRED '97

EFA 128352 / Jul '97 / Hotwire

☐ HOT WIRED MONSTERTRUX

Intro / Wish: *Nine Inch Nails* / Finger on the trigger: *Excessive Force* / Tool and die: *Consolidated* / Godlike: *KMFDM* / Jesus built my hotrod: *Ministry* / Kooler than Jesus: *My Life With The Thrill Kill Kult* / Provision: *Frontline Assembly* / Looking forward: *CNN* / Murder Inc: *Murder Inc.* / Edge of no control: *Meat Beat Manifesto* / Skinflower: *Young Gods* / Motorbike: *Sheep On Drugs* / Headhunter: *Front 242* / Family man: *Nitzer Ebb*

9548318112 / Feb '93 / East West

☐ HOTDOGS, HITS & HAPPY DAYS VOL.1

LPCD 1011 / May '94 / Disky

☐ HOTDOGS, HITS & HAPPY DAYS VOL.10

LPCD 1020 / May '94 / Disky

☐ HOTDOGS, HITS & HAPPY DAYS VOL.2

LPCD 1012 / May '94 / Disky

☐ HOTDOGS, HITS & HAPPY DAYS VOL.3

LPCD 1013 / May '94 / Disky

☐ HOTDOGS, HITS & HAPPY DAYS VOL.4

LPCD 1014 / May '94 / Disky

☐ HOTDOGS, HITS & HAPPY DAYS VOL.5

LPCD 1015 / May '94 / Disky

☐ HOTDOGS, HITS & HAPPY DAYS VOL.6

LPCD 1016 / May '94 / Disky

☐ HOTDOGS, HITS & HAPPY DAYS VOL.7

LPCD 1017 / May '94 / Disky

☐ HOTDOGS, HITS & HAPPY DAYS VOL.8

LPCD 1018 / May '94 / Disky

☐ HOTDOGS, HITS & HAPPY DAYS VOL.9

LPCD 1019 / May '94 / Disky

☐ HOTEL EASY VOL.1 (Golden Cavalcade Casino)

Grandstand / Competitors / Thrills and spills / Where the action is (aka Mono ski) / Guitar gambler / Tycoon / Jackpot / Top chrono / Dangerous assignment / Go getter / Action line / Risk business / Syndicate / City in the sun / Hot property / Sporting highlights / Ill winds / Hollywood scene / Hot module / Organ blower / Trombones in the night / Calender girl / French kick

CDOVD 490 / Jun '97 / Virgin

☐ HOTEL EASY VOL.2 (La Scandale Discotheque)

Boogie juice / Hot pants / Espresso bongo / Young generation / Jet setters / Pulsator / Cutting the funk / Friday feeling / Trend setters / Pop package / Freak out / Thunderbird / Crime squad / World Cup / On the South Side / 49th Street shakedown / Soul city / Making it / Soul organ impromptu / Thunder thighs / Night fever / Disco disco / Mission just possible

CDOVD 491 / Jun '97 / Virgin

☐ HOTEL EASY VOL.3 (Playmates Penthouse)

Penthouse suite / Secret service / Butterfly / Florida playboy / Good thing going / Club 69 / Teen lovers / Call me / Beat me till I'm blue / Time for romance / Gingerbread / Theme for a dream / Satin sounds / Je reviens / Solitaire / Summer love / Young emotions / First affair / Girl with the beautiful hair / Half forgotten daydreams / Kiss in the moonlight / Pussycat / Bed of roses

CDOVD 489 / Jun '97 / Virgin

☐ HOTEL EASY VOL.4 (Paco's Poolside Bar)

Girl in a sportscar / Eurotrash / Fun in the sun / Riviera affair / Lazy day / Sandals in the sand / Clear waters / International playground / Millionaires / Never a dull moment / Beauty Parade / New image / Going places / Holiday commercial / Travelling free / Pacific playground / Caribbean cruise / Montego Bay / Brazil Brazil / Free life / Sunny speed / Summer convertible / Scooter girl

CDOVD 488 / Jun '97 / Virgin

☐ HOTLINES 6

HOT 006 / Dec '96 / Hot Hands

☐ HOTTER THAN HELL

BMCD 50 / Mar '94 / Black Mark

☐ HOTTEST BBQ ALBUM THIS SUMMER, THE

Sweat (a la la la la song) / Baby come back / Sweets for my sweet / I can see clearly now / Bambeleo / Brasil / Soca dance / Dancando lambada / Rivers of Babylon / Kingston Town / Island in the sun / Girl from Ipanema / Calypso medley / One note samba / Samba de Soho / Saudade / O tucano / Best years of our lives / Cuba / Hot hot hot / Spanish Harlem / Lambada

SUMCD 4069 / Sep '96 / Summit

☐ HOTTEST HITS

Those guys: *Sensations* / Come on little girl: *Melodians* / Loving pauper: *Dobson, Dobby* / Midnight hour: *Silvertones* / Heartaches: *Taylor, Vic* / Cry tough: *Ellis, Alton* / Queen majesty: *Techniques* / Right track: *Dillon, Phyllis & Hopeton Lewis* / I'll never fall in love: *Sensations* / Tide is high: *Paragons* / Things you say you love: *Three Tops* / Girl I've got a date: *Ellis, Alton* / Love is a treasure: *McKay, Freddie* / Don't stay away: *Dillon, Phyllis* / You don't need me: *Melodians* / My girl: *Techniques* / La la means I love you: *Ellis, Alton*

TICD 1001 / 15 Sep '97 / Treasure Isle

☐ HOTTEST HITS VOL.2

SOCD 1267 / Oct '96 / Studio One

☐ HOUSE 2 HOUSE MEGA RAVE VOL.1

DCD 5317 / Nov '93 / Disky

☐ HOUSE BOMBS

ZYX 550642 / Nov '96 / ZYX

☐ HOUSE BOX

UCACD 0162 / 3 Aug '98 / UCA

☐ HOUSE CLUB ORIGINALS VOL.1

FUNXD 306 / 16 Mar '98 / RCR

☐ HOUSE COLLECTION (2CD Set)

3024322 / 20 Apr '98 / Techno Import

☐ HOUSE FUNKIN' VOL.1

JAPECD 102 / Sep '94 / Escapade

☐ HOUSE FUNKIN' VOL.2

JAPECD 103 / Feb '95 / Escapade

☐ HOUSE FUNKIN' VOL.3

JAPECD 104 / Jun '95 / Escapade

☐ HOUSE GROOVES VOL.3

HGCD 0062 / 17 Nov '97 / House Grooves

☐ HOUSE IN THE MIX (2CD Set)

ZYX 551032 / 30 Mar '98 / ZYX

☐ HOUSE KISSES VOL.1 (2CD Set)

Feel what you want: *Kristine W* / No love lost: *Rogers, Cece* / Set U free: *Planet Soul* / I like it: *Jomanda* / We can make it: *Mone* / Break night: *Mole People* / Beautiful people: *Tucker, Barbara* / Can we live: *Jesto Funk* / Universal love: *Natural Born Groovers* / Forever and a day: *Brothers In Rhythm* / Sing a song: *Harding, Carolyn & Damon Horton* / You deserve the best: *Wag Ya Tail* / (You're my one and only) True love: *Smith, Ann-Marie* / Don't give up (love will come around): *Morel, George* / I get lifted: *Tucker, Barbara* / Love thang: *Banji Boys* / If Madonna calls: *Vasquez, Junior* / Anything U want: *McCrae, Gwen* / Be sexy: *Justine* / Weekend: *Shock* / (Who) Keeps changing your mind: *South Street Player* / Make the world go round: *Sandy B* / Change: *Daphne* / Freedom (make it funky): *Black Magic* / I'm so grateful: *Kings Of Tomorrow*

ZYX 810962 / Apr '97 / ZYX

☐ HOUSE KISSES VOL.2 (2CD Set)

ZYX 811472 / 27 Apr '98 / ZYX

☐ HOUSE LINE VOL.6 (2CD Set)

DP 260329 / 23 Feb '98 / Dance Paradise

☐ HOUSE LOOP

SM 80262 / Aug '96 / Profile

☐ HOUSE MARKE VOL.2 (25 Brand New & Hot House Trax/2CD Set)

In the morning: *Key* / I want you: *Shandrew* / Baby Baby: *DJ EBO* / My house: *Nap, J. Project* / Party groove: *DJ Kalpa* / Deep side: *Bass Symphony* / Bass: *DJ Micky* / Future: *Big Sound Association* / Ooh yeah: *Syntone* / Wobile: *Boedha* / You got it: *Prophase* / Neuro: *X-Cabs* / Morninglight: *Team Deep* / Ultimate seduction: *Ultimate Seduction* / Summer: *Central Bass* / Magnet: *Klubb Heads* / Rabahouse: *Pro Doctors* / Work: *Fudge* / Guido the killer wimp: *Allium* / House project: *DJ Trax* / Hoover: *Daddy Cool* / Get to this: *Tecmania Rebel* / Solar cycle: *Third Man* / Sirius: *Moon & The Sun* / House show: *Fact Of Life*

DCD 08947272 / Mar '97 / SPV

☐ HOUSE MUSIC MOVEMENT VOL.1, THE (Mixed By Doc Martin)

HMMCD 8091 / 17 Aug '98 / Master Dance Tones

☐ HOUSE MUSIC MOVEMENT VOL.2, THE

Spiral scratch: *Bangalter, Thomas* / Back: *S-Man* / Vibe: *Roger S & The Deep* / Let's do it: *Republic* / Potion: *Narcotic Squad* / Make the beat pound: *DJ Discipline* / Feel the sun: *DJ Dove* / Fade II black: *Kot / Din da da*: *Aviance, Kevin* / Fixation: *Chocolate Fudge* / You: *Dynamo Electrix* / You can't hide: *DJ Sneak* / Last night a DJ saved my life: *King Britt* / Got funk: *Finkjunkeez* / Mighty high: *Revival 3000* / Land of the lost: *Green Velvet* / Answering machine: *Green Velvet* / Fresh and funky: *International Posse*

HMMCD 8094 / 3 Aug '98 / Master Dance Tones

☐ HOUSE MUSIC REVENGE VOL.4 (Nightlife Essentials Presents)

MXD 2098 / 27 Jul '98 / Waako

☐ HOUSE NATION VOL.1

REACTCD 047 / Sep '94 / React

☐ HOUSE NOT JAZZ VOL.1

Struck by luv: *Lectroluv & Alvaughn Jackson* / Sax in the ozone: *Aaron, Robert* / Fired up: *Girl* / Soweto stomp: *Funky Fusion Band* / All the same family: *African Dream* / Critical: *Wall Of Sound* / Rejoice: *250lbs Of Blue* / Thoughts of you: *Wave* / Loving you in Heaven: *Aaron, Robert & Michou* / African dreams: *African Dream*

EBCD 54 / Jan '95 / Eightball

☐ HOUSE OF BAMBOO PRESENTS DANCE AND MOOD MUSIC

No man's land / Ahmedabab theme / Man from nowhere / Strange galaxy / Jungle soul / Land of Marlene / Soft winds / Pictures of oceania / Following you / Magazine / Planification / Psycedelic portrait / Pictures of Saint Tropez / Psychedelic portrait / Ambiance heure zero / Strange valley / Rhythm's dealer / Picture of spring / Picture of summer / Picture of winter / De Paris a Liverpool

CDV 2831 / May '97 / Virgin

☐ HOUSE OF DREAMS (2CD Set)

560042 / Apr '97 / Westcom

☐ HOUSE OF DREAMS VOL.1

ASCCD 2 / Jun '96 / Ascension

☐ HOUSE OF HANDBAG - AUTUMN/ WINTER COLLECTION, THE (2CD Set)

USCD 4 / Oct '95 / Ultrasound

☐ HOUSE OF HANDBAG - SPRING/ SUMMER COLLECTION, THE (2CD Set)

USCD 3 / Jul '95 / Ultrasound

☐ HOUSE OF JOY VOL.1 (2CD Set)

DCD 08947092 / Mar '98 / SPV

☐ HOUSE OF JOY VOL.2 (2CD Set)

DCD 08947482 / Mar '98 / SPV

☐ HOUSE OF JOY VOL.3 (2CD Set)

DCD 08947902 / Mar '98 / SPV

☐ HOUSE OF LIMBO

LIMB 18CD / Jul '93 / Limbo

☐ HOUSE OF LIMBO - TRILOGY

Cry India: *Umboza* / So good: *DJ Fade* / Live in peace: *Tocayo* / It's what's upfront that counts: *Yosh* / Let the love: *Q-Tex* / Funk of tha' month: *Dark Sessions* / Sunshine: *Umboza* / Talk to me: *Planet 95* / Kiss my acid: *Mukkaa* / Screamer: *Yosh* / I trance you: *Gypsy* / Spirit is justified: *Ritmo De Vida* / Thoughts of a tranced love: *Winc* / Gotta get next to you: *Yosh* / Slip: *Soul Surfers* / Best served chilled: *Havana*

LIMB 61CD / Oct '96 / Limbo

☐ **HOUSE OF LIMBO - TRILOGY (Remixed/2CD Set)**
Cry India: *Umboza* / I trance you: *Gypsy* / Best served chilled: *Havana* / Live in peace: *Tocayo* / So good: *DJ Fade* / Funk of the month: *Dark Sessions* / It's what's upfront that counts: *Yosh* / Sunshine: *Umboza* / Let the love: *Q-Tex* / Spirit is justified: *Ritmo De Vida* / Gotta get next to you: *Yosh* / Screamer: *Yosh* / Talk to me: *Planet 95* / Thoughts of a tranced love: *Winc* / Thoughts of a tranced love: *Winc* / Kiss my acid: *Mukkaa* / Slip: *Soul Surfers*
LIMB 61CDX
LIMB 61LE / Oct '96 / Limbo

☐ **HOUSE OF LONDON VOL.1**
OCEANCD 001 / Apr '95 / Ocean

☐ **HOUSE OF LONDON VOL.2**
OCEANCD 002 / Sep '95 / Ocean

☐ **HOUSE OF LOVERS VOL.1**
RECD 01 / Apr '93 / Rupie Edwards

☐ **HOUSE OF LOVERS VOL.2**
RECD 02 / 5 May '98 / Rupie Edwards

☐ **HOUSE OF OLDSCHOOL**
IDTCD 1420 / Mar '97 / ID&T

☐ **HOUSE ON FIRE VOL.1**
RHRCD 58 / Oct '95 / Red House

☐ **HOUSE ON FIRE VOL.2**
RHRCD 100 / Oct '97 / Red House

☐ **HOUSE RARITIES**
XTR 17CDM
XTR 17CDU / Oct '95 / X-Treme

☐ **HOUSE ROCKIN' BLUES**
I got to go: *Little Walter* / Mama talk to your daughter: *Lenoir, J.B.* / Young fashioned ways: *Waters, Muddy* / I have a little girl: *Howlin' Wolf* / You don't love me (you don't care): *Diddley, Bo* / Tired of crying: *Pejoe, Morris* / I'm leaving you: *Spann, Otis* / Rattlesnake: *Brim, John* / Poison Ivy: *Mabon, Willie* / You got to love me: *Arnold, Billy Boy* / Mellow down easy: *Little Walter* / Little girl: *Diddley, Bo* / Date bait: *Blue Smitty* / I would hate to see you go (Be careful): *Brim, John* / If it ain't me: *Rogers, Jimmy* / Who will be next: *Howlin' Wolf* / Close to you: *Waters, Muddy* / Sweet on you baby: *Arnold, Billy Boy* / Goat: *Williamson, Sonny Boy* / He knows the rules: *McCracklin, Jimmy* / I'm satisfied: *Rush, Otis* / Let me love you baby: *Guy, Buddy* / Madison blues: *James, Elmore* / Look out Mabel: *Crockett, G.L.* / Twirl: *Little Luther* / Someday: *Nighthawk, Robert* / Let's go out tonight: *Hooker, John Lee*
CDCHD 610 / Mar '95 / Ace

☐ **HOUSE ROTATION VOL.2 (3CD Set)**
DP 8790032 / 23 Feb '98 / Dance Paradise

☐ **HOUSE THAT TRAX BUILT VOL.1, THE**
Your love: *Knuckles, Frankie* / No way back: *Adonis* / Love can't turn around: *Farley Jackmaster Funk* / I've lost control: *Sleazy D* / Washing machine: *Fingers Inc.* / Move your body: *Jefferson, Marshall* / Rock me: *Screaming Rachel* / House Nation: *House Master Boyz* / U used to hold me: *Rosario, Ralphi*
TRXUKCD 001 / May '96 / Trax UK

☐ **HOUSE THAT TRAX BUILT VOL.2, THE**
R U hot enough: *Virgo* / Liquid love: *Hardy, Ron* / You got the love: *Knuckles, Frankie* / This is acid: *Maurice* / Sensuous woman goes disco: *Jackmaster D* / 7 ways to jack: *Hercules* / Your only friend: *Phuture* / Can U feel it: *Fingers* / Bringing down the walls: *Owens, Robert* / Waiting on my angel: *Knuckles, Frankie* / Real thing: *Screamin' Rachael* / We're rocking down the house: *Adonis*
TRXUKCD 004 / Aug '97 / Trax UK

☐ **HOW BIG IS YOUR WOOFER**
Baia: *Puente, Tito Orchestra & Buddy Morrow Orchestra* / Saturday night in Knightsbridge: *McKuen, Rod* / Breeze and I: *Esquivel, Juan Garcia* / High and the mighty: *Young, Victor & His Orchestra* / Taurus, island meeting: *Jacobs, Dick & His Orchestra* / Delicado: *Faith, Percy & His Orchestra* / Theme from Star Wars: *Cinema Sound Stage Orchestra* / Cas is a gas: *Greenslade, Arthur Trio* / So long San Francisco: *Stanyon Strings* / Listen to the warm: *Greenslade, Arthur & Orchestra* / Woman in love: *Laine, Frankie* / Up a lazy river: *Zentner, Si & His Orchestra* / In someone's shadow: *Greenslade, Arthur & Orchestra* / La marche de Sacco et Vanzetti: *Cinema Sound Stage Orchestra* / Fourth of July in Sioux falls: *San Sebastian Strings* / Bon chance, Jack: *Cinema Sound Stage Orchestra*
12802 / May '97 / Laserlight

☐ **HOW CAN I KEEP FROM SINGING VOL.1 (Early American Rural Religious Music & Song)**
YAZ 2020 / Jun '96 / Yazoo

☐ **HOW CAN I KEEP FROM SINGING VOL.2 (Early American Rural Religious Music & Song)**
YAZ 2021 / Jun '96 / Yazoo

☐ **HOW DO YOU LIKE YOUR BLUES**
Life is a ballgame: *Persuasions* / Can't see for lookin': *Kubek, Smokin' Joe* / You don't drink what I drink: *Wilson, Smokey* / Trombone Porky: *Cohen, Porky & Michelle Willson* / Hot leftover no.1: *Magic Dick & Jay Geils/Bluestime* / Running out of time: *Roomful Of Blues* / Promised land: *Holmes Brothers* / No use talkin': *Thomas, Irma* / Talkin' is over (the walkin' has begun): *Sansone, Jumpin' Johnny* / Longwallin': *Boyack, Pat & The Prowlers* / Check out yourself: *Jones, Tutu* / Let me play with your poodle: *Ball, Marcia* / Hot leftover no.3: *Magic Dick & Jay Geils/Bluestime* / I need time: *Jones, Andrew 'Jr. Boy'* / One foot in the blues: *Adams, Johnny* / Soldier for the blues: *King, Jimmy* / I don't know: *Brown, Ruth & Johnny Adams* / Mean case of the blues: *Clearwater, Eddy*
CDBBAN 27 / Jul '97 / Bullseye Blues

☐ **HOW GREAT THOU ART**
Footsteps / Would you believe / My forever friend / You are the one / One day at a time / You'll never walk alone / Little peace / Amazing Grace / What God has joined together / Whispering hope / Shine your light / Ave Maria / I saw the light / St. Theresa of the roses / Michael / Walk through this world with me / Just a closer walk with thee / Little mountain church house / How far in heaven / How great thou art
RZRCD 569 / 10 Nov '97 / Ritz

☐ **HOW LONG HAS THIS BEEN GOING ON**
CD 20044 / May '86 / Pablo

☐ **HOW SWEET IT IS**
13885892 / 13 Oct '97 / Galaxy

☐ **HOW TO START A FIGHT**
SD 1202 / Oct '96 / Side One

☐ **HOW TO USE MACHINERY**
MA332 / Nov '93 / Machinery

☐ **HOW YOU FE SEY DAT PRESENTS "HOT"**
SONCD 0052 / Jul '93 / Sonic Sounds

☐ **HOWDY (25 Hillbilly All Time Greats)**
Goin' to the barn-dance tonight: *Robinson, Carson & His Pioneers* / It ain't gonna rain no mo': *Hall, Wendell* / Wreck of the old '97: *Dalhart, Vernon* / Runaway train: *Dalhart, Vernon* / Red wing: *Puckett, Riley* / Blue yodel: *Rodgers, Jimmie* / Brakeman's blues: *Rodgers, Jimmie* / My clinch mountain home: *Carter Family* / Foggy mountain top: *Carter Family* / Little Bessie: *Alabama Barnstormers* / She's too good for me: *Cole, Rex Mountaineers* / In the Cumberland mountains: *Robinson, Carson* / When the curtains of the night are pinned back by the stars: *Layman, Zora & The Hometowners* / Atlanta bound: *Autry, Gene* / She came rollin' down the mountain: *Aarons Sisters* / Little old sod shanty on my claim: *Williams, Marc* / Ragtime Cowboy Joe: *Hillbillies* / I want to be a cowboy's sweetheart: *Montana, Patsy & The Prairie Ramblers* / Meet me by the icehouse, Lizzie: *Original Hoosier Hotshots* / Wabash cannonball: *Acuff, Roy & His Crazy Tennesseans* / Golden lariat: *Montana Slim* / New San Antonio Rose: *Wills, Bob & His Texas Playboys* / Walkin' the floor over you: *Tubb, Ernest* / Born to lose: *Daffan, Ted & The Texans* / West ain't what it used to be: *Robinson, Carson & His Pioneers*
CDAJA 5140 / Apr '96 / Living Era

☐ **HOWL (A Farewell Compilation Of Unreleased Songs)**
GRCD 352 / 13 Oct '97 / Glitterhouse

☐ **HUAYNO MUSIC OF PERU VOL.1 1949-89**
ARHCD 320 / Apr '95 / Arhoolie

☐ **HUAYNO MUSIC OF PERU VOL.2 1960-70**
ARHCD 338 / Apr '95 / Arhoolie

☐ **HUBERT GREGG SAYS THANKS FOR THE MEMORY**
China stomp: *Hampton, Lionel & His Orchestra* / Transatlantic lullaby: *Layton, Turner* / There's a small hotel: *Daniels, Bebe* / Scatterbrain: *Brisson, Carl* / Thanks for the memory: *Hope, Bob & Shirley Ross* / Baby face: *Jolson, Al* / Too romantic: *Dorsey, Tommy Orchestra* / Wind in the willows: *Hutchinson, Leslie 'Hutch'* / Physician: *Lawrence, Gertrude* / You're driving me crazy: *Reinhardt, Django & Stephane Grappelli* / After you've gone: *Venuti, Joe & Eddie Lang* / Sugarfoot stomp: *Goodman, Benny Orchestra* / Super special picture of the year: *Yacht Club Jazz Band* / Let's put out the lights and go to sleep: *Howes, Bobby* / Dinah: *Crosby, Bing* / Tea for two: *Tatum, Art* / One I'm looking for: *Buchanan, Jack* / I'm gonna get lit up (when the lights go on in London): *Gregg, Hubert* / Si tu m'aimes: *Sablon, Jean* / At the Darktown strutter's ball: *Dorsey, Jimmy Orchestra* / Jealous of me: *Waller, Fats* / Begin the beguine: *Shaw, Artie* / Princess is awakening: *Laye, Evelyn* / Maybe it's because I'm a Londoner: *Gregg, Hubert*
PASTCD 7024 / Sep '93 / Flapper

☐ **HUGE COMPILATION**
ORBITCD 4 / Aug '92 / Orbital

☐ **HUGE HITS 1996 (2CD Set)**
Virtual insanity: *Jamiroquai* / Breakfast at Tiffany's: *Deep Blue Something* / You're gorgeous: *Baby Bird* / Ooh ahh...just a little bit: *Gina G* / Macarena: *Los Del Rio* / Mysterious girl: *Andre, Peter* / How deep is your love: *Take That* / Fairground: *Simply Red* / Cecilia: *Suggs* / We've got it goin' on: *Backstreet Boys* / Oh what a night: *Clock* / Return of the Mack: *Morrison, Mark* / Creep: *TLC* / Gangsta's paradise: *Coolio* / Children: *Miles, Robert* / X-Files: *DJ Dado* / Gift: *Way Out West* / Don't stop movin': *Livin' Joy* / Firestarter: *Prodigy* / Born slippy: *Underworld* / I wanna be a hippy: *Technohead* / Don't look back in anger: *Oasis* / Tattva: *Kula Shaker* / Design for life: *Manic Street Preachers* / Stupid girl: *Garbage* / One to another: *Charlatans* / Trash: *Suede* / Day we caught the train: *Ocean Colour Scene* / Sale of the century: *Sleeper* / Oh yeah: *Ash* / Wonderwall: *Oasis* / Missing: *Everything But The Girl* / One by one: *Cher* / Falling in to you: *Dion, Celine* / 24/7: *3T* / I will survive: *Savage, Chantay* / Like a woman: *Rich, Tony Project* / I just wanna make love to you: *James, Etta* / Search for the hero: *M-People* / Neighbourhood: *Space* / Three lions: *Lightning Seeds & David Baddiel/Frank Skinner*
MOODCD 50 / Oct '96 / Sony Music

☐ **HUGE HITS 1997 (2CD Set)**
I'll be missing you: *Puff Daddy & Faith Evans/112/The LOX* / Sunchyme: *Dario G* / Just for you: *M-People* / You're the one I love: *Ama, Shola* / Never gonna let you go: *Moore, Tina* / Do ya think I'm sexy: *N-Trance* / Freed from desire: *Gala* / Maria no mercy: *Martin, Ricky* / Where do you go: *No Mercy* / Everybody: *Backstreet Boys* / All I wanna do: *Minogue, Dannii* / Isn't it a wonder: *Boyzone* / Love won't wait: *Barlow, Gary* / Oh la la: *Coolio* / Coco jamboo: *Mr. President* / Fresh: *Gina G* / Clementine: *Owen, Mark* / Love shine a light: *Katrina & The Waves* / All out of love: *OTT* / I believe I can fly: *R Kelly* / Don't speak: *No Doubt* / Nightnurse: *Sly & Robbie/Simply Red* / You showed me: *Lightning Seeds* / Halo: *Texas* / Alright: *Jamiroquai* / Free: *Ultra Nate* / Equador: *Sash* / You're not alone: *Olive* / Professional widow: *Amos, Tori* / Remember me: *Blueboy* / Closer than close: *Gaines, Rosie* / I don't want to: *Braxton, Toni* / Who's the mack: *Morrison, Mark* / Even after all: *Quaye, Finley* / Ready to go: *Republica* / Ain't talkin' bout dub: *Apollo 440* / Underwater love: *Smoke City* / Do you know: *Gayle, Michelle* / Real thing: *Stansfield, Lisa* / Hard to say I'm sorry: *Az Yet* / Hypnotize: *Notorious BIG* / Too gone too long: *En Vogue*
RADCD 75 / Nov '97 / Global TV

☐ **HUMBUGGARY**
BAH 13 / May '95 / Humbug

☐ **HUNGARIAN TRADITIONAL MUSIC**
PS 65117 / Nov '93 / PlayaSound

☐ **HUNGARY - THE LAST PASSAGE**
C 580031 / Oct '94 / Ocora

☐ **HUNTINGDON FOLK**
SVL 04 / Aug '97 / Speaking Volumes

☐ **HURDY GURDY IN FRANCE, THE**
Y 225109CD / Feb '95 / Silex

☐ **HURRA SCHOOL IS OUT (2CD Set)**
Action: *Sweet* / Sky high: *Jigsaw* / Glad all over: *Quatro, Suzi* / Get down: *O'Sullivan, Gilbert* / Over and over: *James Boys* / Hitchin' a ride: *Vanity Fare* / Beach baby: *First Class* / Happy together: *Turtles* / Jeans on: *Dundas, David* / Wild thing: *Fancy* / I feel free: *Amboy Dukes* / Good times: *Easybeats* / I get so excited: *Equals* / Good morning freedom: *Blue Mink* / Hi-Lilli Hi-Lo: *Price, Alan* / Sunglasses: *Ullman, Tracey* / Da doo ron ron: *Cassidy, Shaun* / Surfin' safari: *Beach Boys* / LA International Airport: *Raye, Susan* / Barbados: *Typically Tropical* / Another day in paradise: *Brown, Dennis* / Castles in the air: *McLean, Don* / Stop, girls go crazy: *Moti Special* / L'amour a la Francaise: *Sullivan, Art & Kiki* / Agadoo: *Black Lace* / Africa: *Laurens, Rose* / Kingston Kingston: *Lou & The Hollywood Bananas* / Disco samba: *Two Man Sound* / Let's all chant: *Zager, Michael Band* / Seasons of gold: *Gidea Park* / Red skies: *Fixx* / California sunshine: *Climax Blues Band*
24334 / Jul '96 / Laserlight

☐ **HURRY THE JUG (Classic Songs/ Lilting/Storytelling In The Irish Tradition)**
Talk about Garret Barry and Hurry the jug: *Lenihan, Tom* / Humours of whiskey (Paddy's panacea): *Lenihan, Tom* / Talk about music at Lenihans: *Lenihan, Tom* / John and the farmer: *Byrne, Packie Manus* / Lament to the moon: *Byrne, Packie Manus* / Bold Doherty: *Carolan, Mary-Ann* / Tinker's old budget: *Carolan, Mary-Ann* / Bonny green tree: *Reilly, John* / Raggle taggle gypsy: *Reilly, John* / Waterford boys: *Tunney, Paddy* / Sean O'Dwyer a Gleanna: *Tunney, Paddy* / Peigin is Peader: *Heaney, Joe* / Rocks of Baun: *Heaney, Joe* / Jolly thresher: *Makem, Sarah* / Banks of red roses: *Makem, Sarah* / Drowsy Maggie: *Cinnamond, Robert* / On yonder hill there sits a hare: *Hanna, George* / Erin's lovely home: *Hanna, George* / A stor mo chroi: *MacDonnchadha, Sean* / An buinnean bui: *MacDonnchadha, Sean* / Two strings on a bow: *Mitchell, Kevin* / Boys of Mullaghbawn: *Mitchell, Kevin* / Moorlough Mary: *McDermott, Josie* / Collier's reel/The Bank Of Ireland: *McDermott, Josie*
CDORBD 090 / Jul '96 / Globestyle

☐ **HUSH RECORDS STORY, THE**
Little girl: *Syndicate Of Sound* / Get outta my life: *Syndicate Of Sound* / Someday: *Brogues* / But now I find: *Brogues* / Believe me: *Penn, William & The Quakers* / Hey hey hey: *Penn, William & The Quakers* / I ain't no miracle worker: *Penn, William & The Quakers* / Don't shoot me down: *Brogues* / Looking for the good times (the robot): *Syndicate Of Sound* / That kind of man: *Syndicate Of Sound* / Rumours: *Syndicate Of Sound* / Say I love you: *Syndicate Of Sound* / I like that girl: *Gerry & Leslie* / Ghost of the monks: *Penn, William & The Quakers* / Care free: *Penn, William & The Quakers* / Coming up my way: *Penn, William & The Quakers* / Mary: *Syndicate Of Sound* / Games: *Syndicate Of Sound* / Nothing matters now: *Stop Sign* / Little girl: *Penn, William & The Quakers* / Doctor dear: *Diminished Fifth* / Do you hear: *Diminished Fifth* / Saturday night: *Syndicate Of Sound* / Someday: *Brogues*
CDWIKD 154 / Jan '97 / Big Beat

☐ **HUSTLE, THE**
I feel love: *Summer, Donna* / Ain't nothin' goin' on but the rent: *Guthrie, Gwen* / That's the way I like it: *KC & The Sunshine Band* / Never can say goodbye: *Gaynor, Gloria* / Don't leave me this way: *Houston, Thelma* / You sexy thing: *Hot Chocolate* / Heaven must be missing an angel: *Tavares* / Hang on in there baby: *Bristol, Johnny* / Can't give you anything but my love: *Stylistics* / If I can't have you: *Elliman, Yvonne* / Right back where we started from: *Nightingale, Maxine* / It should have been me: *Fair, Yvonne* / Hustle: *McCoy, Van* / Love's theme: *Love Unlimited Orchestra* / Do what you wanna do: *T-Connection* / Movin': *Brass Construction* / Rock your baby: *McCrae, George* / This will be: *Cole, Natalie* / Got to give it up: *Gaye, Marvin* / You're the first my last my everything: *White, Barry*
5529132 / Oct '97 / Spectrum

☐ **HYMNE AN DIE POSIE**
EFA 127142 / Apr '95 / Weisser Herbst

☐ **HYMNODY OF THE GREEK ORTHODOX CHURCH**
VICG 53462 / Mar '96 / JVC World Library

☐ **HYMNS FROM NORWICH CATHEDRAL**
Praise my soul the king of heaven / Just as I am / We plough the fields and scatter / Holy, holy, holy / Through all the changing scenes of life / Onward Christian soldiers / Abide with me / Christ triuimphant ever reigning / God of Abraham / Lift high the cross / We sing the praise / Crimond / Alleluia sing to Jesus / Angel voices / Be thou my vision / Praise to the holiest / Eternal father / Jesus christ is risen today / O worship the king / For all the saints / Head that once was crowned / Lift up your hearts / All my hope on god is founded
ANT 015 / Nov '96 / Tring

☐ **HYMNS FROM TRURO CATHEDRAL**
O praise ye the lord / Come thou long expected Jesus / O come o come emmanuel / All things bright and beautiful / All creatures of the God and King / Dear Lord and father / My song is love unknown / Forth in thy name o Lord I go / City of god / There is a green hill / When I survey the wondrous cross / Jesus lives / Come down oh loove divine / God be in my head / Oh Jesus I have promised / Fight the good fight / Glorious things / Day thou gavest / Before the ending of the day / Jerusalem
ANT 014 / Nov '96 / Tring

☐ **HYMNS OF OUR FATHERS**
Holy Virgin by God's decree: *Galway Singers* / Be thou my vision: *Galway Singers* / Watch the sunrise: *Galway Singers* / Morning has broken: *Hamilton, Claire* / Lady full of God's own grace: *Galway Singers* / Soul of my saviour: *Galway Singers* / Pie Jesu: *Edwards-Jones, Gill* / Seoladh na Ngamhna: *Galway Singers* / Viderunt Omnes: *Cantus Novus* / Sweet heart of Jesus: *Galway Singers* / Faith of our fathers: *Coppin, Johnny* / Hail Queen of heaven: *Galway Singers* / Daily daily sing to Mary: *Galway Singers* / Ireland, I'll not tell her name: *Sands, Mick* / Ave Maria: *Edwards-Jones, Gill* / Hail glorious St. Patrick: *Galway Singers* / This is my body, broken for you: *Galway Singers* / I heard the voices of Jesus say: *Hamilton, Claire* / Domino fidelium: *Cantus Novus* / Immaculate Mary: *Galway Singers* / Blessed are the pure in heart: *Galway Singers* / Lord's prayer: *Galway Singers*
3036000932 / Mar '97 / Carlton

☐ **HYMNS TO THE FALLEN**
BLACK 013CD / 4 May '98 / Blackend

☐ **HYPE (Life Inside The North West)**
SPCD 371 / Oct '96 / Sub Pop

☐ **HYPER COOL VOL.1**
ZYX 550682 / Nov '96 / ZYX

☐ **HYPER COOL VOL.2**
ZYX 550782 / Feb '97 / ZYX

☐ **HYPERTENSION SAMPLER**
HYCD 200153 / Apr '95 / Hypertension

☐ **HYPNOTIC AND HYPERSONIC (2CD Set)**
HYP 39101922CD / 6 Jul '98 / Hyperium

☐ **HYPNOTIC DRUM 'N' BASS**
Walking on the moon: *DJ Chrome* / Time warp: *Moody Alien* / Chill'em all: *DJ Chrome* / Clockwork: *Trib* / Spaceshore: *Moody Alien* / Run: *Trib* / Drumbient: *Psychochiller* / Eastern groove: *Jangala* / Train's waitin': *Funkless* / Rise and fall: *Psychochiller*
CDSGP 0373 / Feb '98 / Prestige

☐ **HYPNOTIC STATE (3CD Set)**
CLP 0111 / 6 Oct '97 / Hypnotic

☐ **HYPNOTIZING (2CD Set)**
CLP 9971 / Apr '97 / Cleopatra

☐ **HYPOCRITE INNA DANCE HALL STYLE**
JJCD 192 / Apr '96 / Channel One

☐ **HYRDESTUND (Early Norwegian Flutes & Whistles)**
HCD 7116 / Aug '96 / Helio

I

☐ **I AM WALKING**
Through my eyes: *Vasquez, Andrew* / Shi ni sha: *Stroutsos, Gary* / Oweegon: *Little Wolf Band* / Kamui: *Nakai, R. Carlos* / Lost bird: *Stroutsos, Gary & David Lanz* / Across the river: *Vasquez, Andrew* / Wolf song: *Fire Crow, Joseph* / Night of the sun: *Stroutsos, Gary* / Tekanatsyaslitha: *Shenandoah, Joanne* / Tor-Cheney-Nahana: *Sacred Spirit* / Wash your spirit clean: *Walela* / Feather, stone and light: *Nakai, R. Carlos & William Eaton/Will Clipman* / Serenade: *Stroutsos, Gary & David Lanz*
ND 63933 / 17 Nov '97 / Narada

☐ **I ASKED FOR WHISKEY**
IGOCD 2028 / Aug '95 / Indigo

☐ **I CAN EAGLE ROCK (1940-1941)**
TMCD 09 / May '96 / Travellin' Man

☐ **I CAN HEAR MUSIC**
I can hear music: *Beach Boys* / Hippy hippy shake: *Swinging Blue Jeans* / Do wah diddy diddy: *Manfred Mann* / Proud Mary: *Turner, Ike & Tina* / C'mon everybody: *Cochran, Eddie* / Rubber ball: *Vee, Bobby* / Hello Mary Lou: *Nelson, Ricky* / Till I kissed you: *Everly Brothers* / Summer in the city: *Lovin' Spoonful* / Wanderer: *Dion* / Games people play: *South, Joe* / Keep searchin' (we'll follow the sun): *Shannon, Del* / Sloop John B: *Beach Boys* / We've gotta get out of this place: *Animals* / Jenny take a ride: *Ryder, Mitch & The Detroit Wheels* / Some kinda wonderful: *Grand Funk Railroad*
DC 880792 / May '97 / Disky

☐ **I CAN'T BE SATISFIED VOL.1 (Early American Women Blues Singers Town & Country)**
YAZ 2026 / Apr '97 / Yazoo

☐ I CAN'T BE SATISFIED VOL.2 (Early American Women Blues Singers Town & Country)
YAZZ 2027 / Apr '97 / Yazoo

☐ I CAN'T BELIEVE IT'S NOT TRIP HOP
NOR 001CD / Mar '96 / North South

☐ I FALL TO PIECES (Classic Country)
Walkin' after midnight: *Cline, Patsy* / He'll have to go: *Reeves, Jim* / Crystal chandoliers: *Pride, Charley* / White lightning: *Jennings, Waylon* / Take this job and shove it: *Paycheck, Johnny* / Cold cold heart: *Jones, George* / Stranger in my arms: *Cline, Patsy* / Kiss an angel good morning: *Pride, Charley* / I fall to pieces: *Jackson, Wanda* / Have I told you lately that I love you: *Reeves, Jim* / Please help me I'm falling: *Locklin, Hank* / I'm the only hell mama ever raised: *Paycheck, Johnny* / Love of the common people: *Jennings, Waylon* / World's worst lover: *Jones, George* / Four walls: *Reeves, Jim* / Night life: *Nelson, Willie* / Church, a courtroom, then goodbye: *Cline, Patsy* / Help me make it through the night: *Pride, Charley*
CD 6045 / Sep '96 / Music

☐ I GOT IT BAD AND THAT AIN'T GOOD
I got it bad and that ain't good: *Holiday, Billie* / Sad letter: *Waters, Muddy* / Dusty road: *Hooker, John Lee* / Commit a crime: *Howlin' Wolf* / Cool disposition: *Williamson, Sonny Boy* / Little rain: *Reed, Jimmy* / Blues with a feeling: *Little Walter* / Please don't talk about me when I'm gone: *Holiday, Billie* / Mean mistreater: *Waters, Muddy* / Process: *Hooker, John Lee* / Moanin' at midnight: *Howlin' Wolf* / Blue tail fly: *Leadbelly* / Dust my broom: *James, Elmore* / Nice work if you can get it: *Holiday, Billie* / Whiskey and wimmen: *Hooker, John Lee* / Diamonds at your feet: *Waters, Muddy* / I'm in the mood: *Hooker, John Lee* / In New Orleans: *Leadbelly* / Killing floor: *Howlin' Wolf* / Fine and mellow: *Holiday, Billie* / How blue can you get: *King, B.B.* / Off the wall: *Little Walter* / Mean red spider: *Waters, Muddy* / Goin' down slow: *Howlin' Wolf* / Frisco blues: *Hooker, John Lee*
GRF 127 / '93 / Tring

☐ I HAVE TO PAINT MY FACE
ARHCD 432 / Jan '96 / Arhoolie

☐ I KNOW WHAT BOYS LIKE (Great Girl Pop Hits Of 1980/1990's)
SH 5713 / Oct '96 / Shanachie

☐ I LIKE IT (BGP Presents The Vanguard Experience)
EVA: *Perrey, Jean Jacques* / Take yo' praise: *Yarborough, Camille* / I like it: *Players Association* / Rigor mortez: *Burns, Dave* / Work song: *Pazant Brothers* / Funk ain't a word: *Green, Bunky* / Lavendar Thursday: *Natal, Nannette* / Cat in the night: *Perrey, Jean Jacques* / Funky monkey: *Hills, Chris* / Loose and juicy: *Pazant Brothers* / Richie's dream: *Burns, Dave* / Mas que nada: *Perrey, Jean Jacques*
CDBGPD 106 / Jun '96 / Beat Goes Public

☐ I LOVE CUBA SAM
UMD 80495 / 27 Jul '98 / Universal

☐ I LOVE FUSE
FUSE 001CD / Jan '96 / Fuse

☐ I LOVE NY JUNGLE
JSK 011 / Dec '96 / Jungle Sky

☐ I LOVE TECHNO
ILT 01CD / Sep '96 / News

☐ I LOVE YOU (18 Classic Country Love Songs)
Sharing the night together: *Dr. Hook* / Never ending song of love: *Gayle, Crystal* / Take me in your arms and hold me: *Whitman, Slim* / Love me like you used to: *Tucker, Tanya* / What the world needs now is love: *Spears, Billie Jo* / Honey come back: *Campbell, Glen* / Loving him was easier: *Carter, Anita* / Stand by your man: *Jackson, Wanda* / All I have to do is dream: *Newton, Juice* / Crazy: *Nelson, Willie* / Young love: *James, Sonny* / Sweet dreams: *Young, Faron* / Somebody loves you: *Gayle, Crystal* / My blue heaven: *Whitman, Slim* / You love me through it all: *Williams, Don* / When you're in love with a beautiful woman: *Dr. Hook* / Everything a man could ever need: *Campbell, Glen* / Love song: *Newton-John, Olivia*
CDMFP 6281 / Jan '97 / Music For Pleasure

☐ I SHALL SING VOL.1
CDTRL 289 / Mar '94 / Trojan

☐ I SHALL SING VOL.2
Best thing for me: *Powell, June* / I see you my love: *Griffiths, Marcia* / Silly wasn't it: *Forrester, Sharon* / Love that a woman should give a man: *Dillon, Phyllis* / She kept on talking: *Mowatt, Judy* / Please Mr. Please: *Powell, June* / Mother nature: *Sweet, Roslyn* / Heart made of stone (Vocal): *Hall, Audrey* / Heart made of stone (Version): *Hit Squad* / You can wake up with me: *Powell, June* / Love the one you're with: *Dillon, Phyllis* / Promises: *Richard, Cynthia* / You're not my kind: *Naomi* / I can't help it darling: *Jones, Barbara* / Put a little love away: *Forrester, Sharon* / Something about you: *Jordon, Sidonie* / I'll be everything to you (Vocal): *Powell, June* / I'll be everything to you (Version): *Hit Squad*
CDTRL 316 / Mar '94 / Trojan

☐ I TURNED INTO A HELIUM BALLOON
Mirror of your mind: *We The People* / Color of love: *We The People* / You burn me up and down: *We The People* / St. John's shop: *We The People* / In the past: *We The People* / Half of wednesday: *We The People* / My brother, the man: *We The People* / Free information: *We The People* / Too much noise: *We The People* / By the rule: *We The People* / Alfred, what kind of man are you: *We The People* / Beginning of the end: *We The People* / I ain't no miracle worker: *Brogues* / Don't shoot me down: *Brogues* / Let it be: *Blaskey, Lindy & The Lavelles* / You ain't tuff: *Blaskey, Lindy & The Lavelles* / Spinach: *Boston Tea Party* / Words: *Boston Tea Party* / I'm spinning: *Fenwyck* / Mindrocker: *Fenwyck* / State of mind: *Fenwyck* / Away: *Fenwyck* / I wanna die: *Fenwyck* / I lye: *Fenwyck* / Show me the way: *Free For All* / Psychedelic siren: *Daybreakers* / Somebody's son: *Tikis* / Thoughts: *Front Page News* / Lies: *Knickerbockers* / My feet are off the ground: *Knickerbockers*
CDWIKD 130 / Jun '94 / Big Beat

☐ I WALK THE LINE
MACCD 214 / Aug '96 / Autograph

☐ I WILL ALWAYS LOVE YOU (Romantic Panpipes)
I honestly love you / What are you doing / What is this thing called love / With you I'm born again / Softly as I leave you / When you're in love / Someone to watch over me / Miss you nights / Where is the love / Nearness of you / Up where we belong / Speak softly love / Tonight I celebrate my love / I will always love you
CDMFP 6270 / Sep '96 / Music For Pleasure

☐ I WOULDN'T PISS ON IT IF IT WAS ON FIRE (2CD Set)
Hey now: *Perfect Disaster* / Walkin' with Jesus: *Spacemen 3* / Ups: *Blue Aeroplanes* / Let's make some plans: *Close Lobsters* / LA rain: *Rose Of Avalanche* / This is motortown: *Walking Seeds* / Gates of freedom: *Very Things* / Mr. Gas: *Parachute Men* / Big Kahuna: *Harbour Kings* / Rage and storm: *Prophet, Chuck* / You could be mine: *Graney, Dave* / My legendary girlfriend: *Pulp* / My very first nervous breakdown: *Television Personalities* / I won't try: *Midway Still* / I want the moon: *Leatherface* / This town: *Gumball* / Notown: *Anastasia Screamed* / Android dreams: *Mega City Four* / Fire maple song: *Everclear* / Truck train tractor: *Pastels* / God knows it's true: *Teenage Fanclub* / Breakfast: *Eugenius* / Pattern 26: *Manifesto* / Where I find my heaven: *Gigolo Aunts* / So glad: *Thrum* / To one in paradise: *Dando, Evan & HP Zinker* / Girl you'll be a woman soon: *Urge Overkill* / Butterfly girl: *Nightblooms* / Moon don't come up tonight: *Telstar Ponies* / Raymond did you see the red queen: *Moles* / Nowhere nuthin' fuck up: *Built To Spill* / Can't believe it's true: *Halo Benders* / Everything is: *Neutral Milk Hotel* / Baby come down: *Sammy* / Something scratching: *Cottonmouth* / US teens are spoilt bums: *Half Japanese* / Penis size and cars: *Supermodel*
FIRECD 63
FIRECD 63X / 25 May '98 / Fire

☐ I-5 KILLERS VOL.3
What used to be: *Gift* / Blondes: *Everclear* / Crash: *Kpants* / Punch: *Thirty Ought Six* / Lines: *Kaia* / Simeon flick: *Skiploader* / Edward Hopper song: *Whirlees* / Jake's dream: *Time Killing Isabel* / Never win: *Wipers* / It's a lie: *Gravel Pit* / Ugly stick: *Ice Cream Headache* / Get outta my way: *Starlite Trio* / Rock your baby: *Oblivion Seekers* / Evil style: *Anal Solvent* / Josh has a crush: *New Bad Things* / Metropolis 2664: *Caveman Shoestore* / Aloha Steve and Dan-O: *Oswald 5-O* / Your Mom rules: *Supersuckers*
SZ 0213 / Jun '94 / T/K

☐ IBIZA - FOLKLORE Y CANCIONES
31374 / Oct '96 / Divusca

☐ IBIZA '95
Closer: *Mood II Swing* / Ultra flava: *Heller & Farley Project* / One love: *Coccoluto, Claudio* / Do U wanna funk: *Space 2000* / Come with me: *Zero The Hero* / Weekend: *Terry, Todd* / You gotta get up: *Perfectly Ordinary People* / Do you feel: *Effective* / Stick together: *Miss Stuck Up* / Where's my man: *EL Fredo* / Red hot in Ibiza: *DJ Pants* / Born to synthesize: *Mona Lisa Overdrive* / Honk: *Hullabaloo* / Come on y'all: *Rhythm Masters* / Mambo white: *Nox Alba* / Spiritualize: *We Shape Space* / Magic in you: *Sugar Babies*
21 CCCD 001 / Oct '95 / 21st Century Opera

☐ IBIZA ANTHEMS (3CD Set)
Closer than close: *Gaines, Rosie* / Offshore: *Chicane* / Spin spin sugar: *Sneaker Pimps* / Plastic dreams: *Jaydee* / No mas etiendo: *Matador* / Where love lives: *Limerick, Alison* / Somethings do: *Plus 2* / Free: *Ultra Nate* / You got the love: *Source & Candi Staton* / I luv you baby: *Original* / Anytime: *Nu Birth* / See me feel me: *1st Bass* / Gabriel: *Davis, Roy Jr.* / Show melove: *Robin S* / Shattered: *Groove Chronicles* / Encore une fois: *Sash* / Outer limits: *DOA* / Sugar is sweeter: *Bolland, C.J.* / Born slippy: *Underworld* / Dark 97: *Gass* / All night: *Trade*
CLUBCD 1 / 13 Jul '98 / Club Cuts

☐ IBIZA ANTHEMS, THE (3CD Set)
CDBNTW 5 / 27 Jul '98 / Passion

☐ IBIZA HITS (2CD Set)
ZYX 811142 / Aug '97 / ZYX

☐ IBIZA MIX
Beat is pumpin': *Jumpstart* / Jumpin': *Rapture* / Is this love: *Calibre* / Move your body: *Commission* / Bitch: *Queen Party* / My house is your house: *House Experience* / You can feel it: *Shaggy & Scoobie* / Rock da disco: *4 The People* / Back to the floor: *Queen Party* / Original wild style: *Track 2* / Show me your love: *Higher State* / Man to woman: *Higher State* / Facinator: *PK Factory* / Raw to the floor: *Dance Warriors* / Work it: *Session singers* / Rock ya: *Wayward Justice* / I want more: *System 2* / Get up and dance: *Trance Fusion* / Burning like fire: *Big D* / Dance: *Ryder, Mark*
IBMXCD 001 / 15 Sep '97 / Castle

☐ IBIZA UNCOVERED VOL.1 (2CD Set)
VTDCD 168 / 1 Sep '97 / Virgin

☐ IBIZA UNCOVERED VOL.2 (2CD Set)
VTDCD 202 / 10 Aug '98 / Virgin TV

☐ ICH BIN (Mixed By Dr. Motte)
EFA 004202 / Aug '97 / Space Teddy

☐ ICHIBAN BLUES AT CHRISTMAS
(All I want for Christmas is to) lay around: *Willis, Chuck* / Absent minded Santa: *McCain, Jerry* / Lonesome Christmas: *Blues Boy Willie* / Santa Claus is back in town: *Brown, Nappy* / Christmas is here again: *Taylor, Johnny* / Christmas time (comes but once a year): *Lynn, Trudy* / I didn't get nothin' for Christmas: *Garrett, Vernon* / Christmas tears: *Dee, David* / Christmas, don't forget about me: *Drink Small* / Please come home for Christmas: *Willis, Chuck*
ICH 1126CD / Nov '91 / Ichiban

☐ ICHIBAN SAMPLER
ICH 7802CD / Jan '94 / Ichiban

☐ IF A TREE FALLS
Song of the trees: *Trudell, John* / Devil and the trees: *Zero* / Trees: *Hoyt, Robert* / Never alone: *Cockburn, Bruce* / Kiss Mother Nature goodbye: *Williams, Hank Jr.* / Priests of the golden bull: *Sainte-Marie, Buffy* / Cry in the forest: *Fogelberg, Dan* / Where are we gonna work when the trees are gone: *Biafra, Jello & Mojo Nixon* / Trees like to rot in the forest: *Tinklers* / You can't clearcut your way to Heaven: *Cherney, Darryl* / Defend the Earth: *Di Micele, Alicia* / Farewell to Clayoquot sound: *Wyrd Sisters* / Heart of destruction: *Ferron* / Only green world: *Rumors Of The Big Wave*
R 272495 / Nov '96 / Earthbeat

☐ IF IT AIN'T A HIT I'LL EAT MY....BABY
Think twice: *Wilson, Jackie & Laverne Baker* / Two time Slim/Hey, shine: *Snatch & The Poontangs* / Somebody else was suckin' my dick last night: *Wolff, Fred Combo* / Meat man: *Vickery, Mack* / Stoop down baby: *Willis, Chuck* / Deacon Jones/LA women love Uncle Bud: *Chavis, Boozoo* / Don't fuck around with love: *Blenders* / Long John/Short John: *Washington, Dinah* / Rotten cocksuckers' ball: *Clovers* / Hard driving blues: *Milburn, Amos* / Butcher Pete: *Brown, Roy* / Joe's joint: *Ferre, Cliff* / Fuck off (You dirty rooster): *Gaillard, Slim*
CDZ 2009 / Apr '94 / Zu Zazz

☐ IF U CAN BEAT 'EM BREAK 'EM
Eat humble pie: *Small Fish With Spine* / Half price full value: *UMO* / Space gladiator: *Renegade Soundwave* / BSE mon ami: *Le Rosbifs* / Between the 'fro: *Bassbin Twins* / Gotta learn: *Dan Mass* / Freestyle noize: *Freestylers* / One time: *Mantronik, Curtis* / FUNK: *Zum* / Whole meal: *Groove Armada* / Do the turtle: *Cut & Paste* / Moment by moment: *Makesome Breaksome*
SSR 195 / 23 Feb '98 / SSR

☐ IF YOU JUST TUNED IN (Live From The Mean Fiddler's Acoustic Room)
Dollar tree: *Hawkins, Ted* / When we were young: *Orchard, Pat* / Love your shoes: *Cunningham, Andrew* / Rover: *Sons Of The Desert* / Down the wine garden: *Little Big Band* / It's not that bad anymore: *Barely Works* / White cloud: *To Hell With Burgundy* / Spitting: *And All Because The Lady Loves* / Three legged men: *Harding, John Wesley* / Tree to breathe: *Dinner Ladies* / Partisan: *Keineg, Katell* / I ain't got nothin' yet: *Hawkins, Ted*
AWCD 1017 / Apr '90 / Awareness

☐ IF YOU WANT REGGAE VOL.1
TMPCD 028 / Jun '96 / Temple

☐ IF YOU WANT REGGAE VOL.2
TMPCD 029 / Jun '96 / Temple

☐ IF YOU WANT REGGAE VOL.3
TMPCD 030 / Jun '96 / Temple

☐ IFI PALASA - TONGAN BRASS
PANCD 2044 / May '94 / Pan

☐ IGL ROCK STORY VOL.1
AA 046 / Jul '97 / Arf Arf

☐ IL BALLO DEI PAZZI
ACB 07CD / Mar '96 / ACB

☐ IL SUONO DI ROMA
ACVCD 2001 / Oct '94 / ACV

☐ I'LL BE SEEING YOU
I'll be seeing you: *Crosby, Bing* / White cliffs of Dover: *Dorsey, Jimmy* / Lili Marlene: *Anderson, Lale* / Beneath the lights of home: *Durbin, Deanna* / You always hurt the one you love: *Mills Brothers* / Blues in the night: *Herman, Woody Orchestra* / That old black magic: *Miller, Glenn* / Is you is or is you ain't my baby: *Jordan, Louis* / I'll walk alone: *Shore, Dinah* / Moonlight becomes you: *Crosby, Bing* / Somewhere in France with you: *Bowlly, Al* / Don't get around much anymore: *Ellington, Duke* / Sand in my shoes: *Boswell, Connee* / I had the craziest dream: *James, Harry* / Nightingale sang in Berkley Square: *James, Harry* / In the blue of the evening: *Dorsey, Tommy* / This is the army Mr. Jones: *Berlin, Irving* / Long ago and far aways: *Forrest, Helen & Dick Haymes* / Stardust: *Shaw, Artie* / White Christmas: *Crosby, Bing* / London pride: *Coward, Sir Noel* / You'll never know: *Sinatra, Frank* / We'll meet again: *Lynn, Vera*
CECD 2 / 1 Jun '98 / Collector's Edition

☐ I'LL DANCE TILL DE SUN BREAKS THROUGH (Ragtime, Cakewalks & Stomps 1898-1923)
That moaning saxophones rag: *Six Brown Brothers* / Florida rag: *Van Eps Trio* / Bacchanal rag: *Peerless Orchestra* / Alabama skedaddle: *Mitcham, William* / Castle walk: *Europe's Society Orchestra* / From soup to nuts: *Arndt, Felix* / Smoky mokes: *Metropolitan Orchestra* / Eli Green's cake walk: *Cullen & Collins* / Cake walk: *Victor Minstrels* / I'll dance till de sun breaks through: *Joyce, Archibald & His Orchestra* / Ain't nobody's business if I do: *Matson, Charles Creole Serenaders* / Whistling Rufus: *Oakley, Olly* / Wild cherries rag: *Victor Orchestra* / Won't you come home, Bill Bailey: *Collins, Arthur* / Stomp dance: *Victor Military Band* / Calico rag: *Banta, Frank & Howard Kopp* / Smiles and chuckles - A jazz rag: *Six Brown Brothers* / On the Levee: *Victor Minstrels* / Trombone sneeze - a humoresque cakewalk: *Sousa's Band* / Two key rag: *Conway's Band*
CDSDL 336 / Mar '94 / Saydisc

☐ ILL ST. PRESENTS SUBTERRANEAN HITZ VOL.1
WSCD 014 / Jan '97 / Word Sound Recordings

☐ ILLEGAL PIRATE RADIO VOL.1
STHCCD 3 / Aug '93 / Strictly Underground

☐ ILLEGAL PIRATE RADIO VOL.2
STHCCD 4 / Apr '94 / Strictly Underground

☐ ILLEGAL PIRATE RADIO VOL.3
STHCCD 9 / May '95 / Strictly Hardcore

☐ ILLEGAL RAVE VOL.2
STHCCD 2 / Jun '93 / Strictly Underground

☐ ILLEGAL RAVE VOL.3
STHCCD 5 / Jun '94 / Strictly Underground

☐ ILLUMINATIONS (Music To Uplift Relax & Inspire)
Light of the spirit: *Kitaro* / Bike song: *McGarrigle, Kate & Anna* / Kali nichta: *Courage Of Lassie* / Facades: *Glass, Philip* / Missa Greca: *ASHA* / Change we must: *Anderson, Jon* / Dust on the wind: *Kansas* / Transcendental voyage: *Bernhardt, Patrick* / Before summer rain: *Mishra, Sanjay & Jerry Garcia* / In the woods of Krondaal: *Vollenweider, Andreas* / Both sides the Tweed: *Capercaillie* / Last snows of winter: *White, Clifford* / Tara mantra: *Shanti, Oliver* / Mirandor: *Brandenburg, Paul* / Initium: *Corradi, Violaine*
VSOPCD 243 / 29 Sep '97 / Connoisseur Collection

☐ I'M A NO-COUNT
Bad woman: *Fallen Angels* / Caught you red handed: *Jolly Green Giants* / Did ya need to know: *Gregory, Bale & The Shouters* / Go away: *Plague* / Stop it baby: *Heard* / I'm gone: *Continentals* / If you don't come back: *Gents* / Do you believe me: *Byron & The mortals* / 1523 Blair: *Outcasts* / We're pretty quick: *Chob* / Come on baby: *Al's Untouchables* / I'm a no-count: *Wagner, Ty & The Scotchmen* / I'm a nothing: *Magic Plants* / Someday fool: *MG & The Escorts* / It's trash: *Cave Men* / Lively one: *Passions* / I'll be gone: *Opposite Six* / I'm gonna get in that girl's mind: *Reddlemen* / I want your love: *Barking Spyders*
TS 6604CD / 20 Jul '98 / Teenage Shutdown

☐ I'M BEGINNING TO SEE THE LIGHT
Opus one: *Dorsey, Tommy* / Saturday night: *Sinatra, Frank* / I only have eyes for you: *Hawkins, Coleman* / As time goes by: *Holiday, Billie* / Lady Day: *Shaw, Artie* / Somebody loves me: *Condon, Eddie* / Blue Lester: *Young, Lester* / GI jive: *Jordan, Louis* / Red cross: *Parker, Charlie* / I'm beginning to see the light: *Ellington, Duke* / Night and day: *Hall, Edmond* / Down by the riverside: *Johnson, Bunk* / I'm confessin' that I love you: *James, Harry* / Exercise in swing: *Guarnieri, Johnny & Lester Young* / Someone to watch over me: *Wiley, Lee* / All the cats join in: *Goodman, Benny* / Jack Armstrong blues: *Teagarden, Jack & Louis Armstrong* / Sentimental journey: *Day, Doris & Les Brown* / Skyliner: *Barnet, Charlie* / Don't fence me in: *Bailey, Mildred* / Woody 'n' you: *Hawkins, Coleman & Dizzy Gillespie* / There'll be a hot time in the town of Berlin: *Miller, Glenn*
PHONTCD 7672 / Jun '94 / Phontastic

☐ I'M IN THE MOOD FOR BLUES
DCD 5322 / Dec '93 / Disky

☐ I'M IN THE MOOD FOR SAX
I'm in the mood for love / True love / You belong to me / Jane / Secret love / Unforgettable / Dreaming / Send in the clowns / Summer the first time / Nightingale sang in Berkeley Square / Once in a while / Nearness of you / Someone to watch over me / When I fall in love / Certain smile / Evergreen / Scarborough fair / Try to remember / Feelings / Wind beneath my wings / This masquerade
EMPRCD 602 / Jun '96 / Emporio

☐ I'M LEAVING TIPPERARY - CLASSIC IRISH TRADITIONAL MUSIC (Recorded In America In The 1920's & 1930's)
Lord Gordon's reel: *Hanafin, Michael* / I'm leaving Tipperary: *Sullivan, Dan & Shamrock Band* / My darling asleep/Maids on the green: *McGettigan, John* / Martha, the flower of sweet Strabane: *McGettigan, John* / Curlew hills/Peach Blossoms: *Morrison, James* / Frieze breeches: *Ennis, Tom* / Auld blackthorn: *Flanagan Brothers* / My Irish Molly-O: *Flanagan Brothers* / Irish mazurka: *Gillespie, Hugh* / Jenny's welcome to Charlie: *Gillespie, Hugh* / Stone outside Dan Murphy's door: *McGettigan, John* / Tailor's twist/Flower of Spring: *Morrison, James* / Billy Hanafin's reel: *Hanafin, Michael* / Green grow the rushes-o: *Sullivan, Dan & Shamrock Band* / Beggarman song: *Flanagan Brothers* / Tickling Mary Jane: *Rabbet, Murty & Gaelic Band* / Miller's reel/Duffy the dancer: *Nolan, Neil* / Moneymusk/Johnny will you marry me/Keel row: *Morrison, James* / Kildare fancy/Stack of wheat: *Ennis, Tom* / New steamboat/Bucks of Oranmore/Gardeners daughter: *Morrison, James & Tom Ennis* / Erin's lovely lea: *McGettigan, John* / Dowd's No. 9/Jackson's: *Gillespie, Hugh* / Versevanna: *Gillespie, Hugh* / Irish delight: *Flanagan Brothers*
CDORBD 082 / Jan '94 / Globestyle

☐ I'M ROMANTIC
BB 2809 / Aug '96 / Blue Beat

☐ I'M SO LONESOME I COULD CRY
MU 5057 / Oct '92 / Musketeer

☐ I'M SURE WE'RE GONNA MAKE IT
64862 / Jan '97 / Epitaph

☐ IMAGINE (2CD Set)
DEMPCD 008 / Mar '96 / Emporio

☐ IMAGINE ANOTHER IRELAND VOL.1
Summer in Siam: *Pogues* / Strathspey: *Altan* / Harry's game: *Clannad* / All the lies: *Black, Frances* / Idir eatarthu: *O'Suilleabhain, Micheal* / Seo leo'thoil: *Casey, Nollaig & Arty McGlynn* / Lucy's tune: *Spillane, Davy* / Dul dti's raiseanna: *Begley, Seamus & Stephen Cooney* / Gardiner Street blues: *Drew, Ronnie* / Blackbird: *Shannon, Sharon* / Rights of man: *De Danann* / O'Rourke's: *O'Flynn, Liam* / Geantrai: *Anuna* / Pachelbel's frolics: *Ivers, Eileen* / Nocturne: *Irish Chamber Orchestra*
KMCD 63 / Jul '96 / Keltia Musique

☐ IMAGINE ANOTHER IRELAND VOL.2 (Encore)
KMCD 75 / May '97 / Keltia Musique

☐ IMELAND
AMCD 730 / Nov '95 / Amigo

☐ IMMEDIATE BLUES ANTHOLOGY, THE (3CD Set)
I'm your witchdoctor: *Mayall, John & The Bluesbreakers* / Snake drive: *Clapton, Eric* / Ain't gonna cry no more: *McPhee, Tony* / I tried: *Savoy Brown Blues Band* / Tribute to Elmore: *Clapton, Eric* / I feel so good: *Kelly, Jo Ann* / Telephone blues: *Mayall, John & The Bluesbreakers* / You don't love me: *McPhee, Tony* / West coast idea: *Clapton, Eric* / Ain't seen no whisky: *Kelly, Jo Ann* / Flapjacks: *Stone's Masonry* / Cold blooded woman: *Savoy Brown Blues Band* / On top of the world: *Mayall, John & The Bluesbreakers* / Someone to love me: *McPhee, Tony* / Can't quit you baby: *Savoy Brown Blues Band* / Draggin' my tail: *Clapton, Eric & Jimmy Page* / Dealing with the devil: *Dharma Blues Band* / Look down at my woman: *Spencer, Jeremy* / Roll em pete: *Dharma Blues Band* / Choker: *Clapton, Eric & Jimmy Page* / True Blue: *Savoy Brown Blues Band* / When you got a good friend: *McPhee, Tony* / Someday baby: *Davies, Cyril & the Rhythm & Blues All Stars* / Steelin': *All Stars & Jeff Beck* / LA Breakdown: *All Stars & Jimmy Page* / Chuckles: *All Stars & Jeff Beck* / Down in the boots: *All Stars & Jimmy Page* / Piano shuffle: *All Stars & Nicky Hopkins* / Miles road: *Clapton, Eric & Jimmy Page* / Porcupine juice: *Santa Barbara Machine Head* / Howlin for my darling: *Stuff Smith* / Next milestone: *Lee, Albert & Tony Colton* / Someone's gonna get their head kicked in tonight: *Vince, Earl & The Valients* / New death master: *Kelly, Dave* / Back water blues: *Kelly, Jo Ann* / So much to say: *Stewart, Rod* / Married woman blues: *Kelly, Dave* / Water on my fire: *Lee, albert & paul williams* / Kepp your hands out of my pockets: *Kelly, Jo Ann* / Alabama woman: *Kelly, Dave* / Crosstown link: *Lee, Albert* / All night long: *Kelly, Dave* / Down and dirty: *Simon & Steve* / Not fade away: *Davies, Cyril & the Rhythm & Blues All Stars* / Come home baby: *Stewart, Rod & P.P.Arnold* / Life is but nothing: *Arnold, P.P.* / Little miss understood: *Stewart, Rod*
CDIMMBOX 4 / Jun '96 / Charly

☐ IMMEDIATE COLLECTION, THE (16 Legendary Recordings From The Era That Inspired Britpop)
Hello Suzie: *Amen Corner* / Natural born bugie: *Humble Pie* / Out of time: *Farlowe, Chris* / Hang on to a dream: *Nice* / All or nothing: *Small Faces* / Hang on sloopy: *McCoys* / Man of the world: *Fleetwood Mac* / Angel of the morning: *Arnold, P.P.* / First cut is the deepest: *Arnold, P.P.* / Sittin' on a fence: *Twice As Much* / Lazy Sunday: *Small Faces* / Little Miss Understood: *Stewart, Rod* / Handbags and gladrags: *Farlowe, Chris* / (If paradise is) half as nice: *Amen Corner* / Itchycoo park: *Small Faces* / America: *Nice*
SUMCD 4036 / Nov '96 / Summit

☐ IMMORTALES DE CANCION RANCHERA
9944132202 / 3 Mar '98 / Orfeon

☐ IMMORTALES DE LA CANCION MEXICANA
BMCD 2009 / Nov '97 / Blue Moon

☐ IMPERIAL DUB RECORDINGS VOL.1 (Mixed By DJ Mark Farina)
IDR 006 / 22 Sep '97 / Imperial Dub

☐ IN A COCKTAIL MOOD
TCD 1037 / Nov '96 / Tradition

☐ IN BED WITH MARINA
MA 21 / Feb '97 / Marina

☐ IN CASE YOU MISSED IT - JAZZ FESTIVAL VOL.1
Schalle mein prinzchen: *Bue, Papa Viking Jazz Band* / Muskrat ramble: *Collie, Max Rhythm Aces* / Mood indigo: *Ball, Kenny* / Bourbon street parade: *Dutch Swing College Band* / Flyin' house: *Dr. Dixie Jazz Band* / That's a plenty: *Prowizorka Dzezz Bed* / Stranger on the shore: *Bilk, Acker* / Struttin' with some barbecue: *Down Town Jazzband* / Ice cream: *Sunshine, Monty Jazz Band* / Basin Street blues: *Sunshine, Monty Jazz Band* / Jumpin' at the woodside: *Huub Janssen's Amazing Jazz Band* / World is waiting for the sunrise: *Huub Janssen's Amazing Jazz Band* / Bye and bye: *Boutte, Lillian* / Petite fleur: *Lightfoot, Terry* / West End blues: *Mason, Rod Hot Five* / At the jazz band ball: *World's Greatest Jazz Band* / Jambalaya: *Barber, Chris & His Jazz Band* / As I go to the quick river: *Uralsky All Stars*
CDTTD 522 / Feb '95 / Timeless Jazz

☐ IN CASE YOU MISSED IT - JAZZ FESTIVAL VOL.2
Midnight in Moscow: *Ball, Kenny* / Aria: *Bilk, Acker* / It's a sin to tell a lie: *Deep Creek Jazzuits* / Mishka, mishka: *Uralsky All Stars* / What a friend: *Boutte, Lillian* / You are woman: *Jazz Band Ball Orchestra* / Song was born: *Papa Blue's Viking Jazzband* / Royal flush: *Berkhout, Bernard '5'* / Storyville: *Houlind, Doc & His Copenhagen Ragtime Band* / Old rugged cross: *Monty's Sunshine Jazz Band* / Limehouse blues: *Dixie-O-Naires* / Washboard wiggle: *Prowizorka Jazzband* / Kansas City blues: *Collie, Max Rhythm Aces* / Hundred years from today: *Willcox, Spiegle* / Drop that sack: *Mason, Rod Hot Five* / I wish'd I could shimmy like my sister Kate: *Barber, Chris* / Dr. Jazz: *Davison, Bill* / I would do most anything for you love: *Paramount Jazzband Of Boston* / When we danced at the Mardi Gras: *Lightfoot, Terry & His Jazzmen* / Manana: *Dutch Swing College Band* / All the girls go crazy: *Stable Roof Jazzband* / Nagasaki: *Funny House Jazzband* / When I take my sugar to tea: *Revival Jazzband* / Someday you'll be sorry / 'Deed I do
TTD 531532 / Aug '96 / Timeless Jazz

☐ IN CONCERT
186235 / 9 Feb '98 / CMC

☐ IN CONCERT WITH THE PIPES AND DRUMS (The Splendour Of The Pipes)
GRCD 90 / May '98 / Grasmere

☐ IN CROWD, THE (20 Mod Classics 1964-1997)
I can't explain: *Who* / Whatcha gonna do about it: *Who* / In crowd: *Gray, Dobie* / Good morning little school girl: *Stewart, Rod* / Night train: *Brown, James* / I'm the face: *High Numbers* / (I'm a) roadrunner: *Walker, Junior & The All Stars* / Leaving here: *Birds* / There's a ghost in my house: *Taylor, Dean* / I'M A MA: *Taylor, Dean* / Town called malice: *Jam* / Maybe tomorrow: *Chords* / POison ivy: *Lambrettas* / There she goes: *La's* / Snake: *Dodgy* / Getting better: *Shed Seven* / Fightting fit: *Gene* / Sleeping in: *Menswear* / Alright: *Cast* / Into tomorrow: *Weller, Paul*
5359182 / Jun '97 / Deram

☐ IN CRUST WE TRUST
LF 050CD / Aug '93 / Lost & Found

☐ IN DECAY WE TRUST
AV 027CD / 1 Jun '98 / Avantgarde

☐ IN DEFENCE OF ANIMALS VOL.2
Brighton rock: *Elastica* / Electric head: *White Zombie* / Enjoy: *Bjork* / We done it again: *Meat Beat Manifesto* / Chemical beats: *Chemical Brothers* / Son of neckbone: *Beastie Boys* / Tiny meat: *Ruby* / Spaceman: *Belly* / Let's go free: *Moby* / Me-Jane: *PJ Harvey* / Truth: *KRS 1* / Cosmic dub: *Massive Attack & The Mad Professor* / Amnesty report: *Watt, Mike* / Moon pie: *Alice Donut* / Note to a friend: *Aleka's Attic* / Slug dub: *Orb* / Sundayafternoonweightlessness: *Morphine*
BIAS 300CD / Oct '96 / Play It Again Sam

☐ IN DUBLIN'S FAIR CITY (20 Collected Irish Ballads)
DOCDK 111 / 24 Nov '97 / Dara

☐ IN FLIGHT ENTERTAINMENT VOL.1
Mambo mania: *Kaempfert, Bert* / Light my fire: *Ros, Edmundo* / Il fait beau, il fait bon (freedom come, freedom go): *Mauriat, Paul* / Discotheque: *Alguero, Augusto* / Big train: *Greger, Max* / Catwalk: *Moore, Pete* / Blues-a-go-go: *Schifrin, Lalo* / Come Ray come Charles: *Legrand, Michel* / Look of love: *Shaw, Roland* / Paramiribo: *Schroeder, John* / St Tropez: *Bardot, Brigitte* / Tu veut, tu veut pas: *Bardot, Brigitte* / They call me Mr Tibbs: *Chaquito* / Tequila: *Button Down Brass* / Cerveza: *Kaempfert, Bert* / Great expectations: *Alguero, Augusto* / Di-gue-ding-ding: *Legrand, Michel* / I like London in the rain: *Dearie, Blossom* / Let the love come through: *Shaw, Roland*
5353002 / Mar '96 / Deram

☐ IN FLIGHT ENTERTAINMENT VOL.2 (Further In Flight Entertainment)
5531262 / Mar '97 / Deram

☐ IN FLIGHT PROGRAM (Revelation Compilation)
REV 050CD / Dec '96 / Revelation

☐ IN FLUX (Drum 'n' Bass In Movement)
Retrospective: *Dub Alchemist* / Body and soul: *DJ Sensei* / Exalted: *Slok* / Aura: *Skin 4* / Donna Jane: *Dust* / Never still: *Clan Greco* / Arka: *Slok* / Our man in Rio: *Gazzara* / Vectoral 2: *Science Force* / Livin' on borrowed time: *Average White Band* / Loppez bota pra quebar: *DJ Rodriguez* / Simple echo: *Pogo* / Leo leo: *Indo Aminata*
IAM 803CD / 15 Sep '97 / Irma

☐ IN FLUX US
ANDA 228CD / 16 Feb '98 / Au-Go-Go

☐ IN GOTH DAZE
Hex: *Specimen* / Vegas: *Nico* / I walk the line: *Alien Sex Fiend* / Psychotic Louie Louie: *Alien Sex Fiend* / Kicking up the sawdust: *Bone Orchard* / Can't stop smoking: *Alien Sex Fiend* / Sharp teeth pretty teeth: *Specimen* / Last year's wife: *Zero Lacreche* / Carnivale of the gullible: *In Excelsis* / Tenant: *Play Dead* / Beating my head: *Red Lorry Yellow Lorry* / Mind disease: *Ritual* / Creatures of the night: *Screaming Dead* / Hole: *Specimen* / Alone she cries: *Skeletal Family* / Legacy: *Furyo* / Boys 18: *Bauhaus* / Caged 19: *1919* / Hollow eyes: *Red Lorry Yellow Lorry* / So sure: *Skeletal Family*
CDMGRAM 89 / 18 May '98 / Anagram

☐ IN LOVE WITH JAZZ
What a wonderful world: *Armstrong, Louis* / My baby just cares for me: *Simone, Nina* / One I love: *Fitzgerald, Ella* / Ain't misbehavin': *Waller, Fats* / They can't take that away from me: *Lee, Peggy* / Good morning heartache: *Holiday, Billie* / I love Paris: *Crosby, Bing* / Ev'ry time we say goodbye: *McRae, Carmen* / Someone to watch over me: *Webster, Ben* / I want a little sugar in my bowl: *Simone, Nina* / It's wonderful: *Fitzgerald, Ella* / Lover man: *Holiday, Billie* / On the sunny side of the street: *Armstrong, Louis* / Give me the simple life: *Armstrong, Louis* / Get a kick out of you: *McRae, Carmen* / House of the rising sun: *Simone, Nina* / Just an old fashioned girl: *Kitt, Eartha*
ASTCD 4007 / Oct '97 / Go On Deluxe

☐ IN LOVE WITH SOUL VOL.1
261471 / Jun '91 / Ariola

☐ IN LOVE WITH THE 60'S
SELCD 517 / 27 Jun '98 / Castle Select

☐ IN LOVE WITH THE SIXTIES VOL.1
Needles and pins: *Searchers* / Baby now that I've found you: *Foundations* / That's nice: *Christian, Neil* / Here comes my baby: *Tremeloes* / Funny how love can be: *Ivy League* / Michelle: *Overlanders* / Colours: *Donovan* / Girl: *Truth* / Something here in my heart (keeps a tellin' me no): *Paper Dolls* / Venus in blue jeans: *Wynter, Mark* / He's in town: *Rockin' Berries* / (There's) always something there to remind me: *Shaw, Sandie* / Lady Jane: *Garrick, David* / Hi hi Hazel: *Washington, Geno* / Let the heartaches begin: *Baldry, Long John* / That's what love will do: *Brown, Joe* / This is my song: *Clark, Petula* / Cast your fate to the wind: *Sounds Orchestral*
SELCD 514 / 30 Mar '98 / Castle Select

☐ IN LOVE WITH THESE TIMES
FNE 28CD / Mar '94 / Normal

☐ IN MEMORIUM - GILLES DELEUZE (2CD Set)
EFA 006722 / Mar '96 / Mille Plateau

☐ IN ORDER TO DANCE VOL.1
Electrowave: *Space Opera* / Get busy time: *Ceejay* / Here we go: *Project* / Theme of St. Baafs: *Mental Overdrive* / Brasil: *Spectrum* / Acid pandemonium: *Mundo Muzique* / Music: *Sonic Solution* / Poison: *Angel*
RSCD 1 / Nov '91 / R&S

☐ IN ORDER TO DANCE VOL.3
RS 2091CD / 29 Apr '98 / R&S

☐ IN ORDER TO DANCE VOL.4
Andromeda: *Mundo Muzique* / Nightbreed: *Bolland, C.J.* / Rise from your grave: *Phuture* / Bounce back: *Angel, Dave* / Neuromancer: *Source* / Mama: *Neuro* / My definition of house music: *DJ Hell* / Flying dreams: *Afrotrance* / Analogue bubblebath: *Aphex Twin* / Shades: *House Of Usher* / Dream: *Music Of Life Orchestra* / Plastic dreams: *Music Of Life Orchestra*
RS 932CD / Jun '93 / R&S

☐ IN ORDER TO DANCE VOL.5 (2CD Set)
RS 94036CDXX
RS 94036CD / Sep '94 / R&S

☐ IN ORDER TO DANCE VOL.6 (2CD Set)
Loop 2: *Larkin, Kenny* / Glide: *Expansions* / Punk jaz: *Justice, Tony* / Rare tear part 1: *Flytronix* / Destiny: *DJ Pulse* / Stretch: *Ishii, Ken* / Aquisse: *Justice, Tony* / Manhattan melody: *Lemon D* / 5 Miles high: *TMF* / No-one in the world: *Locust* / Detroit: *Reece, Alex* / Eclosed spaces: *Skindivers* / Wind dancer: *Shogun* / Music is the basis of all life: *Mystic Moods* / Kid caprice: *Wax Doctor* / Cool summer breeze: *Original Playboy* / I wanna be there: *Model 500* / Flow: *Model 500* / Solar feelings: *Jacob's Optical Stairway* / Feversih: *Justice, Tony* / Solar system: *Lemon D*
RS 96090CD / May '96 / R&S

☐ IN PRAISE OF GOD
CDDCA 573 / Dec '88 / ASV

☐ IN SEARCH OF THE FREEDOM
CDMF 090 / Nov '93 / Magnum Force

☐ IN SUNDAY MORNING COUNTRY
82551157162 / 5 May '98 / Revelation

☐ IN THA BEGINNING...THERE WAS RAP
Sucker MC's: *Wu Tang Clan* / Fuck tha police: *Bone Thugs n' Harmony* / Big ole butt: *Puff Daddy* / 'N tha mornin': *Master P* / Freaky tales: *Snoop Doggy Dogg* / Knick knack patty wack: *Tha Dogg Pound* / Rapper's delight: *Sermon, Erick & Keith Murray* / *Redman* / I'm still no.1: *Cypress Hill* / I need a freak: *Too Short* / Dopeman: *Mack 10* / Dollar bill y'all: *Coolio* / Show: *Roots*
CDPTY 148 / 24 Nov '97 / Priority/Virgin

☐ IN THE AIR TONIGHT (Synthesizer Hits)
MACCD 310 / Aug '96 / Autograph

☐ IN THE AIR TONIGHT (Virgin's Greatest Hits/2CD Set)
I'd do anything for love (but I won't do that): *Meat Loaf* / I can't help falling in love: *UB40* / That's the way love goes: *Jackson, Janet* / Are you gonna go my way: *Kravitz, Lenny* / Boom boom: *Hooker, John Lee* / Unfinished sympathy: *Massive Attack* / Sailing on the sevens seas: *OMD* / It ain't over 'til it's over: *Kravitz, Lenny* / Stll got the blues: *Moore, Gary* / Sadness: *Enigma* / Close to you: *Priest, Maxi* / You got it: *Orbison, Roy* / Another day in paradise: *Collins, Phil* / Back to life: *Soul II Soul* / Belfast child: *Simple Minds* / Straight up: *Abdul, Paula* / Buffalo stance: *Cherry, Neneh* / Let's stick together: *Ferry, Bryan* / Heaven is a place on Earth: *Carlisle, Belinda* / China in your hand: *T'Pau* / Everything I own: *Boy George* / Sledgehammer: *Gabriel, Peter* / Rise: *Public Image Ltd.* / Separate lives: *Collins, Phil & Marilyn Martin* / Waterfront: *Simple Minds* / Karma chameleon: *Culture Club* / Mama: *Genesis* / Temptation: *Heaven 17* / Ghosts: *Japan* / It must be love: *Madness* / In the air tonight: *Collins, Phil* / Love action: *Human League* / Pretty vacant: *Sex Pistols* / Love is the drug: *Roxy Music* / Tubular bells: *Oldfield, Mike* / Virgin 21: *Wainwright III, Loudon*
VTDCD 26 / Aug '95 / Virgin

☐ IN THE BELLY OF THE WHALE
HCD 7005 / Aug '94 / Hightone

☐ IN THE CEILIDH AND DANCE TRADITION
LC 5246CD / Nov '95 / Lismor

☐ IN THE CELTIC TRADITION
LC 5245CD / Nov '95 / Lismor

☐ IN THE CITY
74321535842 / 22 Nov '97 / RCA

☐ IN THE COUNTRY OF COUNTRY
742412 / May '98 / Compass

☐ IN THE KNOW
ICO 302 / 1 Dec '97 / Infracom

☐ IN THE LAND OF MANTRA
3012132 / Oct '96 / Mantra

☐ IN THE MIX (2CD Set)
IDT 000591 / Dec '96 / ID&T

☐ IN THE MIX '96 VOL.1 (2CD Set)
Every little step: *Brown, Bobby* / Boombastic: *Shaggy* / Hideaway: *De'Lacy* / Renegade master: *Wildchild* / Got myself together: *Bucketheads* / I know the Lord: *Tabernacle* / I believe: *Happy Clappers* / Your love: *Inner City* / Naughty North and the sexy South: *E-Motion* / And I'm telling you: *Giles, Donna* / La luna: *Ethics* / Sunshine after the rain: *Berri* / Little Britain: *Dreadzone* / Common people: *Pulp* / Fee fi fo fum: *Candy Girls* / Runaway: *E'voke* / Mr. Friday night: *Moorish, Lisa* / Sex on the streets: *Pizzaman* / I imagine: *Kiani, Mary* / Gangsta's paradise: *Coolio* / Why you treat me so bad: *Shaggy* / Too hot: *Coolio* / I'm ready: *Size 9* / Mr. Wendal: *Arrested Development* / Chemical beats: *Chemical Brothers* / Passion: *Gat Decor* / Everybody be somebody: *Ruffnecks* / Fairground: *Simply Red* / I love you baby: *Original* / Reach: *Cheeks, Judy* / Boom boom boom: *Outhere Brothers* / He's on the phone: *St. Etienne* / Baby baby: *Corona* / Wham bam: *Candy Girls* / I wanna be a hippy: *Technohead*
VTDCD 77 / Feb '96 / Virgin

☐ IN THE MIX '96 VOL.2 (2CD Set)
Children: *Miles, Robert* / Nightrain: *Kadoc* / Firestarter: *Prodigy* / Keep on jumpin': *Lisa Marie Experience* / Trippin' on sunshine: *Pizzaman* / Not over yet: *Grace* / Klubhoppin: *Klubb Heads* / I need a lover: *Kendoh* / Are you out there: *Crescendo* / Missing: *Everything But The Girl* / Good thing: *Eternal* / State of independence: *Summer, Donna* / Way it is: *Chameleon* / For what you dream of: *Bedrock* / Don't you want me: *Felix* / Satellite: *Beloved* / America (I love America): *Full Intention* / Love is the drug: *Roxy Music* / I got five on it: *Luniz* / Give me a little more time: *Gabrielle* / Lifted: *Lighthouse Family* / Spaceman: *Babylon Zoo* / 1234: *Coolio* / Return of the Mack: *Morrison, Mark* / Giv me luv: *Alcatrazz* / I got the vibration: *Black Box* / Stars: *Dubstar* / Stay another day: *East 17* / Over and over: *Plux* / Eugina: *Salt Tank* / Landslide: *Harmonix* / Be as one: *Sacha & Maria* / Lovelight: *Hanna, Jayn* / Reach up: *Perfecto All Stars* / Theme from S'Express: *S'Express* / Walking wounded: *Everything But The Girl* / So pure: *Baby D*
VTDCD 85 / May '96 / Virgin

☐ IN THE MIX '96 VOL.3 (2CD Set)
I'm alive: *Stretch n' Vern & Maddog* / Krupa: *Apollo 440* / Fastlove: *Michael, George* / Ain't nobody's business if I do: *H2O & Billie* / Where love lives: *Limerick, Alison* / Keep on jumpin': *Terry, Todd* / Disco's revenge: *Gusto* / Don't go: *Third Dimension* / Are you ready for some more: *Reel 2 Real* / Don't stop movin': *Livin' Joy* / My love is for real: *Strike* / Help me make it: *Huff & Puff* / All I wanna do: *Tin Tin Out* / Ooh aah...just a little bit: *Gina G* / There's nothing I won't do: *JX* / Just another groove: *Mighty Dub Katz* / Come on: *Konya* / Higher state of consciousness: *Wink, Josh* / Arms of Loren: *Evoke* / Flava: *Andre, Peter* / That look: *De'Lacy* / Wrong: *Everything But The Girl* / Throb: *Jackson, Janet* / Cuba: *El Mariachi* / That girl: *Priest, Maxi & Shaggy* / Naked: *Louise* / Sunshine: *Umboza* / Want love: *Hysteric Ego* / Love me the right way: *Rapination* / Stamp: *Healy, Jeremy & Amos* / Gift: *Way Out West* / Wannabe: *Spice Girls* / Creep: *TLC* / Bom digi bom (think about the way): *TLC* / Seven days and one week: *BBE* / Macarena: *Los Del Rio* / Born slippy: *Underworld* / You give me love: *Clock*
VTDCD 97 / Oct '96 / Virgin

☐ IN THE MIX '97 VOL.1 (2CD Set)
One and one: *Miles, Robert* / Stupid girl: *Garbage* / Moving on up: *M-People* / Nite life: *English, Kim* / Spinning the wheel: *Michael, George* / Hold that sucker down: *QT Quartet* / Insomnia: *Faithless* / Up to no good: *Porn Kings* / Say my name: *Zee* / Waterfall: *Atlantic Ocean* / Kick up the volume: *Tissera, Rob* / Breathe: *Prodigy* / Jump up to my beat: *Wildchild* / U girls: *Nush* / All I wanna do: *Tin Tin Out* / I am: *Chakra* / Tall 'n handsome: *Outrage* / Sugar is sweeter: *Bolland, C.J.* / Remember me: *Blueboy* / Girls and boys: *Blur* / Space cowboy: *Jamiroquai* / You got the love: *Source & Candi Staton* / Take California: *Propellerheads* / She drives me crazy: *Fine Young Cannibals* / Arkham asylum: *Sasha* / Dreamer: *Livin' Joy* / Atom bomb: *Fluke* / Offshore: *Chicane* / Lost without you: *Hanna, Jayn* / On a ragga tip '97: *SL2* / Bjango: *Lucky Monkeys* / Zoe: *Traxx* / Wiggly world: *Mr. Jack* / Seven days and one week: *BBE* / Passion: *Amendi*
VTDCD 116 / Jan '97 / Virgin

☐ IN THE MIX '97 VOL.2 (2CD Set)
VTDCD 132 / Apr '97 / Virgin

☐ IN THE MIX '97 VOL.3 (2CD Set)
Ecuador: *Sash* / Professional widow: *Amos, Tori* / I wanna be the only one: *Eternal & Bebe Winans* / Age of love: *Age Of Love* / Closer than close: *Gaines, Rosie* / Let the beat hit 'em: *Shena* / Star people: *Michael, George* / Belo horizonti: *Heartists* / I have peace: *Strike* / Fly life: *Basement Jaxx* / Brazen: *Skunk Anansie* / 6 underground: *Sneaker Pimps* / Offshore: *Chicane & Power Circle* / Out of my head '97: *Chicane & Power Circle* / Casual sub: *ETA* / PAPacific melody: *Airscape* / Argentina: *Healy, Jeremy & Amos* / Nightmare: *Brainbug* / Amour: *Porn Kings* / Scooby snacks: *Fun Lovin' Criminals* / Jump around: *House Of Pain* / Block rockin' beats: *House Of Pain* / Lovefool: *Cardigans* / Sandman: *Blueboy* / Hold your head up: *Dlugosch, Boris* / That Elvis track: *Sol Brothers* / Ain't nobody: *Course* / Moment of my life: *D'Ambrosio, Bobby* / Shake your body: *Full Intention* / Freed from desire: *Gala* / Gyspy boy gyspy girl: *Sol Brothers* / Your face: *Slacker* / Latinos del mundo: *Latin Thing* / If wishes were ways: *JDS* / Bellissima: *DJ Quicksilver* / Flaming june: *BT* / Give me love: *Diddy* / Somebody like you: *Elate*
VTDCD 135 / Jul '97 / Virgin

☐ IN THE MIX '98 (2CD Set)
VTDCD 174 / 2 Feb '98 / Virgin

☐ IN THE MIX '98 VOL.2 (2CD Set)
Take control: *State of mind* / Deeper love: *Ruff Driverz* / Rockafeller skank: *Fatboy Slim* / Beat goes on: *All Seeing I* / Treat infamy: *Rest Assured* / Teardrops: *Lovestation* / Spend the night: *Lewis, Danny J.* / Horny: *Mousse T & Hot 'n' Juicy* / Feel it: *Tamperer & Maya* / Found a cure: *Ultra Nate* / Deeper love: *BBE* / Sounds of the wickedness: *Tzant* / Movin' on: *Pender, Debbie* / Feel the beat: *Camisra* /

Sincere: *Cole, MJ* / Love is so nice: *Urban Soul* / Strutt: *Bamboo* / Keep on dancin': *Perpetual Motion* / Truth: *Qattara* / Ruffneck: *Freestylers* / SMDU: *Landars, Brock* / Fight for your right (to party): *NYCC* / One step beyond: *Madness* / It's like that: *Run DMC & Jason Nevins* / Heres where the story ends: *Tin Tin Out* / Word is love: *Voice Of Life* / Anytime: *Nu Birth* / Give me love: *DJ Dado* / One of the people: *Adamski's Thing* / Cafe del mar: *Energy 52* / Ripped in 2 minutes: *A vs. B* / Brimful of Asha: *Cornershop* / Eisbaer: *Groovezone*

VTDCD 195 / 29 Jun '98 / Virgin

☐ IN THE MIX - '90S HITS (2CD Set)

Wrong: *Everything But The Girl* / Two can play that game: *Brown, Bobby* / Show me luv: *Robin S* / Higher state of consciousness: *Wink, Josh* / Is there anybody out there: *Bassheads* / Bomb: *Bucketheads* / Renaissance: *M-People* / Let me show you: *K-Klass* / Chant: *Gusto* / Such a good feeling: *Brothers In Rhythm* / Go: *Moby* / Jazz it up: *Reel 2 Real* / Ain't no love ain't no use: *Sub Sub & Melanie Williams* / Give it up: *Goodmen* / Latin Thing: *Latin Touch* / U sure do: *Strike* / Don't stop movin': *Livin' Joy* / Cry india: *Umboza* / Everybody's free: *Rozalla* / Blurred: *Pianoman* / Girls and boys: *Hed Boys* / Let the music lift you up: *Loveland* / Even better than the real thing: *U2* / Playing with knives: *Bizarre Inc.* / Always something there to remind me: *Tin Tin Out & Espiritu* / Son of a gun: *JX* / Your loving arms: *Martin, Billie Ray* / Key, the secret: *Urban Cookie Collective* / I believe: *Happy Clappers* / Sweet harmony: *Liquid* / Rockin' for myself: *Motiv 8* / Waterfall: *Atlantic Ocean* / Disco 2000: *Pulp* / Let me be your fantasy: *Baby D* / Swamp thing: *Grid* / Born slippy: *Underworld* / Children: *Miles, Robert*

VTDCD 89 / Jul '96 / Virgin

☐ IN THE MIX BY DJ PAVO

IDTMIX 96002 / Mar '97 / ID&T

☐ IN THE MIX IBIZA '97 (2CD Set)

VTDCD 145 / 13 Oct '97 / Virgin

☐ IN THE PIPING TRADITION

LC 5243CD / Nov '95 / Lismor

☐ IN THE POPULAR SONG TRADITION

LC 5244CD / Nov '95 / Lismor

☐ IN THE SMOKE (Classic Traditional London Irish Music 1950-1970's)

Bank of Ireland/Woman of the house/Morning dew: *Casey, Bobby* / Blue riband/Up and away: *Clifford, John & Julia* / Boys of the lough/Trip to Durrow: *Pepper, Noel & Paddy Moran* / Rich man's daughter: *Byrne, Packie* / Jackie Coleman's/The castle: *Power, Jimmy* / Kesh jig/Morrison's/Old Joe's: *Doonan, John* / Bucks of Oranmore/The wind that shakes the barley: *O'Halloran Brothers* / Rights of man/Honeysuckle hornpipe: *Healy, Tommy & Johnny Duffy* / Galway shawl: *Barry, Margaret* / Callaghan's reel: *Curtin, Con & Denis McMahon* / Ballydesmond/Knocknabowl: *Clifford, Julia* / Maid behind the bar: *Wright Brothers & Paddy Neylan* / Coolin': *Pepper, Noel* / Granuaile: *O'Halloran, Des* / Follow me down to Limerick/Hardiman the fiddler: *Power, Jimmy* / Shannon breeze/Heathery breeze/Green fields of America: *Doonan, John* / Cavan lasses/Rose of the heather: *Healy, Tommy & Johnny Duffy* / Creel: *Byrne, Packie* / Moher reel: *Farr, Lucy & Bobby Casey* / Cherish the ladies: *Doonan, John* / Dublin porter/Mountain lark: *Star Of Munster Trio* / Paddy Ryan's dream: *Meehan, Danny* / Flower of sweet Strabane: *Barry, Margaret* / Maguire's favourite/Tralee gaol/Maggie in the wood: *Barry, Margaret* / Coleman's favourite/Promenade: *Power, Jimmy* / Lucy Campbell/Toss the feathers: *McMahon, Tony/Andy Boyce/Mairtin Byrnes* / Blackbird: *Doonan, John*

CDORBD 088 / Mar '95 / Globestyle

☐ IN THE SPIRIT

AL 2801 / Jul '94 / Alligator

☐ IN THE SPOTLIGHT

78067410982 / 27 Apr '98 / Drive Archive

☐ IN THE SUMMERTIME

PLSCD 142 / Apr '96 / Pulse

☐ IN THE SUMMERTIME (18 Scorching Summer Songs)

SUMCD 4142 / Jan '98 / Summit

☐ IN THE SWISS MOUNTAINS

399408 / Jul '91 / Koch

☐ IN THE TRADITION (2CD Set/A Collection Of Classic Blues Recordings)

Dead stray dog: *Louisiana Red* / Don't dog your woman: *McGhee, Brownie* / Hobo blues: *Hooker, John Lee* / Going train blues: *Louisiana Red & Lefty Dizz* / Travelling back home: *Shines, Johnny* / Feel like robbin' the grave: *Terry, Sonny* / Mistake in life: *Sykes, Roosevelt* / Big Walter's boogie: *Horton, Walter* / Mean and evil: *McGhee, Brownie* / Dark room: *Hooker, John Lee* / What has Annie got: *Seward, Alec* / Strollin': *Peg Leg Sam* / Death of Ealare: *Louisiana Red* / Move on up a little higher: *Knight, Marie* / He's a friend of mine: *Wootan Singers* / Trouble's all I see: *Shines, Johnny* / New York boogie: *Sykes, Roosevelt* / First degree: *Louisiana Red & Lefty Dizz* / Bourgeois blues: *Seeger, Pete & Arlo Guthrie* / Selling out: *Terry, Sonny* / Rainy day: *McGhee, Brownie* / I won't be back no more: *Hooker, John Lee* / I know it was the blood: *Lunenberg Travelers* / I got a home: *Peg Leg Sam* / Worried blues ain't bad: *Shines, Johnny* / Stole from me: *Louisiana Red & Lefty Dizz* / Late one Saturday evening: *Seward, Alec* / Florida storm: *Knight, Marie* / Shakey Edmondson's blues: *Horton, Walter* / Keep on loving: *McGhee, Brownie* / Pig meat: *Guthrie, Arlo* / One bourbon, one scotch, one beer: *Hooker, John Lee* / Cold white street: *Louisiana Red*

TBA 2130152 / 3 Nov '97 / Blues Alliance

☐ IN THE WEE SMALL HOURS

Passion flower: *Hodges, Johnny* / It's the talk of the town: *Jacquet, Illinois* / I'll never smile again: *Garner, Erroll* / Laura: *Thielemans, 'Toots'* / Chelsea bridge: *Gillespie, Dizzy* / Tangerine: *Hawkins, Coleman & Ben Webster* / Street scene: *Carter, Benny* / It was a very good year: *Montgomery, Wes* / I can't get started: *Young, Lester & Oscar Peterson* / All across the city: *Evans, Bill & Jim Hall* / Willow weep for me: *Eldridge, Roy* / High and the mighty: *Hampton, Lionel* / In the wee small hours of the morning: *Mulligan, Gerry & His New Sextet* / Child is born: *Peterson, Oscar* / I wrote my song: *Smith, Stuff & Dizzy Gillespie/Oscar Peterson* / I remember Clifford: *Getz, Stan* / Were you there: *Burrell, Kenny*

5526742 / Mar '97 / Spectrum

☐ IN THERE - MUTANT POP HYBRIDS

TBPICD 004 / Jun '96 / T&B

☐ IN TO THE MIX (2CD Set)

Voodoo people: *Prodigy* / Mindstream: *Meat Beat Manifesto* / Instruments of darkness: *Art Of Noise* / Eternal zerne: *Talla 2XLC* / Netherworld: *LSG* / Alpha wave: *System 7* / Re-united mix 4: *Psychic TV* / Renegade soundwave: *Renegade Soundwave* / Clown: *Switchblade Symphony* / Feel the universe: *Juno Reactor* / Trance in time: *Kraftwerk* / Aqualite megga mix: *LCD* / Out of reality: *Sunbeam* / Outface: *Komaidno* / Helium: *Bypass Unit* / Pink button: *Kinder Atom* / Stab: *Din* / Sack says air: *Glez* / In a gentle mood: *Nature* / Concentration: *Surface 10* / Now is forever: *Brain* / Ba and the ka: *Anubian Lights* / Into the abyss: *R-Escape-R* / Funky alienation: *Xylon* / Hymlock: *Cathexis* / Oblivion: *Dilate*

CLP 9991 / Sep '97 / Hypnotic

☐ INCA FLUTES

PS 65192 / Dec '97 / PlayaSound

☐ INCANTATIONS REMEMBERANCE (2CD Set)

SMDCD 155 / 27 Apr '98 / Snapper

☐ INCOMING

SAGCD 01 / 11 May '98 / Saigon

☐ INCREDIBLE MUSIC ALL STARS

IMCD 0015 / Apr '97 / Incredible Music

☐ INCREDIBLY STRANGE - ONLY IN AMERICA

AA 049 / Jul '97 / Arf Arf

☐ INCREDIBLY STRANGE MUSIC VOL.2

0951 / 24 Nov '97 / Asphodel

☐ INCURSIONS IN ILLBIENT

ASP 0968CD / 22 Jun '98 / Asphodel

☐ INDEPENDENCE BREAKS

Bass gunner: *Tipper* / Chemical meltdown: *Santana, Omar* / Miami breaks: *PSS* / Loisiana hayride: *Silicon Valley Def Stars* / Blazer beats: *Roxy Breaks* / Air guitar: *Frog Junkies* / Humaniser: *Humanizer* / Six pak: *Tipper* / Nine ways: *JDS* / QUick release: *Quick Release* / Pulse: *Reel* / Scared: *Altered States*

CDTOT 49 / Jun '97 / Jumpin' & Pumpin'

☐ INDEPENDENCE DAY (The Best New Women Of Country)

Independence day: *McBride, Martina* / On a bus to St. Cloud: *Yearwood, Trisha* / Guys do it all the time: *McReady, Mindy* / One solitary tear: *Austin, Sherrie* / That train don't run: *Berg, Matraca* / Just when I needed you most: *Parton, Dolly & Alison Krauss* / No way out: *Bogguss, Suzy* / Three chords and the truth: *Evans, Sara* / Shut up and drive: *Wright, Chely* / What a woman knows: *Tyler, Kris* / What part of no: *Morgan, Lorrie* / Fool: *Womack, Lee Ann* / Mi vida loco: *Tillis, Pam* / She is his only need: *Judd, Wynonna* / 455 rocket: *Mattea, Kathy* / Mississippi and me: *Campbell, Kate* / I know: *Richey, Kim* / Secret of life: *Peters, Gretchen* / Delta dawn: *Tucker, Tanya* / Sudden gift of fate: *Carpenter, Mary-Chapin*

74321555692 / 11 May '98 / RCA

☐ INDEPENDENT SOUL VOL.1 (14 Hard To Find Tracks From The 80's)

All night love affair: *Roosevelt Carter* / Right track: *Roosevelt Carter* / You must go on: *Junei* / Weak man: *Morris, Lee* / This time it's real: *Nevilles, Larry* / Gotta give your own love story: *Wilkerson, James JD* / I think I'm gonna be blue: *Buford, Larry* / Don't snatch it back: *Daniel, Harold* / Too many irons in the fire: *Hightower, Willie* / Tell me what you want: *Hightower, Willie* / It's no wonder (you drove me crazy): *Dee, Larry* / I could paint a picture: *Hudmon, R.B.* / Caught in the middle: *Cobbin, James & Prime Cut* / Girl you should have known: *Hudson, Johnny*

GSCD 080 / Feb '97 / Goldmine

☐ INDIA O FAST DHRUPAD

SM 1517CD / Oct '94 / Wergo

☐ INDIAN FLUTES OF SOUTH AMERICA VOL.1

PS 65060 / Nov '90 / PlayaSound

☐ INDIAN FLUTES OF SOUTH AMERICA VOL.2

PS 65090 / Jul '92 / PlayaSound

☐ INDIAN KUTCH PEOPLES, THE

926772 / Nov '97 / BUDA

☐ INDIAN MEDITATION

CD 6063 / Apr '97 / Music

☐ INDIAN MUSIC VIRTUOSOS

4301121042 / 27 Apr '98 / ANS

☐ INDIE MIX (2CD Set)

5551002 / 8 Dec '97 / PolyGram TV

☐ INDIGENOUS TRIBES

Alba: *Mounsey, Paul* / Forced to return/Spootisferry: *Rock Salt & Nails* / Reconciliation set: *Runt O' The Litter* / Reprobate's lament: *Imlach, Hamish* / 7 down: *Thoumire, Simon & Fergus MacKenzie* / Irish reels set: *Morrison, Fred* / Scarboro' settler's lament: *Bruce, Ian* / Hooleyganz jig: *Hooleyganz Band* / Henryetta: *Humpff Family* / 70 years/Caber: *New Celeste* / Floggin' set: *Bongshang* / St Francis songs: *Pearlfishers* / Tinne run: *Wolfstone* / Ae fond kiss: *Dalriada* / New pipe order: *Tartan Amoebas*

IRCD 054 / Jul '97 / Lismor

☐ INDIGO AFRICA

Mansa: *Super Rail Band* / Atahora Fabiby: *D'Gary* / Tontobane: *Mahlasela, Vuis* / Le jour du 31: *Traore, Boubacar* / Tsikaholy: *Gisavo, Regis* / Retraite: *Moundanda, Antoine* / Soleye: *Granmoun Lele* / Libodou: *Ki Yi M'Bock* / Bata: *Kouyate, M'Bady* / Ele waye waye: *Jouga, Julien* / Laduma: *Ngema, Mbongeni* / Velono: *Jaojoby* / Idinga: *Lapiro De Mbanga* / Shiria: *Boutella, Safy* / Sheleng: *Kgwanyape Band* / Yemele: *Trogode Banda Linda* / Aia Reheaba: *Vaovy* / N'Gakalenba: *Ngoni, Kamale*

LBLC 2542 / 23 Feb '98 / Indigo

☐ INDIGO BLUES COLLECTION VOL.1 (Budget Sampler)

IGOCD 2033 / Sep '95 / Indigo

☐ INDIGO BLUES COLLECTION VOL.3

IGOCD 2082 / 19 Jan '98 / Indigo

☐ INDUSTRIAL ARMAGEDDON (2CD Set)

AOP 56 / Jun '97 / Age Of Panik

☐ INDUSTRIAL CHRISTMAS CAROL

INV 053CD / Jan '96 / Invisible

☐ INDUSTRIAL MADNESS (4CD Set)

CLP 0045 / 6 Oct '97 / Cleopatra

☐ INDUSTRIAL MIX MACHINE (2CD Set)

CLP 9969 / Jun '97 / Cleopatra

☐ INDUSTRIAL VIRUS (3CD Set)

DTKBOX 61 / Feb '97 / Dressed To Kill

☐ INDUSTRIAL WAR (The Agony & The Ecstasy Of Industrial Music)

SHCD 5722 / Apr '97 / Shanachie

☐ INDUSTRY COMPILATION VOL.1 (Beats & Lyrics)

IR 0022 / 13 Oct '97 / Industry

☐ INESS MEZEL

Wedfel / Ado / Taiga / Aya hedat / Agour / Ifassen / Slassen kan / Laaven yissnay / Our yi nouy / Awah / Lahvev

Y 225066 / May '97 / Auvidis/Ethnic

☐ INFINITE EXCURSIONS VOL.2 (Softer Psychedelic Sounds)

Aspects of nature: *Infinity Project* / Shapeshifter: *Harmonix* / Tower and the star: *Doof* / Dub that never was: *GMS* / Another planet: *Infinity Project* / Landing gear: *Cartoon Killa* / Incandescence: *Infinity Project* / Sneaky Malone: *Excess Head* / Quagmire: *Harmonix* / Behind closed eyelids: *Sphongle* / Outro: *Infinity Project*

TIPCD 15 / 17 Nov '97 / Tip

☐ INFINITE METHODS OF DRUM AND BASS, THE

EMF2CD 003 / 26 May '98 / Emotif

☐ INFINITE SUMMER OF LOVE

TX 2016CD / Jul '94 / Taxim

☐ INFINITY HERZ (2CD Set)

MPTCD 12 / Jul '97 / Matsuri

☐ INFLUENCE, THE

3RDCD 001 / 2 Feb '98 / 3rd Mind

☐ INNOVATORS FUTURE TECHNO

BDRCD 10 / Feb '96 / Breakdown

☐ INNSBRUCK, THE BEAUTIFUL ALPINE CITY

399425 / Jul '91 / Koch

☐ INOLVIDABLES DUOS LATINOS

CCD 902 / Jul '96 / Caney

☐ INSIDE OUT

Inside out / California soul / Liberation song / Eternal journey / Chocolate candy / Blue monsoon / Long goodie / I am the blackgold of the sun / Dancing girl / Prayer for peace

CDARC 513 / Jan '93 / Charly

☐ INSIDE OUT

HLCD 004 / 26 Jan '98 / Hardleaders

☐ INSIDE VOL.1 (Celebrating The Best In British Soul)

When we're making love: *Opaz* / Be still: *French, Michelle* / Me O my: *Mid 8 Production* / Been fooled: *Caitaine, Ria* / Fight: *McKoy* / Whole thing: *Act Of Faith* / Even when you're gone: *Gems For Jem* / Mystery girl: *Green, Tee* / If I knew: *D-Swing* / Hold me closer: *Circle Of Life* / Love away: *Pearce, Mary* / Coming closer: *Feel* / Simple solution: *Dee, Jay* / Running to my baby's arms: *Ipso Facto* / Slow down: *Metropolis* / Through all times: *Perfect Taste*

CDTEP 1 / Nov '92 / Debut

☐ INSIDE VOL.2

Greater love: *Nu Colours* / Reach out: *Perception* / Take me: *D-Swing* / Just don't care: *Funhill* / Visions: *Julianne* / I'll be good to you: *Green, Tee* / Time for love: *Gems For Jem* / Doing it for love: *Act Of Faith* / Get it on: *Solid State Sound* / Sunday morning blue: *Mapp, Chantel* / I know how: *Stevens, Kenni* / Calling her name: *Ipso Facto* / 2 be a friend: *Pearce, Mary* / Love when it's like this: *Antony, Joseph* / Your love my love: *Nazlyn* / Give it (this love song): *Caitaine, Ria*

CDTEP 2 / Jun '93 / Debut

☐ INSIDE VOL.3

Movin' in the right direction: *FM Inc* / Fever (rider): *D-Swing* / So much feeling: *Closer Than Close* / Gotta get it: *Index* / Deeper: *Uschi* / Fallin': *Tyson* / Heaven: *Menzies, Steve* / I Luv U: *Sovereign* / I like the way: *Everis* / Hurt so bad (till U like it): *Marshall, Wayne* / Learned my lesson: *Smith, Charlene* / There ain't enough love: *Zushii* / You belong to me: *Fyza* / Searching: *Robyn*

CDTEP 3 / Mar '94 / Debut

☐ INSIDE VOL.4

Feel the good times: *Smith, Charlene* / If it's to be: *Max* / Feel the heat: *Sugartrain* / We've got here: *Edwards, Kim* / It takes two: *What's Happening* / I can't hide: *Prime, Nathan* / My pain: *LIFE* / You shouldn't lie: *Brown, Dana* / Slow motion: *Groove Nation* / September rain: *Riviera* / I love the summertime: *Silver* / Obsession: *Duverney, Ondrea* / Do without you: *Zaeus* / Where's the sunshine: *Way 2 Go*

CDTEP 5 / Oct '94 / Debut

☐ INSPIRATION - BRAZIL (Forest Of The Amazon)

CDM 5658802 / Mar '96 / EMI Classics

☐ INSPIRATION - INDIA (Duets For Sitar)

CDM 5658812 / Mar '96 / EMI Classics

☐ INSPIRATION - JAPAN (Gagaku - Ancient Japanese Koto Melodies)

CDM 5659102 / Mar '96 / EMI Classics

☐ INSPIRATIONAL SAX

Will you still love me tomorrow / I can't stop loving you / Holding back the years / To all the girls I've loved before / Against all odds / Moonlight shadow / I guess why they call it the blues / How deep is your love

GRF 193 / Jun '92 / Tring

☐ INSPIRE TO PERSPIRE (Best Of Sweat & Underground Vibe) (3CD Set)

SWHCD 1 / Jul '96 / Sweat/ Underground Vibe

☐ INSTRUMENTAL 60'S VOL.3

176282 / Oct '97 / Magic

☐ INSTRUMENTAL 60'S VOL.4

176272 / Oct '97 / Magic

☐ INSTRUMENTAL BLUES

CLACD 432 / Mar '97 / Castle

☐ INSTRUMENTAL BLUES DYNAMITE

CDBT 1135 / Jun '96 / Black Top

☐ INSTRUMENTAL CHRISTMAS VOL.1 (Winter Wonderland)

Jesu joy of man's desiring: *Mantovani Orchestra* / It came upon a midnight clear: *Vaughn, Billy* / Jingle bells: *Erling, Ole* / Santa Claus is coming to town: *Ingmann, Jorgen* / We wish you a merry Christmas: *Hammond King* / Holly and the ivy: *Mantovani Orchestra* / Angels we have heard on high: *Hammond King* / O little town of Bethlehem: *Vaughn, Billy* / Christmas song: *Ingmann, Jorgen* / Winter wonderland: *Erling, Ole* / Ding dong merrily on high: *Mantovani Orchestra* / Hark the herald angels sing: *Vaughn, Billy* / I heard the bells on Christmas day: *Hammond King* / Little drummer boy: *Ingmann, Jorgen* / Christmas chimes are peeling: *Hammond King* / Canticle Noel: *Mantovani Orchestra*

120222 / Oct '97 / Jingle

☐ INSTRUMENTAL CHRISTMAS VOL.2 (Let It Snow Let It Snow)

First Noel: *Vaughn, Billy* / White Christmas: *Erling, Ole* / God rest ye merry gentlemen: *Mantovani Orchestra* / Let it snow let it snow: *Ingmann, Jorgen* / I saw three ships: *Hammond King* / Good king Wenceslas: *Mantovani Orchestra* / Sleigh ride: *Ingmann, Jorgen* / Have yourself a merry little christmas: *Ianescu, Ion Ensemble* / Caroling caroling: *Hammond King* / O holy night: *Vaughn, Billy* / Sleeping beauty (waltz): *Mantovani Orchestra* / O du froliche weinachtszeit: *Ingmann, Jorgen* / Where we come a caroling: *Hammond King* / I saw Mummy kissing Santa Claus: *Erling, Ole* / Joy to the world: *Vaughn, Billy* / Jeanette Isabella: *Hammond King*

120202 / Oct '97 / Jingle

☐ INSTRUMENTAL CHRISTMAS VOL.3 (Mistletoe And Wine)

Silent night: *Mantovani Orchestra* / Mary's boychild: *Erling, Ole* / O christmas tree: *Vaughn, Billy* / Bells of christmas: *Hammond King* / Blue Christmas: *Ianescu, Ion Ensemble* / Morgen kommt der weihnachtsman: *Ingmann, Jorgen* / Greensleeves: *Mantovani Orchestra* / We three kings of Orient are: *Hammond King* / Mistletoe and wine: *Ianescu, Ion Ensemble* / Lasst uns froh und munter sein: *Ingmann, Jorgen* / Rudolph the red-nosed reindeer: *Erling, Ole* / Joy to the world: *Ianescu, Ion Ensemble* / Panic angelicus: *Mantovani Orchestra* / Coventry carol: *Hammond King* / Let it snow: *Ianescu, Ion Ensemble* / Auld lang syne: *Vaughn, Billy*

120212 / Oct '97 / Jingle

☐ INSTRUMENTAL CHRISTMAS, AN (3CD Set)

Jesu joy of man's desiring: *Mantovani & His Orchestra* / It came upon a midnight clear: *Vaughn, Billy* / Jingle bells: *Erling, Ole* / Santa Claus is coming to town: *Ingmann, Jorgen* / We wish you a merry Christmas: *Hammond King* / Holly and the ivy: *Mantovani Orchestra* / Angels we have heard on high: *Hammond King* / O little town of Bethlehem: *Vaughn, Billy* / Christmas song: *Ingmann, Jorgen* / Winter wonderland: *Erling, Ole* / Ding dong merrily on high: *Mantovani & His Orchestra* / Hark the herald angels sing: *Vaughn, Billy* / I heard the bells on Christmas day: *Hammond King* / Little drummer boy: *Ingmann, Jorgen* / Christmas chimes are pealing: *Hammond King* / Canticle noel: *Mantovani & His Orchestra* / First Noel: *Vaughn, Billy* / White Christmas: *Erling, Ole* / God rest ye merry gentlmen: *Mantovani & His Orchestra* / Let it snow let it snow: *Ingmann, Jorgen* / I saw three ships: *Hammond King* / Good king Wenceslas: *Mantovani & His Orchestra* / Sleigh ride: *Ingmann, Jorgen* / Have yourself a merry little Christmas: *Ianescu, Ion* / Caroling caroling: *Hammond King* / O holy night: *Vaughn, Billy* / Sleeping beauty (waltz): *Mantovani & His Orchestra* / O du froliche weinachtszeit: *Ingmann, Jorgen* / Where we come a caroling: *Hammond King* / I saw mummy kissing Santa Claus: *Erling, Ole* / Joy to the world: *Vaughn, Billy* / Jeanette Isabella: *Hammond King* / Silent night: *Mantovani & His Orchestra* / Mary's boy child: *Erling, Ole* / O Christmas tree (O tannenbaum): *Vaughn, Billy* / Bells of Christmas: *Hammond King* / Blue Christmas: *Ianescu, Ion Ensemble* / Morgen kommt der weihnachtsman: *Ingmann, Jorgen* / Greensleeves: *Mantovani & His*

Orchestra / We three kings of orient are: *Hammond King* / Mistletoe and wine: *Ianescu, Ion Ensemble* / Lasst uns froh und munter sein: *Ingmann, Jorgen* / Rudolph the red-nosed reindeer: *Ingmann, Jorgen* / Panic angelicas: *Mantovani & His Orchestra* / Coventry carol: *Hammond King* / Let it snow: *Ianescu, Ion Ensemble* / Auld lang syne: *Vaughn, Billy*

120192 / Nov '97 / Jingle

☐ **INSTRUMENTAL CLASSICS VOL.1**

MODUB 2CD / Aug '92 / Music Of Life

☐ **INSTRUMENTAL DIAMONDS VOL.2 - HIGHLY STRUNG (British 60's Instrumentals)**

Music train: *Honeycombs* / Cleopatra's needle: *Ahab & The Wailers* / Red dragon: *Black Jacks* / Ghoul friend: *Ravens* / Jump Jeremiah: *Ford, Mike & The Consuls* / Ten swinging bottles: *Chester, Peter & The Consulate* / Pompeii: *Checkmates* / Husky: *Nicol, Jimmy* / Packabeat: *Packabeats* / First love: *Clark, Dave Five* / Man in space: *Vigilantes* / Organiser: *Organisers & Harold Smart* / Mad goose: *Sons Of The Piltdown Men* / Eliminator: *Eliminators* / Switch: *Brown, Joe* / Neb's tune: *Ahab & The Wailers* / Traitors: *Packabeats* / Caroline: *Jay, Peter & The Jaywalkers* / Husky team: *Saints* / Dream lover: *Packabeats* / Highly strung: *Rustlers* / Pigtails: *Saints* / Evening in Paris: *Packabeats* / Thunderbirds theme: *Eliminators* / Hurricane: *Honeycombs*

NEXCD 150 / Feb '91 / Sequel

☐ **INSTRUMENTAL FIRE**

SICK 01 / Apr '97 / Musick

☐ **INSTRUMENTAL FOLK MUSIC FROM GREECE**

TSCD 915 / Aug '96 / Topic

☐ **INSTRUMENTAL GEMS VOL.1**

Last night: *Ede, David* / Man in space: *Vigilantes* / John Peel: *Rowena, Jeff Group* / Weekend: *Red Price* / Cleopatra's needle: *Ahab & The Wailers* / Forest fire: *Chester, Pete Group* / Pop corn: *Brown, Joe* / Sunburst: *Fabulous Flee Rekkers* / Raunchy: *McVay, Ray Sound* / Peter Gunn: *Remo Four* / La cucaracha: *Rowena, Jeff Group* / Green man: *Ford, Mike & The Consuls* / Night train: *Nicol, Jimmy & The Shubdubs* / Rockin' minstrel: *Checkmates* / Dream lover: *Packabeats* / Hot toddy: *Original Checkmates* / Exodus: *Eagles* / Tequila: *Shepherd, Bill Orchestra* / Red cabbage: *Jay, Peter & The Jaywalkers* / Matter of who: *Rustlers* / No hats on Ilkley: *Ede, David* / Cerveza: *Wainer, Cherry* / Eliminator: *Eliminators* / Sneeze: *Red Price* / Sleep walk: *Willsher, Pete*

GEMCD 008 / Feb '97 / Diamond

☐ **INSTRUMENTAL LOVE**

I will always love you / (Everything I do) I do it for you / Unchained melody / Power of love / I'm not in love / Annie's song / If you leave me now / Saving all my love for you / Wind beneath my wings / Careless whisper / Fool if you think it's over / He ain't heavy, he's my brother / Have I told you lately / Hero / If you don't know me by now / Jealous guy

QED 219 / Nov '96 / Tring

☐ **INSTRUMENTAL MOODS**

Riverdance: *Anderson, John Concert Orchestra* / Cacharpaya: *Incantation* / Return to innocence: *Enigma* / Yeha noha: *Sacred Spirit* / Celts: *Enya* / Sentinel: *Oldfield, Mike* / Samba pa ti: *Santana* / Albatross: *Fleetwood Mac* / Love's theme: *Moroder, Giorgio* / Adiemus: *Adiemus* / Songbird: *Kenny G* / Cavatina: *Williams, John* / Don't cry for me Argentina: *Shadows* / Inspector Morse theme: *Pheloung, Barrington* / Brideshead revisited: *Burgon, Geoffrey* / Theme from Soldier Soldier: *Parker, Jim* / Chi mai: *Morricone, Ennio* / Stranger on the shore: *Bilk, Acker* / People's Century: *People's Century Orchestra* / Panis Angelicus: *Way, Anthony*

VTCD 65 / Nov '95 / Virgin

☐ **INSTRUMENTAL MUSIC OF THE SOUTHERN APPALACHIANS**

TCD 1061 / 12 Jan '98 / Tradition

☐ **INSTRUMENTAL TANGOS OF THE GOLDEN AGE**

El monito: *De Carlo, Julio* / Colombina: *De Carlo, Julio* / Derecho viejo: *De Carlo, Julio* / Boedo: *De Carlo, Julio* / La cumparsista: *Laurenz, Pedro* / Mala junto: *Laurenz, Pedro* / Orgullo criollo: *Laurenz, Pedro* / Re-fa-si: *De Dois Filiberto, Juan* / El 16: *De Dois Filiberto, Juan* / Fuegos artificiales: *Firpo, Roberto* / El once: *Firpo, Roberto* / La payanca: *Firpo, Roberto* / Don Enrique: *Firpo, Roberto* / Belen: *Di Sarli, Carlos* / La guitarrita: *Di Sarli, Carlos* / Organito de la tarde: *Di Sarli, Carlos* / 9 puntos: *Di Sarli, Carlos* / El amanecer: *Di Sarli, Carlos* / El portentito: *Quinteto Pirincho* / Don Juan: *Quinteto Pirincho* / Rodriguez Pena: *Quinteto Pirincho* / La vuelta da rocha: *Canaro, Francisco* / El gavilan: *Canaro, Francisco* / Punto bravo: *Canaro, Francisco* / Guapeando: *Troilo, Anibal* / La tablada: *Troilo, Anibal*

HQCD 45 / Jun '96 / Harlequin

☐ **INSTRUMENTAL TANGOS OF THE OLD GUARD**

HQCD 70 / May '96 / Harlequin

☐ **INSTRUMENTALLY YOURS**

Blue roofs of Ispahan: *Philippe, Louis* / March of the eligible bachelors: *Monochrome Set* / Constance from Cadaquez: *Marden Hill* / Another conversation with myself: *Watt, Ben* / 1000 guitars of St. Dominiques: *Fantastic Something* / Hasta pronto: *King Of Luxembourg* / All day and all of the night: *Page, Larry Orchestra* / Maestoso con anima: *Deebank, Maurice* / You're the queer one, Les Mun: *Hepburns* / Aperitivo: *Philippe, Louis* / Star trek for jazz guitar: *Posh* / West End: *Leer, Thomas* / Through Eastfields: *Eyeless In Gaza* / Zophia: *Underneath* / Falling: *Beech, Isadora* / Ballet of the red shoes: *Adverse, Anthony* / Execution of Emperor Maximillian: *Marden Hill* / Fantasia, childhood memories: *Fisher-Turner, Simon* / Twangy twangy: *Philippe, Louis* / Park row: *Always* / Flying with lux: *Blind Mr. Jones* / Tender bruises and scars: *Hewick, Kevin* / Geneve: *Fisher, Morgan* / Yo ho ho (and three bottles of wine): *Monochrome Set* / Cavaliere servente: *Philippe, Louis*

MONDE 18CD / 24 Aug '98 / Cherry Red

☐ **INSTRUMENTOS MUSICAIS POPULARES GALEGOS**

H 026CD / Jun '94 / Sonifolk

☐ **INSTRUMENTS (Hannibal Sampler)**

HNCD 8302 / May '93 / Hannibal

☐ **INSTRUMENTS OF FAITH AND VICTORY**

12832 / May '98 / Fairhope

☐ **INSTRUMENTS OF HEALING AND MERCY**

12822 / May '98 / Fairhope

☐ **INSTRUMENTS OF PEACE AND REST**

12812 / May '98 / Fairhope

☐ **INSURGENT COUNTRY VOL.1 (For A Life Of Sin)**

BS 001 / 16 Mar '98 / Bloodshot

☐ **INSURGENT COUNTRY VOL.2 (Hellbent)**

Get it while it's hot: *Whitehead, Earl C. & The Grevious Angels* / Bad times are coming round again: *Waco Brothers* / She took a lot of pills: *Fulks, Robbie* / Little white trash boy: *Starkweathers* / Get down: *Bottle Rockets* / Roulette wheel: *Moonshine Willy* / One I love: *Volebeats* / 22: *Buckner, Richard* / Espoontoon: *Roosevelt, Eleanor* / Tennessee hi-way blues: *Owen, Gwill* / Por favor: *Old 97's* / Walking on my grave: *Cartwrights* / Yellow birds: *Tarnation* / World renowned: *Riptones* / Honky-tonk has-been: *Cornell Hurd Band* / Don't die while I'm alive: *Inbreds* / Mud flap boogie: *World Famous Blue Jays*

BS 004 / 16 Mar '98 / Bloodshot

☐ **INSURGENT COUNTRY VOL.3 (Nashville)**

Hank Williams memorial myth: *House, Tom* / Open flame: *Carroll, Tim* / Daddy's jail: *Lee, Phil & The Sly Dogs* / Your red wagon: *Burch, Paul & His Honky Tonk Orchestra* / Roy: *Morris, R.B.* / God shaped hole: *Hayseed* / Hillbilly train: *George, Sonny & The Tennessee Sons* / One last train: *Jason & The Scorchers* / Cocktail napkin: *Jarvis, Duane* / Whitey: *Lambchop* / Cole Durhew: *House, Tom* / Try it again: *Calvin, Royann* / Lonely at the top: *Baird, Dan* / Safe within your arms: *Garing, Greg* / Rise and shine: *Rose, Kirsti & The Handsome Strangers* / Plans we made: *Lonesome Bob* / No ammunition: *Owen, Gwill* / Those I'll provide: *Courtesy Move*

BS 014 / 16 Mar '98 / Bloodshot

☐ **INTELLIGENT CLUBOVATION VOL.6**

TRC 1022 / 23 Feb '98 / Total Recall

☐ **INTELLIGENT COMPILATION, AN**

K7 035CD / Oct '96 / Studio K7

☐ **INTELLIGENT DRUM & BASS VOL.1**

STHCCD 12 / Jun '95 / Strictly Hardcore

☐ **INTELLIGENT DRUM & BASS VOL.2**

STHCCD 13 / Jul '95 / Strictly Hardcore

☐ **INTELLIGENT INSIDE**

I have no mouth: *Black Lung* / Guardian angel: *Juno Reactor* / Mzeo B: *Download* / Hand: *Velvet Acid Christ* / DRC 2032: *Xyphax* / Depressive tendency: *Individual Totem* / JKTV/Otaku: *Lassigue Bendthaus* / Lost highway 45: *Imminent Starvation* / Gates: *Forma Tadre* / Sub unit one: *Haujobb* / Neuron: *Noise Unit* / Squelch: *Finitribe* / Zap: *Steril* / Plasticity: *Frontline Assembly*

08443622 / 29 Sep '97 / Westcom

☐ **INTELLIGENT SELECTA**

PNCCA 5 / Apr '95 / Production House

☐ **INTENT - NATTY MUSIC (Mixed By Simon 'Bassline' Smith)**

DBM 2035 / Oct '96 / Rogue Trooper

☐ **INTERCITY CRAWL**

Landspeed song: *Donelly, Tanya* / Mixed blood: *Dub Pistols* / Cocksucker blues: *Groop Dogdrill* / Psychopath: *Hardknox* / Don't know how to rock'n'roll: *High Fidelity* / Diamonds are forever yo baby yo: *Lo-Fidelity Allstars* / Out of here: *Monk & Canatella* / Nervous: *Overseer* / Reasons to live: *Silver Sun* / My last girlfriend: *Snow Patrol* / Strange man: *Topper* / Floodlit world: *Ultrasound* / Reprends toi en main: *Velocette* / Liquid: *Vitro* / Down down down: *Warm Jets*

PUBE 18 / 20 Jul '98 / Love Train

☐ **INTERFERENCE LIVE AT LOVE PARADE 94**

EFA 001452 / Aug '95 / Interference

☐ **INTERFERENCE PATTERNS**

KACD 001 / 23 Feb '98 / Kabal

☐ **INTERIORS**

INV 7001CD / 3 Aug '98 / Invisible

☐ **INTERNATIONAL CEILIDH BAND CHAMPIONSHIP, THE**

Strip the willow / Songs and reels / Songs (Keltie Clippie) / Reels / Highland Schottische / Song / Dashing white sergeant / Boston two step / Song (Sound of Pibroch) / Scottische / Dance 13, Jig

LCOM 5218 / Jan '93 / Lismor

☐ **INTERNATIONAL DEEJAY GIGOLOS VOL.1**

EFA 295102 / 10 Nov '97 / International Deejay Gigolos

☐ **INTERNATIONAL DJ SYNDICATE MIX VOL.1-TAKKYU ISHINO**

DDTV u-ziq invade: *Dum Dum T.V.* / Gamer's night: *Mijk's Magic Marble Box* / Voyager: *Beltram, Joey* / Knock knock: *DJ Funk* / Take it to the floor: *K-Hand & Parris Love* / Da mindfuck: *Thee Madkatt Courtship* / Trak 11: *Phylyps* / Acsperience 5: *Hardfloor* / M 04: *Maurizio* / In the bush: *Purpose Maker* / Nagelbrett: *Sensorama* / Don't stop: *Whirlpool Productions* / Das telefon sagt acid: *Ink, Mike & Andreas Dorau* / Fuckin' suckin': *Traxmen* / Mickiee House 2: *Mickiee* / Micro 2: *Tanaka, Fumiya* / Up and down: *Up & Down* / Who da funk: *Dogtrax* / Forerunner: *Natural Born Groovers* / I thought 3, but were 4 in fact: *Ishino, Takkyu*

REACTCD 085 / Sep '96 / React

☐ **INTERNATIONAL DJ SYNDICATE MIX VOL.2-DJ CHER**

Struggle: *Aquatherium* / Future shock: *Seraphim Odyssey* / Listen carefully: *HOW* / Nu energy: *Cosmic Duo* / Canis loopus: *Yekuana* / Passion devotion: *Free Spirit* / Loos caboos: *Electroliners* / Last prayer: *Chapel Of Rest* / Vertigo: *Transcendental Experience* / Ancient forest: *Sun God* / Warning: *Shay, Dan* / Amplexus: *Entropic* / One: *Aria* / Kaleidoscope: *Art Of Trance* / Rain or shine: *Beat Foundation*

REACTCD 103 / Jul '97 / React

☐ **INTERNATIONAL DJ SYNDICATE VOL.3 (Fumiya Tanaka)**

Jamm'in': *Tanaka, Fumiya* / Insistence: *Tanaka, Fumiya* / Speak to me: *Regis* / Pump it: *DJ Funk* / Hangover: *DJ Powerout* / Step to enchantment: *Millsart* / Flash: *Fix* / Armani tracks part 2: *Armani, Robert* / Wiggle: *Long, Wyndell* / Gloss: *Tanaka, Fumiya* / Dancer: *Mills, Jeff* / Language barrier: *Surgeon* / Why + for whom: *Bicknell, Steve* / Leaf: *Morganistic* / Demolition man: *Two Men On Wax* / Toggle: *Tan Ru* / Distortion: *DJ Skull* / Stop screamin': *Wax Master Maurice* / No.2: *Tanaka, Fumiya* / Funky squad: *Karafuto* / Pump the move: *E-Dancer* / Relay: *Blue Maxx* / No.1: *Tanaka, Fumiya* / Wet floor: *Traxmen* / No title: *Dean & Deluca* / Reverting: *Purpose Maker* / Crimes and misdemeanours: *Morganistic* / Encounter: *Outline* / Java: *Mills, Jeff* / It one jah: *Advent* / Allerseelen: *DJ Hell* / Enforcement: *Cyrus* / I9: *Mills, Jeff* / B2: *Mills, Jeff*

REACTCD 111 / Sep '97 / React

☐ **INTERNATIONAL FESTIVAL OF COUNTRY MUSIC, FRUTIGEN (Live May 1987)**

I'm goin', I'm leaving: *Hollow, Traver* / Lonesome, on'ry and mean: *Young, Steven & Tom Russell Band* / Mezcal: *Russell, Tom* / Alkali: *Russell, Tom* / Walkin' after midnight: *Moffatt, Katy & Tom Russell Band* / First taste of Texas: *Bruce, Ed* / Man who turned my mama on: *Bruce, Ed* / Summer wages: *Tyson, Ian & Andrew Hardin* / Someday soon: *Tyson, Ian & Andrew Hardin* / Navajo rug: *Russell, Tom* / Edge of a heartbreak: *Moeller, Dee* / Where is the magic: *Moeller, Dee* / Mamas don't let your babies grow up to be cowboys: *Bruce, Ed*

BCD 15466 / Jun '89 / Bear Family

☐ **INTERNATIONAL GUITAR FESTIVAL**

BEST 1051CD / Jul '94 / Acoustic Music

☐ **INTERNATIONAL RAGGA LOVERS**

TNCD 001 / 23 Feb '98 / Top Nail

☐ **INTIMATE LOVERS VOL.1**

VGCD 015 / Dec '94 / Virgo

☐ **INTIMATE SOUND VOL.1 1989-1993, THE**

Please come back: *Edwards, Dean* / Way we are: *Affair* / There is no way: *Sound Principle* / Bring me back: *Davis, Richard Anthony* / Welcome to yesterday: *Sound Principle* / Keep it comin': *Julianne* / I'm back for more: *Lulu & Bobby Womack* / Getting on with my own life: *Jones Girls* / Lovers for life: *Davis, Richard Anthony* / Is it true: *Drakes, Anthony*

EMHCD 1 / Mar '94 / Intimate

☐ **INTO THE BLUE (The Blue Series Sampler)**

Soul mission: *Bennett, Brian* / Spinning wheel: *Smith, Lonnie* / Blue juice: *McGriff, Jimmy* / Homenagem A Mongo: *Som Tres* / Mamblues: *Kynard, Charles* / High heel sneakers: *Mitchell, Blue* / Idle hands: *Harlem River Drive*

BLUESCD 0997 / 1 Sep '97 / Blue Note

☐ **INTO THE BLUE (2CD Set)**

Seven seconds: *Cherry, Neneh & Youssou N'Dour* / Play dead: *Bjork & David Arnold* / Missing: *Everything But The Girl* / Stars: *Dubstar* / Underwater love: *Smoke City* / Confide in me: *Minogue, Kylie* / Winter in July: *Bomb The Bass* / Milk: *Garbage & Tricky* / Only love can break your heart: *St. Etienne* / Original: *Leftfield & Toni Halliday* / Higher than the sun: *Primal Scream* / Sun rising: *Beloved* / Into the blue: *Moby* / Blue bell knoll: *Cocteau Twins* / Eugina: *Salt Tank* / Box: *Orbital* / Blue room: *Orb* / Stay: *Butler, Bernard* / Genevieve (the pilot of your thighs): *Blake, Perry* / Sunday morning: *Velvet Underground* / When love breaks down: *Prefab Sprout* / Sensual world: *Bush, Kate* / Delicate: *D'Arby, Terence Trent* / Here comes the rain again: *Eurythmics* / Martha's harbour: *All About Eve* / In a lifetime: *Clannad* / Falling: *Cruise, Julee* / Moments in love: *Art Of Noise* / Nightporter: *Japan* / Crying game: *Boy George* / Small blue thing: *Vega, Suzanne* / Perfect day: *Reed, Lou* / Save a prayer: *Duran Duran* / Sleeping satellite: *Archer, Tasmin* / I put a spell on you: *Ferry, Bryan*

5556652 / 23 Mar '98 / PolyGram TV

☐ **INTO THE EIGHTIES (2CD Set)**

Two tribes: *Frankie Goes To Hollywood* / Every breath you take: *Police* / Who's that girl: *Eurythmics* / Sometimes: *Erasure* / Girls on film: *Duran Duran* / Shout: *Tears For Fears* / Call me: *Blondie* / Don't go: *Yazoo* / I go to sleep: *Pretenders* / How soon is now: *Smiths* / Geno: *Dexy's Midnight Runners* / Ghost town: *Specials* / Our lips are sealed: *Fun Boy Three* / House of fun: *Madness* / Do you really want to hurt me: *Culture Club* / Golden Brown: *Stranglers* / It's my life: *Talk Talk* / Look of love: *ABC* / Gold: *Spandau Ballet* / Love plus one: *Haircut 100* / No more I love you's: *Lover Speaks* / Blue Monday: *New Order* / Model: *Kraftwerk* / Temptation: *Heaven 17* / I second that emotion: *Japan* / Enola Gay: *OMD* / Echo Beach: *Martha & The Muffins* / Sound of the crowd: *Human League* / Pop musik: *M* / Somewhere in my heart: *Aztec Camera* / I don't want to talk about it: *Everything But The Girl* / You're the best thing: *Style Council* / Is Vic there: *Department S* / Go wild in the country: *Bow Wow Wow* / Crash: *Primitives* / Killing moon: *Echo & The Bunnymen* / Down in the tube station at midnight: *Jam* / I can't stand up: *Costello, Elvis & The Attractions* / Einstein a go-go: *Landscape* / Vienna: *Ultravox*

RADCD 09 / Apr '95 / Global TV

☐ **INTO THE FORTIES**

Ma I miss your apple pie: *Ambrose & His Orchestra* / There's a land of begin again: *Loss, Joe Band & Chick Henderson* / Don't sit under the apple tree: *Andrews Sisters* / I'll never smile again: *Sinatra, Frank & Tommy Dorsey Orchestra* / You are my sunshine: *Roy, Harry & His Band* / I don't want to walk without you: *Lipton, Celia* / String of pearls: *Miller, Glenn* / When I see an elephant fly: *Leach, Jimmy & His New Organolians* / That lovely weekend: *Carless, Dorothy & Geraldo/Ted Heath* / Moonlight becomes you: *Crosby, Bing* / Someone's rocking my dream boat: *Hutch* / Drummin' man: *Squadronaires* / Who wouldn't love you: *Ink Spots* / Elmer's tune: *Miller, Glenn Orchestra* / Kiss the boys goodbye: *Martin, Mary* / My devotion: *Winstone, Eric Band & Julie Dawn* / Rancho pillow: *Martin, Freddy & His Orchestra* / Beat me daddy eight to the bar: *Shearing, George* / Daybreak: *Sinatra, Frank & Tommy Dorsey Orchestra* / I've got a gal in Kalamazoo: *Andrews Sisters* / Nightingale sang in Berkeley square: *Shelton, Anne & Ambrose* / White Christmas: *Crosby, Bing*

PASTCD 7019 / Mar '97 / Flapper

☐ **INTO THE GROOVE**

SUB 39D / 15 Sep '97 / Subversive

☐ **INTO THE KILTMAKERS**

BSE 001 / 27 Oct '97 / Glass Cow

☐ **INTO THE MIX VOL.2 (2CD Set)**

CLP 194 / 23 Mar '98 / Hypnotic

☐ **INTRODUCING**

101S 77772 / Jun '93 / 101 South

☐ **INTRODUCTION TO AMIATA'S SECRET WORLD, AN**

ARNR 0296 / Apr '97 / Amiata

☐ **INTRODUCTION TO COUNTRY LINE DANCING, AN**

REMCD 505 / Feb '98 / Reactive

☐ **INTRODUCTION TO NEW WORLD, AN**

CD 442 / 6 Jul '98 / New World

☐ **INTROSPECTIVE OF HOUSE - THE ANTHEMS (3CD Set)**

SDIMCD 10 / 24 Nov '97 / Sound Dimension

☐ **INTROSPECTIVE OF HOUSE VOL.1 (3CD Set)**

Do me right: *Inner City* / To be real: *Lady Cop* / Don't leave me this way: *Houston, Thelma* / Love can't turn around: *Heavy Weather* / English 101: *Afrowax* / Real vibration: *Express Of Sound* / Believe in me: *Raw Stylus* / Give me back: *Sensoria* / Looking glass: *I-Spy* / Rok the disco: *Big Echo* / Loveboy: *Foot Club* / Galaxia: *Moonman* / Believer: *DJ Energy* / Gift: *Way Out West* / Never gonna give you up: *Turner, Ruby* / 100%: *Kiani, Mary* / Star: *Shaker* / Don't be afraid: *Moonman* / Voyager: *Mr. Spring* / Horn: *Digi Dance* / Brain bug: *Nightmare* / United nations of house: *United Nations Project* / Diesirae: *Andy & The Lamboy* / Love and respect: *Supa T* / You're surrounded: *Skins/Jules* / So in love with you: *Duke* / Groovebird: *Natural Born Groovers* / French kiss: *Lil' Louis* / Feel the beat: *Sunglasses Ron* / Hi Q: *Stereogen* / Footprint: *Disco Citizens* / All I wanna do: *Tin Tin Out* / Antheum: *Digital Blondes* / Turkish bizzare: *Blade Racer* / U...: *Scott Project* / Petal: *Wubble-U* / Bellissima: *DJ Quicksilver*

SDIMCD 7 / Nov '96 / Sound Dimension

☐ **INTROSPECTIVE OF HOUSE VOL.2 (3CD Set)**

SDIMCD 8 / Jun '97 / Sound Dimension

☐ **INTROSPECTIVE OF HOUSE VOL.3 (3CD Set)**

SDIMCD 9 / 1 Sep '97 / Sound Dimension

☐ **INTUITION...**

At 17: *Ian, Janis* / No frontiers: *Black, Mary* / When I was a boy: *Williams, Dar* / Welcome me: *Baez, Joan* / Jerusalem tomorrow: *Harris, Emmylou* / Words: *Tamalin* / Wonderful thing: *Dowdall, Leslie* / You're in my love: *Lohan, Sinead* / Tenderness: *Ian, Janis* / Bee in the bottle: *Lohan, Sinead* / As cool as I am: *Williams, Dar* / Going back to Harlan: *Harris, Emmylou* / Libertango: *McCall, Kirsty and Sharon Shannon* / Kilkelly: *Shanley, Eleanor* / There's a train that leaves tonight: *Black, Mary* / Down by the sally gardens: *Tamalin* / Rise again: *Rankin Family*

GRACD 224 / 25 Aug '97 / Grapevine

☐ **INUIT GAMES AND SONGS**

AUD 8032 / Mar '93 / Auvidis/Ethnic

☐ **INVICTUS UNCONQUERED VOL.1**

Give me just a little more time: *Chairmen Of The Board* / You've got extra added power in your love: *Chairmen Of The Board* / I shall not be moved: *Barrino Brothers* / Trapped in a love: *Barrino Brothers* / You made me over: *Davis, Melvin* / Can't get enough of you: *Edwards, Tyrone* / She's not just another woman: *8th Day* / You've got to crawl (before you walk): *8th Day* / I need it just as bad as you: *Lee, Laura* / Don't leave me starving for your love: *Lee, Laura* / Don't leave me: *Holland & Dozier* / Why can't we be lovers: *Holland & Dozier* / Giving up the ring: *Glass House* / Crumbs off the table: *Glass House* / Bring the boys home: *Payne, Freda* / Band of gold: *Payne, Freda* / Only time will tell: *General Johnson* / Breakdown: *Parliament* / VIP: *Payne, Sherrie* / Unhooked generation: *Payne, Freda* / I'm so glad: *Holland, Brian* / Roller coaster: *Woods, Danny*

DEEPM 028 / Jul '97 / Deep Beats

☐ **INVICTUS UNCONQUERED VOL.2 (Cherish what is dear to you)**
(You've got me) dangling on a string: Chairmen Of The Board / If I could see the light: 8th Day / Deeper and deeper: Payne, Freda / I had it all: Barrino Brothers / Finders keepers: Chairmen Of The Board / If it ain't love (it don't matter): Glass House / That's love: Hi-Lites / Touch me: Laws, Eloise / New breed kinda woman: Holland & Dozier / Playing games: Glass House / Cherish what is dear to you (while it's near to you): Payne, Freda / Slipping away: Holland & Dozier / Sittin' on a timebomb: Charles, Lee / Eeny meeny miney mo (three's a crowd): 8th Day / Chairmen of the board: Chairmen Of The Board / I got it: New York Port Authority / I don't see me in your eyes anymore: Hunter, Ty / You brought the joy: Payne, Freda / I'm worried: Davis, Melvin / Don't leave me starving for your love: Holland & Dozier
NEMCD 971 / 1 Jun '98 / Sequel

☐ **INVISIBLE ROUTE 666**
INV 666 / Nov '95 / Invisible

☐ **INVISIBLE SOUNDTRACKS (Macro 1)**
Menage a trois: Thomas, Richard / Harsh truth: Zurich / Crater rim cafe: Sons Of Silence / Beachside FX: Nonplace Urban Field / Here I am: Thomas, Richard / Cue: Being / If mountains could sing: Bedouin Ascent / Vistic: Disjecta / Intrusion reported by witness: Thomas, Richard / Sloop B: Twisted Science / Muffin Spencer-Devlin/Hawaii II: Thomas, Richard / Dirt vs Earth: Thomas, Richard / Nevada 2007: Air Miami / Bronchusix: Gescom / Tema: Seymour & Van Hoen / Pendulum: Vendor Refill
REEL 12CD / May '97 / Leaf

☐ **INVISIBLE SOUNDTRACKS (Macro 2)**
Aldrigpunkt: Polyester Orkester / Stepping through a wooden door: B Low / Coarse bitch cop: Small Good Thing / Die dinge des lebens: To Rococo Rot / Aeth: Corwine, Matthew / From the temple to the Nile: Brennan, Max / Beaf: Fridge / Control panel 04: Control Panel / Control Panel 05: Control Panel / Sorry officer: Begg, Si / He who leaves no trace: Miller, Paul D. / Storms and skeeters: Kristian, David / Underwater: Barbed / Driftnet: Eccles-Smith, Ian
REEL 3CD / 9 Mar '98 / Leaf

☐ **INVOCATION**
5244412 / 5 Jan '98 / Six Degrees

☐ **IOWA STATE FARE - MUSIC FROM THE HEARTLAND (Celebrating 150 Years Of Iowa Statehood)**
SFWCD 40083 / Sep '96 / Smithsonian Folkways

☐ **IRAN: MASTERS OF TRADITIONAL MUSIC VOL.1**
C 560024 / Aug '91 / Ocora

☐ **IRAN: MASTERS OF TRADITIONAL MUSIC VOL.2**
C 560025 / Aug '91 / Ocora

☐ **IRAN: MASTERS OF TRADITIONAL MUSIC VOL.3**
C 560026 / Nov '92 / Ocora

☐ **IRANIAN MUSIC - SAZ-E NO**
927162 / 1 Jun '98 / BUDA

☐ **IRELAND - A SONG FOR EVERY COUNTY (2CD Set)**
CHCD 3201 / Mar '96 / Chyme

☐ **IRELAND TODAY**
B 6838 / Nov '96 / Auvidis/Ethnic

☐ **IRELAND'S GREATEST LOVE SONGS (A Collection Of 20 Romantic Ballads From The Emerald Isle)**
On Raglan road: Kelly, Luke / Will ye go lassie go: Barnbrack / Fields of Athenry: Reilly, Paddy / Ringsend Rose: Tara / Song for Ireland: Kelly, Luke / Grace: Brier / Carrickfergus: McCann, Jim / Danny Boy: Locke, Josef / John O'dreams: Dublin City Ramblers / First of May: Close, John / Spanish lady: Dubliners / Sweet sixteen: Fureys & Davey Arthur / Rose of Allendale: Reilly, Paddy / She moved thro' the fair: Locke, Josef / Last farewell: Brier / Town I loved so well: McEvoy, Johnny / Old man: Fureys & Davey Arthur / Mountains of Mourne: Locke, Josef / Lagan love: Shannon Singers / Star of County Down: Barnbrack
CHCD 1099 / Mar '97 / Chyme

☐ **IRIE CHRISTMAS**
RTD 3970035CD / 10 Nov '97 / Institute Of Art

☐ **IRIE IRIE (A Ragamuffin Showcase)**
MSACD 003 / Nov '94 / Munich

☐ **IRIE IRIE (The Ras Sampler)**
MSACD 002 / May '97 / Munich

☐ **IRISH CEILI (Reels & Jigs)**
Piper's Chair/Bill Hart's jig/Nights of St. Patrick: Dubliners / Sheebans/Merry blacksmith/Music in the Glen: Kilfernora Ceili Band / Paddy on the railroad: Gallowglass Ceili Band / Liffey barges: Owens, Jesse / Galway races: Dubliners / Irish soldier: Owens, Jesse / Eavesdropper/Donnybrook boys/A visit to Ireland: Ardellis Ceili Band / Haste to the wedding/Leslie's hornpipe/German Beau: Gallowglass Ceili Band / Queen of Connemara: Ardellis Ceili Band / Claddagh ring: Tulla Ceili Band / Finnegan's wake: Irish National Orchestra & Choir / Donnybrook Fair/Tate's tantrums/Rake of Kildare: Irish National Orchestra & Choir / Johnny I hardly knew ye: Murphy, Mary / Paddy's gone to France/ Skylark: Dubliners / Barn/My own backyard: Dun Carmel Band / Bucks of Oranmore: Gor Jus Wrex
CDMFP 6348 / May '97 / Music For Pleasure

☐ **IRISH CELEBRATION, AN (3CD Set)**
EMTBX 307 / Aug '97 / Emporio

☐ **IRISH COLLECTION**
RZRCD 553 / Oct '95 / Ritz

☐ **IRISH COUNTRY**
Forty shades of green: McBride, Frankie / Gentle mother: Big Tom & The Mainliners / My wild Irish rose: Quinn, Brendan / Two little orphans: Quinn, Philomena / I'll take you home again Kathleen: Coll, Brian / Rose is a rose: McGeegan, Pat / I'll get over you: McCaffery, Helen / Wonderin' what to do: Duffy, Teresa / Mother's love's a blessing: Quinn, Brendan / How are things in Gloccamorra: McBride, Frankie / Rose of Tralee: Coll, Brian / She's got you: Quinn, Philomena / That silver haired daddy of mine: McCaffery, Helen / Sunset years of life: Big Tom & The Mainliners / Nobody's child: Morelli, Tony / Irish way to love: McGoldrick, Anna
EMPRCD 665 / Oct '96 / Emporio

☐ **IRISH DANCE MUSIC**
TSCD 602 / Oct '95 / Topic

☐ **IRISH FAVOURITES**
CPMV 028 / Sep '94 / Cromwell

☐ **IRISH FAVOURITES**
PLSCD 166 / Apr '97 / Pulse

☐ **IRISH FAVOURITES (2CD Set)**
R2CD 4040 / 13 Apr '98 / Deja Vu

☐ **IRISH FAVOURITES**
Bunch of thyme: Shaskeen / Girl: Moore, Barry / Maid at the spinning wheel: Na Fili / Delaney's donkey: Dunphy, Sean / Farewell to Erin: Bothy Band / Loughnames: Shannon, Seamus / Singb Irishmen sing: Barleycorn / Imis dhun ramba: Na Fili / Crosses of Annaghh: Brady, Paul & Matt Malloy / Hills above Drumquin: Margo / I know my love: Crowley, Jimmy / New broom: Bushwackers / Sweetwilliamstown: Na Fili / Shanagolden: Dunphy, Sean / Pipe on the hob: Bothy Band / Dicey Riley: Sweeney's Men / Ceol an Phiobaire: Na Fili / Cherish the ladies: Shannon, Seamus
308932 / 11 May '98 / Hallmark

☐ **IRISH FAVOURITES VOL.1**
DMC 4370 / May '94 / Disky

☐ **IRISH FAVOURITES VOL.2**
DMC 4371 / May '94 / Disky

☐ **IRISH FOLK BALLADS**
MACCD 317 / Aug '96 / Autograph

☐ **IRISH FOLK COLLECTION (3CD Set)**
TBXCD 509 / Jan '96 / TrueTrax

☐ **IRISH FOLK COLLECTION (2CD Set)**
PBXCD 509 / Nov '96 / Pulse

☐ **IRISH FOLK COLLECTION VOL.2**
CCSCD 312 / Feb '93 / Castle

☐ **IRISH FOLK FAVOURITES (4CD Set)**
PBXCD 410 / 20 Apr '98 / Pulse

☐ **IRISH FOLK FEST - BACK TO THE FUTURE**
CDTUT 727490 / '89 / Wundertute

☐ **IRISH FOLK FEST - JUBILEE**
CDTUT 727491 / '89 / Wundertute

☐ **IRISH FOLK LEGENDS**
CDC 013 / Feb '97 / Ceol

☐ **IRISH HEARTBEAT (2CD Set)**
Old Ireland / Old Dungannon Oak / Rare Old Times / Muirsheen Durkin / Galway shawl / Bold O'Donoghue / Fields of Athenry / Wicklow Hills / Dirty Old Town / Hometown on the Foyle / Do you want your old lobby washed down / Four old white lace / Rose of Clare / Lovely lectrim / Pretty little girls from Omagh / Cliffs of Dooneen / I'll tell me ma / Forty shades of green / Spancil hill / Wild rover / Whiskey in the jar / Four country roads / Green fields of France / Irish rover / When you were sweet sixteen / Boys from Killybegs / You seldom come to see me anymore / Boston burglar / Ilse of Innisfree / After all these years / Black velvet band / Our house is not a home / Old bog road / Town I love so well / I'll take you home again Kathleen / Any Tipperary town / Hills of Kerry / Mountains of Mourne / Maggie / Rose of Tralee
DCD 3001 / Jun '97 / Music

☐ **IRISH LOVE SONGS YOU KNOW BY HEART VOL.1**
HBCD 116 / Dec '96 / Outlet

☐ **IRISH LOVE SONGS YOU KNOW BY HEART VOL.2**
HBCD 117 / Dec '96 / Outlet

☐ **IRISH MEMORIES (40 Gems From The Emerald Isle/2CD Set)**
Dermot Hegarty: Black Velvet Band / Sean O'Se: Beautiful City / Barley corn: Sing Irishman Sing / Shaskeen: Shaskeen / Roads and the miles to Dundee: Margo / Pretty little girl from Omagh: Cunningham, Larry / Music in the glen: Owenmore Ceili Band / Far from Erne's shore: Stuart, Gene / Red is the rose: Margo / Paddy McGinty's goat: Dunphy, Sean / Old Claddagh ring: O'Brien, Dermot / Asthoreen Bawn: Coll, Brian / Town I loved so well: Hegarty, Dermot / Green hills of Kerry: Doyle, Danny / West of the old river Shannon: Margo / Golden jubilee: Dunphy, Sean / Give an Irish girl to me: Coll, Brian / Home boys home: O'Brien, Dermot / Rose of Tralee: Curtin, D.J. / When my blue moon turns to gold again: Coll, Brian / You and me, her and him: Lynham, Ray & Philomena Begley / Hold me just one more time: Hurley, Red / Forty shades of green: Cunningham, Larry / Tears on my pillow: Rock, Dickie / Anything's better than nothing: Lynham, Ray & Philomena Begley / I love you because: Cunningham, Larry / If teardrops were pennies: Two's Company / Jimmy Brown the newsboy: Hegarty, Dermot / We go together: Lynham, Ray & Philomena Begley / Fool's castle: Coll, Brian / Poor man's roses: Hurley, Red / Sweet dreams: Two's Company / Daddy was an old time preacher man: Lynham, Ray & Philomena Begley / I've been everywhere: Hegarty, Dermot / Arkansas: Hurley, Red / Petal from a faded rose: Coll, Brian / Made for each other: Two's Company / Sing me back home: Coll, Brian / I'll take you home again Kathleen: McCaffrey, Frank / From a jack to a king: Rock, Dickie
330392 / Mar '97 / Hallmark

☐ **IRISH MEMORIES**
Limerick you're a lady / Irish lullaby / Maggie / Molly my lovely Molly / Here's to my native country / Red is the rose / Beautiful Meath / Moonlight in Mayo / Isle of Innisfree / Cavan girl / Moon behind the hill / Precious memories / Little piece of heaven / County of Fermanagh / Tipperary far away / If we only had old Ireland over here / Spinning wheel / Give an Irish girl to me / Mason's apron / She
RZRCD 568 / 10 Nov '97 / Ritz

☐ **IRISH MUSIC TO SET YOU DANCING**
CHCD 2003 / Dec '96 / Chyme

☐ **IRISH PUB BALLADS COLLECTION**
DOCDK 110 / Aug '96 / Dolphin

☐ **IRISH REELS JIGS AND AIRS**
Hewlett / March of the King of Laoise / Sunny bank / Lament for Limrick / Galtee hunt / West wind/The blackbird / Sheebeg and sheemore / Kid on the mountain / Duke of Fife's welcome to Deeside / Fisherman's lilt / Morgan Magan / Medley / Donegal pilgrim / Blarney pilgrim / Leaving Brittany going to Ireland / Fanteladda/Boys of Ballisidare
SHANCD 97011 / May '98 / Shanachie

☐ **IRISH SHOW BAND YEARS**
CHCD 1060 / Oct '95 / Chyme

☐ **IRISH SHOW BANDS (The Best Of Irish Show Bands)**
PLSCD 176 / Apr '97 / Pulse

☐ **IRISH SHOWBAND COLLECTION, THE**
Papa oo mow mow: Freshmen / Many the memories: Real Mccoy / Crystal chandeliers: Keeling, Tony & The Graduates / Michael Murpheys boy: Dee, Alan & The Chessman / I love you more today: O'Brien, Brendan & The Dixies / Road down by the river: Keynotes / She wears my ring: Fagan, Sean & The Pacific Showband / Down came the rain: Moore, Butch & The Capitol Showband / Showball crazy: Hoedowners / One kiss for old times sake: Quinn, Murty & The Miami / Two of a kind: Dolan, Joe & The Drifters / Santo natale: O'Hara, Shay & The Royal blues / Black velvet band: Kelly, Johnny & The Capitol / Just for old times sake: Rock, Dickie & The Miami Showband / Right or wrong: Reid, Eileen & The Cadets / No one knows: Knowles, Sonny & The Pacific / Our love will go on: Moore, Butch & The Capitol Showband / Leaving of Liverpool: Lynch, Pat & The Airchords / Land of gingerbread: Gregory & The Cadets / Little arrows: O'Brien, Brendan / Quick Joey Small: Real Mccoy / I gave my wedding dress away: Reid, Eileen & The Cadets / He's got you: O'Brien, Brendan & The Dixies / Foolin' time: Moore, Butch & The Capitol Showband / Wishing it was you: Rock, Dickie & The Miami Showband / Anything that's part of you: Keeling, Tony & The Graduates / More than yesterday: Gregory & The Cadets / No one will ever know: Knowles, Sonny & The Pacific / It doesn't matter anymore: O'Brien, Brendan & The Dixies / Irish soldier: Lynch, Pat & The Airchords / Streets of Baltimore: Kelly, Des & The Capitol / Wonderful world of my dreams: Dunphy, Sean & The Hoedowners / Just to see you smile: Freshmen / Jolly tinker: Dolan, Joe & The Drifters / I came to dance with you: Sonny & Sean/The Pacific / Young love: Collins, Donnie Showband & Chris Grace / Walking the streets in the rain: Moore, Butch / Save the last dance for me: O'Brien, Brendan & The Dixies / Bonny Irish boy: Margo & The Keynotes / Ring of fire: Gerry & The Ohio / Born to be with you: Moore, Butch / Together again: O'Brien, Brendan / If I could choose: Dunphy, Sean / Carlingford bay: O'Kelly, Patricia & The Hiltons / We could: Knowles, Sonny & The Pacific / La yenka: Dean, Derek & The Freshmen / Treat my daughter kindly: Lynch, Pat & The Airchords / Bucks polka: Quinn, Clem & The Miami / Distant drums: Fagan, Sean & The Pacific Showband / At the close of a long long day: Gregory & The Cadets / Far away from you: Carroll, Doc / If I had my life to live over: Reid, Eileen & The Cadets / Katie's kisses: O'Brien, Brendan & The Dixies / So many ways: Moore, Butch & The Capitol Showband / Answer to everything: Dolan, Joe & The Drifters / Winter winds: Doherty, Joe & Michael Conn / Round the gum tree: Real Mccoy
PBXCD 323 / 3 Aug '98 / Pulse

☐ **IRISH SINGALONG**
ARAN 3610 / 5 May '98 / Dara

☐ **IRISH SONGBOOK, THE**
Killarney: McCormack, John / Last rose of summer: Austrel, Florence / Father O'Flynn: Santley, Charles / Kathleen Mavoureen: Butt, Clara / Trottin' to the fair: Greene, Harry Plunket / Garden where the praties grow: Greene, Harry Plunket / Minstrel boy: Burke, Tom / I know where I'm going: Sheridan, Margaret / Kerry dance: Dawson, Peter / Next market day: McCormack, John / Boat song: Kirkby-Lunn, Louise / Believe me, if all those endearing young charms: Tibbett, Lawrence / Kitty of Coleraine: O'Doherty, Seamus / Danny Boy: Labette, Dora / Kitty my love will you marry me: McCafferty, James / Open the door softly: McCafferty, James / Love at my heart: Robeson, Paul / Lover's curse: Hill, Carmen / Mother Machree: Crooks, Richard / She moved through the fair: MacEwan, Sydney / Come back to Erin: Sheridan, Margaret / Phil the fluter's ball: Dawson, Peter
MIDCD 006 / Apr '95 / Moidart

☐ **IRISH SONGS YOU KNOW AND LOVE VOL.1**
HBCD 114 / Dec '96 / Outlet

☐ **IRISH SONGS YOU KNOW AND LOVE VOL.2**
HBCD 115 / Dec '96 / Outlet

☐ **IRISH TIMES**
TUT 494 / Oct '94 / Wundertute

☐ **IRISH TIN WHISTLES**
TRADHCD 007 / Jul '93 / GTD

☐ **IRISH TOWN**
HBCD 0006 / May '97 / Hummingbird

☐ **IRISH TRADITIONAL MUSIC (From The UCD Irish Folk Studies Department)**
D 8271 / Nov '97 / Unesco

☐ **IRISH VOICES**
Humours of the King of Ballyhooley: Patrick Street / Stor mo chroi: MacDonnchadha, Sean / Blackwaterside: Kavana, Ron / Traveller all over the world: Harte, Frank / Raggle taggle gypsy: Reilly, John / P for Paddy: Irish Country Four / Rollicking boys of Tandaragee: Tunney, Paddy / Bucket of the mountain dew: McPeake Family Trio / Bean an Leanna: Heaney, Joe / Wind that shakes the barley: Makem, Sarah / Song of the riddles: Clancy, Willie / An sgeilpin droighneach: O'Neachtain, Tomas / Maid on the shore: Lyons, John / Lake of coolfin: Lenihan, Tom / John Reilly: O'Neill, Sarah Ann / Green fields of America: Graham, Len / High on a mountain: Four Men & A Dog
TSCD 702 / Feb '97 / Topic

☐ **IRISH WHISTLES**
HCD 007 / Apr '95 / GTD

☐ **IRON MUSE, THE (A Panorama Of Industrial Folk Music)**
Sangate girl's lament/Elsie Marley: High Level Ranters / Doon the waggonway: High Level Ranters / Miner's life: Gilfellon, Tom / Coal-owner and the pitman's wife: MacColl, Ewan & Peggy Seeger / Trimdon Grange explosion: Killen, Louis / Blackleg miner: Killen, Louis / Auchengeich disaster: Gaughan, Dick & Alistair Anderson / Ee aye, aa cud hew: Pickford, Ed / Durham lockout: Craik, Maureen / Aa'm glad the strike's done: High Level Ranters / Weaver's march: Celebrated working man's band / Spinner's song: Fisher, Ray / Oh, dear me: MacColl, Ewan & Peggy Seeger / Doffin mistress: Briggs, Anne / Little piecer: Brooks, Dave / Hand loom weaver's lament: Boardman, Harry / Dundee lassie: Fisher, Ray / Success to the weavers: Oldham Tinkers / Fourpence a day: MacColl, Ewan & Peggy Seeger / Up the raw: Killen, Louis / Row between the cages: Davenport, Bob / Aw wish pay Friday would come: Killen, Louis & Colin Ross / Keep your feet still Geordie Hinny: Killen, Louis & Colin Ross / Farewell to the Monty: Killen, Louis
TSCD 465 / May '93 / Topic

☐ **IS IT COOL**
Linda who: Crothers, Scott / Blitz: Three Blue Teardrops / Red hot and ready: Memphis Mafia / Rockabilly baby: Erik & The Dragtones / Tear it up: High Noon / Pushrod: Potter, Jeff / Bad cat: Scoffed / Hillibilly hell: Wreckin' Ball / Chicken walk: Mustang Lightning / What'd I do now: Whole Lotsa Papa / Naked cowboy: Rotgut / Rockabilly not fade away: LeVey, Larry / Long hard night: Three Blue Teardrops / Hey baby: Wreckin' Ball / Itchen fer lovin': Scoffed / Blackjack county chains: Whole Lotsa Papa / Wild wild women: Mustang Lightning / Sun # 209: Thompson, Danny / Lonesome road: Rockabilly 88 / Buzz and the flyers: Is It Cool
NERCD 081 / Jun '95 / Nervous

☐ **IS IT LOVE (Music From The Lovers' Guide)**
Theme for lovers / Tender invitation / Touch me / Secret whispers / Echoes of love / I need your love / Toledo / Making love in the rain / Love ocean / Now that you're a part of me / Hold me close
PWKS 4133 / Feb '96 / Carlton

☐ **IS THAT JAZZ**
URCD 007 / Jul '96 / Ubiquity

☐ **IS THIS LOVE (2CD Set)**
NSCD 008 / Feb '95 / Newsound

☐ **ISLAND 40TH ANNIVERSARY VOL.1 1959-1964 (Ska's The Limit)**
5243932 / 29 Sep '97 / Island

☐ **ISLAND 40TH ANNIVERSARY VOL.2 1964-1969 (Rhythm & Blues Beat)**
5243942 / 29 Sep '97 / Island

☐ **ISLAND 40TH ANNIVERSARY VOL.3 1968-1975 (Acoustic Waves)**
Matty Groves: Fairport Convention / (Roamin' thru the gloamin' with) 40,000 madmen: Traffic / Sailing: Sutherland Brothers / Cello song: Drake, Nick / May you never: Martyn, John / Say it ain't so Joe: Head, Murray / Who knows where the time goes: Fairport Convention / I want to see the bright lights tonight: Thompson, Richard & Linda / Island: Renaissance / Where do children play: Stevens, Cat / Poor ditching boy: Thompson, Richard / Dear old battlefield: Incredible String Band / Listen listen: Denny, Sandy / Pavan: Amazing Blondel / Cuckoo's nest: Hutchings & Richard Thompson/Dave Mattacks / Mna na n-eirann: Chieftains
5243762 / 29 Jun '98 / Island

☐ **ISLAND 40TH ANNIVERSARY VOL.4 1967-1975 (Electric Currents)**
Dear Mr. Fantasy: Traffic / Cat's squirrel: Jethro Tull / Court of the crimson king: King Crimson / Mr. big: Free / Better by you better by me: Spooky Tooth / Low spark of the high-heeled boys: Traffic / I just keep singing that same old song: Heavy Jelly / I'd rather be the devil (devil got my woman): Martyn, John / Hard rain's a-gonna fall: Ferry, Bryan / Baby's on fire: Eno, Brian / Do the strand: Roxy Music / From a whisper to a scream: Palmer, Robert / Heartbreak hotel: Cale, John / Feel like makin' love: Bad Company
5244272 / 29 Jun '98 / Island

☐ **ISLAND JAMZ**
JVG 016 / 15 Jun '98 / Shore

☐ **ISLAND MUSIC**
RNCD 2077 / Oct '94 / Rhino

☐ **ISLAND OF ST. HYLARION, THE**
NA 038 / Apr '91 / New Albion

☐ ISLAND OF THE GODS, THE (Balinese Gamelan Gong)
Puspa Wresti / Topeng Keras / Legong / Kepyar Duduk dance - Turuna Jaya / Kupu Kupu Taram / Oleg Tamulilingan / Jauk / Closing instrumental music
SOW 90154 / Jan '97 / Sounds Of The World

☐ ISLAND PARADISE
307092 / Aug '97 / Hallmark

☐ ISLANDS
PUTU 1292 / Jun '97 / Putumayo

☐ ISLE OF GOLDEN DREAMS
Ta-hu-wa-wai: *McIntire, Dick* / Leilani: *McIntire, Dick* / On a coconut island: *Iona, Andy* / My tane: *Iona, Andy* / Let's go for broke: *Iona, Andy* / Hilo march: *Kaonohi, David* / St. Louis blues: *West, Sam Ku* / Vana vana: *Goupil, Augie* / Faa navenave: *Goupil, Augie* / Hawaiian ripple: *Lane, Noi* / Ten tiny toes-one baby nose: *Hoopii, Sol* / Weave a lei flower lei: *Hoopii, Sol* / South Sea Island swing: *Sharpe, A.P. & Honolulu Hawaiians* / Hilo hanakahi: *Kanui & Lula* / Isle of golden dreams: *Smeck, Roy* / Palikiko blues: *Tahiti Beachcombers* / Tomi tomi: *Pineapple, Johnny* / Hanohano Hawaii: *Waikiki Stonewall Boys* / Hanohano hanalei: *South Sea Islanders* / Hula blues: *Moe, Tau* / Papio: *L'ensemble Tamarii Tahiti* / On a beach at Waikiki: *Kilima Hawaiians* / Neath Hawaiian palms: *Wills, Bob* / Steel guitar boogie: *Kaai, Bernie & His Hawaiians*
HQCD 112 / Jun '98 / Harlequin

☐ ISLE OF WIGHT FESTIVAL 1970, THE
EDFCD 327 / Dec '95 / Essential

☐ ISN'T IT ROMANTIC (Songwriters In Jazz)
5297012 / Mar '96 / Verve

☐ ISN'T IT ROMANTIC
ZYX 551122 / 22 Jun '98 / ZYX

☐ ISRAEL'S PSYCHEDELIC TRANCE VOL.1
20552 / 2 Mar '98 / Phonokol

☐ ISRAEL'S PSYCHEDELIC TRANCE VOL.2
20822 / 12 Jan '98 / Phonokol

☐ ISTANBUL 1925
CD 4266 / Dec '94 / Traditional Crossroads

☐ IT 1 ELECTRO
ITCD 1 / May '96 / Psychic

☐ IT AIN'T WHERE YOU'RE FROM...IT'S WHERE YOU'RE AT
LF 281CD / Jun '97 / Lost & Found

☐ IT CAME FROM BENEATH LA
TX 51213CD / Jan '96 / Triple X

☐ IT CAME FROM MEMPHIS
UPSTART 022 / Nov '95 / Upstart

☐ IT CAME FROM OUTER SPACE VOL.1
OUTERSPACE 01 / 6 Oct '97 / Neuton

☐ IT CAME FROM OUTER SPACE VOL.2
OUTERSPACE 23 / Jun '94 / Neuton

☐ IT CAME FROM OUTER SPACE VOL.3
OUTERSPACE 25 / Sep '95 / Neuton

☐ IT DON'T MEAN A THING IF IT AIN'T GOT THAT SWING
My heart belongs to Daddy: *Shaw, Artie* / I got rhythm: *Dorsey, Tommy* / Frankie and Johnny: *Goodman, Benny* / Basin Street blues: *Fitzgerald, Ella & Chick Webb* / Moonlight serenade: *Miller, Glenn* / Taking a chance on love: *Dorsey, Tommy* / Jumpin' at the Woodside: *Basie, Count* / Take the 'A' train: *Ellington, Duke* / September song: *Day, Doris & Les Brown* / Blowin' up a storm: *Herman, Woody* / Skyliner: *Barnet, Charlie* / Linger awhile: *Morgan, Russ* / Fools rush in: *Dorsey, Jimmy* / On the sunny side of the street: *Dorsey, Tommy* / Perdido: *Ellington, Duke* / My heart stood still: *Shaw, Artie* / Jersey bounce: *Goodman, Benny* / Blue and sentimental: *Basie, Count* / Caldonia: *Herman, Woody* / I'm forever blowing bubbles: *Brown, Les*
QED 124 / Nov '96 / Tring

☐ IT STARTED WITH A KISS
(You're) having my baby: *Anka, Paul* / Tonight I celebrate my love: *Bryson, Peabo & Roberta Flack* / Rock me tonight (for old times sake): *Jackson, Freddie* / I thought I'd ring you: *Bassey, Shirley & Alain Delon* / For a moment of your time: *Hammond, Albert* / Could it be I'm falling in love: *Grant, David & Jaki Graham* / Loving you: *Riperton, Minnie* / When I need you: *Sayer, Leo* / I'll fly for you: *Spandau Ballet* / Everytime I think of you: *Babys* / Dedicated to the one I love: *McLean, Bitty* / Move closer: *Nelson, Phyllis* / It started with a kiss: *Hot Chocolate* / When you're in love with a beautiful woman: *Dr. Hook*
WLT 874602 / Oct '96 / Disky

☐ IT TAKES TWO
Don't let the sun go down on me: *Michael, George & Elton John* / You are everything: *Ross, Diana & Marvin Gaye* / Easy lover: *Collins, Phil & Phillip Bailey* / With you I'm born again: *Preston, Billy & Syreeta* / It takes two: *Gaye, Marvin & Kim Weston* / Up where we belong: *Cocker, Joe & Jennifer Warnes* / I've had the time of my life: *Medley, Bill & Jennifer Warnes* / I'm gonna make you love me: *Temptations & Diana Ross/Supremes* / You've lost that loving feeling: *Righteous Brothers* / If you don't know me by now: *Melvin, Harold & The Bluenotes* / Tonight I celebrate my love: *Bryson, Peabo & Roberta Flack* / Midnight train to Georgia: *Knight, Gladys & The Pips* / I got you babe: *Sonny & Cher* / Relight my fire: *Take That & Lulu* / Baby come back: *Pato Banton & Ali Campbell/ Robin Campbell* / Missing: *Everything But The Girl* / Would I lie to you: *Charles & Eddie* / Senza una donna: *Young, Paul & Zucchero* / Every time you go away: *Hall & Oates* / Sisters are doing it for themselves: *Eurythmics & Aretha Franklin* / It's too late: *Quartz & Dina Carroll* / Somethin's gotten hold of my heart: *Pitney, Gene & Marc Almond* / Stop draggin' my heart around: *Nicks, Stevie & Tom Petty & The Heartbreakers* / Say goodbye to Hollywood: *Spector, Ronnie & the E Street Band* / Whole new world: *Bryson, Peabo & Regina Belle* / From now on: *Bolton, Michael & Suzie Benson* / Delicate: *D'Arby, Terence Trent & Des'ree* / Kiss: *Jones, Tom & Art Of Noise* / Up on the roof: *Robson & Jerome* / You're all I need to get by: *Reeves, Martha & G.C. Cameron* / What does it take to win your love: *Bristol, Johnny* / Ain't nothing like the real thing: *Johnson, Marv & Carolyn Gill* / This old heart of mine: *Contours* / It should have been me: *Weston, Kim* / Put yourself in my place: *Edwards, Sandra* / Take me in your arms and love me: *Nero, Frances* / Wholeheartedly: *McNeir, Ronnie* / Reflections: *Syreeta* / It's impossible: *Eckstine, Billy & Sarah Vaughan* / Cry to me: *Crawford, Carolyn* / I'm still waiting: *Payne, Sherrie* / Someday we'll be together: *Bristol, Johnny & Liz Sands* / Every little bit hurts: *Holloway, Brenda* / Try it baby: *Ward, Sammy* / Too many memories: *Terrel, Jean* / Watching the hands of time: *Preston, Billy & Syreeta* / Reunited: *Taylor, Sherri & Sammy Ward* / Hang on there baby: *Bristol, Johnny & Liz Sands* / Love hangover: *Fifth Dimension* / My guy: *Wells, Mary* / We're incredible: *McNeir, Ronnie* / I'll be around: *Cameron, G.C.* / Once upon a time: *Wells, Mary & Marvin Gaye* / Wishing on a star: *Calvin, Billie* / Your precious love: *Nero, Francis & Gino Parks* / Save me I'm all alone: *Dixon, Hank* / Your love is wonderful: *Dixon, Hank* / Come see about me: *Velvette* / You ain't livin' till your lovin': *Weston, Kim & Frankie Gaye* / Everything to me: *Terrel, Jean* / You're so fine: *Stubbs, Joe* / Send some love: *JJ & Ortheia Barnes* / With this ring: *Wylie, Richard*
MOODCD 43 / Apr '96 / Sony Music

☐ IT TAKES TWO
PDSCD 544 / Aug '96 / Pulse

☐ IT WILL TAKE A NATION OF MILLIONS TO HOLD US BACK
BBECD 006 / 15 Sep '97 / Barely Breaking Even

☐ ITALIA - 20 GRANDS SUCCES
3003752 / Jan '97 / IMP

☐ ITALIAN DANCE CLASSICS - DOWN BEAT AND SOUL
4784512 / Jun '97 / Irma

☐ ITALIAN DANCE CLASSICS - FUNKY AND DISCO
4784492 / Jun '97 / Irma

☐ ITALIAN DANCE CLASSICS - HOUSE
4784482 / Jun '97 / Irma

☐ ITALIAN DANCE CLASSICS - TECHNO
4784522 / Jun '97 / Irma

☐ ITALIAN DANCE CLASSICS - UNDERGROUND AND GARAGE
4784502 / Jun '97 / Irma

☐ ITALIAN HOUSE COLLECTION
FIRMCD 5 / Jun '96 / Firm

☐ ITALIAN MANDOLINE
Angelina / Funiculi, funicula (denza) / Firenze mia / Vendetta siciliana / Arrivederci caprl / Comme facette mammeta / Tarentella parigina / Per sempre ti ricordero / Caterina / Tarentella per sofia / Sul mare blu / Sciuri sciurl / Serenata d'estate / Anna amore mio / Sempre domanl / Piove a venezia / Opera comica / Esmeralda / Oi mamma / Malinconica luna
15441 / Nov '91 / Laserlight

☐ ITALIAN POPULAR MUSIC FORMS TODAY
927022 / 24 Apr '98 / BUDA

☐ ITALIAN POPULAR SONGS OF 1930/ 1940S
995872 / 24 Feb '98 / EPM

☐ ITALIAN STRING VIRTUOSI
ROUCD 1095 / Mar '95 / Rounder

☐ ITALO
DASR 004 / 29 Sep '97 / Academy Street

☐ ITALO 2000 (2CD Set)
ZYX 811432 / 30 Mar '98 / ZYX

☐ ITALO 2000 RARITIES (2CD Set)
ZYX 811502 / 15 Jun '98 / ZYX

☐ ITALO CLASSICS (2CD Set)
Dolce Vita: *Paris, Ryan* / Miss Broadway: *Belle Epoque* / Jungle beat: *Roberts, Frankie* / Take the animal: *Bross & The Boss* / Holiday love: *Pao, Sandra* / Let's go down to New York: *Kelly, Aldine* / Take us back: *Ashley, Maida* / By day by night: *DJ Anthony* / Dance across the floor: *Horne, Jimmy 'Bo'* / Shine of rap: *AC & The Others* / Todo lo que pasa: *Martinez, Janet* / Voices: *Mephisto* / It's gonna be alright: *Trancex* / Reach out I'll be there: *DF Girls* / Are you ready to go: *Davis, Sonia* / Djobi djoba: *Crusin' Gang* / Yes we could: *FBI Project* / Iron girls: *Jazilla* / Watcha gonna do for me: *Dr. Fun* / Bette Davis eyes: *Davis, Sonia* / Mcarthur park: *DF Girls* / Sos bandido: *Carrara* / Lucky guy: *Paul Boy* / My first my last my everything: *Taylor, Kim* / Down down Romeo: *Meccano* / Body to body: *Gepo* / I believe: *Anyways* / Disco king: *Carrara* / Night in Chicago: *Reeds* / Spank: *Horne, Jimmy 'Bo'*
SD 885502 / 2 Feb '98 / Disky

☐ ITALO DANCE CLASSICS VOL.2 (2CD Set)
ZYX 811492 / 15 Jun '98 / ZYX

☐ ITALY AFTER DARK - ITALIA NOSTALGICA
Vivere: *Buti, Carlo* / Amami se vuoi: *Fiordaliso, Marisa* / Venezia la luna e tu: *Virgili, Luciano* / Volare: *Arigliano, Nicola* / Bella ragazza dalle trecce bionde: *Buti, Carlo* / Capriccio mazurka: *Gargano, Guiseppe* / Santa Lucia: *De Muro Lomanto, Enzo* / Come prima: *Eigs, Franco* / Sul Lungarno: *Buti, Carlo* / Papavari e papere: *Barimar e La Sua Orchestra* / Reginella: *Buti, Carlo* / Whatever will be will be (Que sera sera): *Power, Romina* / Luna rossa: *Ricci, Franco* / Guaglione: *Carosone, Renato* / Mama: *Gigli, Beniamino* / Anema e core: *De Palma, Jula* / Violino tzigano: *Virgili, Luciano* / Piano fortissimo: *Carosone, Renato* / Stornellando alla toscana: *Villa, Claudio* / Arrivederci Roma: *Gilardini, Renzo*
CDEMS 1458 / Sep '92 / EMI

☐ ITP SELECTED WORKS 1993-1996
ITPAL 03CD / Jul '96 / ITP

☐ IT'S A FAMILY AFFAIR
PRRUKCD 003 / 2 Mar '98 / Planet Rhythm UK

☐ IT'S A HEARTACHE
PLSCD 141 / Apr '96 / Pulse

☐ IT'S A LIFE SENTENCE
LONE 01CD / 15 Dec '97 / SL

☐ IT'S A LOVE THING VOL.1
DTCD 18 / Nov '93 / Discotex

☐ IT'S A LOVE THING VOL.2
DTCD 22 / Apr '95 / Discotex

☐ IT'S A MAN'S MAN'S MAN'S WORLD
Walking the dog: *Thomas, Rufus* / Change is gonna come: *Redding, Otis* / You don't know like I know: *Sam & Dave* / I'll take good care of you: *Mimms, Garnet* / It's a man's man's man's world: *Brown, James* / Summertime: *Stewart, Billy* / Everybody needs somebody: *Pickett, Wilson* / Gimme a little sign: *Wood, Brenton* / I've never found a girl: *Floyd, Eddie* / I forgot to be your lover: *Bell, William* / Walk on by: *Hayes, Isaac* / Only the strong survive: *Butler, Jerry* / Your good thing is about to end: *Rawls, Lou* / Drowning in a sea of love: *Simon, Joe* / I've been lonely for so long: *Knight, Frederick* / Why can't we live together: *Thomas, Timmy* / Take me to the river: *Green, Al* / You and your baby blues: *Burke, Solomon* / It's ecstasy when you're next to me: *White, Barry* / Hang on in there baby: *Bristol, Johnny*
RNBCD 103 / Jul '93 / Connoisseur Collection

☐ IT'S A MAN'S WORLD
I love you always forever: *Rochelle* / No one can love you more than me: *Jones, Hannah* / Call me tonight: *Destiny Love* / I will always love you: *Washington, Sarah* / No more I love you's: *Lipstick* / Anytime: *Obsession* / Gimmie gimmie gimmie (A man after midnight): *Abbacadabra* / Twice the man: *Dionne, Monica* / Windmills of your mind: *Marsh, Sally Ann* / Watching you watching me: *4-2-The Floor* / Wonderwall: *Jackie O* / Let's dance: *E-Male*
BLSTCD 05 / Feb '98 / Blast

☐ IT'S A SHIFTY DISCO THING VOL.1
Senor Nachos: *Dustball* / Building: *Unbelievable Truth* / Cough cap kitty cap: *Nought* / Blah na na: *Impossible Music Force* / Teenage kicks: *DJ Remould* / Magdalen sky: *Gardener, Mark* / Backgarden: *Beaker* / Lubetune: *Spunkle* / Simple: *Cody* / Welcome: *Full Monty* / If everyone I ever loved left me: *Bigger The God* / Son of the human cannonball: *Arthur Turners Lovechild*
SHIFTY 9801 / 23 Feb '98 / Shifty Disco

☐ IT'S A SIXTIES PARTY (2CD Set)
Johnny B. Goode: *Berry, Chuck* / Bye bye love: *Everly Brothers* / Sha la la la lee: *Small Faces* / Tell him: *Davis, Billie* / That'll be the day: *Crickets* / Hats off to Larry: *Shannon, Del* / If paradise is half as nice: *Amen Corner* / Pied piper: *Crispin St Peters* / You're more than a number in my little red book: *Drifters* / I can't help myself: *Four Tops* / Baby now that I've found you: *Foundations* / Let's twist again: *Checker, Chubby* / Sugar and spice: *Searchers* / It's my party: *Gore, Lesley* / She'd rather be with me: *Turtles* / Surf city: *Jan & Dean* / Oh Carol: *Sedaka, Neil* / Rubber ball: *Vee, Bobby* / Dance on: *Shadows* / Fire: *Brown, Arthur* / Bread and butter: *Newbeats* / Judy in disguise with glasses: *Fred, John & The Playboys* / Runaround Sue: *Dion* / Oh pretty woman: *Orbison, Roy* / How do you do it: *Gerry & The Pacemakers* / If I had a hammer: *Lopez, Trini* / Last train to clarksville: *Monkees* / Let's dance: *Montez, Chris* / Give him a great big kiss: *Telstarr* / Shangri-las: *Nut Rockers* / Cur across shorty: *Cochran, Eddie* / Good golly Miss Molly: *Swinging Blue Jeans* / Dimples: *Animals* / Stop in the name of love: *Ross, Diana & The Supremes* / In the middle of nowhere: *Springfield, Dusty* / Out of time: *Farlowe, Chris* / Brown eyed girl: *Morrison, Van* / Si tu dois partir: *Fairport Convention* / March of the mods: *Loss, Joe* / Gimme some lovin': *Davis, Spencer Group* / I can't let go: *Hollies* / Letter box tops: *Berry, Len* / Heartbeat: *Holly, Buddy*
SONYTV 32CD / 6 Oct '97 / Sony TV

☐ IT'S A TRIPLE EARTH
TRECD 114 / Oct '95 / Triple Earth

☐ IT'S ALL BECOMING CLEAR
CLR 400CD / Mar '96 / Clear

☐ IT'S ALL GOOD
SFT 0CD / Apr '98 / Striving For Togetherness

☐ IT'S DOUBLE JAZZ TIME (2CD Set)
ATJCD 5974 / May '93 / Disky

☐ IT'S DOUBLE SWING TIME (2CD Set)
ATJCD 5973 / May '93 / Disky

☐ IT'S FOR LIFE
VD 01CD / Apr '97 / Victory

☐ IT'S FUCKING 'AVIN' IT VOL.2 (2CD Set)
TLCCD 5 / 2 Mar '98 / TLC

☐ IT'S GOT TO BE LOVE
It's got to be love: *Fox, Roy & His Orchestra/Mary Lee* / Embraceable you: *Sinatra, Frank* / Cheek to cheek: *Astaire, Fred* / Life begins when you're in love: *Hildegarde* / Love is the sweetest thing: *Noble, Ray & His Orchestra & Al Bowlly* / I've got my love to keep me warm: *Powell, Dick* / With all my heart: *Boswell, Connee* / There isn't any limit to my love: *Ambrose & His Orchestra/Jack Cooper* / Dearest love: *Coward, Sir Noel* / That sentimental sandwich: *Lamour, Dorothy* / Until today: *Weems, Ted & His Orchestra/Perry Como* / Goodnight my love: *Hylton, Jack & His Orchestra/Bert Yarlett* / Trusting my love: *Matthews, Jessie* / When did you leave Heaven: *Martin, Tony* / You made me love you: *Crosby, Bing & The Merry Macs* / It had to be you: *Gibbons, Carroll & Savoy Hotel Orpheans/Julie Dawn* / You are my love song: *Hutchinson, Leslie 'Hutch'* / Sweet someone: *Fox, Roy & His Orchestra/Denny Dennis* / Nearness of you: *Shore, Dinah* / PS I love you: *Geraldo & His Sweet Music/Cyril Graham* / Man I love: *Langford, Frances* / Long ago and far away: *Haymes, Dick & Helen Forrest*
PPCD 78119 / Mar '95 / Past Perfect

☐ IT'S HARD BUT IT'S FAIR (The Blues Today)
MCCD 147 / Nov '93 / Music Club

☐ IT'S JAZZ (Sampler)
22700 / Feb '96 / Music

☐ IT'S JESUS Y'ALL
Jesus you've been good to me: *Gospel Keynotes* / Hungry child: *Salem travellers* / Thankyou Lord: *Salem travellers* / I can't stop holding on: *Ramey, Troy* / I know a man from Galilee: *Ramey, Troy* / It's Jesus y'all: *Ramey, Troy* / Borrowed time: *Swanee Quintet* / Oh yes he did: *Swanee Quintet* / I've got that feeling: *Swanee Quintet* / I want to be loved: *Ellison, Tommy* / Grandma's hands: *Robinson, Cleophus* / Gamblin' man: *Angelic Gospel Stars* / I'm going to serve Jesus: *Supreme Angels* / Crown of life: *Supreme Angels* / I stood on the banks of Jordan: *Brooklyn Allstars* / People get ready: *Brooklyn Allstars* / That's my son: *Gospel Keynotes* / Won't it be grand: *Consolers* / Lord give me strength: *Boggs, Harold*
CDCHM 381 / Apr '94 / Ace

☐ IT'S ONLY LEISURE TIME
OER 004CD / May '97 / Orange Egg

☐ IT'S PARTY TIME
Monster mash: *Pickett, Bobby 'Boris'* / Seven little girls: *Evans, Paul* / Speedy gonzales: *Boone, Pat* / Rubber ball: *Vee, Bobby* / Does your chewing gum lose its flavour: *Donegan, Lonnie* / Purple people eater: *Wooley, Sheb* / Charlie Brown: *Coasters* / How much is that doggy in the window: *Page, Patti* / I taut I taw a puddy tat: *SJ Group* / Mr. Bass Man: *Cymbal, Johnny* / I'd like to teach the world to sing: *New Seekers* / In the summertime: *Mungo Jerry* / Birds and the bees: *Akins, Jewel* / Freight train: *McDevitt, Chas* / Zip a dee doo dah: *Soxx, Bob B. & The Blue Jeans* / I'm Henry the eighth I am: *Brown, Joe* / My old man's a dustman: *Donegan, Lonnie* / Little arrows: *Lee, Leapy*
ECD 3079 / Jan '95 / K-Tel

☐ IT'S SWING TIME (3CD Set)
55144 / Oct '95 / Laserlight

☐ IT'S THE 50'S
Too young: *Young, Jimmy* / Little shoemaker: *Clark, Petula* / Three bears: *Ellington, Ray Quartet* / I'm walking behind you: *Squires, Dorothy* / Oranges and lemons: *Delaney, Eric & His Band* / West of Zanzibar: *Steel, Anthony & The Radio Revellers* / Cumberland gap: *Donegan, Lonnie & his Skiffle Band* / Young and foolish: *Hockridge, Edmund* / Don't worry: *Brandon, Johnny & The Phantoms* / Dambusters march: *Coates, Eric* / With all my heart: *Clark, Petula* / Wonderful wonderful: *Miller, Gary* / Trudie: *Henderson, Joe 'Mr. Piano'* / Love me forever: *Ryan, Marion* / Hold back tomorrow: *Miki & Griff* / Mr Blue: *MacBeth, David* / Petite fleur: *Barber, Chris Jazz Band & Monty Sunshine* / One more sunrise: *Valentine, Dickie* / Lonnie skiffle: *Donegan, Lonnie & his Skiffle Band* / What do you want to make those eyes at me for: *Ford, Emile & The Checkmates*
MCCD 328 / Nov '97 / Music Club

☐ IT'S THE 70'S (20 Sensational Hits)
Band of gold: *Payne, Freda* / Give me just a little more time: *Chairmen Of The Board* / That same old feeling: *Pickettywitch* / Popcorn: *Hot Butter* / Burlesque: *Family* / Mean girl: *Status Quo* / Alright alright alright: *Mungo Jerry* / Dancing on a Saturday night: *Blue, Barry* / Man who sold the world: *Lulu* / Who do you think you are: *Candlewick Green* / Get dancin': *Disco Tex & The Sexolettes* / Shame shame shame: *Shirley & Company* / Dolly my love: *Moments* / El bimbo: *Bimbo Jet* / Ride a wild horse: *Clark, Dee* / Sky high: *Jigsaw* / Why did you do it: *Stretch* / Lost in France: *Tyler, Bonnie* / Isn't she lovely: *Parton, David* / Fanfare for the common man: *Emerson, Lake & Palmer*
MCCD 300 / Jun '97 / Music Club

☐ IT'S THE REAL THING (2CD Set)
In the summertime: *Mungo Jerry* / What a wonderful world: *Armstrong, Louis* / Happy together: *Turtles* / CC rider: *Lewis, Jerry Lee* / Unforgettable: *Cole, Nat 'King'* / Daydream: *Lovin' Spoonful* / You'll never walk alone: *Gerry & The Pacemakers* / Time of the season: *Zombies* / Will you still love me tomorrow: *Shirelles* / White wedding: *Idol, Billy* / Rescue me: *Bass, Fontella* / Games people play: *South, Joe* / I'm into something good: *Herman's Hermits* / Dancing easy: *Williams, Danny* / C'mon everybody: *Cochran, Eddie* / Be bop a Lula: *Vincent, Gene* / (I don't know why) but I do: *Henry, Clarence 'Frogman'* / Venus: *Avalon, Frankie* / Runaway: *Shannon, Del* / I just want to make love to you: *James, Etta* / Mister Sandman: *Chordettes* / My blue heaven: *Domino, Fats* / Dry bones: *Delta Rhythm Boys* / Country boy: *Cash, Johnny* / Dream a little dream of me: *Mama Cass* / Three steps to heaven: *Cochran, Eddie* / Don't worry be happy: *McFerrin, Bobby* / Beautiful people: *Melanie* / Hawaii Five-O: *Ventures* / Travelin' man: *Nelson, Ricky*
DOU 882472 / 2 Feb '98 / Disky

☐ IT'S THE SENSATIONAL 70'S
Sugar baby love: *Rubettes* / I'm the leader of the gang (I am): *Glitter, Gary* / Save your kisses for me: *Brotherhood Of Man* / Beach baby: *First Class* / Sugar candy kisses: *Kissoon, Mac & Katie* / You won't find another fool like me: *New Seekers* / Doctor's orders: *Sunny* / Boogie on up: *Rokotto* / Where is the love: *Delegation* / Don't throw it all away: *Benson, Gary* / I love you love me love: *Glitter, Gary* / Jukebox jive: *Rubettes* / Love grows (where my Rosemary goes): *Edison Lighthouse* / Falling apart at the seams: *Marmalade* / Figaro: *Brotherhood Of Man* / Don't do it baby: *Kissoon, Mac & Katie* / You've been doing me wrong: *Delegation* / Something old, something new: *Fantastics* / Daddy don't you walk so fast: *Boone, Daniel* / Sweet inspiration: *Johnson, Johnny & Bandwagon*
MCCD 051 / Mar '92 / Music Club

☐ IT'S THE TALK OF THE TOWN
Marie: *Dorsey, Tommy* / It's the talk of the town: *Henderson, Fletcher* / Lonesome nights: *Carter, Benny* / My fine feathered friend: *Miller, Glenn* / Song of India: *Dorsey, Tommy* / Devil's holiday: *Carter, Benny* / Silhoutted in the moonlight: *Miller, Glenn* / Down a Carolina Lane: *Ellington, Duke* / Queer notions: *Henderson, Fletcher* / Stardust: *Dorsey, Tommy* / Blue Lou: *Carter, Benny* / Everyday's a holiday: *Miller, Glenn* / Nagasaki: *Henderson, Fletcher* / Six bells stampede: *Carter, Benny* / Music maestro please: *Dorsey, Tommy* / Don't wake up my heart: *Miller, Glenn* / Night life: *Henderson, Fletcher* / Who: *Dorsey, Tommy* / Sophisticated lady: *Ellington, Duke*
MUCD 9027 / Apr '95 / Musketeer

☐ IT'S TRAD DAD
SELCD 520 / 27 Jun '98 / Castle Select

☐ IT'S WHAT WE DO VOL.1
DRCD 3020 / Feb '96 / Daring

☐ I'VE GOT MY FRIENDS
FR 6869 / Mar '97 / Flat

☐ I'VE LOVED AND LOST AGAIN
MU 5059 / Oct '92 / Musketeer

☐ IVOR NOVELLO - CENTENARY CELEBRATION
GEMMCD 9062 / Nov '93 / Pearl

J

☐ J-GROOVE (The Soul Of Japan/16 Cool Jams)
Embarrassing touch: *Yonekura, Toshinori* / Everytime we walk: *Katsumi* / I've been loving so you long: *Kobayashi, Tomiko* / I want you to say: *Yonekura, Toshinori* / Crimes of love: *Kojima, Michiru* / Early Spring: *Nakanishi, Keizo* / All of this love: *Katoh, Reiko* / 2am: *Nakanishi, Keizo* / Starting over: *Nakanishi, Keizo* / Give me your loneliness: *Katoh, Reiko* / Miracle of love: *Kobayashi, Tomiko* / Dance around: *E-Zee Band* / Dreamin': *Katsumi* / Delicate rain: *Yonekura, Toshinori* / Can't stop my love: *Kobayashi, Tomiko* / Pieces of mind: *Lam, Sandy*
MOCD 3017 / Nov '96 / More Music

☐ J.B. ELIZANBURU - IKUSTEN DUZU GOIZEAN
KD 274CD / Aug '97 / Elkar

☐ JA JA OOMPAH PAH (24 Traditional German Drinking Songs)
Schuplatter / Tiroler holzhackerbaum / O du lieber Augustin / Der frohliche wandersmann / Phyllis und die Mutter / Es war einmal ein treur husar / Oompah polka / Klarinetten polka / Schneewalzer / Zum volksfest / Im schwarzen walfisch / Die dorfmusikanten / Rixdorfer polka / Das war der Herr Von Rodenstein / Bauren polka / Muss I den, muss I den zum / Stadtele 'naus / Bierwalzer / Die lorelei / Anneliese / In Munchen steht ein / Hofbrauhaus / Hans und Liesel / Urbummelied / Lieb heimatland, ade / Alte kameraden
SUMCD 4037 / Nov '96 / Summit

☐ JACKPOT - THE WINNING TICKETS
CDWON 1 / Mar '97 / Jackpot

☐ JACKPOT PRESENTS GUERILLA (2CD Set)
Obession: *Fuzzy Logic* / Alchemy: *Drum Club* / Thee dawn: *Felix Da Housecat* / U make me feel so good: *Drum Club* / Whatever you dream: *React 2 Rhythm* / Prologue: *10th Chapter* / Seven: *Sunshower* / Mercurial: *Euphoria* / Schudelfloss: *Dr. Atomic* / Aquamarine: *Lemon Sol* / Water: *Bogaert, Joe* / Intoxication: *React 2 Rhythm* / Feeling warm: *Eagles Prey* / Obsession: *Fuzzy Logic* / Product: *10th Chapter*
CDWON 004 / 13 Oct '97 / Jackpot

☐ JACKPOT VOL.1
Beauty: *Atlas* / Futura: *Amethyst* / Skin to skin: *Hercules* / Answer my prayer: *Campbell, Danny* / Squeak: *Bubble* / Crash: *Squelch* / Wired: *10th Chapter* / Bodyrock: *Shango* / Crazy thing: *50/50*
CDWON 002 / 8 Sep '97 / Jackpot

☐ JACKSON BLUES 1928-1938
YAZCD 1007 / Jul '91 / Yazoo

☐ JAH JAH DREADER THAN DREAD
You can hold the handle: *Wailing Souls* / Jah jah dreader than dread: *Thompson, Linval* / Lonely man: *McKay, Freddie* / Jah help the people: *McGregor, Freddie* / Come we just a come: *Irie, Welton* / Come closer: *Viceroys* / Humble man: *Wade, Wayne* / Rubadub session: *Palmer, Tristan* / Rock to the riddim: *U-Brown* / Follow fashion: *Sammy Dread* / Follow the dub / Message: *McKay, Freddie* / Round the world: *Wade, Wayne* / Round the dub / Six babylon: *Thompson, Linval* / Six dub / Jah help people dub
MRCD 1005 / May '97 / Majestic Reggae

☐ JAH LOVE INA WI
SKYHIGHCD 2002 / Oct '95 / Sky High

☐ JAH PEOPLE (3CD Set)
DTKBOX 63 / 15 Jun '98 / Dressed To Kill

☐ JAH WISDOM
86102 / Jun '93 / Greensleeves

☐ JAH WORKS
VPFE 3106 / 17 Nov '97 / VP

☐ JAHMENTO RECS
HCD 7006 / Aug '94 / Hightone

☐ J'AI ETE AU BAL VOL.1 (Cajun & Zydeco Music Of Louisiana Vol.1)
ARHCD 331 / Apr '95 / Arhoolie

☐ J'AI ETE AU BAL VOL.2 (Cajun & Zydeco Music of Louisiana)
ARHCD 332 / Apr '95 / Arhoolie

☐ J'AIME LA FRANCE
74321576802 / 6 Jun '98 / Milan

☐ JAKE LEG BLUES
JCD 642 / Jun '94 / Jass

☐ JAKIE JAZZ 'EM 'UP (Old Time Klezmer Music 1912-1926)
GV 101CD / Nov '93 / Global Village

☐ JAM DOWN VIBRATIONS
RR 88812 / Jul '96 / Roadrunner

☐ JAM JAM JAM (Original Full Length Sugarhill 12" Mixes)
Rapper's delight: *Sugarhill Gang* / That's the joint: *Funky 4+1* / Adventures of Grandmaster Flash on the wheels of steel: *Grandmaster Flash* / Rapper's reprise: *Sugarhill Gang & Sequence* / Message: *Grandmaster Flash & The Furious Five* / Making cash money: *Busy Bee* / Mirda rock: *Griffin, Reggie & Technofunk* / White lines (Don't don't do it): *Grandmaster Flash & Melle Mel* / Pump me up: *Trouble Funk*
MUSCD 016 / May '94 / MCI Music

☐ JAM SESSIONS MONTREUX '77
OJCCD 385 / Feb '92 / Original Jazz Classics

☐ JAMAICA SKA
RN 7054 / 10 Aug '98 / Rhino

☐ JAMAICA TODAY IN THE SEVENTIES
SOCD 8022 / Mar '98 / Studio One

☐ JAMAICAN SKA-KORE (3CD Set)
DTKBOX 78 / 23 Feb '98 / Dressed To Kill

☐ JAMIE/GUYDEN DOO WOP COLLECTION VOL.1 (Echoes Of The Vocal Group Era)
Dry your eyes: *Inspirations* / Summertime angel: *Intentions* / I want her to love me: *Larks* / Play those oldies Mr. Bassman: *Anthony & The Sophomores* / My love will follow you: *Continental Gems* / Sweet sweetheart: *Sharps* / Bells: *Creations* / Until then: *Pentagons* / Where is he: *Clickettes* / Girl from across the sea: *Ernie & The Halos* / God gave me you: *Allen, Tony & The Wonders* / For me and my girl: *Four J'S* / No one but you: *Fantasys* / When I get older: *Butlers* / One million years: *Heartbeats* / Maybe you'll be there: *Billy & The Essentials* / I wish on a star: *Pentagons* / Love is like music: *Five Chords* / Foolish one: *Stompers* / One more time: *Four Evers* / Tonight and forever: *Clickettes* / Steamboat: *Webs* / One summer night: *Anthony & The Sophomores* / I see a star: *Little Stevie* / Loveable girl: *Butlers* / I wonder: *Pentagons* / Love: *No Names* / Crazy rock: *Five Chords* / Chapel of love: *Sundials* / Nasty breaks: *Dandevilles* / Loving you: *Allen, Tony & The Wonders* / Come on: *Sharps* / Goodbye: *Inspirations*
BCD 15885 / Jan '97 / Bear Family

☐ JAMIE/GUYDEN DOO WOP COLLECTION VOL.2
Fabulous cars and diamond rings: *Larks* / Steady girl: *Billy & The Essentials* / Here's my heart: *Sharps* / Lookin' for my baby: *Allen, Tony & The Wonders* / Canadian sunset: *Excels* / I'd do anything for you: *Five Chords* / She's mine: *Pentagons* / Why oh why: *Fantasys* / My love my love: *Big John & The Philadelphians* / Darling I want to get married: *Heartbeats* / Everywhere: *Continental Gems* / Have love will travel: *Sharps* / Mr. Misery: *Intentions* / Angel love: *Whirlwind* / Here am I broken hearted: *Four J'S* / How long must a fool go on: *Swallows & The Guides* / I don't wanna go home: *Quarter Notes* / Believe me: *Ervin, Frankie & The Shields* / Help me with my broken heart: *Pentagons* / Dance is over: *Billy & The Essentials* / Everybody south street: *Four Evers* / If I could tonight: *Newports* / Isle of love: *Famous Hearts* / Pretty little Rita: *Mendell, Johnny* / You must try: *Swallows & The Guides* / Whether to resist: *Sundials* / Darling don't make me cry: *Ernie & The Halos* / Don't just stand there: *Five Chords* / She said she loves me: *Four J'S* / There's a reason: *Dandevilles* / Embraceable you: *Intentions*
BCD 15958 / Nov '97 / Bear Family

☐ JAMIE/GUYDEN STORY, THE (2CD Set)
Rebel rouser: *Eddy, Duane* / You'll lose a good thing: *Lynn, Barbara* / Quarter to four stomp: *Stompers* / Pink chiffon: *Torok, Mitchell* / One million years: *Heartbeats* / Maybe you'll be there: *Billy & The Essentials* / Pop pop pop pie: *Sherrys* / Unchained melody: *Blackwells* / Mother nature: *Robinson, Floyd* / Girl from across the sea: *Ernie & The Halos* / Sound off: *Turner, Titus* / Sweet dreams: *McLain, Tommy* / Yes I'm ready: *Mason, Barbara* / Going back to Louisiana: *Channel, Bruce* / I wonder: *Pentagons* / Sea of love: *Kit Kat's* / Dry your eyes: *Brenda & Tabulations* / I really love you: *Ambassadors* / Won't find better than me: *New Hope Singers* / Horse: *Nobles, Cliff* / Let me be your man: *Ashley, Tyrone* / Ain't nothin' but a house party: *Show Stoppers* / Storm warning: *Volcanos* / Tell me: *Ethics* / Here am I broken hearted: *Four J'S* / Oh la la limbo: *Danny & The Juniors* / Hole in the ground: *Rivers, Johnny* / I'm a poor loser: *Davis, Mac* / Time out for tears: *Churchill, Savannah* / Linda Lu: *Sharpe, Ray* / Because they're young: *Eddy, Duane* / Dancing the strand: *Gray, Maureen* / Ring a rockin': *Sedaka, Neil* / Dry your eyes: *Inspirations* / Words mean nothing: *Hazelwood, Lee* / Jam: *Gregg, Bobby* / Need you: *Owens, Donnie* / Have love, will travel: *Sharps* / Dance is over: *Billy & The Essentials* / Never never: *Jordan Brothers* / Darling I want to get married: *Heartbeats* / Come on in: *Alden, Craig* / Forty miles of bad road: *Eddy, Duane* / Son of a gun: *Clark, Sanford* / I'm in love: *Pentagons* / (I cried at) Laura's wedding: *Lynn, Barbara* / Caribbean: *Torok, Mitchell* / Strollin' after school: *Fields, Ernie* / Get out: *Melvin, Harold & The Bluenotes* / Slop time: *Sherrys* / Love (can make you happy): *Merci* / Living doll: *Bond, Bobby* / Oh how it hurts: *Mason, Barbara* / For your prescious love: *Davis, Geater* / Boogaloo down broadway: *Fantastic Johnny C* / Don't make the good girls go bad: *Humphries, Della* / Love addict: *Honey & The Bees* / Right on the tip of my tongue: *Brenda & Tabulations* / Goodbye: *Temptones*
BCD 15874 / Oct '95 / Bear Family

☐ JAMMIN' THE BOOGIE WOOGIE
CD 56025 / Nov '94 / Jazz Roots

☐ JAPAN - KABUKI MUSIC
BCD 6809 / Jan '95 / Auvidis/Ethnic

☐ JAPAN - THE NEW PSYCHEDLIC UNDERGROUND
BOB 107 / Nov '96 / Bob's Airport

☐ JAPAN CONNECTION (East Meets West) (2CD Set)
Set me free: *Hall, Latonia & Satoshi Tomie* / To another galaxy: *Tokyo Ghetto Pussy* / Flashback: *DJ Tonka* / Kotoba: *Oka, Kenichi* / Garden on the palm: *Ishii, Ken* / Quazar gamer's night: *Mijk's Magic Marble Box* / Extra: *Ishii, Ken* / Telecomposer: *Wasaki, Norihiko* / Rendezvous de telepathie: *Biomehanika, Yoji* / Merry Christmas Mr. Lawrence: *Sakamoto, Ryuichi* / Candy girls: *Wham Bam* / Let's get closer baby: *F-Action* / On and on: *Direct Drive* / Did my time: *Timewriter* / Need you: *28 East Boyz* / Find a way: *Yoki Boys* / Shine on: *Sirius 5* / Ain't got no time: *Big Light* / I like house: *Ed's Experience* / SLO: *Spice*
SPV 08968312 / Aug '96 / SPV

☐ JAPAN PUNK KILLS YOU
AMPOP 201CD / Nov '97 / American Pop

☐ JAPANESE KOTO ORCHESTRA
LYRCD 7167 / '91 / Lyrichord

☐ JAPANESE MASTERPIECES FOR THE SHAKUHACHI
LYRCD 7176 / '91 / Lyrichord

☐ JAPPIN' PSYCHO BOMB VOL.1
Jungle boy: *Scamp* / My babe: *Scamp* / Bamboo bomb: *Scamp* / Somebody's gonna get their head kicked in tonight: *Hornets* / Mechagodzilla: *Hornets* / Rebel: *Pharaoh* / Wild cat blues: *Pharaohs* / Ten dollars Bucato: *Tokyo Skunx* / Brand new wagon: *Tokyo Skunx* / Tokyo nuclear niteklub: *Tokyo Skunx* / Bad dream: *Crackpot* / Spray with machine gun: *Crackpot* / Batman: *Biscuits* / Long separation: *Floozy Drippy's* / Tiny cowboy: *Floozy Drippy's* / She's the bad girl: *Jap Kat* / Angry hungry eyes: *Jap Kat*
JRCD 32 / Jun '97 / Jappin' & Rockin'

☐ JAPPIN' PSYCHO BOMB VOL.2
Hallucination: *Mad Mongols* / Indian slap shot: *Mad Mongols* / Chicken choke: *Wood Chuck '91* / Facts of war: *Wood Chuck '91* / No stopping: *Wood Chuck '91* / Here we are nowhere: *Wood Chuck '91* / Tokyo lonesome train: *Jap Kat* / Into the mirror: *Jap Kat* / I'll just stay with rock 'n' roll: *Crazy Billy Rats* / Winter sky: *Crazy Billy Rats* / Love me: *Spikes* / Over heat: *Spikes* / Touch of God's hand: *Dog Eat Dog* / Bounty killer: *Dog Eat Dog* / I'm down: *Wankers* / Rock around the jukebox: *Wankers* / Getting me down: *Dark Ages* / Dark ages: *Dark Ages* / Vanity girl is pretty girl: *Floozy Drippy's* / Phi Phi Island: *Floozy Drippy's*
JRCD 33 / Jun '97 / Jappin' & Rockin'

☐ JARGALANT ALTAI
PAN 2050CD / Apr '96 / Pan

☐ JAVA - ART OF THE GAMELAN DEGUNG
C 560097 / Aug '96 / Ocora

☐ JAVANESE COURT GAMELAN
7559720442 / Jan '95 / Nonesuch

☐ JAW BREAKS
BB 003CD / 23 Feb '98 / Ubiquity

☐ JAZZ - FEMININE
308662 / Feb '96 / Scratch

☐ JAZZ - MASCULINE
308652 / Feb '96 / Scratch

☐ JAZZ 4 YOU VOL.1
BN 047 / Apr '98 / Blue Nite

☐ JAZZ 4 YOU VOL.2
BN 048 / Apr '98 / Blue Nite

☐ JAZZ AFTER HOURS
'Round midnight: *Gales, Larry* / Over the rainbow: *Webster, Ben* / I don't stand a ghost of a chance with you: *Jacquet, Illinois* / Autumn leaves: *Scott, Shirley* / Willow weep for me: *Edison, Harry* / I can't get started: *Gillespie, Dizzy* / Passion flower: *Ellington, Duke* / Tenderly: *Byas, Don* / Body and soul: *Hawkins, Coleman* / Embraceable you: *Eldridge, Roy* / Deep forest: *Hines, Earl 'Fatha'* / You've changed: *Thompson, Lucky* / Mighty low: *Buckner, Milt*
EMPRCD 571 / May '95 / Emporio

☐ JAZZ ALBUM, THE
Leroy Brown: *Kidd, Carol* / Eye witness: *Newton, David* / Moon ray: *Martin, Claire* / Ally: *Smith, Tommy* / Partners in crime: *Martin, Claire* / Gentle rain: *Taylor, Martin* / Don't take your love: *Kidd, Carol* / It's only a paper moon: *Grappelli, Stephane & Martin Taylor* / Lean baby: *Kidd, Carol* / Home from home: *Newton, David* / Old boyfriends: *Martin, Claire* / Angel's camp: *Taylor, Martin* / Please don't talk about me: *Kidd, Carol*
AKD 032 / Sep '94 / Linn

☐ JAZZ AND BIG BAND (4CD Set)
On the sunny side of the street: *Armstrong, Louis* / Everything goes: *Ellington, Duke* / Bird of paradise: *Davis, Miles & Charlie Parker* / Ain't misbehavin': *Waller, Fats* / When my dreamboat comes home: *Rushing, Jimmy* / St. Louis blues: *Witherspoon, Jimmy* / Me and the blues: *Bailey, Mildred* / Moose the mooche: *Davis, Miles* / Sweet Georgie Brown: *Cole, Nat 'King' Trio* / When the saints go marching in: *Armstrong, Louis* / Darktown strutters ball: *Lewis, Meade 'Lux'* / Jazz me blues: *Bechet, Sidney* / My man: *Holiday, Billie* / Street beat: *Parker, Charlie* / Tip toe topic: *Ellington, Duke* / St. Louis blues: *Dorsey, Jimmy* / Smooth sailing: *Fitzgerald, Ella* / Georgia on my mind: *Carmichael, Hoagy Orchestra* / Slow boat to China: *Parker, Charlie* / Honey honey: *Charles, Ray* / C'est si bon: *Armstrong, Louis* / Don't blame me: *Davis, Miles & Charlie Parker* / Harlem speaks: *Ellington, Duke* / Tiger rag: *Henderson, Fletcher* / Mame: *Armstrong, Louis* / Four hands: *Mingus, Charles* / Sonny moon for two: *Rollins, Sonny* / Meet me where they play the blues: *Teagarden, Jack* / South Rampart Street Parade: *Fountain, Pete* / Jelly roll blues: *Morton, Jelly Roll* / Tune of the hickory stick: *Adderley, Cannonball* / Lover man: *Holiday, Billie* / How high the moon: *Wilson, Teddy* / 'Round midnight: *Parker, Charlie* / Crosstown: *Ellington, Duke* / Scrapple from the apple: *Davis, Miles* / Crazeology: *Parker, Charlie & Dizzy Gillespie* / Panama rag: *Ory, Kid & Jimmy Noone* / Tea for two: *Armstrong, Louis* / Yes sir that's my baby: *Cole, Nat 'King' Trio* / April in Paris: *Miller, Glenn* / Begin the beguine: *Shaw, Artie* / Oh Johnny oh johnny oh: *Webb, Chick & Ella Fitzgerald* / Does your heart beat for me: *Morgan, Russ* / Cherokee: *Barnet, Charlie* / In a shanty in old shanty town: *Long, Johnny* / Harlem nocturne: *Barnet, Charlie* / Northwest passage: *Herman, Woody* / Let's dance: *Goodman, Benny* / So rare: *Dorsey, Jimmy* / Opus one: *Dorsey, Tommy* / Indiana: *Ellington, Duke* / Something new: *Basie, Count* / Love me or leave me: *Brown, Les & Doris Day* / I'll never be the same: *Krupa, Gene* / Dipsy doodle: *Clinton, Larry* / Margie: *Lunceford, Jimmie* / Night and day: *Shaw, Artie* / Count steps in: *Basie, Count* / Sultry sunset: *Ellington, Duke* / My heart belongs to daddy: *Shaw, Artie* / I got rhythm: *Dorsey, Jimmy* / Frankie and Johnny: *Goodman, Benny* / Basin street blues: *Webb, Chick & Ella Fitzgerald* / Moonlight serenade: *Miller, Glenn* / Taking a chance on love: *Dorsey, Tommy* / Jumpin' at the woodside: *Basie, Count* / Take the 'a' train: *Ellington, Duke* / September song: *Brown, Les & Doris Day* / Blowin' up a storm: *Herman, Woody* / Skyliner: *Barnet, Charlie* / Linger awhile: *Morgan, Russ* / Fools rush in: *Dorsey, Jimmy* / On the sunny side of the street: *Dorsey, Tommy* / Perdido: *Ellington, Duke* / My heart stood still: *Shaw, Artie* / Jersey bounce: *Goodman, Benny* / Blue and sentimental: *Basie, Count* / Caldonia: *Herman, Woody* / I'm forever blowing bubbles: *Brown, Les*
QUAD 005 / Nov '96 / Tring

☐ JAZZ AND BLUES (Bebop Jazz/2CD Set)
Cheryl: *Parker, Charlie* / Groovin' high: *Gillespie, Dizzy* / Blue room: *Davis, Miles* / Naima: *Coltrane, John* / Minority: *Adderley, Cannonball* / Bluebird: *Parker, Charlie* / Round midnight: *Monk, Thelonious* / Just for laughs (part 2): *Mingus, Charles* / Long long summer: *Gillespie, Dizzy* / Caldonia: *Herman, Woody* / Straight life: *Adderley, Cannonball* / Constellation: *Parker, Charlie* / Doten: *Davis, Miles* / All these things you are: *Gillespie, Dizzy* / Free for all: *Blakey, Art & The Jazz Messengers* / So long Eric: *Mingus, Charles* / Morpheus: *Davis, Miles* / You'd be so nice to come home to: *Adderley, Cannonball* / Hot house: *Gillespie, Dizzy* / Relaxin' in Carmarillo: *Parker, Charlie* / That old devil moon: *Davis, Miles* / Impressions: *Coltrane, John* / Peggy's blue skylight: *Mingus, Charles* / Scavenger: *Adderley, Cannonball* / Klact-orceeseds-tene: *Parker, Charlie* / Squirrel: *Davis, Miles* / All these things you are: *Gillespie, Dizzy* / Monmartre bus ride: *Herman, Woody* / Toy: *Adderley, Cannonball* / Bird feathers: *Parker, Charlie* / Au prirare: *Blakey, Art & The Jazz Messengers* / Emamon: *Gillespie, Dizzy* / Smooch: *Davis, Miles* / Fallen feathers: *Adderley, Cannonball* / Carioca: *Herman, Woody* / Bird's nest: *Parker, Charlie*
BN 218 / Aug '98 / Blue Nite

☐ JAZZ ANTHOLOGY 1942 (2CD Set)
152052 / Mar '94 / EPM

☐ JAZZ ANTHOLOGY 1943-1944 (2CD Set)
152302 / Apr '95 / EPM

☐ JAZZ ANTHOLOGY 1945 (2CD Set)
152342 / Jul '96 / EPM

☐ JAZZ AT RONNIE SCOTT'S
Half a sawbuck: *Hayes, Tubby* / My Mother's eyes: *Stitt, Sonny* / Fly me to the moon: *Feldman, Victor* / It might as well be spring: *Kirk, Rahsaan Roland* / One note samba: *Ranglin, Ernest* / Darn that dream: *Tracey, Stan* / Mi Cosa: *Montgomery, Wes* / What's new: *Scott, Ronnie* / Ben's blues: *Webster, Ben* / DM blues: *Morrissey, Dick*
JHAS 612 / 5 Jan '98 / Ronnie Scott's Jazz House

☐ **JAZZ AT THE CINEMA**
Don't cry for me Argentina: *Getz, Stan* / Autumn leaves: *Baker, Chet* / Laura: *Bryant, Ray* / Something's coming: *Hi-Lo's* / It ain't necessarily so: *Franklin, Aretha* / Get me to the church on time: *Previn, Andre Quartet* / As time goes by: *Supersax & LA Voices* / Blues de la plume: *Grappelli, Stephane* / Exodus song: *Williams, Marion* / Tonight: *Bryant, Ray*
4874602 / 29 Sep '97 / Sony Jazz

☐ **JAZZ AT THE FLAMINGO (2CD Set)**
All star special: *Flamingo All Stars* / Hucklebuck: *Dankworth, John Quintet* / Let's call the whole thing off: *Klein, Harry & Derek Smith Trio* / Yesterday: *Rendell, Don Quartet* / Early one morning: *Crombie, Tony Orchestra* / Basie talks: *Scott, Ronnie & His Orchestra* / Mama, he treats your baby mean: *Ross, Annie & Tony Crombie Orchestra* / C'est si bon: *Ross, Annie & Tony Crombie* / IPA special: *Scott, Ronnie Sextet* / Royal Ascot: *Jazz Couriers* / Plebus: *Jazz Couriers* / Serpent: *Jazz Couriers* / Stompin': *Scott, Ronnie Quintet* / Lucky bean: *Scott, Ronnie Quintet* / 12x5: *Whittle, Tommy Quintet* / Jamba: *Crombie, Tony & Jazz Inc* / Just play: *Thompson, Eddie Trio* / Moveable: *Thompson, Eddie Trio* / Wait and see: *London Jazz Quartet* / Fishin' the blues: *London Jazz Quartet* / Gut bucket: *McNair, Harold Quintet* / Girl in blue: *Kinsey, Tony Quintet* / I only have eyes for you: *Holiday, Billie* / Foggy day in London town: *McRae, Carmen* / Robbin's nest: *Fitzgerald, Ella* / I've got the world on a string: *Torme, Mel* / Misty: *Eckstine, Billy* / Autumn in Cuba: *Le Sage, Bill & Ronnie Ross Quartet* / Gentlemen friend: *Vaughan, Sarah* / Zsa Zsa Gabor: *Moule, Ken & The London Jazz Chamber Group*
FBB 911 / 28 Nov '97 / Ember

☐ **JAZZ AT THE PHILHARMONIC (The First Concert 1944)**
Lester leaps in / Tea for two / Blues / Body and soul / I've found a new baby / Rosetta / Bugle call rag
5216462 / Jan '94 / Verve

☐ **JAZZ AT THE PHILHARMONIC - LONDON 1969 (2CD Set)**
Ow / Stardust / Yesterdays / You go to my head / Tin tin deo / Champ / Woman you must be crazy / Goin' to Chicago / Stormy Monday / Shiny stockings / Undecided / I've got the world on a string / LOVE / Blue Lou / I can't get started (with you) / September song / Body and soul / Bean stalkin' / What is this thing called love
2PACD 26201192 / Apr '94 / Pablo

☐ **JAZZ AT THE PHILHARMONIC - STOCKHOLM '55 (The Exciting Battle)**
Little David / Ow / Sticks / Man I love / I'll never be the same / Skylark / My old flame
CD 23107132 / Apr '94 / Pablo

☐ **JAZZ AT THE PHILHARMONIC: HARTFORD 1953**
Cotton tail / Airmail special / Swinging on a star / Man I love / Seven come eleven / DB blues / I cover the waterfront / Up-'n'-Adam
CD 2308240 / Apr '94 / Pablo

☐ **JAZZ, BLUE & SENTIMENTAL**
DCD 5310 / Dec '93 / Disky

☐ **JAZZ CAFE VOL.1**
So what: *Johnson, J.J.* / Lullaby: *Johnson, J.J.* / Watermelon man: *Hendricks/Lambert* / On Green Dolphin Street: *Burton, Gary* / 'Round midnight: *Rollins, Sonny* / King Porter stomp: *Evans, Gil* / Night in Tunisia: *Gillespie, Dizzy* / Milestones: *Hargrove, Roy* / Every time we say goodbye: *Hollyday, Christopher* / Superwoman: *Woods, Phil* / Expansions: *Woods, L.L.* / Autumn leaves: *Moody, James* / Somewhere over the rainbow: *Baker, Chet* / My funny valentine: *Desmond, Phil* / Just a lucky so and so: *Ellington, Duke* / Take the 'A' train: *Ellington, Duke* / Love me or leave me: *Horne, Lena* / Creole love call: *Nelson, Oliver* / April in Paris: *Davison, 'Wild' Bill* / Naima: *Ruiz, Hilton* / Lady day and john coltrane: *Scott-Heron, Gil*
74321131382 / Feb '93 / Novus

☐ **JAZZ CAFE: AT THE MOVIES**
What a wonderful world: *Armstrong, Louis* / Every time we say goodbye: *Baker, Chet* / My man: *Hawkins, Coleman* / Oh green Dolphin Street: *Hodges, Johnny*
74321263672 / Mar '95 / Jazz Cafe

☐ **JAZZ CAFE: GUITAR**
Blue Lou: *Norvo, Red & Tal Farlow* / Beautiful moons ago: *Pizzarelli, John* / Spoons: *Scofield, John* / For BB King: *Walker, T-Bone*
74321263692 / Mar '95 / Jazz Cafe

☐ **JAZZ CAFE: LATIN**
Manteca: *Gillespie, Dizzy* / Cherry pink: *Prado, Perez* / Mambo Inn: *Ruiz, Hilton* / Manna de carnaval: *Thielemans, Jean 'Toots'*
74321263702 / Mar '95 / Jazz Cafe

☐ **JAZZ CAFE: STANDARDS**
After you've gone: *Basie, Count* / Mood indigo: *Bechet, Sidney* / Georgia on my mind: *Beiderbecke, Bix* / Blue skies: *Goodman, Benny*
74321263722 / Mar '95 / Jazz Cafe

☐ **JAZZ CAFE: TRUMPET & SAXOPHONE**
Wee: *Hargrove, Roy* / Blue Getz blues: *Herman, Woody & Stan Getz* / Angel: *Evans, Gil* / Two of a mind: *Mulligan, Gerry & Paul Desmond*
74321263682 / Mar '95 / Jazz Cafe

☐ **JAZZ CELEBRATION (A Tribute To Carl Jefferson/4CD Set)**
CCD 7005 / Nov '96 / Concord Jazz

☐ **JAZZ CITIES (4CD Set)**
211761 / Feb '97 / Radio France Jazz

☐ **JAZZ CLASSICS**
It's a sin to tell a lie / Potato head blues / Ostrich walk / Riverboat shuffle / Georgia on my mind / Struttin' with some barbecue / Creole jazz / I'm gonna sit right down and write myself a letter / Bourbon Street parade / Snag it / Sweet Georgia Brown / Sophisticated lady / This can't be love / I can't get started (with you) / After you've gone / Old grey bonnet / Old rugged cross / There will never be another you / Ain't misbehavin' / At the woodchoppers' ball
KAZCD 11 / Feb '90 / Kaz

☐ **JAZZ CLASSICS**
Caravan: *Parker, Leon* / Satin doll: *Ellington, Duke* / Perdido: *Vaughan, Sarah* / Better git it in your soul: *Mingus, Charles* / Round midnight: *Monk, Thelonious* / One o clock jump: *Basie, Count & Donna Lee* / Flying home: *Goodman, Benny* / Willow weep for me: *Armstrong, Louis & Jack Teagarden* / Rockin chair: *Armstrong, Louis & Jack Teagarden*
4878062 / 29 Sep '97 / Sony Jazz

☐ **JAZZ CLUB (2CD Set)**
RADCD 87 / 8 Dec '97 / Global TV

☐ **JAZZ CLUB - TENOR SAX**
8400312 / Jun '89 / Verve

☐ **JAZZ COLLECTION (3CD Set)**
TBXCD 507 / Jan '96 / TrueTrax

☐ **JAZZ COLLECTION (2CD Set)**
PBXCD 507 / Nov '96 / Pulse

☐ **JAZZ COLLECTION VOL.1 (When The Saints Go Marching In)**
When the saints go marching in: *Armstrong, Louis* / Moochie: *Ellington, Duke* / King porter stomp: *Goodman, Benny* / It's only a paper moon: *Cole, Nat 'King' Trio* / Something new: *Basie, Count* / My blue heaven: *Shaw, Artie* / How high the moon: *Parker, Charlie* / Indiana: *Armstrong, Louis* / Lover come back to me: *Fitzgerald, Ella* / Cannonball blues: *Adderley, Cannonball Quintet* / I can't remember to forget: *Barnet, Charlie* / At long last love: *Horne, Lena* / Bugle call rag: *Goodman, Benny* / I stuck a match in the dark: *Basie, Count* / Caravan: *Ellington, Duke Orchestra* / My heart stood still: *Shaw, Artie*
101682 / May '97 / A-Play Collection

☐ **JAZZ COLLECTION VOL.2 (Sweet Georgia Brown)**
Sweet georgia brown: *Cole, Nat 'King' Trio* / Honeysuckle rose: *Ellington, Duke* / One o'clock jump: *Basie, Count* / Flying home: *Fitzgerald, Ella* / Somebody stole my girl: *Goodman, Benny* / Nobody knows the trouble I've seen: *Horne, Lena* / No greater love: *Adderley, Cannonball Quintet* / Crosstown: *Ellington, Duke Orchestra* / Bijou: *Herman, Woody* / On the sunny side of the street: *Armstrong, Louis* / Starlit hour: *Fitzgerald, Ella* / My old flame: *Basie, Count Orchestra* / Love me or leave me: *Horne, Lena* / Bird of paradise: *Parker, Charlie* / Embraceable you: *Davis, Miles* / I can't get started with you: *Shaw, Artie*
101692 / May '97 / A-Play Collection

☐ **JAZZ COLLECTION VOL.3 (Basin Street Blues)**
Basin street blues: *Armstrong, Louis* / Sophisticated lady: *Ellington, Duke Orchestra* / Stairway to the stars: *Fitzgerald, Ella* / Get happy: *Goodman, Benny* / Stompin' at the Savoy: *Herman, Woody* / It's a rainy day: *Horne, Lena* / Yes sir that's my baby: *Cole, Nat 'King' Trio* / 'Round midnight: *Parker, Charlie* / Ring dem bells: *Ellington, Duke Orchestra* / Scuttlebutt: *Shaw, Artie* / That old black magic: *Fitzgerald, Ella* / Northwest passage: *Herman, Woody* / Blue juice: *Barnet, Charlie* / Fascinating rhythm: *Goodman, Benny* / Little girl blue: *Horne, Lena* / Trouble with me is: *Cole, Nat 'King' Trio*
101702 / May '97 / A-Play Collection

☐ **JAZZ COLLECTION, THE (3CD Set)**
When the saints go marching in: *Armstrong, Louis* / Mooche: *Ellington, Duke* / King porter stomp: *Goodman, Benny* / It's only a paper moon: *Cole, Nat 'King' Trio* / Something new: *Basie, Count* / My blue heaven: *Shaw, Artie* / How high the moon: *Parker, Charlie* / Indiana: *Armstrong, Louis* / Lover come back to me: *Fitzgerald, Ella* / Cannonball blues: *Adderley, Cannonball* / I can't remember to forget: *Barnet, Charlie* / At long last love: *Horne, Lena* / Bugle call rag: *Goodman, Benny* / I struck a match in the dark: *Basie, Count* / Caravan: *Ellington, Duke Orchestra* / My heart stood still: *Shaw, Artie* / Sweet Georgia Brown: *Cole, Nat 'King' Trio* / Honeysuckle rose: *Ellington, Duke* / One o' clock jump: *Basie, Count* / Flying home: *Fitzgerald, Ella* / Somebody stole my girl: *Goodman, Benny* / Nobody knows the trouble I've seen: *Horne, Lena* / No greater love: *Adderley, Cannonball* / Crosstown: *Ellington, Duke Orchestra* / Bijou: *Herman, Woody* / On the sunny side of the street: *Armstrong, Louis* / Starlit hour: *Fitzgerald, Ella* / My old flame: *Basie, Count Orchestra* / Love me or leave me: *Horne, Lena* / Bird of paradise: *Parker, Charlie* / Embraceable you: *Davis, Miles* / I can't get started with you: *Shaw, Artie* / Basin street blues: *Armstrong, Louis* / Sophisticated lady: *Ellington, Duke Orchestra* / Stairway to the stars: *Fitzgerald, Ella* / Get happy: *Goodman, Benny* / Stompin' at The Savoy: *Herman, Woody* / It's a rainy day: *Horne, Lena* / Yes sir that's my baby: *Cole, Nat 'King' Trio* / Round midnight: *Parker, Charlie* / Ring dem bells: *Ellington, Duke Orchestra* / Scuttlebutt: *Shaw, Artie* / That old black magic: *Fitzgerald, Ella* / Northwest passage: *Herman, Woody* / Blue juice: *Barnet, Charlie* / Fascinating rhythm: *Goodman, Benny* / Little girl blue: *Horne, Lena* / Trouble with me is you: *Cole, Nat 'King' Trio*
101672 / May '97 / A-Play Collection

☐ **JAZZ COLLECTIVE**
Blackbyrds' theme / EBFS / Golden wings / Mambo Inn / African bird / Casa forte / Cornbread / Reggins / Scarborough street fair / Lady smooth / You're gonna lose me / Backed up against the wall / Lifestyles / Quiet storm / Open your eyes you can fly / Ina's song
CDBGPD 076 / Feb '94 / Beat Goes Public

☐ **JAZZ COM BOSSA**
99 1602 / Jul '96 / Ninetynine

☐ **JAZZ COMEDY CLASSICS**
JCD 20 / Jan '87 / Jass

☐ **JAZZ CUTS VOL.1**
TMPCD 010 / Jun '95 / Temple

☐ **JAZZ CUTS VOL.2**
TMPCD 011 / Jun '95 / Temple

☐ **JAZZ CUTS VOL.3**
TMPCD 012 / Jun '95 / Temple

☐ **JAZZ DANCE CLASSICS VOL.1**
LHCD 010 / Jul '96 / Luv n' Haight

☐ **JAZZ DANCE CLASSICS VOL.2**
LHCD 013 / Jul '96 / Luv n' Haight

☐ **JAZZ DANCE CLASSICS VOL.3**
LHCD 015 / Jul '96 / Luv n' Haight

☐ **JAZZ DANCE CLASSICS VOL.4**
LHCD 021 / Jul '96 / Luv n' Haight

☐ **JAZZ DE SCENE VOL.1**
251 278 2 / Mar '90 / Jazztime

☐ **JAZZ DE SCENE VOL.3 1938-1950**
8270962 / Dec '93 / Jazztime

☐ **JAZZ DIVAS**
Take five: *McRae, Carmen* / Smooth sailing: *Fitzgerald, Ella* / I'm a fool I want you: *Holiday, Billie* / Blue rose: *Clooney, Rosemary* / Everything must change: *Simone, Nina* / Murder: *O'Day, Anita* / How deep is the ocean: *Lee, Peggy* / Black coffee: *Vaughan, Sarah* / Thou swell: *Carter, Betty* / Bewitched: *Freelon, Nnenna* / Ain't she sweet: *Humes, Helen* / Day dream: *Wilson, Nancy*
4878072 / 29 Sep '97 / Sony Jazz

☐ **JAZZ ECHOES (A Magical Blend Of Music And The Sounds Of Nature)**
57772 / May '97 / Nature's Harmony

☐ **JAZZ EVENT**
MECCACD 1034 / Nov '94 / Music Mecca

☐ **JAZZ FAVOURITES (3CD Set)**
KBOX 367 / Aug '97 / Collection

☐ **JAZZ FOR A RAINY AFTERNOON**
412320612 / 17 Mar '98 / Thirty Two

☐ **JAZZ FOR EVERYONE (2CD Set)**
When sunny gets blue: *Vaughan, Sarah* / One: *Bennett, Tony* / Moonglow: *Harris, Eddie* / Solitude: *Hawkins, Coleman* / Garden in the rain: *Vaughan, Sarah* / My romance: *Bennett, Tony* / More than you know: *Horne, Lena* / April in Paris: *Basie, Count* / More I see you: *Harris, Eddie* / Five o' clock in the morning: *Williams, Joe* / 'Round midnight: *Monk, Thelonious* / Brown eyed woman: *Turrentine, Stanley* / Mountain greenery: *Bennett, Tony* / One o' clock jump: *Basie, Count* / Mood indigo: *Hawkins, Coleman* / Yesterday: *Mingus, Charles* / Wedding bell blues: *Turrentine, Stanley* / In a mellow tone: *Stitt, Sonny* / Angel eyes: *Blakey, Art* / Fun: *Hampton, Lionel* / I can't get started: *Mingus, Charles* / Moose the mooch: *Davis, Miles* / Anything goes: *Bennett, Tony*
SD 885382 / 2 Feb '98 / Disky

☐ **JAZZ FOR JOY**
5319602 / Nov '96 / Verve

☐ **JAZZ FOR LOVERS**
DCD 5275 / Nov '92 / Kenwest

☐ **JAZZ FOR LOVERS**
TRTCD 170 / Feb '96 / TrueTrax

☐ **JAZZ FOR LOVERS**
CD 3538 / Aug '95 / Cameo

☐ **JAZZ FOR LOVERS**
I've got a crush on you: *Braff, Ruby* / When I fall in love: *Woodard, Rickey* / C'est si bon: *Armstrong, Louis* / Time after time: *Baker, Chet* / Love me: *Sims, Zoot* / More I see you: *Vaughan, Sarah* / Prelude to a kiss: *Vaughan, Sarah* / Blue and sentimental: *Powell, Seldon* / Gee baby ain't I good to you: *Greco, Buddy* / Love story: *Philips, Flip* / I like you you're nice: *Kral, Irene* / Can't we be friends: *Harrow, Nancy* / Teach me tonight: *Newton, David* / When a man loves a woman: *Scott, Shirley*
EMPRCD 635 / Jun '96 / Emporio

☐ **JAZZ FOR LOVERS VOL.1**
Man I love: *Holiday, Billie* / You're nobody til somebody loves you: *Cole, Nat 'King'* / You go to my head: *Vaughan, Sarah* / Love and kisses: *Fitzgerald, Ella* / Liebestraum: *Dorsey, Tommy Orchestra* / Without your love: *Holiday, Billie* / Moonlight serenade: *Miller, Glenn* / For you: *Garner, Erroll* / My kinda love: *Vaughan, Sarah* / Imagination: *Sinatra, Frank & Tommy Dorsey Orchestra* / Prelude to a kiss: *Ellington, Duke* / Love walked in: *Armstrong, Louis* / Embraceable you: *Davis, Miles & Charlie Parker* / Sweet Lorraine: *Cole, Nat 'King'* / Indian love call: *Pastor, Tony & Artie Shaw Orchestra* / With love in my heart: *Terrell, Pha* / Lover come back to me: *Bailey, Mildred* / Body and soul: *Hawkins, Coleman*
CD 3625 / Jul '98 / Cameo

☐ **JAZZ FOR LOVERS VOL.2**
Lover man: *Vaughan, Sarah* / I'm thru with love: *Cole, Nat 'King'* / Sophisticated lady: *Ellington, Duke Orchestra* / Dedicated to you: *Mills Brothers & Ella Fitzgerald* / I love my man: *Holiday, Billie* / (I love you) for sentimental reasons: *Cole, Nat 'King'* / That's when a woman loves a heel: *Washington, Dinah* / I love you much too much: *Andrews Sisters* / I could make you love me: *Vaughan, Sarah* / Love nest: *Cole, Nat 'King'* / 'Round midnight: *Monk, Thelonious* / What is this thing called love: *O'Day, Anita* / Live and love tonight: *Ellington, Duke Orchestra* / Do I love you: *Forrest, Helen & Artie Shaw Orchestra* / It's easy to remember: *Torme, Mel* / I can't give you anything but love: *Garner, Erroll* / Falling in love again: *Small, Paul & Benny Goodman Orchestra* / Just an old love of mine: *Lee, Peggy*
CD 3626 / Jul '98 / Cameo

☐ **JAZZ FOR QUIET TIMES**
60412320972 / 3 Aug '98 / Thirty Two

☐ **JAZZ FOR SENSUAL LOVERS**
STB 2510 / Sep '95 / Stash

☐ **JAZZ FOR SENSUAL LOVERS: ROMANTIC GUITARS**
STB 2515 / Sep '95 / Stash

☐ **JAZZ FOR SENSUAL LOVERS: ROMANTIC SAXOPHONES**
STB 2512 / Sep '95 / Stash

☐ **JAZZ FOR YOU**
NNCD 901 / May '90 / GRP

☐ **JAZZ FROM ATLANTA 1923-1929**
Eskimo song / Black cat blues / Georgia stomp / Home sweet home blues / My pretty girl / After that / Daylight's breaking blues / Hey hey / Atlanta gal / Lonesome lovesick got to have my daddy blues / Mean eyes / Bessie couldn't help it / When my sugar walks down the street / Blues have got me / Cheatin' on me / Go get 'em Caroline / Breakin' the leg / Tweedle dee tweedle doo / Hangin' around / Who'd be blue / Don't take that black bottom away / That's my girl / When Jenny does her low down dance
CBC 1038 / Sep '97 / Timeless Historical

☐ **JAZZ FROM THE WINDY CITY 1927-1930**
Sugar: *McKenzie & Condon's Chicagoans* / China boy: *McKenzie & Condon's Chicagoans* / Nobody's sweetheart: *McKenzie & Condon's Chicagoans* / Liza: *McKenzie & Condon's Chicagoans* / Bullfrog: *Pierce, Charles & his Orchestra* / Jazz me blues: *Pierce, Charles & his Orchestra* / I wish I could shimmy like my sister Kate: *Pierce, Charles & his Orchestra* / There'll be some changes made: *Chicago Rhythm Kings* / I've found a new baby: *Chicago Rhythm Kings* / Friars Point Shuffle: *Jungle Kings* / Darktown strutters ball: *Jungle Kings* / Jazz me blues (III): *Teschemacher, Frank* / Baby, won't you please come home: *Louisiana Rhythm Kings* / Copenhagen: *Schoebel, Elmer* / Prince of wails: *Schoebel, Elmer* / Wailing blues (I and II): *Cellar Boys* / Barrel House stomp (I, II and III): *Cellar Boys*
CBC 1021 / Aug '94 / Timeless Historical

☐ **JAZZ FRUHSCHOPPEN**
ZYX 551102 / 26 May '98 / ZYX

☐ **JAZZ FUNK AND FUSION**
To prove my love: *Doheny, Ned* / Lion dance: *Hiroshima* / Hunt up wind: *Fukumura, Hiroshi* / Thighs high (grip your hips and move): *Browne, Tom* / By all means: *Mouzon, Alphonse & Herbie Hancock* / No problem: *Watanabe, Sadao* / Fly by night: *Ritenour, Lee* / Rag bag: *Grusin, Dave* / Central park: *Corea, Chick* / Disco dancing: *Turrentine, Stanley*
VSOPCD 219 / Aug '95 / Connoisseur Collection

☐ **JAZZ FUNK REVIVAL**
Chameleon: *Jefferson, Eddie* / In the meantime: *Barron, Kenny* / Thank you falletinme be mice elf agin: *Jefferson, Eddie* / Walk that funky dog: *Bronstein, Stan* / Philadelphia bright: *Bishop, Walter Jr.* / In the middle of it all: *Creque, Neal* / Mean street no-bridges: *Ponder, Jimmy* / Black love: *Garnett, Carlos* / Mystery of ages: *Garnett, Carlos* / Let us go (to higher hights): *Garnett, Carlos*
PHOCD 8003 / Sep '95 / Muse

☐ **JAZZ FUSION**
Appetizer / Pulse / Blue love / Slow down / Safari / Elemental force / Razzia 1 / Miles gloriosus / Temesvar / Zick-o-mat / Mys chindli, chum weidli / Mediterranean / Square times on Times Square
303242 / Jun '97 / Hallmark

☐ **JAZZ FUSION VOL.1**
Saxman: *Koz, Dave* / After the dance: *Fourplay* / Anniversary: *Albright, Gerald* / Thinkin' about tomorrow: *Incognito* / My summer vacation: *Patitucci, John* / Sade: *Kenny G* / Tourist in paradise: *Rippingtons* / Heart station: *Laws, Ronnie* / Come with me: *Jordan, Ronny* / Love will make it right: *Watanabe, Sadao* / Up town east: *Special EFX* / Show me the way: *Grant, Tom* / Reed my lips: *Scott, Tom*
FUSIONCD 1 / Jul '94 / Jazz Fusions

☐ **JAZZ FUSION VOL.2**
After the love has gone: *Benoit/Freeman Project* / I don't know: *Wright, Betty* / Back to Memphis: *Sanborn, David* / Wind cries Mary: *Harrison, Donald* / Strutt everette: *Harp, Everette* / Restless: *James, Bob* / Walking in rhythm: *McBride, Joe* / Waiting in vain: *Ritenour, Lee* / Juju: *Miller, Marcus* / Save the best for last: *Meadows, Marion* / That's enough for me: *Austin, Patti* / Rainforest: *Hardcastle, Paul* / Love will find a way: *Lewis, Ramsey* / Justice's groove: *Clarke, Stanley*
FUSIONCD 2 / Oct '94 / Jazz Fusions

☐ **JAZZ FUSION VOL.3**
Undercover: *Porter, Art* / Happy home: *James, Boney* / Doin' it: *Klugh, Earl* / Love is like a river: *Fattburger* / Between the sheets: *Fourplay* / 500 miles to go: *Duke, George* / Daydream: *Johnson, Mark* / For the love of you: *Brown, Norman* / Here to stay: *Metheny, Pat* / Goodbye Manhattan: *Pieces Of A Dream* / Mercy mercy me: *Special EFX* / Fine time to explain: *Spyro Gyra* / Don't get any better: *Scott, Tom* / Laid back: *Breaux, Zachary*
FUSIONCD 3 / Jul '95 / Jazz Fusions

☐ **JAZZ FUSION VOL.4**
Fantasy: *Chinn, Daryle* / Whisk away: *Gable, Tony & 206* / Sunday mornin': *Powell, Doc* / Better days ahead: *Brown, Norman* / Secret garden: *Jones, Quincy* / Take me home to you: *Culbertson, Brian* / Wishful thinking: *Porter, Art* / Going all the way: *Rangell, Nelson* / We belong together: *Ravel, Freddie* / Back in the day: *White, Michael* / Summer nights: *Impromp2* / In the rhythm of my heart: *Mariano, Torcuato* / Play lady play: *Fourplay* / I just wanna stop: *Taylor, Joe*
FUSIONCD 4 / Nov '96 / Jazz Fusions

☐ JAZZ FUTURES (Live In Concert)
Mode for John / Sterling Sylvia / Blue moon / Piccadilly square / Bewitched, bothered and bewildered / Stardust / Medgar Evers blues / You don't know what love is / Public eye
02141631582 / Sep '93 / Novus

☐ JAZZ GOES LATIN (2CD Set)
Carioca: Hawkins, Coleman / Manteca: Gillespie, Dizzy / Samba de uma nota so: Getz, Stan & Charlie Byrd / Chitlins con carne: Burrell, Kenny / Corcovado (Quiet nights of quiet stars): Adderley, Cannonball / Chora tua tristeza (cry your sadness): Rogers, Shorty & His Orchestra / Pantano: Tjader, Cal / Un poquito de tu amor: Parker, Charlie / What is this thing called love: Puente, Tito / Se tudos fossem inquais a voce: Jobim, Antonio Carlos / Duck (d pato): Byrd, Charlie / Chega de daudade (No more blues): Getz, Stan / Con alma: Gillespie, Dizzy / Touch: Tjader, Cal / Bossa nova usa: Brubeck, Dave & Paul Desmond / Mama inez: Parker, Charlie / Manha de carnival: Getz, Stan / That's a Puente: Puente, Tito / Lorraine: Gillespie, Dizzy / Anna: Byrd, Charlie / Armando's quajira: Tjader, Cal / Clouds: Adderley, Cannonball
1807980 / Apr '98 / Jazz Memories

☐ JAZZ GOES TO THE MOVIES
Puttin' on the Ritz / Crazy feet / Alone with my dreams / How I'm doin'/Dinah / One little kiss from you / I like a guy what takes his time / You're hi-de-hi-ing me / Gold diggers song / Pettin' in the park / Wo ist der mann / Nasty man / My future star / Oh I didn't know (you'd get that way) / Lulu's back in town / You are my lucky star / I've got a feeling you're fooling / Got a bran' new suit / Stompin' at the Savoy / Swing Mister Charlie / Smarty (you know it all) / I go for that / Who cares (as long as you care for me) / Just like taking candy from a baby / My my
CBC 1020 / Aug '94 / Timeless Historical

☐ JAZZ GREATS (2CD Set)
DEMPCD 013 / Mar '96 / Emporio

☐ JAZZ GREATS (A Beginner's Guide To Jazz)
Stompin' at the Savoy: Goodman, Benny Orchestra / In the mood: Miller, Glenn Orchestra / What a wonderful world: Armstrong, Louis Orchestra / Song of India: Dorsey, Tommy Orchestra / Take the 'A' train: Ellington, Duke Orchestra / Seventh Avenue express: Basie, Count Orchestra / Begin the beguine: Shaw, Artie Orchestra / Ain't misbehavin': Waller, Fats & His Rhythm / Toledo blade: Hampton, Lionel Orchestra / Sing sing sing (with a swing): Goodman, Benny Orchestra / Mood indigo: Ellington, Duke Orchestra / Moonlight serenade: Miller, Glenn Orchestra
74321499542 / 6 Oct '97 / RCA Victor

☐ JAZZ GUITAR CLASSICS
OJCCD 6012 / Apr '92 / Original Jazz Classics

☐ JAZZ GUITAR IN A SOULFUL MOOD
Satin doll: Burrell, Kenny / Beautiful love: Kessel, Barney / Arubian nights: Coryell, Larry & Emily Remler / You leave me breathless: Alden, Howard Trio / If I should lose you: Ellis, Herb / Nuages: Eschete, Ron Trio / In your own sweet way: Farlow, Tal / Prelude to a kiss: Hall, Jim Quartet / Soon: Byrd, Charlie / 'Round midnight: Smith, Johnny / I'm confessin' (that I love you): Ellis, Herb & Joe Pass / Ecaroh: Bickert, Ed & Lorne Lofsky / I could write a book: Van Eps, George / My funny valentine: Byrd, Charlie / Side track: Palmier, Remo
MCCD 325 / Nov '97 / Music Club

☐ JAZZ GUITAR VOL.1, THE
CD 14528 / Jan '94 / Jazz Portraits

☐ JAZZ GUITAR VOL.1, THE
CD 56007 / Aug '94 / Jazz Roots

☐ JAZZ GUITAR VOL.2, THE
CD 14535 / Jan '94 / Jazz Portraits

☐ JAZZ GUITAR VOL.3, THE
CD 14538 / Jan '94 / Jazz Portraits

☐ JAZZ GUITAR VOL.3, THE
CD 56034 / Jul '95 / Jazz Roots

☐ JAZZ GUITAR VOL.4, THE
CD 14542 / Jan '94 / Jazz Portraits

☐ JAZZ HOURS, THE
SV 0240 / Oct '97 / Savoy Jazz

☐ JAZZ HOUSE GROOVES VOL.1
House jazz: Don Carlos / Ponteio: JD's Jam / Call me: Everyday People / Happy to love: Bradshaw, Ricky / Sax in the ozone: Aaron, Robert / Fuze: Natarel Elamant / People think I'm crazy: Davis, Roy Jr. & Peven Everett / Need: 4th Measure Men / Gabrielle: Davis, Roy Jr. / Capital swing: Jazz Doubt
CDHIGH 4 / Jan '97 / High On Rhythm

☐ JAZZ IN AFRICA VOL.2
Tshona / Stop and start / Umgababa / Kippie's prayer / Te te mbambisa (African day) / Kalahari
CDN 1011 / 15 Jun '98 / Camden

☐ JAZZ IN CALIFORNIA 1923-1930
CBC 1034 / Jun '97 / Timeless Historical

☐ JAZZ IN JAMAICA
LG 21093 / Apr '94 / Lagoon

☐ JAZZ IN ST. LOUIS 1924-1927
CBC 1036 / Jun '97 / Timeless Historical

☐ JAZZ IN TEXAS 1924-1930
CBC 1033 / Jun '97 / Timeless Historical

☐ JAZZ IN THE HOUSE (Mixed By Paul Asher/3CD Set)
Get your mind together: 95 North / Harmonica track: Soulboy / Bassline: DC Track Team / Into the kick with Tito: Deep Audio Penetration / Supreme law: Harmonious Thump / Sublime: Tickle / Our mute horn: Masters At Work / I got jazz in my soul: Just 4 Groovers / Warehouse vs The Ritz: Battle Of The D.J's / Way I feel: Musical Expression / Secret code: Jazz Documents / Sax track: M&J Project / Theme from Change: Daphne / Buff dance: Masters At Work / My Mama said: St. Germain / Foot therapy: Trent, Ron & Chez Damier / I'm leaving you: Ulysses / Innocence and inspiration: Elements Of Life / New Jersey deep: Black Science Orchestra / Tank: Global Logic / Moonshine: Kenlou / Equinox: Code 718 / Acid ensemble: Drivetrain / Wet dreams: Mada / Natural high: Yost, Kevin / Que tal America: Man Called Adam / New Goya: New Sector Movements / Jus' a vibe: Disorient / Stubborn problems: African Jazz / More you want: Groove Box / Never: Kupper/ Campbell Project / Lakou A: Guillaume, Jephte / After the storm: Gigolo Supreme / Carnival: Bah Samba / All that jazz: Ruffneck & Yavahn
SLIPCD 075 / 9 Mar '98 / Slip 'n' Slide

☐ JAZZ IN THE HOUSE VOL.1
Our mute horn: Masters At Work / Gummed: Zig Zag / I got jazz in my soul: Just 4 Groovers / Into the kick with Tito: Deep Audio Penetration / Way I feel: Musical Expression / Sublime: Tickle / Bassline: DC Track Team / Secret code: Jazz Documents / Supreme law: Harmonious Thump / Warehouse Vs the Ritz: Battle Of The D.J's / Sax track: M&J Project / Souffle: Mondo Grosso
SLIPCD 025 / Mar '95 / Slip 'n' Slide

☐ JAZZ IN THE HOUSE VOL.2
Theme from change: Daphne / Buff dance: Masters At Work / My Mama said: St. Germain / Foot therapy: Damier, Chez / I'm leaving you: Ulysses / Innocence and inspiration: Elements Of Life / New Jersey deep: Black Science Orchestra / Tank: Global Logic / Moonshine: Kenlou / Equinox: Code 718 / Acid ensemble: Drivetrain / Wet dreams: Mada
SLIPCD 030 / Sep '95 / Slip 'n' Slide

☐ JAZZ IN THE HOUSE VOL.3 (2CD Set)
SLIPCD 47 / Sep '96 / Slip 'n' Slide

☐ JAZZ IN THE HOUSE VOL.4
Natural high: Yost, Kevin / Que tal America: Man Called Adam / New goya: New Sector Movements / Jus' a vibe: Disorient / Stubborn problems: African Jazz / More you want: Groove Box / Never: Kupper/ Campbell Project / Lakou-a: Guillaume, Jephte / After the storm: Gigolo Supreme / Carnival: Bah Samba / All that jazz: Ruffneck & Yavahn
SLIPCD 60 / Jul '97 / Slip 'n' Slide

☐ JAZZ IN THE HOUSE VOL.5
Do the positive: Black Jazz Chronicles / Criminal kiss: Valentine, Frankie / My history: IG Culture / Time out: Dino & Terry / Uptown: Soul Familia / Escravos de jo: Clausell & Chandler / Plis infinis no.2: Galliano, Frederick / Groove: Global Communication / Summer bummer: Crazy Penis / Reach inside: Bah Samba / Another dae: Blaze
SLIPCD 076 / 4 May '98 / Slip 'n' Slide

☐ JAZZ IN THE THIRTIES (2CD Set)
CDSW 8457/8 / '88 / DRG

☐ JAZZ IS WHERE YOU FIND IT 1924-1930
Blues in A minor / Shanghai shuffle / Savoy rhythm / Rose of the Nile / Drag / My dream ship / Birmingham bound / Postage stomp / Sweet someone / Brainstorm / Maybe sometime / Black Maria
CBC 1048 / 29 Jun '98 / Timeless Historical

☐ JAZZ JAMAICA
SOCD 1140 / Aug '94 / Studio One

☐ JAZZ JAZZ JAZZ
REVCC 003 / Aug '94 / Revco

☐ JAZZ JUICE VOL.1
Miles: Davis, Miles / Jeannine: Jefferson, Eddie / Boss tres bien: Quartette Tres Bien / Cubano chant: Blakey, Art / Rhoda: Mendes, Sergio / Mas que nada: Mendes, Sergio / I'll bet you thought I'd never find you: Hendricks, Jon / It don't mean a thing if it ain't got that swing: Schurr, Diane / I believe in love: Longo, Pat / Crickets sing for anamaria: Valle, Marcus / Do it fluid: Dirty Dozen Brass Band / Take five: McRae, Carmen & Dave Brubeck / Dat dere: Brown, Oscar Jr. / Sidewinder: Herman, Woody & His Herd / Wack wack: Young-Holt Trio / It's a trip: Last Poets
SOUNDSCD 2 / Oct '94 / Street Sounds

☐ JAZZ JUICE VOL.2
Pigmy part 1: Larkin, Billy & The Delegates / Cerveza: Brown, Boots & His Blockbusters / Do it the hard way: Baker, Chet / Who's afraid of Virginia Woolf: Brown, James / Got my mojo working: Smith, Jimmy / Listen love: Lucien, Jon / Jazz jump: King Pleasure / Mardi gras: Smith, Lonnie Liston / Minor chant: Smith, Lonnie / Girl from Ipanema: Rawls, Lou / Ain't nobody here but us chickens: Murphy, Mark / Call me: Wilson, Nancy / Work song: Brown, Oscar Jr. / Fever: Lee, Peggy / Samba: Mullins, Rob / Hit the road Jack: Davison, 'Wild' Bill
SOUNDSCD 4 / Mar '95 / Street Sounds

☐ JAZZ JUICE VOL.3
Hey Leroy, your Mama's callin' you: Castor, Jimmy / Shoshana: Tjader, Cal / Tema da alma Latina: Matos, Bobby / Take five: Puente, Tito / Yumbambe: Sanchez, Poncho / Don't be blue: Jackie & Roy / So high: Lawson, Janet / You've got to have freedom: Sanders, Pharoah / Soul bossa nova: Jones, Quincy / Triste: Shepherd, Cybill / Bossa nova ova: Mitchell, Billy / Boogaloo in room 802: Bobo, Willie / Never was love: Roberts, Judy / Who will buy: Lucien, Jon / Ordinary guy: Bataan, Joe
SOUNDSCD 6 / Jul '95 / Street Sounds

☐ JAZZ JUNGLE
JAZIDCD 142 / Jun '96 / Acid Jazz

☐ JAZZ KANSAS CITY STYLEZ
TPZ 1036 / Jan '96 / Topaz Jazz

☐ JAZZ LADIES VOL.1
CDSGPBJZ 08 / 4 May '98 / Prestige

☐ JAZZ LADIES VOL.2
CDSGPBJZ 09 / 4 May '98 / Prestige

☐ JAZZ LADIES VOL.3
CDSGPBJZ 10 / Jun '95 / Prestige

☐ JAZZ LADIES VOL.4
Burst in with the dawn / Everything must change / I'm coming home / St. Louis blues / Sorrowful blues / Baby doll / My foolish heart / As time goes by / I only have eyes for you / Where or when / It's a blue world / Saving myself for you / You can't be mine / Sugar blues
CDSGPBJZ 29 / May '96 / Prestige

☐ JAZZ LADIES VOL.5
Empty bed blues / Chicago bound blues / Alexander's ragtime band / Back water blues / Georgia on my mind / I cried for you / Love me or leave me / Man I love / Strictly for Dixie / Undecided / Angel eyes / My one and only love / Masquerade is over / Mr. Magic
CDSGPBJZ 30 / 4 May '98 / Prestige

☐ JAZZ LEGENDS VOL.1
CDSGPBJZ 06 / 4 May '98 / Prestige

☐ JAZZ LEGENDS VOL.2
CDSGPBJZ 07 / 4 May '98 / Prestige

☐ JAZZ LIMITED VOL.1
DE 226 / Jun '95 / Delmark

☐ JAZZ LINKX
What's bop: Murata, Yoichi & Solid Brass / Impressions: Kankawa / Hopscotch: Smith, Roger / Real deal: Special EFX / Whisper not: Nakamoto, Mari / Cavendo na rosiera: Yamashita, Yosuke / Willow weep for me: Watts, Ernie / Danae: Malta / Leilani: Minucci, Chieli / Deep focus: Johnson, Mark / Back in love again: Sea, David / Straight no chaser: Holman, Bill Band / I didn't know what time it was: Lundy, Carmen
JVC 90202 / Aug '97 / JVC

☐ JAZZ LIVE (Recorded Live In Paris/2CD Set)
C'est si bon: Grappelli, Stephane & The Five O'Clock Jazz Group / Swanee river rock: Copley, Al Trio / Satin doll: Distel, Sacha & Wild Bill Davis / Dans les rues d'antibes: Luter, Claude & Jacky Milliet Quintet / After you've gone: Doriz, Dany Big Band / Hello Dolly: Grappelli, Stephane & The Five O'Clock Jazz Group / All the jazz band ball: Saury, Maxim Jazz Music / Fourth of June: Milliet, Jackie French Band / Christopher Columbus: Five O'Clock Jazz Group / Moonglow: Doriz, Dany Big Band / South: Ticinum Jazz Band / Riverboat shuffle: Luter, Claude & Jacky Milliet Quintet / After you've gone: Milliet, Jacky French Band & Bonny Taylor / One scotch one bourbon one beer: Copley, Al Trio / Saint Louis blues: Saury, Maxim Jazz Music / Petite fleur: Luter, Claude & Jacky Milliet Quintet / Perdido: Distel, Sacha & Wild Bill Davis / Jumpin' at the woodside: Doriz, Dany Sextet / Saint James infirmary: Ticinum Jazz Band / Johnny B Goode: Copley, Al Trio / Please don't talk about me when I'm gone: Holloway, Nancy & The Stephane Guerault Quintet
24365 / Nov '97 / Laserlight

☐ JAZZ LOFT SESSIONS
ADC 3 / May '97 / Douglas Music

☐ JAZZ LOFT SESSIONS
DM 10003 / 15 Jun '98 / Douglas Music

☐ JAZZ MASTERPIECES VOL.1
PLSCD 151 / Feb '97 / Pulse

☐ JAZZ MASTERPIECES VOL.2
PLSCD 152 / Feb '97 / Pulse

☐ JAZZ MASTERS (The Verve Jazz Masters Sampler)
5198532 / 5 May '98 / Verve

☐ JAZZ MASTERS
BK's broiler: Katz, Bruce / Aurora: Calderazzo, Joey / Sensei: Willis, Larry / Blues on the corner: Palmer, Jeff / Tuda muda: Lewis, Vic / Angels at play: Fambrough, Charles / Mirror puzzle: Akagi, Kei / Suite for Frida Kahlo: Newton, James / Gloria's step: Mokave / Mermaid: Arbuckle, Les / My one and only love: Wallace, Bennie / Free to dream: Binney, David
AQCD 1035 / Mar '96 / Audioquest

☐ JAZZ MASTERS (The Best Of Jazz Masters)
Sweet Georgia Brown: Reinhardt, Django & Stephane Grappelli / Jam blues: Hampton, Lionel & Oscar Peterson / I've got my love to keep me warm: Fitzgerald, Ella & Louis Armstrong / Last night when we were young: Burrell, Kenny & Gil Evans / Polka dots and moonbeams: Young, Lester / Ricardo's dilemma: Nelson, Oliver / Organ grinder's swing: Smith, Jimmy / Stormy weather: Holiday, Billie / Ballad: Mulligan, Gerry / Soul sauce: Tjader, Cal / March on, swan lake: Kirk, Rahsaan Roland / Words can't describe: Vaughan, Sarah / Cocktails for two: Hawkins, Coleman & Ben Webster / Summertime: Baker, Chet / Cherokee: Brown, Clifford & Max Roach / Peanut vendor: Mann, Herbie
5298662 / 5 May '98 / Verve

☐ JAZZ MASTERS (Big Band Jazz)
CDMFP 6294 / Mar '97 / Music For Pleasure

☐ JAZZ MASTERS (Jazz Vocalisers)
CDMFP 6295 / Mar '97 / Music For Pleasure

☐ JAZZ MASTERS (Jazz Superhits Of The 60's)
Cristo redemptor: Byrd, Donald / Song for my Father: Silver, Horace / Moanin': Blakey, Art & The Jazz Messengers / Alligator boogaloo: Donaldson, Lou / Mercy mercy mercy: Adderley, Cannonball / Sidewinder: Morgan, Lee
4934692 / 16 Feb '98 / EMI Jazz

☐ JAZZ MASTERS VOL.2
MATCD 334 / Apr '95 / Castle

☐ JAZZ MEETS AFRICA
5317202 / Feb '97 / MPS Jazz

☐ JAZZ MEETS BRAZIL
5331332 / Mar '97 / MPS Jazz

☐ JAZZ MESSENGERS VOL.2, THE
Yesterdays / Yesterdays / I waited for you / Lady bird / Deciphering the message / Just one of those things / Hank's symphony / Gone with the wind
CD 53129 / Nov '92 / Giants Of Jazz

☐ JAZZ MOODS
TRTCD 126 / Dec '94 / TrueTrax

☐ JAZZ MOODS
MACCD 133 / Aug '96 / Autograph

☐ JAZZ 'N' BASS VOL.2 (2CD Set)
Introduction and wine bar / Stormy weather: DJ SS / Sax therapy: John B / Hornet: Grasscutter / 4th dimension: Codename John / Untitled: Shy FX / Warp factor / Mission impossible: Blue Sonix / Cool: Mental Power / J-break: Perfect Combination / Subway: John B / Protection: Data Flow / Introduction part.2 / I've got you: DJ SS / Snake skin: Matrix / TJS: Tekniq / Turn around: Rayner / Double trouble: Blue Sonix / Strange life: New Mount City Breakers / Sun drif / Jim the jazz: Perfect Combination / Higher place: By Reasonable Force / Split endz: John B / Harlem: DJ SS
NIRCD 03 / 15 Jun '98 / New Identity

☐ JAZZ 'N' STEEL
DE 4013 / Feb '94 / Delos

☐ JAZZ NEW ORLEANS STYLE
TPZ 1049 / Jun '96 / Topaz Jazz

☐ JAZZ NEWBEATS VOL.1 (Good Feelings)
Goodfeelin': DJ First Klas / Rebel: Delaney's Rhythm Section / High hopes: Forest Mighty Black / Moodswing: Outside / Searching: Takemura, Nobukazu & D.C. Lee / Underwater love: Smoke City / Revolutionary woman of the windmill: Up Bustle & Out / Son of mook: Red Snapper / Mella: DJ Food / Strange life: Count Basic / Zitti zitti: Aeroplanitaliani / Psycodelico: Reminiscence Quartet
CDNBT 1 / Jun '96 / New Beats

☐ JAZZ NEWBEATS VOL.2 (Mind Fluid)
Scat attack: Michiru, Monday / Ghittoni: Derek Jarman Blues / At home in space: Fila Brazillia / Pleasure and pain: Project 23 / Creator has a matter plan: Routine / Blowin' it: Herbaliser & Chris Bowden / Jazz hypnosis: First Priority / Cosmic jam: DJ Food / Tutta la notte: Zona 45 / Mind fluid: Nu Yorican Soul / Let the hustlers play: Pulse & Tango / Latin joint: Baby Buddah Heads
CDNBT 2 / Apr '97 / New Beats

☐ JAZZ NEWBEATS VOL.3 (The Blend)
Eva: Perrey, Jean Jacques / Dim's jazz: Dimitri From Paris / Tides: Forest Mighty Black / Friends we'll be: UFO / Man with a suitcase: Josse, Chris / Blend: Herbaliser / Buseki: DJ Krush / Finding a new world: Utsumi / Tuso que voce podia ser: Azymuth / Another sun: Reflection / Finding ALH 84001: Outside / Cong sax: LTJ Bukem
CDNBT 3 / 1 Jun '98 / New Beats

☐ JAZZ NOT HOUSE VOL.1
Satsuki: Giant Step / Vibe Providin': Peace Bureau / Black thoughts: African Dream / Set me free: Watts, Alvin 'Bobby' / Try my lovin': Bluejean / On the sand: Groove Thing / Jazz impressions: African Dream / Hands of a raindrop: Tiny Bubbles
EBCD 53 / Jan '95 / Eightball

☐ JAZZ NOT JAZZ VOL.2 (The New Breed)
New jazz swing: Now School / Yeah: Jazzy Grooves / Love's fantasy: Now School / Ain't really down: Shaft, Jon / Lost: Headshock / Work: Bedroom Boys / Rize: Fuzion / Keep on: Jazz not Jazz
WORLD 003CD / Aug '93 / World Series

☐ JAZZ ODYSSEY, A
I am with you: Bowie, Lester Brass Fantasy / Little boy with the sad eyes: Bowie, Lester Brass Fantasy / Country cooking: McGregor, Chris & Brotherhood Of Breath / Bye bye blackbird: Kirk, Rahsaan Roland / Cherokee: Harris, Eddie / Maleah: McCann, Les / Incident on south street: Lounge Lizards / Children's concerto: Moraz, Patrick & Bill Bruford / Sweet williams: Loose Tubes / Mode forbode: Ballamy, Iain / Sahde 1: Tippett, Keith & Andy Sheppard / Ke a rona: District Six / Daybreak: Tippett, Keith & Julie
CDOVD 493 / 29 Sep '97 / Virgin

☐ JAZZ OF THE 1920'S
Black bottom stomp: Morton, Jelly Roll / Black beauty: Ellington, Duke / Handful of keys: Waller, Fats / San: Whiteman, Paul / Variety stomp: Henderson, Fletcher / Too late: Oliver, Joe 'King' / Bleeding-hearted blues: Johnson, James P. / Waitin' for Katie: Goodman, Benny / One hour: Hawkins, Coleman / Doin' things: Venuti, Joe / Glad rag doll: Hines, Earl 'Fatha' / Four or five times: McKinney's Cotton Pickers / Lonely melody: Beiderbecke, Bix / Delirium: Nichols, Red / That's a serious thing: Teagarden, Jack / Kansas city shuffle: Moten, Bennie / Ain't misbehavin': Waller, Fats
74321584832 / Jun '98 / RCA Victor

☐ JAZZ OF THE 1930'S
Basin Street blues: Armstrong, Louis / Mood indigo: Ellington, Duke / Moten swing: Basie, Count / King Porter stomp: Goodman, Benny / Hocus pocus: Henderson, Fletcher / Song of India: Dorsey, Tommy / Swing is here: Krupa, Gene / Dinah: Waller, Fats / In

the mood: *Miller, Glenn* / Cherokee: *Barnet, Charlie* / Begin the beguine: *Shaw, Artie* / Body and soul: *Hawkins, Coleman* / Hot mallets: *Hampton, Lionel* / Life goes to a party: *James, Harry* / Minnie the moocher: *Calloway, Cab* / Rockin' chair: *Carmichael, Hoagy*

74321584842 / Jun '98 / RCA Victor

☐ JAZZ OF THE 1940'S

Cotton tail: *Webster, Ben* / Yes indeed: *Dorsey, Tommy* / Blues afetr hours: *Teagarden, Jack* / Manteca: *Gillespie, Dizzy* / Your red wagon: *Basie, Count* / Erroll's bounce: *Garner, Erroll* / Summertime: *Shaw, Artie* / Stormy Monday blues: *Hines, Earl 'Fatha'* / All of me: *Carter, Benny* / My heart stood still: *Peterson, Oscar* / Pennies from heaven: *Armstrong, Louis* / Out of nowhere: *Tatum, Art* / Sheik of Araby: *Hawkins, Coleman* / Victory ball: *Parker, Charlie*

74321585012 / 1 Jun '98 / RCA Victor

☐ JAZZ OF THE 1950'S

Chiquito loco: *Rogers, Shorty* / Crimea river: *Cohn, Al & Zoot Sims* / Love me or leave me: *Allen, Henry 'Red'* / Sunday afternoon: *Carter, Benny* / From this moment on: *Horne, Lena* / Perdido: *Ellington, Duke* / I love Paris: *Hawkins, Coleman* / Medley: *Ellington, Duke* / Roses of Picardy: *Norvo, Red* / Salt peanuts: *Powell, Bud* / Tijuana gift shop: *Mingus, Charles* / April in Paris: *Sauter-Finegan Orchestra* / Night at Tony's: *Blakey, Art* / Wailing boat: *Ferguson, Maynard*

74321584852 / 1 Jun '98 / RCA Victor

☐ JAZZ OF THE 1960'S

Without a song: *Rollins, Sonny* / Hello young lovers: *Burton, Gary* / So what: *Johnson, J.J.* / Very thought of you: *Hodges, Johnny* / Sounds of the night: *Terry, Clark* / Where do you go/Girl from Ipanema: *Getz, Stan* / One o' clock jump: *Lambert & Hendricks/Bavan* / All the things you are: *Desmond, Paul & Gerry Mulligan* / Star eyes: *Baker, Chet* / After all: *Ellington, Duke* / Come back baby: *Williams, Joe* / Toin me loose: *Hampton, Lionel*

74321584862 / 1 Jun '98 / RCA Victor

☐ JAZZ ON A SUMMER'S DAY

Take five: *Brubeck, Dave* / Summertime: *Vaughan, Sarah* / Moanin': *Blakey, Art & The Jazz Messengers* / Man I love: *Lee, Peggy* / Girl from Ipanema: *Getz, Stan & Astrud Gilberto* / So what: *Davis, Miles* / Mack the knife: *Armstrong, Louis* / Got my mojo working: *Smith, Jimmy* / Birdland: *Weather Report* / Hymn to freedom: *Peterson, Oscar*

CDGR 196 / Jul '98 / Charly

☐ JAZZ PA NORSK

GMCD 70 / Apr '98 / Gemini

☐ JAZZ PIANO

Jet black boogie: *Memphis Slim* / Ain't misbehavin': *Kellaway, Roger* / Pete and Thomas: *Byard, Jaki* / Blues for Nikki: *Bennett, Don* / Fungii mama: *Barron, Kenny* / Bill: *Di Novi, Gene* / Body and soul: *Monk, Thelonious* / Pagin' Mr Jelly: *Hodes, Art* / Blue sunset: *Hines, Earl 'Fatha'* / Yesterdays: *Hanna, Roland* / So danco samba: *Greco, Buddy* / Soft winds: *Reed, Eric* / Afri song: *Abrams, Muhal Richard* / Rockin' in rhythm: *Ellington, Duke*

EMPRCD 611 / Nov '97 / Music Club

☐ JAZZ PIANO ANTHOLOGY (5CD Set)

Liza: *Johnson, James P.* / Jazzamine concerto: *Johnson, James P.* / Shreveport stomps: *Morton, Jelly Roll* / Dead man blues: *Morton, Jelly Roll* / Shiny stockings: *Hines, Earl 'Fatha'* / Sometimes I'm happy: *Hines, Earl 'Fatha'* / Once in a while: *Hines, Earl 'Fatha'* / Ain't misbehavin': *Waller, Fats* / Honeysuckle rose: *Waller, Fats* / I've got the world on a string: *Wilson, Teddy* / You go to my head: *Wilson, Teddy* / After you've gone: *Wilson, Teddy* / Back home again in Indiana: *Tatum, Art* / Limehouse blues: *Tatum, Art* / I guess I'll have to change my plan: *Tatum, Art* / Ray's idea: *Powell, Bud* / Fool's fancy: *Powell, Bud* / Miguel's party: *Powell, Bud* / 'Round midnight: *Monk, Thelonious* / Light blue: *Monk, Thelonious* / Evidence: *Monk, Thelonious* / Stella by starlight: *Flanagan, Tommy & Kenny Barron* / Kelly's blues: *Kelly, Wynton* / Hear me talkin' to ya: *Silver, Horace* / Home come'n: *Walton, Cedar* / Caravan: *Jones, Hank* / They can't take that away from me: *Jones, Hank* / Take the 'A' train: *Ellington, Duke* / Band call: *Ellington, Duke* / Basie's thought: *Basie, Count* / Blues in B-flat: *Drew, Kenny* / Body and soul: *Garner, Erroll* / Man I love: *Garner, Erroll* / Autumn leaves: *Evans, Bill* / Time remembered: *Evans, Bill* / If I should lose you: *Kellaway, Roger* / Night before: *Hanna, Roland* / Have you met Miss Jones: *Shearing, George* / Rosa Mae: *Williams, Mary Lou* / Gloria: *Williams, Mary Lou* / Straight life: *Cables, George* / Supersonic: *Tristano, Lennie* / Rotunda: *Tyner, McCoy* / We'll be together again: *Tyner, McCoy* / Beautiful love: *Miller, Mulgrew* / Waltz for Bill Evans: *Corea, Chick* / Blues connotation: *Corea, Chick* / Heart to heart: *Corea, Chick & Andy Laverne* / When will the blues leave: *Bley, Paul* / Illusions: *Elias, Elaine* / Day dream: *Mays, Bill*

15954 / Oct '97 / Laserlight

☐ JAZZ PIANO VOL.1 (1935-1942)

251 282 2 / Mar '90 / Jazztime

☐ JAZZ PIONEERS VOL.2 (The Sound Of London)

EX 3392 / Nov '96 / Instinct

☐ JAZZ 'ROUND MIDNIGHT - PIANO

8409372 / Feb '91 / Verve

☐ JAZZ 'ROUND MIDNIGHT - SAXOPHONE

8409512 / Feb '91 / Verve

☐ JAZZ SAMPLER

GMCD 6239 / Dec '89 / Gemini

☐ JAZZ SATELLITES VOL.1 (Electrification/2CD Set)

I am an epigram for life: *Styler, Divine* / Mars in Libra: *Henderson, Eddie* / Karin's mode: *Garbarek, Jan* / Universal conciousness: *Coltrane, Alice* / Gospel comes to New Guinea: *23 Skidoo* / Andromeda strain: *Melle, Gil* / Internal bleeding: *Bedouin Ascent* / Twilight zone: *Connors, Norman* / Satellites are spinning: *Sun Ra* / 3.38: *Pop Group* / Man without a country: *Martin, Stu & John Surman* / Bullroarer: Krakatu / Milk rock: *Organization* / Rated X: *Davis, Miles* / Equals: *Macero, Teo* / Black mystery has been revealed: *Roland* / Beyond games: *Williams, Tony* / Bride of sloth: *Slab* / Goose and lucky: *Cooder, Ry* / Water: *Henderson, Joe* / Rima: *Headhunters* / Brown rice: *Cherry, Don* / Drive towards the smoke: *UI* / New power: *Fat* / Science fiction: *Coleman, Ornette* / Attack impulse: 16-17 / Nobu: *Hancock, Herbie*

AMBT 12 / Jul '96 / Virgin

☐ JAZZ SAXOPHONE IN A SOULFUL MOOD

Blue skies: *Getz, Stan* / I've just seen her: *Mulligan, Gerry & Scott Hamilton* / Here's that rainy day: *Shank, Bud* / Happiness is a thing called Joe: *Holloway, Red & Clark Terry Sextet* / Lover man: *Carter, Kenny* / This is new: *Cohn, Al* / Brother can you spare a dime: *Davern, Kenny* / Stardust: *Woodard, Rickey* / My man Benny: *Woods, Phil Quartet* / I gotta right to sing the blues: *Phillips, Flip* / Rapture: *Land, Harold & Blue Mitchell Quintet* / I'm getting sentimental over you: *Konitz, Lee* / Grooveyard: *Hamilton, Scott*

MCCD 321 / 6 Oct '97 / Music Club

☐ JAZZ SAXOPHONE, THE

Five four train: *Fortune, Sonny* / Sometimes I feel like a Motherless child: *Freeman, Chico* / Celebration: *Giuffre, Jimmy* / If I could be with you one hour tonight: *Hawkins, Coleman* / Passion flower: *Hodges, Johnny* / Thanks for the memory: *Konitz, Lee* / Out of nowhere: *Liebmann, David* / Spanish eyes: *Philips, Flip* / Nuestro bolero: *D'Rivera, Paquito* / Let me tell you why: *Shanky, Bud* / Fred: *Sims, Zoot* / Ballad: *Woods, Phil*

EMPRCD 609 / Jun '96 / Emporio

☐ JAZZ SCENE, THE

5216612 / Feb '95 / Verve

☐ JAZZ SELECTION VOL.1, THE

On the sunny side of the street: *Armstrong, Louis* / Everything goes: *Ellington, Duke* / Bird of paradise: *Davis, Miles & Charlie Parker* / Ain't misbehavin': *Waller, Fats* / When my dreamboat comes home: *Rushing, Jimmy* / St. Louis blues: *Witherspoon, Jimmy* / ME and the blues: *Bailey, Mildred* / Moose the mooche: *Davis, Miles* / Sweet Georgia brown: *Cole, Nat 'King' Trio* / When the Saints go marching in: *Armstrong, Louis* / Darktown strutters ball: *Lewis, Meade 'Lux'* / Jazz me blues: *Bechet, Sidney* / My man: *Holiday, Billie* / Street beat: *Parker, Charlie* / Tip toe topic: *Ellington, Duke* / St. Louis blues: *Dorsey, Jimmy* / Flying home: *Fitzgerald, Ella* / Georgia on my mind: *Carmichael, Hoagy Orchestra* / Slow boat to China: *Parker, Charlie* / Honey honey: *Charles, Ray*

QED 022 / Nov '96 / Tring

☐ JAZZ SELECTION VOL.2, THE

C'est si bon / Don't blame me / Harlem speaks / Tiger rag / Mame / Four hands / Sonny moon for two / Meet me where they play the blues / South Rampart Street Parade / Jelly roll blues / Tune of the hickory stick / Lover man / How high the moon / 'Round midnight / Crosstown / Scrapple from the apple / Crazeology / Panama rag / Tea for two / Yes sir, that's my baby

QED 023 / Nov '96 / Tring

☐ JAZZ SELECTION, THE (4CD Set)

One O'clock jump: *Basie, Count* / 'Round midnight: *Parker, Charlie* / At long last love: *Horne, Lena* / Something new: *Basie, Count* / Out of nowhere: *Davis, Miles* / King Porter stomp: *Goodman, Benny* / Lover come back to me: *Fitzgerald, Ella* / How high the moon: *Parker, Charlie* / Sweet Georgia Brown: *Cole, Nat 'King'* / Mooche: *Ellington, Duke* / More than you know: *Horne, Lena* / Mission to Moscow: *Horne, Lena* / Night in Tunisia: *Davis, Miles* / Basin Street blues: *Fitzgerald, Ella* / Crosstown: *Ellington, Duke* / My blue heaven: *Shaw, Artie* / Street beat: *Parker, Charlie* / All of me: *Basie, Count* / Black and tan fantasy: *Ellington, Duke* / Basin Street blues: *Armstrong, Louis* / Yardbird suite: *Davis, Miles* / I struck a match in the dark: *Basie, Count* / Rumbop concerto: *Gillespie, Dizzy* / Nobody knows the trouble I've seen: *Horne, Lena* / Starlit hour: *Fitzgerald, Ella* / On the sunny side of the street: *Cole, Nat 'King'* / Caravan: *Ellington, Duke* / Fascinating rhythm: *Goodman, Benny* / My heart stood still: *Shaw, Artie* / Ornithology: *Davis, Miles* / Tiger rag: *Armstrong, Louis* / Blue juice: *Barnet, Charlie* / Platterbrains: *Basie, Count* / Blue prelude: *Horne, Lena* / Stompin' at the Savoy: *Horne, Lena* / Yes sir that's my baby: *Cole, Nat 'King'* / Move: *Parker, Charlie* / Bugle call rag: *Goodman, Benny* / Sophisticated lady: *Ellington, Duke* / Moose the mooche: *Davis, Miles* / Cannon's blues: *Adderley, Cannonball* / When the saints go marching in: *Armstrong, Louis* / Embraceable you: *Davis, Miles* / It's only a paper moon: *Cole, Nat 'King'* / Down for double: *Basie, Count* / Little girl blue: *Basie, Count* / Bird of paradise: *Parker, Charlie* / Study in soulphony: *Gillespie, Dizzy* / Stairway to the stars: *Fitzgerald, Ella* / Ring dem bells: *Ellington, Duke* / Sugarfoot stomp: *Ellington, Duke* / Scuttlebutt: *Shaw, Artie* / Northwest passage: *Herman, Woody* / It's a rainy day: *Horne, Lena* / (Back home again in) Indiana: *Armstrong, Louis* / Feather merchant: *Basie, Count* / Riff raff: *Parker, Charlie* / Trouble with me is you: *Cole, Nat 'King'* / Somebody stole my gal: *Goodman, Benny* / There is no greater love: *Adderley, Cannonball* / That old magic: *Fitzgerald, Ella* / Honeysuckle rose: *Ellington, Duke* / Yes sir that's my baby: *Cole, Nat 'King'* / My old flame: *Basie, Count* / Love me or leave me: *Horne, Lena* / On the sunny side of the street: *Armstrong, Louis* / Parker's mood: *Parker, Charlie* / Three hearts in a tangle: *Gillespie, Dizzy* / Bijou: *Herman, Woody* / Don't be that way: *Goodman, Benny* / I can't get started (with you): *Shaw, Artie* / I can't remember to forget: *Barnet, Charlie* / Flying home: *Fitzgerald, Ella* / Ease it: *Adderley, Cannonball* / How high the moon: *Ellington, Duke* / Slow boat to China: *Parker, Charlie* / Don't blame me: *Parker, Charlie* / (Back home again in) Indiana: *Armstrong, Louis* / Fiesta in blue: *Basie, Count* / Bird of paradise: *Davis, Miles* / Get happy: *Goodman, Benny*

TFP 005 / Nov '92 / Tring

☐ JAZZ SHOWCASE

Basie: *Basie, Count Orchestra* / Reunion blues: *Peterson, Oscar* / So wistfully sad: *Brubeck, Dave* / Gone with the wind: *Short, Bobby* / Jo-Wes: *Pass, Joe* / Paraiso: *Mulligan, Gerry & Jane Duboc* / Little suede shoes: *Ruiz, Hilton* / Tour de force: *Hampton, Slide & The Jazz Masters* / Here's to life: *Williams, Joe & George Shearing* / Bird feathers: *Shearing, George* / I'm gonna go fishin': *Torme, Mel* / In the wee small hours of the morning: *Brown, Ray Trio* / Bittersweet: *Bryson, Jeanie* / Lullaby of Birdland: *Jamal, Ahmad*

CD 83342 / Apr '94 / Telarc

☐ JAZZ SINGERS

She was too good to me: *Baker, Chet* / All that jazz: *Torme, Mel* / I'll never be the same: *Rowles, Jimmie & Stan Getz* / Foggy day: *Benson, George* / Ain't she sweet: *Rich, Buddy & the Harry James Orchestra* / I ain't got nobody: *Gonzlaes, Babs & the Johnny Griffin Orchestra* / Flying home: *Gonzlaes, Babs & the Johnny Griffin Orchestra* / FDR Jones: *Calloway, Cab* / Mack the knife: *Armstrong, Louis* / Some minor changes: *Hi-Lo's* / Groove juice special: *Slim & Slam* / Work song: *Brown, Oscar Jr.* / I'm coming Viginia: *Rushing, Jimmy*

4878902 / 29 Sep '97 / Sony Jazz

☐ JAZZ SINGERS 1919-1994 (5CD Set)

3325111302 / 19 May '98 / Smithsonian Folkways

☐ JAZZ THANG (Funk Is The Preacher Jazz Is The Teacher)

Soul guru: *Richardson, Wally* / Black feeling: *Hammond, John* / Bucketful of soul: *Pitts, Trudy* / Tom thumb: *Timmons, Bobby* / Soul fingers: *Nanton, Morris* / Jug eyes: *Ammons, Gene* / I feel the earth move: *Jones, Joe* / Aleiluia: *Person, Houston* / Sweetheart: *Kynard, Charles* / Greasy kid stuff: *Mabern, Harold* / Mission eternal: *Blakey, Art & The Jazz Messengers*

CDBGPD 110 / 29 Sep '97 / Beat Goes Public

☐ JAZZ THAT THE WORLD FORGOT VOL.1 (Jazz Classics Of The 1920's)

YAZ 2024 / Nov '96 / Yazoo

☐ JAZZ THAT THE WORLD FORGOT VOL.2 (Jazz Classics Of The 1920's)

YAZ 2025 / Nov '96 / Yazoo

☐ JAZZ TODAY VOL.1

Sunday in New York: *Cole, Richie* / OTVOG: *Rollins, Sonny* / Scrapple from the apple: *Morgan, Frank Quartet* / If dreams come true: *White, Carla* / Movin' on: *McGriff, Jimmy* / Vicki: *Crawford, Hank* / Underground express: *Campbell, Kerry* / Samba for Isabelle: *Habian, Cliff* / Toc de bola: *Azymuth* / Jacaranda: *Roditi, Claudio*

CDBGP 1026 / Oct '93 / Beat Goes Public

☐ JAZZ TREATS FOR THE HOLIDAYS

ARCD 19122 / Nov '94 / Arbors Jazz

☐ JAZZ TRIBE, THE

1232542 / Nov '92 / Red

☐ JAZZ TRUMPET

Hard sock dance: *Bailey, Benny* / Isn't it romantic: *Baker, Chet* / Open the door: *Curson, Ted* / Red bank shuffle: *Edison, Harry* / Wrap your troubles in dreams: *Eldridge, Roy* / Sallie: *Ellis, Don* / Strength and sanity: *Little, Booker* / What am I here for: *Nance, Ray* / Rua dona Margarida: *Roditi, Claudio* / Casa de luz: *Rogers, Shorty* / No problem: *Terry, Clark* / Ferris wheel: *Williams, Richard*

EMPRCD 610 / Jun '96 / Emporio

☐ JAZZ ULTIMATE

PDSCD 536 / Aug '96 / Pulse

☐ JAZZ UNDERGOUND (Live At Smalls)

Kentucky girl: *Omer Avital Group* / Scenic roots: *Owens, Charles Quartet* / Hexophony: *Linder, Jason Big Band* / Everything happens to me: *Nasser, Zaid Quartet* / Kettle is whistling: *Across 7th Street* / I've never been in love before: *Omer Avital Group* / Prince Albert: *Hewitt, Frank Sextet* / Losing victory: *Owens, Charles Quartet* / Phat: *Linder, Jason Big Band*

IMP 12452 / 9 Feb '98 / Impulse Jazz

☐ JAZZ VALENTINE

MM 65091 / Oct '94 / Music Masters

☐ JAZZ VOCAL GROUPS 1927-1944 (2CD Set)

FA 041 / Sep '95 / Fremeaux

☐ JAZZ VOCALISTS

On the sunny side of the street: *Hampton, Lionel* / Ain't misbehavin': *Waller, Fats* / That ain't right: *Bailey, Mildred* / St. Louis blues: *Teagarden, Jack* / Stars fell on Alabama: *Wiley, Lee* / One o'clock jump: *Lambert, Dave* / Every day I have the blues: *Williams, Joe* / My man's gone now: *Simone, Nina* / Careless love: *Turner, 'Big' Joe* / What a wonderful world: *Armstrong, Louis* / Fine and mellow: *Rushing, Jimmy*

07863660722 / Oct '92 / Bluebird

☐ JAZZ VOCALISTS

Goodnight my love: *Fitzgerald, Ella & Benny Goodman Orchestra* / Marie: *Leonard, Jack & Tommy Dorsey* / Any old time: *Holiday, Billie & Artie Shaw Orchestra* / Ain't misbehavin': *Waller, Fats* / I'll never smile again: *Sinatra, Frank & Tommy Dorsey* / Don't take your love from me: *Horne, Lena & Artie Shaw* / Elmer's tune: *Eberle, Ray & Glenn Miller Orchestra* / One o' clock jump: *Lambert, Hendricks/Bavan* / Don't sit under the apple tree: *Beneke, Tex & Glenn Miller* / Every day I have the blues: *Williams, Joe* / Skylark: *Eckstine, Billy & Earl Hines* / My man's gone now: *Simone, Nina* / Ain't got nothin' but the blues: *Hibbler, Al & Duke Ellington* / What a wonderful world: *Armstrong, Louis* / Fine and mellow: *Rushing, Jimmy*

74321584812 / Jun '98 / RCA Victor

☐ JAZZ VOICE, THE

Doncha go way mad: *Jazz Passengers & Deborah Harry* / You go to my head: *Gallucio, Lo* / Who used to dance: *Lincoln, Abbey* / Stockholm sweetnin': *Mahogany, Kevin* / Moonray: *Brown, Jeri & Cyrus Chestnut* / Prelude to a kiss: *Winstone, Norma* / Baby take a chance with me: *Mingus Big Band* / Music never stopped: *Gallant, Joe & Illuminati* / Since you left: *Gisburg* / Put your quarter in and watch the chicken dance: *Chapin, Thomas Trio* / Everybody's talking about Sammy: *Morgan, Sam Jug Band*

KFWCD 212 / 27 Jul '98 / Knitting Factory

☐ JAZZ YEAR 1935, THE

Bubbling over / Stardust / Solo hop / In a sentimental mood / New Orleans twist / Sleepy time gal / Bouncin' in rhythm / King Porter stomp / Harlem heat / Miss brown to you / Baby won't you please come home / Truckin' / Swingin' em down / Djangology / Every now and then / Facts and figures / In the dark/flashes / Jazz me blues / Rosetta / Buzzard / Willow tree / Muskrat ramble / Chicken and waffles

TPZ 1045 / May '96 / Topaz Jazz

☐ JAZZ YEAR 1946, THE

SNAFU / Mellow mood / I can't escape from you / Confirmation / Allen's alley / Cool breeze / Ten lessons with Timothy / Ornithology / Tippin' out / 52nd Street theme / Five o'clock shadow / Sam beeps and bops / Everything's cool / Under the willow tree / Things to come / Opus in pastels / Opus de bop / Living my life / Cadillac slum / Be bop boogie / She's funny that way / Back talk / Mahogany Hall stomp / Saint

TPZ 1063 / Feb '97 / Topaz Jazz

☐ JAZZ YEAR BOOK 1936, THE (2CD Set)

74321345462 / Feb '97 / Milan

☐ JAZZ YEAR BOOK 1945, THE (2CD Set)

74321313312 / Feb '97 / Milan

☐ JAZZIER RHYTHMS VOL.1

HUBCD 9 / Jun '96 / Hubbub

☐ JAZZIER RHYTHMS VOL.2

Panamanian aire: *Morris, Byron* / Sun shower: *Morris, Byron* / Music in my heart: *Moses, Kathryn* / Brazil: *Gibbs, John* / Known unknown: *Jamal, Khan* / Poquito soul: *One G plus three* / Ron con-con: *El Chicano* / Feelings: *Cheyenne* / Universe: *Semper, George* / Gwee: *Fudoli, Richard* / Moondance: *Feather, Lorraine* / Love for sale: *Anderson, Ernestine*

HUBCD 17 / Mar '97 / Hubbub

☐ JAZZIN' AT RONNIE'S

MCCD 212 / Oct '95 / Music Club

☐ JAZZIN' BABY BLUES

Poor papa: *Jones, Clarence* / Look what a fool I've been: *Johnson, James P.* / Jazzin' baby blues: *Jones, Clarence* / Mama's got the blues: *Waller, Fats* / Mama's gone goodbye: *Montgomery, Mike* / Goodbye: *Montgomery, Mike* / Baby, won't you please come home: *Jones, Clarence* / Play 'em for mama and sing 'em for me: *Baker, Edythe* / He's my man: *Johnson, James P.* / When you're good you're lonesome: *Baker, Edythe* / Cryin' Blues: *Randolph, Mandy* / Blooie blooie: *Baker, Edythe* / Changes: *Lawnhurst, Vee* / Yearning (just for you): *Lawnhurst, Vee* / I'm gonna jazz my way: *Randolph, Mandy*

BCD 117 / Jul '91 / Biograph

☐ JAZZIN' THE BLUES

MCCD 186 / Nov '94 / Music Club

☐ JAZZIN' THE BLUES

Jelly bean blues: *Rainey, Gertrude 'Ma'* / Cold in hand blues: *Smith, Bessie* / Sugar foot stomp: *Oliver, Joe 'King'* / Creole love call: *Ellington, Duke* / West End blues: *Armstrong, Louis* / Good morning blues: *Basie, Count* / I thought I heard Buddy Bolden say: *Morton, Jelly Roll* / Winin' boy blues: *Morton, Jelly Roll* / 2.19 blues: *Armstrong, Louis* / Geechy Joe: *Calloway, Cab* / Rusty dusty blues: *Jordan, Louis* / Across the track blues: *Ellington, Duke* / Trouble in mind: *Millinder, Lucky* / Blue serge: *Ellington, Duke* / What's the use of getting sober: *Jordan, Louis* / Harvard blues: *Basie, Count* / Good Jelly blues: *Eckstine, Billy* / Lady in bed: *Page, Hot Lips* / Hurry hurry: *Millinder, Lucky* / Take me back baby: *Basie, Count*

19133 / Jan '97 / Forlane

☐ JAZZIN' THE BLUES 1936-1946

JPCD 1515 / May '95 / Jazz Perspectives

☐ JAZZIN' THE BLUES VOL.2 (1939-1946)

DOCD 5468 / Jul '96 / Document

☐ JAZZIN' THE BLUES VOL.3 1937-1941

DOCD 5536 / Jun '97 / Document

☐ JDJ ALIVE AT PRIDE 1996

JDJP 1CD / Aug '96 / JDJ

☐ JDJ MARATHON (2CD Set)

ADMCD 1 / Oct '96 / JDJ

☐ JEAN BORELLI PRESENTS DECK WIZARDS VOL.5

PDCD 06 / 10 Nov '97 / Psychic Deli

☐ JEAN COCTEAU EN CHANSONS

108622 / Nov '97 / Musidisc

☐ JESSE'S JUBILEE ALBUM

CD 2030S / Jul '96 / Jesse's Jazz

☐ JEUNES SONNEURS DU CENTRE BRETAGNE

437 / Mar '96 / Arfolk

☐ JEWELS OF CAJUN MUSIC

TRIK 0157 / Oct '94 / Trikont

☐ JEWISH ALTERNATIVE MOVEMENT (A Guide For The Perplexed)
Men trinkt mashke: *Hasidic New Wave* / Hora Attik: *Paradox Trio* / Hava nagila: *Caine, Uri* / Metal: *Naftule's Dream* / Fruit flys: *Dalachinsky, Steve* / Mizmor shir lehanef: *Klezmatics* / Gasn nign: *Krakauer, David* / Secret of the Sabbath: *Brill, Wally* / Denial of the fittest: *Sloan, Judith* / David and Goliath: *Piamenta, Yosi* / Breath of bones: *Lucas, Gary* / Kil N'drei: *Forgiveness* / Gam ki elech: *Carlebach, Anthony* / Hanukkah bush: *Coleman, Anthony* / Alef beit: *Haas, Andy*
KFWCD 216 / 29 Jun '98 / Knitting Factory

☐ JEW'S HARPS OF THE WORLD
PS 66009 / Dec '97 / PlayaSound

☐ JINGLE BELLS IN THE SNOW
CNCD 5931 / Nov '92 / Disky

☐ JITTERBUG JIVE (Texas Swing 1940-1941)
KKCD 19 / Apr '97 / Krazy Kat

☐ JIVE IS JUMPIN', THE (RCA & Bluebird Vocal Groups 1939-1952)
Jive is jumpin': *Four Clefs* / I like pie I like cake: *Four Clefs* / V-Day stomp: *Four Clefs* / When I'm low I get high: *Four Clefs* / Gang busters: *Cats & The Fiddle* / I miss you so: *Cats & The Fiddle* / I'd rather drink muddy water: *Cats & The Fiddle* / Nuts to you: *Cats & The Fiddle* / That's on Jack that's on: *Cats & The Fiddle* / Low down gal blues: *Bronzeville, Lewis Five* / Natchez Mississippi blues: *Bronzeville, Lewis Five* / Comin' in on a wing and a prayer: *Four Vagabonds* / Rosie the riveter: *Four Vagabonds* / Jack you're dead: *Aristo-Kats* / Watch yourself baby: *Aristo-Kats* / That chick's too young to fry: *Deep River Boys* / Elevator boogie: *Johnson, Bill & His Musical Notes* / Shorty's got to go: *Johnson, Bill & His Musical Notes* / One o'clock jump: *Delta Rhythm Boys* / Take the 'A' train: *Delta Rhythm Boys* / I'll never get out of this world alive: *Delta Rhythm Boys* / Boogie woogie on a Saturday night: *Delta Rhythm Boys*
WESA 813 / 15 Jun '98 / Westside

☐ JIVING JAMBOREE
Saturday night fish fry / Ain't got no home / Something's goin' on in my room / They call me big Mama / Honeydripper / Love love of my life / I want you / Buzz buzz buzz / Wet back hop / Ding dong daddy / Music goes 'round and around / Don't stop loving me / Nite life boogie / Opus one / Hit, git and split / Rockin' Robin / My baby's rockin / That's all / You got me reelin' and rockin' / O sole mio boogie / Free and easy / Hey girl, hey boy / Rock that boogie / Flat foot Sam / My man
CDCHD 561 / Apr '95 / Ace

☐ JJ COMPILATION
JJCD 1 / Jun '95 / JJ

☐ JOCKOMO NEW ORLEANS RHYTHM AND BLUES
MCCD 206 / Jul '95 / Music Club

☐ JODLER DU TYROL AU TEXAS
AT 8001 / Jun '97 / ARB

☐ JOE FRASIER PRESENTS
JFCD 4649 / Aug '95 / VP

☐ JOE KING PRESENTS (More Bounce To The Ounce/2CD Set)
LK 154CD / Aug '97 / Lookout

☐ JOURNEY (Vocal Music From India)
Tillvare festival / Drut / Siddi vinayakan seveham / Jhala / Dadra raga maand / Ararara / Composition / Ninnaye rathiyenru / Bhajan aya dwar tumhare / Hymn of praise to the god of love / Tarana / Ganesha stuti srivighna rajam bhaje / Hanuman is reunited with Sita
B 6860 / Mar '98 / Auvidis/Ethnic

☐ JOURNEY DOWN THE RHINE (Popular Music About The Rhine Area)
15371 / '91 / Laserlight

☐ JOURNEY INTO AMBIENT GROOVE VOL.1, A
5243302 / Jan '97 / Quango

☐ JOURNEY INTO AMBIENT GROOVE VOL.2, A
5242242 / Jun '96 / Quango

☐ JOURNEY INTO DRUM 'N' BASS VOL.2 (2CD Set)
Circles: *Adam F* / On and on: *Badu, Erykah* / Gone are the days: *Ganja Kru* / Opaque: *Aquasky* / 2 wicky: *Hooverphonic* / Lucky: *Taylor, Lewis* / Candles: *Reece, Alex* / Sanctuary: *Omni Trio* / I wanted it more and more: *Aphrodite & Gail McLean* / Music that we hear: *Morcheeba* / Sputnik: *Best Boy Electric* / Earthly egos: *Third Wave* / Cover me: *Bjork* / Digital: *Goldie & KRS1* / Brown paper bag: *Roni Size* / You're not alone: *Olive* / KJZ: *Photek* / Lonely without you: *Anderson, Deborah* / Airsign: *Justice* / Escape: *Digital* / 1000 yard stare: *B-Scale* / Planetaria: *4 Hero* / Monokel: *Minsky & Best Boy Electric* / You're gonna miss my face: *Shanie* / If I could fly: *Grace*
5556992 / 26 May '98 / Amber

☐ JOURNEY THROUGH THE UNDERGROUND
PLUGCD 1 / Nov '94 / Produce

☐ JOURNEY TO BRAZIL, A
PS 66508 / Apr '95 / PlayaSound

☐ JOURNEY TO INDIA, A
PS 66512 / Feb '96 / PlayaSound

☐ JOURNEY TO LOUISIANA, A
PS 66511 / Dec '95 / PlayaSound

☐ JOURNEY TO PORTUGAL, A
PS 66507 / Apr '95 / PlayaSound

☐ JOURNEY TO SENEGAL, A
PS 66513 / Oct '96 / PlayaSound

☐ JOURNEY TO THE EDGE (Progressive Rock Classics)
Living in the past: *Jethro Tull* / Joybringer: *Manfred Mann's Earthband* / America: *Nice* / Cirkus: *King Crimson* / In-a-gadda-da-vida: *Iron Butterfly* / Forty thousand headmen: *Traffic* / You keep me hangin' on: *Vanilla Fudge* / Child of the universe: *Barclay James Harvest* / Wishing well: *Free* / Tomorrow night: *Atomic Rooster* / Jerusalem: *Emerson, Lake & Palmer* / Freefall: *Camel* / Back street luv: *Curved Air* / Surprise surprise: *Caravan* / Natural born bugie: *Humble Pie* / Love like a man: *Ten Years After* / Burlesque: *Family* / My room (Waiting for wonderland): *Van Der Graaf Generator*
MUSCD 018 / May '94 / MCI Music

☐ JOURNEY TO VIETNAM, A
PS 66509 / Apr '95 / PlayaSound

☐ JOURNEYS BY DJ PRESENTS DESERT ISLAND MIX (2CD Set) (Peterson, Gilles & Norman Jay)
JDJCD 15 / 22 Sep '97 / JDJ

☐ JOURNEYS BY DJ PRESENTS TRIPTONITE (3CD Set)
Turn off the light: *Shades Of Rhythm* / Private funk: *Private Funk* / Summer bummer: *Crazy Penis* / Klarky Cat: *Gumbo* / Nu odyssey: *Departure Lounge* / Wayward mind: *Homeland* / Lick: *Earl Grey* / Reverberations: *Webster, Charles* / Delirious: *OHMSS* / Terry's house: *Brown, Terry Lee Jr.* / Drop: *Hot Lizard* / Calypso theme: *Pooley, Ian* / Sunseeker: *Solar Perplexed* / You gonna make me love somebody else: *Colourblind* / My love turns to liquid: *Dream 2 Science* / That Elvis track: *Sol Brothers* / Drop the boom: *Freestylers* / Manic jazz day: *DJ Anthony & Georgio* / Renegade: *Hip Hop Renegade* / C and P electric bonus beats: *Cut & Paste* / Chicky disco: *Stout The Dodge* / Auburn: *Skylab 2000* / Shock the beat: *Electric Choc* / What would we do: *Sol Brothers* / Laydown: *2B Continued* / Timeless: *Quake-X* / Energy 52: *Cafe Del Mar* / Encore une fois: *Sash* / Guidance: *Kamillion* / Calm down: *Kamillion* / Fantasy: *Alter Egos* / Thoughts: *Altered States* / Flute lore: *Infinite Wheel* / Luv is all you need: *99 All Stars* / Floorburn: *Chapp'd Out* / Destination eschaton: *Shamen* / Dialogue: *3 Dubs In A Sleeve* / Mickey and Mallory: *Natural Born Groovers* / Scotti deep: *Brooklyn Beats* / Pandomia: *DJ Randy* / Bad man: *Sister Bliss* / Flowtation: *De Moor, Vincent* / Groove seekers allowance: *Swag* / Auburn: *Skylab 2000* / Party: *Fletch* / Acid energy: *DJ Misjah & Groovehend* / State of play: *SNJ Works* / Flamenco trip: *TUSOM*
JDJCD 14 / May '97 / JDJ

☐ JOURNEYS BY DJ VOL.5
JDJCD 5 / Jun '94 / JDJ

☐ JOURNEYS BY DJ VOL.6 (The Ultimate House Party Mix)
JDJCD 6 / Oct '94 / JDJ

☐ JOURNEYS BY DJ VOL.7 (Rocky & Diesel)
JDJCD 7 / Jun '95 / JDJ

☐ JOURNEYS BY DJ VOL.9 (The Ultimate Beach Party)
JDJCD 9 / Dec '95 / JDJ

☐ JOURNEYS INTO JUNGLE
JIJCD 001 / Jun '95 / JDJ

☐ JOURNEYS THROUGH CYBERSEX (Mixed By DJ Alan TG)
TGCD 0012 / Jun '97 / Torture Garden

☐ JOY OF CHRISTMAS, THE (Christmas Crooners/Christmas With Bing Crosby/ Angel Voices)
MCBX 012 / Apr '94 / Music Club

☐ JOY OF CHRISTMAS, THE (2CD Set)
Once in Royal David's city / Ave Maria / Ding dong merrily on high / Silent night / Panis angelicus / Holly and the ivy / Jingle bells/Deck the hall / Good King Wenceslas / O Holy night / O little town of Bethlehem / In dulci jubilo / First Noel / Pastoral sinfonia / O thou that tellest good tidings to Zion / For unto us a child is born / God rest ye merry gentlemen / Away in a manger / What child is this / O come all ye faithful (adeste fidelis) / Twelve days of Christmas / Sussex carol / Star carol / Mary's boy child / King Jesus hath a garden / Up good Christian folk and listen / Child in a manger / Mille cherubini in coro / Lullaby / In the bleak mid Winter / Gesu bambino / Trio for two flutes and a harp / Slumber aria / See amid the Winter's snow / Shepherd's in the field abiding / While shepherds watched / Ave Maria / Hark the herald angels sing
4524502 / Nov '96 / Decca

☐ JOY RIDE VOL.2
DCCD 4001 / Apr '97 / Joe Frazier

☐ JOY TO THE WORLD
Away in a manger: *Nelson, Willie* / What child is this: *Gayle, Crystal* / Deck the halls: *Boxcar Willie* / Silent night: *Mandrell, Louise & Pedro Tomas* / Joy to the world: *Nelson, Willie* / All I want for Christmas: *Nelson, Willie* / Deck the halls: *Nelson, Willie* / O little town of Bethlehem: *Gilley, Mickey* / What child is this: *Carnes, Kim* / O come all ye faithful (adeste fidelis): *Jennings, Waylon* / Hallelujah: *Gayle, Crystal* / It came upon a midnight clear: *Nelson, Willie* / First Noel: *Lettermen*
120332 / Oct '97 / Jingle

☐ JOYEUX NOEL
DCD 5338 / Dec '93 / Disky

☐ JSP JAZZ SESSIONS 1980-1985 (2CD Set)
Dolphin has a message: *Freeman, Bud* / Just past tea time: *Freeman, Bud* / Blues for Brian: *Freeman, Bud* / Cleanheads thing: *Vinson, Eddie 'Cleanhead'* / Fun in London: *Vinson, Eddie 'Cleanhead'* / Racetrack blues: *Vinson, Eddie 'Cleanhead'* / Straight away: *Vinson, Eddie 'Cleanhead'* / Roxanne: *Vinson, Eddie 'Cleanhead'* / Wee Jeanie: *Durham, Eddie* / Sliding along: *Durham, Eddie* / Swinging mood: *Durham, Eddie* / Blue bone: *Durham, Eddie* / Marco's tune: *Connors, Gene 'Mighty Flea'* / Goobers: *Connors, Gene 'Mighty Flea'* / Biscuits: *Connors, Gene 'Mighty Flea'* / Maha's tune: *Connors, Gene 'Mighty Flea'* / Buckjumping: *Casey, Al* / End: *Casey, Al* / Body and soul: *Casey, Al* / Hold out baby: *Casey, Al* / That's the one: *Singer, Hal* / Let's think awhile: *Singer, Hal* / Swing on it: *Singer, Hal* / Point: *Singer, Hal* / Swinging mood: *Durham, Eddie* / Guitar piece no.2: *Durham, Eddie* / Caribbean jam: *Durham, Eddie* / Blue bone: *Durham, Eddie* / Welcase blues: *Casey, Al*
JSPCD 404 / May '98 / JSP

☐ JUBILEE JEZEBELS VOL.1
Drive Daddy drive: *Little Sylvia* / I went to your wedding: *Little Sylvia* / Ain't gonna do it: *Little Sylvia* / Blue heaven: *Little Sylvia* / Everything I need but you: *Little Sylvia* / It must be love: *Watkins, Viola* / Really real: *Watkins, Viola* / There goes my heart: *Watkins, Viola* / I've lost: *Enchanters* / Housewife blues: *Enchanters* / How could you: *Enchanters* / Boogie woogie Daddy: *Enchanters* / Heavenly father: *McGriff, Edna* / It's raining: *McGriff, Edna* / I love you: *McGriff, Edna* / Edna's blues: *McGriff, Edna* / Why oh why: *McGriff, Edna* / I'll surrender anytime: *McGriff, Edna* / It's my turn now: *Fran, Carol* / You can't stop me: *Fran, Carol* / I know: *Fran, Carol* / Any day love walks in: *Fran, Carol* / Just a letter: *Fran, Carol* / World without you: *Fran, Carol*
NEMCD 750 / Aug '95 / Sequel

☐ JUBILEE JEZEBELS VOL.2
Ooh little daddy: *McGriff, Edna* / I'll be around: *McGriff, Edna* / These things shall be: *McGriff, Edna* / I found somebody to love: *Little Sylvia* / Kiss for my baby: *Little Sylvia* / I miss you: *Little Sylvia* / Ring: *Little Sylvia* / Million tears: *Little Sylvia* / Don't blame my heart: *Little Sylvia* / Paint a sky for me: *Watkins, Viola* / Goodnight sweetheart, goodnight: *Mann, Gloria* / Love me boy: *Mann, Gloria* / Today is your birthday: *Enchanters* / When I say my prayer: *Lynne, Gloria* / Uncloudy day: *Lynne, Gloria* / After the lights go down low: *Jerome, Patti* / Johnny has gone: *Jerome, Patti* / I cried for you: *Reese, Della* / Runaround: *Marie Ann* / I can see through you: *Simmons, Fay* / Hangin' around: *Simmons, Fay* / Crying in the chapel: *Fran, Carol* / I'm gonna try: *Fran, Carol* / Let me go: *Big Maybelle* / No better for you: *Big Maybelle*
NEMCD 916 / Jun '97 / Sequel

☐ JUBILEE/JOSIE VOCAL GROUPS VOL.3
NEMCD 756 / Mar '96 / Sequel

☐ JUBILEE/JOSIE VOCAL GROUPS VOL.4
NEMCD 757 / Mar '96 / Sequel

☐ JUBILEE/JOSIE VOCAL GROUPS VOL.5
Cruise to the moon: *Chaperones* / Shining star: *Chaperones* / Man from the moon: *Chaperones* / Teenage paradise: *Volumes* / Sandra: *Volumes* / Night and day: *Til, Sonny* / Shimmy time: *Til, Sonny* / So long: *Til, Sonny* / Crazy love: *Knight, Bob Four* / Memories: *Knight, Bob Four* / Dancing alone: *Emeralds* / Did you ever love a guy: *Emeralds* / This I swear: *Dubs* / Wisdom of a fool: *Dubs* / Our wedding day: *Shells* / Deep in my heart: *Shells* / Lonely road: *Passions* / School bells to chapel bells: *Styles* / I love you for sentimental reasons: *Styles* / Shangri-la: *Parakeets* / Elaine: *Glenwoods* / That's the way it'll be: *Glenwoods* / If you love me, really love me: *Jordan & The Fascinations* / Who needs love: *Ovations* / Remembering: *Ovations* / Two friends: *Knight, Bob Four* / Far from your love: *Appreciations* / Our song: *Volumes*
NEMCD 758 / Jun '96 / Sequel

☐ JUG & WASHBOARD BANDS 1928-1930
SOBCD 35142 / Mar '92 / Story Of The Blues

☐ JUG OF PUNCH, THE (Raising A Glass To Celtic Music)
CELT 9012CD / 9 Mar '98 / Celtophile

☐ JUJU ROOTS 1930S-50S
ROUCD 5017 / Feb '93 / Rounder

☐ JUKE BOX GIANTS (4CD Set)
MBSCD 414 / Nov '93 / Castle

☐ JUKE BOX JIVE (The Birth Of Rock 'n' Roll/2CD Set)
CPCD 82702 / Apr '97 / Charly

☐ JUKE BOX R & B
I got loaded: *Cadets* / Wiggie waggie woo: *Cadets* / Sixty minute man: *Cadets* / Dance the thing: *Dixon, Floyd Orchestra* / Baby, baby every night: *James, Etta* / How big a fool: *James, Etta* / One whole year baby: *Curry, Earl* / This is the night for love: *Flairs* / She wants to rock: *Flairs* / Hit, git and split: *Young Jessie* / Everyday I have the blues: *King, B.B.* / Don't you want a man like me: *King, B.B.* / She moves me: *Watson, Johnny 'Guitar'* / Standing at the crossroads: *James, Elmore* / Rumba rock: *Beasley, Jimmy* / I'm so blue: *Beasley, Jimmy* / Chicken shack: *Turner, Ike & Tina* / Shattered dreams: *Fulson, Lowell* / Let's make with some love: *Berry, Richard & The Flairs* / Double crossin' baby: *Robins* / My darling: *Jacks* / Rock everybody: *Teen Queens*
CDCHD 335 / Sep '91 / Ace

☐ JUKE JOINT BLUES
Statesboro blues: *McTell, 'Blind' Willie* / Good morning schoolgirl: *Williamson, Sonny Boy* / Summertime: *Holiday, Billie* / It hurts me too: *Tampa Red* / Cross road blues: *Johnson, Robert* / Nobody knows when you're down and out: *Smith, Bessie* / You just as well let her go: *Weldon, Casey Bill* / Key to the highway: *Broonzy, 'Big' Bill* / Catfish blues: *Petway, Robert* / Stones in my passway: *Johnson, Robert* / What's the matter with the mill: *Memphis Minnie* / I be troubled: *Waters, Muddy* / Midnight special: *Leadbelly* / I feel so good: *Broonzy, 'Big' Bill* / Midnight hour blues: *Carr, Leroy* / I been dealing with the devil: *Williamson, Sonny Boy* / Baby please don't go: *Williams, 'Big' Joe* / Nobody's fault but mine: *Johnson, 'Blind' Willie* / Roll and tumble blues: *Newbern, 'Hambone' Willie* / Strange fruit: *Holiday, Billie* / Winnie the wailer: *Johnson, Lonnie* / Bull frog blues: *Harris, William* / Lone wolf blues: *Woods, Oscar 'Buddy'* / Ramblin' on my mind: *Johnson, Robert* / Don't you lie to me: *Tampa Red*
EMPRCD 669 / Oct '96 / Emporio

☐ JUKE JOINT'S 5TH ANNIVERSARY COLLECTION, THE
Jumpin' at Deke's: *Abdabs* / Ain't gonna put me down: *Taylor, Matt* / Blues is king: *Grand, Otis* / Can you dig it: *Clayton, Steve 'Big Man' & The 44's* / Long way to go: *Al Morocco 5* / Ain't holding my breath: *Out Of The Blue* / Hedgehog: *Booze & Blues* / Parchment farm: *Receeders* / Let it go: *Rockin' Armadillos* / Shake it and break it: *Marques Brothers* / Brokenhearted blues: *Elmores* / You got me: *Motel Kings* / Fun with the blues: *Packham, Kit One Jump Ahead* / Down in the bottom: *Slim Tim & Lightnin' Phil* / Good morning little school girl: *Bullet Blues Band*
01702002 / Jun '97 / Lunch

☐ JUKEBOX GIANTS
MACCD 107 / Aug '96 / Autograph

☐ JUMP AND SWING WITH BLACK TOP
Trane diggin': *Copley, Al & Hal Singer* / Hit it: *Holmstrom, Rick* / That's it: *Big Joe & The Dynaflows* / Ain't you trouble: *Primich, Gary* / I'll take you back home: *King, Earl* / Mushmouth: *Piccolo, Greg* / Stand by me: *Zimm, Rusty* / I never thought: *Guitar Shorty* / Jumbo: *Gaines, Grady* / Low down dirty dog: *Piazza, Rod & The Mighty Flyers* / Go girl: *Tri-Saxual Soul Champs*
CDBTEL 7007 / May '97 / Black Top

☐ JUMP AROUND - RAP'S HALL OF FAME
XPS 4CD / Jun '96 / X-Press

☐ JUMP BLUE (Rockin' The Joints)
Jump children: *Bartholomew, Dave* / King kong: *Tyler, Big T.* / Hucklebuck with Jimmy: *Five Keys* / Flying home part 1: *Jacquet, Illinois* / Deacon rides again: *McNeely, 'Big' Jay* / Safronia B: *Boze, Calvin & His All Stars* / Messy Bessy: *Jordan, Louis* / I ain't drunk: *Liggins, Joe & Jimmy* / Fine brown frame: *Lutcher, Nellie* / CC rider: *Markham, Pigmeat* / He may be your man: *Humes, Helen* / Yes it's you: *Clovers* / Daybreak: *Crayton, Pee Wee* / When I'm in my tea: *Adams, Jo Jo* / I got loaded: *Harris, Peppermint* / Fool in love: *Turner, Ike & Tina* / Sax shack boogie: *Milburn, Amos* / Cleo's boogie: *Brown, Cleo* / Great big eyes: *Archibald* / Let the four winds blow: *Brown, Roy* / Teenage baby: *Walker, T-Bone* / Don't leave me baby: *Fulson, Lowell* / Wine wine wine: *Dixon, Floyd* / Let the good times roll: *Shirley & Lee* / I need you, I want you: *Parker, Jack* / Jumpin' tonight: *Turner, 'Big' Joe & His Band*
CDP 8543642 / Oct '96 / Blue Note

☐ JUMP JIVE AND HARMONIZE
Jump jive and harmonize: *Thee Midniters* / Busy body: *Jolly Green Giants* / Slippin' and slidin': *Five Americans* / Alligator: *Us Four* / Set me free: *Incrowd* / I wanna be your love: *Cobras* / Can't you see: *Count & The Colony* / Move it on over: *Shannon, Del* / It's alligator time: *Stokely, Jimmy & The Exiles* / El monstruo: *Los Shains* / Monkey man: *Baby Huey & The Baby Sitters* / Gorilla: *Shandells* / 83: *Centurys* / Come on come on: *Esquires* / Who do you love: *Preachers* / Take a look at me: *Lucky & The Gamblers* / Hog: *Groupies* / Ain't that lovin' you baby: *Human Beinz*
TS 6601CD / 20 Jul '98 / Teenage Shutdown

☐ JUMP UP (Best Of Urban Jungle)
FAR 412CD / 16 Jul '97 / Family Affair

☐ JUMP UP THROWDOWN (3CD Set)
CERBAD 6 / 27 Apr '98 / Lacerba

☐ JUMPIN' AND JIVIN'
Something's goin' on in my room: *Daddy Cleanhead* / Tell it like it is: *Milton, Roy* / Lucy Brown: *Henderson, Duke* / Mad lad returns: *Parker, Leo* / Drink up light up: *Alexander, Nelson Trio* / Baby don't do that to me: *Milton, Roy* / Sometimes: *Easton, Amos* / When the rooster crows: *Turner, Joe* / Hep cat boogie: *Liggins, Jimmy* / Baby you don't know: *Milton, Roy* / Red top: *King Pleasure* / Ida Red: *Easton, Amos* / Cool goofin': *Ferguson, Rudy* / Wine woogie: *Phillips, Marvin* / Twisted: *Ross, Annie* / Tiny's boogie: *Easton, Amos* / If you don't know: *Milton, Roy* / I must have been an ugly baby: *Perry, King* / Stop talkin' start walkin': *Jefferson, Eddie* / Gonna leave you baby: *Milton, Roy* / Squattin': *Davis, Eddie 'Lockjaw'* / Hole in the wall: *Dixon, Floyd* / Got a penny Benny: *Carroll, Joe* / Make me know it: *Milton, Roy* / Moody's mood for love: *King Pleasure*
CDCHD 654 / May '97 / Ace

☐ JUMPIN' AND PUMPIN' VS. ELICIT
Papua new guinea: *Future Sound Of London* / Fire when ready: *G Double E* / Visitor: *DJ Space* / Stakker humanoid: *Humanoid* / Dominate: *Flag* / Alchemist: *Genaside II* / Tainted love: *Impedance* / Zum zum: *Love Men* / Check how we jam: *Bass Construction* / We can ride the boogie rock with you: *Bubbles* / Get on the move: *Psychopaths*
CDTOT 6 / Jul '93 / Jumpin' & Pumpin'

☐ JUMPIN' IN CHICAGO
CDGR 175 / Jul '97 / Charly

☐ JUMPIN' JAZZ
Iron city: *Green, Grant* / Speak low: *Sparks, Melvin* / Harold's house of jazz: *Cole, Richie* / Mambo Inn: *Donaldson, Lou* / Possum grease: *Lytle, Johnny* / As time goes by: *Murphy, Mark* / Prodigal son: *Ousley, Harold* / Street song: *Hutcherson, Bobby* / Heavy juice: *Person, Houston* / Things are getting better: *Jefferson, Eddie* / So what: *Lytle, Johnny*
PHOCD 8005 / Jun '96 / PHQ

☐ JUMPIN' JAZZ (The Masters/4CD Set)
SUMBX 4013 / Jan '98 / Summit

☐ JUMPIN' JIVE (2CD Set)
Jumpin' jive: Calloway, Cab / Five guys named Moe: Jordan, Louis & His Tympany Five / Hurry hurry: Harris, Wynonie / All that meat and no potatoes: Waller, Fats / Is you is or is you ain't my baby: Vinson, Eddie 'Cleanhead' / Why don't you do right: Treen, Lil with Broonzy, 'Big' Bill / Watch that jive: Turner, 'Big' Joe & His Band / Caldonia: Herman, Woody & His Orchestra / B-flat blues: King, Saunders & His Blues Band / Pagin' Mr Page: Page, Hot Lips & His Orchestra / Share-croppin' blues: Starr, Kay / 'Taint what you do (it's the way that cha do it): Waller, Fats / Evil gal blues: Washington, Dinah / Shout, sister, shout: Bradshaw, Tiny & His Orchestra / At the swing cat's ball: Jordan, Louis & His Tympany Five / Hey lawdy mama: Kirk, Andy & His Twelve Clouds of Joy / You'se a viper: Smith, Stuff & His Onyx Club Boys / Knock me a kiss: Krupa, Gene & His Orchestra / Ram session: Buck Ram Allstars / Boogie woogie dance: Calloway, Cab Orchestra / What's the use of getting sober (when you're gonna get drunk: Jordan, Louis & His Tympany Five / Your feet's too big: Waller, Fats / Boog it: Armstrong, Louis & Mills Brothers / After hours: Hawkins, Erskine & His Orchestra / Jive (page one of the hepsters dictionary): Calloway, Cab Orchestra / Hamps boogie woogie: Hampton, Lionel & His Orchestra / Here comes the man with the jive: Smith, Stuff & His Onyx Club Boys / Ride Red ride: Millinder, Lucky Orchestra / Rosetta: Newton, Frankie & His Orchestra / Sweet Lorraine: Cole, Nat 'King' Trio / You meet the nicest people in your dreams: Waller, Fats / Do you wanna jump children: Rushing, Jimmy/Count Basie & His Orchestra / Harlem joys: Smith, Willie 'The Lion' & His Cubs / Reefer man: Calloway, Cab Orchestra / Swing with me rhythm: Prima, Louis & His New Orleans Gang / Jumpin' the blues: Cooper, Al & His Savoy Sultans / Roll 'em: Goodman, Benny Orchestra / Squeeze me: Waller, Fats / I got rhythm: Spirits Of Rhythm / Doug the jitterbug: Jordan, Louis & His Tympany Five
330182 / Jul '96 / Hallmark

☐ JUMPIN' LIKE MAD COOL CATS AND HIP CHICKS (2CD Set)
Jumpin' tonight (midnight rockin') / Safronia B / Cow cow boogie / Jumpin' with Symphony Sid / Jump it with a shuffle / Oh babe / Stingy blues / Oo-pa-pa-da / Hypin' women blues / Fine brown frame / Baby, let's be friends / Be baba leba / Frim fram sauce / Solid potato salad / Pork chops and mustard greens / Jack's town / This joint's too hip for me / Marihuana boogie / Pachuko hop / Juice head baby / Cheap old wine and whiskey / Looped / I ain't drunk / All that wine is gone / I seen what'cha done / No more alcohol / Insect ball / Gee / House of blue lights / Hustle is on / Blowin' Red's top / He should'a flip'd when he flop'd / He's a real gone guy / My baby done left me / Chicas patas boogie (oh babe) / Chittlin' ball / Wrong neighbourhood / Jumpin' Jack / Fat and forty / No name boogie / Concentration / Two cats / Yeah yeah yeah / I'll die happy / I may be easy, but I'm no fool / Travellin' baby / Blow man blow / Boogie woogie king / Keep your nose out of my business / Talking that talk / 5 Months, 2 weeks, 2 days
CDEM 1608 / Mar '97 / Capitol

☐ JUMPIN' THE BLUES
Damp rag / New kind of feelin' / Big Bob's boogie / Elephant rock / Riff / Fat man blues / There ain't enough room here to boogie / Dr. Jives / Cadillac boogie / Tra-la-la / Race horse / Pelican jump / Hi-Yo Silver / We're gonna rock this morning
CDCHD 941 / Jun '90 / Ace

☐ JUMPIN' VOL.1
Keep on jumpin': Musique / Runaway: Salsoul Orchestra & Loleatta Holloway / Disco juice: Cloud One / There but for the grace of God go I: Machine / Thousand finger man: Candido / Touch and go: Ecstasy, Passion & Pain / It's all over my face: Loose Joints / Love money: T.W. Funkmasters / Got the feeling: Two Tons Of Fun / Funkanova: Wood, Brass & Steel / Tee's happy: Northend / Go bang: Dinosaur L
HURTCD 002
HURTCDL 002 / Apr '97 / Harmless

☐ JUMPIN' VOL.2
HURTCD 006 / 2 Mar '98 / Harmless

☐ JUMPING AT JUBILEE
Hole in the ground: Kohlman, Freddie Orchestra / You'll never get nothing without trying: Cousin Joe / Ramblin' woman: Cousin Joe / Can't help myself (pts 1 and 2): Powell, Jesse / I'm all alone: Powell, Jesse / Don't pass me by: Brown, Piney / Battle with the bottle: Brown, Piney / 3-D Loving: Brown, Piney / You bring out the wolf in me: Brown, Piney / Ay la bah: Cobb, Danny / Everyday I weep and moan: Willis, Ralph / Somebody's got to go: Willis, Ralph / Blue blues blues: Willis, Ralph / I got a letter: Willis, Ralph / Too late to scream and shout: Willis, Ralph / Hoodoo man: Willis, Ralph / Income tax: Willis, Ralph / Bed tick: Willis, Ralph / Yes he did: La Verne, Ray / Rock on the bop: La Verne, Ray / Drunk, that's all: La Verne, Ray / Rock 'n' roll: La Verne, Ray
NEMCD 749 / Aug '95 / Sequel

☐ JUNGLE - THE EXTREME COLLECTION VOL.2
Junglist raver: Alexander, Dean / Zulu riddim: Major Popular / Authority: Darkus / I believe in love: New Age & C J Nelson / Rass clart money: Darkus / Ruler: Major Popular / Emotions: New Age & C J Nelson / Blessed relief: Darkus / Cafe le jungle: Dubtronix / Special girl: New Age & Phil Joseph / Time is right: Darkus / Vision: Frixion
CDB 9006 / Sep '95 / B9

☐ JUNGLE BOOK
RIVETCD 6 / Aug '95 / Reinforced

☐ JUNGLE CHICH 5
31062 / Dec '95 / Kakchich

☐ JUNGLE COLLECTION, THE
Sucker: Vibe Posse / Do it: Wee Papa Girl Rappers / Rude boy: Wee Papa Girl Rappers / Ethereal: Motive 9 / No pressure: Motive 9 / Aqua marine: Taskmasters / Shimmering light: Tayce / Heaven and earth: Wicked Wayne / Hiding in the tall grass: Hiding In The Tall Grass / Big shot: Wee Papa Girl Rappers / Ethereal: Motive 9 / Sucker: Vibe Posse
QED 170 / Nov '96 / Tring

☐ JUNGLE DUB (14 Jungle Tracks For The Serious Jungalist)
Run 4 da sound clash: Formula 7 / Dance hall massive: DJ Massive / I spy: DJ Monk / Phizical: Roni Size / Feel it: Lemon D / You don't know: Dillinja / Twisted brain: Area 39 / Religion: Formula 7 / Jazz note: DJ Krust / Deep love: Dillinja / Maximum style dubplate: Tom & Jerry & D J Stretch / Bionic: G-Kelly / R 'n' B Collection: Noodles & Wonder / Money in your pocket: Crown Jewels & MC Dett
KICKCD 17 / Dec '94 / Kickin'

☐ JUNGLE DUB EXPERIENCE VOL.1 (Mazaruni)
ARICD 09 / Mar '95 / Ariwa Sounds

☐ JUNGLE DUB EXPERIENCE VOL.2 (Rapununi Safari)
Perry in the dub jungle / Kunte kinte jungle / Organic pressure / Ecologically speaking / Desolate lagoon / Steamy jungle / Natural ras / Beat of the wild beast / Rapununi savannah / Juffre view / Banjui belly
ARICD 111 / Jun '95 / Ariwa Sounds

☐ JUNGLE EXOTICA VOL.1
E 11565CD / Mar '93 / Crypt

☐ JUNGLE EXOTICA VOL.2
EFACD 12888 / Apr '97 / Crypt

☐ JUNGLE HEAT '95
Melody madness: Coolhand Flex & Michelle Thompson / Gangsta: Trinity / Shadow: Dynamic Duo / Living for the night: Stakka & K-Tee / Bastard: Blackman / Bring you down: Tek 9 / Reality: DJ Swift / It's a jazz thing: Roni Size / Wheel up: Lion Man / Set speed: DJ Krust / Jazzmin: Cloud 9 / I'll always be around: Dub Hustlers / Essences so sweet: Jon-E-Z-Bad / Silver haze: Area 39 & Corelle
VTCD 51 / Jun '95 / Virgin

☐ JUNGLE HITS VOL.1
STRCD 1 / Sep '94 / Street Tuff

☐ JUNGLE HITS VOL.2
STRCD 2 / Dec '94 / Street Tuff

☐ JUNGLE HITS VOL.3
STRCD 3 / Jul '95 / Street Tuff

☐ JUNGLE JAZZ VOL.3
Modus operandi: Photek / Brasilian jazz: Slok / It'a allright I feel it: NuYorican Soul / Honolulu spaceship: Dub Alchemist / Tum bin jaya: Sagoo, Bally / Plenilude: Sand / Waiting hopefully: D-Note / Rotation: Clan Greco / Music in my mind: Adam F / Engraved in me: Fast Runna / Why can't we be friends: Black Mighty Wax & Ohm Guru / What is it: Mighty Strinth
IRMA 4912022 / 26 May '98 / Irma

☐ JUNGLE MASSIVE VOL.3
HFCD 44 / Mar '95 / PWL

☐ JUNGLE MASSIVE VOL.4
HF 46CD / Jul '95 / PWL

☐ JUNGLE ON THE STREETS
GTOL 93 / Apr '95 / Land Of The Giants

☐ JUNGLE RENEGADES VOL.1
ANIMATE 3CD / Mar '95 / Re-Animate

☐ JUNGLE ROCK - 1ST EDITION
SUMACD 001 / Nov '92 / Jungle Rock

☐ JUNGLE SKY VOL.4 (Nirvana)
Ali rocks: DJ Soulslinger / Eastern influence: DJ Ani / Bac: Inna-most & Origin / We are not alone: 187 / Mundo civilizado: Lindsay, Arto / Cloze u'r eyez: Kingsize / All natural: Tube / I wish: Marshall H. / Dirty call: Scissor Hands / Flotation device: Neill, Ben
JS 116CD / Mar '97 / Liquid Sky

☐ JUNGLE SOUNDCLASH VOL.1
STHCCD 8 / '94 / Strictly Underground

☐ JUNGLE SOUNDCLASH VOL.2
STHCCD 10 / May '95 / Strictly Underground

☐ JUNGLE SPLASH PRESENTS JUNGLISM VOL.1 (No Retreat No Surrender)
UKBLKCD 1 / Feb '95 / UK Black

☐ JUNGLE TALK
MILL 055CD / 9 Feb '98 / Millenium

☐ JUNGLE TEKNO - IN THE MIX
Drowning: Four Horsemen Of The Apocalypse / Champion sound: Q-Project / We enter: Aphrodite / Phat and phuturistic: Matt / MArvelous cain: Hit Man / See no, hear no: Motherland / War in '94: Badman / State of mind: Sub-Sequence / Tibetan jungel: DJ Rap / Peace in our time: Van Kleef / What kind of world: Ascend & Ultravibe / Scottie: Sub Nation / RAzor's edge: Steve C & Monita / Calling all people: Azone / Gangster lean: NW 1 / Tonight: A-Sides & Nut-E-1 / Breakin free: Slipmatt / Who's that: Coolhand Flex / Wiplash: Coolhand Flex / Hold back: Coolhand Flex
CDTOT 28 / Jun '95 / Jumpin' & Pumpin'

☐ JUNGLE TEKNO VOL.1
Music takes you: Blame / Ten BandH: Freshtrax & Ace / We can ride the boogie: Bubbles / Drop the bass: Out-Phaze / We have it: CMC / Bomb scare: 2 Bad Mice / Run come quick: Audio / Dance with the speaker: Noise Factory / Extreme: Tripper / Jungle mayhem: Primatives / Mind games: Power Zone / Sonata No.6: D-Major / Logical progression: LTJ Bukem / Control: DJ MCM & DJ Smiley / Junglest: Rudeboy / Please your soul: Tomczak
CDTOT 5 / Jun '92 / Jumpin' & Pumpin'

☐ JUNGLE TEKNO VOL.2 (Happiness & Darkness)
Don't need your love: DJ Red Alert & Mike Slammer / Valley of the shadows: Origin Unknown / Euphoria (Nino's dream): Origin Unknown / House Crew: Origin Unknown / Can you feel the rush: Noise Factory / Shining in da darkness: Nookie / Full logic control: Higher Octave / Axis: DJ Solo & DJ Devine / Who's that: Coolhand Flex / Touch: Origin Unknown / Storm trooper: DJ Mayhem / Terminator: Metal Heads / Whiplash: Coolhand Flex / Desire: Weekend Rush / Just a little: M-Beat / Girl it ever: Kenetic
CDTOT 10 / Nov '93 / Jumpin' & Pumpin'

☐ JUNGLE TEKNO VOL.3 (Drum 'n' Bass A Way Of Life)
19.5 HZT: LTJ Bukem & Peshay / Tibetan jungle: DJ Rap / One 2 one: Johnson, Roger / Skyliner: Invisible Man / Let the drummer go: Invisible Man / Gangster lean: NW 1 / Skanka: Hardware / Scottie: Sub Nation / Stay calm: Pulse / Ominous clouds: Interception / Fallen angels: Wax Doctor / Champion sound: Alliance / Breakin' free: Slipmatt / Inesse: DJ Mayhem
CDTOT 14 / Jun '94 / Jumpin' & Pumpin'

☐ JUNGLE TEKNO VOL.4 (Intelligence & Technology)
Sound control: Randall & Andy C / Attitude: Area 39 / What kind of world: Ascend & Ultravibe / Hit man: Marvellous Caine / Jungle warrior: N-ZO & DJ Invincible / What the... remix: Sonz Of A Loop Da Loop Era / Listen up: Higher Sense / Calling all people (remix): Azone / Basher: M6 Crew / Stand easy: JB / Tonight: A-Sides & Nut-E-1 / Natural high: Chaos & Julia Set
CDTOT 15 / Sep '94 / Jumpin' & Pumpin'

☐ JUNGLE TEKNO VOL.5 (The Deep Side)
Resolution: Photek / Music is so special: Brothers With Soul / Twisted girl: Ruff With The Smmoth / Close encounter: Jeep Head / Peace in our time: Van Kleef / Rollin' intelligence: Urban Wax / Dub plate '94 lick: Keith, Ray / License: Krome & Time / Flying remix: Basement Phil / Razor's edge: Steve C & Monita / Fall down on me: Original Substitute / Change: Fast Floor
CDTOT 20 / Nov '94 / Jumpin' & Pumpin'

☐ JUNGLE TEKNO VOL.6 (Phat & Phuturistic)
Phat and phuturistic: Matt / Champion sound: Q-Project / War in '94: Badman / I bring you the future: Noise Factory / Hit man: Marvellous Caine / Dibi DJ: DJ Invincible & Matticus / Presha III: Studio Pressure / Drowning: Four Horsemen Of The Apocalypse / We enter: Aphrodite / See no, hear no: Motherland / State of mind: Sub Sequence / All you wanted: Graham, John
CDTOT 21 / Jan '95 / Jumpin' & Pumpin'

☐ JUNGLE TEKNO VOL.7
Pulse of life: Sentinal / Virtual heaven: Alliance / Switch: DJ Rap / Melody of life: Noise Factory / Respected no accepted: Touch Of Jazz / Fall down on me: Original Substitute / I like it: Jack 'n' Phil / New vision: Big Bud / Deep love: Dillinja / Studio one: Krome & Time / Gangster love: EP Man / Walter jelly: New Jack Pimps
CDTOT 27 / Mar '95 / Jumpin' & Pumpin'

☐ JUNGLE TEKNO VOL.8
Ecstatic: Intense / Oh gosh: Undercover Agent / Twisted brain: Area 39 / 100 Tons of bass: J&J / Rollidge: DJ SS / Free me: Bliss 'n' Tumble / Play the music: Just Intelligence / Hypnosis: Smith, Simon / Unplugged: Appaloosa / Mindscape: Dub Technicians / Peace 'n' luv: Unity / I don't owe you shit: Smak
CDTOT 31 / Jul '95 / Jumpin' & Pumpin'

☐ JUNGLE USA (The New Sound Of The East Coast)
VTX 1CD / Jun '95 / Vortex

☐ JUNGLE VIBES VOL.1
SPVCD 8455362 / Apr '95 / Red Arrow

☐ JUNGLE WARFARE (2CD Set)
MMBK 272 / Apr '95 / Moonshine

☐ JUNGLISM
SOURCDLP 2 / Jul '95 / SOUR

☐ JUNGLIZED
SEL 14 / Jul '96 / Selector

☐ JUNIOR BOYS OWN COMPILATION (2CD Set)
JNR 1001782 / 1 Jun '98 / Junior Boys Own

☐ JURABEG NABIEV (Music From Tadjikstan)
C 560102 / Aug '97 / Ocora

☐ JUS' HOUSE (14 Essential House Grooves)
Slam me baby: 4 To The Bar / Get huh: Ride Committee / Let the music set you free: House Culture / Sax in the ozone: Aaron, Robert / TT Lover: Jus Us / Way I feel: Tears Of Velva / I wanna be your lover: Nuphonic / My prayer: Carroll, Ronnie / Time for change: Ulysses / Come on baby: Faces / Get down: Mixx Vibes / Everything I got: Faces / Must be the music: Serious Rope / Friend not lover: Serenade
CDELV 12 / Jul '93 / Elevate

☐ JUS' JEEPIN' VOL.1
Deep cover: Dr. Dre / I made love (4 da very 1st time): Little Shawn / Live at the barbeque: Main Source / How I could just kill a man: Cypress Hill / You can't see what I can see: Heavy D & The Boyz / Fudge pudge: Organized Konfusion / True fu-schnick: Fu-Schnickens / Blue cheese: UMC's / Lisa baby: Father MC / Scenario: Tribe Called Quest / Half time: Nas / Horny lil devil: Ice Cube / Dwyck: Gang Starr / Daddy: ADL
CDELV 09 / Jun '94 / Debut

☐ JUS' JEEPIN' VOL.2 (Jus' Jeepin' Again)
Electric relaxation: Tribe Called Quest / Wreckx shop: Wreckx n' Effect / Ghetto red hot: Supercat / CREAM: Wu Tang Clan / Chief rocka rumblin': Lords Of The Underground / Down with the king: Run DMC / Make room: Alkaholiks / Zulu war chant: Bambaataa, Afrika / Remains: Gang Starr / Danger: Murray, Keith / 93 Til infinity: Souls Of Mischief / Best kept secret 45: Diamond D & The Psychotic Neurotics / Murdered ova nuttin': Hoodratz / Shit's real: Geronimo, Mic
CDELV 19 / Jun '95 / Elevate

☐ JUS' TRAX
Wair a pear: Carter, Derrick & Chris Nazuka / Living in Brooklyn: Product Of Da Neighbourhood / Stella Sunday: Glasgow Underground / B-Boy black: Heller & Farley Project / Version 1: Swag / Odyssey: 7th Movement / I'm back: Sessomatto / Version 9: Swag / Living in Brooklyn (Roach Motel dub): Product Of Da Neighbourhood / Duro: Ospina, Davidson / Pain in my brain: Outsider
JSTCD 1 / Feb '97 / Jus' Trax

☐ JUST A LITTLE OVERCOME (The Stax Vocal Groups)
No strings attached: Mad Lads / These old memories: Mad Lads / I'm so glad I fell in love with you: Mad Lads / Highway to Heaven: Dramatics / Since I've been in love: Dramatics / Mannish boy: Newcomers / Girl this boy loves you: Newcomers / Just a little overcome: Nightingales / Baby, don't do it: Nightingales / I'm with you: Nightingales / Whole bit of love: Temprees / Your love (is all I need): Temprees / I refuse to be lonely: Stingers / Showered with love: Ollie & The Nightingales / Mellow way you treat your man: Ollie & The Nightingales / All because of you: Limitations / Echo: Epsilons / Make this young lady mine: Mad Lads / Your love was strange: Dramatics / Open up your heart (let me come in): Newcomers / Anyone can: Leaders / Love's creepin' up on me: United Image
CDSXD 019 / Feb '89 / Stax

☐ JUST ANOTHER ASSHOLE
ALP 39CD / Jan '97 / Atavistic

☐ JUST COUNTRY (40 Golden Greats - 2CD Set)
Hello darlin': Twitty, Conway / Streets of Baltimore: Bare, Bobby / She even woke me up to say goodbye: Rogers, Kenny / On her way to being a woman: Williams, Don / Swinging doors: Jones, George / Your cheatin' heart: Shannon, Del / Burning memories: Jennings, Waylon / She thinks I still care: Pitney, Gene / Wild side of life: Thompson, Hank / Honky tonkitis: Walker, Billy / Take these chains from my heart: Gibson, Don / End of understanding: Nelson, Willie / I fall to pieces: Houston, David / King of the road: Miller, Roger / Here comes my baby back again: Young, Faron / Jukebox Charlie: Paycheck, Johnny / Just because: Fender, Freddy / Why baby why: Jones, George & Gene Pitney / Beautiful lady: Greene, Jack / Jambalaya: Russell, Johnny / Me and Bobby McGee: Rogers, Kenny / Good year for the roses: Jones, George / Sweet dreams: Gibson, Don / There's never been a time: Williams, Don / Detroit City: Bare, Bobby / Moment isn't very long: Nelson, Willie / Wine me up: Young, Faron / I recall a gypsy woman: Thompson, Hank / Release me: Paycheck, Johnny / I can't help it: Shannon, Del / Sally was a good old girl: Jennings, Waylon / Almost persuaded: Houston, David / Funny how time slips away: Walker, Billy / Most beautiful girl in the world: Clark, Roy / Heartaches by the number: Miller, Roger / Bridge washed out: Mack, Warner / Luckenbach Texas: Russell, Johnny / It's only make believe: Twitty, Conway / Don't rob another man's castle: Jones, George & Gene Pitney / Green green grass of home: Wagoner, Porter
MUCD 9502 / May '96 / Musketeer

☐ JUST IN TIME TOO LATE
SOHO 16CD / Nov '94 / Suburbs Of Hell

☐ JUST KEEP ON DANCING (Chess Northern Soul)
Look at me now: Callier, Terry / Baby hang on: McAllister, Maurice & The Radiants / After the laughter (here comes the tears): Chandler, Gene / Strange change: Ward, Herb / I just kept on dancing: Banks, Doug / Fat boy can cry: Stewart, Billy / More love that's what we need: Gospel Classics / Tired of being lonely: Jacobs, Eddy / Sweeter than the day before: Valentinos / Landslide: Clarke, Tony / In orbit: Lovejoy, Joy / We go together: Barnum, Eve / Ain't no more room: Kittens / Hold on: Radiants / What can I do: Kirby, George / Love control: Perry, Greg / Do the pearl girl: Matta Baby / Devil made me do it: Natural Four / Why can't I be your man: Chessmen / Seven day fool: James, Etta / Lend me your hand: Kindly Shepherds / I'm so glad: Cato, Joe / Thinkin' about you: Dells / Ol' man river: Stewart, Billy
CDKEND 138 / Oct '96 / Kent

☐ JUST MY IMAGINATION VOL.1
CDTRL 286 / Mar '94 / Trojan

☐ JUST MY IMAGINATION VOL.2
CDTRL 298 / Mar '94 / Trojan

☐ JUST MY IMAGINATION VOL.3
(Sittin' on the) dock of the bay: Brown, Dennis / Private number: Honey Boy / Forgot to be your lover: Dennis, Denzil / Yesterday once more: Woung, Beverley / Stop the war: Parks, Lloyd / Na na hey hey kiss him goodbye: Pioneers / Band of gold: Griffiths, Marcia / It's too late: Now Generation / Look what you've done for me: Boothe, Ken / Everybody plays the fool: Chosen Few / Summertime: Johnson, Domino / If you don't know me by now: Zap Pow / (If loving you is wrong) I don't want to be right: Maytones / One bad people: Briggs, Barry / Boogie on reggae woman: Briggs, Barry / In my life: Robinson, Jackie / Blood brothers: Boothe, Ken / United we stand: Wally Brothers / Man who sold the world: Wally Brothers
CDTRL 311 / Mar '94 / Trojan

☐ JUST MY IMAGINATION VOL.4
I love the way you love me: Chosen Few / Speak softly: Spence, Barrington / It's all in the game: Gaylads / Only you: Gaylads / What'cha gonna do about it: Simpson, Jeanette / What does it take (to win your love): Ellis, Alton / Don't let me be lonely tonight: Forrester, Sharon / Crazy: Dobson, Dobby /

California dreamin': *Francis, Winston* / What's going on: *Pat Satchmo* / Only the strong survive: *Mighty Diamonds* / Queen majesty: *Chosen Few* / Midnight train to Georgia: *Brown, Teddy* / Can't get used to losing you: *Ray, Danny* / Endlessly: *Dobson, Dobby* / Dark end of the street: *Kelly, Pat* / I second that emotion: *Chosen Few* / Lonely for your love: *Uniques* / There's no me without you: *Parks, Lloyd* / I love the way you love me (part 2): *Parks, Lloyd*
CDTRL 328 / Mar '94 / Trojan

☐ **JUST RAGGA**
CRCD 14 / Jul '92 / Charm

☐ **JUST RAGGA VOL.10**
CRCD 50 / Jun '96 / Charm

☐ **JUST RAGGA VOL.11**
CRCD 62 / Mar '97 / Charm

☐ **JUST RAGGA VOL.12**
CRCD 75 / 22 Sep '97 / Charm

☐ **JUST RAGGA VOL.13**
CRCD 82 / 20 Jul '98 / Charm

☐ **JUST RAGGA VOL.2**
CRCD 15 / Oct '92 / Charm

☐ **JUST RAGGA VOL.3**
Action: *Nadine & Terror Fabulous* / Hands on lover: *Brown, Dennis & Lovindeer* / Step aside: *Ninja Ford* / Protein, vitamin and mineral: *Galaxy* / Clap dance: *Red Dragon* / Dead and bury: *Powerman* / Boom bye bye: *Ninja Kid* / Tickie: *Daddy Mite* / Butterfly: *Bailey, Admiral* / Broke wine butterfly: *Terror Fabulous & Daddy Screw* / Don't touch the coke: *Cobra* / No retreat: *Terror Fabulous* / Diseases: *Major Mackerel* / Racist: *Sweetie Irie*
CRCD 16 / Mar '93 / Charm

☐ **JUST RAGGA VOL.4**
CRCD 18 / Jun '93 / Charm

☐ **JUST RAGGA VOL.5**
CRCD 25 / Nov '93 / Charm

☐ **JUST RAGGA VOL.6**
CRCD 28 / Apr '94 / Charm

☐ **JUST RAGGA VOL.7**
CRCD 34 / Oct '94 / Charm

☐ **JUST RAGGA VOL.8**
CRCD 39 / Jun '95 / Charm

☐ **JUST RAGGA VOL.9**
CRCD 47 / Dec '95 / Charm

☐ **JUST THE TWO OF US**
I've had the time of my life: *Medley, Bill & Jennifer Warnes* / Don't wanna lose you: *Estefan, Gloria* / Up where you belong: *Cocker, Joe & Jennifer Warnes* / Too much, too little, too late: *Mathis, Johnny & Deniece Williams* / On the wings of love: *Osborne, Jeffrey* / Through the storm: *Franklin, Aretha & Elton John* / With you I'm born again: *Preston, Billy & Syreeta* / Endless love: *Ross, Diana & Lionel Richie* / Eternal flame: *Bangles* / I know you by heart: *Parton, Dolly & Smokey Robinson* / All the love in the world: *Warwick, Dionne* / Sometimes when we touch: *Wynette, Tammy & Mark Gray* / All I want is forever: *Taylor, James 'JT' & Regina Belle* / I knew you were waiting (for me): *Franklin, Aretha & George Michael* / Wind beneath my wings: *Knight, Gladys*
MOODCD 11 / Mar '90 / Epic

☐ **JUST THE TWO OF US**
JHD 023 / Jun '92 / Tring

☐ **JUSTICE PRESENTS MODERN URBAN JAZZ**
Motoworld: *Krash* / Placid frequency: *Coltrane, Louis* / Blowfish: *Machine* / Savage times: *Justice* / Breath of life: *Tertius* / Cortez: *Steel* / Off the kuff: *Machine* / Tension: *Justice* / Momemto: *Seeka* / Never again: *Krash*
CWCD 001 / 22 Sep '97 / Creative Wax

☐ **JUSTICE SAMPLER VOL.2**
JR 00052 / Mar '94 / Justice

☐ **JUSTIN TIME FOR CHRISTMAS**
JUST 752 / Dec '95 / Justin Time

☐ **JVC WORLD CLASS MUSIC VOL.1**
JD 3307 / Jul '88 / JVC

☐ **JVC WORLD CLASS MUSIC VOL.2**
Maracuja: *Castro-Neves, Oscar* / Donna: *Guitar Workshop In LA* / Face to face: *Okoshi, Tiger* / Cool shadow: *Okoshi, Tiger* / Front runner: *Holman, Bill Band* / Beverly Hills: *Guitar Workshop In LA* / Over the rainbow: *Okoshi, Tiger* / Yamato dawn: *Neptune, John Kaizan* / New face: *Watts, Ernie Quartet*
JD 3319 / Aug '89 / JVC

☐ **JW CALYPSOCA 1997 HITS VOL.1**
JW 127CD / Jun '97 / JW

K

☐ **KALON AR C'HAB**
CDCA 001 / Apr '94 / Diffusion Breizh

☐ **KANSAS CITY**
Blues in the dark: *Basie, Count* / Sittin' in: *Berry, Leon 'Chu'* / Moten swing: *Basie, Count* / How long, how long blues: *Varsity Seven* / Hootie blues: *McShann, Jay* / I surrender dear: *Chocolate Dandies* / Queer notions: *Hawkins, Coleman & Fletcher Henderson* / 627 Stomp: *Johnson, Pete* / Mary's idea: *Kirk, Andy & His Twelve Clouds of Joy* / I left my baby: *Basie, Count Orchestra* / Yeah man: *Basie, Count Orchestra* / Goon drag (gone wid de goon): *Price, Sammy & His Bluesicians* / Froggy bottom: *Kirk, Andy & His Twelve Clouds of Joy* / Blue room: *Moten, Bennie Kansas City Orchestra* / Kansas city stride: *Basie, Count Orchestra* / Pagin' the Devil: *Kansas City Six* / La Fayette: *Page, Hot Lips & His Orchestra* / Solitude: *Ellington, Duke Orchestra* / One o'clock jump: *Basie, Count Orchestra* / Blue Lester: *Young, Lester Quintet*
CD 53300 / Feb '97 / Giants Of Jazz

☐ **KANSAS CITY AND SOUTH WEST**
DCD 8004 / Jan '95 / Disky

☐ **KANSAS CITY LEGENDS 1929-1942**
158432 / Nov '95 / Jazz Archives

☐ **KARAOKE - 50'S & 60'S FAVOURITES**
Teddy bear / Peggy Sue / Lipstick on your collar / Blue suede shoes / Living doll / Shake, rattle and roll / Vaya con dios / Rave on / Be bop a lula / That'll be theday / Love me tender / (We're gonna) Rock around the clock / Hey Jude / Da doo ron ron / Ferry 'cross the Mersey / I want to hold your hand / Bachelor boy / House of the Rising Sun / Congratulations / Delilah / Wooden heart / Return to sender / You'll never walk alone / It's now or never
CC 279 / Nov '91 / Music For Pleasure

☐ **KARAOKE - 60'S SOUL**
AVC 619 / 24 Nov '97 / Avid

☐ **KARAOKE - 70'S**
Mull of Kintyre / Don't go breaking my heart / Hi ho silver lining / Wonder of you / Dancing queen / I love you love me love / Hold me close / Love grows (where my Rosemary goes) / Waterloo / In the summertime / Knock three times / You're the one that I want / I can't tell the bottom from the top / American pie / Summer nights / Sailing
CC 287 / Nov '92 / Music For Pleasure

☐ **KARAOKE - 80'S**
Uptown girl / I should be so lucky / Ebony and ivory / Karma Chameleon / Never gonna give you up / Eye of the tiger / I just called to say I love you / I want to break free / Hello / Winner takes it all / Thank you for the music / Super trouper / Chain reaction / Come on Eileen
CC 288 / Nov '92 / Music For Pleasure

☐ **KARAOKE - 90'S**
Achy breaky heart / All right now / Would I lie to you / Should I stay or should I go / It only takes a minute / Get here / Heartbeat / Baker Street / Heal the world / Tears on my pillow / Too much love will kill you / It must have been love / (Everything I do) I do it for you / Itsy bitsy teeny weeny yellow polka dot bikini
CC 8231 / Nov '93 / Music For Pleasure

☐ **KARAOKE - CHART HITS**
Back for good / Wonderwall / Crazy for you / Stay another day / Re-light my fire / Love me for a reason / Eternal love / If you only let me in / Unchained melody
AVC 581 / Dec '96 / Avid

☐ **KARAOKE - CHRISTMAS KARAOKE**
AVC 621 / 21 Nov '97 / Avid

☐ **KARAOKE - CHRISTMAS KARAOKE PARTY VOL.1**
Merry Christmas everybody / Mistletoe and wine / When a child is born / Jingle bells / Santa Claus is coming to town / Mary's boy child / I wish it could be Christmas every day / Silent night / We three Kings / Last Christmas / Good King Wenceslas / Frosty the snowman / Stop the cavalry / God rest ye merry gentlemen / Saviour's day / Have yourself a merry little Christmas / We wish you a merry Christmas / Auld lang syne
CC 278 / Dec '94 / Music For Pleasure

☐ **KARAOKE - CHRISTMAS KARAOKE VOL.2**
Sleigh ride / Let it snow, let it snow, let it snow / Happy holiday / When Santa got stuck up the chimney / Rudolph the red nosed reindeer / O little town of Bethlehem / I saw mommy kissing Santa Claus / It came upon a midnight clear / Little donkey / Rockin' around the Christmas tree / Winter wonderland / Jolly old St. Nicholas / All I want for Christmas (is my two front teeth) / I saw three ships / Silver bells / Fairy on the Christmas tree / Christmas alphabet / Good Christian men rejoice / Little drummer boy / Ding dong merrily on high / Deck the halls with boughs of holly / Away in a manger / White Christmas
CC 8230 / Dec '94 / Music For Pleasure

☐ **KARAOKE - CLASSIC KARAOKE (Sing Along To The Hits Of The Masters)**
American pie / Can't help falling in love / Do you know the way to San Jose / Ebony and ivory / How deep is your love / I will always love you / New York New York / Olde devil called love again / Wonder of you / Unchained melody / Baby I love your way / Diamonds are forever / If you don't know me by now / It's not unusual / Love is around Crazy
CDMFP 6409 / 27 Oct '97 / Music For Pleasure

☐ **KARAOKE - CLASSICS**
Back for good / YMCA / (The shoop shoop song) it's in his kiss / Summer nights / Unchained melody / Rock around the clock / Summer holiday / New York, New York / Knowing me, knowing you / You can't hurry love / Re-light my fire / Suspicious minds / Don't go breaking my heart / You'll never walk alone / Greatest love of all / (They long to be) close to you
AVC 580 / Dec '96 / Avid

☐ **KARAOKE - GREATEST KARAOKE ALBUM IN THE WORLD (14 Sing-A-Long Party Favourites)**
YMCA / Summer nights / Wake me up before you go go / Fame / Holiday / Saturday night / I will survive / La bamba / Let's twist again / It's not unusual / Cokey cokey / Tiger feet / All shook up / New York, New York
SUMCD 4058 / Nov '96 / Summit

☐ **KARAOKE - IRISH KARAOKE**
With a shillelagh under my arm / If you're Irish come into the parlour / Galway bay / Mountains of Mourne / Minstrel boy / Cockles and mussels / How are things in Glocca Morra / Delaney's donkey / I dream of Jeannie with the light brown hair / When Irish eyes are smiling / It's a long way to Tipperary / Little bit of heaven / Black velvet band / I'll take you home again Kathleen / Believe me, if all those endearing young charms / Rose of Tralee / How can you buy Killarney / Mother Machree / It's a great day for the Irish / Danny boy
CC 8227 / Nov '93 / Music For Pleasure

☐ **KARAOKE - IRISH KARAOKE**
PLSCD 281 / 1 Jun '98 / Pulse

☐ **KARAOKE - IRISH KARAOKE CLASSICS**
AVC 596 / Mar '97 / Avid

☐ **KARAOKE - MORE CHRISTMAS KARAOKE**
I believe in Father Christmas / Jingle bell rock / Here we come a-wassailing / Christmas alphabet / Twelve days of Christmas / Hark the Herald Angels sing / Wonderful Christmas time / First Noel / Do you hear what I hear / Baby it's cold outside / While sheperds watched their flocks by night / Rocking carol
CDSL 8281 / Oct '96 / EMI Solo

☐ **KARAOKE - PARTY CLASSICS**
When a man loves a woman / Dancing queen / When will I see you again / My girl / Sailing / Delilah / Wooden heart / Peggy Sue / Crocodile rock / Love is all around / Can't smile without you / Summer of '69 / Like a virgin / I will survive / Black is black / It only takes a minute
AVC 579 / Dec '96 / Avid

☐ **KARAOKE - PIONEER KARAOKE VOL.1**
Addicted to love / Summer nights / Killing me softly / Candle in the wind / Crazy little thing called love / Great balls of fire / Girls just wanna have fun / All right now / House of the rising sun / I will survive / I heard it through the grapevine / Billie Jean / Locomotion / It's my party / Hey Jude / You'll never walk alone
CDMFP 6124 / Jul '94 / Music For Pleasure

☐ **KARAOKE - PIONEER KARAOKE VOL.2**
It's not unusual / Love shack / Night fever / Stand by your man / He ain't heavy, he's my brother / Let's dance / Hi ho silver lining / Venus / Daydream believer / If you don't know me by now / Crazy / I wanna dance with somebody (who loves me) / Boys are back in town / Summer of '69 / New York, New York / King of the road
CDMFP 6125 / Jul '94 / Music For Pleasure

☐ **KARAOKE - PIONEER KARAOKE VOL.3**
You can't hurry love / Fame / Mony mony / Stop in the name of love / Super trouper / Tainted love / Greatest love of all / Close to you / Blues suede shoes / If I could turn back time / Livin' on a prayer / Up where we belong / Don't it make my brown eyes blue / Bye bye love / Wild thing / Big spender
CDMFP 6126 / Jul '94 / Music For Pleasure

☐ **KARAOKE - PIONEER KARAOKE VOL.4**
American pie / Like a virgin / In the summertime / Hello Dolly / Oh pretty woman / Annie's song / (Sittin' on the) dock of the bay / Daniel / Bachelor boy / Endless love / Help me Rhonda / Hopelessly devoted to you / Geno / Unchain my heart / Bang a gong (get it on) / (We're gonna) Rock around the clock
CDMFP 6140 / Oct '94 / Music For Pleasure

☐ **KARAOKE - PIONEER KARAOKE VOL.5**
Delilah / Hello Mary Lou / Nine to Five / California dreamin' / Crocodile rock / I can see clearly now / Eye of the tiger / Band on the run / Every time we say goodbye / Don't go breaking my heart / Blue moon / We are family / Itchycoo Park / Bobby's girl / All day and all of the night / Ferry across the Mersey
CDMFP 6141 / Oct '94 / Music For Pleasure

☐ **KARAOKE - PIONEER KARAOKE VOL.6**
Are you lonesome tonight / Grease / I left my heart in San Francisco / Best / I will always love you / Dizzy / Groovy kind of love / You're so vain / 2-4-6-8 Motorway / Power of love / I got you babe / Tiger feet / Everybody wants to rule the world / When you're in love with a beautiful woman / Breaking up is hard to do / La bamba
CDMFP 6142 / Nov '94 / Music For Pleasure

☐ **KARAOKE - PIONEER KARAOKE VOL.7**
Love is all around / Centrefold / Unchained melody / Crocodile shoes / All I have to do is dream / Miss you nights / Angie baby / Purple rain / Cry me a river / Knowing me, knowing you / Nothing compares 2 U / With or without you / Lady is a tramp / I'm still standing / I swear / Something gotten hold of my heart
CDMFP 6167 / Jun '95 / Music For Pleasure

☐ **KARAOKE - PIONEER KARAOKE VOL.8**
It's now or never / I'd do anything for love (but I won't do that) / YMCA / Careless whisper / Take a chance on me / Sweet dreams (are made of this) / Dizzy / Baby, I love your way / We are family / Unbelieveable / Singin' in the rain / These dreams / Shine / Moving on up / Mmm mmm mmm mmm / Most beautiful girl in the world
CDMFP 6168 / Jun '95 / Music For Pleasure

☐ **KARAOKE - ROCK 'N' ROLL KARAOKE**
AVC 617 / 17 Nov '97 / Avid

☐ **KARAOKE - SATURDAY NIGHT FEVER KARAOKE**
AVC 623 / 21 Nov '97 / Avid

☐ **KARAOKE - SCOTTISH KARAOKE**
Donald, where's yer troosers / Loch Lomond / Roamin' in the gloamin' / Bluebells of Scotland / Scotland the brave / Dancing in Kyle / Skye boat song / Northern lights of old Aberdeen / My ain folk / Gordon for me / My love is like a red red rose / I love a lassie / Amazing grace / Ye banks and braes o' bonnie Doon / Annie Laurie / I belong to Glasgow / Charlie is my darling / Mull of Kintyre / Westering home / Just a wee deoch an' Doris / Comin' thro' the rye / Auld lang syne
CC 8228 / Nov '93 / Music For Pleasure

☐ **KARAOKE - THE GREATEST KARAOKE**
Killing me softly / Big spender / You'll never walk alone / It's not unusual / Three lions / Yesterday / How deep is your love / (Can't help) falling in love / Always on my mind / Alright / Stand by your man / Crazy / I will survive / Back for good / Hi-ho silver lining / Hey Jude
AVC 578 / Dec '96 / Avid

☐ **KARAOKE BALLADS**
CDSL 8282 / Oct '96 / EMI Solo

☐ **KARAOKE COUNTRY**
Rhinestone cowboy / Coalminer's daughter / Green green grass of home / Here you come again / Honey come back / Nobody's child / I walk the line / Blanket on the ground / Last thing on my mind / Crazy / Wayward wind / Your cheatin' heart / Welcome to my world / Distant drums / Stand by your man / Try a little kindness / Help me make it through the night / Take me home country roads / Jambalaya / Harper Valley PTA / Sixteen tons
CC 280 / Jul '92 / Music For Pleasure

☐ **KARAOKE CROONERS**
Born free / Spanish eyes / Close to you / New York, New York / I left my heart in San Francisco / Magic moments / Strangers in the night / Are you lonesome tonight / Smoke gets in your eyes / Release me / Love is a many splendoured thing / Unforgettable / What a wonderful world / I can't stop lovin' you / Moon river / When I fall in love / Answer me / Unchained melody / More / That's amore / Somewhere
CC 281 / Jul '92 / Music For Pleasure

☐ **KARAOKE DUETS**
Somethin' stupid / Two sleepy people / I got you babe / Don't go breaking my heart / Endless love / It takes two / Cinderella Rockefella / Tonight I celebrate my love / Ebony and ivory / Something's gotten hold of my heart / Especially for you / I'd do anything / Who wants to be a millionaire
CDSL 8263 / Oct '95 / EMI

☐ **KARAOKE GREASE/SATURDAY NIGHT FEVER**
How deep is your love / Jive talking / Night fever / Stayin' alive / If I can't have you / You should be dancing / Rock'n'roll is here to stay / Grease / Hopelessly devoted to you / It's raining on Prom night / Summer nights / You're the one that I want / Tears on my pillow
CDSL 8266 / Oct '95 / Virgin

☐ **KARAOKE LEGENDS - LENNON & McCARTNEY VOL.1**
She loves you / Sergeant Pepper's lonely hearts club band / With a little help from my friends / Help / Penny Lane / All you need is love / Can't buy me love / Love me do / Eleanor Rigby / I want to hold your hand / Back in the USSR / When I'm sixty four / Please please me / Michelle / From me to you / Let it be / Ticket to ride / Yellow submarine / Hard day's night / Yesterday / Hey Jude
CC 8229 / Nov '93 / Music For Pleasure

☐ **KARAOKE LEGENDS - LENNON & McCARTNEY VOL.2**
Magical mystery tour / Nowhere man / Lady Madonna / I should have known / Fool on the hill / Paperback writer / Things we said today / I feel fine / I wanna be your man / Ob-la-di ob-la-da / Long and winding road / Drive my car / Eight days a week / And I love her / Get back / We can work it out / All my loving / Hello goodbye / I saw her standing there / Day tripper / Strawberry fields
CC 8241 / Feb '95 / Music For Pleasure

☐ **KARAOKE LOVE SONGS**
We've only just begun / Suddenly / True love ways / Fever / Silly love songs / Endless love / Power of love / Move closer / When the girl in your arms (is the girl in your heart) / It must have been love / Love letter / And I love you so / Always on my mind / On the wings of love / Fool (if you think it's over) / Three times a lady
CC 286 / Nov '92 / Music For Pleasure

☐ **KARAOKE MILLION SELLING HITS**
Roll over Beethoven / Mona Lisa / Sealed with a kiss / Monday, Monday / Ain't that a shame / Tears / Bright eyes / It's all in the game / Things we do for love / Under the moon of love / Rivers of Babylon / Wichita lineman / He ain't heavy, he's my brother / Anyone who had a heart / World of our own / There's a kind of hush (all over the world) / Diana / He's got the whole world in his hands
CC 8245 / Oct '94 / Music For Pleasure

☐ **KARAOKE NO. 1'S**
Bohemian rhapsody / (Everything I do) I do it for you / Groovy kind of love / You'll never stop me from loving you / Singin' the blues / Long haired lover from Liverpool / Don't go breaking my heart / I remember you / Power of love / Imagine / Whatever will be will be (Que sera sera) / House of the rising sun / Something's gotten hold of my heart / Especially for you / I just called to say I love you
CC 8232 / Nov '93 / Music For Pleasure

☐ **KARAOKE PARTY**
Summertime blues / Good luck charm / Be-bop-a-lula / It's only make believe / Day-o (banana boat song) / You'll never walk alone / He ain't heavy he's my brother / Yellow submarine / Singin' the blues / Cathy's clown / New York New York / Wild thing / Wooly bully / Super trooper / Blowing in the wind / Last waltz
308892 / 11 May '98 / Hallmark

☐ **KARAOKE ROCK 'N' ROLL**
Chantilly lace / It's my party / Bird dog / Locomotion / Shake, rattle and roll / Great balls of fire / Giddy up a ding dong / Lipstick on your collar / That'll be the day / Bye bye love / Rubber ball / Blue suede shoes / Born too late / Peggy Sue / Long tall Sally / Be bop a lula / Teenager in love / Whole lotta shakin' goin' on / Rave on / Good golly Miss Molly / (We're gonna) Rock around the clock / Halfway to paradise / Blueberry Hill / C'mon everybody
CC 296 / Jun '93 / Music For Pleasure

☐ **KARAOKE SHOWTIME**
AVC 622 / 21 Nov '97 / Avid

☐ **KARAOKE SOUL**
Save the last dance for me / (Sittin' on the) dock of the bay / When a man loves a woman / In the midnight hour / It takes two / Reach out, I'll be there / What becomes of the broken hearted / How sweet it is (to be loved by you) / Give me just a little more time / Saturday night at the movies / Band of gold / Try a little tenderness / This old heart of mine / My guy / Stand be me / At the club / Rescue me / My girl / Private number
CC 285 / Nov '92 / Music For Pleasure

☐ **KARAOKE TOP 10 HITS OF THE 60'S**
Summer holiday / Tears / Speedy Gonzales / Anyone who had a heart / Private number / Whiter shade of pale / Seven little girls sitting in the back seat / Do wah diddy diddy / Yeh yeh / What do you want / Puppet on a string / You're sixteen / Pretty flamingo / Boom bang a bang / Lily the pink / Where do you go to my lovely / Tell Laura I love her / What do you want to make those eyes at me for / Blue moon / Three steps to heaven
CC 8246 / Oct '94 / Music For Pleasure

☐ **KARAOKE TOP 10 HITS OF THE 80'S**
Call me / Freedom / True / House of fun / Is there something I should know / When the going gets tough / Wherever I lay my hat (that's my home) / Good heart / With a little help from my friends / Careless whisper / Only way is up / Two hearts
CDSL 8264 / Oct '95 / EMI

☐ **KARAOKE TOP 10 HITS OF THE 90'S**
I'm too sexy / Dizzy / Million love songs / We have all the time in the world / Pray / Rhythm of my heart / Sleeping satellite / Love is all around / Crocodile shoes / Could it be magic
CDSL 8265 / Oct '95 / EMI

☐ **KARENNI**
PAN 2040 / Oct '94 / Pan

☐ **KASIO GEMS**
CD 025C / May '97 / Carotte

☐ **KATZ KEEP ROCKIN' VOL.1 & 2, THE**
LOMACD 39 / Nov '94 / Loma

☐ **KAUSTINEN FOLK MUSIC FESTIVAL 1990**
BHCD 9130 / Jul '91 / Brewhouse

☐ **KAZAAM**
I am Kazaam: *O'Neal, Shaq* / I'll make your dreams come true: *Subway* / I swear I'm in love: *Usher* / Wishes: *Morris, Nathan* / All out on my own: *Shyheim* / No tighter wish: *Tangi & Lisa 'Left Eye' Lopes* / Lay light (one for the money): *Almighty Arrogant* / Show me your love: *Immature* / We genie: *O'Neal, Shaq & Wade Robson* / Dance wit' me: *Weaver, Jason* / If you believe: *Spinderella* / Key to my heart: *Choice* / I get lifted: *Barrio Boyzz* / Get down: *YBTO* / Boys will be boys: *Backstreet Boys* / Best of me: *Jamecia* / Mr. Material: *O'Neal, Shaq*
5490272 / Aug '96 / A&M

☐ **KAZAKH SONGS AND EPIC TRADITION OF THE WEST**
C 580051 / Nov '93 / Ocora

☐ **KEB DARGE'S LEGENDARY DEEP FUNK**
Fun company: *Zambezi* / Dap walk: *Ernie & The Top Notes* / I who have nothing: *Frazier, Ray & The Shades Of Madness* / Gimme some skin: *Penn, Frank* / Kick the habit: *Prophet Soul* / Too hot to hold: *UFO's* / Sagittarus black: *McNealy, Timothy* / Quit jive'in: *Pearly Queen* / Put your own words to it: *Billy/Cross Bronx expressway: Cross Bronx Expressway* / Grease wheels: *Smoki' Shades Of Dub* / (Rockin') courtroom: *Judge Suds & The Soul Detergents* / How about it: *Big Bo Thomas & The Arrows* / Who dun it: *Originals Orchestra* / Soul power: *Lil' Ray & The Fantastic Four* / Ou-wee man: *Serrano, Dave* / Going down for the last time: *Keaton, David* / First thing I do in the morning: *Williams, Joyce* / Can't fight the feeling: *Norwich Street Extension* / I wanna be loved by you: *Family of Eve* / Please be truthful: *Family of Eve*
BBECD 004 / Jun '97 / Barely Breaking Even

☐ **KEB DARGE'S LEGENDARY DEEP FUNK VOL.2**
Silly savage: *Golden Toadstools* / Coffee pot: *BO Junior* / Blues for the Bs: *TJ & The Group* / Power struggle: *Polk, James & The Brothers* / Gettin' soul: *Butler, Aaron & The New Breed* / Firebird: *Rene, Googie* / Psycho: *Fabulous Mark III* / Can we rap: *Carleen & The Groovers* / Get it right: *Calloway, Ricky & His NT Express* / Sissy walk: *Ball, Billy & The Upsetters* / Natural: *Garden, Leon* / Trespasser: *Bad Medicine* / Krunchberry beast: *Rappers* / Blueberry hill: *Washington, Joe* / Society: *Society* / You got it all: *Blenders Ltd.* / That didn't stop me: *Crosby, Beverley* / Spread love: *Harris & Orr* / Love call: *Ramsey & Co.* / Modernisation: *Sons Of The Kingdom*
BBECD 009 / 26 Jan '98 / Barely Breaking Even

☐ **KECAK VOL.1**
VICG 50272 / Mar '96 / JVC World Library

☐ **KECAK VOL.2**
VICG 53512 / Mar '96 / JVC World Library

☐ **KEEP IT ANGRY (Brighton Hunt Saboteur Benefit Album)**
BFRCD 006 / 4 May '98 / Bomb Factory

☐ **KEEP ON COMING THROUGH THE DOOR**
Dance beat / Jack of my trade / Sounds of Babylon / Fire corner / Heart don't leap / To the fields / Mosquito one / Mr. Harry Skank / Alpha and omega
CDTRL 255 / Mar '94 / Trojan

☐ **KEEP ON RUNNING**
CDTRL 334 / Feb '94 / Trojan

☐ **KEEP THE BEAT**
HB8 001 / Oct '96 / Hairball 8

☐ **KEEP THE DREAM ALIVE (Now And Then Singles)**
NTHEN 019CD / May '95 / Now & Then

☐ **KEEP THE FAITH**
Change my darkness into light: *Flirtations* / Time marches on: *Hill, Lainie* / Good little you: *Dee, Joey* / Real thing: *Britt, Tina* / I'd rather die: *Superiors* / Think about the good times: *Washington, Baby* / Heartbreaker: *Barnum, H.B.* / Ecstasy: *Holloway, Patrice* / Hotline: *Garner, Reggie* / You should know: *Notations* / Love is dangerous: *Polk, Frank* / Girl's got it: *Preston, Billy* / What can go wrong: *Thrills* / Love man from Carolina: *Rollins, Bird* / I know the inside story: *Chubby & The Turnpikes* / Take your time and love kill: *Mitchell, Grover* / So Anna just love me: *Johnson, Roy Lee* / La de da I love you: *Foxx, Inez & Charlie* / Livin' in love: *Anthony, Sheila* / Time can change a love: *Scott, Cindy* / Too many people: *Goldsboro, Bobby* / Put your heart in it: *Dee, Joey* / It's too late: *Goldsboro, Bobby* / Love in my heart: *Entertainers* / I can't do it: *Eddie & Ernie*
GSCD 098 / Jun '96 / Goldmine

☐ **KEEP THE HOME FIRES BURNING (Songs & Music From The First World War)**
Here we are, here we are: *Wheeler, F. & Chorus* / Goodbye-ee: *Various Narrators* / Just before the battle mother: *Oakland, Will & Chorus* / Your King and country want you: *Clarke, Helen & Chorus* / Trumpeter: *Newell, Raymond & Ian Swinley* / Deathless army: *Kinniburgh, T.F.* / Medley: *NMB Flying Squadron* / Tramp, tramp, tramp: *Harlan & Stanley/chorus* / Keep the home fires burning: *Various Narrators* / Boys of the old brigade: *NMB Flying Squadron* / Boys in khaki, boys in blue: *Wheeler, F. & Chorus* / Colonel Bogey: *Coldstream Guards Band* / Pack up your troubles in your old kit bag: *Coldstream Guards Band* / It's a long way to Tipperary: *Coldstream Guards Band* / Roses of Picardy: *Murray, Templeton* / Passing Review Patrol: *Not Advised* / What has become of hinkey-dinky-parlay-voo: *Bernard, Al & Chorus*
CDSDL 358 / Mar '94 / Saydisc

☐ **KEEP YOUR ARMS AROUND ME**
IMP 941 / Sep '96 / IMP

☐ **KEEP YOUR SUNNY SIDE UP**
SOW 512 / Jul '94 / Sound Waves

☐ **KEEPING THE FAITH 1990**
CRECD 081 / Jan '91 / Creation

☐ **KEF TIME**
CD 4269 / Feb '95 / Traditional Crossroads

☐ **KENT'S MAGIC TOUCH**
Magic touch: *Moore, Melba* / Things are getting a little tough: *Carlton, Eddie* / You fixed my heartache: *Foxx, Inez & Charlie* / Quit twistin' my arm: *Mitchell, Stanley* / This diamond ring: *Ambrose, Sammy* / Biggest man: *Hunt, Tommy* / Crying like a baby: *Jive Five* / You lie so well: *Knight, Marie* / I got my heart set on you: *Toys* / On top of the world: *SOUL* / Funny how we've changed places: *Anderson, Debra* / You shouldn't have set my soul on fire: *Foxx, Inez* / Tomorrow keeps shining: *Bartley, Chris* / I'm so glad I found you: *Diplomats* / Maybe maybe baby (baby baby baby): *Turner, Dee Dee* / This time round: *SOUL* / I wouldn't come back: *Bethea The Masked Man & The Agents* / Hole in the wall: *Stone, George* / Bricks, broken bottles and sticks: *Parrish, Dean* / You'll fall in love: *Jive Five* / Sweet sweet lovin': *Platters* / Never love a robin: *Hunt, Tommy* / My heart cries for you: *Porgy & The Monarchs* / Don't cry sing along with the music: *Moore, Melba* / That's enough: *Barbara & Brenda* / There comes a time: *Kitt, Eartha* / Long after tonight is all over: *Radcliffe, Jimmy*
CDKEND 146 / May '97 / Kent

☐ **KENTUCKY GOSPEL 1927-1928**
DOCD 8013 / 21 Sep '97 / Document

☐ **KENYA/TANZANIA - WITCHCRAFT & RITUAL MUSIC**
7559720662 / Jan '95 / Nonesuch

☐ **KERALA: THE THAYAMBAKA (Music Of South India)**
C 560047 / Mar '97 / Ocora

☐ **KERRANG VOL.1**
Jesus Christ pose: *Soundgarden* / Another wordly device: *Prong* / Punishment: *Biohazard* / Autosurgery: *Therapy* / Territory: *Sepultura* / Sweating bullets: *Megadeth* / Shedding skin: *Pantera* / Caffeine bomb: *Wildhearts* / My house: *Terrorvision* / Give it away: *Red Hot Chili Peppers* / Warfair: *Clawfinger* / Believe in me: *McKagan, Duff* / Ten miles high: *Little Angels* / Over the edge: *Almighty* / Down in a hole: *Alice In Chains* / Ace of spades (Live): *Motorhead* / Paranoid: *Black Sabbath* / Smoke on the water: *Deep Purple* / Victim of change (Live): *Judas Priest* / Stargazer: *Rainbow* / Bat out of hell: *Meat Loaf* / Cats in the cradle: *Ugly Kid Joe* / In my darkest hour: *Megadeth* / Doctor doctor: *UFO* / Spirit of radio: *Rush* / Epic: *Faith No More* / Angel of death: *Slayer* / Youth gone wild: *Skid Row* / Born to be wild: *Steppenwolf* / Freebird: *Lynyrd Skynyrd*
AHLCD 21 / Jun '94 / Hit

☐ **KERRANG VOL.2 (The Kutting Edge)**
STVCD 27 / Mar '95 / Hit

☐ **KERRANG VOL.3 (2CD Set)**
RR 88572 / Aug '96 / Roadrunner

☐ **KERRY FIDDLES**
OSS 10CD / Mar '94 / Ossian

☐ **KETTLE DRUM**
DBCD 2039 / Feb '96 / Digital B

☐ **KEYBOARD WIZARDS OF THE GERSHWIN ERA VOL.5**
GEMMCD 9205 / Jun '98 / Pearl

☐ **KHARTOUM HEROES**
Cat gut: *Khartoum Heroes* / St. Swithin: *Khartoum Heroes* / Mother Hubbard: *Khartoum Heroes* / Space hopper: *Khartoum Heroes* / Charles and die laughing: *Khartoum Heroes* / Interference: *Khartoum Heroes* / Heaven: *Khartoum Heroes* / Bitter honey: *Khartoum Heroes* / Colossal angel: *Khartoum Heroes* / Song for a flower: *Khartoum Heroes* / Leaves: *Khartoum Heroes* / Out of bounds: *Khartoum Heroes* / Saints within: *Khartoum Heroes* / Moon barking: *Khartoum Heroes*
CDLDL 1222 / Feb '97 / Lochshore

☐ **KICK UP THE 80'S VOL.9**
Never stop: *Echo & The Bunnymen* / I wanna be a flintstone: *Screaming Blue Messiahs* / Life in a northern town: *Dream Academy* / She bangs the drum: *Stone Roses* / More you live, the more you love: *Flock Of Seagulls* / I'm falling: *Bluebells* / Disenchanted: *Communards* / All of my heart: *ABC* / Steppin' out: *Jackson, Joe* / Never take me alive: *Spear Of Destiny* / Whistle down the wind: *Heyward, Nick* / Radio Africa: *Latin Quarter* / Crash: *Primitives* / No memory: *Scarlet Fantastic* / Obsession: *Animotion* / Honey thief: *Hipsway* / Big area: *Then Jerico* / Let my people go go: *Rainmakers*
OG 3528 / Nov '92 / Old Gold

☐ **KICKIN' HOUSE TUNES (2CD Set)**
Promised land: *FUSE* / In the morning: *Key* / Ooo-la-la-la: *Earp, Justine* / Keep on jumpin': *Zoe S* / It's movin': *DJ Linus* / Check your feelings: *Deeper Love* / Music is my life: *Creative House Boys* / Do it now: *Luvly Housebee* / Take me to the top: *MNA Project* / Brooklyn beats: *Deep, Scotti* / Legacy: *Natural Forces* / Secret love: *Magnetic Pulstar* / All night: *BOP Gun* / It's so good: *L&G Project* / U: *DJ Scott Project* / Let the rhythm pump: *Pigalle* / Are you ready: *Moves* / I want you: *Shandrew* / Morning light: *Team Deep* / Candy girls: *Wham Bam* / Magic melody: *Groove Solution* / Tones in my mind: *Cyborg* / Jaba noba: *CYB* / My house: *Nap, J. Project*
DCD 08947292 / Mar '97 / SPV

☐ **KICKIN' HOUSE TUNES VOL.5 (2CD Set)**
Sound of: *Riu Palace Project* / Extension of eternity: *EOE* / Dreaming of you: *Smile Machine* / Dreams: *Sequential One* / Red 5 jumps: *Red 5* / Yah KK: *After Hour* / DJ Pump: *Coma B & Clubnatives* / FRE: *Milk Inc.* / Hardrunner: *Chocolate Milk* / Take me to the top: *Chocolate Milk* / Take you higher: *NU NRG & DJ CRIZ* / Little light: *Novaya* / Like a work: *DJ Nukk* / That's how we do it: *DJ Maui* / Wave: *Sosa* / I want somebody: *Phoenix* / I'm in love with you: *Maximun Score* / Oh what a life: *Gaynor, Gloria* / It's not over: *Nhouse* / True devotion: *Tricky Stuff* / Rockin' your body: *Numf, Fred* / Barbardia: *Duysen, Tim* / I'm gay: *Luky Loke* / I'm your drug: *Maximun Score* / 1000 miles: *Overdog* / Moe your feet: *Phonic*
DCD 08947542 / 2 Feb '98 / SPV

☐ **KICKIN' SOME BRASS**
Rebirth brass band rollin' / Siesta for the fiesta / My feet can't fail me now: *Dirty Dozen Brass Band* / Keep on gwine: *New Orleans Nightcrawlers* / Ms. Lollipop: *New Birth Brass Band* / Wolfing blues: *High Steppers* / Manic depression: *Les Miserables* / Down in honky tonk town: *Coolbone* / Just a closer walk with thee: *Treme Brass Band* / Bourbon street parade: *Olympia Brass Band* / Indians jumping on fire: *Mahogany Brass band* / Lord Lord Lord: *Original Pin Stripe Brass Band*
SHANCD 6028 / 9 Mar '98 / Shanachie

☐ **KICKIN' THE 3 (The Best Of Organ Trio Jazz)**
Kiko: *McGriff, Jimmy* / Kickin' the 3: *Earland, Charles* / Evidence: *DeFrancesco, Joey* / Blues for J: *Smith, Jimmy* / Slouchin': *Smith, Lonnie* / Little green men: *Goldings, Larry* / Misty: *Holmes, Richard 'Groove'* / Lid flippin': *Smith, Johnny 'Hammond'* / After hours: *McDuff, 'Brother' Jack* / Bedeah: *Medeski, John & Billy Martin/Chris Wood* / Monk's dream: *Young, Larry*
SH 5034 / Jun '97 / Shanachie

☐ **KICKIN' THE HILLBILLY**
CLCD 2858 / 29 May '98 / Collector/ White Label

☐ **KID'S RHYTHM 'N' BLUES KAFFEE SUMMER '97**
STINGCD 041 / Jul '97 / Blue Sting

☐ **KILLED BY DEATH VOL.5**
REDRUM 5 / 15 Dec '97 / Redrum

☐ **KILLED BY DEATH VOL.6**
REDRUM 6 / 15 Dec '97 / Redrum

☐ **KILLER VOICES**
What do you want from me: *White, Dougie* / She goes down: *Di'Anno, Paul* / Body rock: *Stratton, Dennis* / Stranger to your heart: *Bodimead, Jackie* / Miles away: *Stratton, Dennis* / No repair: *Di'Anno, Paul* / All shook up: *White, Dougie* / Show some emotion: *Sloman, John* / Cut loose: *White, Dougie* / Forever: *Overland, Steve & Jackie Bodimead* / So far away: *Hart, Lea*
CDTB 177 / Aug '97 / Thunderbolt

☐ **KILLING MUSIC**
Blackfly: *Box Saga* / Initiation: *Sunship* / Alien resident: *Kid Loops* / We are one: *DJ Q* / Porknow fish: *Violet* / At least American Indian people know exactly how they've bee: *Fire This Time* / 13th key: *Sunship* / Waiting hopefully: *D-Note* / Bury the hatchet: *Local Zero* / Urban hustle: *DJ Q* / Nine lives: *Underwolves* / Offshore: *Chicane*
FILT 010CD / Sep '96 / Filter

☐ **KINDA COUNTRY**
PLSCD 170 / Apr '97 / Pulse

☐ **KING JAZZ - THE COMPLETE RECORDINGS VOL.1 (2CD Set)**
BCD 501/02 / Sep '97 / GHB

☐ **KING JAZZ - THE COMPLETE RECORDINGS VOL.2 (3CD Set)**
BCD 503/04/05 / Sep '97 / GHB

☐ **KING KONG 3**
K 180CD / 30 Mar '98 / Konkurrent

☐ **KING KONK VOL.1**
K 152C / Mar '94 / Konkurrel

☐ **KING KONK VOL.2**
K 168 / Aug '96 / Konkurrel

☐ **KING MACKEREL AND THE BLUES ARE RUNNING (Songs & Stories Of The Carolina Coast)**
King Mackerel and the blues are running / Corncake inlet inn / Foodchain / Timeless / Ain't that something / Joyride / Whose idea was this / Down by the edge of the sea / Georgia rose / Sand mountain song / Sound side / Shag baby / Maco light / To catch a king / Home on the river / Mighty storm / I'm the breeze / Beautiful day
SHCD 8503 / Mar '98 / Sugar Hill

☐ **KING OF SKA VOL.1**
KECD 01/02 / Feb '93 / King Edwards

☐ **KING OF SKA VOL.2**
KECD 03/04 / Feb '93 / King Edwards

☐ **KING OF SWING, THE**
MACCD 253 / Aug '96 / Autograph

☐ **KING OF THE BEATS VOL.1, THE (2CD Set)**
TEAMCD 2 / 27 Apr '98 / Team

☐ **KING OF THE BEATS VOL.2, THE**
TEAMCD 3 / 24 Aug '98 / Team

☐ **KING OF THE ROAD**
MU 5058 / Oct '92 / Musketeer

☐ **KING R 'N' B BOX SET, THE (4CD Set)**
KBCD 7002 / Apr '97 / King

☐ **KING SIZE DUB VOL.1 (2CD Set)**
EB 001 / Jun '97 / Echo Beach

☐ **KING SIZE DUB VOL.2 (2CD Set)**
EB 006 / Jun '97 / Echo Beach

☐ **KING SIZE DUB VOL.3 (2CD Set)**
EB 009 / Jun '97 / Echo Beach

☐ **KING SIZE DUB VOL.4**
EB 018 / 25 May '98 / Echo Beach

☐ **KING SIZE SKA**
El torro: *Alphonso, Roland* / King size: *Brooks, Baba* / Hi life: *Williams, Granville Orchestra* / On the move: *Alphonso, Roland* / Cocktails for two: *Ismay, Sammy* / No other love: *Harper, Raymond & His Carib Beats* / Women of the world: *Alphonso, Roland* / Faberge: *Brooks, Baba* / Old McDonald: *Williams, Granville Orchestra* / Nothing for nothing: *Alphonso, Roland* / Riverton city: *McCook, Tommy & The Supersonics* / Atlas: *Bennett, Val* / Jungle bit: *Alphonso, Roland* / First session: *Brooks, Baba* / Popeye ska: *Williams, Granville Orchestra* / Cat: *Alphonso, Roland* / Guantanamera ska: *Alphonso, Roland* / Contact: *Richards, Roy & Baba Brooks* / Amour: *Harper, Raymond & His Carib Beats* / JJ special: *Carib Beats* / Honky tonk ska: *Williams, Granville Orchestra* / Song for my father: *Alphonso, Roland* / Scratch: *Brooks, Baba* / Tear up: *Williams, Granville Orchestra* / Hot nosh: *Johnson, Cluett Orchestra*
CDTRL 399 / Jun '98 / Trojan

☐ **KINGDOM OF METAL (18 Killer Tracks)**
Iron fist: *Motorhead* / (Don't fear) the reaper: *Blue Oyster Cult* / Kingdom of madness: *Magnum* / Urban guerilla: *Hawkwind* / Broken down angel: *Nazareth* / Stay on top: *Uriah Heep* / Angel witch: *Angel Witch* / Race with the devil: *Girlschool* / Sudden life: *Man* / Who do you love: *Juicy Lucy* / Heartline: *George, Robin* / Me and my guitar: *Wishbone Ash* / Nuclear attack: *Moore, Gary* / In league with satan: *Venom* / Come to the sabbat: *Black Widow* / Too hot to handle: *UFO* / Nobody's hero: *Raven* / Bomber: *Headgirl*
SUMCD 4105 / Nov '96 / Summit

☐ **KINGDOM OF THE SUN - FIESTAS OF PERU**
7559791972 / Jan '95 / Nonesuch

☐ **KINGS AND QUEEN OF QAWWALI, THE (Love & Devotion)**
SHCD 64083 / Apr '97 / Shanachie

☐ **KINGS AND QUEENS OF COUNTRY**
CPMV 027 / Sep '94 / Cromwell

☐ **KINGS AND QUEENS OF COUNTRY**
ECD 3360 / 18 Sep '97 / K-Tel

☐ **KINGS OF AFRICAN MUSIC**
NSCD 009 / Nov '96 / Nascente

☐ **KINGS OF BLACK MUSIC, THE**
15169 / Aug '91 / Laserlight

☐ **KINGS OF CAJUN**
Les filles du Canada: Abshire, Nathan / Acadian two step: Balfa Brothers / Triangle special: Pitre, Austin / French fiddle boogie: Bonsall, Joe / Midnight special: Balfa Brothers / Oson two step: Roger, Aldus / La queue de torture: Abshire, Nathan / Love bridge waltz: Duhon, Bessyl / One is a lonely number: Menard, Phil / Fee fee ponchot: Montoucet, Don / Old fashioned two step: Balfa Brothers / Zydeco hee haw: Chavis, Boozoo / That's what makes the cajun dance: Bearb, Ricky / Hick wagon wheel special: Montoucet, Don / Me and my counsin: Doucet, Camey / Mamou hot step: Ardoin Brothers / L'anne tu partit: Fruge, Ronnie / Jolie catin: Chavis, Boozoo / Lacassine special: Balfa Brothers / Johnny can't dance: Ardoin Family Orchestra / Sheryl's special: Cormier, Sheryl
MCCD 066 / '92 / Music Club

☐ **KINGS OF CAJUN (3CD Set)**
MCBX 013 / Dec '94 / Music Club

☐ **KINGS OF CAJUN**
TRIK 0158 / Oct '94 / Trikont

☐ **KINGS OF CAJUN VOL.2**
MCCD 116 / Jun '93 / Music Club

☐ **KINGS OF CAJUN VOL.3**
MCCD 171 / Sep '94 / Music Club

☐ **KINGS OF CALYPSO**
PLSCD 229 / Jul '97 / Pulse

☐ **KINGS OF COUNTRY**
I can't stop lovin' you: Gibson, Don / Talk back trembling lips: Jones, George / Reuben james: Rogers, Kenny / Shelter of your arms: Nelson, Willie / Loves gonna live here: Jennings, Waylon / There goes my everything: Greene, Jack / Send me the pillow that you dream on: Locklin, Hank / Heartaches by the number: Paycheck, Johnny / For the good times: Husky, Ferlin / Where do I go from here: Williams, Don / Sea of heartbreak: Gibson, Don / Almost persuaded: Jones, George / Ruby don't take your love to town: Rogers, Kenny / Broken promises: Nelson, Willie / Son of Hickory Holler's tramp: Darrell, Johnny / Catfish john: Russel, Johnny / Four in the morning: Young, Faron / Things to think about: Jackson, Stonewall / Tears: Williams, Don / Daddy sang bass: Perkins, Carl
300722 / Jul '96 / Hallmark

☐ **KINGS OF COUNTRY**
Home is where you're happy: Nelson, Willie / Sally was a good old girl: Jennings, Waylon / I can't change overnight: Jones, George / Treat me mean treat me cruel: Twitty, Conway / I don't need to know that right now: Paycheck, Johnny / Daddy sang bass: Perkins, Carl / Take my hand for a while: Williams, Don / I can't help it: Young, Faron / Silver wings: Fender, Freddy / So will you my love: Nelson, Willie / White lightnin': Jennings, Waylon / She's just a girl I used to know: Jones, George / Blue is the way I feel: Twitty, Conway / Georgia in a jug: Paycheck, Johnny / What am I living for: Perkins, Carl / Where do we go from here: Williams, Don / Fall to pieces: Young, Faron / Baby I want to love you: Fender, Freddy / I'm building heartaches: Nelson, Willie / Love's gonna live here: Jennings, Waylon
307722 / Aug '97 / Hallmark

☐ **KINGS OF COUNTRY LIVE**
JHD 009 / Jun '92 / Tring

☐ **KINGS OF DUB**
RB 3019 / Jan '96 / Reggae Best

☐ **KINGS OF DUB ROCK VOL.1 & 2 (Sir Coxsone Sound)**
TMCD 3 / Feb '95 / Tribesman

☐ **KINGS OF GYPSY MUSIC**
Son son sera mix / Dale dale al bordon / Gitana / Morena / Venga valiente / Esa amor que me enganaba / Rumba para ti / Amor impoible / Vive a tu manera gitanita nos queremoos / Vete mujer / Juntos los dos / Los lachos te cantan / A-chi-li-pu / No chute / Siego tu vueli / Mejor separanos / Amores pasajeros / Perdido / Amor / Larga espre / Maria dell mar / No vuelvas a sonar
GRF 084 / Apr '93 / Tring

☐ **KINGS OF HIP HOP, THE (4CD Set)**
DAM 003 / Dec '96 / Tring

☐ **KINGS OF KINGS VOL.1**
KOKCD 01 / 5 May '98 / Kings Of Kings

☐ **KINGS OF NEW ORLEANS R&B, THE**
Sea cruise: Ford, Frankie / Rockin' pneumonia and the boogie woogie flu: Smith, Huey / Those lonely, lonely nights: King, Earl / Blow wind blow: Gordon, Junior / Little chickee wah wah: Marchan, Bobby / Just a dream: Clanton, Jimmy / Charlie Brown got expelled: Tex, Joe / At the Mardi Gras: Huey & Curley / Roberta: Ford, Frankie / I love to rock and roll: Bo, Eddie / Rockin' behind the iron curtain: Marchan, Bobby / Happy sax: Tyler, Alvin 'Red' / Grannie stole the show: Tex, Joe / Little Liza Jane: Smith, Huey 'Piano' / Gee baby: Joe & Ann / (Come On) let the good times roll: King, Earl / Have a little mercy: Crawford, Sugar Boy / Rockin' teenage wedding: Angel, Johnny / Don't you just know it: Smith, Huey 'Piano' / Doin' the rock 'n' roll: Spears, Calvin / You little baby faced thing: Tex, Joe / Alimony: Ford, Frankie / Rock: Dorsey, Lee / Everybody's wallin': Smith, Huey 'Piano' / Jockomo: Crawford, Sugar boy & Dr. John / I've got a girl: Cook, Roland / Go Jimmy go: Clanton, Jimmy / Everybody's carried away: King, Earl / Snake eyes: Tyler, Alvin 'Red' / New Orleans: Myles, Big Boy & Dr. John
MCCD 355 / 20 Jul '98 / Music Club

☐ **KINGS OF RHYTHM AND BLUES, THE**
Willie and the hand jive: Otis, Johnny / Brown angel: Liggins, Joe / Bad bad whisky: Milburn, Amos / Outskirts of town: Jordan, Louis / Juice head baby: Vinson, Eddie 'Cleanhead' / Baby baby all the time: Milburn, Amos / Baby I've got news for you: Otis, Johnny / Tanya: Liggins, Joe / Helping hand: Jordan, Louis / Going back to LA: Liggins, Joe / Cleanhead's blues: Vinson, Eddie 'Cleanhead' / Have love will travel: Berry, Richard / Barrelhouse blues: Otis, Johnny / Yama yama pretty mama: Berry, Richard / Corine corine: Turner, 'Big' Joe / I got the walkin' blues: Jordan, Louis / Trackin machine: Berry, Richard / TV mama: Turner, 'Big' Joe / Old maids boogie: Vinson, Eddie 'Cleanhead' / Honey hush: Turner, 'Big' Joe
306002 / Apr '98 / Hallmark

☐ **KINGS OF THE BLUES**
Sweet little angel: King, B.B. / She moves me: Watson, Johnny 'Guitar' / I'll get along somehow: Sims, Frankie Lee / Blues serenade: Turner, Babyface / On my way back home: Flash Terry / Odds against me: Hooker, John Lee / Sittin' here thinkin': Walker, T-Bone / Problem child: Walton, Mercy Dee / Lonesome old feeling: Bumble Bee Slim / I tried: Young Wolf / Cotton picker: Higgins, Chuck & The Melotones / Wild hop: Crayton, Pee Wee / Worried about my baby: Howlin' Wolf / Tavern lounge boogie: Burns, Eddie 'Guitar' / Believe I'll change towns: Hogg, Smokey / Too many rivers: Fulson, Lowell / Yesterday: Chenier, Clifton / Lonesome dog blues: Hopkins, Lightnin' / Hard times: Fuller, Johnny / Riding mighty high: Dixon, Floyd / Please find my baby: James, Elmore
CDCH 276 / Jul '89 / Ace

☐ **KINGS OF WESTERN SWING (2CD Set)**
Crazy cause I love you: Cooley, Spade / Keep a-knockin' but you can't come in: Wills, Bob / She's a rounder: Sunshine Boys / Jive and smile: Skyles, Bob & His Sky Rockets / Everybody's truckin': Modern Mountaineers / Keep on truckin': Wood, Smokey & The Woodchips / Sweet Jennie Lee: Brown, Milton & The Brownies / Jessie: Bruner, Cliff / Oh swing it: Revard, Jimmie / Beer parlour jive: Hi-Flyers / Pipe liner blues: Sunshine Boys / Detour: Cooley, Spade / Milk cow blues: Wills, Johnny Lee / Nickel in the kitty: Stockard, Ocie & his Wanderers / Florene: Selph, Leon / Little Willie Green: Swift Jewel Cowboys / Is it true what they say about Dixie: Rice Brothers / Peach tree shuffle: Penny, Hank & His Radio Cowboys / It's a long way to Tipperary: Revard, Jimmie / Right or wrong: Brown, Milton & The Brownies / Reno Street blues: Hi-Flyers / What's the matter at the mill: Wills, Bob & His Texas Playboys / Gonna get tight: Sunshine Boys / Try it once again: Alley, Shelly Lee / Chill tonic: Penny, Hank & His Radio Cowboys / Swing with the music: Hofner, Adolph / Down hi lo way: Daffan, Ted & The Texans / She's selling what she used to give away: Nettles, Bill / Double crossing Mama: Prairie Ramblers / Sunshine: Dexter, Al / Am I happy: Hofner, Adolph / Tender hearted Sue: Rambling Rogue / I'm telling you: Hughes, Billy / Texahoma boogie: Linville, Charlie & The Fiddlin' Linvilles / Flamin' Mamie: Penny, Hank / Look who's talking: Daffan, Ted & The Texans / I can trust you now: Tyler, Johnny / Sugar baby blues: Nettles, Bill / I'm losing my mind over you: Dexter, Al / New steel guitar rag: Boyd, Bill & His Cowboy Ramblers / Weary trouble on my mind: Smith, Harmie / Talkin' about you: Penny, Hank / What it means to be blue: Russell, Tex / Cotton sack drag: Lindsay, Merle / Road side rag: Boyd, Bill & His Cowboy Ramblers / You don't do right by me anymore: Atchison, Tex / These wild wild women: Penny, Hank / Gals don't mean a thing: Tyler, T. Texas / Gotta little red wagon: Lindsay, Merle / It's been so long darling: Tyler, T. Texas
CDGR 1822 / Nov '97 / Charly

☐ **KINGSTON 14 VOL.1**
JASCD 15 / 20 Apr '98 / Sarge

☐ **KINGSTON TOWN**
HBCD 82 / May '93 / Heartbeat

☐ **KIRGHIZ KOMUZ AND KAZAKH DOMBRA (Music From Turkestan)**
C 560121 / Dec '97 / Ocora

☐ **KISS FM LORDS OF THE UNDERGROUND**
5653502 / 24 Aug '98 / PolyGram TV

☐ **KISS CLUB ANTHEMS VOL.1 (2CD Set)**
Encore une fois: Sash / Scared: Slacker / Born slippy: Underworld / Not forgotten: Leftfield / You got the love: Source & Candi Staton / My love is deep: Parker, Sara / Funk phenomena: Van Helden, Armand / Give me luv: Alcatraz / Higher state of consciousness: Wink, Josh / Keep on jumpin': Terry, Todd & Martha Wash/Jocelyn Brown / Chime: Orbital / Playing with knives: Bizarre Inc. / Sound of Eden: Shades Of Rhythm / Go: Moby / La luna '95: Ethics / Groovebird: Natural Born Groovers / Don't you want me: Felix / Le voie le soleil: Subliminal Cuts / Difference: Funny Walker / Push the feeling on: Nightcrawlers / Tears: Knuckles, Frankie / Beautiful people: Tucker, Barbara / Reach: Lil Mo Yin Yang / Who keeps changing your mind: South Street Players / Missing: Everything But The Girl / Show me love: Robin S / Hideaway: De'Lacy / Get up (everybody): Stingily, Byron / Space cowboy: Jamiroquai / Deeper love: C&C Music Factory / 40 miles: Congress / Testament 1: Chubby Chunks / I'm alive: Stretch n' Vern & Maddog / Not over yet: Grace / Drive me crazy: Partizan / Children: Miles, Robert
5534792 / Apr '97 / PolyGram TV

☐ **KISS CLUB ANTHEMS VOL.2 (2CD Set)**
Sunchyme: Dario G / Stay: Sash & La Trec / Belissima: DJ Quicksilver / I believe: Happy Clappers / Professional widow: Amos, Tori / Something goin' on: Terry, Todd / TI thought it was you: Sex-O-Sonique / Cosmic girl: Jamiroquai / Get up: Stingily, Byron / Saturday: East 57th Street & Donna Allen / Get up go insane: Stretch n' Vern / Magic carpet ride: Mighty Dub Katz / Deeper: Serious Danger / Nightmare: Brainbug / Age of love: Age Of Love / Grooverbird: Natural Born Groovers / Plastic dreams: Jaydee / You got the love: Source & Candi Staton / Closer than closer: Gaines, Rosie / Never gonna let you go: Moore, Tina / Free: Ultra Nate / Belo horizonti: Heartists / RIP groove: Double 99 / Chant: RIP / Digital: Goldie & KRS1 / Spin spin sugar: Sneaker Pimps / Tell me what you want: Industry Standard / Pleasure dome: Soul II Soul / Gabriel: Davis, Roy Jr. & Peven Everett / London thing: Garcia, Scott & MC Styles / Runaway: Nu Yorican Soul / Just gets better: TJR & Xavier / Anytime: Nu-Birth / Don't give up: Weeks, Michelle / Oh boy: Fabulous Baker Boys
5550902 / 17 Nov '97 / PolyGram TV

☐ **KISS GARAGE '98 (2CD Set)**
5558872 / 27 Apr '98 / PolyGram TV

☐ **KISS IN IBIZA**
5259112 / Sep '95 / PolyGram TV

☐ **KISS IN IBIZA '96 (2CD Set)**
I'm alive: Stretch n' Vern / Keep on jumpin': Terry, Todd / Let's all chant: Gusto / Ain't nobody's business if I do: H2O & Billie / Help me make it: Huff & Puff / Want love: Hysteric Ego / Feel my body: O'Moiraghi, Frank / Professional widow: Amos, Tori / Tall and handsome: Outrage / Do that to me: Lisa Marie Experience / That look: De'Lacy / Don't go: 3rd Dimension / High: Hyper Go Go / If I could fly: Grace / Hi energy: Maltese Massive / Tha wildstyle: DJ Supreme / Trans Euro Express: X-Press 2 / 7 days and one week: BBE / Groovebird: Natural Born Groovers / Gift: Way Out West / Bomb scare: 2 Bad Mice / Stamp: Healy, Jeremy & Amos / Jus come: Cool Jack / Sugar is sweeter: Bolland, C.J. / It's gonna be alright: Technocat / Up to no good: Porn Kings / Higher state of consciousness: Wink, Josh / All I want to do: Tin Tin Out / Krupa: Apollo 440 / Horny as funk: Soapy / Nocturnal: Q-Dos / Antheum: Digital Blondes / Believe in me: Mankey / 2nd coming: Libido
5359672 / Oct '96 / PolyGram TV

☐ **KISS IN IBIZA '97 (2CD Set)**
Turn me out (turn to sugar): Praxis & Kathy Brown / Freed from desire: Gala / Gottaman: Pizzaman / Magic carpet ride: Mighty Dub Katz / Dirty cash: Stevie V & Nazlyn / Get up go insane: Stretch n' Vern / Something goin' on: Terry, Todd / Finally: Peniston, Ce Ce / Your face: Slacker / Over me: Whiplash / Swirl: La Casa / Nine ways: JDS / Joanna: Mrs. Wood / Dubbhopping: Klubb Heads / On the run: De Bos / Clouds: Source / Whoosh: Whoosh / Schoenberg: Marmion / Free: Ultra Nate / Never gonna let you go: Moore, Tina / Anytime: Nu Birth / Saturday: East 57th Street & Donna Allen / Plastic dreams: Jaydee / Tell me what you want: Industry Standard / Dreams: Smokin' Beats / Ballistic phunk: Ballistic Brothers & Armand Van Helden / Just gets better: TJR & Xavier / Everythin' is large: Underground Distortion / RIP groove: Double 99 / Sun rising: Beloved / Blue: Way Out West / Pacific melody: Airscape / Offshore: Chicane & Power Circle / Beachball: Nalin & Kane / You're not alone: Olive
5550352 / 15 Sep '97 / PolyGram TV

☐ **KISS IN IBIZA '98 (2CD Set)**
5654102 / 7 Sep '98 / PolyGram TV

☐ **KISS IN THE CAFES**
4898712 / 17 Jul '98 / Irma

☐ **KISS ME I'M IRISH**
If it weren't for the Irish: Parker, Frank / Miss O'Leary's Irish fruitcake: Harrington, Pat / Murphy bed: Harrington, Pat / Which of them will I marry: O'Hara, Maureen / I'm going to be married on Sunday: O'Hara, Maureen / Johnny I hardly knew ye: O'Hara, Maureen / It's a great day for the Irish: Porter, Frank / When Irish eyes are smiling: Porter, Frank / Molly Malone: Porter, Frank / Macushla: Porter, Frank / MacNamara's band: Porter, Frank / Mick McGalligan's ball: Quinn, Carmel & Arthur Godfrey / Humour is on me now: Quinn, Carmel & Arthur Godfrey / Bally McQuilty band: Quinn, Carmel / With my shillelagh under my arm: Quinn, Carmel / There was an old woman: O'Hara, Maureen / Danny boy: O'Hara, Maureen / Macushla: Smith, Kate / Little bit of heaven (sure, they call it Ireland): Smith, Kate
4896802 / 2 Mar '98 / Columbia

☐ **KISS MIX '96 (2CD Set)**
Blurred: Pianoman / Female of the species: Space / Disco frenzy (got to be there): Divine Intervention / It's gonna be alright: Technocat / Latin thing: Latin Thing / Klubhopping: Klubb Heads / On ya way: Helicopter / Le voie le soliel: Subliminal Cuts / Outrageous: Stix 'N' Stoned / Beginning: Dex & Jonesy / Into your heart: 6 By 6 / Theme from S'Express: S'Express / There's nothing I won't do: JX / Deep: Ariel / Schoneberg: Marmion / Baby talk: Future Files / Born slippy: Underworld / Hot and wet (believe it): Tzant / Solution (feels so right): Simonelli, Victor / Keep on jumpin': Lisa Marie Experience / Madagascar: Madagascar / Find your way: Crosby, B.J. / Stand up: Love Tribe / Lover that you are: Pulse / Can't help it: Happy Clappers / Saved my life: Edwards, Todd / Are you gonna be there: Up Yer Ronson / What you want: Future Force / Do me right: Inner City / Pushing against the flow: Ray Stylus
5357012 / Jul '96 / PolyGram TV

☐ **KISS MIX '97 (2CD Set)**
You are the universe: Brand New Heavies / Free: Ultra Nate / RIP groove: Double 99 / Magic carpet ride: Mighty Dub Katz / Invader: Koolworld / Something's goin' on: Terry, Todd / Sunstroke: Chicane / Pacific melody: Airscape / Ecuador: Sash / Catch: Sunscreem / AsceSomeone: Ascension / QuatTruth: Quattara / Blaming June: BT / Frontiers: Spirito / Deep (I'm falling deeper): Ariel / Down to earth: Grace / Sharp tools volume three: Sharp Boys / Freed from desire: Gala / Still a thrill: Sybil / Show me love: Fruit Loop / Get up stand up: Phunky Phantom / Get down to the beat: Brainbashers / Go with the flow: Loop Da Loop / Bring the beat back: De Vit, Tony / Don't be afraid: Moonman / Epidemic: Exit EEE / Rock the turntables: Floorshow / Discohopping: Klubb Heads / Sweet lips: Monaco / Flowtation: De Moor, Vincent
5538402 / Jul '97 / PolyGram TV

☐ **KISS 'N' TELL**
Celebrate your victory: Shirelles / Remember me: Shirelles / You're under arrest: Shirelles / Devil in his heart: Donays / Bad boy: Donays / Party lights: Donays / Silly little girl: Dean & Jean / Casanova: Earline & her girlfriends / Because of you: Earline & her girlfriends / Little girl lost: Brown, Maxine / Peaches 'n' cream: Ikettes / (He's gonna be) fine fine fine: Ikettes / Are you trying to get rid of me: Candy & The Kisses / You did the best you could: Candy & The Kisses / You got it baby: Toys / Try to get you out of my heart: Toys / I just couldn't say: Lorraine & The Delights / Stop, look and listen: Les girls / Kiss and tell: Julie & The Desires / Better be ready: Annette B / Leave us alone: Del-rons / Don't hurt me: Carroll, Bernadette / Nicky: Carroll, Bernadette / Only seventeen: Martin sisters / Stay at home, Sue: Linda Laurie / Hey there, hey there: Gypsies / You don't love me anymore: Dodds, Nella / I wonder why: Chiffons / Foolish little girl: Chiffons / Three dips of ice cream: Chiffons
CDCHD 330 / Feb '93 / Ace

☐ **KISS SMOOTH GROOVES 1997 (2CD Set)**
Cosmic girl: Jamiroquai / Sometimes: Brand New Heavies / Love is all we need: Blige, Mary J. / Doin' it: LL Cool J / I believe I can fly: R Kelly / Wonderful tonight: Damage / Sugar honey ice tea: Goodfellaz / Request line: Zhane / Ain't no playa: Jay-Z & Foxxy Brown / Spirit: Sounds Of Blackness / Let's get down: Tony Toni Tone / Tell me do U wanna: Ginuwine / Don't wanna be a player: Joe / Me and those dreamin' eyes: D'Angelo / Steelo: 702 / Heavenly daughter: Kwesi / Shake it: D-Influence / It's alright: Hines, Deni / I'm not feeling you: Michelle, Yvette / Only you: 112 / Lougin': LL Cool J / Anggel: Simply Red / Touch me tease me: Case & Foxy Brown / Trippin': Morrison, Mark / Nobody knows: Rich, Tony / If you love me: Brownstone / One for the money: Brown, Horace / Creep: TLC / Stressed out: Tribe Called Quest & Faith Evans / 1st of the month: Bone Thugs n' Harmony / Step into a world: KRS 1 / This DJ: Warren G / Sentimental: Cox, Deborah / Ocean drivw: Lighthouse Family / Like this and like that: Monica / Down with the ckique: Aaliyah / Do you know: Gayle, Michelle / Fell so high: Des'ree / Remember me: Blueboy
5333412 / Jun '97 / PolyGram TV

☐ **KISS SMOOTH GROOVES 1998 (2CD Set)**
Phenomenon: LL Cool J / Hypnotize: Notorious BIG / Put my hands where your eyes could see: Busta Rhymes / Ooh la la: Coolio / Rain: Elliott, Missy / High: Lighthouse Family / Happy song: Blackstreet / Everything: Blige, Mary J. / You know my steez: Gang Starr / Guess who's back: Rakim / Wishing on a star: Jay-Z / You should be mine (don't waste time): McKnight, Brian / Sexy Cinderella: Hall, Lynden David / Magic: D-Influence / Shelter: Brand New Heavies / Crush: Zhane / We can get down: Myron / I am the black gold of the sun: NuYorican Soul / Alright: Jamiroquai / I know where its at: All Saints / Sunshine: Jay-Z & Babyface/Foxy Brown / On and on: Badu, Erykah / Iggin' me: DeBarge, Chico / Even after all: DeBarge, Chico / When doves cry: Ginuwine / Ain't that just the way: McNeal, Lutricia / 4 seasons of loneliness: Boyz II Men / Another day: Buckshot Lefonque / Be alone no more: Another Level / Whatever: En Vogue / Good girls: Joe / Playa: Filo / Say nothing: Omar / You bring me up: K-Ci & Jo Jo / It's alright: Queen Latifah / Let me be the one: Mint Condition / Head over heels: Mint Condition / Prince Igor: Warren G
5555742 / 16 Feb '98 / PolyGram TV

☐ **KITTEN ON THE KEYS (Pianorola Favourites)**
Bye bye blackbird / Thora / Miss Annabelle Lee / For me and my gal / Stars and stripes forever / Sweet Genevieve / J'en ai marre / Alexander's ragtime band / I want to be happy / Doll dance / Moon river / Lovable and sweet / Me and Jane in a plane / Kitten on the keys / Stealing / Tippy canoe / Among my souvenirs / More we are together / Three o'clock in the morning
CDJ 115 / Nov '96 / Australian Jazz

☐ **KITTY YO COMPILATION**
9801 / 26 May '98 / Kitty Yo

☐ **KK COMPILATION**
Fire: 2nd Communication / Second episode: Sloppy Wrenchbody / Chasin' the flame: Minister Of Noise / Warp: DRP / BPM: Sterotaxic Device / Curse: Numb / Disobey: Kode IV / What a life: Exquisite Corpse / Burning bodies: Blue Eyed Christ / Point of no return: Cat Rapes Dog / Zoeloe noizz: Insekt / Surely get's me: Swains / Patience: Psychik Warriors Ov Gaia
KK 088CD / Dec '92 / KK

☐ **KK IN THE MIX**
Room for improvement: Riou / Brown leather slouch: RAX / Kraak mix 1: PWOG / Kraak: PWOG / Unit mobius: OK Blaze / Undraped: Starfish Pool / Sick and crazy: GF / Sphengnus: Delta Plan / Light emitting diode: GF / Offday: Starfish Pool / Overflow: Lassigue Bendthaus / Zipper: Unit Moebius / 808 king: RAX / Reset: GF / Spherical perspective: Delta Plan / Collonization: Omicron / Onoreno: Riou
KK 160CD / 29 Sep '97 / KK

☐ **KLEZMANIA (Tradition & Beyond)**
SH 67007 / Mar '97 / Shanachie

☐ **KLEZMER 1993 - TRADITION CONTINUES ON THE LOWER EAST SIDE**
KFWCD 123 / Feb '95 / Knitting Factory

☐ **KLEZMER MUSIC (Early Yiddish Instrumental Music 1908-1927)**
Doina and Hora: Hoffman, Jacob / Sirba: Orchestra Orfeon / Mechutonim Tantz: Jewish Orchestra / Kallarash: Brandwein, Naftule / Yiddish chusedel: Leibowitz, Max / Kleftico vlachiko: Orchestra Goldberg / Fihren die mechutonim aheim: Brandwein, Naftule / Koilen: Ziganoff, Mishka / Ch'sidishe nigunim: Boibriker Kapelle / Haneros haluli: Boibriker Kapelle / Sadigurer-Chusid: Moskowitz, Joseph / Doina: Kosch, S. / Turkische yalle vey uve: Brandwein, Naftule / Sadegurer Chused'l: Schwartz, Abe / Biem Reben's sideh: Yiddisher Orkester / Oi tate, s'is gut: Brandwein, Naftule / Schweir und schwiger tanz: Schwartz, Abe / Rumanische fantasien: Solinski, Joseph / Khosidl: Belf's Rumanian Orchestra / Der shtiller Bulgar: Jewish Orchestra / A Mitzve tenzel: Hochman, I.J. / National hora: Schwartz, Abe / Sher: Schwartz, Abe
ARHCD 7034 / Sep '97 / Arhoolie

☐ **KLEZMER PIONEERS**
ROUCD 1089 / Jun '93 / Rounder

☐ **KLEZMOKUM**
BVHAASTCD 9209 / May '89 / Bvhaast

☐ **KLONED VOL.2**
CDKOPY 102 / Dec '93 / Klone

☐ **KLONED VOL.3**
CDKOPY 103 / Nov '94 / Klone

☐ **KLONED VOL.4**
CDKOPY 104 / Jan '96 / Klone

☐ **KLUBBTRAX VOL.3 (Mixed By The Klubbheads)**
BLUECD 03 / Jun '97 / Dutch Blue

☐ **KLUBHOPPIN' (2CD Set)**
Underwater love: *Smoke City* / Fired up: *Funky Green Dogs From Outer Space* / Ready Or Not: *Course* / People hold on: *Stansfield, Lisa & Dirty Rotten Scoundrels* / Where can I find lovev: *Livin' Joy* / Keep on jumpin': *Terry, Todd & Martha Wash/ Jocelyn Brown* / Funk phenomena: *Van Helden, Armand* / Giv me luv: *Alcatraz* / Can't knock the hustle: *Jay Z & Mary J. Blige* / Release yo'self: *Transatlantic Soul* / Ultra flava: *Heller & Farley Project* / One and one: *Miles, Robert & Maria Naylor* / Hypnotizin': *Winx* / Landslide: *Harmonix* / Show me love: *Robin S* / I'll be your friend: *Owens, Robert* / You got the love: *Source & Candi Staton* / Remember me: *Blueboy* / Ain't talkin' about dub: *Apollo 440* / Breathe: *Prodigy* / Stamp: *Healy, Jeremy & Amos* / Don't you want me: *Felix* / Gift: *Way Out West* / Inferno: *Souvlaki* / Klubhopping: *Klubb Heads* / I'm alive: *Stretch n' Vern & Maddog* / Rollin' on: *Lazy, Doug* / Seven days and one week: *BBE* / Offshore: *Chicane* / Be as one: *Sasha & Maria*
RADCD 60 / Apr '97 / Global TV

☐ **KNEELIN' DOWN INSIDE THE GATE**
ROUCD 5035 / Jul '95 / Rounder

☐ **KNIGHTS OF THE SUAVE HOUSE**
Rider: *Intro* / Heat of the night: *Tele* / Trapped: *Feds* / Just like candy: *Nola* / Questions: *Eightball & MJG* / Starships and rockets: *Thorough Of South Circle* / Life is a crying: *Eightball & Randy* / Ghetto madness: *Nola & Nina Creque* / South circle: *Smoke One Productions* / Death notes: *Feds* / Dusk till dawn: *Feds*
4869052 / 1 Sep '97 / Epic

☐ **KNIGHTS OF THE TURNTABLE VOL.1**
BMRCD 01 / Nov '94 / Boomerang

☐ **KNIGHTS WHO SAY DOT VOL.1, THE**
DOTCD 01 / 20 Oct '97 / Dot

☐ **KNIGHTS WHO SAY DOT VOL.2, THE (2CD Set)**
DOTCD 05 / 27 Apr '98 / Dot

☐ **KNITE FORCE - VINYL IS BETTER**
GUMH 010 / Nov '94 / Gumh

☐ **KNITTING FACTORY BOX SET (5CD Set)**
KFWCD 12345 / Nov '92 / Knitting Factory

☐ **KNITTING FACTORY GOES TO THE NORTH WEST**
KFWCD 101 / Nov '94 / Knitting Factory

☐ **KNITTING FACTORY TOURS EUROPE**
KFWCD 105 / Nov '94 / Knitting Factory

☐ **KNOCK OUT BLUES**
RST 915782 / Jun '94 / RST

☐ **KNOCK OUT IN THE FIRST ROUND**
KOCD 038 / Oct '96 / Knock Out

☐ **KNOCKOUT, IN THE SECOND ROUND**
KOCD 062 / Jun '97 / Knock Out

☐ **KNOW YOUR ENEMY**
EMY 1392 / Sep '97 / Enemy

☐ **KODEX VOL.4**
EFA 119152 / Nov '94 / Kodex

☐ **KOLN KOMPAKT**
KOMPAKTCD 1 / 22 Jun '98 / Kompakt

☐ **KOMM' MIT MIR IN DIE MILCH BAR**
Jacky boy: *Grimm, Monika* / Hatt ich doch ein weisses Sportcoupe: *Parker, Teddy* / Baby komm tanz mit mir: *King, Gaby & Tobby* / My boy lollipop: *Bachert, Hedei* / Seventeen: *Ball, Susi* / Bobby kiss me: *Hinnen, Peterli* / In meinem kalender: *Manuella* / Mama was soll ich nur tun: *Jung, Gissy* / Kusse im mondschien: *Manola, Pirko & Wyn Hoop* / My baby hast du heute frei: *Palmer, Teddy* / Ein junger kavalier: *King, Gabi* / Oh oh ich klopfe an deine tur: *Duvall, Mario & Franco* / Darum traum' ich nur von dir: *Gualdi, Nana* / Dein kleiner bruder: *Herold, Ted* / Nur ein kusschen: *Honey Twins* / I'm sorry: *Gitte* / Lippenstift am jacket: *Froboess, Conny* / Die liebe ist ein seltsames speil: *Francis, Connie* / Die jungen jahre: *James Bros* / Johnny Angel: *Kessler, Alice & Ellen* / Hello Mary Lou: *Kollo, Rene* / Sie war ein madchen von siebzehn jahren: *Michael*
BCD 16179 / Aug '97 / Bear Family

☐ **KONGPILATION**
BJ 999 / Jan '96 / Bananajuice

☐ **KONKOKTING**
PNM 004D / 29 Jun '98 / Pik 'n' Mix

☐ **KONKRETE JUNGLE (Maximum Drum 'N' Bass)**
UTA 25 / 1 Jun '98 / Ultra

☐ **KOOL FM PRESENTS THE FEVER (2CD Set)**
BDRCD 20 / Jun '97 / Breakdown

☐ **KOOL REVOLUTION, A**
TKCD 8 / Aug '95 / 2 Kool

☐ **KORA AND THE XYLOPHONE, THE**
LYRCD 7308 / '91 / Lyrichord

☐ **KOREAN COURT MUSIC**
LYRCD 7206 / '91 / Lyrichord

☐ **KRAFTWORK VOL.1 (Nu Skool Electro/ 2CD Set)**
Into deep space: *Terrace* / Hibernation drive: *Acid Jesus* / Electra: *Slick n' Flash* / Synaps QZ401: *Urban Electro Part 2* / Asphalt: *Kampf, Voigt* / Celestial funk: *Space DJ's* / Voice activated: *Dopplereffekt* / Mind strike: *Operator* / Revenge: *Magic 12* / Countdown: *Mover* / Five-O-nine: *Elektronome* / Track A1: *Interference & That Nigger* / Shorty: *Kennedy, Inigo* / Nautilus: *Dredd, Mike & Peter Green* / 3rd led: *D'Archangelo* / Face the future: *Dredd, Mike* / Predator: *DJ Snug* / RHYTHM: *Euphonic* / I do because I couldn't care less: *I-F* / Electroflair: *Freddie Fresh*
MILL 051CD / 27 Oct '97 / Millenium

☐ **KRAFTWORK VOL.2 (Nu Skool Electro/ 2CD Set)**
MILL 059CD / 5 May '98 / Millenium

☐ **KRALINGEN POP FESTIVAL**
KRCD 1 / Mar '97 / Headlite

☐ **KRANKENHOUSE (2CD Set)**
Transaxual: *Armando* / Alabama blues: *St. Germain* / Old skool: *DJ Tonka* / Organic technology: *Johnson, Paul* / Non stop: *Herbert* / House of God: *DHS* / Rex attitude: *Garnier, Laurent* / Strikeout: *Hardfloor* / Times fade: *Phuture* / Quo vadis: *G-Man* / Pure madness: *Tom Wax* / DJ kicks: *Young, Claude* / Chord memory: *Pooley, Ian* / Praline horse: *Landstrumm, Neal* / Cowgirl: *Underworld* / Kraak: *PWOG* / Terminator: *Westbam* / Who's got the flave: *Kirlian* / Loop 2: *Larkin, Kenny* / Bruce Lee MC: *MC Quincy* / Precipice: *Turntable Terranova* / Circus bells: *Armani, Robert*
SPV 08947162 / Feb '97 / SPV

☐ **KRAUTROCK ARCHIVE VOL.1 (The Cologne Tapes)**
Orion wakes: *Golem* / Leaves are falling: *Temple* / Black light: *Temple* / Dark path: *Cozmic Corriders* / Niemand versteht: *Cozmic Corriders* / Interstellar shortwave: *Astral Army* / Lunarscape: *Galactic Explorers* / Ganz wie du willst: *Feuerrote*
CDOVD 468 / Jul '96 / Virgin

☐ **KRAUTROCK ARCHIVE VOL.2 (Unknown Deutschland)**
Message: *Spirulina* / Innerst: *Ten To Ten* / Heathen temple: *Temple* / Age of ages: *Temple* / Tower of Barad-Dur: *Nazgul* / Godhead dance: *Golem* / Moutainside: *Cozmic Corriders* / Summit: *Cozmic Corriders*
CDOVD 472 / Jun '97 / Virgin

☐ **KRAUTROCK ARCHIVE VOL.3 (Unknown Deutschland)**
Feuerwerk: *Anderson, Neil* / Ethereal jazz: *Galactic Explorers* / Stellar launch: *Golem* / Dead marshes: *Nazgul* / No God/Astaroth: *Baal* / Schaudernacht: *Chronos* / Ship on fire: *Temple*
CDOVD 473 / Jun '97 / Virgin

☐ **KRAZY KATS CAJUN**
TRIK 0167 / Oct '94 / Trikont

☐ **KRIS NEEDS MUST**
Jailbird: *Primal Scream* / Mr Vinegar: *Mr. Parkers Band* / Let the fun begin: *Secret Knowledge* / Lair: *Wulf n' Bear* / Cold house yellow curtains: *Absolute State* / Dreamer: *Longman* / Sonic stiffy: *Kris N' Dave* / Speedway: *Prodigy* / Frontier: *Digital Destroyer* / Rabbits name was: *A&E Dept* / Lazarus: *Boo Radleys*
CDRAID 534 / Mar '97 / Rumour

☐ **KRUSH GROOVES**
GAP 0352 / 20 Apr '98 / Groove Attack

☐ **KUDIYATTAM DANCE DRAMA, THE**
VICG 50372 / Mar '96 / JVC World Library

☐ **KUDOS DIGEST - ISSUE A (IS FOR APPLE), THE**
Electric arc: *Nuron* / Jupiter: *Pluto* / End of an era: *Balony, B.J.* / Chevy rainbow: *Perbec* / Midst of tumult: *Roxy* / Griptape: *Spira* / Check it out: *PVP* / Solitude: *Stasis* / Different emotions: *Insync & Mysteron* / Honda Suzuki's last motorcycle ride: *Le Panel De Pants* / Rustless: *Beautyon*
KUDCD 006 / Jun '95 / Kudos

☐ **KULT DANCE KLASSIX VOL.2**
SPV 79908692 / Aug '93 / SPV

☐ **KUULAS HETKI**
OMCD 46 / Jun '93 / Digelius

☐ **KWANZAA PARTY**
Roaring lion: *Mary Ann* / Ng la banda: *La Expresiva* / I'll take you there: *Staple Singers* / Kanda bongo man: *Liza* / Toinho de Alagoas: *Balanco da Canao* / Sekusile: *Dark City Sisters* / Fidelina: *Duran, Alejo* / Rhythme commercial: *Ensemble Nemours Jean Baptiste* / Gouye gui: *Africando* / Flotation merengue: *Blinky & The Roadmasters* / Shaure Yako: *Orchestre Super Mazembe* / Caliventura: *Afrosound* / Same thing: *Copeland, Johnny* / Ede M chante: *Boukan Ginen*
ROUCD 2153 / Oct '96 / Rounder

☐ **KYOTO JAZZ MASSIVE**
99 2137 / Jul '96 / Ninetynine

L

☐ **LA BANDA (2CD Set)**
Toreador / La Gitana / La Donna e mobile/Quartetto / Deh, non volerli e finale / A me fanciulla / Nessun dorma / E lucevan le stelle / Largo al factotum / Una serenata / Tra la folia, mora, mormora / Time is an empty bottle of wine / Sacra Romana rota
ENJ 932622 / 23 Feb '98 / Enja

☐ **LA CHANRANGA**
283402 / Jan '96 / Total

☐ **LA COLLECTION VOL.1 (2CD Set)**
Lost illusions: *Shazz* / Prelusion: *Deepside* / Aurora Borealis: *Aurora Borealis* / French: *Deepside* / Alabama blues: *St Germain* / How do you plead: *Soofle* / Modus Vivendi: *Modus Vivendi* / Quarter 2: *Orange* / Lost in Alaska: *Alaska* / Yantra: *Scan X* / Acid Eiffel: *Choice* / First time: *Alaska* / Disco inferno: *LN's* / Wake up: *Garnier, Laurent* / Sexual behaviour: *Deep Contest* / Breathless: *Garnier, Laurent* / Weeping waste: *Renegade Legion* / Planet sex: *Garnier, Laurent* / Art of stalking: *Suburban Knight* / Meltdown: *Lunatic Asylum* / Shazz: *Shazz*
3018912 / Dec '96 / FNAC Dance

☐ **LA COLLECTION VOL.2 (2CD Set)**
Deep in it: *St. Germain* / DJGG: *Nova Nova* / Move: *Nuages* / Leave me: *Shazz* / Alabama blues: *St. Germain* / Too late: *Iberian* / Cold fresh air: *Mono, Toni* / Le marias: *Shazz* / Baddest bitch: *Bell, Norma Jean* / Wanna dance: *Aqua Bassino* / Rainforest: *Alaska* / Aleph: *Nova Nova* / Dub experience: *St Germain* / Astral dreams: *Garnier, Laurent* / Rainfall: *Feedback* / Groove is going: *Lady B* / Obtuse corner: *Square* / Jack on the groove: *DS* / Bleu-process cyan: *Scan X* / Crusher: *Iberian* / Louis's cry: *Juantrip* / Milky way: *Borealis, Aurora* / Eternal deep: *Scan X* / 2019: *Taho* / Dance to the music: *Garnier, Laurent* / Orgasm: *Garnier, Laurent* / It's not enough: *Madame B.* / Theisme: *St. Germain* / Cafe bassino: *Aqua Bassino* / Louis' cry: *Juantrip* / Shake it up: *Nova Nova* / Percussion: *St. Germain*
F 045DCD / Jul '96 / F-Communications

☐ **LA CONDITION FEMININE**
983242 / Oct '96 / EPM

☐ **LA FLEUR DE MON SECRET**
Ay amor: *Bola De Nieve* / Tonada de luna llena: *Diaz, Simon* / En el ultimo trago: *Sandoval, Jose Alfredo Jimenez* / Titulos: *Iglesias, Alberto* / Casa con ventanas y libros: *Iglesias, Alberto* / Brevemente: *Iglesias, Alberto* / Retrato de Amanda Gris: *Iglesias, Alberto* / Tango de parla: *Iglesias, Alberto* / En Madrid nunca es tarde: *Iglesias, Alberto* / Facinacion: *Iglesias, Alberto* / Existe alguna posibilidad por pequena que sea de salvar lo n: *Iglesias, Alberto* / Interior: *Iglesias, Alberto* / Escribe compulsivamente: *Iglesias, Alberto* / Duo: *Iglesias, Alberto* / Ingenua: *Iglesias, Alberto* / Mi aldea: *Iglesias, Alberto* / Que Leo: *Iglesias, Alberto* / Vertigo: *Iglesias, Alberto* / Sola: *Iglesias, Alberto* / La flor de mi secreto: *Iglesias, Alberto* / Solea: *Iglesias, Alberto* / Poesia recitada: *Iglesias, Alberto*
4814442 / Jan '96 / Columbia

☐ **LA GALOUBET TAMBOURIN**
C 560073 / Nov '95 / Ocora

☐ **LA GRANDE PARADE DES CHANSONS D'AMOUR (2CD Set)**
983832 / Jul '96 / EPM

☐ **LA HAPPENING (The Mid-60s Soul Sides Of Vault, Fat Fish & Autumn Records)**
Nobody but you: *Wooden Nickels* / I'll never fall in love again: *Freeman, Bobby* / Baby reconsider: *Haywood, Leon* / Wishing and hoping: *Keen, Billy* / My heart's beating stronger: *Fisher, Andy* / That little old heartbreaker me: *Freeman, Bobby* / Tell me tomorrow: *Mandolph, Bobby* / Little girl: *Washington, Lee* / Tender tears: *Montgomery, Bobby* / Ain't no use: *Haywood, Leon* / Head over heels: *Bridges, Chuck & The LA Happening* / Going to a happening: *Neal, Tommy* / Got to get you back: *Mandolph, Bobby* / Fine, fine, fine: *Hughes, Judy* / More than a friend: *Wooden Nickels* / I've been crying: *Jones, Jesse* / Cross my heart: *Keen, Billy* / Mean ol' world: *Casualairs* / I have seniority over your love: *Kimball, Bobby* / I'm your stepping stone: *Montgomery, Bobby* / Wee bit longer: *Fisher, Andy* / Out of sight: *Sly* / Honey: *Averhart, Booker T. & The Mustangs* / You're flying high now baby: *Kimble, Neal* / LA happening: *Bridges, Chuck & The LA Happening* / Soul cargo: *Haywood, Leon*
CDKEND 122 / May '95 / Kent

☐ **LA IGUANA - SONS JAROCHOS FROM MEXICO**
CO 127 / May '96 / Corason

☐ **LA ISLA DE LA MUSICA (2CD Set)**
UMD 80504 / 15 Jun '98 / Universal

☐ **LA KORA DES GRIOTS**
PS 65079 / Nov '91 / PlayaSound

☐ **LA LEGENDE DES CORNOUAILLES**
3015902 / Feb '97 / Arcade

☐ **LA LEGENDE DU MUSETTE**
982732 / Jun '93 / EPM

☐ **LA MACHINE A ZOUKER**
952132 / Nov '97 / Pomme

☐ **LA RESISTANCE (Songs/Poetry Of The French Resistance)**
LDX 274734 / Jul '94 / La Chant Du Monde

☐ **LA RUMBA**
283422 / Jan '96 / Total

☐ **LA SEGUNDA INTERNACIONAL**
MRCD 109 / Nov '96 / Munster

☐ **LA TRADITION AMOUREUSE**
983232 / Oct '96 / EPM

☐ **LA VOIX DES MASQUES DE ZAMBIE**
ARN 58413 / 5 Jan '98 / Arion

☐ **LA YAYA**
HCD 8022 / Jul '94 / Hightone

☐ **LA YELLOW COLLECTION (2CD Set)**
Trailer: *La Yellow 357* / Souvenir de Paris: *Dimitri From Paris* / Peau d'ane: *Vertigo, Louise* / Nangadef maafric: *Galliano, Frederick* / Wrong number: *Kid Loco* / Fort alamo: *Murat, Jean-Louis* / Astral waves: *Papp, Julius* / Quelle sensation bizarre: *La Yellow 357* / Jazzhead: *Ex-Press* / Jazz thing: *Reminiscence Quartet* / Sentiments: *Fresh Lab* / DJ Cam theme: *DJ Cam* / Freestyle linguistique: *Mighty Pop* / Onde anda meu amor: *Reminiscence Quartet* / Return of the forgotten groove: *Bronco* / Rock solid: *Sinclair, Bob* / Ride away: *Mighty Bop* / L'element manquant: *Menelik* / Experience: *Cutee B.* / Psychodelico: *Reminiscence Quartet* / La blues: *De Lambre, Ingrid*
0630183912 / Jul '97 / East West

☐ **LABELLED WITH LOVE**
Magic smile: *Vela, Rosie* / On the wings of love: *Osborne, Jeffrey* / Every breath you take: *Police* / Love and affection: *Armatrading, Joan* / Stuck in the middle with you: *Stealer's Wheel* / Pearl's a singer: *Brooks, Elkie* / Steppin' out: *Jackson, Joe* / Love will keep us together: *Captain & Tennille* / Lady in red: *De Burgh, Chris* / I should have known better: *Diamond, Jim* / Heart on my sleeve: *Gallagher & Lyle* / Wonderful life: *Black* / We're all alone: *Coolidge, Rita* / Babe: *Styx* / Pick up the pieces: *Hudson - Ford* / Labelled with love: *Squeeze* / Will you: *O'Connor, Hazel* / Goodbye to love: *Carpenters* / Oh, Lori: *Alessi*
5518342 / 3 Aug '98 / Spectrum

☐ **LABELLO BLANCO - A DIFFERENT CLASS**
GUMH 9 / Jul '94 / Labello Blanco

☐ **LACHE PAS LA PATATE**
Lache pas la patate: *Newman, Jimmy C.* / La valse de grand basile: *Newman, Jimmy C.* / Jolie blonde: *Newman, Jimmy C.* / Grand Texas: *Newman, Jimmy C.* / Grand Mamou: *Newman, Jimmy C.* / Allons danser colinda: *Newman, Jimmy C.* / J'ai passe devant ta porte: *Newman, Jimmy C.* / La valse du grand chenier: *Newman, Jimmy C.* / Hippy-ty-yo: *Newman, Jimmy C.* / La valse de tolom: *Newman, Jimmy C.* / Allona a Lafayette: *Newman, Jimmy C.* / Cher tout toute: *Newman, Jimmy C.* / Potato song: *Newman, Jimmy C.* / Bayou lafourche: *Guidry, Doc* / Tee Maurice: *Guidry, Doc* / Ton petite couvert: *Guidry, Doc* / Tee Kaplan: *Guidry, Doc* / Over the waves: *Guidry, Doc* / Dans la Louisiane: *Bruce, Vin* / Chere cherie: *Bruce, Vin* / Te petite a te meon: *Bruce, Vin* / Clair de la lune: *Bruce, Vin* / J'ai laisse mon coeur a la maison: *Bruce, Vin* / Pauvre clochard: *Thibodeaux, Rufus* / La valse de amite: *Thibodeaux, Rufus* / Silver lake blues: *Thibodeaux, Rufus* / Draggin' the bow: *Thibodeaux, Rufus* / Port Arthur waltz: *Thibodeaux, Rufus* / Fais do do: *Thibodeaux, Rufus*
CDCHD 501 / 27 Jul '98 / Ace

☐ **LACH'S ANTIHOOT (Live From The Fort At Sidewalk Cafe)**
SH 5707 / Jun '96 / Shanachie

☐ **LADIES AND GENTLEMEN OF SONG (2CD Set)**
Lover man: *Horne, Lena* / Too young: *Lee, Peggy* / Taking a chance on love: *Fitzgerald, Ella* / Them there eyes: *Starr, Kay* / Moon river: *Garland, Judy* / My blue heaven: *Day, Doris* / St Louis blues: *Holiday, Billie* / More I see you: *Vaughan, Sarah* / Manhattan serenade: *Shore, Dinah* / I've got my love to keep me warm: *Starr, Kay* / September in the rain: *Day, Doris* / Yes my darling daughter: *Shore, Dinah* / I'm got the world on a string: *Vaughan, Sarah* / Honeysuckle rose: *Horne, Lena* / Lady is a tramp: *Lee, Peggy* / I'm nobody's baby: *Garland, Judy* / Three little words: *Fitzgerald, Ella* / God bless the child: *Holiday, Billie* / S'wonderful: *Day, Doris* / Are you certain: *Vaughan, Sarah* / All the way: *Sinatra, Frank* / Blue skies: *Como, Perry* / You're a sweet little headache: *Crosby, Bing* / Lazy: *Haymes, Dick* / Darling je vous aime beaucoup: *Cole, Nat 'King'* / My mammy: *Jolson, Al* / I guess I'll have to change my plans: *Bennett, Tony* / Answer me: *Laine, Frankie* / Same one: *Benton, Brook* / On the sunny side of the street: *Sinatra, Frank* / I love you: *Como, Perry* / Apple for the teacher: *Crosby, Bing* / Sonny boy: *Jolson, Al* / Chicago: *Bennett, Tony* / Wheel of fortune: *Laine, Frankie* / Revenge: *Benton, Brook* / Thinking of you: *Haymes, Dick* / Thou swell: *Cole, Nat 'King'* / All through the day: *Como, Perry*
PC 606 / 10 Nov '97 / Platinum Collection

☐ **LADIES OF GASCONY - THE BAGPIPES**
C 560051 / Aug '96 / Ocora

☐ **LADIES OF JAZZ**
Starlit hour: *Fitzgerald, Ella* / Tisket-a-tasket: *Fitzgerald, Ella* / Basin street blues: *Fitzgerald, Ella* / Freight train blues: *Smith, Trixie* / Can't make another day: *Johnson, Edith North* / Trouble in mind: *Hill, Bertha* / Chain gang blues: *Rainy, Ma* / Billie's blues: *Holiday, Billie* / I'm tired of fattening frogs for snakes: *Crawford, Rosetta & James P. Johnson's Hep Cats* / I love you Porgy: *Holiday, Billie* / Stormy weathr: *Horne, Lena* / September song: *Vaughan, Sarah* / What a difference a day makes: *Vaughan, Sarah* / Alone with the blues: *Wiley, Lee* / September in the rain: *Lee, Peggy* / All of me: *Irvin, Frances* / That old gang of mine: *Lee, Peggy* / Moon faced and starry eyed: *Forrest, Helen* / Straighten up and fly right: *McRae, Carmen* / Inside a silent tear: *McRae, Carmen* / Imagination: *McRae, Carmen* / Fine and mellow: *Holiday, Billie*
22727 / Jun '96 / Music

☐ **LADIES OF JAZZ (3CD Set)**
Mad about the boy: *Washington, Dinah* / My favourite thing: *Vaughan, Sarah* / Girl from Ipanema: *Gilberto, Astrud* / I loves you Porgy: *Simone, Nina* / Lover come back to me: *Fitzgerald, Ella* / More than you know: *Horne, Lena* / Summertime: *Vaughan, Sarah* / Do nothing till you hear from me: *Washington, Dinah* / I can't give you anything but love: *Fitzgerald, Ella* / Mississippi goddamn: *Simone, Nina* / That old black magic: *Fitzgerald, Ella* / Meu piao: *Gilberto, Astrud* / I cried for you: *Vaughan, Sarah* / You'll never know: *Fitzgerald, Ella* / My baby just cares for me: *Simone, Nina* / Ain't misbehavin': *Washington, Dinah* / Body and soul: *Vaughan, Sarah* / Don't let me be misunderstood: *Simone, Nina* / Love for sale: *Gilberto, Astrud* / I got love: *Simone, Nina* / What a difference a day made: *Washington, Dinah* / How high the moon: *Fitzgerald, Ella* / Round midnight: *Vaughan, Sarah* / September in the rain: *Lee, Peggy* / Close to you: *Hampton, Lionel & Dinah Washington* / Don't smoke in bed: *Simone, Nina* / Shoo shoo baby: *Washington, Dinah* / In a sentimental mood: *Vaughan, Sarah* / Far away: *Gilberto, Astrud* / You'll have to swing it: *Fitzgerald, Ella* / Black coffee: *Vaughan, Sarah* / Look to the rainbow: *Washington, Dinah* / For all we know: *Simone, Nina* / Sing song swing: *Fitzgerald, Ella* / Hands across the table: *Vaughan, Sarah* / I want a little sugar in my bowl: *Simone, Nina* / Smoke gets in your eyes: *Washington, Dinah* / Willow weep for me: *Washington, Dinah* / Jitterbug waltz: *Washington, Dinah* / Sometimes I feel like a motherless child: *Horne, Lena* / I've got a right to sing the blues: *Lee, Peggy* / It's only a paper moon: *Fitzgerald, Ella* / We can't go on this way: *Fitzgerald, Ella* / Oh lady be good: *Fitzgerald, Ella* / Puppy song: *Gilberto, Astrud* / Black magic: *Gilberto, Astrud* / Thinking of you: *Vaughan, Sarah* / Whatever Lola wants: *Vaughan, Sarah* / More I see you: *Vaughan, Sarah* / Perdido: *Vaughan, Sarah* / Mood indigo: *Simone, Nina* / He needs me: *Simone, Nina* / Love me or leave me: *Simone, Nina* / Sea line woman: *Simone, Nina*
BN 304 / Dec '97 / Blue Nite

☐ **LADIES OF JAZZ (4CD Set)**
SUMBX 4001 / Jan '98 / Summit

☐ **LADIES OF LATIN**
CDHOT 623 / Jul '97 / Charly

☐ **LADIES OF PENTHOUSE**
PHCD 2047 / Oct '96 / Penthouse

☐ **LADIES OF SWING, THE**
Tisket-a-tasket: *Fitzgerald, Ella* / My blue heaven: *Horne, Lena* / What a difference a day made: *Vaughan, Sarah* / On the sunny side of the street: *Lee, Peggy & Woody Herman* / St. Louis blues: *Holiday, Billie* / Body and soul: *McRae, Carmen* / C'est si bon: *Ross, Annie* / Honeysuckle rose: *Horne, Lena* / Little white lies: *Fitzgerald, Ella* / Up a lazy river: *Lee, Peggy & Woody Herman* / Fly me to the moon: *Smith, Keely* / Georgia on my mind: *Holiday, Billie* / September song: *Vaughan, Sarah* / Baby won't you please come home: *Fitzgerald, Ella* / I hear music: *Holiday, Billie* / Somebody loves me: *Lee, Peggy* / Lover man: *Vaughan, Sarah* / Lady is a tramp: *Horne, Lena*
ECD 3290 / Jan '97 / K-Tel

☐ **LADIES SING JAZZ VOL.2 1925-1941**
157762 / Jun '93 / Jazz Archives

☐ **LADIES SING JAZZ VOL.3 1928-1945**
158642 / Jun '97 / Jazz Archives

☐ **LADIES SING THE BLUES**
Downhearted blues: *Bailey, Mildred* / Break o'day blues: *Brown, Ada* / Evil mama blues: *Brown, Ada* / Hangover blues: *Carlisle, Una Mae* / Hard time blues: *Cox, Ida* / Take him off my mind: *Cox, Ida* / Cravin' a man blues: *Glinn, Lillian* / Blues I love to sing: *Hall, Adelaide* / Billie's blues: *Holiday, Billie* / Long gone blues: *Holiday, Billie* / Let your linen hang low: *Howard, Rosetta* / Rosetta blues: *Howard, Rosetta* / Electrician blues: *Miles, Lizzie* / My man o'war: *Miles, Lizzie* / Booze and blues: *Rainey, Gertrude 'Ma'* / Toad frog blues: *Rainey, Gertrude 'Ma'* / Empty bed blues: *Smith, Bessie* / St. Louis blues: *Smith, Bessie* / Jelly jelly look what you done done: *Smith, Clara* / Don't you leave me here: *Smith, Laura* / Goin' crazy with the blues: *Smith, Mamie* / Freight train blues: *Smith, Trixie* / Moaning the blues: *Spivey, Victoria* / I'm a mighty tight woman: *Wallace, Sippie*
CDAJA 5092 / Jun '92 / Living Era

☐ **LADIES SING THE BLUES (Roots Of Rock 'n' Roll Vol.5)**
Blues in my heart: *Miss Rhapsody* / Sugar: *Miss Rhapsody* / Downhearted blues: *Miss Rhapsody* / Sweet man: *Miss Rhapsody* / He may be your man: *Miss Rhapsody* / Night before judgement day: *Miss Rhapsody* / I fell for you: *Miss Rhapsody* / Evil gal blues: *Jones, Albinia* / Salty papa: *Jones, Albinia* / Albinia's blues: *Jones, Albinia* / What's the matter with me: *Jones, Albinia* / Walkin' and talkin' blues: *Hopkins, Linda* / Sad and lonely: *Hopkins, Linda* / Me and dirty blues: *Hopkins, Linda* / Baby please come home: *Hopkins, Linda* / Longing in my heart: *Little Esther* / You can bet your life I do: *Little Esther* / T'ain't what you say: *Little Esther* / If it's news to you: *Little Esther* / So good: *Little Esther* / Do you ever think of me: *Little Esther* / Oo papa do: *Little Esther* / Pitiful: *Big Maybelle* / There I said it again: *Big Maybelle* / So long: *Big Maybelle* / Tell me who: *Big Maybelle* / Ramblin' blues: *Big Maybelle* / Little bird: *Big Maybelle* / Blues early early: *Big Maybelle* / Good man is hard to find: *Big Maybelle*
SV 0275 / Oct '97 / Savoy Jazz

☐ **LADY LOVE**
DCD 5293 / Feb '94 / Disky

☐ **LADY LOVE**
DC 860552 / Mar '96 / Disky

☐ **LADY LOVE - SWEET LOVE GROOVES**
12217 / Jul '93 / Laserlight

☐ **LADYKILLERS VOL.1 (23 Tracks To Die For)**
Stupid girl: *Garbage* / What do I do now: *Sleeper* / Great things: *Echobelly* / Ladykillers: *Lush* / Weak: *Skunk Anansie* / Zombie: *Cranberries* / Drink the elixir: *Salad* / Feed the tree: *Belly* / Lost cat: *Catatonia* / She: *Tiny Monroe* / Rise and shine: *Cardigans* / Crash: *Primitives* / Night in my veins: *Pretenders* / Love your money: *Daisy Chainsaw* / Husband: *Fluffy* / Bright yellow gun: *Throwing Muses* / Fader: *Drugstore* / Ping pong: *Stereolab* / Night: *Intastella* / He's on the phone: *St. Etienne* / Missing: *Everything But The Girl* / Tishbite: *Cocteau Twins* / Fun for me: *Moloko*
5355362 / May '96 / PolyGram TV

☐ **LADYKILLERS VOL.2 (2CD Set)**
5533812 / May '97 / PolyGram TV

☐ **LAFAYETTE SATURDAY NIGHT**
One scotch, one bourbon, one beer: *Roger, Aldus* / Mean woman: *Roger, Aldus* / Zydeco et pas sale: *Roger, Aldus* / Recorded in England: *Bernard, Rod* / 2 fee: *Bernard, Rod* / Kidnapper: *Jewel & The Rubies* / Allons a Lafayette: *Newman, Jimmy C.* / Hippy ti yo: *Newman, Jimmy C.* / Lena Mae: *Walker, Lawrence* / Memphis: *Shondells* / Shine down: *Shondells* / Alligator Bayou: *Raven, Eddy* / I got loaded: *Lil' Bob & The Lollipops* / Come on over: *Gee Gee Shinn* / Colinda: *Guidry, Doc* / What's her name: *Forester, Blackie* / Domino: *Miller, Rodney* / Before I grow too old: *Miller, Rodney* / Just because: *King Karl* / Everybody's feeling good: *King Karl* / I'm cajun cool: *Cajun Born* / Getting late in the evening: *Neal, Raful* / Candy Ann: *Jewel & The Rubies* / That's what's wrong with the church today: *Consoling Clouds Of Joy*
CDCHD 371 / Apr '92 / Ace

☐ **LALABELLA**
FLCD 2057 / Jan '97 / Flames

☐ **LAMBADA**
Lambada / Mar de emocoes / Lambada do galo / Lambada de salvador / Maris Mariazinha / Louca Magia / Mule fubanga / Dancando lambada / Merequeza / Blanco do merengue (el organito) / Isso e bom / Forregae / Brilho Jamaica / Lambada (instrumental)
4660552 / Nov '89 / CBS

☐ **LAMBADA BRAZIL**
Lambada do remelxo: *Banda Cheiro De Amor* / Zorra: *Caldas, Luiz* / Algeria da cidade: *Menezes, Margareth* / Meia lua inteira: *Veloso, Caetano* / Ve estrelas: *Ramalho, Elba* / Roda baiana: *Banda Cheiro De Amor* / Dancando merengue: *Banda Tomalira* / Tenda do amor (magia): *Menezes, Margareth* / La vem o trio: *Banda Tomalira* / Lambada: *Carioca* / Doida: *Ramalho, Elba* / Ode e adao: *Caldas, Luiz* / Vou te pegar: *Nonato Do Cavaquinho* / Grande Gandhi: *Caldas, Luiz* / Careou: *Caldas, Luiz*
8415802 / Nov '89 / Polydor

☐ **LAMBADAS OF BRAZIL**
EMPRCD 512 / Apr '94 / Emporio

☐ **LAMBARENA - BACK TO AFRICA (Gabonese Music Inspired By Bach)**
SK 64542 / Jun '96 / Sony Classical

☐ **LAMBS ON THE GREEN HILLS**
OSS 9CD / Oct '89 / Ossian

☐ **L'AME CORSE**
Pricantula: *Nous Deux* / Manetta: *Chants Corses* / La violetta: *Le Choeur D'Hommes De Sartene* / Padre: *Donnisulana* / U pino tunisianu: *Chants Corses* / Agnes dei: *Micaelli, Jacky* / Bernardinu: *Tavagna* / Lamentu di ghjesu: *Micaelli, Jacky* / Paghjella per agata: *Donnisulana* / U viaghju: *Cesari, Mighela* / Morte de fillicone: *Chants Corses* / Cantu di a tribbiera: *Le Choeur D'Hommes De Sartene* / Lamentu di una minnana: *Tavagna* / Sanctus: *Chants Religieux De Tradition* / Quantu soli: *Nous Deux*
B6849 / May '97 / Auvidis/Ethnic

☐ **LAMENT**
Lament for the dead of the north: *Spillane, Davy* / Bright lady: *Masterson, Declan* / Sean O Duibhir a Ghleanna: *Ni Dhomhnaill, Maighread* / An droighnean donn: *Glackin, Paddy* / Plunkett: *O'Suilleabhain, Micheal* / One breath: *O'Kelly, Alanna* / Port na bpucai: *MacMahon, Tony* / Danny boy: *Moore, Christy* / Taimse I'm chodladh: *Og Potts, Sean* / Sliabh geal gcua: *Conneff, Kevin* / Carolan's devotion: *Sheahan, John* / An bonnan bui: *Potts, Sean* / John O'Dwyer of the glen: *Martin, Neil* / O'Carolan's farewell: *Bell, Derek*
CDRW 27 / Mar '93 / Realworld

☐ **L'AMOUR FOU AU FOL AMOUR (2CD Set)**
FA 155 / 1 Jun '98 / Fremeaux

☐ **LAND OF 1000 DUNCES**
CR 007 / Jun '97 / Candy

☐ **LAND OF BABOON VOL.1**
SR 9607 / Feb '97 / Silent

☐ **LAND OF BABOON VOL.2**
BKA 0005 / 1 Dec '97 / Baraka Foundation

☐ **LAND OF DRUMMERS, A**
VPU 1007CD / May '97 / Village Pulse

☐ **LAND OF HOPE AND GLORY**
Rule Britannia / Strike up the band / British Grenadiers / Here's a health unto her Majesty / Royal ceremony / Marchalong / Cavalry of the clouds / Navy day / Normandy veterans march / Battle of Britain march / Drum and bugle display / Soldiers of the sea / Lionheart / Aces high / Sir John Moore concert march / Abide with me / Land of hope and glory / Life on an ocean wave / Heart of oak / Dam busters march / Bridge too far / On the march
MUCD 9004 / Apr '95 / Musketeer

☐ **LAND OF MY MOTHERS**
CRAICD 048 / Aug '95 / Crai

☐ **LAND OF SONG (Welsh Choral Classics)**
PLSCD 173 / Apr '97 / Pulse

☐ **LAND OF THE BETSIMISRAKA**
Zaza bitiky manambady / Atete aty ragnotra / Mam hely and oz zory e / Pitikilanga siramany / Kiva nariako o zalah / Antsatsa karivo dimanjato / Kaka misy ampondy / Oa oa zaza / Satsoka mangaragna / Tsara ny vary / Zamany / Masombola / Ravoranga / Tirigna ro 'lay dronga / Bakoly / Zanaka tromba
D 8275 / May '98 / Unesco

☐ **LANOR RECORDS STORY 1960-1992, THE**
J'ai fait mon idee: *Bergeron, Shirley* / Parlez vous francais: *Matte, Bill* / I love my baby: *Eltradors* / Life problem: *Anderson, Elton* / Can't stop loving you: *Little Victor* / Drifting cloud: *Drifting Charles* / Keep your arms around me: *Mann, Charles* / Your no longer mine: *Mann, Charles* / I'll be your Jim: *Mallory, Willie* / Runnin' out of fools: *Boynton, Hugh* / Love don't love nobody: *Brown, Ella* / Red red wine: *Mann, Charles* / Crazy face: *Randall, Jay & The Dialtones* / Hot hot lips: *Prescott, Ralph* / I found my woman: *Carrier, Roy* / Chewing gum: *Jacob, Donald* / Walk of life: *Mann, Charles* / Accordion player waltz: *Broussard, Tim* / Drop that ego: *Generation Band* / Zydeco all night: *Walker, Joe* / My name is Beau Jocque: *Jocque, Beau*
ZNCD 1009 / Jul '95 / Zane

☐ **L'APPEL DE LA MUSE VOL.2**
AJE 04CD / Nov '92 / Vinyl Solution

☐ **LARGO**
Chieftans largo: *Chieftains* / Freedom ride: *Taj Mahal* / Cyrus in the moonlight: *Hyman, Rob & Cyndi Lauper* / Gimme a stone: *Forman, Dave & Levon Helm* / Hand in mine: *Hyman, Rob & Joan Osbourne* / Vishnu largo: *Hyman, Rob* / Disorient express: *Forman, Dave & Rob Hyman* / White man's melody: *Lauper, Cyndi* / Needed time: *Taj Mahal* / Banjoman: *Taj Mahal & David Forman/Rob Hyman* / Largo's dream: *Forman, David* / Garth Largo: *Hudson, Garth & Maude* / Star spangled banner: *Forman, Dave & Rob Hyman* / An uncommon love: *Osbourne, Joan & Carole King* / Chieftains Largo: *Chieftains* / Before the mountains: *Little Isidore*
5368772 / 4 May '98 / Blue Gorilla/ Mercury

☐ **LARK IN THE CLEAR AIR**
OSS 13CD / Dec '94 / Ossian

☐ **L'ART DU KHEN (Vietnamese Mouth Organ)**
ARN 60367 / Feb '97 / Arion

☐ **LAS DAMAS DEL TANGO**
EBCD 93 / 24 Apr '98 / El Bandoneon

☐ **LAS VEGAS GRIND VOL.2**
EFA 11512CD / Mar '93 / Crypt

☐ **LAS VEGAS GRIND VOL.5**
EFACD 12887 / Apr '97 / Crypt

☐ **LAST GREAT ROCKABILLY SATURDAY NIGHT, THE**
STCD 3 / Sep '93 / Stomper Time

☐ **LAST GREAT THING YOU DID, THE**
I'll take you there: *Hi-Fives* / Never been caught: *Criminals* / She's coming over: *MTX* / Not you: *Auntie Christ* / Political asshole: *Pansy Division* / Song 2: *Avail* / Cans of love: *Smugglers* / My Jeanette: *Squirtgun* / Drunken staircase: *Potatomen* / Crossover tradegy: *Phantom Surfers* / Chubacabra: *Groovie Ghoulies* / We ain't even married: *Young Pioneers* / Mosquito: *Black Fork* / Life during wartime: *Pinhead Gunpowder* / Snik snak skadullak: *Go-Nuts* / Dead boys too: *Crumbs* / So long sucker: *Mr. T Experience* / Cryin' cryin': *Bomb Bassets* / Hang up: *Parasites* / This scandal shit has got to stop: *Queers* / Split derision: *Uranium 9 Volt* / Valentine: *Groovie Ghoulies* / Fuk shit up: *Blatz*
LK 187CD / 27 Oct '97 / Lookout

☐ **LATE NIGHT BLUES**
MCCD 344 / 20 Apr '98 / Music Club

☐ **LATE NIGHT JAZZ**
What's new: *Paich, Marty* / Summer wishes, winter dreams: *Raney, Sue* / Bewitched: *Chamber Jazz Sextet* / Emily: *Daniels, Eddie* / In a sentimental mood: *Brookmeyer, Bob* / I remember clifford: *Getz, Stan* / Lotus bud: *Shank, Bud* / Please send me someone to love: *De Franco, Buddy* / I waited for you: *Baker, Chet* / Handful of stars: *Konitz, Lee* / On green dolphin street: *Liebmann, David* / I never told you: *Thielemans, 'Toots'* / You go to my head: *Holiday, Billie* / La vie en rose: *Holiday, Billie*
EMPRCD 664 / Oct '96 / Emporio

☐ **LATE NIGHT LATIN**
To be with you: *Cuba, Joe Sextet* / Si te di un beso sin importancia: *Mendoza, Celeste* / Mi pobre corazon: *Duo Los Compadres* / Noro in rumbaland: *Morales, Noro* / Lentamente: *Concepcion, Cesar* / Quien sera: *Lopez, Virginia* / Dandole a la rumba: *Rodriguez, Johnny* / El yoyo: *Puente, Tito* / Mula ta Linda: *Argentino, Carlos* / La noche morena: *Valdes, Vicentico* / De mi no se burla: *Ross, Julita* / Caravan: *Puente, Tito* / No etamos cansao: *Concepcion, Cesar* / Asi son los quereres: *Capo, Bobby* / El rumor de las olas: *Duo Los Compadres* / Eras diferente: *Mendoza, Celeste* / Tu regresso: *Morales, Noro* / Siempre nos pasa lo mismo: *Rodriguez, Johnny* / Y que: *Argentino, Carlos* / Bendicion: *Valdes, Vicentico*
CDHOT 609 / Sep '96 / Charly

☐ **LATE NIGHT LOUNGIN'**
Pursuit: *Milk & Honey* / Chicharrone: *Sub Hash* / DJ in the house: *Brothers Of Soul* / Reach out: *Conscious People* / Everybody: *Papa & Preston Project* / Transformation: *Atomica* / Disco era: *Brothers Of Soul* / U got soul: *Trey Max & Napolean Soul O* / 4th Floor: *Worth, Richard & Naked Music NYC* / Take me there: *Conscious People*
KICKCD 60 / 12 Dec '97 / Kickin'

☐ **LATE NIGHT REGGAE**
Some guys have all the luck: *Harriott, Derrick* / There's a place called Africa: *Byles, Junior* / Give me your love: *McGregor, Freddie* / Long long winter: *Marley, Bob & The Wailers* / You're gonna lose: *Paragons* / Meet me tonight: *Miller, Jacob* / Strange but true: *McKay, Freddie* / Make a move: *U-Roy* / Perfida: *Dillon, Phyllis* / I've got a feeling: *Byles, Junior* / Ride the donkey: *Tenors* / Boom shacka lacka: *Lewis, Hopeton* / I don't know: *Brown, Dennis* / Barbwire: *Dean, Nora* / Hey fat man: *Morgan, Derrick* / Future is here: *Melodians* / Stop loving you: *McGregor, Freddie* / Poor chubby: *Byles, Junior* / Take me back to Africa: *Dekker, Desmond*
CDGR 117 / Jan '97 / Charly

☐ **LATE NIGHT SAX**
Take ten: *Desmond, Paul* / Blue boy: *Getz, Stan* / Stella by starlight: *Washington, Grover Jr.* / Rouse's point: *Rouse, Charlie* / These foolish things: *Jacquet, Illinois* / I loves you porgy: *Tate, Buddy & Marlowe Morris*
4877982 / 29 Sep '97 / Sony Jazz

☐ **LATE NITE R & B**
Two occasions: *Deele* / Rock wit'cha: *Brown, Bobby* / Let's chill: *Guy* / Always: *Pebbles* / Time for love tonight: *Jackson, Freddie* / Baby it's wonderful: *Riff* / On and on: *Portrait* / I can't wait another minute: *Hi-Five* / More of the night: *Whispers* / Come in out of the rain: *Moten, Wendy* / When only a friend will do: *Davis, Mike* / Cry no more: *II D Extreme* / Tender kisses: *Spencer, Tracie* / Something in your eyes: *Bell Biv Devoe* / Show and tell: *Bryson, Peabo*
RB 876622 / 2 Feb '98 / Disky

☐ **LATER VOL.1 (Brit Beat)**
Changing man: *Weller, Paul* / Just lookin': *Charlatans* / Alright: *Supergrass* / Car song: *Elastica* / Girl like you: *Collins, Edwyn* / Day we caught the train: *Ocean Colour Scene* / Goldfinger: *Ash* / Heroine: *Suede* / Yes: *McAlmont & Butler* / Wonderwall: *Oasis* / Bends: *Radiohead* / If you don't want me to destroy you: *Super Furry Animals* / Sleeper: *Audioweb* / Lenny Valentino: *Auteurs* / Fine time: *Cast* / Slight return: *Bluetones* / Universal: *Blur* / Small black flowers that grow in the sky: *Manic Street Preachers* / I spy: *Pulp*
CID 8053 / Sep '96 / Island

☐ **LATER VOL.2 (Slow Beats)**
Karmakoma: *Massive Attack* / Tape loop: *Morcheeba* / Brown sugar: *D'Angelo* / Watusi: *Cherry, Neneh* / Glory box: *Portishead* / I must stand: *Ice-T* / Whipping boy: *Harper, Ben* / Single: *Everything But The Girl* / Suffocated love: *Tricky* / Possibly maybe: *Bjork* / She's a lover: *Martyn, John* / Don't you dream: *Soul II Soul* / Paraffin: *Ruby* / Blues music: *G-Love & Special Sauce* / Feel the music: *Guru* / Inside out: *Nelson, Shara* / People in tha middle: *Spearhead*
CID 8054 / Dec '96 / Island

☐ **LATEX TV OBLIVION**
MHCD 008 / Nov '93 / Minus Habens

☐ **LATIN ALBUM, THE (Guitar Favourites)**
303312 / Jun '98 / Hallmark

☐ **LATIN AMERICAN HOLIDAYS**
CD 62019 / Jan '93 / Saludos Amigos

☐ **LATIN AMERICAN MUSIC**
301062 / Aug '90 / Musidisc

☐ **LATIN AMERICAN PERCUSSION (3CD Set)**
PS 360501 / Sep '96 / PlayaSound

☐ **LATIN BEAT (Latin Beat For The Dancefloor)**
4886882 / 16 Sep '97 / Irma

☐ **LATIN CARNIVAL**
CDHOT 608 / Aug '96 / Charly

☐ **LATIN CARNIVAL (A Musical Celebration Of The Magic Of Latin America)**
Estar Enamorado / Todo se derrumbo / Atrevette / La Ladrona / O me quieres O me dejas / Don diablo / Has nacido libre / Amor ne me ignores / Simple magica / Ella se llambada / Dueno de nada / Preso / Terciopelo y piedra / Si el llama a tu puerta
ECD 3256 / Jan '97 / K-Tel

☐ **LATIN CRUISE, A**
CDHOT 625 / Aug '97 / Charly

☐ **LATIN DANCE PARTY**
CDHOT 637 / 30 Mar '98 / Charly

☐ **LATIN ESSENTIALS**
CDNEW 126 / 3 Aug '98 / Charly

☐ **LATIN FEVER**
Mas que nada: *Tamba Trio* / Toda menina baiana: *Gil, Gilberto* / I like it like that: *Puente, Tito & Blackout Allstars* / Always there: *Bobo, Willie* / Soul sauce: *Tjader, Cal* / Esquina: *Negrocan Aquela* / Chan chan: *Buena Vista Social Club* / Mr. PC: *Snowboy* / Latin America: *Walton, Cedar* / Cantaloupe Island: *Cubana Bop* / Crickets sing for Anamaria: *Bossa Nostra* / Ainda sonhar: *S-Tone Inc.* / Fever: *Puente, Tito & India* / Watermelon man: *Santamaria, Mongo* / Jingo: *Candido* / Chitterings con carne: *Pucho & His Latin Soul Brothers*
JAZZFMCD 10 / 1 Jun '98 / Jazz FM

☐ **LATIN FOR LOVERS**
CDHOT 618 / Mar '97 / Charly

☐ **LATIN FUSION**
TTTCD 006 / 29 Jun '98 / Two To Tango

☐ **LATIN HOUSE JAM**
63326110022 / 3 Aug '98 / Disctel

☐ LATIN JAZZ
Cappuccino: La Sonora Poncena / Diecisiete punto uno: Palmieri, Eddie / Blues a la Machito: Machito & His Afro-Cuban Salseros / Noble cruise: Palmieri, Eddie / Ran kan kan: Puente, Tito / Manteca: Santamaria, Mongo / Night love: La Sonora Poncena / Introvisate: Impacto Crea / Mambo jazz: Ray, Ricardo & Bobby Cruz / Night in Tunisia: Barretto, Ray / Mambo a la tito: Puente, Tito / New one: Santamaria, Mongo
CDHOT 520 / Apr '95 / Charly

☐ LATIN JAZZ
Power struggle / Fiesta a la king / Druma / Sal sangre / Manteca 77 / Camino a casa / Start the world, I want to get on / Zimbabwe
JWD 102220 / Apr '96 / JWD

☐ LATIN JAZZ
Peanut vendor: Winding, Kai & J.J. Johnson / Manteca: D'Rivera, Paquito / Falsa Bahiana: Getz, Stan & Joao Gilberto / Charie: Powell, Baden / La cuna: Barretto, Ray / Blue bossa: Camilo / Tu y mi cancion: Sanchez, David / Brazil: Jobim, Antonio / Carlos / Cuban chant: Ensemble / Why not: Camilo, Michael Orchestra
4875814 / 29 Sep '97 / Sony Jazz

☐ LATIN JAZZ DANCE CLASSICS VOL.1
CBCD 004 / Nov '96 / Cubop

☐ LATIN JAZZ DANCE CLASSICS VOL.2
CBO 10CD / 16 Oct '97 / Cubop

☐ LATIN JAZZ USA
Maria: Martin, Ricky / Guantanamera: Wyclef Jean / Estoy aqui: Shakira / I like it: Blackout sisters / Muevete: Dark Latin Groove / Valga el brillo de tus ojos: Albita / Baila baila: Chayanne / Pantera en la Batista / Naranjo, Monica / Bien pegaito: Merenbooty girls / Muevlo/Move it: Fey / Mi gente latina: Robi Rob's Clubworld & The Wepaman / Ritmo de la noche: Martinez, Lorena / Miami: Smith, Will
4916082 / 3 Aug '98 / Sony Jazz

☐ LATIN JAZZ VOL.1
Nica's dream: Burrell, Kenny / Gunky: Lytle, Johnny / Mambo inn: Taylor, Billy Trio / Caravan: Pucho & His Latin Soul Brothers / Sambop: Adderley, Cannonball / Baion baby: Stitt, Sonny / Tin tin deo: Forrest, Jimmy / Montuneando: Santamaria, Mongo
CDBGP 1023 / Mar '93 / Beat Goes Public

☐ LATIN JAZZ VOL.2
Ping pong: Blakey, Art & The Jazz Messengers / Bag mau: Farmer, Art Septet / Manteca: Garland, Red Trio / Sea food wally: Rodriguez, Willie / Screamin': McDuff, 'Brother' Jack / Fat man: Montego Joe / Mambo nico: Dolphy, Eric & Latin Jazz / Chop sticks: Braith, George
CDBGP 1027 / Aug '89 / Beat Goes Public

☐ LATIN MANHATTAN
CDHOT 633 / Dec '97 / Charly

☐ LATIN ON IMPULSE
IMP 12762 / 24 Aug '98 / Impulse Jazz

☐ LATIN ONLY
El Africano / A mi dios todo le debo / Se me perdio la cadenita / Ligia / El merecumbe / La cocaleca / El beso / La casa de familia / El ciclon / Ella es mi Gloria / La conga / No cuerpo mi corazon / La brujita / Corazol y sincelejo / La pachango del futbol / El tizon / La gorra / La mucura / Ella ma vacila / La muchacha del conejo
DC 880552 / May '97 / Disky

☐ LATIN PASSION (20 Steamy Tangos Rancheras And Boleros)
CDHOT 636 / 16 Mar '98 / Charly

☐ LATIN SOUL BOOGALOO
Bang: Cuba, Joe Sextet / Aye que Rico: Palmieri, Eddie / Para ti mi boogaloo: Cruz, Celia / Aqui Puente, Tito / Ismael y Monchito: Rivera, Ismael / You're looking fine: Orquesta Broadway / Palo de mango: Palmieri, Eddie / Mambo cure: Cortijo, Ralph & Ismael Rivera / El Pito (I'll never go back to Georgia): Cuba, Joe Sextet / Steak-o-lean: Puente, Tito / El reutasi: Barretto, Ray
12913 / Aug '96 / Laserlight

☐ LATIN SUMMER (3CD Set)
KBOX 373 / Aug '97 / Collection

☐ LATINAS
N 17028CD / Aug '95 / Nimbus

☐ LATINO CLUB
Coro miyare: Pacheco, Johnny / Acid: Barretto, Ray / Ajiaco caliente: DR / Fania: Bobalos, Reinaldo / Ay mi cuba: More, Benny / Elpito (I'll never go back to Georgia): Sabater, Cuba / Vente conmigo: Fania Allstars / Taste of latin: Merraro, R. / Nadie se salva de la rumba: Rodriguez, Joe / Que sabroso
CDCHARLY 227 / Jul '90 / Charly

☐ LATINO FIESTA
Come with me: Maria, Tania / Oye como va: Puente, Tito / Bien sabroso: Sanchez, Poncho / Guachi guaro: Tjader, Cal / Smooth operator: Santamaria, Mongo / On Broadway: Puente, Tito / Work song: Barretto, Ray / Besame mucho: Tjader, Cal & Carmen McRae / Funky tamborim: Maria, Tania / Poncho's Passion: Sanchez, Poncho & Carmen McRae / Poncho / Keeper of the flame: Sanchez, Poncho / Good vibes: Tjader, Cal / Ran Kan Kan: Puente, Tito
NSCD 023 / 5 Jan '98 / Nascente

☐ LATINO LATINO
Chacha la vie: Kaoma / Yiri yiri bon: Lemvo, Ricardo / Arranca: Manzanita / Volver a creer: D'Leon, Oscar / Los pasillos de tu conga: Conjunto Cespedes / Besame mama: Sanchez, Poncho / Son flamenco: Del Caney, Los / Asia: Colon, Willie / Chi chi mani: La Momposina, Toto / No me llores: Maestra, Sierra
PUTU 1312 / 29 Sep '97 / Putumayo

☐ LAUGHTER ON THE HOME FRONT (Songs/Comedy That Kept A Nation Going During The Great War)
PASTCD 7047 / Sep '94 / Flapper

☐ LAURIE VOCAL GROUPS - THE 60'S SOUND
Denise: Randy & The Rainbows / Little star: Randy & The Rainbows / Why do kids grow up: Randy & The Rainbows / Don't worry I'm gonna make it: Randy & The Rainbows / Happy teenager: Randy & The Rainbows / Sharin': Randy & The Rainbows / Bye bye: Bon-Aires / Jeannie baby: Bon-Aires / Lovely way to spend an evening: Four Graduates / Candy queen: Four Graduates / Please write: Tokens / Cry and be on my way: Demilles / In the beginning: Illusions / I love you Diane: Four Epics / Dance Joanne: Four Epics / Judy: Rayvons / I'll always love you: Tokens / Away: Concords / Kissin' at the revival: Five Discs / Champaign lady: Teardrops / Walk down the aisle: Monte, Vinnie / Marie: Harps
CDCHD 346 / Feb '92 / Ace

☐ LAURIE VOCAL GROUPS - THE DOO WOP SOUND
Queen of the angels: Orients / I shouldn't: Orients / Zoom, zoom, zoom: Enchords / I need you baby: Enchords / Gloria: Passion / Oh melancholy me: Passion / Just to be with you: Passion / This is my love: Passion / I only want you: Passion / I remember: Four / My dream: Dino & the diplomats / Does my love stand a chance: Del-Satins / Love boat: Karillions / This whole wide world: Ovations / Nicky: Bernadette / You just you: Criterions / Rock 'n' roll revival: Five Discs / Champaign lady: Teardrops / Fou roi pantin: Komintern / Down the road: Les Variations
CDCHD 309 / Feb '91 / Ace

☐ LAZY DAYS OF JAZZ
09026632282 / 10 Aug '98 / RCA Victor

☐ LE CAP VERT D'AUDOURD'HUI
3034262 / 24 Feb '98 / Arcade

☐ LE CHANT DES ENFANTS DU MONDE
ARN 64320 / Jul '95 / Arion

☐ LE COEUR QUI JAZZE
STONE 9573 / 23 Feb '98 / Yellowstone

☐ LE FLOW
CDVIR 73 / 22 Jun '98 / Virgin

☐ LE FRONT POPULAIRE (Songs From Paris 1934-1939/2CD Set)
FA 049 / Jul '96 / Fremeaux

☐ LE FUNK INSTANTE
FR 367CD / 31 Aug '98 / Big Cheese

☐ LE MEJOR DE LA SALSA
BM 516 / Feb '97 / Blue Moon

☐ LE MIROIR D'ARGENT
CVPV 1390CD / Apr '96 / CVPV

☐ LE MONDE DE L'ACCORDEON
3015712 / Apr '97 / Arcade

☐ LE MOULIN ROUGE 1889-1940
983802 / Jul '96 / EPM

☐ LE MUSETTE A PARIS
B 6817CD / Nov '95 / Auvidis/Ethnic

☐ LE PLUS BELLES FRANCAIS
DCD 5321 / Dec '93 / Disky

☐ LE PLUS GRAND ZOUK
4742112 / Jan '97 / AB/Sonodisc

☐ LE SON DE PARIS
325012 / Sep '96 / Melodie

☐ LE TANGO A PARIS 1907-1941 (2CD Set)
FA 012CD / Nov '95 / Fremeaux

☐ LE TEMPS D'UN SLOW (2CD Set)
Comme j'ai toujours envie d'aimer / Un amour de vacances: Rippert, Christophe / Et toute la ville en parle: Torr, Michele / Elle: Barbelivien, Didier / Dinons ce soir en amoureux: Valery, Francois / Je n'aime que toi: Manson, Jean / Si ca va pas on le dit: Barzotti, Claude / Et j'ai le mal de toi: Sweet People / Angelique: Vidal, Christian / Si: Cheryl, Karen / Dis cette melodie: Dumont, Charles / Butterfly: Gerard, Daniel / Fleur du mal: Stephane / Affaire arrangee: Dave / Tous les je vous aime: Roussos, Demis / Envie de t'aimer: Roussos, Demis / Mise au point: Quartz, Jakie / Pour le plaisir: Leonard, Herbert / Un homme et une femme: Croisille, Nicole & Francis Lai / Les maries de vendee: Barbelivien, Didier & Anais / Amoureux fous: Leonard, Herbert & Julie / Maitre pierre: Darel, Sophie & Pierre Perret / Lindberg: Charlebois, Robert & Louise Forestier / Banco en rien, envie de toi: Petter & Sloane / Comme une histoire d'amour: Fugain, Michel & Veronique Sanson / Dream in blue: Valery, Francois & Sophie Marceau / L'enfant de l'univers: Fernandel, Franck & Vincent / Prends une rose: Mardel, Guy & Chantal Goya / Amoureux sans bagages: Seoul, David & Claire Severac / Et si tu pars: Sullivan, Art & Kiki / Aime moi: Barzotti, Claude & Lara Fabian
VPRL 1111 / May '97 / VP

L'aventura: Charden, Stone & Eric / Cet enfant que je t'avais fait: Higelin, Jacques & Brigitte Fontaine / Quoi ca sert l'amour: Piaf, Edith & Theo Sarapo / Si ca fait mal: Hardy, Francoise & Alain Lubrano / Il faut laisser le temps au temps: Gray & Barbelivien
SP 876722 / Nov '96 / Disky

☐ LE TEMPS DES 60'S (2CD Set)
Twist a Saint-Tropez: Les Chats Sauvages & Dick Rivers / Tu marches et tu pleures: Les Dauphins / Les Gaurons: Dona, Alice / C'est pas serieux: Les Chats Sauvages & Dick Rivers / Baby John: Rivers, Dick / Aux jeunes loups: Annoux, Jean Claude / En avant l'amour: Les Chats Sauvages & Dick Rivers / La terre promise: Anthony, Richard / Tu n'es plus la: Rivers, Dick & The Gladiators / La playa: Ciari, Claude / Lecon de twist: Anthony, Richard / Hey pony: Les Chats Sauvages & Dick Rivers / Ya ya twist: Anthony, Richard / Mon train de banlieue: Dona, Alice / Sa grande passion: Les Chats Sauvages & Dick Rivers / Et quelque chose me dit: Bartock, Ria / Alligator: Hector / Les cavaliers du ciel: Les Bourgeois De France / Mauvais garcon: Nelly / Chante alleluia: Les Guitares Seches / Couleurs: Rivers, Dick / Anthony, Richard: Rivers, Dick / Jette-la: Greco, Larry / L'argent de poche: Winter, Pat Et Les Saunders / Mister pitiful: Winter, Pat Et Les Saunders / Sur notre plage: Anthony, Richard / Peut etre demain: Triangle / Fou roi pantin: Komintern / Down the road: Les Variations
SP 876732 / Nov '96 / Disky

☐ LEAD WITH THE BASS CLUB
SD 020 / 15 Jun '98 / Stereo Deluxe

☐ LEAD WITH THE BASS VOL.1
WWCD 8 / Jul '97 / Wibbly Wobbly

☐ LEAD WITH THE BASS VOL.2
WWCD 17 / Mar '96 / Universal Egg

☐ LEADER OF THE PACK (Girl Group Greats From The Rock 'n' Roll Era)
Leader of the pack: Shangri-Las / Soldier boy: Shirelles / One fine day: Chiffons / Chapel of love: Dixie Cups / Da doo ron ron: Crystals / Lover's concerto: Toys / My boyfriend's back: Angels / Remember (walkin' in the sand): Shangri-Las / Will you love me tomorrow: Shirelles / He's so fine: Chiffons / Iko iko: Dixie Cups / Then he kissed me: Crystals / Sally go round the roses: Jaynettes / To know him is to love him: Teddy Bears / He's a rebel: Crystals / Mr. Lee: Bobbettes
SUMCD 4025 / Nov '96 / Summit

☐ LEAF
LEAFCD 1 / May '96 / Psychic

☐ LEAPIN' GUITARS (Rockin' Roulette Instrumentals)
Ramrod: Rogers, Johnny / Sassy: Rogers, Johnny / Chase: Wild Bill & The Blue Denims / Mona my love: Wild Bill & The Blue Denims / Woo hoo: Rock-a-Teens / Pagan: Rock-a-Teens / Offbeat: Rock-a-Teens / Oh, nerves: Rock-a-Teens / Twangy: Rock-a-Teens / War paint: Haley, Bill & The Comets / Riviera: Haley, Bill & The Comets / El Rancho Grande: Eddy, Duane / Poppa's movin' on: Eddy, Duane / Poor boy: Royaltones / Wait: Royaltones / See saw: Royaltones / Little Bo: Royaltones / Cha hua hua: Platt, Eddie / Salty: Castle, Tony & The Raiders / Hi Lili, hi lo: Castle, Tony & The Raiders / Sincerely: Castle, Tony & The Raiders / Taras's theme: Castle, Tony & The Raiders / Leapin' guitar: Chapparals / Beer barrel rock: Chapparals / Bikini: Bikinis / Boogie rock 'n' roll: Bikinis / Down yonder rock: Gone All Stars
NEMCD 923 / Jul '97 / Sequel

☐ LEGACY (A Tribute To The First Generation Of Bluegrass)
Rose of old Kentucky: Berline, Byron & Vince Gill / I'll take the blame: Lonesome River Band / Memories of Mother and Dad: Skaggs, Ricky / Sweetheart you done me wrong: Rowan, Peter / Preachin' prayin' singin': Laurel Canyon Ramblers / Our last goodbye: Lawson, Doyle & Quicksilver / If I should wander back tonight: Hot Rize / Big Mon: Bush, Sam & Jerry Douglas / She's more to be pitied: Seldom Scene / Dark as the night blue as the day: Nashville Bluegrass Band / I'm lonesome without you: Lonesome Standard Time / Get in line brother: Stuart, Marty / Don't this old look rough and rocky: Edwards, Jonathan & The Seldom Scene / I'm going back to the old home: Watson, Doc / Baby girl: Skaggs, Ricky & Tony Rice
SHCD 9202 / Mar '98 / Sugar Hill

☐ LEGACY OF TURLOUGH O'CAROLAN, THE
Planxty Burke: Phillips, Shelley / Planxty Drew: Phillips, Shelley / Squire Parsodns: Orion / Eleanor Plunkett: Deanta / Lord Inchiquin: Deiseal / Hawk of Ballyshannon: Heymann, Ann / Loftus Jones: Dordan / Si Bheag, Si Mhor: Coulter, William / Captain O'Kane: McGuire, Seamus / Colonel John Irwin: Newman, Chris / Mrs. Judge: Long, Donna / Bridget Cruise: Bouchard, Dominic & Cyrille Colas / John O'Connor: Bouchard, Dominic & Cyrille Colas / George Bravazon: Bouchard, Dominic & Cyrille Colas / Fanny Power: McMeen, El / Coralan's farewell to music: O'Sullivan, Jerry
ND 63925 / Jun '96 / Narada

☐ LEGACY'S RHYTHM 'N' SOUL REVUE SAMPLER
Wake up everyone: Melvin, Harold & The Bluenotes / Hot fun in the summertime: Sly & The Family Stone / You're gonna make me love somebody else: Jones / Paul, Billy / Kiss and say goodbye: Manhattans / Ain't no sunshine: Withers, Bill / Piece of my heart: Franklin, Erma / I feel so bad: Willis, Chuck / Backstabbers: O'Jays / Everyone eats when they come to my house: Calloway, Cab / Who loves you but your mother: Isley Brothers / Hey little girl: Major Lance / One girl too late: Brenda & Tabulations / Cowboys and girls: Intruders / My ship is coming in: Jackson, Walter / Love is the message: MFSB / You are my friend: Labelle, Patti / It rocks, it swings: Treniers / Saved: Smith, Lavay
4805122 / May '95 / Columbia

☐ LEGAL TENDER
VPRL 1111 / May '97 / VP

☐ LEGALIZE DE HERB VOL.1
Kaya: Marley, Bob / One draw: Marley, Rita / Herbsman shuffle: King Stitt / Under me sleng teng: Smith, Wayne / Smoking my ganja: Capital Letters / Judge Natty: Jah Lloyd / Better collie: Andy, Horace / Real thing: Levy, Barrington / Legalize it: Clarke, Johnny / Love mi sess: Top Cat / Spliff tail: Palmer, Tristan / Weedfields: Desi Roots
KICKCD 50 / Mar '97 / Kickin'

☐ LEGEND OF NEW ORLEANS, THE
Dr. Jazz / Sweetie dear / Alligator crawl / Too tight / That's a plenty / Pleasure Paul / High society / Astoria strut / Weatherbird / Turtle twist / Maple leaf rag / Perdido Street blues / Clarinet marmalade / Apex blues / Ory's Creole trombone / New Orleans stomp / Sweet lovin' man / Tiger rag / Duet intime / Cannonball blues / Beau Koo Jack / I know that you know / Franklin Street blues / As you like it / Panama
CD 53016 / Jul '88 / Giants Of Jazz

☐ LEGENDARY DIG MASTERS VOL.2 (Dig These Blues)
Old folk's boogie: Simmons, Al / You ain't too old: Simmons, Al / Country home: Sailor Boy / What have I done wrong (parts 1 and 2): Sailor Boy / Hand me down baby: Maden, Sidney / Going back to the plow: Hozay / I've got an expensive woman: Hozay / Wrong doin' woman: John, Moose / Talkin' 'bout me: John, Moose / Springtime blues: Sams, TW / Come on home: Nolen, Jimmy / If you ever get lonesome: Easter, Roy 'Happy' / My woman done quit me: Green, Slim / Moore boogie: Moore, Abe / S and J: Moore, Abe / Singin' the blues: Robbins, Little Bill / Full grown woman: Waters, Larry / Don't tell me that you love me: Waters, Larry / Bring her back to me: Robbins, Billy / Elsm stole my baby (boo hoo): Cane, Sugar / They say you never can miss: Cane, Sugar
CDCHD 334 / Jan '92 / Ace

☐ LEGENDARY DIG MASTERS VOL.3 (Dapper Cats, Groovy Tunes & Hot Guitars)
Telephone boogie: Watson, Johnny & Jeannie / I got a girl (that loves over yonder): Watson, Johnny 'Guitar' / My aching feet: Strogin, Henry / I've been blind, blind, blind: Strogin, Henry / Jimmy's jive: Nolen, Jimmy / Hey little girl: Lewis, Richard / Bingo: Moore, Abe / Talk to me baby: Easter, Roy 'Happy' / Sad stories: Waters, Larry / Check yourself: Allen, Tony & Barbara / Someday: Sams, TW / Country women: Lee, Preston & Orchestra / Get away from here: Lewis, Pete 'Guitar' / Ain't gonna tell: Ray, Dessa / Wiggle walk: Otis, Johnny / Things won't be right without you: Williams, Devonia 'Lady Dee' / Much more: Jessie & Joyce / Itty bitty bee: Johnny / Baby please come home: Robbins, Little Billy / Bolooper: Otis, Johnny & The Jayos / Bad Bad Bulldog: Matthews, Little Arthur / Hot diggity (dog piggity boom): Matthews, Little Arthur / Dead man's shop: Otis, Johnny & His Orchestra
CDCHD 351 / Oct '92 / Ace

☐ LEGENDARY DIG MASTERS VOL.4 (Shoo-Be-Doo-Be-Booh)
Shoobie dooby Mama: Phantoms / My baby doll: Gladiators / Girl of my heart: Gladiators / Another chance: Foster, Cell / Millie's chills: Foster, Cell / Fools prayer: Maye, Arthur Lee / Honey honey: Maye, Arthur Lee / This is the night for love: Maye, Arthur Lee / Whispering wind: Maye, Arthur Lee / Crazy bells: Stevens, Julie / Blue mood: Stevens, Julie / Have a heart: Premiers / My darling: Premiers / Can it be real: Premiers / Take my heart: Stevens, Julie / You think I'm just your fool: Stevens, Julie / Ding a ling a ling: Jayos / Foolish love: Jayos / I plead guilty: Jayos / Wedding ring: Jayos / What am I gonna do: Jayos / In exhange for your love: Jayos / Sweet thing: Ding Dongs
CDCHD 569 / Sep '94 / Ace

☐ LEGENDARY GROUPS OF DOO WOP VOL.1
BMCD 4005 / 5 Jan '98 / Blue Moon

☐ LEGENDARY GROUPS OF DOO WOP VOL.2
BMCD 4006 / 5 Jan '98 / Blue Moon

☐ LEGENDARY SIDEMEN, THE
Beatin' the dog / Black and tan fantasy / Shreveport stomp / Pencil papa / Higginbotham blues / Just blues / I've found a new baby / Yeah man / In a sentimental mood / Clarinet lament / Echoes of Harlem / Swinging at the daisy chain / Jada / Swinging the blues / Prelude to a kiss / Ricky's dream / Till Tom special / Chloe / Portrait of Bert Williams / April in Paris / I want a little girl / Willow weep for me / Jonah joins the Cab
TPZ 1034 / Nov '99 / Topaz Jazz

☐ LEGENDARY SUN ARTISTS VOL.1, THE
One broken heart: Thompson, Hayden / Blue blues: Thompson, Hayden / Rockabilly Gal: Thompson, Hayden / Mama mama mama: Thompson, Hayden / You are my sunshine: Thompson, Hayden / One broken heart: Thompson, Hayden / Love my baby: Thompson, Hayden / Congratulations to you: Joe: Thompson, Hayden / Lonesome feeling: Felts, Narvel & The Rockets / Lonely river: Felts, Narvel & The Rockets / Did you tell me you love: Felts, Narvel & The Rockets / Foolish thoughts: Felts, Narvel & The Rockets / Cry baby cry: Felts, Narvel & The Rockets / Fool in paradise: Felts, Narvel & The Rockets / Kiss a baby: Felts, Narvel & The Rockets / My baby left me: Felts, Narvel & The Rockets / Teen's way: Felts, Narvel & The Rockets / Cry baby Judy: Grayzell, Rudy / I think of you: Grayzell, Rudy / Remember when: Grayzell, Rudy / The ballad of Rock: Grayzell, Rudy
CDSJ 70601 / May '98 / Sun Jay

☐ LEGENDARY VOCAL GROUPS OF THE 1940'S/1950'S, THE
BMCD 2018 / Nov '97 / Blue Moon

☐ LEGENDARY VOICES
CWNCD 2002 / Jun '95 / Javelin

☐ LEGENDS (4CD Set)
Love me tender: Presley, Elvis / Burning love: Presley, Elvis / It's now or never: Presley, Elvis / Heartbreak hotel: Presley, Elvis / I just can't help believing: Presley, Elvis / Girl of my best friend: Presley, Elvis / His latest flame: Presley, Elvis / Always on my mind: Presley, Elvis / Hound dog: Presley, Elvis / All shook up: Presley, Elvis / Can't help falling in love: Presley, Elvis / She's not you: Presley, Elvis / Way down: Presley, Elvis / Suspicious minds: Presley, Elvis / My boy: Presley, Elvis / Elvis has left the building: Presley, Elvis / Everyday: Holly, Buddy / Heartbeat: Holly, Buddy / Learning the game: Holly, Buddy / That'll be the day: Holly, Buddy / True love ways: Holly, Buddy / Oh boy: Holly, Buddy / Not fade away: Holly, Buddy / Wishing: Holly, Buddy / Raining in my heart: Holly, Buddy / Peggy Sue/ Peggy Sue got married: Holly, Buddy / Love's made a fool of you: Holly, Buddy / Fool's paradise: Holly, Buddy / It doesn't matter anymore: Holly, Buddy / Girl in every song: Holly, Buddy / Children of the revolution: Bolan, Marc / Telegram Sam: Bolan, Marc / Ride a white swan: Bolan, Marc / Debora: Bolan, Marc / 20th Century boy: Bolan, Marc / Salamanda palaganda: Bolan, Marc / Child star: Bolan, Marc / Metal guru: Bolan, Marc / Get it on: Bolan, Marc / Solid gold easy action: Bolan, Marc / By the light of the magical moon: Bolan, Marc / Jeepster: Bolan, Marc / Life's an elevator: Bolan, Marc / Hot love: Bolan, Marc / Ain't no sqaure with the corkscrew hair: Bolan, Marc / Melt: Carpenters / We've only just begun: Carpenters / Masquerade: Carpenters / Top of the world: Carpenters / Yesterday once more: Carpenters / For all we know: Carpenters / Superstar: Carpenters / Rain days and Mondays: Carpenters / I won't last a day without you: Carpenters / Only yesterday: Carpenters / Close to you: Carpenters / Hurting each other: Carpenters / Goodbye to love: Carpenters / Solitaire: Carpenters / Calling occupants of interplanetary craft: Carpenters / Melt the years: Carpenters
391282 / Aug '97 / Hallmark

☐ LEGENDS
GFS 085 / Nov '97 / Going For A Song

☐ LEGENDS OF BRITISH ROCK 'N' ROLL, THE
Peggy Sue/Heartbeat: Berry, Mike / Diamonds: Harris, Jet / Good golly Miss Molly: Bennett, Cliff / New Orleans: Sarne, Mike / Peter Gunn: Black, Chris & The Black Cats / Bony Maronie: Bruce, Tommy / Medley: Screaming Lord Sutch / Shakin' all over: Dene, Terry / Ghost riders in the sky: Black, Chris & The Black Cats / Just like Eddie: Heinz / Red planet rock: Lang, Don / Wipe out: Black, Chris & The Black Cats / Somethin' else: Sharpe, Rocky / Boom boom: Bruce, Tommy / Rudy's rock: Black, Chris & The Black Cats / Medley: Conrad, Jess
ECD 2406 / 16 Feb '98 / K-Tel

☐ LEGENDS OF COUNTRY, THE (4CD Set)
SUMBX 4019 / Jan '98 / Summit

☐ LEGENDS OF LATIN MUSIC
Relax and mambo: Machito / Dile que por mi no tema: Cruz, Celia / Que problema: Cuba, Joe Sextet / Camina y ven: La Lupe / Guantanamera: Machito / Kon-kun mambo: Valdes, Minuelito & Machito Orchestra / La plena bomba me llaman: Cruz, Celia / Lindo yambu: Palmieri, Eddie / Guajira: Bobo, Willie / Cha cha chick: Herman, Woody & Tito Puente / Odiame: La Lupe
12916 / Aug '96 / Laserlight

☐ LEGENDS OF MUSIC
322701 / Jul '97 / Koch Presents

☐ LEGENDS OF ROCK 'N' ROLL, THE
Reelin' and rockin': Berry, Chuck / Johnny B Goode: Berry, Chuck / Memphis Tennessee: Berry, Chuck / Nadine: Berry, Chuck / Sweet little sixteen: Berry, Chuck / Rock around the clock: Haley, Bill & The Comets / Shake, rattle and roll: Haley, Bill & The Comets / See you later alligator: Haley, Bill & The Comets / Razzle dazzle: Haley, Bill & The Comets / Saints rock 'n' roll: Haley, Bill & The Comets / This ol' house: Perkins, Carl / Dixie fried: Perkins, Carl / That's right: Perkins, Carl / All Mama's children: Perkins, Carl / Blue suede shoes: Perkins, Carl / Good golly Miss Molly: Little Richard / Lucille: Little Richard / She's got it: Little Richard / Girl can't help it: Little Richard / Tutti frutti: Little Richard
SUMCD 4048 / Nov '96 / Summit

☐ LEGENDS OF SOUL, THE (4CD Set)
SUMBX 4006 / Jan '98 / Summit

☐ LEMON 714
USUXS 73013 / 27 Oct '97 / Zone 6

☐ LEMON LIME VOL.2
SPART 40 / 16 Mar '98 / Spin Art

☐ LES ANTILLES
Ernestine attention / Ce les Antilles / Ba moin un tibo, doudou / Mr. Leonard / Bande Zaoua / La ronde des cuisinieres / Serpent maigre / L'ete en pyjama / Maladie d'amour / Guitare des Antilles / Le rocher / Oh pere / Ninon, merengue, merengue / Danse de gros ca / Guyane, o Guyana / Sans chemise, sans pantalon / Maman, maman / Biguine a Henri / Aye Tumbaye / Roro / Madiana / Papillon vole / Adieu foulard / Adieu madras
ARN 64034 / May '88 / Arion

☐ LES BALALAIKAS DES TZIGANES RUSSES
Les yeux verts / Boublitchki / Ne sois pas jaloux, ne sois pas Fache / Mon bohemien / Ne pars pas / Plaine, ma plaine / Le sarafan rouge / Kalinka / Tzigane et samovar / L'amour s'est enfui / Le vieux Tzigane / Vradanka / Pourquoi m'astu aime
ARN 64019 / May '88 / Arion

☐ LES CHANSONS A VOIX 1900-1920
983952 / Apr '97 / EPM

☐ LES CHANSONS DE 1935
UCD 19094 / Apr '95 / Forlane

☐ LES CHANSONS DE 1936
UCD 19095 / Apr '95 / Forlane

☐ LES CHANSONS DE 1937
UCD 19096 / Apr '95 / Forlane

☐ LES CHANSONS DE 1938
UCD 19097 / Apr '95 / Forlane

☐ LES CHANSONS DE 1939
UCD 19098 / Apr '95 / Forlane

☐ LES CHANSONS DU TROTTOIR
8448642 / 24 Feb '98 / Music Memoria

☐ LES CHANSONS PATRIOTIQUES
984012 / Nov '97 / EPM

☐ LES CINGLES DU MUSIC HALL 1932
Complainte de mackie: Florelle / C'est Parisien: Milton, Georges / Un seul regard: Bauge, Andre & Sim Viva / Il est charmant: Lemonnier, Meg / En parlant un peu de Paris: Garat, Henri / Confessin': Baker, Josephine / One hour with you: Chevalier, Maurice & Jeanette Macdonald / Couches dans le foin: Pills & Tabet / La fiancee du pirate: Gauty, Lys / Beguin-beguine: Sablon, Jean / Zou un peu d'aiou: Alibert, Georges / Quand on est au volant: Mireille & Jean Sablon / Papa n'a pas voulu: Mireille / Si petite: Boyer, Lucienne / Adieu, adieu: Milton, Georges / Mimi: Chevalier, Maurice / Au joyeux tyrol: Milton, Georges / Le doux cabulot: Dubas, Marie / Le doux cabulot: Mirielle / Un soir a la havane: Caire, Reda / Vous ne savez pas: Germaine & Jean Sablon / Je t'ai donne mon coeur: Thunis, Willy / J'ai reve d'une fleur: Alibert, Henri & Jenny Helia / Fleur de Paris: Gilles & Julien
CMH 32 / Oct '96 / Fremeaux

☐ LES CINGLES DU MUSIC HALL 1933
CMH 33 / Jul '96 / Fremeaux

☐ LES CINGLES DU MUSIC HALL 1934
CMH 34 / May '96 / Fremeaux

☐ LES COMEDIAN HARMONISTS (2CD Set)
983782 / Oct '96 / EPM

☐ LES COMIQUES TROUPIERS 1900-1920
984022 / Jun '97 / EPM

☐ LES CONGES PAYES
DEM 019 / Sep '96 / IMP

☐ LES GRANDS MESSIEURS DU MUSIC HALL 1931-1943
983472 / Jul '95 / EPM

☐ LES HARICOTS SONT PAS SALES
CP 0022652 / Oct '97 / Cinq Planetes

☐ LES NUITS DE BAMAKO
381372 / 21 Aug '97 / Melodie

☐ LES PLUS BELLES MUSIQUES CORSES
CDR 127 / 24 Apr '98 / MMED

☐ LES PLUS BELLES VALSES MUSETTE
FA 014CD / Nov '95 / Fremeaux

☐ LES PLUS GRANDS SUCCES DU PUNK
SKYD 622282 / May '97 / Skydog

☐ LES TOPS DU TANGO (2CD Set)
887997 / Feb '97 / Milan Sur

☐ LESS ROCK MORE TALK
ALLIED 87CD / Jul '97 / Allied

☐ LESSON ONE
Tell me why: Freakniks / Miss Thang: Unsung Heroes / Original oddstep: Vert / River: Freakniks / Minkey part 1: Soniq / Action tape 1: Search / One we made earlier: Unsung Heroes / Slide up: Next Men / Cougar: Search / Change of plan: DC 3 / Uncivilized: Freakniks / Lost: Freakniks / Easy alibi: Freakniks / Slow roll '77: Freakniks
SCCD 002 / Jul '97 / Scenario

☐ LESSON ONE REVISED
SCCD 003 / 13 Apr '98 / Scenario

☐ LESSONS FROM THE UNDERGROUND VOL.1
TILTCD 1 / Jun '97 / Tilt

☐ LET 'EM IN
12219 / Nov '93 / Laserlight

☐ LET IT POUR (A Deluge Records Sampler)
DELD 3016 / Oct '96 / Deluge

☐ LET IT RIP
3rd state: Digitalis / Welcome to the world: Digitalis / ALien pets: Prana / Future heaven: Syrinx / Reality check: Visitors / Re-psycle frequency: Joujouka / Monomaniac: Deflo / Lucky 7: Alienated / Dog tag: Environmental Science
MPCD 10 / 22 Oct '97 / Matsuri

☐ LET IT SNOW
Sleigh ride: Williams, Andy / Have yourself a merry little Christmas: Mathis, Johnny / Let it snow, let it snow, let it snow: Day, Doris / White world of winter: Crosby, Bing / Secret of Christmas: Andrews, Julie / Snowfall: Bennett, Tony / Christmas song: Torme, Mel / Joy to the world: Faith, Percy / When a child is born: Mathis, Johnny / Silver bells: Day, Doris / Do you hear what I hear: Williams, Andy / Winter wonderland: Clooney, Rosemary / Pretty paper: Orbison, Roy / Christmas eve in my hometown: Vinton, Bobby / Christmas time again: Humperdinck, Engelbert / Twelve days of Christmas: Conniff, Ray
4746372 / 3 Nov '97 / Columbia

☐ LET THE MINSTRELS PLAY ON (The Best Of The Muse)
Mystery of ages: Garnett, Carlos / SHAKE: Dom Um Romao / Swan lake: Pike, Dave / What am I gonna do: Creque, Neal / Old mam moses: Green, Grant / Chameleon: Jefferson, Eddie / Free spirits: Barr, Walt / El exi-hente: Ousley, Harold / Sly: Ousley, Harold / Why don't cha walk that funky dog: Bronstein, Stan / In the meantime: Baron, Kenny / Let us go: Garnett, Carlos
BBECD 008 / 27 Oct '97 / Barely Breaking Even

☐ LET THERE BE LOVE
TSS 113 / 28 Feb '98 / BMG

☐ LET THERE BE SINGLES
VIRUS 182CD / 10 Nov '97 / Alternative Tentacles

☐ LET'S AGREE UPON THE FUTURE
73572 / 4 Aug '97 / Kitty Yo/Kollaps/ Payola

☐ LET'S DANCE
Night fever: UK Mixmasters / Going back to my roots: Odyssey / Everybody plays the fool: Main Ingredient / Hot hot hot: Poindexter, Buster / Knock three times: Dawn / Hooked on swing: Kings Of Swing Orchestra / Let's twist again: Checker, Chubby / He's a rebel: Crystals / Shout: Isley Brothers / Diana: Anka, Paul / Wooly bully: Sam The Ram & The Fairisles / Ballroom blitz: Sweet
74321339272 / Jan '96 / Camden

☐ LET'S DANCE FOR LOVE '95
FTICD 1 / Jul '95 / Freetown

☐ LET'S DO IT
PHONTCD 7669 / '93 / Phontastic

☐ LET'S GET IT ON
NSCD 021 / May '95 / Newsound

☐ LET'S GO DISCO (2CD Set)
This is it: Moore, Melba / Swing your daddy: Gilstrap, Jim / Nice and slow: Green, Jesse / Ride a wild horse: Clark, Dee / You make me feel like dancing: Sayer, Leo / Highwire: Carr, Linda / Take your mama for a ride: Lulu / Put a little love in me: Delegation / It's a better than good time: Knight, Gladys & The Pips / I'm doin' fine now: New York City / Hold back the night: Trammps / Do it: BT Express / Papa was a rollin' stone: Temptations / Movin': Brass Construction / Zing went the strings of my heart: Trammps / Baby don't change your mind: Knight, Gladys & The Pips / More more more: True, Andrea Connection / Get down: Chandler, Gene / Way you do the things you do: Temptations / Ain't gonna bump no more with no big fat woman: Tex, Joe / Groove me: Kinney, Fern / Flip: Green, Jesse / La la (peace song): Wilson, Al / Where is the love: Delegation / Come to me: Winters, Ruby / I'm on fire: Gilstrap, Jim / Cherry pie guy: Carr, Linda / Saddle up: Christie, David
SD 885312 / 2 Feb '98 / Disky

☐ LET'S GO JIVIN' TO ROCK & ROLL
Say yeah: Salvo, Sammy / I've got a dollar: Dell, Jimmy / Love makes the world go round: Como, Perry / Rock-a-bye boogie: Davis Sisters / Plantation boogie: King, Pee Wee / Tennessee rock 'n' roll: Sons Of The Pioneers / Hubba hubba hubba: Como, Perry / Jackpot: Pedicin, Mike Quintet / TV hop: Morgan Twins / Shape I'm in: Restivo, Johnny / You gotta learn your rhythm and blues: Sedaka, Neil / Kewpie doll: Como, Perry / Blue suede shoes: King, Pee Wee / Fiddle diddle boogie: Davis Sisters / You gotta go: Pedicin, Mike Quintet / Jukebox baby: Como, Perry / Boom de de boom: Baker, Jane / Rock and stroll room: Mickey & Sylvia / When the cats come marching in: Pedicin, Mike Quintet / Idaho red: Ray, Wade
BCD 15533 / Oct '90 / Bear Family

☐ LET'S GO TRIPPIN'
Let's go trippin': Rogers, Milt / Surfer Joe: Surfaris / Wipeout: Surfaris / Three surfer boys: Usher, Gary & The Usherettes / Boss: Rumblers / Move it: Chantays / Pipeline: Chantays / Little stick nomad: Competitors / Samoa: Beachcomas / Beach girl: Boone, Pat / Boss strikes back: Rumblers / Ballad of Bonneville: Brandon, Don / Monsoon: Chantays / Power shift: Competitors / 409: Competitors / You can't sit down: Surfaris / Little Honda: Boone, Pat / It's a gas: Rumblers / Linda's tune: Rancheros / Green onions: Surfaris / Space probe: Chantays / Little deuce coupe: Competitors / Bugged: Rumblers / Angry sea: Rumblers / Milky way: Usher, Gary & The Usherettes / Surfer's stomp: Monroe, Vaughan / Maybe baby: Chantays / Chicago green: Surfaris / Showbiz: Surfaris
CDCHD 630 / Apr '96 / Ace

☐ LET'S GO ZYDECO
Cher catin / Petite et la grosse / Used and abused / Walking down the interstate / Zydeco two step / Crying in the streets / Midland two step / Shake what you got / Lafayette special / Lonesome road / I'm coming home / I've been there / Mardi gras song / Je suis en recolteur / Check out the zydeco / Zolo go / Green's zydeco / King's zydeco / Allons a Lafayette / Moman couche / Two step de grand mallet / Home sweet home
CDCHD 543 / Feb '95 / Ace

☐ LET'S GO, LET'S GO, LET'S GO
12105 / Dec '94 / Laserlight

☐ LET'S HAVE A BLUES BALL
I'm having a ball: Young, Johnny / Dream: Littlejohn, Johnny / Swing it on home: Thornton, Willie Mae 'Big Mama' / Anna Lee: Hooker, Earl / Going back to the country: Bonner, Juke Boy / It's hard: Chenier, Clifton / Come on baby: Hopkins, Lightnin' / Nine below zero: Williamson, Sonny Boy / Gambling blues: Jackson, Lil' Son / Pontiac blues: Williamson, Sonny Boy / I'm in the big city: Bonner, Juke Boy / Meet you at the chicken shack: Hopkins, Lightnin' / Rag around your head: Delafose, John / Blues (Won't let me take my rest): Gray, Henry / Shake your money maker: Littlejohn, Johnny / If trouble was money: Musselwhite, Charley / Wild wild woman: Young, Johnny / Gimme a penny: Thornton, Willie Mae 'Big Mama' / On the road again: Young, Johnny / Mojo in my hand: Robinson, L.C.
CDCHD 590 / Mar '96 / Ace

☐ LET'S HAVE A PARTY
BMCD 4002 / 5 Jan '98 / Blue Moon

☐ LET'S HEAR IT FOR THE GIRLS
All I wanna do: Crow, Sheryl / Girls just wanna have fun: Lauper, Cyndi / Ain't no man: Carroll, Dina / Every day of the week: Jade / Just a step from heaven: Eternal / Whatta man: Salt n' Pepa & En Vogue / Free your mind: En Vogue / Same thing: Carlisle, Belinda / Right beside you: Hawkins, Sophie B. / All I want: Those Two / Little bird: Lennox, Annie / Trouble: Shampoo / Go away: Estefan, Gloria / Jump: Pointer Sisters / It's raining men: Weather Girls / Only way is up: Yazz / I love your smile: Shanice / Gotta get it right: Fiagbe, Lena / Walk like an Eygptian: Bangles / Patience of angels: Reader, Eddi
5165522 / Apr '95 / Polydor

☐ LET'S PARTY (21 Favourites)
Zorba's dance / For he's a jolly good fellow / Congratulations / Hokey cokey / Conga / Superman / Birdie song / Oops upside your head / Celebration / Loco-motion / Saturday night / YMCA / Time warp / Hot hot hot / Anniversary waltz / Lambada / Swing low, sweet chariot / You'll never walk alone / Happy birthday to you / Auld lang syne / Gay Gordons
AVC 562 / May '96 / Avid

☐ LET'S ROCK
Simply the best / Can't get enough / Alright now / Brown sugar / Touch too much / Paranoid / Radar love / Since you've been gone / Summer of '69 / Fool for your lovin' / Get it on / Because the night / Tie your mother down / You give love a bad name / Is this love / Hold the line / If looks could kill / Livin' on a prayer / Shadows of the night / Run to you / Out in the fields / I surrender / Rebel yell / Smokin' / Jeepster / More than a feeling / Ace of spades / Open arms / Tush / Dancing in the moonlight
CDVDB 5 / 4 Aug '97 / Virgin

☐ LET'S ROCK TOGETHER (2CD Set)
NSCD 001 / Feb '95 / Newsound

☐ LETTER FROM MEMPHIS
RR 4693 / 16 Mar '98 / Repertoire

☐ LIBRARY OF CONGRESS ARCHIVE OF FOLK CULTURE (Negro Blues & Hollers)
Camp hollers: House, Son & Willie Brown/Fiddlin' Joe Martin / Cornfield hollers: Berry, Charley / I'm a soldier in the army of the Lord: Silent Grove Baptist Church Congregation / I'm gonna lift up a standard for my King: Church Of God In Christ Congregation / Worried life blues: Edwards, David / Ragged and dirty: Brown, William / Special rider blues: House, Son / Depot blues: House, Son / Mississippi blues: Brown, William / Four o'clock flower blues: Blackwell, William & William Brown / East St. Louis blues: Brown, William / Low down dirty dog blues: House, Son
ROUCD 1501 / May '97 / Rounder

☐ LIBRARY OF CONGRESS ARCHIVE OF FOLK CULTURE (Songs & Ballads Of The Anthracite Miners)
Down down down: Keating, William E. / Avondale mine disaster: Quinn, John J. / Me Johnny Mitchell man: Byrne, Jerry / Boys on the hill: Muldowney, James / On Johnny Mitchell's train: Byrne, Jerry / Rolling on the rye grass: Muldowney, James / Old miner's refrain: Walsh, Daniel / John J Curtis: Rada, Andrew / Celebrated workingman: Walsh, Daniel / When the breaker starts up full time: Byrne, Jerry / Union man: Morgan, Albert / Miner's doom: Walsh, Daniel / Down in a coalmine: Jones, Morgan / Shoofly: Walsh, Daniel
ROUCD 1502 / May '97 / Rounder

☐ LIFE AFTER BLOOM
GRCD 015 / Jun '94 / Guerilla

☐ LIFE IN BLUES
157362 / Feb '93 / Blues Collection

☐ LIFE IS CHANGE VOL.3
EFA 11654 D / Jul '93 / Beri-Beri

☐ LIFE MADE ME BEAUTIFUL AT FORTY
ITM 1498 / Nov '95 / ITM

☐ LIFE ON THE OCEAN WAVE
Sailor's hornpipe / Sailing / Fantasy on British sea songs / Leaving of Liverpool / Cockleshell heroes / A-roving / Blow the man down / Hearts of oak / Skye boat song / Pump shanty / Dartmouth mariner / Shenandoah / Soldiers of the sea / Rollin' home / What shall we do with the drunken sailor / Life on the ocean wave
303772 / Jun '97 / Hallmark

☐ LIFE SUCKS GET A CRASH HELMET
RRCD 001 / Oct '93 / Retch

☐ LIGHTING A MATCH UNDERWATER
DE 1 / Apr '97 / Detroit Electric

☐ LIGHTNING RECORDS PUNK COLLECTION
CDPUNK 79 / Jun '96 / Anagram

☐ LIGHTNING THUNDER AND RAIN
DC 879612 / Oct '97 / Disky

☐ LIKE A GIRL I WANT TO KEEP YOU COMING

Invocation to Papa Legba: *Harry, Deborah* / Sister Ray: *New Order* / Just say no to drugs hysteria: *Burroughs, William S.* / Dead soul: *Burroughs, William S.* / Song for the trees (or) I know sometimes the world is wrong: *Byrne, David* / Tri-power: *Live Skull* / Living on the outside (fucked up world): *Pre-Metal Syndrome* / Party animal: *Finley, Karen* / It's a mistake to think you're special: *Giorno, John* / Hard: *Rollins Band*

VICD 009 / Oct '96 / Visionary/ Jettisoundz

☐ LILITH FAIR (A Celebration Of Women In Music)

7822190072 / 27 Apr '98 / Arista

☐ LIMITLESS (Koyote Collection - 4CD Set)

KRCD 004 / 10 Nov '97 / Koyote

☐ LINE DANCE

Riverdance / Heart's cry / Lift the wings / Cotton eye Joe / Any man of mine / Deadwood stage / Wrong train, wrong line / Fast fingers Freddie / Soft touch / Boys and me

QED 135 / Nov '96 / Tring

☐ LINE DANCE ALBUM VOL.1, THE

Line dancing / Redneck girl / Brown eyed girl / Hey good lookin' / Walking after midnight / Let me dance with you / Start with the talking / I tried at first not to (fall in love with you) / If you don't think I'm leaving / Zydeco ball / When daddy played the fiddle / Cotton eyed Joe / Guitar boogie / You left the water running / Abilene / Gentle on my mind / Orange blossom guitars / Midnight flyer and showboat gambler

SUMCD 4100 / Feb '97 / Summit

☐ LINE DANCE ALBUM VOL.2, THE

Achy breaky heart / Elvira / Shame on me / Black coffee / It's my turn to sing with willie / Sailor soldier christian / Wooden horses / Paul and silas / Fire on the mountain / Southern railroad / Golden slipper / Take a letter marie / Reggae cowboy / Pave your way into tomorrow / Rockabilly girl / Eighteen wheeler / Down the road/Sally Goodin' / Foggy / Mountain breakdown

SUMCD 4136 / Sep '97 / Summit

☐ LINE DANCE COLLECTION, THE (4CD Set)

SUMBX 4008 / Jan '98 / Summit

☐ LINE DANCE FEVER (3CD Set)

Line dancin' days / Goin' country / There you go / EJ's bar / Burnin' fire / Country music hall of fame / This don't feel like dancin' / No honky tonks in heaven / Too easy / Good times come around / Love my car / Love kept it's hold on my heart / I learnt a thing or two / Ain't life wonderful / Louisiana / Daddy's got his blue jeans on / 3 time loser / Situation vacant / Country married rock 'n' roll / Let's hear it for the ladies / I like it I love it / Cotton eye joe / Swamp thing / Little miss honky tonk / Third rock from the sun / I try to think about Elvis / Chattahoochie / Whose bed have your boots been under / XXX's and OOO's (an American girl) / God blessed Texas / Old pop in an oak / Texas cowboys / I want my goodbye back / Mi vida loca (my crazy life) / Third rate romance / Boot scootin' boogie / Mercury blues / My baby loves me / Achy breaky heart / Love's gotta hold on you / Hillbilly rock hillbilly roll / Black coffee / One step forward / Dream baby / He thinks he'll keep her / Cherokee boogie / Guitars and Cadillacs / Ancient history / Elvira / Bug / When will I be loved / Passionate kisses / Honky tonk blues / Wild one / One more last chance

55176 / 29 Sep '97 / Music

☐ LINE DANCE FEVER VOL.1

CURCD 027 / Jul '96 / Curb

☐ LINE DANCE FEVER VOL.2

CURCD 033 / Jan '97 / Curb

☐ LINE DANCE FEVER VOL.3

CURCD 043 / Jun '97 / Curb

☐ LINE DANCE FEVER VOL.4

Jose Cuervo: *Clayton,Kimber* / Mull River Shuffle: *Rankin Family* / Road Runner: *Microwave Dave* / Line Dance Crazy: *Kenny, Sean* / Down on the farm: *McGraw, Tim* / Cowboy boots: *Backsliders* / Dancing shoes: *McDowell, Ronnie* / Crash boom bang: *Cane Honey, T.* / You're not in Kansas: *Messina, JoDee* / Everyday I have to cry: *Woodruff, Bob* / Two more to drive away: *Brannon, Kippi* / Nice work if you can get it: *Burnin' daylight* / Do it again: *Carson, Jeff* / I saw the light: *Wyonna* / Another perfect day: *Blake & Brian* / Race is on: *Brown, Sawyer* / My hat's off to him: *Auston, Jim* / Under the hood: *Anderson, Al*

CURCD 045 / 15 Sep '97 / Curb

☐ LINE DANCE FEVER VOL.5

CURCD 048 / 2 Feb '98 / Curb

☐ LINE DANCE SESSION

(They call me) the breeze: *Moody, George & The Country Squires* / 5678: *Lone Star* / Smoky places: *Memphis Roots* / Save the last dance for me: *Moody, George & The Country Squires* / Honky tonk blues: *Blueberry Hill* / South of the border: *Memphis Roots* / Folsom Prison blues: *Moody, George & The Country Squires* / Loves got a hold on you: *Blueberry Hill* / Cannibals: *Memphis Roots* / Big river: *Blueberry Hill* / Crazy mama: *Memphis Roots* / Gulf of mexico: *Moody, George & The Country Squires* / Fool for you: *Memphis Roots* / Down at the twist and shout: *Bayou Boys* / Me and Bobby McGee: *Moody, George & The Country Squires* / I should have asked her faster: *Memphis Roots*

309042 / 13 Jul '98 / Hallmark

☐ LINE DANCE SPECTACULAR

PLSCD 220 / Jul '97 / Pulse

☐ LINE DANCE SWING

CURCD 053 / 16 Mar '98 / Curb

☐ LINE UP AND DANCE (The Best Of New Country Line Dance 2CD Set)

Achy breaky heart: *Blueberry Hill* / There goes my heart: *Memphis Roots* / One step away: *Bayou Boys* / Elvira: *Memphis Roots* / One more last chance: *Blueberry Hill* / Six days on the road: *Moody, George & The Country Squires* / Passionate kisses: *Blueberry Hill* / Watermelon crawl: *Memphis Roots* / He thinks he'll keep her: *Blueberry Hill* / Tempted: *Memphis Roots* / Hard way: *Blueberry Hill* / I couldn't leave if I tried: *Bayou Boys* / Smokey places: *Memphis Roots* / Cotton eye Joe: *Blueberry Hill* / Fly like a bird: *Memphis Roots* / Crying shame: *Blueberry Hill* / Good noise: *Memphis Roots* / Old flames (can't hold a candle to you): *Moody, George & The Country Squires* / Lovin' all night: *Bayou Boys* / Honky tonk blues: *Blueberry Hill* / Folsom Prison blues: *Moody, George & The Country Squires* / Love's got a hold on you: *Blueberry Hill* / Cannibals: *Memphis Roots* / Big river: *Blueberry Hill* / Crazy Mama: *Memphis Roots* / One step forward: *Blueberry Hill* / Summertime blues: *Bayou Boys* / Gulf of Mexico: *Moody, George & The Country Squires* / Hillbilly rock, hillbilly roll: *Blueberry Hill* / Fool for you: *Memphis Roots* / Mercury blues: *Blueberry Hill* / Living on love: *Moody, George & The Country Squires* / Black coffee: *Memphis Roots* / Cherokee boogie: *Memphis Roots* / Don't close your eyes: *Moody, George & The Country Squires* / Bootscootin' boogie: *Blueberry Hill* / Good hearted woman: *Moody, George & The Country Squires* / Chattahoochee: *Blueberry Hill* / All you ever do is bring me down: *Memphis Roots* / Down at the twist and shout: *Bayou Boys* / Bug: *Blueberry Hill* / Me and Bobby McGee: *Moody, George & The Country Squires* / Fast as you: *Blueberry Hill* / I should have asked her faster: *Memphis Roots* / You got it: *Blueberry Hill* / (They call me) the breeze: *Moody, George & The Country Squires* / You can feel bad: *Blueberry Hill* / South of the border: *Memphis Roots*

3036300175 / Jun '98 / Carlton

☐ LINN SUMMER JAZZ

Makin' whoopee: *Hue & Cry* / Strictly for dancing: *Perfect Houseplants* / Gettin' high: *Martin, Claire* / Going home again: *Taylor, Martin* / Is you is my baby: *Kidd, Carol* / Gold of the azure: *Smith, Tommy* / Virus of love: *Hue & Cry* / Could this be the one: *Martin, Claire* / Gypsy: *Taylor, Martin* / Free like you: *Hue & Cry* / In a mellow tone: *Taylor, Martin* / That's me: *Kidd, Carol* / Midge: *Smith, Tommy*

AKD 072 / Aug '97 / Linn

☐ LION ROARS, THE

(Let me be the) special guest: *Isaacs, Gregory* / Mind what you do: *Prophet, Michael* / Praising the Father: *McKay, Freddie* / Missions are possible: *Mac, Richie* / Set the captive free: *I-Roy* / Gal like you: *Prince Mohammed* / Sam Stone: *George, Earl* / Happy day and night: *Prophet, Michael* / Jah is my light: *Mac, Richie* / Some a them run away: *McKay, Freddie* / Border: *Isaacs, Gregory* / Gal a Christian: *Lone Ranger* / I need a girl: *Levy, Barrington & Trinity* / Song of Zion: *Ethiopians* / Idler's rest: *I-Roy* / Never gonna run away: *Maytones* / Money trouble: *Maytones & I-Roy* / I would be telling you a lie: *George, Earl* / Loving Jah more: *Mac, Richie*

CDGR 205 / 2 Feb '98 / Charly

☐ LIPSTICK ON YOUR COLLAR

Chantilly lace: *Big Bopper* / Summertime blues: *Cochran, Eddie* / Lipstick on your collar: *Francis, Connie* / Be bop a lula: *Vincent, Gene* / Blueberry hill: *Domino, Fats* / Giddy up a ding dong: *Bell, Freddy & The Bellboys* / Wake up little Susie: *King Brothers* / Why do fools fall in love: *Lymon, Frankie & The Teenagers* / Hoots Mon: *Lord Rockingham's XI* / Earth angel: *Crew Cuts* / Little darlin': *Diamonds* / Only sixteen: *Douglas, Craig* / Party doll: *Knox, Buddy* / Cumberland gap: *Vipers Skiffle Group* / Red river rock: *Johnny & The Hurricanes* / Move it: *Richard, Cliff* / Singing the blues: *Steele, Tommy* / Rock island line: *Donegan, Lonnie* / White sports coat: *Dene, Terry* / It's all in the game: *Edwards, Tommy* / It's only make believe: *Twitty, Conway* / Sorry (I ran all the way home): *Impalas* / Ma he's making eyes at me: *Otis, Johnny Show* / Smoke gets in your eyes: *Platters* / Sea of love: *Wilde, Marty*

5529012 / Oct '97 / Spectrum

☐ LIPSTICK TRACES

Boring life / It's too soon to know: *Orioles* / L'amiral cherche une maison a louer: *Tzara, Tristan* / Roadrunner: *Richman, Jonathan* / Excerpt from "Hurlements en faveur de Sade": *Debord, Guy* / Instrumentation verbale: *Brau, Jean-Louis* / Boredom: *Buzzcocks* / One chord wonders: *Buzzcocks* / Phoneme bbbb: *Hausmann, Raoul* / At home he's a tourist: *Gang Of Four* / Gary Gilmore's eyes: *Adverts* / U: *Kleenex* / Excerpt from "Critique de la separation": *Debord, Guy* / Stage talk: *Clash* / Never been in a riot: *Mekons* / Split: *Liliput* / Rohrenhose...: *Blegvad, Peter* / Wake up: *Essential Logic* / You: *Kleenex* / Megapneumanies: *Wolman, Gil* / In love: *Raincoats* / Karawane: *Osmond, Marie* / I wish I was a mole in the ground: *Lunsford, Bascom Lamar* / Building: *Mekons* / Lipstick traces: *Spellman, Benny*

R 2902 / Jul '93 / Rough Trade

☐ LIQUID CALIFORNIA (The Sound Of The West Coast/2CD Set)

SUB 11D / Mar '96 / Subversive

☐ LIQUID SKY ADVENTURE SERIES VOL.1, THE

EBCCD 1 / Apr '97 / Electro Bunker Cologne

☐ LIQUID SKY ADVENTURE SERIES VOL.2, THE

EBCCD 2 / Apr '97 / Electro Bunker Cologne

☐ LISMOR 21ST ANNIVERSARY ALBUM

Rolling in the high grass/Scalloway lasses/Haint dykes o'Voe: *Bain, Aly & Phil Cunningham* / Waulking song: *MacInnes, Mairi* / MacEwan's barn/ Islay teenager/Lewis Road dance/'Horse on' So: *McDonald, Fergie* / Sonny's dream: *Imlach, Hamish* / Links of Forth/Atholl Cummers/MacAllister's dirk: *Strathclyde Police Pipe Band* / We china pig: *Alexander Brothers* / Camptown races/Steamboat Bill/Oh Susanna: *Box & Banjo Band* / Dumbarton's drums: *Gaelforce Orchestra* / Muckin' O' Geordie's byre: *Stewart, Andy* / Gates of Edinburgh reel: *Ellis, John & His Highland Country Band* / Wiggly jig: *New Celeste* / My ain folk: *Anderson, Moira* / Spin and glow/McDowall's breakdown: *Cowie, Charlie* / Sonny's mazurka/Foxhunters: *Mathieson, Pipe Major Robert* / Bonnie lass o'Ballochmyle: *Morrison, Peter* / Bonnie lass o'Bon Accord: *Gordon, Rob & His Band* / Lewis sailing song: *Solley, David* / West Highland way: *McKellar, Kenneth* / Lord Lovat's lament: *78th Fraser Highlander's Pipe Band* / Barren rocks of Aden/Duke of Atholl's Highlanders: *Dancing Strings* / De niand puirt - A Beul: *Runrig*

LCOM 5228 / Apr '94 / Lismor

☐ LISTEN EASY VOL.1 1960'S

WMEM 00204 / 13 Jul '98 / BBC Audio

☐ LISTEN EASY VOL.2 1970'S

WMEM 00162 / 13 Jul '98 / BBC Audio

☐ LISTEN HEAR (Essential Argo/Cadet Grooves)

Listen here: *Soulful Strings* / Either or: *Fisher, Eddie* / I'm a man: *Waters, Muddy* / Voodoo chile: *Upchurch, Phil* / I'm high again: *Diddley, Bo* / Hip judge: *Markham, Pigmeat* / Do what you wanna: *Lewis, Ramsey Trio* / Mr. Kicks: *Young, Eldee* / Hitch hike: *Dushon, Jean* / Timetable: *Land, Harold Quintet* / Black gold: *Upchurch, Phil* / Tales of brave Ulysees: *Rotary Connection* / Les fleurs: *Lewis, Ramsey* / Our day will come: *Bass, Fontella*

CDARC 519 / Mar '95 / Charly

☐ LISTEN TO THE BAND - BRASS SPECTACULAR

WMEM 00032 / 3 Nov '97 / BBC Worldwide

☐ LISTEN TO THE BAND - CLASSICS FOR BRASS

WMEM 00012 / 3 Nov '97 / BBC Worldwide

☐ LISTEN TO THE BAND - ON PARADE

WMEM 00022 / 3 Nov '97 / BBC Worldwide

☐ LISTEN TO THE BAND - REFLECTIONS FOR BRASS

WMEM 00042 / 3 Nov '97 / BBC Worldwide

☐ LISTEN TO THE BANNED (20 Risque Songs 1927-1933)

I've gone and lost my little yo-yo: *Cotton, Billy* / With my little ukelele in my hand: *Formby, George* / Guy what takes his time: *West, Mae* / She was only a postman's daughter: *Durium Dance Band* / Nellie the nudist queen: *Ross & Sargent* / My private affair: *Davies, Dawn* / What's it: *Rodgers, Jimmie* / He hadn't up 'til yesterday: *Tucker, Sophie* / Winnie the worm: *Frankau, Ronald* / I'm a bear in a lady's boudoir: *Edwards, Cliff* / Everyone's got sex appeal for someone: *Frankau, Ronald & Monte Crick* / All poshed up with my daisies in my hand: *Higgins, Charlie* / Pu-leeze Mr. Hemingway: *Carlisle, Elsie* / Let's all be fairies: *Durium Dance Band* / I'm going to give it to Mary with love: *Edwards, Cliff* / Physician: *Lawrence, Gertrude* / No wonder she's a blushing bride: *Fowler, Art* / Flora McDonald: *Byng, Douglas* / Or anything else I've got: *Sutton, Randolph* / And so does he: *Davies, Dawn*

CDAJA 5030 / Oct '88 / Living Era

☐ LISTEN TO THE DRUM

M 00012 / 18 May '98 / Mocca

☐ LISTEN TO THE PLANET (A Musical Journey Around The World)

74321372432 / Oct '96 / Milan

☐ LITTLE BIT OF HEAVEN, A (A Vintage Anthology Of 25 Irish Songs)

Little bit of heaven: *McCormack, John* / Kerry dance: *Dawson, Peter* / Lark in the clear air: *MacEwan, Sydney* / Off to Philadelphia: *McCafferty, James* / Meeting of the waters: *Sheridan, Margaret* / That's how I spell IRELAND: *O'Connor, Cavan* / Kathleen Mavourneen: *McCormack, John* / Tumbledown shack in Athlone: *Munn, Frank* / Garden where the praties grow: *Plunket-Greene, Harry* / Macushla: *Crooks, Richard* / When they sing 'The wearing o'the green' in syncopated blues: *Downey, Morton* / Last rose of summer: *Austral, Florence* / Rose of Tralee: *McCormack, John* / Rory O'Moore: *Lawrence, Brian* / Dawning of the day: *MacEwan, Sydney* / Mountains of Mourne: *Daly, Jackie* / Oft in the stilly night: *Teyte, Maggie* / Mother Machree: *White, Joseph* / Star of County Down: *McCormack, John* / Spinning wheel: *Murphy, Delia* / Green hills of Ireland: *Crooks, Richard* / She moved thro' the fair: *McEwan, Sydney* / Pride of Tipperary: *Davison, Peter* / Danny boy: *Sheridan, Margaret* / Ireland, mother Ireland: *McCormack, John*

CDAJA 5202 / Sep '96 / Living Era

☐ LITTLE BLUES IN YOUR SOUL, A (40 All Time Smooth Blues/Sweet Soul Classics - 2CD Set)

Harlem shuffle: *Bob & Earl* / Shout: *Isley Brothers* / (Your love keeps lifting me) higher: *Wilson, Jackie* / Take me to the river: *Green, Al* / Nutbush City limits: *Turner, Ike & Tina* / I'll take you there: *Staple Singers* / Midnight train to Georgia: *Knight, Gladys & The Pips* / I got you (I feel good): *Brown, James* / Got my mojo working: *Smith, Jimmy* / Dancing in the streets: *Martha & The Vandellas* / I heard it through the grapevine: *Gaye, Marvin* / I put a spell on you: *Simone, Nina* / Going to a go go: *Robinson, Smokey* / (Take a little) piece of my heart: *Franklin, Erma* / Need your love so bad: *Fleetwood Mac* / Mannish boy: *Waters, Muddy* / Thrill is gone: *King, B.B.* / I just wanna make love to you: *James, Etta* / I'd rather go blind: *James, Etta* / Rescue me: *Bass, Fontella* / Smokestack lightnin': *Howlin' Wolf* / Boom boom: *Hooker, John Lee* / Stormy Monday: *Little Milton* / Born under a bad sign: *King, Albert* / Respect: *Franklin, Aretha* / Think: *Franklin, Aretha* / Sweet soul music: *Conley, Arthur* / Stand by me: *King, Ben E.* / Green onions: *Booker T & The MG's* / Knock on wood: *Floyd, Eddie* / Hard to handle: *Redding, Otis* / (Sittin' on) the dock of the bay: *Redding, Otis* / When a man loves a woman: *Sledge, Percy* / What'd I say: *Charles, Ray* / Walking the dog: *Thomas, Rufus* / Soul man: *Sam & Dave* / Everybody needs somebody: *Burke, Solomon* / Mustang Sally: *Pickett, Wilson*

9548362232 / 23 Feb '98 / Warner ESP/ Global TV

☐ LITTLE DARLA HAS A TREAT FOR YOU VOL.6

DRL 030 / Mar '97 / Darla

☐ LITTLE DARLA HAS A TREAT FOR YOU VOL.7

DRL 040 / Jun '97 / Darla

☐ LITTLE DARLA HAS A TREAT FOR YOU VOL.9

DRL 060 / 16 Mar '98 / Darla

☐ LITTLE RAMBLERS 1924-1927, THE

Deep blue sea blues / I'm satisfied behind that sweetie of mine / Those pananma mamas / Prince of wails / Cross words between that sweetie and me / Don't bring Lulu / Look who's here / Gotnot ti me / Melancholy Lou / Deep elm / Fallin' down / I love my baby / Tomorrow mornin' / In your green hat / In your green hat / Could I I certainly could / Here comes Malinda / I wonder whats become of Joe / Hot Henry / And then I forget / My cutey's due at two to two today / Play it / Swamp blues

CBC 1037 / Sep '97 / Timeless Historical

☐ LITTLE RED ROOSTER - ORIGINAL R & B

Tell it like it is / Have you changed your mind / Can't hold out much longer / Through the alley / We're gonna make it / Love you like a woman / Don't you just know it / Tell mama / But I do / Cops and robbers / No money down / Born blind / Get closer together / Say boss man / You never can tell / Ya ya / Cool disposition / Juke / Little red rooster

CDAA 043 / Jun '92 / Tring

☐ LITTLE SOUND BOY

VPCD 1441 / Apr '96 / VP

☐ LITURGY OF TIME, A (Original Interpretations Of Ageless Hymns)

Dear Lord and father of mankind: *Snell, Adrian* / Day thou gavest: *Costello, Julie* / O love that wilt not let me go: *Joseph, Martyn* / Lord's my shepherd: *Joseph, Martyn* / Amazing Grace: *Pope, Mal* / When I survey the wondrous cross: *Pope, Mal* / Great is thy faithfulness: *Pope, Mal* / O Lord my God: *Costello, Julie* / Abide with me: *Fitzgerald, David* / Make me a channel of your peace: *Fitzgerald, David*

WMD 003 / May '98 / Word

☐ LIVE

TUT 781 / Oct '94 / Wundertute

☐ LIVE 1955

JCD 17 / Nov '86 / Jass

☐ LIVE 4 EVER (2CD Set)

Sound of drums: *Kula Shaker* / Road rage: *Catatonia* / Three lions 1998: *Lightning Seeds & David Baddiel/ Frank Skinner* / My star: *Brown, Ian* / Wide open space: *Mansun* / Street spirit: *Radiohead* / There's no other way: *Blur* / Richard III: *Supergrass* / Brimful of Asha: *Cornershop* / Nancy boy: *Placebo* / Under the bridge: *Red Hot Chili Peppers* / New pollution: *Beck* / Push it: *Garbage* / In the meantime: *Spacehog* / Changing man: *Weller, Paul* / Rocks: *Primal Scream* / Breathe: *Prodigy* / Open up: *Leftfield & John Lydon* / Pretty vacant: *Sex Pistols* / Only one I know: *Charlatans* / Groovy train: *Farm* / El president: *Drugstore* / Stay: *Butler, Bernard* / Ballad of Tom Jones: *Space* / History: *Verve* / Australia: *Manic Street Preachers* / Place your hands: *Reef* / Riverboat song: *Ocean Colour Scene* / Fools gold: *Stone Roses* / How soon is now: *Smiths* / Twisted (everyday hurts): *Skunk Anansie* / Reverend black grape: *Black Grape* / Great things: *Echobelly* / Peaches: *Presidents Of The USA* / You and me song: *Wannadies* / I'm free: *Soup Dragons* / Can you dig it: *Mock Turtles* / There she goes: *La's* / Semi-charmed life: *3rd Eye Blind* / All you good good people: *Embrace* / Getting better: *Shed Seven* / Trash: *Suede* / Local boy in the photograph: *Stereophonics* / Love is the law: *Seahorses* / Nanny in Manhatten: *Lilys* / Live forever: *Oasis*

9548364372 / 29 Jun '98 / Warner ESP

☐ LIVE AGAIN

Intro: *Stanley Brothers & The Clinch Mountain Boys* / Cotton eyed Joe: *Stanley Brothers & The Clinch Mountain Boys* / Our darling gone: *Stanley Brothers & The Clinch Mountain Boys* / Molly and tenbrooks: *Stanley Brothers & The Clinch Mountain Boys* / Caclin' hen: *Stanley Brothers & The Clinch Mountain Boys* / Little glass of wine: *Stanley Brothers & The Clinch Mountain Boys* / Blue moon of Kentucky: *Stanley Brothers & The Clinch Mountain Boys* / Lonely tombs: *Stanley Brothers & The Clinch Mountain Boys* / Orange blossom special: *Stanley Brothers & The Clinch Mountain Boys* / PPretty flowers: *Carl & J.P. Sauceman/The Green Valley Boys* / Raod of sadness: *Carl & J.P. Sauceman/The Green Valley Boys* / Baby blue eyes: *Carl & J.P. Sauceman/The Green Valley Boys* / Lifeboat soon is coming: *Carl & J.P. Sauceman/The Green Valley Boys* / Letter that broke my heart: *Carl & J.P. Sauceman/The Green Valley Boys* / Outro: *Carl & J.P. Sauceman/The Green Valley Boys* / Roll in my sweet baby's arms: *Flatt, Lester & Earl Scruggs/The Foggy Mountain Boys* / Rainbow of my dreams: *Flatt, Lester & Earl Scruggs/The Foggy Mountain Boys* / That home above: *Flatt, Lester & Earl Scruggs/The Foggy Mountain Boys* / Old Joe Clark: *Stanley Brothers & The Clinch Mountain Boys* / They're at rest together: *Stanley Brothers & The Clinch Mountain Boys* / White house blues: *Stanley Brothers & The Clinch Mountain Boys* / Standing in the need of prayer: *Stanley Brothers & The Clinch Mountain Boys* / Rding the humpbacked mule: *Stanley Brothers & The Clinch Mountain Boys* / Jealous lover: *Stanley Brothers & The Clinch Mountain Boys* / Goodbye old pal: *Stanley Brothers & The Clinch Mountain Boys* / Just one way to the pearly gate: *Stanley Brothers & The Clinch Mountain Boys* / Intro: *Stanley Brothers & The Clinch Mountain Boys* / Let me be your friend: *Stanley Brothers & The Clinch Mountain Boys* / Short life of trouble: *Stanley Brothers & The Clinch Mountain Boys* / Blackberry

blossom: *Stanley Brothers & The Clinch Mountain Boys* / Rose of old Kentucky: *Stanley Brothers & The Clinch Mountain Boys* / Intro: *Stanley Brothers & The Clinch Mountain Boys* / Intro: *Curly King & The Tennessee Hilltoppers* / Don't forget me: *Curly King & The Tennessee Hilltoppers* / Home furniture ad: *Curly King & The Tennessee Hilltoppers* / I love her now mother's old: *Curly King & The Tennessee Hilltoppers* / Outro: *Curly King & The Tennessee Hilltoppers* / From the manager to the cross: *Wiseman, Mac & The Country Boys* / Broken heart to mend: *Wiseman, Mac & The Country Boys* / Grey eagle: *Wiseman, Mac & The Country Boys*
REBCD 2003 / 9 Mar '98 / Rebel

☐ **LIVE AND DIRECT**
KICKCD 75 / 22 Jun '98 / Kickin'

☐ **LIVE AND WIRED - ROCK ANTHEMS**
Number of the beast: *Iron Maiden* / Black night: *Deep Purple* / Only you can rock me: *UFO* / Trees: *Rush* / Fool for your loving: *Whitesnake* / Rock you like a hurricane: *Scorpions* / Shapes of things: *Moore, Gary* / Freebird: *Lynyrd Skynyrd* / Boys are back in town: *Thin Lizzy* / Show me the way: *Frampton, Peter* / Wheels of steel: *Saxon* / Voodoo chile: *Hendrix, Jimi* / Long live rock 'n' roll: *Rainbow*
CDEMS 1610 / May '97 / EMI

☐ **LIVE AND WIRED - ROCK BALLADS**
November rain: *Guns n' Roses* / Empty rooms: *Moore, Gary* / Sugar mice: *Marillion* / Can't fight this feeling: *REO Speedwagon* / Every rose has it's thorn: *Poison* / I want you to want me: *Cheap Trick* / Still in love with you: *Thin Lizzy* / Ain't no love in the heart of the city: *Whitesnake* / Love walked in: *Thunder* / Two out of three ain't bad: *Meat Loaf* / Smile has left your eyes: *Asia* / Baby I love your way: *Frampton, Peter* / Wind of change: *Scorpions*
CDEMS 1609 / May '97 / EMI

☐ **LIVE AND WIRED - ROCK CLASSICS**
Ace of spades: *Motorhead* / Are you ready: *Thin Lizzy* / 747 strangers in the night: *Saxon* / Neon knights: *Black Sabbath* / Attack of the mad axeman: *Schenker, Michael Group* / Ready and willing: *Whitesnake* / Victims of the future: *Moore, Gary* / All right now: *Free* / Doctor Doctor: *UFO* / Green Manalishi: *Fleetwood Mac* / Bat out of hell: *Meat Loaf* / Run to the hills: *Iron Maiden* / Bastille day: *Rush* / School's out: *Cooper, Alice* / Smoke on the water: *Deep Purple*
CDEMS 1611 / May '97 / EMI

☐ **LIVE AT ANTONE'S ANNIVERSARY ANTHOLOGY VOL.2**
ANT 00016 / Sep '95 / Antones

☐ **LIVE AT DREAMSCAPE**
DSRCD 006 / 24 Aug '98 / Dreamscape

☐ **LIVE AT MIDEM, 1979**
500402 / May '94 / Musidisc

☐ **LIVE AT MOE VOL.1**
WDM 100622 / 29 Jun '98 / World Domination

☐ **LIVE AT RAUL'S**
DJD 3216 / Sep '95 / Dejadisc

☐ **LIVE AT RONNIE SCOTT'S**
This love of mine: *Scott, Ronnie Quintet* / High on you: *Cohn, Al & The Jazz Seven* / Spring can really hang you up the most: *Hayes, Tubby* / Evensong: *Taylor, John Trio* / Never let me go: *Coleman, George Quintet* / J 'n' B: *Sharpe, Jack Big Band* / Over the rainbow: *Webster, Ben Quartet* / La Pastora: *Irakere* / Man I love: *Vaughan, Sarah* / Donna Lee: *Sandoval, Arturo* / This can't be love: *Shaw, Ian* / All the things you are: *Scott, Ronnie Quintet*
3036001132 / Jun '97 / Carlton

☐ **LIVE AT RONNIE SCOTT'S**
PLSCD 236 / Jul '97 / Pulse

☐ **LIVE AT ROSKILDE '94**
STOKES 001 / Jun '95 / Roskilde

☐ **LIVE AT SENSOR VOL.1**
DJBRCD 01UK / 2 Feb '98 / DJ Beat

☐ **LIVE AT SENSOR VOL.2 (Remember)**
DJBRCD 02UK / 2 Feb '98 / DJ Beat

☐ **LIVE AT SUNDANCE IBIZA**
LOL 001CD / 3 Nov '97 / Love Of Life

☐ **LIVE AT THE BIG RUMBLE**
NERCD 066 / Nov '91 / Nervous

☐ **LIVE AT THE CAVEAU DE LA HUCHETTE (45th Anniversary)**
Boogie woogie au Caveau de la Huchette: *Buckner, Milt & Dany Doriz Quintet* / La Huchette: *Saury, Maxim Jazz Music* / O' Caveau: *Laferriere, Marc Dixieland Jazz Band* / Little funky line: *Gerault, Stephanie & Benny Vasseur Quintet* / Gee baby ain't I good to you: *Buckner, Milt & Dany Doriz Quintet* / Fat cat: *Memphis Slim & Michel Denis Quintet* / Tribute to La Huchette: *Vassuer, Benny & Francois Guin Quintet* / Blues at the Huchette: *Fonseque, Raymond & His Original Band* / Birthday boogie: *Hampton, Lionel Big Band*
17154 / Apr '98 / Laserlight

☐ **LIVE AT THE GALWAY SHAWL**
CIC 065CD / Nov '93 / Clo Iar-Chonnachta

☐ **LIVE AT THE KNITTING FACTORY VOL.1**
KFWCD 097 / Nov '94 / Knitting Factory

☐ **LIVE AT THE KNITTING FACTORY VOL.2**
KFWCD 098 / Nov '94 / Knitting Factory

☐ **LIVE AT THE KNITTING FACTORY VOL.3**
KFWCD 099 / Nov '94 / Knitting Factory

☐ **LIVE AT THE KNITTING FACTORY VOL.4**
KFWCD 100 / Nov '94 / Knitting Factory

☐ **LIVE AT THE KNITTING FACTORY VOL.5**
KFWCD 108 / Nov '94 / Knitting Factory

☐ **LIVE AT THE KNITTING FACTORY VOL.6**
KFWCD 161 / Feb '95 / Knitting Factory

☐ **LIVE AT THE ROXY**
Strange boy / Smile and wave goodbye / Relics from the past / I live in a car / Telephone numbers / Get yourself killed / Never wanna leave / Here comes the knife / TV drink / Sniper / Tough on you / Fun, fun, fun / Vertigo / Lullabies lie
CDTB 011 / Mar '95 / Thunderbolt

☐ **LIVE AT THE SOCIAL VOL.1**
Cut man: *Meat Beat Manifesto* / DMX will rock: *Davy DMX* / Mighty hard rocker: *Cash Money & Marvellous* / Yes we can: *Crooklyn Clan* / Doing it after dark: *Berrios, Carlos* / Can't: *Tainted Glass* / Juice: *Eric B & Rakim* / Wesley don't surf: *Red Snapper* / Packet of peace: *Lionrock* / P b4 U go 2 bed: *DJ Who* / To a nation rocking: *Metro* / Get up on it like this: *Chemical Brothers* / Again son: *Love Lee* / Nine acre dust: *Charlatans* / Jack me off: *Funk D'Void* / Mirrorshades: *Webb, Will* / Wede man: *Selectah* / We're doing it (Thang): *Bo, Eddie*
HVNLP 13CD / May '96 / Heavenly

☐ **LIVE AT THE VORTEX**
Can't wait till '78: *Wasps* / Waiting for my man: *Wasps* / Bunch of stiffs: *Mean Street* / Small lives: *Neo* / Tell me the truth: *Neo* / Living for kicks: *Torme, Bernie* / Streetfighter: *Torme, Bernie* / Animal bondage: *Art Attacks* / Frankenstein's heartbeat: *Art Attacks* / Nothing to declare: *Suspects* / You don't break my heart: *Maniacs* / I ain't gonna be history: *Maniacs*
CDPUNK 68 / Nov '95 / Anagram

☐ **LIVE AT YORK MINSTER**
Trumpet prelude / Festive overture / Irish tune from County Derry / Pipe set / Cortege from Mlada / Nimrod / Suite in E flat / Ode to joy / Epilogue from things to come
3036100082 / Apr '96 / Pearls

☐ **LIVE FROM 6A**
5363242 / 23 Feb '98 / Mercury

☐ **LIVE FROM SOUNDSCAPE (Latin Jazz)**
DIW 407 / Oct '97 / DIW

☐ **LIVE FROM SOUNDSCAPE (Latin New York 1980-1983)**
DIW 408 / Oct '97 / DIW

☐ **LIVE FROM THE CHARLOTTE**
RAUCD 010 / Feb '94 / Raucous

☐ **LIVE IN MONTREUX (2CD Set)**
Golden striker: *Modern Jazz Quartet & Manhattan Transfer* / Sad old Red: *Simply Red* / Introduction: *Reeves, Dianne* / For all we know: *Reeves, Dianne* / Crazeology: *Generations* / Portia: *Davis, Miles* / Jack the bear: *Modern Jazz Quartet* / Johnny comes lately: *Davison, 'Wild' Bill* / End of a beautiful friendship: *McRae, Carmen & Dizzy Gillespie* / Stella by starlight: *Morrison, James* / Blues for Nesuhi: *Wein, George & Claude Nobs* / Ponta de areia: *Nascimento, Milton* / Dindi: *Costa, Gal* / Bilhete/ Comecar de Novo: *Lins, Ivan* / Aguas de Marco: *Jobim, Tom* / Gota D'Agua: *Buarque, Chico* / Chega de saudade: *Gilberto, Joao* / Miragem: *Djavan* / Asa Branca: *Regina, Elis & Hermeto Pascal* / Chororo: *Gil, Gilberto* / Tanto Amar: *Matogrosso, Ney* / O Corsario: *Bosco, Joao* / Saudade de Bahia: *Veloso, Caetano* / Santa Clara clareou/Zazueira: *Benjor, Jorge*
ACT 90012 / 29 Jun '98 / Act

☐ **LIVE IT UP**
Fight the power: *Dreadzone* / Love revolution: *Yargo* / Annadin: *Sunscreem* / Are you scared: *Arkarna* / Gulf Breeze: *Eatstatic* / For what you dream of: *Bedrock* / Templehead: *Transglobal Underground* / Golden girls: *Kinetic* / My definition of house music: *DJ Hell* / Do you want to know: *Funtopia* / Sacred cycles: *Lazonby, Pete*
PRIMACD 4 / 27 Apr '98 / Prima Vera

☐ **LIVE PARTY MIX**
DO 476CD / Nov '96 / Dance Opera

☐ **LIVE STIFFS**
I knew the bride: *Lowe, Nick* / Let's eat: *Lowe, Nick* / Semaphore signals: *Wreckless Eric* / Reconnez cherie: *Wreckless Eric* / Police car: *Wallis, Larry* / I just don't know what to do with myself: *Costello, Elvis* / Miracle man: *Costello, Elvis* / Wake up and make love with me: *Dury, Ian* / Billericay Dickie: *Dury, Ian* / Sex and drugs and rock 'n' roll and chaos
DIAB 851 / 3 Nov '97 / Diablo

☐ **LIVERPOOL 1963-1968**
Ferry 'cross the Mersey: *Gerry & The Pacemakers* / Skinny Lizzie: *Gerry & The Pacemakers* / Abyssinian secret: *Black, Cilla* / For no one: *Black, Cilla* / Sandy: *Swinging Blue Jeans* / It's too late now: *Swinging Blue Jeans* / Everything in the garden: *Fourmost* / Breakaway: *Marsden, Beryl* / Whatever will be will be (Que sera sera): *Royce, Earl & The Olympics* / I really do: *Royce, Earl & The Olympics* / America: *Storm, Rory & The Hurricanes* / I got a woman: *Black Knights* / Angel of love: *Black Knights* / I love her: *Kubas* / Magic potion: *Kubas* / First cut is the deepest: *Kubas* / Why don't you love me: *Blackwells* / One way ticket / Don't you do it no more: *Kramer, Billy J. & The Dakotas* / How I won the war: *Musketeer Gripweed & The Third Troop*
SEECD 370 / Aug '94 / See For Miles

☐ **LIVING BEAT HOUSE CLASSICS**
LBLCD 7 / May '97 / Living Beat

☐ **LIVING CHICAGO BLUES VOL.1**
Your turn to cry / Serves me right to suffer / Ain't that just like a woman / Feel like breaking up somebody's home / It's alright / Out of bad luck / Stoop down baby / Sittin' on top of the world / My baby's so ugly / Come home darling / Blues won't let me be / One room country shack / Linda Lou / Too late / Laundromat blues / One day / Woman in trouble
ALCD 7701 / May '93 / Alligator

☐ **LIVING CHICAGO BLUES VOL.2**
Don't answer the door / Two headed man / Cold lonely nights / Move over, little dog / Would you, baby / Worry worry / Sunnyland blues / Cry cry darlin' / Stranded on the highway / Dirty mother for you / Spider in my stew / Don't say that no more / Take it easy, baby / Blues after hours / Little angel child / How much more longer
ALCD 7702 / May '93 / Alligator

☐ **LIVING CHICAGO BLUES VOL.3**
Hard times / She's fine / Moving out of the ghetto / Going to New York / Big leg woman / Careless with our love / Roadblock / Poison ivy / I dare you / Nobody knows my troubles / Sweet little girl / Naptown / Drown in my own tears / Crying for my baby / Feel so bad / Wish me well / Have you ever loved a woman / Berlin Wall / Prisoner of the blues
ALCD 7703 / May '93 / Alligator

☐ **LIVING CHICAGO BLUES VOL.4**
Hard times: *Reed, A.C. & The Spark Plugs* / She's fine: *Reed, A.C. & The Spark Plugs* / Moving out of the ghetto: *Reed, A.C. & The Spark Plugs* / Going to New York: *Reed, A.C. & The Spark Plugs* / Big legged woman: *Scotty & The Rib Tips* / Careless without love: *Scotty & The Rib Tips* / Roadblock: *Scotty & The Rib Tips* / Poison ivy: *Scotty & The Rib Tips* / I dare you: *Lee, Lovie & Carey Bell* / Nobody knows my troubles: *Lee, Lovie & Carey Bell* / Sweet little girl: *Lee, Lovie & Carey Bell* / Nap town: *Lee, Lovie & Carey Bell*
ALCD 7704 / May '93 / Alligator

☐ **LIVING IN THE ICE AGE**
MI 2010 / 23 Feb '98 / Milano 2000

☐ **LIVING MUSIC OF THE STEPPES (Instrumental Music & Song Of Mongolia)**
Blue silk overcoat / Leafy tree / River of Uliastay / Snow crowned Altai Mountain / Hallowed road / Sunder mountain / Altai Mountain paean / Jonon Qara's run / Shiilen boor / Full moon / To run like flowing camel's water / Copper and steel / Flow of the Eveen river / Ayi nan ayi/Two hearts / Bishur appeal / Beloved otter coloured horse / Dungshang googoo / Dugureng zaan / Tale of janggar / Oyrad un daguu / Holbolog a
MCM 3001 / May '97 / Multicultural Media

☐ **LIVING ON THE FRONT LINE**
CDTB 154 / Jul '94 / Thunderbolt

☐ **LIVING THE DREAM**
HIPD 40101 / 27 Jul '98 / Hippo

☐ **LIVING THE NIGHTLIFE**
Carlena: *Just Brothers* / Dearly beloved: *Montgomery, Jack* / Black eyed girl: *Thompson, Billy* / Livin' the nightlife: *Charts* / Groovy guy: *Shirelles* / It's torture: *Brown, Maxine* / Gonna give her all the love I've got: *Gordon, Benny* / I refuse to give up: *Reid, Clarence* / Send my baby back: *Hughes, Freddie* / Good things come to those who wait: *Jackson, Chuck* / Do you love me baby: *Masqueraders* / Please stay: *Ivorys* / Pretty part of you: *Hunt, Tommy* / My sweet baby: *Esquires* / Love ain't what it used to be: *Diplomats* / Yesterday's kisses: *Big Maybelle* / (Happiness will cost you) One thin dime: *Lavette, Bettye* / I want you: *Clay, Judy* / Since I found a love: *Hadley, Sandy* / Love keeps me crying: *Johnson, Walter* / You can't keep a good man down: *Gentlemen Four* / I don't want to lose you: *Wynn, Mel* / Look my way: *Williams, Maurice* / You must be losing your mind: *Raye, Jimmy*
CDKEND 104 / Jun '93 / Kent

☐ **LIVING THING, A**
CDORBD 094 / Jun '97 / Globestyle

☐ **LKJ PRESENTS**
LKJCD 014 / Apr '96 / LKJ

☐ **LO MEJOR DE LA SALSA**
DMA 5011 / Jan '97 / Blue Moon

☐ **LOAD OF..., A (40 Football Favourites/ 2CD Set)**
Liquidator: *Billy Bluebeat* / Keep right on: *Small Heath Alliance* / United United: *Stretford End Boys* / Mr. Bergkamp: *Yeah* / Here we go: *Everton Army* / Up the Spurs: *Cheers* / Smells like team spirit: *Big Blue W* / Ain't no bluff: *Villa Squad* / Celtic's foreign legion: *Broon, James Techno Trio* / We are Rangers: *Sandy Scot* / My favourite Stan: *Red Karaoke Machine* / Santa is a Geordie: *Roden, Harry* / Robin Hood: *Cortez, Hector & His Formation* / Roll out the red carpet: *Arsenal FC 1978 FA Cup Squad* / I'm forever blowing bubbles: *Looking for a Rainbow* / Ballad of Kenny Dalglish: *Big Bad Jock* / Go for it: *Coventry City FC 1987 FA Cup Squad* / Happy Xmas (war is over): *Hoddle, Glenn & Tottenham Hotspur FC 1981/ 2 FA Cup Squad* / One F in Fulham: *Haynes Boys* / Boys in old Brighton blue: *Seagulls* / Jesus with a football: *Formbys* / Z cars: *Gwladys Street End* / We will stand together: *Manchester United FC* / We're coming through: *McCoy, Danny* / Up the Dons: *Shepherd, Robbie* / Every other Saturday: *McLean, Lex & Glasgow Rangers FC* / Viva Scotland: *Gunn, Ben* / Glory glory Ayrshire Killie: *Chosen* / Frank Worthington: *Joe Jordanaires* / Leeds Leeds Leeds (marching on together): *Leeds United FC/ Supporters* / Wembley Wembley Wenbley (Wembley here we come): *Special Duties* / Dancing in the Kippax: *Kinky Singers* / Let 'em come: *Green, Roy* / Thank you Kevin: *Busker* / Gary Lineker a young girl's dream: *Romaine* / Brazil vs. Slough Town '66: *Wembley '66* / You'll never walk alone: *Liverpool FC 1971 Squad* / Do it 'cos you like it: *Fashanu, Justin* / Clarey blue: *Green, Roy* / Crazy games: *Jones, Vinnie*
DEMPCD 026 / Sep '97 / Emporio

☐ **LOADED LOCK IN**
VVR 1000222 / May '97 / V2

☐ **LOCA MIA**
TUMICD 025 / '92 / Tumi

☐ **LOCATED IN THE RECORD CENTRE OF THE SOUTH (The Grand Excello R&B Finale)**
Run Uncle John run: *McCain, Jerry* / Don't let your Daddy slow walk you down: *Good Rockin' Sam* / Teeny weeny baby: *Green, Rudy* / Baby I'm confessin': *Angel, Johnny* / Can't keep from cryin': *Gaines, Earl* / Bad credit: *McCain, Jerry* / I don't need you now: *Gaines, Earl* / Just lonesome that's all: *Offitt, Lillian* / Jig's up: *McCain, Jerry* / Sweetheart please don't go: *Gladiolas* / Guitar rhumbo: *Guitar Gable* / One look at you Daddy: *Fran, Carol* / Walking in the park: *Guitar Gable* / Confusion: *Ballou, Classie* / I quit my knockin': *Fran, Carol* / To you my darlin': *Nelson, Jay* / Late last night: *Harpo, Slim* / My Chinatown gal: *Washington, Leroy* / My true life: *Washington, Leroy* / I got a love (way down in my heart): *Lonesome Sundown* / Because she's gone: *Lazy Lester* / Ponderosa stomp: *Lazy Lester* / I'm gonna cut out on you: *Lonesome Sundown* / Rainin' in my heart: *Harpo, Slim*
CDCHD 686 / Jun '98 / Ace

☐ **LOCKED INTO SURF VOL.1**
WIGCD 002 / Jul '96 / Alopecia

☐ **LOCKED ON VOL.1**
Joy: *Rushmore, Janet* / Space cowboy: *Jamiroquai* / Freak in you: *Jodeci* / Inside your mind: *God* / Saved my life: *Edwards, Todd* / Diamond rings: *X-Presidents* / Misled: *Dion, Celine* / Runnin' away: *Nicole* / Closer: *Mood II Swing* / Let's groove: *Morel's Grooves* / Alabama blues: *St. Germain* / Are u sleeping: *Indo* / Nite life: *English, Kim* / Satisfied: *H2O & Billie* / Spend the night: *Lewis, Danny J.* / Never gonna let you go: *Moore, Tina*
8287512
8287732 / May '96 / London

☐ **LOCKED ON VOL.2**
Closer than close: *Gaines, Rosie* / Experience: *Tuff & Jam* / To deserve you: *Midler, Bette* / Dancing for heaven: *Edwards, Todd* / Just gets better: *TJR & Xavier* / Find the path: *TJR & Xavier* / Anytime: *Nu Birth* / Sugar is sweeter: *Bolland, C.J.* / Sound bwoy burial: *Gant* / Free: *Ultra Nate* / I refuse: *Somore* / Jump to it: *Double 99* / I get a rush: *Tywanda* / Obsessed: *RIP* / Dreams: *Smokin' Beats* / Give me the night: *Crawford, Randy* / Gabrielle: *Davis, Roy Jr.*
CDVRX 3 / 25 Aug '97 / Virgin

☐ **LOGIC TRANCE VOL.2**
Stella: *Jam & Spoon* / Transformation: *Transform* / Trans-o-phobia: *Dance Trance* / Schoneberg: *Marmion* / Midsummernight: *Glass Ceiling* / Fragile: *LSG* / Brainticket 2: *Ramin* / Rez: *Underworld* / Eternal spirit: *4 Voices* / Wake up: *Garnier, Laurent* / Fires of Ork II: *Fires Of Ork* / What is sound: *Blyz* / Little fluffy clouds: *Orb* / Paradise II: *Atlantis* / Papua New Guinea: *Future Sound Of London* / Silence of the water: *Emojonal* / I love you: *Electrotete* / How much can you take: *Visions Of Shiva* / Evolution: *Experience* / Spacetrack: *Cosmic Baby* / Love stimulation: *Humate* / Orbital: *Lush 3.1* / Logic trance: *Microbots*
74321212342 / Jun '94 / Logic

☐ **LOLO SY NY TARINY (Music From Madagascar)**
PS 65121 / Feb '94 / PlayaSound

☐ **LONDON ACID CITY (2CD Set)**
MSS 0034 / 20 Jul '98 / Mutant Sound System

☐ **LONDON BEATS (4CD Set)**
Papua New Guinea: *Future Sound Of London* / Tingler: *Smart Systems* / 'Ard core: *Well Ard* / Harmonik distortion: *DJ Freshtrax & DJ HMS* / Leaps and bounds: *Flag* / I'm not gonna let you do it: *Mental Cube* / Heart beat: *TRIP* / Bring in the pulse: *Indo Tribe* / Braineater: *Danse City* / Summer's child: *Life Form* / Expander: *Future Sound Of London* / Brain of morbius: *Optic Eye* / Stakker humanoid: *Humanoid* / Dominate: *Flag* / Alchemist: *Geneside II* / Tainted love: *Impedance* / Zum zum: *Love Men* / People living today: *Semi Real* / Got to be emotion: *Viginity* / Religion: *Awareness* / Wind theme: *Xpulsion* / We want to be together: *Parkhill* / Eruption: *Flag* / 5 4 3 2 1: *AWOL* / Moscow: *Future Sound Of London* / Melba: *Danse City* / Owl: *Indo Tribe* / Intensity: *Mars, Doom & Fresh Trax* / Coda coma: *Yage* / Let's go: *Hardware* / Out of it: *Spirit Level* / Feel like I'm falling: *Unlimited Dream Company* / Listening: *Unlimited Dream Company* / Pre dawn chaos: *Flag* / Industrial evolution: *Urban Hype* / Bite the bullet baby: *Indo Tribe* / Fire when ready: *G Double E* / Up in dub heaven: *Unlimited Dream Company* / Sunburst: *Optic Eye* / Zip code: *Smart Systems* / Distracted: *Distracted* / Word of mouth: *Parkhill* / Death of a kamikazee: *Geneside II* / Midi overflow: *Danse City* / Feel so good: *TRIP* / Bogeyman: *Happy & Free* / Sanction: *Emtrino* / Mission to love: *Coyaba Tribe* / Far out race: *Optic Eye* / Potion takes effect: *Unlimited Dream Company*
CDBTOT 1 / 22 Sep '97 / Jumpin' & Pumpin'

☐ **LONDON BLUES FESTIVAL (2CD Set)**
ITM 960017 / Feb '94 / ITM

☐ **LONDON JAZZ CLASSICS VOL.1**
Skindo le'le: *Alive* / Jump: *Airto* / Welcome new warmth: *Sardaby, Michel* / Salsa Mama: *Richardson, Doug* / Te' Caliente: *Gallant, Patsy* / Searching: *McClerkin, Corky* / Atlas: *Jones, Robin Seven* / I feel the earth move: *First Gear & Larnelle Harris*
SJRCD 008 / Jul '94 / Soul Jazz

☐ **LONDON JAZZ CLASSICS VOL.2**
Samba de flora: *Moreira, Airto* / Get with it: *Parker, Billy* / Ain't no sunshine: *Sivuca* / Cocoa funk: *Franzetti, Carlos* / Forty days: *Brooks, Billy* / Sophie's gift: *Synthesis* / Feel like makin' love: *Marrero, Ricardo* / Fenway funk: *Paunetto, Bobby*
SJRCD 017 / Jun '94 / Soul Jazz

☐ LONDON JAZZ CLASSICS VOL.3
L'eroe di plastica: *Esposito, Tony* / Mr. Blindman: *McGhee, Donna* / Manha: *Azymuth* / Taz: *Paunetto, Bobby* / A assim que eu sou: *Papete* / Bananas: *Irvine, Weldon* / Bananeira: *Santiago, Emilio* / Mother's land: *Hannibal* / Cascavel: *Adolfo, Antonio*
SJCD 026 / May '95 / Soul Jazz

☐ LONDON PAVILION VOL.1 & 2
Masque / Curry crazy / Trial of Doctor Fancy / You Mary you / Garden of Eden / Amateur detection / Hanging gardens of Reigate: *Would-Be-Goods* / Pop up man / Whoops what a palaver / Lose that long face / Curtain / Valleri / Ruling class / Love / Fire / Paper wraps rock / Dreams of living / Never underestimate the ignorance / If you're missing someone / Libera me / Montague terrace (in blue) / At the end of the corridor
ACME 10CD / 6 Oct '97 / El

☐ LONDON PAVILION VOL.3
ACME 21CD / May '89 / El

☐ LONDON PRIDE (24 Classic Songs Inspired By Britains Capital)
Maybe it's because I'm a Londoner / Mister Brown of London Town / Burlington Bertie from Bow / Life begins at Oxford Circus / With her head tucked underneath her arm / Nightingale sang in Berkeley Square / London pride / Underneath the arches / Mayfair merry-go-round / If it wasn't for the 'ouses in between / Changing of the guard / There's a lovely lake in London / Up the apples and pears / Pretty Polly Perkins of Paddington Green / Down at the old Bull and Bush / London I love / Lambeth walk / I'm going to get lit up / Old Father Thames / Piccadilly / Round the Marble Arch / Percy from Pimlico / 'Ampstead way / Knocked 'em in the Old Kent Road
75605522862 / Mar '98 / Happy Days

☐ LONDON UPDATE OF DRUM 'N' BASS (DJ Wildchild Presents)
MILL 39CD / May '97 / Millenium

☐ LONE STAR BLUES
Houston: *Copeland, Johnny* / Meltdown: *Collins, Albert* / Got my mind back: *Kubek, Smokin' Joe Band & Bnois King* / Shuck 'n' jive: *Boyack, Pat & The Prowlers* / She's a rocket: *Ealey, Robert* / Lone star boogie: *Morgan, Mike & The Crawl* / Hoochie mama: *Jones, Andrew 'Jr. Boy'* / Love and war: *Nulisch, Darrell & Texas Heat* / Say it's not so: *Strehli, Angela* / Dallas Texas: *Primich, Gary* / Texas son: *Reynolds, Teddy*
EDCD 9009 / Nov '97 / Easydisc

☐ LONELY IS AN EYESORE
Hot doggie: *Colourbox* / Acid bitter and sad: *This Mortal Coil* / Cut the tree: *Wolfgang Press* / Fish: *Throwing Muses* / Frontier: *Dead Can Dance* / Crushed: *Cocteau Twins* / No motion: *Dif Juz* / Muscoviet musquito: *Clan Of Xymox* / Protagonist: *Dead Can Dance*
GAD 703CD / 6 Jul '98 / 4AD

☐ LONESOME BABY BLUES (The Lin & Kliff Story/4CD Set)
Crazy mind plus a foolish heart: *Jetton, Wayne* / Meadowlark boogie: *Griffin, Buck* / I'm running for your heart: *Switzer, Bill* / Too fast too wild: *Ray, David* / Just give me time: *Crabb, Larry & Louis* / I love you because: *Shelton, Merle* / Dirty bird song: *Starr, Andy* / Lookin' for the green: *Griffin, Buck* / Pecosita: *Armstrong, Gene* / (I love you baby) all the time: *Ray, David* / My Louisiana home: *Crabb, Larry & Louis* / Bawlin' and squallin' (over you): *Griffin, Buck* / Do you remember: *Buskirk, Paul & Freddy Powers* / Loser: *Buskirk, Paul & Freddy Powers* / Do it right: *Starr, Andy* / Richest man alive: *Gold, Johnny* / Somebody's girl: *Jetton, Wayne* / Chilena my dancing girl: *Shelton, Merle* / Why can't you and I: *Ray, David* / Cochise: *Griffin, Buck* / Round and round: *Starr, Andy* / You're still in my heart: *Crabb, Larry & Louis* / Rough tough man: *Curtis, Dan* / Little red bird: *Switzer, Bill* / Jitterbugging baby: *Ray, David* / Wasted love: *Buskirk, Paul* / I found a new love: *Fuller, Jerry* / Let's elope baby: *Griffin, Buck* / Jessie Lee: *Griffin, Buck* / Dogfight: *Jokers* / Lonely hours: *Armstrong, Gene* / Night air: *Four Mints* / Chapel of my heart: *Buskirk, Paul* / Because I love you: *Gold, Johnny* / Through eternity: *Fuller, Jerry* / Please pardon my tears: *Crabb, Larry & Louis* / Fool again: *Ruff, Ray* / My poor heart: *Strikes* / Still in love with you: *Tu-Tones* / Lonesome feeling: *Ray, David* / Prisoner's farewell: *Mitchell, Woody* / Telegraph: *Atmospheres* / It don't make no nevermind: *Griffin, Buck* / Angel from above: *Fuller, Jerry* / Do you know: *Peck, Bill* / She's somebody's mother: *Mitchell, Woody* / In dreamland: *Ruff, Ray* / Lonesome baby blues: *Ray, David* / Caravan: *Atmospheres* / Lonesome baby blues: *Ray, David* / Rockin' rollin' stone: *Starr, Andy* / Special kind of loving: *Alexander, Don* / Lipstick and rouge: *Fuller, Jerry* / Guitar smoke: *Brinkley, J.B.* / Until you're mine: *Four Mints* / Mother Goose at the bandstand: *Fuller, Jerry* / Knee shakin': *Terry, Don* / Stutterin' Papa: *Griffin, Buck* / I do: *Strikes* / Busy body rock: *Four Mints* / Fanny Brown: *Copeland, Kenny* / My little girl: *Curtis, Don* / Where the Rio de Rosa flows: *Copeland, Ken* / Teenage love: *Fuller, Jerry* / Old man Mose: *Simpson, Bill* / Door is open: *Fuller, Jerry* / Beatle maniacs: *Ruff, Ray* / I took a liking to you: *Ruff, Ray* / Do you love me: *Fuller, Jerry* / Angel blue: *Ruff, Ray* / Blue moonbeam: *Jokers* / If you can't rock me: *Strikes* / I am a fool: *Ray, David* / Whistling rock 'n' roll: *Stubblefield, Bill* / Saccharin Sally: *Tu-Tones* / DJ fever: *Chuckalucks* / I want to go steady with you: *Copeland, Ken* / Pledge of love: *Copeland, Ken* / Blue memories: *Fuller, Jerry* / Dark eyes: *Tanner, Bob Combo* / Fickle chicken: *Atmospheres* / Music box lullaby: *Johnston, Nora* / My girlfriend's car: *Ruff, Ray* / Now I know: *McClarey, Butch* / Rendezvous: *Redd, Ramona* / Kabalo: *Atmospheres* / Someone to love me: *Copeland, Ken* / Late in the evening: *Duncan, Doodle* / Far and distant lands: *Wright, Steve* / You're getting the idea: *Copeland, Ken* / Little Mama tree top: *Four Mints* / Show me the way (to your heart): *Robinson, Margee* / I'll be your baby: *Brinkley, J.B.* / Come back to me: *Strikes* / Twist of lemon: *Wolfe Tanner, R.* / Devil's train: *Chuckalucks* / Certain smile: *Fuller, Jerry* / Jelly roll man: *Simpson, Bill* / And so it goes: *Peck, Bill* / Give me your heart: *Redd, Ramona* / Somewhere angels are smiling: *Johnston, Nora* / Pledge of love: *Ruff, Ray* / Love only me: *Copeland, Ken* / Rock 'n' hall: *McClarey, Butch* / Lonely rhapsody: *Tanner, Bob Combo* / Death row: *Duncan, Doodle* / (Don't leave me) alone: *Four Mints* / Wild wild woman: *Wright, Steve* / Beyond a shadow of a doubt: *Thompson, Virginia* / Suez: *Stubblefield, Bill* / Who am I: *Chuckalucks* / Hurt me: *Robinson, Margee* / Golden grain: *Holman, Dixon* / Locked in the arms of love: *Copeland, Ken* / Fools going home all alone: *Hart, Trella* / Why did she leave me: *Welch, Honee* / It's me girl: *Welch, Honee* / I'm gonna try (to steal her): *Welch, Honee* / Woman child: *Welch, Honee* / Angels can lie: *Welch, Honee* / It must be love: *Welch, Honee*
BCD 15950 / May '98 / Bear Family

☐ LONG JOURNEY HOME
Shenandoah: *Morrison, Van* / Main theme: *Irish Film Orchestra* / Paddy's lamentation/Ships are sailing: *Black, Mary* / Emigration theme: *Irish Film Orchestra* / Bard of Armagh/Streets of Laredo: *Gill, Vince* / Skibbereen: *O'Connor, Sinead* / Night that Larry was stretched/Jig: *Chieftains* / White potatoes: *O'Maonlai, Liam* / Famine theme: *Irish Film Orchestra* / Muldoon the solid man/Grandfathers tune: *Moloney, Mick* / An raibh tu ag an gCarraig: *Sissel* / O'Carolan's farewell to music: *Irish Film Orchestra* / Bean phaidin: *Conneff, Kevin* / O'Donnel's lament/Reel with the beryle: *Ivers, Eileen* / American theme: *Irish Film Orchestra* / Long journey home (anthem): *Costell, Elvis & Anuna*
09026689632 / 5 May '98 / RCA Victor

☐ LONG LIVE LOVE
PLSCD 234 / Jul '97 / Pulse

☐ LONG TALL SALLY (Original Rock 'n' Roll)
(We're gonna) Rock around the clock / Keep a knockin' / Personality / Be bop a lula / Johnny B Goode / At the hop / Great balls of fire / Tutti frutti / Duke of Earl / Shake, rattle and roll / Sea cruise / Stagger Lee / Whole lotta shakin' goin' on / Long tall Sally / Runaway / This ole house / Sweet little sixteen / Yakety yak / Book of love / Roll over Beethoven
CDAA 041 / Oct '92 / Tring

☐ LONG WALK, THE (The Sky Ranch Sampler)
841422 / Sep '96 / Sky Ranch

☐ LOOK OF LOVE, THE
Can't get by without you: *Real Thing* / Best thing that ever happened to me: *Knight, Gladys & The Pips* / Don't throw your love away: *Searchers* / (If paradise is) half as nice: *Amen Corner* / Always something there to remind me: *Shaw, Sandie* / First cut is the deepest: *Arnold, P.P.* / Just when I needed you most: *Vanwarmer, Randy* / Love hurts: *Nazareth* / Isn't she lovely: *Parton, David* / Way we were: *Knight, Gladys & The Pips* / Baby, now that I've found you: *Foundations* / Funny how love can be: *Ivy League* / Angel of the morning: *Arnold, P.P.* / Colour of my love: *Jefferson* / That same old feeling: *Pickettywitch* / You to me are everything: *Real Thing* / Sad sweet dreamer: *Sweet Sensation* / When you walk in the room: *Searchers*
MCCD 039 / Sep '91 / Music Club

☐ LOOK OF LOVE, THE
5351902 / Jan '96 / PolyGram TV

☐ LOOKEY DOOKEY
EFA 11569CD / Jun '93 / Crypt

☐ LOOKING FOR THE LIGHT
Up Chet's alley / Beautiful black eyes / Looking for the light / Margarine / Famous Jacques / Nightbird / You can't go home again / This one's for Chet
RIGHT 002 / 11 May '98 / Right Recordings

☐ LOOKING ON THE BRIGHT SIDE (25 'Cheer Up' Songs 1926-1941)
When you're smiling: *Armstrong, Louis* / Happy days are here again: *Ambrose & His Orchestra* / Looking on the bright side: *Fields, Gracie* / Lucky day: *Revelers & Ed Smalle* / Sunshine: *Smith, Whispering Jack* / Best things in life are free: *Hylton, Jack & His Orchestra* / My blackbirds are bluebirds now: *National Cavaliers Quartet & David Buttolph* / Spread a little happiness: *Hale, Binnie* / Singin' in the rain: *Edwards, Cliff* / Painting the clouds with sunshine: *Marvin, Johnny* / Keep your sunny side up: *Hamps, Johnny & His Kentucky Serenaders* / On the sunny side of the street: *Lewis, Ted & His Band* / Happy feet: *Whiteman, Paul & His Orchestra* / Sunny days: *Layton & Johnstone* / Smile darn ya smile: *Cotton, Billy & His Band* / Today I feel so happy: *Mackey, Percival Kit Cat Band* / Life is just a bowl of cherries: *Hylton, Jack & His Orchestra* / Clouds will soon roll by: *Carlisle, Elsie* / Letting in the sunshine: *Browne, Sam* / There's a new day coming: *Roy, Harry* / When you've got a little springtime in your heart: *Bowlly, Al* / Pennies from Heaven: *Langford, Frances & Louis Armstrong/Bing Crosby* / Things are looking up: *Astaire, Fred* / With a smile and a song: *Rich, Freddie & His Orchestra* / Look for the silver lining: *Boswell, Connee*
CDAJA 5255 / Jun '98 / Living Era

☐ LOOSE (New Sounds Of The Old West)
Tilt-a-whirl: *Bonnevilles* / Penthouse in the woods: *Scud Mountain Boys* / Brother: *Nadine* / Every day is like a birthday party: *Lullaby For The Working Class* / Saddest girl: *Red Star Belgrade* / Lester Lampshade: *Giant Sand* / Moving furniture around: *Handsome Family* / It won't hurt: *Braun, Grace* / Ballet high: *Fuck* / Mood indigo: *Dakota Suite* / Handful of stars: *Bruntnell, Peter* / Calm: *Fontaine, Richmond* / Doris days: *Leach, Tom* / All the luck in the world: *Casal, Neal* / Dreams: *Lincoln '65* / Must've been high: *Supersuckers* / Slag: *Calexico* / Petrified florist: *Lambchop* / All the labour: *Gourds* / Thelma: *Strohm, John P.*
VJCD 004 / 9 Feb '98 / Vinyl Junkie

☐ LORD OF THE DANCE
5337572 / Oct '96 / PolyGram TV

☐ LORD OF THE DANCE
Lord of the dance / Lament of the three Marys / When a man is in love / Fiollaigean / Larry the beer drinker / Merry blacksmith / Our wedding / Abbey reel / Cockles and mussels / Mike Flanagan's barn dance / Suil a run / Star of County Down / Dulman / Gary O'Connors / Swallows tail / Love at the endings / Lord of the dance
3036001242 / 15 Sep '97 / Carlton

☐ LORD OF THE DANCE/RIVERDANCE (And Other Famous Irish Music And Dances/2CD Set)
Lord of the dance / Suil a ruin / Our wedding day (she moved through the fair) / Mike Flanagan's barndance / Medley / Fiollaigean / Star of the county Down / Medley / Medley / Cadineah na d'tri muire / Medley / Medley / When a man's in love / Medley / Medley / In Dublin's fair city / Lord of the dance / Riverdance / Heart's cry / Silver spire / Medley / Galway / Medley / Laugh and half daft / Medley (10) / Medley (11) / Medley (12) / Medley (13) / Miss Murphy / Medley (14) / Corsican melody / Medley (15) / Three Mary's / Riverdance
MPV 100404 / Sep '97 / Movieplay

☐ LORDS OF OI, THE (3CD Set)
DTKBOX 77 / 23 Feb '98 / Dressed To Kill

☐ LORDS OF SVEK VOL.3, THE
SKCD 003 / 2 Feb '98 / Svek

☐ LOS AMIGOS PANAMERICANOS
Pearl harbour / La conga de moda / La conga de D'Arteaga / Cachita / Hay que saber perder / Que me importa / Maracas / Somos diferentes / Viva Mexico / Sonar / Uno dos y tres / Humphrey Bogart rhumba / Cuanto le gusta / Exirana vida / Mama ines / Rhumba jubilee / Pensando en ti / De corazon a corazon / La borrachita / Habla amor / Chiquito montuno / Fiesta en granada / Vamos al campo
HQCD 113 / Sep '98 / Harlequin

☐ LOS GRANDES BANDONEONES
EBCD 100 / 1 Jun '98 / El Bandoneon

☐ LOS MEJORES BOLEROS
BMCD 512 / 24 Apr '98 / Blue Moon

☐ LOS TIEMPOS CAMBIAN
X 55519 / Sep '95 / Aspic

☐ LOST AND FOUND (The Blue Rock Records Story/2CD Set)
5582732 / 31 Aug '98 / Mercury

☐ LOST BLUES TAPES VOL.1
Della Mae: *Hooker, John Lee* / Hound dog: *Thornton, Willie Mae* / Captain Captain: *Waters, Muddy* / I got to cut out: *Williamson, Sonny Boy* / Blues harp shuffle: *Horton, Big Walter* / Strong brain - broad mind: *Dixon, Willie* / Big leg woman: *Dixon, Willie* / You got me runnin': *Desanto, Sugar Pie* / South side jump: *Guy, Buddy* / If I get lucky: *Lenoir, J.B.* / Got a letter this morning: *McDowell, 'Mississippi' Fred* / Sail on: *Sykes, Roosevelt* / Memphis boogie: *Memphis Slim* / Your best friend's gone: *Estes, John & Hammie Nixon* / Farewell baby: *Ross, Dr. Isiah* / Della Mae: *Hooker, John Lee*
92042 / Apr '94 / Act

☐ LOST GROOVES, THE
Hold on I'm comin': *Wilson, Reuben* / It's your thing: *Green, Grant* / Scorpion: *Donaldson, Lou* / Hey western union man: *Green, Grant* / Brother soul: *Donaldson, Lou* / Village lee: *Patton, 'Big' John* / Spooky: *Turrentine, Stanley* / Dancin' in a easy groove: *Smith, Lonnie Liston* / You want me to stop loving you: *Turrentine, Stanley*
CDP 8318832 / Apr '95 / Blue Note

☐ LOST HITS
SKYDOG 622312 / May '97 / Skydog

☐ LOST HITS AND GOLDEN MEMORIES VOL.1
Let's face the music and dance: *Cole, Nat 'King'* / Hit 'n' miss: *Barry, John Seven* / Surfin' USA: *Beach Boys* / Mockinbird: *Foxx, Inez* / Locomotion: *Little Eva* / Lovers' concerto: *Toys* / My heart's symphony: *Lewis, Gary & The Playboys* / Snoopy VS the Red Baron: *Royal Guardsmen* / Footsee: *Wigan's Chosen Few* / But it's alright: *Jackson, J.J.* / Hi ho silver lining: *Beck, Jeff* / Whole lotta love: *CCS* / Here comes that rainy day feeling again: *Fortunes* / Too much foolin' around: *Tams* / Too late to turn back now: *Cornelius Brothers & Sister Rose* / This will be: *Cole, Natalie* / (Take me for) A night in New York: *Bones, Elbow & Racketeers* / Right back from where we started from: *Nightingale, Maxine* / You sexy thing: *Hot Chocolate* / It only takes a minute: *Tavares* / Taste of honey: *Boogie Oogie Oogie* / On the beat: *BB & Q Band* / Loverboy: *Chairmen Of The Board* / Point of view: *Matumbi* / Rock me tonight (for old time's sake): *Jackson, Freddie*
KRLCD 002 / May '96 / KRL

☐ LOST IN SPACE DIVAZ 'N' BASS
CERBAD 8 / 22 Jun '98 / Lacerba

☐ LOST IN SPACE DRUM 'N' BASS 2000 (2CD Set)
CERBAD 7 / 13 Apr '98 / Lacerba

☐ LOST IN SPACE DRUM 'N' BASS VOL.1 (A Smarter Than Average Jungle Collection)
CERBAD 1 / Jul '96 / Lacerba

☐ LOST IN SPACE DRUM 'N' BASS VOL.2 (2CD Set)
CERBAD 2 / Jan '97 / Lacerba

☐ LOST IN SPACE DRUM 'N' BASS VOL.3 (2CD Set)
CERBAD 4 / Jun '97 / Lacerba

☐ LOST MUSIC OF CELTARABIA, THE
GRIN 942CD / Jul '95 / Grinnigogs

☐ LOST SOUL OF DETROIT, THE VOL.1
She's not everybody's girl: *Metros* / That's bad: *Harris, Lafayette Jr.* / I hold the key: *Sanders, Nelson* / I'm leaving baby: *White, Willie* / Leave me alone: *White, Willie* / I gotta know: *Hutcher, Willie* / Standing on the sideline: *Williams, Lloyd* / Can't live without you: *Milner, Reggie* / In the middle: *Reynolds, L.J.* / Stop lost over your past: *Reynolds, L.J.* / I don't mess around: *Reynolds, Jeannie* / People make the world: *Reynolds, Jeannie* / I found the right girl: *Swingers* / Alone in the chapel: *Doe & Joe* / Do you want a love: *Milner, Reggie* / She's alright: *Milner, Reggie* / Somebody help me: *Milner, Reggie* / Uphill climb to the bottom: *Lemons, George* / Nothing can seperate our love: *Turner, Sammy*
GSCD 021 / Aug '93 / Goldmine

☐ LOST TREASURES CONCERTO FOR SONIC CIRCLES (Mixed By DJ Tiesto)
NLGUARD 052 / Jun '97 / Guardian Angel

☐ LOUD, PROUD & PUNK
PLSCD 105 / May '96 / Pulse

☐ LOUDSPEAKER
LU 95052 / 20 Jul '98 / Lunadisc

☐ LOUISIANA BLUES
Blues won't let me take my rest: *Gray, Henry* / Lucky, lucky man: *Gray, Henry* / If I ever get back home: *Kelley, Arthur 'Guitar'* / Talk to me baby: *Kelley, Arthur 'Guitar'* / I got a funny feeling: *Kelley, Arthur 'Guitar'* / I love you baby: *Smith, Moses* / Run around blues: *Hogan, Silas* / Rats and roaches in my kitchen: *Hogan, Silas* / Cold chills: *Gray, Henry* / Hear that rumbling: *Edwards, Clarence* / How many more years: *Edwards, Clarence* / On the dark road crying: *Smith, Moses*
ARHCD 9004 / Sep '97 / Arhoolie

☐ LOUISIANA CAJUN MUSIC SPECIAL VOL.1 (Swallow Records)
Hee haw breakdown: *Cormier, Nolan & the LA Aces* / Pine grove blues: *Abshire, Nathan* / Triangle club special: *Prejean, Leeman* / Louisiana aces special: *Badeaux* / Lacassine special: *Balfa Brothers* / Cypress inn special: *Cormier, Nolan & the LA Aces* / Zydeci Cha Cha: *Mouton* / Cankton two step: *Prejan* / Cajun ramblers special: *Derouen, Wallace* / Eunice two step: *Barzas, Maurice* / Hippy ti yo: *Bonsall, Joe* / I am so lonely: *Herbert, Adam* / Choupique two step: *Abshire, Nathan* / Waltz of regret: *Mate, Doris* / Two steps de vieux temps: *Rambling Aces*
CDCH 914 / Jan '92 / Ace

☐ LOUISIANA CAJUN MUSIC SPECIAL VOL.2 (Swallow Records)
Choupique two step: *Abshire, Nathan* / Cypress inn special: *Cormier, Lionel* / Chinaball blues: *Pitre, Austin* / Cameron two step: *Barro* / Calcasieu rambler's special: *Broussard, August* / Waltz of regret: *Matte, Doris* / Little cajun boy: *Leger, Bobby* / Zydeco cha cha: *Mouzas & Lignos* / Mamou hot step: *Mamou Playboys* / Every night when it's dark: *Hebert, Adam* / La valse de grand bois: *Balfa Brothers* / Cankton two step: *Prejean, Leeman* / She didn't know I was married: *Menard, D.L.* / Family waltz: *Menard, Phil & Don Guillory* / Two steps de vieux temps: *Rambling Aces* / One step de duson: *Cormier, Louis*
CDCH 368 / Mar '92 / Ace

☐ LOUISIANA CHANKY-CHANK
ZNCD 1002 / Oct '95 / Zane

☐ LOUISIANA LIVE FROM MOUNTAIN STAGE
La danse de la vie: *Beausoleil* / Ayiti: *Neville Brothers* / Louisiana two step: *Chenier, Clifton & His Red Hot Louisiana Band* / Long hard journey home: *Radiators* / Such a night: *Dr. John* / Evegeline special: *Sonnier, Jo El* / Mother in law: *Toussaint, Allen* / Lipstick traces: *Toussaint, Allen* / Chere Duloone: *Rapone, Al* / La toussaint: *Riley, Steve & Mamou Playboys* / Choupik two step: *Queen Ida & The Bon Temps Zydeco Band* / Johnny can't dance: *Toups, Wayne & ZydeCajun* / Jeleron: *Buck Wheat Zydeco* / Don't wanna cry no more: *Simien, Terrance*
BPM 306CD / May '97 / Blue Plate

☐ LOUISIANA ROCKERS
Cindy Lou: *Terry, Gene* / Come along with me: *Perrywell, Charles* / Yankee danky doodle: *Wilson, Jimmy* / Baby you been to school: *Page, Charles* / Bye bye baby: *Gerdsen, Ray & the Yellow Jackets* / Catch that train: *Anderson, Elton* / Chickee town rock: *Yellow Jackets* / Clemae: *Morris, Jerry* / I keep cryin': *Cookie* / Why did you leave me: *Lowery, Frankie* / Wiggle rock: *Richards, Jay* / I love you: *Anderson, Elton* / Orelia: *Jackson, Ivory Lee* / Flim flam: *Prevost, Lionel* / No mail today: *Terry, Gene* / Emmagene: *Stevens, Duke* / Slop and stroll jolie blonde: *Dean, Gabe* / Fattie Hattie: *Gerdsen, Ray & the Yellow Jackets* / Do you take me for a fool: *Hillier, Chuck* / Silly dilly: *Nelson, Jay* / Sweet potato mash (Part 1): *Parker, Bill Showboat Band* / Linda Lou: *Little Eddie* / Devil made me say that: *James, Danny* / Muscadine mule: *Ferrier, Al*
CDCHD 491 / Mar '94 / Ace

☐ LOUISIANA ROOTS (The Jay Miller R&B Legacy)
Baby baby come to papa: *King Karl* / If I had my life to live over: *Monroe, Vince* / Cool calm and collected: *King Karl* / Irene: *King Karl* / So long so long: *Skinny Dynamo* / Hoo wee pretty baby: *Hudson, Joe* / Baby give me a chance: *Hudson, Joe* / Emma Lee: *Martin, Chuck* / Crazy mambo: *Ballou, Classie* / That long lost baby: *Hudson, Eddie* / She's sugar sweet: *Hudson, Eddie* / Fool that was blind: *Nelson, Jay* / Knock knock: *Fran, Carol* / Rock 'n' roll train: *Sheffield, Charles 'Mad Dog'* / Kangaroo: *Sheffield, Charles 'Mad Dog'* / Air Force US Navy: *Martin, Sonny* / You're gonna need somebody: *Sheffield, Charles 'Mad Dog'* / I would be a sinner: *Sheffield, Charles 'Mad Dog'* / Flim flam: *Torrance, Lionel* / Red sails in the sunset: *Jay, Bobby* / Popeye train: *Thomas, Tabby* / Here comes the night owl: *Allen, Marva* / How's things with you: *Mayfield, Joe* / Never let me go: *Webster, Katie*
CDCHD 682 / 23 Mar '98 / Ace

☐ LOUISIANA SATURDAY NIGHT
Louisiana man: *Kershaw, Rusty & Doug* / I cried: *Allan, Johnnie* / Mathilda: *Cookie & The Cupcakes* / My jolie blonde: *Bernard, Rod & Clifton Chenier* / She wears my ring: *Bo, Phil* / Feed the flame: *Broussard, Van* / Little cajun girl: *King, Gene* / Big boys cry: *Charles, Bobby* / Sugar bee: *Cleveland Crochet* / Jailbird: *Shurley, Bob & The Vel-Tones* / Legend in my time: *McLain, Tommy* / Diggy liggy lo: *Kershaw, Rusty & Doug* / You had your chance: *White, Margo* / You ain't nothing but fine: *Rockin' Sidney* / Big blue diamonds: *West, Clint* / Rubber dolly: *Allan, Johnnie* / There goes that train: *Martin, Lee* / Let's do the cajun twist: *Randy & The Rockets* / Crazy baby:

Rogers, Buck / Can't stand to see you go: Allen, Dave / Whole lotta shakin' goin' on: Thomas, Prentice / I'm not a fool anymore: Broussard, Van / Back door: Rufus / Whiskey heaven: Ford, Frankie / Seven letters: Storm, Warren / I love my Saturday night: Stutes, Herbie

CDCHD 490 / Oct '93 / Ace

☐ LOUISIANA SCRAPBOOK

Mardi gras in New Orleans: Dirty Dozen Brass Band / New rules: Thomas, Irma / She said the same things to me: Adams, Johnny / We don't see eye to eye: Adams, Johnny / Wondering: Walker, Philip / Song for Renee: Brown, Clarence 'Gatemouth' / It's you I love: Beausoleil / Louisiana blues: Sonnier, Jo El / Bachelor's life: Menard, D.L. & Louisiana Aces / Don't you know I love you: Ball, Marcia / Think it over one more time: Buckwheat Zydeco / Steppin' up in class: Lonesome Sundown & Phillip Walker / No relations: Tyler, Alvin 'Red' / One for the highway: Booker, James / You got me worried: Washington, Walter 'Wolfman' / Gonna cry till my tears run dry: Thomas, Irma / Flintstones meets the president: Dirty Dozen Brass Band / When the saints go marching in: Washington, Isidore 'Tuts'

RCD 20058 / Dec '92 / Rykodisc

☐ LOUISIANA SPICE (25 Years Of Louisiana Music)

ROUCDAN 1819 / Jun '95 / Rounder

☐ LOUNGE-A-PALOOZA

1620722 / 6 Oct '97 / Polydor

☐ LOVE (2CD Set)

5550602 / 2 Feb '98 / PolyGram TV

☐ LOVE ALBUM VOL.1, THE (2CD Set)

Don't be a stranger: Carroll, Dina / If you don't know me by now: Simply Red / Can't help falling in love: UB40 / Searching: China Black / Move closer: Nelson, Phyllis / Again: Jackson, Janet / Against all odds: Collins, Phil / Don't let the sun go down on me: Michael, George & Elton John / It must have been love: Roxette / Don't wanna lose you: Estefan, Gloria / One day I'll fly away: Crawford, Randy / Sweet love: Baker, Anita / Never too much: Vandross, Luther / Piece of my heart: Franklin, Erma / Come in out of the rain: Moten, Wendy / When you tell me that you love me: Ross, Diana / Save the best for last: Williams, Vanessa / Zoom: Fat Larry's Band / Heartbreaker: Warwick, Dionne / Million love songs: Take That / If you leave me now: Chicago / I want to know what love is: Foreigner / I'll stand by you: Pretenders / Why: Lennox, Annie / Crazy: Cline, Patsy / Up where we belong: Cocker, Joe & Jennifer Warnes / Slave to love: Ferry, Bryan / Circle in the sand: Carlisle, Belinda / Rush rush: Abdul, Paula / I'd do anything for love (but I won't do that): Meat Loaf / Good heart: Sharkey, Feargal / (I just) died in your arms: Cutting Crew / Who's that girl: Eurythmics / You're all that matters to me: Stigers, Curtis / Someday (I'm coming back): Stansfield, Lisa / Just another day: Secada, Jon / Don't turn around: Aswad / All that she wants: Ace Of Base / Compliments on your kiss: Red Dragon

VTDCD 38 / Nov '94 / Virgin

☐ LOVE ALBUM VOL.2, THE (2CD Set)

Goodnight girl: Wet Wet Wet / One more night: Collins, Phil / I found someone: Cher / Let's stay together: Turner, Tina / All around the world: Stansfield, Lisa / Ain't no man: Carroll, Dina / I knew you were waiting (for me): Franklin, Aretha & George Michael / Sexual healing: Gaye, Marvin / Endless love: Ross, Diana & Lionel Richie / Unchained melody: Righteous Brothers / When a man loves a woman: Sledge, Percy / My girl: Temptations / Little time: Beautiful South / I don't want to talk about it: Everything But The Girl / Hazard: Marx, Richard / Show me heaven: McKee, Maria / Eternal flame: Bangles / Without you: Nilsson, Harry / Walk on by: Warwick, Dionne / Get here: Adams, Oleta / Power of love: Rush, Jennifer / You don't have to say you love me: Springfield, Dusty / Cry me a river: Welch, Denise / Stand by me: King, Ben E. / When I fall in love: Cole, Nat 'King' / China girl: Bowie, David / It must be love: Madness / Every time you go away: Young, Paul / Damn I wish I was your lover: Hawkins, Sophie B. / Independant love song: Scarlet / China in your hand: T'Pau / I wonder why: Stigers, Curtis / Pray: Take That / Love me for a reason: Boyzone / Crazy for you: Let Loose / Love don't live here anymore: Nail, Jimmy / Jealous guy: Roxy Music / True: Spandau Ballet

VTDCD 69 / Nov '95 / Virgin

☐ LOVE ALBUM VOL.3, THE (2CD Set)

Greatest love of all: Benson, George / You've lost that lovin' feelin': Righteous Brothers / What's love got to do with it: Righteous Brothers / If I could turn back time: Cher / Breakfast at Tiffany's: Deep Blue Something / Hard to say I'm sorry: Chicago / Groovy kind of love: Collins, Phil / Waiting for a girl like you: Foreigner / Living years: Mike & The Mechanics / Missing you: Waite, John / Nothing compares 2 U: O'Connor, Sinead / Angel: Franklin, Aretha / Help me make it through the night: Knight, Gladys & The Pips / Still: Commodores / Tonight I celebrate my love: Flack, Roberta & Peabo Bryson / All the love in the world: Warwick, Dionne / Your song: John, Elton / Make it with you: Bread / It's all coming back to me now: Pandora's Box / Say you'll be there: Spice Girls / Coming home now: Boyzone / I am blessed: Eternal / Babe: Take That / Dreams: Gabrielle / Ocean Drive: Lighthouse Family / Kiss from a rose: Seal / That look in your eye: Campbell, Ali / No more I love you's: Lennox, Annie / Oh pretty woman: Orbison, Roy / Heaven is a place on Earth: Carlisle, Belinda / Easy lover: Collins, Phil & Phillip Bailey / I just want to make love to you: James, Etta / Try a little tenderness: Commitments / Mysterious girl: Andre, Peter / What becomes of the brokenhearted: Ruffin, Jimmy / Unchained melody: Robson & Jerome / Can't stay away from you: Estefan, Gloria / Dance away: Roxy Music / I'd lie for you (and that's the truth): Meat Loaf

VTDCD 104 / Nov '96 / Virgin

☐ LOVE ALBUM VOL.4, THE (2CD Set)

Somebody to love: Queen / Simply the best: Turner, Tina / Two hearts: Collins, Phil / Over my shoulder: Mike & The Mechanics / Lifted: Lighthouse Family / Sacrifice: John, Elton / If you ever: East 17 & Gabrielle / I can't make you love me: Michael, George / I only have eyes for you: Garfunkel, Art / Air that I breathe: Hollies / Words: Boyzone / All by myself: Carmen, Eric / Follow you follow me: Genesis / Is this love: Whitesnake / Alone: Heart / More than this: Roxy Music / Baby I'm a want you: Bread / When you're in love with a beautiful woman: Dr. Hook / Saturday night at the movies: Drifters / Why do fools fall in love: Ross, Diana / Love is all around: Wet Wet Wet / Don't speak: No Doubt / 2 becomes 1: Spice Girls / As long as you love me: Backstreet Boys / Day we find love: 911 / I wanna be the only one: Eternal & Bebe Winans / If you love me: Eternal & Bebe Winans / Give me a little more time: Gabrielle / You might need somebody: Crawford, Randy / Sexual healing: Gaye, Marvin / Never too much: Vandross, Luther / I say a little prayer: Franklin, Aretha / Wherever I lay my hat: Young, Paul / Suddenly: Ocean, Billy / Anything for you: Estefan, Gloria / Wonderful tonight: Damage / Everything: Blige, Mary J. / Will you still love me tomorrow: Shirelles / Moon river: Williams, Danny

VTDCD 156 / 3 Nov '97 / Virgin

☐ LOVE ALBUM, THE

DSPCD 114 / Feb '94 / Disky

☐ LOVE AND DEVOTION

How deep is your love: Take That / Ocean drive: Lighthouse Family / No more I love you's: Lennox, Annie / Love is in my soul: M-People / I believe: Robson & Jerome / Forever love: Barlow, Gary / Nobody knows: Rich, Tony Project / Nothing compares 2 U: O'Connor, Sinead / She makes my day: Palmer, Robert / Love and understanding: Cher / I just want to make love to you: James, Etta / Mysterious girl: Andre, Peter & Bubbler Ranx / Light of my life: Louise / So natural: Stansfield, Lisa / You're all that matters to me: Stigers, Curtis / I will survive: Savage, Chantay / Show me heaven: McKee, Maria / Breathe again: Braxton, Toni / Don't look back in anger: Oasis

74321427282 / Nov '96 / RCA

☐ LOVE AND NAPALM

TR 15CD / Apr '93 / Trance

☐ LOVE BITES

QTVCD 022 / Apr '93 / Quality

☐ LOVE BOX (3CD Set)

Hold me thrill me kiss me: Carter, Mel / My Prayer: Platters / Sweet dreams: Gibson, Don / Four aces: Gibson, Don / Kisses sweeter than wine: Rodgers, Jimmie / Endlessly: Benton, Brook / What in the world's come over you: Scott, Jack / Halfway to paradise: Fury, Billy / Stand by me: King, Ben E. / I remember you: Ifield, Frank / Love letters: Lester, Ketty / Baby it's you: Shirelles / Little things: Berry, Dave / Baby I'm yours: Lewis, Barbara / I think of you: Merseybeats / Somewhere: Proby, P.J. / Silence is golden: Tremeloes / She wears my ring: King, Solomon / I just can't help believin': Everett, Betty & Jerry Butler / Smoke gets in your eyes: Platters / You always hurt the one you love: Henry, Clarence 'Frogman' / Spanish harlem: King, Ben E. / Then he kissed me: Crystals / Way you look tonight: Lettermen / Dedicated to the one I love: Tempo, Nino & April Stevens / Wishin' and hopin': Merseybeats / Remember walkin' in the sand: Shangri-Las / I'd love you to want me: Lobo / When a man loves a woman: Sledge, Percy / So much in love: Tymes / Just one look: Troy, Doris / Come softly to me: Fleetwoods / Half as much: Clooney, Rosemary / Concrete and clay: Unit 4+2 / Chanson D'Amour: Todd, Art & Dotty / For your precious love: Impressions / Kiddio: Benton, Brook / Elusive butterfly: Lind, Bob / Do you want to know a secret: Kramer, Billy J. / I can't stop loving you: Gibson, Don / April love: Boone, Pat / I will: Fury, Billy / This magic moment: Drifters / More than I can say: Vee, Bobby / I'm confessin': Ifield, Frank / Never my love: Association / Love is all around: Troggs / Hey there lonely girl: Holman, Eddie / Behind closed doors: Rich, Charlie / Then you can tell me goodbye: Casinos / Warm and tender love: Sledge, Percy / Goin' out of my head: Little Anthony & The Imperials / Don't let the sun catch you crying: Gerry & The Pacemakers / Since I don't have you: Skyliners / Why: Avalon, Frankie / End of the world: Skeeter Davies / Whispering: Bachelors / Groovy kind of love: Fontana, Wayne

390552 / Aug '97 / Hallmark

☐ LOVE BOX, THE (4CD Set)

PBXCD 413 / 20 Apr '98 / Pulse

☐ LOVE COLLECTION (3CD Set)

TBXCD 510 / Jan '96 / TrueTrax

☐ LOVE COLLECTION (2CD Set)

PBXCD 510 / Nov '96 / Pulse

☐ LOVE COLLECTION VOL.1, THE

Let there be love: Cole, Nat 'King' / Folks who live on the hill: Lee, Peggy / With these hands: Monro, Matt / True love ways: Peter & Gordon / Tonight: Damone, Vic / Where do you go to my lovely: Sarstedt, Peter / Rose Marie: Whitman, Slim / I've got my love to keep me warm: Martin, Dean / What now my love: Bassey, Shirley / Honey: Goldsboro, Bobby / Tears: Dodd, Ken / Let me go, lover: Murray, Ruby / Here in my heart: Martino, Al / Somewhere my love: Sammes, Mike Singers / She wears my ring: King, Solomon / Hymn a l'amour: Piaf, Edith / I pretend: O'Connor, Des / My special angel: Vaughan, Malcolm / He was beautiful: Williams, Iris / Wonder of you: Hilton, Ronnie

CDMFP 5878 / Mar '92 / Music For Pleasure

☐ LOVE COLLECTION VOL.2, THE

Let's fall in love: Cole, Nat 'King' / Autumn leaves: Cole, Nat 'King' / True love: Crosby, Bing & Grace Kelly / Softly as I leave you: Monro, Matt / And we were lovers: Monro, Matt / Something: Bassey, Shirley / Where do I begin: Bassey, Shirley / Lady: Rogers, Kenny / Don't fall in love with a dreamer: Rogers, Kenny / Cry me a river: London, Julie / Spanish eyes: Martino, Al / By the time I get to Phoenix: Campbell, Glen / Don't it make my brown eyes blue: Gayle, Crystal / Somebody loves you: Gayle, Crystal / That's amore (That's love): Martin, Dean / I've got my love to keep me warm: Martin, Dean / Till there was you: Lee, Peggy / La vie en rose: Piaf, Edith / On the street where you live: Damone, Vic / How deep is the ocean: Haymes, Dick

CDMFP 5960 / Dec '92 / Music For Pleasure

☐ LOVE COLLECTION, THE

MACCD 159 / Aug '96 / Autograph

☐ LOVE CONNEXION

DMUT 1363 / Jul '96 / Multitone

☐ LOVE CRAZY MEETS TALAWA

790152 / Nov '93 / Melodie

☐ LOVE FULL OF SOUL (20 Of The Best Soul Hits For Lovin')

With you I'm born again: Syreeta / Tracks of my tears: Contours / Teardrops: Starr, Edwin / Wishing on a star: Calvin, Billie / Special day: Gaye, Frankie / Chalk it up to experience: Thomas, Evelyn / Maybe he forgot: Brown, Miquel / Tearstains: Pennington, Barbara / Every little bit hurts: Holloway, Brenda / If this world were mine: Lawrence, Lynda / Heaven knows: Miracles / Reluctant lover: Griffin, Billy / White lace: Brown, Miquel / Baby I'm for real: Originals / Let's get it on: McNeir, Ronnie / Does your mama know about me: Taylor, Bobby & The Vancouvers / Watching the hands of time: Preston, Billy & Syreeta / Too great a price to pay: Lavette, Bettye / Yes I'm ready: Weston, Kim / Gentle lady: Eckstine, Billy

301132 / Feb '98 / Hallmark

☐ LOVE HURTS (Timeless Rock Classics)

PLSCD 199 / Apr '97 / Pulse

☐ LOVE IS

Unchained melody: Drifters / Rainy night in Georgia: Benton, Brook / What kind of fool (do you think I am): Tams / Will you love me tomorrow: Shirelles / Love letters: Lester, Ketty / Since I don't have you: Skyliners / All I could do was cry: James, Etta / To know him is to love him: Teddy Bears / Only you (and you alone): Platters / Sea of love: Phillips, Phil / I will: Winters, Ruby / You send me: Drifters / If loving you is wrong (I don't want to be right): Sledge, Percy / Don't play that song (you lied): King, Ben E. / Smoke gets in your eyes: Platters / Rhythm of the rain: Cascades / He will break your heart: Butler, Jerry / Dedicated to the one I love: Shirelles

ECD 3076 / Jan '95 / K-Tel

☐ LOVE IS A DOG FROM HELL

My part: Starmarket / Confirmation: Starmarket / Brain nerd: Leopold / Erasmia pulchella: September / Shampoo: Tone Deaf Teens / Fallen star: Cobolt / Sometimes the sun: Cobolt / Twisted: Conway / Words you said: Conway / Good ones: Faint Sound Of Shovelled Earth / Don't feed the heretic: Scared / Ghost: Bob Tilton / Tonight we follow him down: Bob Tilton / Campsite closed: 93 Million Miles From The Sun / This party sucks: 93 Million Miles From The Sun

BLUEEYES 1 / 25 Aug '97 / Birdnest

SIMBA 006 / 17 Nov '97 / Simba

☐ LOVE PARADE 1994 (2CD Set)

D 945013 / Dec '94 / Bunker/D'Vision

☐ LOVE PARADE 1997 (2CD Set)

7702007 / 8 Sep '97 / Omnisonus

☐ LOVE PEACE AND POETRY (American Psychedelic Music)

Shades of blue: Darius / Danny's song: New Tweedy Bros. / White panther: Arcesia / Ride a rainbow: Victoria / Song of a gypsy: Damon / Slave ship: Jungle / Colours: Hunger / Graveyard: Trizio 50 / Nam myo renge kyo: Music Emporium / I'll be on the inside if I can: Brain Police / Oceans of fantasy: Angelo, Michael / I need it higher: Zerfas / There was a time: Lazy Smoke / Mister man: Hickory Wind / Dark thoughts: New Dawn / Wild eyes: Sidetrax / Reflections on a warm day: Patron Saints

QDKCD 021 / Dec '97 / QDK Media

☐ LOVE PEACE AND POETRY (Latin American Psychedelic)

Trema de potato: Almendra / Someday: Lagonia / I'm so glad: Lagonia / Colours: Kaleidoscope / Tomorrow: We All Together / Cuanda llegue el ano 2000: Los Gatos / Yellow moon: Kissing spell / Virgin: Traffic Sound / Obertura: Traffic Sound / Trouble child: Lagonia / De la gente sola: Los Mach's / Oscar Wilde: Los Vidrois Queadros / Super god: Som Imaginario / People: Ladies WC / Degrees: Los Mach's / It's over: Dug Dug's

QDKCD 022 / Dec '97 / QDK Media

☐ LOVE, PEACE AND HAPPINESS (2CD Set)

DBG 53037 / Jun '95 / Double Gold

☐ LOVE POWER (Hard To Find US Hot 100 Hits Of The 60's)

I got rhythm: Happenings / I'm gonna love you too: Hullabaloo / Music to watch girls by: Crewe, Bob Generation / Walkin' my cat named dog: Tanega, Norma / Attack: Toys / Her lover: Dovale, Debbie / Her Royal Majesty: Darren, James / Big wide world: Randazzo, Teddy / When she needs good lovin': Chicago Loopers / Leader of the laundromat: Detergents / But it's alright: Jackson, J.J. / That boy John: Raindrops / Soul heaven: Dixie Drifter / Opportunity: Jewels / Love power: Sandpebbles / Happy: Blades of Grass / You better go: Martin, Derek / Countdown: Cortez, Dave 'Baby' / Double O seven: Detergents

NEMCD 669 / Jun '94 / Sequel

☐ LOVE PROGE (Love Records 1968-1979/2CD Set)

Semi-circle solitude: Blues Section / Somebody keeps calling my name: Baby Grandmothers / Luulosairas: Wigwam / Sisaltani portin loysin: Pekka Streng / Deep thinker: Tasavallan Presidentti / Ajatukset: Willberg, Pepe / Like the purpose told me: Charlies / Elavien hauta: Magyar / Black Friday: Ferris / Lounge: Tasavallan Presidentti / Virtojen kiharat: Pekka Pohjola / Crisader: Wigwam / Ode to eagle: Nimbus / Don't wake me now: Mandala / Persialaisella torilla: Session / No new games: Pembroke, Jim / Tie: Manifest / Do or die: Wigwam / Enema syringe: Hauru, Jukka / Vuorellaistuja: Tabula Rasa / Epilogi: Donna / Atlantis: Nova / Huono juttu: Janus / Summer '72: Hurmerinta, Sami / Passenger to Paramaribou: Tolonen, Jukka / Oh Marlene: Wigwam / Yksin yhdessa (osa): Gustavson, Jukka / Just my situation: Royals / Pablo: Finnforest / Savitaipaleen polkka: Sukellusvene / No why, nobody there: Limousine

LXCD 613 / May '97 / Love

☐ LOVE SONGS (4CD Set)

Will you love me tomorrow: Shirelles / Only you: Platters / Something's gotten hold of my heart: Pitney, Gene / Remember (Walkin' in the sand): Shangri-Las / Fools rush in: Benton, Brook / Save the last dance for me: Drifters / Letter full of tears: Knight, Gladys & The Pips / Ain't no sunshine: Jarreau, Al / Let it be me: Butler, Jerry & Betty Everett / Groovy kind of love: Fontana, Wayne / Build me up buttercup: Foundations / With a girl like you: Troggs / Earth angel: Penguins / I've loved and lost again: Cline, Patsy / Portrait of my love: Clark, Dee / He's so fine: Chiffons / Harbour lights: Platters / Cupid: Drifters / Feelings: Gaynor, Gloria / Hurt: Yuro, Timi / Love is all around: Troggs / One fine day: Chiffons / Everlasting love: Love Affair / Love grows (where my Rosemary goes): Edison Lighthouse / You always hurt the one you love: Yuro, Timi / Smoke gets in your eyes: Platters / Every beat of my heart: Knight, Gladys & The Pips / Chapel of love: Dixie Cups / Run to him: Vee, Bobby / Looking through the eyes of love: Pitney, Gene / Funny how love can be: Ivy League / Baby, now that I've found you: Foundations / Dedicated to the one I love: Shirelles / Under the boardwalk: Drifters / Twilight time: Platters / Can't take my eyes off you: Gaynor, Gloria / There's a kind of hush: Herman's Hermits / You were on my mind: St. Peters, Crispian / Here it comes again: Fortunes / Little things: Berry, Dave / When a man loves a woman: Sledge, Percy / For your precious love: Butler, Jerry / Band of gold: Payne, Freda / It hurts to be in love: Pitney, Gene / Love will keep us together: Sedaka, Neil / Broken promises: Shannon, Del / More I see you: Platters / Gentle on my mind: Campbell, Glen / Rose garden: Anderson, Lynn / This magic moment: Drifters / Guess who: Knight, Gladys & The Pips / It's just a matter of time: Benton, Brook / Feel the need in me: Detroit Emeralds / She even woke me up to say goodbye: Rogers, Kenny / Walkin' after midnight: Cline, Patsy / My heart cries out for you: Mitchell, Guy / Moonlight in Vermont: Fitzgerald, Ella / Night and day: Holiday, Billie / How high the moon: Gaynor, Gloria / Love for sale: Benson, George / Make it easy on yourself: Butler, Jerry / So many ways: Benton, Brook / Warm and tender love: Sledge, Percy / Breaking up is hard to do: Sedaka, Neil / Crying: Campbell, Glen / For the good times: Rogers, Kenny / Godnight my love: Knight, Gladys & The Pips / Stand by me: Drifters / Just out of reach: Cline, Patsy / If you ever should leave me: Fitzgerald, Ella / More than you know: Holiday, Billie / I love how you love me: Yuro, Timi / There will never be another you: Benson, George / Give him a great big kiss: Shangri-Las / To know him is to love him: Shirelles / Let's pretend: Nelson, Willie / Just one smile: Pitney, Gene / Sweet dreams: Young, Faron / It had to be you: Travolta, John

QUAD 018 / Nov '96 / Tring

☐ LOVE SONGS

I'm confessin' that I love you: Horne, Lena / Night and day: Dorsey, Tommy & Frank Sinatra / Heart and soul: Ward, Helen & Larry Clinton / Nearness of you: Miller, Glenn & Ray Eberle / I got ot bad and that ain't good: Anderson, Ivie & Duke Ellington / My one and only love: Ellington, Duke / I've got a crush on you: Laine, Cleo / There will never be another you: Hawkins, Coleman / Stardust: Carmichael, Hoagy / Embraceable you: Vaughan, Sarah & Dizzy Gillespie / Skylark: Eckstine, Billy & Earl Hines / Any old time: Holiday, Billie & Artie Shaw Orchestra / Very thought of you: Carter, Benny & Roy Felton / You're my thrill: Horne, Lena & Charlie Barnet / Song is you: Sinatra, Frank & Tommy Dorsey / Goodnight my love: Fitzgerald, Ella & Benny Goodman Orchestra

74321584802 / Jun '98 / RCA Victor

☐ LOVE SONGS COLLECTION VOL.1

Will you love me tomorrow / Only you / Something's gotten hold of my heart / Remember (walkin' in the sand) / Fools rush in / Save the last dance for me / Letter full of tears / Ain't no sunshine / Let it be me / Groovy kind of love / Build me up buttercup / With a girl like you / Earth angel / I've loved and lost again / Portrait of my love / He's so fine / Harbour lights / Cupid / Feelings / Hurt

QED 004 / Nov '96 / Tring

☐ LOVE SONGS COLLECTION VOL.2

Love is all around / One fine day / Everlasting love / Love grows (where my Rosemary goes) / You always hurt the one you love / Smoke gets in your eyes / Every beat of my heart / Chapel of love / Run to him / Looking through the eyes of love / Funny how love can be / Baby, now that I've found you / Dedicated to the one I love / Under the boardwalk / Twilight time / Can't take my eyes off you / There's a kind of hush / You were on my mind / Here it comes again / Little things

QED 042 / Nov '96 / Tring

☐ LOVE SONGS OF DETROIT (3CD Set)

Ain't no mountain high enough: Payne, Sherrie / Baby I'm for real: Originals / Yes I'm ready: Weston, Kim / If this world were mine: Lawrence, Lynda / Reach for the sky: Jacas, Jake / My heart won't say no: Demps, Louvain / Baby baby: Lewis Sisters / London bridge is falling down: Cameron, G.C. / Slow motion: Barnes, J.J. / Does your Mama know about me: Taylor, Bobby & The Vancouvers / If I were your woman: Royster, Vermettya / It's impossible: Eckstine, Billy / Easy to love: Griner, Linda / Two out of three: Stubbs, Joe / You're love is wonderful: Littles, Hattie / Take me in your arms and love me: Nero, Frances / Give me your love: Royster, Vermettya / Heaven knows: Miracles / You'll be sorry: Fantastic Four / Come back to me: Cameron, G.C. / Special day: Gaye, Frankie / Soul searching: Randolph, Barbara / Cloudy day: Taylor, Bobby & The Vancouvers / Reluctant lover: Griffin, Billy / Hold out my hand: Jacas, Jake / Ain't understanding mellow: Harris, Joey / Sell me soul: Littles, Hattie / Wholeheartedly: McNeir, Ronnie / Smiling faces sometimes: Vee / Teardrops: Starr, Edwin / Keeping my mind on love: Wells, Mary / Ask the lonely: Eckstine, Billy / Watching the hands of time: Preston, Billy & Syreeta / Tracks of my tears: Contours / Every little bit hurts: Holloway, Brenda / Time is on my side: Littles, Hattie / Gentle lady: Eckstine, Billy / Free: Greene, Susaye / Cry to me: Crawford, Carolyn / Love still lives in my heart: Originals / Keep this thought in mind: Bristol, Johnny / You haven't seen my love: Taylor, Bobby & The Vancouvers / With you I'm born again: Syreeta / For old times sake: Jacas, Jake / Too great a price to pay: Lavette, Bettye / Just my imagination: Cameron, G.C. / Let's get it on: McNeir, Ronnie / OOO Baby baby: Robinson, Claudette / Wishing on a

LOVE SONGS OF DETROIT COMPILATIONS R.E.D. CD CATALOGUE

star: Calvin, Billie / Save me I'm all alone: Dixon, Hank / Your precious love: Parks, Fino & Frances Nero / We're incredible: McNeir, Ronnie / Written in stone: Gaye, Frankie / No more heartaches: Bristol, Johnny
3035990065 / Jan '96 / Motor City

☐ **LOVE SONGS OF THE 60'S**
God only knows: Beach Boys / Moon river: Williams, Danny / I'll never fall in love again: Gentry, Bobbie / I remember you: Ifield, Frank / To know you is to love you: Peter & Gordon / If you gotta go, go now: Manfred Mann / She wears my ring: King, Solomon / I could easily fall: Richard, Cliff / Step inside love: Black, Cilla / Softly as I leave you: Monro, Matt / When the girl in your arms (is the girl in your heart): Richard, Cliff / Here I go again: Hollies / Starry eyed: Holiday, Michael / Portrait of my love: Monro, Matt / Love's just a broken heart: Black, Cilla / All I have to do is dream: Campbell, Glen & Bobbie Gentry / Michelle: David & Jonathan / Up on the roof: Lynch, Kenny / As long as he needs me / There's a kind of hush: Herman's Hermits
CDMFP 6041 / Jan '97 / Music For Pleasure

☐ **LOVE SONGS OF THE 70'S**
If I had words: Fitzgerald, Scott & Yvonne Keeley / Loving you: Riperton, Minnie / When you're in love with a beautiful woman: Dr. Hook / And I love you so: McLean, Don / I don't wanna lose you: Kandidate / Love hit me: Nightingale, Maxine / More than a woman: Tavares / Storm in a teacup: Fortunes / I can't tell the bottom from the top: Hollies / Talking in your sleep: Gayle, Crystal / You'll always be a friend: Hot Chocolate / Softly whispering I love you: Congregation / Honey come back: Campbell, Glen / Lay your love on me: Racey / What I've got in mind: Spears, Billie Jo / Let me be the one: Shadows / I honestly love you: Newton-John, Olivia / Summer (the first time): Goldsboro, Bobby / Oh babe what would you say: Smith, Hurricane / Lucille: Rogers, Kenny
CDMFP 5894 / Jan '97 / Music For Pleasure

☐ **LOVE SONGS OF THE 80'S**
Missing you: Waite, John / Crying: McLean, Don / Better love next time: Dr. Hook / Unchain my heart: Cocker, Joe / Round and round: Graham, Jaki / It started with a kiss: Hot Chocolate / Classic: Gurvitz, Adrian / Lady: Rogers, Kenny / Chequered love: Wilde, Kim / Love changes everything: Climie Fisher / Tonight I celebrate my love: Bryson, Peabo & Roberta Flack / Rock me tonight: Jackson, Freddie / Let's go all the way: Sly Fox / Save a prayer: Duran Duran
CDMFP 5927 / Jan '97 / Music For Pleasure

☐ **LOVE SONGS OF VIDYAPATI (Traditional Indian Songs)**
C 580063CD / Apr '95 / Ocora

☐ **LOVE SONGS WITH SOUL**
You bring out the best in me: Bell-Armstrong, Vanessa / Tide is turning: Jackson, Millie / Woman: Jones, Glenn / At this moment: Jones, Glenn / More than friends: Butler, Jonathan / Stay with me tonight: Smith, Richard Jon / Penny lover: Kissoon, Katie / When only a friend will do: Davis, Mike / An imitation of love: Jackson, Millie / Move closer: Jones, Tom / Living in the limelight: Jones, Glenn / In the night: Smith, Richard Jon
EMPRCD 551 / Nov '94 / Emporio

☐ **LOVE THEMES OF THE PAN PIPES (18 Greatest Hits)**
Tears in Heaven / Another day in paradise / Lady in red / Three times a lady / With you I'm born again / Careless whisper / Just the way you are / I don't know much / Fool (If you think it's over) / Wind beneath my wings / Tonight I celebrate my love / Power of love / (Everything I do) I do it for you / If you don't know me by now / Wonderful tonight / I'm not in love / Didn't we almost have it all / Against all odds
PLATCD 156 / Mar '96 / Platinum

☐ **LOVE TO LOVE YOU**
Daniel: John, Elton / Baby makes her blue jeans talk: Dr. Hook / Day by day: Shakatak / Fresh: Kool & The Gang / Nothing's gonna change my love for you: Medeiros, Glenn / Forever and ever: Roussos, Demis / Love me: Elliman, Yvonne / Reason to believe: Stewart, Rod / Soul and inspiration: Walker Brothers / I'm not in love: 10cc / Sun ain't gonna shine anymore: Walker Brothers / Let's put it all together: Stylistics / Don't stop the music: Yarbrough & Peoples / Tahiti: Essex, David
5501442 / Jan '94 / Spectrum

☐ **LOVE TRAIN (The Ultimate Sound Of Philadelphia - 2CD Set)**
Love train: O'Jays / Love I lost: Melvin, Harold & The Bluenotes / You'll never find another love like mine: Rawls, Lou / Me and Mrs. Jones: Paul, Billy / When will I see you again: Three Degrees / Wake up everybody: Melvin, Harold & The Bluenotes / I'll always love my Mama: Intruders / TSOP: MFSB / Backstabbers: O'Jays / Bad luck: Melvin, Harold & The Bluenotes / Take good care of yourself: Three Degrees / Win place or show: Intruders / Love music: O'Jays / Let's make a baby: Paul, Billy / Do it anyway you wanna: People's Choice / Love is the message: MFSB / I'm not in love: Sharp, Dee Dee / Don't let love get you down: Bell, Archie & The Drells / Now that we found love: O'Jays / Sexy: MFSB / Let 'em in: Paul, Billy / Darlin' darlin' baby: O'Jays / Don't leave me this way: Melvin, Harold & The Bluenotes / Year of decision: Three Degrees / Ain't no stoppin' us now: McFadden & Whitehead / If you don't know me by now: Melvin, Harold & The Bluenotes / Show you the way to go: Jacksons / Brandy: O'Jays / Jam jam jam: People's Choice / Lady love: Rawls, Lou / Was that all it was: Carne, Jean / Let's clean up the ghetto: Philadelphia International All Stars / Used ta be my girl: O'Jays / Whole town's laughing at me: Pendergrass, Teddy / Soul City walk: Bell, Archie & The Drells / Put our heads together: O'Jays / Nights over Egypt: Jones Girls / Close the door: Pendergrass, Teddy / Let's groove: Bell, Archie & The Drells / Sweetest pain: Wensel, Dexter / Do you get enough love: Jones, Shirley / Strut your funky stuff: Frantique / Love TKO: Pendergrass, Teddy / Bring the family back: Paul, Billy / If you only knew: Labelle, Patti
MOODCD 56 / 6 Apr '98 / Sony TV

☐ **LOVER'S DELIGHT**
Don't let me be lonely: Kofi / I'll never fall in love: Klearview Harmonix / Children of the night: Cross, Sandra / Give you love: Jones, Vivian / I'm the one who loves you: Hartley, Trevor / Can't hold on: McLean, John / Even though you're gone: Kemi / Hottest shot: Kingpin / Last night: Tajah, Paulette / Love in your heart: Shaloma
ARICD 090 / Oct '93 / Ariwa Sounds

☐ **LOVERS FASHION VOL.1**
FADCD 033 / Mar '96 / Fashion

☐ **LOVERS FASHION VOL.2**
FADCD 034 / Oct '96 / Fashion

☐ **LOVERS FOR LOVERS VOL.1**
WBRCD 901 / Jan '91 / Business

☐ **LOVERS FOR LOVERS VOL.10**
I miss you: Heptones / Just my imagination: Mighty Diamonds / Blackbirds singing: Paragons / Chuck E's in love: Walker, Paulette / Make up to break up: Heptones / Dance the reggae: Harriott, Derrick / Paradise: Gayle, Erica / Last chance: Kelly, Pat / Don't draw the line: Gayle, Erica / Golden touch / All that glitters
WBRCD 910 / Dec '95 / Business

☐ **LOVERS FOR LOVERS VOL.2**
WBRCD 902 / Jan '91 / Business

☐ **LOVERS FOR LOVERS VOL.3**
WBRCD 903 / Jan '91 / Business

☐ **LOVERS FOR LOVERS VOL.4**
WBRCD 904 / Jan '92 / Business

☐ **LOVERS FOR LOVERS VOL.5**
WBRCD 905 / Jan '92 / Business

☐ **LOVERS FOR LOVERS VOL.5 & 6**
WBRCD 905/6 / Oct '95 / Business

☐ **LOVERS FOR LOVERS VOL.6**
WBRCD 906 / Aug '92 / Business

☐ **LOVERS FOR LOVERS VOL.7**
WBRCD 907 / Jan '93 / Business

☐ **LOVERS FOR LOVERS VOL.8**
WBRCD 908 / Dec '93 / Business

☐ **LOVERS FOR LOVERS VOL.9**
WBRCD 909 / Dec '94 / Business

☐ **LOVERS FOREVER**
VPCD 2051 / Jul '96 / VP

☐ **LOVERS FOREVER VOL.3**
JFCD 0004 / Jun '94 / Joe Frazier

☐ **LOVERS LEAP**
ARICD 119 / Oct '96 / Ariwa Sounds

☐ **LOVERS MOODS VOL.2**
VPCD 1447 / Nov '95 / VP

☐ **LOVERS MOODS VOL.3**
VPCD 1458 / Mar '96 / VP

☐ **LOVERS ROCK SERIOUS SELECTIONS VOL.1**
Key to the world: Thomas, Ruddy / Baby my love: Callender, Fil / After tonight: Matumbi / Natty dread a weh she want: Andy, Horace & Tapper / Wide awake in dreams: Biggs, Barry / Let me be your angel: Morgan, Portia / Ting a ling: Tamlins / Betcha by Golly Wow: Dunkley, Errol / Paradise: Adebambo, Jean / Lady of magic: Maloney, Bunny / Walk on by: Motion / Caught you in a lie: Marks, Louisa
CDREG 1 / Feb '95 / Rewind Selecta

☐ **LOVERS ROCK SERIOUS SELECTIONS VOL.2**
CDREG 4 / Jan '96 / Rewind Selecta

☐ **LOVERS ROCK SERIOUS SELECTIONS VOL.3**
CDREG 7 / Mar '97 / Rewind Selecta

☐ **LOVE'S OLD SWEET SONG**
Myself when young: Allin, Norman / Homing: D'Alvarez, Marguerite / Deep river: Anderson, Marian / Fairytales of Ireland: Austral, Florence / Ciribiribin: Bori, Lucrezia / She wandered down the mountainside: Buckman, Rosina / Fairy went a-marketing: Butt, Clara / For you alone: Caruso, Enrico / Blind ploughman: Chaliapin, Feodor / Ich liebe dich, my dear: Crabbe, Armand / Song of songs: Crooks, Richard / Green hills o' Somerset: Dawson, Peter / Love's old sweet song: Galli-Curci, Amelita / I love you truly: Giannini, Dusolina / World is waiting for the sunrise: Hackett, Charles / Danny boy: Labette, Dora / Bird songs at Eventide: McCormack, John / By the waters of Minnetonka: Melba, Nellie / By the bend of the river: Moore, Grace / Last rose of Summer: Patti, Adelina / Love sends a little gift of roses: Piccaver, Alfred / Perfect day: Ponsella, Rosa / Kashmiri song: Tauber, Richard / I know of two bright eyes: Widdop, Walter / Leanin': Williams, Harold
CDAJA 5130 / May '94 / Living Era

☐ **LOVIN' YOU**
MACCD 129 / Aug '96 / Autograph

☐ **LOVING TIME, THE**
Land of love: Brazil, Noel / Farewell to the bad times: Brazil, Noel / To Ramona: Lohan, Sinead / You're in my love: Lohan, Sinead / Deep in your heart: Brady, Paul / Helpless heart: Brady, Paul / All the lies that you told me: Black, Frances / Send him a letter: Black, Frances / Captured: Kennedy, Brian / Forgiveness: Kennedy, Brian / Summer sent you: Black, Mary / Loving time: Black, Mary / Reach out (I'll be there): Goss, Kieran / Wonderful thing: Dowdall, Leslie
TORCD 085 / Jun '97 / Dara
BLX 10034CD / May '97 / Blix Street

☐ **LOVING YOU (4CD Set)**
MBSCD 428 / Nov '93 / Castle

☐ **LOVING YOU**
Do you really want to hurt me: Culture Club / Home on Monday: Little River Band / Baker street: Rafferty, Gerry / When I need you: Sayer, Leo / Spanish stroll: Mink Deville / On the border: Stewart, Al / True: Spandau Ballet / Air that I breathe: Hollies / Winter in America: Ashdown, Doug / Where do you go to my lovely: Sarstedt, Peter / Love hurts: Nazareth / Kids in America: Wilde, Kim / Love is forever: Ocean, Billy / Unforgettable: Rawls, Lou
DC 878542 / Aug '97 / Disky

☐ **LOW BLOWS (An Anthology Of Chicago Harmonica Blues)**
R 2610 / Feb '97 / Rooster

☐ **LUCKY HOUSE (2CD Set)**
SFT 200232 / Oct '96 / Shift

☐ **LULLABIES (A Songbook Companion)**
All through the night / All the pretty little horses / All night all day / Armenian lullaby / Baby's bed's a silver moon / Baloo baleerie / Brahms' lullaby / Brezairola / Traumerei op.15 no.1 / Can ye sew cushions / By'm bye / Bye baby Bunting / Golden slumbers / Dance to your Daddy / Dance little baby / Fais dodo / Goodnight to you all / Berceuse / Hush little baby / Kumbayah / Little boy blue / Suo gan / Matthew Mark Luke and John / Mozart's lullaby / Chanson de nuit op.15 no.1 / Now the day is over - raindrops / Raisins and almonds / Rock-a-bye baby / Rocking - the sandman / O belle nuit / Barcarolle / Skidamarink / Sleep baby sleep / Sweet and low / Swing low sweet chariot / Toora loora loora / Twinkle twinkle little star / When at night I go to sleep
ESSCD 1054 / Mar '98 / ESSAY

☐ **LULLABY FOR THE MOON (Japanese Music For Koto & Shakuhachi)**
Lullaby: Komorluta / Six miles from a mountain pass: Hachi-Ri, Toge / Eternal lights: Kuom No Hikari / Sea fantasy: Umi / Six fragments of koto: Muttsu / Cherry blossoms: Sakura / Moonlight on a ruined castle: Kojo / Plower's songe: Chidorl
HEMIMDCD 104 / 6 Oct '97 / Hemisphere

☐ **LUMPTRONIC VOL.1**
LUMP 02 / 2 Mar '98 / Lumptronic

☐ **LUMPTRONIC VOL.2**
LUMP 03 / 2 Mar '98 / Lumptronic

☐ **LUO ROOTS**
Jadiyana: Kapere Jazz Band / Nath oindo: Kapere Jazz Band / Amagy lando: Kapere Jazz Band / Tuni nyamwalo: Kapere Jazz Band / Samwel adinda: Kapere Jazz Band / Jacob Omolo: Okoth, Ogwang Lelo / Lando nyajomere: Kapere Jazz Band / Amisijamoko: Kapere Jazz Band / John Wangu: Okoth, Ogwang Lelo / Lynette: Onono, Paddy J
CDORBD 061 / Jun '90 / Globestyle

☐ **LUTZ R MASTERHAYER**
SPCD 111287 / Aug '93 / Sub Pop

☐ **LYRICIST LOUNGE VOL.1 (2CD Set)**
Intro: De La Soul / Bring hip hop back: Cipher Complete / Keep pouring: Matrix & Abutta / Blood: Jones, Sarah / Body rock: Mos Def & Q Tip/Tash / Bathroom cipher/Da cipher: Punch & Words / Famous last words: Word A' Mouth / Action guaranteed: OC & Ras Kass / All in my own: Zoot, Mike / Phone call: Bobbito 'The Barber' / OHM: Williams, Saul / Mayday: Natural Elements / Manifesto: Kweli, Talib / Be OK: Bahamadia & Rah Digga / Lyrics: AL / Outside the lounge/Holy water: Lord Have Mercy & DV / Jayou: Jurassic 5 / CIA (Criminal in action): De La Rocha, Zach & KRS-One/ Last Emperor / Society: Problemz / Weight: Indelible MC's / After the show: Words & Rise/Jedi/AL
RWK 11292 / 18 May '98 / Rawkus

☐ **LYRICS PUISSANCE VOL.4**
503822 / Apr '95 / Declic

☐ **LYTIC COCKTAIL**
COMP 025CD / Jan '97 / Compost

M

☐ **M8 - THE ANTHEMS**
MR 021CD / May '96 / Massive Respect

☐ **M8 DJ TECHNOTRANCE**
Natural born killers: DJ Technotrance / Now is the time: Brown, Scott / Pump that body: Scientists / There goes the boom: Eruption / Disco hardcore: DJ Seduction / Chromedome: Active Force / Forbidden territory: Active Force / Gazometer: Brown, Scott / Oh yeah: Ultimate Elation / Shaftman: Shaftman / 123: Digital Nation / On ya knees: Eytronix / Can can party: Sandman / Hardcore science: Q-Tex / Rave dog: Technoterrier / Hardcore euphoria: Sub Source / Fuck the DEA: DJ Technotrance / Don't you want my lovin': DJ Demand / Strobelight: Chill FM / Kiss my ass seduction: DJ Technotrance / Splosh: Water Pistol / Do what you like: Brown, Scott
CDTOT 35 / Jan '96 / Jumpin' & Pumpin'

☐ **M8 EUROPEAN TECHNO HEAVEN**
Only if I had one more: Dyewitness / Ultimate sextrack: Dyewitness / Check your head: Ultrasonic / Power people II: Rhythmic State Crew / Set you free: N-Trance / Feel free: Dougal & Vibes / Sweet in pocket: Justin Time / Anthem: N-Joi / I'm the fuck you man: Wedlock / Sound of Rotterdam: Human Resource / Don't fuck with a redneck: Juggernaut / Cocaine: Neuro-Tek / Strobelight: Chill FM / Believe: Q-Tex
CDTOT 29 / May '95 / Jumpin' & Pumpin'

☐ **M8 EUROPEAN TECHNO HEAVEN**
Luv U more: Elstak, Paul / Back in the UK: Scooter / I wanna be a hippy: Technohead / Now is the time: Brown, Scott / Future: Dyewitness / Fight for your rights: Phonki / On and beyond: Chill FM / Party time: Dougal & Eruption / XTC love: Feranzano, Berto / Go get busy: DJ Weirdo & DJ Sim / Strict stomp: Strictly Verbal
CDTOT 39 / Apr '96 / Jumpin' & Pumpin'

☐ **MACARENA (Swingin' Summer Instrumentals)**
Macarena / Lambada / Una paloma blanca / Mexico / La bamba / Tijuana taxi / Sun of Jamaica / Girl from Ipanema / Ole guapa / Guantanamera / El condor pasa / Ciclito lindo / Un canto a galicia / Jamaica farewell / Volare / Spanish flea / Ticket to the tropics
DGR 1112 / Sep '96 / DGR

☐ **MACEDONIAN DANCES**
PS 65076 / Jul '91 / PlayaSound

☐ **MACHINE CODES COMPILATION 1993-1997**
CODEFCD / Sep '97 / Machine Codes

☐ **MACHINE HEADS**
HEAD 6 / Apr '97 / Machinehead

☐ **MACHINO WEIRDER**
DUKE 017CD / Jun '95 / Hydrogen Dukebox

☐ **MACRO DUB INFECTION VOL.1 (2CD Set)**
Struggle of life: Disciples / Double edge: Spring Heel Jack / Sergio Mendez part 1: 2 Bad Card / Astral altar dub: Automaton / Broadway boogie woogie: Bedouin Ascent / Wadada: Rootsman / Hills are alive: Coil / Half cut: Omni Trio / If you miss: Laika / Crush your enemies: New Kingdom / Goriri: Tortoise / Operation mind control: Skull Vs Ice / Morocco: Alzir, Bud / Beta, seekers of smooth things: Plutobeat / Paranormal in four forms: 4 Hero / This is how it feels: Golden Palominos / Ragga doll: Mad Professor / Phora ride: Wagon Christ / End: Scorn / Ambient pumpkin: Tricky / Iration Steppas vs Dennis Rootical: Iration Steppas / Come forward: Bandulu / Nothingness: Earthling
AMBT 7 / May '95 / Virgin

☐ **MACRO DUB INFECTION VOL.2 (2CD Set)**
M6: Maurizio / Sacred system: Laswell, Bill / Beware soul snatchers: Rome / Altesse: Chatham, Rhys & Martin Wheeler / Libel: Pin / Liquid boy: Him / A presente: Zulutronic / Miles to go: Magnet / Keen as mustard: Plug / Sehn sud: Mouse On Mars / Esoteric red: Tao / When you reach your peak: Alec Empire / Flump: Skull / Shades of nature: Ear Drum / Nautical dub: Porter Ricks / Strong heart: Disciples & Rootsman / El Qadim: Gedulah & Terminal Cheesecake / Revelation of wrath: Andre Gurov Units / Brother no blood: Prince Paul / Handbag dub: Jammin' Unit / Rat day: Bio Muse / Shot in the head: Third Eye Foundation / Sub version: Spectre / Inbred version: Ice & Palace
AMBT 14 / Oct '96 / Virgin

☐ **MAD ABOUT THE BOY (Songs From The Best Known TV Commercials)**
MPV 5521 / Jun '92 / Movieplay

☐ **MAD ABOUT THE BOY VOL.1**
CDKOPY 105 / Oct '96 / Klone

☐ **MAD ABOUT THE BOY VOL.2**
Calling occupants of interplanetary craft: Clune, Jackie / You'll see: Prime / Say what you want: Kamouflage & Louise Ennis / Stay with me till dawn: Illusive / On emore hurt: Parker, Paul & Angie Gold / I'm so happy: Spaghetti Surfers / Feel good: Abigail / Don't speak: Body Double / I'll be there for you: Body Double / Drop dead gorgeous: Boys Of A New Age / Don't cry for me Argentina: Prima / Usin' ma body: Magnetic / Echo beach: Boys Of A New Age / All by myself: Atlanta / I believe I can fly: Kamouflage & Louise Ennis / Saint: Spaghetti Surfers / California dreaming: High Jinks / Summertime: Sinclair, Jenny / Talking in your sleep: Stephanie
CDKOPY 107 / 20 Oct '97 / Klone

☐ **MAD ABOUT THE BOY VOL.3 (2CD Set)**
Bitter sweet symphony: Devorah / Close to you: Clune, Jackie / New year's day: Prima / Stars: Kamouflage / L'amour est partout: Boys Of A New Age / I finally found someone: Parker, Paul & Angie Gold / Dreaming: Miss B & Maxine Barrie / Nobody does it better: Dezire / Dance with you: Bon Bon / Man who sold the world: Boys Of A New Age / Where have all the cowboys gone: Atlanta / Sexy boy: Bon Bon / Pamdise: Devorah / Hot stuff: Men Of Steel / I who have nothing: Miss B & Maxine Barrie / Get up: Disco Dude / Into the groove: Prima / Action man: Jones, G.I
CDKOPY 109 / 22 Jun '98 / Klone

☐ **MAD ABOUT THE GIRLS**
Mad about the boy: Washington, Dinah / All through the night: Lauper, Cyndi / Dreams: Gabrielle / I ain't movin': Des'ree / Our love is here to stay: Fitzgerald, Ella / Shadow of your smile: Gilberto, Astrud / Bewitched, bothered and bewildered: Flyj, Laura / Fever: Lee, Peggy / Don't let me be misunderstood: Simone, Nina / Gone with the wind: Page, Patti / Make yourself comfortable: Vaughan, Sarah / Some of your lovin': Springfield, Dusty / Use me:

Goodman, Gabrielle / Bad day: *Carmel* / Lover man: *Holiday, Billie* / 'Round midnight: *Wilson, Cassandra* / I should care: *London, Julie* / Move over darling: *Day, Doris* / Crazy: *Cline, Patsy* / Perfect year: *Carroll, Dina*
5255552 / Jun '95 / PolyGram TV

☐ **MAD DOG**
NWSCD 5 / Apr '93 / New Sound

☐ **MAD ON ACID (2CD Set)**
3027382 / 2 Mar '98 / Mirakkle/Trax

☐ **MAD SKILLS AND CRAZY VISIONS (2CD Set)**
Do you wanna boogie huh: *Two Tons Of Fun* / My funny Valentine trippy dub: *Big Muff* / Sweet tears: *Nu Yorican Soul* / Clap your hands: *Lil' Louis* / My beat: *Blaze* / Searchin' dub: *Clark, Loni* / Dancing in outer space: *Atmosphere* / Aschewo ara: *Kabbala* / New York style: *Mateo & Matos* / See line woman: *Songstress* / Life is changing: *Costelli, Cricco* / Original disco motion: *Faze Action* / Make me feel: *Freil* / Player: *First Choice* / Monte Carlo: *Sunburst Band* / We had a thing: *Abstract Truth* / Seasons change: *Sylk 130* / Move like this: *NYC Live & Direct*
BBECD 012 / 25 May '98 / Barely Breaking Even

☐ **MADAGASCAR COAST AND TABLELANDS (2CD Set)**
O ry namako o ry mba hitanaero ve ry zanako: *Mpilalao De Fenoarivo* / Ny fifaliana ry lahy tsy feno raha tsy eo anita nareo: *Mpilalao De Fenoarivo* / Tao anatin imano: *Mpilalao De Fenoarivo* / Arie faly aho leitsy: *Mpilalao De Fenoarivo* / Mampahohory ny masandro serania javana: *Mpilalao De Fenoarivo* / Oay lahy e: *Mpilalao De Fenoarivo* / Eny arodo rodgroday ny fanindra: *Choeur Malgache* / Bebesa: *Orchestre Ratianarivo* / Tery mafy loatra ny saina: *Choeur Malgache* / Mazava antisinana ny any aminay: *Mpilalao De Fenoarivo* / Zavy: *Troupe Razanalakona* / Fony hianao mbola kely sakaiza: *Troupe Razanalakona* / Rambalaamanana: *Troupe Razanalakona* / Lahy e: *Orchestre Ratianarivo* / O ry dada sy neny malala o: *Mpilalao De Fenoarivo* / Tanora tsy manaja tena: *Mpilalao De Fenoarivo* / O ravazaha: *Orchestre Ratianarivo* / O ry fody an anala e: *Troupe Razafimahefa* / O ry tsiriy mandalo an itasy: *Troupe Razafimahefa* / Raivo o: *Mpilalao De Fenoarivo* / Ry volon danaitra manga: *Troupe Razafimahefa* / An iza ny basy: *Choeur Malgache* / Afindrafindrao: *Choeur Malgache* / Hadalana hadrisoana: *Mpilalao De Fenoarivo* / Fikasakasana ny eto an tany: *Troupe Razafimahefa* / Indristy mantsy zareo mpilato tsy manantiana: *Troupe Razafimahefa* / Marina ny andro: *Mpilalao De Fenoarivo* / Mitahaza re rabetorimasa: *Troupe Razafimahefa* / Nosy be: *Sakalava* / Andrainjatu: *Betsileo Du Nord* / Ambalavao: *Betsileo du sud* / Majunga: *Sakalava Du Nord* / Befandriana: *Tsimihety*
FA 058 / Nov '97 / Fremeaux

☐ **MADAGASIKARA VOL.1**
Afindrafindraq: *Rakotoarimanana, Rakotofra & Martin* / Feam baliha: *Tombo, Daniel & Marceline Viviroa* / Dia mahaory: *Tombo, Daniel & Marceline Viviroa* / Bonne annee amin ny tanana: *Norbert, Georges & L. Honore Rosa* / Mamakivaky alankiminina: *Norbert, Georges & L. Honore Rosa* / Fambelo eto madagasikara: *Rabenalvo Group* / Nilentika: *Andriamamonjy, David* / Tazana kely: *Andriamamonjy, David* / Mahatsiarotsiaro fanina aeo zeho: *Volambita, Tsimialona* / Nametaa imaintso: *Volambita, Tsimialona* / King's song: *Rakotoarimanana, Martin* / Viavy rosy: *Randriamainty, Emmanuel* / Kilalao: *Ze Ze et groupe son*
CDORBD 012 / Oct '90 / Globestyle

☐ **MADAGASIKARA VOL.2**
Raha mania any / Ento rora / Madirovalo / Tsapika 2000 / Totoy tsara / Sarotra / Voromby / Ny any / Malaza avaratna / Aza mba manary toky
CDORBD 013 / Nov '90 / Globestyle

☐ **MADAGASKAR VOL.1**
FUECCD 704 / Feb '98 / Feuer Und Eis

☐ **MADAGASKAR VOL.2**
FUECCD 706 / Feb '98 / Feuer Und Eis

☐ **MADCHESTER**
MADCCD 1 / Oct '95 / Beechwood

☐ **MADE IN FRANCE VOL.1**
Viens a Paris: *Giraud, Yvette* / Pigalle: *Ulmer, Georges* / J'ais deux amours: *Baker, Josephine* / Valentine: *Chevalier, Maurice* / A Paris dans Chaque faubourg: *Gauty, Lys* / La Java bleue: *Frehel* / Parlez moi d'amour: *Boyer, Lucienne* / La belote: *Alibert* / Nice ma belle: *Alibert* / Ja tire ma reverence: *Sablon, Jean* / Les feuilles mortes: *Vaucaire, Cora* / Fleur de Paris: *Helian, Jacques* / Paris Canaille: *Horner, Yvette* / Douce France: *Trenet, Charles* / Sur les quais du vieux Paris: *Delyle, Lucienne* / La guinguette a ferme ses volets: *Damia* / Frou Frou: *Renaud, Line* / La vie en rose: *Piaf, Edith* / Paris tu m'as pris dans tes bras: *Macias, Enrico* / Paris ferie: *Horner, Yvette*
4931842 / 13 Jul '98 / EMI

☐ **MADE IN GREAT BRITAIN - THE ALBUM**
Much love: *Ama, Shola* / Tingles: *TCB* / Mighty high: *Gaynor, Gloria & Trammps* / Tears: *Colour Girl* / Lift me up: *Harvey, Connie* / My desire: *Amira* / Style: *Ramsey & Fen* / Skip bop: *N&G* / Be the one: *Groove In Motion* / Give you myself: *Sima* / Flava fever: *Cole, MJ* / Hear my word: *Nu Groove* / Endorphins: *Sky Cap* / Theme: *Dreem Teem* / Lessons in love: *Craig, Robbie* / I need your love: *Dubz 4 Klubz* / Get happy: *Underground Solution* / My inspiration: *TJ Cases* / Right before my eyes: *N&G* / Miss the love: *Romy* / Latino: *Mushtaq*
LIBTCD 004 / 8 Jun '98 / 4 Liberty

☐ **MADE ON EARTH (2CD Set)**
BR 026CD / Mar '97 / Blue Room Released

☐ **MADE TO MEASURE RESUME...**
MTM 16 / Mar '88 / Made To Measure

☐ **MADE TO MEASURE VOL.1**
Pieces for nothing / A la recherche: *Lew, Benjamin* / Un chien: *Maboul, Aksak* / Scratch holiday: *Maboul, Aksak* / Verdun: *Tuxedo Moon*
MTM 1CD / '88 / Made To Measure

☐ **MADHOUSE ACTION PACK**
MHCD 001 / Jun '96 / Penthouse

☐ **MADHOUSE CREW LIVE**
793012 / Jan '94 / Jammy's

☐ **MADNESS INVASION VOL.1**
842624 / Jun '94 / EVA

☐ **MADRID MADRID MADRID VOL.1**
20098CD / Aug '97 / Sonifolk

☐ **MADRID MADRID MADRID VOL.2**
20099CD / Aug '97 / Sonifolk

☐ **MAESTRA SIERRA**
74321483922 / 5 May '98 / Milan

☐ **MAESTROS DE LA GUITARRA FLAMENCA VOL.1**
BM 517 / Jan '97 / Blue Moon

☐ **MAESTROS DE LA GUITARRA FLAMENCA VOL.2**
BM 518 / Jan '97 / Blue Moon

☐ **MAESTROS DEL CANTE JONDO**
BMCD 520 / 24 Apr '98 / Blue Moon

☐ **MAESTROS DEL TANGO ARGENTINO (2CD Set)**
BMT 001 / Jan '97 / Blue Moon

☐ **MAGIC AND MYSTERY (Music From Scotland & Ireland)**
Frideray: *Pincock, Dougie & Alan Reid* / Fornethy house: *Heritage* / Lady Iveagh: *Heymann, Ann* / Togail curs air Leodhas: *Battlefield Band* / Air for Jakes: *McCusker, John* / An cailin rua: *McDermott, Josie* / Taimse in', chodladh: *Dykehead Caledonia Pipe Band* / Braidwood waits: *Kinnaird, Alison* / Peace and plenty: *Battlefield Band* / Miss Hamilton: *McNeill, Brian* / She's late but she's timely: *Battlefield Band* / Hollin green hollin/Thomas the rhymer/Young Benjie/Tam Lin: *Battlefield Band* / Planxty sudley: *Maire Ni Chathasaigh* / Mrs. Jamieson's favourite: *Mac-Talla* / Craigs of Ailsa/ Staffa's shore: *Kinnaird, Alison* / A stor mo chroi: *Rigler, Eric* / Brigid's waltz: *McCusker, John*
COMD 2062 / Feb '97 / Temple

☐ **MAGIC CHRISTMAS**
15148 / Nov '95 / Laserlight

☐ **MAGIC FLY (Synthesizer Hits)**
Star Wars suite / Magic fly / Moonraker / St. Elmo's Fire / Rambo / First Blood part II / Oxygene / Aurora / Old and wise / Merry Christmas Mr. Lawrence / Live and let die / Ode to Amadeus / Funky Town / Don't you want me / Don't go / Too shy / Model / Friends of Mr. Cairo / Man with the golden gun / Godfather theme / Going home
MU 5005 / Oct '92 / Musketeer

☐ **MAGIC GROOVE RIDERS VOL.1 (21 House Club Traxx Inside/2CD Set)**
Psychic bounty killers: *Van Helden, Armand & DJ Sneak* / Funky mustique: *Sunday Afternoon* / JW's unreleased tracks: *JW* / Sweet music: *Trancelate* / Don't take your love: *Diesal Disco Jointz* / Ruhr cowboy: *Criss Source* / Leaving: *Digital Disco* / Take control: *Fix To Fax* / You got me: *DJ Eclipse* / Disco town: *Stressman* / Dialogue: *3 Dubs In A Sleeve* / Discodamned nation: *Frank Popp* / U got me: *Belmonthe* / Symphonic days: *Powerplant Revisited* / Nite trax vol.1: *Ultrasonix* / Love hurts: *Paris Red* / Phunky Pheelings: *La Foule* / Dancin: *Mateo & Matos* / Old skool: *DJ Tonka* / Feel that groove: *Farley & Muscle*
560182 / Aug '97 / Nova Tekk

☐ **MAGIC MOMENTS**
CWNCD 2005 / Jun '95 / Javelin

☐ **MAGIC MUSIC TRAXX (2CD Set)**
FRIE 0082 / 3 Aug '98 / Friends

☐ **MAGIC OF BRASS, THE**
Macarthur park / Always on my mind / Don't leave me this way / Bohemian rhapsody / Tritsch tratsch polka / You can call me Al / Carnival for brass / You've lost that lovin' feelin' / Get back / All I ask of you / Shepherd's song / Hello / Pie jesu / Puttin' on the ritz
MUCD 9003 / Apr '95 / Musketeer

☐ **MAGIC OF DETROIT VOL.1, THE**
Find a quiet place and be lonely: *Davis, Melvin* / Don't do nothing I wouldn't do: *Van Dyke, Connie* / Jack the playboy: *Rogers, Lee* / My love looks good on you: *Fabulous Peps* / You got the lovin' touch: *Lamp, Buddy* / His majesty my love: *Edwards, Dee* / They loved to be loved: *Heart, Don* / I wanna tell my baby: *Precisions* / Walk on by: *Rogers, Lee* / Hide and seek: *Dupree, Lillian* / I will give you love: *Dupree, Lillian* / Me and my baby: *Magic Tones* / Detroit, michigan: *Love, Ronnie* / Same thing that makes you laugh: *Rogers, Lee* / Hurt by love: *Hargreaves, Silky* / I'm gonna try to get over: *Hentley, Chuck* / Next best thing: *Lamp, Buddy* / Love and war: *Rogers, Lee* / Too careless with love: *Edwards, Dee* / Too many irons in the fire: *Black, Cody* / With these eyes: *Fabulous Peps* / You're the cream of the crop: *Rogers, Lee* / Together we shall overcome: *Magic Tones* / Cracked up over you: *Rogers, Lee* / Quittin' time': *International Kansas City Playboys*
GSCD 093 / Nov '96 / Goldmine

☐ **MAGIC OF IRELAND, THE (4CD Set)**
EMPRBX 007 / Oct '95 / Emporio

☐ **MAGIC OF IRELAND, THE**
Riverdance / White, orange and green / Scarce O'Tatties / Feilims little boat Phelims / Ballinasloe / Fiddler's green / Three young ladies drinking whisky before breakfast / Port Laige / If you're Irish / Arthur McBride / Morrison merrily kissed the quaker / Ramblin' Irishman / Ministrel boy / Rising of the moon / Little fairy big fairy / Beggarman / Roscabury / Nightingale / Sport of the chase / Whiskey in the jar
CD 6077 / Jun '97 / Music

☐ **MAGIC OF PANPIPES, THE**
Here comes the sun / Maybe / Light my fire / Forse / When you're in love with a beautiful woman / Dim all the lights / On the radio / Feelings / Sailing / Let it be / Dolanne's melody / Don't cry for me Argentina / Un jour d'ete / Autumn dream / Klavier konzert No.1 / Schusscher / Sinfonie / Barcarolle / Largo from the new world symphony / Sleepwalk / Lonely shepherd
QED 020 / Nov '96 / Tring

☐ **MAGIC OF SCOTLAND, THE**
Cumberland medley / Eight men of moidart medley / Bovaglie's plaid / Da tushker reel set medley / Dunoon barn dance medley / Saturday waltz / Laddies who fought and won / Earl of Errol's reel medley / Garry Strathspey / John Worth's jig medley / Campbeltown kiltie ball medley / 6/8 marches lady Dorothea medley / Scottish waltz a rosebud medley / Breakfast in bed / Happy haggis / Cuckoo waltz / St. Johnstoun reel medley / Waltz country dance medley / Sweet Georgia brown / Macdonald of the Isles medley / Strip the willow medley / Flowers of Edinburgh reel selection medley
RECD 515 / Jul '98 / REL

☐ **MAGIC OF THE INDIAN FLUTE VOL.1, THE**
EUCD 1090 / '89 / ARC

☐ **MAGIC OF THE INDIAN FLUTE VOL.2, THE**
EUCD 1129 / '91 / ARC

☐ **MAGIC SOUND OF THE PAN PIPES VOL.1, THE**
El condor pasa / Do that to me one more time / Long and winding road / For your eyes only / Ebony and ivory / If you leave me now / Lady / Unchained melody / Endless love / You light up my life / We've got tonight / Something / Arthur's theme / Feelings
EMPRCD 537 / Nov '96 / Emporio

☐ **MAGIC SOUND OF THE PAN PIPES VOL.2, THE**
Dolanne's melodie / Fernando / Heartbreaker / Strawberry fields forever / Sara / Moonlight shadow / Up where we belong / All time high / Don't cry for me Argentina / Woman in love / Sailing / Yesterday / I have a dream / Bridge over troubled water
EMPRCD 538 / Nov '96 / Emporio

☐ **MAGIC SOUND OF THE PAN PIPES, THE**
EMPRCD 511 / Apr '94 / Emporio

☐ **MAGIC SOUND OF THE PAN PIPES, THE (4CD Set)**
EMPRBX 005 / Sep '94 / Emporio

☐ **MAGIC SOUNDS OF THE PIPES, THE**
CDMFP 5615 / Feb '97 / Music For Pleasure

☐ **MAGIC WONDERLAND VOL.1**
PLUMPCD 100 / Feb '97 / Plumphouse

☐ **MAGIC WURLITZER VOL.1, THE**
PLATCD 31 / Apr '92 / Platinum

☐ **MAGIC WURLITZER VOL.2, THE**
PLATCD 34 / Jul '92 / Platinum

☐ **MAGICAL LUTE**
A 6259 / Jul '98 / Tempo

☐ **MAGICAL PERCUSSION**
A 6257 / Jul '98 / Tempo

☐ **MAGICAL SOUND OF THE PAN PIPES VOL.4**
Un-break my heart / In the air tonight / Man I love / Kiss from a rose / Unforgettable / Careless whisper / Take a look at me now / Your song / Lady in red / Words / (Everything I do) I do it for you / Harry's Game / True / Shadow of your smile / On your shore / Tears in heaven / Love changes everything / All by myself
306452 / May '97 / Hallmark

☐ **MAGICAL SOUND OF THE PANPIPES VOL.3, THE**
Flight of the condor / Do you know where you're going to / Flame trees of Thika / Ballerina girl / No more the fool / Bluebird / Morning has broken / Paradise bird / Sunny / If you leave me now / Autumn breeze / Don't cry for me Argentina / Orinoco flow / Ma baker / Daniel / Mull of kintyre / Once upon a time in the west / El condor pasa
305462 / Oct '96 / Hallmark

☐ **MAGICAL SOUND OF THE PANPIPES, THE**
Up where we belong / He ain't heavy he's my brother / Fernando / Flashdance (what a feeling) / Heartbreaker / MacArthur park / Always on my mind / If only I could / What a wonderful world / I will always love you / Take my breath away / On the radio / Dim all the lights / Beauty and the Beast / Do that to me one more time / Save the best for last / All time high / Unchained melody
302932 / Feb '98 / Hallmark

☐ **MAGICAL SOUND OF THE WURLITZER ORGAN, THE**
Beyond the blue horizon: *Ogden, Nigel* / Sweet and lovely: *Ogden, Nigel* / It's a raggy waltz: *Ogden, Nigel* / In a clock store: *Ogden, Nigel* / Whistler and his dog: *Ogden, Nigel* / Quickstep medley: *Martin, Nicholas* / Tango medley: *Martin, Nicholas* / Rhumba medley: *Martin, Nicholas* / El relicario: *Gledhill, Simon* / These foolish things: *Gledhill, Simon* / My silent love: *Gledhill, Simon* / Veradero: *Gledhill, Simon* / Autumn crocus: *Gledhill, Simon* / Calling all workers: *Sharp, Brian* / Roses of Picardy: *Sharp, Brian* / Coronation Scot: *Sharp, Brian* / In the news: *Sharp, Brian* / I'd give you the world: *Sharp, Brian* / Wurlitzer march: *Loxam, Arnold* / Grasshoppers dance: *Loxam, Arnold* / Narcissus: *Loxam, Arnold* / Windermere march: *Loxam, Arnold* / Dickie bird hop: *Loxam, Arnold*
MCCD 207 / Jul '95 / Music Club

☐ **MAGICAL SOUNDS OF HAWAII**
Honolula dance / Aloha de / Sarina / Hilo march / Beautiful Isle / Terang bular / Aloen ajoen / Hukilau song / Mama / Pau ika lani / Mauna kea / Blue wahini / Imiau ea auwey / Sophisticated Hula / Little cani Joe / Sari nande / Footprints in the sun / Nina bobo / Goro gone no / Mine ha ha / Lime lime / Sejang kene / Honolula / Moon over Maui / Mauri chimes / Kaneuche kiss
GRF 202 / Apr '93 / Tring

☐ **MAGICAL SOUNDS OF THE PANPIPES, THE (4CD Set)**
Up where we belong / He ain't heavy he's my brother / Fernando / Flashdance what a feeling / Heartbreaker / MacArthur park / Always on my mind / If only I could / What a wonderful world / I will always love you / Take my breath away / On the radio / Dim all the lights / Beauty and the beast / Do that to me one more time / Save the best for last / All time high / Unchained melody / Bridge over troubled water / Right here waiting / Mary's boy child / Top of the world / Rose / Strawberry fields forever / When you're in love with a beautiful women / Eternal flame / Norweigan wood / Wind beneath my wings / I'll be there / Got to get you into my life / Let it be me / We've got tonite / Michelle / Island in the sun / Flight of the condor / Do you know where you're going to / Flame trees of Thika / Ballerina girl / No more the fool / Bluebird / Morning has broken / Paradise bird / Sunny / If you leave me now / Autumn breeze / Don't cry for me Argentina / Orinoco flow / Ma Baker / Daniel / Mull of Kintyre / Once upon a time in the west / El condor pasa / Flight of the condor / Do you know where you're going to / Un break my heart / In the air tonight / Kiss froma rose / Unforgettable / Careless whisper / Take a look at me now / Your song / Lady in red / Words / Everthing I do I do for you / Harry's Game / True / Shadow of your smile / On your shore / Tears in heaven / Love changes everything
391272 / Aug '97 / Hallmark

☐ **MAGIE DES ANDES**
GRI 190522 / Feb '96 / Griffe

☐ **MAGNETIC SUBMISSION**
EFA 200792 / Dec '95 / Submission

☐ **MAGNIFICENT 14, THE**
CDTRL 283 / Mar '94 / Trojan

☐ **MAGNIFICENT THUNDERSTORMS**
57702 / May '97 / Nature's Harmony

☐ **MAGNUM ROCKABILLY**
Down on the farm: *Downing, 'Big' Al* / Hip shakin' Mama: *Cochran, Jackie Lee* / Hot dog: *Jones, Corky* / Go go heart: *Doggett, Ray* / Jackson dog: *Brinkley, Larry* / Bip bop boom: *Hawks, Mickey* / Gonna love my baby: *McCollough, Lloyd* / Sunglasses after dark: *Pullen, Dwight* / Satellite hop: *Parchman, Kenny* / What am I gonna do: *Evans, Jimmy* / Fool: *Clark, Sanford* / It hurts the one who loves you: *Doggett, Ray* / Look out Mabel: *Crockett, G.L.* / Move over Rover: *Brinkley, Larry* / Made in the shade: *Dunlap, Gene* / Half my fault: *McCollough, Lloyd* / You bet I do: *Bailey, Don* / Okie's in the Pokie: *Patton, Jimmy* / No doubt about it: *Doggett, Ray* / Lonely heart: *Rickman, Joe* / She won't let me down: *Little, Curtis* / Okie boogie: *Swatley, Hank* / Shackles and chains: *Johnson, B.J.* / Troubles troubles: *Davis, Bobby* / Goin' crazy: *Self, Mack* / Blue swingin' Mama: *Dowd, Larry & The Rockatones* / That'll get it: *Brinkley, Larry* / Puppy love: *Snyder, Tony* / Live your life with care: *Busby, Wayne* / Little Susie: *Evans, Jimmy* / Everytime I see you: *Mobley, Sylvia* / Hard luck: *Blank, Billy* / Rosalie: *Smith, Shelby* / Cotton patch hop: *Williams, Sonny* / Tore up: *Harmonica Ray*
CDMF 100 / 27 Apr '98 / Magnum Force

☐ **MAGYARPALATKA**
SYNCD 152 / Jun '93 / Syncoop

☐ **MAH NA MAH NA (The Complete Remix Project)**
Karmexperience mix: *Karminski Experience* / King of Favelas mix: *Scotti, Paolo* / L'amour mix: *Sebbag, Raphael* / Space go go mix: *Gak Sato & DJ Massive* / Tiki mix: *Sato, Gak* / Mah na mammato mix: *Coccoluto, Claudio & Savino Martinez* / Football club mix: *Sweet Dick Willy & Zbouby/Zebla* / Smash on the beatbox mix: *DJ Smash* / Dub mix: *Coccoluto, Claudio & Savino Martinez*
MET 201204 / Sep '97 / Right Tempo

☐ **MAIDEN VOYAGE**
CMCD 062 / Dec '97 / Celtic Music

☐ **MAILORDER IS FUN**
There's a metal head in the parking lot: *Slapstick* / Slap: *Link 80* / Hava nagilah: *Slow Gherkin* / BA: *Unsteady* / 15 minutes: *Broadways* / Reunion: *Korea Girl* / Hana: *Chinkees* / Boraborinski Brothers: *Johnny Socko* / Goodbyes have been said: *Tuesday* / Xmas: *MU330* / Radio: *Potshot* / Oatmeal for Xmas: *Let's Go Bowling* / Gerry is wrong: *Lee, B. Band* / Dummy room: *Blue Meanies* / To little time to waste: *Schleptones* / For your lungs only: *Alkaline Trio* / Liquor store: *Less Than Jake* / No color no power: *Monkey* / Pitiful: *Pushover* / Howie mobile: *Nicotines* / Plan B: *Impossibles* / Seven: *Animal Chin* / What's your name: *17 Years* / Hot rod: *Supaflies* / Don't bring me down: *J-Church* / Pickle: *Funsize* / Soup: *Discount* / Please: *Hippos* / Efforts wasted: *Beretta, Anne Marie*
AM 026CD / 25 May '98 / Asian Man

☐ **MAIN COURSE**
REDEURO 2 / Nov '94 / Red Eye

☐ **MAINSTREAM MASTERS, THE**
JHR 73529 / May '93 / Jazz Hour

☐ MAIRZY DOATS (24 Original Vintage Comedy Songs)
Sun has got his hat on: *Browne, Sam* / Minnie the moocher: *Calloway, Cab* / Hey little hen: *Loss, Joe* / Mairzy doats: *Merry Macs* / Der fuhrer's face: *Jones, Spike* / Thirty thirsty throats: *O'Shea, Tessie* / Wunga bunga boo: *Formby, George* / Ice cream: *Waring, Fred* / Everything stops for tea: *Buchanan, Jack* / My canary has circles under his eyes: *Summers, Delroy* / Song of the prune: *Crumit, Frank* / La di da di da: *Comber, Bobbie* / Cocktails for two: *Jones, Spike* / Making whoopee: *Cantor, Eddie* / Dry bones: *Waring, Fred* / You can't blame me for that: *Miller, Max* / Teddy Bears' picnic: *Hall, Henry* / Your feets too big: *Waller, Fats* / I wanna banana: *Askey, Arthur* / Mad dogs and Englishmen: *Coward, Sir Noel* / Life begins at forty: *Tucker, Sophie* / Walter, Walter lead me to the altar: *Fields, Gracie* / I took my harp to a party: *Cotton, Billy* / I don't want to go to bed: *Browne, Sam*
308162 / 13 Oct '97 / Hallmark

☐ MAJESTIC REGGAE
Back off ringcraft / Ringcraft dub / Kiss somebody / Kiss kiss dub / Reach the top / Rude boy / Nightfall / Nightfall dubbing / Love comes and goes / Girl of my complexion / Little lover / Turn me on / Marijuana tree / Qua she / Qua she take over / Come along / Qua she dub
MRCD 1006 / Nov '97 / Munich

☐ MAKE IT EASY
Make it easy on yourself: *Walker Brothers* / Unchained melody: *Righteous Brothers* / Green grass of home: *Jones, Tom* / Blue velvet: *Vinton, Bobby* / Most beautiful girl in the world: *Rich, Charlie* / Always on my mind: *Nelson, Willie* / Lovely day: *Withers, Bill* / January February: *Dickson, Barbara* / I can see clearly now: *Nash, Johnny* / Sylvia's mother: *Dr. Hook* / Release me: *Humperdinck, Engelbert* / Nights in white satin: *Moody Blues* / I just don't know what to do with myself: *Springfield, Dusty* / Forever autumn: *Hayward, Justin* / King of the road: *Miller, Roger* / You're a lady: *Skellern, Peter* / Stand by your man: *Wynette, Tammy* / Last farewell: *Whittaker, Roger*
MUSCD 003 / Nov '92 / MCI Music

☐ MAKE MINE MAMBO
NSCD 011 / Nov '96 / Nascente

☐ MAKE THE WORLD GO AWAY (20 Classic Love Songs)
Ain't no pleasing you: *Chas & Dave* / Whispering: *Bachelors* / This is my song: *Clark, Petula* / Make me an island: *Dolan, Joe* / Make the world go away: *Rose Marie* / When my little girl is smiling: *Justice, Jimmy* / Medley: *Knight, Gladys & The Pips* / One day at a time: *Martell, Lena* / Little bitty tear: *Miki & Griff* / Story of my life: *Miller, Gary* / Vaya con dios: *Millican & Nesbitt* / Michelle: *Overlanders* / Isn't she lovely: *Parton, David* / (It's like a) Sad old kinda movie: *Pickettywitch* / Something's gotten hold of my heart: *Pitney, Gene* / Always something there to remind me: *Shaw, Sandie* / Too young: *Young, Jimmy* / Party's over: *Donegan, Lonnie* / Moon river: *Butler, Jerry* / Cry me a river: *Knight, Marie*
TRTCD 112 / 16 Feb '98 / TrueTrax

☐ MAKING UP AGAIN
We've got tonight: *Brooks, Elkie* / It's too late now: *Baldry, Long John* / First cut is the deepest: *Arnold, P.P.* / Out of time: *Farlowe, Chris* / Time in a bottle: *Croce, Jim* / After the goldrush: *Prelude* / Part time love: *Knight, Gladys* / Lost in France: *Tyler, Bonnie* / Can't get by without you: *Real Thing* / Love hurts: *Nazareth* / Second time around: *Shalamar* / Go now: *Moody Blues* / Summer of my life: *May, Simon* / Say you don't mind: *Blunstone, Colin* / Shooting star: *Dollar* / Love is love: *Brooks, Elkie* / Making up again: *Goldie* / Walk on by: *D-Train* / Tired of waiting for you: *Kinks* / It doesn't have to be that way: *Croce, Jim*
TRTCD 140 / Feb '96 / TrueTrax

☐ MALAWI - A KWELA CONCERT
LDX 274972 / Apr '94 / La Chant Du Monde

☐ MALE BLUES OF THE TWENTIES VOL.1 1922
DOCD 5482 / Nov '96 / Document

☐ MALE BLUES OF THE TWENTIES VOL.2 1923-1928
DOCD 5532 / Apr '97 / Document

☐ MALLORCA MIX 1998 (2CD Set)
DNT 100012 / 3 Aug '98 / Dance Network

☐ MAMADOU - THE DRUMS OF MALI
PS 65132CD / Jul '94 / PlayaSound

☐ MAMBA PERCUSSIONS VOL.1
PV 782 91 / '88 / Disques Pierre Verany

☐ MAMBO
CD 62020 / Oct '93 / Saludos Amigos

☐ MAMBO CRAZY
CDHOT 639 / 1 Jun '98 / Charly

☐ MAMBO EN LA HABANA
CD 018 / Mar '96 / Egrem

☐ MAMBO EXPLOSION
Anabacoa: *Prado, Perez & Benny More* / Mambo mucho mambo: *Machito* / Mambo diablo: *Puente, Tito* / Mambo no.5: *Puente, Tito* / Alex Mambo: *Machito* / Maria Cristina: *Prado, Perez & Benny More* / Mamborama: *Puente, Tito* / Clave mambo: *Cuba, Joe Sextet* / Scharneco's mambo: *Morales, Noro* / Baile de san vito: *Valdes, Minuelito*
12911 / Feb '97 / Laserlight

☐ MAMBO KINGS, THE
MPV 5524 / Aug '92 / Movieplay

☐ MAMBO MAMBO MAMBO
TTTCD 7 / 29 Jun '98 / Two To Tango

☐ MAMBO MANIA
Siempre en orbita: *Toro, Yomo* / Mambo para que goche: *Gonzalez, Celio* / Mambo con cha cha cha: *Faz, Roberto* / Donkey serenade: *Puente, Tito* / Guajiriando: *Bienvenido Granda* / Kandela: *Prado, Perez* / El pescador: *Figueroa, Wilfredo* / Otro coco: *Yayo El Indio* / Mambo pide le gente: *Santos, Daniel* / Eslava 22: *Damiron* / Ricci Ricci: *Puente, Tito* / Cachondea: *Feliciano, Jose 'Cheo'* / El cucu: *Capo, Bobby* / Sambrosito: *Santos, Daniel* / Me miraste y te mire: *Machito Y Sus Afro Cubanos* / Oy este mambo: *La Sonora Matancera* / Aguantando: *Paunetto, Bobby* / Go go mambo: *Grand, Rene* / Llegue: *Cuba, Joe Sextet* / Adivinanza: *Machito Y Sus Afro Cubanos*
CDHOT 619 / Apr '97 / Charly

☐ MAN AH BAD MAN
RAW 165146300126 / 8 Jun '98 / Raw Talent

☐ MAN I LOVE, THE
I got rhythm: *Ballew, Smith & Fred Rich Orchestra* / My Marguerita: *Viennese Seven Singing Sisters* / Why do I love you: *Elwin, Maurice & The Rhythmic Eight* / You do something to me: *Dietrich, Marlene* / Uncle Bill has much improved: *Frankau, Ronald* / Copper coloured gal: *Dawn, Dolly & Her Dawn Patrol* / Man I love: *Layton & Johnstone* / Miss Annabelle Lee: *Kent, Betty & Jack Simpson's Sextet* / There's something about a soldier: *Baker, George & Jack Hylton Orchestra* / Have you met Miss Jones: *Hall, Adelaide* / King's a queen at heart: *Rees, Judd* / Pretty girl is like a melody: *Hildegarde* / I must have that man: *Browne, Sam & Jack Hylton Orchestra* / For me and my gal: *Garland, Judy & Gene Kelly* / Ten cents a dance: *Hutchinson, Leslie 'Hutch'* / If you knew Susie (like I know Susie): *Shields, Ella* / Far away in a shanty town: *Grantham, Cyril & Geraldo Orchestra* / Masculine women feminine men: *Mayall, Billy & Gwen Farrar* / Mother's walking round in father's trousers: *Higgins, Charlie* / Sally: *Fields, Gracie* / Cabaret boys: *Bing, Douglas & Lance Lister* / Ida, sweet as apple cider: *Kent, Betty & Jack Simpson's Sextet* / Can't help lovin' dat man: *Layton & Johnstone* / I'm no angel: *West, Mae* / There ain't no sweet man that's worth the salt of my tears: *Rhythm Boys & Paul Whiteman Orchestra*
75605522802 / Aug '96 / Happy Days

☐ MANCHESTER VOL.1
SWDCD 001 / Nov '94 / Swamp Donkey

☐ MANCHESTER VOL.2 (Streetscene)
BOPCD 002 / Dec '95 / Boptop

☐ MANDOLIN BLUES
TCD 6004 / Nov '97 / Testament

☐ MANHATTAN SERENADES (Classic Songs Of New York)
JCD 641 / Nov '93 / Jass

☐ MANIFESTO
MASO 33045CD / Nov '88 / Materiali Sonori

☐ MANIFESTO MONSTERS (2CD Set)
I got the vibration: *Black Box* / Let's all chant: *Gusto* / I'm free: *Robinson, Janice* / Tell it to my heart: *Q-Club* / In de ghetto: *Waters, Crystal* / Vicious circles: *Poltergeist* / I feel love: *Summer, Donna* / Arms of Loren: *E'voke* / Hondy (no access): *Hondy* / Relax: *Waters, Crystal* / Feel tha vibe: *That Kid Chris* / Keep pushin': *Dlugosch, Boris* / State of independence: *Summer, Donna* / Keep on jumpin': *Wash, Martha & Jocelyn Brown* / Disco's revenge: *Gusto* / Stand the test of time: *Wiseass* / Higher state of consciousness: *Wink, Josh* / Say what: *Groove Park* / Voyager: *Mr. Spring* / Can U feel it: *Squad* / La Campana: *DJ Dero*
5341152 / Nov '96 / Manifesto

☐ MANY FACES OF BOOGIE WOOGIE, THE
AMSC 553 / Jun '96 / Avid

☐ MANY MOODS OF LOVE
RN 0036 / May '97 / Runn

☐ MAPUCHE
3001805 / 24 Feb '98 / IMP

☐ MARCHING AROUND THE WORLD
Friedlander march: *Band Of The Royal Tank Regiment* / Radetzsky march: *Band Of The HM Royal Marines* / Gibraltar: *Band Of The HM Royal Marines* / Marche des parachutistes belges: *Band Of The Parachute Regiment* / Army of the nile: *Band Of The Glosters* / Marche lorraine: *Band Of The Cheshire Regiment* / Bridge too far: *Band Of The Parachute Regiment* / Golden mile: *Band Of The Cheshire Regiment* / Cairo road: *Band Of The Cheshire Regiment* / Die soldaten von celle: *Band Of The Royal Tank Regiment* / Hands across the sea: *Band Of The Royal British Legion* / Hyde park: *Band Of The HM Royal Marines* / India, Arabia: *Band Of The Cheshire Regiment* / Arromanches: *Band Of The Royal British Legion* / Valdres march: *Band Of The Royal Tank Regiment* / Road to Vitez: *Band Of The Cheshire Regiment*
300622 / Jun '98 / Hallmark

☐ MARCUS GARVEY CHANT VOL.3
SHCD 2004 / 13 Jul '98 / Sky High

☐ MARDI GRAS - PARADE MUSIC FROM NEW ORLEANS
BCD 107 / Jul '93 / GHB

☐ MARDI GRAS TIME
That's enough of that stuff: *Ball, Marcia* / Mardi Gras mambo: *Richard, Zachary* / Mardi Gras blues: *Jocque, Beau & The Zydeco Hi-Rollers* / I went to the Mardi Gras: *Eaglin, Snooks* / Funkt Liza: *New Orleans Nightcrawlers* / Chanson de Mardi Gras: *File* / Mardi Gras in the city: *King, Earl & Roomful Of Blues* / Do whatcha wanna: *Rebirth Brass Band* / Iko iko: *Dollis, Bo & The Wild Magnolias* / Mardi Gras in New Orleans: *Dirty Dozen Brass Band* / When the saints go marching in: *Washington, Isidore 'Tuts'*
EDCD 9004 / 19 Jan '98 / Easydisc

☐ MARIE CURIE FIELDS OF HOPE (Massed Pipes & Drums)
LCOM 5247 / May '95 / Lismor

☐ MARIJUANA UNKNOWNS VOL.1
THC 001 / Nov '97 / Stoned

☐ MARIJUANA'S GREATEST HITS REVISITED
SKYCD 5024 / Sep '94 / Sky

☐ MARIMAC ANTHOLOGY, THE
ROUCD 0364 / Aug '96 / Rounder

☐ MARINES
DEM 018 / May '96 / IMP

☐ MARK GOODIER SESSIONS
MARK 1 / Mar '92 / Night Tracks

☐ MARK LAMARR'S ACE IS WILD (26 Hot Rockin' Hit Picks From The Vaults Of Ace)
Don't you just know it: *Smith, Huey 'Piano' & The Clowns* / Please don't tell 'em: *Blue dots* / Walkin' with Frankie: *Sims, Frankie Lee* / My love is here to stay: *Myers, Sammy* / High blood pressure: *Smith, Huey 'Piano' & The Clowns* / Josephine: *Ferguson, H-Bomb* / Don't leave me here to cry: *Supremes* / Cut it out: *Tex, Joe* / Is everything alright: *King, Earl* / That moves me (things I don't like): *Dixon, Floyd* / She likes to boogie real low: *Sims, Frankie Lee* / Roberta: *Ford, Frankie* / Saturday night fish fry: *Blue dots* / You can fly high: *King, Earl* / You little baby faced thing: *Tex, Joe* / You can't stop her: *Marchan, Bobby* / Rock 'n' roll bells: *Seacrest, Eddie* / Let's get it on: *Almond, Hershel & Al Good Orchestra* / I love my baby: *Phaetons* / Looking for a woman: *Almond, Hershel* / Love me: *Ray, Danny* / I love you baby: *Almond, Hershel* / Baby it's love: *Angel, Johnny* / Cheatin' woman: *Ford, Frankie* / Dearest darling: *Smith, Huey 'Piano' & The Clowns* / I kneel at your throne: *Emeralds*
WESA 812 / 20 Apr '98 / Westside

☐ MARK OF THE CELTS
Y 225057 / Feb '96 / Silex

☐ MARSEILLE
DEM 020 / Nov '97 / IMP

☐ MARSEILLE, MES AMOURS
878302 / Jun '93 / Music Memoria

☐ MARTINIS BIKINIS AND MEMORIES
Black horse: *Prado, Perez* / Hot toddy: *Flanagan, Ralph* / Moonglow: *Duning, George* / Fly me to the moon: *Hornell, Joe* / I'll catch the sun (Joanna does dinner): *Greenslade, Arthur* / Sagittarius - Gathering of the Centaurs: *Jacobs, Dick & His Orchestra* / One for my baby: *Prado, Perez* / Another man, another harmonica: *Greenslade, Arthur* / Scorpio - Say goodbye: *Jacobs, Dick & His Orchestra* / Marguerita (Maid with tequila): *Little, Big Tiny* / Make it another old fashioned please: *Merman, Ethel* / April in Paris: *Basie, Count* / Another encore, from another man without harmonica: *Greenslade, Arthur* / Chica, chica, boom, chic: *Miranda, Carmen* / Last date: *Cramer, Floyd* / Chant to the night: *Esquivel, Juan Garcia*
12804 / Aug '97 / Laserlight

☐ MAS - A CARIBBEAN CHRISTMAS PARTY
Party for Santa Claus: *Lord Nelson* / Nwel la rive: *Benjamin, Lionel* / Santa Claus (do you ever come to the ghetto): *Davis, Carlene* / Soca santa: *Machel* / Noel pou yo: *Claudette Et Ti Pierre* / Asalto navideno: *El Gran Combo* / Deck the halls with boughs of holly: *Miller, Jacob* / Santa Claus is coming to town: *Spence, Joseph* / Quand j'entends chante Noel: *Gustave, Eddy*
RCD 10150 / Nov '93 / Rykodisc

☐ MAS' HYSTERIA
NSCD 010 / Nov '96 / Nascente

☐ MAS QUE NADA (Brazilian Dance Party)
Peu pia: *Gilberto, Astrud* / One note samba: *Ramiro, Tom* / Aguas de marco: *Familia Jobim & Nova Banda* / Mas que nada: *Brasil Singers* / Desafinado: *Bonfa, Antonio Carlos* / Anos dourados: *Bethania, Maria* / O barquinho: *Ribeiro, Pery* / Olhos coloridos: *Sa, Sandra* / Passarim: *Familia Jobim & Nova Banda* / Agua de beber: *Brasil Singers* / Decisao: *Melodia, Luiz* / Insensatez: *Bonfa, Antonio Carlos* / Vida: *Shock, Obina* / Mar de copacabana: *Gil, Gilberto* / Rabo de comet: *De Vila, Martinho* / Ao velho Pedro: *Moura, Paulo* / Shadow of your smile: *Brasil Singers* / Manha de carnaval: *Ramiro, Tom* / Girl from Ipanema: *Gilberto, Astrud*
ML 51096 / Jul '98 / Musica Latina

☐ MASALA DROP VOL.7 (Music For Meditation)
MASOCD 90099 / 27 Apr '98 / Materiali Sonori

☐ MASCULINE WOMAN AND FEMININE MEN
PASTCD 7072 / May '95 / Flapper

☐ MASHING UP CREATION
CCDUBM 001 / Feb '97 / Dubmission

☐ MASSED CHOIRS (2CD Set)
R2CD 4046 / 13 Apr '98 / Deja Vu

☐ MASSIVE (2CD Set)
AUMASS 1CD / 29 Jun '98 / Au

☐ MASSIVE BREAKBEATS
MSS 0028 / 30 Mar '98 / Mutant Sound System

☐ MASSIVE DANCE '97 (2CD Set)
5553432 / 24 Nov '97 / PolyGram TV

☐ MASSIVE DANCE '98 VOL.2 (2CD Set)
Horny: *Mousse T* / Feel it: *Tamperer & Maya* / Fight for your right: *NYCC* / Found a cure: *Ultra Nate* / La primavera: *Sash* / It's like that: *Run DMC & Jason Nevins* / Deeper love: *Ruff Driverz* / Kung fu: *187 Lockdown* / Life ain't easy: *Cleopatra* / Beat goes on: *All Seeing I* / No way: *Freakpower* / Sounds of wickedness: *Tzant* / Renegade master: *Wildchild* / Get up stand up: *Phunky Phantom* / Jungle brother: *Jungle Brothers* / Rude boy rock: *Lionrock* / Nobody better: *Moore, Tina* / Angel street: *M-People* / Last thing on my mind: *Steps* / Kung fu fighting: *Bus Stop & Carl Douglas* / Doctor Jones: *Aqua* / You make me feel (mighty real): *Stingily, Byron* / Ready for a new day: *Terry, Todd* / Be alone no more: *Another Level* / Treat infamy: *Rest Assured* / Can you feel it: *CLS* / Meet her at the love parade: *Da Hool* / Wizards of the sonic: *Westbam & Red Jerry* / Here I go: *DOP* / Superstar: *Novy, Tom & Eniac* / Sincere: *Cole, MJ* / Anytime: *Nu Birth* / Never ever: *All Saints* / High: *Lighthouse Family* / Show me love: *Robyn* / Uh la la la: *Alexia* / Brimful of Asha: *Cornershop* / Disrememberance: *Minogue, Dannii* / More: *De'Lacy* / Remember: *BT*
5650632 / 1 Jun '98 / PolyGram TV

☐ MASSIVE HITS OF HOUSE (2CD Set)
DRCD 001 / 30 Mar '98 / Dance Reaction

☐ MASSIVE HOUSE HEAVEN (2CD Set)
SMDCD 113 / 9 Feb '98 / Snapper

☐ MASSIVE REGGAE (4CD Set)
SUMBX 4016 / Jan '98 / Summit

☐ MASSIVE REGGAE PARTY 1996
Baby I love your way: *Doctor* / I swear: *Rockets* / Shine: *RR Band* / Games people play: *RR Band* / You don't love me (no no no): *Just A Minute* / Don't turn around: *Just A Minute* / Sweets for my sweet: *George X* / Away from home: *Doctor* / Bayangena Baya Phuma: *Dr. Victor* / Iron lion Zion: *Dr. Victor* / Mr. Loverman: *D&V* / Oh Carolina: *Gringo* / Informer: *Show 2* / Higher ground: *100% Dance* / Can't help falling in love: *100% Dance* / Sweat (a la la la la long): *Easy Groove*
343112 / Jun '96 / Koch International

☐ MASSIVE SOCA '98
HVCD 030 / 9 Feb '98 / Hot Vinyl

☐ MASSIVE SOUND OF RAP, THE (4CD Set)
MSCD 4 / Jun '97 / Mo's Music Machine

☐ MASSIVE SOUNDS OF AURA SURROUND SOUNDS (4CD Set)
NEW generation: *MLO* / One million faces: *Incisions* / Understood: *Must* / Thunderdome: *Thursday Club* / London's on acid: *Cabbage Patch* / Give me a wink: *Fingers Project* / In the heat of the night: *Overhead Noise* / Shofou: *Tyoussi* / Scrumble: *DJ Misjah & Tim* / Temple of acid: *Temple Of Acid* / Deltoid: *Hardline 2* / Overload: *DJ Misjah & Tim* / Dreamlab: *MLO* / Chafs: *Sinus* / Eternal: *Epik* / Dig deep: *Blokka* / Place called acid: *Thursday Club* / Squelch: *Finitribe* / Play D musik: *OCP* / Want you now: *Must* / Breakdown: *Incisions* / Exploration: *Blokka* / Feel it: *Renegade* / What is going on: *Dex* / Man woman love: *DJ Misjah & Groovehend* / Blob: *Epik* / Ice Station Zebra: *Temple Of Acid* / Axiom: *Arcana* / Trancition: *Choci & Freedom Of Sound* / Samarkand: *MLO* / Driver: *Epik* / Midsummers dream: *Blokka*
MSCD 1 / Mar '97 / Aura Surround Sounds

☐ MASSIVE SOUNDS OF RED LIGHTNIN' BLUES, THE (4CD Set)
MSCD 2 / 2 Feb '98 / Red Lightnin'

☐ MASSIVE SOUNDS OF UNDERGROUND VIBE, THE (4CD Set)
MSCD 1 / Mar '97 / Mo's Music Machine

☐ MASTER AND DISCIPLES
CDBM 092 / May '93 / Blue Moon

☐ MASTER BRASS VOL.1 (All England Masters Championship 1990)
French military march / Light Cavalry Overture / Miss blue bonnet / Elegy from a 'Downland Suite' / Coriolanus / Marching through Georgia / Blitz / Someone to watch over me / Sun has got his hat on / Thre negro spirituals / Neapolitan scenes / Blenheim flourishes / Nightfall in camp
QPRL 046D / Oct '97 / Polyphonic

☐ MASTER BRASS VOL.2 (All England Masters Championship 1991)
Morning, Noon and night / Overture: Candide / Allerseelen / Marche slave / Harmony music / American fanfare / Jaguar / Ballet music / Robert le diable / Cornet carillon / Bandology / Great gate of Kiev / Witches sabbath / Evening hymn and sunset
QPRL 048D / Oct '97 / Polyphonic

☐ MASTER BRASS VOL.3 (All England Masters Championship 1992)
Midwest / Overture: Zampa / Summertime / Music from the XVI century / Cambridge variations / Introduction act 3 / Lohengrin / Pineapple Poll / Pantomime / Wedding procession 'Le coq d'or' / Pastime with good company / Procession to the minster / Finlandia
QPRL 052D / Oct '97 / Polyphonic

☐ MASTER BRASS VOL.4 (All England Masters Championship 1993)
Overture: The marriage of Figaro / Sorcerer's apprentice / Pandora / Spider and the fly / Grand march from Aida / English heritage / Blue rondo a la Turk / Lost chord / Festival overture
QPRL 060D / Oct '97 / Polyphonic

☐ MASTER BRASS VOL.5 (All England Masters Championship 1994)
Jubilee prelude / Someone to watch over me / Hailstorm / Eighteenth Variation (On a theme of) / Montage / Folk festival / Pavanne / Take your picc / Russian and Ludmilla / Georgia on my mind / Jerusalem / Entry of the Gods into Valhalla
QPRL 067D / Oct '97 / Polyphonic

☐ **MASTER BRASS VOL.6 (All England Masters Championship 1995)**
Victors' return / Dancing in the park / Deep inside the sacred temple / Paganini variations / La danza / Oberon / Hoe down / Zimba zamba / Dance of the comedians / Bolero
QPRL 073D / Oct '97 / Polyphonic

☐ **MASTER BRASS VOL.7 (All England Masters Championship 1996)**
Washington Grays: *Yorkshire Building Society Band* / Aye waukin' o: *Yorkshire Building Society Band* / Alloway tales: *Yorkshire Building Society Band* / Only love: *Yorkshire Building Society Band* / Savonic rhapsody no.2: *Yorkshire Building Society Band* / Hymns at sunrise: *Williams-Fairey Engineering Band* / Malaguena: *Grimethorpe Colliery Band* / Scottish dances: *Grimethorpe Colliery Band* / Satchmo: *Grimethorpe Colliery Band* / Sugar blues: *Grimethorpe Colliery Band* / In perfect peace: *Grimethorpe Colliery Band* / McArthur Park: *Grimethorpe Colliery Band*
QPRL 083D / Sep '96 / Polyphonic

☐ **MASTER BRASS VOL.8**
Barnum and Bailey's favourite / Overture / Abu Hassan / Carnival cocktail / Elegy from epic symphony / Toccata in D minor / It's alright with me / Riverdance / Jazz / Be a clown / Helter skelter / Priere a Notre Dame / Marianne / Hora staccato / Swing low sweet chariot / Capriccio Espagnol
QPRL 088D / Oct '97 / Polyphonic

☐ **MASTERPIECE VOL.3**
LDRCD 019 / Aug '95 / Londisc

☐ **MASTERS OF FRENCH JAZZ 1937-1944**
2512802 / Feb '91 / Jazztime

☐ **MASTERS OF HARDCORE VOL.2 (2CD Set)**
IDT 000768 / Dec '96 / ID&T

☐ **MASTERS OF HOUSE, THE (2CD Set)**
BB 35243DCD / May '96 / Broken Beat

☐ **MASTERS OF PERCUSSION, THE**
MRCD 1012 / Jan '95 / Moment

☐ **MASTERS OF ROCK, THE (3CD Set)**
DTKBOX 54 / Sep '96 / Dressed To Kill

☐ **MASTERS OF SWING, THE**
It's only a paper moon: *Cole, Nat 'King'* / Jeepers creepers: *Bennett, Tony* / I can't give you anything but love: *Torme, Mel* / Trolley song: *Sinatra, Frank* / Say it isn't so: *Crosby, Bing* / Cottage for sale: *Eckstine, Billy* / Blue skies: *Crosby, Bing* / Surrey with the fringe on top: *Sinatra, Frank* / I've got the world on a string: *Torme, Mel* / That old black magic: *Eckstine, Billy* / Embraceable you: *Cole, Nat 'King'* / Chicago (that toddlin' town): *Bennett, Tony* / I'm getting sentimental over you: *Torme, Mel* / Misty: *Eckstine, Billy* / Cheek to cheek/All by myself: *Crosby, Bing* / Life is a song: *Bennett, Tony* / How deep is the ocean: *Cole, Nat 'King'* / Lullaby of Broadway: *Sinatra, Frank*
ECD 3284 / Jan '97 / K-Tel

☐ **MASTERS OF TECHNOLOGY (2CD Set)**
SMRCD 01 / 3 Nov '97 / Second Movement

☐ **MASTERS OF THE FOLK VIOLIN, THE**
ARHCD 434 / Apr '95 / Arhoolie

☐ **MASTERS OF THE PANPIPES, THE**
EUCD 1318 / Nov '95 / ARC

☐ **MASTERS OF TURKISH MUSIC VOL.2 1906-1949, THE**
ROUCD 1111 / Sep '96 / Rounder

☐ **MASTERS OF ZEN, THE**
PS 65153 / Sep '95 / PlayaSound

☐ **MASTERS SOLO DRUMMING CHAMPIONSHIP 1997**
COMD 2066 / Jul '97 / Temple

☐ **MATADOR'S ARENA VOL.1 (1968-1969)**
JMC 200222 / Jun '95 / Jamaican Gold

☐ **MATADOR'S ARENA VOL.2**
JMC 200223 / Aug '95 / Jamaican Gold

☐ **MATADOR'S ARENA VOL.3**
JMC 200224 / Aug '95 / Jamaican Gold

☐ **MATCHBOX DAYS (Really The English Country Blues)**
Bulldog blues: *Cooper, Mike* / Few short lines: *Kelly, Dave* / Say no to the Devil: *Prager, Simon & Steve Rye* / Nothin' in ramblin': *Kelly, Jo Ann* / Cottonfield blues: *Anderson, Ian A.* / Whitewash station: *Panama Ltd. Jug Band* / Searchin' the desert: *Jones, Al* / Dark road blues: *Missouri Compromise* / Spoonful: *Jones, Wizz* / Meeting house rag: *Cooper, Mike* / Blues walking like a man: *Kelly, Dave* / Stop breaking down: *Prager, Rye & Hall* / Rowdy blues: *Anderson, Ian A.* / Wildcat: *Panama Ltd. Jug Band* / Travellin' blues: *Kelly, Dave* / Bread of heaven: *Rye, Steve* / Black snake moan: *Cooper, Mike* / Cocaine habit: *Panama Ltd. Jug Band* / Friday evening blues: *Anderson, Ian A.* / If I had possession over Judgement Day: *Missouri Compromise* / Black Mary: *Kelly, Jo Ann* / Inverted world: *Anderson, Ian A. & Mike Cooper*
CDWIKD 168 / Feb '97 / Big Beat

☐ **MATERIALISM**
CDNEW 120 / 30 Mar '98 / Charly

☐ **MATRIX DUB**
CEND 1300 / Jan '97 / Century

☐ **MAU MAU JUNGLE**
CD 007 / Jan '93 / Sky High

☐ **MAURITIUS - SEGAS**
C 580060 / Oct '94 / Ocora

☐ **MAX POWER - MAX BASS VOL.1**
BDRCD 15 / Oct '96 / Breakdown

☐ **MAX POWER - MAX BASS VOL.2**
Switch: *Dream Team* / Symetrix: *Future Force* / Wolf: *Shy FX* / Twisted: *Swift* / Style: *Ill Figure* / Stick 'em up: *Remarc* / Mode one: *IQ Collective* / Nightflight: *Andy C & Shimon* / Twister: *Decoder* / International: *MTS* / Who is it: *Firefox* / Reply: *Mask* / Rucus: *Gang Related* / Throat: *Dream Team*
BDRCD 19 / Apr '97 / Breakdown

☐ **MAX THE DOG SAYS... DO THE SKA**
DOJOCD 92 / Dec '92 / Dojo

☐ **MAXI DANCE (2CD Set)**
And the beat goes on: *Whispers* / Just an illusion: *Imagination* / Jump on the rhythm and ride: *Imagination* / From East to West: *Voyage* / Papa was a rolling stone: *Third World* / High energy: *Thomas, Evelyn* / Shoot your shot: *Divine* / Passion: *Flirts* / Can you feel the force: *Real Thing* / Jeopardy: *Kihn, Greg* / Pop muzik: *M* / Rapper's delight: *Sugarhill Gang* / Freedom: *Grandmaster Flash & The Furious Five* / Uptown festival: *Shalamar* / Baby now that I've found you: *Foundations* / Boogie on up: *Rokotto* / Music and lights: *Imagination* / Never can say goodbye: *Gaynor, Gloria* / Feels like I'm in love: *Marie, Kelly* / Ring my bell: *Ward, Anita* / West End girls: *Pet Shop Boys*
24360 / Feb '97 / Laserlight

☐ **MAXI RAI (4CD Set)**
DECLI 845126 / 3 Mar '98 / Munich

☐ **MAXI SALSA (4CD Set)**
DECLI 845131 / 3 Mar '98 / Munich

☐ **MAXI-MUM TENAGLIA**
XTR 18CDM / Nov '95 / X-Treme

☐ **MAXIMUM FREAKBEAT**
I'm a man: *Elois* / You can be my baby: *Elois* / Hey gyp: *Truth* / On my way: *Kings, Lee* / Come on back: *Crying Shames* / Save my soul: *Wimple Winch* / I don't wanna go: *Southern Sound* / You're driving me insane: *Southern Sound* / I'm leaving: *Mark Four* / Roadblock: *Wheels* / Crawdaddy Simone: *Syndicats* / It's shocking what they call me: *GAME* / I want to live: *Mascots* / Lost girl: *Troggs* / Get yourself home: *Fairies* / Going down fast: *Mark Four* / I don't care: *Thor's Hammer* / Searchin' in the wilderness: *Get Rich* / Johnny no: *Primitives* / Action painting: *Ricketts*
REVERB 9 / 20 Apr '98 / Reverb

☐ **MAXIMUM SPEED (2CD Set)**
My desire: *Amira* / Theme: *Dream Team* / Runnin' away: *Nicole* / Gunman: *187 Lockdown* / Bad boys: *Baffled Republic* / Hold your head up high: *Baffled Republic* / Let's groove: *Morel, George* / Don't give up: *Weeks, Michelle* / I refuse: *Weeks, Michelle* / Just gets better: *TJR & Xavier* / Sound bwoy burial: *Gant* / I surrender: *Gant* / Sing a song: *Stingily, Byron* / Free: *Ultra Nate* / I need a miracle: *Coco* / What would we do: *Coco* / Oh boy: *Fabulous Baker Boys* / Belo horizonti: *Heartists* / Got funk: *Heartists* / Turn me out: *Heartists* / Gabriel: *Heartists* / Saved my life: *Edwards, Todd* / Bizzi's party: *Bizzi* / Boss: *Braxtons* / Love shy: *Blond, Kristine* / Get on up: *Jodeci* / Anytime: *Nu-Birth* / To deserve you: *Midler, Bette* / Testify: *Williams, Jay* / Spin spin: *Sneaker Pimps* / Call on me: *Johnny X* / Feel free: *Livin' Large* / London thing: *Garcia, Scott & MC Styles* / Small step: *Victor Goes Ballistic* / Every little time: *Poppers & Aura* / Partay feeling: *B-Crew* / Reach: *Cheeks, Judy* / We can make it happen: *NCA* / Happiness: *Pepper Mashay* / Learn ll love: *English, Kim*
VTDCD 173 / 8 Dec '97 / Virgin

☐ **MAY YOUR SONGS ALWAYS BE SUNG**
All along the watchtower: *Hedges, Michael* / Masters of war: *Feliciano, Jose* / Blowin' in the wind: *Bare, Bobby* / Chimes of freedom: *Carmen, Phil* / Never say goodbye: *Keene, Steven* / Series of dreams: *Zimmerman* / Memphis blues again: *Helmig, Thomas* / Seven days: *Barnes, Jimmy* / Trust yourself: *Carter, Carlene* / Highway 61: *Chiarelli, Rita* / Suterranean homesick blues: *Nilsson, Harry* / Ballad of the thin man: *Sports* / All I really want to do: *Hooters* / Sign on the window: *Warnes, Jennifer* / I shall be released: *Box Tops* / Blind Willie McTell: *Dream Syndicate* / Mighty quinn: *Gotthard* / Knockin' on heaven's door: *Leningrad Cowboys*
743214708828 / Sep '97 / Ariola

☐ **MAYHEM AND PSYCHOSIS VOL.1**
Generation: *Jelly Bean Bandits* / Savage affection: *Holocaust* / Don't lose your mind: *Galaxies IV* / I'm gone: *Magic Mushrooms* / Spider and the fly: *Monacles* / I'm a nothing: *Magic Plants* / Everything there: *Hysterics* / Bad way to go: *Brothers* / 17 years to the end: *Liverpool Set* / I'm a leather boy: *Leather Boy* / Got love: *Front Line* / Why don't you smile: *All Night Workers* / It's trash: *Cavemen* / Original nothing people: *Beatin' Path* / Why: *Dirty Wurds* / Orange rooftop of your mind: *Blue Things* / We're pretty quick: *Chob* / Boil the kettle mother: *ID* / Chocolate moose theme: *Chocolate Moose* / Great train robbery: *Little Boy Blues* / Bad part of town: *Bare Facts* / You're gonna miss me: *Spades* / Love: *Ravin' Blue* / End: *Ruins* / Colours and shapes: *Nobody's Children* / True justice: *Third Stone* / Go your way: *Changing Tymes* / Now you're mine: *Barons*
L 0020CD / Apr '98 / Laroche

☐ **MAYHEM AND PSYCHOSIS VOL.2**
Hipsville 29 BC: *Sparkles* / Evil eye: *Burning Bush* / Lonely weekend: *THEM* / Living Memories: *Trespassers* / Count back: *Purple Underground* / ESP: *Rain* / I can't believe: *Fanatics* / Midnight hour: *Wanted* / I see the light: *Five Americans* / I can only give you everything: *Rainy Daze* / Where you gonna go: *Unrelated Segments* / Brown eyed girl: *Golliwogs* / Bad times: *Clue* / Hydrogen atom: *Bedlam 4* / Baby please don't go: *Moonrakers* / She ain't no use to me: *Ugly Ducklings* / If you want to: *Showstoppers* / Little thing: *Deepest Blue* / Witness people: *Fountain Of Youth* / Voodoo: *Unknowns* / Everything's gone wrong: *Knight, Larry & Upsetters* / Confetti: *Spectrum* / You put me through changes: *Sentrificail Fours* / Slow down: *Swingin' Apollos* / Don't be a dropout: *Oxfords* / Takin' care of business: *Trippers* / Come on into my mind: *Endd* / Evil: *Backdoor Men*
L 0021CD / Apr '98 / Laroche

☐ **MBUKI MVUKI**
OMCD 017 / May '93 / Original Music

☐ **MBUTI PYGMIES OF THE ITURI RAINFOREST**
SFCD 40401 / Sep '94 / Smithsonian Folkways

☐ **ME GONE BUCK WILD (Reggae Dancehall Killers)**
322664 / Apr '97 / Shanachie

☐ **ME NAISET**
KICD 37 / Nov '95 / Kansanmusiikki Instituutti

☐ **MEALTIME**
DMC: *Jega* / Get some sleep tiger: *Red Snapper* / Morpeth Issot: *Wafta* / Eternally: *Point Blank* / Bummy: *AFX* / Utility fog: *Horse Opera* / Sved buttock: *Animals On Wheels* / Fluffy effort: *Mould* / Switch hardflip: *Fastbrook, Elton* / Argos: *Plug* / Mr. Angry: *u-Ziq* / Brace yourself: *u-Ziq*
CDPU 006 / 24 Nov '97 / Planet U

☐ **MEATMEN**
VPCD 2055 / Oct '96 / VP

☐ **MECHANICAL MUSIC HALL**
Burlington Bertie from Bow / After the ball / Nellie Dean / Where did you get that hat / K-K-K-Katy / Flanagan / Down at the old Bull and Bush / Lily of Laguna / If it wasn't for the 'ouses in between / Bill Bailey, won't you please come home / Beside the seaside / Ask a policeman / Don't have any more, Mrs. Moore / Any old iron / My old dutch / Boiled beef and carrots / Ta-ra-ra-boom-de-ay
CDSDL 232 / Jan '92 / Saydisc

☐ **MECHANICAL PARADISE**
NBX 007 / Oct '94 / Haven

☐ **MEDITATION**
22515 / Feb '96 / Music

☐ **MEDLEY TRAIN**
CDTRL 350 / Mar '95 / Trojan

☐ **MEET ME TONIGHT**
BB 2810 / Apr '95 / Blue Beat

☐ **MEETING OF THE WATERS**
Bonnie Mulligan: *Shannon, Sharon* / Wrecking ball: *Harris, Emmylou* / Funny red car: *Cafe Orchestra* / Borders and time: *Rankin Family* / Wonderful thing: *Dowdall, Leslie* / In the morning: *Tamalin* / 17: *Ian, Janis* / Set you free: *Nomos* / Cool as I am: *Williams, Dar* / Da da da: *Nervous* / What do you dream of: *Crenshaw, Marshall* / Song of the rosy cross: *Scott, Mike & Sharon Shannon*
GRACD 232 / 20 Oct '97 / Grapevine

☐ **MEGA BODY BEATS**
Seven days and one week: *BBE* / Soldier soldier: *Captain Jack* / Sing: *Nakatomi* / Freed from desire: *Gala* / Black Betty: *Flashback* / Don't stop movin': *Livin' Joy* / You make me feel: *Real DJ* / Big beat: *Capella* / Believe in the future: *Critical Mass* / My little fantasy: *4 Tune* / Street life: *Peroni Project & Jessica* / Up to no good: *Porn Kings* / Too beautiful: *Blue Zone* / Take my love: *Alitha* / El tiburon: *Project Uno* / U gotta get down: *Pryme*
DC 881652 / Jul '97 / Disky

☐ **MEGA BODY VIBES**
Captain Jack: *Captain Jack* / Jump for joy: *2 Unlimited* / We've got it goin' on: *Backstreet Boys* / I got 5 on it: *Luniz* / Time is up: *Milton, C.B.* / I need your love: *Cappella* / Babies are crazy: *Chakra* / Ultra flava: *Heller & Farley Project* / Children: *Miles, Robert* / Theme from S'Express: *S'Express* / Night train: *Kadoc* / In spirit: *Dilemma* / Give me luv: *Alcatraz* / Party over here: *740 Boyz* / Spank: *D-Xpress & Farida Melville* / Black is black: *Belle Epoque*
WLT 874592 / Oct '96 / Disky

☐ **MEGA DANCE HITS 1997**
ZYX 100482 / 13 Oct '97 / ZYX

☐ **MEGA ITALIA (4CD Set)**
3008002 / Feb '97 / Arcade

☐ **MEGA REGGAE DANCE (4CD Set)**
3008392 / Feb '97 / Arcade

☐ **MEGA SALSA (4CD Set)**
3011972 / Feb '97 / Arcade

☐ **MEGA SOUL (4CD Set)**
3034732 / 24 Feb '98 / Arcade

☐ **MEGA STARS (2CD Set)**
Maria Magdalena: *Sandra* / Bette Davis eyes: *Carnes, Kim* / Baker street: *Rafferty, Gerry* / Skandal im sperbezirk: *Murphy, Spider Band* / Missing you: *Waite, John* / Kids in America: *Wilde, Kim* / Nineteen: *Hardcastle, Paul* / China in your hand: *T'Pau* / Eyes without a face: *Idol, Billy* / Kayleigh: *Marillion* / Locomotive breath: *Jethro Tull* / On the road again: *Canned Heat* / Captain Jack: *Captain Jack* / Apache: *Shadows* / There is a party: *DJ Bobo* / Mississippi: *Pussycat* / If only I could: *Youngblood, Sydney* / Sunshine reggae: *Laidback* / Gimme hope Joanna: *Grant, Eddy* / Do you really want to hurt me: *Culture Club* / Don't let me be misunderstood: *Santa Esmeralda* / Such a shame: *Talk Talk* / Wild boys: *Duran Duran* / Too shy: *Kajagoogoo* / True: *Spandau Ballet* / Showing out: *Mel & Kim* / Good heart: *Sharkey, Feargal* / Words: *David, F.R.* / Don't worry be happy: *McFerrin, Bobby* / Vienna: *Ultravox*
DOU 883112 / 2 Feb '98 / Disky

☐ **MEGA ZOUK (2CD Set)**
3005012 / Feb '97 / Arcade

☐ **MEGARAVE 1998 (2CD Set)**
MR 008 / 29 Apr '98 / Megarave

☐ **MEGASOFT OFFICE '97**
Way form one (so hard): *Elegia* / Saulbass theme: *Ready Made* / Seasons: *Feedback* / Bewildered: *Nova Nova* / No way out: *Chaotik Ramses* / Na Na's waltz: *Aqua Bassino* / Footprints: *Reminiscent Drive* / Downward rush of the stream: *Juantrip* / NYC dharma: *Reminiscent Drive* / Ibiza: *Aqua Bassino*
F 066CD / Jun '97 / F-Communications

☐ **MEGATRIPOLIS (3CD Set)**
FUNKYPCD 1 / Jul '96 / Funky Peace

☐ **MEINE TEXTE, MEINE LIEDER (3CD Set)**
BCD 15603 / Jul '91 / Bear Family

☐ **MELLOW ACID VIBES**
MUSCD 042 / 18 May '98 / MCI Music

☐ **MELLOW TUNES (2CD Set)**
560092 / Apr '97 / Nova Tekk

☐ **MELLOW YELLOW**
Hi ho silver lining: *Beck, Jeff* / Wild thing: *Troggs* / Keep on running: *Davis, Spencer Group* / Mony mony: *James, Tommy & The Shondells* / Don't let me be misunderstood: *Animals* / Doo wah diddy diddy: *Manfred Mann* / Game of love: *Fontana, Wayne & The Mindbenders* / In the middle of nowhere: *Springfield, Dusty* / Then I kissed her: *Beach Boys* / Matthew and son: *Cat Stevens* / Cryin' game: *Berry, Dave* / Kites: *Dupree, Simon & The Big Sound* / Urban spaceman: *Bonzo Dog Band* / Fire: *Crazy World Of Arthur Brown* / On the road again: *Canned Heat* / What you gonna do about it: *Small Faces* / <bBend me shape me: *Amen Corner* / Georgy girl: *Seekers* / Hole in my shoe: *Traffic* / Mellow yellow: *Donovan*
559072 / Oct '97 / Spectrum

☐ **MELLOW'S PLACE**
IDT 000331 / Nov '96 / ID&T

☐ **MELODEON GREATS**
TSCD 601 / Aug '95 / Topic

☐ **MELODIES AND MEMORIES FROM IRELAND (Pan Pipes Collection)**
Red is the rose/Fields of Athenry / Wild colonial boy/ Noreen Bawn / Endearing young charms/Boys from the County Armagh / Teddy O'Neill / Wild Irish rose/ Mothers love's a blessing / Silver threads among the gold / Star of the County Down/Patsy Fagan / If your Irish/Shillelagh under me arm / It's a long way to Tipperary / I'll take you home Kathleen/Rare ould times / Danny boy / When I grow too old to dream / Green glens of Antrim / Irish Molly/Great day for the Irish / When Irish eyes are smiling / Auld lamas fair/ McNamara's band
PADDYCD 4 / 2 Feb '98 / Commercial

☐ **MELODIES FROM MADAGASCAR**
PS 65124 / Apr '94 / PlayaSound

☐ **MELODIES OF LOVE (2CD Set)**
Always on my mind: *Presley, Elvis* / When I fall in love: *Cole, Nat 'King'* / We have all the time in the world: *Armstrong, Louis* / Mad about the boy: *Washington, Dinah* / Unchained melody: *Righteous Brothers* / Fever: *Lee, Peggy* / (I left my heart) in San Francisco: *Bennett, Tony* / Cry me a river: *London, Julie* / That ole devil called love: *Holiday, Billie* / I wanna be loved by you: *Monroe, Marilyn* / Memories are made of this: *Martin, Dean* / Passing strangers: *Vaughan, Sarah & Billy Eckstine* / Summertime: *Fitzgerald, Ella* / As time goes by: *Nilsson, Harry* / I put a spell on you: *Simone, Nina* / Call me irresponsible: *Washington, Dinah* / Nature boy: *Cole, Nat 'King'* / Lover man (oh, where can you be): *Holiday, Billie* / Moonlight serenade: *Miller, Glenn Orchestra* / White Christmas: *Crosby, Bing* / Only the lonely: *Orbison, Roy* / Blue velvet: *Vinton, Bobby* / Will you still love me tomorrow: *Shirelles* / Breaking up is hard to do: *Sedaka, Neil* / Love letters: *Lester, Ketty* / Crazy: *Cline, Patsy* / And I love you so: *Como, Perry* / Stranger in paradise: *Bennett, Tony* / Moon river: *Williams, Andy* / Something's gotten hold of my heart: *Pitney, Gene* / It's now or never: *Presley, Elvis* / Stand by your man: *Wynette, Tammy* / All I have to do is dream: *Everly Brothers* / Oh, Carol: *Sedaka, Neil* / Born free: *Monro, Matt* / Goldfinger: *Bassey, Shirley* / Magic moments: *Como, Perry* / Diamonds are a girl's best friend: *Monroe, Marilyn* / Ain't misbehavin': *Vaughan, Sarah* / What a wonderful world: *Armstrong, Louis*
GLOCD 29 / Jul '97 / Global TV

☐ **MELODIES RUSSES**
3033142 / 24 Feb '98 / Arcade

☐ **MELODY TIME VOL.1 (2CD Set)**
Feeling fine: *Drummond, Don* / If I could rule the world: *Ellis, Alton* / Sinners: *Hinds, Justin & The Dominoes* / Ethiopians: *Mother's Tender Care* / Do it right: *Three Tops* / On the beach: *Paragons* / You don't care: *Techniques* / Don't stay away: *Dillon, Phyllis* / I'll be lonely: *Holt, John* / Moonlight Lover: *Landis, Joya* / Jimmy Brown: *Parker, Ken* / To the other man: *Lewis, Hopeton* / Stampede: *McCook, Tommy & The Supersonics* / Weather report: *Tennors* / Where must I go: *Dunkley, Errol* / Sincerely: *Russell, Dorothy and Ken Parker* / I fell in love: *Conquerors* / Loving wine: *Cole, Stranger and Hortense Ellis* / Dearest: *Dotty and Bonny featuring Don Drummond* / Musical communion: *Brooks, Baba* / Corner stone: *Hinds, Justin & The Dominoes* / Rock steady: *Ellis, Alton* / Ba ba boom: *Jamaicans* / Ride mi donkey: *Tennors* / Don't touch me tomato: *Dillon, Phyllis* / Angel of the morning: *Landis, Joya* / You don't need me: *Melodians* / Everyday is like a holiday: *Sensations* / DJ's choice: *Alcapone, Dennis* / Wear you to the ball: *U.Roy* / Ball a fire: *McCook, Tommy & The Supersonics* / True true true: *Parker, Ken* / Loving pauper: *Dobson, Dobby* / Raindrops: *Silvertones* / You were to be: *Gladiators* / Love up kiss up: *Termites* / Rukumbiine: *Duffus, Shenley* / Next door neighbour: *Grey, Owen and Leon Silvera* / Musical storeroom: *Skatalites*
RN 7025 / 25 Aug '97 / Rhino

☐ **MELT 2000 SAMPLER VOL.1**
BW 085 / 27 Apr '98 / Melt 2000

☐ **MELT 2000 SAMPLER VOL.2**
BW 087 / 27 Apr '98 / Melt 2000

☐ **MELTING PLOT**
SST 249CD / Jan '89 / SST

☐ **MEMORABLE RECORDINGS, THE**
Steamboat stomp / Jazz me blues / Apex blues / Toby / Queer notions / Moods / Maple leaf rag / Nothin' but the blues / Barrelhouse / Boogie woogie stomp / Porter's love song to a chambermaid / Organ grinder's swing / Mood that I'm in / Crazy rhythm / I got rhythm / Shoe shiner's drag / South Rampart Street Parade / I don't stand a ghost of a chance with you / Blues in thirds / When it's sleepy time down South / Perdido / World is waiting for the sunrise / DA blues
TPZ 1035 / Nov '97 / Topaz Jazz

☐ **MEMORIES (18 Love Songs From The 1960's)**
Groovy kind of love: *Fontana, Wayne* / Crying game: *Berry, Dave* / You've got your troubles (I've got mine): *Fortunes* / Bad to me: *Kramer, Billy J.* / You're no good: *Swinging Blue Jeans* / With a girl like you: *Troggs* / Someone, someone: *Poole, Brian* / I think of you: *Merseybeats* / She's not there: *Zombies* / Sweets for my sweet: *Drifters* / Somewhere: *Proby, P.J.* / Rhythm of the rain: *Cascades* / Goin' out of my head: *Little Anthony & The Imperials* / Then you can tell me goodbye: *Casinos* / Woman, woman: *Puckett, Gary & The Union Gap* / Silence is golden: *Tremeloes* / You were on my mind: *Crispin St Peters* / Happy together: *Turtles*
ECD 3078 / Dec '96 / K-Tel

☐ **MEMORIES ARE MADE OF THIS (2CD Set)**
Portrait of my love: *Monro, Matt* / There must be a way: *Vaughan, Frankie* / Moon river: *Williams, Danny* / Diane: *Bachelors* / I love how you love me: *Crawford, Jimmy* / Dreamboat: *Cogan, Alma* / Edelweiss: *Hill, Vince* / No other love: *Hilton, Ronnie* / Wayward wind: *Ifield, Frank* / Greenfields: *Beverley Sisters* / Shifting whispering sands: *Andrews, Eamonn* / Gilly gilly Ossenfeffer katzeneller bogen by the sea: *Bygraves, Max* / Story of my life: *Holliday, Michael* / I pretend: *O'Connor, Des* / Whispering grass: *Davies, Windsor & Don Estelle* / Memories are made of this: *Martin, Dean* / Spanish eyes: *Martino, Al* / Unforgettable: *Cole, Nat 'King'* / Fever: *Lee, Peggy* / You belong to me: *Stafford, Jo* / True love: *Crosby, Bing & Grace Kelly* / Tom Dooley: *Kingston Trio* / Old rivers: *Brennan, Walter* / Sixteen tons: *Ford, Tennessee Ernie* / Under the bridges of Paris: *Kitt, Eartha* / Blueberry Hill: *Domino, Fats* / Cry me a river: *London, Julie* / Honeycomb: *Rodgers, Jimmie* / Night has a thousand eyes: *Vee, Bobby* / Rose Marie: *Whitman, Slim*
DOU 882522 / 2 Feb '98 / Disky

☐ **MEMORIES ARE MADE OF THIS**
Let's face the music: *Cole, Nat 'King'* / Memories are made of this: *Martin, Dean* / Great pretender: *Platters* / Passing strangers: *Vaughan, Sarah & Billy Eckstine* / Who's sorry now: *Francis, Connie* / Fever: *Lee, Peggy* / Kiss me honey honey kiss me: *Bassey, Shirley* / Tulips from Amsterdam: *Bygraves, Max* / Man from Laramie: *Young, Jimmy* / Green door: *Vaughan, Frankie* / This ole house: *Anthony, Billie* / Seven little girls sitting in the back seat: *Avons* / Mr. Sandman: *Valentine, Dickie* / Endless sleep: *Wilde, Marty* / Cara mia: *Whitfield, David* / True love: *Crosby, Bing & Grace Kelly* / Softly softly: *Murray, Ruby* / Story of my life: *Holliday, Michael* / Breeze and I: *Valente, Caterina* / Poor people of Paris: *Atwell, Winifred* / Dreamboat: *Cogan, Alma* / No other love: *Hilton, Ronnie* / Cherry pink and apple blossom white: *Calvert, Eddie* / Rose Marie: *Whitman, Slim* / Here in my heart: *Martino, Al*
5529002 / Oct '97 / Spectrum

☐ **MEMORIES ARE STILL MADE OF HITS VOL.1**
Under the moon of love: *Lee, Curtis* / Baby oh baby: *Shells* / If you gotta make a fool of somebody: *Ray, James* / Million to one: *Charles, Jimmy* / My true story: *Jive Five* / Once in a while: *Chimes* / One track mind: *Lewis, Bobby* / Tell me why: *Belmonts* / It's unbelievable: *Larks* / Pretty little angel eyes: *Lee, Curtis* / All in my mind: *Brown, Maxine* / Itty bitty pieces: *Ray, James* / What time is it: *Jive Five* / Soul twist: *King Curtis* / Tossin' and turnin': *Lewis, Bobby* / I'm in the mood for love: *Chimes* / Come on little angel: *Belmonts* / Til then: *Classics* / I knew it all the time: *Clark, Dave Five* / 81: *Candy & The Kisses* / Barefottin': *Parker, Robert* / Then you can tell me goodbye: *Casinos* / You've gotta be loved: *Montanas* / American boys: *Clark, Petula* / Precious and few: *Climax* / Show and tell: *Wilson, Al*
NEMCD 924 / Mar '97 / Sequel

☐ **MEMORIES ARE STILL MADE OF HITS VOL.2**
Does your chewing gum lose it's flavour: *Donegan, Lonnie* / Midnight in Moscow: *Ball, Kenny & His Jazzmen* / Bumblebee: *Searchers* / Girl don't come: *Shaw, Sandie* / Gotta have your love: *Sapphires* / Canadian sunset: *Sounds Orchestral* / Universal soldier: *Donovan* / Well respected man: *Kinks* / Here comes my baby: *Tremeloes* / Let the heartaches begin: *Long John Baldry* / Ain't nothin' but a houseparty: *Showstoppers* / Ice in the sun: *Status Quo* / Happy heart: *Clark, Petula* / I've been hurt: *Deal, Bill & The Rhondells* / Colour of my love: *Jefferson* / Smile a little smile for me: *Flying Machine* / Reflections of my life: *Marmalade* / That same old feeling: *Pickettywitch* / Something's wrong with me: *Roberts, Austin* / Dancing in the moonlight: *King Harvest* / Delta queen: *Fardon, Don* / I'm doin' fine now: *New York City* / Kung fu fighting: *Douglas, Carl* / Run tell the people: *Boone, Daniel* / I am someone: *James, Jimmy & The Vagabonds* / Let her in: *Travolta, John*
NEMCD 925 / 19 Aug '97 / Sequel

☐ **MEMORIES DU SEGA**
PS 65139CD / Apr '95 / PlayaSound

☐ **MEMORIES OF GREECE**
REWCD 354 / Feb '98 / Reactive

☐ **MEMORIES OF IRELAND**
ECD 3113 / Jun '95 / K-Tel

☐ **MEMORIES OF IRELAND**
Rose of Tralee/Molly Malone / Banks of my own lovely Lee / Flight of the Earls / Teddy O'Neill/The moon behind the hill / Come back Paddy Reilly / Caoineadh an spailpin / Sweet vale of Avoca/ Mountains of Mourne / Spinning wheel / Boolavogue / Down by the Sally Gardens / Danny boy / Carrickfergus / For Ireland I'd not tell her name / Coulin / Green Glens of Antrim/Noreen Bawn/The old bog road / Galway Bay/If only we had ireland over here / Forty shades of green / Wind and the willows
21126 / Aug '97 / Laserlight

☐ **MEMORIES OF SCOTLAND**
ACD 101 / Oct '93 / Koch

☐ **MEMORY LINGERS ON, THE (40 Easy Listening Classics/2CD Set)**
Everybody loves somebody: *Martin, Dean* / I'm in the mood for love: *Day, Doris* / Nancy: *Sinatra, Frank* / Mona Lisa: *Cole, Nat 'King'* / I hear music: *Connor, Chris* / 'Till the end of time: *Como, Perry* / Stormy weather: *Vaughan, Sarah* / I apologise: *Eckstine, Billy* / Old devil moon: *Horne, Lena* / I can't begin to tell you: *Crosby, Bing* / Thou swell: *McRae, Carmen* / Let's face the music and dance: *Astaire, Fred* / One I love (belongs to someone else): *Fitzgerald, Ella* / Love walked in: *Armstrong, Louis* / How about you: *Garland, Judy* / You'll never know: *Haymes, Dick* / Since I fell for you: *Gorme, Eydie* / Our love is here to stay: *Washington, Dinah* / Prelude to a kiss: *Torme, Mel* / Georgia on my mind: *Holiday, Billie* / Saturday night (is the loneliest night in the week): *Sinatra, Frank* / It's only a paper moon: *Fitzgerald, Ella* / I can't believe that your in love with me: *Torme, Mel* / I got it bad and that ain't good: *Day, Doris* / Autumn leaves: *Cole, Nat 'King'* / Send in the clowns: *Gorme, Eydie* / You belong to my heart: *Crosby, Bing* / Let's do it, lets fall in love: *Holiday, Billie* / Foggy day: *Astaire, Fred* / They can't take that away from me: *McRae, Carmen* / Walkin' my baby back home: *Armstrong, Louis* / Love me or leave me: *Horne, Lena* / If I loved you: *Como, Perry* / As long as he needs me: *Vaughan, Sarah* / Misty: *Eckstine, Billy* / It's all right with me: *Connor, Chris* / It can't be wrong: *Haymes, Dick* / Love for sale: *Washington, Dinah* / Boy next door: *Garland, Judy* / You're nobody 'till somebody loves you: *Martin, Dean*
CPCD 81442 / Jun '96 / Charly

☐ **MEMPHIS BLUES 1927-1938**
DOCD 5159 / May '93 / Document

☐ **MEMPHIS JAZZ MEETING**
DIW 613 / Sep '93 / DIW

☐ **MEMPHIS JAZZ MEETING : MEMPHIS CONVENTION**
DIW 874 / Sep '93 / DIW

☐ **MEMPHIS MASTERS: EARLY AMERICAN BLUES CLASSICS 1927-1934**
YAZCD 2008 / Nov '94 / Yazoo

☐ **MEMPHIS SOUL GREATS**
Hey little girl: *West, Norm* / Baby please: *West, Norm* / So good to me: *Jackson, George* / I'm gonna wait: *Jackson, George* / Aretha, sing one for me: *Jackson, George* / Patricia: *Jackson, George* / Let them know you care: *Jackson, George* / Tumbling down: *Fry, James* / Still around: *Fry, James* / Mama's boy: *Fry, James* / I've got enough: *Fry, James* / Without you: *Wright, O.V.* / Rhymes: *Wright, O.V.* / I love my baby: *Hill, Lindell* / Love map: *Hill, Lindell* / Very first time: *Hill, Lindell* / Be good to the one (That's good to you): *Mack, Jimmy* / I love her: *Walker, Willie* / Sweet thing: *Walker, Willie* / Fried chicken: *Thomas, Rufus* / I ain't got time: *Thomas, Rufus*
HILOCD 17 / Jul '95 / Hi

☐ **MEN BEHAVING BADLY**
Boys are back in town: *Thin Lizzy* / Tubthumping: *Chumbawamba* / House of fun: *Madness* / Bad case of loving you (doctor doctor): *Palmer, Robert* / 2468 motorway: *Robinson, Tom* / Spanish stroll: *Mink Deville* / Ever fallen in love: *Buzzcocks* / Walk this way: *Run DMC* / Cool for cats: *Squeeze* / Girl like you: *Collins, Edwyn* / Hit me with your rhythm stick: *Dury, Ian* / Hurry up Harry: *Sham 69* / Love in an elevator: *Aerosmith* / Some kind of bliss: *Minogue, Kylie* / Men behaving badly theme
REP 001CD / 17 Nov '97 / Remedia

☐ **MEN IN COUNTRY**
Storm in the heartland: *Cyrus, Billy Ray* / Third rate romance: *Kershaw, Sammy* / Little more love: *Gill, Vince* / Here comes the rain: *Mavericks* / Maybe we should just sleep on it: *McGraw, Tim* / That's right you're not from Texas: *Lovett, Lyle* / On the verge: *Raye, Collin* / Dirt road: *Brown, Sawyer* / I know where love lives: *Ketchum, Hal* / Ten feet tall and bullet proof: *Tritt, Travis* / Pocket of a clown: *Yoakam, Dwight* / They're playing our song: *McCoy, Neal* / Almost Saturday night: *Woodruff, Bob* / Just like you: *Keb Mo'* / Running out of reasons to run: *Trevino, Rick* / Like the rain: *Black, Clint* / Nobody wins: *Foster, Radney* / Life down on Earth: *Welch, Kevin*
AHLCD 46 / Jul '97 / Hit

☐ **MEN OF HARLECH (Welsh Choral Classics)**
We'll keep a welcome: *Canoldir Male Voice Choir* / How great thou art: *Canoldir Male Voice Choir* / Lord's prayer: *Canoldir Male Voice Choir* / Land of my fathers (Hen wlad fy nhadau): *Moriston Orpheus Choir & The Bedwas, Trethomas & Machin Band* / Where shall I be: *Moriston Orpheus Choir & The Bedwas, Trethomas & Machin Band* / Calon lan: *Moriston Orpheus Choir & The Bedwas, Trethomas & Machin Band* / Rise up shepherd and follow: *Moriston Orpheus Choir* / Anvil chorus: *Moriston Orpheus Choir* / Deep harmony: *Moriston Orpheus Choir* / Goin' home: *Moriston Orpheus Choir* / Mil harddach wyt na'r rhosyn gwyn: *Pontarddulais Male Voice Choir* / Christus redemptor (hyfrydol): *Pontarddulais Male Voice Choir* / Jesu lover of my soul: *Treorchy Male Choir* / Unwaith eto'n nghymru annwyl: *Treorchy Male Choir* / Dove: *Emanuel, Ivor & The Rhos Male Voice Choir* / Ash grove: *Emanuel, Ivor & The Rhos Male Voice Choir* / Deus salutis: *Dunvant Male Choir* / Sarah: *Dunvant Male Choir* / Ar hyd y nos: *Dunvant Male Choir* / My little Welsh home: *Emanuel, Ivor & The Rhos Male Voice Choir* / God bless the Prince Of Wales: *Rhos Male Voice Choir* / Men of Harlech: *Emanuel, Ivor & The Rhos Male Voice Choir*
TRTCD 133 / Oct '94 / TrueTrax

☐ **MERCURY BLUES 'N' RHYTHM STORY 1945-1955 (8CD Set)**
5282922 / Nov '96 / Mercury

☐ **MERCURY BLUES 'N' RHYTHM STORY 1945-1955 (Highlights)**
It's just the blues: *Four Jumps Of Jive* / Bar fly blues: *Witherspoon, Jimmy* / If it's good: *Lee, Julia* / Gonna send you where I got you from: *Vinson, Eddie 'Cleanhead' & Orchestra* / Record ban blues: *Washington, Dinah* / Been fooling around: *Byrd, Roy & His Blues Jumpers* / Streetwalkin' daddy: *Mondy, Alma* / Papa said yes, mama said no, no, no: *Graves, Lee* / West coast lover: *Sims, Robert 'Snake'* / (All alone) I sit and cry: *Hall, Violet* / Let me fly your kite: *Hopkins, Lightnin'* / Get back (black, brown and white): *Broonzy, 'Big' Bill* / No mail blues: *Memphis Slim* / Baby baby blues: *Otis, Johnny* / Hittin' on me: *Johnson, Ella* / Boogie the blues: *Johnson, Ray* / Talk about me: *Hawkins, Jay* / All around the world: *Turner, Titus* / Rhythm rockin' blues: *McGill, Rollee* / Woke up this moring: *Prysock, Arthur*
5329702 / Jan '97 / Mercury

☐ **MERENGUE (Dominican Music & Identity)**
Merengue Cibaeno: *Lora, Nico* / En la batea: *Lora, Nico* / Santiago: *Menendez, Nilo Orquesta* / Juangomero: *Morel, Antonio* / Compadre Pedro Juan: *Vasquez, Nini* / Jardinera: *Mateo, Joseito* / Volvimos de nuevo: *Guandulito* / El virony: *Viloria, Angel & Conjunto Tipico Cibaeno* / Me dejaste sola: *Belkis Concepcion* / Consejo a la mujeres: *Duran, Blas* / El diente de oro: *El Ciego de Nagua* / Merengue Palo Echao: *Mercedes Moreno, Juan A.* / Merengue de Tables: *Mojita, Francisco* / Merengue redondo: *Azolo, Domingo & Pascual Salmon*
ROUCD 1130 / Mar '97 / Rounder

☐ **MERENGUE ONLY**
Sali a papa a mama / El bigote / Cerca de ti / Adivinalo / Son de la loma / La chica gomela / Punta colara / En mi pensamiento / Pan de arroz / Cebiche de camaron / La vendedora de pitos / Mete y saca / Te voy amar / Asegura tu pan / El trencito / Muneca Linda / La matica de yuca / Tu pum pum / Todo todo / Adios
DC 880532 / May '97 / Disky

☐ **MERINGUE**
CO 107 / Jan '94 / Corason

☐ **MERRY AXEMAS (A Guitar Christmas)**
Rudolph the red nosed reindeer: *Shepherd, Kenny Wayne* / First Noel: *Johnson, Eric* / Amazing grace: *Beck, Jeff* / Jingle bells: *Setzer, Brian Orchestra* / Silent night: *Satriani, Joe* / Joy to the world: *Morse, Steve* / Christmas time is here: *Vai, Steve* / Blue Christmas: *Perry, Joe* / Little drummer boy: *Lifeson, Alex* / O Holy night: *Sambora, Richie* / Happy Xmas: *Hotel*
4891692 / 1 Dec '97 / Epic

☐ **MERRY CHRISTMAS**
CNCD 5932 / Nov '92 / Disky

☐ **MERRY CHRISTMAS**
CNCD 5969 / Dec '93 / Disky

☐ **MERRY CHRISTMAS**
I 3896012 / Oct '96 / Galaxy

☐ **MERRY CHRISTMAS**
Stay another day: *East 17* / Step into Christmas: *John, Elton* / Do they know it's Christmas: *Band Aid* / Last Christmas: *Whigfield* / Christmas wrapping: *Waitresses* / Have yourself a merry little Christmas: *Williams, Vanessa* / Funky Christmas: *Sease, Marvin* / Christmas rapping: *Blow, Kurtis* / My Christmas: *Tony Toni Tone* / It may be winter outside: *Love Unlimited Orchestra* / Silent night: *Bryant, Sharon* / Christmas day: *Squeeze* / Spaceman came travelling: *De Burgh, Chris* / Christmas song: *Phillips, Shawn* / Winter's tale: *Essex, David* / Merry Christmas everybody: *Metal Gurus*
5542542 / Oct '97 / Spectrum

☐ **MERRY CHRISTMAS FROM MOTOWN**
Little Christmas tree: *Jackson, Michael* / Christmas lullaby: *Robinson, Smokey & The Miracles* / This Christmas: *Ross, Diana* / Christmas song: *Gaye, Marvin* / Wish you a merry Christmas: *Weston, Kim* / Silent night: *Ross, Diana & The Supremes* / Christmas in the city: *Gaye, Marvin* / Everyone's a kid at Christmas time: *Wonder, Stevie* / Winter wonderland: *Funk Brothers* / I want to come home for Christmas: *Gaye, Marvin* / Just a lonely Christmas: *Ross, Diana & The Supremes* / Won't be long before Christmas: *Ross, Diana & The Supremes* / Miracles of Christmas: *Wonder, Stevie* / Purple snowflake: *Gaye, Marvin*
5507192 / Nov '96 / Spectrum

☐ **MERRY MALADIES (2CD Set)**
CLP 226 / 20 Apr '98 / Cleopatra

☐ **MERRYMENT STORY VOL.1, THE**
CCD 0046 / 15 Jun '98 / CRS

☐ **MERRYMENT STORY VOL.2, THE**
CCD 0045 / 15 Jun '98 / CRS

☐ **MERSEYMANIA (20 Fab Sounds Of The Sixties)**
I saw her standing there / Charmless man / Won't you come out tonight / I'll have to get another girl / She loves you / What shall I do / There I go / Please please me / Tell me now / Your me now / Your kind of love / You don't tell me you don't know / Tell me I'm the one / This is what I mean / This what I mean / In a little while / I want to hold your hand / I don't need you / Joshua / Maybe I will / Seems to me / Baby you can do no wrong / Night without end
306022 / Jan '97 / Hallmark

☐ **MESMER VARIATIONS (Works Inspired By Mesmer/2CD Set)**
ASH 18CD / Oct '95 / Ash International

☐ **METAL BLADE RECORDS 15TH ANNIVERSARY ALBUM**
398414135CD / 28 Jul '97 / Metal Blade

☐ **METAL BOX (3CD Set)**
TBXCD 506 / Jan '96 / TrueTrax

☐ **METAL BOX (2CD Set)**
PBXCD 506 / Nov '96 / Pulse

☐ **METAL COMPILATION, THE**
I'd rather go wild: *Witchfynde* / Take it all away: *Girlschool* / Fighting chance: *Heritage* / Love, guns and money: *Torme, Bernie* / Angels of death: *Hawkwind* / I will survive: *Terraplane* / See you in heaven: *Ace Lane* / First (the only one): *Tygers Of Pan Tang* / Runnin' scared: *Savage* / Sweet dream maker: *Gaskin* / In the stars: *Witchfynde* / Battlezone: *Mournblade* / All the time: *Tiger* / Hardcore: *Torme, Bernie* / Hideaway: *Tygers Of Pan Tang* / Sky's falling down: *Persian Risk* / Eye for an eye: *Savage* / Motorhead: *Hawkwind*
SUMCD 4093 / Jan '97 / Summit

☐ **METAL ERUPTION**
398414212CD / Jun '96 / Metal Blade

☐ **METAL MANIA**
MACCD 158 / Aug '96 / Autograph

☐ **METAL MONOLITHS (2CD Set)**
24076 / Jun '96 / Delta Doubles

☐ **METAL MONSTERS**
CDTB 507 / May '96 / Thunderbolt

☐ **METALHEADZ METALBOX (2CD Set)**
Far out: *Digital* / Special mission: *Digital* / Swarm: *Doc Scott* / Honey: *Doc Scott* / Sabotage: *Ed Rush* / Westway: *Ed Rush* / No guard: *Hidden Agenda* / Big lamp: *Hidden Agenda* / Future state: *Majik J* / Elysian fields: *Majik J* / What's up: *Lemon D* / Urban style music: *Lemon D* / To shape the future: *Optical* / Reckless mission: *Optical* / Desist da black: *Dollis Hill* / Desist da black (remix): *Dollis Hill* / Neptune: *Photek* / Warrior jazz: *Dillinja*
METBX 001 / 29 Jun '98 / FFRR

☐ **METALHEADZ PLATINUM BREAKS VOL.1 (2CD Set)**
VIP rider's ghost: *Rufige Cru* / Psychosis: *Peshay* / Far away: *Doc Scott* / Angels fell: *Dillinja* / Your sound: *J-Majik* / Consciousness: *Photek* / Flute tune: *Hidden Agenda* / Spectrum: *Wax Doctor* / Pulp fiction: *Reece, Alex* / Unofficial ghost: *Doc Scott* / In my life: *Lemon D* / Made up sound: *Source Direct* / Down under: *Digital* / Da base II dark: *Asylum* / Day break: *J-Majik* / Armoured 'D': *Dillinja* / Nocturnal (Back on the firm): *Peshay*
8287832 / 17 Aug '98 / FFRR

☐ **METALHEADZ PLATINUM BREAKS VOL.2 (2CD Set)**
Metro: *Digital* / Pressin' on: *Hidden Agenda* / Arabian nights: *J-Majik* / Stonekiller: *Source Direct* / Metropolis: *Adam F* / Raven: *Rush, Ed* / Dispatch 2: *Hidden Agenda* / On the Nile: *Peshay* / Promise: *Dillinja* / To shape the future: *Optical* / Repertoire: *J-Majik* / Melt: *Sci-Clone* / WARNING: *Codename John* / Your sound: *J-Majik* / Dark metal: *Source Direct* / Swift glide: *Optical* / Chainsaw: *Lemon D*
8289862 / 17 Nov '97 / FFRR

☐ **METAMORPHOSIS (Music From The Ottoman Empire)**
GCD 921001 / Dec '97 / Glossa

☐ **METARD NTAMAGANYA (Rwandan Court And Folk Songs)**
W 260075 / Apr '97 / Inedit

☐ **METEOR ROCKABILLIES**
Mama's little baby: *Thompson, Junior* / Raw deal: *Thompson, Junior* / Tongue tied Jill: *Feathers, Charlie* / Get with it: *Feathers, Charlie* / Rock, roll and rhythm: *McGinnis, Wayne* / Lonesome rhythm blues: *McGinnis, Wayne* / Don't shoot me baby (I'm not ready to die): *Bowen, Bill* / Have myself a ball: *Bowen, Bill* / All messed up: *Hooper, Jess* / Sleepy time blues: *Hooper, Jess* / Latch on to your baby: *Lamberth, Jimmy* / Bop baby bop: *Suggs, Brad* / Charcoal suit: *Suggs, Brad* / Can't steal my way around: *Burcham, Barney* / Much too young for love: *Burcham, Barney* / Curfew: *Carl, Steve & The Jags* / Eighteen year old blues: *Carl, Steve & The Jags* / Gonna shut you off baby: *Haggett, Jimmy* / Women: *Smith, Lendon & The Jesters* / Brother that's all: *Hadley, Red* / Real gone baby: *Velvetones* / Gal named Joe: *Sales, Mac* / Yakety yak: *Mac & Jake* / Don't worry 'bout nothin': *Dixon, Mason*
CDCHM 484 / Jul '93 / Ace

☐ **METRO BREAKS**
CLP 127 / 12 Mar '98 / Hypnotic

☐ **MEVLANA (Music Of The Whirling Dervishes)**
HEMIMDCD 107 / 6 Oct '97 / Hemisphere

☐ **MEXICAN INDIAN TRADITIONS : CELEBRATIONS**
AUD 08304 / Feb '93 / Auvidis/Ethnic

☐ **MEXICAN LANDSCAPES VOL.3**
PS 65903 / Mar '92 / PlayaSound

☐ **MEXICAN LANDSCAPES VOL.4**
PS 65904 / Apr '92 / PlayaSound

☐ **MEXICAN LANDSCAPES VOL.5**
PS 65905 / Sep '92 / PlayaSound

☐ **MEXICAN LANDSCAPES VOL.7**
PS 65907 / Nov '93 / PlayaSound

☐ **MEXICAN REVOLUTION, THE (4CD/ Book Set)**
Ignacio Parra: *Los Alegres De Teran* / Valentin Mancera: *Trio Los Aguilillas* / Corrido de Macario Romero: *Abrego Y Picazo* / Potro Lobo Gateada: *Mariachi Mexico Del Norte* / Jesus Leal: *Robinson, Rafael Herrera* / Jesus Leal: *Rocha, Pedro & Lupe Martinez* / Heraclio Bernal: *Trio Nava* / Benito Canales: *Hernandez Y Sifuentes* / Nuevo corrido de madero: *Comacho, Manuel & Regino Perez* / El cuartelazo: *Los Hermanos Chavarria* / El cuartelazo: *Hermanas Mendoza* / Fusilamiento de General Argumendo: *Hernandez Y Sifuentes* / Benjamin Argumendo: *Berlanga, Andres & Francisco Montalvo* / Fusilamiento de Felipe Angeles: *San Roman Y Vera* / Corrido de durango: *Los Darados De Durango* / Gral Francisco Villa: *Los Cuatezones* / La toma de torreon: *Los Alegres De Teran* / Toma de Guadalajara: *Las Jilguerillas* / La toma de zacatecas: *Los Errantes* / Pancho Villa: *Los Hermanos Chavarria* / La punitiva: *Hernandez Y Sifuentes* / La toma de celaya: *Hermanos Banuelos* / Derrota de villa en celaya: *Rocha, Pedro & Jose Angel Colunga* / Rendecion de pancho villa: *Rocha, Pedro & Lupe Martinez* / Corrido historia y muerte del Gral Francisco Villa: *Rubi Y Vivo* / Adelita: *Trio Gonzalez* / Valentina: *Mendoza, Lydia & Family* / Corrido de Juan Vasquez: *Mendoza, Juanita & Maria* / Corrido de Juan Carrasco: *Meza, Luis Perez* / Corrido de palomon: *Los Montaneses Del Alamo* / Corrido de Juan Villarreal: *Los Hermanos Garza* / La toma de matamoros: *Lara, Augustin & A. Novelo* / Corrido de almazan: *Mendez & Gonzalez* / Amadour maldonado: *Conjunto Tamaulipas* / Corrido de margarito: *Dueto America* / Refugio solano: *Dueto Sandoval* / Julian Del Real: *Hermanos Yanez* / Corrido de Inez Chavez Garcia: *Hermanos Banuelos* / Quirino Navarro: *Trio Los Aguilillas* / Tragedia de Maximiliano Vigueras: *Medellin, Emilio & Lupe Posada* / Corrido de cedillo: *Los Morenos* / Corrido de Yurecuaro y Tanhuato: *Hermanos Banuelos* / Marijuana la soldadera: *Hermanos Banuelos* / Revolucion de Adolfo De La Huerta: *Briceno, Alcides & Jorge Anez* / La pura pelada: *Trio Luna* / El arreglo religioso: *Duo Coahuila* / La nueva revolucion: *San Roman Y Vera* / Ortiz rubio: *La Bella Netty & Jesus Rodriguez* / El corrido del agrarista: *Trovadores Tamaulipecos* / General Obregon: *Trio Luna* / El radiograma: *Guzman & Rosales* / Corrido de toral: *Trovadores Tapatinos* / General Emiliano Zapata: *Trio Luna* / Corrido del General Cardenas: *Del Valle Y Rivas* / El corrido del petroleo: *Ray Y Laurita* / La rielera: *Mendoza, Lydia & Family* / Gral Porfirio Diaz: *Dueto Acosta* / Tiempos amargos: *Dueto America*
ARHCD 7041/44 / Nov '96 / Arhoolie

☐ **MEXICAN-AMERICAN BORDER MUSIC VOL.1 (The Pioneer Recordings Artists 1928-1959)**
ARHCD 7001 / Apr '95 / Arhoolie

☐ **MEXICAN-AMERICAN BORDER MUSIC VOL.3 (Norteno & Tejano Accordion Pioneers)**
ARHCD 7016 / Jan '96 / Arhoolie

☐ **MEXICAN-AMERICAN BORDER MUSIC VOL.4 (Orquestas Tipicas/ Pioneer Dance Orchestras 1926-1938)**
Ofelia: *Enriquez, Jose Perches Orquesta* / Coquetona y juguetona: *Quinteto Tipico Mexicano* / Por vida de dios: *Orquesta Acosta-Rosette* / Alicia: *Enriquez, Jose Perches Orquesta* / Alma mia de mi grandota: *Orquesta Del Norte* / Monterrey alegre: *Orquesta Mexicana Calvillo* / Sonador: *Los Desvelados* / Mondragon: *Orquesta De La Familia* / Aborrecido: *Tipica Martinez* / El manoso: *Orquesta Tipica Fronteriza* / Pensado en ti: *Garza, Alfredo M. Orquesta* / La negra: *Banda Chihuahua* / La prieta, la guera y la chata: *Los Desvelados* / Los canedistas: *Orquesta De Guadalupe Acosta* / Adios mi chaparrita: *Caceres, Emilio Y Su Orquesta Del Club Aguila* / El sueno de califas: *Orquesta Tipica Fronteriza* / La reina de las flores: *Orquesta Tipica Fronteriza* / Adios amor mio: *Orquesta Tipica Fronteriza* / Siempre alegre: *Orquesta Tipica Fronteriza* / Es imposible: *Nunez, Tomas Orquesta* / Las gaviotas: *Nunez, Tomas Orquesta* / Penumbra: *Arredondo, Jose Maria Trio* / Besos y cerezas: *Los Cuatezones* / Celosa: *Garza, Eva Con Orquesta* / Jig in G: *Caceres, Emilio Y Su Orquesta Del Club Aguila* / Alma Angelina: *Las Hermanas Padilla & Orquesta De Manuel S. Acuna*
ARHCD 7017 / Nov '96 / Arhoolie

☐ **MEXICAN-AMERICAN BORDER MUSIC VOL.5 (Orquestas De Cuerdas/ The End Of A Tradition 1926-1938)**
El gato negro: *El Ciego Melquiades* / Sobre las olas: *Quinteto Tipico Mexicano* / No te ruborices: *Orquesta De La Familia Ramos* / La paloma: *Sanchez, Eulalio Y Su Quinteto Mexicao* / A mi juana: *Cuarteto Carta Blanca* / El charrio: *Los Desvelados* / Tamaulipeco: *Trovadores Tamaulipecos* / Ay te va de canto: *El Trio Crudo* / A la orilla de un palomar: *Trio Alegre* / Anhelando: *Trio Alegre* / La maestrita: *Cuarteto De Cuerdo De F. Facio* / Carino: *Cuarteto De Cuerdo De F. Facio* / De aquella crena: *Trio Alegre* / El poder del amor: *Trio Alegre* / La bola: *Cuarteto Monterrey* / Panchita: *Familia Mendoza* / Jesusita en chihuahua: *Los Desvelados* / Marosovia: *Los Alegres* / La respingona: *Morales, Santiago* / Porque eres ansina: *Trio Alamo* / Andale vamos platicando: *Medina River Boys* / Maria Christina: *El Ciego Melquiades* / Jallisco nunca pierde: *El Ciego Melquiades* / Se murio la cucaracha: *Mendoza, Lydia* / Montana: *Marmolejo, Juan Mariachi Tapatio* / New Spanish two step: *Boyd, Bill & His Cowboy Ramblers*
ARHCD 7018 / Nov '96 / Arhoolie

☐ **MEXICO**
CD 62025 / Oct '93 / Saludos Amigos

☐ **MEXICO**
Y 225712 / Dec '96 / Silex

☐ **MEXICO - FIESTAS OF CHIAPAS & OAXACA**
7559720702 / Jan '95 / Nonesuch

☐ **MIAMI BEACH PARTY (Fiesta Latino)**
4930062 / 1 Mar '98 / Atoll

☐ **MIAMI ROCKABILLY**
Any way / Knocked out joint on Mars / I was doing it too: *Roxters* / My baby don't rock me: *Westberry, Kent & The Chaperones* / Hang loose: *Spurlin, Tommy & The Southern Boys* / Heart throb: *Spurlin, Tommy* / No time for heartaches: *Spurlin, Tommy* / So long: *Roxters* / Blues keep knocking: *Trail, Buck* / One eyed Sam: *Spurlin, Tommy & The Southern Boys* / No place to park: *Westberry, Kent & The Chaperones* / My shadow: *Rhythm Rockets* / Boppin' strollin' and messin' around: *Pate, Ray & The Rhythm Rockets* / Kitty Kat rock: *Law, Art* / Oh Janet: *Minimi, Ross* / Lucky day: *Rhythm Rockets* / Here there everywhere: *Pate, Ray & The Rhythm Rockets* / Baby rock: *Minimi, Ross* / Donny's boogie: *Pate, Don & The Rhythm Rockets* / Honky tonk on second street: *Trial, Buck & The Dead Enders* / Let's dance: *Gaye, Bobby & Sparkle Tones* / Sweetest gal in town: *Voytek, Jimmy* / Everybody's gonna do the rock 'n' roll: *Rhythm Rockers* / Dandy sandy: *Gale, Jimmy Imperial* / Rockin' with Rosie: *Deane, Wally & The Flips* / I'm tellin' ya baby: *Deane, Wally & The Flips* / Rock 'n' roll itch: *Curley Jim & The Billey Rocks* / She's mine: *Roxters* / We're gonna rock all night: *Gale, Jimmy Imperial* / Alrforce blues: *Curley Jim & The Billey Rocks* / TV mama: *Frantic Four* / Down by the old millstream: *Frantic Four*
CDCHD 639 / 26 Jan '98 / Ace

☐ **MICK POTTS TRIBUTE CONCERT, THE**
Simon potts introduces the band... / Take the 'A' train / You took advantage of me / Emily / Stealing apples / Isn't it a pity / Digby about Mick / I can't give you anything but love / Jeep is jumpin' / Outro / Micks blues
GBHCD 02 / 19 Jan '98 / Flat Five

☐ **MIDNIGHT BLUE**
Ill wind: *Quebec, Ike* / Please send me someone to love: *Smith, Jimmy* / Lover man: *Marable, Lawrence Quartet & James Clay* / Nearness of you: *Hartman, Johnny* / Smoke gets in your eyes: *Shank, Bud & The Lee Mercer Strings* / Autumn leaves: *Hawkins, Coleman* / Fly me to the moon: *Cole, Nat 'King' & George Shearing* / After the rain: *Pearson, Duke* / Sweet and lovely: *Perkins, Bill & Richie Kamuca* / You don't know what love is: *Wilson, Cassandra* / Nancy: *Green, Grant* / (It will have to do) until the real thing comes along: *Gordon, Dexter* / Willow weep for me: *Turrentine, Stanley & Three Sounds* / I can't get started: *Young, Lester & Nat Cole*
CDP 8543652 / Oct '96 / Blue Note

☐ **MIDNIGHT FLUTE**
If you leave me now / Air that I breathe / Wind of change / Tears in heaven / (Everything I do) I do it for you / All I have to do is dream / Massachussetts / California dreamin' / I will always love you / When a man loves a woman / Fly away / One moment in time / I just called to say I love you / San Francisco / All that she wants / Half a minute / Tenderness / Air on a G string
CD 6043 / Sep '96 / Music

☐ **MIDNIGHT GUITAR**
GRF 194 / Jun '92 / Tring

☐ **MIDNIGHT GUITAR**
Just the way you are / Yesterday / All my love / At seventeen / It's all clear to me now / Something / Moonlight serenade / Mama, I'll be home someday / This can't be love / I write the songs / You needed me / Hey Jude / Feels so good / What are you doing for the rest of your life / At the Copa / Late last night
CD 6027 / Jun '96 / Music

☐ **MIDNIGHT GUITAR MOODS**
What I did for love / Take that look off your face / Evergreen / Close to you / As time goes by / Where is love / On this night of a thousand stars / Do you know where you're going to / He ain't heavy, he's my brother / Crazy / Vaya con dios / Smoke gets in your eyes
CDMFP 6222 / May '96 / Music For Pleasure

☐ **MIDNIGHT HOUR**
RNCD 2090 / Feb '95 / Rhino

☐ **MIDNIGHT IN JAMAICA (2CD Set)**
SMDCD 111 / Jul '97 / Snapper

☐ **MIDNIGHT JAZZ**
JC 98002 / 26 May '98 / Jazz Classix

☐ **MIDNIGHT JAZZ MOODS**
BN 038 / Apr '98 / Blue Nite

☐ **MIDNIGHT JAZZ MOODS VOL.1**
TMPCD 019 / Mar '96 / Temple

☐ **MIDNIGHT JAZZ MOODS VOL.2**
TMPCD 020 / Jul '96 / Temple

☐ **MIDNIGHT JAZZ MOODS VOL.3**
TMPCD 021 / Jul '96 / Temple

☐ **MIDNIGHT MOODS (The Lighter Side Of Jazz)**
Unforgettable: *Cole, Nat 'King'* / Fever: *Lee, Peggy* / Mad about the boy: *Washington, Dinah* / Girl from Ipanema: *Gilberto, Astrud* / Smooth operator: *Sade* / Lily was here: *Stewart, David A. & Candy Dulfer* / It had to be you: *Connick, Harry Jr.* / Take five: *Brubeck, Dave* / Fine romance: *Holiday, Billie* / Every time we say goodbye: *Fitzgerald, Ella* / Misty: *Garner, Erroll* / Cry me a river: *Wilson, Mari* / Goin' out of my head: *Montgomery, Wes* / Take the 'A' train: *O'Day, Anita* / Walk on the wild side: *Smith, Jimmy* / Shadow of your smile: *Peterson, Oscar* / Summertime: *Vaughan, Sarah* / Relax: *Redbone, Leon* / Passing strangers: *Vaughan, Sarah & Billy Eckstine* / What a wonderful world: *Armstrong, Louis*
5158162 / Apr '93 / PolyGram TV

☐ **MIDNIGHT MOODS (Midnight Guitar/ Midnight Sax/Midnight Flute - 3CD Set)**
Just the way you are / Yesterday / All my love / At seventeen / It's all clear to me now / Something / Moonlight serenade / Mama, I'll be home someday / This can't be love / I write the songs / You needed me / Hey Jude / Feels so good / What are you doing for the rest of your life / At the Copa / Late last night / Love is all around / Whiter shade of pale / Long and winding road / Woman / Lean on me / How deep is your love / Just the way you are / When I fall in love / Said I loved you...but I lied / Candle in the wind / Will you be there / You've lost that loving feeling / Blue eyes / Dreamlover / We've only just begun / One sweet day / I can love you like that / Can I touch you...there / If you leave me now / Air that I breathe / Wind of change / Tears in heaven / (Everything I do) I do it for you / All I have to do is dream / Massachussetts / California dreamin' / I will always love you / When a man loves a woman / Fly away / One moment in time / I just called to say I love you / San Francisco / All that she wants / Half a minute / Tenderness / Air on a G string
55160 / Oct '96 / Music

☐ **MIDNIGHT PIANO MOODS**
Heal the world / Goodbye yellow brick road / Next time you fall in love / Lady in red / Day by day / Fool on the hill / Make up my heart / Blue moon / On the street where you live / Can't help falling in love / How to handle a woman / Somethin' stupid
CDMFP 6223 / May '96 / Music For Pleasure

☐ **MIDNIGHT ROCK PRESENTS...**
MR 001CD96 / Jul '96 / Midnight Rock

☐ **MIDNIGHT SAX**
Love is all around / Whiter shade of pale / Long and winding road / Woman / Lean on me / How deep is your love / Just the way you are / When I fall in love / Said I loved you...but I lied / Candle in the wind / Will you be there / You've lost that loving feeling / Blue eyes / Dreamlover / We've only just begun / One sweet day / I can love you like that / Can I touch you...there
CD 6028 / Jun '96 / Music

☐ **MIDNIGHT SAX (2CD Set)**
On Broadway: *Zorn, Pete* / Moon ray: *Zorn, Pete* / Songbird: *Zorn, Pete* / Holding back the years: *Zorn, Pete* / Wonderful world: *Zorn, Pete* / Shadow of your smile: *Zorn, Pete* / Baker Street: *Zorn, Pete* / Misty blue: *Zorn, Pete* / Georgia on my mind: *Zorn, Pete* / Crazy: *Zorn, Pete* / Wild horses: *Zorn, Pete* / Girl from Ipanema: *Zorn, Pete* / Nature boy: *Zorn, Pete* / It ain't necessarily so: *Hastings, Jimmy* / My funny Valentine: *Hastings, Jimmy* / Moon river: *Hastings, Jimmy* / Unforgettable: *Abrams, Frank* / Man I love: *Abrams, Frank* / Lily was here: *Sodout, Chris* / Cry me a river: *Sodout, Chris* / Feelings: *Sodout, Chris* / Manha de carnaval: *Sodout, Chris* / Sax for love: *Sodout, Chris* / Warm and blue: *Gaucher, Michael* / Midnight magic: *Gaucher, Michael* / After hours: *Gaucher, Michael* / Belvedere Hotel: *Gaucher, Michael* / Golden gate: *Gaucher, Michael* / Summertime: *Arnopp, Tony* / Misty: *Arnopp, Tony* / Body and soul: *Arnopp, Tony* / Soul view: *Aspery, Ronnie* / Alright tonight: *Aspery, Ronnie* / Midnight song: *Aspery, Ronnie*
RCACD 210 / Jul '97 / RCA

☐ **MIDNIGHT SAX (38 Safe Sax Sounds For Lovers/2CD Set)**
How deep is your love / Just the way you are / Wonderful tonight / True / Feelings / Unforgettable / Another day in paradise / Lily was here / It ain't necessarily so / Summertime / My funny valentine / Moon ray / Cry me a river / Wonderful world / Georgia on my mind / Moon river / Shadow of your smile / Misty / Everytime you go away / Holding back the years / Baker Street / Air that I breathe / Candle in the wind / Every time we say goodbye / Yesterday / Don't let the sun go down on me / Nature boy / Girl from Ipanema / Save a prayer / You're so vain / My way / I just called to say I love you / Up on the roof / Misty blue / Crazy / On Broadway / Careless whisper / Songbird
SUDCD 4504 / Nov '96 / Summit

☐ **MIDNIGHT SAX MOODS**
Can you feel the love tonight / Mind if I make love to you / Dancing in the dark / Long and winding road / Too much love will kill you / Mona Lisa / I left my heart in San Francisco / It's now or never / Unfogettable / Help me make it through the night / How deep is the ocean / Wherever I lay my hat (that's my home)
CDMFP 6221 / May '96 / Music For Pleasure

☐ **MIDNIGHT SLOWS VOL.1 (2CD Set)**
BB 896 / Apr '97 / Black & Blue

☐ **MIDNIGHT SLOWS VOL.6**
BLE 190932 / Apr '91 / Black & Blue

☐ **MIDNIGHT SLOWS VOL.8**
BLE 193582 / Apr '91 / Black & Blue

☐ **MIDNIGHT SOUL**
Never too much: *Vandross, Luther* / Harvest for the world: *Isley Brothers* / Street life: *Crusaders* / Higher and higher: *Wilson, Jackie* / Never knew love like this before: *Mills, Stephanie* / I'm your puppet: *Purify, James & Bobby* / Have you seen her: *Chi-Lites* / Dance to the music: *Sly & The Family Stone* / Lean on me: *Withers, Bill* / Come into my life: *Sims, Joyce* / Move on up: *Mayfield, Curtis* / I love music: *O'Jays* / It's man's world: *Brown, James* / Love I lost: *Melvin, Harold* / Reunited: *Peaches & Herb* / Rescue me: *Bass, Fontella* / Way we were: *Knight, Gladys & The Pips* / Soul city walk: *Bell, Archie & The Drells*
MUSCD 006 / Nov '92 / MCI Music

☐ **MIDNIGHT SOUL (2CD Set)**
Rock me tonight (for old times sake): *Jackson, Freddie* / Would I lie to you: *Charles & Eddie* / Tonight I celebrate my love: *Bryson, Peabo & Roberta Flack* / Heaven: *Whispers* / Emotionally yours: *O'Jays* / Tender love: *Thomas, Kenny* / Little bit more: *Jackson, Freddie & Melba Moore* / Lovesongs, candlelight and you: *Butler, Jonathan* / Do me baby: *Morgan, Meli'sa* / Call me: *Reynolds, L.J.* / Wanna make love (all night long): *Thomas, Lillo* / Reunited: *Ward, Robert* / Suddenly: *Ocean, Billy* / I'm in love: *Moore, Melba & Kashif* / You bring out the best in me: *Bell-Armstrong, Vanessa* / Two occasions: *Deele* / Rock wit'cha: *Brown, Bobby* / Let's chill: *Guy* / Always: *Pebbles* / Time for love tonight: *Jackson, Freddie* / Baby it's wonderful: *Riff* / On and on: *Portrait* / I can't wait another minute: *Hi-Five* / More of the night: *Whispers* / Come in out of the rain: *Moten, Wendy* / When only a friend will do: *Davis, Mike* / Cry no more: *Il D Extreme* / Tender kisses: *Spencer, Tracie* / Something in your eyes: *Bell Biv Devoe* / Show and tell: *Bryson, Peabo*
DOU 882492 / 2 Feb '98 / Disky

☐ **MIDSUMMER NIGHT DREAMS**
I feel free: *Cream* / Making time: *Creation* / Children of the sun: *Misunderstood* / Season of the witch: *Donovan* / I can hear the grass grow: *Move* / Night of the long grass: *Troggs* / Days of Pearly Spencer: *McWilliams, David* / Paper sun: *Traffic* / Flight from Ashiya: *Kaleidoscope* / Tiny goddess: *Nirvana* / My white bicycle: *Tomorrow* / From the underworld: *Herd* / King Midas in reverse: *Hollies* / I can see for miles: *Who* / Skeleton and the round about: *Idle Race* / Me my friend: *Family* / It's alright, It's only witchcraft: *Family* / Can't find my way home: *Blind Faith*
5535992 / Jun '97 / Debutante

☐ **MIDSUMMER NIGHT DREAMS/SAN FRANCISCAN DAZE (36 British & American Sixties Psychedelic Classics/2CD Set)**
5551782 / Aug '98 / Debutante

☐ **MIGHTY BOX PLAYING**
GTDCD 007 / Jan '95 / GTD

☐ **MIGHTY SESSION**
KMCD 9515 / Mar '98 / Kells

☐ **MIGHTY WURLITZER VOL.1, THE (50 All Time Favourites)**
SWBCD 201 / Sep '94 / Sound Waves

☐ **MIGHTY WURLITZER VOL.1, THE**
Let's twist again/Let's dance/Oh boy / Sweet Caroline/Hi ho silver lining/My boy lollipop / Locomotion/That's livin' alright/Atmosphere / Is this the way to Amarillo/I only want to be with you/Will / Fame/Happy heart/Young ones / What'll I do/At the end of the day/'Till we meet again / Bless 'em all/ After the ball/I'm forever blowing bubbles / My bonnie lies over the ocean/Down at the old bull and bush / It's a sin to tell a lie/Who's taking you home tonight/Alway / Walkin' my baby back home/Maybe it's because I'm a Londoner/ / For me and my gal/ Show me the way to go home / Can't help falling in love/Wonder of you / Birdie song
QED 084 / Nov '96 / Tring

☐ **MIGHTY WURLITZER VOL.2, THE (50 All Time Favourites)**
SWBCD 202 / Sep '94 / Sound Waves

☐ **MIGHTY WURLITZER VOL.2, THE**
Around the world/Pal of my cradle days/Edelweiss / Are you lonesome tonight/When I grow too old to dream / California here I come/Five foot two, eyes of blue/When you' / Don't dilly dally on the way/Happy wanderer/Pack up your tro / Who were you with last night/A long way to Tipperary / American patrol/ Little brown jug/Don't sit under the apple t / Raining in my heart/Downtown/Do wah diddy diddy / Teenager in love/YMCA/Diana / I should be so lucky/ Rockin' all over the world/Knock three / Ob-la-di ob-la-da/Beautiful Sunday/Rhinestone cowboy / Can't take my eyes off you/Sugar sugar / Rock around the clock/Teddy bear/When the saints go marching / Over the rainbow/Unchained melody/You'll never walk alone / In the news
QED 085 / Nov '96 / Tring

☐ **MIGHTY WURLITZER, THE**
Chattanooga choo choo / You'll never know / September in the rain / Jeepers creepers / Pasadena / Happy days are here again / I wonder where my baby is tonight / Saturday rag / Let's face the music and dance / Top hat, white tie and tails / You were never lovelier / Cheek to cheek / I'm beginning to see the light / I've got a gal in Kalamazoo / It don't mean a thing if it ain't got that swing / Fascinating rhythm / They can't take that away from me / Somebody loves me / Someone to watch over me / Wonderful guy / My favourite things / Wonderful day / Mona Lisa / Orange coloured sky / Those lazy crazy days of Summer / I've got a pocketful of dreams / Zing went the strings of my heart / Painting the clouds with sunshine / Me and my girl / Maizy doats and doazy doats / Don't fence me in / We're gonna hang out the washing on the Siegfried line / Oh lady be good / Our love is here to stay / Liza / Embraceable / My fair lady
SUMCD 4030 / Nov '96 / Summit

☐ **MIKEA COUNTRY (Music From Madagascar)**
C 560115 / Dec '97 / Ocora

☐ **MILESTONE AT THE GARDEN**
ROU 1123 / May '96 / Rounder

☐ **MILITANT SCIENCE**
Imaginary world: *Raw Deal* / Ladder: *Purple Kola* / Headless horseman: *Raw Deal* / Renegade: *Tonic* / Mindset: *Native Bass* / Pornagraphica: *Glowball* / Smash and Grab The Flowers: *Asian Dub Foundation & Native Bass* / Tabstramental: *Native Bass* / PKNB: *ADF* / Dalek tune: *Hempolics* / Militant scientist: *ADF & Ramjack Corporation & Master D* / Death is coming: *Todd, Jamie* / Mellow to freedom: *BLIM & MP*
BOSCD 001 / Feb '97 / Botchit & Scarper

☐ **MILITARY BAND SPECTACULAR**
8441742 / Jan '96 / Deram

☐ **MILITARY CLASSICS (2CD Set)**
Blaze away / High on a hill / It's a long way to Tipperary / Colonel Bogey / Soldiers in the park / There's something about a soldier / Beer barrel polka / Quartermaster's store / Lili Marlene / Soldier's chorus / A Scottish soldier / Changing of the guard / Amazing grace / Where have all the flowers gone / Sodiers of the Queen / Royal ceremony / Victory display / Royal salute / Spitfire prelude / Spitfire fugue / La Rejouissance / Army, the navy and the air force / Calling all workers / Guns of Navarone / Lonely bugler / Fanfare for the common man / Aces high / Greensleeves / On Richmond hill baht'at / Boots and saddles / Homeward / Soldiers on parade / Yankee doodle dandy / Soldier alone / Northern echoes suite / Mist covered mountains / Navy day / V for victory / Marchalong / Day thou gavest
330122 / Jul '96 / Hallmark

☐ MILITARY PAGEANT, A (The Massed Bands Of HM Forces)
TRTCD 201 / Jun '95 / TrueTrax

☐ MILK FOR PUSSY
MQCD 9301 / Jan '94 / Mad Queen

☐ MILLENNIUM GROOVES
SPECCD 501 / Mar '97 / Dust II Dust

☐ MILLENNIUM MOODS (2CD Set)
MOODSCD 1 / 15 Jun '98 / Beechwood

☐ MILLENNIUM: ETERNALLY ALIVE
MILL 009CD / Nov '94 / Millenium

☐ MILLION SELLERS - THE BEST OF THE MILLION SELLERS
MSCD 1950 / Apr '94 / Disky

☐ MILLION SELLERS - THE EIGHTIES VOL.1
MSCD 1971 / Apr '94 / Disky

☐ MILLION SELLERS - THE EIGHTIES VOL.2
MSCD 1973 / Oct '94 / Disky

☐ MILLION SELLERS - THE EIGHTIES VOL.3
MSCD 1974 / Oct '94 / Disky

☐ MILLION SELLERS - THE EIGHTIES VOL.4
MSCD 1975 / Oct '94 / Disky

☐ MILLION SELLERS - THE EIGHTIES VOL.5
MSCD 1976 / Oct '94 / Disky

☐ MILLION SELLERS - THE FIFTIES VOL.1
MSCD 1951 / Apr '94 / Disky

☐ MILLION SELLERS - THE FIFTIES VOL.2
MSCD 1952 / Apr '94 / Disky

☐ MILLION SELLERS - THE FIFTIES VOL.3
MSCD 1953 / Apr '94 / Disky

☐ MILLION SELLERS - THE FIFTIES VOL.4
MSCD 1954 / Apr '94 / Disky

☐ MILLION SELLERS - THE SEVENTIES VOL.1
MSCD 1963 / Apr '94 / Disky

☐ MILLION SELLERS - THE SEVENTIES VOL.2
MSCD 1964 / Apr '94 / Disky

☐ MILLION SELLERS - THE SEVENTIES VOL.3
MSCD 1965 / Apr '94 / Disky

☐ MILLION SELLERS - THE SEVENTIES VOL.4
MSCD 1966 / Apr '94 / Disky

☐ MILLION SELLERS - THE SEVENTIES VOL.5
MSCD 1967 / Apr '94 / Disky

☐ MILLION SELLERS - THE SEVENTIES VOL.6
MSCD 1968 / Apr '94 / Disky

☐ MILLION SELLERS - THE SEVENTIES VOL.7
MSCD 1969 / Apr '94 / Disky

☐ MILLION SELLERS - THE SEVENTIES VOL.8
MSCD 1970 / Apr '94 / Disky

☐ MILLION SELLERS - THE SIXTIES VOL.1
MSCD 1955 / Apr '94 / Disky

☐ MILLION SELLERS - THE SIXTIES VOL.2
MSCD 1956 / Apr '94 / Disky

☐ MILLION SELLERS - THE SIXTIES VOL.3
MSCD 1957 / Apr '94 / Disky

☐ MILLION SELLERS - THE SIXTIES VOL.4
MSCD 1958 / Apr '94 / Disky

☐ MILLION SELLERS - THE SIXTIES VOL.5
MSCD 1959 / Apr '94 / Disky

☐ MILLION SELLERS - THE SIXTIES VOL.6
MSCD 1960 / Apr '94 / Disky

☐ MILLION SELLERS - THE SIXTIES VOL.7
MSCD 1961 / Apr '94 / Disky

☐ MILLION SELLERS - THE SIXTIES VOL.8
MSCD 1962 / Apr '94 / Disky

☐ MILLION SELLING HITS OF THE 50'S
Mona Lisa: *Cole, Nat 'King'* / That's amore: *Martin, Dean* / Blueberry Hill: *Domino, Fats* / Rock 'n' roll waltz: *Starr, Kay* / Shotgun boogie: *Ford, Tennessee Ernie* / Mockin' Bird Hill: *Paul, Les & Mary Ford* / Unchained melody: *Baxter, Les* / Come softly to me: *Fleetwoods* / Shrimp boats: *Stafford, Jo* / You send me: *Cooke, Sam* / Fever: *Lee, Peggy* / Here in my heart: *Martino, Al* / On the street where you live: *Damone, Vic* / Oh mein papa: *Calvert, Eddie* / Vaya con dios: *Paul, Les & Mary Ford* / Sixteen tons: *Ford, Tennessee Ernie* / Wheel of fortune: *Starr, Kay* / Ain't that a shame: *Domino, Fats* / Return to me: *Martin, Dean* / Blossom fell: *Cole, Nat 'King'*
CDMFP 6047 / Jan '89 / Music For Pleasure

☐ MIN-YO OF TOHOKU, THE
ARN 64421 / 24 Apr '98 / Arion

☐ MIND CRASHER VOL.1 (2CD Set)
AUM 975003 / 1 Sep '97 / ZYX

☐ MIND OF GOA VOL.1
Keeper of the dream: *Angeles* / No other love: *Blue Amazon* / Goaway: *Power Source* / Tantilus: *Shamanic Tribes On Acid* / Balck rain: *Prana* / Wicked mille: *Orichalcum* / Over drive: *Switchblade* / Riding high: *Evolution* / Bubble: *Bubble* / Anjuna: *V* / Miles and smile: *Sit On The Lungi* / Pulsar glitch: *Total Eclipse* / Acid friction: *Shay, Danny & Danny Clapham* / Awakening: *Fahrenheit* / Endorphin: *Spirit Level* / Ni nuclear mushrooms: *Amanite FX*
CDTOT 41 / May '96 / Jumpin' & Pumpin'

☐ MIND OF GOA VOL.2 (2CD Set)
CDTOT 46 / Nov '96 / Jumpin' & Pumpin'

☐ MIND POLLUTION VOL.1
WOWCD 11 / May '93 / Words Of Warning

☐ MIND POLLUTION VOL.2
WOWCD 29 / Sep '93 / Words Of Warning

☐ MIND THE GAP VOL.14
GC 020 / 17 Nov '97 / Lowlands

☐ MIND THE GAP VOL.15
GC 021 / 19 Jan '98 / Lowlands

☐ MIND THE GAP VOL.17
GC 023 / 9 Mar '98 / Gonzo Circus

☐ MIND THE GAP VOL.18
GC 024 / 6 Jul '98 / Gonzo Circus

☐ MIND THE GAP VOL.2 (Ultimate Breaks & Beats)
Night time: *Mr. Scruff* / Days gone: *Doppelganger* / Astrologikal: *Droppin' Science* / Fuck dub: *Droppin' Science* / Stoned groove: *DJ Die* / Dave Yang and Steve Yin de-wish t'swish: *Fila Brazillia* / O ze (move d's joint): *Shantel* / Homeboy: *Eskubar* / That was no martian: *Airgoose* / Liquid velvet: *J-Majik* / Mad different methods: *Rush, Ed & Trace & Nico* / Jos dis: *DJ DSL*
GAP 00252 / Feb '97 / Groove Attack

☐ MINDCONTROL BY JENS (3CD Set)
PIAS 556450525 / Jun '97 / Plastic Head

☐ MINDY'S REVENGE (20 Killer Cuts)
7019950604 / Nov '97 / Word

☐ MINIATURES (A Sequence Of 51 Tiny Masterpieces)
RSG 159 / Mar '97 / Resurgence

☐ MINIMAL EXPRESSIONS VOL.1
Blowout expressions: *Blowout Express* / Harmonica track: *Soulboy* / Love in return: *Brown, Diana* / It's the time: *Criminal Element Orchestra* / Ultimate: *Pavonia Ave* / You're mine: *Blowout Express* / Let the fun begin: *Secret Knowledge*
MINX 11CD / 11 Aug '97 / Dorado

☐ MINIMALISM (2CD Set)
LA 5CD / 27 Jul '98 / Law & Auder

☐ MINISTRY OF SOUND - CLASSICS (2CD Set)
After the love: *Jesus Loves You* / Always: *MK* / Blow your whistle: *DJ Duke* / Blue: *LaTour* / Energy flash: *Beltram, Joey* / Finaaly: *Peniston, Ce Ce* / For you: *4th Measure Men* / Slve to the vibe: *Aftershock* / Stella: *Jam & Spoon* / Witch doctor: *Van Helden, Armand* / Phantom: *Renegade Soundwave* / Nervous track: *Nu Yorican Soul* / Inside your mind: *Nelson, Grant* / God made me funky: *MD X-Press* / Voices in my mind: *Voices* / (Who) keeps changing: *South Street Players* / Throw: *Paperclip People* / Voodoo ray: *Guy Called Gerald* / Pride: *Clivilles & Cole* / Do you want it right now: *Degrees Of Motion* / Teas: *Knuckles, Frankie* / Passion: *Gat Decor* / French Kiss: *Lil' Louis* / Burning: *MK* / Get busy: *Mr. Lee* / Push the feeling on: *Nightcrawlers* / Progen - move any...: *Shamen* / Alright: *Shamen* / O: *28th Street Crew*
CLACD 1 / Jun '97 / Ministry Of Sound

☐ MINISTRY OF SOUND - LATE NIGHT SESSIONS (Mixed By DJ Harvey)
Bone: *Persuasion* / Garden of Earthly delights: *D-Note* / New Jersey deep: *Black Science Orchestra* / Hiroshi's dub: *TPO* / No excuses dub: *Hunter, Terry* / Jazz y motion: *Batamania* / Souffles H: *Mondo Grosso* / Thank u Mum: *St. Germain* / New day: *Round Two* / Not reggae: *Idjut Boys & LAJ* / Still holdin' on: *Elements Of Life* / Peace: *DJ Food*
SOMCD 4 / Jul '97 / Sound Of Ministry

☐ MINISTRY OF SOUND - THE ANNUAL VOL.1 (2CD Set)
ANNCD 95 / Nov '95 / Ministry Of Sound

☐ MINISTRY OF SOUND - THE ANNUAL VOL.2 (2CD Set)
ANNCD 96 / Nov '96 / Ministry Of Sound

☐ MINISTRY OF SOUND - THE SESSIONS VOL.1 (Mixed By Tony Humphries)
All funked up: *Mother* / Mings incredible disco machine: *Brother Love Dubs* / Let's dance: *Mr. Peach* / Movin' on: *Roach Motel* / Take a ride: *Club 69* / Dreams: *Gabrielle* / Take it to the top: *New Dance Republic* / London x-press: *Xpress 2* / Black sky: *Shakespears Sister* / Question: *Seven Grand Housing Authority* / Slide on the rhythm: *Arizona & Zietia* / Testament one: *Chubby Chunks Vol.1*
MINCD 1 / Jul '97 / Ministry Of Sound

☐ MINISTRY OF SOUND - THE SESSIONS VOL.2 (Mixed By Paul Oakenfold)
MINCD 2 / Jul '97 / Ministry Of Sound

☐ MINISTRY OF SOUND - THE SESSIONS VOL.3 (Mixed By Clivilles & Cole)
MINCD 3 / Jul '97 / Ministry Of Sound

☐ MINISTRY OF SOUND - THE SESSIONS VOL.4 (Mixed By CJ MacKintosh)
MINCDB 4 / Apr '95 / Ministry Of Sound
MINCD 4 / Jul '97 / Ministry Of Sound

☐ MINISTRY OF SOUND - THE SESSIONS VOL.5 (Mixed By Masters Of Work - 2CD Set)
MINCD 5 / Jul '97 / Ministry Of Sound

☐ MINISTRY OF SOUND - THE SESSIONS VOL.6 (Mixed By Frankie Knuckles - 2CD Set)
Good love: *Incognito* / Joy you bring: *Swing 52* / So special: *Spice Of Life & Gina Foster* / I appreciate: *Brown, Kathy* / Race of survival: *Sonz Of Soul & Steven Ville* / Another day: *Sledge, Kathy* / Skyhigh: *Voices & Individual* / I remember dance: *Chuggles* / Freedom (Make it funky): *Black Magic* / Live in unity: *Dangerous Minds* / Day in the life: *Terry, Todd* / Keep movin': *Mone* / Love rendezvous: *M-People* / In the trees: *Faze Action* / Hypnodelic: *FK* / Heavy gospel meeting: *Black Science Orchestra* / I'm so grateful: *Kings Of Tomorrow & Densaid* / Alabama blues: *St. Germain* / Bounce: *Kenlou* / Sound: *X-Press 2* / Limbo of vanished: *Tone Theory* / Theme: *Hot Lizard* / Reach: *Lil' Mo' Yin Yang* / Baby can you reach: *Limelife*
MINCD 6 / Jul '97 / Ministry Of Sound

☐ MINISTRY OF SOUND - THE SESSIONS VOL.7 (Mixed By David Morales - 2CD Set)
MINCD 7 / Jul '97 / Ministry Of Sound

☐ MINISTRY OF SOUND PRESENTS AWOL - LIVE
AWOLCD 1 / Jul '95 / Ministry Of Sound

☐ MINISTRY OF SOUND PRESENTS THE CLUBBERS GUIDE TO IBIZA
MOSCD 1 / 22 Jun '98 / Ministry Of Sound

☐ MINISTRY OF SOUND PRESENTS THE FUTURE SOUND OF NEW YORK
SOMCD 1 / Mar '95 / Ministry Of Sound

☐ MINISTRY OF SOUND SESSIONS VOL.9 (2CD Set)
MINCD 9 / 2 Mar '98 / Ministry Of Sound

☐ MINIT/INSTANT STORY, THE (2CD Set)
CDLAB 101 / Jan '96 / Charly

☐ MINSTREL BANJO STYLE
ROUCD 0321 / Dec '94 / Rounder

☐ MINSTREL BOY, THE (Irish Singers Of Great Renoun)
GEMMCD 9989 / Nov '92 / Pearl

☐ MIRKKOCALBMI
DATCD 21 / Nov '95 / Dat

☐ MISAS Y FIESTAS MEXICANAS
Misa panamericana (messe des mariachis) / Misa tepozteca / La charreada / Sones de michoacan / El taconaso / Hymne au soleil / Danza de los negritos / Danza de los voladores / Danza de los viejitos
ARN 64017 / '88 / Arion

☐ MISCELLANEOUS VOL.1
Under pressure: *Bluefoot* / Unix: *Biomuse* / Lowdown: *Tranquil Elephantizer* / Lunar tunes: *ARC* / Subether: *Endemic Void* / AEA: *Circadian Rhythms* / Moonrise: *Pooley, Ian* / Jinn: *Tao* / Pentax: *Launchdat* / Shapeshifter: *Fantomas* / Living dust: *Toop, David* / Sub evening lullaby: *Takshaka*
WORDD 1 / Jul '95 / Language

☐ MISCELLANEOUS VOL.2
Infinitesimal: *Nad* / Miracle tonic: *Mr. Foster* / Ghost submarine: *Bermuda Triangle* / Sniper: *Occupiers* / Waiting wall: *Steve C* / We R walkin': *Phume* / Alpha Beta Gamma: *Buckfunk 3000* / Why we feel so uncomfortable about the future: *Skrew & Wrap* / Earth hum: *No Sleep* / March of Osiris: *Elixir* / 80's funky: *Decal* / Ouagga: *Phluide* / Zeitgeist: *Isis* / Uncitizen: *Deform*
WORDD 003 / Sep '96 / Language

☐ MISFITS OF SKA VOL.1
AM 002 / Feb '97 / Asian Man

☐ MISFITS OF SKA VOL.2
AM 006 / Feb '97 / Asian Man

☐ MISSED BEATS
BBJCD 002 / Jul '96 / Black On Black

☐ MISSING CHORD, THE
GASH 1 / Feb '97 / Snatch

☐ MISSION
TYCD 001 / Jun '92 / Tan Yah

☐ MISSION IMPOSSIBLE TO FINAL MISSION
SONCD 0058 / Mar '94 / Sonic Sounds

☐ MISSISSIPPI BLUES
TMCD 07 / Oct '91 / Travellin' Man

☐ MISSISSIPPI BLUES (2CD Set)
PBXCD 402 / Dec '96 / Pulse

☐ MISSISSIPPI BLUES
Down the dirt road blues: *Patton, Charlie* / Maggie Campbell blues: *Johnson, Tommy* / Canned heat blues: *Johnson, Tommy* / Big fat Mama: *Johnson, Tommy* / Mississippi jail house groan: *Lacy, Rube* / Dough roller blues: *Akers, Garfield* / M and O blues: *Brown, Willie* / Dry spell blues: *House, Son* / I'm so glad: *James, Skip* / Special rider blues: *James, Skip* / Hard time killin' floor blues: *James, Skip* / 22-20 blues: *James, Skip* / 49 Highway blues: *Williams, 'Big' Joe* / Lead pencil blues: *Temple, Johnny* / Fixin' to die blues: *White, Bukka* / Parchman farm blues: *White, Bukka* / Ride 'em on down: *Petway, Robert* / Black spider blues: *Lockwood, Robert Jr.* / Little boy blues: *Lockwood, Robert Jr.* / Crosscut saw blues: *McClennan, Tommy* / Machine gun blues: *Blackwell, Willie '61'* / If I get lucky: *Crudup, Arthur 'Big Boy'* / Mean old 'Frisco blues: *Crudup, Arthur 'Big Boy'*
IGOCD 2039 / Mar '97 / Indigo

☐ MISSISSIPPI BLUES & GOSPEL (Field Recordings 1934-1942)
DOCD 5320 / Mar '95 / Document

☐ MISSISSIPPI BLUES VOL.1
DOCD 5157 / May '93 / Document

☐ MISSISSIPPI BLUES VOL.2
DOCD 5158 / May '93 / Document

☐ MISSISSIPPI CIVIL RIGHTS MOVEMENT
FE 1419 / Dec '94 / Folk Era

☐ MISSISSIPPI DELTA BLUES
IGOCD 2025 / Jul '95 / Indigo

☐ MISSISSIPPI DELTA BLUES JAM IN MEMPHIS VOL.1
ARHCD 385 / Apr '95 / Arhoolie

☐ MISSISSIPPI DELTA BLUES JAM IN MEMPHIS VOL.2
ARHCD 386 / Apr '95 / Arhoolie

☐ MISSISSIPPI GIRLS 1928-1931
SOBCD 3515 / Mar '92 / Story Of The Blues

☐ MISSISSIPPI MASTERS: EARLY AMERICAN BLUES CLASSICS
YAZ 2008CD / Nov '94 / Yazoo

☐ MISSISSIPPI STRING BANDS VOL.2 1928-1930
DOCD 8028 / Jun '98 / Document

☐ MISSISSIPPI: FROM CANADA TO LOUISIANA
PS 65099 / Nov '92 / PlayaSound

☐ MISSOURI 1950'S ROCKERS
CLCD 4434 / Nov '96 / Collector/White Label

☐ MIST MASTERS - FLEDGLING
Lap of God: *Couch* / Freud's feild day: *Delgados* / Absence: *Supernaturals* / Didn't laugh at all: *Saidflorence* / Spooky: *Love Joy & Happiness* / Eurostar: *Margins* / Bring down the sky: *August* / Fashion victim: *Colour Wheel* / Fugue: *Philo* / Divine in water: *Fuel* / Mary Jane: *Limit Club* / Thank funk it's Friday: *Captain Shifty* / Only one: *Jellyhead* / G 12: *Microwave Babe* / Make it happen: *Skunk Tree* / Awkward: *Geiger Babies* / No reason: *Laughing club* / Coral: *Homecoming* / Banging the drum: *Bond*
IGCD 209 / Jan '95 / Iona

☐ MISTURADA VOL.2
Tempos atraz: *Flytronix* / Preficiao: *4 Hero* / Jazz carnival: *Global Communication* / Ausgang: *Ze's Trip* / Calma: *Lumen* / Faca de conta: *Roni Size* / Tudo que voce podia ser: *Flytronix* / A quem e roupa: *DJ First Klas* / Tempos atraz: *APE* / Orange sour ouica: *Azymuth*
FARO 15CD / Jun '97 / Far Out

☐ MIX TO THE MAX VOL.1
VPCD 2065 / 17 Nov '97 / VP

☐ MIX UNLIMITED
TIMECD 0392 / 2 Feb '98 / Time Unlimited

☐ MIX UNLIMITED - POSITION GOLD
TIMECD 0412 / 15 Jun '98 / Time Unlimited

☐ MIX ZONE, THE (2CD Set)
There's nothing I won't do: *JX* / Blurred: *Pianoman* / On ya way: *Helicopter* / Read my lips: *Alex Party* / Push the feeling on: *Nightcrawlers* / Heaven knows: *Moraes, Angel* / Keep on jumpin': *Lisa Marie Experience* / Nakasaki (I need a lover tonight): *Kendoh* / Klubhopping: *Klubb Heads* / Giv me luv: *Alcatrazz* / Dreamer: *Livin' Joy* / Higher state of consciousness: *Wink, Josh* / Over and over: *Plux & Georgia Jones* / Lover that you are: *Pulse* / Disco's revenge: *Gusto* / I feel love: *Summer, Donna* / Trippin' on sunshine: *Pizzaman* / Trance piano: *Y-*

Traxx / Call on me: Johnny X / Are you out there: Crescendo / Way it is: Chameleon / Yeke yeke: Kante, Mory / Have fun: Coma B / Children: Miles, Robert / Be as one: Sasha & Maria / Let me be your fantasy: Baby D / Theme from S'Express: S'Express / Tempo fiesta: Itty Bitty Boozy Woozy / Resonance: Resonance / Sunshine after the rain: Berri / I need you: Pendulum / For what you dream of: Bedrock & KYO / Access: DJ Misjah & Tim / X files: DJ Dado
5355822 / Jun '96 / PolyGram TV

☐ MIXED EMOTIONS (Jazz In The Eighth Dimension)
I'm on: DJ BMF / To trap a spy: Pimp Daddy Nash / Dub systems go: Dubmarine / Uncertain T: Q-Burns Abstract Message / Funk is free: DJ BMF / Vibe checkin': Q-Burns Abstract Message / Wendy lost in velvet: Pimp Daddy Nash / Feel the sauce: Dubmarine / Wendy lost in jungle: Pimp Daddy Nash / Dubmission: Dubmarine
KOBICD 002 / Jul '96 / On Delancey Street

☐ MIXED EMOTIONS VOL.1 (2CD Set)
If I never see you again: Wet Wet Wet / Alone: Bee Gees / What becomes of the broken hearted: Robson & Jerome / I heard it through the grapevine: Gaye, Marvin / After the love has gone: Earth, Wind & Fire / Love don't live here anymore: Rose Royce / Ain't no sunshine: Withers, Bill / Tired of being alone: Green, Al / You might need somebody: Crawford, Randy / Please don't go: KC & The Sunshine Band / EVERYTime you: KC & The Sunshine Band / Love on the rocks: Diamond, Neil / Sorry seems to be the hardest word: John, Elton / Miss you nights: Richard, Cliff / Without you: Nilsson, Harry / All by myself: Carmen, Eric / Missing you: Waite, John / You've lost that lovin' feelin': Righteous Brothers / Sun ain't gonna shine anymore: Walker Brothers / Power of love: Dion, Celine / Million love songs: Take That / When a man loves a woman: Sledge, Percy / Endless love: Ross, Diana & Lionel Richie / Tonight I celebrate my love: Bryson, Peabo & Roberta Flack / Move closer: Nelson, Phyllis / Get here: Adams, Oleta / On the wings of love: Osborne, Jeffrey / Always and forever: Heatwave / Escaping: Carroll, Dina / Eternal flame: Bangles / When I need you: Sayer, Leo / My love: McCartney, Paul & Wings / Here there and everywhere: Harris, Emmylou / Love and affection: Armatrading, Joan / Lady in red: De Burgh, Chris / She makes my day: Palmer, Robert / Up where we belong: Cocker, Joe & Jennifer Warnes / Glory of love: Cetera, Peter
5536842 / Jun '97 / PolyGram TV

☐ MIXED EMOTIONS VOL.2 (2CD Set)
Yesterday: Wet Wet Wet / Baby can I hold you: Boyzone / Never ever: All Saints / Don't let go (love): En Vogue / Please don't go: No Mercy / Weird: Hanson / If you ever: East 17 & Gabrielle / How do I live: Yearwood, Trisha / I don't wanna lose you: Turner, Tina / Crying: Orbison, Roy / Sail on: Commodores / Slave to love: Ferry, Bryan / I don't want to talk about it: Everything But The Girl / Save a prayer: Hadley, Tony / Everytime you go away: Young, Paul / Unchained melody: Righteous Brothers / Home: Crow, Sheryl / Everything I own: Bread / Mandy: Manilow, Barry / High: Lighthouse Family / I am blessed: Eternal / I need you: 3T / You're still the one: Twain, Shania / Love can build a bridge: Cher & Chrissie Hynde/Neneh Cherry / You've got a friend: Brand New Heavies / Earthbound: Reeves, Conner / Let's stay together: Green, Al / My Cherie amour: Wonder, Stevie / You're the best thing: Style Council / Miracle of love: Eurythmics / Weather with you: Crowded House / Perfect year: Carroll, Dina / I'll be there: Jackson Five / True: Spandau Ballet / Wonderful tonight: Clapton, Eric / Your song: John, Elton / Together we are beautiful: Kinney, Fern
5650342 / 22 Jun '98 / PolyGram TV

☐ MIXED TRAXX
KKT 007CD / 27 Mar '98 / KK

☐ MIXIN'
REVCC 005 / May '95 / Revco

☐ MLLE. SWING ET M. ZAZOU
DEM 017 / Nov '95 / Chansons Actualites

☐ MO' BETTA (St. Louis R&B 1956-1966)
Peg leg woman: King, Willie / Mistreating me: King, Willie / Rock 'n'roll Deacon: Neal, 'Screaming' Joe / Tell me pretty baby: Neal, 'Screaming' Joe / East St. Louis: Little Aaron / My baby: Little Aaron / Teach me how: Williams, Johnny Lee / St. Louis sunset twist: Sharp, Benny / My baby has gone: Little Miss Jessie / She's my baby: Neal, 'Screaming' Joe / Don't quit me baby: Neal, 'Screaming' Joe / Nona baby: Williams, Johnny Lee / Look out pretty baby: Williams, Johnny Lee / Fishtail: Earthworms / My baby don't need changing: Kinglets / Pretty please: Kinglets / Tell me why: Rockers / Condition your heart: Little Herbert & The Arabians / Rumblin' tumblin' baby: Emeralds / Wham slam bam: Green, Fred / My love: Turner, Ike & The Kings Of Rhythm / That's all I need: Turner, Ike & The Kings Of Rhythm / It's alright: Lassiter, Art / Eastside blues: Sain, Oliver / Workin' again: Smith, Robert T
NEMCD 946 / 24 Nov '97 / Sequel

☐ MO' COOKIN'
URCD 004 / Jul '96 / Ubiquity

☐ MO' HOUSE YO MAMA
MM 800242 / Mar '96 / Moonshine

☐ MOBO - THE AWARDS (The Music Of Black Origin Awards)
Closer than close: Gaines, Rosie / Wonderful tonight: Damage / Say nothin': Omar / Love is all we need: Blige, Mary J. / You might need somebody: Ama, Shola / Nightnurse: Simply Red/Sly & Robbie / Even after all: Quaye, Finley / Hypnotise: D-Influence / Free: Ultra Nate / Freed from desire: Gala / Never let you go: Moore, Tina / I believe I can fly: R Kelly / On and on: Badu, Erykah / Remember me: Blueboy / Ocean drive: Lighthouse Family / Virtual insanity: Jamiroquai / C U when you get there: Coolio / GHETTOUT: Changing Faces / Don't let go (love): En Vogue / Sometimes: Brand New Heavies
9548359832 / 3 Nov '97 / Warner Bros.

☐ MOD JAZZ VOL.1 (60's Discotheque Dancers For The Cool School)
Soul shoutin': Scott, Shirley / Collard greens: McCoy, Freddie / Tengo tango: Adderley, Cannonball / Why don't you do right: Murphy, Mark / Money's gettin' cheaper: Witherspoon, Jimmy / Step out and git it: Nomos / Theme from The Carpetbaggers: McDuff, 'Brother' Jack / Theme from NYPD: Smith, Johnny 'Hammond' / Whip it on me: Hawks, Billy / Evil ways: Tjader, Cal / Yeh yeh: Santamaria, Mongo / Watermelon man: Santamaria, Mongo / Seventh son: Allison, Mose / I'm ready: Spann, Otis / Pool shark: Jackson, Willis / Soul shack: Stitt, Sonny / Filthy McNasty: Jefferson, Eddie / Love me right: Witherspoon, Jimmy / I've got your number: Bowie, Pat / Black talk: Earland, Charles / Mama Rufus: Merced Blue Notes / Soul liberation: Bryant, Rusty / Games: Jones, 'Boogaloo' Joe / Kenny's theme: Burrell, Kenny / Pink Panther: McDuff, 'Brother' Jack
CDKEND 139 / Sep '96 / Kent

☐ MOD JAZZ VOL.2 (Mo' Mod Jazz)
Wade in the water: Griffin, Johnny Orchestra / Mission impossible: Gilliam, Johnny / Money (that's what I want): Roach, Freddie / Soul jam: Booker T & The MG's / Got my mojo working (but it just won't work on you): Hawks, Billy / (I got a) stomach ache: Wells, Junior / Got to move your baby: Hopkins, Lightnin' / Eyesight to the blind: Allison, Mose / Georgia on my mind: Allison, Mose / Get the money: Santamaria, Mongo Orchestra / Cholo: Brown Brothers Of Soul / Blue vibes: Lytle, Johnny Trio / Smokey Joe's la la: Rene, Googie Combo / Spider man: McCoy, Freddie / Livin' soul: Holmes, Richard 'Groove' / Right on: Jones, Joe / My train: Saunders, Merl / You can't sit down: Columbo, Chris / Bad luck soul: King, B.B. / You win I lose: Taylor, Little Johnny / Brother Ray: Jackson, Willis / Senor blues: Murphy, Mark
CDKEND 150 / 26 Jan '98 / Kent

☐ MOD PSYCH POWER POP FROM TNT
AA 052 / Sep '97 / Arf Arf

☐ MODALITY
IMP 12402 / 24 Aug '98 / Impulse Jazz

☐ MODEL, THE
Girls on film: Duran Duran / Chant no.1: Spandau Ballet / Fade to grey: Visage / Model: Kraftwerk / Temptation: Heaven 17 / Enola Gay: OMD / Blue Monday: New Order / Is it a dream: Classix Nouveaux / Hyperactive: Dolby, Thomas / Vienna: Ultravox / Mad world: Tears For Fears / Will you: O'Connor, Hazel / Babooshka: Bush, Kate / Love action: Human League / Poison arrow: ABC / Talk Talk: Talk Talk / Living on the ceiling: Blancmange / Rapture: Blondie / Ghosts: Japan / No regrets: Ure, Midge
5529182 / Oct '97 / Spectrum

☐ MODERN ARCHITECTURE OF HOUSE
D 945002 / Jan '95 / Bunker/D'Vision

☐ MODERN ART OF JAZZ, THE
BCD 120 / '92 / Biograph

☐ MODERN CAJUN LOVERS
TRIK 0166 / Oct '94 / Trikont

☐ MODERN CHICAGO BLUES
TCD 5008 / Oct '94 / Testament

☐ MODERN DAY PAINTING BY ORIGINAL ARTISTS
NR 4003 / 17 Nov '97 / Fingerpaint

☐ MODERN ELECTRONICS VOL.1
SUB 2D / Sep '95 / Subversive

☐ MODERN ELECTRONICS VOL.2
SUB 8D / Feb '96 / Subversive

☐ MODERN ELECTRONICS VOL.4
SUB 38D / 29 Sep '97 / Subversive

☐ MODERN JAZZ - THE BEGINNINGS
Romance without finance: Parker, Charlie & Tiny Grimes / Bebop: Gillespie, Dizzy / Salted peanuts: Gillespie, Dizzy / Mean to me: Vaughan, Sarah & Dizzy Gillespie / 52nd Street theme: Gillespie, Dizzy / Night in Tunisia: Gillespie, Dizzy / Ol' man bebop: Gillespie, Dizzy / Anthropology: Gillespie, Dizzy / Lover man: Parker, Charlie / Perdido: Red Rodney / I woke up Dizzy: Hefti, Neal / Loaded: Winding, Kai / Man I love: Gray, Wardell / Dodo's blues: Marmarosa, Dodo / Rifftide: Hawkins, Coleman / Say it isn't so: Hawkins, Coleman / I got rhythm: Young, Lester / Riffamarole: Carter, Benny / Count me out: Allen, Henry 'Red' / Chord-a-bebop: Allen, Henry 'Red' / Apple honey: Herman, Woody / Concerto to end all concertos: Kenton, Stan
RPCD 638 / 10 Nov '97 / Robert Parker Jazz

☐ MODERN JAZZ PIANO ALBUM, THE
Be bop pastel / Seven up / Blues in be bop / Supersonic / On a planet / Air pocket / Celestia / 'S wonderful / Nichols and dimes / Who's blues / My lady gingersnap / Night is young (and you are so beautiful) / Why was I born / My foolish heart / Twins / I'll remember April / Joy bell / I didn't know what time it was / Budo / I married an angel / Jazz message / Frissell frazzle
SV 0272 / Oct '97 / Savoy Jazz

☐ MODERN LOVE (17 Of Today's Classic Love Songs)
Don't let the sun go down on me: Michael, George & Elton John / Save the best for last: Williams, Vanessa / Stay: Shakespears Sister / Goodnight girl: Wet Wet Wet / You: Ten Sharp / Fall at your feet: Crowded House / I wonder why: Stigers, Curtis / Time to make you mine: Stansfield, Lisa / Everytime you go away: Young, Paul / Promise me: Craven, Beverley / Get here: Adams, Oleta / When you tell me that you love me: Ross, Diana / My girl: Temptations / Every kinda people: Palmer, Robert / Coming out of the dark: Estefan, Gloria / Unchained melody: Righteous Brothers / Valerie: Winwood, Steve
5155182 / Jun '92 / PolyGram TV

☐ MODERN NEW ORLEANS MASTERS
ROUCD 11514 / '88 / Rounder

☐ MODERN SOUL VOL.2 (Boss Grooves)
Show me the way: Seville / I can't get over losing you: Butler, Sam / Take another look: Saunders, Frankie / Try love again: Pro-fascination / Let me give love: Empire, Freddie / Give me love: EKG / You keep holding back on love: Sue, Carletta / This time it's real: Nevilles, Larry / Something inside: Raj / What's the use: Troutman, Tony / I'll cry over you: Sheeler, Cynthia / You're gonna wreck my life: Guitar Ray / Where is the love: Caiton, Richard / Very special girl: White, Earl / Man in love: Wright, Bill / Sexy lady: Sideshow / I've got to have your love: Robertson, Chuck
GSCD 015 / May '93 / Goldmine

☐ MODERN SOUL VOL.4
Your love's got me: Satin / Time is right for love: Reed, Bobby / My heart just can't take it: Essex IV / Beggin' for a broken heart: Jackson, Otis / Now you're gone: Smoke / I get groove from you: Shannon, Bobby / One shirt: Marshall, Gene & The Ghetto Sons / This I've gotta see: Shaw, Cecil / Love in my heart: Gunter, Cornell / I know you're leaving me: Hightower, Sy / Here we go: Spread Love / Decisions: Lowe, Freddie / Sexy lady: Giles, Eddie & The Numbers / Breaking training: Brown, Larry / Don't it: Dawson, Roy / I wish our love would last forever: Swiss Movement / You beat me at my game like a lady: Strong, Chuck
GSCD 057 / Jul '95 / Goldmine

☐ MODERN SOUL VOL.5
It takes heart: Perry, Greg / Hardest part: Anderson, Curtis / You're the best thing: Baker, Larom / You got me hung up: King Tutt / What it takes to live: Chosen Few / Paradise: Jewel / I'll make it on my own: Lyde, Cecil / They don't make 'em like you: Horizon / Space lady: Bill / Help is on the way: Whatnauts / Loveland: SPG / My lovely lady: Scott, Moody / What you do to me: Best, William / I'm gonna see you through: Pictures / What am I going to do without your love: Johnson, Willie / Check your direction: Cloud, Michael / Slowly turning to love: Taylor, Alex
GSCD 078 / Mar '96 / Goldmine

☐ MODERN SOUL VOL.6
I can't stop loving you: Love Affair / All alone by the telephone: Bingham, J.B. / Thousand years: Brand New / Ain't nothing for a man in love: Bell, Archie & The Drells / If you want my love: Horne, Jimmy 'Bo' / Can't get along without you: Robinson, Dutch / Don't take your sweet lovin': Ghetto children / Man up in the sky: Strong, Barrett / Key to the world: Reynolds, L.J. / Trying to find a new love: Percy & Them / If you and I had never met: Magic Night / He's comin' in the morning: York, Patti / Gift wrap my love: Reflections / Tryin' to love two women: Persuaders / Tell me you love me: Hill, Bobby / Just to be with you: Dukes, Bobby / Look in the mirror of my eyes: Percy & Them / It's not easy to say goodbye: Ghetto children / Something special: Kirton, Lou / I can't control this feelin': Dean, Snoopy / Tears of the world: Moore, Robert / Lady be mine: King, Willard / Make believe everything's alright: Jones, Jimmy / How can I go on without you: Blake, Cory
GSCD 082 / Sep '96 / Goldmine

☐ MODROPHENIA (2CD Set)
Sha la la la lee: Small Faces / Green onions: Booker T & The MG's / Papa's got a brand new bag: Brown, James / Double barrell: Barker, Dave & Ansell Collins / Israelites: Dekker, Desmond / Baby come back: Equals / Poison ivy: Paramounts / Sunny afternoon: Kinks / Dancing in the street: Reeves, Martha & The Vandellas / Needle in a haystack: Velvelettes / You can't hurry love: Ross, Diana & The Supremes / Out of time: Farlowe, Chris / We've got to get out of this place: Animals / Liquidator: Harry J All Stars / Let your yeah be yeah: Pioneers / You can get it if you really want it: Dekker, Desmond / Band of gold: Payne, Freda / Itchycoo park: Small Faces / With a girl like you: Troggs / Tobacco road: Nashville Teens / Everlasting love: Love Affair / Red red wine: Tribe, Tony / Going to a go go: Robinson, Smokey / Shout: Isley Brothers / Think: Franklin, Aretha / In the midnight hour: Pickett, Wilson / Knock on wood: Floyd, Eddie / Rescue me: Bass, Fontella / (I'm a) roadrunner: Walker, Junior & The All Stars / Wade in the water: Lewis, Ramsey / In crowd: Gray, Dobie / Got my mojo workin': Smith, Jimmy / Letter: Box Tops / Give me just a little more time: Chairmen Of The Board / Young, gifted and black: Bob & Marcia / Wonderful world, beautiful people: Cliff, Jimmy / 007 (shanty town): Dekker, Desmond / Monkey spanner: Barker, Dave & Ansell Collins / Lazy sunday: Small Faces / If paradise is as half as nice: Amen Corner / Mony mony: James, Tommy & The Shondells / Waterloo sunset: Kinks / Pictures of matchstick men: Status Quo / Groovy kind of love: Fontana, Wayne & The Mindbenders
RADCD 62 / May '97 / Global TV

☐ MODS MAYDAY '79
Time for action: Secret Affair / Let your heart dance: Secret Affair / Don't throw your life away: Beggar / Hanging in the balance: Small Hours / Tonight's the night: Mods / Let me be the one: Mods / B-a-b-y baby love: Squire / Midnight to six: Small Hours / Broadway show: Beggar / All night: Beggar / Love only me: Mods / Walking down the King's Road: Squire / Live without her love: Squire / I'm not free (But I'm cheap): Secret Affair / End of the night: Small Hours
DOJOCD 5 / Jun '94 / Dojo

☐ MODS MAYDAY VOL.1
RRCD 225 / May '97 / Receiver

☐ MODS MAYDAY VOL.2
RRCD 228 / Jul '96 / Receiver

☐ MODULATION AND TRANSFORMATION VOL.1
EFA 006652 / Jun '95 / Mille Plateau

☐ MODULATION AND TRANSFORMATION VOL.3 (2CD Set)
EFA 0006932 / 2 Feb '98 / Mille Plateau

☐ MOJO ROCKSTEADY
HBCD 134 / Jun '94 / Heartbeat

☐ MOJO WORKIN'
Got my mojo workin': Waters, Muddy / Rock me baby: King, B.B. / Kansas City: Little Wolf / Spoonful: Howlin' Wolf / I'm in the mood: Hooker, John Lee / Broken hearted blues: Guy, Buddy / Dust my broom: James, Elmore / My babe: Little Walter / Mannish boy: Waters, Muddy / Thrill is gone: King, B.B. / I'm leaving you: Spann, Otis / Little red rooster: Howlin' Wolf / Walkin' the boogie: Hooker, John Lee / Reconsider baby: Fulson, Lowell / Wang dang doodle: Dixon, Willie / Blues for my baby: Memphis Slim / Rollin' stone: Waters, Muddy / Help me: Williamson, Sonny Boy
ASTCD 4006 / Oct '97 / Go On Deluxe

☐ MOJO WORKING (The Best Of Ace Blues)
Dust my blues: James, Elmore / Boogie chillun: Hooker, John Lee / Little school girl: Hogg, Smokey / Happy payday: Littlefield, 'Little' Willie / Blues after hours: Crayton, Pee Wee / Please love me: King, B.B. / Lonesome dog blues: Hopkins, Lightnin' / Riding in the moonlight: Howlin' Wolf / Things that I used to do: Guitar Slim / I miss you so: Turner, Ike / Three hours past midnight: Watson, Johnny 'Guitar' / Baby let's play house: Gunter, Arthur / I'm a mojo man: Lonesome Sundown / I'm a King Bee: Harpo, Slim / Hoodoo blues: Lightnin' Slim / I'm a lover not a fighter: Lazy Lester / Rock me baby: King, B.B. / Part time love: Taylor, Little Johnny / Black nights: Fulson, Lowell / Born under a bad sign: King, Albert
CDCHK 964 / Jan '95 / Ace

☐ MOLTEN GOLD (The Best Of Hot Wax Records)
While you're out looking for sugar: Honey Cone / Day I found myself: Honey Cone / Girls it ain't easy: Honey Cone / Truth will come out: Honey Cone / Want ads: Honey Cone / One monkey don't stop no show: Honey Cone / Women's love rights: Lee, Laura / Wedlock is a padlock: Lee, Laura / Crumbs off the table: Lee, Laura / Rip off: Lee, Laura / Somebody's been sleeping (in my bed): 100 Proof (Aged In Soul) / 90 day freeze: 100 Proof (Aged In Soul) / If I could see the light in the window: 100 Proof (Aged In Soul) / If I could see the light in the window: 100 Proof (Aged In Soul) / I'm mad as hell (and I ain't gonna take no more): 100 Proof (Aged In Soul) & New York Port Authority / Frightened girl: Silent Majority / Colors of my love: Silent Majority / Love machine: Jackson, McKinley & The Politicians / I just want to be loved: Charles, Lee / Free your mind (it's instrumental to be free): Politicians / Westbound no.9: Flaming Ember / Mind, body and soul: Flaming Ember
DEEPM 029 / Jul '97 / Deep Beats

☐ MOMENT RECORDS COLLECTION VOL.1
MR 1008CD / Apr '95 / Moment

☐ MOMENTS IN LOVE VOL.1
You've lost that lovin' feelin': Righteous Brothers / Without you: Nilsson, Harry / Cherish: Kool & The Gang / Keep on loving you: REO Speedwagon / I'm not in love: 10cc / Total eclipse of the heart: Tyler, Bonnie / Broken wings: Mr. Mister / Suddenly: Ocean, Billy / Stay with me 'til dawn: Tzuke, Judie / There's nothing better than love: Vandross, Luther / All the love in the world: Warwick, Dionne / You're the best thing: Style Council / Do what you do: Jackson, Jermaine / Just the way you are: White, Barry / Best thing that ever happened to me: Knight, Gladys & The Pips / Oh girl: Chi-Lites / All out of love: Air Supply / Every day hurts: Sad Cafe
MUSCD 002 / Nov '92 / MCI Music

☐ MOMENTS IN LOVE VOL.3
It started with a kiss: Hot Chocolate / Just the way you are: White, Barry / Almaz: Crawford, Randy / Every time you go away: Young, Paul / Lost without your love: Brad / Fool if yo think it's over: Brooks, Elkie / Rock me tonight: Jackson, Freddie / I don't know how to love him: Elliman, Yvonne / I'm stone in love with you: Mathis, Johnny / He was beautiful: Williams, Iris / Superwoman: White, Karyn / You're the best thing: Style Council / Sign your name: D'Arby, Terence Trent / Mind blowing decisions: Heatwave / Love and affection: Armatrading, Joan / Room in your heart: Living In A Box / Always: Atlantic Starr / Wind beneath my wings: Greenwood, Lee
MUSCD 034 / May '97 / MCI Music

☐ MOMENTS OF LOVE
DCD 5307 / Dec '93 / Disky

☐ MONDO BEAT
ND 45788 / 5 May '98 / Narada

☐ MONDO DRIVE IN
BRCD 5003 / Mar '97 / Blood Red Discs

☐ MONKEY BUSINESS
Tighten up: Untouchables / Fatty fatty: Eccles, Clancy / 54-46 (was my number): Toots & The Maytals / 007: Dekker, Desmond / Liquidator: Harry J All Stars / Fire corner: Eccles, Clancy / Double barrel: Barker, Dave & Ansell Collins / Birth control: Lee, Byron / Herbsman: King Stitt & The Dynamites / Fiddler: Gardiner, Boris / Return of django: Upsetters / Monkey spanner: Barker, Dave & Ansell Collins / Longshot kick de bucket: Pioneers / Young, gifted and black: Bob & Marcia / Monkey man: Toots & The Maytals / Dollar in the teeth: Upsetters / Barbwire: Dean, Nora / Shocks of mighty: Barker, Dave & Ansell Collins / Them laugh and kiki: Soulmates / Cherry oh baby: Donaldson, Eric
CDTRL 188 / Jan '95 / Trojan

☐ MONKEY SKA
Monkey ska: Harriott, Derrick / Really now: Dreamletts / Vat seven: Drummond, Don / I don't need your love: Chuck & Dobby / Don't throw it away: Itals / Out of space: McCook, Tommy & The Supersonics / Sammy no dead: Eccles, Clancy / I'm so in love with you: Techniques / Make yourself comfortable: Los Caballeros Orchestra / Cling to me: Dawkins, Horrell / Open the door: Clive & Naomi / Live wire: Soul Brothers / Seed you sow: Bonny / True confession: Silvertones / Girl next door: Blues Blenders / Jam session: Brooks, Baba / What a good woodman: Perry, Lee 'Scratch' / Tender loving care: Taitt, Lynn / Paradise: Shirley, Roy / Third man theme: Williams, Granville Orchestra
CDTRL 323 / Mar '94 / Trojan

☐ MONOLOGUE (2CD Set)
GEN 005CD / Jul '96 / Generations

☐ MONSTER BOP
Rockin' in the graveyard: *Morningstar, Jackie* / Werewolf: *Bonafede, Carl* / Story that's true: *Bonafede, Carl* / Caveman hop: *Coulston, Jerry* / Cat: *Willis, Rod* / Midnight monsters: *Jack & Jim* / Nightmare: *Stuart, Scottie* / Graveyard: *Bowman, Leroy* / Skeleton fight: *Smith, Allen* / Monster hop: *Dee, Jimmy* / Gorilla: *Convy, Bert* / Leopard man: *Wallace, Joe* / Nightmare hop: *Patterson, Earl* / Monster: *Please, Bobby* / Caveman: *Roe, Tommy* / Mad house jump: *Daylighters* / Jekyll and Hyde: *Burgett, Jim* / Haunted house: *Kevin, Cris* / Head hunter: *Fern, Mike* / I'm the wolfman: *Round Robin* Monopoly / Frankenstein's den: *Hollywood Flames* / Don't meet Mr. Frankenstein: *Casal, Carlos Jr.* / I was a teenage monster: *Keytones* / You can get him Frankenstein: *Castle Kings* / Gila monster: *Johnson, Joe* / Frankenstein rock: *Thomas, Eddie* / I was a teenage cave man: *Luck, Randy* / Frank Frankenstein: *Ivan*
CDBB 55013 / Apr '94 / Buffalo Bop

☐ MONSTER HITS - DRAG CITY
Shut down: *Beach Boys* / Drag city: *Jan & Dean* / Wheel stands: *Super Stocks* / Night rumble: *Cole, Jerry & His Spacemen* / Stick shift: *Duals* / 409: *Beach Boys* / Road runner: *Gants* / Dead Man's Curve: *Jan & Dean* / Four on the floor: *Super Stocks* / Chicken: *Convy, Bert & The Cheers* / Hot rod race: *Dolan, Jimmy* / Black denim trousers and motorcycle boots: *Cheers* / Little deuce coupe: *Beach Boys* / Boss dance: *Cole, Jerry & His Spacemen* / Little old lady: *Jan & Dean* / Fun fun fun: *Beach Boys* / Wide track: *Super Stocks* / Car trouble: *Eligibles* / Little Honda: *Beach Boys* / Brontosaurus stomp: *Piltdown Men* / Mr. Grasser: *Mr. Grasser & The Weirdos* / Street machine: *Super Stocks* / Ballad of Thunder Road: *Mitchum, Robert* / Cheater slicks: *Super Stocks* / Driving little deuce: *Cole, Jerry & His Spacemen* / Shutdown part II: *Beach Boys*
CTMCD 318 / Jun '97 / EMI

☐ MONSTERS OF GOTH (3CD Set)
CLP 0006 / Jul '97 / Cleopatra

☐ MONSTERS OF ROCK
SMR 29 / Jun '94 / Simple Machines

☐ MONSTERS OF ROCK (4CD Set)
MBSCD 435 / Mar '95 / Castle

☐ MONSTERS, ROBOTS & BUG MEN
Tantric porno: *Bardo Pond* / (A) Man Ray: *Long Fin Killie* / Gold teeth: *God* / Sleep: *Third Eye Foundation* / Star: *Hair & Skin Trading Company* / Photon: *Fuxa* / Pretty note: *Run On* / Grand piano: *Ul* / Slow thrills: *Bowery Electric* / Neither yield nor reap: *Brise Glace* / Sea swells and distant squalls: *Pram* / Chance was: *Magic Hour* / *SEDR 77*: *Labradford* / Everlasting arm: *Mercury Rev* / Feedback song: *Flying Saucer Attack* / Ordinary sleep: *Jessamine* / Dancing sumo wrestlers: *Yona Kit* / Preparation: *Windy & Carl* / Crush my soul: *Godflesh* / Lonesome death of Elijah P Woods: *Sabalon Glitz* / Les Yper-Yper sound: *Stereolab* / Doldrums: *Cul De Sac* / Departing the body: *Montgomery, Roy* / Aplomado: *US Maple* / Before I lose my style: *Space Needle* / Good night: *Stars Of The Lid*
AMBT 11 / May '96 / Virgin

☐ MONTE CARLO
ER 1028CD / 19 Jan '98 / Elefant

☐ MONTEREY INTERNATIONAL POP FESTIVAL, THE (16-17 June 1967/4CD Set)
Festival introduction: *Phillips, John* / Along comes Mary: *Association* / Windy: *Association* / Love is a hurtin' thing: *Rawls, Lou* / Dead End Street: *Rawls, Lou* / Tobacco Road: *Rawls, Lou* / San Franciscan nights: *Burdon, Eric & The Animals* / Hey gyp: *Burdon, Eric & The Animals* / Rollin' and tumblin': *Canned Heat* / Dust my broom: *Canned Heat* / Bullfrog blues: *Canned Heat* / Not so sweet Martha Lorraine: *Country Joe & The Fish* / Down on me: *Big Brother & The Holding Company* / Combination of the two: *Big Brother & The Holding Company* / Harry: *Big Brother & The Holding Company* / Roadblock: *Big Brother & The Holding Company* / Ball and chain: *Big Brother & The Holding Company* / Look over yonder wall: *Butterfield Blues Band* / Mystery train: *Butterfield Blues Band* / Born in Chicago: *Butterfield Blues Band* / Double trouble: *Butterfield Blues Band* / Mary Ann: *Butterfield Blues Band* / Mercury blues: *Miller, Steve Band* / Groovin' is easy: *Electric Flag* / Wine: *Electric Flag* / Bajabula bonke: *Masekela, Hugh* / Renaissance fair: *Byrds* / Have you seen her face: *Byrds* / Hey Joe: *Byrds* / He was a friend of mine: *Byrds* / Lady friend: *Byrds* / Chimes of freedom: *Byrds* / So you wanna be a rock 'n' roll star: *Byrds* / Dhun - fast teental: *Shankar, Ravi* / Flute thing: *Blues Project* / Somebody to love: *Jefferson Airplane* / Other side of this life: *Jefferson Airplane* / White rabbit: *Jefferson Airplane* / High flyin' bird: *Jefferson Airplane* / She has funny cars: *Jefferson Airplane* / Booker-Loo: *Booker T & The MG's* / Hip hug-her: *Booker T & The MG's* / Philly Dog: *Booker T & The MG's* / Shake: *Redding, Otis* / Respect: *Redding, Otis* / I've been loving you too long: *Redding, Otis* / Satisfaction: *Redding, Otis* / Try a little tenderness: *Redding, Otis* / Substitute: *Who* / Summertime blues: *Who* / Pictures of Lily: *Who* / Quick one while he's away: *Who* / Happy Jack: *Who* / My generation: *Who* / Killing floor: *Hendrix, Jimi Experience* / Foxy lady: *Hendrix, Jimi Experience* / Like a rolling stone: *Hendrix, Jimi Experience* / Rock me baby: *Hendrix, Jimi Experience* / Hey Joe: *Hendrix, Jimi Experience* / Can you see me: *Hendrix, Jimi Experience* / Wind cries Mary: *Hendrix, Jimi Experience* / Purple haze: *Hendrix, Jimi Experience* / Wild thing: *Hendrix, Jimi Experience* / Straight shooter: *Mamas & The Papas* / Got a feelin': *Mamas & The Papas* / California dreamin': *Mamas & The Papas* / I call your name: *Mamas & The Papas* / Monday, Monday: *Mamas & The Papas* / San Francisco (be sure to wear flowers in your hair): *McKenzie, Scott* / Dancing in the streets: *Mamas & The Papas*
ROKCD 102 / 24 Nov '97 / Essential

☐ MONTREUX FESTIVAL
In view: *Hamilton, Chico* / Let me down easy: *Little Milton* / We're gonna make it: *Little Milton* / Don't make no sense: *Little Milton* / Stormy Monday: *Little Milton* / For the love of a woman: *King, Albert*
CDSXE 070 / Nov '92 / Stax

☐ MOOD MOSAIC VOL.2 (Barnie's Grooves)
Baretta's theme: *Davis, Sammy Jr.* / Sanford And Son: *Forrester, Bobby* / Evil ways: *Wilkins, Ernie* / Streets of San Francisco: *Mancini, Henry* / Call me Mr. Tibbs: *Jones, Quincy* / Rock steady: *Generation Gap* / Desert is a circle: *Jodorowsky, Alexandro* / Super strut: *Port Authority* / Starsky and Hutch: *Blockbusters* / Landlord: *Kooper, Al* / Executive party: *Previn, Andre* / Ruth down: *Smith, Jimmy* / Mission impossible: *4Sound Orchestra* / Road runner: *Bullett* / Contract man: *Bullett*
CDSTONE 9552 / 16 Oct '97 / Stone

☐ MOOD MOSAIC VOL.3 (Sexploitation)
STONE 9561 / 19 Jan '98 / Yellowstone

☐ MOOD MOSAIC VOL.4 (Les Yper Sound)
STONE 9569 / 23 Feb '98 / Yellowstone

☐ MOOD MOSAIC VOL.5 (Supervixens)
STONE 9572 / 23 Feb '98 / Yellowstone

☐ MOOD MOSAIC VOL.6 (Jazz A Go Go)
STONE 9032CD / 19 Jan '98 / Yellowstone

☐ MOODS (A Collection Of Mellow Masterpieces)
Ese amigo de alma: *Vitale, Lito Cuarteto* / El vuelo: *Montes, Osvaldo* / La mer: *Edison* / Un amour dans l'apres-midi: *Edison* / Island: *Argol, Sebastian* / Winds of the stars in their eyes: *Popol Vuh* / Sayoko se souvient: *Edison* / Horseman in the wind: *Argol, Sebastian* / Suitor's visit: *Auckland Philharmonia Orchestra* / A viajem: *Gismonti, Egberto* / Homenaje a Anibal: *Maiz, Sampayo* / So sad: *Faltermeyer, Harold* / Dixie: *Edelman, Randy* / Exuadi-nos: *Musy, Jean* / Genesis: *Shankar, Ravi*
EMPRCD 907 / Jan '97 / Emporio

☐ MOODS FOR LOVER
Chi mai / Concerto de aranjuez / Bilitis / Holding back the years / That old devil called love again / Morning has broken / Crying / Chariots of fire / Aria / Sadness / Cavatina / Piano in the dark / Tara's theme / Imagine / Lily was there / Yesterday / Eternal flame / True
301172 / Jul '96 / Hallmark

☐ MOODS FOR LOVERS (3CD Set)
Power of love / Heartbreaker / Woman in love / September in the rain / Tonight she comes / Cherish / Song for Guy / Imagine / Stranger on the shore / Lady / Glory of love / Somewhere out there / Bright eyes / Just like paradise / Chi mai / El condor pasa / Adagio / Big my secret / As if we never said goodbye / Holding back the years / Eternal flame / I miss you / Nocturne / That ole devil called love / Soleado / Dream on / Edelweiss / Lost in emotion / I'm not in love / Feelings / Love changes everything / Nikita / Spanish eyes / Albatross / Last farewell / Blue moon / Careless whisper / Sadness part 1 / I swear / Aria / We've got tonite / Cavatina / Nights in white satin / Long and winding road / Stand by me / My way / Save a prayer / On my own / Rose / Lara's theme / Time after time / Dreamin'
390222 / Jul '96 / Hallmark

☐ MOODS ORCHESTRAL (4CD Set)
MBSCD 445 / Nov '95 / Castle

☐ MOON OF ROSES
ITM 1487 / Apr '94 / ITM

☐ MOONLIGHT MEMORIES
Night is young and you're so beautiful: *Sinatra, Frank & Dinah Shore* / Indian love call: *McDonald, Jeanette* / Moonlight serenade: *Miller, Glenn* / Moon came up with a grand idea: *Crosby, Bing & Peggy Lee* / My man (Mon homme): *Fitzgerald, Ella* / Stardust: *Sinatra, Frank* / There will never be another you: *Cole, Nat 'King'* / On a slow boat to China: *Haymes, Dick* / Elmer's tune: *Fields, Shep* / Moonlight bay: *Crosby, Bing & Gary Crosby* / Without a song: *Sinatra, Frank* / Mona Lisa: *Cole, Nat 'King'* / Serenade in blue: *Miller, Glenn* / If I didn't care: *Ink Spots* / I'm confessin' (that I love you): *Fitzgerald, Ella* / My funny valentine: *Cole, Nat 'King'* / Just you just me: *Cole, Nat 'King'* / Unforgettable: *Cole, Nat 'King'* / I've heard that song before: *James, Harry* / Polka dots and moonbeams: *Sinatra, Frank* / You made me love you: *Garland, Judy* / String of pearls: *Miller, Glenn* / Cheek to cheek: *Haymes, Dick* / Best things in life are free: *Allyson, June & Peter Lawford* / Thanks for the memory: *Hope, Bob & Shirley Ross* / Zing went the strings of my heart: *Garland, Judy*
ECD 3329 / Mar '97 / K-Tel

☐ MOONRAKER
SPV 08538942 / Sep '94 / SPV

☐ MOONRAKER VOL.3 (2CD Set)
Rain: *Steril* / Cowgirl: *Underworld* / Tabula rasa: *Covenant* / Dizzy divination: *Evil's Toy* / Waterdome: *Signal Aout 42* / City sleeps: *Trauma* / Tied up tied up: *LFO* / Like a flow: *Cyan* / Exile on mainline: *Chemlab* / Kruppel: *Oomph* / Al-Giabr: *Esplendor Geometrico* / Ich bin der Bennende Komet: *Lacrimosa* / Catherine: *Inkubus Sukkubus* / Xodus: *Nefilim* / Democracy: *Killing Joke* / Sick to death: *Atari Teenage Riot* / Wilde kinder: *Sabotage QCQC* / Nezzwerk: *Haujobb* / Let your body die: *Cyber-Tec* / Narcotic influence: *Empirion* / Facer: *X Marks The Pedwalk* / Other world: *Noise Unit* / Red: *Click Click* / Friction friction: *Velvet Acid Christ* / Burn baby burn: *Suicide Commando* / Become an angel: *In Strict Confidence* / You are: *Cobalt 60* / Kerosene: *Think About Mutation* / Circuitry: *Frontline Assembly* / Goodbye horses: *Psyche*
SPV 8747212 / Jun '97 / SPV

☐ MO'PLEN 1000
IRMA 4915692CD / 13 Jul '98 / Irma

☐ MO'PLEN 3000
DOUCE 807CD / 16 Jul '97 / Irma La Douce

☐ MORE CAJUN MUSIC AND ZYDECO
ROUCD 11573 / Aug '95 / Rounder

☐ MORE EROTIC JAZZ (Blue Moves Vol.2)
Urban desire: *Brodka, Eric* / Who's right who's wrong: *Gaskins, Ray* / Lebo: *Masha Bijlsma Band* / Clouds: *Marcelli, Andrea* / When I see the moon: *Vibe Tribe* / First time: *Matalex* / Golden boy greets buddha: *Grey, Carola* / There and back again: *Metro* / Airplan window: *Holzman, Adam* / Freak baby: *Monsters* / Finally: *Kazda* / I love you again: *Gaskins, Ray*
89522 / 13 Oct '97 / Lipstick

☐ MORE GIRLS NIGHT OUT
Free: *Ultra Nate* / Who do you think you are: *Spice Girls* / Ladies night: *Kool & The Gang* / Good times: *Chic* / Remember me: *Blueboy* / You got the love: *Source & Candi Staton* / Come into my life: *Sims, Joyce* / Hideaway: *De'Lacy* / Closer than close: *Gaines, Rosie* / Star people: *Michael, George* / Ain't nobody: *Rufus & Chaka Khan* / We are family: *Sister Sledge* / Boogie wonderland: *Earth, Wind & Fire/The Emotions* / One and one: *Miles, Robert* / Ready or not: *Course* / Everybody's free: *Rozalla* / Show me love: *Robin S* / Beautiful people: *Tucker, Barbara* / Caught in the middle: *Roberts, Juliet* / I wannabe the only one: *Eternal & Bebe Winans* / Professional widow: *Amos, Tori* / Bellissima: *DJ Quicksilver* / There's nothing I won't do: *JX* / Give me love: *Diddy* / Ooh aah just a little bit: *Gina G* / Rhythm of the night: *Corona* / Call me: *Click* / It's raining men: *Weather Girls* / Ride on time: *Black Box* / Relight my fire: *Hartman, Dan* / Jumpin': *Lisa Marie Experience* / Young hearts run free: *Staton, Candi* / I can make you feel good: *Shalamar* / Don't stop movin': *Livin' Joy* / I luv you baby: *Original* / Samba de Janeiro: *Bellini* / Get down tonight: *KC & The Sunshine Band* / It only takes a minute girl: *Taste Of Honey* / Boogie oogie oogie: *Jacksons* / You sexy thing: *Hot Chocolate*
VTDCD 149 / 25 Aug '97 / Virgin

☐ MORE HOTTEST HITS FROM TREASURE ISLE
HB 109CD / Jul '94 / Heartbeat

☐ MORE MIGHTY WURLITZER
Dancing in the dark / Reilly Ace Of Spies / Birth of the blues / Big spender / Wurlitzer march / Grasshopper's dance / Haunted ballroom / Girl from Ipanema / Veradero / I left my heart in San Francisco / Roses of Picardy / Charlatan / Love walked in / Coronation Scot / Somebody stole my girl / Shadow waltz / Celebration march / Mood indigo / Love for sale / When the stars go to sleep
309142 / 13 Jul '98 / Hallmark

☐ MORE OF OUR STUPID NOISE
301242 / 8 Jun '98 / Nettwerk

☐ MORE REGGAE LOVE SONGS
SWCD 001 / 22 Dec '97 / S&WSK

☐ SONGS FOR MUM AND DAD VOL.2
Wayward wind: *Grant, Gogi* / Great pretender: *Platters* / Wonderful time up there: *Boone, Pat* / I believe: *Laine, Frankie* / Never ending story of love: *New Seekers* / Raindrops keep fallin' on my head: *Thomas, B.J.* / Somebody stole my girl: *Ray, Johnnie* / Dark moon: *Guitar, Bonnie* / Those were the days: *Hopkin, Mary* / Mockin' bird hill: *Page, Patti* / Deck of cards: *Martindale, Wink* / Little shoemaker: *Gaylords* / Let me go lover: *Yuro, Timi* / Stranger in paradise: *Four Aces* / Half as much: *Clooney, Rosemary* / Ramona: *Bachelors* / Born free: *Williams, Roger* / You'll never walk alone: *Greenwood, Lee*
ECD 3426 / Feb '98 / K-Tel

☐ MORE THAN A FEELING
You're the voice: *Farnham, John* / Nothing's gonna stop us now: *Starship* / More than a feeling: *Boston* / You took the words right out of my mouth: *Meat Loaf* / Can't fight this feeling: *REO Speedwagon* / Don't stop believin': *Journey* / Rosanna: *Toto* / Satellite: *Hooters* / Final countdown: *Europe* / Broken wings: *Mr. Mister* / When I see you smile: *Bad English* / (Don't fear) The reaper: *Blue Oyster Cult* / Flame: *Cheap Trick* / So tired: *Osbourne, Ozzy* / Rock 'n' roll dreams come through: *Steinman, Jim* / Stairway to heaven: *Far Corporation*
4730452 / Feb '93 / Columbia

☐ MORENTE-OMEGA
EEM 001 / 1 Jun '98 / Karonte

☐ MORLEY, PARLSEY, INGLOTT
PRCD 396 / Jul '92 / Priory

☐ MORNING AFTER
Out of body: *Innersphere* / Repro house: *Justice & Blame* / As fast as I could look away she was still there: *Budd & Zazou* / Indigo: *T-Power* / Flying again: *Spring Heel Jack* / Angry dolphin: *Plaid* / MHT: *Subtropic* / Nautilus: *Appaloosa & Oribit* / T'raenon: *Photek* / Ride: *Soft Ballad* / Night moves: *Foulplay* / Scary HH loop: *Dub Tractor* / Flowers for the moonlight: *Reflections* / String of pearls: *Spacetime Continuum* / Sarcacid part 1: *Alroy Road Tracks & Duke Of Haringay* / F-jam: *Adam F* / Overheated livingroom: *Dub Tractor* / Diosa de la luna: *Baby Doc* / Come with me: *Quattara* / Acid people: *White Trash*
CDTIVAX 1014 / Feb '97 / Positiva

☐ MOROCCAN TRANCE MUSIC VOL.2 (Sufi)
SR 97 / Jul '97 / Sub Rosa

☐ MOROCCO
Mimoun sadie / Bar'ka ti ati a houssa / Gnawi / Hessaoui / Ian minna zin n souss / Moulay' brahim (touichya) / Al ghazzel / Kalali sahib mina nas / Raila / Slam habibi jani / Hadra / Tahdira / Beggar's song / Anta laziz ya Mohamed
YA 225713 / Jul '97 / Silex

☐ MOROCCO/MAROC (Berber Music From High/Anti Atlas Region)
LDX 274991 / Jun '94 / La Chant Du Monde

☐ MOSCOW NIGHTS
MCD 71590 / Jun '93 / Monitor

☐ MOST AWESOME LINE DANCING ALBUM VOL.1, THE
Black coffee: *Dalton, Lacy J.* / Boogie and beethoven: *Gatlin, Larry* / Bop: *Seals, Dan* / It's a little too late: *Tucker, Tanya* / Eat at Joe's: *Boguss, Suzy* / Tricky moon: *Ducas, George* / Lay down Sally: *Asleep At The Wheel* / Honky tonk blues: *Pirates Of The Mississipi* / Even if I tried: *Emilio* / Why baby why: *Palimino Road* / Tennessee two step: *Daniels, Charlie* / Cowboy band: *Dean, Billy* / No chance to dance: *Highway 101* / Cowboys like a little rock and roll: *LeDoux, Chris* / Three nickles and a dime: *Greg, Lynn* / Mama raised me right: *Floyd, Charlie* / Walk that line: *Dalton, Lacy J.* / Find out what's happening: *Pearl River* / Trail of tears: *Tucker, Tanya* / Honky tonk habits: *Emilio*
CDMFP 6411 / 6 Oct '97 / Music For Pleasure

☐ MOST AWESOME LINE DANCING ALBUM VOL.2, THE
Skinny dippin': *Kernaghan, Lee* / Girls night out: *Jeffreys, Gina* / Wild side of life: *Pirates Of The Mississipi* / Roll over: *Horton, Stephen Wayne* / Love hurts: *Dalton, Lacy J.* / Walkin' shoes: *Tucker, Tanya* / Boys in boots: *Kernaghan, Tania* / Fias do do: *Daniels, Charlie* / If I had a cheatin' heart: *Gregg, Ricky Lynn* / Love on arrival: *Seals, Dan* / I feel bad: *Miller, Dean* / Outback club: *Kernaghan, Lee* / Cadillac ranch: *LeDoux, Chris* / Two dollars in the jukebox: *Rabbitt, Eddie* / She came to dance: *Asleep At The Wheel* / Good thing going: *Pearl River* / Life is good: *Emilio* / Kiss me in the car: *Berry, John* / Stay the night: *Ducas, George* / Hammer down: *Dean, Billy*
4949232 / 1 Jun '98 / EMI Gold

☐ MOST BEAUTIFUL SONGS OF AFRICA
EUCD 1239 / Nov '93 / ARC

☐ MOST BEAUTIFUL SOUL ALBUM ON EARTH, THE (40 All Time Soul Classics - 2CD Set)
Kiss from a rose: *Seal* / You might need somebody: *Crawford, Randy* / I believe I can fly: *R Kelly* / Let's stay together: *Turner, Tina* / Just the way you are: *White, Barry* / Goodbye heartbreak: *Lighthouse Family* / (You make me feel like a) Natural woman: *Franklin, Aretha* / Get here: *Adams, Oleta* / So close: *Carroll, Dina* / Everything: *Blige, Mary J.* / When you tell me that you love me: *Ross, Diana* / Earthbound: *Reeves, Conner* / Forget me nots: *Rushen, Patrice* / Being with you: *Robinson, Smokey* / Lovely day: *Withers, Bill* / Woman in love: *Three Degrees* / Never knew love like this before: *Mills, Stephanie* / Love TKO: *Pendergrass, Teddy* / Wishing on a star: *Royce, Rose* / My girl: *Redding, Otis* / Sexual healing: *Gaye, Marvin* / Sign your name: *D'Arby, Terence Trent* / Give me a little more time: *Gabrielle* / Wonderful tonight: *Damage* / Feel so high: *Des'ree* / Killing me softly with her song: *Vandross, Luther* / Tired of being alone: *Green, Al* / How 'bout us: *Champaign* / Between the sheets: *Isley Brothers* / Betcha by golly wow: *Stylistics* / Suddenly: *Ocean, Billy* / Tonight I celebrate my love: *Bryson, Peabo* / Shake you down: *Abbott, Gregory* / Come into my life: *Sims, Joyce* / Do what you do: *Jackson, Jermaine* / Could it be I'm falling in love: *Detroit Spinners* / I care: *Soul II Soul & Charlotte* / Heartbreaker: *Warwick, Dionne* / After the love has gone: *Earth, Wind & Fire* / Give me your love: *Mayfield, Curtis*
TTVCD 2940 / 10 Nov '97 / Telstar TV

☐ MOST BEAUTIFUL TANGOS, THE
Le plus beau tango du monde / Le tango des Fauvettes / J'ai pleure sur tes pas / Tu m'apprendas dis / Je n'attends plus rien / J'aime tes grands yeux / Un tango dans te bras / Un violon dans la nuit / Ne m'ouble pas / Violetta / C'est mon gigolo / C'est un tango parfume / Tango illusion / Tango tango / Un tango c'est un tango / Poema / Antonio / Couer de Parisienne / Olvidame
19140 / Oct '97 / Forlane

☐ MOST BEAUTIFUL YODELLING FROM THE ALPS VOL.1, THE
321122 / Sep '92 / Koch

☐ MOST BEAUTIFUL YODELLING FROM THE ALPS VOL.2, THE
330023 / Sep '92 / Koch

☐ MOST BEAUTIFUL YODELLING FROM THE ALPS VOL.3, THE
330039 / Sep '92 / Koch

☐ MOST POPULAR 34 IRISH AND SCOTTISH SONGS
Scotland the brave / Let's have a ceili / Johnny lad / Donald where's your trousers / Fyfe o / If you're Irish / Agricultural Irish girl / Hannigan's hooley / Northern lights of Old Aberdeen / River Clyde / I belong to Glasgow / Rambles of spring / Finnegan's wake / Town of Ballybay / McNamara's band / Dear old Donegal / Home boys home / Bonnie Charlie / I love a lassie / Loch Lomond / Roamin' in the gloamin' / Keep right on to the end of the road / Ring your mother wore / Gentle mother / Medals for mother / Mother for mine / Cambletown loch / Bonnie wee Jenny McCaul / Fair Isles / I used to love her / Rambling banjo man / Hills of Donegal / Irish rover
PLMCD 30 / Jun '97 / Sharpe

☐ MOST UPLIFTING VOCAL ANTHEMS
CDSAS 1 / Aug '96 / Stage One

☐ MOTHER OF ALL MIX ALBUMS, THE (2CD Set)
TCD 2890 / Feb '97 / Telstar

☐ MOTHER OF ALL SWING ALBUMS, THE (2CD Set)
No diggity: *Blackstreet & Dr. Dre* / Return of the mack: *Morrison, Mark* / Love to love: *Damage* / Ocean Drive: *Lighthouse Family* / Gangsta's paradise: *Coolio* / We've got it goin' on: *Backstreet Boys* / Thank God it's Friday: *R Kelly* / Hit me off: *New Edition* / Woo hah got you all in check: *Busta Rhymes* / Flava: *Andre, Peter* / Forget the world: *Gabrielle* / I'm going down: *Blige, Mary J.* / All the things (your man won't do): *Joe* / Get on up: *Jodeci* / Stressed: *Tribe Called Quest & Faith Evans* / Get money: *Junior MAFIA* / Every little thing I do: *Soul For Real* / Tell me what you like: *Guy* / We got it: *Immature* / Believe in me: *Raw Stylus* / Every little step: *Brown, Bobby* /

Rump steak: Wreckx n' Effect / Poison: Bell Biv Devoe / Boom boom shake the room: DJ Jazzy Jeff & The Fresh Prince / Forget I was a G: Whitehead Brothers / Super woman: White, Karyn / Freek 'n' you: Jodeci / It's too late: Quartz & Dina Carroll
TCD 2877 / Oct '96 / Telstar

□ MOTHER OF ALL SWING VOL.2, THE (2CD Set)
TTVCD 2896 / Jul '97 / Telstar TV

□ MOTHER VOLGA (Recordings From The Banks Of The Volga River)
Recruiting song / An old slow song / An old street song for girls / Wedding dance songs / Wedding song / Song of the soldier's widow / Slow song / Dance chastushki's / Orphan girl song / Funny song from semur region / Dance song / Morkinskaya no. 1 / Old dance song / Morkinskaya no. 2 / Old morkinskaya dance song / If I were a little bird / There is a flock of ducks in the large lake / Lyrical wedding song / Wedding guest song / Guest song / Youth party song / Hey, my heart is bursting / Mari barynya / Our village / An old march / Tjumerli dance melody / Lyrical wedding melody / Lyrical wedding song / Slow song about a forest / Swarm is flying through the field / Wedding dance melody no. 1 / Chuvash dance melody / Wedding dance melody no. 2 / Short wedding song / An old wedding melody / Slow melody from the taryal region / Dance melody from the semur region / Mari wedding dance melody
PANCD 2008 / May '93 / Pan

□ MOTOR CITY (The Music Of Detroit)
TFP 014 / Nov '92 / Tring

□ MOTOR CITY BLUES
NEXCD 274 / Feb '96 / Sequel

□ MOTOR CITY BURNING VOL.1
NER 3014 / 16 Mar '98 / Total Energy

□ MOTOR CITY BURNING VOL.2
NER 3015CD / 14 Apr '98 / Total Energy

□ MOTOWN - THE VERY BEST OF THE 60'S
5306272 / 15 Sep '97 / Motown

□ MOTOWN 40 FOREVER (2CD Set)
5308492 / 7 Sep '98 / Motown

□ MOTOWN CHARTBUSTERS VOL.1
Blowin' in the wind: Wonder, Stevie / You keep me hanging on: Ross, Diana & The Supremes / Standing in the shadow of love: Four Tops / It takes two: Gaye, Marvin & Kim Weston / When can I get away in love: Marvelettes / (I know) I'm losing you: Temptations / What becomes of the broken hearted: Ruffin, Jimmy / Reach out I'll be there: Four Tops / Supremes / 7 rooms of gloom: Four Tops / How sweet it is (to be loved by you): Walker, Junior & The All Stars / I'm ready for love: Reeves, Martha & The Vandellas / Love is here and now you're gone: Ross, Diana & The Supremes / Gonna give her all the love I've got: Ruffin, Jimmy / I was made to love her: Wonder, Stevie / Take me in your arms and love me: Knight, Gladys & The Pips / Jimmy mack: Reeves, Martha & The Vandellas
5541442 / 10 Nov '97 / Spectrum

□ MOTOWN CHARTBUSTERS VOL.2
Ain't nothing like the real thing: Gaye, Marvin & Tammi Terrell / Reflections: Ross, Diana & The Supremes / If you can want: Robinson, Smokey & The Miracles / You keep running away: Four Tops / I could never love another (after loving you): Knight, Gladys & The Pips / I'm wondering: Wonder, Stevie / I've passed this way before: Ruffin, Jimmy / Some things you never get used to: Ross, Diana & The Supremes / Gotta see Jane: Taylor, R. Dean / Shoo-be-doo-be-doo-da-day: Wonder, Stevie / You're my everything: Temptations / Honey chile: Reeves, Martha & The Vandellas / If I were a carpenter: Four Tops / I second that emotion: Robinson, Smokey & The Miracles / If I could build my whole world around you: Gaye, Marvin & Tammi Terrell
5541452 / 10 Nov '97 / Spectrum

□ MOTOWN CHARTBUSTERS VOL.3
I heard it through the grapevine: Gaye, Marvin / I'm gonna make you love me: Ross, Diana & The Supremes/Temptations / My cherie amour: Wonder, Stevie / This old heart of mine (is weak for you): Isley Brothers / I'll pick a rose for my rose: Johnson, Marv / No matter what sign you are: Ross, Diana & The Supremes / I'm in a different world: Four Tops / Dancing in the street: Reeves, Martha & The Vandellas / For once in my life: Wonder, Stevie / You're all I need to get by: Gaye, Marvin & Tammi Terrell / Get ready: Temptations / Stop her on sight (SOS): Starr, Edwin / Love child: Ross, Diana & The Supremes / Behind a painted smile: Isley Brothers / (I'm a) road runner: Walker, Junior & The All Stars / Tracks of my tears: Robinson, Smokey & The Miracles
5541462 / 10 Nov '97 / Spectrum

□ MOTOWN CHARTBUSTERS VOL.4
I want you back: Jackson Five / Onion song: Gaye, Marvin & Tammi Terrell / Let's hit myself: Four Tops / Up the ladder to the roof: Supremes / I can't get next to you: Temptations / Too busy thinking about my baby: Gaye, Marvin / What were the yester- you yesterday: Wonder, Stevie / Someday we'll be together: Ross, Diana & The Supremes / ABC: Jackson Five / Never had a dream come true: Wonder, Stevie / Farewell is a lonely sound: Ruffin, Jimmy / Do what you gotta do: Four Tops / I second that emotion: Ross, Diana & The Supremes / Cloud nine: Temptations / What does it take (to win your love): Walker, Junior & The All Stars / Reach out and touch (somebody's hand): Ross, Diana
5541472 / 10 Nov '97 / Spectrum

□ MOTOWN CHARTBUSTERS VOL.5
Tears of a clown: Robinson, Smokey / War: Starr, Edwin / Love you save: Jackson Five / I'll be there: Jackson Five / Band of gold: Ginger, Freda / That's all in the game: Four Tops / Still water (love): Four Tops / Heaven help us all: Wonder, Stevie / Signed, sealed, delivered (I'm yours): Wonder, Stevie / I'll say forever my love: Wonder, Stevie / Ain't no mountain high enough: Ross, Diana / Stoned love: Supremes /

Abraham, Martin and John: Gaye, Marvin / Forget me not: Reeves, Martha / It's a shame: Motown Spinners / Never had a dream come true: Wonder, Stevie / It's wonderful (To be loved by you): Four Tops
5300602 / Jan '93 / Motown

□ MOTOWN CHARTBUSTERS VOL.5
Tears of a clown: Robinson, Smokey & The Miracles / War: Starr, Edwin / Love you save: Jackson Five / Ball of confusion (that's what the world is today): Temptations / It's all in the game: Four Tops / Heaven help us all: Wonder, Stevie / It's wonderful (to be loved by you): Ruffin, Jimmy / Ain't no mountain high enough: Ross, Diana / Signed sealed delivered I'm yours: Wonder, Stevie / Stoned love: Supremes / Abraham Martin and John: Gaye, Marvin / Still water (love): Four Tops / Forget me not: Reeves, Martha & The Vandellas / It's a shame: Detroit Spinners / I'll be there: Jackson Five / I'll say forever my love: Ruffin, Jimmy
5541482 / 10 Nov '97 / Spectrum

□ MOTOWN CHARTBUSTERS VOL.6
I'm still waiting: Ross, Diana / I don't blame you at all: Robinson, Smokey & The Miracles / We can work it out: Wonder, Stevie / Never can say goodbye: Jackson Five / These things will keep me loving you: Velvelettes / Indiana wants me: Taylor, R. Dean / River deep mountain high: Supremes & Four Tops / Just my imagination (running away with me): Temptations / Nathan jones: Supremes / Simple game: Four Tops / I heard it through the grapevine: Elgins / It's summer: Temptations / Remember me: Ross, Diana / Mama's pearl: Jackson Five / (Come round here) I'm the one you need: Robinson, Smokey & The Miracles / Just seven numbers (can straighten out my life): Four Tops
5541492 / 10 Nov '97 / Spectrum

□ MOTOWN EARLY CLASSICS SAMPLER
Come see about me: Ross, Diana & The Supremes / Baby I need your loving: Four Tops / Way over there: Robinson, Smokey & The Miracles / Wait till my Bobby gets home: Reeves, Martha & The Vandellas / He's the one I love: Wells, Mary / Headline news: Starr, Edwin / Behind a painted smile: Isley Brothers / Ain't too proud to beg: Temptations / Goin' back to Indiana: Jackson Five / Can I get a witness: Gaye, Marvin / I'll say forever my love: Ruffin, Jimmy / People make the world go round: Jackson, Michael
5524342 / Jul '96 / Spectrum

□ MOUNTAIN MUSIC
SFWCD 40038 / Dec '94 / Smithsonian Folkways

□ MOUNTAIN MUSIC OF KENTUCKY VOL.2 (2CD Set)
SFWCD 40077 / May '96 / Smithsonian Folkways

□ MOUNTAIN MUSIC OF PERU VOL.1
CDS 40020 / Aug '94 / Smithsonian Folkways

□ MOUNTAIN MUSIC OF PERU VOL.2
SFWCD 40406 / Aug '95 / Smithsonian Folkways

□ MOUNTAIN MYSTIQUE (The Authentic Sounds Of The Pan Pipes)
Cuando el sole sal / La vierge sola / Carnavalito / Primavera / El indio del Antiplano / Zagoria / El poncho rojo / Sikuereada / Los barriadas / El chuianco / Llamada de los buitres / Rin del angelito / pais / Sol inca / Canto del cuculi / Vicunitas / Las chullpas / Lagrima india / Indiecito soy / La bruja / Rosita / El condor pasa
SUMCD 4031 / Nov '96 / Summit

□ MOUNTAIN SERENITY (A Magical Blend Of Music And The Sounds Of Nature)
57582 / May '97 / Nature's Harmony

□ MOUVANCES TZIGANES - NOMAD'S LAND
PS 65134CD / Jul '94 / PlayaSound

□ MOUWACHAH (Chants Arabo-Andalous)
D 2669 / Nov '97 / Studio SM

□ MOVE CLOSER (19 Romantic Melodies)
Move closer / Ti amo / Right here waiting / Saving all my love for you / Unchained melody / With you I'm born again / It must have been love / Too much / Heaven / How deep is your love / Can't stay away from you / Greatest love of all / Don't wanna lose you now / Anything for you / How am I supposed to live without you / I just can't stop loving you / When a man loves a woman / I'll be there / Eternal flame / Save the best for last
SUMCD 4010 / Nov '96 / Summit

□ MOVE CLOSER (New Recordings)
Move closer: Nelson, Phyllis / Body talk: Imagination / If you're looking for a way out: Odyssey / Maybe: Chantels / With you I'm born again: Syreeta / Love letters: Lester, Ketty / Then you can tell me goodbye: Casinos / My heart and I: Stewart, Amii / I can: Winters, Ruby / When a man loves a woman: Sledge, Percy / Help me make it through the night: Smith, Sammi / He's out of my life: Smith, Sammi / My simple heart: Three Degrees / Way down deep in my soul: Pennington, Barbara / Ben: Jackson Five / Skyliners / You're gonna need me: Lynn, Barbara / Teardrops: Starr, Edwin / Rainy night in Georgia: Benton, Brook
ECD 3308 / 14 Apr '98 / K-Tel

□ MOVE INTO VILLA VILLAKULA
VVK 68 / 29 Dec '97 / Villa Villakula

□ MOVEMENTS IN BULGARIAN FOLK MUSIC
VGR 9405CD / Jul '95 / Van Geel

□ MOVIE MONDO
Newsreader / Thrill Killers trailer / Rat Pfink theme / Rat emerges / You is a Rat Pfink / Running Wild / Big boss a go-go party: Haydock, Ron & The Boppers / ISC trailer / Shock out of shape: Kay, Carol & The Stone Tones / Wild Guitar trailer / Twist fever: Hall, Arch & The Archers / Brain Eaters trailer / Lemon Grove kids: Snyder, Don/Peewee Flyn/Linda & Tickles Steckler / Plan 9 From Outer Space / Night Of The Ghouls / Maniacs Are Loose trailer / Jayne speaks / Bird's the word: Roberts, Rocky & The Airedales / Jayne is dead / Girl From SIN trailer / Another day, another man / Mr. Mari's girls trailer / Get off the road / She Devils instrumental: Lewis, Ruth Band / She speech / Strange Rampage trailer / Spoken intro / Hypnovista trailer / Hell's Angels / Warning
CDWIK 90 / Nov '90 / Big Beat

□ MOVIN' ON VOL.1
Introduce me to love: Absolute / Overjoy: S'Mone, Guy / It's over: Perfect Taste / Searching: China Black / Falling by dominoes: Music & Mystery / Keep it comin': Julianne / Never gonna give you up: Watergates / Takes time: Funkhill / Bring me back: Drakes, Anthony / Pushin' against the flow: Raw Stylus / Mr. Magic: Dreaming A Dream / Reconsider: Bell, Melissa
RUCD 300 / May '92 / Rumour

□ MOVIN' ON VOL.2
Revival: Giralt, Martine / Love guaranteed: Ferrier, Robert / Something inside: Deep Joy / I want you back: Sinclair / Got to be you: Koo Koo / You turn me on: Everis / Call me anytime: FM Inc / One look: Late: Pure Silk / Z.B.A.S.1: Ballin, Chris / Warm love: Law, Joanna / Intimate connection: Delano, Rohan / Yes, yes, yes: Applemountain / Higher love: Naked Funk
RUCD 301 / Oct '92 / Rumour

□ MOVIN' ON VOL.3
Don't go walking (out that door): Watergates / Keep on giving: BCA / Turn me on: Certain Ratio / What you won't do for love: Nu Visions / Girl overboard: Snowboy / It's not alright: Stirling McLean / No man the vibe: Vibe & Delroy Pinnock / Poetical love: Fiyza / Slow and easy: Moving In The Right Direction / Coming on to me: Mo & Beev / No time for change: Outside / Joy is free: Think 2wice / Revelation: Simon, Vannessa / Oh happy day: Beat System
RUCD 302 / Jun '91 / Rumour

□ MOVIN' RECORDS - THE REAL SOUND OF NEW JERSEY
WORLD 004CD / Oct '93 / World Series

□ MOVIN' TO THE COUNTRY
DC 886512 / 2 Feb '98 / Disky

□ MOVING HOUSE VOL.1
SSR 169CD / Sep '96 / SSR

□ MOVING HOUSE VOL.2
Faith hope and happiness: Crazy Gods / Special construction: Afronaught / Halftoo: DJ Profile / Riding high: Yesterday For Today / Full moon: Fuze Action / Rain: DJ Joe Louis / Mass production vol: Fontana, Lenny / Diskoking: Hacienda / Walk on water: Underground Evolution / Shielded: 20/20 Vision / 2 step: 20/20 Vision
SSR 190 / 27 Oct '97 / SSR

□ MOZAMBIQUE VOL.1
Magalango / Mutcico/Munguenisso / Enhipiti esquissirua / Mama na wamina anga monanga / Unabadera unema / N'kissa / Ndiribe nyumba / Tira hikhubula mondlane / Utemdene / N'tabuya mundzuku / Essita zombipiti / Chihire / Komvaravia kovela / Saudamos o grupo ladysmith black mambazo / Nisalili aussiwanini
CDORBD 086 / May '94 / Globestyle

□ MOZAMBIQUE VOL.2
Muticitco / Simbiane / Enhipiti kahi yankhani / Amiravo amutane / Amigos, somos un enxame / Onhipiti ossanta kolowe / Ngaihhe ilanga / Chinhambalala / Ukapata iya, ukapela bai / Mocambicano / Maria, kwadoca / Aliahi ka sialoco wahi wa-salaam / Frelimo quire echemi / Arminda / Mubedo wamina ysati wana wamina / Ndjemu / Onhipiti / Amigos, somos um enxame
CDORBD 087 / Nov '94 / Globestyle

□ MR. MODO'S LUNCHTIME LEGENDS VOL.2
YUMMY 2 / 29 Sep '97 / Mr. Modo's Alient Recordings

□ MR. ROCK GUITAR
Sunshine of your love / Relax / Layla / Samba pa ti / Honky tonk woman / Hey Joe / Wonderful tonight / Crying / Blue time / I shot the sherriff / Every breath you take / How many more time / Whole lotta love / Roccata / All along the watch tower / Stairway to heaven
ANT 017 / Nov '96 / Tring

□ MRG 100
MRG 100CD / Apr '97 / Merge

□ MTM MUSIC VOL.1
Holding on to the night: Axe / When only love can ease the pain: Ten / We'll find a way: Hugo / Fighting the good fight: Stone Soup / Heat of emotion: CITA / After the love has gone: Ten / First strike: the dream: Harlan Cage / No rest for the wounded heart: Tyketto / Robert / Love is the mud: Brunette, Glenn / Life in paradise: Storming Heaven / Talking to Sarah: Cheap / Don't Cry: Ten / Two hearts: CITA / Outlaw: Captive Heart / Don't go the heart: Kyle, Jaime / Wanted man: Burtnick, Glenn
MTM 199618 / Feb '97 / Made To Measure

□ MTV'S AMP 2
Bang on: Propellerheads / Genius: Pitch Shifter / Piku playground: Chemical Brothers / Clocks: Adam F / Digital: Guide & KRS1 / Abandon ship: Hardkiss & Kool Keith / Sexy boy: Air / Jungle brother: Jungle Brothers / Battleflag: Pigeonhed / Release yo'dell: Method Man / How can you heat us: Question Mark / Brown paper bag: Reprazent / War: Chuck D
CDVUS 147 / 13 Jul '98 / Innocent

□ MULTIPLEX
Dirty ride: Jaffa / Cry no more: Prestige Elite / Buddy: Diceman / Tribal woman: Lollipop Revolver / Silver Yoshi: Jaffa / Sugar glide: JP Dup / Face it: JP Dup / Put on your boogie: Prestige Elite / Planet Screech: Diceman / 20 no 6: Lollipop Revolver
KOBICD 007 / 17 Nov '97 / Delancey Street

□ MUMTAZ MAHAL
WLACS 46CD / Jun '95 / Xenophile

□ MUNCHEN - VOLKSANGER 1902-1948
US 0199 / Jul '95 / Trikont

□ MUNDO AFRIKA
African dream: Diop, Wasis & Lena Fiagbe / Sunshine day: Osibisa / Scatterlings of Africa: Juluka Radio Africa & Latin Quarter / Biko: Gabriel, Peter / Nelson Mandela: Special AKA / Jit jive: Bhundu Boys / Diamonds on the soles of her shoes: Simon, Paul / Rain: beautiful rain: Ladysmith Black Mambazo / Shanti: the tree: Gabriel, Peter & Youssou N'Dour / Happy ever after: Fordham, Julia / Sweet lullaby: Deep Forest / Temple head: Transglobal Underground / Father of our nation: Masekela, Hugh / Reckless: Bambaataa, Afrika & UB40 / Yeke yeke: Kante, Mory / Yela: Maal, Baaba / Wombo lombo: Kidjo, Angelique / Africa: Keita, Salif / Shosholoza: Ladysmith Black Mambazo
MOODCD 44 / Jul '96 / Sony Music

□ MUNDO LATINO
Guaglione: Prado, Perez / La cumparsita: Cugat, Xavier / Oye mi canto: Estefan, Gloria / Soul limbo: Mr. Bongo / Something in my eye: Corduroy / La bamba: Los Lobos / Que como va: Santana / Libertango: Piazzolla, Astor / Soul sauce: Tjader, Cal / Soul bossa nova: Jones, Quincy / Mas que nada: Mendes, Sergio / Watermelon man: Santamaria, Mongo / Exciting: Marcovici: Manow / Cherry pink and apple blossom: Sound La Rose / Carmel / Hot hot hot: Arrow / Cuba: Gibson Brothers / Got myself a good man: Pucho / Curveza: Brown, Boots & His Blockbusters / Tequila: Champs
SONYTV 2CD / 29 Jun '98 / Sony TV

□ MURDER ONE (Mixed By Lenny Dee - 2CD Set)
CSCPC 1 / Nov '96 / Crap Shoot

□ MURDER PUNK VOL.1
MPI 001 / Oct '97 / Murder Punk

□ MURDER PUNK VOL.2
MPI 002 / Oct '97 / Murder Punk

□ MURRAY THE K'S HOLIDAY REVUE (Live At The Brooklyn Fox - December 1964)
He's so fine: Chiffons / Denise: Randy & The Rainbows / My boyfriend's back: Randy & The Rainbows / Linda: Jan & Dean / Surf City: Jan & Dean / So much in love: Tymes / Be my baby: Ronettes / She cried: Jay & The Americans / Town without pity: Pitney, Gene / Shop around: Robinson, Smokey & The Miracles / You can't sit down: Dovells / Walk on by: Warwick, Dionne / Having my baby: Temptations / Thou shalt not steal: Dick & DeeDee / Leader of the pack: Shangri-Las / Since I don't have you: Jackson, Chuck / Any day now: Jackson, Chuck / Stand by me: King, Ben E. / Under the boardwalk: Drifters / Saturday night at the movies: Drifters / Baby it's you: Shirelles / Boys: Shirelles / Mama said: Shirelles / Tonight's the night: Shirelles
CDMF 094 / Mar '95 / Magnum Force

□ MUSCLE BUSTLE
Rendezvous stomp: Rhythm Rockers / Slide: Rhythm Rockers / Barefoot adventure: Four Speeds / RPM: Four Speeds / My stingray: Four Speeds / Four on theefloor: Four Speeds / Cheater slicks: Four Speeds / Bite barracuda: Knickerbockers / Mighty barracuda: Knickerbockers / Midsummer night's dream: Jan & Dean / Heart and soul: Jan & Dean / Those words: Jan & Dean / Playmate of the year: Sunsets / Chug-a-lug: Sunsets / CC Cinder: Sunsets / Lonely surfer: Burnin' rubber: Moles, Gene & The Softwinds / Twin pipes: Moles, Gene & The Softwinds / Mag wheels: Usher, Gary / Power shift: Usher, Gary / Competition coupe: Usher, Gary / Burnin' rubber: Moles, Gene & The Softwinds / Four on the floor: Moles / Royal Coachmen / Repeating: Royal Coachmen / Ski storm: Snowmen / 20,000 leagues: Champs
CDCHD 533 / Apr '94 / Ace

□ MUSCLE PACK VOL.1
LOOPCD 102 / Feb '97 / Loop

□ MUSETTE DANCE, THE (Music From Italy)
YA 225056 / Dec '95 / Silex

□ MUSETTE FROM PARIS
15207 / Sep '91 / Laserlight

□ MUSHROOM JAZZ (CD/CDR Set)
OM 005CD / 27 Oct '97 / OM

□ MUSIC AND DANCE OF ITALY VOL.12
TAO 12CD / Mar '96 / Taranta

□ MUSIC AND DANCES OF OLD IRELAND
KAR 987 / Jan '97 / IMP

□ MUSIC AND DANCES OF ROMANIA
KAR 990 / Feb '97 / IMP

□ MUSIC AND SONG OF EDINBURGH, THE
Links of Forth / Rattlin' roarin' Willie / Capernaum / Holyrood House / Lion Wallace saw / Johnny Cope / Loose noose / Deacon Brodie / Sandy Bell's man / Festival lights / Duchess of Edinburgh / Castle / Geordie's / Fisherrow / Mallie Lee / Black swan / Roslin castle / Edinburgh town / Flowers of Edinburgh / Waly waly / Willie's gane tae Melville castle / Union canal / Burning bing / Auld lang syne
CDTRAX 090 / Apr '95 / Greentrax

☐ MUSIC AND SONG OF GREENTRAX
Nodding song / Tunes / Terror time / Venus in tweeds / Eilean m'araich / Set of tunes / Rosie Anderson / Liathach / Sands of the shore / Somewhere in America / Up the Noran water / Dream Angus / Niel Gow's apprentice / Strong woman / No Gods / Nuair bha mi og / '45 Revolution / Summer of '46 / Jamie come try me / Silence of tears / Yellow on the broom / Roy's wife / Chaidh mi' na ghleannan as t-fhoghar / Song of the fishgutters / Culloden's harvest / Moon and St. Christopher
CDTRAX 8696 / Jul '96 / Greentrax

☐ MUSIC AND SONG OF SCOTLAND (A Greentrax Showcase)
Scotland the brave: *Lothian & Borders Police Band* / Bonnie Galloway: *Lothian & Borders Police Band* / Rowan tree: *Lothian & Borders Police Band* / Highland laddie: *Lothian & Borders Police Band* / Dumbarton's drums: *Redpath, Jean* / Rolling hills of the borders: *McCalmans* / Burke and Hare: *Laing, Robin* / Bonnie moorhen: *Heywood, Heather* / Old bean waltz: *Hardie, Ian* / Hospital wood: *Hardie, Ian* / Auchope cairn: *Hardie, Ian* / Glasgow that I used to know: *McNaughtan, Adam* / Bleacher lass o' Kelvinhaugh: *Paterson, Rod* / If wishes were fishes: *Bogle, Eric* / Yonder banks: *Fisher, Archie* / Shipyard apprentice: *Fisher, Archie* / Carls o'Dysart: *Russell, Janet & Christine Kydd* / De'il's awa' wi' tha exciseman: *Russell, Janet & Christine Kydd* / Farm auction: *MacKintosh, Iain* / Donald MacLean's farewell to Oban: *Bain, Aly & Phil Cunningham* / Sands of Burness: *Bain, Aly & Phil Cunningham* / Miller's reel: *Bain, Aly & Phil Cunningham* / Maid of Islay: *MacDonald, Iain* / Canan nan gaidheal: *MacPhee, Catherine-Anne* / Birnie bouzie: *Beck, Jack* / Fife and a' the lands about it: *Heritage* / Freedom come all ye: *Porteous, Lindsay & Friends*
CDTRAX 030 / Dec '89 / Greentrax

☐ MUSIC AND SONGS FROM THE DOGON, MALI
926672 / Jul '97 / BUDA

☐ MUSIC AND SONGS OF MINORITIES, VIETNAM
926692 / Jul '97 / BUDA

☐ MUSIC AT MATT MOLLOY'S
CDRW 26 / Aug '92 / Realworld

☐ MUSIC AT THE EDGE
74321268552 / Jul '95 / RCA

☐ MUSIC CITY SOUL (From Nashville's Black Cats)
When the boy that you love (is loving you): *Gaines, Peggy* / Hold on (a little bit longer): *Hunter, Rufus* / Sound of a crying man: *Hunter, Herbert* / Candy: *Tempo Rhythms* / It's a little bit late: *Waters, Freddie* / I'd like to try it one more time: *Birdsong, Larry* / These are my people: *Shelton, Roscoe* / It's almost sundown: *Allison, Gene* / Foolish lover: *Tig, Jimmy & The Rounders* / Isn't it wonderful to dream: *Hunter, Herbert* / Some day: *Henry, Thomas* / I know the feelin': *Jades* / I want to give my heart to you: *Allison, Levert* / I need a man: *Precious Three* / Tell me baby (who would I be): *Avons* / Just to satisfy my baby: *Gaines, Peggy* / Love is a two way thing: *Waters, Freddie* / My loss your gain: *Jades* / Is it love or imitation: *Henry, Thomas* / Happy go lucky: *Hunter, Herbert* / Push away from the table: *Hunter, Herbert* / You girl: *Watts, Wendell* / Singing a new song: *Watts, Wendell* / Win or lose: *Hunter, Rufus* / Sugar: *Birdsong, Larry & Thomas Henry* / Nobody knows: *Waters, Freddie & Eddie Frierson*
CDKEND 157 / 27 Apr '98 / Kent

☐ MUSIC FOR A CHANGING WORLD
XENO 401CD / Jun '95 / Xenophile

☐ MUSIC FOR COFFEESHOPS (2CD Set)
CDKTB 20 / Mar '96 / Dreamtime

☐ MUSIC FOR DREAMS (2CD Set)
FRCD 6 / 6 Oct '97 / Flex

☐ MUSIC FOR LIFE
Sweet savour / As the deer / After the flood / O perfect love / His love endures for ever / Sixth day / Somebody / Give thanks / Give you the glory / That great day / Second coming (cloudburst, rapture, eternal rest)
GHOUSE CD1 / Dec '96 / Gloryhouse

☐ MUSIC FOR LOVERS
EMPRBX 002 / Sep '94 / Empress

☐ MUSIC FOR MAIDS AND TAXI DRIVERS (Brazil Forro)
Balenco da canoa: *Toinho De Alagaos* / De pernambulco aomaranhao: *Duda Da Passira* / Eu tambem quero beijar: *Orlando, Jose* / Bicho da cara preta: *Toinho De Alagaos* / Comeco de verao: *Heleno Dos Oito Baixos* / Peca licenca pra falar de alagoas: *Toinho De Alagaos* / Recorda cao da passira: *Duda Da Passira* / Agricultor p'ra frente: *Orlando, Jose* / Entra e sai: *Heleno Dos Oito Baixos* / Linda menina: *Orlando, Jose* / Casa de tauba: *Duda Da Passira* / Morena da palmeira: *Orlando, Jose* / Carater duro: *Toinho De Alagaos* / Minha zeze: *Orlando, Jose* / Sonho de amor: *Toinho De Alagaos* / Namoro no escuro: *Toinho De Alagaos* / Forro da minha terra: *Duda Da Passira*
CDORB 048 / Aug '89 / Globestyle

☐ MUSIC FOR MODERN LIVING
LR 00698 / 23 Mar '98 / Lounge

☐ MUSIC FOR MY LOVE
WMCD 5689VT / Feb '94 / Disky

☐ MUSIC FOR RELAXATION
CDCH 606 / Feb '91 / Milan

☐ MUSIC FOR STRINGS FROM TRANSYLVANIA (Romanian Instrumental Dances)
LDX 274937 / Jul '92 / La Chant Du Monde

☐ MUSIC FOR THE ARABIAN DULCIMER AND LUTE
Badru zahur / Nida insan / Zubida / Altaf / Taqsim / Moulana / Salaam / Taqsim raad / Munawaat ablam
CDSDL 415 / Mar '96 / Saydisc

☐ MUSIC FOR THE GODS
RYKO 10315CD / Apr '95 / Rykodisc

☐ MUSIC FOR THE JET SET
TCD 1038 / Nov '96 / Tradition

☐ MUSIC FOR THE QIN, ZHENG AND PIPA
D 8071 / Feb '97 / Unesco

☐ MUSIC FORM THE SHRINES OF AJMER AND MUNDRA
TSCD 911 / Apr '95 / Topic

☐ MUSIC FROM BRAZIL
15497 / Feb '94 / Laserlight

☐ MUSIC FROM BURKINA FASO AND MALI
926932 / 24 Feb '98 / BUDA

☐ MUSIC FROM CAPE VERDE
CAP 21451CD / Nov '95 / Caprice

☐ MUSIC FROM ECUADOR
CAP 22031CD / Nov '95 / Caprice

☐ MUSIC FROM ETHIOPIA
TSCD 910 / Sep '94 / Topic

☐ MUSIC FROM ETHIOPIA
CAP 21432CD / Nov '95 / Caprice

☐ MUSIC FROM KARPATHOS, THE
926442 / Jul '96 / BUDA

☐ MUSIC FROM PORTUGAL
15495 / Jun '94 / Laserlight

☐ MUSIC FROM TAJIKSTAN/ UZBEKISTAN
926392 / Jul '96 / BUDA

☐ MUSIC FROM TANZANIA AND ZANZIBAR VOL.1
CAP 21554CD / Dec '97 / Caprice

☐ MUSIC FROM TANZANIA AND ZANZIBAR VOL.2
CAP 21573CD / Dec '97 / Caprice

☐ MUSIC FROM TANZANIA AND ZANZIBAR VOL.3
CAP 21577CD / Dec '97 / Caprice

☐ MUSIC FROM THE 1997 ROYAL TOURNAMENT
BNA 5097 / 13 Apr '98 / Bandleader

☐ MUSIC FROM THE ANDES & ARGENTINA
CDT 112 / Apr '93 / Topic

☐ MUSIC FROM THE BASQUE COUNTRY (2CD Set)
KD 416/417CD / Nov '96 / Elkar

☐ MUSIC FROM THE EDGE OF EUROPE (Portugal)
Os senhores de guerra: *Madredeus* / Cancao verdes anos: *Paredes, Carlos* / Andanso pela vida: *Vitorino* / Quartertra: *Dancas Ocultas* / Estranha forma de vida: *Rodrigues, Amalia* / June: *Vargas, Antonio Pinho & Maria Joao/Jose Nogueira* / Endachas a Barbara Escrava: *Vargas, Antonio Pinho & Maria Joao/Jose Nogueira* / Milinera: *Trovante* / Carandilheira: *Ne Ladeiras* / Cantiga de ceifa: *Lua Extravagante* / Chora por mim: *Diva* / Os vellos: *Ala Dos Namorados* / Bolero do coronel sensivel que fez amor em monsanto: *Vitorino* / Vem: *Madredeus* / Cancao: *Paredes, Carlos* / Fado portugues: *Rodrigues, Amalia* / Brinquedos: *Vargas, Antonio Pinho & Maria Joao/Jose Nogueira* / O que estrica tenho na rocan: *Ne Ladeiras*
HEMICD 28 / 6 Oct '97 / Hemisphere

☐ MUSIC FROM THE HEART
ELL 3212D / Oct '93 / Ellipsis Arts

☐ MUSIC FROM THE IVORY COAST & FODONON
LDX 274838 / Oct '94 / La Chant Du Monde

☐ MUSIC FROM THE NIGER REGION
D 8006 / Jun '89 / Auvidis/Ethnic

☐ MUSIC FROM THE ORINOCO RIVER
C 560119 / Dec '97 / Ocora

☐ MUSIC FROM THE PUNJAB
ARN 64278 / Oct '94 / Arion

☐ MUSIC FROM THE ROYAL PAGEANT OF THE HORSE
Opening fanfare / Young horse / Rise, rise thou merry lark/Horsey, horsey don't you stop / Queen of Sheba / English country garden / Songs of the country medley / Post horn gallop / John Peel/Old Towler / Devil's gallop / Lilliburlero / Men at arms / Let battle commence / Charge March from Battle of Vittoria / Solitary traveller / Pack up your troubles / Mahler's 5th symphony / Elgar's 1st symphony / O Fortuna / Oranges and lemons / Cockney cavalcade / Pomp and circumstance no.4 / Boys and girls come out to play / Musical joke / Entry of the Gladiators / They're changing the guards at Buckingham Palace / Galloping Major/Charlie is my darlin'/Comin' thro' the rye / We'll keep a welcome/St. Patrick's day / She's a lassie from Lancashire/The Lincolnshire poacher / Blaydon races/Round the Marble Arch / Procession of the knights / Praise my soul / Coronation march from Le Prophete / Zadok the priest / Ode to the horse / National anthem / We said we wouldn't look back / Closing fanfare
3036001032 / Jun '97 / Carlton

☐ MUSIC FROM THE SILK ROADS (Music From China, Mongolia & The C.I.S.)
AUB 6776 / Feb '93 / Auvidis/Ethnic

☐ MUSIC FROM UGANDA VOL.1 (Traditional)
CAP 21495CD / Nov '96 / Caprice

☐ MUSIC FROM UGANDA VOL.2 (Modern Traditional)
CAP 21553CD / Nov '96 / Caprice

☐ MUSIC FROM VIETNAM
CAP 21406CD / Nov '95 / Caprice

☐ MUSIC HALL MEMORIES (24 Great Singalong Favourites)
I belong to Glasgow: *Fyffe, Will* / When I'm cleaning windows (The window cleaner): *Formby, George* / 'Arf a pint of ale: *Elen, Gus* / Laughing policeman: *Penrose, Charles* / Don't have any more, Missus Moore: *Morris, Lily* / Nobody loves a fairy when she's forty: *O'Shea, Tessie* / Lion and Albert: *Holloway, Stanley* / Keep right on to the end of the road: *Lauder, Harry* / Two lovely black eyes: *Coburn, Charles* / League of nations: *Bennett, Billy* / When I take my morning promenade: *Lloyd, Marie* / Ain't it grand to be bloomin' well dead: *Sarony, Leslie* / It's a great big shame: *Elen, Gus* / Because he loves me: *Morris, Lily* / Man who broke the bank at Monte Carlo: *Coburn, Charles* / I'm 94 today: *Fyffe, Will* / Bee song: *Askey, Arthur* / Nice quiet day: *Elen, Gus* / Daddy: *Bennett, Billy* / Coster girl in Paris: *Lloyd, Marie* / Old school tie: *Western Brothers* / I stopped I looked I listened: *Robey, George* / Wait till the work comes round: *Elen, Gus* / What was there was good: *Robey, George*
PLATCD 173 / Mar '96 / Platinum

☐ MUSIC IN A MARRAKESH MARKET SQUARE
LDX 274973 / Jun '94 / La Chant Du Monde

☐ MUSIC IN GHANA
PAMAP 601 / 3 Mar '98 / Munich

☐ MUSIC IN THE WORLD OF ISLAM VOL.1
TSCD 901 / Jul '94 / Topic

☐ MUSIC IN THE WORLD OF ISLAM VOL.2
TSCD 902 / Jul '94 / Topic

☐ MUSIC IN THE WORLD OF ISLAM VOL.3
TSCD 903 / Jul '94 / Topic

☐ MUSIC IS MY OCCUPATION (Ska Instrumentals 1962-1975)
Magic: *McCook, Tommy* / Green island: *Drummond, Don* / Musical store room: *Drummond, Don* / Vitamin A: *Brooks, Baba* / Strolling in: *McCook, Tommy* / River bank parts 1 and 2: *Brooks, Baba* / Silver dollar: *McCook, Tommy & The Skatalites* / Dr. Decker: *Brooks, Baba & Don Drummond* / Eastern standard time: *Drummond, Don* / Yard broom: *McCook, Tommy* / Music is my occupation: *McCook, Tommy & Don Drummond* / Apanga: *McCook, Tommy* / Don de lion: *McCook, Tommy & Don Drummond* / Guns fever: *Brooks, Baba* / Twelve minutes to go: *McCook, Tommy*
CDTRL 259 / Mar '94 / Trojan

☐ MUSIC MAGAZINE - THE 1960'S EDITION
There's always something there to remind me: *Shaw, Sandie* / I'm telling you now: *Freddie & The Dreamers* / I like it: *Gerry & The Pacemakers* / No milk today: *Herman's Hermits* / Bus stop: *Hollies* / Mony mony: *James, Tommy & The Shondells* / Do you want to know a secret: *Kramer, Billy J. & The Dakotas* / Downtown: *Clark, Petula* / Locomotion: *Little Eva* / 5-4-3-2-1: *Manfred Mann* / Foot tapper: *Shadows* / Surf city: *Jan & Dean* / Gregory girl: *Seekers* / House of the rising sun: *Animals* / Hurdy gurdy man: *Donovan* / Got to get you into my life: *Bennett, Cliff & The Rebel Rousers* / Saturday night at the duck pond: *Cougars* / Baby now that I've found you: *Foundations* / Little lovin': *Fourmost* / Runaway: *Shannon, Del*
CDMFP 6273 / Nov '96 / Music For Pleasure

☐ MUSIC MAGAZINE - THE 1970'S EDITION
Union city blue: *Blondie* / This will be: *Cole, Natalie* / Jack in the box: *Moments* / Boogie oogie oogie: *Taste Of Honey* / Don't take away the music: *Tavares* / Now is the time: *James, Jimmy & The Vagabonds* / Haven't stopped dancing yet: *Gonzalez* / Beach baby: *First Class* / You sexy thing: *Hot Chocolate* / Sound your funky horn: *KC & The Sunshine Band* / It's been so long: *McCrae, George* / Living on the front line: *Grant, Eddy* / Sylvia: *Focus* / Motor bikin': *Spedding, Chris* / Romeo: *Mr. Big* / Movie star: *Harpo* / Touch too much: *Arrows* / Bump: *Kenny* / Cat crept in: *Mud* / Devil Gate Drive: *Quatro, Suzi*
CDMFP 6274 / Nov '96 / Music For Pleasure

☐ MUSIC MAGAZINE - THE 1980'S EDITION
Geno: *Dexy's Midnight Runners* / White lines: *Grandmaster Flash & Melle Mel* / Let's do rock steady: *Bodysnatchers* / Solid: *Ashford & Simpson* / We close our eyes: *Go West* / Searchin': *Dean, Hazell* / Dancing tight: *Galaxy & Phil Fearon* / Joy and pain: *Maze & Frankie Beverly* / Respectable: *Mel & Kim* / Somebody help me out: *Beggar & Co* / And the beat goes on: *Beggar & Co* / Movin': *Brass Construction* / Respect: *Adeva* / C'est la vie: *Nevil, Robbie* / Little girl: *Bonds, Gary 'US'* / Intuition: *Linx* / Paint me down: *Spandau Ballet* / Rock me tonight (for old times sake): *Jackson, Freddie* / Is it a dream: *Classix Nouveaux* / Pump up the jam: *Technotronic*
CDMFP 6275 / Nov '96 / Music For Pleasure

☐ MUSIC MERCHANT STORY, THE
Let love grow: *Holloway, Brenda* / Some quiet place: *Holloway, Brenda* / Mama's little baby (loves lovin'): *Brotherly Love* / I don't see you in my eyes anymore: *Brotherly Love* / Growing pains: *Brotherly Love* / Your love controls me: *Jones Girls* / Taster of the honey (not keeper of the bee): *Jones Girls* / You're the only bargain I've got: *Jones Girls* / Come back: *Jones Girls* / Tighten him up: *Laws, Eloise* / You made me an offer I can't refuse: *Laws, Eloise* / Stay with me: *Laws, Eloise* / Love factory: *Laws, Eloise* / (I've been a winner, I've been a loser) I've been in love: *Smith Connection* / I'm bugging your phone: *Smith Connection* / Day you leave: *Smith Connection* / You've been my rock: *Warlock* / Tears ago: *Just Brothers* / You've the love to make me over: *Just Brothers* / Things will be better tomorrow: *Just Brothers* / Sliced tomatoes: *Just Brothers* / Bar-b-q ribs: *Wynglas, Rachel*
DEEPM 024 / Jul '97 / Deep Beats

☐ MUSIC OF AFRICA, THE
MACCD 380 / 30 Mar '98 / Autograph

☐ MUSIC OF AFRICA, THE
Africa / Zomba / Upendo wa bwana / Benyabore / Akotchume / African pounding / Noongoma / Denko / Nandi / N'toum / Bwana asifwee / Tin doro / Bukanga man / Images of Africa / Tambacounda / Ace kwala / Umeinolera / Somoyere / Tama / Afrika
OPMCD 300 / 3 Aug '98 / One Planet

☐ MUSIC OF ARMENIA VOL.5, THE
141192 / Jul '97 / Celestial Harmonies

☐ MUSIC OF ARMENIA VOL.6, THE
131212 / Jul '97 / Celestial Harmonies

☐ MUSIC OF BALI VOL.1, THE (Jegog Music)
131362 / Jul '97 / Celestial Harmonies

☐ MUSIC OF BALI VOL.2, THE (Legong Gamelan)
131372 / Jul '97 / Celestial Harmonies

☐ MUSIC OF BALI VOL.3, THE (Kecack & Tektekan Music)
131382 / Jul '97 / Celestial Harmonies

☐ MUSIC OF BALI, THE
LYRCD 7408 / '91 / Lyrichord

☐ MUSIC OF BALI, THE
1919412 / 24 Apr '98 / EPM

☐ MUSIC OF BAVARIA, THE
Gaudeamus Igitur / Drinking song / Cuckoo yodel / Edelweiss / Bel viso / Golden days / Sherbrooke forest yodel / Wood horn sounds / Wackersberger polka / Walk in the black forest / Mountain boy yodel / Slap dance / White Horse Inn cowbells / Salzkammergut / Lyrebird yodel / Way to your heart / Tegernseer polka / With sack and pack
QED 199 / Nov '96 / Tring

☐ MUSIC OF BRAZIL, THE
Mexa Mexa / Haja Haja / Vem pra Mim / Rasta Fari / Escudo negro / A maluco do mangue / Isso E bom/ Vem ver/Dancando Lambada / O tempero do amor / Delirio do / Carnaval / Vem me / Grito de Igualdade / Sou de Bahia / O Sanho de um Samuray / A colheita / A roda / Brilho Egito / Lambada
QED 194 / Nov '96 / Tring

☐ MUSIC OF BRAZIL, THE (2CD Set)
Mi bahia: *Da Silva, Jorginho* / Saudades de Colonia: *Da Silva, Jorginho* / Canto das tres racas: *Oliveira, Valdeci* / Baiao: *Oliveira, Valdeci* / You needed me: *Almeida, Laurindo* / All my love: *Almeida, Laurindo* / Nada sera como antes: *Oliveira, Valdeci* / Chorinho nr1: *Teran, Sergio* / Guachita: *Da Silva, Jorginho* / Copacabana (at the copa): *Almeida, Laurindo* / Late last night: *Almeida, Laurindo* / Alguem me disse: *Oliveira, Valdeci*
CD 6076 / Jun '97 / Music

☐ MUSIC OF BRAZIL, THE
MACCD 377 / 30 Mar '98 / Autograph

☐ MUSIC OF BRAZIL, THE
Brazil / Descafinado / One note samba / Dancando lambada / Samba carnival / Tema jazz / Meo amigo irmao / Sunset samba / Bonita / Crioulo zouk / She's a carioca / O Barquinho / Copacabana / Dindi / Corcovado / Girl from Ipanema
OPMCD 307 / 31 Aug '98 / One Planet

☐ MUSIC OF CEARA AND MINAS GERAIS, THE
RCD 10404 / 22 Sep '97 / Rykodisc

☐ MUSIC OF CHEN YI, THE
NA 090 / Mar '97 / New Albion

☐ MUSIC OF CHINA VOL.1, THE (The Deben Bhattacharya Collection/2CD Set)
Silk-stringed instruments / Purple peach-flower / Walking along a street / Night by a stream in Spring / Purple bamboo / Fishing music / Suzhou instrumental factory orchestra / Qin / Gu-zhen / Touch of love / She recognized her mother / Farewell cries / An episode from 'Love stories of the west chamber' / Story of love and laughter / Journey to the west
FA 061 / Apr '97 / Fremeaux

□ **MUSIC OF CUBA, THE**
Resumen / La bamba salsa / Yele le / Salscario / Negrita / Patacon / Song tambo / Caravan / High heels mambo / Ritmo cubano / El solitaro / Havana next stop / Que pasa / Resumen (instrumental) / Sun sun babae / Cuba libre / La rumba / Mambo y cha cha cha
OPMCD 309 / 31 Aug '98 / One Planet

□ **MUSIC OF DREAMS, THE**
CEFCD 164 / Jan '94 / Gael Linn

□ **MUSIC OF EGYPT, THE**
RCD 10106 / Nov '91 / Rykodisc

□ **MUSIC OF FRANCE, THE**
WLD 001 / Aug '93 / Tring

□ **MUSIC OF FRANCE, THE**
Milord / I love Paris / Mademoiselle De Paree / Reine de Musette / La mer / Petite fleur / La Goulante de pauvre Jean / Parlez moi d'amour / Song from Moulin Rouge / Et maintenant / C'est magnifique / Padam padam / Mamma / Aline / J'attendrai / L'amour des Poetes / Frere Jacques / Alouette / Sur Le Pont / Aupres de ma blonde / Plaisir d'amour / Hymmne a l'amour
QED 188 / Nov '96 / Tring

□ **MUSIC OF FRANCE, THE**
MACCD 378 / 30 Mar '98 / Autograph

□ **MUSIC OF FRANCE, THE**
La vie en rose / C'est si bon / Pigalle / D'accord / Man and a woman / I wish you love / Sous les ponts de Paris / La vie joyeuse / Love is blue / Mon amour / Enchante / Under Paris skies / Windmills of your mind / Louise / La trapeze / C'est tout / I love Paris / Chez Michel
OPMCD 301 / 3 Aug '98 / One Planet

□ **MUSIC OF GERMANY, THE**
WLD 003 / Aug '93 / Tring

□ **MUSIC OF GERMANY, THE**
Rosamunde (beer barrel polka) / Heidi / Schneewalzer / Volkmusik / Wem Gott will rechte gunst Erweisen/Horsch was kommt von Dra / Das lieben bringt gross' freud/Hoch auf dem gelben wagen / Bayrischer landler/Lustig ist das Zigeunerleben / Die lustigen Holzhackerbaum / Hohe tannen / Rhine medley / Medley / Amboss polka / Annchen von Tharau / Sieben fasser wein / Schone maid / Lilli Marlene / Blau bluht der Einzian / Der frohliche wanderer / Auf wiedersehn
QED 190 / Nov '96 / Tring

□ **MUSIC OF GREECE, THE**
WLD 004 / Aug '93 / Tring

□ **MUSIC OF GREECE, THE**
Zorba's dance / Oniro demento / Doxa to Theo / Kaimos / Aponi Zoi / To Palikari ech Kaimo / Vraho Vraho / Sto Perighiali to Kryfo / Deka Palikaria / Who pays the ferryman / Play bouzouki / Fragossyriani / Otan Simanoun / Varka sto Yialo / Matia Vourkomena / Margarita Margaro / Kalimepa Ilie / Emaste Dio / Safti Gitonia / Baxe Tsifliki
QED 191 / Nov '96 / Tring

□ **MUSIC OF GREECE, THE**
MACCD 379 / 30 Mar '98 / Autograph

□ **MUSIC OF GREECE, THE**
Zorba the Greek / Hellinki psychi / O peripatos to kassafani / Kira giorgena / Maria me ta kitrina / to taxidi / Kalokiernes nostalghies / Kritika perasmata / Kalamatianos / Milisse mou / Roses blanche de Corfu / Francosiriani / Zonaradiko / Hanioti kos syrtos / Night in Plaka / O chorus ton theon / Never on Sunday
OPMCD 302 / 3 Aug '98 / One Planet

□ **MUSIC OF GUADALCANAL, THE (Vocal/Instrumental Music From Solomon Islands)**
C 580049 / Feb '94 / Ocora

□ **MUSIC OF HAWAII, THE**
WLD 005 / Aug '93 / Tring

□ **MUSIC OF HAWAII, THE**
Blue Hawaii / Wini wini / Hula lady / Bora Bora / Paradise Island / Moana rag / Hawaiian wedding song / Lovely hula hands / Kon tiki / Farewell Hawaii / Harbour lights / Aloha land / Hawaii tattoo / Sky of Old Hawaii / Hawaiian war chant / My little hula girl / Song of the islands / On the beach at Waikiki / Vaya con dios / Aloha Oe
QED 192 / Nov '96 / Tring

□ **MUSIC OF HAWAII, THE**
MACCD 383 / 30 Mar '98 / Autograph

□ **MUSIC OF INDIA VOL.1, THE (The Deben Bhattacharya Collection/2CD Set)**
Raga todi on surbahar / Raga miyan-ki-malhar on rudravina / Raga bihag on rudravina / Raga bhairavi on rudravina / Mon eki bhranti tomar / Ki swadeshe ki bideshe / Malay asiya koye gechhe kane / Bhalobeshe bhalo kandale / Mon je nilo / Ay ma sadhan samare / Tomar deoya prane / Shunya e buke / Tomar andhar nisha / Mahasindhur opar theke / Shyam kandano bhalo noy / Bujhi oi sudure / Shaon ashilo phire
FA 060 / Apr '97 / Fremeaux

□ **MUSIC OF INDIA, THE**
Gandhamu pooyyarugal / Thyagaraja keerthana / Varnam / Pahari / Devi Slokam / Meerabhajan/ Mohana kalyani ragam / Bowli / Bhair veen / Momil rano / Siva sthuthi / Kalyani ragam and thanam
OPMCD 308 / 31 Aug '98 / One Planet

□ **MUSIC OF INDONESIA VOL.10, THE (Music Of Biak, Irian Jaya: Wor, Church Songs, Yospan)**
SFWCD 40426 / Feb '97 / Smithsonian Folkways

□ **MUSIC OF INDONESIA VOL.11, THE (Melayu Music Of Sumatra/Riau Isles: Zapin, Mak Yong, Mendu)**
SFWCD 40427 / Feb '97 / Smithsonian Folkways

□ **MUSIC OF INDONESIA VOL.12, THE (Gongs/Vocal Music Of Sumatra:Talempong, Didong, Kulintang)**
SFWCD 40428 / Feb '97 / Smithsonian Folkways

□ **MUSIC OF INDONESIA VOL.13, THE (Kalimantan Strings)**
SFWCD 40429 / Dec '97 / Smithsonian Folkways

□ **MUSIC OF INDONESIA VOL.14, THE**
SFWCD 40441 / Dec '97 / Smithsonian Folkways

□ **MUSIC OF INDONESIA VOL.15, THE**
SFWCD 40442 / Dec '97 / Smithsonian Folkways

□ **MUSIC OF INDONESIA VOL.3, THE (Karya)**
LYRCD 7421 / Feb '94 / Lyrichord

□ **MUSIC OF INDONESIA VOL.7, THE (Music From The Forests Of Riau & Mentawai)**
SFWCD 40423 / Dec '95 / Smithsonian Folkways

□ **MUSIC OF INDONESIA VOL.8, THE (Vocal/Instrumental Music From East/ Central Flores)**
SFWCD 40424 / Dec '95 / Smithsonian Folkways

□ **MUSIC OF INDONESIA VOL.9, THE (Vocal Music From Central/West Flores)**
SFWCD 40425 / Dec '95 / Smithsonian Folkways

□ **MUSIC OF INDONESIA, THE**
SFWCD 40420 / Dec '94 / Smithsonian Folkways

□ **MUSIC OF IRAN, THE**
HMA 190391CD / Oct '94 / Musique D'Abord

□ **MUSIC OF IRELAND, THE**
Danny Boy / Rocky road to Dublin / Galway races, an dearig dun / Welcoming / Sleivenamon / Steal away / Finnegan's wake / Black velvet band / Fields of Atherney / Down by the Sally gardens / Dirty old town / Muirsheen durkin / Molly Malone / O'Carolan's concerto / Wild rover / Bol O'Donaghue / Whiskey in the jar / Softly flows the Clare / Father O'Flynn / Irish washerwoman / Blackberry blossom / It's a long way to Tipperary / Endearing young charms / Eileen Allanah
3036100172 / May '96 / Pearls

□ **MUSIC OF IRELAND, THE**
CD 439CD / May '96 / Arfolk

□ **MUSIC OF IRELAND, THE**
Red is the rose / Donkey's cross / Delaney's fancy / Old boreen / Star of County Down / Gravel walk / Masons apron / Mick McGuire / Humour is on me now / Jig selection / Galway Bay / Green hills of Sligo / Ireland my homeland / Green fields round Ferbane / Home to Donegal / Races of Killadoon / Rambles of spring / Bright silvery light of the moon / Dowd's no.9 / Musical priest / Knocknagow / Carrickfergus
QED 198 / Nov '96 / Tring

□ **MUSIC OF IRELAND, THE**
Danny boy / Bunch of thyme / Black velvet band / Sleivenamon / Molly Malone / Dirty old town / Carrick fergus/Belfast hornpipe / Wild mountain thyme / Down in the Sally gardens / Maid behind the bar/ Gravel walk / Muirsheen durkin / Finnegan's wake / Paddy Ryan's dream/Docherty's reel/McGinneley's reel / Galway races/An dearig dun/Welcoming / I will love you everytime / Riverdance / Whisky in the jar / Irish rovers/rakes of mallow
OPMCD 304 / 3 Aug '98 / One Planet

□ **MUSIC OF ISLAM SAMPLER, THE**
131592 / Apr '98 / Celestial Harmonies

□ **MUSIC OF ISLAM VOL.1, THE (The Classical Music Of Cairo)**
131402 / May '98 / Celestial Harmonies

□ **MUSIC OF ISLAM VOL.10, THE (Qu'an Recitation)**
131502 / Apr '98 / Celestial Harmonies

□ **MUSIC OF ISLAM VOL.11, THE (The Music Of Yemen)**
131512 / Apr '98 / Celestial Harmonies

□ **MUSIC OF ISLAM VOL.12, THE (The Music Of Iran)**
131522 / May '98 / Celestial Harmonies

□ **MUSIC OF ISLAM VOL.13, THE (The Music Of Pakistan)**
131532 / May '98 / Celestial Harmonies

□ **MUSIC OF ISLAM VOL.14, THE (Mystic Music Through The Ages)**
131542 / Apr '98 / Celestial Harmonies

□ **MUSIC OF ISLAM VOL.15, THE (The Music Of Yemen)**
141552 / Apr '98 / Celestial Harmonies

□ **MUSIC OF ISLAM VOL.2, THE (The Music Of the South Sinai Bedouins)**
131412 / May '98 / Celestial Harmonies

□ **MUSIC OF ISLAM VOL.3, THE (The Music Of The Nubians)**
131422 / May '98 / Celestial Harmonies

□ **MUSIC OF ISLAM VOL.4, THE (The Music Of the Arabian Peninsula)**
131432 / Apr '98 / Celestial Harmonies

□ **MUSIC OF ISLAM VOL.5, THE (Aissaoua Sufi Ceremony)**
141442 / Apr '98 / Celestial Harmonies

□ **MUSIC OF ISLAM VOL.6, THE (Al-Maghrib - Gnawa Music)**
131462 / Apr '98 / Celestial Harmonies

□ **MUSIC OF ISLAM VOL.7, THE (Andalusian Music)**
131472 / May '98 / Celestial Harmonies

□ **MUSIC OF ISLAM VOL.8, THE (Folkloric Music Of Tunisia)**
131482 / Apr '98 / Celestial Harmonies

□ **MUSIC OF ISLAM VOL.9, THE (Mawlawiyah Music - The Music Of The Whirling Dervishes)**
131492 / Apr '98 / Celestial Harmonies

□ **MUSIC OF ITALY, THE**
L'Italiano / Parlami d'amore / Gloria / Una lacrima sul viso / Tu sei L'Unica Donna per me / Sharazan / Sara' Perche' ti amo / Per Elisa / Ti amo / Maledetta primavera / O sole mio / Torna a sorriento / Funiculi funicula / O paese d'o sole / Santa Lucia Luntana / Volare / Santa Lucia / O Marenariello / Tu ca nun chiagne / Arrvederci Roma
QED 196 / Nov '96 / Tring

□ **MUSIC OF ITALY, THE**
MACCD 384 / 30 Mar '98 / Autograph

□ **MUSIC OF JAPAN, THE**
WLD 006 / Aug '93 / Tring

□ **MUSIC OF JAPAN, THE**
Autumn sorrow / Moon over Tokyo / Rokudan / Nil Li Zi A / Tanko Bushi / Soran Bushi / Toheganse / Kagome Antagata / Doko sa Hana-Ichi / Sakura instrumental / Sakura / Arirang / Tancha Meh / Chuern Mong / Chidori No Kyoku / Midare / Godan-Kinuta / Outgoing ships / Nite star / Ruined castles / Japanese fisherman / Lotus blossom
QED 193 / Nov '96 / Tring

□ **MUSIC OF KENTUCKY VOL.1, THE**
YAZCD 2013 / Oct '95 / Yazoo

□ **MUSIC OF KENTUCKY VOL.2, THE**
YAZCD 2014 / Oct '95 / Yazoo

□ **MUSIC OF LATIN AMERICA, THE**
Copacabana / Fernando / Quiereme mucho / El lute / Ay no digas / Samba pa ti / Brazil / Quando quando / Argentina / Agua / Oyo como va / Rise / Chiquitita / Mexico / Cuando caliente el sol / El Condor Pasa
QED 189 / Nov '96 / Tring

□ **MUSIC OF LIFE LIVE, THE**
SPOCKCD 1 / Aug '89 / Music Of Life

□ **MUSIC OF LONG AGO 1958-1993, THE (Traditional Croatian Music)**
C 600006 / May '97 / Ocora

□ **MUSIC OF MADAGASCAR, THE (Classic Traditional Recordings From The 1930's)**
YAZCD 7003 / Apr '95 / Yazoo

□ **MUSIC OF MARGINAL POLYNESIA, THE (Fiji, Tuvalu, Wallis & Futuna)**
VICG 52762 / Mar '96 / JVC World Library

□ **MUSIC OF MARTINIQUE 1929-1950, THE**
FLYCD 947 / Jul '96 / Flyright

□ **MUSIC OF MEXICO, THE**
La Felicidad / Corazon Angustiado / Mi Guajira Y mi Caballo / Sueno de Amanecer / Palabra de Mujer / Dentro de mi / Tijuana taxi / Sed de Vivir / Ven / Lonely bull / Hoy soy Feliz / Se que no Volveras / Spanish flea / Cuando pienses en mi / Lamento / La adelita
QED 200 / Nov '96 / Tring

□ **MUSIC OF MEXICO, THE**
La bamba / Mendoza / La raspa / Guadalajara / La cucaracha / La adelita / Cielto lindo / La campa de piedra / El relampago / Las mananitas / Sabor a mi / El rancho grande / El corrido / La madrugada / Jarabe tarito / La negra / Los machettes / El caballito
OPMCD 305 / 31 Aug '98 / One Planet

□ **MUSIC OF MOROCCO, THE**
1919062 / 24 Apr '98 / EPM

□ **MUSIC OF NW ARGENTINA, THE**
824992 / Apr '91 / BUDA

□ **MUSIC OF OUR TIME, THE**
WER 66002 / Nov '97 / Wergo

□ **MUSIC OF PAPUA NEW GUINEA, THE**
925702 / Jun '93 / BUDA

□ **MUSIC OF POLYNESIA VOL.1, THE (Tahiti, Society Islands)**
VICG 52712 / Mar '96 / JVC World Library

□ **MUSIC OF POLYNESIA VOL.2, THE (Tuamoto, Austral Islands)**
VICG 52722 / Mar '96 / JVC World Library

□ **MUSIC OF POLYNESIA VOL.3, THE (Easter Island, The Marquesas Islands)**
VICG 52732 / Mar '96 / JVC World Library

□ **MUSIC OF POLYNESIA VOL.4, THE (Samoa, Tonga)**
VICG 52742 / Mar '96 / JVC World Library

□ **MUSIC OF SARDINIA 1930-1932, THE**
HTCD 20 / Oct '93 / Heritage

□ **MUSIC OF SCOTLAND, THE**
Highland cathederal / Fantasia on mist covered mountains / Bengullion / Isabel T Macdonald / Flora Graham / Loch Lomond / My Bonnie lies over the ocean / Coming through the Rye / Dark Ireland / Skye boat song / Mist covered mountains of home / Mull of Kintyre / Drunken piper / My love she's but a lassie yet / Girl I left behind me / Bonnie Dundee / Off she goes / Donald's awa / Fanfare salute / Scotland the brave / Para Handy / Amazing grace / Auld lang syne / Folk selection / Dashing white sergeant / Galloway house / Roxburgh castle / Auld town march
3036100152 / Jan '97 / Pearls

□ **MUSIC OF SCOTLAND, THE**
Scotland the brave / Loch lomond / Glasgow montage / Bonnie earl o' moray / Sound of iona / Oh gin I were a baron's heir / Piper o' dundee / My love is like a red, red rose / Saturday dance / Dark lochnagar / Killiecrankie / Royal mile / Will ye no come back again
CDALM 5143 / Oct '97 / Almac

□ **MUSIC OF SCOTLAND, THE**
Scotland the brave / Wi'a 100 pipers/Wee muirdie / Flower of Scotland / Mull of Kintyre / Highland cathedral / Bobby Stenhouse/Braes of Gleniffer/ Girl in a blue dress / Crookit bawbee/Lass from Bute / Amazing grace / Mist covered mountains / Loch Lomond/My Bonnie lies over the ocean/Coming through the / Skye boat song / Dashing white sergeant/Galloway house/Roxburgh castle / Riverside polka / Mason's apron / Dark island/Road to the isles/Dream valley of Glendaruel/Old / Auld lang syne
OPMCD 303 / 3 Aug '98 / One Planet

□ **MUSIC OF SOUTH EAST AND EAST ASIA, THE**
VICG 120672 / Feb '96 / JVC World Library

□ **MUSIC OF SPAIN, THE**
Hombrecito
WLD 008 / Aug '93 / Tring

□ **MUSIC OF SPAIN, THE**
Espana Cani / Maria Isabel / Quiereme mucho / Borriquito / Cana de Azucar / Cielito Lindo / La bamba / Agapimu / De Cierto no se Sabe / Granada / Espana / El Porompompero / Sevillanas / Amor Amor / La Cucaracha / Uu rayo del sol / Un canto a Galicia / Ansiedad / Aranjuez mon amour / Y viva Espana
QED 195 / Nov '96 / Tring

□ **MUSIC OF SPAIN, THE**
MACCD 382 / 30 Mar '98 / Autograph

□ **MUSIC OF SPAIN, THE**
Gran Canaria / Hombrecito / Posablanco / E viva Espana / Tango de Malga / Fiesta gitana / Ole ole ole / Morena de mi copla / Concierto de mi copla / Siguiriyas / Espana cani / Alma flamenca / No puede sur / Me enamore / Bamboleo / La primavera / La dorga / Ados Sevilla
OPMCD 306 / 31 Aug '98 / One Planet

□ **MUSIC OF SUNDA, THE (Java)**
VICG 52642 / Feb '96 / JVC World Library

□ **MUSIC OF THE ANDES, THE**
Huajra: *Inti-Illimani* / Subida: *Inti-Illimani* / Fiesta punena (Festival at Punena): *Inti-Illimani* / Amores hallaras: *Inti-Illimani* / La obreras (The working women): *Quilapayun* / Tu (You): *Quilapayun* / Yarvi y Huayno de la quebrada de humahuca (Yaravi and Huayno: *Quilapayun* / Tan alta que est la luna (How high the moon): *Quilapayun* / El canto del cuculi (Song of the turtledove): *Quilapayun* / Dos palomitas: *Quilapayun* / El condor pasa (Flight of the condor): *Conjunto Kollahuara* / Cancion y huayno (Song and huayno): *Conjunto Kollahuara* / Vicunita: *Conjunto Kollahuara* / El tinku: *Jara, Victor* / Baila caporal (Dance master): *Illapu* / Sol de maiz (Sun of corn): *Illapu*
CDEMC 3680 / May '94 / Hemisphere

□ **MUSIC OF THE ARAB AMERICANS, THE**
Fatima / Il-bulbul nagha / Hawwil ya ghannam / Lamma ya albi
ROUCD 1122 / Nov '97 / Rounder

□ **MUSIC OF THE BANSURI, THE (A Flute Of Rajasthan)**
VICG 52202 / Mar '96 / JVC World Library

☐ MUSIC OF THE BUNRAKU THEATRE, THE

VICG 53562 / Mar '96 / JVC World Library

☐ MUSIC OF THE CARIBBEAN, THE

MACCD 381 / 30 Mar '98 / Autograph

☐ MUSIC OF THE FIDDLE, THE

Ceol na fiddlers: *Garioch Fiddlers* / Dumbarton Castle: *Banchory Strathspey & Reel Society* / Forbes Morrison: *Banchory Strathspey & Reel Society* / Left-handed fiddler: *Banchory Strathspey & Reel Society* / Nanny and Betty: *Shetland's Young Heritage* / A yowe cam ta wir door yarmin: *Shetland's Young Heritage* / Up and doon da harbour: *Shetland's Young Heritage* / Bluebells of Scotland: *Duncan, Maurice* / Mull of the cool Bens: *Inverness Fiddlers* / Sheiling song: *Inverness Fiddlers* / Leaving Lismore: *Inverness Fiddlers* / South Georgia whaling song: *Inverness Fiddlers* / Return to the Stewart: *MacDonald, Catriona* / Slanttigart: *MacDonald, Catriona* / Tame her when the snaw comes: *MacDonald, Catriona* / Farewell to Skye: *Banchory Ensemble* / Callum Beag: *Banchory Ensemble* / Juggernaut: *Banchory Ensemble* / Ian Petersen's compliments to Fraser McGlynn: *Banchory Ensemble* / Mackintosh Patrick March: *Aberdeen Strathspey & Reel Society* / Leaving Glen Urquart: *Banchory Strathspey & Reel Society* / South of the Grampians: *Banchory Strathspey & Reel Society* / John McNeil's reel: *Banchory Strathspey & Reel Society* / Sheilis: *Glasgow Reel & Strathspey Society* / Madame Neruda: *Anderson, Paul* / Cradle song: *Anderson, Paul* / Kirrie kebbuck: *Anderson, Paul* / Spey in spate: *Anderson, Paul* / Loch Ruan: *Inverness Fiddlers* / Maid of Flanders: *Inverness Fiddlers* / Sound of Sleat: *Inverness Fiddlers* / Prince Charlie's last view of Scotland: *Leggat, Fiona* / Neil Gow's wife: *Leggat, Fiona* / Old reel: *Leggat, Fiona* / Gu man slan a chi mi: *Shetland's Young Heritage* / Fear a'Bhata: *Shetland's Young Heritage* / Gu man clan a chi mi: *Shetland's Young Heritage* / Herr Roloff's farewell: *Brian, Bill* / Boar's head ceilidh: *Garioch Fiddlers* / Mrs. Forbes Leith: *Anderson, Keith* / Auld Brig O'Doon: *Anderson, Keith* / Beauty of the north: *Anderson, Keith* / Princess Beatrice: *Anderson, Keith* / Ashokan farewell: *Shetland's Young Heritage* / Mrs. McPherson of Cluny: *Banchory Strathspey & Reel Society* / John Grumblie: *Banchory Strathspey & Reel Society* / Anne Fraser McKenzie: *Banchory Strathspey & Reel Society* / Donald Ian Rankine: *Banchory Strathspey & Reel Society* / Ceol na fidhle: *Garioch Fiddlers*

CDLOC 1097 / Nov '96 / Lochshore

☐ MUSIC OF THE FULANI & THE TENDA FROM SENEGAL, THE

C 560043 / May '94 / Ocora

☐ MUSIC OF THE GAMUZ TRIBE SUDAN, THE

D 8072 / Nov '96 / Unesco

☐ MUSIC OF THE GLENS, THE

CDLBP 2025 / Jul '96 / Lochshore

☐ MUSIC OF THE INCAS, THE

LYRCD 7348 / '91 / Lyrichord

☐ MUSIC OF THE INGESSANA & BERTA TRIBES SUDAN, THE

D 8073 / Nov '96 / Unesco

☐ MUSIC OF THE KHOREZM UZBEKISTAN, THE

D 8269 / Nov '96 / Unesco

☐ MUSIC OF THE KOTO, THE

VICG 53582 / Mar '96 / JVC World Library

☐ MUSIC OF THE LOMBOK'S BALINESE COMMUNITY, THE

D 8272 / Jan '98 / Unesco

☐ MUSIC OF THE MILITARY, THE (2CD Set)

Royal Air Force march past / Cavalry of the Steppes / Light of foot / Blaze away / Amazing grace / Men of Harlech/God bless the Prince Of Wales / Aces high / Anchors aweigh / Battle of Britain / Old comrades / Coronation march / Lochanside / Green hills of Tyrol / Dambusters march / Washington post / Sons of the brave / National Emblem / Battle of the Somme / Dagshai hills / Argyll and Sutherland Highlanders / Under the double eagle / Australian march / Redetzky / 633 Squadron / Flower of Scotland / Famous British marches / British Grenadiers / Lilliburlero / All through the night / Highland Laddie / Rule Britannia / Bonnie Anne / Athol cummers / Sheepwife / Macleod of Mull / Semper fidelis / Those magnificent men in their flying machines

CDDL 1078 / May '91 / Music For Pleasure

☐ MUSIC OF THE NILE VALLEY, THE

LYRCD 7355 / Aug '93 / Lyrichord

☐ MUSIC OF THE ORKNEYS, THE

1919072 / 24 Apr '98 / EPM

☐ MUSIC OF THE PALACES AND SECRET SOCIETIES, THE (Cameroun, Bamum)

W 260074 / Feb '97 / Inedit

☐ MUSIC OF THE SHADOWS, THE

MACCD 291 / Aug '96 / Autograph

☐ MUSIC OF THE SHAHNAI, THE

VICG 52212 / Mar '96 / JVC World Library

☐ MUSIC OF THE SHI PEOPLE, THE

VICG 52282 / Mar '96 / JVC World Library

☐ MUSIC OF THE SOUTH PACIFIC, THE

Blue Hawaii / Hawaiian wedding song / Lovely hula hands / Pearly shells / Aloha Oe / Kaimana Hila / Hawaiian tattoo / Polynesian love song / Isa lei / Toai Mai / Papia Tahiti / Farewell (for just a while) / Pania of the reef / Pokarekare Ana / Under the sun / When my Wahine does the Poi / Cheryl Moana Marie / Haere Mai / Now is the hour / Tofa Felengi

QED 197 / Nov '96 / Tring

☐ MUSIC OF THE SOUTH SEAS, THE

PS 360504 / Sep '96 / PlayaSound

☐ MUSIC OF THE STREETS, THE (Mechanical Street Entertainment)

Man who broke the bank at Monte Carlo / I've got a lovely bunch of coconuts / Charmaine / Oh oh Antonio / La Marseillaise / Pomone waltz / Rule Britannia / Honeysuckle and the bee / Just one girl / Bicycle barn dance polka / Bells of St. Mary's / Soldiers of the Queen / Goodbye Dolly Gray / Molly O'Morgan / Little Dolly Daydream / Roamin' in the gloamin' / He had to get out and get under / At Trinity Church / Let the great big world keep turning

CDSDL 340 / Jun '87 / Saydisc

☐ MUSIC OF THE TARTAR PEOPLE, THE

TSCD 912 / Apr '95 / Topic

☐ MUSIC OF THE TUAREG, THE (Ritual Music & Dances From The Hoggar Mountains)

LDX 274974 / May '94 / La Chant Du Monde

☐ MUSIC OF THE VIETNAMESE MONTAGNARDS 1958-1997, THE (2CD Set)

CNR 274108586 / Jan '98 / Le Chant Du Monde

☐ MUSIC OF THE WAYANA TRIBE ON THE LITANI RIVER, THE

926372 / Mar '96 / BUDA

☐ MUSIC OF THE WAYANG KULIT VOL.2, THE

VICG 52662 / Mar '96 / JVC World Library

☐ MUSIC OF THE WAYANG KULIT, THE

VICG 50282 / Mar '96 / JVC World Library

☐ MUSIC OF THE WORLD, THE

PS 66002 / Feb '93 / PlayaSound

☐ MUSIC OF VENEZUALA, THE

El gavan: *Armonia Y Cuerdas* / Sombra en los meadanos: *Raices De Mi Pueblo* / San Rafael: *Chirinos, Ali* / La montuna torpe: *Trio Cabure* / El grillo: *Mendoza, Ricardo Y Su Conjunto* / La jurupera: *Grupo Folklorico Curigna* / Entreverao: *Conjunto Piedemonte* / Zumba que zumba: *Quintana, Luis* / La guarchara: *Fandino, Luis Y Conjunto Piedemonte* / Seis por derecho: *Tapia, Carlos Y Conjunto Piedemonte* / El salto: *Quinteto Montes* / La culebra: *Cabello, Jorge Y Su Conjunto* / Los perros: *Alma Venezolana* / La musicas tuyera: *El Periquito De Miranda* / Barcelonesa: *Grupo Crillo Universitario 'Simon Bolivar'*

CDZ 2018 / Apr '94 / Zu Zazz

☐ MUSIC OF VIETNAM VOL.2, THE

CAP 21463CD / Mar '96 / Caprice

☐ MUSIC OF VIETNAM VOL.3, THE

CAP 21479CD / Mar '96 / Caprice

☐ MUSIC OF WEST BALI, THE

ARN 64271 / Oct '94 / Arion

☐ MUSIC ON THE GYPSY ROUTE VOL.1 (2CD Set)

Hichki / Bhairo singh suro / Kathak dance / Purvi dhun / Heer ranja / Kalyan / Race horse / Bahar de balbul / Battle music / Shur / Mahour / Bedououin love song / Moorish love song / Cepikli / Pontiago 'tig' / Easter procession / Seguiriya / Solea / Malaguena / Canas / Solaeres gitanes / Soleares / Soleares / Flamenco / Songs for Sara's feast day / In praise of Sara

FA 068 / Nov '97 / Fremeaux

☐ MUSIC WAS OUR BUSINESS

Whatcha gonna do when there ain't no swing: *Gonella, Nat & His Georgians* / Japanese sandman: *Gardner, Freddy* / Mirage: *Roy, Harry & His Band* / Swing shoe shop: *Simpson, Jack* / Bottle party: *Winstone, Eric & His Band* / Swing me sweetly: *Davis, Lew* / Song of songs: *Gonella, Nat & His Georgians* / Mind the handle it's hot: *Young, Arthur* / Big noise from Winnetka: *Roy, Harry* / Baby, won't you please come home: *Gardner, Freddy* / Fascinating rhythm: *Clae, John & His Claepigeons* / Swinging to those lies (it's a sin to tell a lie): *Gonella, Nat & His Georgians* / In the mood: *Young, Arthur* / Bitin' the dust: *Winstone, Eric & His Band* / Honeysuckle rose: *Simpson, Jack & His Sextet* / I never knew: *Davis, Lew* / Wednesday night hop: *Roy, Harry & His Band* / Watch the birdie: *Clae, John & His Claepigeons* / Ma (he's making eyes at me): *Young, Arthur* / Booglie wooglie piggy: *Roy, Harry & His Band* / Stay out of the South: *Simpson, Jack & His Sextet* / I got rhythm: *Gonella, Nat & His Georgians*

RAJCD 864 / Mar '96 / Empress

☐ MUSIC WHILE YOU WORK

Calling all workers / National emblem / Gondoliers (Selection) / Listen to liszt / Hits of '39 / Going Greek - selection / Mikado, The - selection / Carefree - medley / Great waltz (selection) / Accordion medley / Banjo on my knee - selection / Fleet's lit up / Hits of the day / Champagne waltz - selection

PASTCD 9791 / Jun '92 / Flapper

☐ MUSIC WHILE YOU WORK (3CD Set)

Calling all workers / Love Parade / New moon / Dancing years / White horse inn / Roberta / Christy Minstrels selection / Whistling Rufus / Sweet nothings / Canadian capers / Alexander's ragtime band / Get out and get under the moon / Cuddle up a little closer / Put your arms around me / Wait for me Mary / If I had my way / East side of heaven / Hit parade / Something in the air / Lisbon story / Sing as we go / French march medley / Ragtime medley / Dixie Lee / Say it with music / Love is the sweetest thing / I'll do my best to make you happy / Pistol packin' Mama / Pony Express / Time on my hands / Close your eyes / But not for me / Embraceable you / Bidin' my time / You are my lucky star / Broadway rhythm / I've got a feelin' you're foolin' / Love walked in / Music goes round and around / Saddle your blues to a wild mustang / Everything I have is yours / Coffee in the morning / Tea for two / Three little words / You're driving me crazy / My heart tells me for the first time I've fallen in love / Ain't misbehavin' / I double dare you / Be a waterfall / Learn to croon / Dreamer / How sweet you are / Very thought of you / Touch of your lips / Just one more chance / Who walks in when I walk out / Keep an eye on your heart / Something for the boys / Leader of the big time band / Hey good lookin' / He's a right guy / Could it be you / Hats / Moonstruck / Country cousins / Mary / Not that kind of person / White city / Bunch of roses / Little bit independent / Let me whisper / Yankee grit / Espana / Shine / Don't be angry / Olf faithfull / Boston bounce / We've got something to sing about / Flash of steel / Girl of the moment / This is new / Suddenly it's spring / Jenny / My ship / Do you ever think of me / Oh how I love my darling / La cinquantaine / Castles in Spain / Maria / Lady of the evening / Vienna blood / One love / There's a new world over the skyline / My prayer / It's like old times / Lilli Marlene / We don't know where we're going / Calling all workers

EMPRESS 1004 / Jul '96 / Empress

☐ MUSIC WHILE YOU WORK

Calling all the workers / Knightsbridge march / If I ruled the world / Rose Marie / Darktown strutters ball / I wish I were in love again / California, here I come / April showers / Swanee / Pagan love song / Moon of Manakoora / Whistle a happy tune / Friends and neighbours / Let there be love / Another openin' another show / Alexander's ragtime band / Oxford Street march / Strike up the band / Music everywhere

304652 / Jun '97 / Hallmark

☐ MUSIC WHILE YOU WORK - CALLING ALL WORKERS VOL.1

Calling all workers: *Victory Band* / Love Parade selection: *Victory Band* / New Moon selection: *Victory Band* / Dancing Years selection: *Fryer, Harry* / White Horse Inn: *Fryer, Harry* / Roberta: *Simpson, Jack* / Christy Minstrels selection: *Troise & His Mandoliers* / Whistling Rufus: *Troise & His Mandoliers* / Sweet nothin's: *Mayerl, Billy* / Canadian capers: *Mayerl, Billy* / Alexanders ragtime band/ Poor butterfly/Get out and get under: *Victory Band* / Flanagan and Allen selection: *Victory Band* / Cuddle up a little closer/Put your arms around me: *Victory Band* / Wait for me Mary: *Victory Band* / If I had my way: *Victory Band* / East side of heaven: *Simpson, Jack* / Hit Parade selection: *Simpson, Jack* / Something in the air: *Fryer, Harry* / Lisbon story: *Fryer, Harry* / Sing as we go: *Mackey, Percival* / French March medley: *Scala, Primo*

RAJCD 819 / Apr '97 / Empress

☐ MUSIC WHILE YOU WORK - CALLING ALL WORKERS VOL.2

Calling all workers: *Victory Band* / Dixie Lee: *Chapman, Wally & His Band* / Say it with music/Love is the sweetest thing: *Simpson, Jack & His Sextet* / I'll do my best to make you happy: *Simpson, Jack & His Sextet* / Pistol packin' Mama/Pony express: *Studio Orchestra* / Time on my hands: *Marsh, Roy & His Orchestra* / Close your eyes: *Chapman, Wally & His Band* / But not for you/Embraceable you/Bidin' my time: *Studio Orchestra* / You are my lucky star/ Broadway rhythm/I got a feelin': *Simpson, Jack & His Sextet* / Love walked in: *Marsh, Roy & His Orchestra* / Music goes 'round and around: *Marsh, Roy & His Orchestra* / Saddle your blues to a wild mustang: *Atkins, Stan & His Band* / Everything I have is yours/Coffee in the morning: *Dodd, Pat & Cecil Norman* / Tea for two: *Marsh, Roy & His Orchestra* / Three little words/You're driving me crazy: *Royal Navy Blue Mariners* / My heart tells me/For the first time I've fallen in love: *Studio Orchestra* / Ain't misbehavin': *Marsh, Roy & His Orchestra* / I double dare you/Boom: *Atkins, Stan & His Band* / By a waterfall/Learn to croon: *Dodd, Pat & Cecil Norman* / Dreamer/How sweet you are: *Studio Orchestra* / Very thought of you: *Chapman, Wally & His Band* / Bei mir bist du schon: *Marsh, Roy & His Orchestra* / Touch of your lips/Just one more chance: *Royal Navy Blue Mariners* / Who walks in when I walk out: *Chapman, Wally & His Band* / Keep an eye on your heart: *Bradley, Josephine & Her Ballroom Orchestra*

RAJCD 847 / May '98 / Empress

☐ MUSIC WHILE YOU WORK - CALLING ALL WORKERS VOL.3

Calling all workers: *Something For The Boys* / Something for the boys: *Something For The Boys* / Leader of the big time band: *Something For The Boys* / Hey good lookin': *Something For The Boys* / He's a right guy: *Something For The Boys* / Could it be you: *Something For The Boys* / Hats: *Green, Phil Orchestra* / Moonstruck: *Green, Phil Orchestra* / Country cousins: *Green, Phil Orchestra* / Mary: *Green, Phil Orchestra* / Not that kind of person: *Green, Phil Orchestra* / White City: *Green, Phil Orchestra* / Bunch of roses: *Burston, Reginald & His Orchestra* / Valse bleue: *Fryer, Harry* / Little bit independent: *Burston, Reginald & His Orchestra* / Let me whisper: *Burston, Reginald & His Orchestra* / Ciribiribin: *Collins, Al & his Orchestra* / Yankee grit: *Crean, Richard & His Orchestra* / Espana: *Davidson, Harry & His Orchestra* / Shine: *Munro, Ronnie & His Orchestra* / Don't be angry: *Munro, Ronnie & His Orchestra* / Old Faithful: *Gardner, Freddy & His Swing Orchestra* / Boston bounce: *Davidson, Harry & His Orchestra* / We've got something to sing about: *Davidson, Harry & His Orchestra* / Flash of steel: *Rabin, Oscar & His Band* / Girl of the moment: *London Coliseum Orchestra* / This is new: *London Coliseum Orchestra* / Suddenly it's Spring: *London Coliseum Orchestra* / Jenny: *London Coliseum Orchestra* / My ship: *London Coliseum Orchestra* / Do you ever think of me: *Green, Phil Orchestra* / Oh how I love my darling: *Green, Phil Orchestra* / La cinquantaine: *Gardner, Freddy* / Castles in Spain: *Crean, Richard & His Orchestra* / Marta: *Burston, Reginald & His Orchestra* / Lady of the evening: *Burston, Reginald & His Orchestra* / Vienna blood: *Gardner, Freddy & His Swing Orchestra* / One love: *Munro, Ronnie & His Dance Orchestra* / There's a new world over the skyline: *Munro, Ronnie & His Dance Orchestra* / My prayer: *Munro, Ronnie & His Dance Orchestra* / It's like old times: *Munro, Ronnie & His Dance Orchestra* / Lili Marlene: *Green, Phil Orchestra* / We don't know where we're going: *Green, Phil Orchestra* / Calling all workers: *Green, Phil Orchestra*

RAJCD 865 / Mar '96 / Empress

☐ MUSIC WORKS PRESENT CHATTY CHATTY MOUTH VERSIONS

GRELCD 196 / Dec '93 / Greensleeves

☐ MUSIC WORKS PRESENTS TWICE MY AGE

GRELCD 144 / Apr '90 / Greensleeves

☐ MUSIC WORKS SHOWCASE 1988

GRELCD 117 / Apr '89 / Greensleeves

☐ MUSIC WORKS SHOWCASE 1989

GRELCD 123 / Jun '89 / Greensleeves

☐ MUSIC WORKS SHOWCASE 1990

Too good to be true / Fatal attraction / Can't make a slip / IOU / Hard road to travel / Big all around / Jealousy / Fall for you again / What's the matter / Report to me / Express love / Break the ice / Easy life

GRELCD 139 / Nov '89 / Greensleeves

☐ MUSIC WORKS SHOWCASE 1990/ 1991

GRELCD 506 / May '90 / Greensleeves

☐ MUSIC WORKS VOL.1 (Gussie Clarke Presents Roots & Culture)

Throw me corn: *Marshall, Larry* / Must be revelation: *Big Youth* / Born to dub you: *Pablo, Augustus* / Dub and gaze: *Big Joe* / In their own way: *Brown, Dennis & Big Youth* / Is it because I'm black: *Wilson, Delroy* / Proud to be black: *Mikey Dread* / Pass the chalice: *Ranking Trevor* / To the foundation: *Brown, Dennis & Hugh Brown* / Jah Jah love people: *Minott, Sugar* / Sensemillia: *Mighty Diamonds* / Guiding star: *Brown, Hugh* / Higher the mountain: *Big Youth & U-Roy* / Skylarking: *Pablo, Augustus* / Don't cuss the daughter: *Trinity* / So much things: *Smart, Leroy* / Love we need: *Brown, Hugh* / No entry: *Pablo, Augustus* / Strictly rockers: *Big Youth & Augustus Pablo*

SPV 0855213 / Aug '96 / SPV

☐ MUSIC WORKS VOL.2 (Gussie Clarke Presents Lovers Dancehall)

I admire you: *Marshall, Larry* / My time: *Isaacs, Gregory* / Love was all I had: *Aitken, Marcia* / Come in Heaven: *Wilson, Delroy* / Mix up girl: *Lindo, Hopeton* / Danger in your eyes: *Mighty Diamonds* / Love you to want me: *Andy, Horace* / Oh no I can't believe it: *Isaacs, Gregory* / Unexpected places: *Ellis, Hortense* / Into the night: *Parks, Lloyd & Hugh Brown* / Children of the night: *Hall, Pam* / Deceiving girl: *Brown, Dennis* / Fools rush in: *Mighty Diamonds* / Love love love: *Wilson, Delroy* / Special lover: *McGregor, Freddie* / I am not the same: *Grier, Merva* / Gonna love you more: *Clarke, Johnny* / Try me: *Stewart, Roman*

SPV 0855214 / Aug '96 / SPV

☐ MUSIC WORTH IT'S WEIGHT IN GOLD

BULLCD 1 / Jun '97 / Bullion

☐ MUSICA DA BALLO IN SICILIA

TA 016CD / Aug '97 / Robi Droli

☐ MUSICA POPULAR DO BRAZIL

GC 900005 / Dec '93 / ITM

☐ MUSICAL BANQUET, A

CDSDLC 397 / Feb '93 / Saydisc

☐ MUSICAL BOX DANCES

CDSDL 359 / '88 / Saydisc

☐ MUSICAL DILEMMAS

Finders kreepers: *Runaways* / Science fu: *Danny Breaks* / Universal: *Raymatics* / Into you: *Blueshift* / Non non non: *Melaaz* / Spanish high noon: *Misterjon* / Miracles: *REQ* / Futurama: *Peshay* / Beauty and the beats: *Runaways* / Phat like a: *Tek 9* / Shifting to blue: *Blueshift* / Seachange: *Misterjon* / Meditations: *REQ* / Lullaby: *Raymatics*

UDRCD 001 / Mar '97 / Universal Dilemma

☐ MUSICAL FEAST

CDHB 84 / Apr '91 / Heartbeat

☐ MUSICAL FEVER 1967-1968

Bad mind grudgeful: *Winston & Robin* / Puppy love: *Bennett & Dennis* / Bad treatment: *Cannon & Soul Vendors* / Get a lick: *Oakley, Bumps* / Hip hug-her: *Sultans* / Let me love you: *Miller, Jacob* / Rub up, push up: *Termites* / Wailing time: *Winston & Robin* / Venus: *Frater, Eric* / Norwegian wood: *Williams, Marshall* / Love me girl: *Soul Vendors* / You shouldn't be the one: *Holness, Winston* / Ram jam: *Jackie & Soul Vendors* / You gonna lose: *Octaves* / Get with it: *Soul Vendors* / Fat fish: *Viceroys* / Grooving steady: *Jackie & Soul Vendors* / Bye bye baby: *Sims, Zoot* / Soul junction: *Soul Vendors* / Mercy mercy: *Slim & Freedom Singers* / Baba boom: *Jackie & Soul Vendors* / Love and unity: *Viceroys* / I don't mind: *Bob & Ty* / Zigaloo: *Sterling, Lester* / Contemplating mind: *Spence, Barrington* / Good girl: *Nangle, Ed* / Musical fever: *Enforcers* / Wiser than Solomon: *Sterling, Lester*

CDTRD 408 / Jul '89 / Trojan

☐ MUSICAL HIGHLIGHTS OF THE BERLIN TATTOO (2CD Set)

All hail to the chief - a king is crowned / Massed pipes and drums / Prince Charles Edward Stuart arrives / King's troop royal horse / Massed bands / Kevock choir / Music for Scottish dancing / Gathering of the clans (finale)

LCOM 9008 / Dec '88 / Lismor

☐ **MUSICAL INSTRUMENTS OF THE WORLD**
CNR 274675 / Dec '96 / Le Chant Du Monde

☐ **MUSICAL JOURNEY**
B 679 / Oct '94 / Auvidis/Ethnic

☐ **MUSICAL LITURGIES OF THE PAKISTAN PUNJAB**
926812 / 21 Aug '97 / BUDA

☐ **MUSICAL ROOTS OF THE NORTH-WEST PROVINCES**
PS 65073 / Jun '91 / PlayaSound

☐ **MUSICAL SPLENDOR VOL.2**
SPCD 126 / 13 Oct '97 / Super Power

☐ **MUSICAL TRADITIONS OF PORTUGAL**
SF 40435CD / Jul '95 / Smithsonian Folkways

☐ **MUSICAL TRADITIONS OF ST. LUCIA**
SF 40416CD / Jan '94 / Smithsonian Folkways

☐ **MUSICAL TRIBUTE TO VICTORY, A (D-Day/VE Day - 2CD Set)**
Spitfire flypast / RAF march past / O peaceful England / Winston Churchill / Highflight / Washing on the siegfried line / Who's this geezer Hitler / Armed forces medley / Knightsbridge march / 633 Squadron / Lie in the dark / D-Day:the landing / American hoedown / Glenn Miller medley / Last enemy / Last post / Speedbird salutes the Allied Armed forces / Now is the hour / Broadcast by General Eisenhower / American patrol / Boogie woogie bugle boy / Chattanooga choo choo / Scotland the brave / Lili Marlene / You belong to me / We'll meet again / You do something to me / Last time I saw Paris / Oh London Bridge / Wish me luck (as you wave me goodbye) / Announcement of German surrender / Rule Britannia / Churchill's victory address / Land of hope and glory / Abide with me / Auld lang syne / Ceasefire announcement / When they sound the last all clear
WARBOX 45CD / Feb '97 / Start

☐ **MUSICAL VOYAGE TO THE AZORES**
YA 225710 / Dec '95 / Silex

☐ **MUSICORA '98**
C 570601 / Jun '98 / Ocora

☐ **MUSICS OF THE EARTH**
D 8105 / Aug '98 / Unesco

☐ **MUSICS OF THE SOVIET UNION**
SFWCD 40002 / May '95 / Smithsonian Folkways

☐ **MUSIQUE DU HAUT XINGU (Music of the Xingu Islands, Brazil)**
C 580022 / Jan '93 / Ocora

☐ **MUSIQUE DU NORDESTE BRAZIL VOL.1**
829602 / 24 Apr '98 / BUDA

☐ **MUSIQUE QUECHUA DU LAC TITICACA (Music From Taquile, Peru)**
C 580015 / Jan '93 / Ocora

☐ **MUSIQUES BRETONNES**
KMCD 01 / Jul '90 / Keltia Musique

☐ **MUSIQUES D'EXTASE ET DE GUERISON (Music From The Baluchi People Of Pakistan & Iran)**
C 580017/18 / Jan '93 / Ocora

☐ **MUSIQUES DES BATAK**
W 260061 / Sep '95 / Inedit

☐ **MUSIQUES DU MALI VOL.1 (Banzoumana/2CD Set)**
389012 / 21 Aug '97 / Melodie

☐ **MUSIQUES DU MALI VOL.2 (2CD Set)**
389022 / 21 Aug '97 / Melodie

☐ **MUSIQUES POUR LES PLANTES VERTES**
Life: *DJ Cam* / ESP: *Hyphen* / Joue Milshtein part 3: *Zein Angelus* / Switch out the sun: *Juantrip* / Dream of the night: *Edoram* / Fleur De Lotus: *Garnier, Laurent* / Sky: *Reminiscent Drive* / Turmoil: *Scan X* / On the way to Paris: *Chaotik Ramses* / Tones: *Nova Nova* / I want to remember this moment always: *Reminiscent Drive*
F 038CD / Apr '96 / Play It Again Sam

☐ **MUSIQUES RITUELLES ET RELIGIEUSES (Music From Sri Lankan Cults & Religions)**
C 580037 / Jan '93 / Ocora

☐ **MUSIQUES TRADITIONNELLES (Music From Sierra Leone)**
C 580036 / Jan '93 / Ocora

☐ **MUSIQUES TRADITIONNELLES - BALI/JAVA**
PS 65110 / Nov '93 / PlayaSound

☐ **MUSIQUES TRADITIONNELLES DE BRETAGNE**
ARN 64380 / Jun '97 / Arion

☐ **MUSLIM MUSIC (Europe & Asia/2CD Set)**
FA 073 / 5 Jan '98 / Fremeaux

☐ **MUST BE MENTAL VOL.2**
PA 011CD / May '95 / Paragoric

☐ **MUST BE SANTA**
ROUCD 3118 / Nov '95 / Rounder

☐ **MUTANT BEATZ**
Heavy handed: *Faceless* / Do yourself some good: *Faceless* / APB: *Lazy K* / My stories: *Rude Culture* / Soul skankin: *Blue Pearl* / Trife: *Soothsayer* / Revolution: *Moonstar* / Matrix: *Pierce, Adam* / Logic: *Faceless* / Dark the day: *Survival Sounds* / Twilight: *Rude Culture* / Shadow: *Black Pearl*
MSS 0017CD / 6 Oct '97 / Mutant Sound System

☐ **MUTANT DISCO**
HURTCD 009 / 13 Apr '98 / Harmless

☐ **MUTILATED**
RR 87772 / 3 Nov '97 / Roadrunner

☐ **MUZIQUE TROPIQUE COLLECTION (2CD Set)**
Stella Sunday: *Glasgow Underground* / Jazz the sea turtle: *4AM* / Back to black: *Urban Revolution* / 90 in the shade: *American Intrigue* / Kingston: *4AM* / Shipwrecked: *4AM* / Gospel song: *Urban Revolution* / Stella Sunday: *Glasgow Underground* / Siesta: *Glasgow Underground* / Kingston: *4AM* / Ice spinner: *West Coast Connection* / Stella Sunday: *Glasgow Underground* / Return of the sea turtle: *4AM* / 4am theme: *4AM* / Montego Bay: *Communication X* / Jazz the sea turtle: *4AM* / 90 in the shade: *American Intrigue* / Dub attraction: *Mystic Soul*
GUCD 001B / 29 Sep '97 / Glasgow Underground

☐ **MUZIQUE TROPIQUE COLLECTION**
Stella Sunday: *Glasgow Underground* / Jazz the sea turtle: *4AM* / Back to black: *Urban Revolution* / 90 in the shade: *American Intrigue* / Kingston: *4AM* / Shipwrecked: *4AM* / Gospel song: *Urban Revolution* / Stella Sunday: *Glasgow Underground*
GUCD 001 / 29 Sep '97 / Glasgow Underground

☐ **MY DUBLIN BAY**
MACCD 201 / Aug '96 / Autograph

☐ **MY HOUSE VOL.1**
SUB 48312 / Feb '97 / Distance

☐ **MY HOUSE VOL.2**
SUB 48432 / Jul '97 / Distance

☐ **MY HOUSE VOL.3 (Mixed By DJ Jef K)**
Justified music: *Papp, Julius* / Home: *Mateo & Matos* / Spirit of the black ghost: *Grant, Mark* / Never can get away: *Hope, Alexander* / New life: *Fresh & Low* / Dreams of you: *Yost, Kevin & Peter Funk* / Don't try: *Trent, Ron & Chez Damier* / I'm grateful: *D'Menace* / Loveiee day: *Blaze* / Lonely: *Joseph, Corrina*
DI 0742 / 30 Mar '98 / Distance

☐ **MY IRISH HOME SWEET HOME**
Phil the fluter's ball / Eileen oge / Danny boy / Mother Machree / It takes an irish heart to sing an irish song / My old Irish mother / Father O'Flynn / Where the Shannon river flows / My wild Irish rose / Down by the glenside / Mountains of mourne / Rose of Tralee / My Irish home sweet home / Spinning wheel / That's how I spell IRELAND / When Irish eyes are smiling / If you're Irish come into the parlour / Three lovely lasses / Kathleen Mavoureen / Laughing Irish eyes / Beautiful Eileen / Did your mother come from Ireland
RAJCD 809 / Apr '97 / Empress

☐ **MY LOVE IS IN AMERICA**
Lord mcdonald's-the fair of ballinasloe (reels) / Lord mcdonald's-the fair of ballinasloe (reels) / Humours of ballyloughlin (double jig) / Joe bane's-the green-gowned lass (reels) / Banks medley / Lament for staker wallace-farewell to erin (airsreels) / Wind that shakes the barley-the tramp's (reels) / Salamanca-trim the velvet (reels) / Aggie whyte's-miss roddy's (reels) / Humours of lissadell (reel) / Untitled-the piper on horseback (reels) / Morning dew-jenny's chickens (reels) / Lad o beirne's-leinster buttermilk (reels) / Flowers of limerick-tommy coen's (reels) / Boys of ballisodare (slip jig) / Plains of boyle-dunphy's hornpipe (hornpipes) / Wandering minstrel medley (double jigs) / My love is in america (reel)
GLCD 1110 / Nov '91 / Green Linnet

☐ **MY WILD IRISH ROSE (22 Favourite Irish Ballads)**
Black velvet band: *Kelly, John* / Shanagolden: *Day, Paddy* / Old maid in a garret: *Sweeneys* / My auld Killarney hat: *Gertrude, Sister Mary* / Enniskillen Dragoons: *Ludlows* / Flower of Macroom: *Dunphy, Sean & The Hoedowners* / Lough sheelin: *Nomads* / Turfman from Ardee: *Gallagher, Bridie* / Arkle: *Behan, Dominic* / Nora: *McEvoy, Johnny* / Beautiful city: *Donal Ring Sound* / Muirsheen durkin: *McEvoy, Johnny* / Sea around us: *Ludlows* / Leaving of Liverpool: *Lynch, Pat* / My wild Irish rose: *Cotton Mill Boys* / Come to the bower: *Dunphy, Sean* / Slaney Valley: *Kinsellas* / McAlpine's Fusiliers: *Kelly, Des* / Curragh Of Kildare: *Johnstons* / Shores of Amerikay: *Broadsiders* / Prisoner: *Day, Paddy* / Bold O'Donoghue: *Dragoons*
TRTCD 124 / Oct '94 / TrueTrax

☐ **MYOHIOACTIONPALBOYGOLD300**
OHIOGOLD 005 / 13 Apr '98 / Ohio Gold

☐ **MYSTERY OF POLYPHONY, THE**
58393 / Mar '96 / World Network

☐ **MYSTERY OF THE YETI**
TIPCD 09 / Nov '96 / Tip

☐ **MYSTERY TRAIN**
Casey Jones: *Cash, Johnny* / Freight train boogie: *Whitstein Brothers* / City of New Orleans: *Goodman, Steve* / Mystery train: *LaBeef, Sleepy* / Cannonball: *Carter Family* / Big black train: *Flatt & Scruggs* / Red ball to Natchez: *Delmore Brothers & Wayne Raney* / Take the 'A' train: *Wills, Bob & His Texas Playboys* / Waiting for a train: *Snow, Hank* / Life's a railway to heaven: *Cline, Patsy* / Old train: *Rice, Tony Unit* / Bringin' in the Georgia Mail: *Rice, Tony Unit* / Train: *Stanley Brothers* / Last cannonball: *McCaslin, Mary*
ROUCD 1129 / Mar '97 / Rounder

☐ **MYSTIC BREW (The Flavour Of Fat City/2CD Set)**
My kinda moves: *Q-Ball & Curt Cazal* / Keep on rockin': *Jigmastas* / Take the train: *Paul, Wayne* / Cissy strut: *Trinidad Steel Drummers* / Great raspberry rip off: *Concrete Puppy* / Creator has a master plan: *Brooklyn Funk Essentials* / Jungle fever: *Izachaar, Hughie* / Tibetan serenity: *Biggs, Travis* / Strait jacket: *Sorgini, Guiliano* / Bad hair blues: *Jimpster* / Rhymes like a scientist: *Third Sight* / Closer: *Essa*
FCCD 001 / 4 May '98 / Fat City

☐ **MYSTIC FIDDLE OF THE PROTO GYPSIES, THE (The Music Of The Baluchi People/Masters Of Trance Music)**
SH 65013 / Aug '97 / Shanachie

☐ **MYSTIC MOODS**
Sailing: *Belmonde, Pierre* / Stranger on the shore: *Bilk, Acker* / Harry's Game: *Light Shadows* / Long and winding road: *Hill & Wiltchinsky* / Chariots of fire: *Masterworks* / Cacharpaya: *Interlude Orchestra* / Aria: *Belmonde, Pierre* / Walking in the air: *Hill & Wiltchinsky* / Theme from Brideshead Revisited: *SRE Band* / Flying: *London Symphony Orchestra* / Meditation from Thais: *Royal Philharmonic Orchestra* / Concierto de aranjuez: *Belmonde, Pierre* / Cavatina: *Hill & Wiltchinsky* / Clair de lune: *Allis, Julie* / Morning: *London Symphony Orchestra* / Spring song: *London Symphony Orchestra* / Morning has broken: *Bilk, Acker* / Canon: *London Symphony Orchestra*
ECD 3131 / Jan '95 / K-Tel

☐ **MYTH AND MAGIC**
CD 408 / 6 Jul '98 / New World

☐ **MYTHS COLLECTION VOL.1**
SUBCD 00316 / Oct '88 / Sub Rosa

☐ **MYTHS COLLECTION VOL.2**
SUBCD 00932 / Dec '90 / Sub Rosa

☐ **MYTHS VOL.1 (Instructions For Survival)**
SR 01 / Feb '97 / Sub Rosa

☐ **MYTHS VOL.2 (System Of Flux And Energies)**
SR 02 / Feb '97 / Sub Rosa

☐ **MYTHS VOL.3 (La Nouvelle Serenite)**
SR 05 / Feb '97 / Sub Rosa

N

☐ **NA ONDA DO FORRONEJO**
RDS 1037 / 12 May '98 / RDS

☐ **NAGEL HEYER SAMPLER VOL.1**
NHRSP 5 / Nov '97 / Nagel Heyer

☐ **NAGEL HEYER SAMPLER VOL.2**
NHRSP 6 / Nov '97 / Nagel Heyer

☐ **NAIM SAMPLER**
CD 023 / 1 Jun '98 / Naim Audio

☐ **NAIVE**
MOSH 076CD / Oct '92 / Earache

☐ **NAKED NASHVILLE**
Good luck 'n' good truckin tonite (naked Nashville theme): *Watson, Dale* / Guys do it all the time: *McCready, Mindy* / Easy come easy go: *Strait, George* / Fancy: *McEntire, Reba* / Honkiest tonkiest beer joint: *Watson, Dale* / Stand by your man: *Wynette, Tammy* / My heroes have always been cowboys: *Nelson, Willie* / It don't get any countrier than this: *McGraw, Tim* / Resurection: *Berg, Matraca* / Rank stranger to me: *Skaggs, Ricky* / Shakin' things up: *Morgan, Lorrie* / Papa bear: *Harling, Keith* / Wrong side of Memphis: *Yearwood, Trisha* / Crazy: *Nelson, Willie* / Strawberry wine: *Berg, Matraca* / Heartaches by the number: *Price, Ray* / I fall to pieces: *Cline, Patsy* / Me and Bobby McGee: *Kristofferson, Kris* / Good luck 'n' good truckin tonite: *Watson, Dale*
74321587572 / 13 Jul '98 / RCA Nashville

☐ **NAME BRAND**
CRCD 30 / Apr '94 / Charm

☐ **NAPALM RAVE VOL.1 (34 Orgasmic Traxx Of Gabba & Hardcore/2CD Set)**
SPV 08638282 / Sep '96 / SPV

☐ **NAPALM RAVE VOL.2 (31 Orgasmic Traxx Of Gabba & Hardcore/2CD Set)**
SPV 08638332 / Sep '96 / SPV

☐ **NAPALM RAVE VOL.3 (30 Orgasmic Traxx Of Gabba & Hardcore/2CD Set)**
It's with us: *Possessed* / Rotterdam: *2 Criminals On The 3rd Floor* / Ill behaviour: *Kill Your Mother* / Under attack: *Organic* / Satanic song: *Apochrypha* / Get the fuck outta my way: *Boldhead Johnnie* / Hemp plant: *DJ Ganja* / Underground: *FAM* / Somebody scream: *Brainlock* / First assault: *Hardtechmedia* / Can you hear this fuckin' beat: *DJ Zicem* / Lestat: *Tonad, Joey* / Fuck a bitch: *Fat Agnus* / Hardcore: *Axl* / Word 2 da mutha fucker: *Federation Against Mellow* / Jesus must die: *Kill Your Mother* / Deeper deeper: *Organic* / Learning experience: *Networxx* / Hardcore: *Axl* / On your own: *Networxx* / U got die: *Fuckface* / Good time: *FAM* / Hardcore: *Axl* / Marijuana gets me high: *Masters Of Da Hardcore* / To the beat of the drum: *DJ Rico & DJ Cain* / I'm gonna dis you right now: *Masters Of Da Hardcore* / Basically the same sex: *MODH* / Sick son of a bitch: *Kill Your Mother* / Basic 1: *Hardtechmedia* / Napalm 2 magamix
SPV 08647022 / Sep '96 / SPV

☐ **NAPALM RAVE VOL.4 (30 Orgasmic Traxx Of Gabba & Hardcore/2CD Set)**
We are at war: *Hardcore Posse* / Start da panic: *Panic Master* / Put your hands together: *Screwhead* / Do you love your hardcore: *Da Jach* / Pump up the base: *Erector* / Don't allow women in here: *Children Of A Dam* / Rock da house: *2 Terror* / Wild and rootsy: *Soundboy* / It is time: *DJ Zicem* / Gimme a white line: *Clan Of Fools* / Bust a freestyle: *DJ Nahho* / I'm on push: *Focus* / War on drugs: *Federation Against Mellow* / Dream your fantasy: *Dreamer* / Life's a bitch: *SHIT* / I love you Mary Jane: *Federation Against Mellow* / Got to go: *Da Bitch & DJ Zicem* / For your souls: *Lords Of Evil* / On my knees: *Warhead* / Sulphur: *Powerstation Holocaust* / Bass disorder: *JJ* / Alternate F1: *Harrotechmedia* / Bow to me: *3x6* / Graveyard: *Audiodoom* / World of the living (Part 1): *Funboy* / World of the living (Part 2): *Funboy* / Demon reserection: *Mercy Me* / Metallic armor: *Autominder* / Naplam rave theme: *Funboy* / This is the end of all: *Unkown Demon*
SPV 08647442 / Apr '97 / SPV

☐ **NAPALM RAVE VOL.5 (2CD Set)**
Welcome to the other side: *Morph* / Can you feel the force: *T.Stone* / Half a christ: *Dark & Evil* / Deadly wishes: *Bunker, Bob* / Demon christ: *Dark & Evil* / Kraoula: *Ronny Reverse* / Alchemy: *Virtual Industries* / Atopsy: *Powerstation Holocaust* / Ravezone sinistra: *Skullbumper* / Dusk: *Nozone Hools* / Shadows of neon maniacs: *Powerstation Holocaust* / Ambientcore: *Deuce Of Doom* / Impaling: *Powerstation Holocaust* / Growing pains: *Skullbumper* / Dr. Aum must die: *Dark & Evil* / Mansonchrist: *Dark & Evil* / Satanchrist: *Planet Hooligan* / New space odyssey: *Boldhyper* / Ultimate goal of evolution: *Bunker, Bob* / Hardcore wannabe: *Agent Punk* / Big bang bang: *Admiral 243* / Pusher: *Rotterdam Resistance* / Humanchrist: *Dark & Evil* / My life in the dark: *Powerstation Holocaust* / Sally slaughter: *Bob & the Assassins* / Uzi love: *Hardnoise*
SPV 08647722 / Sep '97 / SPV

☐ **NAPALM RAVE VOL.6 (2CD Set)**
Sick things: *Powerstation Holocaust* / Hart-core: *Rotterdam Resistance* / Everything is war: *Atomkinder* / G'dd'mned: *Narcotic Empire Corps* / Don't stop (junoattack): *Twin Ion* / No god no home: *Evil Dick On Atari* / Gabba never dies: *No Names* / It's war outthere: *General* / Blow up the world: *Indie Depth* / Blow up: *Indie Depth* / Obey the law: *Da Body* / Bound: *Darian Z* / Rush: *Bosba Ancore* / Enter a world: *Zen* / Brave new world: *Stalking Creep* / Dark time: *Warlord* / Raume: *Atomkinder* / Xinguh: *Keys of kingdom* / On and on it goes: *Bamboo Tribe* / Hardcore business: *Rotterdam Resistance* / So easy: *Rotterdam Resistance* / Your world: *Second Base* / Sick Satan and hate: *Hardware* / Oil tank: *Southside Front* / 30 Years/Earth: *Atomkinder* / Ohhh yeahhhh: *Ssuez, Natas*
SPV 08647952 / 6 Apr '98 / SPV

☐ **NARADA CHRISTMAS COLLECTION VOL.3**
Silver bells: *Arkenstone, David* / God rest ye merry gentlemen: *Whalen, Michael* / O holy night: *Mann, Brian* / O' come all ye faithful: *Lauria, Nando* / It came upon a midnight clear: *Gratz, Wayne* / Ding dong merrily on high: *Rumbel, Nancy* / Good King Wenceslas: *Rumbel, Nancy* / First Noel: *Illenberger, Ralf* / Carol of the bells: *Kostia* / Hark, the herald angels sing: *Tingstad, Eric* / Silent night: *Wynberg, Simon* / We three kings: *Stein, Ira* / Little drummer boy: *Ellwood, William* / O little town of Bethlehem: *Jones, Michael* / Holly and the ivy: *Jones, Michael*
ND 63919 / Dec '95 / Narada

☐ **NARADA COLLECTION VOL.5**
ND 63920 / Aug '95 / Narada

☐ **NARADA DECADE**
ND 263911 / Jun '93 / Narada

☐ **NARADA GUITAR**
72438456362 / 7 Apr '98 / Narada

☐ **NARADA SHOWCASE**
Ruby Tuesday: *Lanz, David* / Cristofori's dream: *Cook, Jesse* / Tomeen O'deas reel: *O'Dea, Tomeen* / Mountain madness: *Fraser, Alasdair & Paul Machlis* / Forgive me: *Lopez, Oscar* / January's journey: *Whelan, John* / Discovery: *Arkenstone, David* / Passage of time: *Whelan, John* / Never was piping so gay: *Whelan, John* / As tears go by: *Lanz, David* / Auld lang syne: *MacLean, Dougie* / Ningal: *Vas* / Mi carmen: *Bastide, Miguel de la* / Seascapes: *Jones, Michael* / Gipsy: *Cook, Jesse* / Whalesong: *Gettel, Michael* / Davey's: *Gettel, Michael* / Laughing wolf: *Fraser, Alasdair & Paul Machlis* / Trip to siglo set: *Dervish*
VNDCD 2 / 11 May '98 / Virgin

☐ **NARADA WORLD (2CD Set)**
Ubi caritas: *Dover, Connie* / Road north: *Fraser, Alasdair* / Sealwoman: *McLaughlin, Mary* / Yundah: *McLaughlin, Mary* / Douce mousitomanie: *Orion* / Planxty Burke: *Phillips, Shelley* / Planxty dew: *Phillips, Shelley* / Chuaigh me 'na rosann: *Scartaglen* / Dancing to a lot of time: *Whelan, John* / Baghdad: *Cook, Jesse* / Gravity: *Cook, Jesse* / Viajero: *De La Bastide, Miguel* / Cactus de paraguana: *Guedes, Carlos* / Back home: *Lauria, Nando* / Doce Morena: *Lauria, Nando* / Lucia: *Lopez, Oscar* / New land: *Rubaja, Bernardo* / Cielo y montana: *Rumillajta* / Mujeres y ninos: *Rumillajta* / Kantico en flor de piedra: *San Miguel, Tomas* / Wind

spirit: Miller, Bill / Precious waters: Nakai, R. Carlos / Kothbiro: Ogada, Ayub / Giant step: Pluznick, Michael / Wasuze otya: Samite / Cheetah hunt: Whalen, Michael / Journey begins: Zimmer, Hans / Ladakh: Ancient Future / Inochi no sharin (Wheel of life): Lee, Riley / Astrae: Vas / Water: Warner, Richard

ND 263935 / May '97 / Narada

☐ NARCOSIS

Silence of water: Emojonal / Game from planet Onchet: Hole In One / My definition of house music: DJ Hell / Come into my life: Abfahrt / New age heart core: Trance Induction / Flash: Fix / Diamond bullet: Effective Force / In the shadow: Morganistic / White darkness: Sandoz / Brother from jazz: Angel, Dave / Ob-selon mi-mos: Mystic Istitute

GRCD 009 / Jul '94 / Guerilla

☐ NARCOSIS (A Dark Ambient Compilation/2CD Set)

9040224 / Apr '97 / Nova Tekk

☐ NASHPOP

NL 046 / 29 Jun '98 / Not Lame

☐ NASHVILLE CLASSICS '40S AND BEFORE

Orange blossom special: Monroe, Bill & His Bluegrass Boys / I'll be back in a year little darlin': Robertson, Texas Jim / There's a star spangled banner waving somewhere: Britt, Elton / Each minute seems a million years: Arnold, Eddy / Shame on you: Boyd, Bill & His Cowboy Ramblers / Stars and stripes on Iwo Jima: Sons Of The Pioneers / Sioux City Sue: Manner, Zeke & His Band / I want to be a cowboy's sweetheart: Allen, Rosalie / Filipino baby: Robertson, Texas Jim / Rose of the Alamo: Allen, Rosalie / My chickashay gal: Rogers, Roy / It's dark outside: Cooley, Spade / I'll never trust you again: Carson, Jenny Lou & Her Tumbleweed Troubadours / Teardrops in my heart: Sons Of The Pioneers / I'll hold you in my heart: Arnold, Eddy / I'm my own Grandpa: Lonzo & Oscar / Garden in my sky: Blue Sky Boys / Tennessee waltz: King, Pee Wee & The Golden West Cowboys / Don't rob another man's castle: Arnold, Eddy / Candy kisses: Britt, Elton / Death at the bar: Wells, Kitty / Birmingham jail: Whitman, Slim / Baby, it's cold outside: Homer & Jethro with June Carter / I wish I knew: Hewitt, Dolph / Marriage vow: Snow, Hank / Prisoner's song: Dalhart, Vernon / Waiting for a train: Rodgers, Jimmie / I'm thinking tonight of my blue eyes: Carter Family

74321317692 / Feb '96 / RCA

☐ NASHVILLE CLASSICS '50S

Take me in your arms and hold me: Arnold, Eddy / Stampede: Rogers, Roy & Sons Of The Pioneers / Quicksilver: Britt, Elton / I'm movin' on: Snow, Hank / Poison love: Johnny & Jack / Down on the trail of aching hearts: Snow, Hank / Slow poke: King, Pee Wee & The Golden West Cowboys / Stop that ticklin' me: Jones, Grandpa / Eddy's song: Arnold, Eddy / (How much is that) hound dog in the window: Homer & Jethro / I forgot more than you'll ever know: Davis Sisters / I found out more than you'll ever know: Cody, Betty / (Oh baby mine) I get so lonely: Johnny & Jack / I don't hurt anymore: Snow, Hank / Satisfied man: Wagoner, Porter / In the jailhouse now No.2: Rodgers, Jimmie / Cattle call: Arnold, Eddy / Yonder comes a sucker: Reeves, Jim / I heard the bluebirds sing: Browns / Oh lonesome me: Gibson, Don / Send me the pillow that you dream on: Locklin, Hank / Blue blue day: Gibson, Don / He'll have to go: Reeves, Jim / Three bells: Browns / Tennessee stud: Arnold, Eddy

74321280222 / Feb '96 / RCA

☐ NASHVILLE CLASSICS '60S

Please help me I'm falling: Locklin, Hank / Last date: Cramer, Floyd / When 2 worlds collide: Miller, Roger / Sea of heartbreak: Gibson, Don / I've been everywhere: Snow, Hank / End of the world: Davis, Skeeter / Abilene: Hamilton, George IV / 500 Miles away from home: Bare, Bobby / Here comes my baby: West, Dottie / Once a day: Smith, Connie / I wouldn't buy a used car from him: Norma Jean / Crystal chandeliers: Belew, Carl / Stop the world (and let me off): Jennings, Waylon / Make the world go away: Arnold, Eddy / Ballad of the Green Berets: Sadler, Sgt. Barry / Distant drums: Reeves, Jim / Just between you and me: Pride, Charley / Mama spank: Anderson, Liz / Pop a top: Brown, Jim Ed / Gentle on my mind: Hartford, John / Last thing on my mind: Parton, Dolly & Porter Wagoner / Caroll County accident: Wagoner, Porter / Plastic saddle: Stuckey, Nat / Bring me sunshine: Nelson, Willie / My blue ridge mountain boy: Parton, Dolly

74321280232 / Feb '96 / RCA

☐ NASHVILLE CLASSICS '70S

Sheriff of Boone county: Price, Kenny / When you're hot, you're hot: Reed, Jerry / Just one time: Smith, Connie / Kiss an angel good morning: Pride, Charley / Country sunshine: West, Dottie / Baptism of Jesse Taylor: Russell, Johnny / There won't be anymore: Rich, Charlie / Pure love: Milsap, Ronnie / I will always love you: Parton, Dolly / This time: Jennings, Waylon / Marie Laveau: Bare, Bobby / Please don't stop loving me: Parton, Dolly & Porter Wagoner / Out of hand: Stewart, Gary / Storms never last: Dottsy / Shadows of my mind: Oxford, Vernon / Door is always open: Dave & Sugar / Suspicious minds: Jennings, Waylon & Jessie Colter / 9999999 tears: Lee, Dickie / Luckenbach, Texas (Back to the basics of love): Jennings, Waylon / Here you come again: Parton, Dolly / Two doors down: Lehr, Zella / What have you got to lose: Hall, Tom T. / If love had a face: Bailey, Razzy / I wanna come over: Alabama / How I miss you tonight: Reeves, Jim & Deborah Allen

74321280242 / Feb '96 / RCA

☐ NASHVILLE CLASSICS '80S

My heart: Milsap, Ronnie / Tennessee river: Alabama / Dukes of Hazzard: Jennings, Waylon / Nine to five: Parton, Dolly / All the roads lead to you: Wariner, Steve / She left love all over me: Bailey, Razzy / Mountain of love: Pride, Charley / Nobody: Sylvia / She got the goldmine (I got the shaft): Reed, Jerry / Somewhere between right and wrong: Conley, Earl Thomas / I got Mexico: Raven, Eddy / Tennessee homesick blues: Parton, Dolly / Moon is still over her shoulder: Johnson, Michael / Eighties ladies: Oslin, K.T. / Cinderella: Gill, Vince / Crazy over you: Foster & Lloyd / Tear stained letter: Sonnier, Jo El / Bluest eyes in Texas: Restless Heart / I'm no stranger to the rain: Whitley, Keith / Dear me: Morgan, Lorrie / Better man: Black, Clint / (Wish I had a) heart of stone: Baillie & the Boys / High cotton: Alabama

74321317682 / Feb '96 / RCA

☐ NASHVILLE CLASSICS - DUETS

Rings of gold: Gibson, Don & Dottie West / Don't let me cross over: Reeves, Jim & Deborah Allen / Mother may I: Anderson, Liz & Lynn / Dear John letter: Bare, Bobby & Skeeter Davis / Looking back to see: Browns / If it's wrong to love you: Snow, Hank & Anita Carter / I love you: Reeves, Jim & Ginny Wright / Under your spell again: Jennings, Waylon & Jessi Colter / Making plans: Parton, Dolly & Porter Wagoner / When my blue moon turns to gold again: Flatt, Lester & Mac Wiseman / I don't want to have to marry you: Brown, Jim Ed & Helen Cornelius / Love is no excuse: Reeves, Jim & Dottie West / Gotta find a bluebird: Davis, Skeeter & Porter Wagoner / Let it be me: Smith, Connie & Nat Stuckey / Promised to John: Snow, Hank & Anita Carter / Hurry my Peters: Tubb, Justin & Lorene Mann / Jeannie's afraid of the dark: Parton, Dolly & Porter Wagoner / Slowly: West, Dottie & Jimmy Dean / Let's get together: Skeeter, Davis & George Hamilton IV / I got you: Jennings, Waylon & Anita Carter / Bluebirds are singing for me: Flatt, Lester & Mac Wiseman / Things: Snow, Hank & Kelly Foxton / Brotherly love: Stewart, Gary & Dean Dillon / Till a tear becomes a rose: Morgan, Lorrie & Keith Whitley / Hold a partner: Black, Clint & Roy Rogers

74321317702 / Feb '96 / RCA

☐ NASHVILLE DREAM (2CD Set)

QTVCD 014 / Oct '92 / Quality

☐ NASHVILLE LINE DANCING ALBUM VOL.2, THE

Bury the shovel: Walker, Clay / Independence day: McBride, Martina / Steppin' stones: Morgan, Lorrie / Party zone: Kentucky Headhunters / Heart is right: Carter, Carlene / Too much fun: Singletary, Daryle / Say I: Alabama / Little drops of my heart: Gattis, Keith / No news: Lonestar / Back in your arms again: Morgan, Lorrie / Limbo: Morris, Jill / Right plan wrong man: Regina Regina / (I'll see you in) Cuba: Oslin, K.T. / I can help: Tippin, Aaron / I should've asked her faster: England, Ty / Seminole wind: Anderson, John / Bad dog no biscuit: Norwood, Daron / Silver tongue gold plated lies: Oslin, K.T.

74321489852 / 18 May '98 / RCA

☐ NASHVILLE ROCK

CURCD 036 / May '97 / Curb

☐ NASTY BLUES VOL.1

Strokin': Carter, Clarence / Trudy sings the blues: Lynn, Trudy / I want to play with your poodle: Willis, Chick / Rainy day: White, Artie / One eyed woman: Coleman, Gary B.B. / I want a big fat woman: Willis, Chick / Ugly man: Taylor, Little Johnny / Watch where you stroke: Coleman, Gary B.B. / Two heads are better than one: Haddix, Travis / Why do I stay here and take all this shit: Carter, Clarence

ICH 1048CD / Mar '94 / Ichiban

☐ NASTY BLUES VOL.2

Jack you up: Willis, Chick / Come back pussy: Williams, Dicky / Cook me: Legendary Blues Band / Grandpa can't fly his kite: Carter, Clarence / Let me funk with you: Blues Boy Willie / Tittie man: Drink Small / Nuts for sale: Willis, Chick / Don't pet my dog: White, Artie / Lemon squeezin' Daddy: Brown, Nappy / Kiss you all over: Carter, Clarence

ICH 1066CD / Oct '93 / Ichiban

☐ NATIONAL ANTHEMS MIX (3CD Set)

FIRMCD 4 / Jun '96 / Firm

☐ NATIONAL ANTHEMS OF THE WORLD

God save the Queen / Star spangled banner / La Marseillaise / Deutschland Lied / Inno di Mameli / Mazurep Dabrowskiego / Marcha Real / Segnorizo Apo Tin Kopsi / Llatikvah / O Canada / Kimiga Yowa Chiyoni / Wilhelmus van Nassouwe / Scotland the Brave / Amthran na bh Fiann / Land of my Fathers / European Anthem

SUMCD 4120 / May '97 / Summit

☐ NATIONAL BRASS BAND CHAMPIONSHIP 1991

Rule Britannia / Showers of gold / Tribute to Ted Heath / Deep inside the sacred temple / Triumphant rhapsody / Energy / Walk in the paradise garden / Pop suite/last movement / David of the white rock / Ouverture solennelle / 1812

QPRL 049D / Oct '97 / Polyphonic

☐ NATIONAL BRASS BAND CHAMPIONSHIP 1992

Happy and glorious / Crimond / Toccata / Temptress for trombones / New Jerusalem / Aida / Air from third suite / Pantomime / In memoriam / Your tiny hand is frozen / Entry of the gladiators

QPRL 056D / Oct '97 / Polyphonic

☐ NATIONAL BRASS BAND CHAMPIONSHIP 1994

Pioneers' march / Bartered bride (overture) / Thoughts of love / Slaughter on 10th Avenue / Theme and co-operation / Dance of the comedians / Better world / Galaxies / Concert etude / Russian Christmas music / Pines of Rome

QPRL 071D / Oct '97 / Polyphonic

☐ NATIONAL BRASS BAND FESTIVAL 1988

Overture / Candide / Fetes / Concerto for cornet / Desert II - horizons / Seascapes / Le petit negre / Phillip McCann salutes Harry Mortimer / Endeavour

QPRL 039D / Oct '97 / Polyphonic

☐ NATIONAL DOWNHOME BLUES FESTIVAL

SCD 21 / Mar '97 / Southland

☐ NATIONAL FOLK FESTIVAL

CIC 068CD / Nov '93 / Clo Iar-Chonnachta

☐ NATIVE AMERICAN DREAM

CD 405 / 6 Jul '98 / New World

☐ NATIVE AMERICAN LEGENDS

PLSCD 277 / 2 Mar '98 / Pulse

☐ NATIVE NEW YORKER (Disco Classics)

Native New Yorker / Yes sir I can boogie / Disco nights / Ms. Grace / Shame / Just don't want to be lonely / Sunny / I can't stand the rain / Jack and Jill / Givin' up givin' in / Rock the boat / La la means I love you / There goes my first love / Blockbuster / It's in his kiss / Fire / Can't get by without you / Dancing on a Saturday night / Jack in the box / Get dancin'

74321476782 / Apr '97 / Camden

☐ NATIVE NORTH AMERICAN COLLECTION (3CD Set)

Night song / Crying rabbit / Eye of the sun / Caller / Flying eagle / Harvest Dreams (part 1) / Harvest dreams (part 2) / Cry for rain (part 1) / Cry for rain (part 2) / Dancing squaws / War song / Like a snake / Spot song / Hungry dog / How the west was lost / Winter ceremony / Counter clockwise circle / Celebrate with wild rice / Credele song / Advice for the young / Wishes of happiness and prosperity / Elevation / Inter tribal song to stop the rain / Heal the soul / Brandishing tomahawk / Horse dance / Dag dance / Death dance / Tree dance / Thunder dance / Light dance / Cry dance / White dance / Spring dance / Travel dance / Squabble dance / Child dance / Wolf dance / Freedom dance

PBXCD 317 / 3 Aug '98 / Pulse

☐ NATIVE SPIRIT

57832 / May '97 / Nature's Harmony

☐ NATIVE WISDOM

Anzala / Soirit / Wiracocha / Healing song: Walking in prayer / An caoineadh / Lawaki / No se muere nunca / Te pure a te fatu / Many feather's chant / Shaman's prayer / Grigogal cridhe / Celebration in the village / Millennium theme

ND 63923 / Apr '96 / Narada

☐ NATIVES

662244 / Jun '93 / FNAC

☐ NATTY REBEL ROOTS

Let jah be praised: Gladiators / Tune in: Isaacs, Gregory / Cry tough: Clarke, Johnny / Natty rebel: U-Roy / Throw away your gun: Prince Far-I / Declaration of rights: Clarke, Johnny / We'll find the blessing: Gladiators / Do you remember: U-Roy / Jah kingdom come: Twinkle Brothers / Slavery let I go: Dr. Alimantado / Crazy baldheads: Clarke, Johnny / Best things in life: Gladiators / Praise jah: Twinkle Brothers / How love divine (dub): Prince Far-I / Uptown top ranking: Althia & Donna

CDFL 9013 / Sep '90 / Frontline

☐ NATURAL BORN TECHNO VOL.1

NZ 030 / Feb '95 / Nova Zembla

☐ NATURAL BORN TECHNO VOL.2

NZ 042CD / Sep '95 / Nova Zembla

☐ NATURAL BORN TECHNO VOL.3

NZ 052CD / Feb '96 / Nova Zembla

☐ NATURAL BORN TECHNO VOL.4

NZ 070CD / Sep '96 / Nova Zembla

☐ NATURAL BORN TECHNO VOL.5

NZ 079CD / Apr '97 / Nova Zembla

☐ NATURAL BORN TECHNO VOL.6

NZ 080CD / Apr '97 / Nova Zembla

☐ NATURAL BORN TECHNO VOL.7

NZ 091 / 1 Dec '97 / Nova Zembla

☐ NATURAL REGGAE HITS

Money in my pocket: Brown, Dennis / Smoke gets in your eyes: Blue Haze / I shot the sheriff: Inner Circle / Cherry oh baby: Donaldson, Eric / Snoopy Vs the Red Baron: Hot Shots / Stop the train: Tosh, Peter / Girl is mine: Yellowman & Peter Metro / Israelites: Dekker, Desmond / Help me make it through the night: Holt, John / Vietnam: Cliff, Jimmy / Young, gifted and black: Bob & Marcia / Double barrel: Barker, Dave & Ansell Collins / Lip town top rankin: Althia & Donna / Norwegian wood disco: Ska Boys / Hot, hot, hot: Arrow / Kingston Kingston: Lou & The Hollywood Bananas

12700 / Apr '96 / Laserlight

☐ NATURAL WOMAN VOL.1

No more I love you's: Lennox, Annie / Oh baby I: Eternal / Breathe again: Braxton, Toni / All woman: Stansfield, Lisa / Independent love song: Scarlet / I'll find you: Gayle, Michelle / Right here: SWV / (Take a little) piece of my heart: Franklin, Erma / Anything for you: Estefan, Gloria / (You make me feel like) a natural woman: Franklin, Aretha / Power of love: Rush, Jennifer / Show me heaven: McKee, Maria / Almaz: Crawford, Randy / (Try to remember) the way we were: Knight, Gladys & The Pips / Move closer: Nelson, Phyllis / Heartbreaker: Warwick, Dionne / Slow hand: Pointer Sisters / Patience of angels: Reader, Eddi / Days: MacColl, Kirsty / Wuthering heights: Bush, Kate

RADCD 14 / Jul '95 / Global TV

☐ NATURAL WOMAN VOL.2

I will survive: Savage, Chantay / No ordinary love: Sade / What's love got to do with it: Turner, Tina / When you tell me that I love you: Turner, Tina / When you tell me you love me: Ross, Diana / Why: Lennox, Annie / Dreams: Gabrielle / Stay: Eternal / All around the world: Stansfield, Lisa / Sweetness: Gayle, Michelle / Get here: Adams, Oleta / Sleeping satellite: Archer, Tasmin / My one temptation: Paris, Mica / It's too late: Quartz & Dina Carroll / Can't stay away from you: Estefan, Gloria / Another sad love song: Braxton, Toni / Holding on: Craven, Beverley / Walking in Memphis: Cher / Rush rush: Abdul, Paula / Save the best for last: Williams, Vanessa / Heaven is a place on earth: Carlisle, Belinda / I just want to make love to you: James, Etta / Time after time: Lauper, Cyndi / Feel so high: Des'ree / You don't love me (no no no): Penn, Dawn / I say a little prayer: Franklin, Aretha / I'm still waiting: Ross, Diana / Best thing that ever happened to me: Knight, Gladys & The Pips / One day I'll fly away: Crawford, Randy / Wishing on a star: Rose Royce / If you're looking for a way out: Odyssey / I'm every woman: Khan, Chaka / No more the fool: Brooks, Elkie / I will always love you: Parton, Dolly / Crazy: Cline, Patsy / At seventeen: Ian, Janis / You're so vain: Simon, Carly / (You make me feel) like a natural woman: King, Carole

RADCD 28 / Mar '96 / Global TV

☐ NATURALLY STONED

MILL 053CD / 1 Dec '97 / Millenium

☐ NATURE ONE (2CD Set)

M&GCD 0102 / 20 Mar '98 / Waterworld

☐ NATURE ONE WATERWORLD VOL.4 (2CD Set)

SPV 08940402 / Nov '97 / SPV

☐ NATURES MORTES

Mr. Clarinet: Birthday Party / Let's have a party: Psychotik Tanks / Feedback song: Rema Rema / Die laughing: In Camera / Rose garden funeral of sores: Bauhaus / You and I: Mass / Like this for ages: Cupol / Gathering dust: Modern English / Marble station: Sort Sol / Controversial subject: The The / Raindance: Past seven days / Re: Dif Juz / Sargaso sea: CVO / So many others: Past seven days / Misguided: Sort Sol / Malignant love: Last Dance / Black and white: The The

CAD 117CD / 1 Dec '97 / 4AD

☐ NAVAJO SONGS FROM CANYON DE CHELLY

804062 / Aug '92 / New World

☐ NAVRANG CHUNDADI

NRCD 3002 / Feb '98 / Navras

☐ NBA - A MUSICAL CELEBERATION

5343232 / Jan '97 / Mercury

☐ NBC'S CHAMBER MUSIC SOCIETY OF LOWER BASIN STREET

HQCD 60 / Jun '96 / Harlequin

☐ NEAT METAL

NM 005CD / Oct '97 / Neat Metal

☐ NEED A SHOT (Essential Recordings Of Urban Blues)

Sail on little girl, sail on: Bumble Bee Slim / Policy wheel blues: Arnold, Kokomo / Trouble in mind: White, Georgia / Bad luck man: Harlem Hamfats / Louise Louise blues: Temple, Johnny / Working man (doing the best I can): Wheatstraw, Peetie / Think you need a shot: Davis, Walter / New little pretty Mama: Gaither, Bill / Night time is the right time: Sykes, Roosevelt / Lonesome bedroom blues: Jones, Curtis / Back door: Washboard Sam / Way down in Louisiana: Weldon, Casey Bill / Want to woogie some more: Johnson, Merline / What is that she got: Broonzy, 'Big' Bill / Lonesome shack blues: Memphis Minnie / Baby take a chance with me: Tampa Red / Key to the highway: Gillum, Bill 'Jazz' / Beer drinking woman: Memphis Slim / County jail blues: Big Maceo / Goin' down slow: St. Louis Jimmy / He's a jelly roll baker: Johnson, Lonnie / Ain't no business we can do: Clayton, Dr. Peter / Big time Mama: Dupree, 'Champion' Jack / New early in the morning: Williamson, Sonny Boy

IGOCD 2040 / May '97 / Indigo

☐ NEGRO CHOIRS 1926-1930

DOCD 5566 / 21 Sep '97 / Document

☐ NEGRO RELIGIOUS FIELD RECORDINGS 1944-46

DOCD 5312 / Dec '94 / Document

☐ NERVOUS SYSTEMS

CDSTUMM 41 / Sep '92 / Mute

☐ NETWORK COLLECTION, THE (4CD Set)

CDBNTW 1 / 30 Mar '98 / Passion

☐ NEU KONSERVATIV

DSA 54046 / Dec '96 / CDSA

☐ NEVER KEPT A DIARY

MC 001 / 23 Feb '98 / Motor Coat

☐ NEVER MIND THE BOLLOCKS 1994

AA 022 / Jul '97 / AA

☐ NEVER MIND THE MOLLUSCS

SPCD 84/255 / Mar '93 / Sub Pop

☐ NEW ACOUSTIC MUSIC

RCD 20002 / May '96 / Rykodisc

☐ NEW ALTERNATIVES VOL.2

NIGHTCD 005 / Sep '96 / Nightbreed

☐ NEW ALTERNATIVES VOL.3 (March Of The Angel Children/2CD Set)

NIGHTCD 009 / Apr '96 / Nightbreed

☐ NEW ALTERNATIVES VOL.4 (2CD Set)

NIGHTCD 020 / 13 Apr '98 / Nightbreed

☐ NEW BEATS OF JAZZ, THE

CDTEP 10 / Jul '97 / Step 2

☐ NEW BLUEBLOODS

ALCD 7707 / Aug '92 / Alligator

☐ NEW BLUES CLASSICS

BBAN 14CD / Aug '94 / Bullseye Blues

☐ NEW BORN BLUE

33WM 101 / Oct '94 / 33 Jazz

☐ NEW BREED

RR 87752 / 3 Nov '97 / Roadrunner

☐ NEW BREED OF DUB, A
Strickley roots: Truth / Astral flame: Disciples / Heavy dub: Dub Specialists / Firing dub: Bush Chemists / Over the rainbow: East Meets West / Conflict: Dub Ghecko / Meditation rock: Dan, Jonah / Take heed: Armagideon / 007 Dub: Dubplate Vibe Crew / Brain damage: Iration Steppas / Tokyo dub: Hi-Tech Roots Dynamics / Hot stepper dub: King General / Right from wrong: Dub Specialists / Falasha dub: Jah Warrior / Dub outernational: East Meets West / Talking dubheadz: All Nation Rockers
DBHD 001CD / Apr '97 / Dubhead

☐ NEW BREED OF RAVERS, A
FORMCD 1 / Nov '93 / Formation

☐ NEW BREED VOL.2, THE
GI 0032 / Mar '97 / GI Productions

☐ NEW BREED VOL.3, THE
GI 0082 / Mar '97 / GI Productions

☐ NEW CLASSICS VOL.1
HYP 39101902CD / 13 Apr '98 / Hyperium

☐ NEW COUNTRY LINE DANCING
Line dancin' days / Goin' country / There you go / EJ's Bar / Burnin' fire / Country music hall of fame / This don't feel like dancin' / No honky tonks in heaven / Too easy / Good times come around / Love my car / Love kept's a hold on my heart / I learn't a thing or two / Ain't life wonderful / Louisiana / Daddy's got his blue jeans on / Time loser / Situation vacant / Country married rock n roll / Let's hear it for the ladies
CD 6072 / Apr '97 / Music

☐ NEW ELECTRIC MUSE VOL.1 (The Story Of Folk Into Rock/3CD Set)
ESBCD 416 / Aug '96 / Essential

☐ NEW ELECTRIC MUSE VOL.2 (The Continuing Story Of Folk Into Rock/ 3CD Set)
King Arthur's servants: Watersons / Agincourt carol: Young Tradition / Bring us in good ale: Young Tradition / Trotto/Saltarello: Renbourn, John / King: Steeleye Span / Hal-an-Tow: Collins, Shirley & The Albion Country Band / Staines Morris: Morris On / Pastime with good company: Gryphon / England be glad: City Waites / Beginning of the world: Kirkpatrick, John & Ashley Hutchings / One-eyed merchant: Pegg, Bob / Carthy's march: Swarbrick, Dave / Four tunes from Terpsichore 1612: Albion Band / Gower wassail: Steeleye Span / Boadicea: Swarbrick, Dave / Jolly bold robber: Brass Monkey / Personent hodie: Albion Band / Medley of four Morris tunes: Kirkpatrick, John / Lovely Joan: McShee, Jacqui / Corbies: Steeleye Span / Annan water: Rusby, Kate / North country maid: Watersons / Lark in the morning: Johnstons / I loved a lass: Pentangle / Lovely on the water: Steeleye Span / Sullivan's John: Briggs, Anne / Bonny May: Tabor, June / Flandyke shore: Jones, Nic / Wishing/The victor's return/The gravel walk: Swarbrick, Dave / Old Grenadier: Brass Monkey / Wonder - The Ridotta Rock: Cock 'n' Bull Band / Radstock jig: Home Service / Galopede: Oyster Band / Byker Hill: Barely Works / 'S Muladach mi/Sad am I and lonely: Mouth Music / Tammienorrie: Shooglenifty / Flower of Magherallyo: Oige / Three reels: Burach / Card song/ Shuffle the pack: Fairport Convention / Thirty foot trailer: Watersons / Dirty old town: Campbell, Ian Folk Group / Tunnel tigers: Johnstons / Go by brooks: Sweeney's Men / Look over the hill and far away: Humblebums / Who knows where the time goes: Fairport Convention / Pond and the stream: Denny, Sandy & Fotheringay / Sally free and easy: Tawney, Cyril / Go your way: Briggs, Anne / When I get to the border: Thompson, Richard & Linda / Dimming of the day: Thompson, Richard & Linda / It's dark in here: Dransfield / I'm a dreamer: Thompson, Linda / Devonside: Thompson, Richard / Pain or paradise: Tabor, June & The Oyster Band / Moving the goalposts: Bragg, Billy / Granite years: Oyster Band / Bede weeps: Lowe, Jez / Sand in your shoes: McTell, Ralph / Hard times heart: Waterson, Norma / Dram for the singer: Pegg, Bob
ESBCD 517 / Aug '97 / Essential

☐ NEW ELECTRONIC GENERATION
CLP 9973 / Apr '97 / Cleopatra

☐ NEW ENGLAND TEEN SCENE VOL.1 1965-1968
AA 060 / Jul '97 / Arf Arf

☐ NEW ENGLAND TEEN SCENE VOL.2 1978-1992
AA 044 / Jul '97 / Arf Arf

☐ NEW FEELING, THE (An Anthology Of World Music)
131242 / May '96 / Celestial Harmonies

☐ NEW FRONTIERS
TMPCD 017 / Oct '95 / Temple

☐ NEW GROOVE, THE (The Blue Note Remix Project Vol.1)
Kofi: Byrd, Donald / Hummin': Adderley, Cannonball / Living for the city: Pointer, Noel / Listen here: Harris, Gene / Friends and strangers: Laws, Ronnie / Down here on the ground: Green, Grant / Summer song: Foster, Ronnie / Move your hand: Smith, Lonnie Liston / Sophisticated hippie: Silver, Horace / Montara: Hutcherson, Bobby / Mixed feelings (The new groove): Terrasson, Jacky / Kofi: Byrd, Donald / Mixed feelings: Terrasson, Jacky
CDP 8365942 / May '96 / Blue Note

☐ NEW HITS 1996 (2CD Set)
How deep is your love: Take That / Return of the mack: Morrison, Mark / Anything: 3T / I will survive: Savage, Chantay / Children: Miles, Robert / Firestarter: Prodigy / Hallo spaceboy: Bowie, David / Ooh ahh, just a little bit: Gina G / Cecilia: Suggs / Stepping stone: PJ & Duncan / Falling into you: Dion, Celine / Creep: TLC / 1,2,3,4 (sumpin' new): Coolio / One by one: Cher / Something so right: Lennox, Annie / Search for the hero: M-People / Missing: Everything But The Girl / Ready or not: Lightning Seeds / I just want to make love to you: James, Etta / Up on the roof: Robson & Jerome / Don't look back in anger: Oasis / Stupid girl: Garbage / Goldfinger: Ash / Charity: Skunk Anansie / Ladykillers: Lush / You and me song: Wannadies / Riverboat song: Ocean Colour Scene / Lump: Presidents Of The USA / No fronts: Dog Eat Dog / Cum on feel the noize: Oasis / Whole lotta love: Goldbug / Passion: Gat Decor / Be as one: Sasha & Maria / My life is in your hands: Meltdown / Landslide: Harmonix / Should I ever (fall in love): Nightcrawlers / Ready to go: Republica / If you wanna party: Molella & The Outhere Brothers / I wanna be a hippy: Technohead / Move move move (the red tribe): Manchester United FC
RADCD 36 / May '96 / Global TV

☐ NEW HITS 1997 (2CD Set)
Underwater love: Smoke City / Unbreak my heart: Braxton, Toni / Where do you go: No Mercy / Don't let go (love): En Vogue / Step by step: Houston, Whitney / Gotta be you: 3T / Fresh: Gina G / Do you know: Gayle, Michelle / Clementine: Owen, Mark / Fugee la: Fugees / Moan and groan: Morrison, Mark / Real thing: Stansfield, Lisa / If you ever: East 17 & Gabrielle / All by myself: Dion, Celine / Rotterdam: Beautiful South / Little wonder: Bowie, David / Consideration: Reef / Australia: Manic Street Preachers / Sugar coated iceberg: Lightning Seeds / Govinda: Kula Shaker / Fired up: Funky Green Dogs / Encore une fois: Sash / You got the love: Source & Candi Staton / Professional widow: Amos, Tori / Ready or not: Course / Remember me: Blueboy / Ain't talkin' 'bout dub: Apollo 440 / Ready to go: Republica / Let me clear my throat: DJ Kool / DISCO: N-Trance / Natural: Andre, Peter / Quit playing games: Backstreet Boys / Day we found love: 911 / Let me in: OTT / It's over: Clock / Pony: Ginuwine / Everytime I close my eyes: Babyface / Cold rock a party: MC Lyte / Love guaranteed: Damage / You might need somebody: Ama, Shola
RADCD 67 / Apr '97 / Global TV

☐ NEW HITS 1998 (2CD Set)
It's like that: Run DMC & Jason Nevins / Brimful of Asha: Cornershop / When the lights go out: Five / Get jiggin' with it: Smith, Will / Cleopatra's theme: Cleopatra / Be alone no more: Another Level / Barbie girl: Aqua / I know where it's at: All Saints / Show me love: Robyn / Spice up your life: Spice Girls / All I have to give: Backstreet Boys / Uh la la la: Alexia / Alane: Wes / Your love gets sweeter: Quaye, Finley / No no no: Destiny's Child / Ain't that just the way: McNeal, Lutricia / Much love: Ama, Shola / All night all right: Andre, Peter & Warren G / Story of love: OTT / Everything she wants: Wham / Big mistake: Imbruglia, Natalie / All around the world: Oasis / Murder and Scully: Catatonia / Avenging angels: Space / Nany in Manhattan: Lilys / High times: Jamiroquai / Raincloud: Dion, Celine / Angel Street: M-People / So good: Roberts, Julie / Hideaway: De'Lacy / Rude boy rock: Lionrock / All about the Benjamins: Puff Daddy / Holler: Ginuwine / Feel so good: Mase / Wishin' on a star: Jay-Z / Disremembrance: Minogue, Dannii / Breathe: Minogue, Kylie / 5678: Stepz / Everlasting love: Cast From Casualty
MOODCD 57 / 23 Mar '98 / Sony TV

☐ NEW JAZZ SPECTRUM VOL.1
Rip a dip: Latin Jazz Quintet / Other side of town: Natural Essence / Things ain't right: Marrow, Esther / Cry: Dickerson, Walt / Modettle: Haynes, Roy / Web: Hawes, Hampton / Taste of honey: Andy & The Bey Sisters / Thang: Matthews, Ronnie / Eli's pork chop: Little Sonny / I've known rivers: Bartz, Gary / Alex the great: Mabern, Harold / Letha: Earland, Charles
CDBGPD 085 / Apr '94 / Beat Goes Public

☐ NEW JAZZ SPECTRUM VOL.2
Nairod: Riverside Jazz Band / One hand: Parker, Maynard / Our generation: Hines, Ernie / Favela: Papaya / Sad song: Williams, Joe / Mucho chupar: Axelrod, David / It's about time: Callier, Terry / Death and taxes: Dickerson, Walt / Song for Pharoah: Cuber, Ronnie / Memphis: Little Sonny / Higgins holler: Walton, Cedar / Everything counts: Axelrod, David
CDBGPD 091 / Oct '94 / Beat Goes Public

☐ NEW JAZZ SPECTRUM VOL.3
Fire eater: Bryant, Rusty / Afro Texas: Mbulu, Letta / No one can love: Cosby, Bill / Shortnin' bread: Three Pieces / Shirley's guanguancho: Aguabella, Francisco / Getting funky round here: Black Nasty / Love them from Spartacus: Lateef, Yusef / Senior boogaloo: Richardson, Wally / Nana: De Souza, Raul / Gibralter: Hubbard, Freddie / Mode: Sonny Red / Sentido-en-seis: Bellson, Louie & Walfredo De Los Reyes / When I die: Marrow, Esther
CDBGPD 095 / May '95 / Beat Goes Public

☐ NEW MOVES
CHILLCD 008 / May '96 / Chillout

☐ NEW MUSIC FROM CHINA - NINE HORSES
WER 62992 / Oct '96 / Wergo

☐ NEW MUSIC FROM MALI
Ka souma man: Sekouba Bambino Diabate / Konifale: Tangra, Kadja / Tchana diani: Traore, Lobi / Ouere: Koita, Dounanke / Faso: Bougouniere Diarrah Sanogo / Sabali: Les Soeurs Sidibe / Fengue: Bagayoga, Issa / Liberia: Diakite, Djenaba / Sinsinbo: Koita, Dounanke / Kulunba: Sidibe, Kagbe / Diarabi: Wassolon Fenin (The Cream Of Wassolon) / Hampate ba: Koita, Ami / N'na djanssama: Kante, Kerfala
CDEMC 3681 / May '94 / Hemisphere

☐ NEW ORLEANS - THE CRADLE OF JAZZ 1917-1946
Tiger rag: Original Dixieland Jazz Band / Ory's creole trombone: Kid Ory's Sunshine Orchestra / Dipper mouth blues: Oliver, Joe 'King' Creole Jazz Band / Tin roof blues: New Orleans Rhythm Kings / Pearls: Jelly Roll Morton / Play that thing: Powers, Ollie Harmony Syncopators / New Orleans wiggle: Piron, A.J. New Orleans Orchestra / Swing: De Droit, Johnny & His New Orleans Orchestra / I wonder where my easy rider's riding now: Bayersdorffer, Johnny & His Jazzola Novelty Orchestra / Stepping on the blues: Austin, Lovie & Her Blue Serenaders / Cake walking babies from home: Williams, Clarence Blue Five / Barataria: Halfway House Orchestra / Careless love: Original Tuxedo Jazz Orchestra / 29th and deadborn: Russell's hot six / Cornet chop suey: Armstrong, Louis & His Hot Five / Snag it: Oliver, Joe 'King' Creole Jazz Band / Gate mouth: New Orleans wanderers / Stock yard strut: Keppard, Freddie Jazz Cardinals / Black bottom stomp: Jelly Roll Morton's Red Hot Peppers / To-wa-bac-a-wa: Dumaine, Louis Jazzola Eight / Wild man blues: Dodds, Johnnie Black Bottom Stompers / As you like it: Celestin's Original Tuxedo Jazz Orchestra / That's a plenty: New Orleans Owls / Potato head blues: Armstrong, Louis & His Hot Seven / Wolverine blues: Jelly Roll Morton / Poutin' papa: Blythe, Jimmy Owls / Bogalousa strut: Morgan, Sam Jazz Band / Hotter than that: Armstrong, Louis & His Hot Five / Panama: Miller, Johnny New Orleans Frollickers / Apex blues: Noone, Jimmie Apex Club Orchestra / She's crying for me: Wynns Creole Jazz Band / Mama stayed out: Dominique, Natty / Old man rhythm: Parenti, Tony / Smoke house blues: Simeon, Omer / Astoria strut: Jones & Collins Astoria Hot Eight / Panama: Russell, Luis & His Orchestra / Tar paper stomp: Barbecue Joe & His Hot Dogs / I've found a new baby: New Orleans Feetwarmers / Way down yonder in New Orleans: Noone, Jimmie New Orleans Band / South Rampart Street Parade: Crosby, Bob & His Orchestra / Really the blues: Ladnier, Tommy Orchestra / High society: Jelly Roll Morton & His New Orleans Jazzmen / King porter stomp: Singleton, Zutty & His Orchestra / Coal cart blues: Armstrong, Louis / Canal street blues: Jones, Richard M. & His Jazzmen / Make me a pallet on the floor: Johnson, Bunk Street Paraders / Muskrat ramble: Miller, Eddie Orchestra / Buddy Bolden blues: Baby Dodds Trio
CDGR 1802 / Oct '97 / Charly

☐ NEW ORLEANS AND DIXIELAND
Polka dot stomp: Bechet, Sidney / Canal street blues: Armstrong, Louis / Blues for Jimmy: Ory, Kid / By and by: Dukes Of Dixieland / Wolverine blues: Condon, Eddie / Kansas city man blues: Bechet, Sidney / Savoy blues: Ory, Kid / Apex blues: Condon, Eddie / Spreading joy: Bechet, Sidney / Tin roof blues: Armstrong, Louis / Mahogany hall stomp: Ory, Kid / Tiger rag: Condon, Eddie
4878172 / 29 Sep '97 / Sony Jazz

☐ NEW ORLEANS BLUES 1923-1940
157612 / Feb '93 / Blues Collection

☐ NEW ORLEANS BLUES PARTY
No city like New Orleans: King, Earl / Something you got: Crawford, Davell / Daddy Daddy Daddy: Fran, Carol & Clarence Holliman / Whole lotta lovin': Professor Longhair / Swannee River Rock: Kazanoff, Mark & Snooks Eaglin / Coconut milk: Dollis, Bo & The Wild Magnolias / Woogie boogie: Porter, George Jr. / Can't straighten your mind: Garbo, Chuck / Oh sweetness: Eaglin, Snooks / Breakaway: Thomas, Irma
EDCD 7028 / Sep '97 / Easydisc

☐ NEW ORLEANS BRASS BANDS
When the saints go marching in / When the saints go marching in / All blues / My song / Down yonder / State of the blues / Auld lang syne / New second line / No, it ain't my fault / Mardi gras in new orleans / Night train / (meet) the flintstones
ROUCD 11562 / Mar '90 / Rounder

☐ NEW ORLEANS DIXIE
Storyville special / Storyville special / When you and I were young maggie / Frankie and johnny / Just a little while to stay here / Pancake rag / 1919 rag / Casey jones / Go down moses / Maryland, my maryland / Swanee river / Midnight in moscow / Just like in the old days / Bill bailey / CC rider / Don't beat about me / Scotch pine swing / Sometimes I feel like a motherless child
22505 / Aug '95 / Music

☐ NEW ORLEANS FUNCTION
CD 3560 / Jul '95 / Cameo

☐ NEW ORLEANS GOSPEL QUARTETS 1947-1956
HTCD 12 / Feb '94 / Heritage

☐ NEW ORLEANS HIT STORY, THE (Twenty Years Of Big Easy Hits 1950-1970)
CDGR 1402 / Apr '97 / Charly

☐ NEW ORLEANS IN THE TWENTIES
CBC 1014 / Jun '93 / Bellaphon

☐ NEW ORLEANS JAZZ
ARHCD 346 / Apr '95 / Arhoolie

☐ NEW ORLEANS JAZZ HERITAGE
8122711112 / Jul '93 / WEA

☐ NEW ORLEANS JAZZ PARTY
ZYX 550952 / 9 Feb '98 / ZYX

☐ NEW ORLEANS JAZZ SCENE OF THE 50'S
CDB 1208 / Apr '92 / Giants Of Jazz

☐ NEW ORLEANS JAZZ VOL.1
WJS 1001CD / Nov '93 / Wolf

☐ NEW ORLEANS JAZZ VOL.2 (1926-1951)
WJSCD 1002 / Jul '96 / Wolf

☐ NEW ORLEANS JOYS (2CD Set)
DCD 8001 / Jan '95 / Disky

☐ NEW ORLEANS LADIES
ROUCD 2078 / '88 / Rounder

☐ NEW ORLEANS TO CHICAGO - THE FORTIES
CJR 1002 / Nov '95 / Gannet

☐ NEW PURE MOODS (2CD Set)
Harry's Game: Clannad / Return to innocence: Enigma / Yeha noha: Sacred Spirit / Sweet lullaby: Deep Forest / Crockett's theme: Hammer, Jan / Oxygene IV: Jarre, Jean Michel / Adiemus: Adiemus / Tubular bells: Oldfield, Mike / Song for Guy: John, Elton / Heart asks pleasure first/The promise: Nyman, Michael / Chi mai: Morricone, Ennio / Theme from Inspector Morse: Pheloung, Barrington / Prelude: Yanni / Aria on air: McLaren, Malcolm / Lilly was here: Stewart, David A. & Candy Dulfer / Cavatina: Williams, John / Don't cry for me Argentina: Shadows / Albatross: Fleetwood Mac / Wild mountain thyme: Silencers / Children: Miles, Robert / Theme from X Files: DJ Dado / Cacharpaya: Incantation / Riverdance: Anderson, John Concert Orchestra / Play dead: Bjork & David Arnold / Protection: Massive Attack / Little fluffy clouds: Orb / Sun rising: Beloved / Ancient person of my heart: Divine Works / Sadness (part 1): Enigma / Only you: Praise / Cantus - song of tears: Adiemus / Theme from The Mission: Morricone, Ennio / Brideshead revisited: Burgon, Geoffrey / Pie Jesu: Pook, Jocelyn / Last Emperor: Byrne, David / Merry Christmas Mr. Lawrence: Sakamoto, Ryuichi / Another green world: Eno, Brian / Schindler's list: Little, Tasmin / Fire walk with me: Badalamenti, Angelo / Woodbrook: O'Suilleabhain, Micheal
VTDCD 158 / 10 Nov '97 / Virgin

☐ NEW REDS SAMPLER
NRAS 001CD / Feb '97 / New Red Archives

☐ NEW ROMANTICS
Chant no.1: Spandau Ballet / Girls on film: Duran Duran / Fascist groove thang: Heaven 17 / Quiet life: Japan / Lawnchairs: Our Daughters Wedding / African and white: China Crisis / Vienna: Ultravox / Model: Kraftwerk / Messages: OMD / Whip it: Devo / Empire State human: Human League / Head over heels: Illustrated Man / Underpass: Foxx, John / Is it a dream: Classix Nouveaux / After a fashion: Ure, Midge & Mick Karn
CDGOLD 1041 / Jul '96 / EMI Gold

☐ NEW SMOKING CLASSICS VOL.1
HYPOXIA 001CD / Sep '95 / Hypoxia

☐ NEW SOUL GROOVES (2CD Set)
No woman no cry: Fugees / C U when U get there: Coolio / Ocean drive: Lighthouse Family / Even after all: Quaye, Finley / My father's son: Reeves, Conner / Everything: Blige, Mary J. / Smokin' me out: Warren G / Virtual insanity: Jamiroquai / Don't leave me: Blackstreet / On and on: Badu, Erykah / Sentimental: Cox, Deborah / I will survive: Savage, Chantay / Pony: Ginuwine / Head over heels: Allure / GHETTOUT: Changing Faces / Anything: 3T / Moan and groan: Morrison, Mark / I believe I can fly: R Kelly / If you ever: East 17 & Gabrielle / Masterplan: Brown, Diana & Barrie K Sharpe / You are the universe: Brand New Heavies / Ain't that just the way: McNeal, Lutricia / Rain: Elliott, Missy / I'm going all the way: Sounds Of Blackness / Love to love: Damage / Shy guy: King, Diana / Forget me nots: Rushen, Patrice / 5 Miles to empty: Brownstone / Closer than close: Gaines, Rosie / Way I feel: Roachford / Don't look any futher: M-People / So many ways: Braxtons / We come to party: N-Tyce / Something about you: New Edition / Fly like an eagle: Seal / Escaping: Carroll, Dina / Feelin': Jodeci / Revival: Girault, Martine / I love your smile: Shanice / Her: Guy
TTVCD 2947 / 17 Nov '97 / Telstar TV

☐ NEW SPIRITS IN JAZZ VOL.1
EFA 015082 / 29 Sep '97 / World's Best

☐ NEW SPIRITS IN JAZZ VOL.2
EFA 015092 / 29 Sep '97 / World's Best

☐ NEW SPIRITS IN JAZZ VOL.3
EFA 015102 / 29 Sep '97 / World's Best

☐ NEW WAVE ARCHIVE
Golden brown: Stranglers / God save the queen: Sex Pistols / Nellie the elephant: Toy Dolls / Gary Gilmour's eyes: Adverts / If the kids are united: Sham 69 / Where have all the boot boys gone: Slaughter & The Dogs / Banana Splits: Dickies / Boredom: Buzzcocks / 12XU: Wire / Oh bondage up yours: X-Ray Spex / World war: UK Subs / Two pints of lager: Splodgenessabounds / New Rose: Damned / Personality crisis: New York Dolls / Babylon's burning: Boys / Do anything you wanna do: Eddie & The Hot Rods / Graveyard groove: Revillos / Jilted John: Jilted John / Seventeen: Jilted John
RMCD 201 / Nov '97 / Rialto

☐ NEW WAVE CLASSICS (2CD Set)
This is not a love song: Public Image Ltd. / Love like blood: Killing Joke / She blinded me with science: Dolby, Thomas / Christian: China Crisis / I ran: Flock Of Seagulls / Unbelievable: EMF / Trouble: Heaven 17 / Golden brown: Stranglers / War song: Culture Club / Reap the wild wind: Ultravox / And she was: Talking Heads / Really saying something: Fun Boy Three & Bananarama / On my radio: Selecter / No rest: New Model Army / Suedehead: Morrissey / Worker: Fischer Z / Wishing: Flock Of Seagulls / Vienna: Ultravox / Cloudbursting: Bush, Kate / Wunderbar: Tenpole Tudor / White wedding: Idol, Billy / Lucky number: Lovich, Lena / Psycho killer: Talking Heads / Black Man Ray: China Crisis / Penthouse and pavement: Heaven 17 / I am the beat: Look / Girls on film: Duran Duran / Hyperactive: Dolby, Thomas / Hans Von Stoffeln: Komtur / Hit me with your rhythm stick: Dury, Ian & The Blockheads
DOU 878282 / 2 Feb '98 / Disky

☐ NEW WAVE NEW DANGER (3CD Set)
DTKBOX 80 / 2 Mar '98 / Dressed To Kill

☐ NEW WAVE OF BRITISH HEAVY METAL COMPILATION
HMRXD 157 / Dec '90 / Heavy Metal

☐ NEW WAVE OF BRITISH HEAVY METAL LIVE, THE
Red skies: Samson / Driving with ZZ: Samson / Riding with angels: Samson / C'mon let's go: Girlschool / Emergency: Girlschool / Take it all away: Girlschool / White witch: Angel Witch / Angel of death: Angel Witch / Angel witch: Angel Witch / Echoes of a distant rattle: Tank / This means war: Tank / That's what dreams are made of: Tank
EMPRCD 714 / Jun '97 / Emporio

☐ NEW WAVE OF BRITISH HEAVY METAL RARITIES VOL.1

Hideaway: *Legend* / Heaven sent: *Legend* / Praying Mantis: *Praying Mantis* / High roller: *Praying Mantis* / Death and destiny: *Mythra* / Killer: *Mythra* / Overlord: *Mythra* / UFO: *Mythra* / Flying high: *Hollow Ground* / War lord: *Hollow Ground* / Rock on: *Hollow Ground* / Don't chase the dragon: *Hollow Ground* / Loser: *Angel Witch* / Suffer: *Angel Witch* / Dr. Phibes: *Angel Witch* / Mony Mony: *Gaskin* / Queen of flames: *Gaskin* / Strange place to be: *Heritage* / Misunderstood: *Heritage*

CDMETAL 2 / Feb '97 / British Steel

☐ NEW WAVE OF BRITISH HEAVY METAL RARITIES VOL.2

CDMETAL 7 / Feb '97 / British Steel

☐ NEW WAVE OF BRITISH HEAVY METAL RARITIES VOL.3

Take it all away: *Girlschool* / It could be better: *Girlschool* / I won't surrender: *Twisted Ace* / Firebird: *Twisted Ace* / Sheralee: *Soldier* / Force: *Soldier* / Back street women: *Jaguar* / Chasing the dragon: *Jaguar* / No way: *Denigh* / Running: *Denigh* / Voice on the line: *Static* / Stealin': *Static* / Metal to the moon: *Seventh son* / Sound and fury: *Seventh son* / This poison fountain: *White Lightning* / Hypocrite: *White Lightning* / I want your life: *Dragonslayer* / Satan is free: *Dragonslayer* / Broken hearts: *Dragonslayer*

CDMETAL 14 / Sep '97 / Anagram

☐ NEW YORK - THE JAZZ AGE (2CD Set)

DCD 8003 / Jan '95 / Disky

☐ NEW YORK DOWNTOWN

KFWCD 200 / Feb '97 / Knitting Factory

☐ NEW YORK JAZZ IN THE ROARING 20'S

BCD 129 / Jun '94 / Biograph

☐ NEW YORK LATIN

Tremendos cumban: *Machito & His Afro-Cubans* / Mambo of the times: *Cuba, Joe Sextet* / Bilongo: *La Plata Sextet* / Ja ja: *Ray, Ricardo & Bobby Cruz* / Caramelos: *Cruz, Celia* / Rumbambola: *Morales, Noro* / Timbalero: *Concepcion, Cesar* / Maquino landera: *Cortijo Y Su Combo* / Mortuno pa' caridad: *Cotto, Joe Y Su Orqesta* / Capullito de aleli: *Campo, Pupi* / Comer lechon: *La Sonora Matancera* / Ponte duro serafin: *Lopez, Johnny Y Su Super Combo* / Descargo combo NY: *Grand, Rene Y Su Super Combo New York* / Tomando soy feliz: *Caney, Rey* / Que buenas son las mujeres: *Valle, Joe Y Su Orquesta* / Caravan: *Puente, Tito* / Arroz con manteca: *Valdes, Miguelito* / Jingle bells: *Cruz, Celia* / Lullaby of Broadway: *Palmieri, Eddie* / Como fue: *Valdes, Vicentico*

CDHOT 615 / Jan '97 / Charly

☐ NEW YORK REALITY CHECK 101A

8289342 / 16 Mar '98 / London

☐ NEW YORK SALSA EXPLOSION

Te Traigo Guajira: *Barretto, Ray* / Ban Ban Quere: *Puente, Tito & His Orchestra* / A Santa Barbara: *Orquesta Broadway* / Vamonos Pa'l Monte: *Palmieri, Eddie* / La Malanga Brava: *Cuba, Joe Sextet* / Candido's Guajiro: *Candido* / Tin Marin: *Ray, Ricardo* / Arrecotin Arrecotan: *Cortijo Y Su Combo* / No quiero piedras en mi Camino: *Rivera, Ismael* / Por Primera Vez: *Sabater, Jimmy*

12907 / Feb '97 / Laserlight

☐ NEW YORK SCHOOL NO.3

ARTCD 6176 / Dec '95 / Hat Art

☐ NEW YORK SOUL SERENADE

I'm stepping out of the picture: *Maestro, Johnny & The Crests* / My arms aren't strong enough: *Clay, Judy* / Am I falling in love: *Brown, Maxine* / I'm gonna have a party: *Bruce, Ed* / Man who has everything: *Lewis, Junior* / Let's play house: *Drake, Tony* / If it's for real: *Porgy & The Monarchs* / Oh lord what are you doing to me: *Big Maybelle* / Don't believe him Donna: *Jackson, Chuck* / New neighbourhood: *Byers, Billy* / Welcome to dreamsville: *Ambrose, Sammy* / In my tenement: *Grier, Roosevelt* / Don't hear speak see no evil: *Platters* / You need me: *Little Charles & The Sidewinders* / Sugar (don't take away my candy): *Jive Five* / It won't hurt: *Gentlemen Four* / Not now but later: *Johnson, Walter* / No easy way down: *Jackson, Walter* / This empty place: *Tangeers* / Haven't got what it takes: *Clay, Judy* / Hurt: *North, Freddie* / See the big man cry: *Bruce, Ed* / False alarm: *Hunt, Tommy* / Who's gonna mention my name: *Sattin, Lonnie* / Would you still say I'm the one you love: *Crossen, Ray* / Little too lonely: *Knight, Marie* / (There goes) the forgotten man: *Radcliffe, Jimmy* / Soul serenade: *O'Dell, Brooks*

CDKEND 149 / 29 Sep '97 / Kent

☐ NEW YORK THRASH

EE 113CD / Nov '94 / ROIR

☐ NEW YORK UNDERCOVER

MCD 11549 / 23 Feb '98 / MCA

☐ NEW YORK VOL.2

DGF 11 / Jan '97 / Frog

☐ NEW YORK'S HARDEST

IJT 001 / Feb '97 / Idjit

☐ NEWPORT ALL STARS

Take the 'A' train / These foolish things / My Monday date / Body and soul / Mean to me / I surrender dear / Please don't talk about me when I'm gone / Pan Am blues

BLCD 760138 / Oct '90 / Black Lion

☐ NEWPORT BROADSIDE (Newport Folk Festival 1963)

Playboys and playgirls: *Dylan, Bob & Pete Seeger* / Willing conscript: *Paxton, Tom* / Ramblin' boy: *Paxton, Tom* / Talking atomic blues: *Hinton, Sam* / Come all ye gallant drivers: *Davenport, Bob* / Fighting for my rights: *Freedom Singers* / I love your dog, I love your dog: *Freedom Singers* / Get on board little children: *Freedom Singers* / I don't want your millions mister: *Garland, Jim* / Ballad of Harry Simms: *Garland, Jim* / Where did you come from: *McCurdy, Ed* / Ballad of Medgar Evers: *Ochs, Phil* / Talking Birmingham jam: *Ochs, Phil* / Coyote my little brother: *La Farge, Peter* / With God on our side: *Baez, Joan & Bob Dylan*

VCD 77003 / Oct '95 / Vanguard

☐ NEWPORT IN NEW YORK

Outside help: *King, B.B.* / Honky tonk train blues: *Glenn, Lloyd* / After hours: *Glenn, Lloyd* / Pinetop's boogie woogie: *Glenn, Lloyd* / Little red rooster: *Thornton, Willie Mae* / Ball and chain: *Thornton, Willie Mae* / Drifter: *Brown, Clarence 'Gatemouth'* / Long distance call: *Waters, Muddy* / Where's my woman / Got my mojo working

CDBM 071 / Apr '91 / Blue Moon

☐ NEWPORT JAZZ FESTIVAL

Sweet Georgia Brown: *Hall, Edmond* / Tin roof blues: *Kaminsky, Max* / Stars fell on Alabama: *McGarity, Lou* / I've found a new baby: *Freeman, Bud* / At the jazz band ball: *Chicago All Stars* / Isle of Capri: *Manone, Wingy* / Relaxin' at the Touro: *Spanier, Muggsy* / I wish I could shimmy like my sister Kate: *Brunis, George* / Royal Garden blues: *Spanier, Muggsy* / I'm in the mood for love: *Thomas, Joe* / Big noise from Winnetka: *Haggart, Bob* / Stealin' apples: *Hucko, Peanuts*

74321218292 / Nov '94 / RCA Victor

☐ NEWPORT JAZZ FESTIVAL ALL STARS

Exactly like you / Centennial blues / I didn't know about you / Nobody knows you (when you're down and out) / Rosetta / Smiles / Jeep is jumpin' / Mooche / Body and soul / Man I love / What's new / Struttin' with some barbecue / Moten swing

CCD 4260 / Dec '87 / Concord Jazz

☐ NEWS '98

HMC 100042 / Feb '98 / Happy Music

☐ NEXT GENERATION

TUT 727492 / Jan '94 / Wundertute

☐ NEXT GENERATION

SR 327CD / Jul '96 / Strictly Rhythm

☐ NEXT STEP ELECTRONICA, THE

AMB 60112 / Jul '97 / Instinct

☐ NEXT STOP (Dub Plate Pressure)

Haunted swing: *Squid Patrol* / To trap a spy: *Pimp Daddy Nash* / I'm on: *DJ BMF* / Spooks anonymous: *Squid Patrol* / Pressures: *13th Sign* / Lazy bomb: *Glamorous Hooligan* / Happytime: *13th Sign* / Outer nation: *12 From A Dozen* / Walk between the raindrops: *Pimp Daddy Nash* / Milkdud: *Soniq* / Moonweed: *13th Sign* / I say: *12 From A Dozen* / Joe dropped the swing: *Pimp Daddy Nash* / Stoned island estate: *Glamorous Hooligan* / Playing with fire: *Extravaganza* / Return of Mark Skids: *Duboniks* / Back in the day: *13th Sign* / Uptown cheese: *Gadgets*

KOBICD 005 / Apr '97 / Delancey Street

☐ NFL JAMS

Start / Way you make me feel: *Jones, Donell & Robert Brooks* / Stay with me: *Richie Rich & Esera Tualo* / Game day: *Phife & Rodney Hampton* / When the cheering stops: *AZ & Ray Buchanan/Scott Galbraith/Zhane* / Bayriders: *Celly Cell & William Floyd* / It's in the game: *Method Man & Ricky Watters* / No doubt: *Havoc & Tyrone Wheatley* / Heads get split: *Channel Live & Corey Harris* / Gotcha looking: *Pharcyde & Raghib 'Rocket' Ismail* / End zone / Fast life: *Ghostface Killah & Andre Rison* / Celebration: *Flip & Lamont 'Law' Warren* / Score

CATCD 101 / Mar '97 / Castle/Pinnacle

☐ NICE AN' RUFF

Sun is shining: *Black Uhuru* / No, no, no: *White, K.C.* / Village of the under priviliged: *Isaacs, Gregory* / Things in life: *Brown, Dennis* / Y mas gan: *Abyssinians* / Bongo red: *Griffiths, Albert & The Gladiators* / Capture rasta: *Culture* / Set de prisoners free: *Mutabaruka* / Dub organizer: *Pablo, Augustus* / Maggie breast: *I-Roy* / Kingston town: *Lord Creator* / Swing and dine: *Melodians* / Love is overdue: *Isaacs, Gregory* / Woman is like a shadow: *Meditations* / Girl I love you: *Andy, Horace* / Good thing going: *Minott, Sugar* / Baltimore: *Tamlins* / Triplet: *Sly & Robbie*

MCCD 092 / Dec '92 / Music Club

☐ NICE UP DANCEE

RCD 20202 / Aug '91 / Hannibal

☐ NIGHT AND DAY

CDHD 187 / '93 / Happy Days

☐ NIGHT AND DAY (2CD Set)

GRP 298662 / Mar '97 / GRP

☐ NIGHT AND DAY

HOMCD 45508 / 24 Mar '98 / Higher Octave

☐ NIGHT AT RONNIE SCOTT'S VOL.1 & 2, A (2CD Set)

Donna Lee: *Sandoval, Arturo* / White caps: *Scott, Ronnie Quintet* / Medley: *Montgomery, Marian* / Falling grace: *Whitehead, Tim* / La Pastora: *Irakere* / Luminous: *Freeman, Chico & Arthur Blythe* / Early Autumn: *Vaughan, Sarah* / Spring is here: *Taylor, John Trio* / Siorra: *Coleman, George* / Sleep late Louie's: *White, Tam Band* / You send me: *Ayers, Roy* / I'm beginning to see the light: *Sharpe, Jack Big Band* / Visiting: *Toussaint, Jean* / Time one: *Fourth World* / My foolish heart: *Delmar, Elaine* / Coming home baby: *Breaux, Zachary* / Hot: *Ayers, Roy* / My love: *Sandoval, Arturo* / Lo que va a pasar: *Irakere* / Serenade to sweden: *Cohn, Al & The Jazz Seven* / Lover man: *Shaw, Ian* / Watching the traffic light change: *National Youth Jazz Orchestra*

NARDCD 001 / 31 Jul '98 / Ronnie Scott's Jazz House

☐ NIGHT AT RONNIE'S VOL.3, A

NARCD 3 / Apr '94 / Ronnie Scott's Jazz House

☐ NIGHT AT RONNIE'S VOL.4, A

NARCD 4 / Mar '95 / Ronnie Scott's Jazz House

☐ NIGHT AT RONNIE'S VOL.5, A

NARCD 5 / Oct '95 / Ronnie Scott's Jazz House

☐ NIGHT AT RONNIE'S VOL.6, A

Foggy day: *Vaughan, Sarah* / This can't be love: *Shaw, Ian* / Stardust: *Delmar, Elaine* / But not for me: *Montgomery, Marian* / You were marvellous, darling: *Howe, Jenny* / Raina da noite: *Purim, Flora* / Haunt me: *Morris, Sarah Jane* / Wild women: *Grimes, Carol* / Good morning heartache: *White, Tam* / It could happen to you: *Brown, Ruth* / Good times: *O'Malley, Tony* / Man I love: *Vaughan, Sarah*

NARCD 6 / Jun '96 / Ronnie Scott's Jazz House

☐ NIGHT AT RONNIE'S VOL.7, A (Brit Jazz)

Jelly mould blues: *Dankworth Generation Big Band* / This I dig of you: *Slater, Holly* / As catch can: *Panayi, Andy Quartet* / Stitch in time: *Kerr, Anthony Quartet* / Un Poco loco: *Melling, Steve Trio* / Playing to the moon: *Garland, Tim Quartet* / African market place: *Critchinson, John & Art Themen Quartet* / Getting on: *King, Peter Quartet* / Have you seen them cakes: *NYJO*

NARCD 7 / 26 May '98 / Ronnie Scott's Jazz House

☐ NIGHT AT THE EMPIRE, A

No no no: *Miller, Max & His Orchestra* / Littul Gel: *Warner, Jack & Joan Winters* / Nothin' else to do all day: *Long, Norman* / You gotta S-M-I-L-E to be H-A-Double-P-Y: *Henderson Twins* / Hawaiian gems: *Mendelssohn, Felix & His Hawaiian Serenaders* / When Dream about Hawaii: *Mendelssohn, Felix & His Hawaiian Serenaders* / Drifting and dreaming: *Mendelssohn, Felix & His Hawaiian Serenaders* / Aloma: *Mendelssohn, Felix* / After all that: *Western Brothers* / You must have been a beautiful baby: *Costa, Sam & Dorothy Carless* / When the steamboat whistle is blowing: *Gonella, Nat & His Georgians* / Two dresden dolls: *Gonella, Nat & His Georgians* / Ode of the fletcher: *Fletcher, Cyril* / Life begins again: *Flanagan & Allen* / I'm just wild about Harry: *Lipton, Celia* / I cried for you: *Lipton, Celia* / You made me love you: *Lipton, Celia* / Three times a day: *Wallace, Nellie* / To mother with love: *Roy, Harry & His Orchestra* / Even a crooner must eat: *Bacon, Max & His Orchestra* / Londone pride... and proud of it too: *Waters, Elsie & Doris* / Sweetest sweetheart: *Mesene, Jimmy* / George Elrick successes: *Elrick, George & His Band* / Music goes 'round and around: *Elrick, George & His Band* / Boo-hoo: *Elrick, George & His Band* / I'm nuts about screwy music: *Elrick, George & His Band* / He never slept a wink all night: *O'Shea, Tessie* / This is my day - gang show of 1939: *Reader, Ralph* / My honey's loving arms: *Oliver, Vic* / Love 'em and leave 'em alone: *King, Hetty & His Orchestra*

PASTCD 9759 / May '92 / Flapper

☐ NIGHT FEVER (2CD Set)

Boogie wonderland: *Earth, Wind & Fire* / Le freak: *Chic* / Lost in music: *Sister Sledge* / Love train: *O'Jays* / Boogie nights: *Heatwave* / Lady marmalade: *Labelle* / Car wash: *Rose Royce* / Celebration: *Kool & The Gang* / That's the way I like it: *KC & The Sunshine Band* / Harvest for the world: *Isley Brothers* / Love really hurts without you: *Ocean, Billy* / You to me are everything: *Real Thing* / When will I see you again: *Three Degrees* / Boogie oogie oogie: *Taste Of Honey* / Heaven must be missing an angel: *Tavares* / Love come down: *King, Evelyn 'Champagne'* / Baby don't change your mind: *Knight, Gladys & The Pips* / Rock your baby: *McCrae, George* / Young hearts run free: *Staton, Candi* / You're the first, the last, my everything: *White, Barry* / (You make me feel) mighty real: *Sylvester* / Oops up side your head: *Gap Band* / I can make you feel good: *Shalamar* / Ain't nobody: *Rufus & Chaka Khan* / Somebody else's guy: *Brown, Jocelyn* / Shaft: *Hayes, Isaac* / And the beat goes on: *Whispers* / Play that funky music: *Wild Cherry* / Best of my love: *Emotions* / Don't leave me this way: *Melvin, Harold* / Use it up and wear it out: *Odyssey* / Rock the boat: *Hues Corporation* / Jump (for my love): *Pointer Sisters* / Disco inferno: *Trammps* / You gave me love: *Crown Heights Affair* / Funkin' for Jamaica: *Browne, Tom* / Shame: *King, Evelyn 'Champagne'* / Family affair: *Sly & The Family Stone* / Blame it on the boogie: *Jacksons* / YMCA: *Village People*

RADCD 24 / Oct '95 / Global TV

☐ NIGHT FEVER

Grease / You're the one that I want / Summer nights / Rasputin / Gimme, gimme, gimme (a man after midnight) / When you're in love with a beautiful woman / Rose garden / Is this the way to Amarillo / At the Copacabana / Bright eyes / We don't talk anymore / It's raining again / Words / Heartbreaker / Video killed the radio star / You're the greatest lover / Lily the pink / Winchester Cathedral / Long live love / Where did our love go / Baby I'm a want you / Summer night city / Stayin' alive / Night fever

CD 6026 / Jun '96 / Music

☐ NIGHT IN HAVANA, A

CDHOT 617 / Mar '97 / Charly

☐ NIGHT MOVES

DBG 53036 / Apr '95 / Double Gold

☐ NIGHT MOVES IN JAZZ

Amandla: *Davis, Miles* / Naima: *Coltrane, John* / B minor waltz: *Evans, Bill* / Lorelei's lament: *Crawford, Hank* / Everything happens to me: *Sullivan, Ira* / Nubian lady: *Lateef, Yusef* / Misty: *Hubbard, Freddie* / Embraceable you: *Farmer, Art & Jim Hall* / Body and soul: *Joseph, Julian* / I'll be seeing you: *Fruscella, Tony* / You go to my head: *Tristano, Lennie* / Summertime: *Mann, Herbie*

9548326342 / Mar '94 / East West

☐ NIGHT MOVES VOL.2

MOCD 002 / May '96 / Da Boops

☐ NIGHT OF THE LIVING PUSSIES

Please don't touch me: *Meteors* / Casting my spell: *Blue Cats* / No more no more no more: *Sergeant Fury* / Street wise: *Guana Batz* / I go wild: *Restless* / Lunatics (are raving): *Frantic Flintstones* / Mad mad bad bad Mama: *Empress Of Fur* / Charlie: *Sharks* / Nothing left but the bones: *Long Tall Texans* / Head on backwards: *Thee Phantom Creeps* / It's gone: *Quakes* / Rock on the moon: *Thee Waltons* / Brand new gun: *Frenzy* / Worms: *Hangmen* / Zulu Joe: *King Kurt* / Pink hearse: *Radium Cats* / Queen of disease: *Demented Are Go* / Throwing my baby out with the bath water: *McCavity's Cat*

CDMGRAM 79 / May '94 / Anagram

☐ NIGHTBUS (Electronic Beats And Breaks From London)

Mindeater: *OOYE* / Impact: *Parker* / Swallow the pill: *Dot UK* / Becks: *Sly Chew* / Borking: *Parker* / Shaka: *Aggressive Beggars* / Timpmove: *OOYE* / Dot 122: *Dot UK* / Last train: *Sly Chew* / Slow symbals: *Aggressive Beggars*

KOBICD 009 / 25 May '98 / Cooking Beats

☐ NIGHTIME ROUNDUP (Collection Of Contemporary Rock Songs From Texas)

TX 2006CD / Jan '94 / Taxim

☐ NIGHTLIFE ESSENTIALS VOL.1 (Mixed By Kenny Carpenter)

WRCD 1253 / 2 Feb '98 / Waako

☐ NIGHTLIFE ESSENTIALS VOL.2

WRCD 1256 / 30 Mar '98 / Waako

☐ NIGHTLIFE ESSENTIALS VOL.3 (New Millennium Mix)

WRCD 63 / 25 May '98 / Waako

☐ NIGHTMARE REMAINS IN THIS OTHER LAND, THE (2CD Set)

OVER 001CD / 17 Aug '98 / Overcome

☐ NIGHTS IN HEAVEN (The Party Anthems - 2CD Set)

It's raining men: *Weather Girls* / We are family: *Sister Sledge* / Your love still brings me to my knees: *Hines, Marcia* / Can you feel it: *Jacksons* / Got to be real: *Lynn, Cheryl* / Relight my fire: *Hartman, Dan* / You make me feel (mighty real): *Hartman, Dan* / Disco inferno: *Trammps* / Don't leave me this way: *Houston, Thelma* / Pilot error: *Mills, Stephanie* / This time I know it's for real: *Summer, Donna* / I want your sex: *Michael, George* / Small town boy: *Bronski Beat* / Could it be magic: *Take That* / Take a chance on me: *Erasure* / Venus: *Bananarama* / Relax: *Frankie Goes To Hollywood* / Only way is up: *Yazz* / What do I have to do: *Minogue, Kylie* / Everybody's free (to feel good): *Rozalla* / I love the nightlife: *Bridges, Alicia* / Supermodel: *Rupaul* / Hey now (girls just want to have fun): *Lauper, Cyndi* / Little bird: *Lennox, Annie* / Losing my mind: *Minnelli, Liza* / Stand by your man: *Wynette, Tammy*

SONYTV 3CD / Aug '95 / Sony TV

☐ NINGS OF DESIRE (The Best Fierce Panda Album In The World Probably)

NONGCD 01 / May '95 / Damaged Goods

☐ NINJA CUTS - FLEXISTENTIALISM (2CD Set)

Cosmic jam: *DJ Food* / Spiral: *DJ Food* / Sunvibes: *DJ Food* / Fungle jungle: *DJ Food* / Scratch your head: *DJ Food* / Consciousness: *DJ Food* / Ninja walk: *DJ Food* / Gentlemen: *DJ Food* / Venus: *Funki Porcini* / B Monkey: *Funki Porcini* / Mother (for your mind): *Herbaliser* / Scratchy noise: *Herbaliser* / Revolutionary woman: *Up Bustle & Out* / Aqui no ma: *Up Bustle & Out* / Ninja's principality: *Up Bustle & Out* / La morena: *Up Bustle & Out* / Atomic moog 2000: *Coldcut* / Shakatakadoodub: *Kruder & Dorfmeister* / Get your head down: *Vibert, Luke* / Junkies bad trip: *London Funk Allstars* / What's in the basket: *London Funk Allstars* / Extreme possibilities: *2 Player* / Do you believe in love: *Uschi* / London and mind state: *DJ Vadim* / Journeyman's electric lazyman: *9 Lazy 9* / Worm turns: *Illuminati Of Hedfuk* / Spoonful of slow: *9 Lazy 9*

ZENCD 022 / Mar '96 / Ninja Tune

☐ NINJA CUTS - FUNKUNGFUSION (2CD Set)

Sordid: *Amon Tobin* / Slipped disc: *Vibert, Luke* / Anger: *Sakamoto, Ryuichi* / Music for body lockers: *Chocolate Weasels* / It's just for you: *Herbaliser* / Clockwork: *Roots Manuva* / Carpel tunnel syndrome: *Kid Koala & Money Mark* / More beats and pieces: *Coldcut* / Emerald alley: *Up Bustle & Out* / No qualms: *Dynamic Syncopation* / Fish: *Mr. Scruff* / Vicious blooms: *Neotropic* / Humerous counterpoint: *Cabbageboy* / Burnt friedman and The Nu Dub Players: *Friedman, Burnt & The Nu Dub Players* / I wish I was a motown star: *Gilberto, Clifford Rhythm Combination* / Goatee vol.1: *Swinscoe, J.* / Surge: *Funki Porcini* / N3: *Irresistable Force* / Crow: *DJ Food* / Soluble ducks: *Animals On Wheels* / Mrs Chombee takes the plunge: *Herbaliser* / Get ready: *Silent Poets & Ursula Rucker* / Theme from the conquest of the irrational: *DJ Vadim* / Independent introduction: *Fink* / River of smack: *Funki Porcini* / Extua textua: *Omnium* / Kickin back: *Wild Palms* / Pac 3: Overide / Lie in king: *Irresistable Force* / Spy: *Journeyman*

ZENCD 033 / 27 Apr '98 / Ninja Tune

☐ NIRVANA (File Under Drum & Bass)

JSK 116 / Feb '97 / Jungle Sky

☐ NISAVA

CDEB 2565 / May '93 / Earthbeat

☐ NITE AT STRAWBERRY SUNDAE, A (2CD Set)

MILL 028CD / Sep '96 / Millenium

☐ NITEBEAT

XTR 15CD / Apr '95 / X-Treme

☐ NITEDANCIN' VOL.1
DFDCD 001 / Jun '95 / Defender

☐ NO CATEGORIES
UR 032 / 23 Mar '98 / Ubiquity

☐ NO COMPROMISE (2CD Set)
DELECCDD 055 / Nov '96 / Delerium

☐ NO EASY WALK TO FREEDOM
Bayeza: Soul Brothers / I'm in love with a rastaman: Mahlathini & The Mahotella Queens / Khoma khoma: Splash / Shebeleza: Mafela, Joe / Kangivumanga: Ladysmith Black Mambazo / Trouble in the night vigil: Chicco / Take it to Jah: Lucky Dube / Ithemba: Sister Phumi / Jive Soweto: Mabuse, Sipho / Mnolawe: Bayete / Don't ask why: Stimela / Sarafina / Now or never: Sankomota / Inkweru: Tananas
NSCD 034 / 15 Jun '98 / Nascente

☐ NO FEAR
VPCD 2067 / 24 Nov '97 / VP

☐ NO FREE RIDES BUDGET BLUES SAMPLER
JSPCDNFR 1 / Jul '95 / JSP

☐ NO FUTURE - THE SINGLES COLLECTION VOL.1
CDPUNK 11 / Mar '97 / Anagram

☐ NO FUTURE - THE SINGLES COLLECTION VOL.2
Someone's gonna die: Blitz / Police story: Partisans / Future must be ours: Blitzkrieg / Banned from the pubs: Peter & The Test Tube Babies / In Britain: Red Alert / Never surrender: Blitz / Today's generation: Attak / Lest we forget: Blitzkrieg / Gangland: Violators / El Salvador: Insane / I've got a gun: Channel 3 / Seventeen years of hell: Partisans / Take no prisoners: Red Alert / Dead hero: Samples / Run like hell: Peter & The Test Tube Babies / Warriors: Blitz / Murder in the subway: Attak / Keep on running: Crux / Summer of '81: Violators / City invasion: Red Alert / Day tripper: Wall / Megalomania: Blood / Wanna riot: ABH / Suffragette City: Rose Of Victory / Night creatures: Screaming Dead / Die with dignity: Violators / There's a guitar burning: Red Alert
CDPUNK 54 / May '95 / Anagram

☐ NO GREATER LOVE (2CD Set)
RADCD 34 / Jun '96 / Global TV

☐ NO JIVE (Authentic Southern Country Blues)
Things gonna change: Leap Frogs / Dirty britches: Leap Frogs / She was all I had: Dixie Doodlers / Best of friends: Dixie Doodlers / Wasted time: Shy Guy Douglas / I'm your country man: Shy Guy Douglas / Gotta have you baby: Campbell, Louis / Natural facts: Campbell, Louis / No place like home: Shy Guy Douglas / She's my kinda girl: Shy Guy Douglas / Welcome home baby: Hunt, Slim / She's mine all mine: Gunter, Arthur / You are doing me wrong: Gunter, Arthur / Honey babe: Gunter, Arthur / No jive: Little Al / Little lean woman: Little Al / Every day brings about a change: Little Al / Easy ridin' buggy: Little Al / Do remember: Garrett, Robert / Quit my drinkin': Garrett, Robert / Everybody drinkin' wine: Dowell, Chas & James Stewart / I've been jumpin' and stompin': Dowell, Chas & James Stewart / Ain't no need to cry: Good Rockin' Bob / I'm bad: Good Rockin' Bob
CDCHD 652 / Apr '97 / Ace

☐ NO LESS THAN WIRELESS
MWCD 2016 / Nov '95 / Music & Words

☐ NO MASTER'S VOICE
NMCD 4 / Feb '96 / No Master's Voice

☐ NO REGRETS (18 Soft Rock Love Songs)
Touched by your presence dear: Blondie / Love changes (everything): Climie Fisher / Missing you: Waite, John / Love walked in: Thunder / Rhythm of my heart: Runrig / Love is a battlefield: Benatar, Pat / French kissing in the USA: Harry, Deborah / Would I lie to you: Charles & Eddie / Love's great adventure: Ultravox / No regrets: Ure, Midge / Strange little girl: Stranglers / Only when you leave: Spandau Ballet / It should have been me: Adeva / C'est la vie: Nevil, Robbie / Kayleigh: Marillion / Power of love: Lewis, Huey & The News / Save a prayer: Duran Duran / When you walked in the room: Carrack, Paul
4954782 / 6 Jul '98 / EMI Gold

☐ NO REPETITIVE BEATS
NRB 58CD / Jan '95 / Six6

☐ NO SWEETER SOUND (2CD Set)
Rough and rocky road: Mello Tones / What are they doing in heaven: Mello Tones / Flying saucers: Mello Tones / When the pearly gates unfold: Mello Tones / Cool by the river banks: Mello Tones / Looking for that city called Heaven: Mello Tones / Run on for a long time: Landford, Bill & The Landfordaires / Touch me Jesus: Landford, Bill & The Landfordaires / You ain't got faith (until you got religion): Landford, Bill & The Landfordaires / Lord I've tried: Landford, Bill & The Landfordaires / Troubled, lord I'm troubled: Landford, Bill & The Landfordaires / Devil is no relation to me: Landford, Bill & The Landfordaires / Don't turn around: RSB Gospel Singers / Oh what a time: RSB Gospel Singers / Father I pray: RSB Gospel Singers / My Lord and I: RSB Gospel Singers / Inside the beautiful gate: RSB Gospel Singers / Just a little talk with Jesus: Deep South Boys / Holy ghost getting us ready: Deep South Boys / My soul is a witness: Deep South Boys / All the way: Sunset Jubilee Singers / Rasslin' Jacob: Sunset Jubilee Singers / Poor pilgrim of sorrow: Sunset Jubilee Singers / There'll be a jubilee: Sunset Jubilee Singers / Jesus is the searchlight: Bailey Gospel Singers / Journey to the sky: Bailey Gospel Singers / Count your blessings: Jackson Gospel Singers / Lord take care of me: Jackson Gospel Singers / Softly and tenderly (Jesus is calling): Jackson Gospel Singers / Sweet hour of prayer: Jackson Gospel Singers / I'm going through: Jackson Gospel Singers / Rock of ages: Jackson Gospel Singers / I know the Lord laid his hands on me: Pearly Gates Spiritual Singers / Not alone: Pearly Gates Spiritual Singers / Man called Jesus: Pearly Gates Spiritual Singers / Jesus at the well: Fields, Sister Myrtle / I'm toiling: Fields, Sister Myrtle
4875042 / 2 Mar '98 / Columbia

☐ NO TIME TO PANIC VOL.2
NOW 0897CD / Feb '97 / Panik

☐ NO.1 60'S ALBUM, THE (Ready Steady Go - 2CD Set)
54321: Manfred Mann / Glad all over: Clark, Dave Five / My generation: Who / Dancing in the street: Reeves, Martha & The Vandellas / For once in my life: Wonder, Stevie / You don't have to say you love me: Springfield, Dusty / You'll never walk alone: Gerry & The Pacemakers / Gimme some lovin': Gerry & The Pacemakers / Tired of waiting: Kinks / Baby love: Ross, Diana & The Supremes / Sun ain't gonna shine anymore: Walker Brothers / All or nothing: Small Faces / Wild thing: Troggs / There's a kind of hush: Herman's Hermits / Carrie anne: Hollies / Onion song: Gaye, Marvin & Tammi Terrell / Mr. Tambourine man: Byrds / Oh pretty woman: Orbison, Roy / I got you babe: Sonny & Cher / Respect: Franklin, Aretha / MY GIRL: Redding, Otis / House of the rising sun: Animals / Good vibrations: Beach Boys / Whiter shade of pale: Procol Harum / Papas got a brand new bag: Brown, James / Reach out I'll be there: Four Tops / Walk on by: Warwick, Dionne / Yeh yeh: Fame, Georgie & The Blue Flames / Shout: Lulu / Bend me shape me: Amen Corner / Jesamine: Casuals / Always something there to remind me: Shaw, Sandie / Twelfth of never: Richard, Cliff / Little bit of me little bit of you: Monkees / Blackberry way: Move / Groovin': Young Rascals / Catch the wind: Donovan / This old heart of mine: Isley Brothers / Will you love me tomorrow: Shirelles / Israelites: Dekker, Desmond / You've got your troubles: Fortunes / Concrete and clay: Unit 4+2 / Needles and pins: Searchers / Twenty four hours from Tulsa: Pitney, Gene / I will: Fury, Billy / I can't let Maggie go: Honeybus / It's my party: Gore, Lesley / Melting pot: Blue Mink / I've gotta get a message to you: Blue Mink
5539342 / 27 Oct '97 / PolyGram TV

☐ NO.1 70'S ALBUM, THE (2CD Set)
Take a chance on me: Abba / Hanging on the telephone: Blondie / Golden years: Bowie, David / Sultans of swing: Dire Straits / Cool for cats: Squeeze / Video killed the radio star: Buggles / Pop muzik: M / Milk and alcohol: Dr. Feelgood / Just what I needed: Cars / Is she really going out with him: Jackson, Joe / Guitar man: Bread & David Gates / Year of the cat: Stewart, Al / Don't go breaking my heart: John, Elton & Kiki Dee / So you win again: Hot Chocolate / Lost in music: Sister Sledge / I will survive: Gaynor, Gloria / I feel love: Summer, Donna / Boogie wonderland: Earth, Wind & Fire / Blame it on the boogie: Jacksons / Le freak: Chic / Candle in the wind: John, Elton / Perfect day: Reed, Lou / Man with the child in his eyes: Bush, Kate / Without you: Nilsson, Harry / All by myself: Carmen, Eric / Three times a lady: Commodores / You're so vain: Simon, Carly / Moonshadow: Cat Stevens / Maggie May: Stewart, Rod / All the young dudes: Mott The Hoople / Twentieth century boy: T-Rex / Spirit in the sky: Greenbaum, Norman / Free bird: Lynyrd Skynyrd / Boys are back in town: Thin Lizzy / Coz I love you: Slade / All right now: Free / School's out: Cooper, Alice / 10538 overture: ELO / Question: Moody Blues / Mull of Kintyre: McCartney, Paul & Wings
5550542 / 20 Oct '97 / PolyGram TV

☐ NO.1 70'S ROCK ALBUM, THE (2CD Set)
5257172 / Aug '95 / PolyGram TV

☐ NO.1 80'S ALBUM, THE (2CD Set)
5356832 / Jul '96 / PolyGram TV

☐ NO.1 ACOUSTIC ROCK ALBUM, THE (2CD Set)
How bizarre: OMC / Not the girl you think you are: Crowded House / More than words: Extreme / All I wanna do: Crow, Sheryl / Stay (I missed you): Loeb, Lisa / Nothing ever happens: Del Amitri / 74-75: Connells / Another cup of coffee: Mike & The Mechanics / Better man: Thunder / To be with you: Mr. Big / Ordinary world: Duran Duran / Cowboy dreams: Nail, Jimmy / Perfect: Fairground Attraction / Constant craving: Lang, k.d. / Martha's harbour: All About Eve / Daniel: John, Elton / Now and forever: Marx, Richard / Please be with me: Clapton, Eric / Big log: Plant, Robert / All I want is you: U2 / Wonderwall: Oasis / Wild wood: Weller, Paul / Walkaway: Cast / On and on: Longpigs / Fake plastic trees: Radiohead / Linger: Cranberries / (I'm gonna) cry myself blind: Primal Scream / There she goes: La's / Some people say: Terrorvision / You and me song: Wannadies / Becoming more like Alfie: Divine Comedy / From the bench at Belvidere: Boo Radleys / Brass in pocket: Pretenders / Psycho killer: Talking Heads / Driving away from home: It's Immaterial / Stuck in the middle with you: Stealer's Wheel / Days: MacColl, Kirsty / I don't wanna talk about it: Everything But The Girl / I was brought to my senses: Sting
5358142 / Sep '96 / PolyGram TV

☐ NO.1 ALL TIME CHRISTMAS ALBUM, THE (2CD Set)
5554032 / 1 Dec '97 / PolyGram TV

☐ NO.1 ALL TIME ROCK ALBUM (2CD Set)
5359542 / Oct '95 / Polydor

☐ NO.1 CHRISTMAS ALBUM (2CD Set)
Stay another day: East 17 / Do they know its Christmas: Band Aid / Pipes of peace: McCartney, Paul / Power of love: Frankie Goes To Hollywood / Fairy tale of New York: Pogues & Kirsty MacColl / Driving home for Christmas: Rea, Chris / Merry Xmas everybody: Slade / Lonely this Christmas: Mud / Another rock n' roll Christmas: Glitter, Gary / Mary's boy child: Boney M / Merry Christmas everybody: Stevens, Shakin' / Keeping the dream alive: Freiheit / Little drummer boy: Jackson, Michael/Jackson Five / Santa Claus is coming to town: Ross, Diana & The Supremes / Last Christmas: Whigfield / Silent night: O'Connor, Sinead / December will be magic again: Bush, Kate / I was born on Christmas day: St. Etienne / Rockin' around the Christmas tree: Mel & Kim / Last Christmas: Wham / Spaceman came travelling: De Burgh, Chris / I believe in Father Christmas: Lake, Greg / Winter's tale: Essex, David / When a child is born: Mathis, Johnny / Pretty paper: Orbison, Roy / Step into Christmas: John, Elton / Walking in the air: Shadows / Merry Christmas darling: Carpenters / Frosty the snowman: Jackson Five / Little St. Nick: Beach Boys / In dulci jubilo: Oldfield, Mike / Only you: Flying Pickets / Walking in the air: Jones, Aled / Mary's boy child: Free The Spirit / Stop the cavalry: Lewie, Jona / I wish it could be Christmas everyday: Wizzard / It may be winter outside: Love Unlimited Orchestra / Winter melody: Summer, Donna / Christmas wrapping: Waitresses / White Christmas: Crosby, Bing
5259782 / 1 Dec '97 / PolyGram TV

☐ NO.1 CLASSIC SOUL ALBUM, THE (2CD Set)
I heard it through the grapevine: Gaye, Marvin / I say a little prayer: Franklin, Aretha / (Sittin' on the) dock of the bay: Redding, Otis / My cherie amour: Wonder, Stevie / Let's stay together: Green, Al / Midnight train to Georgia: Knight, Gladys & The Pips / Tracks of my tears: Robinson, Smokey & The Miracles / Reach out, I'll be there: Four Tops / In the midnight hour: Pickett, Wilson / Dancing in the streets: Reeves, Martha / My guy: Wells, Mary / Soul sister brown sugar: Sam & Dave / I get the sweetest feeling: Wilson, Jackie / Soul city walk: Bell, Archie & The Drells / Piece of my heart: Franklin, Erma / This old heart of mine (is weak for you): Isley Brothers / Just my imagination: Temptations / Hey there lonely girl: Holman, Eddie / If you don't know me by now: Melvin, Harold / Ain't no sunshine: Jackson, Michael / Papa was a rollin' stone: Temptations / Papa's got a brand new bag: Brown, James / Ghetto child: Detroit Spinners / Love train: O'Jays / Nathan Jones: Supremes / Stop her on sight (SOS): Starr, Edwin / Ms. Grace: Tymes / Like sister and brother: Drifters / Family affair: Sly & The Family Stone / Didn't I (blow your mind this time): Delfonics / Homely girl: Chi-Lites / Gonna make you an offer you can't refuse: Helms, Jimmy / I'm still waiting: Ross, Diana / I'll be there: Jackson Five / What becomes of the broken hearted: Ruffin, Jimmy / Walk on by: Warwick, Dionne / Me and Mrs. Jones: Paul, Billy / I'm stone in love with you: Stylistics / Drift away: Gray, Dobie / Easy: Commodores
5256562 / Jan '96 / PolyGram TV

☐ NO.1 COUNTRY ALBUM, THE (2CD Set)
Leaving Las vegas: Crow, Sheryl / Crocodile shoes: Nail, Jimmy / Achy breaky heart: Cyrus, Billy Ray / Everybody's talkin': Nilsson, Harry / House of love: Grant, Amy & Vince Gill / Young at heart: Bluebells / Margaritaville: Buffett, Jimmy / Galveston: Campbell, Glen / It's not you: Dr. Hook / Thing called love: Cash, Johnny / Bargain store: Parton, Dolly / Always on my mind: Nelson, Willie / Talking in your sleep: Gayle, Crystal / You're my best friend: Williams, Don / I don't know why I love you: Pride, Charley / Crying: Orbison, Roy / Crazy: Cline, Patsy / Honey: Goldsboro, Bobby / It's only make believe: Twitty, Conway / I saw the light: Williams, Hank / Stand by your man: Wynette, Tammy / Rawhide: Laine, Frankie / King of the road: Miller, Roger / Peggy Sue got married: Holly, Buddy / Hello Mary Lou: Nelson, Rick / Okie from Muskogee: Haggard, Merle / Good ol' boys: Jennings, Waylon / Devil went down to Georgia: Daniels, Charlie Band / Take this job and shove it: Paycheck, Johnny / Convoy: McCall, C.W. / Guitar town: Earle, Steve / Love hurts: Parsons, Gram & Emmylou Harris / Anchorage: Shocked, Michelle / Take me home, country roads: Newton-John, Olivia / Shut up and kiss me: Carpenter, Mary-Chapin / New kid in town: Yearwood, Trisha / Forever and ever, Amen: Travis, Randy / Walking away a winner: Mattea, Kathy / Whose bed have your boots been under: Twain, Shania / Indian outlaw: McGraw, Tim / Independence day: McBride, Martina / Thousand miles from nowhere: Yoakam, Dwight / Past the point of rescue: Ketchum, Hal / Love can build a bridge: Judds
5357222 / Aug '96 / PolyGram TV

☐ NO.1 DANCE PARTY ALBUM, THE (2CD Set)
Encore une fois: Sash / Free: Ultra Nate / Freed from desire: Gala / Best love: Course / Don't give me your life: Alex Party / Boom boom boom: Outhere Brothers / Boom shake the room: DJ Jazzy Jeff & The Fresh Prince / Pump up the volume: MARRS / Sweets for my sweet: Lewis, C.J. / Two can play that game: Brown, Bobby / Things can only get better: D:Ream / Theme from S'Express: S'Express / I luv U baby: Original / Relight my fire: Take That / Saturday night: Whigfield / Ooh aah...just a little bit: Gina G / Guaglione: Prado, Perez / Macarena: Los Del Rio / Yodel in the canyon of love: Do Re Mi / 5,6,7,8: Steps / Flashdance: Cara, Irene / Ladies night: Kool & The Gang / We are family: Sister Sledge / Night to remember: Shalamar / Bad girls: Summer, Donna / It's raining men: Weather Girls / Only way is up: Yazz / Dancing Queen: Abba / Tainted love: Soft Cell / Relax: Frankie Goes To Hollywood / Dizzy: Reeves, Vic & Wonder Stuff / Come on Eileen: Dexy's Midnight Runners / Tiger feet: Mud / Rock 'n' roll (part 2): Glitter, Gary / Timewarp: Damian / Hillbilly rock, hillbilly roll: Woolpackers / YMCA: Village People / I'm too sexy: Right Said Fred / La bamba: Los Lobos / Don't leave me this way: Communards / Grease mega mix: Travolta, John & Olivia Newton John / I will survive: Gaynor, Gloria / Do ya think I'm sexy: N-Trance & Rod Stewart
5550572 / 10 Nov '97 / PolyGram TV

☐ NO.1 DANCEFLOOR HITS (4CD Set)
DAM 001 / Dec '96 / Tring

☐ NO.1 DRIVE ALBUM, THE (2CD Set)
Halo: Texas / Everyday is a winding road: Crow, Sheryl / You can go your own way: Rea, Chris / Elegantly wasted: INXS / What's the frequency Kenneth: REM / 2468 Motorway: Robinson, Tom / 20th Century boy: T-Rex / Love is the drug: Roxy Music / Cuddly toy: Roachford / Real gone kid: Deacon Blue / Changing man: Weller, Paul / Ready to go: Republica / Girl like you: Collins, Edwyn / Where I find my heaven: Gigolo Aunts / Hey jealousy: Gin Blossoms / Fine time: Cast / Alright: Supergrass / Staying out for the summer: Dodgy / Easy: Terrorvision / How soon is now: Smiths / It's only natural: Crowded House / What if: Lightning Seeds / Not where it's at: Del Amitri / 74-75: Connells / Over my shoulder: Mike & The Mechanics / Cars and girls: Prefab Sprout / Passenger: Iggy Pop / Road to nowhere: Talking Heads / Higher Love: Winwood, Steve / Best friends girl: Cars / Mr. Jones: Counting Crows / Run around: Blues Traveller / Gold: Stewart, John / Good morning Britain: Aztec Camera / How bizarre: OMC / Motortown: Kane Gang / Ocean drive: Lighthouse Family / Serch for the hero: M-People
5539402 / Aug '97 / PolyGram TV

☐ NO.1 HITS
Cocktails for two: Ellington, Duke Orchestra / In the blue of the evening: Dorsey, Tommy & His Orchestra/ Frank Sinatra / Elmer's tune: Miller, Glenn & His Orchestra / It's a sin to tell a lie: Waller, Fats & His Rhythm / Piano concerto in B flat (Tonight we love): Martin, Freddy & His Orchestra / Daddy: Kaye, Sammy Orchestra / Frenesi: Shaw, Artie Orchestra / Merry-go-round broke down: Fields, Shep & His Orchestra / And the angels sing: Goodman, Benny Orchestra / Our love: Dorsey, Tommy & His Orchestra / Heartaches: Weems, Ted & His Orchestra / Where was I: Barnet, Charlie Orchestra / Deep purple: Clinton, Larry & His Orchestra / Over the rainbow: Miller, Glenn Orchestra / They say: Shaw, Artie Orchestra / Symphony: Martin, Freddy & His Orchestra / Two sleepy people: Waller, Fats & His Orchestra / Old lamplighter: Kaye, Sammy Orchestra
74321584792 / Jun '98 / RCA Victor

☐ NO.1 JAZZ ALBUM, THE (2CD Set)
Feeling good: Simone, Nina / Take five: Brubeck, Dave / Manhattan: Fitzgerald, Ella / Girl from Ipanema: Getz, Stan / Milestones: Davis, Miles / Make yourself comfortable: Vaughan, Sarah / Night train: Peterson, Oscar / My funny valentine: Baker, Chet / Goin' out of my head: Montgomery, Wes / So what: Jordan, Ronny / Lily was here: Stewart, Dave & Cindy Duffer / Children of the ghetto: Pine, Courtney / Theme from 'Starsky and Hutch': Taylor, James Quartet / My baby just cares for me: Simone, Nina / Gurney slade: Harris, Max / Lullaby of Birdland: Shearing, George / Mad about the boy: Washington, Dinah / Stranger on the shore: Bilk, Acker / Birdland: Weather Report / Don't you worry 'bout a thing: Incognito / Bossa na praia: Gilberto, Astrud / Desafinado: Getz, Stan / Every time we say goodbye: Fitzgerald, Ella / Walk on the wild side: Smith, Jimmy / I put a spell on you: Simone, Nina / Misty: Garner, Erroll / Fine romance: Holiday, Billie / My ship: Vaughan, Sarah / Rockin' good way: Washington, Dinah & Brook Benton / House of bamboo: Grant, Earl / Everybody loves the sunshine: Ayers, Roy Ubiquity / That's the way love goes: Brown, Norman / Morning dance: Spyro Gyra / Walk on by: Benson, George / Summertime: Fitzgerald, Ella & Louis Armstrong / Unforgettable: Cole, Nat 'King'
5539372 / 1 Sep '97 / PolyGram TV

☐ NO.1 LINE DANCE ALBUM, THE (2CD Set)
5538582 / 22 Sep '97 / PolyGram TV

☐ NO.1 LOVE ALBUM VOL.1, THE (2CD Set)
5352622 / Jan '96 / PolyGram TV

☐ NO.1 LOVE ALBUM VOL.2, THE (2CD Set)
Morning: Wet Wet Wet / Father and son: Boyzone / Rotterdam: Beautiful South / Lifted: Lighthouse Family / Give me a little more time: Gabrielle / Make it with you: Let Loose / Someone to love: East 17 / Pray: Take That / Light of my life: Louise / Oh baby I: Eternal / Love 2 love: Damage / I'll never break your heart: Backstreet Boys / Like a woman: Rich, Tony / One for the money: Brown, Horace / Desire: Nu Colours / Save the best for last: Williams, Vanessa / I can't sleep baby (If I): Kelly, R / Let's get together: O'Neal, Alexander / Don't wanna lose you: Richie, Lionel / Sacrifice: John, Elton / One of us: Osbourne, Joan / In a lifetime: Clannad / Fall at your feet: Crowded House / Don't dream it's over: Young, Paul / Golden eye: Turner, Tina / No more I love you's: Lennox, Annie / Come undone: Duran Duran / Get here: Adams, Oleta / Heaven help my heart: Arena, Tina / Show me heaven: McKee, Maria / Stay: Shakespears Sister / She makes my day: Palmer, Robert / Paris match: Style Council / Something about you: Level 42 / What becomes of the broken hearted: Ruffin, Jimmy / Words: Bee Gees
5531412 / Nov '96 / PolyGram TV

☐ NO.1 MOTOWN ALBUM, THE (2CD Set)
I heard it through the grapevine: Gaye, Marvin / I just called to say I love you: Wonder, Stevie / Tracks of my tears: Robinson, Smokey & The Miracles / Easy: Commodores / Ben: Jackson, Michael / Help me make it through the night: Knight, Gladys & The Pips / Just my imagination (running away from me): Temptations / What becomes of the broken hearted: Ruffin, Jimmy / You are everything: Ross, Diana & Marvin Gaye / You're all I need to get by: Gaye, Marvin & Tammi Terrell / Endless love: Ross, Diana & Lionel Richie / I'm still waiting: Ross, Diana / Three times a lady: Commodores / Do you know where you're going to: Ross, Diana / Go to be there: Jackson, Michael / With you I'm born again: Preston, Billy & Syreeta / Let's get it on: Gaye, Marvin / Still water: Four Tops / Reflections: Ross, Diana & The Supremes / One for the money: Brown, Horace / Your love is a 187: Whitehead Brothers / I'll make love to you: Boyz II Men
5307642 / Jan '97 / Motown

☐ NO.1 PAN PIPE LOVE ALBUM VOL.1, THE (20 Beautiful Pan Pipe Arrangements)
Candle in the wind / Etenal flame / Nothing compares 2 U / China in your hand / Take my breath away / 2 become 1 / How deep is your love / Careless whisper / Without you / Think twice / Power of love / I will always love you / Unchained melody / Killing me softly with his song / One day in your life / I'm not in love / Woman / Lady in red / (Everything I do) I do it for you / Love is all around
ECD 3404 / 3 Nov '97 / K-Tel

☐ NO.1 PUNK ALBUM, THE (2CD Set)
5356582 / Jul '96 / PolyGram TV

☐ NO.1 RAP/HIP HOP ALBUM, THE (2CD Set)
California love: 2Pac / Do you see: Warren G / No: Chuck D / Jump around: House Of Pain / Danger: Blahzay Blahzay / Wopbobalubop: Funkdoobiest / Fight the power: Public Enemy / Television the drug of the nation: Disposable Heroes Of Hiphoprisy / Ince again: Tribe Called Quest / One shot: Brotherhood / Karmacoma: Massive Attack / I got 5

on it: Luniz / I must stand: Ice-T / Getto jam: Domino / I'll be around: Rappin' 4-Tay / Poison: Bel Biv Devoe / Got to keep on: Cookie Crew / Say no go: De La Soul / Eat my goal: Collapsed Lung / Teenage sensation: Credit To The Nation / Hey lover: LL Cool J & Boyz II Men / I will survive: Savage, Chantay / I wish: Skee Lo / Runnin': Pharcyde / Gangsta's paradise: Coolio & LV / Connected: Stereo MC's / Innocent: Addis Black Widow / What's goin down: Honky / Summertime: DJ Jazzy Jeff & The Fresh Prince / People everyday: Arrested Development / It's a shame (my sister): Monie Love & True Image / Buffalo stance: Cherry, Neneh / Why: Ricardo Da Force / Let's talk about sex: Salt n' Pepa / Tease me: Chaka Demus & Pliers / Get a life: Soul II Soul / Rain: Jones, Oran 'Juice' / Mr. Loverman: Shabba Ranks / Throw your hands up: LV / Board game: Collapsed Lung

5358112 / Oct '96 / PolyGram TV

☐ NO.1 REGGAE ALBUM, THE (2CD Set)

Bubblin' hot: Pato Banton & Ranking Roger / You're no good: Aswad / Love and devotion: Real McCoy / Don't turn around: Ace Of Base / Baby come back: Pato Banton / You don't love me (no no no): Penn, Dawn / Searching: China Black / Baby I love your way: Big Mountain / Sweets for my sweet: Lewis, C.J. / Tease me: Chaka Demus & Pliers / Housecall: Shabba Ranks & Maxi Priest / Jamaican in New York: Shinehead / Oh Carolina: Shaggy / Sweat (A la la la la long): Inner Circle / Mr. Loverman: Shabba Ranks / Hot hot hot: Arrow / Shout: Louchie Lou & Michie One / Compliments on your kiss: Red Dragon / Dark heart: Bomb The Bass / Boom shack-a-lack: Apache Indian / Close to you: Priest, Maxi / Swing low, sweet chariot: Ladysmith Black Mambazo & China Black / Keep on moving: Marley, Bob / Hurt so good: Cadogan, Susan / Now that we've found love: Third World / Silly games: Kay, Janet / Dub be good to me: Beats International & Lindy Layton / Good thing going: Minott, Sugar / I don't wanna dance: Grant, Eddy / I want to wake up with you: Gardiner, Boris / Israelites: Dekker, Desmond / I can see clearly now: Nash, Johnny / Double barrel: Barker, Dave & Ansell Collins / Young, gifted and black: Bob & Marcia / Uptown top ranking: Althia & Donna / Don't look back: Tosh, Peter / Love of the common people: Thomas, Nicky / Help me make it through the night: Holt, John / Liquidator: Johnson, Harry & The All-Stars / Wonderful world, beautiful people: Cliff, Jimmy

5256392 / Aug '95 / PolyGram TV

☐ NO.1 ROCK 'N' ROLL ALBUM, THE (2CD Set)

Jailhouse rock: Presley, Elvis / (We're gonna) rock around the clock: Haley, Bill & The Comets / Summertime blues: Cochran, Eddie / Great balls o fire: Lewis, Jerry Lee / Lucille: Little Richard / Johnny B Goode: Berry, Chuck / Wake up little Susie: Everly Brothers / Oh boy: Holly, Buddy & The Crickets / Chantilly lace: Big Bopper / Blueberry hill: Domino, Fats / Great pretender: Platters / Be bop alula: Vincent, Gene / At the top: Danny & The Juniors / Nut rocker: B. Bumble & The Stingers / Let's twist again: Checker, Chubby / Why do fools fall in love: Lymon, Frankie & The Teenagers / Happy Birthday sweet sixteen: Sedaka, Neil / Lipstick on your collar: Francis, Connie / Runaround sue: Dion / Move it: Richard, Cliff / Shake rattle and roll: Haley, Bill & The Comets / Blue suede shoes: Perkins, Carl / Bye byye love: Everly Brothers / La bamba: Valens, Ritchie / Heartbreak hotel: Presley, Elvis / Tutti frutti: Little Richard / No particular place to go: Berry, Chuck / Peggy Sue: Holly, Buddy / Claudette: Everly Brothers / Three steps to heaven: Cochran, Eddie / Poetry in motion: Tillotson, Johnny / AnDiana: Anka, Paul / Rubber ball: Vee, Bobby / Ain't that shame: Domino, Fats / Blue moon: Marcels / See you later alligator: Haley, Bill & The Comets / WILWillie and the hand jive: Otis, Johnny / That's right mama: Perkins, Carl / It's late: Nelson, Rick / Hat's off to Larry: Shannon, Del / Tell Laura I love her: Valance, Ricky / Smoke gets in your eyes: Platters / Sealed with a kiss: Hyland, Brian / Stay: Williams, Maurice & The Zodiacs / Runaway: Shannon, Del / Halfway to paradise: Fury, Billy / It's my party: Gore, Lesley / Book of love: Mudlarks / Sea cruise: Mudlarks / Whole lotta shakin' goin on: Lewis, Jerry Lee

5550172 / 29 Sep '97 / PolyGram TV

☐ NO.1 ROCK BALLADS, THE (2CD Set)

Always: Bon Jovi / I still haven't found what I'm looking for: U2 / China girl: Bowie, David / Believe: John, Elton / I found someone: Cher / Waiting for a girl like you: Foreigner / These dreams: Heart / Wonderful tonight: Clapton, Eric / More than words: Extreme / I'm easy: Faith No More / Only wanna be with you: Hootie & The Blowfish / Missing you: Waite, John / Wind of change: Scorpions / 29 Palms: Plant, Robert / Owner of a lonely heart: Yes / I drove all night: Lauper, Cyndi / I'd do anything for love (but I won't do that): Meat Loaf / Total eclipse of the heart: Tyler, Bonnie / Breakfast at Tiffany's: Deep Blue Something / One of us: Osbourne, Joan / It's only natural: Crowded House / Run baby run: Crow, Sheryl / Always the last to know: Del Amitri / You do something to me: Weller, Paul / Never tear us apart: INXS / It ain't over 'til it's over: INXS / I don't want a lover: Texas / Ode to my family: Cranberries / Perfect day: Reed, Lou / After midnight: Cale, J.J. / Highr love: Winwood, Steve / All out of love: Air Supply / Womankind: Little Angels / Black velvet: Myles, Alannah / Don't want to wait anymore: Tubes / Behind blue eyes: Who / Brothers in arms: Dire Straits

5359412 / Nov '96 / PolyGram TV

☐ NO.1 SAX ALBUM, THE (2CD Set)

I don't want to lose you: Turner, Tina / Jealous guy: Roxy Music / True: Spandau Ballet / Million love songs: Take That / Hands to heaven: Breathe / I wonder why: Stigers, Curtis / You're the best thing: Style Council / Beautiful girl: INXS / Will you: O'Connor, Hazel / Absolute beginners: Bowie, David / Imagination: Belouis Some / Baker Street: Rafferty, Gerry / Year of the cat: Stewart, Al / Lily was here: Stewart, David A. & Candy Dulfer / Walk on the wild side: Reed, Lou / Saxophone song: Bush, Kate / Cowboys and angels: Michael, George / Let's stick together: Ferry, Bryan / Heat is on: Frey, Glenn / Rip it up: Orange Juice / Whole of the moon: Waterboys / Unchain my heart: Cocker, Joe / Maneater: Hall & Oates / Rio: Duran Duran / Pretty in pink: Psychedelic Furs / Dancing in the moonlight: Thin Lizzy / Why did you do it: Stretch / Who can it be now: Men At Work / Rapture: Blondie / Embarrassment: Madness / Hit me with your rhythm stick: Dury, Ian & The Blockheads / Jackie Wilson said (I'm in heaven when you smile): Rowland, Kevin & Dexy's Midnight Runners / Pick up the pieces: Average White Band / Mustang Sally: Commitments / I got you (I feel good): Brown, James / How Gee: Black Machine

5358052 / Aug '96 / PolyGram TV

☐ NO.1 SKA ALBUM, THE (2CD Set)

One step beyond: Madness / Ghost town: Specials / Tears of a clown: Beat / On my radio: Selecter / Special brew: Bad Manners / Gangsters: Special AKA / Double barrell: Barker, Dave & Ansell Collins / Liquidator: Harry J All Stars / People do rocksteady: Bodysnatchers / Rat race: Specials / Return of django: Upsetters / Long shot kick de bucket: Upsetters / Israelites: Dekker, Desmond & The Aces / Missing words: Selecter / Message to you rudy: Specials / Carolina: Rico / Train to skaville: Ethiopians / Monkey spanner: Barker, Dave & Ansell Collins / Monkey man: Maytals / Red red wine: Tribe, Tony / Whisper: Selecter / Walking in sunshine: Bad Manners / Too much too young: Special AKA / Three minute hero: Selecter / Prince: Madness / Lip up fatty: Bad Manners / Ranking full stop: Beat / Nelson Mandela: Special AKA / I can see clearly now: Black, Pauline / Sea cruise: Rico / Selecter: Selecter / You can get it if you really want: Dekker, Desmond / Stereotype: Specials / Can can: Bad Manners / Mantovani: Swinging Cats / Ire feelings(skanga): Edwards, Rupie / I'm in the mood for ska: Lord Tanamo / James Bond: Selecter / Let your yeah be yeah: Pioneers / Sweet sensation: Melodians / Feelings gone: Apollinaires / Skinhead moonstomp: Symarip / 007: Dekker, Desmond / Do nothing: Specials

5534192 / Mar '97 / PolyGram TV

☐ NO.1 SOUL HITS OF THE 60'S VOL.1 (A Brand New Bag)

16112 / Oct '97 / Repeat

☐ NO.1 SOUL HITS OF THE 60'S VOL.2 (Tighten Up)

16102 / Oct '97 / Repeat

☐ NO.1 SOUL HITS OF THE 60'S VOL.3 (Tell It Like It Is)

16092 / Oct '97 / Repeat

☐ NO.1 SUMMER ALBUM, THE (2CD Set)

5356312 / Jul '96 / PolyGram TV

☐ NOBODY TO LOVE

Now that you know: Intruders / Wait 'till the summer: Illusions / Shades of blue: Shandells / There's a flower shop: Paradox / I'm free: Lovin' Kind / Cause of all man kind: Mike's Messengers / Nobody to love: Sonics Inc. / Fool turn round: Answers / Surface world: Jades / It couldn't be true: Twilights / She doesn't know: Viscount V / Abba: Paragons / Outside chance: Sounds Like Us / You better look now: Rogues / Have you for my own: Go Betweens / Please please go away: Answers / Tears from my eyes: Plague / Can't explain: Lovin' Kind

TS 6605CD / 20 Jul '98 / Teenage Shutdown

☐ NOCHE DE AMOUR

TUMICD 024 / '92 / Tumi

☐ NOCHES DE BUENOS AIRES - TANGO VIVO

9100112 / Dec '97 / Winter & Winter

☐ NOCTURNAL (2CD Set)

This corrosion: Sisters Of Mercy / Deliverence: Mission / She's in parties: Bauhaus / Rain: Cult / Moonchild (first seal): Fields Of The Nephilim / Shadow play: Joy Division / Motion of love: Gene Loves Jezebel / Cracking up: Jesus & Mary Chain / Fait accompli: Curve / Snake dance: March Violets / Sex dwarf: Soft Cell / Do you love me: Cave, Nick & The Bad Seeds / Talk about the weather: Red Lorry Yellow Lorry / Ball of confusion: Love & Rockets / I walk the line: Alien Sex Fiend / Kiss kiss bang bang: Specimen / Head like a hole: Nine Inch Nails / Pagan love song: Virgin Prunes / Bela Lugosi is dead: Bauhaus / Love like blood: Killing Joke / Love will tear us apart again: Joy Division / Pink orange red: Cocteau Twins / There is a light that never goes out: Smiths / People are strange: Echo & The Bunnymen / Walking in my shoes: Depeche Mode / Psychonaut: Fields Of The Nephilim / Wasteland: Mission / Day: Xymox / Martha's harbour: All About Eve / Jewel: Cranes / Arane: Dead Can Dance / Ghosts: Japan / Where the wild roses grow: Cave, Nick & Kylie Minogue / Big hollow man: Dax, Danielle / Release the bats: Birthday Party / Never understand: Jesus & Mary Chain

5559082 / 8 Jun '98 / PolyGram TV

☐ NOIR

VICTOCD 022 / Nov '94 / Victo

☐ NOISE ANNOYS

CRECD 171 / Nov '96 / Creation

☐ NOISE LEVEL CRITICAL

Turn me loose: Rock Goddess / Noise level critical: Tigertailz / Losing my grip: Samson / She gives it all: Six Ton Budgie / Sign of the hunted: Lyadrive / King of hearts: Egypt / Marionette: Triarchy / Lest we forget: Stormwitch / My heart is there: Legend / Invaders: Warrior / No stopping it now: No Quarter / No time to kill: Chinatown / Shock 'n' roll: Rhabstallion / Southern: Six Ton Budgie / Steal away the night: Lyadrive / Streets of the city: Rock Goddess / Vice versa: Samson / Love bomb baby: Tigertailz

307822 / Aug '97 / Hallmark

☐ NOISE REDUCTION VOL.2

Crescent cheek: Dijislov / Portadave: Dijislov / Throwing caution: Romance / Sprit: Tribes Of Neurot / Indians: Waterwheel / Windmill: Waterwheel / Cascade florade: Waterwheel / Tone cluster: Waterwheel / Before when we...: TV Pow / Everything: Resident Phase Shifter / Starliner: Solarus / Light: Final / Vessel: Otraslab / Supertrain: Otraslab / Ricardo: Otraslab

INVASO 022CD / 26 Jan '98 / Invisible

☐ NOISE VOL.3

Bass shake: Urban Shakedown / Smoke dis one: Bass Balistic / Caught with a spliff: Hackney Hardcore / Free your mind: Satin Storm / Don Gordon coming: Project One / Peace and loveism: Sonz Of A Loop Da Loop Era / Now hear this: Energy Zone / Up and running: Vocation / Back again: Run Tings / Star preacher: Space Brains / Space: Dionysus / Intensity: Freshtrax & Ace / Let's go: Hardware / What the world needs: Blatant & Dangerous / Out of it: Spirit Level / Bogey man: Happy & Free

CDTOT 8 / Jul '93 / Jumpin' & Pumpin'

☐ NON STOP 60'S PARTY (40 Swinging Favourites)

SUMCD 4042 / Nov '96 / Summit

☐ NON STOP CHRISTMAS PARTY

MCCDX 009 / Nov '94 / Music Club

☐ NON STOP CHRISTMAS TOP 20

Sleigh ride / Lily the pink / Have yourself a merry little Christmas / Jingle bells / White Christmas / Santa Claus is coming to town / We wish you a merry Christmas / Little drummer boy / Rudolph the red nosed reindeer / We wish the merriest / Winter wonderland / I saw Mommy kissing Santa Claus / Do you hear what I hear / Scarlet ribbons / All I want for Christmas (is my two front teeth) / Mary's boy child / First Noel / Hark the herald angels sing / Cokey cokey / Christmas song

SPGCD 8000 / Nov '95 / President

☐ NON STOP COUNTRY ALBUM (A Medley Of 58 Country Favourites)

SUMCD 4040 / Nov '96 / Summit

☐ NON STOP DANCE ANTHEMS (40 Tracks In The Mix - 2CD Set)

It's like that: Run DMC & Jason Nevins / Keep on jumpin': Lisa Marie Experience / La primavera: Sash / Children: Miles, Robert / Insomnia: Faithless / Passion: Gat Decor / Waterfall: Atlantic Ocean / Open your mind: Usura / Barbie girl: Aqua / Freed from desire: Gala / Lovefool: Cardigans / Where love lives: Limerick, Alison / Make the world go around: Sandy B / Feeling good: Huff & Herb / Get up everybody: Stingily, Byron / So in love with you: Duke / Give me rhythm: Black Connection / Love shy: Blond, Kristine / Never gonna let you go: Moore, Tina / Closer than close: Gaines, Rosie / Raed my mind: Reeves, Conner / Hideaway: DeLacy / Brimful of Asha: Cornershop / Jump around: House Of Pain / Who am I: Beenie Man / You sexy thing: Clock / Stayin' alive: N-Trance / Don't stop movin': Livin' Joy / I luv you baby: Original / Keep warm: Jinny / U R the best thing: D:Ream / Son of a gun: JX / Ultra flava: Heller & Farley Project / I love you stop: Red 5 / Encore une fois: Sash / Je regarde le DJ: Encore / Mother's pride: Floribunda / Flylife: Basement Jaxx / Don't stop: Ruff Driverz / Mama used to say: Azure / Show me love: Robin S / Offshore 1997: Chicane / You got the love: Source & Candi Staton / James Bond Theme: Moby

TTVCD 2958 / 23 Mar '98 / Telstar TV

☐ NON STOP DANCE MIX '97 (2CD Set)

Offshore / X-Files / Seven days and one week / Higher state of consciousness / Sunshine after the rain / There's nothing I won't do / Key, the secret / Ooh aah...just a little bit / Born slippy / Night train / Flash / Let me be your fantasy / I like to move it / Boom boom boom / Ready or not / Go / Waterfall / Dreamer / Rhythm of the night / Jump to the beat / Don't give me your life / Encore une fois / Everybody's free / Finally / Hideaway / Don't stop movin' / Read my lips / Keep on jumpin' / Try me out / Move on baby / Baby baby / U got 2 let the music / Humpin' around / Two can play that game / I love you baby / Naughty North and the sexy South / Children / Fable / Bellissima / I love you stop

CDVDB 6 / 8 Aug '97 / Virgin

☐ NON STOP DANCE PARTY

I like to move it: Reel 2 Real / Void: Exoterix / Got to give me love: Dawson, Dana / Omen III: Magic Affair / Give it up: Cut 'n' Move / Elephant paw: Pan Position / Nothing in the world: Mozaic / Give me love: Diddy / Can you hear the voice of Buddha: Voice Of Buddha / Let love shine: Amos / Someday: Eddy / I like to move it (reprise): Reel 2 Real

CDGOLD 1042 / Jul '96 / EMI Gold

☐ NON STOP EUROPA EXPRESS

JAPECD 101 / May '94 / Escapade

☐ NON STOP FREESTYLE MIX

ZYX 87838 / 9 Feb '98 / ZYX

☐ NON STOP HITS (2CD Set)

Vindaloo: Fat Les / Turn back time: Aqua / Dance the night away: Mavericks / Kung fu fighting: Bus Stop & Carl Douglas / Stranded: McNeal, Lutricia / Last thing on my mind: Steps / Happenin' all over again: Shaw, Tracy / Stop: Spice Girls / Brimful of asha: Cornershop / La primavera: Sash / Surfin' USA: Carter, Aaron / Kiss the rain: Myers, Billie / Read my mind: Reeves, Conner / When I need you: Mellor, Will / All I have to give: Backstreet Boys / Kick it: Reggae Boyz / Boom boom: N-Tyce / Beat goes on: All Seeing I / Ballad of Tom Jones: Space / 100 Mile high city: Ocean Colour Scene / Feel it: Tamperer & Maya / Naked in the rain: Blue Pearl / Bamboogie: Bamboo / It's like that: Run DMC / Let me show you: Camisra / Wanna get up: 2 Unlimited / Renegade master: Wildchild / Deeper love: Ruff Driverz / All my love: Queen Pen / Seven days: Blige, Mary J. / Ain't that just the way: McNeal, Lutricia / All my life: K-Ci & Jo Jo / Runnin': 2Pac & Notorious BIG / Fight for your right: NYCC / Je regarde le disque jockey: Encore / Rock your body: Clock / Sounds of the wickedness: Tzant / Been a long time: Fog / Girls just wanna have fun: Happy Nation / Encore un fois: Sash

TTVCD 2962 / 22 Jun '98 / Telstar TV

☐ NON STOP LINE DANCE ALBUM, THE

MCCD 341 / 20 Apr '98 / Music Club

☐ NON STOP LINE DANCE PARTY

CURCD 52 / 23 Mar '98 / Curb

☐ NON STOP PARTY ALBUM, THE (Stars On 45)

MCCD 250 / Jun '96 / Music Club

☐ NON STOP PARTY HITS (3CD Set)

Such a night (to have a party): Racey / Mama loo: Humphries, Les Singers / Under the moon of love: Showaddywaddy / Needles and pins: Smokie / Glass of champagne: Sailor / Stop that train: Sticks 'N' Fire / Stop teasing my heart: Dr. Hook & Ray Sawyer / I see the moon: Goombay Dance Band / Please don't talk to Jessica: Run 4 Fun / Ob la di-ob la da: Marmalade / Agadoo: Black Lace / Since you've been gone: Clout / Sacramento: Middle Of The Road / Medley: Svenne & Lotta / She's in love with you: Quatro, Suzi / Puttin' on the ritz: Taco / Good love can never die: Stardust, Alvin / Traffic jam: Sailor / Saddle up: Christie, David / Walk in the park: Straker, Nick Band / I only wanna be with you: Bay City Rollers / Dancin' party: Showaddywaddy / Have you ever seen the rain: Smokie / Baby makes her blue jeans talk: Dr. Hook & Ray Sawyer / Runaround Sue: Racey / Stay the night: Sailor / Mother and child reunion: Sticks 'N' Fire / Love is in the air: Young, John Paul / It's still rock 'n' roll to me: Marmalade / I will survive: Gaynor, Gloria / Happy together: Turtles / Dance dance dance: Humphries, Les / You and you: Stardust, Alvin / Four letter words: Quatro, Suzi / Let your flow: Bellamy Brothers / Medley: Goombay Dance Band / I love to love: Charles, Tina / I am the music man: Black Lace / Dance rave medley: Mungo Jerry / Singing in the rain: Taco / Everybody is making it big but me: Dr. Hook & Ray Sawyer / Mexico: Humphries, Les Singers / Everybody let's rock: Racey / Lost in your love: Young, John Paul / Wig wam bam: Black Lace / Lay back in the arms of someone: Smokie / Stumblin' in: Quatro, Suzi / Pretty little angel eyes: Showaddywaddy / Portable radio: Clout / Shakin' all over: Stardust, Alvin / Little bit of jazz: Straker, Nick Band / Every little thing: Sticks 'N' Fire / Barbados: Goombay Dance Band / La vie en rose: Taco / Dr. Love: Charles, Tina / When you're in love with a beautiful woman: Dr. Hook & Ray Sawyer / No more reason: Sticks 'N' Fire / Bye bye baby: Bay City Rollers / YMCA/In the navy: Black Lace / Dancing with somebody: Run 4 Fun / Breaking up is hard to do: Svenne & Lotta

10782 / Oct '97 / Go On Deluxe

☐ NON STOP PARTY HITS VOL.1

Let's have a party: Jackson, Wanda / Dynamite: Mud / Be bop a lula: Vincent, Gene & The Bluecaps / Some girls: Racey / Denis: Blondie / Gimme hope Jo'anna: Grant, Eddy / Breakaway: Ullman, Tracey / Can the can: Quatro, Suzi / My sharona: Knack / Bus stop: Hollies / You were made for me: Freddie & The Dreamers / Runaway: Shannon, Del / Forever forever: Domino, Fats / Pretend: Stardust, Alvin / Kids in America: Wilde, Kim / If this is it: Lewis, Huey & The News / Darlin': Miller, Frankie / Right back where we started from: Nightingale, Maxine / Showing out: Mel & Kim / Sex and drugs and rock and roll: Dury, Ian

DC 877452 / May '97 / Disky

☐ NON STOP PARTY HITS VOL.1

Such a night (to have a party): Racey / Mama loo: Humphries, Les Singers / Under the moon of love: Showaddywaddy / Needles and pins: Smokie / Glass of champagne: Sailor / Stop that train: Sticks 'N' Fire / Stop teasing my heart: Dr. Hook & Ray Sawyer / I see the moon: Goombay Dance Band / Please don't talk to Jessica: Run 4 Fun / Ob la di-ob la da: Marmalade / Agadoo: Black Lace / Since you've been gone: Clout / Sacramento: Middle Of The Road / Medley: Svenne & Lotta / She's in love with you: Quatro, Suzi / Puttin' on the ritz: Taco / Good love can never die: Stardust, Alvin / Traffic jam: Sailor / Saddle up: Christie, David / Walk in the park: Straker, Nick Band / I only wanna be with you: Bay City Rollers

10792 / Oct '97 / Go On Deluxe

☐ NON STOP PARTY HITS VOL.2

I hear you knockin': Edmunds, Dave / Rubber ball: Vee, Bobby / Boat that I row: Lulu / Runaround Sue: Dion / Morning train: Easton, Sheena / Magic: Pilot / Cat crept in: Mud / Teenager in love: Dion & The Belmonts / I like it: Gerry & The Pacemakers / Buona sera: Prima, Louis / Mississippi: Pussycat / Walking back to happiness: Shapiro, Helen / Pretty flamingo: Manfred Mann / Good golly miss molly: Swinging Blue Jeans / Nutbush city limits: Turner, Ike & Tina / Coming on strong: Broken English / That's the way I like it: KC & The Sunshine Band / We've gotta get out of this place: Animals / No more heroes: Stranglers

DC 877462 / May '97 / Disky

☐ NON STOP PARTY HITS VOL.2

Dancin' party: Showaddywaddy / Have you ever seen the rain: Smokie / Baby makes her blue jeans talk: Dr. Hook & Ray Sawyer / Runaround Sue: Racey / Stay the night: Sailor / Mother and child reunion: Sticks 'N' Fire / Love is in the air: Young, John Paul / It's still rock 'n' roll to me: Marmalade / I will survive: Gaynor, Gloria / Happy together: Turtles / Dance dance dance: Humphries, Les Singers / You and you: Stardust, Alvin / Four letter words: Quatro, Suzi / Let your love flow: Bellamy Brothers / Medley: Goombay Dance Band / I love to love: Charles, Tina / I am the music man: Black Lace / Dance rave medley: Mungo Jerry / Singing in the rain: Taco / Everybody is making it big but me: Dr. Hook & Ray Sawyer

10802 / Oct '97 / Go On Deluxe

☐ NON STOP PARTY HITS VOL.3

Party doll: Knox, Buddy / Do wah diddy diddy: Manfred Mann / C'mon everybody: Cochran, Eddie / Hippy hippy shake: Swinging Blue Jeans / Barbara ann: Beach Boys / Mony mony: James, Tommy & The Shondells / Hi ho silver lining: Beck, Jeff / Tiger feet: Mud / See my baby jive: Wizzard / Long tall glasses: Sayer, Leo / This little girl: Bonds, Gary 'US' / On the road again: Canned Heat / Roll over Beethoven: ELO / My girl Josephine: Domino, Fats / I'm into something good: Herman's Hermits / Surf city: Jan & Dean / I get around: Beach Boys / Rock your baby: McCrae, George / Don't take away the music: Tavares

DC 877472 / May '97 / Disky

☐ NON STOP PARTY HITS VOL.3

Mexico: Humphries, Les Singers / Everbody let's rock: Racey / Lost in your love: Young, John Paul / Wig wam bam: Black Lace / Lay back in the arms of some one: Smokie / Stumblin' in: Quatro, Suzi / Pretty little angel eyes: Showaddywaddy / Portable radio: Clout / Shakin' all over: Stardust, Alvin / Little bit of jazz: Straker, Nick Band / Every little thing: Sticks 'N' Fire / Barbados: Goombay Dance Band / La vie en rose: Taco / Dr. Love: Charles, Tina / When

you're in love with a beautiful woman: Dr. Hook & Ray Sawyer / No more reason: Sticks 'N' Fire / Bye bye baby: Bay City Rollers / YMCA/In the navy: Black Lace / Dancing with somebody: Run 4 Fun / Breaking up is hard to do: Svenne & Lotta

10812 / Oct '97 / Go On Deluxe

☐ NON STOP PARTY HITS VOL.4

Summertime blues: Cochran, Eddie / Lay your love on me: Racey / Don't let me be misunderstood: Animals / World without love: Peter & Gordon / Baker street: Rafferty, Gerry / Boogie oogie oogie: Taste Of Honey / Heaven must be missing an angel: Tavares / Chequered love: Wilde, Kim / Oh boy: Mud / Tom tom turn around: New World / No milk today: Herman's Hermits / Devil gate drive: Quatro, Suzi / Stuck with you: Lewis, Huey & The News / Centerfold: Geils, J. Band / Stop stop stop: Hollies / Freedom come freedom go: Fortunes / You'll never walk alone: Gerry & The Pacemakers / I'm telling you now: Freddie & The Dreamers / Seven drunken nights: Dubliners / Sloop John B.: Beach Boys / Oh Marie: Prima, Louis / If you can't give me love: Quatro, Suzi / Blueberry hill: Domino, Fats / Do you want to know a secret: Kramer, Billy J. & The Dakotas / Thank u very much: Scaffold

DC 877482 / May '97 / Disky

☐ NON STOP ROCK 'N' ROLL PARTY

Let's have a party: Jackson, Wanda / Good Golly Miss Molly: Swinging Blue Jeans / Under the moon of love: Showaddywaddy / Viva Bobby Joe: Equals / Red river rock: Johnny & The Hurricanes / Tutti frutti: Little Richard / Long tall Sally: Little Richard / Here comes my baby: Tremeloes / Fee-dee-o-dee: Rubettes / Helule helule: Tremeloes / Yellow river: Christie / Tonight: Rubettes / Letter: Box Tops / Windy: Association / Lucille: Little Richard / Bama lama bama loo: Little Richard / Wooly bully: Sam The Sham & The Pharaohs / Da doo ron ron: Crystals / Judy in disguise: John Fred & Playboy Band / He's so fine: Chiffons / Let's twist again: Checker, Chubby / Little honda: Hondells / Keep on dancing: Gentrys / See you later alligator: Haley, Bill & The Comets / Come on let's go: Showaddywaddy / Dancin' party: Showaddywaddy / Say Mama: Showaddywaddy / Shake, rattle and roll: Haley, Bill & The Comets / Rock around the clock: Haley, Bill & The Comets

11982 / Feb '96 / Music

☐ NON STOP ROCK 'N' ROLL PARTY (Non-Stop Party Hits From The 1950's)

SUMCD 4041 / Nov '96 / Summit

☐ NON STOP ROCK 'N' ROLL PARTY MIX

ZYX 100462 / Jan '97 / ZYX

☐ NON STOP SOUL ALBUM, THE

SUMCD 4147 / Jan '98 / Summit

☐ NON STOP SUMMER PARTY

Hot hot hot: Arrow / Is there anybody out there: Bassheads / Young hearts run free: Mazelle, Kym / Reach: Cheeks, Judy / Wiggle it: 2 In A Room / U can't touch this: MC Hammer / Trouble: Shampoo / (We want) the same thing: Carlisle, Belinda / Summertime healing: Eusebe / Don't worry: Appleby, Kim / I thank you: Adeva / Ring my bell: Adeva & Monie Love / Caught in the middle: Roberts, Juliet / Three is family: Dawson, Dana / Sunshine: Umboza / Can you handle it: DNA & Sharon Redd / That's the way I like it: KC & The Sunshine Band / Walking on sunshine: Katrina & The Waves

4959112 / 13 Jul '98 / EMI Gold

☐ NONE OF THESE ARE LOVE SONGS VOL.1

Gonna make you move: Boomshanka / Big bud II: Tranx Project / Reach further: Progression / Ride: Boomshanka / Bug bottom hula: Big Bottom Music / Spirit: Aberration / House of dread: Dread Zone / Agent O: Aloof / Equatorial dawn: Mind Becomes Drum / Who killed the king: Sunz Of Ishen

CVN 001CD / Apr '94 / Caustic Visions

☐ NONE OF THESE ARE LOVE SONGS VOL.2

CVN 003CD / Nov '94 / Caustic Visions

☐ NOOMLIGHT

NOOMCD 0082 / 2 Mar '98 / Noom

☐ NOOMRISE VOL.3

NOOMCD 0052 / Jun '97 / Noom

☐ NORDIC TRAX

MF 005 / 23 Feb '98 / Mo' Funk

☐ NORMANDIE

DEM 011 / Feb '96 / IMP

☐ NORSKE TURDANSAR VOL.1

HCD 7089CD / Apr '95 / Musikk Distribujson

☐ NORSKE TURDANSAR VOL.2

H 7117CD / Aug '97 / Heilo

☐ NORTH CAROLINA BANJO COLLECTION, THE (2CD Set)

Georgia Buck: Thompson, Odell / Corinna: Reid, Babe / Going down the road feeling bad: Baker, Etta / Low baked a hoe cake: Cotten, Libba / Snow a little rain a little: Snipes, John / Fox chase: Roberts, Dink / Going to write a letter: Reed, Ola Belle / Worried blues: Bumgarner, Samantha / Mr. Garfield: Lunsford, Bascom Lamar / Cleveland's marching to the White House: Dickens, Bertie / Old doctor that fell in the well: Gaster, Marvin / Hello coon: Babson, Walter Raleigh / Sugar babe: Wiseman, Scotty / Reuben's train: Watson, Doc / Rambling hobo: Carlton, Gaither / Cumberland Gap: Proffitt, Frank / Roustabout: Cockerham, Fred / Cotton eyed Joe: Kimble, Stella / John Henry: Jarrell, Tommy / Lost Indian: Creed, Kyle / Cripple creek: Lowe, Charlie / Under the double eagle: Marion, Carlie / Big ridge mountain home: Davis, Glenn / Little log cabin in the lane: Sears, Kelly / Royal clog: Helton, Ernest / Arkansas traveller/Old Joe/Sweetheart would you care: Everhart, Clay / Baptist shout: Jenkins, Frank / American and Spanish Fandango: Smith & Allgood / Shuffle feet shuffle: Hendley, Fisher / Missouri waltz: Britt, J.G. & Jerry Wayne / Italian waltz: Nance, Carl / There'll come a time: Poole, Charlie / Man who wrote home sweet home never was a married man: Woolbright, Mark / Cotton mill blues: Watts, Wilmer / Come bathe in that beautiful pool: Walsh, Dock / Biscuits: Watson, Arnold / Whoa mule whoa: Whitener, Hobbie / I left my old home in the mountains: Pegram, George / Short life and it's troubles: Mainer, Wade / Nancy Rowland: Jenkins, Snuffy / Railroad: Overton, A.C. / Nut medley: Best, Carroll

ROUCD 0439/40 / 16 Mar '98 / Rounder

☐ NORTH INDIA-KASHMIR & GANGES PLAIN

ARN 64227 / Jun '93 / Arion

☐ NORTH INDIAN CLASSICAL MUSIC (4CD Set)

Alap: Bhairava, Raga Ahir / Dhamar: Bhairava, Raga Ahir / Kyal: Bhairava, Raga Ahir / Thumri: Bhairava, Raga Ahir / Bhajana in the raga Kaushi kanada: Rupaka, Tala / Tapa in the raga adana vasanta: Khaharava, Tala / Sarangi: Dipachandi, Tala / Vina / Pakhavaj / Tabla tintala / Tabla tala dadra / Sitar / Tila tintala / Raga miyanski malhar / Vichitra vina / Raga vasanta mukhari / Raga desh / Flute / Shamai

ROUCD 5101 / 16 Mar '98 / Rounder

☐ NORTH INDIAN VOCAL MUSIC

Khyal in raga bhairav: Khan, Hafeez Ahmed / Thumri in raga bhairavi: Bhagwat, Neela / Khyal in raga bhupali: Khan, Hafeez Ahmed / Khyal in deshkar: Bhagwat, Neela

CDSDL 404 / Jun '94 / Saydisc

☐ NORTH OF WATFORD VOL.1

Gimme some: Brendon / Shattered glass: Warren, Ellie / Nine times out of ten: Day, Muriel / One minute every hour: Miles, John / Run baby run: Newbeats / Sweet talking guy: Chiffons / You to me are everything: Real Thing / Gotta get along without you: Wills, Viola / Something old, something new: Fantastics / Guilty: Pearls / Ski-ing in the snow: Wigan's Ovation / Touch of velvet: Mood Mosaic / Going to go go: Sharonettes / Shotgun wedding: Roy C / Long after tonight is all over: Radcliffe, Jimmy / Supergirl: Bonney, Graham / Rudi's in love: Locomotive / Man like me: James, Jimmy / Under my thumb: Gibson, Wayne / Out on the floor: Gray, Dobie / Flasher: Mistra / Hold me, thrill me, kiss me: Carter, Mel / Heartache avenue: Maisonettes / I feel love coming on: Taylor, Felice

KRLCD 001 / Apr '95 / KRL

☐ NORTH OF WATFORD VOL.2 (24 Rare Pop & Soul Classics 1964-1979)

Harlem shuffle: Bob & Earl / Cool jerk: Capitols / Holiday: Brasseur, Andre / Do the teasy: Bond, Joyce / I want you to be my baby: Davis, Billie / Something keeps calling me back: Fontana, Wayne / Spooky's day off: Swinging Soul Machine / Never an everyday thing: Bonaparte, Eli / Yesterday: Miles, John / Groovin' with Mr. Bloe: Mr. Bloe / Life: Cats Eyes / Give and take: Cliff, Jimmy / I hear those church bells ringing: Dusk / 3rd finger left hand: Pearls / Trampoline: Davis, Spencer Group / Love on a mountain top: Knight, Robert / Look at what you have done to my heart: Shirley & The Shirelles / If it feels good do it: Reese, Della / Surrender your love: Carrolls / I can prove it: Etoria, Tony / You can do magic: Limmie & Family Cooking / Gonna get along without you now: Wills, Viola / Broken man: Pioneers / Morning glory: Purify, James & Bobby

KRLCD 003 / Jul '97 / KRL

☐ NORTH OF WATFORD VOL.3

Devil's drive: Big Boris / It's too late: Deal, Bill / I've been hurt: Darrell, Guy / Highwire: Carr, Linda / I can't help myself: Elbert, Donnie / pick up your troubles: Vanderbilt, Lee / Don't boogaloo the night away: Hollywood Crestas / Swan lake: Cats / Penny arcade: Orbison, Roy / Wait a minute: Tim Tam & The Turn Ons / Get ready for love: Paintbox / Grazing in the grass: Friends Of Distinction / Wedding bell blues: Fifth Dimension / She's alright: McKenna Mendolson Mainline / Soul coaking: Lefevre, Raymond / Love of my life: Dooleys / Up in a puff of smoke: Brown, Polly / Mr. Universe: Flirtations / Accident: Starr, Edwin / Elusive: Babe Ruth / Chase side shoot up: Bennett, Brian / Who is gonna love me: Imperials / Lovin' is really my game: Brainstorm / Electric slide: Griffiths, Marcia

KRLCD 004 / 20 Jul '98 / KRL

☐ NORTHCORE (The Polar Scene)

BHR 008CD / Feb '95 / Burning Heart

☐ NORTHERN CIRCUITS

ICHILLCD 002 / May '97 / Interchill

☐ NORTHERN EXPOSURE (Mixed By Sasha & John Digweed)

Satellite serenade: Suzuki, Kellchi / Cascade: Future Sound Of London / These waves: Young American Primitive / Raincry: God Within / Out of body experience: Rabbit In The Moon / I am free: King, Morgan / Kites: Ultraviolet / Obsession: Fuzzy Logic / Water from a vine leaf: Orbit, William / Liquid cool: Apollo 440 / Last train to Lhasa: Banco De Gaia / Wave dub: Dope On Plastic / Sound system: Drum Club / Gloom: Castle Trancelot / Wave speech: Lazonby, Peter / Photogenic: Evolution / Dusk: Light / Plan 94 (The voyage): X-Trax / I can't stop: Mellow Mellow / Heliopolis: Banco De Gaia / East: Humate & Rabbit In The Moon / Dark and long: Underworld

NECD 1 / Oct '96 / Ministry Of Sound

☐ NORTHERN EXPOSURE VOL.2 (2CD Set)

NECD 2 / 22 Sep '97 / Ministry Of Sound

☐ NORTHERN LIGHTS (The Cream Of Scotland's Celtic Musicians Live)

Glass of beer: Drop The Box / Barnyards of Dalgety: Old Blind Dogs / Duck: McManus, Tony / Seagull: McManus, Tony / Si Morag: Tannas / Kenny Gillies of Portnalong: Canterach / Bobby MacLeods: Canterach / General gathering 1745: Canterach / Curlew: Canterach / Mich's m'geirigh air bheagan eislein: Mhoireach, Anna / Cape Breton fiddler's welcome to the Shetland Isles: Iron Horse / Morag's No.2: Iron Horse / Lintie: Iron Horse / Bill Powrie: Iron Horse / Andy Renwicks ferret: McManus, Tony / Famous bridge: McManus, Tony / Not coming your way: Drop The Box / Dashing white sergeant: Lorelei / Bodachan cha phos mi: Tannas / Blackthorn stick: Canterach / Calliope house: Canterach / Archie Beag: Canterach / Boys of Ballymote: Canterach / Bennachie: Old Blind Dogs / When she cam' ben she bobbit: Iron Horse / Anvil: Iron Horse / Duncan Johnstone: Iron Horse

CDLDL 1255 / Jan '97 / Lochshore

☐ NORTHERN SOUL - LOST AND FOUND

I won't let her see me cry: Big Frank & The Essences / Dream girl: Griffin, Herman / Lost and found: Carlton, Kenny / Quit while I'm ahead: Cannon, Lorraine / 90's days in the county jail: Woods, Danny / Keep on talking: Prince Phillip / Just like a woman: Fads / Another love: Ambers / She don't deserve you: Honey Bees / I'm leaving: Norman, Jimmy / How lonely: Lamont, Reggie / Hey girl: Festivals / Let me take you out: Duncan, Tommy / Do it all with your heart: Warwick, Dee Dee / Magic saxophone: Castor, Jimmy / Without you: Fashioneers / I'll get over it: Collins, Keanya / Have we met before: Collins, Keanya / I won't share: Paramounts / One room paradise: Hendrix, Margie / Come see what's left of me: Hutton, Bobby / Nobody but you: Leavill, Otis / Get a hold of yourself: Little Rosie Little / Together: Chester Fields / It's gonna be alright: Kilgore, Theola

GSCD 094 / 29 Sep '97 / Goldmine

☐ NORTHERN SOUL - THE CLASSICS VOL.1

Joker: Mylestones / Our love is in the pocket: Barnes, J.J. / Groovin' at the Go-Go: Four Larks / I get the fever: Creation / Nine times out of ten: Day, Muriel / Little piece of leather: Elbert, Donnie / Oh my darlin': Lee, Jackie / Open the door to your heart: Banks, Darrell / Seven day lover: Fountain, James / You don't love me: Epitome Of Sound / They'll never know why: Chavez, Freddie / You can't mean it: Chapter Five / Blowing my mind to pieces: Relf, Bobby / My sugar baby: Clarke, Connie / Baby do the Philly dog: Olympics / Double cookin': Checkerboard Squares / Put your arms around me: Sherrys / If you ever walked out of my life: Barnes, Dena / Man like me: James, Jimmy / What is this: Womack, Bobby / I'm satisfied with you: Furys / Just lovin' you: Andrews, Ruby

GSCD 100 / Jun '97 / Goldmine

☐ NORTHERN SOUL DANCE PARTY

That beatin' rhythm: Temple, Richard / Goose pimples: Scott, Shirley J. / My sugar baby: Clarke, Connie / Double cookin': Checkerboard Squares / Do the philly dog: Olympics / Not me baby: Silhouettes / Yes I love you baby: Dynamics / Eddie's my name: Holman, Eddie / Countdown: Tempos / Going to a happening: Neal, Tommy / Temptation walk: Lee, Jackie / I'm satisfied with you: Furys / There's nothing else to say: Incredibles / My little girl: Garrett, Bobby / I got the fever: Creation / What's the matter baby: Reynolds, L.J. / Let's copp a groove: Wells, Bobby / Get on your knees: Los Canarios / I can't help myself: Ross, Johnny / Earthquake: Lynn, Bobbi / Our love is in the pocket: Banks, Darren / Blowing my mind to pieces: Relf, Bobby

GSCD 046 / Jul '94 / Goldmine

☐ NORTHERN SOUL FEVER VOL.1 (A Compilation Of 60 Legendary Soul Dancers/2CD Set)

Manifesto: Case Of Tyme / My sweet baby: Puzzles / No ifs, no ands, no buts: Young, Mae / Talking eyes: Beatty, Pamela / I don't want to hear it: Exits / Very strong on you: Greer, Cortez / Girl every guy should know: Carrington, Sunny / Bring me all your heartaches: Beavers, Jackie / Don't you need a boy like me: Carlton, Carl / Broken hearted lover: Tojo / I can hear you crying: Hill, Eddie / Try my love: Toni & The Showmen / In my life: Carr, Linda / This heart these hands: Wells, Billy / Just do the best you can: Duke & Leonard / Ain't that love enough: Atkins, Larry / Bad brought the good: Turks / Standing at a standstill: Holmes, Sherlock / Someone else's turn: Clayton, Pat / I ain't got nothin' but the blues: Friendly People / Moments: Bronzettes / Sugar baby: Holland, Jimmy / Real nice: Barnes, Johnny / Beware a stranger: Jones, Bobby / I've got to face: Thunders, Johnny & The Heartbreakers / Turn to me: Chris Towns Unit / Shield all around: Holiday, Jimmy / You better check yourself: La'shell & The Shelletts / I bear witness: Apollo, Vince / No time: John & The Weirdest / I got the fever: Creation / You better believe me: Reeder, Esque / Love can't be modernised: Tripps / Take me back again: Volcanos / Why wonder: And The Echoes / Lean on me: Daye, Eddie / Take back all these things: Majesties / Do what you wanna do: Sindab, Paul / Don't fight the feeling: Newton, Bobby / Airplane song: Kerr, George / Bok to Bach: Father's Angels / Oh yeah yeah yeah: Carroll, Vivian / Everybody's talkin': Baker, Joan / Pretty as a picture: Dillard, Moses / You got it: Dealers / Too much of a good thing: Ambassadors / Ain't gonna cry no more: Charles, Dave / Little things: Moore, Misty / If I only knew: Mike & Ray / Home town boy: Williams, Sebastian / Lonely lover: McFarland, Jimmy / One way lover: Volumes / Somebody help me: Jenkins, Donald & The Delighters / Let nobody love you: Blakley, Virginia / What do you think: Lamarr, Chico / If I could see you now: Sunny & The Sunliners / With these eyes: Fabulous Peps / I want to be free: Admirations / What can a man do: Showstoppers

GSCD 027 / Jan '94 / Goldmine

☐ NORTHERN SOUL FEVER VOL.2 (2CD Set)

Trouble: Agents / Deeper: Chequers / Midnight brew: Carter, Melvin / Hey girl you've changed: Vondells / No one loves you: Hot Cinnamon / You don't need help (Part 1): Garvin, Rex / Hide out: Hideaways / Misery: Strogin, Henry / I'm where it's at: Jades / Case of love: Renfro Bros. / Love bound: Audio Arts Strings / Anyway you want it: Smith, Fred Orchestra / Lonely eyes: Elling, Melvin / I can't stop you: Performers / Sugar pie honey: Promatics / Bounce: Olympics / Gotta get you back: Mandolph, Bobby / I'd best be going: Vito & The Salutations / Permanent vacation: Sodd, Marion / Seven days of loving: Vanelli, Johnny / All that's good: Mills, Tico / Send my baby back: Hughes, Freddie / (Oh oh oh) What a love this is: King, Susan / Actions speak louder than words: Bounty, James / You took my heart: St. Clair, Kelly / Crazy little things: Soul-Jers / Please don't go: Splenders / I'm coming apart at the seams: Kittens Three / Times gone by: Music Track / You'll have to wait: Baby Sitters / Those good times: Nicky C / Keep loving me like you do: Hargreaves, Silky / Soulful jerk: Rumblers / It was true: Big Don's Rebellion / I can take care of myself: Spyders / Dark at the top of my head: Paris, Fred / Stop along the way: Taylor, Robby / Elevator man: Nelson, Roy / Your love keeps drawing me closer: Chandlers / Baby you've got it: Dell, Frank / I didn't know how to: Constellations / I must love you: Wilson, Timothy / I'm tempted: Hollis, Sandy / Love from the Far East: Master Four / Look in the mirror: Vondors / I'll be there: Collection & The Civics / Beware, beware: Compliments / Stop (Don't give up your loving): Two Fellows / I'm losing you: New People / Don't leave me this way: Dynamites / Light drivers: Operator / Love you from the bottom of my heart: Buckner Brothers / So what: Carlton, Carl / If you don't need me: Tyrone Wonder Boy / Your money - my love: Sam & Kitty / (She keeps) Driving me out of my mind: Mighty Lovers / Open the door to your heart: Burdick, Doni / Ain't gonna do you no harm: New Wanderers / Don't give me love: Beery, Dorothy / Some good in everything bad: Fabulous Apollos

GSCD 043 / Aug '94 / Goldmine

☐ NORTHERN SOUL FEVER VOL.3 (Over 2 Hours Of Legendary Soul Dancers/ 2CD Set)

I'll do a little more: Olympics / (All you need is your) Good lovin': Pat & The Blenders / Got to have peace of mind: Peters, Preston / Motown: Cammotions / I love only you: Henry, Edd / We like girls: Scott Bros. / Connie: Servicemen / Gotta wipe away the teardrops: Jackson, Ollie / Poor unfortunate me (I ain't got nobody): Barnes, J.J. / What should I do: Manhattans / Just a dream: Imperial Wonders / Your love: Harrell, Vernon / My baby changes like the weather: Callender, Bobby / Here comes those heartaches: Tripps / Big search is on: Lynn, Dolores / Move it baby: Singin' Sam / It ain't no secret: Dynamic Heartbeats / Some day some way: Traits / Charge: T-K-O-S / I want the good life: Little David / Misunderstood: Kennedy, Joyce / Easily misled: Remarkables / Old days: Furys / Going going gone: Black, Cody / I'm gonna get even with you: Little Ben & The Cheers / I ain't playing baby: Taurus & Leo / Let me render my service: New Wanderers / We go together: Olympics / Just because of you: Rocky Roberts & The Airedales / Number one fool: Fabulous Emotions / You really made it good: Karim, Ty / My kind of girl: Prophets / I'm guilty: Dupree, Leontine / I'm in love with your daughter: Enchantments / Miss Heartbreaker: Ascots / We go together, yes we do: Hammond, Little Walter / I just want to satisfy: Spencer, Bobby / Joey: Petite, Jo Jo / Sad, sad memories: Tempos / Lonely baby: Moonlighters / Blow me a kiss: Anthony, Wayne / Ain't gonna worry about you: Tinley, George / How soon: Wonderettes / Jerk it with soul: Walker, Willie / How good can it get: Lyle, Jay / Under the moon: Wonder, Rufus / Penguin breakdown: Reynolds, L.J. / Open arms - closed heart: Welsh, Janie / If I had my way: Keyes, Troy / Give me your love: Jones, A.C. / Don't you leave me baby: Founders / Giving my love to you: Apis, Fred / That's the way love goes: Disciples Of Soul / No one else can take your place: Inspirations

GSCD 048 / Nov '94 / Goldmine

☐ NORTHERN SOUL FEVER VOL.4 (2CD Set)

Destined to become a loser: Ellingtons / Don't forget to remember: Greater Experience / I'm satisfied just loving you: Bland, Bobbie Jean / I've got to face it: Heartbreaker / I wanna be loved to death: Moore, Bernnie / Auction on love: Bounty, James / Before 2001: Wood, Rufus / Everybody's happy but me: Williams, Cheryl / Front page love: Bee Gee Stans / Good sweet loving: Brown, Roy / Don't turn away: McDougall, Willy / Stay on the case: Innovations / New babe: Invictus / Other side: Five Of A Kind / Darling I love you: Superiors / I know what to do to satisfy you: Robert, Roy / That's not half bad: Woodbury, Gene / On a hot summer day in the big city: King, Ricardo / Sitting in my class: McNier, Ronnie / How can I forget you: Dee, Joey & The Starlighters / Especially for you baby: Four Puzzles / Don't put our the fire: Birchett, Tony / Why did you call: Wood, Eddie / Nobody loves me: Moore, Joe / I gotta have you: Brown, Bobby / You got to steal it: Flairs / I can't get away: Garett, Bobby / We've been together too long: Antony, El / Chinatown: Knight, Victor / I need help: Detroit Land Apples / I love you just the same: Winfield, Parker / Too much for me baby: Florence, Tina / Can we talk: Allen, C / Give me love: Tootsie Love / Nervous breakdown: Forte, Ronnie / Love will conquer all: Two Plus Two / I can feel him slipping away: Brown, Tobbie / It's written all over my face: Holliday, Marva / Together forever: Pardell, Pat & The Powerdrills / Life goes on: Fabulous Sownbeats / False arm: Body Motions / Sensitive mind: General Assembly / I can't fight it: Sain, Lee / Please come back: First Grade / Give it back: Tripps / (I lost love in the) Big city: Daniels / How do you like it: Sheppards / I can't turn my back: Apollo, Vince / Little bit of soul: Gerry & Paul & The Soul Emmissaries / You've got a good thing going: King, Jeanie / Something about you: Spoilers / Peace of mind: Spydels / I ain't got nothin' but the blues: Friendly People / Watch out Mr Lonely: Vaughn, Shirley / First time: Wills, Viola / Lucky we: Sugar & Spice / My lover: Sugar & Sweet / Set me free: Performers / Love and laughter: Anderson, Sonny & Prince Conley

GSCD 074 / May '95 / Goldmine

☐ NORTHERN SOUL FLOORSHAKERS (20 Anthems & Rarities From The RCA Vaults)

Hold to my baby: Cavaliers / I can't change: Chandler, Lorraine / Since I found my baby: Metros / Blowing up my mind: Exciters / I need your love: Dynamics / Tears and misery: Till, Sonny / What's that on your finger: Kendricks, Willie / Some things are better left unsaid: Lester, Ketty / Honest to goodness: Ward, Herb / Could it be you: Scott, Sharon / Lucky to be loved by you: Hutch, Willie / I don't mind: Cooke, Carolyn / It didn't take much (for me to fall in love): Wiggins, Percy / I've gotta know right now: Valentine, Rose / Born a loser: Ray, Don / Don't pity me: Lynne, Sue / You shook me up: Hamilton, Roy / Coz it's you girl: Walsh, James Gypsy Band / Moonlight, music and you: Greene, Laura / Gotta get myself together: Carter, Kenny

MCCD 236 / Apr '96 / Music Club

☐ NORTHERN SOUL GOLDEN MEMORIES VOL.1 (28 Legendary Northern Soul Dancers)

You're everything: Lee, Jackie / (Countdown) Here I come: Tempos / You don't love me: Epitome Of Sound / Let her go: Smith, Otis / Gotta draw this line: Fletcher, Darrow / Gotta find a way: Linsey, Teresa / Quick change artist: Soul Twins / She's puttin' you on: United 4 / I'm satisfied with you: Furys / They're talking about me: Bragg, Johnny / Let's copp a groove: Wells, Bobby / They'll never know why: Chavez, Freddie / Sweet sherry: Barnes, J.J. / Put your arms around me: Sherrys / I need a helping hand: Servicemen / You won't say nothing: Lewis,

Tamala / Since you left: Inticers / Head and shoulders: Young, Patti / Never too young (To fall in love): Moden Redcaps / Heartbroken memories: Ferguson, Sheila / (Come on and be my) Good darlin': Clarke, Jimmy 'Soul' / I never knew: Foster, Eddie / Women's liberation: Topics / This time it's love: Tymes / You don't mean me no good: Jellybeans / New York in the dark: Ad Libs / Lady love: Vontastics

GSCD 062 / Aug '95 / Goldmine

☐ **NORTHERN SOUL LOST AND FOUND VOL.2**

Don't turn away: Diamond, Tony / I cried for: Tempests / Somethin' ain't right: Alston, Ron / Teahouse in Chinatown: Harf, Jimmy / Call me (anytime you want some lovin'): Ellison, Lorraine / Good luck my love: Tears / Take it or leave it: Satisfactions / How come: Williams, Tony / Family tree: Norman, Jimmy / Reason to be lonely: Leavill, Otis / I'm a good girl: Kennedy, Joyce / Let me down slowly: Hall, Carl / Bettin' on love: Jewell, Len / Someone to love tonight: Lewis, Ricky / If it wasn't for love: Bee, Jimmy / Music: Festivals / I'll never go to a party again: Hodges, Charles / Love: Mononrays / Use your head: Wells, Mary / It's all over but the pain: Murphy, Frank / Don't you know: Fashioneers / Nobody loves me like you do: Flamingoes / Girls with big black boots: Paramounts / Restless: Hendrix, Margie / My woman's good to me: Benson, George

GSCD 095 / 20 Jul '98 / Goldmine

☐ **NORTHERN SOUL OF CHICAGO VOL.1, THE**

When I'm with my baby: Magnetics / Stubborn heart: Mosley, Earnest / In other words: Fascinators / Coming back girl: COD's / No right to cry: Galore, Mamie / I love you too: Fantasions / Ain't no good: Copney, Bobby / You can't get away: McCall, Johnny / You've changed my whole life: Farren, Charles / It's mighty nice to know you: Wood, Bobby 'Guitar' / Your wish is my command: Inspirations / Have your fun: Topics / Lost in a city: Majors / She'll come back: Britt, Mel / Love bandit: Collins, Barnabus & Kenya / What you gonna do now: Collins, Lashdown / Two of a kind: Flemons, Wade / I'm gonna love you: Age Of Bronze / Don't say you love me until you do: Maxwell, Holly / I'm satisfied: Gloria & The T-Arias / Cheaper than one: Hunt, Geraldine / Heart of love: Ventures / Go go gorilla: Ideals / Got to be your lover: Profiles / So much love: Taylor, Robert / Love now pay later: Williams, Lee Shot / Is this really love: Gardiner, Don

GSCD 038 / May '94 / Goldmine

☐ **NORTHERN SOUL OF CHICAGO VOL.2, THE**

Count the days: Magnetics / I can't please you: Robins, Jimmy / Jeanette: Flemons, Wade / Pitfall: Savoy, Ronnie / Never let me go: Monique / I really love you: Burns, Jimmy / Don't know what love is: Johnson, Syl / Best is yet to come: Invaders / Running out of years: Gloria & The T-Arias / Urge keeps coming: Armstead, Jo / Thank the Lord for love: Loving Color / Heaven is in your arms: Admirations / Every hurt makes you stronger: Bernard, Chuck / In paradise: Vestel, Lenny / Fight for love: Drake/Ensolids / Wait a minute: Kittens / Lovin' on borrowed time: Orsi, Phil / One day girl: Currington, Harold / I'm running a losing race: Davies, Tyrone / Don't hurt me no more: Woods, Wendy / Please let me: King, Eddie / Change is gonna come: Buckner Brothers / Ain't gonna let me down: Gardner, Don / Lonely was I: Conquistadors / Sweet and lovely: Del-Tours

GSCD 071 / Feb '96 / Goldmine

☐ **NORTHERN SOUL OF LA VOL.1, THE (A Collection Of Rare West Coast 1960's Soul)**

Sweet magic: Servicemen / Wonders of love: Soul Gents / You should have told me: New Yorkers / Under your spell: Paramounts / This is the way I feel: Four Tempos / There's that mountain: Trips / Do this for me: Emotions / It was wrong: Shades Of Jade / Anything for you: Furys / Jealous of you: Mystics / Don't let love get you down: Phonetics / You're good enough for me: Versatiles / (Down in) East L.A.: Angelenos / You'll never make the grade: Sun Lovers / Sad, sad memories: Tempos / No one else can take your place: Inspirations / (I love her so much) it hurts me: Majestics / Hey hey girls: Vines / Is the feeling still there: Remarkables / Save your love: Soul Patrol / Girl, I love you: Sinceres / Just a little: Prominents / Love is a hurting game: Four Sights / My poor heart: Sun Lovers / Beginning of the end: Young Hearts

GSCD 032 / Mar '94 / Goldmine

☐ **NORTHERN SOUL OF LA VOL.2, THE**

I thought you were: Natural Four / Rosie Brooks: Moanin' / Crook his little finger: Heyward, Ann / They didn't know: Goodnight, Terri / Quicksand: Osbourne, Kell / You're welcome: Jackson, June / I'm a bashful guy: Groovers / Shy guy: Mac, Bobby / Closer together: Ster, Eddie / My faith: Dockery, James / Ain't that love enough: Karim, Ty / Ain't that good: Offatield, Bruce / Sleepless nights: Paris / Lost: Darlettes / Love shop: Tater / Try my love: Dodds, Troy / I'm still young: Summers, Johnny / Doctor of love: Abram, J.D. / Pyramid: Soul Brother Inc. / Ooh what you're doing: Capitals / I can't treat her right: Those Two / Specially when: Rumbold, Edwick / To whom it may concern: Sands, Lola / Faith, hope and trust: Roys, Faye / Girl you're so fine: Angelle, Bobby / Strain: Little Stanley / Ain't gonna: Watson, Johnny 'Guitar'

GSCD 039 / Jun '94 / Goldmine

☐ **NORTHERN SOUL OF SWAN, THE**

And in return: Ferguson, Sheila / Are you satisfied: Ferguson, Sheila / Don't leave me lover: Ferguson, Sheila / Walking alone: Valentino, Mark / Put yourself in my place: Mortimor, Azie / Everybody crossfire: Stevens, Sammy / Watch your game: Stevens, Sammy / It will be done: Carlton, Eddie / Misery: Carlton, Eddie / I will love you: Barnet, Richie / Driving me mad: Three Degrees / Spy: Guys From Uncle / Never too young: Modern Redcaps / Empty world: Modern Redcaps / No good: Anthony, Richard / Gonna find the right boy: Sio, Audrey / In love: Galla, Tony / I'm gonna get you: Harris, Leroy / Can't hardly stand it: Lane, Mickey & The Love Tempest / In the paradise: Showmen / Take it baby: Showmen / Hey sah-lo ney: Lane, Mickey Lee / Put that woman down: Leach, John

GSCD 063 / Oct '95 / Goldmine

☐ **NORTHERN SOUL SATISFACTION**

Let's talk it over: Wiggins, Spencer / Something's bad: Nomads / Age of the wolf: Coleman, Susan / These things will keep me lovin' you: Blue Sharks / The orange: Parker, Eddie / Stoney face: Barbara & The Castles / He's alright with me: Keyman Brass / I don't wanna get away from your love: Daniels, Yvonne / My first lonely night: Akens, Jewel / King for a day: Ames, Stuart / I can't wait to see my baby's face: Monticellos / Iceman: Watkins, Bill / I'll give that to you: Wynns, Sandy / I'm gonna hurt you: Lost Soul Band / If this is love: Spencer, Eddie / Angelina, oh Angelina: Ames, Stuart / Better: Winters, Ruby / Could it be: Farrow, Mikki / Tough girl: Arnell, Billy / That's the way: Q / He's a flirt: Sequins / Who am I (you ought to know): Barnes, Dena / Mr. Loser: Blackwell, George / Don't hold back: Monticellos / Satisfy my baby: Sweets / Lucky day: Coff, Theo Invasion / You're too strong: Coleman, Donna / Something about my baby: Sweets / Crying heart: Gilbert, Carl / That's what I want to know: Carr, James

GSCD 088 / Mar '96 / Goldmine

☐ **NORTHERN SOUL SPECTRUM (From Sweet Exuberance To Empty Despair)**

What shall I do: Frankie & The Classicals / You're the love of my life: Jones, Brenda Lee / Can't stop loving the boy: Carolines / Lonely girl: Fox, Annabelle / Prove it: Wheeler, Mary / Sweet thing: Newbag, Johnny / I've got to find her (and tell her): Williams, Scotty / Wrapped around your finger: Poets / Cover girl: Spencer, Carl / You ain't wrapped too tight: Anthony, Wayne / Joker: Elliot, Shawn / Let me down easy: Lavette, Bettye / Hurt is just beginning: Love, Bailey, J.R. / If you and I had never met: Magic Night / Somebody's lying on love: Val & Nick / Don't fight it baby: Humes, Anita / Change my darkness into light: Flirtations / To the bitter end: Hill, Bobby / I'm losing you: Ballard, Kenny & The Fabulous Soul Brothers / Where I'm gonna find her: Lloyd, Mark / Down by the ocean: Sands, George & Sonny / And heaven was here: Irwin, Big Dee / I don't love you no more baby: Prophets / Teardrops are falling: Little Natalie & Henry/The Gifts / Get on your knees: Los Canarios / Let me go: Big Maybelle / You better go: Martin, Derek

CDKEND 144 / Apr '97 / Kent

☐ **NORTHERN SOUL SURVIVORS (30 Northern Soul Classics From Wigan & Beyond)**

Hold on help is on the way: Davis, G. & R. Tyler / Being without you: Williams, Maurice / Come on train: Thomas, Don / Hung up on your love: General Levy / I dedicated to His Majesty: Jones, Vivian & Nico Junior

GSCD 089 / Feb '97 / Goldmine

☐ **NORTHERN SOUL TIME (2CD Set)**

This man in love: New Wanderers / I'm getting tired: Carlettes / Lover: Deltes / That's what I want: McGowan, Syng / I know I'm in love with you: Byrd, George Duke / Nevertheless: Andrews, Lee / She said goodbye: Hambric, Billy / I can't stand to lose you: Chandler, E.J. / Elijah rockin' with soul: Jacobs, Hank / Lighten up baby: Karim, Ty / He's a flirt: Sequins / You got me in the palm of your hands: Richardson, Donald Lee / I need your love: Chaumonts / Oo we let it be me dealer: Evans, Karl / Black power: Coit, James / Easy baby: Adventures / Just a little while: Jackson, Ollie / I'm gonna love you: Hamilton, Edward / Build your house on a strong foundation: Gwen & Ray / Job opening: Del-Larks / What good am I without you: Champion, Mickey / R 'n' B time: Jones, E.J. / Rooney / Airplay song: Jenkins, Norma & The Dolls / Do we let it me the babe: Lewis, Louise / My terms: Ferguson, Helena / Where can my babe: Martels / He must be doing something right: Moody, Joan / You got to love me babe: Millionaires / Oh baby I dig you: Anderson, Gene / Ever again: Woodbury, Gene / Is it all gone: Magicians / Love Baker, Yvonne / Poor unfortunate me: Taylor, Gloria / I wouldn't come back: Mask Man & the Agents / Come on and live: Fabulous Jades / Walkin' by: Boss / Scandalize my name: Casanova Two / Dial L for lonely: Wilson, Madeline / Coalined baby: Love, Dave / I was born to love you: Hunter, Herbert / My heart is calling you: Manificents / Good girl: Stokes, Patti / I can't give up on losing you: Remarkables / Life: Owens, Gwen / Can't get over these memories: Wells, Bobby / Lovin' you baby: Startones / Fascinating girl: Lemons, George / Come go with me: Para-Monts / Just as much: Peterson, Kris / You better think it over: Du-Shons / Yes I love you baby: Dynamics / Ain't nobody's business if I do: Marbray, Ernie / Just lovin' you: Andrews, Ruby / I have faith in you: Burdick, Doni / You're on my mind: Durane, Paula / Heartbreakin' time: Little John / I gotta good thing going: Executive 4

GSCD 077 / Sep '95 / Goldmine

☐ **NORTHERN SOUL'S DIAMONDS AND PEARLS**

I know the meaning: St. John, Rose & The Wanderettes / Please keep away from me: Parker, Eddie / It's not the same: Little Anthony / Cold wave: Daisies / Kissin' her and crying for you: Checkmates / I know the inside story: Chubby & The Turnpikes / Heart harder: Enjoyables / Love and desire: Holloway, Patrice / Stolen hours: Holloway, Patrice / Same old way: Williams, Scott / Hey girl do you love me: Wilson, Timothy / Look at me look at me: Greene, Vernon / He always comes back to me: King, Clydie / My love goes everywhere: Reed, Vernon / You did: Hibson, Herman / 60 Minutes of your love: Banks, Homer / I'm losing you: Ballard, Kenny / Fine young girl: Andrews, Ernie / Can't chance a breakup:

Turner, Ike & Tina / Mr. Soul Satisfaction: Willis, Timmy / Word without sunshine: Philips, Saundra / Love in my heart: Entertainers / What can I do: Prophet, Billy / She's called a woman: Magnificent 7 / To the bitter end: Hall, Willie

GSCD 076 / May '96 / Goldmine

☐ **NORTHUMBRIAN SMALL PIPES**

Keel row: Clough, Tom / Westering home: Blackett-Ord, Diana / Whittingham Green Lane/Ward's Brae: Hepple, John / Wild hills o'wannie: Pigg, Billy / King's hall/John of Carrick: High Level Ranters / Gypsy's lullaby/The Hawk/Memories/Coates Hall: Pigg, Billy / Oh dear, what can the matter be: Atkinson, George / Sir Sidney Smith's march: Hutton, Joe / Lovat scouts/Roxborough Castle/Bonny North Tyne: Alston flower: Hutton, Joe / Sunderland lasses/Lads of Alnwick: Cut & Dry Band / Fenwick of Bywell: High Level Ranters / Barrington hornpipe/Rowley Burn: Hutton, Joe / Proudlock's hornpipe: High Level Ranters / Ho'ley ha'penny/Elsie Marley: Clough, Tom / John Fenwick's the flower among them: Cut & Dry Band / Salmon tails up the water/Herd on the hill/Sweet Hesleyside: Cassley, Colin & Forster Charlton / Coldsfield House/Thorn's march: High Level Ranters / Skye crofters/The Swallow's tail: Pigg, Billy / My laddie sits o'er late up/Shew's the way to Wallington: Cut & Dry Band / Surprise: High Level Ranters / Bonny Woodside/Coffee Bridge: Cut & Dry Band / Dr. Whittaker's hornpipe/Nancy: Cut & Dry Band / Hexham quadrille/Kielder fells: High Level Ranters

TSCD 487 / Nov '96 / Topic

☐ **NORWEGIAN BRASS BAND CHAMPIONSHIPS 1996**

Energy / Partita / Music for the common man / Harmony festival / Variations on an enigma

DOYCD 051 / Jul '96 / Doyen

☐ **NORWEGIAN FOLK MUSIC VOL.1-10 (10CD Set)**

GR 4099CD / Jul '95 / Grappa

☐ **NOT JUST RAGGA**

So real: Sanchez / Thinking about you: McLean, John / Spare me: Wayne Wonder / Rebel woman: Jones, Vivian / Do you remember # 2: Davis, Janet-Lee / Guess I know the reason why: Barry Boom / Perfect lady: Hunningale, Peter / Jungle bungle: Starkey Banton / Run way Mr. Tickle: General Dog / Beaten: Nico Junior / Hyper: Sweetie Irie / One more request: Papa San / Gone down inna mi culture: General Levy / Dedicated to His Majesty: Jones, Vivian & Nico Junior

FADCD 032 / Jan '96 / Fashion

☐ **NOT THE SAME OLD BLUES CRAP**

I'm insane: T-Model Ford / Meet me in the city: Kimbrough, Junior / Come right in: 20 Miles / Snake drive: Burnside, R.L. / Crack whore blues: Neckbones / Lonesome road: Kimbrough, Junior / Have mercy baby: Jelly Roll Kings / If I can't come in: Burnside, R.L. / Been here and gone: Williams, Elmore / Little Eddie blues: Cage, Robert / Your memories: Adkins, Hasil

03122 / 23 Mar '98 / Epitaph

☐ **NOT THE SINGER BUT**

MR 012CD / Apr '92 / Munster

☐ **NOTHIN' BUT THE BLUES (2CD Set)**

DEMPCD 006 / Mar '96 / Emporio

☐ **NOTHIN' BUT THE BLUES (36 Blues Standards - 2CD Set)**

Hoochie coochie man: Waters, Muddy / When my first wife left me: Hooker, John Lee / Shake it for me: Howlin' Wolf / Only fools have fun: Memphis Slim / Don't make me: Hopkins, Lightnin' / You're something else: Reed, Jimmy / Lightnin's boogie: Hopkins, Lightnin' / Oh baby: Lightnin' Slim / Cold and lonesome: Reed, Jimmy / Got my mojo working: Waters, Muddy / No shoes: Hooker, John Lee / Gamblers blues: Memphis Slim / Little rain: Reed, Jimmy / Bad luck blues: Lightnin' Slim / Don't start me talkin': Howlin' Wolf / I'm so excited: Hooker, John Lee / Blues blues: Cage, Robert / Forty years or more: Memphis Slim / Forty four: Hooker, John Lee / Forty four: Howlin' Wolf / Only fool: Reed, Jimmy / Easy on your heels: Hopkins, Lightnin' / Forty four: Baby please don't go: Waters, Muddy / Forty years or more: Reed, Jimmy / Forty years or more: Memphis Slim / Thelma: Hooker, John Lee / Hoodoo blues: Lightnin' Slim / Don't think because: Dusty road: Hooker, John Lee / Don't think because you're pretty: Hopkins, Lightnin' / Howlin' Wolf: Waters, Muddy

330032 / Jul '96 / Hallmark

☐ **NOTHIN' BUT THE BLUES**

EABCD 052 / 24 Nov '97 / Eagle

☐ **NOTHING BUT LOVE SONGS VOL.2**

PILCD 206 / Dec '94 / Pioneer

☐ **NOTHING SHORT OF TOTAL WAR**

Come and smash me said the boy with the magic pen: Sonic Youth / Buggin': Head Of David / Fire in Philly: Lit / He's on fire: Sonic Youth / Kerosene: Big Black / Magic wand: Sonic Youth / Dutch courage: Rapeman / Bulbs of passion: Ranaldo, Lee / Scratchy heart: Cocoanut Youth / Evangelist: Lit / Snake domain: Head Of David / He's a whore: Big Black / Devil's jukebox: Big Stick / 108: Head Of David / Warrenettes / Please keep away from me: Parker, Eddie / Boyd / Sheikh: AC Temple / Just got paped today: Rapeman / Throne of David: King Snake Of Susans / Little is the law: Seahorses / 100 mile high city: Ocean Colour Scene / Old before I die: Williams, Robbie

☐ **NOTHING TO LOSE**

TBCD 1169 / Jul '97 / Tommy Boy

☐ **NOTHING'S GONNA STOP US NOW**

NSCD 015 / Feb '95 / Newsound

☐ **NOVA BALANCO (Brazilian Nu-Beat)**

Boa viagem: Nova Fronteira / Back to music: JD's Jam / Batucada: Forest Mighty Black / Space jazz: Azymuth / Calma: Azymuth / Fuze: Naturel Element / Bandito batucada: Naturel Element / Ritmo: Naturel Element / Tempos atraz: Azymuth / Os grillos: Valle, Marcos & Friends From Rio / Ponteio: Da Lata / Samba perugina: Nova Fronteira

LC 3127 / 3 Nov '97 / Koch International

☐ **NOVEDADES DE CHILE**

Subete a la vereda / Estoy que me muero / Tango / Maquinarias / Para el camino / Se nos pierde la mirada / Comparsa de olvidada tierra / Nuctal lacta / El viejo truco / El mensajero del amor / Corazones partidos / La semilla / Senoritas y caballeros / Refka / Colores de chiloe

68934 / Jul '97 / Tropical

☐ **NOW AND IN TIME TO BE (A Musical Celebration Of The Works Of W.B.Yeats)**

GRACD 219 / Jan '97 / Grapevine

☐ **NOW DANCE '97 (2CD Set)**

Spice up your life: Spice Girls / Samba de Janeiro: Bellini / Freed from desire: Gala / Da ya think I'm sexy: N-Trance / You sexy thing: Hot Chocolate / I wanna be the only one: Eternal & Bebe Winans / Everybody (Backstreet's back): Backstreet Boys / Bodyshakin': 911 / Strangest thing: Michael, George / Closer than close: Gaines, Rosie / Who do you think you are: Spice Girls / Oh la la la: 2 Eivissa / Ecuador: Sash / Belissima: DJ Quicksilver / Every little time: Poppers & Aura / Ready or not: Course / Joy: Staxx / Offshore: Chicane & Power Circle / Arms around the world: Louise / Flash: BBE / Passion: Amen U2 / James Bond theme: Moby / Tubthumping: Chumbawamba / Block rockin' beats: Chemical Brothers / Remember me: Blueboy / You got the love: Source & Candi Staton / Angel of mine: Eternal / Ooh la la: Coolio / Hold your head up high: Dlugosch, Boris & Booom / I need a miracle: Coco / Spiller from Rio: Laguna / Nightmare: Brainbug / Free: DJ Quicksilver / Everybody loves a carnival: Fatboy Slim / Breathe: Prodigy / Choose life: PF Project / Singing stones: Harris, Johnny / Strings for Yasmin: Tin Tin Out / Bentley's gonna sort you out: Bentley Rhythm Ace / Scared: Slacker / Rock da house: Tall Paul / Give me love: Diddy / Circles: Adam F

CDNOD 17 / 20 Oct '97 / Virgin

☐ **NOW THAT'S WHAT I CALL MUSIC 1996 (2CD Set)**

CDNOW 1996 / Oct '96 / EMI

☐ **NOW THAT'S WHAT I CALL MUSIC VOL.35 (2CD Set)**

Say you'll be there: Spice Girls / Fastlove: Michael, George / Flava: Andre, Peter / If you ever: East 17 & Gabrielle / Breakfast at Tiffany's: Deep Blue Something / Se a vida e: Pet Shop Boys / You're gorgeous: Baby Bird / Rotterdam: Beautiful South / If you're thinking of me: Dodgy / Don't dream it's over: Crowded House / Marblehead Johnson: Bluetones / River boat song: Ocean Colour Scene / If it makes you happy: Crow, Sheryl / Milk: Garbage / Woman: Cherry, Neneh / Beautiful ones: Suede / Something changed: Pulp / Flying: Cast / Always breaking my heart: Carlisle, Belinda / Escaping: Carroll, Dina / Words: Boyzone / Someday: Eternal / I'll get over you: Michael, George / Damage / On what a night: Rosie / Strike / Insomnia: Faithless / Seven days and one week: BBE / I'm alive: Stretch n' Vern / Stamp: Jump to my beat: Wildchild / Pearl's girl: Underworld / Neighbourhood: Space / Possibly maybe: Bjork / Chasing rainbows: Shed Seven

CDNOW 35 / Nov '96 / EMI

☐ **NOW THAT'S WHAT I CALL MUSIC VOL.36 (2CD Set)**

Mama: Spice Girls / Say what you want: Texas / Alone: Bee Gees / Don't marry her: Beautiful South / Don't speak: No Doubt / Your woman: White Town / Remember me: Blueboy / Virtual insanity: Jamiroquai / One and one: Miles, Robert & Maria Naylor / Spinning the wheel: Michael, George / Horny: Morrison, Mark / Natural: Andre, Peter / Love guaranteed: Damaged / Don't ya love me true: Eternal / Walk on by: Gabrielle / I can make you feel good: Kavana / Hey child: East 17 / Different beat: Boyzone / Anywhere for you: Backstreet Boys / Placebo / Who do you want from me: Monaco / Everyday is a winding road: Crow, Sheryl / Beetlebum: Blur / Ava's alive: Skunk Anansie / Clouds: Space / Mansun / Free me: Cast / Dark clouds: Space / Waterloo sunset: Dennis, Cathy / Everybody knows (except you): Divine Comedy / Indestructable: Alisha's attic / Shout: Ant & Dec / Free woman: Source & Candi Staton / Encore en fois: Sash / Bellissima: DJ Quicksilver / Flash: BBE / Passion: Amen UK

CDNOW 36 / Mar '97 / EMI

☐ **NOW THAT'S WHAT I CALL MUSIC VOL.37 (2CD Set)**

MMMbop: Hanson / I wanna be the only one: Eternal & Bebe Winans / Lovefool: Cardigans / Just a girl: No Doubt / Ecuador: Sash & Rodriguez / Where do you go: No Mercy / Who do you think you are: Spice Girls / Block rockin' beats: Chemical Brothers / Nancy boy: Placebo / Star people: Michael, George / Don't let go: En Vogue / You might need somebody: Ama, Shola / U U / Too much heaven: Eternal / Ma baker: Boney M / U can't make it coolio: Coolio & 40 Thevz / Smokin' me out: Warren G / Your loving arms: Madison Avenue / Night fever: Boyzone / Hey D Jr. N-Tyce / I'll be: Brown, Foxy & Jay Z / If I never see you again: Wet Wet Wet / Staring at the sun: U2 / Bittersweet Symphony: Verve / Come is the law: Seahorses / 100 mile high city: Ocean Colour Scene / Old before I die: Williams, Robbie / Guiding star: Cast / Young boy: McCartney, Paul / Change would do you good: Crow, Sheryl / Paranoid android: Radiohead / Halo: Texas / Sun hits the sky: Supergrass / Waltzing along: James / On your own: Blur / Scooby snacks: Fun Lovin' Criminals / Saint: Something's going on: Terry, Todd & Martha Wash / Jocelyn Brown / Give me love: Diddy

CDNOW 37 / 14 Jul '97 / EMI

☐ **NOW THAT'S WHAT I CALL MUSIC VOL.38 (2CD Set)**
Tubthumping: *Chumbawamba* / Spice up your life: *Spice Girls* / Where's the love: *Hanson* / Picture of you: *Boyzone* / Angel of mine: *Eternal* / Raincloud: *Lighthouse Family* / Got til it's gone: *Jackson, Janet* / You've got a friend: *Brand New Heavies* / I know where it's at: *All Saints* / Arms around the world: *Louise* / Freed from desire: *Gala* / Stay: *Sash & La Trec* / Sunchyme: *Dario G* / Never gonna let you go: *Moore, Tina* / You sexy thing: *Hot Chocolate* / Do ya think I'm sexy: *N-Trance & Rod Stewart* / Phenomenon: *LL Cool J* / Party people...Friday night: *911* / Maria: *Martin, Ricky* / Samba de Janeiro: *Bellini* / Free: *DJ Quicksilver* / Yesterday: *Wet Wet Wet* / You have dbeen loved: *Michael, George* / Drugs don't work: *Verve* / Stand by me: *Oasis* / All you good good people: *Embrace* / Don't leave: *Faithless* / Karma police: *Radiohead* / Ames Bond theme: *Moby* / Choose life: *PF Project & Ewan McGregor* / Lazy days: *Williams, Robbie* / Life less ordinary: *Ash* / Black eyed boy: *Texas* / Bitch: *Brooks, Meredith* / Janie don't take your love to town: *Bon Jovi, Jon* / Better day: *Ocean Colour Scene* / I'm so lonely: *Cast* / Earthbound: *Reeves, Conner* / Lonely: *Andre, Peter* / 4 Season's of loneliness: *Boyz II Men*
CDNOW 38 / 17 Nov '97 / EMI

☐ **NOW THAT'S WHAT I CALL MUSIC VOL.39 (2CD Set)**
No way no: *Vanilla* / Whine and grine: *Prince Buster* / Ain't that just the way: *McNeal, Lutricia* / Prince Igor: *Warren G & Sissel* / Treat infamy: *Rest Assured* / How do I live: *Rimes, Leann* / All I have to give: *Backstreet Boys* / Weird: *Hanson* / Insane: *Texas* / Kiss the rain: *Myers, Billie* / Tomorrow never dies: *Crow, Sheryl* / Ballad of Tom Jones: *Space* / Torn: *Imbruglia, Natalie* / Renegade master 98: *Wildchild* / You're still the one: *Twain, Shania* / Let me entertain you: *Williams, Robbie* / Mulder and Scully: *Catatonia* / Believe: *Goldie* / Brimful of asha: *Cornershop* / Baby can I hold you: *Boyzone* / Perfect day / No suprises: *Radiohead* / Together again: *Jackson, Janet* / Bamboogie: *Bamboo* / Angels: *Williams, Robbie* / Found a cure: *Ultra Nate* / Lucky man: *Verve* / Never ever: *All Saints* / Her's where the story ends: *Tin Tin Out* / Stop: *Spice Girls* / High: *Lighthouse Family* / Let me show you: *Camisra* / Amnesia: *Chumbawamba* / Planet love: *DJ Quicksilver* / Barbie girl: *Aqua* / Let's go round again: *Louise* / It's like that: *Run DMC & Jason Nevins* / La primavera: *Sash* / 5678: *Steps* / This is hardcore: *Pulp* / Beat goes on: *All Seeing I*
CDNOW 39 / 6 Apr '98 / EMI

☐ **NOW THAT'S WHAT I CALL MUSIC VOL.40 (2CD Set)**
Grease megamix: *Travolta, John & Olivia Newton John* / Viva forever: *Spice Girls* / Looking for love: *Ramirez, Karen* / Because we want to: *Billie* / Lady marmalade: *All Saints* / Horny: *Mousse T & Hot 'n' Juicy* / Feel it: *Tamperer & Maya* / Doctor Jones: *Aqua* / Last thing on my mind: *Steps* / You make me feel like dancing: *Groove Generation & Leo Sayer* / Kung fu dancing: *Bus Stop & Carl Douglas* / New kind of medicine: *Ultra Nate* / Stranded: *McNeal, Lutricia* / Lost in space: *Lighthouse Family* / All that I need: *Boyzone* / All saints: *All Saints* / I get lonely: *Jackson, Janet* / Be careful: *Sparkle & R. Kelly* / Kiss the girl: *Andre, Peter* / Boys of summer: *Henley, Don* / Dance the night away: *Mavericks* / Save tonight: *Cherry, Eagle Eye* / Road rage: *Catatonia* / Big mistake: *Imbruglia, Natalie* / Come back to what you know: *Embrace* / Sonnet: *Verve* / Teardrop: *Massive Attack* / Legacy: *Mansun* / Three lions: *Baddiel & Skinner & Lightning Seeds* / Vinda da loo: *Fat Les* / Rockafeller skank: *Fatboy Slim* / Needin' you: *Morales, David & Face* / I can't help myself: *Lucid* / Keep on dancin: *Perpetual Motion* / Everybody dance: *Tucker, Barbara* / Where are you: *Imaani* / Night fever: *Garcia, Adam* / Do you love me boy: *Kerry-Ann* / No tengo dinero: *Los Umbrellos*
CDNOW 40 / 3 Aug '98 / EMI

☐ **NOWHERE MEN TOO (British Beat 1964-1967)**
LCD 112 / 2 Feb '98 / LCD

☐ **NOWSOUNDS TOP 10 TEXAS**
COLCD 0511 / Jun '97 / Collectables

☐ **NRG RUSH (Mixed By Marc Edwards)**
CDKOPY 108 / 26 Jan '98 / Klone

☐ **NU COOL, THE (2CD Set)**
Spartacus: *Callier, Terry* / I am the black gold of the sun: *NuYorican Soul* / Rush over: *Ndegeocello, Me'shell & Marcus Miller* / Spiritual love: *Urban Species* / Time: *S-Tone Inc.* / Boundaries: *Leena Conquest* / Staten Island groove: *Down To The Bone* / Sucker for your love: *Hit The Boom* / I'll be around: *Soundscape* / Sausolito calling: *Came'lle* / Enjoy the sunshine: *Quiet Boys* / ELBOY: *RAD* / Jesse: *Mother Earth* / Brand new day: *Yada Yada*
JAZZFMCD 9 / 8 Jun '98 / Jazz FM

☐ **NU ENERGY**
Feeling: *Tin Tin Out & Sweet Tee* / Infanta-ci: *Baby Doc & The Dentist* / Cosmonautica: *Virtuolisimo* / First rebirth (Hiroshima nu-energy reconstruction): *Jones & Stephenson* / Casablanca: *Dual Mount* / Energy frenzy: *OCP* / Three minute warning: *Yum Yum* / Catalan rising: *Baby Doc & The Dentist* / For your love: *Elevator* / Mantra to the buddha (Higher state): *Hyperspace* / Dragnet (action hero): *Hiroshima*
CDTOT 19 / Oct '94 / Jumpin' & Pumpin'

☐ **NU GROOVE (4CD Set)**
CDBNTW 3 / 13 Apr '98 / Passion

☐ **NU PERSPECTIVE**
PARTCD 002 / 31 Aug '98 / Partisan

☐ **NU SCHOOL - DANCE MUSIC OF THE CARRIBEAN**
8289312 / 1 Sep '97 / London

☐ **NU SKOOL BREAKZ**
KICKCD 67 / 2 Feb '98 / Kickin'

☐ **NU SKOOL FLAVA**
Flexiwidatel: *Elementz Of Noize* / This style: *Shy FX* / Mid town method level 2: *DJ Trace* / Stick up: *Elementz Of Noize* / Mass hysteria: *Shapeshifter* / Hit the deck: *Shapeshifter* / Let me be: *L-Double* / Amber: *T-Power* / Way it goes down: *DJ Kane* / Funkindem up: *Shy FX* / Difference: *Skyscraper*
SOURCD 006 / Mar '96 / SOUR

☐ **NU SKOOL UPDATE**
Talkin' mad shit: *Shapeshifter* / Nasty: *T-Power* / Let the bass boom: *TC Islam & Alien 3* / Communicate with the world: *Shapeshifter* / Let me recommend: *Dreamteam & MC Det* / Into the beat: *45 Roller* / Punk mutha: *Microburst* / Outcast: *Tonic* / One time: *Elementz Of Noize* / Science: *Elementz Of Noize* / Let the funk flow: *Shy FX* / Body snatcher: *Tonic*
SOURCD 008 / Oct '96 / SOUR

☐ **NU SOUL CLASSICS VOL.1**
HOTTCD 2 / Dec '95 / Hott

☐ **NU YORICA VOL.1 - CULTURE CLASH IN NEW YORK CITY (Experiments In Latin Music 1970-1977 - 2CD Set)**
What are you doing for the rest of your life: *Ocho* / Gumbo: *Cortijo & His Time Machine* / La trompeta y la flauta: *Lopez, Israel 'Cachao' Y Su Descarga* / Babalonia: *Marrero, Ricardo* / Harlem river drive theme: *Harlem River Drive* / Amigos: *Stone Alliance* / Latin strut: *Bataan, Joe* / Anabacoa: *Grupo Folklorico & Experimental Nuevoyorquino* / Tempo 70: *El Gallenton* / Un dia bonita: *Palmieri, Eddie* / Carnaval: *Cortijo & His Time Machine* / Coco may may: *Ocho* / Idle hands: *Harlem River Drive* / Little Rico, little Rico's theme: *Paunetto, Bobby* / Aftershower funk: *Bataan, Joe* / Macho: *Machito & His Orchestra*
SJRCD 029 / Jan '96 / Soul Jazz

☐ **NU YORICA VOL.2 - SHANGO IN THE NEW WORLD (Further Adventures In Latin Music)**
Salute to Elegua: *Cardona, Milton* / O mi shango: *Santamaria, Mongo* / Patato: *Patato, Dicelo* / Spirit of love: *Palmieri, Eddie* / Coro miyare: *Fania Allstars* / Jingo: *Candido* / Odie: *Ponce, Daniel* / Encuentro: *Irakere* / Ko-wo ko-wo: *Cachao* / En orbita: *Fania Allstars* / Barrio nuevo: *Ramirez, Louie* / Lamento borincano: *Libre*
SJRCD 036 / Aug '97 / Soul Jazz

☐ **NU YORICAN HITS**
CDGR 164 / Aug '97 / Charly

☐ **NU YORK NU SKOOL**
Music for the lonely: *Myerson, Jamie* / Drum: *Shooter* / Pressure: *Sub Zero* / Temperature rising: *New Nexus* / Biomagnetics: *DJ Ani* / Nexus apache: *DJ Trance* / Bitch trip: *DJ DB & Tommy D* / Boarder patrol: *Double A & Twist* / Step right in: *Dog Eat Dog* / What's happening now: *Sub Zero* / Funky beeper: *Timezone Vs. Dara* / Smoke: *DJ Dara* / Better world: *Jason Mouse* / Away: *Myerson, Jamie*
SM 80322 / Mar '97 / Profile

☐ **NUBIAN BEATS**
TRIPCD 7 / Oct '96 / Rumour

☐ **NUEVO FLAMENCO**
NSCD 014 / Mar '97 / Nascente

☐ **NUMBER ONE HITS VOL.1**
DCD 5371 / Apr '94 / Disky

☐ **NUMBER ONE HITS VOL.2**
DCD 5372 / Apr '94 / Disky

☐ **NUMBER ONE HITS VOL.3**
DCD 5373 / Apr '94 / Disky

☐ **NUMBER ONE HITS VOL.4**
DCD 5374 / Apr '94 / Disky

☐ **NUMBER ONE HITS VOL.5**
DCD 5375 / Apr '94 / Disky

☐ **NUMBER ONE HITS VOL.6**
DCD 5376 / Apr '94 / Disky

☐ **NUMBER ONE HITS VOL.7**
DCD 5377 / Apr '94 / Disky

☐ **NUMBER ONE HITS VOL.8**
DCD 5378 / Apr '94 / Disky

☐ **NYC HARDCORE**
REV 007CD / May '96 / Revelation

☐ **NYC HOUSE**
ZYX 811052 / Jul '97 / ZYX

O

☐ **O MELHOR DA BOSSA**
1917452 / Apr '97 / EPM

☐ **OBJETS D'ART VOL.1 (2CD Set)**
Clinically inclined: *Future/Past* / Amalia: *As One* / Whirling of spirits: *Balil* / Choke and fly: *Balil* / Neurotic behaviour: *Psyche* / How the West was won: *Psyche* / Chicken noodle soup: *BFC* / Sleep: *BFC* / Exteriors: *Esoterik* / Locators: *Esoterik* / Into the other world: *Phenomyna* / Earthfall: *Phenomyna* / Got the urge: *Phenomyna* / Enseble: *Elegy* / Tone poem: *Elegy* / Kwaidan: *Esoterik* / P switch: *Elegy* / Climatic calm: *Red cell*
ELEC 27 / Mar '96 / New Electronica

☐ **OBJETS D'ART VOL.3**
ELEC 31CD / Feb '97 / New Electronica

☐ **OBLIVAN**
OOR 023CD / Nov '95 / Out Of Romford

☐ **OBRIGADO BATERIA**
CD 1229 / 12 May '98 / CID

☐ **OBSCURE AND ROCKIN'**
CLCD 4431 / Sep '96 / Collector/White Label

☐ **OBSCURE BLUES SHOUTERS VOL.2**
BMCD 6011 / Jan '98 / Blue Moon

☐ **OBSESSIVE HOUSE CULTURE VOL.1**
OBRCD 1 / Mar '94 / Obsessive

☐ **OBSESSIVE HOUSE CULTURE VOL.2**
OBRCD 2 / Aug '94 / Obsessive

☐ **OCEAN DAYBREAK**
DC 879582 / Oct '97 / Disky

☐ **OCEAN OF SOUND**
Dub fi gwan: *King Tubby* / Rain dance: *Hancock, Herbie* / Analogue bubblebath 1: *Aphex Twin* / Empire III: *Hassell, Jon* / Sorban palid: *Suryana, Ujang* / Prelude a l'apres midi d'un faune: *English Chamber Orchestra* / Sunken city: *Baxter, Les* / Loomer: *My Bloody Valentine* / Lizard point: *Eno, Brian* / Shunie Omizutori Buddhist ceremony / Music of horns and whistles: *Vancouver Soundscape* / Howler monkeys / Machine gun: *Brotzmann, Peter Octet* / Yanomami rain song / Bismillah 'rrahmani 'rrahim: *Budd, Harold* / Black satin: *Davis, Miles* / All night flight: *Riley, Terry* / Coyor Panon: *Kurnia, Detty* / Virgin beauty: *Coleman, Ornette* / Chen pe'i pe'i: *Zorn, John & David Toop* / Rivers of mercury: *Schutze, Paul* / I heard her call my name: *Velvet Underground* / Bearded seals / Boat-woman song: *Czukay, Holger & Rolf Dammers* / Fall breaks and back into winter: *Beach Boys* / Faraway chant: *African Headcharge* / Cosmo enticement: *Sun Ra* / Untitled 3: *Music Improvisation Company* / Seven-up: *Deep Listening Band* / In a landscape: *Cage, John* / Vexations: *Marks, Alan* / Suikinkutsu water chime
AMBT 10 / Jan '96 / Virgin

☐ **OCEAN SERENITY (A Magical Blend Of Music And The Sounds Of Nature)**
57752 / May '97 / Nature's Harmony

☐ **OCTANE RATING 98.1**
HOR 001CD / 29 Jun '98 / High Octane

☐ **OCTOBER REVOLUTION, THE**
For Bill Dixon I: *Ali, Rashied & Borah Bergman/Joe McPhee/Wilber Morris* / Death of Danny Love: *Melford, Myra Trio* / For Bill Dixon II: *Ali, Rashied & Borah Bergman/Joe McPhee/Wilber Morris*
ECD 221662 / Oct '96 / Evidence

☐ **ODD SHAPED BALLS (Rugby Songs) (2CD Set)**
When I was youmg / A miner coming home one night / Sterilised heiress / Home on the range / Mother / Roll your leg over / Woodpeckers song / A rovin' / Abdul the bulbul emir / Doodle de doo / Soggy soggy dew / Professions / Big bamboo / Oh sir Jasper / Sing us another one / Ram of Derbyshire / Doggies meeting / Next thanksgiving / Maggie May / If I was the marrying kind / Oh how the money rolls in / Six old ladies / Clementine / Roll me over / Dinah / I used to work in Chicago / Barnacle Bill the sailor / Here's to the good old beer / Horndean school / Frankie and Johnny / She was poor but she was honest / Old King Cole / Sexual life of a camel / Traveller / Virgin sturgeon / Sweet violets
330202 / Jul '96 / Hallmark

☐ **ODDS BODS AND SODS**
Can't believe it's true: *VIP's* / Livin' in the city: *VIP's* / Know what I mean: *Split Screen* / No good for me: *Clerks* / Statik motion: *Justin Case* / Wild boys in cortinas: *Urban Discharge* / Just can't let you go: *VIP's* / Get ready to go: *Squire* / Just don't try: *Squire* / You: *Just Frank* / When the lights go out: *Clerks* / Doing the flail: *Coming Shortly* / Gotta change my life: *Hazard* / Mary Jane: *Blue Movies* / Too far to look inside my head: *Blue Movies* / After my blood: *X-Films* / What's wrong with a pop group: *Zeros* / Decisions: *Action Replay* / Where is johnny: *Innocent Bystanders* / Man in the street: *Debutantes* / TV: *Justin Case* / One out all out: *Straight Up*
MODSKACD 002 / 3 Nov '97 / Captain Mod

☐ **OFF DA HEAD HIP HOP VOL.1**
SUB 42D / 2 Feb '98 / Subversive

☐ **OFF THE TOP VOL.1 (13 Nu-Jazz Beats)**
MA 008 / Mar '97 / M

☐ **OFF THE WALL**
VPCD 2050 / Jul '96 / VP

☐ **OFFERING VOL.1 (The Past & Present Of K7)**
Detroit after dark: *Parker, Terrence* / Black baby: *Kruder & Dorfmeister* / Gangsta shit: *DJ Cam* / Heavybreath: *Impulse* / Wisdom: *Deason, Sean* / World of deep: *E-Dancer* / Claude Young: *Young, Claude* / Walk under a full moon's light: *Kanabis The Edit Assassin* / Black single: *Farda P* / All day: *Nicolette* / Carl Craig: *Craig, Carl* / Columbia: *Varley, Gaz*
K7 059CD / Jun '97 / Studio K7

☐ **OFFERING VOL.2**
Contact/Lezlie: *Terranova* / Tell me why is it oh so hard to be oh so lovely: *Shantel* / No compromise: *Khao* / Man with no thumbs: *Simmonds, Ian* / Wall of pressure: *Impulse* / I don't know: *Smith & Mighty* / Deep off ends: *Sample OS* / Crazy deceased and betrayed: *Khao* / Philosophy: *Shantel* / Bronx theme: *DJ Cam* / Play ah hate ah: *Parker, Terrence* / Wall of deceit: *Impulse* / Helter skelter: *Lame Gold*
K7 070CD / 27 Jul '98 / Studio K7

☐ **OH CANADUH VOL.2**
LRR 031CD / 29 Jun '98 / Lance Rock

☐ **OH CHERRY OH BABY**
LG 21047 / Feb '93 / Lagoon

☐ **OH HAPPY DAY**
Step by step: *Hawkins, Edwin Singers* / He saved my soul: *Swan Silvertones* / Nobody knows: *Highway QC's* / God is moving: *Martin, Sallie Singers* / Walk with me: *Highway QC's* / Get your soul right: *Swan Silvertones* / We shall overcome: *Swan Silvertones* / Oh happy day: *Hawkins, Edwin Singers* / I can see evrybody's mother: *5 Blind Boys of Alabama* / Pray on: *Staple Singers* / He has the way: *Greatest Harvest Choir* / Good news: *Staple Singers* / Too close to heaven: *Bradford, Alex* / Father I stretch my hand to thee: *Harmonizing Four* / See how he kept me: *Argo Singers* / I'm going through: *Caravans*
307942 / 15 Sep '97 / Hallmark

☐ **OH JULIE (Teen Group Sounds From Nashville & The South)**
Oh Julie: *Crescendos* / My little girl: *Crescendos* / School girl: *Crescendos* / Crazy hop: *Crescendos* / Young and in love: *Crescendos* / Rainy Sunday: *Crescendos* / I've tried: *Crescendos* / Gawk 'n' stroll: *Crescendos* / Lucky love: *Crescendos* / Teenage angel: *Crescendos* / Jackie: *Green, Janice* / With all my heart: *Green, Janice* / I'm waiting: *Fortune, Billy* / My pretty baby: *Plaids* / Til the end of the dance: *Plaids* / Still love you baby: *Tabs* / Will we meet again: *Tabs* / You know baby: *Meloaires* / I'm so glad: *Meloaires* / Teacher don't keep me in: *Martels* / Where did my woman go: *Martels* / That's how I go for you: *Butler, Cliff Group* / I've got my heart in my hand: *Storm, Warren Group* / Love you a thousand ways: *Bob & Ray* / Isle of Sue Saint Marie: *Bob & Ray* / Sweet Nancy: *Bob & Ray* / Mr. Blues (poor old lonely me): *Lindsey Brothers* / Maybe: *Trends* / Candy to my sherry: *Moffett, Kenny*
CDCHD 647 / Apr '97 / Ace

☐ **OH KASIO BOY**
CD 024C / May '97 / Carotte

☐ **OH WHAT A NIGHT (2CD Set)**
December '63 (Oh what a night): *Valli, Frankie & Four Seasons* / Love train: *O'Jays* / Shaft: *Hayes, Isaac* / Dance to the music: *Sly & The Family Stone* / Get up I feel like being a sex machine: *Brown, James* / Lady Marmalade: *Labelle* / Get down on it: *Kool & The Gang* / I'll go where your music takes me: *James, Jimmy & The Vagabonds* / Boogie nights: *Heatwave* / I love to love: *Charles, Tina* / You make me feel like dancing: *Sayer, Leo* / Strut your funky stuff: *Frantique* / Ladies night: *Kool & The Gang* / Hang on in there baby: *Bristol, Johnny* / Wishing on a star: *Rose Royce* / Rock the boat: *Hues Corporation* / Blame it on the boogie: *Jacksons* / Boogie wonderland: *Earth, Wind & Fire* / Oops upside your head: *Gap Band* / Use it up and wear it out: *Odyssey* / YMCA: *Village People* / Play that funky music: *Wild Cherry* / Best of my love: *Emotions* / Red light spells danger: *Ocean, Billy* / Move on up: *Mayfield, Curtis* / You to me are everything: *Real Thing* / Rasputin: *Boney M* / Stayin' alive: *N-Trance* / DISCO: *Ottawan* / Always and forever: *Heatwave* / When I need you: *Sayer, Leo* / Harvest for the world: *Isley Brothers* / I will survive: *Gaynor, Gloria* / Disco inferno: *Trammps* / I'm in the mood for dancing: *Nolans* / Celebration: *Kool & The Gang* / Ain't no stopping us now: *McFadden & Whitehead* / We are family: *Sister Sledge* / Heaven must be missing an angel: *Tavares* / Young hearts run free: *Staton, Candi* / December '63 (Oh what a night): *Kid Creole* / Love train: *Kid Creole*
SONYTV 38CD / 9 Mar '98 / Sony TV

☐ **OH WHAT A YEAR 1955-1959 (3CD Set)**
KBOX 378 / 29 Jun '98 / Collection

☐ **OH WHAT A YEAR 1960-1964 (3CD Set)**
KBOX 379 / 29 Jun '98 / Collection

☐ **OH WHAT A YEAR 1965-1969 (3CD Set)**
KBOX 380 / 29 Jun '98 / Collection

☐ **OH WHAT A YEAR 1970-1974 (3CD Set)**
KBOX 381 / 29 Jun '98 / Collection

☐ **OH WHAT A YEAR 1975-1979**
KBOX 382 / 29 Jun '98 / Collection

☐ **OHM GURU PRESENTS THE FUTURE SOUND OF ITALY**
PAZ 803CD / Sep '97 / La Plaza

☐ **OI CHARTBUSTERS VOL.1 & 2**
GLC: *Menace* / Mania: *Strike* / Five minute fashion: *Infa Riot* / Suburban rebels: *Business* / Two pints of lager: *Splodgenessabounds* / Stark raving normal: *Blood* / Police car: *Cockney Rejects* / Blind ambition: *Partisans* / Time bomb: *Blitz* / Rapist: *Combat 84* / Runnin' riot: *Cock Sparrer* / Clockwork skinhead: *4 Skins* / Murder of liddle towers: *Angelic Upstarts* / Violence in our minds: *Last Resort* / Give a dog a bone (live): *Sham 69* / Riot riot: *Infa Riot* / Borstal breakout: *Accident* / Get outta my 'ouse: *Business* / Two little boys: *Splodgenessabounds* / Such fun: *Blood* / Motorhead: *Cockney Rejects* / Daily news: *Exploited* / 4Q: *Blitz* / Poseur: *Combat 84* / Run for cover: *Cock Sparrer* / Plastic gangsters: *4 Skins* / Leave me alone: *Angelic Upstarts* / Held hostage: *Last Resort*
STEPCD 011 / 4 May '98 / Step 1

☐ **OI IT'S A WORLD INVASION VOL.3**
STEPCD 109 / 24 Nov '97 / Step 1

☐ **OI IT'S STREETPUNK VOL.1**
HOO 11 / Oct '97 / Helen Of Oi

☐ **OI IT'S STREETPUNK VOL.2**
HOO 39CD / 6 Jul '98 / Helen Of Oi

☐ **OI OF JAPAN**
AA 016CD / Mar '97 / AA

☐ **OI OI THAT'S YER LOT**
STEPCD 026 / 23 Mar '98 / Step 1

☐ **OI THE ALBUM**
Oi oi oi: *Cockney Rejects* / Rob a bank: *Peter & The Test Tube Babies* / Wonderful world: *4 Skins* / Have a cigar: *Postmen* / Daily news: *Exploited* / Generation of scars: *Terrible twins* / Guns for the Afghan rebels: *Cock Sparrer* / Sunday stripper: *Cock Sparrer* / Last

night another soldier: *Angelic Upstarts* / Chaos: *4 Skins* / Here we go again: *Cockney Rejects* / Isubeleeene: *Splodge, Max* / Beardsmen: *Postmen* / Cranked up realy high: *Slaughter & The Dogs* / Bootboys: *Barney & the Rubbles* / Intensive care: *Barney & the Rubbles* / I still believe in anarchy: *Exploited*

AHOYCD 072 / 3 Nov '97 / Captain Oi

☐ OI THE DEMOS

I want you: *Crack* / 999: ABH / War hero: *Distortion* / By the way: *Case* / Listen to the silence: *Angelic Upstarts* / In my time: *Sub Culture* / Backstreet child: *Burial* / House of the rising sun: *Anti Establishment* / Surfin' dream: *Anti Establishment* / Crazy town: *Case* / Teenage oppression: *ABH* / Liddle Towers: *Crux* / Chaos is: *Distortion* / She don't cry anymore: *Angelic Upstarts* / I can't forget: *Angelic Upstarts* / Perfect society: *Foreign Legion* / Criminal ways: *Case* / Never change: *Skin Deep* / Navy: *Postmen* / In the underworld: *Cockney Rejects*

AHOYCD 081 / 24 Nov '97 / Captain Oi

☐ OI THE TIN

Oi oi oi: *Cockney Rejects* / What have we got: *Sham 69* / GLC: *Menace* / One law for them: *4 Skins* / Woring class kids: *Last Resort* / Harry May: *Business* / 2 Million voices: *Angelic Upstarts* / Kids of the '80's: *Angelic Upstarts* / England belongs to me: *Cock Sparrer* / In Britain: *Red Alert* / Evil: *4 Skins* / Someone's gonna die: *Blitz* / Police story: *Partisans* / Tucker's ruckers ain't no suckers: *Gonads* / Violence in our minds: *Last Resort* / Banned from pubs: *Peter & The Test Tube Babies* / Borstal breakout: *Sham 69* / We can do anything: *Cockney Rejects* / Eat end kids: *Ejected* / England: *Angelic Upstarts*

CANCAN 002CD / 3 Nov '97 / Can Can

☐ OI/SKAMPILATION VOL.1

700092 / Mar '97 / Radical

☐ OI/SKAMPILATION VOL.2

700132 / Mar '97 / Radical

☐ OI/SKAMPILATION VOL.3

RAD 700162 / 8 Sep '97 / Radical

☐ OKEH - A NORTHERN SOUL OBSESSION VOL.1

You're gonna make me love you: *Sheldon, Sandi* / Gonna get along without you now: *Vibrations* / I'm coming to your rescue: *Triumphs* / I still love you: *Seven Souls* / Gone but not forgotten: *Robinson, Johnny* / This heart of mine: *Artistics* / Quitter never wins: *Williams, Larry & Johnny Watson* / Come back: *Williams, Ken* / Wish I had known: *Phillips, Sandra* / Bring it back home: *Chimes* / Call me tomorrow: *Harris, Major* / You don't want me no more: *Major Lance* / What's the use of me trying: *Tangier* / I'm so afraid: *Opals* / My heart is hurtin': *Butler, Billy & The Enchanters* / Hurt: *Church, Jimmy* / Somebody's always trying: *Taylor, Ted* / He who picks a rose: *Carstairs* / I don't want to discuss it: *Little Richard* / I can do it: *Autographs* / Take me to paradise: *Cheers* / So glad your love don't change: *Little Foxes* / I'm taking on pain: *Tate, Tommy* / It's an uphill climb to the bottom: *Jackson, Walter*

CDKEND 132 / Mar '96 / Kent

☐ OKEH - A NORTHERN SOUL OBSESSION VOL.2

Ain't gonna move: *Williams, Larry & Johnny Watson* / End up crying: *Vibrations* / I'll leave it up to you: *Artistics* / Let my heart and soul be free: *Tan Geers* / Memories: *Triumphs* / Your good girls gonna go bad: *Jackson, Cookie* / You ask for one good reason: *Williams, Larry* / Cool breeze: *Sims, Gerald* / Rhythm: *Major Lance* / You're gonna be sorry: *Opals* / Just another dance: *Mars, Marlina* / After you there can be nothing: *Jackson, Walter* / I can't make it without you: *Hayes, Malcolm* / South like West: *Watson, Johnny* / Let me show it to you: *Fundamentals* / Yesterday is gone: *Variations* / You can't take it away: *Mortimor, Azie* / Little bit of something: *Little Richard* / Second class lover: *Dushon, Jean* / Train: *Belgianettes* / Can't live without her: *Butler, Billy* / Hello heartaches, goodbye love: *Davis, Joyce* / I can't work no longer: *Butler, Billy* / That's what Mama say: *Jackson, Walter*

CDKEND 142 / Feb '97 / Kent

☐ OKRA ALL-STARS

OKCD 33021 / Mar '94 / Okra

☐ OLD BELIEVERS (Songs Of The Nekrasov Cossaks)

SFWCD 40462 / Oct '95 / Smithsonian Folkways

☐ OLD BULL AND BUSH, THE

GEMMCD 9913 / Feb '92 / Pearl

☐ OLD REGULAR BAPTISTS (Lined Out Hymnody From South Eastern Kentucky)

SFWCD 40106 / Aug '97 / Smithsonian Folkways

☐ OLD SCARS AND UPSTARTS

DISA 002CD / 11 May '98 / Revelation

☐ OLD SCHOOL BREAKZ

Soundclash: Kicksquad / Sanity clause: *Zero Zero* / ScientiBee: *Scientist* / Temple of dreams: *Messiah* / 5678: *Shut Up & Dance* / There is no law: *Messiah* / Evil surrounds us: Wishdokta / 20000 surrounds us: *Wishdokta* / Exorcist: *Scientist*

KICKCD 71 / 5 May '98 / Kickin'

☐ OLD SCHOOL HARDCORE

DB 47782 / 1 Dec '97 / Deep Blue

☐ OLD SCHOOL RAP - THE ROOTS OF RAP

King Tim III (personality jock): *Fatback Band* / Money (dollar bill y'all): *Spicer, Jimmy* / Rockin' it: *MC Flex & The FBI Crew* / Please stay: *Fatback & Gerry Bledsoe* / Alarm (XX rated): *Hawk* / Rock me down: *Young, Monalisa* / Step by step: *Simon, Joe* / Heobah: *Rae, Fonda* / If I can't have your love: *Brown, Jocelyn* / Workin' out: *Ritz* / We come to jam: *Blaze* / Can you guess what groove this is: *Glory* / Live it up: *Rae, Fonda* / Go with the feeling: *Krystal* / Got to have your lovin': *Feel*

CDSEWD 048 / Jun '92 / Southbound

☐ OLD SKOOL REUNION (2CD Set)

RADCD 69 / Jul '97 / Global TV

☐ OLD SKOOL SKA (2CD Set)

SMDCD 139 / 22 Sep '97 / Snapper

☐ OLD SKOOL, THE (2CD Set)

Never too much: *Vandross, Luther* / And the beat goes on: *Whispers* / Just be good to me: *SOS Band* / Hanging on a string: *Loose Ends* / She's strange: *Cameo* / Risin' to the top: *Burke, Keni* / Running away: *Ayers, Roy* / Love come down: *King, Evelyn* / Don't look any further: *Edwards, Dennis* / All night long: *Mary Jane Girls* / I can make you feel good: *Shalamar* / Native New Yorker: *Odyssey* / I found lovin': *Fatback Band* / Forget me nots: *Rushen, Patrice* / Juicy fruit: *Mtume* / 'Ain't nothing goin' on but the rent: *Guthrie, Gwen* / Roses are red: *Mac Band & McCampbell Brothers* / I specialize in love: *Brown, Sharon* / Low rider: *War* / Summer madness: *Kool & The Gang* / I want your love: *Chic* / Thinking of you: *Sister Sledge* / I love music: *O'Jays* / Harvest for the world: *Isley Brothers* / Don't leave me this way: *Melvin, Harold & The Bluenotes* / Best of my love: *Emotions* / Car wash: *Rose Royce* / Love TKO: *Pendergrass, Teddy* / Feel the need in me: *Detroit Emeralds* / Nights over Egypt: *Jones Girls* / Behind the groove: *Marie, Teena* / Feel so real: *Arrington, Steve* / Circles: *Atlantic Starr* / Just a touch of love: *Slave* / Never knew love like this before: *Mills, Stephanie* / I'll be around: *Wells, Terri* / I wonder if I take you home: *Lisa Lisa & Cult Jam* / Shame: *King, Evelyn* / Funkin' for Jamaica: *Browne, Tom* / Me and Mrs Jones: *Paul, Billy*

RADCD 59 / Mar '97 / Global TV

☐ OLD TIME MOUNTAIN GUITAR (Vintage Recordings 1926-1931)

Lonesome weary blues: *Harvey, Roy & Leonard Copeland* / Buck Dancer's choice: *McGee, Sam* / Guitar rag: *Harvey, Roy & Jess Johnson* / Charlotte hot-step: *Fletcher, David* / Jailhouse rag: *Miller, David* / Logan county blues: *Hutchison, Frank* / Greasy wagon: *Harvey, Roy & Leonard Copeland* / Augusta rag: *Dupree, Melvin* / Franklin blues: *McGee, Sam* / Blue grass twist: *South Georgia Highballers* / Take me to the land of jazz: *Stokes, Lowe & His North Georgians* / Red rose rag: *Fletcher, David & Gwen Foster* / Back to the blue ridge: *Harvey, Roy & Leonard Copeland* / Fresno blues: *Crockett, Johnny* / Jefferson Street rag: *Harvey, Roy & Jess Johnson* / Norfolk flip: *Dupree, Melvin* / Spanish fandango: *Silleshaw, John & The String Marvel* / Jamestown exhibition: *Baylesse Rose*

COUNTY 3512 / Jul '98 / County

☐ OLD TIME MUSIC ON THE AIR VOL.1

ROUCD 0331 / Sep '94 / Rounder

☐ OLD TIME MUSIC ON THE AIR VOL.2

ROUCD 0391 / Aug '96 / Rounder

☐ OLD TIME PARTY FAVOURITES VOL.1

SWBCD 203 / Sep '94 / Sound Waves

☐ OLD TIME PARTY FAVOURITES VOL.2

SWCD 204 / Sep '94 / Sound Waves

☐ OLD TOWN & BARRY SOUL STIRRERS

Think smart: *Fiestas* / I'm so glad: *Howard, Frank* / Oh oh here comes the heartbreak: *Jones, Thelma* / Try love one more time: *Sparkels* / If I had known: *Houston, Freddie* / You can't trust your best friend: *Height, Donald* / My foolish heart: *Coleman, David* / Gotta find a way: *Jones, Thelma* / We're gonna make it: *Reid, Irene* / Stop, take another look: *Divine Men* / Could this be love: *Rosco & Barbara* / Jerk it: *Gypsies* / Cross my heart: *Yvonne & The Violets* / Baby I need: *Lorraine & The Delights* / Left out: *Johnson, Jesse* / My heart's on fire: *Bland, Billy* / Chills and fever: *Houston, Freddie* / Drown my heart: *Coleman, David* / Barefootin' time in Chinatown: *Young, Tester* / I want a chance for romance: *Rivera, Hector* / It's a woman's world (you better believe it): *Gypsies* / Soul stirrer: *Bobby & Betty Lou* / Gypsy said: *Fiestas* / Things have more meaning now: *Scott, Peggy*

CDKEND 111 / Jun '94 / Kent

☐ OLD TOWN BLUES VOL.1 (Downtown Sides)

Uncle Bud: *Terry, Sonny & Brownie McGhee* / Climbing on top of the hill: *Terry, Sonny & Brownie McGhee* / Sweet sweet woman: *Terry, Sonny & Brownie McGhee* / Evil hearted woman: *Wayne, James* / Rock reel rock: *Wayne, James* / Where you been: *Wayne, James* / True blues: *Wayne, James* / Slidin': *Terry, Sonny & Brownie McGhee* / Crazy about you baby: *Terry, Sonny & Brownie McGhee* / Chicken hop: *Bland, Billy* / I need a woman: *Terry, Sonny & Brownie McGhee* / Playboy: *Littlefield, 'Little' Willie* / Sweet little girl: *Littlefield, 'Little' Willie* / Hard luck baby: *Littlefield, 'Little' Willie* / Work out: *Littlefield, 'Little' Willie* / Love's a disease: *Terry, Sonny & Brownie McGhee* / She loves so easy: *Terry, Sonny & Brownie McGhee* / Confusion: *Terry, Sonny & Brownie McGhee* / Reap what you sow: *Terry, Sonny & Brownie McGhee* / Things that I used to do: *Gaddy, Bob* / Could I would I: *Dixon, Willie* / Ugly girls: *Dixon, Willie*

CDCHD 469 / Sep '93 / Ace

☐ OLD TOWN BLUES VOL.2 (The Uptown Sides)

CDCHD 498 / Jun '94 / Ace

☐ OLD TOWN DOO WOP VOL.1

There's a moon out tonight: *Capris* / Zu zu: *Bonnevilles* / Fool in love: *Keytones* / Walking along: *Solitaires* / On Sunday afternoon: *Harptones* / Never let me go: *Royaltones* / Have you ever loved someone: *Vocaleers* / Later later baby: *5 Crowns* / Message of love: *Laurels* / It all depends on you: *Harptones* / Love you baby all the time: *Co-eds* / Last night I dreamed: *Fiestas* / Two in love: *McFadden, Ruth & The Royaltones* / Last rose of summer: *Symbols* / Remember then: *Earls* / Magic rose: *Solitaires* / Tonight Kathleen: *Valentines* / Seven wonders of the world: *Keytones* / Hey Norman: *Royaltones* / Lorraine: *Bonnevilles* / Why oh why: *Tru-Tones* / I love an angel: *Co-eds* / You could be my love: *5 Crowns* / Mambo boogie: *Harptones* / Crying my heart out: *Symbols* / I need your love so bad: *Vocaleers* / I fell in love: *Esquires*

CDCHD 433 / Jun '93 / Ace

☐ OLD TOWN DOO WOP VOL.2

So fine: *Fiestas* / My dearest darling: *Cleftones* / What did she say: *Solitaires* / Day we fell in love: *Ovations* / Where I fell in love: *Capris* / Zip boom: *Supremes* / Little girl (I love you madly): *Cleftones* / Life is but a dream: *Harptones* / Ding dong: *Packards* / Lullaby of the bells: *Five Crowns* / My broken heart: *Chimes* / Hong Kong jelly wong: *Royaltones* / School boy: *Harptones* / Love and devotion: *Vocaleers* / Why does the world go round: *Escorts* / Angels sang: *Solitaires* / My babe (she don't want me no more): *Supremes* / (I'm afraid) the masquerade is over: *Cleftones* / Good luck darling: *Five Crowns* / Mexico: *Chimes* / Dream of love: *Packards* / Gee what a girl: *Hummers* / There's something awful nice about you: *Escorts* / I've got a notion: *Harptones* / I give you my word: *Royaltones* / Do you know what I mean: *Hummers* / Our anniversary: *Fiestas* / My lullabye: *Ovations*

CDCHD 470 / Aug '93 / Ace

☐ OLD TOWN DOO WOP VOL.3

Crazy love: *Royaltones* / Indian girl: *Capris* / Starlight tonight: *Inspirators* / You know you're doin' me wrong: *Harptones* / I beg your forgiveness: *Co-eds* / Possibility: *Crowns* / My heart (I'm blue without you): *Keytones* / Jingle jingle: *Tremaines* / Wedding: *Solitaires* / My faith: *Fi-Tones* / Darling listen to the words of this song: *McFadden, Ruth & The Supremes* / I love you baby: *Farmer, Peggy & The Harptones* / Give me your love: *Four Pharaohs* / Gloria: *Cleftones* / Last round-up: *Supremes* / I'm in love: *Co-eds* / Please give me one more chance: *Mumford, Gene & The Serenaders* / Why must I love you: *Esquires* / Life is but a dream: *Earls* / Tonight: *Supremes* / Think: *Universals* / Oh what a feeling: *Inspirators* / School girl: *Harptones* / Latin lover: *Royaltones* / Guess who: *Cleftones* / China girl: *Four Pharaohs* / Moon shining bright: *Tremaines* / You're gonna need my help someday: *Harptones*

CDCHD 471 / Oct '93 / Ace

☐ OLD TOWN DOO WOP VOL.4

Round goes my heart: *Solitaires* / Some people think: *Capris* / I call to you: *Burgess, Vicki* / I won't tell the world: *Blenders* / Night is over: *Gems* / I'll be there: *Vocaleers* / Lonely: *Solitaires* / My heart: *Fi-Tones* / Why do I cry: *Capris* / Night: *Nick & The Nacks* / Walkin' and talkin': *Solitaires* / Lover lover lover: *Symbols* / You for me: *McFadden, Ruth* / It's you: *Earls* / Girl of mine: *Solitaires* / My island in th esun: *Capris* / Summer love: *Valentines* / Crazy love: *Royaltones* / Girl in my dreams: *Capris* / But I know: *Blenders* / Pretty thing: *Solitaires* / Life is but a dream: *Harptones* / Nursery rhymes: *Gems* / Thrill of love: *Solitaires* / When you're smiling: *Mumford, Gene & The Serenaders* / Listen listen baby: *Unknowns*

CDCHD 570 / Jan '95 / Ace

☐ OLDIES BUT GOLDIES VOL.1

15028 / Dec '94 / Laserlight

☐ OLDIES BUT GOLDIES VOL.2

15029 / Dec '94 / Laserlight

☐ OLDIES BUT GOLDIES VOL.3

12388 / Feb '95 / Laserlight

☐ OLDIES BUT GOLDIES VOL.4

12389 / May '95 / Laserlight

☐ OLDIES BUT GOODIES

Mrs. Brown: *Cooter* / Johnny B Goode: *5 Driver* / Mr. Sandman: *Gob* / Blue moon: *MXPX* / Be my baby: *Lounge* / I gotta know: *Lounge* / Runaround Sue: *Latex Generation* / Oh boy: *McCrackin, Bill* / Leader of the pack: *Good Riddance* / Da doo run run: *Another Joe* / Kalamazoo: *Bounder* / Wonderful world: *Lipmonger* / Book of love: *Sumo Grimace* / Be bop a lula: *Grieving Eucalyptus* / Sweet rock 'n' roller: *Automatic 7*

NGPR 010CD / 20 Jul '98 / Vagrant

☐ OLDIES GREATEST HITS

SONCD 0059 / Mar '94 / Sonic Sounds

☐ OLDIES KEEP SWINGING

SONCD 0057 / Jan '94 / Sonic Sounds

☐ OLDTIME FESTIVAL

BLR 84005 / May '91 / L&R

☐ OLE - BULLFIGHT MUSIC FROM SPAIN

Espana cani / Opera flamenca / Vaya capes / La entrada

15161 / '91 / Laserlight

☐ OLYMPIC - THE ALBUM

Stay with me forever: *Prolific* / So deep: *Scope* / Question: *7 Grand Housing Authority* / Feel the love: *Perez, Eric* / Shiver: *Powerzone* / Another man: *Shy One* / Your love: *Mr. Peach* / Lies: *Perez, Eric* / You can turn around: *Bottom Dollar* / More to love: *Volcano*

ELYACD 001 / Feb '94 / Olympic

☐ ON A DANCE TIP '95 (2CD Set)

Fairground: *Simply Red* / Gangsta's paradise: *Coolio & LV* / Boom boom boom: *Outhere Brothers* / Stayin' alive: *N-Trance* / Scatman: *Scatman John* / Try me out: *Corona* / Missing: *Everything But The Girl* / Hideaway: *De'Lacy* / Runaway: *Real McCoy* / I got a little something for you: *MN8* / U sure do: *Strike* / Two can play that game: *Brown, Bobby* / Right in the night: *Jam & Spoon* / Don't you want me: *Felix* / Move your body: *Xpansions* / Happy just to be with you: *Gayle, Michelle* / Shoot me with your love: *D:Ream* / Sight for sore eyes: *M-People* / Surrender your love: *Nightcrawlers* / Not over yet: *Grace* / You remind me of something: *Kelly, R* / Dreamer: *Livin' Joy* / Turn on tune in cop out: *Freakpower* / I luv u baby: *Original* / Walking in Memphis: *Cher* / Son of a gun: *JX* / Bomb: *Bucketheads* / Don't stop (wiggle wiggle): *Outhere Brothers* / 3 is family: *Dawson, Dana* / Whoomph (there it is): *Clock* / Set you free: *N-Trance* / Tell me when: *Human League* / Baby baby: *Corona* / Here comes the hotstepper: *Kamoze, Ini* / Total eclipse of the heart: *French, Nicki* / Your loving arms: *Martin, Billie Ray* / Reach up (papa's got a brand new pig bag): *Perfecto All Stars* / Always something there to remind me: *Tin Tin Out & Espiritu* / First the last eternity: *Snap* / Zombie: *ADAM & Amy* / Guaglione: *Prado, Perez* / Cotton eye Joe: *Rednex*

RADCD 27 / Nov '95 / Global TV

☐ ON A DANCE TIP VOL.1

Cotton eye Joe: *Rednex* / Sight for sore eyes: *M-People* / Tell me when: *Human League* / Runaway: *MC Sar & The Real McCoy* / Set you free: *N-Trance* / Reach up: *Perfecto All Stars* / Let me be your fantasy: *Baby D* / Them girls: *Zig & Zag* / Saturday night: *Whigfield* / No matter what you do (I'm gonna get with U): *Flavour* / Total eclipse of the heart: *French, Nicki* / Here comes the hotstepper: *I'm A Kamikaze* / Welcome to tomorrow (are you ready): *Snap* / Sweetness: *Gayle, Michelle* / None of your business: *Salt n' Pepa* / Saved: *Mr. Roy* / U sure do: *Strike* / Sweet love: *M-Beat* / Good life: *EVE* / My heart belongs to you: *Jodeci* / Bump 'n' grind: *R Kelly*

RADCD 07 / '95 / Global TV

☐ ON A DANCE TIP VOL.2

Don't stop (wiggle wiggle): *Outhere Brothers* / Dreamer: *Livin' Joy* / Scatman: *Scatman John* / Two can play that game: *Brown, Bobby* / Baby baby: *Corona* / Love and devotion: *Real McCoy* / Love city groove: *Love City Groove* / Open your heart: *M-People* / U sure do: *Strike* / Guaglione: *Prado, Perez* / Push the feeling on: *Nightcrawlers* / First the last eternity: *Snap* / Not over yet: *Grace* / Axel F: *Clock* / Always something there to remind me: *Tin Tin Out* / Conway: *Reel 2 Real & The Mad Stuntman* / It's a love thing: *Milton, C.B.* / I'm going down: *Blige, Mary J.* / Every day of the week: *Jade* / Your body's callin': *Kelly, R*

RADCD 12 / May '95 / Global TV

☐ ON A DANCE TIP VOL.3

La la hey hey: *Outhere Brothers* / Happy just to be with you: *Gayle, Michelle* / Hideaway: *De'Lacy* / I luv u baby: *Original* / Everybody: *Clock* / Party up the world: *D:Ream* / Don't let the feeling go: *Nightcrawlers* / Son of a gun: *JX* / Don't you want me: *Felix* / Move your body: *Xpansions* / Scatman's world: *Scatman John* / Morning after (free at last): *Strike* / I want to live: *Grace* / Try me out: *Corona* / Come and get your love: *Real McCoy* / Search for the hero: *M-People* / Zombie: *ADAM & Amy* / Running around town: *Martin, Billie Ray* / Catch a fire: *Haddaway* / Loving you more: *BT & Vincent Covello* / Destination eschaton: *Shamen* / Kiss from a rose: *Seal*

RADCD 20 / Jul '95 / Global TV

☐ ON A DANCE TIP VOL.4

Missing: *Everything But The Girl* / Whole lotta love: *Goldbug* / Loving you more: *BT* / Electronic pleasure: *N-Trance* / I wanna be a hippy: *Technohead* / Passion: *Gat Decor* / Got myself together: *Bucketheads* / If you wanna party: *Molella & The Outhere Brothers* / Itchycoo park: *M-People* / Release the pressure: *Leftfield* / Waterfalls: *TLC* / Fairground: *Simply Red* / Too hot: *Coolio* / Skin on skin: *Grace* / I don't wanna be a star: *Corona* / Do it for love: *4Mandu* / Let's push it: *Nightcrawlers* / Is this a dream: *4Mandu* / One by one: *Cher* / And I'm telling you I'm not going: *Giles, Donna*

RADCD 26 / Feb '96 / Global TV

☐ ON A WINTER'S EVENING

Don't it make my brown eyes blue: *Gayle, Crystal* / Cryin': *McLean, Don* / Move closer: *Nelson, Phyllis* / When I fall in love: *Cole, Nat 'King'* / Orchard road: *Sayer, Leo* / All I have to do is dream: *Everly Brothers* / Feelings: *Albert, Morris* / Sharing the night together: *Dr. Hook* / Home on Monday: *Little River Band* / Everybody's gotta learn sometime: *Korgis* / Winter in America: *Ashdown, Doug* / Anyone who had a heart: *Black, Cilla* / They shoot horses don't they: *Racing Cars* / Where do you go to my lovely: *Sarstedt, Peter* / Love don't live here anymore: *Nail, Jimmy* / Classic: *Gurvitz, Adrian*

WLT 874612 / Oct '96 / Disky

☐ ON CHANTAIT QUAND MEME

DEM 013 / Feb '96 / IMP

☐ ON DA REGGAE TIP

TVT 63502 / 18 May '98 / Blunt

☐ ON GUARD FOR THEE

ANDA 204 / Jan '97 / Au-Go-Go

☐ ON MANA 689 - NEW MUSIC INDONESIA VOL.2

LYRCD 7420 / Aug '93 / Lyrichord

☐ ON MARCO POLO'S ROAD (The Musicians Of Kunduz & Faizabad/ Afghanistan)

Badakhshani charbaiti / Charbaiti batcha moshi mosh / Tajik charbaiti / Tajik charbaiti and mondanabosh / Zirbaghali solo / Uzbek pashtun herati folk songs / Badakhshani folk songs / Falak

MCM 3003 / May '97 / Multicultural Media

☐ ON TARGET (20 Direct Hits From The Mod Revival)

When you're young: *Jam* / Maybe tomorrow: *Chords* / Time for action: *Secret Affair* / Millions like us: *Purple Hearts* / You need wheels: *Merton Parkas* / Walking down the Kings Road: *Squire* / Your side of heaven: *Back To Zero* / Strength of the nation: *Teenbeats* / Go steady: *Lambrettas* / Biff bang pow: *Times* / See saw: *Jolt* / By your love: *Long Tall Shorty* / My world: *Secret Affair* / British way of life: *Chords* / Gabrielle: *Nips* / Love is dead: *Small World* / Jimmy: *Purple Hearts* / SX 225: *Killermeters* / I helped Patrick McGoohan escape: *Teenage Film Stars* / Angry voices: *Circles*

MUSCD 038 / 6 Oct '97 / MCI Music

☐ ON THE BANKS OF THE DEVERON

Vancouver / Diddler / Hugh MacDonald / Granny Fraser's flitting / Farewell to the creeks / Leaving port Askaig / MacPhersons' lament / Silver darlings / Highland cathederal / Sandy's new chanter / Tak a dram / Dumbarton castle / Craigellachie brig / Left

handed fiddler / Trawler song / Rowan tree / Bonnie Gallowa / Old rustic bridge / Carillon / Spirit of Glen Deveron / Here's to Scottish whisky / Dr. Ross's 50th welcome to the Argyllshire gathering / 10th Bn H.L.I. Crossing the Rhine

CDGR 151 / Dec '95 / Ross

□ ON THE BEACH

Summer on the beach: Thomas, Evelyn / Lazin' on the beach: Gidea Park / Miami heatwave: 7th Avenue / Hotter than Summer days: Edwards, Sandra / On the beach: Demps, Louvain / Summertime City: Gidea Park / Footprints in the sand: 7th Avenue / Boys (summertime love): Sabrina / Itsy bitsy teenie weenie yellow polkadot bikini: Sha Na Na / I wanna hold your hand: Dollar / Limbo rock: Checker, Chubby / Remember (walkin in the sand): Shangri-Las / Sandy: Travolta, John / Beach baby: Regents / It's my party: Gore, Lesley / If I had a hammer: Lopez, Trini / Build me up a buttercup: Foundations / Love letters in the sand: Boone, Pat / Caribbean: Torok, Mitchell / Surfin': Beach Boys / Pipeline: Chantays / Hula love: Knox, Bobby / Barbara Ann: Regents / Surfin' safari: Beach Boys / Wipe out: Surfaris

ECD 3432 / Aug '98 / K-Tel

□ ON THE BEACH AT WAIKIKI 1914-1952

HQCD 57 / Aug '95 / Harlequin

□ ON THE MODERN SIDE

Janice: Mahoney, Skip / I don't do this: Qualls, Sidney Joe / Case of too much makin' love: Scott, Gloria / Top of the stairs: Collins & Collins / Circles: Atlantic Starr / Too late: Mandrill / Love don't come no stronger: Perry, Jeff / Get into your life: Bevoy D / Sweet little girl: Williams, Mel / Ain't nothin' like your love: Charisma Band / Once I've been there: Connors, Norman & Phillip Mitchell / It ain't like it used to be: Brown, Randolph / Shake off that dream: Phillips, Eddie / Boss thing together: Phillips, Eddie / He sent me to you: Perry, Oscar / I wanna give you tomorrow: Perry, Oscar / I just wanna spend: Warner, Pete / Memories: Warner, Pete / All alone by the telephone: Checkmates / Thank you baby: Moore, Johnny

CSCD 124 / 30 Mar '98 / Goldmine

□ ON THE PHILADELPHIA BEAT VOL.1

Girl across the street: Smith, Moses / Got what you need: Fantastic Johnny C / Standing in the darkness: Ethics / Help wanted: Volcanos / This gets to me: Hudson, Pookie / If I'm all you got (I'm all you need): Ambassadors / Don't set me up for the kill: Dorothy & The Hesitations / Ain't it baby: Gamble, Kenny / Dynamite exploded: Honey & The Bees / Storm warning: Volcanos / I want my baby back: Ashley, Tyrone / Bobby, is my baby: Mason, Barbara / Don't let it happen to you: Harper, Benny / Girl I Love you: Temptones / Joke's on you: Gamble, Kenny / Won't find better than me: Kit Kat's / Why do you hurt the one who love's you: Honey & The Bees / You gave me somebody to love you: Ambassadors / Don't ever want to lose your love: Mason, Barbara / Till then: Pentagons / Trying to work out a plan: Dorothy & The Hesitations / Let's have a good time: Nobles, Cliff / You're number one: Volcanos / Love you can depend on: Brenda & Tabulations / Let's talk it over: Kayettes / Don't give away my love: Soul Brothers Six / Better to have loved and lost: Irwin, Big Dee

BCD 15844 / Aug '95 / Bear Family

□ ON THE ROAD

TUT 771 / Oct '94 / Wundertute

□ ON THE ROAD AGAIN

Truck drivin' outlaw: Olsen, Denis / Girl on the billboard: Reeves, Del / Truck drivin' son of a gun: Dudley, Dave / CB Savage: Brown, Steven / Highway 40 blues: Ricks, Earl / Truck driver's prayer: Ricks, Earl / Tennessee is home to me: Blueboy, David / That's trucking: Ricks, Earl / Roll truck roll: Simpson, Red / Mystery maiden: Bennet, George / Truckers way of life: Blueboy, David / Hold everything: Spooks, Grover / Roll on: McRoad, John & The Texas Liner / It's hard to love a man: Bennet, George / Freightliner fever: McBrown, Mel / I'm a truck: Simpson, Red / He took me for a ride: La Costa Tucker / I didn't jump the fence: King, Don / On the road again: McRoad, John & The Texas Liner / Day time friends: McRoad, John & The Texas Liner / Ode to 10-33: McRoad, John & The Texas Liner

22504 / Feb '96 / Music

□ ON THE ROAD AGAIN (Country Blues Recordings From The Deep South 1969-1974)

When a gal cross the bottom: Murrell, Lattie / Spoonful: Murrell, Lattie / Blues for Mattie Mae: Murrell, Lattie / Good morning little school girl: Murrell, Lattie / Railroad blues: Guffin, Lum / Johnny Wilson: Guffin, Lum / On the road again: Guffin, Lum / Old country blues: Guffin, Lum / Moaning and groaning blues: Guffin, Lum / Loping blues: Jackson, Lincoln / Kennedy moan: Tills, Perry / Tell me why you like Roosevelt: Tills, Perry / Denomination blues: Tills, Perry / Why did I have to leave Cairo: Floyd Davis, William / Sweet peace: Thompson, Ashley / Take your burdens to the lord: Townsend, Joe / Stuttgart, Arkansas: Miller, Walter / Sherman's blues: Miller, Walter / Hop's boogie: Miller, Walter / Fool's blues: Corley, Dewey / Don't the peaches look mellow: Broadnax, Othar / Sally got a big leg: Daughters Of Zion

FLYCD 58 / Oct '97 / Flyright

□ ON THE ROCKS VOL.1

Light my fire: Zacharias / Sunshine superman: Torme, Mel / Incense and peppermints/It's a beautiful morning: Denny, Martin / Uptight: Jerome, Henry / Green tambourine: Sir Julian / Tired of waiting: Hollyridge Strings / Mellow yellow/We gotta get out of this place: Hollyridge Strings / Gimme a little sign: Morrow, Buddy / Hard day's night: Lee, Peggy / Whiter shade of pale: Moreno, Mario / Heartbreak hotel: Hollyridge Strings / Don't be cruel: Hollyridge Strings / As tears go by: New Classic Singers / Evil ways: Delory, Al / Get back: Little Big Horns / Hello I love you/Touch me: Lettermen / Dizzy: Royal Blue / Shaft: Hollyridge Strings / Mighty Quinn: London, Julie / Day in the life: Tartaglia / I am the walrus: Tartaglia / Daydream believer: Tartaglia / Winchester cathedral: Riddle, Nelson / Love grows (where my rosemary grows): Newton, Wayne

CDEMS 1612 / May '97 / EMI

□ ON THE ROCKS VOL.2

Heart full of soul: Mann, Johnny Singers / Satisfaction: McCallum, David / Carry the weight: Lai, Francis / Games people play: Torme, Mel / I get around/California girls: Hollyridge Strings / Summer in the city: Morrow, Buddy / Everyday people: Ledd, Peggy / Mrs Robinson: Lombard, Guy / Hush: Royal Blue / Blue jay way/Blackbird: Lord Sister & Sandler/Young / Heard it through the grapevine: Little Big Horns / Pretty woman: Jerome, Henry / Wear your love like heaven/Working on a groovy train: Rose, David / Yummy yummy yummy: London, Julie / Superfly: Duchin, Peter / Holiday: Moreno, Mario / Baby love/Respect: Zacharias / I can see for miles: Lord Sitar / Happy together: Torme, Mel / Can't buy me love: Hollyridge Strings / Sergeant Pepper: Hollyridge Strings / Light my fire: Tartaglia / These boots are made for walking: Mrs. Miller

CDEMS 1613 / May '97 / EMI

□ ON THE STREETS

WB 1166CD / Jun '97 / We Bite

□ ON THE SUNNY SIDE OF THE STREET 1934

PHONTCD 7653 / '93 / Phontastic

□ ON THE WILD SIDE

NSCD 003 / Feb '95 / Newsound

□ ON-U SOUND (A Party Of Dubbers And Toasters)

CLP 9919 / Feb '97 / Cleopatra

□ ON-U SOUND DUB XPERIENCE (The Dread Operators)

CLP 9825 / Oct '96 / Cleopatra

□ ONCE IN A LIFETIME (2CD Set)

TCD 2889 / Feb '97 / Telstar

□ ONCE UPON A TIME IN THE WEST

Bonanza / Once upon a time in the West / Good, the bad and the ugly / Magnificent seven / Green leaves of summer / High noon / Fist full of dollars / Hondo / Man with the harmonica / Professional gun / Yankee doodle / Dynamite ringo / Return of the seven / Wandering star / Hang 'em high / Man from Laramie / How the West was won / Alamo / Comancheros / True grit

GRF 041 / Feb '93 / Tring

□ ONE AD

WF 841012 / Jun '94 / Waveform

□ ONE AND ONLY, THE

Year of the cat: Stewart, Al / Baker Street: Rafferty, Gerry / Weight: Band / It's a long way there: Little River Band / Classic: Gurvitz, Adrian / Bon voyage: Carnes, Kim / Border: America / Sharing the night together: Dr. Hook / He ain't heavy, he's my brother: Hollies / I go to pieces: Cotton/Lloyd/Christian / No more fear of flying: Brooker, Gary / It's a heartache: Tyler, Bonnie / I love you so: McLean, Don / Release me: Wilson Phillips / Don't you write her off: Hillman, Chris & Roger McGuinn / We've got tonight: Brooks, Elkie

DC 880132 / May '97 / Disky

□ ONE FOOT IN THE GROOVE - AMERICAN BIG BANDS

American patrol: Miller, Glenn / Take the 'A' train: Ellington, Duke / One o'clock jump: James, Harry / Dipsy doodle: Clinton, Larry / Sunny side of the street: Dorsey, Tommy / Dinah: Hampton, Lionel / Mississippi mud: Beiderbecke, Bix / Jersey bounce: Nelson, Ozzie / Dippermouth blues: Dorsey, Jimmy / Christopher Columbus: Goodman, Benny / Begin the beguine: Shaw, Artie / South Rampart Street Parade: Crosby, Bob / Wrap your troubles in dreams: Gray, Glen / Honeysuckle rose: Basie, Count / In a sentimental mood: Jurgens, Dick / In the mood: Miller, Glenn / Sugarfoot stomp: Henderson, Fletcher / Perdido: Ellington, Duke / Ciribiribin: James, Harry / Woodchopper's ball: Herman, Woody

ONEC 001 / Apr '96 / Tring

□ ONE FOOT IN THE GROOVE - CROONERS

Where the blue of the night: Crosby, Bing / Imagination: Eberle, Bob / All or nothing at all: Sinatra, Frank / Sonny boy: Jolson, Al / Amapola: Rey, Monte / This can't be love: Vallee, Rudy / East of the sun: Tracy, Arthur / Mimi: Chevalier, Maurice / Where are you: Hutchinson, Leslie 'Hutch' / Georgia on my mind: Carmichael, Hoagy / Oh Buddy, I'm in love: Gibbons, Carroll / I'll see you later: Coward, Sir Noel / I'm in a dancing mood: Buchanan, Jack / Elmer's tune: Eberle, Ray / Fine romance: Astaire, Fred / Lulu's back in town: Powell, Dick / Brother, can you spare a dime: Crosby, Bing / Rock a bye your baby: Jolson, Al / You lucky people you: Sinatra, Frank / Very thought of you: Bowlly, Al

ONEC 004 / Apr '96 / Tring

□ ONE FOOT IN THE GROOVE - LADIES

Tisket a tasket: Fitzgerald, Ella / Every time we say goodbye: Horne, Lena / I hear a rhapsody: Shore, Dinah / Everybody sings: Garland, Judy / I like a guy what takes his time: West, Mae / Nobody knows you when you're down and out: Smith, Bessie / Beyond the blue horizons: McDonald, Jeanette / Darling, je vous aime beaucoup: Hildegarde / Swing me a lullaby: Boswell, Connee / Let yourself go: Rogers, Ginger / Everything I have is yours: Etting, Ruth / With every breath I take: Boswell, Connee / You've done something to my heart: Jones, Gwen / There's something about a soldier: Courtneidge, Cicely / Life begins at forty: Tucker, Sophie / Miss Brown to you: Holiday, Billie / On the good ship lollipop: Temple, Shirley / I've got you under my skin: Day, Frances / We'll meet again: Lynn, Vera / You brought a new kind of love to me: Waters, Ethel

ONEC 002 / Apr '96 / Tring

□ ONE FOOT IN THE GROOVE - WAR SONGS

We'll meet again: Lynn, Vera / There'll always be an Egland: Lynn, Vera / Umbrella song: Flanagan & Allen / When they sound the last all clear: Lynn, Vera / When the lights go on: Monroe, Vaughan / You've done something to my heart: Trent, Bruce / Run rabbit run: Flanagan & Allen / Leaning on a lamp post: Formby, George / There's something about a soldier: Courtneidge, Cicely / Hey little hen: Loss, Joe / Nightingale sang in Berkeley Square: Lombardo, Guy / Boogie woogie bugle boy: Andrews Sisters / All over the place: Trinder, Tommy / Lili Marlene: Anderson, Lale / Don't sit under the apple tree: Miller, Glenn / There'll be bluebirds over the white cliffs of Dover: Stone, Lew / Homecoming waltz: Benson, Ivy / My devotion: Winston, Eric / We're gonna hang out the washing on the Siegfried line: Flanagan & Allen / I'll be seeing you: Crosby, Bing

ONEC 003 / Apr '96 / Tring

□ ONE HALF OF A WHOLE DECADE (Five Years At Ministry Of Sound)

Voices in my mind: Voices / Good feelin': Swing Kids / This is the only way: Lovebeads & Courtney Grey / Nothing better: Colourblind / Deliver me: Urban Blues Project / Helpless: Urbanised & Silvano / Pride, a deeper love: C&C Music Factory / It's gonna be a lovely day: SOUL System / Beautiful people: Tucker, Barbara / Carry on: Wash, Martha / I'll be your friend: Owens, Robert / Pennies from heaven: Inner City / Raise me: Bizarre Inc. / Not forgotten: Leftfield / Love me tonight: White, Anthony / Plastic dreams: Jaydee / Yeke yeke: Kante, Mory / Kinetic: Golden Girls / Believe in me: Mankey / Melody of love: Summer, Donna / When: Sunscreem / Satellite: Beloved / Take me higher: Lucas, Jennifer / O: 28th Street Crew / Rays of the rising sun: Mozaic / Destiny: Hieroglyphix / Solar system: Q-Project / Night train: Appaloosa & DJ Dream / Above and beyond: PHD / Universal music: Seb & Lo Tek / Music: LTJ Bukem / Jazz lick: Peshay / Senses: DJ Addiction / Reflections: New Balance / Euphony: Axis

MOS 5CD / Sep '96 / Ministry Of Sound

□ ...ONE LAST KISS

SPART 1 / Feb '97 / Spin Art

□ ONE LITTLE INDIAN GREATEST HITS VOL.1

TPCD 7 / Dec '88 / One Little Indian

□ ONE LITTLE INDIAN GREATEST HITS VOL.2

TPCD 17 / Apr '90 / One Little Indian

□ ONE LITTLE INDIAN TAKES ON THE COWBOYS

TPCD 6 / May '88 / One Little Indian

□ ONE LOVE (20 Caribbean Classics)

Rivers of babylon: Boney M / Brown girl in the ring: Boney M / Help me make it through the night: Holt, John / Killing me softly: Holt, John / Everything I own: Booth, Ken / Hurt so good: Cadogan, Susan / Nice and easy: Cadogan, Susan / Many rivers to cross: Cliff, Jimmy / Wonderful world, beautiful people: Cliff, Jimmy / Banana boat song (Day O): Belafonte, Harry / Side show: Biggs, Barry / Dat: Shevington, Pluto / Israelites: Dekker, Desmond / First time: Griffiths, Marcia / Ever I saw your face: Griffiths, Marcia / When will I see you again: Griffiths, Marcia / I want to wake up with you: Gardiner, Boris

PLATCD 3913 / Mar '92 / Platinum

□ ONE LOVE (The Very Best Of Reggae)

I want to wake up with you: Holt, John / Wonderful world: Heptones / Rhythm body: Minott, Sugar / Sweet sensation: Melodians / Good thing going: Isaacs, Gregory / Tide is high: Paragons / Keep on moving: Marley, Bob & The Wailers / Guns don't argue: Alcapone, Dennis / Pressure drop: Toots & The Maytals / I will always love you: Holt, John / Satisfy my soul: Marley, Bob & The Wailers / One my love: Sly & Robbie / If I were a carpenter: Winston Groovy / Guns of Navarone: Upsetters / Jah Jah bless the dreadlocks: Mighty Diamonds / Clint Eastwood rides again: Perry, Lee 'Scratch' / Wet dream: Max Romeo / Cocaine in my brain: Dillinger / Monkey man: Toots & The Maytals / One love: Marley, Bob & The Wailers

CD 6030 / Sep '96 / Music

□ ONE LOVE PRESENTS SENTIMENTAL RAGGA VOL.1

KICKCD 16 / Oct '94 / Kickin'

□ ONE LOVE VOL.2 (Another 20 Caribbean Classics)

Amigo: Black Slate / Hot hot hot: Arrow / Ready for it now: Lovelady, Bill / Cupid: Nash, Johnny / Let your yeah be yeah: Pioneers / I am what I am: Greyhound / Peace to the man: Hot Chocolate / Uptown top ranking: Althia & Donna / Barbados: Typically Tropical / Sing a little song: Dekker, Desmond / I'm in the mood for love: Lord Tanamo / Hold me tight: Nash, Johnny / Double barrel: Barker, Dave & Ansell Collins / Liquidator: Harry J All Stars / Real fashion, reggae style: Johnson, Carey / Money in your pocket: Brown, Dennis / You never know what you've got: Me & You / Love of the common people: Thomas, Nicky / Suzanne beware of the devil: Livingstone, Dandy / All in one: Marley, Bob

PLATCD 3920 / Oct '93 / Platinum

□ ONE MAN ONE VOTE

GRELCD 160 / Apr '91 / Greensleeves

□ ONE MORE SONG

CDPH 1197 / Aug '96 / Philo

□ ONE NATION (2CD Set)

CARTCD 1 / 3 Nov '97 / Beechwood

□ ONE NATION EXPERIENCE

RTD 3970034CD / 10 Nov '97 / Institute Of Art

□ ONE NATION UNDER HOUSE (Yoshitoshi Allstars/2CD Set)

Dedicated to all believers: Heiko Laux / Love revolution: Mysterious People / In your soul: Latino Circus / Fly away: Mysterious People / House music: Amador, Eddie / Rock: Lofty Love / Tick-tock: Chia Pet / Gak trak: Dished Out Bums / Love revolution: Mysterious People / Dedicated to all believers: Heiko Laux / True (the faggot is you): Morel / Sensurround: Mysterious People / Laavburds: Dished Out Bums / Want: Kings Of Tomorrow / On the dark side: Brother Brown / Fade II black: Kings Of Tomorrow / Love revolution: Mysterious People / Frequency ride: Mysterious People / Go insane: Joystick / House step: Joystick / Up 'n' down: Faders Inc. / Wake up: Morel

TWCD 90004 / 25 May '98 / Twisted UK

□ ONE O'CLOCK JUMP

One o'clock jump: Basie, Count / Moose the mooch: Davis, Miles / Bugle call rag: Goodman, Benny / It's only a paper moon: Cole, Nat 'King' / Basin Street blues: Armstrong, Louis / Rumbop concerto: Gillespie, Dizzy / 'Round midnight: Parker, Charlie / Stompin' at the Savoy: Herman, Woody / My heart stood still: Shaw, Artie / At long last love: Horne, Lena / That old black magic: Fitzgerald, Ella / Yardbird suite: Davis, Miles / Love me or leave me: Horne, Lena / Tiger rag: Armstrong, Louis / Feather merchant: Basie, Count / Move: Parker, Charlie / Get happy: Goodman, Benny / Blue prelude: Horne, Lena / Three hearts in a triangle: Gillespie, Dizzy / Slow boat to China: Gillespie, Dizzy

GRF 125 / '93 / Tring

□ ONE STEP AHEAD - TWO TONE DANCE CRAZE

BHR 028CD / Oct '95 / Burning Heart

□ ONE VOICE (Vocal Music From Around The World)

Izithembiso Zenkosi: Ladysmith Black Mambazo / Prochula se moma Nedelya: Trio Bulgarka / Tender comrade: Bragg, Billy / Jerusalem revisited: Coope Boyes & Simpson / Ever widening circles of remorse: Sublette, Ned & Lawrence Weiner/The Persuasions / Cantu a balluu seriu: Tenores Di Bitti / Heilani Saattelin Amerikkahan: Liedes, Anna-Kaisa / Puisque je t'aime, pars: Revey, Laurence / Irijirie (my dawn): Pearl Divers Of Bahrain / Bean an leanna: Heaney, Joe / Blood and gold/Mohacs: Prior, Maddy & June Tabor / Grey cock: Carthy, Eliza / E ho hi: MacKenzie, Talitha / Bazali Bethu: Black Umfolosi / Himene tarava: Tamarii Pirae of Tahiti / Throat singing: Shu-De / Benza guru: Tibetan Buddhist Monks / Introitus - Da Pacem: Cantori Gregoriani / Study war no more: Sweet Honey In The Rock

RGNET 1014CD / Aug '97 / World Music Network

□ ONE WORLD

ROUAN 15 / Oct '94 / Rounder

□ ONE WORLD (2CD Set)

RADCD 74 / 19 Jan '98 / Global TV

□ ONE WORLD OR NONE (The Conscious Compilation)

Northern sulphuric soul: Rae & Christian / Kalimba: Freakniks / Chicken ina box: Mr. Scruff / Jive talk: Fourth World / Universal highness: Thievery Corporation / Duden: Atlas, Natacha / Zed and two L's: Fila Brazillia / Dub systems go: Dubmarine / Garden: Riz Allstars / Dub oppression: Riz Allstars & Ishuru

WDM 004CD / Feb '97 / World Development

□ ONE WORLD, ONE VOICE

CDV 2632 / Jun '90 / Virgin

□ ONGAKU=MUSIC

ONGAKUCD 1 / 17 Nov '97 / Ongaku

□ ONLY CLUB ALBUM YOU'LL EVER NEED, THE

5407862 / Aug '97 / A&M

□ ONLY FOR THE HEADSTRONG (2CD Set)

Rock the dancefloor: Forbes, Davie / Pop goes the world: Third Man / Rock this place: DJ Elevation / Any last words: DJ Psycangle / Resident evil: Tailbone / Dark and darker: DJ Flare / End of an era: Luna-C / As yet untitled: Brothers Mayhem / Energy flux: El Bruto / I got something: DJ Reno & Eatsum / Is stupid when: DJ Psycangle / Let me go: Toxic Avengers / Time to party: DJ E-Rick & Tactic / Crazy: Brotherhood

DBM 2774 / Feb '97 / Death Becomes Me

□ ONLY FREEWAYS TO SKINNER KAT

RAUCD 12 / Oct '94 / Raucous

□ ONLY GUITAR (2CD Set)

24042 / Jun '96 / Delta Doubles

□ ONLY THE POORMAN FEEL IT

Izinziswa / Giya / Siyaya / Mayibuye / Shosholoza / No easy road / Skorokoro / Yivumeni we zinsizw / Uthando lami / Ihlathi / Intsizwa / Thula / Madambadamba

CDEMC 3706 / Sep '97 / EMI

□ ONLY THE STRONG

VR 010CD / Jun '94 / Victory

□ ONLY WAY IS UP, THE

Walking on sunshine: Katrina & The Waves / Nelson Mandela: Specials / I feel love: Bronski Beat & Marc Almond / Nineteen: Hardcastle, Paul / Dancing with tears in my eyes: Ultravox / Reflex: Duran Duran / Small town boy: Bronski Beat / We close our eyes: Go West / My ever changing moods: Style Council / If I was: Ure, Midge / Living in a box: Living In A Box / Only way is up: Yazz / Respectable: Mel & Kim / Don't leave me this way: Communards / Breakout: Swing Out Sister / Something's gotten hold of my heart: Almond, Marc & Gene Pitney / Walk the dinosaur: Was Not Was / Don't worry be happy: McFerrin, Bobby / Don't turn around: Aswad / She drives me crazy: Fine Young Cannibals

5529232 / Oct '97 / Spectrum

□ ONLY YOU (20 Great Hits Of The Sixties)

That's what love will do: Brown, Joe / When my little girl is smiling: Justice, Jimmy / Only you (And you alone): Wynter, Mark / Sailor: Clark, Petula / Who put the bomp: Viscounts / March of the Siamese children: Ball, Kenny / Party's over: Donegan, Lonnie / Up on the roof: Grant, Julie / I wonder who's kissing her now: Ford, Emile / Swinging on a star:

Irwin, Big Dee & Little Eva / It's almost tomorrow: Wynter, Mark / Where are you now: Trent, Jackie / Counting teardrops: Ford, Emile / Alone at last: Wilson, Jackie / Ramona: Bachelors / Picture of you: Brown, Joe / Sukiyaki: Ball, Kenny / Michael, row the boat ashore: Donegan, Lonnie / Spanish Harlem: Justice, Jimmy / Ya ya twist: Clark, Petula
TRTCD 102 / 18 May '98 / TrueTrax

☐ **ONLY YOU**
Room in your heart: Living In A Box / When will I see you again: Brother Beyond / Don't turn away: Go For It / Until forever: Rogers, Evan / I'll fly for you: Spandau Ballet / What becomes of the broken hearted: Boy George / Caravan of love: Housemartins / Rise to the occasion: Fisher, Climie / Orchard Road: Sayer, Leo / Turn back the clock: Johnny Hates Jazz / Mistake no.3: Culture Club / Only you: Flying Pickets / You're in love: Wilson Phillips / Don't want to wait anymore: Tubes / Won't let you go: Sly Fox / Every rose has it's thorn: Poison
DC 870532 / Mar '97 / Disky

☐ **OOH OOH - THE POETS OF RHYTHM: HOTPIE & CANDY RECORDS (Original Raw Soul Vol.1)**
Working on the line: Soul Saints Orchestra / Spooky grinder: Woo Woo's / South Carolina: Bus People Express / Fifty yards of soul: Whitefield Brothers / Funky train: Poets Of Rhythm / ORF (Pts 1 and 2): Organized Raw Funk / Funky Sex Machine: Baral, Bo / Cooking on a piece of meat: Whitefield Brothers / Augusta, Georgia (Here I come): Bus People Express / Ooh ooh: Woo Woo's / Hotpie's popcorn: Poets Of Rhythm / Bag of soul: Soul Saints Orchestra / Sticky sticky sock-a-poo: Mighty Continentals / It's your thing
ME 000372 / Sep '95 / Soulciety

☐ **OPEN HOUSE**
Super sonic surfer: Fractal Shark / Open house: Monolith / Free for all: Deep Quest / House of reality: Monolith / Silver dollar: Balloon / Sunrise surprise: Deep Quest / Infect: Fractal Shark / Kling klang: Deep Quest / Islands in the sun: Monolith / Mercury mission: Balloon
306172 / Jan '97 / Hallmark

☐ **OPEN T - ON THE ROAD**
TMPCD 018 / Dec '95 / Temple

☐ **OPERATION BEATBOX**
REC 023 / Oct '96 / Re-Constriction

☐ **OPERATION D**
DBTXCD 2 / Nov '95 / Sting Ray

☐ **OPSCENE 50**
GAP 032CD / Sep '96 / Gap Recordings

☐ **ORANGE COUNTY PUNK VERSUS SKA VOL.1**
SV 001CD / Mar '97 / Revelation

☐ **ORANGE PEEL**
EFA 006292 / 14 Sep '98 / Source

☐ **ORBITS VOL.1**
CDC 001 / Mar '95 / Out Of Orbit

☐ **ORCHESTRAL DANCE PARTY**
SGP 300003CD / 23 Mar '98 / Desco

☐ **ORDER ODONATA VOL.1**
BFLCD 13 / 1 Sep '98 / Butterfly

☐ **ORGAN RADIO VOL.1**
ORGAN 025CD / Mar '97 / Org

☐ **ORGAN RADIO VOL.2 (Another Taste of UK 'Core)**
ORGAN 031CD / 27 Oct '97 / Org

☐ **ORGANIC TECHNOLOGI**
BOSCDLP 003 / 26 Jan '98 / Botchit & Scarper

☐ **ORGANISED SOUND**
JFRCD 005 / Sep '96 / Jazz Fudge

☐ **ORGANISM VOL.1**
EFAD 84632 / Oct '94 / Dossier

☐ **ORGANISM VOL.2**
EFA 084642 / Mar '95 / Dossier

☐ **ORGANISM VOL.3**
EFA 084682 / Nov '95 / Dossier

☐ **ORGANISM VOL.4**
EFA 08469CD / Jun '96 / Dossier

☐ **ORGANIST ENTERTAINS YOU**
Here we are again: Foort, Reginald / Ta ra ra boom de ay: Foort, Reginald / Down at the old Bull and Bush: Foort, Reginald / Melody in F: MacPherson, Sandy / Change partners: Cleaver, Robinson / Yam: Cleaver, Robinson / I used to be colour blind: Cleaver, Robinson / Las Cuatro Milpas: Ramsey, Harold / Rhythm of the clock (tick a tick tock): Torch, Sidney / Rhapsody in blue: Ramsey, Harold & Patricia Rossborough / Parade of the tin soldiers: MacLean, Quentin / Mosquitos parade: MacLean, Quentin / My love parade: MacLean, Quentin / Why shouldn't we: Foort, Reginald / Door of my dreams: Foort, Reginald / Indian love call: Foort, Reginald / You're a sweetheart: Torch, Sidney / Invitation to the waltz: Cleaver, Robinson & Patricia Rossborough / My dream garden: Foort, Reginald / Love's a garden of roses: Foort, Reginald / Trees: Foort, Reginald / Lullaby of the leaves: Foort, Reginald / Bees' wedding: Foort, Reginald / I'm knee deep in daisies: Foort, Reginald / Narcissus: Foort, Reginald / Brown bird singing: Foort, Reginald / Spring song: Foort, Reginald / Country gardens: Foort, Reginald / Grandma said: Dixon, Reginald / I miss you in the morning: Dixon, Reginald / Isn't this a lovely day: Torch, Sidney / Why stars come out at night: Torch, Sidney / Cheek to cheek: Torch, Sidney / Keep smiling: Foort, Reginald / Music Maestro please: Dixon, Reginald / Little lady make believe: Dixon, Reginald / Whistler and his dog: Cleaver, Robinson / Washington Post: Ramsey, Harold / Semper fidelis: Ramsey, Harold / Hungarian march: Ramsey, Harold / I shall always remember you smiling: Dixon, Reginald / Where the Shannon flows down to the sea: Dixon, Reginald / Dainty Miss: Cleaver, Robinson / Miss Annabelle Lee: Cleaver, Robinson / Somebody stole my gal: Cleaver, Robinson / St. Louis blues: Ramsey, Harold
RAJCD 862 / May '96 / Empress

☐ **ORGASMIC HOUSE**
DOWN 1CD / Jun '95 / Sun Down

☐ **ORIENT OF THE GREEKS, THE**
926592 / Apr '97 / BUDA

☐ **ORIENTAL DREAMS**
PS 65075 / Jul '91 / PlayaSound

☐ **ORIENTAL GARDEN, AN**
RFLCD 217 / 6 Oct '97 / Reflection

☐ **ORIGIN UNKNOWN (2CD Set)**
RAMMLPCD 2 / 6 Apr '98 / Ram

☐ **ORIGIN UNKNOWN - THE SPEED OF SOUND**
RAMMLPCD 1 / May '97 / Ramm

☐ **ORIGINAL ART FORM (2CD Set)**
Kiss Fm radio promo: Tycoon Tosh & Terminator Troops / Love and peace: Tycoon Tosh & Terminator Troops / That's the jail: Boy Ken / Love break: Tagaki Kan / Sax hoodlum: Major Force West / Last orgy: Tiny Panx / Yes we can can: Orchids / Meet the rhythm: Tagaki Kan / Hand made: ECD / In tempo: ECD / Santastic mix: SDP / Love formula: Tagaki Kan / Version: Hiroshi & Kudo / Bed jam sesson: Tycoon Tosh & Terminator Troops / Club of steel: DJ Doc Holiday / Prop master's party: Kool DJ Red Alert / Midnight: Tycoon Tosh / Get happy: Tycoon Tosh & Terminator Troops / Freakedout: Tagaki Kan / Nice guy: SDP / Essential dub: Major Force West / Copy '88-'99: Tycoon Tosh & Terminator Troops / I will call you: Orchids / Shinco about it: SDP / Economic animal in concrete jungle: Tycoon Tosh / Hiroshi's dub: TPO / Life in science: Orchids / Family stoned beat: TPO / Return of the original art form: Hiroshi & Kudo
MW 082CD / 6 Oct '97 / Mo Wax

☐ **ORIGINAL BEATS FROM THE CONCRETE STREETS**
Bass machine retuned: Mantronik, Curtis / Sunrise: Bas Kittens / ARG: DJ HZ / Safe: Melting Pot / Thrill is gone: Elements Of Life / Lesson six: Cut Chemist / Nobody knows my name: T-Love / GOD theme: Glimmer Of Dope / Space fritters: Lo Phat Hi Fi / Fugu: Small Fish With Spine
992164 / 20 Apr '98 / Oxygen/Music Works

☐ **ORIGINAL CHILLOUT (2CD Set)**
XSP 3CDM / 17 Aug '98 / X-Treme

☐ **ORIGINAL CLUB SKA**
CDHB 055 / Feb '91 / Heartbeat

☐ **ORIGINAL DJ CLASSICS**
ROCKY 1 / Apr '96 / Rocky One

☐ **ORIGINAL FUNK (The Sound Of New Orleans)**
325062 / 21 Aug '97 / Melodie

☐ **ORIGINAL HITS OF THE 60'S AND 70'S**
PKL 514911 / Jul '93 / K&K

☐ **ORIGINAL JAZZ MASTERS VOL.1, THE (5CD Set)**
DAMUSIC 76032 / Dec '95 / DA Music

☐ **ORIGINAL JAZZ MASTERS VOL.2, THE (5CD Set)**
DAMUSIC 76042 / Dec '95 / DA Music

☐ **ORIGINAL JUKEBOX HITS VOL.1 (2CD Set)**
There goes my heart again: Domino, Fats / Lollipop: Chordettes / Bye bye love: Everly Brothers / Little girl: Valens, Ritchie / Without you: Tillotson, Johnny / Venus: Avalon, Frankie / You don't know me: Welch, Lenny / Hippy hippy shake: Romero, Chan / Big John: Shirelles / Rockin' ghost: Bleyer, Archie / Keep searching (we'll follow the sun): Shannon, Del / 24 hours from Tulsa: Pitney, Gene / La bamba: Valens, Ritchie / Rumours: Crawford, Johnny / Twist and shout: Isley Brothers / Let's dance: Montez, Chris / It hurts to be in love: Pitney, Gene / Mama said: Shirelles / Forever, forever: Domino, Fats / Bird dog: Everly Brothers / Stranger in town: Shannon, Del / Canadian sunset: Williams, Andy / Donna: Valens, Ritchie / Ballad of Davy Crockett: Hayes, Billy / Cherry stone: Addrisi Brothers / It keeps right on a-hurtin': Tillotson, Johnny / Never on Sunday: Chordettes / Hernando's hideaway: Bleyer, Archie
SD 885432 / 2 Feb '98 / Disky

☐ **ORIGINAL JUKEBOX HITS VOL.2 (2CD Set)**
Red sails in the sunset: Domino, Fats / Wake up little Susie: Everly Brothers / Runaway: Shannon, Del / Butterfly: Williams, Andy / Poetry in motion: Tillotson, Johnny / Man who shot Liberty Valence: Pitney, Gene / Cindy's birthday: Crawford, Johnny / Dedicated to the one I love: Shirelles / We belong together: Valens, Ritchie / Rumble: Wray, Link / Little town flirt: Shannon, Del / Ginger bread: Avalon, Frankie / My uncle used to love me but she died: Miller, Roger / Kansas city: Domino, Fats / Only love can break a heart: Pitney, Gene / Who cares: Domino, Fats / Born to be with you: Chordettes / Bye bye love: Everly Brothers / Send me the pillow that you dream on: Tillotson, Johnny / I like your kind of love: Williams, Andy / King of the road: Miller, Roger / I'm a lonesome fugitive: Vincent, Gene / I'm gonna knock on your door: Hodges, Eddie / De de Dinah: Avalon, Frankie / Walkin' after midnight: Cline, Patsy / Will you still love me tomorrow: Shirelles / Come on let's go: Valens, Ritchie / Hats off to Larry: Shannon, Del
SD 885342 / 2 Feb '98 / Disky

☐ **ORIGINAL MAMBO KINGS, THE**
5138762 / Jan '93 / Verve

☐ **ORIGINAL MEMPHIS FIVE VOL.1 1922-1923**
My honey's lovin' arms / Cuddle up blues / Hopeless blues / Lonesome mama blues / Hot lips / Yankee doodle blues / I wish I could shimmy like my sister Kate / Achin' hearted blues / Chicago / Running wild / Ivy / That barking dog / Stop your kidding / Loose feet / Aggravatin' / Great white way blues / Four o'clock blues / Shufflin' Mose / Jelly roll blues / Bunch of blues / Sweet papa Joe / Hootin' de hoot
COCD 16 / Mar '95 / Collector's Classics

☐ **ORIGINAL MEMPHIS ROCK 'N' ROLL**
CLCD 4404 / Nov '96 / Collector/White Label

☐ **ORIGINAL MUSIC REVIVE REGGAE CLASSICS**
Lion Train: Prophet, Michael / Lion train: Prophet, Michael / Sataland: Jah Woosh / Sataland: Jah Woosh / Fight on my own: Reggae George / Fight on my own: Reggae George / Free up the blackman: Joseph Ear Lock / Free up the blackman: Joseph Ear Lock / Run run: Delgado, Junior / Run run: Delgado, Junior / Marcus say: Jah Woosh / Marcus say: Jah Woosh / Tonight: Andy, Horace / Tonight: Andy, Horace / Come down sun: Mackay, Freddy / Come down sun: Mackay, Freddy / What sweet you so: Sherman, Bim
OMCD 035 / 1 Sep '97 / Original Music

☐ **ORIGINAL REGGAE HITS OF THE 60'S & 70'S VOL.1, THE**
PKCD 33194 / Sep '94 / K&K

☐ **ORIGINAL REGGAE HITS OF THE 60'S & 70'S VOL.4, THE**
PKCD 040898 / 5 May '98 / K&K

☐ **ORIGINAL RHUMBAS**
995312 / Aug '93 / EPM

☐ **ORIGINAL SEEDS**
74321552312 / 22 Jun '98 / Rubber

☐ **ORIGINAL STALAG 17-18 AND 19**
WRCD 1684 / Oct '92 / Jet Star

☐ **ORIGINAL VERSIONS OF SONGS BY THE COMMITMENTS**
Mustang Sally / Chain of fools / Hard to handle / Mr. Pitiful / I never loved a man (the way I love you) / In the midnight hour / Slip away / Please please please / Shaft / Show me / Try a little tenderness / Dark end of the street / I've got dreams to remember / Do right man / Do right woman, do right man
7567918132 / Feb '94 / East West

☐ **ORIGINALS VOL.1**
Wonderful world: Cooke, Sam / I heard it through the grapevine: Gaye, Marvin / Stand by me: King, Ben E. / When a man loves a woman: Sledge, Percy / C'mon everybody: Cochran, Eddie / Mannish boy: Waters, Muddy / Ain't nobody home: King, B.B. / Can't get enough: Bad Company / Joker: Miller, Steve Band / Should I stay or should I go: Clash / Twentieth century boy: T-Rex / Mad about the boy: Washington, Dinah / Piece of my heart: Franklin, Erma / Heart attack and vine: Hawkins, Screamin' Jay
MOODCD 29 / May '93 / Columbia

☐ **ORIGINATION 1974-1984**
SHCD 6012 / Oct '95 / Sky High

☐ **ORIGINATORS, THE**
Let the power fall: Max Romeo / Kaya dub: King Tubby & The Aggrovators / Village: Isaacs, Gregory / Someday: Ellis, Alton / Reggae hits the town: Ethiopians / Originator: U-Roy / Zion gate: Andy, Horace / Left me with a broken heart: Paragons / Love me forever: Brown, Dennis / Guns don't argue: Alcapone, Dennis / King Tubby's special: Pablo, Augustus / Three times a lady: Sanchez / I'm in the mood for love: Edwards, Jackie / If it don't work out: Kelly, Pat / You're my desire: Marley, Rita & The Soulettes / Jam in the street: Holt, John / Gonna take a miracle: Boothe, Ken / Just once in my life: McGregor, Freddie
CDBM 124 / Jan '97 / Blue Moon

☐ **ORIGINS OF MAN, THE**
PRMTCDX 001 / 22 Sep '97 / Primate

☐ **ORISSI DANCE MUSIC**
VICG 52682 / Mar '96 / JVC World Library

☐ **ORKNEY SESSIONS**
ATCD 041 / Oct '95 / Attic

☐ **ORKUS COLLECTION VOL.1**
EFA 616002 / 1 Dec '97 / Orkus

☐ **ORQUESTAS TEJANAS (Tejano Roots)**
ARHCD 368 / Apr '95 / Arhoolie

☐ **ORTHODOX CHANTS**
AUB 006770 / Dec '92 / Auvidis/Ethnic

☐ **OS IPANEMAS**
MRBCD 001 / May '95 / Mr. Bongo

☐ **OSLO AGREEMENT, THE**
BASE 002 / 15 Sep '97 / Homebase

☐ **OTHER STUFF VOL.1**
In essance: Isis / Vorn: Idjut Boys / Intertwining sexuality: Sensory Productions / Nothin's been the same: DJD & NYN / Landing: Sutra / Other / Other / Eso lo que va: Beach Flea & Magic Juan / Future: Other Project & RMA / Feel the warmth: Reel Houze / Brinca: Rosario, Ralphi / Hard to dye: Paramour / Love triangle: Coco Steel & Lovebomb / It's a party: Man Called Adam
THECD 106 / Apr '97 / Other

☐ **OTHER STUFF VOL.2**
Der bauch: MC Sultan / This is London: Coco, Chris / Rumble in Brazil: Arce, Aaron / Bloo Monday: Arce, Aaron / Apollo: Cujo / Slip away: Idjut Boys / Great ocean road: Coco Steel / Portal drift: Benz / Are you ready: Mighty Clouds Of Joy / French boy: Garcons
THECD 110 / 26 May '98 / Other

☐ **OTHERWORLD (Dance Trance & Magic Plants)**
TRANR 610CD / 1 Sep '97 / Transient

☐ **OTTOMAN ART MUSIC**
AAA 130 / Apr '97 / Club Du Disque Arabe

☐ **OUD, THE**
LYRCD 7160 / Dec '94 / Lyrichord

☐ **OUIJAWHAMMY**
AB 002CD / Mar '96 / Holistic

☐ **OUR FAVOURITE THINGS**
Please don't talk about me when I'm gone: Holiday, Billie / Stolen moments (aka you belong to her): Carter, Betty & Carmen McRae / Squatty roo: Fitzgerald, Ella / Crazy he calls me: Washington, Dinah / If I were a bell: Dearie, Blossom / Up jumped spring: Lincoln, Abbey / They didn't believe me: Anderson, Ernestine / Sometimes I'm happy: Vaughan, Sarah / You're lucky to me: Merrill, Helen / I've got the world on a string: O'Day, Anita / Only trust your heart: Gilberto, Astrud / Blue and sentimental: Humes, Helen / My favourite things: Carter, Betty / Don't explain: Simone, Nina / Just in time: Horn, Shirley / If you could see me now: King, Morgana
5526402 / Mar '97 / Spectrum

☐ **OUR FRIENDS ELECTRIC (2CD Set)**
TCD 2814 / Feb '96 / Telstar

☐ **OUR SALVATION IS IN HAND**
TP 05 / May '97 / Theme Park

☐ **OUT LOUD (For Gay & Lesbian Human Rights)**
KFWCD 169 / Oct '96 / Knitting Factory

☐ **OUT OF IRELAND (Irish Emigration To America)**
Timothy Cashman theme / Devereux brothers theme / Optimism theme / Mary Rush theme / T. McIntyre theme / William Murphy theme / Discrimination theme / Richard O'Gorman theme / Mary Ann Rowe theme / Tom Brick theme / Religion theme / Tim O'Brien theme / Closing credits
SHCD 79092 / 23 Mar '98 / Shanachie

☐ **OUT OF MANY ONE VOL.1 (Jamaican Music 1962-1975)**
Music is my occupation: Drummond, Don / Owe me no pay me: Ethiopians / Jack of my trade: Sir Lord Comic / Run for your life: Bryan, Carl / Sick and tired: Grant, Neville / Don't look back: Brown, Buster / Only yesterday: Parker, Ken / Place called Africa: Byles, Junior / Hopeful village: Tennors / Better must come: Wilson, Delroy / Stop that man: Crystalites / Space flight: I-Roy / Sun is shining: Marley, Bob & The Wailers / Fever: Byles, Junior / Satan side: Hudson, Keith / Skank in bed: Scotty / Let's start again: Campbell, Cornell & Friends
CDTRS 1 / Jan '89 / Trojan

☐ **OUT OF MANY ONE VOL.2**
CDTRS 2 / Nov '90 / Trojan

☐ **OUT OF THE BOX VOL.2**
BMCD 119 / 17 Nov '97 / Black Mark

☐ **OUT OF THE BRONX VOL.1**
Guardian angel: Camerons / Please be mine: Consorts / Baby don't you know: Camerons / Cheryl: Camerons / Time after time: Consorts / Little girl: Dreamers / Mashed potato Mary: Villari, Guy / On the street where you live: Chuckles / Cheryl: Reno, Al / Day before yesterday: Darnell & The Dreams / At the start of a new romance: Dials / Tell Gina: Elgins / I'm not the one for you: Dee, Sonny / He's a lover/I got fired: Chesterfields / I had a love: Darnell & The Dreams / Here I stand: Dee, Sonny / Star above: Consorts / Carrie: Consorts / Laura: Camerons / Bad girl: Rue Teens / I made the biggest mistake of my life: Bi-Tones / Dance with me: Rue Teens / Lorraine: Excellents / She's not coming home: Excellents / She's got it: Camerons
BB 55047 / Aug '97 / Buffalo Bop

☐ **OUT OF THE BRONX VOL.2**
Cheryl: Elgins / Boom chic-a-boom: Camerons / Congratulations: Reno, Al / Girl that I marry: Camerons / Because of you: Dreamers / I'll wait: Chuckles / Time after time: Consorts / These foolish things: Dials / Mi-a-suri talk: Taylor, Mike / I'm all alone: Villari, Guy / Red red robin: Camerons / Barbara Ann: Darts / Fool in love: Darts / Runaround: Darts / Mother's love: Darts / Trying: Dials / I made the biggest mistake of my life: Excellents / Jeanette Jeanette: Bi-Tones / You and I: Teardrops / Unchained melody: Dials / It's much better (to make her love me): Montereys / Romeo and Juliet: Montereys / Playing the game: Montereys / Two lovers: Montereys / Wouldn't you cha cha with me: Orientals / You can't run away: Tommy & The Del Royals / I cried: Orientals / Trust in love: Tommy & The Del Royals / New love: Darnell & The Dreams / Time to say goodbye: Elegant Four
BB 55048 / Aug '97 / Buffalo Bop

☐ **OUT OF THE DARK**
CM 77160CD / Mar '97 / Century Media

☐ **OUT OF THE MOUNTAINS (The Essential Bluegrass Collection)**
Duelling banjos: Jackson, Carl / Doorstep of trouble: *Nashville Bluegrass Band* / Man of constant sorrow: Rowan, Peter / Big Sciota: Douglas, Barenberg & Meyer / One love/People get ready: *New Grass Revival* / Long time gone: *Nashville Bluegrass Band* / Ramblin' on my mind: *Front Range* / Rock my soul: Lawson, Doyle & Quicksilver / Anything Southbound: *Lonesome Standard Time* / I don't believe you've met my baby: *Douglas, Jerry* / Away on the mountain: *O'Brien, Tim & Mollie* / Honey don't: *Country Gentlemen* / Last thing on my mind: *Chesapeake* / Moth to a flame: *Rowan, Peter & The Nashville Bluegrass Band* / Third stone form the sun: *Psychograss* / Bluegrass widow: *Keen, Robert Earl* / Were you there: *Front Range* / Possession's nine tenths of the law: *Lonesome Standard Time* / Black Mountain rag: *Crary, Dan* / Your friendship carries me: *Blue Rose* / Can't you hear me calling: *Boone Creek* / Foggy mountain breakdown: *Jackson, Carl*
NSCD 035 / 15 Jun '98 / Nascente

☐ **OUT OF THEIR MOUTH VOL.2**
ALP 38CD / Jan '97 / Atavistic

☐ **OUT ON THE FLOOR (Legendary Northern Soul Club Classics)**
Seven days too long: *Wood, Chuck* / She blew a good thing: *Poets* / Girls are out to get you: *Fascinations* / Looking for you: *Mimms, Garnet* / I can't get a hold of myself: *Curry, Clifford* / Snake: *Wilson, Al* / Stay close to me: *Stairsteps* / I'll do anything: *Troy, Doris* / Breakout: *Ryder, Mitch* / What's wrong with me baby: *Invitations* / Queen of fools: *Mills, Barbara* / Nobody but me: *Human Beinz* / I dig your act: *O'Jays* / Shake a tail feather: *Purify, James & Bobby* / This thing called love: *Wyatt, Johnny* / Our love will grow: *Showmen* / Try a little harder: *Fidels* / Backfield in motion: *Mel & Tim* / Don't be sore at me: *Parliaments* / Reaching for the best: *Exciters* / Somebody somewhere needs you: *Banks, Darrell* / Oh my darlin: *Dee, Jackie* / Groovin' at the go-go: *Four Larks* / Little piece of leather: *Elbert, Donnie* / Out on the floor: *Gray, Dobie*
GSCD 058 / Jun '95 / Goldmine

☐ **OUT ON THE FLOOR TONIGHT (26 Classic Northern Floor Fillers)**
Boomerang: *Leavill, Otis* / Many's a slip: *Present* / I wanna know: *Paul, John E.* / On a magic carpet ride: *Dee, Kiki* / He's my kind of fellow: *Sandy & The Pebbles* / Broken heart attack: *Sweet* / What's it gonna be: *Springfield, Dusty* / Put me in your pocket: *Harper, Jeanette* / Baby make your own sweet music: *Jay & The Techniques* / One night affair: *Butler, Jerry* / He loves me: *Chalafontes* / You can't close the windows: *Petals* / Joker went wild: *Hyland, Brian* / Mr. Love: *Wright, Nat* / I wish I was: *Garrigan, Eddie* / Woman: *Newarkers, Nicky* / Big hurt: *Farrell, Susan* / He will break your heart: *Groovers* / I'll do anything: *Gamble, Lenny* / Girl don't make me wait: *Time Box* / You don't know where your interest lies: *Five A Penny* / Closer she gets: *Drevar, John* / Little darlin': *Flirtations* / Daylight saving time: *Keith* / Who can I turn to: *Copage, Marc*
GSCD 107 / May '97 / Goldmine

☐ **OUT THE LIGHTS VOL.3**
DTCD 12 / Jul '92 / Discotex

☐ **OUT THE LIGHTS VOL.4**
DTCD 14 / Nov '92 / Discotex

☐ **OUT THE LIGHTS VOL.5**
DTCD 17 / Jun '93 / Discotex

☐ **OUT THE LIGHTS VOL.6**
DTCD 24 / Apr '96 / Discotex

☐ **OUT THERE (A Thread Through Time/ 2CD Set)**
TBCD 001 / Nov '94 / T&B

☐ **OUTER SPACE COMMUNICATIONS**
DIS 007CD / Apr '94 / Minus Habens

☐ **OUTLAWS IN MY EYE (Texas)**
CA 001 / 20 Apr '98 / Cardiac Arrest

☐ **OUTLAWS IN MY EYE VOL.1**
CA 002 / 20 Apr '98 / Cardiac Arrest

☐ **OUTLAWS IN MY EYE VOL.2**
CA 003 / 20 Apr '98 / Cardiac Arrest

☐ **OUTSIDE THE REACTOR VOL.1**
BR 1CD / Feb '97 / Blue Room Released

☐ **OVCCI VUOMI OVTAA VEAIGGIS**
DATCD 20 / Nov '95 / Dat

☐ **OVER THE EDGE**
Got to be emotion: *Virginity* / I'm coming up: *Love Boutique* / Love bizarre: *Fratelli* / Can't stop: *Plez* / How to win your love: *ECA* / Throwdown: *Bitch* / Religion: *Awareness* / 550 state: *Blood Brothers* / Feel that feelin': *T-Boom* / Wind theme: *Xpulsion* / Summer's child: *Life Form* / Acperience 1: *Hardfloor* / (You give me) All your love: *Pro-gressive*
CDTOT 9 / May '93 / Jumpin' & Pumpin'

☐ **OVER THE TOP**
TRTCD 180 / Jun '95 / TrueTrax

☐ **OVER THERE 1942**
PHONTCD 7670 / Apr '94 / Phontastic

☐ **OVERDOSE OF HEAVY SPINACH**
AA 063 / 16 Mar '98 / Arf Arf

☐ **OVERPOWERED BY FUNK**
Shaft: *Hayes, Isaac* / One nation under a groove: *Funkadelic* / Get up off that thing: *Brown, James* / Fire: *Ohio Brothers* / Move on up: *Mayfield, Curtis* / Beginning of the end: *Funky Nassau* / Funkin' for Jamaica: *Browne, Tom* / Are you ready (do the bus stop): *Fatback Band* / Express: *BT Express* / Strawberry letter 23: *Brothers Johnson* / I need it: *Watson, Johnny 'Guitar'* / Family affair: *Sly & The Family Stone* / Papa's got a brand new pig bag: *Pig Bag* / Word up: *Cameo* / Ain't gonna bump no more: *Tex, Joe* / Pick up the pieces: *Average White Band* / Play that funky music: *Wild Cherry* / Sunshine day: *Osibisa* / We got the funk: *Positive Force* / Expansion: *Smith, Lonnie Liston*
RENCD 109 / Oct '95 / Renaissance Collector Series

☐ **OW (All Star Jam Session)**
MCD 075 / Dec '95 / Moon

☐ **OWLS' HOOT, THE**
DGF 2 / May '95 / Frog

☐ **OXFORD ARTISTS**
Famous: *Thurman* / Dowee oowee oo: *Arthur Turners Lovechild* / 24 Hours (Used): *Candyskins* / Sally said: *Beaker* / See you: *Mystics* / Warts 'n' all: *Bigger The God* / Arc weld: *Blue Kite* / Yeah: *Dustball* / If I was Barry White: *Daisies* / Falling down: *Wonderland* / Snail trail: *Heavenly* / Ulcer: *Sky Drive* / Shopping: *Egg* / U are my sunshine: *Oxford United FC*
OXCD 2000 / Aug '97 / Rotator

☐ **OYE LISTEN (Compacto Caliente)**
Defiendeme Santa Barbara: *Leida, Linda* / Arroz con manteca: *Leida, Linda* / Olvidame: *Rodriguez, Bobby* / La mulata cubana: *Valdes, Alfredo* / Con carino a Panama: *Santamaria, Monguito* / Festival in Guarare: *La Sonora De Baru* / Ay se paso la serie: *Rolando la serie* / Ocana sordi: *Los guaracheros de oriente* / Como se baila el son: *La India Del Oriente* / Ban-con-tim: *Super All Star* / Prende la vela: *Calzado, Rudy* / Saludando a los rumberos: *Marti, Virgilio*
CDORB 014 / Jan '87 / Globestyle

☐ **OZARK FRONTIER**
Bury me beneath the willow: *Riddle, Almeda* / Merry golden tree: *Riddle, Almeda* / Titanic: *Riddle, Almeda* / Alan Bain: *Riddle, Almeda* / Rainbow 'mid life's willows: *Riddle, Almeda* / Lonesome dove: *Riddle, Almeda* / Down in Arkansas: *Riddle, Almeda* / Anything: *Morris, Neil* / Music has no end: *Morris, Neil* / Irish soldier and the English lady: *Morris, Neil* / Turnip greens: *Morris, Neil* / Rock all the babies to sleep: *Morris, Neil* / Willow green: *Gilbert, Ollie* / Once I courted a lady beauty bright: *Gilbert, Ollie* / It rained a mist: *Gilbert, Ollie* / Lord Batesman: *Gilbert, Ollie* / Pretty Polly Oliver: *Gilbert, Ollie* / Sally Goodin: *Everidge, Charlie* / Buffalo gals: *Shannon, Bookmiller* / Eighth of January: *Shannon, Bookmiller* / Cotton-eyed Joe: *Shannon, Bookmiller* / Scotch musick: *Morrison, Absie* / My prettiest girl is gone: *Morrison, Absie* / Nancy's got a pretty dress on: *Morrison, Absie* / Down in Arkansas among the sticks: *Shannon, Bookmiller*
ROUCD 1707 / Sep '97 / Rounder

P

☐ **P&B PRODUCTIONS - RITUALS**
PB 96010 / Mar '97 / P&B

☐ **PACHA IBIZA (2CD Set)**
VENCDA 114 / 1 Jun '98 / Vendetta

☐ **PACIFIC STATE (Electronica Made In Japan - 2CD Set)**
Warning: *Oe, Tatsuye* / Dinosaur R.: *Ishii, Ken* / Soul screamer: *Boom Boom Satellites* / Bote: *Ishino, Takkyu* / Slient speaker: *Inaoko, Ken* / Worker: *Subvoice* / Quadra loops: *Quadra* / Synfunk: *DJ Q'Hey* / Auq boogie: *Co-Fusion* / Cross: *Takemura, Nobukazu* / Creepy crawly: *Web* / Secret samba: *Doctor YS & The Cosmic Drunkards* / Emotion: *Hoodrum* / Elegant space: *Sunahara, Yoshinori* / Matsuri: *DJ Krush* / Paradise V2: *DJ Krush* / Device versa: *Harakami, Rei* / Soft tone: *Prism* / Cool pot: *Hagio, Masahiko* / Shake down: *Bust Boom Choker* / Techattack: *Dazzle T & Quicky*
DVNT 030CD / 13 Oct '97 / Deviant

☐ **PADDY IN THE SMOKE**
TSCD 603 / Jul '97 / Topic

☐ **PAID IN FULL**
BSCD 3000 / 27 Jul '98 / Black Shadow

☐ **PAISLEY POP (Pye Psych & Other Colours 1966-1969)**
Quiet explosion: *Uglys* / Good idea: *Uglys* / Bitter thoughts of little Jane: *Timon* / Too much on my mind: *Gates Of Eden* / I wish I was five: *Scrugg* / Lavender popcorn: *Scrugg* / All the love in the world: *Consortium* / You're all things bright and beautiful: *Christian, Neil* / Blessed: *Kytes* / Goodbye Thimble Mill Lane: *Schadel* / Smile a little smile for me: *Flying Machine* / Dreamtime: *Rainbow People* / Cave of clear light: *Bystanders* / I wonder where my sister's gone: *Anan* / Black veils of melancholy: *Status Quo* / Dreams secondhand: *Blinkers* / That's when happiness begins: *Montanas* / Tamaris Khan: *Onyx* / Major to minor: *Settlers* / Stop, look, listen: *Fresh Air* / Captain Reale: *Gentle Influence* / Morning way: *Trader Horne*
NEXCD 188 / Mar '92 / Sequel

☐ **PAKISTAN - THE MUSIC OF THE QAWAL**
AUD 8082 / Jun '91 / Unesco

☐ **PAKISTAN TREASURES**
PS 65082 / Nov '91 / PlayaSound

☐ **PAKISTANI SOUL MUSIC**
Dhol: *Sain, Pappu & Joora* / Naat: *Qawwal, Bahauddin Qutbuddin & Party* / Way of Shah Abdul Latif: *Fakir, Qurban & Ensemble* / Poem of Khwaja Ghulam Farid: *Bhagat, Faqira* / Way of Shah Abdul Latif: *Ali, Zulfiqar & Nazer Hussain/Mazher Hussain* / Kafi of Khwaja Ghulam Farid: *Khan, Allah Dad* / Naat: *Qawwal, Asif Ali Kahn & Party* / Alap and dhrupad in rag patdeep: *Khan, Mallikzada Muhammed Hafeez & Mallikzada Afzal*
SM 15292 / Jun '97 / Wergo

☐ **PALACE OF WORMS**
PO 2WCD / Jan '97 / Nightbreed

☐ **PALAIS DE YOGYAKARTA VOL.4 (Concert Music From Java)**
C 560087 / Oct '95 / Ocora

☐ **PALO, PALO VOL.1**
CD 8477452 / May '96 / Soul Head

☐ **PALO, PALO VOL.2**
CD 8477462 / May '96 / Soul Head

☐ **PAN ALL NIGHT (The Steel Bands Of Trinidad & Tobago)**
Birthday party: *Phase II Pan Groove* / Dus' in dey face: *Exodus* / All night (reprise): *Moods* / Mystery band: *Amoco Renegades* / Pan in yuh pan: *Courts Laventille Sound Specialists* / Miss supporter: *Cordettes* / All night: *Vat 19 Fonclaire*
DE 4022 / Feb '94 / Delos

☐ **PAN FLUTE COLLECTION VOL.1, THE (The Lonely Shepherd)**
Lonely shepherd / Largo / El Condor Pasa / Dolanne's melody / Aolha Oe / I dream of you / Mexican sun / L'ete Indien / What a wonderful world / Forse / Un jour d'ete / White clouds / Bye bye September / Maybe / Diana's song / Just in time
101082 / May '97 / A-Play Collection

☐ **PAN FLUTE COLLECTION VOL.2, THE (Sailing)**
Sailing / Yesterday / Heartbreaker / I have a dream / Michelle / Top of the world / Something / Fernando / Island in the sun / Ebony and ivory / Woman in love / Let it be / Beauty and the beast / Bridge over troubled water / Groovy kind of love / Here comes the sun
101092 / May '97 / A-Play Collection

☐ **PAN FLUTE COLLECTION VOL.3, THE (I Will Always Love You)**
I will always love you / Tears in heaven / From a distance / Some broken hearts never mend / Sleepwalk / Moonlight shadow / Forever and ever / Unchained melody / Do that to me one more time / Up where we belong / Save the best for last / Wind beneath my wings / Nothing's gonna change my love for you / I'll be there for you / Wonderland / Touch of you
101102 / May '97 / A-Play Collection

☐ **PAN FLUTE COLLECTION, THE (The Lonely Shepherd/Sailing/I Will Always Love You/3CD Set)**
Lonely shepherd / Largo / El Condor Pasa / Dolanne's melody / Aloha oe / I dream of you / Mexican sun / L'ete Indien / What a wonderful world / Forse / Un jour d'ete / White clouds / Bye bye September / Maybe / Diana's song / Just in time / Sailing / Yesterday / Heartbreaker / I have a dream / Michelle / Top of the world / Something / Fernando / Island in the sun / Ebony and ivory / Woman in love / Let it be / Beauty and the beast / Bridge over troubled water / Groovy kind of love / Here comes the sun / I will always love you / Tears in Heaven / From a distance / Some broken hearts never mend / Sleepwalk / Moonlight shadow / Forever and ever / Unchained melody / Do that to me one more time / Up where we belong / Save the best for last / Wind beneath my wings / Nothing's gonna change my love for you / I'll be there / Wonderland / Touch of you
101072 / May '97 / A-Play Collection

☐ **PAN GLOSSARY NO.1**
PAN 2000A / Oct '94 / Pan

☐ **PAN IS BEAUTIFUL VOL.1 - THE WORLD'S BEST STEELBANDS (Calypso & Soca)**
Hammer: *Trinidad All Stars Steel Band* / Get something and wave: *Tropical Angel Harps* / Jericho: *Solo Harmonites* / Exodus: *Exodus* / Musical Volcano: *Witco Desperadoes* / Nah do that: *National Quarries Cordettes* / Govenor's ball: *Trintoc Invaders*
68962 / Apr '97 / Tropical

☐ **PAN IS BEAUTIFUL VOL.2 - THE WORLD'S BEST STEELBANDS (Classics)**
Academic festival overture: *Exodus* / 5th symphony 4th movement: *Trintoc Invaders* / Capriccio Espagnol: *Solo Harmonites* / Overture to the bartered bride: *Witco Desperadoes* / Jupiter: *Courts Laventille Sound Specialists* / 5th symphony 4th movement: *Trinidad All Stars Steel Band* / William Tell overture: *National Quarries Cordettes*
68963 / Jun '97 / Tropical

☐ **PAN JAZZ 'N' CALYPSO**
California shower / We kinda music / Rhythm in the groove / Take me there / Hydra / Never can say goodbye / East river drive / Philmore's dream / Sitting through the notes / Iron man / Fire down below
DE 4016 / Jan '94 / Delos

☐ **PAN JAZZ CONVERSATIONS (Caribbean Carnival Series)**
Mauby beach / Dry river blues / What's the name of this song / Reflection / Dadu / De hustler / Karnaval people / Fingers
DE 4019 / Apr '94 / Delos

☐ **PAN PIPE CHRISTMAS, A**
Silent night / Winter wonderland / White Christmas / Deck the halls / I saw Mummy kissing Santa Claus / Jolly old St. Nicholas / It came upon a midnight clear / It's beginning to look like Christmas / Adagio / Air / Lonely shepherd / Reverie / Papa petit Noel / Still still / Sleigh ride / Il est ne le divine enfant / First Noel / O little town of Bethlehem / Jingle bells / Auld lang syne
CDVIP 145 / Nov '96 / Virgin VIP

☐ **PAN PIPE CLASSICS (3CD Set)**
KBOX 376 / Aug '97 / Collection

☐ **PAN PIPE DREAMS (Inspirations/20 Contemporary Love Songs)**
Unchained melody / Can you feel the love tonight / Holding back the years / Riverdance / Kiss from a rose / Perfect year / I swear / Have you ever really loved a woman / Love is all around / We've got tonight / Fields of gold / Power of love / Careless whisper / El condor pasa / Caribbean blue / Time after time / Constant craving / Theme from harry's game / Get here / Colours of the wind
PMCD 7016 / Sep '95 / Pure Music

☐ **PAN PIPE DREAMS**
Change the world / Because you loved me / Someday / Kiss from a rose / Earth song / Without you / Breathe again / After the love has gone / Jesus to a child / All woman / One day in your life / Reunited / This masquerade / Desperado / Show me heaven / Waiting to exhale / Hero / Power of love
CDVIP 151 / Apr '97 / Virgin VIP

☐ **PAN PIPE HORIZONS (2CD Set)**
Jesus to a child / Candle in the wind / Romeo and Juliet / Songbird / Satellite of love / Heart of gold / Don't dream it's over / Just the way you are / Is this the world we created / Don't let the sun go down on me / Love is all around / You're so vain / Midnight at the oasis / One day in your life / Wonderful tonight / Harry's game / American tune / Brothers in arms / Air that I breathe / I will always love you / Think twice / Another day in paradise / Save a prayer / America / Knockin' on heaven's door / Sail on / I won't last a day without you / Wild world / How deep is your love / Every time you go away / Let's stay together / Being with you / Hotel California / Up on the roof / Baker street / Father and son / Don't give up / Wonderwall / You've got a friend / Belfast child
330242 / Jul '96 / Hallmark

☐ **PAN PIPE INSPIRATION**
PMCD 7011 / Apr '95 / Pure Music

☐ **PAN PIPE MOODS**
Up where we belong / Unchained melody / You light up my life / Do that to me one more time / Feelings / Let it be / Even the nights are better / Rose / Aranjuez mon amour / If you leave me now / For your eyes only / Michelle / You needed me / I have a dream / Don't cry for me argentina / Lonely shepherd / Yesterday / Sleepwalk / Something
QED 097 / Nov '96 / Tring

☐ **PAN PIPE MOODS**
PLSCD 160 / Feb '97 / Pulse

☐ **PAN PIPE MOODS IN PARADISE**
Forever and ever / Spanish eyes / Spanish harlem / Moon river / Strangers in the night / La Isla Bonita / Begin the beguine / Don't want to lose you / Guantanamera / Fernando / Chiquitita / Hey / Summertime / Rise / Have you ever really loved a woman / Don't let the sun go down on me / Feelings / Hello / You'll see / Amor
5319612 / May '96 / Polydor

☐ **PAN PIPE MOODS VOL.2**
5293952 / Oct '95 / PolyGram TV

☐ **PAN PIPE SOUNDS OF CHRISTMAS, THE**
Silent night / White Christmas / Mary's boy child / Mistletoe and wine / First Noel / When a child is born / O come all ye faithful (adeste fidelis) / Haapy Christmas war is over / Last Christmas / Little drummer boy / Winter's tale / Walking in the air / Do they know it's Christmas / Winter wonderland / Away in a manger / Pipes of peace
RECD 505 / Dec '97 / REL

☐ **PAN PIPE SOUNDS OF SCOTLAND, THE**
Amazing grace / My love is like a red, red rose / Wild mountain thyme / Over the sea to Skye / Flower of Scotland / Ae fond kiss / Ye banks and braes / Scottish soldier / Loch Lomond / Dark island / Will ye no come back again / Caledonia / Brides of Glenshiel / Island song / Auld lang syne
RECD 510 / Dec '97 / REL

☐ **PAN PIPES (3CD Set)**
EMTBX 302 / Aug '97 / Emporio

☐ **PAN PIPES COLLECTION (2CD Set)**
DEMPCD 005 / Mar '96 / Emporio

☐ **PAN PIPES FOR LOVERS**
Power of love / (I've had the) Time of my life / We've got tonight / Eternal flame / You light up my life / Up where we belong / (Everything I do) I do it for you / Heartbreaker / Forever and ever / Do that to me one more time / When you're in love with a beautiful woman / Love changes everything / And I love her / Groovy kind of love / Have you ever really loved a woman / Light my fire / Woman in love / For your eyes only / (I can't help) Falling in love with you / I will always love you
CD 6022 / Jun '96 / Music

☐ **PAN PIPES OF THE ANDES VOL.2**
El condor pasa: *Santiago y su conjunto* / Chasquinanes: *Patoruzu Y Su Conjunto* / Hacia el carnaval: *Los Indios De Cuzco* / Sol inca: *Santiago y su conjunto* / Pajaritos: *Patoruzu Y Su Conjunto* / Bosque: *Los Indios De Cuzco* / Poncho color del viento: *Los Indios De Cuzco* / Diecinueve de enero: *Patoruzu Y Su Conjunto* / Baila cholita: *Los Indios De Cuzco* / Kena misky: *Patoruzu Y Su Conjunto* / Tutalla manta: *Los Indios De Cuzco* / Zagoria:

Santiago y su conjunto / El zaino: Patoruzu Y Su Conjunto / La piojosa: Patoruzu Y Su Conjunto / Mascarita: Los Indios De Cuzco / Viento andino: Los Indios De Cuzco / Carro podrido: Los Indios De Cuzco / Carnavalito: Santiago y su conjunto
305902 / Jan '97 / Hallmark

☐ PAN PIPES PLAY LOVE SONGS
I don't wanna cry / Wind beneath my wings / Ebony and ivory / Fernando / I'll be there / Bridge over troubled water / Always on my mind / Can you feel the love tonight / Music of the night / Orinoco flow / What a feeling / Top of the world / Norwegian wood / Tears in heaven / Moonlight shadow / He ain't heavy, he's my brother / Michelle / Just when I needed you most / Begin the beguine / Take my breath away
CD 6032 / Sep '96 / Music

☐ PAN PIPES SELECTION (2CD Set)
I have a dream / Strawberry fields forever / Dark side of the sun / Scarborough fair / Sailing / Unchained melody / Amazing grace / If you leave now / Something / Feelings / Here comes the sun / Sara / Yesterday / MacArthur park / Bird of paradise / House of the rising sun / Don't cry for me Argentina / Banks of the Ohio / Autumn dream / Let it be / Power of love / (I've had the) Time of my life / We've got tonight / Eternal flame / You light up my life / Up where we belong / (Everything I do) I do it for you / Heartbreaker / Forever and ever / Do that to me one more time / When you're in love with a beautiful woman / Light my fire / Woman in love / For your eyes only / (I can't help) falling in love / I will always love you
DCD 3012 / Jun '97 / Music

☐ PAN PIPES XMAS MOODS
Happy Xmas (war is over) / I believe in Father Christmas / Medley No.1 / Fairytale of New York / In Dulci Jubilo / Medley No.2 / Walking in the air / Last Christmas / Lonely this Christmas / Chestnuts roasting on an open fire / Santa Claus is coming to town / Medley No.3 / Do they know it's Christmas / Rudolph the red nosed reindeer / Stop the cavalry / Mistletoe and wine / Winter wonderland / When a child is born / White Christmas / Medley No.4
5338582 / Dec '96 / PolyGram TV

☐ PAN WOMAN
Pan woman / Pan woman / Monday night / Steelband times / Woman on the bass / Soca baptist / Is this love / Pan blues / Pan rising / Saaj sameelan / Granny / Curry tabanca
DE 4017 / Feb '94 / Delos

☐ PANAUNIE
RRTGCD 7705 / '88 / Rohit

☐ PANDEMONIUM NO.1
PAN 0100A / Oct '94 / Pan

☐ PANGAEA 2097
PAGCD 001 / May '97 / Pagoda

☐ PANNARAMA
BFISHCD 1 / Apr '94 / Big Fish

☐ PANORAMA (Steel Bands Of Trinidad And Tobago)
Woman is boss / Poom poom / Steel of wheels / Par by storm / Pan in uyh ruckungkertungkung / Ramajay / Iron man / Ramjay (reprise)
DE 4015 / Jan '94 / Delos

☐ PANPIPE CHRISTMAS, A (3CD Set)
White Christmas / Jingle bells / Do they know it's Christmas / I heard the bells on Christmas day / Oh Christmas tree / I saw the ships/Serenade/A child is born / Little drummer boy / Oh little town of Bethlehem / O come all ye faithful / German medley / Away in a manger / Holly and the ivy / We wish you a merry Christmas / Ave Maria / Winter wonderland / French medley / Merry Christmas / Christmas song / Winter's tale / God rest ye merry gentlemen / German medley / Silver bells / When a child is born / Joseph my dear Joseph / Twelve days of Christmas / Deck the halls / Oh du frohliche / Ding dong merrily on high / Silent night / Mary's boy child / Mistletoe and wine / Blue Christmas / Sleigh ride / First Noel / Season of joy / Have yourself a merry little Christmas / Hark the herald angels sing / Unto us a child is born / Alpenlandisches medley / Christmas is here / Rudolph the red-nosed reindeer / Auld lang syne
120272 / Nov '97 / Jingle

☐ PANPIPE COLLECTION, THE (4CD Set)
SUMBX 4007 / Jan '98 / Summit

☐ PANPIPES AT CHRISTMAS
Good King Wenceslas / God rest ye merry gentlemen / We wish you a merry Christmas / Ding dong merrily on high / Winter wonderland / Angels from the realms of glory / Christmas song / Auld lang syne / Holly and the ivy / Away in a manger / Little drummer boy / Rudolph the red nosed reindeer / Under the mistletoe / Unto us a child is born / Once in Royal David's City / Here we come a wassailing / Jingle bells / Season of joy / Christmas is here / When a child is born / Hark the herald angels sing / Deck the halls
XMAS 012 / Nov '96 / Tring

☐ PANPIPES OF THE ANDES
TRTCD 183 / Feb '96 / TrueTrax

☐ P'ANSORI (Korea's Epic Vocal Art & Instrumental Music)
7559720492 / Jan '95 / Nonesuch

☐ PANTASTIC WORLD OF STEEL MUSIC VOL.1
68940 / Jul '97 / Tropical

☐ PA'QUE BAILEN MUCHACHOS (2CD Set)
BMT 001/002 / Feb '97 / Blue Moon

☐ PARADIGM SHIFT
08643462 / May '97 / Westcom

☐ PARADISE CITY (One World One Love/ 2CD Set)
UKK 4106 / Oct '94 / UKK

☐ PARADISE FOUND (Rare Exotic Sounds Vol.1)
HBCD 1001 / 8 Jun '98 / Hibiscus

☐ PARADISE IN PARAGUAY
4301121032 / 27 Apr '98 / ANS

☐ PARAGUAYAN HARP
PS 65128 / May '94 / PlayaSound

☐ PARAMOUNT BLUES (Home Town Skiffle)
BSCD 30 / Dec '97 / Black Swan

☐ PARAMOUNT BLUES VOL.3
HCD 12013 / Oct '93 / Black Swan

☐ PARAMOUNT RECORDINGS CHICAGO 1926-1928
DGF 13 / May '97 / Frog

☐ PARIS AFTER DARK
La mer: Trenet, Charles / Hymne a l'amour: Piaf, Edith / J'attendrai: Rossi, Tino / Ma Tonkinoise: Baker, Josephine / Valentine: Chevalier, Maurice / Je cherche un millionaire: Mistinguett / Embrasse-moi cherie: Delyle, Lucienne / Pigalle: Ulmer, Georges / Le chaland qui passe: Gauty, Lys / Sur ma vie: Les Compagnons De La Chanson / La vie en rose: Piaf, Edith / Parlez-moi d'amour: Boyer, Lucienne / Ces petites choses: Sablon, Jean / Mon homme: Mistinguett / J'ai deux amours: Baker, Josephine / Boum: Trenet, Charles / La java bleue: Frehel / Le fiacre: Sablon, Jean / Les trois cloches: Piaf, Edith et Les Compagnons De La Chansons / C'est a Capri: Rossi, Tino
CZ 140 / Sep '88 / EMI

☐ PARIS BY NIGHT
Milord: Piaf, Edith / Douce France: Trenet, Charles / Briu d'amour: Alexander, Maurice / Sur les quais du vieux Paris: Delyle, Lucienne / Vieni vieni: Rossi, Tino / Seul ce soir: Marjane, Leo / J'aime Paris au mois de mai: Aznavour, Charles / Puisque vous partez en voyage: Sablon, Mireille & Jean / Moulin rouge: Les Compagnons De La Chanson / A Paris dans chaque faubourg: Gauty, Lys / Sur le pont d'Avignon: Sablon, Jean / Ou est-il donc: Frehel / Ma Louise: Chevalier, Maurice / La clocher de mon coeur: Busch, Eva / Nuages: Reinhardt, Django / Depuis que les bals sont fermes: Damia / Qur reste t'Il de nos amours: Trenet, Charles / Ma cabane au Canada: Renaud, Line / Un seul couvert, please, James: Sablon, Jean / Bal dans ma rue: Piaf, Edith
CZ 316 / Jun '90 / EMI

☐ PARIS GROOVE UP
Arabesques / Christ'al / Gardez l'ecoute / Pardonne / Go go motion / K-talk 2 / Elles aimant ca / Bola / Mic mac / Fantaisy / Really groovy / Funky takini / Boom bastic / Just comme ca / Ame saoul-am soul
4509961722 / Jul '94 / Warner Bros.

☐ PARIS HOT CLUB STYLE
REWCD 356 / Feb '98 / Reactive

☐ PARIS MUSETTE
Under Paris skies / Man and a woman / Promenade a montmartre / D'accord / I wish you love / Mon amour / Les matelots / Love is blue / C'est tout / La vie joyeuse / La vie en rose / Windmills of your mind / Ma petite / Enchante / Chez michel / Madame sophie / Canal du midi
SUMCD 4149 / Sep '97 / Summit

☐ PARIS MUSETTE VOL.3
CDLLL 217 / Jan '98 / La Lichere

☐ PARIS, OH QUE J'AIME
PASTCD 7069 / Mar '95 / Flapper

☐ PARIS WASHBOARD VOL.2
SOSCD 1261 / Oct '93 / Stomp Off

☐ PARIS...CAFE-CONCERT
C'est un mauvais garcon' / Boum / Gigolette / Maitre Pierre / J'attendrai / Sur le pont d'avignon / C'est un bureaucrate / Un p'tit bock / Chez moi / Vous oubliez votre cheval / Tel qu'il est / Guitare d'amour / Ma douce vallee / Place pigalle / Sombreros et mantillas / As dis ah dis / C'est un chagrin de femme / Je ne donnerais pas ma place / J'ai connu do vous / Oh Suzanna youp youp-la-la / La vie qui va
PASTCD 9797 / Aug '92 / Flapper

☐ PAROXYSN
MKTCD 001 / Aug '91 / Mute

☐ PARTISAN COMPILATION
Mauve flow: Justice / Life support: Future Engineers / Deceptive emotion: Banaczech / Synthetic bitch: Foul Play Production / Remember: Perfect Combination / Structure: Tertius / Espionage: Total Science / Black cell: System 4 / Live at the jazz club: DJ Addiction / Ipcress file: Banaczech
PARTCD 001 / 29 Jun '98 / Partisan

☐ PARTNERS (20 Timeless Duets From A Golden Era)
Friendship: Garland, Judy & Johnny Mercer / Gone fishin': Crosby, Bing & Louis Armstrong / Into each life some rain must fall: Fitzgerald, Ella & The Ink Spots / Indian love call: MacDonald, Jeanette & Nelson Eddy / Moon came up with a great idea: Crosby, Bing & Peggy Lee / Pistol packin' mama: Andrews Sisters & Bing Crosby / Moonlight bay: Crosby, Bing & Gary Crosby / Best things in life are free: Allyson, June & Peter Lawford / Put it there pal: Crosby, Bing & Bob Hope / 42nd Street: Keeler, Ruby & Dick Powell / Shine: Crosby, Bing & The Mills Brothers / For me and my gal: Garland, Judy & Gene Kelly / Night is young and you're so beautiful: Sinatra, Frank & Dinah Shore / Zing a little zong: Crosby, Bing & Jane Wyman / Civilization (bongo bongo bongo): Andrews Sisters & Danny Kaye / Spaniard that blighted my life: Jolson, Al & Bing Crosby / Little Miss Broadway: Temple, Shirley & George Murphy / Connecticut: Garland, Judy & Bing Crosby / Bob White (whatcha gonna swing tonight): Boswell, Connee & Bing Crosby / Thanks for the memory: Hope, Bob & Shirley Ross
ECD 3295 / Feb '97 / K-Tel

☐ PARTY FAVOURITES
Happy birthday to you / I'm 21 today / Celebration / Wally dance medley / Congratulations / I am the music man / Hokey cokey / Birthday medley / Happy birthday / Simon says / Agadoo / Charleston / Conga / Wedding / Wedding march / Anniversary waltz / Last waltz / Can can / Birdie song / Knees up mother Brown / Big Ben striking twelve o' clock / Auld lang syne / God save the Queen
301582 / Feb '98 / Hallmark

☐ PARTY FEVER
SONCD 0062 / Mar '94 / Sonic Sounds

☐ PARTY HITS (2CD Set)
Let's have a party: Jackson, Wanda / Yellow river: Christie / Sugar baby love: Rubettes / Hippy hippy shake: Swinging Blue Jeans / Da doo ron ron: Crystals / I'm into something good: Herman's Hermits / Baby come back: Equals / Walkin' back to happiness: Shapiro, Helen / Silence is golden: Tremeloes / You'll never walk alone: Gerry & The Pacemakers / Runaway: Shannon, Del / Just walkin' in the rain: Ray, Johnnie / Something's gotten hold of my heart: Pitney, Gene / Speedy Gonzales: Boone, Pat / Charlie Brown: Coasters / Papa-oom-mow-mow: Rivingtons / Ob-la-di ob-la-da: Marmalade / Nut rocker: B. Bumble & The Stingers / Words: David, F.R. / Under the moon of love: Showaddywaddy / Tonight: Rubettes / In the bad bad old days: Foundations / Keep searchin' (we'll follow the sun): Shannon, Del / Walk don't run: Ventures / Viva Bobby Joe: Equals / I'm telling you now: Freddie & The Dreamers / Ferry cross the Mersey: Gerry & The Pacemakers / When a man loves a woman: Sledge, Percy / Someone: Tremeloes / Windy: Association / Wishin' and hopin': Merseybeats / Sheila: Roe, Tommy / Mr. Bassman: Cymbal, Johnny / It's my party: Gore, Lesley
DCD 3005 / Jun '97 / Music

☐ PARTY HITS VOL.1
10472 / Jun '97 / A-Play Collection

☐ PARTY HITS VOL.2
10482 / Jun '97 / A-Play Collection

☐ PARTY HITS VOL.3
10492 / Jun '97 / A-Play Collection

☐ PARTY IS FOR LIFE, NOT JUST FOR CHRISTMAS
CD 02 / Jul '97 / Cabbaged

☐ PARTY MEGAMIX (Over 100 Sensationally Sequenced Songs)
PLATCD 3917 / Sep '93 / Platinum

☐ PARTY NIGHT IN IRELAND (Music, Craic & Song)
If you're Irish/McNamara's band/Hannigan's holiday: Erin's Isle Singers / Nedeen: Grace, Brendan / Fasten the leggin/Munster buttermilk: Fitzgerald, Richard Ceili Band / Peggy O'Neill/Sweet Rosie O'Grady/My wild Irish rose: Erin's Isle Singers / Pup: Toibin, Niall / Pigeon on the gate/Foxhunters: Shaskeen / Rose of Tralee: Erin's Isle Singers / Incoming call: Kelly, Frank / Cooley's ceili: Crossroads Ceili / I'll take you home again Kathleen/ Green glens of Antrim: Erin's Isle Singers / Caravan man: Toibin, Niall / Rights of man: Crossroads Ceili / Dear old Donegal/It's a long way to Tipperary/Hello Patsy Fa: Erin's Isle Singers
CHCD 034 / Oct '96 / Chart

☐ PARTY OF FIVE
9362464312 / Feb '97 / Warner Bros.

☐ PARTY PARTY (The Non Stop Party 4 Pack/4CD Set)
SUMBX 4015 / Jan '98 / Summit

☐ PARTY TIME
I 3896062 / Oct '96 / Galaxy

☐ PARTY TIME AT STUDIO ONE (2CD Set)
3021522 / Jun '97 / Arcade
RN 7018 / 30 Mar '98 / Rhino

☐ PASODOBLES DE CORRIDA 1925-1945
995812 / 21 Aug '97 / EPM

☐ PASS THE VIBES ON
5352212 / Jan '96 / PolyGram TV

☐ PASSCHENDAELE SUITE
Dodendans: Panta Rhei / Land of the long white cloud: Simpson, Lester / Een schip: Panta Rhei / Ao tea roa: Coope Boyes & Simpson / Robin's song: Panta Rhei / Lay me low: Coope Boyes & Simpson / Bloody fields of Flanders: Panta Rhei & Lester Simpson / Still in the night: Boyes, Jim & Barry Coope/Fabien Degryse / Ein Schottisch tantz: Panta Rhei / (Mad old, sad old) Shuffling Jack: Coope Boyes & Simpson/Panta Rhei / Tyne cot at night/I want to go home: Coope Boyes & Simpson / Largo: Pilartz, luc & Aurelie Dorzee/Kathy Adam / New Jerusalem: Coope Boyes & Simpson/Panta Rhei
NMCD 10 / Nov '96 / No Master's Cooperative

☐ PASSING OF THE REGIMENTS
BNA 5065 / May '92 / Bandleader

☐ PASSION (Music For Guitar)
Proven by fire / Love on the beach / Good question / Parasol days / Passion and pride / Gentle touch / Running games / New face / Lover's promise / Explorations / Joy of life
ND 61044 / Oct '94 / Narada

☐ PASSION TRAX
CDPASH 1 / Feb '93 / Passion

☐ PAST AND PRESENT AND FUTURE (2CD Set)
MPCD 05 / 16 Mar '98 / Mulitplex

☐ PAST PERFECT SAMPLER (The Great Sound Of The 1920-1940s)
I never knew: Armstrong, Louis / Doug the Jitterbug: Jordan, Louis / I let a song go out of my heart: Ellington, Duke / King Porter stomp: Crosby, Bob / Home Guard blues: Formby, George / Cuban overture: Whiteman, Paul & Rosa Linda / Carolina shout: Waller, Fats / Just let me look at you: Coward, Sir Noel / La danza: Gigli, Beniamino / Miss Annabelle Lee: Reinhardt, Django & Stephane Grappelli / Muddy water: Lunceford, Jimmie / I guess I'll have to change my plan: Fitzgerald, Ella / Let yourself go: Rogers, Ginger / Taking a chance on love: Fitzgerald, Ella / Shall we dance: Astaire, Fred
PPCD 78100 / Feb '95 / Past Perfect

☐ PAST PRESENT AND FUTURE
MRCD 022 / Nov '96 / M8

☐ PATIO COLLECTION VOL.2
SMLX 007 / Apr '97 / Smilex

☐ PATROLLING THE EDGE OF DEEP HOUSE - DEEP STATES
Tribe: MATO / I love: Paradise Deep Groove / Needs (needs not wants): Mood Life / Within without: Read, Jaime / Moov: Francois K / Erotic illusions: Abacus / Black oceans: Heard, Larry / Vesuvius: Stranger / If you lose your shadow: Aberation / Netherlands: Louis, Joe
SLIPCD 53 / Mar '97 / Slip 'n' Slide

☐ PATTERNS OF JEWISH LIFE (Highlights Of Series - Traditional & Popular Jewish Music)
SM 16042 / Feb '94 / Wergo

☐ PAX RECORDS PUNK COLLECTION
CDPUNK 75 / May '96 / Anagram

☐ PAY IT ALL BACK - US
RESTLESS 7269 / Aug '94 / On-U Sound

☐ PAY IT ALL BACK VOL.2
Train to doomsville: Perry, Lee 'Scratch' & Dub Syndicate / Billy Bonds MBE: Barmy Army / Circular motion: Forehead Bros / What a wonderful day: African Headcharge / No alternative (but to fight): Dub Syndicate & Dr. Pablo / Run them away: Sherman, Bim & Singers & Players / Water the garden: Prince Far-I & Singers & Players / Throw it away: African Headcharge / Digital: Eskimo Fox
ONULP 42CD / Dec '88 / On-U Sound

☐ PAY IT ALL BACK VOL.3
Disconnection: Strange Parcels / Heart's desire: Singers & Players / You thought I was dead: Perry, Lee 'Scratch' & Dub Syndicate / Stoned immaculate: Dub Syndicate & Akabu / I think of you: Little Annie / Jack the biscuit: Fairley, Andy / Hey ho: Dub Syndicate / These things happen: Stewart, Mark / Ennio: Frederix, Martin / To be free: Strange Parcels & Bernard Fowler / My God: African Headcharge / Spirit soul: Pillay, Alan / False leader: Clail, Gary / Jacob's pillow: Rae, Jesse / Devo: Barmy Army / Blue moon: Barmy Army / Nightmare: Sherman, Bim
ONUCD 53 / May '91 / On-U Sound

☐ PAY IT ALL BACK VOL.4
ONUCD 20 / Feb '93 / On-U Sound

☐ PAY IT ALL BACK VOL.5
ONUCD 75 / Apr '95 / On-U Sound

☐ PAY IT ALL BACK VOL.6
ONUCD 96 / Aug '96 / On-U Sound

☐ PE DE SERRA FORRO BAND, BRAZIL
SM 15092 / Oct '92 / Wergo

☐ PEACE AND LOVE
UPCD 001 / Sep '96 / Upsetter

☐ PEACE AND LOVE
SKIP 52CD / Nov '96 / Broken

☐ PEACE COMPILATION
WB 3156CD / Oct '96 / We Bite

☐ PEACE ON EARTH (3CD Set)
DTKBOX 75 / 30 Mar '98 / Dressed To Kill

☐ PEACEFUL EASY FEELING
It should have been you: Blacknuss / Cigarette: Wall Of Sound / Music: Shogunn / Crazy life: Winnie / Modus operandi: Ol / Peaceful easy feeling: Alexander, Rob / Things you make me do: Thomas, Carla / Hold on to love: Cameron, Marie / Our love: Black, Sassy / What did I do: Zaeus / Committed: Renaizzance / I'll keep you warm: Serenade / Chance: Gallimore, Khaline / I like: Everis
CDTEP 8 / Sep '95 / Debut

☐ PEACEFUL WATERS (A Magical Blend Of Music And The Sounds Of Nature)
57812 / May '97 / Nature's Harmony

☐ PEACEVILLE 10TH ANNIVERSARY COMPILATION
One of the few: Anathema / Shout: Anathema / Some velvet morning: My Dying Bride / Roads: My Dying Bride / Better off dead: Dominion / Song of joy: Thine / Girl who lives on heaven hill: Blackstar / Oh baby: Acrimony / Crazy horses: Blood Divine / Love will tear us apart: Blood Divine / Paint it black: Dominion / Running back: Blackstar / Don't let me down: Lid / Goodbye cruel world: Anathema
CDVILE 77 / 13 Apr '98 / Peaceville

☐ PEAK RUSH
HKCDXY 04 / 24 Aug '98 / Hook

☐ PEASANT MUSIC FROM HAITI
926802 / Jul '97 / EPM

☐ PEBBLES VOL.1
AIPCD 5016 / Jul '92 / Archive

☐ PEBBLES VOL.10
AIPCD 5027 / Feb '97 / AIP

☐ PEBBLES VOL.2
AIPCD 5019 / Jul '92 / Archive

☐ PEBBLES VOL.3
AIPCD 5020 / Jul '92 / Archive

☐ PEBBLES VOL.4
AIPCD 5021 / Jul '92 / Archive

☐ PEBBLES VOL.5
No good woman: *Tree* / Go away: *Plague* / You don't know me: *Magi* / It's a crying shame: *Gentlemen* / Writing on the wall: *5 Canadians* / Why: *Dirty Wurds* / Universal vagrant: *Merry Dragons* / I wanna come back: *Fe Fi Four Plus 2* / I tell no lies: *Escapades* / You need love: *Danny & The Escorts* / Yesterday's heroes: *Satyrs* / Way it used to be: *Little Phil & The Night Shadows* / Move: *State Of Mind* / I need love: *State Of Mind* / Time stoppers: *State Of Mind* / You'll never be my girl: *Thursday's Children* / Way I feel: *12 am*
AIPCD 5022 / Jul '92 / Archive

☐ PEBBLES VOL.6
AIPCD 5023 / Feb '95 / Archive

☐ PEBBLES VOL.7
AIPCD 5024 / Feb '95 / Archive

☐ PEBBLES VOL.8
AIPCD 5025 / Feb '96 / Archive

☐ PEBBLES VOL.9
AIPCD 5026 / Feb '97 / AIP

☐ PELHAM'S SOCA PARTY VOL.1
CSSCD 001 / Jun '94 / Cott

☐ PENSIONERS ON ECSTACY
CRECD 082 / Nov '90 / Creation

☐ PENTHOUSE CLASSIC COMBINATIONS VOL.2
PH 2006 / Jun '96 / Penthouse

☐ PENTHOUSE CULTURE CENTRE
PHRICD 28 / Jan '96 / Penthouse

☐ PENTHOUSE DAMSEL PANDEMONIUM
SVCD 2044 / May '96 / Shocking Vibes

☐ PENTHOUSE DANCEHALL HITS VOL.7
PHCD 2029 / May '96 / Penthouse

☐ PENTHOUSE LOVERS ROCK VOL.1
PHCD 2002 / Jun '96 / Penthouse

☐ PENTHOUSE LOVERS ROCK VOL.2
PHCD 2009 / Jun '96 / Penthouse

☐ PENTHOUSE LOVERS ROCK VOL.3
PHCD 2010 / Jun '96 / Penthouse

☐ PENTHOUSE PARTY MIX VOL.7
PHCD 2076 / 27 Apr '98 / Penthouse

☐ PENTHOUSE SAMPLER VOL.1
PHCD 22 / Aug '93 / Penthouse

☐ PEOPLE'S CHOICE, THE
JD 002 / 20 Apr '98 / Ffrench Production

☐ PEPPERMINT STICK PARADE
BUS 10012 / May '95 / Bus Stop

☐ PEQUENO DICIONARIO DA MPB VOL.1
CD 3698 / 17 Aug '98 / CID

☐ PEQUENO DICIONARIO DA MPB VOL.2
CD 3704 / 17 Aug '98 / CID

☐ PEQUENO DICIONARIO DA MPB VOL.3
CD 3711 / 17 Aug '98 / CID

☐ PERCUSSION MUSIC OF MADRAS
VICG 53492 / Mar '96 / JVC World Library

☐ PERCUSSIONS D'AMERIQUE LATINE
Butucada au carnaval de Rio / Tehuantepec / Cumbia cienaguera / El hombre celoso / Conga au carnival de Santiago de Cuba / Janitzio / Josefa Matia / La llorona / El Ferrocarril de Los Altos / Bateria a Salvador de Bahia / Cancion mixteca / Mapale / El rey Quiche / Descarga barbacoana / Bateria au carnaval de Manaus / Currulao / Chiapas
ARN 64023 / '88 / Arion

☐ PERCUSSIONS OF KERALA
PS 65201 / Jun '98 / PlayaSound

☐ PERFECT DAY (2CD Set)
Perfect day / Up where we belong: *Cocker, Joe & Jennifer Warnes* / Perfect day / Lifted: *Cocker, Joe & Jennifer Warnes* / Perfect day / You've got a friend: *Lighthouse Family* / Healing hands: *Lighthouse Family* / I believe I can fly: *R Kelly* / I am blessed: *Eternal* / Harvest for the world: *Isley Brothers* / Through the storm: *Franklin, Aretha & Elton John* / I'll stand by you: *Pretenders* / Marvellous: *Lightning Seeds* / Things can only get better: *D:Ream* / Power of love: *Dion, Celine* / Something inside so strong: *Siffre, Labi* / Lovely day: *Withers, Bill* / I can see clearly now: *Nash, Johnny* / I say a little prayer: *Franklin, Aretha* / Wind beneath my wings: *Knight, Gladys* / Don't know much: *Ronstadt, Linda & Aaron Neville*
SONYTV 42CD / 16 Mar '98 / Sony TV

☐ PERFECT INSTRUMENTAL COLLECTION VOL.1
HRCD 8048 / Dec '93 / Disky

☐ PERFECT INSTRUMENTAL COLLECTION VOL.2
DCD 5253 / Aug '92 / Disky

☐ PERFECT INSTRUMENTAL LOVE ALBUM
CNCD 5993 / Feb '94 / Disky

☐ PERFECT LOVE
Happy just to be with you: *Gayle, Michelle* / Don't walk away: *Jade* / I'm so into you: *SWV* / Captured: *Kennedy, Brian* / Unchained melody: *Robson & Jerome* / You're all that matters to me: *Stigers, Curtis* / Find my love: *Fairground Attraction* / There must be an angel: *Eurythmics* / I wanna sex you up: *Color Me Badd* / Baby I love your way: *Big Mountain* / Confide in me: *Minogue, Kylie* / All woman: *Stansfield, Lisa* / Without you: *Nilsson, Harry* / All by myself: *Carmen, Eric* / Theme from Harry's Game: *Clannad* / What becomes of the broken hearted: *Robson & Jerome* / I will always love you: *Robson & Jerome* / Perfect day: *Reed, Lou*
74321578202 / 11 May '98 / Camden

☐ PERFECT LOVE, A (2CD Set)
Love is all around: *Wet Wet Wet* / Don't speak: *No Doubt* / I believe I can fly: *R Kelly* / Unbreak my heart: *Braxton, Toni* / I'll never break your heart: *Backstreet Boys* / Back for good: *Take That* / Love me for a reason: *Boyzone* / Lifted: *Lighthouse Family* / Search for the hero: *M-People* / If you ever: *East 17 & Gabrielle* / You might need somebody: *Ama, Shola* / Love II Love: *Damage* / I love you always forever: *Lewis, Donna* / Love won't wait: *Barlow, Gary* / Don't leave: *Blackstreet* / If you love me: *Brownstone* / Yearnin': *Jones, Donell* / Nobody knows: *Rich, Tony Project* / My father's son: *Reeves, Conner* / Stay I missed you: *Loeb, Lisa* / One moment in time: *Houston, Whitney* / If you don't know me by now: *Simply Red* / Your song: *John, Elton* / Time after time: *Lauper, Cyndi* / Have I told you lately: *Stewart, Rod* / How deep is your love: *Bee Gees* / Jealous guy: *Roxy Music* / It must be love: *Madness* / Get here: *Adams, Oleta* / Perfect day: *Reed, Lou* / Kiss from a rose: *Seal* / Wherever I lay my hat: *Young, Paul* / All around the world: *Stansfield, Lisa* / I'll never fall in love again: *Deacon Blue* / Show me heaven: *McKee, Maria* / Everything I own: *Bread* / Wonderful tonight: *Clapton, Eric* / Romeo and Juliet: *Dire Straits* / Power of love: *Rush, Jennifer* / Always on my mind: *Presley, Elvis*
RADCD 80 / 8 Nov '97 / Global TV

☐ PERFECTO FLUORO
Adagio for strings / Moon / Sugar rush / Revisions / Lost in love / Real nightmare / Play dead / Atlantis / Prophase / Love remembered / Kabalah / Craven leaves / Miserere / Banks of babylon / Cute name / Conspiracy / Little buddha / This love / Mystery land / Merry christmas mr lawrence / We're not alone / Jungle hip / New kicks / If I could fly / Floor space / Teleport
0630166942 / Oct '96 / Perfecto/East West

☐ PERFUMED GARDEN VOL.3, THE
REVERB 6 / Sep '97 / Reverb

☐ PERRIER YOUNG JAZZ AWARDS 1998
JAZZFMCD 7 / 30 Mar '98 / Jazz FM

☐ PERSIAN LOVE SONGS
LYRCD 7235 / '91 / Lyrichord

☐ PERSIAN NIGHTS
340552CD / Jul '95 / Koch

☐ PERU - HUAYNO, VALSE CREOLE & MARIERA
PS 65133CD / Jul '94 / PlayaSound

☐ PERUVIAN HARPS AND GUITARS
PS 65158 / Dec '95 / PlayaSound

☐ PETER WAS A FISHERMAN (1939 Trinidad Field Recordings)
You know one Joseph Keeba / Invocation / Yan mi yan mi / John Gilman want tobaco / E-ajo / Bay road girls / Enyin olowo / Roll Jordan roll / Yard o yaddo / I want a pretty woman / Oh send me she back / Eshu bara / Mureau mureau / We don't want no rice / Ye ekun ara wa la mi sun / Ou bel marie coolie / In eine / Ikubo / Bucco bay young girl / You abd you bad / What a friend we have in Jesus / Paulie say she love me / Ye iwo / Texas sailor coming down / WHen me baby born / Peter was a fisherman / Zutula dead / Summo / Donnie willie / Da night a de wake / Jesus lover of my soul / I wish I was a little girl
ROUCD 1114 / Feb '98 / Rounder

☐ PETITE O' REILLE
BP 1044 / 23 Mar '98 / Boucherie Productions

☐ PHASE 6 (Super Stereo)
Mattino di fuoco: *Boga, Dom* / Senza archi: *Roelens, Puccio* / Diodo: *Tical, H.* / Disperazione: *Sciascia, Armando* / Obsessively: *Hamilton, Peter* / Desert heat: *Hamilton, Peter* / Assonanza in mi: *Sciascia, Armando* / Mas que nada: *Battisti, Bruno* / Su delicia: *Battisti, Bruno* / I'm a man: *Billy & His Friends* / Segura o sambura: *Battisti, Bruno* / Hua hua rock: *Battisti, Bruno* / I found my love in Portofino: *Battisti, Bruno* / Le grisbi: *Collins, Cat Sextet* / Caravan: *Roelens, Puccio*
CDPL 005 / 18 May '98 / Plastic

☐ PHIALS OF ACID JAZZ VOL.1 (16 Intoxicating Grooves From The Vaults Of Acid Jazz)
Mr. Freedom: *Mother Earth* / Whole lotta love: *Taylor, James Quartet* / Mother's tongue: *Brand New Heavies* / Taurus woman: *Subterraneans* / Love will keep us together: *Taylor, James Quartet & Alison Limerick* / I'm the one: *D-Influence* / Everything's going to the beat: *Ace Of Clubs* / Quiet dawn: *Humble Souls* / Bad trip: *Night Trains* / Living life your own way: *Windross, Rose* / Change your mind: *Callier, Terry* / Eyes that burn: *Emperor's New Clothes* / Don't you let me down: *Planet* / Peace and love: *Cloud 9* / Motorhead: *Corduroy* / Nothing like this: *Snowboy*
MUSCD 032 / Jan '97 / MCI Music

☐ PHIALS OF ACID JAZZ VOL.2
MUSCD 041 / 18 May '98 / MCI Music

☐ PHILIDELPHIA SOUL CLASSICS VOL.1
STCD 1000 / Jun '93 / Disky

☐ PHILIPPINE MUSIC KALINGA PEOPLE
CDMANU 1518 / Feb '97 / ODE

☐ PHILLY DUST KREW
TOODAMNY 52 / Feb '95 / Too Damn Hype

☐ PHILO SO FAR: 20TH ANNIVERSARY FOLK SAMPLER
AN 12 / Apr '94 / Rounder

☐ PHOENIX - THE ALBUM (Live At The Phoenix Festival 1996)
So let me go far: *Dodgy* / On a Tuesday: *Linoleum* / Percolator: *Stereolab* / This is fake DIY: *Bis* / Come out 2nite: *Kenickie* / Plastic ashtray: *Urusei Yatsura* / Bug in a breeze: *Baby Bird* / Hello spaceboy: *Bowie, David* / From despair to where: *Manic Street Preachers* / 36 degrees: *Placebo* / Weak: *Skunk Anansie* / Alice what's the matter: *Terrorvision* / Get some sleep tiger: *Red Snapper* / La madrugada: *Zion Train* / Smoke 'em: *Fun Lovin' Criminals* / Way beyond blue: *Catatonia*
PHNXCD 1 / Jun '97 / NMC

☐ PHOENIX PANORAMA (The Viv Labels/ 3CD Set)
How about me: *Johnson, Jimmy* / It's you, you, you: *Spellman, Jimmy* / Give me some of yours: *Spellman, Jimmy* / Cat Daddy: *Johnson, Jimmy* / Lover man: *Spellman, Jimmy* / Mama Lou: *Burnam, Buzz* / Time wounds all heels: *Clingman, Loy* / Don't hate me: *Lane, Jack* / Wings: *Combo, Copa* / Queen of hearts: *Adair, Ronnie* / Mr. Blues (is my shadow): *Lane, Jack* / Whisper to me: *Silvers, Johnny* / Five more miles to folsom: *Hardin, Doug* / King fool: *Lane, Jack* / Blue and lonesome mood: *Silvers, Johnny* / Talk to me: *Hardin, Doug* / All through the night: *Lane, Jack* / Restless: *Lane, Jack* / Blue I am: *Rollins, Don* / That's the way it happend: *Rollins, Don* / Other woman: *Rollins, Don* / Other woman (demo): *Rollins, Don* / If I'm wrong (demo): *Rollins, Don* / Don't hate me (demo): *Rollins, Don* / Good bartender (demo): *Rollins, Don* / Mirror mirror (demo): *Rollins, Don* / Crazy arms: *Lee, Garry* / Long John's flagpole rock: *Roller, Long John* / Hay Mama: *Roller, Long John* / If I'm wrong: *Owens, Donnie* / Need you: *Owens, Donnie* / Tomorrow: *Owens, Donnie* / Shy: *Perkins, Dal* / Raindance: *Self, Alvie* / Where, when and how: *Self, Alvie* / Things I can't forget: *Ryan, Ronnie* / Devil's den: *Turley, Duane* / Long gone cat: *Turley, Duane* / Between midnight and dawn: *Owens, Donnie* / Ask me anything: *Owens, Donnie* / On and on: *Owens, Donnie* / Cry little girlie: *Banta, Benny* / Gotta get with it: *Lemaire, Eddie* / Little more wine: *Hawks* / I ask of you: *Johnson, Miriam* / Boppin' blue jeans: *Leonard Bros* / Do da da do: *Leonard Bros* / Still of the night: *Langford, Gerry* / Tell me: *Langford, Gerry* / Lonely walk: *Self, Alvie* / Round and round: *Casey, Al* / Rockin' down Mexico way: *Clinkscale, Jimmy* / Doggone lonesome town: *Lane, Barry* / Rain on the mountain: *Q-Zeen* / There'll come a day: *Wilson, Easy Deal* / I don't wantcha: *Wilson, Easy Deal* / You're still my baby: *Banta, Benny* / Cruisin' central: *Warmer, Faron* / Stop: *Cole, Don* / Fussin: *Ray, Gerald* / Panic: *Ray, Gerald* / I've got a girl: *Smith, Gary* / Shummyin' John: *Roustabouts* / Scotch and soda: *Thome, Henry* / Scarlett: *Thome, Henry* / I feel the blues coming on: *Clingman, Loy* / Li'l O'Bug: *Wagoners* / Ali Baba: *Morgan Condello Combo* / Tip: *Clingman's Clan* / Freshman girl, senior boy: *Dansfords* / Hard times: *McAllisters* / Saro Jane: *Clingman, Loy* / Silly dilly: *Terry & Peggy* / Cindy's crying: *Gray, Jimmie* / Forgotten: *Versales* / Nobody but you: *Contessas* / Gingerbread: *Alan & The Alpines* / Was it make believe: *Essex, Herb* / Bumble bee: *Tads* / Me, my shadow, and I: *Fullylove, Leroy* / I want to know: *Fullylove, Leroy* / Oo, what you do to me: *Fullylove, Leroy* / One of these days: *Fullylove, Leroy* / Day after day (master): *Fullylove, Leroy* / Man like myself: *Wild Flowers* / More than me: *Wild Flowers* / Times past: *Hobbits* / Top of the morning: *Hobbits* / Sidewalks and avenues: *Second Edition* / Sad now: *Solid Ground* / Tell her: *Riffs* / Don't move girl: *Lost & Found* / Big wave: *Scallywags* / Hi-fi baby: *Door Knobs* / For me: *Destiny's Children*
BCD 15824 / Jun '95 / Bear Family

☐ PHOSPHORESCENT
TIPCD 08 / Oct '96 / Tip

☐ PHRENTIC DRUMS (Destructive Hardstep Drum 'n' Bass)
CLP 00862 / 26 Aug '97 / Hypnotic

☐ PHUTURE BEATS (2CD Set)
MM 08941802 / Jan '96 / Independence

☐ PHUTURE PHUNK
Dust bucket: *Nitrate* / Hayfever: *Speedy J* / Innocent: *Tribes Of Krom* / Freshness: *Hookian Mindz* / Riots: *Freshness on Wax* / Blast: *Stalker* / Playa: *Flava Unit* / King of the beats: *Amazon II* / Lyca journey: *Freshness on Wax* / Interpret: *Atkins, Juan* / Citation: *Tons Of Tones* / Natural high: *Warp 69* / Matter: *Sunrise Society* / System address: *ISM* / Sqelch: *Finitribe*
DBM 31514 / 29 Sep '97 / Fierce

☐ PHUTURISTIC PHUNK
TKH 004 / Dec '96 / Tekhed

☐ PHYSICAL FATNESS
Olive me: *NOFX* / Stand: *Good Riddance* / What happened to the likely lads: *Snuff* / Ultimate devotion: *Strung Out* / Biggest joke: *Strung Out* / My sweet dog: *Hi-Standard* / Cool kids: *Screeching Weasel* / Raise a family: *Lagwagon* / Stour: *Bracket* / Next in line: *Swinging Utters* / On the outside: *No Use For A Name* / My pop the cop: *No Use For A Name* / Painless: *Screw 32* / True: *Propaghandi* / Partial birth: *Tilt* / Go away: *88 Fingers Louie* / Me and Julio...: *Me First & The Gimme Gimmes* / Arsehole: *Snuff*
FAT 560CD / 24 Nov '97 / Fatwreck Chords

☐ PIANO (3CD Set)
EMTBX 314 / 20 Apr '98 / Emporio

☐ PIANO BLUES DALLAS 1927-1929
PYCD 15 / '92 / Magpie

☐ PIANO BLUES VOL.1
DOCD 5192 / Oct '93 / Document

☐ PIANO BLUES VOL.1 1923-1930
SOBCD 35112 / Mar '92 / Story Of The Blues

☐ PIANO BLUES VOL.1 1928-1932
PYCD 01 / Apr '90 / Magpie

☐ PIANO BLUES VOL.2
PYCD 02 / Jul '90 / Magpie

☐ PIANO BLUES VOL.2 1927-1940
DOCD 5220 / Jan '94 / Document

☐ PIANO BLUES VOL.2 1930-1939
SOBCD 35122 / Mar '92 / Story Of The Blues

☐ PIANO BLUES VOL.3 1924-1931
DOCD 5314 / Dec '94 / Document

☐ PIANO BLUES VOL.3: VOCALION 1928-30 (Shake Your Wicked Knees)
Back in the alley / Cow cow blues / Slum gullion stomp / Texas shout / Michigan River blues / You can't come in / I'm so glad / Mexico bound blues band
PYCD 03 / Oct '90 / Magpie

☐ PIANO BLUES VOL.4 1923-1928
DOCD 5336 / May '95 / Document

☐ PIANO BLUES VOL.5 1929-1936
DOCD 5337 / May '95 / Document

☐ PIANO BLUES VOL.5: POSTSCRIPT 1927-33 (Hot Box On My Mind)
PYCD 05 / Apr '91 / Magpie

☐ PIANO BOOGIE WOOGIE
GR boogie: *Rodgers, Gene* / GR blues: *Rodgers, Gene* / Rhapsody boogie: *Rodgers, Gene* / GR blues: *Rodgers, Gene* / GR boogie: *Rodgers, Gene* / Blues boogie: *Sampson, Deryck* / Boogie express: *Sampson, Deryck* / Boogie in C: *Sampson, Deryck* / Hen house boogie: *Sampson, Deryck* / Basin street boogie: *Sampson, Deryck* / Kansas city boogie woogie: *Sampson, Deryck* / Canal street boogie woogie: *Sampson, Deryck* / Boogie seranade: *Sampson, Deryck* / Table top boogie: *Sampson, Deryck* / If things don't get better: *White, Beverley* / Don't stop now: *White, Beverley* / You ain't had no blues: *Hayes, Billy* / Man shortage blues: *Hayes, Billy* / I'm a doctor for women: *Dupree, 'Champion' Jack* / Lover's lane: *Dupree, 'Champion' Jack* / She makes good jelly: *Dupree, 'Champion' Jack*
PYCD 22 / Sep '98 / Magpie

☐ PIANO DISCOVERIES (Newly Found Titles & Alt. Takes 1928-43)
BDCD 6045 / Jan '94 / Blues Document

☐ PIANO DREAMS
Watermark / Right here waiting / Up where we belong / Evergreen / (Everything I do) I do it for you / Song for Guy / Missing / Wonderful tonight / Shepherd moons / All out of love / Always on my mind / Yesterday / Memories of green / Imagine / How deep is your love / I want to know what love is / Love is blue
CDVIP 149 / Apr '97 / Virgin VIP

☐ PIANO IN BLUES
157172 / Feb '93 / Blues Collection

☐ PIANO MOODS
I will always love you / Have you ever really loved a woman / Stay another day / Fragile / Love can build a bridge / Miss you like crazy / Right here waiting / Back for good / No more I love you's / Get here / Think twice / Chains / Key to my life / Endless love / Best in me / Total eclipse of the heart / Whiter shade of pale / Unchained melody / Love is all around
3036000062 / Oct '95 / Carlton

☐ PIANO MOODS
75605512862 / Sep '96 / Happy Days

☐ PIANO PLAYTIME
I'd know you anywhere: *Thorburn, Billy* / Do I love you: *Thorburn, Billy* / I want my Mama: *Thorburn, Billy* / Message from the man in the moon: *Moore, Gerry* / Sophisticated lady: *Layton, Turner* / Ace of clubs: *Mayerl, Billy* / Ace of hearts: *Mayerl, Billy* / Jammin': *Moore, Gerry* / Sweet Sue: *Moreton, Ivor & Dave Kay* / Heebie jeebies: *Moreton, Ivor & Dave Kay* / I wonder where my baby is tonight: *Moreton, Ivor & Dave Kay* / In the shade of the old apple tree: *Carroll, Eddie & Bobby McGee* / My blue heaven: *Carroll, Eddie & Bobby McGee* / Running wild: *Carroll, Eddie & Bobby McGee* / Marigold: *Mayerl, Billy* / Roses in December: *Thorburn, Billy* / Blossoms on Broadway: *Thorburn, Billy* / Here comes the sandman: *Thorburn, Billy* / Little Sir Echo: *Renara* / Rosetta: *Moore, Gerry* / It don't mean a thing if it ain't got that swing: *Moreton, Ivor & Dave Kay* / Happy feet: *Moreton, Ivor & Dave Kay* / Everybody loves my baby: *Moreton, Ivor & Dave Kay* / I got rhythm: *Moreton, Ivor & Dave Kay* / Ace of diamonds: *Mayerl, Billy* / Ace of spades: *Mayerl, Billy* / Ain't misbehavin': *Young, Arthur* / March winds and April showers: *Moore, Gerry* / Man I love: *Rossborough, Patricia* / Marie: *Rossborough, Patricia* / My heart stood still: *Rossborough, Patricia* / No more you: *Moore, Gerry* / Blind man's buff: *Young, Arthur* / No

souvenirs: Carroll, Eddie / You made me love you: Carroll, Eddie / Let the curtain come down: Carroll, Eddie / We're in the money: Rossborough, Patricia / Shadow waltz: Rossborough, Patricia / When two love each other: Moore, Gerry / Merry widow waltz: Bradbury, Stan / Destiny: Bradbury, Stan / Yip I addy: Bradbury, Stan
RAJCD 860 / 2 Feb '98 / Empress

☐ **PIANO SOLITUDE (A Magical Blend Of Music And The Sounds Of Nature)**
57642 / May '97 / Nature's Harmony

☐ **PIANO TALK**
ISCD 105 / '88 / Intersound

☐ **PICADILLY STORY, THE (2CD Set)**
Crazy mixed up kid: Brown, Joe & The Bruvvers / Half of my heart: Ford, Emile / There, I've said it again: Saxon, Al / Honest I do: Storm, Danny / Z-cars: Keating, Johnny / Don't come cryin' to me: Jones, Davy / Picture of you: Brown, Joe & The Bruvvers / Rivers run dry: Hill, Vince / I knew it all the time: Hill, Vince / It might as well rain until September: De Laine Sisters / All of me: Lynton, Jackie / Long gone baby: Britten, Buddy & The Regents / Ferryboat ride: Cudley Dudley / Walk right in: Kestrels / Hey Paula: Elaine & Derick / Heavenly: Eager, Vince / Let's make a habit: Guv'nors / Ain't gonna kiss ya: Jackson, Simone / He's so near: Douglas, Donna / Tip of my tongue: Quickly, Tommy / Don't lie to me: Jeannie & The Big Guys / To know her is to love her: Storme, Robb & Whispers / He don't want your love anymore: Doll, Linda & the Sundowners / Is it true: Tony D & The Shakeouts / Sally go round the roses: Remo Four / Where did our love go: Jay, Peter & The Jaywalkers / Cast your fate to the wind: Sounds Orchestral / Don't cry for me: Peters, Mark / You've lost that lovin' feelin': Ann, Barbara / Girl who wanted fame: Wackers / Baby do it: McKenna, Val / Lonely room: Ryder, Mal & the Spirits / Poor man's son: Rockin' Berries / She's about a mover: Britten, Buddy & The Regents / Tossin' and turnin': Ivy League / Take a heart: Sorrows / Leave my baby alone: Britt / Leave it to me: Band Of Angels / That's my life (my love and my home): Lennon, Freddie / Why don't I run away from you: Antoinette / Ask the lonely: Rio, Bobby / I know (you don't love me no more): Felders Orioles / You don't know like I know: Powell, Keith & Billie Davis / Dear Mrs. Applebee: Garrick, David / Ain't that peculiar: Loving Kind / Whatever will be will be (Que sera sera): Washington, Geno & The Ram Jam Band / Ain't love good, ain't love proud: James, Jimmy & The Vagabonds / It keeps rainin': Powell, Keith & The Valets / Run to the door: Ford, Clinton / 98.6: Bystanders / I'll always love you: Time Box / Almost but not quite there: Traffic Jam
NEDCD 240 / Oct '93 / Sequel

☐ **PICCADILLY NIGHTS (British Dance Bands Of The 1920's)**
That girl over there / Swing on the gait / It's a million to one you're in love / What'll you do / Make my cot where the cot-cot-cotton grows / How long has this been going on / Miss Annabelle Lee / Lila / That's my weakness now / Sunny skies / Matilda Matilda / Saskatchewan / There's a blue ridge 'round my heart, Virginia / 'S wonderful / Crazy rhythm / I'm a one man girl / Spread a little happiness / Out of the dawn / Ida, sweet as apple cider / I don't know why I do it but I do
DHAL 17 / Sep '93 / Halcyon

☐ **PICK AND MIX (2CD Set)**
Higher sun: Moom / Time to fly: Aardvarks / Ease it: Suicidal Flowers / Gil: Kava Kava / Corcucopia: Steppes / Of the first water: Sons Of Selina / Tribal elders: Riff, Nick / Let the powers: Nova Express / Dissolving: Treatment / Watching the sky: Kryptasthesie / Annihilation: Omnia Opera / Inner days: Nukli / Solstice song: Mandagora / Voyage 34: Porcupine Tree / Warmth within: Dead Flowers / Psychomuzak: Extasie / Root verses of the six bardos: Liberation Through Hearing / Goat faced girl: Zuvuya / Nindia: Electric Orange / Arc of ascent: Bazaar, Saddar / Ormithology: Praise Space Electric / Can you play: Praise Space Electric / Ornithology: Praise Space Electric / Purple haze: Boris & His Bolshie Balalaika / Gospel according to IEM: Incredible Expanding Mindfuck
DELECCDD 023 / Oct '95 / Delerium

☐ **PICTURE YOURSELF BELLY DANCING**
MCD 71780 / Sep '93 / Monitor

☐ **PILGRIM, THE**
Himlico's map / Gair na gairbe / Walk in the ocean / Pilgrim / Columcille's farewell to Ireland / Land of the picts / Iona / Briochan and columba / Storm at sea / Whita waves foam over / Ymadawiad Arthur / St Manchans prayer / Samson peccator episcopus / St Mathews point / Danse plin / Bal plin / Danse an dro / Santiago / Vigo / Deer's cry / God be with me / A'ghrian
TARACD 3032 / Aug '94 / Tara

☐ **PILLOW TALK**
Pillow talk: Sylvia / Be thankful for what you've got: DeVaughan, William / Sad sweet dreamer: Sweet Sensation / Girls: Moments / Stay with me baby: Redding, Wilma / Can't get by without you: Real Thing / So sad the song: Knight, Gladys & The Pips / There it is: Shalamar / Red red wine: James, Jimmy / Loving you - losing you: Hyman, Phyllis / It's a love thing: Whispers / Suspicious minds: Staton, Candi / Betcha by golly wow: Hyman, Phyllis & Michael Henderson / Come back and finish what you started: Knight, Gladys & The Pips / You'll never know: Hi-Gloss / Have you seen her: Chi-Lites / Valentine love: Connors, Norman / You gave me love: Crown Heights Affair
TRTCD 117 / Feb '96 / TrueTrax

☐ **PILLOWS AND PRAYERS (A Cherry Red Compilation 1982-1983)**
Portrait: Five Or Six / Eine symphonie des grauns: Monochrome Set / All about you: Leer, Thomas / Plain sailing: Thorn, Tracey / Some things don't matter: Watt, Ben / Love in your heart: Coyne, Kevin / Modi 2: Milesi, Pierro / Compulsion: Crow, Joe / Lazy ways: Marine Girls / My face is on fire: Felt / No noise: Eyeless In Gaza / Xoyo: Passage / On my mind: Everything But The Girl / Bang and a wimpey: Attila The Stockbroker / I unseen: Misunderstood / Don't blink: Nightingales / Stop the music for a minute: Crisp, Quentin
CDMRED 41 / Apr '96 / Cherry Red

☐ **PINARENO**
PIR 372 / Oct '92 / Piranha

☐ **PIONEER CHRISTMAS**
Mistletoe and wine / Frosty the snowman / Step into Christmas / Christmas song / Last Christmas / Stop the cavalry / Lonely this Christmas / Rockin' around the Christmas tree / Blue Christmas / Santa Claus is coming to town / Winter wonderland / Wonderful Christmas time / I saw Mommy kissing Santa Claus / White Christmas
CDMFP 6178 / Nov '95 / Music For Pleasure

☐ **PIONEERS OF THE BOUNCING BEAT**
EFFS 1001CD
EFFS 1001CDR / Oct '94 / Effective

☐ **PIPES AND DRUMS**
LBP 2028CD / Jun '96 / Lochshore

☐ **PIPES AND DRUMS FROM THE BORDERS (Berwick Tattoo 1996)**
Opening fanfare / Pipes and drums / King's division Waterloo band / Northumbria police band / Northumberland band of the royal regiment of fusiliers / Highland band of the Scottish division / Massed military bands / Final: pipes, drums and bands
BNA 5130 / Dec '96 / Bandleader

☐ **PIPES AND DRUMS OF IRELAND**
925592 / Jun '93 / BUDA

☐ **PIPES AND DRUMS OF SCOTLAND**
EUCD 1213 / Sep '93 / ARC

☐ **PIPES AND STRINGS OF SCOTLAND VOL.1**
From scotland with love / Sailing / Scotland forever / Marching home / Mull of kintyre / Plaisir d'amour / Going home / Sands of time / Amazing grace / Home of mine / Il silenzio / Mcwhinnie's salute / Remembrances / Auld lang syne / Loch lomond / Skye boat song
CD ITV 362 / Dec '86 / Scotdisc

☐ **PIPING CENTRE 1997 RECITAL SERIES VOL.1, THE**
COMD 2075 / 10 Aug '98 / Temple

☐ **PIPING CENTRE 1997 RECITAL SERIES VOL.2, THE**
COMD 2076 / 10 Aug '98 / Temple

☐ **PIPING CONCERT (Celtic Connections)**
Strathspeys/Reels: Macdonald, Angus / 4/4 Marches: Macdonald, Angus / Stathspeys and reels: Macdonald, Angus / Johnny's tune: Keenan, Paddy / Flagstone of memories: Keenan, Paddy / Song and three reels: Duncan, Gordon / Jigs and reels: Duncan, Gordon / Golden eagle: Cato, Pauline & Tom McConville / Alexander's hornpipe: Cato, Pauline & Tom McConville / Herr Roloff's farewell: Cato, Pauline & Tom McConville / Slow air march and dances: Molard, Patrick
CDLDL 1270 / Jan '98 / Lochshore

☐ **PIPING HOT (A Celtic Bagpipe Collection)**
Good drying set: Tannahill Weavers / Larry Redican's hornpipe/The green banner: O'Sullivan, Jerry / Onward blindly onward: Rare Air / Blackbirds and thrushes: Connolly, Matty / Sean Reid's/Toss the feathers: Moloney, Mick & Joe McKenna / Grimstock: House Band / Clueless: Wolfstone / Brian O'Lynn/The woods of old Limerick: Patrick Street / Rainy day/The merry blacksmith/The silver spear: Ennis, Seamus / Bells of Tipperary/Miss Galvin's: Burke, Joe & Michael Cooney/Terry Corcoran / Dear Irish boy/The stone in the field: Reck, Tommy / Colonel Fraser: O'Sullivan, Jerry / Kintail: Tannahill Weavers
CELT 9004 / May '97 / Celtophile

☐ **PITCH CONTROL**
Slowmo: Surreal Madrid / Mexico: Kings Of The Wild Frontier / George best: Jeep Beat Collective / Head top lick: Koku / Moog lose the world cup: Moog / Route 1: Push squad / Street football: Laidback / Line up: Shrink 2 Fit / Stretcher'd off: Lee Van Cleef / Crowd control: Meat Katie / Mexican wave form: Scope
SPECCD 506 / 26 May '98 / Dust II Dust

☐ **PITCH, THE**
MONCD 001 / Mar '93 / Montana

☐ **PITCH, THE**
Hi / Dustbin man / Razor / Monkey man / Killing for the headlines: Velma / Come undone: 2000 / Nullify me: Tinlip / In our own cage: Gazebo / Pulse: Bushbaby / Thief: Velma / Scandinavian girlfriend: Superhero / Circular: Dragdoll
BACWCD 1 / 18 Aug '97 / Big & Complex World

☐ **PLACE IN THE SUN, A**
CRECD 088 / May '94 / Creation

☐ **PLANET DUB (2CD Set)**
BARKCD 015 / Oct '95 / Planet Dog

☐ **PLANET E PRESENTS INTERGALACTIC BEATS**
PE 010CD / May '97 / Planet E

☐ **PLANET OF DRUMS**
LCDCD 01 / 15 Jun '98 / Planet Of Drums

☐ **PLANET RADIO (2CD Set)**
ZYX 811252 / 6 Oct '97 / ZYX

☐ **PLANET RADIO VOL.3 (2CD Set)**
ZYX 811542 / 29 Jun '98 / ZYX

☐ **PLANET RAMPANT VOL.2**
SUB 10D / Apr '96 / Subversive

☐ **PLANET SKA**
PHZCD 57 / Feb '95 / Unicorn

☐ **PLANET SQUEEZE BOX (3CD Set)**
ELLIPSIS 347 / Jun '96 / Ellipsis Arts

☐ **PLANETARY PEBBLES VOL.1**
AIPCD 1057 / 29 Sep '97 / AIP

☐ **PLANETARY PEBBLES VOL.2 (Exitos A Go Go - 60's Teenbeat South Of the Border)**
AIPCD 1061 / 10 Aug '98 / AIP

☐ **PLANETE FLAMENCO**
DECLI 845250 / 3 Mar '98 / Munich

☐ **PLANETE RAI**
Let me cry: Mami, Cheb / La Camel: Khaled, Cheb / N'sel fik: Fadela, Cheb / Sel dem drai: Kada, Cheb / Dawili Mali: Tati, Cheb / Ana Mazel: Mami, Cheb / Rani Meute: Kada, Cheb / Zini: Rai, Raina / Kutche: Khaled, Cheb / Gouloulima: Zahouani, Cheb / El awama: Kada, Cheb / Rih el gharei: Moumen, Cheb / Chabba bent: Khaled, Cheb / Douha alia: Mami, Cheb
GUMBOCD 004 / Jan '93 / Cooking Vinyl

☐ **PLANETE REGGAE VOL.1**
8411352 / Oct '96 / Declic

☐ **PLANETE REGGAE VOL.2**
172032 / Oct '96 / Declic

☐ **PLANETE ROCK 'N' ROLL**
302129 / May '94 / Total

☐ **PLATIPUS RECORDS VOL.1**
PLAT 10CD / 18 May '98 / Platipus

☐ **PLATIPUS RECORDS VOL.2**
PLAT 20CD / 18 May '98 / Platipus

☐ **PLATIPUS RECORDS VOL.3**
Anomaly/Calling your name: Libra / Now and zen: Quietman / Hidden of venus: LSG / Awakening: POB / Seadog: Clanger / All because of you: Universal State Of Mind / Journey: Loveclub / Kaleidoscope: Art Of Trance / Floating: Terra Firma / Yeti: Union Jack
PLAT 35CD / 6 Oct '97 / Platipus

☐ **PLAY**
EFA 123352 / Aug '97 / Sideburn

☐ **PLAY ME A POLKA**
ROUCD 6029 / Dec '94 / Rounder

☐ **PLAY NEW ROSE FOR ME**
ROSE 100CD / Jan '87 / New Rose

☐ **PLAY THE BLUES**
Lonely guitar man: Dawkins, Jimmy / Drivin' me crazy: Shadows / Keep it: Watts, Noble / Little red rooster: Drink Small / Looking up at the bottom: Ealey, Theodis / Locksmith: Nelson, 'Chicago' Bob / In order: Principato, Tom / Ain't no blues in town: Rhodes, Sonny / House without a home: Turner, Troy / Sky is crying: Coleman, Gary B.B. / Three wives: McCain, Jerry / I like to hear my guitar sing: Benton, Buster
ICH 11892 / Jun '96 / Ichiban

☐ **PLAYING FOR LOVE**
BLR 84 026 / May '91 / L&R

☐ **PLAYING HARD TO GET (West Coast Girls)**
You're so fine: Berry, Dorothy / Little bit of soap: Carroll, Yvonne / Stop shovin' me around: Delicates / Dreamworld: Loren, Donna / Crying on my pillow: Berry, Dorothy / He's a big deal: Medina, Renee / Goodbye Jimmie: Berry, Panda / You haven't seen nothing: Young, Dee Dee / Don't mess around with me: Sister Rachel / Nothing to write home about: Francettes / Love bells: Galens / Date bait: Maxwell, Diane / You better watch out boy: Accents / Chinese lanterns: Galens / Boy I love: Medina, Renee / Write me a letter: Blossoms / I've been hurt: Delicates / How long must this fool pay: Carroll, Yvonne / I'll wait: Blossoms / I want to get married: Delicates / Search is over: Blossoms / Hard to get: Blossoms / Come on everybody: Delicates / I gotta tell it: Blossoms / Big talkin' Jim: Blossoms / Mr. Loveman: Carroll, Yvonne / Comin' down with love: Delicates / Muscle bustle: Loren, Donna
CDCHD 559 / May '95 / Ace

☐ **PLAYING THE BLUES**
Still got the blues (for you): Moore, Gary / Boom boom: Hooker, John Lee / Down in Mississippi: Staples, Pops / Trouble blues: Hammond, John / Too many cooks: Evans, Terry / I'll be good: Washington, Walter 'Wolfman' / Back to my baby: Sanne / Iceman: Collins, Albert / Green all over: Jumpin' The Gunn / Witchin' moon: McCray, Larry / Too early to tell: Kinsey Report / She likes to boogie real low: Winter, Johnny / Rule the world: Robillard, Duke
CDVIP 130 / Oct '94 / Virgin VIP

☐ **PLAYING WITH FIRE (Contemporary Celtic Instrumentals)**
Reel Beatrice/Abbey reel / Sprig of Shillelagh/ Planxty penny / Two reels / Lord Gordon's reel / Foggy dew / Copper plate / Waltz from Orsa / In and out the harbour / Rolling waves/Market town/ Scatter the mud / Jenny's welcome to Charlie/ Father Francis Cameron / Marquis of Huntly / Con Cassidy's and Nelly O'Boyle's highland reels / Gavotten / Walkin' o' the Fauld / Carraigin ruadh / Curlew/McDermott's reel/Three scones of Boxty
GLCD 1101 / Feb '93 / Green Linnet
CELT 9011CD / 9 Mar '98 / Celtophile

☐ **PLEASURES AND TREASURES (A Kaleidoscope of Sound)**
March by Mr Handel: Hacker, Alan / Mira O Norma: Polyphon musical box / Jean's reel: Tickell, Kathryn / Lezghinka: Best Of Brass / Prelude to lute suite in E major: North, Nigel / Colette: Whiteman, Paul & His Orchestra / John come kiss me now: Townsend, Dave / Music from Compline: Stanbrook Abbey Nuns & Prinknash Abbey Monks / Le coucou: Preston, Stephen / Whistling Rufus: Sound In Brass Handbells / Limerick's lamentation: Monger, Eileen / La quinte estampie real: Canter, Robin / I've got a lovely bunch of coconuts: Barrel Organ / Love at the fair: Jing Ying Soloists / Miss Annabelle Lee: Pianola Roll / Scherzo: Holmes, Ralph / Wibbly wobbly walk: Charman, Jack / Jenny Lind medley: Couza, Jim / Turkish rondo: Burnett, Richard / O Sanctissima: Schmitt, Georges / Reve gourmand: Pauly, Danielle / Sportive little trifler: Canterbury Clerkes & London Serpent Trio
CDSDLC 362 / Sep '86 / Saydisc

☐ **PLUS FROM US**
Obiero: Ogada, Ayub / Keep on marching: Meters / Oasis: Hammill, Peter / Pine tree and on the street: Pokrovsky, Dmitri / Best friend paranoia: Orbit, William / Lone bear: Levin, Tony / Morecambe bay: Gifford, Alex / Down by the river: Rhodes, David / Triennale: Eno, Brian / Rose rhythm: Serra, Eric / Silence: Katche, Manu / Baladi we hetta: Ramzy, Hossam / Dreams: Shankar 'N' Caroline / Suheyla: Erguner, Kudsi / El Conquistador: Lanois, Daniel
CDRW 33 / May '93 / Realworld

☐ **PLUS GRANDS SUCCES DU PUNK VOL.2**
622522 / Apr '97 / Skydog

☐ **PM SCIENTISTS DROP THE BEATS (2CD Set)**
CERBAD 9 / 18 May '98 / Lacerba

☐ **POETRY OF IRA COHEN, THE**
SR 62 / Mar '96 / Sub Rosa

☐ **POETRY PUT TO SONG**
7992382 / Jan '95 / Hispavox

☐ **POETRY PUT TO SONG**
7996512 / Jan '95 / Hispavox

☐ **POINT TO BE MADE VOL.1, A (2CD Set)**
Got to believe: Ramos & Supreme / What cannado: Midas & Supreme / Groove control: Midas / Here beside me: DJ Stompy & Supreme / Crowd control: Ramos & Supreme / Knightraver: Ramos & Supreme/Sunset Regime / Harmonize: Ramos & Supreme/Sunset Regime / Journey: Ramos & Supreme / How could you do that: Joshua / Goodtimes: Edy C / Love is the only way: DJ Storm / Can't stop: Midas / Meadowland: Edy C / Eternity: DJ Justice / Wings of love: Go Mental / Always in my dreams: DJ Supreme & UFO / Body rock: DJ Stompy / All alone: MC Marley & UFO / Pump it up: DJ Dream / I believe: DJ Stompy / Broken wings: DJ Supreme & UFO / Love somebody else: Ikon / Critical heights: Unknown Project / Are you ready: DJ Sy & Unknown / Summertime vibe: Druid & Vinyl Groover / Higher and higher: Ramos & Supreme/Sunset Regime / I believe in the beat: DJ Stompy / Three little words: DJ Stompy / What's going on: DJ Dream & DJ Ell / Heart is jumpin': Midas / Through the night: DJ Webley & Sensation / We are unity: DJ Sy & Unknown / Calypso summer: Vinyl Groover / Pure love: Midas & Donna Grassie / Instant love: Underground Movement
FUSCD 003 / 10 Nov '97 / Fusion

☐ **POINT TO BE MADE VOL.2, A (2CD Set)**
FUSCD 004 / 16 Mar '98 / Fusion

☐ **POINTS WEST (New Horizons In Country Music)**
HCD 8021 / Oct '94 / Hightone

☐ **POLISH MOUNTAIN FIDDLE MUSIC VOL.2 (Fire In The Mountains)**
YAZ 7013 / Aug '97 / Yazoo

☐ **POLISH VILLAGE MUSIC 1927-1933**
ARHCD 7031 / Jun '95 / Arhoolie

☐ **POLITICAL PARTY BROADCAST (2CD Set)**
Treatment: Kektex / Mushrooms on daleks: Sacroblast / Slut fuck: Immersion / Godstopper: Kektex / Piston: Kektex / Techno slut: Immersion / Lock: Kektex / New wave of acid techno: Lochi / Sonar: Sacroblast / What is soul: Temperature Drop / Bug swat: Kektex / Techno slut: Immersion / Paroxysm: Lochi / Roland abuse: Sacroblast / Trip wire: Lochi / London acid city: Lochi / In the forehead: Kektex / New wave of acid techno 92): Kektex / Quasar: Kektex / Control: Secret Hero / Hoover baby: Tasha Killer Pussies / Lock: Kektex / Slut fuck: Immersion
ROUTEPILE 1 / Jun '97 / Routemaster

☐ **POLITPARADE (4CD Set)**
Der Geist weht: Strauss, Franz Joseph / Ich glaube nicht: Von Hassel, Kai Uwe / Wir nehmen nicht Abschied: Erhard, Ludwig / Wir wunschen Frieden Heinrich: Barzel, Rainer / Die Reise: Lubke, Heinrich / Das Lied von der unzefriedenen Gruppe: Kiesinger, Georg / Berliner jam session: Diverse 1 / Deutschland braucht Bayern: Strauss, Franz Joseph / We do not want to fight: Schroder, Gerhard / Die NPD ist wieder weg: Schmidt, Helmut / Made in Germany: Scheel, Walter / Wir wollen mehr Demokratie wagen: Brandt, Willy / Etwas lernen - etwas leisten: Schmidt, Helmut / Nach allem was ich sehe: Barzel, Rainer / Der song mit den kurzen Beinen: Wehner, Herbert / Das ist gut: Brandt, Willy / Das Lied von der Vaterlandsliebe: Carstens, Karl / Vertrauen in die Wahrung: Schmidt, Helmut / Wo steht denn geschrieben: Genscher, Hans Dietrich / Es gibt nur eine Mitte: Strauss, Franz Joseph / Tai tik: Strauss, Franz Joseph / Was wir wollen: Barzel, Rainer / Trimm dich trilogie / Dichterlesung Franz Josef / Afghanistan: Strauss, Franz Joseph / Kein schoner land: Strauss, Franz Joseph / Sicher kann keiner sein: Schmidt, Helmut / Ach du lieber Gott: Strauss, Franz Joseph / Ich kenne die sprache des Volkes: Strauss, Franz Joseph / Der Rechsstaat muss Zahne bekommen: Strauss, Franz Joseph / Die Krise: Schmidt, Helmut / Practa Sunt Servanda: Schmidt, Helmut / Mara Durimeh: Schmidt, Helmut /

Wir Deutschen sind des shiessens satt: Schmidt, Helmut / Wir werden siegen: Strauss, Franz Joseph / Das duell: Schmidt, Helmut & Franz Josef Strauss / Wenn das Benehmen Glucksache ist: Schmidt, Helmut & Franz Josef Strauss / Bruder Josef: Schmidt, Helmut & Franz Josef Strauss / Kaloriengehalt: Schmidt, Helmut & Franz Josef Strauss / Menschliche Herkunft: Schmidt, Helmut & Franz Josef Strauss / Produktion von Eiern: Schmidt, Helmut & Franz Josef Strauss / Sportliche Betatigung: Schmidt, Helmut & Franz Josef Strauss / Meine damen und herren: Schmidt, Helmut & Franz Josef Strauss / Wenn Pferde immer noch nicht so recht saufen: Schmidt, Helmut & Franz Josef Strauss / Das kann ich nicht: Schmidt, Helmut & Franz Josef Strauss / Meine sehr verehrten damen und herren: Schmidt, Helmut & Franz Josef Strauss / Es gibt auch pillen fur Manner: Schmidt, Helmut & Franz Josef Strauss / Bonner nachtgebet: Schmidt, Helmut & Franz Josef Strauss / Eigene Geschichte: Schmidt, Helmut & Franz Josef Strauss / Wer raus geht muss auch wieder reinkommen: Schmidt, Helmut & Franz Josef Strauss / Ein paar bemerkungen: Schmidt, Helmut & Franz Josef Strauss / Darf ich sie fragen: Schmidt, Helmut & Franz Josef Strauss / Fahren sie in ihren Ausfuhrungen fort: Schmidt, Helmut & Franz Josef Strauss / Da mussen sie ich eine bessere Frage einfallen lassen: Schmidt, Helmut & Franz Josef Strauss / Meine Damen und Herren: Schmidt, Helmut & Franz Josef Strauss / Herr Abgeordneter, fahren sie in ihrer Rede fort: Schmidt, Helmut & Franz Josef Strauss / Noch eine Bemerkung: Schmidt, Helmut & Franz Josef Strauss / Das ist gut das lassen wir weg: Schmidt, Helmut & Franz Josef Strauss / Heinrich Lubke: Einigkeit und Recht und Freiheit: Schmidt, Helmut & Franz Josef Strauss / Vorwurfe: Schmidt, Helmut & Franz Josef Strauss / Einigkeit und Recht und Freheit 2: Schmidt, Helmut & Franz Josef Strauss / Ausserdem konnen wir leicht nachweisen: Schmidt, Helmut & Franz Josef Strauss / Gartenschau: Schmidt, Helmut & Franz Josef Strauss / Literatur und Dichtung: Schmidt, Helmut & Franz Josef Strauss / Moderne Baukunst: Schmidt, Helmut & Franz Josef Strauss / Deutsche Vereinigung: Schmidt, Helmut & Franz Josef Strauss / Zum Schluss: Schmidt, Helmut & Franz Josef Strauss

BCD 16008 / Nov '96 / Bear Family

☐ POLKAS OF THE WORLD
995832 / Nov '97 / EPM

☐ POLLYCOUNTRY VOL.1
PCM 002 / Apr '97 / Pollytone

☐ POLYPHONIC CHANTS OF THE MONGO PEOPLE
C 580050 / Sep '93 / Ocora

☐ POLYPHONIES (Southern Alps)
926652 / Feb '97 / BUDA

☐ POLYPHONIES OF THE SOLOMON ISLANDS
LDX 274663 / Nov '90 / La Chant Du Monde

☐ POLYPHONIES VOCALES (Music From Albania)
W 260065 / Dec '95 / Inedit

☐ POLYPHONY FOR HOLY WEEK (Religious Vocal Music From Sardinia)
LDX 274936 / Jul '92 / La Chant Du Monde

☐ POLYPHONY OF SVANETI
LDX 274990 / May '94 / La Chant Du Monde

☐ POLYPHONY OF THE DORZE (Ethiopia)
2746461 / Jan '95 / La Chant Du Monde

☐ PONDOU FEVER
PEYOTE 011CD / 22 Sep '97 / Peyote

☐ POP AND DANCE VS. DRUM AND BASS
UE 01505 / 27 Apr '98 / Urban Essentials

☐ POP BOUTIQUE VOL.2
SWCD 1003 / 20 Apr '98 / Spinning Wheel

☐ POP CLASSICS
Born to be wild: Steppenwolf / Sweet home Alabama: Lynyrd Skynyrd / Don't believe a word: Moore, Gary / Broken wings: Mr. Mister / Saturday night: Brood, Herman / Radio girl: Hiatt, John / LB Boogie: Livin' Blues / Lola: Kinks / American woman: Guess Who / We built this city: Starship / Radio Africa: Latin Quarter / Rocky mountain way: Walsh, Joe / Feelin' alright: Mason, Dave / Elvira: Oak Ridge Boys / Woodstock: Matthew's Southern Comfort / Joy to the world: Three Dog Night
MCD 30199 / Mar '94 / Ariola Express

☐ POP CLASSICS
DSPCD 105 / Sep '93 / Disky

☐ POP ELECTRONIQUE
SWCD 1004 / 8 Jun '98 / Spinning Wheel

☐ POP GOES THE 70'S
Beautiful Sunday: Boone, Daniel / Freedom come freedom go: Fortunes / In the summertime: Mungo Jerry / Come and get it: Badfinger / Witch queen of New Orleans: Redbone / Radancer: Marmalade / Son of my father: Chicory Tip / Fox on the run: Connolly, Brian / Dancin, on a Saturday night: Blue, Barry / Goodbye my love: Glitter Band / Sugar baby love: Rubettes / I'd like to teach the world to sing (in perfect harmony): New Seekers / Billy don't be a hero: Paper Lace / Chirpy chirpy cheep cheep: Kissoon, Mac & Katie / I'd love you to want me: Lobo / Indiana wants me: Taylor, Dean / Rock your baby: McCrae, George / That same old feeling: Brown, Polly
ECD 3075 / Jan '95 / K-Tel

☐ POP HITS DELUXE
HRCD 8042 / Jul '94 / Disky

☐ POP HITS GO ON
MU 5051 / Oct '92 / Musketeer

☐ POP HITS OF THE 60'S
PWKS 4181 / Nov '94 / Carlton

☐ POP INSIDE THE SIXTIES VOL.3
SEECD 400 / Jun '94 / See For Miles

☐ POP JINGU VOL.1
SONOCD 4 / Jun '97 / Sonorama

☐ POP MUSIC FROM AFRICA VOL.1
15285 / '91 / Laserlight

☐ POP MUSIC FROM AFRICA VOL.2
15286 / '91 / Laserlight

☐ POP UNDER THE SURFACE
YES 0001 / Dec '97 / Yesterday

☐ POPCORN'S DETROIT SOUL PARTY
Nothing no sweeter: Carlton, Carl / Ooh boy: Adorables / Down in the dumps: Hester, Tony / Hurting: Erik & Vikings / Turn on the heat: Popcorn & Soul Messengers / Somebody stop that boy: Boo, Betty / Hanky panky: Wylie, Richard 'Popcorn' / Tell her: Clarke, Jimmy 'Soul' / Gotta kind a way: Lindsay, Therese / Mighty lover: Ideals / Saving all my love for you: Popcorn Orchestra / Spaceland: Hester, Tony / My baby ain't no play thing: Harvey, Willy / Sweet Darling: Clarke, Jimmy 'Soul' / Arrest me: Thomas, Jano / If it's all the same to you babe: Ingram, Luther / Nobody love me like you: Mercer, Barbara / Going to a happening: Popcorn Orchestra / I'll be your champion: Clarke, Jimmy 'Soul' / Let the sun shine in your window: Mann, Columbus / Cool off: Detroit Executives / You knew what you was gettin': Williams, Juanita / G I Joe we love you: Fantasions
GSCD 059 / Nov '95 / Goldmine

☐ POPPIES (3CD Set)
DTKCD 70 / 29 Sep '97 / Dressed To Kill

☐ POPTARTZ (4CD Set)
Movin to music: Finito / My love: Shades Of Rhythm / DJ Dubs: Lock, Eddie / We got the love: Erik / Comes over me: Stylofoam / Mooncat: Shaker / Changeling: Tan Ru / Move and groove: Basement Of Sound / Raise the feeling: Shades Of Rhythm / Protein: Tata Box / Storm: Space Kittens / Let the fun begin: Fluffy Toy IQ / Think about it: Stylofoam / Do me: Aquarius / Electroluv: 4th Wave / Hideaway: De'Lacy / Deliver me: Urban Blues Project / Feeling: Jasper Street Family / One love: Coccoluto, Claudio / I won't waste your time: Joi & Jorio / Reeboot 144: OLN / Everlasting picture: B-Zet / You can't turn around: Bottom $ / Do it to me: Dark, Frankie / Let no man put a sunder: First Choice / Welcome to the factory: Moraes, Angel / Work 2 do: Roach Motel / Dancing in the year 2000: From The Soul / So everbody (get off it): Sound Design / Club America: Club America / Dreamtime: Zee / Same thing in reverse: Boy George / El metro: Disco Volante / Joanna: Mrs. Wood / Fee fi fo fum: Candy Girls / Out come the freaks: Lippy Lou / Never felt this way: Hi-Lux / Indoctrinate: Castle Trancelot / Florubunda: Mothers Pride / Do you want me: Mambo / Don't you want me: Felix / Rollerskate disco: Pooley, Ian / Shake your body: Ill Disco / C'mon y'all: Rhythm Masters / Come together: Double FM / Dive: Club 69 / Transform: Mijangos / Happiness (is just around the bend): Brooklyn's Poor & Needy / Let the rythm flow: Diva Rhythms / Lost in you: Matt Bianco / Geel good: B-Code / Forerunner: Natural Born Groovers / Who's the badman: De Patten / Rock 2 the beat: RM Project / In my brain: Mark NRG / Unbe: RAW / La Casa: Adrian & Alfarez / Energy tax: RMS / If we lose our lovin': DMB
REACTCD 067 / Nov '95 / React

☐ POPULAR FOLK SONGS FROM NORTH GERMANY
EUCD 1180 / '91 / ARC

☐ POPULAR MUSIC FROM RAJASTHAN
Satara / Tandura (Bhajan) / Morchang solo / Shehnai and nagara / Basuri solo / Marriage orchestra / Ravanahattha solo / Dhol and thali / Murli / Narh / Morchang / Kamayacha / Narh song / Narh and song / Ravanahattha and song / Nagara
PS 65184 / Jun '97 / PlayaSound

☐ POPULAR MUSIC OF CHILE
PS 65094 / Aug '92 / PlayaSound

☐ POPULAR PROFESSIONAL MUSICIANS OF RAJASTHAN
C 580044 / May '94 / Ocora

☐ POPULAR SONGS OF IRELAND
995802 / Apr '97 / EPM

☐ POPULAR SPANISH SONGS OF THE 1930'S
BMCD 2011 / Apr '97 / Blue Moon

☐ POPULAR SPANISH SONGS OF THE 1940'S
BMCD 2012 / Apr '97 / Blue Moon

☐ POPULAR SPANISH SONGS OF THE 1950'S
BMCD 2013 / Apr '97 / Blue Moon

☐ PORN BEATS
Oscar winners: 12 From A Dozen / Beef nets: Shrink 2 Fit / Trevor Slemmons: Mr. Dan / Je t'aime: Danmass / Bangin' the head: Mother Nature's Cloud & Shower Show / Can't let you go: Mellowtrons / Spank da moog: Moog / Sex with the neightbours: IHB / Slack: Snappy Sid / 0898: Clam Leppers / Jazz mag: Suburban Ghetto / Scarlet letter: Mike Flowers & The Mellowtrons
SPECCD 503 / Jul '97 / Dust II Dust

☐ PORTER RECORDS STORY, THE
There goes my heart: Stevens, Randy / Everyone will know: Loren, Frankie / Hip monkey: Loren, Frankie / Wonderful way: Loren, Frankie / Mexicali baby: Rio Rockers / Mexican rock and roll: Rio Rockers / Stop: Red 'Hot' Russell / Pedro Joe: Red 'Hot' Russell / Slinky: Isabell, Rusty / Jaybi: Isabell, Rusty / Little Miss Butte: Isabell, Rusty / Yi yi: Isabell, Rusty / Mixed up mama: Tads / Hey little girl: Tads / Glowing moon: Tads / You're my girl: Pepper, Pete / Cherry cherry red: Pepper, Pete / Purple people eater: Pepper, Pete / Peepin' John: Ward, Darby / Crazy: Ward, Darby / Ring the wedding bells: Porter, Frank / Wolf call: Anthony, Mark / Beluah mae: Cole, Don / True blue: Thirtythrees / No one in my heart but you: Thirtythrees / Satelite: Rocks / Cry blue baby: Chamberlain Brothers / Ring chimes: Leaguers / You heard me knocking: Adams, Billy
BCD 16272 / Jul '98 / Bear Family

☐ PORTRAIT OF BOOGIE WOOGIE PIANO, A (2CD Set)
Pinetop's boogie woogie: Smith, Pine Top / Chicago stomp: Blythe, Jimmy / Cow Cow blues: Davenport, Cow Cow / Chimes blues: Davenport, Cow Cow / Five o'clock blues: Yancey, Jimmy / Fives: Thomas, Hersal / Suitcase blues: Ammons, Albert / Honky tonk train blues: Lewis, Meade 'Lux' / Dearborn Street Breakdown: Avery, Charles / I don't know: Loften, Cripple Clarence / Detroit rocks: Taylor, Montana / Heifer dust: Ezell, Will / Chain 'em down: Garnett, Blind Leroy / St. Louis stomp: Speckled Red / Thirty one blues: Callaway, Bob / Pratt City blues: Williams, Jabo / Texas stomp: Rice, Dot / Farish Street jive: Montgomery, Little Brother / Carolina shout: Johnson, James P. / Echoes of spring: Smith, Willie 'The Lion' / Handful of keys: Waller, Fats / Honeysuckle rose: Waller, Fats / Ain't misbehavin': Waller, Fats / Pinetop's boogie woogie: Brown, Cleo / Boogie woogie stomp: Ammons, Albert / St. Louis blues: Ammons, Albert / Mr. Freddie Blues: Lewis, Meade 'Lux' / Six wheel chaser: Lewis, Meade 'Lux' / Basement boogie: Johnson, Pete / Death ray boogie: Johnson, Pete / Boogie woogie prayer: Boogie Woogie Trio / Yancey stomp: Yancey, Jimmy / Slow and easy blues: Yancey, Jimmy / Sixth Avenue express: Ammons, Albert & Pete Johnson / Barrelhouse boogie: Ammons, Albert & Pete Johnson / Boogie rocks: Ammons, Albert / Dive bomber: Johnson, Pete / Hold 'em Hootie: McShann, Jay / Central Avenue breakdown: Hampton, Lionel / Cecil boogie: Gant, Cecil / On the sunny side of the street: Hines, Earl 'Fatha' / Cheek to cheek: Turner, 'Big' Joe / St. Louis blues: Chittison, Herman / Tiger rag: Tatum, Art / Smashing thirds: Waller, Fats / Alligator crawl: Waller, Fats / Viper's drag: Waller, Fats
GALE 423 / 6 Oct '97 / Gallerie

☐ PORTRAIT OF FRENCH CAFE SONGS, A (2CD Set)
Boum: Trenet, Charles / Mon legionnaire: Piaf, Edith / Quand on s'promene au bord de l'eau: Gabin, Jean / Felice aussie: Fernandel / Paris sera toujours Paris: Chevalier, Maurice / Qu'est-ce qu'on attend pour etre heureux: Ventura, Ray / Y'a d' la joie: Trenet, Charles / Tchi tchi: Rossi, Tino / Les roses blanches: Sylva, Berthe / Escale: Solidor, Suzi / Comme de bien entendu: Prejean, Albert / Cane cane canebiere: Alibert / Je cherche un millionnaire: Mistinguett / Ma pomme: Chevalier, Maurice / Johnny Palmer: Lajon, Annette / Je suis swing: Hess, Johnny / Le vagabond: Piaf, Edith / Le chant du guardian: Rossi, Tino / La mome caoutchhouc: Gabin, Jean / Mon amant de la St.Jean: Delyle, Lucienne / Le fils de la femme poisson: Frehel / Confessin: Baker, Josephine / Le fanion de la legion: Piaf, Edith / Mam'selle Clio: Trenet, Charles / Ah si vous connaissiez ma poule: Chevalier, Maurice / Le plus beau tango du monde: Alibert, Henri / L'accordeoniste: Piaf, Edith / Le temps qu'une hirondelle: Mireille / C'est a Capri: Rossi, Tino / Tout va tres bien madame la marquise: Ventura, Ray / Leo lea elie: Gabin, Jean / Le soleil et la lune: Trenet, Charles / Le petite tonkinoise: Baker, Josephine / Prosper ou youp la boum: Chevalier, Maurice / La java bleue: Frehel / Ignace: Fernandel / Ca c'est de la bagnole: Georgius / Elle frequentait la rue pigalle: Piaf, Edith / Quand un vicomte: Chevalier, Maurice / Je chante: Trenet, Charles / Barnabe: Fernandel / Ou sont-ils trous mes copains: Piaf, Edith / Le marche' de menilmontant: Chevalier, Maurice / Avec ma p'tite gueule: Gabin, Jean
GALE 418 / 6 Oct '97 / Gallerie

☐ PORTRAIT OF GOSPEL, A (2CD Set)
Oh my Lord: Jackson, Mahalia / God shall wipe all tears away: Jackson, Mahalia / I want Jesus to walk around my bedside: Selah Jubilee Singers / When the saints go marching in: Davis, Blind Willie / When I stand before the King: Taggart, Blind Joe / Tell me what kind of man Jesus is: Chicago Sanctified Singers / Gabriel: Beck, Elder Charles / Twelve gates to the city: Davis, Rev. Gary / Moan you moaners: Smith, Bessie / Do Lord send me: Peach, Georgia / Shake Mother's hand for me: Golden Eagle Gospel Singers / I'm free at last: Southern Sons / Wade in the water: Charioteers / If you see my saviour: Dorsey, Thomas A. / Wonder where the gambling man: Norfolk Jubilee Quartet / I want God's bosom to be mine: Birmingham Jubilee Singers / Praise him shining angels: Second Zion Four / Them bones: Mitchell's Christian Singers / Handwriting on the wall: Heavenly Gospel Singers / When the gates swing open: Heavenly Gospel Singers / Walk in the light: Heavenly Gospel Singers / He knows just how much we can bear: Selah Jubilee Singers / I saw the light: Selah Jubilee Singers / I looked down the line: Dixie Hummingbirds / My Lord is writing all the time: Heavenly Gospel Singers / King Jesus knows I'm coming: White, Josh & The Carolinians / Ezekiel saw the wheel: Charioteers / One day when the Lord will call me: Southern Sons / To the rock: Golden Gate Quartet / Massa's in the cold cold ground: Golden Gate Quartet / John the revelator: Golden Gate Quartet / Travellin' shoes: Golden Gate Quartet / Rock my soul: Golden Gate Quartet / Jonah in the whale: Golden Gate Quartet / Didn't it rain: Golden Gate Quartet / Just a closer walk with thee: Tharpe, Sister Rosetta / Lonesome road: Tharpe, Sister Rosetta / Rock me: Tharpe, Sister Rosetta / Rock Daniel: Tharpe, Sister Rosetta / God don't like it: Tharpe, Sister Rosetta / Precious Lord hold my hand: Tharpe, Sister Rosetta / Shadrack: Armstrong, Louis / Nobody knows the trouble I've seen: Armstrong, Louis / Lord you made the night too long: Armstrong, Louis / I hope Gabriel likes my music: Armstrong, Louis / Going to shout all over God's heaven: Armstrong, Louis / Cain and Abel: Armstrong, Louis
GALE 425 / 6 Oct '97 / Gallerie

☐ PORTRAIT OF MY LOVE
Ramblin' rose: Cole, Nat 'King' / Portait of my love: Monro, Matt / As long as he needs me: Bassey, Shirley / Secret love: Kirby, Kathy / Mack the knife: Fitzgerald, Ella / Stranger on the shore: Bilk, Acker / You'll answer to me: Laine, Cleo / It might as well rain September: King, Carole / Charmaine: Bachelors / Wonderful land: Shadows / Hey Paula: Paul & Paula / Why: Newley, Anthony / What a mouth: Steele, Tommy / Fings ain't what they used to be: Bygraves, Max / 76 trombones: King Brothers / Wheels cha cha: Loss, Joe / James Bond theme: Barry, John / You're driving me crazy: Temperance Seven / Paper roses: Kaye Sisters / Theme from Dr.Kildare: Chamberlain, Richard
5529032 / Oct '97 / Spectrum

☐ PORTRAIT OF NEW ORLEANS JAZZ, A (2CD Set)
Tiger rag: Original Dixieland Jazz Band / Canal street blues: Oliver, Joe 'King' Creole Jazz Band / New Orleans joys: Jelly Roll Morton / Milenberg joys: New Orleans Rhythm Kings / Play that thing: Powers, Ollie Harmony Syncopators / New Orleans wiggle: Piron, A.J. New Orleans Orchestra / Swing: De Droit, Johnny & His New Orleans Orchestra / I wonder where my easy rider's riding now: Raversdorffer, Johnny & His Jazzola Novelty Orchestra / Cake walking babies from home: Williams, Clarence Blue Five / Barataria: Halfway House Orchestra / Black rag: Original Tuxedo Jazz Orchestra / 29th and Dearborn: Russell's hot six / She keeps it up all the time: Jackson, William / Wa wa wa: Oliver, Joe 'King' Dixie Syncopators / Here comes the hot tamale man: Cookie's Gingersnaps / Gate mouth: New Orleans wanderers / Black bottom stomp: Jelly Roll Morton's Red Hot Peppers / To-wa-bac-a-wa: Dumaine, Louis Jazzola Eight / Pearls: Jelly Roll Morton / Black bottom stomp: Jelly Roll Morton / St. Louis blues: Armstrong, Louis / Heebie jeebies: Armstrong, Louis / Cornet chop suey: Armstrong, Louis / As you like it: Celestin's Original Tuxedo Jazz Orchestra / That's a plenty: New Orleans Owls / Ory's creole trombone: Armstrong, Louis & His Hot Five / Bogalousa strut: Morgan, Sam Jazz Band / Savoy blues: Armstrong, Louis & His Hot Five / Panama: Miller, Johnny New Orleans Frollickers / BBull fiddle blues: Dodds, Johnny Washboard Band / She's crying for me: Wynn's Creole Jazz Band / Old man rhythm: Parenti, Tony / Astoria strut: Jones & Collins Astoria Hot Eight / Smilin' the blues away: Jelly Roll Morton / Panama: Russell, Luis & His Orchestra / Way down yonder in New Orleans: Noone, Jimmie New Orleans Band / Wolverine blues: Crosby, Bob & His Orchestra / Weary blues: Ladnier, Tommy / Winin' boy blues: Jelly Roll Morton / King Porter stomp: Singleton, Zutty & His Orchestra / Canal street blues: Jones, Richard M. & His Jazzmen / Canal street blues: Oliver, Joe 'King' / High society rag: Oliver, Joe 'King' / Chattanooga stomp: Oliver, Joe 'King' / Potato head blues: Armstrong, Louis / West end blues: Armstrong, Louis / St. James Infirmary: Armstrong, Louis
GALE 422 / 6 Oct '97 / Gallerie

☐ PORTRAIT OF SWING, A
GALE 426 / 20 Apr '98 / Gallerie

☐ PORTRAIT OF TANGO, A (2CD Set)
Le plus beau de tous les tangos du monde: Alibert / J'ai pleure sur tes pas: Claveau, Andre / J'aime tes grands yeux: Gauty, Lys / Violetta: Dassary, Andre / Vous, qu'avez-vous fait de mon amour: Lumiere, Jean / Serenade sans espoir: De Lyle, Lucienne / Etoile de Rio: Plana, Jaime / Tes mensonges: Bory, Louis / Un jour sans toi: Celis, Elyane & Lecuona Cuban Boys / Le tango des fauvettes: Marino, Robert / Bandoneon: Caire, Reda / Si tu reviens: Aubert, Jeanne / Porquoi loin de toi: Ketty, Rina / Sans toi: Boyer, Lucienne / C'est la fumee: Sirjo, Jean / Tout s'efface: Ketty, Rina / Le secret de tes caresses: Lumiere, Jean / Loin de toi: Marie-Jose / Un violon dans la nuit: Rossi, Tino / Parle-moi d'autre chose: Boyer, Lucienne / Le tango de Ramona: Plana, Jaime / Baisse un peu L'abatjour: Celis, Elyane & Lecuona Cuban Boys / Le tango chinois: Lumiere, Jean / Partir: Chacun, Jean / Caminito: Gardel, Carlos / Mi Buenos Ayres querido: Gardel, Carlos / Misa de once: Gardel, Carlos / La violeta: Gardel, Carlos / A media Luz: Pizzaro, Manuel / Un viejo amor: Pizzaro, Manuel / Poema: Bianco, Eduardo / Ilusion: Bianco, Eduardo / Clavel del aire: Corsini, Ignacio / Yira yira: Corsini, Ignacio / La cumparsita: Orchestra Tipica Victor / El Choclo: Orchestra Tipica Victor / Mama, yo quiero un novio: Vila, Alberto / Garufa: Vila, Alberto / Las Vueltas de la vida: Charlo / Tango del querer: Gomez, Alberto / Soy un arlequin: Gomez, Alberto / Decime: Genaro, Tano / Por ultima vez: Genaro, Tano / Adios muchachos: Magaldi, Augustin / Vagabundo: Magaldi, Augustin / Dondo estas corazon: Orchesta Bachicha
GALE 424 / 6 Oct '97 / Gallerie

☐ PORTUGAL ROCKERS
RNRCD 001 / Feb '96 / Metralha

☐ PORTUGUESE LANDS
PS 66003 / May '94 / PlayaSound

☐ PORTUGUESE STRING MUSIC
HTCD 05 / Feb '91 / Heritage

☐ POSITION CHROME
EFA 813682 / 10 Nov '97 / Chrome

☐ POSITIVE ENERGY
MM 800282 / Jun '95 / Moonshine

☐ POSITIVE VIBRATIONS
Meaning of life: Heptones / Change: Wilson, Delroy / Don't show off: Maytones / Engine 54: Ethiopians / Ten ton woman: Jah Stone / In a de runnings: Jarrett, Winston & The Righteous Flames / Sweet and sour you: McKay, Freddie / Madness: Maytones / My number one: Isaacs, Gregory / Jamaica collie: Lone Ranger / Promise is a comfort: Prince Mohammed / Give thanks and praises: George, Earl / Love your brother man: Levy, Barrington / Who feels it: Maytones / (You're my) soul and inspiration: Jones, Barbara & Trinity / (I'm in a) dancing mood: Wilson, Delroy / Righteous stand: Prince Mohammed / Set me go free: Ethiopians / Africa: Lone Ranger
CDGR 206 / 2 Feb '98 / Charly

☐ POSSE VOL.1 & 2, THE
UPTCD 21 / Nov '96 / Uptempo

☐ **POSSESSION & POETRY (Vezo, Mahafaly & Masikoro From Madagascar)**
C 580046 / Nov '93 / Ocora

☐ **POSSESSION SONGS (North Vietnam)**
926572 / Feb '97 / BUDA

☐ **POST PUNK PRIMER, A**
Gentlemen take polaroids: Japan / Requiem: Killing Joke / Song from under the floorboards: Magazine / Peek a boo: Devo / Monochrome set: Monochrome Set / Cold imagination: Devoto, Howard / Albatross: Public Image Ltd. / Are you receiving me: XTC / Betrayal: Jah Wobble / Commerciality: Partridge, Andy / Empire state human: Human League / Five miles of you: Verlaine, Tom / Never take me alive: Spear Of Destiny / Pick up: Quine, Robert
CDOVD 498 / 29 Sep '97 / Virgin

☐ **POT OF GOLD VOL.1**
VPRSCD 3101 / Mar '97 / VP

☐ **POUR CEUX QUI S'AIMENT**
DCD 5294MM / Apr '94 / Disky

☐ **POW WOW SONGS (Songs Of The Plains Indians)**
Slow war dance songs / Contest songs for straight dancers / Contest songs for fancy dancers / Round dance / Sioux flag song / War dance song / Slow war dance, Vietnam song / Grass dance song
803432 / Aug '92 / New World

☐ **POWER & SOUL**
Perfect year: Carroll, Dina / Come in out of the rain: Moten, Wendy / Get here: Adams, Oleta / No more tears (enough is enough): Mazelle, Kym & Jocelyn Brown / I will survive: Gaynor, Gloria / Ain't no mountain high enough: Ross, Diana / River deep, mountain high: Turner, Tina / Respect: Franklin, Aretha / Piece of my heart: Franklin, Erma / Help me make it through the night: Knight, Gladys / And I'm telling you I'm not going: Holliday, Jennifer / All woman: Stansfield, Lisa / Save the best for last: Williams, Vanessa / Sweet love: Baker, Anita / It should have been me: Fair, Yvonne / Stay with me baby: Turner, Ruby / Piano in the dark: Russell, Brenda / I will: Winters, Ruby / Superwoman: White, Karyn / Power of love: Rush, Jennifer
5168962 / Aug '94 / PolyGram TV

☐ **POWER AND SOUL (2CD Set)**
5654422 / 31 Aug '98 / PolyGram TV

☐ **POWER DANCE '98**
085703402 / 23 Mar '98 / Dance Street

☐ **POWER OF A WOMAN (2CD Set)**
I know where it's at: All Saints / 2 become 1: Spice Girls / Don't let go love: En Vogue / Just a step from heaven: En Vogue / You're the one I love: Ama, Shola / Ain't that just the way: McNeal, Lutricia / Missing: Everything But The Girl / Lovefool: Cardigans / One of us: Osbourne, Joan / Whats up: 4 Non Blondes / Hedonism: Skunk Anansie / Cornflake: Amos, Tori / I am I feel: Alisha's Attic / Stay: Loeb, Lisa / Give me a little more time: Gabrielle / Evrything: Blige, Mary J. / Man child: Cherry, Neneh / Arms around the world: Louise / Telefunkin': N-Tyce / Rhythm of life: Adams, Oleta / Constant craving: Lang, k.d. / I love you always forever: Lewis, Donna / Independent love song: Scarlet / Where have all the cowboys gone: Cole, Paula / I'll stand by you: Pretenders / Marlene on the wall: Vega, Suzanne / What I am: Brickell, Edie / Stupid girl: Garbage / Patience of angels: Reader, Eddi / Let's stay together: Turner, Tina / Respect: Franklin, Aretha / I'm only human: Franklin, Aretha / Ain't no mountain high enough: Ross, Diana / I'm every woman: Khan, Chaka / On and on: Badu, Erykah / Confide in me: Minogue, Kylie / Delicious: Hines, Deni / You were meant for me: Jewel / Sleeping satellite: Archer, Tasmin / All woman: Stansfield, Lisa
TTVCD 2950 / 23 Feb '98 / Telstar TV

☐ **POWER OF HARD TRANCE VOL.1**
IG 0072 / 2 Feb '98 / Progressive Nation

☐ **POWER OF HARD TRANCE VOL.2**
IG 0092 / 15 Jun '98 / Progressive Nation

☐ **POWER OF METAL VOL.2 (Second Attack)**
Atlantis failing: Iron Savior / Darcer: Elegy Shadow / Valley of the kings: Gamma Ray / Angel: Conception / Kiss of Judas: Stratovarius / Rise again: Kamelot / Obsessions: Virgin Steele / Against the fears: Sanvoisen / Loder Jolly Roger: Running Wild / Future world: Helloween / Dial 911: Superior / Greedmachine: Stigmata / Don't fear the winter: Rage / Minute man: Mercury Rising
N 02892 / 12 Jan '98 / Noise

☐ **POWER OF POP, THE**
Kids in America: Wilde, Kim / Centerfold: Geils, J. Band / Love is a Battlefield: Benatar, Pat / Do you really want to hurt me: Culture Club / (I just) Died in your arms tonight: Cutting Crew / True: Spandau Ballet / Temptation: Heaven 17 / Kayleigh: Marillion / If only I could: Youngblood, Sydney / Bette Davis eyes: Carnes, Kim / Sylvia: Focus / Heroes: Meat Loaf / When you're in love with a beautiful woman: Dr. Hook / Movie star: Harpo / Don't worry be happy: McFerrin, Bobby / It started with a kiss: Hot Chocolate / Roll over Beethoven: ELO / Never ending story: Limahl
KS 875082 / Jul '97 / Disky

☐ **POWER OF THE TRINITY**
SH 45030 / Feb '97 / Shanachie

☐ **POWER PLAYS (19 Classic Tracks)**
In my chair: Status Quo / Go now: Moody Blues / No more the fool: Brooks, Elkie / Out of time: Farlowe, Chris / First cut is the deepest: Arnold, P.P. / Tin soldier: Small Faces / America: Nice / Natural born bugie: Humble Pie / Man of the world: Fleetwood Mac / Are you growing tired of my love: Status Quo / You really got me: Kinks / Strange band: Family / Love hurts: Nazareth / Iron man: Black Sabbath / Lay down (Candles in the rain): Melanie & The Edwin Hawkin Singers / In my own time: Family / It's a heartache: Tyler, Bonnie / Operator (That's not the way it feels): Croce, Jim / This flight tonight: Nazareth
TRTCD 114 / 2 Feb '98 / TrueTrax

☐ **POWER TRACKS VOL.2**
ZYX 300092 / Nov '96 / ZYX

☐ **POWER TRAIN**
VPCD 2072 / 18 May '98 / VP

☐ **POWERDANCE 1997 (2CD Set)**
DST 305252 / Nov '96 / Dance Street

☐ **POWERHOUSE**
PHCD 01 / Mar '93 / Midtown

☐ **POWERHOUSE LIVE VOL.1 (Mixed By Nigel Benn/DJ Ride)**
POWCD 1001 / 27 Oct '97 / Powerhouse

☐ **POWERPLAY VOL.1**
FORMCD 02 / Jul '94 / Formation

☐ **PRAISE**
301202 / May '97 / Carlton

☐ **PRAISE AND GLORY**
Praise my soul: Choir Of Guildford Cathedral / Thine by the glory: Secombe, Harry / Onward Christian soldiers: Pontarddulais Male Voice Choir / Rejoice the Lord is King: Choir Of Guildford Cathedral / Amazing Grace: Anderson, Moira / Let all the world in every corner sing: Pontarddulais Male Voice Choir / Love divine: Choir Of Guildford Cathedral / There's a friend for little children: Choir Of Guildford Cathedral / Abide with me: Secombe, Harry / Guide me o thou Great Jehovah: Secombe, Harry / Old rugged cross: Anderson, Moira / How great thou art: Pontarddulais Male Voice Choir / All things bright and beautiful: Children Of Scisset Middle School / When I survey the wonderous cross: Anderson, Moira / Lord's my sheperd: Pontarddulais Male Voice Choir / God be with you till we meet again: Secombe, Harry
SUMCD 4123 / Jun '97 / Summit

☐ **PRAISE BE (15 Harmonious Masterpieces)**
Pomp and circumstance No.1 / Irish tune from County Derry / Praise my soul the King of Heaven / Hear my prayer / Come down o love divine / Eternal father strong to save / O praise ye the Lord / Dear Lord and father of mankind / How lovely are thy dwellings fair / Ave verum corpus / Psalm 23 - the Lord is my shepherd / All creatures of our God and King / Thou wilt keep him in perfect peace / Lord is my shepherd / I was glad
GRF 334 / Apr '93 / Tring

☐ **PRE-WAR GOSPEL STORY 1902-1944, THE (2CD Set)**
BOG 21 / Nov '95 / Best Of Gospel

☐ **PRE-WAR VOCAL JAZZ STORY, THE (2CD Set)**
BOJCD 22 / Oct '96 / Best Of Jazz

☐ **PREACHERS AND CONGREGATIONS VOL.1 1927-1938**
DOCD 5529 / Apr '97 / Document

☐ **PREACHERS AND CONGREGATIONS VOL.2 1926-1941**
DOCD 5530 / Apr '97 / Document

☐ **PREACHERS AND CONGREGATIONS VOL.3 1925-1929**
DOCD 5547 / Jul '97 / Document

☐ **PREACHERS AND CONGREGATIONS VOL.4 1924-1931**
DOCD 5548 / Jul '97 / Document

☐ **PREACHERS AND CONGREGATIONS VOL.5 1926-1931**
DOCD 5559 / 21 Sep '97 / Document

☐ **PREACHERS AND CONGREGATIONS VOL.6 1924-1936**
DOCD 5560 / 21 Sep '97 / Document

☐ **PREACHERS AND CONGREGATIONS VOL.7 1925-1928**
DOCD 5567 / 21 Sep '97 / Document

☐ **PREACHING TO THE PERVERTED**
PERVCDLP 001 / Jun '97 / Naked

☐ **PRECIOUS LORD (The Best Of Gospel Music)**
Move on up a little higher: Jackson, Mahalia / Take my hand precious Lord: Franklin, Aretha / Anyhow: Golden Gate Jubilee Quartet / There is a fountain filled with blood: Franklin, Aretha / When I stand before the King: Taggart, Blind Joe / Oh my Lord what a morning: Jackson, Mahalia / You grow closer: Franklin, Aretha / Stand on the right side of the road: Blue Chips / Where we'll never grow old: Franklin, Aretha / I want Jesus to to walk around my bedside: Salem Jubilee Singers / Day is past and gone: Franklin, Aretha / Jezebel: Golden Gate Jubilee Quartet / He'll wash you whiter than snow: Franklin, Aretha / Shout, Sister shout: Tharpe, Sister Rosetta / While the blood runs warm: Franklin, Aretha / Twelve gates to the city: Davis, Rev. Gary / Moan you moaners: Smith, Bessie / Yield not to temptation: Franklin, Aretha / Sun didn't shine: Golden Gate Jubilee Quartet / Rock me: Tharpe, Sister Rosetta / Wade in the water: Charioteers / Take my hand precious Lord: Franklin, Aretha
CD 6091 / Aug '97 / Music

☐ **PRECIOUS METAL**
TMPCD 014 / Mar '95 / Temple

☐ **PRECIOUS WATERS, RIVER OF LIFE**
Precious waters / Stormlight / Dawn / Mountain shadows / Tears of the Gods / Celebration / First snow / Where the rivers are born / Lonely birds / Shadows of eternity / Snow dreams of becoming water / Warm wind / Return of the sun / Falling water / First sun on the winter ice / Melting waters / In the mountain lake / Raging waters / Desert call / Through the parched land / Flowing toward heaven / Desert flower / River dreams / Cycle continues
ND 63917 / May '95 / Narada

☐ **PRECOLOMBIAN (Forgotten Spirit)**
14908 / Feb '97 / Spalax

☐ **PRECOLOMBIAN MUSIC (Prehispanic)**
14907 / Feb '97 / Spalax

☐ **PRECOLOMBIAN MUSIC (Ritual)**
14909 / Feb '97 / Spalax

☐ **PRELUDE - THE SOUND OF NEW YORK (2CD Set)**
I am music: Mastermind / Pranian man: Prana People / Mosquito walk: Sine / Hustle bus stop: Mastermind / Walking on music: Jacques, Peter Band / Never: Centre Stage / Stretchin' out: Adams, Gayle / You got my love: Redd, Sharon / I know you feel like I feel: Thurston, Bobby / Happy ever after: Unlimited Touch / I'm totally yours: High Gloss / Take a risk: Empress / Searching to find the one: Unlimited Touch / Let's work it out: Next Movement / Let's go all the way: Adams, Gayle / Tryin' to get over: D-Train / Your good lovin': Joli, France / Groove it to your body: Wilson, Mike / Body movement: Conquest / Funn: Gunchback Boogie Band / Lay it down on me: Mallory, Gerald / Video freak: Frazier, Cliff & Co. / Do you love me: Secret Weapon / Good lovin': Unlimited Touch / Key: Wuf Ticket
DEEPD 017 / Apr '97 / Deep Beats

☐ **PREMIER COLLECTION OF INSTRUMENTAL HITS VOL.1**
KNEWCD 733 / Apr '94 / Kenwest

☐ **PREMIER COLLECTION OF INSTUMENTAL HITS VOL.2**
KNEWCD 734 / Apr '94 / Kenwest

☐ **PREMIER COLLECTION OF INSTUMENTAL HITS VOL.3**
KNEWCD 735 / Apr '94 / Kenwest

☐ **PRENDS DONC COURAGE: SWAMP MUSIC VOL.6**
US 0202 / Apr '95 / Trikont

☐ **PRESS START**
DFDCD 13 / 27 Oct '97 / Defender

☐ **PRESTIGE FUNKY BEATS**
PCD 24148 / Jun '95 / Pablo

☐ **PRESTIGE JAZZ SAMPLER**
CDRIVM 002 / Mar '88 / Riverside

☐ **PRESTIGE SOUL - JAZZ ENCYCLOPAEDIA VOL.1**
PCD 24137 / Jun '95 / Pablo

☐ **PRESTIGE/FOLKLORE YEARS VOL.1 (All Kinds Of Folks)**
New York town: Elliott, Jack / Railroad Bill: Elliott, Jack / Rollin' in my sweet baby's arms: Elliott, Jack / Duncan and Brady: Rush, Tom / Rag Mama: Rush, Tom / Barb'ry Allen: Rush, Tom / Wagoner's lad: Seeger, Peggy / Chickens they are crowing: Seeger, Peggy / Green rocky road: Van Ronk, Dave / Whoa Buck: Van Ronk, Dave / Maggie Lauder: Redpath, Jean / Fife overgate: Redpath, Jean / Joshua gone Barbados: Von Schmidt, Eric / She's like a swallow: Dobson, Bonnie / Irish exile song: Dobson, Bonnie / Long chain: Sellers, Maxine / Single girl: Sellers, Maxine / Jesus met the woman at the well: Len & Judy / This life I'm living: Len & Judy
CDWIKD 134 / Feb '95 / Big Beat

☐ **PRESTIGE/FOLKLORE YEARS VOL.2 (The New City Blues)**
Cocaine blues: Van Ronk, Dave / Death letter: Van Ronk, Dave / Red river blues: Fuller, Jesse / How long blues: Fuller, Jesse / San Francisco Bay blues: Fuller, Jesse / Sleepy man blues: Muldaur, Geoff / Aberdeen Mississippi blues: Muldaur, Geoff / Motherless child blues: Nelson, Tracy / Starting for Chicago: Nelson, Tracy / Ramblin' man: Nelson, Tracy / Crow Jane: Von Schmidt, Eric / Light rain: Von Schmidt, Eric / Kennedy blues: Von Schmidt, Eric / Orphan's blues: Rush, Tom / If you don't want me baby: Larry & Hank / Watchdog blues: Larry & Hank / Four women blues: Larry & Hank / Alberta: New Strangers
CDWIKD 135 / Feb '95 / Big Beat

☐ **PRESTIGE/FOLKLORE YEARS VOL.3 (Roots And Branches)**
Let us get together right down here: Davis, Rev. Gary / Twelve gates to the city: Davis, Rev. Gary / Maple leaf rag: Davis, Rev. Gary / Bound to lose: Holy Modal Rounders / Euphoria: Holy Modal Rounders / Crowley waltz: Holy Modal Rounders / Blues in the bottle: Holy Modal Rounders / St. Louis tickle: Van Ronk, Dave / Goodbye Maggie: Lilly Brothers / I'm coming back, but I don't know when: West, Harry & Jeanie / I'd like to be your shadow in the moonlight: West, Harry & Jeanie / Beautiful brown eyes: Charles River Valley Boys & Tex Logan / Sally Goodin: Charles River Valley Boys & Tex Logan / Uncle Penn: Charles River Valley Boys & Tex Logan / Salty dog: Keith & Rooney / Teardrops in my eyes: Keith & Rooney / Maggie rag: Greenhill, Mitch / Blues, just blues, that's all: True Endeavor Jug Band / Jug band blues: True Endeavor Jug Band / She's gone: Traum, Artie / High society: Folk Stringers / I don't feel at home in this world anymore: New Strangers
CDWIKD 136 / Feb '95 / Big Beat

☐ **PRESTIGE/FOLKLORE YEARS VOL.4 (Singing Out Loud)**
Mule skinner blues: Elliott, Jack / Night herding song: Elliott, Jack / Talking fishing blues: Elliott, Jack / Fisherman's luck: Seeger, Mike & Sonny Miller / Sally Ann: Seeger, Mike & Sonny Miller / John Hardy: Seeger, Mike & Sonny Miller / Fiddler's bagpipe: Seeger, Mike & Sonny Miller / Peter Emberly: Dobson, Bonnie / First time: Dobson, Bonnie / If I had my way: Davis, Rev. Gary / Sally, where you get your liquor from: Davis, Rev. Gary / You got to move: Davis, Rev. Gary / Devil's dream: Keith & Rooney / Ain't gonna work tomorrow: Keith & Rooney / Gypsy Davey: Aaron, Tossi / I don't want your millions Mister: Seeger, Pete / Here's to Cheshire, here's to cheese: Seeger, Pete
CDWIKD 137 / Feb '95 / Big Beat

☐ **PRICELESS JAZZ**
Bye bye blackbird: McRae, Carmen / In crowd: Lewis, Ramsey / Blackberry winter: Jarrett, Keith / Street life: Crusaders / Poinciana: Jamal, Ahmad / Desire: Scott, Tom / Spirits: Yellow Jackets / Where flamingos fly: Evans, Gil
GRP 99012 / 23 Mar '98 / GRP

☐ **PRIDE '95**
SR 321CD / Jul '95 / Strictly Rhythm

☐ **PRIDE OF INDEPENDENTS**
TT 6CD / Jun '93 / Beechwood

☐ **PRIDE OF IRELAND, THE (Heart Of Ireland/Seven Drunken Nights/Home/ 3CD Set)**
Whiskey in the jar / Four country roads / Green fields of France / Irish Rover / When you were sweet sixteen / Boys from Killybegs / You seldom come to see me anymore / Boston burgler / Isle of Innisfree / After all these years / Black velvet band / Our house is not a home / Old bog road / Town I love so well / I'll take you home again Kathleen / Any Tipperary town / Hills of Kerry / Mountains of Mourne / Maggie / Rose of Tralee / Bold O'Donaghue / Paddle me own canoe / Molly Malone / Medley / Ferryman / Cod liver oil/ Coolies / Home boys home / Father O'Flynn / Irish washerwoman / Blackberry blossom / Lannigan's ball / All for me grog / Wild rover / Medley / Muirsheen durkin / Paddy Fathy's reel/Dinny's fancy / Spanish lady maid behind the bar/Gravel walk / Holy ground / Finnegan's wake / Irish rover/Rakes of Mallow / Seven drunken nights / Ramblin' Irishman / Rising of the moon / Road to Sligo/Tripping up the stairs / Ashplant / Medley / O'Catolan's dream / White, orange and green / High road to Linton/Mrs Mcleods reel / Foxhunters / Fiddler's green / Rocky road to Dublin / Arthur McBride / Medley / Gravelwalk
55159 / Oct '96 / Music

☐ **PRIDE OF SCOTLAND, THE (Scottish Pipe Bands/3CD Set)**
LB 868392 / Aug '96 / Disky

☐ **PRIDE OF SCOTLAND, THE (3CD Set)**
Scotland the brave / Skye boat song / Amazing grace / Road to the Isles / Old rustic bridge by the mill / Towsay Castle / Money musk / Miss McLeod O'Raasey / Cock o' the North / Old rustic bridge by the mill / Route march / When the battle is over / 79th farewell to Gibraltar / Colonel Robertson / Dovecote Park / Prince Charles welcome to Lochaber / Mingulay boat song / Silver spear / Curlew / Captain Horne / MacFarlane's reel / Inverness gathering / Drunken piper / 79th's farewell to Gibraltar / Earl of Mansfield / Drum salute / Up in the morning / Muckin' o' Geordie's Byre / Cock o' the North / Royal Scots polka / Conundrum / Highland wedding / Smith of Chilliehassie / Boghall and Bathgate / Redundancy / Train journey North / Reveille / Miss Kirkwood / Song of the Clyde / Westering home / Keep right on to the end of the road / Northern lights of old Aberdeen / Bonnie Kirkwall Bay / Bonnie banks of Loch Lomond / Football crazy / Here's to Scottish whisky / Land for all seasons / Star o' Rabbie Burns / Man's a man for a' that / Romin' in the Gloamin' / Just a wee Deoch an' Doris / Ye banks and braes / Tobermory Bay / Marching through the heather / Auld lang syne / Lord and Lady Elgin of Broomhall: Shand, Jimmy / Maresland twostep: Shand, Jimmy / Lady Angela Alexander/Sir Kenneth Alexander: Shand, Jimmy / Threave Castle polka: Shand, Jimmy / Suptd. Ian Thomson's farewell to the Fife Police: Shand, Jimmy / Francis Wright's waltz: Shand, Jimmy / Memories of Willie Smith: Shand, Jimmy / Ian Powrie's welcome to Dunblane: Shand, Jimmy / Windy edge barn dance: Shand, Jimmy / Lunan Bay/Tom and Mary Lyon's waltz: Shand, Jimmy / It's grand among your ain folk: Shand, Jimmy / David Anderson Shand's 40th birthday: Shand, Jimmy / Geordie Watson the co-worker: Shand, Jimmy / Heather mixture twostep: Shand, Jimmy / Compliments to Harry Lawson/Compliments to Dr. A.K. Tulloch: Shand, Jimmy / Whitley Chapel barndance: Shand, Jimmy / John McDonald's march: Shand, Jimmy / Miss Jean Thompson's 100th birthday: Shand, Jimmy / Bruce Laing's welcome to Auchtermuchty: Shand, Jimmy / Guardians of the Gulf: Shand, Jimmy / Royal Guard Regiment of HM the Sultan of Oman: Shand, Jimmy / Willie Merrilees OBE: Shand, Jimmy / Margaret and Robert Innes of Pitterweem: Shand, Jimmy
55163 / Apr '97 / Music

☐ **PRIDE OF SCOTLAND, THE**
PLSCD 276 / 2 Mar '98 / Pulse

☐ **PRIDE VOL.1 (The Very Best Of Scotland - 2CD Set)**
Dignity: Deacon Blue / Baker Street: Rafferty, Gerry / Vienna: Ultravox / Real gone kid: Deacon Blue / Why: Lennox, Annie / Caledonia: Miller, Frankie / Sweet dreams (are made of this): Eurythmics / There must be an angel: Eurythmics / Inside: Stiltskin / Perfect: Fairground Attraction / Patience of angels: Reader, Eddi / Party fears two: Associates / If I was: Ure, Midge / Let's go round again: Average White Band / I can feel it: Silencers / Miracle of being: Capercaillie
74321284372 / Oct '95 / RCA

☐ **PRIDE VOL.2 (2CD Set)**
Julia says: Wet Wet Wet / No more I love yous: Lennox, Annie / I'll never fall in love again: Deacon Blue / She's a river: Simple Minds / King of the road: Proclaimers / Find my love: Fairground Attraction / Love is a stranger: Eurythmics / You wear it well: Stewart, Rod / Miracle of being: Capercaillie / Loch Lomond: Runrig / Labour of love: Hue & Cry / Brand new friend: Cole, Lloyd & The Commotions / Club country: Associates / Fisherman's blues: Waterboys

/ Cath: Bluebells / Summer of love: Danny Wilson / Thorn in my side: Eurythmics / An ubhal as airde: Runrig / Girl like you: Collins, Edwyn / Saturday night: Blue Nile / Queer: Garbage / Move any mountain: Shamen / Movin' on up: Primal Scream / Sparky's dream: Primal Scream / Iceblink luck: Cocteau Twins / You could be forgiven: Horse / Scottish rain: Silencers / Rattler: Goodbye Mr. Mackenzie / I would 500 miles: Proclaimers / Prospect Street: Big Dish / Real McCoy: Silencers / Big Country: Big Country / Chains: River Detectives / Fergus sings the blues: Deacon Blue / April skies: Jesus & Mary Chain / Oblivious: Aztec Camera

74321371542 / May '96 / RCA

☐ PRIMAL BLUE

Bass blues / Uno dos adios / Primal blue / Dear Ruth / Stolen moments / You go to my head

HIBD 8006 / Oct '95 / Hip Bop

☐ PRIME CHOPS VOL.2 (Blind Pig Sampler)

BP 8002CD / May '94 / Blind Pig

☐ PRIME CHOPS VOL.3

BPCD 8003 / Dec '95 / Blind Pig

☐ PRIME CUTS (From Funky Breaks To Funky House)

Talkin' about the power: Blade & Liam Nabb / Simone Fabbroni / We got the funky: Blade & Liam Nabb / Simone Fabbroni / Afro t: Black & Brown / Funky guitar: TC 92 / Wild bass: Nabb, Liam & Simone Fabbroni / Feel free: Last Minister / First job: Kekkotronics & LTJ / Two hearts together: Soul Etico / Trouble jazz: Blender / Funk my ass: Ohm Guru / I'm gonna love you: Jesto Funk / Nightlife: Typhorns / Basta: Ruggeri, Gemelli

IAM 804CD / 15 Sep '97 / Irma

☐ PRIME CUTS VOL.4

PRMTCD 004 / Nov '96 / Primate

☐ PRIME NUMBERS VOL.2

PRIME 051CD / May '96 / Prime

☐ PRISON BLUES OF THE SOUTH

17026 / Sep '94 / Laserlight

☐ PRISON SONGS VOL.1 (Murderer's Home)

ROUCD 1714 / Aug '97 / Rounder

☐ PRISON SONGS VOL.2 (Hear Poor Mother Call)

ROUCD 1715 / Aug '97 / Rounder

☐ PRISON WORKSONGS

Berta: Big Louisiana & Rev. Rogers/Roosevelt Charles / Take this hammer: Guitar Welch & Hogman Maxey/Andy Mosely / Stewball: Rev. Rogers & Big Louisiana/Jose Smith / Five long years for one man: Mathews, Odea / Alberta let your bangs grow long: Guitar Welch & Hogman Maxey/Andy Mosely / I had five long years: Russell, James / Early in the mornin': Butler, John / All teamed up in Angola's mule lot: Roosevelt Charles & Arthur Davis/Big Louisiana / I got a hurtin' in my right side: Rafus, Willy & Work Gang / Let your hammer ring: Big Louisiana & Willy Rafus/Arthur Davis / Cleaning this highway: Rafus, Willy & Andy Mosely/Johnny Butler / John Henry: Guitar Welch & Hogman Maxey/Robert Pete Williams / Something within me: Mathews, Odea / Jesus cares: Macon, Murray / Working on the levee part 1: Dunn, Emanuel / Working on the levee part 2: Dunn, Emanuel / Take this hammer: Big Louisiana / Pickin' cotten all day long: Scott, Creola & Ceola / My mule Grey: Dunn, Emanuel

ARHCD 448 / Nov '97 / Arhoolie

☐ PRIVATE COLLECTION OF GERMAN UNDERGROUND...

ABB 85CD / Apr '95 / Big Cat

☐ PRIVATE LIFE OF AN INDEPENDENT

BUR 001 / Apr '97 / British Underground Productions

☐ PRIVILEGE IBIZA (2CD Set)

VENCDA 112 / 1 Jan '98 / Vendetta

☐ PRO-CANNABIS

EFA 119662 / Jun '94 / Dope

☐ PROCESS

CAI 20052 / 27 Oct '97 / Caipirinha

☐ PRODUCER'S TROPHY

HCD 7011 / Dec '94 / Hightone

☐ PRODUCT MUSIC (Original Music From US Commercials)

HA 294004 / 9 Mar '98 / Honest Abe

☐ PROGFEST '97 (2CD Set)

In the dead of the night: Wetton, John Band / Rendezvous 602: Wetton, John Band / Starless: Wetton, John Band / Madre mia/Prima aqua: Le Orme / Ii vecchio: Le Orme / Ii fiume: Le Orme / Felona and serona: Le Orme / Medusa: Arena / Retropolis: Flower Kings / Humanizzimo: Flower Kings / Thoughts: Spock's Beard / Go the way you go: Spock's Beard / Mindbender: Spock's Beard / Sell out: Spock's Beard / Neuropsychopathic eye: Spock's Beard / Atestupan: Sinkadus / Sirens: Sinkadus

OM 1010CD / 4 May '98 / Outer Music

☐ PROGRAM ANNIHILATOR VOL.2

SST 213CD / Feb '90 / SST

☐ PROGRESSION

PROG 292 / Feb '94 / Progression

☐ PROGRESSIVE AND ART ROCK PRIMER, A

Germ patrol: Egg / Soup song: Wyatt, Robert / How beautiful you are: Blegvad, Peter / Wingful of eyes: Gong / Spectral mornings: Hackett, Steve / My experience: Hammill, Peter / Theme one: Van Der Graaf Generator / Hang on to a dream: Nice / TNK: Manzanera, Phil / Out in the sun: Moraz, Patrick / Casablanca moon: Slapp Happy / In the dead of might: UK / Nothing to lose: Weston, John

CDOVD 497 / 29 Sep '97 / Virgin

☐ PROGRESSIVE CITY VOL.2

FRIE 004 / Jun '97 / Friends

☐ PROGRESSIVE CITY VOL.3

FRIE 0052 / 17 Nov '97 / Friends

☐ PROGRESSIVE HOUSE CLASSICS

Intoxication: React 2 Rhythm / Difference: Djum Djum / Sack the drummer: Soundclash Republic / LionRock: Lionrock / Speed controller: Acorn Arts / Get out on this dancefloor: DOP / Mighty Ming: Brother Love Dubs / Big mouth: Lemon Interupt / Londress strutt: Smells Like Heaven / Not forgotten: Leftfield / Future le funk: DOP / Who's the badman: Patern, Dee / Pure pleasure: Digital Excitation / Body Medusa: Supereal / Funkatarium: Jump

FIRMCD 1 / Feb '96 / Firm

☐ PROGRESSIVE POP INSIDE THE 70'S

Who can I trust: Walrus / Yes you do: Pacific Drift / I wrapped her in ribbons: Galliards / I've been moved: Hollywood Freeway / Never gonna let my body touch the ground: Walrus / Goodbye to Baby Jane: Campbell, Junior / Cloudy day: Vehicle / Maybe: Granny's Intentions / Dan the wing: Mellow Candle / Pretty Belinda: Clan / Mr. Horizon: Hemlock / Standing on the corner: Youlden, Chris / Rebels rule: Iron Virgin / Back street luv: Curved Air / Candy baby: Beano / Sweetest tasting candy sugar: Sheriden, Lee / Ultrastar: Rococo / Whizmore kid: Principal Edwards / Sweet illusion: Campbell, Junior / Candy eyes: Fresh Meat / One night affair: Areety, Colin / Jesus come back: Matthews's Revelation / Two sisters: Wolf / Bye and bye: Beano

SEECD 424 / May '95 / See For Miles

☐ PROGRESSIVE SAMPLER

PSCD 1 / Dec '97 / Progressive

☐ PROGRESSIVE TRANCE

MILL 066CD / 3 Aug '98 / Millenium

☐ PROLE LIFE

Grand monophonic: Yummy Fur / Fiery Jack: Yummy Fur / Typical of boys: Yummy Fur / All women are robots: Yummy Fur / Vanilla maneli: Yummy Fur / Cosmonauts and carbonauts: Yummy Fur / Eyeball popping madness: Yummy Fur / Skunk rap: Trout / Scary costumes: Trout / Human boing: Trout / Owl in the tree: Trout / Divorce at high noon: Blisters / Post-feminist business woman: Blisters / Patrick meets the courgettes: Blisters / Christian chorus: Blisters / Mommy is a punker: Pink Cross / Chopper chix: Pink Cross / Punk outfit: Pink Cross / No time for bimbo: Pink Cross / Toby Mangel: Lugworm / Sweaty says: Lugworm / Disco: Lugworm / Barmitzvah: Lugworm

CDKRED 121 / Jul '95 / Cherry Red

☐ PROLEKULTURE

Pilgrimage to paradise: Sourmash / Sleepless: Razors Edge / Acid voices: Traumatic / First rebirth: Jones & Stephenson / Trope: Amphetamine / Neurodancer: Wippenberg / High on the edge: Housetrap II / Global phases: Jon The Dentist / Mighty machine: Dream Plant / Digital mass: DJ Randy / Cut the midrange: Watchman

KULTCDX 1

KULTCD 1 / May '97 / Prolekult

☐ PROMISED LAND VOL.3 (4CD Set/ Mixed By Peshay & Slipmaster J)

Elemental: Special EFX / 2012: Helen T / Jazz adiction: Addiction & Helen T / 8 Bars: N-Jay / Smash n grab: Addiction & Helen T / Pure jazz: Special EFX / Jakes progress: Helen T / Within a dream: Helen T / Derelict love: Nookie & Larry Heard / Sweet power: Time Signature / Stay calm: Helen T / Polaris: Helen T / Electro solution: In Deep / Showshenk: Helen T / You and me: Nookie & Larry Heard / Minds: Mind 21 / Sax tune: Helen T / Where are: Futurebound / Earls dream: Helen T / Losin: Helen T / Water colours: In Deep / Ambient Nature: Collektive / Revibe: N-Jay / Jakes progress 97: Helen T / Jazzed out: Fokus / Losing: Helen T / Chocolate sushi: Drawback Hill / Jazz u like it: Addiction & Helen T / Rebound: Personelle / Midnite: Simon Bassline Smith / Music: LTJ Bukem / Vocal tune: Peshay / Aromatherapy: Adam F / Music Box: Roni Size / Millenium: Big Bud / Meditation: DJ Crystal / Let it roll: DJ Crystal / Heaven: Skanna / Sorrow: Futurebound

HLPCD 4 / 15 Sep '97 / Higher Limits

☐ PROPER COMP VOL.1

Grande bassito: Acid Farm / On and on: DJ K. Alexi Shelby / Greg Metzger: McBride, Woody / Electric: Stoll, Steve / Infrared: Wild, Damon / Fuken around: Hunt, Gene / Personal carrier: Henze, W.J. / MMMM: Freddie Fresh / Third wave: DJ Capricorn / Dig it: Carbon Boys

PROPS 008CD / Jun '95 / Proper

☐ PROPER COMP VOL.2

PROPS 016CD / Jul '96 / Proper

☐ PROUD

In the neighbourhood: Sisters Underground / Tuesday's blues: Pacifican Descendants / We're the OMC: Otara Millionaires Club / Based on a lost cause: Radio Backstab & DJ Payback / Pass it over: Pacifican Descendants / Dawn of the eve: Di-Na-Ve / One too many: Vocal Five / I don't need you: Semi MC's / Ain't it true: Sisters Underground / Save New Zealand: Vocal Five / Pacific beats: Puka Puka / Prove me wrong: MC Slam / Groove me: Rhythm Harmony / Trust me: Semi MC's

VOLTCD 77 / Oct '95 / Volition

☐ PROUD TO BE LOUD

Rainbow in the park: Dio / Knocking at your back door: Deep Purple / Rosalie: Thin Lizzy / Get the funk out: Extreme / You've gone wild: Almighty / Jet boy/ Jet girl: New York Dolls / Madhouse: Anthrax / Eyes shut tight: Downset / Bone china: Mother Love Bone / Crying over you: Gun / Rising force: Malmsteen, Yngwie / Temple of the king: Rainbow / Closer to the heart: Rush / Snorting whiskey: Travers, Pat / Just a shadow: Big Country / Wishing well: Free / Ramblin' man: Allman Brothers / Gypsy road: Cinderella

5533292 / Feb '97 / Debutante

☐ PRY CLUB DANCE

HMC 100032 / Feb '98 / Happy Music

☐ PSALMS FOR SOLOMON

BLKMCD 012 / Jun '95 / Blakamix

☐ PSALMS OF DRUMS

Psalms of drums: King Tubby / Healing stream: Dillinger / Liberation: Kalphat, Bobby / Sabotage: King Tubby / I hold the handle: Michael Scotland / Natty contractor: Trinity / Weatherman skank: I-Roy / Stumbling block: Dillinger / Page One: King Tubby / King at the controls: King Tubby / Wash wash: Patterson, Carlton / Watchman dub: King Tubby / Internal feelings: Trinity / Love is a treasure: Michael Scotland / Let me go girl: Patterson, Carlton

PSCD 12 / Jan '97 / Pressure Sounds

☐ PSEUDONYM SAMPLER VOL.2

CDP 1051DD / 19 Jan '98 / Pseudonym

☐ PSY KREMBO VOL.2

KRBCD 005 / 10 Nov '97 / Krembo

☐ PSYCHEDELIA

MUSCD 021 / Sep '94 / MCI Music

☐ PSYCHEDELIA (Rare Blooms From The English Summer Of Love)

Flight from Ashiya: Kaleidoscope / Peter's birthday: World Of Oz / Catherine's wheel: Laine, Denny / Brother can you spare a dime: St. Valentine's Day Massacre / Turquoise tandem cycle: Crest, Jason / Magic potion: Open Mind / Portcullis gate: Bulldog Breed / Weekdaze: Principal Edwards / Out of your own little world: Megaton / Niagara: Megaton / Meditations: Felius Andromeda / Gone is the sad man: Timebox / I can't sleep: Quik / Thursday morning: Giles, Giles & Fripp / Scream in the ears: Fay, Bill / My organ grinder: Vehicle / Sycamore Sid: Focal Point / Some good advice: Fay, Bill / Soul full of sorrow: Quik / Baby get your head: Double Feature / Halo in your hair: Bulldog Breed / Nite is a comin' / Smeta Murgaty: Warm Sounds

SEECD 463 / Oct '96 / See For Miles

☐ PSYCHEDELIA (2CD Set)

Eight miles high: Byrds / White rabbit: Jefferson Airplane / Daydream: Lovin' Spoonful / Itchycoo Park: Small Faces / Living in the past: Jethro Tull / Here comes the nice: Small Faces / California dreamin': Mamas & The Papas / Come up the years: Jefferson Airplane / Electricity: Captain Beefheart / Summer in the city: Lovin' Spoonful / See my friends: Kinks / Flowers in the rain: Move / Kites: Dupree, Simon & The Big Sound / Light my fire: Feliciano, Jose / Pictures of matchstick men: Status Quo / Light flight: Pentangle / Black magic woman: Santana / Sitting on a fence: Twice As Much / Feel a whole lot better: Byrds / Tin soldier: Small Faces / Hi ho silver lining: Beck, Jeff / Sunshine superman: Donovan / Night of fear: Move / Monday monday: Mamas & The Papas / Green tambourine: Lemon Pipers / Days of Pearly Spencer: McWilliams, David / Somebody to love: Jefferson Airplane / Lazy Sunday: Small Faces / Mad John: Small Faces / Goo goo barabajagal (Love is hot): Donovan & Jeff Beck Group / Candles in the rain: Melanie / Let's go to San Francisco: Flowerpot Men / I'm the urban spaceman: Bonzo Dog Band / Mirror man: Captain Beefheart & His Magic Band / Thoughts of Emerlist Davjack: Nice / Man of the world: Fleetwood Mac

RCACD 211 / Jul '97 / RCA

☐ PSYCHEDELIC BEER

EFA 215542 / 15 Dec '97 / High Society

☐ PSYCHEDELIC CLUB TRAX

CLP 9987 / Jun '97 / Cleopatra

☐ PSYCHEDELIC CROWN JEWELS VOL.1

GF 104 / Nov '97 / Gear Fab

☐ PSYCHEDELIC FREQUENCIES

White rabbit: Jefferson Airplane / King Midas in reverse: Hollies / War in peace: Spence, Skip / Keep your mind open: Kaleidoscope / Broken arrow: Buffalo Springfield / Evening of light: Nico / Loved one: George, Lowell / Frantic desolation: Sopwith Camel / Defecting grey: Pretty Things / Omaha: Moby Grape / Happenings ten years time ago: Yardbirds / Electricity: Captain Beefheart / Psychotic reaction: Count Five / I just don't know: Banshee / Can you please crawl out your window: Vacels / Golden Earrings: Gandalf / Land of their dreams: Auto Salvage / Standing on the moon (space hymn): Lothar & The Hand People

TMPCD 027 / May '96 / Temple

☐ PSYCHEDELIC GOA TEST

CLP 0002 / Jun '97 / Cleopatra

☐ PSYCHEDELIC PERCEPTIONS

TMPCD 025 / May '96 / Temple

☐ PSYCHEDELIC VIBES VOL.1

20602 / 2 Mar '98 / Trust In Trance/ Phonokol

☐ PSYCHEDELIC VIBES VOL.4

21012 / 30 Mar '98 / Trust In Trance/ Phonokol

☐ PSYCHEDELIC VISIONS

TMPCD 026 / May '96 / Temple

☐ PSYCHEDELIC VOODOO (2CD Set)

Klm: Christof & DJ Mael / Stardust: Nervasystem / Jaws: Growling Mad Scientists / Do androids dream of electric sheep: Growling Mad Scientists / Progress: Growling Mad Scientists / Pulse III: Anti Matter / Too pure: Koxbox / Dawn on epsilon: Deviation / Space puppy: SYB Unity Nettwerk Experience / Yemaya: Elysium & Worm / Toxic brainwaves: Ominus / Subtropical forrest: Miranda / Sleepless nation: Psychlopedia / Different species: Crop Circles / Shapeshifter: Encens / Spider: Chakra / Project oblivion: Conspiracy Theory / Internal horizon: Process / Angel hair: Manmademan

SPV 08947662 / Sep '97 / SPV

☐ PSYCHEDELIC VOYAGE VOL.1 & 2

CAN 1 / 22 Jun '98 / Bon Voyage

☐ PSYCHO CIVILIZED

ELM 009CD / 2 Mar '98 / Elevator

☐ PSYCHO KILLERS (3CD Set)

DTKBOX 84 / 25 May '98 / Dressed To Kill

☐ PSYCHOBILLY SAMPLER VOL.2

DAGCD 4 / Sep '96 / Fury

☐ PSYCHOSERENADE

BEWARECD 002 / May '97 / Beware

☐ PSYCHOTHRILL

Mosainga: Mills, Jeff / Drugsky 0023: Dusk / Bass fishing: DJ ESP & Fuzz Face / Double decker: RBR / Killing field: Polygen / New beginning: Graphite / Loosing child: Haderlapp, Walter / Hen-Fruit: Casper, Roland / Dynamics: Clemen, Jana / Down by law: Co-Jack / Sh-punch: Flaptrack / Runner: DMP

ESS 42992 / Feb '97 / Essence

☐ PSYCHOTRANCE VOL.1

MM 800072 / Aug '94 / Moonshine

☐ PSYCHOTRANCE VOL.2

MM 800202 / Jan '95 / Moonshine

☐ PSYCHOTRANCE VOL.3

MM 800402 / Oct '95 / Moonshine

☐ PSYCHOTRANCE VOL.4 (Slam)

MM 800562 / Oct '96 / Moonshine

☐ PUB PIANO SING-A-LONG

Swanee medley / Slow boat to China medley / I'm gonna sit right down and write myself a letter / Lili Marlene medley / Roll out the barrel medley / Tavern in the town medley / You made me love you medley / Johnny's so long at the fair medley / Little old wine drinker me medley / Wish me luck as you wave me goodbye medley / Tiptoe through the tulips

CD 6080 / Jun '97 / Music

☐ PUB ROCK (Paving The Way For Punk)

61767210142 / 14 Apr '98 / Beloved

☐ PUCK ROCK VOL.1

WRONG 11 / Apr '94 / Wrong

☐ PULP FUSION VOL.1

Shifting gears: Hammond, John / Chitterlings con carne: Pucho & His Latin Soul Brothers / Don't it drive you crazy: Pointer Sisters / Inner city blues: Wilson, Reuben / First come first serve: Wilson, Reuben / Melting pot: Booker T & The MG's / Every time he comes around: Riperton, Minnie / Burning spear: SOUL / Bump: Freeman, George / Crab apple: Muhammad, Idris / Hang up your hang ups: Hancock, Herbie / Afrodesia: Smith, Lonnie

HURTCD 003 / Aug '97 / Harmless

☐ PULP FUSION VOL.2

HURTCD 007 / 16 Mar '98 / Harmless

☐ PULP SURFIN'

DOCD 700222 / Jan '97 / Del-Fi

☐ PULSATING HITS

PULSE 16CD / Nov '94 / Pulse 8

☐ PULSATING RHYTHMS VOL.1

PULSECD 1 / Aug '91 / Pulse 8

☐ PULSATING RHYTHMS VOL.2

PULSECD 4 / Jun '93 / Pulse 8

☐ PULSATING RHYTHMS VOL.4

PULSECD 10 / Jul '93 / Pulse 8

☐ PULSE

Babes on broomsticks: Synchro / Foxglove: Shakta / Deliverance: Butler & Wilson / Black rain: Amanite Fx & Prana / Trashish: Transwave / Radiation: Blot / San yacid: Cosmosis / Dawn to dusk: Asia 2001 / Smells electric: Metal Spark / Viton: NDMA / Pulsar glitch: Total Eclipse / Kabalah: Astral Projection / Tinkerbell: Power Source / X-Files: Chakra & Edi Mis / Bong incus: Eat Static / Triplexus: Miranda / Touch the sun: Sundog / Miles and smiles: Sit On The Lunch / Afterlife: Astralasia

SPV 08947122 / Oct '96 / SPV

☐ PULSE OF LIFE

ELL 3210C / Oct '93 / Ellipsis Arts

☐ PULSE VOL.1 (This Is Psychedelic Trance/2CD Set)

Placid: Shanti, Stanley & The Chillum Wallahs / Cor: Green Nuns Of The Revolution / Portamento: Blenn, Boris / Orange acid: Brain Accent / Axonal: Transwave / Prana: Rainbow Spirit / Born again: Doof / Moon raker: Disco Volante / Blessing: Sourmash / Transparent mind: Total Eclipse / Key: Indoor / Bodynamique: Phreax / Secret of Mana: Amanite FX / Dancing spirit: Soluna / Quatermass: Kali / Antidote: Blue Planet Co-operation

SPV 08938592 / Jun '96 / Subterranean

☐ **PULSE VOL.2 (2CD Set)**
Loin sleeps tonight: Infernal Machine / Between the nothing: Shakta & Ping Pong / Howling at the moon: Cosmosis / Interforce: Acid Rockers / Creatures: Reflecta / Free return: Alienated / Angelina: Doof / Ten years after: Mindfield / Masters of the universe: UX / Great spirit: Space Tribe / Whirlpool: Astralasia / Magnetic activity: MFG / Ushuaya: Ushuaya / Screwdriver: Planet Ben
DCD 08947402 / May '97 / Subterranean

☐ **PULSE VOL.6 (2CD Set)**
SPV 09247992 / 6 Apr '98 / SPV

☐ **PULSE VOL.7 (The 7th Stage/2CD Set)**
DCD 08939192 / 3 Aug '98 / SPV

☐ **PUMP HARDER**
MM 800512 / Jun '96 / Moonshine

☐ **PUMP IT UP MR. DJ (Check Out The DJ's Playlist)**
Now that we found love / Vogue / Going back to my roots / Everlasting love / Easy lover / Trapped / Don't take away the music / This is it / Deeper love (the salsa track) / You keep me hangin' on / Show me love / Dreams
ECD 3199 / Mar '95 / K-Tel

☐ **PUMP UP EUROPE**
LDCD 8823 / Aug '89 / Play It Again Sam

☐ **PUMPIN' AND THUMPIN'**
BB 003 / May '96 / BB

☐ **PUNK**
What do I get: Buzzcocks / EMI: Sex Pistols / Personality crisis: New York Dolls / Angels with dirty faces: Sham 69 / Born to lose: Thunders, Johnny / Bored teenagers: Adverts / Looking for a kiss: New York Dolls / Rip off: Sham 69 / One track mind: Thunders, Johnny / Boston babies: Slaughter & The Dogs / Pretty vacant: Sex Pistols / No time to be 21: Adverts / Hear nothing, see nothing, say nothing: Discharge / Brickfield nights: Boys / Time's up: Buzzcocks
MCCD 015 / Feb '91 / Music Club

☐ **PUNK (3CD Set)**
MCBX 017 / Dec '94 / Music Club

☐ **PUNK - LIVE AND NASTY**
I live in a car: UK Subs / In a rut: Damned / White riot: Sham 69 / Babylon's burning: Ruts / I am the hunted: GBH / Submission: Sex Pistols / No time to be 21: Adverts / What do I get: Buzzcocks / Nights in white satin: Dickies / Runaway: Slaughter & The Dogs / Don't need it: Eater / New guitar in town: Boys / C'mon everybody: Vicious White Kids / Hard loving man: Moped, Johnny / Urban kids: Chelsea / Wolf at the door: Lurkers
EMPRCD 586 / Oct '95 / Emporio

☐ **PUNK - THE WORST OF TOTAL ANARCHY (2CD Set)**
Anarchy in the UK: Sex Pistols / Hersham boys: Sham 69 / Catholic school girls rule: Red Hot Chili Peppers / Butcher baby: Plasmatics / King rocker: Generation X / Gary Gilmore's eyes: Adverts / Ever fallen in love: Buzzcocks / Nobody's hero: Stiff Little Fingers / C30, C60, C90, go: Bow Wow Wow / Nasty nasty: 999 / Born to lose: Thunders, Johnny & The Heartbreakers / Babylon's burning: Ruts / No survivors: GBH / Heroin it's all over: Lurkers / Come dancing: No Dice / My way: Vicious, Sid / Get up and jump: Red Hot Chili Peppers / God save the Queen: Sex Pistols / Love you more: Buzzcocks / Sound of the suburbs: Members / Homicide: 999 / Sheena is a punk rocker: Ramones / Something better change: Stranglers / Never again: Discharge / Warhead: UK Subs / Stand strong stand proud: Vice Squad / Tight black pants: Plasmatics / Badman: Cockney Rejects / Why sugar: No Dice / Day the world turned day-glo: X-Ray Spex / Kids on the streets: Angelic Upstarts / No time to be 21: Adverts
SP 871952 / Nov '96 / Disky

☐ **PUNK ALERT**
EMPRCD 678 / Apr '97 / Emporio

☐ **PUNK AND DISORDERLY**
AABT 100CD / Sep '94 / Abstract

☐ **PUNK AND DISORDERLY (The Best Of Punk & Disorderly)**
CLP 9824 / Oct '96 / Cleopatra

☐ **PUNK AND DISORDERLY (4CD Set)**
SUMBX 4012 / Jan '98 / Summit

☐ **PUNK AND DISORDERLY VOL.2 (Further Changes)**
Sick boy: GBH / Dreaming: Expelled / El salvador: Insane / Stab the judge: One Way System / Gotta get out: Court Martial / London bouncers: Action Pact / Masque: Dark / Gangland: Violators / I've got a gun: Channel 3 / Vicious circle: Abrasive Wheels / Fallen hero: Enemy / Death to humanity: Riot / Hobby for a day: Wall / More than fights: Disorder / Shellshock: Erazerhead / Resurrection: Vice Squad / How much longer: Alternative TV / Corgi crap: Drones / I hate school: Suburban Studs / Run like hell: Peter & The Test Tube Babies
CDPUNK 22 / Dec '93 / Anagram

☐ **PUNK AND DISORDERLY VOL.3 (The Final Solution)**
Burn 'em down: Abrasive Wheels / Give us a future: One Way System / Kick out the tories: Newtown Neurotics / Police state: UK Subs / Jailbait: Destructor / Government policy: Expelled / Dead hero: Samples / Woman in disguise: Angelic Upstarts / Viva la revolution: Adicts / Dragnet: Vibrators / Computers don't blunder: Exploited / New barbarians: Urban Dogs / Have you got 10p: Ejected / Outlaw: Chron Gen / Suicide bag: Action Pact / Summer of '81: Violators
CDPUNK 23 / Dec '93 / Anagram

☐ **PUNK AND NASTY (2CD Set)**
DEMPCD 010 / Mar '96 / Emporio

☐ **PUNK BITES VOL.1**
F 019CD / Apr '97 / Fearless

☐ **PUNK BITES VOL.2**
Calling all punks: Bickley / Two on glue: NOFX / Simply fly: Pulley / Gimme gimme gimme: Pennywise / Subhumanitarian homewrecked blues: 30 Foot Fall / Falling down: Big Wig / On the counter: Discount / Self appointed leader: Gob / GSP: MXPX / Just like me: Strung Out / Basement diaries: Drapes / Revolve: Straight Faced / My so called real world: Slick Shoes / 7 Minutes: Backside / Police truck: Whitekaps / Holiday road: Whippersnapper / More than friends: Homegrown / Another boring day: 98 Mute / Nutso smasho: Quincy Punx / Charmed: Dynarmite Boy / Pulley worms apart: Hoboken / POC: Chuck / Excuses: Sam The Butcher / Bruce Wayne: Assorted Jelly Beans / Go to the dentist: Crowd / Feel better today: Krhissy / Just around the corner: Pinker, Horace / Detroit: Ballgagger / Dumb as rocks: Boredoms / Fit: Outside
F 030CD / 26 Jan '98 / Fearless

☐ **PUNK CHARTBUSTERS VOL.1**
WRR 028 / Dec '96 / Wolverine

☐ **PUNK CITY ROCKERS (4CD Set)**
MBSCD 440 / Nov '95 / Castle

☐ **PUNK COMPILATION**
Summer of '81: Violators / Shellshock: Erazerhead / Four minute warning: Chaos UK / Complete disorder: Disorder / When he kissed me: Hollywood Brats / Chinese rocks: Thunders, Johnny / Tomorrow's sunset: Buzzcocks FOC / Women in disguise: Angelic Upstarts / Baby baby: Vibrators / Black flowers for the bride: 999 / Teenage rampage: 999 / Great rock and roll swindle: Chaotic Dischord / 1000 marching feet: Xpozez / Razors in the night: Blitz / Follow the leader: Saints / Bone idol: Drones / I hate school: Suburban Studs / Action time vision: ATV / Run like hell: Peter & The Test Tube Babies / Bad hearts: Tights / Love sucks: Adicts / Give us a future: One Way System / 17 years of hell: Partisans / I've got a gun: Channel 3 / Outside view: Eater
EMPRCD 550 / Nov '94 / Emporio

☐ **PUNK GENERATION (4CD Set)**
MBSCD 419 / Nov '95 / Castle

☐ **PUNK LEGENDS (The American Roots)**
FREUDCD 056 / 24 Nov '97 / Jungle

☐ **PUNK LIVES**
TRTCD 146 / May '95 / TrueTrax

☐ **PUNK LOST & FOUND**
Saints and sinners: Johnny & The Self Abusers / Shakin' all over: Generation X / Justifiable homicide: Professionals / Keys to your heart: 101'ers / Where's Captain Kirk: Spizz Energi / I'm in love with the girl on the Manchester megastore check: Freshies / Television screen: Radiators From Space / Johnny won't go to heaven: Killjoys / Terminal stupid: Snivelling Shits / Waiting for the man: Eater / (I want to be an) Anglepoise lamp: Soft Boys / Gabrielle: Nips / New order: Generation X / Smash it up: Damned / Cosmonaut: Bragg, Billy
SH 5705 / May '96 / Shanachie

☐ **PUNK ROCK LOSERS**
ALBR 1 / Jun '97 / Al's

☐ **PUNK ROCK RARITIES VOL.1**
On me: Bears / Hard time: Mutants / School teacher: Mutants / Lady: Mutants / Office girl: Stoat / Little Jenny: Stoat / Crazy paving: Karloff, Billy / Backstreet Billy: Karloff, Billy / I'm different: Embryo / You know he did: Embryo / Here comes the night: Rivals / Both sides: Rivals / Sound so false: Murder Inc. / Polythene dream: Murder Inc. / Nobody cares: Murder Inc. / Lord of the dance: Jump Squad / Debt: Jump Squad / Kings cross: Charge / Brave new world: Charge / God's kids: Charge
CDPUNK 63 / Oct '95 / Anagram

☐ **PUNK ROCK RARITIES VOL.2**
CDPUNK 83 / Oct '96 / Anagram

☐ **PUNK SUCKS**
Slowdown: Pennywise / Soulmate: No Use For A Name / Racer X: Ten Foot Pole / All you need: Sublime / Face in the crowd: Home Grown / Descendent's song: Voodoo Glowskulls / Germs: White Kaps / Too Many: 88 Fingers Louie / Sometimes: Neighbors / Old school pride: HFL / I hate you: Everready / New dreams: Boll Weevils / Cpk: Unwritten law / Mother superior: Good Riddance / Support your troops: Strung Out / Right Now: Naked Aggression / 49 and 61: Jughead's Revenge / Damn you: Funeral Oration / Song 9: Overlap / Ballad of Johnny X: Bouncing Souls / All my time: Boris The Sprinkler / Skate the Haight: Glue Gun / Cereal killer: Quincy Punx / Can't figure it: Fed Up / Omit: Straight Faced / 2000 AD: FYP / Bummers: Fighting Cause / Out on the grass: Supernovice / Deadbeat: Living End
LIB 37801CD / 3 Aug '98 / Liberation

☐ **PUNK, THE BAD AND THE UGLY, THE**
CLP 9959 / Mar '97 / Cleopatra

☐ **PUNK UPRISINGS VOL.1**
LOOKOUT 139CD / Feb '96 / Lookout

☐ **PUNK UPRISINGS VOL.2**
GK 034 / 15 Jun '98 / Go-Kart

☐ **PUNK VOL.2**
Anarchy in the UK: Sex Pistols / Babylon's burning: Ruts / Nobody's hereo: Stiff Little Fingers / Borstal breakout: Sham 69 / Dead cities: Exploited / Ain't got a clue: Lurkers / Maniac: Peter & The Test Tube Babies / Feeling alright with the crew: 999 / Chinese takeaway: Adicts / Right to work: Chelsea / Holidays in the sun: Sex Pistols / Alternative Ulster: Stiff Little Fingers / Two pints of lager: Splodgenessabounds / Stand strong, stand proud: Vice Squad / Something that I said: Ruts / I hate people: Anti Nowhere League / Teenage warning: Angelic Upstarts / Flares and slippers: Cockney Rejects / Punk's not dead: Exploited / Warriors: Blitz
MCCD 027 / May '91 / Music Club

☐ **PUNK VS. SKA VOL.2**
SRR 01CD / 15 Dec '97 / Revelation

☐ **PUNKORAMA VOL.1**
E 864482 / Nov '94 / Epitaph

☐ **PUNKORAMA VOL.2**
64842 / Dec '96 / Epitaph

☐ **PUNKS FROM THE UNDERGROUND**
622432 / Apr '97 / Skydog

☐ **PUNKS NOT DREAD**
For adolf's only: Chaos UK / Bone idol: Chaos UK / Brain bomb: Chaos UK / Defiant pose: Raw Noise / GLC: Raw Noise / No one: Red Flag '77 / Borstal breakout: Extreme Noise Terror / Johnny won't get to heaven: Extreme Noise Terror / Naive: Filth Kick / Sonic reducer: Filth Kick / Sad so sad: Red Flag '77 / New rose: Poison Idea
PREACH 002CD / 10 Nov '97 / Rhythm Vicar

☐ **PUNKS ON DRUGS**
DOTECD 1 / Jun '97 / Antidote

☐ **PUNKS SKINS AND HERBERTS VOL.1**
HOO 32CD / 15 Jun '98 / Helen Of Oi

☐ **PUNKS UNDERCOVER**
CLP 9930 / Mar '97 / Cleopatra

☐ **PURE ABSTRAKT (Adventures In Dub)**
SDW 0422 / 20 Jul '98 / Shadow

☐ **PURE ATTRACTION**
You're my best friend: Queen / Right beside you: Hawkins, Sophie B. / Easy: Faith No More / Just a step from heaven: Eternal / Patience of angels: Reader, Eddi / Return to innocence: Enigma / Don't dream it's over: Crowded House / Now that the magic has gone: Cocker, Joe / Where does my heart beat now: Dion, Celine / Hold me, thrill me, kiss me: Estefan, Gloria / Stay: Shakespears Sister / Someone saved my life tonight: John, Elton / Independent love song: Scarlet / Now and forever: Marx, Richard / Total eclipse of the heart: Tyler, Bonnie / Hold me now: Logan, Johnny / I'll never fall in love again: Deacon Blue / Every breath you take: Police / Careless whisper: Michael, George / Power of love: Rush, Jennifer / Jealous guy: Roxy Music / In dreams: Orbison, Roy / When I fall in love: Dion, Celine / Nothing compares 2 U: O'Connor, Sinead / (Sittin' on the) dock of the bay: Bolton, Michael / In a broken dream: Python Lee Jackson / Eternal flame: Bangles / Always and forever: Vandross, Luther / Time after time: Lauper, Cyndi / Only to be with you: Roachford / Love hurts: Capaldi, Jim / Show me heaven: McKee, Maria / I wonder why: Stigers, Curtis / I'll stand by you: Pretenders / Ordinary world: Duran Duran / Take my breath away: Berlin / Miracle of love: Eurythmics / Whole new world (Aladdin's theme): Bell, Regina
SONYTV 1CD / Jun '95 / Sony TV

☐ **PURE AUDIOSEX VOL.1 (Kraft Presents Modern Techno House Trax/ 2CD Set)**
Elements: Stoll, Steve / Bite and scratch: Vogel, Christian / Home delivery: Landstrumm, Neal / I'll have some: Winx, Josh & DJ ESP / Killer train: Miss Djax / Fax wars: Innersound / To the sky: Pump Panel / Acid wiss L: DJ Skull / Dr. J: McBride, Woody / Snare rolls and back ups: Righteous Men / Transaxual: Armando / Loop 2: Larkin, Kenny / How deep is your love: Love Inc. / Shuffle this: Broom, Mark / Extra: New John / G-man: El Jem / Flash: Kosmik Messenger / Instant: Beltram, Joey / Get funky, get down: Micronauts / In from the night: Planetary Assault Systems / Chord memory: Pooley, Ian / Hibernia: Mont Cenis Trax
SPV 08938722 / Sep '96 / SPV

☐ **PURE AUDIOSEX VOL.2 (2CD Set)**
Mommy why: Thee Madkatt Courtship / In da jungle: Playboy / Beavis at bat: Hardfloor / Power hour: DJ ESP / No way back: Adonis / F5: DJ Misjah / Forklift: Beltram, Joey / Drumcode 20: Beyer, Adam / Club NCN: Love Inc. / I need to freak: Aux 88 / First premonition: Gianelli, Fred / Dragnet: Stoll, Steve / When love comes down: Righteous Men / Bud shake: Lindsey, Patrick / Alien spoke: Broom, Mark / Ice fractions: Silvershower / Dark forces: SLAM / Overlap: Ishii, Ken / Vertigo: Steve Bug & Acid Maria / Les plates verdes: Mont Cenis Trax / 'Ang my pickcha: Partycrashers
DCD 08947512 / Jun '97 / SPV

☐ **PURE DANCE '96 (2CD Set)**
Born slippy: Underworld / Ain't nobody's business if I do: H2O & Billie / Keep on jumpin': Lisa Marie Experience / Don't stop movin': Livin' Joy / Everybody's free: Rozalla / Nighttrain: Kadoc / Higher state of consciousness: Wink, Josh / Keep on jumpin': Terry, Todd & Martha Wash/Jocelyn Brown / Hello honky tonks (rock your body): Pizzaman / We've got it goin' on: Backstreet Boys / Mysterious girl: Andre, Peter / Good intentions: Nelson, Shara & G.Corp / Sunshine: Umboza / Jazz it up: Reel 2 Real / Let's all chant: Gusto / There's nothing I won't do: JX / Children: Miles, Robert / Arms of Loren: E'voke / Walking wounded: Everything But The Girl / Firestarter: Prodigy / Nagasaki EP (I need a lover tonight): Kendoh / State of independence: Summer, Donna / Disco 2000: Pulp / Klubbhopping: Klubb Heads / Give me luv: Alcatraz / Disco's revenge: Gusto / Hideaway: De'Lacy / Passion: Gat Decor / Krupa: Apollo 440 / So pure: Baby D / Good thing: Eternal / Do you still: East 17 / Macarena: Los Del Mar / I wish: Skee Lo / I got 5 on it: Luniz / Too hot: Coolio / Thank God it's Friday: R Kelly / Can't help it: Happy Clappers / Theme from S Express: S'Express / Le voie de soleil: Subliminal Cuts
5357892 / Aug '96 / PolyGram TV

☐ **PURE DANCE '97 (2CD Set)**
Where's the love: Hanson / As long as you love me: Backstreet Boys / I know where it's at: All Saints / Free: DJ Quicksilver / Black eyed boy: Texas / Every little time: Poppers & Aura / Somethin' goin' on: Terry, Todd / Saturday: East 57th Street & Donna Allen / Freed from desire: Gala / Encore une fois: Sash / Finally: Peniston, Ce Ce / Lovefool: Cardigans / Magic carpet ride: Mighty Dub Katz / I believe: Happy Clappers / Professional widow: Amos, Tori / I'm alive: Stretch n' Vern / Firestarter: Prodigy / Born slippy: Underworld / Bellisima: DJ Quicksilver / Dreamer: Livin' Joy / Blurred: Pianoman / There's nothing I won't do: JX / Just a little bit: Gina G / Let me be your fantasy: Baby D / Missing: Everything But The Girl / Seven day and one week: BBE / I luv u baby: Original / Ready or not: Course / You got the love: Source & Candi Staton / Disco's revenge: Gusto / Loving you more: BT / Your loving arms: Martin, Billie Ray / Not over yet: Grace / I like the way: Kaleef / Klubbhopping: Klubb Heads
5550842 / 6 Oct '97 / PolyGram TV

☐ **PURE DISCO CLASSICS VOL.1**
Uptown festival part one: Shalamar / And the beat goes on: Whispers / Wet my whistle: Midnight Star / Fantastic voyage: Lakeside / Shame shame shame: Shirley & Co. / Give me just a little more time: Chairmen Of The Board / Can you feel the force: Real Thing / Kung Fu fighting: Douglas, Carl / I wanna dance wit choo: Disco Tex & The Sexolettes / Feels like I'm in love: Marie, Kelly / High energy: Thomas, Evelyn / Walk in the park: Straker, Nick Band / Ring my bell: Ward, Anita / Footsteps following me: Nero, Frances / Girls: Moments / First impressions: Impressions / Galaxy of love: Crown Heights Affair / Superfly: Mayfield, Curtis / Pillow talk: Sylvia
SELCD 515 / 2 Mar '98 / Castle Select

☐ **PURE ECSTATIC ENERGY**
GLOBECD 1 / May '93 / All Around The World

☐ **PURE FILTH**
74321565062 / 29 Jun '98 / Filth

☐ **PURE GROOVES (18 Dance Hits)**
Sunchyme / You make me wanna / Frozen / Stay / You're not alone / Young hearts run free / I say a little prayer / Free / Dancehall queen / Closer than close / You're the one I love / Blood on the Dance floor / You might need somebody / I don't want to / Smokin' me out / Alright / It's alright / Together again
308982 / 11 May '98 / Hallmark

☐ **PURE HITS (The 90's Collection)**
Stop / Dr. Jones / Bamboogie / Alane / All I have to give / Ain't that just the way / Rain clouds / Let's go round again / My oh my / Are you Jimmy Ray / Uh la la la / Maria / Barbie girl / Picture of you / Casanova / I know where it's at / Spice up your life / Everybody
308992 / 11 May '98 / Hallmark

☐ **PURE JAZZ SAMPLER**
CDGATE 1001 / Oct '90 / Kingdom Jazz

☐ **PURE LOVE SONGS**
Too much / Never ever / I believe I can fly / Tell him / Butterfly / I wiil come to you / How come how long / Different beat / I need you / If I never see you again / Tell me / Wishes / As long as you love me / Torn / I'll be missing you
308972 / 13 Jul '98 / Hallmark

☐ **PURE LOVERS VOL.1**
CCD 101 / Oct '92 / Charm

☐ **PURE LOVERS VOL.10**
CCD 110 / Mar '97 / Charm

☐ **PURE LOVERS VOL.11**
CCD 111 / Mar '98 / Charm

☐ **PURE LOVERS VOL.2**
CCD 102 / Sep '90 / Charm

☐ **PURE LOVERS VOL.3**
CCD 103 / Apr '91 / Charm

☐ **PURE LOVERS VOL.4**
I'm so alone: Davis, Richie / Master vibes: Hunningale, Peter / Love u down: Brown, Lloyd / Morning after: Rich, Anthony / I won't stop loving you: Hall, Pam / Daydreaming: Robotiks & Jocelyn Brown / Hypnotic love: Leo, Phillip / Can you feel the love: Pure Silk & Trevor Walters / Hold me: Pinchers / Miss wire waist: Scotty / Emptiness inside: Hammond, Beres / Ecstasy of love: Levi, Sammy / Fire burning: Griffiths, Marcia / I'm only human: Wayne Wonder / Mrs. Jones: Kofi / Make my dream a reality: Pure Silk & Wendy Walker / Stranger in love: Dave Fluxe
CCD 104 / Nov '91 / Charm

☐ **PURE LOVERS VOL.5**
CCD 105 / Aug '92 / Charm

☐ **PURE LOVERS VOL.6**
CCD 106 / Apr '93 / Charm

☐ **PURE LOVERS VOL.7**
CCD 107 / Feb '94 / Charm

☐ **PURE LOVERS VOL.8**
CCD 108 / Feb '95 / Charm

☐ **PURE NOSTALGIA**
Bei mir bist du schon: Andrews Sisters / Puttin' on the Ritz: Astaire, Fred / When I take my sugar to tea: Boswell Sisters & Dorsey Brothers Orchestra / Very thought of you: Bowlly, Al / Minnie the moocher: Calloway, Cab / Rockin' chair: Carmichael, Hoagy & Louis Armstrong / Louise: Chevalier, Maurice / Temptation: Crosby, Bing / Falling in love again: Dietrich, Marlene / Ten cents a dance: Etting, Ruth / Sally: Fields, Gracie / Leaning on a lamp-post: Formby, George / Over the rainbow: Garland, Judy / All the things you are: Hutchinson, Leslie 'Hutch' / Java jive: Ink Spots / Sonny boy: Jolson, Al / Medley: Layton & Johnstone / We'll meet again: Lynn, Vera / Dancing on the ceiling: Matthews, Jessie / Moonlight serenade: Miller, Glenn / Tiger rag: Mills Brothers / My curly headed baby: Robeson, Paul / Without a song: Sinatra, Frank & Tommy Dorsey / Marta: Tracy, Arthur / Some of these days: Tucker, Sophie
CDAJA 5118 / Mar '94 / Living Era

☐ **PURE POP (18 Original Hits/3CD Set)**
Nutbush city limits: Turner, Ike & Tina / Emma: Hot Chocolate / Dyna-mite: Mud / Rock your baby: McCrae, George / All around my hat: Steeleye Span / Hit me with your rhythm stick: Dury, Ian & The Blockheads / True: Spandau Ballet / Too shy: Kajagoogoo / Stuck with you: Lewis, Huey & The

News / Nineteen: *Hardcastle, Paul* / Heart and soul: *T'Pau* / Are you my baby: *Wendy & Lisa* / U can't touch this: *MC Hammer* / Back to life: *Soul II Soul* / Unbelieveable: *EMF* / Don't worry: *Appleby, Kim* / One and only: *Hawkes, Chesney* / Oh Carolina: *Shaggy*
LAD 873382 / Nov '96 / Disky

☐ **PURE PUREPECHA**
CO 119CD / Aug '94 / Corason

☐ **PURE REGGAE**
VSOPCD 198 / Jun '94 / Connoisseur Collection

☐ **PURE REGGAE (4CD Set)**
Red red wine: *Boothe, Ken* / Kingston town: *Ricketts, Glen* / Tide is high: *Holt, John* / Love you baby: *Biggs, Barry* / Singer man: *Blues Busters* / People get ready: *Kelly, Pat* / Rivers of Babylon: *Boothe, Ken* / Exodus: *Mafia & Fluxy* / Wild world: *Blues Busters* / If it is fire you want: *Hinds, Justin & The Dominoes* / Sweet sensation: *Lee, Byron & The Dragonaires* / I shot the sheriff: *Ricketts, Glen* / Wear to the ball: *Holt, John* / Busted lad: *Dekker, Desmond* / Ram goat liver: *Pluto* / What's happening: *Gardiner, Boris* / One big happy family: *Ruffin, Bruce* / Get up stand up: *Thomas, Ruddy* / Love again: *George, Sophia* / Sweet Jamaica: *Donaldson, Eric* / Last farewell: *Edwards, Jackie* / Let's stay together: *Gardiner, Boris* / Can't you see: *Wilson, Delroy* / Swing low: *Heptones* / Redemption song: *Fraser, Dean* / Uno fi move: *Shabba Ranks* / Can't test me: *Chaka Demus & Pliers* / War: *Marley, Kymani* / Down in the ghetto: *Paul, Frankie* / Shock out: *Chaka Demus* / Final decision: *George, Sophia* / You and your smiling face: *Brown, Dennis* / Some sweet day: *Hammond, Beres* / Milk and honey: *In Crowd* / Buffalo soldier: *Thomas, Ruddy* / Come back Charlie: *Charlie Chaplin* / Kool and deadly: *Eastwood & Saint* / Soul rebel: *Max Romeo* / Judgement day: *Paragons* / Don't go nowhere: *Dunkley, Errol* / Ambition: *Reedy, Winston* / Tell me if you ready: *Seaton, B.B.* / Keep on doing it: *Blues Busters* / What you're doing to me: *Donaldson, Eric* / Power of love: *Thriller U* / Do you really want to hurt me: *Heptones* / Everybody join hands: *Dekker, Desmond* / Time is going to come: *Admiral Tibet* / Born in Ethiopia: *In Crowd* / I'm a peaceful man: *Edwards, Jackie* / Queen majesty: *Kelly, Pat* / If you wanna make love: *Biggs, Barry* / Nice time: *Dunkley, Errol* / Could you be loved: *Mafia & Fluxy* / Rainy night in Georgia: *Holt, John* / If you could see me now: *Pioneers* / No man is an island: *Andy, Horace* / Send me the pillow you dream on: *Schloss, Cynthia* / Sweet cherrie: *Honey Boy* / Caught you in a lie: *McFarlin, Sandra* / Long and winding road: *Brown, Dennis* / Love me for a reason: *Miller, Maxine* / Massachusetts: *McGregor, Freddie* / Power of love: *Minott, Sugar* / No woman no cry: *Marley, Kymani* / I think I love you: *Donaldson, Eric* / Wide awake in a dream: *Biggs, Barry* / Raindrops keep falling on my head: *Gardiner, Boris* / Once upon a time: *Wilson, Delroy* / Love light: *Isaacs, Gregory* / Baby I need your loving: *Smith, Slim* / Never gonna give you up: *Adebambo, Jean* / If you don't know me by now: *Hammond, Beres* / Paradise in your eyes: *Reedy, Winston* / Just a little more time: *Seaton, B.B.* / We play reggae: *In Crowd* / Money in my pocket: *Edwards, Jackie* / Lively up yourself: *Lee, Byron & The Dragonaires* / Terror: *Chaka Demus & Spana Bana* / Money and friends: *Dekker, Desmond* / Sister love: *Isaacs, Gregory* / Who cares: *Wilson, Greg* / I let you go boy: *Penn, Dawn* / You never know: *George, Sophia* / Night like this: *Biggs, Barry* / Midnight hour: *Kelly, Pat* / Bring your love to me: *Pliers* / I see you my love: *Griffiths, Marcia* / Natural mystic: *Andy, Horace* / Many rivers to cross: *Boothe, Ken* / Mississippi: *Schloss, Cynthia* / Save the people: *Ruffin, Bruce* / Never will I hurt you: *Paragons* / Take life easy: *Honey Boy* / Come down: *Pioneers* / Private lessons: *Seaton, B.B.* / Whiter shade of pale: *Kelly, Pat* / Story book children: *Isaacs, Gregory* / Sweet dreams: *Pioneers* / They can't get me out: *Campbell, Cornell* / While there's life there's hope: *Ruffin, Bruce*
ECD 3350 / Jun '97 / K-Tel

☐ **PURE REGGAE (2CD Set)**
Baby come back: *Pato Banton & Ali Campbell/Robin Campbell* / Boombastic: *Shaggy* / Mr. Loverman: *Shabba Ranks* / Baby I love your way: *Big Mountain* / Soul rebel: *Marley, Bob & The Wailers* / I can see clearly now: *Cliff, Jimmy* / Close to you: *Priest, Maxi* / You don't love me (no no no): *Penn, Dawn* / Compliments on your kiss: *Red Dragon & Brian & Tony Gold* / Searching: *China Black* / Here comes the hotstepper: *Kamoze, Ini* / Shy guy: *King, Diana* / Now that we've found love: *Third World* / Tomorrow people: *Marley, Ziggy & The Melody Makers* / Boom shack-a-lak: *Apache Indian* / Shine: *Aswad* / Let your yeah be yeah: *Pioneers* / Uptown top ranking: *Althia & Donna* / Israelites: *Dekker, Desmond* / Many rivers to cross: *Cliff, Jimmy* / Twist and shout: *Chaka Demus & Pliers* / Mysterious girl: *Andre, Peter* / All that she wants: *Ace Of Base* / D'yer mak'er: *No Mercy* / Sweets for my sweet: *Lewis, C.J.* / Dancing on the floor: *Third World* / Oh Carolina: *Shaggy* / Cecilia: *Suggs* / Informer: *Snow* / Sweat (a la la la la long): *Inner Circle* / Love of the common people: *Thomas, Nicky* / Wonderful world beautiful people: *Cliff, Jimmy* / Silly games: *Kay, Janet* / Come give me your love: *Stephens, Richie & General Degree* / Summer breeze: *One Love* / Fudgie: *Goofy* / Good thing going: *Minott, Sugar* / Pressure drop: *Toots & The Maytals* / Young gifted and black: *Bob & Marcia* / Double barrell: *Barker, Dave & Ansell Collins* / Liquidator: *Harry J All Stars* / Red red wine: *Tribe, Tony*
RADCD 71 / Sep '97 / Global TV

☐ **PURE ROCK BALLADS (2CD Set)**
5555892 / 9 Feb '98 / PolyGram TV

☐ **PURE ROLLERS (20 Rolling Drum & Bass Tracks/2CD Set)**
New dawn: *X* / Raw dogs: *Joker* / Remember me: *Benny Blanco* / Check dis: *De Elite* / Easy dread: *Serious Intent* / Shit: *L-Double & Shy FX* / Rolling number: *Dynamic Duo* / Super bad: *Bonafide* / World of music: *Dred Bass & The JB* / 16 track ting: *Dream Team* / On the beat: *Swift* / Let's roll: *Darkman* / Tonics jazz lick: *Joker* / P-funk era: *P-Funk* / Yea: *Paul Z.* / Ride: *Dynamic Duo* / Roll on: *Andy C* / Take away: *Joint Venture* / Roll that shit: *Marvellous Caine* / Just roll: *Swift*
BDRCD 11 / Mar '96 / Breakdown

☐ **PURE SILK**
SGCD 11 / Jun '93 / Sir George

☐ **PURE SOCA '98**
HVCD 031 / 9 Feb '98 / Hot Vinyl

☐ **PURE SOCA VOL.2**
HVCD 029 / 15 Sep '97 / Smokey

☐ **PURE SOFT METAL**
TMPCD 015 / Mar '95 / Temple

☐ **PURE SOUL VOL.1 (The Best Of Expansion - 30 Awesome Soul Gems/ 2CD Set)**
Give me the sunshine: *Leo's Sunshipp* / You can't turn me away: *Striplin, Sylvia* / Pick up the pieces: *Gardner, Joanna* / On and on: *Hewett, Howard* / Make love: *Carne, Jean* / Give me your love: *Rogers, Richard* / Candles: *James, Josie* / It's alright: *Burke, Keni* / Say you will: *Jackson, Nicole* / Later tonight: *Chandler, Omar* / I'll treat u rite: *Perry, Trina* / Rockin' you tonight: *Gary* / I'll keep a light on: *King, Evelyn 'Champagne'* / Tic toc: *Lorenzo* / I'm so in love with you baby: *McNeir, Ronnie* / My favourite thing: *Brooks, Calvin & Hari Paris* / Any way: *Garmon, Terry* / Oasis: *Baylor, Helen* / Time after time: *Taylor, Gary* / Let them talk: *Bofill, Angela* / Let me know: *Mannsfield, Rodney* / Love won't let me wait: *Haynes, Victor* / On my own: *Andrea* / My joy is you: *Wanda* / Love to love you: *On The Contrary* / Show me some love: *Benito* / Give me all your love: *Ballin, Chris* / Cream of love: *Ware, Leon* / Do it right: *Act Of Faith* / I'll be what you need: *Serenade*
EXCDP 12 / Dec '96 / Expansion

☐ **PURE SOUL VOL.2 (2CD Set)**
Rhythm of life / Strip it down: *Velma* / This dedication: *Burke, Keni* / Walk on water: *Graham, Jaki* / It's time: *Wanda* / Crystal clear: *Hewett, Howard* / Galaxy of love: *Bofill, Angela* / Pleasure: *Act Of Faith* / Falling for you: *Carne, Jean* / Keep giving me love: *Rogers, Richard* / Can't run: *Zee, Dawn* / I didn't mean to hurt you: *Valentine, Billy* / Shoo be doo: *Candy J* / Animal: *Cunningham, Woody* / Hey boy: *Jackson, Rebbie* / Love to love you: *On The Contrary* / Call me: *Mannsfield, Rodney* / I can't get enough: *Perry, Trina* / Mind over matter: *Adkins, Gary* / I don't wanna lose it: *James, Josie* / Eye to eye: *Taylor, Gary* / Stormy love affair: *Hatcher, Roger* / It really doesn't matter: *King, Evelyn 'Champagne'* / Special feelings: *Gardner, Joanna* / Real love: *Lorenzo* / Back to back: *Ware, Leon* / It's only natural: *Thomas, Keith* / Stay away from you: *Ballin, Chris* / For the love of you: *Chandler, Omar* / Just a little taste of your love: *Pedicin, Michael Jr.*
EXCDP 14 / May '97 / Expansion

☐ **PURE SOUL VOL.3 (2CD Set)**
Feast or famine: *Valentine, Billy* / Once you find a good thing: *Amiekoleh* / Don't abuse my love: *Emotions* / Worth the wait: *De Lange, Andre* / Tomorrow: *Special Gift* / Diamond in me: *Willis, Chris* / Holding on: *Parkes* / You will always be there: *Parkes* / I get off on you: *Burke, Keni* / Any time any place: *Gary* / We can make it: *Gardner, Joanna* / Show me: *Chandler, Omar* / Tell me where you are: *Haynes, Victor* / Beverley: *Jamariah* / Winter love: *Mason, Barbara* / How can this be: *Mannsfield, Rodney* / All she wants is love: *Bofill, Angela* / Come live with me angel: *Ware, Leon* / Have I told you that I love: *Carne, Jean* / Woop de woo: *Rogers, Richard* / Take a little time: *James, Josie* / Baby you're wrong: *McNeir, Ronnie* / Take a ride: *Beverly & Duane* / Starchild: *King, Evelyn 'Champagne'* / Know him: *Candy J* / You got what I want: *Jous* / If you don't want my love: *Taylor, Lewis* / I'm back for more: *Leo's Sunshipp* / Starlite: *Ballin, Chris* / Jive: *Jive*
EXCDP 17 / 8 Dec '97 / Expansion

☐ **PURE SPEED VOL.2**
Wherever love is found: *Darbyshire, Richard* / Be strong: *Gaines, Rosie* / Love lady: *Damage* / Tears: *Underground Solution* / London thing: *Garcia, Scott & MC Styles* / Answer my prayer: *Rhythm Street* / I refuse (what you want): *Somore* / Just open your mind: *Zoo Experience* / Anytime: *Nu Birth* / Gabriel: *Davis, Roy Jr.* / My family depends on me: *Simone* / Secret love: *Shah* / Got funk: *Funk Junkeez* / Don't think about it: *Adeva* / All over: *Slip'd By* / Don't lose the magic: *Master Jam* / Don't stop: *Ruff Driverz*
EVOKE 2CD / 23 Mar '98 / Evocative

☐ **PURE SPUN SUGAR**
AMPOP 203 / 20 Apr '98 / American Pop

☐ **PURE TRADITIONAL IRISH ACCORDION**
PTICD 1027 / Mar '97 / Pure Traditional Irish

☐ **PURE VINTAGE BLUES VOL.1 (You Dirty Mistreater)**
Deep water blues: *Thomas, Hociel* / Jealous woman like me: *Wallace, Sippie* / Mail train blues: *Wallace, Sippie* / Dead drunk blues: *Wallace, Sippie* / Lazy man blues: *Wallace, Sippie* / Lovesick blues: *Hill, Bertha* / Trouble in mind: *Hill, Bertha* / You dirty mistreater: *Wilson, Grant* / Come on coot do that thing: *Wilson, Grant* / Down hearted blues: *Smith, Bessie* / My sweetie went away: *Smith, Bessie* / Sobbin' hearted blues: *Smith, Bessie* / Livin' high: *Taylor, Eva* / Coal cart blues: *Taylor, Eva* / Mandy, make up your mind: *Taylor, Eva* / Was it a dream: *Christian, Lillie Delk* / How do you do it that way: *Spivey, Victoria* / Ain't misbehavin': *Ellis, Segar* / Nobody knows the way I feel this morning: *Hunter, Alberta* / Broken busted blues: *Smith, Clara* / You've got to beat me to keep me: *Smith, Trixie*
RAJCD 870 / Oct '95 / Empress

☐ **PURE VINTAGE BLUES VOL.2 (Mining Camp Blues)**
He likes it slow: *Butterbeans & Susie* / St. Peter's blues: *Welsh, Nolan* / Find me at the Greasy Spoon (if you miss me here): *Grant, Coot & 'Kid' Wesley Wilson* / You've got to go home on time: *Mack, Baby* / Last night I dreamed you kissed me: *Christian, Lillie Delk* / I ain't gonna play no second fiddle (if I can play lead): *Christian, Lillie Delk* / Flood blues: *Wallace, Sippie* / Anybody here want to try my cabbage: *Jones, Maggie* / Funny feathers: *Spivey, Victoria* / I can give you everything but love: *Christian, Lillie Delk* / JC Holmes blues: *Smith, Bessie* / Any woman's blues: *Smith, Bessie* / I must have that man: *Christian, Lillie Delk* / Good time flat blues: *Jones, Maggie* / Lowland blues: *Hill, Bertha* / Careless love blues: *Smith, Bessie* / What kind o' man is that: *Mack, Baby* / Too busy: *Christian, Lillie Delk* / Bridewell blues: *Welsh, Nolan* / Mining camp blues: *Smith, Trixie* / Baby: *Christian, Lillie Delk*
RAJCD 880 / Apr '96 / Empress

☐ **PURE VOL.1**
PCD 001 / 13 Jul '98 / Desco

☐ **PURPLE**
CRELP 032CD / '88 / Creation

☐ **PURPLE KNIF SHOW**
622462 / 23 Feb '98 / Melodie

☐ **PURPLE PAIN**
DOL 020CD / Jun '95 / Dolores

☐ **PURVEYORS OF TASTE (Creation Compilation)**
CRECD 010 / May '94 / Creation

☐ **PUSSY GALORE**
PUSSYCD 007 / Oct '96 / Pussy Foot

☐ **PUT YA HAND ON DE BUMPER**
CCD 0021 / Aug '95 / CRS

☐ **PUTTING ON AIRS (A Collection Of Celtic Airs)**
CELT 9009CD / 9 Mar '98 / Celtophile

☐ **PUTUMAYO BLEND, A (Music From The Coffee Lands)**
PUTU 1352 / 27 Oct '97 / Putumayo

☐ **PWEEP (2CD Set)**
BFFP 94 / Apr '95 / Blast First

☐ **PYGMIES OF THE LOBAYE, THE**
PS 65175 / Dec '96 / PlayaSound

Q

☐ **Q - COUNTRY**
AHLCD 16 / May '94 / Hit

☐ **Q - RHYTHM & BLUES**
Brown eyed girl / I'll go crazy: *Brown, James* / It's all over now: *Cooder, Ry* / I'd rather go blind: *Stewart, Rod* / Fool in love: *Turner, Ike & Tina* / Dr. Brown: *Fleetwood Mac* / Nadine: *Berry, Chuck* / Mockingbird: *Foxx, Inez & Charlie* / Blue Monday: *Domino, Fats* / Everybody needs somebody to love: *Burke, Solomon* / Stepping out: *Mayall, John & Eric Clapton* / Born under a bad sign: *King, Albert* / Young blood: *Coasters* / Gimme some lovin': *Davis, Spencer Group* / Hi-heel sneakers: *Tucker, Tommy* / House of the rising sun: *Animals* / Let the good times roll: *Shirley & Lee* / We're gonna make it: *Little Milton* / Roadrunner: *Diddley, Bo* / Long tall shorty: *Kinks* / You'd better move on: *Alexander, Arthur* / Got my mojo working: *Manfred Mann* / My babe: *Little Walter*
AHLCD 7 / Mar '93 / Hit

☐ **Q - THE BLUES**
AHLCD 1 / Jun '92 / Hit

☐ **Q MUSIC VOL.1**
51RCD 1 / Jan '97 / 51st

☐ **QAWWALI - THE ART OF THE SUFIS VOL.2**
VICG 50302 / Mar '96 / JVC World Library

☐ **QED**
Organofonia ramovs: *Laibach* / Ataxia: *Dieform* / Untitled excerpt: *2'EV* / Ebony tower in the Orient water: *Radio Rabotnik TV* / Kennen sie koein: *Der Plan* / Delerium 2: *Chris & Cosey* / HLA: *Non Toxique Lost* / Tribal noise 2: *Het Zweet* / Anyway don't do the sport fuck: *Spring As Der Wolken* / Call: *Banabila, Michel* / Restimulation: *Hafler Trio* / Mutation waltz: *Manoton, K. B.* / Menegins: *Einsturzende Neubauten* / Eleven: *De Executie/Klec* / E and E: *Pig D4* / Getuich der miljoenen: *Zegueld, Peter* / L'espirit domine l'etoile: *Etant Donnes* / Oirat / I wanna be injured, l'ace d'or: *Club Moral* / Liberal 1:13: *Zero Kama* / CBA: *SBOTHI* / Demonomania: *Test Department*
NLCD 001 / Sep '88 / N L Centre

☐ **QUAD SQUAD, THE (4CD Set)**
SUMBX 4009 / Jan '98 / Summit

☐ **QUADRUPED**
BARKCD 006 / Oct '94 / Planet Dog

☐ **QUALITY PUNK ROCK**
BTR 006CD / Mar '96 / Bad Taste

☐ **QUANGO SPORT**
5243322 / Jan '97 / Quango

☐ **QUANTUM MECHANICS (2CD Set)**
RJCD 01 / 9 Feb '98 / Renegade Hardware

☐ **QUARKNOSIS**
Dolcevita: *Optica* / Utopia: *Transfinite* / Tapestry: *Quad* / Zoophite: *Optica* / Technozone: *Output & DJ Oz* / Moonshine: *Eyetek* / Aquaville: *Quad* / Trance dance: *Optic Eye* / Shimmer: *Alien Mutation* / Tokyo: *Centuras* / Something inside: *Deep Joy*
KINXCD 1 / Apr '94 / Kinetix

☐ **QUARTER TO TWELVE**
VPCD 2039 / Sep '95 / VP

☐ **QUARTIN**
Obnoxious: *Mauro, Jose* / Chao Vermelho: *Piri* / Wave: *Brasil, Victor Assis* / So Tinha de ser com voce: *Brasil, Victor Assis* / Reza Brava: *Piri* / Apocalipse: *Mauro, Jose* / Dindi: *Brasil, Victor Assis* / Children: *Brasil, Victor Assis* / Bonita: *Brasil, Victor Assis* / As Increvis Peripecias de Danilo: *Piri* / Voces Querem mate: *Piri* / Ginger bread boy: *Brasil, Victor Assis* / Quarenta graus a sombra: *Brasil, Victor Assis* / Sombra morta: *Piri* / Memoria: *Mauro, Jose* / Ao amigo quartin: *Brasil, Victor Assis*
FARO 019CD / 2 Mar '98 / Far Out

☐ **QUEENS OF AFRICAN MUSIC**
Akwaba: *Kidjo, Angelique* / Awuthele kancane: *Mahotella Queens* / 8/10: *Bel, M'Bilia* / Tsy kivy: *Tarika* / Click song: *Makeba, Miriam* / Mutumbo: *Muana, Tshala* / Farfina dambe: *Doumbia, Nahawa* / Lok' dance: *Soukous Stars* / Soamn: *Koita, Ami* / Djorolen: *Sangare, Oumou* / Christiana: *Diuobate, Oumou* / Legends: *Chaka Chaka, Yvonne* / Oukaladado: *Bell, Nayanka*
NSCD 019 / 6 Oct '97 / Nascente

☐ **QUEENS OF COUNTRY**
Rose garden: *Anderson, Lynn* / Misty blue: *Spears, Billie Jo* / Just out of reach: *Cline, Patsy* / Crazy: *Jackson, Wanda* / Both sides now: *Murray, Anne* / Harper Valley PTA: *Riley, Jeannie C.* / End of the world: *Davis, Skeeter* / DIVORCE: *West, Dottie* / When I dream: *Anderson, Lynn* / You never can tell: *Spears, Billie Jo* / Poor man's roses: *Cline, Patsy* / It's only make believe: *Jackson, Wanda* / Last thing on my mind: *Murray, Anne* / Box of memories: *Riley, Jeannie C.* / Release me: *Mandrell, Barbara* / No charge: *Montgomery, Melba* / I wish I could fall in love again: *Howard, Jan* / Dallas: *Spears, Billie Jo* / Wishful thinking: *Fargo, Donna* / Blue bayou: *Anderson, Lynn*
MUCD 9014 / Apr '95 / Musketeer

☐ **QUEENS OF COUNTRY**
Blue bayou: *Anderson, Lynn* / You never can tell: *Spears, Billie Jo* / Misty blue: *Spears, Billie Jo* / Wishful thinking: *Fargo, Donna* / It's only make believe: *Jackson, Wanda* / Box of memories: *Riley, Jeannie C.* / Both sides now: *Murray, Anne* / No charge: *Montgomery, Melba* / I wish I could fall in love again: *Howard, Jan* / Poor man's roses: *Cline, Patsy* / Release me: *Mandrell, Barbara* / Rose garden: *Anderson, Lynn* / DIVORCE: *West, Dottie* / Harper Valley PTA: *Riley, Jeannie C.* / Last thing on my mind: *Murray, Anne* / Crazy: *Jackson, Wanda* / When I dream: *Anderson, Lynn* / End of the world: *Davis, Skeeter* / Just out of reach: *Cline, Patsy* / Dallas: *Spears, Billie Jo*
300882 / Jun '98 / Hallmark

☐ **QUEENS OF COUNTRY, THE**
JHD 011 / Jun '92 / Tring

☐ **QUIET NIGHTS IN (Romantic Melodies)**
Love's theme / Just the way you are / What I did for love / Ballade pour Adeline / You light up my life / Arthur's theme / Under the influence of love / Don't it make my brown eyes blue / When I need you / Daydream believer / Bright eyes / You don't bring me flowers / One day in your life / Talking in your sleep / What's another year / Strangers in the night / Lady / Crockett's theme / Man and a woman
QED 064 / Nov '96 / Tring

R

☐ **R & B CONFIDENTIAL NO.1 - THE FLAIR STORY**
Romp and stomp blues: *Walton, Mercy Dee* / Baby beat it: *Henderson, Duke* / Cuban getaway: *Turner, Ike Orchestra* / Please find my baby: *James, Elmore* / You better hold me: *Reed, Jimmy* / Night howler: *Gale, Billy* / This is the night for love: *Flairs* / Let's make with some love: *Flairs* / Go Robbie go: *Robinson, Robbie & Binky* / Send him back: *Gunter, Shirley* / Baby, I love you so: *Gunter, Shirley* / Oop shoop: *Gunter, Shirley* / Hey Dr Kinsey: *Henderson, Duke* / Next time: *Berry, Richard* / Hard times: *Fuller, Johnny* / Chop house: *Allen, Blinky* / Have you ever: *Walton, Mercy Dee* / My baby left town: *Dixie Blues Boys* / People are wonderin': *Parham, Baby 'Pee Wee'* / Baby please: *Cockrell, Mat* / Quit hangin' around: *King, Saunders*
CDCHD 258 / Feb '89 / Ace

☐ **R & B HEROINES (Goldner's Golden Girls)**
Gee what a boy: *Joytones* / Let it be: *Smith, Savannah* / Repeat after me: *Delvetts* / What I don't know won't hurt me: *Essex* / Second hand love: *King, Mabel* / If you want to you can come: *Carousels* / I'll walk alone: *Chantels* / Don't stop the wedding: *Cole, Ann* / My foolish heart: *Joytones* / Every fortune teller tells me: *Kaye, Anne* / My valentine: *Sweet Teens* / You and I can climb: *Span, Patricia & The Cleftones* / Pretty little thing: *Carousels* / Anytime anyplace anywhere: *Smith, Savannah* / Bring it to me: *Essex* / Symbol of love: *King, Mabel* / Have fun: *Cole, Ann* / My darling: *Chantels* / Been so long: *Humes, Anita* / Jimbo jambo: *Joytones* / What did I do wrong: *Blades, Carol* / With this ring: *Sweet Teens* / Dilly dally darling: *Kaye, Anne* / Is this really the end: *Joytones*
NEMCD 918 / Jun '97 / Sequel

☐ **R & B HITS 1942-1945, THE (2CD Set)**
Take it and git: *Kirk, Andy & His Twelve Clouds of Joy* / I'm gonna leave you on the outskirts of town: *Jordan, Louis & His Tympany Five* / Stormy Monday blues: *Eckstine, Billy & Earl Hines* / Let's be friends: *Green, Lil* / What's the use of getting sober: *Jordan, Louis* / See See rider blues: *Bea Booze* / That ain't right: *Cole, Nat 'King' Trio* / Let me play with your poodle: *Tampa Red* / Let's beat out some love: *Johnson, Budd Orchestra* / Apollo jump: *Millinder, Lucky Orchestra* / Why don't you do right: *Lee, Peggy* / Riffette: *Slack, Freddie & His Orchestra* / Flying home: *Hampton, Lionel Orchestra* / Rusty dusty blues: *Rushing, Jimmy & The Count Basie*

R & B HITS 1942-1945, THE
Band / Hey lawdy Mama: Richmond, June / Five guys named Moe: Jordan, Louis / Ration blues: Jordan, Louis / Hurry hurry: Churchill, Savannah / When my man comes home: Johnson, Ella & Buddy Johnson / Straighten up and fly right: Cole, Nat 'King' Trio / Evil gal blues: Washington, Dinah / GI jive: Jordan, Louis / Cherry red blues: Vinson, Eddie 'Cleanhead' & Cootie Williams Orchestra / Is you is or is you ain't my baby: Jordan, Louis / Hamp's boogie woogie no.1: Hampton, Lionel / Gee baby, ain't I good to you: Cole, Nat 'King' Trio / I wonder: Gant, Cecil / Somebody's gotta go: Vinson, Eddie 'Cleanhead' & Cootie Williams Orchestra / Mop mop: Jordan, Louis / You can't get that no more: Jordan, Louis / SK blues: Turner, Joe / Strange things happening every day: Tharpe, Sister Rosetta / Rock me Mama: Crudup, Arthur 'Big Boy' / Caldonia: Jordan, Louis / Lover man (oh where can you be): Holiday, Billie / Who threw the whisky in the well: Harris, Wynonie / Somebody done changed the lock on my door: Jordan, Louis / That's the stuff you gotta watch: Johnson, Budd Orchestra / Honeydripper: Liggins, Joe & His Honey Drippers / Honeydripper: Liggins, Joe & His Honey Drippers / Jimmy's blues: Rushing, Jimmy & Count Basie Orchestra / Things have changed: Big Maceo / Blues at sunrise: Hunter, Ivory / Joe / Be-baba-leba: Humes, Helen
IGODCD 100 / Sep '97 / Indigo

R & B HITS 1946
Buzz me: Jordan, Louis / Honey dripper: Galloway, Cab / Drifting blues: Moore, Johnny & Charles Brown / Voo-it, voo-it: Andrews Sisters / Hey, ba-ba-re-bop: Hampton, Lionel / RM blues: Milton, Roy / Got a right to cry: Liggins, Joe / I know: Kirk, Andy & His Twelve Clouds of Joy / Tanya: Liggins, Joe / (Get your kicks on) Route 66: Cole, Nat 'King' Trio / Shorty's got to go: Millinder, Lucky / Stone cold dead in the market (he had it coming): Fitzgerald, Ella & Louis Jordan / I know who threw the whiskey (in the well): Jackson, Bull Moose / My gal's a jockey: Turner, Joe / Choo-choo ch'boogie: Jordan, Louis / Sunny road: Sykes, Roosevelt / Playful baby: Harris, Wynonie / So glad your mind: Crudup, Arthur / Gotta gimme what'cha got: Lee, Julia / Ain't that just like a woman: Jordan, Louis / Let the good times roll: Jordan, Louis
IGOCD 2060 / Feb '97 / Indigo

R & B HITS 1947
Bobby sox blues: Walker, T-Bone / Shake the boogie: Williamson, Sonny Boy / Open the door Richard: Fletcher, Dusty / Texas and Pacific: Jordan, Louis / Old maid boogie: Vinson, Eddie / Blow top blues: Washington, Dinah / Kidney stew blues: Vinson, Eddie / That's my desire: Brooks, Hadda / Jack you're dead: Jordan, Louis / I know your putting me down: Brown, Jordan, Louis / New Orleans blues: Brown, Charles & Johnny Moore's Three Blazers / True blues: Milton, Roy / Hurry on down: Lutcher, Nellie / Boogie woogie blue plate: Jordan, Louis / Red top: Ammons, Gene / He's a real gone guy: Ammons, Gene / Snatch and grab it (opportunity knocks but once): Lee, Julia / Early in the morning: Jordan, Louis / Look out: Jordan, Louis / Thrill me: Jackson, Bull Moose / I love you: Jackson, Bull Moose / Merry Christmas baby: Brown, Charles & Johnny Moore's Three Blazers
IGOCD 2081 / 19 Jan '98 / Indigo

R & B VOCAL GROUPS VOL.1
It's too soon to know: Orioles / Lemon squeezin' daddy: Sultans / Make me thrill again: Marylanders / Hey baby: Four Bars / Girl that I marry: Starlings / I've lost: Enchanters / Can't get you off my mind: Dreamers / Don't play no mombo: Charioteers / You captured my heart: Sultans / Prayer: Teardrops / Paint a sky for me: Watkins, Viola & The Crows / How you move me: Four Bars / I'm so all alone: Marylanders / Fried chicken: Marylanders / Getting tired tired tired: Orioles / Music maestro please: Powell, Sandy / You'll never understand: Bowlly, Al / I love you (I got my heart on my sleeve): Charioteers / Grief by day, grief by night: Four Bars / Blues at dawn: Sultans / Fool: Teardrops / Today is your birthday: Enchanters / These things I miss: Dreamers / Teardrops on my pillow: Orioles / Don't be angry: Sultans / Good old 99: Marylanders / If I give my heart to you: Four Bars
NEMCD 736 / Jun '95 / Sequel

R & B VOCAL GROUPS VOL.2
I'd rather have you under the moon: Orioles / Hold me: Clicks / Tears of love: Kari, Sax & Quailtones / Why do you treat me this way: Four Bars / Please love me: Marylanders / You are so beautiful: Five Notes & The Hamil-Tones / Baby let me bang your box: Toppers / My heart: Teardrops / You broke my heart: Clicks / Fine brown frame: Starlings / How I'd feel without you: Marylanders / Only you: Four Bars / Jamie low: Orioles / I've love blues: Four Bars / Ooh baby: Teardrops / One fried egg: Charioteers / Peace and love contentment: Clicks / I'm a sentimental fool: Marylanders / Stop it quit it: Four Bars / I fell for your loving: Cues / Broken hearted baby: Five Notes & The Hamil-Tones / My plea for love: Starlings / Stars are out tonight: Teardrops / Grandpa's love: Four Bars / Come back to me: Clicks
NEMCD 743 / Jun '95 / Sequel

R & B'S LOST AND FOUND
72065776002 / 7 Apr '98 / Thump

RA DA BANG BASEL (2CD Set)
910020 / Mar '98 / Winter

RABID/TJM PUNK SINGLES COLLECTION
Cranked up really high: Slaughter & The Dogs / Bitch: Slaughter & The Dogs / Ain't been to no music school: Nosebleeds / Facist pigs: Nosebleeds / Innocents: Cooper Clarke, John / Suspended sentence: Cooper Clarke, John / Psycle sluts: Cooper Clarke, John / Central detention centre: Gyro / Jilted John: Jilted John / Kinnel Tommy: Banger, Ed / Who is innocent: Out / Man in a box '47: When the world isn't there: V2 / It doesn't bother me: Distractions / It's alright: Slaughter & The Dogs / Edgar Allen Poe: Slaughter & The Dogs / Twist and turn: Slaughter & The Dogs / UFO: Slaughter & The Dogs / Where have all the boot boys gone: Hit & run / You're a bore: Elti / Fast breeder: Slaughter & The Dogs
RRCD 227 / Aug '96 / Receiver

COMPILATIONS

RADICAL BEAUTY (2CD/CD Rom Set)
Dip in the trip: Vicious Circle / 50cc: Journeyman / Sphere: Sphere Vs. Nick Philip / Hall of mirrors: Mixmaster Morris / Interlude: Pemberton, Daniel / Hypnotizing: PFM / Sonic winds: Seeba & Lotek / Hedge: Sharpe, Jonah / Sound bites: T-Power / Yusei ramen: Pemberton, Daniel
OM 007CD / 22 Sep '97 / OM

RADIO 1 SOUND CITY LEEDS 1996
CTYCD 96 / Aug '96 / Harmless

RADIO 2 - SOUNDS OF THE 60'S
Who put the bomp: Viscounts / When we get married: Dreamlovers / Have a drink on me: Donegan, Lonnie / Venus in blue jeans: Winter, Mark / Welcome home baby: Brook Brothers / Spanish harlem: Justice, Jimmy / Count on me: Grant, Julie / He's in town: Rockin' Berries / Tossing and turning: Ivy League / Thunderbirds theme: Gray, Barry Orchestra / Round every corner: Clark, Petula / Take a heart: Sorrows / Lady Jane: Garrick, David / Sittin' on a fence: Twice As Much / Baby now that I'v found you: Foundations / Green tambourine: Lemon Pipers / Handbags and gladrags: Farlowe, Chris / David Watts: Kinks / Something here in my heart: Paper Dolls / Ain't nothing but a house party: Showstoppers
NEMCD 693 / Sep '94 / Sequel

RADIO DAYS (Thanks For The Melody)
DEX 250CD / Nov '96 / Australian Jazz

RADIO DAYS
Runaway: Shannon, Del / At the hop: Danny & The Juniors / Leader of the pack: Shangri-Las / Will you love me tomorrow: Shirelles / Save the last dance for me: Drifters / It's in his kiss (shoop shoop song): Everett, Betty / Duke of earl: Chandler, Gene / My boyfriend's back: Angels / Lucille: Little Richard / Do you wanna dance: Freeman, Bobby / Sweet talkin' guy: Chiffons / Chapel of love: Dixie Cups / Surf city: Jan & Dean / Let's hear it again: Checker, Chubby / Charlie Brown: Coasters / Rebel rouser: Eddy, Duane / Singing the blues: Mitchell, Guy / Come go with me: Del Vikings / Little darlin': Diamonds / Earth angel: Crew Cuts
SUMCD 4195 / 11 May '98 / Summit

RADIO DAYS - BRITISH 30'S DANCE
Radio Times: Hall, Henry & The BBC Dance Orchestra / I don't do things like that: Trinder, Tommy / Scrimpleshop's talcum (commercial): Long, Norman / Coronation girls: Waters, Elsie & Doris / Tale of Hector Cramp: Fletcher, Cyril / Radio time signal: Taunton, Peter / Schottzelheimer's suspenders (commercial): Long, Norman / All for ten shillings a year: Stanelli & Edgar / There's a small hotel: Daniels, Bebe & Ben Lyon / Football commentary: Koys, Nelson & Ivy St. Helier / Little Betty Bouncer: Flotsam & Jetsam / British mother's big fight: Desmond, Florence & Max Kester / Ye BBC: Flanagan & Allen / Hi de ho: Revnell, Ethel & Gracie West / Cindy granules (commercial): Taunton, Peter / In 1992: Campbell, Big Bill & His Rocky Mountain Rhythm / I know that sailors do cause: O'Shea, Tessie / Radio Baloni close-down: Taunton, Peter / Ding dong bell: Askey, Arthur / Mr. and Mrs. Ramsbottom went off: Holloway, Stanley / We can't let you broadcast that: Long, Norman / Cricket commentary: Clapham & Dwyer / Jubilee baby: Driver, Betty / Henry's motors (commercial): Ratcliffe / Come on the good ship Ballyhoo: Warner, Jack & Jeff Darnell / Five-in-one practice: Pola, Eddie / Adventures of Featherston-Haugh DSO: Taunton, Peter
CDHD 163 / Feb '97 / Happy Days

RADIO FREEDOM
ROUCD 4019 / Jun '96 / Rounder

RADIO GOLD
Promised land: Allan, Johnnie / La Bamba: Valens, Ritchie / When the boy's happy (the girl's happy too): Four Pennies / Wake up little Susie: Everly Brothers / Wanderer: Dion / My true love: Jive Five / Dizzy: Roe, Lizzy: Williams, Larry / Mr. Sandman: Chordettes / I fought the law: Fuller, Bobby Four / Hush-a-bye: Mystics / Hello this is Joanie: Evans, Paul / Will you still love me tomorrow: Shirelles / Where or when: Dion & The Belmonts / Venus: Avalon, Frankie / Sixteen candles: Crests / When will I be loved: Everly Brothers / One fine day: Chiffons / Rockin' robin: Day, Bobby / Twist and shout: Isley Brothers / Little bit of soap: Jarmels / I'll come running back to you: Cooke, Sam / Earth angel: Penguins / Runaround Sue: Dion / Since I don't have you: Skyliners / Good golly Miss Molly: Little Richard / Poetry in motion: Tillotson, Johnny / Denise: Randy & The Rainbows / Tell it like it is: Neville, Aaron / Sweet dreams: McLain, Tommy / Goodnight my love: Belvin, Jesse
CDCHD 347 / Feb '92 / Ace

RADIO GOLD VOL.2
Long tall Sally: Little Richard / Runaway: Shannon, Del / Donna: Valens, Ritchie / Bye bye love: Everly Brothers / Bony Maronie: Williams, Larry / Soldier boy: Shirelles / Nut rocker: B-Bumble & The Stingers / My baby: Paul & Paula / Let's dance: Montez, Chris / Hey baby: Channel, Bruce / Nobody needs your love (like I do): Pitney, Gene / Lollipop: Chordettes / Hippy hippy shake: Romero, Chan / Dedicated follower (of fashion): Kinks / Happy: McLain, Tommy / You'll never get to heaven: Warwick, Dionne / Crying in the rain: Everly Brothers / I'll keep you satisfied: Kramer, Billy J. & The Dakotas / Needles and pins: Searchers / Shakin' all over: Kidd, Johnny & The Pirates / It's all over now: Womack, Bobby / Al / Old smokey: Weavers / It's my party: Gore, Lesley
CDCHD 446 / Sep '93 / Ace

RADIO GOLD VOL.3
Love is strange: Mickey & Sylvia / Willie and the hand jive: Otis, Johnny / Sweet nothin's: Lee, Brenda / I'm in love again: Domino, Fats / Stardust: Ward, Billy & The Dominoes / Charms of amour: Todd, Art & Dotty / I'm gonna sit right down and write myself a letter: Williams, Billy / Susie darlin': Luke, Robin / Lion sleeps tonight: Tokens / Make it easy on yourself: Butler, Jerry / If it is in his kiss (The shoop shoop song): Everett, Betty / Halfway to paradise: Orlando, Tony / That'll be the day: Crickets / Only the lonely: Orbison, Roy / When: Kalin Twins / White sports coat and a pink carnation: Robbins, Marty / On the rebound: Cramer, Floyd / Banana boat song (Day O): Belafonte, Harry / Singin' the blues: Mitchell, Guy / Twelfth of never: Mathis, Johnny / Freight train: McDevitt, Chas & Nancy Whisky / Big man: Four Preps / At the hop: Danny & The Juniors / Just walking in the rain: Ray, Johnnie / Garden of Eden: Valino, Joe / Green door: Lowe, Jim / I hear you knocking: Lewis, Smiley / Seven little girls sitting in the back seat: Evans, Paul / Witch doctor: Seville, David / I go ape: Sedaka, Neil
CDCHD 557 / May '95 / Ace

RADIO INFERNO
RTD 19715982 / Dec '93 / Our Choice

RADIO JUNGLE
RR 105CD / Jul '96 / Roots

RADIO ODYSSEY (WRAS Live On-Air Compilation)
Cut me out: Toadies / Music is love: G-Love & Special Sauce / Radar: Morphine / Morphine / Of course you can: Morphine / Life and death: Low Pop Suicide / Hazing: Throwing Muses / Tibetan music: Drepung Loseling Monks
D 2248762 / May '96 / Ichiban

RADIO RAP
Boom boom boom: Outhere Brothers / Here comes the hotstepper: Kamoze, Ini / Whatta man: Salt n' Pepa & En Vogue / Regulate: Warren G & Nate Dogg / Who am I (what's my name): Snoop Doggy Dogg / People everyday: Arrested Development / Now that we've found love: Heavy D & The Boyz / Boom shake the room: DJ Jazzy Jeff & The Fresh Prince / I like to move it: Reel 2 Real / Power: Snap / U can't touch this: MC Hammer / Informer: Snow / Boom rock soul: Benz / Homie lover friend: R Kelly / Can I kick it: Tribe Called Quest / Cantaloop (Flip fantasia): US 3 / Big poppa: Notorious BIG / Trivia of you: Usher / On a ragga tip: SL2 / Deep: East 17
RADCD 22 / Oct '95 / Global TV

RADIO ROMANCE (2CD Set)
Please don't talk about me when I'm gone: Martin, Dean / In the still of the night: Damone, Vic / Don't get around much anymore: Christy, June / You'll never know: Cole, Nat 'King' / There is no greater love: King Singers / Foolish things: Manning, Bob / There must be a way: Martino, Al / My kind of girl: Matt / C'est magnifique: Starr, Kay / Nightingale sang in Berkeley Square: Darin, Bobby / I'm beginning to see the light: Lee, Peggy / On the sunny side of the street: Stafford, Jo & The Pied Pipers / Crazy she calls me: Cole, Nat 'King' / Baby it's cold outside: Martin, Dean / Zing went the strings of your heart: Garland, Judy / Until the real thing comes along: Cole, Nat 'King' / Heal live girl: Morro, Matt / It's a long long time: Lee, Peggy / It's alright with me: Manning, Bob / You're nobody 'til somebody loves you: Martin, Dean / Standing on a corner: Darin, Bobby / Night lights: Cole, Nat 'King' / Takin' a chance on love: Shore, Dinah / It's great to be alive: Stafford, Jo & Jonny Mercer / Change partners: Damone, Vic / Canadian sunset: Williams, Andy / Long long ago: Martin, Dean & Nat 'King' Cole / I've got the world on a string: Starr, Kay / Ragtime cowboy Jo: Stafford, Jo
DOU 886702 / 2 Feb '98 / Disky

RAGE TEAM, THE
Back from the grave: Nekromantix / We did nothing wrong: Adolescents UK / Am I crazy: Mad Heads / Jeff's head: Pikehead / Rude: Grind / Self destruct: Plastic Bag / Big wide world: Strange Behaviour / And it hurts: Psycho Bunnies / Drop dead: Switchblade / Everything's so perfect: Dead Lillies / Monster metal: Nekromantix / Mrs. Thatcher's on the dole: Adolescents UK / Now or never: Mad Heads / Individuality eagle: Pikehead / Paparazzi: Grind / Right to remain silent: Plastic Bag / It's alright to love: Strange Behaviour / Not with you: Psycho Bunnies / I'm your slave: Switchblade / Freak show: Dead Lillies
RAGECD 112 / Sep '93 / Rage

RAGGA BEAT
Oh carolina / Sweat (a la la la la long) / Mr. Loverman / Try jah love / Iron lion zion / Flex / Bad boys / Deep / Red red wine / Baby I love your way / Sweets for my sweet / Wheel of fortune / Shine / Twist and shout / can't help falling in love with you / Dedicated to the one I love / I can see clearly now / Buffalo soldier
ECD 3215 / Mar '95 / K-Tel

RAGGA CLASH VOL.1
FADCD 021 / Sep '92 / Fashion

RAGGA CLASH VOL.2
FADCD 022 / Sep '92 / Fashion

RAGGA CLASH VOL.3
FADCD 029 / Nov '93 / Fashion

RAGGA CLASH VOL.4
FADCD 031 / Dec '95 / Fashion

RAGGA DOM
097042 / Apr '95 / Declic

RAGGA HITS VOL.1
MACCD 279 / Aug '96 / Autograph

RAGGA HITS VOL.2
MACCD 280 / Aug '96 / Autograph

RAGGA HOUSE
Ragamuffin hip hop: Asher D & Daddy Freddie / DC Dance: Asher D & Daddy Freddie

Mannix, Joe / Dance hall clash: Daddy Freddie & Tenor Fly / Blo' dem brains: Leslie Lyrics / Shadow and arrow: Nitty Gritty / Brutality: Asher D & Daddy Freddie / Killing me softly: Mikey General / Grand finale: Demon Boyz & Asher D/Daddy Freddie / Ragga house (all night long): Harris, Simon / Don't stop rocking: Daddy Freddy & Sugar Minott / Lanndlord monologue: Cotton, Joseph / Africa: Daddy Freddie
QED 051 / Nov '96 / Tring

RAGGA IN THE JUNGLE
STRJCD 1 / Apr '95 / Street Tuff

RAGGA JUNGLE ANTHEMS VOL.1
GREZCD 3001 / Dec '95 / Greensleeves

RAGGA JUNGLE ANTHEMS VOL.2
GREZCD 3002 / Mar '96 / Greensleeves

RAGGA MANIA
FABCD 001 / Sep '95 / Fashion

RAGGA MANIA VOL.1
CHEMCD 001 / 5 May '98 / Chemist

RAGGA MANIA VOL.2
CHEMCD 002 / Aug '95 / Chemist

RAGGA MANIA VOL.3
CHEMCD 003 / Feb '96 / Chemist

RAGGA MANIA VOL.4
CHEMCD 004 / Feb '96 / Chemist

RAGGA MEGA MIX VOL.1
SONCD 0054 / Aug '93 / Sonic Sounds

RAGGA MEGA MIX VOL.2
SONCD 0084 / Apr '96 / Sonic Sounds

RAGGA PARTY VOL.1 (Dancing On The Roof)
RN 0016 CD / Jul '92 / Runn

RAGGA PARTY VOL.2 (More Than Just Dancehall)
RN 017CD / Nov '92 / Runn

RAGGA PARTY VOL.3 (Don't Stop Ragga)
RN 0018 CD / Nov '92 / Runn

RAGGA PARTY VOL.4
RN 0019 CD / Nov '92 / Runn

RAGGA PITCH
MONCD 002 / Nov '93 / Montana

RAGGA RAGGA RAGGA VOL.1
Don't know: Jigsy King / Husband goody-goody: Capleton / Movie star: Galaxy P / Intimate: Bounty Killer & Redrose / Woman fi look good: Snagapuss / Living in a dream: Capleton & Brian & Tony Gold / Mek noise: Mad Cobra / Top gun: Cocoa T & Buju Banton / Galong so: Major Mackerel / Red alert: Spragga Benz / Work the body good: Jigsy King / Sake a yuh body: Daddy Screw & Major Christie / Informer: Snagapuss, Redrose, Lizard & More / Return father and son: Ninjaman & Ninja Ford / Bwoy need a pension: Grindsman / Money: Galaxy P / Holy moly: Bajja Jedd / Jessica: Red Fox
GRELCD 192 / Nov '93 / Greensleeves

RAGGA RAGGA RAGGA VOL.10
Who am I: Beenie Man / I don't give a damn: Cobra / Tight up skirt: Red Rat / Pet and pamper: Mad Cobra / Boom boom: General Degree / Tell me: Beenie Man / Big ninja bike: Stephens, Tanya / Work dem: Merciless / Please it on the jar (in): Captain Barkey / Dolly house secret: Red Rat & Hawkeye / Infiltrate: Paul, Sean / Girls selector: Slingshot & Mexican / Superman: General Degree / Strong performer: Spragga Benz / Trouble mi piece: Merciless / Wink me: Goofy / Nike air: Vegas / Mach 11 arena: Mad Cobra
GRELCD 247 / 2 Mar '98 / Greensleeves

RAGGA RAGGA RAGGA VOL.11
GRELCD 249 / 15 Jun '98 / Greensleeves

RAGGA RAGGA RAGGA VOL.2
Bad boy nuh club scout: Bounty Killer & Ninjaman / Dis di program: Beenie Man / Sireen: Papa San / Run come: Terror Fabulous / Wap dem girl: Sabba Tooth / Trespass: Bounty Killer / Fat piece of goose: Duck Man / Hollow point bad boy: Ninjaman / Burning up: Red Dragon / Not another word: Bounty Killer / You must be mania: Daddy Screw / Wood stitchie: Lieutenant Stitchie / Dem bawling out: Galaxy P / Jockey wid di distance: Tumpa Lion / Run gal run: Daddy Lizard / Hotness: Mad Cobra / Spermrod: Simpleton / Nuh have no heart: Bounty Killer
GRELCD 204 / Jun '94 / Greensleeves

RAGGA RAGGA RAGGA VOL.3
World dance: Beenie Man / War is not a nice thing: Tony Rebel & Garnet Silk / Mr. wiper: Turbo Belly / Angel in a Silver Cat / Woman no cuss: Buju Banton / Make a muscle: Jigsy King / Hey boy red Indian: Pinchers / Gallowas: Mad Cobra / World dance: Ninjaman / Nozzle and stagger: Judas / Only master: General Degree / Coming in style: Daddy Lizard / Riding through South: Red Dragon / Chuckleberry / Joker gangster: Merciless
GRELCD 212 / Dec '94 / Greensleeves

RAGGA RAGGA RAGGA VOL.4
GRELCD 214 / May '95 / Greensleeves

□ **RAGGA RAGGA RAGGA VOL.5**
GRELCD 218 / Aug '95 / Greensleeves

□ **RAGGA RAGGA RAGGA VOL.6**
GRELCD 223 / Nov '95 / Greensleeves

□ **RAGGA RAGGA RAGGA VOL.7**
Mr. War War: *Merciless* / Benz and bimma: *Bounty Killer* / Mad house tek him: *Spragga Benz* / Explode gal: *Red Dragon* / Hotter this year: *Buccaneer* / Girls way: *Beenie Man* / In and out: *General Degree* / Gal fi get wock: *Bounty Killer* / Want the lumber: *Simpleton* / More gyal: *Red Dragon* / Matey anthem
GRELCD 228 / May '96 / Greensleeves

□ **RAGGA RAGGA RAGGA VOL.8**
Yaw yaw: *Beenie Man* / Model: *Bounty Killer* / Hammer: *Merciless* / Buccaneer medley: *Buccaneer* / Gal dem wining: *Chuck Fender* / Blackboard: *Beenie Man* / Serve me long: *Frisco Kid* / You've got me waiting: *Bounty Killer & Nitty Kutchie/Angel Doolas* / Ban mi fi di truth: *Beenie Man* / Hot girl: *Spragga Benz* / Gal fi di future: *Daddy Screw* / Man confuse: *Merciless* / Me a wine her: *Bailey, Admiral* / It's me it's me: *Chuck Fender* / Ready or not: *Scare Dem* / Nah nuh sense Bruce: *Merciless* / Pure gal: *Harry Toddler* / Woa woa: *General Degree*
GRELCD 233 / Nov '96 / Greensleeves

□ **RAGGA RAGGA RAGGA VOL.9**
Dwayne: *Red Rat* / Pleasure tour: *General Degree* / Ill na na: *Monster Shock* / Good boy: *Red Rat* / Fudgie: *Goofy* / My gal dem: *Beenie Man* / Postman: *Hawkeye* / Bad man sonata: *Buccaneer* / Italee: *Red Rat* / Girls dem man: *Scare Dem* / Dog bark: *Goofy* / Who badda: *General Degree & Lady Saw* / Cheap clothes: *Mad Cobra* / Second place: *Buccaneer* / My man: *Lady G* / Cartoon character: *General Degree* / Little Miss Cutie: *Ghost* / Mr. McCoy: *Merciless*
GRELCD 240 / 31 Aug '97 / Greensleeves

□ **RAGGA REVOLUTION**
Getting blacker: *Macka B* / Bills: *Thriller Jenna* / Equal rights / Righteous way: *Yabby You* / Kick up a rumpus: *Pepper Seed* / Father of creation: *Harris, Bobby* / Give the poor man a bly: *Pepper Seed* / What's happening to our world: *Shaloma* / Good friend / Tomorrow is another day: *Stewart, Tinga* / Set things straight: *Pepper Seed* / Righteous dub: *Mad Professor*
ARICD 086 / Sep '93 / Ariwa Sounds

□ **RAGGA RIDDIM BHANGRA**
DMUT 1259 / Aug '93 / Multitone

□ **RAGGA SOCA HITS VOL.2**
JW 013 / Jan '96 / JW

□ **RAGGA SUN HIT**
0092 / Apr '95 / Declic

□ **RAGGA TO THE MAX**
032012 / Jan '97 / Melodie

□ **RAGGA'S GOT SOUL**
DTCD 23 / Aug '95 / Discotex

□ **RAGGA'S GOT SOUL VOL. 3**
DTCD 28 / 27 Jul '98 / Discotex

□ **RAGGASOCA 1997 HITS VOL.2**
JW 126CD / Jun '97 / JW

□ **RAGGEDY JOE**
VPCD 2063 / 23 Feb '98 / VP

□ **RAGING RIVERS**
DC 879532 / Oct '97 / Disky

□ **RAGTIME**
TRTCD 181 / Jun '95 / TrueTrax

□ **RAGTIME BLUES GUITAR 1928-1930**
One way gal: *Moore, William* / Ragtime crazy: *Moore, William* / Midnight blues: *Moore, William* / Ragtime millionaire: *Moore, William* / Tillie Lee: *Moore, William* / Barbershop rag: *Moore, William* / Old country rock: *Moore, William* / Raggin' the blues: *Moore, William* / Brownie blues: *Gay, Tarter* / Unknown blues: *Gay, Tarter* / Jamestown exposition: *Baylesse Rose* / Black dog blues: *Baylesse Rose* / Original blues: *Baylesse Rose* / Frisco blues: *Baylesse Rose* / Dupree blues: *Walker, Willie* / Sould Caroline rag: *Walker, Willie*
DOCD 5062 / Oct '92 / Document

□ **RAGTIME TO JAZZ VOL.1 (1912-1919)**
CBC 1035 / Jun '97 / Timeless Historical

□ **RAGTIME TO JAZZ VOL.2**
Teasing the cat / At the jazz band ball / Jazz de luxe / Good man is hard to find / Lonesome road / Yellow dog blues / Hello hello / Weeping willow blues / Bluin' the blue / Dixieland one-step / Left alone blues intro: Good night boat / Railroad blues / Blues naughty sweetie gives to me / Tiger rag / Sounds of Africa / Saxophone blues / Shake it and break it / Muscle shoals blues / Decatur street blues / Virginia blues / Truly / Hot lips / Loose feet / Telephone blues
CBC 1045 / Sep '97 / Timeless Historical

□ **RAGTIME VOL.1 1897-1919**
159052 / 24 Feb '98 / Jazz Archives

□ **RAILROAD SONGS AND BALLADS**
ROUCD 1508 / Aug '97 / Rounder

□ **RAIN DROPPING ON A BANANA TREE**
ROUCD 1125 / Feb '96 / Rounder

□ **RAINDANCE**
Raindance / Return from River Island / Circle of fire / Intertribal pow wow / Thunder cloud mountain / Dance of the warrior / Seeds of future happiness / Nighthawk / Honouring the horse / Dance of the bear / Song of the harvest / Celebration of the young
5298622 / Apr '96 / PolyGram TV

□ **RAINFOREST RHYTHMS (A Magical Blend Of Music And Sounds Of Nature)**
57682 / May '97 / Nature's Harmony

□ **RAJASTHAN - MUSICIANS OF THE DESERT**
C 580058CD / Jul '95 / Ocora

□ **RAJASTHANI FOLK MUSIC**
CDSDL 401 / Mar '94 / Saydisc

□ **RALLY BACK**
SPCD 0133 / Mar '98 / Super Power

□ **RAM JAM A GWAAN**
HBST 161CD / Aug '94 / Heartbeat

□ **RAMPANT COMPILATION VOL.1**
SUB 1D / Aug '95 / Subversive

□ **RANDALL LEE ROSE'S DOO WOP SHOP**
I wonder why: *Dion & The Belmonts* / Remember then: *Earls* / Why do kids grow up: *Randy & The Rainbows* / Please love me forever: *Cathy Jean & The Roommates* / You were mine: *Cathy Jean & The Roommates* / Babalu's wedding day: *Eternals* / Church bells may ring: *SC Cadets* / Pretty little angel eyes: *Lee, Curtis* / I'll follow you: *Jarmels* / Angel baby: *Rosie & The Originals* / Earth angel: *Penguins* / On Sunday afternoon: *Harptones* / Denise: *Randy & The Rainbows* / Eyes: *Earls* / Possibility: *Crowns* / We belong together: *Belmonts* / I'll never know: *Del-Satins* / Once in a while: *Chimes* / Rockin' in the jungle: *Eternals* / Shoudn't I: *Orients* / I remember: *Five Discs* / Eddie my love: *Teen Queens* / To be loved (forever): *Pentagons* / My true story: *Jive Five* / Who's that knocking: *Genies* / Angels listened in: *Crests* / Hush-a-bye: *Mystics* / There's a moon out tonight: *Capris* / This I swear: *Skyliners* / Till then: *Classics*
CDCHD 392 / Oct '92 / Ace

□ **RANDOM**
BBQCD 195 / Jun '97 / Beggars Banquet

□ **RAP A CITE**
FR 366 / 23 Feb '98 / Plug It

□ **RAP ATTACK (2CD Set)**
Rapper's delight: *Sugarhill Gang* / Message: *Grandmaster Flash & Melle Mel* / Spoonin' rap: *Spoonie Gee* / Doggie dance: *Mr. Lee* / Go see the doctor: *Kool Moe Dee* / Self destruction: *Stop The Violence Movement* / Magic wand: *Whodini* / Wee rule: *Wee Papa Girl Rappers* / I left my wallet in El Segundo: *Tribe Called Quest & Jungle Brothers* / Parents just don't understand: *DJ Jazzy Jeff & The Fresh Prince* / U can't touch this: *MC Hammer* / It's a shame: *Monie Love & True Image* / Rent thugarism: *Assault Team* / PYT: *Smooth & 2Pac* / Oregano flow: *Digital Underground* / Ghetto: *Too Short* / Can I kick it: *Tribe Called Quest* / Dog talk: *K-9 Corporation* / That's when ya lost: *Souls Of Mischief* / Doo-wop sh'bob: *TOC & Rocca* / La schmoove: *Fu-Schnickens* / Time to flow: *D-Nice* / Whoomp (there it is): *Tag Team* / Jack of spades: *Boogie Down Productions* / He's the DJ I'm the rapper: *DJ Jazzy Jeff & The Fresh Prince* / Faith: *Wee Papa Girl Rappers* / Mind blowin': *Smooth* / Get busy: *Mr. Lee* / Whites lines: *Grandmaster Flash & Melle Mel*
DOU 878312 / 2 Feb '98 / Disky

□ **RAP AUTHORITY, THE**
ICH 7803CD / Apr '94 / Ichiban

□ **RAP DECLARES WAR**
Rap declares war: *War & Friends* / Funky 4 U: *Nice & Smooth* / New Jack swing: *Wreckx n' Effect* / Feels so good: *Brand Nubian* / Potholes in my lawn: *De La Soul* / Short but funky: *Too Short* / Heartbeat: *Ice-T* / Young black male: *2Pac* / Don't let no-one get you down: *War & Hispanic MC's* / Low rider (on the boulevard): *Latin Alliance* / Ya estuvo (that's it): *Kid Frost* / Slow ride: *Beastie Boys* / Drums of steel: *7A3* / Rhyme fighter: *Mellow Man Ace* / Summatymz ova: *Brotherhood Creed* / Spill the wine: *Lighter Shade Of Brown* / Join me please (homeboys make some noise): *Mantronix*
74321305252 / Sep '95 / Avenue

□ **RAP FROM BRAZIL**
KAR 981 / Nov '96 / IMP

□ **RAP HITS**
Gangsta's paradise / Get a life / White lines (Don't do it) / U can't touch this / Let's talk about sex / Set adrift on memory bliss / Push it / Me myself and I / Jump around / Walk this way / Hip hop hooray / Funky cold medina / Mr. Wendal / Informer / Come baby come / Now that we found love / Here we go / It's a shame (my sister) / Can I kick it
306342 / Jan '97 / Hallmark

□ **RAP HOUSE DANCE PARTY**
15376 / Aug '91 / Laserlight

□ **RAP IT UP**
NBCD 95010 / 18 May '98 / Nite & Blue

□ **RAP LEGENDS ARCHIVE VOL.1**
BLIPCD 103 / Oct '96 / Urban London

□ **RAP LEGENDS ARCHIVE VOL.2**
BLIPCD 104 / Oct '96 / Urban London

□ **RAP REVIVAL**
Part time sucker: *KRS 1* / I think I can beat Mike Tyson: *DJ Jazzy Jeff & The Fresh Prince* / Luck off Lucien: *Tribe Called Quest* / Get in the groove: *Wee Papa Girl Rappers* / Set the pace: *Skinny Boys* / Ghetto: *Too Short* / Sue me: *Dr. Ice* / Illegal business: *Boogie Down Productions* / Verses from the abstract: *Tribe Called Quest* / Hands across the ocean: *She Rockers* / Haunted house of rock: *Whodini* / My imagination: *2 Too Many* / 808 is comin': *D-Nice* / Big mouth: *Whodini* / No respect: *Kool Moe Dee* / I can go crazy: *DJ Jazzy Jeff* / Nasty girls: *Steady B*
EMPRCD 554 / Nov '94 / Emporio

□ **RAP RULES**
What's up doc (can we rock): *Fu-Schnickens & Shaquille O'Neal* / La Raza: *Kid Frost* / Smoke some kill: *Schoolly D* / Shoot pass slam: *Shaquille O'Neal* / I think I can beat Mike Tyson: *DJ Jazzy Jeff & The Fresh Prince* / This is how we rip shit: *Casual* / On and on: *Shyheim aka The rugged Child* / Ruff karnage: *Silver Bullet* / Something 2 smoke 2: *MC Breed* / Victim of the ghetto: *College Boyz* / Streit up menace: *MC Eiht* / Nasty girls: *Steady B* / Mentirosa: *Mellow Man Ace* / Thugarism: *Assault Team* / Flow on: *Lords Of The Underground* / Trigga gots no heart: *Spice 1*
DC 881352 / Jul '97 / Disky

□ **RAP STREET**
ITM 001459CD / Jun '93 / ITM

□ **RAPE OF HOLY TRINITY, THE**
SHAGRATH 007CD / Mar '97 / Hot

□ **RAPPAZ 'N' DA HOOD (4CD Set)**
DTKBOX 62 / Jun '97 / Dressed To Kill

□ **RAPPER'S PARADISE**
MCD 87037 / 1 Dec '97 / NRJ Energy

□ **RAPSODY OVERTURE**
Intrumental / E lucean le stelle: *Xzibit* / Dear Mallika: *LL Cool J* / E lucean le stelle: *Xzibit* / Prince Igor: *Warren G & Sissel* / Belle nuit: *Mother Superia* / Praludium: *Jay* / Ach so fromm: *Jay* / Syrinx: *Redman* / Vissi d'arte: *Onyx* / Schwanensee: *Scoota* / Recondita armonica: *Nikki D* / Nessun dorma: *Mobb Deep* / Prince Igor: *Warren G & Sissel*
5368552 / 19 Jan '98 / Mercury

□ **RARE 60'S BEAT TREASURES VOL.1**
BTCD 77010 / Nov '97 / Gone Beat

□ **RARE 60'S BEAT TREASURES VOL.2**
BTCD 77011 / Nov '97 / Gone Beat

□ **RARE 60'S BEAT TREASURES VOL.3**
BTCD 77012 / 24 Nov '97 / Gone Beat

□ **RARE BLUES 1934-1937**
DOCD 53331 / Apr '95 / Document

□ **RARE BLUES 1938-1948**
DOCD 5427 / Jul '96 / Document

□ **RARE BRAZIL VOL.5**
RB OO5CD / May '97 / Batacuda

□ **RARE BRAZIL VOL.6**
RB 006CD / May '97 / Batacuda

□ **RARE CHICAGO BLUES 1962-1968**
CDBB 9530 / Jun '93 / Bullseye Blues

□ **RARE COLLECTABLE AND SOULFUL VOL.1 (RCA - Northern Soul's Holy Grail)**
Ooh it hurts me: *Cavaliers* / Push a little bit harder: *Metros* / Change your ways: *Kendricks, Willie* / What can I do: *Chandler, Lorraine* / (Putting my heart under) lock and key: *Scott, Sharon* / Take me away: *Cooke, Carolyn* / What's that on your finger: *Carter, Kenny* / It hurts too much to cry: *Barnum, H.B.* / Today is my day: *Courtney, Dean* / Since you're gone: *Barons* / Lovesick: *Dynamics* / She'll be leaving you: *Kendricks, Willie* / It's better: *Scott, Sharon* / Mend the torn pieces of my heart: *Chandler, Lorraine* / Having fun: *Bobbettes* / Don't you know (a true love when you see one): *Mason, Tony* / Crackin' up over you: *Hamilton, Roy* / I'm just a man: *Insiders* / I'm leaving: *Nash, Johnny* / Let the music play: *Hamilton, Roy* / What have I done wrong: *Crawford, Faye* / Come on strong: *Wilcox, Nancy* / It didn't take much (for me to fall in love): *Wiggins, Percy* / I'll never forget you: *Metros*
CDKEND 141 / Jan '97 / Kent

□ **RARE COLLECTABLE AND SOULFUL VOL.2**
I can't hold on: *Chandler, Lorraine* / You only live twice: *Chandler, Lorraine* / Happy go lucky me: *Bobbettes* / Love is so wonderful: *Courtney, Dean* / It's guaranteed: *Cavaliers* / Dance little girl: *Cavaliers* / Girl's got soul: *Dynamics* / She's foolin' you: *Kendricks, Willie* / My imagination: *Metros* / Don't wait too long: *Scott, Sharon* / I'm not afraid: *Scott, Sharon* / Let me correct myself: *Mason, Tony* / Chain reaction: *Celestrals* / Three rooms with running water: *Nash, Johnny* / What kind of love is this: *Nash, Johnny* / Reach out for me: *Hamilton, Roy* / Anything you do: *Channels* / Stronger than me: *Lumley, Rufus* / I've got to find her: *Carter, Kenny* / Tears and misery: *Til, Sonny* / Movin' too slow: *Exciters* / Can't let you go: *Geminis*
CDKEND 156 / 24 Nov '97 / Kent

□ **RARE GROOVE**
Boogie wonderland: *Earth, Wind & Fire/The Emotions* / Shake your body: *Jacksons* / That's the way I like it: *KC & The Sunshine Band* / Use it up and wear it out: *Odyssey* / And the beat goes on: *Whispers* / Contact: *Starr, Edwin* / More than a woman: *Tavares* / If I can't have you: *Elliman, Yvonne* / I will survive: *Gaynor, Gloria* / Ring my bell: *Ward, Anita* / Hang on in there baby: *Bristol, Johnny* / Rock your baby: *McCrae, George* / You bet your love: *Hancock, Herbie* / Now that we've found love: *Third World* / Play that funky music: *Wild Cherry* / It's a disco night (rock don't stop): *Isley Brothers* / Le freak: *Chic* / We are family: *Sister Sledge* / Boogie nights: *Heatwave* / You make me feel (mighty real): *Sylvester* / Don't stop the music: *Yarbrough & Peoples* / Working my way back to you: *Detroit Spinners* / Rock the boat: *Hues Corporation* / Funky town: *Lipps Inc.* / Love come down: *King, Evelyn 'Champagne'* / I can make you feel good: *Shalamar* / Celebration: *Kool & The Gang* / Haven't stopped dancing yet: *Gonzales* / Right back where we started from: *Nightingale, Maxine* / Get along without you now: *Wills, Viola* / Jump to the beat: *Lattisaw, Stacy* / Searching: *Change*
QTVCD 016 / Nov '92 / Quality

□ **RARE GROOVE CLASSICS VOL.1**
SGCD 16 / Jul '93 / Sir George

□ **RARE JAZZ AND BLUES PIANO 1935-1937**
DOCD 5388 / Dec '95 / Document

□ **RARE MEXICAN CUTS FROM THE SIXTIES**
EVAB 23 / 1 Jun '98 / EVA

□ **RARE REGGAE FROM THE VAULTS OF STUDIO ONE**
HBCD 47 / May '89 / Heartbeat

□ **RARE SOUL HARMONY OF THE 60'S**
I need your love: *Chandlers* / No no no: *Appreciations* / On a little island: *Enchanters* / Call on me: *Four Reputations* / Today I kised my new love: *Arabians* / I want you to be my baby: *De-Lites* / Love: *Ascots* / Did I make a mistake: *Revlons* / Easy to be true: *People's Choice* / Baby baby: *Premonitions* / So lonely: *Perfections* / You are: *Executive 4* / You should have told me: *New Yorkers* / Boy next door Frankie: *Karl & The Chevrons* / You don't love me anymore: *Limelights* / I'll hold on: *Four Perfections* / Forever: *Seminoles* / Good night: *Celebrities* / Go on: *United Four* / Why do I do these foolish things: *United Four* / I need your love: *Reflections* / How was your weekend: *Mac, Bobby* / Steal away: *Flint Emeralds* / You've been gone so long: *Tomangoes*
GSCD 115 / 23 Mar '98 / Goldmine

□ **RARE SOUL UNCOVERED VOL.1 (Chicago Twine Time)**
CDNEW 131 / 1 Jun '98 / Charly

□ **RARE TERRITORY BANDS**
IAJRCCD 1002 / Oct '93 / IAJRC

□ **RAREST ROCKABILLY & HILLBILLY BOOGIE/BEST OF ACE ROCKABILLY**
Nothin' but a nuthin': *Stewart, Jimmy & His Nighthawks* / Darlin': *Dale, Jimmie* / Baby doll: *Dale, Jimmie* / Pretending is a game: *Jeffers, Sleepy & The Davis Twins* / My blackbirds are bluebirds now: *Jeffers, Sleepy & The Davis Twins* / Don't sweep that dirt on me: *Shaw, Buddy* / No more: *Shaw, Buddy* / My baby left me: *Rogers, Rock* / Little dog blues: *Price, Mel* / Henpecked daddy: *Johnson, Ralph & The Hillbilly Show Boys* / Umm boy you're my baby: *Johnson, Bill & The Dabblers* / Stoney mountain boogie: *Stoney Mountain Playboys* / Big black cat: *Hendon, R.D.* / It's a Saturday night: *Mack, Billy* / Rockin' daddy: *Fisher, Sonny* / Everybody's movin': *Glenn, Glen* / One cup of coffee: *Glenn, Glen* / I can't find the doorknob: *Jimmy & Johnny* / My big fat baby: *Hall, Sonny & The Echoes* / How come it: *Jones, Thumper* / Trucker from Tennessee: *Davis, Link* / Little bit more: *LaBeef, Sleepy* / I'm through: *LaBeef, Sleepy* / Jitterbop baby: *Harris, Hal* / Let's get it on: *Almond, Hershel* / I'm a hobo: *Reeves, Danny* / Rock it: *Jones, George* / Sneaky Pete: *Fisher, Sonny*
CDCHD 311 / Jul '91 / Ace

□ **RAS PORTRAITS (2CD Set)**
Somewhere: *McGregor, Freddie* / Break free: *Minott, Sugar* / One stone: *Culture* / Crysis: *Lodge, J.C.* / Give it with caution: *Isaacs, Gregory* / Jah Jah hear my plea: *Don Carlos* / Great train robbery: *Black Uhuru* / De di doo: *Eek-A-Mouse* / No wanga gut: *Tiger* / License to kill: *Charlie Chaplin* / Showers of blessings: *Reid, Junior* / Righteous: *Mystic Revealers* / Don't let the children cry: *Broggs, Peter* / Same song: *Israel Vibration* / Songs of freedom: *Paul, Frankie* / Natty dread rise again: *Congos* / Prayer: *Yellowman* / Victory is mine: *Brown, Dennis* / Little children cry: *Levy, Barrington* / Corrupt cop: *Mighty Diamonds* / Rocking dolly: *Cocoa T* / Lay it on the line: *Wailing Souls* / Kunte kinte: *Mad Professor* / Squeeze me: *Macka B* / Nah give up: *Sizzla* / Unforgettable: *Fraser, Dean*
RASMP 33903 / Jun '97 / Ras

□ **RAS PORTRAITS (Harmony Trios)**
Dread in the mountain: *Black Uhuru* / Cool and calm: *Israel Vibration* / One stone: *Culture* / Something is wrong: *Link & Chain* / Teach the children: *Heptones* / Get up and dance: *Melodians* / Natty dread rise again: *Congos* / Posse are you ready: *Mighty Diamonds* / Joy in the morning: *Psalms*
RAS 3306 / Jul '97 / Ras

□ **RAS PORTRAITS (Dancehall DJ's)**
Nice up dance: *Natural Beauty* / No wanga gut: *Tiger* / Firing strong: *Tony Rebel* / Nah give in: *Sizzla* / Blackness awareness: *Michigan & Smiley* / Lyrics of mine: *Brigadier Jerry* / Music addict: *U-Roy* / Reggae on the move: *Yellowman* / Alms house: *Capleton* / Ruff this year: *Chaka Demus & Pliers* / Oh Lord: *Tappa Zukie* / Love mi sess: *Top Cat* / Charlie in the party: *Charlie Chaplin* / Gun in a baggy: *Little Lenny* / Mother culture: *Sister Carol*
RAS 3311 / Jul '97 / Ras

□ **RAS PORTRAITS (The Ariwa Label)**
Never risk: *McLean, John* / You are the one: *Intense* / We play reggae: *Kofi* / Armagedeon: *Andy, Horace* / Squeeze me: *Macka B* / Kill the Police Bill: *Ranking Ann* / DJ Mama: *Thriller Jenna* / True born African: *U-Roy* / King step: *Pato Banton* / Rebel on the roots corner: *Tippa Irie* / Speed rap: *Papa Levi* / Mystic warrior: *Perry, Lee 'Scratch'* / One million man dub: *Jah Shaka & Mad Professor* / Doppler in de jungle: *Mad Professor & William The Conqueror/King O' Di Jungle* / Kunte kinte jungle: *Mad Professor & Douggie Digital/Juggler*
RAS 3320 / Jul '97 / Ras

□ **RAS PORTRAITS (The Live & Learn Label)**
Hear the River Jordan: *Ras Michael & The Sons Of Negus* / Le' go me hand: *Josey Wales* / Teach me culture: *Levy, Barrington* / Reggae-lution: *Mighty Diamonds* / Chanting: *Reid, Junior & Don Carlos* / Black history: *Reid, Junior & Don Carlos* / Hold tight: *Brown, Dennis* / Where is Garvey: *Mighty Diamonds* / Them a fret: *Wailing Souls* / Kingston 14: *Wailing Souls* / Run around child: *Hammond, Beres & Barrington Levy* / Some girls are trouble: *Hammond, Beres & Barrington Levy* / Jam session: *Mighty Diamonds* / Play on: *Wailing Souls* / Cease fire: *Prophet, Michael* / Forward natty: *Campbell, Al*
RAS 3330 / Jul '97 / Ras

☐ **RAS RECORDS PRESENTS A REGGAE CHRISTMAS**
We wish you a merry Christmas / Jingle bells: *Don Carlos & Glenice Spencer* / Joy of the world: *Lodge, J.C.* / O come all ye faithful (Adeste fidelis): *McGregor, Freddie* / Drummer boy: *Michigan & Smiley* / Twelve days of Christmas: *Broggs, Peter* / Silent night: *Black, Pablo* / Feliz Navidad: *McGregor, Freddie* / Night before Christmas: *Eek-A-Mouse*
RASCD 3101 / Jan '89 / Ras

☐ **RAS, REGGAE AND RYKODISC**
RCD 20151 / Aug '91 / Hannibal

☐ **RAST DESTAGAH**
PANCCD 2017 / May '93 / Pan

☐ **RASTA**
BB 2808 / Aug '96 / Blue Beat

☐ **RASTA REGGAE**
RB 3018 / Jan '96 / Reggae Best

☐ **RASTA SHOWCASE**
CC 2708 / Jan '94 / Crocodisc

☐ **RASTAFARI LIVETH IN THE HEART**
JLCD 5001 / Jul '97 / Uptempo

☐ **RASTAFARI TEACHINGS VOL.1**
ROTCD 004 / Jun '95 / Reggae On Top

☐ **RASTAFARI TEACHINGS VOL.2**
ROTCD 014 / 6 Apr '98 / Reggae On Top

☐ **RAUNCHY BUSINESS - HOT NUTS AND LOLLIPOPS**
Sam the hot dog man: *Johnson, Lil* / My stove's in good condition: *Johnson, Lil* / Wipe it off: *Johnson, Lonnie* / Best jockey in town: *Johnson, Lonnie* / Shave 'em dry: *Bogan, Lucille* / He's just my size: *Kirkman, Lillie Mae* / If it don't fit (don't force it): *Barrel House Annie* / Furniture man blues: *Johnson, Lonnie & Victoria Spivey* / My pencil don't write no more: *Carter, Bo* / Banana in your fruit basket: *Carter, Bo* / Get 'em from the peanut man (hot nuts): *Johnson, Lil* / Get 'em from the peanut man (the new hot nuts): *Johnson, Lil* / Drivin' that thing: *Mississippi Sheiks* / Bed spring poker: *Mississippi Sheiks* / Lollypop: *Hunter & Jenkins* / Meat cuttin' blues: *Hunter & Jenkins* / You got to give me some of it: *Moss, Buddy* / Butcher shop blues: *Edwards, Bernice*
4678892 / May '91 / Columbia

☐ **RAUSCHEN VOL.10**
FIM 1017 / Oct '95 / Force Inc.

☐ **RAUSCHEN VOL.11**
FIM 1018 / Mar '96 / Force Inc.

☐ **RAUSCHEN VOL.12 (2CD Set)**
FIM 1022 / Oct '96 / Force Inc.

☐ **RAUSCHEN VOL.13**
EFA 044272 / 27 Apr '98 / Force Inc.

☐ **RAUSCHEN VOL.7**
FIM 1013 / Jun '94 / Force Inc.

☐ **RAUSCHEN VOL.9**
FIM 1016 / Apr '95 / Force Inc.

☐ **RAVE - JUST DO IT (2CD Set)**
560022 / Jan '97 / Westcom

☐ **RAVE AND CRUISE (The Odyssey - 2CD Set)**
Odyssey: *Novy, Tom* / Feel it: *Bruisin' Hool* / La maree: *Charles L'Admiral* / Smilin' faces: *Romanto* / Swing it: *Future Funk* / Air royo: *Disko Pogo* / Croissant show, me gusta mucha: *Acis Maris* / Vor mentera: *Bug, Steve* / Vibrations: *X-Men* / SOS bells: *Houzer, Felix* / La onda: *Dune, Alex* / Flying jazz: *Pussylover* / Drums: *Westbam* / Get wicked: *Hardsequencer* / Drop da bass: *Raver's Nature* / T2: *Tanith* / Flashing teardrops: *Resistance* / Freak tonight: *Pascal* / Descent III: *Talla 2XLC* / No more pain: *Rixen, Gerrit* / Bass for life: *DJ Felipe* / Mr. Brown's ice coffee: *Yamul* / Goody goody: *Dook Mayza* / Paraguys: *DJ Dick* / Maschuge: *Genlog*
74321382462 / Jun '96 / Kosmonaut

☐ **RAVE COLLISION**
EWM 41872 / Aug '95 / Broken Beat

☐ **RAVE DA NATION (2CD Set)**
SPV 09240442 / Nov '97 / SPV

☐ **RAVE FLOOR MUSIC FOR RAVE FLOOR PEOPLE VOL.1 (2CD Set)**
BB 04209DCD / Jan '96 / Broken Beat

☐ **RAVE GENERATION**
CDSOR 003 / Feb '97 / Sound Of Rome

☐ **RAVE MASSACRE**
SPV 08938962 / Oct '94 / SPV

☐ **RAVE MASSACRE VOL.5 (2CD Set)**
Way we rocked it: *DJ Delirium & Guitar Rob* / Don't fuck with a roughneck: *Juggernaut* / Music that lasts forever: *DJ Roy* / Speedy recovery: *Source Code* / Intelligent hardcore: *Dark Raver & DJ Vince* / Vandaag: *Gabbers Voor Gabbers* / Vocoder: *DJ Devon* / Aboriginal: *Bioforce & Mike Oh'man* / Braingeyser: *El Bruto* / Mindblower: *Ectomorph* / Hootimack: *Enfusia* / Get down: *Liberator* / Hell is coming: *Zelator* / Mindcrushing: *Da Mindcrusher* / Impulsive: *Dark Destination* / Fuck (what else): *Scum* / Stylewarrior: *Bazooka* / Filled with power: *Predator* / Raid over Moscow: *Nuclear System* / Got up hardcore: *Out Of Key* / Break it down: *Viper* / Fight: *Speedfreak* / Satanic cults: *Coremat Inc.* / No happy shit: *Rotterdam Terror Corps* / Drunken bonehead: *Drugzone* / Let's drum the boomstick: *Revolution Team & The Snake* / Sign of the void: *Rapid S* / Kick this party: *Bioforce & Mike Oh'man* / New style: *DJ Alex* / Wake up: *Hough & Dr. Pille* / WWRU: *Reactor*
SPV 08947492 / Jun '97 / SPV

☐ **RAVE MISSION**
09238508 / Jan '96 / SPV

☐ **RAVE MISSION (The Dream Edition/ 2CD Set)**
Traumzeit: *Dreamplant* / Secret love: *Magnetic Pulstar* / Waterfall: *Atlantic Ocean* / Our dream: *Caucasuss* / Alcatraz: *Peyote* / Paraglide: *Paragliders* / Transfiguration: *DJ Dave Davis* / Dreamgarden: *Hardworld* / Space girl: *DJ Hooligan* / Dreams: *Quench* / Tower of Naphatali: *C.J. Bolland* / Love stimulation: *Humate* / Oasis: *Paragliders* / 3rd rebirth: *Jones & Stephenson* / World of aqua: *Aqua* / Beyond your dreams: *Homahino* / 16 reasons to love: *Niholai* / Source: *Redeye* / My world: *Van Dyke, Paul* / Herzsprung: *Caunos* / Planet: *Mystic Forces* / How much can you take: *Visions Of Shiva*
SPV 09247382 / Feb '97 / SPV

☐ **RAVE MISSION CLASSICS VOL.1 (2CD Set)**
Catching the scent of mystery: *4-Voice* / Herzsprung: *Caunos* / Waterfront: *Kamasutra* / Stuck on a spacetrip: *Demonic Emotions* / Torus: *Green, Marc* / Evolution: *Mandala* / Evolver: *De Niro* / Human beings: *Interstate* / Let's celebrate: *DJ Thoka* / Static: *Eisley, Mos* / I likem like that: *Digital Mama* / Inside your head: *Paraphobia* / Heulunder wolf: *Future Breeze* / Rubycon: *Top, Emmanuel* / Meditation spiritualism and love: *Wax Trax* / Brainchild: *Nostrum* / Time: *Mega'lo Mania* / Nothing is over: *Possible Words* / I wanna dance: *Final Fantasy* / Green flow: *DJ Khetama* / Lost souls: *Secret Alloy* / Dark melody: *Faxe Inc* / Alright: *Magnetic Slides* / Ganesha: *Karma*
SPV 08539122 / 29 Jun '98 / SPV

☐ **RAVE MISSION VOL.1 (2CD Set)**
SPV 08838952 / Aug '94 / Subterranean

☐ **RAVE MISSION VOL.10 (3CD Set)**
Headlines: *Gargano, Pablo* / Solid session: *Format* / Intialize: *DJ Yanny & The Paragod* / Orange juice: *E-Max* / Accelerator: *Nuclear Hyde* / Listen to the fat bass: *Loving Loops* / Fiesta: *Aircraft* / Black arrows: *Gary D* / Forbidden fruit: *Canyon* / Innocent game: *Planet Groove* / Rage: *Planet Groove* / Believe in me: *Load Michall* / Uberschall: *Scoozy, Mark* / Firmly underground: *Hide & Seek* / Awakening: *POB & Xavia* / Sensoria II: *DJ Marcelo* / Enervate: *Transa* / What to be: *Racoon* / Guava: *Caucasuss* / Vicious circle: *Club Quake* / Cost control: *Steady State* / Blue planet: *Blue Planet* / Psylophone: *Unison* / Cydonia: *Dark Bones & De Chile*
SPV 09247712 / Sep '97 / SPV

☐ **RAVE MISSION VOL.11 (2CD Set)**
SPV 09247822 / 2 Feb '98 / SPV

☐ **RAVE MISSION VOL.12 (2CD Set)**
Confusion: *APE* / Enter the darkroom: *Plastic Angel* / Millenium: *Cores* / It's a dream: *DJ Manga* / Sleeper: *Quietman* / Paranoid: *Silent Harmony* / Vision of life: *Hand's Burn* / Come on: *Interstate* / Chase: *Trance Atlantic Air Waves* / Sex machine: *Taylor, Norman* / Happiness: *DJ Crack* / La mosca: *Esperanza, Tony* / Let it flow: *Clinix* / Silent wishes: *Planet Fuse* / Deep blue: *Planet Ocean* / Send me an angel: *Modern Art* / Outback: *Aqualite* / Move your feet: *DJ Mellow D* / In my dream: *Scoopex*
DCD 08939012 / 30 Mar '98 / SPV

☐ **RAVE MISSION VOL.13 (2CD Set)**
DCD 08939172 / 3 Aug '98 / SPV

☐ **RAVE MISSION VOL.2 (Entering Lightspeed/2CD Set)**
SPV 08938232 / Dec '94 / Subterranean

☐ **RAVE MISSION VOL.3 (2CD Set)**
SPV 08938292 / May '95 / Subterranean

☐ **RAVE MISSION VOL.4 (2CD Set)**
SPV 08938352 / Jul '95 / Subterranean

☐ **RAVE MISSION VOL.5 (The Jubilee Box Set/3CD Set)**
TCD 09238480 / Dec '95 / Subterranean

☐ **RAVE MISSION VOL.7 (2CD Set)**
Stuck on a spacetrip: *Demonic Emotions* / Whiplash: *Overcharge & G.Meter* / Unicorn: *DJ Tomicraft* / Nothing is over: *Possible Words* / Cosmic wave: *DJ Warlock* / Ganesha: *Karma* / That's the way it should be: *De Luxe, Tom* / People: *Indris* / Evolver: *De Niro* / Electronically entertained: *Technology* / Human beings: *Interstate* / Secret love: *Magnetic Pulstar* / Twilight zone: *Aqualoop* / Trance research: *E-Space* / Erotmania: *DJ Randy* / Baby: *Nostrum* / Error 129: *Greenforce* / What is: *DJ Thoka* / Beyond the clouds: *Omega Force* / Give me all you got: *Soulslider* / Sweet gravity remix: *LSG* / Soccer boys: *XXL*
09247232 / Nov '96 / SPV

☐ **RAVE MISSION VOL.8 (2CD Set)**
Perfect: *Scope* / Planet hunter: *Third Man* / Monosphere: *Liquid Bass* / Lost Genesis: *Backdraft* / E volution: *Virtual Atmosfear* / Great bear: *Little Jam* / Crazy: *Global Control* / Sleepless: *Greenforce* / Metropolis: *Changall* / Other worlds: *Proxyma* / Vulcan: *Commander Tom* / My love emotions: *Creams* / Meta morph VI: *Error 010* / Tears: *Solid Sleep* / Overdrive: *Mass In Orbit* / In heaven: *Oson* / Mind over matter: *Sloane Strangers* / Yesterday: *Sonic Tool* / What was it like: *Framic* / ATOMIC JUNKIES: *Atomic Junkies* / Luke: *Planet E Team* / Human beings: *Interstate*
SPV 09247372 / Feb '97 / SPV

☐ **RAVE MISSION VOL.9 (2CD Set)**
SPV 09247502 / May '97 / SPV

☐ **RAVE OF THE WORLD**
CLP 9920 / Mar '97 / Hypnotic

☐ **RAVE POWER (3CD Set)**
ZYX 811092 / Jul '97 / ZYX

☐ **RAVE RELIGION VOL.1**
Energy: *DJ Tibby* / Pagemaster: *DJ Gollum* / Secret (don't tell it): *D-Lay* / Lonely days: *Comma* / Alright: *Magnetic Slides* / Any time any place: *Alien Factory* / Credits: *Celysys, Tom* / Albion: *Twisted* / Journey: *Oaks, Oliver & DJ Luna* / Peaceful harmony: *Plastic Enemy* / Now and zen: *Quiet Man* / Revolver: *De Niro* / Megalomania: *Mega Lomania* / Pulse: *Magnetic Pulstar* / Don't be afraid: *Moonman* / Let there be light: *Moonman* / Achtung: *Timo Maas & Digital City* / Get back to the growlers: *Growlers* / Good music: *DJ Meltron* / Running dream: *Levy 9* / Hold back: *Edge & Dentist* / Overland: *Dawntreader*
560113 / Aug '97 / Nova Tekk

☐ **RAVE ZONE '95**
Speed freak: *Speed Freak* / Move me up: *Surreal Deal Featuring Anji* / Camel: *Yekuana* / Partytime: *Katclub* / Indian summer: *Atomix* / Rockin' to the music: *Savannah* / I'm so real: *Miss Ferguson* / Kingdom: *Yekuana* / Ready steady: *Tomorrow people* / Heaven: *Positive Connection* / Jump jump (a little higher): *Progen 7* / Everybody get up: *Angel Deluxe*
ECD 3100 / Jan '95 / K-Tel

☐ **RAVEALATION**
STHCCD 11 / Jun '95 / Strictly Underground

☐ **RAVEHEART - THE FUBAR ALBUM**
FACD 2 / Nov '96 / Fubar

☐ **RAVEMASTER VOL.2**
ZYX 81088 / Oct '96 / ZYX

☐ **RAVEMEISTER CLASSICS VOL.1 (2CD Set)**
SPV 08547942 / 2 Feb '98 / SPV

☐ **RAVEMEISTER VOL.1 (2CD Set)**
SPV 08938362 / Jun '95 / Subterranean

☐ **RAVEMEISTER VOL.2 (2CD Set)**
SPV 08938452 / Dec '95 / Subterranean

☐ **RAVEMEISTER VOL.3 (2CD Set)**
Black is black: *All Nighters* / Read my lips: *Future Breeze* / Put your house in order: *Toja* / Magma: *Dual Mount* / Stargate custodian: *Stargate* / Forcing beat: *Casseopaya* / Comix: *L'Age Synthetique* / Acid invasion: *Pneumonia* / Capturing matrix: *Rexanthony* / You can't stop the groove: *Fusion* / Watchman's theme: *Watchman* / Open da house: *Lords Of Octagon* / Northern lights: *Mr. Oz & Larry Lush* / Baby: *Nostrum* / Photon: *Tool & Sakin* / Double orange: *D-Fense & Confusion* / Container dreams: *Elasticoculture* / Poisoned strawberry: *Tranceatlantic*
SPV 08938652 / May '96 / Subterranean

☐ **RAVEMEISTER VOL.4 (2CD Set)**
Get up: *Picard, Etienne* / Blow back: *Nostrum* / Make your wish: *Microgroove* / Spin: *Exithone* / Matabu: *Cores* / Interceptor: *Van Basten* / Lash v 11: *Rubicon Massacre Ltd.* / Favorite: *DJ Ed* / Numa: *Phonetics* / Space party: *Space Frog* / Voice: *D-Fense & Confusion* / Bob km: *Friends, Lovers & Family* / Stepping energy: *Ultrashock* / Force: *Omega Force* / Connect: *Mass In Orbit* / Evolution: *Mandala* / Lostsideon: *Lostideon* / Mediation, spiritualism and love: *Wax Trax 2* / Intoxication: *Unison* / Turn it up: *Huntemann* / Based on acid: *DJ Ablaze* / Synthetic Mankind: *State Of House* / Pandora's box: *Zaffarano, Marco*
SPV 09247142 / Nov '96 / Subterranean

☐ **RAVEMEISTER VOL.5 (2CD Set)**
Running man: *Nuclear Hyde* / Bad house music: *Loving Loops* / Human beings: *Interstate* / Monastery: *Nostrum* / Sleepless: *Greenforce* / Snavalo: *TB-Tuner* / Mystery: *Code 16* / Allright: *Patchwork* / My love: *Datas* / Acid squid: *Asys* / Like it: *Pneumonia* / Maen cetti: *Pendragon & Taffrican* / Status X: *Framic* / Pandorras: *Raptor* / Research: *X-Ite* / Overdrive: *Mass In Orbit* / Take me to the top: *MNA-Project* / Sound: *De Donatis* / Stairclimbing: *Lunar Trip* / Every night: *Virtual Elements* / Liquid loop: *Aqualite* / Sonnenschein: *Perpetuum Mobile*
SPV 09247352 / Feb '97 / Subterranean

☐ **RAVEMEISTER VOL.6 (2CD Set)**
Ayla: *Ayla* / Love is solution: *Exit EEE* / Matter in question: *Riva* / La vache: *Milk Inc.* / Club art: *Rees, John* / Pandomia: *DJ Randy* / Alright: *Magnetic Slides* / Run off: *Rave Bass* / Accident: *Skylab* / Scream: *Avalonge* / Nothing but deluxe: *Deluxe* / End: *Nostrum* / Nighttripper: *Equator* / Lonely days: *Comma* / Best: *Plug 'n' Play* / Humanoid: *N-Son-X* / Organic: *Phuture Punk* / What does he think: *Nooroom* / Organix: *Code 25* / My life: *Vegas Soul* / Too deep: *DJ Philip* / Interlude: *Paraphobia* / Nowhere: *Matthews, Mike*
SPV 09247452 / Jun '97 / Subterranean

☐ **RAVEMEISTER VOL.7 (2CD Set)**
SPV 09247582 / Sep '97 / SPV

☐ **RAVEMEISTER VOL.8**
SPV 09247752 / Nov '97 / SPV

☐ **RAVERMEISTER CLASSICS VOL.2 (2CD Set)**
SPV 08539212 / 1 Jun '98 / SPV

☐ **RAVERMEISTER VOL.10**
Eternal rhapsody: *Stephano, Marino* / Trance emotions: *Usura* / Gliding: *Mercedes* / Bell song: *McLaren, Malcolm* / Dream: *Lissat & Brain* / Summer of love: *Scoope* / Flashback 2: *Slotmachine Allstars* / Opus 5: *Digital Domain* / Logical device: *Panama* / Honey buzz: *Holden, Paul* / Call: *Neverland* / Fly away: *Plastic Angel* / Supernatural: *Superspy* / Nightingale: *DJ Mind-X* / Starship: *Magnetic Slides* / Imfinite: *Adventist* / Visions: *Whacky Visions* / Talking about sex: *DJ Session One & DJ Slug* / You must smile: *Overcharge & G.Meter* / Feel your way: *DJ Cyglas* / Trancemission: *Nevo & Avavi* / Tranceformer: *Code 34* / F-active: *Sound Inc.*
DCD 08939132 / 3 Aug '98 / SPV

☐ **RAVERMEISTER VOL.9 (2CD Set)**
SPV 09247962 / 6 Apr '98 / SPV

☐ **RAVER'S NIGHT VOL.2 (2CD Set)**
483808 / 29 Apr '98 / Ruff Neck

☐ **RAVER'S PARADISE VOL.2 (2CD Set)**
IDTCOMP 004 / Dec '96 / ID&T

☐ **RAVING MAD**
Trip to Trumpton: *Urban Hype* / Sesame's treet: *Smart E's* / Searching for my rizla: *Ratpack* / Closer to all your dreams: *Rhythm Quest* / Temple of dreams: *Messiah* / Gun: *Nino* / On a rubbish tip: *Progression* / Papua new guinea: *Future Sound Of London* / Hot chilli: *NAM* / No other: *Nightbreed* / Humanoid: *Stakker* / What's E for dad: *Little Jack* / Trip to the moon (Part 2): *Acen* / Reset: *Output & DJ Oz* / Feel the vibe: *Tequila Carter*
CDELV 01 / Jul '92 / Elevate

☐ **RAW BLUES VOL.1**
CDSGP 026 / Jan '93 / Prestige

☐ **RAW BLUES VOL.2 (2CD Set)**
Blues in my blood: *Smith, Gregg* / Crawling King snake: *Hooker, John Lee* / My baby's gone: *Hopkins, Lightnin'* / Ain't that lovin' you baby: *Reed, Jimmy* / Ray Charle's blues: *Charles, Ray* / Angels laid him away: *Hurt, 'Mississippi' John* / Song for Frank: *Skeleton Crew* / Lend me your love: *Memphis Slim* / Blues before sunrise: *Hooker, John Lee* / Say boss man: *Diddley, Bo* / Cherry red: *Bloomfield, Mike* / She's mine: *Ciotti, Roberto* / May be the last time: *Little Walter & Otis Rush* / Hoodoo blues: *Lightnin' Slim* / Baby what's wrong with you: *Hurt, 'Mississippi' John* / Come here Mama: *Thomas, Rufus* / Her talkin': *Hopkins, Lightnin'* / Rock me baby: *Memphis Slim*
CDSGP 081 / Aug '94 / Prestige

☐ **RAW BLUES VOL.3 (36 Great Blues Tracks/2CD Set)**
Got my mojo working: *Perkins, Willie 'Pinetop'* / Hobo blues: *Hooker, John Lee* / CC rider: *Charles, Ray* / Spoonful: *Canned Heat* / Gotta find my baby: *Memphis Slim* / I didn't mean to hurt your feelings: *Howlin' Wolf* / Hoochie coochie man: *Waters, Muddy* / Caress me baby: *Reed, Jimmy* / Boogie woogie blues: *Brown, Roy* / Nothing but the blues: *Hopkins, Lightnin'* / Every day I have the blues: *Mayfield, Percy* / My babe: *Lightnin' Slim* / Goodnight Irene: *Leadbelly* / Baby please don't go: *Williams, 'Big' Joe* / South side boogie: *Cotton, James* / Just keep on drinking: *Perkins, Willie 'Pinetop'* / Rockin' the house: *Memphis Slim* / High heel sneakers: *Perkins, Willie 'Pinetop'* / Slim's blues: *Memphis Slim* / Screamin' and cryin': *Waters, Muddy* / Goin' down slow: *Howlin' Wolf* / Boogie in the dark: *Reed, Jimmy* / Evil hearted woman: *Hopkins, Lightnin'* / Dimples: *Canned Heat* / Crazy about you babe: *Lightnin' Slim* / Two years of torture: *Mayfield, Percy* / When my first wife left me: *Hooker, John Lee* / Sloppy drink blues: *Williams, 'Big' Joe* / I was robbed last night: *Electric Flag* / John Handy: *Leadbelly* / V8 Ford blues: *Cotton, James* / Lightnin' boogie: *Hopkins, Lightnin'* / Travellin' blues: *Brown, Roy* / All my life: *Howlin' Wolf* / Howlin' wolf: *Waters, Muddy*
CDSGP 0273 / Aug '97 / Prestige

☐ **RAW COMPILATION VOL.1**
FNARRCD 009 / May '92 / Damaged Goods

☐ **RAW JAMS VOL.1**
HOMEGROWNCD 3 / Jun '95 / Homegrown

☐ **RAW 'N' UNCUT HIP HOP**
EFA 127772 / Nov '95 / Ruff 'n' Raw

☐ **RAW POWER SAMPLER**
Parisienne walkways: *Moore, Gary* / Run to your mama: *Moore, Gary* / Gypsy: *Uriah Heep* / Wizard: *Uriah Heep* / In nomine satanus: *Venom* / Devil's answer: *Atomic Rooster* / Walking in the park: *Colosseum* / Chase is better than the catch: *Motorhead* / Bang the drum all day: *Rundgren, Todd* / In the beginning: *Magnum*
RAWCD 1000 / Mar '88 / Raw Power

☐ **RAW RAW DUB**
CEND 2000 / Jan '97 / Century

☐ **RAW RECORDS PUNK COLLECTION, THE**
Sick of you: *Users* / I'm in love with today: *Users* / Johnny won't go to heaven: *Killjoys* / Naive: *Killjoys* / Withdrawal: *Unwanted* / Bleak outlook: *Unwanted* / 1984: *Unwanted* / New religion: *Some Chicken* / Blood on the wall: *Some Chicken* / Radio call sign: *Lockjaw* / Young ones: *Lockjaw* / Arabian daze: *Some Chicken* / Number seven: *Some Chicken* / It's my life: *Gorillas* / My soul's alive: *Gorillas* / Secret police: *Unwanted* / These boots are made for walking: *Unwanted* / Journalist jive: *Lockjaw* / I'm not me: *Unwanted* / End is nigh: *Unwanted* / Bondage boy: *Sick Things* / Kids on the street: *Sick Things* / So young: *Psychos* / Straight jacket: *Psychos* / At night: *Killjoys* / I wish you dead: *Acme Sewage Co.* / I don't need you: *Acme Sewage Co.* / Millionaire: *GT'S* / Young British and white: *Psychos* / I can see you: *Acme Sewage Co.*
CDPUNK 14 / Sep '93 / Anagram

☐ **RAW RUB A DUB VOL.2: EINSTEIN'S THEORY OF DUB**
GPCD 003 / Oct '94 / Gussie P

☐ **RAZOR CUTS (2CD Set)**
74321531742 / 27 Oct '97 / Logic

☐ **RAZOR RECORDS PUNK COLLECTION**
CDPUNK 45 / Feb '95 / Anagram

☐ RCA VICTOR 80TH ANNIVERSARY SAMPLER

Livery stable blues: Original Dixieland Jazz Band / Dr. Jazz: Morton, Jelly Roll / In the mood: Miller, Glenn / Night in Tunisia: Gillespie, Dizzy / Tijuana gift shop: Mingus, Charles / Without a song: Rollins, Sonny / What a wonderful world: Armstrong, Louis / Truth is spoken here: Roberts, Marcus / Labyrinth: Harrell, Tom

09026687852 / Apr '97 / RCA Victor

☐ RCA VICTOR 80TH ANNIVERSARY VOL.1 (1917-1929)

Livery Stable blues: Original Dixieland Jazz Band / Meanest blues: Original Memphis Five / She's crying for me: New Orleans Rhythm Kings / Smokehouse blues: Morton, Jelly Roll & His Red Hot Peppers / Kansas city shuffle: Moten, Bennie Kansas City Orchestra / Dr. Jazz: Morton, Jelly Roll & His Red Hot Peppers / My pretty girl: Goldkette, Jean & His Orchestra / Davenport blues: Red & Miffs Stompers / St. Louis shuffle: Henderson, Fletcher Orchestra / Wolverine blues: Morton, Jelly Roll / Clementine: Goldkette, Jean & His Orchestra / Feeling no pain: Red & Miffs Stompers / Black and tan fantasy: Ellington, Duke Orchestra / San: Whiteman, Paul & His Orchestra / Doing things: Venuti, Joe Blue Four / Four or five times: McKinney's Cotton Pickers / South: Moten, Bennie Kansas City Orchestra / Boy in the boat: Johnson, Charlie & His Paradise Orchestra / I'm gonna stomp Mr. Henry Lee: Eddie's Hot Shots / Everybody loves my baby: Hines, Earl 'Fatha' Orchestra / Ozark mountain blues: Missourians / It should have been you: Allen, Henry & His New York Orchestra / Ain't misbehavin': Waller, Fats / Too late: Oliver, Joe 'King' Orchestra / Hello Lola: Mound City Blues Blowers

09026687772 / Apr '97 / RCA Victor

☐ RCA VICTOR 80TH ANNIVERSARY VOL.2 (The Second Decade 1930-1939)

Rockin' chair: Carmichael, Hoagy Orchestra / Mood indigo: Ellington, Duke Cotton Club Orchestra / Sugarfoot stomp: Henderson, Fletcher Orchestra / Heebie jeebies: Mills Blue Rhythm Band / Lafayette: Moten, Bennie Kansas City Orchestra / St. Louis blues: Armstrong, Louis Orchestra / Minnie the Moocher: Calloway, Cab Orchestra / Jazznocracy: Lunceford, Jimmie Orchestra / After you've gone: Goodman, Benny Trio / Swing is here: Krupa, Gene Swing Band / King Porter stomp: Hill, Teddy NBC Orchestra / Honeysuckle rose / Jivin' the vibres: Hampton, Lionel Orchestra / I can't get started: Berigan, Bunny Orchestra / Don't be that way: Goodman, Benny Orchestra / Begin the beguine: Shaw, Artie Orchestra / Boogie woogie: Dorsey, Tommy Orchestra / Really the blues: Ladnier, Tommy Orchestra / Limehouse blues: Manone, Wingy Orchestra / Cherokee: Barnet, Charlie Orchestra / In the mood: Miller, Glenn Orchestra / Hot mallets: Hampton, Lionel Orchestra / Body and soul: Hawkins, Coleman Orchestra / You're letting the grass grow: Waller, Fats & His Rhythm / Relaxin' at the Touro: Spanier, Muggsy Ragtime Band

09026687782 / May '97 / RCA Victor

☐ RCA VICTOR 80TH ANNIVERSARY VOL.3 (The First Label In Jazz 1940-1949)

Sheik of Araby: Hawkins, Coleman / Cotton tail: Ellington, Duke / Summit ridge drive: Shaw, Artie / Blues in thirds: Bechet, Sidney / All of me: Carter, Benny / One o'clock jump: Metronome All Stars / Yes indeed: Dorsey, Tommy / Things ain't what they used to be: Hodges, Johnny / St Louis Blues: Kirby, John & His Orchestra / Stormy Monday blues: Hines, Earl 'Fatha' / Night in Tunisia: Gillespie, Dizzy / Spotlite: Hawkins, Coleman / Cadillac Slim: Carter, Benny & Chocolate Dandies / Epistrophy: Clarke, Kenny / Buckin' the blues: Esquire All American Award Winners / Out of nowhere: Tatum, Art / Blues after hours: Teagarden, Jack / Erroll's bounce: Garner, Erroll / Ain't misbehavin': Armstrong, Louis / I don't stand a ghost of a chance with you: Tristano, Lennie / Your red wagon: Tristano, Lennie / Algo bueno (Woody'n you): Gillespie, Dizzy / Overtime: Metronome All Stars / My heart stood still: Peterson, Oscar Trio

9026687792 / Jul '97 / RCA Victor

☐ RCA VICTOR 80TH ANNIVERSARY VOL.4 (The First Label In Jazz 1950-1959)

Roses of Picardy: Norvo, Red Septet / Tijuana gift shop: Mingus, Charles / Two degrees East, three degrees West: Lewis, John / Chiquito loco: Rogers, Shorty Orchestra & Art Pepper / Crimea river: Cohn, Al & Zoot Sims / Love me or leave me: Allen, Henry 'Red' All Stars / Concerto for Billy The Kid: Russell, George Smalltet & Bill Evans / Sunday afternoon: Carter, Benny Orchestra / Let me love you: Horne, Lena / Coscrane: Powell, Bud Trio / Perdido: Ellington, Duke Orchestra / Moanin': Blakey, Art & The Jazz Messengers / I love Paris: Hawkins, Coleman & Manny Albam Orchestra

09026687802 / Aug '97 / RCA Victor

☐ RCA VICTOR 80TH ANNIVERSARY VOL.5 (The First Label In Jazz 1960-1969)

Without a song: Rollins, Sonny / All the things you are: Desmond, Paul & Gerry Mulligan / Hello young lovers: Burton, Gary Quartet / After all: Ellington, Duke Orchestra / Sounds of the night: Terry, Clark Quintet / Very thought of you: Hodges, Johnny / So what: Johnson, J.J. Orchestra / Imagination: Desmond, Paul / Star eyes: Baker, Chet / Old folks: McLean, Jackie Quartet / One o'clock jump: Lambert, Hendricks/Bavan / Round midnight: Rollins, Sonny & Co. / Turn me loose: Hampton, Lionel & His All-Star Alumni Big Band

09026687812 / 20 Oct '97 / RCA Victor

☐ RCA VICTOR 80TH ANNIVERSARY VOL.6 (The First Label In Jazz 1970-1979)

Quadrille anyone: Akiyoshi, Toshiko & Lew Tabackin Big Band / Four brothers: Herman, Woody & The New Thundering Herd / Pusher: Simone, Nina / Dancing men: Rich, Buddy & His Orchestra / Up from the skies: Evans, Gil Orchestra / Good medicine: Severinsen, Doc / Ridin' high: Laine, Cleo / Inside out: Brecker Brothers / Expansions: Smith, Lonnie Liston / What a wonderful world: Armstrong, Louis

09026687822 / 20 Oct '97 / RCA Victor

☐ RCA VICTOR 80TH ANNIVERSARY VOL.7

Whisper not: Marcus, Roberts / Truth is spoken here: Marcus, Roberts / 'Round midnight: McRae, Carmen / Uptownship: Masekela, Hugh / Imagination: Baker, Chet / I'll be around: Laine, Cleo & Dudley Moore / Jacknife: Brecker Brothers / Blue monk: Roberts, Marcus / Tschanz: Coleman, Steve / Almost blue: Baker, Chet

09026687832 / 10 Nov '97 / RCA Victor

☐ RCA VICTOR 80TH ANNIVERSARY VOL.8

Pinocchio: Hargrove, Roy / Cherokee: Roberts, Marcus / Winelight: Braden, Don / I'll be seeing you: McRae, Carmen / Labyrinth: Harrell, Tom / Just sittin' and rockin': Laine, Cleo / Drop kick live: Coleman, Steve / Moon ray: Eade, Dominique / Voyage: Perez, Danilo / Our love is here to stay: Rubin, Vanessa / Uptown traveller: Hart, Antonio

09026687842 / 10 Nov '97 / RCA Victor

☐ RE-SEARCH PRESENTS INCREDIBLY STRANGE MUSIC VOL.2

EFA 709512 / Sep '96 / Asphodel

☐ REACT TEST VOL.1

REACTCD 31 / Nov '93 / React

☐ REACT TEST VOL.2

REACTCD 052 / Nov '94 / React

☐ REACT TEST VOL.3

Joanna: Mrs. Wood / Shinny: Elevator / Magic: Blu Peter / Sugar shack: Seb / Orange theme: Cygnus X / Tip of the iceberg: GTO / Spirit: Kitachi / Witch doktor: Van Helden, Armand / Untitled: Sharp Tools / PARTY: Movin' Melodies / Do me: Aquarius / Bring it back 2 luv: Project

REACTCD 070 / Nov '95 / React

☐ REACT TEST VOL.4

Shoenberg: Marmion / Flagship: Blu Peter / Whodunnit: Mrs. Wood / Hopper: Armadillo / Amphetamine: Trope / Ignition: Madame Dubois / Sparkling: Little Matt / Scratch: Kitachi / Sabor de verano: Padilla, Jose / Indoctrinate: Castle Trancelot / TMF 61: Fowlkes, Eddie 'Flashin' / Do it to me: Dark, Frankie

REACTCD 081 / Jun '96 / React

☐ REACT TEST VOL.5

Heartbreak: Mrs. Wood / Pictures in your mind: Blu Peter / Rainbow islands: Seb / Magnitude 7: Sonic Animation / Fusion: Atkins, Juan / Heavyweight: Kitachi / Enlightenment: Aldo Bender / In my brain: Mark NRG / Transamazonia: Shamen / Walking on air: Padilla, Jose / Mighty machine: Dream Plant / Jus a lil' dope: Masters At Work

REACTCD 092 / Nov '96 / React

☐ REACT TEST VOL.6

Age of love: Age Of Love / Fever: SJ / Evil queen: Shimmon & Woolfson / Vertigo: Transcendental Experience / Force: Garnier, Laurent / E dancer: Saunderson, Kevin / Ohm: Wamdue Kids / Disco hall: Crump, Harrison / I'm the baddest bitch: Bell, Norma Jean / Remember me: Blue Boy / Night's interlude: Nightmares On Wax / You got the love: Source & Candi Staton

REACTCD 108 / Aug '97 / React

☐ REACTIVATE CLASSICS (2CD Set)

Technarchy: Cybersonik / Techno trance: D-Shake / Pure: GTO / Magic orchestra: B-Sides / Rubb it in: Fierce Ruling Diva / Quadrophonia: Quadrophonia / Mentasm: Second Phase / Sonar system: Meng Syndicate / House of God: DHS / Can you feel it: CLS / Der klang der familie: 3 Phase / Horsepower: Bolland, C.J. / Age of love: Age Of Love / La musika tremenda: Ramirez / Acperience: Hardfloor / Come into my life: Abfahrt / Circus bells: Armani, Robert / Schoneberg: Marmion / Pilgramige to paradise: Sourmash / Loops and tings: Jens / Anything you want: Delta Lady / Shinny: Elevator

REACTCDX 114
REACTCD 114 / 26 Jan '98 / React

☐ REACTIVATE VOL.10

Osaka acid: Sushi / Lost in love: Legend B / First rebirth: Jones & Stephenson / Access: X-Trax / Ready to flow: Urban Trance Plant / Sizzling love: PHI / Ice man on the beach: Pan & Trex / Que vous etez: Friends, Lovers & Family / Can't stop: Komakino / Superstitious: Luxor / Point zero: Li Kwan / Cybertrance: Blue Alphabet / Flagship: Blu Peter / Mighty machine: Dream Plant / Octopus: Art Of Trance / Under siege: Project X / Acid NRG: NRG Jams / Future world: Cenobyte

REACTCD 060 / May '95 / React

☐ REACTIVATE VOL.10 - REMIX

REACTCDX 060 / May '95 / React

☐ REACTIVATE VOL.11 (Stinger Beats And Techno Rays/2CD Set)

Rainbow islands: Seb / Positivity's knirvana: Positivity / Evolver: De Niro / This is for: Albion / Tribe: Hoschi / Borg destroyer: Kinetic A.T.O.M. / Aura infinity: Acid Bottle / Believer: DJ Energy / Whiplash: Overcharge & G.Meter / Blow your mind: Gargano, Pablo / Ultrafilter: RND / Accelerate: Zzino / Give it to me: Choci & DJ E.C. / Planet hunters: Third Men / Techidat: Pro Active / Gospel 2000: 16C+ / Strings of heaven: DJ Jamo & Jack Knives / U: DJ Scot Project / Gonna getcha: Fierce Child / Accident: Skylab / Yum yum: Baby Doc / Rok da house: Wicked Wipe

REACTCDX 088
REACTCD 088 / Oct '96 / React

☐ REACTIVATE VOL.12 (2CD Set)

Arms of heaven: Sunbeam / Evil Queen: Shimmon & Woolfson / Chemical air: Mark 1 / Wise man: Tsunami / Waters: Taucher / Everyones future: Gargano, Pablo / Trance in Saigon: Gargano, Pablo / Sound: De Donatis / Pandomia: DJ Randy / Prophase: Transa / Remember last summer: Extract / Up-Riser: Quake-X / Axis: Nuclear Hyde / One million faces: Incisions / Flowtation: De Moor, Vincent / Pipeman: Nomination 1 / Groovebird: Natural Born Groovers / Roadrunner: Mach 1 / Tune in turn out: Obsessive / Greetings from the exile: Tranceliner / Pili Pili: M

REACTCDX 102
REACTCD 102 / Jun '97 / React

☐ READING FESTIVAL '73

Hands off: Gallagher, Rory / Feathered friends: Greenslade / Losing you: Faces / Earth mother: Duncan, Lesley / Hang onto a dream: Hardin, Tim / Person to person: Hardin, Tim / Roadrunner: Strider / Don't waste my time: Status Quo / Long legged Linda: Bown, Andy

SEECD 343 / Mar '92 / See For Miles

☐ READY STEADY BOOGALOO

Come one come all: Dale, Syd / Wild elephants: Clarke, James / Groupie: Dale, Syd / Lucky seven: Dale, Syd / Cool stepper: Harris, Max / Carnaby chick: Lusher, Don / Running from danger: Gray, Steve / Disco tek: Dale, Syd / Boogalo: Dale, Syd / Go for broke: Gray, Steve / Double take: Clarke, James / London life: Dale, Syd / Spanish charade: Hatch, Tony / Say something sweet: Clarke, James / Gentle giant: Dale, Syd / Hacienda happening: Walter, Dick / Portobello road: Reed, Les / News travels fast: Lawless, Jim

SUMCD 4185 / 23 Feb '98 / Summit

☐ READY STEADY GO (The Motown Album - 2CD Set)

Yester-me, yester-you, yesterday: Wonder, Stevie / Dancing in the street: Reeves, Martha & The Vandellas / Stop in the name of love: Ross, Diana & The Supremes / I heard it through the grapevine: Gaye, Marvin / Reach out I'll be there: Four Tops / My girl: Temptations / What becomes of the broken hearted: Ruffin, Jimmy / I'm gonna make you love me: Ross, Diana & The Supremes/Temptations / It takes two: Gaye, Marvin & Kim Weston / Standing in the shadows of love: Four Tops / Stop her on sight (SOS): Starr, Edwin / (I'm a) roadrunner: Walker, Junior & The All Stars / Uptight (everything's alright): Wonder, Stevie / How sweet it is (to be loved by you): Gaye, Marvin / This old heart of mine (is weak for you): Isley Brothers / Heatwave: Reeves, Martha & The Vandellas / I can't help myself: Four Tops / Baby love: Ross, Diana & The Supremes / Take me in your arms and love me: Knight, Gladys & The Pips / Tears of a clown: Robinson, Smokey & The Miracles / Onion song: Gaye, Marvin & Tammi Terrell / For once in my life: Wonder, Stevie / Ooo baby baby: Robinson, Smokey & The Miracles / My guy: Wells, Mary / Reflections: Ross, Diana & The Supremes / Do you love me: Contours / Twist and shout: Isley Brothers / Please Mr. Postman: Marvelettes / Can I get a witness: Gaye, Marvin / Nowhere to run: Reeves, Martha & The Vandellas / You keep me hangin' on: Ross, Diana & The Supremes / Walk away Renee: Four Tops / Tracks of my tears: Robinson, Smokey & The Temptations / Good lovin' ain't easy to come by: Gaye, Marvin & Tammi Terrell / I'll pick a rose for my rose: Johnson, Marv / My cherie amour: Wonder, Stevie / You can't hurry love: Ross, Diana & The Supremes / Get ready: Temptations / Jimmy Mack: Reeves, Martha & The Vandellas / Too busy thinking about my baby: Gaye, Marvin / Headline news: Starr, Edwin / What does it take (to win your love): Walker, Junior & The All Stars / Bernadette: Four Tops / Ain't nothing like the real thing: Gaye, Marvin & Tammi Terrell / Gonna give her all the love I've got: Ruffin, Jimmy / Behind a painted smile: Isley Brothers / I second that emotion: Robinson, Smokey & The Miracles / You're all I need to get by: Gaye, Marvin & Tammi Terrell / Where did our love go: Ross, Diana & The Supremes / Place in the sun: Wonder, Stevie

5308652 / 9 Mar '98 / PolyGram TV

☐ READY STEADY GO & WIN

Hyde 'n' seek: Thyrds / I'll miss you: Harbour Lights / Bo Street runner: Bo Street Runners / Did you ever hear the sound: Knight, Tony & The Livewires / Lonely one: Deltones & Tony Lane / She loves to be loved: Falling Leaves / Our love feels new: Echolettes / You make me go 'oooh': Dynamos / Not guilty: Falling Leaves / And I do what I want: Bo Street Runners / Tell me what you're gonna do: Bo Street Runners / I'm leaving you: Royal, Jimmy & The Hawkes / So much love: Planets / Every time I look at you: Five Aces / Anytime: Scene Five / Ain't it a shame: Vibrons / Mistletoe love: Fenda, Jaymes & The Vulcans / Think of me: Olympics / You've come back: Leasides / Only girl: Fenda, Jaymes & The Vulcans / Get out of my way: Bo Street Runners / Baby never say goodbye: Bo Street Runners

SEECD 202 / Feb '92 / See For Miles

☐ REAL AUTHENTIC SOUND OF STUDIO ONE, THE

Musically crucial: Earl 16 / Gimme fe me corn: Martin, Horace / Who beg no get: Little John / So secure: Griffith, Hugh / Dance hall session: Griffith, Hugh / Sweetheart: Ellis, Hortense / Predicting your future: Livingston, Carlton / Get your green card: Jarrett, Mikey / Jamaican Collie: Dillinger / Asking you to leave: Brown, Barry / Thank you Jah: Michigan & Smiley / Africa here I come: McGregor, Freddie / Full up: Wild Mix / What a gwan: Tennessee / Three mile shank: Lone Ranger / Rub a dub dub with feeling: Paul, Frankie / New give up: Ethiopians

RASCD 9001 / Mar '97 / Ras

☐ REAL BAHAMAS, THE

7559793002 / 26 Jan '98 / Nonesuch

☐ REAL BIRTH OF FUSION, THE

Miles runs the voodoo down: Davis, Miles / Birds of fire: Mahavishnu Orchestra / Cucumber slumber: Weather Report / Chameleon: Hancock, Herbie / Silly putty: Clarke, Stanley / Mr. Spock: Williams, Tony / Sorceress: Corea, Chick & Return To Forever / Opus Pocus: Pastorius, Jaco / Phenomenon:compulsion: McLaughlin, John

4841452 / Aug '96 / Columbia

☐ REAL BLACK RHYTHM

STCD 1156 / May '97 / Collector/White Label

☐ REAL DEAL VOL.1

CDRAID 514 / Feb '94 / Rumour

☐ REAL DEAL VOL.2

CDRAID 517 / May '94 / Rumour

☐ REAL EXCELLO R&B, THE

Little queen bee (got a brand new king): Harpo, Slim / I need money (keep your alibis): Harpo, Slim / Still rainin' in my heart: Harpo, Slim / I tried so hard: Smith, Whispering / Cryin' blues: Smith, Whispering / I'm goin' in the valley: Hogan, Silas / Dark clouds rollin': Hogan, Silas / I'm so glad: Austin, Leon / I had a dream last night: Lonesome Sundown / She's my crazy little baby: Lonesome Sundown / Goin' crazy over TV: Anderson, Jimmy / You're playin' hookey: Lonesome Sundown / It's love baby: Gaines, Earl / Nothing in this world (gonna keep you from me): Anderson, Jimmy / Let's play house: Gunter, Arthur / Winter time blues: Lightnin' Slim / Pleasin' for love: Shelton, Roscoe / Whoa now: Lazy Lester / It's your voodoo working: Sheffield, Charles 'Mad Dog' / Rock-a-me all night long: Nelson, Jay / Leavin' Tennessee: Garner, Alan / Baby, kiss me gain: Sweet Clifford / Crazy over you: Shelton, Roscoe / Baby I'm stickin' to you: Friday, Charles

CDCHD 562 / Nov '94 / Ace

☐ REAL IBIZA (2CD Set)

Orange sunshine: Superstars Of Rock / Glide: Afterlife / One day in paradise: Padilla, Jose / Amm my favourite people: Man Called Adam / Sunday afternoons: Daou, Vanessa / Great ocean round: Coco Steel & Lovebomb / Silent life: Fluff / My funny valentine: Big Muff / Would you like me to seduce you: Krystal / Cinematic sundown: Los Olivadados / Lazy living: Ibizarre / Overheated livingroom: Dub Tractor / Peace: DJ Food / Prayer: Guillaume, Jephte / Float: Ibizarre / Groovin' with you: Gentle People / Flower garden: Alania / Freedom from pity: Jhelisa / Glass bead game: Thievery Corporation / Juggs: Philadelphia Bluntz / Haunted kind: Omni Trio / Are you high: Wamdue Project / See line woman: Songstress

REACTCD 132 / 24 Aug '98 / React

☐ REAL INTELLIGENCE VOL.2

RI 041CD / Dec '96 / Rather Interesting

☐ REAL LOVE

TSS 101 / 2 Feb '98 / BMG

☐ REAL MUSIC BOX, THE (25 Years Of Rounder Records/9CD Set)

ROUCDAN 25 / Feb '96 / Rounder

☐ REAL MUSIC OF PERU, THE

Maria Alejandrina: Picaflor De Los Andes / Un pasajero en el camino: Picaflor De Los Andes / Fiesta de mayo: Picaflor De Los Andes / Aguas del Rio Rimac: Picaflor De Los Andes / Carrito de pasajos: Picaflor De Los Andes / Verbenita, verbenita: La Pallasquinta / Oreganito: La Pallasquinta / El guapachoso: Orquesta Sensacion Del Mantaro / Llorando a mares: Flor Pucarina / Airampito: Flor Pucarina / Noche de luna: Flor Pucarina / Para que quiero la vida: Flor Pucarina / Pichiusita: Flor Pucarina / Rompe Macarios: Orquesta Los Tarumas De Tarma / Alianza Corazon: Orquesta Los Tarumas De Tarma / Dos Clavelles: La Princesita De Yungay / Tus ojos: Los Borbones Del Peru / Ya te gane: Orquesta Los Rebeldes De Huancayo

CDORBD 064 / Feb '91 / Globestyle

☐ REAL RUMBA FROM CUBA

CO 110 / May '96 / Corason

☐ REAL STONES

Come on: Berry, Chuck / I just want to be loved: Waters, Muddy / Bye bye Johnny: Berry, Chuck / You better move on: Alexander, Arthur / Money: Strong, Barrett / Route 66: Berry, Chuck / Carol: Berry, Chuck / Mona: Diddley, Bo / Fortune teller: Spellman, Benny / Confessin' the blues: Berry, Chuck / Around and around: Berry, Chuck / Don't lie to me: Berry, Chuck / Memphis: Berry, Chuck / Roadrunner: Diddley, Bo / Roll over Beethoven: Berry, Chuck / Cops and robbers: Diddley, Bo / Down the road apiece: Diddley, Bo / I can't be satisfied: Waters, Muddy / You can't catch me: Berry, Chuck / Suzie Q: Hawkins, Dale / Little red rooster: Howlin' Wolf / Talkin' about you: Berry, Chuck / Look what you've done: Waters, Muddy / Little Queenie: Berry, Chuck / Let it rock: Berry, Chuck / Run Rudolph run: Berry, Chuck / Crackin' up: Diddley, Bo / I'm a man: Diddley, Bo / Rollin' stone: Waters, Muddy

PRD 70122 / Dec '89 / Provogue

☐ REAL WORLD SAMPLER 1995

Le voyageur: Papa Wemba / Hazo avo: Rossy / Mwanuni: Eyuphuro / Al nahla al 'Ali: Eyuphuro / Shahbaaz qalandar: Khan, Nusrat Fateh Ali / Ya sahib-ul-Jamal: Sabri Brothers / Nibiro ghon andare: Sabri Brothers / Raga bhairavi: Sridhar, K. & K Shivakumar / Enchantment: Chandra, Sheila / Sgariunt na Gcompanagh (The parting of friends): Malloy, Matt

RWSAM 4 / Oct '95 / Realworld

☐ REALLY GOT THE BLUES

BN 037 / Apr '98 / Blue Nite

☐ REANIMATOR (Black Market Science)

ION 20052 / 5 Jan '98 / Ion

☐ REBEL MUSIC (An Anthology of Reggae Music - 2CD Set)

You don't know: Andy, Bob / Loser: Harriott, Derrick / High school dance: McKay, Freddie / Russians are coming: Bennett, Val / Tonight: Keith & Tex / Ain't that lovin' you: U-Roy / Them a fe get a beatin': Tosh, Peter / God helps the man: Smart, Leroy / Hypocrite: Heptones / S90 skank: Big Youth / Hard tighter: Little Roy / Eedding skank: Brown, Glen / Anywhere but nowhere: White, K.C. / Beat down Babylon: Byles, Junior / Concentration: Brown, Dennis / Screaming target: Big Youth / Slaving: Parkes, Lloyd / You are my angel: Andy, Horace / Melody maker: Hudson, Keith / Money in my pocket: Brown, Dennis / Cheater: Brown, Dennis / Blackman time: I-Roy / Satan side: Andy, Horace & Earl Flute / Give praises: Big Youth / Rock away: Isaacs, Gregory / Saturday night special: Dyke, Michael / Cool rasta: Heptones

CDTRD 403 / Mar '94 / Trojan

☐ REBEL ROCKABILLY

RAUCD 019 / Jun '96 / Raucous

☐ REBIRTH OF COOL VOL.2

I've lost my ignorance (and don't know where to find it): *Dream Warriors* / La raza: *Kid Frost* / Senga abele (lion roar): *Dibango, Manu & MC Mello* / Cool and funky: *Jordan, Ronny* / I should've known better: *Paris, Mica* / All for one: *Brand Nubian* / One to grow on: *UMC's* / Family: *McKoy* / Try my love: *Washburn, Lalomie* / Kickin' jazz: *Outlaw* / Looking at the front door: *Main Source* / Free your feelings: *Slam Slam* / Go with the flow: *Rock, Pete & C.L. Smooth* / Set me free: *Bygraves* / Black whip: *Chapter & Verse* / Slow jam: *Dodge City Productions*

BRCD 582 / Feb '92 / 4th & Broadway

☐ REBIRTH OF COOL VOL.3

BRCD 590 / Apr '93 / 4th & Broadway

☐ REBIRTH OF COOL VOL.4

Just wanna touch her: *DJ Krush* / Play my funk: *Simple E* / Rent strike: *Groove Collective* / R U conscious: *Buchanan, Courtney* / My favourite things: *Jordan, Ronny* / Otha fish: *Pharcyde* / Cantamilla: *Tranquility Bass* / Aftermath: *Tricky* / Earthsong: *Batu* / Cool like the blues: *Warfield, Justin* / Straight plays: *F-Mob* / Crazy: *Outside* / Spock with a beard: *Palmskin Productions* / World mutations: *Tone Productions* / Tree, air and rain on Earth: *Mondo Grosso* / Great men's dub: *Burning Spear* / Soul of the people: *Bread & Butter*

BRCD 607 / Jun '94 / 4th & Broadway

☐ REBIRTH OF COOL VOL.5 (Subterranean Abstract Blues)

Friendly pressure: *Jhelisa* / Eine kleine hedmusik: *Coldcut* / Karmacoma: *Massive Attack* / Boundaries: *Conquest, Leena* / Whipping boy: *Harper, Ben* / Deep shit: *Kruder & Dorfmeister* / Hell is round the corner: *Tricky* / Turn on, tune in, find joy: *Freakpower* / Revenge of the number: *Portishead* / Bug powder dust: *Bomb The Bass* / United Future Airlines: *United Future Organisation* / Iniquity worker: *D-Note* / Release yo' delf: *Method Man* / Kosmos: *Weller, Paul* / Nouveau Western: *MC Solaar* / Get it together: *Beastie Boys*

BRCD 617 / Jul '95 / 4th & Broadway

☐ REBIRTH OF COOL VOL.6 (On Higher Sound)

Underwater love: *Smoke City* / Claire: *IO* / To forgive but not forget: *Outside* / You are Heaven sent: *Nicolette* / Cotton wool: *Lamb* / Horizons: *LTJ Bukem* / Migration: *Sawhney, Nitin* / Ponteio: *Da Lata* / Jazz garage: *Akasha* / Feel the sunshine: *Reece, Alex* / Surfin': *Ranglin, Ernest* / Who could it be: *Luciano & Jungle Brothers* / Bittersweet: *Taylor, Lewis* / Street player: *DJ Pulse & The Jazz Cartel* / Rudiments: *Angel, Dave*

BRCD 620 / Aug '96 / 4th & Broadway

☐ REBIRTH OF COOL VOL.7 (2CD Set)

Get another plan: *Abstract Truth* / Monkey jazz: *O'Brien, Ian* / My beat: *Blaze* / Size of an elephant: *Universal Being* / Contrazoom: *Spacer* / Redeemer: *Spacer* / Where my mind is at: *DJ Skitzo* / My history - feel the spirit: *New Sector Movements* / Escaravos de Jo: *Kerri & Jo* / African elation: *Fraser, Dean* / Tears for Yazd: *Amalgamation Of Soundz* / Chemical imbalance: *Kendra, Karime* / Elephant ride: *State Of Bengal* / Life: *Luciano* / Plans and designs: *Faze Action* / Ma-Da: *Tala Quintet* / In at the deep end: *Riley, Bill* / Ballet dance: *Roni Size* / Impressions: *Fused Up* / What is it: *Mighty Strinth*

CIDD 8065 / 23 Mar '98 / Island

☐ RECKLESS ROOTS ROCKERS

WRCD 0038 / 12 Jan '98 / Wackies

☐ RECOLLECTIONS OF 1945 (Vocalists)

I begged her: *Sinatra, Frank* / I'll close my eyes: *Squires, Dorothy* / There I've said it again: *Hutchinson, Leslie 'Hutch'* / Accentuate the positive: *Crosby, Bing & The Andrews Sisters* / Together: *Layton, Turner* / There goes that song again: *Hall, Adelaide* / I'm so alone: *Conway, Steve* / Gipsy: *Squires, Dorothy* / Kiss me again: *Sinatra, Frank* / My dreams are getting better all the time: *Lynn, Vera* / It could happen to you: *Crosby, Bing* / Laura: *Shelton, Anne* / Dream: *Hutchinson, Leslie 'Hutch'* / I fall in love too easily: *Sinatra, Frank* / Coming home: *Squires, Dorothy* / June comes round every year: *Green, Johnny* / Pablo the dreamer: *Shelton, Anne* / You're so sweet to remember: *Hutchinson, Leslie 'Hutch'* / I'm gonna love that guy: *Hall, Adelaide* / Moment I saw you: *Conway, Steve* / Out of this world: *Conway, Steve* / Let the rest of the world go by: *Squires, Dorothy*

RAJCD 875 / May '96 / Empress

☐ RECOLLECTIONS OF 1945 (Dance Bands)

More and more: *Ambrose & His Orchestra* / Accentuate the positive: *Payne, Jack & His Orchestra* / I should care: *Winstone, Eric & His Orchestra* / Laura: *Gibbons, Carroll & Savoy Hotel Orpheans* / You moved right in: *Roy, Harry & His Band* / Saturday night: *Silvester, Victor & His Jive Orchestra* / Let him go let him tarry: *Loss, Joe & His Orchestra* / No one else will do: *Geraldo & His Orchestra* / Bell bottom trousers: *Payne, Jack & His Orchestra* / Candy: *Roy, Harry & His Band* / Dream: *Geraldo & His Orchestra* / I walked in: *Winstone, Eric & His Orchestra* / There I've said it again: *Loss, Joe & His Orchestra* / I'm gonna love that guy: *Winstone, Eric & His Orchestra* / Ma-Ma: *Gonella, Nat & His Georgians* / Trolly song: *Geraldo & His Orchestra* / Little on the lonely side: *Geraldo & His Orchestra* / Robin Hood: *Geraldo & His Orchestra* / Can't you read between the lines: *Geraldo & His Orchestra* / Can't help singing: *Ambrose & His Orchestra* / Gipsy: *Roy, Harry & His Orchestra* / You belong to my heart: *Gibbons, Carroll & Savoy Hotel Orpheans* / Just a prayer away: *Payne, Jack & His Orchestra*

RAJCD 876 / May '96 / Empress

☐ RECORD FACTORY IN THE JUNGLE

792502 / Apr '96 / Melodie

☐ RECORD MIRROR PRESENTS COOL CUTS

Reaching up: *Oscar G & Marck Michel* / Feel my body: *O'Moiraghi, Frank & Amnesia* / Got myself together: *Bucketheads* / Everybody needs a 303: *Fatboy Slim* / Keep hope alive: *Crystal Method* / Forerunner: *Natural Born Groovers* / Race of survival: *Sonz Of Soul & Steven Ville* / Change: *Daphne* / Freedom: *Lil' Louis* / Is this the rhythm: *Rhythm & Vibe* / Another day: *Sledge, Kathy* / Happy days: *Sweet Mercy & Joe Roberts*

CDLIV 1 / Feb '96 / Skratch

☐ RECORDS FOR THE WORKING CLASS

DER 369CD / 6 Jul '98 / Deep Elm

☐ RED BIRD SOUND VOL.2

Boy from New York: *Ad Libs* / Kicked around: *Ad Libs* / He ain't no angel: *Ad Libs* / Ask anybody: *Ad Libs* / On the corner: *Ad Libs* / Oo wee oh me oh my: *Ad Libs* / I'm just a down home girl: *Ad Libs* / Johnny my boy: *Ad Libs* / Slime: *Ad Libs* / Somethin' you got: *Robinson, Alvin* / Searchin': *Robinson, Alvin* / Down home girl: *Robinson, Alvin* / Fever: *Robinson, Alvin* / How can I get over you: *Robinson, Alvin* / I'm gonna put some hurt on you: *Robinson, Alvin* / Bottom of my soul: *Robinson, Alvin* / Let the good times roll: *Robinson, Alvin* / Take me for a little while: *Sands, Evie* / Run home to your mama: *Sands, Evie* / I can't let you go: *Sands, Evie* / You've got me uptight: *Sands, Evie* / Having a party: *Mitchell, Ronnie* / I'm loving you more every day: *Mitchell, Ronnie* / Hold on baby: *Hawkins, Sam* / Bad as they come: *Hawkins, Sam* / I know it's all right: *Hawkins, Sam* / I know it's all right: *Hawkins, Sam* / It hurts so bad: *Hawkins, Sam* / Keep it up: *Soul Brothers* / I got a dream: *Soul Brothers*

GEMCD 017 / 26 Jan '98 / Diamond

☐ RED BIRD SOUND VOL.3

Bossa nova baby: *Tippie & The Clovers* / My heart said: *Tippie & The Clovers* / He ain't no angel: *Leola & The Lovejoys* / Wait around the corner: *Leola & The Lovejoys* / Go now: *Banks, Bessie* / It sounds like my baby: *Banks, Bessie* / Standing by: *Warwick, Dee Dee* / Don't think my baby's coming: *Warwick, Dee Dee* / Something you got: *Robinson, Alvin* / Searchin': *Robinson, Alvin* / It's mighty nice: *Lovejoys* / Payin': *Lovejoys* / It won't be me anymore: *Donna, Vic* / Dance Marie: *Donna, Vic* / Big bad world: *Saint, Cathy* / Mr.Heartbreak: *Saint, Cathy* / Trophy run: *Moore, Bobby & Friends* / Braggin': *Moore, Bobby & Friends* / My baby loves me: *Tams* / Here I am: *Tams* / Everybody come clap your hands: *Moody & The Deltas* / Monkey climb: *Moody & The Deltas*

GEMCD 019 / 26 Jan '98 / Diamond

☐ RED BIRD SOUND VOL.4

GEMCD 025 / 6 Apr '98 / Diamond

☐ RED BIRD STORY, THE (2CD Set)

Chapel of love: *Dixie Cups* / I wanna love him so bad: *Jellybeans* / People say: *Dixie Cups* / Remember (walkin' in the sand): *Shangri-Las* / Goodnight baby: *Butterflies* / Leader of the pack: *Shangri-Las* / Gee baby gee: *Dixie Cups* / Iko iko: *Dixie Cups* / Give him a great big kiss: *Shangri-Las* / Gee the moon is shining bright: *Dixie Cups* / I can never go home anymore: *Shangri-Las* / Boy from New York City: *Ad Libs* / Give us your blessing: *Shangri-Las* / He ain't no angel: *Ad Libs* / Past, present and future: *Shangri-Las* / I'm just a down home girl: *Ad Libs* / Down home girl: *Robinson, Alvin* / I hurt on the other side: *Barnes, Sidney* / Something you got: *Robinson, Alvin* / Bad as they come: *Hawkins, Sam* / Let the good times roll: *Hawkins, Sam* / Come on baby: *Hawkins, Sam* / Fever: *Robinson, Alvin* / Go now: *Banks, Bessie* / Bossa nova baby: *Tippie & The Clovers* / My heart said (the bossa nova): *Tippie & The Clovers* / I can't let go: *Sands, Evie* / Take me for a little while: *Sands, Evie* / Standing by: *Warwick, Dee Dee* / I don't think my baby's coming back: *Warwick, Dee Dee* / New York's a lonely town: *Tradewinds* / I know it's alright: *Jeff & Ellie*

CDLAB 105 / Apr '96 / Charly

☐ RED EYE APPETISER

REDCD 32 / Mar '94 / Red Eye

☐ RED HOT (The Best Of Sun Blues)

Mystery train: *Little Junior's Blue Flames* / We all gotta go sometime: *Hill-Louis, Joe* / Chicken: *Gordon, Rosco* / Beggin' my baby: *Little Milton* / Boogie disease: *Ross, Dr. Isiah* / Bear cat: *Thomas, Rufus* / Baker shop boogie: *Nix, Willie* / No greater love: *Emerson, Billy 'The Kid'* / Shoobie oobie: *Gordon, Rosco* / Looking for my baby: *Little Milton* / Fussin' and fightin': *Little Junior's Blue Flames* / Straighten up baby: *Cotton, James* / Chicago breakdown: *Ross, Dr. Isiah* / Ain't that right: *Snow, Eddie* / Bourbon street jump: *Hill, Raymond* / Red hot: *Emerson, Billy 'The Kid'*

308602 / 20 Apr '98 / Hallmark

☐ RED HOT BLUES

MACCD 198 / Aug '96 / Autograph

☐ RED HOT JAZZ

AVM 533 / May '94 / Avid

☐ RED HOT REGGAE (18 Original Hits/ 3CD Set)

Don't look back (you've gotta walk): *Tosh, Peter* / Sideshow: *Biggs, Barry* / Girlie girlie: *George, Sophia* / Cool and deadly: *Eastwood & Saint* / Gal wine: *Chaka Demus & Pliers* / Cocaine: *Dillinger* / Everything I own: *Boy George* / Bush doctor: *Tosh, Peter* / Gimme hope Jo'anna: *Grant, Eddy* / Feel my riddim: *Skibby* / Someone loves you honey: *T-Spoon* / I want to wake up with you: *Gardiner, Boris* / No woman no cry: *Marley, Kymani* / Nightshift: *Winston Groovy* / Israelites: *Dekker, Desmond* / It keeps rainin' (tears from my eyes): *McLean, Bitty* / Amigo: *Black Slate* / Do you really want to hurt me: *Culture Club*

LAD 873862 / Nov '96 / Disky

☐ RED HOT ROCKABILLY VOL.1

Hip shakin' mama / Bip bop boom / Look out Mabel / Grits / Sunglasses after dark / Okies in the pokie / Hot dog / Made in the shade / Down on the farm / Fool / Oakie boogie / Blue swingin' mama

CDMF 030 / Jul '90 / Magnum Force

☐ RED HOT ROCKABILLY VOL.7

Rock 'n' roll on a Saturday night / Rock-a-sock a hop / Grandma rock 'n' roll / Servant of love / Knocking on the backside / Walking and a' strolling / Black Cadillac / DJ blues / Don't cry little darling / Linda Lou / Teenage lover / So help me gal / Snake eyed woman / Depression blues / Quick sand love / Nicotine

CDMF 069 / Aug '89 / Magnum Force

☐ RED HOT ROCKABILLY VOL.8

Forty nine women / That'll get it / Lonely heart / Clickety clack / Satellite hop / Dig that crazy driver / My baby's still rockin' / Crawdad hole / Go go heart / You bet I do / It hurts the one who loves you / Puppy love / No doubt about it / Roll over Beethoven / No. 9 train / Rock on Mabel / Long tall Sally / Jitterbuggin' baby / One way ticket / Elvis stole my gal / Fool about you / You don't mean to make me cry / Tore up / Jackson dog / Move over Rover

CDMF 082 / Feb '92 / Magnum Force

☐ RED HOT SOCA

CR 004 / 13 Oct '97 / Charlie's

☐ RED RIVER BLUES 1934-1943

TMCD 08 / '92 / Travellin' Man

☐ RED ROAD CROSSING (Native American Chant)

Invocation of the great spirit / Welcome song / Flag song / Jingle dance / Sun dance / Grass dance of the northern tribes / Butterfly dance / Intertribal chant / Warrior's chant / Red chant / Desert song / Closing rights

IN 57362 / Jul '98 / Interra

☐ RED ZONE, THE (The Essential Collection Of Classic Dub)

SH 45034 / Oct '97 / Shanachie

☐ REDISCOVERED BLUES VOL.2 (2CD Set)

You can't be lucky all the time: *Sykes, Roosevelt* / Sweet old Chicago: *Sykes, Roosevelt* / Jailbait: *Sykes, Roosevelt* / Bloodstains: *Sykes, Roosevelt* / Hush oh hush: *Sykes, Roosevelt* / Cannonball: *Sykes, Roosevelt* / I'm tired: *Sykes, Roosevelt* / Crazy fox: *Sykes, Roosevelt* / Direct South: *Sunnyland Slim* / Wake up in the morning: *Sunnyland Slim* / Driftin' blues: *Sunnyland Slim* / Puppy love: *Sunnyland Slim* / New B and O blues: *Sunnyland Slim* / Midnight special: *Sunnyland Slim* / In the evening: *Sunnyland Slim* / Meet me in the bottom: *Sunnyland Slim* / Wee wee baby: *Sunnyland Slim* / I'm the one: *Sunnyland Slim* / You used to love me: *Bumble Bee Slim* / My past life: *Bumble Bee Slim* / She's got a thing going on: *Bumble Bee Slim* / Substitute woman: *Bumble Bee Slim* / Canada walk: *Bumble Bee Slim* / Blue and lonesome: *Bumble Bee Slim* / Goin' back to Memphis: *Bumble Bee Slim* / Blue and lonesome: *Bumble Bee Slim* / Dust my broom: *Bumble Bee Slim* / Come day, go day: *Bumble Bee Slim* / Well alright: *Bumble Bee Slim* / Devil is a busy man: *Bumble Bee Slim* / Pinetop's boogie woogie: *Bumble Bee Slim* / Goin' back to Memphis: *Bumble Bee Slim* / Dust my broom: *Bumble Bee Slim* / Unlucky one: *Bumble Bee Slim* / Canada walk: *Bumble Bee Slim* / Jumpin' after midnight: *Bumble Bee Slim* / Hot house stuff: *Bumble Bee Slim* / Got to get my baby: *Sunnyland Slim* / Miss Bessie Mae: *Sunnyland Slim* / Everytime I get to drinkin': *Sunnyland Slim* / Midnight stomp: *Sunnyland Slim* / Little girl blues: *Sunnyland Slim* / I don't worry: *Crudup, Arthur 'Big Boy'* / Room and board: *Crudup, Arthur 'Big Boy'* / Long curly mane: *Crudup, Arthur 'Big Boy'* / Reebuck man: *Crudup, Arthur 'Big Boy'* / Before you go: *Crudup, Arthur 'Big Boy'* / Boogie in the morning: *Crudup, Arthur 'Big Boy'* / What are you trying to do: *Crudup, Arthur 'Big Boy'* / Burying ground: *Crudup, Arthur 'Big Boy'* / Death Valley blues: *Crudup, Arthur 'Big Boy'* / Kerrina Kerrina: *Crudup, Arthur 'Big Boy'*

CDEM 1588 / Apr '96 / Premier/EMI

☐ REEFER SONGS (23 Original Jazz and Blues Vocals)

JASSCD 7 / Oct '91 / Jass

☐ REFERENCE JAZZ

RRS 2CD / '91 / Reference Recordings

☐ REFLECTIONS (Haunting Sound Of The Pan Pipes)

Time to say goodbye / I belive I can fly / Love shine a light / Mama / You might need somebody / Always on my mind / If you're thinking of me / Don't speak / If I never see you again / Angel / Child / Say what you want / Lifted / Wind beneath my wings / Unbreak my heart / You'll see / Don't marry her / One and one

ECD 3389 / 3 Nov '97 / K-Tel

☐ REFLECTIONS IN THE LOOKING GLASS

CLP 9806 / Oct '96 / Cleopatra

☐ REGAL RECORDS IN NEW ORLEANS

I'll never be free: *Gayten, Paul* / Yeah yeah yeah: *Gayten, Paul* / You ought to know: *Gayten, Paul* / You shouldn't: *Gayten, Paul* / Confused: *Gayten, Paul* / Bear hug: *Gayten, Paul* / Oooh la la: *Gayten, Paul* / My last goodbye: *Gayten, Paul* / I ain't gonna let you in: *Gayten, Paul* / Kickapoo juice: *Gayten, Paul* / Each time: *Gayten, Paul* / Fishtails: *Gayten, Paul* / Suzette: *Gayten, Paul* / Happy birthday to you: *Gayten, Paul* / For you my love: *Gayten, Paul* / Back trackin' aka Dr. Daddy-o: *Gayten, Paul* / Gold ain't everything: *Gayten, Paul* / Baby what's new: *Laurie, Annie* / My rough and ready man: *Laurie, Annie* / Low down feeling: *Laurie, Annie* / Three times seven equals twenty one: *Laurie, Annie* / I don't marry too soon: *Laurie, Annie* / Messy Bessy: *Bartholomew, Dave* / Nickel wine: *Bartholomew, Dave* / Riding high: *Brown, Roy* / Brand new baby: *Brown, Roy*

CDCHD 362 / Jan '92 / Ace

☐ REGGAE 4 U (3CD Set)

KBOX 371 / Aug '97 / Collection

☐ REGGAE AFRICA

Lion in a sheep skin: *Harley & The Rasta Family* / Amagni: *Dembele, Koko* / Show biz to requin: *Tangara Speed Ghoda* / Veto de dieu: *Alpha Blondy* / Nothing but prayer: *Senzo* / C'est pas da ni blo: *Kassy, Serges* / Wondogbo: *Kouame, Lystrone* / Unlucky man: *Ice T Cool* / Sweet reggae: *Harley & The Rasta Family* / Politic warrior: *Ray, P.I.* / Elle: *Jah Gunt* / Lord say: *Tangara Speed Ghoda* / N'ka yere: *Dembele, Koko* / Children of Africa: *Ismael Isaac Les Freres Keita*

CDEMC 3679 / May '94 / Hemisphere

☐ REGGAE ARCHIVE

Rivers of Babylon: *Melodians* / It mek: *Dekker, Desmond & The Aces* / Love of the common people: *Thomas, Nicky* / Monkey spanner: *Barker, Dave & Ansell Collins* / Young gifted and black: *Bob & Marcia* / Crying over you: *Boothe, Ken* / Suzanne beware of the devil: *Livingstone, Dandy* / Red red wine: *Tribe, Tony* / Wonderful world beautiful people: *Cliff, Jimmy* / Let your yeah be yeah: *Pioneers* / Dollar in your teeth: *Upsetters* / Israelites: *Dekker, Desmond & The Aces* / Black and white: *Greyhound* / Everything I own: *Boothe, Ken* / Uptown top rankin': *Althia & Donna* / Help me make it through the night: *Holt, John* / Black pearl: *Faith, Horace* / Money in my pocket: *Brown, Dennis* / Hurt so good: *Cadogan, Susan* / You can get it if you really want: *Dekker, Desmond*

RMCD 203 / Nov '97 / Rialto

☐ REGGAE ARCHIVE - US

RESTLESS 7268 / Aug '94 / On-U Sound

☐ REGGAE ARCHIVES VOL.1

African land/Africa we want to go: *Kalphat, Carol & Clint Eastwood* / African melody: *Dr. Pablo & The Cry Tuff All-Stars* / Dub from creation: *Creation Rebel* / Creation cycle: *Creation Rebel* / Love by everyone/ Rebel no devil: *Prince Far-I & DJ Buzz* / Golden locks: *Sherman, Bim* / Slummy ghetto: *Sherman, Bim* / Party time: *Sherman, Bim* / Sweet reggae music: *Holt, Errol* / Barber salon: *Prince Far-I* / African space: *Creation Rebel* / Mother don't cry: *Creation Rebel* / Drum don't talk: *Creation Rebel*

ONUCD 21 / Mar '93 / On-U Sound

☐ REGGAE ARCHIVES VOL.2

ONUCD 22 / Apr '93 / On-U Sound

☐ REGGAE BABYLON

RB 3031 / Mar '95 / Reggae Best

☐ REGGAE BASHMENT

ECCD 00052 / 17 Nov '97 / East Coast

☐ REGGAE BLASTERS VOL.1

D 19960 / Sep '96 / Far I

☐ REGGAE BLASTERS VOL.2

D 19969 / Sep '96 / Far I

☐ REGGAE BLASTERS VOL.3

D 19970 / Oct '96 / Far I

☐ REGGAE BLASTERS VOL.4

D 19971 / Oct '96 / Far I

☐ REGGAE CELEBRATION

D 31517 / Oct '96 / Far I

☐ REGGAE CHRISTMAS

Silent night / I saw mommy kiss a dreadlocks / Dub it for Christmas / Santa Claus / Flash your dread / Sensimillia

PCD 1422 / Nov '91 / Profile

☐ REGGAE CHRISTMAS

CDTRL 364 / Nov '95 / Trojan

☐ REGGAE CHRISTMAS (2CD Set)

Peace and love: *Bradshaw, Sonny* / Jingle bells: *Studio Three* / Santa Claus is ska ing to town: *Williams, Granville Orchestra* / Merry merry Christmas: *Ellis, Anton & The Lipsticks* / Christmas time again: *Anderson, Rueben* / Christmas parade: *Edwards, Rupie* / Ding dong bell: *Ethiopians* / Christmas in JA: *Willoughby, Neville* / We three kings: *Kingstonians* / Christmas day: *Gaylads* / Drummer boy: *Studio Three* / I saw mommy kissing Santa Claus: *Clarke, Johnny* / Santa Claus dub: *Aggrovators* / Merry Christmas: *Winston Groovy* / White Christmas: *Edwards, Jackie* / Blue Christmas: *Holt, John* / Reggae Christmas: *Gable Hall School Choir* / Holy Christmas: *Cimarons* / Merry Christmas happy new year: *Robinson, Sandra* / I believe in Father Christmas: *Holt, John* / Last Christmas: *Holt, John* / Lonely this Christmas: *Holt, John* / White Christmas: *Holt, John* / Happy Xmas: *Holt, John* / Spaceman came travelling: *Holt, John* / When a child is born: *Holt, John* / Santa Claus is comin' to town: *Holt, John* / My oh my: *Holt, John* / Blue Christmas: *Holt, John* / Auld lang syne: *Holt, John*

CDTBX 101 / Dec '97 / Trojan

☐ REGGAE CHRISTMAS FROM STUDIO ONE

HBCD 118 / Nov '92 / Heartbeat

☐ REGGAE CLASSICS - SERIOUS SELECTIONS VOL.1

Love the way it should be: *Royal Rasses* / Back a yard: *In Crowd* / Bucket bottom: *Prince Alla* / Here I come: *Brown, Dennis* / Fade away: *Byles, Junior* / No man is an island: *Motion* / Natural collie: *McGregor, Freddie* / Time is the master: *Holt, John* / Easy: *Lindsay, Jimmy* / I'm still waiting: *Wilson, Delroy* / Man in me: *Matumbi* / Mr. Ska Beena: *Ellis, Alton*

CDREG 2 / Mar '95 / Rewind Selecta

☐ REGGAE CLASSICS - SERIOUS SELECTIONS VOL.2

CDREG 5 / Jun '96 / Rewind Selecta

☐ REGGAE COLLECTION, THE (4CD Set/ 100 Reggae Classics)

Lively up yourself: *Marley, Bob* / Baby I love you: *Ellis, Alton* / Maximum respect: *Isaacs, Gregory* / Lately girl: *Brown, Dennis* / Girl is in love: *Minott, Sugar* / Got to tell the people: *Campbell, Cornell* / She want it: *Holt, John* / Do it sweet: *Edwards, Jackie* / Falling in love with you: *Russell, Devon* / You and I: *Blackstones* / Hammer: *Marley, Bob* / Yellow a the best: *Yellowman & The Paragons* / Train to skaville: *Dillon, Leonard* / Have I told you lately that I love you: *Fifth, George* / Kaya: *Marley, Bob* / Mark my word: *Griffiths, Marcia* / Diana: *Heptones* / Do that to me one more time: *Wilson, Delroy* / Let love in:

Brown, Dennis / All night session: Edwards, Jackie / First time I saw you: Paragons / Good thing going: Minott, Sugar / Why: Ellis, Alton / Born to lose: Holt, John / Love to the people: Russell, Devon / Lover's paradise: Brown, Dennis / You better come good: Yellowman & The Paragons / Good vibes: Heptones / Let me go girl: Edwards, Jackie / Valley of decision: Ellis, Alton / Homely girl: Holt, John / Soul rebel: Marley, Bob / Youv'e lost that loving feeling: Minott, Sugar / Feel like jumping: Griffiths, Marcia / Wilson, Delroy: Wilson, Delroy / There she goes: Marley, Bob / We the people who are darker than blue: Russell, Devon / She is not my kind: Isaacs, Gregory / Brandy: Scott, Audrey / I need her: Paragons / Children of Israel: Brown, Dennis / I want you girl: Ellis, Alton / Survival: Griffiths, Marcia / Children of the world: Blackstones / Suzette: Burrell, Roland / Hey love: Holt, John / Suspicious minds: Johnson, Anthony / Make it with you: Minott, Sugar / Once upon a time: Faith, George / Natural mystic: Marley, Bob / Full metal jacket: Yellowman & The Paragons / Mellow wood: Marley, Bob / Spanish harlem: Wilson, Delroy / You are mine: Ellis, Alton / Souls keep burning: Brown, Dennis / Melody life: Griffiths, Marcia / Only a smile: Blackstones / Here I come: Holt, John / Place called Zion: Paragons / My heart is bleeding: Isaacs, Gregory / Lover's rock: Minott, Sugar / Boasting: Brown, Dennis / Please stay: Faith, George / Soul shake down party: Marley, Bob / Move on up: Russell, Devon / Sweet inspiration: Johnson, Anthony / Special thanks: Yellowman & The Paragons / Same song: Blackstones / Love comes from unexpected places: Scott, Audrey / Put it on: Marley, Bob / Girl you can't be my wife: Ellis, Alton / Missing you: Minott, Sugar / Stay: Griffiths, Marcia / Any day now: Brown, Dennis / Oh girl: Holt, John / In the midnight hour: Holt, John / Drifter: Campbell, Cornell / Trenchtown rock: Marley, Bob / Cry not for me: Ellis, Alton / Drift away: Heptones / Lonely days: Minott, Sugar / You are sugar and spice: Brown, Dennis / Lonesome feeling: Griffiths, Marcia / Love and affection: Faith, George / Makings of version: Russell, Devon / Soul captives: Marley, Bob / Dedicated to you: Yellowman & The Paragons / Black race: Burrell, Roland / Sha-la-la-la: Heptones / Best thing that ever happened to me: Scott, Audrey / Togetherness: Johnson, Anthony / If loving you is wrong: Faith, George / Come a little closer: Paragons / Hooligan: Brown, Dennis / Do you love me: Holt, John / Treat you right: Marley, Bob / Now we know: Minott, Sugar / In the heart of the city: Isaacs, Gregory / Love you for more reasons than one: Ellis, Alton / Dreamland: Griffiths, Marcia

391302 / Aug '97 / Hallmark

☐ REGGAE COLLECTION, THE (3CD Set)

Heartache: Isaacs, Gregory / Unchained melody: Ricks, Glen / You sexy thing: Osbourne, Johnny / Suspicious minds: Heptones / Endless love: Edwards, Jackie / How deep is our love: Silvertones / Save the last dance for me: Morgan, Derrick / One life to live: Dillon, Phyllis / Give me some more of your loving: Smith, Slim / Rock your baby: Cimarons / Girl I'm out of my mind: Ricks, Glen / Land of love: Heptones / Seven letters: Morgan, Derrick / Love that a woman should give a man: Dillon, Phyllis / I'll take you home: Originals / It's time for love: Ricks, Glen / Let it be me: Edwards, Jackie / Where do broken hearts go: Starr, Sandy / Penny for your song: Thompson, Linval / We belong together: Dillon, Phyllis / Gimme gimme: Dekker, Desmond & The Aces / Here I stand: Hinds, Justin & The Dominoes / Yeah ho: Cliff, Jimmy / Wicked a go feel it now: Campbell, Al / Boom shaka laka: Lewis, Hopeton / Ba ba ri ba skank: Alcapone, Dennis / Cultural roots: Mr. Badman / Tide is high: U-Roy / Shine eye gal: Clint Eastwood / Two time: Morgan, Derrick / This feeling: Smith, Slim / Rasta time: Campbell, Al / Good man: Chris Irie / Sweet soul music: Gladiators / Samba reggae: Cliff, Jimmy / People get ready: Osbourne, Johnny / In my life: Rondo, Geno / Sweet reggae music: Trinity / Every day is a holiday: Sensations / Watch this sound: Smith, Slim / Unity: Dekker, Desmond & The Aces / Rub a dub: Cliff, Jimmy / Rock on: Isaacs, Gregory / Kung fu fighting: Cimarons / Just groove with me: Don Carlos / African roots: Clint Eastwood / You can get if you really want: Cimarons / Joyful locks: U-Roy / Oh Carolina: Ricks, Glen / Big big man: Trinity / Some woman must cry: Morgan, Derrick / Peace and love: Jamaicans / Chatty chatty mouth: Mello Ladds / Ball of fire: Dillinger / Love fever: Cobra / Let go the dread: Minott, Sugar / What will your Mama say: Isaacs, Gregory / Eddie oh baby: Dillon, Phyllis / Super boss: U-Roy / Trying youthman: Brown, Barry

PBXCD 324 / 3 Aug '98 / Pulse

☐ REGGAE CULTURE

HBAN 13CD / Jul '94 / Heartbeat

☐ REGGAE DANCE (15 Red Hot Reggae Hits)

Sweets for my sweet / I can see clearly now / Baby come back / Sweat (a la la la la long) / Don't turn around / Dedicated to the one I love / Baby I love your way / It keeps rainin' tears / Bombastic / Shy guy / Informer / Can't help falling in love / Kingston Town / Sign / All that she wants

SUMCD 4061 / Nov '96 / Summit

☐ REGGAE DANCE PARTY

304862 / Jun '98 / Hallmark

☐ REGGAE ESSENTIALS

343992 / Apr '97 / Koch International

☐ REGGAE FAVOURITES

Sweat (A la la la la long) / Iron lion zion / Nightshift / Pass the dutchie / Many rivers to cross / Electric avenue / Reggae night / I got you babe / To love somebody / Everything I own / Could you be loved / Red red wine

399010 / Sep '93 / Koch

☐ REGGAE FEELING

322719 / Apr '97 / Koch

☐ REGGAE FEELING VOL.3

3411252 / Aug '94 / Koch

☐ REGGAE FOR KIDS VOL.1

RASCD 3095 / May '92 / Ras

☐ REGGAE FOR KIDS VOL.2

Day-o: Isaacs, Gregory / Hush daddy's baby: Mystic Revealers / Children of the world: Yvad / Didn't you know: Wailer, Bunny / Rasta row the boat ashore: Charlie Chaplin / Big ship: McGregor, Freddie / What about the children / One love: McGregor, Freddie / Hello goodbye: Don Carlos / Reggae for kids: Roots Radics / Smart, smart, smart: Brigadier Jerry / School done rule: McGregor, Steven / Raindrops/I can see clearly now: Yami Bolo / What the world needs now: Yami Bolo

RAS 3232 / Dec '97 / Ras

☐ REGGAE FOR LOVERS

Be my friend: Pinchers / When: Pinchers / Playmate: Pinchers / Fever: Osbourne, Johnny / Only the strong survive: Osbourne, Johnny / Keep on telling me: Admiral Tibet

DCD 5273 / Nov '92 / Kenwest

☐ REGGAE FOR LOVERS

I can't wait: Sanchez / Pretty looks: Sanchez / Who cares: Sanchez / True believer: Sanchez / Get ready: Ricks, Glen / Sitting in the backseat: Ricks, Glen / Closer together: Ricks, Glen / Hooked: Isaacs, Gregory / Place in your heart: Garnet Silk / Move on slow: Garnet Silk / 100% of love: Smart, Leroy / Body is hear with me: Smart, Leroy

SUMCD 4110 / Mar '97 / Summit

☐ REGGAE FOR LOVERS

Betcha by golly wow: Dunkley, Errol / Give me: Tony Tuff / I never knew love: Chalice / Girl is mine: Yellowman & Peter Metro / True love: Undivided Roots / Without love: Tamlins / My devotion: Brown, Junior / I'm in the mood: Naturalites / Nice time: Don Carlos / It's you girl: Prophet, Michael / How can I: Holt, John / Shine eye gal: Levy, Barrington / You move me: Douglas, Keith / No time to lose: Campbell, Al / My time: Isaacs, Gregory / My love: Viceroys

307642 / Jul '97 / Hallmark

☐ REGGAE FREEDOM

D 31518 / Sep '96 / Far I

☐ REGGAE FROM JAMAICA VOL.1 (Redder Than Red)

BB 2801 / Dec '94 / Blue Beat

☐ REGGAE FROM JAMAICA VOL.2 (Blowin' In The Wind)

BB 2802 / Dec '94 / Blue Beat

☐ REGGAE FROM JAMAICA VOL.3 (Rock Steady)

BB 2803 / Dec '94 / Blue Beat

☐ REGGAE FROM JAMAICA VOL.4 (Mellow Mood)

BB 2804 / Dec '94 / Blue Beat

☐ REGGAE FROM JAMAICA VOL.5 (Girlie Girlie)

BB 2805 / Dec '94 / Blue Beat

☐ REGGAE FROM JAMAICA VOL.6 (Rivers Of Babylon)

BB 2806 / Dec '94 / Blue Beat

☐ REGGAE GOLD

VPCD 15092 / 18 Aug '97 / VP

☐ REGGAE GOLD 1996

VPCD 1479 / May '96 / VP

☐ REGGAE GOLD 1997

VPCD 15092 / Aug '97 / VP

☐ REGGAE GOLD 1998

VPCD 15292 / 18 May '98 / VP

☐ REGGAE GOT SOUL (2CD Set)

Hey love: Holt, John / Try once more: Crucial Vibes / That's all I want: Paragons / Do it sweet: Edwards, Jackie / She's faced the hardest times: Johnson, Anthony / You are sugar and spice: Brown, Dennis / Make it with you: Minott, Sugar / Never too much love: Russell, Devon / When you're in love with a beautiful woman: Wilson, Delroy / In the heart of the city: Isaacs, Gregory / Perhaps, perhaps, perhaps: Scott, Audrey / Suspicious minds: Johnson, Anthony / Tell me now: Griffiths, Marcia / Murder in the dancehall: Isaacs, Gregory / Children of Israel: Brown, Dennis / You got me going crazy: Wilson, Delroy / Suzette: Burrell, Roland / Sweet Marie: Edwards, Jackie / Brother's don't give up: Isaacs, Gregory / I need her: Paragons / One step forward (and two steps back): Dillon, Leonard / Trick on the book: Campbell, Cornell / Truly: Griffiths, Marcia / Lately girl: Brown, Dennis / Lovers paradise: Brown, Dennis / Move on up: Russell, Devon / Have I told you lately that I love you: Faith, George / Spanish Harlem: Wilson, Delroy / I'll be lonely: Holt, John / Promise to be true: Isaacs, Gregory / Where I stand: Campbell, Cornell / Wolves and Leopards: Brown, Dennis / What's going on: Wilson, Delroy / Good thing going: Minott, Sugar / Trumpet sounding: Crucial Vibes / Do that to me one more time: Wilson, Delroy

330152 / Jul '96 / Hallmark

☐ REGGAE GREATEST HITS

DCD 5068 / Jul '89 / Disky

☐ REGGAE GREATS

TFP 019 / Nov '92 / Tring

☐ REGGAE GROOVES VOL.1

TJCD 002 / 13 Oct '97 / Smokey Joe

☐ REGGAE HEAT (2CD Set)

Baby I love your way: Big Mountain / Living on the front line: Grant, Eddy / I can see clearly now: Nash, Johnny / Ghost town: Specials / Monkey man: Toots & The Maytals / You can get it if you really want: Dekker, Desmond / Tears of a clown: Beat / Uptown top rankin': Althia & Donna / Young, gifted and black: Bob & Marcia / I wanna wake up with you: Gardiner, Boris / Funky Kingston: Toots & The Maytals / Think twice: Marie, Donna / Suzanne beware of the devil: Livingstone, Dandy / I don't wanna dance: Grant, Eddy / Israelites: Dekker, Desmond / Hurt so good: Cadogan, Susan / Love of the common people: Thomas, Nicky / Stir it up: Nash, Johnny / In the dard: Toots & The Maytals / Many rivers to cross: Cliff, Jimmy / Small axe: Marley, Bob & The Wailers / Montego Bay: Notes, Freddie / I shot the sherrif: Inner Circle / Everything I own: Boothe, Ken / Good thing going: Minott, Sugar / Rivers of Babylon: Melodians / 007: Dekker, Desmond / Message to you Rudy: Specials / Money in my pocket: Brown, Dennis / Gal wine: Chaka Demus & Pliers / Know your culture: Big Mountain / Let your yeah be yeah: Pioneers / Mad about you: Ruffin, Bruce / Wonderful world, beautiful people: Cliff, Jimmy / Wondering wanderer: Misty In Roots / You gotta walk (don't look back): Tosh, Peter

RCACD 205 / Jul '97 / RCA

☐ REGGAE HEAT (2CD Set)

Don't look back: Tosh, Peter / Amigo: Black Slate / Money in my pocket: Brown, Dennis / Gimme hope Joanna: Grant, Eddy / Wonderful world beautiful people: Cliff, Jimmy / Do you really want to hurt me: Culture Club / OK Fred: Dunkley, Errol / Girlie girlie: George, Sophia / Midnight rider: Davidson, Paul / I want to wake up with you: Gardiner, Boris / Israelites: Dekker, Desmond / Could you be loved: Thomas, Ruddy / Mockingbird hill: Migil 5 / Nightshift: Winston Groovy / Sideshow: Biggs, Barry / Feel my riddum: Skibby / Everything I own: Boy George / Storybook children: Isaacs, Gregory / No woman no cry: Marley, Kymani / Lady: Wade, Wayne / Lay down (wet dreams): Invaders & George Hughes / Stir it up: Thomas, Ruddy / Tomorrow: Marley, Ziggy / Reckless: Bambaataa, Afrika & UB40 / Bush doctor: Tosh, Peter / I don't wanna dance: Grant, Eddy / It keeps rainin': McLean, Bitty / I wanna be your man: Chaka Demus & Pliers / Love of the common people: Thomas, Nicky / Many rivers to cross: Dekker, Desmond

DOU 878332 / 2 Feb '98 / Disky

☐ REGGAE HITS

Don't look back (you've gotta walk): Tosh, Peter / Amigo: Black Slate / Money in my pocket: Brown, Dennis / Gimme hope Jo'anna: Grant, Eddy / Wonderful world, beautiful people: Cliff, Jimmy / Do you really want to hurt me: Culture Club / OK Fred: Dunkley, Errol / Girlie girlie: George, Sophia / Midnight rider: Davidson, Paul / I want to wake up with you: Gardiner, Boris / Israelites: Dekker, Desmond / Could you be loved: Thomas, Ruddy / Mockingbird hill: Migil 5 / Nightshift: Winston Groovy

WLT 874582 / Nov '96 / Disky

☐ REGGAE HITS BOX SET VOL.4

RHBCD 4 / Nov '95 / Jet Star

☐ REGGAE HITS BOX SET VOL.5

RHBCD 5 / Nov '95 / Jet Star

☐ REGGAE HITS BOX SET VOL.6

RHBCD 6 / Nov '95 / Jet Star

☐ REGGAE HITS FOREVER

SPCD 0131 / 13 Oct '97 / Super Power

☐ REGGAE HITS JUGGLIN'

BWCD 0019 / 20 Jul '98 / Brickwall

☐ REGGAE HITS VOL.1

Under me sensi: Levy, Barrington / Herbman hustling: Minott, Sugar / Mix me down: Tony Tuff / Haul and pull up: Brown, Neville / Lover's magic: Isaacs, Gregory / Someone special: Brown, Dennis / Gimme good loving: Natural Touch / Feel so good: Reid, Sandra / Between me and you: Campbell, Carol / 'Cause you love me baby: Tajah, Paulette / Roots rockin': Aswad / Woman I need your loving: Investigators

JECD 1001 / Jun '88 / Jet Star

☐ REGGAE HITS VOL.1

MACCD 283 / Aug '96 / Autograph

☐ REGGAE HITS VOL.1

Money in my pocket / Soul rebel / I show you how to reggae / Soul shakedown party / Prisoner of love / Stop the train / Can you feel it / Caution / Reggae fever / Dock of the bay / Soul captive / Uptight / Cause you love my baby / Go tell it on the mountains / Green green grass of home / Roots rock

GRF 0103 / Apr '93 / Tring

☐ REGGAE HITS VOL.1 & 2

RHBCD 1 / Dec '93 / Jet Star

☐ REGGAE HITS VOL.10

JECD 1010 / Jul '91 / Jet Star

☐ REGGAE HITS VOL.12

JECD 1012 / Apr '92 / Jet Star

☐ REGGAE HITS VOL.13

Big up: Shaggy & Rayvon / Man kind: Capleton / I spy: General TK / How the world a run: Buju Banton / Second class: Gonzalez, Carol / Woman a you: Terror Fabulous / Ring the alarm quick: Tenor Saw & Buju Banton / Discovery: Griffiths, Marcia & Tony Rebel/Cutty Ranks/Buju Banton / Missing you now: Sanchez / I was born a winner: McGregor, Freddie / Where is the love: Hammond, Beres & Sugar Minott/ Tony Rebel / Who say man nuh cry: Buju Banton & Beres Hammond / Can this be real: Boom, Barry & Cutty Ranks / I love you too much: Wade, Wayne / You are my lady: Lefty Banton / End of the road: Paul, Frankie / Go round: Jack Reuben & The Riddler / Save the best for last: Singing Sweet

JECD 013 / Dec '92 / Jet Star

☐ REGGAE HITS VOL.14

JECD 1014 / Aug '93 / Jet Star

☐ REGGAE HITS VOL.15

JECD 1015 / Dec '93 / Jet Star

☐ REGGAE HITS VOL.16

JECD 1016 / Aug '94 / Jet Star

☐ REGGAE HITS VOL.17

JECD 1017 / Dec '94 / Jet Star

☐ REGGAE HITS VOL.18

JECD 1018 / Sep '95 / Jet Star

☐ REGGAE HITS VOL.19

JECD 1019 / Dec '95 / Jet Star

☐ REGGAE HITS VOL.2

Wildfire: Holt, John & Dennis Brown / I'll be on my way: Isaacs, Gregory / Inferiority complex: Paul, Frankie / Country living: Mighty Diamonds / Curly locks: Byles, Junior / Senci addick: Fergeson, Horace / Baby be true: Thompson, Carroll / Caught you in a lie: Reid, Sandra / I love you: Sister Audrey / Jazzy: Paula / I'm gonna fall in love: Stewart, Tinga / Horsemove (giddiup): Horseman / House is not a home: Minott, Sugar

JECD 1002 / '88 / Jet Star

☐ REGGAE HITS VOL.2

MACCD 284 / Aug '96 / Autograph

☐ REGGAE HITS VOL.2

Don't rock my boat / Love me / Key to the world / Riding high / Upside down / Only heaven can wait / Fussin' and fightin' / I will love you (like ABC) / Three little birds / Lively up yourself / You are to me / Rebels hop / Make it with you / Sun is shining / Peace love and happiness / Maga dog

GRF 104 / Apr '93 / Tring

☐ REGGAE HITS VOL.21

JECD 1021 / Mar '97 / Jet Star

☐ REGGAE HITS VOL.21 (In The Mix - Chris Goldfinger/Glamma Kid)

JECDRX 1021 / Jun '97 / Jet Star

☐ REGGAE HITS VOL.22

I'm not a king: Cocoa T / Call me on the phone: Sanchez / Africa here I come: Morgan Heritage / Jah by my side (why be afraid): Tony Rebel / Ghetto people song: Everton Blender / Romie: Beenie Man / Moschino: Glamma Kid / No can do: Lindo, Kashief / Hold on: Mikey Spice / I believe I can fly: Sanchez / Nobody knows: Beenie Man / Dwayne: Red Rat / Goggle: Stephens, Tanya / She's having my baby: Ricardo, Don / I'll keep loving you: Nerious Joseph / Real love: Brown, Lloyd / Searching for love: Livingston, Andy / Good girl: Jack Radics & Bounty Killer/Frisco Kid / Mr. Whodini: Merciless / Lift up your head: Everton Blender / Bad news: Hammond, Beres

JECD 1022 / Jul '97 / Jet Star

☐ REGGAE HITS VOL.22 (In The Mix - DJ Village)

JECDRX 1022 / 19 Jan '98 / Jet Star

☐ REGGAE HITS VOL.23

JECD 1023 / 27 Apr '98 / Jet Star

☐ REGGAE HITS VOL.3

Sweet reggae music: Nitty Gritty / Shub in: Paul, Frankie / Watch how the people dancing: Knots, Kenny / Greetings: Half Pint / Dear Boopsie: Hall, Pam / Boops: Supercats / Girlie girlie: George, Sophia / Members only: Taylor, Tyrone / One dance won't do: Hall, Audrey / Sixth street: Wilson, Jack / Hello darling: Tippa Irie / Be my lady: Hunningale, Peter / It's you: Cross, Sandra / Party nite: Undivided Roots / Guilty: Gardiner, Boris

JECD 1003 / Mar '87 / Jet Star

☐ REGGAE HITS VOL.3

MACCD 285 / Aug '96 / Autograph

☐ REGGAE HITS VOL.3 & 4

RHBCD 2 / Jan '94 / Jet Star

☐ REGGAE HITS VOL.4

Wings of love: Sparks, Trevor / Girlfriend: Fraser, Dean / She's mine: Levy, Barrington / She's my lady: Administrators / Holding on: Cross, Sandra / If I give my heart to you: McLean, John / Guilty for loving you: St. Clair, Carl / Dangerous: Smith, Conroy / Chill out: Tenor Saw & Doggie / Debi Debi girl: Peter Metro & Sister Charmaine / Bad boy: Courtney Melody / Get ready: Paul, Frankie / Tears: Turner, Chuck / Big in bed: Lilly Melody

JECD 1004 / Jun '88 / Jet Star

☐ REGGAE HITS VOL.4

MACCD 286 / Aug '96 / Autograph

☐ REGGAE HITS VOL.5

Woman of moods: Dixon, Trevor / Black pride: Kofi / No way no better than yard: Bailey, Admiral / Am I losing you: Schloss, Cynthia / Ooh la la: LJM / Mi love mi girl bad: Flourgan & Sanchez / Proud to be black: Crucial Robbie / Power of love: Gibbons, Leroy / Cover me: Stewart, Tinga & Ninga Man / Very best: Intense / Life: Frighty & Colonel Mite / I still say yes: Parkings, Juliet / Man in the mirror: Little Kirk

JECD 1005 / Dec '88 / Jet Star

☐ REGGAE HITS VOL.5

MACCD 287 / Aug '96 / Autograph

☐ REGGAE HITS VOL.5 & 6

RHBCD 3 / Jan '94 / Jet Star

☐ REGGAE HITS VOL.6

My commanding wife: Gardiner, Boris / Bun and cheese: Clement Irie & Robert French / Looking over love: Kofi / Baby can I hold you tonight: Sanchez / New way to say I love you: Wayne Wonder / Stick by me: Marley, Bob / I want to get next to you: Manifest / Love me ses: Top Cat & Tenor Fly / On my mind: Intense / Lovers affair: Roni / Fatal attraction: Taxman / Mix up: UU Madoo & Captain Barky / Sweet and nice: Douglas, Lambert & Wayne Fire

JECD 1006 / Jul '89 / Jet Star

☐ REGGAE HITS VOL.7

JEÇD 1007 / Dec '89 / Jet Star

☐ REGGAE HITS VOL.8

Your love: Prophet, Michael & Ricky Tuff / Know fi move your waist: Major Danger / Ku-klung-klung: Red Dragon / Spirit: Chaka Demus / Burrp: Nardo Ranks / Money honey: Sweetie Irie / Body tune up: Johnny P / Buck wild: Paul, Frankie & Papa San / Careless whisper: Thriller U / Mrs. Jones: Levi, Sammy / Sharing the night: Brown, Lloyd / Finders keepers: Leroy Mafia / One night: Wayne Wonder & Brian/Tony Gold / 2 a.m.: Calvin / Do you ever think about me: Pure Silk / Ticket to ride: Trisha

JECD 1008 / Jun '90 / Jet Star

☐ **REGGAE HITS VOL.9**
JECD 1009 / Dec '90 / Jet Star

☐ **REGGAE IN YOUR JEGGAE**
CDTRL 358 / Aug '95 / Trojan

☐ **REGGAE KOLOR**
8419712 / Oct '96 / Declic

☐ **REGGAE LEGEND**
VPCD 1421 / Aug '95 / VP

☐ **REGGAE LEGENDS VOL.1**
RB 3011 / Nov '94 / Reggae Best
RNCD 2105 / Apr '95 / Rhino

☐ **REGGAE LOVE SONGS (16 Big Hits)**
Longshot kick de bucket: *Pioneers* / Let your yeah be yeah: *Pioneers* / Who's loving you: *Boothe, Ken* / Dark end of the street: *Boothe, Ken* / Never never: *Brown, Dennis* / Closer I get to you: *Brown, Dennis* / Something inside so strong: *Griffiths, Marcia* / Just don't want to be lonely: *Griffiths, Marcia* / Everything I own: *Boothe, Ken* / Crying over you: *Boothe, Ken* / Concrete jungle: *Brown, Dennis* / Ain't that loving you baby: *Brown, Dennis* / Sweet bitter love: *Griffiths, Marcia* / First time ever I saw your face: *Griffiths, Marcia* / I man born ya: *Shervington, Pluto* / Your honour: *Shervington, Pluto*
PLATCD 167 / Mar '96 / Platinum

☐ **REGGAE MAGIC VOL.1**
BWCD 0017 / 22 Jun '98 / Brickwall

☐ **REGGAE MEDAL VOL.1**
CRBCD 001 / Jan '94 / Carib Jems

☐ **REGGAE MELODIES**
RB 3016 / Oct '95 / Reggae Best

☐ **REGGAE MIX-TURES**
Danger zone: *Jah Stitch* / Proverbs: *McLeod, Enos & Pat Kelly* / I wish it would rain: *McLeod, Enos & Pat Kelly* / Nice time: *Uprising* / Uprising in dub: *Uprising* / Temptation woman: *McLeod, Enos* / Black man pickney: *McLeod, Enos* / Black dub: *McLeod, Enos* / Blood and fire: *McLeod, Enos* / Dub with fire: *McLeod, Enos* / Whipping dub: *McLeod, Enos* / Greedy girl: *Prince Ugly* / Natty dread something: *Prince Ugly & Searcher* / Mash mouth: *Jah Stitch* / Musso in dub: *Jah Stitch* / Three the hard way: *Campbell, Al & Dillinger/Trinity* / I'm a Joseph: *Trinity* / Whip them Jah: *Clint Eastwood*
PRCD 609 / May '97 / President

☐ **REGGAE MOOD SWINGZ**
WL 00072 / 9 Feb '98 / Wild Life Muzik

☐ **REGGAE MUSIC ALL NIGHT LONG (4CD Set)**
CDNCBOX 2 / Sep '91 / Charly

☐ **REGGAE MUSICAL MADNESS**
BSCD 2000 / Mar '98 / Black Shadow

☐ **REGGAE NOW**
ANCD 09 / Jan '94 / Heartbeat

☐ **REGGAE ON THE SEAS**
SONCD 0075 / Mar '95 / Sonic Sounds

☐ **REGGAE REFRESHERS SAMPLER VOL.1**
RRCDS 101 / Jun '90 / Reggae Refreshers

☐ **REGGAE REFRESHERS SAMPLER VOL.2**
Very well: *Wailing Souls* / Prophecy: *Fabian* / Gates of Zion: *Prophet, Michael* / Hypocrite: *Wailer, Bunny* / Botanical roots: *Black Uhuru* / Handsworth revolution: *Steel Pulse* / Jah heavy load: *Ijahman Levi* / One step forward: *Perry, Lee 'Scratch'* / Croaking lizard: *Upsetters* / Invasion: *Burning Spear* / Fade away: *Byles, Junior* / Independent intavenshan: *Johnson, Linton Kwesi* / Border: *Isaacs, Gregory* / Jailbreak: *Sly & Robbie* / Dub fire: *Aswad* / Sata: *Jah Lion*
RRCDS 102 / Apr '95 / Reggae Refreshers

☐ **REGGAE REVELATION**
REO 97CD / Nov '94 / ROIR

☐ **REGGAE REVOLUTION**
LG 21087 / Jun '92 / Lagoon

☐ **REGGAE REVOLUTION VOL.1**
RE 097CD / Jul '97 / ROIR

☐ **REGGAE ROCK VOL.2**
RRCD 9111 / Mar '96 / Reggae Rock

☐ **REGGAE ROOTS (2CD Set)**
I want to wake up with you: *Holt, John* / Rhythm body: *Minott, Sugar* / Tide is high: *Paragons* / Guns don't argue: *Alcapone, Dennis* / I willa lways love you: *Holt, John* / One my love: *Sly & Robbie* / Guns of Navarone: *Upsetters* / Clint Eastwood rides agian: *Perry, Lee 'Scratch'* / Cocaine in my brain: *Dillinger* / One love: *Marley, Bob & The Wailers* / Wonderful world: *Heptones* / Sweet sensation: *Melodians* / Keep on moving: *Marley, Bob & The Wailers* / Pressure drop: *Toots & The Maytals* / Satisfy my soul: *Marley, Bob & The Wailers* / If I were a carpenter: *Winston Groovy* / Jah jah bless the dreadlocks: *Mighty Diamonds* / Wet dream: *Max Romeo* / Monkey man: *Toots & The Maytals*
DCD 3004 / Jun '97 / Music

☐ **REGGAE SELECT VOL.1**
ECCD 00042 / Jun '97 / East Coast

☐ **REGGAE SONGS OF PRAISE**
VPCD 2070 / 20 Apr '98 / VP

☐ **REGGAE STARS**
Mount Zion: *Brown, Dennis* / Forgive her: *Davis, Ronnie* / Choose me: *Taylor, Tyrone* / (This world is a) Stage: *Davis, Ronnie* / My heart is in danger: *Holt, Errol & Roots Radics* / Keep away son: *Brown, Dennis* / Why must I: *Brown, Dennis* / See a man's face: *McLeod, Enos* / Gain experience: *McLaren, Frederick* / Comin' home: *Davis, Ronnie* / Lovie dovie: *Davis, Ronnie* / Chasin' you: *Davis, Ronnie* / Let it be me: *Davis, Ronnie* / Raindrops: *Davis, Ronnie* / I'm in love: *Andy, Horace* / Sparkling light: *Skyers, Nathan* / Write myself a letter: *Isaacs, Gregory*
PRCD 607 / May '97 / President

☐ **REGGAE SUPERSTARS**
RRTGCD 7732 / Mar '89 / Rohit

☐ **REGGAE SUPERSTARS**
RNCD 2076 / Dec '94 / Rhino

☐ **REGGAE SUPERSTARS (CD/CD Rom Set)**
WWCDR 010 / Apr '97 / Weton-Wesgram

☐ **REGGAE SUPERSTARS BONANZA**
RNCD 2022 / Sep '93 / Rhino

☐ **REGGAE SUPERSTARS OF THE 80'S**
BSLCD 12003 / Feb '88 / Rohit

☐ **REGGAE TIME**
GLD 63303 / Jul '94 / Goldies

☐ **REGGAE TOP 20 VOL.1**
SONCD 0029 / Jun '92 / Sonic Sounds

☐ **REGGAE TOP 20 VOL.2**
SONCD 0030 / Jun '92 / Sonic Sounds

☐ **REGGAE TRAIN, THE**
CBHB 174 / Feb '96 / Heartbeat

☐ **REGGAE UP (2CD Set)**
DEMPCD 001 / Mar '96 / Emporio

☐ **REGGAEMANIA**
Keep on movin' / Roll on a rolling stone / Originator / Ba ba riba skank / Everyday is like a holiday / Mabrouk / Concrete jungle / Let's build our dream / Travelling man / Too much / I'll forever keep on loving you / Red ash / Bam bam / You are like Heaven to me / I'll never get burn / Garden of love
74321360622 / Jun '96 / Milan

☐ **REGGAE'S GREATEST HITS**
After you who could there be: *Sanchez* / I will never look for love again: *Paul, Frankie* / Have a heart: *Brown, Dennis* / Lady of your calibre: *Isaacs, Gregory* / No one can take my place: *Glasgow, Deborahe* / Betcha by golly wow: *Minott, Sugar* / Mad house: *General Pecos* / Smile: *Ricks, Glen* / Groove my mind: *Thriller U* / Overjoyed: *Brown, Dennis* / Momentum: *Major Cat* / Can't hide my feelings: *Harvey, Maxine*
WRCD 019 / 9 Mar '98 / World

☐ **REGGAE'S GREATEST HITS VOL.1**
CDHB 3601 / Feb '96 / Heartbeat

☐ **REGGAE'S GREATEST HITS VOL.2**
CDHB 3602 / Feb '96 / Heartbeat

☐ **REGGAE'S GREATEST HITS VOL.3**
CDBH 3603 / Feb '96 / Heartbeat

☐ **REGGAE'S GREATEST HITS VOL.4**
CDHB 3604 / Feb '96 / Heartbeat

☐ **REGGAE'S GREATEST HITS VOL.5**
CDHB 3605 / Feb '96 / Heartbeat

☐ **REGGAE'S GREATEST HITS VOL.6**
CDHB 3606 / Feb '96 / Heartbeat

☐ **REGGAE'S GREATEST HITS VOL.7**
CDHB 3607 / Feb '96 / Heartbeat

☐ **REGGAE'S GREATEST HITS VOL.8**
CDHB 3608 / Feb '96 / Heartbeat

☐ **REGGAE'S GREATEST HITS VOL.9**
CDHB 3609 / Mar '96 / Heartbeat

☐ **REGGATTA MONDATTA**
ELDCD 006 / 7 Sep '98 / Ark 21

☐ **REINCARNATION (Street Parade/2CD Set)**
SPV 09240452 / Nov '97 / SPV

☐ **REJECTED VOL.2**
REJ 1000011 / 15 Dec '97 / Rejected

☐ **REJOICE (Celebration Of Christian Music/2CD Set)**
Magnificat / Feria / Lord's prayer / Most worthy Lord / Praise my soul the King of Heaven / Ave Maria / Callanish / Jesus Lord / Pie Jesu / Give me Jesus / I was glad / Hear and I will speak / Armenian mass / When I survey the wondrous cross / St. Mark's passion / Simple faith / You are so precious / God who fell to earth / We declare again / Cross / I will give thanks / Far away / My senses fly / Rock the rollin' stone / Melody of the morning / Hem me in / Sun goes down / Deep peace
330482 / Mar '97 / Hallmark

☐ **RELAXATION AND MEDITATION WITH MUSIC AND NATURE (Distant Thunder)**
12259 / Jul '97 / Laserlight

☐ **RELAXATION AND MEDITATION WITH MUSIC AND NATURE (Ocean Voyages)**
12260 / Jul '97 / Laserlight

☐ **RELEASE YOUR MIND VOL.2 (3CD Set)**
RR 69612 / 26 Jan '98 / Relapse

☐ **RELEASE: 22 CLASS A TRACKS (2CD Set)**
RLSCDX / 18 Sep '97 / Release

☐ **RELICS OF THE 60'S VOL.1 & 2**
PR 290 / Nov '97 / Phoarward

☐ **RELIGIONS OF THE WORLD**
A 6232 / Jan '97 / Tempo

☐ **RELIGIONS OF THE WORLD (7CD Set)**
A 6240 / Feb '98 / Tempo

☐ **RELIGIONS OF THE WORLD - BUDDHISM**
Introduction and song of praise from the Ramayana / Madmen of God / Evocation of the clouds/Prologue to the Gitagovinda / Buddhist chant / Dai hannya tendoku E overture / Dai hannya tendoku E Yuri chant / Dai hannya tendoku E sugu chant / Ho sho shu excerpt / Bhuddist chants and prayers / Invocation to the goddess Yeshiki Mamo
A 6233 / Jul '97 / Tempo

☐ **RELIGIONS OF THE WORLD - ISLAM**
A 6235 / Mar '97 / Tempo

☐ **RELIGIONS OF THE WORLD - JUDAISM**
Schofar / Shema Israel: *Kamann, Emile* / Music for the feast of tabernacles: *Philharmonic Ensemble Of Paris* / Song for Pesach: *Rabbi Papo* / El melekh yochev: *Nissan, Moshe* / Shadai emor na daile-galuteinu: *Tsubeiri, Tsadoq & Joseph Ozeiri* / Az yashir moshe: *Tsubeiri, Tsadoq & Joseph Ozeiri* / Al ted'ag leche avar yavo ha-go'el: *Habba, David* / Dror yikra: *Rahaminov, Mordashai & Elie Balkiyov* / Adon hakol mahayyyeh kol nesamah: *Habush, Aharon & Israel* / Feast of Hanukka: *Aguado, Bienvenida 'Berta'* / Nichmat kol hai tibarekh et chimkha: *Buzaldo, Mordakai* / Three songs for circumcision / Ana avda dkudcha: *Rakovski, Shalom* / Keyser bulgar: *Kasbek Ensemble* / Djankoye: *Kasbek Ensemble*
A 6236 / Dec '97 / Auvidis Tempo

☐ **RELIGIONS OF THE WORLD - ORTHODOXY**
Bells of Novodevichy convent / Oura I sourp yeghehetzi / Qadish qadish qadish: *JJ Moran Mar Ignatius Yaacoub III* / Akh tagore h'achire: *Daoud, Evelyne* / Madroshe in the 7th mode: *Daoud, Evelyne* / Creation: *Aga, Alemu* / Why weep why lament: *Alexeyevka Folk Ensemble* / Belarussian Christmas carol / Vitay Mary / May the heavens rejoice / O ye apostles / Liturgy of St. John Chrisostom / Otche nach / Sovet prevechnii: *Balakova, Iskra & The Great Bulgarian Voices/Zdravo Mihaylov* / Great Ektene from the divine lithurgy of St. John Chrisostom: *Russian State Symphony Cappella & Valery Polyansky*
A 6237 / Dec '97 / Auvidis Tempo

☐ **RELIGIONS OF THE WORLD - PROTESTANTISM**
Ein fest burg ist unser Gott / Kumm zu uns Schopfer / Ainsi qu'on oit le cerf bruire: *Oratoire De Louvre* / Ein kind ist uns geboren: *Oratoire De Louvre* / Vater unser im Himmelreich: *Chapuis, Michel* / Mass in B minor / Toccata in D minor / Magnificat fecit potentiam / Seht den sieger: *Berlin Radio Symphony & Chamber Orchestra* / Messiah Alleluia chorus / Might I in the sight appear: *Gonville & Caius College Choirs* / Roi david je t'aimerai seigneur d'un amour tendre: *Gulbenkian Chorus & Orchestra/Michel corboz* / Standing in the need of prayer: *Littleton, John* / Joshua at the battle of Jericho: *Mellotones* / Oh happy day: *Williams, Marion & The Gospel Caravan*
A 6238 / Dec '97 / Auvidis Tempo

☐ **RELIGIONS OF THE WORLD - TRADITIONAL RELIGIONS (Tribal Religious Music From Africa Australia And Americas)**
A 6239 / Sep '97 / Auvidis Tempo

☐ **RELIGIOUS CHANTS OF NORTH AFRICA VOL.2**
AAA 125 / Feb '97 / Club Du Disque Arabe

☐ **RELIGIOUS EXPRESSION IN THE CENTRAL BLUE RIDGE (2CD Set)**
Children of the heav'nly King / Testimony/Satan your Kingdom must come down / Philip in Samaria / How long has it been / I'm going down by the river of Jordan / What a time we're living in / When the redeemed are gathering in / How happy are they / Must Jesus bear the cross alone / Prayer / Jesus is coming soon / Doxology / Blessing / Baptizing at Carson Creek / Palms of victory / Holding to his hand of love / Lord will make a way somehow / Keep on the firing line / On the other side of Jordan / Twilight is falling / Home in heaven / Preaching by inspiration / Vision in a Tobacco Barn / I'll make you a fisherman of men / I used to be wild as a buck / Vision of the end of time
ROUCD 1506/7 / Jun '98 / Rounder

☐ **RELIGIOUS MUSIC FROM GUJARAT**
PS 65193 / Jan '98 / PlayaSound

☐ **RELIX 20TH ANNIVERSARY**
RRCD 2066 / Jul '97 / Relix

☐ **RELIX BAY ROCK VOL.5**
RRCD 2053 / Jul '97 / Relix

☐ **REMEMBER THE 50'S**
12106 / Jan '93 / Laserlight

☐ **REMEMBER THE 60'S - THE GROUPS**
Sabre dance: *Love Sculpture* / Quartermaster's stores: *Shadows* / It's my life: *Animals* / Seven daffodils: *Cherokees* / I'll never get over you: *Kidd, Johnny & The Pirates* / Greenback dollar: *Kingston Trio* / Don't let the sun catch you crying: *Gerry & The Pacemakers* / From a window: *Kramer, Billy J. & The Dakotas* / William Tell: *Sounds Incorporated* / You're no good: *Swinging Blue Jeans* / We're through: *Hollies* / Livin' above your head: *Jay & The Americans* / Three rooms with running water: *Bennett, Cliff & The Rebel Rousers* / One in the middle: *Manfred Mann* / Heart's symphony: *Lewis, Gary & The Playboys* / She's lost you: *Zephyrs* / I think we're alone now: *James, Tommy & The Shondells* / Going up the country: *Canned Heat* / For whom the bell tolls: *Dupree, Simon & The Big Sound* / Break away: *Beach Boys*
CDSL 8249 / Jul '95 / EMI

☐ **REMEMBER THE 70'S**
KBOX 351 / Nov '95 / Collection

☐ **REMEMBER THE 70'S - THE GROUPS**
Whole lotta love: *CCS* / Cotton fields: *Beach Boys* / Let's work together: *Canned Heat* / Rag mama rag: *Band* / Malt and barley blues: *McGuinness Flint* / Mocking bird: *Barclay James Harvest* / Strange kind of woman: *Deep Purple* / Long cool woman in a black dress: *Hollies* / Do ya: *Move* / 10538 overture: *ELO* / Brother Louie: *Hot Chocolate* / Judy teen: *Harley, Steve & Cockney Rebel* / Overnight sensation (Hit record): *Raspberries* / Forgotten roads: *If* / Millionaire: *Dr. Hook* / Ships in the night: *Be-Bop Deluxe* / Walk on by: *Stranglers* / Promises: *Buzzcocks* / My Sharona: *Knack* / Dance stance: *Dexy's Midnight Runners*
CDSL 8250 / Jul '95 / EMI

☐ **REMEMBER WHEN SINGERS COULD REALLY SING**
I left my heart in San Francisco: *Bennett, Tony* / Born free: *Williams, Andy* / Crazy: *Cline, Patsy* / Moon river: *Williams, Danny* / Portrait of my love: *Monro, Matt* / Mr. Wonderful: *Lee, Peggy* / Love letters in the sand: *Lester, Ketty* / Cry: *Ray, Johnnie* / On the street where you live: *Damone, Vic* / Return to me: *Martin, Dean* / Who's sorry now: *Francis, Connie* / Around the world: *Crosby, Bing* / Release me: *Humperdinck, Engelbert* / Move over darling: *Day, Doris* / Rose Marie: *Whitman, Slim* / I'm sorry: *Lee, Brenda* / It's only make believe: *Twitty, Conway* / This is my song: *Clark, Petula* / Distant drums: *Reeves, Jim* / It's impossible: *Como, Perry*
AHLCD 3 / Nov '92 / Hit

☐ **REMEMBERING KATE WOLF (Treasures Left Behind)**
RHRCD 114 / 1 Sep '98 / Red House

☐ **REMIXED REMODELLED**
CDALMY 1 / May '95 / Almighty

☐ **RENAISSANCE WORLDWIDE: LONDON (2CD Set)**
Underwater love: *Smoke City* / Soothe: *Furry Phreaks* / Easy rider blues: *Bulkhead* / Milk: *Garbage* / Everytime: *Lustral* / Western approaches: *Pako* / Mind, body and soul: *Carroll, Dina* / Saint and sinner: *Stone Factory* / Cowgirl: *Underworld* / Twisted: *Skunk Anansie* / Sea: *St. Etienne* / Gorecki: *Lamb* / Absurd: *Fluke* / Drive by: *Way Out West* / BETA: *Empirion* / Split second: *Landlord* / Koea 954: *DJ Supernova* / Misbehavinit: *Rebel Yelle* / Houston: *Moogability* / Smells electric: *Metal Spark* / Drop: *Ascendance* / Gel gor beni ask n'eyledi: *Sultan* / As a child I could walk on the ceiling: *Delta* / Alien nation: *Children Of Paradise* / Mind merge: *Darshan*
RENWW 1CD / 6 Oct '97 / Renaissance Worldwide

☐ **RENDEZVOUS VOL.1**
SJRCD 001 / Jul '96 / Street Jazz

☐ **RENDEZVOUS VOL.2**
SJRCD 002 / Jul '96 / Street Jazz

☐ **RENEGADE SOUNDSCAPES**
Code: *Absolute Zero & Subphonics* / Silence: *Future Engineers* / Sqaure waves: *Genotype* / Capacity: *Monochrome & Subphonics* / Shaft: *Mastermind* / Fugitive: *Absolute Zero & Subphonics* / Shattered: *Future Engineers* / 70's flava: *Mastermind*
RSSCD 01 / 10 Aug '98 / Renegade Recordings

☐ **RENEWAL MUSIC - BEHOLD THE LAMB (Songs Of Worship For The New Millenium)**
Kyrie / Come and rejoice / Glory glory to the King / Because we believe / At the name of Jesus / I saw Heaven opened / Jesus we enthrone you / Come to the table / We will meet you there / Faithful to your call / Give thanks / Gloria in excelsis deo
11422 / Oct '97 / Integrity

☐ **RENT PARTIES AND GOOD TIMES (Shake Your Wicked Knees)**
YAZOO 2035 / 16 Mar '98 / Yazoo

☐ **RER QUARTERLY - SELECTIONS FROM VOL.2**
RERQCD 2 / Jul '93 / ReR/ Recommended

☐ **RER QUARTERLY VOL.4 NO.1**
RER 0401 / Jun '94 / ReR/ Recommended

☐ **RER QUARTERLY VOL.4 NO.2**
RER 0402 / Jun '97 / ReR/ Recommended

☐ **RESONANCE MOOD**
Target eye: *Sandman* / Tio mate: *Deflo* / Slugfest: *Slug* / Intensive psychedelic care: *Chakra & Nada* / Jaws: *Growling Mad Scientists* / Shadow five: *Lunar Asylum* / Decoder: *Nervasystem* / Athalon: *Manmademan* / Pulse 2: *Anti Matter*
MPCD 06 / May '97 / Matsuri

☐ RESOUNDING POLYPHONY OF THE CAUCAUSUS, THE (Georgia)
Mravaljamieri / Shemodzakhili / Kalospiruli / Nana / Alilo / Shen bicho anagurelo / Gaprindi shavo mertskhalo / Hassanbegura / May peace be with us / Shavi shashvi / Song of friendship / Vakhtangura / Batonebo / Nanina / Tsmindao gmerto / Ailuya / Tsintskaro / Shen khar venakhi / Suliko
MCM 3004 / May '97 / Multicultural Media

☐ RESPECT TO STUDIO ONE (2CD Set)
HBCD 181/182 / Nov '94 / Heartbeat

☐ RESTLESS WIND (Shades Of Music From The Heart Of India)
Punjabi sunrise / Morning prayer / Village life / Slow train / Santura / Zar gul / Restless wind / Hunting chant / Chase / Maila / Monkey fingers / Evening prayer
DC 882202 / 29 Aug '97 / Disky

☐ RESURRECTING THE BLUES
REMCD 515 / Feb '98 / Reactive

☐ RETREAT RECORDS (History Of A Label)
GEMCD 024 / 24 Aug '98 / Diamond

☐ RETROSPECTIVE 1929-1963, A (2CD Set)
One hour (if I could be with you one hour tonight): *Mound City Blues Blowers* / Hello Lola: *Mound City Blues Blowers* / Miss Hannah: *McKinney's Cotton Pickers* / Wherever there's a will, baby: *McKinney's Cotton Pickers* / Sugarfoot stomp: *Henderson, Fletcher Orchestra* / Hocus pocus: *Henderson, Fletcher Orchestra* / When the lights are low: *Hampton, Lionel* / One sweet letter from you: *Hampton, Lionel* / Dinah: *Hampton, Lionel* / Meet Mr Foo: *Hawkins, Coleman* / Fine dinner: *Hawkins, Coleman* / She's funny that way: *Hawkins, Coleman* / Body and soul: *Hawkins, Coleman* / When day is gone: *Hawkins, Coleman* / Sheikh of araby: *Hawkins, Coleman* / My blue heaven: *Hawkins, Coleman* / Bouncing with bean: *Hawkins, Coleman* / Bugle call rag: *Metronome All Star Band* / One o'clock jump: *Metronome All Star Band* / Say it isn't so: *Hawkins, Coleman* / Spotlite: *Hawkins, Coleman* / Indian winter: *Esquire Jazz All Stars* / Indian summer: *Esquire Jazz All Stars* / How did she look: *Hawkins, Coleman & His Orchestra* / April in Paris: *Hawkins, Coleman & His Orchestra* / How strange: *Hawkins, Coleman & His Orchestra* / Half step down please: *Hawkins, Coleman & His Orchestra* / Angel face: *Hawkins, Coleman & His Orchestra* / There will never be another you: *Hawkins, Coleman & His Orchestra* / Bean stalks again: *Hawkins, Coleman & His Orchestra* / I love Paris: *Hawkins, Coleman* / Under Paris skies: *Hawkins, Coleman* / I've got the world on a string: *Allen, Henry 'Red' & His Orchestra* / Sweet Lorraine: *Allen, Henry 'Red' & His Orchestra* / Watermelon man: *Lambert, Hendricks/Bavan* / All the things you are: *Rollins, Sonny*
786366172 / Aug '95 / Bluebird

☐ RETROSPECTIVE OF HOUSE VOL.1
SDIMCD 3 / Jul '95 / Sound Dimension

☐ RETROSPECTIVE OF HOUSE VOL.2 (2CD Set)
SDIMCD 4 / Nov '95 / Sound Dimension

☐ RETROSPECTIVE OF HOUSE VOL.3 (4CD Set)
SDIMCD 5 / May '96 / Sound Dimension

☐ RETROSPECTIVE OF HOUSE VOL.4 (1991-1996/De Vit/Graham Gold/Sister Bliss - 3CD Set)
Around the world: *East 17* / Pacific symphony: *Transformer 2* / Movin' melodies: *Indica* / Joanna: *Mrs. Wood* / Age of love: *Age Of Love* / Schoneburg: *Marmion* / Freedom: *U-People* / Latin intruder: *Latin Thing* / Bits and pieces: *Artemesia* / Just can't get enough: *Transformer 2* / Deep house: *Triple J* / Back to my roots: *Rich In Paradise & FPI Project* / Who's the badman: *Patten, Dee* / Crazy man: *Blast* / Bells of New York: *Slo Moshun* / Raw: *Asuca* / Tester-don't stop: *Z100* / I know: *New Atlantic* / Made in 2 minutes: *Plastic Jam* / Closer to our dreams: *Rhythm Quest* / Club mix: *Desert Moods* / Crystal clear: *Grid* / This love: *Red Sun* / Just come 2 vocal: *Cool Jack* / 7 Days and 1 week: *BBE* / Way out west: *Montana* / Yeke yeke: *Kante, Mory* / Smokebelch II: *Sabres Of Paradise* / Energy flash: *Beltram, Joey* / Papua New Guinea: *Future Sound Of London* / Land of rhythm: *Marascia* / Is there anybody out there: *Friends Of Matthew* / Lionrock: *Lionrock* / Bad man: *Sister Bliss* / Don't leave: *Faithless* / Morel's grooves Vol.4 : let's groove: *Morel, George*
SDIMCD 6 / Aug '96 / Sound Dimension

☐ RETURN OF THE DJ VOL.1, THE
BOMB 2002CD / Jul '97 / Bomb

☐ RETURN TO SENDER
NORMAL 205CD / Aug '96 / Normal

☐ RETURN TO THE PLANET FUNK (2CD Set)
Movin': *Brass Construction* / Fire: *Ohio Players* / Slide: *Slave* / Baby brother: *War* / Fantastic voyage: *Lakeside* / Funk funk: *Cameo* / Get the funk out ma face: *Brothers Johnson* / Do the bus stop: *Fatback Band* / Ffun: *Con Funk Shun* / Dazz: *Brick* / Reach for it: *Duke, George* / Unlock the funk: *Locksmith* / Real mother for ya: *Watson, Johnny* / Stretchin' out: *Bootsy's Rubber Band* / Tear the roof of the sucker: *Parliament* / Shake your rump to the funk: *Bar-Kays* / Fight the power: *Isley Brothers* / Happy music: *Blackbyrds* / Saturday night: *Earth, Wind & Fire* / Joy and pain: *Maze* / I thought of you: *Hancock, Herbie* / New york city: *Miroslav Virous* / Keep your body workin': *Kleeer* / Sun is here: *Sun* / Potential: *Cazbo, Jimmy Bunch* / Do it any way you wanna: *People's Choice* / Do ya wanna get funky with me: *Brown, Peter* / Funky stuff: *Kool & The Gang* / Make it funky: *Brown, James*
743215083528 / 8 Sep '97 / Ariola

☐ RETURN TO THE SOURCE (Sacred Sites)
Hill of shining beings: *Man Made Man* / Tribedelic nomads: *Insectocide* / Ama no kawa: *Insectocide* / Energy transition: *Quirk* / Flight of the pteradactil: *Parasonix* / Supernature: *Medicine Drum* / Rites of Ra: *Anubis* / Tapu: *Laughing Buddha* / Ilias: *Buzzcraft* / Dawn of man: *Masa* / Sky spirit: *Ceiba* / Disciplinic flow: *Tribal Drift* / Reaper girl: *Kat Von Trapp* / Hypnofly: *UVW* / Mootawinjee: *TRipitaka* / Newgrange: *Azukx* / Every mother's sun: *Astralasia* / Time gate: *Yokota* / Freefall: *Youth* / Stone henge: *Universal Sound* / Sacred reunion: *Star Children*
RTTSCD 4 / Jun '97 / Positiva

☐ RETURN TO THE SOURCE (Shamanic Trance)
Nom butu: *Der Stern Von Afrika* / Sloworm: *Germinating Seeds Of Doda* / Dance with the devil: *Quirk* / Stranded: *Bley, Johann* / Alien funk: *Maskalin* / Tango electro: *Dino & Avi Algranati* / Amma: *Nommos* / Universal minds: *Psychopod* / Saturnalia: *Slide* / Octofunk: *Green Nuns Of The Revolution*
4942092 / 30 Mar '98 / Positiva

☐ RETURN TO THE TECNODROME
RPTCD 010 / Feb '97 / Replicant

☐ RETURN TO UMOJA
CONCD 001 / Jul '96 / Conqueror

☐ REUNION MAURITIUS RODRIGUEZ
Y 225716 / Apr '98 / Auvidis Silex

☐ REVELATION
BB 2813 / Oct '95 / Blue Beat

☐ REVENGE OF THE KILLER CRASH HELMETS/UNTAXED
RRCD 015 / 13 Apr '98 / Retch

☐ REVENGE OF THE KILLER PUSSIES
Wild women: *Alien Sex Fiend* / Swamp baby: *Sunglasses After Dark* / Jazz Butcher meets Count Dracula: *Jazz Butcher* / Fats terminal: *Bone Orchard* / Graveyard stomp: *Meteors* / Seven deadly sins: *Outcasts* / Running wild: *Ricochets* / Red headed woman: *Panther Burns* / Hellbag shuffle: *Sunglasses After Dark* / Werewolf blues: *Guana Batz* / She's got fever: *Brilliant Corners* / Long necked daddy-o: *Boneasaurus Wrecks* / Hills have eyes: *Meteors* / Shearing machine: *Very Things* / Zulu beat: *King Kurt* / I don't wanna get thin: *Blubbery Hellbellies* / I wanna be like you: *Turnpike Cruisers* / Your good girl's gonna go bad: *Screaming Sirens* / Pointed bra: *Orson Family* / Stomp it: *Raunch Hands*
CDMPSYCHO 11 / Jan '96 / Anagram

☐ REVERBERATION VOL.4
REVERB 4 / Dec '97 / Reverb

☐ REVERBERATION VOL.5 (Chocolate Soup)
REVERB 5 / 16 Mar '98 / Reverb

☐ REVIVAL HITS VOL.1 & 2
MFCD 8 / May '94 / Mafia/Fluxy

☐ REVIVING A TRADITION
PS 65116 / Nov '93 / PlayaSound

☐ REVOLUTIONARY GENERATION
ASHADOW 3CD / Jan '96 / Moving Shadow

☐ REVOLUTIONS
Wildstyle groove: *Paninaro* / Make it rock: *Cotton Club* / Rollercoaster: *Chapter 9* / Love the groove: *Alpha Motion* / Lover number 6: *Daydreamer* / De dah dah (Spice of life): *Mac, Keith* / Shock the beat: *Electric Choc* / In your dance: *E-Lustrious* / Funkin' crazy: *KGB* / Rok da house: *Tall Paul* / It was meant to be: *D'Enrico* / We are going down: *Deadly Sins* / Warehouse days of glory: *New Deep Society* / Club for life: *Chris & James* / Reach: *Cheeks, Judy*
CDHIGH 1 / Sep '94 / High On Rhythm

☐ REVOLVER
REVXD 219 / Feb '98 / Revolver

☐ REZ VOL.2 (2CD Set)
REZCD 102 / Apr '96 / Rezerection

☐ RHINESTONE COWBOY
Rhinestone cowboy: *Campbell, Glen* / Ring of fire: *Cash, Johnny* / Crying: *McLean, Don* / Little bit more: *Dr. Hook* / Don't it make my brown eyes blue: *Gayle, Crystal* / Banks of the Ohio: *Newton-John, Olivia* / Funny how time slips away: *Nelson, Willie* / King of the road: *Miller, Roger* / All I have to do is dream: *Gentry, Bobbie* / Rose Marie: *Whitman, Slim* / Blanket on the ground: *Spears, Billie Jo* / We're all alone: *Coolidge, Rita* / Under the gun: *Bogguss, Suzy* / Mississippi: *Pussycat* / Convoy: *McCall, C.W.* / Six days on the road: *Dudley, Dave* / It's four in the morning: *Young, Faron* / San Antonio stroll: *Tucker, Tanya* / It's only make believe: *Twitty, Conway* / Release me: *Lewis, Jerry Lee*
5529142 / Oct '97 / Spectrum

☐ RHYTHM AND BLUES (WITH A LITTLE SOUL) (At Abbey Road 1963-1967)
Baby please don't go: *Patterson, Ottilie* / Wade in the water: *Bond, Graham Quartet* / Bye bye Johnny: *Wayne, Pat & The Beachcombers* / I saw her standing there: *Power, Duffy* / My babe: *Pirates* / Pretty face: *Beat Merchants* / Tired broke busted: *Power, Duffy* / Down in Mexico: *Boston Crabs* / Litty bitty pretty ones: *Paramounts* / Turn on your lovelight: *Goins, Herbie & The Nightimers* / I believe to my soul: *Boston Dexters* / Voodoo blues: *Shades Of Blue* / Baby what you want me to do: *Sons of Fred* / Groovin': *Manfred Mann* / I just got some: *Stewart, Rod* / Hoochie coochie man: *Baldry, Long John & The Hoochie Coochie Men* / Got to get you into my life: *Bennett, Cliff & The Rebel Rousers* / How: *Jynx* / I'll be there: *Sons of Fred* / Bye bye bird: *Toggery Five* / I put a spell on you: *Manfred Mann* / Gypsy woman: *Ryan, Phil & The Crescents* / 634 5789: *Bennett, Cliff & The Rebel Rousers* / No.1 in your heart: *Goins, Herbie & The Nightimers* / Shake: *Stewart, Rod* / Land of 1000 dances: *Action*
4934532 / 23 Feb '98 / EMI

☐ RHYTHM AND BLUES EXPRESS
TOLL 002CD / Jun '92 / Tollhaus

☐ RHYTHM IS A DANCER (2CD Set)
55524 / Nov '94 / Laserlight

☐ RHYTHM 'N' BLUES LEGENDS VOL.1
BMCD 4003 / Jan '98 / Blue Moon

☐ RHYTHM 'N' BLUES LEGENDS VOL.2
BMCD 4004 / Jan '98 / Blue Moon

☐ RHYTHM OF BRAZIL, THE
Mother Brasilier / Bizantina bizancia: *Ben, Jorge* / Moenda: *Machado, Elaine* / Tatmiro: *De Moraes, Vincius* / Banda da carmen mirandes: *Armandinho & Trio Electrico* / Jovelina perola negro: *O Dia Se Zanoou* / Cinco criancas: *Lobo, Edu* / Roberto corta essa: *Ben, Jorge* / Festejando / A Voz doz morro: *Melodia, Luiz* / Mulato latino: *Melodia, Luiz* / A bencao bahia: *Toquinho & Vincius De Moraes* / Salve simpatia: *Ben, Jorge* / Como diza o poeta: *Toquinho & Vincius De Moraes* / Viva meu samba / Casa de samba
MCCD 013 / Feb '91 / Music Club

☐ RHYTHM OF RESISTANCE
U mama uyajabula: *Mlangeni, Babsy* / Ke ya le leboha: *Mlangeni, Babsy* / Perefere: *Malomba* / Pampa madiba: *Malomba* / Jesu otsoile: *Mparanyana & The Cannibals* / Umthombowase golgota: *Ladysmith Black Mambazo* / Yinhleleni: *Ladysmith Black Mambazo* / Inkunzi ayi hlabi ngokusima: *Johnny & Sipho* / Igula lamasi: *Mahotella Queens* / Ubu gowelle: *Baseqhudeni, Abafana*
SHANCD 43018 / Apr '88 / Shanachie

☐ RHYTHM OF THE ISLANDS
HQCD 92 / Jan '97 / Harlequin

☐ RHYTHM REPUBLIC
AVEXCD 40 / Jun '96 / Avex

☐ RHYTHM REPUBLIC DISCO VOL.1
AVEXCD 35 / Mar '96 / Avex

☐ RHYTHM REPUBLIC JAZZ VOL.1
AVEXCD 36 / Jun '96 / Avex

☐ RHYTHM TRACK EXPLOSION VOL.1
GSR 70017 / Apr '92 / Ras

☐ RHYTHM WAS OUR BUSINESS
Tiger rag / Mama don't allow it / Hold tight / Apple for the teacher / I can't dance / Bill tell / Anything goes / Out every Friday / Chinatown, my Chinatown / Who's sorry now / Clarinet marmalade / Sea food squabble / Weather man / Give out / It don't mean a thing if it ain't got that swing / Nagasaki / Way down yonder in New Orleans / Potomac jump / I'm forever blowing bubbles / Promenade / Twelfth street rag / Russian salad / Seven day's leave / Someday sweetheart
RAJCD 810 / 1 Jun '98 / Empress

☐ RHYTHMICAL SKUNK ABUSE
HEMP 14CD / 26 Jan '98 / Recordings Of Substance

☐ RHYTHMS OF AFRICA
REACD 003 / Jun '98 / Reactive

☐ RHYTHMS OF AFRICA
9006231032 / 24 Mar '98 / Miramar

☐ RHYTHMS OF LIFE, SONGS OF WISDOM (Akan Music Of Ghana)
SFWCD 40463 / Mar '96 / Smithsonian Folkways

☐ RHYTHMS OF RAPTURE (Sacred Music Of Haitian Voodoo)
SFWCD 40464 / Oct '95 / Smithsonian Folkways

☐ RICKY MONTANARI PRESENTS RIVIERA HOUSE TRAXX
PAZ 801CD / Sep '97 / La Plaza

☐ RIDE DADDY RIDE
Ride daddy ride: *Noel, Fats* / Sure cure for the blues: *Four Jacks* / Big ten inch record: *Jackson, Bull Moose* / Smooth slow easy: *Drivers* / Drill daddy drill: *Ellis, Dorothy* / Roll roll pretty baby: *Swallows* / Walkin' blues: *Hunter, Fluffy* / Rocket 69: *Rhodes, Todd* / I knew he would: *Sharps & Flats* / Grandpa can boogie too: *Greenwood, Lil* / I want a bowlegged woman: *Jackson, Bull Moose* / I want my Fanny Brown: *Harris, Wynonie* / My hatch'l man: *Hunter, Fluffy* / Chocolate pork chop man: *Lewis, Pete 'Guitar'* / It ain't the meat: *Swallows* / Ride jockey ride: *Lamplighters* / Mountain oysters: *Davis, Eddie 'Lockjaw'* / Triflin' woman: *Harris, Wynonie* / My ding a ling: *Bartholomew, Dave* / Last of the good rockin' men: *Four Jacks* / Your daddy's doggin' around: *Rhodes, Todd*
CDCHARLY 272 / Feb '91 / Charly

☐ RIDE THE BASSLINE
UCACD 0152 / 3 Aug '98 / UCA

☐ RIDE THE WILD SURF
Surf city: *Jan & Dean* / Wipeout: *Surfaris* / Surfin' safari: *Beach Boys* / Little deuce coupe: *Jan & Dean* / Beach baby: *Regents* / Luau: *Beach Boys* / Little old lady from Pasadena: *Jan & Dean* / Batman theme: *Marketts* / Surfin' bird: *Trashmen* / Ride the wild surf: *Jan & Dean* / Barbie: *Beach Boys* / GTO: *Regents* / Fun fun fun: *Jan & Dean* / Pipeline: *Chantays* / Surfin': *Beach Boys* / Surfer stomp: *Marketts* / Sidewalk surfin': *Jan & Dean* / Hey little cobra: *Regents* / Surfer girl: *Beach Boys* / Dead man's curve: *Jan & Dean*
308812 / Jun '98 / Hallmark

☐ RIDIM FE RIDIM
RFCD 006 / Jun '97 / Record Factory

☐ RIDING HIGH
SRFN 001CD / Feb '96 / Srfn

☐ RIDING THE ROOTS CHARIOT
PSCD 20 / 27 Jul '98 / Pressure Sounds

☐ RIG ROCK DELUXE
Truck driving man: *Walser, Don* / Will there be big rigs in heaven: *Owens, Buck & The Buckaroos* / Nitro express: *Red Simpson & Junior Brown* / Miss Marie and The Bedford Blaze: *Red Simpson & Junior Brown* / Truckstop girl: *Willis, Kelly* / Mother trucker: *Shaver* / Lookin' at the world through a windshield: *Volt, Son* / Diesel diesel diesel: *Reeves, Del & Jim Lauderdale* / Wagon of clay: *Knight, Cheri* / White freight liner blues: *Earle, Steve* / Highway junkie: *Yayhoos* / Semi truck: *Kirchen, Bill & Too Much Fun* / Mama was a rock (daddy was a rollin stone): *Kirchen, Bill & Too Much Fun* / I'm coming home: *Lowe, Nick & The Impossible Birds* / Truck drivin' man (give it all I can): *Bottle Rockets* / Six days on the road: *Rig Rock Deluxe*
UPSTART 025 / Sep '96 / Upstart

☐ RIGHT DIRECTION (20 Northern Soul Stormers)
Weakspot: *Thomas, Evelyn* / Make sure (you have someone who loves you): *Jiani, Carol* / Out on the floor: *Nero, Frances* / Breaking down the walls of heartache: *Starr, Edwin* / Let me down easy: *Lavette, Bettye* / Wiht this ring: *Wylie, Richard 'Popcorn'* / Night: *Johnson, Marv* / Sking in the snow: *Pallas, Laura & The Reputations* / Reaching for the best: *Exciters* / Ain't no soul (left in these old shoes): *Fantastic Four* / You hit me where it hurt me: *Weston, Kim* / You're gonna be my baby: *McNair, Barbara* / That's when the tears start: *Velvelettes* / Six by six: *Van Dyke, Earl* / Right direction: *Littles, Hattie* / Key to my happiness: *Lovetones* / Your magic put a spell on me: *Lovetones* / He's so irreplaceable: *Jones, Doris* / Look what you've done to my heart: *Elgins* / What's wrong with me baby: *Valadiers*
SUMCD 4132 / Jun '97 / Summit

☐ RIGHT TOUCH, THE
RR 102CD / Jul '96 / Roots

☐ RIGHT TRACKS, THE
RNCD 2008 / May '93 / Rhino

☐ RIGHTS OF MAN, THE
GLCD 1111 / Feb '92 / Green Linnet

☐ RIGODON SAUVAGE
C 560053 / Nov '95 / Ocora

☐ RIKK AGNEW'S SMASH DEMOS VOL.2
EFA 122392 / May '96 / Musical Tragedies

☐ RIME OF THE ANCIENT SAMPLER
VP 141CD / Jun '93 / Voiceprint

☐ RINCE COMPLETE IRISH DANCING SET
CHCD 1050 / Jan '95 / Chyme

☐ RING RING FESTIVAL '96
RINGRING 001 / Jun '98 / ReR/ Recommended

☐ RINGBANG REBEL DANCE
951902 / Apr '96 / Ice

☐ RINGING CLEAR (The Art of Handbell Ringing)
Entry of the gladiators / Linden Lea / Stephen Foster selection / Grandfather's clock / On wings of song / Lord of the dance / Girl with the flaxen hair / Country gardens / Ashgrove / Ragtime dance / Parade of the tin soldiers / Isle of Capri / Lullaby / Original rags / Silver threads among the gold / Intermezzo from cavalleria rusticana / Bells of St. Mary's / O waly waly / Flow gently sweet Afton / Syncopated clock / O guter mond / Whistling Rufus
CDSDL 333 / Oct '91 / Saydisc

☐ RIOT CITY SINGLES COLLECTION VOL.1
Last rockers: *Vice Squad* / Young blood: *Vice Squad* / Politics: *Insane* / Vicious circle: *Abrasive Wheels* / Gotta get out: *Court Martial* / Four minute warning: *Chaos UK* / Undead: *Undead* / Dreaming: *Expelled* / Army song: *Abrasive Wheels* / Fuck the world: *Chaotic Dischord* / No solution: *Court Martial* / No security: *Chaos UK* / Dogsbody: *Mayhem* / Have you got 10p: *Ejected* / Dead revolution: *Undead* / Burn em' down: *Abrasive Wheels* / Make it alone: *Expelled* / Nottingham problem: *Resistance 77* / Fast 'n' loud: *Ejected* / Cream of the crop: *No Choice* / Points of view: *Emergency* / Never trust a friend: *Chaotic Dischord* / Back on the piss again: *Sex Aids* / Gentle murder: *Mayhem* / Crime for revenge: *Ultraviolent* / East of dachau: *Underdogs* / Die for your government: *Varukers* / Russians: *Ejected* / Led to the slaughter: *Varukers* / Cliff: *Chaotic Dischord*
CDPUNK 15 / Mar '97 / Anagram

☐ RIOT CITY SINGLES COLLECTION VOL.2
Living on dreams: *Vice Squad* / Humane: *Vice Squad* / Dead and gone: *Insane* / Voice of youth: *Abrasive Wheels* / Fight for your life: *Court Martial* / Kill your baby: *Chaos UK* / It's corruption: *Undead* / What justice: *Expelled* / Juvenile: *Abrasive Wheels* / You're gonna die: *Chaotic Dischord* / Too late: *Court Martial* / What about a future: *Chaos UK* / Street fight: *Mayhem* / Class of '82: *Ejected* / Place is burning: *Undead* / Urban rebel: *Abrasive Wheels* / Government policy: *Expelled* / Join the army: *Resistance 77* / I don't care: *Ejected* / Sadist dream: *No Choice* / City fun: *Emergency* / Pop stars: *Chaotic Dischord* / We are the road crew: *Sex Aids* / (Your face fits) Lie and die: *Mayhem* / Dead generation: *Ultraviolent* / Johnny go home: *Underdogs* / All systems fail: *Varukers* / Twenty four years: *Ejected* / End is nigh: *Varukers*
CDPUNK 55 / May '95 / Anagram

☐ RIOT ZONE
Sick to death: Atari Teenage Riot / New kick: *Shizuo* / I don't want to be part of this: *EC8OR* / We all die: *Alec Empire* / You're a hero: *Patric C* / Destroy 2000 years of culture: *Atari Teenage Riot* / Lory vs bomb 20: *Bomb 20* / Cocaine ducks: *EC8OR* / Sweat: *Shizuo* / Sex with annemone: *Patric C* / Show: *Elias, Hanin* / Peak: *Alec Empire* / Donutz and blood: *Bomb 20* / Atari teenage riot: *Atari Teenage Riot* / Cook cook: *DJ Mowgli* / My confession: *De Babalon, Christoph* / Residum: *De Babalon, Christoph*
DHRCD 010 / 3 Nov '97 / Digital Hardcore

☐ RIP IT UP
Rip it up: Monday, Floria / I turned them all down: *Madden, Gregg* / Red headed woman: *Worley, Wayne* / Tornado: *Jiants* / Lot of lovin': *Lewis, Diana Lee* / If I had me a woman: *Vale, Blacky* / Tough enough: *Raven, Marc* / Ruby Lee: *Dean, Donnie* / Sweet rockin' mama: *Hi-Tombs* / Betty Jo: *Brazell, Nicky* / She's my woman: *Jiants* / Whole lotta shakin' goin' on: *Thunderbirds* / Love me love me love me: *Faucett, Ed* / Sweet love: *Bond, Bobby* / I've got a baby: *Arnold, Clyde* / Messed up: *Cavaliers* / Livin' doll: *Bond, Bobby* / Crocodile hop: *Thomas, Dale* / Lovin': *Monday, Floria* / Let's all rock 'n' roll: *Lombardie, Joe* / Pizza pizza pizza pie: *Alan, Neil* / Walk spin shake and rock: *Griffith, Joe* / Whatcha gonna do tomorrow: *Killen, Buddy* / She sure can rock me: *Radar, Don* / Suzanne: *Travis, Dave* / Solid rock: *John, Jimmie* / Little boy blue: *Bel-Tones* / I don't like him: *Travis, Dave* / Rockin' the blues: *Hall, Roy* / Crazy rock: *King, Bobby*
CDBB 55063 / Oct '97 / Buffalo Bop

☐ RIP IT UP
Love will tear us apart: *Joy Division* / Procession: *New Order* / Gangsters: *Specials* / Lunatics (have taken over the asylum): *Fun Boy Three* / On my radio: *Selecter* / Say hello wave goodbye: *Soft Cell* / Treason: *Teardrop Explodes* / Picture this: *Blondie* / Rip it up: *Orange Juice* / Christian: *China Crisis* / Thinking of you: *Colourfield* / Wonderful life: *Black* / Come live with me: *Heaven 17* / Golden brown: *Stranglers* / Mirror man: *Human League* / Don't tell me: *Blancmange* / Hit that perfect beat: *Bronski Beat* / White wedding: *Idol, Billy* / Down in the tube station at midnight: *Jam*
5529172 / Oct '97 / Spectrum

☐ RIP PRESENTS THE REAL SOUND OF THE UNDERGROUND (2CD Set)
Theme: *Dreem Teem* / Pump it up: *Mowatt, Andy* / Marbles: *Black Grape* / Magic carpet ride: *Mighty Dub Katz* / Yeah: *RIP* / Gabriel: *Davis, Roy Jr.* / Deep inspiration: *RIP* / Chant: *RIP* / Free: *Ultra Nate* / I refuse what you want: *Somore* / Moment in my life: *D'Ambrosio, Bobby* / My desire: *Amira* / Love is what we need: *RIP* / Back to life: *Ragga's Revenge* / Rush me: *Ten Degrees Below* / Flava fever: *MJ Cole* / Hideaway: *De'Lacy* / Oh baby: *RIP* / Industry standard vol.1 what you want: *Industry Standard* / Walking zero: *Sneaker Pimps* / Spend the night: *Lewis, Danny J.* / Rip groove: *Double 99* / Naked and scared: *Nayler, Maria* / Freedom: *Miles, Robert* / Gunman: *187 Lockdown* / Oh boy: *Fabulous Baker Boys* / Gangsta boogie: *Too Ruff* / Proffesional widow: *Amos, Tori* / Burning: *RIP* / Hold your head up high: *ADR*
VTDCDX 178
VTDCD 178 / 20 Apr '98 / Virgin TV

☐ RIPE MASTERS VOL.2
Let me love you for tonight: *Kariya* / Scandalise: *Afterlife* / Move on: *Ray, Cecilia* / Need you: *Davis, Alvin* / Share my love: *Waters, Kim* / Don't you want it: *Edwards, Sandi* / Ordinary girl: *P-Ski Mac* / Naughty but nice: *Spice* / Money or love: *Davis, Alvin* / Walking on sunshine: *Rockers Revenge* / I'll always love my Ma: *P-Ski Mac* / Round 'n' round: *Ray, Cecilia* / Lost in the storm: *Waters, Kim* / I wonder where you are: *Edwards, Sandi* / Byzantium: *Afterlife*
RIPECD 216 / Nov '95 / Ripe

☐ RISE
SCENTCD 001 / Jun '97 / Fragrant

☐ RISE IN PROGRESS
RCD 001 / Apr '96 / Rise

☐ RISE OF EUROPEAN CIVILISATION, THE
PBRCD 001 / Oct '96 / Point Break

☐ RISING HIGH COLLECTION, THE
Sweet home Chicago: *Louisiana Red* / Sweet little angel: *Louisiana Red* / King bee: *Louisiana Red* / Lightnin' blkues: *Hopkins, Lightnin'* / Trouble in mind: *Hopkins, Lightnin'* / Blues ain't nothin' but a feelin': *Hopkins, Lightnin'* / I'm gonna get on my feet's afterwhile: *Terry, Sonny & Brownie McGhee* / Oh ja bo: *Terry, Sonny & Brownie McGhee* / Walk on: *Terry, Sonny & Brownie McGhee* / My father's words: *Terry, Sonny & Brownie McGhee* / Good morning blues: *Terry, Sonny & Brownie McGhee* / I've never felt like this before: *Terry, Sonny & Brownie McGhee*
RSCD 0011 / May '96 / Just A Memory

☐ RISQUE BLUES VOL.1
KCD 6021 / 20 Apr '98 / King

☐ RISQUE BLUES VOL.2
KCD 6022 / 20 Apr '98 / King

☐ RITMO BRASILEIRO
Swing da cor / Ile de luz / Soy loco por ti America / Sei de cor / Mistura e manda / Diamante / Solidao / Banda dos negros / Vida / Canto da cor / Tempos felizes / O menino / A Deusa do amor / Maravilhe / Esphina da bacalhau
MPG 74038 / Apr '97 / Movieplay Gold

☐ RITMO DE LA NOCHE
DCD 5393 / Jul '94 / Disky

☐ RITMO LATINO (Los Clasicos Y La Nueva Generacion/2CD Set)
ARC 336 / 29 Jun '98 / Arcade

☐ RITUAL MOUTH ORGANS OF THE MURUNG
W 260084 / Jun '98 / PlayaSound

☐ RITUAL MUSIC FROM THE MEDITERRANEAN
FMM 001 / Mar '98 / Robi Droli

☐ RITUAL, THEATRE AND CHAMBER MUSICS FROM SOUTH VIETNAM
D 8070 / Nov '96 / Unesco

☐ RIVE GAUCHE
GTY 20009 / 23 Mar '98 / Gravity

☐ RIVER OF SOUND, A
Ah sweet dancer: *O'Suilleabhain, Micheal* / Johnny Dohertys: *Tourish, Ciaran/Dermot Byrne* / Two Conneeleys: *Moore, Christy & Micheal O'Suilleabhain* / Real blues reel: *Power, Brendan* / Si bheag, si mhor: *O'Suilleabhain, Micheal/C. Breatnach* / Pulsus / Three jigs: *Kelly, Laoise* / River of sound / Caoineadh na dtri mhuire: *O'Lionaird, Iarla* / Three reels: *Ivers, Eileen* / Wind in the woods: *O'Connor, M./M. Murray* / Turas go tir na nog: *O'Suilleabhain, Micheal* / O'Keefe's slides: *Begley, Seamus & Stephen Cooney* / Roaring water reels: *Vallely, Niall* / Barn dances: *Gavin, Frankie & Martin O'Connor* / Port na bpucai: *Browne, Ronan*
CDV 2776 / Dec '95 / Virgin

☐ RIVER REEL
Rights of man / Banks of the Uilleann/Scartaglen reel / Cooley's waltzes / Ships a sailing/Creggs pipes/ Dublin reel / When sick is it tea you want/Apples in winter / Daniel O'Connell / Last nights fun/Toss the feathers/Farrel O'Gara / Dave Hennessey's polka/ Brendan Begley's favourite / Trip to Durrow/Cup of tea / Jackson's jig/Joe Ryan's / Queen of the Fair selection / Crowley's 1 and 2 / Begley's fancy / Munster buttermilk selection / Green fields of Rossbeigh/The wise maid/Concerting reel
21114 / Aug '97 / Laserlight

☐ RIVERDANCE (The Very Best Of Traditional Irish Music And Song)
Riverdance / Spindle shanks / Sean ban / Roly poly / Miss Murphy / An dro / Corsican melody / Off to California / Galway / Hearts cry / Silver spire / Siamsa / Laugh and half daft / Paddy taylor's / Jimmy Lyon's jig / Swinging on the gate / Terry Teahan's polka / Three Marys / Riverdance
3036001232 / 15 Sep '97 / Carlton

☐ RIVERSIDE HISTORY OF CLASSIC JAZZ (3CD Set)
I'm going to heaven if it takes my life: *Gates, Rev. J.M. & Congregation* / I've got the blues for Rampart Street: *Cox, Ida* / Big Bill blues: *Broonzy, 'Big' Bill* / Cascades: *Joplin, Scott* / Perfect rag: *Morton, Jelly Roll* / Pearls: *Morton, Jelly Roll* / Froggie Moore rag: *Oliver, Joe 'King' Jazzband* / Memphis maybe man: *Cook, Doc & His Dreamland Orchestra* / Mama stayed out: *Barrelhouse Five* / Fives: *Yancey, Jimmy* / Lone star blues: *Johnson, Pete* / Royal garden blues: *Beiderbecke, Bix & The Wolverines* / Friars Point Shuffle: *Jungle Kings* / Harlem strut: *Johnson, James P.* / Cake walkin' babies from home: *Red Onion Jazz Babies* / Stampede: *Red & Miffs Stompers* / Eccentric: *Davison, 'Wild' Bill* / Muskrat ramble: *Spanier, Muggsy* / Hop off: *Henderson, Fletcher Orchestra* / Rainy nights: *Ellington, Duke Washingtonians* / Make me a pallet on the floor: *Johnson, Bunk* / Weary blues: *Ory, Kid* / Antigua blues: *Watters, Lu & The Yerba Buena Jazz Band*
RBCD 005 / Oct '93 / Riverside

☐ RIVERSIDE RECORDS STORY, THE (4CD Set)
It don't mean a thing if it ain't got that swing: *Monk, Thelonious* / Watermelon man: *Santamaria, Mongo* / This here: *Adderley, Cannonball* / Brilliant corners: *Monk, Thelonious* / Four on six: *Montgomery, Wes* / Waltz for Debby: *Evans, Bill* / African waltz: *Adderley, Cannonball* / Meditation: *Byrd, Charlie* / Village caller: *Little, Johnny* / Blues for Dracula: *Jones, Philly Joe* / Wade in the water: *Griffin, Johnny* / Smooth as the wind: *Mitchell, Blue* / Big P: *Heath, Jimmy* / Freedom suite: *Rollins, Sonny* / Cariba: *Montgomery, Wes* / Ruby my dear: *Monk, Thelonious & Coleman Hawkins* / Ruby my dear: *Monk, Thelonious & John Coltrane* / 'Round midnight: *Mulligan, Gerry & Thelonius Monk* / One foot in the gutter: *Monk, Thelonious & Clark Terry* / Peace piece: *Evans, Bill* / Know what I mean: *Adderley, Cannonball* / Things are getting better: *Adderley, Cannonball* / Delilah: *Jackson, Milt & Wes Montgomery* / Trav'lin' light: *Webster, Ben & Joe Zawinul* / Tickletoe: *Davis, Eddie 'Lockjaw' & Johnny Griffin* / Work song: *Adderley, Nat* / If you could see me now: *Baker, Chet* / One by one: *Blakey, Art* / On a misty night: *Dameron, Tadd* / My old flame: *Dorham, Kenny* / Come rain or come shine: *Drew, Kenny* / Circle waltz: *Friedman, Don* / Out of the past: *Golson, Benny* / Mutattra: *Harris, Barry* / Laura: *Hawkins, Coleman* / Autumn leaves: *Henry, Ernie* / Eyes so beautiful as yours: *Hope, Elmo* / Invitation: *Jackson, Milt* / Letter from home: *Jefferson, Eddie* / Blue low: *Johnson, Budd* / Some kinda mean: *Jones, Sam* / On Green Dolphin Street: *Kelly, Wynton* / West coast blues: *Land, Harold* / I'm just a lucky so-and-so: *Lateef, Yusef* / I am in love: *Lincoln, Abbey* / Invitation: *Mance, Junior* / Out of this world: *Murphy, Mark* / Nardis: *Russell, George* / Fools rush in (where angels fear to tread): *Sims, Zoot* / Come Sunday: *Terry, Clark* / So tired: *Timmons, Bobby* / Zulu: *Weston, Randy*
RCD 44222 / Jan '98 / Ace

☐ RIVERSIDE ROCKABILLY
RAUCD 014 / Jul '97 / Raucous

☐ RIVIERA - THE HI-LIFE COMPILATION (2CD Set)
Time for love: *English, Kim* / Joy and happiness: *Stabbs* / I see only you: *Nootropic* / Fantasy: *Angel Heart* / Pleasure: *Medium High* / Oohhh baby: *Simpson, Vida* / I know a place: *English, Kim* / Lost in love: *Up Yer Ronson* / Renegade master: *Wildchild* / Bailando con lobos: *Cabana* / Nite life: *English, Kim* / Another night: *Kitsch In Synch* / Prayer to the music: *Polo, Marco* / Manifest your love: *DOP* / Raise: *Boston Bees* / Manifest your love: *DOP*
5294002 / Aug '96 / Hi-Life

☐ RMM MEGAMIX
RMD 81354 / 24 Mar '98 / RMM

☐ RMO VOL.1
Hypnodelic: *Francois K* / Burnin up: *Morales, Angel* / Never stop: *Reflexion* / Live in unity: *Dangerous Minds* / Deeper: *Flat Earth Society* / Radical noise: *DJ Tonka* / Invasion: *Freakforce* / Manual: *Continious Cool* / State of time: *Gage* / Theme from Blue Cucaracha: *Innocent* / Gliding: *Compass* / Disappear: *Underground People* / Latin kaos: *El Bandolero* / Deep love: *D. dact* / Sensation 2: *Nelson, G & R Purser* / Dance, dance, dance: *Fruitloops* / Tonite: *Sleaze*
SPV 08468382 / Oct '96 / SPV

☐ ROAD MARCH (Trinidadian Carnival Hits 1980)
RHP 1001CD / 1 Dec '97 / RHP

☐ ROAD OF BROKEN HEARTS - ORIGINAL COUNTRY ROOTS
Wild side of life / Making believe / I can't forget / She's the steppin' out kind / Heartache to recall / Ball and chain / Wabash cannonball / Honky tonk merry go round / Take my hand / Me and my gin / Cowpoke / Lukenbach Texas / Jenny Lou / Wings of a dove / Ol' blue / Send me the pillow that you dream on / DJ for a day / I don't like you anymore / I'm a regular daddy / Road of broken hearts
CDAA 042 / Jan '92 / Tring

☐ ROAD TO RHYTHM 'N' BLUES AND ROCK 'N' ROLL VOL.1
Hastings Street / Milkcow blues / Boogie woogie stomp / My Daddy was a lovin' man / We gonna pitch a boogie woogie / Boogie woogie (I may be wrong) / Trucking little woman / Blues ain't nothin' but... / Roll 'em Pete / Baby don't / On me / Jumpin' at the Savoy / After hours / Confessin' the blues / Hootie's ignorant oil / I want a tall skinny Papa / Cow cow boogie / Hey lawdy Mama / Hurry hurry / I know how to do it / Boogie rocks / Boogie woogie on a Saturday night / Groovin' the blues / Bellvue for you / Somebody's gotta go / You need coachin'
PASTCD 7811 / Feb '97 / Flapper

☐ ROAD TO RHYTHM 'N' BLUES AND ROCK 'N' ROLL VOL.2
Strange things happening every day / That's the stuff you gotta watch / Rock me Mama / Caldonia / Southpaw serenade / Schoolday blues / Honeydripper / T-Bone boogie / Juice head baby / Here comes the blues / Be baba leba / Chicago breakdown / Bartender breakdown / Choo choo ch'boogie / Wedding day blues / Boogie woogie Hannah / Jump the boogie / Let the good times roll / Postman blues / Bottoms up / Amos blues / Pencil broke / Wake up old maid / Miss Brown blues
PASTCD 7812 / Feb '97 / Flapper

☐ ROARING 20'S, THE
If you knew Susie like I know Susie: *Shilkret, Jack & His Orchestra* / Sheikh of Araby: *Pianola Roll* / I'm tellin' the birds, tellin' the bees: *Smith, Jack 'Whispering'* / That's my weakness now: *Pianola Roll* / Canadian capers: *Biese, Paul Trio* / Rose Marie: *Pianola Roll* / Colette: *Whiteman, Paul & His Orchestra* / Where the lazy daisies grow: *Pianola Roll* / Ain't misbehavin': *Hylton, Jack & His Orchestra & Sam Browne* / My inspiration is you: *Pianola Roll* / Wedding of the painted doll: *Pianola Roll* / Don't bring Lulu: *Garber, Jan & His Orchestra* / Always: *Pianola Roll* / Where, oh where do I live: *Douglas, Fred & Orchestra* / Birth of the blues: *Pianola Roll* / I miss my Swiss: *Golden Gate Orchestra* / Ain't she sweet: *Pianola Roll* / Hello Swanee, hello: *Syncopated Four* / Ramona: *Pianola Roll* / Charleston
CDSDL 344 / Mar '94 / Saydisc

☐ ROARING TWENTIES
DCD 5334 / Dec '93 / Disky

☐ ROBERT BURNS - THE MERRY MUSES (Gill Bowman, Tich Frier, Fiona Forbes, Robin Laing & More)
Yellow, yellow yorlin' / My girl she's airy, she's buxom and gay / Nine inch will please a lady / Logan water / Ye haelien wrang, lassie / Bonniest lass / As I cam o'er the Cairneymount / O gie the lass her fairin' lad / Cuddie the cooper / Wad ye do that / Ye jovial boys who loved the joys / Dainty Davie / Muirland Meg / How can I keep my Maidenhead / Nae hair on't / In Edinburgh town they've made a law / There was a jolly gauger, a gauging he did ride / Duncan Gray / Duncan MacLeerie
IRCD 035 / Feb '96 / Iona

☐ ROBERT BURNS COLLECTION - THE BURNS SUPPER
Selkirk grace / Address to the haggis / Immortal memory of Robert Burns / Toast to the lassies / Reply to the toast to the lassies / Tam o'shanter / Man's a man/Auld lang syne
LCOM 6039 / Nov '95 / Lismor

☐ ROBERT BURNS COLLECTION - THE MUSIC
Of a' the airts / Bonnie lass of Ballochmyle / Green grow the rashes / Afton water / Ca' the ewes / Aye waukin' o / Trilogy / John Anderson my jo / Star of Rabbie Burns / Ye banks and braes / O my love is like a red red roae / Ae fond kiss / Man's a man / Bonnie wee thing / Auld lang syne
LCOM 6041 / Nov '95 / Lismor

☐ ROBERT BURNS COLLECTION - THE SONGS
Man's a man / O my love is like a red red rose / Ae fond kiss / Afton water / Bonnie lass of Ballochmyle / Ye banks and braes / Aye waukin' o / De'il's awa' wi' tha exciseman / Rosebud by my early walk / Scots wha hae / I'm ower young to marry yet / There was a lad / Birks o' Aberfeldy / MacPherson's farewell / John Anderson my jo / Auld lang syne
LCOM 6040 / Nov '95 / Lismor

☐ ROBERTO CLEMENTE UN TRIBUTO MUSICAL
Roberto / Sueno de un nino / Somos la fuerza latina / Roberto y Tirabala / Orgullo de Borinquen / Clemente (Estrella 21) / Jugando la pelota / Jardinero del amor / Lo mejor que dios ha hecho
RLCD 1021 / 20 Jul '98 / Ryko Latin

☐ ROCK
Baby baby baby: *Little Ted* / Nitebeats: *Nitebeats* / 309: *Rockin' Continentals* / Annie Mae: *Dewitt, Bobby* / Crazy about you: *Gallagher, James* / I'm a-ready baby: *Garmon, Bob* / How about a date: *Honorables* / Bob-a-lena: *Frils, Jim & The Vallants* / Hot dog: *Jones, Gorkey* / Blankety blank: *Summers, Ronnie* / Shape up: *White, Otis* / I wanta: *Starr, Billy* / Linda Lou: *Ford, Bubba* / Please have mercy: *Dane, Jimmy* / What's the use: *Maupin, Ramon* / Go go heart: *Doggett, Ray* / She's my baby: *Holmes, Leon* / Wiggling blond: *Ford, Bubba* / Baby baby: *Waggoner, Mike* / Raised on rock 'n' roll: *Gotroe, Jackie* / Rock 'n' roll Grandpa: *Radar, Don* / Let's rock tonight: *Grubbs, Jimmy* / Just one more time: *Deckelman, Sonny* / Goodbye little darling goodbye: *Shelton, Gary* / Teenage bop: *Night, Rocky* / It's a lonely world: *Deckelman, Sonny* / Twenty one: *Danton, Tommy* / Rocking Rufus: *Maupin, Ramon* / No doubt about it: *Doggett, Ray* / Basher no.5: *Waggoner, Mike*
BB 55060 / Aug '97 / Buffalo Bop

☐ ROCK & POP BALLADS
12202 / May '94 / Laserlight

☐ ROCK AND LOVE
HMC 100012 / 27 Oct '97 / Happy Music

☐ ROCK AND METAL FACTORY (2CD Set)
Symphony of destruction: *Megadeth* / Mistaken identity: *Biohazard* / Like broken glass: *Crowbar* / Voracious souls: *Death Angel* / Dungeons are calling: *Savatage* / Where U want it: *Boo-Yaa TRIBE* / Behind the sun: *Dearly Beheaded* / World circus: *Toxik* / War pigs: *Sacred Reich* / Burned device: *Flotsam & Jetsam* / Agent orange: *Sodom* / Digital dictator: *Vicious Rumors* / Terror: *Armored Saint* / Valley of the dolls: *Fates Warning* / Objection overruled: *Exodus* / Thunder kiss '65: *White Zombie* / As I die: *Paradise Lost* / Into the pit: *Testament* / Institutionalised: *Suicidal Tendencies* / America must be destroyed: *GWAR* / Syn.kill 1: *Annihilator* / Fortune in lies: *Dream Theater* / Face down in the gutter: *XYZ* / Freedom: *Cooper, Alice* / Misery shows: *Trouble* / Black tiger: *Y&T* / Clouds in my house: *Voivod* / Hole in the sky: *Pell, Axel Rudi* / Am I evil: *Diamond Head* / So fine: *Waltari*
DOU 882442 / 2 Feb '98 / Disky

☐ ROCK AND WATER
ECLCD 9411 / Jan '96 / Eclectic

☐ ROCK AROUND THE CLOCK
MACCD 211 / Aug '96 / Autograph

☐ ROCK AROUND THE JUKEBOX
Long tall Sally / Stagger Lee / Rebel rouser / Runaway / Night has a thousand eyes / Tequila / Little darlin' / He's so fine / Be bop a lula / Under the moon of love / Mr. Bass Man / Blue Monday / Angels listened in Kansas City / Rockin' Robin / Personality / So long baby / Lucille / Dance with the guitar / Duke of Earl
QED 007 / Nov '96 / Tring

☐ ROCK AROUND THE LOCK
Crazy 'bout my baby: *Rimshots* / Wanted man: *Number 9* / Crash landed: *Space Cadets* / Little Miss Pancake: *Playboys* / No way out: *Big Six* / De bop: *Bach, Johnny & The Moonshine Boozers* / I fell in love: *Rimshots* / 20th century boy: *Big Six* / Like trash: *Flaming Stars* / Froffee coffee: *Stargazers* / Golden hair: *Restless* / Rattleshakin' daddy: *Marshall & The Shooting Stars* / Bring her here to me: *Kid Rocker* / Put me down: *Restless* / Are you ready to rumble: *Curtis, Mac*
JRCD 28 / Nov '97 / Jappin' & Rockin'

☐ ROCK BALLADS
Once in a lifetime: *Kansas* / Parisienne walkways: *Moore, Gary* / Amanda: *Boston* / Winning man: *Krokus* / On and on: *Bishop, Stephen* / Surrender: *Trixter* / Thrill is gone: *King, B.B.* / Pusher: *Trixter* / She's gone: *Steelheart* / Sara: *Starship* / Still believe: *Starship* / Washable ink: *Hiatt, John* / Gail: *Cooper, Alice* / Just one precious moment: *Emergency* / Stairway to heaven: *Far Corporation*
MCD 30202 / Mar '94 / Ariola Express

☐ ROCK BEFORE ELVIS
STBCD 25162617 / Aug '95 / Stash

☐ ROCK BLASTS FROM THE PAST VOL.2
Devil doll: *Orbison, Roy* / You're my baby: *Orbison, Roy* / Whole lotta shakin' goin' on: *Haley, Bill & The Comets* / Razzle dazzle: *Haley, Bill & The Comets* / Baby baby bye bye: *Lewis, Jerry Lee* / I need you all the time: *Platters* / Bonnie B: *Lewis, Jerry Lee* / Maggie doesn't work here anymore: *Platters* / Ooby dooby: *Orbison, Roy* / Saints rock 'n' roll: *Haley, Bill & The Comets* / Down the line: *Lewis, Jerry Lee* / Voo vee ah vee: *Platters*
EMBCD 3427 / 27 Apr '98 / Ember

☐ ROCK CLASSICS
I want you to want me: *Cheap Trick* / Barracuda: *Heart* / Carrie: *Europe* / She's not there: *Santana* / Up around the bend: *Hanoi Rocks* / Breaking the law: *Judas Priest* / Ride like the wind: *Saxon* / Silver machine: *Hawkwind* / Rock 'n' me: *Miller, Steve Band* / Show me the way: *Frampton, Peter* / I surrender: *Rainbow* / Waiting for an alibi: *Thin Lizzy* / Radar love: *Golden Earring* / Closer to the heart: *Rush* / Whatever you want: *Status Quo* / Victims of circumstance: *Barclay James Harvest* / Lady in black: *Uriah Heep* / This flight tonight: *Nazareth*
VSOPCD 194 / Apr '94 / Connoisseur Collection

☐ ROCK CLASSICS VOL.1
11851 / Feb '95 / Laserlight

☐ ROCK CLASSICS VOL.2
11852 / Feb '95 / Laserlight

☐ ROCK CLASSICS VOL.3
11853 / Feb '95 / Laserlight

☐ ROCK DA CIDADE
12050011 / 12 May '98 / Paradoxx

R.E.D. CD CATALOGUE

☐ ROCK DON'T RUN VOL.2
SPINCD 0023 / Jan '97 / Spinout

☐ ROCK GIANTS
12402 / Feb '95 / Laserlight

☐ ROCK IT FOR ME - 1937
One o'clock jump: Basie, Count / Sailboat in the moonlight: Holiday, Billie & Her Orchestra / I can't get started (with you): Berigan, Bunny / Honeysuckle rose: Hawkins, Coleman / Boo hoo: Lombardo, Guy / When we're alone: James, Harry / Alabamy home: Ellington, Duke / Getting some fun out of life: Holiday, Billie & Orchestra/Barney Kessel / Carry me back to old Virginny: Armstrong, Louis / Song of India: Dorsey, Tommy / I can't give you anything but love: Goodman, Benny / Who's sorry now: Crosby, Bob / Loch Lomond: Sullivan, Maxine / Posin': Lunceford, Jimmie / I've got my love to keep me warm: Norvo, Red / Rock it for me: Webb, Chick / Whose babe: Hampton / I must have that man: Wilson, Teddy / Caravan: Ellington, Duke / Topsie
PHONT CD 7663 / Apr '90 / Phontastic

☐ ROCK LEGENDS
This flight tonight: Nazareth / NIB: Black Sabbath / Sweet Lorraine: Uriah Heep / Silver machine: Hawkwind / Down the dustpipe: Status Quo / Race with the devil: Girlschool / Dancin': Moore, Gary / Motorhead / Who do you love: Juicy Lucy / Ace of spades: Motorhead / Natural born bugie: Humble Pie / Broken down angel: Nazareth / Levitation: Hawkwind / Ice in the sun: Status Quo / Wizard: Uriah Heep / All of my life: Magnum / Parisienne walkways (lives): Moore, Gary
MCCD 045 / Sep '91 / Music Club

☐ ROCK LEGENDS (2CD Set)
MBSCD 406 / Nov '93 / Castle

☐ ROCK LEGENDS (4CD Set)
PBXCD 412 / 20 Apr '98 / Pulse

☐ ROCK LIVE FROM THE MOUNTAIN STAGE
Alright guy: Snider, Todd / 8 Piece box: Southern Culture On The Skids / Ain't hurtin' nobody: Prine, John / I believe: Blessid Union Of Souls / I must be high: Wilco / Poor boy blues: Bonepony / Blue: Jayhawks / Welfare music: Bottle Rockets / Jackopierce / Send me on my way: Rusted Root
BPM 307CD / May '97 / Blue Plate

☐ ROCK ME SLOWLY
MUSCD 020 / Sep '94 / MCI Music

☐ ROCK 'N' ROLL (2CD Set)
R2CD 4017 / 13 Apr '98 / Deja Vu

☐ ROCK 'N' ROLL CHRISTMAS
Rudolph the red nosed reindeer: Dixie Cups / White Christmas: Ford, Frankie / Frosty the snowman: Coasters / Christmas song: Drifters / Deck the halls: Crickets / Sleigh ride: Diamonds / If I could spend Christmas with your Hoe, Tommy / Little drummer boy: Tokens / Silent night: Shirelles / New baby for Christmas: Preston, Johnny / Winter wonderland: Rockin' Robin / Rockin' around the Christmas tree: Jones, Davy
XMAS 009 / Nov '96 / Tring

☐ ROCK 'N' ROLL CLASSICS (2CD Set)
Why do fools fall in love: Lymon, Frankie & The Teenagers / Oh Carol: Sedaka, Neil / Duke of Earl: Chandler, Gene / Under the moon of love: Lee, Curtis / Get a job: Silhouettes / Sealed with a kiss: Hyland, Brian / At the hop: Danny & The Juniors / Poetry in motion: Tillotson, Johnny / I only have eyes for you: Flamingos / Heartbeat: Holly, Buddy / All I have to do is dream: Everly Brothers / Runaway: Shannon, Del / Since I don't have you: Skyliners / One fine day: Chiffons / Will you still love me tomorrow: Shirelles / Bye bye love: Everly Brothers / Breaking up is hard to do: Sedaka, Neil / Rock around the clock: Haley, Bill / Leader of the pack: Shangri-Las / Shoop shoop song: Everett, Betty / Remember (walkin' in the sand): Shangri-Las / Goodnight sweetheart, goodnight: Spaniels / 24 hours from Tulsa: Pitney, Gene / Hey Paula: Paul & Paula / Wanderer: Dion / Diana: Anka, Paul / Johnny B Goode: Vee, Bobby / Sea cruise: Ford, Frankie / In the still of the night: Five Satins / Rubber ball: Vee, Bobby / C'mon everybody: Cochran, Eddie / Stay: Williams, Maurice & The Zodiacs / Born too late: Poni-Tails / Baby it's you: Shirelles / Come go with me: Del-Vikings / I'm gonna be strong: Pitney, Gene / Blue moon: Marcels
RCACD 203 / Jul '97 / RCA

☐ ROCK 'N' ROLL CLASSICS
MACCD 154 / Aug '96 / Autograph

☐ ROCK 'N' ROLL CLASSICS (4CD Set)
SUMBX 4018 / Jan '98 / Summit

☐ ROCK 'N' ROLL DANCE PARTY
This ole house: Clooney, Rosemary / Good golly Miss Molly: Little Richard / Rebel rouser: Eddy, Duane / Yakety yak: Coasters / Party doll: Knox, Buddy / Red river rock: Johnny & The Hurricanes / Green door: Lowe, Jim / At the hop: Danny & The Juniors / Runaway: Shannon, Del / Nut rocker: B Bumble & The Stingers / Night has a thousand eyes: Vee, Bobby / Wooly bully: Sam The Sham & The Pharaohs / Poetry in motion: Tillotson, Johnny / Running bear: Preston, Johnny / Rock and roll is here to stay: Danny & The Juniors / Boy from New York City: Ad Libs
SUMCD 4189 / 11 May '98 / Summit

COMPILATIONS

☐ ROCK 'N' ROLL ESSENTIALS
CDNEW 124 / 1 Jun '98 / Charly

☐ ROCK 'N' ROLL FEVER (The Wildest From Specialty)
Justine: Don & Dewey / Moose on the loose: Jackson, Roddy / Thunderbird: Hall, Rene / My baby's rocking: Monitors / Cherokee dance: Landers, Bob / She said 'Yeah': Williams, Larry / Don't stop loving me: Church, Eugene / Don't you just know it: Titans / Twitchy: Hall, Rene / Haunted house: Fuller, Johnny / Chicken, baby, chicken: Harris, Tony / Sack: Hughes, Ben / Arlene: Titans / Little bird: Hollywood Flames / I've got my sights set on someone new: Jackson, Roddy / Lights out: Byrne, Jerry / It's spring again: Pentagons / Goodbye baby goodbye: Lowery, Sonny / Ooh little girl: Dixon, Floyd / Rock 'n' roll fever: Dixon, Floyd / Swingin' at the creek: Fuller, Johnny / Frankenstein's den: Hollywood Flames / Carry on: Byrne, Jerry / Hiccups: Jackson, Roddy / Satisfied: Casualairs
CDCHD 574 / Jul '94 / Ace

☐ ROCK 'N' ROLL FOREVER
DCD 5306 / Dec '93 / Disky

☐ ROCK 'N' ROLL GOLD (2CD Set)
D2CD 4017 / Jun '95 / Deja Vu

☐ ROCK 'N' ROLL GREATS (2CD Set)
Matchbox: Perkins, Carl / Woman in black: Vincent, Gene / Whole lotta shakin' goin' on: Lewis, Jerry Lee / Reet Petite: Wilson, Jackie / Baby I don't care: Richard / Little Queenie: Lewis, Jerry Lee / Rip it up: Haley, Bill / Blue Monday: Domino, Fats / Doby dooby: Orbison, Roy / Maybelline: Elvis, Scotty & Bill / Lucille: Little Richard / Boppin' the blues: Perkins, Carl / Be bop a lula: Vincent, Gene / Shake rattle and roll: Haley, Bill / Runaway: Shannon, Del / Red hot: Haley, Bill / Ain't that a shame: Domino, Fats / Let's have a party: Jackson, Wanda / Lonely weekend: Rich, Charlie / That's why: Wilson, Jackie / High school confidential: Lewis, Jerry Lee / Blueberry hill: Lewis, Jerry Lee / Speedy gonzales: Boone, Pat / Wake up little Suzie: Everly Brothers / Blue suede shoes: Perkins, Carl / Rock around the clock: Haley, Bill / Rave on: Jackson, Wanda / Hats off to Larry: Shannon, Del / Great balls of fire: Lewis, Jerry Lee / That's alright mama: Elvis, Scotty & Bill / Unsquare dance: Smith, Warren / Honey don't: Perkins, Carl / See you later alligator: Haley, Bill / Raunchy: Justis, Bill / Hello Mary Lou: Nelson, Rick / Good golly Miss Molly: Little Richard / Rockhouse: Orbison, Roy / Be my guest: Domino, Fats / Sea cruise: Ford, Frankie / Long tall Sally: Little Richard
330212 / Jul '96 / Hallmark

☐ ROCK 'N' ROLL GREATS VOL.1
Tutti frutti: Little Richard / That'll be the day: Holly, Buddy & The Crickets / Blueberry Hill: Domino, Fats / Take good care of my baby: Vee, Bobby / Walk don't run: Ventures / Say mama: Vincent, Gene / Bird dog: Everly Brothers / Sweet little sixteen: Berry, Chuck / Something else: Cochran, Eddie / (We're gonna) Rock around the clock: Haley, Bill & The Comets / I'm walkin': Domino, Fats / Oh boy: Holly, Buddy & The Crickets / Don't ever change: Crickets / Why do fools fall in love: Lymon, Frankie & The Teenagers / Be bop a lula: Vincent, Gene / Summertime blues: Cochran, Eddie / You're sixteen: Burnette, Johnny Rock 'N' Roll Trio / Rubber ball: Vee, Bobby
CDMFP 5744 / Apr '92 / Music For Pleasure

☐ ROCK 'N' ROLL GREATS VOL.2
C'mon everybody: Cochran, Eddie / Ain't that a shame: Domino, Fats / Willie and the hand jive: Otis, Johnny Show / Memphis Tennessee: Berry, Chuck / Dreamin': Burnette, Johnny / Bony Moronie: Paul Rock river rock: Johnny & The Hurricanes / Git it: Vincent, Gene / I'm not a juvenile delinquent: Lymon, Frankie & The Teenagers / Whole lotta shakin' goin' on: Lewis, Jerry Lee / At the hop: Danny & The Juniors / Great balls of fire: Lewis, Jerry Lee / Peggy Sue: Holly, Buddy & The Crickets / Claudette: Everly Brothers / Three steps to heaven: Cochran, Eddie / Blue Monday: Domino, Fats / Blue jean bop: Vincent, Gene / Johnny B Goode: Berry, Chuck / Good golly Miss Molly: Little Richard
CDMFP 5745 / Apr '92 / Music For Pleasure

☐ ROCK 'N' ROLL HALL OF FAME CONCERT
4837932 / Sep '96 / Sony Music

☐ ROCK 'N' ROLL JAMBOREE
PT 650001 / Jun '96 / Part

☐ ROCK 'N' ROLL LEGENDS
Shake, rattle and roll: Haley, Bill / Rock around the clock: Haley, Bill / See you later alligator: Haley, Bill / Rip it up: Haley, Bill / Memphis Tennessee: Lewis, Jerry Lee / Good golly Miss Molly: Lewis, Jerry Lee / Tutti frutti: Lewis, Jerry Lee / Long tall Sally: Lewis, Jerry Lee / Whole lotta shakin' goin' on: Lewis, Jerry Lee / Great balls of fire: Lewis, Jerry Lee / Boogie woogie man from Tennessee: Lewis, Jerry Lee / Be bop a Lula: Vincent, Gene / Pistol packing Mama: Vincent, Gene / Bird doggin': Vincent, Gene / Blue jean bop: Vincent, Gene / Blue suede shoes: Perkins, Carl / This ole house: Perkins, Carl / All Mama's children: Perkins, Carl / That's right: Perkins, Carl
PLATCD 138 / Feb '97 / Platinum

☐ ROCK 'N' ROLL LOVE SONGS
Save the last dance for me: Platters / It keeps right on hurtin': Tillotson, Johnny / More than I can say: Vee, Bobby / You belong to me: Duprees / Mr. Blue: Fleetwoods / So much in love: Tymes / I love the way you love me: Johnson, Marvin / Rock 'n' roll lullaby: Thomas, B.J. / My heart is an open book: Dobkins, Carl Jr. / Hey baby: Channel, Bruce / Chapel of love: Dixie Cups / Dedicated to the one I love: Shirelles / Some kind of wonderful: Drifters / Lavender blue: Turner, Sammy / Sea of love: Phillips, Phil / My own true love: Duprees / Hurt: Kuro, Timi / Only you (and you alone): Platters
ECD 3114 / Jan '95 / K-Tel

☐ ROCK 'N' ROLL LOVE SONGS
SUMCD 4139 / Jan '98 / Summit

☐ ROCK 'N' ROLL MEGAMIX
JHD 107 / Aug '93 / Tring

☐ ROCK 'N' ROLL ORGY VOL.1
FLESHDEN 6901 / Nov '95 / Flesh Den

☐ ROCK 'N' ROLL ORGY VOL.2
FLESHDEN 6902 / Nov '95 / Flesh Den

☐ ROCK 'N' ROLL ORGY VOL.3
FLESHDEN 6903 / Nov '95 / Flesh Den

☐ ROCK 'N' ROLL ORGY VOL.4
FLESHDEN 6904 / Jan '97 / Flesh Den

☐ ROCK 'N' ROLL PARTY
Good golly miss molly: Little Richard / This ole house: Clooney, Rosemary / Yakety yak: Coasters / Rebel rouser: Eddy, Duane / Red river rock: Johnny & The Hurricanes / Party doll: Knox, Buddy / At the hop: Danny & The Juniors / Green door: Lowe, Jim / Nut rocker: B Bumble & The Stingers / Runaway: Shannon, Del / Night has a thousand eyes: Vee, Bobby / Poetry in motion: Tillotson, Johnny / Wooly bully: Sam The Sham & The Pharaohs / Duke of earl: Chandler, Gene / Running bear: Preston, Johnny / Boy from New York City: Ad Libs / Rock 'n' roll is here to stay: Danny & The Juniors / Let's twist again: Checker, Chubby
ECD 3055 / Dec '96 / K-Tel

☐ ROCK 'N' ROLL PARTY 1957-1962
Motorbiene (Motorcycle) / Buona Sera / My happiness / Ein engel ohne fliguel (I can see an angel) / Lippenstift am jacket / Oh oh ah ah (witch doctor) / Ritsch ratsch (splish splash) / Speedy Gonzalez / Rock-a-hula baby / Fur gabi tu ich alles / Fraulein / Norman / Yes tonight Josephine / Kuba / Wunderbares madchen (catch a falling star) / Oh, das war schon (oh lonesome me) / Lollipop / Two farbe der liebe (a white sports coat) / Zahn Hag / Japanisches abscieldsleid
BCD 15235 / Nov '86 / Bear Family

☐ ROCK 'N' ROLL RIOT
Rockin' roll riot: Stoltz Brothers / Savage: Barnicoat, Alan / Betty Ann: Cruisers / Tough 'n rough: Saladin / Itch: Cherry, Carl / That cat: Brown, Tommy / Rock 'n' roll saddles: Edwards, Johnny / Baby Sue: Rhythm Tones / Rock 'n' roll rock: Kelly, Roy / Is that wrong: Wynnewoods / Bloodshot: String Kings / Granny went rockin': Scott, Rodney / My baby's casual: Flaharty, Sonny / Rockin' and boppin': Newman, Carl / Rockin' teens: Puckett, Dennis / Little jewel: Taylor, Bill / Keep it swinging: Skelton, Eddie / Rock 'n' roll guitar: Knight, Johnny / Woman can make you blue: Porter, Royce / Wild wild woman / Wright, Steve / Rock rhythm roll: Dash, Frankie / Where's my baby: Giant, Ethan / I know why: Clark, Billy / Scratching on my screen: Cartey, Ric / Rock 'n' roll romance: Big Rocker / Blues in the morning: Foley, Jim / Hard luck: Blank, Billy / Bootleg rock: Bonny, Billy / Robinson Cruise bop: Cole, Sonny / By by blues: Puckett, Dennis
CDBB 55004 / Apr '94 / Buffalo Bop

☐ ROCK 'N' ROLL ROMANCE
Will you still love me tomorrow: Shirelles / Sealed with a kiss: Hyland, Brian / Young love: Hunter, Tab / Venus: Avalon, Frankie / Come go with me: Del-Vikings / Born too late: Poni-Tails / Since I don't have you: Skyliners / Every breath I take: Pitney, Gene / Thousand stars: Young, Kuen & The Innocents / Love letters in the sand: Boone, Pat / Heartbeat: Holly, Buddy / Donna: Valens, Ritchie / Till I kissed you: Everly Brothers / Hey baby: Channel, Bruce / My true love: Scott, Jack / Oh Julie: James, Crazy / Sweet nothin's: Lee, Brenda / I'm sorry: Lee, Brenda / (We're gonna) Rock around the clock: Haley, Bill / Rock 'n' roll is here to stay: Danny & The Juniors / All by myself: Barry, Len / Pipeline: Chantays / Wipeout: Surfaris / Mona (Diddley, Bo / Suzie Q: Hawkins, Dale / Come go with me: Del-Vikings / Great, gosh and mighty: Richard
MCD 30200 / Mar '94 / Ariola Express

☐ ROCK 'N' ROLL SUPERSTARS (CD/CD Rom Set)
WWCDR 008 / Apr '97 / Weton-Wesgram

☐ ROCK 'N' ROLL WITH PIANO VOL.1
CLCD 4435 / Mar '97 / Collector's Edition

ROCKABILLY PARTY

☐ ROCK 'N' ROLL WITH PIANO VOL.3
CLCD 4445 / 31 Jul '98 / Collector/ White Label

☐ ROCK N' ROLL WITH PIANO VOL.2
CLCD 4437 / Apr '97 / Collector/White Label

☐ ROCK OF AGES
RENCD 104 / Jul '95 / Renaissance Collector Series

☐ ROCK OF AMERICA
NSCD 018 / May '95 / Newsound

☐ ROCK ON VOL.1
CDTMR 8014 / Jul '95 / Candor

☐ ROCK OUT (2CD Set)
DEMPCD 007 / Mar '96 / Emporio

☐ ROCK PROGRESSION (2CD Set)
SMDCD 114 / 9 Feb '98 / Snapper

☐ ROCK STEADY 1966-1967 (Bobby Aitken Presents)
NXBACD 01 / 23 Mar '98 / Next Step

☐ ROCK STEADY RAVE
CPCD 8023 / Feb '94 / Charly

☐ ROCK STEADY/FUNKY REGGAE
RB 3008 / May '94 / Reggae Best

☐ ROCK THE DANCEFLOOR (2CD Set)
Paradise city: N-Trance / Up to the wildstyle: Pom Kings & DJ Supreme / Tha horns of Jericho: DJ Supreme / Your caress is all I need): DJ Flavours / Rok da floor: Primo / Take me away (paradise): Mix Factory / Do you love me baby: Fly guys / Self preservation society: Headrush / Is this a dream: Love Decade / Let the bass kick: 2 For Joy / Everyday of my life: House Traffic / Space invaders: Hit 'N Hide
GLOBECD 9 / 10 Aug '98 / All Around The World

☐ ROCK THE PLANET (2CD Set)
One vision: Queen / Who's gonna ride your wild horses: U2 / On the shoreline: Genesis / Crazy: Seal / Fragile: Sting / Zombie: Cranberries / Bad blame: REM / Steam: Gabriel, Peter / Under Afrikan skies: Simon, Paul / Over: John, Elton / Disappear: INXS / Here comes the rain again: Eurythmics / Mmm Mmm Mmm: Crash Test Dummies / How many people: McCartney, Paul / I will do anything for love: Meat Loaf / Learning to fly: Pink Floyd / Prayer for the dying: Seal / It's the end of the world as we know it (and I feel fine): REM / I still haven't found what I'm looking for: U2 / Don't give up: Gabriel, Peter & Kate Bush / Is this the world we created: Queen / I'm still standing: John, Elton / Yes we can: Artists United For Nature / Damn I wish I was your lover: Hawkins, Sophie B / Silent scream: MacLowan, Shane / Sowing the seeds of love: Tears For Fears / Walk of life: Dire Straits / Brazilian: Genesis / Wake me up on time: Scott, Jack / Oh for you baby: Brown, judgement day: Winwood, Steve / Miracle of love: Eurythmics / Jealous: Judah / Spirit of the forest: Spirit Of The Forest
5334282 / Aug '96 / PolyGram TV

☐ ROCK THERAPY
We will rock you: Queen / Let's get rocked: Def Leppard / Livin' on a prayer: Bon Jovi / Tragic comic: Extreme / Here I go again: Whitesnake / Wind of change: Scorpions / Backstreet symphony: Thunder / Wishing well: Free / Rockin' all over the world: Status Quo / Living after midnight: Jethro Tull / Burning of the Midnight lamp: Hendrix, Jimi / Too old to rock 'n' roll, too young to die: Jethro Tull / Fanfare for the common man: Emerson, Lake & Palmer / Breeze: Lynyrd Skynyrd / Won't get fooled again: Who / Run to the hills: Iron Maiden
5168612 / Jun '94 / PolyGram TV

☐ ROCK THERAPY '96
Keep the faith: Bon Jovi / What's the frequency Kenneth: REM / Desire: U2 / Live forever: Oasis / Salvation: Cranberries / Word up: Gun / Only thing that looks good on me is you: Adams, Bryan / New sensation: INXS / Waterfront: Simple Minds / Don't stop: Fleetwood Mac / Total eclipse of the heart: Dire Straits / Jean & The Dominoes / Whiskey in the jar: Thin Lizzy / Bat out of hell: Meat Loaf / Baba O'Riley: Who / Another brick in the wall: Pink Floyd / Kashmir: Page, Jimmy & Robert Plant
5530172 / Oct '96 / PolyGram TV

☐ ROCKABILLY HOODLUMS
CLCD 4438 / Apr '97 / Collector/White Label

☐ ROCKABILLY PARTY
It's many miles from me to you: Monroe, Homer / Carmen-Sue: Melson, Lee 'Red' / Lonesome old jail: Blankenship Brothers / Don't shoot me: Bowen, Bill / Party: Sims, Al / Nuthin' but nuthin': Stewart, Jimmy / Hard up blues: Blankenship Brothers / I'm long gone: Belew, Carl / Pretty baby: Pruitt, Lewis / Rockin' thru the tunnel of love: Reed, Carl / All messed up: Hooper, Jess / Wilson blues no.1: Wilson, James / Way up Alaska: Oster, Al / Have yourself a ball: Bowen, Bill / Time will tell: Beasley, Art / You're gonna reap what you sow: Strong, Ray / Pack up and go: Triplett, Sid / Track down baby: James, Tom / That's why I am blue: Blankenship Brothers / Where there's a will: Trantham, Carl / Married life: Boogie: Triplett, Sid / Bubble gum boogie: Rash, Curley / Hey baby: James, Tom / Tore my playhouse down: Saunders, Robert / Sleep time: Hooper, Jess / Behave little red caboose: Sims, Al / I'm baby blues / Heart break attention: Hamby, 'Guzzy' / Bill
CDBB 55064 / Oct '97 / Buffalo Bop

☐ ROCKABILLY PSYCHOSIS
Surfin' bird: *Trashmen* / Psycho: *Sonics* / Crusher: *Novas* / Paralysed: *Legendary Stardust Cowboy* / She said: *Adkins, Hasil 'Haze'* / My daddy is a vampire: *Meteors* / Radioactive kid: *Meteors* / Dateless nites: *Falco, Tav Panther Burns* / Jack on fire: *Gun Club* / Folsom Prison blues: *Geezers* / Catman: *Stingrays* / Just love me: *Guana Batz* / Love me: *Phantom* / Red headed woman: *Dickinson, Jimmy & the Cramps* / Scream: *Nielsen, Ralph & The Chancellors* / Hidden charms: *Wray, Link* / Run chicken run: *Milkshakes*
CDWIK 18 / Oct '89 / Big Beat

☐ ROCKABILLY RECORD CO. (Goofin' Rockabilly Sampler)
Rockin' blues: *Lewis, Willie* / Rock 'n' roll religion: *Lewis, Willie* / Oh, baby babe: *Lewis, Willie* / Crazy boogie: *Lewis, Willie* / Workin' man blues: *Lewis, Willie* / Mary Lou rock: *Billy & The Bob Cats* / Train of misery: *High Noon* / Glory bound: *High Noon* / Baby let's play house: *High Noon* / All night long: *High Noon* / Who was that cat: *High Noon* / Crazy fever: *High Noon* / I ain't in love with you/Tonight: *Pharaohs* / I want my whiskey: *Pharaohs* / Dollar bill boogie: *Pharaohs* / A-bop-a-baby: *Roadhouse Rockers* / Be my baby: *Kevin & Todd* / Beat up Ford: *Leyland, Carl 'Sonny'* / I like the boogie woogie: *Leyland, Carl 'Sonny'* / Whiskey straight up: *Frantic Flattops* / Rockabilly Willie: *King Cat & The Pharaohs* / It's Saturday night: *King Cat & The Pharaohs* / You got no sense: *King Cat & The Pharaohs* / Ran down Daddy: *Three Cats & The Kittens*
GRCD 6036 / Jan '97 / Goofin'

☐ ROCKABILLY SHAKEDOWN
Cats were jumpin': *Worthan, John* / Grandpa's twist: *Monte, Avery* / Shake down: *Thomas, Bill* / Rockin' and a knockin': *Griffith, Gayle* / It's a cryin' shame: *Perkins, Howard* / Too too many: *Worthan, John* / They're learning: *Pratt, Lynn* / Rock 'n' roll fever: *Ray, Gene* / Aquacell blues: *Burch, Woody* / I'm lonesome baby: *Philmon, Hiram* / Pine mountain boogie: *Lewis, Arvel* / Come here mama: *Pratt, Lynn* / Ten horned devil: *Prince Arky* / Look what I found: *Hubbard, Orangie* / I'm lost without your love: *Lee, Wibby* / Strange woman's love: *Worthan, John* / You gotta love me baby: *Philmon, Hiram* / I wanta make love: *Dobson, Leroy* / Big foot Annie: *Boots, Don* / Hep cat boogie: *Hanna, Fletcher* / Music to my ears: *Speck & Doyle* / She's gone: *Pedigo Brothers* / High steppin' daddy: *Gaddie, Grover* / Whhel keep a-rollin': *Sovine, Eddie* / Gee whiz Miss Liz: *Jackson, Marvin* / You gotta quit cheatin': *Wilcox, Coye* / All alone at night: *Rivers, Chuck* / Straw room boogie: *Spain, Dick* / Kool it baby: *Blake, Tommy* / Don't cry baby: *Veale, Cal*
CDBB 55070 / Mar '98 / Buffalo Bop

☐ ROCKABILLY SHAKEOUT VOL.1
Shadow my baby: *Barber, Glen* / Atom bomb: *Barber, Glen* / I don't know when: *Harris, Hal* / My little baby: *Jimmy & Johnny* / True affection: *Johnson, Byron* / Slippin' and slidin': *Davis, Link* / Hey hey little boy blue: *Lindsay, Merle* / Gee whiz: *Dee & Patty* / All the time: *LaBeef, Sleepy* / Spin the bottle: *Joy, Benny* / Chicken bop: *Truitt Forse* / My big fat baby: *Hall, Sonny & The Echoes* / Cat's just got back in town: *Mack, Billy* / Tennessee rock: *Scoggins, Hoyt* / Uranium fever: *Gaddis, Ruddy* / Prettiest girl at the dance: *Wyatt, Gene*
CDCH 191 / Feb '92 / Ace

☐ ROCKERS AND BALLADEERS VOL.1
PLATCD 341 / Oct '90 / Platinum

☐ ROCKERS AND BALLADEERS VOL.2
PLATCD 342 / Oct '90 / Platinum

☐ ROCKET FUEL
MIDDLE 6CD / Jul '96 / Middle Earth

☐ ROCKETS
ZYX 550902 / Nov '97 / ZYX

☐ ROCKETSHIP
Flying saucer rock 'n' roll: *Love Brothers* / Rock rock rocket ship: *Rockers* / Satellite rock: *Rebelaires* / Blast off: *Holloway, Alden* / Rock it on Mars: *Dunavan, Terry* / Rock the universe: *Vaughn, Dell* / Knocked out joint on Mars: *Trail, Buck* / Cape Caneveral: *Mead, Monte* / Moon beat: *Fabulous Imperials* / Rock on the moon: *Stewart, Jimmy* / Rock it to the moon: *Gotroe, Jackie* / Moon twist: *Nix, Billy* / Good old Sputnik: *Young, Nelson* / Shooting for the moon: *Carl & Norman* / Satellite: *Rocks* / Light my rockets: *Alan, Neil* / Satellite rock: *Copeland, James* / Space dance: *Simpson, Royco* / Rockin' on the moon: *Deacon & The Rock 'n' Rollers* / Got a rocket in my pocket: *Beaver, Stan* / Little moon men: *George, Lee* / Trip to the moon: *Reynolds, Wesley* / Countdown 4321: *Lanzl, Geno* / Rocking on the moon: *Sando, Ronnie* / Boppin' Martian: *Robinson, Dick* / Shake it over Sputnik: *Hogan, Billy* / Rock moon rock: *James, Daniel* / Man from Mars: *Paulson, Butch* / Orbit twist: *Shoffner, Rufus* / Rocket to the moon: *Caves, John Wesley* / Moon rocketin': *Vogt, Les* / Moon twist: *Dallis, Chuck* / Honeymoon trip to Mars: *Tucker, Jack* / Rockin' space girl: *Grubbs, Jimmy*
BB 55052 / Aug '97 / Buffalo Bop

☐ ROCKIN' AT THE TAKE 2 VOL.1 & 2
LOMACD 30 / Aug '94 / Loma

☐ ROCKIN' AT TOWN HALL
RFDCD 06 / Apr '91 / Country Routes

☐ ROCKIN' BLUES
Fool in heah: *Dawkins, Jimmy* / TROUBLE: *Nighthawks* / I got the blues all over me: *McCain, Jerry* / Evil gal: *Reed, Francine* / Cigarette blues: *Rhodes, Sonny* / Rock me baby: *Lynn, Trudy* / Honey hush: *Principato, Tom & Danny Gatton* / Born under a bad sign: *Bell, William* / High and lonesome: *Shadows* / I need to love you: *Hall, Sandra* / Rockin' Daddy: *Johnson, Luther 'Houserocker'*
D 2248782 / Sep '96 / Ichiban

☐ ROCKIN' D-DAY
Bruce Fuckin' Lee: *Mad Mongols* / Cheat: *Earls Of Suave* / Shake it up: *Guana Batz* / I fought the rawhide: *Tokyo Skunx* / Bitch attack: *Sharks* / Get on the right track: *Polecats* / Tiny cowboy: *Floozy Drippy's* / Cadillac baby: *Hamilton, Colbert & The Nitros* / See you later alligator: *Stargazers* / Rebel: *Pharaohs* / Animal special: *Marshall & The Shooting Stars* / Bip bop boom: *Rockings* / Rockabilly guy: *Polecats* / Terminaton: *Jasons* / Rock that boogie: *Stargazers* / El camino: *Spikes* / Rollercoaster rock: *Hamilton, Colbert & The Nitros* / Walking the devil's foot: *Chicken Jump Skips* / Lady rock 'n' roll: *Harman, Mark*
JRCD 13 / Sep '97 / Jappin' & Rockin'

☐ ROCKIN' DOO WOP VOL.1 1954-1964
NEMCD 692 / Apr '95 / Sequel

☐ ROCKIN' DOO WOP VOL.2
I want you to be my girl: *Lymon, Frankie & The Teenagers* / Hindu baby: *Emanons* / Hey babe: *Cleftones* / Too young: *Lymon, Lewis & The Teenagers* / Sugar sugar: *Cadillacs* / Teenager rock: *Classmates* / My heart beats for you: *Echoes* / Come my little baby: *Chantels* / Goody goody: *Lymon, Frankie & The Teenagers* / Speedo is back: *Cadillacs* / Flip flop: *Teenagers* / Lymon, Lewis and The Teenagers: *Teenagers* / (I need some) money: *Miracles* / You're the one to blame: *Starlighters* / Never let go: *Chantels* / Shimmy shimmy ko-ko bop: *Little Anthony* / Lover boy: *Cleftones* / Barbara Ann: *Regents* / Heart and soul: *Cleftones* / Travelling strangers: *Little Anthony*
NEMCD 767 / Apr '96 / Sequel

☐ ROCKIN' FROM COAST TO COAST
Buzz buzz a-diddle-it: *Cannon, Freddy* / Skippy is a sissy: *Gaines, Roy* / Bim bam: *Butera, Sam* / I'm snowed: *South, Joe* / Sapphire: *Oliver, Big Danny* / Rock the bop: *Lee, Brenda* / Mexicali baby: *Rio Rockers* / Hocus pocus: *Raiders* / Too much rockin': *Lewis, Tiny* / Cool off baby: *Barrix, Billy* / Flirty Gertie: *Jivatones* / Please Mr. Mayor: *Clark, Roy* / New shoes: *Denson, Lee* / Dirty dishes: *Mack, Jeani* / Good golly Miss Molly: *Valiants* / You're right, I'm left, she's gone: *Schmidling, Tyrone* / Rockin' in the graveyard: *Morningstar, Jackie* / Rockin' the joint: *Esquerita* / Eager boy: *Lonesome Drifter* / Honey don't: *Schmidling, Tyrone* / Why did you leave me: *Josie, Lou* / Frieda Frieda: *Valiants* / Wee Willie Brown: *Graham, Lou* / Swing Daddy swing: *Hawkins, Jerry* / Long gone Daddy: *Cupp, Pat & His Flying Saucers* / Let's go baby: *Eldridge, Billy*
CDCHD 496 / Sep '96 / Ace

☐ ROCKIN' GOOD CHRISTMAS
Winter wonderland: *Overland, Steve & Jackie Bodimead* / White Christmas: *Di'Anno, Paul* / Santa Claus is coming to town: *Di'Anno, Paul* / Have yourself a merry little Christmas: *Sloman, John* / This Christmas: *Overland, Steve & Jackie Bodimead* / Merry Xmas everybody: *McAuliffe, Kim* / Another rock and roll Christmas: *Di'Anno, Paul* / Silent night: *Di'Anno, Paul* / Was that the night: *Callcut, Ray* / I wish it could be Christmas everyday: *Laine, Denny* / Little drummer boy: *Creator, Carlos*
CH 880952 / 30 May '97 / Disky

☐ ROCKIN' IN NEW YORK
Can't do sixty no more: *Du-Droppers* / Cry baby: *Scarlets* / Won't you come home baby: *Topps* / Runaround baby: *Kodaks* / Mary Lee: *Rainbows* / Bye bye baby: *Channels* / Part time sweetheart: *Pretenders* / What can the matter be: *Quadrells* / Honey honey: *Lymon, Lewis & The Teen Chords* / Go back: *Du-Droppers* / Tonight and forever: *Whirlers* / Stars in the sky: *Channels* / Come back: *Harmonaires* / Castle in the sky: *Bop Chords* / All night long: *Du Mauriers* / Fine fine frame: *Continentals* / Come on and love me baby: *Du-Droppers* / My baby and me: *Kodaks* / Why can't you treat me right: *Sequins* / Bobby Lee: *Riviera, Bobby & The Hemlocks* / Tonight: *Love Notes* / So why: *Bop Chords* / Counting the stars: *Ladders* / I want to run to you: *Tellers* / In my thunderbird: *Thunderbirds*
CDGR 198 / Nov '97 / Charly

☐ ROCKIN' IT UP VOL.1&2
LMCD 1217 / Jun '97 / Lost Moment

☐ ROCKIN' SEVENTIES
I can do it: *Rubettes* / Angel face: *Glitter Band* / Who put the bomp: *Showaddywaddy* / You little trustmaker: *Tymes* / Keep on dancin': *Bay City Rollers* / Juke box jive: *Rubettes* / Hey rock 'n' roll: *Showaddywaddy* / Hold back the night: *Trammps* / Pinball wizard: *New Seekers* / It's been so long: *McCrae, George* / Sugar baby love: *Rubettes* / Greased lightning: *Travolta, John* / Rock 'n' roll lady: *Showaddywaddy* / Foe-dee-o-dee: *Rubettes* / Shang-a-lang: *Bay City Rollers* / Let's get together again: *Glitter Band* / Witch Queen of New Orleans: *Redbone* / Multiplication: *Showaddywaddy* / Rock your baby: *McCrae, George* / Bye bye baby: *Bay City Rollers*
GRF 222 / Apr '93 / Tring

☐ ROCKIN' THE BLUES
PLSCD 193 / Apr '97 / Pulse

☐ ROCKIN' THE CROSSROADS
ANT 9904CD / Jul '94 / Antones

☐ ROCKTASTIC
CLACD 999 / Jul '94 / Castle

☐ ROCKY MOUNTAIN RETREAT
DC 879562 / Oct '97 / Disky

☐ ROCKYGRASS
BPCD 100 / Mar '96 / Blue Planet

☐ RODIGAN'S DUB CLASSICS VOL.1
CDREG 6 / Aug '96 / Rewind Selecta

☐ RODNY KRAJ
CR 00212 / Nov '95 / Czech Radio

☐ ROGUE TROOPER SAMPLER
DBMTR 35 / Nov '95 / Rogue Trooper

☐ ROLL ON ROLLING STONE
BB 2807 / Aug '96 / Blue Beat

☐ ROLLIN' AND TUMBLIN'
IGOCD 2029 / Apr '95 / Indigo

☐ ROLLIN' ROCK GOT THE SOCK VOL.1
HMG 4002 / Nov '97 / Hightone

☐ ROLLIN' ROCK GOT THE SOCK VOL.2
HMG 4004 / Feb '98 / Hightone

☐ ROLLING RIVERS AND SMILING VALLEYS
QPRZ 011D / Jan '93 / Polyphonic

☐ ROLLING THUNDER
Eye of the tiger: *Survivor* / I surrender: *Rainbow* / Strange kind of woman: *Deep Purple* / Night games: *Bonnet, Graham* / Trouble: *Gillan* / Don't let me be misunderstood: *Moore, Gary* / Incommunicado: *Marillion* / Final countdown: *Europe* / She's a little angel: *Little Angels* / 747 (Strangers in the night): *Saxon* / Rhythm of love: *Scorpions* / Hey you: *Quireboys* / Living after midnight: *Judas Priest* / Never say die: *Black Sabbath* / Ace of spades: *Motorhead* / Easy livin': *Uriah Heep* / Race with the devil: *Girlschool*
RENCD 107 / Oct '95 / Renaissance Collector Series

☐ ROMANCE (Music For Piano)
Shape of her face / Old family portrait / Sister bay / I always come back to you / Sacred dance / Reasons for moving / Minor truths / Beginning of love / Melusina / In the path of the heart / First light / Over shallow water / State of grace / First kiss / Summer fields / As I fall / Land of seduction
ND 61045 / Nov '94 / Narada

☐ ROMANCE OF PARIS, THE
La mer: *Trenet, Charles* / La vie en rose: *Piaf, Edith* / Si j'aime Suzy: *Sablon, Jean & Eliane De Creus* / A Paris dans chaque Faubourg: *Gauty, Lys* / Mon cocktail d'amour: *Chevalier, Maurice* / Tant qu'il y aura des etoiles: *Rossi, Tino* / Il ne faut pas briser un reve: *Busch, Eva* / Les pieds dans l'eau: *Sablon, Jean* / De temps en temps: *Baker, Josephine* / Les prenomes effaces: *Tranchant, Jean* / La romance de Paris: *Trenet, Charles* / Prends moi dans tes bras: *Gauty, Lys* / C'est un passe un dimanche: *Chevalier, Maurice* / Le grand frise: *Damia* / La ballade du cordonnier: *Gauty, Lys* / Parce que je vous aime: *Sablon, Jean & Eliane De Creus* / C'est merveilleux: *Piaf, Edith* / Tout me sourit: *Trenet, Charles* / C'est une petite etoile: *Aubert, Jeanne* / Barnabe: *Fernandel* / C'est vrai: *Mistinguett* / Les trois cloches: *Piaf, Edith* / La Marseillaise: *Thill, Georges & Chorus/Band Of The Grand Republicaine*
PASTCD 7819 / Jul '97 / Flapper

☐ ROMANCE OF THE SAX, THE (3CD Set)
Love is all around: *Sinatra, Frank & Gene Kelly* / Whiter shade of pale / Long and winding road / Woman / Lean on me / How deep is your love / Just the way you are / When I fall in love / Said I loved you...but I lied / Candle in the wind / Will you be there / You've lost that loving feeling / Blue eyes / Dreamlover / We've only just begun / One sweet day / I can love you like that / Can I touch you there / Up where we belong / Can you feel the love tonight / Seven seconds / Everlasting love / Talking in your sleep / Anytime you need a friend / I'd lie for you (and that's the truth) / Secret / Holding back the years / All I wanna do / Get on your feet / Forever young / Heal the world / I'd do anything for love / Saturday night / Words / Make it happen / Simply the best / Wind beneath my wings / As tears go by / Close to you / Don't dream it's over / Farewell my summer love / First time ever I saw your face / He ain't heavy he's my brother / True colours / Love is in the air / Greatest love of all / I guess that's why they call it the blues / Way we were / Girl from Ipanema / Goodbye to love / Don't know much / We've got tonight / Without you / Always on my mind
55175 / Oct '97 / Music

☐ ROMANCING THE HARP
When I fall in love / Wonderful tonight / And I love you so / Lady / Tonight I celebrate my love / Spanish eyes / Most beautiful girl in the world / Unchained melody / Love me tender / Mona Lisa / Close to you / True love / Cry me a river / Move closer / Moon river / Greatest love of all
CDMFP 6283 / Jan '97 / Music For Pleasure

☐ ROMANIAN GEMS
Incantation / Prelude d'amour / Romance au Claire De Lune / Frenesia / Fiancailles / Pan danse pour la nymphs sprinz / Complaint d'amour / Caprices au bord de l'eau / Taquineries / Consolation / Allegresse en mineur / Porcession nuptiale
PV 750004 / Jul '94 / Disques Pierre Verany

☐ ROMANTIC CHRISTMAS
DCD 5312 / Dec '93 / Disky

☐ ROMANTIC CLASSICS
DCD 5210 / Jul '92 / Disky

☐ ROMANTIC CLASSICS
DSPCD 104 / Sep '93 / Disky

☐ ROMANTIC CLASSICS
GCC 1002 / Sep '94 / Disky

☐ ROMANTIC CLASSICS BOX SET (3CD Set)
HRCD 8016 / Feb '93 / Disky

☐ ROMANTIC CLASSICS VOL.3
DCD 5279 / Nov '92 / Disky

☐ ROMANTIC CLASSICS VOL.4
DCD 5280 / Feb '93 / Disky

☐ ROMANTIC GUITAR
GRF 240 / Aug '93 / Tring

☐ ROMANTIC GUITAR
Here comes the sun / Bright eyes / Cavatina / Have you ever really love a woman / Heartbreaker / Endless love / Words / Unchained melody / Have you ever really loved a woman / I know him so well / Here, there and everywhere / Without you / Lady in red / Albatross / Imagine / Take that look off your face / Lara's theme (Somewhere my love) / Spanish eyes
CD 6069 / Apr '97 / Music

☐ ROMANTIC GUITAR MOODS (3CD Set)
Careless whisper / My love / Cavatina / All by myself / Last farewell / Feelings / Imagine / Adagio / What a wonderful world / There'll be sad songs / Bilitis / Yesterday / Albatross / At this moment / Long and winding road / Lady in red / Lara's theme / Say you will / Glory of love / I wanna dance with somebody / Always / Midnight / Under the boardwalk / She's like the wind / Could've been / (Sittin' on the) dock of the bay / Take my breath away / Moonlighting / Midnight blue / Just like paradise / Sailing / Mandolin rain / Se la / On my own / Nothing's gonna stop us now / Everybreath you take / Baker street / Save a prayer / Soleado / Here comes the sun / More than I can say / Sara / Heat of the night / Watermelon man / Take that look off your face / Please don't go / Tender love / Strawberry fields forever / Words / Just my imagination / Waiting for a star to fall / Miss you like crazy / As time goes by
390152 / Jul '96 / Hallmark

☐ ROMANTIC GUITARS VOL.2
Love is all around: *Thompson, Keith* / (Everything I do) I do it for you: *Thompson, Keith* / Sara bossa: *Abell, Dick* / Any time at all: *Abell, Dick* / Air that I breathe: *Thompson, Keith* / Romeo and Juliet: *Thompson, Keith* / If you leave me now: *Thompson, Keith* / Rose: *Aprile, J.C.* / I will always love you: *Thompson, Keith* / Wonderful tonight: *Thompson, Keith* / Shadow of your smile: *Angelo Et Ses Guitares* / Think twice: *Thompson, Keith* / Manha de carnaval: *Angelo Et Ses Guitares* / La playa: *Angelo Et Ses Guitares* / Tears in heaven: *Thompson, Keith*
306622 / Jun '97 / Hallmark

☐ ROMANTIC INSTRUMENTAL COLLECTION (3CD Set)
HRCD 8015 / Nov '92 / Disky

☐ ROMANTIC JAZZ VOL.1
Somewhere: *Brubeck, Dave* / Easy to love: *Garner, Erroll* / Goodnight my love: *Vaughan, Sarah* / My funny valentine: *Baker, Chet* / Satin doll: *Hampton, Lionel* / Mood indigo: *Ellington, Duke* / Moonlight serenade: *Miller, Glenn* / Body and soul: *Goodman, Benny* / 'Round midnight: *Davis, Miles* / Summertime: *Holiday, Billie* / I can't stand the rain: *Phillips, Esther* / Fair weather: *Baker, Chet* / Theme from "Summer of 42": *Benson, George* / If I could be with you one hour tonight: *Holiday, Billie* / I've got a message to you: *Laws, Hubert*
4811542 / Dec '95 / Columbia

☐ ROMANTIC JAZZ VOL.2
Time after time: *Davis, Miles* / Medley: *Fitzgerald, Ella* / Bewitched: *Goodman, Benny* / It might as well be Spring: *Vaughan, Sarah* / Night and day: *Ellington, Duke* / It's the same old story: *Holiday, Billie* / You'd be so nice to come home to: *Desmond, Paul* / I got it bad and that ain't good: *Lee, Peggy* / Song is you: *Brubeck, Dave* / Honeysuckle rose: *Armstrong, Louis Allstars* / Come rain or come shine: *Vaughan, Sarah* / Sophisticated lady: *Ellington, Duke* / Am I blue: *Ellington, Duke* / Stella by starlight: *Davis, Miles* / Squeeze me: *Armstrong, Louis Allstars* / Summertime: *Benson, George*
4844812 / Aug '96 / Columbia

☐ ROMANTIC JAZZ VOL.3
When I fall in love: *Washington, Grover Jr.* / Ligia: *Getz, Stan* / Quiet nights of quiet stars: *Bennett, Tony* / When you wish upon a star: *Brubeck, Dave* / Over the rainbow: *Franklin, Aretha* / Sophisticated lady: *Ellington, Duke* / After hours: *Vaughan, Sarah* / She was too good to me: *Baker, Chet* / Where did I go: *McRae, Carmen* / 'Til I get it right: *Whalum, Kirk* / I get along without you very well: *Whalum, Kirk* / Two lonely people: *Evans, B* / I could write a book: *Carter, Betty & Ray Bryant* / Imagine: *Lee, Heiko* / My romance: *Webster, Ben* / Isn't she lovely: *Gordon, Dexter*
4871242 / 26 Jan '98 / Columbia

☐ ROMANTIC LATIN BALLADS
CDHOT 626 / Aug '97 / Charly

☐ ROMANTIC LOVE THEMES
DCD 5300 / Dec '93 / Disky

☐ ROMANTIC PIANO
Where do I begin (Love Story) / I just called to say I love you / You don't bring me flowers / Don't cry for me Argentina / Yesterday / Way we were / How deep is your love / If you leave me now / Feelings / Greatest love of all / Memory / Just the way you are / Power of love / Something / Mandy / Unforgettable / Just the two of us / To all the girls I've loved before / For your eyes only / Let it be
CD 6068 / Apr '97 / Music

☐ ROMANTIC POP MELODIES
DCD 5304 / Dec '93 / Disky

☐ ROMANTIC RAGGA VOL.1
SIDCD 004 / Feb '93 / Sinbad

☐ ROMANTIC RAGGA VOL.2
SIDCD 005 / Feb '94 / Sinbad

☐ ROMANTIC REGGAE
I wanna wake up with you: *Holt, John* / Choose me: *Pierre, Marie* / Moon river: *Greyhound* / You are everything: *Chosen Few* / Stand by me: *Junior Soul* / Sweet inspiration: *Pioneers* / Everything I own: *Boothe, Ken* / Side show: *Biggs, Barry* / Hurt so good: *Cadogan, Susan* / Only a smile: *Brown, Dennis* / Prisoner of love: *Barker, Dave* / All I have is love: *Isaacs, Gregory* / Black pearl: *Faith, Horace* / Spanish harlem: *Edwards, Jackie* / First time ever I saw your face: *Griffiths, Marcia* / Runaway with love: *Charmers, Lloyd* / Crying over you: *Boothe, Ken* / Everybody plays the fool: *Chosen Few* / You make me feel brand new: *Gardiner, Boris* / Still in love: *Ellis, Alton* / Montego bay: *Notes, Freddie & The Rudies* / You are everything to me: *Holt, John* / Let us be: *Thomas, Nicky* / Save the last dance for me: *Heptones*
VSOPCD 133 / May '89 / Connoisseur Collection

☐ ROMANTIC REGGAE MIX VOL.2
BWCD 0018 / 20 Jul '98 / Brickwall

☐ **ROMANTIC ROSES OF IRELAND**
My lovely rose of Clare / Rose of Castlerea / Red is the rose / Rose of Killarney / My rose of the mountain / My lovely Irish rose / Rosie / Rose of mooncoin / Rose of Aranmore / Ringsend rose / Rose of Kilkenny / Connemara rose / Rose of Allendale / Sweet Rosie O'Grady / My wild Irish rose / My beautiful Irish rose
EMPRCD 549 / Nov '94 / Emporio

☐ **ROMANTIC SAX**
MACCD 164 / Aug '96 / Autograph

☐ **ROMANTIC SAX**
Wind beneath my wings / As tears go by / Close to you / Don't dream it's over / Farewell my summer love / First time ever I saw your face / He ain't heavy he's my brother / True colours / Love is in the air / Greatest love of all / I guess that's why they call it the blues / Way we were / Girl from Ipanema / Goodbye to love / Don't know much / We've got tonight / Without you / Always on my mind
CD 6093 / Oct '97 / Music

☐ **ROMANTIC SOUND SAMPLER VOL.2**
EFA 910092 / May '95 / Zillo

☐ **ROMANTICA**
PUTU 1362 / 9 Feb '98 / Putumayo

☐ **RONDELET PUNK SINGLES COLLECTION**
No government: *Anti Pasti* / Two years too late: *Anti Pasti* / Another dead soldier: *Anti Pasti* / Six guns: *Anti Pasti* / Burial: *Fits* / Violent society: *Special Duties* / Colchester Council: *Special Duties* / Bomb scare: *Dead Man's Shadow* / Another Hiroshima: *Dead Man's Shadow* / East to the West: *Anti Pasti* / Muscles: *Membranes* / Police state: *Special Duties* / Go to hell: *Threats* / Fuck the Tories: *Riot Squad* / We are the Riot Squad: *Riot Squad* / Bullshit Crass: *Special Duties* / Riot in the city: *Riot Squad* / Caution in the wind: *Anti Pasti* / Flower in the gun: *Dead Man's Shadow* / High Street Yanks: *Membranes* / Politicians and ministers: *Threats* / Last laugh: *Fits*
CDPUNK 49 / Mar '95 / Anagram

☐ **ROOF INTERNATIONAL**
HCD 7008 / Aug '94 / Hightone

☐ **ROOTS ALL OVER THE GODAMN PLACE**
EFA 800272 / Oct '94 / T-Wah

☐ **ROOTS AND CULTURE (Serious Selections Vol.1)**
True Rastaman (So Jah seh): *Fred Locks* / Wolfs and leopards: *Brown, Dennis* / Forward to Zion: *Abyssinians* / His majesty is coming: *In Crowd* / Prophecy: *Fabian* / Diverse doctrine: *Ras Ibuna* / Tenement yard: *Miller, Jacob* / Rough ole life: *Minott, Sugar* / Kingston 11: *Royal Rasses* / Marcus Garvey: *Burning Spear* / Black is our colour: *Wade, Wayne* / Back to Africa: *Aswad*
CDREG 3 / Jul '95 / Rewind Selecta

☐ **ROOTS AND ROCKERS REGGAE VOL.1**
PWD 7438 / Jun '96 / Pow Wow

☐ **ROOTS DAUGHTERS**
Guide and protect: *Aisha* / Catch the boat: *Live Wya* / English girl: *Sister Audrey* / Free South Africa: *Cross, Sandra* / Fire: *Faybienne* / Until you come back to me: *Just Dale & Robotniks* / Place in the sun: *Kofi* / Mr. Roots man: *Rasheda*
ARICD 039 / Sep '88 / Ariwa Sounds

☐ **ROOTS DUB**
SOCD 50153 / May '97 / Studio One

☐ **ROOTS 'N' CULTURE (21 Mighty Reggae Cuts)**
Right time: *Mighty Diamonds* / Train to Rhodesia: *Big Youth* / Legalize it: *Tosh, Peter* / Rockers time now: *Clarke, Johnny* / International herb: *Culture* / Never get burn: *Twinkle Brothers* / Universal tribulation: *Isaacs, Gregory* / Jah loves: *Abyssinians* / Message from the King: *Prince Far-I* / Soul rebel: *Gladiators* / House of dreadlocks: *Big Youth* / Free Africa: *Twinkle Brothers* / Sun is shining: *Tamlins & Sly Dunbar* / Roots natty roots natty congo: *Clarke, Johnny* / Behold: *Culture* / Declaration of rights: *Clarke, Johnny* / Looks is deceiving: *Gladiators* / Freedom fighters: *Washington, Delroy* / Since I threw the comb away: *Twinkle Brothers* / Africa: *Mighty Diamonds* / It dread inna Inglan: *Johnson, Linton Kwesi*
NSCD 016 / Jul '97 / Nascente

☐ **ROOTS OF ACID JAZZ, THE**
Swing low, sweet Cadillac: *Gillespie, Dizzy* / For mods only: *Hamilton, Chico* / Hard sock dance: *Jones, Quincy* / Stolen moments: *Nelson, Oliver* / Big city: *Horn, Shirley* / Beat goes on: *Szabo, Gabor* / Hold 'em Joe: *Rollins, Sonny* / Winchester Cathedral: *Jones, Hank* / Ciao, ciao: *Turrentine, Stanley* / La podrida: *Barbieri, Gato* / Southern smiles: *Jarrett, Keith* / Creator has a masterplan: *Sanders, Pharoah* / Go Li'l Liza: *Hawkins, Coleman* / Slippin' and slidin': *Lateef, Yusef*
IMP 12042 / Dec '96 / Impulse Jazz

☐ **ROOTS OF DOO WOP**
RTS 33021 / May '90 / Roots

☐ **ROOTS OF GARAGE**
AVEXCD 44 / Jul '96 / Avex

☐ **ROOTS OF INNOVATION**
EFA 186922 / Jun '97 / On-U Sound

☐ **ROOTS OF MODERN JAZZ, THE (The 1948 Sensation Sessions)**
Baggy's blues: *Jackson, Milt & His All Stars* / In a beautiful mood: *Jackson, Milt & His All Stars* / Slits: *Jackson, Milt & His All Stars* / Baggy eyes: *Jackson, Milt & His All Stars* / Nobility bop: *Thompson, Sir Charles* / Yesterdays: *Thompson, Sir Charles* / It's my turn now: *Thompson, Sir Charles* / Charles boogie: *Thompson, Sir Charles* / Don't blame me: *Thompson, Sir Charles* / Robbin's nest: *Thompson, Sir Charles* / In a garden: *Thompson, Sir Charles* / Someone to watch over me: *Thompson, Sir Charles* / You go to my head: *Thompson, Sir Charles* / Relaxin': *Jacquet, Russell & His All Stars* / Lion's roar: *Jacquet, Russell & His All Stars* / Suede Jacquet: *Jacquet, Russell & His All Stars* / Scamper roo: *Jacquet, Russell & His All Stars* / Stardust: *Lord Nelson & His Boppers* / Red shoes: *Lord Nelson & His Boppers* / Body and soul (Time to dream): *Lord Nelson & His Boppers* / Ratio and proportion: *Lord Nelson & His Boppers* / Royal weddings: *Lord Nelson* / Be bop blues: *Lord Nelson* / Fine and Dandy: *Lord Nelson* / Third Song: *Lord Nelson*
CDBOPD 017 / May '94 / Boplicity

☐ **ROOTS OF NORTHERN SOUL, THE (30 All-Nighter Classics From The Early Days)**
Let's go baby (where the action is): *Parker, Robert* / Mr. Bang Bang man: *Little Hank* / Don't mess with my man: *Thomas, Irma* / Roll with the punch: *Shelton, Roscoe* / Walkin' up a one way street: *Tee, Willie* / Love's holiday: *Scott, Peggy & Jo Jo Benson* / Touch me kiss me hold me: *Inspirations* / Fortune teller: *Spellman, Benny* / Nothing's worse than being alone: *Ad Libs* / Sweet and easy: *McCoy, Van Strings* / No sad songs: *Simon, Joe* / Don't talk like that: *Murray, Clarence* / Happy feet: *Parker, Robert* / Getting mighty crowded: *Everett, Betty* / In your heart: *Dontells* / You can't take it away: *Hughes, Freddie* / Sufferin' city: *Johnny & Lilly* / Hard nut to crack: *Neville, Aaron* / Billy's bag: *Preston, Billy* / I caught you in a lie: *Parker, Robert* / You gotta pay the price: *Taylor, Gloria* / Baby you've got it: *Murray, Clarence* / Nothing can stop me: *Chandler, Gene* / Hey sugar: *Dells* / Trouble over the weekend: *Everett, Betty* / Don't let me down: *Hughes, Freddie* / So glad she's mine: *Carter Brothers* / Do you like you do me: *Williams, John* / Hot potato: *Clark, Dee* / I'm evil tonight: *Harris, Betty*
GSCD 083 / Feb '97 / Goldmine

☐ **ROOTS OF OK JAZZ**
CRAW 7 / Jan '96 / Crammed World

☐ **ROOTS OF POWERPOP, THE**
BCD 4060 / Feb '97 / Bomp

☐ **ROOTS OF RAP, THE (Classic Recordings From The 1920's & 1930's)**
YAZCD 2018 / May '96 / Yazoo

☐ **ROOTS OF REGGAE VOL.1, THE**
Soul shakedown party: *Marley, Bob* / Everything I own: *Boothe, Ken* / You can get it if you really want: *Dekker, Desmond* / Black and white: *Greyhound* / Hurt so good: *Cadogan, Susan* / Man in the street: *Drummond, Don* / Barber saloon: *Mikey Dread* / Let me down easy: *Brown, Dennis* / I'm a madman: *Perry, Lee 'Scratch'* / Israelites: *Dekker, Desmond* / Help me make it through the night: *Holt, John* / 54-46 (was my number): *Toots & The Maytals* / Kaya: *Marley, Bob* / Let your yeah be yeah: *Pioneers* / Young, gifted and black: *Bob & Marcia* / Rock me in dub: *Thompson, Linval* / Java: *Pablo, Augustus* / What you gonna do on judgement day: *Prince Far-I*
MCCD 014 / Feb '91 / Music Club

☐ **ROOTS OF REGGAE VOL.1-3, THE (3CD Set)**
MCBX 003 / Sep '95 / Music Club

☐ **ROOTS OF REGGAE VOL.2, THE**
Message to you Rudy: *Livingstone, Dandy* / Train to Skaville: *Ethiopians* / 007: *Dekker, Desmond* / Perfidia: *Dillon, Phyllis* / Liquidator: *Harry J All Stars* / Longshot kick de bucket: *Pioneers* / Phoenix City: *Alphonso, Roland* / Return of Django: *Upsetters* / Confucius: *Skatalites* / Double barrel: *Barker, Dave & Ansell Collins* / Trenchtown rock: *Marley, Bob* / Pressure drop: *Toots & The Maytals* / East of the River Nile: *Pablo, Augustus* / Skinhead moonstomp: *Symarip* / All I have is love: *Isaacs, Gregory* / I shot the sheriff: *Inner Circle* / Hit the road Jack: *Big Youth* / Book of rules: *Heptones* / Three eye gal: *Levy, Barrington* / Blood and fire: *Niney The Observer*
MCCD 041 / Sep '91 / Music Club

☐ **ROOTS OF REGGAE VOL.3, THE**
Caution: *Marley, Bob & The Wailers* / Miss Jamaica: *Cliff, Jimmy* / Monkey man: *Toots & The Maytals* / People funny boy: *Perry, Lee 'Scratch'* / It mek: *Dekker, Desmond* / Pied Piper: *Bob & Marcia* / Suzanne beware of the devil: *Livingstone, Dandy* / Rock steady train: *Evan & Jerry/Carib Beats* / Stop that train: *Tosh, Peter & The Wailers* / Skank in bed: *Scotty* / Keep moving: *Marley, Bob & The Wailers* / Bartender: *Aitken, Laurel* / Whip: *Ethiopians* / Sweet sensation: *Melodians* / Dreader than dread: *Honey Boy Martin* / I'm in the mood for ska: *Lord Tanamo* / Montego bay: *Notes, Freddie & The Rudies* / Oh ba-a-by (sick and tired): *Techniques* / African Queen: *Pablo, Augustus* / Rock steady: *Ellis, Alton*
MCCD 072 / Jun '92 / Music Club

☐ **ROOTS OF RHYTHM AND BLUES 1939-1945, THE (2CD Set)**
FA 050 / Apr '96 / Fremeaux

☐ **ROOTS OF ROCK 'N' ROLL VOL.1 1927-1938, THE (2CD Set)**
FA 351 / Nov '96 / Fremeaux

☐ **ROOTS OF ROCK 'N' ROLL VOL.1, THE (Big Band, Blues & Boogie)**
Flyin' Home: *Hampton, Lionel* / Honeydripper: *Jackson, Bull Moose* / Walk 'em: *Johnson, Budd* / Minnie the moocher: *Calloway, Cab* / Countless blues: *Kansas City Six* / I know my love is true: *Liggins, Joe* / We ain't got nothin' (but the blues): *Jackson, Bull Moose* / Floogie boo: *Williams, Cootie* / If it's good: *Lee, Julia* / I want a tall skinny papa: *Tharpe, Sister Rosetta* / Caldonia: *Jordan, Louis* / Boogie beat'll getcha: *Red Caps* / Bartender boogie: *McVea, Jack* / Boogie woogie stomp: *Ammons, Albert* / Roll 'em Pete: *Turner, Joe & Pete Johnson* / Who threw the whiskey in the well: *Harris, Wynonie* / Rock me: *Tharpe, Sister Rosetta* / Shout sister shout: *Tharpe, Sister Rosetta* / Voot oreene: *Gaillard, Slim* / Hit that jive Jack: *Gant, Cecil* / SK groove: *King, Saunders* / It's all right baby: *Turner, Joe & Pete Johnson* / Slim Gaillard's boogie: *Gaillard, Slim* / Ee-bobaliba: *Trenier, Claude & Big Jim Wynn* / Five guys named moe: *Jordan, Louis* / Rock woogie: *Wiley, Pee Wee & Big Jim Wynn* / I'm woke up now: *Broonzy, 'Big' Bill & Chicago 5* / Dirt road blues: *Crudup, Arthur 'Big Boy'*
PLCD 551 / Nov '96 / President

☐ **ROOTS OF ROCK 'N' ROLL VOL.2, THE (Stompin' Western Swing)**
Easy ridin' Papa: *Brown, Milton & The Brownies* / South Texas Swing: *Hofner, Adolph* / Eyes of Texas: *Boyd, Bill & His Cowboy Ramblers* / Hot time Mama: *Penny, Hank* / Knocky knocky: *Light Crust Doughboys* / Bass man jive: *Stockard, Ocie & his Wanderers* / Oozlin' Daddy blues: *Wills, Bob* / Gettin' that lowdown swing: *Modern Mountaineers* / Hot Mama stomp: *Universal Cowboys* / High geared Daddy: *Davis, Jimmie* / Pipeliner blues: *Modern Mountaineers* / Shame on you: *Cooley, Spade* / Sweet talkin' Mama: *Penny, Hank* / Everybody's tryin' to be my baby: *Newman, Roy* / Southern belle: *Williams, Curly* / No good for nuthin' blues: *Sunshine Boys* / Up jumped the Devil: *Tune Wranglers* / Don't let the deal go down: *O'Daniel, W. Lee & His Hillbilly boys* / Milk cow blues: *Bruner, Cliff* / Hi-flyer stomp: *Hi-Flyers* / Sundown blues: *Texas Wanderers* / Somebody's been using that thing: *Brown, Milton & The Brownies* / Texas stomp: *Newman, Roy* / Bringing home the bacon: *Bruner, Cliff* / Alabama jubilee: *Rice Brothers* / Joe Turner blues: *Hofner, Adolph* / Fort Worth stomp: *Crystal Springs Playboys* / Give me my money: *Blue Ridge Playboys*
PLCD 552 / Nov '96 / President

☐ **ROOTS OF ROCK 'N' ROLL VOL.3, THE (1947/2CD Set)**
FA 353 / Jan '98 / Fremeaux

☐ **ROOTS OF ROCK 'N' ROLL VOL.5, THE (Adam Blew His Hat)**
Adam blew his hat / There's good blues tonight / It's just the blues / Big fat Mama / I want to rock / Flat rock / Milk shake stand / Fine brown frame / Boogie woogie ball / My baby's boogying / Texas stomp / Old Taylor / Down the road apiece / Groovin' boogie / Jack you're dead / Fifth avenue woman / Boogie woogie's mother-in-law / That's the stuff you gotta watch / Come on over to my house / What's the matter with me / Night before judgement day / My lovin' Papa / Buzz buzz buzz / 2.00 am hop / Diggin' my potatoes No.2 / I want my lovin'
PLCD 561 / May '97 / President

☐ **ROOTS OF ROCK 'N' ROLL VOL.7, THE (Stompin' At The Honky Tonk)**
If you can't take five take two: *Brown, Milton & The Brownies* / Sugar: *Bruner, Cliff Texas Wanderers* / Rockin' it back: *Texas Wanderers* / Daddy's got the deep elm blues: *Revard, Jimmie & His Oklahoma Playboys* / You gotta ho-de-ho: *Swift Jewel Cowboys* / Who calls you sweet mama now: *Modern Mountaineers* / Riding to glory now: *Wood, Smokey & The Woodchips* / Cotton eyed Joe: *Wills, Bob & His Texas Playboys* / Tulsa twist: *McBride, Dickie & The Village Boys* / Stompin' at The Honky Tonk: *Dunn, Bob Vagabonds* / Sadie Green (the vamp of New Orleans): *Newman, Roy & his boys* / I love my fruit: *Sweet Violet Boys* / Three way boogie: *Cooley, Spade Orchestra* / Bring it down to my house honey: *Wills, Luke* / Somebody's rose: *Atchison, Tex* / South Texas swing: *Hofner, Adolf & His San Antonians* / Hot as I am: *Saddle Tramps* / You are my sunshine: *Rice Brothers* / Devil's great grandson: *Sons Of The Pioneers* / Al viva tequila: *Ritter, Tex & Sons Of The Pioneers* / Oklahoma stomp: *Cooley, Spade Orchestra* / Mama's getting hot and papa's getting cold: *Davis, Jimmie* / Who's cryin' sweet papa now: *Modern Mountaineers* / Jones stomp: *Port Arthur Jubileers* / New falling rain blues: *Bruner, Cliff & His Boys/Moon Mulligan* / Detour: *Walker, Jimmy*
PLCD 563 / May '97 / President

☐ **ROOTS OF RUMBA ROCK VOL.1 (Zaire Classics Vol.1)**
CRAW 4 / Jan '96 / Crammed World

☐ **ROOTS OF RUMBA ROCK VOL.2**
CRAM 010 / Jul '95 / Crammed Discs

☐ **ROOTS OF SWEDISH POP, THE**
5314862 / Jul '97 / Uppers

☐ **ROOTS OF THE BLUES**
Louisiana: *Ratcliff, Henry* / Field song from Senegal: *Bakari Badji* / Po' boy blues: *Dudley, John* / Katy left Memphis: *Tangle Eye* / Berta berta: *Miller, Leyroy & A Group Of Prisoners* / Old original blues: *McDowell, 'Mississippi' Fred & Miles Pratcher* / Jim and John: *Young, Ed & Lonnie Young* / Emmaline, take your time: *Askew, Alec* / Buttermilk: *Pratcher, Miles & Bob* / Mama Lucy: *Gary, Leroy* / I'm gonna live, anyhow till I die: *Pratcher, Miles & Bob* / No more my lord: *Tangle Eye & A Group Of Prisoners* / Lining hymn and prayer: *Crenshaw, Rev. & The Congregation* / Death comes a creepin' in my room: *McDowell, 'Mississippi' Fred* / Church house moan: *Congregation Of New Brown's Chapel* / Beggin the blues: *Jones, Bessie* / Rolled and tumbled: *Hemphill, Rose & Fred McDowell* / Goin' down to the races: *McDowell, 'Mississippi' Fred & Miles Pratcher/Fannie Davis* / You gotta cut that out: *Forest City Joe*
802522 / Aug '92 / New World

☐ **ROOTS OF UB40, THE (17 Reggae Classics)**
MCCD 276 / Dec '96 / Music Club

☐ **ROOTS PIRANHA**
PIR 482 / Oct '92 / Piranha

☐ **ROOTS REALITY**
Heartache: *Jolly Brothers* / Silver and gold: *Osbourne, Johnny* / Time to unite: *Black Uhuru* / Ain't gonna turn back: *Brown, Barry* / Hell and sorrow: *Ellis, Hortense* / Colly George: *Jones, Frankie* / Last train to Africa: *Prince Alla* / Angel of the morning: *Lara, Jennifer* / Only love can conquer: *Fantells* / Jah Jah blessing: *Fantells* / Right track: *Minott, Sugar* / Dat song: *Castell, Lacksley*
MENT 001CD / Jan '96 / Mention

☐ **ROOTS ROCKERS REGGAE VOL.1**
OK Fred: *Dunkley, Errol* / Sing a little song: *Dekker, Desmond* / Work all day: *Biggs, Barry* / Eighteen yellow roses: *Gardiner, Boris* / Back a yard: *In Crowd* / Johnny too bad: *Suckers* / Thank you Lord: *Max Romeo* / I cried a tear: *Schaffer, Doreen* / Do you really want to hurt me: *Heptones* / Island music: *Calendar, Fip* / Three ring circus: *Biggs, Barry* / Rock my soul: *Biggs, Barry* / Smiling faces: *Holt, John* / I want to wake up with you: *Holt, John* / Sunshine people: *Holt, John* / Elizabethan reggae: *Gardiner, Boris*
EMPRCD 617 / Jun '96 / Emporio

☐ **ROOTS ROCKERS REGGAE VOL.2**
Girlie girlie: *George, Sophia* / Happy anniversary: *Schloss, Cynthia* / Dynamic: *Paula* / Wide awake in a dream: *Biggs, Barry* / Dat: *Shervington, Pluto* / Busted lad: *Dekker, Desmond* / First cut is the deepest: *Penn, Dawn* / Place in the sun: *Winjama* / I don't need your love: *Griffiths, Marcia* / Slave ship: *In Crowd* / Uptown Sharron: *Isaacs, Gregory* / When she was my girl: *Wilson, Delroy* / Land of my birth: *Donaldson, Eric* / Mad about you: *Ruffin, Bruce* / You're no good: *Boothe, Ken* / No woman no cry: *Clarke, Johnny*
EMPRCD 618 / Jun '96 / Emporio

☐ **ROOTS TRADITION FROM THE VINEYARD**
Come on over: *Frazer, Phillip* / Housing scheme: *Peter & Lucky* / Natty roots: *Toyan & Errol Scorcher* / Natty twelve tribe dub / Only jah jah know: *Frazer, Phillip & Toyan* / Sweetest thing: *Sammy Dread* / Vineyard: *Peter & Lucky* / Planter dub / True history: *Taylor, Rod* / Black people: *Toyan* / See a man face: *Ranking, Peter* / Robe: *Little John* / Gun fever: *Toyan* / When I fall in love: *Jah Bible* / Jah Jah knowledge: *Soul Syndicate*
MRCD 1004 / May '97 / Majestic Reggae

☐ **ROOTSMAN SHOWCASE '94**
RMCD 014 / Nov '94 / Roots Man

☐ **ROSA PARKS TRIBUTE**
VTYCD 002 / Mar '96 / Verity

☐ **ROSE OF TRALEE, THE**
MU 5065 / Oct '92 / Musketeer

☐ **ROSES ARE RED, VIOLETS ARE BLUE (Timeless Love Songs)**
Roses are red: *O'Donnell, Daniel* / Donegal shore: *O'Donnell, Daniel* / Mary from Dungloe: *O'Donnell, Daniel* / Grace: *McCann, Jim* / Back in love by Monday: *Lynam, Ray* / Mona Lisa lost her smile: *Lynam, Ray* / Before the next teardrop falls: *McCann, Susan* / Morning glory: *Foster & Allen* / When I dream: *Foster & Allen* / Fields of Athenry: *Reilly, Paddy* / Star of County Down: *Reilly, Paddy* / Red is the rose: *Begley, Philomena* / When you were sweet sixteen: *Fureys & Davey Arthur* / Crazy: *Kelly, Sandy* / Calypso: *Hogan, John* / Pretty little girl from Omagh: *Duncan, Hugo* / Invisible tears: *Williamson, Ann* / Bunch of violets blue: *Big Tom* / Tie that binds: *Durkin, Kathy* / Wild flowers: *Flavin, Mick* / Pal of my cradle days: *Breen, Ann* / Spancil hill: *Duff, Mary*
IHCD 56 / Jul '89 / Irish Heritage

☐ **ROT RECORDS PUNK SINGLES COLLECTION**
Lost cause: *Riot Squad* / I'm OK fuck you: *Riot Squad* / There ain't no solution: *Riot Squad* / Wet dreams: *Clockwork Soldiers* / Flowers in the gun: *Dead Man's Shadow* / Enemy: *Resistance 77* / Model soldier: *Animal Farm* / Shattered glass: *Paranoia* / Last but not least: *Enemy* / Don't criticise: *Patrol* / Russia: *Resistance 77* / Hate the law: *Riot Squad* / Massacred millions: *Varukers* / Will they never learn: *Varukers* / Incisor: *English Dogs* / Boot down the door: *Oi Polloi* / Return to hell: *Skeptix* / Evil will win: *Rattus* / Forward into battle: *English Dogs* / Killed by my mans own hands: *Varukers* / Bloody road to glory: *Rabid* / Boys in blue: *Rejected* / Cider: *Expelled* / Cities: *Cult Maniax*
CDPUNK 40 / Oct '94 / Anagram

☐ **ROTTEN RICH**
VPCD 2060 / 17 Nov '97 / VP

☐ **ROUGH AND FAST**
EFA 127012 / Jan '95 / Riot Beats

☐ **ROUGH GUIDE TO BRAZIL**
Provei: *Lins, Ivan* / Volta da asa branca: *Dominguihos & Convidados* / Baton vermelho: *Ze Paulo* / Negada da lapa: *Tiscatti, Adil* / Isso: *Ribeiro, Rita* / Tchori tchori: *Miranda, Marlui & Uakti* / Danca do maniero pau: *Friere, Paulo* / Taina: *Nascimento, Dinho* / Charles Anjo 45: *Muzenza* / Mil amargos: *Monteiro, Gilberto* / Anabela: *Braz, Renato* / Caymmi mostra ao mundo o que a bahia mangueira tem: *Da Vai-Vai, Thobias* / Voce vai ver: *Andrade, Leny* / Rio de exageros: *Guinga* / E luxo so: *Passos, Rosa* / Dente de ouro: *Papete* / Rondeio dos ventos: *Souza, Cristaldo* / Santos reis: *Branca, Pena & Xavantinho* / Carinhoso: *Nascimento, Joel & Radames Gnattali/Camerata Carioca*
RGNET 1021CD / 13 Apr '98 / World Music Network

☐ **ROUGH GUIDE TO CAJUN AND ZYDECO MUSIC**
One step at a time: *Chenier, Clifton* / Zydeco boogaloo: *Buckwheat Zydeco* / Balfa waltz: *Doucet, David* / La tit chord: *Newman, Jimmy C.* / La misere m'a fait brallier: *Delafose, John & The Eunice Playboys* / Rolling pin: *Beausoleil* / Grande bosco: *LeJeune, Eddie* / Bayou pon pon: *LeJeune, Eddie* / Savoy DTwo step d'amende: *Savoy-Doucet Cajun Band* / Disco et fais do-do: *Daigrepont, Bruce* / BeausoKolinda: *Beausoleil* / Slow horses and fast women: *Nathan & Zydeco Cha Cha's* / La pointe aux pins: *Riley, Steve* / Fiddle stomp: *Read, Wallis 'Cheese'* / Jolie petit Juliette: *Abshire, Nathan & The Pinegrove Boys* / Chicot two step: *California Cajun Orchestra* / J'etais au bal: *Sonnier, Jo El* / Let the good times roll: *Buckwheat Zydeco* / I passed in front of your door: *Menard, D.L.*
RGNET 1028CD / 13 Apr '98 / World Music Network

☐ **ROUGH GUIDE TO CLASSIC JAZZ**
Dr Jazz: *Morton, Jelly Roll & His Red Hot Peppers* / Smoke house blues: *Morton, Jelly Roll & His Red Hot Peppers* / Original dixieland one step: *Original Dixieland Jazz Band* / Dippermouth blues: *Oliver, Joe 'King' & His Creole Jazz Band* / Mr Jelly Lord: *New Orleans Rhythm Kings* / Sugar foot stomp: *Henderson, Fletcher Orchestra* / Potato head blues: *Armstrong, Louis Hot Seven* / West end blues: *Armstrong, Louis Hot Five* / Hear me talking to you: *Rainey, Gertrude 'Ma'* / Nobody knows you when

you're down and out: *Smith, Bessie* / Shake the Jelly-Roll: *Cobb, J.C. & His Grains Of Corn* / Stomp your stuff: *State Street Ramblers* / Pinetop's boogie woogie: *Smith, Pine Top* / Nobody's sweetheart: *McKenzie & Condon's Chicagoans* / Since my girl turned me down: *Beiderbecke, Bix & His Gang* / Beale street blues: *Charleston Chasers* / Imagination: *Mole, Miff Molers* / Makin' friends: *Condon, Eddie* / Minor drag: *Waller, Fats & His Buddies* / Log cabin blues: *Williams, Clarence* / South: *Morton, Benny* / Creole Love call: *Ellington, Duke Orchestra* / Hot and anxious: *Redman, Don & His Orchestra* / New King Porter Stomp: *Henderson, Fletcher*

RGNET 1012CD / May '97 / World Music Network

☐ ROUGH GUIDE TO ENGLISH ROOTS MUSIC, A

Lucky break: *Hank Dogs* / Trip: *Carthy, Eliza & The Kings Of Calicutt* / Sail on by: *Oyster Band* / Claudy banks: *Waterson, Norma & Martin/Eliza Carthy* / Be my rambling woman: *McLeod, Rory* / Gypsy's lullaby/Hawk memories/Coates Hall: *Pigg, Billy* / Begging song: *Carthy, Martin & Dave Swarbrick* / Lord of steam and iron: *Kirkpatrick, John* / Falling slowly: *Coope Boyes & Simpson* / Hopping down in Kent: *Fuller, Louise* / Country life: *Watersons* / Byker Hill: *Barely Works* / Brilliant pebbles: *Edward II* / Yellow dress: *Albion Band* / Red wing polka / Bold fisherman: *Cox, Harry* / Baker: *Tabor, June & Danny Thompson/Savourna Stevenson* / New England: *Bragg, Billy*

RGNET 1018CD / 20 Jul '98 / World Music Network

☐ ROUGH GUIDE TO FLAMENCO

Venta zoraida: *Morente, Enrique* / Mi tempo: *Riqueni, Rafael* / Veloz hacia su sino: *Pardo, Jorge* / Buleria de la mocita/Buleria a palo seco: *La Macanita, Tomasa* / Del molinete: *Linares, Carmen* / Pozo del deseo: *Ketama* / La voz del tiempo: *Tomatito* / Y yo que culpa tengo: *Poveda, Miguel* / Bodas de sangre: *Negra, Pata* / Serrana que te olvidara: *Duquende* / Del calvario: *Soto, Jose* / A quien contarie: *Lobato, Chano* / Dicen de mi: *Benavent, Carles* / A mi tio lele: *Potito* / A mi Manuel: *Habichuela, Pepe* / Nana de colores: *Carrasco, Diego* / Abuello Pacote/Buleria por solea: *El Barullo*

RGNET 1015CD / Sep '97 / World Music Network

☐ ROUGH GUIDE TO IRISH MUSIC

Solid ground: *Keane, Dolores* / Tommy Peoples/ Windmill/Fintan McManus's: *Altan* / Coinleach ghlas an fromhair: *Clannad* / On horseback: *Ivers, Eileen* / Season of mists: *Crawford, Kevin* / Lakes of Pontchartrain: *Deanta* / White petticoat/Kerry jig/ Katy is waiting: *Patrick Street* / Terry Cuz Teahans polka/Murphy's polka/O'Sullivan's polka: *Sliabh Notes* / Molly and Johnny: *Dervish* / Humours of Lissadell/Music in the glen/Johnson's: *Derance, Joe* / Boys of Malin/Gravel walks: *Tourish, Ciaran & Dermot McLaughlin* / Dulman/Charlie O'Neil's highland: *Cran* / Mist on the mountain/Three little drummers': *Larrissey, Brendan* / Untitled/Untitled/ Hand me down the tackle: *O'Donnell, Siobhan & Karen Tween/Andy Cutting* / Colm cille na feile: *Ni Dhomhnaill, Maighread* / Sod of turf/Katie goes to granny: *Murray, Martin* / 'O' Connell's march/ Galway bay hornpipe/Banshee's wail/Over: *Hayes, Martin*

RGNET 1006CD / Sep '96 / World Music Network

☐ ROUGH GUIDE TO NORTH AFRICAN MUSIC

RGNET 1011CD / 27 Oct '97 / World Music Network

☐ ROUGH GUIDE TO REGGAE

Broadway jungle: *Maytals* / Chinatown: *Drummond, Don & The Skatalites* / Tide is high: *Paragons* / Rivers of Babylon: *Melodians* / Too late: *Pablo, Augustus* / Great stone: *King Tubby & The Soul Syndicate* / Conquering lion: *Yabby You & The Prophets* / Slavery days: *Burning Spear* / Fisherman: *Congos* / Warrior charge: *Aswad* / Rough neck: *Isaacs, Gregory* / This a lover's corner: *General Echo* / Entertainment: *Palmer, Tristan* / Cockney translation: *Smiley Culture* / We can work it out: *Davis, janet-Lee & Peter Hunningal* / Living dangerously: *Levy, Barrington & Bounty Killer* / Untold stories: *Buju Banton* / Slave: *Lucky Dube*

RGNET 1016CD / 27 Oct '97 / World Music Network

☐ ROUGH GUIDE TO SALSA

Carruseles: *La Sonora Carruseles* / Pegaso: *Latin Brothers* / Pal bailador: *Arroyo, Joe Y La Verdad* / Azulito: *Bauza, Mario* / El lenguaje del son: *Ritmo Y Candela/Patato* / Guateque campesino: *Conjunto Campesino Cuyaguateje* / Se quema la chumbamba: *Familia Valera Miranda* / Mulence: *Cubanismo* / Mulata coqueta: *D'Leon, Oscar* / Del monton: *La Sonora Dinamita* / Manyoma: *Fruko Y Sus Tesos* / LALa negra tomasa: *Grupo El Organo Pinareno* / Tumbao a peruchin: *Rodriguez, Alfredo* / Fiesta a la king: *Palmieri, Charlie*

RGNET 1017CD / 27 Oct '97 / World Music Network

☐ ROUGH GUIDE TO SCOTTISH MUSIC

Ballavanich: *Wolfstone* / Chi mi'n greamhradh: *MacPhee, Catherine-Anne* / Claire in heaven: *Capercaillie* / 8 Step waltz: *Iron Horse* / Seinn O: *MacKenzie, Talitha* / Wigtown fanfare: *Ring 'O' Steall* / Scotts Callan O'Bonnie Dundee: *Cast* / Erin-go-bragh: *Gaughan, Dick* / Unicorn set: *Tannahill Weavers* / Midwinter waltz: *Boys Of The Lough* / Sally Gardens: *Heywood, Heather* / Mairead nan cuiread: *Tannas* / Bob Parsons strathspey: *Tannas* / Galicia revisited: *Ceolbeg* / Brown milk maid: *Ceolbeg* / Dunnottar castle: *Ceolbeg* / Maid of Glengarrysdale: *Ceolbeg* / Disused railway: *Battlefield Band* / Just a dream: *Jansch, Bert* / Malcolm Ferguson: *Old Blind Dogs* / Finbar Saunders: *Old Blind Dogs*

RGNBET 1004CD / May '96 / World Music Network

☐ ROUGH GUIDE TO THE MUSIC OF CUBA

En casa del Trompo No Bailes: *Orquesta Riverside* / Rucu Rucu a Santa Clara: *Irakere* / Santa Barbara: *Gonzalez, Celina* / Un meneito na mas: *Vieja Trova Santiaguera* / A Orillas del Cauto: *Saquito, Nico* / Descarga en Faux: *Ritmo Y Candela* / Amiga Mia: *Los Van Van* / Oyelo Sonar: *Bellita* / Descarga Numero dos: *O'Farrill, Chico & Allstars Cubano* / Mambo Rincon: *Bauza, Mario* / Dundunbanza: *Sierra Maestra* / Elegba: *Ros, Lazaro* / El Vendedor de Agua: *Valera Miranda Family* / Alafia: *Conjunto Cespedes* / Caballo Viejo: *Estudiantina Invasora* / Tinguiti 'ta Durmiendo: *Los Terry*

RGNET 1022CD / 26 Jan '98 / World Music Network

☐ ROUGH GUIDE TO THE MUSIC OF INDIA AND PAKISTAN

RGNET 1008CD / Oct '96 / World Music Network

☐ ROUGH GUIDE TO THE MUSIC OF KENYA AND TANZANIA

RGNET 1007CD / Oct '96 / World Music Network

☐ ROUGH GUIDE TO THE MUSIC OF PORTUGAL, A

Saudades de coimbra: *Alfonso, Jose* / Fado da sina: *Dulce Pontes* / Cancao do Gaitero: *Realejo* / Verdes sao os campos: *Carvalho, Teresa Silva* / Despertar: *Paredes, Carlos* / Ai mouraria: *Rodrigues, Amalia* / Conta danca I: *Vai De Roda* / O rapaz do cosaquito: *Terra A Terra* / Decadas: *V Imperio* / Barquinho do mar: *Lendas & Mitos* / Avenidas: *Anabela* / Quem o fado Calunia: *Da Fe, Maria* / Fala da mulher sozinha: *Bessa, Margarida* / Menina estas a Janela: *Vitorino* / Fado em cinco Estilos: *De Noronha, Marie Teresa* / Sou um fado desta idade: *Gentil, Lenita* / Maldito fado: *Zel, Carlos* / A alma do ganhao: *De Almeida, Carlos* / Cravo roxo: *Ronda Dos Quatro Caminhos* / E na vila di Redondo: *Grupo Cantadores Do Redondo* / Grandola Vila Morena: *Alfonso, Jose*

RGNET 1025CD / 20 Jul '98 / World Music Network

☐ ROUGH GUIDE TO THE MUSIC OF SOUTH AFRICA

Nigizongena Kanjani: *Izingqungqulu Zomhlaba* / Nyamphemphe: *Mahlathini & The Mahotella Queens* / Groovin' jive no.1: *Khanyile, Noise & The Jo'burg City Stars* / House of exile: *Lucky Dube* / Motherland: *Chaka Chaka, Yvonne* / My kind of jazz: *Tebogo* / Meva: *Mashiyane, Spokes* / Jive township: *African Jazz Pioneers* / Yaze yangala: *Elite Swingsters* / Celebration: *Mseleku, Bheki* / Ungithatha Kanjani: *West Nkosi* / Udlame: *Soul Brothers* / Tsotsi: *Boyoyo Boys* / Inkomo Zodwa: *Makeba, Miriam & The Skylarks* / Mbube: *Linda, Solomon & Original Evening Birds* / Kangivumanga: *Ladysmith Black Mambazo*

RGNET 1020CD / 26 Jan '98 / World Music Network

☐ ROUGH GUIDE TO THE MUSIC OF THE ANDES

RGNET 1009CD / Oct '96 / World Music Network

☐ ROUGH GUIDE TO THE MUSIC OF ZIMBABWE

RGNET 1010CD / Oct '96 / World Music Network

☐ ROUGH GUIDE TO WEST AFRICAN MUSIC

RGNET 1002CD / Oct '95 / World Music Network

☐ ROUGH GUIDE TO WORLD MUSIC, THE

Rebellion: *Arroyo, Joe* / Sama rew: *Africando* / Dugu kamelenba: *Sangare, Oumou* / Zaiko wa wa: *Zaiko Langa L* / Diandioli: *De Dakar, Etoile* / Rwanamiza: *Kayirebwa, Cecile* / Jono: *Tarika* / Tsaiky mboly hely: *Georges, Roger* / Henna: *Kuban, Ali Hassan* / Goodbye again: *Yue, Guo & Joji Hirota* / Tanola nomads: *Sainkho* / Khosid wedding dances: *Muszikas* / When I'm up I can't get down: *Oyster Band* / Hot tamale baby: *Buckwheat Zydeco* / Theid mi ddhach: *MacKenzie, Talitha*

RGNET 1001CD / Oct '94 / World Music Network

☐ ROUGH STUFF

Rock baby rock: *Hicks, Bob* / Teenage baby: *Anderkin, Lonnie* / Pink shoes: *Matts, Merle* / Ready to go steady: *King, Jack* / Lovin' at night: *Accent* / Everybody rocks: *Tiny Morrie* / I'm a wise ole cat: *Mitchell, Thomas* / Walking blues: *Beach, Ray* / Grandpa's rock: *Trailblazers* / Tell 'em: *Anderkin, Lonnie* / My little jewel: *Beam, Tommy 'Jim'* / Babystiin' all the time: *Hicks, Bob* / Somebody's stealin' my baby: *White, Roger* / Have heart will love: *King, Jack* / Shake with me baby: *Matts, Merle* / Tell me baby: *Smith, Billy* / Pinch me quick: *Smith, Jimmy* / Boppin' the stroll: *Welz, Joey* / She told a lie: *Mishoe, Watson* / Walking out: *Bryan, Jerry* / Little boogie ding dong: *Chewing Ray* / Study hall blues: *Rockin' Rebels* / That's the way: *Clendening, Jimmie & Keetie Kats* / Stomping to the beat: *Wolf* / Jo jo rock 'n' roll: *Martin, Bobby* / Thinkin' about you: *Rhythm Rockers* / Rock 'n' roll blues: *Blattner, Jules* / Oh my Linda: *Holt, Jim* / Tuff-e-nuff baby: *Keynotes* / Fluffy dog: *Pack, Charlie*

CDBB 55065 / Oct '97 / Buffalo Bop

☐ ROUGH TECHNIQUE VOL.1

FNTCD 3 / 20 Jul '98 / Freskanova

☐ ROULETTE ROCK 'N' ROLL COLLECTION VOL.1

Satellite: *Tate, Joe* / I'm free: *Tate, Joe* / Rock 'n' roll Mama: *Tate, Joe* / I guess it's love: *Tate, Joe* / I got a rocket in my pocket: *Lloyd, Jimmy* / You're gone baby: *Lloyd, Jimmy* / Where the Rio de Rosa flows: *Lloyd, Jimmy* / Rock-a-bop-a-lina: *Hart, Billy & Don* / Hole in my bucket: *Davis, Bob* / Rock to the music: *Davis, Bob* / Never anymore: *Davis, Bob* / Leapin' guitar: *Chapparals* / Goin' wild: *Isle, Jimmy* / Baby take me back: *Larue, Roc* / You've got what it takes: *Strickland, Johnnie* / That's baby: *Strickland, Johnnie* / Sweet talkin' baby: *Strickland, Johnnie* / Crazy about you: *Malloy, Vince* / Hubba hubba ding dong: *Malloy, Vince* / Girls, girls, girls: *Hammer, Jack* / Private property: *Lanier, Don* / Ponytail girl: *Lanier, Don* / Only one: *Roberts, Don 'Red'* / Goin' back to St. Louis: *Vickery, Mack* / Romeo Joe: *Skee Brothers* / Daisy Mae: *Dio, Andy*

NEMCD 619 / Jul '92 / Sequel

☐ ROULETTE ROCK 'N' ROLL COLLECTION VOL.2

Strange: *Hawkins, Screamin' Jay* / Whammy: *Hawkins, Screamin' Jay* / Bloodshot eyes: *Harris, Wynonie* / Sweet Lucy Brown: *Harris, Wynonie* / Spread the news: *Harris, Wynonie* / Saturday night: *Harris, Wynonie* / Josephine: *Harris, Wynonie* / Did you get the message: *Harris, Wynonie* / Everybody's gonna rock 'n' roll: *Isley Brothers* / I wanna know: *Isley Brothers* / Drag: *Isley Brothers* / Rockin' McDonald: *Isley Brothers* / 7-11: *Gone All Stars* / Screamin' Ball at Dracula Hall: *Duponts* / Hippy dippy Daddy: *Cookies* / Roll over Beethoven: *Four Chaps* / Hindu baby: *Emanons* / Ding dong: *Echoes* / Woo woo train: *Valentines* / Dance with me: *Chaperones* / Ain't you gonna: *Powell, Jimmy & the Caddies* / Alabama rock 'n' roll: *King, Mabel*

NEMCD 670 / Jun '94 / Sequel

☐ ROULETTE ROCK 'N' ROLL COLLECTION VOL.3

You're driving me mad: *Campbell, Jo Ann* / Don't say maybe: *Roberts, Don 'Red'* / Come dance with me: *Ackoff, Bob* / Don't stop: *Trider, Larry* / Ha ha song: *Trider, Larry* / Sittin' at home with the blues: *Elgin, Johnny* / High school blues: *Vickery, Mack* / Hot dog: *Lee, Curtis* / Sweetness: *Lanier, Don* / Need your love: *Lanier, Don* / Hey doll baby: *Kelly, Pat* / Cloud 13: *Kelly, Pat* / Patsy: *Kelly, Pat* / Glow of love: *Moonlighters* / Broken heart: *Moonlighters* / School bus: *Shades* / Baby baby: *Shades* / Jeri Lee: *Shades* / Guitar hop: *Shades* / I looked for you: *Gracie, Charlie* / Race: *Gracie, Charlie* / Sorry for you: *Gracie, Charlie* / Scenery: *Gracie, Charlie* / Wassa matter with you baby: *Campbell, Jo Ann*

NEMCD 754 / Aug '95 / Sequel

☐ ROULETTE ROCK'N'ROLL COLLECTION VOL.4 (Lotta Boppin')

Party doll: *Hawkins, Screamin' Jay* / Party doll: *Hawkins, Screamin' Jay* / Whammy: *Hawkins, Screamin' Jay* / Hard day's night: *Hawkins, Screamin' Jay* / Hard day's night: *Hawkins, Screamin' Jay* / Hard day's night: *Hawkins, Screamin' Jay* / Feast of the Mau Mau: *Hawkins, Screamin' Jay* / Feast of the Mau Mau: *Hawkins, Screamin' Jay* / Feast of the Mau Mau: *Hawkins, Screamin' Jay* / Long, long walk: *Rivers, Johnny* / Baby come back: *Rivers, Johnny* / That's rock'n'roll: *Rivers, Johnny* / One man woman: *Rivers, Johnny* / Lover's plea: *Vickery, Mack* / Meant to be: *Vickery, Mack* / My kind of woman: *Haley, Bill & The Comets* / Spanish twist: *Haley, Bill & The Comets* / Checkmated and bingoed: *Hart, Billy & Don* / I'm not ashamed: *Larue, Roc* / Rockabilly yodel: *Larue, Roc* / I've heard that line before: *Strickland, Johnnie* / Don't leave me lonely: *Strickland, Johnnie* / Fool's hall of fame: *Strickland, Johnnie* / I was born to rock: *Rock-a-Teens* / Doggone it baby: *Rock-a-Teens* / Dance to the bop: *Rock-a-Teens* / Story of a woman: *Rock-a-Teens* / Janis will rock: *Rock-a-Teens* / That's my Mama: *Rock-a-Teens* / Lotta boppin': *Rock-a-Teens*

NEMCD 921 / Jul '97 / Sequel

☐ 'ROUND MIDNIGHT

Let there be love: *Cole, Nat 'King'* / Manhattan: *Fitzgerald, Ella* / My baby just cares for me: *Simone, Nina* / Your love is king: *Sade* / Desafinado: *Getz, Stan* / Air on a G string: *Loussier, Jacques* / Very thought of you: *Bennett, Tony* / Call me irresponsible: *Washington, Dinah* / Imagination: *Eckstine, Billy* / I get a kick out of you: *Holiday, Billie* / Unsquare dance: *Brubeck, Dave* / Shiny stockings: *Basie, Count* / Makin' whoopee: *Armstrong, Louis & Oscar Peterson* / Lover man: *Vaughan, Sarah* / When I fall in love: *Webster, Ben* / 'Round midnight: *Torme, Mel* / Meditation: *Gilberto, Astrud* / Lullaby of Birdland: *Shearing, George* / Cat: *Smith, Jimmy* / What's new: *Benson, George*

5164712 / Sep '93 / Verve

☐ ROUND TOWER MUSIC VOL.1

If that's the way you want it / Past the point of rescue / Jesus in a leather jacket / Ordinary town / Fabulous thunderbirds / Putting me in the ground / Only dancing / Drive-in movies / Sister and brother / My love is in America / Lead the knave / Refugee from heaven / Limbo people / Walking on seashells / My love is yours

RTMCD 33 / Dec '91 / Round Tower

☐ ROUND TOWER MUSIC VOL.2

RTMCD 70 / Jun '96 / Round Tower

☐ ROUND TOWER SAMPLER

RTMCD 87 / Feb '97 / Round Tower

☐ ROUNDER BANJO

ROUCD 11542 / '88 / Rounder

☐ ROUNDER BLUEGRASS GUITAR

ROUCD 11576 / Feb '97 / Rounder

☐ ROUNDER EUROPE BLUES REVUE (3CD Set)

I had a dream: *Ealey, Robert* / Santa's messin with the kid: *Campbell, Eddie C.* / Soul that's been abused: *Sumlin, Hubert & Mighty Sam* / Baby that what you want me to do: *Holmes Brothers* / Get outta my way: *Smith, Byther* / My abay told me: *Hughes, Joe* / I want to keep you: *Clark, W.C.* / Beatrice, Beatrice: *Walker, Philip* / Missing person: *Funderburgh, Anson & Sam Myers* / Black bottom: *Ward, Robert* / How long: *Legendary Blues Band* / Blues for breakfast: *Clearwater, Eddy* / Nobody's fool: *Shannon, Preston* / Can't see for lookin': *Kubek, Smokin' Joe Band* / Eddie's gospel groove: *Earl, Ronnie* / Shuck 'n' jive: *Boyack, Pat & The Prowlers* / Stranger blues: *Harman, James Band* / I don't wanna know: *Lamont Cranston Blues Band* / Bones in the closet: *Suhler, Jim & Monkey Beat* / Rainy day women: *Little Mike & The Tornados* / Worried no more: *Morgan, Mike & The Crawl* / Lover and a friend: *Welch, Mike* / Baby please set a date: *Thorogood, George & The Destroyers* / Bad boy: *Zinn, Rusty* / Bad poker hand: *Primich, Gary* / Shoulda coulda woulda: *Robillard, Duke* / Feeling good: *Piazza, Rod & The Mighty Flyers* / You're so mean to me: *Willson, Michelle* / Peaches tree: *Hummel, Mark* / One hundred miles: *Hawkins, Ted* / Step it up and go: *Rishell, Paul & Annie Raines* / Guess I'll walk alone: *Thomas, Jesse* / That's alright: *King, Freddie* / Ride that train: *Ball, Tom & Kenny Sultan* / I can hardly get along: *Brozman, Bob* / It hurt's me too: *Hammond, John* / Worried life blues: *Little Antony & Sugar Ray* / Like a shotgun: *Block, Rory* / Sweet home Chicago: *Pitchford, Lonnie* / Pretty thing: *Dyer, Johnny* / Baby couldn't be found: *Little Buster* / Members only: *Persuasions* / I'm good: *Amundson, Monti*

CBHCD 5013 / May '97 / CRS

☐ ROUNDER FIDDLE

ROUCD 11565 / Dec '90 / Rounder

☐ ROUNDER GUITAR

ROUCD 11541 / '88 / Rounder

☐ ROUNDER OLD TIME MUSIC

ROUCD 11510 / '88 / Rounder

☐ ROUTE 66 (A Musical Journey Thru America's Heartland - 2CD/MC Set)

Route 66 / Tous les temps en temps / Southbound train / Key to the highway / Ain't that the blues / Pick-up boogie / Flying on the wings of America / Country boy with a rock and roll heart / Wreck of the ol' 43 / Border song / My West Virginia home / Hobo's lullabye / Saturday rolling around / Baby, what you want me to do / Blues don't love you / Long and lonesome cry / Bottleneck blues / Promised land / Baby let me follow you down / Country blues / Down in the Lafayette / Crawdaddy stomp / Factory / Soul man / Memphis blues / Song for Doc / Hey hey hey / I still miss someone / Shenandoah / Creole hoedown / Leve tes fenetres haut / Treat her right / Bourbon Street march / Knockin' on Heaven's door

330072 / Jul '96 / Hallmark

☐ ROUTES FROM THE JUNGLE

We are E: *Lennie Di Ice* / Waking up: *Nicolette* / You held my hand: *Manix* / Open your mind: *Foulplay* / Last action hero: *DJ Doc Scott* / Bludclot artattack: *Ed Rush* / Secret summer fantasy: *Bodysnatch* / Dark strangers: *Boogie Times Tribe* / Nazinja nazaka: *Guy Called Gerald* / Music box: *Roni Size* / Deeper love: *Dillinja* / Apollo 9: *Jo* / Believe: *E-Z Rollers* / Flowers: *Flynn & Flora* / Feel it: *Randall & Andy C* / Wrinkles in time: *4 Hero* / Droppin' science Vol.2: *Droppin' Science* / Asian love dance: *DJ Krust*

VTDCD 46 / Apr '95 / Virgin

☐ ROXCALIBUR

No point runnin': *Black Rose* / Brands hatch: *Brands Hatch* / Burn this town: *Battleaxe* / Oppression: *Satan* / Battlefield: *Marauders* / Wings of the night: *Unter den Linden* / Exodus: *Skitzofrenik* / Battleaxe: *Battleaxe* / Woman of the night: *Marauders* / Ridin' high: *Black Rose* / Man at the bottom: *Unter den Linden* / Keep right on: *Skitzofrenik* / Executioner: *Satan* / No return: *Brands Hatch*

CDMETAL 15 / 13 Oct '97 / Anagram

☐ ROYAL MEMPHIS SOUL (4CD Set)

HIBOOK 11 / Feb '97 / Hi

☐ ROYAL PALACE OF YOGYAKARTA, JAVA

C 560069CD / Jul '95 / Ocora

☐ ROYAL TOURNAMENT 1989

Firebird suite / I don't want to join the Air Force / Bold aviator was dying / Another thousand revs wouldn't do him any harm / There were three huns sat on his tail / I left the mess room early / Far far away / Glory flying regulations / RAF march past / Bonnie Dundee / Old Towler / Garry Owen / Hunting the hare / Round the Marble Arch / Come lasses and lads / Galloping major / Light cavalry / Post horn gallop / John Peel / Campbells are coming / Royal Artillery slow march / Keel row / In the mood / Little brown jug / String of pearls / Moonlight serenade / St. Louis blues march / Bugle calls from St. Mary's church / Cracow / Sky eagles / March march Polonia / Brothers it is time to fight / Uhlans have come / War, my little war / How nice it is on a little war / March of the 1st brigade / Oka / Victory victory / General Maczek's salute / General salute / Fanfare - Oranges and lemons / Maybe it's because I'm a Londoner / Heart of oak / HMS Pinafore / All the nice girls love a sailor / Alla Marcia / Glorious victory / Bond of friendship / Trumpet prelude / Symphony no. 3 in C minor / Last post and evening hymn / Hands across the sea / National anthem

BNA 5089 / Aug '89 / Bandleader

☐ ROYAL TOURNAMENT 1990

Fanfare / Sea solider / British Grenadiers / Belle Isle / Early one morning / Soldier an' solder too / Symphonic marches of John Williams / Cockleshell heroes / Begone dull care / Heaven in my hand / Love in the first degree / Better the devil you know / I should be so lucky / Too many broken hearts / Heart of oak / HMS Pinafore / All the nice girls love a sailor / Caernarvon Castle / Sarie Marais / Blue devils / Semper fidelis / Sing sing sing / Apotheosis / Song of the Marines / Follow me / HM Jollies / Finalanda / Dear Lord and Father of mankind / Sunset / Britannic salute / National anthem / Life on the ocean wave

BNA 5090 / '91 / Bandleader

☐ ROYAL TOURNAMENT 1991

BNA 5091 / Jun '91 / Bandleader

☐ ROYAL TOURNAMENT 1993

BNA 5093 / Aug '93 / Bandleader

☐ ROYAL TOURNAMENT 1994

BNA 5094 / Jul '94 / Bandleader

☐ ROYAL TOURNAMENT 1996 (2MC Set)

BNA 5096 / Jul '96 / Bandleader

☐ ROYALTY & EMPIRE (Patriotic Classics From UK's Military Bands/2CD Set)

Rule Brittania: *Royal Marines* / Crown imperial: *Life Guards Band* / Silver bugles: *Light Infantry Bands* / Birdcage walk: *Blues & Royals Band* / Orb and sceptre: *Life Guards Band* / Governors guard: *Light Infantry Bands* / India/Arabia: *Yorkshire Volunteers* / Navy day: *Royal Marines* / Vivat regina: *Light Division* / God bless the Prince Of Wales: *Queen's Dragoon Guards* / Gibraltar: *Royal Marines* / Royal ceremony: *RAOC Staff Band* / Abide with me: *Queen's Royal*

Hussars / Here's a health unto her majesty: *Blues & Royals Band* / Standard of St. George: *Blues & Royals Band* / Royal standard: *Royal Engineers* / I was glad: *Coldstream Guards Choir* / Fame and glory: *Royal Engineers* / Fantasy on British sea songs: *Central Band Of Royal British Legion* / Jerusalem: *Central Band Of Royal British Legion* / Spirit of pageantry: *Prince Of Wales Yorkshire Regiment* / Imperial echoes: *Royal Marines* / Glorious victory: *Queen's Dragoon Guards* / Britannic salute: *Royal Marines* / Land of hope and glory: *Royal Marines* / Day thou gavest and last post: *Burma Band*

330472 / Mar '97 / Hallmark

☐ **RUBAB ET DUTAR (Music From Afghanistan)**

C 560080 / Dec '95 / Ocora

☐ **RUCKUS JUICE AND CHITLINS VOL.1**

Low down blues: Whistler's Jug Band / Giving it away: *Birmingham Jug Band* / Cocaine habit blues: *Memphis Jug Band* / Try and treat her right: *Harris, John* / Ferguson, Ben / Glad and sorry blues: *Harris, John* / What's that taste like gravy: *King David's Jug Band* / Newport blues: *Cincinnati Jug Band* / Big railroad blues: *Cannon's Jug Stompers* / Fourth street mess around: *Memphis Jug Band* / Banjoreno: *Dixieland Jug Blowers* / Tear it down: *King David's Jug Band* / Ticket agent blues: *Lewis, Noah Jug Band* / You ought to move out of town: *Davenport, Jed & Beale Street Jug Band* / Cold from bed: *Kelly, Jack & His South Memphis Jug Band* / Bill Wilson: *Birmingham Jug Band* / Cash money blues: *Clifton, Kaiser* / That's my rabbit my dog caught it: *Walter Family* / Spiders next: *Memphis Jug Band* / She's in the graveyard now: *McDonald, Earl Original Louisville Jug Band* / Please don't holler mama: *Ferguson, Ben* / Vamps of 28: *Whistler's Jug Band* / Rukus juice and chittlin': *Memphis Jug Band*

YAZCD 2032 / 9 Mar '98 / Yazoo

☐ **RUCKUS JUICE AND CHITLINS VOL.2**

Bring it with you when you come: *Cannon's Jug Stompers* / German blues: *Birmingham Jug Band* / Selling the jelly: *Lewis, Noah Jug Band* / You may leave but this will bring you back: *Memphis Jug Band* / Walkin' cane stomp: *Kentucky Jug Band* / Rising sun blues: *King David's Jug Band* / Old folks started it: *Wallace, Minnie* / Memphis shake: *Dixieland Jug Blowers* / Stealin' stealin': *Memphis Jug Band* / Sweet potato blues: *King David's Jug Band* / RFC blues: *Kelly, Jack & His South Memphis Jug Band* / Brown jug blues: *Buzzington, Ezra Rustic Revellers* / Last chance blues: *Cannon's Jug Stompers* / He's in the jailhouse now: *Memphis Jug Band* / George Street stomp: *Cincinnati Jug Band* / Casey Bill: *McDonald, Earl Original Louisville Jug Band* / Greenville strut: *Mississippi Sarah & Daddy Stovepipe* / Boodle and shake: *Dixieland Jug Blowers* / Jug band special: *Whistler's Jug Band* / Smackin' the sax: *Louisville, Phillips Jug Band* / What makes my baby cry: *Five Harmaniacs* / Piccolo blues: *Davenport, Jed & Beale Street Jug Band* / Jug rag: *Prairie Ramblers*

YAZCD 2033 / 9 Mar '98 / Yazoo

☐ **RUDE AWAKENING VOL.1, THE**

AWAKE 1CD / Jun '89 / Beechwood

☐ **RUDE AWAKENING VOL.2, THE**

AWAKE 2CD / Jul '90 / Beechwood

☐ **RUDIES ALL ROUND**

Don't be a rude boy: *Rulers* / Rudie gets plenty: *Spanishtonians* / Preacher: *Ellis, Alton* / Blam blam fever: *Valentines* / Soldiers take over: *Rio Grandes* / Curfew: *Aitken, Bobby* / Copasetic: *Rulers* / Rudie bam bam: *Clarendonians* / Cool off rudies: *Morgan, Derrick* / Denham town: *Winston & George* / Drop the ratchet: *Cole, Stranger* / Blessings of love: *Ellis, Alton* / Rude boy train: *Dekker, Desmond* / Beware: *Overtakers* / Rudies all round: *White, Joe* / Rudies are the greatest: *Pioneers* / Stop the violence: *Valentines* / What can I say: *Tartans* / Judge Dread in court: *Morgan, Derrick* / Set them free: *Perry, Lee 'Scratch'*

CDTRL 322 / Mar '94 / Trojan

☐ **RUDIE'S CHOICE VOL.1**

CDBM 116 / Jul '96 / Blue Moon

☐ **RUDIE'S CHOICE VOL.2**

Clipper: *Rodriguez, Rico* / Pork pie hat: *Aitken, Laurel* / It sucks: *Big 5* / Ska beat boogie: *International Beat* / Market trading: *One Step Behind* / Home and family: *Rodriguez, Rico* / Sexy boogie: *Aitken, Laurel* / Yeah yeah yeah: *International Beat* / Universe: *Big 5* / Reselecterization: *Selecter* / Embarassment: *One Step Behind* / Lamsbread: *Rodriguez, Rico*

CDBM 126 / 23 Jan '98 / Blue Moon

☐ **RUDIE'S NIGHT OUT**

On my radio: *Selecter* / Are you ready: *International Beat* / Orange Street: *Big 5* / James Bond: *Selecter* / Too nice to talk to: *International Beat* / Live injection: *Big 5* / Too much pressure: *Selecter* / Hard world: *International Beat* / Big 5: *Big 5* / Jackpot: *International Beat* / Can can: *Big 5* / Train to Skaville: *Selecter*

CDBM 104 / Jun '95 / Blue Moon

☐ **RUF DIAMONDS VOL.1**

RUF 012CD / Jan '97 / Ruf Beats

☐ **RUFF CUT (The Original & Authentic Sound Of Jah Works)**

RUSCD 8230 / Feb '97 / ROIR

☐ **RUFF RAGGA**

RNCD 2052 / Mar '94 / Rhino

☐ **RUFFNECK COLLECTION VOL.4**

RUF 49 / 28 Jan '98 / Ruff Neck

☐ **RUFFNECK COLLECTION VOL.6**

RUF 037 / Oct '96 / Ruff Neck

☐ **RUGBY SONGS**

Swing low, sweet chariot / Bye bye blackbird / She's the most immoral lady / If I were the marrying kind / Here's to the good old beer / Good ship Venus / Ivan Skavinski Skavar / Madamoiselle from Armentier / Ring dang doo / Ram from Derbyshire / Dinha Dinha show us your leg / In the shade of the old apple tree / Sing us another one / Horndean school / Doggies meeting / Roll me over / Quartermaster's stores / There was an old segeant / Mayor of Bayswater / In mobile / Poor old Angeline / Bye bye blackbird (version 2) / Bring back seven old ladies / Swing low, sweet Chariot (reprise)

C5MCD 571 / Feb '95 / See For Miles

☐ **RUN RHYTHM RUN (Instrumental Scorchers From Treasure Isle.)**

CDHB 104 / Sep '96 / Heartbeat

☐ **RUNNIN' WILD (The Original Sounds Of The Jazz Age 1921-1931)**

Running wild: *Ellington, Duke* / Loveable and sweet: *Hanshaw, Annette* / There's a rainbow 'round my shoulder: *Jolson, Al* / My song: *Vallee, Rudy* / Heebie jeebies: *Boswell Sisters* / Loveless love: *Waller, Fats* / Magnolia: *California Ramblers* / Any old time: *Rodgers, Jimmie* / Egyptian Ella: *Lewis, Ted* / How many times: *Lucas, Nick* / She's got 'It': *Weems, Ted* / Makin' whoopee: *Whiteman, Paul* / California here I come: *Edwards, Cliff* / Me: *Etting, Ruth* / Four or five times: *McKinney's Cotton Pickers* / Without that gal: *Austin, Gene* / Home again blues: *Original Dixieland Jazz Band* / Lindy: *Original Dixieland Jazz Band* / Oh you have no idaea: *Tucker, Sophie* / You brought a new kind of love to me: *Chevalier, Maurice* / St. James Infirmary: *Bloom, Rube* / Three little words: *Crumit, Frank* / Painting the clouds with sunshine: *Hylton, Jack*

CDAJA 5017 / Jan '96 / Living Era

☐ **RURAL BLUES**

157182 / Feb '93 / Blues Collection

☐ **RURAL BLUES 1934-1956**

DOCD 5223 / Apr '94 / Document

☐ **RURAL STRING BANDS OF TENNESSEE**

Greenback dollar: *Weems String Band* / Everybody two step: *Roane County Ramblers* / Tennessee mountain fox chase: *Vance's Tennessee Breakdowners* / Saro: *Caplinger, Warren Cumberland Mountain Entertainers* / Forked deer: *Bowman, Charlie & His Brothers* / Johnson boys: *Grant Brothers* / Boll weevil: *Lindsey & Conder* / Going down the Lee Highway: *Grayson & Whitter* / Preacher got drunk and laid his bible down: *Tennesse Ramblers* / Davy: *Weems String Band* / Alabama trot: *Roane County Ramblers* / Baby call your dog off: *Ridgel's Fountain Citians* / Green valley waltz: *McCartt Brothers & Patterson* / Moonshiner and his money: *Bowman, Charlie & His Brothers* / On the banks of the old Tennessee: *Baker, Mr. & Mrs. J.W.* / Old hen cackled: *Davenport, Homer & The Young Brothers* / I'm sad and blue: *Perry County Music Makers* / Tennessee breakdown: *Vance's Tennessee Breakdowners*

COCD 3511 / Jul '97 / County

☐ **RUSH HOUR VOL.3, THE**

REACTCD 048 / Oct '94 / React

☐ **RUSH-TRIA - THE CONCEPT (2CD Set)**

DPARACD 1 / Apr '96 / Dance Paradise

☐ **RUSHY MOUNTAIN**

Top of Maol/Humours of Ballydesmons: *Kerry Fiddles* / Callaghan's/Right of man: *O'Keeffe, Padraig* / Tom Sullivan's/Johnny Leary's/Jim Keefe's reel: *Daly, Jackie* / Lark in the bog: *Star Of Munster Trio* / Uppercurch polkas: *Clifford, Billy* / Humours of Lisheen: *Clifford, John & Julia* / Doyle's polka: *O'Leary, Johnny* / Chase me Charlie: *Kerry Fiddles* / Kennedy's favourite/Woman of the house: *Murphy, Dennis* / Banks of Sullane: *Daly, Jackie* / Bill Black's: *Star Of Munster Trio* / Willie Doherty's/Up on the wagon: *Clifford, Billy* / Brosna slide/Scartaglen/Padraig O'Keefe's favourite: *O'Leary, Johnny* / Julia Clifford's/Bill the waiver's: *Clifford, Julia* / Humours of Galtymore/Callaghan's/New mown meadows: *Murphy, Dennis & Julia Clifford* / Trip to the jacks/Where is the cat: *Daly, Jackie* / Palatine's daughter: *Clifford, John & Julia* / Fermoy lasses/Honeymoon: *Clifford, Billy* / Worn torn petticoat/Denis O'Keefe's favourite: *O'Leary, Johnny* / Mountain road/Paddy Cronin's: *Clifford, Julia & Billy Clifford* / Walsh's hornpipe: *Daly, Jackie* / Mrs. Ryan's/Danny Green's polkas: *Clifford, Billy* / Taimse I'm chodladh: *Clifford, Julia* / Tourmore polkas: *O'Leary, Johnny* / Johnny when you die/Swallow's tail/Miss McLeod's: *Kerry Fiddles* / Danny Ab's: *Clifford, Julia & Dennis Murphy* / Matt Haye's jigs: *Clifford, Billy* / Glenside cottage/Taim gan airgead: *Daly, Jackie* / John Clifford's polka/Behind the bush in the garden/Going fo: *Clifford, John & Julia*

CDORBD 085 / Aug '94 / Globestyle

☐ **RUSSIAN FAR NORTH - THE CHUKCHI**

PS 65189 / Oct '97 / PlayaSound

☐ **RUSSIAN ORTHODOX MUSIC/GREAT VOICES OF BULGARIA**

AUB 6786 / Feb '94 / Auvidis/Ethnic

☐ **RYKODISC 1996 SAMPLER**

Buena: *Morphine* / Walking through a wasted land: *Thompson, Richard* / Devon: *Dr. Didg* / My guitar wants to kill your Mama: *Zappa, Frank* / Black rage: *Last Poets* / Hazy Jane 1: *Drake, Nick* / Devoiko mome: *Sebestyen, Marta* / Ain't hurtin' nobody: *Prine, John* / Ndaweh's dream: *Baka Beyond* / Pure and easy: *Townshend, Pete* / Put you down: *Escovedo, Alejandro* / There ain't no sweet man (Who's worth the salt of my tears): *Waterson, Norma* / Good night Eddie: *Collins, Bootsy* / Thoughless kind: *Cale, John* / Rockin' the res: *Trudell, John* / Stories: *O'Connell, Maura* / On the beach: *Golden Smog* / Last song: *Hart, Mickey*

RSCD 1996 / Jul '96 / Rykodisc

S

☐ **SABA SABA**

Saba saba: *Mil Quilhento 1500 & Conjunto Popombo de Nampula* / Noijukuru: *Conjunto Nimala de lalauah* / Kufera povo: *Mil Quilhento 1500 & Conjunto Popombo de Nampula* / Bainxa: *Conjunto Nimala de lalauah* / Josina: *Mil Quilhento 1500 & Conjunto Popombo de Nampula* / Na munthamana nau: *Conjunto Nimala de lalauah* / Mariana: *Mil Quilhento 1500 & Conjunto Popombo de Nampula* / Nonmualana: *Conjunto Nimala de lalauah* / Arminda: *Mil Quilhento 1500 & Conjunto Popombo de Nampula* / Nampula: *Conjunto Nimala de lalauah* / Omahie wa mama kihala e flore: *Mil Quilhento 1500 & Conjunto Popombo de Nampula* / Kamueire Kiwereiaka: *Conjunto Nimala de lalauah*

CDORBD 077 / Nov '92 / Globestyle

☐ **SACRED CEREMONIES (Music Of South Asia)**

Allah Muhammad char ya: *Khan, Nusrat Fateh Ali* / Sangwa duepa Budddist chant: *Monks Of The Gyuto Monastery* / Silhet song: *Brahmachari, Prahlad* / Raga multani: *Dagar Brothers* / Raga bageshri: *Das, Partho* / Raga kausik dhwani, tala kaharwa: *Ganguly, Rita* / Orissi, pallavi: *Mohapatra, Guru Kelucharan & Manjula Mathur* / Morning prayer in praise of Lord Shiva and Lord Vishnu / Nagasvaram: *Kamber, Murukesha*

VIGC 130682 / Mar '97 / JVC

☐ **SACRED HARP SINGING**

ROUCD 1503 / 19 Jan '98 / Rounder

☐ **SACRED KORAN, THE (Islamic Chants Of The Ottoman Empire)**

VICG 50062 / Mar '96 / JVC World Library

☐ **SACRED MUSIC OF THE SIKHS**

VICG 50352 / Mar '96 / JVC World Library

☐ **SACRED MUSIC, SACRED DANCE**

CD 736 / Oct '92 / Music & Arts

☐ **SACRED SONGS 1925-1934 (Original Performances Classic Years In Digital Stereo)**

Sacred hour: *Dawson, Peter* / Bless this house: *McCormack, John* / Lord's prayer: *Thomas, John Charles* / Lost chord: *Butt, Dame Clara* / Star of Bethlehem: *Crooks, Richard* / Rosary: *Novis, Donald* / Ave Maria: *Fields, Gracie* / All through the night: *Crooks, Richard* / Wings of a dove: *Lough, Master Ernest* / Still night holy night: *Robeson, Paul* / Jesus Christ is risen today: *Crooks, Richard* / Abide with me: *Thomas, John Charles* / Hear my prayer: *Lough, Master Ernest* / Ave Maris: *Schumann, Elisabeth*

RPCD 313 / Sep '96 / Robert Parker Jazz

☐ **SACRED SONGS FOR CHRISTMAS**

Ave Maria / Nun seid ihr wohl gerochen / O Holy night / In dulci jubilo / Panis angelicus / Il est ne / O divine redeemer / Hark the herald angels sing / Virgin's slumber song / Sinfonia / Silent night / Great and mighty wonder / Nun's chorus / Lord's prayer / Come all ye shepherds / Mille cherubin in coro / Away in a manger / Ave Maria

4612402 / Nov '96 / Belart

☐ **SACRED STEEL GUITARS VOL.1**

ARHCD 450 / Feb '97 / Arhoolie

☐ **SACRED TIBETAN CHANTS FROM THE GREAT PRAYER FESTIVAL**

CD 735 / Oct '92 / Music & Arts

☐ **SAD SWEET DREAMER**

PLSCD 154 / Apr '97 / Pulse

☐ **SAFE SOUL VOL.1**

Just loving you: *Green, Garland* / Once you fall in love: *McLoyd, Eddie* / I'll see you in hell first: *Mitchell, Phillip* / Rising cost of love: *Jackson, Millie* / It takes both of us: *Act One* / If I can't have your love: *Brown, Jocelyn* / Plenty of love: *C-Brand* / Stay with me: *Martin, Daltrey* / Still in love with you: *Bailey, J.R.* / My shining star: *Fatback Band* / Sweet music, soft lights and you: *Jackson, Millie & Isaac Hayes* / I'll see you in hell first (alt. take): *Mitchell, Phillip* / Feed me your love: *Fatback Band*

CDSEW 020 / Jan '90 / Southbound

☐ **SAFE SOUL VOL.2**

Never like this: *Two Tons* / Hooked on you: *Simmons, David* / I think I love you: *Shock* / It's way too late: *Watson, Johnny 'Guitar'* / Love starved: *Brown, Shirley* / What'cha see is what'cha get: *Dramatics* / Lovin': *Hurtt, Phil* / Shouting out love: *Emotions* / Ghettos of the mind: *Pleasure* / Always there: *Side Effect* / Everybody's singing love songs: *Sweet Thunder* / Ladies night out: *Pleasure*

CDSEWD 022 / Aug '90 / Southbound

☐ **SALSA (The Caliente Compilation)**

Taka taka-ta: *Irakere* / El coco: *Irakere* / Locas por el mambo: *More, Benny* / Mi chiquita: *More, Benny* / El bobo de la yuca: *More, Benny* / Lo que me paso en la guagua: *Alvarez, Adalberto & Su Son* / Longina: *Burke, Malena & NG La Banda* / Santa Barbara: *Gonzalez, Celina* / Pare Cochero: *Orquesta Aragon* / Yo no quiero que seas celosa: *Reve Y Su Charangon* / Los sitios entero: *Ng La Banda* / La protesta de los chivos: *Ng La Banda* / Coge el Camaron: *La Origina De Manzanillo* / Se muere la tia: *La Origina De Manzanillo* / Eso que anda: *Los Van Van*

PSCCD 1007 / Feb '95 / Pure Sounds From Cuba

☐ **SALSA**

3003732 / Jan '97 / IMP

☐ **SALSA AND TRADITION**

PS 65097 / Oct '92 / PlayaSound

☐ **SALSA BOLERO CUBAN (3CD Set)**

PSCBOX 001 / Feb '95 / Pure Sounds From Cuba

☐ **SALSA CUBANA GOLD COLLECTION, THE (2CD Set)**

R2CD 4064 / 20 Apr '98 / Deja Vu

☐ **SALSA DE AMOR**

UMD 80496 / 27 Jul '98 / Universal

☐ **SALSA ES MP**

9819562372 / 5 May '98 / MP

☐ **SALSA FLAMENCA - CON FUERZA Y CON BONDAD**

EUCD 1262 / Mar '94 / ARC

☐ **SALSA GREATS**

Mi negra Mariana: *Rodriquez, Pete* / Che che cole: *Colon, Willie* / Pedro Navaja: *Blades, Ruben* / Arsenio: *Harlow, Larry* / Senor Serano: *Miranda, Ismael* / Aguzate: *Ray, Ricardo* / Oye como va: *Puente, Tito* / Quitate la mascara: *Barretto, Ray* / Juan pena: *Colon, Willie* / El Malecon: *Orchestra Harlow* / Muneca: *Palmieri, Eddie* / Richies jala jala: *Ray, Ricardo* / Tu loco locoy yo traquillo: *Roena, Roberto* / Huracan: *Valentin, Bobby*

CDCHARLY 131 / Aug '88 / Caliente

☐ **SALSA HITS**

9819562352 / 7 Apr '98 / Musical Productions

☐ **SALSA JAZZ**

ML 51026 / 14 Apr '98 / Musica Latina

☐ **SALSA MAGIC**

Oye come va: *Santana* / La cumparsita: *Cugat, Xavier* / Soul limbo: *Mr. Bongo* / Que hay de malo: *Rivera, Jerry* / La manana: *Enriquez, Luis* / Rumbera: *Chirino, Willy* / Me dara el consentimineto: *Manuelle, Victor* / Mi media mitad: *Ruiz, Rey* / Sin voluntad: *Rosa, Gilberto Santa* / La gallinita de los huevos de oro: *Grupo Niche* / Creo en ti: *Blades, Ruben* / Mama: *Arroyo, Joe* / No podras: *Giro* / Como un haracan: *Blades, Ruben* / Gitano: *Santana* / I like it like that: *Blackout allstars*

48444802 / 3 Aug '98 / Columbia

☐ **SALSA MERENGUE MAMBO**

La maxima expression: *Ensamble Latino* / La cosecha de Mujeres: *Tribu Band* / El Sonero: *Grupo Raices* / Son de Cuba a Puerto Rico: *Delgado, Isaac* / Como se queda: *Ensamble Latino* / Mamaita no quiere: *Alvarez, Adalberto* / Adios Carcelero y Carcel: *Rivas, Maria* / Que ganas: *Delgado, Isaac* / Tres Deseos: *Nazario, Ednita* / Que te pasa mami: *Alvarez, Adalberto* / Tu serenata: *Grupo Raices* / Mapale: *Rivas, Maria* / No aparentes que no sientes: *Silva, Mauricio* / Fracaso: *Ensamble Latino* / Palanque: *Tribu Band*

CDEMC 3701 / Mar '95 / EMI

☐ **SALSA ONLY**

A ritmo de la: *Basta una mirada* / *Mi mujer es celosa* / *Mi vecina* / El emigrante latino / El patillero / Te propongo / Sobre las olas / Cuando aparezca el amor / Oasis / El concinero mayor / Pegaso / Todos bailan salsa / Ban ban / La suegra / Dime que paso / Rosa Angelina / Managua / Nicaragua / Barranquillero arrebatao / Papi papa

DC 880542 / May '97 / Disky

☐ **SALSA ROMANTICA**

7894868572 / 12 May '98 / Irma

☐ **SALSA SABROSA**

Soy antillana: *Cruz, Celia* / Sipriano: *Ray, Ricardo & Bobby Cruz* / Sabo los rumberos: *Canales, Angel* / Sale el sol: *Rivera, Ismael* / Canion: *La Sonora Poncena* / Mi debilidad: *Quintana, Ishmael* / Quiero saber: *Fania Allstars* / Arrepientete: *Barretto, Ray* / Anoranzas: *La Serie, Rolando & Johnny Pacheco* / El raton: *Feliciano, Jose 'Cheo'* / No bebo mas: *La Sonora Poncena* / De toros maneras rosas: *Rivera, Ismael* / La maleta: *Blades, Ruben* / Periodico de ayer: *Lavoe, Hector*

CDHOT 517 / Apr '95 / Charly

☐ **SALSAMANIA**

Ganas / El rey de la punctualidad / Sonaremos el tambo / Nabuco donosor / Dile / Le flor do los lindos campos / Cucala / Yo no soy guapo / Llamame / To loco loco y yo tranquilo / Che che cole / Laye laye

CDHOT 515 / Sep '94 / Charly

☐ **SALSAMANIA (4CD Set)**

BMCD 99901 / Jul '96 / Palladium

☐ **SALSOUL (The Best Of Salsoul Records)**

MCCD 282 / Dec '96 / Music Club

☐ **SALSOUL ESSENTIALS VOL.1 (16 Stompin' Classics From Salsoul/2CD Set)**

If you're looking for fun: *Weeks & Co.* / Take some time out: *Salsoul Orchestra* / Step out of my dream: *Strangers* / Make up your mind: *Aurra* / I know you will: *Logg* / Falling in love: *Surface* / Sadie (she smokes): *Bataan, Joe* / Moment of my life: *Inner Life* / Love sensation: *Holloway, Loleatta* / Let no man put asunder: *First Choice* / Ain't no mountain high enough: *Inner Life* / Ten percent: *Double Exposure* / Runaway: *Holloway, Loleatta* / Dr. Love: *First Choice* / I love NY: *Metropolis* / Beat goes on and on: *Ripple*

CDNEW 1042 / Jan '97 / Charly

☐ **SALSOUL ESSENTIALS VOL.2 (16 Stompin' Classics From Salsoul/2CD Set)**

I got my mind made up: *Instant Funk* / Love thang: *First Choice* / Bottle: *Bataan, Joe* / Salsoul 3001: *Salsoul Orchestra* / Just as long as I've got you: *Love Committee* / Nice 'n' naasty: *Salsoul Orchestra* / Can you see where I'm coming from: *Instant Funk* / Sing sing: *Gaz* / Mama don't, Papa won't: *Holloway,*

Loleatta / Ooh I love it: *Salsoul Orchestra* / My love is free: *Double Exposure* / You're just the right size: *Salsoul Orchestra* / Hit and run: *Holloway, Loleatta* / Double cross: *First Choice* / Dreaming: *Holloway, Loleatta* / Everyman: *Double Exposure*
CDNEW 1072 / Apr '97 / Charly

☐ **SALSOUL ESSENTIALS VOL.3 (2CD Set)**
Jingo: *Candido* / Catch me on the rebound: *Holloway, Loleatta* / Let's celebrate: *Skyy* / I picked a winner: *Inner Life* / Ling Ching Tong: *Botton, Joe* / Let's get it off: *Cameron, Rafael* / This will be a night to remember: *Holman, Eddie* / Love is finally coming my way: *True Example* / Love is you: *Williams, Carol* / Time will tell: *Holman, Eddie* / Are you single: *Aurra* / I've got the hots for you baby: *Double Exposure* / Call me: *Skyy* / Dancing in the stars: *Skyy* / How high: *Cognac* / All my lovin': *Williams, Jimmy*
CDNEW 1132 / Sep '97 / Charly

☐ **SALUDOS AMIGOS**
CD 62048 / Nov '93 / Saludos Amigos

☐ **SALUTE TO THE BIG BANDS**
PLSCD 232 / Jul '97 / Pulse

☐ **SALZBURG - VOLKSMUSIK 1910-1949**
US 0197 / Jul '95 / Trikont

☐ **SAMARKAND TO BUKHARA**
7122038 / Jun '97 / Long Distance

☐ **SAMBA**
To voltando: *Simone* / Tristeza pe no chao: *Nunes, Clara* / Saxofone, por que choras: *Ferreira, Abel* / Roendo as unhas: *Paulinho Da Viola* / Quisera ser eu: *Jurema* / Samba do iraja/No foi ela: *Moreira, Wilson & Nei Lopes* / Tiro ao alvaro: *Regina, Elis & Adoniran Barbosa* / De noite, na cama: *Monteiro, Doris* / Geraldinos e arquibaldos: *Gonzaguinha* / A primeira vez: *Pinheiro, Leila* / Samba da minha terra: *Caymmi, Dorival* / Corcovado: *Gilberto, Joao* / Samba dobrado: *Djavan* / Antes que seja tarde: *Lins, Ivan* / Tie: *Agora E Samba* / Dingue li bangue: *Conjunto Sal Da Terra* / Na glerra, dingu: *Os Choroes* / O que e que a baiana tem: *Miranda, Carmen & Dorival Caymmi*
PRMDCD 15 / Oct '96 / Hemisphere

☐ **SAMBA ENREDO (2CD Set)**
KAR 271 / Sep '96 / IMP

☐ **SAMBA IN THE HOUSE**
Dance with me: *Latin Impact* / Drums of life: *Abraxas, Ray & Rafael Torres* / Mamba: *Latin Kings* / Can you dig it: *That Kid Chris* / Tocame: *Paso Latino* / Yeah babe: *Latin Impact* / Chunga chunga: *Kings From Queens* / Drums of life: *Abraxas, Ray & Rafael Torres* / Me hace sentir tan bien: *Private Ize* / Negrita ven: *Private Ize* / Toma: *El Cantor* / El ritmo: *Latin Impact* / Un ritmo baila: *Ospina, David Going Deep* / Something duro: *IZE 1* / Timbala: *4 Six Drums*
KICKCD 43 / Jan '97 / Kickin'

☐ **SAMBA LATINO**
ZYX 550812 / Jun '97 / ZYX

☐ **SAMBA ONLY**
Brasiliana / Medley argumento / Medley recomecar / Medley saudosa maloca / Melody tristeza / Brazil nao seremos jamais ou seremos / Medley cidade maravilhosa / Medley o teu cabelo nao nega / Medley piada de salao / Medley marcha do cordao do bola preta / Medley fogao / Medley hino rubro negro / Medley as pastorinhas / Medley do jeito que o rei mandou / Medley reza forte / Medley quando vim de minas / Medley serenou / Me leva me leva / Amarre o inimigo no cipo / O amanha
DC 880572 / May '97 / Disky

☐ **SAMBA RUMBA CONGA**
PASTCD 7071 / Aug '95 / Flapper

☐ **SAMPLE CITY VOL.1**
FILECD 442 / Aug '93 / Profile

☐ **SAMPLE CITY VOL.2**
FILECD 450 / Jun '94 / Profile

☐ **SAMPLE SOME OKRA**
OKSP 001 / Mar '94 / Okra

☐ **SAMPLE 'THE WORLD OF SERIES...', THE**
I'd like to teach the world to sing: *New Seekers* / Mighty Quinn: *Manfred Mann* / You've got your troubles: *Fortunes* / Cara mia: *Whitfield, David* / Shout: *Lulu & The Luvvers* / It's only make believe: *Twitty, Conway* / King of the road: *Miller, Roger* / Answer me: *Dickson, Barbara* / Diane: *Bachelors* / Durham Town: *Whittaker, Roger* / Do you love me: *Poole, Brian & The Tremeloes* / You're a lady: *Skellern, Peter* / Drinkin' wine spo-dee-o-dee: *Lewis, Jerry Lee* / Game of love: *Fontana, Wayne & The Mindbenders* / Tower of strength: *Vaughan, Frankie* / Welcome home: *Peters & Lee* / Juliet: *Four Pennies* / Moon river: *Francis, Connie* / Your cheatin' heart: *Williams, Hank Jr.* / Singin' the blues: *Steele, Tommy*
5523702 / Jun '96 / Spectrum

☐ **SAMPLE THIS...**
BYO 045CD / 4 Aug '97 / Better Youth Organisation

☐ **SAN ANTONIO BLUES 1937**
DOCD 5232 / Apr '94 / Document

☐ **SAN ANTONIO'S CONJUNTOS IN THE 1950'S**
ARHCD 376 / Apr '95 / Arhoolie

☐ **SAN DIEGO BLUES JAM**
TCD 5029 / Oct '95 / Testament

☐ **SAN FRANCISCAN DAZE**
San Franciscan nights: *Burdon, Eric & The Animals* / Diddy wah diddy: *Captain Beefheart* / Summertime blues: *Blue Cheer* / Mendocino: *Sir Douglas Quintet* / (We ain't got) nothin' yet: *Blues Magoos* / No time like the right time: *Blues Project* / Sea train: *Sea Train* / Desiree: *Left Banke* / I can take you to the sun: *Misunderstood* / Like to get to know you: *Spanky & Our Gang* / White light, white heat: *Velvet Underground* / Let's get together: *We Five* / Do you know what I mean: *Michaels, Lee* / You're a very lovely woman: *Merry Go Round* / Cave song: *Linn County* / Sunshine girl: *Parade* / Let it hang out (let it all hang out): *Hombres*
5536722 / Jun '97 / Debutante

☐ **SAN FRANCISCO - MUSIC CITY COMPILATION 1998 (2CD Set)**
TR 20092 / 5 May '98 / Trocadero

☐ **SAN FRANCISCO BLUES**
Should've been gone: *Hooker, John Lee* / Evil: *Hammond, John* / Elvin's blues: *Bishop, Elvin* / Willie and the hand jive: *AB Skhy* / Jorma's blues: *Jefferson Airplane* / Milk cow blues: *Commander Cody* / Hard times: *Hooker, John Lee* / Hey Bo Diddley: *Hammond, John* / Hesitation blues: *Taj Mahal* / Country blues: *Watson, Doc* / Hobo blues: *Hooker, John Lee* / Guitar blues 2: *Taj Mahal* / So many roads, so many trains: *Hammond, John* / Sally May: *Hooker, John Lee* / Mustang Sally: *Chambers Brothers*
3036000712 / Feb '97 / Carlton

☐ **SAN FRANCISCO BLUES FESTIVAL-1980**
157732 / Feb '93 / Blues Collection

☐ **SAN FRANCISCO COLLECTION VOL.2, THE**
SFCD 1 / 2 Apr '98 / Royal Scottish Country Dance Society

☐ **SAN FRANCISCO HOUSE CULTURE (2CD Set)**
SPV 08638442 / Jan '96 / Subterranean

☐ **SAN FRANCISCO LEGENDS**
Casey Jones: *Grateful Dead* / Uncle John's band: *Grateful Dead* / Black dog: *Winchester, Jesse* / Somebody to love: *Jefferson Airplane* / Baby please don't go: *Chambers Brothers* / What made Milwaukee famous (has made a loser out of me): *Commander Cody* / I wish you would: *Hammond, John* / Guitar blues: *Taj Mahal* / Hot summer day: *It's A Beautiful Day* / I feel alright: *Hooker, John Lee* / Gambler's blues: *Hammond, John* / Might have to cry: *Scaggs, Boz* / Make my life shine: *Scaggs, Boz* / Don't do this to me: *Valente, Dino* / Home in my hand: *Commander Cody* / Daddy roll on: *Town Cryers & Marty Balin*
307682 / Jul '97 / Hallmark

☐ **SAN FRANCISCO LEGENDS GOLD COLLECTION, THE (2CD Set)**
R2CD 4065 / 20 Apr '98 / Deja Vu

☐ **SAN FRANCISCO NIGHTS**
Twelve ducks: *Clover* / No vacancy: *Clover* / Milk of human kindness: *Clover* / High coin: *Charlatans* / Blues ain't nothing: *Charlatans* / Superman: *New Riders Of The Purple Sage* / Garden of Eden: *New Riders Of The Purple Sage* / All I ever wanted: *New Riders Of The Purple Sage* / She's a bad news baby: *Mojo Men* / New York City: *Mojo Men* / Candle to burn: *Mojo Men* / Happiness is you: *Mojo Men* / You didn't even say goodbye: *Mojo Men*
CDTB 167 / 27 Feb '98 / Thunderbolt

☐ **SANCTIFIED JUG BANDS 1928-1930**
Master came and called me / Master came and called me / Come over here / How much I owe for love divine / Lord, lord he sure is good to me / Watch, ye, but god know'd it / A wild man in town / He shut the lion's mouth / A lie was told / Everybody was there / He's got the whole world in his hands / I will meet you at the station / Thou carest lord, for me / Jesus throwed up a highway for me / Sinner, I'd make a change / When I get inside the gate
DOCD 5300 / Dec '94 / Document

☐ **SANCTUARY SESSIONS - LIVE AT CRUISE'S HOTEL, ENNIS**
CCD 001CD / Oct '94 / CCD

☐ **SANTA AND SATAN - ONE AND THE SAME**
DD 9497 / Nov '96 / Dr. Dream

☐ **SANTA CLAUS BLUES**
JASSCD 3 / Aug '89 / Jass

☐ **SANTA'S BAG**
O come, o come Emmanuel / O tannenbaum / Silver bells / White Christmas / Have yourself a merry little Christmas / Away in a manger / Christmas song / Christmas blues / It's the time of the year / Jingle bells / Let it snow, let it snow, let it snow / Santa Claus is coming to town / Blue Christmas
CD 83352 / Oct '94 / Telarc

☐ **SANTA'S GOT A GTO**
ID 123353CD / Nov '97 / Dionysus

☐ **SANTIC PRESENTS AN EVEN HARDER SHADE OF BLACK**
CDPS 001 / Mar '95 / Pressure Sounds

☐ **SARAH 100 THERE AND BACK AGAIN LANE**
Sensitive: *Field Mice* / Atta girl: *Heavenly* / Ahprahran: *Sugargliders* / Peaches: *Orchids* / Joy of living: *Blueboy* / Six o'clock is rosary: *Ministers* / Inside out: *Brighter* / Make a deal with the city: *East River Pipe* / English rain: *Wake* / Temporal: *Secret Shine* / All of a tremble: *St. Christopher* / Pristine Christine: *Sea Urchins* / He gets me so hard: *Boyracer* / Mustard gas: *Action Painting* / Tell me how it feels: *Sweetest Ache* / Rio: *Another Sunny Day* / In Gunnersbury Park: *Hit Parade* / Drown: *Even As We Speak*
SARAH 100 / 29 Jun '98 / Sarah

☐ **SATIN AND STEEL**
If I could turn back time: *Cher* / Will you be there (in the morning): *Heart* / Same thing: *Carlisle, Belinda* / I believe: *Detroit, Marcella* / Running up that hill: *Bush, Kate* / Sexcrime (1984): *Eurythmics* / All fired up: *Benatar, Pat* / Black velvet: *Myles, Alannah* / Better be good to me: *Turner, Tina* / Feel like making love: *Henry, Pauline* / I want that man: *Harry, Deborah* / Monsters and angels: *Voice Of The Beehive* / Going down to Liverpool: *Bangles* / Stop draggin' my heart around: *Nicks, Stevie & Tom Petty & The Heartbreakers* / Faster than the speed of night: *Tyler, Bonnie* / I want your love: *Transvision Vamp* / Pretend we're dead: *L7* / Gloria: *Branigan, Laura* / Bette Davis eyes: *Carnes, Kim* / Echo beach: *Martha & The Muffins*
5169712 / Aug '94 / PolyGram TV

☐ **SATIN SHEETS**
Looking in the eyes of love: *Loveless, Patty* / I've already loved you in my mind: *Twitty, Conway* / Feelings: *Twitty, Conway* / Leave my heart the way you found it: *Greenwood, Lee* / Hopeless romantics: *Earle, Steve & the Dukes* / Anyone can be somebody's fool: *Griffith, Nanci* / Satin sheets: *Pruett, Jeanne* / Crying: *Jennings, Waylon* / Don't worry baby: *Thomas, B.J.* / Break it to me gently: *Lee, Brenda* / She's got you: *Lynn, Loretta* / Am I blue (yes I'm blue): *Strait, George* / Love song: *Oak Ridge Boys* / Wind beneath my wings: *Greenwood, Lee* / He called me baby: *Cline, Patsy* / (Turn out the lights) and love me tonight: *Williams, Don*
PWKS 4268 / Feb '96 / Carlton

☐ **SATISFACTION GUARANTEED (Hits Of The Seventies)**
MU 5047 / Oct '92 / Musketeer

☐ **SATTA**
BWCD 0012 / Mar '98 / Brickwall

☐ **SATURDAY NIGHT (The Best Of Pub Rock)**
Sweet Gene Vincent: *Dury, Ian & The Blockheads* / Down the road apiece: *Gibbons, Steve Band* / Who do you love: *Juicy Lucy* / Looked out my window: *Johnson, Wilko & Len Lewis Band* / Amsterdam dog: *Ducks Deluxe* / Milk and alcohol: *Dr. Feelgood* / Down in the bottom: *Groundhogs* / Goin' back home: *Pirates* / On the street: *Das Luftwaffegeschaft* / Absolutely gone: *Gibbons, Steve Band* / Baby Jane: *Dr. Feelgood* / Please don't touch: *Pirates* / Burnin' rubber: *Green, Mick* / Something's goin' on: *Ducks Deluxe* / Bottle up and go: *Johnson, Wilko* / Do anything you wanna do: *Eddie & The Hot Rods* / Saturday night: *Juicy Lucy* / Shakin' all over: *Pirates* / Shake for me: *Groundhogs* / To be alone with you: *Gibbons, Steve Band*
3036000782 / Jun '97 / Carlton

☐ **SATURDAY NIGHT AFTER HOURS SESSION**
MMCCD 008 / 30 Mar '98 / Massive

☐ **SATURDAY NIGHT AT HEAVEN, A**
SATCD 1 / Mar '94 / Prime Cuts

☐ **SATURDAY NIGHT BLUES**
SP 1172CD / Oct '93 / Stony Plain

☐ **SATURDAY NIGHT'S ALRIGHT**
I'm in you: *Frampton, Peter* / Eighth day: *O'Connor, Hazel* / Paper plane: *Status Quo* / Ramblin' man: *Allman Brothers* / Saturday night's alright for fighting: *John, Elton* / I'm waiting for the man: *Velvet Underground* / Stairway to heaven: *Far Corporation* / Letter: *Box Tops* / Freebird: *Lynyrd Skynyrd* / Funk 49: *James Gang* / Liar: *Three Dog Night* / Warrior: *Wishbone Ash* / Parisienne walkways: *Moore, Gary* / Who do you love: *Juicy Lucy* / Broken down angel: *Nazareth* / Lady in the black: *Uriah Heep* / Ace of spades: *Motorhead* / America: *Nice* / You took the words right out of my mouth: *Meat Loaf* / Rosanna: *Toto* / God gave rock 'n' roll to you: *Argent* / All day and all of the night: *Stranglers* / Holding out for a hero: *Tyler, Bonnie* / Livin' thing: *ELO*
3220 / Oct '92 / Carlton

☐ **SAVE THE LAST DANCE FOR ME**
Save the last dance for me: *Heptones* / Will you still love me tomorrow: *Barker, Dave* / Shotgun wedding: *Campbell, Cornell* / Then he kissed me: *Marvels* / Hang on sloopy: *Chosen Few* / Da doo ron ron: *Heyward, Winston* / Darling you send me: *Max Romeo* / Oh Carol (Vocal): *McKay, Freddie* / Oh Carol: *Brown, Lennox* / Sincerely: *Edwards, Jackie* / (Sittin' on the) dock of the bay: *McKay, Freddie* / Light my fire: *Soul Sam* / Come on over to my place: *Robinson, Jackie* / Wonderful world: *Donaldson, Eric* / It's in his kiss (The shoop shoop song): *Marvels* / Blue moon: *Platonics* / Duke of Earl (Version): *McCook, Tommy & The Aggrovators*
CDTRL 317 / Mar '94 / Trojan

☐ **SAVE THE LAST DANCE FOR ME**
Do you want to know a secret: *Kramer, Billy J.* / Tossing and turning: *Ivy League* / Little loving: *Fourmost* / My guy: *Wells, Mary* / You were made for me: *Wells, Mary* / Just like Eddie: *Heinz* / Do you love me: *Poole, Brian* / Pied piper: *St. Peters, Crispian* / Bobby's girl: *Maughan, Susan* / Save the last dance for me: *Drifters* / Juliet: *Four Pennies* / Hello little girl: *Fourmost* / Little children: *Kramer, Billy J.* / Um um um um um um: *Fontana, Wayne* / But I do: *Henry, Clarence* / Crying game: *Berry, Dave* / Wimoweh: *Denver, Karl* / Tell me when: *Applejacks* / Baby now that I've found you: *Foundations* / Jesamine: *Casuals*
CD 6042 / Oct '96 / Music

☐ **SAX AT MIDNIGHT (Cool Jazz Classics)**
CDGR 110 / Dec '96 / Charly

☐ **SAX BY THE SEA (A Magical Blend Of Music And The Sounds Of Nature)**
57852 / May '97 / Nature's Harmony

☐ **SAX COLLECTION, THE (2CD Set)**
Up where we belong / Can you feel the love tonight / Seven seconds / Everlasting love / Talking in your sleep / Anytime you need a friend / I'd lie for you (and that's the truth) / Secret / Holding back the years / All I wanna do / Get on your feet / Forever young / Heal the world / I'd do anything for love / Saturday night / Words / Make it happen / Simply the best / Love is all around / Whiter shade of pale / Long and winding road / Woman / Lean on me / How deep is your love / Just the way you are / When I fall in love / Said I loved you.. but I lied / Candle in the wind / Will you be there / Blue eyes / Dreamlover / We have only just begun / One sweet day / I can love you like that / Can I touch you.. there
DCD 3003 / Jun '97 / Music

☐ **SAX FOR LOVERS**
MACCD 332 / Aug '96 / Autograph

☐ **SAX FOR LOVERS**
Up where we belong / Can you feel the love tonight / Seven seconds / Everlasting love / Talking in your sleep / Anytime you need a friend / I'd lie for you (and that's the truth) / Secret / Holding back the years / All I wanna do / Get on your feet / Forever young / Heal the world / I'd do anything for love / Saturday night / Words / Make it happen / Simply the best
CD 6052 / Feb '97 / Music

☐ **SAX FOR ROMANTICS (4CD Set)**
MBSCD 447 / Nov '95 / Castle

☐ **SAX MOODS**
MACCD 333 / Aug '96 / Autograph

☐ **SAX ON SILK**
MACCD 356 / 26 Jan '98 / Autograph

☐ **SAXOMANIA (Honkers & Screamers)**
Wiggles: *Prysock, Red House Rockers* / Crying my heart out: *Prysock, Red House Rockers* / Hard rock: *Prysock, Red House Rockers* / Jump for George: *Prysock, Red House Rockers* / Hammer: *Prysock, Red House Rockers* / Jackpot: *Prysock, Red House Rockers* / Earthquake: *Singleton, Charlie* / Bobby's boogie: *Lane, Morris* / Last call: *Holloway, Red* / Foolin' around slowly: *Holloway, Red* / Buttermilk: *Holloway, Red* / Big Jay's hop: *McNeely, 'Big' Jay* / Zero: *Dash, Julian* / Give it up: *Watts, Noble 'Watts' & Paul Williams Orchestra* / Pass the buck: *Watts, Noble 'Watts' & Paul Williams Orchestra* / Big two four: *Watts, Noble 'Watts' & Paul Williams Orchestra* / South shore drive: *Watts, Noble 'Watts' & Paul Williams Orchestra* / Sack o'woe: *King Curtis & The Knoble Knights* / Soul twist: *King Curtis & The Knoble Knights* / Twistin' with the King: *King Curtis & The Knoble Knights*
CPCD 8163 / Nov '96 / Charly

☐ **SAXON DANCEHALL SPECIALS VOL.1**
SAXCD 001 / Apr '94 / Saxon Studio

☐ **SAXOPHONE DREAMS**
End of the road / Songbird / Why / Piano in the dark / Right here waiting / Can you feel the love tonight / Jealous guy / Jesus to a child / I will always love you / Love won't let me wait / Get here / If you were here tonight / Summer (the first time) / Save the best for last / True / Suddenly / Careless whisper / Giving you the best that I got
CDVIP 147 / Apr '97 / Virgin VIP

☐ **SAXOPHONE PHENOMENOM, THE**
Wayward balladeer: *Coxhill, Lol* / Gossip: *Haslam, George* / Dayday: *Dean, Elton* / New worlds: *Dunmall, Paul* / Landscape gardening: *Dunmall, Paul* / Life after room service: *Biscoe, Chris* / Song: *Parker, Evan* / Hasta pronto: *Haslam, George* / Odeon's dropout piece: *Wilkinson, Alan*
SLAMCD 401 / Oct '96 / Slam

☐ **SAXOPHONY (Honkers & Shouters)**
Easy rockin': *Kohlman, Freddie Orchestra* / Flashlight: *Wright, Jimmy* / Move over: *Wright, Jimmy* / 2.20 AM: *Wright, Jimmy* / Blowin' awhile: *Hall, Rene* / Rene's boogie: *Hall, Rene* / Blue creek hop: *Hall, Rene* / Downbeat: *Hall, Rene* / Jubilee jump: *Hall, Rene* / Jesse's blues: *Hall, Rene* / Turnpike: *Powell, Jesse* / Sopping molasses: *Powell, Jesse* / Whooping blues: *Lucas, Buddy* / Pea lily: *Lucas, Buddy* / Undecided: *Lucas, Buddy* / Big Bertha: *Lucas, Buddy* / One taste calls for another: *Hall, Rene*
NEMCD 748 / Aug '95 / Sequel

☐ **SCI FI CAFE**
00972 / 6 Oct '97 / Hypnotic

☐ **SCI FI**
EFA 628212 / 24 Nov '97 / Superstition

☐ **SCIENCE FICTION JAZZ VOL.2**
MOLECD 003 / Jun '97 / Mole

☐ **SCIENCE FICTION JAZZ VOL.3**
MOLECD 0082 / 30 Mar '98 / Mole

☐ **SCORED 1-0**
JTI 1CD / Jul '97 / JTI

☐ **SCORPIO RECORDS STORY, THE**
Brown eyed girl: *Golliwogs* / You better be careful: *Golliwogs* / Fight fire: *Golliwogs* / Fragile child: *Golliwogs* / Walking on the water: *Golliwogs* / You better get it before it gets you: *Golliwogs* / Call it pretending: *Golliwogs* / Boots: *Spokes* / Stop calling me: *Group B* / She's gone: *Group B* / I know your name girl: *Group B* / I never really knew: *Group B* / Time: *Tokays* / Hole in the wall: *Tokays* / It's up to you: *Shillings* / Made you cry: *Shillings* / Losin' you: *Newcastle 5* / Yes I'm cryin': *Newcastle 5* / Gotta get away: *Penn, William* / Blow my mind: *Penn, William* / Far and away: *Penn, William* / Weatherman: *Squires* / Anyhow anywhere: *Squires* / It must be love: *Squires* / Read all about it: *Tears* / Rat race: *Tears* / People through my glasses: *Tears*
CDWIKD 129 / Apr '94 / Big Beat

☐ **SCOTLAND - ACCORDION, HARP & FIDDLE**
PS 65109 / Nov '93 / PlayaSound

☐ **SCOTLAND - THE MUSIC OF A NATION**
Caddam Woods: *Golden Fiddle Orchestra* / Strathspeys and reels: *Burgess, John* / Bonnie lass o'Bon Accord: *Ford, Tommy* / Medley: *Gonnella, Ron* / 4/4 marches: *Dysart & Dundonald Pipe Band* / Slow air and marches: *MacKay, Rhona* / Mrs. Hamilton of Pencaitland: *Glasgow Caledonian Strathspey & Reel Society* / Gay Gordons: *Ellis, John & His Highland Country Band* / Free and easy: *Hunter, Karen* / Petronella: *Brock, Robin & His*

R.E.D. CD CATALOGUE COMPILATIONS SCOTTISH VOICES

Dance Band / March, strathspey and reel: MacFadyen, Iain / Hangman's reel: MacLean, Calum / Waltzes: Dysart & Dundonald Pipe Band / Reels: Currie Brothers / Cro cheann T Saile: MacKay, Rhona / Marches: Glasgow Caledonian Strathspey & Reel Society / Dumbarton's drums: Gaelforce Orchestra / Mary of Argyll: Gaelforce Orchestra / Trilogy: Gaelforce Orchestra

LCOM 9004 / Aug '87 / Lismor

☐ SCOTLAND FOREVER

PDSCD 520 / Sep '97 / Pulse

☐ SCOTLAND NOW VOL.1 (The Dances & The Dance Bands)

Eightsome reel: Holmes, Ian & Scottish Dance Band / Strip the willow: Johnstone, Jim & His Band / West Highland waltz: MacDonald, Fergie & Highland / Dashing white Sergeant: MacPhail, Ian & His Scottish Dance Band / Canadian barn dance: Johnstone, Jim & His Band / Waltz country dance: Keith, Lex & His Scottish Band / Irish jiggery: MacDonald, Fergie & Highland / Grand march: Wilson, Callum / Jig strathspey and reel: Lothian Scottish Dance Band / St. Bernard's waltz: Johnstone, Jim & His Band / Boston Two Step: Ellis, John & His Highland Country Band / Reel (hoop her and gird her): Glendaruel Scottish Dance Band / Pride o' erin waltz: MacLeod, Bobby & His Music / Gay Gordons: Campbell, Colin & His Highland Band / Two highland schottissches: Ellis, John & His Highland Country Band / Military two step: Johnstone, Jim & His Band / Lothian lads: Lothian Scottish Dance Band / Palais glide: Johnstone, Jim / Hebridean waltz: Carmichael, John / Irish military two step: McDonald, Fergie

LCOM 9003 / Jul '87 / Lismor

☐ SCOTLAND NOW VOL.2 (The Music & The Song)

Fiddle and pipe medley: Hardie, Ian / Forth bridge song: Laing, Robin / Who pays the piper: McCalmans / Wild geese: Redpath, Jean / Slow air and pipe medley: McCallum, Craig Scottish Dance Band / Chi Mi'n Geamhradh: MacPhee, Catherine-Anne / See the people run: Ceolbeg / Coorie doon: Stramash / Atlantic reels: McNeill, Brian / MacCrimmon's Lament and slow air: Heywood, Heather / Across the hills of home: Bogle, Eric / Storm in Edinburgh/The streaker: Bogle, Eric / Oor Hamlet: McNaughtan, Adam / Tha Mo Chridhe Sa Ghaidhealtachd: Scott, Elfrida / Fiddle tune medley: Robertson, Arthur Scott / I wish I was in Glasgow: MacKintosh, Iain / Bell: Jackson, William Billy / Rollin' home: McCalmans

CDTRAX 060 / Dec '92 / Greentrax

☐ SCOTLAND THE BRAVE

Scotland the brave: Daly, Glen / Songs of the borders: Alexander Brothers / Scottish trilogy: Martell, Lena / Lass of bon accord: Alexander Brothers / MacNamara's band: Daly, Glen / Marching home: Alexander Brothers / Mary of Skye: Kennedy, Calum / Sky is bluer in Scotland: Daly, Glen / Cuckoo waltz: Starr, Will / Auld Scotch sang medley: Alexander Brothers / Grand march: MacLeod, Jim & His Band / Guid Scotch night: Stewart, Andy & Jimmy Blue Band / There's nae toon: Alexander Brothers / Little street where old friends meet: Daly, Glen / Scotish soldier: Stewart, Andy / Duke and Duchess of Edinburgh: MacLeod, Jim & His Band / Dear old Glasgow town: Daly, Glen / Amazing grace: Royal Scots Dragoon Guards / Flower of Scotland: Alexander Brothers

TRTCD 136 / Oct '94 / TrueTrax

☐ SCOTLAND THE BRAVE

EUCD 1321 / Nov '95 / ARC

☐ SCOTLAND THE BRAVE

Scotland the brave / Highland cathedral / Mull of kintyre / Auld town march / Pipe major Willie Ross / Highland lassie / Going to the fair / Lady Ramsey's strathspey / Lady Carmichael's strathspey / Leezy Lindsay / Brolam / Pulteney reel / Isle of barley / Newmarket house / Doune of Inverochty / Mist covered mountains / Old toastie / Lady MacKenzie of Fairburn / Strathspey king / Gin I were a baron's heir / Barbara's jig / Mason's apron / Amazing grace / Duncan McInnes / Stirling castle / Kilt is my delight / Dr. Ross / 50th welcome to Argyllshire gathering / Dark island / Road to the isles / Dream valley of Glendural / Old rustic bridge / Paddy's leather breaches / Last minute friendship / Graugach / O'er the bows to Ballindalloch / Miss Girdle / Three girls of Portree / Mary Anderson / Campbell town kiltie / Moving cloud / Famous bridge / Eriskay love song / Ass in the graveyard / Merrily dance the quaker's wife / Queen of the rushes / Heilan' laddie

300752 / Feb '97 / Hallmark

☐ SCOTLAND THE BRAVE

Old rustic bridge by the mill/Towsay Castle/Money musk: Gordon Highlanders / Miss McLeaod O'Raasey/Cock of the North: Gordon Highlanders / Route March/When the battle is over: Gordon Highlanders / 79th farewell to Gibraltar: Massed Pipes & Drums / Colonel Robertson: Massed Pipes & Drums / Dovecote Park: Massed Pipes & Drums / Prince Charles welcome to Lochaber/Mingulay boat song: Massed Pipes & Drums / Silver spear/The curlew/Captain Horne: Massed Pipes & Drums / MacFarlane's reel/O'Leudh: Massed Pipes & Drums / Inverness gathering: Edinburgh City Police Pipe Band / Drunken piper/79th's farewell to Gibraltar: Edinburgh City Police Pipe Band / Earl of Mansfield: Edinburgh City Police Pipe Band / Drum salute: Boghall & Bathgate Caledonia Pipe Band / Royal Scots polka/Conundrum: Boghall & Bathgate Caledonia Pipe Band / Highland wedding/The Smith of Chilliehassie: Boghall & Bathgate Caledonia Pipe Band / Boghall and Bathgate: Boghall & Bathgate Caledonia Pipe Band / Train journey North/The redundancy: Boghall & Bathgate Caledonia Pipe Band / Up in the morning/The muckin' o'Geordie's byre: Turriff & District Pipe Band / Cock o'the North: Turriff & District Pipe Band / Reveille: Gordon Highlanders / Miss Kirkwood: Gordon Highlanders / Scotland the Brave: Gordon Highlanders

CD 6060 / Feb '97 / Music

☐ SCOTLAND THE BRAVE

PLSCD 178 / Apr '97 / Pulse

☐ SCOTLAND THE BRAVE

Piping hot / Bonnie Dundee / Barren rocks of Aden / Rose of Allendale / Skye boat song / Duncan McInnes / Kilworth hills / Gaelic air / Pipers waltz / Crusaders / Wooden heart / Scotland the brave / AA Cameron / Mist covered mountains / Murdo's wedding / Brigadier Snow / Ae fond kiss / Saffron kilt / Rowan tree / Archie McKinlay / Amazing grace

RECD 516 / Dec '97 / REL

☐ SCOTLAND'S MUSIC (Selected Works From the History Of Scottish Music/ 2CD Set)

9th century bells / Jubente petrus / Sanctorum piissime Columba / O Columba / Pi li li liu / Airs by Fingal / Deidre's lament / Sanctus ierarchia / Kyrie / Hac in anni janua / Gowans are gay / Ex te lux oritur / Pleugh sang / Salve festa dies / Dicant nunc judei / O bone Jesu / Support your servant / Galliarde la roine d'ECosse / Golden pavan / Come my children dear / Why should I be so sad on my wedding day / Dic mihi saeve puer / Sonata on Scot's tunes / Symphony in B flat / Bagatelle / Drei lieder No.1 keiner von den schonheit tochtern / O would that I could see again / I will think of thee my love / In the glen / Benedictus / Calgacus

CKD 008 / Apr '93 / Linn

☐ SCOTS DANCE PARTY FAVOURITES

Grand march and reels: MacLeod, Jim & His Band / Scottish waltzes: MacLeod, Jim & His Band / Strip the willow: MacLeod, Jim & His Band / Marches: MacLeod, Jim & His Band / Britannia two step: MacLeod, Jim & His Band / Dashing white Sergeant: MacLeod, Jim & His Band / Dunoon barn dance: Shand, Jimmy & His Band / Gay Gordons: Shand, Jimmy & His Band / Set of reels: Shand, Jimmy & His Band / Hesitation waltz: Shand, Jimmy & His Band / Westering home selection of waltzes: Shand, Jimmy & His Band / Set if jigs: Shand, Jimmy & His Band / Piper's polka: Shand, Jimmy & His Band / Ulist trampings song: Cameron, Mary / Dancing in Kyle: Cameron, Mary / These are my mountains: Cameron, Mary / Road to the isles: Cameron, Mary / Eriskay love lilt: Cameron, Mary / Mull of Kintyre: Cameron, Mary / Down in the glen: Cameron, Mary / White heather foxtrot: Shand, Jimmy Jr. & His Band

303600892 / Apr '97 / Carlton

☐ SCOTS SPECTACULAR, A

BNA 5139 / 13 Apr '98 / Bandleader

☐ SCOTS WHA'HAE

PWKS 4265 / Jan '97 / Carlton

☐ SCOTTISH BAGPIPES

B6829CD / May '96 / Auvidis Travelling

☐ SCOTTISH BAGPIPES & DRUMS

12249 / Sep '94 / Laserlight

☐ SCOTTISH CEILIDH MUSIC

Galloway House/Aitken drum/Rakes o' Mallow / Claverhouse reel/C.M. Barbour / Apple tree/CTS Empress/Agnes Ritchie/Pottinger's reel / Arther Bignold of Loch Rosque/Sprig of Ivy / Gravel walk/ The big reel / Marches and reels / My Mother/ Leaving Skye/Sine Bahn / College hornpipe/Miss Gaytons/Braes of Gleniffer/The navvie / Donald MacLean/The Ross battery / Sally was a good 'un/ Bowing the strings / Jig of slurs/Corkhill/Ness Bothan / Air and Shetland reels / Madame Bonaparte/Harvest home/Seven stars / Teetotaller/ Anne's reel/Perrie hoose a' hint the burn / Miss Susan Cooper / Border polka / Alison and Bobby's farewell to the Chase/Captain Campbell / Glens of Angus/We'd better bide a wee/The road to Dundee / My mother / Paddy's leather breeches/The curlew/ The tenpenny bit / Inverness gathering/The man from Skye / Radio-Valse / Daashing white sergeant/ The Bore stone / Highland lassie/Miss Mary Douglas

RECD 494 / Jan '98 / REL

☐ SCOTTISH CHRISTMAS, A

MMCD 215 / Nov '96 / Maggie's Music

☐ SCOTTISH COLLECTION (3CD Set)

TBXCD 511 / Jan '96 / TrueTrax

☐ SCOTTISH COLLECTION (2CD Set)

PBXCD 511 / Nov '96 / Pulse

☐ SCOTTISH COLLECTION - PIPES & DRUMS

CDLBP 2028 / Mar '96 / Lochshore

☐ SCOTTISH COLLECTION - SCOTTISH EVENING LIVE

CDLBP 2027 / Mar '96 / Lochshore

☐ SCOTTISH COLLECTION - SINGERS AND THE SONGS

CDLBP 2021 / Mar '96 / Lochshore

☐ SCOTTISH COLLECTION - SONGS OF THE GAELS

CDLBP 2022 / Mar '96 / Lochshore

☐ SCOTTISH COLLECTION, THE (2CD Set)

Amazing grace: Kevock Choir & Massed Pipes/ Drums / Song of the Clyde: Mallan, Peter / Westering home: McPartland, Joe / Road to the Isles: McPartland, Joe / Right on to the end of the road: Miller, Ina / Nothern lights of old Aberdeen: Miller, Ina / Bonnie Kirkwall bay: Miller, Ina / Bonnie banks of Loch Lomond: Miller, Ina / Football crazy: Beattie, Johnny / Here's to Scottish whisky: Tartan Lads / Land for all seasons: Urquhart, Jimmy / Star o'Robbie Burns: McPartland, Joe / Man's a man for all that: Laurie, John / Roamin' in the gloamin': McPartland, Joe / Jus a wee doech an doris: McPartland, Joe / Skye boat song: Miller, Ina / Ye banks and braes: Miller, Ina / Tobermory bay: Miller, Ina / Marching through the heather: Hughes, Ken & Alan / Auld lang syne: Laurie, John / Pipe set 1: Gordon Highlanders / Route march: Gordon Highlanders / When the battle is over: Gordon Highlanders / 79th farewell to Gilbraltar: Gordon Highlanders / Medley: Gordon Highlanders / Inverness gathering medley: Edinburgh City Police Pipe Band / Drum salute: Boghall & Bathgate Caledonia Pipe Band / Up in the morning: Turriff & District Pipe Band / Royal Scots polka medley: Boghall & Bathgate Caledonia Pipe Band / Highland wedding medley: Boghall & Bathgate Caledonia Pipe Band / Redundancy: Gordon Highlanders / Revelle: Gordon Highlanders / Miss Kirkwood: Gordon Highlanders / Scotland the brave: Gordon Highlanders

DCD 3006 / Jun '97 / Music

☐ SCOTTISH COUNTRY DANCING VOL.1

PACD 032 / Mar '94 / Music Masters

☐ SCOTTISH DANCE BANDS

CDSL 8283 / Feb '97 / EMI Gold

☐ SCOTTISH EVENING LIVE VOL.2, A

CDLBP 2029 / Jul '96 / Lochshore

☐ SCOTTISH EVENING, A

O'er the sea/Lad wi' the plaidie/Troy's wedding/ Highland lad: Johnstone, Jim & His Band / Over the sea to Skye: Cameron, Mary / Mairi's wedding: Cameron, Mary / Loch Maree: Cameron, Mary / Land for all seasons: Cameron, Mary / Dark Island: Cameron, Mary & Bill Torrance / Muckin' o' Geordies Byre/Glasgow Gaelic club/The fairy dance: Johnstone, Jim / Ken Muir's up and awa': Johnstone, Jim / Fiddle set: Fielding, Marie / Annie Laurie: Torrance, Bill / Laird o' Drumblair/The mason's apron: Johnstone, Jim / Earl of Earl/Battle of the Somme/Scottish horse: Johnstone, Jim / Victoria hornpipe/The poppy leaf/Kirk's hornpipe: Fielding, Marie / Dashing white Sergeant/Rose tree/ My love she's but a lassie: Johnstone, Jim / Cock o' the north/Drum solo/Amazing Grace/Gillie Callum / Scotland the Brave / Lovat Scouts/Roaring Jelly/My home/De'il amang the tailors: Johnstone, Jim / Loch Lomond: Cameron, Mary & Bill Torrance / Man's a man for a' that/Will ye no come back again: Cameron, Mary & Bill Torrance / Auld lang syne: Cameron, Mary & Bill Torrance

RECD 490 / Jan '98 / REL

☐ SCOTTISH FAMILY CHRISTMAS

Santa on parade / Sleigh ride / Holly jolly Christmas / Deck the halls / Have yourself a merry little Christmas / Winter wonderland / Have a merry Christmas / Earl of Mansfield / Atholl highlanders / Piping hot Christmas / Louden's bonnie woods and braes / O'er the bows to Ballindalloch / Miss Ada Crawford / Because he was a bonnie lad / High road to Linton / Piper of Drummond / Cutting bracken / Rudolph the red nose reindeer / Frosty the Snowman / Santa Claus is coming to town / Here comes Santa Claus / I saw mommy kissing Santa Claus / Have yourself a merry little Christmas / Away in a manger / O come all ye faithful (adeste fidelis) / Good King Wenceslas / Silent night / Amazing Grace / Auld lang syne / We wish you a merry Christmas

CDITV 621 / Nov '96 / Scotdisc

☐ SCOTTISH FIDDLE RALLY (Concert Highlights 1985-1995)

Boston Scottish fiddle club / Sands of muirness / Duchess of Bedford / Dundee clog / Baddeck gathering / Iron man / Hunter, Charlie / Da cross reel / Arthur Muise / Mrs Crawford / Smiths a gallant fireman / Duke of Gordon Birthday / Battle of the Somme / Little cascade / Athole rose / Devil in the kitchen

CDTRAX 154 / 2 Mar '98 / Greentrax

☐ SCOTTISH FIDDLER'S RALLY

Fiddler's welcome/Bearsden fiddlers: Fiddler's Patrol / Arran shepherd/Dunlop strathspey/ Drumadoon: Currie, Rev. James / Rantin' Scottish jigs / Hamish the boot/Betty's reward / Orcadian / Celtic waltzes / Circassion circle / Neil Gow's lament for James Murray of Abercairney / Leaving Glenurquhart / Stirling castle / Inver lassies / Speed the plough / Pipe march selection / Music of J. Scott Skinner / Mary Cameron Johnston/Jenny's jig

RECD 509 / Jan '98 / REL

☐ SCOTTISH FOLK FESTIVAL

FMS 2036CD / Jul '94 / Fenn Music Services

☐ SCOTTISH FOLK FESTIVAL '93

FMS 2040CD / Jul '94 / Fenn Music Services

☐ SCOTTISH FOLK FESTIVAL '94

FMS 2050CD / Jun '94 / Fenn Music Services

☐ SCOTTISH GOLD (In The Celtic Tradition)

LCOM 5245 / May '95 / Lismor

☐ SCOTTISH GOLD (In The Ceilidh & Dance Tradition)

LCOM 5246 / May '95 / Lismor

☐ SCOTTISH GOLD (In The Popular Song)

LCOM 5244 / May '95 / Lismor

☐ SCOTTISH GOLD (In The Piping Tradition)

LCOM 5243 / May '95 / Lismor

☐ SCOTTISH HARPS

CDTRAX 5007 / Jul '98 / Greentrax

☐ SCOTTISH MOODS

Loch Lomond / Dark island / My love is like a red, red rose / Over the sea to Skye / Island song / Amazing Grace / Caledonia / Ae fond kiss / Flower of Scotland / Brides of Glenshiel / Wild mountain thyme / Auld lang syne

RECD 506 / Dec '97 / REL

☐ SCOTTISH PIPES & DRUMS

PS 65113 / Nov '93 / PlayaSound

☐ SCOTTISH REFLECTIONS PAST AND PRESENT

Angels of Dunblane: Pattullo, Gordon Trio & Pipe Major Andy Scott / Durisdeer: Huband, John & Ron Kerr / Lord of the dance: Huband, John & Ron Kerr / Earl of Errol: Huband, John & Ron Kerr / Marching through the heather: Haynes, Ken & Alan / Happy haggis: Glen Lomond Scottish Dance Band / Jigs: Ochil Players / Hills of Galloway: Campbell, Joe / Miss Rhoda W Hammond: Anderson, Stuart / Mrs. MacDonald of Dunach: Anderson, Stuart / Raasay House: Anderson, Stuart / JD MacLennan: Anderson, Stuart / Here's to Scottish whisky: Tartan Lads / Captain Campbell: MacAndrew, Hector / Mozart Allan Tulchan Lodge: MacAndrew, Hector / Burn o' Forgie: MacAndrew, Hector / My dear and only love: Bell, Paddie / Scott Skinner's compliments to Dr. MacDonald: Fitchet, Angus & His Scottish Dance Band / Lord Huntly's cave: Fitchet, Angus & His Scottish Dance Band / Fitba crazy: Beattie, Johnny / Hills of Glenorchy: Harvey, Bobby / Sons of Glenorchy: Harvey, Bobby / Who'll be King but Charlie: Glen Lomond Scottish Dance Band / Stool of repentance: Glen Lomond Scottish Dance Band / Buildings: Fisher, Ray & Archie / Captain Norman Orr Ewing: Anderson, Stuart / Murdo MacKenzie of Torridon: Anderson, Stuart / Dowie dens of Yarrow: Bell, Paddie / I'll aye ca' in by yon toun: Sumner, Bernard / Sarah Jane: JSD Band / Harry Carmichael: Fitchet, Angus & His Scottish Dance Band / Provost Tonge of Monifeith: Fitchet, Angus & His Scottish Dance Band / Jim Johnstone: Fitchet, Angus & His Scottish Dance Band / Amazing grace: Kevock Choir & Massed Pipes/Drums

CDGR 157 / Oct '96 / Ross

☐ SCOTTISH SERENADE

AVC 616 / 1 Jun '98 / Avid

☐ SCOTTISH SONGBOOK, THE

Auld Scotch sangs: McCormack, John / Comin' thro' the rye: Gluck, Alma / My love is like a red red rose: Hislop, Joseph / Annie Laurie: McCormack, John / Turn ye tae me: McCormack, John / Bonnie Mary of Argyle: Hislop, Joseph / Afton water: Hislop, Joseph / Ye banks and braes o' bonnie Doon: Melba, Nellie / Road to the isles: Lauder, Harry / Ca' the yowes: Baillie, Isobel / Flowers of the forest: Labette, Dora / March March Ettrick and Teviotdale: Dawson, Peter / Jock O'Hazeldean: Kirkby-Lunn, Louise / Robin Adair: Brola, Jeanne / An Eriskay love lilt: Robeson, Paul / My ain folk: Butt, Clara / Ae fond kiss: Coleman, Esther & Foster Richardson / Will ye no' come back again: MacEwan, Sydney / John Anderson, my Jo: Hill, Carmen / Bonnie banks of Loch Lomond: Hislop, Joseph

MIDCD 001 / Jan '95 / Moidart

☐ SCOTTISH TRADITION VOL.1 (Bothy Ballads)

Muckin' O' Geordie's byre: Macbeath, Jimmy / Stool of repentance: Bothy Band / As I came ower the Muir O' Ord: Bowie, James / Bold Princess Royal: Taylor, Jamie / Shepherd lad o'rhynie: MacDonald, John / My last farewell to Stirling: Murray, Charlie / Whistle o'er the lave o't: Macbeath, Jimmy / Stumpie strathspey: Macbeath, Jimmy / Mason's apron: Macbeath, Jimmy / Lochiel's welcome to Glasgow march: Macbeath, Jimmy / Airlin's fine braes: Elvin, Bill / Mrs. Grieg: Taylor, Jamie / Hairst o'rettie: Murray, Charlie / Smith's a gallant fireman: Murray, Charlie / Haill week o' the fair: Taylor, Jamie / Old horned sheep-jig: Taylor, Jamie / Athol highlanders/ March played in jig time: Taylor, Jamie / Medley: Steele, Frank

CDTRAX 9001 / May '93 / Greentrax

☐ SCOTTISH TRADITION VOL.2 (Music From The Western Isles)

He mandu / Dheanainn sugradh / Oran do bhean mhie fhraing / Puirt a buel / Cha tillmaccrimmon

CDTRAX 9002 / Nov '92 / Greentrax

☐ SCOTTISH TRADITION VOL.3 (Songs From Barra)

We're you in the mountains / My love Alan / One day as I roamed the hills / Woman over there who laughed / Silver whistle / Early today I set out

CDTRAX 9003 / Jan '94 / Greentrax

☐ SCOTTISH TRADITION VOL.4 (Shetland Fiddle Music)

CDTRAX 9004 / Jan '94 / Greentrax

☐ SCOTTISH TRADITION VOL.5 (The Muckle Sangs)

Gypsy laddie / False knight on the road / Bonnie banks o'fordie / Tam lin, the bold pedlar / Two sisters / Young Johnston

CDTRAX 9005 / Nov '92 / Greentrax

☐ SCOTTISH TRADITION VOL.6 (Gaelic Psalms From Lewis)

Martyrdom / Coleshill / Stroudwater / Dundee / London New / Martyrs

CDTRAX 9006 / Aug '94 / Greentrax

☐ SCOTTISH TRADITION VOL.9 (The Fiddler & His Art)

Lady Madelina Sinclair/Sandy Cameron: MacDonnel, Donald / Mackintosh's lament: MacDonnel, Donald / Medley: MacDonnel, Donald / Gabhaidh sinn an rathad mor: MacDonnel, Donald / Renfrewshire Militia/Inganess: Inkster, Hugh / Stronsay Waltz/Jock Halcrow: Shearer, Pat & David Linklater / Medley: Shearer, Pat & David Linklater / Braes of Tullymet/Captain Keeler: Reid, John Sr. & John Reid Jr. / Medley: Poleson, Andrew & William Williamson / Neil Gow's lament for whiskey: Stewart, Albert / Medley: MacAndrew, Hector & Sandie Edmondson / James F Dickie/JF Dickie's delight: MacAndrew, Hector & Sandie Edmondson / My heart is broken since thy departure: MacAndrew, Hector & Sandie Edmondson / Medley: MacAndrew, Hector & Sandie Edmondson

CDTRAX 9009 / May '93 / Greentrax

☐ SCOTTISH VOICES

Erin go bragh: Gaughan, Dick / For a' that and a' that: Exiles / Fire in the glen: Stewart, Andy M./Phil Cunningham/Manus Lunny / My last farewell to Stirling: Battlefield Band / MacCrimmon's lament: Robertson, Jeannie / Wi' my rovin' eye: Kennedy, Norman / Will ye gang love: Fisher, Archie / Corncrake: Kentigern / Cruel Mither: Campbell, Ian / Maid of Glenshee: Higgins, Lizzie / Sweet kumadee: Manuel, Ian / Norland winds: Fisher, Cilla & Artie Trezise / Freedom call all ye: Exiles / Gillie mor: Gaughan, Dick / Bawbie allan: McCulloch, Gordeanna & The Clutha / Will ye no come back again: MacColl, Ewan

TSCD 703 / Feb '97 / Topic

☐ **SCOTTY STORY, THE**
AA 043 / Jul '97 / Arf Arf

☐ **SCREAM**
0022822CIN / Jun '97 / Edel

☐ **SCREAMS OF THE GUTTER**
JABSC 014CD / 3 Aug '98 / Sidekicks

☐ **SCREWED**
ARR 67010CD / Jan '96 / Amphetamine Reptile

☐ **SCUM OF THE EARTH (2CD Set)**
SS 011 / 22 Jun '98 / SND Stories

☐ **SEA OF SERENITY**
DC 879542 / Oct '97 / Disky

☐ **SEA SONGS & SHANTIES (Traditional English Songs From The Last Days Of Sail)**
Stormy weather boys: *Roberts, A.V. 'Bob'* / Rio Grande: *Fishermen's Group* / Mr. Stormalong: *Roberts, A.V. 'Bob'* / Warlike seamen: *Copper, Bob & Ron* / Worst old ship: *Roberts, A.V. 'Bob'* / Yarmouth fishermen's song: *Cox, Harry* / Maggie May: *Roberts, A.V. 'Bob'* / Caroline and her young sailor bold: *Makem, Sarah* / Whisky Johnny: *Roberts, A.V. 'Bob'* / What shall we do with the drunken sailor: *Fishermen's Group* / Can't you dance the polka: *Roberts, A.V. 'Bob'* / Sailor's alphabet: *Jenkins, Clifford* / Haul away Joe: *Roberts, A.V. 'Bob'* / Cruisin' 'round Yarmouth: *Cox, Harry* / Windy old weather: *Roberts, A.V. 'Bob'* / Farewell and adieu (we'll rant and we'll roar): *Fishermen's Group* / High barbaree: *Roberts, A.V. 'Bob'* / Liverpool packet: *Barber, Bill* / Little boy billee: *Roberts, A.V. 'Bob'* / Johnny Todd: *Roberts, A.V. 'Bob'* / Banks of Claudy: *Copper, Bob & Ron* / Bold Princess Royal: *Roberts, A.V. 'Bob'* / Jack Tarr on the shore: *Cox, Harry* / Smuggler's boy: *Roberts, A.V. 'Bob'* / Smacksman: *Brown, Tom* / Hanging Johnny: *Roberts, A.V. 'Bob'*
CDSDL 405 / Feb '94 / Saydisc

☐ **SEASON OF MISTS (A Collection Of Celtic Moods)**
Wishing tree: *McGuire, Seamus* / Ceol na nollag: *Kilbride, Pat* / Grimstock: *House Band* / Miss Gordon of Gight: *Sileas* / Sound of Taransay: *Tannahill Weavers* / Lorraine's waltz: *Whelan, John & Eileen Ivers* / Glenglass: *Wolfstone* / Marcus Hernon's air: *Madden, Joanie* / An raibh tu ag an gcarraig: *Deanta* / Pockets of gold: *Reeltime* / L'hiver sur richelieu/ Miss B's dream: *Orealis* / Season of mists: *Crawford, Kevin*
CELT 9003 / May '97 / Celtophile

☐ **SEASON ROUND (Carols For The Whole Year)**
Come all you true good Christmas: *Valley Folk* / Shepherds arise: *Oak* / Here we come a wassailing: *Watersons* / Pace egging song: *Watersons* / Holly bears a berry: *Watersons* / Cambridgeshire May carol: *Collins, Shirley* / Hal-an-tow: *Watersons* / Two brethren: *Watersons* / EArlsdon sword dance: *Watersons* / Harvest song we gets up in the morn: *Watersons* / Souling song: *Watersons* / Cherry tree carol: *Watersons* / Herod and the cock: *Watersons* / Babe of Bethlehem: *Watersons* / Wassail song: *Watersons* / Idumea: *Watersons* / Green fields: *Watersons* / Sleep on beloved: *Watersons*
TSCD 700 / 16 Mar '98 / Topic

☐ **SEASONS IN THE SUN (2CD Set)**
NSCD 014 / Feb '95 / Newsound

☐ **SECOND FLIGHT**
AFRCD 11 / 29 Jun '98 / Flying Rhino

☐ **SECOND GRAND CONCERT OF SCOTS PIPING**
La quenoville: *St. Laurence O'Toole Pipe Band Quartet* / Caledonian Society of London: *St. Laurence O'Toole Pipe Band Quartet* / Blonde haired maid: *St. Laurence O'Toole Pipe Band Quartet* / Cathy's Willie: *St. Laurence O'Toole Pipe Band Quartet* / Lieutenant Colonel George Latham's fancy: *St. Laurence O'Toole Pipe Band Quartet* / New crossroads: *St. Laurence O'Toole Pipe Band Quartet* / Old Joe: *St. Laurence O'Toole Pipe Band Quartet* / Sean Coughlans: *St. Laurence O'Toole Pipe Band Quartet* / Banks of the Lee: *St. Laurence O'Toole Pipe Band Quartet* / Little bag: *St. Laurence O'Toole Pipe Band Quartet* / Hills of Kesh: *St. Laurence O'Toole Pipe Band Quartet* / Boys of Malin: *St. Laurence O'Toole Pipe Band Quartet* / Lord Ramsey's: *St. Laurence O'Toole Pipe Band Quartet* / Transfusion: *St. Laurence O'Toole Pipe Band Quartet* / Tiolfaidh tu abhaile liom: *St. Laurence O'Toole Pipe Band Quartet* / Anna Kloareg: *Molard, Patrick* / Al Letenant Schmidt o Kimiad ar 5ved Kompagnunez: *Molard, Patrick* / Donatien Laurent: *Molard, Patrick* / Al Lez-vamm: *Molard, Patrick* / Gwerz Mari-Louiz: *Molard, Patrick* / Gavotenn ar menez: *Molard, Patrick* / Ton cranhuel: *Molard, Patrick* / Kas a barh: *Molard, Patrick* / Laride: *Molard, Patrick* / Devil in the kitchen: *Maclean, John* / Calum Crubach: *Maclean, John* / Black snuff mill: *Maclean, John* / Sleepy Maggie: *Maclean, John* / Scotsville reel: *Maclean, John* / Roddy MacDonald's fancy: *Maclean, John* / Caberfeidh: *Maclean, John* / Hamish and the stone: *Maclean, John* / Ed Neigh's welcome to Cape Breton: *Maclean, John* / Allan Gillis' reel: *Maclean, John* / Kennedy Street march: *Maclean, John* / Miller o' Drone: *Maclean, John* / Lady Carmichael: *Maclean, John* / Unknown: *Maclean, John* / Night we had the goats: *Maclean, John* / Unknown: *Maclean, John* / Marry me now: *Maclean, John* / Snuff wife: *Robertson, Malcolm* / Martha's vineyard: *Robertson, Malcolm* / Maid on the green: *Robertson, Malcolm* / Donnie MacGregor: *Robertson, Malcolm* / Nelly Mahony's: *Robertson, Malcolm* / Pete Bradley's: *Robertson, Malcolm* / Jim Keefe's: *Robertson, Malcolm* / Sweeney's polka: *Robertson, Malcolm* / Mike Ward's polka: *Robertson, Malcolm* / Glen polka: *Robertson, Malcolm* / Mediana a pipia: *Mascia, Orlando & Franco Melis* / Fiorassiu: *Mascia, Orlando & Franco Melis* / Fiuda: *Mascia, Orlando & Franco Melis*
CDTRAX 128 / May '97 / Greentrax

☐ **SECRET LIFE OF ARABIA, THE**
AAA 166 / Nov '97 / Club Du Disque Arabe

☐ **SECRET LIFE OF PUNKS, THE**
Dogs of war: *Exploited* / One law for them: *4 Skins* / Kids of the 80's: *Infra Riot* / No U turns: *Partisans* / Employers black list: *Business* / Youth: *Blitz* / Harry may: *Business* / Jet boy jet girl: *Chron Gen* / King of the jungle: *Last Resort* / Maniac: *Peter & The Test Tube Babies* / Catch 22: *Infra Riot* / Yesterdays heroes: *4 Skins* / Army life: *Exploited* / I lost my love to a UK sub: *Gonads*
DOLECD 108 / Jan '96 / Dojo

☐ **SECRET LIFE OF TRANCE VOL.1**
RSNCD 6 / May '93 / Rising High

☐ **SECRET LIFE OF TRANCE VOL.3**
RSNCD 20 / Jul '94 / Rising High

☐ **SECRET LIFE OF TRANCE VOL.4**
RSNCD 28 / Dec '94 / Rising High

☐ **SECRET LIFE OF TRANCE VOL.6**
RSNCD 40 / Aug '95 / Rising High

☐ **SECRET LIFE OF TRANCE VOL.7 (2CD Set)**
RSNCD 50 / Feb '97 / Rising High

☐ **SECRET MUSEUM OF MANKIND - CENTRAL ASIA (Ethnic Music Classics 1923-1948)**
YAZ 7007 / Jul '96 / Yazoo

☐ **SECRET MUSEUM OF MANKIND - NORTH AFRICA (Ethnic Music Classics: 1925-1948)**
YAZCD 7011 / Mar '97 / Yazoo

☐ **SECRET MUSEUM OF MANKIND VOL.1**
YAZCD 7004 / Oct '95 / Yazoo

☐ **SECRET MUSEUM OF MANKIND VOL.2**
YAZCD 7005 / Oct '95 / Yazoo

☐ **SECRET MUSEUM OF MANKIND VOL.3. (Ethnic Music Classics 1923-1948)**
YAZ 7006 / Jul '96 / Yazoo

☐ **SECRET MUSEUM OF MANKIND VOL.4 (Ethnic Music Classics: 1925-1948)**
YAZCD 7010 / Mar '97 / Yazoo

☐ **SECRET RECORDS PUNK SINGLES COLLECTION VOL.1**
Dogs of war: *Exploited* / Army life: *Exploited* / Exploited barmy army: *Exploited* / Kids of the 80's: *Infa Riot* / One law for them: *4 Skins* / Dead cities: *Exploited* / Harry May: *Business* / Yesterday's heroes: *4 Skins* / Jet boy jet girl: *Chron Gen* / Attack exploited: *Chron Gen* / I lost my love to a UK sub: *Gonads* / Punk city rockers: *Gonads* / Smash the discos: *Business* / H-Bomb: *Business* / TOP: *Exploited* / Computers don't blunder: *Exploited* / Troops of tomorrow: *Exploited* / Feel the rage: *Infa Riot* / Clouded eyes: *Chron Gen* / Outlaw: *Chron Gen* / Victim: *Strike* / Low life: *4 Skins* / Seems to me: *4 Skins*
CDPUNK 13 / Sep '93 / Anagram

☐ **SECRET RECORDS PUNK SINGLES COLLECTION VOL.2**
Blown to bits: *Exploited* / Fuck the mods: *Exploited* / I belive in anarchy: *Exploited* / Hitler's in the charts again: *Exploited* / Alternative: *Exploited* / Addiction: *Exploited* / Brave new world: *4 Skins* / Justice: *4 Skins* / Employers blacklist: *Business* / Disco girls: *Business* / Subway sadist: *Chron Gen* / Behind closed doors: *Chron Gen* / Disco tech: *Chron Gen* / Punk rock will never die: *Gonads* / Got any Wrggly's John: *Gonads* / She can't whip me: *Gonads* / School's out: *Infa Riot* / Fight for your life: *Angela Rippon's Bum* / I'm thick: *Skin Disease* / Where's dock green: *Venom* / Way it's got to be: *East End Badoes*
CDPUNK 60 / Sep '95 / Anagram

☐ **SEDUCTIVE SOUNDS OF TEKNOTIKA, THE**
One step beyond / When the planets align / Twinge / Seduction of the virgin princess / Arvesche-tam / Kfi stanbouich / Swing sexy / Shake it / Interview with an alien '97 / Universal love / Afterglow / Aftermath
EYEUKCD 014 / Jul '97 / Eye Q

☐ **SEE WITH YOUR EARS (The Red Seal Surround Sound Sampler)**
09026683182 / Feb '96 / RCA Red Seal

☐ **SEEDMOUTH**
CSR 12CD / May '96 / Cold Spring

☐ **SEEDS**
So small: *Showgirls* / Judy Garland life: *Gretschen Hofner* / Miss bunny romp: *Dragstripper* / Absolutely, positively nothing: *GEN* / Michaela: *Pippi & The Butcherbirds* / It's a game: *Minty* / Marianne Fame: *Showgirls* / Pervert upstairs: *Dragstripper* / How's that: *Theaudience* / MIA: *Tubetop* / Glug glug car: *Sexton Ming* / RnB international: *Zbons* / Klassy with a kapital k: *Gretschen Hofner* / Isadora grand prix: *That Donald* / Mirror of me: *Pippi & The Butcherbirds* / Bubble song: *Genteels*
OPIUM 1 / 15 Sep '97 / Poppy

☐ **SEGADANCE (Music From Mauritius)**
PS 65126 / May '94 / PlayaSound

☐ **SELECTED CIRCUITS**
UPCD 06 / Sep '95 / Nitro

☐ **SELECTED SIGNS VOL.1 (An Anthology)**
5378052 / Sep '97 / ECM

☐ **SELECTED WORKD FOR MOVING PICTURES VOL.1**
PIAS 556460120 / Nov '96 / Antler

☐ **SELECTED WORKS FOR MOVING PICTURES VOL.2**
FREI 002CD / 15 Sep '97 / Freibank

☐ **SELECTION OF COUNTRY (2CD Set)**
DCD 704 / Dec '96 / Gold Sound

☐ **SELECTOR DUB NARCOTIC**
KCD 82 / 11 May '98 / K

☐ **SELEKTA SHOWCASE '89**
My prerogative: *Sanchez* / Enquirer: *One-two crew* / Lick out: *Ninjaman* / Jah is the way: *Minott, Sugar* / Nice and cute: *Johnny P* / Special lady: *Gel, Ny* / Vanity crazy: *Chaka Demus* / Rawborn rub a dub: *Meakes, Carl* / Me no know why: *General Trees* / Step it up: *Antony, Pad*
GRELCD 130 / Nov '89 / Greensleeves

☐ **SEND ME THE PILLOW YOU DREAM ON**
Send me the pillow that you dream on: *Locklin, Hank* / Reuben James: *Rogers, Kenny* / I feel sorry for him: *Nelson, Willie* / Come on in: *Cline, Patsy* / Hey good lookin': *Cash, Johnny* / You'll always have someone: *Nelson, Willie* / Six days on the road: *Dudley, Dave* / Always leaving, always gone: *Rogers, Kenny* / Burning memories: *Jennings, Waylon* / Walkin' after midnight: *Cline, Patsy* / Singin' the blues: *Mitchell, Guy* / Take these chains from my heart: *Drusky, Roy* / Mule train: *Laine, Frankie* / Don't think twice, it's alright: *Jennings, Waylon* / If I don't understand: *Nelson, Willie* / Ramblin' rose: *Lee, Johnny* / Rose garden: *Anderson, Lynn* / Heart you break may be your own: *Cline, Patsy* / Ticket to nowhere: *Rogers, Kenny* / Release me: *Mandrell, Barbara* / I can't find the time: *Nelson, Willie* / Waterloo: *Jackson, Stonewall* / Last letter: *Drusky, Roy* / Wild side of life: *Fender, Freddy* / Sunshine: *Rogers, Kenny*
GRF 120 / Feb '93 / Tring

☐ **SEND ME THE PILLOW YOU DREAM ON**
MACCD 213 / Aug '96 / Autograph

☐ **SENHORAS DO FADO (Lisboa 1925-1945)**
3004080 / 24 Feb '98 / IMP

☐ **SENSATIONAL 70'S VOL.1**
PLSCD 182 / Apr '97 / Pulse

☐ **SENSATIONAL 70'S VOL.2**
PLSCD 183 / Apr '97 / Pulse

☐ **SENSATIONAL SIXTIES VOL.1**
Hippy hippy shake: *Swinging Blue Jeans* / Tell him: *Davis, Billie* / For your love: *Clapton, Eric & The Yardbirds* / Moon river: *Williams, Danny* / I'm into something good: *Herman's Hermits* / Baby now that I've found you: *Foundations* / Well I ask you: *Kane, Eden* / Spicks and specks: *Bee Gees* / Dear Mrs. Applebee: *Garrick, David* / Wild one: *Rydell, Bobby* / Sugar sugar: *Archies* / Dimples: *Animals* / Rollin' and tumblin': *Canned Heat* / With a girl like you: *Troggs* / Fool in love: *Turner, Ike & Tina* / Down in the boondocks: *Royal, Billy Joe* / Call up the groups medley: *Barron Knights*
CDSGP 0354 / 10 Nov '97 / Prestige

☐ **SENSATIONAL SIXTIES, THE (2CD Set)**
You never walk alone: *Gerry & The Pacemakers* / Silence is golden: *Tremeloes* / Runaway: *Shannon, Del* / Happy birthday sweet sixteen: *Sedaka, Neil* / Wild thing: *Troggs* / I'm into something good: *Herman's Hermits* / Rubber ball: *Vee, Bobby* / Something's gotten hold of my heart: *Pitney, Gene* / I'm sorry: *Lee, Brenda* / Da doo ron ron: *Crystals* / When a man loves a woman: *Sledge, Percy* / I'm telling you now: *Freddie & The Dreamers* / Because they're young: *Eddy, Duane* / Little town flirt: *Shannon, Del* / It's my party: *Gore, Lesley* / Breaking up is hard to do: *Sedaka, Neil* / Walkin' back to happiness: *Shapiro, Helen* / Wishin' and hopin': *Merseybeats* / Rescue me: *Bass, Fontella* / Dancing in the street: *Reeves, Martha* / Do you want to know a secret: *Kramer, Billy J.* / Tossing and turning: *Ivy League* / Little loving: *Fourmost* / Um, um, um, um: *Fontana, Wayne* / You were made for me: *Freddie & The Dreamers* / Just like Eddie: *Heinz* / Do you love me: *Poole, Brian* / Pied piper: *St. Peters, Crispian* / Bobby's girl: *Maughan, Susan* / Save the last dance for me: *Drifters* / Juliet: *Four Pennies* / Hello little girl: *Fourmost* / Little children: *Kramer, Billy J.* / My guy: *Wells, Mary* / But I do: *Henry, Clarence 'Frogman'* / Crying game: *Berry, Dave* / Wimoweh: *Denver, Karl* / Tell me when: *Applejacks* / Baby now that I've found you: *Foundations* / Jesamine: *Casuals*
DCD 3002 / Jun '97 / Music

☐ **SENSATIONAL SIXTIES, THE**
I'm into something good: *Herman's Hermits* / Always something there to remind me: *Shaw, Sandie* / Pretty flamingo: *Manfred Mann* / Sloop John B.: *Beach Boys* / Needles and pins: *Searchers* / Happy together: *Turtles* / Walking back to happiness: *Shapiro, Helen* / Do you want to know a secret: *Kramer, Billy J.* / I'm telling you now: *Freddie & The Dreamers* / Hi ho silver lining: *Beck, Jeff* / We've gotta get out of this place: *Animals* / Hold me: *Proby, P.J.* / Bus stop: *Hollies* / Judy in disguise: *Fred, John & The Playboys*
DC 881402 / 2 Feb '98 / Disky

☐ **SENSATIONAL SOUL**
Soul man: *Sam & Dave* / Gimme little sign: *Wood, Brenton* / Backfield in motion: *Mel & Tim* / Rescue me: *Bass, Fontella* / Harlem shuffle: *Bob & Earl* / Letter: *Box Tops* / Under the boardwalk: *Drifters* / Knock on wood: *Floyd, Eddie* / In crowd: *Gray, Dobie* / Dancing in the street: *Reeves, Martha* / Rock your baby: *McCrae, George* / I just can't stop dancing: *Bell, Archie & The Drells* / (Sittin' on the) dock of the bay: *Sledge, Percy* / Hey girl don't bother me: *Tams* / Spanish Harlem: *King, Ben E.* / Love I lost: *Melvin, Harold & The Bluenotes* / Indiana wants me: *Taylor, R. Dean* / What becomes of the broken hearted: *Ruffin, Jimmy*
ECD 3056 / Jan '95 / K-Tel

☐ **SENSE OF DIRECTION, A**
Sense of direction / Aunt Monk / Theme for a new day / Long as you're living / I'm trying to find a way / Keep the faith / Panther / Cleopatra and the African Knight / To the establishment / Red clay / Communication / Dorian
CDBGPD 099 / Oct '95 / Beat Goes Public

☐ **SENSES**
Play dead: *Bjork & David Arnold* / Robin (The hooded man): *Clannad* / Love theme: *Vangelis* / Between the lines: *Lindes, Hal* / Cockeye's song: *Morricone, Ennio* / Love's theme: *Moroder, Giorgio* / Robinson Crusoe: *Art Of Noise* / Nomads of the wind: *Bennett, Brian* / Oboe concerto in D minor: *Academy Of Ancient Music* / Gymnopedie no.1: *Satie, Erik* / Equinoxe part 4: *Jarre, Jean Michel* / Eve of war: *Wayne, Jeff* / Cacharpaya: *Incantation* / Coisich a ruin (walk my beloved): *Capercaillie* / Rowena's theme: *Edge* / Cavatina: *Williams, John* / Snowman: *Blake, Howard* / Concierto de Aranjuez: *De Angelis, Nicolas* / Oxygene part IV: *Marvin, Hank* / Going home: *Knopfler, Mark*
5166272 / Sep '94 / PolyGram TV

☐ **SENSUAL CLASSICS**
SPLCD 044 / Apr '96 / Sloane

☐ **SENSUAL RHYTHMS**
Would I lie to you: *Charles & Eddie* / Back to life: *Soul II Soul* / Ain't no sunshine: *Youngblood, Sydney* / Big fun: *Inner City* / Magic: *Defunkt* / Thinking about your love: *Thomas, Kenny* / Walk on by: *Carroll, Dina* / Love zone: *Ocean, Billy* / Take good care of me: *Butler, Jonathan* / Caught in the middle: *Roberts, Juliet* / Endlessly: *Jones, Glenn* / Still water: *O'Bryan* / Heartbeat: *Ward, Robert* / I wanna love somebody: *Bofill, Angela* / Let be your baby: *Williams, Geoffrey* / She's playing hard to get: *Hi-Five*
DC880832 / Aug '97 / Disky

☐ **SENSUAL SAX COLLECTION, THE (3CD Set)**
EMTBX 306 / Aug '97 / Emporio

☐ **SENSUOUS PANPIPES**
Sexual healing / We've got tonight / Jealous guy / Mad about the boy / I guess that's why they call it the blues / Dock of the bay / Move closer / Mist blue / Killing me softly / Just the way you are / Endless love / When a man loves a woman / Help me make it through the night / Cry me a river
CDMFP 6271 / Sep '96 / Music For Pleasure

☐ **SENTIMENTAL JOURNEY**
It's only a paper moon: *Cole, Nat 'King'* / Nightingale can sing the blues: *Lee, Peggy* / Along the Navajo trail: *Crosby, Bing* / Things ain't what they used to be: *Ellington, Duke* / Stardust: *Shaw, Artie* / May you always: *Stewart, Sandy* / As the world turns: *Gibson, Ginny* / Cherokee canyon: *Miller, Glenn* / I don't mind: *Boswell, Connee* / Who put the devil in Evelyn's eyes: *Mills Brothers* / Far from the madding crowd: *Haymes, Dick* / Just another blues: *Cole, Nat 'King'* / Gold cadillac: *Waring, Fred & His Pennsylvanians* / And the angels sing: *Goodman, Benny* / In the mood: *Miller, Glenn* / Mad about him blues: *Shore, Dinah* / I'll never smile again: *Dorsey, Tommy* / On the Atchison, Topeka and the Santa Fe: *Herman, Woody* / My very good friend the milkman: *Waller, Fats* / That's how love comes: *Gibson, Ginny* / April fool: *Ellis, Peggy-Ann* / Don't cry crybaby: *Cole, Nat 'King'* / You ain't got nothin': *Boswell, Connee* / (I'm getting) Corns for my country: *Andrews Sisters* / It takes a long, long train with a red caboose: *Page, Patti* / Casanova cricket: *Carmichael, Hoagy* / Finders keepers: *Mitchell, Guy* / I tipped my hat (and slowly rode away): *James, Harry Orchestra*
3036100142 / Feb '96 / Pearls

☐ **SENTIMENTAL JOURNEY**
DCD 5308 / Dec '93 / Disky

☐ **SENTIMENTAL JOURNEY**
GALE 429 / 20 Apr '98 / Gallerie

☐ **SENTIMENTAL SWING - 12 HITS**
UP 005 / Sep '92 / Hindsight

☐ **SENTIMENTS OF LOVE**
VPCD 2044 / Mar '96 / VP

☐ **SENZA VOLTO (The Eve Collection)**
EVECD 97001 / Jun '97 / Eve

☐ **SEODA CHONAMARA VOL.1 (Connemara Favourites Vol.1)**
Inis Caltrach/Toss the feathers: *Althneach, Iorras* / Galtee mountain boy: *O'Flaharta, John Beag* / Stack of wheat/Stack of barley/Johnny will you marry me: *O'Hiarnain, P.J.* / Green brooms: *Ac Dhonncha, Sean* / Currachai na Tra Baine: *O'Beaglaoich, Sean* / Peigin leitir moir: *O'Beaglaoich, Sean* / All the way to Galway fair: *O'Lochluinn, Paidraig* / My own dear native land: *MacDonnchadha, Johnny Mhairtin Learai* / Sweet Biddy Daly: *Walsh, John G* / My pretty fair maid: *Walsh, John G* / Cliff, Belfast and Sweeps hornpipes: *O'Ceannabhain, Padraig Tom Photch* / Neansin Bhan: *O'Ceannabhain, Padraig Tom Photch* / Wise maid/Last night's fun: *Connolly, John* / Si do Mhaimeo: *Ni Chathain, Brid* / High reel: *Learai, Sonai Choilm* / Whistling thief: *Ac Dhonncha, Sean* / Charlie Mulvihill/Plains of Boyle: *Na Hancairi* / An hunter: *Rathcliffe, Peter* / Amhran na gCualain: *Sheainn, Mairtin* / Irish washerwoman: *Ghabha, Michael Mhaire* / An Merican mor: *O'Flaharta, John Beag* / First house in Connaught: *O'Hiarnain, P.J.* / Queen of Connemara: *MacEoin, Tomas*
CICD 019 / Dec '93 / Clo Iar-Chonnachta

☐ **SEPTETOS CUBANOS - SONES DE CUBA (2CD Set)**
MT 113/4 / Jan '94 / Corason

☐ **SERENADA (Classic Fado And Guitar Serenades From Portugal)**
Balada de outono: *Alfonso, Jose* / Flores para cointra: *Bernardino, Antonio* / Pavara: *Antonio Portugal* / Variacoes em si menor: *Paredes, Carlos* / La longe: *Santos, Almeida* / Suadades de coinbra: *Alfonso, Jose* / Trova do vento que pasa: *Bernardino, Antonio* / Crucificado: *Alfonso, Jose* / Desfoliada: *Paredes, Artur* / Estudo em la moir: *Brojo, Antonio* / Cancao de flores: *De Oliveira, Adriano Correla* / Variacos em re menor: *Antonio Portugal* / Cantiga para os que partem: *Bernardino, Antonio* / Mar alto: *Alfonso, Jose* / Balada de montego: *Paredes, Artur* / Guitarras do men pais: *Bernardino, Antonio* / Variacas em la menor: *Paredes, Carlos* / O meu fado: *Lacerda E Megre* / Roque, Sutil: *Lacerda E Megre* / Samaritana: *Bernardino, Antonio*
NSCD 020 / 6 Oct '97 / Nascente

☐ **SERENADE OF LOVE, A (2CD Set)**
DEMPCD 107 / Mar '96 / Emporio

☐ **SERESTAS DA MINHA TERRA**
99348 / 12 May '98 / Minas

☐ **SERIALEMENT VOTRE**
SVCD 2 / May '97 / Commando

☐ **SERIOUS LISTENING MUSIC VOL.1**
DELSDC 1 / Jan '94 / Delirium

☐ **SERIOUS LISTENING MUSIC VOL.2**
DELSCD 02 / Jun '94 / Delirium

☐ **SERIOUS REGGAE ALBUM VOL.1, THE**
CDSGP 0260 / Sep '96 / Prestige

☐ **SERIOUS REGGAE ALBUM VOL.2, THE**
CDSGP 0141 / Aug '95 / Prestige

☐ **SERIOUS REGGAE ALBUM VOL.3, THE**
CDSGP 077 / Jul '94 / Prestige

☐ **SERVE CHILLED**
Mr. Wendal: *Arrested Development* / Summertime: *DJ Jazzy Jeff & The Fresh Prince* / Manchild: *Cherry, Neneh* / Ghetto jam: *Domino* / Set adrift on memory bliss: *PM Dawn* / Karmacoma: *Massive Attack* / Rebirth of slick: *Digable Planets* / Spiritual love: *Urban Species* / Eye know: *De La Soul* / Gotta lotta love: *Ice-T* / It was a good day: *Ice Cube* / Can I kick it: *Tribe Called Quest* / Feel me flow: *Naughty By Nature* / I'll be around: *Rappin' 4-Tay* / In the summertime: *Shaggy* / Save it 'til the morning after: *Shut Up & Dance* / My definition of a bombastic jazz style: *Dream Warriors* / That's how I'm livin': *Ice-T* / I need love: *LL Cool J* / People everyday: *Arrested Development*
VTCD 56 / Aug '95 / Virgin

☐ **SERVICE BANDS ON THE AIR VOL.1**
Flying home: *Miller, Glenn & The Army Airforce Orchestra* / I couldn't sleep a wink last night: *Skyrockets* / Barrel house boogie: *Skyrockets* / On the sunny side of the street: *Skyrockets* / Swinging on a star: *Skyrockets* / March of the toys: *Canada Dance Band* / It's love love love: *Royal Air Force Dance Orchestra* / Leapfrog: *Royal Air Force Dance Orchestra* / I'll get by: *Royal Air Force Dance Orchestra* / Milkman keep those bottles quiet: *Royal Air Force Dance Orchestra* / Dear old southland: *Royal Air Force Dance Orchestra* / I can't give you anything but love: *US Navy Dance Band* / LST party: *US Navy Dance Band* / With my head in the clouds: *Miller, Glenn & AAF Band* / No compree: *Miller, Glenn & AAF Band* / Lark leaps in: *Royal Marines Commando Forces Band* / Wartime medley: *Canadian Army Radio Orchestra* / Out of this world: *Canadian Army Radio Orchestra* / More than you know: *Royal Army Ordanance Corps Dance Orchestra* / Mr. Ghost goes to town: *Royal Navy Swing Octet* / With a song in my heart: *British Band Of The AEF*
VJB 19442 / May '94 / Vintage Jazz Band

☐ **SERVICE BANDS ON THE AIR VOL.2 (VE Day Party)**
Introduction / Music makers / Let's get lost / Dance with a dolly / My blue heaven / Long ago and far away / Jumpin' Jiminy / Angry / I'm beginning to see the light / Holiday for strings / My heart isn't in it / Introduction / African war dance / All this and heaven too / Down for double / Comedy routine / Jazz me blues / What a difference a day makes / My heart tells me / Woodchopper's ball / Tess's torch song / Way down yonder in New Orleans / I'll be seeing you / When Johnny comes marching home
VJB 19462 / May '95 / Vintage Jazz Band

☐ **SETTING THE SCENE (From The Vaults Of KPM)**
GAP 0292 / 24 Nov '97 / Groove Attack

☐ **SEVEN SEALS, THE**
To you: *Nature & Organisation* / Seven seals: *Current 93* / My inspiration is you: *Tiny Tim* / Nit pick: *Nurse With Wound*
DURTRO 033CD / Aug '97 / Durtro

☐ **SEVENTEEN AND A HALF**
NITR 007 / Feb '97 / Demolition Derby

☐ **70'S COLLECTION, THE (3CD Set)**
KBOX 369 / 27 Apr '98 / Collection

☐ **SEVENTIES DOWNUNDER VOL.1**
RVCD 22 / 8 Jun '98 / Raven

☐ **SEVENTIES DOWNUNDER VOL.2 (Do Y'Self A Favour - The Countdown Years 1975-1979)**
RVCD 35 / Jan '94 / Raven

☐ **SEX, DRUGS & ROCK 'N' ROLL (3CD Set)**
Sex and drugs and rock 'n' roll: *Dury, Ian* / Golden brown: *Dury, Ian* / Legalise it: *Tosh, Peter* / Wild places: *Browne, Duncan* / Acid queen: *Turner, Ike & Tina* / Whole lotta love: *CCS* / Amphetamine Annie: *Canned Heat* / Brother Louie: *Quireboys* / Bad boys like to rock 'n' roll: *Quireboys* / Hit me with your best shot: *Benatar, Pat* / Party girls: *Mink Deville* / Love stinks: *Geils, J. Band* / Milk and alcohol: *Dr. Feelgood* / OD'd on life itself: *Blue Oyster Cult* / Ain't ni high like rock 'n' roll: *Helix* / Psycho killer: *Talking Heads* / You are my heroin: *Boy George* / Hit me with your rhythm stick: *Dury, Ian* / Sex party: *Quireboys* / Orgasm addict: *Buzzcocks* / I like to rock: *April Wine* / Jeopardy: *Kihn, Greg Band* / Talk dirty to me: *Poison* / Lebanon: *Untouchables* / Only you can rock me: *UFO* / Gimme shelter: *Grand Funk Railroad* / Sexcrime: *Eurythmics* / Voyeur: *Fish* / No more heroes: *Stranglers* / Pretty paracetamol: *Fischer Z* / Cruisin' and boozin': *Hagar, Sammy* / Courvoiser concerto: *Schenker, Michael Group* / Gimme some lovin': *Thunder* / Sugar walls: *Easton, Sheena* / House of the rising sun: *Animals* / Who do you love: *Juicy Lucy* / Paranoid: *Black Sabbath* / Ace of spades: *Motorhead* / I've been drinking: *Beck, Jeff & Rod Stewart* / Animal: *WASP* / Don't let the needle win: *WASP* / Little river band: *Little River Band* / I want a new drug: *Lewis, Huey & The News* / Wake up and make love with me: *Dury, Ian* / Cocaine: *Dillinger* / I got stoned and missed it: *Dr. Hook* / Heaven is in the back seat of my Cadillac: *Hot Chocolate* / Sex as a weapon: *Benatar, Pat* / Body rock: *Vidal, Maria*
HR 868612 / Sep '96 / Disky

☐ **SEXOPOLIS**
FAN 002CD / 16 Sep '97 / Fantomas

☐ **SEXTETOS CUBANOS VOL.2**
ARHCD 7006 / Sep '95 / Arhoolie

☐ **SEXUAL HEALING (18 Sensual Masterpieces)**
Sexual healing / Black velvet / Boombastic / I want your sex / Crazy / Erotica / How deep is your love / Unchained melody / Je t'aime / Do that to me one more time / I will always love you / Just a step from heaven / Endless love / Deeper and deeper / No ordinary love / You gotta love someone / Theme from 'Emanuelle' / Let's talk about sex
305752 / Oct '96 / Hallmark

☐ **SEYCHELLES - THE FORGOTTEN ISLANDS**
ARN 60402 / Jul '97 / Arion

☐ **SHACK, THE**
DOJOCD 145 / Sep '93 / Dojo

☐ **SHADES, GUITARS, STRIPES AND STARS (American Alternative Rock Classics)**
Battleship chains: *Georgia Satellites* / Satellite: *Hooters* / Crashin' down: *Jason & The Scorchers* / Don't want to know if you're lonely: *Husker Du* / Final wild son: *Long Ryders* / Copperhead Road: *Earle, Steve* / Trail of tears: *Guadalcanal Diary* / Behind the wall of sleep: *Smithereens* / I believe I'm in love: *Fabulous Thunderbirds* / Future's so bright I gotta wear shades: *Timbuk 3* / Bigger stones: *Beat Farmers* / Will the wolf survive: *Los Lobos* / Let my people go: *Rainmakers* / Time ain't nothing: *Green On Red* / Don't run wild: *Del-Fuegos*
VSOPCD 225 / Jul '96 / Connoisseur Collection

☐ **SHADES OF COUNTRY VOL.1**
PLSCD 107 / Apr '96 / Pulse

☐ **SHADES OF COUNTRY VOL.2**
PLSCD 108 / Apr '96 / Pulse

☐ **SHADES OF SOUL VOL.2 (2CD Set)**
RADCD 66 / Aug '97 / Global TV

☐ **SHADOW MUSIC OF JAVA**
ROU 5060 / May '96 / Rounder

☐ **SHAG AND BLUES VOL.1 (Beach Blast)**
Strokin': *Carter, Clarence* / Messin' with my mind: *Carter, Clarence* / Hit and run lover: *Nelson, 'Chicago' Bob* / Something's mighty wrong: *Davis, Tyrone* / Lil' brown eyes: *Ealey, Theodis* / I want a big fat woman: *Willis, Chuck* / One slick woman: *Willis, Chuck* / Something you got: *Johnson, Luther 'Houserocker'* / Fish girl blues: *Lynn, Trudy* / Ain't no blues in town: *Rhodes, Sonny* / Only you: *Chi-Lites* / First impressions: *Impressions* / I need you so bad: *Legendary Blues Band* / Woman like you: *Dr. Hector & The Groove Injectors* / Honky tonk: *Doggett, Bill & The King Allstars* / Crosscut saw: *Coleman, Gary B.B.* / I'd rather be blind: *Bell, William*
DOG 91042 / Aug '97 / Wild Dog

☐ **SHAG AND BLUES VOL.2 (Beach Boogie)**
Slip away: *Carter, Clarence* / Been there done that: *Reed, Francine* / You don't want me: *Dawkins, Jimmy* / Find you a job: *Hall, Sandra* / Trying to love you: *Bell, William* / Knife and a fork: *Anderson, Kip* / Brenda: *Smith, O.C.* / Pump up your love: *Hall, Sandra* / I'll be doggone: *Garrett, Vernon* / Prove my love: *Davis, Tyrone* / I'm trouble: *Jackson, Yvonne* / Lisa: *Lee, Darrell* / You bug me: *Reed, Francine & Delbert McClinton* / How long have you been lovin' me: *Jackson, Chuck* / I'm the man you need: *Ealey, Theodis* / Hold me in your arms: *Gooding, Cuba* / Fell in love: *Smith, Gregg*
DOG 91112 / Aug '97 / Wild Dog

☐ **SHAKE 'EM ON DOWN (The Real Country Blues)**
Shake 'em on down / Sloppy drunk blues / Alabama blues / Need more blues / Judge bushay blues / Pardon denied again / Rabbit blues / Take me out of the bottom / Fred's worried life blues / Poor black Mattie / Come home to me baby / Smokestack lightnin' / Write me a few lines / Mississippi river / Just tippin' in / She left me a mule to ride / Canned heat / Three o'clock in the morning / 'Bout a spoonful / You call yourself a cadillac / Keep your nose out of my business / Oh baby
CDCHD 527 / Oct '94 / Ace

☐ **SHAKE, JUMP, SHOUT**
Hold me back: *Westbam* / Callas: *Vox Mystica* / Heavy mental: *Heavy Mental* / Saxophone: *Westbam* / Exzess: *Dick* / Alarm clock: *Westbam* / Time: *Beat In Time* / On a mission: *Dick* / Hell or heaven: *LUPO* / Dreams: *Darling, Grace* / Is it raw enough: *Heavy Mental* / Aka aka: *Eastbam*
YOBCD 1 / Jun '90 / Yobro

☐ **SHAKE, RATTLE & ROCK 'N' ROLL (2CD Set)**
Great balls of fire: *Lewis, Jerry Lee* / Personality: *Price, Lloyd* / Tutti frutti: *Little Richard* / Great pretender: *Platters* / My true love: *Scott, Jack* / Wild one: *Rydell, Bobby* / It's only make believe: *Twitty, Conway* / Ain't misbehavin': *Bruce, Tommy* / That'll be the day: *Crickets* / Handy man: *Jones, Jimmy* / Charlie Brown: *Coasters* / Running Bear: *Preston, Johnny* / Bobby's girl: *Maughan, Susan* / Shakin' all over: *Dene, Terry* / Singin' the blues: *Mitchell, Guy* / Blueberry hill: *Domino, Fats* / Tell him: *Davis, Billie* / Stay: *Williams, Maurice & The Zodiacs* / School day: *Berry, Chuck* / I want to walk you home: *Domino, Fats* / Moonlight gambler: *Laine, Frankie* / Rock 'n' roll music: *Berry, Chuck* / Oh boy: *Crickets* / Good golly Miss Molly: *Little Richard* / Stagger Lee: *Price, Lloyd* / Blue suede shoes: *Perkins, Carl* / Dream lover: *Darin, Bobby* / Spanish Harlem: *King, Ben E.* / Memphis Tennessee: *Berry, Chuck* / Cradle of love: *Preston, Johnny* / Be bop a lula: *Vincent, Gene* / Yakety yak: *Coasters* / Sheila: *Roe, Tommy* / Maybe baby: *Crickets* / Sway: *Rydell, Bobby* / Ain't that a shame: *Domino, Fats* / My heart's a symphony: *Lewis, Gary & The Playboys* / Born to be a rolling stone: *Vincent, Gene* / Whole lotta shakin' goin' on: *Lewis, Jerry Lee*
330312 / Mar '97 / Hallmark

☐ **SHAKE, RATTLE AND ROLL**
MACCD 212 / Aug '96 / Autograph

☐ **SHAKE THAT THING (America's Top Bands Of The 20's)**
I wanna be loved by you: *Broadway Nitelites* / Shakin' the blues away: *Selvin, Ben & His Orchestra* / Hello Swanee, hello: *Lentz, Al & His Orchestra* / Mighty blue: *Waring's Pennsylvanians* / What a day: *Weems, Ted & His Orchestra* / Melancholy Lou: *Lanin, Howard & His Ben Franklin Dance Orchestra* / Confessin': *Lombardo, Guy & His Royal Canadians* / Shake that thing: *Lyman, Abe & His California Orchestra* / Everything's made for love: *Lopez, Vincent & His Orchestra* / Wabash blues: *Charleston Chasers* / Smile: *Whiteman, Paul & His Orchestra* / Let's misbehave: *Aaronson, Irving & His Commanders* / Just a night for meditation: *Crumit, Frank* / Bugle call rag: *Lewis, Ted & His Band* / S'posin': *Vallee, Rudy & His Connecticut Yankees* / He's the last word: *Bernie, Ben & His Hotel Roosevelt Orchestra*
CDAJA 5002 / Apr '89 / Living Era

☐ **SHAKE THE BONES (Hydrogen Dukebox Compilation)**
033CD / Mar '97 / Hydrogen Dukebox

☐ **SHAKE YOUR CONGAS**
Big bang conga: *Los Albinos* / Chiquito: *Calzado, Ruben & His Latin Orchestra* / When the world was mine: *Golden Dream Orchestra* / Aquarella: *Carlier, Jo* / Loin de mes yeux pres de mon coeur: *Pelletier, Jean-Claude* / Go go conga: *Los Albinos* / Blue candlelight: *Evans, Jean & His Piano Strings* / Los patatos: *Boxeros* / Obsession: *Owen, Reg* / Pancho: *Dee Dee & Her Panchos* / Chinese conga: *Los Albinos* / Blue sunrise: *Sadi Quartet* / La cucarachacha: *Loland, Peter* / Birds of paradise: *Kreuder, Peter* / A la salud: *La Baum, Stan & His Orchestra* / Swinging conga: *Los Albinos* / Forever: *Clippers* / Headin' north: *Albimore, Willy* / Marijuana brass: *Mertens, Teddy* / Frere jacques conga: *Los Albinos*
74321421462 / Jun '97 / RCA Victor

☐ **SHAKEN NOT STIRRED**
James Bond theme: *Bond, James* / Goldfinger: *Bond, James* / Green eyes: *Florence, Bob* / It happened in Monterrey: *Florence, Bob* / Caravan: *Lyman, Arthur* / Taboo: *Lyman, Arthur* / Sunny: *Lyman, Arthur* / Mambo burger: *Burger, Jack* / Boulevard of broken dreams: *Burger, Jack* / Man with the golden gun: *In Group* / If I had a hammer: *In Group* / Orchids in the moonlight: *Zimmerman, Harry*
RCD 50337 / Feb '96 / Rykodisc

☐ **SHAKIN' ALL OVER**
Locomotion: *Little Eva* / Runaway: *Shannon, Del* / Three steps to heaven: *Cochran, Eddie* / Shakin' all over: *Kidd, Johnny & The Pirates* / Bobby's girl: *Maughan, Susan* / Where the boys are: *Francis, Connie* / I remember you: *Ifield, Frank* / Tell Laura I love her: *Valance, Ricky* / Blue moon: *Marcels* / Tower of strength: *Vaughan, Frankie* / Island of dreams: *Springfields* / Wimoweh: *Denver, Carl* / Dreamin': *Burnette, Johnny* / Poor me: *Faith, Adam* / Well I ask you: *Kane, Eden* / Are you sure: *Allisons* / Good timin': *Jones, Jimmy* / When my little girl is smiling: *Douglas, Craig* / Running bear: *Preston, Johnny* / Apache: *Shadows*
5529022 / Oct '97 / Spectrum

☐ **SHAKIN' FIT**
CRD 006 / May '97 / Candy

☐ **SHAKUHACHI AND ORGAN**
PS 65199 / May '98 / PlayaSound

☐ **SHAM ROCKS, THE**
STOMP 002 / Nov '96 / Sleeping Giant

☐ **SHAMANIC SONGS OF SIBERIAN AMUR BASIN**
926712 / Jun '97 / BUDA

☐ **SHAMROCK AND THISTLE**
PLATCD 336 / Jul '92 / Platinum

☐ **SHAPESHIFTER VOL.1 (A Jazz Step Injection)**
Deep blue C: *Unguided Lights* / Jazz 163: *N-Jay* / One man dead: *Native Bass* / 125th St: *Click & Cycle* / Jeamland '96: *BLIM* / J-Funk: *Unguided Lights* / Tripple: *Elementz Of Noize* / Encephalia: *N-Jay* / Police state: *T-Power* / Astral: *Elementz Of Noize* / Dallas: *Morf*
SOURCD 007 / Aug '96 / SOUR

☐ **SHAPESHIFTER VOL.2 (Millennial Jazz)**
Purple haze: *Purple Kola* / Spell: *Morf* / Memorex in deep water: *Amnesia* / 125th Street: *Click & Cycle* / Refraction edit: *T-Power* / Mental orgasm: *Freq Nasty* / Lord of the rings: *Bangers United* / Conspiracy: *Unguided Lights* / Fruitcake: *BLIM* / Transcend: *Urbanites* / Sweet daze: *Click & Cycle* / Take me to summer: *Minx* / Alternative universe: *Morf*
SOURCD 9 / Apr '97 / SOUR

☐ **SHARING THE NIGHT TOGETHER**
10612 / Jun '97 / A-Play Collection

☐ **SHARING THE NIGHT TOGETHER**
Midnight lady: *Norman, Chris* / Just when I needed you most: *Vanwarmer, Randy* / Three steps to heaven: *Showaddywaddy* / Sharing the night together: *Dr. Hook & Ray Sawyer* / I can't help falling in love: *Rogers, Kenny* / Every beat of my heart: *Marian* / Midnight blue: *Tucker, Louise* / Love is in the air: *Young, John Paul* / Everybody's got to learn: *Korgis* / Guardian angel: *Masquerade* / Streets of London: *McTell, Ralph* / If you think you know how to love me: *Smokie* / It's only make believe: *Showaddywaddy* / Substitute: *Clout* / Hello baby: *Marmalade* / You were on my mind: *Crispin St Peters* / Aloha Oe until we meet again: *Goombay Dance Band* / Love me for a reason: *As We Speak* / If we only had the time: *Svenne & Lotta*
10892 / Oct '97 / Go On Deluxe

☐ **SHARP PUNK AND OI**
STEPCD 112 / 23 Feb '98 / Step 1

☐ **SHAWMS FROM NE CHINA VOL.1**
926132 CD / Jul '95 / BUDA

☐ **SHAWMS FROM NE CHINA VOL.2**
926122 CD / Jul '95 / BUDA

☐ **SH'BOOM, SH'BOOM**
Book of love: *Monotones* / Boy from New York City: *Ad Libs* / Sincerely: *Moonglows* / Oh what a night: *Dells* / Sixteen candles: *Crests* / Goodnight sweetheart, goodnight: *Spaniels* / Duke of Earl: *Chandler, Gene* / Hasppy, happy birthday baby: *Tune Weavers* / Come go with me: *Del-Vikings* / At my front door: *El Dorado* / Since I don't have you: *Skyliners* / Once in a while: *Chimes* / Sea of love: *Phillips, Phil & The Twilights* / It's in his kiss (The shoop shoop song): *Everett, Betty* / My true story: *Jive Five* / Long lonely nights: *Andrews, Lee* / Over and over: *Day, Bobby* / For all we know: *Orioles* / Mr. Sandman: *Chordettes* / Alley oop: *Hollywood Argyles*
MCCD 091 / May '92 / Music Club

☐ **SHEEN (2CD Set)**
KK 141CD / Oct '95 / KK

☐ **SHERBET-LICK IT**
REACTCD 057
REACTCDX 057 / Feb '95 / React

☐ **SHE'S A REBEL (Alternative Women Rock For A Cure)**
Oh Nina: *Muffs* / Mendo hoo-ha: *Tribe 8* / Jack shit: *Teen Angels* / Tranny chaser: *Tribe 8* / Suck: *Cake Like* / Give it to the dog: *Bandit Queen* / Starsucker: *Die Cheerleader* / Loose and undubdued: *Bell* / Sycophant: *Nitocris* / Ego: *Flower S.F.* / Rock-a-bye-baby: *7 Year Bitch* / Prick: *Batter Shell* / No yawk: *Cocktaillica* / Isosceles: *Dirt Merchants* / Goodnight now: *Muffs*
SH 5714 / Mar '97 / Shanachie

☐ **SHESHWE (Sounds Of The Mines)**
ROUCD 5031 / '88 / Rounder

☐ **SHETLAND DIALECT**
VK 001CD / Aug '97 / Veesink

☐ **SHETLAND SESSIONS VOL.1, THE**
LCOM 7021 / Mar '92 / Lismor

☐ **SHETLAND SESSIONS VOL.2, THE**
LCOM 7022 / Mar '92 / Lismor

☐ **SHINE (The Best Of 1997)**
5550732 / 24 Nov '97 / PolyGram TV

☐ **SHINE EYE GAL (Brukdon From Belize)**
CO 118CD / May '94 / Corason

☐ **SHINE ON**
I 3896032 / Oct '96 / Galaxy

☐ **SHINE ON SWEET STARLET**
SFTRI 537CD / 20 Apr '98 / Sympathy For The Record Industry

☐ **SHINE VOL.1**
Parklife: *Blur* / Cigarettes and alcohol: *Oasis* / Regret: *New Order* / Zombie: *Cranberries* / Animal nitrate: *Suede* / Connection: *Elastica* / Do you remember the first time: *Pulp* / So let me go far: *Dodgy* / Speakeasy: *Shed Seven* / Welcome to paradise: *Green Day* / How soon is now: *Smiths* / Sit down: *James* / Getting away with it: *Electronic* / Size of a cow: *Wonder Stuff* / Altogether now: *Farm* / Dragging me down: *Inspiral Carpets* / Weirdo: *Charlatans* / International bright young thing: *Jesus Jones* / Feel the pain: *Dinosaur Jr.* / Shine on: *House Of Love*
5255672 / May '95 / Polydor

☐ **SHINE VOL.10 (2CD Set)**
5650472 / 17 Aug '98 / PolyGram TV

☐ **SHINE VOL.2**
Some might say: *Oasis* / Changing man: *Weller, Paul* / Girl from Mars: *Ash* / Love spreads: *Stone Roses* / Girl like you: *Collins, Edwyn* / Wake up Boo: *Boo Radleys* / Change: *Lightning Seeds* / Staying out for the summer: *Dodgy* / Fine time: *Cast* / Waking up: *Elastica* / Ridiculous thoughts: *Cranberries* / Vegas:

Sleeper / Where I find my heaven: Gigolo Aunts / Haunted by you: Gene / Now they'll sleep: Belly / Sparky's dream: Teenage Fanclub / Stay together: Suede / Kinky Afro: Happy Mondays / Love will tear us apart: Joy Division / Underwear: Pulp
5258582 / Aug '95 / Polydor

☐ SHINE VOL.3
Common people: Pulp / Roll with it: Oasis / Alright: Supergrass / Marvellous: Lightning Seeds / What do I do now: Sleeper / Stardust: Menswear / Alright: Cast / Only happy when it rains: Garbage / King of the kerb: Echobelly / Angel interceptor: Ash / End of a century: Blur / One love: Stone Roses / From the bench at Belvidere: Boo Radleys / Olympian: Gene / Just when you're thinkin' things over: Charlatans / Fantasy: Levellers / Let's all go together: Marion / Where have you been tonight: Shed Seven / Might be stars: Wannadies / Step on: Happy Mondays
5259652 / Oct '95 / Polydor

☐ SHINE VOL.4
Sandstorm: Cast / Mis-shapes: Pulp / Mansize rooster: Supergrass / Sleeping in: Menswear / Getting better: Shed Seven / From a window: Northern Uproar / Riverboat song: Ocean Colour Scene / Weak: Skunk Anansie / Divebomb: Number One Cup / Time: Marion / Far: Longpigs / Universal: Blur / Dark therapy: Echobelly / For the dead: Gene / Ten storey love song: Stone Roses / Just: Radiohead / Lucky you: Lightning Seeds / Carnival: Cardigans / Anywhere: Dubstar / Come together: Smokin' Mojo Filters / Fade away: Oasis & Friends
5353212 / Feb '96 / Polydor

☐ SHINE VOL.5
5356892 / Jul '96 / PolyGram TV

☐ SHINE VOL.6 (2CD Set)
Peacock suit: Weller, Paul / One to another: Charlatans / Design for life: Manic Street Preachers / Trash: Suede / Good enough: Dodgy / Circle: Ocean Colour Scene / On stand by: Shed Seven / We love you: Menswear / Love fool: Cardigans / Charmless man: Blur / Underground: Folds, Ben Five / Becoming more like Alfie: Divine Comedy / 12 reasons why I love her: My Life Story / Sale of the century: Sleeper / Goodnight: Baby Bird / Rush hour: Joyrider / What's in the box: Boo Radleys / Lump: Presidents Of The USA / On a rope: Rocket From The Crypt / Free to decide: Cranberries / Forbidden City: Electronic / Champagne supernova: Oasis / Walkaway: Cast / Something changed: Pulp / On and on: Longpigs / Bad actress: Terrorvision / Exodus: Levellers / Stripper vicar: Mansun / You're one: Imperial Teen / Livin' it up: Northern Uproar / Chinese burn: Heavy Stereo / Look at you now: Elcka / 500 (shake baby shake): Lush / Elevator song: Dubstar / Anymore: Cracknell, Sarah / Valentine's Day: Ruth / Beyond safe ways: Bawl / One in a million: Sussed / Punka: Kenickie / 36 degrees: Placebo
5359202 / Sep '96 / PolyGram TV

☐ SHINE VOL.7 (2CD Set)
Flying: Cast / Beautiful ones: Suede / Everything must go: Manic Street Preachers / Fighting fit: Gene / Twisted: Skunk Anansie / Lost myself: Longpigs / Disco 2000: Pulp / Ready or not: Lightning Seeds / You've got it bad: Ocean Colour Scene / C'mon kids: Boo Radleys / Lava: Silver Sun / Kandy pop: Bis / Teenage angst: Placebo / Burden in my hands: Soundgarden / Celebrity hitlist: Terrorvision / Boy wonder: Speedy / No one speaks: Geneva / Great things: Echobelly / Nice guy Eddie: Sleeper / Sparkle: My Life Story / Morning glory: Oasis / Milk: Garbage & Tricky / 6 Underground: Sneaker Pimps / If you're thinking of me: Dodgy / Chasing rainbows: Shed Seven / For you: Electronic / You're gorgeous: Baby Bird / Patio song: Gorky's Zygotic Mynci / Neighbourhood: Space / Girls and boys: Blur / Frog princess: Divine Comedy / Whatever: Oasis / Lazy lover: Supernaturals / Lenny: Supergrass / If you don't want me to destroy you: Super Furry Animals / Broken stones: Weller, Paul / If I could talk I'd tell you: Lemonheads / Street spirit: Radiohead / Not so manic now: Dubstar / You've got a lot to answer for: Catatonia / One night stand: Aloof
5530512 / Nov '96 / PolyGram TV

☐ SHINE VOL.8 (2CD Set)
Free me: Cast / North country boy: Charlatans / Swallowed: Bush / Place your hands: Reef / Nancy boy: Placebo / Sixty mile smile: 3 Colours Red / Kevin Carter: Manic Street Preachers / Wide open space: Mansun / Tattva: Kula Shaker / What do you want from me: Monaco / She's a star: James / We could be kings: Gene / Farewell to twilight: Symposium / Sugar coated iceberg: Lightning Seeds / King of kissingdom: My Life Story / Your woman: White Town / Diamond dew: Gorky's Zygotic Mynci / Everybody knows (except you): Divine Comedy / Found you: Dodgy / Masterplan: Oasis / Lazy: Suede / Beetlebum: Blur / It's no good: Depeche Mode / Novocaine for the soul: Eels / Hedonism (just because you feel good): Skunk Anansie / Babies: Pulp / Bully boy: Shed Seven / Shady lane: Pavement / Someone always gets there first: Bennet / Statuesque: Sleeper / I don't know: Ruth / Go: Jocasta / Monday morning: Candyskins / RACE: Tiger / 1962: Grass Show / U16 girls: Travis / Hit: Wannadies / Caught by the fuzz: Supergrass / Skyscraper: Intastella / Bankrobber: Audioweb
5534522 / Apr '97 / PolyGram TV

☐ SHINE VOL.9 (2CD Set)
D'you know what I mean: Oasis / Film star: Suede / Heavy soul: Weller, Paul / How high: Charlatans / Sun hits the sky: Supergrass / Bruise pristine: Placebo / 100 mile high city: Ocean Colour Scene / Drop dead gorgeous: Republica / What a beautiful day: Levellers / On your own: Blur / Where it's at: Beck / Your new cuckoo: Cardigans / Julia: Silver Sun / International language of screaming: Super Furry Animals / Sweet lips: Monaco / Tomorrow: James & Brian Eno / Come back brighter: Reef / Paranoid android: Radiohead / Blinded by the sun: Seahorses / Guiding star: Cast / Nothing lasts forever: Echo & The Bunnymen / Speak to me someone: Gene / You showed me: Lightning Seeds / I don't want control of you: Teenage Fanclub / No more talk: Dubstar / Post modern sleaze: Sneaker Pimps / Love has passed away: Supernaturals / Best regrets: Geneva / Girl I once knew: Northern Uproar / Thousand trees: Stereophonics / Fairweather friend: Symposium / Shorty: Wannadies / Promise: Delirious / Hurricane: Warm Jets / Electricity: Spiritualized / Brimful of Asha: Cornershop / Fear of flying: Ruth / Susan's house: Eels / Taxloss: Mansun
5539752 / 1 Sep '97 / PolyGram TV

☐ SHIT FACTORY, THE (6CD Set)
DTKBOX 5053 / 15 Jun '98 / Dressed To Kill

☐ SHIVA SPACE TECHNOLOGY
SHIVACD 001 / 3 Nov '97 / Shiva Space Technology

☐ SHOCK ROCK VOL.1
She won't rock: Di'Anno, Paul / All shook up: White, Dougie / Show some emotion: Sloman, John / These dreams: Barden, Gary / Cut loose: White, Dougie / Big beat no heart: McAuliffe, Kim / Two hearts in love: Stratton, Dennis / An' that ain't all: Moore, Nicky / It ain't over: Stratton, Dennis / Caught you life: Hart, Lea / Miles away: Stratton, Dennis / Fine line: Hart, Lea / I've had enough: Stratton, Dennis / Lucky to lose: Di'Anno, Paul / Listen to what your heart says: Di'Anno, Paul
CDTB 189 / 29 May '98 / Thunderbolt

☐ SHOCK THERAPY
EFA 008792 / Jul '97 / Shockwave

☐ SHOESTRING CHARTBUSTERS
SHOECD 001 / 2 Feb '98 / Shoestring

☐ SHOOP - THE DEFINITION OF TECHNO (3CD Set)
ZBDCD 001 / Jul '96 / Shoop

☐ SHORT SHARP SHOCK
OVER 47CD / May '96 / Overground

☐ SHOUT AND SCREAM
DRCD 001 / Jul '95 / Detour

☐ SHOUT BROTHER SHOUT
AL 2800 / Jul '94 / Alligator

☐ SHOUT IT OUT 1946-1952
RST 915792 / Jun '94 / RST

☐ SHOUT THE FUTURE TRIBE
CDACV 2005 / Jun '95 / ACV

☐ SHOUTING THE BLUES
Adam bit the apple: Turner, 'Big' Joe / Still in the dark: Turner, 'Big' Joe / Feelin' happy: Turner, 'Big' Joe / Midnight is here again AKA Dawn is breakin' through: Turner, 'Big' Joe / I want my baby: Turner, 'Big' Joe / Life is a card game: Turner, 'Big' Joe / After a while you'll be sorry: Turner, 'Big' Joe / Just a travellin' man: Turner, 'Big' Joe / Big city blues: Big Maceo / Do you remember: Big Maceo / Just tell me baby: Big Maceo / One Sunday morning: Big Maceo / State street boogie: Johnson, Don Orchestra / Jackson's blues: Johnson, Don Orchestra / Chesterfield baby: Johnson, Don Orchestra / Lonesome lover blues: Smilin' Smokey Lynn / Run rabbit run: Smilin' Smokey Lynn / Feel like ballin' tonight: Smilin' Smokey Lynn / Rock-a-bye baby: Smilin' Smokey Lynn / Hometown baby (Hip Cat): Smilin' Smokey Lynn / She's been gone: H-Bomb Ferguson / You made me baby: H-Bomb Ferguson
CDCHD 439 / Jan '93 / Ace

☐ SHOVE IT
My man, a sweet man: Jackson, Millie / Night fever: Fatback Band / Can you get to that: Funkadelic / Pain: Ohio Players / Baby let me take you (in my arms): Detroit Emeralds / Man size job: LaSalle, Denise / Keep on stepping: Fatback Band / Get down, get down (get on the floor): Simon, Joe / Pleasure: Ohio Players / It's all over but the shouting: Jackson, Millie / Funky dollar bill: Funkadelic
CDSEWX 015 / Oct '89 / Westbound

☐ SHOW AND TELL
WHI 666CD / 1 Sep '97 / Which

☐ SHOWTIME
VPXLCD 3110 / Mar '98 / Xtra Large Productions

☐ SHOWTIME JAM
VPXL 3109 / 8 Dec '97 / VP

☐ SHREDS VOL.4
SH 43CD / Oct '97 / Shredder

☐ SHREDS VOL.5
SH 44CD / Oct '97 / Shredder

☐ SHREVEPORT STOMP
Ba Da: Perkins, Roy / Red beans and rice: Patin, Scatman & The Ram Rods / Cheater's can't win: Lewis, Margaret / Flat foot Sam: TV Slim / Mailman mailman: Williamson, Sonny Boy / Come back Betty: Steel, L.C. / I'm leaving: Brannon, Linda / Bow wow puppy love: Bonin, Jimmy / Drop top (TK1): Perkins, Roy / Reconsider me: Lewis, Margaret / Hippy Ti Yo: Page, Bobby / Wherever you are: Brannon, Linda / Pow wow: Tennessee, Grace / Let me feel it: Brown, Elgie / Girl in the street: Williams, Vince / Ginning: Patin, Scatman & The Ram Rods / Baby please forgive me: Webb, Troy / What did you do last night: Rocky Robin & the Riff Raffs / Night creature: Run-a-ways / Anyway you do: Brannon, Linda / Eager boy: Lonesome Drifter / Lonesome heart: Hunter, Charlotte / El Rancho Grande Rock: Starmakers / Lover's land: Walker, Ernest / Louisiana twist: Bailey, June Bug
CDCHD 495 / Jun '94 / Ace

☐ SHRINE
CSR 4 CD / Jun '93 / NMC

☐ SHRINE - THE RAREST SOUL LABEL
Stop overlooking me: Cairos / Guess who loves you: Daye, Eddie & Four Bars / Don't let him hurt you: Les Chansonettes / I won't believe it 'til I see it: Parker, Bobby / Watch your step: Cautions / I'm so devoted: Epsilons / Huh baby: Prophets / Wait 'til I get there: Tippie & The Wisemen / I won't be coming back: Bryant, J.D. / Mind in a bind: Epsilons / Do what I want: Cavaliers / I'll never let you get away: Dennis, Bill / I'll take you back: Enjoyables / No more like me: Pollard, Ray / Take it from me: Traci / I know about her: DC Blossoms / Dream my heart: Edwards, Shirley / My only love: Counts / Fall guy: Cautions / Mystery: Armstrong, Jimmy / Weekend: Hall, Sidney / I'll understand: Taylor, Leroy & The Four Kays / She went away: Linda & The Vistas / Let me walk away: Tippie & The Wisemen
CDKEND 160 / 27 Jul '98 / Kent

☐ SHUFFLIN' ON BOND STREET (Jamaican R&B/Ska Instrumentals)
CDTRL 275 / Aug '94 / Trojan

☐ SHUT THE GATE SUZY
NITR 002 / Jan '97 / Demolition Derby

☐ SHUT UP AND PLAY YER BLUES
MCCD 216 / Oct '95 / Music Club

☐ SHUT UP AND POGO
NV 50 / Jun '97 / Nasty Vinyl

☐ SI SAFAA (New Music From The Middle East)
Ghallo Tara: Ahmed, Hamdi / Agulak: Khairy, Saleh / Anta Al Hakam: Sahir, Kazim Al / Matajarahnish: Hanan / Nami: Ayubi, Aida / Sif Safaa: Mounir, Mohamed / Khafet Dhamon: Fouad, Mohamed / Tasadig Wala Ahliflak: Ahmed, Hamdi / Leh Alkhiyana: Hilal, Abu / Ya Leyl A'ah: Hanan / Hawad: Fouad, Mohamed / Alashan Al Malih: Khairy, Saleh
CDEMC 3700 / Mar '95 / Hemisphere

☐ SICK SICK SICK (Live At The Klub Foot 1987)
Vibrate / Vibrate / Cast iron arm / Pvc chair / Rubber bucaneer / Pervy in the park / Rubber love / Holy hack jack / Love is for skitzos / I want your loving / Possessed / Werewolf bitch / Natural born lover / Uncle willy / Wind up dead
DOJOCD 23 / Jun '94 / Dojo

☐ SIDEREAL REST
SCRATCH 21 / Dec '96 / Scratch

☐ SIGNS OF LIFE
BR 036CD / 6 Oct '97 / Blue Room

☐ SILENT CRYING
TT 00272 / Feb '97 / T&T

☐ SILK & STEEL
I found someone: Cher / Night in my veins: Pretenders / Independent love song: Scarlet / Heaven is a place on earth: Carlisle, Belinda / Walking on broken glass: Lennox, Annie / Look: Roxette / Whole world lost its head: Go-Go's / Change of heart: Lauper, Cyndi / We belong: Benatar, Pat / Total eclipse of the heart: Tyler, Bonnie / Rubber band girl: Bush, Kate / Mandinka: O'Connor, Sinead / I touch myself: Divinyls / Crash: Primitives / You're history: Shakespears Sister / Hazy shade of winter: Bangles / Rush hour: Wiedlin, Jane / What I am: Brickell, Edie & New Bohemians / Self control: Branigan, Laura / Baby I don't care: Transvision Vamp
5255692 / May '95 / Polydor

☐ SILKY SOUL
It don't get no better han this: Burke, Solomon / Just you just me: Peebles, Ann / Personally: Kelly, Paul / Neither one of us: Adams, Johnny / I'd rather beg: Garbo, Chuck / Gonna take my heart's advice: Clay, Otis / Whatever it takes: Little Buster / Willing and able: Reed, Dalton / Can't you hear it in my tears: Thomas, Irma / Out of the dark: Washington, Walter 'Wolfman'
EDCD 7008 / Nov '96 / Easydisc

☐ SILLY SYMPHONIES
70700271363 / Nov '95 / Essential Dance

☐ SILLY SYMPHONIES VOL.3
707003 / Jul '96 / Essential Dance

☐ SILOS AND UTILITY SHEDS
GRCD 361 / Nov '96 / Glitterhouse

☐ SILVER PLANET COLLECTION VOL.1
SILVER 7CD / 26 Jan '98 / Silver Planet

☐ SILVER TOP COLLECTION, THE
MILCD 002 / 15 Jun '98 / Milk

☐ SIMPLY HYMNS
All creatures of our God and King / Doxology / Praise to the Lord / Almighty / Holy Holy Holy / When I survey the wondrous cross / Stand up stand up for Jesus / There is power in the blood / Are you washed in the blood / Victory is Jesus / All hail the power / Nothing but the blood / Saviour like a shepherd lead us / There is a fountain filled with blood / Fairest Lord Jesus / My Jesus I love thee / What a friend we have in Jesus / Solid rock / Crown him with many crowns / Great is thy faithfulness / Amazing grace / It is well with my soul / Come thou font of every blessing / And can it be / Joyful joyful we adore thee
12262 / Mar '98 / Integrity

☐ SIMPLY PAN PIPES
Stars / Fairground / She'll have to go / Sad old red / You've got it / Never never love / Your mirror / It's only love / To be with you / For your babies / Something's got me started / Remembering the first time / Wonderland / New flame / Holding back the years / Ev'rytime we say goodbye / Do the right thing / Thrill me / We're in this together / If you don't know me by now
303000982 / Apr '97 / Carlton

☐ SIMPLY SOUL (4CD Set)
Barefootin': Parker, Robert / When a man loves a woman: Sledge, Percy / For your precious love: Butler, Jerry / So many ways: Benton, Brook / Save the last dance for me: Drifters / Operator: Knight, Gladys & The Pips / Soul man: Sam & Dave / Me and Mrs. Jones: Paul, Billy / If you don't know me by now: Melvin, Harold & The Bluenotes / Feel the need in me: Detroit Emeralds / Walking the dog: Thomas, Rufus / Show and tell: Wilson, Al / I stand accused: Butler, Jerry / It's just a matter of time: Benton, Brook / I got you (I feel good): Brown, James / There goes my baby: Drifters / Soul sister, brown sugar: Sam & Dave / You've made me so very happy: Whispers / Try a little tenderness: Sledge, Percy / Knock on wood: Floyd, Eddie / Warm and tender love: Sledge, Percy / Under the boardwalk: Drifters / Every beat of my heart: Knight, Gladys & The Pips / Rainy night in Georgia: Benton, Brook / I thank you: Sam & Dave / Make it easy on yourself: Butler, Jerry / Papa's got a brand new bag: Brown, James / Woman in love: Three Degrees / I've never found a girl to love me like you do: Floyd, Eddie / Band of gold: Payne, Freda / Portrait of my love: Clark, Dee / Let it be me: Butler, Jerry & Betty Everett / Needle in a haystack: Whispers / I've been loving you too long: Sledge, Percy / Ain't no sunshine: Jarreau, Al / Up on the roof: Drifters / Hold on I'm coming: Sam & Dave / Letter full of tears: Knight, Gladys & The Pips / Challenge: Butler, Jerry / Duke of Earl: Chandler, Gene / On no not my baby: Brown, Maxine / You don't know what you mean to me: Sam & Dave / Please please please: Brown, James / I got the feelin': Brown, James / On broadway: Drifters / Heatwave: Reeves, Martha / Stoned love: Supremes / Dancing in the street: Weston, Kim / First I look at the purse: Contours / Beachwood 4-5789: Marvelettes / Dance with me: Drifters / If ever I should fall in love: Knight, Gladys & The Pips / Just my imagination: Cameron, G.C. / Ain't no mountain high enough: Payne, Sherrie / Touch me in the morning: Littles, Hattie / This old heart of mine: Contours / My cherie amour: Moy, Sylvia / You are the sunshine of my life: Nero, Frances / I'm still waiting: Payne, Sherrie / I'll pick a rose for my rose: Johnson, Marv / Used to be a playboy: Marvelettes / Jimmy mack: Lavette, Bettye / Tracks of my tears: Contours / Love hangover: 5th Dimension / My smile is just a frown: Crawford, Carolyn / Reach out I'll be there: Taylor, Bobby / He was really sayin' somethin': Velvelettes / Reflections: Syreeta / Remember me: Lewis, Pat / With you I'm born again: Syreeta / Too busy thinking 'bout my baby: Cameron, G.C. / Ready or not here I come: Contours / Rescue me: Lewis, Pat / Nathan Jones: Supremes / Reunited: Satintones / Going to a go go: Monitors / Love child: Supremes / Emotion: Weston, Kim
QUAD 002 / Nov '96 / Tring

☐ SIMPLY THE BEST (Classic Soul/2CD Set)
Let's stay together: Green, Al / Tired of being alone: Green, Al / (You make me feel) Like a natural woman: Franklin, Aretha / I say a little prayer: Franklin, Aretha / Respect: Franklin, Aretha / Stand by me: King, Ben E. / Green onions: Booker T & The MG's / Express yourself: Wright, Charles / Could it be I'm falling in love: Detroit Spinners / Ain't no mountain high enough: Ross, Diana / You are everything: Ross, Diana / You can't hurry lovve: Ross, Diana & The Supremes / Walk on by: Warwick, Dionne / You'll never get to heaven: Warwick, Dionne / Under the boardwalk: Drifters / Up on the roof: Drifters / Knock on wood: Floyd, Eddie / (Take a little) piece of my heart: Franklin, Erma / Reach out I'll be there: Four Tops / If you don't know me by now: Melvin, Harold & The Bluenotes / (Your love keeps lifting me) Higher and higher: Melvin, Harold & The Bluenotes / I got the sweetest feeling: Wilson, Jackie / I'll be there: Jacksons / (I feel like I'm being a) sex machine: Brown, James / I got you (I feel good): Brown, James / What becomes of the brokenhearted: Ruffin, Jimmy / Dancing in the streets: Martha & The Vandellas / When you're young and in love: Marvelettes / Ain't nothin' like the real thing: Gaye, Marvin / Heard it throught the grapevine: Gaye, Marvin / Too busy thinkin' about my baby: Gaye, Marvin / Got to be there: Jackson, Michael / My baby just cares for me: Simone, Nina / (Sittin' on the) dock of the bay: Redding, Otis / My girl: Redding, Otis / Try a little tenderness: Redding, Otis / When a man loves a woman: Sledge, Percy / Where is the love: Flack, Roberta & Donny Hathaway / Soul man: Sam & Dave / Tears of a clown: Robinson, Smokey & The Miracles / Tracks of my tears: Robinson, Smokey & The Miracles / I second that emotion: Robinson, Smokey & The Miracles / Everybody needs somebody to love: Burke, Solomon / My cherie amour: Wonder, Stevie / Stop in the name of love: Supremes / Baby love: Supremes / Ain't too proud to beg: Supremes / Papa was a rolling stone: Supremes / In the midnight hour: Pickett, Wilson / Mustang sally: Pickett, Wilson / Groovin': Young Rascals
9548352042 / Mar '97 / Warner Bros.

☐ SIMPLY THE BEST CHRISTMAS (2CD Set)
White Christmas: Crosby, Bing / Christmas song: Cole, Nat 'King' / Blue Christmas: Presley, Elvis / Mary's boy child: Belafonte, Harry / All alone at Christmas: Love, Darlene / Good night Wenceslas: Torme, Mel / God rest ye merry gentlemen: Como, Perry / Jingle bells: Reeves, Jim / Away in a manger: Andrews, Julie / Winter wonderland: Green, Al / Peace on earth/Little drummer: Crosby, Bing & David Bowie / Hark the herald angels sing: Como, Perry / Bleak midwinter: Pierce Petit / I believe: Robson & Jerome / We wish you a merry Christmas: Crosby, Bing / Sleigh ride: Parton, Dolly / Warm in December: London, Julie / Deck the halls: Cathedral Choir / O come all ye faithful (adeste fidelis): Grant, Amy / Frosty the snowman: Jackson Five / Rudolph the red nosed reindeer: Carpenters / Let it snow let it snow let it snow: Day, Doris / O little town of Bethlehem: Nelson, Willie / Rockin' around the Christmas tree: Lee, Brenda / Have yourself a very merry Christmas: Garland, Judy / In dulce jubilo: Oldfield, Mike / Oiche chiun: Enya / First Noel: Williams, Andy / Amazing grace: Collins, Judy / When you wish upon a star: Ronstadt, Linda / I'll be home for Christmas: Day, Doris / It came upon a midnight clear: Cash, Johnny / Do you hear what I hear: Crosby, Bing / Holly and the ivy: De Grassi, Alex / Ave MAria: Carreras, Jose / Christmas alphabet: Valentine, Dickie / While shepherds watched: Oxford Chapel Choir / Away in manger: Take 6
9548360072 / 24 Nov '97 / Warner Bros.

☐ SIMPLY THE BEST DISCO (2CD Set)
I will survive: Gaynor, Gloria / Funky Town: Lipps Inc. / Boogie nights: Heatwave / I'm every woman: Khan, Chaka / Lady Marmalade: Labelle / Blame it on the boogie: Jacksons / That's the way I like it: KC & The Sunshine Band / Ain't nobody: Rufus & Chaka Khan / Night to remember: Shalamar / You to me are everything: Real Thing / It is love you're after: Rose Royce / And the beat goes on: Whispers / Forget me nots: Rushen, Patrice / Heaven must be missing an angel: Tavares / We are family: Sister Sledge / Use it up and wear it out: Odyssey / Let's groove: Earth, Wind & Fire / I feel love: Summer, Donna / You make me feel (mighty real): Sylvester / Disco inferno: Trammps / Play that funky music: Wild Cherry / Hang on in there baby: Bristol, Johnny / Going back to my roots: Odyssey / If I can't have you: Elliman, Yvonne / Good times: Chic / Best of my love: Emotions /

Hustle: McCoy, Van / Lost in music: Sister Sledge / Shaft: Hayes, Isaac / Young hearts run free: Staton, Candi / Le freak: Chic / IOU: Freeez / Jump to the beat: Lattisaw, Stacy / Celebration: Kool & The Gang / Yes sir, I can boogie: Baccara / Working my way back to you: Detroit Spinners / Boogie oogie oogie: Taste Of Honey / Ring my bell: Ward, Anita / Rasputin: Boney M / Boogie wonderland: Earth, Wind & Fire

9548354282 / 16 Mar '98 / Warner Bros.

☐ SIMPLY THE BEST LOVE SONGS VOL.1 (2CD Set)

9548351122 / Feb '97 / Warner Bros.

☐ SIMPLY THE BEST LOVE SONGS VOL.2 (2CD Set)

Greatest love of all: Benson, George / Hard habit to break: Chicago / Crazy for you: Madonna / (You make me feel like) a natural woman: Franklin, Aretha / Rainy night in Georgia: Crawford, Randy / I don't wanna talk about it: Stewart, Rod / (Sittin' on the) dock of the bay: Redding, Otis / Superwoman: White, Karyn / Don't let go love: En Vogue / Waiting for a girl like you: Foreigner / Purple rain: Prince / Near wild heaven: REM / Wonderful tonight: Clapton, Eric / You might need somebody: Ama, Shola / Stand by me: Oasis / Love is strange: Everything But The Girl / If you don't know me by now: Simply Red / Fool if you think it's over: Rea, Chris / Patience of angels: Reader, Eddi / Baby can I hold you: Chapman, Tracy / 2 become 1: Spice Girls / Cuts both ways: Estefan, Gloria / True colours: Lauper, Cyndi / Every time you go away: Young, Paul / One day in your life: Jackson, Michael / Sacrifice: John, Elton / Easy: Commodores / How deep is your love: Bee Gees / Love is all around: Wet Wet Wet / Lifted: Lighthouse Family / I believe I can fly: R Kelly / What's love got to do with it: Turner, Tina / Nothing compares 2 U: O'Connor, Sinead / You're gorgeous: Baby Bird / Everytime we say goodbye: Simply Red / Time to say goodbye: Brightman, Sarah & Andrea Bocelli/Andrew Lloyd Webber / No more I love yous: Lennox, Annie / What becomes of the broken hearted: Ruffin, Jimmy / Back for good: Take That / Fall at your feet: Crowded House

9548362252 / 2 Feb '98 / Warner Bros.

☐ SIN ALLEY VOL.1

E 11564CD / Mar '93 / Crypt

☐ SING DE CHORUS

Country club scandal / Madame Khan / Songs of long ago / Dew and rain / Worker's plea / St. Peter's day / Black market / Leave me alone Dorothy / Ugly woman - trouble and misery / Los iros / Gold in Africa / Treasury scandal / Reign too long / Louise / Graf Zeppelin / Adolf Hitler / Love me or leave me / Matilda / Money is king / Victory calypso / Coldness of the water / Let the white people fight / Sedition law / Mother's love / Woman called Dorothy / Tribute to executor / Sing de chorus

DE 4018 / Feb '94 / Delos

☐ SING ME A SWING SONG

Troubled waters: Anderson, Ivie / Thanks a million: Armstrong, Louis / More than you know: Bailey, Mildred / What'd ja do to me: Boswell Sisters / I let a song go out of my heart: Boswell, Connee / Zaz zul zaz: Calloway, Cab / Don't try your jive on me: Carlisle, Una Mae / Louisiana: Crosby, Bing / When I grow too old to dream: Dandridge, Putney / Ten cents a dance: Etting, Ruth / Sing me a swing song: Fitzgerald, Ella / Lovable and sweet: Hanshaw, Annette / 1-2 Button your shoe: Holiday, Billie / Thursday: Humes, Helen / Isle of Capri: Manone, Wingy / Three little words: Rhythm Boys / I just couldn't take it baby: Teagarden, Jack / I wish I were twins: Valaida / Dream man: Waller, Fats / Restless: Ward, Helen / Am I blue: Waters, Ethel / Drop in next time you're passing: Welch, Elisabeth

CDAJA 5077 / Jan '91 / Living Era

☐ SING MY BLUES TONIGHT (The Ace Mississippi Blues Masters Vol.1)

That moves me (things I don't like): Dixon, Floyd / Black night: Brown, Charles / Let's just be friends: Brown, Charles / Way down in Louisiana: Dixon, Floyd / Nobody knows I'm in love with you: Ferguson, H-Bomb / Educated fool: Brown, Charles & Amos Milburn / I wanna go home: Brown, Charles & Amos Milburn / Wake up and live: Dixon, Floyd / Darlin' how long: Milburn, Amos / Sing my blues tonight: Brown, Charles / Trouble blues: Brown, Charles / Josephine: Ferguson, H-Bomb / Floyd's after hours: Dixon, Floyd / Love like a river: Brown, Charles / Driftin' blues: Brown, Charles / Never know about a woman: Dixon, Floyd / Merry Christmas baby: Brown, Charles / Don't cry: Brown, Charles / Me quieres: Dixon, Floyd / Baby don't go: Ferguson, H-Bomb / Lost in a dream: Brown, Charles / So much to remember you by: Brown, Charles / What would you be: Dixon, Floyd / Too late to cry anymore: Brown, Charles / Baby please write me: Dixon, Floyd

WESM 530 / 19 Jan '98 / Westside

☐ SING SING SO

VICG 52192 / Feb '96 / JVC World Library

☐ SINGALONG BANJO PARTY

Baby face / Toot toot tootsie / Let's all go down The Strand / You are my sunshine / Pennies from Heaven / Any old iron / Bye bye blackbird / Mammy / Underneath the arches / Shine on harvest moon / On Mother Kelly's doorstep / Birdie song

PLATCD 01 / Dec '88 / Platinum

☐ SINGER AND THE SONGS VOL.2, THE

CDBLP 2023 / Jul '96 / Lochshore

☐ SINGERS MEET THE DJ'S

RNCD 2106 / Jun '95 / Rhino

☐ SINGERS OF IMPERIAL RUSSIA VOL.1

GEMMCDS 99979 / Sep '92 / Pearl

☐ SINGERS OF IMPERIAL RUSSIA VOL.2

GEMMCDS 90013 / Oct '92 / Pearl

☐ SINGERS OF IMPERIAL RUSSIA VOL.3

GEMMCDS 90046 / Nov '92 / Pearl

☐ SINGERS OF JAZZ

Cutting out blues: Shavers, Charlie / Lullaby in boogie: Duffy, Jack / Dream weaver: Amorosa, Johnny / Mr. Sandman: Mills Brothers / I've got my fingers crossed: Waller, Fats / Christopher Columbus: Waller, Fats / She walks like a kangaroo: Sheppard, Ollie / Tiger rag: Mills Brothers / Robin Hood: Prima, Louis / Boogie woogie (I may be wrong): Rushing, Jimmy / You do me any old way: Broonzy, 'Big' Bill / Moon glow: Mills Brothers / Oop bop sh'bam: Gillespie, Dizzy / Jumping jive: Calloway, Cab / Minnie the moocher: Calloway, Cab / El rancho vego: Culver, Dick / I don't know why (I just do): Martin, Kenny / Sweet Lorraine: Cole, Nat 'King' / You're the cream in my coffee: Cole, Nat 'King' / Abraham: Torme, Mel / Velvet moon: Nelson, Skip / Music maestro please: Mills Brothers

22728 / Jun '96 / Music Box

☐ SINGERS ON TOP

792512 / Dec '95 / Melodie

☐ SINGERS SELECTIONS VOL.1

ZZCD 020 / Sep '96 / Zola & Zola

☐ SINGERS VOL.1

PHCD 2052 / Jan '97 / Penthouse

☐ SINGIN' THE GOSPEL

Nobody's fault but mine: Johnson, 'Blind' Willie / If I had my way: Johnson, 'Blind' Willie / Dark was the night: Johnson, 'Blind' Willie / I'm gonna run: Johnson, 'Blind' Willie / Dear old southland: Armstrong, Louis / Sha drack: Armstrong, Louis / Goin' to shout all over God's heaven: Armstrong, Louis / Nobody knows the trouble I've seen: Armstrong, Louis / Jonah and the whale: Armstrong, Louis / Bye and bye: Armstrong, Louis / Gospel train: Golden Gate Quartet / I'm on my way: Golden Gate Quartet / What more can Jesus do: Mitchell's Christian Singers / My poor mother died a-shoutin': Mitchell's Christian Singers / All God's chillun got rhythm: Ellington, Duke Orchestra / Swing low, sweet chariot: Ellington, Duke Orchestra / All God's chillun got wings: Ellington, Duke Orchestra / Go down Moses: Ellington, Duke Orchestra / Deep river: Ellington, Duke Orchestra / Sometimes I feel like a Motherless child: Waller, Fats / Strange things happened everyday: Tharpe, Sister Rosetta

19126 / 1 Jun '98 / Musidisc

☐ SINGIN' THE GOSPEL 1933-1936

DOCD 5326 / Mar '95 / Document

☐ SINGING IN AN OPEN SPACE (Zulu Rhythm & Harmony)

ROUCD 5027 / Dec '90 / Rounder

☐ SINGING THE MOTHER COUNTRIES

RIVCD 9912 / May '97 / Riverside

☐ SINGING VALLEYS, THE

SCDB 7054 / Feb '97 / Sain

☐ SINGLE MINDED

CDWIKD 109 / Jun '92 / Big Beat

☐ SINGLES BAR, THE

Achtung salaam: Sparkes, Neil & The Last Tribe / Is the 'erb dope: Mr. Electric Triangle / Omshanti: Solar Plexus / When you feel good, things can turn: Peanutbutter Wolf / Strong vibrations: Improvised Explosive / Bite the bullet: Nobby Stylus / Mr. kiss kiss bong bong: James Bong / Quelle aventure: Nose & Menelik / Everybody loves the sunshine: Quiet Boys / Causeway: Reality Drip / Jihad: Man Called Adam

TKCDM 45 / Apr '97 / 2 Kool

☐ SINGLES COLLECTION VOL.4

Cranked up really high: Slaughter & The Dogs / Bitch: Slaughter & The Dogs / I need nothing: Menace / Electrocutioner: Menace / Bad man: Cockney Rejects / New song: Cockney Rejects / England: Angelic Upstarts / Sticks diary: Angelic Upstarts / 17 Years of hell: Partisans / Power and the greed: Partisans / Bastards in blue: Partisans / Winner: Infa Riot / School's out: Infa Riot / Jerusalem: One Way System / Jackie was a junkie: One Way System / Stark raving normal: Blood / Mesrine: Blood

AHOYCD 071 / 3 Nov '97 / Captain Oi

☐ SINNERS & SAINTS

DOCD 5106 / Nov '92 / Document

☐ SIPSI OF YAYLA, THE (Turkey)

C 560103 / Aug '98 / Ocora

☐ SIR LLOYD HITS VOL.2

SLGRCD 001 / Mar '96 / Sir Lloyd

☐ SISSY MAN BLUES (Straight/Gay Blues & Jazz Vocals)

JASSCD 13 / Oct '91 / Jass

☐ SISTERS (Folksong)

SOW 1001 / Oct '95 / Sisters Of The World

☐ SISTERS IN REGGAE VOL.1

D 19972 / Sep '96 / Far I

☐ SISTERS IN REGGAE VOL.2

D 31520 / Sep '96 / Far I

☐ SISTERS OF SOUL

Rescue me: Bass, Fontella / I heard it through the grapevine: Reeves, Martha / Gee whiz (look at his eyes): Thomas, Carla / My guy: Wells, Mary / Love makes a woman: Acklin, Barbara / Baby it's you: Shirelles / Midnight at the oasis: Muldaur, Maria / He's a rebel: Crystals / Just one look: Troy, Doris / I will: Winters, Ruby / Heatwave: Reeves, Martha / It's in his kiss (the shoop shoop song): Everett, Betty / I'm a woman: Muldaur, Maria / BABY: Thomas, Carla / I know (you don't love me no more): George, Barbara / There's no other (like my baby): Crystals / Will you still love me tomorrow: Shirelles / Two lovers: Wells, Mary

SUMCD 4160 / 26 Jan '98 / Summit

☐ SISTERS OF SWING 1998 (2CD Set)

Under the bridge: All Saints / Life ain't easy: Cleopatra / All my love: Queen Pen / Boom boom: N-Tyce / Stranded: McNeal, Lutricia / You think you own me: McNeal, Lutricia / Much love: Ama, Shola / Rose is still a rose: Franklin, Aretha / Love shy: Blond, Kristine / Show me love: Robyn / Rewind: Celetia / Big bad mama: Brown, Foxy / You've got a friend: Brand New Heavies / Don't you love me: Eternal / Falling: D-Influence / Strawberries: Smooth / I want you to want me: Solid Harmonie / Closer than close: Gaines, Rosie / Horny: Mousse T & Hot 'n' Juicy / Don't let go: Mousse T & Hot 'n' Juicy / Everything: Blige, Mary J. / On and on: Badu, Erykah / Never gonna let you go: Moore, Tina / GHETTOUT: Changing Faces / Head over heels: Allure / Kiss and tell: Brownstone / Revival: Girault, Martine / Slow flow: Braxtons / Crush: Zhane / I like the way: Hines, Deni / Days of youth: Laurnea / Age ain't nothing but a number: Aaliyah / Special kind of lover: Nu Colours / No doubt: 702 / I'm not feeling you: Michelle, Yvette / It's alright: Queen Latifah / Distant lover: Hicks, Taral

5650762 / 29 Jun '98 / PolyGram TV

☐ SISTERS OF SWING VOL.1

5352252 / Jan '96 / PolyGram TV

☐ SISTERS OF SWING VOL.2

Twenty foreplay: Jackson, Janet / I can't tell you why: Brownstone / Sweet funky thing: Eternal / I'm goin' down: Blige, Mary J. / Desire: Nu Colours / Celebration of life: Truce / Sweetness: Gayle, Michelle / Will you be my baby: Infiniti / Gimme that body: Q-Tee / Whatta man: Salt n' Pepa & En Vogue / Give me a little more time: Gabrielle / Mama said: Anderson, Carleen / I fell (so you could catch me): Nelson, Shara / Never knew love like this: Henry, Pauline & Wayne Marshall / Moving on up: Knight, Beverley / I wanna love you: Jade / I'm so into you: SWV / Love groove: Smooth / (At your best) You are love: Aaliyah

5354752 / Apr '96 / PolyGram TV

☐ SISTERS OF SWING VOL.3 (2CD Set)

You're makin' me high: Braxton, Toni / Sometimes: Brand New Heavies / Do you know: Gayle, Michelle / If you really cared: Gabrielle / Waterfalls: TLC / Grapevyne: Brownstone / Request line: Zhane / Tell me: Groove Theory / Revival: Girault, Martine / Steelo: 702 / I'm not feeling you: Michelle, Yvette / You will rise: Sweet Back / Runaway: Nu Yorican Soul / Remember me: Blueboy / Mr. Big Stuff: Queen Latifah / Ain't no player: Jay-Z & Foxxy Brown / Can't knock the hustle: Jay-Z & Mary J. Blige / Shoop: Salt n' Pepa / Shy guy: King, Diana / You've got the love: Source & Candi Staton / Walk on by: Gabrielle / You're the one I love: Ama, Shola / Sentimental: Cox, Deborah / Over and over: Johnson, Puff / You're the one: SWV / Escaping: Carroll, Dina / I will survive: Savage, Chantay / Don't walk away: Jade / There ain't nothing like the love: Montage / Thing I like: Aaliyah / Before you walk out of my life: Monica / Undercover lover: Smooth / True spirit: Anderson, Carleen / Stay: Ndegeocello, Me'shell / I was made to love you: Cato, Lorraine / Show me: Dawson, Dana / Keep on movin': Soul II Soul & Caron Wheeler / Down that road: Nelson, Shara / Feel so high: Des'ree

5534652 / May '97 / PolyGram TV

☐ SIX 6 COLLECTION, THE (4CD Set)

CDBNTW 2 / 30 Mar '98 / Passion

☐ SIX STAGE PHASER

VC 108CD / Mar '97 / Vinyl Communication

☐ SIX STRING BOOGIE (The Power Of Blues Guitar)

Enter the tornado: Wilson, U.P. & Paul Aorta/The Kingpins / Hold on baby: Wilson, U.P. & Paul Aorta/The Kingpins / Prancing: Turner, Ike / Bessie Mae: Gibson, Lacy & Sunnyland Slim / House rent boogie: Hooker, John Lee / Leave me alone: Benton, Buster / Somebody loan me a dime: Robinson, Fenton / Texas love: Pollock, Mark / Blue light: Mighty Houserockers / Shake 'em on down: McDowell, 'Mississippi' Fred / You're gonna need me: Allison, Luther / All by myself: Murphy, Matt & Memphis Slim / Walked all night long: Smith, Byther / Well alright then: Morgan, Mike / First time I met the blues: Guy, Buddy / Little bit worried: Sharpville, Todd / Dust my broom: Hooker, Earl / Way you dance: Green, Peter & Mick/Enemy Within / Little Stevie's shuffle: Elmores

MCCD 151 / Feb '94 / Music Club

☐ SIZHU/SILK BAMBOO

PAN 2030CD / Feb '95 / Pan

☐ SIZZLIN' SUMMER HITS

Macarena: Trio Del Sol / Rio-mix: Trio Del Sol / Girl from Ipanema: Gilberto, Astrud / Limbo rock: Checker, Chubby / Abele: Osibisa / Lambada de Americana: Brazil / Banana boat song: Trio Del Sol / We wanna go dancing: Trio Del Sol / Mamae eu quero: Gilberto, Astrud / (Sittin' on the) dock of the bay: Club Safari / One note Samba: Shaw, Sandie / (Do the) Salsa: Jackson, Latoya / Time is right: Osibisa / Let your sunshine: Trio Del Sol / Saragossa: Trio Del Sol / Lambadie lambadia: Brazil / Let's limbo some more: Checker, Chubby / La bamba: Lopez, Trini

DGR 1113 / Sep '96 / DGR

☐ SIZZLING COUNTRY DANCING (2CD Set)

MCD 211612 / Mar '97 / MCA

☐ SIZZLING THE BLUES (New Orleans 1927-1929)

I haven't got a dollar to pay the house rent man: Davis, Genevieve / I've got that something: Davis, Genevieve / Pretty Audrey: Dumaine, Louis Jazzola Eight / To-wa-bac-a-wa: Dumaine, Louis Jazzola Eight / Franklin Street blues: Dumaine, Louis Jazzola Eight / Red onion drag: Dumaine, Louis Jazzola Eight / Mama cookie: Cook, Ann / He's the sweetest black man in town: Cook, Ann / Panama: Miller, Johnny New Orleans Frollickers / Dippermouth blues: Miller, Johnny New Orleans Frollickers / Sizzling the blues: Hazel, Monk & His Bienville Roof Orchestra / High society: Hazel, Monk & His Bienville Roof Orchestra / Git wit it: Hazel, Monk & His Bienville Roof Orchestra / Ideas: Hazel, Monk & His Bienville Roof Orchestra / Astoria strut: Jones & Collins Astoria Hot Eight / Duet stomp: Jones & Collins Astoria Hot Eight / Damp weather: Jones & Collins Astoria Hot Eight / Tip easy blues: Jones & Collins Astoria Hot Eight

DGF 5 / May '95 / Frog

☐ SKA (3CD Set)

EMTBX 312 / 20 Apr '98 / Emporio

☐ SKA - THE ALBUM

CLP 214 / 20 Apr '98 / Cleopatra

☐ SKA - THE THIRD WAVE VOL.2

SH 5709 / Jun '96 / Shanachie

☐ SKA - THE THIRD WAVE VOL.3

SH 5723 / May '97 / Shanachie

☐ SKA AFTER SKA AFTER SKA

CDHB 105 / Apr '98 / Heartbeat

☐ SKA ARCHIVE

Train to Skaville: Ethiopians / Skinhead moonstomp: Symarip / On my radio: Selecter / Guns of Navarone: Skatalites / Monkey man: Maytals / Rudy, a message to you: Dandy / Return of Django: Upsetters / Phoenix city: Alphonso, Roland / Longshot kick de bucket: Pioneers / Gangsters: Specials / Bonanza ska: Malcolm, Carlos / Liquidator: Harry J All Stars / Carry go bring come: Hinds, Justin / Tide is high: Paragons / Israelites: Dekker, Desmond / Red red wine: Tribe, Tony / Tears of a clown: Special Beat / Double barrel: Barker, Dave & Ansell Collins / I'm in the mood for ska: Lord Tanamo / Wonderful world, beautiful people: Cliff, Jimmy

RMCD 202 / Nov '97 / Rialto

☐ SKA BEATS

Just a feeling: Bad Manners / On my radio: Selecter / Big six: Judge Dread / Sally Brown: Aitken, Laurel & The Loafers / Universe: Big 5 / Mirror in the bathroom: International Beat / Al Capone: Hot Knives / I can see cleary now: Black, Pauline / Ska pig: Mark Foggo's Skasters / Prince of peace: Maroon Town / Ska'd for life: Ska-Dows / Darling: Riffs / Samson and Delilah: Bad Manners / Right on King Hammond: King Hammond / Ska skank: Natural Rhythm / Look at me now: Volcanos / Long shot kick de bucket: Ska Boom / Limehouse lady: Kay, Arthur Originals

EMPRCD 646 / Oct '96 / Emporio

☐ SKA BEATS VOL.1

Mental ska (the rap): Longsy D / Just keep rockin': Double Trouble & Rebel MC / Force ten from Navarone: Roughneck / Musical scorcha: Rackit Allstar / Resolution '99: Maroon Town / Rock to dis (house mix): Jamaica Mean Time / We play ska: Children Of The Night / This is ska (Buster's original ska mix): Longsy D & Buster Bloodvessel / Skanking with the toreadors: Ministry Of Ska / Rude boy shuffle: Rude Boys / Swingin' thing: Flowers Ltd & BMG

SKACID 001CD / Nov '89 / Beechwood

☐ SKA BONANZA (2CD Set)

CDHB 86 / Feb '92 / Heartbeat

☐ SKA CRAZY

PLSCD 104 / Apr '96 / Pulse

☐ SKA DOWN HER WAY (Women Of Ska)

Lyin' ass bitch: Fishbone / You're wondering: Skatalites / Rotten banana legs: Skankin' Pickle / Hung up: Bim Skala Bim / Darling boy: Checkered Cabs / High school: Green, Isaac & The Skalars / Look at you now: Agent 99 / I wish you were a beer: Skandalous Allstars / Cloven: Skahumbug

SH 5725 / Jun '97 / Shanachie

☐ SKA DOWN JAMAICA WAY

TDCD 101 / Mar '97 / Top Deck

☐ SKA FANTASTIC

RB 3012 / Mar '95 / Reggae Best

☐ SKA GIANTS (3CD Set)

DTKBOX 72 / 13 Oct '97 / Dressed To Kill

☐ SKA HITS VOL.1 (3CD Set)

DTKBOX 89 / 25 May '98 / Dressed To Kill

☐ SKA IS THE LIMIT

On my radio: Selecter / Too much too young: Specials / Gangsters: Special AKA / Really saying something: Fun Boy Three & Bananarama / Free yourself: Untouchables / Work out: Dekker, Desmond / Message to Rudy: Specials & Rico / Three minute hero: Selecter / Ghost town: Specials / I spy for the FBI: Untouchables / Please don't bend: Dekker, Desmond / What I like most about you is your girlfriend: Special AKA / It ain't what you do it's the way that you do it: Fun Boy Three & Bananarama / Wild child: Untouchables

DC 880742 / May '97 / Disky

☐ SKA IS THE LIMIT/HISTORY OF SKA

RNCD 2073 / Oct '94 / Rhino

☐ SKA ISLAND (A New Skauthentic Compilation)

5243922 / 29 Sep '97 / Island

☐ SKA RIFFS (18 Ska Classics)

Too much pressure: Selecter / Rocksteady party: Aitken, Laurel & The Potato 5 / Magical feeling: International Beat / My girl lollipop: Bad Manners / Viva suspenders: Judge Dread / Peter Gunn: Riffs / Living in a suitcase: Loafers / Rough rider: Big 5 / Watching the rich kids: Kay, Arthur Originators / Won't you try to be different: Volcanos / Jimmy Jazz: Off The Shelf / Double barrel: Hot Knives / Hello: Foggo, Mark Skasters / Travellin' light: Maroon Town / Another way: Skin Deep / South London boy: Originals / Sheila: Burial / Best friend: Bugsy Malone

EMPRCD 647 / 8 Sep '97 / Emporio

☐ SKA SPECTACULAR VOL.1
CPCD 8021 / Feb '94 / Charly

☐ SKA SPECTACULAR VOL.2
CPCD 8022 / Feb '94 / Charly

☐ SKA STARS OF THE 80'S
GAZCD 006 / Apr '90 / Gaz's Rockin' Records

☐ SKA SUCKS
He wants me back: *Dance Hall Crashers* / Marcus Garvey: *Hepcat* / Maggie Mae: *Pietasters* / Skagasm: *Ocean 11* / We go together: *Less Than Jake* / Spy market: *Let's Go Bowling* / Suicide: *Choking Victim* / Stop looking at me: *Unsteady* / Jerry: *Mustard Plug* / Introduction to the yellow passion: *Mephiskapheles* / Orange boy: *Usuals* / Kind of: *Link 80* / Asleep at the wheel: *Hippos* / Clear color: *Limp* / Believer: *Chickenpox* / Da strike: *Millencolin* / Hangin' out: *Home Grown* / Tune me out: *MU330* / Dream girl: *Jeffries Fan Club* / Almost punk enough: *Slapstick* / Oceanside putt putt: *Attaboy skip* / Face first: *Against all Authority* / Share: *Cousin Oliver* / Teen Idol: *Rx Bandits* / Full trucker effect: *Johnny Socko* / Not your pet: *Chinkees* / Kick the bucket: *Liberator* / Day in the life of: *Homeless Wonders* / We are potshot: *Potshot*
37809 / 3 Aug '98 / Liberation

☐ SKA TRAX - THE NEXT GENERATION VOL.1
EFA 119962 / Dec '94 / Heatwave

☐ SKA TRAX - THE NEXT GENERATION VOL.2
EFA 127882 / Jan '96 / Heatwave

☐ SKA WARS (4CD Set)
MBSCD 439 / Nov '95 / Castle

☐ SKA ZONE
TX 51200CD / Jun '97 / Triple X

☐ SKAMPLER
SR 9708 / 19 Jan '98 / Skam

☐ SKANARCHY VOL.1
ELM 004CD / 2 Mar '98 / Elevator

☐ SKANARCHY VOL.2
ELM 008CD / 2 Mar '98 / Elevator

☐ SKANARCHY VOL.3
ELM 019CD / 30 Mar '98 / Elevator

☐ SKANDALOUS VOL.1 (I've Gotcha Covered)
Secret agent man: *Toasters* / Guns of Navarone: *Skatalites* / Paranoid: *Ruder Than You* / Sanford and Son: *PErfect ThYroID* / Sunshine of your love: *Bim Skala Bim* / Brown eyed girl: *Magadog* / Scooby Doo: *Jinkies* / Flintstones: *Benuts* / Lonesome track: *Regatta 69* / Batman movie theme: *Skavoovie & the Epitones* / Come together: *PErFect ThYroID* / Police woman: *Skatalites* / For the turnstiles: *Bim Skala Bim* / Hawa negila: *Bluekilla*
SH 5717 / Dec '96 / Shanachie

☐ SKANDALOUS VOL.2 (I've Gotcha Covered)
SH 5726 / Aug '97 / Shanachie

☐ SKANK VOL.1 (Licensed To Ska)
Skinhead love affair: *Buster's All Stars* / Fire: *Bluebeat* / Julie Julie: *Braces* / Orion: *Busters* / Laughing loafers: *Loafers* / Ska skank down party: *Skaos* / Jump start: *Forest Hillbillies* / Pipeline: *Buster's All Stars* / Safety guards: *Bluebeat* / Letter: *Braces* / Keen on games: *Busters* / Melancholy Sally: *Loafers* / Struggle: *Skaos* / Shocker: *Toasters*
SMMCD 553 / 29 Jun '98 / Snapper

☐ SKANK VOL.2 (Ska For Ska's Sake)
Skadansk: *Mark Foggos's Skasters* / It's so easy: *Loafers* / WLN: *Hot Knives* / King Hammond shuffle: *King Hammond* / City riot: *Maroon Town* / Off The Shelf tonight: *Off The Shelf* / Blind date: *Riffs* / Another town: *Mr. Review* / Driving me to drink: *Skandal* / One eyed lodger: *Judge Dread* / Ska sax: *Pick it up* / Woman: *Pork Hunts*
SMMCD 552 / 29 Jun '98 / Snapper

☐ SKANK VOL.3 (15 Commandments)
SMMCD 551 / 29 Jun '98 / Snapper

☐ SKANKIN' IN THE PIT
HR 17CD / Feb '97 / Hopeless

☐ SKANKIN' ROUND THE WORLD VOL.1
DOJOCD 175 / Nov '93 / Dojo

☐ SKANKIN' ROUND THE WORLD VOL.2
DOJOCD 176 / Nov '93 / Dojo

☐ SKANKIN' ROUND THE WORLD VOL.3
DOJOCD 185 / Feb '94 / Dojo

☐ SKANKIN' ROUND THE WORLD VOL.4
DOJOCD 186 / Feb '94 / Dojo

☐ SKANKIN' ROUND THE WORLD VOL.5
DOJOCD 190 / Jan '96 / Dojo

☐ SKANKING IN THE PIT
HR 6172 / 16 Feb '98 / Hopeless

☐ SKARA BRAE
CEFCD 031 / 24 Aug '98 / Gael Linn

☐ SKA'S THE LIMIT (2CD Set)
RNCD 2075 / Oct '94 / Rhino

☐ SKATERS HAVE MORE FUN
EFA 610602 / Jul '97 / Skate

☐ SKAVILLE USA VOL.1
SKANKCD 001 / Jan '98 / Skank

☐ SKAVILLE USA VOL.2
SKANKCD 002 / Jan '98 / Skank

☐ SKAVILLE USA VOL.3
SKANKCD 003 / Jan '98 / Skank

☐ SKAVILLE USA VOL.4
SKANKCD 004 / Jan '98 / Skank

☐ SKAVILLE USA VOL.5
SKANKCD 005 / Jan '98 / Skank

☐ SKAVILLE USA VOL.6
SKANKCD 006 / Jan '98 / Skank

☐ SKAVILLE USA VOL.7
SKANKCD 007 / Jan '98 / Skank

☐ SKIN FULL VOL.1
Freeform: *Grand Unified* / Coffee: *Dogs Deluxe* / Chang 500: *King Kooba* / You blow my mind: *DJ Food* / Release the cracken: *King Kooba* / You were my sunshine: *Meateaters* / Quorma: *Underwolves* / All of one: *Dogs Deluxe* / Dig deeper: *Grand Unified* / Assid bahn: *Fifa* / Wing it: *Palmskin Productions* / You were my sunshine: *Herbaliser*
SKINCD 001 / 3 Nov '97 / Second Skin

☐ SKIN TWO - PERVY VIBEZ AND KINKY CUTS
MIL 047CD / 13 Oct '97 / Millenium

☐ SKINHEAD REVOLT
Skinhead revolt: *Joe The Boss* / What will your mother say: *Jones, Clancy* / If it don't work out: *Kelly, Pat* / Champion: *GG All Stars* / Little better: *Parks, Lloyd* / Left with a broken heart: *Paragons* / In the spirit: *Charmers, Lloyd* / Reggae girl: *Tennors* / Death a come: *Charmers, Lloyd* / Skinhead speaks his mind: *Hothead All Stars* / Dark end of the street: *Kelly, Pat* / Shu be du: *Eccles, Clancy* / Come a little closer: *Donaldson, Eric* / Barbabus: *GG All Stars* / Loving reggae: *Maytones* / Ease me up officer: *Soul Ofrus* / Got to get away: *Paragons* / To love somebody: *Brown, Buster* / Place called happiness: *Mills, Rudy* / Last call: *Silver Stars*
CDTRL 329 / Mar '94 / Trojan

☐ SKINNINGROVE BAY
Save a place for me / Carlin how / Skinningrove Bay / Filten castle / Deep green / Old man of the ocean / North country girl / Abess St. Hilda
C5CD 580 / Mar '97 / See For Miles

☐ SKINT PRESENTS BRASSIC BEATS VOL.1
BRASSIC 1CD / Jul '96 / Skint

☐ SKINT PRESENTS BRASSIC BEATS VOL.2
BRASSIC 4CD / Apr '97 / Skint

☐ SKINT PRESENTS BRASSIC BEATS VOL.3
BRASSIC 6CD / 9 Feb '98 / Skint

☐ SKIRL OF PIPES VOL.1, THE
PACD 031 / Mar '94 / Music Masters

☐ SKOKIAN INA AFRICAN BEAT
LMLP 3003 / Sep '97 / Jah Life

☐ SKUNK - THIS SOME BAD WEED VOL.1
Dances with fire: *Mojo Risin'* / Return of Rasputin: *Aardvark* / Movement, the message: *Soundcraft* / Sinister footwork: *3rd Alternative* / All of your mind: *Blood Runs Dry* / Out of my paradise: *Aardvark* / Chant 4 freedom: *Vu 2* / Won't cry you: *SULO* / Fox on the cut: *Babyfox* / No apologies: *3rd Alternative* / Slider: *Paingang* / One love: *Molara* / 20,000 feet: *Vu 2* / Wibbler: *Soundcraft* / This some bad weed: *Soundcraft*
POOCD 001 / Dec '93 / Skunk

☐ SKUNK - THIS SOME BAD WEED VOL.2
POOCD 2 / Oct '94 / Skunk

☐ SKYE SCENE
SSCD 01 / Jul '98 / Skye Scene

☐ SLAMMED
RR 87792 / 3 Nov '97 / Roadrunner

☐ SLAMMIN' SETS VOL.1
Where's the hip hop: *Active Force* / Back in business: *Ultimate Buzz* / Merlins funfair: *Forbes, Davie* / Keeping alive: *Forbes, Davie* / Reach out: *Forbes & Cyclone* / Don curly wurly: *Forbes & Cyclone* / Breakdown on the floor: *Active Force* / Foreever and a day: *Active Force* / Apoclypse now: *Forbes, Davie* / Getting there: *Forbes, Davie*
DCSR 009 / Jun '97 / Clubscene

☐ SLAMMIN' VINYL PRESENTS ABSOLUTE HARDCORE (2CD Set)
Distant love: *DJ Sy & Unknown Artist* / Deeper: *DJ Sy & DJ Demo* / Hopscotch: *Midnight Express* / Bang the beat: *DJ Sy & Unknown Artist* / Scratchin': *DJ Sy & Unknown Artist* / Shooting star: *Bang* / Jump a little higher: *Breeze* / Take my love: *DJ Brisk* / Thunder and rain: *DJ Brisk* / Sailaway: *Bang* / Back in your arms: *DJ Huxley* / Power of love: *Brown, Scott* / You and me: *Brown, Scott* / Jump around: *Slippery Project* / On and on: *DJ Brisk & DJ Ham* / Musik: *Happy Rollers* / Life: *Ham* / Is anybody out there: *Ham* / Coming on strong: *DJ Slam & Charlie B* / Listen to the Ace: *DJ Sy & Unknown Artist* / Devotion: *DJ Demo & DJ Sy* / Music is my life: *Monty & D'Skys* / U had it all: *Monty & D'Skys* / Come together: *DJ Demo* / Sensation: *DJ Demo & DJ Sy* / Wicked sound: *DJ Tap-It & B&H* / (Still untitled): *DJ Hixxy*
SVCD 001 / 9 Mar '98 / Slammin' Vinyl

☐ SLANGED
EFA 04914CD / Nov '92 / City Slang

☐ SLAUGHTERED VOL.1
SPV 07725162 / Feb '94 / SPV

☐ SLAUGHTERED VOL.2
SPV 07725172 / Jun '94 / SPV

☐ SLEEPY'S THEME (The Vinyl Room)
65901720012 / 14 Jul '98 / BGNT

☐ SLENG TENG EXTRAVAGANZA
GRELCD 209 / May '95 / Greensleeves

☐ SLIDE GUITAR BLUES
IGOCD 2030 / Oct '95 / Indigo

☐ SLIDE GUITAR CLASSICS VOL.1
REP 4664 / 19 Jan '98 / Repertoire

☐ SLIDE GUITAR GOSPEL 1944-1964
DOCD 5222 / Apr '94 / Document

☐ SLIDE GUITAR MASTERS
Guitar rag: *Weaver, Sylvester* / Spoonful blues: *Patton, Charlie* / Rock and tumble blues: *Newbern, 'Hambone' Willie* / Love changing blues: *McTell, 'Blind' Willie* / Lord I just can't keep from crying: *Johnson, 'Blind' Willie* / Kingfish blues: *Tampa Red* / Preachin' the blues: *House, Son* / Goin' up the country: *Barbecue Bob* / Sagefield woman blues: *Arnold, Kokomo* / Special streamline: *White, Bukka* / Evil hearted woman blues: *Woods, Oscar 'Buddy'* / You just as well let her go: *Weldon, Casey Bill* / Ramblin' on my mind: *Johnson, Robert* / Country blues: *Waters, Muddy* / Combination boogie: *Hutto, J.B.* / Dust my broom: *James, Elmore* / Crossroads: *Homesick James* / Blue guitar: *Hooker, Earl* / Had a date with Barbara last night: *Louisiana Red* / Shake 'em on down: *McDowell, 'Mississippi' Fred*
CDGR 219 / 2 Feb '98 / Charly

☐ SLIDE GUITAR VOL.1 (Bottles, Knives & Steel)
Bottleneck blues: *Weaver & Beasley* / Untitled: *Barbecue Bob* / God don't never change: *Johnson, 'Blind' Willie* / Dark was the night: *Johnson, 'Blind' Willie* / St. Louis blues: *Weaver & Beasley* / Experience blues: *Willis, Ruth & Blind Willie McTell* / Guitar rag: *Weaver, Sylvester* / You can't get that stuff no more: *Tampa Red* / High sheriff blues: *Patton, Charlie* / Homesick and lonesome blues: *Fuller, Blind Boy* / Packin' trunk blues: *Leadbelly* / I believe I'll make a change: *Weldon, Casey Bill* / Don't sell it (don't give it away): *Woods, Oscar 'Buddy'* / Muscat Hill blues: *Woods, Oscar 'Buddy'* / Travelling riverside blues: *Johnson, Robert* / Bukka's jitterbug swing: *White, Bukka* / Special stream line: *White, Bukka* / Swing low, sweet chariot: *Terrell, Sister O.M.* / Pearline: *House, Son*
4672512 / Oct '90 / CBS

☐ SLIDE GUITAR, THE (An Anthology)
Country blues: *Taj Mahal* / Packin' trunk: *Leadbelly* / Preachin' blues: *Johnson, Robert* / Don't sell it (don't give it away): *Woods, Buddy* / Two timin' woman: *Weldon, Casey Bill* / Homesick and lonesome blues: *Fuller, Blind Boy* / Special streamline: *White, Bukka* / Bottleneck blues: *Weaver & Beasley* / Moanin' the blues: *Shaw, Allen* / High sheriff blues: *Patten, Charley* / Diddle da diddle: *Georgia Cotton Pickers* / Decatur St 81: *Georgia Browns* / Travelin' blues: *McTell, 'Blind' Willie* / No matter how she done it: *Tampa Red & Georgia Tom* / Hard times: *Moss, Buddy* / You're gonna need somebody on your bond: *Johnson, 'Blind' Willie* / Preachin' blues: *House, Son* / I feel like going home: *Waters, Muddy* / Sitting in the jail house: *Winter, Johnny* / I can stand to see you die: *Otis, Shuggie* / I feel so bad: *Bloomfield, Mike* / Am I wrong: *Keb Mo'*
4898902 / 20 Jul '98 / Sony Blues

☐ SLIDIN'...SOME SLIDE
BB 9533CD / Jan '94 / Bullseye Blues

☐ SLIP 'N' SLIDE VOL.3
SLIPCD 51 / Oct '96 / Slip 'n' Slide

☐ SLIP 'N' SLIDE VOL.4
Never can get away: *Hope, Alexander* / Mama: *Restless Soul* / Rock steady: *McKnight, Julie* / Only you: *Smith, Lynette* / Tunnel: *House Of Jazz* / C docks traffic jam: *Dockin, Charles* / My desire: *Amira* / I want you for myself: *McKnight, Julie* / Alright: *Mijan* / Sykodelik: *Restless Soul* / TBC: *Rivera, Sandy* / Funky people: *Funky People*
SLIPCD 074 / 15 Dec '97 / Slip 'n' Slide

☐ SLOVENIA IRP
CD 13255 / Mar '93 / Nika

☐ SLOVENIAN FOLK MUSIC AND SONGS 1975-1995
C 600007 / Feb '98 / Ocora

☐ SLOW MO
Shaolin satelite: *Thievery Corporation* / Cicu catiena: *Sie* / Chocolate Elvis: *Tosca* / GI blus: *Kaleidoscope* / On the other side: *Jadell* / Departure lounge: *Hightower Set* / Freedom: *DJ Food* / Noktorno: *Boqus* / Interlude: *Faceless* / Look 4 a style: *Bantam* / Subways: *Strange Brew* / Bluehouse: *Dol-Lop* / Pickled eggs and sherb: *All Seeing I*
SD 015 / 13 Apr '98 / Stereo Deluxe

☐ SLOW MOTION (14 Urban Contemporary Love Ballads)
Your body's calling: *R Kelly* / Let me do U: *POV* / All night: *Me 2 U* / Please tell me tonight: *Motiv* / Don't go nowhere: *Riff* / Always: *Mint Condition* / When I need somebody: *Tresvant, Ralph* / I got a thang 4 ya: *Low Key* / La la love: *Avila, Bobby Ross* / Make love 2 me: *Lorenzo* / Baby it's real: *Serenade* / I'll be there for you: *ML* / Wait for me: *Chalant* / Gangsta lean: *DRS*
CDELV 16 / Jun '94 / Elevate

☐ SLOW 'N' MOODY, BLACK 'N' BLUESY
Nothing can change this love: *Hill, Z.Z.* / You messed up my mind: *Hammond, Clay* / I can't stand it: *Holiday, Jimmy* / Directly from my heart: *Little Richard* / I don't need: *Turner, Ike & Tina* / Let's get together: *Arthur & Mary* / Darling I'm standing by you: *Jones, Jeanette* / Baby I'll come right away: *Love, Mary* / If I'd lose you: *Day, Jackie* / I don't wanna lose you: *Young, Tami* / Baby, come to me: *Little Henry & The Shamrocks* / Ain't nobody's business if I do: *King, B.B.* / Every dog has his day: *Copeland, Johnny* / Baby, what you want me to do: *Little Richard* / Baby I'll come: *Love, Mary* / Everybody needs somebody: *Love, Mary* / Weep no more: *Terry & The Tyrants* / It's real: *Robbins, Jimmy* / Can't count the days: *Robbins, Jimmy* / Whenever I can't sleep: *Gauff, Willie & The Love Brothers* / Last one to know: *Haywood, Joe* / Mr. President: *Haywood, Joe* / Woman needs a man: *Baker, Yvonne* / Farewell: *Gauff, Willie & The Love Brothers* / Why should I be the one: *Gauff, Willie & The Love Brothers* / I'll come back to you: *Mighty Hannibal* / Consider yourself: *Johnson, Stacey*
CDKEND 003 / Nov '94 / Kent

☐ SLOW PUNANY
GPCD 006 / Dec '93 / Gussie P

☐ SMALL BAND SWING VOL.1 1935-1937 (Made In Swinton)
CVA 7993 / Jan '97 / Jazz Document

☐ SMALL GROUP SWING
Upstairs: *Smith, Stuff* / I ain't got nobody: *Webb, Chick* / In a little Spanish town: *Webb, Chick* / Chicken and waffles: *Berigan, Bunny* / Swingin' in the coconut trees: *Jordan, Louis* / Doug the Jitterbug: *Jordan, Louis* / Baby, won't you please come home: *Spencer Trio* / Lorna Doone shortbread: *Spencer Trio* / Three little words: *Freeman, Bud* / Raggin' the scale: *Venuti, Joe* / Josephine: *Rollini, Adrian* / Dr. Livingstone, I presume: *Shaw, Artie* / When the quail come back to San Quentin: *Shaw, Artie* / Countless blues: *Kansas City Six* / Home James: *James, Harry* / Body and soul: *Tatum, Art* / I'll take the South: *Brown, Cleo* / Minor Drag: *Waller, Fats* / Oh Susannah, dust off that old piano: *New Orleans Rhythm Kings* / 29th and dearborn: *Dodds, Johnny* / China boy: *Goodman, Benny* / When the midnight choo-choo leaves for Alabam': *Dorsey, Tommy*
PPCD 78102 / Feb '95 / Past Perfect

☐ SMALL WONDER PUNK SINGLES COLLECTION VOL.1
Mucky pup: *Puncture* / Hungry: *Zeros* / Radio wunderbar: *Carpettes* / Safety pin stuck in my heart: *Fitzgerald, Patrick* / GLC: *Menace* / Buy me sell me: *Fitzgerald, Patrick* / Nineteen and mad: *Leyton Buzzards* / Puppet life: *Punishment Of Luxury* / Small wonder: *Carpettes* / Little Miss Perfect: *Demon Preacher* / Never been so stuck: *Nicky & The Dots* / New way: *Wall* / Disco love: *Molesters* / End: *Cravats* / Last year's youth: *Menace* / DNA: *Murder The Disturbed* / End of civilisation: *Molesters* / Flares and slippers: *Cockney Rejects* / Violence grows: *Fatal Microbes* / Exchange: *Wall* / Time tunnel: *English Sub-titles* / Soft ground: *Prole* / Precinct: *Cravats* / You're driving me: *Cravats* / Off the beach: *Cravats* / They've got it all wrong: *Anthrax*
CDPUNK 29 / Mar '94 / Anagram

☐ SMALL WONDER PUNK SINGLES COLLECTION VOL.2
Can't play rock n roll: *Puncture* / Radio fun: *Zeros* / How about me and you: *Carpettes* / Set we free: *Fitzgerald, Patrick* / I'm civilised: *Menace* / Little dippers: *Fitzgerald, Patrick* / Irrelevant battles: *Fitzgerald, Patrick* / Youthanasia: *Leyton Buzzards* / Demon: *Punishment Of Luxury* / 2 NE 1: *Carpettes* / Linoleum walk: *Nicky & The Dots* / Suckers: *Wall* / Uniforms: *Wall* / Burning bridges cravats: *Cravats* / I am the dreg: *Cravats* / Who's in here with me / Commuter man: *Molesters* / Carry no banners: *Menace* / Walking corpses: *Murder The Disturbed* / Girl behind the curtain: *Molesters* / Police car: *Cockney Rejects* / Beautiful picture: *Fatal Microbes* / Sweat: *English Sub-titles* / SMK: *Prole* / What will tomorrow: *Anthrax*
CDPUNK 70 / Jan '96 / Anagram

☐ SMALLTALK
Colonel Fraser / Mary Ann MacInnes / Famous bridge / Kail and pudding / Cumha coire a 'cheathaich / Jock Hawk / New claret / Low country dance / Advasar Blacksmith / Black haired lad / Shetland fiddler / Over the sea to nova scotia / Rose Anderson / Les vielles bottiness / Heights of casino / 'S truagh nach do dh'fhuirich / Fhorton jig / James Byrne's jig / Duncan McKillop / Bee in the knickers / Fil o ro
CDTRAX 079 / Sep '94 / Greentrax

☐ SMASH HITS MIX '97 (2CD Set)
Wannabe: *Spice Girls* / Flava: *Andre, Peter* / We've got it goin' on: *Backstreet Boys* / Naked: *Louise* / When I fall in love: *Ant & Dec* / Spinning the wheel: *Michael, George* / Don't stop movin': *Livin' Joy* / Love sensation: *911* / Don't make me wait: *911* / Jazz it up: *Reel 2 Real* / Gangsta's paradise: *Coolio & LV* / I got 5 on it: *Luniz* / Good thing: *Eternal* / Freedom: *Williams, Robbie* / Love II love: *Damage* / If you leave me now: *Upside Down* / Crazy chance: *Kavana* / Oh what a night (December '63): *Clock* / That girl: *Priest, Maxi & Shaggy* / X Files theme: *DJ Dado* / Don't look back in anger: *Oasis* / Day we caught the train: *Ocean Colour Scene* / Breakfast at Tiffany's: *Deep Blue Something* / You're gorgeous: *Baby Bird* / Spaceman: *Babylon Zoo* / Breathe: *Prodigy* / Trash: *Suede* / Charmless man: *Blur* / Female of the species: *Space* / Oh yeah: *Ash* / Stars: *Dubstar* / Stupid girl: *Garbage* / Going out: *Supergrass* / Something for the weekend: *Divine Comedy* / Wrong: *Everything But The Girl* / Atom bomb: *Fluke* / Stamp: *Healy, Jeremy & Amos* / Seven days and one week: *BBE* / Born slippy: *Underworld* / I wanna be a hippy: *Technohead*
VTDCD 110 / Dec '96 / Virgin

☐ SMASH HITS MIX '98 (2CD Set)
VTDCD 164 / 24 Nov '97 / Virgin

☐ SMASH HITS OF THE 1960'S VOL.1
DCC 866792 / Aug '96 / Disky

☐ SMASH HITS OF THE 1960'S VOL.2
DC 866802 / Aug '96 / Disky

☐ SMASH HITS OF THE 1960'S VOL.3
DC 866812 / Aug '96 / Disky

☐ SMASH HITS SUMMER '97 (2CD Set)
I wannabe the only one: Eternal & Bebe Winans / I believe I can fly: Kelly, R / Wonderful tonight: Damage / Quit playin' games with (my heart): Backstreet Boys / Who do you think you are: Spice Girls / Ld before I die: Williams, Robbie / Ready to go: Republica / Bellisima: DJ Quicksilver / Encore une fois: Sash / Star people '97: Michael, George / Professional widow: Amos, Tori / Ready or not: Course / Fresh: Gina G / Body shakin': 911 / Natural: Andre, Peter / I can make you feel good: Kavana / Clementine: Owen, Mark / Let me in: OTT / One kiss from heaven: Louise / Extremis: Hal & Gillian Anderson / Words: Boyzone / Forever: Boyzone / I need you: 3T / Moan and groan: Morrison, Mark / Do you know: Gayle, Michelle / Walk on by: Gabrielle / Remember me: Blueboy / I have peace: Strike / You got the love: Source & Candi Staton / Underwater love: Smoke City / Shout: Ant & Dec / Your woman: White Town / North country boy: Charlatans / Tattva: Kula Shaker / Song 2: Blur / Richard III: Supergrass / Smile: Supernaturals / Kowalski: Primal Scream / Nightmare: Brainbug / Flash: BBE / Theme from the Professionals: Johnson, Laurie London Big Band
VTDCD 144 / Jun '97 / Virgin

☐ SMASH HITS SUMMER '98 (2CD Set)
Where are you now: Imaani / Top of the world (ole ole ole): Chumbawamba / It's like that: Run DMC & Jason Nevins / Are you Jimmy Ray: Ray, Jimmy / Brimful of asha: Cornershop / Mmmbop: Hanson / True to us: Vanilla / All I want is you: Vanilla / Here's where the story ends: Tin Tin Out / I want you to want me: Solid Harmonie / Last thing on my mind: Steps / Be alone no more: Another Level & Jay-Z / Doctor Jones: Aqua / No no no: Destiny's Child & Wyclef Jean / Feel it: Tamperer / Let me entertain you: Williams, Robbie / Uh la la la: Alexia / Eat my goal: Collapsed Lung / La primavera: Sash / Ain't that just the way: McNeal, Lutricia / Cleopatra's theme: Cleopatra / Ballad of Tom Jones: Space / Show me love: Robyn / Perfect day / Zorba's dance: LCD / Keep on dancin' (let's go): Perpetual Motion / I get lonely: Jackson, Janet / Angels: Williams, Robbie / All I have to give: Backstreet Boys / All that matters: Louise / Never ever: All Saints / Big mistake: Imbruglia, Natalie / Teardrop: Massive Attack / Raincloud: Lighthouse Family / Baby can I hold you tonight: Boyzone / Too much: Spice Girls / All the man that I need: May, Shernette / No way no way: Vanilla / Stop: Spice Girls / Best days: Juice / Mulder and Skully: Catatonia
VTDCD 186 / 18 May '98 / Virgin

☐ SMELL THE FUZZ
398417010CD / Oct '96 / Metal Blade

☐ SMELLS LIKE TEAM SPIRIT VOL.1
D 00041CD / 3 Nov '97 / Displeased

☐ SMELLS LIKE TEAM SPIRIT, VOL.2
D 00050CD / 3 Nov '97 / Displeased

☐ SMILE JAMAICA (40 Totally Tropical Reggae Hits) (2CD Set)
Funkin' for Jamaica: Browne, Tom / Lively up yourself: Marley, Bob / Mr Loverman: Shabba Ranks / Stranded: McNeal, Lutricia / Oh Carolina: Shaggy / Don't worry be happy: McFerrin, Bobby / Sweets for my sweet: Lewis, C.J. / Here comes the hotstepper: Kamoze, Ini / Sweat (a la la la la long): Inner Circle / Mr Big Stuff: Knight, Jean / 54-46 (was my number): Toots & The Maytals / Who am I: Beenie Man / Dwayne: Red Rat / Kick it: Reggae Boyz / Mysterious girl: Andre, Peter & Bubbler Ranx / Wild world: Priest, Maxi / Baby come back: Equals / You don't love me (no no no): Penn, Dawn / Travelling man: Studio 2 / Rude boy rock: Lionrock / Hot hot hot: Arrow / Soul limbo: Booker T & The MG's / Samba de janeiro: Carrilio / Naked in the rain: Blue Pearl / Oye como va: Puente, Tito / Lambada: Kaoma / Macarena: Los Del Mar / Guaglione: Prado, Perez / Jingo: Candido / Mas que nada: Los Delanteros / Tu vuo fa l'Americano: Cozzo, Gisella & Maarco Guerzoni / Funky Nassau: Beginning Of The End / Bossa nova: Tippie & The Clovers / Watermelon Man: Santamaria, Mongo / Money in my pocket: Brown, Dennis / You can get it if you really want: Dekker, Desmond / Good thing going: Minott, Sugar / Electric Avenue: Grant, Eddy / Dancing on the floor: Third World / I can see clearly now: Nash, Johnny
TTVCD 2976 / 8 Jun '98 / Telstar TV

☐ SMILE MIX SESSION VOL.2
SM 80302 / Feb '97 / Profile

☐ SMITHSONIAN FOLKWAYS AMERICAN ROOTS COLLECTION
SFWCD 40062 / Jul '96 / Smithsonian Folkways

☐ SMITHSONIAN FOLKWAYS WORLD MUSIC COLLECTION
SFWCD 40471 / Aug '97 / Smithsonian Folkways

☐ SMOKE RINGS
PHONTCD 7641 / '93 / Phontastic

☐ SMOKERS INC.
SINCCD 001 / Nov '96 / No Smoking

☐ SMOOCHER IS BACK, THE (12 Class X Soul Tracks)
Every time you're near me: Scott, Gloria / I only wanted to love you: Sass / Fill you up: Mystique / Pick up: Ace Spectrum / My love is your love: Isley Brothers / Got to see u soon: Checkmates Unlimited / Let's stay together: Joseph, Margie / This kind of love: Valentine Brothers / Sharing: Vitamin E / Open up your soul: Franklin, Erma / I just didn't hear me the first time: Sandpebbles / Sing a love song: Connors, Norman
FR 363CD / 16 Dec '97 / Big Cheese

☐ SMOOCHIN' IN CHICAGO
For all we know: Orioles / Golden teardrops: Flamingos / Secret love: Moonglows / Fool's prayer: Five Echoes / Lonely one: Sherrif & The Ravels / You have two (I have none): Sherrif & The Ravels / Ozeta: Magnificents / Oh baby you have to go: El Cincos / Baby please: Moonglows / Happy til the letter: Orioles / Blues in the letter: Flamingos / Now that it's over: Falcons / Judy: Prodigals / Fools will be fools: Orioles / Hello dear: Hi-Liters / Festival of love: Dukays / Lost lover: Magnificents / My only love: Falcons / Oh what a night: Dells / You're still in my heart: Dells / Why did she go: Magnificents / Big lie: Dukays / Glitter in your eye: Sheppards / Lover's prayer: Deltones / Much in need: Five Royales
CDGR 199 / Nov '97 / Charly

☐ SMOOCHIN' IN NEW YORK
CDGR 174 / Jul '97 / Charly

☐ SMOOTH JAZZ SLOW JAMS (The Romantic Side Of Contemporary Jazz)
SH 5039 / Oct '97 / Shanachie

☐ SMOOTH ONE, A
CECD 3 / 29 Jun '98 / Collector's Edition

☐ SMOOTH SOUNDS OF SAXON, THE
VPCD 2054 / 22 Dec '97 / VP

☐ SMYRNAIC SONG IN GREECE 1928-1935, THE
HTCD 27 / Feb '95 / Heritage

☐ SNAKEBITE CITY
BLU 06 / Apr '95 / Blue Fire

☐ SNAKEBITE CITY VOL.4
BLU 07 / Mar '97 / Blue Fire

☐ SNAKEBITE CITY VOL.5
BLU 08 / Oct '96 / Blue Fire

☐ SNAKEBITE CITY VOL.6
BLU 09 / Apr '97 / Blue Fire

☐ SNAKEBITE CITY VOL.7
BLU 10 / 1 Dec '97 / Blue Fire

☐ SNAKEBITE CITY VOL.8
BLU 12 / 10 Aug '98 / Blue Fire

☐ SNAP (The Essential Mix Show/2CD Set)
Oasis: Paragliders / Vicious circle: Poltergeist / Love above: Finitribe / Where are you: 16 Bit / Original: Leftfield / Flying souls: Sequencer / Luck spray: Redeye / Survive: Brothers Grimm / Raise your hands: Boston Bruins / Drive: Trancesetters / Melt: Leftfield / Aqualite: Wavemaker / Happy rose: Arcus / Tension: Reunification / Dark side of the Moog: Schulze, Klaus / Classix: Arcus / Mushroom shaped: Finitribe / Raven: 16 Bit
5286752 / Jul '96 / Mercury

☐ SNAPOLOGY
Cherry man: Wannadies / It's absence: Souls / On your bedroom floor: This Perfect Day / Sheena: Eggstone / Under surface: Baby Lemonade / Miss thing-a-magic: Simpkins / It's not that easy: Poverty Stinks / SU song: Singer / Seven years: Scents / Marine love (demo): Easy / Million dollar project: Whipped Cream / Blind: Poodle
SNAP 008 / Oct '93 / Soap

☐ SNOWBOARD GENERATION (2CD Set)
Everybody needs a 303: Fatboy Slim / Song 2: Blur / Sure shot: Beastie Boys / Smack my bitch up: Prodigy / Ultrafunkula: Van Helden, Armand / Brown paper bag: Roni Size / Midlander: Bentley Rhythm Ace / Burnin' wheel: Primal Scream / High noon: DJ Shadow / Renegade master: Wildchild / Outer space: Tenor, Jimi / Dirt: Death In Vegas / Black steel: Tricky / Berry meditation: UNKLE / Block rockin' beats: Chemical Brothers / Digital: Goldie & KRS1 / Triumph: Wu Tang Clan / Bang: Propellerheads / Jungle brother: Jungle Brothers / Post modern sleaze: Sneaker Pimps / Theme from Control Centre: Herbaliser / Blue flowers: Dr. Octagon / New pollution: Beck / Karma coma: Massive Attack
SNOWCD 1 / 9 Mar '98 / Beechwood

☐ SNOWDANCE
Cyberspace / Heigh hoo heigh hoo / Send me an angel / Stop this dream / Bee in my bonnet / Marcelo Mastroianni / Take my hand / Redwire desire / 2 The top / Girl / Summer of love / Stay tuned / Paradiso / Fly to the sky / XTC / Grober bar
399842 / Jun '97 / Koch Presents

☐ SO BLUE SO FUNKY VOL.1 (Heroes Of The Hammond)
All about my girl: McGriff, Jimmy / Silver metre: Patton, 'Big' John / I'm movin' on: Smith, Jimmy / Wine, wine, wine: Roach, Freddie / Brown sugar: Roach, Freddie / Hootin' 'n' tootin': Jackson, Fred / Face to face: Willette, 'Baby Face' / Fat Judy: Patton, 'Big' John / Plaza De Toros: Young, Larry / Boop bop bing bash: Braith, George / Everything I do gohn be funky: Donaldson, Lou / Hot rod: Wilson, Reuben / Butter for yo' popcorn: McDuff, 'Brother' Jack / Ain't it funky now: Green, Grant
BNZ 267 / May '91 / Blue Note

☐ SO BLUE SO FUNKY VOL.2 (Heroes Of The Hammond)
Where it's at: McGriff, Jimmy / Meetin' here: Amy, Curtis & Paul Bryant / When Malindy sings: Roach, Freddie / Mary had a little lamb: Braith, George / Can heat: Smith, Jimmy / Morris the minor: Holmes, Richard 'Groove' / Minor soul: Lytell, Jimmy / Somethin' strange: Willette, 'Baby Face' / I want to go home: Patton, 'Big' John / Street scene: Young, Larry / Kid: Donaldson, Lou
CDP 8290922 / Jun '94 / Blue Note

☐ SO WIE ES DAMALS WAR
BCD 15712 / Mar '93 / Bear Family

☐ SOARING CLASSICS (A Magical Blend Of Music And The Sounds Of Nature)
50562 / May '97 / A-Play Collection

☐ SOCA BEYOND THE HORYZON
HVCD 033 / 27 Jul '98 / Hot Vinyl

☐ SOCA CARNIVAL '96
960102 / May '96 / Tattoo

☐ SOCA CROSSOVER
CMBCD 35 / 15 Jun '98 / Caribbean

☐ SOCA EXPLOSION (The Soul Of Calypso)
68935 / Jun '97 / Tropical

☐ SOCA GOLD 1997
VPCD 1499 / Aug '97 / VP

☐ SOCA GOLD VOL.1
HVCD 015 / Apr '92 / Hot Vinyl

☐ SOCA GOLD VOL.2
HVCD 016 / Apr '92 / Hot Vinyl

☐ SOCA GOLD VOL.3
HVCD 020 / Jan '93 / Hot Vinyl

☐ SOCA GOLD VOL.4
HVCD 021 / Jan '93 / Hot Vinyl

☐ SOCA GOLD VOL.5
HVCD 023 / Sep '95 / Hot Vinyl

☐ SOCA GOLD VOL.6
HVCD 024 / Sep '95 / Hot Vinyl

☐ SOCA GREATEST HITS VOL.1
Fire in the back seat: Curtis, Yvonne / Lay with me: Campbell, Bill / Teaser: Curtis, Yvonne / Let it go: Johnny Rhythm / Sexy feeling: Curtis, Yvonne / Heat in the place: Campbell, Bill / Celebrate with me: Campbell, Bill / Lady lady: Campbell, Bill / Soca dance party: Lucky / Whine on something: Campbell, Pete / 11-7 (Carnival party time): Campbell, Pete / Hot hot hot: Lillete / Sugar bum bum: Lord Diamond / Ah feeling the feelings: Lord Diamond / Don't rock the ting so: Sam, Jeff
WSRCD 101 / Sep '96 / World Sound

☐ SOCA GREATEST HITS VOL.2
Somebody: Campbell, Pete / Cool it down: Melanesse / Got to see you: Campbell, Pete & Roy Alton / Rock the music: Wavet / Sabina: Parker, Belinda / Mama Africa: Campbell, Bill / Maria Tebbola: Campbell, Bill / Serious: Campbell, Pete / Nearest to my heart: Campbell, Bill / Closer: Campbell, Bill / Break away: Lucky / Only for lovers: Curtis, Yvonne / Easy dancing: Davis, Teddy / Let me love you: Davis, Teddy
WSRCD 102 / Sep '96 / World Sound

☐ SOCA HITS VOL.5
WSRCD 106 / 18 Aug '97 / World Sound

☐ SOCA PARTY VOL.4
CSS 018 / 17 Nov '97 / Coral

☐ SOCA PRESSURE
KMP 003CD / Mar '97 / KMP

☐ SOCA SAMPLER
HVCD 025 / Jul '96 / Hot Vinyl

☐ SOCA SWITCH
TSS 01CD / Mar '97 / SJP

☐ SOCA SWITCH VOL.3, THE
JWCL 005CD / Mar '98 / JW

☐ SOCCER ROCKERS (Football Favourites)
Land of hope and glory / We shall not be moved / Battle hymn of the republic / BBC Grandstand theme / I'm forever blowing bubbles / You'll never walk alone / We will rock you / When the saints go marching in / Back home / He's got the whole world in his hands / We are the champions / Stars and stripes forever / Match Of The Day theme / Give peace a chance / Red flag
3036000072 / Oct '95 / Carlton

☐ SOCIAL HARP, THE
ROUCD 0094 / Oct '94 / Rounder

☐ SOCIEDAD = SUCIEDAD
BYO 047CD / 27 Oct '97 / Better Youth Organisation

☐ SOFT METAL
TMPCD 013 / Mar '95 / Temple

☐ SOFT REGGAE
Baby come back: Pato Banton / Baby I love your way: Big Mountain / Searching: China Black / Complimnets on your kiss: Red Dragon / You don't love me (no no no): Penn, Dawn / Mr. Loverman: Shabba Ranks / Best of my love: Lewis, C.J. / Wonderful world, beautiful people: Cliff, Jimmy / Shine: Aswad / Sweat (a la la la la long): Inner Circle / It's raining: McLean, Bitty / Oh Carolina: Shaggy / Close to you: Priest, Maxi / I can see clearly now: Nash, Johnny / Let your yeah be yeah: Pioneers / Love of the common people: Thomas, Nicky / Young, gifted and black: Bob & Marcia / Dancing on the floor: Third World / Good thing going: Minott, Sugar / Silly games: Kay, Janet / Everything I own: Boothe, Ken / I shall sing: Griffiths, Marcia / I will always love you: Hall, Pam
RADCD 4 / Jan '95 / Global TV

☐ SOFT REGGAE (18 Romantic Reggae Classics)
Wide awake in a dream: Biggs, Barry / Sweetest thing: Blues Busters / Lady: Wade, Wayne / Don't need your love: Griffiths, Marcia / Sister Love: Isaacs, Gregory / Woman behind the man: Gardiner, Boris / Sit and cry over you: Dunkley, Errol / Mississippi: Scloss, Cynthia / Let's fall in love: Hammond, Beres / Forgot to say I love you: Holt, John / If you could see me now: Pioneers / Moving away: Boothe, Ken / Baby lay down: Schaffer, Doreen / If it's fire you want: Hinds, Justin / If you wanna make love: Biggs, Barry / Take life easy: Honey Boy / Twilight time: Sanchez / Rockers in the rain: George, Sophia
ECD 3292 / Jan '97 / K-Tel

☐ SOFT ROCK
5352482 / Jan '96 / PolyGram TV

☐ SOFT ROCK
PDSCD 504 / Sep '97 / Pulse

☐ SOFT ROCK CLASSICS VOL.1
You're the voice: Farnham, John / Nothing's gonna stop us now: Starship / Maneater: Hall & Oates / Kyrie: Mr. Mister / You took the words right out of my mouth: Meat Loaf / I hear you knockin': Edmunds, Dave / Bridge to your heart: Wax / Runaway boys: Stray Cats / Mean girl: Status Quo / American woman: Guess Who / Perfect day: Reed, Lou / Every day hurts: Sad Cafe / How long: Ace / Living next door to Alice: Smokie / Human touch: Springfield, Rick / Who's that girl: Eurythmics
74321400252 / Jul '96 / Camden

☐ SOFT ROCK CLASSICS VOL.2
Blinded by the light: Manfred Mann's Earthband / War baby: Robinson, Tom / Broken wings: Mr. Mister / Love hurts: Nazareth / It's a heartache: Tyler, Bonnie / My oh my: Sad Cafe / Promise you made: Cock Robin / Satellite of love: Reed, Lou / White rabbit: Jefferson Airplane / In a broken dream: Python Lee Jackson / Lily was here: Stewart, David A. / Can't fight this feeling: REO Speedwagon / Lost in love: Air Supply / Rock the night: Air Supply / Modern girl: Meat Loaf / Spirit in the sky: Greenbaum, Norman
74321446892 / Feb '97 / Camden

☐ SOLDIER SOLDIER (16 Military Band Favourites)
Rule Britannia: Royal British Legion Band / Knightsbridge march: Blues & Royals Band / Dambusters march: Blues & Royals Band / Bridge too far: Parachute Regiment Band / Royal ceremony: Staff Band Of The RAOC / Normandy veterans: Duke Of Wellington Regiment / Amazing grace: Blues & Royals Band / Royal standard: Royal Engineers / It's a long way to Tipperary: Royal Irish Rangers / High on a hill: Royal Green Jackets / American patrol: 9th/12th Royal Lancers / Pipe medley: Irish Guards Band / Here's a health unto her majesty: Royal Tank Regiment / Abide with me: Queen's Royal Irish Hussars / Old comrade: Blues & Royals Band / Boys of the old brigade/Old soldiers never die: Royal Tank Regiment
SUMCD 4032 / Nov '96 / Summit

☐ SOLID GOLD
MMGV 014 / Jan '93 / Magnum Video

☐ SOLID GOLD 70'S (3CD Set)
I will survive / Reflections of my life: Marmalade / Open up: Mungo Jerry / Get dancin': Disco Tex & The Sexolettes / Freedom come freedom go: Fortunes / Saddle up: Christie, David / Beautiful sunday: Boone, Daniel / Midnight at the oasis: Muldaur, Maria / Build me up buttercup: Foundations / Indiana wants me: Taylor, R. Dean / Ballroom blitz: Sweet / Devils answer: Atomic Rooster / Band of gold: Payne, Freda / I like you: Nelson, Phyllis / Nice and slow: Green, Jesse / Rock your baby: McCrae, George / I wanna dance with choo: Disco Tex & The Sexolettes / Rose garden: Anderson, Lynn / Yellow river: Christie / Love grows where my rosemary goes: Edison Lighthouse / Love don't live here anymore: Rose Royce / Baby jump: Mungo Jerry / Play me like you play your old guitar: Eddy, Duane / Hey there lonely girl: Holman, Eddie / Can you do it: Georgie & Brian Johnson / Bye bye baby: Bay City Rollers / Up with the cock: Judge Dread / Four in the morning: Young, Faron / Angel face: Glitter Band / Girls: Moments & Whatnauts / Stop in the name of love: Gaynor, Gloria / Garden party: Gaynor, Gloria / Feel the need in me: Detroit Emeralds / Love really hurts without you: Ocean, Billy / Dancin' on a saturday night: Blue, Barry / I love to love: Charles, Tina / Billy don't be a hero: Paper Lace / You little trustmaker: Paper Lace / If you don't know me by now: Melvin, Harold & The Bluenotes / Sing me: Brothers / Wishing on a star: Rose Royce / Goodbye my love: Glitter Band / Cousin norman: Marmalade / Do the funky chicken: Thomas, Rufus / Big seven: Judge Dread / Don't let it die: Hurricane smith / Good lookin' woman: Dolan, Joe / I'd like to teach the world to sing: New Seekers / My heart's symphony: Lewis, Gary & The Playboys / Me and you and a dog named boo: Lobo / Cat crept in: Mud / Heaven must be missing an angel: Tavares / Give a little love: Bay City Rollers / Dance little lady dance: Charles, Tina / You want it you got it: Detroit Emeralds / Oh boy: Mud / Juke box jive: Rubettes / Alright alright alright: Mungo Jerry / Pepper box: Peppers / Whodunnit: Tavares
390022 / Jul '96 / Hallmark

☐ SOLID GOLD COXSONE STYLE
CDHB 80 / May '92 / Heartbeat

☐ SOLID GOLD FROM THE VAULTS VOL.1
Shocks 71: Barker, Dave / DJ's choice: Williams, Winston / People's choice: Williams, Winston / Ease up: Bleechers / Everything for your fun: Bleechers / Help wanted: Cole, Stranger / I'm movin' on: Johnny & The Attractions / Hot sauce: Barker, Dave / New love: Herman / Music keep on playing: Campbell, Cornell / Soup: JJ Allstars / Cloudburst: Hippy Boys / Proud feeling: Rhythm Rulers / Red ash: Carl / Walk with love: Toots & The Maytals / Skanky dog: Scotland, Winston
CDTRL 291 / Mar '94 / Trojan

☐ SOLID GOLD FROM THE VAULTS VOL.2
CDTRLS 293 / Nov '91 / Trojan

☐ SOLID GOLD FROM THE VAULTS VOL.3
CDTRL 295 / Feb '92 / Trojan

☐ SOLID GOLD FROM THE VAULTS VOL.4
CDTRL 302 / Mar '94 / Trojan

☐ SOLID GOLD HITS
Blue suede shoes: *Perkins, Carl* / Lucille: *Little Richard* / Reelin and rockin: *Berry, Chuck* / Runaway: *Shannon, Del* / Red river rock: *Johnny & The Hurricanes* / Poetry in motion: *Tillotson, Johnny* / Oh Carol: *Sedaka, Neil* / Be bop a lula: *Vincent, Gene* / (Dance with the) Guitar man: *Eddy, Duane* / Twenty four hours from Tulsa: *Pitney, Gene* / Duke of Earl: *Chandler, Gene* / Venus: *Avalon, Frankie*
74321339322 / Jan '96 / Camden

☐ SOLID GOLD SEVENTIES (3CD Set)
YMCA: *Village People* / Never can say goodbye: *Gaynor, Gloria* / All the young dudes: *Mott The Hoople* / Chestnut mare: *Byrds* / I can do it: *Rubettes* / Behind closed doors: *Rich, Charlie* / Son of my father: *Chicory Tip* / Never ending song of love: *New Seekers* / Me and you and a dog named Boo: *Lobo* / Love I lost: *Melvin, Harold* / Goodbye my love: *Glitter Band* / I can't leave you alone: *McCrae, George* / In Zaire: *Wakelin, Johnny* / Undercover angel: *O'Day, Alan* / Blockbuster: *Sweet* / Reflections: *Marmalade* / Patches: *Carter, Clarence* / Billy don't be a hero: *Paper Lace* / Black skin blue eyed boy: *Equals* / In the summertime: *Mungo Jerry* / Love grows: *Edison Lighthouse* / Come and get it: *Badfinger* / Raindrops keep falling on my head: *Thomas, B.J.* / Do it any way you wanna: *People's Choice* / Midnight at the oasis: *Muldaur, Maria* / Beautiful Sunday: *Boone, Daniel* / Indiana wants me: *Taylor, R. Dean* / Something old something new: *Fantastics* / Freedom come freedom go: *Fortunes* / Run run run: *Jo Jo Gunne* / Brandy (you're a fine girl): *Looking Glass* / Pepper box: *Peppers* / Drift away: *Gray, Dobie* / Dancing on a Saturday night: *Blue, Barry* / Rose garden: *Anderson, Lynn* / Hey girl don't bother me: *Tams* / Love on a mountain top: *Knight, Robert* / Falling in love: *Hamilton, Joe & Frank Reynolds* / Hitchin' a ride: *Vanity Fare* / Yellow river: *Christie* / Rock your baby: *McCrae, George* / Angel face: *Glitter Band* / Be thankful for what you've got: *De Vaughn, William* / More more more: *True, Andrea Connection* / Night Chicago died: *Paper Lace* / Sugar baby love: *Rubettes* / Hey there lonely girl: *Holman, Eddie* / In the navy: *Village People* / Radancer: *Marmalade* / Alright alright alright: *Mungo Jerry* / I'd love you to want me: *Lobo* / I'd like to teach the world to sing: *New Seekers* / All the way from Memphis: *Mott The Hoople* / Get dancin': *Disco Tex & The Sexolettes* / Most beautiful girl: *Rich, Charlie* / I'm doing fine now: *New York City* / Ballroom blitz: *Sweet* / If you don't know me by now: *Melvin, Harold* / Witch queen of New Orleans: *Redbone* / I will survive: *Gaynor, Gloria*
390542 / Aug '97 / Hallmark

☐ SOLOMON ISLANDS - FATALEKE & BAEGU MUSIC
AUD 8027 / Jun '91 / Unesco

☐ SOL'S STORY (The Baton Label)
Thousand stars: *Rivileers* / Lonely nights: *Hearts* / (I love you) for sentimental reasons: *Rivileers* / Things I love: *Fidelitys* / Got my mojo working (but it just won't work on you): *Cole, Ann* / Oo-wee: *Hearts* / Pepper-hot baby: *Belvederes* / I thought I told you not to tell them: *Knight, Marie* / Easy easy baby: *Cole, Ann* / My tearful heart: *Cole, Ann* / Each day: *Cole, Ann* / No star is lost: *Cole, Ann* / You're mine: *Cole, Ann* / I've got nothing working now but my real old fashioned love: *Cole, Ann* / TV baby: *Suburbans* / I remember: *Suburbans* / Will you ever say you're mine: *Mello-Maids* / Careless love: *Pilgrims* / I remember dear: *Mello-Maids* / We two: *Belvederes* / Until the real thing comes along: *Hearts* / Are you satisfied: *Cole, Ann* / Gone gone gone: *Hearts* / My wish: *Lonely Ones* / Deep down inside: *Rivileers* / I told them: *Suburbans* / Clock of love: *Cole, Ann* / Hard times (the slop): *Watts, Noble*
CDCHD 505 / 3 Nov '97 / Ace

☐ SOLUTIONS AND REMEDIES
FERN 2 / 22 Jun '98 / Claire

☐ SOMA 50
Painless: *SLAM* / Bit player: *Percy X* / Acres of space: *Envoy* / Sex with a stranger: *Audio Spectrum* / Fallen arches: *Maas* / Utah jazz: *Rejuvination* / Kincho: *Funk D'Void* / Feelin' horny: *Brown, Earl* / C-Horse: *Equus* / On epsilon: *Skintrade*
SOMA 50CD / Mar '97 / Soma

☐ SOMA COMPILATION VOL.1
SOMACD 1 / Nov '94 / Soma

☐ SOMA COMPILATION VOL.2
SOMACD 003 / Nov '95 / Soma

☐ SOMA COMPILATION VOL.3
SOMACD 6 / Nov '96 / Soma

☐ SOMA COMPILATION VOL.4
Emelia's first tooth: *Otaku* / Manouvers: *Envoy* / Boogie bus: *Bush Funk* / V Ger: *Funk D'Void* / Dark forces: *SLAM* / Lights: *Space DJ's* / Prelude: *New Soul Fusion* / Day 3: *Percy X* / Raw spirit: *Pressure Funk* / House train: *Hutton Drive* / Bad coffee: *Funk D'Void* / Future remembrance: *20:20 Vision* / Look at me know: *Maas*
SOMACD 009 / 20 Oct '97 / Soma

☐ SOME GIRLS
10432 / Jun '97 / A-Play Collection

☐ SOME LOVE
DOG 009CD / Sep '94 / Mrs. Ackroyd

☐ SOME OF THESE WERE HOOJ VOL.1
HOOJCD 1 / Apr '94 / Hooj Choons

☐ SOME OF THESE WERE HOOJ VOL.2
HOOJCD 2 / Aug '95 / Hooj Choons

☐ SOME OF THESE WERE HOOJ VOL.3
HOOJCD 3
HOOJCDX 3 / Nov '96 / Hooj Choons

☐ SOME SONGS
New radio: *Bikini Kill* / Hating in d: *Unwound* / Firefly: *Heavens To Betsy* / Some song: *Smith, Elliot* / Hand grenade: *Team Dresch* / Elephantitus of the night: *Godheadsilo* / Grease: *Peechees* / Be good: *Frumpy* / Grape juice plus: *Cupid Car Club* / Young savage: *Thrones* / Bad ciculation: *Witchy Poo* / Hillarys eyebrows: *Phranc* / Four letter love: *Mukiliteo Fairies* / Stargirl and blood on the saddle: *Starpower*
KRS 276CD / 22 Sep '97 / Kill Rock Stars

☐ SOMEONE TO LOVE (The Birth Of The San Francisco Sound)
She's my baby: *Mojo Men* / Fire in my heart: *Mojo Men* / Why can't you stay: *Mojo Men* / Girl won't you go: *Mojo Men* / Girl: *Great Society* / Father Bruce: *Great Society* / You can't cry: *Great Society* / Born to be burned: *Great Society* / Daydream nightmare love: *Great Society* / Heads up: *Great Society* / Double triptamine superautomatic everlovin' man: *Great Society* / Ain't it babe: *Charity Shayne* / Last thing on my mind: *Vejtables* / Mansion of tears: *Vejtables* / Let's get together: *Valente, Dino* / That's how it is: *Great Society* / Right to me: *Great Society* / Where: *Great Society* / Cold dreary morning: *Ashton, Jan* / I'm a fool: *Engle, Butch & The Styx* / Smile smile smile: *Engle, Butch & The Styx* / Someone to love: *Great Society* / Free advice: *Great Society* / Bye bye bye: *Tikis* / Lost my love today: *Tikis* / More and more and more: *Tikis* / True love is hard to find: *Tikis* / Happy with you: *Tikis* / Mad: *Tikis* / About my tears: *Tikis*
CDWIKD 170 / Oct '96 / Big Beat

☐ SOMETIMES DEATH IS BETTER
SHR 007CD / Aug '95 / Shiver

☐ SOMETIMES GOD HIDES
DGM 9605 / Oct '96 / Discipline

☐ SOMETIMES THE DEVIL DRESSES AS A WOMAN
BAH 24 / Sep '97 / Humbug

☐ SON OF BASTARD TRACKS
Hammer house of hip hop: *Schizoid Man* / Duplicate: *Euphonic* / Phasing saddles: *Soundproof* / Theme from Dylan: *Buckley, Chuck Experience* / Full nelson: *Appaloosa* / Lost: *Tiny Lion* / Casino nights: *Looptroop* / Fiend of dope island: *Brains Unchained* / Space race 2000: *Tapeheads* / Shuffler: *DJ Bigfoot* / Planar 1: *Short Fuse* / Atlantis: *Lomax*
DIFCD 4 / 10 Aug '98 / Different Drummer

☐ SON OF OI
AHOYCD 009 / 3 Nov '97 / Captain Oi

☐ SON OF SEA (1997 - 20 Barbershop Quartets)
1509537062 / 27 Apr '98 / Intersound

☐ SON OF SLAM CHOPS
TX 51204CD / Feb '97 / Triple XXX

☐ SONG CREATORS IN EASTERN TURKEY
SF 40432CD / Jan '94 / Smithsonian Folkways

☐ SONG FOR EUROTRASH
St.Tropez: *Bardot, Brigitte* / Save your kisses for me: *Kenickie* / Poupee de cire poupee de san: *Dubstar* / Ding a dong: *Collins, Edwyn* / La la la: *Martin, Dean* / Volare: *St. Etienne* / All kinds of everything: *Hall, Terry & Sinead O'Connor* / What's another year: *McGowan, Shane* / Ooh yeah: *Henger, Eva* / A ba ni be: *Fox Force 5* / Congratulations: *Annie Christian* / Waterloo: *Abba* / Variations on te deum: *808 State* / Song for Eurotrash: *De Caunes, Antoine*
4950622 / 4 May '98 / EMI

☐ SONG RETAINS THE SAME
SHR 8801CD / 22 Jun '98 / Safe House

☐ SONGBIRDS
MCCD 174 / Sep '94 / Music Club

☐ SONGS AND DANCES FROM CUBA, THE
EUCD 1235 / Nov '93 / ARC

☐ SONGS AND DANCES FROM THE FAROE ISLANDS
ARN 60329 / Jul '97 / Arion

☐ SONGS AND DRUMS OF BAGA WOMEN, GUINEA
926272 / Sep '96 / BUDA

☐ SONGS AND MELODIES FROM THE EMERALD ISLE
CDMFP 6347 / May '97 / Music For Pleasure

☐ SONGS AND RHYTHMS OF MALAWI, THE
PS 65140CD / Apr '95 / PlayaSound

☐ SONGS AND RHYTHMS OF MOROCCO, THE
LYRCD 7336 / Feb '94 / Lyrichord

☐ SONGS BY NDEBELE WOMEN, SOUTH AFRICA
926562 / Sep '96 / BUDA

☐ SONGS FOR LOVERS
DCD 5278 / Nov '92 / Kenwest

☐ SONGS FOR MUM AND DAD VOL.1 (18 Wonderful Memories)
I'd like to teach the world to sing (in perfect harmony) / I remember you: *Ifield, Frank* / Charmaine: *Bachelors* / My prayer: *Platters* / April love: *Boone, Pat* / Jealousy: *Laine, Frankie* / Tennessee waltz: *Page, Patti* / Autumn leaves: *Williams, Roger* / Heartaches by the number: *Mitchell, Guy* / Walkin' my baby back home: *Ray, Johnnie* / Kisses sweeter than wine: *Rodgers, Jimmie* / Ivory tower: *Carr, Cathy* / My happiness: *Pied Pipers* / Freight train: *McDevitt, Chas* / Green door: *Lowe, Jim* / Whispering grass: *Ink Spots* / Stranger on the shore: *Bilk, Acker* / This ole house: *Clooney, Rosemary*
ECD 3198 / Mar '95 / K-Tel

☐ SONGS FOR MUMS & DADS (2CD Set)
TSCD 227 / Mar '97 / Outlet

☐ SONGS FOR POLITICAL ACTION 1926-1953 (Folk Music, Topical Songs & The American Left - 10CD Set)
Boll weevil: *Sandburg, Carl* / Patriotic diggers: *Allison, John* / London bridge is falling down: *Seeger, Charles* / Risselty Rosselty: *Seeger, Charles* / Hands: *Seeger, Charles* / Old grey mare: *Crawford-Seeger, Ruth* / Ragged hungry blues part 1: *Jackson, Aunt Molly* / Ragged hungry blues part 2: *Jackson, Aunt Molly* / I'm going to organise, baby mine: *Gunning, Sarah Ogun* / I don't want your millions Mister: *Cadle, Tillman* / Raggedy raggedy: *Handcox, John* / No more mourning: *Handcox, John* / Join the Union tonight: *Handcox, John* / We're going to roll the Union on: *Handcox, John* / There is mean things happening in this land: *Handcox, John* / Farmer's letter to the President: *Ferguson, Bob* / Farm relief blues: *Miller, Bob* / 11 cent cotton, 40 cent meat: *Bob's Boys* / Hootenanny song: *Miller's Bullfrog Entertainers* / Bank failures: *Ferguson, Bob* / Rich man and the poor man: *Miller, Bob* / Poor forgotten man: *Palmer, Bill* / Soup song: *New Singers* / Internationale: *New Singers* / Rise up: *New Singers* / United front: *New Singers* / Forward, we've not forgotten: *New Singers* / In praise of learning: *New Singers* / On the picket line: *Manhattan Chorus* / Hold the Fort: *Manhattan Chorus* / Casey Jones: *Manhattan Chorus* / Sit down: *Manhattan Chorus* / Write me out my union card: *Manhattan Chorus* / We shall not be moved: *Manhattan Chorus* / Join the Union: *Manhattan Chorus* / Solidarity forever: *Manhattan Chorus* / Strange funeral in Braddock: *Baumann & Siegmeister* / Abraham Lincoln: *Robinson, Earl* / Joe Hill: *Robinson, Earl* / Spring song: *Robinson, Earl* / Old Chisholm trail: *Kraber, Tony* / Old paint (the horse with the Union label): *Aarons, Saul* / Capitalistic boss: *Aarons, Saul* / Little theater on the left: *Dowd, Harrison* / Little theater on the right: *Dowd, Harrison* / Nine foot shovel: *White, Joshua* / Chain gang boun': *White, Joshua* / Trouble: *White, Joshua* / Goin' home boys: *White, Joshua* / Cryin' who, cryin' you: *White, Joshua* / Told my Captain: *White, Joshua* / Jerry: *White, Joshua* / Southern exposure: *White, Joshua* / Uncle Sam says: *White, Joshua* / Jim Crow train: *White, Joshua* / Bad housing blues: *White, Joshua* / Hard times blues: *White, Joshua* / Defense factory blues: *White, Joshua* / Strange death of John Doe: *Almanac Singers* / Billy Boy: *Almanac Singers* / C for conscription: *Almanac Singers* / Washington breakdown: *Almanac Singers* / Lisa Jane: *Almanac Singers* / Ballad of October 16th: *Almanac Singers* / Plow under: *Almanac Singers* / Talking Union: *Almanac Singers* / Union train: *Almanac Singers* / Which side are you on: *Almanac Singers* / Get thee behind me Satan: *Almanac Singers* / Union maid: *Almanac Singers* / All I want: *Almanac Singers* / Songs for bridges: *Almanac Singers* / Babe o' mine: *Guthrie, Woody* / Blow ye winds, heigh ho: *Almanac Singers* / Haul away Joe: *Almanac Singers* / Blow the man down: *Almanac Singers* / Golden vanity: *Almanac Singers* / Away, Rio: *Almanac Singers* / Coast of high Barbary: *Almanac Singers* / Greenland fishing: *Almanac Singers* / Dodger song: *Almanac Singers* / Ground hog: *Almanac Singers* / State of Arkansas: *Almanac Singers* / Hard, ain't it hard: *Almanac Singers* / I ride an old paint: *Almanac Singers* / House of the rising sun: *Almanac Singers* / Weaver's song: *Almanac Singers* / Dear Mr. President: *Almanac Singers* / Belt line girl: *Almanac Singers* / Round, round Hitler's grave: *Almanac Singers* / Side by side: *Almanac Singers* / Deliver the goods: *Almanac Singers* / Reuben James: *Almanac Singers* / Boomtown Bill: *Almanac Singers* / Keep the oil a rollin': *Almanac Singers* / I'm looking for a home: *Priority Ramblers* / Amsterdam maid: *Priority Ramblers* / Song of the free: *Priority Ramblers* / In Washington: *Priority Ramblers* / Overtime pay: *Priority Ramblers* / Jarama Valley: *Glazer, Hawes & Lomax* / Quinta Brigada T: *Seeger, Glazer, Hawes & Lomax* / Spanish marching song: *Seeger, Glazer, Hawes & Lomax* / Cook house: *Seeger, Glazer, Hawes & Lomax* / Young man from Alcala: *Seeger, Glazer, Hawes & Lomax* / Quinte regimento: *Seeger, Glazer, Hawes & Lomax* / Quartermaster song: *Seeger, Glazer, Hawes & Lomax* / Little man on a fence: *White, Joshua* / Jim Crow: *Union Boys* / You better get ready: *Union Boys* / Hold the Fort: *Union Boys* / We shall not be moved: *Union Boys* / Hold on: *Union Boys* / Solidarity forever: *Ives, Burl* / Dollar ain't a dollar anymore: *Union Boys* / Horace Greeley: *Robinson, Earl* / Kevin Barry: *Robinson, Earl* / House I live in: *Robinson, Earl* / Man's a man for a' that: *Robinson, Earl* / Drill ye tarriers drill: *Robinson, Earl* / Frozen logger: *Robinson, Earl* / Jefferson and liberty: *Robinson, Earl* / Sweet Betsy from Pike: *Robinson, Earl* / Dirty miner: *Robinson, Earl* / Grand Coolee Dam: *Robinson, Earl* / Free and equal blues: *Robinson, Earl* / Century of the common man: *Sir Lancelot* / I'm a Native American Nazi: *Partlow, Vern* / Join the UAW-CIO: *Partlow, Vern* / Keeping score for '44: *Partlow, Vern* / UAW train: *Partlow, Vern* / Susan's in the Union: *Partlow, Vern* / Rollback blues: *Partlow, Vern* / Mama don't allow: *Partlow, Vern* / Farmer-Labor train: *Guthrie, Woody* / So long, it's been good to know you: *Guthrie, Woody* / Talking sailor: *Guthrie, Woody* / Sally, don't you grieve: *Guthrie, Woody* / Citizen CIO: *Glazer, Tom & Joshua White* / No more blues: *White, Joshua* / We've got a plan: *Glazer, Tom* / Social worker's talking blues: *Glazer, Tom* / I'm gonna put my name down: *Glazer, Tom* / Freedom Road: *White, Joshua* / Landlord: *White, Joshua* / Beloved Comrade: *White, Joshua* / Johnny has gone for a soldier: *White, Joshua* / Beloved comrade: *White, Joshua* / Man who couldn't walk around: *White, Joshua* / I'm the guy: *White, Joshua* / Little man sitting on a fence: *White, Joshua* / When the country is broke: *Glazer, Tom* / Money in the pocket: *Glazer, Tom* / Our fight is yours: *Glazer, Tom* / Moses Green: *Hays, Lee* / Rankin tree: *Hays, Lee* / Talking Bilbo: *Hays, Lee* / This old world: *Hays, Lee* / No one stooge: *Claiborne, Bob* / Song of my hands: *Asbel, Bernie* / Mad as I can be: *Asbel, Bernie & Pete Seeger* / Jackie Robinson: *Lord Invader* / High price blues: *McGhee, Brownie* / Black, brown and white: *McGhee, Brownie* / Nix on Mundt/Nixon: *Beyer, Anna* / Daily worker's song: *Levine, George* / Taft-Hartley blues: *Levine, George* / Parnell Thomas blues: *Cunningham, Sis* / Turn me loose: *Reynolds, Malvina* / Snowball: *Berries* / Swingin' on a scab: *Berries* / On to Sacramento: *Casetta, Mario* / Atomic talking blues: *Partlow, Vern* / Newspapermen meet such interesting people: *Partlow, Vern* / Passing through: *Blakeslee, Dick* / Listen Mr. Bilbo: *Seeger, Hawes, Hays & Wood* / Joe Hill: *Seeger, Hawes, Hays & Wood* / OPA shout: *Seeger, Pete & Bob Claiborne* / Voting union: *Seeger, Hawes, Hays & Wood* / Get out the vote: *Seeger, Hawes, Hays & Wood* / Dollar ain't a dollar anymore: *Glazer, Tom* / Dollar for a PAC: *Seeger, Hawes, Hays & Wood* / What congress done to me: *Seeger, Hawes, Hays & Wood* / Four PAC nursery rhymes: *Seeger, Hawes, Hays & Wood* / DDT: *Seeger, Hawes, Hays & Wood* / Fare ye well bad congressman: *Seeger, Hawes, Hays & Wood* / No, no, no discrimination: *Seeger, Glazer, Hays & Wood* / Voter, oh voter: *Seeger, Glazer, Hays & Wood* / Commonwealth of toil: *Wood, Gilbert, Seeger & Glazer* / We've got our eyes on you: *Wood, Gilbert, Seeger & Glazer* / Preacher and the slave: *Wood, Gilbert, Seeger & Glazer* / Talking Union: *Wood, Gilbert, Seeger & Glazer* / Which side are you on: *Wood, Gilbert, Seeger & Glazer* / Solidarity forever: *Wood, Gilbert, Seeger & Glazer* / Whole wide world around: *Wood, Gilbert, Seeger & Glazer* / Hold the fort: *Wood, Gilbert, Seeger & Glazer* / Talking PAC: *Seeger, Pete* / Conversation with a mule: *Seeger, Pete* / Farmer is the man: *Seeger, Pete* / Join the Farmer's Union: *Seeger, Pete* / Talking atom: *Seeger, Pete* / Newspapermen meet such interesting people: *Seeger, Pete* / Skillet good and greasy: *Seeger, Pete* / T for Texas: *Seeger, Pete* / Cumberland Mountain bear chase: *Seeger, Pete* / Walk in peace: *Sir Lancelot* / Atomic energy: *Sir Lancelot* / Old lady with a rolling pin: *Sir Lancelot* / Red boogie: *Goodson & Vale* / Unity rhumba: *Goodson & Vale* / Elephant and the ass: *Goodson & Vale* / Hungry rhapsody: *Goodson & Vale* / Housing: *Goodson & Vale* / People's songs chorus ballad of FDR: *Goodson & Vale* / Jim Crow: *Goodson & Vale* / Mein schtele belz: *Berries* / Zhonkoye: *Berries* / Travelin': *Seeger, Pete* / Black, brown and white blues: *Seeger, Pete* / Death of Harry Simms: *Seeger, Pete* / Winnsboro cotton mill blues: *Seeger, Pete* / No Irish need apply: *Seeger, Pete* / Unemployment: *Casetta, Mario* / Compensation blues: *Casetta, Mario* / Fireship: *Sanders, Betty* / Johnny, I hardly knew you: *Sanders, Betty* / Peekskill story: *Weavers* / Wasn't that a time: *Weavers* / Dig my grave: *Weavers* / Freight train blues: *Weavers* / Love song blues: *Weavers* / Hammers song: *Weavers* / We're keeping score in '44: *Robinson, Earl* / No more blues: *White, Joshua* / Lay that ballot down: *Oliver, Bill* / Fertilizer song: *Partlow, Vern* / Talking FTA: *Partlow, Vern* / Kiss the boys goodbye: *Partlow, Vern* / Round and round in the canneries: *Partlow, Vern* / My name is Cannery Bill: *Partlow, Vern* / Bosses' gang: *Alexander, Mara* / Bye bye bosses: *Alexander, Mara* / New walls of Jericho: *Huey, Richard* / Henry Wallace is the man: *Royal Harmonaires* / Corrido to Wallace and Taylor: *Alvarez, Abigail* / Second corrido to Wallace and Taylor: *Alvarez, Abigail* / Battle hymn of '48: *Robeson, Paul* / Same old merry-go-round: *Loring, Michael* / I've got a ballot: *Loring, Michael* / Great day: *Loring, Michael* / Wallace button: *Levine, George* / Goodbye Harry: *Levine, George* / Henry Wallace: *Cunningham, Sis* / We can win with Wallace: *Oliver, Bill* / Work with Wallace: *Reynolds, Malvina* / Century of the common man: *Sir Lancelot* / Wallace is the man for me: *Sir Lancelot* / Yankee Doodle, tell the boss: *Loring, Michael & Alan Lomax* / New York city: *Weavers* / Marcantonio for me: *Hellerman, Fred* / Skip to the polls: *Weavers* / Marcantonio for Mayor: *Hellerman, Fred* / Now, right now: *Duncan, Laura* / We shall not be moved: *Weavers* / Oh freedom: *Seeger, Pete* / Ben Davis: *Seeger, Pete* / People's choice: *Seeger, Pete* / Keep a-goin' and a-growin': *Seeger, Pete* / Riddle of Thurman Towns: *Decormier, Bernardi & Booth* / Grapes to pick: *Gallant, Gerald* / I don't want to be adjusted: *Hellerman, Fred* / Stand up and be counted: *Hellerman, Fred* / We will overcome: *Hellerman, Fred* / Progressive Party is here to stay: *Hellerman, Fred* / Pity the downtrodden landlord: *Hill, Bob* / Hammer song: *Weavers* / Banks of marble: *Weavers* / Spring song: *Lieberman, Ernie & Hope Foye* / My old man: *Lieberman, Ernie* / Song of my hands: *Lieberman, Ernie* / I'm on my way: *Lieberman, Ernie* / In contempt: *Lieberman, Duncan & Smith* / Die gedenken sind frei: *Lieberman, Duncan & Smith* / Walk along together: *Lieberman, Duncan & Smith* / Put my name down: *Lieberman, Duncan & Smith* / Hold on: *Lieberman, Duncan & Smith* / Didn't my Lord deliver Daniel: *Smith, Osborne* / I've got a right: *Duncan, Laura* / We shall overcome: *Jewish Young Folksingers* / Talking Un-American blues: *Sanders, Betty* / Old Bolshevik song: *Glazer, Joe & Bill Friedland* / Cloakmaker's Union: *Glazer, Joe & Bill Friedland* / Land of the daily worker: *Glazer, Joe & Bill Friedland* / Our line's been changed again: *Glazer, Joe & Bill Friedland* / In old Moscow: *Glazer, Joe & Bill Friedland* / Unite for unity: *Glazer, Joe & Bill Friedland* / Bill Bailey: *Glazer, Joe & Bill Friedland* / Last Internationale: *Glazer, Joe & Bill Friedland* / Giveaway boys in Washington: *Glazer, Joe* / Joe McCarthy's band: *Glazer, Joe* / I've got to know: *Guthrie, Woody* / This land is your land: *Guthrie, Woody*
BCD 15720 / May '96 / Bear Family

☐ SONGS FOR SOPHISTICATS (40 Cool Jazz Vocals/2CD Set)
Lulu's back in town: *Torme, Mel* / Old devil moon: *McRae, Carmen* / I'm glad there is you: *Carr, Helen* / I get a kick out of you: *Hartman, Johnny* / Time after time: *Roche, Betty* / Foggy day: *London, Julie* / Midnight sun: *Troup, Bobby* / Blame it on my youth: *Connor, Chris* / Sometimes I'm happy: *Winters, Jerrie* / Yardbird suite: *Dorough, Bob* / If you could see me now: *Morris, Audrey* / You're not the kind: *Morel, Terry* / Angel eyes: *Jeffries, Herb* / Trouble is a man: *Moore, Marilyn* / With the wind and rain in your hair: *Ryan, Sue* / Let's fall in love: *Elliott, Don* / Thou swell: *Moran, Pat Quartet* / My baby just cares for me: *Simone, Nina* / Woman is a sometime thing: *Rosolino, Frank* / Ridin' high: *Connor, Chris* / You're getting to be a habit with me: *Carr, Helen* / Fascinating rhythm: *Torme, Mel* / Last time for love: *McRae, Carmen* / All too soon: *Roche, Betty* / I fall in love too easily: *Hartman, Johnny* / Don't worry about me: *London, Julie* / Thrill is gone: *Connor, Chris* / Skylark: *Troup, Bobby* / There'll never be another you: *Winters, Jerrie* / Blue turning grey over you: *Morris, Audrey* / Devil may care: *Dorough, Bob* / Too late now: *Morel, Terry* / Lover come back to me: *Moore, Marilyn* / Dinner for one please James: *Jeffries, Herb* / I'll be around: *Moran, Pat Quartet* / I loves you Porgy: *Simone, Nina* / What is there to say: *Hartman, Johnny* / You make me feel so young: *Blair, Sally* / September in the rain: *Faye, Frances* / Girl next door: *Torme, Mel*
CDGR 2002 / 2 Feb '98 / Charly

☐ SONGS FOR THE 90'S
BRAM 1991172 / Nov '93 / Brambus

R.E.D. CD CATALOGUE
COMPILATIONS
SOPHISTICATION VOL.1

☐ SONGS FROM BENGAL
ARN 64214 / Jun '93 / Arion

☐ SONGS FROM ERITREA (2CD Set)
RPM 0122 / 9 Mar '98 / Rags Productions

☐ SONGS FROM JAHL
RB 3005 / May '94 / Reggae Best

☐ SONGS FROM THE EMERALD ISLE (2CD Set)
Galway Bay: Locke, Josef / Spinning wheel: Murphy, Delia / Star of County Down: McCormack, John / Ballyhoe: McGoldrick, Anna / Old bog road: Drennan, Tommy / Courtin' in the kitchen: Murphy, Delia / Mother Machree: MacEwan, Father Sydney / Trottin' to the fair: Murray, Ruby / Banks of my own lovely Lee: O'Se, Sean / When Irish eyes are smiling: Jones, Sandie / Pretty Irish girl: O'Dowda, Brendan & Ruby Murray / Mountains of Mourne: O'Dowda, Brendan / Castlebar Fair: Gallagher, Bridie / Rose of Tralee: O'Dowda, Brendan / Eileen O'Grady: Gallagher, Bridie / Danny boy: O'Se, Sean / Connemara: O'Dowda, Brendan & Ruby Murray / Doonaree: Murray, Ruby / Sweet Marie: O'Dowda, Brendan / Flower of sweet Strabane: Gallagher, Bridie / Whiskey in the jar: Dubliners / Three drunken maidens: Planxty / Galway races: Dubliners / Kitty of Coleraine: Bunratty Singers / Bantry Bay: O'Se, Sean
CDDL 1104 / Nov '92 / EMI

☐ SONGS FROM THE EMERALD ISLE
Road to Sligo / Muirsheen Durkin / Donegal Danny / O'Carolan's concerto / Finnegan's wake / Green fields of Rossbeigh / Corney is coming / Joe Cooley's reel / Black velvet band / Cod liver oil/ Coolies / Dirty old town / Jolly beggarman/Hunter's purse / Fields of Athenry / Pinch of snuff / Cherish the ladies/Paddy Clancy's jig / Gillan's apples/Father O'Flynn / Into the rain / Wild rover / Whisky in the jar / Irish rover/Rakes of mallow / Farewell to Ireland
SUMCD 4059 / Nov '96 / Summit

☐ SONGS FROM THE EMERALD ISLE (20 Classic Irish Ballads)
CDIRL 501 / Apr '97 / Outlet

☐ SONGS FROM THE EXOTIC
BML 012 / Jan '96 / British Music

☐ SONGS FROM THE HADRAMAWT (Yemen 1985-1995)
Ataha rasuli / Dan tarab / Hayya layali jamila / Dan jammala / Tahwida and khuwaib / Jalsat dan / Dan tarab / Ana wa khilli trradina / Dan jammalla / Ghina bani maghra / Tarhib / Bushrak hadha-i yaumu id / Dan tarab / Khalli ahuf waddak ya danin
D 8273 / Mar '98 / Unesco

☐ SONGS FROM THE HEART (A Collection Of Irish Ballads)
CELT 9010CD / 9 Mar '98 / Celtophile

☐ SONGS FROM THE NAKED CITY (2CD Set)
RS 7004 / 8 Sep '97 / Red Star

☐ SONGS FROM THE PENALTY BOX
TND 1090CD / 13 Apr '98 / Tooth & Nail

☐ SONGS FROM THE PENALTY BOX VOL.2
TNR 1110CD / 3 Aug '98 / Tooth & Nail

☐ SONGS FROM THE SHORES OF THE BLACK SEA
LDX 274980 / Jun '94 / La Chant Du Monde

☐ SONGS FROM THE SMOKE (15 New Songs About London)
Springboard: Big Steve Tree & The Famous Times / Blue skies over Battersea: Ansell, Martin / Dog in brownian motion W5: Brown, Diego & The Good Fairy / Spring in the suburbs: Cassell, Debbie / Homeless: Colette / Remember this: Johnson, Robb / London kisses: McLeod, Rory / I love London: Bowen, Lorraine / On Primrose Hill: Chawner, Suzanna / Mind how you go: Ray, Lucy / Shadowlands: Wob / Far flung wastes of Harringay: Grey, Tamsin / Quicksand hornpipe: Ryder, Anna / I was born and raised in Croxley Green: Weston, Wilf / For all and none: Orchard, Pat
CYCLECD 010 / 9 Mar '98 / Cycle

☐ SONGS KALINA AMERINDIANS
927052 / 24 Apr '98 / BUDA

☐ SONGS OF BAKHSHI WOMEN
W 260064 / Sep '95 / Inedit

☐ SONGS OF CHRISTMAS
Silent night: Drifters / When a child is born: Benton, Brook / Jingle bells: Clooney, Rosemary / White Christmas: Armstrong, Louis / We wish you a merry Christmas: Drifters / Blue Christmas: Platters / Silver Bells: Crosby, Bing & Ella Fitzgerald / Jingle bells rock: Sherman, Bobby / Please come home for Christmas: Platters / New baby for christmas: Preston, Johnny / Little drummer boy: Clooney, Rosemary / Oh, come all ye faithful: Crosby, Bing / Auld lang syne: Drifters / Santa claus is coming to town: Cole, Nat 'King'
SCD 1000 / 13 Oct '97 / Start

☐ SONGS OF CHRISTMAS
11702 / Dec '97 / Fairhope

☐ SONGS OF EARTH, WATER, FIRE AND SKY (Music Of The American Indian)
802462 / Aug '92 / New World

☐ SONGS OF INDIA
MNWCD 156 / Mar '89 / MNW

☐ SONGS OF IRELAND, THE
ETCD 192 / Apr '96 / Etude

☐ SONGS OF IRELANDS' 1916 UPRISING, THE
Freedom sons: Wolfhound / Roger Casement: Wolfhound / Foggy dew: Hunt, Declan / Brave volunteers: Hunt, Declan / Men of Easter week: Hunt, Declan / Memory of the dead: Hunt, Declan / Who is Ireland's enemy: Hunt, Declan / Old howth gun: Hunt, Declan / James Connolly: McEldowney, Eugene / Eireann go bragh: McEldowney, Eugene / Arbour hill: McEldowney, Eugene / Rebel: Dubliners / Grace: Shamrog / Michael Collins: Moore, Brian / Frank Ryan: Close, John / James Larkin: Mark's Men / Dawning of the day: O'Neill, Terry / Blood stained bandage: McAreavey, Ray / Gra mo choroi: McGorman, Fee / Connolly was there: McAreavey, Ray / Erin's flag: McAreavey, Ray / Gallipoli: Irish Ramblers / Soldiers song: Irish Ramblers / Off to Dublin in the green: O'Brien, Dermot / Cathal Bruga: Hunt, Declan / Only our rivers run free: Corrib Folk / Easter prophecy: Long Kesh Internees / Ireland's fight for freedom: Bogside Volunteers / Who fears to speak of Easter week: Behan, Brendan / Proclamation of the Irish Republic: Grant, Gearoid
CDIRL 1916 / Jun '98 / Outlet

☐ SONGS OF LOVE AND DANCE - KURDISTAN
AAA 128 / Sep '97 / Club Du Disque Arabe

☐ SONGS OF LOVE AND JOY
Amazing love / As high as the heavens / I rejoice in your love / I will sing / In your presence / Let the heavens rejoice / Mourning into dancing / Such joy / Think about his love / Your love
11692 / Apr '98 / Fairhope

☐ SONGS OF LOVE, LUCK, ANIMALS AND MAGIC
Love Song: Douglas, Frank A. / Grizzly bear war song: Douglas, Frank A. / Rabbit song: Douglas, Frank A. / Gambling songs: Douglas, Frank A. / Basket song: Figuerosa, Aileen / Brush dance: Figuerosa, Aileen / Brush dance song: Figuerosa, Aileen / Seagull song: Norris, Ella / Song to stop the Rain: Norris, Ella / Hunting Song: Shaughnessy, Florence / Pelican song: Bommelyn, Loren / Ceremonial dance / Ending ceremonial dance
8029722 / Sep '92 / New World

☐ SONGS OF MUKANDA, THE (Music Of The Secret Society Of The Luvale People Of Africa)
Ndumbamwelela / Lilombola songs / Sunrise songs / Sunset songs / Meal ritual / Water bearing songs / Greeting and bidding farewell to guests / Kukuwa songs / Jingunda songs / Eve of the purification ceremony / Purification ceremony / Final ceremony
MCM 3008 / May '97 / Multicultural Media

☐ SONGS OF OLD RUSSIA
MCD 71560 / Sep '93 / Monitor

☐ SONGS OF PEACE
God of peace / When you lie down / I have overcome the world / Grace mercy and peace / Cast thy burden / Perfect peace / Undying love / He stilled the storm / God of hope / Meditate on these things
10982 / Mar '98 / Integrity

☐ SONGS OF PRAYER AND BLESSING
Be magnified / Blessed be the Lord God almighty / Blessing glory and honour / I offer my life / Live in me / Our heart / Ever let it be / O God you are my god / Song for the nations / Use me
11662 / Apr '98 / Fairhope

☐ SONGS OF SCOTLAND
Man's a man for a' that: Caern Folk Trio / Highland lullaby: McDonald, Alastair / Piper o' Dundee: Caern Folk Trio / Farewell my love: McBennett, Helen / Wee kirkcudbright centipede: McDonald, Alastair / Sailing up the clyde: Sutherland, Alex Singers / Water is wide: McBennett, Helen / Peat fire flame: MacDonald Sisters / Bonnie wee Jeanne McColl: Sutherland, Alex Singers / Bog Kilmarnock Bunnett: Sutherland, Alex Singers / Northern lights of Aberdeen: Sutherland, Alex Singers / I belong to Glasgow: Sutherland, Alex Singers / Go away from my window: Sutherland, Alex Singers / Auld lang syne: Stewart, Andy
EMPRCD 590 / Oct '95 / Emporio

☐ SONGS OF SCOTLAND (A Celebration Of The Magic Of Scotland)
Amazing grace / Song of the Clyde / Westering home / Road to the Isles / Keep right on to the end of the road / Northern lights of old Aberdeen / Bonnie Kirkwall Bay / Bonnie banks of Loch Lomond / Football crazy / Heres to Scottish whiskey / Land for all seasons / Star O'Rabbie Burns / Man's a man for a that / Roamin in the gloamin / Just a wee deoch an' Doris / Skye boat song / Ye banks and braes / Tobermory bay / Marching through the heather / Auld lang syne
CD 6062 / Apr '97 / Music

☐ SONGS OF SCOTLAND
Home to the Kyles (Tighnabruaich) / Auld meal seal mill / Bonnie Gallawa' / Misty islands of the highlands / Wee sprig o' heather / Our ain fireside / Loch Lomond / Island of Arran / Rowan tree / Roses of Prince Charlie/The old rustic brig / Scotland the brave / Old rustic brig / Home that I love / Flower of Scotland / Hills of Lorne / Annie Laurie/Fiona / Inverary Inn / Lochnagar / My love is like a red red rose / Westering home/Skye boat song / Northern lights of Aberdeen/Loch Lomond / Auld Scots mother mine / Ae fond kiss / Mary of Argyll / Will ye no come back again
CDLOC 1100 / Sep '97 / Lochshore

☐ SONGS OF SUNSHINE (The Very Best Of Classic Organ Music)
Crown imperial / Trumpet sonata in D major / Prelude in E flat major / Salut d'amour / Festal flourish / Fantasia in D minor / Tuba tune / Will O' the wisp / Nimrod / Larghetto / Festive march / Air in C major / Trumpet minuet / Grand choeur / Irish tune from County Derry / Song of sunshine
301592 / Jun '97 / Hallmark

☐ SONGS OF THE ABORIGINES
LYRCD 7331 / '91 / Lyrichord

☐ SONGS OF THE BALKANS
CNCD 5982 / Apr '94 / Disky

☐ SONGS OF THE BRITISH ISLANDS
Early one morning / My Bonnie lies over the ocean / Oak and the ash / Lass with the delicate air / I live not where I love / Vicar of Bray / Jerusalem / One man went to mow / What shall we do with the drunken sailor / Ten green bottles / A-roving / Lass of Richmond hill / Greensleeves / Lincolnshire poacher / O no John / Summer is a-coming in / Land of hope and glory / Cockles and mussels / Last rose of summer / Salley gardens / Spinning wheel / Danny boy / Annie Laurie / Ye banks and braes / Bonnie bonnie banks o' Loch Lomond / Comin' thro' the rye / Auld lang syne / Flower of Scotland / Men of Harlech / All through the night / Ash grove / Land of my fathers / God save the Queen
BHCD 9707 / Dec '97 / Brewhouse

☐ SONGS OF THE CIVIL WAR
I wish I was in Dixies' land / All quiet along the Potomac tonight / We are coming, Father Abra'am / Mother, is the battle over / Drummer boy of Shiloh / Beauregards's retreat from Shiloh / Jeff in petticoats / Weeping, sad and lonely / It's a gold old rebel
NW 202 / '88 / New World

☐ SONGS OF THE DEPRESSION
JASSCD 639 / May '94 / Jass

☐ SONGS OF THE EARTH
D 8104 / Aug '98 / Unesco

☐ SONGS OF THE GAELS
LBP 2022CD / Jun '96 / Lochshore

☐ SONGS OF THE GARIFUNA
VICG 53372 / Mar '96 / JVC World Library

☐ SONGS OF THE HAWAIIAN ISLANDS, THE
73842782022 / 14 Jul '98 / Coconut Grove

☐ SONGS OF THE INUIT
VICG 53332 / Mar '96 / JVC World Library

☐ SONGS OF THE ISLES
MM 214 / 11 May '98 / Musurgia Graeca

☐ SONGS OF THE JU'HOANSI BUSHMEN, THE (Music From Namibia)
C 560117 / Aug '97 / Ocora

☐ SONGS OF THE LAKOTA SIOUX (North America)
2741000 / Jan '95 / La Chant Du Monde

☐ SONGS OF THE RUSSIAN PEOPLE
274978 / Jan '95 / La Chant Du Monde

☐ SONGS OF THE SEA
EMPRCD 786 / 16 Mar '98 / Emporio

☐ SONGS OF THE SPIRIT
Coyote dance: Little Wolf / Medicine flute: Coyote Oldman / Song of union: Shenandoah, Joanne / Hunter's twilight: Nakai, R. Carlos / Son of the sun: Kastin / Red cloud: Way West / Oweegon: Little Wolf / Summoning winds: Native Flute Ensemble / Return of the red hat: Stearns, Michael & Ron Sunsinger / My child: Primeaux, Mike & Attson / Nez Perce: 500 Nations / Cherokee: Coolidge, Rita
41372 / Nov '96 / Triloka

☐ SONGS OF THE TRAVELLING PEOPLE
Won't you buy my sweet blooming lavender: Penfold, Janet / Come a' ye tramps an' hawkers: Stewart, Davie / Blarney stone: Barry, Margaret / Berryfields o'Blair: Stewart, Belle / Muckin' o' geordie's byre: McBeath, Jimmy & Willie Kelby / Choring song: Robertson, Jeannie / Beggar wench: Stewart, Davie / Blacksmith courted me: Smith, Phoebe / Barnyards o' Delgaty/Gin I were where the Gadie rins: Kelby, Willie / On the bonny banks o' the roses: McPhee, Duncan / Bard of Armagh: Barry, Margaret / Dandling song/Bonny lassie-o/Cuckoo's nest: Robertson, Jeannie / I am a romany: Smith, Phoebe / Devonshire time and 2 gipsy hornpipes: Connor, Frank O / Higher Germanie: Smith, Phoebe / Little beggar man: Doran, Paddy / Kathleen: Barry, Margaret / Lady o' the dainty doon-by: Robertson, Jeannie / Tenpenny bit/She moves through the fair: Stewart, Belle / Poor smuggler's boy: Brasil, Angela / Aul' jockey Bruce o' the Fornet: Stewart, Davie / Tuning up: Hughes, Carolyne & Charlie Lindsay / Twa heids are better than yin: Stewart, Kathie / Moss O'Burreldale: McBeath, Jimmy / Gay Gordons: Kelby, Willie / Overgate: Robertson, Jeannie / Macpherson's rant: Stewart, Donald & Albert / Macpherson's lament: Stewart, Davie
CDSDL 407 / Nov '94 / Saydisc

☐ SONGS OF THE ULSTER PROTESTANT, THE
Union cruiser / Aghalee heroes / Green grassy slopes / Derry's walls / Protestant boys / Orange and blue / Blackman's dream / Battle of Garvagh / Lily O / Boyne water / Sash / Sprigs of Kilrea / Auld orange flute / No surrender
CDUCD 10 / Apr '97 / Ulster Music

☐ SONGS OF WARTIME
RAJCD 925 / Jun '94 / Empress

☐ SONGS THAT WON THE WAR
PLATCD 3928 / May '94 / Platinum

☐ SONGS WE TAUGHT THE FUZZTONES (32 Garage Classics)
MMCD 66002 / 10 Nov '97 / Music Maniac

☐ SONGWRITER SERIES VOL.5 (The Birth Of The Blues - De Sylva/Brown/ Henderson)
Best things in life are free / Birth of the blues / Black bottom / Don't tell him what happened to me / Varsity drag / Button up your overcoat / One more time / If you haven't got love / Used to you / My lucky star / Forgetting you / Little pal / My sin / I'm in seventh heaven / I want to be bad / Good for you bad for me / Without love / You wouldn't fool me would you / Sonny boy / You're the cream in my coffee / I'm a dreamer (aren't we all) / If I had a talking picture of you / Good news
PASTCD 7803 / 4 May '98 / Flapper

☐ SONGWRITERS EXCHANGE
STCD 529 / Jan '93 / Stash

☐ SONIC BOOM
BOOMCD 1 / Jul '97 / Boom

☐ SONIC COLLECTION, THE
SONCD 0070 / Sep '94 / Sonic Sounds

☐ SONIC INTERFERENCE
9010752 / Mar '97 / Immediate

☐ SONICS EVERYWHERE
Year zero: PCM / In for: Scorn / Every bit of it: Scorn / SIMM Nowhere: Scorn / Heads of children: Jupiter Crew / Tracking: Ambush / Stir: Quoit / Inside out: Ambush / Last bad trip: Interceptor / In the cooler: PCM / Noticed off: Scorn / These days: Scorn / Rhino charged: Jupiter Crew / Detatchment: Ambush / Slowly drying: Interceptor
INVPOSSO 01CD / 26 Jan '98 / Invisible

☐ SONRISAS DE TEXAS
MSA 007 / Feb '94 / Modern Blues

☐ SONS AND LOVERS
RVCD 27 / Feb '93 / Raven

☐ SOOTHERS AND MOVERS
What greater love: Little Anthony / I'll make you happy: Hunt, Tommy / Consider the source: Haywood, Leon / Face up to the truth: Troy, Doris / Love won't wear off: Bailey, J.R. / Tried and convicted: Womack, Bobby / Bring on the heartaches: Tee, Willie / You had it made: Terrell, Freddie / I've got love for my baby: Younghearts / Soft and gentle ways: King, Clyde / No time for you: O'Jays / Mamma's love: Tribulations / You can bring me all your heartaches: Rawls, Lou / Where were you: Andrews, Ernie / Isn't it just a shame: Wells, Kenny / I'm gonna make it: Pacesetters / Turn to me: Towns, Chris / Outcast: Eddie & Ernie / Who is it gonna be: Dee & Joe / Because I love you: Hightower, Willie / I'm lonely for you: Swan, Bettye / I'm sorry: Black, Cody / And heaven was here: Big Dee Irwin
GSCD 081 / Sep '96 / Goldmine

☐ SOPHISTICATED GENTLEMEN (2CD Set)
Dance ballerina dance: Cole, Nat 'King' / From Russia with love: Monro, Matt / That's amore: Martin, Dean / You're getting to be a habit with me: Torme, Mel / Way you look tonight: Haymes, Dick / Fascinating rhythm: Damone, Vic / Smile: Cole, Nat 'King' / Story of Tina: Martino, Al / Stranger in paradise: MacRae, Gordon / Return to me: Martin, Dean / Portrait of my love: Monro, Matt / Spanish eyes: Martino, Al / On the street where you live: Damone, Vic / Blue moon: Torme, Mel / Do you love me: Haymes, Dick / Begin the beguine: MacRae, Gordon / Pretend: Cole, Nat 'King' / Granada (Lara): Martino, Al / Impossible dream: Monro, Matt / Younger than Springtime: Damone, Vic / When I fall in love: Cole, Nat 'King' / It might as well be Spring: MacRae, Gordon / I've got my love to keep me warm: Martin, Dean / How deep is the ocean: Haymes, Dick / Again: Torme, Mel / Most beautiful girl in the world: Damone, Vic / Unchained melody: Monro, Matt / Wanted: Martino, Al / Volare: Martin, Dean / Bewitched, bothered and bewildered: Torme, Mel / Memories are made of this: Martin, Dean / My funny valentine: MacRae, Gordon / Who can I turn to: Monro, Matt / Til there was you: Damone, Vic / Autumn leaves: MacRae, Gordon / Blossom fell: Cole, Nat 'King' / Kiss: Martin, Dean / On days like these: Monro, Matt / Isn't it a lovely day (to be caught in the rain): Haymes, Dick / Very thought of you: Cole, Nat 'King'
CDDL 1299 / Nov '95 / Music For Pleasure

☐ SOPHISTICATED LADIES (2CD Set)
Fever: Lee, Peggy / Something: Bassey, Shirley / Wheel of fortune: Starr, Kay / What the world needs now is love: Horne, Lena / It must be him: Carr, Vikki / I can't give you anything but love: Garland, Judy / I've got you under my skin: Bassey, Shirley / Folks who live on the hill: Lee, Peggy / Comes a-long a'love: Starr, Kay / Over the rainbow: Garland, Judy / Cry me a river: London, Julie / By the time I get to Phoenix: Carr, Vikki / Unchained melody: Horne, Lena / Changing partners: Starr, Kay / Long ago (and far away): Stafford, Jo / Fools rush in: Bassey, Shirley / Occasional man: London, Julie / Zing went the strings of my heart: Garland, Judy / Manana: Lee, Peggy / I (who have nothing): Bassey, Shirley / Side by side: Starr, Kay / It's a good day: Lee, Peggy / Old devil moon: Garland, Judy / Fly me to the moon: London, Julie / Fine romance: Horne, Lena / Walk away: Carr, Vikki / Cheek to cheek: Lee, Peggy / Nearness of you: Bassey, Shirley / Diamonds are a girl's best friend: London, Julie / In love in vain: Horne, Lena / Play me a simple melody: Stafford, Jo & Starlighters / My heart belongs to Daddy: London, Julie / As long as he needs me: Bassey, Shirley / Hello young lovers: Horne, Lena / Only love can break a heart: Carr, Vikki / I won't dance: Lee, Peggy / Always true to you in my fashion: London, Julie / That's entertainment: Garland, Judy / Yesterdays: Stafford, Jo / Puttin' on the Ritz: Garland, Judy
CDDL 1302 / Nov '95 / Music For Pleasure

☐ SOPHISTICATION VOL.1 (Songs Of The Thirties)
Top hat, white tie and tails: Gibbons, Carroll / Things are looking up: Astaire, Fred / Way you look tonight: Astaire, Fred / Touch of your lips: Hildegarde / Darling je vous aime beaucoup: Hildegarde / Just let me look at you: Coward, Sir Noel / Where are the songs we sung: Coward, Sir Noel / Limehouse blues:

Lawrence, Gertrude / You were meant for me: Lawrence, Gertrude / Do do do: Lawrence, Gertrude / Someone to watch over me: Lawrence, Gertrude / Cup of coffee: Lawrence, Gertrude / Wild thyme: Lawrence, Gertrude / Experiment: Lawrence, Gertrude / Nightfall: Carter, Benny / So little time: Keller, Greta / I poured my heart into a song: Hutchinson, Leslie 'Hutch' / You do something to me: Dietrich, Marlene / Falling in love again: Dietrich, Marlene / Dancing honeymoon: Buchanan, Jack / And her mother came too: Buchanan, Jack / Fancy our meeting: Buchanan, Jack / Who: Buchanan, Jack / Two little bluebirds: Buchanan, Jack / Goodnight Vienna: Buchanan, Jack / It's not you: Buchanan, Jack / There's always tomorrow: Buchanan, Jack / Drop in next time you're passing: Welch, Elisabeth / One little kiss from you: Matthews, Jessie / Let me give my happiness to you: Matthews, Jessie / When you've got a little springtime in your heart: Matthews, Jessie / Over my shoulder: Matthews, Jessie / I nearly let love go slipping through my fingers: Matthews, Jessie / Got to dance my way to heaven: Matthews, Jessie / Everything's in rhythm with my heart: Matthews, Jessie / I can wiggle my ears: Matthews, Jessie

PPCD 78108 / Feb '95 / Past Perfect

☐ **SOPHISTICATION VOL.2**

PPCD 78121 / Mar '96 / Past Perfect

☐ **SOPRANO SUMMIT 1976 (Live At The Illiana Club)**

STCD 3254 / Mar '97 / Storyville

☐ **SORTED (2CD Set)**

Push it: Garbage / Corpses: Brown, Ian / Bad old man: Baby Bird / Stay: Butler, Bernard / Nothing lasts forever: Echo & The Bunnymen / This feeling: Puressence / Summertime: Sundays / Rise and shine: Cardigans / I'm leaving: Lodger / Lazy: Suede / She's a star: James / Venus as a boy: Bjork / If you don't want me to destroy you: Super Furry Animals / She cries your name: Orton, Beth / I will be your girlfriend: Dubstar / Hedonism (just because you feel good): Skunk Anansie / Brick: Folds, Ben Five / Your woman: White Town / Ballad of Tom Jones: Space / You and me song: Wannadies / Sleep on the left side: Cornershop / Late in the day: Supergrass / Love me and leave me: Seahorses / Ten storey love song: Stone Roses / El President: Drugstore / More than us: Travis / I'm so lonely: Cast / Lost myself: Longpigs / Consideration: Reef / Wild wood: Weller, Paul / It's a beautiful thing: Ocean Colour Scene / Found you: Dodgy / You showed me: Lightning Seeds / I don't want control of you: Teenage Fanclub / Going for gold: Shed Seven / Olympian: Gene / Bury you: Symposium / Sorted for E's and whizz: Pulp / Star: Primal Scream

5581122 / 25 May '98 / PolyGram TV

☐ **SORTED, SNORTED AND SPORTED**

CRECD 117 / Dec '91 / Creation

☐ **SOUFFLE (A BUDA Sampler)**

927042 / 24 Apr '98 / BUDA

☐ **SOUL AFTER HOURS**

All I know is the way I feel: Thomas, Irma / I can take you to heaven tonight: Clay, Otis / Love is all that matters: Burke, Solomon / Still in love: Adams, Johnny / Without you: Washington, Walter 'Wolfman' / Baby I will: Shannon, Preston / Ever since: Little Buster / Nobody but you: Peebles, Ann / I'm gonna hold you to your promise: Kelly, Paul / You can't hold on to a love that's gone: Holmes Brothers

EDCD 7009 / Nov '96 / Easydisc

☐ **SOUL ALBUM VOL.1, THE (2CD Set)**

Let's get it on: Gaye, Marvin / Let's stay together: Turner, Tina / Search for the hero: M-People / Ocean drive: Lighthouse Family / You gotta be: Des'ree / I am blessed: Eternal / Always and forever: Vandross, Luther / Move closer: Nelson, Phyllis / My girl: Temptations / (Take a little) piece of my heart: Franklin, Erma / Tired of being alone: Green, Al / Rainy night in Georgia: Crawford, Randy / Why can't we live together: Thomas, Timmy / Caravan of love: Isley-Jasper-Isley / Be thankful for what you've got: De Vaughn, William / Unfinished sympathy: Massive Attack / Woman: Cherry, Neneh / Back to life: Soul II Soul / If you love me: Brownstone / I will survive: Savage, Chantay / It takes two: Gaye, Marvin & Kim Weston / Band of gold: Payne, Freda / Give me just a little more time: Chairmen Of The Board / Don't leave me this way: Melvin, Harold & The Bluenotes / What a fool believes: Doobie Brothers / Respect yourself: Staple Singers / Private number: Clay, Judy & William Bell / I can't stand the rain: Peebles, Ann / Change is gonna come: Redding, Otis / Ain't no sunshine: Withers, Bill / Me and Mrs Jones: Paul, Billy / Until you come back to me: Franklin, Aretha / Ready or not here I come (can't hide from love): Delfonics / Betcha by golly wow: Stylistics / Zoom: Fat Larry's Band / I'm doin' fine now: New York City / Solid: Ashford & Simpson / Slowhand: Pointer Sisters / After the love has gone: Earth, Wind & Fire / Rock me tonight (for old times sake): Jackson, Freddie / Piano in the dark: Russell, Brenda / Nightshift: Commodores

VTDCD 115 / Feb '97 / Virgin

☐ **SOUL ALBUM VOL.2, THE (2CD Set)**

VTDCD 165 / 1 Dec '97 / Virgin

☐ **SOUL ALONE (The Art Of The Solo)**

131262 / Sep '96 / Celestial Harmonies

☐ **SOUL ATTITUDE**

3003642 / Jul '97 / IMP

☐ **SOUL BOX (3CD Set)**

TBXCD 503 / Jan '96 / TrueTrax

☐ **SOUL BOX (2CD Set)**

I can make you feel good: Shalamar / I'm doin' fine now: New York City / Hold back the night: Trammps / Can you feel the force: Real Thing / My girl: Whispers / Walk on by: D-Train / Headlines: Midnight Star / Zoom: Fat Larry's Band / Make it easy on yourself: Butler, Jerry / Be thankful for what you've got: DeVaughan, William / Stay with me baby: Redding, Wilma / Love on a two way street: Moments / Best thing that ever happened to me: Knight, Gladys & The Pips / My guy: Wells, Mary / Loving you, losing you: Hyman, Phyllis / Pillow talk: Sylvia / Galaxy of love: Crown Heights Affair / Come back and finish what you started: Knight, Gladys & The Pips / It's a love thing: Whispers / I owe you one: Shalamar / You gave me love: Crown Heights Affair / I wanna dance wit' choo: Disco Tex & The Sexolettes / Knock on wood: Floyd, Eddie / Suspicious minds: Staton, Candi / Still in love: Lucas, Carrie / Harlem shuffle: Bob & Earl / In the name of love: Redd, Sharon / Hold on I'm coming: Burke, Solomon / No one can love you more: Hyman, Phyllis / Midnight train to Georgia: Knight, Gladys & The Pips / Love fever: Adams, Gayle / Valentine love: Connors, Norman / Can't get by without you: Real Thing / Sad sweet dreamer: Sweet Sensation / Zing went the strings of my heart: Trammps / You'll never know: Hi-Gloss / Lean on me: Moore, Melba / Where did our love go: Elbert, Donnie / More, more, more: True, Andrea Connection / Friends: Shalamar / Beat goes on: Whispers / Check out the groove: Thurston, Bobby / Can you handle it: Redd, Sharon / Midas touch: Midnight Star / Give me your love: Mason, Barbara / So sad the song: Knight, Gladys & The Pips / You'll never know what you're missing: Real Thing / Betcha by golly wow: Hyman, Phyllis & Michael Henderson / Oh no, not my baby: Brown, Maxine / You are my starship: Connors, Norman

PBXCD 503 / Nov '96 / Pulse

☐ **SOUL BROTHERS, SOUL SISTERS**

Sweet soul music: Sam & Dave / Operator: Knight, Gladys / Stand by me: King, Ben E. / Under the boardwalk: Drifters / Dancing in the street: Reeves, Martha / Rock your baby: McCrae, George / Hey girl don't bother me: Tams / Band of gold: Payne, Freda / When a man loves a woman: Sledge, Percy / Something old, something new: Fantastics / Baby: Thomas, Carla / Love really hurts without you: Ocean, Billy / Harlem shuffle: Bob & Earl / It's in his kiss (The shoop shoop song): Everett, Betty / What becomes of the broken hearted: Ruffin, Jimmy / If you don't know me by now: Melvin, Harold & The Bluenotes / Rescue me: Bass, Fontella / Knock on wood: Floyd, Eddie / Hey there lonely girl: Holman, Eddie / You'll lose a good thing: Lynn, Barbara

MUCD 9026 / Apr '95 / Musketeer

☐ **SOUL CHASERS VOL.1**

Got to get away: Brown, Sheree / Be for real: Miller, Cat / Do it any way you want: Winters, Robert / Trying to get to you: Carter, Valerie / (A case of) Too much love makin': Scott, Gloria / Top of the stairs: Collins & Collins / I want to be your everything: High Fashion / Would you believe in me: Lucien, Jon / All of my love: Jeter, Genobia / Looking up to you: Wycoff, Michael / And so it begins: Syreeta / Never stopped loving you: Davis, Tyrone / Hold tight: Magic Lady / Call me: Reynolds, L.J.

CDEXP 4 / Nov '92 / Expansion

☐ **SOUL CHASERS VOL.2**

Come into my life: Ndugu / Keep on doin': Jones, Glenn / Say you will: Kitajima, Osamu / It only happens (When I look at you): Franklin, Aretha / I don't want wanna live without you: Platinum Hook / I can't tell you: New Horizon / Good times: Gaines, Rosie / Love love love: Hathaway, Donny / Ripe for the pickin': Trumains / Overdose of joy: Record, Eugene / Fragile handle with care: Dees, Sam / I'm not ready: Ujima / We're in love: Austin, Patti / I can't forget about you: Matlock, Ronn

CDEXP 8 / Nov '94 / Expansion

☐ **SOUL CLASSICS**

This is it: Moore, Melba / Can't get by without you: Real Thing / Hold back the night: Trammps / Come back and finish what you started: Knight, Gladys & The Pips / Dancing in the street: Reeves, Martha / Little piece of leather: Elbert, Donnie / Soul man: Dam & Dave / Harlem shuffle: Bob & Earl / Higher and higher: Wilson, Jackie / Knock on wood: Floyd, Eddie / Your little trustmaker: Tymes / Rock your baby: McCrae, George

74321339282 / Jan '96 / Camden

☐ **SOUL CLASSICS**

4892672 / 23 Feb '98 / Irma

☐ **SOUL CLASSICS (2CD Set)**

Midnight train to Georgia: Knight, Gladys & The Pips / Have you seen her: Chi-Lites / Misty blue: Moore, Dorothy / Members only: Bland, Bobby / Just my imagination: Temptations / Tell it like it is: Neville, Aaron / Buying a book: Tex, Joe / I will: Winters, Ruby / Didn't I blow your mind: Delfonics / Give the little man a great big hand: DeVaughan, William / Gloria: Enchantments / That's the way: Tex, Joe / Do you remember yesterday: New York City / Love Jones: Jenkins, Norma / Daddy's home: Toots & The Maytals / Only a fool: Lee, Byron & Mighty Sparrow / Move closer: Nelson, Phyllis / La la means I love you: Delfonics / Be thankful for what you've got: DeVaughan, William / Can't go on without you: New York City / Together we are beautiful: Kinney, Fern / Where is the love: Delegation / Hold on: LaSalle, Denise / Oh girl: Chi-Lites / Show and tell: Wilson, Al / I believe I'm gonna make it: Tex, Joe / My girl: Temptations / Ask the lonely: Four Tops

SD 885332 / 2 Feb '98 / Disky

☐ **SOUL COLLECTION**

Warm and tender love: Sledge, Percy / Under the boardwalk: Drifters / Every beat of my heart: Knight, Gladys & The Pips / Rainy night in Georgia: Benton, Brook / Thank you: Sam & Dave / Make it easy on yourself: Butler, Jerry / Papa's got a brand new bag: Brown, James / Woman in love: Three Degrees / I've never found a girl to love me like you do: Floyd, Eddie / Band of gold: Payne, Freda / Portrait of my love: Clark, Dee / Let it be me: Butler, Jerry & Betty Everett / Needle in my haystack: Whispers / I've been loving you too long: Sledge, Percy / Ain't no sunshine: Jarreau, Al / Up on the roof: Drifters / Hold on I'm comin': Sam & Dave / Letter full of tears: Knight, Gladys & The Pips / Challenge: Butler, Jerry / Duke of Earl: Chandler, Gene

QED 180 / Nov '96 / Tring

☐ **SOUL CONNECTION**

La la means I love you: Delfonics / Boss: Brown, James / Everybody loves the sunshine: Ayers, Roy / Put yourself in my place: Isley Brothers / Letter to myself: Chi-Lites / I'm stone in love with you: Stylistics / Few more kisses to go: Hayes, Isaac / Make it with you: Whispers / Win lose or show: Intruders / Walk away from love: Ruffin, David / Special lady: Goodman, Ray / Baby come close: Robinson, Smokey / Miss Grace: Tymes / Heaven must have sent: Elgins / Just my imagination: Temptations / Cherish: Kool & The Gang / Zoom: Fat Larry's Band / Hello stranger: Elliman, Yvonne / Could it be I'm falling in love: Detroit Spinners / I've been so lonely for so long: Knight, Frederick / If you don't know me by now: Melvin, Harold & The Bluenotes

5651382 / 6 Jul '98 / Debutante

☐ **SOUL DESIRE VOL.1**

Sexual healing: Gaye, Marvin / Sign your name: D'Arby, Terence Trent / Shake you down: Abbott, Gregory / Rock me tonight: Jackson, Freddie / After the love has gone: Earth, Wind & Fire / Loving you: Riperton, Minnie / Give me the reason: Vandross, Luther / How 'bout us: Champaign / I still haven't found what I'm looking for: Chimes / Smooth operator: Sade / Ain't no sunshine: Withers, Bill / I need your lovin': Williams, Alyson / Mated: Grant, David & Jaki Graham / Always and forever: Heatwave / Tonight I celebrate my love: Bryson, Peabo & Roberta Flack / If you don't know me by now: Melvin, Harold & The Bluenotes

4717322 / Jun '92 / Columbia

☐ **SOUL EMOTION (2CD Set)**

NSCD 011 / Feb '95 / Newsound

☐ **SOUL EXPLOSION (14 Dynamite Cuts)**

Feel the need in me: Detroit Emeralds / Something old, something new: Fantastics / Saturday night at the movies: Drifters / Soul man: Sam & Dave / Knock on wood: Floyd, Eddie / Do the funky chicken: Thomas, Rufus / Hold on I'm coming: Sam & Dave / You want it, you got it: Detroit Emeralds / Is it love you're after: Rose Royce / Car wash: Rose Royce / We are family: Sister Sledge / Lost in music: Sister Sledge / Heaven must be missing an angel: Tavares / Whodunit: Tavares

SUMCD 4024 / Nov '96 / Summit

☐ **SOUL FOR LOVERS**

DCD 5274 / Nov '92 / Kenwest

☐ **SOUL FOR SALE**

0444122 / 27 Oct '97 / Jet Set

☐ **SOUL GIANTS (4CD Set)**

CDBELV 1 / 25 May '98 / Elevate

☐ **SOUL HEAVEN (The Ultimate Smoocher's Mellow Groove Collection)**

CDNEW 132 / 29 Jun '98 / Charly

☐ **SOUL IN THE HOLE**

Game of life: Dead Press / Diesel: Wu Tang Clan / Against the grain: Sauce Money / Ride: MOP / You ain't a killer: Big Punisher / LA Times: Xzibit / Main aim: Dwellas / Rare species: Mobb Deep / High expectations: Common / Child is born: Brand Nubian / Won on won: Cocoa Brovaz / Sole in a hole: Wu All Stars / Visions of blur: Darc Mind / Late night action: Organised Confusion / Your life: OC

078636753126 / 24 Nov '97 / Loud

☐ **SOUL INSPIRATION**

NSCD 020 / May '95 / Newsound

☐ **SOUL JAZZ LOVE STRATA-EAST**

Peace go with you, brother: Scott-Heron, Gil / Well you needn't: Ridley, Larry / Prince of peace: Sanders, Pharoah / Changa chikuyo: Ridley, Larry / John Coltrane: Jordan, Clifford / Hopscotch: Rouse, Charlie / Bottle: Scott-Heron, Gil / Travelling man: Cowell, Stanley / First impressions: Farrah, Shamek / Dance of the little children: Parker, Billy / Eddie Harris: Jordan, Clifford / Smiling Billy suite: Heath Brothers

SJRCD 019 / Oct '94 / Soul Jazz

☐ **SOUL JAZZ VOL.1**

Honky tonk: Butler, Billy / Return of the prodigal son: Green, Byrdie / I've got the blues: Moody, James / Mom and dad: Earland, Charles / 322 wow: Lytle, Johnny / Up to date: Smith, Johnny 'Hammond' / Dat dere: Adderley, Cannonball Quartet / Light: Ammons, Gene

CDBGP 1028 / Jun '89 / Beat Goes Public

☐ **SOUL JUKE BOX HITS (2CD Set)**

DCD 5064 / Jul '89 / Disky

☐ **SOUL MAN**

22513 / Jul '95 / Music

☐ **SOUL MESSENGER VOL.1**

RNGCD 002 / Mar '95 / EC1

☐ **SOUL MOODS (2CD Set)**

NSCD 009 / Feb '95 / Newsound

☐ **SOUL MOTION (CD/CDR Set)**

OM 004CD / Mar '97 / OM

☐ **SOUL NIGHTS**

Searching: China Black / Just a step from heaven: Eternal / Don't be a stranger: Carroll, Dina / End of the road: Boyz II Men / Let's get it on: Gaye, Marvin / Night shift: Commodores / Rainy night in Georgia: Crawford, Randy / Where is the love: Paris, Mica & Will Downing / Just another day: Secada, Jon / So close to love: Moten, Wendy / Now I know what made Otis blue: Young, Paul / Stop loving me, stop loving you: Hall, Daryl / Because of you: Gabrielle / Let's stay together: Pasadenas / So amazing: Vandross, Luther / Shake you down: Abbott, Gregory / Everybody's gotta learn sometime: Yazz / Drift away: Gray, Dobie / Tonight I celebrate my love: Bryson, Peabo & Roberta Flack / Midnight at the Oasis: Muldaur, Maria

5250052 / Aug '94 / PolyGram TV

☐ **SOUL NIGHTS (2CD Set)**

Move closer: Nelson, Phyllis / Toast of love: Three Degrees / It takes two: Barry, Claudja / Forever mine: O'Jays / Love TKO: Pendergrass, Teddy / Lets make a baby: Paul, Billy / Sweeter pain: Wansel, Dexter / In the ghetto: White, Barry / Expressway to your heart: Soul Survivors / You can make it if you try: Allison, Gene / Warm and tender love: Sledge, Percy / Sweet woman like you: Tex, Joe / When you smile: Hutson, Leroy / Stay in my corner: Dells / Didn't we make it: Broadway Express / Don't let love get you down: Bell, Archie & The Drells / For your precious love: Butler, Jerry / Down the aisle: Labelle, Patti & The Bluebells / This love is sweet: Mayfield, Curtis / Soul sister: Jones, Ronnie / Get on up: Esquires / Unforgettable: Rawls, Lou / We do it: Stone, R. & J. / Midnight love affair: Douglas, Carl / Every beat of my heart: Barry, Claudja / Love me like a lover: Charles, Tina / Smarty pants: First Choice / Girls got soul: Indeep / In and out of love: Imagination / Guilty: Pearls / Glad to be your lover: Aiken, Ben / Any day now: Jackson, Chuck / He will break your heart: Butler, Jerry / Twilight time: Platters / Oogum boogum song: Wood, Brenton / Mystery of the world: MFSR

24323 / May '96 / Laserlight

☐ **SOUL NIGHTS**

TSS 107 / 28 Feb '98 / BMG

☐ **SOUL OF A WOMAN VOL.1**

RENCD 102 / Jul '95 / Renaissance Collector Series

☐ **SOUL OF A WOMAN VOL.2**

RENCD 113 / Mar '96 / Renaissance Collector Series

☐ **SOUL OF BLACK PERU, THE**

Yo no soy jaqui (i am not jaqui) / Samba malato / Azuca de cana (sugarcane) / Lando / Son de los diablos (dance of the devils) / Toro mat (bull kills) / Zapateo en menor / Maria lando / No me cumben (that's not for me) / Una larga noche (a long night) / Enciendente candela (light the flame) / Lando / Canterurias / Prendeme la vela (light my candle) / Mario lando

9362458782 / Jun '95 / Warner Bros.

☐ **SOUL OF CAPE VERDE, THE**

68978 / Apr '97 / Tropical

☐ **SOUL OF EIGHTBALL, THE**

8536542502 / 21 Apr '98 / Lightyear

☐ **SOUL OF GOSPEL, THE**

I'll take you there: Staple Singers / You're all I need to get by: Franklin, Aretha / Rescue me: Bass, Fontella / Lean on me: Withers, Bill / (Your love keeps lifting me) higher and higher: Wilson, Jackie / People get ready: Impressions / Oh happy day: Hawkins, Edwin Singers / (Take another little) piece of my heart: Franklin, Erma / Let's stay together: Green, Al / I say a little prayer: Franklin, Aretha / Stand by me: King, Ben E. / Yah mo be there: Ingram, James & Michael McDonald / I'm going all the way: Sounds Of Blackness / Message is love: Baker, Arthur & Backbeat Disciples/Al Green / Let my people go: Winans / I knew you were waiting (for me): Franklin, Aretha & George Michael / I still haven't found what I'm looking for: Chimes / Anytime you need a friend: New Jersey Gospel Choir / Up where we belong: South Carolina Baptist Choir / If you're ready (come go with me): Staple Singers / Mercy mercy me: Gaye, Marvin

RADCD 31 / Nov '95 / Global TV

☐ **SOUL OF GOSPEL, THE**

CDEXM 1 / Jul '97 / Exhale

☐ **SOUL OF JAMAICA/HERE COMES THE DUKE**

Angel of the morning: Landis, Joya / My willow tree: Ellis, Alton / Heatwave: McCook, Tommy & The Supersonics / (Mummy) out of the light: Landis, Joya / My best girl: Paragons / What the world needs now: McCook, Tommy & The Supersonics / I can't stand it: Ellis, Alton / Long time no nice time: Dillon, Phyllis / Ride me donkey: McCook, Tommy / Love letters: Ellis, Alton & Phyllis Dillon / Woman go home: Jamaicans / Flying home: McCook, Tommy & The Supersonics / Laba laba reggae (the lonely goat herd): McCook, Tommy & The Supersonics / Second fiddle: McCook, Tommy & The Supersonics / Mary Poppins: Simpson, Danny/Tommy McCook & The Supersonics / Soul remedy: McCook, Tommy & The Supersonics / I'm in the mood for love: Techniques / I'm yours forever: Soul Lads / True true true: Parker, Ken / Run come celebrate: Techniques / Sweet soul music: Gladiators / Kansas City: Landis, Joya / Love up kiss up: Termites / Funny: Soul Lads

CDTRL 383 / May '97 / Trojan

☐ **SOUL OF JAZZ PERCUSSION, THE**

FSRCD 210 / Oct '96 / Fresh Sound

☐ **SOUL OF RHYTHM 'N' BLUES REVUE (Live At The Lone Star Roadhouse)**

SHAN 9005CD / Oct '93 / Shanachie

☐ **SOUL OF SPRING, THE**

What did I do wrong: Mayberry Movement / You didn't love me anyhow: Act One / I'm the other half of you: Godfrey, Ray / Please come home: Green, Garland / I can't believe you said you love me: Jackson, Lou / It's the same old story: Act One / House for sale: Jackson, Millie / Can I get a witness: Verdell, Jackie / C'mon and give it up: Bathe, Clare / But not for me: Determinations / There's another in my life: Mitchell, Phillip / Mirror don't lie: Simon, Joe / Lead me on: Internationals / Come through me: Green, Garland / I think I'm in love: Mayberry Movement / 28 ways (she loves me): Parker, Winfield / I wanna get over: Street People / Things are not the same: Luv co. / Love doctor: Jackson, Millie / No one else will do: Walker, Ronnie / If I can't have your love: Brown, Jocelyn / Alakazam: Ross, Sonny / Time: Williams, Don & The Exchange

CDKEND 151 / 24 Nov '97 / Kent

☐ **SOUL OF THE 80'S VOL.2**

JHD 043 / Jun '92 / Tring

☐ **SOUL ON THE STREETS VOL.1**

Take care of yourself: Dan-Elle / Love and devotion: Marshall, Wayne / 24-7 Love: Irini / Save your love: SLO / Hooked on you: Everis / Don't let them know: Irini / You turn me on: Everis / Sexual thing: Marshall, Wayne / Sweet lovin': 3rd Zone / Fire and desire: Dan-Elle / Everybody's gotta rave: Marshall, Wayne / Don't let them know (remix): Irini / She want's a 24/7: Hyper Man

SCGCD 201 / May '94 / SCG

☐ **SOUL ON THE STREETS VOL.2**

SCGCD 3 / Dec '94 / SCG

☐ SOUL POWER
Footsteps following me: Nero, Frances / All over the world: Jackson, Chuck / Girl with a broken heart: Pree, Karen / Billy Griffin: Technicolor / It's a shame: Cameron, G.C. / Free: Green, Susaye / Man up in the sky: Bristol, Johnny / Andantes: Boss / Seperation: Lewis, Pat / You see the trouble with me: Littles, Hattie / My brother: Gaye, Frankie / Hurt the one I love: Ruffin, David / Hit and miss: Jean, Scherrie & Lynda / Case of too much love making: Weston, Kim / Surrender: Lavette, Bettye / Give me your love: Royster, Vermettya
SUMCD 4184 / 23 Feb '98 / Summit

☐ SOUL PRESSURE VOL.1
Treat U right: Truce / Flavour of the old school: Knight, Beverley / You can count on me: Graham, Jaki / Turn out the light: Haynes, Victor / Slap 'n' tickle: Kreuz / From me 2 U: Everis / More I try: Just Good Friends / If only: Walker, Daniel / Do it right: Act Of Faith / Only you: Serenade / Good man: Mutual Concept / Angel: Riviera / Nobody knows: LIFE / Women's intuition: Attitude
CDMISH 2 / Jun '95 / Mission

☐ SOUL PRESSURE VOL.2 (14 Urban Soul Flavours)
Never knew love: Troi / Total satisfaction: Heron, Dee / Could you be mine: Ballin, Chris / Get down on it: Kreuz / Something good tonight: Trichelle / Do me that way: Damage / Come go away: Truce / First time: Haynes, Victor / Giving my all: Philips, Jennifer / In love: Campbell, Roger / Lover come back: Sha Sha / Heaven: SCG & Irini / Closer than close: McNeish, Carol / Do you really: Ruude
CDMISH 4 / Dec '95 / Mission

☐ SOUL QUEENS, THE
15168 / Aug '91 / Laserlight

☐ SOUL SALAD
Come back to me: Cheyenne / Tenderness: Pennbrooke, Annie / It's real: Eastside Connection / More love: Love, Mary / Don't be afraid of love: Robinhood / Ridin' high: New Establishment / This love is mine: Perfect Circle / Just you and me: Murray, Juggy / I apologise: Big Foot
HUB 019 / Jun '97 / Hubbub

☐ SOUL SAMPLER VOL.1
I'll be your winner: Clarke, Jimmy 'Soul' / Oh my darlin': Lee, Jackie / Pizza pie man: Grier, Roosevelt / Hide out: Hideaways / Girl across the street: Smith, Moses / Lady love: Vontastics / I've been trying: Chants / I need your love: Woods, Ella / This love: Joytones / Streets got my lady: Brandon, Bill / Girl I love you: Fisher, Shelly / Given up on love: Thompson, Johnny / Searching for soul: Wade, Jake & The Soul Searchers / Everything's gonna be alright: Moore, Robert / You: Wilson, Spanky
GSCD 013 / Aug '96 / Goldmine

☐ SOUL SAMPLER VOL.2
Your heart makes me lonely: Chandlers / I don't want to hear it: Exits / Give in to the power of love: Committee / Ain't gonna do you no harm: Willis, Betty / Lighten up baby: Karim, Ty / Don't cha tell nobody: Vontclaires / Candle: Burdick, Doni / I don't mess around: Reynolds, Jeanie / What have I got now: Fletcher, Darrow / All of a sudden: Incredibles / I found out: Lacour, Bobby / I'll cry over you: Sheeler, Cynthia / I'll cry 1000 tears: Holman, Eddie / Let's get together: George, Cassietta / Crumbs off the table: Young Disciples / Breakdown: Memphians / Cool off: Detroit Executives
GSCD 034 / Aug '96 / Goldmine

☐ SOUL SAMPLER VOL.3
False alarm: Volcanos / So is the sun: World Column / Shotgun and the duck: Lee, Jackie / Long run: Blandon, Curtis / This thing called love: Wyatt, Johnny / I'll hold you: Frankie & Johnny / I wanna testify: Parliaments / Angel baby: Banks, Darrell / Times are bad: Barnes, Bobby / Jenkins, diane: Barnes, Bobby / This I've gotta see: Shaw, Cecil / Let's get together: George, Cassietta / Over the top: Dawson, Roy / Paradise: Jewel / I can't lie to my heart: Fykes, Betty
GSCD 096 / Jul '96 / Goldmine

☐ SOUL SELECTION VOL.1
Last night changed it all (I really had a ball): Williams, Esther / Hang on in there: Kirkland, Mike James / Is it because I'm black: Johnson, Syl / Help is on the way: Whatnauts / Now that I have you: McGee, Tommy / Do you believe in fate: Roberts, Sir John / Do you really love me: Bullock, Janice / Remember to remember: Holmes, Rick
HUBCD 8 / Jun '96 / Hubbub

☐ SOUL SELECTION VOL.2
Nightlife: Blair / Lovely lady: Burch, Vernon / Here is where the love is: Wilson, Bobby / Lovely weekend: Ron & Candy / Elijah rockin' with soul: Jacobs, Hank / I love her so much it hurts: Majestics / You're so right for me: Eastside Connection / Speed up: Moorer, Betty / You should have told me: McGhee, Donna / Phone home: Chingas, Johnny
HUBCD 11 / Nov '96 / Hubbub

☐ SOUL SENSATION (2CD Set)
NSCD 012 / Feb '95 / Newsound

☐ SOUL SENSATIONS (4CD Set)
SUMBX 4017 / Jan '98 / Summit

☐ SOUL SENSITIVITY (2CD Set)
NSCD 010 / Feb '95 / Newsound

☐ SOUL SOLDIERS
I'm the one who loves you: Banks, Darrell / No one blinder (than a man who won't see): Banks, Darrell / Just because your love has gone: Banks, Darrell / Only the strong survive: Banks, Darrell / Got to get rid of you: Barnes, J.J. / Snowflakes: Barnes, J.J. / I like everything about you: Hughes, Jimmy / I'm so glad: Hughes, Jimmy / Did you forget: Hughes, Jimmy / Chains of love: Hughes, Jimmy / Just ain't strong as I used to be: Hughes, Jimmy / Since I lost my baby's love: Major Lance / I wanna make up (before we break up): Major Lance / That's the story of my life: Major Lance / Girl come on home: Major Lance / Ain't no sweat: Major Lance / Beautiful feeling: Banks, Darrell / When a man loves a woman: Banks, Darrell / Let 'em down baby: Hughes, Jimmy / I'm not ashamed to beg or plead: Hughes, Jimmy / Sweet Sherry: Barnes, J.J. / Baby, please come back home: Barnes, J.J.
CDSX 012 / Aug '88 / Stax

☐ SOUL SOUNDS OF THE 90'S
What is black music: Williams, Cunnie / Life with you: Buchanan, Courtney / London kills me: Groove Nation / My destiny: Mr. C / Status symbol: Great Unknown / I can't help it: Glenn, Chris / Keep the groove: Freestyle / Drift away: Thompson, Carroll / Warm weather: Mother Of Pearl / If we loose our way: Johnson, Paul / Mr. Groove: McCord, Kevin / What the child needs: Ronald, Terry
SOUNDSCD 7 / Oct '95 / Street Sounds

☐ SOUL SOUNDS OF THE SEVENTIES
Boogie nights: Heatwave / I'll go where the music takes me: Charles, Tina / Love really hurts without you: Ocean, Billy / Love don't live here anymore: Rose Royce / Car wash: Rose Royce / More than a woman: Tavares / Heaven must be missing an angel: Tavares / Can you feel the force: Real Thing / You to me are everything: Real Thing / Doctor Love: Charles, Tina / Always and forever: Heatwave / Magic fly: Space / Love machine: Miracles / Stoned love: Supremes / Heaven must have sent you: Elgins / Hang on in there baby: Bristol, Johnny & Liz Sands
QED 187 / Nov '96 / Tring

☐ SOUL SOURCE (The Best Of Expansion/4CD Set)
CDBEXP 1 / 16 Mar '98 / Expansion

☐ SOUL SPECTRUM (Selected By Dr. Bob Jones/The Legendary Keb Darge)
You hit my love: Paris, Hari / Not by bread alone: Tamango, Kim / Whole lotta you in me: Brotherly Love / Hardest part: Anderson, Curtis / Space lady: Bill / Take it or leave it: Cory / I was born to love you: Timeless Legend / All of a sudden: Moore, Melvin / What it's all about: Veda / Making new friends: Tracy, Jeanie / You've got so much feeling (in your love): Armstrong, Tal / Keep on getting down: Franko, Lee / Movin' on: GD & The Big J / Ain't gonna be no fool (for you): Fabulous Playmates / Watchin' out: Split Decision Band / Love at first taste: Walker, Johnnie / She's so good: Solid Gold Revue & Ray Crumley / I wanna be with you: Parker, Winfield / Music slave: Jade / Peace love not war: King, Johnny & The Fatback Band
BBECD 013 / 29 Jun '98 / Barely Breaking Even

☐ SOUL STIRRERS
Walk around: Soul Stirrers / Sleep on mother: Soul Stirrers / Precious Lord: Soul Stirrers / I want to rest: Soul Stirrers / Lord I've tried: Soul Stirrers / Remember me: Soul Stirrers / This is my prayer: Soul Stirrers / Does Jesus care: Soul Stirrers / I'm going to tell God: Five Blind Boys Of Mississippi / I was praying: Five Blind Boys Of Mississippi / Will Jesus be waiting: Five Blind Boys Of Mississippi / Vacant room glory: Nightingales / See how they done my Lord: Sensational Nightingales / I'm coming up Lord: Sensational Nightingales / Somewhere to lay my head: Sensational Nightingales
SFCD 1001 / Mar '98 / Spirit Feel

☐ SOUL SUPREME (2CD Set)
DEMPCD 016 / Mar '96 / Emporio

☐ SOUL SUPREME VOL.2
Wanted: Johnson, Paul / Dom Perignon: Don-E / Look no more: Occasions / Love is all you need: Clark, Rick & Gina Foster / It's on: Hilary / Rumours and lies: Kareem / Do me right: Laverne, Elisha / Cry: Ballin, Chris / Meant to be: Dutchy / Dance with me: 5 AM / More than a lover: Cole, Errol / Searchin': Stevens, Mike / Cast all your cares: Knight, Beverley
DOMECD 10 / Feb '97 / Dome

☐ SOUL SURVIVORS (40 Northern Soul Anthems - 2CD Set)
Move on up: Mayfield, Curtis / SOS: Starr, Edwin / It takes two: Gaye, Marvin & Kim Weston / Needle in a haystack: Velvelettes / What: Street, Judy / Do I love you (Indeed I do): Wilson, Frank / This old heart of mine (is weak for you): Isley Brothers / 1-2-3: Barry, Len / Backfield in motion: Mel & Tim / Let's wade in the water: Shaw, Marlena / My man, a sweet man: Jackson, Millie / Love makes a woman: Acklin, Barbara / Sweetest feeling: Wilson, Jackie / You're gonna love my baby: McNair, Barbara / Be young, be foolish, be happy: Tams / Better use your head: Little Anthony & The Imperials / There's a ghost in my house: Taylor, R. Dean / Out on the floor: Gray, Dobie / Sweet soul music: Conley, Arthur / Bok to bach: Father's Angels / You know how to love me: Hyman, Phyllis / Queen of clubs: KC & The Sunshine Band / Don't take away the music: Tavares / Love machine: Miracles / Snake: Wilson, Al / Show me: Tex, Joe / Time is tight: Booker T & The MG's / Here I go again: Bell, Archie / Sweet talkin' guy: Chiffons / Rescue me: Bass, Fontella / Can't satisfy: Impressions / Girl (why you wanna make me blue): Temptations / Green door: Frog, Wynder K. / I'm gonna run away from you: Lynn, Tammi / Zoo (The Human Zoo): Commodores / Go go power: De Santo, Sugar Pie / Dearly beloved: Montgomery, Jack / Long after tonight is all over: Radcliffe, Jimmy / Time will pass you by: Legend, Tobi / I'm on my way: Parrish, Dean
TCD 2869 / Apr '97 / Telstar

☐ SOUL TIME
Soul time: Ellis, Shirley / Help me: Spellbinders / Temptation is calling my name: David, Lee / I worship you baby: Glories / I don't want to talk about it: Ames, Nancy / Cause your mine: Vibrations / Angel baby: Carrow, George / You don't know where your intrests lie: Valery, Dana / I'm in a world of pain: Sweet Things / Stranger in my arms: Randell, Lynne / Are we ready for love: Austin, Patti / Ain't that a lot of love: Taj Mahal / I feel alright: Richards, Turley / There's a pain in my heart: Poppies / I want to tell you: Wilson, Orbrey / STOP: Lorelei / Of hopes and dreams and tombstones: Fraser, Jimmy / Walk like a man: Moore, Johnny B.
4888402 / 29 Sep '97 / Epic

☐ SOUL TRAIN CHRISTMAS
Let it snow: Boyz II Men / Every day every Christmas: Vandross, Luther / God bless the dreamer: Hines, Simon / O Come all ye faithful: Az Yet / Silent night: En Vogue / Special gift: Isley Brothers / Have yourself a merry little Christmas: Rome / Christmas song: Cole, Natalie / Santa Claus is coming to town: Immature / Silver bells: Total Commitment / This Christmas: Labelle, Patti / Someday at Christmas: Wonder, Stevie / It's Christmas all over the world: New Edition / Santa Claus goes straight to the ghetto: Brown, James / There's no Christmas without you: Franklin, Kirk & The Family / Give love on Christmas day: Gill, Johnny
4893642 / 1 Dec '97 / Epic

☐ SOUL TRAIN VOL.1 (2CD Set)
CDSGP 0149 / Jan '95 / Prestige

☐ SOUL TRAIN VOL.2 (2CD Set)
CDSGP 0262 / Feb '96 / Prestige

☐ SOUL UNDERGROUND VOL.1
Two sides to every story: Love, Jimmy / Baby I'm serious: Tillman, Charlotta / Don't accuse me: Squires / I feel good (all over): Lavette, Bettye / Come back baby: Stoppers / (I know) Your love has gone away: Drapers / Only your love can save me: Lavette, Bettye / He's got the nerve: True Tones / Another time another place: Starr, Harry / If you ask me (because I love you): Williams, Jerry / Fell in love with you baby: Elliot, Linda / Dance dance dance: Casualeers / What shall I do: Frankie & The Classicals / Don't refuse my love: Intrigues / Stand up like a man: Lavette, Bettye / Nothing can help you now: Curtis, Lenny / I'll do anything: Troy, Doris / Too long without some loving: Clovers / What did I do: Humes, Anita & The Essex / Walkin': Jones, Jimmy / I'm just a fool for you: Lavette, Bettye / Mama's got a bag of her own: King, Anna / Can't help lovin' dat man: Vann, Ila / Step into my world: Vann, Ila
NEMCD 759 / Oct '95 / Sequel

☐ SOUL UNDERGROUND VOL.2 (Time Marches On)
Three dollar bill: Gibson, Beverley-Ann / I'll never let you go: Cadillacs / Never ever leave me: Hunt, Geraldine / Please don't go: Kathy & The Calenders / Everything is fine: Skyliners / Spinnin' top: Orlons / No better for you: Big Maybelle / Try my loving on you: Clovers / I'm in such misery: Gardner, Don / We'll be makin' out: James, Jessica & The Outlaws / I'm so glad: Neal, Robert / Help me (get over my used to be lover): Honey & The Bees / I've got my baby: Livingston, Patty / Now that you left me: Thurmond, Duff / Condition red: Baltimore & Ohio Marching Band / Time marches on: Hill, Lainie / Turns to me: Towns, Chris Unit / Human race: Adams, June / Isn't it just a shame: Wells, Kenny / Stop hurting me baby: Purple Mundi / Never had a love so good: Johnson, Charles / I need you like a baby: Janice / Nobody but you: Phillips, Esther / It seems like I've been here before: Jackson, J.J.
NEMCD 841 / Apr '96 / Sequel

☐ SOUL'D TOGETHER VOL.2 (The Soul Of Black America)
Ain't no way: Gibson, Anthony T. / Say it isn't so: Gibson, Anthony T. / Special kinda woman: Gibson, Anthony T. / My heart: Gibson, Anthony T. / Sitting in the park: Gibson, Anthony T. / I need a lover: Gibson, Anthony T. / If you need: Gibson, Anthony T. / Sidelines: Gibson, Anthony T. / Is it for real: Gibson, Anthony T. / Take the money: Gibson, Anthony T. / At this moment: Gibson, Anthony T.
ATCD 016 / Nov '92 / ATR

☐ SOUL'D TOGETHER VOL.3 (The Soul Of Black America)
Close to you: Bush, Charles / I want you: Smith, Antoine / Second go around: Cornelious, Eve / House my love: Blount, Carlton / Never go back: Ledford, Kenne / Good times: DeBarge / I knew I could always count on you: Brown, Shirley / Thank you lady: Brittan, James / Nine to five (who said it): Floyd, Jeff / Reaching for the sky: Riley, Walter / Drug free society: Mozie B / Never give up: Mathis, Diane / One more night: Gaines, Rosie / Let me kiss you where it hurts: Burris, Warren / Girl I miss you: Group Life / If you need it: Bush, Charles
ATCD 017 / Aug '93 / ATR

☐ SOUL'D TOGETHER VOL.4 (The Soul Of Black America)
Walking in rhythm: Foxx Empire / I'll give my love: Thin Line / Take U to the top: Bush, Charles / Taking it as it comes: Desi / Time to stay: Kiass / Reach out your hand: Mason, Laverna / Baby I know: McNeir, Ronnie / Nothing like this: Greene, Mark / Call me: Nash, Kevin / Straight from the heart: Brittan, James / Throw her love: Floyd, Jeff / Peaceful: Eddie M
ATCD 023 / Aug '95 / ATR

☐ SOULED ON REGGAE (3CD Set)
EMTBX 313 / 20 Apr '98 / Emporio

☐ SOULED ON REGGAE VOL.1
Ain't no sunshine: Boothe, Ken / I'll be there: Biggs, Barry / Tears of a clown: Chosen Few / Only the strong survive: Mighty Diamonds / Me and Mrs Jones: White, Joe / You make me feel brand new: Wilson, Delroy / Baby I need your loving: Wilson, Delroy / Homely girl: Inner Circle / Papa was a rolling stone: Pioneers / Just my immagination: London, Jimmy / Dock of the bay: Brown, Dennis / Band of gold: Griffiths, Marcia / Rainy night in Georgia: Thomas, Nicky / BAckstabbers: Lee, Byron & The Dragonaires / Didn't I blow your mind: Cables / You keep me hangin' on: Dorane, Mike
EMPRCD 577 / Jul '95 / Emporio

☐ SOULED ON REGGAE VOL.2 (16 Soul Classics In A Reggae Style)
I second that emotion: Chosen Few / Don't leave me this way: Wilson, Delroy / Put yourself in my place: Campbell, Cornell / My girl: Brown, Dennis / Let's get it on: Boothe, Ken / First time ever I saw your face: Griffiths, Marcia / Thin line between love and hate: Seaton, B.B. / Ain't nothing like the real thing: Bob & Marcia / Didn't I blow your mind: Cables / You keep me hanging on: Dorane, Mike / Private number: Honey Boy / My cherie amour: Harry J All Stars / If loving you is wrong: Maytones / What does it take to win your love: Ellis, Alton / Midnight train to Georgia: Brown, Teddy / When will I see you again: Inner Circle
EMPRCD 667 / Oct '96 / Emporio

☐ SOULED ON REGGAE VOL.3 (16 Soul Classics In A Reggae Style)
Just my imagination: Biggs, Barry / Didn't we almost have it all: Pliers / If you don't know me by now: Ricks, Glen & The Taxi Gang / Endless love: Edwards, Jackie / Three times a lady: Sanchez / Ain't no sunshine: Andy, Horace / When she was my girl: Wilson, Delroy / Love of the common people: Donaldson, Eric / Brandy: McGregor, Freddie / Ain't too proud to beg: Alcapone, Dennis / Rainy night in Georgia: Holt, John / You're the best thing that ever happened to me: Blues Busters / Everybody plays the fool: Pioneers / Let's stay together: Gardiner, Boris / Never gonna give you up: Reedy, Winston / Just don't want to be lonely: Blues Busters
EMPRCD 755 / 8 Sep '97 / Emporio

☐ SOULFUL
LHCD 014 / Jul '96 / Luv n' Haight

☐ SOULFUL DIVAS VOL.1 (Pop & Soul Sirens)
HIPD 40094 / 19 May '98 / Hippo

☐ SOULFUL DIVAS VOL.2 (Dance Queens)
HIPD 40097 / 19 May '98 / Hippo

☐ SOULFUL KINDA 70'S (2CD Set)
Shy guy: Baker, Johnny / Man of value: Berklay, Tyrone / Your smallest wish: 21st Century Ltd / Dancing on a daydream: Soulvation Army / You live only once: Imperial Wonders / Happy: Velvet Hammer / It's not where you start: Davis, Luckey / Like taking candy from a baby: Brown, J.T. / Ain't nothing wrong: Jones, Jimmy / This economy: Michel, Lee / Shady lady: Newton, Bobby / Baby hard times: Love, Dave / In a world so cold: St. Germain, Tyrone / Over the top: Dawson, Roy / Secret place: Brothers / If it wasn't for you: Four Sonics / Loneliness: Will, David / Let's spend some time together: Houston, Larry / Dance all night: Masterplan / You're my main squeeze: Crystal Motion / Game players: Silverspoon, Dooley / Wrong crowd: Prince George / Bet you if you ask around: Velvet / You better keep her: Holmes, Marvin / You can win: Bileo / Heartache and pain: Pages / He's always around: Gerrard, Donny / I can't make it: Simmons, Vessie / I want to be loved: Stevens & Foster / Love's built on a strong foundation: Big Jim's Border Crossing / Ho happy day: Flame 'n' King / Turning point: Simmons, 'Little' Mack / Honey baby: Innervision / Have love will travel: Jones, Rosey / When the fuel runs out: Ambitions / Spellbound: Everett, Frank / I wonder: Family Circle / Come back: Fantastic Puzzles / What goes up: Cody, Black / Don't you leave: Hughes, Freddie / Operator operator: Baker, Johnny / Some kinda man: Pride & Passion / All I want: Neal, C.C. / Come and ask me: 5 Wagers / From the bottom of your heart: Steelers / Give in to the power of love: Committee / Let's get nasty: Stephens, Chuck / What: Weathers, Oscar / Love will turn around: Entertains / I'm a winner: Just Bobby
GSCD 050 / Nov '95 / Goldmine

☐ SOULFUL-DELIVERY THE MESSAGE
IMP 12392 / 24 Aug '98 / Impulse Jazz

☐ SOUND BOY KILLING
SH 45018 / Dec '94 / Shanachie

☐ SOUND COLORS
XTR 47CDM / 8 Jun '98 / X-Treme

☐ SOUND GALLERY VOL.1
Oh Calcutta: Pell, Dave / Black rite: Mandingo / Headhunter: Mandingo / Snake pit: Mandingo / Punch bowl: Parker, Allan / Night rider: Hawkshaw, Alan / Girl in a sportscar: Hawkshaw, Alan / It's all at the co-op now: Hawkshaw, Alan / Blarney's stoned: Hawkshaw, Alan / Riviera affair: Richardson, Neil / Jetstream: Gregory, John / Jaguar: Gregory, John / Half forgotten daydreams: Gregory, John / Life of leisure: Mansfield, Keith / Young scene: Mansfield, Keith / Music to drive by: Loss, Joe / Detectives: Tew, Alan / Boogie juice: Bennett, Brian / Penthouse suite: Dale, Syd / I feel the earth move: Keating, Johnny / Jesus Christ superstar: Keating, Johnny / Earthmen: Kingsland, Paddy / Shout about pepsi: Wright, Denny / Funky fever: Morehouse, Alan
CDTWO 2001 / Apr '95 / Premier/EMI

☐ SOUND GALLERY VOL.2
Jason King theme: Johnson, Laurie / Powerhouse pop: Mansfield, Keith / Good word: Scotsman / Two lane blacktop: Clarke, James / Zodiac: Lindup, David / That's nice: Moorhouse, Alan / I can see for miles: Lord Sitar / Accroche toi, Caroline: Paris Studio Group / Marsellaise Generique: Lai, Francis / Francais Francais: Pourcel, Franck / Left Bank two: Noveltones / Light my fire: Andrews, John / Avengers tag: Johnson, Laurie / Open house: Fahey, Brian / Mama Elephant: E-Cap / International flight: Snell, David / Up to date: Park, Simon / On the brink: Vickers, Mike / Sports car special: Pearson, Johnny / Countdown: Fahey, Brian / Miss World: Dale, Syd / Enter the dragon: Parnell, Jack / Breakaway: Karman, Steve / Caesar Smith: Johnson, Laurie / Rat catchers: Pearson, Johnny / At the sign of the Swinging Cymbal: Fahey, Brian / Theme One: Martin, George
CDTWO 2002 / Jul '96 / Premier/EMI

☐ SOUND INFORMATION
WWCD 9 / Feb '95 / Wibbly Wobbly

☐ SOUND INFORMATION COLLECTIVE
EBSC 06 / 20 Apr '98 / Echo Beach

☐ SOUND NAVIGATOR (Setting Sail For An Outernational Reggae Style)
BTT 0332 / Oct '95 / Buback

☐ SOUND OF A MOUNTAIN STREAM (Music For Relaxation)
SUMCD 4153 / Sep '97 / Summit

☐ SOUND OF A STORM
SUMCD 4155 / Jan '98 / Summit

☐ SOUND OF ACID, THE (2CD Set)
3014782 / 20 Apr '98 / Techno Import

☐ SOUND OF CHRISTMAS PANPIPES, THE
When a child is born / Have yourself a very merry Christmas / Sleigh ride / O little town of Bethlehem / Way in a manger / In Dulci jubilo / Once in Royal David's City / Hark the Herald angels sing / Silent night / God rest ye merry gentlemen / White Christmas / Christmas dreams / First Noel / Little Drummer Boy / Walking in the air (The snowman) / In the bleak mid winter / Happy Christmas (war is over) / I'll be home for Christmas / Mistletoe and wine / Christmas song / Go rest ye merry gentlemen
3036000052 / Oct '95 / Carlton

☐ SOUND OF CLEVELAND CITY, THE
Testament 1: *Chubby Chunks* / Don't stop: *Direct 2 Disc* / Herbal hand: *B-Line* / Excuse me: *Direct 2 Disc* / Whose no.1: *Dig The New Breed* / Hey Mr. DJ: *Screen II* / Real thing: *Di Bart, Tony* / Morning: *Direct 2 Disc* / Saturday night party: *Alex Party* / Cast: *B-Line* / Drive in one: *TST Fever Posse* / Swing man: *Rhyme Time Productions*
CLECD 333 / Aug '94 / Cleveland City

☐ SOUND OF CLUB KINETIC VOL.2 (2CD Set)
VKCD 02 / Oct '96 / Club Kinetic

☐ SOUND OF CLUB KINETIC VOL.3 (2CD Set)
VKCD 3 / Oct '96 / Club Kinetic

☐ SOUND OF CLUB KINETIC VOL.4
VKCD 4 / Aug '97 / Club Kinetic

☐ SOUND OF COLUMBIA, THE (Highlights From The 9th Cartegena Festival)
CPCD 8135 / Jan '96 / Charly

☐ SOUND OF DETROIT/RARE STAMPS/ HERE TO STAY (Don Davis Presents)
Baby, please come back home: *Barnes, J.J.* / Chains of love: *Barnes, J.J.* / Now that I got you back: *Barnes, J.J.* / Easy living: *Barnes, J.J.* / Sweet Sherry: *Barnes, J.J.* / Don't make me a storyteller: *Mancha, Steve* / Love like yours: *Mancha, Steve* / Keep the faith: *Mancha, Steve* / I don't wanna lose you: *Mancha, Steve* / Hate yourself in the morning: *Mancha, Steve* / Just keep on loving me: *Mancha, Steve* / Just because your love has gone: *Banks, Darrell* / Forgive me: *Banks, Darrell* / Only the strong survive: *Banks, Darrell* / Don't know what to do: *Banks, Darrell* / When a man loves a woman: *Banks, Darrell* / We'll get over: *Banks, Darrell* / Beautiful feeling: *Banks, Darrell* / I could never hate her: *Banks, Darrell* / Never alone: *Banks, Darrell* / No one blinder (than a man who won't see): *Banks, Darrell* / My love is strictly reserved: *Banks, Darrell*
CDSXD 061 / Jul '92 / Stax

☐ SOUND OF FUNK VOL.1, THE
Damph F'aint: *Johnson, Herb Settlement* / Sad chicken: *Leroy & The Drivers* / How long shall I wait: *Fields, James Lewis* / Hector: *Village Callers* / Let the groove move you: *Lewis, Gus 'The Groove'* / Groovy world: *Fabulous Caprices* / Jan jan: *Various Narrators* / Iron leg: *Mickey & The Soul Generation* / You got to be a man: *Williams, Frank* / Searching for soul: *Various Narrators* / Push and pull: *Sons Of Slum* / Take this woman off the corner: *Spencer, James* / Everything gonna be alright: *Various Narrators* / Tramp Part 1: *Showmen Inc.* / I'm the man: *Showmen Inc.* / Whip: *Brown, Al* / You: *Wilson, Spanky* / Brother Brown: *Bob, Camille* / Happy soul: *Cortez, Dave & The Moon People* / Let my people go: *Darondo* / Nefertiti: *Wysdom*
GSCD 007 / Nov '92 / Goldmine

☐ SOUND OF FUNK VOL.10, THE (Serious 70's Heavyweight Rarities)
Super funky (part 1): *Thunder, Lightning And Rain* / Quit jivin': *Pearly Queen* / Pick and shovel: *Touch* / Georgia walk: *Raw Soul* / Soul block (of rocking people): *Len And The Pa's* / Rare back and stretch (part 1): *Sandifer, McKinley* / Chicken and rice: *Soul Serenaders* / I gotta see my baby: *Ellis, Jamie* / I don't want to cry: *Cole, Bennie & His Soul Bros.* / She broke down (ran right out on me): *Little Richard III* / No names will be called: *Road Runners* / Chicken peck (part 2): *Pronouns* / You have come into my life: *Swindell, Earl* / Man hunt: *Ross, Mitzi* / Charge: *Bronc-Glows* / Down home publicity: *Apple And The 3 Oranges* / Allen's party: *Matthews, Allen* / Can you dig it: *Soul Setters* / Who's the blame: *Jessie, Obe* / So called friends: *Barnes, J.J.*
GSCD 097 / Oct '96 / Goldmine

☐ SOUND OF FUNK VOL.2, THE
Gat or bat / Humpty dumpty: *Vibrettes* / I've got reasons: *Hooper, Mary Jane* / Got to get me a job: *Alford, Ann* / Love got a piece of your mind: *5 Ounces Of Earth* / African strut: *Westbrook, Lynn* / Spin-II jug: *Brooks, Smokey* / Girl chooses the boy: *Collins, Lashdown* / Funk I-Tus: *Warm excursion* / Chocolate sugar: *Six Feet Under* / Screwdriver: *Austin, Lee* / Skin II black: *Bush, Tommy* / Communication is where it's at: *Billy the baron* / World: *1619 Bab* / Fun and funk: *Fantastic epics* / Marvin's groove: *BW Souls* / Hot butter 'n' all: *Darondo*
GSCD 012 / Apr '93 / Goldmine

☐ SOUND OF FUNK VOL.3, THE
Got a thing for you baby: *Mr. Percolator* / Funky funky hot pants: *Mason, Wee Willie* / JB's latin: *Spittin' Image* / New bump and twist: *Kats* / Hit drop: *Explosions* / Africana: *Propositions* / Got a gig on my back: *Kelly & The Soul Explosion* / Soul drippin's: *Interns* / Let's get together: *George, Cassietta* / Baby I've got it: *King George & The Fabulous Souls* / Fon-kin love: *Love International* / Campbell lock: *Campbell, Don* / Funky soul shake: *White, E.T. & The Potential Band* / Hot pants: *20th Century* / Closed mind: *Different Bags* / Give a damn: *Gordon, Benny* / Stop (what'cha doing to me): *Roberts, Roy* / Gimme some tonight: *Holmes Justice, Marvin* / How you get higher: *Hunter & His Games*
GSCD 023 / Sep '93 / Goldmine

☐ SOUND OF FUNK VOL.4, THE
Funky buzzard: *Little Oscar* / Fun in your thang: *Phelps, Bootsey & The Soul Invaders* / Funky fat man: *Bynum, Burnett & The Soul Invaders* / Keep on brother keep on: *Fatback Band* / Crumbs for the table: *Young Disciples & Co.* / Moon walk: *King Solomon* / Bumping: *Chestnut, Tyrone* / Open up your heart: *Raw Soul & Frankie Beverly* / Get some: *Wee Willie & The Winners* / (Ride on) iron horse: *Marlboro Men* / Funky funk: *Big Al & The Star Treks* / Funky moon meditation: *Moonlighters* / Wait a minute: *Xplosions* / Do the funky donkey: *Turner, Otis & The Mighty Kingpins* / Funky line part 1: *Fabulous Shalimars* / Hold tight: *McNutt, Bobby* / Funky hump: *Cook, Little Joe* / Be black baby: *Tate, Grady* / Can you dig it: *Chico & Buddy*
GSCD 028 / Jan '94 / Goldmine

☐ SOUND OF FUNK VOL.5, THE
Dynamite: *Colt, Steve* / Crazy legs: *Soul Tornadoes* / Breakdown: *Memphians* / Revolution rap (Part 1): *Green, Cal* / Wait a minute: *Xplosions* / Funkie moon: *Johnson, Smokey & Company* / Soul combination: *Soul Combination* / Afro bush: *Gaunichaux, E. & The Skeptics* / Football: *Mickey & The Soul Generation* / Whip (Part 1): *Simpkins, Darnell & the Family Tree* / Give a man a break: *Mintz, Charles* / I laugh and talk (but I don't play): *Strong, Zeke & the Ladyetts* / Kuri kuri: *Diety* / Hot pants: *Bee, Jimmy* / Bear funk: *Revolution Funk* / Do the yum yum man: *Contributors Of Soul* / Whip (Part 2): *Simpkins, Darnell & the Family Tree* / I laugh and talk (instrumental): *Strong, Zeke & the Ladyetts* / Revolution rap (Part 2): *Green, Cal*
GSCD 036 / Apr '94 / Goldmine

☐ SOUND OF FUNK VOL.6, THE
Gigolo: *Anderson, Gene* / You did it: *Robinson, Ann* / Foxy little Mama: *Stone, Bob & His Band* / Oof (Do anything I want): *Colbert, Chuck* / Sweet thing: *Campbell, Milton & The R-D-M Band* / Rerun: *King Hannibal* / Atlanta boogaloo: *Inclines* / Rough nut: *Zodiacs* / Fussin and cussin (Part 1): *Four Wheel Drive* / (Get ready for) Changes: *Marva & Melvin* / Funky John: *Cameron, Johnny & The Camerons* / Soul chills: *Soul, Dede & The Spidels* / Loneliest one: *Anderson, Gene* / Life is like a puzzle: *Village Soul Choir* / Sunshine: *Scacy & The Sound Service* / Take it where you found it: *Jackson, Lorraine* / Fussin and Cussin (Part: *Four Wheel Drive* / Soul chills (Part 2): *Soul, Dede & The Spidels* / Boogie man: *Jones, Rufus R.*
GSCD 045 / Aug '94 / Goldmine

☐ SOUND OF FUNK VOL.7, THE
Super cool: *Hunt, Pat* / Branded: *Leach, C.J.* / Funky strut: *Fabulous Soul Eruption* / Hook and boogie: *Abraham* / It's your love: *Theron & Darrell* / Dap walk: *Ernie & The Top Notes* / Gimme some: *General Crook* / Boilin' water: *Soul Stoppers Band* / Bad luck: *Carbo, Hank* / Fish head: *Slim & Soulful Saints* / Green power: *Wallace, Sir Sidney* / Slow down: *Elliott, Don* / Do your own thing: *Moultrie, Sam* / Soul chicken: *Allen, Bobby* / Soul power: *Willis, Jamie* / Whip: *Brown, Al* / Hook and boogie: *Abraham* / Gimme some: *General Crook* / Slow down: *Elliott, Don*
GSCD 060 / Dec '94 / Goldmine

☐ SOUND OF FUNK VOL.8, THE
Ain't no other way: *Hitson, Herman* / Baby don't cry: *Third Guitar* / Do the Bobby Dunn: *Dunn, Bobby* / Popcorn baby: *Hench, Freddy* / Check your battery: *Talbot, Johny* / Baby I've got it: *Fabulous Souls* / You lost your thing: *Johnson, Hank* / Sagittarius: *Landlord & Tennants* / Ain't that fun: *Harris, Tyrone* / Movin' and Groovin': *Volcanos* / Lady: *Superiors Band & Their Soul Singers* / Funky donkey: *Illusions* / Groove penguin: *Wonsley, Excell* / Soul encyclopedia: *Jones, Geraldine* / Get off your butt: *Hines, Debbie* / Jungle: *Young Senators* / Funky jive: *Soul Crusaders* / Village sound: *Village Sound*
GSCD 064 / Jun '95 / Goldmine

☐ SOUND OF FUNK VOL.9, THE
Free and easy: *Apples & The Oranges* / Take it and get: *Zere & The Soul Sisters* / I don't want to hear it now: *Brinson, Jimmy* / Cool it: *Morris, Guy* / Do the train: *Thrillers* / Number one prize: *Bare Faxx* / Cookies: *Brother Soul* / What it is: *Apollis* / Funky wah wah: *La Mar, Tony* / Tormented: *Holliday, Johnny* / What you do it good: *Williams, Gene* / Sound success: *Wallis, Joe* / Funky mule: *Holmes, Martin & The Uptights* / Times are bad: *Barnes, Bobby* / I got a new thing: *Smith, Willie* / Akiwawa: *Village Crusaders* / Nabbit juice: *Eastwind* / Happy fool: *Belva* / Sock it to me: *Moore, Henry* / Do it good: *Brother Soul*
GSCD 067 / Jan '96 / Goldmine

☐ SOUND OF GARAGE CITY, THE
CTC 0404 / May '95 / Coast 2 Coast

☐ SOUND OF GONDWANA, THE
150262 / Aug '97 / Black Sun

☐ SOUND OF HAPPYCORE '97 VOL.2, THE (2CD Set)
Follow the sun: *Triple J* / Dreaming: *DJ Slam* / Bassline kickin': *MC Lust* / La la song: *Cru-L-T* / Eternity: *Triple J* / You're the voice: *Waxman* / Oceans apart: *DJ Kaos* / Give me your love: *DJ Stompy* / Guardian angel: *DJ Vinyl Groover* / See the light: *Brisk & Trixxy* / Devotion: *DJ Sy & DJ Demo* / Another lonely day: *Eruption*
CDRAID 538 / 27 Oct '97 / Rumour

☐ SOUND OF ILLEGAL TECHNO, THE (2CD Set)
3021302 / 27 Apr '98 / Techno Import

☐ SOUND OF INFINITY (Trip Hop From Outer Space)
IM 802CD / 16 Sep '97 / Irma

☐ SOUND OF IRISH FOLK, THE
DOCDZ 8801 / 20 Apr '98 / Dara

☐ SOUND OF LIGHT, THE
ND 63914 / Oct '94 / Narada

☐ SOUND OF MOTORCITY, THE (3CD Set)
Crazy 'bout the guy: *Supremes* / On the beach: *Demps, Louvain* / Mister wonderful: *Randolph, Barbara* / Back in circulation: *Fantastic Four* / Merry go round: *Lewis, Pat* / Straight in the eye: *Cameron, G.C.* / What's wrong with me baby: *Valadiers* / Pull myself together: *Johnson, Marv* / Release this love: *Starr, Edwin* / Gonna win you back: *Contours* / Ten out of ten: *Elgins* / You're my lucky number: *McNeir, Ronnie* / You're my luck number: *McNeir, Ronnie* / One too many reasons: *Littles, Hattie* / I need you: *Jacas, Jake* / Nowhere to go but up: *Nero, Frances* / You're so fine: *Stubbs, Joe* / Hurt the one you love: *Ruffin, David* / Don't take my kindness for weakness: *Starr, Edwin* / Hit and miss: *Supremes* / Got the big city blues: *Eckstine, Billy* / It's a rough world: *Satintones* / Face to face with love: *McNair, Barbara* / You're what's missing in my life: *Cameron, G.C.* / Girls are out to get you: *Andantes* / Angel: *Griffin, Billy* / Lost and found: *Demps, Louvain* / Waiting 'round the corner: *Mike & The Modifiers* / Can't give you up: *McNeir, Ronnie* / Sweet as a honey bee: *Barnes, J.J.* / Reach for the sky: *Lavette, Bettye & Jake Jacas* / Your love is wonderful: *Littles, Hattie* / Where did our love go: *Three Ounces Of Love* / Step into my shoes: *Reeves, Martha & The Vandellas* / Not this time: *Griner, Linda* / Stop in the name of love: *Supremes* / Running a fever: *Littles, Hattie* / Lonely lonely girl am I: *Velvelettes* / After dark: *Campbell, Choker* / It's a pleasure: *Nero, Frances* / Heatwave: *Motor City Allstars* / With you I'm born again: *Syreeta* / Fighting for what's right: *Holloway, Brenda* / Keep on giving me love: *McNeir, Ronnie* / Starting all over again: *Lands, Liz* / Turning my back and walking away: *Randolph, Barbara* / Working on a building of love: *Fantastic Four* / Let the music take you away: *Van Dyke, Earl* / Rescue me: *Lewis, Pat*
390242 / Jul '96 / Hallmark

☐ SOUND OF MUSIC, THE
CZ 33CD / Nov '93 / Bring On Bull

☐ SOUND OF ONE MAN CLAPPING, THE
OMC 0012 / 20 Apr '98 / One Man Clapping

☐ SOUND OF PHILADELPHIA VOL.1, THE
HURTCD 008 / 30 Mar '98 / Harmless

☐ SOUND OF PHILADELPHIA, THE (2CD Set)
When will I see you again: *Three Degrees* / Love I lost: *Melvin, Harold & The Bluenotes* / Show you the way to go: *Jacksons* / Love train: *O'Jays* / I'll always love my mama: *Intruders* / Soul city walk: *Bell, Archie & The Drells* / For the love of money: *O'Jays* / Love is the message: *MFSB* / Me and Mrs. Jones: *Paul, Billy* / Ooh child: *Sharp, Dee Dee* / I wanna know your name: *Intruders* / Bad luck: *Melvin, Harold & The Bluenotes* / Dirty ol' man: *Three Degrees* / Find me a girl: *Jacksons* / Your song: *Paul, Billy* / Sound of Philadelphia: *MFSB*
488696 / 3 Aug '98 / Columbia

☐ SOUND OF PHILADELPHIA, THE (2CD Set)
Love train: *O'Jays* / Satisfaction guaranteed: *Blue Notes* / Do it anyway you wanna: *People's Choice* / Dirty ol' man: *Three Degrees* / Only the strong survive: *Paul, Billy* / You are everything: *Stylistics* / TSOP (The sound of Philadelphia): *Three Degrees* / Shout: *Trammps* / I love music: *O'Jays* / You'll never find another love like mine: *Rawls, Lou* / Lady marmalade (Voulez-vous coucher avec moi ce soir): *La Belle* / Soul city walk: *Bell, Archie & The Drells* / Ain't no stoppin' us now: *McFadden & Whitehead* / Let 'em in: *Paul, Billy* / Hold back the night: *Trammps* / Let's clean up the ghetto: *Philadelphia International All Stars* / Back stabbers: *O'Jays* / Love epidemic: *Trammps* / Me and Mrs.Jones: *Paul, Billy* / Year of decision: *Three Degrees* / Ms.Grace: *Tymes* / Don't leave me this way: *Melvin, Harold & The Bluenotes* / You make me feel brand new: *Stylistics* / Family affair: *MFSB* / Your song: *Paul, Billy* / When will I see you again: *Three Degrees* / Shiftless shady Jealous kind of people: *O'Jays* / (Win place or show) She's a winner: *Intruders* / Zing went the strings of my heart: *Trammps* / If you don't know me by now: *Melvin, Harold & The Bluenotes*
DBP 102017 / Jan '98 / Double Platinum

☐ SOUND OF REVOLUTION
RENCD 111 / Mar '96 / Renaissance Collector Series

☐ SOUND OF ROME
ACV 204 CD / Oct '95 / ACV

☐ SOUND OF SKA, THE
Lip up fatty / On my radio / Can can / Too much too young / Night boat to cairo / One step beyond / Mirror in the bathroom / Nee nee na na nu nu / Special brew / Baggy trousers / Hand's off she's mine / Three minute hero / Buster's groove
QED 091 / Nov '96 / Tring

☐ SOUND OF SKA, THE
Sound of skaaa medley: *Bad Manners* / On my radio: *Black, Pauline* / Mirror in the bathroom: *Rankin' Roger* / Special Brew: *Rankin' Roger* / Night boat to Cairo: *Bad Manners* / Can can: *Bad Manners* / Missing words: *Black, Pauline* / Baggy trousers: *Bad Manners* / One step beyond: *Bad Manners* / Lip up fatty: *Bad Manners* / Hands off she's mine: *Rankin' Roger* / Too much too young: *Rankin' Roger* / Three minute hero: *Black, Pauline* / Buster's groove: *Bad Manners* / One stop beyond: *Bad Manners*
SUMCD 4124 / Jun '97 / Summit

☐ SOUND OF SOUND VOL.2
111902 / Feb '94 / Musidisc

☐ SOUND OF STONE, THE
Sound of stone: *Dennehy, Tim* / May morning dew: *Spillane, Davy* / Fertile rock: *Bloom, Luka* / Pup jig: *Shannon, Sharon* / Miss Burren, Co Clare: *Lane, Frankie* / Rodney Millar's: *Custy, Mary Band* / For Mullaghmore: *Bushplant* / Bonny Portmore: *McKennitt, Niall* / Progress of man: *Sheedy, Niall* / Mountain twig: *Crawford, Kevin & Pat Marsh* / One starry night: *Tyrrell, Sean* / An gleann cuin: *Peoples, Tommy & Siobhan/Gary O'Briain* / Ambran na boirne: *Flanagan, John* / Limestone rock: *Moving Cloud* / Laurel bush: *Moving Cloud* / Silver spear: *Moving Cloud* / Battering ram: *Custy, Mary Band* / Donegal reel: *Crawford, Kevin & Pat Marsh* / Daisyfield: *Peoples, Tommy & Siobhan/Gary O'Briain*
BAGCD 001 / Jul '93 / Bag

☐ SOUND OF SUMMER, THE (The Ultimate Beach Party)
Surf city: *Jan & Dean* / Surfin' safari: *Beach Boys* / Hey little cobra: *Regents* / Little Honda: *Hondells* / Tequila: *Cannon, Ace* / Indian lake: *Cowsills* / Ride the wild surf: *Jan & Dean* / Wipeout: *Surfaris* / Surfer girl: *Beach Boys* / Baby talk: *Jan & Dean* / GTO: *Regents* / Remember (walkin' in the sand): *Shangri-Las* / Summer song: *Chad & Jeremy* / Beach baby: *Regents* / Surfin': *Beach Boys* / Pipeline: *Chantays*
ECD 3047 / Jan '95 / K-Tel

☐ SOUND OF SUMMER, THE (16 Sun-Drenched Classics)
Tequila: *Cannon, Ace* / Indian lake: *Cowsills* / Hey little cobra: *Regents* / Little honda: *Hondells* / GTO: *Regents* / Surf city: *Jan & Dean* / Surfin' safari: *Beach Boys* / Wipe out: *Surfaris* / Pipeline: *Chantays* / Remember (walking in the sand): *Shangri-Las* / Surfin': *Beach Boys* / Surfer girl: *Beach Boys* / Summer song: *Chad & Jeremy* / Baby talk: *Jan & Dean* / Ride the wild surf: *Jan & Dean* / Beach baby: *Regents*
SUMCD 4148 / Sep '97 / Summit

☐ SOUND OF SUPERSTITION VOL.4, THE (2CD Set)
SUPER 2050 / Mar '96 / Superstition

☐ SOUND OF SUPERSTITION VOL.6, THE (2CD Set)
EFA 620882 / 9 Mar '98 / Superstition

☐ SOUND OF THE ABSOLUTE
OM 001CD / Mar '94 / OM

☐ SOUND OF THE BAGPIPES, THE
302782 / Feb '97 / Hallmark

☐ SOUND OF THE DOLPHINS (Music For Relaxation)
SUMCD 4152 / Sep '97 / Summit

☐ SOUND OF THE HOOVER, THE (2CD/ Unmixed Set)
Cyanide: *Hiroshima* / Baloney: *Lectrolux* / Age of love: *Age Of Love* / Are am eye: *Commander Tom* / Amok: *Interactive* / House is surrounded: *Lectrolux* / Rok da house: *Wicked Wipe* / Tremora del terra: *Illuminatae* / Mantra 95: *Baby Doc & The Dentist* / Terradome: *Karlton* / Are you all ready: *De Vit, Tony* / Yum yum: *Baby Doc* / Astralia: *Mandala* / Big drum: *Digital Man* / Exigent: *Baby Doc & The Dentist* / Slave: *Ironik* / Epidemic 96: *Exit EEE*
TEC 25CDM
TEC 25CD / 13 Oct '97 / Truelove

☐ SOUND OF THE STREETS, THE (4CD Set)
LF 226 / 27 Oct '97 / Lost & Found

☐ SOUND OF THE SUBURBS, THE
Eton rifles: *Jam* / Ant music: *Adam & The Ants* / Ever fallen in love: *Buzzcocks* / Another girl another planet: *Only Ones* / Teenage kicks: *Undertones* / Echo beach: *Martha & The Muffins* / Happy birthday: *Altered Images* / Oliver's army: *Costello, Elvis* / 2-4-6-8 Motorway: *Robinson, Tom Band* / Hit me with your rhythm stick: *Dury, Ian & The Blockheads* / Call me: *Blondie* / Reward: *Teardrop Explodes* / I don't like Mondays: *Boomtown Rats* / Pretty in pink: *Psychedelic Furs* / No more heroes: *Stranglers* / Turning Japanese: *Vapors* / Do anything you wanna do: *Eddie & The Hot Rods* / Sound of the suburbs: *Members*
4888252 / 6 Oct '97 / Columbia

☐ SOUND OF THE SYNTHS VOL.2
15426 / Jun '93 / Laserlight

☐ SOUND OF THE UNDERGROUND VOL.1 (SOUR Cream)
SOURCD 1 / Feb '95 / SOUR

☐ SOUND OF THE UNDERGROUND VOL.1, THE (UK/Mixed By The Lisa Marie Experience)
SOTUCD 8234 / 17 Aug '98 / Master Dance Tones

☐ SOUND OF THE UNGERGROUND VOL.2, THE (Ibiza)
SOTUCD 8236 / 18 May '98 / Master Dance Tones

☐ SOUND OF THE WHALE (Music For Relaxation)
SUMCD 4154 / Sep '97 / Summit

☐ SOUND SPECTRUM, THE
Get carter: *Budd, Roy* / Love is a four letter word: *Budd, Roy* / Getting nowhere in a hurry: *Budd, Roy* / Plaything: *Budd, Roy* / Hurry to me: *Budd, Roy* / Grow your own: *Schroeder, John Orchestra* / Headband: *Schroeder, John Orchestra* / Touch of velvet: *City Of Westminster String Band* / Split level: *City Of Westminster String Band* / Stiletto: *Rey, Chico & The Jett Band* / Heavy Water: *Davies, Ray & His Funky Trumpet* / Mach 1: *Davies, Ray & His Funky Trumpet* / Speakin' of spoken: *Lovin' Spoonful* / Supershine No.9: *Sister Goose And The Ducklings* / Loner: *Hunter, Milton* / Busy body: *Dicks, Ted* / Birds: *Hatch, Tony Orchestra* / 2001: *Holmes, Cecil Soulful Sound* / Pegasus: *Vickers, Mike* / Hot wheels: *Badder Than Evil*
WENCD 005 / Nov '95 / When

☐ SOUND STAGE 7 STORY, THE (2CD Set)
Easy going fellow: *Shelton, Roscoe* / Hymn no. 5: *Gaines, Earl* / I'm his wife, you're just a friend: *Sexton, Ann* / I love you: *Baker, Sam* / Only time you say you love me: *Smith, Charles* / You keep me hangin' on: *Simon, Joe* / Whole lot of man: *Davis, Geator* / All the time: *Washington, Ella* / Sometimes you have to cry: *Baker, Sam* / Chokin' kind: *Simon, Joe* / He called me baby: *Washington, Ella* / Your heart is so cold: *Davis, Geator* / Strain on my heart: *Shelton, Roscoe* / You're gonna miss me: *Sexton, Ann* / I'll take care of you: *Gaines, Earl* / I'm not

through loving you: Brown, Lattimore / I don't care who knows: Church, Jimmy / Soon as darkness falls: Shelton, Roscoe / What made you change your mind: King, Bobby / Human / Judge of hearts: Hobbs, Willie / Someone bigger than you or me: Baker, Sam / We've got to save it: Scott, Moody / Let me come on home: King, Bobby / I'm ready to love you now: Shelton, Roscoe / Just a glance away: Baker, Sam / Try something new: Billups, Eddie / Ooh I love you: Cashmeres / I got love: Byrd, Leon / Woman's touch: Scott, Moody / My faith in you: Church, Jimmy / I know your heart has been broken: Shelton, Roscoe

CDLAB 103 / Mar '96 / Charly

☐ SOUNDBOMBING

RWK 11312 / 9 Feb '98 / Rawkus

☐ SOUNDBOX (4CD Set)

WASH 0012 / 2 Feb '98 / Wash

☐ SOUNDS AND PRESSURE VOL.1

Barbican dub: Hudson, Keith / Problems: Andy, Horace / Ras menilik Congo: Pablo, Augustus / Red blood: Black Skin The Prophet / Mansion of invention: Prince Far-I & The Arabs / Black belt Jones: Hudson, Keith / Tribal war: Little Roy / Sinners: Hudson, Keith / Bass ace: Prince Far-I & The Arabs / Same song: Israel Vibration / King Tubby's dub song: Pablo, Augustus

PSCD 005 / Jul '97 / Pressure Sounds

☐ SOUNDS AND PRESSURE VOL.2

Poor Marcus: Mighty Diamonds / Columbus ship: Little Roy / Thriller: Don D Jr. / In God we trust: Morwells / In time to come: Earth & Stone / Who have eyes to see: Prince Far-I & Mike Brooks / Shepherd rod: Upsetter / Jestering: Shorty The President & Enos 'Genius' McLeod / Shame and pride: Mighty Diamonds / Right way: Prince Far-I & The Arabs / I'll go through: Israel Vibration

PSCD 10 / Jul '97 / Pressure Sounds

☐ SOUNDS AND PRESSURE VOL.3

Disco Jack: Mittoo, Jackie / Too late: Ellis, Alton / Purify dub: Techniques / Down santic way: Big Joe / King at the control's: King Tubby / Woman of silo: Brooks, Mike / Shaka the great: Overnight Players / Brother Joe: Prince Far-I / Disco Jack: Mittoo, Jackie

PSCD 16 / 27 Oct '97 / Pressure Sounds

☐ SOUNDS COLOMBIAN

Momposina: Pinedo, Nelson & La Sonora Matancera / Quien pueda interesar: Forero, Esther / Pila pilandera: Cruz, Celia / Senorita (la llave y la cerradura): Penaranda, Jose Maria / Entre palmeras: Los Ases Del Ritmo / La levita: Forero, Esther / Dejenla llorar: Velasquez, Anibal / El vaquero: Pinedo, Nelson & La Sonora Matancera / El ano viejo: Valdes, Vicentico / Oye mi cumbia: Los Ases Del Ritmo / Por mi no te preoccupes: Forero, Esther / El demonio son los hombres: Penaranda, Jose Maria / Estas delirando: Pinedo, Nelson & La Sonora Matancera / A la orilla del mar: Flores, Isodoro Conjunto / El pajaro bobo: Penaranda, Jose Maria / No quiero llorar: Cruz, Celia / La cosquillita: Velasquez, Anibal / La mafafa: Torruellas, Angel Luis / Mi cafetal: Trio Maravilla / Ay cosita Linda: Argentino, Carlos & La Sonora Matancera

CDHOT 620 / Apr '97 / Charly

☐ SOUNDS CUBAN

CDHOT 607 / Aug '96 / Charly

☐ SOUNDS EASY

Kiss me honey honey kiss me: Bassey, Shirley / Love is blue: Mauriat, Paul Orchestra / Sunny: Hebb, Bobby / Walk in the black forest: Jankowski, Horst & Orchestra / Don't let the rain come down: Serendipity Singers / Adam Adamant theme: Lee, Dave & Orchestra / Say wonderful things: Carroll, Ronnie / Colorado: Del Parana, Luis Alberto Y Los Paraguayos / Summer place theme: Gregory, John Orchestra / What are you doing for the rest of your life: Gillies, Stuart / Air for G string: Swingle Singers & Modern Jazz Quartet / On a clear day you can see forever: Laine, Cleo / Love letters: Arthey, Johnny Orchestra / Girl talk: Coffee Set / Scarborough fair: South, Harry Stereo Brass / Sway: Cugat, Xavier & His Orchestra / Troubleshooters: Tew, Alan Latin Sound / How are things in glocca morra: Gray, Johnnie & His Saxophones / Long daddy green: Dearie, Blossom / America: Cortez & His New Latin / Eso beso: McGuiffe, Bill / Wedding: Rogers, Julie / Man without love: Henderson, Joe / In the hall of the mountain king: Smith, Pete Orchestra / Somethin' stupid: Button Down Brass / Sisters: Beverley Sisters

5354212 / Jun '96 / Mercury

☐ SOUNDS FROM THE ELECTRONIC LOUNGE

Theme from The Electric Lounge: Scanner & Signs Ov Chaos / Channel vacuum: Scanner / Sonic dub no.2: Sonic Man / Ultrasonic: Techno Animal / Olematon: O / Vul QX: Huber, Alois / Counterpoint: Signs Ov Chaos / Lift (dense): To Rococo Rot / Duo sonic no.5: Potuznik, Gerhard & Gerhard Deluxe / Hapatus: Panasonic / Thee devil's tongue: Signs Ov Chaos / Paper napkin: Trawl / Mothlight: Scanner / Dead acid society: Starfish Pool / POWER: Kirlian / MH: Riou / Tight: 6K / Comparitive vandalism: Aphasic & DJ Send / Art gallery: Eight Miles High / Logan's run: Mazda / Vampires and robots: Signs Ov Chaos

REACTCD 123 / 15 Jun '98 / React

☐ SOUNDS LIKE GLASGOW

Bedroom hustler: East End Trax / Wind on water: Fresh & Low / Sides of iron: Chaser / Ode to the MIC: Stunts Blunts & Beats / Sole inflection: Oscuro P / 90 degrees: SLAM / Brown sauce: H-Foundation / Catalyst dub: Mount Florida / Aquan's realm: Urb-N-Ri / Funk de fino: Gypsy / Deep down: Robinson Wall Project

PAN 1002CD / 27 Oct '97 / Pan

☐ SOUNDS LIKE PARIS

South of heaven: Zend Avesta / Psychotic phunk reaction: Daphreephunkateers & Adelph / Fllying fingers: Motorbass / Non non non: Melaaz / Soul salsa soul: Melaaz / Cut a rug: Dirty Jesus / My family: Elegia / Le voyage: Mighty Bop / 357 Magnum Fries: La Funk Mob / Affaires a faire: La Chatte Rouge / Toujours l'amour: Dimitri From Tokyo

PAN 1001CD / Jul '97 / Pan

☐ SOUNDS LIKE TRIP HOP VOL.1 (2CD Set)

Caffeine effect: Taran / Prequel: Triad / Ohresohold: Alchemist / Cuban blend: Herbaliser / Knockout drops: Single Cell Orchestra / Stickleback: Small Fish With Spine / Prophets of peace: Poke / Did you know: Beanfield / Qamar: Der Alte Mann Vom Berg / Fuckdub baby: Tosca / Find the shrinkables: Fauna Flash / People of Alderaan: Poke / Diamond bullet: Effective Force / Good shot kit: Dharma Bums / Combat squad: Futurecore/Synchromesh / Friends of peace: Weedstar / Phatty's lunch box: Mekon / Finally: Swandive / Beats and ines: DJ D Love

560212 / 23 Feb '98 / Nova Tekk

☐ SOUNDS OF A GENERATION, THE (2CD Set)

Sweet home Alabama: Lynyrd Skynyrd / Feeling alright: Grand Funk Railroad / Nutbush city limits: Turner, Ike & Tina / Eve of destruction: MacGuire, Barry / Smoke on the water: Deep Purple / Rocky Mountain way: Walsh, Joe / Home on Monday: Little River Band / Night they drove old Dixie down: Band / American pie: McLean, Don / Dedicated to the one I love: Mamas & The Papas / Good vibrations: Beach Boys / Eli's coming: Three Dog Night / Let's work together: Canned Heat / I don't want to go to Vietnam: Hooker, John Lee / Baby night: Sweet Smoke / Black night: Deep Purple / We're an American band: Grand Funk Railroad / Weight: Band / Horse with no name: America / Air that I breathe: Hollies / Tears in the morning: Beach Boys / Sooner or later: Grass Roots / Monday Monday: Mamas & The Papas / Pretty flamingo: Manfred Mann / You make my life so beautiful: Harvey, Alex Band / Dream a little dream of me: Mama Cass / I can hear music: Beach Boys / On the road again: Canned Heat / We've gotta get out of this place: Animals / Free bird: Lynyrd Skynyrd

DOU 882532 / 29 Aug '97 / Disky

☐ SOUNDS OF AFRICA

SOW 90120 / Jan '94 / Sounds Of The World

☐ SOUNDS OF BAMBOO, THE (Instrumental Music Of The 'Are'are People/Solomon Islands)

Music to raise the house / Swine shrieks / Love song piece/Ho'osia ritual / Parrot piece / Mound bird / Introduction piece / Haridata's grief / Popora's weeping / Frogs of darana / Closing piece / Rihe piece / Kinkina bird piece / Infant's cry / Stop and go / Moaning piece / Mice piece / Dove piece / Sound of the river piece / Bats piece / Thunder piece / Lamentation / Eagle piece / Tree roots piece / Moths / Rat / Thunder / Dog / Sacred taro pudding to the wild man / Divination song / Kiroha deconstruction / Lament solo / Lament duo / Lament hummed / Lullaby / Love song

MCM 3007 / May '97 / Multicultural Media

☐ SOUNDS OF CALEDONIA

RECD 499 / Dec '97 / REL

☐ SOUNDS OF EVOLVING TRADITIONS, THE (Central Andean Music & Festivals/Peru & Bolivia)

Farewell to Ayacucho Town / El condor pasa / Sacsayhuaman / Arisal tree / Golden basket / Huallancayo / Pio pio / Chacarera / Guadalquivir River / Sicu ensemble / Wayruru / Auki auki / Unbundled panpipes / Takitas / Wedding music from Amarete / Church bells / Mule music / Music for chica beer / Festival finale music

MCM 3009 / May '97 / Multicultural Media

☐ SOUNDS OF NATURE

Fingals cave / Pearl Fisher / Peer Gynt / Moonlight sonata / Tosca / Adagio for strings / New World symphony / Gymnopedie / Pavane / Air on a G string / Romeo and Juliet overture / Pathetique / Memories of green / Fragile / Earth song / Ommadawn / Almost a whisper / Watermark / Chi mai / Summer the first time / Rain must fall / Etude / Revolutions / Missing / Sheperd moons

CDVDB 1 / 4 Aug '97 / Virgin

☐ SOUNDS OF NATURE (3CD Set)

CN 303 / Dec '97 / Call Of Nature

☐ SOUNDS OF NEW HOPE, THE (3CD Set)

AIW 045CD / Dec '96 / Nightbreed

☐ SOUNDS OF NEW ORLEANS VOL.10

STCD 6017 / Jul '96 / Storyville

☐ SOUNDS OF OLD MEXICO

CDHOT 640 / 29 Jun '98 / Charly

☐ SOUNDS OF PHILADELPHIA, THE (Live In London)

Love I lost: Melvin, Harold & The Bluenotes / If you don't know me by now: Melvin, Harold & The Bluenotes / Hope that we can be together soon: Melvin, Harold & The Bluenotes / Don't leave me this way: Melvin, Harold & The Bluenotes / Wake up everybody: Melvin, Harold & The Bluenotes / Me and Mrs. Jones: Paul, Billy / Sound of Philadelphia: Three Degrees Orchestra / My simple heart: Three Degrees / Medley: Three Degrees / Woman in love: Three Degrees / Dirty ol' man: Three Degrees / When will I see you again: Three Degrees / Love train

308252 / 13 Oct '97 / Hallmark

☐ SOUNDS OF SCOTLAND

MACCD 125 / Aug '96 / Autograph

☐ SOUNDS OF SCOTLAND VOL.1, THE

Scottish soldier: Stewart, Andy / Amazing grace: Scots Guards 1st Battalion Pipes/Drums / 6.20: Shand, Jimmy / Auld scotch sangs: Anderson, Moira / Down in the glen: Wilson, Robert / Wild rover: Tartan Lads / Isle of Skye: Corries / I love a lassie: Logan, Jimmy / Miss Elspeth Campbell / Inverary Castle: Argyll & Sutherland Highlanders / Mrs. McPherson of Inveran: Argyll & Sutherland Highlanders / Scotland the brave: Wilson, Robert / My ain house: Anderson, Moira / Campbeltown Loch / Sky is bluer in Scotland: Tartan Lads / Drunken piper: Blackwatch 1st Battalion Pipes/Drums / Highland laddie: Blackwatch 1st Battalion Pipes/Drums / Black bear: Blackwatch 1st Battalion Pipes/Drums / Road to the Isles: Stewart, Andy / Victory polkas: Gordon Highlanders 1st Battalion Pipes/Drums / Willie the woodcutter: MacLeod, Jim / Tom Clements reel: MacLeod, Jim / Trumpet hornpipe: MacLeod, Jim / Bonnie Galloway / Here's to scotch whiskey: Tartan Lads / Bonnie Dundee: Corries / Liberton pipe band polka: Wick Scottish Dance Band & Wick Fiddlers / Heather bells will bloom again: Stewart, Andy / My ain folk: Anderson, Moira / Rothesay Bay: Anderson, Moira / When you and I were young Maggie: Tartan Lads / Gathering of the clans: Wilson, Robert / Hills O' the Clyde: Wilson, Robert / Gay gordons: Johnstone, Jim & His Band / Fifty first Highland division: Johnstone, Jim & His Band / Far o'er: Johnstone, Jim & His Band

CDMFP 6316 / Feb '97 / Music For Pleasure

☐ SOUNDS OF SCOTLAND VOL.2, THE

CDMFP 6317 / Feb '97 / Music For Pleasure

☐ SOUNDS OF SUDAN

WCD 018 / Jan '91 / World Circuit

☐ SOUNDS OF THE 70'S (4CD Set)

MBSCD 402 / Nov '95 / Castle

☐ SOUNDS OF THE 70'S (4CD Set)

PBXCD 408 / 20 Apr '98 / Pulse

☐ SOUNDS OF THE CITY

SCCD 1 / Jan '96 / Sounds Of The City

☐ SOUNDS OF THE DETONATOR VOL.1 (Mixed by DJ's Vibes, Seduction & Dougal/2CD Set)

DPRCD 01 / Jun '97 / Dance Planet

☐ SOUNDS OF THE DETONATOR VOL.2 (Mixed By DJ's Sy, SS, Grooverider & Ralphie Dee/2CD Set)

DPRCD 02 / Jun '97 / Dance Planet

☐ SOUNDS OF THE DETONATOR VOL.3 (Mixed By DJ Seduction & DJ Sy/DJ Vibes/3CD Set)

IKSCD 1 / 18 May '98 / IKS

☐ SOUNDS OF THE SEA (3CD Set)

CN 304 / Dec '97 / Call Of Nature

☐ SOUNDS OF THE SEASONS (3CD Set)

CN 301 / Dec '97 / Call Of Nature

☐ SOUNDS OF THE SEVENTIES (4CD Set)

Band of gold: Payne, Freda / I can do it: Rubettes / Angel face: Glitter Band / I only wanna be with you: Bay City Rollers / I love to love: Charles, Tina / I wanna dance wit' choo: Disco Tex & The Sexolettes / Greased lightning: Travolta, John / (Dancing) on a Saturday night: Blue, Barry / Hitchin' a ride: Vanity Fare / Baby jump: Mungo Jerry / Love really hurts without you: Ocean, Billy / Here comes that rainy day feeling again: Fortunes / I will survive: Gaynor, Gloria / Juke box jive: Rubettes / Goodbye my love: Glitter Band / Sahng a lang: Bay City Rollers / Now is the time: James, Jimmy & The Vagabonds / Run back: Douglas, Carl / If you don't know me by now: Melvin, Harold & The Bluenotes / Woman in love: Three Degrees / Hey there lonely girl: Holman, Eddie / Dance little lady dance: Charles, Tina / Black and white: Greyhound / People like you and people like me: Glitter Band / Sandy: Travolta, John / In the summertime: Mungo Jerry / Get dancin': Disco Tex & The Sexolettes / Somerlove sensation: Bay City Rollers / Never can say goodbye: Gaynor, Gloria / Kung fu fighting: Douglas, Carl / I'm on fire: 5000 Volts / Ring my bell: Ward, Anita / Hold back the night: Trammps / Indiana wants me: Taylor, R. Dean / Yellow river: Christie / Freedom come freedom go: Fortunes / I'll go where your music takes me: James, Jimmy & The Vagabonds / Wake up everybody: Melvin, Harold & The Bluenotes / Dirty ol' man: Three Degrees / Me and Mrs.Jones: Paul, Billy / I'll go where your music takes me: Charles, Tina / Stoned love: Supremes / Boogie nights: Heatwave / Car wash: Royce, Rose / Can you feel the force: Real Thing / You to me are evrything: Real Thing / Heaven must have sent you: Elgins / Magic fly: Space / Hang on in there baby: Bristol, Johnny / Love don't live here anymore: Royce, Rose / Doctor love: Charles, Tina / More than a woman: Tavares / Always and forever: Heatwave / Rainforest: Biddu Orchestra / Reaching for the best: Exciters / Patches: Carter, Clarence / Come and get it: Badfinger / Never ending song of love: New Seekers / Foe dee o dee: Rubettes / Hey girl don't bother me: Tams / More more more: True, Andrea Connection / You don't have to be in the army to fight in the war: Mungo Jerry / Troglodyte (caveman): Castor, Jimmy Bunch / Treat her like a lady: Cornelius Brothers & Sister Rose / What have they done to my song ma: New Seekers / Something old something new: Fantastics / I get a little sentimental over you: New Seekers / Let's get together again: Glitter Band / I'd like to teach the world to sing: New Seekers / I'm doin' fine now: New York City / Alright alright: Mungo Jerry / Lady rose: Mungo Jerry / Pinball wizard/See me feel me: New Seekers / Sugar baby love: Rubettes / Up in a puff of smoke: Brown, Polly / Open up: Mungo Jerry / Beg steal or borrow: New Seekers / Love grows (where my rosemary grows): Edison Lighthouse / You little trustmaker: Tymes

QUAD 013 / Nov '96 / Tring

☐ SOUNDS OF THE SEVENTIES (2CD Set)

Get it on: Bolan, Marc & T-Rex / Virginia Plain: Roxy Music / School's out: Cooper, Alice / All the young dudes: Mott The Hoople / Crocodile rock: John, Elton / I'm the leader of the gang: Glitter, Gary / Blockbuster: Sweet / Walk on the wildside: Reed, Lou / Make me smile (come up and see me): Cockney Rebel / Mama weer all crazee now: Slade / See my baby jive: Wizzard / Love train: O'Jays / Show you the way to go: Jacksons / Best of my love: Emotions / That lady: Isley Brothers / Le freak: Chic / We are family: Sister Sledge / Boogie wonderland: Earth, Wind & Fire / I will survive: Gaynor, Gloria / You're the first, my last, my everything: White, Barry / Ladies night: Kool & The Gang / Band on the run: McCartney, Paul & Wings / Mr. Blue Sky: ELO / Baker street: Rafferty, Gerry / So you win again: Hot Chocolate / Down down: Status Quo / Oliver's army: Costello, Elvis / Hit me with your rhythm stick: Dury, Ian / Heart of glass: Blondie / Message in a bottle: Police / Maggie Mae: Stewart, Rod / Without you: Nilsson, Harry / Vincent: McLean, Don / I'm not in love: 10cc / Horse with no name: America / Seasons in the sun: Jacks, Terry / Lean on me: Withers, Bill / Right thing to do: Simon, Carly / Every day hurts: Sad Cafe / Wishing on a star: Rose Royce

RADCD 01 / Nov '94 / Global TV

☐ SOUNDS OF THE SEVENTIES-REGGAE STYLE

I can't get next to you: Charmers / You're a big girl now: Chosen Few / Rainy night in Georgia: Thomas, Nicky / Groove me: Beckford, Keeling / Just my imagination: Barker, Dave / Sister big stuff: Holt, John / Shaft: Charmers, Lloyd / Help me make it through the night: Parker, Ken / Ben: Elaina, Margaret / Lean on me: Seaton, B.B. / Have you seen her: Harriott, Derrick / First time ever I saw your face: Griffiths, Marcia / Let me down easy: Brown, Dennis / Break up to make up: Sibbles, Leroy / Hurt so good: Cadogan, Susan / Too late to turn back: Ellis, Alton / Living a little, laughing a little: Spence, Barrington / If you're ready: Richards, Cynthia / You make me feel brand new: Gardiner, Boris / When will I see you again: Inner Circle

CDTRL 321 / Mar '94 / Trojan

☐ SOUNDS OF THE SIXTIES (4CD Set)

Runaway: Shannon, Del / He's so fine: Chiffons / Will you love me tomorrow: Shirelles / 24 hours from Tulsa: Pitney, Gene / Leader of the pack: Shangri-Las / Every beat of my heart: Knight, Gladys & The Pips / Fools rush in: Benton, Brook / Under the boardwalk: Drifters / Rubber ball: Vee, Bobby / Harbour lights: Platters / Walk don't run: Ventures / Mr. bass man: Cymbal, Johnny / Judy in disguise: Fred, John & His Playboy Band / I believe: Bachelors / Tossin' and turnin': Ivy League / Don't let the sun catch you crying: Gerry & The Pacemakers / Silhouettes: Herman's Hermits / Tabacco road: Nashville Teens / Baby now that I've found you: Foundations / Love is all around: Troggs / Remember (walkin' in the sand): Shangri-Las / Surfin' safari: Beach Boys / I'm gonna be strong: Pitney, Gene / Chapel of love: Dixie Cups / Duke of Earl: Chandler, Gene / Oh no not my baby: Brown, Maxine / Barefootin': Parker, Robert / Soldier boy: Shirelles / Hats off to Larry: Shannon, Del / Save the last dance for me: Drifters / Ramona: Bachelors / Hippy hippy shake: Swinging Blue Jeans / You'll never walk alone: Gerry & The Pacemakers / There's a kind of hush: Herman's Hermits / Wild thing: Troggs / Here it comes again: Fortunes / Tell Laura I love her: Valance, Ricky / Walkin' back to happiness: Shapiro, Helen / Hurt: Yuro, Timi / Dizzy: Roe, Tommy / Night has a thousand eyes: Vee, Bobby / Up on the roof: Drifters / Do you love me: Poole, Brian / Little town flirt: Shannon, Del / Bobby's girl: Maughan, Susan / Last night in Soho: Dave Dee, Dozy, Beaky, Mick & Tich / With a girl like you: Troggs / Do you want to know a secret: Kramer, Billy J. / How do you do: Gerry & The Pacemakers / You were on my mind: St. Peters, Crispian / Mama: Berry, Dave / I think of you: Merseybeats / Roses are red: Carroll, Ronnie / Love grows: Edison Lighthouse / Jesamine: Casuals / Dimples: Hooker, John Lee / Devil or angel: Vee, Bobby / Little lovin': Fourmost / No milk today: Herman's Hermits / That's why I'm crying: Ivy League / Sugar sugar: Archies / Everlasting love: Love Affair / Run to him: Vee, Bobby / Swiss maid: Shannon, Del / Town without pity: Pitney, Gene / Shake me, wake me: Rodgers, Clodagh / Legend of Xanadu: Dave Dee, Dozy, Beaky, Mick & Tich / I can't control myself: Troggs / Crying Game: Berry, Dave / Ferry 'cross the Mersey: Gerry & The Pacemakers / Pied piper: St. Peters, Crispian / Wishin' and hopin': Merseybeats / He's in town: Rockin' Berries / Jack the ripper: Screaming Lord Sutch / Letter full of tears: Knight, Gladys & The Pips / Funny how love can be: Ivy League / Diane: Bachelors / Step by step: Crests / Winchester cathedral: New Vaudeville Band / Boom boom: Hooker, John Lee

QUAD 001 / Nov '96 / Tring

☐ SOUNDS OF THE STREET AND FAIRGROUND ORGAN (18 Musical Crowd Pleasers)

New colonial march / Marching strings / Good old bad old days / Coronation bug / Hello bluebird / Too many kisses in summer / Brown eyes why are you blue / Waltzing Matilda / Espana / El capitan / Old comrades / Twelth street rag / I do like to be beside the seaside / If I had a golden umbrella / Household brigade / Cuckoo waltz / Anchors aweigh / Beer barrel polka

305792 / Oct '96 / Hallmark

☐ SOUNDS OF THE WINDS (3CD Set)

CN 302 / Dec '97 / Call Of Nature

☐ SOUNDS OF THE WORLD VOL.1, THE (Latin America)

PS 65991 / Mar '93 / PlayaSound

☐ SOUNDS OF WALES, THE

We'll keep a welcome: Morriston Orpheus Choir / Myfanwy: Monmouthshire Massed Choir / Speed your journey: Second Festival Of One Thousand Welsh Male Voices / March of the men of Harlech: Morriston Orpheus Choir / Soldier's chorus: Monmouthshire Massed Choir / Land of song: Morriston Orpheus Choir / All through the night / Men of Wales: Band of the 1st Bat The Welsh Regiment / Steal away: Morriston Orpheus Choir / Battle hymn of the Republic / Thou gavest: Monmouthshire Massed Choir / Tros y garreg: Morriston Orpheus Choir / Counting the goats / Cartref: Morriston Orpheus Choir / Sanctus / Hiraeth: Morriston Orpheus Choir / Laudamus: Festival of Massed Welsh Choirs / When I survey the wondrous cross / Elizabethan serenade: Morriston Orpheus Choir & The Band of the Welsh Guards / Comrades in arms / Llef (Deus salutis): Monmouthshire Massed Choir / Unwaith eto'n nghymru annwyl: Morriston Orpheus Choir / Silver birch: Second Festival Of One Thousand Welsh Male Voices / Guide me o thou great Redeemer: Third Festival Of One Thousand Welsh Male Voices / Land of my fathers (Hen wlad fy nhadau): Third Festival Of One Thousand Welsh Male Voices

CDMFP 6368 / May '97 / Music For Pleasure

☐ **SOUNDS PUERTO RICAN**
Tequila: Cortijo Y Su Combo / El buen borincano:
Santiago, Ismael / Vuelve carinito: Yayo El Indio / Lo
deje llorando: Cortijo Y Su Combo / La rena:
Rodriguez, Tito / Pa le lo: Ray, Ricardo & Bobby Cruz
/ Altagracia: Conjunto Típico Cibaeno / Alegría y
bomba: Cortijo Y Su Combo / Mujer: Feliciano, Jose
'Cheo' / Yauco: Valle, Joe / Dejalo que suba: Rivera,
Ismael / Algeria y bomba: Cortijo Y Su Combo /
Sangre: Ray, Ricardo & Bobby Cruz / Yauco:
Hernandez, Mario / Vamos ya: Rodriguez, Tito /
Todo es para ti: Pizarro, Tony / Las ingratitudes:
Cortijo Y Su Combo / La cartita: Valle, Joe / Para ti:
Hernandez, Mario / Sere feliz: Feliciano, Jose 'Cheo'
/ Toda una eternidad: Valle, Joe
CDHOT 629 / Oct '97 / Charly

☐ **SOUNDWORKS EXCHANGE VOL.1,
THE**
**SWECD 1 / Jul '97 / Sound Work
Recordings**

☐ **SOUNDWORKS EXCHANGE VOL.2,
THE**
**SWRCD 2 / Jul '97 / Sound Work
Recordings**

☐ **SOURCE LAB 3 X**
Faithful: Fantom / Nite fly: Hi-Way / Sonic 75: Tele
Pop Musik / Symphony of sickness: Aleph /
Monodrama: Chateau Flight / Antisocial: Extra Lazy
/ Power Sandwich: I-Cube / What about your love:
Low Tone Priority / Mais ou est Geneviève: Les
Petroleuses / Inflammable b-boy: DJ Cam / Post it:
Scratch Pet Land
CDVIRX 58 / Jul '97 / Virgin

☐ **SOURCE LAB 3 X/Y (2CD Set)**
Faithful: Fantom / Nite fly: Hi-Way / Sonic 75: Tele
Pop Musik / Symphony of sickness: Aleph /
Monodrama: Chateau Flight / Antisocial: Extra Lazy
/ Power sandwich: I-Cube / What about your love:
Low Tone Priority / Mais ou est Geneviève: Les
Petroleuses / Inflammable b-boy: DJ Cam / Post it:
Scratch Pet Land / Magik: Bel Air Project / Paris
methodie rose: ODC / Magik: Bel Air Project / Paris
interdite: Krell / Man and woman = Infinity: Dimitri
From Paris / Ghost town: Dr. L / La couleur: Ollano /
Gordini mix: Golpher, Alex / Technical Jed: Extra
Lucid / Gasoana 70: 3-Air
CDVIR 58 / Jul '97 / Virgin

☐ **SOURCE LAB 3 Y**
Jean-Jacques et les Dauphins: Le Tone / Sunshine:
Mozesli / Lapheetphunkateerz: Maisons Lafitte /
Doctor F: Influx / Obsession: Magic Malik / Salami
man: Grand-Popo Football Club / La methode rose:
ODC / Magik: Bel Air Project / Paris acid city: Black
Strobe / No pain without your love: DJ Gregory /
ABCD mental: Djhama, Taka / Cosmic bird: Perrey,
Jean Jacques
CDVIRY 58 / Jul '97 / Source

☐ **SOURCE LAB VOL.2**
Neither sing-song nor baden baden: Bang Bang /
Free jah: Avesta, Zend / Hunt one connection: Main
Basse (Sur La Ville) / Musique: Daft Punk / Bomb de
Bretagne (Bombe Breizh): Le Tone / Planete
interdite: Krell / Man and woman = Infinity: Dimitri
From Paris / Ghost town: Dr. L / La couleur: Ollano /
Gordini mix: Golpher, Alex / Technical Jed: Extra
Lucid / Gasoana 70: 3-Air
CDVIR 52 / Jul '96 / Virgin

☐ **SOUTH AMERICA - HISPANIC**
AUB 006782 / Sep '93 / Auvidis/Ethnic

☐ **SOUTH AMERICA - INDIAN**
AUB 006783 / Sep '93 / Auvidis/Ethnic

☐ **SOUTH AMERICAN WAY**
CIN 050 / Apr '97 / IMP

☐ **SOUTH INDIA - RITUAL MUSIC &
THEATRE OF KERALA**
**LDX 274910 / Nov '90 / La Chant Du
Monde**

☐ **SOUTH OF THE BORDER (Sound Of
Tex Mex)**
MCCD 245 / Jun '96 / Music Club

☐ **SOUTH OF THE BORDER (A Touch Of
Latin)**
Besame mucho: Dorsey, Jimmy Orchestra / Brazil:
Baker, Josephine / Frenesi: Shaw, Artie Orchestra / I
yi yi yi yi I like you very much: Miranda, Carmen /
South America take it away: Crosby, Bing & The
Andrews Sisters / What a difference a day: Healer:
Barnet, Charlie Orchestra / Carioca: Boswell,
Connee / Begin the beguine: Shelton, Anne / Tico
tico: Smith, Ethal / Mexican bus song: Dorsey, Jimmy
Orchestra / Amapola: Durbin, Deanna / Continental:
Stone, Lew & His Band / Time was: Cugat, Xavier &
His Waldorf-Astoria Orchestra / Breeze and I:
Dorsey, Jimmy Orchestra / You belong to my heart:
Crosby, Bing / Perfidia: Miller, Glenn Orchestra /
South of the border: Bowlly, Al / My swash: Sinatra,
Frank / Down Argentina way: Shore, Dinah / Peanut
vendor: Kenton, Stan Orchestra
306712 / Jun '98 / Hallmark

☐ **SOUTH OF THE BORDER**
CDHOT 622 / Jul '97 / Charly

☐ **SOUTH PACIFIC JAZZ**
Royal garden blues / St. Louis blues / Mood indigo /
Perido / Man with the horn / Oh Lady be good /
Stormy weather / Stompin' at the Savoy / Body and
soul / One o'clock jump / Don't blame me / Harvest
time
SV 0219 / Oct '97 / Savoy Jazz

☐ **SOUTH SIDE BLUES - CHICAGO:
LIVING LEGENDS**
Wonderful thing: Mississippi Sheiks / I knew you
were kiddin' all the time: Mississippi Sheiks / Things
'bout comin' my way: Mississippi Sheiks / Four
o'clock blues: Mama Yancey / How long blues:
Mama Yancey / Mama Yancey's blues: Mama
Yancey / Make me a pallet on the floor: Mama
Yancey / Jelly Jelly: Benson, Henry / Jelly Roll Baker:
Benson, Henry / New satellite blues: Montgomery,
Little Brother
**OBCCD 508 / Apr '94 / Original Blues
Classics**

☐ **SOUTH TEXAS POLKA PARTY**
El Barrilito: De La Rosa, Tony / La Chicharonera:
Martinez, Narciso / La Espanola: Longoria, Valerio /
La Chapaneca: Villa, Beto & Tony De La Rosa / Mi
chula polka: Zimmerle, Fred Rio San Antonio / Las
tres conchitas: Ayala, Pedro / El Taconazo: Guzman,
Ricardo / Tacho's polka: Los Regionales De Texas /
Nona: Lopez, Juan / Flor de Mexico: Conjunto Bernal
/ El Camino: Silva, Hermanos / Nuevo Laredo
polka: Lopez, Gilberto / El Rancho Grande polka:
Los Gavilanes / Con Alma Chiquitita: Zuniga,
Agapito / Las Gaviotas: Mariachi Matamoros /
Vamos Al Baile: Martinez, Freddie Orquesta
ARHCD 9005 / Sep '97 / Arhoolie

☐ **SOUTHEND ROCK VOL.2**
Wine, women and song: Dr. Feelgood / Muskrat:
Johnson, Wilko / Crawlin' king snake: Marques
Brothers / Fake: Kicking K / Dragging my heels:
Hypocrites / Henry's eyes: Pocrackor / Standing at
the crossroads: Judy, Mockey / Look at the purse: Al
Morocco 5 / Hercules: Basey Brothers / Going down
to Leigh-On-Sea: Famous Potatoes /
Misunderstood: Noxcuse / Watch your step: Phaze
/ Route 666: Hamsters / Clear but confusing: Bullet
Blues Band / Against the grain: Jody / Colouresound:
22 Arlington Square / Laurel: Trampoline Situation /
Revelation time: Accidub / La cuero: Snowboy
01702001 / Oct '96 / Lunch

☐ **SOUTHERN DOO WOP VOL.1 (Shoop
Shoop)**
Shoop shoop: Gladiolas / Love you love you love
you: Marigolds / Won't you let me know: King
Krooners / Now that she's gone: King Krooners / Bee
bop baby: Peacheroos / Little darlin': Gladiolas /
Love love baby: Rhythm Casters / Don't say
tomorrow: Marigolds / Pretty little girl: King Krooners
/ Memoirs: King Krooners & Little Rico / My china
doll: Glad Rags / Bee bop girl: Gladiolas / They little girl:
Gladiolas / Rollin' stone: Marigolds / There's been a
change: King Krooners / Sweetheart please don't
go: Gladiolas / School daze: King Krooners / Playboy
lover: King Krooners / Everyday my love is true:
Peacheroos / Two strangers: Marigolds / Oh my
darling: Rhythm Casters / Just one love: Glad Rags /
Don't ever get married: Meloaires / Indebted to you:
Meloaires
CDCHD 529 / Jun '95 / Ace

☐ **SOUTHERN DOO WOP VOL.2
(Krooning)**
Jukebox rock'n'roll: Bragg, Johnny & The Marigolds
/ School daze: King Krooners / There's been a
change: King Krooners / Comin' home to you:
Gladiolas / High school affair: Five Chums / One day,
one day: King Krooners / It's you darling it's you:
Bragg, Johnny & The Marigolds / Little darlin':
Gladiolas / Sloo foot Soo: Seniors / Yes that's love:
Marigolds / One day, one day: King Krooners / Be
me know: King Krooners / Run, run Little Joe:
Gladiolas / Rollin' stone: Marigolds / Steps of love:
King Krooners / I wanta know: Gladiolas / Give me
the power: Five Chums / Why don't you: Marigolds /
What does the future hold: King Krooners / Say you'll
be mine: Gladiolas / Magic of you: Themes / Don't
say tomorrow: Hollyhocks / You for me: Hollyhocks /
Why did you leave me: Seniors
CDCHD 629 / Nov '96 / Ace

☐ **SOUTHERN FRIED SOUL**
You're so good to me baby: Spencer, Eddie / It takes
a whole lotta woman: Gauff, Willie & The Love
Brothers / When she touches me: Martin, Rodge /
Good man is hard to find: Martin, Rodge / Can you
handle it: Allison, Levert / You can get it now:
Middleton, Gene / Man who will do anything:
Middleton, Gene / So many times: Lewis, Levina /
Look a little higher: Up Tights / Just a dream: Up
Tights / Sad, sad song: Crawford, Charles / Fa fa fa fa
fa (sad song): McDade, Joe / My girl's a soul girl:
Rogers, Lon / Too good to be true: Rogers, Lon /
You're being unfair to me: Sample, Hank / So in love
with you: Sample, Hank / I'll always love you:
Moultrie, Sam / I found what I wanted: Lacour,
Bobby / Cry like a baby: Lacour, Bobby / Love waits
for no man: Curlee, Bobby & The Preachers / Why is it
taking so long: Baxter, Tony / I'm surprised: Vann,
Paul
GSCD 025 / Nov '93 / Goldmine

☐ **SOUTHERN GROOVES**
You can't have your cake (and eat it too): Young,
Tommie / Full grown lovin' man: Brandon, Bill / How
do you spell love: Patterson, Bobby / Annie got hot
pants power: Johnson, Syl / Love connection: Snell,
Annette / Big legged woman: Hobbs, Willie / Sticky
Sue: Murray, Mickey / Stick in your earhole: Jackson,
Eddie / Get to me: Ingram, Luther / You been doing
me wrong for so long: Sexton, Ann / It takes two to do
wrong: Patterson, Bobby / Tomorrow (I'll begin to
make new plans): Hobbs, Willie / Do you think there's
a chance: Ingram, Luther / I don't care about your
past: Washington, Ella / Everybody's got a little devil
in their soul: Young, Tommie / Just because the
package has been unwrapped and opened: Black,
Alder Ray & The Fame Gang / Sugar Daddy: Sexton,
Ann / You made your bed: Bradford, Eddie / It's not
how long you make it: Holiday, Shay / Dango: African
Music Machine
CPCD 8067 / Apr '97 / Charly

☐ **SOUTHERN JOURNEY VOL.10 (And
Glory Shone Around)**
Newburgh / Eternal day / Heavenly vision / Sardis /
Windham / New Jerusalem / Present joys / Logan /
Ocean / Alabama / Dear creek / Misiom / Protection /
Notes almost divine / Morgan / Melancholy day /
Cross fr me / Anthem on the word: Jesus blood /
Victoria / Sinner's friend / Promise land / New jordan
/ Ragan / Commentary / Hallelujah / Closing prayer
ROUCD 1710 / Feb '98 / Rounder

☐ **SOUTHERN JOURNEY VOL.12
(Georgia Sea Islands)**
Moses / Moses don't get lost / Turkle dove / Adam in
the garden / Daniel / Daniel in the lion's den / Little
David / Eli you can't stand / John / Sign of judgement
/ One of these days / O day / Rock in the weary land /
It just suits me / I'm gonna lay down my life for my lord
/ Before this time another year / On death / Goodbye
everybody
ROUCD 1712 / Feb '98 / Rounder

☐ **SOUTHERN JOURNEY VOL.13 (Earliest
Times - Georgian Seas Islands)**
Live humble / Buzzard lope / Ain't I right / Row the
boat child / You got the rope child / You got my letter
/ Riley / See Aunt Dinah / Pay me / Carrie belle / Reg
lar regalr / You better mind / Carrie bell
ROUCD 1713 / Feb '98 / Rounder

☐ **SOUTHERN JOURNEY VOL.9 (Harp Of
A Thousand Strings)**
ROUCD 1709 / 19 Jan '98 / Rounder

☐ **SOUTHERN RHYTHMS**
Banana split: King, Kid Combo / Skip's boogie: King,
Kid Combo / Brass rail: King, Kid Combo / Gimmick:
King, Kid Combo / Chocolate sundae: King, Kid
Combo / Greasy feat: King, Kid Combo / Bus station
blues: Brooks, Louis & His Hi-Toppers / Waddle trot:
Brooks, Louis & His Hi-Toppers / Double shot:
Brooks, Louis & His Hi-Toppers / Time out: Brooks,
Louis & His Hi-Toppers / Chicken shuffle: Brooks,
Louis & His Hi-Toppers / X-cello rock: Brooks, Louis
& His Hi-Toppers / Mambino: King, Kid Combo /
Strollin' time: King, Kid Combo / Thing-a-ma-jig:
King, Kid Combo / Hob nob: King, Kid Combo /
Shaggy dog: King, Kid Combo / Fina: King, Kid
Combo / Overton Lea Drive: Brooks, Louis & His Hi-
Toppers / Frisco: Brooks, Louis & His Hi-Toppers /
Riding home: Brooks, Louis & His Hi-Toppers / Stand
it: Brooks, Skippy / Dim lights: Brooks, Skippy /
Doin' the horse: Brooks, Skippy
CDCHD 662 / 27 Oct '97 / Ace

☐ **SOUTHERN STATES SOUND**
MCCD 135 / Jan '92 / Music Club

☐ **SOUTHPORT WEEKENDER (2CD Set)**
AVEXCD 56 / Sep '97 / Avex

☐ **SOUVENIR DE PARIS (The Great
French Stars)**
C'est un p'tit rien: Mistinguett & Jean Gabin / Tango
de Marilou: Rossi, Tino / Si j'etais Blanche: Baker,
Josephine / Oui, papa: Chevalier, Maurice / Parlez-
moi d'amour: Boyer, Lucienne / St. Louis blues:
Ventura, Ray & His Collegians / Plaisir d'amour:
Printemps, Yvonne / Pauvre grand: Frehel / Vous
permettez madame: Chevalier, Maurice / J'attendrai:
rien, je n'ai plus rien qu'un chien: Sablon, Jean / Ca
c'est Paris: Mistinguett / Ca c'est fou: Alibert / Le
chaland qui passe: Gauty, Lys / Valentine: Chevalier,
Maurice / C'est mon gigolo: Damina / La petite
Tonkinoise: Baker, Josephine / Couche dans le foin:
Pills & Tabet / Papa n'a pas voulou: Mirielle / La
Marseillaise: Thill, Georges
CDAJA 5028 / ' / Living Era

☐ **SOUVENIR DES GUINGUETTES**
FA 971 / Sep '96 / Fremeaux

☐ **SOUVENIR OF WALES IN SONG**
SCD 9006 / Feb '95 / Sain

☐ **SOVEREIGN SOLOISTS**
DOYCD 003 / Jun '93 / Doyen

☐ **SOWETO NEVER SLEEPS**
SHANCD 43041 / Apr '88 / Shanachie

☐ **SOY UN ARLEQUIN (Tango Ladies
1923-1954)**
HQCD 98 / Jun '97 / Harlequin

☐ **SPACE - THE ALBUM (3CD Set)**
FIRMCD 7 / Jul '96 / Firm

☐ **SPACE AGE**
**BLACKHOLECD 02 / 17 Aug '98 / Black
Hole**

☐ **SPACE AGE POP VOL.1 (Melodies And
Mischief)**
Delicado: Three Suns / Caravan: Sir Julian / Little
black box: Thompson, Bob Orchestra / Foolin'
around: Esquivel, Juan Garcia / Whispering: Rene,
Henri / Third Man theme: Klein, John / Sentimental
journey: Gold, Marty / Rollercoaster: Rene, Henri /
Jungle drums: Denny, Martin / Springtime for Hitler:
Mancini, Henry / Scheherazade: Polo, Markko
Adventurers / Diga diga doo: Thompson, Bob
Orchestra / Why wait: Prado, Perez / Doll dance:
Case, Russ / Smoke: Three Suns / Powerhouse:
Bass, Sid
07863666452 / Mar '96 / RCA

☐ **SPACE AGE...THE NEW ATLANTIS**
ORBIT 004CD / 27 Apr '98 / Space Age

☐ **SPACE BOX (3CD Set)**
CLP 9772 / Oct '96 / Cleopatra

☐ **SPACE DAZE (The History And Mystery
Of Electronic Ambient Space Rock)**
CLEO 76162 / Jan '95 / Cleopatra

☐ **SPACE DAZE 2000**
CLEO 1844 / Jul '96 / Cleopatra

☐ **SPACE IBIZA (2CD Set)**
VENCDA 113 / 1 Jun '98 / Vendetta

☐ **SPACE INVADERS**
RE 201CD / Aug '95 / Panorama

☐ **SPACE LOG 1.1**
GAMMA 01 / Mar '95 / Gamma

☐ **SPACE MOOD AND ELECTRIC SOUL**
PLRCD 001 / Jun '97 / Plastic

☐ **SPACE MOUNTAIN**
JAC 002CD / Oct '95 / Oasis

☐ **SPACED OUT (2CD Set)**
Dancing in outer space: Atmosfear / Cocomotion: El
Coco / Go bang: Dinosaur L / For the love of money:
Disco Dub Band / Just in time: Raw Silk / Mi sabrina
tequana: Ingram / Feelin' good: McGee, Francine /
Double journey: Powerline / Space funk: Manuel /
Time machine: Chocolate Milk / Dancing in outer
space (Masters At Work remix): Atmosfear / For the
love of money (Harvey remix): Disco Dub Band / For
the love of money (Underdog remix): Disco Dub Band
SUSHI 4CD / Jun '97 / Disorient

☐ **SPACEFROGS VOL.2**
EFA 290102 / Dec '95 / Superstition

☐ **SPANGLE EP NO.3**
SPANG 003 / Feb '96 / Spangle

☐ **SPANISH GUITAR**
REWCD 352 / Feb '98 / Reactive

☐ **SPANISH GUITAR MUSIC (2CD Set)**
R2CD 4030 / 13 Apr '98 / Deja Vu

☐ **SPANISH RAGGA**
SM 3110 / Apr '95 / Declic

☐ **SPECIAL BREW**
Numb: U2 / One to one religion: Bomb The Bass /
Blue print: Attica Blues / Army of me: Bjork / Release
the beats: Way Out West / Connected (Danny remix):
Stereo MC's / Doin' it (remix): Redhead Kingpin / No
flush: Red Snapper / Perpetual motion: DJ Crystal /
Inner city life: Goldie / Wild wood: Weller, Paul / Cry:
Money Mark / Away again: Howie B
5355992 / Aug '96 / London

☐ **SPECIAL GIFT**
Special gift: Isley Brothers / All I want for Christmas:
Winbush, Angela / This Christmas: Dru Hill / Hark the
herald angels sing: Nneka & Myron / Little drummer
boy: Myron / Remember love: Blount, Tanya /
Christmas time is here: Chapman, Tracy / Silent night:
Jordan, Ronny / Don't give up: Island Ark Stars /
Silent night: Mona Lisa / Christmas rappin': Blow,
Kurtis / Christmas time is party time: Luke / No dark
there: Luke
5243072 / 24 Nov '97 / Island

☐ **SPECIAL GUITARS VOL.2 1943-1956**
7899522 / Jan '95 / Jazztime

☐ **SPECIAL REQUEST TO ALL BAD BOYS**
JJCD 6197 / 29 Sep '97 / Channel One

☐ **SPECIAL REQUEST TO ALL
DANCEHALL FANS**
JJCD 6200 / 29 Sep '97 / Channel One

☐ **SPECIAL REQUEST TO ALL LOVERS**
JJCD 6199 / 29 Sep '97 / Channel One

☐ **SPECIALTY LEGENDS OF BOOGIE
WOOGIE**
X-temporaneous boogie: Howard, Camille / Rock
that voot: Alexander, Nelson Trio / Rockin' boogie:
Lutcher, Joe & His Society Cats / Heavy on the
woogie: Alexander, Nelson Trio / Cuttin' the
boogie: Luther, Joe & His Society Cats / Barcarolle boogie:
Howard, Camille / Instantaneous boogie: Howard,
Camille / 12th street boogie: Johnson, Don
Orchestra / Miraculous boogie: Howard, Camille /
Milton's boogie: Milton, Roy / Ferocious boogie:
McDaniel, Willard / Boogie woogie nu: Liggins, Joe
/ Fire-ball boogie: Howard, Camille / Boogie woogie
barber shop: Milton, Roy / 3 a.m. boogie: McDaniel,
Willard / Bangin' the boogie: Howard, Camille /
Ciribiribin boogie: McDaniel, Willard / Unidentified
boogie woogie no. 1: McDaniel, Willard / Million dollar
boogie: Howard, Camille / Boogie in the groove:
Jackson, Jo Jo
CDCHD 422 / Sep '92 / Ace

☐ **SPECIALTY LEGENDS OF JUMP
BLUES VOL.1**
Honeydripper: Liggins, Joe / Oh babe: Milton, Roy /
Blues for sale: Lutcher, Joe / Duck's yas yas yas:
King, Perry & His Pied Pipers / I can't stop it: Liggins,
Jimmy / That song is gone: Liggins, Jimmy / Well,
well baby: Alexander, Nelson Trio / Rag mop:
Liggins, Joe / One sweet letter: Liggins, Joe / Pink
champagne: Liggins, Joe / Happy home blues:
Banks, Buddy / Muffle shoe shuffle: Wynn, Big Jim / I
ain't got a dime: Perry, King / Saturday night boogie
woogie man: Liggins, Joe / Jack of diamonds:
Thomas, Jesse / I dare you baby: Mayfield, Percy /
I'm your rockin' man: Manzy, Herman / Natural born
lover: King, Perry & His Pied Pipers / I wonder who's
boogin' my woogie: King, Perry & His Pied Pipers / I
can't lose with the stuff I use: Liggins, Joe /
Country girl: Henderson, Duke / Hucklebuck: Milton,
Roy / Heavy weight baby: Motley, Frank / Traffic
boogie: Lutcher, Joe
CDCHD 573 / Jul '94 / Ace

☐ **SPECIALTY ROCK'N'ROLL**
Lights out: Bryne, Jerry / Moose on the loose:
Jackson, Roddy / Bim bam: Don & Dewey / Don't you
just know it: Titans / (We're gonna) Rock around the
clock: Millet, Lil / My baby's rockin': Monitors /
Hickory dickory dock: Myles, Big Boy / Flip: Marvin &
Johnny / Good golly Miss Molly: Little Richard /
Sonny / Short fat Fannie: Williams, Larry / Rock 'n'
roll dance: Price, Lloyd / Girl can't help it: Little
Richard / Haunted house: Fuller, Jerry / Slow down:
Williams, Larry / Cherokee dance: Landers, Bob /
Hiccups: Jackson, Roddy / Zing zing: Neville, Art /
Carry on: Byrne, Jerry
CDCH 291 / May '90 / Ace

☐ **SPECTABULAR SYNTHESIZER**
MACCD 101 / Aug '96 / Autograph

☐ **SPECTRUM**
Westside: *DJ Dazee* / Control: *Markee* / Own thing: *DJ Dazee* / Own way: *Substance* / Blonix: *Markee* / Dazee age: *Decoder* / No one knows: *Markee* / L F ant: *Substance* / Get down: *Substance* / Glitch: *Pure Instinct* / Homeboyz: *DJ Dazee* / Pure one: *Pure Instinct*
RNTCD 001 / 20 Apr '98 / Ruff Neck Ting

☐ **SPECTRUM FEST (A Relapse Sampler)**
RR 66622 / Jan '97 / Relapse

☐ **SPEED CITY**
UE 01504 / 27 Apr '98 / Urban Essentials

☐ **SPEED FREAKS**
Bad boys: *Baffled Republic* / Future dreams: *Maxim* / Best friend: *Flava* / Sunrise: *Dangerous Dubz* / Shabeen: *And Gone* / I need you: *Part 2* / Don't hold back: *Dangerous Dubz* / Let me tell you: *Jump Up Crew* / Do it baby: *Fontaine, Miles* / Give me joy: *Wood, Kathy* / Metronome: *Freaks Of Nature* / Get up on your feet: *Vissal*
CDHIGH 8 / 10 Nov '97 / High On Rhythm

☐ **SPEED GARAGE ANTHEMS VOL.1 (2CD Set)**
RADCD 78 / 1 Dec '97 / Global TV

☐ **SPEED GARAGE ANTHEMS VOL.2 (40 Classic Underground Speed Garage Cuts - 2CD Set)**
Another groove: *Another Level & Double 99* / Spend the night: *Lewis, Danny J.* / Back to life: *Ragga's Revenge* / Make the world go round: *Sandy B* / Rock the funky beat: *Natural Born Chillers* / Dubplate culture: *Soundscape* / Don't stop: *Ruff Driverz* / Move on baby: *Cappella* / Let the bass roll: *DJ Pooch* / Theme: *Dream Team* / Freedom: *Miles, Robert & Kathy Sledge* / Burnin': *ADR* / Let me be your fantasy: *Baby D* / Everythin' is large: *Underground Distortion* / Deeper: *Serious Danger & Sarjant D* / Over you: *M-Dubs* / Can you feel it: *CLS* / Get up: *Stingily, Byron* / Slip and slide: *Pied Piper & Unknown MC* / Industry standard: *Industry Standard* / Spin spin sugar: *Sneaker Pimps* / Living in danger: *Ace Of Base* / So good: *Roberts, Juliet* / Gunman: *187 Lockdown* / I will survive: *Savage, Chantay* / Never gonna let you go: *Moore, Tina* / Be alone no more: *Another Level* / Renegade master: *Wildchild* / Feel da groove: *G-Flame & Mr. G* / Wherever land is found: *Darbyshire, Richard* / R U sleeping: *Indo* / Hideaway: *De'Lacy* / Freek 'n you: *Jodeci* / Two can play that game: *Brown, Bobby* / Ohh la la: *Coolio* / Gabriel: *Davis, Roy Jr.* / Love struck energy: *London Connection & Tempo O'Neal* / Do it right: *G-Flame & Mr. G* / Insomnia: *Faithless* / Space cowboy: *Jamiroquai*
RADCD 83 / 9 Feb '98 / Global TV
RADCD 83X / 23 Feb '98 / Global TV

☐ **SPEED GARAGE EXPLOSION**
EFA 044292 / 13 Jul '98 / Force Inc.

☐ **SPEED LIMIT**
MM 890502 / Jan '96 / Moonshine

☐ **SPEED LIMIT CLASSICS**
MM 890512 / Jul '96 / Moonshine

☐ **SPEED OF THE SOUND**
GRCD 314 / Apr '94 / Glitterhouse

☐ **SPEED REVOLUTION (2CD Set)**
24066 / Jun '96 / Delta Doubles

☐ **SPEEDCORE (2CD Set)**
HURTCD 011 / 27 Apr '98 / Harmless

☐ **SPICE OF LIFE REMIXES VOL.1**
HOTTCD 1 / Feb '95 / Hott

☐ **SPIKED**
Something better change: *Stranglers* / Babylons burning: *Ruts* / Ever fallen in love: *Buzzcocks* / Sweet suburbia: *Skids* / Alternative Ulster: *Stiff Little Fingers* / Turning Japanese: *Vapors* / Wild wild life: *Talking Heads* / Shot by both sides: *Magazine* / Don't dictate: *Penetration* / King Rocker: *Generation X* / Emergency: *999* / Outdoor miner: *Wire* / Glad to be gay: *Robinson, Tom Band* / What do I get: *Buzzcocks* / I'm not a fool: *Cockney Rejects* / Sheena is a punk rocker: *Ramones* / Suspect device: *Stiff Little Fingers* / Hanging around: *Stranglers*
CDGOLD 1057 / Oct '96 / EMI Gold

☐ **SPIKED**
Judy says: *Vibrators* / London girls: *Vibrators* / Inside out: *999* / English wipeout: *999* / Ain't got a clue: *Lurkers* / Solitaire: *Lurkers* / 42nd Street: *Angelic Upstarts* / Burglar: *Angelic Upstarts* / Virginia plain: *Spizz Energi* / Cold city: *Spizz Energi* / Teenage depression: *Eddie & The Hot Rods* / Quit this town: *Eddie & The Hot Rods* / Stepping stone: *Thunders, Johnny* / Too much junkie business: *Thunders, Johnny* / No faith: *Suburban Studs* / Take it or leave it: *Vice Squad* / We are the boys: *Blitz* / Two years too late: *Anti Pasti* / Peacehaven wild kids: *Peter & The Test Tube Babies*
SUMCD 4094 / Jan '97 / Summit

☐ **SPINNIN' THE CHAMBER**
LRR 008 / Oct '96 / Last Resort

☐ **SPIRALLING OUT**
DIVINE 015CD / 4 Nov '97 / Taste/Divine

☐ **SPIRIT CRIES, THE**
Abelagudahani / Grating song / Abaimahani / Paranda / Combination / Punta / Dugu song / Healing song / Shipibo song / Ashaninka song / Aleke / Songe / Lonsei / Mato (Solo) / Mato (Leader and chorus) / Awasa / Kumanti / Agwado song / Susa / Dance song / Love song / Papa / Tambu
RCD 10250 / Mar '93 / Rykodisc

☐ **SPIRIT OF AFRICA**
AHLCD 42 / Oct '96 / Hit

☐ **SPIRIT OF AFRICA VOL.2, THE**
AHLCD 54 / 18 May '98 / Hit

☐ **SPIRIT OF AFRICAN SANCTUS (Compiled By David Fanshawe)**
Acholi bwala dance / Call to prayer / Egyptian wedding / Islamic prayer school / Reed pipe and grass cutting song / Courtship dances / Four men on the prayer mat / Zebaidir song with Rebabah / Hadandua cattle boys song / Hadandua love songs and bells / Zande song of flight and frogs / Tamboura song / Edongo dance / Busoga fishermen / Bowed harp / Teso fishermen / Acholi enanga / Dingy dingy dance / Rainsong of latigo oteng / Bunyoro madinda / Bwala dance / Rowing chant of the Samia / Song of Lamentation / Masai milking song / Song of the river, Karamoja / Karamajong children's song / Turkana cattle song / Luo ritual burial dance / War drums / Aluar horns
CDSDL 389 / Mar '94 / Saydisc

☐ **SPIRIT OF CHRISTMAS PAST, THE (Nostalgic Christmas Memories From The 1930's/1940's)**
White Christmas: *Crosby, Bing* / Savoy Christmas medley: *Noble, Ray* / Christmas carols: *London Church Carol Choir* / Santa Claus express: *Hall, Henry* / Say it with carols: *Mayerl, Billy* / Christmas bells at Eventide: *Fields, Gracie* / Fairy on the Christmas tree: *Hall, Henry & The Three Sisters* / Winter wonderland: *Stone, Lew* / Santa Claus is coming to town: *Reser, Harry* / I'll walk alone (thru every Christmas): *Shore, Dinah* / 'Twas the night before Christmas: *Waring, Fred & His Pennsylvanians* / Jingle bells: *Waller, Fats* / Coventry carol: *Schumann, Elisabeth* / Noel: *Thill, Georges* / Sleep my saviour sleep: *Celebrity Quartette* / Christmas message to the empire 1932: *King George V* / Christmas dinner: *Miller, Max* / Have yourself a merry little Christmas: *Garland, Judy* / Christmas night in Harlem: *Teagarden, Jack & Johnny Mercer* / Mary had a baby, yes Lord: *Robeson, Paul* / Silent night, holy night: *Crosby, Bing* / Charles Dickens' Christmas: *Williams, Bransby* / Auld lang syne: *Dawson, Peter*
CDAJA 5178 / Sep '96 / Living Era

☐ **SPIRIT OF CHRISTMAS, THE**
AMPCD 036 / Dec '97 / AMP

☐ **SPIRIT OF HEALING, THE (3CD Set)**
SPIRICD 3 / 11 May '98 / Beechwood

☐ **SPIRIT OF INDIA**
AHLCD 48 / Jul '97 / Hit

☐ **SPIRIT OF INDIA, THE (The Best Of Indian Classical Music)**
Raga mishra piloo / Raga pahadi / Bhajan / Tal ektal / Dhun bhairavi / Raga bhairavi
PLATCD 3931 / Mar '95 / Platinum

☐ **SPIRIT OF MEDITATION, THE (3CD Set)**
SPIRICD 2 / 3 Nov '97 / Beechwood

☐ **SPIRIT OF MICRONESIA**
CDSDL 414 / Oct '95 / Saydisc

☐ **SPIRIT OF POLYNESIA**
Aitutaki drum dance / Himene tarava / Poipoi - taro pounding / Song of Papa Teora / Himene Ruau / Bird dance hula / Haka Maori welcome / Song of Papa Kiko / Kai kai of Mama Amelia / Hoko war dance / Meke wesi spear dance / Tau 'a' alo / Fangufangu nose flute / Faikava love song / Chiefs and orators sasa / Tagi lullaby / Tawhoe - oar dance / Copra bugle call / Mokaone's harmonica / Song of Anili / Frigate bird dance, Nauru / Funafuti chorus, Tuvalu / Imenetuki - Gospel chant / Mire of Eamaki / Ute - cutting nuts / Tapa cloth beating / Palmerston shanties / Imenetuki / Mako of Mama Lulutangi / Canoe racing and wrestling / Children's games / Akatikatika drum dance / Mako chant / Haka tapatapa / Pig dance/Ruu chant / Himene tarava (Tahiti) / Himene Nota / Otea drum dance
CDSDL 403 / Mar '94 / Saydisc

☐ **SPIRIT OF PRAISE, THE (The New Songs)**
I draw near / For every worry that troubled our hearts / Jesus Christ (once again) / God is good all the time / God of grace / My Jesus my saviour / I need you / You turn my night (though ten thousand fall) / Whole hearted / Joined together in this place (under one banner) / He can make the blind to see (I believe it now) / Search me
SPND 011 / Oct '97 / Spirit Of Praise

☐ **SPIRIT OF RAGTIME 1910-1947, THE**
Maple leaf rag: *Joplin, Scott* / Temptation rag: *Pryor, Arthur Band* / Waiting for the Robert E. Lee: *Connolly, Dolly* / Tiger rag: *Original Dixieland Jazz Band* / Carolina shout: *Johnson, James P.* / Snake rag: *Oliver, Joe 'King' & His Creole Jazz Band* / Ragtime oriole: *Van Eps, Fred & John F. Burckhardt* / Alexander's ragtime band: *Smith, Bessie Band* / Pearls: *Morton, Jelly Roll & His Red Hot Peppers* / Southern rag: *Blake, Arthur 'Blind'* / Weather bird rag: *Armstrong, Louis & Earl Hines* / Numb fumblin': *Waller, Fats* / Darktown strutter's ball: *Teagarden, Jack & Paul Whiteman Orchestra* / Eccentric: *Spanier, Muggsy Ragtime Band* / Twelfth Street rag: *Waller, Fats & His Rhythm* / Thriller rag: *Johnson, Bunk* / Echoes of spring: *Smith, Willie 'The Lion'* / Panama rag: *Ory, Kid* / Tiger rag: *Tatum, Art* / Harlem rag: *Watters, Lu & The Yerba Buena Jazz Band* / Music box rag: *Roberts, Luckey* / Swipsey cakewalk: *Parenti, Tony Ragtime Band* / Joplin's sensation: *Carey, Mutt New Yorkers* / Entertainer: *Joplin, Scott* / Maple leaf rag: *Bechet, Sidney New Orleans Feetwarmers*
CDAJA 5256 / Apr '98 / Living Era

☐ **SPIRIT OF RELAXATION (3CD Set)**
SPIRICD 1 / Jul '97 / Beechwood

☐ **SPIRIT OF SCOTLAND, THE**
Black Isle/Banks of Lossie/Abbeyville: *Pipes & Drums Of Queen's Own Highlanders* / Bonnie Strathyre/Rothsay Bay/My mother: *Tartan Lads* / Last o' the Lairds: *Scottish Fiddle Orchestra* / Galloway House/Aitken Drum/Claverhouse reel/C.M. Barbour: *Traditional Scottish Country Dance Band* / Sands of Kersal / Puirt-a-Buil / Scottish soldier: *Tartan Lads* / New Caledonian: *Scottish Fiddle Orchestra* / Apple tree/CTS Empress/Agnes Ritchie/Pottinger's reel: *Scottish Fiddle Orchestra* / Skye boat song/Auld rustic bridge/The black bear: *Scottish Fiddle Orchestra* / Gay Gordons / Mist covered mountains: *Gordon Highlanders* / Airs and jigs: *Gordon Highlanders* / Strathspey: *Stewart, John* / Reel: *Morrison, John* / Over the sea to Skye: *Sandeman, Mary* / Wild mountain thyme / Rose of Allandale/The Rowan tree/The bonnie hoose o' Airlie: *Pipes & Drums Of Queen's Own Highlanders* / Scottish country dance waltzes / Summer road: *Tartan Lads* / Eightsome reels: *Scottish Fiddle Orchestra*
RECD 473 / Jan '98 / REL

☐ **SPIRIT OF THE AGE, THE (The Time Of Progressive Rock)**
Master of the universe: *Hawkwind* / Funk angel: *Brinsley Schwarz* / Locomotive breath: *Jethro Tull* / Love like a man: *Ten Years After* / Do it: *Pink Fairies* / Butterfly: *Barclay James Harvest* / Debora: *T-Rex* / Fire and water: *Free* / I am the walrus: *Spooky Tooth* / Starship trooper: *Yes* / Back street love: *Curved Air* / Oh yeah: *Can* / Devil's answer: *Atomic Rooster* / America: *Nice* / Brain salad surgery: *Emerson, Lake & Palmer* / Burlesque: *Family*
RENCD 118 / Mar '97 / Renaissance Collector Series

☐ **SPIRIT OF THE AZTEC, THE**
5371742 / Mar '97 / PolyGram TV

☐ **SPIRIT OF THE EAST, THE (Music For Meditation)**
CD 6025 / Jun '96 / Music

☐ **SPIRIT OF THE INCAS, THE (2CD Set)**
R2CD 4044 / 13 Apr '98 / Deja Vu

☐ **SPIRIT OF THE NEW AGE VOL.1, THE**
Crossing the ridge: *Dada Wa* / Sadness: *Enigma* / Floating: *Hypnosis* / Mad Alice Lane (a ghost story): *Lawlor* / X-Files: *DJ Dado* / Twin peaks: *DJ Dado* / Nocturnal spirit: *Q-Dos* / Fanfare of life: *Leftfield* / Raindance: *Aura* / Indian spirit: *Slavik, Andi & Susanne Kemler* / On Earth as it is in Heaven: *Incantation* / Entre dos aguas: *De Lucia, Paco & Ramon Algeciras* / Baila verena: *Potschka, Potsch* / Scandalise: *Afterlife* / Dusk pressure: *Drop* / Secret call: *Ginko Garden* / Kama kami: *Keiles, Glenn & Caroline MacKendrick*
MCD 80346 / Jun '97 / MCA

☐ **SPIRIT OF THE NEW AGE VOL.2, THE**
UMD 80425 / 9 Feb '98 / Universal

☐ **SPIRIT OF THE PLAINS, THE (2CD Set)**
How the West was lost: *Nakai, R. Carlos & Peter Kater* / Earth: *Nakai, R. Carlos & Peter Kater* / Gathering: *Youngblood, Mary* / Dakota justice: *Kater, Peter & White Oak Singers* / Kahalu'nyuhe matriarch: *Shenandoah, Joanne* / Centering: *Nakai, R. Carlos & Peter Kater* / Last of the buffalo: *Nakai, R. Carlos & Peter Kater* / Memoir chaco warrior: *Mirabal, Robert* / Creation story: *Harjo, Joy & PJ.* / West: *Nakai, R. Carlos & Peter Kater* / Honourable sky: *Nakai, R. Carlos & Peter Kater* / Stating intention: *Nakai, R. Carlos & Peter Kater* / Path of beauty: *Shenandoah, Joanne* / Tu tu teshcote: *Fox, Lorain* / Moaning cavern: *Youngblood, Mary* / Rainsong: *Mirabal, Robert* / Good day to die: *Nakai, R. Carlos & Peter Kater* / Warrior/magician: *Mirabal, Robert* / Cat tails and wild rice: *Nakai, R. Carlos & Peter Kater* / Katisitsy tha: *Shenandoah, Joanne* / Embracing the darkness: *Nakai, R. Carlos & Peter Kater* / Caribou dream/Omaha song: *Nakai, R. Carlos & Peter Kater* / Initiation: *Nakai, R. Carlos & Peter Kater* / Circle of friendship: *Shenandoah, Joanne* / Mic mac lullaby: *Philbrook, Mary* / Tears for Kientepoos: *Youngblood, Mary* / White river utes: *Nakai, R. Carlos & Peter Kater* / She had some horses: *Harjo, Joy & PJ.* / Chief Ouray's death song: *Nakai, R. Carlos & Peter Kater* / If ghosts could dream: *Mirabal, Robert* / Flight song: *Nakai, R. Carlos & Peter Kater* / Kanekotsy tha: *Shenandoah, Joanne* / Gathering of souls: *Nakai, R. Carlos & Peter Kater* / Lullaby: *Mirabal, Robert* / Miles ahead: *Nakai, R. Carlos & Peter Kater* / Hand in hand: *Nakai, R. Carlos & Peter Kater*
SDVSOPCD 254 / 22 Jun '98 / Connoisseur Collection

☐ **SPIRIT OF THE RHYTHM VOL.2, THE**
RHP 1003CD / Oct '97 / RHP

☐ **SPIRIT OF THE STREET VOL.1, THE (11 Urban Jazz Flavours)**
Watusi strut: *Quiet Boys* / Brooklyn heights: *Down To The Bone* / Esquema da bossa: *Quintetto X* / A second thought: *Common Cause* / I really like that girl: *Flux* / Round trip: *Yada Yada* / Solaris: *S-Tone Inc.* / East side: *Four 80 East* / Nightlife: *Typhoons* / On the sly: *Peace Of Mind* / Solaris: *Bossa Nostra*
JAZZFMCD 4 / 15 Sep '97 / Jazz FM

☐ **SPIRIT OF THE STREET VOL.2, THE**
Mardi gras: *Sambada* / Toy r us: *Greyboy Allstars* / Latin joint: *Baby Buddah Heads* / Indian summer: *Neos* / Adventures of F-F man: *NFL Horns Project* / Full metal boob tube: *Bums Rush* / Ombre: *Achenza, Paolo Trio* / Fuse one: *Yada Yada* / Joy is a good groove: *Down To The Bone* / Sentimental song: *Man Sueto* / Shades of youth: *Millenium Project* / Jihad: *Mo Nazam*
JAZZFMCD 8 / 6 Apr '98 / Jazz FM

☐ **SPIRIT OF TRANQUILITY, THE (2CD Set)**
Rose / Morning mist / Mountain spring / Voice of calm / Harmonious / Snowdrop / Night owl / Utopia / Healing hands / Uplifting / New life / Magic canvas / Soothing / Chorale / Freedom / True faith / Rhythm of the rainforest / South American spirit / Serengeti sunrise / Tunnel of light / Sanctuary of the whale / Scuba dive / Peace chant / Andalucian shores / Breath of fresh air / Sunburst / Romeo and Juliet / Silent hymn / Aura / Gentle touch / Fantasy / Gymnopedie no.1 / Awakening
RADCD 79 / Mar '98 / Global TV

☐ **SPIRIT OF VAMPYROS LESBOS, THE**
Spirit of vampyros lesbos: *Minus 8* / Stroemberg: *Higher Than God* / Lions and the cucumber: *Rockers Hi-Fi* / Vampya Killa: *Dr. Israel* / Lion and the cucumber: *Dr. Rockitt* / Frauleinsuppe: *Project Pollen* / Necromix: *DJ Wally* / Future fruit: *De Chico* / People's playground: *Witchman* / Nadine de Uskuder: *Vogel, Christian* / Morpho: *DJ Hell* / Les Boss Electros: *Two Lone Swordsmen* / Six wisdoms of Aspasia: *Alec Empire* / Necromancer: *Spectre*
EFA 123332 / 15 Sep '97 / Sideburn

☐ **SPIRITS OF NATURE**
Sweet lullaby: *Deep Forest* / Little fluffy clouds: *Orb* / Sun rising: *Beloved* / X-Files: *DJ Dado* / Return to innocence: *Enigma* / Stars: *Dubstar* / Way it is: *Hornsby, Bruce* / Play dead: *Bjork & David Arnold* / Aria on air: *McLaren, Malcolm* / Adiemus: *Adiemus* / Only you: *Praise* / Falling: *Cruise, Julee* / Mad Alice Lane (A ghost story): *Lawlor* / Sentinel: *Oldfield, Mike* / Theme from the mission: *Morricone, Ennio* / Heart asks pleasure first: *Nyman, Michael* / Fashion shoe II from "Three Colours Red": *Preisner, Zbigniew* / Chariots of fire: *Vangelis*
VTCD 87 / Jun '96 / Virgin

☐ **SPIRITS OF NATURE (A Collection Of Native American Inspired Music & Chants)**
Dance of the warrior / Brandishing the tomahawk / Circle of fire / Thunder cloud mountain / Celebration of the young / Elevation / Return from river island / Winter ceremony / Counterclockwise circle of dance / Seeds of future happiness
307612 / Jul '97 / Hallmark

☐ **SPIRITUAL CLEANSING**
Believe in the spirit: *Line Of Flight* / Something's going wrong: *Balagan* / Glond ar skogens gud: *Koop* / Sanctury: *Forces Of Nature* / Template: *Hunch* / Fly: *Livonia* / Very serious smoking: *Control Freaks* / Rollercoaster: *Outcast* / Pushin' and shovin': *August* / Roll on: *Sneaker Pimps* / Beautiful: *Essen* / This feelin': *Magnificent Three*
CUP 031CD / 16 Feb '98 / Clean Up

☐ **SPIRITUAL HIGH**
OM 002CD / Mar '97 / OM

☐ **SPIRITUAL HIGH**
TSS 115 / 28 Feb '98 / BMG

☐ **SPIRITUAL LIFE MUSIC**
Prayer: *Guillaume, Jephte* / All loved out: *Ten City* / Lakou-a: *Guillaume, Jephte* / Karipe: *Guillaume, Jephte* / Escravos de jo: *Claussel, Joe & Kerri Chandle* / Mixed moods: *Mateo & Matos* / Stubborn problems: *African Jazz* / Symbols of life: *Lucho*
NUX 118CD / 3 Nov '97 / Nuphonic

☐ **SPIRITUAL VIBES**
CLEO 01063 / 2 Feb '98 / Hypnotic

☐ **SPIRITUALLY IBIZA VOL.2**
FIRMCD 6 / Jun '96 / Firm

☐ **SPLENDOUR OF JAPANESE INSTRUMENTS (3CD Set)**
PS 360503 / Sep '96 / PlayaSound

☐ **SPLENDOUR OF SCOTLAND, THE (A Tribute In Music & Song)**
I belong to Glasgow / Northern lights of old Aberdeen / Road and miles to Dundee / Song of the Clyde / Master David Cleland / Dunblane hydro march / Isle of Arran / Mull of the cool high bens / Banjo breakdown / Land for all seasons / Of A' the airts / Man's a man for a' that / Whistle o'er the alve o't / My heart is sair / This is no' my ain lassie / My love she's but a lassie yet / What'd be king but Charlie / Johnny Cope / Charlie is my darling / Braemar highland gathering
CDGR 156 / Jul '96 / Ross

☐ **SPLENDOUR OF THE KOTO**
PS 65131 / May '94 / PlayaSound

☐ **SPLENDOUR OF THE SHAKUHACHI**
PS 65130 / May '94 / PlayaSound

☐ **SPLENDOUR OF THE SHAMISEN**
PS 65129 / May '94 / PlayaSound

☐ **SPLINTER (Paper Recordings Present)**
Molde: *Those Norwegians* / Cut the rug: *Dirty Jesus* / Got change for a twenty: *Salt City Orchestra & Derrick Carter* / Plants animals H2O: *Cine City* / Downtime: *Paper music issue one* / Summer bummer: *Crazy Penis* / Origami: *Wastepaper* / Phunk theory theme: *New Phunk Theory* / Book: *Salt City Orchestra* / Bustabubble: *Shaboom*
PAPCD 002 / 25 May '98 / Paper

☐ **SPOOKY TUNES AND TALES**
POMP 013 / 3 Nov '97 / Vesuvius

☐ **SPOONFUL OF BLUES**
422490 / May '94 / New Rose

☐ **SPOTLIGHT ON BLUES**
Boom boom boom: *Hooker, John Lee* / Honest I do: *Reed, Jimmy* / Dust my broom: *James, Elmore* / Baby, let me hold your hand: *Charles, Ray* / Need him: *Little Richard* / Rooster blues: *Lightnin' Slim* / I put a spell on you: *Hawkins, Screamin' Jay* / Caldonia: *Jordan, Louis* / Blueberry Hill: *Domino, Fats* / Dimples: *Hooker, John Lee* / She's a winner: *Taylor, Ted* / When the sun goes down: *Turner, 'Big' Joe* / Moppers blues: *Stewart, Rod* / Shame shame shame: *Reed, Jimmy* / Rollin' and tumblin': *Canned Heat* / Polk salad Annie: *White, Tony Joe*
HADCD 146 / Feb '94 / Javelin

☐ **SPOTLIGHT ON COUNTRY**
Ruby, don't take your love to town: *Rogers, Kenny* / Rawhide: *Laine, Frankie* / Walkin' after midnight: *Cline, Patsy* / Wasted days and wasted nights: *Fender, Freddy* / Singin' the blues: *Mitchell, Guy* / Harper Valley PTA: *Riley, Jeannie C.* / It's only make believe: *Twitty, Conway* / Six days on the road: *Dudley, Dave* / Are you proud of America: *Skaggs, Ricky* / Primrose Lane: *Wallace, Jerry* / Four in the morning: *Young, Faron* / Teddy bear song: *Fairchild, Barbara* / Ballad of the Green Berets: *Sadler, Sgt. Barry* / Home is where you're happy: *Nelson, Willie* / Wings of a dove: *Husky, Ferlin* / Good year for the roses: *Jones, George*
HADCD 149 / Feb '94 / Javelin

☐ **SPOTLIGHT ON COUNTRY - LIVE**
Stand by your man: *Wynette, Tammy* / Behind closed doors: *Rich, Charlie* / Delta dawn: *Tucker, Tanya* / Jambalaya: *Fender, Freddy* / Rose garden: *Anderson, Lynn* / Medley: *Boxcar Willie* / Here comes my baby: *West, Dottie* / Let it be me: *Tillotson,*

Johnny / Let your love flow: Bellamy Brothers / Ball and chain: Mattea, Kathy / He stopped loving her today: Jones, George / Mr. Bojangles: Nitty Gritty Dirt Band / Total woman: Riley, Jeannie C. / Key largo: Higgins, Bertie / Okie from Muskogee: Haggard, Merle / Wine me up: Young, Faron

HADCD 150 / Feb '94 / Javelin

☐ SPOTLIGHT ON HITS OF THE SIXTIES

Sweets for my sweet: Searchers / You've got your troubles: Fortunes / Love is all around: Troggs / Wild thing: Troggs / I am the world: Bee Gees / Ferry 'cross the Mersey: Gerry & The Pacemakers / When you walk in the room: Searchers / Storm in a teacup: Fortunes / I can't control myself: Troggs / Needles and pins: Searchers / How do you do it: Gerry & The Pacemakers / Caroline: Fortunes / Monday's rain: Bee Gees / Sugar and spice: Searchers

HADCD 143 / Feb '94 / Javelin

☐ SPOTLIGHT ON JAZZ

In the mood: Miller, Glenn / One o'clock jump: Basie, Count / Tuxedo junction: Hirt, Al / Misty: Vaughan, Sarah / Ring dem bells: Hampton, Lionel / C Jam blues: Ellington, Duke / How high the moon: Fitzgerald, Ella / Scraple from the apple: Parker, Charlie / Sawnuff: Davis, Miles / Sweet Georgia Brown: Cole, Nat 'King' / Tip toe topic: Ellington, Duke / Mr. Paganini: Fitzgerald, Ella / Curros: Byrd, Donald / Court: Hubbard, Freddie / If you could see me now: Vaughan, Sarah / All the things you are: Benson, George

HADCD 144 / Feb '94 / Javelin

☐ SPOTLIGHT ON PAUL SIMON PLUS

Play me a sad song: Simon, Paul / It means a lot: Simon, Paul / Flame: Simon, Paul / While I dream: Sedaka, Neil / Ring-a-rock: Sedaka, Neil / Ding dong: Orlando, Tony / You're the one: Rivers, Johnny / Hole in the ground: Rivers, Johnny / This is real: Valli, Frankie / Comme si bella: Valli, Frankie / Please me forever: Edwards, Tommy / It's all in the game: Edwards, Tommy

HADCD 141 / Feb '94 / Javelin

☐ SPOTLIGHT ON REGGAE

RGCD 0011 / Nov '94 / Rocky One

☐ SPOTLIGHT ON ROCK 'N' ROLL

(We're gonna) Rock around the clock: Haley, Bill & The Comets / Tutti frutti: Little Richard / Rockin' robin: Day, Bobby / Blue suede shoes: Perkins, Carl / Venus: Avalon, Frankie / Red river rock: Johnny & The Hurricanes / Let's dance: Montez, Chris / Surfin' bird: Trashmen / Louie Louie: Kingsmen / Walk don't run: Ventures / I fought the law: Fuller, Bobby / Hey little girl: Clark, Dee / Tiger: Fabian / Ooby dooby: Orbison, Roy / Ring-a-rock: Sedaka, Neil / Great balls of fire: Lewis, Jerry Lee

HADCD 147 / Feb '94 / Javelin

☐ SPOTLIGHT ON ROCK 'N' ROLL - LIVE

Rubber ball: Vee, Bobby / I'm gonna make you mine: Christie, Lou / Twilight time: Platters / Ginny come lately: Hyland, Brian / Charlie Brown: Coasters / Runaway: Shannon, Del / Motor running: Lewis, Jerry Lee / Dizzy: Roe, Tommy / Way down yonder in New Orleans: Cannon, Freddy / Why do fools fall in love: Diamonds / Roberta: Ford, Frankie / La bamba: Tokens / Peggy Sue: Crickets / Keep on running: Davis, Spencer / My guy: Wells, Mary / Rock 'n' roll is here to stay: Original Juniors

HADCD 148 / Feb '94 / Javelin

☐ SPOTLIGHT ON SOUL

Soul man: Sam & Dave / Knock on wood: Floyd, Eddie / Harlem shuffle: Bob & Earl / My guy: Wells, Mary / Stay: Williams, Maurice & The Zodiacs / Stagger Lee: Price, Lloyd / Tell it like it is: Neville, Aaron / Every beat of my heart: Knight, Gladys & The Pips / So fine: Turner, Ike & Tina / Mockingbird: Foxx, Inez / Oh no, not my baby: Brown, Maxine / Precious and few: Climax Blues Band / Show and tell: Wilson, Al / Seems like I gotta do wrong: Whispers / Stand by me: King, Ben E. / When a man loves a woman: Sledge, Percy

HADCD 145 / Feb '94 / Javelin

☐ SPOTLITE JAZZ SAMPLER

If I should use you / What's next / My funny valentine / Three little words / White in the moon / Isn't it / Everywhere calypso / Day by day / Dream dancing / Behind the mask / Maids of Cadiz / Conception / My romance / Shadowy light / Interlude / Promised land

SPJCD 301 / Feb '97 / Spotlite

☐ SPRING AGAIN

Love is all: Glover, Roger & Guests / Place in the sun: Hammond, Albert / Happy together: Turtles / Air that I breath: Hollies / Spring again: Rawls, Lou / Don't worry be happy: McFerrin, Bobby / All around my hat: Steeleye Span / Wonderful world: Herman's Hermits / You make me feel like dancing: Sayer, Leo / If I had words: Fitzgerald, Scott & Yvonne Keeley / Freedom come, freedom go: Fortunes / Birds and the bees: Akens, Jewel / Wonderful world, beautiful people: Cliff, Jimmy / Oh happy day: Hawkins, Edwin Singers

DC 879192 / Mar '97 / Disky

☐ SPRING STORY, THE (Essential 70s Soul)

Tom the pepper: Act 1 / My man, a sweet man: Jackson, Millie / Step by step: Simon, Joe / I can see him making love to you: Mayberry Movement / Too through: Brown, Jocelyn / I found lovin': Fatback Band / I gotta get away: Godfrey, Ray / He didn't know (he kept on talkin'): Green, Garland / You've come a long way baby: Flower Shoppe / Baby you got it all: Street People / Just a little misunderstanding: Jones, Busta / SOS (stop her on sight): Parker, Winfield / Get ready: Harris, Eva / Uptight: Harris, Eva / (Are you ready) Do the bus stop: Fatback Band / It's my life: Mainstreeters / Jody, come back and get your shoes: Newsome, Bobby / If we get caught I don't know you: Mitchell, Phillip / Drowning in the sea of love: Simon, Joe / (If loving you is wrong) I don't wanna be right: Jackson, Millie / Friends or lovers: Act 1 / Magic's in the air: Walker, Ronnie / Loves contest: Joneses / How about a little hand (for the boys in the band): Boys In The Band / Bumpin' and stompin': Green, Garland / Come and get these memories: Godfrey, Ray

CDSEWD 103 / Oct '95 / Southbound

☐ SPUNK JAZZ

Hate me: Animals On Wheels / You're on your own: Begg, Si / Dirty great mable: Bubbah's Tum / Wetwang: Paddington Breaks / Fat dog (12 O'Clock): Come On Feel The Nothing / Old school knee clicker: Value Ape / Holiby's Theorem: Mould / Blue tea: Hoarse Operator / FYA: Animals On Wheels / Spare parts: Paddington Breaks / Ballad of Terry Ping: Milky Boy / Tense and learning: Vert

ILLCD 001 / 22 Sep '97 / Ill

☐ SQUASBOX

Y 225107CD / Jul '95 / Silex

☐ SQUEEZE PLAY (A World Accordion Anthology)

Tarantella Teggianese: D'Elia, / Dormi e Risposa: Gangone, G / Drunkard's last will: Polak, Wladyslaw / Best friend's song (Kumotersko): Orkiestra Karol Stoch / Pawel Walc (Paul's waltz): Rudzinski, Bruno / Mason's apron: Murphy, Frank / Rodney's glory: Hanafin, Michael / In Padure La Ghergani: Radulescu, Margarita / Girl from Ardeal: Jivan, George / Song of the bus drivers: Trio Huracan / La Piedrera: Jimenez, Santiago Jr. / Ulele Izweni: Luthuli, Mahlautini / Nonyembezi: Dingaan, Joseph / Besarabia Doina: Ziganoff, Mishka / Tsygansky Hopak: Ziganoff, Mishka / Miss Jessie Smith/The Kirrie Kebbuck/Petronella: McHardy & Hosie / Brig o' Perth: Dalrymple, Bob & David / Inverness gathering: Dalrymple, Bob & David / Politkos Sirtos: Papatzis-Tsakiris / Saut Crapaud: Fruge, Columbus / Ne buvez pilus jamais: Falcon, Joseph / Reel de Berthier: Vagabonds de Montreal / Italijanski Valcek: Strukelj Trio / Apaga la Luz: Quintero, Luis

ROUCD 1090 / Feb '97 / Rounder

☐ SST ACOUSTIC

SST 276CD / May '93 / SST

☐ ST. LOUIS 1927-1933

DOCD 5181 / Oct '93 / Document

☐ ST. LOUIS BLUES 1925-1941

158392 / Sep '95 / Blues Collection

☐ ST. LOUIS BLUES REVUE (The Classic Bobbin Sessions)

Hucklebuck twist: Sain, Oliver Orchestra / Honey bee: Bass, Fontella & Oliver Sain Orchestra / Bad boy: Bass, Fontella & Oliver Sain Orchestra / Brand new love: Bass, Fontella & Oliver Sain Orchestra / I don't hurt anymore: Bass, Fontella & Oliver Sain Orchestra / Limited love: Love, Clayton & Roosevelt Marks Orchestra / Unlimited love: Love, Clayton & Roosevelt Marks Orchestra / Bye bye baby: Love, Clayton & Roosevelt Marks Orchestra / Mistreated: Love, Clayton & Roosevelt Marks Orchestra / It's you: Love, Clayton & Roosevelt Marks Orchestra / Year after year: Love, Clayton & Roosevelt Marks Orchestra / Baby bring your clothes back home: Westbrook, Walter & His Phantom Five / Midnight jump: Westbrook, Walter & His Phantom Five / That will never do: Little Milton & Oliver Sain Orchestra / I'm a lonely man: Little Milton & Oliver Sain Orchestra / Long distance operator: Little Milton & Oliver Sain Orchestra / I found me a new love: Little Milton & Oliver Sain Orchestra / I'm tryin': Little Milton & Oliver Sain Orchestra / Strange dreams: Little Milton & Oliver Sain Orchestra / Hold me tight: Little Milton & Oliver Sain Orchestra / (I have the) same old blues: Little Milton & Oliver Sain Orchestra / Dead love: Little Milton & Oliver Sain Orchestra / My baby pleases me: Little Milton & Oliver Sain Orchestra / Let it be known: Little Milton & Oliver Sain Orchestra / Hey girl: Little Milton & Oliver Sain Orchestra / Cross my heart: Little Milton & Oliver Sain Orchestra / I'm in love: Little Milton & Oliver Sain Orchestra / My mind is troubled: Little Milton & Oliver Sain Orchestra / Harlem nocturne: Sain, Oliver Orchestra

CDCHD 633 / Aug '96 / Ace

☐ ST. LOUIS GIRLS 1927-1934

DOCD 5182 / Oct '93 / Document

☐ ST. LOUIS GIRLS 1929-1937

SOB 035362 / Oct '92 / Story Of The Blues

☐ ST. LOUIS TOWN 1929-1933

YAZCD 1003 / Apr '91 / Yazoo

☐ ST. LUCIA JAZZ

PD 007 / May '96 / Ebony

☐ ST. PATRICK'S DAY CELEBRATION

Haste to the wedding: Gallowglass Ceili Band / Irish washerwoman: Gallowglass Ceili Band / Flaherty's drake: O'Dowda, Brendan / Paddy McGinty's goat: Harrington, Pat / Irish jubilee: Harrington, Pat / Plough and the stars: Gallowglass Ceili Band / Mrs. Crotty's reel: Gallowglass Ceili Band / Muirsheen Durkin: Dubliners / Kelly the boy from Killan: Dubliners / Croppy boy: Dubliners / It's the same old shillelagh: Downey, Morton / When Irish eyes are smiling: Downey, Morton / Mother Machree: Smith, Kate / Molly Malone: Smith, Kate / Heather breeze: Gallowglass Ceili Band / St. Anne's reel: Gallowglass Ceili Band / Peeler's jacket: Gallowglass Ceili Band / Outlawed reparee: Clancy Brothers & Tommy Makem / Port Lairge: Clancy Brothers & Tommy Makem / I'm a free born man of the travelling people: Clancy Brothers & Tommy Makem / March from Oscar and Malvina: Chieftains / When a man's in love: Chieftains

4896812 / 2 Mar '98 / Columbia

☐ STAND BY ME (Love Songs From TV Commercials)

Stand by me: King, Ben E. / Only you: Platters / Drift away: Gray, Dobie / Will you still love me tomorrow: Shirelles / When a man loves a woman: Sledge, Percy / Rescue me: Bass, Fontella / Games people play: South, Joe / I'm into something good: Herman's Hermits / My blue heaven: Domino, Fats / Walkin' the dog: Thomas, Rufus / I got you (I feel good): Brown, James / Be bop a lula: Vincent, Gene / Up on the roof: Drifters / Leader of the pack: Shangri-Las / I put a spell on you: Hawkins, Screamin' Jay / Warm and tender love: Sledge, Percy / But I do: Henry, Clarence 'Frogman' / Venus: Avalon, Frankie / Runaway: Shannon, Del / Goodnight sweetheart, well it's time to go: Spaniels

MU 3013 / Oct '95 / Musketeer

☐ STAND UP VOL.3

701996060X / Oct '97 / Word

☐ STANDARDS ON IMPULSE

Summertime: Blakey, Art / In a sentimetal mood: Ellington, Duke & John Coltrane / I concentrate on you: Johnson, J.J. & Kai Winding / Body and soul: Carter, Benny / Sister Sadie: Evans, Gil / Unforgettable: Hartman, Johnny / Oh lady be good: Basie, Count / Mood indigo: Mingus, Charles / Fly me to the moon: Haynes, Roy / What's new: Coltrane, John / Satin doll: Tyner, McCoy / Stardust: Webster, Ben / Cherokee: Manne, Shelly / Do nothin' 'til you hear from me: Terry, Clark / Solitude: Ellington, Duke & Coleman Hawkins / Girl from Ipanema: Shepp, Archie

IMP 12032 / Dec '96 / Impulse Jazz

☐ STANDING ON THE VERGE (The Roots Of Funk 1964-1974)

Out of sight: Brown, James / Cissy strut: Meters / Funky broadway: Meters / Kool and the gang: Kool & The Gang / She lookin' good: Collins, Rodger / Ain't got time: Collins, Rodger / Boogaloo down broadway: Fantastic Johnny C / Right on for the darkness: Mayfield, Curtis / Bra: Cymande / It's your thing: Isley Brothers / Dance girl: Mighty Tomcats / Funky judge: Bull & the Matadors / Horse: Nobles, Cliff & Co.

SHANCD 9008 / 9 Mar '98 / Shanachie

☐ STANDING ROCK, SPIRIT OF SONG

14944 / Jan '97 / Spalax

☐ STANDING STONES

NAGE 5CD / Feb '86 / Art Of Landscape

☐ STAR O'RABBIE BURNS, THE

Star O'Rabbie Burns: Dawson, Peter / Auld lang syne: Dawson, Peter / Man's a man for a' that: Watson, Bobby / My love is like a red red rose: Hislop, Joseph / Of a'the airts the wind can blaw: Hislop, Joseph / My love she's but a lassie yet: Hislop, Joseph / Corn rigs: Hislop, Joseph / Afton water: Hislop, Joseph / Ye banks and braes o' bonnie Doon: MacEwan, Sydney / Comin' thro' the rye: Teyte, Maggie / Blue eyed lassie: Burnett, Robert / Ca' the yowes: Brunskill, Muriel / Green grow the rashes: MacKinley, Jean Sterling / I'll meet thee on the Lea rig: Murray, Laidlaw / Mary Morrison: Harrison, John / Tam Glen: Day, Jean / De'il's awa' wi' tha exciseman: Henderson, Roy / Oh Willie brewed a peck o'malt: Henderson, Roy / I'm owre young tae marry yet: Baillie, Isobel / John Anderson, my Jo: Baillie, Isobel / Bonnie wee thing: McCormack, John / Ae fond kiss: Coleman, Esther & Foster Richardson / Scots wha hae: Glasgow Orpheus Choir / Charming Chloe: Suddaby, Elsie / O'whistle an' I'll come tae ye, my lad: Scotney, Evelyn / Mary Morison: MacGregor, Alexander

MIDCD 004 / Jan '95 / Moidart

☐ STAR POWER

EFA 201172 / May '95 / Pravda

☐ STAR TREK STRIKES BACK

CDR 004 / Mar '97 / ACV

☐ STARS OF BIRDLAND ON TOUR

Lullabye of birdland: Basie, Count & His Orchestra / Why not: Basie, Count & His Orchestra / Basie talks: Basie, Count & His Orchestra / Jumpin' at the Woodside: Young, Lester & Count Basie & His Orchestra / I'm confessin': Young, Lester & Count Basie & His Orchestra / Every tub: Young, Lester & Count Basie & His Orchestra / Every day I have the blues: Young, Lester & Count Basie & His Orchestra / Shake rattle and roll: Young, Lester & Count Basie & His Orchestra / Dinner with friends: Young, Lester & Count Basie & His Orchestra / Lullabye of birdland: Shearing, George Quintet / Medley/East of the sun/ Roses of Picardy/I'll remember April/: Shearing, George Quintet / Jumpin' with symphony sid: Shearing, George Quintet / George Shearing speaks: Shearing, George Quintet / Man I love: Shearing, George Quintet / Yesterdays: Shearing, George Quintet / Mambo inn: Shearing, George Quintet / Little pony: Shearing, George Quintet / Easy living: Getz, Stan & Count Basie Orchestra / Blues: Getz, Stan & Count Basie Orchestra / Blee bop blues: Getz, Stan & Count Basie Orchestra / I get a kick out of you: Garner, Erroll Trio / Laura: Garner, Erroll Trio / Idaho: Garner, Erroll Trio / There's a small hotel: Garner, Erroll Trio / Medley/Will you still be mine/Gypsy in my soul: Garner, Erroll Trio / 'Swonderful: Vaughan, Sarah & Count Basie Orchestra / Easy to remember: Vaughan, Sarah & Count Basie Orchestra / East of the sun: Vaughan, Sarah & Count Basie Orchestra / How important can it be: Vaughan, Sarah & Count Basie Orchestra / That old devil moon: Vaughan, Sarah & Count Basie Orchestra / Idle gossip: Vaughan, Sarah & Count Basie Orchestra / Make yourself comfortable: Vaughan, Sarah & Count Basie Orchestra / Perdido: Vaughan, Sarah & Count Basie Orchestra / Chris crossed: Basie, Count & Joe Williams / Comeback: Basie, Count & Joe Williams

JZCL 5015 / Feb '97 / Jazz Classics

☐ STARS OF COUNTRY MUSIC, THE

Oh lonesome me: Gibson, Don / Peace in the valley: Jordanaires / Mexican Joe: Reeves, Jim / Crazy arms: Lewis, Jerry Lee / Next in line: Cash, Johnny / These boots are made for walking: Hazelwood, Lee / World's worst loser: Jones, George / Sally was a good old girl: Jennings, Waylon / Rose Marie: Whitman, Slim / Settin' the woods on fire: Williams, Hank / Honky tonk angels: Parton, Dolly / Race is on: Jones, George / Yonder comes a sucker: Reeves, Jim / Broken heart: Twitty, Conway / El Paso: Robbins, Marty / Train of love: Cash, Johnny / Please release me: Parton, Dolly

22518 / Dec '95 / Music

☐ STARS OF MOTORCITY VOL.2, THE

With you I'm born again: Syreeta / Look into the eyes of a fool: Bristol, Johnny / Got the big city blues: Eckstine, Billy / Needle in a haystack: Velvelettes / Keep this thought in mind: Bristol, Johnny / Better late than never: Velvelettes / Gentle lady: Eckstine, Billy / He was really saying something: Velvelettes / Love fire: Syreeta / What does it take to win your love: Bristol, Johnny / Ask the lonely: Eckstine, Billy / One door closes, another one opens: Bristol, Johnny / Don't keep your distance: Bristol, Johnny / Moment of weakness: Syreeta / I dig everything about you: Eckstine, Billy / One plan of action: Syreeta

302752 / Jul '97 / Hallmark

☐ STARS OF REGGAE SUNSPLASH

CPCD 8025 / Feb '94 / Charly

☐ STARS OF ROCK 'N' ROLL

Tutti frutti: Little Richard / Rock around the clock: Haley, Bill / Mr. Bassman: Cymbal, Johnny / Wooly bully: Sam The Sham & The Pharaohs / Da doo ron ron: Crystals / Tallahassie lassie: Cannon, Freddy / Rubber ball: Vee, Bobby / Good golly Miss Molly: Swinging Blue Jeans / Shake, rattle and roll: Haley, Bill / Maybelline: Berry, Chuck / Keep a knockin': Little Richard / Lucille: Little Richard / Long Tall Sally: Little Richard / Wild thing: Troggs / Sheila: Roe, Tommy / At the hop: Danny & The Juniors / Speddy Gonzalez: Boone, Pat / It's my party: Gore, Lesley

22524 / Dec '95 / Music

☐ STARS OF THE LONDON PALLADIUM (The Greatest Performers Of Yesteryear)

I believe: Bachelors / Charmaine: Bachelors / I remember you: Ifield, Frank / Lovesick blues: Ifield, Frank / Say wonderful things: Carroll, Ronnie / Ring a ding girl: Carroll, Ronnie / Midnight in Moscow: Ball, Kenny / Green leaves of summer: Ball, Kenny / Does your chewing gum lose its flavour: Donegan, Lonnie / My old man's a dustman: Donegan, Lonnie / Singin' the blues: Mitchell, Guy / Knee deep in the blues: Mitchell, Guy / Cry: Ray, Johnnie / Just walkin' in the rain: Ray, Johnnie / Rose, Rose I love you: Laine, Frankie / Jezebel: Laine, Frankie / My prayer: Platters / Only you (and you alone): Platters

ECD 3282 / Jan '97 / K-Tel

☐ STARS SING CHRISTMAS FAVOURITES, THE

Christmas song / Have yourself a merry little Christmas / Santa Claus is coming to town / Frosty the snowman / O come all ye faithful (adeste fidelis) / Hark the herald angels sing / This time of the year / White Christmas / Blue Christmas / Let it snow, let it snow, let it snow / When a child is born / Silver bells / We wish you a merry Christmas / Please come home for Christmas / What child is this / Silent night / Little drummer boy / You're all I want for Christmas / Jingle bells / Auld lang syne

XMAS 013 / Nov '96 / Tring

☐ STARTRAX CLUB DISCO COLLECTION, THE

Startrax club disco / More than a woman / Night fever / Tragedy / Love you inside out / Jive talkin' / Edge of universe / Boogie child / Too much heaven (Our love) / Don't throw it all away / Wind of change / You stepped into my life / If I can't have you / New York mining disaster / 1941 / Stayin' alive / Night on Broadway / Search find / Lights went out in (Massachusetts) / How deep is your love / Reaching out / You should be dancing / Spirits (having flown) / Keep a good man down / I've got to get a message to you / Fanny (be tender with your love) / Love so right / First of May / Children of the world / IOIO / Saved by the bell / Words / Black is black / She's not there / In the navy / One way ticket / YMCA / I can see clearly now / Sunny / Kissin' in the back row of the movies / Bad girls / Instant replay / Three steps to heaven / Keep on dancing / Love hangover / Working my way back to you / DISCO / Use it up and wear it out / That's the way (I like it) / Band of gold / Alright now / Love train / Que sera mi vida / Ladies night / Go west / Kung fu fighting / Year 2525 (Exordium and terminus) / I will survive / Le freak / Because the night / When you're in love with a beautiful woman / Feels like I'm in love

306822 / May '97 / Hallmark

☐ STASH SAMPLER VOL.2, THE

STCD 599 / Jan '93 / Stash

☐ STATE OF PLAY VOL.2

BLCDXY 02 / 30 Mar '98 / Bellboy

☐ STATE OF THE ART VOL.5

PIAS 213003928 / May '97 / Play It Again Sam

☐ STATE OF THE NU-ART VOL.1, THE

PLAN 7CD / May '97 / Blue Planet

☐ STATE OF THE NU-ART VOL.2, THE (2CD Set)

PLAN 11CD / 26 Jan '98 / Silver Planet

☐ STATE OF THE UNION

DIS 32CD / Mar '95 / Dischord

☐ STATE OF THE UNION (2CD Set)

ALP 69CD / Jan '97 / Atavistic

☐ STATEMENT OF INTENT

ELM 8003CD / 22 Jun '98 / E-Melt

☐ STATEMENTS OF INTENT

Shattered: Haunted / Deserted: Gardenian / Goliaths disarm their Davids: In Flames / Black earth: Arch Enemy / To kill without emotion: December Wolves / Carry the torch: Gandalf / Shall they come forth unto us: Elysian Fields / Nerve: Katatonia / Autumn's ablaze: Primordial / 12th rising: Naglfar / In death's embrace: Dimmu Borgir / Poison: Crown / High on blood: Deranged / Dissolving: Eucharist / Razorfever: Dark Tranquillity / Traveller of unknown plains: Thy Serpent

WICK 001 / 20 Jul '98 / Wicked World

☐ STATESIDE SMASHES

PLATCD 345 / Oct '90 / Platinum

☐ STATESIDE SWEET MUSIC

Love and learn: Fields, Shep / If the moon turns green: Kassel, Art / Little rendezvous in Honolulu: Lopez, Vincent / I have eyes: Shaw, Artie Orchestra / One cigarette for two: Martin, Freddy & His Orchestra / Pessimistic character: Ayres, Mitchell & His Orchestra / Can't get Indiana off my mind: Gordon, Gay & The Mince Pies / I don't want to cry anymore: Barnet, Charlie / Apple blossom and chapel bells: Martin, Freddy & His Orchestra / I threw a bean bag at the moon: Kassel, Art / That sentimental sandwich: Nelson, Ozzie & His Orchestra / On a little bamboo bridge: Fields, Shep / Whispering grass: Dorsey, Jimmy Orchestra / Strange enchantment: Nelson, Ozzie & His

Orchestra / Meet the sun halfway: Ayres, Mitchell & His Orchestra / Afterglow: Whiteman, Paul & His Orchestra / Never took a lesson in my life: Gordon, Gray & His Orchestra / Why don't we do this more often: Martin, Freddy & His Orchestra / That's for me: Barnet, Charlie Orchestra / Moonlight and shadows: Shaw, Artie Orchestra / Who's afraid of love: Berigan, Bunny & His Orchestra / Flamingo: Martin, Freddy & His Orchestra
PASTCD 9787 / Apr '92 / Flapper

☐ STATESIDE VOL.1
ZEN 006CD / Feb '96 / Indochina

☐ STAX BLUES MASTERS VOL.1 (Blue Monday)
They want money: Little Sonny / Drivin' wheel: King, Albert / Creeper: Robinson, Freddie / Eight men, four women: Little Milton / Things that I used to do: Little Sonny / Bad luck: King, Albert / More bad luck: King, Albert / Born under a bad sign: King, Albert / Blues with a feeling: Little Sonny / Married woman: Little Milton / Ronettes: Robinson, Freddie / Blue Monday: Little Milton / After hours: Robinson, Freddie / Open the door to your heart: Little Milton / Blues after hours: Robinson, Freddie / River's invitation: Robinson, Freddie / It's hard going up (but twice as hard coming down): Little Sonny
CDSXE 080 / Nov '92 / Stax

☐ STAX FUNK - GET UP AND GET DOWN
Shaft: Hayes, Isaac / Castle of joy: Fat Larry's Band / What goes around (must come around): Sons Of Slum / Dark skin woman: Rice, Sir Mack / What'cha see is what'cha get: Dramatics / Son of Shaft: Bar-Kays / Dryer part 1: Johnson, Roy Lee & The Villagers / Cool strut part one: Hayes, Bernie / Mr. Big Stuff: Knight, Jean / Funkasize you: Sho Nuff / Holy ghost: Bar-Kays / Men: Hayes, Isaac / Circuits overloaded: Foxx, Inez & Charlie / FLB: Fat Larry's Band / Black: Mar-Keys / Get up and get down: Dramatics / Moving on: Dynamic Soul Machine / You chose me: Sho Nuff / Dryer part 2: Johnson, Roy Lee & The Villagers / Cool strut part 1: Hayes, Bernie
CDSX 020 / May '89 / Stax

☐ STAX FUNK - SON OF STAX FUNK
Title theme (Tough guys): Hayes, Isaac / Type thang: Hayes, Isaac / Steppin' out: Sho Nuff / Mix match man: Sho Nuff / What does it take: Sons Of Slum / Man: Sons Of Slum / Getting funky round here: Black Nasty / Nasty soul: Black Nasty / Watch the dog: Shack / Patch it up: Johnson, Roy Lee / Funky hot grits: Thomas, Rufus / Soul town: Forevers / Shake your big hips: Tolbert, Israel / Bump meat: Rice, Sir Mack / Do me: Knight, Jean / In the hole: Bar-Kays / Watch me do it: Sho Nuff / Right on: Sons Of Slum / Talkin' to the people: Black Nasty / I'll kill a brick for my man: Hot Sauce / Carry on: Knight, Jean / Song and dance: Bar-Kays / Do the funky chicken: Thomas, Rufus / Devil is dope: Dramatics
CDSXD 075 / Feb '93 / Stax

☐ STAX FUNX
Run Ray run: Hayes, Isaac / LAS: South Memphis Horns / Grab a handful: Miller, Art Jerry / Sweetback's theme: Van Peebles, Melvin / Got it together: Robinson, Rudy & The Hungry Five / Wes: Soul Merchants / End theme/Truck Turner: Hayes, Isaac / Ghetto - misfortune's wealth: 24 Carat Black / Rock back: Thomas, Rufus / Do the sweetback: March Wind / Too many lovers: Shack / My thing is a moving thing: TSU Tornadoes / Broadway freeze: Scales, Harvey / Coldblooded: Bar-Kays / Hi-jacking love: Taylor, Johnny / Fancy: Hamilton, Chico / I feel good: Sons Of Truth / Love's gonna tear your playhouse down: Brooks, Chuck / (What's under) the natural do: Kasandra, John / Dirty tricks: Sweet Inspirations / One pair of pants: Johnson, L.V.
CDSXD 110 / Apr '97 / Stax

☐ STAX GOLD (Hits 1968-1974)
Soul limbo: Booker T & The MG's / Time is tight: Booker T & The MG's / Private number: Clay, Judy & William Bell / Who's making love: Taylor, Johnnie / Bring it on home to me: Floyd, Eddie / I forgot to be your lover: Bell, William / I like what you're doing (to me): Thomas, Carla / Do the push and pull (part 1): Thomas, Rufus / Mr. Big Stuff: Knight, Jean / What'cha see is what'cha get: Dramatics / Respect yourself: Staple Singers / I'll take you there: Staple Singers / Shaft: Hayes, Isaac / Son of Shaft: Bar-Kays / I've been lonely for so long: Knight, Frederick / Starting all over again: Mel & Tim / Woman to woman: Brown, Shirley / I'll be the other woman: Soul Children / So I can love you: Emotions / I have learned to do without you: Staples, Mavis / In the rain: Dramatics / Dedicated to the one I love: Temprees / Short stoppin': Brown, Veda / Cheaper to keep her: Taylor, Johnnie
CDSXD 043 / Sep '91 / Stax

☐ STAX O' SOUL: SAMPLER OF STAX TRAX
Will you still love me tomorrow: Bell, William / Stolen angel: Tonettes / Zip a dee doo dah: Booker T & The MG's / Little boy: Thomas, Carla / Last clean shirt: Thomas, Rufus / Cupid: Redding, Otis / Sweet devil: John, Mable / Need your love so bad: Johnson, Ruby / I've never found a girl: Floyd, Eddie / I could never be president: Taylor, Johnnie / What side of the door: Hughes, Jimmy / Open the door to your heart: Little Milton / I can't break away (from your love): Lewis, Barbara / When something is wrong with my baby: Weston, Kim / I finally got you: McCracklin, Jimmy / Takin' all the love I can: Joseph, Margie / Wade in the water: Little Sonny / I've been lonely for so long: Knight, Frederick / Respect yourself: Staple Singers / Getting funky round here: Black Nasty / Flat tire: King, Albert / We need each other, girl: Hayes, Isaac / Move me move me: Brown, Shirley
CDSXX 100 / Oct '93 / Stax

☐ STAX REVUE LIVE AT THE 54 BALLROOM
Green onions: Booker T & The MG's / You can't sit down: Booker T & The MG's / Summertime: Booker T & The MG's / Soul twist: Booker T & The MG's / Boot-leg: Booker T & The MG's / Don't have to shop around: Mad Lads / Candy: Astors / Last night: Mar-Keys / Any other way: Bell, William / You don't miss your water: Bell, William / Every ounce of strength: Thomas, Carla / Do the dog: Thomas, Rufus / Walking the dog: Thomas, Rufus
CDSXD 040 / Sep '91 / Stax

☐ STAX SIRENS AND VOLT VAMPS
Try a little tenderness: Sweet Inspirations / I've got to go on without you: Brown, Shirley / Take it off her (and put it on me): Brown, Veda / Love slave: Alexander, Margie / Shouldn't I love him: John, Mable / Got to be the man: Emotions / Save the last kiss for me: Knight, Jean / Nobody: Joseph, Margie / Who could be loving you: Ross, Jackie / Standing in the need of your love: Jeanne & The Darlings / I'll never grow old: Charmells / Give love to save love: Clay, Judy / You hurt me for the last time: Foxx, Inez & Charlie / I like what you're doing (to me): Thomas, Carla / If I had it my way: Weston, Kim / How can you mistreat the one you love: Love, Katie / Love changes: Charlene & The Soul Serenaders / What happened to our good thing: Haywood, Kitty / Where would you be today: Ilana
CDSX 013 / Jun '88 / Stax

☐ STAX/VOLT REVUE VOL.3 (Live In Europe)
Introduction (London): Emperor Rosko / Red beans and rice: Booker T & The MG's / Booker-loo: Booker T & The MG's / Green onions: Booker T & The MG's / Hip hug-her: Booker T & The MG's / Introduction (Paris): Hubert / Let me be good to you: Thomas, Carla / Yesterday: Thomas, Carla / Something good: Thomas, Carla / B-A-B-Y: Thomas, Carla / Introduction (London) 2: Emperor Rosko / I don't want to cry: Floyd, Eddie / Raise your hand: Floyd, Eddie / Knock on wood: Floyd, Eddie / Introduction (London) 3: Emperor Rosko / Respect: Redding, Otis / My girl: Redding, Otis / Shake: Redding, Otis / Day tripper: Redding, Otis / Introduction: Redding, Otis / Fa fa fa fa fa (Sad song): Redding, Otis / Introduction: Redding, Otis / Try a little tenderness: Redding, Otis
CDSXD 044 / May '92 / Stax

☐ STAYIN' HOME WITH THE BLUES
Bedroom blues: Wallace, Sippie & Albert Ammons Rhythm Kings / Willie Mae: Broonzy, 'Big' Bill / Sad news from Korea: Hopkins, Lightnin' / Jet propelled Papa: Humes, Helen & Buck Clayton Orchestra / West coast blues: Edwards, J.D. / Sweet patooty boogie: Ammons, Albert & His Rhythm Kings / Water coast blues: Broonzy, 'Big' Bill Fat Four / Oil man blues: Vinson, Eddie 'Cleanhead' & Orchestra / Dust my broom: Lockwood, Robert Jr. / Brown skinned woman: Sunnyland Slim Trio / St. Louis blues: Ammons, Albert & His Rhythm Kings / No mail blues: Memphis Slim Orchestra / Beer drinking baby: Valentine, Billy / My man's an undertaker: Washington, Dinah / Sweet home Chicago: King, Freddie / Garfield Avenue blues: McShann, Jay Boogie Woogie Sextet & Crown Prince Waterford / Shipyard woman blues: McShann, Jay Sextet & Jimmy Witherspoon / Byrd's blues: Byrd, Roy & His Blues Jumpers
5540542 / Oct '97 / Spectrum

☐ STEEL BAND MUSIC OF THE CARIBBEAN
Fire down below / Grass skirt / Mary Ann / Out of my dreams / Spear dance / Zulu chant / La paloma / Jungle / Native mambo / Spur dance / Flag woman / Wings of a dove / Endless vibrations / Calypso eine kleine nachtmusik
12176 / Mar '96 / Laserlight

☐ STEEL BANDS OF TRINIDAD AND TOBAGO
Sunset / Pan in the minor / Love's theme / To be continued / Unknown band / I just called to say I love you / Sparrow medley / Calypso music / Brisad del zolla / Somewhere out there / Hammer
DE 4011 / Jan '94 / Delos

☐ STEEL DRUM FESTIVAL
TCD 1039 / Nov '96 / Tradition

☐ STEEL MUSIC VOL.2 (Calypsos And Socas)
68941 / Apr '97 / Tropical

☐ STEEL RAILS (Classic Railroad Songs Vol.1)
Wabash Cannonball: Acuff, Roy / Orange blossom special: Johnson Mountain Boys / Daddy, what's a train: Phillips, Utah / Jimmie the kid: Rodgers, Jimmie / Ramblin' man: Kane, Kieran / Steel rails: Krauss, Alison / Trainwreck of emotion: McCoury, Del / Slow moving freight train: Moffatt, Hugh / Lord of the trains: Russell, Tom / LAst train: Rowan, Peter / Nine pound hammer: Grisman, David / When the golden train comes down: Sons Of The Pioneers / Texas, 1947: Clark, Guy / Pan American boogie: MacKenzie, Kate
ROUCD 1128 / Mar '97 / Rounder

☐ STEEPED IN THE BLUES TRADITION
TCD 1016 / May '96 / Tradition

☐ STEP BACK TO THE SIXTIES
Nitty gritty/Something's got a hold on me: Hollies / I call your name: Kramer, Billy J. & The Dakotas / In crowd: Fourmost / I don't want to see you again: Peter & Gordon / Around and around: Swinging Blue Jeans / Talking about you: Hollies / It's gonna be alright: Gerry & The Pacemakers / Lost city: Shadows / I just can't lose the blues: Ifield, Frank / Let there be love: Bassey, Shirley
4950332 / 29 Jun '98 / EMI

☐ STEP ON
Step on: Happy Mondays / Unbelievable: EMF / Dub be good to me: Beats International & Lindy Layton / Gypsy woman: Waters, Crystal / Mr. Wendall: Arrested Development / Don't let it go to your head: Brand New Heavies / Mercy mercy me: Palmer, Robert / It's my life: Talk Talk / Stay: Shakespears Sister / Hold on: Wilson Phillips / Road to nowhere: Talking Heads / Real real real: Jesus Jones / Can't touch this: MC Hammer / You make me feel mighty real: Somerville, Jimmy / Ic eice baby: Vanilla Ice / Whatta man: Salt n' Pepa / It's a shame: Monie Love / Shake oyour head: Was Not Was / House of love: East 17 / Dizzy: Reeves, Vic & Wonder Stuff
5529242 / Oct '97 / Spectrum

☐ STEP, WRITE, RUN (2CD Set)
TONE 6CD2 / Nov '96 / Touch

☐ STEPPIN' OUT - THE ALBUM VOL.3
STEP 3CDN / Sep '96 / Steppin' Out

☐ STEPPIN' OUT - THE ALBUM VOL.5 (2CD Set)
STEP 5CD / 31 Jul '98 / Steppin' Out

☐ STEPPING IT OUT
VT 1CD / Oct '93 / Veteran Tapes

☐ STEREO COCKTAIL
EFA 610512 / May '96 / Platten Meister

☐ STEREO ULTRA
Ok Chicago: Resonance / Le crocodile porte cle: Gerard, Bernard / Nues dans l'eau: Garvarentz, Georges / Petrol pop: Magne, Michel & Jean Yanne / Kidnapping: Schafer, Karl-Heinz / Ten and medor: Gorageur, Alain / Batacuda: Delerue, Georges / Hashisch party: Garvarentz, Georges / Full speed: Bolling, Claude / Sexopolis: Mirouze, Jean Pierre / La theme d'Olivier: Lai, Francis / La course d'auto: Dumont, Charles / Take one: Golden Pot / Grand theme malka: Magne, Michel
FR 364CD / 30 Mar '98 / Big Cheese

☐ STEREOPOLY
HADCD 002 / 27 Oct '97 / Hadshot Haheizart

☐ STICKY WHIPPET (The Best Of New Ground Records)
Live in taffeta: Secret Order / Manoible man: Floating Bloke / Shiny woman: Conemelt / Glowing trees: Meek / Two days: Corridor / All over hair piece: Conemelt / Beetlecrusher: Floating Bloke / Agnostic stomp: Conemelt / New Ground office: Grant
OUCH 003CD / 6 Oct '97 / Spiky

☐ STILETTO VAMP (3CD Set)
DTKBOX 68 / 13 Oct '97 / Dressed To Kill

☐ STILL COOKIN'
URCD 005 / Jul '96 / Ubiquity

☐ STILL DIZZY AFTER ALL THESE YEARS (2CD Set)
Paranoid: Black Sabbath / Dear Miss lonely hearts: Lynott, Phil / Delilah: Harvey, Alex / Crawfish: Streetwalkers / 5705: City Boy / In my box: Fairfield Parlour / I don't know: May Blitz / Hey Lord don't ask me questions: Parker, Graham / My Heaven: Clear Blue Sky / Mwenga sketch: Jade Warrior / Cry for everyone: Gentle Giant / Catch you on the rebop: Davis, Spencer Group / Get your dog off me: Beggar's Opera / Torrid zone: Nucleus / No time like the present: Downes, Bob / Those about to die: Colosseum / Joybringer: Manfred Mann's Earthband / It's all over now: Stewart, Rod / Mr. Joy: Stewart, Rod / Paper plane: Status Quo / Dreammare: Uriah Heep / To play your little games: Cressida / Half baked: Campbell, Jimmy / Lady's changing home: Tudor Lodge / Living at the end of time: Atlantis / Four horseman the spencer: Aphrodite's Child / Warm red glow: Patto / Time for leaving: Magna Carta / Who do you love: Juicy Lucy
5552022 / 6 Jul '98 / Vertigo

☐ STILL FROM THE HEART
WB 1152CD / Jun '97 / We Bite

☐ STILL GOT THE BLUES
EMPRBX 004 / Sep '94 / Empress

☐ STILL GOT THE BLUES (2CD Set)
Shame shame shame: Guy, Buddy / Wake up call: Mayall, John / Blue mood: Winter, Johnny / World in motion: Staples, Pops / Fear no evil: Ward, Robert / Cork up that bottle: Blue Lou & The Headhunters / Home at last: Harris, Hi Tide / Your mind is on vacation: Rogers, Roy / I guess that says it all: Croker, Brendan / Oh say you can see the red, white and blues: Graham, John / Since I fell for you: Diesel, Johnny / Frustrated baby: McCray, Larry / Feels like rain: Guy, Buddy / Too many cooks: Evans, Terry / I can tell: Trout, Walter Band / Lord have mercy on me: Ward, Robert / All those heroes: Mayall, John / No money at all: Croker, Brendan & The 5 O'Clock Shadows / Look now baby: Glass, James / Down in Mississippi: Staples, Pops / Some kind of wonderful: Guy, Buddy / Iceman: Collins, Albert / Hole in my heart: McCray, Larry / Third degree: Blue Lou & The Headhunters / You keep sayin' that you're leavin': Winter, Johnny / Trouble blues: Hammond, John / One in a million: Mayall, John / Glamour girl: Robillard, Duke Band / Chokin' kind: Washington, Walter 'Wolfman' / I miss you so: Harris, Hi Tide
DOU 882402 / 29 Aug '97 / Disky

☐ STILL GOT THE BLUES VOL.1
EMPRCD 502 / Apr '94 / Emporio

☐ STILL GOT THE BLUES VOL.2
EMPRCD 508 / Apr '94 / Emporio

☐ STILL SEARCHIN' (A Collection Of Electro Beats)
My beatbox: Deejay Punk-Roc / Bass alarm: DJ Ex-Fx / Toke it out: Rude Cubans / Ladies rock the house: Real Rulers / Lazy afternoon: Swoon / Bass-a-go-go: DJ Ex-Fx / I'm not a bitch: E Funk Sound Surgeon / Bouncing bomb: Jaywalk / Never let u go: Jaywalk / Still searchin': Cape Canaveral
ILLCD 1013 / 30 Mar '98 / Airdog

☐ STILL SMOKIN'
GLINECD 001 / Apr '97 / Ganja/ Frontline

☐ STILL SPICY GUMBO STEW
I don't want to be hurted: George, Barbara / Losing battle: Adams, Johnny / Check Mr. Popeye: Bo, Eddie / Now let's Popeye: Bo, Eddie / Shrimp boat: Dr. John / Somebody's got to go: Tick tocks / Why lie: Tee, Willie / I found a little girl: Bo, Eddie / Love as true as mine: Johnson, Wallace / I got a feelin': Nooky Boy / Money (that's what I want): Afo executives / Who knows: Tee, Willie / Heart for sale: Lee, Robbie / Point: Dr. John / Roamin-itis: Bo, Eddie / Baby: Lynn, Tammi / Love love love: Wood Brothers / Nancy: Afo executives / Serpent woman: Robinson, Alvin / Soulful woman: Robinson, Alvin / Sho' 'bout drive me wild: Robinson, Alvin / End of a dream (Booker's ballad): Booker, James / Cry cry cry: Robinson, Alvin
CDCHD 520 / Jun '94 / Ace

☐ STINGRAY - THE COLLECTION VOL.1
STINGCD 1 / Feb '95 / Sting Ray

☐ STIRRING WITH SOUL
TCD 1040 / Nov '96 / Tradition

☐ STOLEN MOMENTS - RED, HOT & COOL (2CD Set)
Time is moving on: Byrd, Donald & Guru / Un angel en danger: MC Solaar & Ron Carter / Positive: Franti, Michael / Nocturnal sunshine: Ndegeocello, Me'shell / Flyin' high in the Brooklyn sky: Digable Planets/Lester Bowie/Wah Wah Watson / Stolen moments: UFO / Rubber's song: Pharcyde / I shall proceed: Roots & Roy Ayers / Trouble don't last always: Incognito/Carleen Anderson/Ramsey Lewis / Rent strike: Groove Collective & Bernie Worrell / Scream: Us 3 & Joshua Redman/Tony Remy / This is madness: Last Poets & Pharoah Sanders / Apprehension: Cherry, Don & The Watts Prophets / Love supreme: Marsalis, Branford / Love supreme: Coltrane, Alice / Creator has a master plan: Sanders, Pharoah
GRP 97942 / Oct '94 / GRP

☐ STOMPERS (2CD Set)
Shame shame shame: Lewis, Smiley / Fat man: Domino, Fats / Wine woman and whiskey: Lightfoot, Papa George / For you my love: Lutcher, Nellie & Nat 'King' Cole / Jumpin' at capitol: Cole, Nat 'King' Trio / Who drank my bear while I was in the rear: Bartholomew, Dave / Prancin': Turner, Ike & Tina's Kings Of Rhythm / Hucklebuck with Jimmy: Five Keys / Variations on a theme: Lewis, Meade 'Lux' / That's all I need: Turner, Ike & The Kings Of Rhythm / Hole in my heart: Esquerita / Trouble up the road: Brenston, Jackie / Boogie woogie Memphis: Memphis Slim / Down the road apiece: Milburn, Amos / Save your money baby: Shakey Jake & The All Stars / Mother fuyer: Dirty Red / Let the good times roll: Shirley & Lee / Proud Mary: Turner, Ike & Tina / No mo do yakomo: Dr. Feelgood / You can't catch me: Love Sculpture / King kong: Tyler, Big T. / Big fat: Canned Heat / Be baba leba: Humes, Helen / Little bitty pretty one: Harris, Thurston & The Sharps / Rockin' by myself: Gowans, Sammy / I need you I want you: Parker, Jack / Red hot: Luman, Bob / Slow smooth and easy: Gene & Eunice / Oo wee: Jordan, Louis / Fujiyama mama: Allen, Annisteen / Come back to me: Walker, T-Bone / Down the road: Lewis, Smiley / Baby get it on: Turner, Ike & Tina / Sandra B: Boze, Calvin & His All Stars / Hurt by love: Foxx, Inez / I got booted: James, Sonny / Back in the night: Dr. Feelgood / Lookin' for a love: Womack, Bobby / Low down in lodi: King, Freddie / So long good luck and goodbye: Rogers, Weldon
CDEM 1622 / Jul '97 / EMI

☐ STOMPIN' AT THE KLUB FOOT VOL.5
DOLECD 105 / Jan '98 / Dojo

☐ STOMPIN' AT THE SAVOY
Stompin' at the Savoy: Armstrong, Louis / In the mood: Miller, Glenn / It started all over again: Dorsey, Tommy / Nutcracker suite: Brown, Les / Northwest passage: Herman, Woody / Tea for two: Armstrong, Louis / April in Paris: Miller, Glenn / Nearness of you: Dorsey, Jimmy / Nightmare: Shaw, Artie / How about you: Brown, Les / C'est si bon: Armstrong, Louis / Frankie and Johnny: Goodman, Benny / Chattanooga choo choo: Miller, Glenn / Fools rush in: Dorsey, Jimmy / Pretty woman: Ellington, Duke / Good for nothin' Joe: Barnet, Charlie / Tiger rag: Armstrong, Louis / After glow: Herman, Woody / I've got rhythm: Dorsey, Jimmy / That old black magic: Miller, Glenn
GRF 129 / '93 / Tring

☐ STONE COLD FUNK
MCCD 337 / 16 Mar '98 / Music Club

☐ STONE ROCK BLUES
CHLD 19264 / Oct '94 / Chess/MCA

☐ STONED REVOLUTION
RNDL 98022CD / 27 Jul '98 / Rough Trade

☐ STONES OF CALLANISH, THE (A Folk Opera 2CD Set)
Stones on the hill: Tabor, June / Crucified on your old broken cross: Paterson, Rod / Don't say goodbye: Davies, Lesley / Across the wide ocean: Russell, Janet / Latha dhomh's mi gabhail a'mhonaidh: MacPhee, Catherine-Anne / Going down to metal bridge: Dow, Nick & Bernard Wrigley / You ebb and flow: Russell, Janet / I stand here alone on the beach: Davies, Lesley / On me way to Dover: Dow, Nick / Towers of London: Simpson, Fiona / You ebb and flow: Paterson, Rod / Tasdan a'righ's feileadh an t-saighdeir: MacPhee, Catherine-Anne / Down from the hills: Paterson, Rod & Fiona Simpson/ Catherine Ann MacPhee / Sleep on my darling: Davies, Lesley / Stones on the hil: Tabor, June / Another pint: Paterson, Rod / Reconciliation: Paterson, Rod & Lesley Davies / Take me back to Lewis: Davies, Lesley
DOG 005/6 / Feb '97 / Mrs. Ackroyd

☐ STONEWALL (3CD Set)
DTKBOX 91 / 6 Jul '98 / Dressed To Kill

☐ STOP AND LISTEN VOL.1
BBECD 001 / Nov '96 / Barely Breaking Even

☐ STOP AND LISTEN VOL.2
Monkey that became president: Brotherhood / It's too funky in here: P-Funk All Stars / Tribute to the JB's: Last Minister / Power (out of sight): Hip Hop Traxx / Summertime lovin': Arrington, Steve / Soul power '74: Maceo & The Macks / Walk into the sun: Organised Confusion / Cut me loose: Push / Que si que: Pac Man / Got to get back to Louisiana: Parker, Elmer / Zambezi: Kynard, Charles / More mess on my thing: Poets Of Rhythm
BBECD 003 / Mar '97 / Barely Breaking Even

☐ **STOP AND LISTEN VOL.3 (Compiled By Bobbi & Steve)**
Trinidad: Jumbo Caribbean Disco / I really love you: Heaven & Earth / Till you surrender: Brown, Rainbow / Saturday night, Sunday morning: Houston, Thelma / Trip to your mind: Hudson People / Love don't live: Proctor, Michael / My desire: Next Phase & Helen Bruner / Just follow the vibe: Zoo Experience / We can make it: Zoo Experience / Everybody: Preston Project / Love and happiness: Second Crusade / Keep the faith: Ramirez, Philip
BBECD 007 / Jul '97 / Barely Breaking Even

☐ **STOP AND LISTEN VOL.4**
Mosquito coast 94-96: Mr. Gone / Guiro electro: Matos, Bobby / Straight ahead: Brooklyn Express / Nothing's changed: Ten City / Motivation: Atmosfear / African mailman: Simone, Nina / Bummer summer: Crazy Penis / Berimbau de ossanha: Easydelics / In good faith: Harris, Norman / Spring again: Yost, Kevin / Send in the clowns: Alexandria, Lorez / Way we live: Raw Soul Express
BBECD 011 / 27 Apr '98 / Barely Breaking Even

☐ **STOP SAMPLER**
74321308452 / Sep '95 / Arista

☐ **STORM FROM THE EAST VOL.1 (JMJ Mix Tape)**
ASHADOW 4CD / May '96 / Moving Shadow

☐ **STORM FROM THE EAST VOL.2**
Storm from the east Vol.2 / Eleventh hour: PFM / Reed breeze: Hyper On Experience / Illicit groove: JMJ & Richie / Overcast swing: Flytronix / Sunset phobia: E-Z Rollers / Gravitational pull: JMJ / Altitude of dreams: Universal / Horizontal movements: Kudos / True: Tekniq / Control: Banks, Alex
ASHADOW 8CD / Mar '97 / Moving Shadow

☐ **STORM OF DRONES (3CD Set)**
ASP 0966CD / 22 Jun '98 / Asphodel

☐ **STORMY WEATHER**
PHONTCD 7647 / '94 / Phontastic

☐ **STORMY WEATHER**
LMLP 3002 / Sep '97 / Jah Life

☐ **STORY OF FADO, THE (Music From Portugal)**
A casa de Mariquinhas: Marceneiro, Alfredo / Nao venhas tarde: Ramos, Carlos / Tia macheta: Cardoso, Berta / A tendinha: Silva, Hermina / A rosinha dos limoes: Max / Rosa enjeitada: Teresa de Noronha, Maria / Partir e morer um pouco: Dos Santos, Antonio / Foi na travessa da palha: Do Carmo, Lucilia / Foi deus: Rodrigues, Amalia / Lisboa a noite: De Matos, Tony / Aquela janela virada pro mar: Da Silva, Tristao / Fado das caldas: Da Camara, Vicente / Belos tempos: Farinha, Fernando / Colchetes de oiro: Da Camara, Hermano / Fadista louco: Mourao, Antonio / Saudade vai-te embora: Maria, Fernanda / Embucado: Rosa, Joao Ferreira / Amar: Carvalho, Teresa Silva / Saudade mal do fado: Do Carmo, Carlos / Arraial: Braga, Joao / Ate que a voz me doa: Da Fe, Maria / Carvalo ruco: Pereira, Nuno Da Camara
HEMIMDCD 100 / Feb '97 / Hemisphere

☐ **STORY OF FLAMENCO, THE**
Serranita me publicaste: De La Matrona, Pepe / Me valgo de mi saber: De Cadiz, Perla / Subasta de cuadras antiguos: De Cadiz, Pericon / Moritos a caballo: De Jerez, Sernita / Yo tengo tres corazones: Isidro, Paco / Mujer malina: Caracol, Manolo / Le pido a dios: De Utrera, Fernanda / En al estribo: Moreno, Gabriel / Los andaluces: Flores De Gaditano / La zagala: La Nina De La Puebla / Me pongo a pregonar: De Jerez, Terremoto / Fiesta en el Barrio De Santiago: De Jerez, Terremoto & Romerito/El Borrico/Diamante Negro / A linares que us mi pueblo: Linares, Carmen / Tabernas de triana: El Pali / Nochebuena en el alosno: Toronjo, Hermanos / Nana de la cebollas: Morente, Enrique / Me guesta estar en la Sierra: Marchena, Pepe
HEMIMDCD 103 / Feb '97 / Hemisphere

☐ **STORY OF GOLDBAND RECORDS, THE**
Stormy weather: Phillips, Phil / Let's boogie: Bonner, Juke Boy / Sugar Bee: Cleveland Crochet / Let's go boppin' tonight: Ferrier, Al / Crawl: Guitar Junior / So what: Duhan, Johnny / Cindy Lou: Terry, Gene / You're lonesome now: Perrywell, Charles / Boogie in the mud: James, Danny / Going crazy baby: Guitar Junior / Rooster strut: Savoy, Ashton / No future: Rockin' Sidney / You're so fine: Kershaw, Pee Wee / Frosty: James, Danny / San Antonio: Big Walter / Please accept my love: Wilson, Jimmy / Blue bayou shuffle: Cookie & The Cupcakes / Teenage baby: Herman, Sticks / Secret of love: Anderson, Elton / Chicken stuff: Wilson, Hop / Teardrops in my eyes: Terry, Gene / Puppy love: Parton, Dolly / Don't leave me: Phillips, Phil
CDCHD 424 / Nov '92 / Ace

☐ **STORY OF ROCK 'N' ROLL (2CD Set)**
Leader of the pack: Shangri-Las / He's so fine: Chiffons / Stagger lee: Price, Lloyd / Runaway: Shannon, Del / Shake rattle and roll: Haley, Bill / Sheila: Roe, Tommy / Wooly bully: Sam The Sham & The Pharaohs / Speedy gonzales: Boone, Pat / Venus: Avalon, Frankie / Only sixteen: Cooke, Sam / Shakin' all over: Allen, Chad & The Guess Who / Party doll: Knox, Buddy / Lucille: Little Richard / Keep on dancing: Gentrys / Viva Bobby Joe: Equals / Red river rock: Johnny & The Hurricanes / Rock around the clock: Haley, Bill / Letters: Box Tops / Tallahassee road: Nashville Teens / Dancing in the street: Reeves, Martha / Da doo ron ron: Crystals / It's my party: Gore, Lesley / Let's have a party: Jackson, Wanda / Teen beat: Nelson, Sandy / Maybelline: Berry, Chuck / Good golly Miss Molly: Swinging Blue Jeans / Raunchy: Justis, Bill / Blueberry hill: Domino, Fats / Charlie Brown: Coasters / Baby come back: Equals / Rock 'n' roll is here to stay: Danny & The Juniors
DCD 3009 / Jun '97 / Music

☐ **STORY OF TANGO, THE**
La cumparsita: Basso, Jose / El choclo: Sexteto Mayor / De vuelta y media: Varela, Francisco / Quejas de bandoneon: Troilo, Anibal / Verano porteandon: Garello, Paul / La cachila: Pugliese, Osvaldo / El dia que me quieras: Gardel, Carlos / Grisel: Mores, Mariano / La pu me qui: Canaro, Francisco / Yira, yira: Sassone, Florindo / La yumba: Pugliese, Osvaldo / Adios nonino: Sexteto Mayor / Margerita de Agosto: Garello, Paul / El firulete: Basso, Jose / Taquito militar: Mores, Mariano / La tablada: Canaro, Francisco / Danzarin: Troilo, Anibal / Palomita blanca: Varela, Francisco / Adios muchachos: Sassone, Florindo / Mi Buenos Aires querido: Gardel, Carlos
HEMIMDCD 101 / Feb '97 / Hemisphere

☐ **STORY OF THE BLUES, THE**
Hot time in the old town tonight: Hurt, 'Mississippi' John / Casey Jones: Hurt, 'Mississippi' John / Goodnight Irene: Leadbelly / Bollweevil: Leadbelly / Nothin' but the blues: Hopkins, Lightnin' / Evil hearted woman: Hopkins, Lightnin' / Things I used to do: Lightnin' Slim / My babe: Lightnin' Slim / Jump for joy: Turner, 'Big' Joe / Honest I do: Reed, Jimmy / Dust my broom: Howlin' Wolf / Shake it for me: Howlin' Wolf / Terraplane blues: Williams, 'Big' Joe / I got my mojo working: Waters, Muddy / Hoochie coochie man: Waters, Muddy / Corrina Corrina: Waters, Muddy / Baby, please don't go: Waters, Muddy / Whiskey and wimmen: Hooker, John Lee / Dimples: Hooker, John Lee / Boom boom: Hooker, John Lee
CD 6100 / Oct '97 / Music

☐ **STORY OF THE CIVIL RIGHTS MOVEMENT THROUGH ITS SONG, THE**
SFWCD 40032 / Dec '94 / Smithsonian Folkways

☐ **STRAIGHT AHEAD (A Journey Through Acid Jazz)**
Mission impossible: Taylor, James Quartet / Day at the seaside: Brand New Heavies / Bolivia: Sandberg, Ulf Quartet / Bad ass weed: Mother Earth / I don't want to see myself (without you): Callier, Terry / Spinning wheel: New Jersey Kings / Manteca: Jazz Renegades / Dat's slammin': Gordon, Robbie / Ain't no sunshine: Beaujolais Band / Beyond the snowstorm: Snowboy / Mercy mercy me: Jazz Apostles / Throttle back: Emperor's New Clothes
MUSCD 033 / Jan '97 / MCI Music

☐ **STRAIGHT EDGE AS FUCK VOL.3**
DFR 18 / Jun '97 / Desperate Flight

☐ **STRAIGHT FROM THE SOUL**
Hot wild unrestricted crazy love: Jackson, Millie / At last: Jones, Glenn / Bad attitude: Sha Sha / Vibe is right: Turner, Ruby / No stoppin' us now: Davis, Mike / High on desire: Winstanley, Liz / Children of the ghetto: Real Thing / Heal our land: Butler, Jonathan / Every step of the way: Jones, Glenn / Merry go round: Turner, Ruby / Jewel of the Nile: Wilson, Precious / I need you: Smith, Richard Jon / Love is a dangerous game: Jackson, Millie / Overflowing: Butler, Jonathan / Pressing on: Bell-Armstrong, Vanessa / I'll be your friend: Wilson, Precious
EMPRCD 548 / Nov '94 / Emporio

☐ **STRAIGHT FROM THE STREET VOL.1 (The Hip-Hottest New R&B & Rap)**
Creep: TLC / Flava in ya ear: Mack, Craig / Big poppa: Notorious BIG / Think of you: Users / Tonite: AFGM / Don't take it personal: Arnold, Monica / Git up, git out: Outkast / We gets busy: Illegal / Just a little flava: Unorthodox / Player's ball: Outkast / Beware of rampshack: Rampage / Get down: Mack, Craig / I miss you: N II U
74321276912 / Feb '97 / Arista

☐ **STRAIGHT NO CHASER**
Pee Wee Marquette's intro / Cantaloupe island / Ronnie's bonnie / Comment on ritual / Alfie's theme / Cool blues / Crisis / Straight no chaser / Sookie sookie / Goin' down south / Song for my Father / Blind man / Filthy McNasty / Jeannine / Steppin' into tomorrow
CDS 8282632 / Apr '94 / Blue Note

☐ **STRAIGHT OUTTA BOONE COUNTY**
Hamtramck mama: Volebeats / Run mountain: Flathead / I'm lonesome without you: Hazeldine / No vacancy: Holler / Wedding of the bugs: Fulks, Robbie / No more nuthin': Lucky Stars / Dark as a dungeon: Slobberbone / Hangman's boogie: Caution Horse / In the jailhouse: Grievous Angels / Southern moon: One Riot One Ranger / Tennessee waltz: Timms, Sally / Won't you ride in my little red wagon: Gunter, Hardrock & The Dalhart Imperials / Why don't you haul off and love me: Belly, Scroat / If I lose: Cowslingers / Bottom of the glass: Whiskeytown / Barbara Allen: Handsome Family / I wanna be hugged to death by you: Waycross / Hucklebuck: Riptones / Big big city: Showoffs / Nine pound hammer: Waco Brothers
BS 019CD / Jun '97 / Bloodshot

☐ **STRAIGHT TALK VOL.1**
PHCD 2051 / Jan '97 / Penthouse

☐ **STRANGE GAMES AND THINGS**
Strange games and things: Love Unlimited Orchestra / If I can't stop you: Bristol, Johnny / Mademoiselle: Foxy / You can't run away: Bar-Kays / Reasons: Riperton, Minnie / Bring your sweet loving back: Starpoint / Hollywood dreaming: Father's Children / Hunk of heaven: Lemuria / Elevate your mind: Williams, Linda / 90% of me is you: McCrae, Gwen / Another day: Goodman, Ray & Brwon / Girl you need a change of mind: Kendricks, Eddie
BBECD 005 / Jun '97 / Beechwood

☐ **STRANGE KIND OF LOVE**
Look of love: ABC / Love action (I believe in love): Human League / Golden brown: Stranglers / Only you: Yazoo / Love is a wonderful colour: Icicle Works / Rip it up: Orange Juice / Love will tear us apart: Joy Division / I'm in love with a German film star: Passions / I go to sleep: Pretenders / It must be love: Madness / Boys don't cry: Cure / Picture this: Blondie / Treason (it's just a story): Teardrop Explodes / Enola Gray: OMD / Bitterest pill (I ever had to swallow): Jam / It's different for girls: Jackson, Joe / Love my way: Psychedelic Furs / Party fears two: Associates / Back of love: Echo & The Bunnymen / Story of the blues (part 1): Mighty Wah
5355162 / Apr '96 / PolyGram TV

☐ **STRAWBERRY SUNDAE VOL.2 (2CD Set)**
Oh yeah: Syntone / Passion: Amen / Devotion: 88.3 / Feel so alive: Boomerang & Anna J. / Can you feel it: Solid Collective / It's about time: KGB / O: 28th Street Crew / Alright: Blu Room / I heat up: One Of A Kind / I feel you: Ispirazione / Comprided: Edge, Gordon / Feel so good: Brainbashers / Rock it: Atomic / Somebody scream: Warriors Of Love / If you really want somebody: McAteer, Grace / Beat: Dreamon / DBL: DJ Alan X / Round and round: RM Project / Slammin': RM Project / Lust not love: Ya Programme / Piano head: Rhythm Robbers / Do you feel what I'm feeling: Rhythm Robbers / Trading faces: Cadenza / Body working: Grand Larceny / Radiate: Brother Grim / Dirty minds: Tyrant / Love will take me higher: Pele & Gaston
MILL 040CD / Aug '97 / Millenium

☐ **STREET JAMS (The Very Best Of R&B Hip Hop & Street Soul - 2CD Set)**
No diggity: Blackstreet & Dr. Dre / Phenemenon: LL Cool J / I know where it's at: All Saints / All my life: K-Ci & Jo Jo / Gangsta's paradise: Coolio & LV / Ain't that just the way: McNeal, Lutricia / All my love: Queen Pen / This is how we do it: Jordan, Montell / Jump around: House Of Pain / She's got that vibe: Kelly, R / Boom boom: N-Tyce / I'll be there for you: Method Man & Mary J. Blige / Whatta man: Salt n' Pepa / Sometimes: Brand New Heavies / Love to love: Damage / Lifted: Lighthouse Family / If you want me: Hicks, Hinda / My father's son: Reeves, Conner / On and on: Badu, Erykah / It's like that: Run DMC & Jason Nevins / Now that we found love: Heavy D & The Boyz / Stranded: McNeal, Lutricia / Motownphilly: Boyz II Men / It's alright I feel it: NuYorican Soul / Always there: Incognito / Travelling man: Studio 2 / Real love: Driza Bone / Can I kick it: Tribe Called Quest / Apparently nothin': Young Disciples / Mary Jane (all night long): Blige, Mary J. / I'm going all the way: Sounds Of Blackness / Where you are: Patterson, Rashsaan / Guess who's back: Rakim / Iggin' me: DeBarge, Chico / Rewind: Celetia / Something about you: New Edition / Freek n' you: Jodeci / Every little thing I do: Soul For Real
TTVCD 2963 / 11 May '98 / Telstar TV

☐ **STREET JAZZ VOL.1**
Natasha: Like Young / Klute: FRISK / Theme from the underground bowling alley: TUBA / West by South West: As One / Be bop breakdance: Little Eye / Candyfloss: Forest Mighty Black / AWOL: British Underground Productions / Get up, get down: Fishbelly Black / London kills me: Groove Nation / Don't rub another man's rhubard: Innuendo / You know what it's like: Duverney, Ondrea / Free your mind: Action People / Seasons of my mind: Batu / Apple strudle: Up Bustle & Out
CDTEP 4 / Jun '94 / Step 2

☐ **STREET JAZZ VOL.2**
Better dreams: Family Construction / Fricasse de funk: Malka Family / 22 Steps ahead: Katch 22 / Life: Vibrazioni Productions / Heavyweight round: Sharpshooters / All black station: Progetto Tribale / It's a pleasure to see you: Tandy, George / Retro future: Retrovibe Movement / Where's Will: Zaeus / Moocow: Banana / Skiff: Bongo, Bud / Brixton Hill: Love Universal / Out of tune: Independent Colours / Summer: Pushmipulyu / Catwalk: Shakatak
CDTEP 6 / Dec '94 / Step 2

☐ **STREET JAZZ VOL.3**
Children of the world: Ghetto Swing / Too hot: Browne, Tom / Cilantro: Big Up Jazz / Power of seven: Bassism / I've to to know: Zaeus / Walking: Love Universal / Shadow run: Diferenz / Dig deep the funk: Alliance / Sweet talkin': Sharpshooters / Down to the bone groovers: Statem Island Groove / Rodo mundo: Reminiscence Quartet / Splie: Bongo, Bud
CDTEP 7 / Aug '95 / Step 2

☐ **STREET LIFE VOL.1**
GACCD 9301 / Aug '96 / GAC

☐ **STREET MUSIC OF PANAMA**
OMCD 008 / Nov '90 / Original Music

☐ **STREET ORGAN IN HOLLAND, THE**
ARN 64418 / 24 Feb '98 / Arion

☐ **STREET PARADE '95**
Sound: Humate / C5: DJ Edge / Level X: Bad Boy: Advent / Eclos: Random Fluctuations / Pure energy: Freakazoid / Mecha tech: Mijk's Magic Marble Box / I like that: Awex / I feel so detuned: No Soul / Clap your hands: Koenig / Audio strike: Synectics
SUPER 2043CD / Aug '95 / Superstition

☐ **STREET PARTY SING-A-LONG - 45 ENGLISH FAVOURITES**
PLATCD 3937 / Mar '95 / Platinum

☐ **STREET SOUL (2CD Set)**
Two can play that game: Brown, Bobby / She's got that vibe: R Kelly / Motownphilly: Boyz II Men / Right here: SWV / Flavour of the old school: Knight, Beverley / Just a step from heaven: Eternal / Don't walk away: Jade / Back and forth: Aaliyah / I love your smile: Shanice / That's the way love goes: Jackson, Janet / I swear: All 4 One / Down that road: Nelson, Shara / Don't look any further: M-People / Don't be a fool: Loose Ends / Back to life: Soul II Soul / One: Paris, Mica / Searching: China Black / Some girls: Ultimate Kaos / Sweetness: Gayle, Michelle / Unfinished sympathy: Massive Attack / Bump 'n' grind: R Kelly / Sensitivity: Tresvant, Ralph / Cry for you: Jodeci / 69: Father MC / Poison: Bel Biv Devoe / Can't stop: After 7 / Ghetto heaven: Family Stand / My lovin': En Vogue / Express: Carroll, Dina / Finally: Peniston, Ce Ce / Midnight at the oasis: Brand New Heavies / Mama said: Anderson, Carleen / Real love: Driza Bone / Carry me home: Gloworm / Down 4 whatever: Nuttin' Nyce / Hey DJ: Lighter Shade Of Brown / Buddy X: Cherry, Neneh / Whatta man: Salt n' Pepa & En Vogue / People everyday: Arrested Development / Summertime: DJ Jazzy Jeff & The Fresh Prince
VTDCD 41 / May '95 / Virgin

☐ **STREET SOUNDS ANTHEMS VOL.1 (The Official Week-Enders Album)**
I found lovin': Fatback Band / Funkin' for Jamaica: Browne, Tom / Bring the family back: Paul, Billy / Ain't no stoppin' us now: McFadden & Whitehead / Dominoes: Byrd, Donald / Movin': Brass Construction / Encore: Lynn, Cheryl / Hard work: Handy, John / Groove: Franklin, Rodney / Prance on: Henderson, Eddie
SOUNDSCD 3 / Mar '95 / Street Sounds

☐ **STREET SOUNDS ANTHEMS VOL.2**
Running away: Ayers, Roy / Expansions: Smith, Lonnie Liston / Let the music play: Earland, Charles / Six million steps: Harris, Rahni / Shame: King, Evelyn 'Champagne' / You can do it: Hudson, Al & The Partners / Which way is up: Starguard / Don't stop the music: Yarbrough & Peoples / You know how to love me: Hyman, Phyllis / Risin' to the top (give it all you got): Burke, Keni
SOUNDSCD 5 / May '95 / Street Sounds

☐ **STREET VIBES (2CD Set)**
RADCD 95 / 3 Aug '98 / Global TV

☐ **STREET WALKIN' BLUES**
JASSCD 626 / Oct '92 / Jass

☐ **STREETS OF FEAR**
Streets of fear: Caldonia / Goin' to Albert Lea: Higham, Darrel / Hot rhythm blue love: Kyme, Peter / Rollin' Danny: Phillips, Dave / Do you have to go: Hayward, Ronnie / You better watch out: Blue Jeans / Sleepless night: Vortex, Eddie / Rattlin' man: Twenty Flight Rock / Blue moon: Lightnin' Jay / Money: Muskrats / Say what you mean: Flapjacks / 1000 miles: Outer Miles / Too fast to live, too young to die: Sabrejets / Rock 'n' roll planet: Chalky The Yorkie / C'mon little girl: Cobras / Rattlesnake: Haywire / Cosmic star of rock 'n' roll: Power, Will / That's you: Rimshots / Down in the jungle: Clive's Jive Five / Losers never win: Caldonia
FCD 3037 / Mar '95 / Fury

☐ **STREETS OF NEW ORLEANS, THE**
Basin Street blues / Burgundy Street blues / St. Phillip Street breakdown / Beale Street blues / South Rampart Street Parade / Basin Street blues / Canal Street blues / South Rampart Street blues / Canal Street blues / Bourbon Street parade / Perdido Street blues
8747052 / Jul '96 / DA Music

☐ **STREETS OF SKA**
CDHB 198 / Nov '95 / Heartbeat

☐ **STREETWALKING BLUES**
JCD 626 / Feb '91 / Jass

☐ **STREETWISE RAP AND HIP HOP (2CD Set)**
Summertime: DJ Jazzy Jeff & The Fresh Prince / Wild wild West: Kool Moe Dee / Check yourself: D-Nice & Too Short / Can I kick it: Tribe Called Quest / Faith: Wee Papa Girl Rappers / Magic wand: Whodini / Go see the doctor: Kool Moe Dee / Down 4 whatever: Nuttin' Nyce / Keeper of the funk: Steady B / Livin' in a jungle: Schoolly D / I like the girls: Mr. Lee / Ghetto: Too Short / Self destruction: Stop The Violence Movement / Doo wop sh'bop: TOC & Rocca / Smoke some kill: Schoolly D / I think I can beat Mike Tyson: DJ Jazzy Jeff & The Fresh Prince / This is how we rip shit: Casual / Shoot pass slam: O'Neal, Shaq / Bonita applebum: Tribe Called Quest / Nasty girls: Steady B / Why is that: Boogie Down Productions / Call me D-Nice: D-Nice / '93 til infinity: Souls Of Mischief / What's up doc (can we rock): Fu-Schnickens / Infinite mass: Mah Boyz / Get in the groove: Wee Papa Girl Rappers / Jam it jam: She Rockers / Rise and shine: Kool Moe Dee
SD 886192 / 2 Feb '98 / Disky

☐ **STRESS BUSTERS**
STRESSCD 1 / 18 May '98 / Beechwood

☐ **STRICTLY BUSINESS (2CD Set)**
Intro / Like dis: Cool Hand Flex / Keep it real: Dextrous / Interlude: Stretch & T-Bone / Operating correctly: DJ Stretch / Interlude: Digital FX / Amazing: Shy FX / Raw: DJ Rap / Strumming dubs: Jonnie Blaze / Shaoling style: Tom & Jerry / Chill: Mr. Time / Bugle: T-Bone / Bruton: DJ Kane / Physical battle: Ken, Kenny / Can't take no more: Fusion Forum / Passing Phases: Mar, Leon / Interlude: Randall / Hard noize: Randall / Top gun: Dream Team / Rollin inside: MC Go / Don't take the shit: MC Fats / Interlude: Goldie / Hornet 127: Rufige Cru / Outro
RIDTMCD 01 / Jul '97 / Riddim Track
RIDTCD 01 / 23 Mar '98 / Riddim Track

☐ **STRICTLY DANCING (18 Strict Tempo Dance Favourites)**
Happy music / Secret love / Go tango / Granada / Spanish gypsy dance / La bamba / Green door / No reply / If I fell / How deep is your love / Look of love / Love letters / That's amore / I just called to say I love you / Violins / Lambada / Never gonna give you up / Que sera mi vida
SUMCD 4078 / Nov '96 / Summit

☐ **STRICTLY HARDCORE**
STHCCD 1 / '92 / Strictly Underground

☐ **STRICTLY INSTRUMENTAL VOL.1**
Outta tune: Big Four / Downshiftin': Ruo-Gents / Bandstand rocket: Twislors / Chicken: Cells, Ronnie / Don't call me flyface: Roekers / Spitfire: Harold & Bob / Rockin' hall: Howie & The Crystals / Fast track: Stingrays / Road block: Teen Rockers / Ce'ny: Jerry & The Silvertones / Vibrations: Royal Jokers / Tranquilizer boogie: Qual, Rex / Rock-a-mo: Adkinson, Billy / Round rock boogie: Rel-Yeas / Chicken rock: Wood, Scott / Devil's run: Kliebe, Herb Nervous Kats / Ghost train: Electro-Tonos / Ducks flying backward: Volk Brothers / Dancin' little thing: Riehle, Nick / Torpedo: Rhythm Rockers / Rampage: Rockaways / High time: Rock-Tonos / Teen rock: Teen Rockers / Workout: Journeymen / Talking crickets: Off Beats / Scramble: Night Trains / Wild cat: Sensations / Beatnik: Royal Jokers / Robot: Continental Cousins / All keyed up: Big Four
BB 55050 / Aug '97 / Buffalo Bop

☐ STRICTLY INSTRUMENTAL VOL.2
Midnight express: *Dawnbeats* / 234: *Rockin' Continentals* / Earthquake boogie: Dunavan, Terry / Bedlam: *Sounds* / Wolf call: Dent, Lord / Upspring: *Casuals* / Viking twist: *Vikings* / Moanin' bass: *Vibrations* / Shaften: *Corvetlos* / Firewater: *Premiers* / Roulette rock: *Varlatones* / Sabotage: Goode, B. / Heartbeat: *Daywins* / Ad lib: *Galaxies* / Red ants: *Off Beats* / Deep in the heart of Texas rock: *Dawnbreakers* / Spitfire: *Royal Notes* / Confusion: *Celts* / Flea: Reynolds, Larry / Venus rock: *Rollettes* / Do the fly: *Rovin' Gamblers* / Hot wire: *Crew* / Chicken rock: Holmes, Fat Daddy / Rock and a half: *Millionaires* / Rise: *St. John's Cardinals* / Endsville: Don, Al / Speed zone: *Impacts* / Troubled streets: *Night People* / Everybody twist: *Enchanters* / *Wibcee*: Williams, J.L.
BB 55051 / Aug '97 / Buffalo Bop

☐ STRICTLY RHYTHM VOL.3
REACTCD 043 / Jul '94 / React

☐ STRICTLY RHYTHM VOL.4
Theme: Loop 7 / Unnecessary changes: *Morel's Grooves* / Let's talk about me: *Androgeny* / Tearin' me apart': *Inner Soul* / Goin' clear: *Caucasian Boy* / Witch doktor: *Van Helden, Armand* / Sumba luma: *Tribal Infusion* / Paul's pain: *Nightman* / Project blast: *Photon Inc.* / Chosen path: *Sole Fusion* / Get up and get soulful: *Morel's Grooves* / Flavor of love: *Logic*
REACTCD 058 / Mar '95 / React

☐ STRICTLY RHYTHM VOL.5
SR 322CD / Oct '95 / Strictly Rhythm

☐ STRICTLY SOCA VOL.1
SJCM 108CD / Mar '97 / Crosby

☐ STRICTLY SOCA VOL.2
JWCM 111CD / 2 Feb '98 / Crosby

☐ STRICTLY THE BEST
VPCD 1227 / Apr '92 / VP

☐ STRICTLY THE BEST VOL.15
VPCD 1459 / Nov '95 / VP

☐ STRICTLY THE BEST VOL.18
VPCD 1460 / Nov '95 / VP

☐ STRICTLY THE BEST VOL.19
VPCD 15192 / 17 Nov '97 / VP

☐ STRICTLY THE BEST VOL.20
VPCD 15202 / 17 Nov '97 / VP

☐ STRICTLY THE BEST VOL.4
VPCD 1186 / Jul '92 / VP

☐ STRICTLY THE BEST VOL.7
VPCD 1251 / Nov '92 / VP

☐ STRICTLY THE BEST VOL.8
VPCD 1252 / Nov '92 / VP

☐ STRICTLY TRANCE VOL.1 (2CD Set)
GR 3708 / May '96 / Groovey

☐ STRICTLY UNDERGROUND VOL.1
Protein: *Sonic Experience* / Moonstompin': *Undercover Movement* / Mind, body and soul: *Fantasy UFO* / Burial: *Soundclash* / Let's go: *Noise Engineer* / Answer: *Equation* / Thru the night: *Noise Engineer* / Music's gonna rule the world: *Sonic Experience* / Untitled revolution: *Tigers In Space* / Best: *Full Dread* / Check it out: *Masters Of The Universe* / Do you want me: *Skeletor*
STURCD 1 / Nov '91 / Strictly Underground

☐ STRICTLY UNDERGROUND VOL.2
STURCD 3 / Feb '94 / Strictly Underground

☐ STRICTLY UNDERGROUND VOL.3
STURCD 5 / Oct '94 / Strictly Underground

☐ STRICTLY WORLDWIDE VOL.3
PIR 36 / Jun '94 / Piranha

☐ STRIKE A DEEP CHORD
JR 000032 / Dec '92 / Justice

☐ STRIKE UP THE BAND
What am I here for: *Basie, Count* / Midnight sun: *Hampton, Lionel* / Skyliner: *Barnet, Charlie* / Change of pace: *Jones, Quincy* / Harry, not Jesse: *James, Harry* / Pork pie: *Ferguson, Maynard* / One for Duke: *Nelson, Oliver* / Leave us leap: *Krupa, Gene* / I would do most anything for you: *Goodman, Benny* / Dateless Brown: *Rich, Buddy* / Birk's works: *Gillespie, Dizzy* / Br'er rabbit: *Vinson, Eddie 'Cleanhead'* / Boot 'em up: *Jacquet, Illinois* / Claxton Hall Swing: *Bellson, Louie* / Jazz me blues: *Herman, Woody* / Detour ahead: *Brookmeyer, Bob* / Jam with Sam: *Ellington, Duke*
5526442 / Mar '97 / Spectrum

☐ STRING BANDS 1926-1929
DOCD 5167 / May '93 / Document

☐ STRINGS OF AFRICA (Madagascar/ Burundi/Sierra Leone/3CD Set)
C 570301 / Mar '97 / Ocora

☐ STROBOSCOPICA (Sonorizzazioni Pyscho Beat)
Mark 4: *Matto Grosso* / Freedom power: *Dopping 2000* / Duo balls: *I-Gres* / Affano: *Micalizzi, F.* / Leyla theme: *Freedom Power* / Hide park: *Mark 4* / Walking at sunshine: *Pulsar* / Voleyr: *I-Gres* / Il porto: *Alessandroni, Alessandro* / Restless: *I-Gres* / Vortice freedom: *POWER* / Cat theme: *Pulsar* / Feasing: *Freedom Power* / To Jimmy: *I-Gres* / Altaena party: *De Masi, Francesco* / Reaction: *Freedom Power*
PLREC 003CD / 8 Dec '97 / Plastic

☐ STRUMMIN' MENTAL VOL.1
EFACD 11571 / 16 Mar '98 / Crypt

☐ STRUMMIN' MENTAL VOL.2
EFA 11579 / 16 Mar '98 / Crypt

☐ STUC CENTENARY ALBUM (If It Wisnae For The Union)
Battle of the Somme: *Dubliners* / Freedom come all ye: *Dubliners* / Four stone walls: *Capercaillie* / Both sides the tweed: *Gaughan, Dick* / Ravenscraig: *Runrig* / If it wisnae for the union: *Imlach, Hamish* / Bawbee birlin: *McCulloch, Gordeanna* / James Connolly: *Moore, Christy* / North by north: *Johnstone, Arthur* / Contract: *Bogle, Eric* / Gauteng: *Louw, Mara* / I am the common man: *Battlefield Band* / Blantyre explosion: *MacColl, Ewan* / Farewell tae the haven: *McCalmans* / Sell your labour, not your soul: *McNeill, Brian* / Three nights and a sunday: *McGinn, Matt* / Mothers, daughters, wives: *Small, Judy* / Te recuerdo Amanda: *Jara, Victor* / Stand together: *Ceolbeg*
CDTRAX 5005 / Feb '97 / Greentrax

☐ STUDIO DJ (2CD Set)
3017032 / Nov '96 / Fairway

☐ STUDIO K7 COMPILATION
K7 040CD / Oct '96 / Studio K7

☐ STY WARS
Bizarre love pentangle: *Muzz* / Tread lightly: *Moss, Bernard* / Drawing straws: *Bullitnuts* / Cinquante piquante: *Baby Mammoth* / Poodle calf: *Brazil Nuts* / Kingsblood royale: *Fila Brazillia* / Punctus contra punctum: *Solid Doctor* / Honey melon: *Mammoth Nuts* / Aim low: *Sheik & Beige* / Tone poem: *Third Face*
PORK 050 / 27 Apr '98 / Pork

☐ SUB LEVEL UK (15 Nu Breed Garage Tracks Mixed By DJ Dexter)
BULLCD 2 / 24 Nov '97 / Bullion

☐ SUB POP 200
TUPCD 4 / Jul '89 / Tupelo

☐ SUBBASE SAMPLER
SUBBASECD 4 / Oct '96 / Suburban Base

☐ SUBCULTURE
Chance: *Reel Houze* / Solo: *Biosphere* / Rhythmix: *That Kid Chris* / Pressure dub: *Ability II* / Renegade: *DJ Camacho* / UNI: *Soul Searchers* / Climax: *Smooth & Simmons* / Deep down: *Robinson Wall Project* / Let's get jazzy: *KC Flight* / Spring once more: *Unknown Factor* / Jazz journey: *DJ Assassin* / UNI: *Soul Searchers* / Sunburst: *Takabayashi* / Relics: *Abacus*
74321505752 / 29 Sep '97 / Arista

☐ SUBLIME HARMONIE (Victorian Musical Boxes & Polyphons)
March of the Toreadors / Hallelujah Chorus / Ave Maria / War march of the priests / Lost chord / Waltz from Faust / Largo / Wedding song / Wedding march / I have a song to sing / Behold the Lord High Executioner / Valse des fees
CDSDL 303 / Feb '93 / Saydisc

☐ SUBMERGED (A Collection Of Blooming Breaks And Buldging Beats)
Cheesey spillane: *Smart Alec & Clever Cloggs* / Summertime: *Lemongrass* / Mental stength: *Megashira* / La belle du jardin: *Pilgrims of the Mind* / Local spasm: *Nonplace Urban Field* / Spring: *Elektronauten* / Turn the screw: *Haynes, Graham* / 4am Electric: *Short Fuse* / Reminder: *Skrupel & Dani B* / Cee mix ree mix: *Crazy Baldheads* / Theme from fluturism: *Naid* / So happy: *Kriz PD*
INCCD 3313 / 8 Sep '97 / Incoming

☐ SUBMISSION VOL.1 (2CD Set)
Headlines: *Gargano, Pablo* / Purple phaze: *Canyon* / Now and zen: *Quietman* / Psalm 604: *Mobeus* / State of mind: *Floorplay* / Planet hunter: *Third Man* / Submerge 2: *Surge* / Let's turn on: *Doof* / Silver bullet: *Van Basten* / Arpa del mar: *Diveman* / Ancient forest: *Sungod* / Fahrenheit: *Love Loop* / Revolver: *De Niro* / Acid sunshine: *Transmasters* / Power of dreams: *Genetik* / Alternative: *Kulprit* / Meta morph 5: *Error 010* / Train of thought: *Matrix* / Growla: *Cage, Luke* / Jarred the mind: *Beach Buddha* / Party spirit: *Deep Sound*
9110224 / 23 Feb '98 / Nova Tekk

☐ SUBTERRANEAN HITZ VOL.2
EFA 012252 / 2 Feb '98 / Word Sound Recordings

☐ SUBTONAL
E 11100CD / Mar '98 / Electrolux

☐ SUBURBS FROM HELL
SOHO 13CD / Jan '94 / Suburbs Of Hell

☐ SUCCOUR (2CD Set)
POTCD 1 / Nov '96 / Backs

☐ SUCK IT AND SEE (2CD Set)
PUSSYCDLP 069 / 27 Jul '98 / Pussy Foot

☐ SUDANESE MUSIC FROM WEST JAVA
SM 16072 / Feb '96 / Wergo

☐ SUDDEN IMPACT VOL.1
VPCD 1241 / Jul '92 / Shocking Vibes

☐ SUGAR BABY
I 3896072 / Oct '96 / Galaxy

☐ SUGAR HITS (2CD Set)
Something goin' on: *Terry, Todd* / Free: *Ultra Nate* / Fresh: *Gina G* / MFEO: *Kavana* / Natural: *Andre, Peter* / 911: *911* / Closer than close: *Gaines, Rosie* / Isn't it a wonder: *Boyzone* / Let me in: *OTT* / Clementine: *Owen, Mark* / WAaterloo sunset: *Dennis, Cathy* / Do you know: *Gayle, Michelle* / CardLovefool: *Cardigans* / Statuesque: *Sleeper* / Girl power: *Shampoo* / Good enough: *Dodgy* / Disco 2000: *Pulp* / Dark clouds: *Space* / Candy girl: *Baby Bird* / 6 underground: *Sneaker Pimps* / Different beats: *Boyzone* / Forever love: *Barlow, Gary* / Anywhere for you: *Backstreet Boys* / I need you: *3T* / Last night: *Az Yet* / I believe I can fly: *R Kelly* / Wonderful tonight: *Damage* / One kiss from heaven: *Damage* / How deep is your love: *Take That* / If you ever: *East 17 & Gabrielle* / I love you always forever: *Lewis, Donna* / Walk on by: *Gabrielle* / Shout: *Ant & Dec* / Hey child: *East 17* / Make it with you: *Let Loose* / One more chance: *One* / Happy: *MN8* / We got it: *Immature* / Sometimes when we touch: *Newton* / Twelfth of never: *Carter Twins*
5536982 / Jun '97 / PolyGram TV

☐ SUGAR LUMP
Sweet as she can be: *Adkinson, Billy* / Scrapirion: *Slade, Prentis* / Rock me: *Dunn, David* / You're a cheater: *Sessions, Don* / Back to school again: *Michael, Teddy Lee* / Gonna be nice tonight: *Phantoms* / Sugar lump: *Adkinson, Billy* / Cry woman cry: *Wheeler, Larry* / Candy stone: *Furr, Curt* / Rocking at school: *Dunavan, Terry* / Redwood fence: *Shadows* / Katy D: *Billy & The Jokers* / Mine all mine: *Cuno, Fred* / Home run: *Halladay, Chance* / There ain't nothing true: *Nelson, Bobby* / No use knocking on my door: *Walker, Lanie* / No chance: *Maupin, Ramon* / Sugaree: *York, Rusty* / You lied to me honey: *Gavley, Junior* / Little more loving: *Comer, Chuck* / Eenie meenie miney mo: *Walker, Lanie* / Tennessee border: *Work, Jimmy* / Come over rover: *Mooney, Glenn* / Uh huh: *Bowman, Leroy* / Oh Pattie: *Kaye, Johnnie* / Please please baby: *Brown, Bobby* / Bette Loe: *Bowman, Bow* / Sweet love: *York, Rusty* / Down at big Mary's house: *Brown, Bobby* / Love gone: *Maupin, Ramon*
BB 55061 / Aug '97 / Buffalo Bop

☐ SUGAR PLUMS (Holiday Treats From Sugar Hill)
SHCD 3796 / Jan '97 / Sugar Hill

☐ SUGARHILL - THE 12" REMIXES
Message: *Grandmaster Flash & The Furious Five* / Freedom: *Grandmaster Flash & The Furious Five* / Apache: *Sugarhill Gang* / Rapper's delight: *Sugarhill Gang* / Eighth wonder: *Sugarhill Gang* / White lines (don't don't do it): *Grandmaster Flash & Melle Mel*
CLACD 345 / Jun '94 / Castle

☐ SUITCASE FULL OF BLUES, A
HCD 23 / Dec '95 / Black Swan

☐ SUITE '98
Moustique: *Stereo Total* / Bilitis: *France, Laila* / From Imola to Mexico: *Le Hammond Inferno* / Funky huxley: *Experimental Pop Band* / Muso: *Pop Tarts* / Most important man alive: *Momus* / Gemuese: *Dauerfisch* / Au revoir: *Dob* / Natacha: *Czerkinsky* / Puerto Habana: *Spring* / Jet ski: *Maxwell Implosion* / MFRFM: *Sunihara, Yoshinori* / L'aventure fantastique: *Fantastic Plastic Machine*
BUNG 0332 / 25 May '98 / Bungalow

☐ SULT: SPIRIT OF THE MUSIC
HBCD 0009 / Feb '97 / Hummingbird

☐ SULTRY LADIES OF JAZZ (3CD Set)
Miss Brown to you: *McRae, Carmen* / As long as I live: *Clooney, Rosemary* / In the wee small hours of the morning: *Christy, June* / All of me: *Vaughan, Sarah* / First time ever I saw your face: *Houston, Thelma* / This October: *London, Julie* / Gentleman friend: *Wilson, Nancy* / Spring cam really hang you up the most: *Kral, Irene* / I concentrate on you: *Sommers, Joanie* / Old folks: *Anderson, Ernestine* / Down with love: *Southern, Jeri* / I've got a right to cry: *Alexandria, Lorez* / Zing went the strings of my heart: *Harper, Toni* / You're blase: *Vaughan, Sarah* / September in the rain: *London, Julie* / Tabby the cat: *O'Day, Anita* / All night long: *Wilson, Nancy* / Sometimes I'm happy: *Vaughan, Sarah* / East Street: *Christy, June* / Look out, it's love: *Sommers, Joanie* / Talk about cozy: *Alexandria, Lorez* / More than you know: *Carpenter, Thelma* / About a quarter to nine: *Rivers, Mavis* / Sunday blues: *London, Julie* / Spring will be a little late this year: *Southern, Jeri* / It's a wonderful world: *Kral, Irene* / C'est la vie: *Franklin, Lynn* / On Green Dolphin Street: *Wilson, Nancy* / You better go now: *Sommers, Joanie* / I'm gonna lock my heart: *McRae, Carmen* / I'll take romance: *Christy, June* / Street of dreams: *Alexandria, Lorez* / Life is just a bowl of cherries: *Harper, Toni* / Don't worry 'bout me: *Clooney, Rosemary* / Lullaby in rhythm: *Christy, June* / Just a gigolo: *McRae, Carmen* / I hadn't anyone 'til you: *Southern, Jeri* / Detour ahead: *Kral, Irene* / Best is yet to come: *Alexandria, Lorez* / I'll close my eyes: *Sommers, Joanie* / One for my baby (and one more for the road): *Franklin, Lynn* / Feeling good: *Anderson, Ernestine* / What is this thing called love: *Vaughan, Sarah* / My old flame: *Clooney, Rosemary* / One minute to one: *Rivers, Mavis* / Nearness of you: *Wilson, Nancy* / Blues: *O'Day, Anita* / Tall boy: *London, Julie* / Just in time: *McRae, Carmen* / Bewitched, bothered and bewildered: *Harper, Toni* / Nobody else but me: *Kral, Irene*
HBCD 505 / Dec '96 / Hindsight

☐ SULTRY SUMMER BREEZE
DC 879502 / Oct '97 / Disky

☐ SUMMER BREEZE
Summer breeze: *Isley Brothers* / (Sittin' on the) dock of the bay: *Redding, Otis* / Walking in rhythm: *Blackbyrds* / Back to life: *Soul II Soul* / Under the broadwalk: *Drifters* / Girl from Ipanema: *Cole, Nat 'King'* / Gimme the sunshine: *Leo's Sunshipp* / Lovely day: *Withers, Bill* / Walking in sunshine: *Rockers Revenge* / Funky Nassau: *Beginning Of The End* / Hot hot hot: *Poindexter, Buster* / Funkin' for Jamaica: *Browne, Tom* / I can see clearly now: *Nash, Johnny* / Midnight at the oasis: *Muldaur, Maria* / Summer madness: *Kool & The Gang* / Love city groove: *Love City Groove* / Everybody's got summer: *Atlantic Starr* / Summertime: *DJ Jazzy Jeff & The Fresh Prince*
74321383172 / Jun '97 / RCA

☐ SUMMER CLUB CLASSICS
Children: *Miles, Robert* / Don't you want me: *Felix* / Hideaway: *DeLacy* / Not forgotten: *Leftfield* / Move your body: *Xpansions* / Swamp thing: *Grid* / Another night: *Real McCoy* / What is love: *Haddaway* / It's my life: *Dr. Alban* / Rhythm is a dancer: *Snap* / Funkin' for Jamaica: *Browne, Tom* / I wanna sex you up: *Color Me Badd* / Good thing going: *Minott, Sugar* / Baby I love your way: *Big Mountain* / Scatman: *Scatman John* / Macarena: *Los Del Rio*
74321588112 / 15 Jun '98 / Camden

☐ SUMMER COLLECTION (2CD Set)
KBOX 228 / Jul '98 / Collection

☐ SUMMER DANCE '98 (2CD Set)
C'est la vie: *B-Witched* / Gimmie love: *Alexia* / Diva: *Dana International* / Last thing on my mind: *Steps* / Heart's lone desire: *Marsden, Matthew* / Kung fu fighting: *Bus Stop & Carl Douglas* / Turn back time: *Aqua* / Life ain't easy: *Cleopatra* / Boom boom: *N-Tyce* / This is how we party: *Soap* / Rock your body: *Clock* / Breathe: *Minogue, Kylie* / Do you really want me: *Robyn* / Cup of life: *Martin, Ricky* / Happenin' all over again: *Shaw, Tracy* / I'll be there for you: *Solid Harmonie* / Delicious: *Kulay* / Carnival de Paris: *Dario G* / Feel it: *Tamperer & Maya* / Found a cure: *Ultra Nate* / Never ever: *All Saints* / Everybody (backstreet's back): *Backstreet Boys* / Uh la la la: *Alexia* / La primavera: *Sash* / It's over: *Pianoheadz* / It's like that: *Run DMC & Jason Nevins* / Renegade master '98: *Wildchild* / Deeper love: *Ruff Driverz* / Spend the night: *Lewis, Danny J.* / Get up stand up: *Phunky Phantom* / No good for me: *Bruce Wayne* / Strong: *Liquid* / Reason/Gettin' into it: *Sylk 130* / Superhero: *Daze* / Carry on: *Summer, Donna & Giorgio Moroder*
SONYTV 50CD / 13 Jul '98 / Sony TV

☐ SUMMER DANCE ENERGY
JHD 106 / Aug '93 / Tring

☐ SUMMER DANCE PARTY
Boom boom boom: *Outhere Brothers* / Whoomph (there it is): *Clock* / Right in the night (fall in love with the music): *Jam & Spoon* / Humpin' around: *Brown, Bobby* / Scatman: *Scatman John* / Be my lover: *La Bouche* / Rhythm of the night: *Corona* / Another night: *MC Sar & The Real McCoy* / It's my life: *Dr. Alban* / What is love: *Haddaway* / Rhythm is a dancer: *Snap* / Could it be magic: *Take That* / Guaglione: *Prado, Perez* / Tequila: *Champs* / Lambada: *Lambada* / Miami hit mix: *Estefan, Gloria* / Hot hot hot: *Arrow* / Baby come back: *Pato Banton* / Baby I love your way: *Big Mountain* / Sweat (a la la la la long): *Inner Circle* / Cotton eye Joe: *Rednex* / Summertime: *DJ Jazzy Jeff & The Fresh Prince*
RADCD 18 / Jul '95 / Global TV

☐ SUMMER DANCE PARTY
Keep it comin' love: *KC & The Sunshine Band* / Rock your baby: *McCrae, George* / Boogie oogie oogie: *Taste Of Honey* / Get off: *Foxy* / Sun is here: *Sun* / Saddle up: *Christie, David* / Gonna get along without you now: *Wills, Viola* / Movin': *Brass Construction* / Whodunit: *Tavares* / Swing your daddy: *Gilstrap, Jim* / Let's all chant: *Zager, Michael Band* / Saturday night: *T-Connection* / You can do it: *Hudson, Al & The Partners* / Carwash: *Rose Royce* / Float on: *Floaters* / This is it: *Moore, Melba* / Do it: *BT Express* / That's the way I like it/Shake your body/Get down/ Give it up: *KC & The Sunshine Band*
DC 880782 / Aug '97 / Disky

☐ SUMMER DAZE (20 Scorching Summer Hits)
In the Summertime: *Mungo Jerry* / You to me are everything: *Real Thing* / Swing your Daddy: *Gilstrap, Jim* / Now is the time: *James, Jimmy & The Vagabonds* / Uptown festival medley: *Shalamar* / Beach baby: *First Class* / I'm gonna make you mine: *Christie, Lou* / La bamba: *Feliciano, Jose* / Mexico: *Baldry, Long John* / Let's go to San Francisco: *Flowerpot Men* / Sunshine superman: *Donovan* / Daydream: *Lovin' Spoonful* / Build me a buttercup: *Foundations* / Yummy yummy yummy: *Ohio Express* / Simon says: *1910 Fruitgum Company* / El bimbo: *Bimbo Jet* / Born with a smile on my face: *De Sykes, Stephanie* / Egyptian reggae: *Richman, Jonathan & Modern Lovers* / Sunshine day: *Osibisa* / Walking on sunshine: *Rockers Revenge*
SUMCD 4103 / Nov '96 / Summit

☐ SUMMER FOLK COLLECTION
High level hornpipe/Uncle George's: *Sawdust Band* / To Ireland I made my way: *Hutchings, Ashley* / Dear landlord: *Fairport Convention* / Four hands reel/St Annes reel: *Albion Country Band* / Plunder town: *Christmas, Keith* / I thought you'd come: *Downes, Paul* / Hard hats: *Beer, Phil* / LIB/Hayeswood reel: *Hutchings, Ashley Dance Band* / This blessed plot: *Albion Band* / Spring air: *Amazing Blondel* / Blind fiddler: *Beer, Phil* / Nameless kind of hell: *Albion Band* / Butterfly dreams: *Rose Among Thorns* / Flandyke shore: *Albion Band* / War behind walls: *Christmas, Keith* / Lovers: *Downes, Paul* / Colours of love: *Albion Band* / Telstar: *Big Beat Combo* / Wings: *Hutchings, Ashley & Ken Nicol*
HTDCD 64 / Aug '96 / HTD

☐ SUMMER FUN
MUSCD 027 / Jul '95 / MCI Music

☐ SUMMER FUN (2CD Set)
KBOX 227 / Jul '98 / Collection

☐ SUMMER GROOVE (2CD Set)
9548353822 / May '97 / Warner Bros.

☐ SUMMER HEAT (2CD Set)
Don't look back: *Tosh, Peter* / Money in my pocket: *Brown, Dennis* / Wonderful world, beautiful people: *Cliff, Jimmy* / OK Fred: *Dunkley, Errol* / Could you be loved: *Thomas, Ruddy* / No woman no cry: *Marley, Kymani* / I wanna be your man: *Chaka Demus & Pliers* / Reckless: *Bambaataa, Afrika* / Bush doctor: *Tosh, Peter* / I don't wanna dance: *Grant, Eddy* / Many rivers to cross: *Dekker, Desmond* / Walking on sunshine: *Katrina & The Waves* / Gimme hope Jo'anna: *Grant, Eddy* / Sunshine reggae: *Laidback* / Amigo: *Black Slate* / Karma chameleon: *Culture*

Club / Carribean queen: Ocean, Billy / Don't let me be misunderstood: Santa Esmeralda / Kalimba de luna: Esposito, Tony / Lion sleeps tonight: Tight Fit / Love is in the air: Jones, Tom / Hot hot hot: Arrow / In the summertime: Mungo Jerry / Bring back (sha na na): Mixed Emotions / Going back to my roots: Odyssey / Summer in the city: Lovin' Spoonful / Good vibrations: Beach Boys / Dancing in the city: Hain, Marshall / Happy together: Turtles / Soul rebel: Marley, Kymani

DC 880022 / 30 May '97 / Disky

☐ SUMMER HIT MIX 1998 (2CD Set)

ZYX 811522 / 22 Jun '98 / ZYX

☐ SUMMER HOLIDAY (A Trade Compilation - 2CD Set)

Cro-Magnon: Constipated Monkeys / Found a cure: Ultra Nate / Funky fresh: International Posse / Lost in space: Thompson, Alan / Good love: Richard F / Shake it on up: T-Total / Beat the street: Gordon, Lonnie / Where: Sun God / Samplitude vol.2: Basoski, Olav / Freaks come out: Fisher, Cevin / House music: Amador, Eddie / Uprising: Ecomo, Silvio / Samplitude vol.3: Basoski, Olav / Spin me wild: Freak & Mac Zimms / Everybody: Backstreet Boys / Don't walk just wander: Square Window / London town: JDS / Flew over Central Park: Ecomo, Sylvio / Caned: Dynamite / Infidelity: Roach, Joff / Raise your hands: Knuckleheadz / Set you free: Thomas, Steve / Just let go: Petra & Co / Novopain: Daisy, Pete / Let's groove: DJK / Get to the back: Fantazia / Thermo element: Rush, Gene / Don't stop: F1 / Leader: Captain & Steve Thomas

0521202

0521612 / 29 Jun '98 / Jive

☐ SUMMER IN THE CITY

PLSCD 187 / Apr '97 / Pulse

☐ SUMMER LOVE (2CD Set)

KBOX 230 / Jul '98 / Collection

☐ SUMMER NIGHTS (2CD Set)

KBOX 231 / Jul '98 / Collection

☐ SUMMER NRG

Abba medley: Unlimited Beat / Can't take my eyes off you: Jay, Jessica / Summertime: Cicero / Alone: Heartclub & 3 Boys / In your dreams: Ultimate Buzz / 2 becomes 1: Wildside / Deadwood stage: Brown, Beccy / Angels: A-Tension / Take That medley: Unlimited Beat / Hold me: Lovelife / Forever and a day: Active Force / Boom boom: Joshua / I'm in the mood for dancin': Nolans

DASR 002 / 29 Sep '97 / Academy Street

☐ SUMMER OF LOVE

MUSCD 022 / Sep '94 / MCI Music

☐ SUMMER OF LOVE (2CD Set)

San Francisco: McKenzie, Scott / Eight miles high: Byrds / Going up the country: Canned Heat / Hole in my shoe: Traffic / Flowers in the rain: Move / Carrie-Anne: Move / Excerpt: West, Keith / Something in the air: Thunderclap Newman / Windy: Association / Happy together: Turtles / Waterloo sunset: Kinks / Weight: Band / Sunshine superman: Donovan / Friday on my mind: Donovan / Good vibrations: Beach Boys / 98.6: Keith / 59th Street Bridge song: Harpers Bizarre / Groovin': Rascals / California dreamin': Mamas & The Papas / This wheels on fire: Driscoll, Julie & The Brian Auger Trinity / Love is all around: Troggs / Rainy day women nos.12 and 35: Dylan, Bob / San Fransciscan nights: Burdon, Eric & The Animals / For what it's worth: Buffalo Springfield / Paper sun: Traffic / Strange brew: Cream / Somebody to love: Jefferson Airplane / Living in the past: Jethro Tull / DuKites: Dupree, Simon & The Big Sound / Massachusetts: Bee Gees / Let's go to San Francisco: Flowerpot Men / Mr Tambourine man: Byrds / Mighty Quinn: Manfred Mann / Ride my see-saw: Moody Blues / Alone again or: Love / Whiter shade of pale: Procol Harum / Itchychoo park: Small Faces / Mama told me not to come: Three Dog Night / Fresh garbage: Spirit / Fire: Crazy World Of Arthur Brown / Eve of destruction: McGuire, Barry / Woodstock: Matthew's Southern Comfort / PucYoung girl: Puckett, Gary & The Union Jack / Purple haze: Hendrix, Jimi

5538622 / Jul '97 / PolyGram TV

☐ SUMMER OF LOVE (3CD Set/Interview Discs)

55645 / Oct '97 / Laserlight

☐ SUMMER OF LOVE (CD/Book Set)

SB 09 / 23 Feb '98 / Sonic Book

☐ SUMMER OF LOVE

REACD 001 / 6 Apr '98 / Reactive

☐ SUMMER OF LOVE GOES ON, THE (2CD Set)

5651312 / 20 Jul '98 / PolyGram TV

☐ SUMMER PARTY (3CD Set)

KBOX 372 / Aug '97 / Collection

☐ SUMMER RAIN

307042 / Aug '97 / Hallmark

☐ SUMMER REGGAE

Sunshine people: Hammond, Beres & Mikey Zappow / We play reggae: In Crowd / Work all day: Biggs, Barry / Everyday is just a holiday: Thomas, Ruddy / Whiter shade of pale: Kelly, Pat / You never knew: George, Sophia / Mississippi: Schloss, Cynthia / Red red wine: Boothe, Ken / Sunshine for me: Isaacs, Gregory / Baby my love: Callender, Fil / Honey: Honey Boy / I'm in the mood for love: Biggs, Barry / No woman no cry: Clarke, Johnny / Kingston town: Boothe, Ken / Massachusetts: McGregor, Freddie / Love again: George, Sophia / Ain't no sunshine: Andy, Horace / Sun is shining: Wilson, Delroy / Time for love: Thomas, Ruddy / Rock my soul: Griffiths, Marcia

ECD 3387 / 1 Sep '97 / K-Tel

☐ SUMMER ROCK

If this is it: Lewis, Huey & The News / Alone: Heart / Rock me tonight: Squier, Billy / White wedding: Idol, Billy / No doubt about it: Hot Chocolate / Hymn: Ultravox / Temptation: Heaven 17 / Baker Street: Rafferty, Gerry / Sebastian: Cockney Rebel / Love is a battlefield: Benatar, Pat / Nutbush city limits: Turner, Ike & Tina / Lonesome loser: Little River Band / Locomotive breath: Jethro Tull / Don't forget me: Glass Tiger / Smoke on the water: Deep Purple / Girls on film: Duran Duran / Shadow on the wall: Oldfield, Mike

DC 881252 / Aug '97 / Disky

☐ SUMMER SIZZLERS

Walking on sunshine: Katrina & The Waves / Fantastic day: Haircut 100 / Beach baby: First Class / Hot hot hot: Arrow / In the summertime: Mungo Jerry / Happy together: Turtles / Sunny afternoon: Kinks / Lazy Sunday: Small Faces / Summer in the city: Lovin' Spoonful / Remember (walking in the sand): Shangri-Las / Seasons in the sun: Jacks, Terry / Hang on sloopy: McCoys

74321339292 / Jan '96 / Camden

☐ SUMMER SWING

Humpin' around: Brown, Bobby / Freak like me: Howard, Adina / Party all night: Kreuz / Candy rain: Soul For Real / Oh baby, I: Eternal / Freek 'n you: Jodeci / Your body's callin': R Kelly / Down with the clique: Aaliyah / I wanna be down: Brandy / Your love is a 187: Whitehead Brothers / Here comes the hotstepper: Kamoze, Ini / Rump shaker: Wreckx n' Effect / Hoochie booty: Ultimate Kaos / Real love: Blige, Mary J. / Everyday: Incognito / Apparently nothin': Anderson, Carleen / Too many fish: Knuckles, Frankie & Adeva / Lifted: Lighthouse Family / Joy: Blackstreet / There's nothing like this: Omar

VTCD 53 / Jul '95 / Virgin

☐ SUMMER VYBES (2CD Set)

Disco's revenge: Gusto / Trippin' on sunshine: Pizzaman / Keep on jumpin': Lisa Marie Experience / Get down (you're the one for me): Backstreet Boys / Sunshine after the rain: Berri / Always there: Incognito & Jocelyn Brown / Rhythm of the night: Corona / Two can play that game: Brown, Bobby / Swing low, sweet chariot: China Black / She's got that vibe: R Kelly / In the summertime: Shaggy / Boom shack-a-lack: Apache Indian / Sweets for my sweet: Lewis, C.J. / Whoomp (there it is): Clock / U R the best thing: D:Ream / Another night: MC Sar & The Real McCoy / Rhythm is a dancer: Snap / Baby come back: Pato Banton / Mr. Vain: Culture Beat / Summertime: DJ Jazzy Jeff & The Fresh Prince / Too hot: Coolio / Something 4 da honeyz: Jordan, Montell / I got 5 on it: Luniz / Thank God it's Friday: R Kelly / Throw your hands up: LV / Lifted: Lighthouse Family / Brand new day (I'm no puppet): Darkman / Tease me: Chaka Demus & Pliers / Mr. Loverman: Shabba Ranks / Compliments on your kiss: Red Dragon / Here comes the hotstepper: Kamoze, Ini / Don't turn around: Aswad / You don't love me (no no no): Penn, Dawn / Love city groove: Love City Groove / Searching: China Black / Shout (it out): Louchie Lou & Michie One / Runnin': Pharcyde / Close to you: Priest, Maxi / Sweat (a la la la la long): Inner Circle / Back to life: Soul II Soul

5356442 / Jun '96 / PolyGram TV

☐ SUMMER WIND

BLR 84017 / May '91 / L&R

☐ SUMMERPARTY (2CD Set)

Macarena: Oliveira, Valdeca Y Banda Tropical / Don't let me be misunderstood: Santa Esmeralda / Yes sir I can boogie: Baccara / I don't want to: Real Pop Collektive / Kingston, Kingston: Lou & The Hollywood Bananas / Barbados: Typically Tropical / Save your kisses for me: Brotherhood Of Man / Paloma Blanca: Baker, George Selection / Agadoo: Black Lace / Beachboy gold: Gidea Park / Da doo Ron Ron: Cassidy, Shaun / Beach baby: First Class / Sugar sugar: Archies / Sweets for my sweet: Searchers / In the summertime: Mungo Jerry / Beautiful Sunday: Boone, Daniel / Knock on wood: Stewart, Amii / 5000 volts: Stewart, Amii / Live is life: Opus / Stop in the name of love: Supremes / Let your love flow: Bellamy Brothers / La mia musica: Cutugno, Toto / Dolce Vita: Paris, Ryan / Disco samba: Two Man Sound / Let's all chant: Zager, Michael Band / Substitute: Clout / Fire in the night: Hotshots / Samba de Janeiro: Real Pop Collektive / On the beach: Flirts / Native love: Divine / Happy children: Lion, P / Dance yourself dizzy: Liquid Gold / Sunglasses: Ullman, Tracey / Hot lips: Kenny / Sky high: Jigsaw

24381 / Aug '97 / Laserlight

☐ SUMMERTIME HITS FROM THE WORLD

DCD 5305 / Nov '93 / Disky

☐ SUMMERTIME SOUL

5258002 / Aug '95 / PolyGram TV

☐ SUN AND BASS

TKCD 47 / Mar '97 / 2 Kool

☐ SUN GODS, THE (3CD Set)

DTKBOX 66 / 6 Jul '98 / Dressed To Kill

☐ SUN LEGENDS

EABCD 061 / 24 Nov '97 / Eagle

☐ SUN ROCK 'N' ROLL VOL.1

You better dig it: Johnson, Bill / Walkin' and talkin': Owen, Mark / Diamond ring: Isle, Jimmy / Oh wee: Suggs, Brad / There will be no teardrops tonight: McVoy, Carl / More pretty girls than one: Howard, Edwin / Hey baby doll: Bush, Eddie / Your cheatin' heart: Greaves, Cliff / Let 'em talk: Dorman, Harold / Tuff: Cannon, Ace / Shut your mouth: Barton, Ernie / Hula hop: Baugh, Smokey Joe / Shake 'em up baby: Ballard, Frank / Hambone: Anthony, Rayburn / Boogaloo: Johnson, Bill / I've got it made: Wayne, Thomas / Belle of Swannee: Pendarvis, Tracy / Wait 'til Saturday night: Dorman, Harold / I wanna make sweet love: McGill, Jerry / Mean old world: Thomas, Cliff / Rocking history: Williams, Jimmy / I'm losing you: Williams, Red / Tragedy: Wayne, Thomas / Have a little party: Gilley, Mickey / No more crying the blues: Alton & Jimmy / Good gracious: Vel-Tones / I'm getting better all the time: Pittman, Barbara / Baby doll: Four Dukes / All I want is you: Williams, Jimmy / Memories never grow old: Lee, Dickie & The Collegiates

CPCD 8277 / Jan '97 / Charly

☐ SUN ROCK 'N' ROLL VOL.2

Forty days: Cagle, Wade & Escorts / Oowee oowee: Cagle, Wade & Escorts / Lovestruck: McGill, Jerry & The Topcoats / She's a woman: Baugh, Smokey Joe / Trouble: Powers, Johnny / Gonna give a party: Woods, James / Lock you in my heart: Woods, James / Hey Mr. Shoes: Woods, James / Somehow I'll find a way: Fakes, Roger / Why do I love you: Alton & Jimmy / I just don't know: Alton & Jimmy / What's the use: Alton & Jimmy / Don't be runnin' wild (Problem child): Cook, Ken / I was a fool: Cook, Ken / Stairway to nowhere: Barton, Ernie / Little bitty pretty girl: Janes, Roland & Eddie Cash / Baby I don't care: Bush, Eddie / Stop the world and let me off: Mann, Carl / Without a love: Isle, Jimmy / I'll be satisfied: McVoy, Carl / Born to lose: McVoy, Carl / It makes no difference now: McVoy, Carl / Yes ma'am: Rich, Charlie / Trip into love: Hoback, Curtis & Stardusters / Bagpipe rock: Honeycutt, Glenn / Hula lula: Honeycutt, Glenn

CPCD 8318 / Oct '97 / Charly

☐ SUN, SEA AND SALSA (A Cocktail Of Caribbean Grooves)

NSCD 015 / Mar '97 / Nascente

☐ SUN SINGLES VOL.1 (4CD Set)

Flat tire: London, Johnny / Drivin' slow: London, Johnny / Got my application baby: Garth, Gay / Trouble (will bring you down): Jackson, Handy / We all gotta go sometime: Hill-Louis, Joe / Some may be like yours: Hill-Louis, Joe / Baker shop boogie: Nix, Willie / Seems like a million years: Nix, Willie / Easy: Jimmy & Walter / Before long: Jimmy & Walter / Bear cat: Thomas, Rufus / Walkin' in the rain: Thomas, Rufus / Heaven or fire: Brooks, Dusty / Tears and wine: Brooks, Dusty / Lonesome old jail: Hunt, D.A. / Greyhound bloues: Hunt, D.A. / Call me anything, but call me: Big Memphis Marainey / Baby no no: Big Memphis Marainey / Take a little chance: De Berry, Jimmy / Time has made a change: De Berry, Jimmy / Baby please: Prisonaires / Just walking in the rain: Prisonaires / Feelin' good: Parker, Junior & The Blue Flames / Fussing and fighting: Parker, Junior & The Blue Flames / Tiger man: Thomas, Rufus / Save that money: Thomas, Rufus / My God is real: Prisonaires / Softly and tenderly: Prisonaires / Blues waltz: Ripley Cotton Choppers / Silver bells: Ripley Cotton Choppers / Prosoner's prayer: Prisonaires / I know: Prisonaires / Mystery train: Parker, Junior & The Blue Flames / Love my baby: Parker, Junior & The Blue Flames / Come back baby: Ross, Dr. Isiah / Chicago breakdown: Ross, Dr. Isiah / Beggin' my baby: Little Milton / Somebody told me: Little Milton / No teasing around: Emerson, Billy 'The Kid' / If love is believing: Emerson, Billy 'The Kid' / Wolf call boogie: Hot Shot Love / Harmonica jam: Hot Shot Love / Boogie blues: Peterson, Earl / In the dark: Peterson, Earl / Troublesome waters: Seratt, Howard / I must be saved: Seratt, Howard / My baby: Cotton, James / Straighten up baby: Cotton, James / If you love me: Little Milton / Alone and blue: Little Milton / Gonna dance all night: Gunter, Hardrock / Fallen angel: Gunter, Hardrock / Now she cares no more for me: Poindexter, Doug / My kind of carryin' on: Poindexter, Doug / I'm not going home: Emerson, Billy 'The Kid' / Woodchuck: Emerson, Billy 'The Kid' / Bourbon street jump: Hill, Raymond / Snuggle: Hill, Raymond / Great medical menagerist: Floyd, 'Harmonica' Frank / Rockin' chair Daddy: Floyd, 'Harmonica' Frank / Cotton crop blues: Cotton, James / Hold me in your arms: Cotton, James / There is love in you: Prisonaires / What'll you do next: Prisonaires / Right or wrong: Cunningham, Buddy / Who do I cry: Prisonaires / That's alright Mama: Presley, Elvis / Blue moon of Kentucky: Presley, Elvis / Good rockin' tonight: Presley, Elvis / I don't care if the sun don't shine: Presley, Elvis / Drinkin' wine spo-dee-o-dee: Yelvington, Malcolm / Just rolling along: Yelvington, Malcolm / Boogie disease: Ross, Dr. Isiah / Jukebox boogie: Ross, Dr. Isiah / Look to Jesus: Jones Brothers / Every night: Jones Brothers / Move baby move: Emerson, Billy 'The Kid' / When it rains it pours: Emerson, Billy 'The Kid' / Milkcow blues boogie: Presley, Elvis / You're a heartbreaker: Presley, Elvis / Don't believe: Rhodes, Slim / Uncertain love: Rhodes, Slim / I'm left, you're right, she's gone: Presley, Elvis / Baby let's play house: Presley, Elvis / I feel so worried: Lewis, Sammy & Willie Johnson / So long baby, goodbye: Lewis, Sammy & Willie Johnson / Red hot: Emerson, Billy 'The Kid' / There is no greater love: Emerson, Billy 'The Kid' / Homesick for my baby: Little Milton / Lookin' for my baby: Little Milton / Cry cry cry: Cash, Johnny / Hey porter: Cash, Johnny / Don't do that: Five Tinos / Sitting by my window: Five Tinos / I forgot to remember to forget: Presley, Elvis / Let the jukebox keep on playing: Perkins, Carl / Gone gone gone: Perkins, Carl / House of sin: Rhodes, Slim / Are you ashamed of me: Rhodes, Slim / Ain't that right: Snow, Eddie / Bring your love back home to me: Snow, Eddie / Just love me baby: Gordon, Rosco / Weeping blues: Gordon, Rosco / Signifying monkey: Smokey Joe / Listen to my baby: Smokey Joe / Movie magg: Perkins, Carl / Turn around: Perkins, Carl / Lonely sweetheart: Taylor, Bill / Split personality: Taylor, Bill / I've been deceived: Feathers, Charlie / Peepin' eyes: Feathers, Charlie / Someday you will pay: Miller Sisters / You didn't think I would: Miller Sisters

BCD 15801 / Nov '94 / Bear Family

☐ SUN SINGLES VOL.2 (4CD Set)

Daydreams come true: Wimberly, Maggie Sue / How long: Wimberly, Maggie Sue / There's no right way to do me wrong: Miller Sisters / You can tell me: Miller Sisters / Defrost your heart: Feathers, Charlie / Wedding gown of white: Feathers, Charlie / Folsom Prison blues: Cash, Johnny / So doggone lonesome: Cash, Johnny / Little fine healthy thing: Emerson, Billy 'The Kid' / Something for nothing: Emerson, Billy 'The Kid' / Blue suede shoes: Perkins, Carl / Honey don't: Perkins, Carl / Sure to fall: Perkins, Carl / Tennessee: Perkins, Carl / No more, no more: Haggett, Jimmy / They call our love a sin: Haggett, Jimmy / Chicken: Gordon, Rosco / Love for you baby: Gordon, Rosco / Gonna romp and stomp: Rhodes, Slim / Bad girl: Rhodes, Slim / Rock 'n' roll Ruby: Smith, Warren / I'd rather be safe then sorry: Smith, Warren / Slow down: Earls, Jack / Fool for loving you: Earls, Jack / Get rhythm: Cash, Johnny / I walk the line: Cash, Johnny / Ooby dooby: Orbison, Roy / Go go go: Orbison, Roy / Boppin' the blues: Perkins, Carl / All Mama's children: Perkins, Carl / Welcome to the club: Chapel, Jean / I won't be rockin' tonight: Chapel, Jean / Trouble bound: Riley, Billy Lee / Rock with me baby: Riley, Billy Lee / Rockin' with my baby: Yelvington, Malcolm / It's me baby: Yelvington, Malcolm / Red headed woman: Burgess, Sonny / We wanna boogie: Burgess, Sonny / Fiddle bop: Rhythm Rockers / Jukebox help me find my baby: Rhythm Rockers / I'm sorry: Perkins, Carl / I'm not sorry: Perkins, Carl / Dixie fried: Perkins, Carl / Black Jack David: Smith, Warren / Unbangi stomp: Smith, Warren / You're my baby: Orbison, Roy / Rock house: Orbison, Roy / Love crazy baby: Parchman, Kenny / I feel like rockin: Parchman, Kenny / I need a man: Pitman, Barbara / No matter who's to blame: Pitman, Barbara / Come on little Mama: Harris, Ray / Where'd you stay last night: Harris, Ray / Ten cats down: Miller Sisters / Finders keepers: Miller Sisters / Take and give: Rhodes, Slim / Do what I do: Rhodes, Slim / Shoobee doobee: Gordon, Rosco / Cheese and crackers: Gordon, Rosco / There you go: Cash, Johnny / Train of love: Cash, Johnny / Crazy arms: Lewis, Jerry Lee / End of the road: Lewis, Jerry Lee / Flyin' saucer rock 'n' roll: Riley, Billy Lee / I want you baby: Riley, Billy Lee / Matchbox: Perkins, Carl / Your true love: Perkins, Carl / Feelin' low: Chaffin, Ernie / Lonesome for my baby: Chaffin, Ernie / Restless: Burgess, Sonny / Ain't got a thing: Burgess, Sonny / I'll be around: Honeycutt, Glenn / I'll wait forever: Honeycutt, Glenn / Sweet and easy: Orbison, Roy / Devil doll: Orbison, Roy / Don't make me go: Cash, Johnny / Nest in line: Cash, Johnny / It'll be me: Lewis, Jerry Lee / Whole lotta shakin' goin' on: Lewis, Jerry Lee / So long I'm gone: Smith, Warren / Miss Froggie: Smith, Warren / Bop bop baby: Wake & Dick / Don't need your lovin' baby: Wake & Dick / Please don't cry over me: Williams, Jimmy / That depends on you: Williams, Jimmy / Fools hall of fame: Richardson, Rudi / Why should I cry: Richardson, Rudi / Greenback dollar: Harris, Ray / Foolish heart: Harris, Ray / Easy to love: Self, Mack / Every day: Self, Mack / Forever yours: Perkins, Carl / That's right: Perkins, Carl / I'm lonesome: Chaffin, Ernie / Laughin' and jokin': Chaffin, Ernie / More than yesterday: Bruce, Edwin / Rock boppin' baby: Bruce, Edwin / Red hot: Riley, Billy Lee / Pearly Lee: Riley, Billy Lee / Flat foot Sam: Blake, Tommy / Lordy hoody: Blake, Tommy

BCD 15802 / Jun '95 / Bear Family

☐ SUN SINGLES VOL.3 (4CD Set)

Give my love to Rose: Cash, Johnny / Home of the blues: Cash, Johnny / Good lovin': Lee, Dickey / Memories never grow old: Lee, Dickey / Great balls of fire: Lewis, Jerry Lee / You win again: Lewis, Jerry Lee / Cindy Lou: Penner, Dick / Your honey love: Penner, Dick / Ballad of a teenage Queen: Cash, Johnny / Big river: Cash, Johnny / Chicken hearted: Orbison, Roy / I like love: Orbison, Roy / My bucket's got a hole in it: Burgess, Sonny / Sweet misery: Burgess, Sonny / I've got love if you want it: Smith, Warren / I fell in love: Smith, Warren / Lend me your comb: Perkins, Carl / Glad all over: Perkins, Carl / Breathless: Lewis, Jerry Lee / Down the line: Lewis, Jerry Lee / Baby please don't go: Riley, Billy Lee / Wouldn't you know: Riley, Billy Lee / Judy: Grayzell, Rudy / I think of you: Grayzell, Rudy / Ten years: Clement, Jack / Your lover boy: Clement, Jack / Sweet woman: Bruce, Edwin / Part of my life: Bruce, Edwin / Love is a stranger: Sunrays / Lonely hours: Sunrays / I feel so blue: Priesman, Magel / Memories of you: Priesman, Magel / I guess things happen that way: Cash, Johnny / Come in stranger: Cash, Johnny / High School confidential: Lewis, Jerry Lee / Fools like me: Lewis, Jerry Lee / Dreamy nights: Lee, Dickey / Fool fool fool: Lee, Dickey / Right behind you baby: Smith, Ray / So young: Smith, Ray / Drinkin' wine: Simmons, Gene / I done told you: Simmons, Gene / I dig you baby: Blake, Tommy / Sweetie pie: Blake, Tommy / Return of Jerry Lee: Lewis, Jerry Lee / Lewis Boogie: Lewis, Jerry Lee / Ways of a woman in love: Cash, Johnny / You're the nearest thing to heaven: Cash, Johnny / Break up: Lewis, Jerry Lee / I'll make it all up to you: Lewis, Jerry Lee / Thunderbird: Burgess, Sonny / Itchy: Burgess, Sonny / Torro: Gordon, Rosco / Sally Jo: Gordon, Rosco / Diamond ring: Isle, Jimmy / I've been waitin': Isle, Jimmy / Born to lose: Chaffin, Ernie / My love for you: Chaffin, Ernie / Yu made a hit: Smith, Ray / Why why why: Smith, Ray / It's just about time: Cash, Johnny / I just thought you'd like to know: Cash, Johnny / Breeze: Taylor, Vernon / Today is a blue day: Taylor, Vernon / Black haired man: Clement, Jack / Wrong: Clement, Jack / I'll sail my ship alone: Lewis, Jerry Lee / It hurt me so: Lewis, Jerry Lee / Down by the riverside: Riley, Billy Lee / No name girl: Riley, Billy Lee / Sweet, sweet girl: Smith, Warren / Goodbye Mr. Love: Smith, Warren / Jump right out of this jukebox: Wheeler, Onie / Tell 'em off: Wheeler, Onie / Luther played the boogie: Lewis, Jerry Lee / Thanks a lot: Lewis, Jerry Lee / Lovin' up a storm: Lewis, Jerry Lee / Big blon' baby: Lewis, Jerry Lee / Without a love: Isle, Jimmy / Time will tell: Isle, Jimmy / Rockin' bandit: Smith, Ray / Sail away: Smith, Ray / Don't ever leave me: Chaffin, Ernie / Miracle of you: Chaffin, Ernie / I forgot to remember to forget: Cash, Johnny / Katy too: Cash, Johnny / Got the water boiling: Riley, Billy Lee / One more time: Riley, Billy Lee / No more crying the blues: Isle, Jimmy / Have faith in my love: Isle, Jimmy / Let's talk about us: Lewis, Jerry Lee / Ballad of Billy Joe: Lewis, Jerry Lee / Mystery train: Taylor, Vernon / Sweet and easy to love: Taylor, Vernon / Lovestruck: McGill, Jerry / I wanna make sweet love: McGill, Jerry / Be mine, all mine: Powers, Johnny / With your love, with your kiss: Powers, Johnny / Winnie the parakeet: Crane, Sherry / Willie Willie: Crane, Sherry

BCD 15803 / Nov '96 / Bear Family

☐ SUN SINGLES VOL.4 (4CD Set)

You're just my kind: Mercer, Will / Ballad of St. Mark's: Mercer, Will / Little Queenie: Lewis, Jerry Lee / I could never be ashamed of you: Lewis, Jerry Lee / You tell me: Cash, Johnny / Goodbye little darlin': Cash, Johnny / What a life: Isle, Jimmy / Together: Isle, Jimmy / Alice blue gown: Anthony, Rayburn / St. Louis blues: Anthony, Rayburn / Straight A's in love: Cash, Johnny / I love you because: Cash, Johnny / Thousand guitars: Pendarvis, Tracy / Is it too late: Pendarvis, Tracy / Walkin' and talkin': Owen, Mack / Somebody just like you: Owen, Mack / Old black Joe: Lewis, Jerry Lee / Baby baby bye bye: Lewis, Jerry Lee / Legend of the big steeple: Richey, Paul / Broken hearted Willie: Richey, Paul / Who's gonna shoe your pretty little feet: Anthony, Rayburn / There's no tomorrow: Anthony, Rayburn / Bobaloo: Johnson, Bill / Bad times ahead: Johnson, Bill / Great pretender: Wilson, Sonny / I'm gonna take a walk: Wilson, Sonny / You burned the bridges: Bobbie Jean / Cheaters never win: Bobbie Jean / Story of a broken heart: Cash, Johnny / Down the street to 301: Cash, Johnny / John Henry: Lewis, Jerry Lee / Hang up my rock 'n' roll shoes: Lewis, Jerry Lee / Is it me: Pendarvis, Tracy / Southbound line: Pendarvis, Tracy / Guess I'd better go: Strength, 'Texas' Bill / Senorita: Strength, 'Texas' Bill / Mean eyed cat: Cash, Johnny / Port of lonely hearts: Cash, Johnny /

Good guys always win: *Roberts, Lance* / Time is right: *Roberts, Lance* / I gotta know: *Rossini, Tony* / Is it too late: *Rossini, Tony* / Rockin' lang syne: *Rockin' Stockin'* / Yuleville USA: *Rockin' Stockin'* / You don't love me anymore: *Jay, Ira* / More than anything: *Jay, Ira* / When I get paid: *Lewis, Jerry Lee* / Love made a fool of me: *Lewis, Jerry Lee* / Sweet and easy to love: *Orbison, Roy* / Devil doll: *Orbison, Roy* / Sad news: *Sheridan, Bobby* / Red man: *Sheridan, Bobby* / Oh lonesome me: *Cash, Johnny* / Life goes on: *Cash, Johnny* / What'd I say: *Lewis, Jerry Lee* / Livin' lovin' wreck: *Lewis, Jerry Lee* / UT party: *Klein, George* / Belle of the swannee: *Pendarvis, Tracy* / Eternally: *Pendarvis, Tracy* / Groovy train: *Cagle, Wade* / Highland rock: *Cagle, Wade* / I'll wait forever: *Wood, Anita* / I can't show how I feel: *Wood, Anita* / I'll stick by you: *Dorman, Harold* / There they go: *Dorman, Harold* / Sugartime: *Cash, Johnny* / My treasure: *Cash, Johnny* / Cold cold heart: *Lewis, Jerry Lee* / It won't happen with me: *Lewis, Jerry Lee* / I forgot to remember to forget: *Sisk, Shirley* / Other side: *Sisk, Shirley* / Well I ask ya: *Rossini, Tony* / Darlena: *Rossini, Tony* / Save the last dance for me: *Lewis, Jerry Lee* / As long as I live: *Lewis, Jerry Lee* / Since I met you: *Hosea, Don* / Uh huh uh: *Hosea, Don* / Everybody's searching: *Wood, Bobby* / Human emotions: *Wood, Bobby* / Uncle Jonah's place: *Dorman, Harold* / Just one step: *Dorman, Harold* / Money: *Lewis, Jerry Lee* / Bonnie B: *Lewis, Jerry Lee* / Travellin' salesman: *Smith, Ray* / I won't miss you: *Smith, Ray* / How well I know: *Anthony, Rayburn* / Big dream: *Anthony, Rayburn* / I've been twistin': *Lewis, Jerry Lee* / Ramblin' Rose: *Lewis, Jerry Lee* / Candy doll: *Smith, Ray* / Hey boss man: *Smith, Ray* / Blue train: *Cash, Johnny* / Born to lose: *Cash, Johnny* / In the beginning: *Dorman, Harold* / Wait 'til Saturday night: *Dorman, Harold* / After school: *Rossini, Tony* / Just around the corner: *Rossini, Tony* / Sweet little sixteen: *Lewis, Jerry Lee* / How's my ex treating you: *Lewis, Jerry Lee*

BCD 15804 / Apr '97 / Bear Family

☐ SUN SINGLES VOL.5 (4CD Set)

You make it sound so easy: *Rossini, Tony & The Chippers* / New girl in town: *Rossini, Tony & The Chippers* / Midnight soiree: *Four Upsetters* / Crazy arms: *Four Upsetters* / Good golly Miss Molly: *Lewis, Jerry Lee* / I can't trust me (in your arms anymore): *Lewis, Jerry Lee* / Seasons of my heart: *Lewis, Jerry Lee & Linda Gail* / Teenage letter: *Lewis, Jerry Lee* / Nothin' shakin': *Lewis, Linda Gail* / Sittin' thinkin': *Lewis, Linda Gail* / Surfin' calliope: *Four Upsetters* / Wabash cannonball: *Four Upsetters* / Moved to Kansas City: *Rossini, Tony* / Nobody: *Rossini, Tony* / Ain't gonna let you (break my heart): *Teenangels* / Tell me my love: *Teenangels* / Betty and Dupree: *Adams, Billy* / Got my mojo workin': *Adams, Billy* / Don't step on my dog: *Yates, Billy & The T-Birds* / Stop wait and listen: *Yates, Billy & The T-Birds* / Lookin' for my Mary Ann: *Adams, Billy* / Trouble in mind: *Adams, Billy & Jesse Carter* / Wide open road: *Cash, Johnny & The Tennessee Two* / Belshazar: *Cash, Johnny & The Tennessee Two* / Signifying monkey: *Smokey Joe* / Listen to me baby: *Smokey Joe* / Reconsider baby: *Adams, Billy* / Ruby Jane: *Adams, Billy* / Mountain' high: *Randy & The Radiants* / Peek-a-boo: *Randy & The Radiants* / Carry me back to old Virginia: *Lewis, Jerry Lee* / I know what it means: *Lewis, Jerry Lee* / Too late to right my wrong: *Gorgeous Bill* / Carleen: *Gorgeous Bill* / My way of thinking: *Randy & The Radiants* / Truth from my eyes: *Randy & The Radiants* / Big big world: *Yates, Billy* / I dropped my M and M's: *Yates, Billy* / My babe: *Jesters* / Cadillac man: *Jesters* / Open the door Richard: *Adams, Billy* / Rock me baby: *Adams, Billy* / Don't knock what you don't understand: *Stinit, Dane* / Always on the go: *Stinit, Dane* / Sherry's lips: *Houston, David* / Miss Brown: *Houston, David* / No you for me: *Climates* / Breaking up again: *Climates* / Sweet country girl: *Stinit, Dane* / Muddy ole river (near Memphis Tennessee): *Stinit, Dane* / I'm gonna move in the room with the Lord: *Anderson, Brother James* / My soul needs resting: *Anderson, Brother James* / I'm a lover: *Load Of Mischief* / Back in my arms again: *Load Of Mischief* / You pass me by: *Blake, Buddy* / Please convince me: *Blake, Buddy* / Love my baby: *Thompson, Hayden* / One broken heart: *Thompson, Hayden* / Two young fools in love: *Pittman, Barbara* / I'm getting better all the time: *Pittman, Barbara* / Raunchy: *Justis, Bill Orchestra* / Midnite man: *Justis, Bill Orchestra* / That's the way I love: *Carroll, Johnny* / I'll wait: *Carroll, Johnny* / Treat me right: *Thomas, Cliff & Ed/Barbara* / I'm on my way home: *Thomas, Cliff & Ed/Barbara* / College man: *Justis, Bill Orchestra* / Stranger: *Justis, Bill Orchestra* / Point of view: *Powers, Wayne* / My love song: *Powers, Wayne* / After the hop: *Pinky, Bill & The Turks* / Sally's got a sister: *Pinky, Bill & The Turks* / Wild rice: *Justis, Bill Orchestra* / Scroungie: *Justis, Bill Orchestra* / You are my sunshine: *McVoy, Carl* / Tootsie: *McVoy, Carl* / Everlasting love: *Pittman, Barbara & Bill Justis* / Cold cold heart: *Pittman, Barbara & Bill Justis* / Stairway to nowhere: *Barton, Ernie* / Raining the blues: *Barton, Ernie* / Cattywampus: *Justis, Bill Orchestra* / Summer holiday: *Justis, Bill Orchestra* / Frog: *Mitchell, Lee & Curly Money* / Little blue bird told me: *Mitchell, Lee & Curly Money* / Sorry I lied: *Thomas, Cliff & Ed/Barbara* / Leave it to me: *Thomas, Cliff & Ed/Barbara* / Whirlwind: *Rich, Charlie* / Philadelphia baby: *Rich, Charlie* / Somehow without you: *Milan, Mickey & Bill Justis* / Picture: *Milan, Mickey & Bill Justis* / Crazy baby: *Cook, Ken* / I was a fool: *Cook, Ken* / Bop train: *Justis, Bill Orchestra* / String of pearls-cha hot cha: *Justis, Bill Orchestra* / Minstrel show: *Clement Travellers* / Three little guitars: *Clement Travellers* / Hopeless love: *Demopoulos, Jimmy* / If I had my way: *Demopoulos, Jimmy* / I'm the only one: *Thomas, Cliff & Ed/Barbara* / Tidewind: *Thomas, Cliff & Ed/Barbara*

BCD 15805 / Feb '98 / Bear Family

☐ SUN SUN

So quero un xodo / Montreux a Marseille / Summer freestyle / M'boka ya bisengo / Calle ocho beija flor / Tress cun deo la / One love Africa / Rain dancer / In search of M'baoudi

4891132 / 4 May '98 / Columbia

☐ SUNDAY BEST

SPECCD 505 / 4 May '98 / Dust II Dust

☐ SUNDAY FLAVAZ VOL.1 (2CD Set)

74321538802

74321570692 / 30 Mar '98 / Logic

☐ SUNDAY MORNING SESSIONS

MRCD 176 / Sep '95 / Munich

☐ SUNDAZED SAMPLER, THE

Water baby boogie: *Maphis, Joe / Nancy: Barker Bros.* / Ain't that too much: *Vincent, Gene* / Rockabilly yodel: *Larue, Roc & The Three Pals* / Loophole: *Royal Coachmen* / Four in the floor: *Shutdowns* / Bustin' floor boards: *Tornadoes* / Twist and shout: *Isley Brothers* / Mama here comes the bride: *Shirelles* / Western Union: *Five Americans* / One track mind: *Knickerbockers* / Cadillac: *Colony Six* / Dirty water: *Standells* / Little latin lupe lu: *Ryder, Mitch & The Detroit Wheels* / Louie Louie: *Kingsmen* / Surfin' bird: *Trashmen* / Dimples: *Animals* / I got my mojo working: *Shadows Of Knight* / I've been wrong before: *HP Lovecraft* / Rollercoaster: *13th Floor Elevators* / I ain't no miracle worker: *Brogues* / Spend your life: *First Crow To The Moon* / Last time around: *Delvetts* / Anyway I can: *Choir* / Sweetgina: *Things To Come*

CDSC 01 / Apr '94 / Sundazed

☐ SUNNY AFTERNOON (The Hits Of Summer)

In the summertime: *Mungo Jerry* / Beach baby: *First Class* / Hello Susie: *Amen Corner* / Do you wanna dance: *Blue, Barry* / Let's go to San Francisco: *Flowerpot Men* / El bimbo: *Bimbo Jet* / Baby, now that I've found you: *Foundations* / Sunny afternoon: *Kinks* / Green tambourine: *Lemon Pipers* / Simon says: *1910 Fruitgum Company* / Sunshine day: *Osibisa* / Egyptian reggae: *Richman, Jonathan & Modern Lovers* / Sky high: *Jigsaw* / Brand new key: *Melanie* / Summer in the city: *Lovin' Spoonful* / Itchycoo Park: *Small Faces* / I wanna hold your hand: *Dollar* / That same old feeling: *Pickettywitch* / Swing your daddy: *Gilstrap, Jim* / Elenore: *Turtles*

TRTCD 145 / 18 May '98 / TrueTrax

☐ SUNNY AFTERNOONS

Sunny afternoon: *Kinks* / Daydream: *Lovin' Spoonful* / 59th Street Bridge song: *Simon & Garfunkel* / Happy together: *Turtles* / Wouldn't it be nice: *Beach Boys* / Lazy Sunday: *Small Faces* / Daydream believer: *Monkees* / Sunshine superman: *Donovan* / Sitting in the park: *Fame, Georgie* / Sunny: *Hebb, Bobby* / Dedicated to the one I love: *Mamas & The Papas* / Mr. Tambourine Man: *Byrds* / San Francisco: *McKenzie, Scott* / Woodstock: *Matthew's Southern Comfort* / Paper sun: *Traffic* / Badge: *Cream* / Green tambourine: *Lemon Pipers* / Let's go to San Francisco: *Flowerpot Men* / For what it's worth: *Buffalo Springfield* / I can't let Maggie go: *Honeybus* / 98.6: *Keith* / Kites: *Dupree, Simon & The Big Sound* / Good vibrations: *Beach Boys* / Itchycoo Park: *Small Faces* / Mellow yellow: *Donovan* / Waterloo sunset: *Kinks* / She'd rather be with me: *Turtles* / Friday on my mind: *Cure* / Jesamine: *Casuals* / Love grows (Where my Rosemary grows): *Edison Lighthouse* / My name is Jack: *Manfred Mann* / Early in the morning: *Vanity Fare* / Jennifer Eccles: *Hollies* / Flowers in the rain: *Move* / I'm a believer: *Monkees* / Summer in the city: *Lovin' Spoonful* / We gotta get out of this place: *Animals* / With a girl like you: *Troggs* / Monday Monday: *Mamas & The Papas* / Morning has broken: *Stevens, Cat* / Good day sunshine: *Tremeloes* / Judy in disguise: *Fred, John & His Playboy Band* / Sorrow: *Merseys* / Elusive butterfly: *Lind, Bob* / Windy: *Association* / Groovy kind of love: *Mindbenders* / Goo goo Barabajagal (Love is hot): *Donovan & Jeff Beck Group* / Hole in my shoe: *Traffic*

5256002 / Jul '95 / PolyGram TV

☐ SUNNY HOLIDAY

ISCD 166 / May '98 / Intersound

☐ SUNNY SUNDAY SMILE

SUNDAY 640CD / May '94 / Sunday

☐ SUNNYSIDE UP (Mixed By DJ Drew And Skol/2CD Set)

SSUCD 001 / 20 Apr '98 / Sunnyside Up

☐ SUNSET SWING

BLC 760171 / Oct '92 / Black Lion

☐ SUNSHINE BOX (4CD Set)

ECD 3430 / 6 Jul '98 / K-Tel

☐ SUNSHINE GIRLS (TK Deep Soul 2)

Make me feel like a woman: *Moore, Jackie* / Jazz freak: *Reades, Philette* / Puttin' it down to you: *Moore, Jackie* / One woman's trash: *Brandye* / Your real good thing's about to come to an end: *Reades, Philette* / It's harder to leave: *Moore, Jackie* / Loving you, loving me: *Serton, Ann* / Secret lover: *Reades, Philette* / Tired of hiding: *Moore, Jackie* / I'll be right here (when you return): *Wilson, Ruby & The Blue Chips* / Bridge that lies between us: *Moore, Jackie* / God bless this man of mine: *Reades, Philette* / Hurtin' inside out: *Moore, Jackie* / Man and a baby boy: *Wilson, Ruby* / Somebody loves you: *Moore, Jackie*

NEMCD 744 / Jun '95 / Sequel

☐ SUNSHINE HITS VOL.1

MNF 05452 / 8 Jun '98 / Manifold

☐ SUNSHINE REGGAE

SBCD 009 / Jul '95 / Soul Beat

☐ SUNSPLASH SHOWCASE

TWCD 1055 / Nov '95 / Tamoki Wambesi

☐ SUNTRANCE GOA 1996

Youth of the galaxy: *Doof* / Atomic armadillo: *Green Nuns Of The Revolution* / Supernatural: *Slinky Wizard* / LSD: *Hallucinogen* / China zones: *Castle Trancelot* / Tempest: *Salamander* / Magic frequencies: *Witchcraft* / Arcana: *Orion* / 3 Minute warning: *Yum Yum* / Technossomy: *Rejuvination* / Sonar eclipse: *U4EA*

CDTOT 38 / Mar '96 / Jumpin' & Pumpin'

☐ SUNTRANCE VOL.3

Scared: *Slacker* / State of mind: *Floorplay* / Extraterrestrial lover: *Shamanic Tribes On Acid* / Running up that hill: *Levy 9* / Kaleidoscope: *Art Of Trance* / L'architecture: *South Of Trance* / Great ruaha: *Vee* / Canis loopus(thousand rains): *Yekuana* / Amplexus: *Yekuana* / Everything: *Tallulah*

CDTOT 48 / Apr '97 / Jumpin' & Pumpin'

☐ SUONO LIBERO

DOUCE 806CD / 16 Jul '97 / Irma La Douce

☐ SUPER ALL STAR

Francisco guayabal / El platanal de bartolo / Tres linda cubanas / Ban-con-tim / Alto songo / Malanga / El sopon / La cascara

CDORB 017 / Jul '90 / Globestyle

☐ SUPER BRAVISSIMO (2CD Set)

HIT 150002 / 29 Jun '98 / ZYX

☐ SUPER DANCE GROOVE (2CD Set)

Deep in you: *Tanya Louise* / Make my love: *Christopher, Shawn* / Children: *Miles Inc.* / Someone loves you honey: *T-Spoon* / Don't give me your life: *Alex Party* / Knockin': *Double Vision* / You got me up: *Dajae* / Got myself together: *Bucketheads* / Follow me: *E-Lyte* / Theme from S'Express: *S'Express* / Ultra flava: *Heller & Farley Project* / Break 4 love: *Raze* / Black is black: *Belle Epoque* / Wiggle it: *2 In A Room* / Satisfy my love: *Johnston, Sabrina* / In spirit: *Dilemma* / Captain Jack: *Captain Jack* / Let me be free: *Fox, Samantha* / Saturday night: *Whigfield* / Whammer slammer: *Warp 9* / Cotton eye Joe: *Rednex* / Spontaneous: *Spymaster & Eric Nouhan* / Get off your high horse: *Rollo Goes Camping* / Rockstar: *T-Spoon* / All right: *Double Vision* / Rich in paradise: *FPI Project* / Jump for joy: *2 Unlimited* / Living in a fantasy: *Unicorn* / Whomp (there it is): *Tag Team* / Fred come to bed: *Erotic*

DOU 878292 / 2 Feb '98 / Disky

☐ SUPER DANCE VOL.12 (2CD Set)

ZYX 810982 / Apr '97 / ZYX

☐ SUPER DANCING TO REGGAE AND SKA

3020772 / Jul '97 / Arcade

☐ SUPER DUB SESSIONS

WRCD 1720 / 12 Jan '98 / Wackies

☐ SUPER HIT TROPICAL

VGCD 670017 / Jan '93 / Vogue

☐ SUPER HITS OF THE 1970'S VOL.1

DC 866822 / Aug '96 / Disky

☐ SUPER HITS OF THE 1970'S VOL.2

DC 866832 / Aug '96 / Disky

☐ SUPER HITS OF THE 1970'S VOL.3

DC 866842 / Aug '96 / Disky

☐ SUPER MERENGAZO

Que no me adivinas / Amandote / Caliente / Que la pasa a mi mujer / Cuando me enamoro / Toitico tuyo / Rodando / Ala talala / Suegra / Merengue internacional / Mambo mix

RMD 81425 / 24 Mar '98 / RMM

☐ SUPER MUSIKBOX VOL.1

Berliner luft: *Lincke, Paul* / 100 mal Berlin: *Hahnemann, Helga* / Konig der Welt: *Karat* / Major Tom: *Schilling, Peter* / He kleine Linda: *Muck* / Gold in deinen Augen: *Schobel, Frank* / Gwendolina: *Adamo* / Wem: *Carpendale, Howard* / Es fahrt ein Zug nach Nirgendwo: *Anders, Christian* / Ein Bett im Kornfeld: *Drews, Jurgen* / Heute male ich dein Bild, Cindy Lou: *Manuella* / Blue night in Rio: *Bottcher, Martin* / Geld wie heu: *Bottcher, Gerd* / Siebenmal in der woche: *Torriani, Vico* / Souvenirs: *Ramsey, Bill* / Heimweh: *Quinn, Freddy* / Siebenmeilenstiefel: *Bonney, Graham* / Schmidtchen Schleicher: *Haak, Nico* / Beautiful morning: *Rehnbein, Herbert* / Kaiserwalzer: *Stolz, Robert*

BCD 17007 / Nov '96 / Bear Family

☐ SUPER MUSIKBOX VOL.2

Sugar sugar: *Archies* / Popcorn: *Hot Butter* / Hang on Sloopy: *McCoys* / Save all your kisses for me: *Brotherhood Of Man* / Sugar baby love: *Rubettes* / Barbara Ann: *Beach Boys* / Santa Maria: *Onions, Oliver* / Dolce vita: *Paris, Ryan* / Paloma blanca: *Baker, George Selection* / Let your love flow: *Bellamy Brothers* / Ma belle Amie: *Tee Set* / It's a real good feeling: *Kent, Peter* / Love is in the air: *Young, John Paul* / Yellow river: *Christie* / Winchester Cathedral: *New Vaudeville Band* / San Francisco: *McKenzie, Scott* / Chantilly lace: *Big Bopper* / Ring of fire: *Cash, Johnny* / Just walkin' in the rain: *Ray, Johnnie* / Moon river: *Butler, Jerry* / 'S wonderful: *Conniff, Ray*

BCD 17008 / Nov '96 / Bear Family

☐ SUPER SALSA HITS

Abueleta: *Colon, Willie* / Indestructible: *Barretto, Ray* / Abandonada fue: *Orchestra Harlow* / Nina Y semora: *Puente, Tito* / Mi desengana: *Roena, Roberto* / Cafe: *Palmieri, Eddie* / Acuzar mami: *Pacheco, Johnny* / Senora: *Ray, Ricardo* / Soy Boricua: *Valentin, Bobby* / Acere Ko: *La Sonora Poncena*

CDHOT 500 / Oct '93 / Charly

☐ SUPER SELLERS OF THE 50'S (2CD Set)

Lollipop: *Chordettes* / Till I kissed you: *Everly Brothers* / Only you: *Platters* / Canadian sunset: *Williams, Andy* / Ballad of Davy Crocket: *Hayes, Billy* / Walkin' after midnight: *Cline, Patsy* / Let me be the one: *Locklin, Hank* / Donna: *Valens, Ritchie* / Tiger: *Fabian* / Why: *Avalon, Frankie* / Wake up little Susie: *Everly Brothers* / Danny boy: *Twitty, Conway* / Rockin' robin: *Day, Bobby* / Rockin' ghost: *Bleyer, Archie* / All I have to do is dream: *Everly Brothers* / My prayer: *Platters* / Born to be with you: *Chordettes* / Honky tonk merry go round: *Cline, Patsy* / Venus: *Avalon, Frankie* / La bamba: *Valens, Ritchie* / Hound dog man: *Fabian* / All American boy: *Bare, Bobby* / Bird dog: *Everly Brothers* / Anywhere I wonder: *Larosa, Julius* / You don't know me: *Welch, Lenny* / Butterfly: *Williams, Andy* / Hernando's hideaway: *Bleyer, Archie* / Man in the raincoat: *Marlowe, Marion*

SD 885352 / 2 Feb '98 / Disky

☐ SUPER SOUNDS OF BOSWORTH VOL.2

BARKED 2CD / Oct '96 / Trunk

☐ SUPER SUMMER HITS

Mon amour: *BZN* / Ticket to the tropics: *Joling, Gerard* / Rio: *Maywood* / Juanita: *MacKenzie, Nick* / Everybody join hands: *Debby* / Una paloma blanca: *Baker, George Selection* / Ma belle amie: *Tee Set* / Windsurfin': *Surfers* / Sweet love: *Ferrari* / January February: *Dutch Rhythm Steel Band* / Sevilla: *BZN* / Vaya con dios: *Cats* / Doin' la bamba: *Pussycat* / Comment ca va: *Shorts* / See the sun: *Teach In* / Dr. Rhythm: *G'Race* / Weekend: *Earth & Fire* / You and me: *Spargo*

DC 880762 / May '97 / Disky

☐ SUPERHEROES SERIES VOL.1 (Dr. Strange Vs. Asian Man)

MC 001CD / 22 Jun '98 / Mission Control

☐ SUPERMARKET

EFA 122682 / Apr '95 / Disko B

☐ SUPERSONIC 70'S (20 Sensational Smash Hits)

Shooting star: *Dollar* / (Dancing) on a Saturday night: *Blue, Barry* / Sky high: *Jigsaw* / Kung fu fighting: *Douglas, Craig* / Popcorn: *Hot Butter* / Man who sold the world: *Lulu* / Who do you think you are: *Candlewick Green* / Born with a smile on my face: *De Sykes, Stephanie* / Beach baby: *First Class* / More than a lover: *Tyler, Bonnie* / Life is too short girl: *Sheer Elegance* / Sad sweet dreamer: *Sweet Sensation* / Whenever you want my love: *Real Thing* / I'll go where your music takes me: *James, Jimmy & The Vagabonds* / Why did you do it: *Stretch* / Black superman: *Wakelin, Johnny* / This flight tonight: *Nazareth* / Indian reservation: *Fardon, Don* / Shake it down: *Mud* / Lady Rose: *Mungo Jerry*

SUMCD 4101 / Nov '96 / Summit

☐ SUPERSONIC SEVENTIES

Rainbow: *Marmalade* / Love grows (where my Rosemary goes): *Edison Lighthouse* / Wake up everybody: *Melvin, Harold & The Bluenotes* / Baby jump: *Mungo Jerry* / Me and you and a dog named Boo: *Lobo* / Midnight at the Oasis: *Muldaur, Maria* / Do you wanna dance: *Blue, Barry* / Let's get together again: *Glitter Band* / Beg steal or borrow: *New Seekers* / Here comes that rainy day feeling again: *Fortunes* / Son of my father: *Chicory Tip* / You little trustmaker: *Tymes* / It's been so long: *McCrae, George* / I will survive: *Gaynor, Gloria* / Roll away the stone: *Mott The Hoople* / Everlasting love: *Knight, Robert* / Chestnut mare: *Byrds* / Juke box jive: *Rubettes* / Wig wam bam: *Connolly, Brian* / Billy don't be a hero: *Paper Lace*

308562 / 20 Apr '98 / Hallmark

☐ SUPERSTAR LINE UP VOL.2

CDNNM 005 / Jun '92 / New Name

☐ SUPERSTARS

HADCD 201 / Jul '96 / Javelin

☐ SUPERSTARS AT THE DANCE HALL

RNCD 2093 / Mar '95 / Rhino

☐ SUPERSTARS HIT PARADE VOL.8

SPCD 0124 / May '97 / Superpower

☐ SUPERSTARS HIT PARADE VOL.9

SPCD 0132 / 9 Feb '98 / Super Power

☐ SUPERSTARS OF COUNTRY, THE

Sea of heartbreak: *Gibson, Don* / Oh, lonesome me: *Gibson, Don* / Blue blue day: *Gibson, Don* / Give myself a party: *Gibson, Don* / I can't stop loving you: *Gibson, Don* / End of the world: *Davis, Skeeter* / Gonna get along without you now: *Davis, Skeeter* / I can't stay mad at you: *Davis, Skeeter* / What does it take: *Davis, Skeeter* / Am I that easy to forget: *Davis, Skeeter* / King of the road: *Miller, Roger* / England swings: *Miller, Roger* / Husbands and wives: *Miller, Roger* / In the summertime: *Miller, Roger* / Walkin' in the sunshine: *Miller, Roger* / Behind closed doors: *Rich, Charlie* / Good time Charlie's got the blues: *Rich, Charlie* / My elusive dreams: *Rich, Charlie* / There won't be anymore: *Rich, Charlie* / Most beautiful girl: *Rich, Charlie*

ECD 3368 / Jun '97 / K-Tel

☐ SUPERSTARS OF REGGAE

ECD 3365 / 18 Sep '97 / K-Tel

☐ SUPERSTARS OF ROCK 'N' ROLL, THE

Lucille: *Little Richard* / Good golly Miss Molly: *Little Richard* / Keep a knockin': *Little Richard* / Tutti frutti: *Little Richard* / Baby face: *Little Richard* / Be bop a lula: *Vincent, Gene* / Say mama: *Vincent, Gene* / Lonely street: *Vincent, Gene* / Lotta lovin': *Vincent, Gene* / Pistol packin' mama: *Vincent, Gene* / Ain't that a shame: *Boone, Pat* / Wonderful time up there: *Boone, Pat* / Don't forbid me: *Boone, Pat* / Why, baby, why: *Boone, Pat* / Speedy Gonzales: *Boone, Pat* / (Dance with) the guitar man: *Eddy, Duane* / Peter Gunn: *Eddy, Duane* / Shazam: *Eddy, Duane* / Yep: *Eddy, Duane* / Movin' and groovin': *Eddy, Duane*

ECD 3367 / Jun '97 / K-Tel

☐ SUPERSTARS OF SOUL, THE

Spanish harlem: *King, Ben E.* / Stand by me: *King, Ben E.* / I (who have nothing): *King, Ben E.* / Don't play that song (you lied): *King, Ben E.* / Supernatural thing: *King, Ben E.* / Wake up everybody: *Melvin, Harold & The Bluenotes* / If you don't know me by now: *Melvin, Harold & The Bluenotes* / Love I lost: *Melvin, Harold & The Bluenotes* / Bad luck: *Melvin, Harold & The Bluenotes* / Satisfaction guaranteed (or take your love back): *Melvin, Harold & The Bluenotes* / When a man loves a woman: *Sledge, Percy* / Warm and tender love: *Sledge, Percy* / Take time to know her: *Sledge, Percy* / It tears me up: *Sledge, Percy* / Cover me: *Sledge, Percy* / Soul man: *Sam & Dave* / Hold on I'm comin': *Sam & Dave* / Soul sister, brown sugar: *Sam & Dave* / I thank you: *Sam & Dave* / Sweet soul music: *Sam & Dave*

ECD 3366 / Jun '97 / K-Tel

☐ SUPERSTARS OF THE 40'S, THE

On the sunny side of the street: *Cole, Nat 'King'* / Do nothing 'til you hear from me: *Cole, Nat 'King'* / I'm a shy guy: *Cole, Nat 'King'* / This will make you laugh: *Cole, Nat 'King'* / Is you is or is you ain't my baby: *Cole, Nat 'King'* / That old black magic: *Fitzgerald, Ella* / I want to be happy: *Fitzgerald, Ella* / Basin Street blues: *Fitzgerald, Ella* / If dreams come true:

Fitzgerald, Ella / Lover come back to me: Fitzgerald, Ella / In the mood: Miller, Glenn / Chattanooga choo choo: Miller, Glenn / Pennsylvania 6-5000: Miller, Glenn / (I've got a girl in) Kalamazoo: Miller, Glenn / Moonlight serenade: Miller, Glenn / Fools rush in: Sinatra, Frank / Embraceable you: Sinatra, Frank / Stardust: Sinatra, Frank / Sunshine of your smile: Sinatra, Frank / I'll be seeing you: Sinatra, Frank
ECD 3357 / Jun '97 / K-Tel

☐ SUPERSTARS OF THE 50'S, THE
Just walkin' in the rain: Ray, Johnnie / Cry: Ray, Johnnie / Little white cloud that cried: Ray, Johnnie / Walkin' my baby back home: Ray, Johnnie / Hernando's hideaway: Ray, Johnnie / This ole house: Clooney, Rosemary / Hey there: Clooney, Rosemary / Botch-a-me: Clooney, Rosemary / Half as much: Clooney, Rosemary / Come on-a my house: Clooney, Rosemary / Jealousy: Laine, Frankie / I believe: Laine, Frankie / Love is a golden ring: Laine, Frankie / Rose, rose I love you: Laine, Frankie / Jezebel: Laine, Frankie / Tennessee waltz: Page, Patti / Old cape cod: Page, Patti / How much is that doggie in the window: Page, Patti / Changing partners: Page, Patti / Mockin' bird Hill: Page, Patti
ECD 3358 / Jun '97 / K-Tel

☐ SUPERSTARS OF THE 60'S, THE
Rubber ball: Vee, Bobby / More than I can say: Vee, Bobby / Devil or angel: Vee, Bobby / Run to him: Vee, Bobby / Night has a thousand eyes: Vee, Bobby / Wild one: Rydell, Bobby / Volare: Rydell, Bobby / We got love: Rydell, Bobby / Swingin' school: Rydell, Bobby / Forget him: Rydell, Bobby / Everybody: Roe, Tommy / Dizzy: Roe, Tommy / Sweet pea: Roe, Tommy / Jam up jelly tight: Roe, Tommy / Sheila: Roe, Tommy / Poetry in motion: Tillotson, Johnny / It keeps right on a-hurtin': Tillotson, Johnny / You're the reason: Tillotson, Johnny / Without you: Tillotson, Johnny / Talk back trembling lips: Tillotson, Johnny
ECD 3359 / Jun '97 / K-Tel

☐ SUPERSTARS OF THE BLUES
Whiskey and wimmin': Hooker, John Lee / Good rockin' mama: Hooker, John Lee / Dusty road: Hooker, John Lee / I'm so excited: Hooker, John Lee / My first wife left me: Hooker, John Lee / Shaggy dog: Hopkins, Lightnin' / Good times: Hopkins, Lightnin' / Lightnin's stomp: Hopkins, Lightnin' / Talk of the town: Hopkins, Lightnin' / My baby's gone: Hopkins, Lightnin' / Sassy Mae: Memphis Slim / Wish me well: Memphis Slim / Blue and lonesome: Memphis Slim / Stepping out: Memphis Slim / Comeback: Memphis Slim / Hoochie coochie man: Waters, Muddy / Caldonia: Waters, Muddy / I got my mojo working: Waters, Muddy / Garbage man: Waters, Muddy / Baby please don't go: Waters, Muddy
ECD 3388 / 23 Feb '98 / K-Tel

☐ SUPERSTARS OF THE SEVENTIES (2CD Set)
Get ready: Rare Earth / In the summertime: Mungo Jerry / Rock your baby: McCrae, George / Ring my bell: Ward, Anita / That's the way I like it: KC & The Sunshine Band / Ballroom blitz: Sweet / Dynamite: Mud / Tonight: Rubettes / Lay down (candles in the rain): Melanie / Give up your gun: Buoys / (Dancing) on a Saturday night: Blue, Barry / Do it anyway you wanna: People's Choice / Dreams are ten a penny: Kincaid / Matrimony: O'Sullivan, Gilbert / More more more: True, Andrea Connection / Popcorn: Hot Butter / Son of my father: Chicory Tip / Troglodyte: Castor, Jimmy Bunch / Shame shame shame: Shirley & Company / Jukebox jive: Rubettes / Save all your kisses for me: Brotherhood Of Man / Yellow river: Christie / Get down: O'Sullivan, Gilbert / Tiger feet: Mud / Night Chicago died: Paper Lace / Beach baby: First Class / Freedom: Kissoon, Mac & Katie / Get dancin': Disco Tex & The Sexolettes / Love really hurts without you: Ocean, Billy / I'd like to teach the world to sing: New Seekers / Brandy: Looking Glass / Jungle rock: Mizell, Hank / Love grows: Edison Lighthouse / Beautiful Sunday: Boone, Daniel / Rosetta: Fame, Georgie & The Blue Flames / Day after day: Badfinger
TNC 96229 / Aug '96 / Natural Collection

☐ SUPERSTITION VOL.5 (3CD Set)
EFA 620752 / May '97 / Superstition

☐ SUPERWOMAN (2CD Set)
VTDCD 179 / 9 Mar '98 / Virgin

☐ SUPREME SOUL VOL.1 (4CD Set)
Loving you: Massivo / Someday we'll all be free: Green, Tee / When love calls: Kudos / If U believe: Act Of Faith / Searchin': Robyn / Take my hand: Massivo / Surprise surprise: Zushii / I found someone: Gaines, Billy & Sarah / Love can make you feel so happy: Ipso Facto / How can this be: Mannsfield, Rodney / Angel: Riviera / Starlite: Ballin, Chris / Don't be so distant: Taylor, Gary / Real love: Bofill, Angela / Shoulda been you: Ware, Leon / Falling for you: Carne, Jean / Are you ready: Robbins, Rockie / Movin' on: Ipso Facto / I'll be a freak for you: Layton, Lindy / Don't keep me waiting: Rhythm Within / I like: Serenade / You know what it's like: Duverney, Ondrea / Mystery girl: Green, Tee / Ain't nobody: Wallace, Lucy / Love come down: Jackson, Nicole / I know how: Stevens, Kenni / Do without you: Zaeus / I know what's on your mind: Chandler, Omar / Love to love you: On The Contrary / Even when you're gone: Gems For Jem / I like your style: Green, Tee / Friend not a lover: Serenade / Follow your heart: McNeir, Ronnie / Give it (this love song): Caitaine, Ria / Something good inside: Rogers, Richard / Piano in the dark: AMP / I wanna know you: Hewett, Howard / We got one: Covington, Matt / Living in a world: Beverly & Duane / Love me for a reason: As We Speak / I think about you: King, Evelyn 'Champagne' / Committed: Renaizzance / Oasis: Baylor, Helen / Move closer: Zee / In love: Campbell, Roger / Looking for a man: James, Josie / Do you wanna chill with me: Solid State Sound / Shine: Aja / Calling up old memories: Haynes, Victor / Where is the love: J&G
CDBDEB 1 / 8 Dec '97 / Debut

☐ SUPREME SOUL VOL.2 (4CD Set)
CDBDEB 2 / 2 Mar '98 / Debut

☐ SUPREME SOUL VOL.3 (4CD Set)
CDBDEB 3 / 29 Jun '98 / Debut

☐ SURF GUITAR GREATS (One Dozen Surf-Rock Instrumentals)
Mission Impossible: Laika & The Cosmonauts / Miserlou: Laika & The Cosmonauts / Tailspin: Los Straitjackets / Itchy chicken: Los Straitjackets / Pacifica: Los Straitjackets / Fadeaway: Laika & The Cosmonauts / Suicide bay: Halibuts / Hammerhead: Halibuts / Pier pressure: Del Rey, Teisco / Seville: Del Rey, Teisco / Surf the wild Gowanus: Chardiet, Simon / Tico Tico: Tailgators
EDCD 7036 / Sep '97 / Easydisc

☐ SURF PARTY
295720 / Jul '93 / Ariola

☐ SURRENDER TO THE VIBE
PTM 132 / Sep '95 / Phantasm

☐ SURVIVAL
Survival theme / Citizens of coral / Valley beneath the sea / Dwellers of the deep / Suite for silver shoals / Dreams of emSonata for the seal / Creatures of the ocean / Glide with a matinee / Song of the river / Empire of the elephant / Rhythm of hells gate / In the heart of Africa / Animal outback / Empire of the plains / East of eden / Amazonian journey / Web of the spider monkey / Apalachian heights / Madagascar land of hope / Mountains of snow leopard / Tarantulas reach / Andes landscape / Night raiders / Queen of the beasts / Red in tooth and claw / Leaders of the pack / Gorillas shatterred kingdom / Wings over the world / Humming bird calypso / Flight of the snow geese / Fly to the stars / Angels of the orient / Mysterious skies / Sumatra dawn / Through the eye of a needle
VTCD 148 / 28 Jul '97 / Virgin

☐ SURVIVAL OF THE FATTEST
FAT 538CD / Jun '96 / Fatwreck Chords

☐ SURVIVAL SOUNDS
Fallen angel: Robertson, Robbie / Sina (Soumbouya): Keita, Salif / Tahi: Moana & The Moahunters / Pundela: Robin, Thierry & Gulabi Sapera / Bring 'em all in: Scott, Mike / Mapoto: Mapfumo, Thomas & The Blacks Unlimited / Didgeridoo solo/Baru (crocodie): Sunrize Band / Modernise, westernise: Rough Image / Exile: Oryema, Geoffrey / Om mani padme hung: Lhamo, Yungchen / Whirl-y-reel 1: Afro Celt Sound System / Take me to God: Jah Wobble's Invaders Of The Heart / Navega sola: Martin, Mayte / I want to go home: Ongala, Remmy / My country: Midnight Oil
WSSS 1 / Nov '96 / Womad Survival

☐ SURVIVAL-THE DANCE COMPILATION
One nation: Supereal / Little bullet part 1: Spooky / Boss drum: Shamen / Choice: Orbital / Djapana: Yothu Yindi / King of the funky zulus: Moody Blues / Release the dub: Leftfield / Aquarium: Grid / Flowing nile: Zion Train / Freeality: Freeality / Predator: Spiral Tribe
GRCD 008 / May '93 / Guerilla

☐ SUSHI 303
RTD 34600062 / Sep '96 / City Slang

☐ SVENSK JAZZHISTORIA VOL.2 (Hot Epoken - Swedish Jazz 1931-1936/ 2CD Set)
CAP 22038CD / Aug '97 / Caprice

☐ SVG CARNIVAL 1998
GSCD 2418 / 13 Jul '98 / Strakers

☐ SWAMP BLUES
Looking the world over: Smith, Whispering / Thousand miles from nowhere: Smith, Whispering / SDeep South Mose: Smith, Whispering / Cold black mare: Smith, Whispering / Storm in Texas: Smith, Whispering / Baton Rouge breakdown: Smith, Whispering / Baby please don't go: Smith, Whispering / Somebody stole my baby and gone: Kelley, Arthur 'Guitar' / How can I stay when all I have is gone: Kelley, Arthur 'Guitar' / I don't know why: Kelley, Arthur 'Guitar' / Number ten is at the station: Kelley, Arthur 'Guitar' / Just give me a chance: Hogan, Silas / Dry chemical blues: Hogan, Silas / I didn't tell her to leave: Hogan, Silas / Hoodoo blues: Hogan, Silas / Honey bee blues: Hogan, Silas / Lonesome bedroom blues: Edwards, Clarence / Let me love you baby: Edwards, Clarence / I want somebody: Edwards, Clarence / Can't last too long: Gray, Henry / Gray's bounce: Gray, Henry / Showers of rain: Gray, Henry / Worried life blues: Gray, Henry / Cooling board: Edwards, Clarence
CDCHD 661 / Jul '97 / Ace

☐ SWAMP MUSIC VOL.9 (New Trail Raiders)
US 0206 / Apr '95 / Trikont

☐ SWAMP SURFING IN MEMPHIS
ANDA 047CD / 23 Feb '98 / Au-Go-Go

☐ SWAN'S SOUL SIDES
Run tun: Persianettes / You're everything: Showmen / Misery: Carlton, Eddie / Never too young (to fall in love): Modern Redcaps / In love: Galla, Tony / Trying to find my baby: Dodds, Troy / I'm just your clown: Teddy & The Twilights / Two steps ahead: Johnson, Herb / No sign of you: Modern Redcaps / Put yourself in my place: Mortimor, Azie / In return: Ferguson, Sheila / Have faith in me: Sugar & Spice / Handsome boy: Ladybirds / Gotta find a way: Wilson, Naomi / Hey sah-lo-ney: Lane, Mickey Lee / No good: Anthony, Richard / Our love will grow: Showmen / Hot hot: Buena Vistas / You got to tell me: Rivieras / Who do you love: Sapphires / Gotta draw the line: Three Degrees / Hearbroken memories: Ferguson, Sheila / I do love you: Styles / Put that woman down: Leach, John / It will be done: Carlton, Eddie / Everybody crossfire: Stevens, Sammy
CDKEND 120 / Jan '96 / Kent

☐ SWARM OF DRONES (2CD Set)
ASP 0953CD / 22 Jun '98 / Asphodel

☐ SWEDISH FOLK MUSIC
C 600010 / May '98 / Ocora

☐ SWEDISH JAZZ FROM THE 70'S
2002 / Nov '89 / Caprice

☐ SWEDISH SINS
March of the SOD: Entombed / Suckerpunch: Leadfoot / 5 years ahead of my time: Nomads / Ferrytale: Hellacopters / Stars: Backyard Babies / Down: Haystack / Horrorboy: Kids Are Sick / Citylife: Skelett / Rats inc.: Sewergrooves / Laff track: Robots / Just for fun: Zen / Silverdollarflip: A-Bombs / Tractor beam: Superbee / Girlfriend: Henry Fiat's Open Sore / What I want: Let's Gos / Sub. way: Misdemeanor / Happiness: Silvermachine / Louisville lip: Friends / Evil matcher: Gluecifer
JAZZ 006CD / 24 Nov '97 / White Jazz

☐ SWEET CITY SOUL (4CD Set)
I can't help myself: Four Tops & The All Stars / Stop her on sight (SOS): Starr, Edwin / Hang on in there baby: Bristol, Johnny / Technicolour: Griffin, Billy / All over the world: Jackson, Chuck / When you're young and in love: Marvelettes / Love hangover: 5th Dimension / Baby love: Supremes / You are the sunshine of my life: Nero, Frances / Reach out and touch somebody's hand: Demps, Louvain / It takes two: Gaye, Frankie & Kim Weston / Band of gold: Payne, Freda / Ain't no mountain high enough: Payne, Sherrie / Standing still: Monitors / Love machine: Miracles / Light a nightmare: Andantes / It should have been me: Weston, Kim / Ain't too proud to beg: Willie, Richard / With you I'm born again: Syreeta / I'm gonna make you love me: Originals & The Supremes / Footsteps following me: Nero, Frances / Nathan Jones: Supremes / Breaking down the walls: Starr, Edwin / Heatwave: Reeves, Martha & The Vandellas / My guy: Wells, Mary / Dancing in the street: Weston, Kim / Heaven must have sent you: Elgins / This old heart of mine: Contours / Wishing on a star: Calvin, Billie / What does it take to win your love: Bristol, Johnny / My brother: Gaye, Frankie / I'll be around: Cameron, G.C. / Date with the rain: Griffin, Billy / Reflections: Syreeta / All around the motorcity: Andantes / Wholeheartedly: McNier, Ronnie / Put yourself in my place: Edwards, Sandra / Day by day: Monitors / Love child: Supremes / Gentle lady: Eckstein, Billy / Stop in the name of love: Supremes / I'll pick a rose for my rose: Johnson, Marv / Going to a go-go: Monitors / Rescue me: Lewis, Pat / Relight my fire: Jackson, Chuck / Someday we'll be together: Bristol, Johnny / Sweet sherry: Barnes, J.J. / Tell a fool goodbye: Edwards, Sandra / It's a shame: Cameron, G.C. / Darlin' darlin' baby: Starr, Edwin / Back by popular demand: Supremes & The Originals / Tracks of my tears: Contours / Ten out of ten: Elgins / I'm still waiting: Payne, Sherrie / On the beach: Demps, Louvain / Something incredible: Griffin, Billy / Let me down easy: Lavette, Bettye / Save me I'm all alone: Dixon, Hank / My cherie amour: Moy, Sylvia / Needle in a haystack: Velvelettes / Ain't nothing but a house party: Contours / Stoned love: Supremes / Man up in the sky: Bristol, Johnny / Tears of a clown: Monitors / Jimmy mack: Lavette, Bettye / 25 miles: Starr, Edwin / Ain't nothing like the real thing: Johnson, Marv & Carolyn Gill / Just my imagination: Cameron, G.C. / Special day: Gaye, Frankie / Free: Greene, Susaye / It's the same old song: Stubbs, Joe / Remember me: Lewis, Pat / He was really saying something: Velvelettes / It wouldn't change the man he is: Blinky / You're all I need to get by: Reeves, Martha & G.C. Cameron / Man in my life: Laurence, Lynda / Crazy 'bout the guy: Supremes / Lost and found: Demps, Louvain / You're my first, my last, my everything: Littles, Hattie / It's impossible: Eckstein, Billy & Susaye Greene
MBSCD 449 / Sep '96 / Castle

☐ SWEET DREAMS
Sweet dreams: Young, Faron / I've loved and lost again: Cline, Patsy / Don't think twice: Jennings, Waylon / I can't find the time: Nelson, Willie / (I never promised you a) Rose garden: Anderson, Lynn / Always leaving, always gone: Rogers, Kenny & The First Edition / Hello walls: Drusky, Roy / Wishful thinking: Fargo, Donna / I can't get enough of you: Jackson, Stonewall / Before the next teardrop falls: Fender, Freddy / Release me: Mandrell, Barbara / Have I told you lately that I love you: Reeves, Jim / Lonely wine: Gilley, Mickey / Making believe: Wells, Kitty / Four in the morning: Young, Faron / Your tender years: Jones, George / Hungry for your love: Cline, Patsy / She even woke me up to say goodbye: Rogers, Kenny & The First Edition / Last letter: Drusky, Roy / I don't know why I love you but I do: Fender, Freddy
QED 021 / Nov '96 / Tring

☐ SWEET EMOTIONS
EX 3592CD / 16 Oct '97 / Instinct

☐ SWEET GUITAR
Windmills of your mind / Air on a g-string / Lady in red / Without you / Sweet sixteen / If you leave me now / WHile my guitar gently weeps / Mona Lisa / You've got a friend / Step inside love / Dreams / Morning song / As I roved out / Ministal boy / Music of the night / Elvira Madigan / Autumn leaves / Fur elise / Fool on the hill / Gymnopedie
EMPRCD 682 / Apr '97 / Emporio

☐ SWEET HEAVEN
Just look: Arizona Dranes / Sweet heaven is my home: Arizona Dranes / Dark was the night cold was the ground: Johnson, 'Blind' Willie / Let your light shine on me: Johnson, 'Blind' Willie / Lord stand by me: Davis, Gary / I belong to the band hallejulah: Davis, Gary / God don't like it: Thorpe, Sister Rosetta / I looked down the line (and I wondered): Thorpe, Sister Rosetta / God's gonna seperate the wheat from the chares: Jackson, Mahalia / Move on up a little higher: Jackson, Mahalia / Amazing grace: Jackson, Mahalia / Every time I feel the spirit: Golden Gate Quartet / Preacher and the bear: Golden Gate Quartet / Go down Moses: Southern Sons / Moan you mourners: Smith, Bessie / My record will be there: Washington, Sister Ernestine / What could I do: Washington, Sister Ernestine / Book of the seven seals: Dixie Hummingbirds / Jonah in the belly of the whale: Norfolk Jubilee Quartet / You better run: Norfolk Jubilee Quartet / Ain't no grave can hold my body down: Sturdivant, Bozie / I got a key to the kingdom: White, Joshua / My soul is gonna live with God: White, Joshua / I want two wings: Smith, Rev. Utah
PASTCD 7823 / 2 Feb '98 / Flapper

☐ SWEET HOME BLUE CHICAGO (Red Hot Mamas)
Sweet home Chicago: Carroll, Karen / Mama: Jordan, Lynne / 20 percent alcohol: Greeson, Liz Mandville / Meet me with your black drawers on: Lee, Bonnie / Something you got: Scott, Patricia / Unchain my heart: Johnson, Shirley / One good man: Jordan, Lynne / Honey don't: Staten, Little Mary / What have I done wrong: Greeson, Liz Mandville / Wee baby blues: Lee, Bonnie / Not that kind of girl: Scott, Patricia / Hold what you've got: Johnson, Shirley / Blue Chicago blues: Carroll, Karen
BC 5001 / Dec '97 / Blue Chicago

☐ SWEET HOME BLUE CHICAGO (Clark Street Ramblers)
Kokomo me baby: Moore, Johnny B. / Park my car: Baze, George / Sun is shining: Clearwater, Eddy / Turn up the heat: Vaughn, Maurice John / I been foolin' around: Coleman, Michael / I wonder why: Kent, Willie / Nothing: Kent, Willie / I'm tired: Shaw, Eddie / Don't lie to me: Moore, Johnny B. / Hush hush: Baze, George / It's my fault: Vaughn, Maurice John / You're going to miss me: Coleman, Michael / All night long: Kent, Willie
BC 5002 / Dec '97 / Blue Chicago

☐ SWEET HOME CHICAGO
DD 618 / Mar '95 / Delmark

☐ SWEET LORD (Charly Gospel Greats)
Uncloudy day: Staple Singers / Jesus is the answer: Argo Singers / No coward soldier: Caravans / Have I told you about my religion: Bells Of Joy / I'm thinkin': Five Blind Boys Of Mississippi / My loved ones: Soul Stirrers / His eye is on the sparrow: Harmonizing Four / Somewhere to lay my head: Highway QC's / What he's done for me: Five Blind Boys Of Alabama / He saved my soul: Swan Silvertones / He has a way: Greater Harvest Choir / Too close to heaven: Bradford, Alex / Will the circle be unbroken: Pilgrim Travellers / God is moving: Sallie Martin Singers / Step by step: Original Gospel Harmonettes / Precious Lord (part 1): Franklin, Aretha / Precious Lord (part 2): Franklin, Aretha / We shall overcome: Jackson, Mahalia
CPCD 8090 / Apr '95 / Charly

☐ SWEET MEMORIES FROM BIG BAND
UP 004 / Sep '92 / Hindsight

☐ SWEET 'N' TOUGH (Blues From Chicago)
MCCD 280 / Dec '96 / Music Club

☐ SWEET SOUL CLASSICS
PDSCD 517 / Sep '97 / Pulse

☐ SWEET SOUL DREAMS
290426 / Dec '92 / Ariola

☐ SWEET SOUND OF SUCCESS
You've got the power: Esquires / If I had you: O'Dell, Brooks / There's still tomorrow: Diplomats / Same old story: Big Maybelle / Don't say goodnight and mean goodbye: Shirelles / Invisible: Miles, Lenny / That's enough: Robinson, Roscoe / Baby take me: Jackson, Chuck / Keep on searchin': Candy & The Kisses / Finders keepers, losers weepers: Dodds, Nella / If I catch you: Shaw, Timmy / Hand it over: Jackson, Chuck / He's no good: Hughes, Freddie / Love of my man: Kilgore, Theola / Look over your shoulder: Jackson, Chuck / One step at a time: Brown, Maxine / Door is open: Hunt, Tommy / It's mine: Montgomery, Tammy / Lonely people do foolish things: Clay, Judy / How much pressure: Robinson, Roscoe / Come see about me: Dodds, Nella / Half a man: Cooke, L.C. / This world's in a hell of a shape: Ross, Jackie / Do it now: Banks, Bessie / Ask me: Brown, Maxine / Can't let you out of my sight: Jackson, Chuck & Maxine Brown / Gonna send you back to Georgia: Shaw, Timmy / Don't believe him Donna: Miles, Lenny
CDKEND 112 / Jun '94 / Kent

☐ SWEET, SOFT AND LAZY
12203 / Dec '94 / Laserlight

☐ SWEET SWEET SKA (3CD Set)
TX 51169CD / 8 Dec '97 / Triple XXX

☐ SWEET SWEET SOCA
SCR 334 / 13 Oct '97 / Charlie's

☐ SWEET SWING (4CD Set)
78067421082 / 14 Jul '98 / Drive Archive

☐ SWEET TASTE OF WESTBOUND, A
Walt's third trip: Morrison, Junie / Rhythm changes: Counts / Baby let me take you (in my arms): Detroit Emeralds / Walked away from you: Ohio Players / Cookie jar: Haskins, Fuzzy / Get up off my mind: LaSalle, Denise / You can't miss what you can't measure: Funkadelic / What am I gonna do: Houston Outlaws / Funky Sunday afternoon: Person, Houston / Back to funk: Lowe, Robert / You're messin' up my mind: Washington, Albert / Ain't I been good to you: Fantastic Four / Your love is my desire: Erasmus Hall / Crazy legs: Austin, Donald / Sweet taste of sin: Coffey, Dennis / Bull: Theodore, Mike Orchestra / Deadeye Dick: CJ & Co. / Everything's gonna be alright: Clark Sisters
CDSWX 150 / Mar '96 / Westbound

☐ SWEETER THAN SWEETS
CMS 01CD / Mar '97 / Canopy

☐ SWEETER THAN THE DAY BEFORE (28 Classic Cuts From The Chess Stable)
Strange change: Ward, Herb / Baby you've got it: McAllister, Maurice & The Radiants / Such a pretty thing: Chandler, Gene / Chained to your heart: Moore, Bobby & The Rhythm Aces / Love reputation: LaSalle, Denise / Let's wade in the water: Shaw, Marlena / Make sure (you have someone who loves you): Dells / What can I do: Kirby, George / Lucky boy: Hutton, Harold / Later than you think: Mack, Andy / Sweeter than the day before: Valentinos / If I would marry you: Montgomery, Tammy / Is it a sin: Timiko / Whole new plan: Garrett, Joan / Look at me now: Callier, Terry / Strange feeling: Nash, Johnny / Mighty good lover: Vashonettes / My baby's good: Williams, Johnny / Sometimes: Little Milton / Can't you hear the beat: Carltons / I can't stand it: Seminoles / I just kept on dancing: Banks, Doug / Pay back: James, Etta / Pain: Collier, Mitty / Landslide: Clarke, Tony / Thinkin' about you: Dells / Ain't got no problems: Sunday / Count me out: Stewart, Billy
CDARC 515 / Jun '91 / Charly

Column 1

☐ SWEETEST FEELING - THE GOLDEN AGE OF SOUL (4CD Set)
CDDIG 7 / Feb '95 / Charly

☐ SWEETEST HARMONY (25 Vintage Harmony Ensembles)
Breezin' along with the breeze: Revelers & Ed Smalle / Whisper song: California Hummingbirds / Too busy: Four Rajahs / Dear on a night like this: National Cavaliers Quartet & David Buttolph / That's my weakness now: Rhythm Boys & Paul Whiteman Orchestra / Girl in the little green hat: Four Musketeers & Mabel Pearl / At the baby parade: Harmonians Quartet / Sweet Jennie Lee: Big Four / Dinah: Cole Brothers / Oh by jingo: Three Keys / Stormy weather: Three Admirals / Cuban tango: Viennese Seven Singing Sisters / America calling medley: Carlyle Cousins & Brian Lawrence Quaglino Quartet / Why don't you practice what you preach: Boswell Sisters & Victor Young Orchestra / In the shade of the old apple tree: Four Aces / Caravan: Mills Brothers / Everybody step: Three Peters Sisters & Harry Bidgood Rhythm Boys / Mandy: Four Modernaires & Paul Whitman Swing Wing Group / Bidin' my time: Foursome / Undecided: Dandridge Sisters / Tuxedo junction: Andrews Sisters & Vic Schoen Orchestra / Shakespeare in rhythm: Cavendish Three & Bruce Campbell / Java jive: Ink Spots / Breathless: Merry Macs / Auf wiedersehn my dear: Comedy Harmonists & Emil Gerhardt
CDAJA 5216 / Sep '97 / Living Era

☐ SWEETS FOR MY SWEET
TMPCD 008 / Jan '95 / Temple

☐ SWING BROTHER SWING (16 Big Band Greats)
Life is a song: Bennett, Tony & Count Basie Orchestra / Stormy weather: Vaughan, Sarah & Billy Eckstine Orchestra / I'll walk alone: Kallen, Kitty & Harry James Orchestra / Do something to me: Walters, Teddy & Artie Shaw Orchestra / Gone with the wind: Johnson, Jay & Stan Kenton Orchestra / Love me or leave me: Vaughan, Sarah & Dizzy Gillespie Orchestra / And the angels sing: Tilton, Martha & Benny Goodman Orchestra / Jump for joy: Nance, Ray & Duke Ellington Orchestra / Chatanooga choo choo: Modernaires & Glenn Miller Orchestra / C'est si bon: Ross, Annie & Tony Crombie Orchestra / Ain't misbehavin': Williams, Joe & Count Basie Orchestra / Taking a chance on love: Christie, June & Stan Kenton Orchestra / Goodnight my love: Fitzgerald, Ella & Benny Goodman Orchestra / Mack the knife: Nance, Ray & Duke Ellington Orchestra / What is this thing called love: Torme, Mel & Artie Shaw Orchestra / It beggars in Sun Valley: Modernaires & Glenn Miller Orchestra
SUMCD 4039 / Nov '96 / Summit

☐ SWING CARAIBE (Paris 1929-1946/ 2CD Set)
Hallelulah: Valvert, Felix / Sonny Boy: Valvert, Felix / He's my secret passion: Notte & His Creole Band / I found a wonderful girl: Notte & His Creole Band / Shuffle of to Buffalo: Mayambe & San Jazz / Sweet low sweet chariot: Achille, Louis-Thomas / Kenny meeny miney mo: Jazz Sam Castendet / Sweet Georgia Brown: Jazz Sam Castendet / My heart: Del's Jazz Biguine / Swing but sweet: Louise, Pierre & Albert Lirvat / Cet air convient a ma melancolie: Louise, Pierre & Albert Lirvat / Oh cette musique: Jumbo, Freddy Ensemble / Seul ce soir: Jumbo, Freddy Ensemble / Begine swing: Jumbo, Freddy Ensemble / Swing 42: Jumbo, Freddy Ensemble / Boogie woogie: Jumbo, Freddy Ensemble / Ce soir: Jumbo, Freddy Ensemble / La va di wa wa ou: Jumbo, Freddy Ensemble / Voyage au long cours: Jumbo, Freddy Ensemble / Inspiration: Cooper, Harry Orchestra / Nuages: Cooper, Harry Orchestra / La cigale: Cooper, Harry Orchestra / Allegro: Cooper, Harry Orchestra / Nos impressions: Cooper, Harry Orchestra / Caprice en ut: Cooper, Harry Orchestra / Lune rosse: Cooper, Harry Orchestra / Partie da plaisir: Visuer, Gus Orchestra / Hot club parade: Chauliac, Leo & Son Orchestre / Swing guitars: Ferret, Jean Sixtette / Georgina: Ensemble Swing Du Hot Club Colonial / J'adore la musique: Ensemble Swing Du Hot Club Colonial / Misty sunrise: Ensemble Swing Du Hot Club Colonial
FA 069 / Nov '97 / Fremeaux

☐ SWING DE MUSETTE
IMP 047 / Apr '97 / IMP

☐ SWING ERA, THE
CDDIG 2 / Feb '95 / Charly

☐ SWING FOR A CRIME
842623 / May '94 / EVA

☐ SWING GIRLS, THE
That old devil called love: Holiday, Billie / St Louis Blues: Holiday, Billie / Georgia on my mind: Holiday, Billie / I hear music: Holiday, Billie / Over the rainbow: Garland, Judy / Forty second street: Keeler, Ruby & Dick Powell / Pistol packin' Mama: Andrews Sisters & Bing Crosby / I want to be happy: Fitzgerald, Ella / A tisket, a tasket: Fitzgerald, Ella / Little white lies: Fitzgerald, Ella / Baby won't you please come home: Fitzgerald, Ella / Bob White (Watcha gonna swing tonight): Boswell, Connee & Bing Crosby / For me and my gal: Garland, Judy & Gene Kelly / Rum and coca cola: Andrews Sisters / My blue heaven: Horne, Lena / A honeysuckle rose: Horne, Lena / Lady is a tramp: Horne, Lena / Honeysuckle rose: Horne, Lena / What a difference a day made: Vaughan, Sarah / Honeysuckle rose: Horne, Lena / A honeysuckle rose: Holiday, Billie / Release me: Little Esther / My heart belongs to Daddy: Fitzgerald, Ella / Our love is here to stay: Washington, Dinah / Summertime: Holiday, Billie / Sometimes I feel like a Motherless child: Vaughan, Sarah / I ain't got no, / Judy lee: Simone, Nina / Getting mighty crowded: Everett, Betty / What a difference a day makes: Vaughan, Sarah / Smoke gets in your eyes: Washington, Dinah / That ole devil called love again: Everett, Betty
ECD 3326 / Mar '97 / K-Tel

☐ SWING GUYS, THE
I haven't time to be a millionaire: Sinatra, Frank / Trolley song: Sinatra, Frank / Lullaby of broadway: Sinatra, Frank / Surrey with a fring on top: Sinatra, Frank / Straighten up and fly right: Cole, Nat 'King' / It's only a paper moon: Cole, Nat 'King' / Embraceable you: Cole, Nat 'King' / How deep is the ocean: Cole, Nat 'King' / Pretty baby: Jolson, Al / Spaniard that display my life: Jolson, Al & Bing Crosby / Gone fishin': Armstrong, Louis & Bing Crosby / Jeepers creepers: Bennett, Tony / Life is a song: Bennett, Tony / Cottage for sale: Eckstine, Billy / That old black magic: Eckstine, Billy / I can't give you anything but love: Torme, Mel / I've got the world on a string: Torme, Mel / I'm getting sentimental over you: Torme, Mel /

Column 2

Say it isn't so: Crosby, Bing / Blue skies: Crosby, Bing / Cheek to cheek: Crosby, Bing / All by myself: Crosby, Bing / On the sunny side of the street: Armstrong, Louis / Chicago: Bennett, Tony / Put it there pal: Hope, Bob & Bing Crosby
ECD 3327 / Mar '97 / K-Tel

☐ SWING INTO BOP
TPZ 1028 / Oct '95 / Topaz Jazz

☐ SWING INTO CHRISTMAS
Cradle in Bethleham: Washington, Grover Jr. / Blue Christmas: Washington, Grover Jr. & Terence Blanchard / O come all ye faithful (adeste fidelis): Roberts, Marcus / Winter wonderland: Roberts, Marcus / Christmas time is here: Blanchard, Terence / Amazing grace: Hawkins, Tramaine / Carols of the bells: Marsalis, Wynton Septet / Let it snow, let it snow, let it snow: Marsalis, Wynton Septet
4814112 / Nov '95 / Sony Jazz

☐ SWING, JIVE & DOO WOP - THE COLLECTION
PEPCD 114 / Feb '96 / Pollytone

☐ SWING OUT
I'm coming Virginia: Berigan, Bunny / How'm I doin': Prima, Louis / Wire brush stomp: Krupa, Gene / What's the reason: Waller, Fats / Sometimes I'm happy: Goodman, Benny / London bridge is falling down: Basie, Count / Pennies from heaven: Prima, Louis / Panasie stomp: Basie, Count / Japanese sandman: Goodman, Benny / There'll be some changes made: Waller, Fats / Love bug will get you: Prima, Louis / Last round up: Krupa, Gene / Solo hop: Miller, Glenn Orchestra / Strictly jive: Webb, Chick & His Orchestra / Flea on a spree: Powell, Tony & His Orchestra / Flat foot floogie: Manone, Wingy & His Orchestra / Darktown strutters ball: Dorsey, Jimmy Orchestra / Keep a-knockin': Jordan, Louis & His Tympany Five / And the angels sing: Elman, Ziggy & His Orchestra / Don't you miss your baby: Basie, Count / Swinging em down: Jenkins, Freddie & Harlem 7 / Miss Otis regrets: Lunceford, Jimmie & His Orchestra / Dusk in upper sandusky: Dorsey, Jimmy Orchestra / In a little spanish town: Miller, Glenn Orchestra
300422 / Jul '96 / Hallmark

☐ SWING OUT JAZZ
BN 036 / Apr '98 / Blue Nite

☐ SWING OUT...SISTERS
Mad about the boy: Washington, Dinah / My baby just cares for me: Simone, Nina / You're no good: Everett, Betty / Tisket-a-tasket: Fitzgerald, Ella / Gentleman friend: Vaughan, Sarah / God bless the child: Holiday, Billie / Release me: Little Esther / My heart belongs to Daddy: Fitzgerald, Ella / Our love is here to stay: Washington, Dinah / Summertime: Holiday, Billie / Sometimes I feel like a Motherless child: Vaughan, Sarah / I ain't got no, / Judy lee: Simone, Nina / Getting mighty crowded: Everett, Betty / What a difference a day makes: Vaughan, Sarah / Smoke gets in your eyes: Washington, Dinah / That ole devil called love again: Everett, Betty
SUMCD 4026 / Nov '96 / Summit

☐ SWING TIME
CWNCD 2007 / Jun '95 / Javelin

☐ SWING TIME (4CD Set)
Night is young and you're so beautiful: Sinatra, Frank / Indian love ca,ll: McDonald, Jeanette / Moonlight serenade: Miller, Glenn / Serenade in blue: Miller, Glenn / String of pearls: Miller, Glenn / Moon came up with a bright idea: Crosby, Bing & Peggy Lee / My man (Mon homme): Fitzgerald, Ella / I'm confessin' (That I love you): Fitzgerald, Ella / Stardust: Sinatra, Frank / Without a song: Sinatra, Frank / Polka dots and moonbeams: Sinatra, Frank / There will never be another you: Cole, Nat 'King' / Mona Lisa: Cole, Nat 'King' / My funny valentine: Cole, Nat 'King' / Unforgettable: Cole, Nat 'King' / Just you, just me: Cole, Nat 'King' / On a slow boat to China: Haymes, Dick / Cheek to cheek: Haymes, Dick / Elmer's tune: Fields, Shep / Moonlight bay: Crosby, Bing & Gary Crosby / If I didn't care: Ink Spots / I've heard that song before: James, Harry / You made me love you: Garland, Judy / Best things in life are free: Allyson, June & Peter Lawford / Thanks for the memory: Hope, Bob & Shirley Ross / Zing went the strings of my heart: Garland, Judy / Room 66: Cole, Nat 'King' / You're the cream in my coffee: Cole, Nat 'King' / Too marvellous for words: Cole, Nat 'King' / When you're smiling (The whole world smiles with you): Cole, Nat 'King' / Fools rush in: Sinatra, Frank / Sunshine of your smile: Sinatra, Frank / How about you: Sinatra, Frank / I'll be seeing you: Sinatra, Frank / Into each life some rain must fall: Fitzgerald, Ella & The Ink Spots / I'm in the mood: Miller, Glenn / Chattanooga choo choo: Miller, Glenn / Friendship: Garland, Judy & Johnny Mercer / Opus No.1: Dorsey, Tommy / Shine: Crosby, Bing & The Mills Brothers / Macpherson is rehearsin' (It's swing): Fitzgerald, Ella / Taking a chance on love: Fitzgerald, Ella / Darktown strutters' ball: Fitzgerald, Ella / Take the "A" train: Ellington, Duke / In a moment of weakness: Powell, Dick / Zing a little zong: Crosby, Bing & Jane Wyman / Ida, sweet as apple cider: Mills Brothers / Civilization (Bongo, bongo, bongo): Andrews Sisters & Danny Kaye / Little Miss Broadway's: Temple, Shirley & George Murphy / You were never lovelier: Astaire, Fred / Connecticut: Garland, Judy & Bing Crosby / I haven't got time to be a millionaire: Sinatra, Frank / Straighten up and fly right: Cole, Nat 'King' / Pretty baby: Jolson, Al / Gone fishin': Armstrong, Louis & Bing Crosby / It's only a paper moon: Cole, Nat 'King' / Trolley song: Sinatra, Frank / Surrey with a fring on top: Sinatra, Frank / Lullaby of broadway: Sinatra, Frank / How deep is the ocean: Cole, Nat 'King' / Blue skies: Crosby, Bing / Dogtown blues: Crosby, Bob / Savoy blues: Crosby, Bob / Dippermouth blues: Dorsey, Jimmy & Louis Armstrong / Tin roof blues: Dorsey, Tommy & St. Louis blues: Dorsey Brothers / Diga diga doo: Ellington, Duke / Roll 'em: Goodman, Benny / Memphis blues: Henderson, Fletcher / At the woodchoppers' ball: Herman, Woody / Sweet sorrow blues: Hughes, Spike / That too, do: Moten, Bennie / Hot and anxious: Redman, Don / New call of the freaks: Russell, Luis / Blues: Shaw, Artie / Ridin' but walkin': Waller, Fats
CDAJA 5088 / Oct '91 / Living Era

Column 3

(Watcha gonna swing tonight): Boswell, Connee & Bing Crosby / For me and my gal: Garland, Judy & Gene Kelly / Rum and coca cola: Andrews Sisters / My blue heaven: Horne, Lena / Lady is a tramp: Horne, Lena / Honeysuckle rose: Horne, Lena / What a difference a day made: Vaughan, Sarah / September song: Vaughan, Sarah / Lover man: Vaughan, Sarah / Body and soul: McRae, Carmen / C'est si bon: Ross, Annie / Up a lazy river: Lee, Peggy & Woody Herman / Fly me to the moon: Smith, Keely / Baby won't you please come home: Fitzgerald, Ella / Somebody loves me: Lee, Peggy
ECD 3325 / Mar '97 / K-Tel

☐ SWING TRUMPET KINGS (2CD Set)
Memories for the count / Ballin' the jack / Canal street blues / Just a closer walk with thee / Snowy morning blues / Fidgety feet / All of me / Struttin' with some barbecue / Bugle call rag
5332632 / Feb '97 / Verve

☐ SWING WAS OUR BUSINESS
St. Louis blues / Don't try your jive on me / Ridin' high / Spring fever / Frankie and Johnny / How'm I doin / China boy / Sing sing sing / Calling all keys / Chopsticks / Dedication / Get hot / Mozelton / Fate let's go / Ol' man river / Sheik of araby / Archer street drag / Patty cake patty cake / There's a plenty / Yankee doodle plays fugue / Hot lips
RAJCD 859 / 2 Feb '98 / Empress

☐ SWINGERS (2CD Set)
Let's face the music and dance: Cole, Nat 'King' / Volare: Martin, Dean / Come fly with me: Sinatra, Frank / I left my heart in San Francisco: Bennett, Tony / Blue velvet: Vinton, Bobby / Misty: Mathis, Johnny / I can't give you anything but love: Armstrong, Louis / Stardust: Carmichael, Hoagy / What a difference a day: Vaughan, Sarah / No such thing as love: Como, Perry / You'll never know: Haymes, Dick / April love: Boone, Pat / You made me love you: Jolson, Al / Puttin' on the ritz: Astaire, Fred / Wives and lovers: Jones, Jack / Swinging on a star: Crosby, Bing / Can't get used to losing you: Williams, Andy / Louise: Chevalier, Maurice / What a wonderful world: Armstrong, Louis / Mack the knife: Darin, Bobby / Magic moments: Como, Perry / Little she wine drinker me: Martin, Dean / Good life: Bennett, Tony / Born free: Monro, Matt / Walking in the rain: Ray, Johnnie / What kind of fool am I: Newley, Anthony / On the street where you live: Damone, Vic / I believe: Laine, Frankie / It might as well be spring: Haymes, Dick / Lollipops and roses: Jones, Jack / After you've gone: Jolson, Al / Love letters in the sand: Boone, Pat / Thanks for the memory: Hope, Bob & Shirley Ross / Moon river: Williams, Andy / Christmas song: Torme, Mel / White Christmas: Crosby, Bing
TTVCD 2937 / 17 Nov '97 / Telstar TV

☐ SWINGIN' JAZZ FOR HIPSTERS VOL.1
Candy man: Brown, Ray & Monty Alexander/Sam Most / Goin' out of my head: McDuff, Jack / Walk between the raindrops: Torme, Mel / Isn't she lovely: Grappelli, Stephane / Slidin': Meurkens, Hendrik / Honeysuckle rose: Scaggiari, Stefan / I can do it: Jones, Jack / Swinging on a star: Braff, Ruby / Sleepwalk: Eschete, Ron / 59th Street Bridge song: Anderson, Ernestine / Lady wants to know: Roberts, Howard / Girl from Ipanema: Byrd, Charlie Trio
CCD 47921 / 17 Nov '97 / Concord Jazz

☐ SWINGIN' JAZZ FOR HIPSTERS VOL.2
Bemsha swing: Hall, Jim / Mr. Gentle and Mr. Cool: Peplowski, Ken / Frenesi: Byrd, Charlie / Tossed salad and scrambled eggs: Burton, Gary / Tico Tico: Vignola, Frank / Dave's face: Heath Brothers / Age of Aquarius: McDuff, Jack / Gone: Mulligan, Gerry / Heatwave: Tjader, Cal & Carmen McRae / Look of love: Hamilton, Scott / Fly me to the moon (in other words): Alexander, Monty / I'm hip: Torme, Mel & George Shearing
CCD 47922 / 17 Nov '97 / Concord Jazz

☐ SWINGIN' THE CLASSICS
March of the toys: Dorsey, Tommy / Prelude in c# minor: Dorsey, Tommy / Liebestraum: Cole, Nat 'King' Trio / Wearing of the green: Berigan, Bunny / Moon love: Miller, Glenn & Ray Eberle / Russian sailors dance: Crosby, Bob / Barcarolle: Barnet, Charlie / Anitra's dance: Teagarden, Jack / Old black joe: James, Harry / Slavonic dance: Byas, Don / Polish dance: Spivak, Charlie / Song of India: Dorsey, Tommy / Finiculi finicula: Teagarden, Jack / Blue danube: Cole, Nat 'King' Trio / Spanish dance: Krupa, Gene / Ave Maria: Beneke, Tex
VN 1010 / Feb '97 / Viper's Nest

☐ SWINGIN 60'S LATIN
Deletreado: Gutierrez, Noel / Con la punta del pie teresa: Cortijo Y Su Combo / Volvio la plena: Kalaff, Luis / El tubo: Granda, Bienvenido / De Cuba a Mexico: Granda, Bienvenido / Recordando mi borinquen: Valle, Joe Y Su Orquesta / Quien tomo la bronca: Lopez, Antonio Y Su Super Combo / Yo me pa'ver: Cuba, Joe Sextet / Samana: Beltran, Alberto / Tu indiferencia: Beltran, Alberto / Noche de ronda: Grand, Rene / Vengan a la charanga: Cruz, Celia / Ají picante: Morel, Manolin / El Maton: Ray, Ricardo & Bobby Cruz / Tremendo cocito: Cuba, Joe Sextet / Alegría y bomba: Rivera, Ismael / Imoye: Cruz, Celia / Todo el mundo escucha: Granda, Bienvenido / La vida: Ricardo, Ray & Bobby Cruz / Guaracha y bembe: Feliciano, Jose 'Cheo'
CDHOT 627 / Aug '97 / Charly

☐ SWINGING AT THE SAVOY
158442 / Mar '96 / Jazz Archives

☐ SWINGING GROOVES FROM 20 PHONTASTIC YEARS
PHONTCD 9315 / Nov '95 / Phontastic

☐ SWINGING THE BLUES
Swingin' the blues: Basie, Count / Jelly roll blues: Berigan, Bunny / Just blues: Connie's Inn Orchestra / Dogtown blues: Crosby, Bob / Savoy blues: Crosby, Bob / Dippermouth blues: Dorsey, Jimmy & Louis Armstrong / Tin roof blues: Dorsey, Tommy / St. Louis blues: Dorsey Brothers / Diga diga doo: Ellington, Duke / Roll 'em: Goodman, Benny / Memphis blues: Henderson, Fletcher / At the woodchoppers' ball: Herman, Woody / Sweet sorrow blues: Hughes, Spike / That too, do: Moten, Bennie / Hot and anxious: Redman, Don / New call of the freaks: Russell, Luis / Blues: Shaw, Artie / Ridin' but walkin': Waller, Fats
CDAJA 5088 / Oct '91 / Living Era

Column 4

☐ SWINGING THE BLUES (1931-1939)
DOCD 5354 / Jun '95 / Document

☐ SWINGING THE SIXTIES
Ticket to ride / Cracklin' Rosie / She loves you / Bridge over troubled water / Michelle / Woodstock / Spinning wheel / Norwegian wood / In the ghetto / Yesterday / Both sides now / Can't buy me love / Little green apples / Eleanor Rigby / Without her / All you need is love / Your song / Strawberry fields forever / Suzanne / Hard days night / Anna / All my loving / Didn't we
303882 / Jul '97 / Hallmark

☐ SWINGING WEST (1940's Western Swing From Southern California)
KKCD 15 / 3 Sep '97 / Krazy Kat

☐ SWINGSATION
Jumpin' at the woodside: Basie, Count & His Orchestra / Sent for you yesterday: Basie, Count & His Orchestra / Oh lady be good: Basie, Count & His Orchestra / Rhythm is our business: Lunceford, Jimmie & His Orchestra / Organ grinder's swing: Lunceford, Jimmie & His Orchestra / For dancers only: Lunceford, Jimmie & His Orchestra / Flyin' home: Hampton, Lionel & His Orchestra / Blow top blues: Hampton, Lionel & His Orchestra / Midnight sun: Hampton, Lionel & His Orchestra / When I get that old black magic: Fitzgerald, Ella & Chick Webb / Crazy rhythm: Fitzgerald, Ella & Chick Webb / Undecided: Fitzgerald, Ella & Chick Webb / One o' clock jump: Goodman, Benny Orchestra / Peg o' my heart: Miller, Glenn & His Orchestra / Room: Dorsey, Tommy & His Orchestra / Continental: Shaw, Artie Orchestra
GRP 99242 / 24 Aug '98 / GRP

☐ SWITCHED ON (18 Great Live & Acoustic Tracks)
Chocolate cake: Crowded House / Just another day: Secada, Jon / Circle in the sand: Carlisle, Belinda / I can't help falling in love with you: Marx, Richard / Ordinary world: Duran Duran / Sleeping satellite: Archer, Tasmin / Mr. Wendel: Arrested Development / Respect: Deaz's Midnight Runners / Blank expression: Specials / Kayleigh: Marillion / Year of the cat: Stewart, Al / Vienna: Ultravox / Would I lie to you: Charles & Eddie / True: Spandau Ballet / Carry the blame: River City People / I heard it through the grapevine: Turner, Ike & Tina / Dirty love: Thunder / Loch Lomond: Runrig
4954772 / 6 Jul '98 / EMI Gold

☐ SWITCHED ON COUNTRY (50 Non-Stop Country Hits)
Hello I love you / Sundown / Woman, beautiful woman / Ruby, don't take your love to town / Gentle on my mind / Jolene / Let your love flow / Rhinestone cowboy / Oh, lonesome me / Half the way / I'll said you had a beautiful body / Detroit city / Down the mississippi / Some days are diamonds / Slow hand / I don't wanna play house / Your cheatin' heart / Listen to the radio / You never gave up on me / Always on my mind / Love me tender / Honey / Teddy bear / Only love / Annie's song / Me and Bobby McGee / Help me make it through the night / When you were sweet sixteen / Love hurts / You needed me / Blue eyes crying / I will always love you / Wolverton mountain / Coward of the county / Some broken hearts never mend / Take me home country roads / You asked me to / Before the next teardrop falls / Banks of the Ohio / If you love me let me know / You're my best friend / I recall a gypsy woman / Shelter of your eyes / Silver threads and golden needles / Honey come back / Most beautiful girl / Have I told you lately that I love you
CD 6071 / Apr '97 / Music

☐ SWITCHED ON COUNTRY: THE RANCH HANDS
Hello I love you / Sundown / Woman, beautiful woman / Ruby don't take your love to town / Gentle on my mind / Jolene / Let your love flow / Rhinestone cowboy / Oh lonesome me / Half the way / I'll said you had a beautiful body / Detroit city / Down the mississippi / Mississippi / Some days are diamonds / Slow hand / I don't wanna play house / Your cheatin' heart / Listen to the radio / You never gave up on me / Always on my mind / Love me tender / Honey / Sweetest thing / Only love / Annie's song / Me and bobby mcgee / Help me make it through the night / When you were sweet sixteen / Love hurts / You needed me / Blue eyes crying in the rain / I will always love you / Wolverton mountain / Coward of the county / Some broken hearts never mend / Take me home country roads / You asked me to / Before the next teardrop falls / Banks of the Ohio / If you love me let me know / You're my best friend / I recall a gypsy woman / Shelter of your eyes / Silver threads and golden needles / Honey come back / Most beautiful girl / Have I told you lately that I love you
GRF 214 / Mar '93 / Tring

☐ SWITCHED ON THE SIXTIES
Le cage aux folles / Caravan / Best of times / Harlem nocturne / Bandstand boogie / Puttin' on the ritz / Boogie woogie / Satin doll / Tuxedo junction / Chameleon days / Le cage aux folles / Hooked on dixie / Hooked on swing / Save the last dance for me / Hooked on the roaring 20's / Swingin' the classics / Swing with bing
EMPRCD 519 / Jul '94 / Emporio

☐ SWITZERLAND - YODELS OF APPENZELL
AUD 8026 / Jun '91 / Unesco

☐ SYDE TRIPS VOL.1
WHCD 002 / Mar '97 / Wooden Hill

☐ SYMPATHY IN CHAOS VOL.1
13th floor spectrum: VVX / Zentrical wheel: Mantaray / Floating through the air on gossamer wings: Liquid Dub Connection / Geomantik: Prana / Monkey on a cloud: TRiptaka / Pizza: Ju Ju Space Jazz / Vice: Massimo Vivona / Atmosphere: Anand / Space is the place: Irresistable Force
MPCD 7 / Jul '97 / Matsuri

☐ SYMPATHY IN CHAOS VOL.2 (Compiled By Tsuyoshi Suzuki)
MPCD 17 / 13 Jul '98 / Matsuri

☐ **SYMPHONIC BOSSA NOVA**
4509908772 / Feb '95 / WEA

☐ **SYMPHONY OF NATURE**
D 8106 / Aug '98 / Unesco

☐ **SYNCHROMIX (Electronic Dance Mixes)**
Wannabe / Discotheque / Step by step / Return of the mack / Don't cry for me Argentina / I shot the sheriff / Don't let go (love) / Space jam / Ooh aah, just a little bit / Cold rock a party / Virtual insanity / Tonight is the night
SMCD 71 / Jun '97 / Start

☐ **SYNEWAVE NEW YORK VOL.1**
KICKCD 27 / Sep '95 / Kickin'

☐ **SYNEWAVE NEW YORK VOL.2**
KICKCD 37 / May '96 / Kickin'

☐ **SYNOPTICS**
EFA 003162 / May '95 / Reflective

☐ **SYNTHESIS**
XTR 48CDM / 17 Aug '98 / X-Treme

☐ **SYNTHESISER ALBUM, THE**
Chariots of fire / Oxygene / Love theme from Midnight Express / Miami vice / Autobahn / Axel F / Magic fly / Popcorn / Metropolis / Mammagamma / Aurora / I hear you now / Equinoxe / Forbidden colours / Lucifer / Das madchen auf der treppe / Chi mai / Song for Guy
MCCD 061 / Mar '92 / Music Club

☐ **SYNTHESISER COLLECTION (2CD Set)**
DEMPCD 012 / Mar '96 / Emporio

☐ **SYNTHESIZER CLASSICS**
Theme from Antarctica / Eve of war / Equinoxe part 5 / Tubular bells / Autobahn / Aurora / Magnetic fields part 2 / Theme from 'Rain Man' / Tubbs and Valerie / To the unknown man / Electric salsa / Model / Rockit / Chariots of fire / Living on video / I'll find my way home
EMPRCD 650 / Oct '96 / Emporio

☐ **SYNTHESIZER DREAMS**
Fields of gold / Father figure / Another day in paradise / Forever love / Nikita / Words / Moments in love / These dreams / Broken wings / These are the days of our lives / Diamonds and pearls / No more I love you's / Shine on you crazy diamond / Groovy kind of love / Crockett's theme / Father and son / Merry Christmas Mr Lawrence / Drive
CDVIP 150 / Apr '97 / Virgin VIP

☐ **SYNTHESIZER GOLD**
HRCD 8052 / Apr '94 / Disky

☐ **SYNTHESIZER HITS**
55137 / Oct '95 / Laserlight

☐ **SYNTHESIZER HITS (4CD Set)**
MBSCD 446 / Nov '95 / Castle

☐ **SYNTHESIZER HITS (2CD Set)**
One night in Bangkok / Pop musik / Private dancer / Purple rain / California dreamin' / Delta lady / Love shack / Blue Monday / Sound of silence / Who's that girl / Smooth operator / Tubular bells / Vienna / Walk like an Egyptian / Rhythm is a dancer / Popcorn / One night in heaven / Never gonna give you up / We are the champions / Venus / Another day in paradise / Bohemian rhapsody / Justify my love / Crazy for you / In the air tonight / I want your sex / Eleanor Rigby / Just the way you are / Can't help falling in love / Locomotion / Beat it / (Everything I do) I do it for you / Hot in the city / I will always love you / Memories / Most beautiful girl in the world / Radio gaga / Yellow submarine
MUCD 9510 / May '96 / Musketeer

☐ **SYNTHESIZER HITS (Purple Rain)**
MACCD 309 / Aug '96 / Autograph

☐ **SYNTHESIZER HITS (Tubular Bells)**
MACCD 308 / Aug '96 / Autograph

☐ **SYNTHESIZER HITS**
Eve of the war / Tubular bells / Antarctica / Equinoxe (part 5) / Model / Chariots of fire / Magnetic fields (part 2) / Magic fly / Popcorn / Miami Vice / Pulstar / Oxygene (part 4) / Axel F / Chase / Pepperbox / Crockett's theme / Maid of Orleans / Autobahn
301062 / Jun '98 / Hallmark

☐ **SYNTHETIC PLEASURES VOL.1**
MM 800462 / Sep '96 / Moonshine

☐ **SYNTHETIC PLEASURES VOL.2**
CAI 20012 / Apr '97 / Caipirinha

☐ **SYRIA: MUEZZINS D'ALEP**
C 580038 / Nov '92 / Ocora

☐ **SYRIAN ORTHODOX CHURCH**
Mass in first mode / B'utho according to St. Ephraim / Gnez / Takhshifto
D 8075 / Jul '98 / Unesco

T

☐ **T IN THE PARK**
8287822
8287922 / Jul '96 / Go Discs

☐ **T IN THE PARK (The Best Of T In The Park 1994-1996 - 3CD Set)**
Do you rememeber the first time: *Pulp* / Shakermaker: *Oasis* / Jump around: *House Of Pain* / Swamp thing: *Grid* / Radio: *Teenage Fanclub* / Word up: *Gun* / Belaruse: *Levellers* / La tristesse durera (scream to a sigh): *Manic Street Preachers* / White love: *One Dove* / Always the last to know: *Del Amitri* / To the end: *Blur* / Good as gold (stupid as mud): *Beautiful South* / Open your heart: *M-People* / Wake up Boo: *Boo Radleys* / Can't get out of bed: *Charlatans* / Broken stones: *Weller, Paul* / Strange ones: *Supergrass* / Stutter: *Elastica* / Twisted and bent: *Trash Can Sinatras* / Charity: *Skunk Anansie* / Confide in me: *Minogue, Kylie* / Rez: *Underworld* / Poison: *Prodigy* / High and dry: *Radiohead* / Alright: *Cast* / Staying out for the Summer: *Dodgy* / Release the pressure: *Leftfield* / Into my world: *Audioweb* / Accelerate: *Drugstore* / Jesus Christ: *Longpigs* / Carnival: *Cardigans* / Tishbite: *Cocteau Twins* / Life is sweet: *Chemical Brothers*
8287762 / Jul '96 / Go Discs

☐ **T-BIRD PARTY**
EFA 115962 / Dec '95 / Crypt

☐ **TAARAB MUSIC OF ZANZIBAR VOL.3**
Mapenzi kiapo / Wembe / Mwana mtifu / Mbaya kufanya jema / Sitakila wama / Juwa toka / Sema / Wambea / Machozi yananimwaika / Mpeni pole / Pakacha
CDORBD 040 / Jul '90 / Globestyle

☐ **TAHITI: BELLE EPOQUE VOL.3**
S 65811 / Nov '92 / Manuiti

☐ **TAHITI: SONGS OF THE ATOLLS & ISLANDS**
S 65816CD / Aug '94 / Manuiti

☐ **TAJIK MUSIC OF BADAKHSHAN**
AUD 0082212 / Dec '93 / Auvidis/Ethnic

☐ **TAKE MY BREATH AWAY VOL.1**
Unchained melody / Groovy kind of love: *Royal Philharmonic Orchestra* / Lily was here: *Royal Philharmonic Orchestra* / (Everything I do) I do it for you: *Royal Philharmonic Orchestra* / Show me heaven: *Royal Philharmonic Orchestra* / Take a look at me now: *Royal Philharmonic Orchestra* / Take my breath away: *Royal Philharmonic Orchestra* / My girl: *Royal Philharmonic Orchestra* / Time of my life: *Royal Philharmonic Orchestra* / Twin peaks (falling): *Royal Philharmonic Orchestra* / Stand by me: *Royal Philharmonic Orchestra* / Hero (the wind beneath my wings): *Royal Philharmonic Orchestra* / It must have been love: *Royal Philharmonic Orchestra*
EMPRCD 597 / Jun '96 / Emporio

☐ **TAKE NO PRISONERS (The Best Of British Punk)**
Vicious circle: *Abrasive Wheels* / Television's over: *Adverts* / How much longer: *Alternative TV* / Forty second street: *Angelic Upstarts* / Let them free: *Anti Pasti* / New age: *Blitz* / Teenage depression: *Eddie & The Hot Rods* / Sick boy: *GBH* / Just thirteen: *Lurkers* / Nasty nasty: *999* / Cum on feel the noize: *One Way System* / Take no prisoners: *Red Alert* / Lost cause: *Riot Squad* / Punk rocker: *Special Duties* / Soldier soldier: *Spizz Energi* / My generation: *Suburban Studs* / London girls: *Vibrators* / You'll never know: *Vice Squad* / Something else: *Vicious, Sid*
CD 6149 / Jul '98 / Music

☐ **TAKE THE FLOOR**
CDC 014 / Feb '97 / Ceol

☐ **TAKE THE MUSIDISC JAZZ TRAIN**
500772 / Sep '96 / Musidisc

☐ **TAKE THE ROUGH WITH THE SMOOTH**
EFA 116802 / May '95 / Mzee

☐ **TAKIN' A DETOUR VOL.1**
Catastrophe theory: *Dilemmas* / Jenny Diablo: *Protectors* / Piece of the action: *Most* / Doin' me in: *Mourning After* / Emily against the world: *Curtains* / You know I need you: *Route 66* / Rackin' my mind: *Clique* / Down the tubestation a midnight: *Persuaders* / Keeps your hand of Felicity: *Blocked* / Threw her a line: *Aardvarks* / Secondry modern Miss: *Now* / Harder I try: *Nuthins* / Airwaves: *Strike* / Mr. Cooper: *Sharp Kiddie* / Wish you were here: *Buzz* / Water: *Knave*
DRCD 006 / Jan '96 / Detour

☐ **TAKIN' LIBERTIES**
TTPCD 005 / Nov '94 / Totem

☐ **TAKING IT EASY (2CD Set)**
DEMPCD 004 / Mar '96 / Emporio

☐ **TAKOMA ECLECTIC SAMPLER**
World boogie: *White, Bukka* / She's lookin' good: *Canned Heat & Harvey Mandel* / I keep wishing for you: *Sir Douglas Quintet* / Just like an eagle: *Muldaur, Maria* / Cha dooky-doo: *Barron, Ronnie* / Mama blues: *Ross, Dr. Isiah* / Ferns: *Hand, Cal* / Heart of a country song: *Maddox, Rose* / I'm shakin': *Thompson, Ron & The Resistors* / Wine, women and rock 'n' roll: *Swamp Dogg* / My darlin' New Orleans: *Cuccia, Ron* / Tennessee rock 'n' roll: *Winski, Colin* / Crossfire: *Davis, Spencer* / Your friends: *Bloomfield, Mike* / Indian-Pacific: *Fahey, John* / Last days of the suicide kid: *Bukowski, Charles* / Washington Post march: *Santa Monica Pier Merry-Go-Round*
CDTAK 8904 / Jul '97 / Takoma

☐ **TALE OF ALE, THE**
FRCD 23 / Nov '93 / Free Reed

☐ **TALES OF THE UNEXPECTED**
RFCD 001 / Jun '95 / Rainforest

☐ **TALK ME DADDY (Anthology Of Women Singers From Gothic)**
FLYCD 37 / Oct '91 / Flyright

☐ **TALKIN' JAZZ VOL.1**
Hip walk: *Herbolzheimer, Peter* / See you later: *Grauer, Joanne* / New morning: *Winter, Kitty* / Join us: *Reith, Dieter* / Someday: *Duke, George* / Upa neguinho: *Lobo, Edu* / My soul: *Duke, George* / Sconsolato: *Murphy, Mark* / Carmell's black forest waltz: *Davis, Nathan* / Secret life: *Novi Singers* / All blues: *Ross, Annie & Pony Poindexter* / Colours of excitement: *Francis, Rimona* / Frog child: *Grauer, Joanne*
5188612 / Nov '93 / Talkin' Loud

☐ **TALKIN' JAZZ VOL.2**
Mathar: *Pike, Dave Set* / Take off your shoes to feel the setting sun: *Dauner, Wolfgang* / Love me: *Teupen, Johnny* / Get out of my life woman: *Barry, Dee Dee & The Movements* / Big schlepp: *Pike, Dave Set* / Roll on the left side: *Kiesewetter, Knut Train* / Onkel Joe: *Catch Up* / Wives and lovers: *Reith, Dieter Trio* / Nude: *Velebny, Karel* / Espresso loco: *Boland, Francy* / Cantaloupe Island: *Krog, Karin* / Feel: *Duke, George*
5235292 / Sep '94 / Talkin' Loud

☐ **TALKIN' JAZZ VOL.3**
Yaad: *Jazz Meets India* / Burungkaka tua: *Scott, Tony* / Sakara: *Boland, Clarke* / North beach: *Duke, George* / Stars and rockets: *Thomas, Peter* / Colour: *Lehn, Erwin Orchestra* / Sunshine of your love: *Fitzgerald, Ella* / Things we did today: *London Jazz Quartet* / Un graso de areia: *Boland, Clarke* / Just give me time: *Murphy, Mark* / Little bird: *Bianchi, Elsie Trio* / Waldmachen: *Brom, Gustav* / Suite pour San Remo overture: *Gilson, Jef Nonet* / Big P: *Modern Jazz Group* / Blue dance: *Kovac, Roland* / Model forces gratuliere: *Pauer, Fritz* / First movement: *Evans, Bill*
5535852 / Jul '97 / Talkin' Loud

☐ **TALKIN' LOUD SAMPLER VOL.1**
Young Disciples Theme: *Young Disciples & MC Mello* / Get it: *Steps Ahead* / Mean machine 90: *Jalal* / Step right on: *Young Disciples & Outlaw Posse* / Glide: *Incognito* / Tribal knight: *Ace Of Clubs* / Wild and peaceful: *Bassic* / Little ghetto boy: *Galliano*
8467922 / Sep '90 / Talkin' Loud

☐ **TALKIN' LOUD SAMPLER VOL.2**
Hide and seek: *Urban Species* / Hungry like a baby: *Galliano* / Colibri: *Incognito* / You've got to move: *Omar* / Back to the real world: *K-Creative* / All I have in me: *Young Disciples* / Theme from Marxman: *Marxman* / Qui semme le vente recolte le tempo: *MC Solaar* / Serious love: *Perception* / I commit: *Powell, Bryan* / Take me now: *Payne, Tammy* / Apparently nothin': *Young Disciples* / There's nothing like this: *Omar* / Prince of peace: *Galliano* / Always there: *Incognito*
5159362 / Jan '93 / Talkin' Loud

☐ **TALKIN' LOUDER**
No Government: *Nicolette* / Natural thing: *Reprazent* / Always there: *Incognito* / I've known rivers: *Pine, Courtney* / Mission impossible: *United Future Organisation* / Religion and politics: *Urban Species & Terry Callier* / Hanging by a thread: *Lee, Shawn* / Chemical imbalance: *Kendra, Karime* / Some came: *Galliano* / What's my name: *Native Sol*
5325932 / May '96 / Talkin' Loud

☐ **TALKIN' VERVE - GROOVY**
Chain of fools: *Smith, Jimmy* / Ain't too proud to beg: *Bobo, Willie* / I got you (I feel good): *Jones, Quincy* / Vehicle: *Baker, Chet* / (Sittin' on) the dock of the bay: *Smith, Jimmy* / Ain't that peculiar: *Jones, Quincy* / Everydays: *Burrell, Kenny* / (I can't get no) satisfaction: *Peterson, Oscar* / California dreaming: *Montgomery, Wes* / Sunny: *Smith, Jimmy* / Evil ways: *Baker, Chet* / Papa's got a brand new bag: *Jones, Quincy* / I heard it through the grapevine: *Bobo, Willie* / Spinning wheel: *Baker, Chet* / Spill the wine: *Smith, Jimmy* / Goin' out of my head: *Montgomery, Wes*
5570812 / 26 May '98 / Verve

☐ **TALKIN' VERVE - MAMBO MANIA**
Hip hug her: *O'Farrill, Chico* / El Limpiabotas: *Valdes, Miguelito* / South of the border: *Montgomery, Wes* / Mas que nada: *Valdaz, Carlos & Eugene Arango* / Fiebre Cuban: *Boland, Francy & Kenny Clarke* / Sabre dance: *Schifrin, Lalo* / Man and a woman: *O'Farrill, Chico* / Curacao: *Tjader, Cal* / Ya yo e: *Valdaz, Carlos & Eugene Arango* / Los companedores: *Valdes, Miguelito* / Peanut vendor: *Schifrin, Lalo* / Guaguanco Africano: *Valdes, Miguelito* / Cuban patato chip: *Mann, Herbie* / Mambo de las Brujas: *Boland, Francy & Kenny Clarke* / Negra Leono: *Valdes, Miguelito* / Descarga numera 1000: *O'Farrill, Chico*
5573632 / 29 Jun '98 / Verve

☐ **TALKIN' VERVE - WITH A TWIST**
5379142 / 15 Sep '97 / Verve

☐ **TALKING AND PREACHING TROMBONES**
158862 / Apr '97 / Jazz Archives

☐ **TALKING BLUES**
LG 21067 / May '93 / Lagoon

☐ **TALKING SPIRITS (Native American Peublo Music)**
CDT 126 / Apr '93 / Topic

☐ **TANGO**
Jealousy: *Geraldo's Gaucho Tango Orchestra* / There's heaven in your eyes: *La Plata Tango Band* / Marushka: *Sesta, Don Gaucho Tango Band* / From a kiss springs happiness: *La Plata Tango Band* / Madame, you're lovely: *Mantovani & His Tipica Orchestra* / Tangled tangos No. 1 (part 1): *Rinaldo, Don & His Tango Orchestra* / Dolores: *Geraldo & His Gaucho Tango Orchestra* / Spider of the night: *Mantovani & His Tipica Orchestra* / Summer evening in Santa Cruz: *Silvester, Victor & His Ballroom Orchestra* / I could be happy with you: *Geraldo's Gaucho Tango Orchestra* / Dear madam: *Silvester, Victor & His Ballroom Orchestra* / Te quiero dijiste: *Geraldo & His Orchestra* / Tangled tangos No. 1 (part 2): *Rinaldo, Don & His Tango Orchestra* / At the balalaika: *Geraldo & His Orchestra* / Blue sky: *Mantovani & His Tipica Orchestra* / If the world were mine: *Geraldo & His Orchestra* / South of the border (Down Mexico way): *Harris, Jack & His Orchestra* / El pescador: *Loss, Joe Band* / Isle of Capri: *Geraldo & His Gaucho Tango Orchestra* / Serenade in the night: *Mantovani & His Tipica Orchestra* / Flowers I may not offer: *La Plata Tango Band* / Lamento gitano: *Loss, Joe Band*
PASTCD 9752 / Jan '92 / Flapper

☐ **TANGO**
CDHOT 624 / Jul '97 / Charly

☐ **TANGO AND MAMBO CALIENTE (2CD Set)**
R2CD 4021 / 13 Apr '98 / Deja Vu

☐ **TANGO ARGENTINO**
Vuelo al sur / Ventanita florida / Voy cantando tangos por el mundo / Sur / Volver / Tango-tango / Yuyo verde / Los argentinos / Comos dos extranos / Loca bohemia / Buenos aires conoce / Los suenos / Maipo / La vida es Linda, pibe / Milonga del tartamundo / Corrientes arriba / Tango del eco / Ausencias / Adios arrabal / Oblivion / Tal vez no tenga fin / Como abrazado a un rencor / Typical one
MCCD 098 / Mar '93 / Music Club

☐ **TANGO LADIES**
HQCD 34 / Feb '94 / Harlequin

☐ **TANGO LADIES 1923-1954**
HQCD 52 / Jun '95 / Harlequin

☐ **TANGO ONLY**
Delusion / El velo azul / A media luz / El choclo / Bombonicito / El flete / Uno / Que falte que me haces / Asi / Andre de sepato novo / Yo te canto / Beunos Aires / Pecho helado / Con mil amores / Caminito / Alma / Tengo cuidado / Historia di un amor / Maula / Tango bolero / Feline
DC 880562 / May '97 / Disky

☐ **TANGOS PARA AFICIONADOS VOL.2 (The 1950s)**
PHONTCD 7582 / Jun '94 / Phontastic

☐ **TANTRANCE VOL.1 (A Trip To Psychedelic Trance/2CD Set)**
Mahadeva: *Astral Projection* / Robostyx: *Transwave* / Let's turn on: *Doof* / Powergen: *Astral Projection* / Le lotus bleu: *Total Eclipse* / Vicious circles: *Poltergeist* / Pulseman vs. Sineman: *Ninjahead* / Guardian angel: *Juno Reactor* / Telepathy: *Infinity Project* / Planet Sex: *Garnier, Laurent* / Flouro neuro sponge: *Hallucinogen* / Dig a jig: *Baba G* / Stud stunners: *Bassline Baby* / Scarab: *Prana*
08938582 / Apr '96 / Subterranean

☐ **TANTRANCE VOL.2 (A Trip To Psychedelic Trance/2CD Set)**
Rotorblade: *Juno Reactor* / Jack in the box: *Man With No Name* / Rezwalker: *Transwave* / Fuel on: *Koxbox* / Democracy: *Killing Joke* / Microdive: *Etnica* / Kalki's coming: *Astralasia* / Spiritual transgression: *Encens* / Entropy: *Satori* / Morphic resonance: *Cosmosis* / One love: *Electric Universe* / Enlightened Evolution: *Astral Projection* / Paranormal activity: *Phreaky* / Camel: *In Door* / Forbidden: *Disco Volante* / Earth: *Prana* / Flash of fire: *Green Nuns Of The Revolution* / Trip tonite: *Etnica* / Monzoon: *Elysium*
SPV 08947032 / Aug '96 / Subterranean

☐ **TANTRANCE VOL.3 (2CD Set)**
Trommelmaschine: *Der Dritte Raum* / Narcotic influence: *Empirion* / Furnace: *Total Eclipse* / Satellite: *Moon & The Sun* / Astral voyage: *Electric Universe* / Sundown: *Overlords* / Hear the air: *Brainman* / Kicking test: *Antidote* / Kage: *Ree K* / Nobody: *Psyko Disko* / Alien love song: *Astralasia* / Second room: *X-Dream* / Slick witch: *Slinky Wizard* / Overload: *MFG* / Soothsayer: *Hallucinogen* / Pale: *Semsis* / Back to Earth: *Satori* / Freak show: *Cydonia* / Celtic alchemy: *Spectral* / Jana: *Killing Joke* / Mr. Redeemer: *Zodiac Youth*
DCD 08947362 / May '97 / Subterranean

☐ **TANTRANCE VOL.4 (2CD Set)**
SPV 08947532 / Sep '97 / SPV

☐ **TANTRANCE VOL.6 (2CD Set)**
SPV 08939022 / May '98 / SPV

☐ **TANZANIA SOUND**
OMCD 018 / May '93 / Original Music

☐ **TAPPAN ZEE IS 20 (The Best Of Tappan Zee)**
King Tut: *Colby, Mark* / Changes: *Harris, Allen Band* / Good morning: *Longmire, Wilbert* / Virginia Sunday: *Tee, Richard* / Watermelon man: *Santamaria, Mongo* / Song for my daughter: *Colby, Mark* / Winding river: *James, Bob & Earl Klugh* / El Mayorazgo: *Brackeen, Jo Anne* / Scat talk: *Colby, Mark* / Now: *Tee, Richard* / Hawkeye: *Longmire, Wilbert* / Carmel tea: *Brackeen, Jo Anne* / Tappan Zee: *James, Bob*
RENCD 121 / Mar '97 / Renaissance Collector Series

☐ **TARANTINO CONNECTION, THE**
Misirlou: *Dale, Dick & His Del-Tones* / Dark night: *Blasters* / Little green bag: *Baker, George Selection* / Graceland: *Sexton, Charlie* / Girl you'll be a woman soon: *Urge Overkill* / Waiting for the miracle: *Cohen, Leonard* / Little bitty tear: *Ives, Burl* / Stuck in the middle with you: *Stealer's Wheel* / You never can tell: *Berry, Chuck* / Love is: *Palmer, Robert* / Sweet Jane: *Cowboy Junkies* / Six blade knife: *Dire Straits* / Foolish hearts: *Mavericks* / Vertigo: *Combustible Edison*
MCD 80325 / Oct '96 / MCA

☐ **TARD AND FURTHUR'D**
SB 52CD / 27 Oct '97 / Siltbreeze

☐ **TARQUIN RECORDS ALL STAR HOLIDAY EXTRAVAGANZA**
TQ 019 / 29 Dec '97 / Tarquin

☐ **TARTAN DISC, THE (Scotland The Brave)**
CDITV 480 / Jul '89 / Scotdisc

☐ **TASTE OF 3RD STONE RECORDS VOL.1, A**
Sooner or later: State Of Grace / Smile: State Of Grace / Deep blue breath: AR Kane / I know: Bark Psychosis / So cold: Popguns / Someone to dream of: Popguns / Basking: Mali Rain / Callow hill 508am: Mali Rain / Alaska: Transambient Communications / River: Transambient Communications / California nocturne: Experimental Audio Research / Ecstasy in slow motion: Spacemen 3 / Revolution: Spacemen 3 / Paddington Bear: Goober Patrol / Grabbers: Goober Patrol
STONE 021CD / 30 Mar '98 / 3rd Stone

☐ **TASTE OF 3RD STONE RECORDS VOL.2, A**
All life long: Insides / Sweetside silver night: No Man / Fancy swim: Reverberation / In the presence of angels: Mali Rain / V5: Transambient Communications / Crushed: Popguns / Stalker: Olympia Hurricanes / Hello: State Of Grace / Cool as moons: AR Kane / Murder city: Bark Psychosis / It won't be long: Chapterhouse / Friendly: Vanilla Pod / Downward mobility: Goober Patrol / I want you right now: Spacemen 3 / Little angel: Colorsound / Ring modulator: Experimental Audio Research / Stairs leading up: Octal / Forever alien: Spectrum
STONE 029CD / 16 Mar '98 / 3rd Stone

☐ **TASTE OF ASIA, A**
NI 7025 / Mar '95 / Nimbus

☐ **TASTE OF BRAZIL, A**
Lambadas medley / Mexa mexa / Lambadie lambadia / Lambada da Americana / Lambadas medley / Te futaco / Memina moca / Quero ser seu grande amor / Mata papi (Ja que e gostoso deixa) / Lambadas medley / Por cima de mim / Amor de piranha / Do jeito que voce vier
QED 080 / Nov '96 / Tring

☐ **TASTE OF CHINA, A**
REWCD 355 / Feb '98 / Reactive

☐ **TASTE OF INDIA, A**
REWCD 353 / Feb '98 / Reactive

☐ **TASTE OF INTERNAL BASS, A**
Brooklyn heights: Down To The Bone / Manwa: NFL Horns Project / Freefall: Peace Of Mind / Back to the flat: Diamond Wookie / Mosquito coast 94-96: Mr. Gone / Gold medal kid: Panamar Reed / Joy is a good groove: Down To The Bone / Adventures of FF man: NFL Horns Project / Le club contemporaine: Tarantulas / Casa del ritmo: Afro Elements
IBCD 10 / 19 Jan '98 / Internal Bass

☐ **TASTE OF IRELAND, A (2CD Set)**
DEMPCD 009 / Mar '96 / Emporio

☐ **TASTE OF IRELAND, A**
MACCD 315 / Aug '96 / Autograph

☐ **TASTE OF IRELAND, A (Irish Traditional Music)**
NI 7035 / Feb '97 / Nimbus

☐ **TASTE OF OLD IRELAND, A**
HCD 115 / Apr '95 / GTD

☐ **TASTE OF TEX MEX, A (40 Tejano Titbits/2CD Set)**
Beer barrel polka: Longoria, Valerio / El temblor de San Francisco: Jordan, Steve / Viva San Antonio: Vela, Ruben Y Su Conjunto / Rio rebelde: Grupo Badd / Al mirar tu cara: Jimenez, Santiago Jr. / Chulas fronteras: Los Terribles Del Norte / Contrabando de nogales: Beltran, Martin / La Calandria: Campeones De Raul Ruiz / Conchita la viuda alegre: Texas Revolution / Santa amalia: Ramirez, Janie C. / El gambler: Escobar, Linda / Donde voy a vivar: Mardigal, Conjunto / Hasta cuando: Zamora, Albert Y Talento / Flor sin retono: Zamora, Albert Y Talento / Tu corazon y el mio: Grupo Badd / Ojitos verdes: Los Arcos/Hermanos Pena / Amor amor: Joslin, Rena / Quiero verte: Lopez Y Los Muchachos / Corazon de mi amor: Los Truenos De Tejas / Cuiden su amor: Saldivar, Mingo / Flor de Mexico: Jordan, Steve / Cuatro vidas: Grupo Badd / Se me olvido: Longoria, Valerio / La carga ladiada: Los Fronterizos De Cd Acuna / La monedade dos caras: Los Dos Gilbertos / Polly want's a craker: Zimmerle, Henry / Oh lonesome me: Jerry & The Ruf-Nex / Que me lleve el diablo: Ruiz, Raul Campeones / Mejor solo: De La Rosa, Tony / Sera por los tacos: Los Truenos De Tejas / Pobre palomita: Eva Y Barra / Me agarro la imigracion: Los Terribles Del Norte / El corrido de emilio cabrerra: Jimenez, Santiago Jr. / Lo nuestro termino: Vela, Ruben Y Su Conjunto / A medias de la noche: Zamora, Albert Y Talento / Con la tierra encima: Los Dorados / Voy a llorar: Caballeros Del Norte / Hay que sentimiento traigo: Escobar, Linda / Los ilegales: Longoria, Valerio / Hey Jude: Grupo Coahuila
DEMPCD 028 / 6 Oct '97 / Emporio

☐ **TASTE OF TRANSIENT, A**
TRANR 606CD / Oct '96 / Transient

☐ **TASTER**
PRKCD 37 / Jul '97 / Park

☐ **TATHATA VOL.1**
EFA 028652 / Jun '97 / Spirit Zone

☐ **TATHATA VOL.2**
Ololuiqui: Ololluqui / Machine planet: Shiva Chandra / Supersonic wind: Mos-Fet / Das pr e4parat: Psy Psy 6 / Atomic children: Tarsis / Stardiver: Electric Universe / Cacophonix: Space Tribe / Star traveller: Hara Gobi / Frisco machine: Sun Project
EFA 028832 / 8 Dec '97 / Spirit Zone

☐ **TEACHIN' THE BLUES (21 Blues Originals Which Inspired Eric Clapton)**
CDGR 224 / 1 Jun '98 / Charly

☐ **TEACHING YOU NO FEAR**
BHR 015CD / Feb '95 / Burning Heart

☐ **TEARDROPS, LOVE, HEARTBREAK**
DCD 5302 / Nov '93 / Disky

☐ **TEARS OF A CLOWN, THE**
Tears of a clown: Robinson, Smokey & The Miracles / I heard through the grapevine: Gaye, Marvin / Reach out I'll be there: Four Tops / My cherie amour: Wonder, Stevie / It's a man's man's world: Brown, James / I put a spell on you: Simone, Nina / War: Starr, Edwin / I'll be there: Jackson Five / Someday we'll be together: Ross, Diana & The Supremes / Nowhere to run: Reeves, Martha & The Vandellas / Just my imagination: Temptations / Heaven must have sent you: Elgins / Farewell is a lonely sound: Ruffin, Jimmy / Love is life: Hot Chocolate / Behind a painted smile: Isley Brothers / Stoned love: Supremes / What does it take: Walker, Junior & The All Stars / Help me make it through the night: Knight, Gladys & The Pips / Few more kisses to go: Hayes, Isaac / You see the trouble with me: White, Barry
5529092 / Oct '97 / Spectrum

☐ **TECHNIQUES VAULT**
VPCD 2040 / Apr '96 / VP

☐ **TECHNO BALLADS VOL.2 (2CD Set)**
Hymn: Moby / Crazy: Global Cee / Summer spent: Beaumont Hannant / Happy shades: Full Moon Fashions / Codeine bullets: Ryman, John / Time flies: Vegas Soul / Clones: Spicelab / Surrender: Interloper / Seing sense: 7th Plain / Time is an illusion: World Of Chocolate / 39: Full Moon Fashions / Mind colours: Beaumont Hannant / Forever: Auto Union / Reich: LA Synthesis / Global Zero: Auto Union / Existential: Tribes Of Krom / Blau: Marzipan & Mustard / Vibes of style: Tribes Of Krom / Mhahalonovis: Osgood, Tim / Philadelphia experiment: Headman / Laut: Marzipan & Mustard / Jazzzy H: Elexir Vitae
MILL 043CD / Jul '97 / Millenium

☐ **TECHNO BALLADS VOL.3 (2CD Set)**
MILL 057CD / 23 Feb '98 / Millenium

☐ **TECHNO CELEBRATION**
7702395 / Apr '97 / Omnisonus

☐ **TECHNO CLASSICS (3CD Set)**
Pull over: Speedy J / Crowd control: Tranzformer / OK alright: Digital Boy / BOTTROP: DJ Hooligan / Raw: OTT / Dukkha: Precious / Bonzai channel: Thunderball / Magic feet: Dunn, Mike / Work that motherfucker: Poindexter, Steve / God of abraham: MNO / Who is Elvis: Phenomania / Rave alarm: Khan, Praga / Sueno Latino (HOG Ocean beats): Sueno Latino / Le seigneur des tenebres: Pleasure Game / Je n'aime que toi: Angel Ice / Cosmotrash: Trashman / Fairydust: Set Up System / Ballet: JNJ / New York Chicago: Soup / Wave: Belgica Wave / Hablando: Ramirez & Pizarro / 100% of dishin' you: Armando / Nana: NUKE featuring Marilyn Mariani / Animals: De Ruyter, Yves / Night in motion: Cubic 22 / Dark symphony: Phrentic system / Soushkin: Dream Your Dream / Circus bells: Armani, Robert / Altered states: Trent, Ron / Orgasmico: Ramirez / Schoom: Dee, Lenny & Darien Kelly / 99.9: Koenig Cylinders / Bountyhunter: DJ Bountyhunter / Work it: Search & Destroy / El punto final: Final Analysis / Rockin' to the rhythm: Convert / Insominiac: DJPC / F 16: F 16 / Extrasyn: RFTR
HR 882122 / Jul '97 / Disky

☐ **TECHNO CLASSICS VOL.1**
FRCD 003 / '95 / Flex

☐ **TECHNO CLASSICS VOL.2**
RSNCD 3 / Oct '92 / Rising High

☐ **TECHNO EXPLOSION (4CD Set)**
Slammin': Pandemic / 550 state: Blood Brothers / Stakker humanoid: Humanoid / Innate: Future Sound Of London / Wonderful day: Flag / Nightmares: Psychopaths / Q: Mental Cube / Too sexy to dance: Bass Construction / Hard head: Future Sound Of London / Meet your makers: Danse City / AST: AST / Feel it: Sugarmen / So this is love: Mental Cube / We can ride the boogie: Bubbles / We came to party: Flag / Turn on the music: Ramraiders / Killer Mummy: Psychopaths / Nasty rhythm: DJ Splix / Paradise: Flag / Space virus: Smart Systems / Feel that feelin': T-Boom / Journey: Residential Area / Proximity: DJ Fresh Trax / I've become what you were: Indo Tribe / Pulse State: Future Sound Of London / Burnin' love: Critical Mass / Hypnotised: Flag / M2: Danse City / Flight: Blood Brothers / Fuzzy logic: Yage / It is: Yeow Man / Esus flow: AST / Eleanor Rigby: Lonely people / Divine distortion: DJ Fresh Trax / Invasion: Clockhouse Hours / I don't owe you sh..: Smak / Parsley: DJ Splix / Beats and culture: Psychopaths / Keep on: Blood Brothers / 1000 feet: Coma Kid / Make me feel: Bass Construction / Come with me: Techno Excursion / Passion for science: Flag / Livin' for the love: Yage / Mangler: Mars, Doom & Fresh Trax / RV theme: Vee, Ray / Revenge of Betty Bleep: Bleeps Anonymous / Understand our destiny: Suzy Shoes / Partytime: Armitage & Shanks
CDBTOT 2 / 24 Nov '97 / Jumpin' & Pumpin'

☐ **TECHNO HEAD VOL.3 (Out Of Control)**
REACTCD 051 / Oct '94 / React

☐ **TECHNO HEAD VOL.4 (Sound Wars The Next Generation - 2CD Set)**
Majik: Technohead / Party trance: DJ Freak / Paranoid beauty: Future Viper / Droppin' bombs: DJ Fury / Cocaine: Technohead / Intellectual killer: Nasenbluten / Knight of visions: Knight Vision / Shaftman: Shaftman / Pope and the president: DJ Raffe / Extreme terror: DJ Skinhead / King of the street: Alec Empire / Abduction exp: DJ Freak / Raw toy: Lorenz Attractor / Dubious: DJ Yubba & DJ Deviant / Hyper bitch: Burning Lazy Persons / Axis: UVC / What is your name: Beatlejuice / Bullen raus: Agro / Incubation: Somatic Responses / Flohwalzer: Dummy / Voice only: Smily Slayers / Imploding head: Johnny Violent
REACTCDX 098
REACTCD 098 / Mar '97 / React

☐ **TECHNO MACHINE (2CD Set)**
3025712 / 22 Sep '97 / ID&T

☐ **TECHNO MASTERS**
Meet your maker: Dance City / Groove me: Jems For Jem / E-go: Real Masters / Turn your love: Clockhouse Hours / Feel like I'm falling: Unlimited Dream Company / RV theme: Vee, Ray / 1am goodnight: Coma Kid / Sunburst: Optic Eye / Come with me: Techno Explosion / Eleanor Rigby: Lonely people / Adrenalin: Jargon / Dominate: Flag / Coda coma: Yage / I think I want some more: Auto-Logic / I don't owe you: Smak / Nightmare: Psychopaths
305092 / Jun '97 / Hallmark

☐ **TECHNO NATIONS (A History Of Techno 1992-1996 - 4CD Set)**
KICKCD 45 / Aug '96 / Kickin'

☐ **TECHNO NATIONS VOL.2**
KICKCD 9 / Apr '94 / Kickin'

☐ **TECHNO NATIONS VOL.3**
KICKCD 14 / Jan '95 / Kickin'

☐ **TECHNO NATIONS VOL.4**
KICKCD 25 / Jun '95 / Kickin'

☐ **TECHNO NATIONS VOL.5**
KICKCD 34 / Mar '96 / Kickin'

☐ **TECHNO NATIONS VOL.6 (2CD Set)**
Dial: Clark & Lofthouse / Intensity: Maney, Ron & Cari Lekebusch / Eniac: Octave One / Conception: Astrocat & Kenny S. / Black sea: Drexciya / Take control: Universal addictions Vol.3 / Prewax: Ratio / Gruve: Planetary Assault Systems / Freeky deeky: Kosmic Messenger / Alistairs theme: Voorn, Orlando / Squeaky: Sir Real / Break down: Bryant, Akilah / Relax 2000: 6th Sense Approach / Encounter: Outline / Pimp slave: Denham, Jay / Style wars: Bartz, Richard / Lights: Space DJ's / Sunshower 2: Pooley, Ian / Real timez: Advent / Curb: Beltram, Joey
KICKCD 47 / Mar '97 / Kickin'

☐ **TECHNO NATIONS VOL.7**
KICKCD 68 / 16 Feb '98 / Kickin'

☐ **TECHNO PHUNK**
BAZZCD 2 / Mar '95 / Rumour

☐ **TECHNO PLANET**
Get down everybody / Holy noise / Dreams of santa anna / Man with the masterplan/Quadrophonia / Inscrutable/Problem house / Brainwasher/Defcon / Successor/2 hard 2 / Caramba/Tera WAN / It's not a dream/Diabolico / Epilepsa/Epilesia / Bronto beat/Cas stewart / Jesus left the house/Father techno / Dream/Flanger / Rotterdam/High profile / Natural system/Hyper space / Let my people go/In god we trust
DC 881062 / Jul '97 / Disky

☐ **TECHNO POWERTRAX (15 Extended Hard-Edged Jams)**
Groovy beat / Feel the rhythm / Speed freak / Read my lips / Overdrive to the maximum / Ready steady go / Move now (I got a feeling) / Rocking to the music / Trance fiction (parts 1 and 2) / Movin' on / I can feel the beat / Wolf spirit / Tribal key / Sonic groove / Night and day
EMPRCD 621 / Jun '96 / Emporio

☐ **TECHNO RAVE**
Let's go: Accelerator / Club Overdue: Synchron / Out of control: Cosmic Ray / Hypnotich: Delirium / Dominator: 909 Surprise / Secrets of sexual attraction: Ministers Of Sex / Tek-no-body: Technophobia / Total recall: Noise Attack / Ultra bass: Q-Inzest & DJ Raw / Oriental dream: Alpha X / Let me outta here: Elektro-Teknik
QED 125 / Nov '96 / Tring

☐ **TECHNO SOUND OF DISTANCE**
DI 182 / Dec '95 / Distance

☐ **TECHNO TO THE CORE**
Rainbow in the sky: Elstak, Paul / Church of house: Perplexer / You make me feel so good: DJ Thoka / Dancing together: Critical Mass / It's gonna be a fine night: Micado / Wonderful days: DJ Charly Lownoise & Mental Theo / Do what ya like: Brown, Scott / Make you dance: Smooth But Hazardous / Renegade rewind: Eko / Music is ecstasy: Love Nation & Justin Time / Take it from the groove: Midas / Into the blue: Moby
CDTOT 36 / Feb '96 / Jumpin' & Pumpin'

☐ **TECHNO TRAVEL (2CD Set)**
702671 / Oct '96 / Omnisonus

☐ **TECHNO TRAX VOL.17 (2CD Set)**
ZYX 810902 / Jan '97 / ZYX

☐ **TECHNO TRAX VOL.18**
ZYX 811012 / May '97 / ZYX

☐ **TECHNO TRAX VOL.19 (2CD Set)**
ZYX 811262 / 10 Nov '97 / ZYX

☐ **TECHNO TRAX VOL.20 (2CD Set)**
ZYX 811392 / 16 Feb '98 / ZYX

☐ **TECHNO UNIVERSE**
Noise (X-treme sounds) / Bass-X instinct/DJ Fab / 88 to piano/Holy noise / Dope man/Lenny D versus DJ Paul / Hallelluja/Problem house / Unarmed and dangerous/MC Hughie Babe / Nightmare/Global insert project / Defcon / R 001/Trade mark / Housy hip hop/Rave gang / Total distortion/Spirit of distortion / Nativity/Hardware / Better than better/TNT / Assasin/Rich in paradise / It's time to party/Techno matic
DC 881082 / Jul '97 / Disky

☐ **TECHNO VISIONS VOL.1**
CDRAID 510 / Mar '93 / Rumour

☐ **TECHNO VISIONS VOL.2**
CDRAID 512 / May '93 / Rumour

☐ **TECHNO WORLD**
Wave of the future: Quadrophonia / Rock sensation: American force / Piano junkie: DJ Caligula / Feel the rhythm: DJ Rob / Starnoise: Millennium / Party zone: Problem House / Boom boom: TNT / Blob: Defcon / Hardcore will never die: Holy Noise / Let the groove move: Second wave / Put your hands in the air: Unknown Artist / Sex instructor: Ultra Sonic / Mikado: Zo ro / Amore: 2 for love
DC 881072 / Jul '97 / Disky

☐ **TECHNO ZONE**
OZONCD 24 / Mar '92 / Ozone

☐ **TECHNOBOTANIAC TRYPTAMINES**
EFA 009622 / 1 Dec '97 / Nephilim

☐ **TECHNOLOGICAL ELEMENTS**
NR 703014 / Jun '96 / Essential Dance

☐ **TECHNOMANIA**
Lie: Fading Colours / Quick meditation: Gargarin 108 / Plug and play: Freenternetry / Transmigration of souls: Mesmerisa / Run: Trib / Clockwork: Trib / Occident: MOA / Lie: Fading Colours
CDSGP 0374 / Feb '98 / Prestige

☐ **TECHSTEPPIN'**
Zone: Hydro / Machines: DJ Doc Scott / Check me out: Ed Rush / Mach II: Skyscraper / Haze: Rollers Instinct / Liberty one: Skyscraper / Black marbles: Cronic Crew / Get stoned: Limit / Mutant: Rollers Instinct / Headless horseman: Raw Deal / Tha bomb shit: Hydro / Difference: Skyscraper
EMFCD 001 / Apr '96 / Emotif

☐ **TECSTEP TROOPERS**
GYCD 01 / 15 Jun '98 / Gyration

☐ **TEDDY BOY ROCK 'N' ROLL**
PEPCD 104 / Jan '95 / Pollytone

☐ **TEDDY BOY ROCK 'N' ROLL - 5TH ANNIVERSARY**
PEPCD 118 / Nov '96 / Pollytone

☐ **TEDDYBOY ROCK 'N' ROLL VOL.6**
PEPCD 121 / 10 Nov '97 / Pollytone

☐ **TEEN BEAT**
Wipeout: Safaris / Batman: Marketts / Let there be drums: Nelson, Sandy / Walk don't run: Ventures / Predator: Billy Joe & The Checkmates / Red river rock: Johnny & The Hurricanes / Let's go: Routers / Sleep walk: Santo & Johnny / Rebel rouser: Eddy, Duane / Teen beat: Nelson, Sandy / Pipeline: Chantays / Hawaii Five-O: Ventures / Reveille rock: Johnny & The Hurricanes / Happy organ: Cortez, Dave 'Baby' / Forty miles of bad road: Eddy, Duane / Raunchy: Justis, Bill / Tequila: Cannon, Ace / Nut rocker: B-Bumble & The Stingers
ECD 3058 / Jan '95 / K-Tel

☐ **TEEN BEAT TEQUILA**
12546 / Jun '95 / Laserlight

☐ **TEEN BEAT VOL.1**
Teen beat: Nelson, Sandy / Swanee river hop: Domino, Fats / Raunchy: Freeman, Ernie / Rumble: Wray, Link / Green mosquito: Tune Rockers / Poor boy: Royaltones / Topsy II: Cole, Cozy / So rare: Dorsey, Jimmy Orchestra / Tequila: Champs / Happy organ: Cortez, Dave 'Baby' / Clouds: Spacemen / Twitchy: Hall, Rene / Guitar boogie shuffle: Virtues / Wild bird: Jive-A-Tones / Midnighter: Champs / Fast freight: Allens, Arvee / In the mood: Fields, Ernie Orchestra / So what: Yellow Jackets / Wild weekend: Rockin' Rebels / Torquay: Fireballs / Bongo rock: Epps, Preston / Walk don't run: Ventures / Nut rocker: B-Bumble & The Stingers / Wheels: String-A-Longs / Bulldog: Fireballs / Rockin' crickets: Hot-Toddys / Wham: Mack, Lonnie / Slumber party: Van-Dells / Spunky: Jenkins, Johnny / Memphis: Mack, Lonnie
CDCHD 406 / Sep '93 / Ace

☐ **TEEN BEAT VOL.2**
Califf boogie: Teenbeats / El rancho rock: Champs / Mathilda: String-A-Longs / Flip flop and bop: Cramer, Floyd / Mule train stomp: Buchanan, Roy / Manhattan spiritual: Owen, Reg / Wiggle wobble: Cooper, Les / Ramrod: Eddy, Duane / Boo boo stick beat: Atkins, Chet / Fickle chicken: Atmospheres / Cerveza: Brown, Boots / Wild twist: Roller Coasters / Blue eagle: Rivers, Jimmy / Big jump: Nelson, Sandy / Patricia: Prado, Perez / Teensville: Atkins, Chet / Mardi gras: Cortez, Dave 'Baby' / Carioca: Fireballs / Rebel rouser: Eddy, Duane / Cast your fate to the wind: Guaraldi, Vince / Machine gun: Rip Tides / Power shift: Usher, Gary / Kabalo: Atmospheres / Hucklebuck: Fields, Ernie / Guitar rhumbo: Guitar Gable / Pretty please: Buchanan, Roy / Apple knocker: B-Bumble & The Stingers / Doin' the horse: Brooks, Skippy / Soul twist: King Curtis & The Knoble Knights / Dish rag: Kendrick, Nat
CDCHD 522 / Aug '94 / Ace

☐ **TEEN BEAT VOL.3**
Quite a party: Fireballs / Perfida: Ventures / Slop beat: Teen Beats / Mau mau: Wailers / You can't sit down: Upchurch, Phil Combo / Ghost riders in the sky: Ramrods / Walking with Mr. Lee: Allen, Lee & His Band / Big guitar: Bradley, Owen Quintet / Woo-hoo: Rock-a-Teens / Stick shift: Duals / Velvet waters: Megatrons / Moovin' 'n' groovin': Eddy, Duane / Ramrod: Casey, Al / Pipeline: Chantays / Blue jean shuffle: Johnson, Plas / Heat: Rockin' R's / Wipeout: Surfaris / Yellow bird: Lyman, Arthur / Baja: Astronauts / Twistle: Troy & The T-Birds / Back beat: Rondels / Hot pastrami: Dartells / Brass buttons: String-A-Longs / Sumpin' jumpin': Blackwell, Bumps / Wolf call: Dent, Lord & His Invaders / Too much tequila: Champs / Telegraph: Atmospheres / I want to know: Lucas, Buddy / Jay-Dee's boogie woogie: Dorsey, Jimmy Orchestra
CDCHD 602 / Feb '96 / Ace

☐ **TEEN BEAT VOL.4**
Brontosaurus stomp: Piltdown Men / Bust out: Busters / Image: Levine, Hank / Peter gunn: Anthony, Ray / Chicken pickin': Mack, Lonnie / Rinky dink: Cortez, Dave 'Baby' / Raunchy: Justis, Bill / Scratchy: Wammack, Travis / Tuff: Cannon, Ace / Sidewinder: Dakus, Wes / Nite rock: Nite Rockers / Swingin' shepherd blues: Koffman, Moe Quartette / Honky tonk: Fields, Ernie / Church key: Meyers,

Dave & The Surftones / Green monkey: Cooper, Garnell & The Kinfolks / Wiggle tail II: Rene, Googie / Asia minor: Kokomo / Bullwinkle II: Centurions / Unitar rock: Willie J / Sandstorm: Fatimas / Trollin': Brown, Boots & His Blockbusters / Lonely dragster: Fuller, Bobby Four / Drums-a-go-go: Hollywood Persuaders / Take ten: Troy & The T-Birds / Astronauts: Busters / Smokie: Black, Bill Combo

CDCHD 655 / Aug '97 / Ace

□ TEEN IDOLS

Poetry in motion: Tillotson, Johnny / Poor little fool: Nelson, Ricky / Do you want to know a secret: Kramer, Billy J. / Under the moon of love: Lee, Curtis / Crying in the rain: Everly Brothers / Turn me loose: Fabian / Hello Mary Lou: Nelson, Ricky / Little children: Kramer, Billy J. / Venus: Avalon, Frankie / Tell Laura I love her: Valence, Ricky / Pretty little angel eyes: Lee, Curtis / Till I kissed you: Everly Brothers / Tiger: Fabian / Bad to me: Kramer, Billy J. / It's late: Nelson, Ricky / Why: Avalon, Frankie

308132 / 13 Oct '97 / Hallmark

□ TEEN TOWN

Say you'll be mine: Ballard, Jimmy Lee / Lovin' baby: Perkins, Howard / I wonder: Killen, Billy J. / Poor little fool: Angel, Johnny / Teen town: Blattner, Jules / I'm gone Mama: Murphy, Jim / Gone again: Davis, Ken / All about cha baby: Irwin, Kim / Fingertips: Fisher, Brian / Green stuff: Blattner, Jules / Baby baby: Dante / Deep blue sea: Pearson, Ronnie / Just say: Denny Al / You broke my heart: O'Neal, Jackie / Evelina Malony: Worthan, John / Our love will last: Zambon, Frankie / Wayward wind: Royal Rhythms / Take me back: Speck, Darrell / Tell me quick tell me true: St. Clair, Butch / He can't love you: Sparkles / Spin the bottle: Dukes, Earl / Be mine: Catalinas / You break my heart: Echo Man / Till I'm with you: Blattner, Jules / Cindy Mary: Cochran, Wayne / I'm crying again: Popiel, Joe / What more: Loveless, Doug / Starlight: Del-Rays / I'm hypnotized: Shepherd, Buddy / Coconut girl: Loveless, Doug

CDBB 55071 / Mar '98 / Buffalo Bop

□ TEENAGE CRUSH

Sea of love: Phillips, Phil & The Twilights / You don't know what you've got: Donner, Ral / What in the world's come over you: Scott, Jack / How the time flies: Wallace, Jerry / Born too late: Poni-Tails / Tell Laura I love her: Peterson, Ray / Sweet dreams: Gibson, Don / It's only make believe: Twitty, Conway / Bobby sox to stockings: Avalon, Frankie / Sealed with a kiss: Hyland, Brian / Pretty blue eyes: Lawrence, Steve / Diary: Sedaka, Neil / Devil or angel: Vee, Bobby / Hold me, thrill me, kiss me: Carter, Mel / Close to Cathy: Clifford, Mike / Way you look tonight: Lettermen / Tragedy: Fleetwoods / My heart is an open book: Dobkins, Carl Jr. / My special angel: Helms, Bobby / It's all in the game: Edwards, Tommy / Love me warm and tender: Anka, Paul / Teen angel: Dinning, Mark / Chances are: Mathis, Johnny / Guess who: Belvin, Jesse / Take good care of her: Wade, Adam / Teenage crush: Sands, Tommy / Cry me a river: London, Julie / I understand (just how you feel): G-Clefs

CDCHD 640 / Jan '97 / Ace

□ TEENAGE IDOLS, THE

Poetry in motion: Tillotson, Johnny / Run to him: Vee, Bobby / Hats off to Larry: Shannon, Del / Wild one: Rydell, Bobby / Venus in blue jeans: Clanton, Jimmy / Maybe tomorrow: Fury, Billy / Why: Avalon, Frankie / Party doll: Knox, Buddy / Ain't that a shame: Boone, Pat / Wondrous place: Fury, Billy / You're the reason: Tillotson, Johnny / Tiger: Fabian / Just a dream: Clanton, Jimmy / Swingin' school: Rydell, Bobby / Susie darlin': Luke, Robin / Venus: Avalon, Frankie / Hula love: Knox, Buddy / Rubber ball: Vee, Bobby

SUMCD 4191 / 11 May '98 / Summit

□ TEENAGE KICKS

Pretty vacant: Sex Pistols / Going underground: Jam / My perfect cousin: Undertones / Do anything you wanna do: Eddie & The Hot Rods / If the kids are united: Sham 69 / Pump it up: Costello, Elvis & The Attractions / No more heroes: Stranglers / She's so modern: Boomtown Rats / Hit me with your rhythm stick: Dury, Ian & The Blockheads / Ever fallen in love: Buzzcocks / Working for the Yankee dollar: Skids / Turning Japanese: Vapors / King rocker: Generation X / Germ free adolescents: X-Ray Spex / What a waste: Dury, Ian & The Blockheads / Is Vic there: Department S / Go wild in the country: Bow Wow Wow / Eighth day: O'Connor, Hazel / Automatic lover: Vibrators / Lucky number: Lovich, Lena / Rich kids: Rich Kids / Start: Jam / Teenage kicks: Undertones / Hanging on the telephone: Blondie / Brass in pocket: Pretenders / Airport: Motors / Take me, I'm yours: Squeeze / Can't stand losing you: Police / I got you: Split Enz / Pretty in pink: Psychedelic Furs / 2-4-6-8 Motorway: Robinson, Tom / I want you to want me: Cheap Trick / Shake some action: Flamin' Groovies / Swords of a thousand men: Tenpole Tudor / Back of my hand: Jags / My best friend's girl: Cars / My Sharona: Knack / Time for action: Secret Affair / Generals and Majors: XTC / Reward: Teardrop Explodes / Clean clean: Buggles / Roxette: Dr. Feelgood / Hey Lord don't ask me questions: Parker, Graham / Spanish stroll: Mink Deville / Roadrunner: Richman, Jonathan / Real wild child: Iggy Pop

5253382 / Jul '95 / PolyGram TV

□ TEENAGE KICKS

L 37806 / Jun '97 / Liberation

□ TEENAGE LOVE

MACCD 166 / Aug '96 / Autograph

□ TEENAGE REPRESSION VOL.1

642041 / May '94 / EVA

□ TEENAGE ROCK 'N' ROLL PARTY (Crazy Kids...Living To A Wild Rock 'n' Roll Beat)

All night long / Old folk's boogie / Slow down / Blue jeans and a boy's shirt / That's alright baby / Sweetheart please don't go / Crying my heart out / Roll hot rod roll / Jump Jack jump / Yama yama pretty mama / You know you're doin' me wrong / These golden rings / My desire / Night of the werewolf / Dance to it / Have mercy Miss Percy / Hands off / Can't believe you wanna leave / (I'm afraid) the masquerade is over / Those lonely, lonely nights / Wet back hop / Hey girl, hey boy / Let's go boppin' tonight / Hit, git and split / Right now / Shake your hips / Look out Miss James / Who's been jivin' you / Sweet dreams

CDCHD 555 / Sep '94 / Ace

□ TEENBEAT 50

Earle Hotel: Scaley Andrew / Sketch for Sleepy: Bastro / Marbles: Circus Lupus / Block of wood: Vomit Launch / Strange pair: Vomit Launch / Capitalist joyride: Unrest / Dr. Seuss: Autoclave / Time loop: Cohen, Johnny / On tape: Teenage Gang Debs / California: Sexual Milkshake / I'm going to blow your fucking head off: Superconductor / Not at all: Velocity Girl / It's hard to be an egg: Eggs / Shaniko: Love, Courtney / Teenbeat theme: Love, Courtney / Teenbeat epilogue: Love, Courtney / Sweet Georgia Brown: Krokodiloes / Look out: Helter Skillet / Teenage suicide: Naomi Wolff / Love affair is over: Clarence / Merry go round: Coral / Equator of her navel: Jungle George / Holiday New England: Superstar, Mark E / You fucking English bastard: SCUD / 23rd rocker: Wills, Butch / Peace: Wall Drug

OLE 0252 / Mar '94 / Matador

□ TEENBEAT SAMPLER

TEENBEAT 141CD / Sep '94 / Teenbeat

□ TEENBEAT SAMPLER 1998

TB 251 / 9 Feb '98 / Teenbeat

□ TEJANO ROOTS (24 Hits From Discos Ideal 1946-1966)

ARHCD 341 / Apr '95 / Arhoolie

□ TEJANO ROOTS - THE WOMEN

ARHCD 343 / Apr '95 / Arhoolie

□ TEKNO ACID BEATS

TOPY 39CD / Feb '89 / Temple

□ TEKTEKAN

VICG 52262 / Mar '96 / JVC World Library

□ TELARC SURROUND SOUNDS

Cybergenesis/terminator: Cincinnati Pops Orchestra/Erich Kunzel / Jurassic lunch: Cincinnati Pops Orchestra/Erich Kunzel / Also sprach zarathustra: Cincinnati Pops Orchestra/Erich Kunzel / Chiller/Phantom of the opera: Cincinnati Pops Orchestra/Erich Kunzel / La donna e mobile: Cincinnati Pops Orchestra/Erich Kunzel / Hopper dance: Empire Brass Quintet / Tambourin: Empire Brass Quintet / Two part inventions in F and B flat: Carlos, Wendy / 2 a day in Tunisia: Spies / Use me: Wells, Junior / You don't miss your water: Bell, William & The Memphis Horns / Bachianas Brasileiras #4: Coral/Tristan and Isolde: Prelude: Lopez-Cobez, Jesus / Salve virgo: Ensemble PAN

CD 80447 / Apr '96 / Telarc

□ TELARCHIVE

Seven come eleven / Line for Lyons / Cherokee / So long Eric / I know that you know / Stardust / Sweet Sue, just you / Slop / Gerry meets Hamp

83318 / Jun '92 / Telarc

□ TELECOM 331

PIAS 458001126 / May '96 / Pop

□ TELECONNED VOL.1 (We Want The Airwaves)

36505893802 / 5 May '98 / TRGR

□ TELEPATHY

BDRCD 8 / Jun '95 / Breakdown

□ TELL ME THE RIDDUM

VPCD 2071 / 25 May '98 / VP

□ TEMPETE POUR SORTIR

KMCD 58 / Mar '96 / Keltia Musique

□ TEMPLE OF ELECTRONICA

TEMPNYC 2CD / Oct '95 / Temple

□ TEMPLE RECORDS VOL.1

TEMPNYC 1CD / Oct '95 / Temple

□ TEMPLE SAMPLER, THE

COMD 2049 / Feb '94 / Temple

□ TEMPO JAZZ

RTCL 801CD / Jul '96 / Right Tempo

□ TEN YEARS LATER

BNR 01CD / 29 Sep '97 / Revelation

□ TENDANCE VOL.4

ZYX 550692 / Nov '96 / ZYX

□ TENDER LOVE

Tender love: Thomas, Kenny / Tonight I celebrate my love: Bryson, Peabo & Roberta Flack / I don't wanna lose you: Kandidate / Coming home: Hain, Marshall / Solid: Ashford & Simpson / This will be: Cole, Natalie / More than a woman: Tavares / It's been so long: McCrae, George / Please don't go: KC & The Sunshine Band / Rock me tonight: Jackson, Freddie / Fantasy real: Fearon, Phil / Sexy girl: Thomas, Lillo / Other side of the rainbow: Moore, Melba / Cross your mind: King, Evelyn 'Champagne' / Woman of the world: Mazelle, Kym / Free love: Roberts, Juliet / Why can't we live together: Thomas, Timmy / Loving you: Riperton, Minnie

CDGOLD 1030 / Jan '97 / EMI Gold

□ TENOR SAX & TROMBONE SPECTACULAR

PCD 7019 / Jun '93 / Progressive

□ TEQUILA MAN, THE

Margarita: Chuck Rio & The Originals / Denise: Chuck Rio & The Originals / Midnighter: Champs / Surfin' blues: Persuaders / Tequila: Champs / El Rancho rock: Champs / Bruce: Flores, Danny & The Fans / Antonilla: Chuck Rio & The Originals / C'est la vie: Chuck Rio & The Originals / Whip: Chuck Rio & The Originals / TNT: Champs / Mama Inez: Chuck Rio & The Originals / Wildman: Contenders / Taking off on a wall: Persuaders / Hanging ten: Creshendoes / Surfer strip: Creshendoes / Surfer's lullaby: Persuaders / Gremmie bread: Persuaders / Kreshendo stomp: Creshendoes / Toes on the nose: Persuaders / Caught in the soup: Persuaders / Surfer's nightmare: Persuaders / Raid: Persuaders / Don't go baby: Danny Boy / Crazy street / You are my sunshine: Flores, Danny & The Fans / Bad boy: Chuck Rio & The Originals / Call me baby: Chuck Rio & The Originals / Worried restless and sad: Flores, Danny & The Fans

CDCHD 688 / 29 Jun '98 / Ace

□ TERMINAL CITY RICOCHET

VIRUS 75CD / Nov '89 / Alternative Tentacles

□ TERRA SERPENTES (A World Serpent Compilation)

T 2901E: Arkkon / Bahnhofstrasse: Bates, Martyn / One minute more: Chris & Cosey / Frolicking: Current 93 / May you never be alone like me: Dall, Bryin / Only Europe knows: Kapo / Dark scenery court games: Doyle, Roger / Wise words of Eve: Elijah's Mantle / Still water bonne: In Gowan Ring / What the cat brought in: Lemon Kittens / Love is regret: Loretta's Doll / Untitled: Moon Lay Hidden Beneath A Cloud / By a foreign river: Nature & Organisation / All God's dogs: Neither Neither World / Window of possible organic development: Nurse With Wound / Come unto me: Orchis / Music from Pearls Before Swine: Rice, Boyd / On the corner: Sand / Some colossus: Scorpionwind / Oblivion extract: Shock Headed Peters / Did you see: Sol Invictus / Oblique realities: Somewhere In Europe / Ways to strength and beauty: Strength Through Joy / Live: Tiny Tim / Scavenging soul: Zone

WSDCD 016 / Apr '97 / World Serpent

□ TERRORDROME VOL.1 (Hardcore Nightmare)

DB 47982 / Mar '95 / Deep Blue

□ TERRORDROME VOL.1 (Darkside From Hell)

0041512COM / Jul '97 / Edel

□ TERRORDROME VOL.2 (Hardcore Cyberpunk)

Introdrome: Chosen Few / Tyrannofuck: DJ Fistfuck / String X: Cyanide / I'll show you my gun: Annihilator / Base U (Smash TV): Shadowrun / Accelerator 4: Technohead / One day: Wedlock / Maniac: Chosen Few / Cocksuckers: Tellurian / FTS: Vinyl Killer / Domestic moves: Maniac Of Noise / Victim of trance: Analyzer / Cause a riot: Blunted Vision, A / Power dominion: Dee, Lenny & Ralphie Dee / 20,000 volt: High Energy / Suck it: Oral Maniac / Terrordrome: High Energy / Fuck this: Re-Animator / Accelerator 3: Technohead / Fucking Speedloader: Speedloader / Relatic: Cyanide / Mokummania: Maniac Of Noise / Goddamn mind: Noisegate / Invasion of the intruders: Sons of Aliens / In 16 beats time second: Vitamin / CTX: Original Gabber / Eat zat pizza: Salami Brothers / Insane: Strontium 9000 / Psychic 909: Milan / Move it faster: Triplet / Quetsch: Haardcore / Outrodrome: Original Gabber / I control your body: Dee, Lenny & Ralphie Dee / Maniac (mix): Chosen Few / Suck it (mix): Oral Maniac / Accelerator: Technohead / Mokummania (mix): Maniac Of Noise / Relatic (mix): Cyanide / My house is your house: Vitamin / Victim of trance (mix): Analyzer / Eat zat pizza (mix): Salami Brothers / Cocksuckers (mix): Tellurian / 20,000 volt (mix): High Energy

DB 47972 / Mar '95 / Deep Blue

□ TERRORDROME VOL.4 (Supersonic Guerilla)

DB 47962 / Apr '95 / PolyGram TV

□ TERRORDROME VOL.7 (2CD Set)

0041822CON / Jun '96 / Edel

□ TERRY'S CAFE

PLACCD 0112 / 30 Mar '98 / Plastic City UK

□ TESSERACT COMPILATION VOL.3

TES 030 / 1 Dec '97 / Tesseract

□ TEST 7

Joanna: Mrs. Wood / Sundance: Sundance / Age of love: Age Of Love / I bring you love: Blu Peter / Revolution: Sharkey / Spirit: Kitachi / Work mi body: Monkey Mafia / Shadow boxing: Doc Scott / Tune in turn out: Obsessive / Alarm clock: Westbam / Kaleidoscope: Westbam / Blow your mind: Gargano, Pablo

REACTCD 117 / 24 Nov '97 / React

□ TEST 8

I feel devine: SJ / Tell me what you want: Blu Peter / Feels so good: Mrs. Wood / Bitch: Hellfire Club / Roadrage: Madame Dubois / Everyone's future: Gargano, Pablo / Loops and tings: Jens / Welcome to the future: Shimmon & Woolfson / B boy stance: Freestylers / Sundance: Sundance / Who's the badman: Patten, Dee / Sunstroke: Chicane

REACTCD 127 / 27 Apr '98 / React

□ TESTAMENT RECORDS SAMPLER

TCD 4001 / May '95 / Testament

□ TESTCARD MUSIC VOL.1

Flying over San Jose: Gale, Simon / Girl I love: Fox, John / Now or never: Polish Radio Orchestra / Pondering: Polish Radio Orchestra / Look out: Gale, Simon / Up and up: Privsek, Joze / February: Budapest Radio Orchestra / Tropicano: Budapest Radio Orchestra / Canzona d'amore: Gale, Simon / My fate and you: Robeznik, Jure / Lights of Hong Kong: Budapest Radio Orchestra / When you smile: Arcon, Lem / Better luck next time: Polish Radio Orchestra / Golubchik: Thon, Franz Big Band / Janice in wonderland: Budapest Radio Orchestra / So lovingly: Fox, John / Enjoy yourself: Polish Radio Orchestra / My dear cousin Julia: Bergenson, Jorg & Igor Molescu / Danger: Polish Radio Orchestra / There will be yet another day: Polish Radio Orchestra

ASCD 206 / 1 Sep '97 / Apollo Sound

□ TESTCARD MUSIC VOL.2 (From The Archives)

APSCD 208 / 30 Mar '98 / Apollo Sound

□ TEX-MEX (The Full Enchilada)

Beer barrel polka: Longoria, Valerio / El tremblor de San Francisco: Jordan, Steve / Viva San Antonio: Vela, Ruben Y Su Conjunto / Al Mirar tu Cara: Los Campeones De Raul Ruiz / Santa Amalia: Ramirez, Janie C. / Ojitos verdes: Los Arcos/Hermanos Pena / Amor amor: Joslin, Rena / Flor de Mexico: Jordan, Steve / Cuatro vidas: Grupo Badd / Jambalaya: Fender, Freddy / Oh lonesome me: Jerry & The Ruf-Nex / Mejor solo: De La Rosa, Tony / Me agarro la imaginacion: Los Terribles Del Norte / El corrida de Emilo Cabrerra: Jimenez, Santiago Jr. / Lo nuestra termino: Vela, Ruben / Voy a llorar: Caballeros Del Norte / Hay que sentimiento traigo: Escobar, Linda / Los ilegales: Longoria, Valerio / Tu y las nubes: Fender, Freddie & Janie C. Ramirez

NSCD 033 / 15 Jun '98 / Nascente

□ TEX-MEX FIESTA

Ay te dejo en San Antonio / La ratita / Amor bonito / Corine Corina / La tracionera / El desperado / Caballo viejo / Que cobarde / Viva seguin / La duena de la llave / Por esos montes / Cuatro o cinco farolazos / Quiereme vidita / Las gaviotas / Tomando y fumando / Puentes quemados / Saludamos a texas / Mi unico camino real / Medio vuelo / Tarde pa' appepentirnos / Magia de amor / Juarez

CDCHD 528 / Oct '94 / Ace

□ TEX-MEX FIESTA (A Round Up Of Classic Conjunto Singles From Texas)

El chubasco: Los Colores / El adolorido: Vela, Ruben Y Su Conjunto / Vencido: Vela, Ruben Y Su Conjunto / Alegra serenata: Los Cuatitos Cantu / Como un amanecer: Los Cuatitos Cantu / Declarate inocente: Los Cuatitos Cantu / Que bonito es querer: Los Tremendos Gavilanes / Pero Maria: Los Tremendos Gavilanes / Le llorona loca: Jordan, Steve / La dame de Espana: Jordan, Steve

EDCD 7039 / Jul '97 / Easydisc

□ TEXANS LIVE FROM MOUNTAIN STAGE

(Is anybody going to) San Antone: Texas Tornados / Shake your hips: Barton, Lou Ann / Portales: Hubbard, Ray Wylie / Whatever way the wind blows: Willis, Kelly / Shadow boxing: Hickman, Sara / Just a wave: Gilmore, Jimmie Dale / Buckskin stallion blues: Van Zandt, Townes / Georgia on a fast train: Shaver, Billy Joe / I had my hopes up high: Ely, Joe / Esperate (wait for me): Hinojosa, Tish / St. Gabriel: Ball, Marcia / She ain't goin nowhere: Clark, Guy / Miles and miles of Texas: Asleep At The Wheel

BPM 304CD / May '97 / Blue Plate

□ TEXAS AND TENNESSEE TERRITORY BANDS

Sugar babe I'm leavin' / Happy / Goofus / Sadness will be gladness / Goose creek / Better than nothin' / That's a-plenty / Mississippi stomp / Memphis kick up / You never did that before / Down on Biscayne Bay / We can't use each other anymore / Down where the blue bonnets grow / I ain't got no gal now / I don't love nobody but you / Honey child / All muggled up / Shooin' flies / Come easy go easy love / When I can't be with you

RTR 79006 / Jul '97 / Retrieval

□ TEXAS BLACK COUNTRY DANCE 1927-1935

DOCD 5162 / May '93 / Document

□ TEXAS BLUES

ARHCD 352 / Apr '95 / Arhoolie

□ TEXAS BLUES (2CD Set)

Stubborn woman: Jones, Tutu / Young devil: Walker, Philip / You're a dog: Jones, Andrew 'Jr. Boy' / Meet me in the bottom: Fulson, Lowell / Come back baby: Fulson, Lowell / Going back to Texas: Kirkpatrick, Bob / Old friend of mine: Kirkpatrick, Bob / What the woman's done to me: Coronado, Joe / Sunrise sorrow: Coronado, Joe / Don't leave me baby: Dixon, Floyd / Heroes of the blues: Jones, Tutu / Jacksboro highway: Williams, Alanda / Camilla's hop: Houston, Joe & Otis Grand / Blues for T-Bone: Houston, Joe & Otis Grand / Blame it on me: Little Nikki & Andrew 'Jr. Boy' Jones / Need the need: Wilson, U.P. / Long time: Wilson, U.P. / Blues for the iceman: Ray, Kenny 'Blue' / Looking for my baby: Williams, Alanda / Alone at Christmas: Williams, Alanda / Meat's too high: Vinson, Eddie 'Cleanhead' / Racetrack blues: Vinson, Eddie 'Cleanhead' / She torture me: Walker, Philip & Otis Grand / What happened to you: Morello, Jimmy / Bet you do it real good: Coronado, Joe / Little girl: Kirkpatrick, Bob / Tribute to Freddie: Jones, Andrew 'Jr. Boy' / Tell me tell me: Watson, Johnny 'Guitar' / Moon is rising: Littlefield, 'Little' Willie / Made up my mind: Wilson, U.P.

JSPCD 403 / 21 Sep '97 / JSP

□ TEXAS BLUES 1927-1937

DOCD 5161 / May '93 / Document

□ TEXAS BLUES GUITAR

Claim jumper: Copeland, Johnny / Love me with a feeling: Funderburgh, Anson & The Rockets / Insomnia: Walker, Philip & Otis Grand / Texas Cadillac: Kubek, Smokin' Joe Band / Sometimes I slip: Brown, Clarence 'Gatemouth' / Texas guitar slinger: Hughes, John 'Guitar' / I'm worried: Morgan, Mike & The Crawl / Rough edges: Clark, W.C. / Half step: Wilson, U.P. / Blues for Carol: Holliman, Clarence

EDCD 7037 / Jun '97 / Easydisc

□ TEXAS BLUES GUITAR 1929-1935

SOB 35332CD / Apr '95 / Story Of The Blues

□ TEXAS BLUES GUITAR SUMMIT

Fast woman: Jones, Andrew 'Jr. Boy' / That's your woman but she comes to see me sometime: Wilson, U.P. / Chankety chank: Wilson, U.P. / I just can't help it: Wilson, U.P. & Bobby Gilmore / I can't be this way no more: Gilmore, Bobby / Strange bed: Gilmore, Bobby / Party tonight: Quall, Henry / Rosie Mae: Quall, Henry / Are you sticking with me baby: Wynne, J.B. / All alone blues: Wynne, J.B. / Dynamite: Wynne, J.B. / Stinky dink: Jones, Andrew 'Jr. Boy'

JSPCD 293 / Feb '98 / JSP

☐ **TEXAS BLUES PARTY**
Dollar got the blues: Brown, Clarence 'Gatemouth' / Young devil: Walker, Philip & Otis Grand / Texas party: Copeland, Johnny / Soul king shuffle: Wilson, U.P. / You're my brand: Kubek, Smokin' Joe Band / I want to shout about it: Clark, W.C. / 20 miles: Funderburgh, Anson & The Rockets / Why oh why: Houston, Joe & Otis Grand / 'Big D' shuffle: Morgan, Mike & The Crawl / It's been a mistake: Jones, Tutu
EDCD 7038 / Jun '97 / Easydisc

☐ **TEXAS BLUES PARTY VOL.2 (The Very Best Of Texas Blues Today)**
WCD 120631 / Dec '96 / Wolf

☐ **TEXAS BOHEMIA**
TRIKONTUS 201 / Jan '95 / Trikont

☐ **TEXAS COUNTRY**
Second fiddle / Night life / Funny how time slips away / Take me as I am (or let me go) / Hello walls / Crazy / Wasted days and wasted nights / When I didn't love you / Mean woman / Holy one / Before you stopped loving me / Cherokee boogie / Drivin' nails in my coffin / I've been everywhere / Take me back to Tulsa / Faded love / Milk cow blues / My shoes keep walking back to you / San Antonio rose / Stay a little longer
BGOCD 391 / 3 Aug '98 / Beat Goes On

☐ **TEXAS COUNTRY BLUES 1948-1951**
FLYCD 941 / Aug '94 / Flyright

☐ **TEXAS FIELD RECORDINGS 1934-1939**
DOCD 5231 / Apr '94 / Document

☐ **TEXAS FLASHBACKS VOL.1**
MMCD 66061 / Sep '97 / Music Maniac

☐ **TEXAS FLASHBACKS VOL.2**
MMCD 66062 / Dec '97 / Music Maniac

☐ **TEXAS GARAGE BANDS (West Texas Rarities)**
COLCD 0663 / Jun '97 / Collectables

☐ **TEXAS GARAGE BANDS (AOK Records Story)**
COLCD 0595 / Jun '97 / Collectables

☐ **TEXAS GARAGE BANDS (Corpus Christie Rarities)**
COLCD 0664 / Jul '97 / Collectables

☐ **TEXAS GIRLS**
DOCD 5163 / May '93 / Document

☐ **TEXAS PIANO 1923-1935**
DOCD 5224 / Apr '94 / Document

☐ **TEXAS PIANO 1927-1938**
DOCD 5225 / Apr '94 / Document

☐ **TEXAS PIANO BLUES 1929-1948**
SOB 35092CD / Apr '95 / Story Of The Blues

☐ **TEXAS: A COLLECTION OF TEXAS GARAGE**
ANDA 198 / Jan '97 / Au-Go-Go

☐ **TFSM 03**
EFA 127662 / Jul '95 / Gaia

☐ **THAI (Spirituality & Technology For The Manga Consciousness)**
CDZ 001 / Sep '96 / Zone

☐ **THANK YOU BOB**
PB 001 / May '97 / Bob

☐ **THANKS FOR THE MEMORY**
MCCD 164 / Jul '94 / Music Club

☐ **THAT BEATIN' RHYTHM (A Collection Of Mirwood Northern Soul Classics)**
Where there's a will: Thomas, Jimmy / I can't get away: Garrett, Bobby / Ooh honey baby: Cosby, Earl / Same old thing: Olympics / Let me do it: Belles / Set me free: Performers / Duck: Lee, Jackie / Temptation walk: Lee, Jackie / He's alright with me: Mirettes / Day she needed me: Performers / Could it be: Temple, Richard / Send for me I'll be there: Cosby, Earl / Stubborn heart: Sheppards / My little girl: Bob & Earl / My little girl: Garrett, Bobby / That beatin' rhythm: Temple, Richard / Baby do the philly dog: Olympics / I'm satisfied with you: Furys / Don't pretend: Belles / I'll do a little bit more: Olympics / Whether it's right or wrong: Lee, Jackie & Delores Hall / How do you like it: Sheppards / Cigarette ashes: Conwell, Jimmy / Big brother: Garrett, Bobby / Leave a light in the window until I come home: Alexander, J.W. / Secret agents: Olympics / Mine exclusively: Olympics
GSCD 010 / Feb '96 / Goldmine

☐ **THAT GROOVSVILLE SOUND**
I'll never forget you: O'Jays / Sweet Sherry: Barnes, J.J. / No one to love: Lewis, Pat / Friday night: Mancha, Steve / Our love is in the pocket: Banks, Darrell / Don't be sore at me: Parliaments / Please let me in: Barnes, J.J. / Hit and run: Batiste, Rose / That's why I love you: Professionals / Making up time: Holidays / Loving you takes all of my time: Debonaires / I lost you: Holidays / Keep the faith: Mancha, Steve / Chains of love: Barnes, J.J. / Warning: Lewis, Pat / I must love you: Davis, Melvin / Stone broke: Ward, Sam / Headache in my heart: Debonaires / Just keep on loving me: Mancha, Steve / Look at what I almost missed: Lewis, Pat / I miss my baby (that lonely feeling): Batiste, Rose / Somebody, somewhere needs you: Banks, Darrell / I think I found a love: Barnes, J.J. / I'm the one who loves you: Track
GSCD 105 / Mar '97 / Goldmine

☐ **THAT HIGH LONESOME SOUND (The Best Of Bluegrass Through The Years)**
If I should wander back tonight: Hot Rize / Looking for the stone: O'Brien, Tim & Mollie / Blue yodel no.3: Johnson Mountain Boys / My hands are tied: Lonesome Standard Time / I'm going back to the old home: Watson, Doc / Blue moon of Kentucky: Osborne Brothers / Trains make me lonesome: Auldridge, Mike / Rock salt and nails: Crowe, J.D. & The New South / I ain't brok but I'm badly bent: Grisman, David / I was left on the street: McCoury Brothers / Where the soul man never dies: Skaggs, Ricky & Tony Rice / When God dips his pen of love in my heart: Krauss, Alison / Running hard on a broken heart: Lonesome River Band / Kentucky King: Lonesome Standard Time / That high lonesome sound: Rowan, Peter & The Nashville Bluegrass Band / Molly and tenbrooks: Crowe, J.D. / Blue ridge express: Munde, Alan / One way track: Boone Creek / Darlin' Corey: Clifton, Bill / Roll jordan roll: Nashville Bluegrass Band / Foggy mountain chimes: Here Today / Tramp on the street: Blue Sky Boys / Come on home: Clements, Vassar
REMCD 522 / 27 Apr '98 / Reactive

☐ **THAT HIGH LONESOME SOUND**
ACD 19 / Mar '96 / Acoustic Disc

☐ **THAT'LL FLAT GIT IT VOL.1 (Rockabilly & Rock 'n' Roll From The Vaults Of RCA Victor)**
Sixteen chicks: Clay, Joe / Born to love one woman: Cartey, Ric / Sugar sweet: Houston, David / New shoes: Denson, Lee / Little boy blue: Johnson, Hoyt / Drug store rock 'n' roll: Martin, Janis / Rosie let's get cozy: Rich, Dave / Catty Town: Glasser, Dick / Star light, star bright: Castle, Nan / TV hop: Morgan Twins / Honky tonk mind: Blake, Tommy / Teen billy baby: Sprouts / Don't bug me baby: Allen, Milt / Now stop: Carson, Martha / Milkcow blues: Rodgers, Jimmie / Duck tail: Clay, Joe / Heart throb: Cartey, Ric / One and only: Houston, David / I've got a dollar: Dell, Jimmy / Lovin' honey: Morris, Gene / Barefoot baby: Martin, Janis / Rock-a-bye baby: Bonn, Skeeter / That ain't nothing but right: Castle, Joey / Mary Nell: Inman, Autrey / Hey jibbo: Wood, Art / All night long: Blake, Tommy / Full grown cat: McCoys / Just thought I'd set you straight: Harris, Ted / Oooh-wee baby: Cartey, Ric / Shake it up baby: Dee, Frankie / Lovin' honey: Morris, Gene
BCD 15622 / May '93 / Bear Family

☐ **THAT'LL FLAT GIT IT VOL.11 (Rockabilly From The Vaults Of Mercury Records)**
Rockin' daddy: Bond, Eddie & His Stompers / Slip slip slippin' in: Bond, Eddie & His Stompers / Flip flop mama: Bond, Eddie & His Stompers / Boppin' Bonnie: Bond, Eddie & His Stompers / All the time: LaBeef, Sleepy / Love bug crawl: Edwards, Jimmy / That's my reward: Wallace, Billy & The Bama Drifters / What'll I do: Wallace, Billy & The Bama Drifters / Burning the wind: Wallace, Billy & The Bama Drifters / Mean mistreatin' baby: Wallace, Billy & The Bama Drifters / I've changed my mind, wild mind: Talley, Johnny 'T' / Lonesome train: Talley, Johnny 'T' / You're my big baby now: Moss, Roy / You don't know my mind: Moss, Roy / Corrine corrina: Moss, Roy / You nearly lose your mind: Moss, Roy / Done gone: George & Earl / Better stop look and listen: George & Earl / Draggin': Gordon, Curtis / Mobile Alabama: Gordon, Curtis / Sitting on top of the world: Gordon, Curtis / Let's get wild: Grayzell, Rudy / Yes I do: Porter, Royce / You're the one that done it: Wayne, Thomas / I can't help it: Day, Bing / Maybelle: Cray, Jackie / Born to love one woman: Johnston, Don / Rock a bye baby rock: Dycus, Connie / Sugar doll: Jay, Johnny / Dance me to death: Hi-Liters
BCD 16101 / Jul '98 / Bear Family

☐ **THAT'LL FLAT GIT IT VOL.12 (Rockabilly From The Vaults Of Imperial Records)**
Red hot: Luman, Bob / So long good luck goodbye: Rodgers, Weldon / Play my boogie: Mack, Billy / Let's go baby: Eldridge, Billy / Bop bop ba doo bop: Williams, Lew / Please give me something: Allen, Bill / Hip shakin' baby: Brown, Roy / Make with the lovin': Herrold, Dennis / If you can't rock me: Strikes / Centipede: Williams, Lew / Don't wait up: Perkins, Laura Lee / Didi didi: Garner, Johnny / Everybody's got a baby but me: Miller, Warren / Warm love: Burnette Brothers / Abracadabra: Williams, Lew / Rockin': Strikes / Hip hip baby: Herrold, Dennis / Sweet baby doll: Burnette, Johnny / Loretta: Jones, Al / Cat talk: Williams, Lew / Hey baby: Lawrence, Bill / I don't want to cry over you: Strikes / All night long: Luman, Bob / Kiss me sweet: Garner, Johnny / Gone ape man: Williams, Lew / You arouse my curiosity: Herrold, Dennis / Dirty dog: Banks, Dick / Baby I'm sorry: Strikes / Something I said: Williams, Lew / Rockin' by myself: Gowans, Sammy
BCD 16102 / Aug '97 / Bear Family

☐ **THAT'LL FLAT GIT IT VOL.14 (Rockabilly From The Vaults Of Sun Records)**
Rock all night: Honeycutt, Glenn / Move baby move: Penner, Dick / Pop and mama: Simmons, Gene / Rock me baby: Haggett, Jimmy / Take me (garden of evil): Wages, Jimmy / Hula bop: Smokey Joe / Drive-in: Vickery, Mack / Somehow we'll find a way: Fakes, Roger / Treat me right: Parchman, Kenny / Christine: Hall, Roy / Problem child: Cook, Ken / Chain gang charlie: Money, Curley / My one desire: Williams, Jimmy / Tough tough tough: Anderson, Andy / Gonna give a party: Wood, James / Wood, James: Wood, James / Wampus cat: Chandler, Howard / Take me to that place: Earls, Jack / That's the way I feel: Pritchett, Jimmy / Apron strings: Hoback, Curtis / Miss Pearl: Wages, Jimmy / Wages, jimmy: Wages, Jimmy / Lonely wolf: Harris, Ray / Me and my rhythm guitar: Powers, Johnny / Don't you worry: Thompson, Hayden / Got me a trumpet: Yelvington, Malcolm / She's gone away: Barton, Ernie / Peroxide blonde and a hopped up model Ford: Simmons, Gene / Uh huh oh yeah: Pendarvis, Tracy / Put me down: Turner, Jesse Lee / What a beat / Red hen hop / Rakin' and scrapin': Beard, Dean
BCD 16210 / Aug '97 / Bear Family

☐ **THAT'LL FLAT GIT IT VOL.2 (Rockabilly & Rock 'n' Roll From The Vaults Of US Decca)**
Hot rock wild: Carroll, Johnny / Wild women - crazy: Carroll, Johnny / Crazy lovin': Carroll, Johnny / Tryin' to get you: Carroll, Johnny / Corine Corina: Carroll, Johnny / Rock 'n' Roll Ruby: Carroll, Johnny / Flip, flop and fry: Carroll, Johnny / Baby don't leave me: Five Chavis Brothers / Way out there: Chuck & Bill / Ruby Pearl: Cochran, Jackie Lee / Mamy don't you think I know: Cochran, Jackie Lee / Lorraine: Covelle, Buddy / Cool it baby: Fontaine, Eddie / Whole lotta shakin' goin' on: Hall, Roy / Off beat boogie: Hall, Roy / See you later alligator: Hall, Roy / Three alley cats: Hall, Roy / Diggin' the boogie: Hall, Roy / I wanna bop: Harlan, Billy / I would be a doggone lie: Harlan, Billy / Be bop baby: Harlan, Billy / Sweet love on my mind: Jimmy & Johnny / Teenage love is misery: Kennedy, Jerry / Crazy baby: Maltais, Gene / Ten little women: Noland, Terry / Teenage boogie: Pierce, Webb / Cast iron arm: Wilson, Peanuts / You're barking up the wrong tree: Woody, Don / Make like a rock and roll: Woody, Don
BCD 15623 / Jun '92 / Bear Family

☐ **THAT'LL FLAT GIT IT VOL.3 (Rockabilly & Rock 'n' Roll From The Vaults Of Capitol)**
You oughta see Grandma rock: McDonald, Skeets / Heartbreakin' Mama: McDonald, Skeets / My little baby: Maddox, Rose / Sebbin' come elebbin: Heap, Jimmy / Go ahead on: Heap, Jimmy / Try me: Luman, Bob / Cash on the barrelhead: Louvin Brothers / Red hen hop: Louvin Brothers / Worryin' kind: Sands, Tommy / Playin' the field: Sands, Tommy / My gal Gertie: Dickerson, Dub / When I found you: Reed, Jerry / I've had enough: Reed, Jerry / Mr. Big feet: Charlie Bop Trio / Cool down Mame: Farmer Boys / My baby done left me: Farmer Boys / Party kiss: Fallin, Johnny / Party line: Fallin, Johnny / There's gonna be a ball: Grayzell, Rudy / Bop cat bop: Crum, Simon / Jeopardy: Shepard, Jean / He's my baby: Shepard, Jean / Alone with you: Young, Faron / I can't dance: Young, Faron / Black cat: Collins, Tommy / I chickened out: Loran, Kenny / Slow down brother: Husky, Ferlin / I went rockin': Norris, Bobby / You mostest girl: Trammell, Bobby Lee
BCD 15624 / Jun '92 / Bear Family

☐ **THAT'LL FLAT GIT IT VOL.4 (Rockabilly & Rock 'n' Roll From The Vaults Of Festival)**
They call me Willie: Barry, Billy / Wild one: Barry, Billy / My love is true: Barry, Billy / Baby I'm a king: Barry, Billy / Weepin' and wailin: Barry, Billy / Oh no: Barry, Billy / I love you now: Barry, Billy / Do the oop-poo-pah-doo: Dio, Ronnie / Love pains: Dio, Ronnie / Motorcycle: Balls, Billy / Till time stands still: Starr, Charlie / Sick and tired: Starr, Charlie / You ain't my number one: Starr, Charlie / Black jack Joey: Starr, Charlie / Christmas twist: Starr, Charlie / One broken heart for sale: Blackwell, Otis
BCD 15630 / Apr '94 / Bear Family

☐ **THAT'LL FLAT GIT IT VOL.5 (Rockabilly & Rock 'n' Roll From The Vaults Of Dot)**
Circle rock: Copas, Lloyd / Love me: Phantom / Carry on: Newman, Jimmy C. / Lonesome for a letter: Clark, Sanford / Big door: Brown, Gene / Skinny Minnie: Denton, Bob / Dogonnit: Spellman, Jimmy / Step it up and go: Wiseman, Mac / Oh my baby's gone: Sharpe, Ray / Rock sock the boogie: Flowers, Pat / I'm low low low: Clingman, Loy / Call me shorty: Gilley, Mickey / Pucker paint: Wolfe, Danny / You're late Miss Kate: Dee, Jimmy / It's all over: Sullivan, Niki / Boogie woogie: Tucker, Billy Jo / You heard me knocking: Adams, Billy / Mary Lou: Burdette, Lew / I like this kind of music: Ringo, Jimmy / Trapped love: Courvale, Keith / Playboy: Denton, Bob / Chicken shack: Van Dyke, Leroy / Ballroom baby: Lory, Dick / That's the way I feel: Sharpe, Ray / Johnny Johnny Johnny: Jones, Kay Cee / It ain't me: Campi, Ray / Come on baby: Gilley, Mickey / Put me down: Lucas, Matt / Let's flat get it: Wolfe, Danny / Henrietta: Dee, Jimmy / Love me: Phantom
BCD 15711 / May '97 / Bear Family

☐ **THAT'LL FLAT GIT IT VOL.6 (Rockabilly & Rock 'n' Roll From The Vaults Of US Decca)**
All by myself: Hall, Roy / Rock it down to my house: Tubb, Justin / Alligator come across: Duff, Arlie / Wee Willie Brown: Graham, Lou / Hey babe let's go downtown: Therien, Joe Jr. / Everybody's tryin' to be my baby: York Brothers / Morse code: Woody, Don / Juke joint Johnny: Sovine, Red / Don't stop now: Hall, Roy / Come back to me darling: Therien, Joe Jr. / You gotta move: Smith, Chester / Knock knock: Allen, Rex / Crazy little guitar man: Foley, Red / Sputnik (satellite girl): Engler, Jerry / You're long gone: Therien, Joe Jr. / Baby's gone: Claud, Vernon / Sweet Willie: Allen, Barbara / Move on: Hall, Roy / She wanna rock: Derksen, Arnie / Wheels: Therien, Joe Jr. / Crazy chicken: Gallagher, James / Don't go baby (don't go): Coker, Al / School house rock: Harlan, Billy / Bring my cadillac back: Knightmares / Rockabilly boogie: Therien, Joe Jr. / Roc-a-chicka: Mack, Warner / Cheat on me baby: Rockin' Saints / Tennessee Tody: Billy & Western Okies / One and only: Fontaine, Eddie / Shake baby shake: Raney, Wayne
BCD 15733 / Nov '94 / Bear Family

☐ **THAT'LL FLAT GIT IT VOL.7 (Rockabilly & Rock 'n' Roll From The Vaults Of MGM)**
Rockin' rollin' stone: Starr, Andy / Rock 'n' roll fever: Campbell, Cecil / Mr. Blues: Rainwater, Marvin / Watchin' the 710 roll by: Griffin, Buck / Rootie tootie: Berry Kids / My square dancin' Mama: Gallion, Bob / Rock old rock: Early, Bernie / Long black train: Twitty, Conway / Rocking guitar: Campbell, Cecil / Go, go, go right into town: Berry Kids / Rockin' chair on the moon: Wellington, Rusty / Round and round: Starr, Andy / Your kisses kill me: Early, Bernie / Latch on: Hargrave, Ron / Country cattin': Swan, Jimmy / Love me love: Berry Kids / Dixieland rock: Campbell, Cecil / Hot and cold: Rainwater, Marvin / Stutterin' Papa: Griffin, Buck / There's good rockin' tonight: Wills, Billy Jack / Baby, love me: Gallion, Bob / Big money: Davis, Paul / Buttercup: Hargrave, Ron / You're my teenage baby: Berry Kids / Cuddle lovin' baby: Charley & Junior / All she wants to do is rock: Wills, Billy Jack / Let's go rock'n'roll: Sandy, Frank / I wanta waltz: Blackmon, Thelma / Drive-in movie: Hargrave, Ron / Rockin' and rollin' with Grandmaw: Robinson, Carson
BCD 15789 / May '96 / Bear Family

☐ **THAT'LL FLAT GIT IT VOL.8 (Rockabilly & Rock 'n' Roll From The Vaults Of Fabor/Abbott)**
You mostest girl: Trammell, Bobby Lee / Cool cat: Montgomery, Joe / Let's fall in love: Burnette, Dorsey / Meadowlark: Coker, Sandy / Bawlin' baby: Horton, Johnny & Billy Barton / Long sideburns: Barry, Boelean / Shirley Lee, I sure do love you: Trammell, Bobby Lee / Stop the clock rock: Creel Sisters / Shotgun boogie: Horton, Johnny / I love you girl: Podolor, Dickie / That's alright with me: Luman, Bob / No use in lying: Luman, Bob / Hello baby: Luman, Bob / We're gonna bop: Coker, Alvadean / Hot Rod is her name: Tall, Tom / Salt and pepper: Summers, Ronnie / Rockin' Maraccas: Rose, Dusty / Hula rock: Rose, Dusty / Klondike: Lanham, Roy / Love is over: Guitar, Bonnie / Frantic party: Guitar, Bonnie / Stop talkin', start lovin': Harshman, Robert Luke / Love what'cha doin' to me: Harshman, Robert Luke / Jumping with the shadows: Shadows / Shadow rock: Shadows / Creep: Shadows / Don't you know: Tall, Tom & Ruckus Tyler / Whose little pigeon are you: Tall, Tom & Creel Sisters / Rock town rock: Tyler, Ruckus / Rollin' and a-rockin': Tyler, Ruckus / We're gonna bop: Coker, Alvadean
BCD 15936 / May '96 / Bear Family

☐ **THAT'S ALL FOLK (2CD Set)**
CML 5741015/6 / Aug '97 / Le Chant Du Monde

☐ **THAT'S JAZZ VOL.1**
BN 039 / Apr '98 / Blue Nite

☐ **THAT'S JAZZ VOL.2**
BN 040 / Apr '98 / Blue Nite

☐ **THAT'S JAZZ VOL.3**
BN 041 / Apr '98 / Blue Nite

☐ **THAT'S JAZZ VOL.4**
BN 042 / Apr '98 / Blue Nite

☐ **THAT'S LAMBADA**
Lambada / Lambada Copacabana / Para ser so whoman / Outra vez / Apita / Ja passou / O mato / Fantasia / Rio / Chega / Jogo de fogo / Nao sei / Lambada quente / Lambada
QED 167 / Nov '96 / Tring

☐ **THAT'S ROCK 'N ROLL (2CD Set)**
Great balls of fire: Lewis, Jerry Lee / Bobby Sox to stockings: Avalon, Frankie / Dedicated to the one I love: Shirelles / Be bop a lula: Everly Brothers / Doggin': Vincent, Gene / It keeps right on a hurting: Tillotson, Johnny / Keep searching (we'll follow the sun): Shannon, Del / There goes my heart again: Domino, Fats / I met him on a Sunday: Shirelles / Ooby dooby: Orbison, Roy / Honey don't: Perkins, Carl / I won't be rockin' tonight: Chapel, Jean / We belong together: Valens, Ritchie / Jailhouse rock: Jordanaires / Forever forever: Domino, Fats / I'm gonna knock on your door: Domino, Fats / Do you wanna dance: Shannon, Del / Bird dog: Everly Brothers / That's alright mama: Everly Brothers / Poetry in motion: Tillotson, Johnny / Whole lotta shakin' goin' on: Lewis, Jerry Lee / Blue suede shoes: Perkins, Carl / Will you still love me tomorrow: Shirelles / You're my baby: Orbison, Roy / Hound dog man: Fabian / Why: Avalon, Frankie / Love crazy baby: Parchman, Kenny / I want you baby: Riley, Billy Lee
SD 885402 / 2 Feb '98 / Disky

☐ **THAT'S WHY WE'RE MARCHING (World War II & The American Folk Song Movement)**
SFWCD 40021 / Apr '96 / Smithsonian Folkways

☐ **THEATRE OF SOUND**
KICKCD 62 / 1 Jun '98 / Kickin'

☐ **THEIR ORIGINAL SINS (20 Tracks From The Vaults Of Scooch Pooch)**
Jesus is on my side: Teen Angels / Poppa Hoodoo: Lord High Fixers / End of the devil dogs: La Donnas / My side of town: Rayons / Ghetto blaster: Countdowns / 23: Gomez / Dead End days: Jesus Christ Superfly / 18 squeeler: Steerjockey / It's alright: Zeke / Mighty Ranxerox: Bottom Feeders / Who's who: Dead End Cruisers / Dialudid: Zeke / Is paranoia a form of awareness: Lord High Fixers / Ain't it a shame: Detroit Cobras / Bath mat: Hectics / Every day is a Brenda day: Popdefact / Networks: Hamicks / Go away: Teen Angels / Hello ladies and gentlemen: Zeke / Teenage head: Nine Pound Hammer
PO 28 / Oct '96 / Scooch Pooch

☐ **THEIR SYMPATHETIC MAJESTIES REQUEST (2CD Set)**
SFTRI 200CD / 3 Aug '98 / Sympathy For The Record Industry

☐ **THELMA RECORD CO STORY, THE (Legendary Detroit Soul)**
Love is the only solution: Star, Martha / I'm a peace loving man: Laskey, Emanuel / Lucky to be loved by you: Hargreaves, Silky / I just can't leave you: Inst / You got the best of me: Hill, Eddie / I just cant leave you: Batiste, Rose / Sorry ain't good enough: Matthews, Joe / I love you: Inst / Gonna cry a river: Ward, Robert / I've got to run for my life: Laskey, Emanuel / Someday: Batiste, Rose / Whirlpool: Inst / You better mend your ways: Matthews, Joe / No part time love for me: Star, Martha / Nobody loves me like my baby: Gilford, Jimmy
GSCD 055 / Nov '94 / Goldmine

☐ **THELMA'S DETROIT COLLECTIVE**
I'm lonely: Starr, Martha / She's my beauty queen: Matthews, Joe / Groovy generation: Kennedy, Billy / I can hear you cryin': Hill, Eddie / It's too bad baby: Starr, Martha / Making up time: Holidays / Honky tonk woman: Fabulous Playboys / This love I have for you: Fabulous Peps / Lucky to be loved by you: Laskey, Emanuel / Sweet love: Starr, Martha / Whirlpool: Mancha, Steve / Still hungry: San Remo Strings / I love you: Storm, Tom / Is it worth it all: Matthews, Joe / What did I do wrong: Laskey, Emanuel / I wanna be your girl: Starr, Martha / Sweet things: Kennedy, Billy / Do right my baby call: Kingfish, Joey / She's going to leave you: Fabulous Peps / Let's party: Thelma All Stars / Miracles: O'Jays / That's the way loves: Storm, Tom / I'll love you forever: Holidays / Hit and run: Reeves, Martha
GSCD 069 / Aug '96 / Goldmine

☐ **THEM DIRTY BLUES (2CD Set)**
JASSCD 11/12 / Oct '91 / Jass

☐ **THEME FROM THE DANCE**
63676700012 / Jul '97 / Aquarius

☐ **THEMES AND DREAMS**
Return to innocence: *Enigma* / Only you: *Praise* / Sentinel: *Oldfield, Mike* / Harry's Game: *Clannad* / Brideshead theme: *Burgon, Geoffrey* / Crocket's theme: *Hammer, Jan* / Twin Peak's theme: *Badalamenti, Angelo* / Mission: *Morricone, Ennio* / Aria: *Yanni* / Songbird: *Kenny G* / Lily was here: *Stewart, Dave & Cindy Duffer* / City never sleeps: *Eurythmics* / Albatross: *Fleetwood Mac* / Samba pa ti: *Santana* / Scarborough fair: *In Tune* / So, relax: *Redbone, Leon* / An ubhal as airde: *Runrig* / Inspector morse main theme / Between the lines theme: *Lindes, Hal* / Spiritual high (state of independence): *Moodswings* / Deep forest: *Deep Forest* / Concerto de Aranjuez: *Hall, Jim*
RADCD 11 / Jun '95 / Global TV

☐ **THEMES FOR DREAMS (The Magic Sound Of The Panpipes)**
Light of experience / Bright eyes / Feelings / Miss you nights / Whiter shade of pale / Don't cry for me Argentina / Love story / Ave Maria / Stranger on the shore / Annie's song / Concierto de aranjuez / You don't bring me flowers / Aria / Forever autumn / Sailing / Nights in white satin / Amazing grace / I can't stop loving you
MCCD 156 / May '94 / Music Club

☐ **THEN AND NOW (San Francisco Sound Vol.1)**
SFS 03931 / 23 Mar '98 / SF Sound

☐ **THEN HE KISSED ME**
MACCD 210 / Aug '96 / Autograph

☐ **THEN THAT'S WHAT THEY CALL DISCO**
We got the funk: *Positive Force* / Lookin' for love tonight: *Fat Larry's Band* / Hi tension: *Hi-Tension* / Can you feel the force: *Real Thing* / You can do it: *One Way & Al Hudson* / Shake your groove thing: *Peaches & Herb* / Sir Dancealot: *Olympic Runners* / You make me feel (mighty real): *Sylvester* / Space bass: *Slick* / Get down: *Chandler, Gene* / Everything is great: *Inner Circle* / White lines (don't don't do it): *Grandmaster Flash & Melle Mel*
CDELV 05 / May '93 / Elevate

☐ **THEORY OF EVOLUTION**
TRANR 613CD / 2 Feb '98 / Transient

☐ **THERE ARE MANY DIFFERENT COLOURS**
ORCCD 1 / Sep '96 / Octopus

☐ **THERE ARE TOO MANY FOOLS FOLLOWING TOO MANY RULES (2CD Set)**
501 RDOOM2CD / Jun '95 / Irdial

☐ **THERE GOES THE NEIGHBOUR**
COLCD 0508 / Jun '97 / Collectables

☐ **THERE IS SOME FUN GOING FORWARD (Dandelion - Rarities)**
Only do what is true: *Medicine Head* / Anticipation: *Ward, Clifford T.* / Pretty little girl: *Coxhill-Bedford Duo* / Nell's song: *Hart, Mike* / All ends up: *Tractor* / Fly high: *St. John, Bridget* / Sky dance: *Trevor, John* / Mama keep your big mouth shut: *Stackwaddy* / Colour is blue: *Country Sun* / Sand all yellow: *Coyne, Kevin* / Vorblifa exit: *Coxhill, Lol* / Fetch me my woman: *Siren* / War is over: *Siren* / Autumn lady dancing: *Principal Edwards Magic Theatre* / Early morning song: *St. John, Bridget* / Sleeping town: *Beau* / Girl from Ipanema: *Stackwaddy*
SEECD 427 / Jul '95 / See For Miles

☐ **THERE WAS A LADY (The Voice Of Celtic Woman)**
Willie Taylor: *Dillon, Mary & Deanta* / Mo choill: *Ni Mhaonaigh, Mairead & Altan* / Fogsail an dorus/ Nighean bhuaidh' ruadh: *Matheson, Karen & Capercaillie* / Roisin dubh: *Ryan, Cathie & Cherish The Ladies* / Siuil a run: *Fahy, Mairin & Reeltime* / Maid that sold her barley: *Dillon, Mary & Deanta* / There was a lady: *Ni Dhomhnaill, Triona & Relativity* / Ranntai fheilinidh na fidile: *Ni Dhomhnaill, Maighread* / Jug of punch: *Ni Mhaonaigh, Mairead & Altan* / Am buachaille ban: *Matheson, Karen & Capercaillie* / Green grow the rushes oh: *Clancy, Aoife & Cherish The Ladies* / Casadh cam na feadarnaighe: *Ni Dhomhnaill, Triona & Touchstone* / Dark inisheoghain: *Dillon, Mary & Deanta*
CELT 9002 / May '97 / Celtophile

☐ **THERE WHERE THE AVALANCHE STOPS (Albanian Folk Festival)**
T 3311 / '90 / Touch

☐ **THERE'LL ALWAYS BE AN ENGLAND (24 War-Time Songs From 1939)**
There'll always be an England: *Loss, Joe* / Wishing: *Lynn, Vera* / We must all stick together: *Geraldo* / Songs the Tommies sang: *Stone, Lew* / Adolf: *Ambrose* / FDR Jones: *Flanagan & Allen* / We're gonna hang out the washing on the Siegfried Line: *Waters, Elsie & Doris* / Handsome Territorial: *Gonella, Nat* / Till the lights of London shine again: *Henderson, Chick & Joe Loss* / They can't black out the moon: *Roy, Harry* / Kiss me goodnight, Sergeant Major: *Cotton, Billy* / We'll meet again: *Henderson, Chick & Joe Loss* / If a grey-haired lady says How's yer father: *Flanagan & Allen* / Wish me luck as you wave me goodbye: *Hylton, Jack* / Goodnight children everywhere: *Henderson, Chick & Joe Loss* / Wings over the navy: *Cotton, Billy* / Run rabbit run: *Flanagan & Allen* / I'm sending a letter to Santa Claus: *Fields, Gracie* / Nasty Uncle Adolf: *Ambrose* / Somewhere in France with you: *Henderson, Chick & Joe Loss* / Mother's prayer at twilight: *Lynn, Vera* / Rhymes of the times: *Ambrose*
CDAJA 5069 / Feb '90 / Living Era

☐ **THERE'S A GRIOT GOING ON**
FMS 5029 / Jan '94 / Rogue

☐ **THERE'S A MOVEMENT UNDERGROUND**
PLUGCD 3 / Feb '96 / Produce

☐ **THEY CALL IT IRELAND**
Little bit of heaven (sure they call it Ireland): *Parker, Frank* / Kitty my love won't you marry me: *Parker, Frank* / Kerry dance/My wild Irish rose: *Parker, Frank* / It's true that the women are worse than the men: *O'Hara, Maureen* / Kerry cow: *O'Hara, Maureen* / Galway baby: *Quinn, Carmel* / Green glens of Antrim: *Quinn, Carmel* / Where the river Shannon flows: *Smith, Kate* / That's how I spell IRELAND: *Downey, Morton* / Kevin Barry: *Downey, Morton* / Back to Donegal: *Harrington, Pat* / If there'd never been an Ireland: *Harrington, Pat* / Rich man died: *O'Hara, Maureen* / There was an old man: *O'Hara, Maureen* / Wee Hughie: *O'Hara, Maureen* / Isle of Innisfree: *Quinn, Carmel* / Whistling gypsy: *Quinn, Carmel* / Drumcolliher: *O'Dowda, Brendan* / Rose of Tralee: *Parker, Frank*
4896822 / 2 Mar '98 / Columbia

☐ **THEY CALLED IT CROONING (Recordings From 1928-1932)**
Where the blue of the night meets the gold of the day: *Crosby, Bing* / Cheerful little earful: *Ellis, Segar* / My song: *Bullock, Chick* / She's a new kind of old-fashioned girl: *Smith, Jack* / Got a date with an angel: *O'Malley, Pat* / Living in dreams: *Columbo, Russ* / Orange blossom time: *Edwards, Cliff* / She's wonderful: *Shalson, Harry* / Am I blue: *Bellew, Smith* / Here lies love: *Browne, Sam* / Thrill is gone: *Vallee, Rudy* / Ain't misbehavin': *Austin, Gene* / My sweet Virginia: *Bowlly, Al* / Please: *Rosing, Val* / Little by little: *Marvin, Johnny* / You're a real sweetheart: *Coslow, Sam* / Sweet Sue, just you: *Metaxa, George* / Thank your father: *Richman, Harry*
CDAJA 5026 / ' / Living Era

☐ **THEY PLAYED THE HACKNEY EMPIRE**
Summer sweetheart: *Cortez, Leon & His Coster Band/Dorren Harris* / Beer barrel polka: *Cortez, Leon & His Coster Band/Guv'nor & The Boys* / He said Kiss Me: *O'Shea, Tessie & Her Banjulele & Orchestra* / Hymie and Amy sing sing: *O'Shea, Tessie & Her Banjulele & Orchestra* / Serenade in the night: *Loss, Joe Band* / When the poppies bloom: *Loss, Joe Band* / Again: *Loss, Joe Band* / Did I remember: *Loss, Joe Band* / Forty four fousand and five: *Sarony, Leslie & Leslie Holmes* / Cut yourself a little piece of cake: *Sarony, Leslie & Leslie Holmes* / He's an angel: *Masters, Kitty & Orchestra* / Ready for the river: *Gonella, Nat & His Georgians* / Deep river: *Gonella, Nat & His Georgians* / Two rivers flow through: *Gonella, Nat & His Georgians* / Harlem: *Gonella, Nat & His Georgians* / Sandy furnishes the home: *Powell, Sandy & Company* / Arp experience: *Miller, Max* / Grand old man: *Miller, Max* / Swimming instructor: *Miller, Max* / Georgia's got a moon: *Roy, Harry* / I'm looking for the Sheik Of Araby: *Millward, Sid & His Nitwits* / Good morning: *Murgatroyd & Winterbottom* / Lonesome trail ain't lonesome anymore: *Campbell, Big Bill* / London pride: *Waters, Elsie & Doris* / Button up your shoes and dance: *Wall, Max* / My Alf: *Tarri, Suzette* / Stormy weather: *Carless, Dorothy* / Lady of Spain: *Geraldo & His Gaucho Tango Orchestra*
RAJCD 848 / 6 Apr '98 / Empress

☐ **THEY SHALL NOT PASS**
Lean on me: *Redskins* / Unionize: *Redskins* / Adrenochrome: *Sisters Of Mercy* / Body electric: *Sisters Of Mercy* / Mindless violence: *Newtown Neurotics* / Kick out the tories: *Newtown Neurotics* / Pink headed bug: *Three Johns* / Men like monkeys: *Three Johns*
AABT 400CD / Jul '91 / Abstract

☐ **THEY SOLD A MILLION (The Swinging 1930's)**
One o'clock jump: *James, Harry* / Honeysuckle rose: *Reinhardt, Django* / After you've gone: *Reinhardt, Django* / Marie: *Dorsey, Tommy* / Boogie woogie: *Dorsey, Tommy* / Begin the beguine: *Shaw, Artie* / Nightmare: *Shaw, Artie* / Black Bay shuffle: *Shaw, Artie* / Traffic jam: *Shaw, Artie* / Body and soul: *Hawkins, Coleman* / April in Paris: *Hawkins, Coleman* / Sugar foot stomp: *Hawkins, Coleman* / Little brown jug: *Miller, Glenn* / In the mood: *Miller, Glenn* / Sunrise serenade: *Miller, Glenn* / Moonlight serenade: *Miller, Glenn*
74321366612 / Apr '96 / Camden

☐ **THEY SOLD A MILLION (The Fabulous 1940's)**
Pennsylvania 6-500: *Miller, Glenn* / Tuxedo Junction: *Miller, Glenn* / I've got a girl in Kalamazoo: *Miller, Glenn* / American patrol: *Miller, Glenn* / Chattanooga choo choo: *Miller, Glenn* / Frenesi: *Shaw, Artie* / Stardust: *Shaw, Artie* / Summit Ridge Drive: *Shaw, Artie* / Opus 1: *Dorsey, Tommy* / On the sunny side of the street: *Dorsey, Tommy* / Chinatown, my chinatown: *Dorsey, Tommy* / I'm getting sentimental over you: *Dorsey, Tommy* / When the midnight choo choo leaves for Alabama: *Dorsey, Tommy* / Holiday for strings: *Rose, David* / There I've said it again: *Monroe, Vaughan* / Riders in the sky: *Monroe, Vaughan*
74321366622 / Apr '96 / Camden

☐ **THEY SOLD A MILLION (The Vintage Years)**
Ida, sweet as apple cider: *Nichols, Red* / Spaniard who blighted my life: *Jolson, Al* / Sonny boy: *Jolson, Al* / Rainbow on my shoulder: *Jolson, Al* / Wang wang blues: *Whiteman, Paul* / Japanese sandman: *Whiteman, Paul* / Three o'clock in the morning: *Whiteman, Paul* / Linger awhile: *Whiteman, Paul* / Prisoner's song: *Dalhart, Vernon* / Dardanella: *Whiteman, Paul* / Who: *Olson, George* / My blue heaven: *Austin, Gene* / Ramona: *Austin, Gene* / It ain't gonna rain no more: *Hall, Wendell* / Some of these days: *Tucker, Sophie*
74321366602 / Apr '96 / Camden

☐ **THEY SOLD A MILLION (2CD Set)**
Rum and coca cola: *Andrews Sisters* / I've got a gal in Kalamazoo: *Miller, Glenn Orchestra* / I'm making believe: *Fitzgerald, Ella & The Ink Spots* / Besame mucho: *Dorsey, Jimmy & His Orchestra* / Too ra loo ra loo ra: *Crosby, Bing* / Dancing in the dark: *Shaw, Artie Orchestra* / Oklahoma / There are such things: *Sinatra, Frank* / Don't fence me in: *Crosby, Bing & The Andrews Sisters* / Chattanooga choo choo: *Miller, Glenn Orchestra* / I've heard that song before: *James, Harry Orchestra* / GI jive: *Jordan, Louis & His Tympany Five* / Swinging on a star: *Crosby, Bing* / You always hurt the one you love: *Mills Brothers* / Into each life some rain must fall: *Fitzgerald, Ella & The Ink Spots* / Is you is or is you ain't my baby: *Jordan, Louis & His Tympany Five* / In the mood: *Miller, Glenn Orchestra* / Paper doll: *Mills Brothers* / Begin the beguine: *Shaw, Artie Orchestra* / Jumpin' jive: *Calloway, Cab Orchestra* / You made me love you: *James, Harry Orchestra* / Sunday, Monday or always: *Crosby, Bing* / You'll never know: *Haymes, Dick* / Moonlight serenade: *Miller, Glenn Orchestra* / Amapola: *Dorsey, Jimmy Orchestra* / At the woodchoppers ball: *Herman, Woody Orchestra* / Sweet Leilani: *Crosby, Bing* / Marie: *Dorsey, Tommy Orchestra* / Bei mir bist du schon: *Andrews Sisters* / All or nothing: *Sinatra, Frank* / New San Antonio Rose: *Wills, Bob & His Texas Playboys* / Tisket-a-tasket: *Fitzgerald, Ella*
330372 / Mar '97 / Hallmark

☐ **THEY'RE PLAYING OUR SONG**
It had to be you / Way you look tonight / I'm in the mood for love / What a difference a day made / Where or when / Folks who live on the hill / Two sleepy people / Night and day / Embraceable you / Long ago and far away / You were never lovelier / That old feeling / Very thought of you / Man I love / Why do I love you / All the things that are you / Song is you / As long as I love / Every time we say goodbye / There I've said it again / You do something to me / Too marvellous for words / Love letters / Don't blame me
PASTCD 7802 / Nov '96 / Flapper

☐ **THINGS BEEN BAD**
Babayaga: *Pagans* / Why am I alone: *Choab* / What I want you to say: *Barracudas* / I found a new love: *Ognir & The Nite People* / Girl with the long black hair: *Other Half* / Gotta find a new love: *Yo Yo's* / I found a peanut: *Thee Midniters* / Bad apple: *Pilgrimage* / Never mistaken: *Debonaires* / Bar the door: *Roaming Toga's* / Only everything: *Peter & The Wolves* / Lost one: *Roots & Wyld* / 1000 miles: *Inner Thoughts* / She was good: *Talisman* / Things have been bad: *Saxons* / Now and then: *Stains* / Do you remember: *Lost Soles* / She taught me love: *Kama-Del-Sutra*
TS 6603CD / 20 Jul '98 / Teenage Shutdown

☐ **THINKING OF YOU**
Here we are: *Estefan, Gloria* / Fool (if you think it's over): *Brooks, Elkie* / I'll never fall in love again: *Deacon Blue* / Promise me: *Craven, Beverley* / Two out of three ain't bad: *Meat Loaf* / All cried out: *Moyet, Alison* / Everytime you go away: *Young, Paul* / Neither one of us: *Knight, Gladys & The Pips* / If you were here tonight: *O'Neal, Alexander* / Sorry seems to be the hardest word: *John, Elton* / Ain't no sunshine: *Withers, Bill* / Blue velvet: *Vinton, Bobby* / Stay with me 'til dawn: *Tzuke, Judie* / How am I supposed to live without you: *Bolton, Michael* / Eternal flame: *Bangles* / Let's stay together: *Green, Al* / Still: *Commodores*
MOODCD 15 / Feb '91 / CBS

☐ **THIRD GENERATION**
IG 0052 / Jun '97 / Intergroove

☐ **THIRTY YEARS OF BLUES**
DCD 7819 / 6 Mar '98 / Avid

☐ **THIS AIN'T TRIP HOP VOL.1**
MM 800212 / Feb '95 / Moonshine

☐ **THIS AIN'T TRIP HOP VOL.2**
MM 800392 / Oct '95 / Moonshine

☐ **THIS AIN'T TRIP HOP VOL.3**
MM 800482 / May '96 / Moonshine

☐ **THIS BEING HUMAN**
RGM 198CD / Apr '98 / Red Gold Music

☐ **THIS ENGLAND (Special Double Compilation)**
GCMD 508 / 10 Nov '97 / GCM

☐ **THIS FILM'S CRAP LET'S SAMPLE THE SOUNDTRACK**
First and last: *Dunderhead* / Extention: *Skematicks* / Petrushka: *Pentatonik* / Catalonia: *Pentatonik* / Pentaura: *Pentaura* / Pulsation: *Lumo* / Trouble shooter: *Love Rears* / Black and white: *Slowly*
FILMCRP 007CD / Sep '96 / North South

☐ **THIS FUNKY THING VOL.1**
This funky thing: *Pierce, Don* / Your love and my money: *Davis, Curtis* / Hot pants: *Carleen & The Groovers* / Right on brother, right on: *Soul Controllers* / I've been searchin': *Wright, Lonzine* / Soul groove: *Mato & The Mystics* / Hump the bump: *Soul Company* / When ya git through wit it put it back: *Blenders Ltd.* / Go for it: *Smith, Kenny & The Loveliters* / Bury the hatchet: *Count Rockin' Sidney* / Garden of four trees: *Explosions & Juanita Brooks* / Dynamite: *Soul Merchants* / So sharp: *Soul Clinic* / Do the rope 'Dee Dope': *Lil Waters' Burning Flame* / Gettin' T'gether man: *Classitors* / Stay together: *Soul Excitement* / Stormy Jazzmin: *Stormy Jazzmin*
GSCD 116 / Jun '97 / Goldmine

☐ **THIS HOUSE IS NOT A MOTEL**
EFA 4481 CD / Jul '89 / Glitterhouse

☐ **THIS IS 2 KOOL**
TKCD 1 / Mar '95 / 2 Kool

☐ **THIS IS ACID JAZZ**
Runaway: *Nu Yorican Soul* / Don't let it go to your head: *Brand New Heavies* / Frederick lies still: *Galliano* / Chillin': *Movement '97* / Mini: *Corduroy* / Shine: *Breeze* / After dark: *Laverna, Michelle* / Step off: *Rhythm* / Apparently nothin': *Young Disciples* / Always there: *Incognito* / Bomb: *Supa Star* / You blow my mind: *Jasmine* / Lucky fellow: *Snowboy & Noel McKoy* / Good thing: *Future Collective* / Jesse: *Mother Earth* / Loving you: *Meateaters* / Turn on tune in drop out: *Freakpower* / Trust me: *Vibraphonic & Alison Limerick* / Jazzatude: *Bud* / Whole lotta love: *Goldbug* / Do you: *Shades Of Rhythm* / Shake it loose: *United States*
BEBOXCD 12 / Jun '97 / Beechwood

☐ **THIS IS ACID JAZZ VOL.3 (New Voices)**
EX 3382 / Nov '96 / Instinct

☐ **THIS IS AFROWAX**
085703772 / 29 Jun '98 / House Nation

☐ **THIS IS BAD TASTE VOL.2**
BTR 26CD / 25 May '98 / Bad Taste

☐ **THIS IS BIG BEAT (3CD Set)**
Bentleys gonna sort you out: *Bentley Rhythm Ace* / Going out of my head: *Fatboy Slim* / Patrol: *Charlatans* / Devil in a sports shirt: *Midfield General* / Poison: *Prodigy* / Lion generation: *Mono Man* / Reactor A: *Ladder* / Magic carpet ride: *Mighty Dub Katz* / This nation: *Adelphi* / Gritty shaker: *Holmes, David* / Kowalski: *Primal Scream* / Sub zero: *Red Myers* / More beats and pieces: *Coldcut* / Dirt: *Death In Vegas* / Switch: *Howie B* / Hello darlin': *Fuzz Townshend* / Boned: *Meat Katie* / Take California: *Propellerheads* / High noon: *DJ Shadow* / Full circle: *Essence* / Black orchid: *Appleseed* / Mind party: *DJ Stix*
BEBOXCD 16 / 17 Nov '97 / Beechwood

☐ **THIS IS BLACK TOP**
I can't stop loving you: *Funderburgh, Anson & Sam Myers* / Iron cupid: *King, Earl* / That certain door: *Eaglin, Snooks* / Woman's gotta have it: *Neville Brothers* / Stick around: *Radcliff, Bobby* / Can't call you no: *Sumlin, Hubert & Mighty Sam* / Lemonade: *Funderburgh, Anson & Sam Myers* / Young girl: *Eaglin, Snooks* / If I don't get involved: *Medwick, Joe & Grady Gaines* / Hello sundown: *Davis, James 'Thunderbird'* / Party in Nogales: *Levy, Ron*
BTSCD 1 / Dec '89 / Black Top

☐ **THIS IS CLUB ANTHEMS (3CD Set)**
Don't stop movin': *Livin' Joy* / I believe: *Happy Clappers* / I luv U baby: *Original* / Let me show you: *K-Klass* / Weekend: *Terry, Todd Project* / I'm so in luv with U: *Da Boss & Blu* / Don't stop the music: *Supernature* / If Madonna calls: *Vasquez, Junior* / Let me be your fantasy: *Baby D* / La Serenissima: *DNA* / Release yourself: *Blue Mast* / Krupa: *Apollo 440* / Everybody be somebody: *Ruffneck* / Renegade master: *Wildchild* / Wanted: *K Crushed One* / Atlantic ocean: *Degrees Of Motion* / Who do you love: *Supernature* / Do you: *Airwaves* / Are you out there: *Crescendo* / Do that to me: *Lisa Marie Experience* / Bette Davis eyes: *Cover Up*
BEBOXCD 6 / Oct '96 / Beechwood

☐ **THIS IS CLUB NATION VOL.1 (3CD Set)**
Bellisima: *DJ Quicksilver* / Show me love: *Robin S* / Encore une fois: *Sash* / Fired up: *Funky Green Dogs* / Total overload: *Sister Spirits* / Insomnia: *Faithless* / Funk phenomena: *Van Helden, Armand* / Hot sweat: *Fever* / Underwater love: *Smoke City* / Flash: *BBE* / Together: *Liberty* / Passion: *Amen* / Deep Freeze: *Universal* / Talkin' 'bout dub: *Apollo 440* / Mind assault: *Altered States* / Alright: *Jamiroquai* / Nightmare: *Brainbug* / Hot love: *DJ Kinky* / Prophet: *Bolland, C.J.* / Sunstroke: *Chicane* / Ready or not: *Course*
BEBOXCD 13 / Jun '97 / Beechwood

☐ **THIS IS CLUB NATION VOL.2 (3CD Set)**
Stay: *Sash & La Trec* / Benedictus: *Brainbug* / I thought it was you: *Sex-O-Sonique* / Free: *Ultra Nate* / Way out: *Bubble* / Open your mind: *Usura* / Choose life: *PF Project & Ewan McGregor* / Pressure: *Indigo* / Never stop: *Cutmaster* / Feeling good: *Huff & Herb* / It's over love: *Terry, Todd* / Pray: *Opaz* / Changes: *Groove connexion* / Dreams: *Smokin' Beats* / Lift me up: *Red 5* / Do what ya want: *Supa* / Forgiven (I feel love): *Space Brothers* / So good: *Roberts, Juliet* / Liquid: *Abstrac* / Renegade master: *Wildchild* / Never seen before: *Expressions* / Your'e gonna miss me: *JC*
BEBOXCD 18 / 23 Feb '98 / Beechwood

☐ **THIS IS DRUM 'N' BASS VOL.1 (3CD Set)**
Do you know where you're coming from: *Jamiroquai* / Come to me: *Bjork* / Candles: *Reece, Alex* / Rollin': *Solid State* / Game: *Cutmaster* / So many dreams: *Guy Called Gerald* / Spice of life: *Slim* / Metropolis: *Adam F* / Sonic sixes: *Dimension* / Trip: *Skylab* / Loop 2: *Larkin, Kenny* / ER: *DOA* / Outlands: *Subversive* / Beautiful day: *Nicolette* / Destiny: *DJ Pulse* / Elemental breaks: *Nova* / Digital ultramagnetic: *Boss* / Sea: *St. Etienne* / Ultraworld: *Motion* / Sound and vision: *Loot* / Downlow: *Aquarius* / Something always happens: *Art Of Noise*
BEBOXCD 10 / Mar '97 / Beechwood

☐ **THIS IS DRUM 'N' BASS VOL.2 (3CD Set)**
Share the fall: *Roni Size* / It's alright: *Nu Yorican Soul* / This is disco: *Angel, Dave* / Landcruiser: *Raxmus* / Post modern sleaze: *Sneaker Pimps* / Summer breeze: *Aphrodite* / Off centre: *Voyager Kru* / Joy and pain: *Eternity* / Isobel: *Bjork* / Plugged: *Voodoo* / One of many: *Lemon D* / Ultimate bass: *Pacific* / Circles: *Adam F* / On the time: *DJ Die* / Silverblade: *Dillinja & Cybotron* / Kemistry: *Goldie* / Soul in motion: *DJ Krust* / New York: *Reece, Alex* / Chain reaction: *Phaser* / Love peace and unity: *DJ Hype* / Technology: *Rush, Ed & Nico* / Freeform: *Force ID*
BEBOXCD 15 / 20 Oct '97 / Beechwood

☐ **THIS IS EASY (2CD Set)**
Champions: *Hatch, Tony* / Superstars / Spanish flea: *World Of Tijuana* / Sentimental journey: *Esquivel, Juan Garcia* / Swingin' safari: *Kaempfert, Bert* / Animal Magic / Pink panther: *Mancini, Henry* / Big Match / Up up and away: *5th Dimension* / Strange report: *Love, Geoff* / In crowd: *Faith, Percy Orchestra* / Taste of honey: *World Of Tijuana* / New Avengers: *Johnson, Laurie Orchestra* / Asteroid: *Moore, Pete* / Riviera Affair / Avenues and alleyways: *Christie, Tony* / Man in a suitcase: *Grainer, Ron* / Do you know the way to San Jose: *Goodwin, Ron & His Orchestra* / Music to watch girls by: *Williams, Andy* / 1-2-3: *Faith, Percy Orchestra* / Misirlou: *Denny, Martin* / Classical gas: *Williams, Mason* / Black beauty / Always something there to remind me: *Shaw, Sandie* / Crossroads: *Hatch, Tony* / Good, the bad and the ugly: *Montenegro, Hugo* / Girls in a sportscar / Walk on by: *Warwick, Dionne* / Windmills of your mind: *Harrison, Noel* / Raindrops keep falling on my head: *Thomas, B.J.* / Anyone who had a heart: *Bacharach, Burt* / Summer breeze: *Conniff, Ray & Singers* / Un homme et une femme: *Lai, Francis* / Get Carter: *Budd, Roy* / I can't let Maggie go: *Honeybus* / Light my fire: *Feliciano, Jose* / Close to you: *Monro, Matt* / As tears go by: *Sinatra, Nancy* / This Is Your Life / Call me: *Montez, Chris* / Chelsea morning: *Mendes, Sergio* / It never rains in Southern California: *Conniff, Ray & Singers* / What the world needs now is love: *Goodwin, Ron* / Aujourd hui c'est

toi: Lai, Francis / House is not a home: Bacharach, Burt / Wives and lovers: Jones, Jack / Go-between: Barry, John / I say a little prayer: Franklin, Aretha / Unknown love: Count Indigo / Look of love: Hayes, Isaac
VTDCD 80 / Mar '96 / Virgin

☐ **THIS IS EUROVISION (39 Songs For Europe - 2CD Set)**
Ne partez pas sans moi: Dion, Celine / Congratulations: Richard, Cliff / Making your mind up: Bucks Fizz / Save your kisses for me: Brotherhood Of Man / What's another year: Logan, Johnny / Beg, steal or borrow: New Seekers / Ein bisschen frieden: Nicole / Apres toi: Leandros, Vicky / Tu te reconnaitras: David, Anne-Marie / Why me: Martin, Linda / J'aime la vie: Kim, Sandra / Rock 'n' roll kids: Harrington, Paul & Charlie McGettigan / Hallelujah: Harrington, Paul & Charlie McGettigan / Let me be the one: Shadows / Poupee de cire, poupee de son: Gall, France / Voice: Quinn, Eimaer / Un blanc, un abre, une rue: Severine / Love games: Belle & The Devotions / Jack in the box: Rodgers, Clodagh / He gives me love (la la la): Massiel / Power to all our friends: Richard, Cliff / Hold me now: Logan, Johnny / Puppet on a string: Shaw, Sandie / Long live love: Newton-John, Olivia / Boom bang a bang: Lulu / I love the little things: Monro, Matt / All kinds of everything: Dana / Ding a dong: Teach In / Aba ni bi: Cohen, Izhar / In your eyes: Kavanagh, Niamh / Bad old days: Coco / I belong: Kirby, Kathy / Parlez vous Francais: Baccara / Sing little birdie: Carr, Pearl / Message to your heart: Janus, Samantha / L'oiseau et l'enfant: Myriam, Marie / Rock bottom: De Paul, Lynsey & Mike Moran / Lonely symphony: Ruffelle, Frances / One step further: Bardo
VTDCD 142 / Apr '97 / Virgin

☐ **THIS IS FOLK**
Step back: Jansch, Bert / Spring is returning/ Dosvedanya: McLeod, Rory / Turn things upside down: Happy End / Maybe then I'll be a rose: Stevenson, Savourna / Doctor calls: Tabor, June / Byker hill: Barely Works / It's raining (my eyes are filled with clouds): Ancient Beatbox / Seventeen years of sorrow: Prior, Maddy / Rhythm of time: WAZ / Whistle daughter whistle: God's Little Monkeys / Madman mora blues: Boiled In Lead / Hush little baby: Horseflies / Bridges: Phillips, Utah & Ani Di Franco / Promises: Wired To The Moon / All tomorrow's parties: Tabor, June & The Oyster Band / Manchester rambler: MacColl, Ewan & Peggy Seeger / Why should I stand up: Colorblind James Experience
GRILLCD 012 / 29 Jun '98 / Cooking Vinyl

☐ **THIS IS HARDCORE (3CD Set)**
Jumpin' pumpin': DJ Demand / Paradise: Unknown Project / Techno wonderland: Smeetit, Steve / Music's so wonderful: Vibes & Wishdokta / Journey: Ramos & Supreme / Sun always shines: DJ Supreme & UFO / Slippery Project: Slippery Project / Anything for you: Vibes / Can you dig it: Sharky & Dee / You're mine: DJ Demo / Hold me now: Go Mental / Gizmo music: Future Vinyl Collective / Smiling eyes: DJ Stompy / Eternity: Jimmy JT Time / Nothing is forever: Happy Tunes / Comin' on strong: Slam & Charly B / I believe: Force & Styles / Setting you free: DJ Unknown / Doesn't have to be: Vinyl Groover / Total recall: Full Action / Groove control: Midas & Dougal / All you need (is an angel): DJ Edy C
BEBOXCD 11 / Apr '97 / Beechwood

☐ **THIS IS HIP HOP (3CD Set)**
Loungin': LL Cool J / Big Bad Mama: Brown, Foxy & Dru Hill / If heaven got a ghetto: 2Pac / Step into my world: KRS 1 / Ganstas paradise: Coolio / Bail out: Full Bass / Smokin' me out: Warren G / Jungle Brothers: Jungle Brothers / 4 more: De La Soul & Zhane / Echoes: DFX / Fight the power: Public Enemy / Innocent: Addis Black Widow / Let me clear my throat: DJ Kool / Checkpoint: Missile / I left my wallet: Tribe Called Quest / Peter Piper: Run DMC / Worst: Onyx & Wu Tang Clan / Royalty: Gang Starr / Pressure: MC Silky / Unexplained: Gravediggaz & RZA / Superman: Mafia Posse / This is how we do it: Jordan, Montell
BEBOXCD 19 / 30 Mar '98 / Beechwood

☐ **THIS IS HIP HOP VOL.2 (26 Of The Biggest Licks - 2CD Set)**
USCD 5 / Apr '96 / Ultrasound

☐ **THIS IS HOME ENTERTAINMENT VOL.1**
HE 002 / Dec '96 / Home Entertainment

☐ **THIS IS HOME ENTERTAINMENT VOL.2**
HE 008 / Dec '96 / Home Entertainment

☐ **THIS IS HOME ENTERTAINMENT VOL.3**
HE 120CD / May '97 / Home Entertainment

☐ **THIS IS HOUSE (3CD Set)**
I've got you: 2 Minds / Where love lies: Limerick, Alison / Beautiful people: Tucker, Barbara / Is anybody out there: Bassheads / Gonna take you: Beatserver / Jingo: Candido / Hideaway: De'Lacy / My love is free: Double Exposure / Dr. Love: First Choice / Can't you see: G'Street Project / Lets groove: Morels, George / Dominator: Human Resource / Your love: Inner City / Space cowboy: Jamiroquai / Live and direct: Juice On The Loose / French Kiss: Lil' Louis / Hit'n'run: Holloway, Loleatta / Someday: M-People / Something about you: Mr. Roy / Blue Monday: New Order / Salsa house: Richie Rich / Take me away: True Faith
BEBOXCD 4 / Jul '96 / Beechwood

☐ **THIS IS IBIZA (3CD Set)**
Free: Ultra Nate / Age of love: Age Of Love / Feel what you want: Kristine W / Offshore: Chicane / Spin spin sugar: Sneaker Pimps / Something goin' on: Terry, Todd / Ecuador: Sash & Rodriguez / Bellisima: DJ Quicksilver / Freed from desire: Gala / Chapter 9: Mac, Keith Project / Born slippy: Underworld / La nuela: Maltese Massive / Discohopping: Klubb Heads / Can't wait: Funky Dory / Cycle of life: Atlantic Ocean / I'll be there: 88.3 / Higher state of conciousness: Wink, Josh / Seven days and one week: BBE / Plastic dreams: Jaydee / Your face: Slacker / Sandman: Blueboy / Classic love: Los Dios
BEBOXCD 14 / 29 Sep '97 / Beechwood

☐ **THIS IS IT**
MCCD 196 / Mar '95 / Music Club

☐ **THIS IS JAZZ (10CD Set)**
Cornet chop suey: Armstrong, Louis / Heebie jeebies: Armstrong, Louis / Potato head blues: Armstrong, Louis / West End blues: Armstrong, Louis / Memories of you: Armstrong, Louis / Stardust: Armstrong, Louis / When you're smiling: Armstrong, Louis / Dinah: Armstrong, Louis / Tiger rag: Armstrong, Louis / Lazy river: Armstrong, Louis / Basin street blues: Armstrong, Louis / Big butter and egg man: Armstrong, Louis / Ain't misbehavin': Armstrong, Louis / When it's sleepy time down south: Armstrong, Louis / I've got the world on a string: Armstrong, Louis / Between the devil and the deep blue sea: Armstrong, Louis / Little duet (for Zoot and Chet): Baker, Chet / Love walked in: Baker, Chet / You don't know what love is: Baker, Chet / I'm through with love: Baker, Chet / You'd better go now: Baker, Chet / Wind: Baker, Chet / Autumn leaves: Baker, Chet / She was too good to me: Baker, Chet / Tangerine: Baker, Chet / What'll I do: Baker, Chet / Take five: Brubeck, Dave / Gone with the wind: Brubeck, Dave / Someday my prince will come: Brubeck, Dave / Blue rondo a la Turk: Brubeck, Dave / Pennies from heaven: Brubeck, Dave / When you wish upon a star: Brubeck, Dave / Jeepers creepers: Brubeck, Dave / For all we know: Brubeck, Dave / Sing sing sing (with a swing): Goodman, Benny / Flying home: Goodman, Benny / Wang wang blues: Goodman, Benny / Don't be that way: Goodman, Benny / Running wild: Goodman, Benny / King Porter stomp: Goodman, Benny / Limehouse blues: Goodman, Benny / Mission to Moscow: Goodman, Benny / You turned the tables on me: Goodman, Benny / Avalon: Goodman, Benny / Memories of you: Goodman, Benny / 'Round midnight: Monk, Thelonious / Well you needn't: Monk, Thelonious / Bemsha swing: Monk, Thelonious / Ruby my dear: Monk, Thelonious / Straight, no chaser: Monk, Thelonious / Blue Monk: Monk, Thelonious / Rhythm-a-ning: Monk, Thelonious / Monk's dream: Monk, Thelonious / Misterioso: Monk, Thelonious / Epistrophy: Monk, Thelonious / Better git it in your soul: Mingus, Charles / Goodbye pork pie hat: Mingus, Charles / Fable of Faubus: Mingus, Charles / Self portrait in 3 colors: Mingus, Charles / Slop: Mingus, Charles / Song with orange: Mingus, Charles / Gunslinging bird: Mingus, Charles / Far Wells, Mill Valley: Mingus, Charles / New now, know how: Mingus, Charles / Shoes of the fisherman's wife are some jive ass slippers: Mingus, Charles / Please don't come back from the moon: Mingus, Charles / East St Louis toodle-oo: Ellington, Duke / In a sentimental mood: Ellington, Duke / Stompy Jones: Ellington, Duke / Prelude to a kiss: Ellington, Duke / C jam blues: Ellington, Duke / Sentimental lady: Ellington, Duke / Take the 'A' train: Ellington, Duke / Satin doll: Ellington, Duke / In a mellotone: Ellington, Duke / Solitude: Ellington, Duke / Mood Indigo: Ellington, Duke / Diminuendo and crescendo in blue: Ellington, Duke / 'Round midnight: Davis, Miles / Stella by starlight: Davis, Miles / Springsville: Davis, Miles / Summertime: Davis, Miles / So what: Davis, Miles / Someday my prince will come: Davis, Miles / Seven steps to heaven: Davis, Miles / Walkin': Davis, Miles / ESP: Davis, Miles / Clockwise: Benson, George / Myna bird blues: Benson, George / Willow weep for me: Benson, George / Stormy weather: Benson, George / Cooker: Benson, George / Borgia stick: Benson, George / Ode to a Kudu: Benson, George / Take five: Benson, George / I remember Wes: Benson, George / Good King Bad: Benson, George / Summertime: Benson, George / From now on: Benson, George / Birdland: Weather Report / Remark you made: Weather Report / Black market: Weather Report / Man in the green shirt: Weather Report / Young and fine: Weather Report / Teen town: Weather Report / Moors: Weather Report / Mysterious traveller: Weather Report / Orange lady: Weather Report
4843942 / Sep '96 / Sony Jazz

☐ **THIS IS JAZZ**
Wave / Retratro en branco e prieto (Picture in black and white) / Sabia / Dindi / Ponteio / Obsession / Corcovado / Double rainbow / Vera cruz / Miracle of the fishes / Nrazil
CK 65045 / May '97 / Sony Jazz

☐ **THIS IS JAZZ - SAMPLER**
Ain't misbehavin': Armstrong, Louis / Mood indigo: Ellington, Duke / One o'clock jump: Basie, Count / Four: Davis, Miles / This years kisses: Holiday, Billie / Blue rondo a la Turk: Brubeck, Dave / It might as well be a spring: Vaughan, Sarah / Peacocks: Getz, Stan / Remark you made: Weather Report / Dance of Maya: McLaughlin, John / Port of entry: Shorter, Wayne
CK 65008 / Oct '96 / Sony Jazz

☐ **THIS IS JAZZ VOL.1 (2CD Set)**
JCD 1025/26 / Nov '96 / Jazzology

☐ **THIS IS JAZZ VOL.2 (The Rudi Blesh Broadcasts/2CD Set)**
JCD 1027/1028 / Sep '97 / Jazzology

☐ **THIS IS JUNGLE**
USCD 001 / Sep '94 / Ultrasound

☐ **THIS IS JUNGLE (3CD Set)**
Feel the sunshine: Reece, Alex / Inner city life: Goldie / Trippin' on broken beats: Omni Trio / Definition of a track: Perfect Combination / Smooth note: Jason Mouse / Witchcraft: Roni Size / Sky high: St. Files / T'raenon: Photek / Danger: Sub Sequence / Mr. Kirk's nightmare: 4 Hero / Distance: By Pass / Musik: LTJ Bukem / Western tune: PFM / Spectrum: Wax Doctor / Jazz creation: Universal Flava / I've known rivers: Pine, Courtney / Piano tune: Peshay / Too unique: Cool Breeze & Stepz Ahead / Subtrakt: Tiefenentzerrer / Sax lick: Intense / Tear down (da whole place): Dillinja / State of mind: Analyse
BEBOXCD 7 / Nov '96 / Beechwood

☐ **THIS IS JUNGLE SKY VOL.1**
JSK 004 / Dec '96 / Jungle Sky

☐ **THIS IS JUNGLE SKY VOL.2**
JSK 008 / Dec '96 / Jungle Sky

☐ **THIS IS JUNGLE SKY VOL.5 (2CD Set)**
JS 130CD / 6 Apr '98 / Jungle Sky

☐ **THIS IS LATINAMYL**
FABRLAT 1CD / 8 Sep '97 / Fused & Bruised

☐ **THIS IS LIVING JOY**
Getting harder: Time Span / Boom: Sub State / I want your love: Infernus / Come to the rescue: DJ Happy Raver & The Smile-E / Take me away: Jimmy J & Cru-L-T / Rock the dancefloor: Forbes, Davie / Motorway madness: DJ Vibes & Wishdokta / Gotta get down: DJ Poosie / Hypnotic spectrum: El Bruto / It never fucking happens: DJ Psycangle / Pop goes the world: 3rd Mann / Morning, please don't come: DJ Ham / Something good: Brown, Scott / Feel free: DJ Reno & Eatsum & The Kidz / I like bouncing: Cru-L-T
DBM 2262 / Apr '97 / Death Becomes Me

☐ **THIS IS MOD VOL.1 (Rarities 1979-1981)**
Opening up: Circles / Billy: Circles / We can go dancing: Amber Squad / You should see what I do to you in my dreams: Amber Squad / Can't sleep at night: Cigarettes / It's the only way to live: Cigarettes / All I want is your money: Cigarettes / I've forgotten my number: Cigarettes / They're back again: Cigarettes / Choose you: Deadbeats / Julies new boyfriend: Deadbeats / Oh no: Deadbeats / Nobody loves me: Letters / Don't want you back: Letters / Happy song: Nips / Nobody to love: Nips / Saturday night: Odds / Not another love song: Odds / Circles: Circles / Summer nights: Circles
CDMGRAM 98 / Oct '95 / Anagram

☐ **THIS IS MOD VOL.2**
Twisted wheel: Killermeters / SX 225: Killermeters / Plane crash: Purple Hearts / Scooby doo: Purple Hearts / Gun of life: Purple Hearts / Fashion plague: Exits / Cheam: Exits / Need somebody to love: VIP's / One more chance: VIP's / Stuttgart special: VIP's / Who knows: VIP's / Janine: VIP's / Modern boys: Crooks / Beat goes on: Crooks / Wild about you: Same / Movements: Same / All the time in the world: Crooks / Banging my head: Crooks / Odd man out: Teenage Film Stars / I apologise: Teenage Film Stars / Just a little Mod: Tonik, Terry / Smashed and blocked: Tonik, Terry
CDMGRAM 101 / Mar '96 / Anagram

☐ **THIS IS MOD VOL.3 (Diamond Collection)**
CDMGRAM 106 / Jun '96 / Anagram

☐ **THIS IS MOD VOL.4 (Modities)**
CDMGRAM 107 / Oct '96 / Anagram

☐ **THIS IS MOD VOL.5**
I can't put my finger on you: Amber Squad / Tell you a lie: Amber Squad / Why should it happen to me: Killermeters / Cardiac arrest: Killermeters / If you want it: Graduates / Hey young girl: Graduates / One way street: Aces / First impressions: Small World / Stupidity Street: Small World / Tomorrow never comes: Small World / Win or lose: Long Tall Shorty / Ain't done wrong: Long Tall Shorty / Even if I know: Sema 4 / Sema 4 messages: Sema 4 / Actors all: Sema 4 / Do you know your friends: Sema 4 / My life's a jigsaw: Purple Hearts / Guy who made her a star: Purple Hearts / Just to please you: Purple Hearts / Strength of the nation: Teenbeats / If I'm gone tomorrow: Teenbeats
CDMGRAM 110 / May '97 / Anagram

☐ **THIS IS MOD VOL.6**
CDMGRAM 116 / 17 Nov '97 / Anagram

☐ **THIS IS MODERN FOLK**
Boy done good: Bragg, Billy / Both hands (live): Di Franco, Ani / Sail on by: Oyster Band / Call it democracy: Cockburn, Bruce / England's new chains: Rev Hammer / Burford stomp: Leveller's Mutiny / Desolation blues: Leven, Jackie / Arranmore: Goats Don't Shave / Between a man and a woman: White, Andy / Run runaway: Great Big Sea / Band of dreams: Rockingbirds / Father's day: Weddings, Parties & Anything / Spivaye solovey: Ukrainians / New year's day: Prophet, Chuck / Hard: Robinson, Tom / Runaway train driver: Smith, TV / Kathleen: Thomas, David / Bjorn again polka: Edward II & The Red Hot Polkas / Bonny besses: Reader, Eddi
GRILLCD 011 / 29 Jun '98 / Cooking Vinyl

☐ **THIS IS NORTHERN SOUL**
Silent treatment: Demain, Arin / My sugar baby: Clark, Connie / Double cookin': Checkerboard Squares / I've got to get myself together: Turner, Spyder / Love makes me lonely: Chandlers / Walk with me heart: Smith, Bobby / Emperor of my baby's heart: Harris, Kurt / Nobody knows: Wonder, Diane / You're on top girl: Empires / Are you angry: Servicemen / No right to cry: Galore, Mamie / So sweet so satisfying: Treetop, Bobby / Not me baby: Silhouettes / Love's just begun: Grayson, Calvin / Falling in love with you baby: Cook, Little Joe / Those lonely nights: Soul Communicators / Bar track: Burdock, Doni / He broke your game wide open: Dell, Frank / I've had it: Andrews, Lee / I'll always love you: Moultrie, Sam / Sister Lee: Ward, Sam / Prove yourself a lady: Bounty, James / Psychedelic soul: Russell, Saxie
GSCD 014 / Jun '93 / Goldmine

☐ **THIS IS NORTHERN SOUL VOL.1 (A Collection Of 24 Tamla Motown Northern Soul Rarities)**
Reconsider: Holloway, Brenda / Do I love you: Wilson, Frank / Your love can save me: Marvelettes / This love starved heart of mine: Gaye, Marvin / Goodbye cruel world: Griner, Linda / You're gonna love my baby: McNair, Barbara / Share a little love: Monitors / Come on back to me baby: Temptations / I'm still loving you: Weston, Kim / He's all I got: Supremes / Just walk in my shoes: Knight, Gladys & The Pips / Suspicion: Originals / Keep on lovin' me: Nero, Frances / Cryin' in the night: Monitors / You hit me: Weston, Kim / Like a nightmare: Andantes / I've been blessed: Taylor, Bobby / Thrill a minute: Weston, Kim / I'll keep holding on: Marvelettes / Truly yours: Temptations / When I'm gone: Holloway, Brenda / Just a little misunderstanding: Contours / No one's gonna love you more: Knight, Gladys / You ain't saying nothing new: Henry, Vigil / Goodnight Irene: Originals / I gotta find a way: Temptations / What more could a boy ask for: Spinners / It's never too late: Knight, Gladys
5308182 / Sep '97 / Debutante

☐ **THIS IS PARADISE**
CDBNTW 4 / 25 May '98 / Passion

☐ **THIS IS RAP**
Fantastic voyage: Coolio / I wish: Skee Lo / Connected: Stereo MC's / Sneakers: Black Bean Sauce / Jump around: House Of Pain / Walk this way: Run DMC / Call it what you want: Credit To The Nation / Skin-Tact: Loco Spengo / People everyday: Arrested Development / It's a summer thang: M-Doc & Chantay Savage / Blazang: Blazang / Say no go: De La Soul / Can I kick it: Tribe Called Quest / Once upon a time: Smoothe Da Hustler / I'll be there for you/You're all I need to get by: Method Man & Mary J. Blige / Time is ticking: Smith, Eddie & Paul Nathan / Gangstas boogie: LV / We here you ain't seen nothing yet: Da Bomb & Euphemia Burke / Summertime: DJ Jazzy Jeff & The Fresh Prince / Try: Melly & Eddie Smith/Paul Nathan / Paid in full: Eric B & Rakim / Make ya mark: Bell, Melissa & Chojin
BEBOXCD 5 / Sep '96 / Beechwood

☐ **THIS IS REGGAE**
Soul rebel / Money in my pocket / I show you how to reggae / Love me / Prisoner of your love / Soul shake down party / Reggae fever / (Sittin' on the) dock of the bay / Upside down / Stop that train / Green green grass of home / Key to the world / Only heaven can wait for love / Caution / Roots rock / I will love you like abc / Three little birds / You are to me / Soul captives / Make it with you
QED 008 / Nov '96 / Tring

☐ **THIS IS REGGAE (4CD Set)**
PBXCD 406 / 20 Apr '98 / Pulse

☐ **THIS IS REGGAE MUSIC (2CD Set)**
RN 7002 / Aug '96 / Rhino

☐ **THIS IS SCOTLAND**
Hundred thousand welcomes / Amazing grace / Come to the Ceilidah-John Worth's jig / Dancing in Kyle / Abide with me / Massacre of Glencoe / Jaqueline waltz / Always Argyll / Punch bowl reel / Archaracle midgie / Bonnie Mary of Argyle / Skyline of Skye / Reels / 4/4 marches
CDITV 354 / Aug '88 / Scotdisc

☐ **THIS IS SKA**
Sound of ska (medley) / On my radio / Mirror in the bathroom / Special brew / Night boat to Cairo / Can can / Missing words / Baggy trousers / One step beyond / Lip up fatty / Hands off she's mine / Too much too young / Three minute hero / Buster's groove
ECD 3147 / Mar '95 / K-Tel

☐ **THIS IS SOCA (Carnival Hits)**
Barbara: Superblue / Rang bang katang: Ajala / Billie Jean: Stephenson, Andy / Jump up and play de mas: Raw / Free up: Herbert, 'Tambu' Chris / Trini slam: Daddy D / Caribbean party: Rudder, David / Short pants: Chinese Laundry / Shake: Atlantik / Wukerman: Miranda, Marcia / Jouvert morning: Third Bass / Maturity: Rustee & Karla / Aghen aghen: Kindred / Carnival is woman: Rukshun
NSCD 025 / 16 Feb '98 / Nascente

☐ **THIS IS SOUL (2CD Set)**
For the good times: Green, Al / You're gonna make me cry: Wright, O.V. / Buying a book: Tex, Joe / Dirty man: Lee, Laura / I've been loving you too long: Thomas, Irma / We're gonna make it: Little Milton / Part time love: Peebles, Ann / I'd rather go blind: James, Etta / Tell it like it is: Neville, Aaron / Pledging my love: Ace, Johnny / Any day now: Jackson, Chuck / Anna (go to him): Alexander, Arthur / Searchin' for my love: Moore, Bobby & The Rhythm Aces / Teardrops: Andrews, Lee & The Hearts / Oh what a night: Dells / How can you mend a broken heart: Green, Al / Bcak for a taste of your love: Johnson, Syl / Eight men four women: Wright, O.V. / Nine out of ten times: Kelly, Paul / Miss Pittiful: Kelly, Paul / Let me wrap my arms around you: Burke, Solomon / Love is a 4 letter word: Phelps, James / Good to me: Thomas, Irma / That's the way I feel about cha: Womack, Bobby / I gotta sit down and cry: Marchan, Bobby / O-o I love you: Dells / I wake up crying: Jackson, Chuck / I'll coming running back to you: Cooke, Sam / You oughta be here with me: Snell, Annette / God is standing by: Snell, Annette
DOU 886652 / 2 Feb '98 / Disky

☐ **THIS IS SOUL VOL.1**
Barefootin': Parker, Robert / When a man loves a woman: Sledge, Percy / For your precious love: Butler, Jerry / So many ways: Benton, Brook / Save the last dance for me: Drifters / Operator: Knight, Gladys & The Pips / Soul man: Sam & Dave / Me and Mrs Jones: Paul, Billy / If you don't know me by now: Melvin, Harold & The Bluenotes / Feel the need in me: Detroit Emeralds / Walking the dog: Thomas, Rufus / Show and tell: Wilson, Al / I stand accused: Butler, Jerry / It's just a matter of time: Benton, Brook / I got you (I feel good): Brown, James / There goes my baby: Drifters / Soul sister, brown sugar: Sam & Dave / You've made me so very happy: Whispers / Try a little tenderness: Sledge, Percy / Knock on wood: Floyd, Eddie
QED 006 / Nov '96 / Tring

☐ **THIS IS SPACE (4CD Set)**
Space lab: Kraftwerk / Star too far: Psychic TV / Adjust me: Hawkwind / Blue room: Orb / Point of no return: Helios Creed / Evolution: Legendary Pink Dots / Other side of the sky: Gong / Sploosh: Ozric Tentacles / Mrs. Fiend goes to outer space: Ozric Tentacles / Elements: Spiral Realms / Here come the warm jets: Eno, Brian / Silverbird/Mastodon: Pressurehed / Lanky: Barrett, Syd / Nass Arab: Coil / Wie der wind: Amon Duul II / Slo bio/Rock God: Turner, Nik / 2000 flushes: Din / Movements of a visionary: Tangerine Dream / Rain: Sky Cries Mary / Eternity: Clock DVA / Spineless jelly: Future Sound Of London / Wind of change: Hawkwind / Out of the blue: Roxy Music / Anubian light destiny: Anubian Lights / Wahnfried: Schulze, Klaus / All saints:

Bowie, David / Venusian skyline: *Melting Euphoria* / Last lagoon: *Orbit, William* / Trip to G9: *Spiral Realms* / Space does not care: *Zero Gravity* / Antenna: *Kraftwerk* / Number 9: *Aphex Twin* / Wind on water: *Fripp, Robert & Brian Eno* / Cylos: *Dilate*

CLP 9974 / Apr '97 / Cleopatra

☐ **THIS IS SPEED GARAGE VOL.1 (3CD Set)**

Closer than close: *Gaines, Rosie* / London ting: *Garcia, Scott* / Gabriel: *Davis, Roy Jr.* / Anytime: *Nu Birth* / Double life: *Soul Sonique* / Don't think about it: *Adeva* / My message: *Urban Generation* / Spin spin sugar: *Sneaker Pimps* / Just gets better: *TJR & Xavier* / Passion life: *Rise* / Never love again: *Jay, Sarah* / Oh boy: *Fabulous Baker Boys* / I refuse what you want: *Somore* / Urban spirit: *Progress* / Trapped: *Dream Team* / Deep inside: *Substance* / Need good love: *Tuff & Jam* / End of the line: *Inc. Force* / Love vibration: *Kubrick* / We can make it happen: *Craig, Robbie* / Movement: *Ultralife* / Desire: *Nu Skool*

BEBOXCD 17 / 19 Jan '98 / Beechwood

☐ **THIS IS SPEED GARAGE VOL.2 (3CD Set)**

Pleasuredome: *Soul II Soul* / Pressure: *Sounds Of Blackness* / Somebody else's guy: *Peniston, Ce Ce* / Analogue tower: *Rough Selecta* / Dreams: *Smokin' Beats* / Outlander: *Rascal* / Don't stop: *Ruff Driverz* / Pure: *Irresistable Force* / Ohh la la: *Coolio* / Sound bwoy burial: *Gant* / Vapour dub: *Sniper* / All night long: *MA1* / Free: *Ultra Nate* / Spend the night: *Lewis, Danny J.* / Underground: *Usual Suspects* / MAximum force: *DIY* / Make the world go round: *Sandy B* / Get up: *Stingily, Byron* / Step up: *VIP* / Insomnia: *Faithless* / Frequency dimension: *DJ Q* / Distirtion overload: *Product 105*

BEBOXCD 20 / 27 Apr '98 / Beechwood

☐ **THIS IS SWING (3CD Set)**

Back and forth: *Aaliyah* / Poison: *Bel Biv Devoe* / Humpin around: *Brown, Bobby* / Grapevine: *Brownstone* / Whats not yours: *Darkman* / Stay: *Nelson, Evon* / Back to the lab: *Font La Roy & Darkman* / Close to you: *Treverson, George* / Her: *Guy* / Be mine tonight: *George, Jacqui* / Just the way: *Ishmael, Jeff* / Freak'n you: *Jodeci* / Gangsta's paradise: *LV* / Happy: *MN8* / Real love: *Blige, Mary J.* / Don't take it personal (just one of dem days): *Monica* / Bump and grind: *Kelly, R* / Up town: *Rugged & Raw* / Right here: *SWV* / Keep on giving me love: *Truce* / Take you home: *Frazer, Wayne*

BEBOXCD 1 / Feb '96 / Beechwood

☐ **THIS IS TECHNO VOL.1 (3CD Set)**

Digeridoo: *Aphex Twin* / We no longer understand: *As One* / 2 paintings and a drum: *Cox, Carl* / Dreamland: *Craig, Carl* / Air bourne: *Angel, Dave* / Tour: *De Force* / Collision: *Eclipse* / Hypnotic state: *Fantasy Flight* / IFO: *IFO* / Higher state of consciousness: *Wink, Josh* / Open up: *Leftfield* / Progression: *Mantra* / Time: *Broom, Mark* / Go: *Moby* / Stormwatch: *Morph* / Cuban timewarp: *Neuropolitique* / Little fluffy clouds: *Orb* / Spastik: *Plastikman* / Poison: *Prodigy* / Above your eyes: *Scanner* / Boss drum: *Shamen* / Harlequin: *Vath, Sven* / Below and above: *Trio* / Dark and long: *Underworld*

BEBOXCD 3 / Jun '96 / Beechwood

☐ **THIS IS TECHNO VOL.2 (3CD Set)**

Breathe: *Prodigy* / Born slippy: *Underworld* / Box: *Orbital* / Source: *Phazer* / Sugar is sweeter: *Bolland, C.J.* / Maximum impact: *X-Wing* / All that rises: *Pure* / Alpha waves: *System 7* / Astral dreams: *Garnier, Laurent* / Dominions complete: *Florence* / Fall out: *Q-Bass* / Tribal jedi: *Cox, Carl* / Hypnotizin': *Winx* / Move any mountain: *Shamen* / Planet surfing: *Masquerade* / Plastic love: *Delta* / Girl boy: *Aphex Twin* / Shambala: *As One* / Dark forces: *SLAM* / Astrofarm: *Digital Source* / Blue chip: *Future Funk* / Time zone: *Logic* / Bonus mix by Mark EG

BEBOXCD 9 / Feb '97 / Beechwood

☐ **THIS IS TECHNO VOL.3 (3CD Set)**

Papua New Guinea: *Future Sound Of London* / Smack my bitch up: *Prodigy* / Sleeping giants: *Mills, Jeff* / Pearls girl: *Underworld* / Dream the dream: *Florence* / On the brink: *Ultramarine* / Crispy bacon: *Garnier, Laurent* / Naughty sisters in Rio: *Neuropolitique* / Energy flash: *Beltram, Joey* / Freek funk: *Slater, Luke* / Metamorpheus: *2000 & One* / Armchair education: *Voorn, Orlando* / Mantra: *Bolland, C.J.* / Witch dokter: *Van Helden, Armand* / Asa nisi masa: *As One* / Shape peace: *East Island* / How's the music: *Winx* / Acperience: *Hardfloor* / Stroke: *Terrace* / Pacific state: *808 State* / Outer limit: *Origins* / Circuit breaker: *Fourth Element*

BEBOXCD 21 / 15 Jun '98 / Beechwood

☐ **THIS IS THE 80'S**

I don't want to talk about it / Oblivious / Each and everyone / Life in a northern town / Money's too tight (to mention) / Somewhere in my heart / Perfect / Fairytale of new york / Golden brown / Who's that girl / Enola gay / Only you / Life's what you make it / Do you really want to hurt me / Save a prayer / To cut a long story short / Fools gold / Reward / Look of love (part one) / Favourite shirts (boy meets girl) / Ghost town / Our house / Geno / Beat surrender / Alive and kicking / Don't you want me / Blue monday / Two tribes / Relax / Tainted love / How soon is now / This charming man / Imperial / Close (to the edit) / Killing moon / What is love / Brass in pocket / Since yesterday

9548342052 / Feb '96 / WEA

☐ **THIS IS THE ANIMAL LIBERATION FRONT**

MORTCD 90 / 27 Apr '98 / Mortarhate

☐ **THIS IS THE BLUES (24 Electric Blues Hits)**

Mona: *Diddley, Bo* / You can't judge a book by the cover: *Diddley, Bo* / I'm a man: *Diddley, Bo* / Who do you love: *Diddley, Bo* / Spoonful: *Howlin' Wolf* / Smokestack lightnin': *Howlin' Wolf* / Help me: *Williamson, Sonny Boy* / I'd rather go blind: *James, Etta* / Rock me baby: *James, Etta* / Almost grown: *Berry, Chuck* / Memphis: *Berry, Chuck* / I just want to make love to you: *Waters, Muddy* / Hoochie coochie man: *Waters, Muddy* / Baby, please don't go: *Waters, Muddy* / Got my mojo working: *Waters, Muddy* / Let's work together: *Harrison, Wilbert* / Kansas City: *Harrison, Wilbert* / Rollin' and tumblin': *James, Elmore* / Dust my broom: *James, Elmore* / Bright lights big city: *Reed, Jimmy* / Dimples: *Hooker, John Lee* / Boom boom: *Hooker, John Lee* / Born under a bad sign: *King, Albert* / Hi-heel sneakers: *Tucker, Tommy*

PLATCD 3909 / Oct '90 / Platinum

☐ **THIS IS THE FUNK**

68914 / Apr '97 / Tropical

☐ **THIS IS THE NEW SOUND OF POPCORE**

DB 47852 / Sep '96 / Deep Blue

☐ **THIS IS TRIP HOP VOL.1 (3CD Set)**

Age of consent: *New Order* / Far out son of a lung: *Future Sound Of London* / Fly by night: *Substance* / Floot: *Wagon Christ* / Aphrohead: *Bluntz* / Nights interlude: *Nightmares On Wax* / Chase: *Smiler* / Kosmos SX dub 2000: *Weller, Paul* / Tides: *Agent Orange* / Jail bird: *Primal Scream* / Rising star: *Holy Haze* / Vibes: *Tempest* / Karma coma: *Massive Attack & DJ Shadow* / Birth: *Howie B* / Mudskipper: *Junk Waffel* / Anxiety: *Maad* / Mass observation 95: *Scanner* / Under the influence: *Pusher* / Filthy: *St. Etienne* / Early lady: *Yogi* / Thirst: *Solo* / Source: *Assassin* / Reverb disaster: *Bubbles* / Mellow madness: *Perpetual Motion*

BEBOXCD 2 / Mar '96 / Beechwood

☐ **THIS IS TRIP HOP VOL.2 (3CD Set)**

La tristesse durera (scream to a sigh): *Manic Street Preachers* / Release four: *Leftfield* / Flippin' tha bird: *Ruby* / Backyard: *Clearzone* / Sidewinder: *Submarine* / Snapper: *Red Snapper* / ESP: *Ratio* / Oxbow lakes: *Orb* / Bug powder dust: *Bomb The Bass* / Full force: *Yella* / Dusted: *Toolez* / Cry: *Howie B* / Milk: *Garbage* / Raxmus: *Black Dog* / Sonic surveillance: *Alpha* / Abstract truth: *DJ Abandon* / Trigger hippie: *Morcheeba* / Memories of the future: *Edge Of Motion* / Voodoo people: *Prodigy* / Dark side: *Renegade* / Disco lab: *Scout* / State of mind: *Blosense* / Bonus mix by Naked Funk

BEBOXCD 8 / Feb '97 / Beechwood

☐ **THIS LAND (Inspired By The Show Riverdance)**

CDMFP 6237 / Aug '96 / Music For Pleasure

☐ **THIS YEAR'S LOVE 1996 (2CD Set)**

MOODCD 48 / Nov '96 / Sony Music

☐ **THIS YEAR'S LOVE 1997 (2CD Set)**

If I never see you again: *Wet Wet Wet* / Don't speak: *No Doubt* / Say what you want: *Texas* / Even after all: *Quaye, Finley* / Love fool: *Cardigans* / Isn't it a wonder: *Boyzone* / Don't marry her: *Beautiful South* / Indestructable: *Alisha's Attic* / You showed me: *Lightning Seeds* / Way I feel: *Roachford* / Call the man: *Dion, Celine* / So help me girl: *Barlow, Gary* / I'm kissing you: *Des'ree* / All out of love: *OTT* / Gotta be you: *3T* / I can make you feel good: *Kavana* / Love shine a light: *Katrina & The Waves* / T shirt: *Gina G* / Waterloo sunset: *Dennis, Cathy* / I believe I can fly: *R Kelly* / Quit playing games with my heart: *Backstreet Boys* / Fix: *Blackstreet* / Everything: *Blige, Mary J.* / 5 Miles to empty: *Brownstone* / When doves cry: *Ginuwine* / Real thing: *Stansfield, Lisa* / You are the universe: *Brand New Heavies* / Everytime I close my eyes: *Babyface* / My father's son: *Reeves, Conner* / All cried out: *Allure* / Hey child: *East 17* / You're not alone: *Olive* / Underwater love: *Smoke City* / Walk on by: *Gabrielle* / Horny: *Morrison, Mark* / Body shakin': *911* / All about us: *Andre, Peter* / Falling: *Ant & Dec* / Wonderful tonight: *Damage*

MOODCD 54 / 10 Nov '97 / Sony TV

☐ **THIS YEARS LOVE**

Think twice: *Dion, Celine* / Back for good: *Take That* / Stay another day: *East 17* / Oh baby I: *Eternal* / Missing: *Everything But The Girl* / No more I love you's: *Lennox, Annie* / Love me for a reason: *Boyzone* / If you love me: *Brownstone* / I'll find you: *Gayle, Michelle* / I'll make love to you: *Boyz II Men* / Your body's callin': *Boyz II Men* / Always and forever: *Vandross, Luther* / Hold me thrill me kiss me: *Estefan, Gloria* / Chains: *Arena, Tina* / Jesse: *Kadison, Joshua* / You gotta be: *Des'ree* / Search for the hero: *M-People* / Independent love song: *Scarlet* / Unchained melody: *Robson & Jerome* / Careless whisper: *Michael, George*

MOODCD 42 / Nov '95 / Sony Music

☐ **THOSE DOO WOP DAYS (18 Classic Tracks)**

Come go with me: *Del-Vikings* / Oh what a night: *Dells* / Maybe: *Chantels* / For your precious love: *Impressions* / Little darlin': *Diamonds* / Earth angel (will you be mine): *Penguins* / Stay in my corner: *Dells* / Little star: *Elegants* / If you don't know me by now: *Melvin, Harold & The Bluenotes* / Sorry (I ran all the way home): *Impalas* / Whispering bells: *Del-Vikings* / Blue moon: *Marcels* / Sixteen candles: *Crests* / Since I don't have you: *Skyliners* / Gee whiz: *Innocents* / Great pretender: *Platters* / Stroll: *Diamonds* / Then you can tell me goodbye: *Casinos*

ECD 3304 / Feb '97 / K-Tel

☐ **THOSE FABULOUS FORTIES**

Boogie woogie bugle boy: *Andrews Sisters* / It's a sin to tell a lie: *Ink Spots* / Golden wedding: *Herman, Woody* / For me and my gal: *Garland, Judy* / There, I've said it again: *Monroe, Vaughan* / Frenesi: *Shaw, Artie* / Chica chica boom chic: *Miranda, Carmen* / Paper doll: *Mills Brothers* / Honey hush: *Waller, Fats & his Rhythm Orchestra* / Skylark: *James, Harry* / Daybreak: *Dorsey, Tommy* / My adobe Hacienda: *Baker, Kenny* / Harlem nocturne: *Anthony, Ray* / Fools rush in: *Martin, Tony* / In the mood: *Miller, Glenn* / Tangerine: *Dorsey, Jimmy*

HADCD 159 / May '94 / Javelin

☐ **THOSE WERE THE DAYS**

KWCD 809 / Jul '94 / Kenwest

☐ **THOUGHTS OF COUNTRY VOL.1**

Stand beside me: *O'Donnell, Daniel* / Almost persuaded: *Kirwan, Dominic* / Jennifer Johnson and me: *Flavin, Mick* / Dear God: *Duff, Mary* / Four in the morning: *Pride, Charley* / Way old friends do: *Begley, Philomena* / Back in love by Monday: *Lynam, Ray* / Still got a crush on you: *Hogan, John* / Daisy chain: *Begley, Philomena & Mick Flavin* / Apologising roses: *Spears, Billie Jo* / Queen of the Silver Dollar: *Begley, Philomena* / Travellin' light: *Flavin, Mick* / Amy's eyes: *Pride, Charley* / Forever and ever Amen: *Duff, Mary* / Just between you and me: *Begley, Philomena & Mick Flavin* / I'm no stranger to the rain: *Curtis, Sonny* / Take good care of her: *O'Donnell, Daniel* / Don't fight the feeling: *Hogan, John* / Sweethearts in heaven: *Margo* / Sea of heartbreak: *Kirwan, Dominic*

RZRCD 518 / May '92 / Ritz

☐ **THOUGHTS OF COUNTRY VOL.2**

RZRCD 561 / Jul '96 / Ritz

☐ **THOUGHTS OF IRELAND VOL.1**

Summertime in Ireland: *O'Donnell, Daniel* / Isle of Innisfree: *Foster & Allen* / Beautiful meath: *Duff, Mary* / Golden dreams: *Kirwan, Dominic* / Shanagolden: *Margo* / Home to Donegal: *Flavin, Mick* / Red is the rose: *Begley, Philomena* / Spancil Hill: *Duff, Mary* / If we only had old Ireland over here: *McCaffrey, Frank* / Carrickfergus: *Quinn, Brendan* / Girl from Wexford town: *Flavin, Mick* / Bunch of thyme: *Foster & Allen* / Galway Bay: *Begley, Philomena* / Give an Irish girl to me: *Nerney, Declan* / Noreen Bawn: *Kirwan, Dominic* / Moonlight in Mayo: *McCaffrey, Frank* / Lady from Glenfarne: *Quinn, Brendan* / Rose of Allendale: *Morrisey, Louise* / Forty miles to Donegal: *Margo* / Sing me an old Irish song: *O'Donnell, Daniel*

RZRCD 519 / May '92 / Ritz

☐ **THOUGHTS OF IRELAND VOL.2**

RZRCD 560 / Jul '96 / Ritz

☐ **THOUGHTS OF LOVE**

RZRCD 562 / Jul '96 / Ritz

☐ **THOUGHTS OF YESTERDAY**

I need you: *O'Donnell, Daniel* / Do what you do do well: *Pride, Charley* / Crazy: *Duff, Mary* / More than I can say: *Curtis, Sonny* / Maggie: *Foster & Allen* / Before the next teardrop falls: *Kirwan, Dominic* / Pal of my cradle days: *Gloria* / Seven lonely days: *Spears, Billie Jo* / Sentimental old you: *Begley, Philomena* / More than yesterday: *McCaffrey, Frank* / Roses are red: *O'Donnell, Daniel* / China doll: *Hogan, John* / Say you'll stay until tomorrow: *Kirwan, Dominic* / After all these years: *Foster & Allen* / Ramblin' rose: *Pride, Charley* / Little things mean a lot: *Dana* / It's our anniversary: *McCaffrey, Frank* / Yellow roses: *Duff, Mary* / He stopped loving her today: *Lynam, Ray* / Old flames: *Begley, Philomena*

RZRCD 520 / Apr '92 / Ritz

☐ **THRACE ANTHOLOGY VOL.3 (Bulgaria)**

274977 / Jan '95 / La Chant Du Monde

☐ **THRASHED**

RR 87782 / 3 Nov '97 / Roadrunner

☐ **THREADGILL'S SUPPER SESSIONS VOL.1**

WM 1013CD / May '94 / Watermelon

☐ **THREADGILL'S SUPPER SESSIONS VOL.2**

WMCD 1052 / Jun '96 / Watermelon

☐ **THREE CHORDOPHONE TRADITIONS (Music From Ethiopia)**

D 8074 / Nov '96 / Unesco

☐ **THREE PHENOMENA**

VC 120CD / Oct '97 / Vinyl Communication

☐ **THREE SHADES OF THE BLUES**

BCD 107 / '92 / Biograph

☐ **THREE STEPS TO HEAVEN**

QTVCD 011 / Aug '92 / Quality

☐ **THREE WAY MIRROR**

Treme terra / Misturada / Return / Three-way mirror / San Francisco River / Starting over again / Lilia / Plane to the trane

RR 24CD / Sep '91 / Reference Recordings

☐ **THREE WORLDS OF TRIKOLA, THE (The Collection)**

3201932 / Jul '92 / Triloka

☐ **THRONE OF DRONES (2CD Set)**

ASP 0952CD / 22 Jun '98 / Asphodel

☐ **THROUGH THE DECADES WITH THE MIGHTY WURLITZER 1920'S**

OS 233 / 13 Apr '98 / Bandleader

☐ **THROUGH THE DECADES WITH THE MIGHTY WURLITZER 1930'S**

OS 234 / 13 Apr '98 / Bandleader

☐ **THROUGH THE SKIES (Mixed By Faze Action)**

XTR 43CDM / 23 Feb '98 / X-Treme

☐ **THUNDERBOLT (Searing RNB Sax Instrumentals)**

Paradise rock / Thunderbolt / Paradise roll / Fish bait / Melancholy horn / Jay bird / Strollin' out / Flying with the king / King is blue / Big wind / Royal crown blues / Sweet Georgia Brown / Easy ridin' / Joyride

FLYCD 29 / Apr '91 / Flyright

☐ **THUNDERDOME VOL.18 (Psycho Silence/2CD Set)**

ARC 332 / 8 Sep '97 / Arcade

☐ **THUNDERDOME VOL.21 (2CD Set)**

9902349 / 29 Jun '98 / Arcade

☐ **THUNDERING DRAGON**

SM 1519CD / Oct '94 / Wergo

☐ **THUNDERSTORM**

DC 879552 / Oct '97 / Disky

☐ **THURSDAY'S TANGOS OF THE GOLDEN AGE**

Jueves: *De Caro, Julio* / Mi queja: *De Caro, Julio* / Donde estas corazon: *Bachicha* / Te vi muy triste: *Racho, Pippo* / Perdon: *Racho, Pippo* / Bells of Hawaii: *Canaro, Francisco* / Zaraza: *Canaro, Francisco* / Milonga classica: *Canaro, Francisco* / Bandoneon de mis amores: *Canaro, Francisco* / Cara sucia: *Canaro, Francisco* / Clavel del aire: *De Dois Filiberto, Juan* / Botines viejos: *De Dois Filiberto, Juan* / La quinterita: *De Dois Filiberto, Juan* / Lo quevieron tus ojos: *Lomuto, Francisco* / Mar de fondo: *Lomuto, Francisco* / Se han sentado las carretas: *Lomuto, Francisco* / Sabato: *Di Sarli, Carlos* / Don Jose Maria: *Di Sarli, Carlos* / El pollo Ricardo: *Di Sarli, Carlos* / Marianito: *Di Sarli, Carlos* / Los Mareados: *Ortiz, Ciriaco* / Madame Ivonne: *Ortiz, Ciriaco* / Galleguita: *Ortiz, Ciriaco* / Milonguita: *Ortiz, Ciriaco*

HQCD 120 / Sep '98 / Harlequin

☐ **TIBET - HEART OF DHARMA**

ELLICD 4050 / May '97 / Ellipsis Arts

☐ **TIBETAN BUDDHISM - RITUAL ORCHESTRA/CHANTS**

7559720712 / Jan '95 / Nonesuch

☐ **TIBETAN FREEDOM ALBUM (3CD Set)**

Ground on one: *Harper, Ben* / Blues explosion man: *Spencer, Jon Blues Explosion* / About a boy: *Smith, Patti* / Fake plastic trees: *Radiohead* / Oh my god: *Tribe Called Quest* / One: *U2* / Cast no shadow: *Gallagher, Noel* / Meija: *Sonic Youth* / Wildflower: *Porno For Pyros* / This is a call: *Foo Fighters* / Bridge is over/Black cop/South Bronx: *KRS 1* / Nobody beats the wiz/Star spangled banner: *Biz Markie* / Yellow ledbetter: *Vedder, Eddie/Mike McCready* / Type slowly: *Pavement* / Heads of the goverment: *Perry, Lee 'Scratch'* / She caught the katy: *Taj Mahal* / Beetlebum: *Blur* / Electrolite: *Stipe, Michael & Mike Mills* / Wake up: *Morissette, Alanis* / Hyper ballad: *Bjork* / Harder they come: *Rancid* / Root down: *Beastie Boys* / Birthday cake: *Cibo Matto* / Asshole: *Beck* / Me myself and I: *De La Soul* / Fu gee la: *Fugees* / Bulls on parade: *Rage Against The Machine*

8591102 / 17 Nov '97 / Parlophone

☐ **TIBETAN INCANTATIONS**

Om mani padme hum / Mantra of Avalokiteshvara / Om mani padme hum

NSCD 028 / 16 Feb '98 / Nascente

☐ **TIBETAN RITUAL MUSIC**

LYRCD 7181 / '91 / Lyrichord

☐ **TIGER FEET**

Saturday night's alright for fighting: *John, Elton* / Tiger feet: *Mud* / This town ain't big enough for the both of us: *Sparks* / Can the can: *Quatro, Suzi* / Cum on feel the noize: *Slade* / Bump: *Kenny* / See my baby jive: *Wizzard* / January: *Pilot* / Touch too much: *Arrows* / Hallelujah freedom: *Campbell, Junior* / Sugar baby love: *Rubettes* / Sylvia: *Focus* / Dance with the Devil: *Powell, Cozy* / One and one is one: *Medicine Head* / Motorbikin': *Spedding, Chris* / Silver dream machine: *Essex, David* / Make me smile (come up and see me): *Harley, Steve & Cockney Rebel* / Life is a minestrone: *10cc* / Oh no not my baby: *Stewart, Rod* / Rockin' all over the world: *Status Quo*

5529122 / Oct '97 / Spectrum

☐ **TIGER MASK TRASH AU GO GO**

ID 123358 / 1 Jun '98 / Dionysus

☐ **TIGER RAG**

PHONTCD 7619 / '93 / Phontastic

☐ **TIGHTEN UP VOL.1 & 2**

Tighten up: *Perry, Lee 'Scratch'* / Kansas City: *Landis, Joya* / Spanish Harlem: *Bennett, Val* / Place in the sun: *Isaacs, David* / Win your love: *Penny, George A.* / Donkey returns: *Brother Dan Allstars* / Ob-la-di ob-la-da: *Bond, Joyce* / Angel of the morning: *Landis, Joya* / Fat man: *Morgan, Derrick* / Soul limbo: *Lee, Byron* / Mix it up: *Kingstonians* / Watch this squad: *Uniques* / Longshot kick de bucket: *Pioneers* / John Hones: *Mills, Rudy* / Fire corner: *Eccles, Clancy* / Wreck a buddy: *Soul Sisters* / Reggae in your jeggae: *Livingstone, Dandy* / Fattie fattie: *Eccles, Clancy* / Return of Django: *Upsetters* / Sufferer: *Kingstonians* / Moonlight lover: *Landis, Joya* / Come into my parlour: *Bleechers* / Them a laugh and a ki ki: *Soulmates* / Live injection: *Upsetters*

CDTRL 306 / Mar '94 / Trojan

☐ **TIGHTEN UP VOL.3 & 4**

Monkey man / Shocks of mighty / Freedom Street / Raining in my heart / Man from Carolina / Leaving Rome / Singer man / Suffering / Herbsman / Barbwire / Stay a little bit longer / Queen of the world / Blood and fire / Johnny too bad / Selah / One eye enos / Hard life / I shall sing / Grooving out on life / Starvation / Bush doctor / Good ambition / I got it / Stand by your man

CDTRL 307 / Mar '94 / Trojan

☐ **TIGHTEN UP VOL.5 & 6**

Better must come: *Wilson, Delroy* / In paradise: *Edwards, Jackie & Julie Anne* / Hello mother: *Dynamites* / Rod of correction: *Eccles, Clancy* / Ripe cherry: *Alcapone, Dennis* / Three in one: *Dunkley, Errol* / Joy to the world: *Julien & The Chosen Few* / Know Far I: *Herman, Bongo & Bunny* / It's you: *Toots & The Maytals* / Bridge over troubled water: *London, Jimmy* / Shaft: *Chosen Few* / Duppy conqueror: *Marley, Bob & The Wailers* / Pitta patta: *Smith, Ernie* / Do your thing: *Chosen Few* / Breezing: *Chung, Mikie* / As long as you love me: *Maytones* / Down side up: *Harry J All Stars* / Suzanne beware of the devil: *Livingstone, Dandy* / Struggling man: *Cimarons* / Redemption song: *Toots & The Maytals* / Hot bomb: *I-Roy & The Jumpers* / President mash up the resident: *Shortie* / Who told you so: *Edwards, Jackie* / Unite tonight: *Eccles, Clancy*

CDTRL 320 / Mar '94 / Trojan

☐ **TIME FOR LOVE (More Songs For Lovers)**

It's time for love: *Chi-Lites* / Zoom: *Fat Larry's Band* / Time in a bottle: *Croce, Jim* / Now is the time: *James, Jimmy* / I can see clearly now: *Knight, Gladys* / Hot love: *Marie, Kelly* / Girls: *Moments* / Can't get by without you: *Real Thing* / Night to remember: *Shalamar* / Purely by coincidence: *Sweet Sensation*

/ Band of gold: *Sylvester* / Pillow talk: *Sylvia* / Hold back the night: *Trammps* / And the beat goes on: *Whispers* / I get the sweetest feeling: *Wilson, Jackie* / It's in his kiss (The shoop shoop song): *Everett, Betty* / She'd rather be with me: *Turtles* / Gimme little sign: *Wood, Brenton* / Caroline goodbye: *Blunstone, Colin*

TRTCD 159 / Feb '96 / TrueTrax

☐ **TIME FOR LOVING, A (2CD Set)**

NSCD 005 / Feb '95 / Newsound

☐ **TIME FOR TECHNO**

Gonna make u feel so good / Axel F / Jump / Oxygene / Cocoon / Sonic groove / Popcorn / Energize / Action / Magic fly / Acid bird / Roffos theme v the hitman

ECD 3129 / Jan '95 / K-Tel

☐ **TIME MOTION TRANCE (2CD Set)**

OXA 20042 / 1 Jun '98 / OXA

☐ **TIME PASSAGES (2CD Set)**

Home on Monday: *Little River Band* / Don't you write her off: *McGuinn, Roger & Gene Clark/Chris Hillman* / On and on: *Bishop, Stephen* / True love: *Frey, Glenn* / American dream: *Dirt Band* / Sweet home Alabama: *Lynyrd Skynyrd* / Love will find a way: *Nitty Gritty Dirt Band* / Weight: *Band* / California dreamin': *Beach Boys* / Baker Street: *Rafferty, Gerry* / Year of the cat: *Stewart, Al* / Hard rock cafe: *King, Carole* / I go to pieces: *Cotton, Lloyd & Christian* / Classic: *Gurvitz, Adrian* / Horse with no name: *America* / Time passages: *Stewart, Al* / Lonesome loser: *Little River Band* / Save it for a rainy day: *Bishop, Stephen* / Great pretender: *Band* / All I wanted: *Kansas* / Right down the line: *Rafferty, Gerry* / Margaritaville: *Buffett, Jimmy* / Need a little taste of love: *Doobie Brothers* / They shoot horses don't they: *Racing Cars* / No more fear of flying: *Brooker, Gary* / Cool change: *Little River Band* / You've lost that loving feeling: *Baldry, Long John* / Tired of toein' the line: *Burnette, Rocky* / Border: *America* / Whatever's written in your heart: *Rafferty, Gerry*

DOU 882412 / 29 Aug '97 / Disky

☐ **TIME TO REMEMBER 1937, A (20 Original Chart Hits)**

Free: *Flanagan & Allen* / Fine romance: *Astaire, Fred & Ginger Rogers* / Shall we dance: *Roy, Harry* / It looks like rain in cherry blossom lane: *Loss, Joe & His Orchestra* / Where are you: *Hutch* / Bessie couldn't help it: *Gonella, Nat* / Greatest mistake of my life: *Messene, Jimmy* / Let's put our heads together: *Roy, Harry* / September in the rain: *Loss, Joe* / Love bug will bite you: *Gonella, Nat* / Night is young: *Hutch* / Broken hearted clown: *Messene, Jimmy* / Boo hoo: *Hall, Henry* / There's a small hotel: *Roy, Harry* / Way you look tonight: *Astaire, Fred* / Goodnight my love: *Gibbons, Carroll & Savoy Hotel Orpheans* / Hometown: *Flanagan & Allen* / May I have the next romance with you: *Hutch* / They can't take that away from me: *Roy, Harry* / Pennies from heaven: *Gonella, Nat*

ATTR 1937 / Mar '97 / Baktabak

☐ **TIME TO REMEMBER 1946, A (20 Original Chart Hits)**

Fine romance: *Tilton, Martha & Johnny Mercer* / Candy: *Roy, Harry & His Band* / Takin' the trains out (chasin' after you): *Foster, Teddy* / I get a kick out of you: *Whiting, Margaret* / I'll be with you in apple blossom time: *Stafford, Jo* / Sentimental journey: *Foster, Teddy & The Band* / I dream of you more you dream I do: *Lewis, Archie & Geraldo* / Anywhere: *Winstone, Eric* / We'll gather lilacs: *Geraldo* / Coming home: *Squires, Dorothy* / Take the 'A' train: *Ellington, Duke* / Did you ever get that feeling in moonlight: *Preager, Lou & His Band* / One-zy, two-zy, I love you-zy: *Simpson, Jack & His Sextet* / Fools rush in: *Stafford, Jo* / I'd rather be me: *Roy, Harry & His Band* / Dreams of yesterday: *Squires, Dorothy* / Little things that mean so much: *Payne, Jack & His Orchestra* / In the land of beginning again: *Lewis, Archie & Geraldo* / I walked right in: *Winstone, Eric* / If I had you: *Whiting, Margaret*

ATTR 1946 / Mar '97 / Baktabak

☐ **TIME TO REMEMBER 1947, A (20 Original Chart Hits)**

Hurry on down: *Lutcher, Nellie* / Gal in calico: *Loss, Joe & His Orchestra* / Sowing machine: *Hutton, Betty* / Temptation: *Stafford, Jo & Red Ingle* / Stars will remember: *Conway, Steve* / People will say we're in love: *Hutch* / Moonlight serenade: *Rabin, Oscar* / Danger ahead: *Squires, Dorothy* / I'm not in love: *Rabin, Oscar* / Tell me Marianne: *Loss, Joe & His Orchestra* / How lucky you are: *Layton, Turner* / He's a real gone guy: *Lutcher, Nellie* / I wish I didn't love you so: *Hutton, Betty* / Time after time: *Conway, Steve* / If I can help somebody: *Wilson, Robert* / Smoke dreams: *Stafford, Jo* / I've got the sun: *Stafford, Jo* / Come back to Sorrento: *Locke, Josef* / Song is ended: *Lutcher, Nellie* / I'll make up for everything: *Conway, Steve*

ATTR 1947 / Apr '97 / Baktabak

☐ **TIME TO REMEMBER 1956, A (20 Original Chart Hits)**

Be bop a Lula: *Vincent, Gene* / 16 tons: *Ford, Tennessee Ernie* / Teach you to rock: *Crombie, Tony* / Experiments with mice: *Dankworth, John Quintet* / Tumbling tumbleweeds: *Whitman, Slim* / Zambesi: *Calvert, Eddie* / Robin Hood: *James, Dick* / Cindy O Cindy: *Brent, Tony* / No other love: *Hilton, Ronnie* / Blueberry Hill: *Domino, Fats* / You are my first love: *Murray, Ruby* / Memories are made of this: *Martin, Dean* / Pickin' a chicken: *Boswell, Eve* / Too young to go steady: *Cole, Nat 'King'* / Bad penny blues: *Lyttelton, Humphrey* / Cat came back: *James, Sonny* / Why do fools fall in love: *Lymon, Frankie & The Teenagers* / Rock Island Line: *Freberg, Stan* / Hot diggity: *Holliday, Michael* / True love: *Crosby, Bing & Grace Kelly*

ATTR 1956 / Mar '97 / Baktabak

☐ **TIME TO REMEMBER 1957, A (20 Original Chart Hits)**

When I fall in love: *Cole, Nat 'King'* / Young love: *James, Sonny* / Kisses sweeter than wine: *Rodgers, Jimmie* / Wisdom of a fool: *Wisdom, Norman* / Party doll: *Knox, Buddy* / My special angel: *Vaughan, Malcolm* / Wonderful wonderful: *Hilton, Ronnie* / Be my girl: *Hilton, Ronnie* / You, me and us: *Cogan, Alma* / Ma he's making eyes at me: *Otis, Johnny* / Blue Monday: *Domino, Fats* / White sport coat: *King Brothers* / Dark moon: *Brent, Tony* / I'm not a juvenile delinquent: *Lymon, Frankie & The Teenagers* / Any old iron: *Sellers, Peter* / Cumberland Gap: *Vipers Skiffle Group* / He's got the whole world in his hands: *London, Laurie* / Man that plays the mandolin: *Martin, Dean* / School day: *Lang, Don* / I'll take you home again Kathleen: *Whitman, Slim*

ATTR 1957 / Mar '97 / Baktabak

☐ **TIME TO REMEMBER 1960, A (20 Original Chart Hits)**

Poor me: *Faith, Adam* / That's you: *Cole, Nat 'King'* / Walk don't run: *Ventures* / Dreamin': *Burnette, Johnny* / Staccato's theme: *Bernstein, Elmer* / Ain't misbehavin': *Bruce, Tommy* / You got what it takes: *Johnson, Marv* / Shakin' all over: *Kidd, Johnny & The Pirates* / As long as he needs me: *Bassey, Shirley* / Goodness gracious me: *Sellers, Peter & Sophia Loren* / Pistol packin' Mama: *Vincent, Gene* / Starry eyed: *Holliday, Michael* / Apache: *Shadows* / Pretty blue eyes: *Douglas, Craig* / Tell Laura I love her: *Valance, Ricky* / Hit and miss: *Barry, John* / Tie me kangaroo down: *Harris, Rolf* / Beatnik fly: *Johnny & The Hurricanes* / Walkin' to New Orleans: *Domino, Fats* / Three steps to heaven: *Cochran, Eddie*

ATTR 1960 / Mar '97 / Baktabak

☐ **TIME TO REMEMBER 1961, A (20 Original Chart Hits)**

Take good care of my baby: *Vee, Bobby* / Walkin' back to happiness: *Shapiro, Helen* / Kontiki: *Shadows* / Michael: *Highwaymen* / Hello Mary Lou: *Nelson, Rick* / Time has come: *Faith, Adam* / Let true love begin: *Cole, Nat 'King'* / I love how you love me: *Crawford, Jimmy* / Weekend: *Cochran, Eddie* / Till there was you: *Lee, Peggy* / Climb every mountain: *Bassey, Shirley* / You're drivin' me crazy: *Temperance Seven* / Moon river: *Williams, Danny* / Blue moon: *Marcels* / Magnificent seven: *Barry, John* / Let there be drums: *Nelson, Sandy* / Hundred pounds of clay: *Douglas, Craig* / My girl Josephine: *Domino, Fats* / Runaway: *Shannon, Del* / You're sixteen: *Burnette, Johnny*

ATTR 1961 / Mar '97 / Baktabak

☐ **TIME TO REMEMBER 1962, A (20 Original Chart Hits)**

Locomotion: *Little Eva* / I remember you: *Ifield, Frank* / Don't ever change: *Crickets* / James Bond theme: *Barry, John* / Wonderful world of the young: *Williams, Danny* / Young world: *Nelson, Rick* / Ramblin' rose: *Cole, Nat 'King'* / Little Miss Lonely: *Shapiro, Helen* / English country garden: *Rogers, Jimmy* / Old rivers: *Brennan, Walter* / Cindy's birthday: *Fenton, Shane & The Fentones* / Jambalaya: *Domino, Fats* / Dance on: *Shadows* / Hole in the ground: *Cribbins, Bernard* / When my little girl is smiling: *Douglas, Craig* / Peppermint twist: *Dee, Joey & The Starlighters* / Forever kind of love: *Vee, Bobby* / As you like it: *Faith, Adam* / It might as well rain until September: *King, Carole* / Sun arise: *Harris, Rolf*

ATTR 1962 / Mar '97 / Baktabak

☐ **TIME TO REMEMBER 1963, A (20 Original Chart Hits)**

Surfin' USA: *Beach Boys* / Bad to me: *Kramer, Billy J.* / Night has a thousand eyes: *Vee, Bobby* / Stay: *Hollies* / From Russia with love: *Monro, Matt* / Little town flirt: *Shannon, Del* / From a Jack to King: *Miller, Ned* / Cruel sea: *Dakotas* / First time: *Faith, Adam* / Tell him: *Exciters* / You were made for me: *Freddie & The Dreamers* / My little girl: *Crickets* / I'll never get over you: *Kidd, Johnny & The Pirates* / Foot tapper: *Shadows* / Let's turkey trot: *Little Eva* / Hippy hippy shake: *Swinging Blue Jeans* / Red sails in the sunset: *Domino, Fats* / Surf city: *Jan & Dean* / Wayward wind: *Ifield, Frank* / You'll never walk alone: *Gerry & The Pacemakers*

ATTR 1963 / Mar '97 / Baktabak

☐ **TIME TO REMEMBER 1964, A (20 Original Chart Hits)**

I'm into something good: *Herman's Hermits* / Do wah diddy diddy: *Manfred Mann* / Little loving: *Fourmost* / I get around: *Beach Boys* / World without love: *Peter & Gordon* / You're no good: *Swinging Blue Jeans* / Walk away: *Monro, Matt* / Fever: *Shapiro, Helen* / Little children: *Kramer, Billy J.* / Ferry cross the Mersey: *Gerry & The Pacemakers* / One way love: *Bennett, Cliff & The Rebel Rousers* / Happiness: *Dodd, Ken* / Tobacco road: *Nashville Teens* / I understand: *Freddie & The Dreamers* / Anyone who had a heart: *Black, Cilla* / Just one look: *Hollies* / Message to Martha: *Faith, Adam* / House of the rising sun: *Animals* / They call he (la bamba): *Crickets* / Goldfinger: *Bassey, Shirley*

ATTR 1964 / Mar '97 / Baktabak

☐ **TIME TO REMEMBER 1965, A (20 Original Chart Hits)**

All I really want to do: *Cher* / I'm alive: *Hollies* / True love ways: *Peter & Gordon* / Stingray: *Shadows* / Yesterday: *Monro, Matt* / No regrets: *Bassey, Shirley* / California girls: *Beach Boys* / Maria: *Proby, P.J.* / I'll be there: *Gerry & The Pacemakers* / Carnival is over: *Seekers* / You've lost that lovin' feelin': *Black, Cilla* / Trains, boats and planes: *Kramer, Billy J.* / This little bird: *Nashville Teens* / Must to avoid: *Herman's Hermits* / Paradise: *Ifield, Frank* / Windmill in old Amsterdam: *Ifield, Frank* / Hard days night: *Sellers, Peter* / If you've gotta go gonow: *Manfred Mann* / Little you: *Freddie & The Dreamers* / We've got to get out of this place: *Animals*

ATTR 1965 / Mar '97 / Baktabak

☐ **TIME TO REMEMBER 1966, A (20 Original Chart Hits)**

Sunshine superman: *Donovan* / Alfie: *Black, Cilla* / Supergirl: *Bonney, Graham* / Lady Godiva: *Peter & Gordon* / You've come back: *Proby, P.J.* / Sloop John B: *Beach Boys* / No milk today: *Beach Boys* / No one will ever know: *Ifield, Frank* / Morningtown ride: *Seekers* / Hanky panky: *James, Tommy & The Shondells* / Bang bang my baby shot me down: *Cher* / Take me to your heart again: *Hill, Vince* / I met a girl: *Shadows* / Don't make me over: *Swinging Blue Jeans*

ATTR 1966 / Mar '97 / Baktabak

☐ **TIME TO REMEMBER 1967, A (20 Original Chart Hits)**

Hi ho silver lining: *Beck, Jeff* / Gregory girl: *Seekers* / Carrie Anne: *Hollies* / I've been a bad bad boy: *Jones, Paul* / With a little help from my friends: *Young Idea* / There's a kind of hush: *Herman's Hermits* / Then I kissed her: *Beach Boys* / It must be him: *Carr, Vikki* / Boat that I row: *Lulu* / Thank you very much: *Scaffold* / Big spender: *Bassey, Shirley* / Seven drunken nights: *Dubliners* / There must be a way: *Vaughan, Frankie* / Mellow yellow: *Donovan* / Kites: *Dupree, Simon & The Big Sound* / Up up and away: *Mann, Johnny Singers* / On a carousel: *Hollies* / Excerpt from a teenage opera: *West, Keith* / Heroes and villains: *Beach Boys* / Ode to Billy Joe: *Gentry, Bobbie*

ATTR 1967 / Mar '97 / Baktabak

☐ **TIME TO REMEMBER 1968, A (20 Original Chart Hits)**

Weight: *Band* / I'm the urban spaceman: *Bonzo Dog Band* / Mony mony: *James, Tommy & The Shondells* / Hurdy gurdy man: *Donovan* / Listen to me: *Hollies* / Sunshine girl: *Herman's Hermits* / Nevertheless: *Vaughan, Frankie* / Darlin': *Beach Boys* / She wears my ring: *King, Solomon* / On the road again: *Canned Heat* / I'm a tiger: *Lulu* / For whom the bell tolls: *Dupree, Simon* / Lily the pink: *Scaffold* / May I have the next dream with you: *Roberts, Malcolm* / Honey: *Goldsboro, Bobby* / Love is blue: *Beck, Jeff* / Jennifer juniper: *Donovan* / Blue eyes: *Partridge, Don* / Do it again: *Beach Boys* / Jennifer Eccles: *Hollies*

ATTR 1968 / Mar '97 / Baktabak

☐ **TIME TO REMEMBER 1969, A (20 Original Chart Hits)**

He ain't heavy he's my brother: *Hollies* / Mocking bird: *Foxx, Inez & Charlie* / I'll never fall in love: *Gentry, Bobbie* / Wichita lineman: *Campbell, Glen* / Love is all: *Roberts, Malcolm* / I can hear music: *Beach Boys* / Where do you go to my lovely: *Sarstedt, Peter* / My sentimental friend: *Herman's Hermits* / Nobody's child: *Young, Karen* / Love at first sight: *Sounds Nice* / Goo goo barabajagal: *Donovan & Jeff Beck Group* / Deal: *Campbell, Pat* / Going up the country: *Canned Heat* / Aquarius: *Jones, Paul* / Gin gan goolie: *Scaffold* / Good morning starshine: *Oliver* / Breakfast on pluto: *Partridge, Don* / Breakaway: *Beach Boys* / Games people play: *South, Joe* / Boom boom a bang: *Lulu* / Stop stop: *Hollies* / Stop stop stop: *Hollies* / High time: *Jones, Paul* / Got to ge you into my life: *Bennett, Cliff & The Rebel Rousers* / Pretty flamingo: *Manfred Mann* / WITCHES BREW: *Jones, Janie* / Good vibrations: *Beach Boys*

ATTR 1969 / Mar '97 / Baktabak

☐ **TIME TO REMEMBER 1970, A (20 Original Chart Hits)**

Whole lotta love: *CCS* / Love is life: *Hot Chocolate* / Cotton fields: *Beach Boys* / Can't tell the bottom from the top: *Hollies* / Lady Barbara: *Herman's Hermits* / Something: *Bassey, Shirley* / Let's work together: *Canned Heat* / Grandad: *Dunn, Clive* / Black night: *Deep Purple* / When I'm dead and gone: *McGuiness Flint* / Raindrops keep falling on my head: *Gentry, Bobbie* / Song of joy: *Rios, Miguel* / Man from Nazareth: *Joans, John Paul* / Honey come back: *Campbell, Glen* / Out demons out: *Broughton, Edgar* / Gasoline alley bred: *Hollies* / Sugar bee: *Canned Heat* / Rag Mama rag: *Band* / Years may come years may go: *Herman's Hermits* / I hear you knocking: *Edmunds, Dave*

ATTR 1970 / Mar '97 / Baktabak

☐ **TIME TO REMEMBER 1971, A (20 Original Chart Hits)**

Don't let it die: *Smith, Hurricane* / Strange kind of woman: *Deep Purple* / Tonight: *Move* / Walkin': *Move* / For all we know: *Bassey, Shirley* / You could've been a lady: *Hot Chocolate* / Freedom come freedom go: *Fortunes* / Banks of the Ohio: *Newton-John, Olivia* / Apache dropout: *Broughton, Edgar Band* / Softly whispering I love you: *Congregation* / Ernie: *Hill, Benny* / Rose garden: *New World* / Look around: *Hill, Vince* / Hey Willie: *Hollies* / Mozart 40: *Sovereign Collection* / Chinatown: *Move* / Fireball: *Deep Purple* / Dream baby: *Campbell, Glen* / Tap turns on the water: *CCD* / I believe (in love): *Hot Chocolate*

ATTR 1971 / Mar '97 / Baktabak

☐ **TIME TO REMEMBER 1972, A (20 Original Chart Hits)**

American pie: *McLean, Don* / 10538 Overture: *ELO* / Long cool woman in a black dress: *Hollies* / Conquistador: *Procol Harum* / Storm in a teacup: *Fortunes* / Who was it: *Hurricane smith* / Journey: *Brown, Duncan & Sebastian Graham-Jones* / California man: *Move* / What is life: *Newton-John, Olivia* / Pugwudgie: *Drake, Charlie* / Sister Jane: *New World* / Baby: *Hollies* / Never before: *Deep Purple* / Just out of reach: *Dodd, Ken* / Brother: *CCS* / You'll always be my friend: *Hot Chocolate* / Ball park incident: *Wizzard* / Vincent: *McLean, Don* / Oh babe what would you say: *Hurricane smith* / Silver machine: *Hawkwind*

ATTR 1972 / Mar '97 / Baktabak

☐ **TIME TO REMEMBER 1973, A (20 Original Chart Hits)**

Nutbush City limits: *Turner, Ike & Tina* / Summer (The first time): *Goldsboro, Bobby* / Dance with the devil: *Powell, Cozy* / Heart of stone: *Kenny* / Roll over Beethoven: *ELO* / Gaudette: *Steeleye Span* / Day that Billy shot crazy Bobby: *Hollies* / Why can't we live together: *Thomas, Timmy* / Dyna-mite: *Mud* / Everyday: *McLean, Don* / Take me home country road: *Newton-John, Olivia* / Urban guerrilla: *Hawkwind* / Brother Louie: *Hot Chocolate* / You smiled: *Monro, Matt* / Band played the boogie: *CCS* / See my baby jive: *Wizzard* / Never never never: *Bassey, Shirley* / Sylvia: *Focus* / Dear Elaine: *Wood, Roy* / Can the can: *Quatro, Suzi*

ATTR 1973 / Mar '97 / Baktabak

☐ **TIME TO REMEMBER 1974, A (20 Original Chart Hits)**

Magic: *Pilot* / Judy Teen: *Harley, Steve & Cockney Rebel* / Going down that road: *Wood, Roy* / You're having my baby: *Anka, Paul* / Devil gate drive: *Quatro, Suzi* / Hello summertime: *Goldsboro, Bobby* / Bump: *Kenny* / Tell him: *Hello* / Rock me gently: *Kim, Andy* / Air that I breathe: *Hollies* / Queen of clubs: *KC & The Sunshine Band* / Mr Soft: *Harley, Steve & Cockney Rebel* / Happy anniversary: *Whitman, Slim* / Man in black: *Powell, Cozy* / School love: *Blue, Barry* / Tiger feet: *Mud* / I honestly love you: *Newton-John, Olivia* / Pinball: *Protheroe, Brian* / Emma: *Hot Chocolate* / Rock your baby: *McCrae, George*

ATTR 1974 / Mar '97 / Baktabak

☐ **TIME TO REMEMBER 1975, A (20 Original Chart Hits)**

Make me smile: *Harley, Steve & Cockney Rebel* / That's the way (I like it): *KC & The Sunshine Band* / Rhinestone cowboy: *Campbell, Glen* / Right back where I started from: *Nightingale, Maxine* / Motorbikin': *Spedding, Chris* / Lovin' you: *Riperton, Minnie* / Secrets that you keep: *Mud* / Fancy pants: *Kenny* / Angie baby: *Reddy, Helen* / Yin and yan: *Reddy, Helen* / Pandora's box: *Procol Harum* / Where is the love: *Wright, Betty* / It's been so long: *McCrae, George* / New York groove: *Hello* / Blanket on the ground: *Spears, Billie Jo* / Your Mama won't like me: *Quatro, Suzi* / You sexy thing: *Hot Chocolate* / Pilot: *January* / Oh boy: *Mud* / All around my hat: *Steeleye Span*

ATTR 1975 / Mar '97 / Baktabak

☐ **TIME TO REMEMBER 1976, A (20 Original Chart Hits)**

Little bit more: *Dr. Hook* / Ships in the night: *Be-Bop Deluxe* / Sing me an old fashioned song: *Spears, Billie Jo* / Man to man: *Hot Chocolate* / Heaven must be missing an angel: *Tavares* / Loves a prima donna: *Harley, Steve & Cockney Rebel* / Movie star: *Harpo* / Honey: *McCrae, George* / Shake shake your booty: *KC & The Sunshine Band* / If not you: *Dr. Hook* / Rodrigo's guitar concerto: *Manuel & The Music Of The Mountains* / Wurzels: *Wurzels* / Mississippi: *Pussycat* / Maid in heaven: *Be-Bop Deluxe* / Movin': *Brass Construction* / Don't take away the music: *Tavares* / What I've got in mind: *Spears, Billie Jo* / Don't stop it now: *Hot Chocolate* / Better use your head: *Little Anthony & The Imperials* / Here comes the sun: *Harley, Steve & Cockney Rebel*

ATTR 1976 / Mar '97 / Baktabak

☐ **TIME TO REMEMBER 1977, A (20 Original Chart Hits)**

Get a grip on yourself: *Stranglers* / Be good to yourself: *Miller, Frankie* / Lucille: *Rogers, Kenny* / So you win again: *Hot Chocolate* / Love hit me: *Nightingale, Maxine* / Spanish stroll: *Mink Deville* / I'm your boogie man: *KC & The Sunshine Band* / Year of the cat: *Stewart, Al* / Tear me apart: *Quatro, Suzi* / Perfect day: *Saints* / Southern nights: *Campbell, Glen* / They shoot horses don't they: *Racing Cars* / Smoke on the water: *Deep Purple* / Do what you wanna do: *T-Connection* / Don't it make my brown eyes blue: *Gayle, Crystal* / Whodunnit: *Tavares* / Little girl: *Banned* / Dancing easy: *Williams, Danny* / 2468 Motorway: *Robinson, Tom Band* / Sneakin suspicion: *Dr. Feelgood*

ATTR 1977 / Mar '97 / Baktabak

☐ **TIME TO REMEMBER 1978, A (20 Original Chart Hits)**

Baker Street: *Rafferty, Gerry* / Ever fallen in love: *Buzzcocks* / Dancing in the street: *Hain, Marshall* / Talking in your sleep: *Gayle, Crystal* / 5 Minutes: *Stranglers* / More like the movies: *Dr. Hook* / Lay your love on me: *Racey* / If I had words: *Fitzgerald, Scott & Yvonne Keeley* / Darlin': *Miller, Frankie* / Don't cry for me Argentina: *Shadows* / Every one's a winner: *Hot Chocolate* / On fire: *T-Connection* / If you can't give me love: *Quatro, Suzi* / More than a woman: *Tavares* / Boogie boogie oogie: *Taste Of Honey* / Coming home: *Hain, Marshall* / What do I get: *Buzzcocks* / Nice 'n' sleazy: *Stranglers* / Don't take no for an answer: *Robinson, Tom Band* / Down at the doctors: *Dr. Feelgood*

ATTR 1978 / Mar '97 / Baktabak

☐ **TIME TO REMEMBER 1979, A (20 Original Chart Hits)**

When you're in love with a beautiful woman: *Dr. Hook* / Please don't go: *KC & The Sunshine Band* / Milk and alcohol: *Dr. Feelgood* / Duchess: *Strangers* / Mindless boogie: *Hot Chocolate* / She's in love with you: *Quatro, Suzi* / Gertcha: *Chas & Dave* / I don't wanna lose you: *Kandidate* / Tired of toein' the line: *Burnette, Rocky* / Some girls: *Racey* / Theme from the Deer Hunter: *Shadows* / Freedoms' prisoner: *Harley, Steve & Cockney Rebel* / My sharona: *Knack* / At home he's a tourist: *Gang Of Four* / Night owl: *Rafferty, Gerry* / Straw dogs: *Stiff Little Fingers* / Livin' on the frontline: *Grant, Eddy* / Doctor Doctor: *UFO* / Outdoor miner: *Wire* / Everybody's happy nowadays: *Buzzcocks*

ATTR 1979 / Mar '97 / Baktabak

☐ **TIME TO SAY GOODBYE (2CD Set)**

Time to say goodbye / How deep is your love / We are the world / Killing me softly / Everytime I see you / Lemon tree / Macarena / From Vienna to LA / Viel zu nah am himmel / Only you / Ebony and ivory / Summer love / Blue eyes / Don't cry for me Argentina / Isla romantica / Lonely day / Greensleeves / Ballade pour adeline / Winner takes it all / First love / Liebst du mich / Wind of change / Moon river / Le reve / One moment in time / Sleepless in Vienna / Conquest of paradise / Hotel calafornia / Bob's pop / I do it for you / Your eyes / When I need you / Liebe ist starker / Fly away / Nights are endless / Amazing grace

330228 / Sep '97 / Koch

☐ **TIMELESS**

CDSGP 0304 / Aug '96 / Prestige

☐ **TIMELESS CLASSICS (2CD Set)**

AMSC 629 / 27 May '98 / Avid

☐ **TIMELESS COMPILATION**

PWMCD 1 / Oct '89 / Total

☐ **TIMELESS FLIGHT**

CDTB 187 / 27 Mar '98 / Thunderbolt

☐ **TIMELESS TRADITIONAL JAZZ FESTIVAL**

Schlafe mein prinzchen: *Bue, Papa Viking Jazz Band* / Muskrat ramble: *Collie, Max Rhythm Aces* / Mood indigo: *Ball, Kenny & His Jazzmen* / Bourbon Street Parade: *Dutch Swing College Band* / Flyin' house: *Dr. Dixie* / That's a plenty: *Prowizorka Dzez Bed* / Stranger on the shore: *Bilk, Acker & His Paramount Jazz Band* / Struttin' with some barbecue: *Down Town Jazzband* / Ice cream: *Sunshine, Monty Jazz Band* / Basin Street blues: *Sunshine, Monty Jazz Band* / Jumpin' at the Woodside: *Jansens, Huub* / World is waiting for the sunrise: *Jansens, Huub* / Bye

and bye: *Boutte, Lillian* / Petite fleur: *Lightfoot, Terry* / West End blues: *Barber, Chris & Rod Mason's Hot Five* / At the Jazz Band Ball: *World's Greatest Jazz Band* / Jambalaya: *Barber, Chris & His Jazz Band* / As I go to the Quick River: *Uralsky All Stars*
CDTTD 52223 / Jul '94 / Timeless Traditional

☐ TINSEL TUNES (More Holiday Treats From Sugar Hill)
Blue Christmas lights: *Hillman, Chris & Herb Pedersen* / Sleigh ride: *Bush, Sam* / In the bleak midwinter: *O'Brien, Mollie* / Christmas story: *Nashville Bluegrass Band* / All I want is Mary for Christmas: *Lonesome River Band* / Ring the bells at midnight: *Kallick, Kathy & The Little Big Band* / Christmas is coming to town: *Laurel Canyon Ramblers* / Bring a torch Jeanette Isabella: *Thile, Chris* / I'll be home for Christmas: *Brother Boys* / On a quiet night: *Psychograss* / Last month of the year: *Fairfield Four & NBB* / Every day will be like a holiday: *Dixon, Don & Marti Jones* / Christmas swing: *Chesapeake* / Merry Christmas from the family: *Keen, Robert Earl*
SHCD 3855 / Mar '98 / Sugar Hill

☐ TIP CLASSICS (GMS Tweaked Mix)
TIPCD 20 / 3 Aug '98 / Tip

☐ TIP SINGLES VOL.2
Universal mind: *Psychopod* / Human oscillator: *Psychopod* / Karma: *Laughing Buddha* / Hyperspaced: *Infinity Project* / Weird karma: *Doof* / See you later oscillator: *Synchro* / Soothsayer: *Hallucinogen* / STC: *Deviant* / Scorch: *Snake Thing*
TIPCD 16 / 13 Oct '97 / Tip

☐ TIP SINGLES VOL.3
Growlmonizer: *Growlmonizer* / Stun gun: *Slinky Nuns* / Autopilot: *Xtra Terresticle* / Lighthouse: *Lotus Omega* / Skuffed: *System Busters* / Overwind: *Infinity Project* / Murora my love: *Deviant* / Stop the carnage: *Psychopod* / One small creature: *GMS* / Star above Parvathi: *Doof*
TIPCD 17 / 16 Feb '98 / Tip

☐ TIR MO CHRAIDH
BRCD 0003 / May '97 / B&R Heritage

☐ TIROLER-ABEND
499422 / Jul '91 / Koch

☐ TITANIC (Melodies From The White Star Music Book On The Titanic)
Mikado / Stars and stripes forever: *Philadelphia Orchestra* / Nell Gwynn dances: *New Symphony Orchestra* / Spring song: *Victor Concert Orchestra* / Minuet: *Sandler, Albert & His Orchestra* / El capitan: *Sousa's Band* / Faust: *Sandler, Albert & His Orchestra* / Humoreske no.7: *Primrose, William & Victor Symphony Orchestra* / Salut d'amour: *Victor Concert Orchestra* / Serenade: *Victor String Ensemble* / Orpheus in the underworld: *Light Symphony Orchestra* / Mosquitoes parade: *Campoli, Alfredo & His Salon Orchestra* / Henry VIII: *New Symphony Orchestra* / Rosary: *Primrose, William & Victor Symphony Orchestra* / God save the King: *BBC Symphony Orchestra*
PASTCD 7822 / Nov '97 / Flapper

☐ TJOPLUSTA PART 2
BROOL 006CD / Mar '96 / Brool

☐ TO HAVE AND TO HOLD
IONIC 15CD / Oct '96 / Mute

☐ TO THE BEAT Y'ALL - OLD SCHOOL RAP
Rapper's delight: *Sugarhill Gang* / Radio commercial: *Sugarhill Gang* / That's the joint: *Funky 4+1* / Adventures of grandmaster flash on the wheels of steel: *Grandmaster Flash* / Birthday party: *Grandmaster Flash* / Good times: *Grandmaster Flash* / Another one bites the dust: *Grandmaster Flash* / Rapture: *Grandmaster Flash* / Flash to the beat: *Grandmaster Flash* / White lines (don't don't do it): *Grandmaster Flash & Melle Mel* / Drop the bomb: *Trouble Funk* / Pump me up: *Trouble Funk* / Hey fellas: *Trouble Funk* / Freedom: *Grandmaster Flash & The Furious Five* / Message: *Grandmaster Flash & The Furious Five* / It's nasty (genius of love): *Grandmaster Flash & The Furious Five* / Scorpio: *Grandmaster Flash & The Furious Five* / Spoonin' rap: *Gee, Spoonie* / And you know that: *Sequence* / Funk you up: *Sequence* / To the beat y'all: *Lady B* / Super wolf can do it: *Super-Wolf* / Eighth Wonder: *Sugarhill Gang* / Monster jam: *Spoonie Gee & The Sequence* / Yes we can-can: *Treacherous Three* / Break dancin': *West Street Mob* / Electric boogie: *West Street Mob* / Busy bee's groove: *Busy Bee* / Making cash money: *Busy Bee* / Jesse: *Grandmaster Flash & Melle Mel* / Message II (Survival): *Melle Mel & Duke Bootee* / We are known as emcees (we turn the party out): *Crash Crew* / Breaking bells (take me to the mardi gras): *Crash Crew* / Scratching: *Crash Crew* / Check it out: *Wayne & Charlie* / All night long (Waterbed): *Kevie Kev* / Mirda rock: *Griffin, Reggie* / King heroin: *Funky Four* / Mayor: *Melle Mel*
NXTCD 217 / Oct '92 / Sequel

☐ TO THE BEST MUM IN THE WORLD (16 Songs For Mothers Everywhere)
For mama / Whatever will be will be (Que sera sera) / I'll always love my mama / Shop around / Teenager's mother / Mama / Mother in my eyes / Silver threads among the gold / Mama used to say / Say mama / I saw mommy kissing Santa Claus / My mommy's eyes / Mama said / Mother of mine / No charge / Reading me stories
306122 / Jan '97 / Hallmark

☐ TODOS ESTOS ANOS
21067CD / Nov '95 / Sonifolk

☐ TOE THE LINE VOL.1 (20 Linedance Classics)
Wild Horse Saloon theme: *Wild Horse Saloon* / Watermelon crawl: *Byrd, Tracy* / What the cowgirls do: *Gill, Vince* / Easy come, easy go: *Strait, George* / Going through the big D: *Chesnutt, Mark* / Out with a bang: *Murphy, David Lee* / Why haven't I heard from you: *McEntire, Reba* / If I ain't got you: *Stuart, Marty* / Let the picture paint itself: *Crowell, Rodney* / Dust in the bottle: *Murphy, David Lee* / 4 To 1 in Atlanta: *Byrd, Tracy* / High tech redneck: *Jones, George* / Gonna get a life: *Chesnutt, Mark* / One more last chance: *Gill, Vince* / Adalida: *Strait, George* / I wanna got too far: *Yearwood, Trisha* / All you ever do is bring me down: *Mavericks* / Trouble: *Chesnutt, Mark* / Copperhead road: *Earle, Steve* / Walking to Jerusalem: *Byrd, Tracy*
MCD 11455 / 8 Sep '97 / MCA

☐ TOE THE LINE VOL.2 (The Next Step)
Honky tonkin's what I do best: *Stuart, Marty* / Everytime I get around you: *Murphy, David Lee* / Swing city: *Brown, Roger* / Wrong place, wrong time: *Chesnutt, Mark* / Every cowboys dream: *Akins, Rhett* / Missing you: *Mavericks* / Out of control raging fire: *Byrd, Tracy* / Tangled up in Texas: *River, Frazier* / Where the sidewalk ends: *Strait, George* / Little more love: *Gill, Vince* / Texas is bigger than it used to be: *Chesnutt, Mark* / Hillbilly rock: *Stuart, Marty* / Honkytonk dancing machine: *Byrd, Tracy* / Guitar town: *Earle, Steve* / Southside of Dixie: *Gill, Vince* / I brake for brunettes: *Akins, Rhett* / Highways and heartaches: *Ely, Joe* / Walk on: *Withers, Janeen* / Don't be cruel: *Stuart, Marty* / Lovebug: *Strait, George* / Rose of Memphis: *Crowell, Rodney* / Love on the loose, heart on the run: *McBride & The Ride* / Holdin' heaven: *Byrd, Tracy* / One dance with you: *Gill, Vince* / Tempted: *Stuart, Marty* / Strut your stuff: *Sheriff, Dave* / If I ain't got you: *Yearwood, Trisha* / Children: *Mavericks* / Hard lovin' woman: *Collie, Mark* / You better think twice: *Gill, Vince* / Honky tonk twist: *Lee, Scooter* / What they're talkin' about: *Akins, Rhett* / Blame it on Texas: *Chesnutt, Mark* / Hillbilly highway: *Earle, Steve* / Western women: *Brown, Roger* / Big love: *Byrd, Tracy* / Rocky top: *Osborne Brothers*
MCD 11591 / Feb '97 / MCA

☐ TOE THE LINE VOL.3 (2CD Set)
MCD 72022 / 17 Nov '97 / MCA

☐ TOES ON THE NOSE (32 Surf Age Instrumentals)
Squad car: *Eddie & The Showmen* / Midnight run: *Super Stocks* / Voodoo juice: *Ghouls* / Quiet surf: *Allen, Richie & The Pacific Surfers* / Movin': *Eddie & The Showmen* / Mr. Rebel: *Eddie & The Showmen* / Moon probe: *Vulcans* / Coffin nails: *Ghouls* / Newport beach: *Super Stocks* / Casbah: *Nelson, Sandy* / We are the young: *Eddie & The Showmen* / Trophy run: *Super Stocks* / Legends: *Ho-Dads* / Outer limits: *Cole, Jerry & His Spacemen* / Twilight city: *Vulcans* / Ventura: *Super Stocks* / Toes on the nose: *Eddie & The Showmen* / Surf man: *Allen, Richie & The Pacific Surfers* / Faraway places: *Eddie & The Showmen* / Lanky bones: *Eddie & The Showmen* / Pipeline: *Cole, Jerry & His Spacemen* / Bucket seats: *Rally packs* / Last walk: *Super Stocks* / Border town: *Eddie & The Showmen* / Oceanside: *Super Stocks* / Midnight surfer: *Cole, Jerry & His Spacemen* / Space race: *Ho-Dads* / Dracula's theme: *Ghouls* / Young and lonely: *Eddie & The Showmen* / Redondo beach: *Super Stocks* / Gridiron goodie: *Super Stocks* / Scratch: *Eddie & The Showmen*
CDCHD 634 / Sep '96 / Ace

☐ TOGETHER
I knew you were waiting (for me): *Franklin, Aretha & George Michael* / Sometimes love just ain't enough: *Smyth, Patty & Don Henley* / Where is the love: *Paris, Mica & Will Downing* / Baby, come to me: *Austin, Patti & James Ingram* / Don't know much: *Ronstadt, Linda & Aaron Neville* / We've got tonight: *Rogers, Kenny & Sheena Easton* / If you were with me now: *Minogue, Kylie & Keith Washington* / You are everything: *Ross, Diana & Marvin Gaye* / Ain't nothing like the real thing: *Gaye, Marvin & Tammi Terrell* / Up where we belong: *Cocker, Joe & Jennifer Warnes* / Endless love: *Ross, Diana & Lionel Richie* / With you I'm born again: *Preston, Billy & Syreeta* / Tonight I celebrate my love: *Bryson, Peabo & Roberta Flack* / You're all I need to get by: *Gaye, Marvin & Tammi Terrell* / Stop, look, listen (to your heart): *Gaye, Marvin & Diana Ross* / It takes two: *Gaye, Marvin & Kim Weston* / Too much, too little, too late: *Mathis, Johnny & Deniece Williams* / Reunited: *Peaches & Herb* / Solid: *Ashford & Simpson* / Teardrops: *Womack & Womack*
5254612 / Mar '95 / Polydor

☐ TOGETHER - THE EASTBOUND JAZZ YEARS
Baby let me take you (in my arms): *Chandler, Gary* / Crazy legs: *Person, Houston* / For the love of you: *Person, Houston* / Gettin' off: *Mason, Bill* / Lester leaps in: *Person, Houston* / Blow top blues: *Jones, Etta* / Flamingo: *Chandler, Gary* / Gathering together: *Sparks, Melvin* / When I'm kissing my love: *Wilson, Spanky* / Jet set: *Chandler, Gary* / Mr. Jay: *Mason, Bill*
CDBGPD 071 / Aug '93 / Beat Goes Public

☐ TOGETHER AGAIN (2CD Set)
Make no mistake he's mine: *Carnes, Kim & Barbra Streisand* / Tonight I celebrate my love for you: *Bryson, Peabo & Roberta Flack* / Do that to me one more time: *Captain & Tennille* / Especially for you: *Trachta, Jeff & Bobbie Eakes* / If you go: *Barry & Eileen* / I'd thought I'd ring you: *Bassey, Shirley & Alain Delon* / Could it be I'm falling in love: *Grant, David & Jaki Graham* / Soemtimes when we touch: *Grant & Forsyth* / Together we are beautiful: *Neville, Gordon & Marilyn David* / Two of us: *Kissoon, Mac & Katie* / What becomes of the brokenhearted: *Turner, Ruby & Jimmy Ruffin* / Until forever: *Rogers, Evan & Deitra Hicks* / I'll keep your dreams alive: *Benson, George & Patti Austin* / Little bit more: *Jackson, Freddie & Melba Moore* / Heaven's justa step away: *McCook, John & Bobbie Eakes* / Maybe: *Bryson, Peabo & Roberta Flack* / If you're ready: *Butler, Jonathan & Ruby Turner* / Mated: *Grant, David & Jaki Graham* / Having my baby: *Anka, Paul & Odia Coates* / More than I can say: *Justian & Mandy* / I'm in love: *Moore, Melba* / Somewhere between: *Grant & Forsyth* / Love story: *Tempo, Nino* / Precious thing: *Charles, Ray & Dee Dee Bridgewater* / All I have to do is dream: *Campbell, Glen & Bobbie Gentry* / Only a fool: *Lee, Byron & Mighty Sparrow* / You need a woman tonight: *Captain & Tennille* / Sugar candy kisses: *Kissoon, Mac & Katie* / I'm gonna love you forever: *Kissoon, Mac & Katie*
DOU 886722 / 2 Feb '98 / Disky

☐ TOGETHER FOREVER
GFS 079 / Nov '97 / Going For A Song

☐ TOKYO FLASHBACK VOL.1
PSFD 12 / 16 Mar '98 / PSF

☐ TOKYO FLASHBACK VOL.2
PSFD 24 / 16 Mar '98 / PSF

☐ TOKYO FLASHBACK VOL.4
PSFD 69 / Dec '95 / PSF

☐ TOKYO TRASHVILLE
ANDA 181 / Mar '97 / Au-Go-Go

☐ TOLEKI BANGO
CRAW 1 / Jan '96 / Crammed World

☐ TOM-TOM ARABESQUES
VICG 50092 / Mar '96 / JVC World Library

☐ TOM-TOM FANTASY
VICG 50102 / Mar '96 / JVC World Library

☐ TOMMY ARMSTRONG OF TYNESIDE
TSCD 484 / Jul '97 / Topic

☐ TOMORROW'S HITS TODAY
SHINECD 002 / 24 Nov '97 / Summershine

☐ TONE TALES FROM TOMORROW VOL.2 (Ntone Compilation)
2005: *Transcend* / Cymatic frequency: *Coldcut* / First time ever I saw your face: *Law, Joanna* / Weeds: *Neotropic* / Gather: *Path* / 50cc: *Journeyman* / 2003: *Transcend* / Hypobank: *Drome* / Sleeper: *MLO* / Zen in Africa: *Bogus Order* / Dubmunculus: *Hex* / Shark dance: *Real Life* / Alien community: *Alien Community* / Pressure: *Continuum* / Harmonic: *Hex* / Float on: *Purr*
NTONECD 009 / Apr '96 / Ntone

☐ TONIGHT AT MEZZO
Street walk: *Sambada* / Speak easy: *Four 80 East* / Smetana: *Borenius, Louis Coup D'Etat* / What's the best thing to do tomorrow: *Street Jazz Unit* / Samba royale: *Achenza, Paolo Trio* / Crusader: *Fishbelly Black* / Take one: *Yada Yada* / Equation: *Mr. Gone* / Original untitles: *Neos* / Chad's valley: *Diamond Wookie* / Magic night: *Bentley, Ed* / Keep on it: *Three Deuces*
MZCD 001 / 28 Feb '98 / Mezzo

☐ TOO GLAMOROUS (2CD Set)
MM 00012 / 17 Aug '98 / Miss Moneypenny's

☐ TOO GOOD TO BE FORGOTTEN
CDTRL 362 / Oct '95 / Trojan

☐ TOO HOT FOR ME (The JSP Sampler)
You're one woman: *Wilson, U.P.* / Woman is dangerous: *Shields, Lonnie* / I'm talking about love: *Butler Twins* / Hip guy: *Sayles, Charlie* / Doggy style: *Cosse, Ike* / Hey brother: *Morello, Jimmy* / Too hot for me: *Parker, Kenny* / Everlastin' tears: *Edwards, Willie* / Going back to Texas: *Kirkpatrick, Bob* / Light in a dark place: *Singleton, T-Bone* / Funky thang: *Patterson, Jordan* / One eyed man: *Tre'* / Here we go: *Rawls, Johnny* / You're a dog: *Jones, Andrew 'Jr. Boy'* / Fine as wine: *Coronado, Joe* / Aunt Nancey's Bull: *Griswalds* / Walk that way: *Wilson, U.P.*
JSPCD 2H1 / Apr '97 / JSP

☐ TOO LATE
True love: *Half Pint* / It's true: *Minott, Sugar* / Jealousy: *Sanchez, David* / Passing judgement: *Garnet Silk* / Wish it would rain: *Jack Radics* / Too late: *Brown, Dennis & Deborah Glasgow* / Action speak louder than words: *Simpleton* / Me won't prove: *Grindsman* / Don't dis the flex: *Pinchers* / Good body girls: *Ninja Kid* / Gummy glue don: *General Pecos* / Needed in the tabernacle: *Major Cat*
WRCD 004 / Dec '97 / World

☐ TOO LATE TOO LATE VOL.10
DOCD 5061 / 15 Jun '98 / Document

☐ TOO LATE TOO LATE VOL.2 1897-1935
DOCD 5216 / Jan '94 / Document

☐ TOO LATE TOO LATE VOL.4 1892-1937
DOCD 5321 / Mar '95 / Document

☐ TOO LATE TOO LATE VOL.7 1927-1955
DOCD 5525 / Apr '97 / Document

☐ TOO LATE TOO LATE VOL.8
DOCD 5574 / 21 Sep '97 / Document

☐ TOO LATE TOO LATE VOL.9 1922-1945
DOCD 5590 / 5 Feb '98 / Document

☐ TOO PURE SAMPLER
PURECD 034 / Apr '94 / Too Pure

☐ TOO UNTOUCHABLE
CASTE 6CD / 1 Sep '98 / OutCaste

☐ TOO YOUNG TO KNOW, TOO WILD TO CARE
New dawn fades: *Joy Division* / For Belgian friends: *Durutti Column* / And then again: *Certain Ratio* / Age of consent: *New Order* / Talk about the past: *Wake* / Brighter: *Railway Children* / Hymn from a village: *James* / Smiling monarchs: *Abecedarians* / Reach out for love: *King, Marcel* / Looking from a hilltop: *Section 25* / Genius: *Quando Quango* / WFL: Happy Mondays / My rising star: *Northside* / Moves like you: *Carroll, Cath* / Getting away with it: *Electronic*
8287002 / Mar '97 / Factory Too

☐ TOOTH AND NAIL ROCK SAMPLER VOL.1
TN 1091CD / 13 Apr '98 / Tooth & Nail

☐ TOP 12 DISCO SINGLES
PKCD 03893 / Jul '93 / K&K

☐ TOP COUNTRY (100 Of Country Music's Greatest Tracks-4CD Set)
Swingin' doors: *Haggard, Merle* / Riverboat: *Young, Faron* / Just one time: *Gibson, Don* / Behind closed doors: *Rich, Charlie* / Nobody but a fool would love you: *Smith, Connie* / Cool water: *Bandy, Moe* / Eat drink and be merry: *Wagoner, Porter* / If teardrops were silver: *Shepard, Jean* / BJ the DJ: *Jackson, Stonewall* / Good year for the roses: *Paycheck, Johnny* / Room full of roses: *Husky, Ferlin* / Don't touch me: *Seely, Jeannie* / Fingerprints: *Cline, Patsy* / Make the world go away: *Price, Ray* / In the summertime (You don't want my love): *Miller, Roger* / Geisha girl: *Locklin, Hank* / I'll repossess my heart: *Wells, Kitty* / Company you keep: *Phillips, Bill* / It takes a lot of money: *Mack, Warner* / Southern loving: *Brown, Jim Ed* / DJ for a day: *Newman, Jimmy C.* / No help wanted: *Carlisle, Bill* / Down Yonder: *Wood, Del* / Loose talk: *Smith, Carl* / Top of the world: *Anderson, Lynn* / For the good times: *Price, Ray* / I take a lot of pride in whwt I am: *Haggard, Merle* / Chug-a-lug: *Miller, Roger* / Little boy sad: *Phillips, Bill* / Country girl: *Riley, Jeannie C.* / Mornin' ride: *Greenwood, Lee* / To a sleeping beauty: *Dean, Jimmy* / Tender years: *Paycheck, Johnny* / Midnight train to Georgia: *Anderson, Lynn* / Let me be the one: *Locklin, Hank* / This white circle on my finger: *Wells, Kitty* / Back up buddy: *Smith, Carl* / Second hand rose: *Drusky, Roy* / Far far away: *Gibson, Don* / Comancheros: *King, Claude* / Will you remember mine: *Nelson, Willie* / Sittin' in an all nite cafe: *Mack, Warner* / Most beautiful girl: *Rich, Charlie* / Take time to love her: *Stuckey, Nat* / Then and only then: *Smith, Connie* / My elusive dreams: *Houston, David* / She called me baby baby: *Husky, Ferlin* / I can see an angel: *Cline, Patsy* / Sherrif of Boone county: *Price, Kenny* / Street of laredo: *Bandy, Moe* / Old rugged cross: *Price, Ray* / What would you do (If Jesus came to your house): *Wagoner, Porter* / Turn your radio on: *Davis, Skeeter* / There is power in the blood: *Gibson, Don* / Whispering hope: *Brown, Jim Ed* / Jesus is your ticket to heaven: *Smith, Connie* / Amen: *Greenwood, Lee* / Softly and tenderly: *Russell, Johnny* / Just a closer walk with thee: *Cline, Patsy* / You light up my life: *Smith, Margo* / Rock of ages: *Felts, Narvel* / Standing on the promises: *Pruett, Jeanne* / Little delta Church: *Darrell, Johnny* / One day at a time: *Greenwood, Lee* / What a friend we have in Jesus: *Price, Ray* / Life's railway to heaven: *Dalton, Lacy J.* / In the sweet bye and bye: *Kilgore, Merle* / Church in the wildwood: *Houston, David* / Uncloudy day: *Pruett, Jeanne* / Why me Lord: *Greene, Jack* / Baptism of Jesse Taylor: *Russell, Johnny* / Leaning on the everlasting arms: *Butler, Carl & Pearl* / Put your hand in the hand: *Posey, Sandy* / Peace in the valley: *Price, Kenny* / Amazing grace: *Greenwood, Lee* / Okie from Muskogee: *Haggard, Merle* / Good time Charlie's got the blues: *Rich, Charlie* / Night life: *Price, Ray* / Wine me up: *Young, Faron* / It's a little more like heaven: *Locklin, Hank* / Give myself a party: *Gibson, Don* / High noon (Do not forsake me): *Bandy, Moe* / Tiger woman: *King, Claude* / See the big man cry: *Louvin, Charlie* / I love you honey: *Cline, Patsy* / Country Bumpkin: *Smith, Cal* / I hope so: *Nelson, Willie* / Me and Bobby McGee: *Miller, Roger* / Race is on: *Paycheck, Johnny* / San Antonio rose: *Husky, Ferlin* / Lonely women make good lovers: *Luman, Bob* / Baby doll: *Fairchild, Barbara* / Fool's gold: *Greenwood, Lee* / Juanita Jones: *Phillips, Stu* / Am I that easy to forget: *Davis, Skeeter* / Nobody's darlin' but mine: *Jackson, Stonewall* / Cry: *Anderson, Lynn* / Hey Joe: *Smith, Carl* / Sea of love: *Houston, David*
ECD 3285 / Aug '97 / K-Tel

☐ TOP COUNTRY STARS
15214 / Aug '91 / Laserlight

☐ TOP GEAR ANTHEMS (2CD Set)
VTDCD 192 / 8 Jun '98 / Virgin

☐ TOP GEAR VOL.1
Jessica: *Allman Brothers* / Killer queen: *Queen* / Sharp dressed man: *ZZ Top* / You took the words right out of my mouth: *Meat Loaf* / Two princes: *Spin Doctors* / We don't need another hero: *Turner, Tina* / More than a feeling: *Boston* / Big log: *Plant, Robert* / Inside: *Stiltskin* / Wishing well: *Free* / Roll away the stone: *Mott The Hoople* / Maggie May: *Stewart, Rod* / Tuff enuff: *Fabulous Thunderbirds* / Because the night: *Smith, Patti* / Call me: *Blondie* / Rhiannon (Will you ever win): *Fleetwood Mac* / You: *Frampton, Peter* / When tomorrow comes: *Eurythmics* / Power of love: *Lewis, Huey & The News* / Do anything you wanna do: *Eddie & The Hot Rods* / 2-4-6-8 Motorway: *Robinson, Tom* / Bad case of lovin' you (Doctor Doctor): *Palmer, Robert* / Boys are back in town: *Thin Lizzy* / Brown eyed girl: *Morrison, Van* / Rocky mountain way: *Walsh, Joe* / Talking back to the night: *Cocker, Joe* / Show me the way: *Frampton, Peter* / I want you to want me: *Cheap Trick* / Long train runnin': *Doobie Brothers* / American pie: *McLean, Don* / Black magic woman: *Santana* / Everybody wants to rule the world: *Tears For Fears* / Walk on the wild side: *Reed, Lou* / Wicked game: *Isaak, Chris* / Venus in furs: *Velvet Underground*
MOODCD 33 / May '94 / Columbia

☐ TOP GEAR VOL.2
I want to break free: *Queen* / I drove all night: *Lauper, Cyndi* / My brother Jake: *Free* / Drive: *Cars* / Change: *Lightning Seeds* / Can't get enough: *Bad Company* / Final countdown: *Europe* / Peace pipe: *Cry Of Love* / Africa: *Toto* / Damn, I wish I was your love: *Hawkins, Sophie B.* / Owner of a lonely heart: *Yes* / Heart of stone: *Stewart, Dave* / Atomic: *Blondie* / Since you've been gone: *Rainbow* / Satellite: *Hooters* / Once bitten twice shy: *Hunter, Ian* / Addicted to love: *Palmer, Robert* / Free bird: *Lynyrd Skynyrd* / Dead ringer for love: *Meat Loaf* / Little Miss can't be wrong: *Spin Doctors* / Seven wonders: *Fleetwood Mac* / Driver's seat: *Sniff 'n' The Tears* / Good feeling: *Reef* / Gimme all your lovin': *ZZ Top* / Flame: *Cheap Trick* / If I could turn back time: *Cher* / Twenty nine palms: *Plant, Robert* / Hold your head up: *Argent* / Life's been good: *Walsh, Joe* / Cars and girls: *Prefab Sprout* / On the road again: *Canned Heat* / Poison: *Cooper, Alice* / Missing you: *Waite, John* / Night games: *Bonnet, Graham* / Motorcycle emptiness: *Manic Street Preachers* / (Don't fear) The reaper: *Blue Oyster Cult*
MOODCD 41 / May '95 / Columbia

☐ TOP GEAR VOL.3 (The Rock Ballads)
Rock 'n' roll dreams come through: *Meat Loaf* / Rhiannon: *Fleetwood Mac* / Always the sun: *Stranglers* / 74-75: *Connells* / Couldn't get it right: *Climax Blues Band* / Stainsby girls: *Rea, Chris* / Mmm mmm mmm mmm: *Crash Test Dummies* / Creep: *Radiohead* / Driving away from home: *It's Immaterial* / So far away: *Dire Straits* / When will you (make my telephone ring): *Deacon Blue* / I don't want

to talk about it: Everything But The Girl / Johnny and Mary: Palmer, Robert / If I was: Ure, Midge / It's my life: Talk Talk / Alive and kicking: Simple Minds / Yes: McAlmont & Butler / Bette Davis eyes: Carnes, Kim / Walking in Memphis: Cher / Lucky you: Lightning Seeds / He's on the phone: St. Etienne / Manic Monday: Bangles / Mary's prayer: Danny Wilson / No more I love you's: Lennox, Annie / Somewhere down the crazy river: Robertson, Robbie / Come together in the morning: Free / Parisienne walkways: Moore, Gary / Ghost in you: Psychedelic Furs / Wonderful life: Black
SONYTV 12CD / Feb '96 / Sony TV

☐ **TOP OF THE HILL BLUEGRASS (The Sugar Hill Collection)**
SHCD 9201 / Dec '95 / Sugar Hill

☐ **TOP OF THE POPS**
CECD 6 / Jun '96 / Collector's Edition

☐ **TOP OF THE POPS - THE CUTTING EDGE**
Design for life: Manic Street Preachers / Tattva: Kula Shaker / Oh yeah: Ash / Peaches: Presidents Of The USA / Trash: Suede / One to another: Charlatans / Good night: Baby Bird / Me and you versus the world: Space / What's in the box (see watcha got): Boo Radleys / Born slippy: Underworld / Out of the sinking: Weller, Paul / Becoming more like Alfie: Divine Comedy / Alright: Cast / Mario man: Super Furry Animals / Day we caught the train: Ocean Colour Scene / Shark: Throwing Muses / All nighter: Elastica / Mouse in a hole: Heavy Stereo / Crazy: Nut / Saved: Octopus / Possibly maybe: Bjork / Virtual insanity: Jamiroquai / Tape loop: Morcheeba / Stupid girl: Garbage / Nice guy Eddie: Sleeper / Ready or not: Lightning Seeds / 500 (Shake baby shake): Lush / Someone somewhere: Wannadies / Elevator song: Dubstar / Celebrity hit list: Terrorvision / In a room: Dodgy / Exodus: Levellers / Sitting at home: Honeycrack / Ski jump nose: Mansun / Men in black: Black, Frank / Hours and the times: 18 Wheeler / To you I bestow: Mundy / Anymore: Cracknell, Sarah / Krupa: Apollo 440 / Chemical beats: Chemical Brothers
SONYTV 19CD / Sep '96 / Sony TV

☐ **TOP OF THE POPS SUMMER '98 (2CD Set)**
All that I need: Boyzone / Feel it: Tamperer & Maya / Last thing on my mind: Steps / Doctor Jones: Aqua / When the lights go out: Five / Uh la la la: Alexia / I will come to you: Hanson / All I have to give: Backstreet Boys / High: Lighthouse Family / No no no: Destiny's Child / Put your arms around me: Texas / Old before I die: Williams, Robbie / Angel street: M-People / Show me love: Robyn / Party people...Friday night: 911 / Story of love: OTT / Treat infamy: Rest Assured / It's like that: Run DMC & Jason Nevins / Brimful of Asha: Cornershop / Ballad of Tom Jones: Space / Never ever: All Saints / Big mistake: Imbruglia, Natalie / Kiss the rain: Myers, Billie / Who do you think you are: Spice Girls / Found a cure: Ultra Nate / Here's where the story end: Tin Tin Out / Sounds of wickedness: Tzant / La primavera: Sash / All my life: K-Ci & Jo Jo / Arms around the world: Louise / Cleopatra's theme: Cleopatra / Father: LL Cool J / Be alone no more: Another Level / I want you to want me: Solid Harmonie / Breathe: Minogue, Kylie / My star: Brown, Ian / All around the world: Oasis
5557132 / 4 May '98 / PolyGram TV

☐ **TOP OF THE POPS VOL.2**
Fairground: Simply Red / Gangsta's paradise: Coolio / Shy guy: King, Diana / Baby it's you: Dion, Celine / Pour que tu m'aimes encore: Dion, Celine / Power of love: Vandross, Luther / Walking in Memphis: Cher / Never forget: Take That / Heaven help my heart: Arena, Tina / If you leave me now: Riverseries / U krazy katz: PJ & Duncan / We've got it goin' on: Backstreet Boys / Stay with me: Erasure / He's on the phone: St. Etienne / I'm only sleeping: Suggs / Girl like you: Collins, Edwyn / Raoul and the Kings of Spain: Tears For Fears / You do: McAlmont & Butler / 74-75: Connells / Where the wild roses grow: Cave, Nick & Kylie Minogue / Wonderwall: Oasis / Lucky you: Lightning Seeds / Common people: Pulp / What do I do now: Sleeper / Kings of the kerb: Echobelly / From the bench at Belvidere: Boo Radleys / Love rendevous: M-People / Missing: Everything But The Girl / Hideaway: De'Lacy / Happy just to be with you: Gayle, Michelle / I can't tell you why: Brownstone / You remind me of something: R Kelly / Stayin' alive: N-Trance / Found love: Double Dee & Dany / My prerogative: Brown, Bobby / 1st of tha month: Bone Thugs n' Harmony / Exodus: Sunscreem / Transamazonia: Shamen / La la la hey hey: Outhere Brothers / Angel: Jam & Spoon
SONYTV 9CD / Nov '95 / Sony TV

☐ **TOP RANK EXPLOSION**
LG 21096 / May '94 / Lagoon

☐ **TOP ROCK STEADY**
LG 21070 / Feb '93 / Lagoon

☐ **TOP SOLOISTS, THE**
Singin' the blues / Savoy blues / Swing out / Moonglow / Limehouse blues / Vibraphone blues / Heckler's hop / I can't get started / Lazy afternoon / Just a hood / Rocks / Roy meets horn / Tea for two / Lester leaps in / Body and soul / Rosetta / Cotton tail / Day dream / Solo flight / Swingmatism / Little John special
TPZ 1032 / Nov '97 / Topaz Jazz

☐ **TOP SOUNDS FROM TOP DECK VOL.1 (Ska-Ra-Van)**
Ska-ra-van: Alphonso, Roland / Yogi man: Moore, Johnny / Everyday: Avalons / Cleo's back: Alphonso, Roland / Love will find a way / Red is danger: Moore, Johnny / Love in the afternoon: Drummond, Don / Ten virgins: Angelic Brothers / 5 o'clock whistle: Brooks, Baba / Money or love: Al & The Vibrations / Scattered lights: McCook, Tommy / Ti-pi-tin: Harper, Raymond / Shot in the dark: Alphonso, Roland / El Cid: King Sporty & Justin Yap
WESM 509 / 22 Sep '97 / Westside

☐ **TOP SOUNDS FROM TOP DECK VOL.4 (Ska-Ta-Shot)**
Ska ta shot: Taitt, Lynn / Shock resistant: Brooks, Baba / Please leave me alone: Andy & The Avalons / Sweet dreams: Bibby & The Astronauts / Rolli rollin': Alphonso, Roland / Red is danger: Moore, Johnny / Come back pretty baby: Schoolboys / Because of you: Alphonso, Roland / Too young to love: Marshall, Larry / Determination: Alphonso, Roland / Ambition of men: Anderson, Rueben / Warlock: Mittoo, Jackie / Fresh out of love: Jetts / Ska down Jamaica way: Nelson, Ferdie & Ivan Yap
WESM 521 / 19 Jan '98 / Westside

☐ **TOP TEN**
NWSCD 6 / Apr '93 / New Sound

☐ **TOP TEN HITS OF THE 60'S**
House of the rising sun: Animals / Do it again: Beach Boys / Got to get you into my life: Bennett, Cliff & The Rebel Rousers / Someone else's baby: Faith, Adam / Little lovin': Fourmost / Ferry 'cross the Mersey: Gerry & The Pacemakers / Something is happening: Herman's Hermits / In the country: Richard, Cliff / Look through my window: Hollies / High time: Jones, Paul / I'm a tiger: Lulu / FBI: Shadows / Hippy hippy shake: Swinging Blue Jeans / Pasadena: Temperance Seven / Twelfth of never: Richard, Cliff / Let's go to San Francisco: Flowerpot Men / Seven little girls sitting in the back seat: Avons / You were made for me: Freddie & The Dreamers
CDMFP 6040 / Sep '88 / Music For Pleasure

☐ **TOP TEN HITS OF THE 60'S VOL.1**
PLSCD 216 / Apr '97 / Pulse

☐ **TOP TEN HITS OF THE 60'S VOL.2**
PLSCD 217 / Apr '97 / Pulse

☐ **TOP TEN HITS OF THE 70'S**
Wuthering Heights: Bush, Kate / American pie: McLean, Don / Baker Street: Rafferty, Gerry / Roll over Beethoven: ELO / Tap turns on the water: CCS / 2-4-6-8 motorway: Robinson, Tom / You sexy thing: Hot Chocolate / Angie baby: Reddy, Helen / Air that I breathe: Hollies / Make me smile (come up and see me): Harley, Steve & Cockney Rebel / Let's work together: Canned Heat / Some girls: Racey / Heaven must be missing an angel: Tavares / 48 crash: Quatro, Suzi / Cotton fields: Beach Boys / Cat crept in: Mud / Little bit more: Dr. Hook / Years may come years may go: Herman's Hermits
CDMFP 6078 / Oct '89 / Music For Pleasure

☐ **TOP TEN HITS OF THE 70'S**
Nutbush City limits: Turner, Ike & Tina / Walking: CCS / I can't tell the bottom from the top: Hollies / I hear you knocking: Edmunds, Dave / Love is life: Hot Chocolate / Right back where we started from: Nightingale, Maxine / Night owl: Rafferty, Gerry / Don't it make my brown eyes blue: Gayle, Crystal / If you can't give me love: Quatro, Suzi / Summer (the first time): Goldsboro, Bobby / That's the way (I like it): KC & The Sunshine Band / Mr. Soft: Cockney Rebel / Rock me gently: Kim, Andy / Oh boy: Mud / Don't take away the music: Tavares / Them heavy people: Bush, Kate / Angel fingers: Wizzard / Vincent: McLean, Don
CDMFP 6211 / Feb '96 / Music For Pleasure

☐ **TOP TEN HITS OF THE 80'S**
Girls on film: Duran Duran / Running up that hill: Bush, Kate / Geno: Dexy's Midnight Runners / Golden brown: Stranglers / Kids in America: Wilde, Kim / Harder I try: Brother Beyond / Bette Davis eyes: Carnes, Kim / Tonight I celebrate my love: Bryson, Peabo & Roberta Flack / Kayleigh: Marillion / Set me free: Graham, Jaki / Model: Kraftwerk / Too shy: Kajagoogoo / Turning Japanese: Vapors / Searchin': Dean, Hazell / Walking on sunshine: Katrina & The Waves / Tarzan boy: Baltimora / Election day: Arcadia / Sexy eyes: Dr. Hook / No doubt about it: Hot Chocolate / Let's go all the way: Sly Fox
CDMFP 5893 / Sep '90 / Music For Pleasure

☐ **TOP TEN HITS OF THE 80'S**
It started with a kiss: Hot Chocolate / For your eyes only: Easton, Sheena / Strange little girl: Stranglers / Chequered love: Wilde, Kim / Classic: Gurvitz, Adrian / I could be so good for you: Waterman, Dennis / Solid: Ashford & Simpson / Road to nowhere: Talking Heads / I don't wanna dance: Grant, Eddy / Missing you: Waite, John / Set me free: Graham, Jaki / Love changes (everything): Climie Fisher / Incommunicado: Marillion / Respectable: Mel & Kim / Big apple: Kajagoogoo / Crying: McLean, Don
CDMFP 6212 / Feb '96 / Music For Pleasure

☐ **TOP TEN HITS OF THE 80'S - VOL.2**
Reflex: Duran Duran / Perfect: Fairground Attraction / Babooshka: Bush, Kate / Lifeline: Spandau Ballet / Lavender: Marillion / System addict: Five Star / Fantastic day: Haircut 100 / Living in a box: Living In A Box / We close our eyes: Go West / Better love next time: Dr. Hook / Atomic: Blondie / Use it up and wear it out: Odyssey / Tunnel of love: Fun Boy Three / Broken wings: Mr. Mister / Girl you know it's true: Milli Vanilli / Rat race: Specials / You'll never stop me loving you: Sonia / Rise to the occasion: Climie Fisher / Who's leaving who: Dean, Hazell / There there my dear: Dexy's Midnight Runners
CDMFP 5975 / Dec '92 / Music For Pleasure

☐ **TOP TIMING**
FANT 005 / 31 Aug '98 / Fantomas

☐ **TOPAZ BOX, THE (5CD Set)**
TPZS 1030 / Nov '95 / Topaz Jazz

☐ **TORCH SONGS**
Am I blue: Holiday, Billie / My old flame: Holiday, Billie / He's gone blues: Smith, Bessie / You've got me crying again: Wiley, Lee / Tears in my heart: Bailey, Mildred / Love me or leave me: Grace, Teddy / I'm up a tree: Fitzgerald, Ella / I'm gonna cry you out of my heart: Fitzgerald, Ella / Stormy weather: Anderson, Ivie / I got it bad and that ain't good: Anderson, Ivie / It's torture: Humes, Helen / Somebody else is taking my place: Lee, Peggy / You took my love: Stafford, Jo / Friend of yours: Stafford, Jo / Good-for-nothin' Joe: Horne, Lena / One for my baby: Horne, Lena / There must be a way: Boswell, Connee / There will never be another you: Knight, Evelyn
RPCD 324 / Apr '97 / Robert Parker Jazz

☐ **TORONTO SOCA X-PLOSION VOL.1**
CD 0011 / Jan '97 / Oss

☐ **TORONTO TATTOO**
LCOM 8015 / Oct '93 / Lismor

☐ **TORQUE (2CD Set)**
NUTCD 1 / Mar '97 / No U Turn

☐ **TOTAL DEF JAM (The Definitive Collection)**
Fight for your right to party: Beastie Boys / Rain: Jones, Oran 'Juice' / Don't believe the hype: Public Enemy / Mama said knock you out: LL Cool J / Fight the power: Public Enemy / Slam: Onyx / Ghetto jam: Domino / Regulate: Warren G / You're all I need: Method Man & Mary J. Blige / This is how we do it: Jordan, Montell / What's love got to do with it: Warren G & Adina Howard / Whateva man: Redman / Touch me, tease me: Case / Hey lover: LL Cool J / I like: Jordan, Montell / Get me home: Brown, Foxy / Ain't nobody: LL Cool J / I shot the sheriff: Warren G
5360722 / Jun '97 / PolyGram TV

☐ **TOTAL RECALL VOL.1 (Calling The Classics)**
Get up, stand up: Tosh, Peter / Why did you do it: McGregor, Freddie / Here I am baby: Brown, Al / My time: Brown, Dennis / I roots: Third World / Pomp and pride: Toots & The Maytals / Come see Jah: Miller, Jacob / Suspicious minds: Heptones / Never get weary: Culture / Nature planned it: Struggle / Israel: Paul, Frankie / Birds follow Spring: Griffiths, Hugh / Mother miserable: Captain Barkey / Style with fashion: Papa Bruce / Oh no not my baby: McGregor, Freddie / Rub-a-dub: Johnny Ringo / Daddy mix: Purpleman / I'm living: Griffiths, Hugh / Crystal blue persuasion: Heptones / 54-46 (was my number): Toots & The Maytals
CDGR 114 / Jan '97 / Charly

☐ **TOTAL RECALL VOL.10**
VPCD 1508 / Mar '98 / VP

☐ **TOTAL RECALL VOL.7**
VPCD 1303 / Mar '96 / VP

☐ **TOTAL RECALL VOL.8**
VPCD 1334 / Aug '94 / VP

☐ **TOTAL RECALL VOL.9**
VPCD 1384 / Mar '96 / VP

☐ **TOTAL TOGETHERNESS VOL.1**
CRCD 27 / Mar '94 / Charm

☐ **TOTAL TOGETHERNESS VOL.2**
CRCD 37 / Nov '94 / Charm

☐ **TOTAL TOGETHERNESS VOL.3**
FAMCD 001 / Jul '95 / Famous

☐ **TOTAL TOGETHERNESS VOL.4**
Nah fi watch nuh mate: Cobra / Oh yes no guess: Beenie Man / Babylon drop: Bounty Killer / Noise of the ghetto: Tony Rebel / Darness thing: Lady Saw / Oh Mama: Jigsy King / Dis: Galaxy P / House mouse: Shabba Ranks / Turn around: Beenie Man / No interview: Bounty Killer / Search: Louie Culture / Top rankin: Althia & Donna / Tek yuh man: Buccaneer / Want you back: Lady G
FAMCD 002 / Jan '96 / Famous

☐ **TOTALLY ACID JAZZ**
Astral space: Quiet Boys / 3 mile island: Taylor, James Quartet / Spinning wheel: New Jersey Kings / Stoned woman: Mother Earth / Lucky fellow: Snowboy / BNH: Brand New Heavies / London England: Corduroy / Monkey drop: New Jersey Kings / Find our love: City Lix / Keep it coming: K-Collective / Whole lotta love: Goldbug / Dream come true: Brand New Heavies / Feeling sad tonight: Isaacs, Gregory / Mr. Jeckle: Beesley's, Max High Vibes / Mr. Freedom: Mother Earth
EAMCD 003 / Apr '98 / Eagle

☐ **TOTALLY BLUES GUITAR**
Don't answer the door: King, B.B. / Hoochie coochie man: Waters, Muddy / Dust my broom: James, Elmore / Stormy Monday blues: Bland, Bobby / Real mother for ya: Watson, Johnny 'Guitar' / Statesboro blues: Taj Mahal / St. Louis blues: Brown, Clarence 'Gatemouth' / Dimples: Hooker, John Lee / Stone crazy: Guy, Buddy / Tell me what's the reason: Walker, T-Bone / Ain't that loving you baby: Reed, Jimmy / Pretty baby blues: Tampa Red / Got a good thing goin': Collins, Albert / Morning at midnight: Howlin' Wolf / Bony moronie: Winter, Johnny / John the revelator: House, Son / Smokestack lightning: Thorogood, George / Sky is crying: Vaughan, Stevie Ray
VSOPCD 239 / Jul '97 / Connoisseur Collection

☐ **TOTALLY CELTIC ROCK**
Mandinka: O'Connor, Sinead / I'm gonna be: Proclaimers / Protect and survive: Runrig / Whistler: Jethro Tull / Darlin': Miller, Eddie & Lou Stein / No regrets: Ure, Midge / When I'm dead and gone: McGuiness Flint / Get it right next time: Rafferty, Gerry / Wonderland: Big Country / Loch Lomond: Runrig / Letter from America: Proclaimers / If I was: Ure, Midge / Love of the common people: Stiff Little Fingers / Geno: Dexy's Midnight Runners / Good heart: Sharkey, Feargal / Year of the cat: Stewart, Al / Irish rover: Gor Jus Wrex
4954762 / 6 Jul '98 / EMI Gold

☐ **TOTALLY CHRISTMAS**
White Christmas: Martin, Dean / Christmas song: Cole, Nat 'King' / Winter wonderland: Mercer, Johnny / Deck the halls: Lee, Peggy / Here is Christmas: Wilson, Ann & Nancy / Ring out the solstice bells: Jethro Tull / Rudolf the red nosed reindeer: Martin, Dean / Santa Claus is coming to town: Gleason, Jackie / Little drummer boy: Lynn, Vera / Twelve days of Christmas: Adams, Cliff / Mary's boy child: Monro, Matt / Christmas waltz: Lee, Peggy / Silent night: Paul, Les & Mary Ford / Walking in the air: Jones, Aled / God rest ye merry gentlemen: Fitzgerald, Ella / While sheperd's watched: King's Singers / Ding Dong merrily on high: Bach Choir / First Noel: Canterbury Cathedral Choir
CDGOLD 1100 / 13 Oct '97 / EMI Gold

☐ **TOTALLY CLASSICAL GUITAR**
Nocturno: Segovia, Andres / Fandanguillo: Barrueco, Manuel / Miller's dance: Bream, Julian / Suite espanola asturias: Fernandez, Eduardo / Cavatina: Sollscher, Goran / Suite espanola granada: Bream, Julian / Heitor villa lobos (prelude 1): Yepes, Narciso / Heitor villa lobos (etudes 1): Romero, Pepe / Ritual fire dance: Hill, Robin / Estudios: Lendle, Wolfgang / Andaluza: Sapnish Art Quartet / Aranjuez: Martin, Juan
VSOPCD 258 / 10 Aug '98 / Connoisseur Collection

☐ **TOTALLY COMMERCIALS**
My special angel: Vaughan, Malcolm / Angelina: Prima, Louis / Fever: Lee, Peggy / I'm sitting on top of the world: Darin, Bobby / Wild is the wind: Simone, Nina / Put a little love in your heart: De Shannon, Jackie / Call me irresponsible: De Shannon, Jackie / Night rider: Hawkshaw, Alan / Stompin' at the Savoy: Goodman, Benny / Stripper: Loss, Joe Orchestra / I love you Porgy: Simone, Nina / Story of my life: Holliday, Michael / Fly me to the moon: London, Julie / In the mood: Loss, Joe Orchestra / Love is the sweetest thing: Bowlly, Al / Teach me tiger: Stevens, April / Mellow yellow: Donovan / Air that I breathe: Hollies
4954752 / 6 Jul '98 / EMI Gold

☐ **TOTALLY COUNTRY GUITAR**
Yakety axe: Atkins, Chet / Take me to your lovin' place: Gatlin, Larry / Guitar town: Earle, Steve / Return of the grievous angel: Parsons, Gram / Everybody's had the blues: Haggard, Merle / Blue Kentucky girl: Harris, Emmylou / Wild and blue: Anderson, John / Touch me when I'm dancing: Alabama / Love's gonna get you some day: Skaggs, Ricky / Texas: Jennings, Waylon / Down at the twist and shout: Carpenter, Mary-Chapin / Another place another time: Williams, Don / Down on the corner: Reed, Jerry / Don't be so cruel: Moore, Scotty / Six pack to go: Thompson, Hank / Hello love: Snow, Hank / Hey good lookin': Mavericks / Forever and ever Amen: Travis, Randy
VSOPCD 241 / Jul '97 / Connoisseur Collection

☐ **TOTALLY DISCO**
More than a woman: Tavares / Haven't stop dancin' yet: Gonzalez / Get off: Oxy / Do what you wanna do: T-Connection / Movin': Brass Construction / I'll go where you're music takes me: James, Jimmy & The Vagabonds / You're my everything: Garrett, Lee / Boogie oogie oogie: Taste Of Honey / That's the way I like it: KC & The Sunshine Band / Dance across the floor: Horne, Jimmy 'Bo' / Shame shame shame: Shirley & Company / Galaxy of love: Crown Heights Affair / Do you wanna get funky with me: Brown, Peter / Rock me gently: Kim, Andy / Groove on: Hale, Willie 'Little Beaver' / Rock your baby: McCrae, George
CDGOLD 1101 / 15 Sep '97 / EMI Gold

☐ **TOTALLY IRISH (The Essential Irish Album)**
Riverdance: Kennedy, Fiona / Black velvet band: Dubliners / Seven drunken nights: Dubliners / Three drunken maidens: Planxty / Paddy on the railroad/ Miss McLeod: Gallowglass Ceili Band / Sheebans/ Merry blacksmith/Music in the Glen: Kilfernora Ceili Band / Dan Malone: Hasson, Gemma / Phil the fluters ball: O'Dowda, Brendan / It's a great day for the Irish: Murray, Ruby / Dear old Donegal: Locke, Josef / When Irish eyes are smiling: Jones, Sandie / Danny Boy: O'Se, Sean / Johnny I hardly knew ye: Murphy, Mary / Behind the bush and the garden: Dun Carmel Band / Over the road to Maggie/The Sailor's bonnet: Dun Carmel Band / Crossing: Wilson, Alexia & Paul Brennan / This land: Kennedy, Fiona
CDGOLD 1096 / May '97 / EMI Gold

☐ **TOTALLY JAZZ**
CDGOLD 1088 / Mar '97 / EMI Gold

☐ **TOTALLY JAZZ GUITAR**
Stella by midnight: Kessel, Barney Trio / Night and day: Pass, Joe / Fingerpickin': Montgomery, Wes / You'd be so nice to come home to: Hall, Jim / I concentrate on you: Ellis, Herb / Desafinado: Byrd, Charlie & Stan Getz / Sweet Georgia brown: Reinhardt, Django / Fascinating rhythm: Farlow, Tal / Song for my Father: Benson, George / Midnight blue: Burrell, Kenny / Sweet syncopation: Ritenour, Lee / Touch of silk: Gale, Eric / Georgia on my mind: Jordan, Stanley / So what: Jordan, Ronny / My favourite things: McLaughlin, John Trio / Meant to be: Scofield, John / Flight over Rio: Di Meola, Al / Mountains greenery: Barnes, George & Ruby Braff
VSOPCD 240 / Jul '97 / Connoisseur Collection

☐ **TOTALLY LOVE**
Mercy mercy me: Palmer, Robert / Save a prayer: Duran Duran / True: Spandau Ballet / Power of love: Lewis, Huey & The News / Thinking about your love: Thomas, Kenny / Love changes everything: Fisher, Climie / Put your love in me: Hot Chocolate / Darlin': Miller, Frankie / Me and Mrs Jones: Jackson, Freddie / Please don't go: KC & The Sunshine Band / Missing you: Waite, John / You're having my baby: Anka, Paul / Tracks of my tears: Go West / Loving you: Riperton, Minnie / Tonight I celebrate my love: Bryson, Peabo & Roberta Flack / Sexy eyes: Dr. Hook / Let's get married: Proclaimers / Something's gotten hold of my heart: Almond, Marc & Gene Pitney
4932802 / 12 Jan '98 / EMI Gold

☐ **TOTALLY NINETIES**
Unbelieveable: EMF / Only living boy in New Cross: Carter USM / Real real real: Jesus Jones / Sleeping satellite: Archer, Tasmin / Mr. Wendall: Arrested Development / Trouble: Shampoo / Well did you evah: Harry, Deborah & Iggy Pop / Rubberhand girl: Bush, Kate / I'll be your baby tonight: Palmer, Robert & UB40 / It should have been me: Adeva / Live your life be free: Carlisle, Belinda / Trippin' on your love: Thomas, Kenny / I like to move it: Reel 2 Real / Independence: Lulu / Careful: Horse / Ice ice baby: Vanilla Ice
CDGOLD 1102 / 15 Sep '97 / EMI Gold

☐ **TOTALLY NO.1'S OF THE 60'S**
Sweets for my sweet: Searchers / Pretty flamingo: Manfred Mann / Do it again: Beach Boys / I'm alive: Hollies / Ob-la-di, ob-la-da: Marmalade / I remember you: Ifield, Frank / Go now: Moody Blues / You'll never walk alone: Gerry & The Pacemakers / Anyone who had a heart: Black, Cilla / Little children:

Column 1

Kramer, Billy J. & The Dakotas / Tell Laura I love her: Valance, Ricky / Carnival is over: Seekers / House of the rising sun: Animals / I'm into something good: Herman's Hermits / Foot tapper: Shadows / Runaway: Shannon, Del / Mony mony: Jones, Tommy & The Shondells / Three steps to heaven: Cochran, Eddie / You're driving me crazy: Temperance Seven / Shakin' all over: Kidd, Johnny & The Pirates

CDGOLD 1085 / Feb '97 / EMI Gold

☐ **TOTALLY NO.1'S OF THE 70'S**

Sunday girl: Blondie / So you win again: Hot Chocolate / Tiger feet: Mud / David gate drive: Quatro, Suzi / January: Pilot / Rock your baby: McCrae, George / Make me smile (come up and see me): Harley, Steve & Cockney Rebel / See my baby jive: Wizzard / I hear you knocking: Edmunds, Dave / In the summertime: Mungo Jerry / Can the can: Quatro, Suzi / Heart of glass: Blondie / Kung fu fighting: Douglas, Carl / You to me are everything: Real Thing / When you're in love with a beautiful woman: Dr. Hook / Vincent: McLaughlin, Pat / Oh boy: Mud / Wuthering heights: Bush, Kate

CDGOLD 1086 / Feb '97 / EMI Gold

☐ **TOTALLY NO.1'S OF THE 80'S**

Is there something I should know: Duran Duran / When the going gets tough, the tough get going: Ocean, Billy / Give it up: KC & The Sunshine Band / Respectable: Mel & Kim / Feels like I'm in love: Marie, Kelly / Nineteen: Hardcastle, Paul / If I was: Ure, Midge / Something's gotten hold of my heart: Almond, Marc & Gene Pitney / True: Spandau Ballet / Crying: McLean, Don / Move closer: Nelson, Phyllis / Too shy: Kajagoogoo / I don't wanna dance: Grant, Eddy / Tide is high: Blondie / Ghost town: Specials / Geno: Dexy's Midnight Runners / Too much too young: Special AKA / Atomic: Blondie

CDGOLD 1087 / Feb '97 / EMI Gold

☐ **TOTALLY NORTHERN SOUL VOL.1 (25 Classic Forgotten Northern Oldies)**

Prepared to love you: Lindsay, Thelma / She tried to kiss me: Beverly, Frankie / All of my life: Detroit Soul / Lost in a world of a dream: Sharpetts / I've got the feeling: Bel Aires / You'd better believe it baby: Charades / Your turnin': Soul Shakers / Don't make me love you: Huw's Review / I'm not strong enough: Four Perfections / Gotta get closer to you my love: Showstoppers / Now that I found you baby: Mirrettes / You gonna miss a good thing: Bowie, John / Educated fool: Billy Story / Groovin' at the go-go: Four Larks / Words can't explain: Belles / Pearl: Jones, Tamiko / Monkey see monkey: Handy, Roy / I can't find her: Rolantos / Run by our love: Ingram, Luther / I need a love: Barbour, Connie / Dance little Earl: Hammond, Clay / Play time: Hedges, Pat / Take a giant step: Hedges, Pat / Somebody new: Moore, Danny / Stronger than her love: Flirtations

GSCD 106 / 20 Oct '97 / Goldmine

☐ **TOTALLY NORTHERN SOUL VOL.2**

That's how much I love you: Wheeler, Art / I've caught you cheating: Adventurers / Catwalk: Gerry & Paul / Music with soul: Georgia Prophets / You're the one: Twilights / Don't you make me cry: Bridges, Chuck / You kind ain't good: Mirettes / Them love blues: Wright, Earl / I'm coming apart at the seams: Kittens Three / Detroit soul city: Thrillers / You wouldn't have anything: Remarkables / Got to have it now: Invitations / Without a warning: Brown, Rocky / I can't stay away: Caressers / Stride: Strides / Sweet baby: Gardner, Al / Is she in your town: Lee, Curtis / Little angel: Performers / I struck it rich: Harner, Billy / Isn't she a pretty girl: McNeir, Ronnie / Since I lost my baby: Furys / I'll bet you: Linsey, Teresa / Talk about a shindig: Barnes, Sidney / Tee ta: Neal, Tommy / Day has gone: Williams, Maurice / Move over baby: Wylie, Richard 'Popcorn' / That one: Fantastics

GSCD 132 / 23 Mar '98 / Goldmine

☐ **TOTALLY ROCK**

Love is a battlefield: Benatar, Pat / Some like it hot: Powerstation / Nutbush city limits: Turner, Ike & Tina / Power of love: Lewis, Huey & The News / Simply irresistible: Palmer, Robert / Doctor: Doobie Brothers / Comin' on strong: Broken English / When you walk in the room: Carrack, Paul / Talk talk: Talk Talk / Freeze frame: Geils, J. Band / Baker Street: Rafferty, Gerry / Fall to love: Diesel Park West / Isn't it time: Babys / Betty Davies eyes: Carnes, Kim / Missing you: Waite, John / Road to nowhere: Talking Heads / Love walked in: Thunder / Lawnmower: Marillion

CDGOLD 1095 / 15 Sep '97 / EMI Gold

☐ **TOTALLY ROCK 'N' ROLL**

C'mon everybody: Cochran, Eddie / Hello Mary Lou: Nelson, Ricky / Runaway: Shannon, Del / Be-bop-a-lula: Vincent, Gene / Rave on: Holly, Buddy / Heartbeat: Vee, Bobby / Shakin' all over: Kidd, Johnny & The Pirates / Stupid cupid: Jackson, Wanda / Party doll: Knox, Buddy / Willie and the handjive: Otis, Johnny / At the hop: Danny & The Juniors / Runaround Sue: Dion / Why do fools fall in love: Lymon, Frankie & The Teenagers / Blue moon: Marcels / Don't ever change: Crickets / Tallahassee lassie: Jan & Dean / I'm walkin': Domino, Fats / You're sixteen: Domino, Fats / Ruby baby: Darin, Bobby / High school confidential: Faith, Adam / Maybelline: Santo Family / Lonely weekends: Proby, P.J. / Memphis: Rivers, Johnny / Hey Miss Ruby: Fenton, Shane & The Fentones / Do you wanna dance: Freeman, Bobby

4954742 / 6 Jul '98 / EMI Gold

☐ **TOTALLY ROCK GUITAR**

Hold the line: Toto / China groove: Doobie Brothers / Paranoid: Black Sabbath / Beck's bolero: Beck, Jeff / Don't believe a word: Thin Lizzy / Confessor: Anderson, Ian / Highway star: Deep Purple / Stealer: Free / Natural born bugie: Humble Pie / Hold on: Santana / Black magic woman: Fleetwood Mac / Cactus boogie: Howe, Steve / I pity the fool: Page, Jimmy / Shake I'm in: Band / More than a feeling: Boston / Sweet home alabama: Lynyrd Skynyrd

VSOPCD 238 / Jul '97 / Connoisseur Collection

☐ **TOTALLY SENSATIONAL 70'S 1970-1973**

I hear you knocking: Edmunds, Dave / Let's work together: Canned Heat / Rag mama rag: Band / Whole lotta love: CCS / Don't let it die: Hurricane smith / Malt and barley blues: McGuinness Flint / Strange kind of women: Deep Purple / 10583 overture: ELO / Ball park incident: Wizzard /

Column 2

California man: Move / All because of you: Geordie / Long cool women in a black dress: Hollies / Standing in the road: Blackfoot Sue / Silver machine: Blackfoot Sue / I've been drinking: Beck, Jeff & Rod Stewart / Roll over Beethoven: ELO / Son of my father: Chicory Tip / American pie: McLean, Don

4949432 / 1 Jun '98 / EMI Gold

☐ **TOTALLY SENSATIONAL 70'S 1973-1976**

48 crash: Quatro, Suzi / Angel fingers: Wizzard / Dance with the devil: Powell, Cozy / Dyna-mite: Mud / Hello hello I'm back again: Glitter, Gary / Bump: Kenny / Touch too much: Arrows / Judy teen: Harley, Steve & Cockney Rebel / Magic: Pilot / Ballroom blitz: Sweet / Tell him: Hello / Motor bikin': Spedding, Chris / Ships in the night: Be-Bop Deluxe / Disco queen: KC & The Sunshine Band / Get down tonight: Hot Chocolate / It's been so long: McCrae, George / Don't take away the music: Tavares / Little bit more: Dr. Hook

4949442 / 1 Jun '98 / EMI Gold

☐ **TOTALLY SENSATIONAL 70'S 1977-1979**

2 4 6 8 motorway: Robinson, Tom / Little girl: Banned / Peaches: Stranglers / Spanish stroll: Mink Deville / Down at the doctor's: Dr. Feelgood / Ever fallen in love: Buzzcocks / Rich kids: Rich Kids / Valley of the dolls: Generation X / Picture this: Blondie / My sharona: Knack / Romeo: Mr. Big / They shoot horses don't they: Racing Cars / Everyday hurts: Sad Cafe / Wow: Tosh, Peter / Don't look back: Bush, Kate / Living on the front line: Grant, Eddy / Gangsters: Special AKA / Night owl: Rafferty, Gerry

4949452 / 1 Jun '98 / EMI Gold

☐ **TOTALLY SOLID HITBOUND**

Good things: Hatcher, Willie / Our love (is in this pocket): Barnes, J.J. / My darling: Griffin, Herman / Never alone: Holidays / Hit and run: Revilot / Somebody somewhere (needs you): Lebaron Orchestra / I lost you: Holidays / You better wake up: Debonaires / Love that never grows cold: Beavers, Jackie / Did my baby call: Mancha, Steve / Girl crazy: Gigi & The Charmaines / I need you like a baby: Henry, Andrea / I must love you: Davis, Melvin / When you lose the one you love: Smith, Buddy / Poor unfortunate me: Gigi & The Charmaines / I won't hurt anymore: Anderson, Eddie / Happiness is here: Topper Ensemble / Open the door to your heart: Banks, Daryl

GSCD 070 / Jan '96 / Goldmine

☐ **TOTALLY SPANISH GUITAR**

Malaguena: Sabicas / Callejon del carmen: Sanlucar, Manolo / Mi tierra: Platas, Manitas De / Taranta: Marchena, Melchor de / Granadina: Cano, Manuel / Almez de san pedro: Hickstein, Thomas / Aurora: Martin, Juan / La feria: Martin, Juan / Zapateado: Ricardo, Nino / Bulerais: Serrano, Juanito / Fandangos por verdiales: Romero, Pepe / Liberte: Gipsy Kings / Recuerdos de la alhambra: Williams, John

VSOPCD 257 / 10 Aug '98 / Connoisseur Collection

☐ **TOTALLY SUMMER**

Summer holiday: Richard, Cliff / Surfin' USA: Beach Boys / Beach baby: First Class / Surf city: Jan & Dean / Summer sun: Barracudas / In the summertime: Mungo Jerry / Walking on sunshine: Katrina & The Waves / Summertime blues: Cochran, Eddie / Summertime: Fun Boy Three / Here comes the sun: Harley, Steve & Cockney Rebel / Summer (the first time): Goldsboro, Bobby / Under the boardwalk: Drifters / Summer breeze: Seals & Crofts / California dreamin': Mamas & Papas / Sunshine superman: Donovan / Sunshine girl: Herman's Hermits / California girls: Beach Boys / Hello sunshine: Goldsboro, Bobby

CDGOLD 1099 / Jun '97 / EMI Gold

☐ **TOTALLY TRADITIONAL TIN WHISTLES**

OSS 53CD / Jan '94 / Ossian

☐ **TOTALLY TRANCED**

Your touch: R2001 / Purity: Aloof / Feel: Chameleon Project / Hello San Francisco: Dance 2 Trance / Slide: Contact / Music is movin': DIKK: Fargetta / World evolution: Trance / La yerba del diablo: Datura / Spirit in me: Vibe Alive / Land of oz: Spooky / Peace and happiness: Humanoid / Orcana: Void / Mi piace: Marmalade / Passing thru' the surface: Flux / Time to rock: Industrial / Forever people: Biologix

CDELV 03 / Dec '92 / Debut

☐ **TOTALLY WIRED IN DUB**

DUBIDCD 5 / Feb '96 / Acid Jazz Roots

☐ **TOTALLY WIRED ITALIA**

JAZIDCD 079 / Sep '93 / Acid Jazz

☐ **TOTALLY WIRED SWEDEN**

JAZIDCD 103 / Aug '94 / Acid Jazz

☐ **TOTALLY WIRED VOL.10**

Time and space theme: Time & Space / Would you believe in me: Lucien, Jon / Corduroy orgasm club: Corduroy / Ladder: One Creed / Real gone turn it on: Cloud 9 / It's all in: Whole Thing / Sweet feeling: Esperanto / Ladder: One Creed / Real gone turn it on: Cloud 9 / It's all in: Whole Thing / Sweet feeling: Esperanto / Curcarea deaupa: Michaelson, Hilmar Orn / I remain...: Hafler Trio / Mara river at night: Watson, Chris / Supermarket slight becommes part of the Earth: Seymour, Daren & Mark Van Hoen / Mule river

JAZIDCD 072 / Jul '93 / Acid Jazz

Column 3

☐ **TOTALLY WIRED VOL.11**

Three mile island: Taylor, James Quartet / Fresh in my mind: Forest Mighty Black / Never will I stop loving you: Clark, Alice / Freakin': Freakpower / Joyous: Pleasure / Theme from Millenium Falcon: Square Window / To the bone: Children Of Judah / Who me: Ghost / Monsieur Taylor's new brand: Monsieur Kamayatsu / Do you like it: Skunkhour / Anger: Mondo Grosso / Clever girl: Purdey, Samuel / Astral space: Quiet Boys

JAZIDCD 101 / Jun '94 / Acid Jazz

☐ **TOTALLY WIRED VOL.12**

Life eternal: Mother Earth / Akimbo: Bartholomew, Simon / Funky jam: Primal Scream / Mental: Dub War / Swinging foot: Swinging Foot / Gimme one of those: Brand New Heavies / Couldn't take missing you: Square Window / Summertime: OOKE / Art is the message: Stickman / Don't you let me down: Planet / Work on a dream: Birtha / In deep: Red Snapper / Indian rope man: Phaze

JAZIDCD 120 / Mar '95 / Acid Jazz

☐ **TOTALLY WIRED VOL.2**

Beads, things and flowers: Humble Souls / Monkey drop: New Jersey Kings / Trinkets and trash: Cool Beats / APB: Man Called Adam / Break for jazz: Break for jazz / Nzuri beat: White, Steve & Gary Wallace / Homegrown: Jones, Ed / Tildens: Sandberg, Ulf Quartet / Gimme one of those: Brand New Heavies / Killer: Night Trains

JAZIDCD 016 / Nov '93 / Acid Jazz

☐ **TOTALLY WIRED VOL.3**

JAZIDCD 022 / Nov '93 / Acid Jazz

☐ **TOTALLY WIRED VOL.4**

JAZIDCD 028 / Nov '93 / Acid Jazz

☐ **TOTALLY WIRED VOL.5**

JAZIDCD 031 / Dec '91 / Acid Jazz

☐ **TOTALLY WIRED VOL.6**

JAZID 36CD / May '91 / Acid Jazz

☐ **TOTALLY WIRED VOL.7**

Theme from riot on 103rd street: Mother Earth / Taurus woman: Subterraneans / That's how it is: Grand Oral Disceminator / Machine shop: Untouchable Machine Shop / Don't you care: Clark, Alice / Sunship: Sunship / Sim ting: Quiet Boys / Believe in me: Vibraphonic / Change had better come: Dimond, Mark

JAZIDCD 043 / Nov '91 / Acid Jazz

☐ **TOTALLY WIRED VOL.8**

JAZIDCD 050 / Apr '92 / Acid Jazz

☐ **TOTALLY WIRED VOL.9**

Mr. Jeckle: Beesley's, Max High Vibes / Warlock of pendragon: Mother Earth / Dat's slammin': Gordon, Robert / Reprise for the wolf in sheep's clothing: Sons Of Judah / Got a groove: Wiggs, Supa & Jonzi / Stand it: George, Brenda / Electric soup: Corduroy / That's it: Grass Snakes / Dreams: Raw

JAZIDCD 057 / Oct '92 / Acid Jazz

☐ **TOTENTANZ VOL.2 (The History Of Zoth Ommog)**

CLP 0005 / Jul '97 / Cleopatra

☐ **TOUCH**

NRCDCOM 2 / 6 Apr '98 / Neoteric

☐ **TOUCH ME IN THE MORNING**

CDTRL 337 / Apr '94 / Trojan

☐ **TOUCH OF ACID JAZZ VOL.1**

FARCD 401 / Jul '96 / Family Affair

☐ **TOUCH OF DEATH, A**

Perpetual dawn: Fleshcrawl / Primeval transubstantiation: Agressor / Where the rivers of madness stream: Cemetary / Who will not be dead: Seance / Within the silence: Rosicrucian / Excursion demise: Invocator / Solace: Necrosanct / Born bizarre: Tribulation / Enigma: Edge Of Sanity / Blood And Iron: Bathory

BMCD 026 / Sep '92 / Black Mark

☐ **TOUCH OF ROMANCE VOL.1, A**

KNEWCD 725 / Apr '94 / Kenwest

☐ **TOUCH OF ROMANCE VOL.2, A**

KNEWCD 726 / Apr '94 / Kenwest

☐ **TOUCH OF ROMANCE VOL.3, A**

KNEWCD 727 / Apr '94 / Kenwest

☐ **TOUCH OF ROMANCE VOL.4, A**

KNEWCD 728 / Apr '94 / Kenwest

☐ **TOUCH OF ROMANCE, A**

I'm beginning to see the light: Williams, Joe & Count Basie / Top hat, white tie and tails: Armstrong, Louis / Goin' to Chicago: Hibbler, Al / Tenderly: Eckstine, Billy / Charge account: Latimore, Clark / Stockholm sweatnin': Hendricks, Jon / I want a little girl: McShann, Jay / Song is you: Crosby, Bing / Between the devil and the deep blue sea: Rich, Buddy / Touch of your lips: Baker, Chet / T'ain't so honey, t'ain't so: Tangerain, Jack / Is you is or is you ain't my baby: Jordan, Louis / You can't have your cake and eat it: Fabulous Ellingtonians / I could have told you: Bukky Quintet / Frederic: less still: Gaillarde, Latin jam: Haryon / Lock out: Hip Joints / Playing for real: Jazz Renegades / Batu casu: Bangs A Bongo / Freedom principle: Leo, Bukky & Galliano / Sweet cakes: New Jersey Kings

5526392 / Mar '97 / Spectrum

☐ **TOUCH OF THE MASTER'S HAND, A**

RTECD 191 / Mar '96 / RTE/Europe 1

☐ **TOUCH SAMPLER VOL.1**

Mind loss: H3OH / PS one: Jeck, Philip / Valley of the Kings and Queens: Gamil, Soliman / Orgasmatron: Sandoz / Sudurgate: Michaelson, Hilmar Orn / I remain...: Hafler Trio / Mara river at night: Watson, Chris / Supermarket slight becommes part of the Earth: Seymour, Daren & Mark Van Hoen / Mule river

Column 4

of Grebene: Fara, Eli & Luiza Mica / Ghettoes of the mind: Sweet Exorcist / Mesmerised: Drome / In the compound: Rax Werx / Radio KPFK: Z'Ev / Knowledge: SETI / Supplication: Gamil, Soliman / Calcutta: Marutani, Koji

T 01 / Oct '95 / Touch

☐ **TOUCH SAMPLER VOL.3**

TZERO 3 / 6 Apr '98 / Touch

☐ **TOUCHED BY THE HAND OF GOTH VOL.1 (2CD Set)**

SPV 08638302 / Aug '95 / SPV

☐ **TOUCHED BY THE HAND OF GOTH VOL.2 (2CD Set)**

Painted flowers in a picture: Placebo Effect / See you in hell: Suicide Commando / Wheel: Sleeping Dogs Wake / Inside me: Revenge Of Nephthys / November morning: Love Is Colder Than Death / Angel light: This Ascencion / Gedanken eines vampires: Dimstra Et Imago / EST Trip to the moon: Alien Sex Fiend / Rat kill: Blok 57 / Slavesex: Die Form / Smell of decay: Sixth / Die liebe: Atrocity / Realtives menschsein: Misanthrope / Painkilling suicide: Love Like Blood / No blind eyes can see: Lacrimosa

SPV 08738642 / May '96 / SPV

☐ **TOUGHER THAN TOUGH**

CDTRL 304 / Mar '94 / Trojan

☐ **TOUGHER THAN TOUGH (The Story Of Jamaican Music - 4CD Set)**

Oh Carolina: Folkes Brothers / Boogie in my bones: Aitken, Laurel / Midnight track: Gray, Owen / Easy snappin': Beckford, Theophilus / Housewives' choice: Derrick & Patsy / Forward march: Morgan, Derrick / Miss Jamaica: Cliff, Jimmy / My boy lollipop: Millie / Six and seven books of Moses: Toots & The Maytals / Simmer down: Wailers / Man in the street: Drummond, Don / Carry go bring home: Hinds, Justin / Guns of navarone: Skatalites / Al Capone: Prince Buster / Hard man fe dead: Prince Buster / Tougher than tough: Morgan, Derrick / Girl I've got a date: Ellis, Alton / Happy go lucky girl: Paragons / Dancing mood: Wilson, Delroy / Train is coming: Boothe, Ken / Take it easy: Lewis, Hopeton / Ba ba boom: Jamaicans / 007: Dekker, Desmond / I've got to go back home: Andy, Bob / Queen majesty: Techniques / Loving pauper: Dobson, Dobby / Don't stay away: Dillon, Phyllis / Israelites: Dekker, Desmond / 54-46 (was my number): Toots & The Maytals / Reggae hit the town: Ethiopians / Wet dream: Max Romeo / My conversation: Uniques / Upsetters / Liquidator: Harry J / All Stars / Rivers of Babylon: Melodians / Harder they come: Cliff, Jimmy / Young, gifted and black: Bob & Marcia / Wake the town: Q-Roy / How long: Kelly, Pat / Double barrel: Barker, Dave & Ansell Collins / Blood and fire: Niney The Observer / Cherry oh baby: Donaldson, Eric / Better must come: Wilson, Delroy / Money in my pocket: Brown, Dennis / Stick by me: Holt, John / Teach the children: Alcapone, Dennis / 500 watts: Big Youth / Everything I own: Boothe, Ken / Westbound train: Brown, Dennis / Move out a Babylon: Clarke, Johnny / Curly locks: Byles, Junior / Country boy: Heptones / Welding: I-Roy / Marcus Garvey: Burning Spear / Right time: Mighty Diamonds / Natty sing hit songs: Stewart, Roman / Ballistic affair: Smart, Leroy / Tenement yard: Miller, Jacob / War in a Babylon: Max Romeo / Police and thieves: Murvin, Junior / Two sevens clash: Culture / I'm still waiting: Wilson, Delroy / No woman, no cry: Marley, Bob & The Wailers / Uptown top ranking: Althia & Donna / My number one: Isaacs, Gregory / Breeda gravalicious: Welling Souls / River Jordan: Minott, Sugar / Armagideon time: Willams, Millie / Guess who's coming to dinner: Black Uhuru / Fort Augustus: Delgado, Junior / Jogging: Marshall, Freddie / Sitting and waiting: Brown, Dennis / Night nurse: Isaacs, Gregory / Mad over me: Yellowman / Diseases: Michigan & Smiley / Water pumping: Osbourne, Johnny / Pass the tu-sheng-peng: Smith, Wayne / Tempo: Brown, Dennis / Boops: Super Cat / Greetings: Half Pint / Punanny: Bailey, Admiral / Hol' a fresh: Red Dragon / Rumours: Isaacs, Gregory / Cover me: Stewart, Tinga & Ninjaman / Legal rights: Papa San & Lady Saw / Bubble With Me: Shaba / Telephone love: J.C. Lodge / Bogle dance: Buju Banton / Murder she wrote: Chaka Demus & Pliers / O Carolina: Shaggy

IBXCD 1 / Oct '93 / Mango

☐ **TOUR DE CHANT**

DCD 5325 / Nov '93 / Disky

☐ **TOURNEE 95**

GWP 010CD / Nov '95 / Gwerz

☐ **TOUVAN CHANTS FROM CENTRAL ASIA**

Y 225222CD / Jul '95 / Silex

☐ **TOWN HALL PARTY 1958-1961**

RFDCD 15 / Dec '95 / Country Routes

☐ **TOWNSHIP JAZZ 'N' JIVE (18 South African Urban Swing Classics From The Jivin' 50's)**

Ubuhlungu: Four Yanks / Clarinet kwela: Moeketsi, Kippie & The Marabi Kings / Banana ba rustenburg: Mashiyane, Spokes / De makeba: Jazz Dazzlers / Omyakane: Royal Players / Something new in Africa: Solven Whistlers / Hololo: Skylarks / Nteziani: na: Huddlestone, Father Band / Baby are yeng: Jacobs, Nancy & Her Sisters / Dudu wam: Four Yanks / Tladi la bayeta: Motaung, Reggie / Nqaba Mabvu: Masuka, Dorothy / Ploho / Loafers corner: Orlando Seven / Isomeloshelo: Manhattan Brothers / Kwela blues: Mabuse, Kenny / Ngi namba ngekwa: Masuka, Dorothy / Phata tsea: Manhattan Brothers / Mbube: Linda, Solomon & Original Evening Birds / Mtsaba: Msomi, Reggie Hollywood Jazz Band

NSCD 022 / Oct '97 / Nascente

☐ **TOWNSHIP SWING JAZZ VOL.1 (1954-58)**

HQCD 08 / Oct '91 / Harlequin

☐ **TOWNSHIP SWING JAZZ VOL.1**

668932 / Apr '96 / Melodie

☐ TOX UTHAT VOL.2
SR 9465 / Jul '94 / Silent

☐ TRACKSPOTTING (2CD Set)
Saint: Orbital / Theme from Mission: Impossible: Clayton, Adam & Larry Mullen / Lovefool (Tee's club radio): Cardigans / Shallow grave: Leftfield / Born slippy: Underworld / Papau New Guinea: Future Sound Of London / Crash and carry: Orbital / Slid: Fluke / Wake up: Stereo MC's / Wildwood: Weller, Paul / This is not America: Bowie, David & Pat Metheny / Downtown: Cole, Lloyd / Wait for the sun: Supergrass / Natural one: Folk Implosion / Gone: Holmes, David & Sarah Cracknell / Play dead: Bjork & David Arnold / Small plot of land: Bowie, David / Forbidden colours: Sylvian, David / Falling: Cruise, Julee / Hold me, thrill me, kiss me, kill me: U2 / 36 degrees: Placebo / Sunshine shakers: Reef / Begging you: Stone Roses / Let's all got together: Marion / I spy: Pulp / There she goes: La's / You and me song: Wannadies / Bad behaviour: Super Furry Animals / Lust for life: Iggy Pop / That woman's got me drinking: MacGowan, Shane & The Popes / Perfect crime: Faith No More / Sugar ray: Jesus & Mary Chain / Misirlou: Dale, Dick & His Del-Tones / 5:15: Who / Pet semetary: Ramones / Pretty in pink: Psychedelic Furs / Girl you'll be a woman soon: Urge Overkill / Left of centre: Vega, Suzanne / Stuck in the middle with you: Stealer's Wheel / How can we hang on to a dream: Hardin, Tim
5534302 / May '97 / PolyGram TV

☐ TRAD AT HEART
Barn dances: Arcady / Tomasín A Rí: Begley & Cooney / Donal Agus Morag: Altan / Cat chase mouse: O'Connor, Martin / Moving cloud: O'Connor, Gerry / Ril an Spideal: De Danann / Liquid sunshine: O'Connor, Martin / Snowy path: Altan / Hennessey's: Arcady / Funk the cajun blues: O'Connor, Gerry / Bruach na Carraige Baine: Begley & Cooney / Jimmy Byrnes and Dinkies: De Danann
DART 3171 / Jun '97 / Dara

☐ TRAD FIDDLE IN FRANCE
Y 225110CD / Feb '95 / Silex

☐ TRADE VOL.1 (2CD Set)
Back from the dead EP: Sound Design / Up and down: Raw Junkies / Horny toad: Cajmere / Fusion journey: Aqua Boogie / Don't you want me: PV Project / Everybody reach: Millennium / Kick it in: Hit Junkie / Movin' me: Millennium / Feel: Zone 1 / I feel good: K-Hand / Fanaklo: Underground Vibes Sessions III / Can you feel what I feel: Bell, Louise / Itty bitty boozy woozy: Tempo fiesta / Industrial cartel: Castle Trancelot / It's alright: SAIN / Cut the midrange: Watchman / May I have the mayonnaise: Movin' Melodies / If we lose our lovin': DMB / Ultimate: Antic / Ga ga: Yo Yo / Let's rock: E-Trax / Forces of nature: Sneo, Eric / Feel the generation: Mind X / Underwave: Disciples / Chemical hostage: Sigma 2 / Eine kleine nacht musik: Kleinboiz / Controller: Sigma 2
FVRCD 1001 / Sep '95 / Feverpitch

☐ TRADE VOL.2 (3CD Set)
Disco daze: Rhythm Construction Co. / That sound: Musaphia, Joey / Rhumba: S-Man / Get it together: Criso, Filthy Rich / Day in the life: Terry, Todd / Addiction: DJ Lil'tai / Do it: Glenn Underground / Disko dreams: 100 Proof (Aged In Soul) / Back to front: Rocato, Ralph / Groove melody: Johnson, Paul / I need GU: GU / In da closet: Hardrive / Blessing: Sourmash / Eternal: Epik / Set up: Edge 18 / Dreams: Quench / Lover man: Bad Man / X: DJ Scott / Neurodancer: Whompound / Yum yum: Baby Doc / Trancedo: Dywwitness / Crisis: Ganesh / Are am Eve: Commander Tom / Avandanza: Yum! / Wham bam: Candy Girls & Sweet Pussy Pauline / Caterpillar: Keoki / Live as one: Sam Tranx / Into your heart: 6 By 6 / Labia: Prins, Patrick / Got to learn: Bit Boys Action Squad / Watch me shine: Silvester, Stretch / Just can't get enough: Transformer 2 / Nightrain: Kadoc / My house is your house (and your house is mine): Montini Experience
FVRCD 2 / Apr '96 / Feverpitch

☐ TRADE VOL.3 (Mixed By Tony De Vit & Steve Thomas/2CD Set)
Sharp tools Vol.2: Sharp Boys / Soaking wet: 99 All Stars / Lick it: Black & Brown / Sharp tools Vol.2: Sharp Boys / Luxor: Strange Attractor / Totally insane: Scoff Boys / Up to no good: Pom Kings / Forerunner: Natural Born / Let me tell you something: Three Guys On Warwick & Devone / Pulse fiction: Trex, Andy / Keep rollin': Katy's Lips / Take you there: Experts / System: Starfish / Pump 1: Beyer, Adam / Greatest: Mount / Ma' definition of house EP: De Luxe, Tom & Waterhouse / You're no good: Billabong / Avalatonal: Doubell, E. J. / What happened: Donni & Choci / South: Randall, Dave / Bonkers EP: Code Blue / Ultimate Seduction: Ultimate Seduction / Biggest and baddest: Brainbashers / Bird: King Of House / Drum fire: King Of House / Welcome: Committee / Bonkas: Kinky Roland / Trance line: Committee / Get loose: Mangrove / Are you ail ready: De Vit, Tony / Elevate: Format One / NWA: Base, D.R. & Karim
FVRCD 3 / Oct '96 / Feverpitch

☐ TRADE VOL.4 (3CD Set)
Clear: Artist Formerly Known As Technique / Set yourself free: Torres, Liz / Parade: Pierce, Mike / Drums are us: DJ Sneak / VIP EP Vol.1: Hip Hoperation / Psychic bounty killaz: DJ Sneak & Armand Van Helden / Body, soul and spirit: Miquel, Michael / Higher: Saeed / Tantra's circus: Christian, James & Tantra's Circus / I want music: Fisher, Cevin / Rough and raw: Roberts, Andy / Elevation: 95 North / Disco life (check dis' out): Linear Science / Rock the turntable: Floorshow / Sharp tools Vol.3: Sharp Boys / Sexy thing: JP Presents / Distant stab: Freak & Mac Zimms / Dirty habits: Monk Mac: Ha-Lo / Show me love: Fruit Loop / Syncrasp: Bubblegum Crisis / Black science: Wooden 'N' Farley / Return of the borg: Kinetic A.T.O.M. / Phunkee muzeek: Shazzamm / Londons burning/Me mum said: Daisy, Pete & Jamie Rainbow / Frank's birthday: Bigfoot Spira / 6 hours: Mould Impression / Burning desire: Incisions / Katoomba: Roughage / Pick it up: Kulac / Flowtation: De Moor, Vincent / Have fun: Coma B / Never enough: NRG / Give me love: Diddy / Jungle high: Juno Reactor / Flash: BBE / Baloney: Lectrolux / XTC phase one: Ethos / F18 / Overdose (my heart is pumping): F18 / Machine gun: Autumn, Rachel / Chemical imbalances: Mark & Amind / Give it to me: Choci & EC1 / Tardis to Brooklyn: Bang The Future / Hellfire: 200 Degrees
FVRCD 5 / Mar '97 / Feverpitch

☐ TRADITIONAL AND MODERN JAZZ MASTERWORKS
Back o' town blues: Armstrong, Louis Allstars / Panama: Armstrong, Louis Allstars / Jack-Armstrong blues: Armstrong, Louis Allstars / Beale Street blues: Nichols, Red & His Five Pennies / Pennies a bum: Nichols, Red & His Five Pennies / Pennies / Music goes 'round and around: Dorsey, Tommy & His Clambake Seven / Maple leaf rag: Condon, Eddie / Polka dot stomp rag: Condon, Eddie / Carolina shout: Condon, Eddie / Margie: Condon, Eddie / Riverboat shuffle: Condon, Eddie / Walkin' my baby back home: Condon, Eddie / Running wild: Condon, Eddie / Aunt Hagar's blues: Condon, Eddie / Sand dip music: Condon, Eddie / Heebie jeebies: Condon, Eddie / Oh babe: Prima, Louis & Swing Band / How high the moon: Prima, Louis & Swing Band
17052 / Nov '95 / Laserlight

☐ TRADITIONAL ANDEAN FOLK SONGS
Ingrata no llores: Mallku, Jach'a / Hoja de otono: Mallku, Jach'a / Jucku: Mallku, Jach'a / Jesus & Quimantu / Pachamama: Rumillajta / Kusga quilla: Inti-Raymi / La partita: Rumillajta / Ohawanakuy: Rumillajta / Tierra de condores: Mallku, Jach'a / Carnaval de la feria: Rumillajta / Iscanqaya: Rumillajta / Fuego de los Andes: Mallku, Jach'a / Puerto del sol: Rumillajta / Zuki: Rumillajta / Tus lagrimas: Nan, Karu / Maria Juana: Quimantu
NSCD 026 / 16 Feb '98 / Nascente

☐ TRADITIONAL ARABIC MUSIC
D 8002 / Jun '89 / Auvidis/Ethnic

☐ TRADITIONAL CHILEAN MUSIC
D 8001 / Jun '89 / Auvidis/Ethnic

☐ TRADITIONAL DANCE MUSIC OF IRELAND
Sally gardens/Masons apron: Hogan, Jimmy Trio / Gurty's frolic: Doherty, John / Louis Quinn's: Hogan, Jimmy / David delight: Turkington, Tom / Sweep's: Taylor, Paddy / Bunker hill/Tommy Whelan's: Hogan, Jimmy Trio / Please give a penny to the poor old man: Doherty, John / Stormy weather: Doherty, John / Gosson that beats his father: McGuire, Sean / Copperplate/The boys of the spuds: Hogan, Jimmy Trio / Carracastle lasses: Gorman, Michael & Margaret Barry / Biddy the bowl wife/I lost my love and I care not/King of th: McCusker Brothers Ceilidh Band / New lough isle castle: Doherty, John / Hares when you're young: Doherty, John / Lord Gordons: Doherty, John / Boys of the lough/Lark: Hogan, Jimmy Trio / Down the glen: Taylor, Paddy / Hare among the heather/woman of the house: Gorman, Michael & Margaret Barry / Paddy O'Brien's: Hogan, Jimmy / Tinker's apron and antrim reel: McCusker Brothers Ceilidh Band / Red haired boys: Turkington, Tom / O'Malleys/The Luck Penny: Hogan, Jimmy Trio / Banks of the llen: Hogan, Jimmy / First of may: Doherty, John / Trumpet/Locomotive: Hogan, Jimmy / Banks of the llen: Taylor, Paddy / Dark girl dressed in blue: Doherty, John / Floggin: Doherty, John / Johnson's/Golden eagle: Hogan, Jimmy Trio / Mason's apron: Turkington, Tom / Independent: Hogan, Jimmy / Paddy's own/Launch: Breen, Paddy / Music at the gate: Ennis, Seamus / Basket of oysters: Doherty, John / O'Brien's fancy: Hogan, Jimmy Trio / Garret Barry's: Hogan, Jimmy Trio / Boys of Ballisodare: Gorman, Michael & Margaret Barry / Passing cloud: Hogan, Jimmy Trio
CDSDL 420 / Mar '97 / Saydisc

☐ TRADITIONAL FIDDLE MUSIC OF KENTUCKY VOL.1 (Up The Ohio & Licking Rivers)
Portsmouth airs: Thomas, Buddy / Bumble bee in a jug: Hawkins, George Lee / Meg Gray: Hawkins, George Lee / Lansing Quadrille: Bailey, Alfred / Weddington's reel: Bailey, Alfred / Indian squaw: Greene, Alva / Pet Indian: Greene, Alva / Getting George Bush upstairs: Riley, Perry / Getting wild again: Riley, Perry / Lost tomahoe: Kinney, Charlie / Blackeyed peas and cornbread: Prater, Bob / Grand hornpipe: Prater, Bob / bakewheather: Thomas, Buddy / Humphrey's jig: Hawkins, George Lee / Darling girl: Hawkins, George Lee / Rat's gone to rest: Hawkins, George Lee / Big Indian hornpipe: Bailey, Alfred / Alexander waltz: Bailey, Alfred / Turkey gobbler: Thomas, Buddy / I've got a Grandpa: Greene, Alva / Blind man's lament: Greene, Alva / McClanahan's march: Greene, Alva / Callahan: Hawkins, George Lee / Boatin' up Sandy: Hawkins, George Lee / Pumpkin vine: Thomas, Buddy / Kicked up a devil of a row: Rigdon, Clarence / Bell cow: Kinney, Charlie / Onion tops and turnip greens: Prater, Bob / Feed my horse on corn and hay: Thomas, Buddy / Jaybird in a high oak tree: Riley, Perry / Warfield: Riley, Perry / Bonaparte's retreat: Bailey, Alfred / Fiden to the White House: Bailey, Alfred / Jenny run: Greene, Alva / Buck Hord: Hawkins, George Lee / Flannery's dream: Greene, Alva / Winding sheep: Greene, Alva / Buck Hord: Greene, Alva / Addison: Thomas, Buddy
ROUCD 0376 / Feb '97 / Rounder

☐ TRADITIONAL FIDDLE MUSIC OF KENTUCKY VOL.2 (Along The Kentucky River)
She danced all night in the fiddler's shoes: Fulks, Darley / Atlanta Schottische: Fulks, Darley / Snowstorm: Fulks, Darley / Downfall of Paris: Fulks, Darley / Greenup creek: Fulks, Darley / Pharoah: Fulks, Darley / Everybody's favourite: Todd, Lelia / Boatin' up Sandy: Thomas, Earl / Red lick: Stamper, Billy / Poor girl waltz: Williams, Columbus / Last gold dollar: Kidwell, Van / Johnny in the low ground: Woodward, Jim / Morgan on the railroad: Barnes, Ed 'Buck' / Snowbird in the Ashbank: Masters, John / Shippingport: Masters, John / Camp Nelson blues: Masters, John / Garfield march: Masters, John
ROUCD 0377 / Feb '97 / Rounder

☐ TRADITIONAL FOLK MUSIC FROM NORTHERN IRELAND
CDNI 101 / Aug '96 / Outlet

☐ TRADITIONAL IRISH DRINKING SONGS (Sing-A-Long Medley)
SUMCD 4169 / 26 Jan '98 / Summit

☐ TRADITIONAL IRISH MUSIC FROM BELFAST
Shaskeen / Trim the velvet / Out on the ocean / Hog with the money / Boys of Blue Hill / Plains of Boyle / Gan Anim / Sligo maid / Sally Gardens / Coolin / Gold spear / Road to Ballymac / Toss the feathers / Night Larry was stretched / Hardyman the fiddler / Three Kerry polkas / Rights of man / Chief O'Neill's hornpipe / Ships are sailing / Cup of tea / Trip to Athlone / Rambling pitchfork / Frost is all over / Spindle shanks / George White's favourite / Se fath mo bhuartha / Boys of the town / Metal bridge / Old bush / Bucks of Oranmore
PTICD 1095 / May '96 / Pure Traditional Irish

☐ TRADITIONAL JAZZ FAVOURITES
PLSCD 235 / Jul '97 / Pulse

☐ TRADITIONAL JAZZ MASTERWORKS
Trouble in mind: Armstrong, Louis & Chippie Hill / New York blues: Graves, Roosevelt / I ain't no iceman: Davenport, Cow Cow / You do me any old way: Broonzy, 'Big' Bill / I'm tired of fatterin' frogs for snakes: Crawford, Rosetta & James P. Johnson's Hep Cats / Freight train blues: Smith, Trixie / Cherry red: Turner, 'Big' Joe & Pete Johnson's Boogie Woogie Boys / Billie's blues: Holiday, Billie & Her Orchestra / Boogie woogie: Rushing, Jimmy & The Jones-Smith Inc. / Lockwood boogie: Lockwood, Robert Jr. & The Aces / Jumpin' in the woodpile: Williams, 'Big' Joe & J.D. Short / Sykes gumboogie: Sykes, Roosevelt & King Kolax Band / Good morning blues: Snyder/Ake Anderson/Dino Alvarez / Young Hawk's blues: J.B. & His Hawks / Everyday I have the blues: Rush, Otis Blues Band / Blues and trouble: Lockwood, Robert Jr. & The Aces / Things I used to do: Young, 'Mighty' Joe Chicago Blues Band
17050 / Nov '95 / Laserlight

☐ TRADITIONAL MEDITERRANEAN OBOES AND BRASS
926822 / Nov '97 / BUDA

☐ TRADITIONAL MUSIC
D 8004 / Jun '89 / Auvidis/Ethnic

☐ TRADITIONAL MUSIC FROM CONNEMARA (The Gaelic Heritage)
C 580029 / Mar '93 / Ocora

☐ TRADITIONAL MUSIC FROM CROATIA
D 8276 / Jun '93 / Unesco

☐ TRADITIONAL MUSIC FROM MALAWI
D 8625 / Feb '96 / Unesco

☐ TRADITIONAL MUSIC FROM PERU
Pap hallmay / Papa asllay / Papa ch'utay / Carnaval de tinkuy I / Puka chaki wallata / Anu niwu de lawata / Carnaval de tinkuy II / Carnaval de tinkuy III / Kacharpari y Diana I / Linguayqu qcchachaqip / Cruzata puchñu / Linda gavotita / Q'ellabamba campanity / Danza q'anchi de canas / Punch'ay qhashwa / Tupay chita kasarachiru / Toqroyoq plazapi / Tuytunki tuytunki / Descanso q'asay / Kasarakuy mallkiyuq / Chita mamalla / Tupay sabura juygo
D 8268 / Jul '97 / Unesco

☐ TRADITIONAL MUSIC FROM THE AZORES
PS 65125 / Apr '94 / PlayaSound

☐ TRADITIONAL MUSIC FROM THE CARPATHIANS
QUI 903029 / Jul '91 / Quintana

☐ TRADITIONAL MUSIC FROM THE UKRAINE
Y 225216CD / Apr '95 / Silex

☐ TRADITIONAL MUSIC OF CAPE BRETON
NIM 5383CD / Nov '93 / Nimbus

☐ TRADITIONAL MUSIC OF CHINA
824912 / Nov '90 / BUDA

☐ TRADITIONAL MUSIC OF ETHIOPIA
PS 65074 / Jun '91 / PlayaSound

☐ TRADITIONAL MUSIC OF GREECE
QUI 903060 / Nov '91 / Quintana

☐ TRADITIONAL MUSIC OF IRELAND
Four courts/Katie's fancy: Buttons & Bows / William / Taylor: Patrick Street / Cameronian set: Cherish The Ladies / Brian Boru's march/Sporting Paddy: The traveller: Burke, Joe & Michael Cooney/Terry crabbe / Drowsie Maggie set: Watt, Robin / Corcoran / Loftus: Patrick Street / An cailin gaelach: Altan / Seanbhean bhocht/Sweeney's: Mou artha Cloud / Green fields of Canada: Deanta / Sword in the hand/ The providence cradle: Old bush: McIlroy, Matt & Sean Keane: / Jimmy Keane/Robbie O'Connell/Liz Carroll / Blind Mary: Madden, Joanie / Yellow tinker/Lady Montgomery/The merry harriers: Altan
CELT 9006 / Jun '97 / Celtophile

☐ TRADITIONAL MUSIC OF OMAN, THE
927032 / 24 Feb '98 / BUDA

☐ TRADITIONAL MUSIC OF PERU VOL.1 (Festivals Of Cusco)
SFWCD 40466 / Dec '95 / Smithsonian Folkways

☐ TRADITIONAL MUSIC OF PERU VOL.2 (The Mantaro Valley)
SFWCD 40467 / Dec '95 / Smithsonian Folkways

☐ TRADITIONAL MUSIC OF PERU VOL.3
SFWCD 40468 / Dec '96 / Smithsonian Folkways

☐ TRADITIONAL MUSIC OF SCOTLAND
Tae the weaver's gin ye go: Stewart, Andy M. & Manus Lunny / Carls o' Dysart: Tannahill Weavers / Log splitter set: Tannahill Weavers / Iain ghlinn' cuaich: Capercaillie / Bellavinich: Wolfstone / Secret portrait/Wha'll be king but Charlie: Silly Wizard / Jim's jig/The snuff wife/Eileen MacDonald: Thoumire, Simon Three / Archibald McDonald of Keppoch: Cunningham, John / Are ye sleeping Maggie/The noose and the gillie: Tannahill Weavers / Hut on Staffin Island/Sandy MacLeod Garafad/Soft horse reel: Relativity / Puirt a beul/Snug in a blanket: Capercaillie / Land o' the leal: Stewart, Andy M.
CELT 9005 / Oct '97 / Celtophile

☐ TRADITIONAL MUSIC OF THE MAORI
VPS 489 / Sep '96 / Viking

☐ TRADITIONAL MUSIC OF VIETNAM
ARN 64303 / Jul '95 / Arion

☐ TRADITIONAL POLYPHONIC SONGS
927062 / 24 Apr '98 / BUDA

☐ TRADITIONAL PORTUGUESE MUSIC
D 8008 / Jun '89 / Auvidis/Ethnic

☐ TRADITIONAL PUB SONGS
Roll out the barrel / Who were you with last night / Hold your hand out you naughty boy / Hello, hello / Who's your lady friend / Ship ahoy / It's a long way to Tipperary / I do like to be beside the seaside / Pack up your troubles (in your old kit bag) / Baby face / Don't dilly dally on the way / Run, rabbit, run / Waiting at the church / Strollin' / Underneath the arches / Side by side / Lambeth walk / Daddy wouldn't buy me a bow wow / I'm henry the eight I am / Goodbye Dooly Gray / When you're smiling the whole world smiles with you / Bye bye blackbird / Home town / Lily of Laguna / On mother Kelly doorstep / I'm forever blowing bubbles / Boiled beef and carrots / Any old iron / My old man's a dustman / I've got a lovely bunch of coconuts / Knees up mother brown
SUMCD 4130 / Jun '97 / Summit

☐ TRADITIONAL ROMANIAN MUSIC
Asa zice mandra mea / Marie poale ciurate si joc de doi / Doamne bate lumea rea / Frunzulita margarit / Folae verde de salcuta
YA 225714 / Nov '97 / Terres

☐ TRADITIONAL SINGING FROM BULGARIA
C 5600009 / Aug '98 / Ocora

☐ TRADITIONAL SONGS OF EASTER ISLAND, THE
ARN 64345 / Sep '96 / Arion

☐ TRADITIONAL SONGS OF IRELAND
Warrior's chant: McPeake Family Trio / Moorlough shore: O'Neill, Jim / Wild colonial boy: Barry, Margaret / My singing bird: McPeake Family Trio / Whistling thief: Ennis, Seamus / Factory girl: Barry, Margaret / When you go to the fair: Devaney, Hudie / Jug of punch: McPeake Family Trio / Moses ritooralay: Barry, Margaret / Keening song: Gallagher, Kitty / Verdant braes of skreen: McPeake Family Trio / Her mantle so green: O'Neill, Jim / As I roved out: Ennis, Seamus / Factory girl: Makem, Sarah / Wild mountain thyme: Moran, Thomas / Hawk and the crow: O'Connor, Liam / She moves through the fair: Barry, Margaret / Bridget O Mally: Devaney, Hudie / Wild mountain thyme: McPeake Family Trio / Blacklot: McKeann, Francis / Turfman from Ardee: Barry, Margaret / Nursemaid: Gallagher, Kitty / Monaghan fair: McPeake, Frank / Magpie's nest: Kelly, Annie Jane / Dance to your daddy: Cronin, Elizabeth / Spailshan ni dhuibhir: McPeake Family Trio
CDSDL 411 / May '95 / Saydisc

☐ TRADITIONAL THAI MUSIC
D 8007 / Jun '89 / Auvidis/Ethnic

☐ TRADITIONALLY IRISH
ARAN 3602 / 22 Jun '98 / Dara

☐ TRADITIONS OF BALI
926002 CD / Oct '94 / BUDA

☐ TRADITIONS OF BRITTANY - BAGPIPES
SCM 026CD / Apr '94 / Diffusion Breizh

☐ TRADITIONS OF BRITTANY - CLARINET
SCM 025CD / Apr '94 / Diffusion Breizh

☐ TRADITIONS OF BRITTANY - HURDY GURDY
SCM 024CD / Apr '94 / Diffusion Breizh

☐ TRADITIONS OF BRITTANY - VIOLIN
SCM 031CD / Apr '94 / Diffusion Breizh

☐ **TRAIN TICKET VOL.2 (2CD Set)**
Lowgo: *Magoo Project* / Synaesthesia: *Synaesthesia* / Sweet gravity: *LSG* / Channel feedback: *LSG* / Refunktion: *Scan Carriers* / To eclipse: *Apach* / Spellbound: *Cwithe* / Pulse: *Magnetic Pulstar* / Flow: *Model 500* / State of time: *Gage* / Rama: *Recycle* / Extra: *Ishii, Ken* / Mark NRG: *Mark NRG* / Endogenous rhythm: *R-Factor* / Structur der seele: *Rob Acid* / Pylorus: *Hypnopedia*
SPV 08992322 / Jun '96 / SPV

☐ **TRAINS ON THE HIGHWAY**
IMP 942 / Sep '96 / IMP

☐ **TRANCE**
NT 6755CD / Nov '96 / New Tone

☐ **TRANCE CENTRAL**
PCCD 0012 / 6 Jul '98 / Planetary Conciousness

☐ **TRANCE CENTRAL VOL.1**
KICKCD 18 / Mar '95 / Kickin'

☐ **TRANCE CENTRAL VOL.1-3 (3CD Set)**
KICKCD 53 / Jun '97 / Kickin'

☐ **TRANCE CENTRAL VOL.2**
KICKCD 22 / May '95 / Kickin'

☐ **TRANCE CENTRAL VOL.3**
KICKCD 30 / Nov '95 / Kickin'

☐ **TRANCE CENTRAL VOL.4**
KICKCD 36 / Mar '96 / Kickin'

☐ **TRANCE CENTRAL VOL.5 (2CD Set)**
KICKCD 44 / Nov '96 / Kickin'

☐ **TRANCE CENTRAL VOL.6 (Psychedelic Moments - 2CD Set)**
Snake dance: *Nemesis* / Howling at the moon: *Cosmosis* / Violent violet: *Three State Logic* / Cynabs: *Orion* / Triplexus: *Miranda* / Karma 209: *Talking Souls* / Atlantis: *Section X* / Destination: *Guidance* / Water margin: *Lunar Asylum* / Braindance: *Kaaya* / Loin king: *Infernal Machine* / X plore: *Montauk-P* / Second room: *X-Dream* / Destination Bom: *Doof* / Alien earth activity: *UX*
KICKCD 51 / Apr '97 / Kickin'

☐ **TRANCE CENTRAL VOL.7 (2CD Set)**
KICKCD 61 / 27 Oct '97 / Kickin'

☐ **TRANCE CLUB VOL.1**
MNF 05422 / 30 Mar '98 / Manifold

☐ **TRANCE CORE**
Rainbow island: *Seb* / Dreamland: *Q-Tex* / Movin' on: *Cortex* / Whistle tune: *Aurora 7* / Natural born killer: *Dominion* / Acid sunshine: *Trance Masters* / Better day: *GBT Inc* / Revolution: *DJ Fury* / My mind: *Cru-L-T* / Music hypnotizing: *DJ Ham* / Before your eyes: *Helix* / Truth: *Smith & Sharkey* / Oresis (parts 1 and 2): *Cicero*
CDTOT 47 / Nov '96 / Jumpin' & Pumpin'

☐ **TRANCE EUROPE**
CLEO 92432 / Mar '94 / Cleopatra

☐ **TRANCE EXPERIENCE**
DR 0012 / Mar '97 / Discobole

☐ **TRANCE MISSION VOL.1**
AUM 004062 / Dec '96 / AMS

☐ **TRANCE MISSION VOL.2 (2CD Set)**
AUM 975001 / 1 Sep '97 / ZYX

☐ **TRANCE MIX VOL.8**
MR 1005 / 2 Mar '98 / Melodia

☐ **TRANCE MUSIC**
LDX 2741008 / Sep '95 / La Chant Du Monde

☐ **TRANCE PACIFIC EXPRESS (2CD Set/ Booklet)**
DVNT 020CD / Jun '97 / Deviant

☐ **TRANCE PLANET VOL.1**
4444772062 / 24 Feb '98 / Triloka

☐ **TRANCE PLANET VOL.2**
Kothbiro / Walk like a pygmy / Sacred stones / Angelica in delirium / Boto / Matinal / Monsoon / Through the hill / Touba fame ke / Third chamber part 4 / True to the times / Improvisation / N'cosi sikelel' afica
3202102 / 24 Feb '98 / Triloka

☐ **TRANCE PLANET VOL.3**
Valencia: *Taha, Rachid* / Ave Maria: *Kagen-Paely, Vyatchescav* / Saa magni: *Sangare, Oumou* / Ghost dance: *Tulku* / Elalama Helalla: *Shehan, Steve & Baly Othmani* / Zephyrus: *Stellamara* / Cool wind is blowing: *Gasparyan, Djivan* / Lovelorn: *Levy, Iki* / To the evening child: *Micus, Stephan* / Alimatou salia: *Cissokho, Milang* / Like water: *Azrie, Abed* / Guru bandana: *Khan, Ali Akbar* / Nwahulwana: *Orchestra Marrabenta Star De Mocambique*
6971241102 / 24 Feb '98 / Triloka

☐ **TRANCE PLANET VOL.4**
3145557282 / 5 May '98 / Triloka

☐ **TRANCE RAVER VOL.5**
SFT 2000242 / May '97 / Shift

☐ **TRANCE SPOTTING**
CLP 9913 / Mar '97 / Hypnotic

☐ **TRANCE TRIBUTE TO THE 80'S, A**
Tainted love / Fade to grey / Vienna / Enola Gay / Blue Monday / Cars / Don't you want me
CLP 99002 / Jan '97 / Cleopatra

☐ **TRANCE TRIPPIN'**
Sanction: *Emtorino* / Kollo: *Pan Pacific* / Bandos: *Villivaru* / Shadow: *Nyali* / Argentine dawn: *Mullos* / Insatiable: *Emtorino* / Mission to love: *Coyaba Tribe* / Three walls two ceilings: *Delirious Pink Dog* / Topkapi: *Canabisis* / 5 a.m. in Barringo: *Mashed* / Satyagrahi: *Meallo*
CDTOT 11 / Jun '94 / Jumpin' & Pumpin'

☐ **TRANCE VOL.2**
CDRAID 509 / Dec '92 / Rumour

☐ **TRANCE VOL.3**
CDRAID 511 / May '93 / Rumour

☐ **TRANCE VOL.4**
CDRAID 513 / Oct '93 / Rumour

☐ **TRANCE VOL.5**
Dreams: *Quench* / Kruspolska: *Hedningarna* / Fluid: *Marine Boy* / Rich girl: *Crimes, Tori* / Agent o: *Aloof* / Move in motion: *Hanson & Nelson* / Torwart: *Deep Piece* / Kiss the baby: *United State Of Sound* / X-tribe: *X-Tribe* / Space man: *Miro* / Solar VS1: *Remould*
CDRAID 515 / Mar '94 / Rumour

☐ **TRANCE VOL.6**
CDRAID 521 / Feb '95 / Rumour

☐ **TRANCE XPERIENCE VOL.1**
I 3884402 / Jul '97 / Galaxy

☐ **TRANCE XPERIENCE VOL.2**
I 3884412 / Jul '97 / Galaxy

☐ **TRANCED OUT AND DREAMING**
BARKCD 023 / Jan '97 / Planet Dog

☐ **TRANCED OUT VOL.888**
DIVINE 018CD / 7 Oct '97 / Taste/Divine

☐ **TRANCED OUT VOL.999 (The Blue One)**
DIVINE 021CD / 4 Nov '97 / Taste/Divine

☐ **TRANCEFLOOR**
XPS 2CDM
XPS 2CDU / Oct '95 / X-Press

☐ **TRANCENTRAL BOXED (6CD Set)**
KICKCD 56 / 22 Sep '97 / Kickin'

☐ **TRANCEOGRAPHY**
AQUACD 4 / 29 Sep '97 / Aquarius

☐ **TRANCEPORTER**
70001271363 / Jan '95 / Essential Dance

☐ **TRANCESEXUAL**
CLEO 9701CD / May '96 / Cleopatra

☐ **TRANQUIL IRISH MELODIES**
HCD 006 / Apr '95 / GTD

☐ **TRANQUIL MOODS (4CD Set)**
SUMBX 4023 / Jan '98 / Summit

☐ **TRANQUILITY (Music For The Mind & Body - 2CD Set)**
Mystery of the mountains: *Midori* / Saphire: *Moon, Ashley* / Communion: *Larsen, Lou* / Transformation: *Midori* / Cirrus: *Moon, Ashley* / Beauty of the mountains: *Midori* / New horizons: *Midori* / Beyond the valleys: *Moon, Ashley* / Rainbow dancing: *Glassfield, Chris* / Price of peace: *Volker Cat* / Fireside: *L'Esprit* / Passage of time: *Lawrie, Susie* / Swans: *Glassfield, Chris* / Contemplation: *Laurie, Susie* / Ripples: *L'Esprit* / Echoes of eternity ii: *Volker Cat* / Eternal silence: *Laurie, Susie*
RCACD 219 / Jul '97 / RCA

☐ **TRANQUILITY (Rainforest)**
Rainforest / Deep green / Sounds of the forest / Clearing
307072 / 13 Jul '98 / Hallmark

☐ **TRANQUILITY (Wild Waters)**
River dawn / Flowing streams / Wild waters
307002 / 13 Jul '98 / Hallmark

☐ **TRANQUILITY (Gentle Tides)**
Gentle tides
307012 / 13 Jul '98 / Hallmark

☐ **TRANQUILITY (Woodland Morning)**
Woodland morning / Stream / Birds in the trees / Noon in the woods
307022 / 13 Jul '98 / Hallmark

☐ **TRANQUILITY (Country Sunset)**
Country sunset
307052 / 13 Jul '98 / Hallmark

☐ **TRANQUILLITY (The Seasons - Spring)**
305872 / May '97 / Hallmark

☐ **TRANQUILLITY (Relationships)**
306972 / Jun '97 / Hallmark

☐ **TRANQUILLITY (The Seasons - Summer)**
305882 / Jun '97 / Hallmark

☐ **TRANS CONTINENTAL TECHNO (4CD Set)**
032505 CD / Jan '97 / Nite & Blue

☐ **TRANS SLOVENIA EXPRESS**
CDSTUMM 131 / Aug '94 / Mute

☐ **TRANSATLANTIC SAMPLER**
TRACD 102 / Apr '96 / Transatlantic

☐ **TRANSATLANTIC TICKET**
Light flight: *Pentangle* / Fhir a' bhata: *Johnstons* / Angie/Work song: *Jansch, Bert* / Up to now: *Dransfield* / Vestapol/That's no way to get along: *Grossman, Stefan* / Come by the hills: *Furey, Finbar & Eddie* / Three pieces by O'Carolan: *Renbourn, John* / Ploughboy's dream: *Gryphon* / Burn the witch: *McCalmans* / Grey daylight/The hawk/The ten pound fiddle: *Swarbrick, Dave* / Tom Dooley: *Sweeney's Men* / Heliotrope bouqet: *James, John* / England's green and pleasant land: *Digance, Richard* / All the good times: *Mr. Fox* / Twa recruiting sergeants: *Campbell, Ian Folk Group* / Silk pyjamas: *Humblebums* / Black scrag: *Lee, Philip John* / Pretty Polly: *Jansch, Bert* / John Barleycorn: *Young Tradition* / Sugar babe: *Renbourn, John* / Goodbye pork pie hat: *Pentangle*
ESMCD 577 / Jul '97 / Essential

☐ **TRANSCENDENCE (Impulse In A Spiritual Groove)**
IMP 12432 / 24 Aug '98 / Impulse Jazz

☐ **TRANSCENTRAL CONNECTION VOL.1**
ASHADOW 7CD / Nov '96 / Moving Shadow

☐ **TRANSCENTRAL CONNECTION VOL.2**
ASHADOW 11CD / 30 Mar '98 / Moving Shadow

☐ **TRANSFORMATIONS & MODULATIONS**
EFA 6512 / Apr '94 / Mille Plateau

☐ **TRANSIENT DAWN**
Ambience: *Astral Projection* / Hypnosys: *Messiah* / Searching slowly: *Slide* / Vision: *Cosmix & Elysium* / Temple of the moon: *Anubis* / Slipstream: *Medicine Drum* / Blue sun shrine: *Doof* / Dawn of an era: *Cosmosis*
TRANR 609CD / Jun '97 / Transient

☐ **TRANSIENT VOL.1 (New Energy & Trance)**
TRANR 601CD / Apr '95 / Transient

☐ **TRANSIENT VOL.3**
TRANR 603CD / Apr '96 / Transient

☐ **TRANSIENT VOL.4**
TRANR 605CD / Sep '96 / Transient

☐ **TRANSIENT VOL.5**
TRANR 608CD / Apr '97 / Transient

☐ **TRANSIENT VOL.6 (Theory Of Evolution)**
Chaos to order: *Psychaos* / Flooob: *Lumen* / Mummy machine: *Schuldt, Tim* / Creepy crawly: *Process & Slide* / Ceremoniak: *Spies* / Barbequed mind: *Radiation* / Julz: *Tristan & Man Made Man* / Megabyte: *Element Over Nature* / Eighth hole: *Coma*
TRAN 613CD / 9 Feb '98 / Transient

☐ **TRANSISTOR REVENGE**
IRB 59992 / Jan '96 / Deep Blue

☐ **TRANSMISSIONS**
SECTCD 002 / 9 Mar '98 / Secret

☐ **TRANZMISSION**
TRANZ 001CD / Sep '95 / Dance Net

☐ **TRAS-OS-MONTES (BEYOND THE MOUNTAINS)**
C 580035 / Mar '93 / Ocora

☐ **TRAUMHAFT DEUTSCH**
Hello again: *Carpendale, Howard* / Du entschuldige-ich kenn' dich: *Brink, Bernard* / Ich wollt' nur mal mit dir reden: *Lavi, Daliah* / Bis ans ende der welt: *Purple Schulz* / Du gehst fort: *Sheer, Ireen & Bernard Brink* / Wei mei Herzschlag: *Heller, Andre* / Bleib bei mir heut'nacht: *Borg, Andy* / Herz an herz gefuhl: *Deutscher, Drafi* / Auf den mond schieben: *Petry, Wolfgang* / Deine flugelfangen feuer: *Martin, Andreas* / Die lebe bleibt: *Lage, Klaus* / Schickeria: *Spuder Murphy GAng* / Bye bye my love: *Foos, Black* / Niemals geht man so ganz: *Herr, Trude*
DC 862412 / Oct '96 / Disky

☐ **TRAVEL THE WORLD WITH PUTUMAYO**
PUTU 1302 / Jun '97 / Putumayo

☐ **TRAVELLING ARTISTS OF THE DESERT (The Vernacular Musical Culture Of Rajasthan/India)**
Drawing water/Camel's cry/Festival day pilgrimage song / Nara / Gorbandh / Charka / Morchang and dholak performance / Morbhai / Warshawa / Ghoomar / Panihari / Hichiki / Harjas / Arani / Proclaimation for the village leader / Mehndi / Ohmpoori / Moomal / Narrative with dhol / Bhajan / Hanumanji
MCM 3002 / May '97 / Multicultural Media

☐ **TRAVELLING THROUGH THE JUNGLE (Fife & Drum Bands From The Deep South)**
TCD 5017 / Mar '95 / Testament

☐ **TRAVELOGUE - BALI**
YA 225709 / Aug '96 / Silex

☐ **TRAVELOGUE - CHINA**
YA 225701 / Jan '95 / Silex

☐ **TRAVELOGUE - GREECE**
YA 225706 / Jan '95 / Silex

☐ **TRAVELOGUE - IRELAND**
YA 225704 / Jan '95 / Silex

☐ **TRAVELOGUE - MADAGASCAR**
YA 225702 / Jan '95 / Silex

☐ **TRAVELOGUE - PORTUGAL**
YA 225703 / Jan '95 / Silex

☐ **TRAVELOGUE - QUEBEC**
YA 225705 / Jan '95 / Silex

☐ **TRAVIS COUNTY PICKIN' (Country Jazz Guitar Austin Texas Style)**
HMG 3001 / Aug '97 / Hightone

☐ **TRAX UNLIMITED VOL.7**
TIMECD 0442 / 6 Jul '98 / Time Unlimited

☐ **TREACLE PEOPLE PRESENT STREET HOUSE, THE**
KICKCD 81 / 13 Jul '98 / Kickin'

☐ **TREASURE CHEST OF NORTHERN SOUL, A**
I must love you: *Wilson, Timothy* / Remember: *Whispers* / I'll be there: *Gems* / Day my heart stood still: *Jackson, Ollie* / I found true love: *Hambric, Billy* / Watch yourself: *Hester, Tony* / Hole in the wall: *Barnes, J.J.* / You will never get away: *Maye, Cholli* / Shin-a-ling: *Cooperettes* / Mixed up: *Furys* / What is this: *Womack, Bobby* / You don't mean it: *Barnes, Towanda* / What good am I without you: *Fletcher, Darrow* / I gotta find that girl: *Hambric, Billy* / I'll never let you go: *O'Jays* / Going going gone: *Black, Cody* / Lovingly yours: *Wilson, Timothy* / My kind of woman: *Starr, Edwin* / Now you've got the upper hand: *Staton, Candi* / Daddy-o: *Lindsay, Therese* / What is this (vox): *Womack, Bobby* / This won't change: *Tipton, Lester* / Lies: *Owens, Gwen* / Feel good all over: *Huey, Claude 'Baby'* / I still wait for you: *Batiste, Rose* / Love bandit: *Chi-Lites* / Very next time: *Marlynns* / Gee baby: *Wilson, Micky* / I got the power: *Masqueraders* / My baby ain't no plaything: *Harvey, Willy*
GSCD 075 / Oct '95 / Goldmine

☐ **TREASURE ISLE DUB VOL.1 & 2**
LG 21090 / Aug '93 / Lagoon

☐ **TREASURE ISLE GREATEST HITS**
SONCD 0041 / Sep '95 / Sonic Sounds

☐ **TREASURE ISLE HOTTEST HITS VOL.1 (Treasure Isle Recordings From The 1960's)**
RMM 1134 / Mar '96 / Treasure Isle

☐ **TREASURE ISLE HOTTEST HITS VOL.2**
RMM 1267 / Jan '94 / Treasure Isle

☐ **TREASURE ISLE MEETS TIPTOP**
SONCD 0047 / Jul '93 / Sonic Sounds

☐ **TREASURE ISLE MOOD**
CBHB 195 / Oct '95 / Heartbeat

☐ **TREASURE ISLE TIME**
RNCD 2092 / Feb '95 / Rhino

☐ **TREASURE ISLE TIME**
CDHB 196 / Oct '95 / Heartbeat

☐ **TREASURE OF MY HEART**
Munster Buttermilk: *Andrews, William* / Johnny will you marry me: *Sullivan, Dan & Shamrock Band* / Farewell to Ireland: *Morrison, James* / Paddy in London: *Flanagan Brothers* / Me husband's flannel shirt: *McGettigan, John* / Dowd's favourite: *Gillespie, Hugh* / Tippin' it up to Nancy: *Reilly, John* / Bruachna carriage baine: *Clancy, Willie* / Bunch of keys/Buckley's dream: *Rowsome, Leo* / My father's a hedger and ditcher: *Carolan, Mary-Ann* / Muckross Abbey/Mulvihill's: *Murphy, Dennis* / Turfman from Ardee: *Barry, Margaret* / Choice wife: *Clancy, Willie* / Cunnla: *Heaney, Joe* / Wild mountain thyme: *McPeake Clan* / Roaring Mary: *Doherty, John* / Off to California: *Russell, Micho* / Wind that shakes the barley: *Makem, Sarah* / Rakish Paddy: *Doran, Felix* / Rollicking boys around Tandaragee: *Tunney, Paddy* / New demesne: *Ennis, Seamus* / Micko Russell's reel/trip to Birmingham: *McDermott, Josie* / He rolled her to the wall: *Harte, Frank* / Silver spear/Flax in bloom: *Glackin, Paddy* / Murphy's/Going to the well for water: *Daly, Jackie* / Eclipse/Tailor's twist: *Boys Of The Lough* / Willie Clarke's/Green grow the rushes-o: *Holmes, Joe* / Micho Russels/Sporting nell: *Four Men & A Dog*
ORB 081CD / Oct '93 / Globestyle

☐ **TREASURY OF IRISH MUSIC VOL.1, A**
CDTCD 004 / Aug '95 / Gael Linn

☐ **TREASURY OF IRISH MUSIC VOL.2, A**
CDTCD 005 / 20 Oct '97 / Gael Linn

☐ **TREASURY OF IRISH MUSIC VOL.3, A**
CDTCD 006 / 20 Oct '97 / Gael Linn

☐ **TREASURY OF IRISH SONG, A**
MCCD 278 / Dec '96 / Music Club

☐ **TREASURY OF IRISH SONGS, A**
SHCD 79094 / Oct '95 / Shanachie

☐ **TREASURY OF THE LIBRARY OF CONGRESS FIELD RECORDINGS, A**
Bonaparte's retreat: *Stepp, W.H* / Rock island's line: *Pace, Kelly* / Pretty Polly: *Ball, E.C.* / Pullin' the skiff: *Graham, Ora Dell* / Shortenin' bread: *Graham, Ora Dell* / Sea lion woman: *Shipo, Christine & Katherine* / Soldier's joy: *Nashville Washboard Band* / Another man done gone: *Hall, Vera* / Northfield: *Denson, Paine* / When I lay my burden down: *Johnson, Turner Junior* / Grub springs: *Claunch, W.E.* / Ain't no grave can hold my body down: *Sturdivant, Bozie* / Iron merrimac: *Learned Hand* / Creek lullaby: *Margaret* / Coal creek march: *Steele, Pete* / Worried life blues: *Edwards, David 'Honeyboy'* / One morning in May: *Gladden, Texas* / Blood-strained banders: *Strothers, Jimmie* / Goodbye old paint: *Morris, Jess* / Lead me to the rock: *Dennis, Wash & Charlie Sims* /

Glory in the meeting house: Strong, Luther / Avondale mine disaster: Quinn, John J. / Roll on the ground: Willingham, Thaddeus C. / Diamond Joe: Butter, Charlie / Lost John: Terry, Sonny / Sept ans sur mer: Hoffpauir, Elita & Mary/Ella / East Texas rag: Casey, Smith / Old Joe Clark: Ward, Wade / Gypsy Davy: Guthrie, Woody / Kiowa story of the flute: Cozad, Belo
ROUCD 1500 / Nov '97 / Rounder

☐ **TREESTAR REVIEW**
BCNCD 10142 / Mar '98 / Beacon

☐ **TRENCH TOWN DUB**
OMCD 27 / Oct '93 / Original Music

☐ **TREND LINE VOL.2**
DP 260330 / 23 Feb '98 / Dance Paradise

☐ **TRENDANCE VOL.5**
ZYX 550822 / Jul '97 / ZYX

☐ **TRENDANCE VOL.6**
ZYX 550872 / 27 Oct '97 / ZYX

☐ **TRESOR 100**
EFA 561002 / 3 Aug '98 / Tresor

☐ **TRESOR VOL.2**
CDNOMU 14 / May '93 / Nova Mute

☐ **TRESOR VOL.3**
Solid sleep: Mills, Jeff / Ten four: Beltram, Joey / Rhythm of vision: Hood, Robert / Science fiction: Bell, Daniel / Allerseelen: DJ Hell / Motor musicmaerz: 3 Phase / Energizer: Baxter, Blake / Protection: Vision / Monolith: Sun Electric / Schizophrenia: Schizophrenia
NOMU 43CD / Apr '95 / Nova Mute
EFA 393972 / 29 Jun '98 / Tresor

☐ **TRESOR VOL.4 (Solid/2CD Set)**
M6: Maurizio / Shadow chaser: Scan 7 / M 69 starlight: Model 500 / Relish: Substance / La beff: TV Victor / What: Vogel, Christian / Cooper's coffee: Pacou / Instant: Beltram, Joey / Think quick: Infiniti / Domina: Domina / Zombie assassin: Holy Ghost Inc. / Where's your child: Bam Bam / Art Lukm: Holy Ghost Inc. / Energizer: Baxter, Blake / Lyot: Vainquer / Skyscratch: Ingator / Sonic destroyer: X-101 / Der klang der familie: 3 Phase & Dr. Motte / Dark territory: Scan 7 / Reel techno: Pacou / Dark corridor: Scan 7 / Minnia (The Queen's Theme): X-103
29263CD / Feb '97 / Tresor

☐ **TRESOR VOL.5**
EFA 292642 / May '97 / Tresor

☐ **TRIANGLE DUB CLASH**
ZD7CD / Apr '96 / Zip Dog

☐ **TRIBAL ARTISTS (2CD Set)**
Give myself to you: Daou / Get your hands off my man: Vasquez, Junior / Theme: Kupper, Eric / So get up: Underground Sound Of Lisbon / Dream: Deep Dish / Casa de x: Deep Dish / Bottom heavy: Tenaglia, Danny / Look ahead: Tenaglia, Danny / Love to heart: Atom / Storm: Salt City Orchestra / That's what I got: Liberty City / There will come a day: Absolute / Horn ride: En / Accident: Roxy / Up in this house: NYDC / Planet K: K-Scope / Dancin': TNT / So get up: Underground Sound Of Lisbon / Accident: Roxy / Horn ride: En / Dream: Deep Dish / Bottom heavy: Tenaglia, Danny / That's what I got: Liberty City / Storm: Salt City Orchestra / Theme: K-Scope
PAGANCD 1004 / 16 Mar '98 / Pagan

☐ **TRIBAL GATHERING '96 (Gayle San/ Marshall Jefferson/James Lavell - 3CD Set)**
Tribal: San, Gayle / Digital domain: Shi-Take / Circuit sex: Blunted Boy Wonder / AI: Subvoice 007 / Breakdown: RND Technologies / Meantime: Space DJ's / Barcode population: USS Severe / Sensual sign: Tesox / Funky drive: X-Connection / Horny ass Fred: Fred / Accelerate: Zzino / Resize: Colone / Book: Salt City Orchestra / Samba magic: Basement Jaxx / Chord memory: Pooley, Ian / Happy days: Hope, Alexander / Gotta keep pushin': Z-Factor / Be free: Basement Jaxx / Calling: Vudu / Joy: Bresoul / Jump on it: Jefferson, Marshall / Your wildest dreams: Swingtime Dee / Sexy thing: Avianche, Jean Phillipe / One love: Northside / This could be the night: Aphroqueens / Quiddity: Max 404 / Latin nights: Shogun / Allergy: Howie B / Spiral dub: DJ Food / Murderah style: DJ Spooky & Mr. Scruff / Headless horseman: Raw Deal / Attention please: 4th Wave / Duality: DJ Krush & DJ Shadow / Your destiny: DJ Crystl / Real thing: Peshay / Papua New Guinea: Future Sound Of London / One for MAW: Jedi Knights / Ladies and gentlemen: 69
UNV 001CD / Oct '96 / Universe

☐ **TRIBAL HEART**
AIM 1042 / May '95 / Aim

☐ **TRIBAL VOICES (Songs Of Native Americans)**
R 272538 / Nov '96 / Earthbeat

☐ **TRIBES OF DA UNDERGROUND VOL.2 (2CD Set)**
IC 012CD / Jan '96 / Infracom

☐ **TRIBES OF DA UNDERGROUND VOL.3**
IC 0252 / Jun '97 / Infracom

☐ **TRIBULATION DUB VOL.4**
WSPLP 008 / Feb '96 / WSP

☐ **TRIBUTE TO BERRY GORDY, A**
5304362 / Jul '95 / Motown

☐ **TRIBUTE TO MARCUS GARVEY, A**
GRELCD 147 / Jul '90 / Greensleeves

☐ **TRIBUTE TO PECKINGS, A**
SOCD 7786 / 2 Feb '98 / Studio One

☐ **TRIBUTE TO THE QUEEN OF HEARTS, A**
LJRCD 015 / 13 Oct '97 / LJR

☐ **TRIBUTE TO TI FRERE, A**
C560019 / Jun '91 / Ocora

☐ **TRIBUTE TO..., A**
CDZOT 179 / Jul '97 / Zoth Ommog

☐ **TRICKED OUT**
Crystal jelly: Hard Hop Heathen / Oh-zone layer: Dark Side Of The Shroom / Green mushroom: Dark Side Of The Shroom / Pure havoc: Hard Hop Heathen / Off to demention X: Wizard Of Oh / Chemical meltdown: Tales From The Hardside / Terminal intensity: Tales From The Hardside / Double dove: Hard Hop Heathen / Temple of boom: Tales From The Hardside / Ohterior motive: Hard Hop Heathen / White beats: Wizard Of Oh / Free bass: Hard Hop Heathen / Beat bastik: Hard Hop Heathen / Panaramic: Dark Side Of The Shroom
MM 800632 / Apr '97 / Moonshine

☐ **TRIGGER**
HAIR 5 / May '94 / Hair

☐ **TRIKI VOL.1 (Diatonic Dynamite)**
KD 431CD / Nov '96 / Elkar

☐ **TRINIDAD HOT TIMES**
68979 / Apr '97 / Tropical

☐ **TRIO DE TRIOS**
9944132282 / 31 Mar '98 / Orfeon

☐ **TRIP 7 (2CD Set)**
DO 475CD / Nov '96 / Dance Opera

☐ **TRIP HOP AND JAZZ VOL.3**
EX 364 / 13 Oct '97 / Instinct

☐ **TRIP HOP AND JAZZ VOL.4**
EX 387 / 20 Jul '98 / Instinct

☐ **TRIP 'N' GROOVE - LE SON DE RADIO NOVA**
325022 / Nov '95 / Melodie

☐ **TRIP THROUGH SOUND VOL.1**
BR 021CD / Feb '97 / Blue Room

☐ **TRIP THROUGH SOUND VOL.2**
BR 069CD / 26 May '98 / Blue Room Released

☐ **TRIP TO MARS VOL.1 (2CD Set)**
SPV 899605 / Feb '94 / SPV

☐ **TRIP TO MARS VOL.2 (2CD Set)**
SPV 899626 / Jul '94 / SPV

☐ **TRIP TO THE ANDES**
TMDCD 2 / Mar '97 / Tumi Dance

☐ **TRIPHOP SHOP**
DOUCE 803CD / Nov '96 / Irma La Douce

☐ **TRIPHOPRISY VOL.1**
SQUCD 1 / Jun '95 / Rumour

☐ **TRIPHOPRISY VOL.2**
SQUCD 2 / Nov '95 / Rumour

☐ **TRIPHOPRISY VOL.3**
SQUCD 3 / May '96 / Rumour

☐ **TRIPHOPRISY VOL.4 (2CD Set)**
SQUCD 4 / Apr '97 / Squat

☐ **TRIPLE TWIN SPIN**
SPCD 0125 / May '97 / Superpower

☐ **TRIPNOTIZED VOL.3 (2CD Set)**
MNF 05242 / Jan '97 / Manifold

☐ **TRIPNOTIZED VOL.4 (2CD Set)**
MNF 05262 / Jun '97 / Manifold

☐ **TRIPNOTIZED VOL.5**
MNF 05302 / 29 Sep '97 / Manifold

☐ **TRIPNOTIZED VOL.6**
MNF 05332 / 26 Jan '98 / Manifold

☐ **TRIPOLI TRAX PRESENT VOL.1 (2CD Set)**
Let the rhythm flow: Dancing divas / Bells of revolution: Lemon 8 / Clap your hands: Junior Camp / Rock the turntables: Floorshow / Set you free: Thomas, Steve / Noize: DJ Eclipse / Emptiness: Da Junkies / Shake it: Fruitloop / Raise your hands: Knuckleheadz / Take you there: Experts / House rocca: Knuckleheadz / Recoil: F1 / Don't stop: Mark NRG / Epidemic: Exit EEE / Tic toc: Rizzo
TTRAXCD 001 / 31 Jul '98 / Tripoli Trax

☐ **TRIPPIN' ON NORTHERN SOUL (Dose - 20 Classic Northern Soul Stompers)**
Trip: Mitchell, Dave / You'd better go-go: Lucas, Matt / Satisfy me baby: Sweets / Show me how to love: Forrest, Jackie / Right combination: Brody, Marsha / Try a little harder: Keyman Strings / Get it baby: Mitchell, Stanley / With a lonely heart: Four Voices / Queen of the go-go: Garvin, Rex / Bring it on home: Lee, Jackie / It's OK with me: Wright, Larry / Airplane song: Jenkins, Norma / I'm a sad girl: Johnson, Diane / There can be a better way: Smith Bros / Don't pretend: Mirwood Orchestra / Hold your horses: Clarke, Jimmy 'Soul' / Train keep on movin': Fifth Dimension / Woman's liberation: Topics / Just can't leave you: Hester, Tony / Papa oo mow mow: Sharonettes
GSCD 091 / Jul '96 / Goldmine

☐ **TRIPPIN' ON RHYTHMS**
Midnight at the oasis: Brand New Heavies / Happy friends: Greyboy Allstars / Last xt: Ayers, Roy / Love in return: Brown, Diana / In full swing: Jordan, Ronny / On the sand: Groove Thing / Ricky's hat: Liquid Soul / Sneaky: Groove Collective / MD blew: Jones, Victor / Heavy rotation: Slide 5 / Like water: Abstract Truth / Poppy's song: Big Muff
SHANCD 5041 / 9 Mar '98 / Shanachie

☐ **TRIPPIN' TUNES**
BRACD 5 / 12 Jan '98 / Braintist

☐ **TRISKEDEKAPHILIA**
ANKST 61CD / Oct '95 / Ankst

☐ **TROJAN EXPLOSION (20 Reggae Hits)**
You can get it if you really want: Desmond Dekker & The Aces / Reggae in your jeggae: Livingstone, Dandy / Johnny too bad: Slickers / Liquidator: Harry J All Stars / Wonderful world, beautiful people: Cliff, Jimmy / Them a laugh and a kiki: Soulmates / 54-46 (was my number): Toots & The Maytals / Cherry oh baby: Donaldson, Eric / Let your yeah be yeah: Pioneers / Dollar of soul: Ethiopians / Young, gifted and black: Bob & Marcia / Sweet sensation: Melodians / Elizabethan reggae: Gardiner, Boris / Mama look deh: Pioneers / Double barrel: Barker, Dave & Ansell Collins / Small axe: Marley, Bob / Pomp and pride: Toots & The Maytals / Return of Django: Upsetters / 007: Dekker, Desmond & The Aces / Phoenix city: Alphonso, Roland
CDTRL 246 / Mar '94 / Trojan

☐ **TROJAN JUNGLE VOL.1**
CDTRL 368 / Mar '96 / Trojan

☐ **TROJAN JUNGLE VOL.2**
CDTRL 378 / Feb '97 / Trojan

☐ **TROJAN SINGLES COLLECTION VOL.1**
CDTRL 367 / Mar '96 / Trojan

☐ **TROJAN SINGLES COLLECTION VOL.2**
Suzanna beware of the devil: Livingstone, Dandy / Brandy: English, Scott / Return of Django: Upsetters / Big seven: Judge Dread / Double barrel: Barker, Dave & Ansell Collins / Lonely days, lonely nights: Dowling, Don / 007: Dekker, Desmond / Young, gifted and black: Bob & Marcia / Big six: Judge Dread / Monkey spanner: Barker, Dave & Ansell Collins / Dollar in the teeth: Upsetters / Red red wine: Tribe, Tony / Big eight: Judge Dread / It mek: Dekker, Desmond / Train to skaville: Ethiopians / Big nine: Judge Dread / Guns of Navarone: Skatalites / Pickney girl: Dekker, Desmond / I'm in the mood for ska: Lord Tanamo / Money in my pocket: Brown, Dennis / Israelites: Dekker, Desmond / Snoopy vs. The Red Baron: Hot Shots / Je t'aime (moi non plus): Judge Dread / Hurt so good: Cadogan, Susan / Irie feelings: Edwards, Rupie
CDTRL 373 / Sep '96 / Trojan

☐ **TROJAN STORY VOL.1**
Bartender: Aitken, Laurel / Humpty dumpty: Morris, Eric / Housewives' choice: Derrick & Patsy / Don't stay out late: Patrick, Kentrick / Rough and tough: Cole, Stranger / Man to man: Patrick, Kentrick / Confucius: Drummond, Don / Soon you'll be gone: Blues Busters / Yeah yeah: Riots / Dreader than dread: Martin, Honeyboy / Syncopate: Astronauts / Keep the pressure on: Winston, George / Oh babe: Techniques / Train to Skaville: Ethiopians / Pretty Africa: Cliff, Jimmy / Rock steady: Ellis, Alton / Perfidia: Dillon, Phyllis / Way of life: Taitt, Lynn / Second fiddle: Tennors / Nana: Slickers / Black and white
CDTAL 100 / Mar '94 / Trojan

☐ **TROJAN STORY, THE (2CD Set)**
Guns of Navarone: Skatalites / Phoenix City: Alphonso, Roland / Oh ba-a-by: Techniques / Rock steady: Ellis, Alton / Do the reggae: Toots & The Maytals / Stand by your man: Webber, Marlene / Red red wine: Tribe, Tony / Miss Jamaica: Cliff, Jimmy / Version galore: U-Roy / Screaming target: Big Youth / Cassius Clay: Alcapone, Dennis / Black man time: I-Roy / Silhouette: Brown, Dennis / Jimmie Brown: Parker, Ken / Just can't figure it out: Diamonds / Enter into his gates: Clark, Johnnie / Pretty African: Dekker, Desmond / Save the last dance for me: Heptones / Nice nice time: Zap Pow / Take me home country roads: Toots & The Maytals / Time is the master: Simon, Tito / Mama look deh: Pioneers / Big 8: Judge Dread / Them a fe get a beatin': Tosh, Peter / Montego Bay: Notes, Freddie & The Rudies / Elizabethan reggae: Lee, Byron & The Dragonaires / 007: Dekker, Desmond / Crying over you: Boothe, Ken / Return of Django: Upsetters / Mr. Bojangles: Holt, John / Reggae in your jeggae: Livingstone, Dandy / Longshot kick de bucket: Pioneers
CDTRD 402 / Mar '94 / Trojan

☐ **TROMBONE ALBUM, THE**
Boneology / Down Vernon's Alley / Riffette / Rubberneck / Mean to me / Sweet and lovely / Take me out to the ballgame / Lo-fi / Wanting you / You'll do / Walkin' / Jan Cee Brown / Playgirl stroll / Playgirl stroll / Accident / Darryl's minor / Judiful
SV 0276 / Oct '97 / Savoy Jazz

☐ **TROPICAL BEACH PARTY (16 Exotic Sun Soaked Scene Setters)**
Tropicallo / Samba rio / Carnaval do Brasil / Yellow bird / Kingston nights / Salsarico / Antigua / Sailing with the sun / Cuba libre / Copacabana sunrise / Una flor no cabello / Deep Kingston / Solitario / La bamba salsa / Yele le / Latino paradiso
304522 / Jun '98 / Hallmark

☐ **TROPICAL EXTRAVAGANZA**
TUMICD 028 / Oct '92 / Tumi

☐ **TROPICAL FESTIVAL**
Kwassa kwassa: Kanda Bongo Man / Cachita: La Charanga Almendra / Forward Jah Jah children: Inner Circle / La revancha: Los Diablitos / Bomba camara: Grupo Melao / Cuban medley: La Origina De Manzanillo / Workey workey: Burning Flames / Cascara Bellagua: Castro, Poldo / Suma sume: Godzom / Mara La Hoz: Grupo Caneo
CPCD 8131 / Oct '95 / Charly

☐ **TROPICAL ISLAND PARADISE**
Yarbero moderno: Cruz, Celia / Traffic mambo: Lamy, Ernest Orchestra / Cogelo que eso es tuyo: Kalaff, Luis / Descarga: Ray, Ricardo & Bobby Cruz / Habana rumba: Trio Matamoros / En el monte: Duo Los Compadres / Pardon caporal: Nemours Jean-Baptiste / La maricutana: Damiron Y Capuseaux / Compay lobo: La Sonora Matancera / El automovil: Hernandez, Mario Y Sus Diablos Del Caribe / Por eso es que yo te quiento: Kalaff, Luis / Mambo tata: Ray, Ricardo & Bobby Cruz / En cadenas: Faz, Roberto Y Su Conjunto / El chivo: La Sonora Matancera / El jarro pichao: Damiron Y Capuseaux / Yo teno pena: Duo Los Compadres / Mango mangue: Cruz, Celia / Besame donde te: Hernandez, Mario Y Sus Diablos Del Caribe / Jamaicuba: Faz, Roberto Y Su Conjunto
CDHOT 613 / Dec '96 / Charly

☐ **TROPICAL RAIN FOREST**
DC 879602 / Oct '97 / Disky

☐ **TROPICAL SUMMER (2CD Set)**
KBOX 229 / Jul '98 / Collection

☐ **TROPICAL SUMMER HITS (2CD Set)**
Walking on sunshine: Katrina & The Waves / Karma chameleon: Culture Club / Gimme hope Joanna: Grant, Eddy / Carribean Queen: Ocean, Billy / Don't let me be misunderstood: Santa Esmeralda / Kalimba de luna: Esposito, Tony / Lion sleeps tonight: Tight Fit / Love is in the air: Jones, Tom / La colegiala: Low, Gary / Sopha de caracol: Banda Blanca / Hot hot hot: Arrow / That's the way I like it: KC & The Sunshine Band / Swing your daddy: Gilstrap, Jim / In the summertime: Mungo Jerry / Paloma blanca: Baker, George Selection / Sunshine reggae: Baker, George Selection / Amigo: Black Slate / Papa chico: Esposito, Tony / Bring back: Mixed Emotions / Turn to gold: Austin, David / Dancing easy: Williams, Danny / Everybody's laughing: Fearon, Phil & Galaxy / Going back to my roots: Odyssey / Everybody join hands: Dekker, Desmond / Beach baby: First Class / Walking on sunshine: Rockers Revenge / Summer in the city: Lovin' Spoonful / Good vibrations: Beach Boys / Dancing in the city: Hain, Marshall / Happy together: Turtles
DOU 878322 / 2 Feb '98 / Disky

☐ **TROUBLE ON THE DANCEFLOOR (2CD Set)**
XTR 39CDM / 13 Oct '97 / X-Treme

☐ **TROUBLE ON THE TERRACES**
STEPCD 091 / 6 Jul '98 / Step 1

☐ **TRUCK DRIVIN' MAN (20 Truckin' Country Classics)**
Truck drivin' man: Campbell, Glen / Movin' on: Haggard, Merle / Big wheels in the moonlight: Seals, Dan / Truckers paradise: Reeves, Del / I'm a truck: Simpson, Red / I've been everywhere: Asleep At The Wheel / Big wheel cannonball: Curless, Dick / Six days on the road: Dudley, Dave / Six days awaiting: Adams, Kay / Big Joe: Stewart, John / Rollin' rig: Dudley, Dave / Roll truck roll: Simpson, Red / Girl on the billboard: Reeves, Del / White line fever: Haggard, Merle / Little pink mack: Adams, Kay / Tombstone every mile: Curless, Dick / Truck drivers blues: Simpson, Red / Texas Ruby: Dudley, Dave / Lookin' at the world through a windshield: Reeves, Del / Trucker and the UFO: Arbor, Brush
4949192 / 1 Jun '98 / EMI Gold

☐ **TRUCKIN' MY BLUES AWAY (Collection Of Contemporary Blues Songs From Texas)**
TX 1009CD / Jan '94 / Taxim

☐ **TRUE**
Up where we belong: Cocker, Joe & Jennifer Warnes / Your song: John, Elton / Tonight I celebrate my love: Bryson, Peabo & Roberta Flack / Three times a lady: Commodores / One day in your life: Jackson, Michael / Do that to me one more time: Captain & Tennille / With you I'm born again: Preston, Billy & Syreeta / Just the way you are: White, Barry / I'm not in love: 10cc / Steppin' out: Jackson, Joe / I should've known better: Diamond, Jim / First time: Beck, Robin / Something's gotten hold of my heart: Almond, Marc & Gene Pitney / Room in you're heart: Living In A Box / Long hot summer: Style Council / Goodbye girl: Go West / Get here: Adams, Oleta / I'm still waiting: Ross, Diana / Under your thumb: Godley & Creme / True: Spandau Ballet
5529212 / Oct '97 / Spectrum

☐ **TRUE BRIT (The Best Of Brit Pop)**
5354792 / Jun '96 / PolyGram TV

☐ **TRUE LOVE (16 Songs From The Heart)**
True love: Cline, Patsy / Blue velvet: McCann, Susan / May I have the next dream with you: Roberts, Malcolm / As usual: Lee, Brenda / Marianne: O'Donnell, Daniel / Portrait of my love / He used to give me roses: Ray, Stacey / Let it be me: Everly Brothers / Take good care of my baby: Vee, Bobby / Country hits medley: McCann, Susan / It's our anniversary: McCaffrey, Frank / Tennessee waltz / If those lips could only speak: Foster & Allen / I'll never find another you: Seekers / When I dream: Gayle, Crystal / All I have to do is dream: Everly Brothers
PLATCD 3912 / '91 / Platinum

☐ **TRUE LOVE (All Time Classic Love Songs - 3CD Set)**
MCBX 007 / Sep '95 / Music Club

☐ **TRUE LOVE (2CD Set)**
A Star Is Born / Blue velvet / People / When I fall in love / Someone to watch over me / Stand by me / My girl / True love / It must have been love / Groovy kind of love / Wind beneath my wings / Unchained melody / (Everything I do) I do it for you / Twin peaks (falling) / Show me heaven / Take my breath away / Against all odds (take a look at me now) / Time of my life / Somewhere / Tara's theme / Edelweiss / As time goes by / Some enchanted evening / Over the rainbow / Moon river / Secret love / Summertime / Lara's theme / Way we were / Where do I begin / Up where we belong / Love changes everything / Look of love / Music of the night / Speak softly love / Any dream will do / Memory / Send in the clown / Summer place / True love ways
PC 621 / 1 Jun '98 / Platinum Collection

☐ **TRUE LOVE (18 Soulful Classics From The Heart)**
Unchained melody: *Drifters* / Rainy night in Georgia: *Benton, Brook* / What kind of fool (do you think I am): *Tams* / Will you love me tomorrow: *Shirelles* / Love letters: *Lester, Ketty* / Since I don't have you: *Skyliners* / All I could do was cry: *James, Etta* / To know him is to love him: *Teddy Bears* / Only you (and you alone): *Platters* / Sea of love: *Phillips, Phil* / I will: *Winters, Ruby* / You send me: *Drifters* / If loving you is wrong (I don't want to be right): *Sledge, Percy* / Don't play that song (you lied): *King, Ben E.* / Smoke gets in your eyes: *Platters* / Rhythm of the rain: *Cascades* / He will break your heart: *Butler, Jerry* / Dedicated to the one I love: *Shirelles*
SUMCD 4197 / 11 May '98 / Summit

☐ **TRUE LOVE COLLECTED VOL.1**
TLCCOL 1 / 6 Apr '98 / Truelove

☐ **TRUE LOVE WAYS**
MCCD 119 / Aug '93 / Music Club

☐ **TRUE LOVE WAYS**
Unchained melody: *Righteous Brothers* / Love is all around: *Troggs* / Groovy kind of love: *Mindbenders* / True love ways: *Peter & Gordon* / Hey Paula: *Paul & Paula* / Carrie Ann: *Hollies* / You don't have to say you love me: *Springfield, Dusty* / My guy: *Wells, Mary* / Baby it's you: *Berry, Dave* / Jesamine: *Casuals* / You've got your troubles: *Fortunes* / God only knows: *Beach Boys* / I'll never find another you: *Seekers* / Don't let the sun catch you crying: *Gerry & The Pacemakers* / No milk today: *Herman's Hermits* / Alfie: *Black, Cilla* / Boys cry (when no one can see them): *Kane, Eden* / Rain and tears: *Aphrodite's Child* / All I really want to do: *Cher* / Sun ain't gonna shine anymore: *Cher*
5529052 / Oct '97 / Spectrum

☐ **TRUE PEOPLE: THE DETROIT TECHNO ALBUM (2CD Set)**
Davy Jones Locker: *Dresciya* / Aura: *KT 19941* / Life of a planet rider: *Shakir, Anthony* / Fusion part 2: *Atkins, Juan* / Wiggin: *May, Derrick* / RMF 60: *Fowlkes, Eddie* / 8th Wonder: *Pullne, Stacey* / Zephyr: *Kech & B Bonds* / Carma: *Young, Claude* / Morph: *Larkin, Kenny* / Where is the love: *Baxter, Blake* / Sources: *Echols, Santonio* / TMF 61: *Fowlkes, Eddie* / Operation 10: *Barnett, Thomas* / E-Dancer: *Saunderson, Kevin* / D May 87: *Oldham, Alan* / Don't blame it on me: *365 Black* / Art of stalking: *Suburban Knight* / Gama: *Brown, Tom* / CRX: *Little Joe*
REACTCD 071 / Jan '96 / React

☐ **TRUE STORY OF COUNTRY, THE**
Rose garden: *Anderson, Lynn* / It's only make believe: *Jackson, Wanda* / Big bad John: *Dean, Jimmy* / Harper Valley PTA: *Riley, Jeannie C.* / Mad: *Dudley, Dave* / Girl on the billboard: *Reeves, Del* / Heartbreak USA: *Wells, Kitty* / Hallo walls: *Young, Faron* / Tennessee: *Jack & Misty* / He took me for a ride: *La Costa Tucker* / I'm a truck: *Simpson, Red* / Rednecks, white socks, blue ribbon beer: *Russell, Johnny* / No charge: *Montgomery, Melba* / Nashville: *Houston, David* / It only hurts for a little while: *Smith, Margo* / Help me make it through the night: *Smith, Sammi*
11813 / Dec '95 / Music

☐ **TRUE UNDERGROUND, THE**
SR 324CD / Apr '96 / Strictly Rhythm

☐ **TRULY UNFORGETTABLE (32 Truly Unforgettable Songs)**
When I fall in love: *Cole, Nat 'King'* / Be my love: *Lanza, Mario* / Only you: *Platters* / It's all in the game: *Edwards, Tommy* / Spanish eyes: *Martino, Al* / On the street where you live: *Damone, Vic* / He'll have to go: *Reeves, Jim* / Misty: *Mathis, Johnny* / Can't get used to losing you: *Williams, Andy* / Dream lover: *Darin, Bobby* / Move over darling: *Day, Doris* / Never be anyone else but you: *Nelson, Rick* / It's only make believe: *Twitty, Conway* / End of the world: *Davis, Skeeter* / More than I can say: *Vee, Bobby* / It's over: *Orbison, Roy* / Cry me a river: *London, Julie* / Love letters: *Lester, Ketty* / I left my heart in San Francisco: *Bennett, Tony* / Make it easy on yourself: *Walker Brothers* / Joanna: *Walker, Scott* / You don't have to say you love me: *Springfield, Dusty* / Look homeward angel: *Ray, Johnnie* / Every time we say goodbye: *Fitzgerald, Ella* / God bless the child: *Holiday, Billie* / Passing strangers: *Eckstine, Billy & Sarah Vaughan* / What a wonderful world: *Armstrong, Louis* / Folks who live on the hill: *Lee, Peggy* / Stand by me: *King, Ben E.* / Save the last dance for me: *Drifters* / Unforgettable: *Cole, Nat 'King'*
CDEMTVD 55 / Nov '90 / EMI TV

☐ **TRUMPET SPECTACULAR**
PCD 7015 / Jun '93 / Progressive

☐ **TRUMPETS IN JAZZ**
CDCH 556 / Feb '91 / Milan

☐ **TRUMPETS IN MODERN JAZZ**
Will you still be mine: *Farmer, Art* / For now: *Baker, Chet* / Swingin' the blues: *Clark, Terry* / Bubba and the whale: *Conexion Latina* / Adriatica: *Goykovich, Dusko* / One bright glance: *D'Earth, John* / Jeffuso: *Brooks, Roy* / Little song: *Blue Box* / Kush: *Gillespie, Dizzy* / Body and soul: *Jones, Elvin* / Fairy boat to Rio: *Ambrosetti, Franco* / Siempre junto a ti: *Gonzalez, Jerry*
ENJ 80002 / Mar '94 / Enja

☐ **TRUST IN ME (The Old America On The Air)**
Soon: *Crosby, Bing* / I hear a rhapsody: *Boswell, Connee* / This love of mine: *Sinatra, Frank* / I only have eyes for you: *Powell, Dick* / Honey in the bee ball: *Jordan, Louis* / Lazy: *Jolson, Al* / Old piano plays the blues: *Cole, Nat 'King'* / He's my guy: *Shore, Dinah* / After school swing session: *Jordan, Louis* / Sinner kissed an angel: *Sinatra, Frank* / I'm in love with the honourable Mr. So and so: *Crawford, Joan* / Thousand goodnights: *Powell, Dick* / Out of nowhere: *Crosby, Bing* / Trust in me: *Boswell, Connee* / Nat meets June: *Cole, Nat 'King'* / Yes indeed: *Crosby, Bing & Connie Boswell* / Why can't you: *Jolson, Al* / Imagination: *Sinatra, Frank* / You'll never know: *Powell, Dick* / It's all so new to me: *Crawford, Joan* / Don't come cryin' on my shoulder: *Jordan, Louis* / On the sentimental side: *Crosby, Bing* / Sunrise serenade: *Boswell, Connee* / Everything happens to me: *Sinatra, Frank*
RY 82 / Aug '97 / Radio Years

☐ **TRUST IN TRANCE PSYCHEDELIC VIBES VOL.2**
20772 / 2 Mar '98 / Phonokol

☐ **TRUST IN TRANCE PSYCHEDELIC VIBES VOL.3**
20942 / 2 Mar '98 / Phonokol

☐ **TRUTH AND RIGHTS**
HBCD 78 / Jun '94 / Heartbeat

☐ **TULIKULKKU**
KICD 30 / Dec '93 / Kansanmusiikki Instituutti

☐ **TUMBAO ALL STARS**
TCD 501 / 24 Apr '98 / Tumbao

☐ **TUMI CUBA CLASSICS VOL.1 (Son)**
TUMICD 049 / Aug '95 / Tumi

☐ **TUMI CUBA CLASSICS VOL.3 (Rumba)**
TUMICD 052 / Aug '95 / Tumi

☐ **TUMI CUBA CLASSICS VOL.4 (The Big Sound)**
TUMICD 053 / Aug '95 / Tumi

☐ **TUMI CUBA CLASSICS VOL.5 (Son, The Future)**
TUMICD 055 / Sep '95 / Tumi

☐ **TUMI CUBA CLASSICS VOL.6 (Musica Campesino)**
TUMICD 056 / Dec '95 / Tumi

☐ **TUMMY RE TOUCH**
TUCH 017CD / 27 Jul '98 / Tummy Touch

☐ **TUNE OF CROP OVER WINNERS 1979-1995**
RHP 1005CD / 15 Jun '98 / RHP

☐ **TUNES FROM LOWLANDS, HIGHLANDS AND ISLANDS**
58394 / Mar '96 / World Network

☐ **TUNNEL MIXES (3CD Set)**
LIMB 56CD / May '96 / Limbo

☐ **TURDS ON A BUM RIDE VOL.1 & 2**
ANT 1/2 / May '97 / Anthology

☐ **TURDS ON A BUM RIDE VOL.3**
ANT 311 / May '97 / Anthology

☐ **TURDS ON A BUM RIDE VOL.4**
ANT 2211 / May '97 / Anthology

☐ **TURDS ON A BUM RIDE VOL.5**
ANT 32 / 19 Jan '98 / Anthology

☐ **TURDS ON A BUM RIDE VOL.6**
ANT 33 / 19 Jan '98 / Anthology

☐ **TURKEY - THE MUSIC OF THE YAYLA**
C 560050 / Aug '94 / Ocora

☐ **TURN ME LOOSE (Contemporary American Country)**
Let's do something: *Gill, Vince* / Dancin' on the wire: *Berg, Matraca* / Big bad broken heart: *Regina Regina* / It's a done deal: *Foster & Lloyd* / Wild at heart: *White, Lari* / We got the love: *Restless Heart* / What more do you want from me: *Vincent, Rhonda* / Many many many beers ago: *Tippin, Aaron* / Woman of the world: *White, Lari* / Truth hurts: *Restless Heart* / She made a memory out of me: *Restless Heart* / What a woman wants: *White, Lari* / Somewhere between right and wrong: *Conley, Earl Thomas* / Walkin' after midnight: *Oak Ridge Boys* / Baby walk on: *Berg, Matraca* / Turn me loose: *Gill, Vince*
74321588092 / 15 Jun '98 / Camden

☐ **TURN ME ON (15 Grinding Slow Jams)**
APB: *Taylor, Gary* / You can't turn me away: *Striplin, Sylvia* / This is for the lover in you: *Hewett, Howard* / Call me: *Mannsfield, Rodney* / Good thing goin' on: *Carne, Jean & Billy Paul* / Sweet funky thing: *King, Evelyn 'Champagne'* / Give me the sunshine: *Leo's Sunshipp* / Love won't let me wait: *Voices In Control* / Pick up the pieces: *Gardner, Joanna* / Keep giving me love: *Rogers, Richard* / Cream of love: *Ware, Leon* / Let them talk: *Bofill, Angela* / Tic toc: *Lorenzo* / Let's settle down: *Chandler, Omar* / Win your love: *James, Josie*
MUSCD 040 / 6 Oct '97 / MCI Music

☐ **TURN ON, TUNE IN, DROP OUT (A Trip In Psychedelia)**
Coloured rain: *Traffic* / Rainbow chaser: *Nirvana* / Venus in furs: *Velvet Underground* / San Franciscan nights: *Burdon, Eric* / Turn on, tune in, drop out: *Fugs* / Alone again or: *Love* / You keep me hangin' on: *Vanilla Fudge* / In a gadda da vida: *Iron Butterfly* / Walk on gilded splinters: *Dr. John* / Ball and chain: *Big Brother* / Hey Grandma: *Moby Grape* / Eight miles high: *Byrds* / Animal zoo: *Spirit* / Somebody to love: *Jefferson Airplane* / Evil ways: *Santana* / Willie the pimp: *Zappa, Frank* / Pusher: *Steppenwolf* / Catch the wind: *Donovan*
RENCD 119 / Mar '97 / Renaissance Collector Series

☐ **TURNING OVER VOL.1**
IGNCD 01 / Oct '96 / Ignition

☐ **TURNING OVER VOL.2**
IGNCD 02 / 12 Jan '98 / Ignition

☐ **TURNING THE WORLD BLUE**
SKIZ 003 / Dec '96 / Skizmatic

☐ **TURQUERIE**
SPNO 11 / Oct '94 / Spin

☐ **TUVALU**
PAN 2055CD / Dec '94 / Pan

☐ **TWENTY BEST OF TODAY'S FOLK MUSIC**
EUCD 1071 / '89 / ARC

☐ **TWINIGHT'S CHICAGO SOUL HEAVEN**
Nevermore: *Domino, Renaldo* / Thank you baby: *Johnson, Syl* / Main squeeze: *Evans, Nate* / New day: *Notations* / Falling in love: *Dynamic Tints* / Wayward dream: *Poindexter, Annette* / I've made up my mind: *Taylor, Josephine* / Temptation's hard to fight: *McGregor, George* / That's the reason: *Benton, Buster* / Tearing me up inside: *Harrison & The Majestic Kind* / Same kind of thing: *Johnson, Syl* / Don't wanna face the truth: *Radiants* / Lift this hurt: *Spencer, Elvin* / To love someone (that don't love you): *Kaldirons* / So good to have you home again: *Mystiques* / Yesterday's mistakes: *Jones, Jimmy* / Maggie: *Williams, Johnny* / Life walked out: *Mist* / I won't stop to cry: *Stormy* / You need to be loved on: *Domino, Renaldo* / Soul heaven: *Friends Of E. Rodney Jones* / Powerful love: *Chuck & Mac* / Which one am I: *Perfections* / Just you and me: *Notations*
CDKEND 131 / Nov '96 / Kent

☐ **TWIST**
TBCD 003 / Sep '95 / T&B

☐ **TWIST THIS PUSSY**
Elements: *Tenaglia, Danny* / Drama: *Club 69* / Dear father in heaven: *Dangerous, Johnny* / Magic Orgasm: *House Heroes* / Calypso breakdown: *Karnak* / K-hole: *Size Queen* / Goosebumps: *Nylx* / Get this: *Superchumbo* / Salva Mea: *S&H* / Voodoo drums: *Kult Of Krameria* / Bambo: *Moogroove* / Love of life: *Yohan Square* / Perfect love: *House of prince* / Much better: *Club 69*
TWCD 90005 / 3 Aug '98 / Twisted UK

☐ **TWISTED (2CD Set)**
TVCD 1 / Dec '95 / Twisted Vinyl

☐ **TWISTED WHEEL (ONE MORE TIME), THE**
Talk of the grapevine: *Height, Donald* / More more of your love: *Brady, Bob* / Kid: *Brasseur, Andre* / Soul serenade: *Dollar, Beau* / Everybody dance now: *Soul City* / I can't see the love: *Ballads* / Just like a yo-yo: *Winters, Ruby* / Soul sauce: *Tjader, Cal* / Oh how happy: *Shades Of Blue* / If this is love: *Precisions* / Make me yours: *Swann, Bettye* / Let love come between us: *Purify, James & Bobby* / Scratchy: *Wammack, Travis* / Hole in the wall: *Packers* / I can't please you: *Robins, Jimmy* / Cheater: *Kuban, Bob* / In a moment: *Intrigues* / Going to a happening: *Neal, Tommy* / Restless: *Hendrix, Margie* / Get on up: *Esquires* / I spy: *Thomas, Jano* / Freedom train: *Carr, James* / Nitty gritty: *Ray, Ricardo*
GSCD 112 / 24 Nov '97 / Goldmine

☐ **TWISTED WHEEL STORY, THE**
Good time tonight: *Soul Sisters* / Shotgun and the duck: *Lee, Jackie* / Fife piper: *Dynatones* / You get your kicks: *Ryder, Mitch* / Everybody's going to a love in: *Brady, Bob* / Karate boogaloo: *Jerry O* / Gonna fix you good: *Little Anthony* / Lil lovin' sometimes: *Patton, Alexander* / Ain't no soul: *Milsap, Ronnie* / Humphrey stomp: *Harrison, Earl* / That driving beat: *Mitchell, Willie* / There's nothing else to say: *Incredibles* / Any day now: *Jackson, Chuck* / Dr. Love: *Sheen, Bobby* / Love is after me: *Rich, Charlie* / Little Queenie: *Blacks, Bill* / Secret agent: *Olympics* / Tightrope: *Foxx, Inez & Charlie* / I got what it takes: *Foxx, Inez & Charlie* / That's enough: *Robinson, Roscoe* / Open the door to your heart: *Banks, Darrell* / My elusive dreams: *Dillard, Moses & Joshua* / Next in line: *Lands, Hoagy* / It keeps rainin: *Domino, Fats* / Get out of my heart: *Dillard, Moses & Joshua* / Never love a robin: *Barbara & Brenda*
GSCD 066 / Nov '95 / Goldmine

☐ **TWO DOZEN DODGY BRITISH COVERS**
Why do fools fall in love: *Ryan, Marion* / Story of my life: *Miller, Gary* / Lah dee dah: *Hicks, Colin* / Itchy twitchy feeling: *Wainer, Cherry* / Teenager in love: *Valentine, Dickie* / Mr. Blue: *McBeth, David* / Rockin' little angel: *Viscounts* / Little bit of soap: *Justice, Jimmy* / Ecstasy: *Reed, Oliver* / It might as well rain until September: *DeLaine Sisters* / Your nose is gonna grow: *Ford, Emile* / Patches: *Davis, Danny* / He's a rebel: *Breakaways* / Pop-pop-pop-pie: *Jackson, Simone* / I wanna stay here: *Miki & Griff* / (Just like) Romeo and Juliet: *Peter's Faces* / In crowd: *First Gear* / Let's lock the door (and throw away the key): *Lancastrians* / Trains and boats and planes: *Harris, Anita* / Younger girl: *Knack* / I washed my hands in muddy water: *Hungry* / (Your gonna) hurt yourself: *Bystanders* / Snoopy versus the red baron: *Gates Of Eden* / (We ain't got) nothin' yet: *Spectres* / Captain of the ship: *JSO*
GEMCD 011 / 26 Jan '98 / Diamond

☐ **TWO FRIENDS TING AND TING**
Sound ting: *Gold, Brian & Tony* / Idle talk ting: *Cutty Ranks* / Keeping a fat ting: *Redrose* / Gun ting: *Lindo, Hopeton* / Pretend ting: *Papa San* / Love ting: *Home T* / Oil ting: *Cocoa T* / Bow ting: *Flourgan* / Procrastinate ting: *Mann, Peter* / Bun ting / Cheat ting: *Chevelle* / Gyow ting: *Sister Charmaine*
GRELCD 155 / Feb '91 / Greensleeves

☐ **TWO RIDDIMS CLASH**
GPCD 002 / Jun '92 / Gussie P

☐ **TWO RYDIM CLASH**
NWSCD 9 / May '94 / New Sound

☐ **TWO TO TANGO (2CD Set)**
CDG 2332 / 3 Aug '98 / Charly

☐ **TWO TONE JUMP**
RKCD 9306 / May '93 / Rockhouse

☐ **TYPES - A KUDOS SAMPLER**
About this: *Pentatonik* / Rotation: *Angel, Dave* / Zycoon: *Synectics* / Point of no return: *Stasis* / Contrapoint: *Fugue* / Isatai: *As One* / Penguins: *Eco Tourist* / Tknoh: *Germ* / Intelligence: *Sandoz* / Vein: *Scanner* / All over hair piece: *Conemelt* / Crystalline existences: *White Funks On Dope*
KUDCD 005 / Jul '94 / Kudos

☐ **TYRANNY OF THE BEAT VOL.1**
SPV 05622172 / May '95 / SPV

☐ **TYRANNY OF THE BEAT VOL.2**
5722352 / May '96 / Westcom

☐ **TYRANNY OF THE BEAT VOL.3**
05743272 / Feb '97 / Westcom

☐ **TYRANNY OF THE BEAT VOL.4**
06843732 / 9 Mar '98 / Westcom

☐ **TYROLEAN EVENING, A**
399422 / Sep '92 / Koch

☐ **TZIGANES (2CD Set)**
3032172 / Nov '97 / Arcade

U

☐ **UBU DANCE PARTY (2CD Set)**
DATACD 2 / Mar '97 / Datapanik

☐ **UFO'S ARE REAL**
BBLP 001 / Nov '93 / Bionic Beats

☐ **UGANDA: AUX SOURCES DU NIL**
C 560032 / Nov '92 / Ocora

☐ **UILLEANN PIPES - BEAUTIFUL IRELAND**
Isle of Innisfree / Coolin / Eddie's favourite / Rathlin Island / My Lagan love / Cliffs of Dooneen / Shoe the donkey / Galway bay / Carrickfergus / Old Ardboe / Dark island / Lonesome boatman / Sally Gardens
PLMCD 21 / Jan '97 / Sharpe

☐ **UK GARAGE FEVER VOL.1 (The Sound Of Speed Garage)**
SUB 44D / 24 Nov '97 / Subversive

☐ **UK GARAGE FEVER VOL.2 (The Sound Of Speed Garage)**
SUB 45D / 23 Feb '98 / Subversive

☐ **UK GARAGE FEVER VOL.3**
SUB 49D / 29 Jun '98 / Subversive

☐ **UK GAY ANTHEMS VOL.1**
I am what I am: *Respect* / Don't make me wait: *Loveland* / I will always love you: *Washington, Sarah* / Put your hands up in the air: *Living Proof* / Love love love-Here I come: *Rollo Goes Mystic* / Only wanna be with you: *Obsession* / Hold that sucker down: *OT Quartet* / Santa Maria: *Tatjana* / Voulez vous: *Abbacadabra* / He's on the phone: *St. Etienne* / You spin me round: *Kinky Boyz* / You keep me hangin' on: *Hannah & Her Sisters* / Atomic: *Blondie*
BLSTCD 03 / 2 Feb '98 / Blast

☐ **UK GAY ANTHEMS VOL.2 (It's A Man's World)**
ALMYCD 16 / 2 Feb '98 / Blast

☐ **UK MEETS US RAP**
MOLCD 42 / Apr '97 / Music Of Life

☐ **UK REGGAE ALL STARS**
CONQ 999CD / Nov '94 / Conqueror

☐ **UK SPACE TECHNO VOL.1**
MILL 020CD / Mar '96 / Millenium

☐ **UK SPACE TECHNO VOL.2 (2CD Set)**
MILL 026CD / Jul '96 / Millenium

☐ **UK SPACE TECHNO VOL.3**
MILL 037CD / Mar '97 / Millenium

☐ **UK SPACE TECHNO VOL.4 (2CD Set)**
MILL 054CD / 23 Feb '98 / Millenium

☐ **UK SWING (2CD Set)**
MCD 11805 / 29 Jun '98 / MCA

☐ **UK UNDERGROUND**
AZNY 1001 / Oct '92 / Azuli

☐ **UK/DK**
USA: *Exploited* / Joker in the pack / No security: *Chaos UK* / Life: *Disorder* / Blind justice: *Business* / Things that need / Fighter pilot: *Vibrators* / Ignite: *Damned* / You talk, we talk: *Pressure* / Viva la revolution / Jerusalem: *One Way System* / Soldier boy: *Varukers* / 42nd Street: *Angelic Upstarts* / Stand strong, stand proud: *Vice Squad* / USA
CDPUNK 47 / Feb '95 / Anagram

☐ **UKHC COMPILATION**
HAUS 007CD / 10 Nov '97 / Household Name

☐ **UKRAINIAN VOICES**
PS 65114 / Nov '93 / PlayaSound

☐ ULTIMATE 50'S R&B SMASHES
Drinkin' wine spo-dee-o-dee: McGhee, Stick & His Spo-Dee-O-Dee Buddies / Teardrops from my eyes: Brown, Ruth / One mint julep: Clovers / Honey hush: Turner, 'Big' Joe Band / Money honey: McPhatter, Clyde & The Drifters / Sh'boom: Chords / I've got a woman: Charles, Ray Band / Since I met you baby: Hunter, Ivory Joe / Jim Dandy: Baker, LaVern & The Gliders / Without love (there's nothing): McPhatter, Clyde / CC rider: Willis, Chuck / Searchin': Coasters / There goes my baby: Drifters / What'd I say: Charles, Ray
8122729612 / 4 May '98 / Atlantic

☐ ULTIMATE 60'S SOUL SENSATIONS
Sweet soul music: Conley, Arthur / Chain of fools: Franklin, Aretha / In the midnight hour: Pickett, Wilson / Green onions: Booker T & The MG's / Got to get you off my mind: Burke, Solomon / Tighten up: Bell, Archie & The Drells / Hold on I'm comin': Sam & Dave / You don't miss you water: Bell, William / Hello stranger: Lewis, Barbara / Tramp: Otis & Carla / Walking the dog: Thomas, Rufus / Show me: Tex, Joe / Soul finger: Bar-Kays / Last night: Mar-Keys / Sitting on the dock of the bay: Redding, Otis
8122729622 / 4 May '98 / Atlantic

☐ ULTIMATE 60'S SOUL SMASHES
Soul man: Sam & Dave / Respect: Franklin, Aretha / In the midnight hour: Wilson Pickett / When a man loves a woman: Sledge, Percy / On broadway: Drifters / Baby I'm yours: Lewis, Barbara / Hold what you've got: Tex, Joe / Cool jerk: Capitols / Knock on wood: Floyd, Eddie / Slip away: Carter, Clarence / Last night: Mar-Keys / Land of 1000 dances: Wilson Pickett / Memphis soul stew: King Curtis / Baby: Thomas, Carla / Try a little tenderness: Redding, Otis
8122729632 / 4 May '98 / Atlantic

☐ ULTIMATE 70'S R&B SMASHES
Patches: Carter, Clarence / Ghetto: Hathaway, Donny / Don't knock my wood: Wilson Pickett / Rock steady: Franklin, Aretha / I'll be around: Spinners / Right place wrong time: Dr. John / Sideshow: Blue Magic / Pick up the pieces: Average White Band / Bertha butt boogie: Castor, Jimmy Bunch / Supernatural thing: King, Ben E. / Disco inferno: Trammps / Slide: Slave / Firecracker: Mass Production / We are family: Sister Sledge
8122729642 / 4 May '98 / Atlantic

☐ ULTIMATE 80'S
Under pressure: Queen & David Bowie / New year's day: U2 / It's a sin: Pet Shop Boys / Sexcrime (1984): Eurythmics / Relax: Frankie Goes To Hollywood / Is there something I should know: Duran Duran / Need you tonight: INXS / I'm still standing: John, Elton / Everywhere: Fleetwood Mac / Every breath you take: Police / Road to hell: Rea, Chris / I want to know what love is: Foreigner / Big log: Plant, Robert / Wonderful life: Black / Love of the common people: Young, Paul / Road to nowhere: Talking Heads / Reward: Teardrop Explodes / Something about you: Level 42 / Do you really want to hurt me: Culture Club / She drives me crazy: Fine Young Cannibals / Money for nothing: Dire Straits / Wonderland: Big Country / White wedding: Idol, Billy / Start: Jam / Big area: Then Jerico / Dead ringer for love: Meat Loaf / Atomic: Blondie / I'm your man: Wham / Look of love: ABC / Young at heart: Bluebells / Come on Eileen: Dexy's Midnight Runners / Blue Monday: New Order / Only you: Yazoo / (Keep feeling) Fascination: Human League / Enola Gay: OMD / Shout: Tears For Fears / To cut a long story short: Spandau Ballet / Tainted love: Soft Cell / We close our eyes: Go West / Vienna: Ultravox
5168312 / Jun '94 / Polydor

☐ ULTIMATE 80'S
74321271042 / Aug '95 / RCA

☐ ULTIMATE 80'S BALLADS
Save me: Queen / Different corner: Michael, George / All I want is you: U2 / Absolute beginners: Bowie, David / Every little thing she does is magic: Police / Sweet surrender: Wet Wet Wet / Save a prayer: Duran Duran / True: Spandau Ballet / Power of love: Frankie Goes To Hollywood / Eternal flame: Bangles / Here comes the rain again: Eurythmics / I go to sleep: Pretenders / Don't dream it's over: Crowded House / Avalon: Roxy Music / Waiting for a girl like you: Foreigner / Hard habit to break: Chicago / She makes my day: Palmer, Robert / Little lies: Fleetwood Mac / Total eclipse of the heart: Tyler, Bonnie / Romeo and Juliet: Dire Straits / Right here waiting: Marx, Richard / Wherever I lay my hat (that's my home): Young, Paul / One day in your life: Jackson, Michael / Leaving me now: Level 42 / Long hot summer: Style Council / Hands to heaven: Breathe / Love don't live here anymore: Nail, Jimmy / It's different for girls: Jackson, Joe / Golden brown: Stranglers / Chance: Big Country / Kayleigh: Marillion / All of my heart: ABC / No regrets: Ure, Midge / Human: Human League / Souvenir: OMD / One of us: Abba / China in your hands: T'Pau / I second that emotion: Japan / Hold me now: Thompson Twins / Victims: Culture Club
5251132 / Nov '94 / PolyGram TV

☐ ULTIMATE ACCAPELLA VOL.1, THE
ZYX 100532 / 3 Aug '98 / ZYX

☐ ULTIMATE ACCAPPELLA VOL.2, THE
ZYX 100542 / 3 Aug '98 / ZYX

☐ ULTIMATE CAJUN COLLECTION
J'aime grand gueydan: Allan, Johnnie / Colinda: Raven, Eddy / Jolie blon: Thibodeaux, Rufus / Grand Texas: Roger, Aldus / Gabriel: Broussard, Alex / Cajun two-step: Forester, Blackie / Le sud de la Louisianne: Bruce, Vin / Allons a Lafayette: Thibodeaux, Rufus / Pine grove blues: Abshire, Nathan / Creole stomp: Roger, Aldus / Tout son amour: Foret, L.J. / Pauvre hobo: Thibodeaux, Rufus / Married life: Cormier, Louis / La Lou special: Broussard, Pee-Wee / Tous les deux pour la meme: Forester, Blackie / Crawfish festival time: Raven, Eddy / Mon tit baille: Newman, Jimmy C. / Chere Alice: Richard, Zachary / One scotch, one bourbon, one beer: Roger, Aldus / Tee Maurice: Guidry, Doc / Mamou two-step: Walker, Lawrence / La valse de amite: Thibodeaux, Rufus / Comment ca se fait: Newman, Jimmy C. / I'm Cajun cool: Storm, Warren / Evangeline: Dusenberry Family / La maison a deux portes: Storm, Warren / La valse de KLFY: Doucet, Michael / Fais do do: Thibodeaux, Rufus / La valse d'anniversaire: Forester, Blackie / Le two-step de l'acadien: Abshire, Nathan / Grand mamou: Thibodeaux, Rufus / Chemin des coeurs casser: Foret, L.J. / Le nouveau two-step: Richard, Zachary / One more chance: Roger, Aldus / Dans la Louisianne: Bruce, Vin / Alligator Bayou: Raven, Eddy / Lake Arthur stomp: Thibodeaux, Rufus / Ma belle Evangeline: Allan, Johnnie / Le two-step de choupique: Abshire, Nathan / Bayou Sam: Forester, Blackie / Elle n'est pas la plus belle: Foret, L.J. / Tu es la mienne pour toujours: West, Clint / La valse de Quebec: Thibodeaux, Rufus / Lafayette two-step: Roger, Aldus / Le blues Francais: Abshire, Nathan / Cotton fields: Forester, Blackie
DCD 5254 / Aug '92 / Disky

☐ ULTIMATE CLUB MIX VOL.2 (2CD Set)
5652922 / 3 Aug '98 / PolyGram TV

☐ ULTIMATE COUNTRY (2CD Set)
Dance the night away: Mavericks / Soft place to fall: Moorer, Alison / Oh romeo: McCready, Mindy / Thousand miles from nowhere: Yoakam, Dwight / Wind beneath my wings: Greenwood, Lee / Brown eyed girl: Morrison, Van / Islands in the stream: Rogers, Kenny / Crazy: Cline, Patsy / Me and Bobby McGee: Kristofferson, Kris / I fall to pieces: Lynn, Loretta / One piece at a time: Cash, Johnny / Rhine stone cowboy: Campbell, Glen / Wimoweh: Denver, Karl / Twelfth of never: Lansborough, Charlie / When soul meets soul: Couldwell, Adam / Behind closed doors: Rich, Charlie / Blanket on the ground: Spears, Billie Jo / From a distance: Griffiths, Nancy / I've cried: Gayle, Crystal / Jolene: Parton, Dolly / How do I live: Yearwood, Trisha / Bitch: Brooks, Meredith / Achy breaky heart: Cyrus, Billy Ray / Whoever's in New England: McEntire, Reba / I honestly love you: Newton-John, Olivia / Don't it make your brown eyes blue: Gayle, Crystal / Stand by your man: Wynette, Tammy / What I am: Brickell, Edie / I was country when country wasn't cool: Mandrell, Barbara / Love can build a bridge: Judds / Bobbie Sue: Oak Ridge Boys / I recall a gypsy woman: Thompson, Hank / Devil went down to Georgia: Daniels, Charlie / Forever and ever amen: Travis, Randy / Help me make it through the night: Pride, Charley / Talking in your sleep: Normansell, Amanda / You're my best friend: Williams, Don / I will always love you: Rogers, Kenny
TTVCD 2986 / 17 Aug '98 / Telstar TV

☐ ULTIMATE COUNTRY COLLECTION (2CD Set)
Most beautiful girl in the world: Rich, Charlie / I recall a gypsy woman: Williams, Don / I fall to pieces: Cline, Patsy / Crystal chandeliers: Pride, Charley / Stand by your man: Wynette, Tammy / Walk on by: Van Dyke, Leroy / Before the next teardrop falls: Fender, Freddy / Poor boy blues: Atkins, Chet & Mark Knopfler / Blanket on the ground: Spears, Billie Jo / Make the world go away: Arnold, Eddy / He'll have to go: Reeves, Jim / He stopped loving her today: Jones, George / Ring of fire: Cash, Johnny / Rose garden: Anderson, Lynn / I couldn't leave you if I tried: Crowell, Rodney / Lucille: Rogers, Kenny / Legend in my time: Milsap, Ronnie / Rhinestone cowboy: Campbell, Glen / I'm movin' on: Snow, Hank / Feel so right: Alabama / Always on my mind: Nelson, Willie / Please help me, I'm falling: Locklin, Hank / For the good times: Price, Ray / Coal miner's daughter: Lynn, Loretta / Oh lonesome me: Gibson, Don / Hillbilly girl with the blues: Dalton, Lacy J. / Abilene: Hamilton, George IV / Four in the morning: Young, Faron / Loving her was easier (than anything I'll ever do again): Kristofferson, Kris / Baby don't get hooked on me: Davis, Mac / Lone star state of mind: Griffith, Nanci / If I said you had a beautiful body: Bellamy Brothers / Here you come again: Parton, Dolly / Dukes of Hazzard: Jennings, Waylon / Down at the twist and shout: Carpenter, Mary-Chapin / El Paso: Robbins, Marty / Don't close your eyes: Whitley, Keith / Wind beneath my wings: Greenwood, Lee / Talking in your sleep: Gayle, Crystal / Don't rock the jukebox: Jackson, Alan
MOODCD 26 / Oct '92 / Columbia

☐ ULTIMATE COUNTRY LINE DANCING PARTY, THE (3CD Set)
Bootin' scootin' boogie / I feel lucky / Money in the bank / Trouble / Lost and found / Don't rock the jukebox / Blame it on your heart / Workin' man's PH.D / Texas tatoo / Great balls of fire / Watermelon crawl / Wink / That's my story / If Bubba can dance / American honky tonk bar association / Move over Madonna / If the good die young / He thinks he'll keep her / Third rock from the sun / Fast as you can / Ain't goin' down till the sun comes up / Cowboy boogie / Be my baby tonight / Indian outlaw / Baby likes to rock it / Rock my world / Holdin' heaven / Achy breaky heart / Chattahoochee / Swingin' / One more last chance / Born to boogie / Guitars / Cadillacs / Down at the twist and shout / God bless Texas / All my rowdy friends / John Deere Green / Renegades / Rebels and rogues / Elvisand Andy
CDTRBOX 292 / 6 Oct '97 / EMI Gold

☐ ULTIMATE DISCO COLLECTION
QTVCD 021 / Mar '93 / Quality

☐ ULTIMATE DISCO MIX (2CD Set)
He's the greatest dancer: Sister Sledge / I'm coming out: Ross, Diana / Play that funky music: Wild Cherry / And the beat goes on: Whispers / Turn the music up: Players Association / I thought it was you: Hancock, Herbie / Get down: Chandler, Gene / Lady Maramalade: Labelle / Boogie nights: Heatwave & Jocelyn Brown / Hot stuff: Summer, Donna / Cuba: Gibson Brothers / Let's all chant: Zager, Michael Band / Use it up and wear it out: Odyssey / Instant replay: Hartman, Dan / Boogie wonderland: Earth, Wind & Fire / Can you feel the force: Real Thing / Contact: Starr, Edwin / You make me feel (mighty real): Sylvester / Can you feel it: Jacksons / Shame: King, Evelyn 'Champagne' / Knock on wood: Stewart, Amii / Move on up: Mayfield, Curtis / Don't stop the music: Yarbrough & Peoples / Do the bus stop (are you ready): Fatback Band / Brick house: Commodores / Funkin' for Jamaica: Browne, Tom / Ladies night: Kool & The Gang / Night to remember: Shalamar / Best of my love: Emotions / I will survive: Gaynor, Gloria / I shoulda loved ya: Walden, Narada Michael / You gave me love: Crown Heights Affair / Strutt your funky stuff: Frantique / Feel so real: Arrington, Steve / Walking on sunshine: Rockers Revenge / Love come down: King, Evelyn 'Champagne' / You can't hide (your love from me): Joseph, David / Funkytown: Lipps Inc. / Ai no corrida: Jones, Quincy / Searching: Change / Southern freeez: Freeez / It's a disco night (rock don't stop): Isley Brothers / I feel for you: Khan, Chaka
5556622 / 23 Mar '98 / PolyGram TV

☐ ULTIMATE DOO-WOP COLLECTION
NEMCD 618 / Feb '92 / Sequel

☐ ULTIMATE DRUM 'N' BASS
CLP 9979 / Apr '97 / Cleopatra

☐ ULTIMATE DRUM 'N' BASS VOL.1 (2CD Set)
Sound control: Randy & Andy C / 6 Million ways to die: Uncle 22 / Babylon: Splash / Scottie: Sub Nation / Bonber: Aphrodite / Drum and bass wise: Remarc / Screwface 2: Dubtronix / Sound murderer: Remarc / Tearin' (informer): X-Men / Deep in dub: DJ Scoobie / Helicopter: Deep Blue / Time stretch: Size, Roni / Champion dub: Dub Selector / Vibe: Drum & Bass / Dread bass: Dead Dred / Selector: Gangster Sound / Rudie: Hackney Hardcore / It's the way: DJ Tactics / 100 tons of bass: J&J / Rollidge: DJ SS / Hey baby: Intel Inside / Wait for the bass: DJ Scoobie / Terrorist: Renegade & Ray Keith / Valley of the shadows: Origin Unknown / Illusions: A-Sides / Step: Double A / FBI: Drum & Bass
MMCCD 006 / 2 Mar '98 / Massive

☐ ULTIMATE DRUM 'N' BASS VOL.2 (2CD Set)
QPMCD 5 / Apr '96 / QPM

☐ ULTIMATE DRUM 'N' BASS VOL.2 (2CD Set)
Lighter: Sound Of The Future / No war business: Xclusive / Physics: J&J / Horn 494: DJ Tactics / Armed and dangerous: Soundclash / Oh gosh: Undercover Agent / No surrender: Jungle Warrior / Hearing is believing: MA2 / Together: Universal Love / Calling all the people: Azone / Booya: Amazon II / Spiritual aura: Engineers Without Fears / Lucky: Jazz Vibes / Drowning: 4 Horsemen / Exclusive: Xclusive / Jungle Jesus: Jungle Warrior / Zone 6: Infinity & Basics / What kind of world: Ascend & Ultravibe / Warp drive: DJ Crystl / We enter: Aladdin / Future: Noise Factory / Free: Uncle 22 / Music is the vibe: Sub Sequence / We come back: Drum & Bass / Renegade snares: Omni Trio / It's a jazz thing: Size, Roni & DJ Die
MMCCD 007 / 2 Mar '98 / Massive

☐ ULTIMATE EIGHTIES MIX
5652852 / 27 Jul '98 / PolyGram TV

☐ ULTIMATE HAPPY HARDCORE COLLECTION VOL.2, THE (3CD Set)
Love boy: DJ Dougal & Mickey Skeedale / Died in your arms tonight: Go Mental / Can can you do it: Sharkey & Dee / All over: Force & Styles / Let the music: Eruption / Kounter attak: Druid & Vinyl Groover / Higher and higher: Ramos & Supreme/ Sunset Regime / Never give up: Midas / Vampire: DJ Sy & Unknown / Wannabe forever: Jimmy J & Cru-L-T / Take it from the groove: Billy Bunter / So real: DJ Vinyl Groover / SMD 3: SMD / Love is the only way: DJ Storm / Can't stop: DJ Ham / Breaking free: Slipmatt / Play the theme: DJ Sy & Unknown / Falling for you: DJ Justice / Pure love: Midas & Donna Grassie / Got to get up: Kriston / On top: Sence of summer / Hold on: DJ Justice / Take it easy: Edy C / Hold me now: Midas & Fade / You got me jumpin': Ikan / Never give up: Midas / Love boy: DJ Dougal & Mickey Skeedale / Real love: DJ Sy & Unknown / Woo woo wanting you: Ikon / Died in your arms tonight: Go Mental / Let the music: Eruption / So real: DJ Vinyl Groover / It's going to be alright: Vibes & Wishdokta / Wannabe forever: Jimmy J & Cru-L-T / Break thru: Midas & Sunset Regime / We need a blue sky: Greenpeace Release / Love of my life: DJ Dougal / Vampire: DJ Sy & Unknown / Kounter attak: Druid & Vinyl Groover / Take it from the groove: Billy Bunter / Higher and higher: Ramos & Supreme/ Sunset Regime / Just can't stop: Midas / Can can you do it: Sharkey & Dee / All over: Menace & USD / All over: Force & Styles
MMCCD 005 / 9 Feb '98 / Massive

☐ ULTIMATE HOTWIRE SAMPLER
EFA 128172 / May '95 / Hotwire

☐ ULTIMATE HOUSE
CHAMPCD 1016 / Oct '88 / Champion

☐ ULTIMATE HOUSE, THE
GRF 210 / Mar '93 / Tring

☐ ULTIMATE INSTRUMENTAL COLLECTION (3CD Set)
COLBX 001 / Feb '97 / Focus

☐ ULTIMATE JAZZ FUNK (2CD Set)
Always there: Laws, Ronnie / Funkin' for Jamaica: Browne, Tom / Movin': Brass Construction / Bottle: Scott-Heron, Gil / Expansions: Smith, Lonnie Liston / Shaker song: Spyro Gyra / Love will bring us back together: Ayers, Roy / Come with me: Maria, Tania / Westchester Lady: James, Bob / Dancing in outer space: Atmosfear / Killer Joe: Golson, Benny / To prove my love: Doheny, Ned / BCahnge: Byrd, Donald / I thought it was you: Hancock, Herbie / Poo poo la la: Ayers, Roy / Rotation: Alpert, Herb / Summer madness: Kool & The Gang / Street life: Crusaders / Easy: Jarreau, Al / Chicago song: Sanborn, David / Jazz carnival: Azymuth / Strawberry letter: Brothers Johnson / Pick up the pieces: Band / For the love of money: O'Jays / Dominoes: Byrd, Donald / Dance anthems: Byrd, Donald
ULTIMCD 1 / 13 Oct '97 / Beechwood

☐ ULTIMATE LINE DANCING ALBUM, THE
Hillybilly rock hillybilly roll: Woolpackers / Boot scootin' boogie: Brooks & Dunn / Achy breaky heart: Cyrus, Billy Ray / I feel lucky: Carpenter, Mary-Chapin / Chatahoochie: Jackson, Alan / Romeo: Parton, Dolly / Honky tonk man: Yoakam, Dwight / Baby likes to rock it: Tractors / Honky tonk attitude: Diffie, Joe / Line king: Sunset Stampede / Cotton eyed Joe: Rednex / Swamp thing: Grid / Life's a dance: Montgomery, John Michael / My baby loves me: McBride, Martina / Copperhead road: Earle, Steve / Cleopatra Queen of denial: Tillis, Pam / Money in the bank: Anderson, John / Funky cowboy: McDowell, Ronnie / Adalida: Strait, George / 1-800-used to be: Morgan, Lorrie / No-one else on earth: Wyonna
RADCD 41 / Jan '97 / Global TV

☐ ULTIMATE LOOPS VOL.1, THE
ZYX 100552 / 3 Aug '98 / ZYX

☐ ULTIMATE LOOPS VOL.2, THE
ZYX 100562 / 3 Aug '98 / ZYX

☐ ULTIMATE LOVE COLLECTION, THE (4CD Set)
When a man loves a woman: Sledge, Percy / Move closer: Nelson, Phyllis / What becomes of the broken hearted: Ruffin, Jimmy / If you don't know me by now: Melvin, Harold & The Bluenotes / Love really hurts without you: Ocean, Billy / With you I'm born again: Syreeta / How sweet it is (to be loved by you): Sam & Dave / Don't you dare call it love: Gaynor, Gloria / Letter: Box Tops / Marvellettes: Box Tops / When you're young and in love: Marvelettes / Stop her on sight: Starr, Edwin / My prayer: Platters / Save the last dance for me: Drifters / Band of gold: Payne, Freda / Will you love me tomorrow: Shirelles / Love don't live here anymore: Royce, Rose / Bring it on home to me: Floyd, Eddie / Love potion no.9: Clovers / Love makes a woman: Acklin, Barbara / BABY: Thomas, Carla / You belong to me: Duprees / Maybe: Chantels / Every beat of my heart: Knight, Gladys / Baby (you've got what it takes): Benton, Brook / Baby love: Supremes / Inside out: Odyssey / Tell it like it is: Neville, Aaron / Rainy night in Georgia: Benton, Brook / Suddenly: Gaynor, Gloria / Teardrops: Starr, Edwin / True love: Sister Sledge / Mr. Blue: Floyd, Eddie / If loving you is wrong (I don't want to be right): Drifters / Emotion: Weston, Kim / I'll pick a rose for my rose: Johnson, Mary / Letter full of tears: Knight, Gladys / Stop in the name of love: Supremes / Behind closed doors: Sledge, Percy / You're all that I need to get by: Reeves, Martha & G.C. Cameron / Good lovin': Sam & Dave / I can't give you back the love I feel for you: Syreeta / I've passed this way before: Ruffin, Jimmy / Got to get you off my mind: Burke, Solomon / Wishing on a star: Royce, Rose / Power of love: Simon, Joe / You beat me to the punch: Wells, Mary / Misty: Price, Lloyd / Turn back the hands of time: Davis, Tyrone / He will break your heart: Butler, Jerry / My heart and I: Stewart, Amii / Love letters: Lester, Ketty / If you're looking for a way out: Odyssey / Where do you go to my lovely: Sarstedt, Peter / Words: David, F.R. / Ring my bell: Ward, Anita / Sweets for my sweet: Drifters / Poetry in motion: Tillotson, Johnny / Hey baby: Channel, Bruce / Gimme little sign: Wood, Brenton / Birds and the bees: Atkins, Jewel / Remember (walking in the sand): Shangri-Las / Sixteen candles: Crests / You got what it takes: Johnson, Marv / Somewhere: Proby, P.J. / Last night was made for love: Fury, Billy / Don't let it die: Smith, Hurricane / Night has a thousand eyes: Vee, Bobby / Everlasting love: Knight, Robert / Groovy kind of love: Fontana, Wayne / Venus in blue jeans: Clanton, Jimmy / Susie darlin': Luke, Robin / Woman woman: Puckett, Gary & The Union Gap / I'm gonna make you mine: Christie, Lou / You little trustmaker: Tymes / So this is love: Castells / Baby now that I've found you: Foundations / I will: Fury, Billy / Hey Paula: Paul & Paula / Don't let the sun catch you crying: Gerry & The Pacemakers / Run to him: Vee, Bobby / Tell him: Davis, Billie / Hurt so bad: Little Anthony & The Imperials / Stand by me: King, Ben E. / This magic moment: Drifters / Hold me: Proby, P.J. / I love how you love me: Crawford, Jimmy / Love is all around: Troggs / Tell Laura I love her: Peterson, Ray / You were made for me: Freddie & The Dreamers / I've been a bad bad boy: Jones, Paul / Tradgedy: Fleetwoods / You've got your troubles (I've got mine): Fortunes / Forget him: Rydell, Bobby / You were on my mind: St. Peters, Crispian / Someone someone: Poole, Brian / Juliet: Four Pennies / I think of you: Merseybeats / Tossin' and turnin': Ivy League / Young girl: Puckett, Gary & The Union Gap / Happy together: Turtles
ECD 3420 / 23 Feb '98 / K-Tel

☐ ULTIMATE LOVERS VOL.1
ARKCD 101 / Nov '92 / Arawak

☐ ULTIMATE LOVERS VOL.2
ARKCD 104 / Dec '93 / Arawak

☐ ULTIMATE MEMPHIS COUNTRY COLLECTION VOL.1, THE (2CD Set)
Hey porter: Cash, Johnny / Cold cold heart: Lewis, Jerry Lee / (Tell me) Who: Smith, Warren / Turn around: Perkins, Carl / Uncertain love: Rhodes, Slim / Daisy bread boogie: Steele, Gene / Feelin' low: Chaffin, Ernie / Chains of love: Miller Sisters / My kind of carryin' on: Poindexter, Doug / Show me: Bond, Eddie / Blues in the bottom of my shoes (Way down blues): Yelvington, Malcolm / When you stop loving me: King, Cast / Easy to love: Self, Mack / Home of the blues: Cash, Johnny / Let the jukebox keep on playing: Perkins, Carl / Tonight will be the last night: Smith, Warren / Will the circle be unbroken: Lewis, Jerry Lee / Standing in your window: Bond, Eddie / Down on the border: Simmons, Gene / How long: Wimberly, Maggie Sue / Heartbreakin' love: Wages, Jimmy / I'm bluer than anyone can be: Mann, Carl / Muddy ole river: Stinit, Dane / Tragedy: Wayne, Thomas / Your the nearest thing to heaven: Cash, Johnny / This old heart of mine: Bond, Eddie / That black haired man: Clement, Jack / Who will the next fool be: Rich, Charlie / Wayward wind: Mann, Carl / Bummin' around: Feathers, Charlie / In the dark: Peterson, Earl / Just rolling along: Yelvington, Malcolm / Fool for loving you: Earls, Jack / Jump right out of this jukebox: Wheeler, Onie / I'd rather be safe than sorry: Smith, Warren / Someday you will pay: Miller Sisters / That's what I tell my heart: McDaniel, Luke / Country boy: Cash, Johnny / Sure to fall: Perkins, Carl / Jambalaya: Lewis, Jerry Lee / Take and give: Rhodes, Slim / We're getting closer to being apart: Feathers, Charlie / Tell 'em off: Wheeler, Onie / Everyday: Self, Mack / I'm lonesome: Chaffin, Ernie / When I dream: Earls, Jack / Nothing to lose but my heart: Peterson, Earl / I've been deceived: Feathers, Charlie / Day I found you: Bond, Eddie / Ten years: Clement, Jack / Sittin' and thinkin': Rich, Charlie / Goodbye Mr. Love: Smith, Warren / If I could change you: Mann, Carl / Who's gonna shoe your pretty little feet: Anthony, Rayburn / I know what it means: Lewis, Jerry Lee / Tennessee: Perkins, Carl
MEMPHIS 01 / Jan '93 / Disky

☐ ULTIMATE NON-STOP PARTY ALBUM
Stars on 45 / Swing the mood / Do you remember / That's what I like / Caribbean show / Stars on 45
SUMCD 4033 / Nov '96 / Summit

☐ ULTIMATE PAN PIPE COLLECTION, THE (2CD Set)
Candle in the wind / How deep is your love / Your song / Wonderful tonight / Killing me softly / Just the way you are / Everything I do I do it for you / Kiss from a rose / I will always love you / Lady in red / Can you feel the love tonight / Love is all around / Man I love / Love changes everything / If you leave me now /

ULTIMATE PAN PIPE COLLECTION, THE

Back for good / Don't dream it's over / Everytime you go away / Misteru: Flute Indienne / Prolocu: Los Ponchos / Altiplano: Sudamerica / Pito pito: Viracocha / La gaviotta borracha: Los Ponchos / La feria de puno: Los Craneos / Totoras: Sudamerica / Cuequita de los koyos: Viracocha / Desdenosa: Viracocha / Palo alto: Karumanta / Balicha: Viracocha / Mambo di machaguay: Viracocha / Taquirai: Los Craneos / Huyano alegre: Los Craneos / Pichaski: Karumanta / Fiesta aymara: Viracocha / Rosita: Los Craneos / Diecinueve de enero: Patoruzu Y Su Conjunto / Pa'ti cholita: Patoruzu Y Su Conjunto / Vicunitas: Patoruzu Y Su Conjunto / Tutaita manta: Los Indios De Cuzco / El condor pasa: Los Craneos / El chuianco: Flute Indienne / Canto del cuculi: Los Indios De Cuzco / Charaumita: Los Indios De Cuzco / Nace el carnaval: Los Indios De Cuzco / Kena Misky: Patoruzu Y Su Conjunto / Indiecito soy: Los Indios De Cuzco / Soi inca: Los Indios De Cuzco / Pajaritos: Patoruzu Y Su Conjunto / El pajaron: Patoruzu Y Su Conjunto / El zaino: Patoruzu Y Su Conjunto / La piojosa: Patoruzu Y Su Conjunto / Bosque: Los Indios De Cuzco / Fiestarka: Los Indios De Cuzco / sudamerica quiaquenita: Los Indios De Cuzco / Baila cholita: Los Indios De Cuzco

PBXCD 322 / 3 Aug '98 / Pulse

□ ULTIMATE PARTY ANIMAL (2CD Set)
Saturday night: Whigfield / Ooh ahh just a little bit: Gina G / Dreamer: Livin' Joy / Moving on up: M-People / Things can only get better: D:Ream / We are family: Sister Sledge / Let me be your fantasy: Baby D / Ride on time: Black Box / Rhythm of the night: Corona / Power: Snap / Sunshine after the rain: Berri / Twist and shout: Chaka Demus & Pliers / Don't stop (wiggle wiggle): Outhere Brothers / No limit: 2 Unlimited / Boom shake the room: DJ Jazzy Jeff & The Fresh Prince / Stayin' alive: N-Trance / Two can play at that game: Brown, Bobby / Killer: Adamski / I wanna be a hippy: Technohead / Saturday night at the movies: Robson & Jerome / Grease Megamix / Wake me up before you go go: Wham / Relight my fire: Take That / Loco motion: Kylie / Never gonna give you up: Astley, Rick / I'm too sexy: Right Said Fred / Macarena: Los Del Rio / Timewarp: Damian / Saving the mood: Jive Bunny / Can can: Bad Manners / Anniversary waltz: Status Quo / Cotton eye Joe: Rednex / Flava: Andre, Peter / Help yourself: Ferrino, Tony / Cum on feel the noize: Slade / Blockbuster: Sweet / Hit me with your rhythm stick: Dury, Ian & The Blockheads / I'll be there for you: Friends / YMCA: Village People / Boney M megamix: Boney M / Celebration: Kool & The Gang / Boogie wonderland: Earth, Wind & Fire / You make me feel (mighty real): Sylvester / Contact: Starr, Edwin / Oops upside your head: Gap Band / Back to the sixties: Tight Fit / Abba Medley / Beatles medley / Beatles medley: Take That / Guaglione: Prado, Perez

RADCD 47 / Nov '96 / Global TV

□ ULTIMATE PSYCHOBILLY COLLECTION
REMCD 516 / Feb '98 / Reactive

□ ULTIMATE PUB SING-A-LONG ALBUM
MCCD 248 / Jun '96 / Music Club

□ ULTIMATE RAP ACCAPELLA, THE
ZYX 100572 / 3 Aug '98 / ZYX

□ ULTIMATE RAVE CLASSICS
QPMCD 4 / Mar '96 / QPM

□ ULTIMATE RECORDING COMPANY, THE
TOPPCD 004 / Jul '94 / Ultimate

□ ULTIMATE ROCK (2CD Set)
CDEMTVD 148 / Feb '97 / EMI TV

□ ULTIMATE ROCK 'N' ROLL COLLECTION (2CD Set)
(We're gonna) Rock around the clock: Haley, Bill & The Comets / Chantilly lace: Big Bopper / Johnny B Goode: Berry, Chuck / Say mamma: Vincent, Gene / Little bitty pretty one: Lymon, Frankie / Sea cruise: Ford, Frankie / Girl can't help it: Little Richard / Something else: Cochran, Eddie / Reet petite: Wilson, Jackie / Tequila: Champs / Good golly miss molly (Live): Lewis, Jerry Lee / That's alright: Parkins, Carl / I'm walkin': Domino, Fats / Hats off to Larry: Shannon, Del / Sweet little sixteen: Berry, Chuck / Johnny & The Hurricanes / Baby let's play house: Feathers, Charlie / Claudette: Everly Brothers / Barbara Ann: Regents / That'll be the day: Holly, Buddy / Crying: Bopper / Little darlin': Diamonds / Primrose lane: Wallace, Jerry / Let's have a party: Nelson, Wanda / Jennie Lee: Jan & Arnie / Raunchy: Justis, Bill / You've got what it takes: Johnson, Marv / Let's twist again: Checker, Chubby / Runaround Sue: Dion / Ali Mama's children: Parkins, Carl / Bony moronie: Williams, Larry / Nut rocker: B Bumble & The Stingers / Blue suede shoes: Cochran, Eddie / At the hop: Danny & The Juniors / Oh boy: Holly, Buddy / Little darlin': Diamonds / Rebel rouser: Eddy, Duane / I'm number one rock 'n' roll C and W boogie blues man: Gilley, Mickey / Whole lotta shakin' goin' on: Lewis, Jerry Lee / Rip it up: Haley, Bill & The Comets / Shame shame shame: LaBeef, Sleepy / Oh baby: Berry, Chuck

MOODCD 36 / Oct '94 / Columbia

□ ULTIMATE SIXTIES COLLECTION, THE (4CD Set)
Here comes my baby: Tremeloes / Hippy hippy shake: Swinging Blue Jeans / Twist and shout: Poole, Brian / Twist: Checker, Chubby / How do you do it: Gerry & The Pacemakers / Sweets for my sweet: Searchers / Leader of the pack: Shangri-Las / Happy together: Turtles / You were made for me: Freddie & The Dreamers / Baby now that I've found you: Foundations / Here it comes again: Fortunes / Do you want to know a secret: Kramer, Billy J / Are you sure: Allisons / Love on a mountain top: Knight, Robert / Everybody: Roe, Tommy / Lightning strikes: Christie, Lou / Tossin' and turnin': Ivy League / My boyfriend's back: Angels / Saturday night at the movies: Drifters / When will you say I love you: Fury, Billy / San Franciscan nights: Animals / Any way that you want me: Troggs / Wishin' and hopin': Merseybeats / Come back and shake me: Rogers, Kenny / Lay down (candles in the rain): Melanie / Hurt so bad: Little Anthony & The Imperials / Sweet talkin' guy: Chiffons / So much in love: Tymes / Wonderful

wonderful: Tymes / Bobby's girl: Maughan, Susan / More than I can say: Vee, Bobby / Shelia: Roe, Tommy / You'll never walk alone: Gerry & The Pacemakers / Don't throw your love away: Searchers / Ain't misbehavin': Bruce, Tommy / Limbo rock: Checker, Chubby / It keeps right on a-hurtin': Tillotson, Johnny / Valare: Rydell, Bobby / Diamonds: Harris, Jet / Just like Eddie: Heinz / 98.6: Keith / Shout: Dee, Joey & The Starlighters / Don't treat me like a child: Shapiro, Helen / Winchester cathedral: New Vaudeville Band / Where do yo go to (my lovely): Sarstedt, Peter / Funny how love can be: Ivy League / Groovy kind of love: Fontana, Wayne / You were on my mind: Crispin St Peters / Tell him: Davis, Billie / Juliet: Four Pennies / Crying game: Berry, Dave / I like it: Gerry & The Pacemakers / Thousand stars: Fury, Billy / Make me an island: Dolan, Joe / Let's go to San Francisco: Flowerpot Men / With a girl like you: Troggs / Google eye: Nashville Teens / I think of you: Merseybeats / I understand: Freddie & The Dreamers / Good golly Miss Molly: Swinging Blue Jeans / Bad to me: Kramer, Billy J / Walking back to happiness: Shapiro, Helen / I love how you love me: Crawford, Jimmy / Tell me when: Applejacks / Those were the days: Hopkin, Mary / Woman woman: Puckett, Gary & The Union Gap / Needles and pins: Searchers / Little loving: Fourmost / Candy man: Poole, Brian / Love letters: Lester, Ketty / If you don't know me by now: Melvin, Harold & The Bluenotes / Turn turn turn: Byrds / Warm and tender love: Sledge, Percy / Then you can tell me goodbye: Casinos / Soul sister brown sugar: Sam & Dave / Up on the roof: Drifters / I've passed this way before: Ruffin, Jimmy / He's a rebel: Crystals / For your precious love: Impressions / He's so fine: Chiffons / Blue moon: Marcels / Early in the morning: Vanity Fair / Little town flirt: Shannon, Del / Come back when you grow up: Vee, Bobby / Jam up and jelly tight: Roe, Tommy / Wild one: Rydell, Bobby / Revenge: Benton, Brook / Heatwave: Reeves, Martha / Hey baby: Channel, Bruce / Johnny get angry: Sommers, Joanie / Bumble boogie: B Kimble & The Stingers / Lil' red riding hood: Sam The Sham & The Pharaohs / Walk a mile in my shoes: South, Joe / Oh happy day: Hawkins, Edwin Singers

ECD 3415 / 16 Feb '98 / K-Tel

□ ULTIMATE SKA COLLECTION
DCD 5295 / Nov '93 / Disky

□ ULTIMATE SOUL COLLECTION VOL.1
Rainy night in georgia / Walking the dog / Knock on wood / Land of 1 000 dances / Thin line between love and hate / Save the last dance for me / I say a little prayer / Under the boardwalk / What'd I say / Soul finger / Soul man / Everybody needs somebody to love / What's goin' on / (sittin' on) the dock of the bay / Green onions / Hold on I'm comin' / Baby I'm yours / I'm still in love with you / It's a man's man's man's world / Sweet soul music / Tears of a clown / I'm gonna make you love me / Have you seen her / Tribute to a king / La la means I love you / Try a little tendeness / Love won't let me wait / Clean up woman / Stand by me / Patches / In the midnight hour / Memphis soul stew / Why can't we live together / (your love keeps lifting me) higher and higher / Recovery / I got you (I feel good) / Rescue me / I'm your puppet / See saw / Respect / Spanish harlem / When a man loves a woman / B-a-b-y / Stay with me / Warm and tender love

9548333402 / Feb '95 / Warner Bros.

□ ULTIMATE SOUL COLLECTION VOL.2, THE
Tracks of my tears / Tighten up / Harlem shuffle / Best thing that ever happened to me / Please please please / When something is wrong with my baby / Papa's got a brand new bag / Private number / Mercy mercy / Lovin' you / Oh girl / Be thankful for what you've got / Give me just a little more time / Hey girl don't bother me / Backfield in motion / Grazing in the grass / Tired of being alone / I get the sweetest feeling / Shout / Got to get you off my mind / Gee whiz (look at his eyes) / Just one look / Band of gold / Ain't no sunshine / Move on up / I'm so proud / You keep me hangin' on / I thank you / It tears me up / Take time to know her / There goes my baby / You don't treat me no good / I'm been loving you too long / Up on the roof / Funky nassau / 634 5789 / I'll be around / Could it be I'm falling in love / Respect yourself / Ghetto / Soul dressing / Think / (you make me feel like) a natural woman / Mustang sally

9548338402 / Oct '95 / Warner Bros.

□ ULTIMATE SPEED GARAGE VOL.1
TIDCD 003 / 13 Apr '98 / Tidalwave

□ ULTIMATE SUMMER PARTY (2CD Set)
Horny: Mousse T & Hot 'n Juicy / Feel it: Tamperer & Maya / La promanara: Sash / Beat goes on: All Seeing I / Free: Ultra Nate / Fight for your right: NYCC / Kung fu fighting: Bus Stop & Carl Douglas / Last thing on my mind: Steps / All I wanna do: Mongue, Danni / U sure do: Strike / U sexy thing: Clock / Sunshine after the rain: Berri / U got to let the music: Cappella / Don't give me your life: Alex Party / Let me be your fantasy: Baby D / Fire we the secret: Urban Cookie Collective / Real thing: Di Bart, Tony / Just a little bit: Gina G / Another night: Real McCoy & MC Sar / Rhythm of the night: Corona / (How does it feel to be) On top of the world: England United / Night fever: Garcia, Adam / Dr. Jones: Aqua / Saturday night: Whigfield / Uh la la la: Alexia / Lamatada: Kaoma / La bamba: Los Lobos / Hot hot hot: Arrow

5650502 / 15 Jun '98 / PolyGram TV

□ ULTIMATE SUMMER PARTY ANIMAL (2CD Set)
RADCD 63 / Jun '97 / Global TV

□ ULTIMATE SUN COUNTRY COLLECTION (56 Legendary Original Sun Recordings)
Hey porter: Cash, Johnny / Cold cold heart: Lewis, Jerry Lee / (Tell me) who: Smith, Warren / I turn around: Perkins, Carl / Uncertain love: Rhodes, Slim / Daisy bread boogie: Steele, Gene / Feelin' low: Chaffin, Ernie / Drums of love: Miller Sisters / My kind of carryin' on: Poindexter, Doug / Show me: Bond, Eddie / Blues in the bottom of my shoes (way down blues): Yelvington, Malcolm / When you gotta hang me king: Cast / Easy to love: Self, Mack / Home of the blues: Cash, Johnny / Let the jukebox keep on playing: Perkins, Carl / Tonight will be the last night: Scott, Ramsey / I'll sail my ship alone: Lewis, Jerry Lee / Standing in your window: Bond, Eddie / Down on the border: Simmons, Gene / How long: Wimberly, Maggie Sue / Heartbreakin' love: Wages, Jimmy / I'm bluer than anyone can be: Mann, Carl / Muddy ole river: Stirit, Dane / Tragedy: Wayne, Thomas / You're the nearest thing to heaven: Cash,

Johnny / This old heart of mine: Bond, Eddie / That black haired man: Clement, Jack / Who will the next fool be: Rich, Charlie / Wayward wind: Mann, Carl / Bummin' around: Feathers, Charlie / In the dark: Peterson, Earl / Just rolling along: Yelvington, Malcolm / Fool for loving you: Earls, Jack / Jump right out of this jukebox: Wheeler, Onie / I'd rather be safe than sorry: Smith, Warren / Someday you will pay: Miller Sisters / That's what I tell my heart: McDaniel, Luke / Country boy: Cash, Johnny / Care to fall: Perkins, Carl / Jambalaya: Lewis, Jerry Lee / Take and give: Rhodes, Slim / We're getting closer to being apart: Feathers, Charlie / Tell 'em off: Wheeler, Onie / Everyday: Self, Mack / I'm lonesome: Chaffin, Ernie / When I dream: Earls, Jack / Nothing to lose but my heart: Peterson, Earl / I've been deceived: Miller Sisters / Charlie / Day I found you: Bond, Eddie / Ten years: Clement, Jack / Sittin' and thinkin': Rich, Charlie / Goodbye Mr. Love: Smith, Warren / If I could change you: Mann, Carl / Who's gonna shoe your pretty little feet: Anthony, Rayburn / I know what it means: Lewis, Jerry Lee / Tennessee: Perkins, Carl

DCD 5201 / Aug '91 / Disky

□ ULTIMATE SURFING ALBUM
JHD 012 / Jun '92 / Tring

□ ULTIMATE SWEDISH (Slash & Burn Vol.1)
SPV 08453752 / Aug '96 / SPV

□ ULTIMATE SWING
Love is all we need: Blige, Mary J. & Nas / Grapevine: Brownstone / She's got that vibe: R Kelly / It your girl only knew: Aaliyah / Freakin': Jodeci / No diggity: Blackstreet / My perogative: Brown, Bobby / Humpshaker: Wrecks n' Effect / Sensitivity: Tresvant, Ralph / Poison: Bel Biv Devoe / You make me wanna: Usher / Creep: TLC / Don't take it personal: Monica / Right here: SWV / Before you walk out the door: Brandy / Something for da honeyz: Jordan, Montell / Doin' it: LL Cool J / Hold on: En Vogue / Request line: Zhane / Don't wanna be a player: Joe / So you like what you see: Samuelle / Return of the mack: Morrison, Mark / Get me home: Brown, Foxy & Blackstreet / You might need somebody: Ama, Shola

ULTIMCD 2 / 20 Apr '98 / Beechwood

□ ULTIMATE TANGO
MACCD 376 / 30 Mar '98 / Autograph

□ ULTRA DANCE (Mixed By Boris Dlugosch) (2CD Set)
All of me: Backroom Boys & Takiya Dixon / Stay gold: Deep Dish / Lift me up: MK & Claire Rivers / Jump to my beat: Wildchild / Release yo self: Transatlantic Soul / Love each other: Wildchild / It's your life: Naked Music NYC & Motivation / You've got love: Tribe / This love we've found: Reel Soul & Carolyn Harding / Keep on dreaming: Lisa Marie Experience / Super sweeter: Bolland, C.J. / Keep on jumpin': Lisa Marie Experience

ULTRA 1002 / Mar '97 / Ultra

□ ULTRA LOUNGE (TV Town)
Bubbles in the wine: Martin, Freddy & His Orchestra / May, Billy & His Orchestra / Man from UNCLE: Caiora, Al / Spies: Caiora, Al / Thanks for the memory: Pell, Dave / Munsters: Marshall, Jack / Fugitive: Zentner, Si / Dick Van Dyke: Riddle, Nelson & Orchestra / Alvin Show: Riddle, Nelson & Orchestra / Human jungle: Barry, John / Batman: McCallum, David / Maxine: May, Billy & His Orchestra / One step beyond (fear): Ventures / Twilight zone: Ventures / Mr. Lucky: Zentner, Si / Mod squad: Caiora, Al / My three sons: Riddle, Nelson & Orchestra / Burle's law suite: Zentner, Si / Soundtrack orchestra / Bewitched: Lee, Peggy / Melancholy serenade: Gleason, Jackie / Power / Jones, Spike

CDEMS 1616 / Jul '97 / EMI

□ ULTRA LOUNGE (Bossa Novaville)
So danco samba: De Sah, Wanda / Meditation: Almeida, Laurindo & Bossa Nova All Stars / Little bird: Perkins, Bill / Little toat: Perkins, Bill / Samba de orfeu: Anthony, Ray / Amy's theme: Denny, Martin / Rico vacilon: Barbour, Dave / Rey: Lawrence, Steve / One note samba: Holmes, Leroy / Recado bossa nova: Holmes, Leroy / Triste: Roberts, Howard / Holiday: May, Billy / Look of love: May, Billy & His Orchestra / Desafinado: Zentner, Si / Dick / Poinciana: Martin, Dean / Manha de carneval: Almeida, Laurindo / Mas que nada: Mitchell, Rubin / So nice: De Sah, Wanda & Sergio Mendes / Fly me to the moon: London, Julie

CDEMS 1617 / Jul '97 / EMI

□ ULTRA LOUNGE (Wild Cool & Swingin' Too)
Frenesi: Gorme, Eydie / Night and day: Lawrence, Steve / Charade: Darin, Bobby / A lot of livin' to do: Wilson, Nancy / 5 months, 2 weeks, 2 days: Prima, Louis / Wives and lovers: Damone, Vic / Boy from ipanema: Lee, Peggy / Strangers in the night: Newton, Wayne / With plenty of money and you: Bennett, Tony / Call me irresponsible: Darin, Bobby / Is you is or is you ain't my baby: Washington, Dinah / Snootie little cutie: Troup, Bobby / Daddy: London, Julie / Just in time: Martin, Dean / Perdido: Vaughan, Sarah / Angel eyes: Jones, Jack / Just a gigolo: Prima, Louis / I ain't got nobody: Prima, Louis / Swingin' down the lane: Rodriguez, Tito / Watch what happens: Horne, Lena / Hawaiian war chant: Fitzgerald, Ella

CDEMS 1618 / Jul '97 / EMI

□ ULTRA LOUNGE (Mondo Hollywood)
Experiment in terror: Caiora, Al / Man and a woman: May, Billy & Jerry Holmes / Love theme: Baxter, Les / Leroy Holmes / Barbarella: Ferrante & Teicher / Cool: Denny, Martin / Hot rod rumble: Courage, Sandy / Pink panther: Johnson, Plas / It had better be tonight: Johnson, Plas / Beat girl: Barry, John / You only live twice: Barry, John / Girl friend of the whirling dervish: Denny, Martin / Bali ha'i: Shindo, Tak / Pyramid of the sun: Baxter, Les / Quiet village: Denny, Martin / Wimowch: Sumac, Yma

CDEMS 1619 / Jul '97 / EMI

□ ULTRA LOUNGE (Bongoland)
Deep night: Snyder, Terry / Softly as in a morning sunrise: Snyder, Terry / Latin fever: Costanzo, Jack / Taboo: Arnaud, Leo / Nightmare: Loco, Joe / On Green Dolphin Street: Denny, Martin / Hernando's hideaway: Denny, Martin / Dr. No's fantasy: Fisher, Elliott / Night in Tunisia: Latin Jazz Sextet / Cherry pink and apple blossom white: Baxter, Les & Billy May / Bernie's June: Caiora, Al / Brazil: Contreras, Tino / Caravan: Hyman, Dick / Inch worm: Costanzo, Jack / Misiriou: Perito, Nick / Quien sera: Perito, Nick / Young savages: Denny, Martin / Balinese bongos: Baxter, Les / Club caballeros: Almeida, Laurindo & The Danzaneros / Moderna muchachas: Loco, Joe / La cumparsa: Costanzo, Jack / Harlem nocturne: Costanzo, Jack / Colon: Savage Beat Of Augie Colon

CDEMS 1620 / Jul '97 / EMI

□ ULTRA LOUNGE (Bottoms Up)
Fandango: Denny, Martin / Big noise from winnekta: Caiora, Al / Midnight swim: Caiora, Al / Hot toddy: London, Julie / Mah-na mah-na: Holmes, Leroy / Music to watch girls by: May, Billy / Slick: May, Billy / Oh honey: Wood, Gloria / Guys and dolls: Snyder, Terry / Cute: McLain, Danny / No matter what shape your stomach is in: New Classic Singers / Tijuana taxi: New Classic Singers / Sing sing sing: Denny, Martin / Baby elephant walk: Caiora, Al & Billy May / Java: Caiora, Al & Billy May / Potluck: La Salle, John Quartet / Rots-o-ruck: Marino, Richard / Squatty roo: Buzon, John Trio / Twang: Costanzo, Jack / Latin dance: Hoffman, Dr. Samuel / S wonderful: Hoffman, Dr. Samuel / Quiet village: Denny, Martin / Lisbon Antigua: Riddle, Nelson

CDEMS 1621 / Jul '97 / EMI

□ ULTRA LOUNGE VOL.1 (Mondo Exotica)
Swamp fire: Denny, Martin / Moon Mis: Out-Islanders / Caravan: 80 Drums Around The World / Hypnotique: Denny, Martin / Atlantis: Baxter, Les / Aika: Edwards, Webley / Miserlou: Denny, Martin / Lust: Sheva, Bas / Hana maui: Floyd, Chick / 10 voodoo dreams: Baxter, Les / Jungle madness: Denny, Martin / 12 Babalo: Sumac, Yma / Simba: Denny, Martin / Bali h'ai: Shindo, Tak / Pyramid of the sun: Baxter, Les / Quiet village: Denny, Martin / Wimowch: Sumac, Yma

CDEMS 1584 / Apr '96 / Premier/EMI

□ ULTRA LOUNGE VOL.10 (A Bachelor In Paris)
I love Paris: Butera, Sam / Song from Moulin Rouge: Jones, Jonah Quartet / Milord: Baxter, Les / Under Paris skies: Car, Joe 'Fingers' / La la Collette: Car, Joe 'Fingers' / Valentina: Bernstein, Elmer / Parisian women: Coleman, Cy / Mon amour, I love amour: Baxter, Les / C'est magnifique: Riddle, Nelson / Viva l'amour: Doo, Dicky & The Don'ts / April in Paris: Mighty Accordian Band / Poor people of Paris: May, Billy / French cat rule: Double Six Of Paris / Petite fleur: Rene, Henri / Clown on the Eiffel tower: Baxter, Les / La vie en rose: Butera, Sam / C'est si Ben: Cooper, Jack / I love Paris: Constanzo, Jack / Can can: Shard, Jerry

CDEMS 1597 / Apr '96 / Premier/EMI

□ ULTRA LOUNGE VOL.11 (Organs In Orbit)
Rockhouse: Freeman, Ernie / III wind: Buzon, John Trio / Girl from Ipanema: McLain, Danny / Love is just around the corner: Davis, Jackie / Movin' at midnight: Sir Julian / Voce e eu: Wanderley, Walter / Li'l darlin': Bucci, Joe Trio / Patricia: May, Billy & His Orchestra / Third Man theme: Baxter, Dio Trio / Man and a woman: Sir Julian / Mr. Ghost goes to town: Buzon, John Trio / Laura: McLain, Danny / More: McLain, Danny / Perfida: Davis, Jackie / Late, Late show: Buckner, Milt / Fever: Freeman, Ernie / Comin' home baby: Freeman, Ernie / Flying fiddles: Torrent, Manuel / Shay / Song of joy: Denny, Martin / Enchanted farm: Forbidden Five

CDEMS 1598 / Aug '96 / Premier/EMI

□ ULTRA LOUNGE VOL.12 (Saxophobia)
I dig: Baxter, Les / Street scene: Butera, Sam / All or nothing at all: Auld, George / Bernie's June: Hamner, Curley & Milt Buckner / Watermelon man: King Curtis / Volare: Riddle, Nelson / Tanya: Johnson, Plas / Samba de Orfeu: Perkins, Bill / Peter Gunn twist: Anthony, Ray / Goldfinger: Basie, Count / Caravan: Jenkins, Gordon / Speakeasy blues: Riddle, Nelson / One mint julep: Palmer, Earl Trio / Ebb tide: Out-Islanders / Big twist: Johnson, Plas / Moanin': Basie, Count / Misfits: Costa, Don / Bong bash: Domiguin, Pepe

CDEMS 1599 / Aug '96 / Premier/EMI

□ ULTRA LOUNGE VOL.13 (Christmas Cocktails)
Rudolph, the red-nosed reindeer mambo: May, Billy / Winter wonderland: Lee, Peggy / Christmas trumpets / We wish you a merry Christmas: Anthony, Ray / Christmas is: Rawls, Lou / Santa Claus is comin' to town/White Christmas: McGriff, Jimmy / I'd like you for Christmas: London, Julie / Holiday on skis: Caiora, Al & His Orchestra / (Everybody's waitin' for) the man with the bag: Starr, Kay / Jingle bells/Jingle bell rock: Hollyridge Strings / Rudolph, the red-nosed reindeer: May, Billy / Baby it's cold outside: Gleason, Jackie & Jack Marshall / What are you doing New Year's Eve: Nancy / Cha cha all the way: Capitol Studio Orchestra / Christmas song (Merry Christmas to you): Cole, Nat 'King' / Nutcracker suite: Brown, Les & His Band Of Renown / Ring those Christmas bells: Waring, Fred & His Pennsylvanians / Violets for your furs: Continental / Tag: Unknown Artist / Capitol promo: Unknown Artist

CDEMS 1600 / Nov '97 / Premier/EMI

□ ULTRA LOUNGE VOL.2 (Mambo Fever)
Hooray for Hollywood: Swan, Don / Manana: Davis, Mavis / Jackie / Peter Gunn mambo: Constanzo, Jack / Chili con mambo: Anthony, Ray & George Shearing / Hernando's hideaway: Davis, Jackie / Mambo No. 8: Loco, Joe / Mambo of love: Anthony, Ray / Taboo: Duarte, Carmen / Chihuahua: Oliver, Dick / I don't want to set the world on fire: Buzon, John / Jungle drums: Barbour, Dave / Cuban nightmare: Buzon, John / Mambo jambo: Costanzo, Jack / Soy / Poinciana: Costanzo, Jack / Mambo gallego / Mambo No. 5: Prado, Perez / Medley: Sumac, Yma / Way down yonder in New Orleans: Prado, Perez

yonder in New Orleans: Alexander, Van / Oink oink mambo: Reves, Chuy / Diga diga doo: Buzon, John Trio / Hernando's hideaway: May, Billy & His Orchestra / Tico tico: Swan, Don / Glow worm cha cha cha: Davis, Jackie / Malambo: Sumac, Yma / Can can overture: Constanzo, Jack / Oye negra: Snyder, Terry
CDEMS 1585 / Apr '96 / Premier/EMI

☐ **ULTRA LOUNGE VOL.3 (Space Capades)**
Gay spirits: Rose, David / Lover: Marino, Richard / Moon moods: Baxter, Les / Power house: Hammock, Bobby / Drivin' around the block: Harrell, Dickie / Calcutta: Baxter, Les / Holiday for strings: Schumann, Walter / You're the top: Elliott, Dean / Istanbul (not Constantinople): Carr, Joe 'Fingers' / Stumbling: Shindo, Tak / Sabre dance: Baxter, Les / This room is my castle of quiet: May, Billy / I get a kick out of you: Slatkin, Felix / Satan takes a holiday: Malmsten, Jack / Puttin' on the ritz: Snyder, Terry / Blues in the night: Roy, Alvin / Saturday night on Saturn: Baxter, Les / Lonesome Road: Elliott, Dean
CDEMS 1586 / Apr '96 / Premier/EMI

☐ **ULTRA LOUNGE VOL.4 (Bachelor Pad Royale)**
Route 66 theme: Riddle, Nelson & Orchestra / Caravan: Buzon, John Trio / Sexe: Renaud, Line / Cool: Busch, Lou & His Orchestra / Beast: Buckner, Milt / Our man Flint theme: Fisher, Elliott / Spring, sprang, sprung: Fascinato, Jack / Night train: Rey, Alvino / Harlem nocturne: Denny, Martin / Boulevard of broken dreams/Fever: Butera, Sam / Topsy: Bucci, Joe Trio / Like young: Pell, Dave / Street scene '58: Busch, Lou & His Orchestra / Playboy's theme: Coleman, Cy / Shot in the dark: Haskell, Jimmie / Shangri-la: Jones, Spike New Band / Black coffee: London, Julie / Melancholy serenade: King Curtis
CDEMS 1591 / May '96 / Premier/EMI

☐ **ULTRA LOUNGE VOL.5 (Wild, Cool & Swingin')**
Ain't that a kick in the head: Martin, Dean / Dig that crazy chick: Butera, Sam & The Witnesses / More: Darin, Bobby / Fever: Lee, Peggy / Jump, jive an' wail: Prima, Louis / Please don't talk about me when I'm gone: Davis, Sammy Jr. / Danke schoen: Newton, Wayne / French poodle: Butera, Sam & The Witnesses / What is this thing called love: Smith, Keely / Sunday in New York: Darin, Bobby / Closer to the bone: Prima, Louis / Nobody but me: Rawls, Lou / Little girl: Damone, Vic / LOVE: Cole, Nat 'King' / Volare: Martin, Dean / That old black magic: Prima, Louis & Keely Smith / You'd be so nice to come home to: London, Julie / Hello Dolly: Darin, Bobby
CDEMS 1592 / May '96 / Premier/EMI

☐ **ULTRA LOUNGE VOL.6 (Rhapsodesia)**
Girl talk: Roberts, Howard / Serenata: Jones, Jonah Quartet / Sleep walk: Rene, Henri & His Orchestra / Smoke gets in your eyes: Mallet Men / Go slow: London, Julie / Ebb tide: Anthony, Al / If I should lose you: Shearing, George / Willow weep for me: Marcellino, Muzzy / Dansero: Baker, Don Trio / Lunar rhapsody: Baxter, Les / You're my thrill: Gray, Dolores / Fever: Marino, Richard & His Orchestra / Blues in my heart: Buzon, John Trio / Tenderly: Gleason, Jackie / Picnic theme: Snyder, Terry / Turquoise: Buckner, Milt / Do it again: Stevens, April / Ruby: Baxter, Les Orchestra
CDEMS 1593 / May '96 / Premier/EMI

☐ **ULTRA LOUNGE VOL.7 (The Crime Scene)**
Dragnet/Room 43: Anthony, Ray / I Spy: Hagen, Earle / Thinking of baby: Bernstein, Elmer / From Russia with love: Basie, Count / Big town: Almeida, Laurindo / Man with the golden arm: May, Billy / Untouchables: Riddle, Nelson / James Bond theme: Holmes, Leroy / Mission Impossible: May, Billy / Harlem nocturne: Jones, Spike / Walk on the wild side: Zentner, Si / Mister Kiss Kiss Bang Bang: Fisher, Elliott / Wild ones: Busch, Lou / Staccato's theme: Bernstein, Elmer / Search for Vulcan: Holmes, Leroy / Peter Gunn suite: Anthony, Ray / Silencers: Carr, Vikki / Music to be murdered by: Alexander, Jeff Singers
CDEMS 1594 / Jul '96 / Premier/EMI

☐ **ULTRA LOUNGE VOL.8 (Cocktail Capers)**
Rollercoaster: Baxter, Les / Hey bellboy: Wood, Gloria / This could be the start of something: Pell, Dave / Pink Panther theme: Hollywood Studio Orchestra / Like young: Rose, David / Underwater chase: Caiora, Al / Binga banga bonga/Percolator: Snyder, Terry / Call me: New Classic Singers / Mountain greenery: Freeman, Bernie Combo / Charade: Zentner, Si / Shooting star/Jungalero: Baxter, Les / Honorable Hong Kong rock: Out-Islanders / Odd job man/I wanna be a James Bond girl: Holmes, Leroy / Heap big chief: Marcellino, Muzzy / Blue Danube rock: Jones, Jesse / Pussy cat: Coleman, Cy / Teach me Tiger: Stevens, April / Lolita Ya Ya: Riddle, Nelson
CDEMS 1595 / Jul '96 / Premier/EMI

☐ **ULTRA LOUNGE VOL.9 (Cha Cha De Amor)**
Sway: Martin, Dean / Recado bossa nova: Almeida, Laurindo / You're my thrill: Auld, Georgie / It must be true: Buzon, John Trio / Carioca: Denny, Martin / Whatever Lola wants: Baxter, Les / A Nega Se Vingou: Wanderley, Walter / Dark eyes/It happened in Monterey: Mallet Men / Gropher mambo: Sumac, Yma / Zelda's theme: Prado, Perez / Magnificent seven: Rodriguez, Tito / Cha cha cha d'amour: Martin, Dean / Desafinado: Almeida, Laurindo / Bei mir bist du schon/La furiosa: Costanzo, Jack & Don Swan / Choo choo cha cha: Rinks Dinks / So nice: May, Billy / Rock-cha-rhumba / Sway: London, Julie
CDEMS 1596 / Jul '96 / Premier/EMI

☐ **ULTRA TECHNO VOL.1**
IR 006CD / Apr '96 / Independence

☐ **ULTRAMETAL**
MONITOR 1 / Jan '92 / Monitor

☐ **ULTRATUBES MEKTAR (Remixes)**
PV 0182 / 27 Apr '98 / Planet Vision

☐ **UNCHAINED MELODIES**
You'll never walk alone: Gerry & The Pacemakers / When a man loves a woman: Sledge, Percy / Smoke gets in your eyes: Platters / Halfway to paradise: Fury, Billy / Raindrops keep fallin' on my head: Thomas, B.J. / Stranger on the shore: Bilk, Acker / Spanish harlem: King, Ben E. / Love letters in the sand: Boone, Pat / What becomes of the broken hearted: Ruffin, Jimmy / Unchained melody: Drifters / You've lost that loving feeling: Yuro, Timi / Will you love me tomorrow: Shirelles / Somewhere: Proby, P.J. / Moon river: Butler, Jerry / Bright eyes: Belmonde, Pierre / My own true love: Duprees / I don't know why, but I do: Henry, Clarence 'Frogman' / Help me make it through the night: Smith, Sammi
ECD 3196 / Mar '95 / K-Tel

☐ **UNCHARTED TERRITORIES VOL.1**
Central line: Alroy Road Tracks & Duke Of Haringay / Tranquillity: Aquasky / Saxx: Fourth World / Visible from space: Hunch / Cool breeze: Ken, Kenny & Cool Breeze / Cotton wool: Lamb / Melting pot: Melting Pot / Harp of gold: Nice, Peter Trio / Mutant jazz: T-Power / Freefall: Terresa / Touch me / Never as good: Wax Doctor
SOUNDSCD 9 / Jul '96 / Street Sounds

☐ **UNCHARTED TERRITORIES VOL.2**
SOUNDSCD 11 / Feb '97 / Street Sounds

☐ **UNCLE SAM BLUES**
Army blues: White, Bukka / GI blues: Lightnin' Slim / Red's dream: Louisiana Red / Vietnam blues: Lenoir, J.B. / Stormy desert: Terry, Cooper / Overseas blues: Borum, 'Memphis' Willie / Uncle Sam don't take my man: Pryor, Snooky / Back to Korea blues: Sunnyland Slim / Vietcong blues: Wells, Junior / Million lonesome women: McGhee, Brownie / '41 blues: Clayton, Dr. Peter / Pearl Harbour blues: Clayton, Dr. Peter / Give me a 32-20: Crudup, Arthur 'Big Boy' / Win the war blues: Williamson, Sonny Boy / Army blues: Edwards, David / Atomic bomb blues: Harris, Homer / So cold in Vietnam: Shines, Johnny / Sad news from Korea: Hopkins, Lightnin'
CD 52043 / Oct '96 / Blues Encore

☐ **UNCOVERED**
Walk on by: Franklin, Aretha / Let's stay together: Pasadenas / Every night: Snow, Phoebe / They won't go when I go: Michael, George / Until you come back to me: Williams, Deniece & Johnny Mathis / (Sittin' on the) dock of the bay: Bolton, Michael / Don't dream it's over: Young, Paul / Stop lovin' me, stop lovin' you: Hall, Daryl / What's going on: Lauper, Cyndi / Summertime: Benson, George / Stand by me: White, Maurice / Why can't we live together: Sade / Still haven't found what I'm looking for: Chimes / Superstar (Don't you remember): Vandross, Luther / I'll never fall in love again: Deacon Blue / Georgia on my mind: Nelson, Willie
MOODCD 38 / Feb '95 / Sony Music

☐ **UNDARK 3396**
EMIT 3396 / Dec '96 / Time Recordings

☐ **UNDEAD (A Gothic Masterpiece - 3CD Set)**
DTKBOX 51 / Sep '96 / Dressed To Kill

☐ **UNDER A GROOVE VOL.1**
PIAS 378960320 / May '96 / Mix It

☐ **UNDER A HAVANA MOON (2CD Set)**
R2CD 4058 / 9 Mar '98 / Deja Vu

☐ **UNDER DOCTORS ORDERS**
VPCD 02038 / Sep '95 / VP

☐ **UNDER GREEN CORN MOON (Native American Lullabies)**
2158509162 / 24 Mar '98 / Silver Wave

☐ **UNDER ME SLENG TENG EXTRAVAGANZA**
TRD 2385 / 20 Jul '98 / TRD

☐ **UNDER THE SIGN OF THE SACRED STAR**
CDVILE 66 / May '96 / Peaceville

☐ **UNDER THE SUN**
Hot summer salsa: Jive Bunny / Making your mind up: Bucks Fizz / Light up the world with sunshine: Ocean, Billy / Heat is on: Gaynor, Gloria / Summertime: Drifters / Endless summer: Gidea Park / California girl: Floyd, Eddie / It's in his kiss (The shoop shoop song): Everett, Betty / Surf City: Jan & Dean / Just one look: Troy, Doris / Seasons in the sun: Fortunes / Summer love sensation: Bay City Rollers / Sunshine girl: Herman's Hermits / Hot days: Troggs / Turn turn turn: Byrds / Good morning sunshine: Oliver / Me and you and a dog named Boo: Lobo / Look it's raining sunshine: Johnson, Marv / Guantanamera: Lopez, Trini / Speedy Gonzales: Boone, Pat / Summer song: Chad & Jeremy / Close to perfection: Brown, Miquel / Apples peaches pumpkin pie: Jay & The Techniques / Too hot: Kool & The Gang / Bring back those surfin days: Gidea Park
ECD 3431 / Aug '98 / K-Tel

☐ **UNDERCOVER VOL.3**
SPV 08438202 / Jul '95 / SPV

☐ **UNDERGROUND FLAVAS**
Deeper: Lady Penelope & Abstract / All night long: Gant / Bad boys: Baffled Republic / Things are never: Operator & Baffled / Odyssey one: Federation X / Tonite: Underground Solution / Let me tell you: Jump Up Crew / Was she ever mine: Anthill Mob / Mixed up: Bell, Melissa / Music: Benson, Shawn
BDRCD 23 / Aug '97 / Breakdown

☐ **UNDERGROUND GARAGE (2CD Set)**
DCID 001 / 16 Mar '98 / Dance Club International

☐ **UNDERGROUND HOUSE PARTY VOL.3 (Mixed By Tony Humphries)**
Hideway: De'Lacy / Underground: System VIIII / No pay day: Gayland / Get yourself together: Moods Of Madness / Respect: Adeva / You don't know: Serious Intention / Check this out: Hardhouse / In and out of my life: Adeva / Victim: Moods Of Madness / I like you: Cassio & The Funky People / Release the tension: Harris, Cassandra
NBCD 950004 / Jul '96 / Nite & Blue

☐ **UNDERGROUND HOUSE PARTY VOL.4 (Mixed By Camcho)**
Body work: Hot Streak / Thee industry made me do it: Aphrohead / Get huh: Ride Committee / Jungle kisses: Roc & Kato / Givin it all I get: Solution / Plastic disco: DJ Duke / I'm a sex maniac: Storm / Keep on dancing: Dixon, Daniel / Hear the music: Gypsymen / Funky horns: Fierce Factor / Ma foom bey: Cultural Vibe / In and out of my life: Adeva / Thee: Felix Da Housecat / Pickin up the promises: Brown, Jocelyn / Do you wanna dance: Bad Boy Orchestra
NBCD 95005 / Jul '96 / Nite & Blue

☐ **UNDERGROUND HOUSE PARTY VOL.5 (Mixed By Rodger S)**
2101535 / Jul '96 / Nite & Blue

☐ **UNDERGROUND HOUSE PARTY VOL.6 (Smack Da House)**
Lonely: Donald O / So proud: Abrams, Colonel / Flute song: Moods Of Black / Special: Donald O / Happy: Rock, Calvin / I'll do anything: Inner Vision / Vacum: Mental Instrum / Makin' love (To Nicole): Cassio Ware / Goin' thru the motion: Jenkins, Keshia / Reach for the sky: Supa / Brothers and sisters: Hope, Alexander / Give it: Sir Charles / Watcha gonna do: Pseudo & Colonel Abrams / Luv changes: Chicago People / Celebrate: Rush, Donell / Old fashioned love: Pollard, Karen
032501CD / Jul '96 / Nite & Blue

☐ **UNDERGROUND LONDON**
KICKCD 31 / Dec '95 / Kickin'

☐ **UNDERGROUND UK**
KICKCD 38 / Jul '96 / Kickin'

☐ **UNDERTONES VOL.1**
OMCD 10 / Jul '96 / One Movement

☐ **UNDERTONES VOL.2**
OMCD 12 / Jul '96 / One Movement

☐ **UNDERWOOD**
SR 100 / Apr '96 / Sub Rosa

☐ **UNDERWOOD VOL.2**
SR 125 / Jul '97 / Sub Rosa

☐ **UNDISPUTED (2CD Set)**
Found a cure: Ultra Nate / It's like that: Run DMC & Jason Nevins / Brimful of Asha: Cornershop / Never ever: All Saints / Renegade master: Wildchild / I thought it was you: Sex-O-Sonique / Word is love: Voices Of Life / Where are you: Patterson, Rashsaan / Make the world go round: Sandy B / Shout to the top: Fire Island & Loleatta Holloway / Movin' on: Pender, Debbie / Love shy: Blond, Kristine / So good: Roberts, Juliet / Dreams: Smokin' Beats & Lyn Eden / Give me a rhythm: Black Connection / Le disc jockey: Encore / Move on up: Trickster / Bamboogie: Bamboo / Let me show you: Camisra / Choose life: PF Project & Ewan McGregor / RIP groove: Double 99 / Digital: Goldie & KRS1 / Somebody else's guy: Peniston, Ce Ce / Hideaway: De'Lacy / Gunman: 187 Lockdown / Smack my bitch up: Prodigy / Repeated love: ATGOC / Strings for Yasmin: ATGOC / Desire: BBE / Meet her at the Love Parade: Da Hool / I can't help myself: Lucid / Sunchyme: Dario G / I refuse: Somore / You make me feel (mighty real): Stingily, Byron / Benedictus: Brainbug / Planet Love: DJ Quicksilver / Flaming June: BT / Stay: Sash
5556952 / 30 Mar '98 / PolyGram TV

☐ **UNEARTHED GOLD OF ROCK STEADY VOL.1**
OHCD 004 / Nov '95 / Ossie

☐ **UNFINISHED, THE**
SR 103 / Jan '97 / Sub Rosa

☐ **UNFORGETTABLE**
Unforgettable: Washington, Dinah / Red sails in the sunset: Washington, Dinah / Where of when: Washington, Dinah / You're nobody till somebody loves you: Washington, Dinah / Misty: Vaughan, Sarah / That old black magic: Vaughan, Sarah / Careless: Vaughan, Sarah / You stepped out of a dream: Vaughan, Sarah / Too marvellous for words: Holiday, Billie / Say it isn't so: Holiday, Billie / Our love is here to stay: Holiday, Billie / Stars fell on Alabama: Holiday, Billie / My way: Simone, Nina / Chain gang: Simone, Nina / Angel of the morning: Simone, Nina / I ain't got no...I got life: Simone, Nina
74321449262 / Jan '97 / Camden

☐ **UNFORGETTABLE**
I'll be home: Boone, Pat / Hey there: Clooney, Rosemary / My special angel: Helms, Bobby / Heartaches by the number: Mitchell, Guy / Ivory tower: Carr, Cathy / Band of gold: Cherry, Don / My happiness: Pied Pipers / Three coins in the fountain: Four Aces / Kisses sweeter than wine: Rodgers, Jimmie / Love is a golden ring: Laine, Frankie / Only you (and you alone): Platters / Walkin' my baby back home: Ray, Johnnie / I went to your wedding: Page, Patti / With all my heart: Sands, Jodie / PS I love you: Hilltoppers / Hold my hand: Cornell, Don / Suddenly there's a Valley: Grant, Gogi / So rare: Dorsey, Jimmy
ECD 3077 / Dec '96 / K-Tel

☐ **UNFORGETTABLE (Hits Of The Fifties)**
PLSCD 158 / Apr '97 / Pulse

☐ **UNFORGETTABLE BIG BANDS**
UP 006 / Sep '92 / Hindsight

☐ **UNFORGETTABLE LOVE SONGS VOL.1 (2CD Set)**
Giving it all away: Sayer, Leo / How am I supposed to live without you: Puckett, Gary / Move closer: Nelson, Phyllis / I'm doin' fine now: New York City / They don't know: Ullman, Tracey / Man who sold the world: Lulu & David Bowie / Many rivers to cross: Dekker, Desmond / Be thankful for what you've got: DeVaughan, William / My girl: Temptations / One and only: Knight, Gladys & The Pips / You've still got a place in my heart: Stardust, Alvin / I go to pieces: Sweet, Rachel / Only love can break your heart: Mint Juleps / Come to me: Jones, Tom / When I need you: Sayer, Leo / Is this love: Puckett, Gary / Just my imagination: Temptations / Only love can break a heart: Pitney, Gene / Daniel: Feliciano, Jose / Midnight train to Georgia: Knight, Gladys & The Pips / Reflections of my life: Marmalade / Won't somebody dance with me: De Paul, Lynsey / Daydream: Lovin' Spoonful / I'm so lonesome I could cry: Thomas, B.J. / Words: Shaw, Sandie / Don't give up on us: Soul, David / Sandy: Travolta, John / Beautiful people: Melanie
SD 885452 / 2 Feb '98 / Disky

☐ **UNFORGETTABLE LOVE SONGS VOL.2 (2CD Set)**
Only a fool: Lee, Byron & Mighty Sparrow / If I sing you a love song: Jones, Tom / Love is all: Humperdinck, Engelbert / Vaya con dios: Orlando, Tony / When will I see you again: Three Degrees / Raindrops keep falling on my head: Thomas, B.J. / Only you: Platters / When a man loves a woman: Sledge, Percy / I'm gonna make you love me: Supremes / Save your love: Renee & Renato / To all the girls I loved before: Keel, Howard / Red sails in the sunset: Domino, Fats / Unchained melody: Domino, Fats / Ask the lonely: Four Tops / You've got a friend: Jones, Tom / All I have to do is dream: Everly Brothers / Love me tender: Jordanaires / My special prayer: Sledge, Percy / Woman in love: Three Degrees / You're all I need to get by: Orlando, Tony / Sugar candy kisses: Kissoon, Mac & Katie / Going in with my eyes open: Soul, David / Hooked on a feeling: Thomas, B.J. / Broken dreams: Guys & Dolls / He don't love you: Orlando, Tony / Lady: Keel, Howard / Let me call you sweetheart: Domino, Fats / MacArthur Park: Four Tops
SD 885462 / 2 Feb '98 / Disky

☐ **UNFORGETTABLE MELODIES (2CD Set)**
Bridge over troubled water: Goodwin, Ron & His Orchestra / Never on a Sunday: Love, Geoff & His Orchestra / Honeymoon song: Manuel & The Music Of The Mountains / Snowbird: Pourcel, Franck & His Orchestra / What the world needs now is love: Goodwin, Ron & His Orchestra / Moon river: Manuel & The Music Of The Mountains / True love: Love, Geoff & His Orchestra / Godfather love theme: Pourcel, Franck & His Orchestra / Misty: Love, Geoff & His Orchestra / Fool on the hill: Goodwin, Ron & His Orchestra / Spanish Harlem: Manuel & The Music Of The Mountains / Forever and ever: Pourcel, Franck & His Orchestra / Spartacus love theme: Love, Geoff & His Orchestra / Love story: Goodwin, Ron & His Orchestra / Autumn leaves: Manuel & The Music Of The Mountains / She: Pourcel, Franck & His Orchestra / Ballade pour Adeline: Love, Geoff & His Orchestra / Walk on by: Goodwin, Ron & His Orchestra / White rose of Athens: Manuel & The Music Of The Mountains / Blue moon: Pourcel, Franck & His Orchestra / Walk in the Black Forest: Love, Geoff & His Orchestra / Rhapsody on a theme by Paganini: Goodwin, Ron & His Orchestra / Waltz from serenade for strings: Manuel & The Music Of The Mountains / Summertime: Pourcel, Franck & His Orchestra / When I fall in love: Love, Geoff & His Orchestra / Elizabethan serenade: Goodwin, Ron & His Orchestra / Shadow of your smile: Manuel & The Music Of The Mountains / On a clear day (You can see forever): Pourcel, Franck & His Orchestra
CDDL 1120 / Aug '91 / Music For Pleasure

☐ **UNFORGETTABLE SESSION, AN**
CD 53097 / Jan '95 / Giants Of Jazz

☐ **UNHOLY BIBLE (The Cacophonous Label Sampler)**
Witch storm: Bal Sagoth / Shikigami: Sigh / In the name of darkness: 13 Candles / Pale nocturnal majesty: Ancient Ceremony / Splendour of a thousand swords gleaming beneath the b: Bal Sagoth / Her harvest is my prey: Vergelmer / Destroyer: Bloodstorm / Together we summon the dark: Abyssos / Ravens of the night: Twilight Ophera / Curse of Izanaghi: Sigh
NIHIL 028CD / 10 Nov '97 / Cacophonous

☐ **UNIDENTIFIED FLOATING AMBIENCE**
SR 9454 / May '94 / Silent

☐ **UNIFIED COLOURS OF DRUM 'N' BASS (2CD Set)**
FORMCD 06 / Aug '97 / Formation

☐ **UNISSUED SUN MASTERS**
CPCD 8137 / Nov '95 / Charly

☐ **UNITED ARTISTS OF MESSIDOR SAMPLER**
MES 158232 / Apr '93 / Messidor

☐ **UNITED DANCE VOL.3 (2CD Set)**
FBRCD 334 / Jan '96 / 4 Beat

☐ **UNITED DANCE VOL.4 (2CD Set)**
FBRCD 336 / May '96 / 4 Beat

☐ **UNITED DANCE VOL.5 (2CD Set)**
FBRCD 337 / Oct '96 / 4 Beat

☐ **UNITED DANCE VOL.6 (2CD Set)**
12 Of love: Sly / Cape fear: Sly / Devotion: Sly / Don't you want me: Eruption / Reach out: Eruption / Right thing: Eruption / Behind closed doors: Eruption / Come on: Walford Project / After dark: Thunder & Joy / Sunshine: Slipmatt & Eruption / Jump around: Slippery Project & Benz / Scream: DJ Hixxy & Sunset Regime / Hardcore passion: DJ Hixxy & Sunset Regime / Hyper space: Druid & Sharkey / Simply electric: Force & Styles / Field of dreams: Force & Styles / Pacific sun: Force & Styles / Cutting deep:

Force & Styles / Pretty green eyes: Force & Styles / Paradise and dreams: Force & Styles / Apollo 12 pt 2: Force & Styles / Heart of gold: Force & Styles / Tardis to Brooklyn: Bang The Future / Ease your mind: Bunter, Billy & Sunset / Gates of oblivion: Bang The Future / Let the music: Eruption / Beginning of a new era: Bang The Future / Blinding light: DJ Magical / Feel the hype: Generation / Ever lasting love: Seduction / Rushing: Iyduction & Sy / On the road: Iyduction & Sy / In the mix: Seduction / Hey yeah: Seduction
FBRCD 338 / Apr '97 / 4 Beat

☐ UNITED FLAVA OF BRITISH RAP
Listen urban species: Urban Species / Here we go: NSO Force / Hang 'em high: Kaliphz / Bring it on: Cash Crew / Who you know: Krispy Three / Making moves: MC NI / Big trouble in little Asia: Hustlers HC / Yabba dabba doo: Darkman / Free man: 11-59 / Colourcode: Gunshot / Coming eqipped: 3pm / Hell hath no fury: Evey / Wha cha' all paid: Scientists Of Sound / How's life in London: London Posse / What's going on: Blak Twang / All about Eve: Marxman
WOLCD 1063 / Jul '95 / Ticking Time/ China

☐ UNITED FLAVA OF DRUM 'N' BASS
Honeytrap revolution: Tacye / Lofy site: Rationa L / United flava: Davenport, Mikey / Whose name happens: Esoteria 3B Squared / Troy: Resistance Quad / Iguana: Microcosm / Sub pocket book oblivion: Hiding In The Tall Grass / International hitman: Vibe Posse / Hesters last retreat: DJ Tyrone / Baby Jane: Fledgling & DJ Tyrone/Aries Project / Swansgate hopper incident: Greaves, Sally / Lofy optimum: Rationa L / Dubtrap: Ideal Lodgers / Oceanic quest: DVS / United flava: Davenport, Mikey
TOYCD 1006 / 4 May '98 / Intrinsic

☐ UNITED FREQUENCIES OF TRANCE VOL.6
E 11943/2 / Dec '93 / United Frequencies Of Trance

☐ UNITED MUTATIONS
LCD 03 / 9 Feb '98 / Lo Recordings

☐ UNITED RAVERS COMPILATION VOL.1
URRC 1 / Nov '95 / United Ravers

☐ UNITED SPEAKEASY COLLECTIVE NU JAZZ PRINCIPLES
MM 890002 / Jun '95 / Moonshine

☐ UNITED TRIBES POW WOW VOL.1
SPALAX 14942 / Oct '96 / Spalax

☐ UNITED TRIBES POW WOW VOL.2
SPALAX 14943 / Oct '96 / Spalax

☐ UNITED WORLD OF AMBIENT
97006 / 29 Jun '98 / United World Of Dance

☐ UNITED WORLD OF TRANCE
97002 / 29 Jun '98 / United World Of Dance

☐ UNIVERSAL EGG VOL.1
EB 004 / 20 Apr '98 / Universal Egg

☐ UNIVERSAL SOUNDS OF AMERICA
Space 2: Durrah, David / Theme de yoyo: Art Ensemble Of Chicago / Lions of judah: Reid, Steve / Astral travelling: Sanders, Pharoah / Space odyssey: Belgrave, Marcus / Empty street: Reid, Steve / Kitty bey: Morris, Byron / Space 1: Durrah, David / Space is the place: Sun Ra
SJRCD 027 / Jul '95 / Soul Jazz

☐ UNIVERSE - WORLD TECHNO TRIBE (The Most Progressive Dance Party Organisation In The World)
Pioneers of the universe: Hypnotist / Springyard: Bolland, C.J. / .215061: AFX / List 2: Suburban Hell / Tremora del terra: Illuminatae / Virtual reality: Two Thumbs / Jojba: Dr. Fernando / Flying deeper: Skyflyer / Cosmic love (approach and identify): Resistance D / Virtual breakdown (mind your head): Garnier, Laurent / Sequential (the dune mix): Sequential / First symphony: Angel, Dave / Barbarella: Vath, Sven
VERSECD 1 / Apr '93 / Universe/Rising High

☐ UNIVERSE PRESENTS THE TRIBAL GATHERING (2CD Set)
Are we here (who are they): Orbital / Voodoo people: Prodigy / Song for life: Leftfield / Spastik: Plastikman / Infinite mass: Faith Department / Every time you touch me: Moby / Starship universe: Bolland, C.J. / Crisis a gwan: Bandulu / Lagoon: Angel, Dave / Her jazz: Chemical Brothers / Mother Earth: Dubtribe / Det 29-62: Cox, Carl / Heart: Loop 8.2 / Hypnotic Eastern rhythm: Soundclash Republic / Violator: Transmakus / Bug: Drum Club / Dark and long: Underworld
8284522 / Jul '95 / Internal

☐ UNIVERSO TROPICAL
UMD 80482 / 25 May '98 / Universal

☐ UNLIMITED AMBIENT
MASOCD 90092 / Jul '97 / Materiali Sonori

☐ UNLIMITED BEAT
Abba medley / Bee Gees medley / Take That medley / Police medley / Michael Jackson medley / Elton John medley / Donna Summer medley
DACSR 005 / 10 Nov '97 / Academy Street

☐ UNLOCK THE FUNK (The Very Best Of Club Classics - 2CD Set)
Funkin' for Jamaica: Browne, Tom / Are you ready (do the bus stop): Fatback Band / Back to my roots: Odyssey / Ride on time: Black Box / Rapp payback: Brown, James / Holy ghost: Bar-Kays / Freeway of love: Franklin, Aretha / We got the funk: Positive Force / You make me feel (mighty real): Sylvester / Night to rememeber: Shalamar / Can you feel the force: Real Thing / Troglodyte: Castor, Jimmy Bunch / Get up before the night is over: Technotronic / Sisters are doin' it for themselves: Franklin, Aretha & Annie Lennox / Rapper's delight: Sugarhill Gang / Unlock the funk: Locksmith / Use it up wear it out: Odyssey / Do you wanna funk: Sylvester / Love come down: King, Evelyn / Jump (for my love): Pointer Sisters / Midas touch: Midnight Star / Shut d funk up: Dr. John / You're the one for me: Train / Shut 'um down: Scott-Heron, Gil / Last night a DJ saved my life: Indeep / Pump up the jam: Technotronic / Got to use my imagination: Knight, Gladys / Shame shame shame: Shirley & Co. / Message: Grandmaster Flash / Let the music play: Shannon / We just funkers: Hampton, Michael
RCACD 216 / Jul '97 / RCA

☐ UNMETERED TAXI
JJCD 169 / Apr '96 / Channel One

☐ UNO MELODIC STORY, THE
CDNEW 121 / 30 Mar '98 / Charly

☐ UNPAVED ROADS VOL.3
70001671363 / Mar '96 / Essential Dance

☐ UNPLUGGED ROCK AND POP CLASSICS (3CD Set)
Mr Tambourine man / Ruby Tuesday / Waterloo sunset / Ride a white swan / Brown eyed girl / Honey don't think / All apopogies / Four seasons in one day / Meet me on the corner / Every night / When you were sweet sixteen / Make me smile / Sweet Jane / Sorrow / Any other guy / Passenger / Losing my religion / Horse with no name / Catch the wind / Itchycoo park / Live forever / Kooks / Love her madly / Heart of gold / So young / Jesus don't want me for a sunbeam / Made of stone / It ain't me babe / Constant craving / There is a light that never goes out / Femme fatal / Sun ain't gonna shine anymore / Be bop a lula / Milkcow blues / Peggy Sue / Rip it up / Almost grown / That'll be the day / C'mon everybody / Not fade away / Rave on / That's alright Mama / 20 Flight rock / Rock around the clock / Whole lotta shakin' goin' on / Blue moon of Kentucky / All shook up / Reelin' and rockin' / Strollin' / Baby I don't care
HR 879452 / May '97 / Disky

☐ UNPROGGED
HUDROK 001CD / Dec '96 / Blueprint

☐ UNRELEASED VOL.11
Moodz: Pooley, Ian / Assasin: Baxter, Blake / Away and beyond: Broom, Mark / Una pequena melodia en domingo: Curtin, Dan / Nervous: Neuropolitique / William drive by disaster: Lazermusik / ID clones: Shake / Puter vibes: Landstrumm, Neal / Thinking mans dream: Young, Claude / Aware and awake / Veil: Blue Binary / Practopia: B12
ELEC 28CD / Apr '96 / New Electronica

☐ UNSUNG HEROES (The Phase II Mod Collection)
PHZCD 17 / Nov '94 / Unicorn

☐ UNTITLED VOL.1 (2CD Set)
Live forever: Oasis / Stupid girl: Garbage / Girls and boys: Blur / Wake up boo: Boo Radleys / Lady killers: Lush / Change: Lightning Seeds / King of the kerb: Echobelly / Waking up: Elastica / Uh huh oh yeh: Weller, Paul / Girl like you: Collins, Edwyn / Countdown: Pulp / Waterfall: Stone Roses / Movin' on up: Primal Scream / Creep: Radiohead / Stay together: Suede / Can you dig it: Mock Turtles / Weak: Skunk Anansie / Neighbourhood: Space / You and me song: Wannadies / Dizzy: Reeves, Vic & Wonder Stuff / Regret: New Order / Get the message: Electronic / This charming man: Smiths / Made of stone: Stone Roses / Can't be sure: Sundays / I'll stand by you: Pretenders / Road to nowhere: Talking Heads / I scare myself: Dolby, Thomas / Love shack: B-52's / Shipbuilding: Wyatt, Robert / Just the one: Levellers / Fisherman's blues: Waterboys / Message in a box: World Party / Mary's prayer: Danny Wilson / Like lovers do: Cole, Lloyd / Somewhere in my heart: Aztec Camera / Don't go: Hothouse Flowers / King of rock 'n' roll: Prefab Sprout / Twist and shout: Deacon Blue / Missing: Everything But The Girl
RADCD 32 / Apr '96 / Global TV

☐ UNTITLED VOL.2 (2CD Set)
Wonderwall: Oasis / Country house: Blur / Sale of the century: Sleeper / Going out: Supergrass / Queer: Garbage / Female of the species: Space / Riverboat song: Ocean Colour Scene / Alright: Cast / Goldfinger: Ash / Street spirit: Radiohead / Connection: Elastica / Yes: McAlmont & Butler / Something for the weekend: Divine Comedy / Charity: Skunk Anansie / Stars: Dubstar / Not bad enough: Eggman / Sleeping in: Menswear / 13th: Cure / He's on the phone: St. Etienne / Born slippy: Underworld / What's the frequency Kenneth: REM / Hung up: Weller, Paul / From despair to where: Manic Street Preachers / True faith: New Order / Lucky you: Lightning Seeds / Dark therapy: Echobelly / Rocks: Primal Scream / Love will tear us apart: Joy Division / Fools gold: Stone Roses / Only one I know: Charlatans / Personal Jesus: Depeche Mode / How soon is now: Smiths / Good morning Britain: Aztec Camera & Mick Jones / Real gone kid: Deacon Blue / When love breaks down: Prefab Sprout / Each and everyone: Everything But The Girl / I fell back alone: World Party / Crash: Primitives / Might be stars: Wannadies / Wild ones: Suede
RADCD 39 / Jul '96 / Global TV

☐ UNTITLED VOL.3 (2CD Set)
You're gorgeous: Baby Bird / Some might say: Oasis / Trash: Suede / Sandstorm: Cast / In a room: Dodgy / Circle: Ocean Colour Scene / Nice guy Eddie: Sleeper / Peacock suit: Weller, Paul / Design for life: Manic Street Preachers / On a rope: Rocket From The Crypt / 6 underground: Sneaker Pimps / One to another: Charlatans / All I want: Skunk Anansie / High and dry: Radiohead / Only happy when it rains: Garbage / Oh yeah: Ash / Boy wonder: Speedy / Great things: Echobelly / She said: Longpigs / What's in the box: Boo Radleys / Firestarter: Prodigy / Pearl's girl: Underworld / Protection: Massive Attack / Wrong: Everything But The Girl / Play dead: Bjork & David Arnold / Elevator song: Dubstar / Kinky afro: Happy Mondays / Sally cinnamon: Stone Roses / Loaded: Primal Scream / There she goes: La's / Love your money: Daisy Chainsaw / Animal nitrate: Suede / Disappointed: Electronic / Blue glow: Pulp / New England: MacColl, Kirsty / 500 (shake baby shake): Lush / Perfect: Lightning Seeds / Rise and shine: Cardigans / I wanna be adored: Stone Roses / She cries your name: Orton, Beth
RADCD 44 / Nov '96 / Global TV

☐ UNTOUCHABLE OUTCASTE BEATS
CASTE 3CD / Aug '97 / OutCaste

☐ UP & DOWN CLUB SESSIONS VOL.2
'Round midnight: Hueman Flavour / As I reach: Hueman Flavour / Up: Up & Down Allstars / Here on earth: Jones, Josh Ensemble / Cherry suite: Hueman Flavour / Acalona yare: Jones, Josh Ensemble / Blues in Havana: Jones, Josh Ensemble / Vision sets you free: Hueman Flavour / Destiny: Hueman Flavour / Down: Up & Down Allstars / Ache: Jones, Josh
MR1042 / Aug '95 / Mammoth

☐ UP 4 IT
CDRAID 532 / Sep '96 / Rumour

☐ UP ALL NIGHT VOL.1 (30 Northern Soul Classics)
Nothing can stop me: Chandler, Gene / Getting mighty crowded: Everett, Betty / Nothing worse than being alone: Ad Libs / That other place: Flemons, Wade / I keep tryin': Hughes, Freddie / You're the dream: Shelton, Roscoe / I hurt on the other side: Barnes, Sidney / Lonely for you baby: Dee, Sonny / Come on train: Thomas, Don / Breakaway: Valentines / You're gonna need me: Ford, Ted / Being without you: Williams, Maurice / Why don't you write: Bates, Lee / But I couldn't: Harper, Willie / Just another heartbreak: Little Ritchie / Touch me, hold me, kiss me: Inspirations / Tear stained face: Varner, Don / Hung up on your love: Montclairs / Running for my life: Shelton, Roscoe / My man don't think I know: Davies, Gwen / Hold on: Beavers, Jackie / You've been gone too long: Sexton, Ann / That's enough: Robinson, Roscoe / I'd think it over twice (if I were you): Fletcher, Sam / You'll always be in style: Barnes, Sidney / Don't let me down: Hughes, Freddie / Sweet and easy: McCoy, Van / Power of love: Humphrey, Amanda / Now I'm in love with you: Sims, Marvin L. / I'm a fool, I must love you: Falcons
CPCD 8216 / Apr '97 / Charly

☐ UP ALL NIGHT VOL.2 (30 Hits From The Original Soul Underground)
That's my girl: Clark, Dee / Black eyed girl: Thompson, Billy / Return: Williams, Maurice / Dearly beloved: Montgomery, Jack / Toast to the lady: Wilson, Eddie / That's no way to treat a girl: Knight, Marie / Please stay: Ivorys / You hit me like TNT: Jones, Linda / Let's get back together: Honey Bees / Carlena: Just Brothers / Get it baby: Mitchell, Stanley / Love slipped through my fingers: Ohio Players / Do you love me baby: Masqueraders / You can't keep a good man down: Gentlemen Four / One bo-dillion years: Little Ritchie / Check yourself: Chandler, Gene / I love you always: Rivingtons / Welcome to Dreamsville: Ambrose, Sammy / Use it before you lose it: Valentin, Bobby / I'm gonna do it myself: Ellie, Jimmy 'Preacher' / Lost love: Irma & The Fascinations / Stop and get hold of myself: Knight, Gladys & The Pips / If there's anything else you want (Let me know): Joy, Roddie / I'm stepping out of the picture: Maestro, Johnny & The Crests / Wrong girl: Showmen / Johnny my boy: Ad Libs / That girl: Porgy & The Monarchs / One in a million: Brown, Maxine / It used to be: Burns, Jimmy & The Fantastic Epics / Long after tonight is all over: Radcliffe, Jimmy
CPCD 8217 / May '97 / Charly

☐ UP COUNTRY
Lonesome me / Sea of heartbreak / Birmingham turnaround / Goodnight irene / Maggie / And so it goes / (turn out the light and) love me tonight / Louisiana saturday night / Blanket on the ground / Sing me an old fashioned song / He'll have to go / I won't forget you / Anna marie / Follow me / Beautiful body / Ruby / Folsom Prison blues / Rawhide / Riders in the sky / Cold cold heart / Take these chains / Rambling rose / Walk right back / Cheating heart / Putting on the style
SOV 014CD / Jan '93 / Sovereign

☐ UP JUMPED THE BLUES
MCCD 241 / Mar '96 / Music Club

☐ UP MAYO
UM 1CD / Dec '97 / Up Mayo

☐ UP THE PSYCHO MELLOW
Rolling space: Expo 80 / Holiday in Monte Carlo: Bobbio, Reddy / Neutral: Bobbio, Reddy / Mondo di domani: Mondo Di Domani / Binairement: Paris Studio Group / Cha ba da ba da: Paris Studio Group / Rush: Black Fire / Upa neguiho: Expo 80 / Hot heels: Vocal Shades & Tones / Drugpop: Sounds Pop / Alcoholic: Black Fire / Discesa libera: Discesa Libera / Tout casser: Paris Studio Group / Flash: Paris Studio Group / Don't let go: Hawksworth Big Band / Tic splash: Paris Studio Group / Tube: Psycheground Group / Easy: Psycheground Group
SCEB 904CD / 15 Jun '98 / Schema

☐ UP TO ZION
I hear a sound / Day of the Lord / He is good / Bless the Lord / Let us rejoice and be glad / Praise the Lord / Ascribe unto the Lord / He shall reign / We give you thanks / By your blood / Who is like me / Worthy is the lamb / Great and marvellous / Sond of Moses / Come let us get up to Zion / Come let us get up
HMD 41 / Mar '92 / Hosanna

☐ UP WITH THE CURTAIN (Stars of the Variety Theatre)
That's what you think: Bermon, Len / Stormy weather: Carless, Dorothy / I'll take romance: Driver, Betty / Can't we meet again: Flanagan & Allen / Million tears: Flanagan & Allen / Underneath the arches: Flanagan & Allen / Caught in the act: Forsythe, Seamon & Farrell / I have an ear for music: Geraldo & Arthur Tracy / Love in bloom: Geraldo / Pretty girl is like a melody: Geraldo & Arthur Tracy / Up with the curtain: Geraldo / I'm a different me they say: Hutchinson, Leslie 'Hutch' / Melody maker: Hutchinson, Leslie 'Hutch' / Oh they're tough, mighty tough in the West: Hylton, Jack / Was it rain: Hylton, Jack / Me and my girl: Lane, Lupino & Teddie St. Denis / Every Sunday afternoon: Miller, Max / You can't go away like that: Miller, Max / Georgia's got a moon: Nesbitt, Max & Harry / Hit medley: Reid, Billy Accordion Band / My honey's loving arms: Rosing, Val / On behalf of the working classes: Russell, Billy / I don't do things like that: Trinder, Tommy / Lads tell a few: Western Brothers
CDAJA 5076 / '91 / Living Era

☐ UP YER RONSON - ORIGINAL SOUNDTRACK VOL.1
You can't touch me: Pollack, Karen & Fire Island / U: Clark, Loni / I know a place: English, Kim / Back to love: Brand New Heavies / I believe: Sounds Of Blackness / Another sleepness night: Christopher, Shawn / Lost in love: Up Yer Ronson / Where love lives: Limerick, Alison / Lover: Roberts, Joe / Keep the jam goin': Ill Disco / Nite life: English, Kim / Colour of my skin: Swing 52 / Gimmie luv: Bad Yard Club / Real: Allen, Donna / Take me back to love: Sledge, Kathy / Mings incredible disco machine: Brother Love Dubs / All over me: Carr, Suzi / Blow your whistle: DJ Duke / Dreamer: Livin' Joy / Theme from Outrage: Outrage / On the dance floor: DJ Disciple / U girls: Nush / Will you love me in the morning: Mollison, Sam / Get yourself together: Hustlers Convention / Someday: M-People / 100% pure: Waters, Crystal / Renegade master: Wildchild / On ya way: Helicopter / Everybody dance: Evolution
5350762 / Nov '95 / Hi-Life

☐ UP YER RONSON - THE SUMMER OF NINETY SIX (3CD Set)
Come back to love: Mr. Happy / Skyplus: Nylon Moon / Nightrain: Kadoc / Klubbhopping: Klubb Heads / Heartbeat: Somerville, Jimmy / Up side my head: Funkysensual / Howler: HMM / Fire: Belief / Indica: Movin' Melodies / Bring me luv: Crystal / Disco frenzy: Divine Intervention / Access: DJ Misjah & Tim / I'm coming hardcore: MANIC / Goodtimes: Funkydory / Groovy beat: DOP / Desire: Nu Colours / Movin': Mone / Reach: Lil' Mo' Yin Yang / Giv me luv: Alcatraz / Heaven: Washington, Sarah / Imperial grooves: Musaphia, Joey / Freedom: Black Magic / Let me take you away: Temperance / Stand up: Love Tribe / Never stop: Reflexion & Laura Alford / Find our way: Key To Life / Lover that you are: Pulse / Are you gonna be there: Up yer Ronson & Mary Pearce / Are you with me love: Elements Of Life / Now when I see you: Nordenstam, Stina / Bee charmer: Schroeder, Ingrid / King of Woolworths: Exact Life / Doesn't mean that much to me: Eg & Alice / Kant kino: Simple Minds / Dream beam: Hypnotone / Latin joint: Baby Buddah Heads / Ending: Eno, Brian / Gulls 'n' bouys: Adam & Eve Project / Siolim: Small Fish With Spine / Three steps to Heaven: Beloved / Dream time: Jackson / Killing: Olive
5332422 / Oct '96 / Hi-Life

☐ UPFRONT SPEED GARAGE VOL.1
Give it all you've got: Part 2 / Experience: Tuff & Jam / Give it up: DJ Fuzz Buzz & Rice Fernandez / I got ya: Colour 3 / Timeless groove: Flite Crew / Chronic's theme: Groove Chronicles / Coming at cha: Memzee & MJ Cole / Sweet thing: Maxim / Organized chaos: Organized Chaos / Deeper: DJ Infinity / I get high: Fontaine, Miles
SPEEDCD 001 / 8 Dec '97 / Speed

☐ UPFRONT SPEED GARAGE VOL.2
Don't know baby: DJ Jack & Jill / Can't get enough: Old Soul / Take me up: Hurley, Ray / Vol.2: Maximum Pleasure / Tell the world: Rhythm Inc. / Coolthamenta: Surburban Science / 'Til da break: Freestyle Orchestra / Love fantasy vol.2: Maxim / Crosswordz: Hi-Life International / Love is the message: Rocksteady / Ultrafunka: Urban Funk / No way back: Groove Elastic / What I dream: King, Michael / 9 to 5: MF Project / Big bird: Clarke, Warren
SPEEDCD 002 / 16 Mar '98 / Speed

☐ UPPERS ON THE SOUTH DOWNS
DOJOCD 196 / Nov '94 / Dojo

☐ UPROOTED
Buck starts here: Fulks, Robbie / He don't care about me: Willis, Kelly / Pity party: Watson, Dale / Beer and kisses: Rigby, Amy / Dissatisfied: Gordon, Kevin / Box of visions: Russell, Tom / John Deere tractor song: Walser, Don / Thunderstorms and neon signs: Hancock, Wayne / River under the road: Egge, Ana / Boiling water: Murphy, Trish / Mother Nature and Father Time: Owen, Gwill / Jackson TN: Burch, Paul / East Texas pines: Bosworth, Libbi / Take that ride: Morris, R.B.
SHANCD 6031 / Jul '98 / Shanachie

☐ UPTEMPO (The Sound Of Speed Garage)
DBM 33484 / 16 Feb '98 / Death Becomes Me

☐ UPTOWN, DOWN SOUTH
I've got to hold back / Sweetest girl in the world / Judy / That's loving you / I'm not your regular woman / Since I met you baby / Don't let our love fade away / Even if the signs are wrong / Childhood days / Just another guy / Bigger and better / Cryin' days are over / Save a foolish man / That's my man / No more tears / Set your soul on fire / Our love is getting better / Crystal blue persuasion / What price for love / Thanks a lot / I would if I could / Keep on running away / Running away from love / Just the other day
CDKEND 121 / Feb '95 / Kent

☐ URAL: TRADITIONAL MUSIC FROM BASHKORTOSTAN
PAN 2018CD / Mar '95 / Pan

☐ URB MIX VOL.2
Boogie star: Liquitek Pimps / Disco recovery: Lumpheads / Talkin' about the power: Blade & Liam / Central park: Candelari, Benji / Indoctrinate: Castle Trancelot / Radiate: Brother Grim / Party: Casanova's Revenge / Ha ha: Antony Acid / Kick up the volume: Tissera, Rob / Bell tup: UFG Sound System / Bounce: Fabbroni, Simone / Planet acid: Newton, Nick / Ghetto train: Electroliners / Rampant prankster: Slab / Terminator beats: Dave Trance
SM 80292 / 20 Oct '97 / Smile Communications

☐ URBAN DANCE CLASSICS VOL.1
URCD 001 / May '97 / Urban Dance

☐ URBAN ESSENCE (2CD Set)
DUGCD 1 / Feb '97 / De Underground

☐ URBAN RHYMES (2CD Set)
It's like that: *Run DMC & Jason Nevins* / Loungin': *LL Cool J* / I shot the sheriff: *Warren G* / Woo Haa got you all in check: *Busta Rhymes* / C U when U get there: *Coolio* / Think of you: *Usher* / Feels so good: *Mase* / Wishing on a star: *Jay-Z* / Be alone no more: *Another Level* / Whatta man: *Salt n' Pepa & En Vogue* / I wish: *Skee Lo* / I will survive: *Savage, Chantay* / Summertime: *DJ Jazzy Jeff & The Fresh Prince* / Can I kick it: *Tribe Called Quest* / Waterfalls: *TLC* / Boom shack-a-lack: *Apache Indian* / Here comes the hotstepper: *Kamoze, Ini* / Magic number: *De La Soul* / Message: *Grandmaster Flash & The Furious Five* / Rapper's delight: *Sugar Hill Gang* / Gangsta's paradise: *Coolio* / Tha Crossroads: *Bone Thugs n' Harmony* / Set adrift on memory bliss: *PM Dawn* / Prince Igor: *Warren G & Sissel* / Rain: *Elliott, Missy* / Jump around: *House Of Pain* / Cantaloop: *US 3* / Like this and like that: *Monica* / Triumph: *Wu Tang Clan* / Flava in ya ear: *Mack, Craig* / Ain't no player: *Jay-Z* / Walk this way: *Run DMC & Aerosmith* / White lines (don't do it): *Grandmaster Flash & Melle Mel* / It takes two: *Rob Base & DJ E-Z Rock* / Only you: *112* / Golden brown: *Kaleef* / She's got that vibe: *R Kelly* / Mind blwin': *Smooth* / Now that we found love: *Heavy D & The Boyz* / Push it: *Salt n' Pepa*
RADCD 89 / Apr '98 / Global TV

☐ URBAN SHAKEDOWN (Flavour Records Presents Over One Hour Of R 'n' B Killers)
Can't hang: *Xscape* / Tonight: *Shai* / Stay with me: *Weaver, Jason* / Touch myself: *T-Box* / Stressed out: *Tribe Called Quest* / Floatin' on your love: *Isley Brothers* / Think of you: *Usher* / No diggity: *Blackstreet* / Just the way: *Hunter, Alfonzo* / How we stay: *Lesha* / Rhyme: *Murray, Keith* / Movin on: *Peniston, Ce Ce* / Forget I was a G: *Whitehead Brothers* / Do thangz: *Men O Vision* / Tell me: *Groove Theory* / Realize: *Weaver, Jason* / Get up: *Masters At Work* / Lover in you: *Baby Face* / Every little thing: *Soul For Real* / Get money: *Junior MAFIA*
URB 001CD / Jan '97 / Flavour

☐ URBAN SYMPHONIES
BUMPCD 001 / Jul '96 / Bumpin'

☐ US HOMEGROWN (2CD Set)
OPD 30011 / Jul '97 / Outpost

☐ UTOM - SUMMONING THE SPIRIT (Music In The T'Boli Heartland)
RCD 10402 / 22 Sep '97 / Rykodisc

☐ UZLYAU (Music Of The Tuva, Sayan, Altai & Urals)
PAN 2019CD / Jan '94 / Pan

V

☐ V AS IN VICTIM
AVANT 027CD / Oct '94 / Avant

☐ V CLASSIC VOL.2
UL 0232 / 20 Apr '98 / Ultra

☐ V CLASSICS (3CD Set)
Maintain: *DJ Krust* / It's jazzy: *Roni Size* / Calling: *Goldie* / War and peace: *DJ Die & Suv* / Blaze dis one: *DJ Krust* / Change: *Lemon D* / Reckoning: *Keith, Ray* / On time: *DJ Die* / Only a dream: *Roni Size* / Li-li: *Scorpio* / Unexplored terrain: *Dillinja*
VECD 01 / Apr '97 / V

☐ V DISC COLLECTION (4CD Set)
269032 / Dec '95 / Milan

☐ V DISC COLLECTION VOL.1 (The Big Bands)
269042 / Jun '95 / Milan

☐ V DISC COLLECTION VOL.2 (Combos & Soloists)
269052 / Jun '95 / Milan

☐ V DISC COLLECTION VOL.3 (The Singers)
269062 / Jun '95 / Milan

☐ VALDES MERCEDIT AY QEU BUENO
74321430512 / 6 Apr '98 / Milan

☐ VALIS 2 (Everything Must Go/2CD Set)
33: *Laswell, Bill* / Angry lone nut: *Babu* / In there: *Scorn* / Cab iii: *DXT* / Black loop: *SIMM* / World of destruction: *Spectre & Dr. Israel* / Trawl/ Disappearance: *Scanner* / I wanna be like Ike: *Full Cone* / Dustbuster: *Shining Path* / L'insigne des pires: *APC* / Sepolta: *Full Cone & Buckethead* / Hip hop pooray 19-poo-96: *Ohtake, Shinro* / Explicit sound: *We Olive & L Loop/Once II* / Beaver claus: *Disk* / Metal beat 2: *DXT* / Atoms to suns: *Laswell, Bill* / Twirling: *Him* / Perfect shadow: *SIMM* / Advice from God on getting a face: *Corporal Blossom* / Rockin' it: *Torture* / Metatron dub: *Praxis* / Peanut: *Full Cone* / Phonoprophic: *Electric Soul* / Letter be: *Buckethead* / Ananvoice: *Junexxon S*
ION 20022 / 5 Jan '98 / Ion

☐ VALLENATO, THE (Traditional Music From Colombia)
C 560093 / Nov '96 / Ocora

☐ VALLEY AND PAMPAS
PS 65152 / Sep '95 / PlayaSound

☐ VALLEY OF DEATH
VPCD 1443 / Nov '95 / VP

☐ VALLEY RECALLS VOL.1, THE (Love Peace And Harmony)
NRCD 0066 / Jul '96 / Navras

☐ VALLEY RECALLS VOL.2, THE (Raga Bhoopali)
NRCD 0067 / Jul '96 / Navras

☐ VALLEYS SING, THE
Old rugged cross / Love divine / Day thou gavest Lord is ended / All in the April evening / Guide me o thou great / Jehovah / Where you there / What a friend we have in Jehovah / Lord's prayer / Give thanks / There is a redeemer / Majesty / Steal away / Kymbayah / Abide with me / Onward Christian soldiers / When I survey the wondrous cross / You'll never walk alone / Praise my soul the king of heaven
WSTCD 9725 / Apr '92 / Word

☐ VAMPIRE THEMES
CLP 0003 / Jun '97 / Cleopatra

☐ VAMPIROS LESBOS: SEXADELIC DANCE PARTY
EFA 119502 / Aug '96 / Crippled Dick Hot Wax

☐ VAMPYRES (6CD Set)
DTKBIG 5160 / May '97 / Dressed To Kill

☐ VANGUARD BLUES SAMPLER
VMD 74002 / Oct '96 / Vanguard

☐ VANGUARD DANCE CLASSICS
VMD 79487 / Oct '96 / Vanguard

☐ VANGUARD FOLK SAMPLER
VMD 74001 / Oct '96 / Vanguard

☐ VANGUARD NEWPORT FOLK FESTIVAL SAMPLER
VMD 74003 / Oct '96 / Vanguard

☐ VANGUARD SAMPLER, THE (A Collection Of Folk, Country, Blues & Rock)
Walk right in: *Rooftop Singers* / Old train: *Dillards* / All the pretty little horses: *Odetta* / Swallow song: *Farina, Mimi & Richard* / Goodnight Irene: *Weavers* / Leaving of Liverpool: *Clancy Brothers* / Saro Jane: *Kingston Trio* / Universal soldier: *Sainte-Marie, Buffy* / Come all ye fair and tender ladies: *Ian & Sylvia* / Did you hear John Hurt: *Paxton, Tom* / Sassy Mama: *Thornton, Willie Mae 'Big Mama'* / Turn, turn, turn, (to everything there is a season): *Collins, Judy* / Over in the gloryland: *Kentucky Colonels* / My buddy buddy friends: *Musselwhite, Charley* / Mystery train: *Wells, Junior* / Corrinna Corrinna: *Hurt, 'Mississippi' John* / So many road, so many trains: *Hammond, John* / I feel like I'm fixing to die rag: *Country Joe & The Fish* / Lady Coryell: *Coryell, Larry* / Rock 'n' roll music: *Frost*
VCD 001 / Jun '97 / Vanguard

☐ VANITY
Funk phenomena: *Van Helden, Armand* / Keep on jumpin': *Fruit Loops 2* / Nervous breakdown: *Constance* / Love's gonna get you: *Modernique & Larry Wood* / Drillzone: *GAME* / Just be good to me: *Groove Box & Leena Marie* / I just can't stop it: *Rim 'n' Stuff* / Happy days: *Aquarius Recordings* / Got to get up: *DJ Tonka* / Feel's alright: *Nightbreed* / Shake it: *Adam P* / Ain't missing: *Pancake* / Strut your funky stuff: *No Box*
MOC 59482 / Feb '97 / Mocca

☐ VANS WARPED TOUR
WARPEDCD 1 / 23 Feb '98 / Shock

☐ VARIACOES EM FADO
KAR 986 / Oct '96 / IMP

☐ VARIATIONS ON A CHILL (2CD Set)
SSR 147 / Aug '95 / SSR

☐ VARIATIONS VOL.2
PD 05 / May '98 / Paradigm

☐ VASSAR
KFWCD 120 / Nov '94 / Knitting Factory

☐ VAULT CLASSICS VOL.1
DGVCD 2023 / Jun '93 / Dynamite & Grapevine

☐ VAULTAGE PUNK COLLECTION
Jilly: *Piranhas* / Virginity: *Piranhas* / Tension: *Piranhas* / Girls get nervous: *Nicky & The Dots* / Wrong street: *Nicky & The Dots* / Lord Lucan is missing: *Dodgems* / Elvis is dead: *Peter & The Test Tube Babies* / Bank holidays: *Vandells* / Bloody: *Golinski Brothers* / Nervous wreck: *Lillettes* / Hey operator: *Lillettes* / I want to be my girl: *Woody & The Splinters* / Sweetie: *Chefs* / Thrush: *Chefs* / Happy families: *Piranhas* / 24 hours: *Chefs* / Let's make u: *Chefs* / Sinking gondola: *Exclusives* / Extradition: *Reward system*
CDPUNK 101 / 15 Sep '97 / Anagram

☐ VAYA RUMBA
Alguien canto: *Gonzalez, Antonio* / Esta tarde vi Llover: *Gonzalez, Antonio* / Voy voy: *Peret* / Rumba pa ti: *Peret* / Don toribio carambola: *Peret* / Retrato a Sevilla: *Los Del Rio* / Mama Mamita: *Los Del Rio* / Achilipu: *Vargas, Dolores* / No se no se: *Rumba Tres* / Son son sera: *De Vega, Manola* / Mia mia: *El Fary* / Rumbera de seda: *El Principe Gitano* / Que me coma el Tigre: *Flores, Lola* / Yeke yeke: *Los Lachos* / La Piragua: *Vargas, Dolores* / Que Bonite es mi Nina: *De Huelva, Perlita* / La balsa: *Perez, Gato* / La rumbera: *Escobar, Manola*
NSCD 036 / 15 Jun '98 / Nascente

☐ VE DAY - THE DANCE BANDS
Germany surrenders: *Churchill, Winston* / I've got a heart filled with love: *Preager, Lou & His Band* / Together: *Weir, Frank & His Astor Club Seven* / Marlene: *Loss, Joe & His Orchestra* / If I had only known: *Geraldo & His Orchestra* / Opus one: *Heath, Ted & His Music* / Sitting on a cloud: *Simpson, Jack & His Sextet* / Swinging on a star: *Geraldo & His Orchestra* / Barrelhouse boogie: *Roy, Harry & His Band* / So dumb but so beautiful: *Geraldo & His Orchestra* / Shine on harvest moon: *Geraldo & His Orchestra* / You're in love: *Preager, Lou & His Band* / Don't sweetheart me: *Geraldo & His Orchestra* / It had to be you: *Loss, Joe & His Orchestra* / Dance with a Dolly: *Ambrose & His Orchestra* / Time on my hands: *Gonella, Nat & His Georgians* / Someday I'll meet you again: *Geraldo & His Orchestra* / What do you think those ruby lips were made for: *Thorburn, Billy & Robinson Cleaver* / That's sabotage: *Geraldo & His Orchestra* / Don't ask me why: *Gibbons, Carroll & The Savoy Hotel Orpheans* / Undecided: *Silvester, Victor & His Jive Orchestra* / Amor amor: *Ambrose & His Orchestra* / I'll get by: *Barriteau, Carl Orchestra* / You'll be a happy little sweetheart in the spring: *Cotton, Billy & His Band* / I'm going to build a future world around you: *Geraldo & His Orchestra*
RAJCD 844 / Feb '95 / Empress

☐ VE DAY - THE OFFICIAL BRITISH LEGION COLLECTION (2CD Set)
Run rabbit run: *Flanagan & Allen* / We'll meet again: *Lynn, Vera* / (We're gonna hang out the) washing on the Siegfried Line: *Cotton, Billy & His Band* / Over the rainbow: *Garland, Judy* / In the mood: *Loss, Joe Band* / Boys in the backroom: *Dietrich, Marlene* / If I had my way: *Crosby, Bing* / Nightingale sang in Berkley Square: *Hutchinson, Leslie 'Hutch'* / Beer barrel polka: *Andrews Sisters* / I'll never smile again: *Dorsey, Tommy* / I've got sixpence: *Organ Dance Band & Me* / Room 504: *Hale, Binnie* / Last time I saw paris: *Coward, Sir Noel* / Frensi: *Shaw, Artie Orchestra* / Beneath the lights of home: *Geraldo* / I yi yi yi yi (I like you very much): *Miranda, Carmen* / London pride: *Coward, Sir Noel* / Yours: *Lynn, Vera* / American patrol: *Loss, Joe Band* / Anniversary waltz: *Crosby, Bing* / You made me love you: *Foster, Teddy* / White cliffs of Dover: *Lynn, Vera* / I don't want to walk without you: *Gibbons, Carroll* / You are my sunshine: *Crosby, Bing* / Don't sit under the apple tree: *Andrews Sisters* / Chattanooga choo choo: *Miller, Glenn* / Deep in the heart of Texas: *Crosby, Bing* / Silver wings in the moonlight: *Shelton, Anne* / Whispering grass: *Ink Spots* / Moonlight becomes you: *Crosby, Bing* / Praise the Lord and pass the ammunition: *Macs, Merry* / As time goes by: *Layton, Turner* / Begin the beguine: *Haywood, Eddie* / I had the craziest dream: *Gibbons, Carroll* / I'm gonna get lit up (when the lights go on in London): *Loss, Joe Band* / Coming in on a wing and a prayer: *Ambrose* / Tico tico: *Smith, Ethel* / You'll never know: *Haymes, Dick* / This is the army Mr. Jones: *Berlin, Irving* / Besame mucho: *Dorsey, Jimmy* / Roll me over: *Cotton, Billy & His Band* / Paper doll: *Mills Brothers* / Lovely way to spend an evening: *Gibbons, Carroll* / I'll be seeing you: *Crosby, Bing* / Lili Marlene: *Shelton, Anne* / Swinging on a star: *Crosby, Bing* / No love, no nothin': *Carless, Dorothy* / Dance with a dolly: *Geraldo & His Dance Orchestra* / Jukebox Saturday night: *Miller, Glenn* / My guy's come home: *Loss, Joe*
CDEM 1549 / Apr '95 / EMI

☐ VE DAY - THE VOCALISTS
Victory: *Churchill, Winston* / There's a new world: *Lynn, Vera* / Shine on Victory moon: *Bonn, Issy* / It's been a long, long time: *Hall, Adelaide* / Let me love you tonight: *Melachrino, George* / I got it bad and that ain't good: *Davis, Beryl* / (All of a sudden) My heart sings: *Hall, Adelaide* / Goodnight wherever you are: *Green, Johnny* / It could happen to you: *Lynn, Vera* / Tonight I kissed you: *Shelton, Anne* / Come out come out where ever you are: *Green, Johnny* / Don't believe everything you dream: *Bonn, Issy* / Then you kissed me: *Green, Johnny* / Long ago and far away: *Lynn, Vera* / You're in love: *Peers, Donald* / Pistol packin' Mama: *Dennis, Johnny* / Shine on harvest moon: *Flanagan & Allen* / In a friendly little harbour: *Layton, Turner* / It's love love love: *Morrow, Dorothy* / Dreaming: *Flanagan & Allen* / Lili Marlene: *Shelton, Anne* / MacNamara's band: *Morrow, Dorothy* / Dare I love you: *Hutchinson, Leslie 'Hutch'* / Things that mean so much to me: *Bonn, Issy* / Fool with a dream: *O'Connor, Cavan*
RAJCD 845 / Feb '95 / Empress

☐ VE DAY MUSICAL TRIBUTE - NOW IS THE HOUR
VEDAY 1945 / Feb '97 / Start

☐ VE DAY PARTY
PASTCD 7063 / May '95 / Flapper

☐ VEDIC PRESENTS RHYTHMIC INTELLIGENCE
SR 123CD / Jul '97 / Sub Rosa

☐ VEE JAY STORY, THE (2CD Set)
CDLAB 104 / Apr '96 / Charly

☐ VELVET VOICES
Run to Jesus for refuge: *Barnet, Charlie* / Joe Turner: *Young, Ed & Hobart Smith* / Titanic: *Jones, Bessie & Hobart Smith* / Witness for my Lord: *Silver Leaf Quartette Of Norfolk* / Dark day: *Silver Leaf Quartette Of Norfolk* / Very same God: *Silver Leaf Quartette Of Norfolk* / Gospel train: *Silver Leaf Quartette Of Norfolk* / I got a home: *Rahmings, Nat & Hobart Smith/Ed Young* / Hey hey honey: *Bright Light Quartet* / Menhaden chanteys: *Bright Light Quartet* / I'm tired: *Bright Light Quartet* / Just beyond the river: *Bright Light Quartet* / Christian automobile: *Bright Light Quartet* / Walk on the bay: *Rahmings, Nat & Hobart Smith/Ed Young* / Join the revelator: *Belleville A Capella Choir* / Walk, Billy Abbott: *Proctor, Willis* / How could I live: *Peerless Four* / Noah: *Peerless Four* / Trouble in my way: *Peerless Four* / I'm a soldier in the army of the Lord: *Peerless Four*
ROUCD 1708 / Sep '97 / Rounder

☐ VERABRA RETROSPECTIVE '80/'90
Bob the bob: *Lounge Lizards* / Minha rua: *Xiame* / Sundown: *Cerletti, Marco* / Pipeland: *Schaffer, Janne* / Bagus: *Toshiyuki Honda* / Act natural: *Grolnick, Don* / DUV: *De Winkel & Hattler* / Yellow fellow: *Mynta* / No name: *Von Senger, Dominik* / Algodoal: *Herting, Mike* / Flamencos en Nueva York: *Nunez, Gerardo* / Lilo and Max: *De Winkel, Torsten* / Azure treasure: *Shlomo Bat-Ain* / Cousin butterfly: *Never Been There* / Joyride: *Thompson, Barbara Paraphernalia* / At the top of the hill: *Marsh, Hug* / De sabado pra dominguinhes: *Pascoal, Hermeto*
VBR 20402 / Nov '90 / Vera Bra

☐ VERSION 1.1
NOMU 17CD / Oct '93 / Mute

☐ VERVE'S GRAMMY WINNERS
5214852 / May '94 / Verve

☐ VERY BEST OF 100% PURE GROOVE, THE (80's Dancefloor Classics - 2CD Set)
Ain't nobody: *Khan, Chaka* / Funkin' for Jamaica: *Browne, Tom* / Last night a DJ saved my life: *Indeep* / Got to have your love: *Mantronix* / Ghetto heaven: *Family Stand* / Cross the track: *Maceo & The Macks* / You to me are everything: *Real Thing* / Pick up the pieces: *Average White Band* / Runaway: *Salsoul Orchestra* / I believe in miracles: *Jackson Sisters* / Rock Creek Park: *Blackbyrds* / Rappers delight: *Sugarhill Gang* / And the beat goes on: *Whispers* / Ain't no stopping us now: *McFadden & Whitehead* / He's the greatest dancer: *Sister Sledge* / Forget me nots: *Rushen, Patrice* / Roadblock: *Stock/Aitken/Waterman* / You're the one for me: *D-Train* / Message: *Grandmaster Flash* / Somebody else's guy: *Brown, Jocelyn* / Too hot: *Kool & The Gang* / I can make you feel good: *Shalamar* / Down on the street: *Shakatak* / Walking on sunshine: *Rockers Revenge* / Running away: *Ayers, Roy* / Behind the groove: *Marie, Teena* / Jingo: *Candido* / All this love I'm giving: *McCrae, Gwen* / She's strange: *Cameo* / I found loving: *Fatback Band* / Hangin' on a string: *Loose Ends* / Fools paradise: *Morgan, Meli'sa* / Outstanding: *Gap Band* / London town: *Light Of The World* / All night long: *Mary Jane Girls* / Don't look any further: *Edwards, Dennis* / Don't let your love get me down: *Bell, Archie & The Drells* / Feel like making love: *Heatwave*
TTVCD 2957 / 15 Jun '98 / Telstar TV

☐ VERY BEST OF BLUES GUITAR, THE
VBCD 306 / Jan '96 / Charly

☐ VERY BEST OF BRASS BANDS, THE
Puttin' on the ritz: *Britannia Building Society Foden Band* / Over the rainbow: *Williams-Fairey Engineering Band* / You'll never walk alone: *Britannia Building Society Foden Band* / Gladiator's farewell: *Williams-Fairey Engineering Band* / Tea for two: *Britannia Building Society Foden Band* / Solveig's song: *Britannia Building Society Foden Band* / Pretty girl is like a melody: *Britannia Building Society Foden Band* / Dance of the comedians: *Sun Life Band* / Sorcerer's apprentice: *Sun Life Band* / Folk festival: *Williams-Fairey Engineering Band* / Swing low, sweet chariot: *Williams-Fairey Engineering Band* / Fest musik der stadt Wien: *Williams-Fairey Engineering Band* / Tritsch tratsch polka: *Williams-Fairey Engineering Band*
3036000772 / Feb '97 / Carlton

☐ VERY BEST OF COUNTRY, THE
AHLCD 23 / Sep '94 / Hit

☐ VERY BEST OF DISCO FOX, THE (2CD Set)
ZYX 811422 / 30 Mar '98 / ZYX

☐ VERY BEST OF HOUSE NATION VOL.3, THE (3CD Set)
089704102 / 3 Aug '98 / House Nation

☐ VERY BEST OF IRISH CEILI MUSIC, THE
CHCD 1039 / Aug '94 / Chyme

☐ VERY BEST OF IRISH COUNTRY, THE
Come down the mountain Katie Daly: *Duncan, Hugo* / Cottage by the lee: *Cunningham, Larry* / Village in County Tyrone: *Begley, Philomena* / Sweet forget me not: *Anderson, Big Jim* / Among the Wicklow hills: *Ely, Pat* / Travellin' people: *McCann, Susan* / Galway Bay: *O'Donnell, Daniel* / Three leaf shamrock from Greenore: *Margo* / Road to Malinmore: *Henry, Bernhard* / Little country town in Ireland: *Glenn, John* / Donegal shore: *O'Donnell, Daniel* / Old cross of Ardboe: *Begley, Philomena* / Lovely Derry: *Cunningham, Larry* / Time is rolling on: *Henry, Bernhard* / Rose of Allendale: *Woods, Pat* / Old Claddagh ring: *Margo* / Any Tipperary town: *Ely, Pat* / Rose of Tralee: *McCann, Susan* / Boys from the County Armagh: *Glenn, John* / Westmeath bachelor: *Duncan, Hugo* / Alice is in wonderland: *Kirwan, Dominic*
CDIRISH 011 / May '97 / Outlet

☐ VERY BEST OF JAZZ FM, THE
Too darn hot: *Fitzgerald, Ella* / Cat: *Smith, Jimmy* / My baby just cares for me: *Simone, Nina* / Miles: *Davis, Miles* / Take 5: *Brubeck, Dave & Carmen McRae* / Senor blues: *Taj Mahal* / Wade in the water: *Lewis, Ramsey* / Song for my Father: *Bridgewater, Dee Dee & Horace Silver* / Tin tin deo: *Gillespie, Dizzy* / Johnny and Mary: *Taylor, Martin* / Work song: *Adderley, Nat* / Killer Joe: *Three Of A Kind* / So what: *Jordan, Ronny* / Theme from Starsky and Hutch: *Taylor, James Quartet* / Pastime paradise: *Barretto, Ray* / Lady Day and John Coltrane: *Scott-Heron, Gil* / Cantaloupe island: *Pucho & His Latin Soul Brothers* / Some cow fonque: *Buckshot Lefonque* / Pick up the pieces: *Average White Band* / Watermelon man: *Sanchez, Poncho* / Skaravan: *Jazz Jamaica* / Oye como va: *Puente, Tito* / Brooklyn heights: *Down To The Bone* / Bebop props: *Ping Pong*
JAZZFMCD 6 / 19 Jan '98 / Jazz FM

☐ VERY BEST OF JAZZ MOODS, THE (2CD Set)
TTVCD 2970 / 27 Jul '98 / Telstar TV

☐ VERY BEST OF LATIN JAZZ, THE (2CD Set)
Ran kan kan: *Puente, Tito* / Mais que nada: *Mendes, Sergio* / Watermelon man: *Santamaria, Mongo* / Cantaloupe Island: *Pucho & His Latin Soul Brothers* / Ponteio: *Gilberto, Astrud* / Vera cruz: *Turrentine, Stanley* / Aguas de Marco: *Getz, Stan* / Bien sabroso: *Sanchez, Poncho* / Ode to cachao: *Puente, Tito* / Yatra-ta: *Maria, Tania* / Samba de sausalito: *Santana* / Little train: *Benson, George* / Brazilian love affair: *Duke, George* / Jazz carnival: *Azymuth* /

Rain forest: *Hoggard, Jay* / Come with me: *Maria, Tania* / Smooth operator: *Santamaria, Mongo* / Double rainbow: *Getz, Stan* / Agua de beber: *Gilberto, Astrud* / Favela: *Jobim, Antonio Carlos* / Wave: *Peterson, Oscar* / If you want to be a lover: *Henrique, Luiz* / So danco samba: *Bonfa, Luiz* / Tide: *Jobim, Antonio Carlos* / Samba para dos: *Schifrin, Lalo & Bob Brookmeyer* / Samba d'Orpheu: *Desmond, Paul* / Conceirto de Aranjuz: *Hall, Jim*

RADCD 96 / 11 May '98 / Global TV

☐ VERY BEST OF SCOTLAND VOL.1, THE

Amazing Grace: *Royal Scots Dragoon Guards* / Campbell town loch: *Stewart, Andy* / Caledonian two step: *MacLeod, Jim & His Band* / Scotland the brave: *Wilson, Robert* / Wee MacGregor Highland Patrol: *Scots Guards* / Black Douglas: *Corries* / Castles in the air: *Johnstone, Jim & His Band* / Down in the Glen: *Wilson, Robert* / National emblem: *Gordon Highlanders* / March selection: *Holmes, Ian & His Band* / Gathering of the clans: *Scots Guards* / Lintons ploughmans jig: *Shand, Jimmy & His Band* / With a hundred pipers: *2nd Battalion Scots Guards* / Bonnie lass of Bon accord: *Johnstone, Jim & His Band* / Steadfast and true: *Gordon Highlanders* / Middleton medley: *Glen Lomond Scottish Band*

4936062 / 16 Feb '98 / Music For Pleasure

☐ VERY BEST OF SCOTLAND VOL.2, THE

Flower of Scotland: *Royal Scots Dragoon Guards* / Gathering of the clans: *Wilson, Robert* / My ain house: *Anderson, Moira* / Sky is blue in Scotland: *Tartan Lads* / Teviot brig jig: *Johnstone, Jim & His Band* / Garb of old call: *Scots Guards* / Scottish soldier: *Stewart, Andy* / Isle of Skye: *Corries* / Para handy: *Houliston, Max & his Scottish Band* / Holyrood: *Gordon Highlanders* / My ain folk: *Anderson, Moira* / Ye banks and braes: *McEwan, Sydney* / Mull of Kintyre: *Royal Scots Dragoon Guards* / Roamin' in the gloamin': *Royal Scots Dragoon Guards* / Toronto Scottish regiment: *Black Watch Band* / Duntroon: *Black Watch Band*

4936072 / 16 Feb '98 / Music For Pleasure

☐ VERY BEST OF SCOTLAND VOL.3, THE

Donald where's your troosers: *Stewart, Andy* / Drunken piper: *Black Watch Band* / Auld scot songs: *Anderson, Moira* / Wild rover: *Tartan Lads* / West awake hornpipe: *Johnstone, Jim & His Band* / Robertson Hornpipe: *Johnstone, Jim & His Band* / I love a lassie: *Logan, Jimmy* / My home: *Royal Scots Dragoon Guards* / Sky boat song: *Royal Scots Dragoon Guards* / Hiking group: *Gay Gordons* / Bonnie Dundee: *Corries* / Scottish waltzes selection: *Wick Scottish Dance Band* / Back to bonnie Scotland: *Wick Scottish Dance Band* / Auld house: *Wick Scottish Dance Band* / Road to the isles: *Stewart, Andy* / Cock o the North: *Scots Guards* / Rowan tree: *Anderson, Moira* / Northern lights of old Aberdeen: *Shand, Jimmy* / Circle waltz: *Glenlomand Scottish Band* / Queen Mary queen Mary: *Glenlomand Scottish Band* / If you will Marry me: *Glenlomand Scottish Band* / Kate Bardier: *Glenlomand Scottish Band* / My wee lauds a sojer: *Glenlomand Scottish Band* / I belong to Glasgow: *Fyffe, Will*

4936082 / 16 Feb '98 / Music For Pleasure

☐ VERY BEST OF SMOOTH JAZZ GUITAR, THE

After hours: *Jordan, Ronny* / Night rhythms: *Ritenour, Lee* / Smiles and smiles to go: *Carlton, Larry* / Promenade: *White, Peter* / Playing for time: *Acoustic Alchemy* / Feel like making love: *Coryell, Larry* / Anything and everything: *Minucci, Chieli* / Just between us: *Brown, Norman* / Cafe Reggio: *Breaux, Zachary* / Quiet volcano: *Traum, Artie* / Music inside: *Loeb, Chuck* / Anything's possible: *Fattburger*

SHANCD 5043 / Apr '98 / Shanachie

☐ VERY BEST OF SUN ROCK 'N' ROLL, THE

Whole lotta shakin' goin' on: *Lewis, Jerry Lee* / Ain't got a thing: *Burgess, Sonny* / Boppin' the blues: *Perkins, Carl* / Devil doll: *Orbison, Roy* / Red hot: *Riley, Billy Lee* / Got love if you want it: *Smith, Warren* / All night rock: *Honeycutt, Glenn* / Love my baby: *Thompson, Hayden* / Flatfoot Sam: *Blake, Tommy* / Love crazy baby: *Parchman, Kenny* / Put your cat clothes on: *Perkins, Carl* / Baby, please don't go: *Riley, Billy Lee* / Wild one: *Lewis, Jerry Lee* / Domino: *Orbison, Roy* / My bucket's got a hole in it: *Burgess, Sonny* / Blue suede shoes: *Perkins, Carl* / Come on little mama: *Harris, Ray* / Ubangi stomp: *Smith, Warren* / Break up: *Smith, Ray* / Madman: *Wages, Jimmy* / We wanna boogie: *Burgess, Sonny* / That don't move me: *Perkins, Carl*

MCCD 024 / May '91 / Music Club

☐ VERY BEST OF SUN ROCKABILLY, THE (2CD Set)

CDGR 1412 / Apr '97 / Charly

☐ VERY BEST OF TEXAS BLUES PIANO, THE

WCD 120629 / Jul '97 / Wolf

☐ VERY BEST OF WELSH MALE CHOIRS, THE (Goreuon Corau Meibion Cymru)

Arwelfa: *United Choirs* / Now the day is over: *LLanelli Choir* / Y goedwig werdd: *Godre'r Aran Choir* / Deep harmony: *Pendyrus Choir* / Last words of David: *United Choirs* / With a voice of singing: *Cwmbach Choir* / Ol' arks a-moverin: *Trelawnyd Choir* / Lost chord: *Pontarddulais Male Voice Choir* / Pilgrim's chorus: *United Choirs* / Iechyd da: *Rhos Male Voice Choir* / Gloria: *Pendyrus Choir & Cory Band* / Kwmbayah: *Trelawnyd Choir* / Gwn Dafydd Ifan: *Twm O'r Nant Choir* / Amen: *United Choirs* / Pie Jesu: *LLanelli Choir* / Bandit's chorus: *Cwmbach Choir* / Ar derfyn dydd: *Godre'r Aran Choir* / Where shall I be: *Pontarddulais Male Voice Choir* / Love could I only tell thee: *Rhos Male Voice Choir* / Mae d'eisiau di bob awr: *United Choirs*

SCD 2012 / Nov '96 / Sain

☐ VERY NOSTALGIC CHRISTMAS, A (The 1930/1940's)

White Christmas: *Crosby, Bing* / Winter wonderland: *Walsh & Parker* / I'm sending a letter to Santa Claus: *Robins, Phyllis* / God rest ye merry gentlemen: *Crosby, Bing* / Fairy on the Christmas tree: *Hall, Henry Orchestra* / Little boy that Santa Claus forgot: *Tracy, Arthur* / Silent night: *Langford, Frances* / O come all ye faithful (Adeste Fidelis): *Langford, Frances* / Christmas bells at Eventide: *Fields, Gracie* / Jingle bells: *Miller, Glenn* / I'm spending Christmas with the old folks: *Rabin, Oscar* / Christmas bells are ringing: *Winn, Max* / Santa Claus express: *Wilbur, Jay* / I'm going home for Christmas: *Hall, Henry Orchestra* / I took my harp to a party: *Fields, Gracie* / Jolly old Christmas: *Cotton, Billy* / Cradle song: *Miller, Glenn* / Ave Maria: *Lynn, Vera* / Good morning blues: *Lynn, Vera* / Aladdin - A potty pantomime: *Payne, Jack*

RAJCD 839 / 6 Oct '97 / Empress

☐ VERY SERIOUS SMOKIN' VOL.2

GR 101012 / Dec '96 / Gravity

☐ VERY SPECIAL CHRISTMAS VOL.1, A

Santa Claus is coming to town: *Pointer Sisters* / Winter Wonderland: *Eurythmics* / Do you hear what I say: *Houston, Whitney* / Merry Christmas baby: *Springsteen, Bruce & The E Street Band* / Have yourself a merry little Christmas: *Pretenders* / I saw Mommy kissing Santa Claus: *Mellencamp, John Cougar* / Gabriel's message: *Sting* / Christmas in Hollis: *Run DMC* / Christmas (baby please come home): *U2* / Santa baby: *Madonna* / Little drummer boy: *Seger, Bob & The Silver Bullet Band* / Run Rudolph run: *Adams, Bryan* / Back door Santa: *Bon Jovi* / Coventry carol: *Moyet, Alison* / Silent night: *Nicks, Stevie*

CDA 3911 / Nov '94 / A&M

☐ VERY SPECIAL CHRISTMAS VOL.2, A

Christmas all over again: *Petty, Tom & The Heartbreakers* / Jingle bell rock: *Travis, Randy* / Christmas song: *Vandross, Luther* / Santa Claus is coming to town: *Sinatra, Frank & Cyndi Lauper* / Birth of Christ: *Boyz II Men* / Please come home for Christmas: *Bon Jovi, Jon* / What Christmas means to me: *Young, Paul* / O Christmas tree: *Franklin, Aretha* / Rockin' around the Christmas tree: *Spector, Ronnie & Darlene Love* / White Christmas: *Bolton, Michael* / Christmas is: *Run DMC* / Christmas time again: *Extreme* / Merry Christmas baby: *Raitt, Bonnie & Charles Brown* / O holy night: *Campbell, Tevin* / Sleigh ride: *Gibson, Debbie* / What child is this: *Williams, Vanessa* / Blue Christmas: *Wilson, A.N.* / Silent night: *Wilson Phillips* / I believe in you: *O'Connor, Sinead*

5400032 / Nov '95 / A&M

☐ VERY SPECIAL CHRISTMAS VOL.3, A

5407642 / 1 Dec '97 / A&M

☐ VERY THOUGHT OF YOU, THE (18 Croonin' Love Songs)

Portrait of my love: *Monro, Matt* / That's amore: *Martin, Dean* / I love you because: *Martino, Al* / Wind beneath my wings: *Tarmey, Bill* / (They long to be) close to you: *Hill, Vince* / You're getting to be a habit with me: *Torme, Mel* / Nightingale sang in Berkley square: *Darin, Bobby* / Till there was you: *Damone, Vic* / On the street where you live: *Hilton, Ronnie* / My funny valentine: *MacRae, Gordon* / Stairway of love: *Holliday, Michael* / Sweet Lorraine: *Monro, Matt* / All I do is dream of you: *Martin, Dean* / May I have the next dream with you: *Roberts, Malcolm* / Roses of Picardy: *Darin, Bobby* / True love: *Crosby, Bing* / Story of my life: *Holliday, Michael* / Very thought of you: *Haymes, Dick*

CDMFP 6282 / Jan '97 / Music For Pleasure

☐ VETERAN COMPILATION

VTC 1 / Jun '93 / Veteran Tapes

☐ VIA UFO TO MERCURY

ALP 84CD / Jan '97 / Atavistic

☐ VIBE MUSIC - THE SOULFUL SOUND OF CHICAGO

PLUGCD 2 / Jul '95 / Produce

☐ VIBE VOL.1 (The Sound Of Swing)

Love no limit: *Blige, Mary J.* / Realize: *Wilson, Charlie* / That's the way love is: *Brown, Bobby* / If you feel the need: *Shomari* / I like your style: *Bubba* / Don't keep me waiting: *Rhythm Within* / Real love: *Lorenzo* / One night stand: *Father MC* / Do you wanna chill with me: *Solid State Sound* / Yo - that's a lot of body: *Ready For The World* / Baby, baby, baby: *TLC* / Right here: *SWV* / Helluva: *Brotherhood Creed* / I dream, I dream: *Jackson, Jermaine*

CDELV 07 / Jul '93 / Elevate

☐ VIBE VOL.2

Skip to my Lu: *Lisa Lisa* / Back and forth: *Aaliyah* / Satisfy you: *Hall, Damion* / All through the night: *POV* / Oh my God: *Tribe Called Quest* / You told me: *Motiv* / Want U back: *Me 2 U* / Are you free: *Mint Condition* / In my nature: *Nuttin' Nyce* / Tell me I'm not dreaming: *Titiyo* / She's playing hard to get: *Hi-Five* / Show me you love me: *Serenade* / 69: *Father* / Get with you tonight: *Montage*

CDELV 17 / Jun '94 / Elevate

☐ VIBRATIONS

PHCD 2063 / 26 Jan '98 / Penthouse

☐ VICIOUS

DRESS 602 / 25 May '98 / Dressed To Kill

☐ VICTIMS OF HOUSE (3CD Set)

TCD 09247182 / Mar '97 / SPV

☐ VICTORIAN MUSICAL BOXES

CDSDL 408 / Sep '94 / Saydisc

☐ VICTORIAN SUNDAY, A

Abide with me / Judas Maccabaeus / Lost chord / When I survey the wondrous cross / How sweet the name of Jesus sounds / Lead kindly light / Nearer my god to thee / Shall we meet beyond the river / Only an armour bearer / I will sing of my redeemer / Scatter seeds of kindness / Shall we gather at the river / Beaulah land / Hold City / Morning hymn / Evening hymn / Onward Christian Soldiers / Rescue the perishing / What shall the harvest be / We'll work 'til Jesus comes / Washed in the blood of the lamb / What a friend we have in Jesus / Sicilian mariners / Helmsley / Luther's hymn / London new / Mountain Ephraim / God save the Queen

CDSDL 331 / Oct '91 / Saydisc

☐ VICTORY SINGLES VOL.2

VR 079CD / 11 May '98 / Victory

☐ VICTORY STYLE

VR 033CD / Apr '96 / Victory

☐ VICTORY THE SINGLES VOL.3

VR 082CD / 20 Jul '98 / Victory

☐ VIENNA NIGHTS

CDMOIR 419 / Apr '95 / Memoir

☐ VIENNATONE

Speechless drum and bass: *Count Basic* / Nova schuhu: *Bask* / Chocolate Elvis: *Tosca* / East West (et moi): *Mama Oliver* / Each and everyday: *Potuznik & Sokol* / Resistance: *Blackwing* / Hawk: *Planet E* / A1: *Farmer's Manual* / Sit dub: *Huber, Alois* / Connection: *Showroom Recording Series* / Family affair: *Dannin, Puck*

K7 055CD / May '97 / Studio K7

☐ VIETNAM - THE DAN TRANH

C 560055CD / Aug '94 / Ocora

☐ VIETNAM - TRADITION DU SUD

C 580043 / Nov '92 / Ocora

☐ VILE VIBES

CDVILE 15 / Feb '90 / Peaceville

☐ VILLAGE VANGUARD LIVE SESSIONS (3CD Set)

Lover come back to me / Blues for Max / Tour de force / Birks' works / Lullaby of the leaves / Stella by starlight / 13 Avenue 'B' / On the trail / Sweet Georgia Brown / Don't git sassy / Little pixie / Second race / Willow tree / Ah that's freedom / Quietude / Bachafillen

55605 / Oct '97 / Laserlight

☐ VINE YARD REVIVAL SERIES VOL.1

VYDCD 1 / Sep '95 / Vine Yard

☐ VINE YARD REVIVAL SERIES VOL.2

VYCD 010 / Jul '96 / Vine Yard

☐ VINTAGE BANDS, THE

Music, Maestro, please: *Hylton, Jack & His Orchestra* / Alexander's ragtime band: *Roy, Harry & His Orchestra* / Nagasaki: *Gonella, Nat & His Georgians* / Nobody loves a fairy when she's forty: *Cotton, Billy & His Band* / My brother makes the noises for the talkies: *Payne, Jack & The BBC Dance Orchestra* / Stay as sweet as you are: *Stone, Lew & His Orchestra* / In the mood: *Loss, Joe & His Orchestra* / Let's face the music and dance: *Fox, Roy & His Orchestra* / Nightingale sang in Berkeley Square: *Gibbons, Carroll & The Savoy Hotel Orpheans* / Dancing in the dark: *Ambrose* / Here's to the next time: *Hall, Henry & The BBC Dance Orchestra* / Say it with music: *Payne, Jack & The BBC Dance Orchestra* / I'm gonna get lit up (when the lights go on in London): *Gibbons, Carroll & The Savoy Hotel Orpheans* / Change partners: *Loss, Joe & His Orchestra* / Did you ever see a dream walking: *Hall, Henry & The BBC Dance Orchestra* / Shine: *Cotton, Billy & His Band* / She had to go and lose it at the Astor: *Roy, Harry & His Orchestra* / Easy to remember: *Stone, Lew & His Orchestra* / Have you met Miss Jones: *Hylton, Jack & His Orchestra* / I can't dance: *Gonella, Nat & His Georgians* / Night is young and you're so beautiful: *Fox, Roy & His Orchestra* / Let's put out the lights: *Ambrose*

CC 206 / May '88 / Music For Pleasure

☐ VINTAGE CHRISTMAS, A

Little boy that Santa Claus forgot / Winter wonderland / Gracie Fields' christmas party / I'm sending a letter to Santa Claus / Gert and Daisy make a christmas pudding / Silent night / I'm going home for christmas / Christmas in the rockies / Gracie with the Air Force at christmas / Santa Claus express / Lambeth walk christmas party / O come all ye faithful (Adeste Fidelis) / Christmas bells at eventide / Robinson cleaver's christmas medley / White Christmas

PASTCD 9768 / Nov '91 / Flapper

☐ VINTAGE COUNTRY

My little lady: *Rodgers, Jimmie* / Daddy and home: *Rodgers, Jimmie* / Waiting for a train: *Rodgers, Jimmie* / Any old time: *Rodgers, Jimmie* / Back in the saddle again: *Autry, Gene* / It makes no difference now: *Autry, Gene* / You are my sunshine: *Autry, Gene* / Time changes everything: *Wills, Bob & His Texas Playboys* / New San Antonio Rose: *Wills, Bob & His Texas Playboys* / Take me back to Tulsa: *Wills, Bob & His Texas Playboys* / Great speckled bird: *Acuff, Roy & His Smokey Mountain Boys* / Night train to Memphis: *Acuff, Roy & His Smokey Mountain Boys* / Wreck on the highway: *Acuff, Roy & His Smokey Mountain Boys* / Mule skinner blues: *Monroe, Bill & His Bluegrass Boys* / No letter in the mail: *Monroe, Bill & His Bluegrass Boys* / Orange blossom special: *Monroe, Bill & His Bluegrass Boys*

HADCD 161 / May '94 / Javelin

☐ VINTAGE JAZZ VOL.1

CDSGPBJZ 01 / 4 May '98 / Prestige

☐ VINTAGE JAZZ VOL.12

Struttin' with some barbecue / Hotter than that / Muskrat ramble / Wild man blues / New Orleans shout / Stinagree blues / West End blues / Edna / Henderson stomp / St. Louis shuffle / Easy money / King Porter stomp / My melancholy baby / Beale Street blues

CDSGPBJZ 23 / May '96 / Prestige

☐ VINTAGE JAZZ VOL.13

So mnay times / Peg o' my heart / Swingin' on the Teagarden gate / Can't we talk it over / Melancholy blues / West End blues / Knockin' a jug / St. Louis blues / Flat hat blues / Tenor king / Swingin' at Milts / Begin the beguine / Donkey serenade / Let's walk

CDSGPBJZ 24 / May '96 / Prestige

☐ VINTAGE JAZZ VOL.14

Royal Garden blues / Song of India / Beale Street blues / Boogie woogie / Swing low, sweet clarinet / I got it bad / Fan it / There'll be some changes made / Love of my life / My heart belongs to Daddy / Nightmare / Dinah / Everybody loves my baby / Heebie jeebies are rockin' the town

CDSGPBJZ 25 / May '96 / Prestige

☐ VINTAGE JAZZ VOL.15

O natural blues / Variety stomp / I'm coming Virginia / Stockholm stomp / Lonesome road / Muggles / Save it pretty Mama / Willie the weeper / Rockin' in rhythm / Thursday / Table in the corner / I'll remember / Muddy river blues / Somewhere a voice is calling

CDSGPBJZ 26 / 16 Mar '98 / Prestige

☐ VINTAGE JAZZ VOL.16

Rhythm club stomp / Showboat shuffle / Shake it and break it / Mule face blues / It's only a paper moon / Sunday / Sad eyes / Runnin' wild / This heart of mine / I surrender dear / Swanee river / Sheik of Araby / Tin roof blues / After you've gone

CDSGPBJZ 27 / 4 May '98 / Prestige

☐ VINTAGE JAZZ VOL.17

Apple honey / Stardust / Northwest passage / Good Earth / Drum stomp / Rhythm rhythm (I got rhythm) / House of Morgan / Willie the weeper / Ory's creole trombone / Lamp is low / What is this thing called love / Octaroon / Blues / Stop kicking my heart around

CDSGPBJZ 28 / May '96 / Prestige

☐ VINTAGE JAZZ VOL.2

CDSGPBJZ 02 / 4 May '98 / Prestige

☐ VINTAGE JAZZ VOL.3

CDSGPBJZ 03 / 4 May '98 / Prestige

☐ VINTAGE JAZZ VOL.4

CDSGPBJZ 04 / 4 May '98 / Prestige

☐ VINTAGE JAZZ VOL.5

CDSGPBJZ 05 / 4 May '98 / Prestige

☐ VINTAGE JAZZ VOL.6

CDSGPBJZ 15 / 4 May '98 / Prestige

☐ VINTAGE MELODIES (Songs of the Victorian era)

Come into the garden Maud / Won't you buy my pretty flowers / Mistletoe bough / End of a perfect day / My pretty Jane / Drinking / I'll be your sweetheart / Silent worship / In the gloaming / Road to Mandalay / Mother take the wheel away / Excelsior

LCDM 9040 / Oct '90 / Lismor

☐ VINTAGE MUSIC FROM INDIA

ROUCD 1083 / May '93 / Rounder

☐ VINTAGE PIANO VOL.1

CDSGPBJZ 11 / 4 May '98 / Prestige

☐ VINTAGE PIANO VOL.2

CDSGPBJZ 12 / 4 May '98 / Prestige

☐ VINTAGE PIANO VOL.3

CDSGPBJZ 13 / 4 May '98 / Prestige

☐ VINTAGE PIANO VOL.5

On the sunny side of the street / She's funny that way / Over the rainbow / All of me / Moon mist / Passion flower / Paris blues / C jam blues / Messin' around / Six wheel chaser / Chicago flyer / Blues de lux / Every time we say goodbye / Memories of you

CDSGPBJZ 21 / May '96 / Prestige

☐ VINTAGE PIANO VOL.6

Two's and few's / Honky tonk train blues / Rising tide blues / Far ago blues / I'm confessin' that I love you / I surrender dear / I'm in the mood for love / Undecided / If dreams come true / Stompin' at the Savoy / Bugle call rag / I can't get started / Hiya Sue / Creole rhapsody

CDSGPBJZ 22 / May '96 / Prestige

☐ VINTAGE R&S VOL.2

Stella: *Jam & Spoon* / Infinition: *Quadrant* / Zeta 3: *Zeta 3* / Jam the box: *69* / Macrocosm: *Mike Dred* / Kinetic: *Golden Girls* / Alcatraz: *Peyote* / Vamp: *Outlander* / Desire: *69* / Elektra: *Source Experience* / Camargue: *Bolland, C.J.*

RS 96104CD / Oct '96 / R&S

☐ VINTAGE REGGAE HITS

RDCD 196 / Feb '96 / Andy Presents

☐ VINTAGE SOUL TRACKS

CWNCD 2011 / Jul '96 / Javelin

☐ VINYL FRONTIER (2MC Set)

SOUN 23CD / 1 Sep '97 / Soundclash

☐ VIOLIN JAZZ 1927-1944 (2CD Set)

Body and soul: *Grappelli, Stephane* / Them their eyes: *Grappelli, Stephane* / I wonder where my baby is tonight: *Grappelli, Stephane* / Calling all keys: *Rignold, Hugo* / Wild cat: *Venuti, Joe Trio* / My syncopated melody man: *McKenzie, Red & His Music Box* / Goin' places: *Venuti, Joe* / Four string Joe: *Venuti, Joe Blue Four* / Running ragged: *Venuti, Joe Blue Four* / Kansas City Kitty: *Sissle, Noble Orchestra* / After you've gone: *Smith, Stuff & His Onyx Club Boys* / Onyx Club spree: *Smith, Stuff & His Onyx Club Boys* / Skip it: *Smith, Stuff Trio* / C jam blues: *Ellington, Duke Orchestra* / Moon mist: *Ellington, Duke Orchestra* / My melancholy baby: *Asmussen, Svend* / It don't mean a thing if it ain't got that swing: *Asmussen, Svend* / Ring dem bells: *Asmussen, Svend* / Smart Alec: *Hampton, Lionel Orchestra* / Eddie's blues: *South, Eddie* / Oh lady be good: *South, Eddie* / Fiddle ditty: *South, Eddie* / Concerto pour deux violins en re mineur: *South, Eddie* / Minor swing: *Laurence, Claude & Orchestra* / Vous et moi: *Reinhardt, Django* / Strange harmony: *Warlop, Michel & Orchestra* / Harmoniques: *Warlop, Michel* / Oui: *Warlop, Michel* / Christmas swing: *Warlop, Michel* / Jig in G: *Caceres, Emilio Trio* / Solo: *Nero, Paul Trio*

FA 052 / Oct '96 / Fremeaux

☐ **VIOLINS OF EUROPE (France/ Romania/Sweden/Norway/3CD Set)**
C 570304304 / Mar '97 / Ocora

☐ **VIPER MAD BLUES (25 Songs Of Dope & Depravity)**
Kicking the gong around: *Calloway, Cab & his Cotton Club Orchestra* / Dope head blues: *Spivey, Victoria & Lonnie Johnson* / Cocaine habit blues: *Memphis Jug Band* / Pipe dream blues: *Meyers, Hazel* / Smoking reefers: *Adler, Larry* / Take a whiff on me: *Leadbelly* / Killin' jive: *Cats & The Fiddle* / You're a viper: *Smith, Stuff & His Onyx Club Boys* / Reefer man: *Lee, Baron Blue Rhythm Band* / Stuff is here and it's mellow: *Brown, Cleo* / Onyx hop: *Newton, Frankie Uptown Serenaders* / Knocking myself out: *Green, Lil* / Junker's blues: *Dupree, 'Champion' Jack* / Reefer hound blues: *Jones, Curtis* / Reefer song: *Waller, Fats* / I'm feelin' high and happy: *Krupa, Gene & His Orchestra* / When I get low, I get high: *Fitzgerald, Ella & Chick Webb Orchestra* / Ol' man river (smoke a little tea): *Williams, Cootie & His Rug Cutters* / Blue reefer blues: *Jones, Richard M. & His Jazz Wizards* / Cocaine: *Justice, Dick* / Reefer head woman: *Gillum, Bill 'Jazz' & His Jazz Boys* / Willie the weeper: *Jaxon, Frankie 'Half Pint'* / Cocaine blues: *Jordan, Luke* / Blue drag: *Taylor, Freddy & His Swing Men* / Viper's moan: *Bryant, Willie & His Orchestra*
CDMOJO 306 / Nov '96 / Mojo

☐ **VIRGINIA TRADITIONS (Ballads & Songs)**
GVM 1004CD / Jul '95 / Global Village

☐ **VIRGINIA TRADITIONS - SECULAR BLACK MUSIC**
GVM 1001CD / Jul '95 / Global Village

☐ **VIRTUAL DJ - DRUM 'N' BASS**
Enta da dragon: *DJ Red* / Dub moods: *Aphrodite* / Mad apache: *Shy FX* / Nu gen: *Decoder* / Behold: *Swift* / Star Wars: *Dream Team* / Beats back: *Spice* / Untouchables: *Ill Figure* / Switch: *Special K* / Opinion: *Swoosh* / Nobody: *Phiziks*
BDRCD 21 / Jul '97 / Breakdown

☐ **VIRTUAL DJ - UNDERGROUND GARAGE**
BDRCD 22 / Jul '97 / Suburban Base

☐ **VIRTUAL LABEL COMPILATION**
MOCD 0012 / Oct '96 / Virtual

☐ **VIRUS THAT WOULD NOT DIE, THE (Alternative Tentacles Records Sampler)**
VIRUS 209CD / 10 Nov '97 / Alternative Tentacles

☐ **VISION MASTERMIXERS VOL.1 (The Immaculate Mixes Vol.1)**
QED 092 / Dec '96 / Tring

☐ **VISION MASTERMIXERS VOL.2 (The Immaculate Mixes Vol.2)**
QED 093 / Dec '96 / Tring

☐ **VISION MASTERMIXERS VOL.3 (The Sixties)**
QED 094 / Nov '96 / Tring

☐ **VISION MASTERMIXERS VOL.4 (The Seventies)**
QED 095 / Nov '96 / Tring

☐ **VISION MASTERMIXERS VOL.5 (Disco Hits)**
QED 096 / Nov '96 / Tring

☐ **VISION ONE (2CD Set)**
AUM 007/8 / 6 Jul '98 / Aum Fidelity

☐ **VISIONS OF THE PAST VOL.2**
AS 711351 / Oct '97 / As

☐ **VISIONS OF THE PAST VOL.3**
AS 711352 / Oct '97 / As

☐ **VISIONS OF THE PAST VOL.4**
AS 711353 / Oct '97 / As

☐ **VISITATION VOL.1**
MEYCD 17 / Sep '96 / Magick Eye

☐ **VISITATION VOL.2**
Electronic meditation: *Children Of Dub* / Three monkeys: *Under The Honeytunnel* / Beyond the blue 2: *Spiralhead* / Alien love song: *Spiralhead* / In the heart of a blazing sun: *SYT* / Carpenter: *Black Hole* / Shape of life: *UVX* / ESP: *Children Of Dub* / Slap tongue squeeky bonk: *Mushroom* / Big fish: *Another Green World*
MEYCD 21 / 13 Oct '97 / Magick Eye

☐ **VIVA AMERICANA**
Americana: *Taylor, Chip* / Has been: *Thompson Brothers* / Painful days and sleepless nights: *Derailers* / TAble top dancer: *Kane, Kieran* / I don't believe it yet: *Craig, Cathryn* / This side of heaven: *Campbell, Kate* / Cadillac Elvis: *Griffin, Sid* / One last question: *Jason & The Scorchers* / Only one angel: *LaFave, Jimmy* / I don't think of her: *Neuwirth, Bob* / Litst of reasons: *Watson, Dale* / Nobody's girl: *Peters, Gretchen* / Black sanke gilmore: *Gilmore, Jimmie Dale* / Pyramid of tears: *Escovedo, Alejandro* / Ourland: *Allen, Terry* / Gourds: *Gourds*
BOKA 001CD / 9 Mar '98 / Abokadisc

☐ **VIVA BRASIL**
NSCD 037 / 18 May '98 / Nascente

☐ **VIVA DIABLO BLANCO (Freestyle Beats Vol.1)**
Lopez: *808 State* / Song for Lindy: *Fatboy Slim* / Airport: *Supercharger* / Shakey shakey: *Philadelphia Bluntz* / Ain't talkin' 'bout dub: *Apollo 440* / Timber: *Grantby* / Bend: *Egg* / Finders and creepers: *Runaways* / One night: *Aloof* / Who do you trust: *Arkarna* / Tales from the hard side: *Santana, Omar* / Moog island: *Morcheeba* / Something always happens: *Art Of Noise*
ZEN 013CD / Mar '97 / Indochina

☐ **VIVA EURO POP**
Fantasy / Rhythm of the night / Don't stop (wiggle wiggle) / Baby baby / Power / U got 2 let the music / Real thing / Right in the night / Ain't no love (ain't no use) / La danse d'helene / Key the secret / It's my life / Doop / Saturday night / Another night / What is love / Viva la bamba (hot hot hot) / No limit / Scatman / Cotton eye joe / Don't give me your life / Dreamer / Run to you / Get-a-way / Mr vain / Get ready for this / Pump up the jam / Stayin' alive / Children / Whoomph (there it is) (short stab) / Let me be your fantasy / U sure do / Just a little bit / Zombie / Boom boom boom / Always something there to remind me / Missing / Pump up the volume / Theme from s-express / Rockin' for myself
0630152072 / May '96 / East West

☐ **VIVA HACIENDA (3CD Set)**
Dirty talk: *Klein & The MBO* / Confusion: *New Order* / Al nafish: *Hashim* / Boogie down Bronx: *Man Parrish* / Let the music play: *Shannon* / Beat the street: *Redd, Sharon* / Don't make me wait: *Peech Boys* / Seventh heaven: *Guthrie, Gwen* / Twilight: *Maze* / All in all: *Sims, Joyce* / This brutal house: *Nitro Deluxe* / No way back: *Adonis* / Give yourself to me: *Farley, Farley, Farley* / Can U feel it: *Mr. Fingers* / Pump up Chicago: *Mr. Lee* / Slam: *Phuture* / Carino: *T-Coy* / Dream 17: *Annette* / I'm in love: *Shalor* / There's an acid house going on: *London Beat* / Dream girl: *Pierre's Pfantasy Club* / Where love lives: *Limerick, Alison* / M'baby: *Karma* / Know how: *Young MC* / Slasa house: *Richie Rich* / Wild times: *Deee-Lite* / I like it: *Landlord* / French kiss: *Lil' Louis* / Love sensation: *Holloway, Loleatta* / Strings of life: *Rhythm Is Rhythm* / I'll be waiting: *Griffin, Clive* / Rise from your grave: *Phuture* / Been a long time: *Fog* / Bone: *Persuasion* / Oddyssey: *7th Movement* / An instrumental need: *Rosario, Ralphi* / Funk phenomena: *Van Helden, Armand* / Throw: *Paperclip People* / Bomb: *Bucketheads* / Fired up: *Funky Green Dogs* / You can't hide from your bud: *DJ Sneak* / Fly life: *Basement Jaxx* / Do da doo: *Robotman* / Book: *Salt City Orchestra*
74321486552 / May '97 / De-Construction

☐ **VIVA MEXICO (20 Mariachi Favourites)**
CDHOT 605 / Jun '96 / Charly

☐ **VIVA MEXICO**
Cielito lindo: *Parraguez, Luis* / Adelita: *Tobar, Rodrigo* / Malaguena: *Oliveira, Valdeci* / Volver: *Gonzalez* / La vikina: *Jerez, Mauricio* / Besame mucho: *Oliveira, Valdeci* / Siempre adios: *Duo Yucatan* / La cucaracha: *Tobar, Rodrigo* / Cucurucucu Paloma: *Gonzalez* / Solamente una vez: *Oliveira, Valdeci* / Indio Camaye: *Duo Yucatan* / La bamba: *Parraguez, Luis* / Tempo: *Oliveira, Valdeci* / Senora Morena: *Casco, Oscar* / Perdone me: *Duo Yucatan*
12728 / Aug '96 / Laserlight

☐ **VIVA SEVILLA (Flamenco Alhama)**
39840762 / 21 Aug '97 / Blue Flame

☐ **VOCAL AND INSTRUMENTAL MUSIC OF MONGOLIA**
TSCD 909 / Sep '94 / Topic

☐ **VOCAL BLUES AND JAZZ VOL.1 1921-1930**
DOCD 1004 / Apr '97 / Document

☐ **VOCAL BLUES AND JAZZ VOL.2 1921-1938**
DOCD 1012 / Jul '98 / Document

☐ **VOCAL DUETS 1924-1931**
DOCD 5526 / Apr '97 / Document

☐ **VOCAL GROUP HARMONY FROM TAURUS RECORDS**
You're for me: *Escorts* / At seventeen: *Vocal Lords* / So so long: *Knight, Bob Four* / I'm selling my heart: *Knight, Bob Four* / Pretty little Joanie: *Filler, Marty* / You tease me: *Knight, Bob Four* / So lonely: *Donnie & The Del-Chords* / When you're alone: *Donnie & The Del-Chords* / Yeah bom dom de dubi dubi: *Filler, Marty* / Place in your heart: *Joey* / She comes of age: *Filler, Marty* / I don't care: *Donnie & The Del-Chords* / Happy: *Escorts* / Be with you: *Donnie & The Del-Chords* / My prayer for you: *Fireflies* / Take you back again: *Jovations* / I found heaven: *Donnie & The Del-Chords* / You were mine: *Fireflies* / I need you: *Colombo, Joe* / This is the last time: *Huffman, Donnie* / Tell her: *Sinceres* / Could you mean more: *Fireflies* / That old feeling: *Donnie & The Del-Chords* / Tell me why: *Donnie & The Del-Chords* / Please say you want me: *Donnie & The Del-Chords* / I'm in the mood for love: *Donnie & The Del-Chords* / Guardian angel: *Donnie & The Del-Chords* / At the hop: *Donnie & The Del-Chords* / That's my desire: *Donnie & The Del-Chords* / Oh what a night: *Donnie & The Del-Chords* / Out of sight out of mind: *Donnie & The Del-Chords*
BB 55049 / Aug '97 / Buffalo Bop

☐ **VOCAL GROUPS (Coast To Coast)**
Call on me: *Mello Moods* / I tried and tried and tried: *Mello Moods* / I'm lost: *Mello Moods* / When I woke up this morning: *Mello Moods* / Christmas song: *Mello Moods* / Each time: *Cabineers* / My my my: *Cabineers* / Lost: *Cabineers* / Baby, where'd you go to: *Cabineers* / What's the matter with you: *Cabineers* / Baby mine: *Cabineers* / Thrill me baby: *Pierce, Henry* / Hey fine Mama: *Pierce, Henry* / That's bad: *Metronomes* / Come on and rock: *Dukes* / I was a fool: *Dukes* / Oh Kay: *Dukes* / Ooh bop she bop: *Dukes* / Zindy Lou: *Chimes* / Gone: *Belvin, Jesse* / One little blessing: *Belvin, Jesse* / Honey dew: *Gipson, Byron 'Slick' & The Sliders* / How do you kiss an angel: *Green, Vernon & The Phantoms* / Why oh why: *Church, Eugene* / Can it be: *Titans* / Red sails in the sunset: *Monitors*
CDCHD 594 / Oct '96 / Ace

☐ **VOCAL GROUPS, THE**
PLATCD 343 / Oct '90 / Platinum

☐ **VOCAL QUARTETS VOL.1 1928-1940**
DOCD 5537 / Jun '97 / Document

☐ **VOCAL QUARTETS VOL.2 1929-1932**
DOCD 5538 / Jun '97 / Document

☐ **VOCAL QUARTETS VOL.3 1927-1936**
DOCD 5539 / Jun '97 / Document

☐ **VOCAL QUARTETS VOL.4 1927-1943**
DOCD 5540 / Jul '97 / Document

☐ **VOCAL QUARTETS VOL.5 1924-1928**
DOCD 5541 / Jul '97 / Document

☐ **VOCAL QUARTETS VOL.6 1928-1944**
DOCD 5542 / Jul '97 / Document

☐ **VOCAL QUARTETS VOL.7 1925-1943**
DOCD 5543 / Jul '97 / Document

☐ **VOCAL REFRAIN**
MAK 103 / Nov '94 / Avid

☐ **VOCAL TRADITIONS OF ALBANIA**
Shqiptaria bashke gjithmone / Nje thelleze e shkruar prilli / Smarte moj / Kenge vaji / Ne gjume isha dhe u zgjova / Kenge popullore qytetare / Ne maje te shelgut / Kam shtepine me rasa / Larg nga vendi i bardhe flori / Fyell i tanes / Bec patani / Ra nje lot dhe lagu syt / Me muar malli me muar / Djale te bukur te beri nena / Vajta nje dite ne pazar / Qaj moj zemer qaj / Zani i nanes / Kenge per meco bonen / Ymer aga / Lan vasha ne gure te lumit / Moj kosove trimneshe dardane / Medet o riza medet / Dasmore sot asht tan shqipnija
CDSDL 421 / Oct '97 / Saydisc

☐ **VOCAL TRADITIONS OF BULGARIA**
Mari Maro / Snoshti vecher u vas byah / Polegnala bela pshenitza / Momne le mari hubava / Vido dva vetra veyat / Ziadi mi rayo / Dosto, mome dosto / Shto yubavo sofiskoto pole / Zamurknaya petstotin aiduka / Senkya pada / Bre Nikola Nikola / Devoiko Mari Hubava / Rechenski kamuk reka zaglavya / Rasti bore / Zazhena se niva / Pominalo e devoiche / Rodilo se muzhko dete / Zluntzeto trepti zauda / Pusni ma maicho / Doide mi obed pladnina / Done ide ot manastir
CDSDL 396 / Mar '94 / Saydisc

☐ **VOCALS & INSTRUMENTALS POLYPHONIES OF ETHIOPIA (2CD Set)**
C 580055/56 / May '94 / Ocora

☐ **VOICE OF FOLK, THE**
When I first came to Caledonia: *Waterson, Norma* / Old horse: *Carthy, Martin* / Grey cock: *Carthy, Eliza* / Bonnie lass amang the heather: *Gaughan, Dick* / Little pot stove: *Jones, Nic* / Somewhere along the road: *Prior, Maddy* / Four loom weaver: *MacColl, Ewan* / Old man Jones: *Kirkpatrick, John* / King of Rome: *Tabor, June* / Shipyard apprentice: *Battlefield Band* / False true lover: *Collins, Shirley* / Joh: *Four Men & A Dog* / Time to ring some changes: *Thompson, Richard* / Striking for another land: *Albion Band* / Dr. Fausters tumblers/The night of Trafalgar/Prince William: *Brass Monkey*
TSCD 705 / Oct '96 / Topic

☐ **VOICE OF SPAIN 1927-1931**
HTCD 38 / Sep '96 / Heritage

☐ **VOICE OF THE BLUES (Bottleneck Masterpieces)**
Goin' up the country: *Barbecue Bob* / Decatur Street 81: *Georgia Browns* / Ground hog blues: *Ramblin' Thomas* / Keep on trying: *Tampa Kid* / She's coming back some cold rainy day: *Georgia Cotton Pickers* / Jefferson country blues: *Butler, Sam* / Come over to my house baby: *Woods, Oscar 'Buddy'* / When the saints go marchinh in: *Davis, Blind Willie* / Voice of the blues: *Scruggs, Irene* / She's a hum dum dinger from Dingersville: *Davis, Jimmie* / Corrine corrina blues: *Too Bad Boys* / Laughing rag: *Smeck, Roy* / Selling that stuff: *Hokum Boys* / I want you to lead me on: *Terrell, Sister O.M.*
YZZCD 1046 / May '98 / Yazoo

☐ **VOICE OF THE FULBE - BURKINA FASO**
LDX 2741079 / Jul '97 / Le Chant Du Monde

☐ **VOICES (Hannibal Sampler)**
HNCD 8301 / Feb '90 / Hannibal

☐ **VOICES (English Traditional Songs)**
FE 087CD / Nov '95 / Fellside

☐ **VOICES FROM LONG DISTANCE**
3018652 / Apr '97 / Long Distance

☐ **VOICES FROM THE GHETTO - YIDDISH**
242066 / Aug '93 / FNAC

☐ **VOICES IN CONTROL (The R&B Flavours Album)**
Cold world: *Haynes, Victor* / Slow down boy: *Cambell, Jackie* / Everything's alright: *Haynes, Victor* / Can't run: *Zee, Dawn* / Don't make me wait: *Haynes, Victor & Kenny T* / Slow jam/Interlude: *Haynes, Victor* / Do me right: *Zee, Dawn & Victor Haynes* / Love won't let me wait: *Haynes, Victor* / Surrender: *Sani* / Slow jam tonight: *Zee, Dawn & Victor Haynes* / For the love of you: *Haynes, Victor* / Out of luck: *Cambell, Jackie* / That's what love can do: *Shelton, Yvonne*
EXCDP 10 / May '96 / Expansion

☐ **VOICES OF AMERICA (Vocal Harmony Groups: Then & Now)**
Whispering bells: *Del-Vikings* / For your precious love: *Butler, Jerry & The Impressions* / Oh what a night: *Dells* / Everybody plays the fool: *Main Ingredient* / Thousand stars: *Rivileers* / Blue moon: *Marcels* / PS I love you: *Four Vagabonds* / Catalina I love you: *Four Preps* / Till then: *Mills Brothers* / Morse code of love: *Capris* / Sincerely: *Moonglows* / Have you seen her: *Chi-Lites* / Count every star: *Ravens* / I got rhythm: *Happenings* / Crying in the chapel: *Orioles* / I don't want to set the world on fire: *Ink Spots* / Chapel of dreams: *Valentinos* / (Now and then there's) A fool such as I: *Robins* / Please don't say you want me: *Schoolboys* / Don't sit under the apple tree: *Andrews Sisters* / Crazy for you: *Heartbeats* / Do it again: *Beach Boys* / Gang that sang heart of my heart: *Four Aces* / Opportunity: *Jewels* / I wonder why: *Dion & The Belmonts* / If I ever fall in love: *Shai*
CDCHD 416 / Jun '96 / Ace

☐ **VOICES OF DRUM N' BASS**
MILL 062CD / 11 May '98 / Millenium

☐ **VOICES OF IRELAND**
ECD 3396 / 23 Feb '98 / K-Tel

☐ **VOICES OF SARDINIA VOL.1 (Tenore De Orosei)**
9100212 / Apr '98 / Winter & Winter

☐ **VOICES OF SARDINIA VOL.2 (Concordu De Orosei)**
9100222 / Apr '98 / Winter & Winter

☐ **VOICES OF THE ORIENT (North India/ Iran/Syria/3CD Set)**
C 570305 / Mar '97 / Ocora

☐ **VOICES OF THE RAIN FOREST**
From morning night to real morning / Making sago / Cutting trees / Clearing the brush / Bamboo Jew's harp / From afternoon to afternoon darkening / Evening rainstorm / Drumming / Song ceremony / From night to inside night / Relaxing by the creek
RCD 10173 / Jul '91 / Rykodisc

☐ **VOICES OF THE SPIRITS - SONGS AND CHANTS**
ELL 3210A / Oct '93 / Ellipsis Arts

☐ **VOICES OF THE UKRAINE**
PS 65145CD / Jul '95 / PlayaSound

☐ **VOICES OF THE WORLD (An Anthology Of Vocal Expression/3CD Set)**
CMX 374101012 / Dec '96 / Le Chant Du Monde

☐ **VOIX CELTIQUE**
KMCD 77 / Dec '97 / Keltia Musique

☐ **VOLCANO (20 Super Hits)**
SONCD 0005 / Oct '90 / Sonic Sounds

☐ **VOLCANO ERUPTION, THE**
SONCD 0050 / Jul '93 / Sonic Sounds

☐ **VORSPRUNG DURCH DRUM 'N' BASS**
SPV 08947672 / Nov '97 / SPV

☐ **VORTEX ENERGIZE**
IRB 59982 / Sep '96 / Deep Blue

☐ **VOX HUMANA (Voices Through Time)**
0630200312 / 16 Feb '98 / Erato

☐ **VOYAGE INTO TRANCE VOL.1, A**
BFLCD 14 / 1 Sep '98 / Butterfly

☐ **VOYAGE INTO TRANCE VOL.2, A**
BFLCD 20 / 1 Sep '98 / Butterfly

☐ **VOYAGE TO PLANET DOG**
Dream messages: *Timeshard* / Discovery: *Future Loop Foundation* / Area 51: *Eat Static* / Sheesha: *Banco De Gaia* / Visitor: *Children Of The Bong* / Spirit catcher: *Future Loop Foundation* / Last train to Lhasa: *Banco De Gaia* / Brain: *Eat Static*
BARKCD 027 / 23 Feb '98 / Planet Dog

☐ **VYBIN' - THE BEST OF VYBIN' (2CD Set)**
Return of the mack: *Morrison, Mark* / I got 5 on it: *Luniz* / Nobody knows: *Rich, Tony* / Waterfalls: *TLC* / Tha crossroads: *Bone Thugs n' Harmony* / Shy guy: *King, Diana* / Bump 'n' grind: *Kelly, R* / I will survive: *Savage, Chantay* / One for the money: *Brown, Horace* / You're the one: *SWV* / How many ways: *Braxton, Toni* / If I ruled the world: *Nas* / Mutual feeling: *Knight, Beverley* / Woo hah got you all in check: *Busta Rhymes* / I wanna be down: *Brandy* / Feels so good: *Xscape* / Like this and like that: *Monica* / G-spot: *Marshall, Wayne* / Kissin' you: *Total* / Gangsta's paradise: *Coolio* / Virtual insanity: *Jamiroquai* / Good thing: *Eternal* / Bombastic: *Shaggy* / Ocean drive: *Lighthouse Family* / Love enuff: *Soul II Soul* / 24/7: *3T* / Sweetness: *Gayle, Michelle* / If you love me: *Brownstone* / Every day of the week: *Jade* / Like a playa: *La Ganz* / Back and forth: *Aaliyah* / Down 4 whateva: *Nuttin' Nyce* / Undercover lover: *Smooth* / Freak like me: *Howard, Adina* / Only you: *112 & Notorious BIG* / (Can't always have) sunshine: *SC223* / Get it on: *Clash Of Culture* / Sentimental: *Cox, Deborah* / Je t'aime: *SS Soul* / Boom biddy bye bye: *Cypress Hill*
RADCD 45 / Nov '96 / Global TV

☐ **VYBIN' VOL.1 (New Soul Rebels)**
Sight for sore eyes: *M-People* / Bump 'n' grind: *R Kelly* / Breathe again: *Braxton, Toni* / My lovin': *En Vogue* / Stay: *Eternal* / Body and soul: *Baker, Anita* / Right here: *SWV* / Be happy: *Blige, Mary J.* / I wanna be down: *Brandy* / Revival: *Girault, Martine* / Dream on dreamer: *Brand New Heavies* / Apparently nothing: *Young Disciples* / Always there: *Incognito* /

VYBIN' VOL.1 COMPILATIONS R.E.D. CD CATALOGUE

Down that road: *Nelson, Shara* / Unfinished sympathy: *Massive Attack* / Don't walk away: *Jade* / Back and forth: *Aaliyah* / G-Spot: *Marshall, Wayne* / Stroke you up: *Changing Faces* / Back to life: *Soul II Soul*

RADCD 05 / Feb '95 / Global TV

☐ **VYBIN' VOL.2 (2CD Set)**

Creep: *TLC* / Gangsta's paradise: *Coolio & LV* / Sentimental: *Cox, Deborah* / She's got that vibe: *Kelly, R* / I can't tell you why: *Brownstone* / Two can play that game: *Brown, Bobby* / How many ways: *Braxton, Toni* / Freek 'n' you: *Jodeci* / Freak like me: *Howard, Adina* / Down 4 whateva: *Nuttin' Nyce* / Party all night: *Kreuz* / Candy rain: *Soul For Real* / Been thinking about you: *Girault, Martine* / G-spot: *Marshall, Wayne* / Down for the one: *Knight, Beverley* / Finest: *Truce* / Most beautiful boy: *Mayte* / If I ever fall in love: *Shai* / (You make me feel like a) natural woman: *Blige, Mary J.* / Don't take it personal: *Monica* / Best friend: *Brandy* / I like: *Kut Klose* / Age ain't nothing but a number: *Aaliyah* / You remind me of something: *Kelly, R* / Think of you: *Usher* / Just kickin: *Xscape* / Rock wit'cha: *Brown, Bobby* / Flavour of the old school: *Knight, Beverley* / Right here: *SWV* / Free/sail on: *Moore, Chante* / Hey Mr DJ: *Zhane* / I know: *Thompson, Tony* / Good life: *Ebony Vibe Everlasting* / Crazy: *Morrison, Mark* / Let's get it on: *Jade* / One more chance/stay with me: *Notorious BIG* / You used tolove me: *Evans, Faith* / Je t'aime: *SS Soul* / Mind blowin: *Smooth*

RADCD 19 / Feb '96 / Global TV

☐ **VYBIN' VOL.3 (2CD Set)**

Return of the mack: *Morrison, Mark* / Diggin' on you: *TLC* / I got 5 in it: *Luniz* / If you love me: *Brownstone* / Your body's callin': *Kelly, R* / Rock wit'cha: *Brown, Bobby* / Love enuff: *Soul II Soul* / I wish: *Skee Lo* / Tell me what you like: *Guy* / Who can I run to: *Jordan, Montell* / Brokenhearted: *Brandy* / Regulate: *Warren G* / Moving on up (on the right side): *Knight, Beverley* / Gimme that body: *Q-Tee* / Circles: *Don-E* / So good (to come home to): *Matias, Ivan* / Throw your hand up: *Aaliyah* / (Can't always have) sunshine: *C 223* / Search for the hero: *M-People* / I will survive: *Savage, Chantay* / 1,2,3,4 (sumpin' new): *Coolio* / Cruisin': *D'Angelo* / Every day of the week: *Jade* / All the things (your man won't do): *Joe* / I'm so into you: *SWV* / Love u 4 life: *Jodeci* / Like this and like that: *Monica* / Hump tonight: *Marshall, Wayne* / Down low (nobody has to know): *Kelly, R* / Love city groove: *Love City Groove* / Freedom: *Gayle, Michelle* / Keep on groovin': *Kreuz* / Are u ready: *Celetia* / Celebration of life: *Truce*

RADCD 33 / Apr '96 / Global TV

☐ **VYBIN' VOL.4 (2CD Set)**

Nobody knows: *Rich, Tony Project* / Thank god it's Friday: *R Kelly* / Lifted: *Lighthouse Family* / Waterfalls: *TLC* / Where love lives: *Limerick, Alison* / You're the one: *SWV* / Everyday: *Incognito* / Mary Jane (all night long): *Blige, Mary J.* / I'll be there for you/You're all I need to get by: *Method Man & Mary J. Blige* / Humpin' around: *Brown, Bobby* / Who do u love: *Cox, Deborah* / Something 4 da honeyz: *Jordan, Montell* / Taste your love: *Brown, Horace* / Young nation: *Aaliyah* / Movin' on: *Brandy* / Woo hah got you all in check: *Busta Rhymes* / Get on up: *Jodeci* / I'll be around: *Rappin' 4-Tay* / Too hot: *Coolio* / Sound of da police: *KRS 1* / Good thing: *Eternal* / Undercover lover: *Smooth* / Love of mine: *Earth Gyrlz* / Desire: *Nu Colours* / Everyday and evrynight: *Michelle, Yvette* / Feels so good: *Xscape* / Before you walk out of my life: *Monica* / Grapevine: *Brownstone* / Remedy: *Knight, Beverley* / Lay my body down: *Kut Klose* / Soon as I get home: *Evans, Faith* / My cherie amour: *Thompson, Tony* / Tell somebody: *Thompson, Tony* / Don't look any further: *M-People* / Every little thing I do: *Soul For Real* / Missing your love: *Celetia* / Get down on it: *Kreuz* / Robyn: *Kreuz* / Don't come to stay: *Hot House* / I will survive: *Savage, Chantay*

RADCD 38 / Jul '96 / Global TV

W

☐ **WA-CHI-KA-NOCKA**

Wigwam Willie: *Phillips, Carl* / Indian Joe: *Adams, Art* / Warrior Sam: *Willis, Don* / Warpath: *Lenny & The Star Chiefs* / Cherokee stomp: *Tidwell, Bobby* / Cherokee rock: *Wheeler, Chuck* / Indian rock and roll: *Jerome, Ralph* / War paint: *Warriors* / Kaw-liga: *Porter, Bruce* / Rock my warriors rock: *Jackson, Joe* / Wa-chic-ka-noka: *Holmes, Tommy* / Witchapoo: *Cathey, Frank* / Geronimo: *Renegade* / Indian squaw: *Kellwoods* / Geronimo stomp: *Darvell, Barry* / Big indian: *Downs, Tommy* / Chief whoopin' koff: *Royal Knights* / Little brave: *Smalling, Eddie* / Little bull and buttercup: *Homer, Chris* / Massacre: *Ronny & Johnny* / Wahoo: *Bennett, Arnold* / Bobby sox squaw: *Impacts* / Tomahawk: *Brown, Tom* / Rockin' redwing: *Masters, Sammy* / Red wing: *Wayne, Gordon* / Indian moon: *Chieftones* / Medicine man: *Warren, Bobby Five* / Rattlesnake: *Bayou, Billy* / Cowboys and indians: *Brent, Ronnie* / Indian rock: *Musical Lynn Twins*

CDBB 55011 / Apr '94 / Buffalo Bop

☐ **WADE IN THE WATERS VOL.1 (Spirituals)**

SFWCD 40072 / Jun '94 / Smithsonian Folkways

☐ **WADE IN THE WATERS VOL.2 (Congregation Singing)**

SFWCD 40073 / Jun '94 / Smithsonian Folkways

☐ **WADE IN THE WATERS VOL.3 (Gospel Pioneers)**

SFWCD 40074 / Jun '94 / Smithsonian Folkways

☐ **WADE IN THE WATERS VOL.4 (Community Gospel)**

SFWCD 40075 / Jun '94 / Smithsonian Folkways

☐ **WAIL DADDY (Excello Nashville Jump Blues)**

Chicken hearted woman: *Samuels, Clarence* / Dyna-flow: *Cooley, Jack* / Tom Tom boogie: *Cooley, Jack* / Glad I don't worry no more: *Fat Man* / Back alley boogie: *Johnson, Sherman* / Allotment blues: *Dowell, Charlie & Willie Lee Patton* / Wail Daddy: *Dowell, Charlie & Willie Lee Patton* / Down south in Birmingham: *Thorne, Del & Her Trio* / New Memphis blues: *Shy Guy Douglas* / Detroit arrow: *Shy Guy Douglas* / Happy go lucky: *Good Rockin' Beasley* / Drive soldiers drive: *Bailey, Little Maxie* / My baby's blues: *Bailey, Little Maxie* / Goof train: *Thorne, Del & Her Trio* / Fly chick blues: *Thorne, Del & Her Trio* / Yeh it's true: *Hardison, Bernie* / Love me baby: *Hardison, Bernie* / Watch on: *Blue Flamers* / Lazy Pete: *Roosevelt, Lee* / Late every evening: *McGhee, Tommy* / Poppin': *McGhee, Tommy* / Prize fightin' papa: *Bryant, Beulah* / Too many keys: *Prince, Bobby* / Driving down the highway: *Blue Flamers*

CDCHD 653 / Jun '97 / Ace

☐ **WAITING TO BE OLD**

OPPROBRIUM 1 / 25 Aug '97 / Opprobrium

☐ **WAKE UP DEAD MAN**

ROUCD 2013 / Aug '94 / Rounder

☐ **WAKE UP JAMAICA**

CDTRL 331 / Mar '94 / Trojan

☐ **WALK ON THE WILD SIDE (Soft Rock Classics - 2CD Set)**

Walk on the wild side: *Reed, Lou* / All around the world: *Stansfield, Lisa* / Rapture: *Blondie* / If you let me stay: *D'Arby, Terence Trent* / Would I lie to you: *Eurythmics* / Golden brown: *Stranglers* / Simply irresistible: *Palmer, Robert* / Storm music: *Scott-Heron, Gil* / High powered love: *Harris, Emmylou* / Never met a girl like you before: *Collins, Edwyn* / All through the night: *Lauper, Cyndi* / Power of love: *Lewis, Huey & The News* / In the name of love: *Thompson Twins* / This city never sleeps: *Eurythmics* / Blinded by the light: *Manfred Mann's Earthband* / Unchained melody: *Robson & Jerome* / Rich girl: *Hall & Oates* / I scare myself: *Dolby, Thomas* / These dreams: *Heart* / Perfect day: *Reed, Lou* / You're the voice: *Farnham, John* / Kyrie: *Mr. Mister* / Nothing's gonna stop us now: *Starship* / Guaranteed: *Level 42* / Move closer: *Nelson, Phyllis* / We've got tonight: *Brooks, Elkie* / Atmospherics: *Robinson, Tom* / Ship of fools: *Erasure* / Maneater: *Hall & Oates* / Signed, sealed, delivered: *Turner, Ruby* / You took the words right out of my mouth: *Meat Loaf* / Ain't no sunshine: *Withers, Bill* / Hand on my heart: *Shriekback* / Wherever I lay my hat (that's my home): *Young, Paul*

RCACD 213 / Jul '97 / RCA

☐ **WALK RIGHT IN (Essential Memphis Blues)**

My money never runs out: *Cannon, Gus* / Mr. Crump don't like it: *Beale Street Sheiks* / Twelve pound daddy: *Dickson, Pearl* / Ain't nobody's business if I do: *Stokes, Frank* / Happy blues: *Dickson, Tom* / I will turn your money green: *Lewis, Furry* / Judge Harsh blues: *Lewis, Furry* / Rolling stone: *Wilkins, Robert* / That's no way to get along: *Wilkins, Robert* / Walk right in: *Canon's Jug Stompers* / KC moan: *Memphis Jug Band* / Cocaine habit blues: *Memphis Jug Band* / Travelling Mama blues: *Calicott, Joe* / Bedside blues: *Thompkins, Jim* / Ticket agent blues: *Lewis, Noah Jug Band* / Hesitation blues: *Jackson, Jim* / Can I do it for you: *Memphis Minnie & Kansas Joe* / Granpa and Grandma blues: *Memphis Minnie Jug Band* / Highway No.61 blues: *Kelly, Jack & His South Memphis Jug Band* / Moanin' the blues: *Shaw, Allen* / Sugar farm blues: *Rachell, Yank* / Need more blues: *Estes, 'Sleepy' John* / Renewed love blues: *Doyle, Little Buddy*

IGOCD 2038 / Jun '97 / Indigo

☐ **WALK THE LINE**

Southern kickin' finger lickin': *Cane Honey, T.* / That's my story: *Nashville Cats* / Hang in there Superman: *Nashville Cats* / Walkin' the line: *Sheriff, Dave* / Back in your arms again: *Nashville Cats* / Cannibals: *Nashville Cats* / I forgot to remember: *Dean Brothers* / Cowboy stomp: *Nashville Cats* / Life is good: *Nashville Cats* / Set me free: *Horsfall, Des* / Black coffee: *Nashville Cats* / Daddy's money: *Nashville Cats* / I need somebody: *Cheap Seats* / My Maria: *Nashville Cats* / Cherokee boogie: *Nashville Cats* / Party's over: *Ambler, Tim*

TRMCD 001 / May '97 / Thorny Rose

☐ **WALK THE LINE VOL.2**

TRMCD 002 / 27 May '98 / Thorny Rose

☐ **WALKING ON SUNSHINE (2CD Set)**

NSCD 016 / Feb '95 / Newsound

☐ **WALL OF PUSSY (Wall Of Sound/Pussy Foot Compilation)**

WALLPUSSCD 1 / May '96 / Wall Of Sound

☐ **WALL OF SOUND VOL.1 (The First XI)**

Macarena madness: *E-Klektik* / Phatty's lunchbox: *Mekon* / Jazzadelica: *Akasha* / Kicks: *Agent Provocateur* / 'D'Ecoutez: *Rootless* / Fly to sangeetha: *Zoot Woman* / Dollar: *Artery* / Nil by mouth: *Wiseguys* / Trickshot: *Ceasefire* / Gettin' stupid: *Dirty Beatniks* / Painiac: *Mekon & Artery*

WALLCD 004 / 22 Sep '97 / Wall Of Sound

☐ **WALL OF SOUND VOL.2 (The Second XI)**

Revenge of the mekon: *Mekon & Mad Frankie Fraser* / Salvage: *Wreckage* / Kickin' off: *Hustlers Of Culture* / Go faster: *Propellerheads* / Red tape: *Agent Provocateur* / We keep on: *Wiseguys & Sense Live* / Kontakte: *Les Rhythmes Digitales* / Spanish fly: *Akasha* / Beatnik bounce: *Dirty Beatniks* / Welcome to tackletown: *Mekon & Evil B. & Jah Norris* / Hot pursuit: *Naked All Stars*

WALLCD 014 / 22 Sep '97 / Wall Of Sound

☐ **WALTZING AROUND IRELAND**

Black velvet band / Do you want your oul lobby washed down / One day at a time / Accordion selection / Rose of mooncoin / Rose of Tralee / Rose of Aranmore / My Eileen is waiting for me / 40 Shades of green / County Armagh / Mountains of Mourne / Green glens of Antrim / Der little Ireland / Red rose cafe / Galway bay / Girl from Donegal / If those lips can only speak / Old claddagh ring / Irish harvest day / Love is teasing / Cockles and mussels

RBCD 523 / Jun '97 / Sharpe

☐ **WALTZING MATILDA (Australian Folk Tunes)**

IMCD 3005 / Feb '96 / Image

☐ **WANG WEIPING (Pipa Lute)**

C 560128 / Apr '98 / Ocora

☐ **WANTED**

HAGCD 003 / May '97 / Hag

☐ **WANTED - THE OUTLAWS**

My heroes have always been cowboys: *Jennings, Waylon* / Honky tonk heroes (Like me): *Jennings, Waylon* / Slow movin' outlaws: *Jennings, Waylon* / (I'm a) Ramblin' man: *Jennings, Waylon* / I'm looking for blue eyes: *Colter, Jessi* / You mean to say: *Colter, Jessi* / Why have you been gone so long: *Colter, Jessi* / Suspicious minds: *Jennings, Waylon & Willie Nelson* / Good hearted woman: *Jennings, Waylon & Willie Nelson* / Heaven and hell: *Jennings, Waylon & Willie Nelson* / Under your spell again: *Jennings, Waylon & Willie Nelson* / I ain't the one: *Jennings, Waylon & Willie Nelson* / Nowhere road: *Jennings, Waylon & Willie Nelson* / Me and Paul: *Nelson, Willie* / Yesterdays wine: *Nelson, Willie* / T For Texas: *Glaser, Tompall* / Put another log on the fire: *Glaser, Tompall* / You left a long, long time ago: *Nelson, Willie* / Healing hands of time: *Nelson, Willie* / If she's where you like livin' (You won't feel at home with: *Colter, Jessi* / It's not easy: *Colter, Jessi*

7863668412 / Jun '96 / RCA

☐ **WAR COMPILATION**

WAR 005CD / Apr '96 / Wrong Again

☐ **WAREHOUSE RAVES VOL.1**

Numero uno: *Starlight* / Guitarra: *Raul* / Love is life: *Candy Flip* / Te amo: *Navarro, Raimunda* / Love sensation: *Holloway, Loleatta* / 69: *Brooklyn Express* / Paradhouse: *Koxo Club Band* / Why can't we live together: *Illusion* / It's a dream: *Amnesia* / Let me love you for tonight: *Kariya* / Just a little bit: *Total Science* / Strings of life: *Rhythim Is Rhythim*

CDRUMD 101 / Sep '89 / Rumour

☐ **WAREHOUSE RAVES VOL.2**

CDRUMD 102 / May '92 / Rumour

☐ **WAREHOUSE RAVES VOL.3**

CDRUMD 103 / Mar '90 / Rumour

☐ **WARP FACTOR 1 (Space Funk And Cosmic Beats)**

Fedime's flight: *Jazzanova* / Heavy handed: *Raw Airs* / Slide: *OOTOP* / Chrystalline: *Fantomas* / La theme: *Mighty Bop* / Callin' W2: *DJ Bi-Cen* / Con bass: *Cortiz, Alex* / 1000 nudes: *Divine Sounds Orchestra* / Wavesea: *Mira, Elisa Calmo* / I'm not here: *Soul Quality Quartet* / Sidewinder: *Cubana Bop & Pucho* / Baby lush: *Rikki Blue*

GIO 001CD / 23 Feb '98 / Kingkladze

☐ **WARRIOR ON THE BATTLEFIELD, A (1920s/1940s A Capella)**

Daniel in the lion's den: *Norfolk Jubilee Quartet* / I got a home in that rock: *TCI Womens Four* / Jog a-long boys: *Pullman Porters Quartet* / So glad I've got the stone: *Bethel Quartet* / Jesus the light of the world: *Bethel Quartet* / I am a pilgrim: *Silver Leaf Quartette Of Norfolk* / Our Father: *Silver Leaf Quartette Of Norfolk* / My soul is a witness for my Lord: *Silver Leaf Quartette Of Norfolk* / You better let that liar alone: *Silver Leaf Quartette Of Norfolk* / Sleep on mother: *Silver Leaf Quartette Of Norfolk* / Ship is at the landing: *Silver Leaf Quartette Of Norfolk* / I'm going home on the Chickasaw train: *IC Glee Quartet* / Do you want to be a lover of the Lord: *Davis Bible Singers* / Daniel saw the stone: *Davis Bible Singers* / Light of the world: *Dunham Jubilee Singers* / I'm leaning on the Lord: *Famous Blue Jay Singers* / New dry bones: *Heavenly Gospel Singers* / Going back with Jesus: *Heavenly Gospel Singers* / Warrior on the battlefield: *Golden Eagle Gospel Singers* / Prodigal Son: *Golden Eagle Gospel Singers* / Jonah: *Golden Gate Jubilee Quartet* / Found a wonderful saviour: *Golden Gate Jubilee Quartet* / Blind Barnabus: *Golden Gate Jubilee Quartet* / He never said a mumblin' word: *Golden Gate Jubilee Quartet* / Run on: *Golden Gate Jubilee Quartet*

ROUCD 1137 / Nov '97 / Rounder

☐ **WARTIME FAVOURITES VOL.1 - THE EARLY YEARS**

They can't black out the moon: *Roy, Harry & His Orchestra* / God bless you Mr. Chamberlain: *Roy, Harry & His Orchestra* / Oh ain't it grand to be in the navy: *Roy, Harry & His Orchestra* / Nasty Adolf Hitler: *Ambrose & His Orchestra* / Rhymes of the times: *Ambrose & His Orchestra* / Spitfire song: *Loss, Joe & His Orchestra* / Adolf: *Ambrose & His Orchestra* / One certain soldier: *Carless, Dorothy* / We're going to hang out the washing: *Ambrose & His Orchestra* / When that man is dead and gone: *Geraldo & His Dance Orchestra* / Run rabbit run: *Roy, Harry & His Orchestra* / Wings over the navy: *Cotton, Billy & His Band* / Kiss me goodnight, Sergeant Major: *Cotton, Billy & His Band* / FDR Jones: *Roy, Harry & His Orchestra* / Lords of the air: *Loss, Joe Band* / Tiggerty boo: *Roy, Harry & His Band* / It's a paor of wings for me: *Gonella, Nat & His Georgians* / Nice kind Sergeant Major: *Long, Norman* / There'll always be an England: *Loss, Joe Band*

RAJCD 825 / 3 Aug '98 / Empress

☐ **WARTIME FAVOURITES VOL.2 - SONGS OF D-DAY**

Homeward bound: *Hall, Henry Orchestra* / Don't ask me why/Whistling in the dark/Hey good looking: *Preager, Lou & His Orchestra* / I never mention your name: *Roy, Harry & His Band* / Milkman keep those bottles quiet: *Squadronaires* / I heard you cry last night: *Preager, Lou & His Orchestra* / My heart tells me: *Roy, Harry & His Band* / San fernando valley: *Skyrockets Dance Orchestra* / Shoo shoo baby: *Preager, Lou & His Orchestra* / How sweet you are: *Roy, Harry & His Band* / Do you believe in dreams: *Skyrockets Dance Orchestra* / I'll get by/A lovely way to spend an evening/All of my life: *Melachrino, George & His Orchestra* / So dumb but so beautiful: *Skyrockets Dance Orchestra* / Macnamara's band: *Geraldo & His Orchestra* / Padulah: *Hall, Henry Orchestra* / I left my heart at the stage door canteen: *Ambrose & His Orchestra* / Is you is or is you ain't my baby: *Skyrockets Dance Orchestra* / Spring will be a little late this year: *Skyrockets Dance Orchestra* / Dreamer: *Hall, Henry Orchestra* / Close to you: *Ambrose & His Orchestra* / Is my baby blue tonight: *Crowe, George & The Blue Mariners* / Chocolate soldier from the USA: *Parry, Harry & His Radio Rhythm Club Sextet* / Mairzy doats and dozy doats: *Preager, Lou & His Orchestra* / October mood: *Skyrockets Dance Orchestra*

RAJCD 826 / Aug '94 / Empress

☐ **WARTIME FAVOURITES VOL.3 - VICTORY**

Keep an eye on your heart: *Geraldo & His Orchestra* / What more can I say: *Thorburn, Billy* / Don't sit under the apple tree: *Crosby, Bob & His Orchestra* / In my arms: *Geraldo & His Orchestra* / It costs so little: *Thorburn, Billy* / Smiths and the Jones: *Geraldo & His Orchestra* / All over the place: *New Mayfair Dance Orchestra* / You are my sunshine: *Roy, Harry & His Band* / You can't say no to a solider: *Geraldo & His Orchestra* / It's foolish but it's fun: *Thorburn, Billy* / Five o'clock whistle: *Loss, Joe & His Orchestra* / We three: *Gonella, Nat & His Georgians* / Hey Mabel: *Winstone, Eric* / Aurora: *Dorsey, Jimmy Orchestra* / Jingle jangle jingle: *Winstone, Eric & His Band* / Sailor with the navy blue eyes: *Roy, Harry & His Band* / Six lessons from Madame La Zonga: *Dorsey, Jimmy Orchestra* / I've got a gal in Kalamazoo: *Geraldo & His Orchestra* / I'm nobody's baby: *Gonella, Nat & His Georgians* / Yours: *Winstone, Eric & His Band* / Why don't you fall in love with me: *Roy, Harry & His Band* / Zoot suit: *Crosby, Bob & His Orchestra* / White cliffs of Dover: *Thorburn, Billy* / Pennsylvania polka: *Roy, Harry & His Band*

RAJCD 827 / Aug '94 / Empress

☐ **WARTIME MEMORIES 1939-1945 (The Sounds And Songs That Inspired The Nation)**

Mars / God of war / Battle of Britain march / Guns of Navarone / Longest day / Victory at sea / Dambusters march / 633 squadron / Colditz march / Marches medley / Keep the home fires burning / Lillie Marlene/We're gonna hang out the washing / White cliffs of Dover / It's a long way to Tipperary/Pack up your troubles / Bless 'em all / Medley / I'll be seeing you/We'll meet again / Dance hall medley / In the mood / Sweet Georgia Brown / Jumpin' at the Woodside / Jerusalem / Land of hope and glory / Rule Britannia

SUMCD 4091 / Jan '97 / Summit

☐ **WASHINGTON DC GARAGE**

COLCD 0523 / Jun '97 / Collectables

☐ **WASSAIL**

FE 125CD / Mar '98 / Fellside

☐ **WASSOULOU SOUND VOL.1**

STCD 1035 / Oct '91 / Stern's

☐ **WASSOULOU SOUND VOL.2**

Kani kassi / Gnoumna ke la / Kankeletigui / Nale nale / Ni la kani / Mougakan / Ita dia / Simbo / Barika bognala / Djina Mousso

STCD 1048 / Mar '94 / Stern's

☐ **WATCH HOW YOU FLEX (Reggae Dancehall)**

SHCD 45002 / Jun '93 / Shanachie

☐ **WATER AND ARCHITECTURE**

SR 120CD / 2 Mar '98 / Sub Rosa

☐ **WATER COMMUNICATION (2CD Set)**

Spaced in: *Newman, Colin* / Metal sea: *Immersion* / Immerse: *Pablo's Eye* / Last hand: *Ronnie & Clyde* / Quo vardis: *G-Man* / Limbic: *Lobe* / Hide: *Spigel, Malka* / Cypher: *Pablo's Eye* / Kiss: *Plastic Venus* / Automation: *Newman, Colin* / World gardening: *Oracle* / Water walker: *Trawl* / Flow motion: *Earth* / Hacol zaram beyachad: *Spigel, Malka* / Affective: *Lobe* / Cinnebar: *Ronnie & Clyde* / Train: *Plastic Venus* / How long (is a piece of string): *Immersion* / Shadow: *Dol-Lop* / Chinned: *G-Man*

DWM 20 / Feb '97 / Swim

☐ **WATERHOUSE REVISITED VOL.2**

HCD 7013 / Mar '95 / Hightone

☐ **WATERLOO SUNSET STORY, THE**

I want to sleep with you: *Eleanor Rigby* / Till the end of the day: *Eleanor Rigby* / Take another shot of my heart: *Eleanor Rigby* / 1995: *Eleanor Rigby* / Where have all the good times gone: *Eleanor Rigby* / Mad Xmas: *Eleanor Rigby* / Kiss me quickly it's Xmas: *Eleanor Rigby* / Make up your mind: *Reaction* / 4 X 4: *Reaction* / Over and over: *Eleanor Rigby* / Last night in Soho: *Eleanor Rigby* / See my friend: *Eleanor Rigby* / Honeydipper: *Beatboy* / Please please: *Beatboy* / Man from uncle: *Grave* / Airport blues: *Beatboy* / Love on the phone: *Eleanor Rigby* / Think for yourself: *Eleanor Rigby* / Teenage sex: *Psychomatics* / Gotta move: *Psychomatics* / Censorship: *Eleanor Rigby*

FLEG 10CD / Aug '97 / Future Legend

☐ **WATERMELON FILES OF TEXAS MUSIC, THE**

MSACD 9 / Dec '94 / Munich

☐ **WATT WORKS FAMILY ALBUM**

Fleur carnivore: *Bley, Carla* / Best of friends: *Mantler, Karen* / Walking batteriewoman: *Bley, Carla* / A l'abattoir: *Mantler, Michael* / Crab alley: *Swallow, Steve* / When I run: *Mantler, Michael* / I can't stand...: *Weisberg, Steve* / Alien (part 2): *Mantler, Michael* / Talking hearts: *Bley, Carla* / Twenty: *Mantler, Michael* / I hate to sing: *Bley, Carla* / Movie six: *Mantler, Michael* / AD infinitum: *Bley, Carla* / Doubtful guest: *Mantler, Michael* / Funny bird: *Bley, Carla*

8414782 / Jan '90 / Watt

☐ **WAVE (The Biggest New Wave Hits/ 3CD Set)**
To cut a long story short: *Spandau Ballet* / White wedding: *Idol, Billy* / So long: *Fischer Z* / Asylum in Jerusalem: *Scritti Politti* / Don't dictate: *Penetration* / Everybody's gotta learn sometime: *Korgis* / Wishing if I had a photograph of you: *Flock Of Seagulls* / All stood still: *Ultravox* / Girls: *Twilly, Dwight* / She blinded me with science: *Dolby, Thomas* / Wishful thinking: *China Crisis* / Golden brown: *Stranglers* / Hit me with your rhythm stick: *Dury, Ian* / My Sharona: *Knack* / Hot in the city: *Idol, Billy* / Telephone always ring: *Fun Boy Three* / Love like blood: *Killing Joke* / I ran: *Flock Of Seagulls* / Dear God: *XTC* / Chant no.1: *Spandau Ballet* / Sinful: *Wylie, Pete* / Reasons to be cheerful: *Dury, Ian & The Blockheads* / Slippery people: *Talking Heads* / Love of the common people: *Talking Heads* / Drowning: *Stiff Little Fingers* / Drowning in Berlin: *Mobiles* / Big apple: *Kajagoogoo* / Independence day: *Kajagoogoo* / Temptation: *Heaven 17* / Musclebound: *Spandau Ballet* / Hyperactive: *Dolby, Thomas* / Good heart: *Sharkey, Feargal* / Shouldn't have to be like that: *Fra Lippo Lippi* / At home he's a tourist: *Gang Of Four* / Dream kitchen: *Frazier Chorus* / Echo beach: *Martha & The Muffins* / Worker: *Fischer Z* / Turning Japanese: *Vapors* / Day one: *Comsat Angels* / Money: *Flying Lizards* / Church of the poison mind: *Culture Club* / Sex and drugs and rock 'n' roll: *Dury, Ian* / Psycho killer: *Talking Heads*
HR 868442 / Sep '96 / Disky

☐ **WAVE FORUM (WAVE RECORDS COMPILATION)**
WAVE 222 / Jun '97 / Cleveland City

☐ **WAVE PARTY**
Goody two shoes: *Adam Ant* / Feels like heaven: *Fiction Factory* / This is the day: *The The* / Skin deep: *Stranglers* / Pretty in pink: *Psychedelic Furs* / Doot doot: *Fruer* / Who can it be now: *Men At Work* / You spin me round: *Dead Or Alive* / Don't talk to me about love: *Altered Images* / Talking in your sleep: *Romantics* / Real gone kid: *Deacon Blue* / Wheel: *Spear Of Destiny* / Birth, school, work, death: *Godfathers* / Heaven: *Psychedelic Furs* / Be free with your love: *Spandau Ballet* / Dutch mountains: *Nits*
4758322 / Dec '95 / Columbia

☐ **WAVE ROMANTICS VOL.2**
Do you love me: *Cave, Nick* / Green and grey: *New Model Army* / Golden brown: *Stranglers* / Beside you: *Iggy Pop* / Vienna: *Ultravox*
SPV 08438992 / Feb '95 / SPV

☐ **WAVY GRAVY VOL.1 (For Adult Enthusiasts)**
BEWARECD 001 / May '97 / Beware

☐ **WAVY GRAVY VOL.2**
BEWARECD 003 / Feb '97 / Beware

☐ **WAY FOR BRITTANY, A**
CD 819 / Aug '93 / Escalibur

☐ **WAY FOR IRELAND, A**
CD 314 / Aug '93 / Arfolk

☐ **WAY FOR SCOTLAND, A**
CD 313 / Aug '93 / Arfolk

☐ **WAY IT IS, THE**
LF 250CD / Jun '96 / Lost & Found

☐ **WAY OF LIFE**
Retry: *Majistrate* / Five tones: *Undercover Agent* / Hard disk: *MTS* / Inspiration: *MTS* / Dub plate circles: *Undercover Agent* / Slaughter: *Undercover Agent* / Warriors: *Undercover Agent* / Babylon: *Splash* / Computer rock: *Embee* / Oh gosh: *Undercover Agent* / Hypnosis: *Undercover Agent* / Walk tall: *Embee*
ECIUJCD 1 / 8 Jun '98 / Juice

☐ **WAY OUT CHAPTER, THE**
HLCD 2 / Jul '97 / Hard Leaders

☐ **WAY OUTTA LINE (Line Dance Competition)**
Cryin' season: *West, Adam* / Happy doin' what we're doin': *Maken, Sarah* / Wanderer: *Pernot, Clifton* / Louisianna blues: *Tex Pistols* / Big bad dog: *Balham Alligators* / Deep in the heart of Texas: *Makem, Sarah* / Honky tonk man: *Makem, Sarah* / Bayou teche: *Balham Alligators* / One last time: *Walsh, Errol* / Better to have and not need: *Youlden, Chris* / From the eyes of the faraway dancer: *Dockery, Doc* / Always late: *Pernot, Clifton* / Bad feet: *Pernot, Clifton*
PRPCD 4 / Dec '97 / Proper

☐ **WAY WITH THE GIRLS (30 Female Soul Rarities From The 1960's)**
You will never get away: *Maye, Cholli* / Here come the heartaches: *Lovells* / I'm a sad girl: *Johnson, Deena* / If you can stand me: *Lewis, Tamala* / Thrills and chills: *Smith, Helene* / I feel strange: *Wonderettes* / Lost without your love: *Carlettes* / Now that I found you baby: *Mirettes* / It's over: *Lindsay, Terry* / It's all over: *Gee's* / Why weren't you there: *Lindsay, Thelma* / Step aside baby: *Lollipops* / It happens every day: *Persianettes* / Source of love: *Marie, Gina* / Sweet sweet love: *Durettes* / Pretty boy: *Hall, Dora* / Big man: *Starr, Karen* / Ain't gonna hurt my pride: *Judi & The Affections* / You're the guy: *Argie & The Arketts* / There's something the matter: *Cynthia & The Imaginations* / Wonderful one: *Lindsey, Theresa* / My, my sweet love: *Lee, Barbara* / If you love me (show me): *Monique* / Sugar boy: *Charmettes* / Don't cha tell nobody: *Vont Claires* / Don't cry: *Irma & The Larks* / My fault: *Passionettes* / Try my love: *Sequins* / How can I get to you: *Soul, Sharon* / His way with the girls: *Lornettes*
GSCD 029 / Mar '94 / Goldmine

☐ **WAYS OF LOVE, THE**
Careless whisper: *Michael, George* / Your love is king: *Sade* / So amazing: *Vandross, Luther* / Softly whispering I love you: *Young, Paul* / I'll never fall in love again: *Deacon Blue* / Eternal flame: *Bangles* / Time and tide: *Basia* / Wishing you were here: *Moyet, Alison* / Through the barricades: *Spandau Ballet* / Castle in the clouds: *Craven, Beverley* / Stay with me 'til dawn: *Tzuke, Judie* / Unconditional love: *Hoffs, Susanna* / Toy soldiers: *Martika* / Baby I love your way/Freebird: *Will To Power*
4720732 / Aug '92 / Columbia

☐ **WAYZ OF THE DRAGON, THE**
DDRAGCDLP 01 / 15 Jun '98 / Dope Dragon

☐ **WBCN NAKED DISC (Stop Handgun Violence Benefit)**
WIC 10082 / 16 Feb '98 / Wicked Disc

☐ **WE ARE ICERINK**
Birth of Sharon: *Earl Brutus* / When I get to heaven: *Sensuround* / Don't destroy me: *Golden* / V neck: *Elizabeth City State* / Supermarket: *Supermarket* / (Why don't you) Ring me: *Hard Muscle* / Love hour: *Oval* / Bob cool: *Spring* / Don't worry baby: *Melody Dog* / Bouffant headbutt: *Shampoo* / Dub to the stars (instrumental): *Parallel Universe* / New electric pop and soul: *World Of Twist*
DAVO 001CD / May '94 / Icerink

☐ **WE ARE ONE (Griot Songs From Mali)**
PAN 2015CD / Aug '94 / Pan

☐ **WE ARE REASONABLE PEOPLE**
Freeman Hardy and Willis acid: *Squarepusher & AFX* / Orange Romeda: *Boards Of Canada* / Hammer without a master: *Broadcast* / Ilasas: *Plaid* / Stop look listen: *Autechre* / Fishtail parker: *Nightmares On Wax* / Wear my bikini: *Tenor, Jimi* / Plaything: *Plone* / 4 dead monks: *Red Snapper* / Umchunga locks: *Calix, Mira* / Circulation: *Two Lone Swordsmen* / Salute to those people who say fuck you: *Bell, Mark*
WAP 100CD / 29 Jun '98 / Warp

☐ **WE ARE THE BLUES**
5238382 / Feb '95 / PolyGram Jazz

☐ **WE ARE THE CHAMPIONS (20 Football Fantasies)**
Come on you gunners: *Arsenal FC* / Come on you Villa: *Aston Villa FC* / Army swing: *Blackburn Rovers FC* / We'll keep the flag flying high: *Chelsea FC* / Go for it: *Coventry City FC* / Going back to Derby: *Derby County FC* / Everyone is cheering the blues: *Everton FC* / Leeds, Leeds, Leeds (marching on together): *Leeds United FC* / This is the season for us: *Leicester City FC* / Anfield rap '96: *Liverpool FC* / Glory glory Man United: *Manchester United FC* / We're coming through: *Middlesbrough FC* / Black 'n' white (toon army): *Newcastle United FC* / Nottingham Forest is my rock 'n' roll: *Nottingham Forest FC* / We are the owls: *Sheffield Wednesday FC* / Legend of the saint: *Southampton FC* / Daydream believer (cheer up Peter Reid): *Sunderland AFC* / Tottenham, Tottenham: *Tottenham Hotspur FC* / Forever blowing bubbles: *West Ham United FC* / We are Wimbledon: *Wimbledon FC*
SUMCD 4076 / Nov '96 / Summit

☐ **WE BITE 100**
WB 1100CD / Jan '96 / We Bite

☐ **WE BITE TOO**
WB 100012 / Jan '96 / We Bite

☐ **WE CAME TO DANCE**
SPV 08438822 / Jul '95 / SPV

☐ **WE CAME TO DANCE VOL.10 (2CD Set)**
Morphedus: *Skinny Puppy* / Isolation: *Die Krupps* / Deliverance: *Atrocity* / Ich bin der brennede kamet: *Lacrimosa* / I can't enjoy it: *Blind Passengers* / San Diego: *Cyan* / Erkaufte traume: *Goethes Erben* / Der trieb: *Umbra Et Imago* / Dusk: *Dreadful Shadows* / This empty ocean: *Love Like Blood* / Small world: *Secret Discovery* / Santos inocentes: *Calva Y Nada* / Kill a raver (I came to dance): *Leaether Strip* / Misery: *Psyche* / Der unbesiegte sonnegott: *Forthcoming Fire* / November day: *Inside* / Can I do what I want: *Shock Therapy* / Touch: *Klinik* / Furnace: *New Mind* / Shockwaved: *Still Silent* / Chameleon: *Still Patient* / Suchtig: *Dorsetshire* / Violent world: *Ravenous* / Fragile tomorrow: *Aqua* / Organics: *Evil's Toy* / Die for Jehovah: *Birmingham 6* / Become an angel: *In Strict Confidence* / Sun: *Under The Noise* / Game: Abscess / Radioactive love: *Daily Planet* / Blind man dreams: *Elegant Machinery* / In power we entrust to love: *Chandeen*
DCD 08647302 / Apr '97 / SPV

☐ **WE CAME TO DANCE VOL.4**
Non stop violence: *Apoptygma Berzerk* / Soul cremation: *Delay* / Barcode: *Frontline Assembly* / Another day: *Ichor* / Under your skin: *Bischoff, Silke* / We deserve it all: *Leaether Strip* / Colour of truth: *Girls Under Glass* / Du riechst so gut: *Rammstein* / Metalmorphosis: *Die Krupps* / Hey fuck da world: *Klute* / Figurehead: *Covenant* / Toys for Alice: *Sleeping Dogs Wake* / Spiderdust: *Bel Canto* / Sorciere: *La Floa Maldita* / Looking glass men: *Forma Tadre* / Prophecy: *Delerium*
SPV 08538632 / Apr '96 / SPV

☐ **WE CAME TO DANCE VOL.9 (Dark Wave & Electro)**
TOMAM: *Cobalt 60* / Deep red: *Apoptygma Berzerk* / Free and alive: *X Marks The Pedwalk* / Don't turn around: *Blind Passengers* / Agony of ecstasy: *Image Transmission* / I try, I die: *Leaether Strip* / This blackness: *Gracious Shades* / Pictures: *Derriere Le Miroir* / Vampire: *Inside* / Beneath the skin: *Collide* / Programmed for hell: *Fracture* / Levitation: *Individual Totem* / Cybegod: *Rame* / I beg for you: *Distain* / L'oasis: *La Floa Maldita* / To protect and to serve: *Bischoff, Silke*
SPV 08547042 / Sep '96 / SPV

☐ **WE CAN STILL BE FRIENDS**
MMR 001 / 16 Mar '98 / Magic Marker

☐ **WE DIED IN HELL - THEY CALLED IT PASSCHENDAELE**
MAPCD 93004CD / Jan '94 / Map

☐ **WE DIG DIXIELAND JAZZ**
Tiger rag / Village blues / Black and blue / Who's sorry now / When it's sleepy time down South / Clarinet marmalade / Joe's blues / Some of these days / I told you once / Georgia on my mind
SV 0197 / Oct '97 / Savoy Jazz

☐ **WE GOT A PARTY (Best Of Ron Records Vol.1)**
ROUCD 2076 / ' / Rounder

☐ **WE LOVE THE PIRATE STATIONS**
BX 4342 / Dec '97 / BR Music

☐ **WE LOVE TO ROCK 'N' ROLL (New Orleans Rock 'N' Roll R&B Party)**
Sea cruise: *Smith, Huey & Gerri Hall* / I've got a girl: *Cook, Roland* / I love to rock 'n' roll: *Bo, Eddie* / Snake eyes: *Tyler, Alvin 'Red' & The Gyros* / You aim to please: *Clanton, Jimmy & His Rockets* / Everybody's carried away: *King, Earl* / What I learned about you: *Hall, Gerri* / Teenage rock: *Little Booker* / Loberta: *Marchan, Bobby* / Come on home: *Spears, Calvin* / Little Liza Jane: *Smith, Huey & His Rhythm Aces* / Standing at the door: *Joe & Ann* / Yes I got you: *Garbo, Chuck* / Mercy: *Gene & Als Spacemen* / Charlie Brown got expelled: *Tex, Joe & His X-Classmates* / You can't stop her: *Marchan, Bobby & The Clowns* / I wanna know why: *Cook, Roland* / Everybody's whalin': *Smith, Huey & His Rhythm Aces* / Walk on: *Tyler, Alvin 'Red' & The Gyros* / New Orleans: *Myles, Big Boy & Mac Rebennack Orchestra*
WESM 544 / May '98 / Westside

☐ **WE RULE DANCEHALL**
KGCD 002 / Jan '96 / Keeling

☐ **WE THREE KINGS (3CD Set)**
DTKBOX 83 / 25 May '98 / Dressed To Kill

☐ **WE WISH YOU A MERRY CHRISTMAS**
MACCD 206 / Aug '96 / Autograph

☐ **WEDDING ALBUM, THE (To Have And To Hold)**
QTVCD 006 / Jun '92 / Quality

☐ **WEDDING MUSIC OF MARAMURES**
C 580052 / Jan '94 / Ocora

☐ **WEEK IN THE REAL WORLD VOL.1, A**
CDRW 25 / Jul '92 / Realworld

☐ **WEEK OR TWO IN THE REAL WORLD**
CDRW 30 / Jul '94 / Realworld

☐ **WEEKENDER (12 Extended Dance Classics)**
MUSCD 010 / Sep '93 / MCI Music

☐ **WEEKENDER**
Fools gold: *Stone Roses* / Only one I know: *Charlatans* / There's no other way: *Blur* / Shine on: *House Of Love* / This is how it feels: *Inspiral Carpets* / Groovy train: *Farm* / Crash: *Primitives* / International bright young thing: *Jesus Jones* / Can you dig it: *Mock Turtles* / There she goes: *La's* / Truth: *Real People* / Give give give me more more more: *Wonder Stuff* / Take it: *Flowered Up* / Chelsea girl: *Ride* / Hello: *Beloved* / Pacific state: *808 State* / Lemonstone desired: *Rain* / Shall we take a trip: *Northside* / I'm free: *Soup Dragons* / Come together: *Primal Scream*
4911132 / 18 May '98 / Columbia

☐ **WEEKENDERS**
Common people: *Pulp* / Girls and boys: *Blur* / Stars: *Dubstar* / Spooky: *New Order* / Voodoo people: *Prodigy* / In dust we trust: *Chemical Brothers* / Blow the whole joint up: *Monkey Mafia* / Big time sensuality: *Bjork* / Weirdo: *Charlatans* / Dubdreamer: *Menswear* / Lazarus: *Boo Radleys* / Halcyon: *Orbital* / Vow: *Garbage* / La tristessa durerra: *Manic Street Preachers* / Hallelujah: *Happy Mondays* / Kosmos: *Weller, Paul* / Waterfall: *Stone Roses*
8287662 / Apr '96 / London

☐ **WELCOME TO IRELAND**
Two recruiting sergeants / Four strong winds / Highlevel / Cregan white hare / Honey and wine / Orange maid of Sligo / Bottles of black porter: *Caern Folk Trio* / Ballinderry: *Caern Folk Trio* / Flight of Earls: *Caern Folk Trio* / German clock winder: *Caern Folk Trio* / I know my love: *Caern Folk Trio* / Guns and drums: *Caern Folk Trio* / Ball o' yarn: *Caern Folk Trio* / I am a rover: *Caern Folk Trio*
EMPRCD 713 / Apr '97 / Emporio

☐ **WELCOME TO NORTHERN IRELAND**
CDNI 001 / May '96 / Outlet

☐ **WELCOME TO NY NOW GO HOME**
BSR 103CD / Jan '97 / Bittersweet

☐ **WELCOME TO PLANET REVCO**
REVCC 009 / Jul '96 / Revco

☐ **WELCOME TO SCOTLAND**
Teviot brig: *Shand, Jimmy Jr.* / Quaker's wife: *Shand, Jimmy Jr.* / Ishbel's jig: *Shand, Jimmy Jr.* / Comin' thro' the rye: *MacLeod, Jim* / My love is like a red red rose: *MacLeod, Jim* / Bonnie Galloway: *MacLeod, Jim* / Soft lowland tongue: *MacLeod, Jim* / Uist tramping song: *Anderson, Moira* / Roamin' in the gloamin': *Shand, Jimmy Jr.* / I love a lassie: *Shand, Jimmy Jr.* / Stop your ticklin' jock: *Shand, Jimmy Jr.* / Wee Deoch an' Doris: *Shand, Jimmy Jr.* / Northern lights of old Aberdeen: *Logan, Jimmy* / Battle o'er: *Shand, Jimmy Jr.* / I see mull: *Anderson, Moira* / Mairi's wedding: *MacLeod, Jim & His Band* / Bill Thomson's farewell to Dublane: *MacLeod, Jim & His Band* / Rabbie's visit: *MacLeod, Jim & His Band* / Carronades: *MacLeod, Jim & His Band* / Pheonix: *MacLeod, Jim & His Band* / Lassie come and dance with me: *MacLeod, Jim & His Band* / I lo'e nae a laddie: *MacLeod, Jim & His Band* / Muckin' O' Geordie's byre: *MacLeod, Jim & His Band* / Wi' a hundred pipers: *MacLeod, Jim & His Band* / Dancing in Kyle: *Anderson, Moira* / Jock McKay: *Shand, Jimmy Jr.* / Gordon for me: *Shand, Jimmy Jr.* / Lass of lowrie: *Shand, Jimmy Jr.* / Down in the Glen: *Logan, Jimmy* / Memories of Orkney: *Shand, Jimmy Jr.* / Macfarlane O' the sproats: *MacLeod, Jim & His Band* / Bonnie lass o'Fyvie: *MacLeod, Jim & His Band* / Barnyards o'Delgaty: *MacLeod, Jim & His Band* / Mormond braes: *MacLeod, Jim & His Band* / Polka danska: *Shand, Jimmy Jr.* / My ain' folk: *Logan, Jimmy*
CDMFP 6314 / Feb '97 / Music For Pleasure

☐ **WELCOME TO SKANNECTICUT**
ELM 018CD / 2 Mar '98 / Elevator

☐ **WELCOME TO THE BLUES VOL.1**
157572 / Feb '93 / Blues Collection

☐ **WELCOME TO THE BLUES VOL.2**
157592 / Feb '93 / Blues Collection

☐ **WELCOME TO THE FUTURE VOL.1**
TPLP 50CD / Mar '93 / One Little Indian

☐ **WELCOME TO THE FUTURE VOL.2**
Human behaviour: *Bjork* / Beautiful morning: *Soul Family Sensation* / Sugar daddy: *Secret Knowledge* / Comin' on: *Shamen* / Devo: *Crunch* / God: *Hypnotist* / UK : USA: *Eskimos & Egypt* / FU2: *FUSE* / Obsession: *Wishdokta & Vibes*
TPLP 60CD / Jan '94 / One Little Indian

☐ **WELCOME TO THE FUTURE VOL.3**
TPLP 80CD / Oct '95 / One Little Indian

☐ **WELCOME TO THE FUTURE VOL.4**
SUB 27D / Feb '97 / Subversive

☐ **WELCOME TO THE LAND OF HONEYDIPPED**
DIPAL 001CD / Sep '95 / Honeydipped

☐ **WELCOME TO THE WORLD OF DEMI-MONDE**
DMCD 1030 / Oct '95 / Demi-Monde

☐ **WELCOME TO TRANSWORLD**
TRANNYCD 1 / Apr '96 / Transworld

☐ **WELCOME TO WHITE CLOUD'S WORLD OF MUSIC**
WCL 110302 / Jul '97 / White Cloud

☐ **WELL CHARGED VOL.1**
PSCD 14 / Jun '97 / Pressure Sounds

☐ **WE'LL MEET AGAIN (2CD Set)**
DBG 53038 / Jan '95 / Double Gold

☐ **WE'LL MEET AGAIN**
We're gonna hang out the washing on the Siegfried Line: *Two Leslies* / White cliffs of Dover: *Lynn, Vera* / Could you please oblige us with a bren gun: *Coward, Sir Noel* / Run rabbit run: *Flanagan & Allen* / Ma, I miss your apple pie: *Blue Rockets Dance Orchestra* / This is the army Mr. Jones: *Berlin, Irving* / I'm going to get it up (when the lights go on in London): *Gibbons, Carroll* / Fleet's in Port again: *Breeze, Alan* / Painting the clouds with sunshine: *Hylton, Jack* / I'll be seeing you: *Gibbons, Carroll* / Hey little hen: *Loss, Joe* / Imagine me in the Maginot Line: *Formby, George* / Deepest shelter in town: *Desmond, Florence* / Beer barrel polka (Roll out the barrel): *Andrews Sisters* / Der Fuhrer's face: *Jones, Spike & His City Slickers* / Goodnight, wherever you are: *Leader, Harry & His Band* / I did what I could with my gas mask: *Formby, George* / In the mood: *Miller, Glenn* / We'll meet again: *Lynn, Vera*
QED 171 / Nov '96 / Tring

☐ **WELL TRODDEN PATH, THE**
CR 00092 / Nov '95 / Czech Radio

☐ **WELSH CHOIRS**
Land of my fathers / God bless the Prince of Wales / You'll never walk alone / Soldiers chorus / All through the night / Guide me o thou great redeemer / Old man river / With cat like tread / Battle hymn of the republic / Old folks at home / Cwm Rhondda / Selection from les miserables / Steal away
300822 / Jul '96 / Hallmark

☐ **WELSH CHORAL FAVOURITES**
My little Welsh home: *Dunvant Male Choir* / Soldier's farewell: *Dunvant Male Choir* / Close thing eyes: *Dunvant Male Choir* / Stodole pumpa: *Gwalia Male Choir* / Heimat: *Gwalia Male Choir* / Marching song: *Gwalia Male Choir* / Steal away: *Gwalia Male Choir* / Hiraeth: *Morriston Orpheus Choir* / Hyder: *Morriston Orpheus Choir* / American trilogy: *Morriston Orpheus Choir* / My dearest dear: *Morriston Orpheus Choir* / Martyrs of the arena: *Morriston Orpheus Choir* / My hero: *Morriston Orpheus Choir* / Ride the chariot: *Pontarddulais Male Voice Choir* / Windmills of your mind: *Pontarddulais Male Voice Choir* / Mil harddach wyt na'r rhosyn Gwyn: *Pontarddulais Male Voice Choir* / Memory: *Canoldir Male Voice Choir* / Eli Jenkin's prayer: *Canoldir Male Voice Choir* / My love is like a red red rose: *Canoldir Male Voice Choir*
CDMFP 6367 / May '97 / Music For Pleasure

☐ **WELSH MALE VOICE CHOIRS**
CDMFP 6366 / May '97 / Music For Pleasure

☐ **WELSH SOLOS AND SONGS**
SCD 2109 / Feb '96 / Sain

☐ **WEMBLEY MILITARY TATOO**
PLSCD 180 / Apr '97 / Pulse

☐ **WENDY**
Never ending dream: *X-Perience* / Do it for love: *Caught In The Act* / Break it up: *Scooter* / One and one: *Miles, Robert* / Falling in love: *Bed & Breakfast* / All the places: *BND* / Show me the way: *Mr. President* / Don't make me wait: *911* / Who wants to

live forever: *Dune* / Rainbows in the sky: *Yasmin* / Don't speak: *Clueless* / So strung out: *C-Block* / Crimson and clover: *2 Young* / And the beat goes on: *Lorenza* / I was born to love you: *Worlds Apart* / Pray: *DJ Bobo* / Right way: *Mark Oh* / Bolingo: *La Bouche*
ZYX 550702 / Apr '97 / ZYX

☐ WE'RE HERE BECAUSE WE'RE HERE - PASCHENDALE
NMCD 9CD / Jul '95 / No Master's Voice

☐ WE'RE HERE BECUASE WE'RE HERE
NMCD 8 / Jan '96 / No Master's Voice

☐ WE'RE SO PRETTY VOL.1 (3CD Set)
DTKBOX 58 / Dec '96 / Dressed To Kill

☐ WE'RE SO PRETTY VOL.2 (3CD Set)
DTKBOX 59 / Dec '96 / Dressed To Kill

☐ WEST 25TH CLASSICS
CHIP 152 / Oct '94 / Jive

☐ WEST 25TH VOL.1
CHIP 151 / Aug '94 / Jive

☐ WEST 25TH VOL.2
CHIP 157 / Jul '95 / Jive

☐ WEST 25TH VOL.3
CHIP 167 / Feb '97 / Jive

☐ WEST BY NORTH-SOUTH
VR 322C / Feb '97 / Vagrant

☐ WEST COAST RADIO HITS (Rock)
Drown in your ocean: *Walker, Brett & The Railbirds* / Right kind of love: *Drury, Timothy* / Working man: *King Of Hearts* / What's still left: *Walker, Brett & The Railbirds* / Silver and gold: *Walker Zapper Overdrive* / I know you: *Waybill, Fee* / Yesterday has gone: *Walker, Brett & The Railbirds* / All the love we kill: *Spiro, Mark* / Lessons of the heart: *Feehan, Tim* / Tell me why: *Walker, Brett & The Railbirds* / Can't help ourselves: *Drury, Timothy* / Surprise yourself: *Waybill, Fee* / Confidential: *D'Avesta, Delin* / Wherever this road may lead you: *Steel Horses* / Stay young: *Spiro, Mark* / American dreamer: *Walker, Brett & The Railbirds* / Blue lights: *Rake & The Surftones*
WESTCD 13 / Mar '97 / West Coast

☐ WEST COAST RADIO HITS (Love)
Wishful thinking: *Drury, Timothy* / It's a good thing: *Walker, Brett & The Railbirds* / Don't call my name: *King Of Hearts* / In the dark: *Spiro, Mark* / Haunt me tonight: *Marx, Richard* / Where is your love: *Jordan, Marc* / Fallin' in love: *Clewer, Janey* / I don't miss you too: *Feehan, Tim* / Just to be loved: *Champlin, Bill* / I'll set you free: *Drury, Timothy* / Everything I want: *Walker, Brett & The Railbirds* / King of hearts: *King Of Hearts* / Somewhere deep inside: *Waybill, Fee* / I'll be over you: *Goodrum, Randy* / October in Oxnard: *Rake & The Surftones* / After the love is gone: *King Of Hearts* / It still stings: *Drury, Timothy*
WESTCD 12 / Mar '97 / West Coast

☐ WEST COAST RAP VOL.1
CDSEWM 050 / Jul '92 / Southbound

☐ WEST COAST RAP VOL.2
CDSEWM 051 / Jul '92 / Southbound

☐ WEST COAST RAP VOL.3
CDSEWM 052 / Jul '92 / Southbound

☐ WEST COAST WAILERS VOL.1 (Harmonica Blues)
DTCD 3036 / Oct '96 / Double Trouble

☐ WEST END STORY VOL.1
Heartbeat: *Gardner, Taana* / Let's go dancin': *Sparque* / Heat you up (melt you down): *Lites, Shirley* / Do it to the music: *Raw Silk* / Can't you feel it: *Michelle* / Rescue me: *Thomas, Sybil* / Time: *Stone* / You can't have your cake: *Taylor, Brenda*
110652 / Jun '93 / Musidisc

☐ WEST END STORY VOL.2
Work that body: *Gardner, Taana* / It's all over my face: *Loose Joints* / Another man: *Mason, Barbara* / Give your body up to music: *Nichols, Billy* / Ride on the rhythm: *Mahogany* / Girl I like the way you move: *Stone* / Doin' the best that I can: *Lavette, Bettye* / Just in time: *Rawsilk*
110692 / Aug '93 / Musidisc

☐ WEST END STORY VOL.3
When you touch me: *Gardner, Taana* / Let me feel your heartbeat: *Glass* / Music turns me on: *Sparque* / When the shit hits the fan: *Master Boogie's song & dance* / Disco dance: *Michele* / Chillin' out: *Brooks, Inez* / Speak well: *Philly USA* / Keep on dancin': *Phrase II*
110942 / Nov '93 / Musidisc

☐ WEST END STORY VOL.4
No frills: *Gardner, Taana* / Take some time: *Sparque* / Searchin' for some lovin': *Trusty, Debbie* / I get lifted: *Sweet Life* / Hot summer nights: *Love Club* / Don't I ever cross your mind: *Mason, Barbara* / Hold me, squeeze me: *Michele* / People come dance: *Holt, Ednah & Starluv*
111872 / Jan '94 / Musidisc

☐ WEST INDIES - AN ISLAND CARNIVAL
7559720912 / Jan '95 / Nonesuch

☐ WEST SOUND CIRCLE
EFA 004552 / Mar '96 / Interference

☐ WESTBOUND SOUND OF DETROIT
Gonna spread the news: *Unique Blend* / Yes I'm in love: *Unique Blend* / Does he treat you better: *Unique Blend* / Monny and Daddy: *Unique Blend* / Old fashioned woman: *Unique Blend* / Lonely in a crowd: *Superlatives* / I don't know how (to say I love you) don't walk away: *Superlatives* / Things are looking up: *Detroit Emeralds* / Rosetta Stone: *Detroit Emeralds* / That's all I got: *Detroit Emeralds* / If you need me, call me (and I'll come running): *Fantastic Four* / I'm falling in love (I feel good all over): *Fantastic Four* / What's it all about: *Counts* / Happy days: *Magictones* / Everything's gonna be alright: *Magictones* / I've changed: *Magictones* / I'll make it up to you: *Magictones* / Trying real hard (to make the grade): *Magictones* / I don't what it is but it sho is funky: *Mighty Elegant* / I find myself falling in love with you: *Mighty Elegant* / What am I gonna do: *Houston Outlaws* / I'm loving you, you're leaving me: *Motivations* / I love you: *Motivations* / My baby ain't no plaything: *New Holidays* / When I'm back on my feet: *Various Narrators*
CDSEWD 065 / Aug '94 / Westbound

☐ WESTERN SWING ON THE AIR 1948-1961
RFCD 07 / Oct '91 / Country Routes

☐ WE'VE GOT ONE WICKED BOGLE
SGCD 12 / Dec '92 / Sir George

☐ WE'VE GOT TONIGHT (Classic Love Songs)
PLSCD 179 / Apr '97 / Pulse

☐ WHAAM BAM THANK YOU DAN
In the afternoon: *Revolving Paint Dream* / I know where Syd Barrett lives: *TV Personalities* / Never find time: *Mixers* / You're my kind of girl: *Page Boys* / Only the sky children know: *Page Boys* / Too shy: *Direct Hits* / Dream inspires: *TV Personalities* / Still dreaming: *Marbie Staircase* / Art of love: *1000 Mexicans* / Dancing with the dead / I'm sad: *Dmochowski, Jedrez* / Wouldn't you: *Laughing Apples* / Bike: *TV Personalities* / I'm in love with you: *Page Boys* / Naughty little boys: *Direct Hits* / My favourite films: *Gifted Children* / Dark ages: *Marble Staircase* / Love hurts: *Mixers* / Painting by numbers: *Gifted Children* / News of you: *1000 Mexicans* / No one's little girl: *TV Personalities* / What killed Alesiter Crowley: *Direct Hits*
ASKCD 043 / May '95 / Vinyl Japan

☐ WHALES OF THE PACIFIC
DC 879622 / Oct '97 / Disky

☐ WHAT A BAM BAM (Women in Reggae: Dancehall Queens)
SH 45028 / Nov '96 / Shanachie

☐ WHAT A DIFFERENCE A DAY MADE
AVC 526 / Nov '93 / Avid

☐ WHAT A FEELING (2CD Set)
Flashdance (what a feeling): *Cara, Irene* / Celebration: *Kool & The Gang* / Oops upside your head: *Gap Band* / Ain't nobody: *Rufus & Chaka Khan* / If I can't have you: *Elliman, Yvonne* / Hang on in there baby: *Bristol, Johnny* / Think: *Franklin, Aretha* / Car wash: *Royce, Rose* / Hustle: *McCoy, Van* / Heaven must be missing an angel: *Tavares* / Let's groove: *Earth, Wind & Fire* / Native New Yorker: *Odyssey* / You're the first, my last, my everything: *White, Barry* / Let's hear it for the boy: *Williams, Deniece* / Best of my love: *Emotions* / Lost in music: *Sister Sledge* / Play that funky music: *Wild Cherry* / Dance to the music: *Sly & The Family Stone* / Can you feel it: *Jacksons* / Stayin' alive: *N-Trance* / Footloose: *Loggins, Kenny* / Fame: *Cara, Irene* / Young hearts run free: *Staton, Candi* / Love train: *O'Jays* / We are family: *Sister Sledge* / That's the way (I like it): *KC & The Sunshine Band* / It's raining men: *Weather Girls* / You make me feel (Mighty real): *Sylvester* / Sound of Philadelphia: *MFSB* / You gave me love: *Crown Heights Affair* / I can make you feel good: *Shalamar* / Knock on wood: *Stewart, Amii* / You to me are everything: *Real Thing* / Kissin' in the back row of the movies: *Drifters* / I'm doin' fine now: *New York City* / Get dancin': *Disco Tex & The Sexolettes* / Rock the boat: *Hues Corporation* / Shoop shoop song (It's in his kiss): *Cher* / Boogie Wonderland: *Earth, Wind & Fire* / It's a love thing: *Whispers* / You're the one that I want: *Gibson, Debbie & Craig McLachlan*
SONYTV 26CD / May '97 / Sony TV

☐ WHAT A WAY TO COME DOWN (Nuggets From The Golden State)
I saw you: *Gold* / No parking: *Gold* / I stole the goodyear blimp: *Book of changes* / Suddenly I'm desperately in love: *Book of changes* / Good times: *Transatlantic railroad* / Now she's gone: *Transatlantic railroad* / Left hand girl: *Engle, Butch & The Styx* / No matter what you say: *Engle, Butch & The Styx* / She is love: *Engle, Butch & The Styx* / My kind of people: *Just Slightly Richer* / Solitude: *Just Slightly Richer* / Wet chant: *Immediate Family* / Rubiyat: *Immediate Family* / Highway highway: *Short Yellow* / Start seeing: *Short Yellow* / Colours: *Staff* / Mr misfortune: *Staff* / Shoot me through: *Collection* / He was a friend of mine: *Collection* / Love is the greatest thing: *Royal Family* / Signed bs: *Royal Family* / Let's be friends again: *Transatlantic railroad* / Mirrors: *Transatlantic railroad* / Purple orange: *Strawberry window*
CDWIKD 173 / Aug '97 / Big Beat

☐ WHAT DID YOU COME DOWN FOR
NEKO 001 / Jun '96 / Neko
NEK 1D / Aug '97 / Genki

☐ WHAT DO YOU WANT A JAPANESE TO DO
Just ask why: *Revs* / Big yellow taxi: *Elmerhassel* / She's gone: *Saturn V* / House of god: *Monochrome Set* / Pistols of colour: *Tokyo Skunx* / Dead head baby: *Fat Tulips* / Back again: *Grape* / I never loved you: *Strawberry Story* / Orange county: *Bluebells* / Cathedral high: *St. Christopher* / Come clean: *BMX Bandits* / I won't be there: *Milkshakes* / My boyfriend's learning karate: *Thee Headcoatees* / My favourite girl: *Hit Parade* / Locks and bolts: *Carousel* / Special to me: *Speedway Stars* / Aware of all: *McCluskey Brothers* / Mirror man: *Looking Glass* / Rosanna: *Haywains* / Nobody better: *SKAW* / Nine or seven: *Beatnik Filmstars* / Christmas tears: *Fletcher, Amelia & Hit Parade*
ASKCD 015 / Feb '93 / Vinyl Japan

☐ WHAT GOES AROUND COMES AROUND
PROCD 17 / Mar '97 / MC Projects

☐ WHAT GOES ROUND
Medusa: *Solitaria* / Skits: *Primordial Soup* / Physche: *Phlex* / Domo arigato: *Phreax* / Got a 'BBD' 4 u: *Beat Junkies* / 575: *DJ Shufflemaster* / I kid you not my man: *Teasdale, Anthony* / SDFG: *Phlex* / Jack goes home: *Teasdale, Anthony*
PROCD 017 / Feb '97 / MC Projects

☐ WHAT IS CRUST WHAT IS MELOCORE BE DIFFERENT HARDCORE
DISCCD 15 / 13 Apr '98 / Discipline

☐ WHAT IS JAZZ
KFWCD 109 / Nov '94 / Knitting Factory

☐ WHAT IS JAZZ 1996
KFWCD 195 / Oct '96 / Knitting Factory

☐ WHAT IS THIS THING CALLED LOVE (Cool Love Songs Of The 1930's/ 1940's)
Taking a chance on love: *Fitzgerald, Ella* / Sweet Lorraine: *Cole, Nat 'King'* / What is this thing called love: *Dorsey, Tommy & Connie Haines* / Sunshine of your smile: *Dorsey, Tommy & Frank Sinatra* / All of me: *Dorsey, Jimmy & Helen O'Connell* / Sposin': *Crosby, Bing* / Say it with a kiss: *Shaw, Artie & Helen Forrest* / May I never love again: *Weems, Ted & Perry Como* / He's funny that way: *Hawkins, Coleman & Thelma Carpenter* / These foolish things: *Goodman, Benny* / More than you know: *Wilson, Teddy & Billie Holiday* / When somebody thinks you're wonderful: *Waller, Fats* / Body and soul: *Shore, Dinah* / Why do I love you: *Langford, Frances & Tony Martin* / I can't give you anything but love: *Armstrong, Louis* / Think it over: *Wynn, Nan* / Old fashioned love: *Mills Brothers* / Here's love in your eyes: *Wilson, Teddy & Helen Ward* / Two in love: *Krupa, Gene, Anita O'Day & Johnny Desmond* / Journey to a star: *Garland, Judy* / Nearness of you: *Miller, Glenn & Ray Eberle* / Man I love: *Lamour, Dorothy*
PPCD 78114 / Feb '95 / Past Perfect

☐ WHAT IT IS
LHCD 008 / Jul '96 / Luv n' Haight

☐ WHAT SWEET MUSIC THEY MAKE VOL.1
VAMPCD 001 / Nov '96 / Raven/Vampire Guild

☐ WHAT SWEET MUSIC THEY MAKE VOL.2
VAMPCD 002 / Nov '96 / Raven/Vampire Guild

☐ WHAT SWEET MUSIC THEY MAKE VOL.3
RIP 100CD / Nov '96 / Raven/Vampire Guild

☐ WHATCHA GONNA SWING TONIGHT
RHRCD 50 / Oct '95 / Red House

☐ WHAT'S COOKIN'
URCD 014 / Jul '96 / Ubiquity

☐ WHAT'S HAPPEN' IN GARAGE (3CD Set)
WATSCD 2 / 6 Oct '97 / Premium

☐ WHAT'S HAPPENIN' DRUM AND BASS VOL.1
Gotta have your love: *McCrae, Gwen* / F-jam: *Adam F* / Run away bass: *Filthy Rich & Hermion* / We can make it happen: *Nookie & NCA* / Money: *BLIM* / Galcier: *BLIM* / Urban blues: *Girley, Steve* / Traces of guilt: *Expresso* / Ladder: *Tonic & Purple Kola* / Rock the funky beat: *Natural Born Chillers* / Let the bass boom: *TC & Slam* / Chillin' on da phunk: *Elementz Of Noize* / Danger: *Ed Solo* / Comin' thru: *Urbanites* / JSA 1: *Rude Bwoy Monty* / Nasty: *Shy FX* / Dub moods: *Aphrodite* / Summer dub: *Aladdin*
WATSCD 1 / Jun '97 / Au

☐ WHAT'S IN THE PUB IN 1996
PUB 001CD / Jun '96 / Pub

☐ WHAT'S MINE IS YOURS (The Emo Diaries)
DER 362 / 15 Sep '97 / Deep Elm

☐ WHAT'S SHAKIN'
Good time music: *Lovin' Spoonful* / Almost grown: *Lovin' Spoonful* / Spoonful: *Butterfield, Paul Blues Band* / Off the wall: *Butterfield, Paul Blues Band* / Can't keep from cryin' sometimes: *Kooper, Al* / I want to know: *Clapton, Eric & The Powerhouse* / Crossroads: *Clapton, Eric & The Powerhouse* / Lovin' cup: *Butterfield, Paul Blues Band* / Good morning little school girl: *Butterfield, Paul* / Steppin' out: *Clapton, Eric & The Powerhouse* / I'm in love again: *Rush, Tom* / Don't bank on it baby / Searchin' / One more mile: *Butterfield, Paul Blues Band*
7559613432 / Dec '95 / Elektra

☐ WHAT'S THE SCORE
FMCD 006 / Apr '97 / Fatman

☐ WHAT'S THE WORD (Diggin' In The Crates)
Sister Ruth: *Patterson, Don & Booker Ervin* / My favourite things: *Earland, Charles* / El hombre: *Martino, Pat* / Strut: *Wright, John* / Blue odyssey: *Person, Houston* / Swamp people: *Pucho & His Latin Soul Brothers* / Moanin': *Blakey, Art* / Mau Mau: *Farmer, Art* / Cattin' Latin: *Pike, Dave* / Bahia: *Coltrane, John* / Ubangi that got away: *Terry, Buddy* / Gettin' it togetha: *Timmons, Bobby* / Summertime: *Gryce, Gigi*
CDBGPD 111 / 24 Nov '97 / Beat Goes Public

☐ WHAT'S UP MATADOR (2CD Set)
Piano song no.2: *Chavez* / Strike: *Come* / One step forward: *Railroad Jerk* / Dig my shit: *Spencer, Jon Blues Explosion* / My thoughts are a gas: *Guided By Voices* / Telamon Bridge: *Spoon* / Killing moon: *Pavement* / Hangman: *Silkworm* / Don't say a word: *Yo La Tengo* / Blood of feeling: *Manning, Barbara* / Life is an imbecile: *Bettie Serveert* / Stuck on an island: *Phair, Liz* / Alfredo's welcome: *For Carnation* / Days away: *Run On* / Hurricane watch: *Mecca Normal* / Lucy: *Helium* / Back of your head: *Cat Power* / Small parade: *Tobin Sprout* / Riverdale: *Liquor Giants* / Traile: *Bardo Pond* / Kawasaki ZII 750 rock 'n' roll: *Guitar Wolf* / Happy birthday: *Pizzicato 5* / Tom Courtenay: *Yo La Tengo* / Texas never whispers: *Pavement* / Catholic education: *Teenage Fanclub* / For tension: *Superchunk* / Vandal X: *Unsane* / Splat: *Bailter Space* / Pat's trick: *Helium* / Nude as the news: *Cat Power* / Tomboy: *Bettie Serveert* / Couldn't you wait: *Silkworm* / Don't buy the realistic: *Spoon* / Stratford on Gy: *Phair, Liz* / Twiggy twiggy: *Pizzicato 5* / Hey student: *Fall* / Bang the drum: *Railroad Jerk* / In/Out: *Come* / Dang: *Spencer, Jon Blues Explosion* / Son of Sam: *Chain Gang* / Adam and Steve: *Frogs* / Unreal is here: *Chavez* / Motor away: *Guided By Voices* / Still: *SF Seals* / My pal the tortoise: *Thinking Fellas Union Local 282* / Water cuts my hands: *Mecca Normal*
OLE 1632 / 29 Sep '97 / Matador

☐ WHEELS OF STEEL
PLSCD 192 / Apr '97 / Pulse

☐ WHEELS OF THE WORLD VOL.1
YAZ 7008 / Feb '97 / Yazoo

☐ WHEELS OF THE WORLD VOL.2
YAZ 7009 / Feb '97 / Yazoo

☐ WHEN A MAN LOVES A WOMAN
HRCD 8053 / May '94 / Disky

☐ WHEN A MAN LOVES A WOMAN (16 Love Songs With Soul)
When a man loves a woman: *Sledge, Percy* / Higher and higher: *Wilson, Jackie* / Have you seen her: *Chi-Lites* / So in love: *Mayfield, Curtis* / I'd rather go blind: *James, Etta* / That's the way I feel about cha: *Womack, Bobby* / It's in his kiss (The shoop shoop song): *Everett, Betty* / Gimme little sign: *Wood, Brenton* / Rescue me: *Bass, Fontella* / Ruler of my heart: *Thomas, Irma* / Tell it like it is: *Neville, Aaron* / I had a talk with my man: *Collier, Mitty* / (If loving you is wrong) I don't want to be right: *Ingram, Luther* / Every beat of my heart: *Knight, Gladys & The Pips* / You send me: *Cooke, Sam* / Hold what you've got: *Tex, Joe*
CPCD 8057 / Feb '95 / Charly

☐ WHEN A MAN LOVES A WOMAN
When a man loves a woman: *Sledge, Percy* / Sitting on the dock of the bay: *Sledge, Percy* / Blue moon: *Marcels* / My special angel: *Vogues* / Hey Paula: *Paul & Paula* / Softly whispering I love you: *New English Congregation* / Solitaire: *Yarborough, Glenn* / Deep purple: *Tempo, Nino* / I'd love you to want me: *Lobo* / Silence is golden: *Tremeloes* / Whispering: *Tempo, Nino* / Come softly to me: *Fleetwoods* / Rainy night in Georgia: *Benton, Brook* / Little darlin': *Diamonds* / Where have all the flowers gone: *Kingston Trio*
22503 / Dec '95 / Music

☐ WHEN EYES MEET (A Global Celebration Of Love)
SH 64084 / Jun '97 / Shanachie

☐ WHEN HEMP WAS HIP
VN 167 / Aug '95 / Viper's Nest

☐ WHEN I WAS A COWBOY VOL.1 (Early American Songs Of The West)
YAZ 2022 / Sep '96 / Yazoo

☐ WHEN I WAS A COWBOY VOL.2 (Early American Songs Of The West)
YAZ 2023 / Sep '96 / Yazoo

☐ WHEN I'M HUNGRY I EAT
GMZ 001 / Sep '97 / Gourmandizer

☐ WHEN THE MAY IS ALL IN BLOOM (Traditional Singing From SE England)
VT 131CD / Jul '95 / Veteran Tapes

☐ WHEN THE SAINTS GO MARCHING IN
When the saints go marching in: *Armstrong, Louis* / Something new: *Basie, Count* / Bird of paradise: *Davis, Miles* / Street beat: *Parker, Charlie* / Basin Street blues: *Fitzgerald, Ella* / More than you know: *Horne, Lena* / Sweet Georgia Brown: *Cole, Nat 'King'* / Northwest passage: *Herman, Woody* / Don't blame me: *Davis, Miles* / (Back home again in) Indiana: *Armstrong, Louis* / Study in Soulphony: *Gillespie, Dizzy* / Somebody stole my gal: *Goodman, Benny* / All of me: *Basie, Count* / Scuttlebut: *Shaw, Artie* / Flying home: *Fitzgerald, Ella* / Little girl blue: *Horne, Lena* / Bijou: *Herman, Woody* / Yes sir that's my baby: *Cole, Nat 'King'* / On the sunny side of the street: *Armstrong, Louis* / Blue juice: *Barnet, Charlie*
GRF 124 / '93 / Tring

☐ WHEN VICTORIA WAS QUEEN
Tribute to pageantry / Crimond / Lily of Laguna / Grand march from Aida / Love's old sweet song / Radetsky march / Wellington march / Nimrod / Pageantry of Gilbert and Sullivan / Jerusalem / Don't dilly dally on the way / Land of hope and glory / Imperial echoes / Soldiers of the Queen/There's something about a soldier / Evening hymn
306382 / Jan '97 / Hallmark

☐ WHEN YOUR LOVER HAS GONE
When your lover has gone: *Holiday, Billie* / Dimples: *Hooker, John Lee* / Baby, please don't go: *Waters, Muddy* / Who's been talkin': *Howlin' Wolf* / Catfish blues: *King, B.B.* / Ain't nobody's business if I do: *Holiday, Billie* / Hand in hand: *James, Elmore* / Born blind: *Williamson, Sonny Boy* / Boogie chillun: *Hooker, John Lee* / Trainfare blues: *Waters, Muddy* / Wang dang doodle: *Howlin' Wolf* / Easy to remember: *Holiday, Billie* / BB boogie: *King, B.B.* / Coming home: *James, Elmore* / Poor Howard green corn: *Leadbelly* / Settin' here drinkin': *Waters, Muddy* / Tupelo: *Hooker, John Lee* / Down in the bottom: *Howlin' Wolf* / My babe: *Little Walter* / Don't explain: *Holiday, Billie* / Don't lose your eye: *Williamson, Sonny Boy* / Everyday I have the blues: *King, B.B.* / You gonna miss me: *Waters, Muddy* / Look on yonder wall: *James, Elmore* / Drug store woman: *Hooker, John Lee*
GRF 126 / '93 / Tring

☐ WHEN YOUR SMILING (Honky Tonky Hits)
PLSCD 175 / Apr '97 / Pulse

☐ WHERE BLUES MEETS ROCK
PRD 70912 / Jun '96 / Provogue

☐ WHERE BLUES MEETS ROCK VOL.3
Bessie Mae: Omar & The Howlers / Obstacles in my way: Trout, Walter Band / You got the blues: Hole, Dave / Lucky lucky lucky: Katon, Michael / Hip shake: Mack, Bobby / Hey baby: Hamsters / Stones and colours: Tognoni, Rob / Cold pillow: Taino, Joe / Under saturn rings: Verheyen, Carl / Fun missing you: Siburn, Innes / Laugh: Tiven, Jon Group
PRD 71142 / 3 Aug '98 / Provogue

☐ WHERE JAZZ WAS BORN
CD 56021 / Aug '94 / Jazz Roots

☐ WHERE THE GIRLS ARE VOL.1
Condition red: Goodees / Look in my diary: Reparata & The Delrons / Don't drop out: Parton, Dolly / Little things like that: Wallis, Suzy / Live and learn: Heatherton, Joey / I'm thru: Carter, Carolyn / Anything worth having (is well worth waitin' for): Moody, Joan / Love kitten: Corcoran, Noreen / Oowee baby: Day, Doris / Please don't kiss me again: Charmettes / How much is that doggie in the window: Baby Jane & The Rockabyes / Your ya ya is gone: Tren-Teens / Hula hoppin': Boyd, Idalia / Push a little harder: Avons / That boy of mine: Sherrys / Young girl: Charmaine / Sometimes I wonder: Brown, Barbara / What kind of girl (do you think I am): Franklin, Erma / Mixed up shook up girl: Patty & The Emblems / Who's that guy: Kolettes / Friend of mine: Geminis / Oh what a night for love: Victorians / Hey there lonely boy: Ruby & The Romantics / Lonely girl: Lovettes
CDCHD 648 / May '97 / Ace

☐ WHERE YOU'RE GOING
Cold summer: Buffalo Daughters / Butter of 69: Butter 08 / New song: Lee, Ben / Arizona: Wiggs, Josephine Experience / Red Umbrella: Kostars / OJ: BS 2000 / Pop song: Lee, Ben / Root down: Beastie Boys / 16: Noise Addict / Silver turkey: Buffalo Daughters / Good morning America: Moistboyz / Under your skin: Luscious Jackson / Hard to hold: Butter 08 / Brand new: Beastie Boys / Mr.B goes surfing: Wiggs, Josephine Experience
GR 054 / 16 Mar '98 / Grand Royal

☐ WHERE'S THE BEEF
DT 002 / Nov '97 / Drive Through

☐ WHICH SIDE ARE YOU ON (Coal Mining Women)
Coal mining woman: Dickens, Hazel / Blue diamond mines: Boyens, Phyllis / Dreadful memories: Gunning, Sarah Ogun / Yablonski murder: Dickens, Hazel / Lawrence Jones: Boyens, Phyllis / Draglines: Reel World String Band / Coal miner's grave: Dickens, Hazel / Come all you coal miners: Gunning, Sarah Ogun / Black lung: Dickens, Hazel / Dream of a miner's child: Boyens, Phyllis / Mannington Mine disaster: Dickens, Hazel / 25c that you paid: Gunning, Sarah Ogun / Clay County miner: Dickens, Hazel / Clara Sullivan's letter: Dickens, Hazel / What she aims to be: Reel World String Band / Coal tattoo: Dickens, Hazel / Hello coal miner: Gunning, Sarah Ogun / Battle of Jericol: Reel World String Band / Which side are you on: Reece, Florence / They'll never keep us down: Dickens, Hazel
ROUCD 4026 / Oct '97 / Rounder

☐ WHIP 1983-1993 (Various Goths)
FREUDCD 43 / Sep '93 / Jungle

☐ WHIPLASH
RNCD 2051 / Mar '94 / Rhino

☐ WHIRL-Y-WAVES VOL.1 & 2 (2CD Set)
WHIRL 1 / 20 Jul '98 / Whirly Gig

☐ WHISKEY IN THE JAR
Whiskey in the jar: Thin Lizzy / Wishing well: Free / Black night: Deep Purple / Maggie May: Stewart, Rod / You ain't seen nothing yet: Bachman-Turner Overdrive / 10538 overture: ELO / Lay down: Strawbs / When I'm dead and gone: McGuiness Flint / Something in the air: Thunderclap Newman / Lets work together: Canned Heat / Together: Wood, Roy / Whole lotta love: CCS / Giving it all away: Daltrey, Roger / I hear you knocking: Edmunds, Dave / California man: Edmunds, Dave / Darlin': Miller, Frankie / Rag mama rag: Band / Ball park incident: Wizzard / Coz I love you James: Slade / Down down: Status Quo
5529102 / Oct '97 / Spectrum

☐ WHITE BOX OF JAZZ, THE (4CD Set)
PBXCD 405 / 20 Apr '98 / Pulse

☐ WHITE BOY BLUES
TRTCD 161 / Dec '94 / TrueTrax

☐ WHITE BOY BLUES
PLSCD 184 / Feb '97 / Pulse

☐ WHITE BOY BLUES VOL.1
Snake drive: Clapton, Eric / West coast idea: Clapton, Eric / Choker: Clapton, Eric & Jimmy Page / I'm your witch doctor: Mayall, John & The Bluesbreakers / Tribute to Elmore: Clapton, Eric / Freight loader: Clapton, Eric & Jimmy Page / Miles road: Clapton, Eric & Jimmy Page / Telephone blues: Mayall, John & The Bluesbreakers / Draggin' my tail: Clapton, Eric & Jimmy Page / Down in the boots: All Stars & Jimmy Page / Stealin': All Stars & Jeff Beck / Chuckles: All Stars & Jeff Beck / LA breakdown: All Stars & Jimmy Page / Piano shuffle: All Stars & Nicky Hopkins / Some day baby: Davies, Cyril & The All Stars / Porcupine juice: Santa Barbara Machine Head / Rubber monkey: Santa Barbara Machine Head / Albert: Santa Barbara Machine Head / Who's knocking: Spencer, Jeremy / Look down at my woman: Spencer, Jeremy
CCSCD 816 / 26 Jan '98 / Castle

☐ WHITE BOY BLUES VOL.2
Tried: Savoy Brown Blues Band / Cold blooded woman: Savoy Brown Blues Band / Can't quit you baby: Savoy Brown Blues Band / True blue: Savoy Brown Blues Band / I feel so good: Kelly, Jo Ann / Ain't gonna cry no more: McPhee, Tony / You don't love me: McPhee, Tony / When you got a good friend: McPhee, Tony / Someone to love me: McPhee, Tony / Dealing with the devil: Dharma Blues Band / Roll 'em Pete: Dharma Blues Band / Water on my fire: Lee, Albert / Crosstown link: Lee, Albert / Flapjacks: Masonry, Stones / Not fade away: Davis, Cyril & The All Stars / So much to say: Stewart, Rod / On top of the world: Mayall, John & The Bluesbreakers / Hideaway: Mayall, John & The Bluesbreakers / Supernatural: Mayall, John & The Bluesbreakers / Standing at the crossroads: Ten Years After / I want to know: Ten Years After / Next milestone: Lee, Albert
CCSCD 817 / 26 Jan '98 / Castle

☐ WHITE CHRISTMAS (28 Famous Christmas Melodies)
CNCD 3132 / Nov '92 / Disky

☐ WHITE CHRISTMAS (A Selection Of Classic Festive Songs)
Christmas alphabet: Valentine, Dickie / Rudolph the red nosed reindeer: Scala, Primo Banjo/Accordian Band / Christmas and you: King, Dave / Away in a manger: Shelton, Anne & The George Mitchell Choir / Christmas island: Valentine, Dickie / I'm sending a letter to Santa Claus: Lynn, Vera / Silent night: Lewis, Archie / St. Nicholas waltz: Roza, Lita / Must be Santa: Steele, Tommy & The Childrens Chorus / Santo Natale: Whitfield, David / Jingle bells rock: Bygraves, Max / Little boy that Santa Claus forgot: Roza, Lita / Jingle bells: Scala, Primo Banjo/ Accordian Band & The Keynotes / White Christmas: Lynn, Vera / Christmas song: Shelton, Anne & The Wardour Singers / I saw Mommy kissing Santa Claus: Cotton, Billy Band & The Mill Girls/The Bandits / Little donkey: Beverley Sisters / Christmas in Killarney: Four Ramblers / Merry Christmas: Shelton, Anne / O come all ye faithful (adeste fidelis): Whitfield, David
5525682 / Nov '96 / Spectrum

☐ WHITE CHRISTMAS
White Christmas / Have yourself merry little Christmas / Jingle bells / Silent night / O Holy night / First Noel / Silver bells / Skater's waltz / Winter wonderland / Mary's boy child / Away in a manger / Christmas song / Sleigh ride / Christmas waltz / Holly and the ivy
4610782 / Nov '96 / Belart

☐ WHITE CHRISTMAS
White Christmas: Crosby, Bing / Santa Claus is coming to town: Sinatra, Frank / Have yourself a merry little Christmas: Clooney, Rosemary / Zat you Santa Claus: Armstrong, Louis / Silent night: Jackson, Mahalia / God rest ye merry gentlemen: Sinatra, Frank & Bing Crosby / First Noel: Vaughn, Billy / Sleigh bells: Autry, Gene / Merry Christmas to you: Sinatra, Frank / I saw Mummy kissing Santa Claus: Sherman, Bobby / O little town of Bethlehem: Jackson, Mahalia / Rudolph the red-nosed reindeer: Clooney, Rosemary / Little drummer boy: Sinatra, Frank & Midnight Strings / C-h-r-i-s-t-m-a-s: Wells, Kitty / O holy night: Butler, Jerry / Hitch a ride with Santa Claus: Crosby, Bing
120062 / Oct '97 / Jingle

☐ WHITE CHRISTMAS (A Christmas Present From The Past)
GCMD 510 / 17 Nov '97 / GCM

☐ WHITE CHRISTMAS (3CD Set)
We wish you a merry Christmas: Drifters / Silent night: Jackson, Mahalia / Christmas makes the town: Benton, Brook / Ave Maria: Lanza, Mario / O little town of Bethlehem: Adams, Johnny / Jingle bells: Clooney, Rosemary / Away in a manger: Wells, Kitty / First Noel: Sinatra, Frank & The Midnight Strings / O holy night: Butler, Jerry / It came upon a midnight clear: Crosby, Bing & Rosemary Clooney / Hark the herald angels sing: Jackson, Mahalia / Auld lang syne: Drifters / Christmas just ain't Christmas (Without the one I love): Drifters / Child: Benton, Brook / Amazing grace: Phillips, Ann / Deck the halls: Cranberry Singers, The / O come all ye faithful: Sinatra, Frank & Bing Crosby / Christmas in New Orleans: Armstrong, Louis / Ding dong merrily on high: Cranberry Singers, The / Come home for Christmas: Platters / God rest ye merry gentlemen: Sinatra, Frank & Bing Crosby / Good King Wenceslas: Cranberry Singers, The / Lord's prayer: Adams, Johnny / Jolly old saint Nicholas: Cranberry Singers, The / Christmas feeling: Sinatra, Frank & Bing Crosby / Go tell it on the mountain: Jericho Group / Joy to the world: Lanza, Mario / We wish you a merry Christmas: Liberace / White Christmas: Armstrong, Louis / Lonely this Christmas: Mud / Wonderful Christmas time: Cranberry Singers, The / I'll be home for Christmas: Campbell, Glen / O little town of Bethlehem: Jackson, Mahalia / I wish everyday could be like Christmas: Benton, Brook / Santa Claus is coming to town: Sinatra, Frank / Little boy that Santa Claus forgot: Lynn, Vera / Blue Christmas: Platters / Silver bells: Clooney, Rosemary / Rudolph the red nosed reindeer: Sinatra, Frank & Bing Crosby / Frosty the snowman: Autry, Gene / Zat you Santa Claus: Armstrong, Louis / Winter wonderland: Drifters
JB 302 / Dec '97 / K-Box

☐ WHITE CHRISTMAS, A
White Christmas / Sleigh ride / Winter wonderland / Jolly old St. Nicholas / Twelve days of Christmas / Silver bells / Rudolf the red nosed reindeer / Happy holiday / Have yourself a merry little Christmas / Here we come a wassailin / March of the toys / Santa Claus is coming to town / I heard the bells on Christmas day / Oh Christmas tree / Up on the housetop / Silent night / Let it snow, let it snow, let it snow / Holly jolly Christmas
XMAS 014 / Nov '96 / Tring

☐ WHITE ELEPHANTS AND GOLDEN DUCKS (Enchanting Musical Treasures From Burma)
SHCD 64087 / May '97 / Shanachie

☐ WHITE HEATHER CLUB, THE
CC 263 / May '91 / Music For Pleasure

☐ WHITE HEATHER SHOW, THE (21 Scottish Favourites)
303972 / Jan '97 / Hallmark

☐ WHITE LABEL HOUSE SESSION VOL.1
WLCD 5001 / 10 Nov '97 / White Label

☐ WHITE LABEL VOL.2
WLCD 3002 / Jan '95 / White Label

☐ WHITE MAN BLUES
Dock of the bay: Spatz / Hungry man blues: Sumlin, Willie / It's too late: Head, Roy / Black cat bone: Blanchard, Pierre / I need someone: Long, Joey / Mercury blues: Owens, Steve / Milk cow blues: Terrapin Jackson / Red neck blues: Holzhaus, Chris / Please come home for Christmas: Winter, Johnny & Edgar / Rough girl: Maly, Ed / Gonna get my baby: Brooks, Bruce / Lay down gal of mine: Winter, Johnny / Nobody but me tells me when my eagle to fly: Head, Roy / Something to ease my pain: Long, Joey
CDTB 168 / Oct '95 / Thunderbolt

☐ WHITE MANSIONS (A Tale From The American Civil War 1861-65)
Story to tell / Dixie, hold on / Join around the flag / White trash / Last dance and the Kentucky racehorse / Southern boys / Union mare and confederate grey / No one would believe a summer could be so cold / Southland's bleeding / Bring up the twelve pounders / They laid waste to our land / Praise the lord / King has called me home / Bad man / Dixie now your done
CDMID 182 / '93 / A&M

☐ WHITE RHINO
AFRCD 8 / 3 Nov '97 / Flying Rhino

☐ WHITE RIVER REGGAE BASH VOL.1
RN 0052 / 6 Jul '98 / Runnetherlands

☐ WHITE ROOTS VOL.1 (From American Folk To Country Rock)
Good time Charlie's got the blues: Presley, Elvis / Queen Jane approximately: Dylan, Bob / Brown eyed girl: Morrison, Van / Hickory wind: Byrds / Wild horses: Flying Burrito Brothers / Song for you: Parsons, Gram / Sleepless nights: Harris, Emmylou / I don't want to talk about it: Crazy Horse / Willin': Little Feat / Mandolin wind: Stewart, Rod / Eve of destruction: McGuire, Barry / Buzzin' fly: Buckley, Tim / For what it's worth: Buffalo Springfield / She don't have to see you: Golden Smog / So long, Marianne: Cohen, Leonard / Other kind: Earle, Steve / I shall be released: Weller, Paul / Cause cheap is how I feel: Cowboy Junkies
74321382952 / Jun '96 / RCA

☐ WHITE ROOTS VOL.2 (From American Folk To Psychedelia)
American pie: McLean, Don / Summer in the city: Lovin' Spoonful / Father and son: Stevens, Cat / Alone again or: Love / Don't talk: Beach Boys / I'm a believer: Monkees / Get together: Youngbloods / Green tambourine: Lemon Pipers / California dreamin': Mamas & The Papas / San Francisco: McKenzie, Scott / I need a man to love: Big Brother & The Holding Company / Mr. Tambourine man: Dylan, Bob / Purple haze: Hendrix, Jimi / Eight miles high: Byrds / Venus in furs: Velvet Underground / Man of the world: Fleetwood Mac / Light your windows: Quicksilver Messenger Service / White rabbit: Jefferson Airplane / American woman: Guess Who / Tight rope: Russell, Leon
74321382962 / Jun '96 / RCA

☐ WHITE ROSE, THE (A Festival Of Yorkshire Music)
Soldier's chorus / Monte christe / Prelude to Act III / Lohengrin / Portrait of my love / Westminster waltz / Fishermen of England / Tribute to Ivor Novello / White rose / Battle hymn of the Republic / Gladiator's farewell / Love could I only tell thee / Lost chord / Colonel Bogey / Roman war song / Long day closes / Fantasia on British sea songs / On Ilkley moor baht'at
QPRZ 016D / Oct '97 / Polyphonic

☐ WHITE SPIRITUALS FROM THE SACRED HARP
802052 / Aug '92 / New World

☐ WHITER SHADE OF DOO-WOP, A
Little star: Elegants / Little boy blue: Elegants / I'll close my eyes: Skyliners / Door is still open: Skyliners / Little Eva: Locomotions / Adios my love: Locomotions / Read between the lines: Dell-Satins / I'll pray for you: Dell-Satins / Bermuda: Four Seasons / Spanish lace: Four Seasons / Barbara Ann: Regents / Over the rainbow: Regents / Runaround: Regents / Cruise to the moon: Chaperones / Shining star: Chaperones / Picture in my wallet: Darrell & Oxfords / Roses are red: Darrell & Oxfords / Can't you tell: Darrell & Oxfords / Reasons for love: Darrell & Oxfords / Rip Van Winkle: Devotions / (I love you) for sentimental reasons: Devotions / Snow White: Devotions / Zindy Lou: Devotions / Tears from a broken heart: Devotions / Sunday kind of love: Devotions
NEMCD 715 / Nov '94 / Sequel

☐ WHO FEARS TO SPEAK
RTE 209CD / Mar '98 / RTE/Europe 1

☐ WHO GAVE THE PERMISSION
RIZ 00032 / Nov '95 / Riz

☐ WHO WILL CALM THE STORM
SCR 26 / Jul '95 / Strictly Country

☐ WHOLE LOTTA HARDCORE (3CD Set)
KICKCD 66 / 15 Dec '97 / Kickin'

☐ WHOLE LOTTA ROCK 'N' ROLL (3CD Set)
MCBX 011 / Apr '94 / Music Club

☐ WHOLE LOTTA SOUL (2CD Set)
AOP 52 / Oct '97 / Age Of Panik

☐ WHOOP RECORDS COLLECTION VOL.1 (2CD Set)
WHCD 01 / Nov '96 / Whoop

☐ WHO'S ZOOMIN' WHO VOL.2 (Mixed By DJ Corrie)
Pentagon: Dextra / When I was falling: Aquanauts / Funky ass music: Aquanauts / Fallen: Manuel / One 4 the road: Barb Wired / Drum code 2: Beyer, Adam / Spirit: Sourmash / Digital doman: Shi-Take / Blanks: Mo Whack / X-tension: DJ Misjah & Tim / Hyperventilate: Scoff Boys / Cyklik: Maurer, Herwig / Tycho: Modern Anominal Techno Project / Digital islands: Harpon / Anaalogical rhythm: Biological / Feathers: Spicelab
ZOOMCD 3 / Apr '97 / Zoom

☐ WHY CAN'T WE HATE MORE VOL.1
BIRD 112CD / 27 Apr '98 / Birdnest

☐ WIBBLY WOBBLY WALK, THE (From Original Phonograph Cylinders)
Wibbly wobbly walk: Charman, Jack / Oh by jingo, oh by gee: Premier Quartet / I miss my Swiss: Tennessee Happy Boys / Everything's at home except your wife: Van Brunt, Walter / Spaniard that blighted my life: Merson, Billy / Tickle me Timothy: Williams, Billy / Little Ford rambled right along: Williams, Billy / Wallaperoo: Osmond, Arthur / I love me: Broadway Dance Orchestra / Come back to Georgia: Hickman, Art & His Orchestra / All by yourself in the moonlight: Sarony, Leslie / Little wooden whistle wouldn't whistle: Columbia Novelty Orchestra / Why did I kiss that girl: Savoy Havana Band / Felix keeps on walking: Savoy Havana Band / I parted my hair in the middle: Formby, George / There's a rickety rackety shack: Kit Kat Band / Down south: International Novelty Quartet / Parade of the wooden soldiers: International Novelty Orchestra
CDSDL 350 / Mar '94 / Saydisc

☐ WIBBLY, WOBBLY WORLD
WWCD 4 / Mar '94 / Wibbly Wobbly

☐ WICKED A GO FEEL IT (Classic Roots & Culture 1976-1985)
This is a true true love: Campbell, Al / Revelation: Levy, Barrington / Never gonna give Jah up: Minott, Sugar / Judgement come: Campbell, Cornell / Moving on to Zion: Clarke, Johnny / Enter the kingdom of Zion: Brown, Barry / Captivity: Levy, Barrington / Intelligence of her mind/They can't stop us now: Viceroys / Africa is the black man's home: Minott, Sugar / Have faith in Jah: Palmer, Michael / Friend indeed: Brown, Neville / What a gathering: Brooks, Mike / Propaganda: Smart, Leroy / No weak heart: Davis, Ronnie / Lead us to Jah Jah: Brown, Barry / Informer: Campbell, Cornell / Give the people what they want: Davis, Ronnie / Dread are the controller: Thompson, Linval / Politician: Brown, Barry / Yeh weh deh: Levy, Barrington / Wicked a go feel it: Campbell, Al
CDTRL 375 / Nov '96 / Trojan

☐ WIDESCREEN VERSIONS
Leo 9: Klute / Perception: Klute / Silent weopons: Klute / Dakota: Lexis / Hynotise: Lexis / Zonation: Paradox & DMR / Relics: Studio Pressure
CERT18CD 002 / 10 Aug '98 / Certificate 18

☐ WIDOW'S UNIFORM, THE (A Folk Opera)
REAL 0101CD / Nov '96 / Realisations

☐ WIEN - VOLKSMUSIK 1906-1937
US 0198 / Jul '95 / Trikont

☐ WIGAN CASINO STORY VOL.1, THE
Flasher: Mistura / Long after tonight is all over: Radcliffe, Jimmy / We go together: August & Duneen / Tears: Roye, Lee / You've been away: Roye, Lee / Take away the pain stain: Austin, Patti / Live Adam and Eve: Reflections / Dance, dance, dance: Casualeers / If you ask me: Williams, Jerry / Better use your head: Imperials / Joker: Myslestones / Skiing in the snow: Invitations / Time will pass you by: Legend, Tobi / I can't help lovin' you: Anka, Paul / I'll always need you: Courtney, Dean / Stick by me baby: Salvadors / You don't love me: Epitome Of Sound / I never knew: Foster, Eddie / Put your arms around me: Sherrys / I really love you: Tomangoes / I'm on my way: Parrish, Dean
GSCD 051 / Sep '94 / Goldmine

☐ WIGAN CASINO STORY VOL.2, THE
Baby mine: Houston, Thelma / Love slipped through my fingers: Williams, Sam / Superlove: David & The Giants / Hey little way out girl: Construction / Double cookin': Checkerboard Squares / Take me home: King, Donna / Panic: Reparata & The Delrons / My sugar baby: Clarke, Connie / Psychedelic soul: Russell, Saxie / Ten miles high: David & The Giants / What shall I do: Frankie & The Classicals / Hey little girl: Phillips, D.D. / Rosemary: Wylie, Richard / If that's what you wanted: Beverly, Frankie / Champion: Mitchell, Willie / Ever again: Williams, Bernie / So is the sun: World Column / Breakaway: Carmen, Steve / I'm where it's at: Jades / I'm comin' home in the morning: Pride, Lou / I'm gettin' on life: Wombats / You got me where you want me: Santos, Larry / I travel alone: Ragland, Lou / End of our love: Wilson, Nancy / Meet me halfway: Little Bryany / Manifesto: Case Of Tyme / I walked away: Paris, Bobby
GSCD 072 / Sep '95 / Goldmine

☐ WIGAN CASINO STORY VOL.3, THE (The Final Chapter)
They'll never know why: Chavez, Freddie / Gallop: Wright, Milton / Psychedelic soul part 2: Russell, Saxie / Sad girl: Anderson, Carol / We were made for each other: Terrible Tom / Paris blues: Middleton, Tony / Say it isn't so: Boo, Betty / Just another heartache: Little Ritchie / He'll never love you: Grace, Charlie / Once: Hale, Larry / Hang on: Wall Of Sound / Woman love thief: Stemmons Express / Let me make you happy: Woods, Billy / Coloured man: Vann, Teddy / Just say you're wanted and needed: Owens, Gwen / How to make a sad man glad: Capreez / Set my heart at ease: Farrow, Mikki / Halos are for angels: Carter, Blanche / Captain of my ship:

Seventh Wonder / Take my heart: Saxton, Mary / I can take care of myself: Chandler, Gene / Out of my mind: Rain / Tainted love: Jones, Gloria / Sidras theme: Ronnie & Robyn / Don't bring me down: Dacosta, Rita

GSCD 090 / Sep '96 / Goldmine

☐ WILD AND EXCELLENT INSTROS

CLCD 4442 / Nov '97 / Collector/White Label

☐ WILD AND WET

Land of a thousand dances: Geils, J. Band / Mustang sally: Commitments / Willie and the hand jive: Thorogood, George / Some kinda wonderful: Grand Funk Railroad / Ain't got no home: Band / Jenny take a ride: Ryder, Mitch & The Detroit Wheels / You'd better move on: Mink Deville / Turn the music down: Bonds, Gary 'US' / In the midnight hour: Commitments / Your mama don't dance: Poison / Gimme some lovin': Thunder / (Sittin' on the) Dock of the bay: Hagar, Sammy / Brother Louie: Quireboys / Feelin' alright: Heights

DC 880842 / May '97 / Disky

☐ WILD AT HEART VOL.1 (18 Rock Classics)

I surrender: Rainbow / Cold as ice: Foreigner / Dead ringer for love: Meat Loaf / Strange kind of woman: Deep Purple / Whatever you want: Status Quo / Tom Sawyer: Rush / Incommunicado: Marillion / Witch queen of New Orleans: Redbone / Breaking the law: Judas Priest / Run run run: Jo Jo Gunne / Magic carpet ride: Steppenwolf / Your mama don't dance: Poison / Paranoid: Black Sabbath / Elected: Cooper, Alice / Prime mover: Zodiac Mindwarp / Sylvia: Focus / Feel like makin' love: Bad Company / Final Countdown: Europe

MUSCD 028 / Jan '97 / MCI Music

☐ WILD AT HEART VOL.2

Do anything you want to: Thin Lizzy / Caroline: Status Quo / Neon knights: Status Quo / Iron fist: Motorhead / Eye of the tiger: Survivor / Legs: ZZ Top / Still loving you: Scorpions / Who do you love: Juicy Lucy / Wheels of steel: Saxon / Take on the world: Judas Priest / Good lovin' gone bad: Bad Company / St. Elmo's fire: Parr, John / Scream until you like it: WASP / Urgent: Foreigner / Backstreet Symphony: Thunder / Poison: Cooper, Alice / Superstitious: Europe / Total eclipse of the heart: Tyler, Bonnie

MUSCD 037 / May '97 / MCI Music

☐ WILD BUNCH (27 Instrumental Reggae Classics)

CDTRL 346 / Mar '95 / Trojan

☐ WILD CONNECTION

Save a place for me / Deep green / Carlin How / Old man of the ocean / Skinningrove Bay / North country girl / Kilten Castle / Abess St. Hilda

101222 / May '97 / A-Play Collection

☐ WILD CONSERVES - THE FLAVOURS OF SCOTLAND (In Aid Of Scottish Wildlife Trust)

LCOM 5226CD / Jan '94 / Lismor

☐ WILD HEARTED WOMAN (2CD Set)

These dreams: Heart / Hold on: Wilson Phillips / China in your hand: T'Pau / Bette Davis eyes: Carnes, Kim / We belong: Benatar, Pat / I touch myself: Divinyls / Walking on sunshine: Katrina & The Waves / All for love: Wilson, Nancy / Rush hour: Wiedlin, Jane / French kissin' in the USA: Harry, Deborah / Love blonde: Wilde, Kim / Broken heart: Rush, Jennifer / Marc Anthony's tune: Nelson, Tyka / Happy ever after: Fordham, Julia / You could have been with me: Easton, Sheena / You're in love: Wilson Phillips / Love is a battlefield: Benatar, Pat / Kids in America: Wilde, Kim / Again: Roberts, Juliet / Universal song: Carnes, Kim / In the heat of the night: Sandra / For your eyes only: Easton, Sheena / All I wanna do is make love to you: Heart / Suddenly last summer: Motels / Are you my baby: Wendy & Lisa / Rush rush: Abdul, Paula / Do me baby: Morgan, Meli'sa / Tide is high: Blondie / Heart and soul: T'Pau / Tell me your plans: Shirts

DOU 882482 / 2 Feb '98 / Disky

☐ WILD IRISH ROSE (Popular Irish Ballads)

PLSCD 188 / Apr '97 / Pulse

☐ WILD MEN BOP

MCG 20030 / May '98 / Vampirella

☐ WILD PUNK (18 Punk Greats)

I hate people: Anti Nowhere League / Disco in Mosco: Vibrators / Lookalikes: Drones / Soldier soldier: Spizz Energi / Suspect device: Stiff Little Fingers / Smash the discos: Business / Banned from the pubs: Peter & The Test Tube Babies / Burn 'em down: Abrasive Wheels / Lost cause: Riot Squad / I'm alive: 999 / Death to disco: Not Sensibles / Lock it up: Eater / Two pints of lager: Splodge / Babylon's burning: Ruts / Wanna world: Urban Dogs / Outlaw: Chron Gen / Right to work: Chelsea

EMPRCD 679 / 8 Sep '97 / Emporio

☐ WILD ROVER (A Feast Of Irish Folk)

Rocky road to Dublin: Dubliners / Lonesome boatman: Furey, Finbar & Eddie / Medley: Renbourn, John / Barleycorn: Johnstons / Leaving of Liverpool: Johnstons / Medley: Maloney, Michael / Foggy dew: Imlach, Hamish / Flowers in the valley: Furey, Finbar & Eddie / Newry highwayman: Johnstons / Wild rover: Dubliners / Bill Hart's favourite: Furey, Finbar & Eddie / Killarney boys of pleasure: Swarbrick, Dave / Medley: Renbourn, John / Spanish cloak: Furey, Finbar & Eddie / I'll tell me ma: Dubliners / Reels: Kilfernora Ceili Band / Norwegian song: Maloney, Michael / Golden jubilee: Glenside Ceilidh Band / Leitram fancy: Maloney, Michael / Home boys home: Dubliners

TRTCD 125 / Dec '94 / TrueTrax

☐ WILD SUMMER WOW (A Creation Sampler)

CRECD 002 / May '94 / Creation

☐ WILD THING

TRTCD 182 / Feb '96 / TrueTrax

☐ WILD THINGS VOL.2

ZERO 0004 / 5 Jan '98 / Zero

☐ WILD WOMEN DO GET THE BLUES

Love's calling: Joseph, Margie / Save your love: Freeman, Louise / I'm trouble: Jackson, Yvonne / What a mean feeling: Synethia / It be's that way sometime: Synethia / One monkey (don't stop no show): Reed, Francine / I got the will: Hall, Sandra / Do I need you (too): Lynn, Trudy / Instant breakfast: Lynn, Trudy

ICH 11902 / Jun '96 / Ichiban

☐ WILDERNESS RETREAT (A Magical Blend Of Music And The Sounds Of Nature)

57792 / May '97 / Nature's Harmony

☐ WILL YOU STILL LOVE ME

CDGFR 130 / Jun '92 / Tring

☐ WIND AND REED

Sunderlal: Rumbel, Nancy / Rose water: Siebert, Budi / Meisoroku (edit): Lee, Riley / Thunder's windmill: Brewer, Spencer / To the willow: Wynberg, Simon / Night tribe: Rumbel, Nancy / Guinevere's tears: Arkenstone, David / Sad memories: Illenberger, Ralf / Awakening: Stein, Ira / Surrender: Gettel, Michael / Northeast wind: Lauria, Nando

ND 61037 / Nov '93 / Narada

☐ WIND DOWN ZONE VOL.1

Happy: Surface / Stay: Controllers / Curious: Midnight Star / Sometehing in the way you make me feel: Mills, Stephanie / Gotta get you home tonight: Wilde, Eugene / Oasis: Baylor, Helen / It never rains in southern california: Tony Toni Tone / Portugese love: Marie, Teena / Everybody loves the sunshine: Ayers, Roy / Why people fall in love: McNeir, Ronnie / Heaven sent you: Clarke, Stanley / Tik tok: Lorenzo / Don't be so distant: Taylor, Gary / Buttercup: Anderson, Carl

CDELV 4 / Jun '96 / Elevate

☐ WIND DOWN ZONE VOL.3

Sexy girl: Thomas, Lillo / Every little bit: Scott, Millie / Genie: BB&Q Band / There ain't nothin' (like your lovin'): Laurence, Paul / I'm the one for you: Whispers / Get in touch with me: Collage / Your smile: Rene & Angela / I need your lovin': Williams, Alyson / My sensitivity: Vandross, Luther / Addictive love: Winans, Bebe & Cece / Never say goodbye to love: Moore, Rene / Can't wait: Payne, Freda / When we're making love: LaSalle, Denise / Are you ready: Robbins, Rockie

CDELV 11 / Dec '93 / Elevate

☐ WIND DOWN ZONE VOL.4

Make it last forever: Sweat, Keith / Games: Booker, Chuckii / Please be mine: Belle, Regina / Let's start love over: Jaye, Miles / Nite and day: Sure, Al B. / You can't turn me away: Striplin, Sylvia / I believe in love: Harris, Major / Rockin' you eternally: Ware, Leon / Don't stop doin' what cha' do: Mills, Stephanie / In the mood: Davis, Tyrone / Warm weather: Pieces Of A Dream / Feels like I'm falling in love: Bar-Kays / Strung out for your love: Four Tops / Lovers everywhere: LTD

CDELV 14 / Apr '94 / Elevate

☐ WIND DOWN ZONE VOL.5

Let's get closer: Cooper, Michael / Love's got a hold on me: Tisha / Sex on the beach: Truth Inc / All because of you: Sherrick / Headline news: Bell, William / Loving you: Byrd, Donald / Make me love the rain: Wright, Betty / Keep it up: Wright, Milton / Tears: Tamara & The Seen / Fade to black: Lynn, Cheryl / We are one: Maze / You're No.1 (In my book): Knight, Gladys / Love you give to me: Lewis, Webster / Touch me again: Williams, Deniece

CDELV 18 / Dec '94 / Elevate

☐ WIND DOWN ZONE VOL.6

Crazy love: Bryson, Peabo / Tell me: Wooten Brothers / Mutual attraction: Change / Feels so good: Midnight Star / Show me where you're coming from: Lucas, Carrie / Love crazy: Atlantic Starr / You know I love you: Break Water / Intimate friends: Kendricks, Eddie / If it isn't love: New Edition / Tropical love: Bofill, Angela / Sparkle: Cameo / Stay: Jones, Glenn / Read my mind: Tashan / Here is my love: Sylvester

CDELV 20 / Jun '95 / Elevate

☐ WIND DOWN ZONE VOL.7

Never gonna give you up: Mills, Stephanie / It's only love: Dante, Steven / What can a miracle do: Warwick, Dionne / It's just the way I feel: Dunlap, Gene / Imaginary playmates: Rene & Angela / You bring out the best in me: Bell-Armstrong, Vanessa / All my love: Rushen, Patrice / I think my heart is telling: King, Evelyn 'Champagne' / Passion and pain: McClean, Janice / In search of: Taylor, Gary / Strangers: Williams, Deniece / Turn out the nightlight: Tavares / I want to touch you: Hall, Randy / I wanna know you: Hewett, Howard

CDELV 21 / Mar '96 / Elevate

☐ WIND IN THE WILLOWS (A Rock Concert)

INAK 9010 / Feb '96 / In Akustik

☐ WINDHAM HILL - A MUSICAL EXPLORATION

Angel eyes: Brickman, Jim / Call of the child: Nightnoise / Norwegian mountains: Sevag, Oystein / Chava's song: Hedges, Michael / Castille: Obiedo, Ray / Last look: Mariano, Torcuato / World's getting louder: De Grassi, Alex / Over easy: Lynch, Ray

01934111732 / Jan '96 / Windham Hill

☐ WINDHAM HILL - BACH VARIATIONS

01934111502 / Jan '95 / Windham Hill

☐ WINDHAM HILL - CELTIC SEASON

01934111782 / Nov '95 / Windham Hill

☐ WINDHAM HILL - GUITAR SAMPLER

Momentary change of heart: De Grassi, Alex / Deep at night: De Grassi, Alex / Sunday on the violet sea: Torn, David / Lion of Boaz: Torn, David / Ritual dance: Hedges, Michael / If I needed someone: Hedges, Michael / Selene: Manring, Michael / Red right returning: Manring, Michael / Sweet pea: Andress, Tuck / Betcha by golly wow: Andress, Tuck

01934111106 / Jan '95 / Windham Hill

☐ WINDHAM HILL - IMPRESSIONISTS

01934111162 / Jan '95 / Windham Hill

☐ WINDHAM HILL - IN SEARCH OF ANGELS

01934111532 / Jan '95 / Windham Hill

☐ WINDHAM HILL - PATH (An Ambient Journey From Windham Hill)

Tibet (part 2): Isham, Mark / On the forest floor: Holroyd, Bob / Le desert bleu: Descarpentries, Xavier / White spirits: Uman / Ghost dancer: De Roth & The Mirrors / To tree or not to tree: Evenson, Dean / Lydia: Story, Tim / Ancient evenings: Hughes, Gary / Riding windhorse (Buddafields): Heavenly Music Corporation / 12.18: Global Communication

01934111632 / Apr '95 / Windham Hill

☐ WINDHAM HILL - PIANO COLLECTION

01934111492 / Sep '95 / Windham Hill

☐ WINDHAM HILL - SANCTUARY (20 Years Of Windham Hill - 2CD Set)

Rocket to the moon: Brickman, Jim / Night slip: Ackerman, Will / Intermezzo: Silverman, Tracy / Ariel boundaries: Hedges, Michael / Wide asleep: Manring, Michael / Wedding rain: Story, Liz / Children's dance: De Grassi, Alex / Hand picked rose of a faded dream: Childs, Billy / House made of dawn light: Douglas Spottedd Eagle / Siri's arrival: Melamora / Night in that land: Nightnoise / Hummingbird: Winston, George / Redonde: Modern Mandolin Quartet / Turning twice: Turtle Island String Quartet / Ivory: Lynch, Ray / Asleep snow came flying: Story, Liz / Fionnghuiala (Mouth music): Nightnoise / Manhattan underground: Gossu, Scott / Daydreams: Schonherz & Scott / Very special place: Mariano, Torcuato / Transit: Stein, Ira & Russel Walder / We kindda music: Narell, Andy / Thousand teardrops: Shadowfax / Every deep dream: Aaberg, Philip / There's a monk in my garden: Sevag, Oystein / Blue kiss: Obiedo, Ray / To be: Montreux Band / Rameau's nephew: Saisse, Philippe / Pittsburg 1901 (Edit): Isham, Mark / Dolphins: Marshall, Mike & Darol Anger / View of you: Simon, F. / Tears of joy: Tuck & Patti / Underground (Edit): Stein, Ira & Russel Walder

1934111802 / Jul '96 / Windham Hill

☐ WINDHAM HILL - THE FIRST TEN YEARS (2CD Set)

Bricklayer's beautiful daughter: Ackerman, Will / White rain: De Grassi, Alex / Colors/dance: Winston, George / Angel's flight: Shadowfax / Bradley's dream: Storey, Liz / Afternoon postlude soliloquy: Hecht, Daniel / Second gymnopedie (1888): Quist, Bill / Homefeild suite: Qualey, David / Rickover's dream: Hedges, Michael / Variations on clair de lune: Basho, Robbie / Oristano sojourn: Cossu, Scott / Clockwork: De Grassi, Alex / Peace: Winston, George / Aerial boundaries: Hedges, Michael / Egrets: Montreux Band / On the threshold of liberty: Isham, Mark / Welcoming: Manring, Michael / 19a: Nightnoise / Montana half light: Aaberg, Philip / Shadowdance: Shadowfax / Pittsburgh 1901: Isham, Mark / Calling: Stein & Walder / Gwenlaise: Cossu, Scot & Friesen, Eugene / Dolphins: Marshall, Mike & Darol Anger / Wishing well: Schonherz & Scott / Theme for Naomi Uemura: Aaberg, Philip / Toys not ties: Nightnoise / Close cover: Mertens, Wim / To the well: Mathieu, W.A. / Hot beach: Interior / New waltz: Dalglish, Malcolm / Processional: Ackerman, Will / Woman at the well: Story, Tim

01934110952 / Jan '95 / Windham Hill

☐ WINDHAM HILL - THE ROMANTICS

01934111712 / Jan '95 / Windham Hill

☐ WINDHAM HILL - WINTER'S SOLSTICE VOL.1

01934111742 / Nov '95 / Windham Hill

☐ WINDHAM HILL SAMPLER '96

Last look: Mariano, Torcuato / When the snow melts: Cunningham, Phil / Theme from 'In search of angels': Story, Tim / White spirit: Umah / Playground: Curtis, Henry Adam / Differetn shore: Nightnoise / Jenny's room: Nightnoise / Southern jukebox music: Penguin Cafe Orchestra / If you believe: Brickman, Jim / Madchenile: Horovitz, Wayne / Prelude in C Minor: Erquiaga, Steve / Picture this: Brickman, Jim / Rio Amazonas: Sevag, Oystein / Castille: Obiedo, Ray

1934111792 / Jun '96 / Windham Hill

☐ WINNER'S CIRCLE

BET 6027 / Jan '95 / Bethlehem

☐ WINNERS

RZRCD 551 / Nov '95 / Ritz

☐ WINNERS CIRCLE VOL.2

Romantically inspired: Tashan / Light of love: Angie & Debbie / Wanna make love 2U: Mannsfield, Rodney / You can't go wrong: Vertical Hold / Come a little closer: Rice, Gene / Quiet time: Belle, Regina / Love tonight: Walker, Chris / Where do we go from here: Steele, Jevetta / I wanna love: Moore, Chante / If you ever loved someone and lost: Beasley, Walter / Never too late: Goodman, Gabrielle / Wait a minute: Mahogany Blue / More today than yesterday: Company / Wonderin': Moten, Wendy

CDEXP 7 / Dec '93 / Expansion

☐ WINNERS, THE (The Great British Country Music Awards)

Follow your dream: O'Donnell, Daniel / Light years away: West Virginia / Before I call it love: Jory, Sarah / Charlie: Froggatt, Raymond / Your love is like a flower: Down County Boys / Fireside dreaming: Landsborough, Charlie / If tomorrow never comes: Pride, Charley / Born to run: Young Country / You're the first thing I think of: O'Donnell, Daniel / Never had it so good: Jory, Sarah / Just between you and me: Pride, Charley / Going nowhere fast: Young Country / Don't make me cry again: Froggatt, Raymond / Come and sit by the river with me: Down County Boys / Blue rendezvous: West Virginia / What colour is the wind: Landsborough, Charlie

RCD 551 / Nov '95 / Ritz

☐ WINNETOU, DU WARST MEIN FREUND

Winnetou du warst mein freund: Brice, Pierre / Meine roten bruder: Brice, Pierre / Ribanna: Brice, Pierre / Ich steh allein: Brice, Pierre / Keineer weiss den tag: Brice, Pierre / Wunderschon: Brice, Pierre / Die nacht beginnt: Brice, Pierre / Lonely: Brice, Pierre / Faire l'amour: Brice, Pierre / Mehr als alles kann man nicht: Brice, Pierre / Madchen in samt und seide: Barker, Lex / Ich oin morgen auf dem weg zu dir: Barker, Lex / Karl May: Lubke, Heinrich / Das hat uns schon Karl May erzalt: Micky & Gaby / Das war die welt von winnetou: Winnetous / Der schatz im silberse: Medium Terzett / Winnetou: Stephan, Karl / Winnetou's bester freund: Silbersee trio / Old shatterhand: Flusspiraten / Nscho-tschi rote rose der prarie: Silbersee trio / Der rot mohn von missouri: Gaby & Petra / Winnetou's schwester: Weiss, Anneli / Lebe wohl, Winnetou: Medium Terzett

BCD 15984 / Jul '96 / Bear Family

☐ WINTER (2CD Set)

Holly and the ivy: De Grassi, Alex / First Noel: Silverman, Tracy & Thea Suits-Silverman / Snow on high ground: Nightnoise / Silent night: Erquiaga, Steve / Walking in the air: Winston, George / Abide the winter: Ackerman, Will / Third gymnopedie: De Grassi, Alex / God rest ye merry gentlemen: Erquiaga, Steve / Little star: Brickman, Jim / We three kings: Higbie, Barbara / Variations on the Kanon by Johann Pachabel: Winston, George / Jesu joy of man's desiring: Qualey, David / Christmas song: Erquiaga, Steve / Little drummer boy: Schonherz & Scott / By the fireside: Mathieu, W.A. / Petite Aubade: Shadowfax / Carol of the bells / In the bleak midwinter: Petti, Pierce

RADCD 49 / Nov '96 / Global TV

☐ WINTER WONDERLAND

Winter wonderland: Day, Doris / Jingle bells: Streisand, Barbra / Santa Claus is coming to town: Bennett, Tony / Christmas spirit: Charles, Ray / Christmas song: Mathis, Johnny / It came upon a midnight clear: Andrews, Julie / O holy night: Vinton, Bobby / When a child is born: Mathis, Johnny & Gladys Knight / Blue Christmas: Nelson, Willie / Little drummer boy: Cash, Johnny / First Noel: Williams, Andy / Silent night: Wynette, Tammy / Christmas time is here again: Robbins, Marty / Mary's boy child: Humperdinck, Engelbert / White Christmas: Sinatra, Frank

4677042 / 3 Nov '97 / Columbia

☐ WINTER'S ROMANCE (18 Romantic Ballads)

Lady: Rogers, Kenny / Cryin': McLean, Don / Move closer: Nelson, Phyllis / When I fall in love: Cole, Nat 'King' / Cry me a river: London, Julie / All I have to do is dream: Everly Brothers / Don't it make my brown eyes blue: Gayle, Crystal / Feelings: Albert, Morris / Sharing the night together: Dr. Hook / Home on Monday: Little River Band / Everybodies gotta learn sometime: Korgis / Winter in America: Ashdown, Doug / Anyone who had a heart: Black, Cilla / They shoot horses don't they: Racing Cars / Where do you go to my lovely: Sarstedt, Peter / Love don't live here anymore: Nail, Jimmy

DCB 864842 / Nov '96 / Disky

☐ WIPEOUT

Afro ride: Leftfield / Chemical beats: Chemical Brothers / Blue Monday: New Order / Age of love: Jam & Spoon / Wipeout (PETROL): Orbital / One love: Prodigy / La tristesse durera (Scream to a sigh): Manic Street Preachers / When: Sunscreem / Good enough: BB & Angie Brown / Circus bells: Armani, Robert / Captain dread: Dreadzone / Transamazonia: Shamen

SONYTV 6CD / Nov '95 / Sony TV

☐ WIPEOUT 2097 (Playstation Soundtrack)

We have explosive: Future Sound Of London / Atom bomb: Fluke / Loops of fury: Chemical Brothers / Tin there: Underworld / Third sequence: Photek / Leave home: Chemical Brothers / We have explosive (Herd killing): Future Sound Of London / Firestarter: Prodigy / V 6: Fluke / Musique: Daft Punk / 2097: Source Direct / Titan: Photek / Petrol: Orbital / Afro ride: Leftfield

CDV 2815 / Sep '96 / Virgin

☐ WIRED (2CD Set)

Breathe: Prodigy / Leave home: Chemical Brothers / Atom bomb: Fluke / Sugar is sweeter: C.J. Bolland / La tristesse durera (scream to a sigh): C.J. Bolland / Stupid girl: Garbage / Pearl's girl: Underworld / Rollercoaster: Grid / Satan: Orbital / Call a cab: Lionrock / Born slippy: Underworld / Rocco: Death In Vegas / Blue Monday: New Order / Offshore: Chicane / If I could fly: Grace / Inner city life: Goldie / Acid lab: Reece, Alex / Milk: Garbage & Tricky / 6 Underground: Sneaker Pimps / Tape loop: Morcheeba / Sly: Massive Attack / Single: Everything But The Girl / One night stand: Aloof / Dance of the bad angels: Booth, Tim & Angelo Badalamenti / Release the pressure: Leftfield / Perpetual dawn: Orb / Londinium: Archive / Stars: Dubstar / Fool's gold: Stone Roses / Disco 2000: Pulp / Satellite: Beloved / Little Britain: Dreadzone / Disappointed: Electronic / In yer face: 808 State / Move any mountain '96: Shamen

5532572 / Jan '97 / PolyGram TV

☐ WITH A SONG IN OUR HEARTS AGAIN (2CD Set)

They say it's wonderful: Crosby, Bing / Sentimental me: Anthony, Ray Orchestra / Undecided: Anthony, Ray Orchestra / It's magic: Anthony, Ray Orchestra / Steppin' out with my baby: Anthony, Ray Orchestra / How lucky are you: Andrews Sisters / Do you love me: Haymes, Dick / You're getting to be a habit with me: Torme, Mel / Again: Torme, Mel / I'll string along with you: Stafford, Jo & Gordon MacRae / To each his own: Ink Spots / No orchids for my lady: Ink Spots / Where or when: Dinning Sisters / I can't begin to tell you: Crosby, Bing & Carmen Cavallaro / Hurry on down: Lutcher, Nellie / My mother's eyes: Lutcher, Nellie / Song is ended (but the melody lingers on): Lutcher, Nellie / Put 'em in a box: Cole, Nat 'King' / My one and only highland fling: Haymes, Dick & Dorothy Carless / Hop scotch polka: Garber, Jan & His Orchestra / That lucky old sun: Martin, Dean /

Powder your face with sunshine: Martin, Dean / Day by day: Crosby, Bing / Riders in the sky: Crosby, Bing / Teresa: Haymes, Dick & The Andrews Sisters / I get sentimental over nothing: Cole, Nat 'King' / Tenderly: Dennis, Clark / Bluebird of happiness: Stafford, Jo & Gordon MacRae / With a song in my heart: Day, Dennis / This is the moment: Stafford, Jo / There's a train out for dreamland: Cole, Nat 'King' / Kiss in the dark: MacRae, Gordon / Far away places: Whiting, Margaret / Manana: Lee, Peggy / How high the moon: Cole, Nat 'King' / Jealous heart: Garber, Jan / On a slow boat to China: Goodman, Benny / Buttons and bows: Dinning Sisters / You was: Lee, Peggy & Dean Martin / When my dreamboat comes home: Crosby, Bing

CDDL 1266 / May '94 / Music For Pleasure

☐ **WITH LOVE TO MY VALENTINE**

I 3896222 / Feb '97 / Galaxy

☐ **WIZARD OF OZ**

JASSCD 629 / Feb '92 / Jass

☐ **WIZARDRY OF OZ, THE**

TRANR 611CD / 29 Sep '97 / Transient

☐ **WOHLSTAND - GERMAN/JAPANESE NOISE COMPILATION**

EFA 127712 / Oct '95 / Human Wreckords

☐ **WOLFE TONE (Rebel Songs Of 1798)**

Aims of the united Irishmen: MacLachlainn, Gearoid / Croppies who will not lie down: Moore, Brian / Who fears to speak of '98: Hunt, Declan / Boulavogue: Dubliners / Henry Joe McCracken: Irish Ramblers / Grave of Wolfe Tone: Hunt, Declan / Rising of the moon: Irish Ramblers / Four green fields: Dubliners / Bold Robert Emmett: Irish Ramblers / Three flowers: Moore, Brian / Kelly the boy from Killane: Irish Ramblers / Irish ways and Irish laws: Close, John / General Munro: Hunt, Declan / Only our rivers run free: Irish Ramblers / Croppy boy: Hunt, Declan / 20 men from Dublin town: O'Brien, Dermot / Roddy McCorley: Hunt, Declan / West's awake: Innisfree Ceoil

CDUI 1798 / Jun '98 / Outlet

☐ **WOMAD LIVE 1996 (What Summer Is Made For)**

Khosha hawraman: Kamkars / Nyamaropa: Mapfumo, Thomas & The Blacks Unlimited / Karayib leve: Kali / Magulo: Wagogo Women's Drum & Dance Ensemble / Da eye wifie: Shooglenifty / Anticipate: Di Franco, Ani / La salio de la mar le galaria: Yannatou, Savina & Primavera En Salonico / Aisha: Ashkhabad / Habibti: Slimani, Abdel Ali / In this dis-united Kingdom: Land Of My Mothers / E te fatu: Te Ava Piti / Renggong manis: Banyumas Bamboo Gamelan / Pole pole: Ongala, Remmy Band

WSVEN 3 / Jun '97 / Womad Select

☐ **WOMAN IN LOVE, A**

MACCD 118 / Aug '96 / Autograph

☐ **WOMAN IN LOVE, A**

PLSCD 191 / Apr '97 / Pulse

☐ **WOMAN IN ME, THE (18 Superb Vocal Performances)**

I say a little prayer: Franklin, Aretha / Right thing to do: Simon, Carly / Love me: Elliman, Yvonne / Don't it make my brown eyes blue: Gayle, Crystal / I just don't know what to do with myself: Springfield, Dusty / Something: Bassey, Shirley / One day I'll fly away: Crawford, Randy / Every time we say goodbye: Fitzgerald, Ella / Anyone who had a heart: Warwick, Dionne / Cry me a river: London, Julie / Loving you: Riperton, Minnie / Memory: Paige, Elaine / Torn between two lovers: MacGregor, Mary / Best thing that ever happened to me: Knight, Gladys & The Pips / Ain't got no...I got life: Simone, Nina / This is my song: Clark, Petula / Wishing you were somehow here again: Brightman, Sarah / We're all alone: Coolidge, Rita

MUSCD 019 / May '94 / MCI Music

☐ **WOMAN TO WOMAN (2CD Set)**

Mighty love: Stansfield, Lisa / Everyday people: Franklin, Aretha / Love is a stranger: Eurythmics / From a distance: Griffith, Nanci / Ce leis: Griffith, Nanci / Thanks to you: Harris, Emmylou / Natural thing: M-People / Walk like an Egyptian: Bangles / Rapture: Blondie / Show me heaven: McKee, Maria / Street life: Crawford, Randy / So natural: Stansfield, Lisa / Walking on sunshine: Katrina & The Waves / Bette Davies eyes: Carnes, Kim / Whole of the moon: Warnes, Jennifer / Another siutase in another hall: Dickson, Barbara / That's what friends are for: Dickson, Barbara / Sisters (are doin' it): Franklin, Aretha & Annie Lennox / Mignight train to Georgia: Knight, Gladys / See the day: Lee, Dee C. / You came: Wilde, Kim / Total eclipse of the heart: Tyler, Bonnie / Dream a little dream of me: Mama Cass / No secrets call of the wild: Brooks, Elkie / Don't go: Yazoo / Rubberband girl: Bush, Kate / What you do with what you got: Reader, Eddi / Heartbreaker: Warwick, Dionne / I've learned to respect the power of love: Mills, Stephanie / Move closer: Nelson, Phyllis / Friends: Stewart, Amii / Livin' in the light: Wheeler, Caron / It's in his kiss: Lewis, Linda / Star: Dee, Kiki / Slowhand: Pointer Sisters / Woman to woman: Brown, Shirley

RCACD 215 / Jul '97 / RCA

☐ **WOMAN TO WOMAN - THE BEST OF WOMAN TO WOMAN**

Can't cry anymore: Crow, Sheryl / Baby baby: Grant, Amy / As I lay me down: Hawkins, Sophie B. / Big white room: Garside, Melanie / Independent love song: Scarlet / Precious: Lennox, Annie / Here we are: Estefan, Gloria / Whispering your name: Moyet, Alison / Constant craving: Lang, k.d. / Power of love: Rush, Jennifer / I drove all night: Lauper, Cyndi / I know: Ferris, Dionne / What I am: Brickell, Edie & New Bohemians / Magic smile: Vela, Rosie / Luka: Vega, Suzanne / And so is love: Bush, Kate / Thank you for hearing me: O'Connor, Sinead / I believe: Detroit, Marcella / Show me heaven: McKee, Maria / Give me a little more time: Gabrielle / You gotta be: Des'ree / No ordinary love: Sade / So natural: Stansfield, Lisa / In your care: Archer, Tasmin / Love...thy will be done: Martika / See the day: Lee, Dee C. / Love and affection: Armatrading, Joan / Stop: Brown, Sam / It's too late: King, Carole / At seventeen: Ian, Janis / I don't know why: Colvin, Shawn / (Love moves in) Mysterious ways: Fordham, Julia / Patience of angels: Reader, Eddi / Walking down Madison: MacColl, Kirsty / You're so vain: Simon, Carly / Hold on: Wilson Phillips / Eternal flame: Bangles / Woman to woman: Craven, Beverley

5353572 / Feb '96 / PolyGram TV

☐ **WOMAN'S HEART VOL.1, A**

Only a woman's heart: McEvoy, Eleanor & Mary Black / Caledonia: Keane, Dolores / Vanities: Keane, Dolores / Blackbird: Shannon, Sharon / Wall of tears: Black, Frances / Summerfly: O'Connell, Maura / Island: Keane, Dolores / I hear you breathing: McEvoy, Eleanor / Sonny: Black, Mary / Coridinio: Shannon, Sharon / Living in these troubled times: O'Connell, Maura / After the ball: Black, Frances

DARA 3158 / Jan '95 / Dara

☐ **WOMAN'S HEART VOL.2, A**

DARA 3063 / Jan '95 / Dara

☐ **WOMAN'S LOVE, A**

Fare thee well, my own true love: Black, Mary / Amhran Peter Baille: Black, Mary / Casting my shadow on the road: Murray, Sinead / New love story: Murray, Sinead / Chomaraigh Aoibhinn O: O'Sullivan, Maire / Carraig: O'Sullivan, Maire / Johnny lovely Johnny: Keane, Dolores / Low low lands of Holland: Keane, Dolores / Pluirin na mBan Don Og: Na Chathain, Brid / Aililiu na Gamha: Na Chathain, Brid / Memories of Father Angus MacDonald: Roach, Nancy / Golden keyboard: Roach, Nancy / An Seanduine: Ni Bheaglaoich, Eilin / Jimmy Mo Mhile Stor: Ni Bheaglaoich, Eilin / Workin' man: Taggart, Mairead / Scolar: Taggart, Mairead / Cre na Cille: Dhonncha, Ann Marie Nic / Slan leis an Oige: Dhonncha, Ann Marie Nic

CICD 091 / Dec '93 / Clo Iar-Chonnachta

☐ **WOMAN'S WORLD**

EFA 064612 / Oct '94 / Metalimbo

☐ **WOMEN IN (E)MOTION FESTIVAL**

T&M 109 / Jan '95 / Tradition & Moderne

☐ **WOMEN IN COUNTRY VOL.1**

He thinks he'll keep her: Carpenter, Mary-Chapin / Till you love me: McEntire, Reba / One way ticket: Rimes, Leann / Crescent City: Harris, Emmylou / Walking away a winner: Mattea, Kathy / From a distance: Griffith, Nanci / Lonely too long: Loveless, Patty / Another little piece of my heart: Hill, Faith / On a bus to St. Cloud: Yearwood, Trisha / Give me some wheels: Boguss, Suzy / To be loved by you: Judd, Wynonna / Love can build a bridge: Judds / I'll take my sorrow straight: DeMent, Iris / Circus girl: Peters, Gretchen / Something in red: Kasset, Angela / Romeo: Parton, Dolly / You wanna make something out of it: Messina, JoDee / Past the point of rescue: Black, Mary

AHRCD 41 / Feb '97 / Curb

☐ **WOMEN IN COUNTRY VOL.2**

AHLCD 47 / Jun '97 / Curb

☐ **WOMEN IN COUNTRY VOL.3**

AHLCD 53 / 9 Mar '98 / Hit

☐ **WOMEN IN REGGAE**

VYDCD 016 / Sep '96 / Vine Yard

☐ **WOMEN LIVE AT MOUNTAIN STAGE**

Strange fire: Indigo Girls / Lock stock and teardrops: Lang, k.d. / Egos like hairdos: Di Franco, Ani / Amsterdam: Baez, Joan / I kissed a girl: Sobule, Jill / Sweet sorrow in the wind: Harris, Emmylou / When I was a boy: Williams, Dar / Battle of Evermore: Wilson, Ann & Nancy / Crazy Mary: Williams, Victoria / Half of a woman: Eatman, Heather / Iron horse: Kennedy Rose / Reach for the rhythm: Lynne, Shelby

BPM 308CD / May '97 / Blue Plate

☐ **WOMEN OF BLUE CHICAGO**

Baby, what you want me to do: Lee, Bonnie / Vicksburg blues: Carroll, Karen / As the years go passing by: Johnson, Shirley / I'm shakin': Jordan, Lynne / Thrill is gone: Big Time Sarah / Walking blues: Lee, Bonnie / Goin' down slow: Carroll, Karen / It hurts me too: Johnson, Shirley / If I can't sell it: Jordan, Lynne / Wild about that thing: Davis, Katherine / Why my man won't treat me right: Big Time Sarah

DD 690 / Jun '97 / Delmark

☐ **WOMEN OF BRITTANY**

KMCD 74 / Jun '97 / Keltia Musique

☐ **WOMEN OF FAITH**

I'll be believing: Point Of Grace / Beauty for ashes: Lewis, Crystal / Waiting in the wings: Anointed / He came through: Baylor, Helen / Shout to the Lord: Zschech, Darlene / Exalt the name: Patty, Sandi / Master's hand: Morgan, Cindy / Flower in the rain: Velasquez, Jaci / Saviour like a shepherd: Walsh, Sheila / Joy of the Lord: Caesar, Shirley

12802 / Apr '98 / Integrity

☐ **WOMEN OF GOSPEL'S GOLDEN AGE VOL.1**

More like Jesus: Griffin, Bessie / Blessed mother: Griffin, Bessie / Whosoever will: Griffin, Bessie / Heaven: Griffin, Bessie / Nobody but you: Griffin, Bessie / All of my burdens (ain't that good news): Griffin, Bessie / Sit dowm children: Robinson, Helen Youth Choir / I'm not gonna let nobody stop you: Princess Stewart / Tired, Lord: Princess Stewart / Bring back those days: Argo Singers / Lookin' this way: Argo Singers / Get away Jordan: Love Coates, Dorothy / Every day will be Sunday (by and by): Love Coates, Dorothy / I'm going to die with the staff in my hand: Love Coates, Dorothy / Take your burden to the Lord and leave it there: Love Coates, Dorothy / I must see Jesus: Greenwood, Lil / Tell Jesus all: Simmons-Akers Trio / Going to Canaan's shore: Simmons-Akers Trio / Glory to his name: Simmons-Akers Trio / God is a battle axe: Carr, Sister Wynona / I'm a pilgrim traveller: Carr, Sister Wynona / See his blessed face: Carr, Sister Wynona / How good God is: Carr, Sister Wynona / Till we meet again: Martin, Sallie Singers & Cora Martin / Jesus: Martin, Sallie Singers & Cora Martin / Thank you Jesus: Martin, Sallie Singers & Cora Martin / How far am I from Canaan: Famous Ward Singers of Philadelphia

CDCHD 567 / Mar '94 / Ace

☐ **WOMEN OF SONG**

JD 159 / Nov '97 / Chesky

☐ **WOMEN OF THE PO VALLEY**

Nella citta di Genova / O marinaio che cosa rimirì / La mia Mamma l'e 'na ruffiana / Sento il fischio del vapore / Moretto o bel moretto / Lavoro e molto poco / O cancellier che tieni la penna in mano / L'oi bella va in giardino / La vien giu dalle montagne / La strada delle pioppe / O cara Mamma ni voi maritar / Se otto ore / Vedo spuntar fra gli alberi / O macchinista getta carbone / La biondina di voghera / Vien morettina vien / Mamma mia voi marita / Donna Lombarda / In casa mia cinque sorelle / Peppino entra in camera / Al me murus al sta de la del seri

B 6846 / May '97 / Auvidis/Ethnic

☐ **WOMEN OF THE WORLD (Celtic Vol.1)**

PUTU 1332 / Jun '97 / Putumayo

☐ **WOMEN OF THE WORLD (Celtic Vol.2)**

PUTU 1342 / 27 Oct '97 / Putumayo

☐ **WOMEN WITH VOICES**

I'm glad there is you: Kent, Shirley / Infant eyes, missing: Fox, Mandy / Play with light and shade: Mackness, Vanessa / Isadora and Kryia: Alquimia / January thaw: Hodgson, Liz / Lot to answer for: Hammon, Marion / Mele honua: Dogan-Corringham, Viv / Bit of a risk maybe: Bentley, Alison / Fox's revenge: Bolton, Polly / Cradle song: Tippett, Julie & Maggie Nichols / If I don't love you: Shaw, Dorothy / Mm-chuh-agh: Ox Vox / Pig war: Welch, Linda Lee / Everything: Alquimia

SLAMCD 402 / Oct '96 / Slam

☐ **WOMEN'S WORK**

PUTU 1282 / Mar '97 / Putumayo

☐ **WONDERFUL BABY (16 Classic Baby Songs)**

You're having my baby / All that she wants / Naughty lady of Shady Lane / Baby sittin' boogie / Where will the baby's dimple be / When a child is born / Summertime / Beautiful boy / Wonderful baby / Twenty tiny fingers / When I first met you / Hush little baby / Isn't she lovely / Rock 'n' roll baby / Baby mine / Heaven sent

304932 / Jun '97 / Hallmark

☐ **WONDERFUL CHRISTMAS**

DCD 5346 / Dec '93 / Disky

☐ **WONDERFUL WORLD, BEAUTIFUL PEOPLE (2CD Set)**

SMDCD 109 / Jul '97 / Snapper

☐ **WONDERFUL WURLITZER, THE (Featuring Robert Wolfe & Nicholas Martin)**

RAF march past / Medley 1 / Medley 2 / Parade of the tin soldiers / Medley 3 / Medley 4 - Me and my girl / Gymnopedie no.1 / Our director / Tiger rag / Kitten on the keys / Medley 5 / Medley 6 / Rondo all turce / Medley 7 / Eleanora / Buffoon / Light of foot march

12722 / Nov '95 / Laserlight

☐ **WONDERLAND (The Final/2CD Set)**

SPV 08992542 / Mar '97 / ID&T

☐ **WONDROUS WATERFALL**

DC 879592 / Oct '97 / Disky

☐ **WOODSTOCK GENERATION**

EDL 28612 / Oct '94 / Edel

☐ **WOODSTOCK MOUNTAINS**

ROUCD 11520 / '88 / Rounder

☐ **WORD IS BLACKNESS - THE SOUND IS SOUL, THE**

Shower the world: Aleshure / I like it: Johnson, Dewaine / Don't shoot: Knyght, Doug / Only wanna be in your arms: Gaines, Rosie & Kevin Nash / Lonely: Nash, Kevin / Loving you: D Macon / Step 2 U: Marqo / Time heals (a wounded heart): Kenyada / This feeling of love: Graves, Cynthia / After the rain: Gaines, Rosie & Kevin Nash / You're the one: Jharris / I'm ready: Mighty Clouds Of Joy / All of my love: Nash, Kevin & Monet / Realise: For The Gospel / Just wanna give you my love: Aleshure

ATCD 025 / Jan '97 / ATR

☐ **WORD SOUN' 'AVE POWER**

HBCD 15 / Jun '94 / Heartbeat

☐ **WORKING THE ROAD (The Golden Age Of Chicago Gospel)**

Come in the room: Anderson, Robert / Trust in Jesus: Anderson, Robert / How could it be: Anderson, Robert / Oh Lord is it I: Anderson, Robert / How I got over: Anderson, Robert / Sow righteous seeds: Anderson, Robert / He's pleading in glory: Anderson, Robert / He's pleading in glory: Anderson, Robert / My expectation: Anderson, Robert / How could it be: Anderson, Robert / Working the road: Ballinger, Reverend Robert / Standing in the safety zone: Ballinger, Reverend Robert / I John saw the number: Ballinger, Reverend Robert / Drop your net: Ballinger, Reverend Robert / My soul loves Jesus: Ballinger, Reverend Robert / I'm heaven bound: Lewis, Sammy / Come unto me: Smith, Lewis Singers / Jesus lover of my soul: Smith, Lewis Singers / Down on my knees: Smith, Lewis Singers / I just had to call his name: Smith, Lewis Singers / He'll make you happy: Smith, Lewis Singers / He's my everything: Smith, Lewis Singers / Hold the light: Smith, Lewis Singers / Hold the light: Smith, Lewis Singers

DE 702 / Jan '98 / Delmark

☐ **WORLD ACCORDING TO CRAMMED**

Shimmering warm and bright: Canto, Bel / Granite and sand: Lone, Kent / Look of love: Dalcan, Dominique / Nautical dream: Avalon / If I sleep will the plane crash: Lurie, John / L'oeill de la nuit: Matta, Ramuntcho / I don't care: Gruesome Twosome / Tanola nomads: Sainkho / Brrrlak: Zap Mama / No tears: Tuxedo Moon / Ay triste: Bobvan / Amdyaz: Zazou, Hector / Soul magic: YBU & Jonell / Monna: Black Maria / Dragoste de la clejani: Taraf De Haidouks / Et tout est parti de la: Lew, Benjamin / Banzanza: Roots Of OK Jazz

CRAM 087 / Jan '94 / Crammed Discs

☐ **WORLD CLASS PUNK**

RUSCD 8243 / 20 Jul '98 / ROIR

☐ **WORLD DANCE - THE DRUM AND BASS EXPERIENCE (2CD Set)**

Let me in: DJ Harmony / Circles: Adam F / Renegade: Keith, Ray / Champion sound: Alliance / Inner city life: Goldie / Everyman: DRS & Kenny Ken / Bomber: Aphrodite / Arsonist: Urban Shakedown / Set speed: DJ Krust / DOPE: Dope On Plastic / Lockdown: Dee, Ellis / Breakage vol.4: Noise Factory / Rumble: DJ Rap / Lighter: DJ SS / MA2: DJ SS / Fuckin' em up: Shy FX / Get raw: Engineers Without Fears / Quest: Shimmon & Andy C / Funkula: Shimmon & Andy C / License: Krome & Time / This Style: Shy FX / Chopper: Shy FX / Real killer: Dee, Ellis & MC Fearless / P-Funk Era: P-Funk / We must unite: DJ Hype / Six million ways to die: Dope Skillz / Love and unity: DJ Hype & MC Fats Peace / Warning: DJ Hype & MC Fats Peace / Bonaza kid: Firefox / Truly one: Origin Unknown / Valley of the shadows: Origin Unknown / Ganja man: DJ Krome & Mr. Time / Oh Gosh: Undercover Agent / Babylon (dog bark): Splash / Screwface: Brainkillers / Angles: DJ Krust / Super sharp shooter: DJ Zinc / R-Type: Jo / Pulp fiction: Reece, Alex / Dictation: Mask / Numbers: Gang Related & Mask / Remember the rollers: Dr. S. Gachet / Metropolis: Adam F

FIRMCD 10 / Dec '96 / Firm

☐ **WORLD DANCE VOL.3 (3CD Set)**

Scottie: Subnation / Warhead: DJ Krust / Trouble: Scorpio / One: Mampi swift / Jazz steppin': Rogue Unit / Five times: Undercover Agent / Mutation: C, Andy & Shimmon / It's like that: DJ Zinc / Whose the bad man: Pascal / Stretched: Dope Skillz / Beep me 911: Elliott, Missy / Yeah you: Step / Love will find a way: Romero, Victor / Gem for gems: One Tribe / Make you whole: Andronicus / Case of funk: Nightmares On Wax / Your love: Prodigy / Feel good: Manix / Far out: Sons of loop da loop era / Bomb scare: 2 Bad Mice / Living in darkness: Top Buzz / Sound of eden: Shades Of Rhythm / Made in two minutes: Bug Kann & Plastic Jam / Don't go: Awesome 3 / Feel the rhythm: New Class A / Body heat: 2 as 1 / Sassy lady: New Horizons / Long time coming: Bump & Flex / Who needs enemies: Red Light / Love peace and happiness: Something Else / Keep on: M&S & Jaye Ella Ruth / Take control: State Of Mind / Spirit of the sun: Fontana, Lenny / Always: Ramsey & Fen / Masquerade: Gerideau / Casanova: Taylor & Burton / If you want me: Hicks, Hinda

WORLDCD 3 / 17 Aug '98 / Beechwood

☐ **WORLD DOMINATION LIVE (2CD Set)**

OPCD 068 / 22 Jun '98 / Osmose

☐ **WORLD DOMINATION VOL.1**

OPCD 032 / May '95 / Osmose

☐ **WORLD DOMINATION VOL.2, THE**

OPCD 056 / Apr '97 / Osmose

☐ **WORLD DOMINATION VOL.3**

OPCD 067 / 13 Apr '98 / Osmose

☐ **WORLD FUSION COMPILATION**

O zokye: Malagache Connexion / Pudela: Robin, Thierry / Laaven yissna: Mezel, Iness / Pale amende si abeau: Gutsa, Nicolae / Al pasar por el puerto: Bares, Equidad / Marv eo ma mestrez: Marchand, Erik / Toutrakansko rondo: Quintet Clarinettes / Kicsi kicsi kem: Robin, Thierry / Ottomar: Quintet Clarinettes / Et la roue de la vie: Clastrier, Valentin / Ou en vas-tu: Chabenat, Giles & Frederic paris / Li barquetas de Sant Joan: Tesi, Riccardo & Patrick Vaillant/Gianluigi Trovesi / Filugana: Ledda, Elena / Lo temps vai e ven e vire: Carlotti, Jean-Marie / La balada de Felis Galean: Tesi, Riccardo & Patrick Vaillant / Manetta: Chants Corses / El di de la me muart: Quatuor Vocal De Giovanna Marini / Une anche pasee: Vaurien, Scopolamine / Lo ezin egínaren kanta: Achiary, Benat / Comme dans un train pour une etoile: Clastrier, Valentin / Farewell: Pellen, Jaques / Tio vivo: Achiary, Benat / Se yu sabio: Gilbert, Alain

Y 225063 / Nov '97 / Silex

☐ **WORLD IN MOTION**

Radio Africa: Bhundu Boys / Kachembere: Bhundu Boys / Wende zako: Real Sounds / Uchandifunga: Four Brothers / Rudo chete: Four Brothers / Kana vatsvene vopinda: Manureke, M / Cain na Abel: Manureke, M / Out of Africa: Biggie Tembo / Big banana: Jolly Boys / Mother and wife: Jolly Boys / My lovely Elizabeth: Rogie, S.E. / I wish I was a cowboy: Rogie, S.E. / Ganado ferez: Incantation / Ojos azules: Incantation / Breaths: Sweet Honey In The Rock / Waters of Babylon: Sweet Honey In The Rock / Polítya: Ukrainians / Koroleva ne polerma: Ukrainians

GRILLCD 013 / 29 Jun '98 / Cooking Vinyl

☐ **WORLD IN OUR BACKYARD**

CHUB 1005CD / Mar '98 / Chubby Dragon

☐ **WORLD IN UNION ANTHEMS**

World in union '95: Ladysmith Black Mambazo / Swing low, sweet chariot: Ladysmith Black Mambazo & China Black / Bread of heaven: Ball, Michael & Ladysmith Black Mambazo / Haka 95/ Pokarekare Ana: Union & Ngati Ranana / Burning in your heart: Union / Y dale alegria a mi Corazon: Union & Marie Claire D'Ubaldo / Shoshaloza: Ladysmith Black Mambazo / Samoa Tula'i: Union & The Samoan Choir / Sakura: Union / Flower of Scotland: Dickson, Barbara / Otua Mafimafi: Union & The Tongan Choir / Ireland's call: Strong, Andrew & The Irish Rugby Squad / Va Pensiero: Union / O Canada: Union / Vis-a-vis: Union & Monique Seka / Mocanita Cu Trifoi: Union & Nick Magnus / Run wallaby run: Parkinson, Doug / Le monde uni: Union

5278072 / Jul '95 / PolyGram TV

☐ **WORLD INSTRUMENTAL COLLECTION, A**

PUTU 1232 / Oct '96 / Putumayo

☐ **WORLD IS A WONDERFUL PLACE, THE**
HPR 2003CD / May '93 / Hokey Pokey

☐ **WORLD MOODS (2CD Set)**
VTDCD 201 / 17 Aug '98 / Virgin TV

☐ **WORLD MUSIC**
NI 7008 / Sep '94 / Nimbus

☐ **WORLD MUSIC ALBUM**
Finale: Piazzolla, Astor / Neend koyi: Najma / Bolingo: Doudongo, M Poto / Puente de Los Alunados: Nunez, Gerardo / Milagre dos peixes: Nascimento, Milton / Humpty dumpty: Palmieri, Eddie / Alvorada: Mariano / Souareba: Keita, Salif / Flash of the spirit (laughter): Hassell, Jon & Farafina / Chebba: Khaled, Cheb / Galapagos: Nuemann & Zapf
INT 30102 / May '91 / Intuition

☐ **WORLD MUSIC FROM ISRAEL (2CD Set)**
FA 079 / 24 Apr '98 / Fremeaux

☐ **WORLD MUSIC OF AMERICA, THE**
WLD 002 / Aug '93 / Tring

☐ **WORLD MUSIC SAMPLER VOL.2**
NI 7014 / Sep '94 / Nimbus

☐ **WORLD MUSIC THAT SPEAKS TO THE SPIRIT**
5346582 / 5 Jan '98 / Triloka

☐ **WORLD MUSIC VOL.1 (N. Europe/S. America)**
825052 / Jul '91 / BUDA

☐ **WORLD OF AEROBICS, THE (2CD Set)**
ZYX 11062 / Jan '98 / ZYX

☐ **WORLD OF AMERICAN LOVE SONGS, THE (2CD Set)**
ZYX 110922 / 1 Sep '97 / ZYX

☐ **WORLD OF BRASS, THE**
Stars and stripes forever / Ash grove / Scottish rhapsody / Flowert duet / Blue danube waltz / Last spring / Australian fantasy / Excerpts from Capriccio Espagnol / Largo / Blaydon races / Rose of tralee / Three tenors fantasy / Russian fantasy
CHAN 4511 / Aug '92 / Chandos

☐ **WORLD OF CHA CHA CHA/RUMBA/ SAMBA/JIVE, THE (2CD Set)**
ZYX 110862 / 1 Sep '97 / ZYX

☐ **WORLD OF COVER VERSIONS, THE (2CD Set)**
ZYX 111052 / Jan '98 / ZYX

☐ **WORLD OF DELIRIUM VOL.1**
DELWCD 01 / '95 / Delirium

☐ **WORLD OF DELIRIUM VOL.2**
DELWCD 002 / Jul '94 / Delirium

☐ **WORLD OF DELIRIUM VOL.3**
DELWCD 03 / May '95 / Delirium

☐ **WORLD OF DREAM VOL.2, THE (2CD Set)**
ZYX 111352 / 1 Jun '98 / ZYX

☐ **WORLD OF DRUMS AND PERCUSSION, THE**
CMPCD 5004 / 3 Aug '98 / CMP

☐ **WORLD OF FIESTA DE SAMBA, THE (2CD Set)**
ZYX 110972 / 1 Sep '97 / ZYX

☐ **WORLD OF FOOTBALL, THE (The Good The Bad And The Ugly Of World Football/3CD Set)**
This time we'll get it right: England World Cup Squad 1982 / Boys in green: Republic Of Ireland FC / Say it with pride: Scotland FC / Come on Northern Ireland: Northern Ireland FC / Wales: Wales FC / Re-sepp-ten: Denmark FC / Gascoigne please: Mr. Martini / England '66: Silvester, Victor Orchestra / Ally's tartan army: Cameron, Andy / Who nicked the ball: Hurst, Geoff & Martin Peters / Viva Scotland: Gunn, Ben / World in motion: Cortez, Hector & His Formation / Brazil vs. Slough Town FC 1966: Wembley '73 / Roger Milla is my no.9 dream: Rainbow Choir / Can we kick it (no we can't): Wall Of Orange / Maradonna hand ball: Business / Soccer fan: Real Sounds Of Africa / Super Marco Van Basten: Rainbow Choir / We are the champions: Hoddle, Glen / Mr. Bergkamp: Yeah / Crazy games: Jones, Vinnie / Do the Wright thing: Wright, Ian / Oh sweet England: Moore, Bobby & Geoff Hurst/Martin Peters / Jackie's Geordie Sunday: Charlton, Jack / Fabrizio Ravenelli: Mannion / Ooh ooh Tony Adams: A-Team / Ryan Giggs we love you: Rainbow Choir / Viva Bobby Moore: Business / Gio: Phoenix, Kevin / South Africa: Revelation Time & Ruud Gullit / Duncan Duncan Ferguson: Duncan's Army / Shearer Shearer: Dingo / Psycho: Merry Men / Juninho jest: Mannion / You'll never walk alone: Kop Choir / Football football I like football: Randall, Alan / Pass shoot goal: Fields, Gracie / Match Of The Day: Soccer Rockers / When the Saints go marching in: Soccer Rockers / Football crazy football mad: Hall, Robin & Jimmy MacGregor / BBC Grandstand: Soccer Rockers / Jesus with a football: Formbys / On the ball: Supporters / Sports Report: Soccer Rockers / Young footballer: Lees, Ian 'Sludge' / I'm forever blowing bubbles: Lees, Ian 'Sludge' / Oh no not football: Goal To Goal & Jazzie J / My oh my: Oxford United & Prism / Battle of the Republics (glory glory hallelujah): Soccer Rockers
390605 / 20 Apr '98 / Hallmark

☐ **WORLD OF GABBA, THE (2CD Set)**
ZYX 110882 / 1 Sep '97 / ZYX

☐ **WORLD OF GOA TRANCE, THE (2CD Set)**
ZYX 111402 / 1 Jun '98 / ZYX

☐ **WORLD OF HIP HOP, THE (2CD Set)**
ZYX 110872 / 1 Sep '97 / ZYX

☐ **WORLD OF HOLIDAY HITS, THE**
ZYX 110692 / Jul '97 / ZYX

☐ **WORLD OF HOUSE MUSIC (2CD Set)**
EFA 063312 / Jul '96 / Ausfahrt

☐ **WORLD OF MALLORCA PARTY, THE (2CD Set)**
ZYX 110892 / 1 Sep '97 / ZYX

☐ **WORLD OF MUSIC, THE (Israel)**
Hava naguila nora / Zemer atick / Kalou raglayim / Mazeltov/Similtov/Yevele lecha / Fraylekh / Veahaya ketz shatul / Polka tcherkesse / Banor alena / Zum gali gali / Shalom alehem / Tehilim / Yedid ne fesh / Vilno / Kindelita / Emek / Roeh veroah / Ma naavou / Kaddish
308952 / 11 May '98 / Hallmark

☐ **WORLD OF MUSIC, THE (Cuba)**
Lo que me paso en la: Alvarez, Adalberto & Su Son / Se meure la tia: Los Van Van / Coge el camaron: La Origina De Manzanillo / Bacalo con pan: Grupo Irakere / Unicornio: Rodriguez, Silvio / Mi son mi son mi son: Miguelito Cuni Con Chappottin / Cantido Celina: Gonzales, Celena / Ese sentimiento que se llama amor: Alonso, Pacho / La chica mamey: Orquesta Ritmo Oriental / El diapason: Orquesta Original De Manzanillo / Me falbas tu: Alonso, Pacho Y Su Orquestra / Que es lo que hace ud: Gomez, Tito Con Jorrin / De mis recuerdos: Burke, Elena / A bayomo en coche: Son 14 / Por encima del nivel: Orquestra Los Van Van
309152 / 13 Jul '98 / Hallmark

☐ **WORLD OF MUSIC, THE (India)**
Varnum / Keerthana / Samajavaragamana / Keerthana / Kalyani ragam / Nidichalasukhama / Adigoalladigo / Meerabhajan / Ayyappa ashtakam / Gandhamu pooyyaruga / Folk song 1 / Hindi folk song / Folk song 2 / Purandaradasa keertana / Hinki tune / Siva sthuthi / Hanuman chalisa / Devi slokam / Wedding bells 1 / Wedding bells 2 / Vedam / Las carretas del rocio / Castellana / Sevillanas de la loteria / Farruca / Junto a una rosa llonaba / Sevillanas / Los gitanos canasteros / Fantasia inca
309232 / 13 Jul '98 / Hallmark

☐ **WORLD OF MUSIC, THE (Iberia)**
Guajira: Caca De Azacur / No lo beses en la boca / Ritmos del Paraguay / La luna por el rocio / Verdias / Fandangos de huelva / Carcelera
309242 / 13 Jul '98 / Hallmark

☐ **WORLD OF PUNK, THE**
ZYX 110722 / Jul '97 / ZYX

☐ **WORLD OF RAP VOL.2, THE (2CD Set)**
ZYX 111072 / Jan '98 / ZYX

☐ **WORLD OF RAVE PARADES, THE (2CD Set)**
ZYX 110952 / 1 Sep '97 / ZYX

☐ **WORLD OF SALSA, THE (2CD Set)**
ZYX 110702 / 1 Sep '97 / ZYX

☐ **WORLD OF SOCA, THE (2CD Set)**
GC 900003/4 / Dec '93 / ITM

☐ **WORLD OF TECHNO VOL.3, THE (2CD Set)**
ZYX 111392 / 1 Jun '98 / ZYX

☐ **WORLD OF TRADITIONAL MUSIC, THE**
C 56006166 / May '94 / Ocora

☐ **WORLD OF TRUCKERS, THE (2CD Set)**
ZYX 110762 / 1 Sep '97 / ZYX

☐ **WORLD OUT OF TIME VOL.3, A (The Music Of Madagascar)**
SHCD 64069 / Sep '96 / Shanachie

☐ **WORLD PIPE BAND CHAMPIONSHIPS 1987**
Selection / March, strathspey and reel / Selection / Selection / March, strathspey and reel / Selection / Selection / March, strathspey and reel / Selection / March, strathspey and reel / Selection / March, strathspey and reel / March, strathspey and reel
LCOM 9005 / '87 / Lismor

☐ **WORLD PIPE BAND CHAMPIONSHIPS 1989**
March, strathspey and reel: Strathclyde Police Pipe Band / Selection: Strathclyde Police Pipe Band
LCDM 9019 / '89 / Lismor

☐ **WORLD PIPE BAND CHAMPIONSHIPS 1990**
CDMON 810 / Sep '90 / Monarch

☐ **WORLD PIPE BAND CHAMPIONSHIPS 1991**
CDMON 816 / Jul '94 / Monarch

☐ **WORLD PIPE BAND CHAMPIONSHIPS 1992**
CDMON 818 / Jul '94 / Monarch

☐ **WORLD PIPE BAND CHAMPIONSHIPS 1993**
MON 820CD / Nov '93 / Monarch

☐ **WORLD PIPE BAND CHAMPIONSHIPS 1994**
MON 825CD / Oct '94 / Monarch

☐ **WORLD PIPE BAND CHAMPIONSHIPS 1995**
CDMON 827 / Sep '95 / Monarch

☐ **WORLD PIPE BAND CHAMPIONSHIPS 1996**
CDMON 830 / Oct '96 / Monarch

☐ **WORLD PIPE BAND CHAMPIONSHIPS 1997**
Caledonia selection: Shotts & Dykehead Caledonia Pipe Band / Strathspey and reel: Shotts & Dykehead Caledonia Pipe Band / March, strathspey and reel: Fraser, Simon University Pipe Band / Victoria Police selection: Victoria Police Pipe Band / March, strathspey and reel: Victoria Police Pipe Band / Caledonia selection: Boghall & Bathgate Caledonia Pipe Band / Scottish Power selection: Scottish Power Pipe Band / March, strathspey and reel: Montgomery, Field Marshall Pipe Band / Selection: Strathclyde Police Pipe Band / March, strathspey and reel: 78th Fraser Highlander's Pipe Band
CDMON 831 / 6 Oct '97 / Monarch

☐ **WORLD RECORDS SAMPLER VOL.1**
Token for two: Brown, Dennis / Dreaming: Isaacs, Gregory / Easy squeeze: Minott, Sugar / Passing judgement: Garnet Silk / Woke up crying: Ricks, Glen / Love me so bad: General Pecos / Bring back the world: Sanchez / Rebel with a cause: Brown, Dennis / Mind is willing: Glasgow, Deborahe / Ebony eyes: Thriller U / New York City: London, Jimmy / Heaven me reach: Simpleton
WRCD 012 / Dec '97 / World

☐ **WORLD RECORDS SAMPLER VOL.2**
Slapper dapper: Isaacs, Gregory / Waiting for you: Brown, Dennis / Trust me too much: Sanchez / Out of my mind: Ricks, Glen / Speak the truth: Minott, Sugar / Dem fe hear: Simpleton / I really love you: Campbell, Al / Diplomatic fools: Isaacs, Gregory / Impossible: Sanchez / Gimme your love: Glasgow, Deborahe / Run come: General Pecos
WRCD 014 / Dec '97 / World

☐ **WORLD ROOTS LIVE 1992-1993**
MWCD 3007 / Jun '94 / Music & Words

☐ **WORLD SONIC DOMINATION**
KICKCD 11 / Jul '94 / Kickin'

☐ **WORLD STILL WON'T LISTEN**
TDH 0018 / Feb '97 / Too Damn Hype

☐ **WORLD TECHNO ALLIANCE**
DBMPCHD 3 / Jun '96 / Punch

☐ **WORLD WAR TWO MEMORIES**
Rule Brittania: Band Of The Royal Marines / Royal Fleet Auxiliary: Band Of The Royal Marines / D-Day drum display: Band Of The Royal Marines / Colonel bogey/Semper Fidelis/Liberty bell: Band Of The Royal Marines / Marche Militaire Francaise: Band Of The Royal Marines / Stars and stripes forever: Band Of The Royal British Legion / Hands across the sea: Band Of The Royal British Legion / Popular songs of World War Two: Band Of The Royal British Legion / Longest day: Band Of The Royal British Legion / V for victory: Band Of The Royal British Legion / Marches of the British Armed Forces: Band Of The Royal British Legion / Heave ho my lads/The Army Air Corps: Band Of The Royal British Legion / National emblem: Royal Regiment Of Fusiliers Band / Normandy veterans: Duke Of Wellington Regiment / Ever glorious: Band Of The Cheshire Regiment / SSAFA march: Staff Band Of The RAOC / Glorious victory: Western Band Of The RAF / Boys of the Old Brigade/Old soldier's never die: Band Of The Royal Tank Regiment / Evening hymn/Last Post: Worcestershire & Sherwood Foresters Regiment
3036000942 / Jun '97 / Carlton

☐ **WORLD WIDEST YOUR GUIDEST**
CDORBD 073 / May '92 / Globestyle

☐ **WORLD'S BEST POWER POP COMPILATION...REALLY, THE**
Plastic moon rain: Moptops / Exit to stay: DT'S / It's a shame: This Perfect Day / Just another day: Twenty Cent Crush / Love you like a King: Clevenger, Walter / Brenda revisited: Lennon, Martin Luther / Colours: Rooks / Easy on the eye: Howes, Kenny / Waking from a dream: Gilbert, Micah / Miss July: Jones, Brad / What goes around: Barely Pink / Go: Willie Wisely / Yes yes hey hey: Wanderband / Today will be yesterday: Big Hello / Waterfall: Heavy Into Jeff / Almost something there: Beatifics / Wave to ride: Living Daylights / Throw me down: Cool Blue Halo / Try not to care: DGS Younger / Nervous man: Stellaluna / So low: Dead Flowers / Take me or leave me: Time Bomb Symphony
NL 0038 / May '97 / Not Lame

☐ **WORLD'S BEST, THE**
House of the rising sun: Burdon, Eric / Man who sold the world: Lulu / I am the beat: Look / (Don't fear) the reaper: Blue Oyster Cult / Clap for the wolfman: Guess Who / Couldn't get it right: Climax Blues Band / Alone: Puckett, Gary / Lost in fantasy: Bachman-Turner Overdrive / Parchement farm: Winter, Johnny / Don't do that: Geordie / Tomorrow night: Atomic Rooster / 2-4-6-8 Motorway: Robinson, Tom / In the skies: Green, Peter / Polka salad Annie: White, Tony Joe
DC 865582 / May '97 / Disky

☐ **WORLD'S GREATEST JAZZ BALLADS (2CD Set)**
'Round midnight: Monk, Thelonious / Autumn leaves: Getz, Stan / On green dolphin street: Wilson, Teddy / Time on my hands: Holiday, Billie / My funny valentine: Blakey, Art & The Jazz Messengers / Sophisticated lady: Ellington, Duke Orchestra / Summer of '42: Thielemans,toots / I can't get started: Webster, Ben / Time out for tears: Washington, Dinah / Lover man: Brubeck, Dave Quartet / People: Jamal, Ahmad / Stardust: Grappelli, Stephane Quartet / Will you still be mine: Burrell, Kenny / Misty: Hampton, Lionel & Earl Hines / I remember clifford: Art Farmer & Benny Golson Jazztet / My foolish heart: McRae, Carmen / I should care: Gordon, Dexter / What are you doing the rest of your life: Evans, Bill / Deep in a dream: Sims, Zoot / Man I love: Baker, Chet / Imagination: Lewis, Ramsey Trio / Black and blue: Armstrong, Louis / Look of love: Kessel, Barney / Tenderly: Kenton, Stan Orchestra / Moonlight in Vermont: Mulligan, Gerry / Our love is here to stay: Kirk, Rahsaan Roland
DBG 53048 / Jul '96 / Double Gold

☐ **WORLD'S GREATEST JAZZ CONCERT VOL.1**
JCD 301 / Oct '93 / Jazzology

☐ **WORLD'S GREATEST JAZZ CONCERT VOL.2**
JCD 302 / Oct '93 / Jazzology

☐ **WORLD'S GREATEST LIVE ALBUM, THE (2CD Set)**
Slippery people: Talking Heads / Notorious: Duran Duran / Gold: Spandau Ballet / All fall down: Ultravox / Kayleigh: Marillion / Every rose has it's thorn: Poison / Love is the drug: Roxy Music / Dreadlock holiday: 10cc / New kid in town: Frey, Glenn / Love is like oxygen: Sweet / Radar love: Golden Earring / Born to be wild: Steppenwolf / Sweet home Alabama: Lynyrd Skynyrd / Lonesome loser: Little River Band / Horse with no name: America / Sylvia's mother: Dr. Hook / Sebastian: Harley, Steve & Cockney Rebel / Hocus pocus: Focus / I'm going home: Ten Years After / Smoke on the water: Deep Purple
DOU 882512 / 2 Feb '98 / Disky

☐ **WORLD'S GREATEST ROCK 'N' ROLL HITS (2CD Set)**
(We're gonna) Rock around the clock: Haley, Bill & The Comets / Shake, rattle and roll: Haley, Bill & The Comets / Summertime blues: Cochran, Eddie / C'mon everybody: Cochran, Eddie / Three steps to heaven: Cochran, Eddie / Sweet little sixteen: Berry, Chuck / Maybellene: Berry, Chuck / Stagger Lee: Price, Lloyd / Personality: Price, Lloyd / Be bop a lula: Vincent, Gene / Long tall Sally: Little Richard / Good golly Miss Molly: Little Richard / Ain't that a shame: Boone, Pat / Love letters in the sand: Boone, Pat / Whole lotta shakin' goin' on: Lewis, Jerry Lee / Blue suede shoes: Perkins, Carl / Blueberry hill: Domino, Fats / Red river rock: Hurricanes / Bo Diddley: Diddley, Bo / At the hop: Danny & The Juniors / Tequila: Champs / Rockin' Robin: Day, Bobby / Sea Cruise: Ford, Frankie / Rebel rouser: Eddy, Duane / Kansas City: Harrison, Wilbert / Do you want to dance: Freeman, Bobby / I'm walkin': Domino, Fats / 40 Days: Hawkins, Ronnie / Great balls of fire: Lewis, Jerry Lee / Happy organ: Cortez, Dave 'Baby' / Book of love: Monotones / Suzie Q: Hawkins, Dale / Boppin' the blues: Perkins, Carl / Rock 'n' roll is here to stay: Danny & The Juniors / Love you most of all: Cooke, Sam / Earth angel: Penguins / It's all in the game: Edwards, Tommy / I love you so: Chantels / Sealed with a kiss: Hyland, Brian / I only have eyes for you: Flamingoes / Donna: Valens, Ritchie / Little darlin': Diamonds / Daddy's home: Shep & The Limelites / Don't break the heart that loves you: Francis, Connie / It's only make believe: Twitty, Conway / Oh what a nite: Dells / I'm gonna get married: Price, Lloyd / He's so fine: Chiffons / Only you: Platters / Tears on my pillow: Little Anthony & The Imperials / Chapel of love: Dixie Cups / Tell Laura I love her: Peterson, Ray / Ten commandments of love: Moonglows / Dedicated to the one I love: Shirelles / My special angel: Helms, Bobby / But I do: Henry, Clarence 'Frogman' / Remember (Walkin' in the sand): Shangri-Las / Only love can break a heart: Pitney, Gene / Goodnite, sweetheart, goodnite: Spaniels
DBG 53049 / Jul '96 / Double Gold

☐ **WORLD'S GREATEST VOICES OF THE CENTURY**
HADCD 203 / Jul '96 / Javelin

☐ **WORLDWIDE: TEN YEARS OF WOMAD**
Live at real world (extract): Drummers Of Burundi / Amina: Kanda Bongo Man / Allah hoo allah hoo: Khan, Nusrat Fateh Ali / Invaders of the heart: Jah Wobble / Lion - Gaiende: N'Dour, Youssou / Pacifica and pacifica medley inc aloha: Sandii / If things were perfect: James / Runidera: Orquesta Reve / Gun: Scott-Heron, Gil / Wake of the Medusa: Pogues / Sina: Keita, Salif / Diaka: Toumant Diarate / Legend of the old mountain man: Terem Quartet / Entrada: Cabral, Pedro Caldiera / Muchadura: Mapfumo, Thomas / Will the circle be unbroken: Holmes Brothers
RWBK 1 / Jul '92 / Realworld

☐ **WORSHIP HIM ON THE STRING QUARTET**
Give thanks with a grateful heart / Jesus we enthrone you / When I look into your holiness / Tenderness / Lord send me / Behold the wood of the cross / Pachelbel's canon/You laid aside your majesty / Spirit of God in splendour come / Spirit of the living God / Son of man / Nimrod from the enigma variations
SPND 015 / Jun '98 / Spirit Of Praise

☐ **WOW 1998 (The World's Top 30 Christian Artists & Songs/2CD Set)**
Did you hear the mountains tremble: Delirious / Reality: Newsboys / Overjoyed: Jars Of Clay / Coloured people: DC Talk / Hope to carry on: Caedmon's Call / My hope is you: Third Day / Missing person: Smith, Michael W. / Man of God: Audio Adrenaline / Disappear: Out Of The Grey / Mission: Carman / We can make a difference: Velasquez, Jaci / People get read Jesus is comin': Lewis, Crystal / Saving the world: Crosse, Clay / More than you know: Out Of Eden / Heatseekers: World Wide Message Tribe / Ineed your love: Raze / I need your love: Raze / Once again: Redman, Matt / Let us pray: Chapman, Steven Curtis / Carry you: Grant, Amy / Up where we belong: Winans, Bebe & Cece / Circe of friends: Point Of Grace / On my way to paradise: Carlisle, Bob / Measure of a man: 4HIM / Give it up: 4HIM / I call him love: Troccolli, Kathy / Adore you: Anointed / Just one: Phillips, Craig & Dean / You move me: Ashton, Susan / Breathe on me: Patty, Sandi / One of two: Chapman, Gary / Whisper heard around the world: Duncan, Bryan / My utmost for his highest: Paris, Twila
4943972 / 20 Apr '98 / EMI

☐ **WOW GOSPEL 1998 (The Year's 30 Top Gospel Artists & Songs/2CD Set)**
01241431092 / Mar '98 / Word

☐ WOW WHAT A RUSH
Dynamite: *Becks* / U R everything: *Becks* / Sweet in pocket: *Helix & Becks/Marlon* / Feel the love: *Donna* / Musical foundations: *Love Nation* / All I ever wanted: *Love Nation* / Show me love: *Citadel Of Kaos* / Higher love: *JDS* / Crazy daze: *Adem* / Let it lift you: *Bunter, Billy & JDS* / I believed: *Donna* / Eternity: *Triple J* / Follow the sun: *Triple J* / Touch my heart: *DNA & Justin time* / Here I am: *DJ Ham & DJ Demo/ Justin Time* / Have it all: *Triple J*
CDWOW 1 / 17 Aug '98 / Stage One

☐ WURLITZER CHRISTMAS
AVC 545 / Nov '94 / Avid

X

☐ X-MIX
Deep space intro: *Saunderson, Kevin* / Ritual beating system: *Bango EP* / Ribosomal: *Tata Box Inhibitors* / Love songs: *Chocolate City* / Spadet: *Jarl Prongo* / Merlouche ideale: *Rene & Gaston* / Night illusions: *Octave One* / Use me: *R-Tyme* / Mind machine: *69* / Siege: *Octave One* / In da jungle: *Playboy* / World of the deep: *E-Dancer* / Vamp: *Outlander* / Neurodisco: *Trancesetters* / Sharp tools: *Sharp Boys* / Razorback: *Deason, Sean* / Bloated: *Strand* / 10 ex-pr: *Electric* / Bar: *Dark Comedy* / Velocity funk: *E-Dancer* / Deep space outro: *Saunderson, Kevin*
K7 061CD / 6 Oct '97 / Studio K7

☐ X-MIX VOL.2 (Destination Planet Dream)
K7 027CD / Apr '94 / Studio K7

☐ X-MIX VOL.3
K7 032CD / Nov '94 / Studio K7

☐ X-RATED GANG VOL.1, THE
RN 0037 / Nov '94 / Runn

☐ X-RATED GANG VOL.2
RN 0051 / Jul '97 / Runnetherlands

☐ X-RATED GANG VOL.3
RN 0054 / 30 Mar '98 / Runn

☐ X-THEMES VOL.2, THE
DC 887082 / 2 Feb '98 / Disky

☐ X-TRANCE VOL.3 (2CD Set)
ZYX 811512 / 8 Jun '98 / ZYX

☐ X-TREME FIVE, THE (DJ Nervous/ Eightball/Cutting/Definitive/Nitebeat - 5CD Set)
XTR 21 / Apr '96 / X-Treme

☐ X-TREME POWER (DJ Duke Vs. Power)
XTR 19CDU
XTR 19CDM / Jan '96 / X-Treme

☐ XL RECORDINGS VOL.5
XLCD 116 / Jul '95 / XL

☐ XOURCISE YOUR MIND (Rare Nordic Ethno-Grooves)
Herr holger: *Garmarna* / Hoglorfven: *Hedningarna* / Grovhalling: *Hoven Droven* / Sugghugg: *Vasen* / Adam i paradis: *Trio Patrekatt* / Gycklaren: *Malmquist, Dan Gisen* / Overtime: *Urban Turban* / Traces of pangaea: *Almqvist, Thomas* / Pinewood 3 step: *Hakansson, Kenny* / Vanner and frander: *Folk & Rackere* / Menuett fran oravais: *JP Nystroms* / Everybody's neighbour: *Foundland*
XOUCD 115 / May '97 / Xource

☐ XTRA BASS
KPSVCD 5 / Jan '97 / Shocking Vibes

☐ XYLOPHONES FROM OUHAM PENDE
CCD 560094 / May '96 / Ocora

Y

☐ Y LLEGO LA CUBANITIS
UMD 80497 / 27 Jul '98 / Universal

☐ Y VIVA ESPANA
16124 / Aug '94 / Laserlight

☐ YA GOTTA HAVE MOXIE
AIPCD 1059 / 29 Jun '98 / AIP

☐ YAMANTAKA TROCHU RITE (The Diamond Path - Rituals Of Tibetan Buddhism)
SHANCD 66006 / 9 Mar '98 / Shanachie

☐ YARD VIBES
ICD 951 / 5 May '98 / Imaj

☐ YARDBIRD SWEETS VOL.1
YRB 001CD / Jul '96 / Yardbird Suite

☐ YEAR IN SEVEN INCHES, THE
DIS 14CD / Jul '96 / Dischord

☐ YEAR ZERO SURROUND SOUNDBITES VOL.1
SUSCD 1 / Jan '95 / Aura Surround Sounds

☐ YEH YEH
TMPCD 007 / Jan '95 / Temple

☐ YELE BRAZIL
Yele congo / Coche viejo (carro velho) / Venha me amar / Kizomba festa da raca / Embala eu / Volte para o seu lar / Felicidade / Epilogo / Jogo de angola / Swqura este samba (ogunhe) / De onde eu vim / Nego laranja / Alagados / Canto de nana / Toque e seducao / Canto da cor
CDEMC 3694 / Nov '94 / Hemisphere

☐ YELLOW PILLS VOL.4
BD 9043 / Oct '97 / Big Deal

☐ YELLOW UNLIMITED
EFA 2222CD / May '89 / Yellow

☐ YEMEN (Music Of The High Plateaux)
PS 65179 / Mar '97 / PlayaSound

☐ YESTERDAYS VOL.1
12101 / Dec '94 / Laserlight

☐ YESTERDAYS VOL.2
12102 / Dec '94 / Laserlight

☐ YESTERDAYS VOL.3
12103 / Dec '94 / Laserlight

☐ YIDDISH MUSIC AND SONG
304692 / May '97 / Carlton

☐ YODELLING AND SCHULPLATTER FOLK DANCE
399200 / Sep '92 / Koch

☐ YONDER COMES THE BLUES (Jazz Classics)
SOSCD 1061 / Nov '92 / Stomp Off

☐ YORUBA DRUMS FROM BENIN (The World's Musical Traditions No.8)
SFWCD 40440 / Mar '96 / Smithsonian Folkways

☐ YOU ARE SO BEAUTIFUL
When your in love with a beautiful women: *Dr. Hook & Ray Sawyer* / I wanna do it with you: *Dr. Hook & Ray Sawyer* / Stumblin' in: *Quatro, Suzi* / Take good care of my baby: *Smokie* / Nickelodeon nights: *Sailor* / Why do lovers break each others hearts: *Showaddywaddy* / You are so beautiful: *Rogers, Kenny* / Let it be me: *Svenne & Lotta* / Day after day: *Goombay Dance Band* / Reflections of my life: *Marmalade* / Just to hear your voice: *Stardust, Alvin* / Always crying over you: *Dr. Hook & Ray Sawyer* / My guy: *Surprise Surprise* / For you my love: *Gaynor, Gloria* / Give a little love: *Bay City Rollers* / When will you be mine: *Clout* / Let a good thing die: *Marian* / Are you looking for someone: *Andrews, Chris* / I'm still lovin' you: *Goombay Dance Band* / I'll never get over you: *Showaddywaddy*
10882 / Oct '97 / Go On Deluxe

☐ YOU ARE THERE - A LEGENDARY LABEL
4425412 / Feb '95 / Mercury

☐ YOU CAN'T GET THAT STUFF NO MORE (The Slide Guitar)
IMP 938 / Sep '95 / IMP

☐ YOU DESERVE EVEN WORSE
LF 083CD / Jun '94 / Lost & Found

☐ YOU GOTTA KNOW WHAT YOU STAND FOR
IS 889850CD / 8 Dec '97 / I Scream Music

☐ YOU HAVE TO LAUGH, DON'T YOU (22 Gems Of Vintage Comedy)
Laughing policeman: *Penrose, Charles* / I should say so: *Wilton, Robb* / Under the bed: *Wallace, Nellie* / Trains: *Gardiner, Reginald* / Mad dogs and Englishmen: *Coward, Sir Noel* / Joe Ramsbottom buys a piano: *Evans, Norman* / Everything is fresh today: *Hodges, Jack* / Battle of Hastings 1066: *Edgar, Marriott* / My Mother doesn't know I'm on the stage: *Bennett, Billy* / What can you give a nudist on his birthday: *Fields, Gracie* / Surrealist alphabet: *Clapham & Dwyer* / When I'm cleaning windows: *Formby, George* / Gardening - what to do with your aspidistra: *Wakefield, Oliver* / There are fairies at the bottom of the garden: *Lillie, Beatrice* / Woman improver: *Miller, Max* / Bee song: *Askey, Arthur* / Yorkshire pudding: *Holloway, Stanley* / Dance of the cuckoos: *Laurel & Hardy* / Insurance salesman: *Crumit, Frank* / Cocktails for two: *Jones, Spike* / Jim goes up, I come down: *Durante, Jimmy* / Thing: *Harris, Phil*
CDAJA 5210 / May '97 / Living Era

☐ YOU KNOW THE SCORE
DCSR 003 / Oct '94 / Clubscene

☐ YOU MUST REMEMBER THIS
You'll never know: *Lynn, Vera* / Night and day: *Astaire, Fred* / As time goes by: *Hale, Binnie* / Folks who live on the hill: *Sullivan, Maxine* / I'd climb the highest mountain: *Ink Spots* / Love walked in: *Baker, Kenny* / It's always you: *Crosby, Bing* / Stairway to the stars: *Keller, Greta* / Please believe me: *Froman, Jane* / Falling in love again: *Dietrich, Marlene* / How deep is the ocean: *Goodman, Benny & Peggy Lee* / I wish I knew a bigger word than love: *Gideon, Melville* / All the things you are: *Martin, Tony* / Starlight serenade: *Rey, Monte* / There, I've said it again: *Carter, Benny & Roy Felton* / Nearness of you: *Welch, Elisabeth* / Two sleepy people: *Geraldo & Al Bowlly* / I only have eyes for you: *Hutchinson, Leslie 'Hutch'* / Dream lover: *MacDonald, Jeanette* / When a man loves a woman: *Robins, Phyllis* / You were meant for me: *Boswell, Connee* / Man I love: *Langford, Frances* / Nightingale sang in Berkeley Square: *Layton, Turner* / I know why: *Miller, Glenn & Paula Kelly* / Night is young and you're so beautiful: *Sinatra, Frank & Dinah Shore* / As time goes by (extract): *Wilson, Dooley & Ingrid Bergman*
UCD 252 / Feb '97 / Happy Days

☐ YOU MUST REMEMBER THIS (2CD Set)
Signature tune: *Payne, Cy* / Who is that man who looks like Charlie Chaplin: *Handley, Tommy* / Wish me luck as you wave me goodbye: *Fields, Gracie* / I didn't really oughter 'ave went: *Hare, Doris* / I did what I could with my gas mask: *Formby, George* / Washing of the Siegfried Line: *2 Leslies* / Kiss me Goodnight, Sergeant Major: *Askey, Arthur* / It was a lover and his lass: *Bowlly, Al* / We'll meet again: *Lynn, Vera* / As time goes by: *Wilson, Dooley* / Coming in on a wing and a prayer: *Shelton, Anne* / Calling all workers: *Coates, Eric* / Yes my darling daughter: *Shore, Dinah* / Thingummy Bob: *Fields, Gracie* / All over the place: *Trinder, Tommy* / London pride: *Coward, Sir Noel* / Deepest shelter: *Desmond, Florence* / Grand old man: *Miller, Max* / Run rabbit run: *Flanagan & Allen* / When can I have a banana again: *Roy, Harry* / Thanks for dropping in Mr. Hess: *Askey, Arthur* / Moonlight serenade: *Miller, Glenn* / This is the army: *Berlin, Irving* / Why don't you right: *Lee, Peggy* / In the mood: *Miller, Glenn* / That lovely weekend: *Geraldo* / My British buddy: *Berlin, Irving* / Jersey bounce: *Squadronaires* / Tico tico: *Smith, Ethel* / Lili Marlene: *Andersen, Lale* / Cocktails for two: *Jones, Spike* / Oh what a surprise for the duce: *Carlisle, Elsie* / Swing out to victory: *Waller, Fats* / I'd climb the highest mountain: *Ink Spots* / Victory roll rag: *Roy, Harry* / Wings over the navy: *Stones, Lew & His Band* / You'd be so nice to come home to: *Shelton, Anne* / Last time i saw paris: *Coward, Sir Noel* / White cliffs of Dover: *Lynn, Vera* / Body and soul: *Miller, Glenn* / Saturday night is the loneliest night of the week: *Sinatra, Frank* / Don't fence me in: *Crosby, Bing*
CDHD 2652 / Feb '97 / Happy Days

☐ YOU MUST REMEMBER THIS (20 Everlasting Memories From Days Gone By)
Over the rainbow: *Garland, Judy* / Pretty baby: *Jolson, Al* / That old devil called love: *Holiday, Billie* / Straighten up and fly right: *Cole, Nat 'King'* / Blue skies: *Sinatra, Frank* / Tisket-a-tasket: *Fitzgerald, Ella* / If I didn't care: *Ink Spots* / Take the 'A' train: *Ellington, Duke* / Mississippi mud: *Beiderbecke, Bix* / Thanks for the memory: *Hope, Bob* / On the sunny side of the street: *Armstrong, Louis* / Rum and coca cola: *Andrews Sisters* / Moonlight serenade: *Miller, Glenn* / Sun has got his hat on: *Brown, Sam* / Leaning on a lamp post: *Formby, George* / Teddy bears' picnic: *Hall, Henry* / Ida sweet as apple cider: *Mills Brothers* / Walter walter lead me to the alter: *Fields, Gracie* / Louise: *Chevalier, Maurice* / We'll meet again: *Lynn, Vera*
ECD 3294 / Feb '97 / K-Tel

☐ YOU MUST REMEMBER THIS - CHRISTMAS FAVOURITES
God rest ye merry gentlemen: *Crosby, Bing* / Let it snow, let it snow, let it snow: *Boswell, Connee* / See amid the winter's snow: *McCormack, John* / I'm sending a letter to Santa Claus: *Fields, Gracie* / Gesu bambino: *Dawson, Peter* / Sam's Christmas pudding: *Holloway, Stanley* / While shepherds watched: *Fleet Street Choir* / Nazareth: *Allin, Norman* / Have yourself a merry little Christmas: *Garland, Judy* / Adeste fideles (O, come all ye faithful): *McCormack, John* / Es hat sich halt eroffnet (Tyrolean nativity hymn): *Vienna Boys Choir* / Cantique de Noel (O holy night): *Journet, Marcel* / Coventry carol (Lully, thou little tiny child): *Schumann, Elisabeth* / Angels, from the realms of glory: *Cathedral Singers* / Silent night: *Sinatra, Frank* / O du frohliche: *Tauber, Richard* / Little boy that Santa Claus forgot: *Robins, Phyllis* / Noel en mer (Christmas on the sea): *Rossi, Tino* / Christmas bells are ringing (a Yuletide fantasy): *Midnight Minstrels (Debroy Somers Band)* / Ninna-nanna della vergine (cradle song of the Virgin Mary): *Muzzio, Claudia* / Star of Bethlehem: *Crooks, Richard* / Virgin Mary had a baby boy: *Connor, Edric* / Sleep my saviour, sleep: *Celebrity Quartette* / Auld lang syne: *Dawson, Peter*
75605522822 / Nov '96 / Happy Days

☐ YOU MUST REMEMBER THIS - THE GREAT LOVE SONGS
If you are but a dream: *Sinatra, Frank* / Dedicated to you: *Fitzgerald, Ella & Mills Brothers* / Moonlight and shadows: *Lamour, Dorothy* / Things are looking up: *Astaire, Fred* / Out of this world: *Stafford, Jo* / When somebody thinks you're wonderful: *Waller, Fats & his Rhythm Orchestra* / Let the rest of the world go by: *Squires, Dorothy* / Touch of your lips: *Crosby, Bing* / Blue skies: *Sullivan, Maxine* / Penthouse serenade (when we're alone): *Hope, Bob & Shirley Ross* / And the angels sing: *Tilton, Martha & Benny Goodman* / You happen once in a lifetime: *Hutchinson, Leslie 'Hutch'* / My melancholy baby: *Froman, Jane* / Yes sir that's my baby: *Cantor, Eddie* / Spinning wheel: *Murphy, Delia* / Time on my hands: *Dennis, Denny* / Like someone in love: *Shore, Dinah* / Wherever there's love: *Wiley, Lee & Eddie Condon* / Embraceable you: *Cole, Nat 'King' Trio* / All through the day: *Whiting, Margaret* / Sweet and lovely: *Layton, Turner* / I'm in the mood for love: *Langford, Frances* / They didn't believe me: *Haymes, Dick* / I can't give you anything but love: *Boswell, Connee* / I'm gonna love that guy (like he's never been loved before): *Hall, Adelaide*
75605522622 / Feb '97 / Happy Days

☐ YOU MUST REMEMBER THIS - THE HAPPY ALBUM
Shout for happiness: *Bowlly, Al & Ray Noble & His New Mayfair Orchestra* / Back to those happy days: *Hutchinson, Leslie 'Hutch'* / Happy feet: *Rhythm Boys* / Singin' in the rain: *Valaida* / Let me sing and I'm happy: *Jolson, Al* / Happy days are here again: *O'Malley, Pat & Jack Hylton* / Got a bran' new suit: *Waller, Fats & his Rhythm Orchestra* / Smile, darn ya, smile: *Browne, Sam/The Carlyle Cousins/Ambrose* / Spread a little happiness: *Hale, Binnie & Al Starita* / Livin' in the sunlight, lovin' in the moonlight: *Chevalier, Maurice* / I'm happy when you're happy: *Cooper, Jack/Ronnie Munro/New Mayfair Dance Orchestra* / Happy: *Layton & Johnstone* / Accentuate the positive: *Green, Johnny/Three Boys & A Girl/Geraldo* / It's a hap-hap-happy day: *Davis, Beryl/Stephane Grappelli/Arthur Young* / Make yourself a happiness pie: *Payne, Jack & The BBC Dance Orchestra* / Tea for two: *Crosby, Bing & Connie Boswell/Bob Crosby's Bob Cats* / When the red red robin (comes bob bob bobbin' along): *Smith, Whispering Jack* / May all your troubles be little ones: *Sarony, Leslie* / Say to yourself I will be happy: *Browne, Sam/Max Bacon/The Blue Mountaineers/ Joe Brannelly* / My blue heaven: *Lanceford, Jimmy Trio* / That's why I'm happy: *Kane, Helen* / Happy as the day is long: *O'Malley, Pat & Jack Hylton* / Sing a happy-go-lucky song: *Trinder, Tommy* / My troubles are over: *Sunshine Boys* / Happy ending: *Scott Coomber, Billy & Jack Payne* / Holiday for strings: *Jones, Spike & His City Slickers*
75605522612 / Feb '97 / Happy Days

☐ YOU MUST REMEMBER THIS - VINTAGE COMEDY SONGS
When I'm cleaning windows: *Formby, George* / My kid's a crooner: *Carlisle, Elsie & Ambrose* / Mrs. Worthington: *Coward, Sir Noel* / La de da: *Miller, Max* / Short'nin' bread: *Waller, Fats* / Olga Pulloffski the beautiful sky: *Berman, Len & Henry Hall/BBC Dance Orchestra* / Stone cold dead in the market: *Fitzgerald, Ella & Louis Jordan Tympany Five* / 1,2,3,4,5,6,7: *Frankau, Ronald* / It's a great big shame: *Elen, Gus* / How d'ya keep 'em down on the farm: *Cantor, Eddie* / Mr. Jones (are you coming to bed): *Desmond, Florence* / Bee song: *Askey, Arthur* / Start off each day with a song: *Durante, Jimmy & Eddie Jackson* / She was poor but she was honest: *Bennett, Billy* / Let's have a tiddley at the milk bar: *Wallace, Nellie* / Drinking: *McEachern, Malcolm* / (I'll be glad when you're dead) you rascal you: *Armstrong, Louis* / Thank you so much Mrs. Lowsborough goodbye: *Byng, Douglas* / Song of the prune: *Crumit, Frank* / Oh Mr. Porter: *Blaney, Norah* / When I met Connie in the cornfield: *Handley, Tommy* / Nobody loves a fairy when she's forty: *O'Shea, Tessie* / My little sweet Austin Seven: *Long, Norma* / Chloe: *Ingle, Red & Spike Jones/City Slickers* / Busy busy: *Picon, Molly* / She had to go and lose it at The Astor: *Currie, Bill & Harry Roy Chorus*
75605522722 / Feb '97 / Happy Days

☐ YOU SEXY THING
You sexy thing: *Hot Chocolate* / Hot hot hot: *Arrow* / Rock you baby: *McCrae, George* / Sexy girl: *Thomas, Eddie* / Kiss you all over: *Exile* / Would I lie to you: *Charles & Eddie* / I just wanna make love to you: *Rawls, Lou* / Body talk: *Imagination* / Disco queen: *Hot Chocolate* / Body rock: *Vidal, Maria* / Let's go all the way: *Sly Fox* / Get down tonight: *KC & The Sunshine Band* / Forget me nots: *Jackson, Freddie* / Stripper: *Loss, Joe & His Orchestra*
4939032 / 2 Mar '98 / EMI Gold

☐ YOU THRILL MY SOUL (Female & Girl Groups From The Early Stax Sessions)
Same thing: *Thomas, Carla* / Here it comes again: *Thomas, Carla* / I can't stay: *Thomas, Carla* / Heavenly angel: *Tonettes* / Stolen angel: *Tonettes* / Unhand that man: *Tonettes* / Gone for good: *Rene, Wendy* / Same guy: *Rene, Wendy* / Love at first sight: *Rene, Wendy* / If she should ever break your heart: *Stephens, Barbara* / Heartbreaker: *Parker, Deanie* / Ask him: *Parker, Deanie* / Love is like a flower: *Stephens, Barbara* / Just one touch: *Parker, Deanie* / Ain't enough hours in the day: *Thomas, Carla* / Gosh I'm lucky: *Thomas, Carla* / He hasn't failed me yet: *Rene, Wendy* / Crying all by myself: *Rene, Wendy* / Last love: *Rene, Wendy* / Crowded park: *Rene, Wendy* / Can't stay away: *Rene, Wendy* / Tell me: *Tonettes* / Come to me: *Tonettes* / Do boys keep diaries: *Thomas, Carla*
CDSXD 088 / Sep '93 / Stax

☐ YOU TREATED ME BAD
Wait: *Gremlins* / Get a move on: *Moxies* / Why did God make girls: *Rogues, JD.* / I'm cryin': *Monday's Mondos* / Hurray for Hazel: *Davidson, Terry & The Barracudas* / Long hair: *Little John & The Sherwoods* / Scream loud: *Quests* / I've been through it before: *Plague* / Girl from Liverpool: *Twilighters* / Pain: *Midnights* / She's loving me: *Possums* / It's gonna take a while: *Morticians* / I feel like crying: *Sound Extraction* / I've seen you around: *Messengers* / Leavin' you baby: *Saints* / She don't love me: *Dead Beats* / I've got a feeling: *Mystery Men* / She's bad: *Shoremen* / You treat me bad: *Ju Ju's*
TS 6602CD / 20 Jul '98 / Teenage Shutdown

☐ YOU WEAR IT WELL
Rocket man: *John, Elton* / American pie: *McLean, Don* / Baker street: *Rafferty, Gerry* / Make me smile: *Harley, Steve & Cockney Rebel* / You wear it well: *Stewart, Rod* / Stuck in the middle with you: *Stealer's Wheel* / When you're in love with a beautiful woman: *Dr. Hook* / Emma: *Hot Chocolate* / Got to be ther: *Jackson, Michael* / Air that I breathe: *Hollies* / I wanna stay with you: *Gallagher & Lyle* / Widde eyes and legless: *Fairweather-Low, Andy* / Game s people play: *South, Joe* / I'd like to teach the world to sing: *New Seekers* / Oh you pretty thing: *Noone, Peter/SmDon't let it die: Smith, Hurricane* / You're a lady: *Skellern, Peter* / Softly whispering I love ou: *Congregation* / Easy: *Commodores* / Night in white satin: *Moody Blues*
5529112 / Oct '97 / Spectrum

☐ YOU'LL NEVER WALK ALONE (The Hits Of The 1960's)
You'll never walk alone: *Gerry & The Pacemakers* / Silence is golden: *Tremeloes* / Runaway: *Shannon, Del* / Happy birthday sweet sixteen: *Sedaka, Neil* / Wild thing: *Troggs* / I'm into something good: *Herman's Hermits* / Rubber ball: *Vee, Bobby* / Something's gotten hold of my heart: *Pitney, Gene* / I'm sorry: *Lee, Brenda* / Da doo ron ron: *Crystals* / When a man loves a woman: *Sledge, Percy* / I'm telling you now: *Freddie & The Dreamers* / Because they're young: *Eddy, Duane* / Little town flirt: *Shannon, Del* / It's my party: *Gore, Lesley* / Breaking up is hard to do: *Sedaka, Neil* / Walkin' back to happiness: *Shapiro, Helen* / Wishin' and hopin': *Merseybeats* / Rescue me: *Bass, Fontella* / Dancing in the street: *Reeves, Martha*
CD 6031 / Sep '96 / Music

☐ YOU'LL NEVER WALK ALONE (The Hillsborough Benefit Album)
VVR 1000342 / Jun '97 / V2

☐ YOUNG AT HEART
Young at heart: *Bluebells* / Do you really want to hurt me: *Culture Club* / Nikita: *John, Elton* / Johnny come home: *Fine Young Cannibals* / Too shy: *Kajagoogoo* / Lifeline: *Spandau Ballet* / Is there something I should know: *Duran Duran* / Poison arrow: *ABC* / Fame: *Cara, Irene* / Come on Eileen: *Dexy's Midnight Runners* / Call me: *Go West* / Never ending story:

Limahl / Rise to the occasion: *Fisher, Climie* / Sun goes down: *Level 42* / Electric avenue: *Grant, Eddy* / Our lips are sealed: *Fun Boy Three* / Robert De Niro's waiting: *Bananarama* / Speak like a child: *Style Council* / Tide is high: *Blondie* / Labelled with love: *Squeeze*

5529192 / Oct '97 / Spectrum

☐ **YOUNG FLAMENCOS, THE**

HNCD 1370 / Dec '91 / Hannibal

☐ **YOUNG FOGIES VOL.1**

ROUCD 0319 / Jul '94 / Rounder

☐ **YOUNG FOGIES VOL.2**

ROUCD 0369 / Oct '95 / Rounder

☐ **YOUNG LIONS AND OLD TIGERS - A 75TH BIRTHDAY CELEBRATION**

Roy Hargrove / How high the moon / Michael Brecker waltz / Here comes McBride / Joe Lovano tango / In your own sweet way / Joshua Redman / Together / Moody / Gerry-go-round / Ronnie Buttacavoli / Deep in a dream

CD 83349 / Nov '95 / Telarc

☐ **YOUNG PIPERS OF SCOTLAND**

2/4 Marches: *Armstrong, Christopher* / Strathspeys and reels: *Armstrong, Christopher* / Slow air and two jigs: *Armstrong, Christopher* / 2/4 Marches: *MacLean, Gordon* / 6/8 Marches: *MacLean, Gordon* / Strathspey and reel: *MacLean, Gordon* / Slow air and jigs: *MacLean, Gordon* / Slow air and jigs: *Cassells, Stuart* / Strathspeys and reels: *Cassells, Stuart* / Marches: *Cassells, Stuart* / 2/4 marches: *Wright, Andrew* / Waltz, hornpipe and jig: *Wright, Andrew* / Piobaireachd: *Wright, Andrew*

CDTRAX 125 / Mar '97 / Greentrax

☐ **YOUNG, WILD AND FREE**

DCD 5360 / May '94 / Disky

☐ **YOUNG ZYDECO DESPERADOS: SWAMP MUSIC VOL.8**

US 0204 / Apr '95 / Trikont

☐ **YOUNGBLOOD STORY VOL.1**

Do wah diddy diddy: *Dave Dee, Dozy, Beaky, Mick & Tich* / Brandy: *English, Scott* / Get ready for love: *Easybeats* / Planetary cruiser: *McGlynn, Pat* / Sea trip: *Shelley, Peter* / On the run: *Ocean, Billy* / Rhythm on the radio: *ABC* / True love forgives: *Kissoon, Mac & Katie* / Crazy feeling: *Douglas, Carl* / Ain't nothing but a house party: *Show Stoppers* / Personality crisis: *New York Dolls* / Take a heart: *Fardon, Don* / Mr. Station Master: *Harper, Roy* / Morning bird: *Damned* / C'mon round to my place: *Wayne, Carl* / When I was 16: *Page, Jimmy* / Captain man: *Powell, Jimmy* / Let the live live: *Fardon, Don* / You keep me hangin' on: *Kissoon, Mac* / Don't ever change: *Berry, Mike* / Spread myself around: *King, Ben E.* / Can you feel it: *Ocean, Billy* / Sleepwalk: *Los Indianos*

C5CD549 / '89 / See For Miles

☐ **YOUR GENERATION (18 Punk & New Wave Classics)**

MUSCD 009 / Sep '93 / MCI Music

☐ **YOUR GENERATION (2CD Set)**

Design for life: *Manic Street Preachers* / Hey dude: *Kula Shaker* / Caught by the fuzz: *Supergrass* / Neighbourhood: *Space* / Teenage angst: *Placebo* / Ginger: *David Devant & His Spirit Wife* / Sleeper: *Audioweb* / Sleep well tonight: *Gene* / Imaginary friends: *Lightning Seeds* / King of kissingdom: *My Life Story* / Monday morning: *Candyskins* / Not so manic now: *Dubstar* / Promised land: *Cast Of Bread* / Exodus: *Levellers* / Life's a cinch: *Mundy* / All hype: *Longpigs* / Middle class hereos: *Divine Comedy* / Queen is dead: *Smiths* / Too handsome to be homeless: *Baby Bird* / Stripper vicar: *Mansun* / Mis-shapes: *Pulp* / Mr. Robinson's quango: *Blur* / Planet telex: *Radiohead* / Nuclear holiday: *3 Colours Red* / Little baby swastikka: *Skunk Anansie* / Sick of drugs: *Wildhearts* / Punka: *Kenickie* / Prozac Beats: *18 Wheeler* / Trigger hippie: *Morcheeba* / Open up: *Leftfield* / Born slippy: *Underworld* / Little Britain: *Dreadzone* / Ebeneezer Goode: *Shamen* / Where's me jumper: *Sultans Of Ping FC* / Anarchy in the UK: *Sex Pistols*

SONYTV 25CD / Apr '97 / Sony TV

☐ **YOUR INVITATION TO SUICIDE**

MRCD 040 / May '94 / Munster

☐ **YOUR MIND WORKS IN REVERSE**

COLCD 0713 / 8 Jun '98 / Collectables

☐ **YOUR OWN, YOUR VERY OWN (Stars Of The Music Hall 1901-1929)**

Don't do it again, Matilda: *Champion, Harry* / Every little movement has a meaning of its own: *Lloyd, Marie* / Two lovely black eyes: *Coburn, Charles* / Mrs. Kelly: *Leno, Dan* / One of the boys: *Formby, George* / Jocular joker: *Chergwin, G.H.* / Let's all go where all the crowd goes: *Williams, Billy* / Photo of the girl I left behind me: *Merson, Billy* / I'm twenty-one today: *Pleasante, Jack* / Flower of the heather: *Lauder, Harry* / If the managers only thought the same as mother: *Scott, Maidie* / She sells seashells: *Bard, Wilkie* / By the sea: *Sheridan, Mark* / Don't have any more, Mrs. Moore: *Morris, Lily* / Dinah: *Elliott, G.H.* / Hello, sunshine, hello: *Whelan, Albert*

CDAJA 5004 / Apr '92 / Living Era

☐ **YOUR PRECIOUS LOVE**

Your precious: *Butler, Jerry* / When a man loves a woman: *Sledge, Percy* / My guy: *Wells, Mary* / I heard it through the grapevine: *Gaye, Marvin* / Have you seen her: *Chi-Lites* / Woman in love: *Three Degrees* / Let's get it on: *McNeir, Ronnie* / You're all that I need to get by: *Reeves, Martha* / Love don't live here anymore: *Royce, Rose* / Just my imagination: *Cameron, G.C.* / Cherish: *Kool & The Gang* / Tracks of my tears: *Young, Paul* / Every beat of my heart: *Knight, Gladys* / Wishing on a star: *Royce, Rose* / With you I'm born again: *Syreeta* / Rainy night in Georgia: *Benton, Brook* / Careless whisper: *Gaynor, Gloria* / Up on the roof: *Drifters*

CD 6114 / Jan '98 / Music

☐ **YOU'RE DRIVING ME CRAZY**

Ring dem bells / Confessin' / Rockin' chair / Happy feet / Somebody loves me / You're driving me crazy / New Orleans hop scop blues / Sheikh of Araby / Mood indigo / I got rhythm / Here comes Emily Brown / If I could be with you one hour tonight / When I'm alone / Heebie jeebies / I can't believe that you're in love with me / Okay baby

PHONTCD 7618 / '93 / Phontastic

☐ **YOU'VE LOST THAT LOVIN' FEELIN'**

You've lost that lovin feelin': *Righteous Brothers* / Sun ain't gonna shine anymore: *Walker Brothers* / Ain't nothing like the real thing: *Gaye, Marvin & Tammi Terrell* / You don't say to say love me: *Springfield, Dusty* / Where do you go to my lovely: *Sarstedt, Peter* / I'll never fall in love again: *Gentry, Bobbie* / As tears go by: *Faithfull, Marianne* / You don't know: *Shapiro, Helen* / Step inside love: *Black, Cilla* / Michelle: *David & Jonathan* / Somwhere: *Proby, P.J.* / Trains and boats and planes: *Kramer, Billy J. & The Dakotas* / Up on the roof: *Lynch, Kenny* / Jennifer Eccles: *Hollies* / Don't let the sun catch you crying: *Gerry & The Pacemakers* / There's a kind of hush: *Herman's Hermits* / Love is all: *Roberts, Malcolm* / Je t'aime moi non plus: *Birkin, Jane & Serge Gainsbourg* / I'm gonna make you love me: *Ross, Diana & The Supremes*

5529084 / Oct '97 / Spectrum

☐ **YOYO A GO GO (2CD Set)**

YOYO 4CD / Sep '96 / K

☐ **YU BODY GOOD**

WRCD 38 / Dec '93 / Techniques

☐ **YUGOSLAVIA: LES BOUGIES DU PARADIS**

C 580041 / Nov '92 / Ocora

☐ **YULE BE BOPPIN'**

Cool yule: *Elling, Kurt* / Santa Claus is coming to town: *Martino, Pat* / Jingle bells: *Reeves, Dianne* / I've ogt my love to keep me warm: *Elias, Elaine* / Blue x-mas: *Dorough, Bob* / You're a mean one Mr. Grinch: *Haque, Fareed* / Santa baby: *Jackson, Javon* / Be-bop Santa: *Sweet Daddy Lowe & The Blue Note Ad Hoc Orchestra* / I'd like you for Christmas: *Silvano, Judi* / Adeste fideles: *Terrasson, Jacky* / Zat you Santa Claus: *Green, Benny & Miles Griffith* / Cristo redentor: *Watson, Bobby & Jack Walrath* / Peace on earth: *Ferrell, Rachelle* / Christmas time is here: *Hunter, Charlie* / Carol of the bells: *Lovano, Joe*

8569912 / 24 Nov '97 / Blue Note

☐ **YULE COOL (2CD Set)**

I wish it could be Christmas forever: *Como, Perry* / Happy holiday: *Crosby, Bing* / Little boy that Santa Claus forgot: *Cole, Nat 'King'* / Senor Santa Claus: *Reeves, Jim* / Holly and the ivy: *Steeleye Span* / White Christmas: *Boone, Pat* / Let it snow, let it snow, let it snow: *Martin, Dean* / I want Elvis for Christmas: *Cochran, Eddie* / Jingle bells: *Paul, Les* / It came upon a midnight clear: *Fitzgerald, Ella* / Wonderful land: *Shadows* / Mary's boy child: *Monro, Matt* / Frosty the snowman: *Ventures* / What Christmas means to me: *Green, Al* / Baby's first Christmas: *Francis, Connie* / Song angels sing: *Lanza, Mario* / Snow coach: *Conway, Russ* / Never do a tango with an eskimo: *Cogan, Alma* / Lonely pup (in a Christmas shop): *Faith, Adam* / Christmas waltz: *Lee, Peggy* / Warm December: *London, Julie* / Silent night: *Locke, Josef* / Bells of St. Mary's: *Neville, Aaron* / Holly jolly Christmas: *Ives, Burl* / Rockin' around the Christmas tree: *Lee, Brenda* / Christmas on the range: *Wills, Bob* / Christmas is paintin' the town: *Oak Ridge Boys* / Rockin' around the Christmas tree: *Cannon, Ace* / Deck the halls with boughs of holly: *Crickets* / Sleigh ride: *Ferrante & Teicher* / O'Holy night: *Rodgers, Jimmie* / Parade of the wooden soldiers: *Garber, Jan* / I saw Mommy kissing Santa Claus: *Gleason, Jackie* / Jingle bell rock: *Hollyridge Strings* / Silver bells: *Dunstedter, Eddie* / Christmas trumpets: *Anthony, Ray* / Auld lang syne: *Alexander, Van* / Christmas song: *Mancini, Henry* / O Holy night: *Danny & The Juniors* / Must be Santa: *Steele, Tommy* / Baby, it's cold outside: *Montgomery, Wes & Jimmy Smith*

VTDCD 36 / Oct '95 / Virgin

☐ **YULETUNES**

BV 125912 / Nov '96 / Black Vinyl

Z

☐ **ZAIRE: SUPER GUITAR SOUKOUS**

Sana: *Kanda Bongo Man* / Africa: *Depeu, Dave* / Sango ya mawa: *Dabany, Patience* / Mukaji wani: *Yogo, Dindo* / Guelo: *Gueatan System* / Pa moi: *Delly, Joyce* / N'nanele: *Zoukunion* / Guede guina: *Guede, Olives* / Mosolo na ngai: *General Defao* / Soso ya tongo: *Empire Bakuba Et Pepe Kalle* / Makoule: *Seliko*

CDEMC 3678 / May '94 / Hemisphere

☐ **ZAMBIANCE**

Kambowa: *Shalawambe* / Mao: *Amayenge* / Nyina kataila: *Kalambo hit parade* / By air / Tai yaka: *Julizya* / Icupo cha kuala pa mpapa: *Shalawambe* / Itumba: *Kalusha, Alfred Chisala Jr.* / Ni Maggie: *Kalusha, Alfred Chisala Jr.*

CDORB 037 / Jun '89 / Globestyle

☐ **ZEITGEIST (New Wave Club Culture - 3CD Set)**

Theme from pm3: *Palefield Mountain* / Who am I: *Coyote* / Alive: *Innerself* / Set in stone: *Bedrock* / Unbound: *Freelance Icebreakers* / Shrug: *Freefall* / Etana's flight: *Sunday Club* / Diddley squat: *Gloat* / Retrospace: *Genetica* / Leone: *Almighty Beatfreakz* / Strobelight serenade: *Superstars Of Rock* / Dancin' in outer space: *Hustlers Convention* / Spy who dubbed me: *OST* / In the streets: *Full Intention* / Anti skate: *Genetica* / Ghosts: *Chris & James/Sally Rodgers* / Sonic boom: *Desert* / Waiting: *Manitou* / Slipping in and out of consciousness: *Assasins Of Sound* / Dreams: *Eros Euphony* / For what you dream of: *Bedrock* / Horse with no name: *Sasha* / America: *Full Intention* / Up all night: *Superstars Of Rock* / Ghosts: *Chris & James* / Love and the light: *Genetica* / Healing dream: *Sunday Club*

ZEITCD 1 / 6 Oct '97 / Stress

☐ **ZEPHYR SWINGS INTO 1997**

Lester leaps in: *Masso, George & Brian Lemon/Roy Williams* / You'll never know: *Vache, Warren & Brian Lemon* / Farewell blues: *Poplowski, Ken & Alan Barnes/Brian Lemon/Roy Williams* / This is all I ask: *Braff, Ruby & Brian Lemon* / Moon glow: *Barnes, Alan & Brian Lemon Octet* / Dearly beloved: *Barnes, Alan & Brian Lemon* / Watch what happens: *Masso, George & Brian Lemon/Roy Williams* / Jeepers creepers: *Vache, Warren & Brian Lemon* / When it's sleepy time down south: *Peplowski, Ken & Alan Barnes/Brian Lemon/Roy Williams* / Bill: *Barnes, Alan & Brian Lemon* / Wouldn't it be lovely: *Braff, Ruby & Brian Lemon* / Boar jibu: *Barnes, Alan & Brian Lemon Octet*

ZECD 10 / Nov '96 / Zephyr

☐ **ZHENG MELODIES: ABOVE THE CLOUDS (Chinese Han Music)**

Resentment of Zhaojun / Entertainment / Song of the western chamber / Tranquil lake / Du-yu-hun / Jade chain / Dan-Dian-Tou and Luang-Cha-Hua / Lotus / Bai-Jia-Chun / Halcyon at a pond / Morning of the Ya Mountain / Yi-Dian-Jin / Bei-Jin-Gong / Nan-Jin-Gong

SOW 90157 / Jan '97 / Sounds Of The World

☐ **ZILLO MUSIC MACHINE (Club Hits Vol. 3)**

Dir flut: *Witt Heppner* / Spiel mit mir: *Rammstein* / Gekreuzigt: *Oomph* / Futile: *Velvet Acid Christ* / Totes fleisch: *Terminal Choice* / Destillat: *Das Ich* / Xodus: *Nefilim* / You didn't want me: *Mesh* / War: *Wumpscut* / Kill a raver: *Lecether Strip* / Snakedressed: *Dive* / Cantus: *Faith & The Muse* / Misery: *Die Verbannten Kinder Evas* / Lay Down: *Velianov*

SPV 08526002 / 1 Sep '98 / SPV

☐ **ZIMBABWE - THE SOUL MUSIC OF MBIRA**

7559720542 / Jan '95 / Nonesuch

☐ **ZONOPHONE PUNK SINGLES COLLECTION, THE**

Greatest cockney rip off: *Cockney Rejects* / Inside out: *Stiffs* / I'm forever blowing bubbles: *Cockney Rejects* / We can do anything: *Cockney Rejects* / We are the firm: *Cockney Rejects* / Last night another soldier: *Angelic Upstarts* / England: *Angelic Upstarts* / Volume control: *Stiffs* / Turn me on turn me off: *Honey Bane* / Kids on the street: *Angelic Upstarts* / I understand: *Angelic Upstarts* / Easy life: *Cockney Rejects* / On the streets again: *Cockney Rejects* / Jimmy (listen to me): *Honey Bane* / Different strokes: *Angelic Upstarts* / Never say die: *Angelic Upstarts* / Out of reach: *Vice Squad* / Stand strong stand proud: *Vice Squad* / Everybody jitterbug: *Toy Dolls* / Citizen: *Vice Squad*

CDPUNK 97 / May '97 / Anagram

☐ **ZOO IBIZA VOL.1**

ZOO 001CD / Jul '96 / Steppin' Out

☐ **ZOO IBIZA VOL.2**

ZOO 002CD / Jul '96 / Steppin' Out

☐ **ZOO, THE**

DCD 001 / Oct '90 / Document

☐ **ZOOM CLASSICS**

ZOOMCD 2 / Sep '95 / Zoom

☐ **ZOOM, ZOOM, ZOOM**

Get a job / Stranded in the jungle / Remember then / Come go with me / Zoom, zoom, zoom / Stay / I understand / Sixteen candles / Lover's island / One summer night / Church bells may ring / Earth angel / Since I don't have you / For all we know / When you dance / Deserie / At last up on a mountain / Why don't you write me / Crazy over you / Clock / Music music music / Tears on my pillow / You painted pictures

CPCD 8000 / Oct '93 / Charly

☐ **ZOOP, ZOOP, ZOOP (Traditional Music Of The Virgin Islands)**

804272 / Mar '96 / New World

☐ **ZORBA'S DANCE (Memories From Greece)**

15180 / '91 / Laserlight

☐ **ZULU BEATS**

FILECD 466 / Oct '95 / Profile

☐ **ZULU JIVE**

HNCD 4410 / Aug '93 / Hannibal

☐ **ZYDECO - THE EARLY YEARS 1961-1963**

ARHCD 307 / Apr '95 / Arhoolie

☐ **ZYDECO CHAMPS**

ARHCD 328 / Apr '95 / Arhoolie

☐ **ZYDECO DANCE HALL**

Motor dude special: *Chavis, Boozoo & The Majic Sounds* / Git it, Beau Jocque: *Jocque, Beau & The Zydeco Hi-Rollers* / I don't want nobody here but you: *Delafose, John & The Eunice Playboys* / Miquen: *August, Lynn* / Madeline: *Zydeco Force* / I'm on my way: *Zydeco Force* / Couche dehors ce soir: *Jocque, Beau & The Zydeco Hi-Rollers* / Suzy Q: *Chavis, Boozoo & The Majic Sounds* / Gotta find my woman: *Delafose, John* / Tante Nana: *Nathan & Zydeco Cha Cha's*

EDCD 7035 / Sep '97 / Easydisc

☐ **ZYDECO DANCE PARTY**

Gator man / Chere duloone / Hello Rosa Lee / Zydeco round the world / Capitaine Gumbo / Boogie in New Orleans / Just a little girl / They all ask for you / Tyrone / Mazuka / Ay tet fee / Zydeco / I'm gonna take you home tonight / Creole de Lake Charles / My baby she's gone / Fais deaux deaux / Bayou polka / La bas two step

GNPD 2220 / Sep '95 / GNP Crescendo

☐ **ZYDECO FEVER**

It's a zydeco groove: *Li'l Brian & Zydeco Travelers* / Paper in my shoe: *Chavis, Boozoo* / Make it stank: *Jocque, Beau* / My feet can't fail me now: *Buckwheat Zydeco* / Choo choo ch'boogie: *August, Lynn* / Big chief: *Richard, Zachary* / Modern waltz: *Zydeco Force* / Don't mess with my ya ya: *Pee Wee & The Zydeco Boll Weevils* / I'm goin' to the country to get me a majo hand: *Chavis, Boozoo* / Baby please don't go: *Jocque, Beau* / Black gal: *Nathan & Zydeco Cha Cha's* / I don't want nobody here but you: *Delafose, John* / Hot tamale baby: *Buckwheat Zydeco* / Lula, Lula don't go out to bingo: *Chavis, Boozoo* / Knockin' on heaven's door: *Jocque, Beau* / Louisiana Saturday night: *Caesar, Warren* / My woman is a sally dog: *Prudhomme, Willis* / Z-Funk: *Li'l Brian & Zydeco Travelers*

NSCD 029 / 11 May '98 / Nascente

☐ **ZYDECO PARTY**

Zydeco groove: *August, Lynn* / I'm on my way: *Zydeco Force* / I'm coming home: *Brothers, Sam Five* / Johnny can't dance: *Chenier, Clifton* / Zydeco hee haw: *Chavis, Boozoo* / Jalapena lena: *Rockin' Sidney* / Whatever boils your crawfish: *August, Lynn* / Leon's Zydeco: *Brothers, Sam Five* / Dopsie's Cajun Stomp: *Rockin' Dopsie* / Down east: *Zydeco Brothers* / Loan me your handkerchief: *Delafose, John* / Do it all night long: *Chavis, Boozoo* / Fun in acadiana: *Francis, Morris* / Eh mon allons dancer le zydeco: *Chavis, Wilfred* / You used to call me: *Chenier, Clifton* / Shake, rattle and roll: *Rockin' Dopsie* / You ain't nothing but fine: *Rockin' Sidney* / Keep on dreaming: *Chavis, Wilfred* / Deacon Jones: *Chavis, Boozoo* / Reach out: *Zydeco Brothers*

CDCHD 430 / Oct '92 / Ace

☐ **ZYDECO PARTY**

Oh 'tit fille: *Delafose, John & The Eunice Playboys* / Ardoin two step: *Ardoin, Chris & Double Clutchin'* / Festival Zydeco: *Nathan & The Zydeco Hi Rollers* / Wedding day waltz: *Delafose, Geno* / Lache pas la patate: *Buckwheat Zydeco* / Hippy ty o: *August, Lynn* / Zydeco dreamer: *L'il Brian & The Zydeco Travellers* / Bye bye Lucille: *Arceneaux, Fernest* / I'm going to the country to get me a mojo hand: *Chavis, Boozoo & The Majic Sounds*

EDCD 7045 / 19 Jan '98 / Easydisc

☐ **ZYDECO SHOOTOUT AT EL SID O'S**

ROUCD 2108 / Sep '91 / Rounder

☐ **ZYDECO STOMP (Instrumental)**

Zydeco stomp: *Arceneaux, Fernest* / Geno's two-step: *Delafose, Geno* / Tang the hump: *Li'l Brian & Zydeco Travelers* / Buck's boogie: *Buckwheat Zydeco* / Kinder 2-step: *Jocque, Beau* / Boozoo's shuffle: *Chavis, Boozoo* / Rockin' accordion: *August, Lynn* / Two step farouche: *Delafose, John & The Eunice Playboys* / El Sid O's zydeco boogaloo: *Nathan & Zydeco Cha Cha's* / Blues in June: *Rockin' Sidney*

EDCD 7065 / 20 Apr '98 / Easydisc

☐ **ZYDECO'S GREATEST HITS**

Ya ya: *Buckwheat Zydeco* / Give him cornbread: *Jocque, Beau* / Your Mama don't know: *Nathan & Zydeco Cha Cha's* / French rockin' boogie: *Delafose, Geno* / My toot toot: *Rockin' Sidney* / Hot tamale baby: *Chenier, Clifton* / Turning point: *Buckwheat Zydeco* / Uncle Bud: *Chavis, Boozoo* / Broken hearted: *Delafose, John* / Follow me chicken: *Nathan & Zydeco Cha Cha's*

EDCD 7025 / Nov '96 / Easydisc

Soundtracks

☐ **12 MONKEYS**
Rockmaster, Paul *c*
Introduction / Cole's first dream/Volunteer duty/ Topside / Silent night / Spider research/Introduction (We did it)/Propostion / Time confusion to the mental ward/Planet Ogo / Wrong number/Coles's second dream/Dormitory spider / Vivisection: Olins, Charles / Sleepwalk: Cole, B.J. / Introduction (Escape to nowhere)/Scanner room/Capture and se / Cole's third dream / Interrogation/Time capsule/Cole kidnaps Railly / Blueberry Hill: Domino, Fats / What a wonderful world: Armstrong, Louis / Cole's fourth dream / Comanche: Wray, Link & The Wraymen / Earth died screaming: Waits, Tom / Introduction (Quest for twelve monkeys) / Fateful bullet/Boot from the trunk/Cole's longing / Photo search/Mission brief / Back in '96 / Fugitives/Fateful love/Home dentistry / Introduction (12 monkeys theme/reprise)/ Giraffes and flaming / This is my dream/Cole's call/ Louis and Jose / Peters does his worst / Dreamers awake
MCD 11392 / Mar '96 / MCA

☐ **24-7**
Tim and Darcy no.3: Hewerdine, Boo & Neil MacColl / Courtroom no.2: Hewerdine, Boo & Neil MacColl / Wild night: Morrison, Van / Monkey dead: Sunhouse / Look at the fool: Buckley, Tim / I wish I never saw the sunshine: Orton, Beth / Blue Danube waltz: Vienna Philharmonic Orchestra / Blues no.3: Hewerdine, Boo & Neil MacColl / Damaged: Primal Scream / Ramble on love: Strauss Hofmannsthal Grainger / Long time man: Rose, Tim / Fruit tree: Drake, Nick / Funeral: Hewerdine, Boo & Neil MacColl / Broken stones: Weller, Paul
ISOM 6CD / 30 Mar '98 / Independiente

☐ **32 SHORT FILMS ABOUT GLENN GOULD**
Gould, Glenn *con*
SK 46686 / Jan '94 / Sony Classical

☐ **42ND STREET (1980 Broadway Cast)**
Warren, Harry *c*
Dubin, Al *l*
Overture / Audition / Shadow waltz / Young and healthy / Go into your dance / You're getting to be a habit with me / Getting out of town / We're in the money / Dames / Sunny side to every situation / Lullaby of Broadway / About a quarter to nine / Shuffle off to Buffalo / 42nd Street / Finale / 42nd Street (reprise)
BD 83891 / '85 / RCA Victor

☐ **42ND STREET (CC Productions)**
Warren, Harry *c*
Dubin, Al *l*
42nd Street overture / Shadow waltz / Young and healthy / You're getting to be a habit with me / We're in the money / Dames / Lullaby of Broadway / About a quarter to nine / Shuffle off to Buffalo / 42nd Street finale
QED 215 / Nov '96 / Tring

☐ **55 DAYS AT PEKING**
Tiomkin, Dimitri *c*
VSD 5233 / Feb '90 / Varese Sarabande

☐ **70 GIRLS 70 (1991 London Cast)**
Kander, John *c*
Ebb, Fred *l*
CDTER 1186 / Sep '91 / TER

☐ **70 GIRLS 70 (1971 Broadway Cast)**
Kander, John *c*
Ebb, Fred *l*
Kosarin, Oscar *con*
SK 30589 / Nov '92 / Sony Broadway

☐ **100 RIFLES**
Goldsmith, Jerry *c*
W 9101 / 14 Apr '98 / Taran

☐ **101 DALMATIANS (Live Action)**
WD 699402 / Oct '96 / Disney Music & Stories

☐ **101 DALMATIONS - LIVE ACTION (Singalong)**
WD 740324 / Nov '96 / Disney Music & Stories

☐ **187**
Slack hands: Galliano / Spying glass: Massive Attack / Release yo' delf: Method Man / Stem: DJ Shadow / Flipside: Everything But The Girl / Karmacoma: Massive Attack / In November: Darling, David / Neither sing sing nor Baden Baden: Bang Bang / Raincry: God Within / Pregao: Madredeus / Wilderness: V-Love / Mankind (part II): Jalal
7567927602 / 15 Sep '97 / Atlantic

☐ **1000 ACRES, A**
VSD 5870 / 6 Jul '98 / Varese Sarabande

☐ **1776 (Broadway Cast)**
Edwards, Sherman *c*
Howard, Peter *con*
SK 48215 / Nov '92 / Sony Broadway

☐ **1941**
Williams, John *c*
Williams, John *con*
March / Invasion / Sentries / Riot at the USO / To Hollywood and glory / Swing swing swing / Battle of Hollywood / Ferris wheel sequence / Finale
VSD 5832 / 30 Mar '98 / Varese Sarabande

☐ **1984 (For The Love Of Big Brother) (Eurythmics)**
Stewart, David A./Annie Lennox *c*
I did it just the same / Sexcrime (1984) / For the love of big brother / Winston's diary / Greetings from a dead man / Julia / Doubleplusgood / Ministry of love / Room 101
CDVIP 135 / Sep '95 / Virgin

☐ **2001: A SPACE ODYSSEY (Alex North Score) (National Philharmonic Orchestra)**
North, Alex *c*
Goldsmith, Jerry *con*
Main title / Foraging / Eat meat and the kill / Bluff / Night terrors / Dawn of man / Space station docking / Trip to the moon / Moon rocket bus / Space talk / Interior Orion / Main theme
VSD 5400 / Oct '93 / Varese Sarabande

☐ **2001: A SPACE ODYSSEY**
North, Alex *c*
Overture: Sudwesfunk Orchestra/Ernest Bour / Main title/Also sprach zarathustra: Vienna Philharmonic Orchestra/Herbert Von Karajan / Requiem for soprano/Mezzo soprano/Two mixed choirs/Orch: Bavarian Radio Orchestra/Francis Travis / Blue Danube: Berlin Philharmonic Orchestra/Herbert Von Karajan / Lux aeterna: Stuttgart Schola Cantorum/Clytus Gottwold / Gayane ballet suite: Leningrad Philharmonic Orchestra/Gennadi Rezhdestuensky / Jupiter and beyond: Vienna Philharmonic Orchestra/Herbert Von Karajan / Atmospheres: Vienna Philharmonic Orchestra/Herbert Von Karajan / Adventures: Vienna Philharmonic Orchestra/Herbert Von Karajan / Also sprach zarathustra: Vienna Philharmonic Orchestra/Herbert Von Karajan / Blue Danube: Berlin Philharmonic Orchestra/Herbert Von Karajan / Also sprach zarathustra: Sudwesfunk Orchestra/Ernest Bour / Lux aeterna: Stuttgart Schola Cantorum/Clytus Gottwold / Adventures: Internationale Musikinstitut Darmstadt/Gyorgi Ligeti / Hal 9000
CDODEON 28 / Jan '97 / Soundtracks

A

☐ **A LA FOLIE (Nyman, Michael Band)**
Nyman, Michael *c*
399492 / Nov '94 / Delabel

☐ **ABOVE THE RIM**
Anything: SWV / Old time's sake: Sweet Sable / Part time lover: H-Town / Big pimpin': Dogg Pound Gangstas / Didn't mean to turn you on: 2nd II None / Doggie style: D.J. Rogers / Regulate: Warren G. & Nate Dogg / Pour out a little liquor: Thug Life / Gonna give it to ya: Jewell & Aaron Hall / Afro puffs: Lady Of Rage / Jus' so ya no: CPO - Boss Hog / Hoochies need love too: Paradise / I'm still in love with you: Sure, Al B. / Crack 'em: OFTB / U bring da dog out: Rhythm & Knowledge / Blowed away: Rezell, B / It's not deep enough: Jewell / Dogg pound 4 life: Dogg Pound Gangstas
IND 92359 / Feb '97 / Interscope

☐ **ABSOLUTE POWER**
Niehaus, Lennie *c*
Mansion / Christy dies / Mansion chase / Christy's dance / Waiting for Luther / Wait for my signal / Dr Kevorkian / Presume / Sullivan's revenge / Kate's theme / End credits
VSD 5808 / Apr '97 / Varese Sarabande

☐ **ABYSS, THE**
Silvestri, Alan *c*
Main title / Search the Montana / Crane / Manta ship / Pseudopod / Fight / Sub battle / Lindsey drowns / Resurrection / Bud's big dive / Bud on the ledge / Back on the air / Finale
VSD 5235 / Oct '89 / Varese Sarabande

☐ **ACE VENTURA I (Pet Detective)**
Power of suggestion: Stevens, Steve / All Ace's: Stevens, Steve / Lion sleeps tonight: John, Robert / Psychoville/Ace Race: John, Robert / Mission impossible / Ace of hearts / Hammer smashed face: Cannibal Corpse / Warehouse / Ficklo and Einhorn / Ace in the hole / Ace is in the house: Tone Loc
5230002 / May '94 / Polydor

☐ **ACROSS 110TH STREET (Womack, Bobby & Peace)**
Womack, Bobby *c*
Across 110th street / If you don't want my love give it back / Quicksand / Do it right / Hang on in there / Across 110th street / Harlem clavinette: Johnson, J.J. Orchestra / Harlem love theme: Johnson, J.J. Orchestra
RCD 10706 / 12 Jan '98 / Rykodisc
CPCD 8340 / May '98 / Charly

☐ **ACT OF PIRACY/THE GREAT WHITE**
Stevens, Morton *c*
PCD 111 / '92 / Prometheus

☐ **ACT, THE (Broadway Cast)**
Kander, John *c*
Ebb, Fred *l*
Shine it on / It's the strangest thing / Bobo's / Turning / Little do they know / Arthur in the afternoon / Money tree / City lights / There when I need him / Hot enough for you / Little do they know (reprise) / My own space / Walking papers
DRGCD 6101 / '87 / DRG

☐ **AD - ANNO DOMINI (Paris Philharmonic Orchestra)**
Schifrin, Lalo *c*
Golgatha / Valerius and Sarah / King Herod's march / Eternal land / Fisherman / Peter and Thomas trek / Roman celebration / Road to Damascus / New love / Gladiator school / Majesty of Rome / Corina and Caleb / Roman legion / Wedding procession / Nero the lover / Martyrdom / Exalted love
PCD 112 / Apr '92 / Prometheus

☐ **ADDAMS FAMILY VALUES (Score)**
Shaiman, Marc *c*
It's an Addams / Sibling rivalry / Love on a tombstone / Debbie meets the family / Camp Chippewa / Fester's in love / Big date / Tango / Fester and Debbie's courtship / Wednesday and Joel's courtship / Honeymoon is over / Escape from Debbie / Eat us / Wednesday's revolt / Debbie's big scene / Some time later
VSD 5465 / Dec '93 / Varese Sarabande

☐ **ADJUSTER (& Music For The Films Of Atom Egoyan)**
Danna, Mychael *c*
VSD 5674 / Jul '96 / Varese Sarabande

☐ **ADVENTURES OF MARK TWAIN, THE/ THE PRINCE AND THE PAUPER (Brandenburg Philharmonic Orchestra/ Choir)**
Steiner, Max/Erich Wolfgang Korngold *c*
Stromberg, William T. *con*
9026626602 / Jun '96 / RCA Victor

☐ **ADVENTURES OF PRISCILLA, QUEEN OF THE DESERT**
I've never been to me: Charlene / Go west: Village People / Billy don't be a hero: Paper Lace / My baby loves lovin': White Plains / I love the nightlife: Bridges, Alicia / Can't help lovin' dat man: Richards, Trudy & Billy May / I will survive: Gaynor, Gloria / Fine romance: Horne, Lena / Shake your groove thing: Peaches & Herb / I don't care if the sun don't shine: Page, Patti / Finally: Peniston, Ce Ce / Take a letter Maria: Peniston, Ce Ce / Mamma mia: Abba / Save the best for last: Williams, Vanessa
MUMCD 9416 / Oct '94 / Mother

☐ **ADVENTURES OF ROBIN HOOD, THE (Utah Symphony Orchestra)**
Korngold, Erich *c*
EK 57568 / Jan '93 / Silva Screen

☐ **ADVENTURES OF ROBIN HOOD, THE**
Korngold, Erich *c*
CDTER 1066 / May '89 / TER

☐ **ADVENTURES OF ROBIN HOOD, THE/ REQUIEM FOR A CAVALIER**
Korngold, Erich *c*
Korngold, Erich *con*
VSD 47202 / Aug '91 / Varese Sarabande

☐ **ADVENTURES OF ROBINSON CRUSOE, THE**
Mellin, Robert & Gian-Piero Reverberi *c*
Reverberi, Gian-Piero *con*
Opening titles / Main theme / Friday / Crusoe's youth remembered / Away from home / Adrift / Solitude / Shelter / Scanning the horizon/Flashback - escapdes in York / Cannibals / Wild goats / Palm trees / In search of rescue / Civilised man / Distant shores / Alone / Catching dinner / Poor Robinson / Danger / Closing titles
FILMCD 705 / Apr '96 / Silva Screen

☐ **AFTER DARK MY SWEET**
Jarre, Maurice *c*
After dark my sweet / Collie and Fay / Uncle Bud / Kidnapping
VSD 5274 / Jul '90 / Varese Sarabande

☐ **AFTER THE FOX**
Bacharach, Burt *c*
RCD 10716 / 6 Apr '98 / Rykodisc

☐ **AGONY AND THE ECSTASY, THE**
North, Alex *c*
VSD 5901 / 10 Aug '98 / Varese Sarabande

☐ **AGUIRRE (& Heart Of Glass/Nosferatu) (Popul Vuh)**
SPALAX 14703 / Oct '96 / Spalax

☐ **AGUIRRE/HERZ AUS GLAS/ NOSFERATU (Soundtracks For Werner Herzog/Film Can Set) (Popul Vuh)**
Popul Vuh *c*
14703 / Jul '97 / Spalax

☐ **AIN'T MISBEHAVIN' (1979 Broadway Cast)**
Waller, Fats *c*
Ain't misbehavin' / Honeysuckle Rose / Squeeze me / Handful of keys / I've got a feeling I'm falling / How ya baby / Jitterbug waltz / Ladies who sing with the band / Yacht Club swing / When the nylons bloom again / Cash for your trash / Off-time / Joint is jumpin' / Entr'acte / Spreadin' rhythm around / Lounging at the Waldorf / Viper's drag/The reefer song / Mean to me / Your feet's too big / That ain't right / Keepin' out of mischief now / Find out what they like / Fat and greasy / Black and blue / I'm gonna sit right down and write myself a letter / Two sleepy people/I've got my fingers crossed
BD 82965 / Aug '90 / RCA Victor

☐ **AIN'T MISBEHAVIN' (1979 London Cast)**
Waller, Fats *c*
CASTCD 53 / Apr '96 / First Night

☐ **AIR FORCE ONE**
Goldsmith, Jerry *c*
Goldsmith, Jerry *con*
VSD 5825 / Aug '97 / Varese Sarabande

☐ **AIRPORT**
Newman, Alfred *c*
Airport / Airport love theme / Inez' theme / Guerreo's goodbye / Ada Quonsett stowaway / Mel and Tanya / Airport love theme 2 / Joe Patroni plane or plows / Triangle / Inez lost forever / Emergency landing / Airport (End Title)
VSD 5436 / Aug '93 / Varese Sarabande

☐ **AKIRA (Japanese Score)**
Shoji, Yamashiro *c*
DSCD 6 / Nov '93 / Demon

☐ **AKIRA**
Shoji, Yamashiro *c*
Kaneda / Battle against clown / Tetsuo / Akira / Winds over Neo-Tokyo / Doll's polyphony / Shohmyoh / Mutation / Exodus from the underground fortress / Illusion / Requiem
DSCD 7 / May '95 / Demon

☐ **ALADDIN (1958 Television Cast)**
Porter, Cole *c*
Perelman, S.J. *l*
Emmett Dolan, Robert *con*
SK 48205 / May '95 / Sony Broadway

☐ **ALADDIN**
Menken, Alan *c*
Ashman, Howard & Tim Rice *l*
WD 742602 / Mar '96 / Disney Music & Stories

☐ **ALEXANDER NEVSKY (& Scythian Suite) (Finnie, Linda/Royal Scottish National Orchestra/Chorus)**
Prokofiev, Sergei *c*
Jarvi, Neeme *con*
CHAN 8584 / Jul '94 / Chandos

☐ **ALEXANDER NEVSKY (St. Petersburg Philharmonic Orchestra/Chorus)**
Prokofiev, Sergei *c*
Temirkanov, Yuri *con*
09026619262 / Feb '96 / RCA Victor

☐ **ALEXANDER THE GREAT/BARABBAS**
Nascimbene, Mario *c*
Nascimbene, Mario *con*
DRGCD 32964 / Nov '96 / DRG

☐ **ALICE'S RESTAURANT (Guthrie, Arlo)**
Guthrie, Arlo *c*
Alice's restaurant massacre / Chilling of the evening / Ring around a rosy rag / Now and then I'm going home / Motorcycle song / Highway in the wind
244045 / Feb '94 / Reprise

☐ **ALICE'S RESTAURANT (30th Anniversary Edition) (Guthrie, Arlo)**
Guthrie, Arlo *c*
Alice's restaurant massacre / Chilling of the evening / Ring around a rosy rag / Now and then I'm going home / Motorcycle song / Highway in the wind
379592 / Aug '97 / Koch International

☐ **ALIEN (National Philharmonic Orchestra)**
Goldsmith, Jerry *c*
Newman, Lionel *con*
Main title / Face hugger / Breakaway / Acid test / Landing / Droid / Recovery / Alien planet / Shaft / End titles
FILMCD 003 / Jun '87 / Silva Screen

☐ **ALIEN EMPIRE (The Ocellus Suite) (Munich Symphony Orchestra)**
Kiszko, Martin *c*
Journey to the Alien Empire / Ocellus voyage / Battle zone / Angels and warriors / Slipstreams / Earthstalkers / Insectarium / Solus odyssey / Ancient enemies / Three visions / Firstborn / Distant swarm / Colony and metropolis / Earthrise / Return voyage
CDEMC 3730 / Jan '96 / Soundtrack Music

☐ **ALIEN III**
Goldenthal, Elliot *c*
Sheffer, Jonathan/N. Nackley *con*
Agnus Dei / Bait and chase / Beast within / Lento / Candles in the wind / Wreckage and rape / First attack / Lullaby elegy / Death dance / Visit to the wreckage / Explosion and aftermath / Dragon / Entrapment / Adagio
MCD 10629 / 8 Sep '97 / MCA

☐ **ALIEN IV (Alien Resurrection)**
Frizzell, John *c*
09026689552 / 24 Oct '97 / RCA Victor

☐ **ALIEN NATION - THE SERIES (Dorff, Steve/Larry Herbstritt/David Kurtz)**
Dorff, Steve/Larry Herbstritt/David Kurtz *c*
GNPD 8024 / '94 / GNP Crescendo

☐ **ALIEN TRILOGY**
Goldsmith, Jerry & James Horner *c*
VSD 5753 / Nov '96 / Varese Sarabande

☐ **ALL AMERICAN (1962 Broadway Cast)**
Strouse, Charles *c*
Adams, Lee *l*
Morris, John *con*
SK 48216 / Nov '92 / Sony Broadway

☐ **ALL OVER ME**
8110 / Sep '97 / TVT

☐ **ALL THAT JAZZ**
On Broadway: *Benson, George* / Michelle: *Burns, Ralph* / Take off with us: *Bergman, Sandahl & Chorus Vavaldi* / Ponte vecchio: *Burns, Ralph* / Everything old is new again: *Allen, Peter* / South Mt Sinai parade: *Burns, Ralph* / After you've gone: *Palmer, Leland* / There'll be some changes made: *Reinking, Ann* / Who's sorry now: *Burns, Ralph* / Some of these days: *Foldi, Erzsebet* / Going home now: *Burns, Ralph* / Bye bye love: *Vereen, Ben & Roy Scheider* / Vivaldi concerti in G: *Burns, Ralph* / Main Title: *Burns, Ralph*
5512692 / Sep '95 / Spectrum

☐ **ALL THE BROTHERS WERE VALIANT**
Rozsa, Miklos *c*
Rozsa, Miklos *con*
PCD 131 / Jan '95 / Prometheus

☐ **ALL THE KING'S MEN**
5390662 / Aug '97 / Polydor

☐ **ALLONSANFAN/METELLO**
Morricone, Ennio *c*
OST 103 / Jan '95 / Milano Dischi

☐ **ALMOST AN ANGEL**
Jarre, Maurice *c*
Jarre, Maurice *con*
VSD 5307 / Jan '91 / Varese Sarabande

☐ **ALTA MAREA/VATERLAND (Harvey, Mick)**
IONIC 6CD / Mar '93 / The Fine Line

☐ **AMADEUS (Academy Of St. Martin In The Fields)**
Mozart, W.A. *c*
Marriner, Neville *con*
8251262 / Feb '85 / London

☐ **AMAHL AND THE NIGHT VISITORS, THE (Royal Opera House)**
Menotti, Gian Carlo *c*
CDTER 1124 / Nov '97 / TER

☐ **AMATEUR**
Taylor, Jeff/Ned Rifle *c*
Mind full of worry: *Aquanettas* / Only shallow: *My Bloody Valentine* / Water: *PJ Harvey* / Japanese to English: *Red House Painters* / Shaker: *Yo La Tengo* / Tom boy: *Bettie Serveert* / Girls Girls Girls: *Phair, Liz* / Then comes Dudley: *Jesus Lizard* / Here: *Pavement*
7567925002 / Jan '95 / Warner Bros.

☐ **AMATEUR, THE/OF UNKNOWN ORIGIN/THE LATE SHOW**
Wannberg, Ken *c*
PCD 137 / Apr '96 / Prometheus

☐ **AMAZING GRACE AND CHUCK**
Bernstein, Elmer *c*
VCD 47285 / Jan '89 / Varese Sarabande

☐ **AMBUSH OF GHOSTS, AN (In The Nursery)**
TM 90382 / Mar '96 / Roadrunner

☐ **AMERICA IS DYING SLOWLY**
America / Decisions / (Lately) I've been thinking / Check ya self / Games / Street life / Listen to me now / Blood / No rubber no backstage pass / Suckas PH / Sport that raincoat / (sat away from the) nasty hoes / What I represent / Hustle / I breaks 'em off / Yearn
7559619252 / Jun '96 / WEA

☐ **AMERICAN BUFFALO**
Newman, Thomas *c*
VSD 5751 / Oct '96 / Varese Sarabande

☐ **AMERICAN CHRISTMAS, AN**
VSD 5441 / Dec '93 / Varese Sarabande

☐ **AMERICAN GIGOLO (Moroder, Giorgio)**
Moroder, Giorgio *c*
Call me: *Blondie* / Love and passion: *Barnes, Cheryl* / Night drive / Hello Mr. WAM / Apartment / Palm Springs Drive / Night drive (reprise) / Seduction (Love Theme)
5511032 / Sep '95 / Spectrum

☐ **AMERICAN GRAFFITI**
(We're gonna) Rock around the clock: *Haley, Bill & The Comets* / Sixteen candles: *Crests* / Runaway: *Shannon, Del* / Why do fools fall in love: *Lymon, Frankie & The Teenagers* / That'll be the day: *Holly, Buddy & The Crickets* / Maybe baby: *Holly, Buddy & The Crickets* / Fannie Mae: *Brown, Buster* / At the hop: *Flash Cadillac & The Continental Kids* / She's so fine: *Flash Cadillac & The Continental Kids* / Goodnight well it's time to go: *Spaniels* / See you in September: *Tempos* / Surfin' safari: *Beach Boys* / All summer long: *Beach Boys* / He's the great imposter: *Fleetwoods* / Almost grown: *Berry, Chuck* / Johnny B Goode: *Berry, Chuck* / Smoke gets in your eyes: *Platters* / Only you: *Platters* / Great pretender: *Platters* / Little darlin': *Diamonds* / Stroll: *Diamonds* / Peppermint twist: *Dee, Joey & The Starlighters* / Ya Ya: *Dorsey, Lee* / Ain't that a shame: *Domino, Fats* / I only have eyes for you: *Flamingos* / Get a job: *Silhouettes* / To the aisle: *Five Satins* / Do you wanna dance: *Freeman, Bobby* / Party doll: *Knox, Buddy* / Come go with me: *Del-Vikings* / You're sixteen: *Burnette, Johnny Rock 'N' Roll Trio* / Love potion no.9: *Clovers* / Since I don't have you: *Skyliners* / Chantilly lace: *Big Bopper* / Teen angel: *Dinning, Mark* / Crying in the chapel: *Till, Sonny & The Orioles* / Thousand miles away: *Heartbeats* / Heart and soul: *Cleftones* / Green onions: *Booker T & The MG's* / Barbara Ann: *Regents* / Book of love: *Monotones*
MCLDD 19150 / Apr '97 / MCA

☐ **AMERICAN IN PARIS, AN**
Gershwin, George *c*
Main title / Paris narration/Left bank / Nice work if you can get it / Adam Cork monologue / Nice work if you can get it (outtake) / Embraceable you / Fascinatin' rhythm / By Strauss / Street exhibition / I got rhythm / But not for me / Medley / Someone to watch over me / I've got a crush on you (outtake) / Tra la la / Love is here to stay / Medley 2 / Love walked in (outtake) / (I'll build) A stairway to paradise / I don't think I'll fall in love today / Concerto in F / Kiss me / What time is it / 'S wonderful / Lise I love you / Strike up the band (extended version) / Liza (extended version) / Oh lady be good/'S wonderful / That certain feeling/Clap yo' hands / I got rhythm (extended version) / Tra la la (outtake) / Utrillo did it / But not for me (outtake) / American in Paris ballet / Finale / My cousin in Milwaukee (outtake) / Foggy day (outtake) / Half of it dearie blues / Nice work if you can get it (rehearsal)
CDODEON 20 / Sep '96 / Soundtracks

☐ **AMERICAN WEREWOLF IN PARIS, AN**
1621312 / 24 Nov '97 / Polydor

☐ **AMISTAD**
DRD 50035 / 16 Feb '98 / Dreamworks

☐ **ANACONDA**
Edelman, Randy *c*
Edelman, Randy *con*
Anaconda / Watching and waiting / Night attack / This must be heaven / Down river / Seduction / Travelogue / Baiting the line / My beautiful Anna..(conda) / Totem's sacred ground / Sarone's last stand
0022812CIN / Jul '97 / Edel

☐ **ANASTASIA**
Rumour in St Petersburg / Journey to the past / Once a upon a December / In the dark of the night / Learn to do it / Learn to do it / Paris holds the key (to your heart) / At the beginning: *Marx, Richard & Donna Lewis* / Journey to the past: *Aaliyah* / Once upon a December: *Carter, Deanne* / Prologue / Speaking of Sophie / Nightmare / Kidnap and reunion / Reminiscing with grandma / Finale
7567807532 / 16 Mar '98 / Atlantic

☐ **AND DO THEY DO (Nyman, Michael Band)**
Nyman, Michael *c*
CDTER 1123 / 1 Sep '98 / TER

☐ **AND THE BAND PLAYED ON**
Burwell, Carter *c*
Burwell, Carter *con*
VSD 5449 / Apr '94 / Varese Sarabande

☐ **ANDRE**
Rowland, Bruce *c*
Thanks to you: *Collins, Tyler* / Yakety yak: *Coasters* / Rama rama ding dong: *Edsels* / This magic moment: *Drifters* / I only have eyes for you: *Flamingos* / You talk too much: *Jones, Joe* / Peppermint twist: *Dee, Joey & The Starlighters* / Lover's concerto: *Toys* / Don't say nothin' bad (about my baby): *Cookies* / Johnny Angel: *Faboures, Johnny* / Green onions: *Booker T & The MG's* / Along came Jones: *Coasters* / You're my best friend: *Craig 'n' Co.*
8122718022 / Jan '95 / Warner Bros.

☐ **ANDY WARHOL'S DRACULA/ANDY WARHOL'S FRANKENSTEIN**
Gizzi, Claudio *c*
OST 119 / Jan '94 / Milano Dischi

☐ **ANGEL AT MY TABLE, AN**
McGlashan, Don *c*
A 8925 / Jan '92 / Alhambra

☐ **ANGEL AT MY TABLE, AN**
McGlashan, Don *c*
DRGCD 12603 / Jan '95 / DRG

☐ **ANGEL BABY**
74321443592 / Dec '96 / Milan

☐ **ANGEL HEART**
Jones, Trevor *c*
Harry Angel: *Jones, Trevor & Courtney Pine* / Honeymoon blues: *Smith, Bessie* / Nightmare: *Jones, Trevor & Courtney Pine* / Girl of ...: *Gray, Glen & The Casa Loma Orchestra* / I got this thing about chickens: *Jones, Trevor & Courtney Pine* / Right key but the wrong keyhole / Rainy rainy day: *McGhee, Brownie* / Looking for Johnny: *Jones, Trevor & Courtney Pine* / Soul on fire: *Baker, LaVern* / Bloodmare: *Jones, Trevor & Courtney Pine* / Johnny Favourite: *Jones, Trevor & Courtney Pine*
IMCD 76 / '89 / Island

☐ **ANGELI BIANCHI ANGELI NERI**
Umiliani, Piero *c*
ET 903CD / 14 Apr '98 / Easy Tempo

☐ **ANGELIQUE**
Magne, Michel *c*
Angelique Marquise des Anges / Angelique devant la statue antique / Angelique se jette au cou de Peyrac / Angelique apprend que Peyrac a ete arrete / Angelique traquee au Louvre / Angelique reprend espoir / Merveilleuse Angelique / Angelique et le Poete Crotte / Angelique et le Roy / Angelique retrouve la statue antique / Angelique decouvre les traces de Peyrac / Peyrac s'enfuit dans les souterrains
MSA 99011 / Sep '97 / Movies Select Audio

☐ **ANGELS AND INSECTS (Balanescu Quartet)**
CDSTUMM 147 / Dec '95 / Mute

☐ **ANGIE**
Goldsmith, Jerry *c*
Goldsmith, Jerry *con*
VSD 5469 / Jun '94 / Varese Sarabande

☐ **ANGST (Schulze, Klaus)**
Schulze, Klaus *c*
Freeze / Pain / Memory / Surrender / Beyond
CDTB 027 / Feb '86 / Thunderbolt

☐ **ANIMA MUNDI**
Glass, Philip *c*
Journey / Ark / Garden / Beginning / Living waters / Perpetual motion
7559793292 / Jan '94 / Nonesuch

☐ **ANIMAL HOUSE**
Faber College theme / Louie Louie: *Belushi, John* / Twistin' the night away: *Cooke, Sam* / Tossin' and turnin': *Lewis, Bobby* / Shama lama ding dong / Hey Paula: *Paul & Paula* / Animal house: *Bishop, Stephen* / Money (that's what I want): *Belushi, John* / Let's dance: *Montez, Chris* / Dream girl: *Bishop, Stephen* / What a wonderful world: *Cooke, Sam* / Shout / Intro
MCLD 19086 / Jun '92 / MCA

☐ **ANJO MAU INTERNACIONAL**
10372 / 14 Apr '98 / Som Livre

☐ **ANNA KARENINA (Gorchakova, Galina & Maxim Vengerov/St. Petersburg Philharmonic Orchestra)**
Solti, George *con*
4553602 / May '97 / Decca

☐ **ANNE OF GREEN GABLES (London Cast)**
Campbell, Norman *c*
Campbell, Norman & Donald Harron *l*
Goldstein, Martin *con*
SMK 53495 / Dec '91 / Sony West End

☐ **ANNIE (1982 Film Cast)**
Strouse, Charles *c*
Charnin, Martin *l*
Tomorrow / It's the hard-knock life / Maybe / Dumb dog / Sandy / I think I'm gonna like it here / Little girls / We got Annie / Let's go to the movies / Sign / You're never fully dressed without a smile / Easy Street / Tomorrow reprise / Finale
4676082 / Dec '90 / CBS

☐ **ANNIE**
Strouse, Charles *c*
Charnin, Martin *l*
Overture / Maybe / It's the hard-knock life / Tomorrow / We'd like to thank you / Little girls / I think I'm going to like it here / NYC / Easy Street / You're never fully dressed without a smile / I don't need anything but you / New deal for Christmas
SHOWCD 041 / Jan '97 / Showtime

☐ **ANNIE GET YOUR GUN (Criswell, Kim & Thomas Hampson/Studio Cast/ Ambrosian Chorus/London Sinfonietta)**
Berlin, Irving *c*
Fields, Dorothy *l*
McGlinn, John *con*
CDANNIE 1 / Aug '91 / EMI Classics

☐ **ANNIE GET YOUR GUN (1986 London Cast)**
Berlin, Irving *c*
Fields, Dorothy *l*
Overture / Colonel Buffalo Bill / I'm a bad bad man / Doin' what comes natur'lly / Girl that I marry / You can't get a man with a gun / There's no business like show business / They say it's wonderful / Moonshine lullaby / My defenses are down / Wild horse ceremonial dance / I'm an Indian too / I got lost in his arms / I got the sun in the morning / Old fashioned wedding / Anything you can do / Finale
OCRCD 6024 / Oct '95 / First Night

☐ **ANNIE GET YOUR GUN (Broadway Cast)**
Berlin, Irving *c*
Fields, Dorothy *l*
ZDM 7647652 / Apr '93 / EMI Classics

☐ **ANNIE GET YOUR GUN (Cast Recording)**
Berlin, Irving *c*
Fields, Dorothy *l*
CDTER 1229 / Aug '95 / TER

☐ **ANNIE WARBUCKS (Broadway Cast)**
CDQ 5550402 / Mar '94 / EMI

☐ **ANTARCTICA (Vangelis)**
Vangelis *c*
Antarctica / Antarctica echoes / Kinematic song of white / Life of Antarctica / Memory of Antarctica / Other side of Antarctica / Deliverance
8157322 / Mar '96 / Polydor

☐ **ANTARTIDA (Cale, John)**
Cale, John *c*
TWI 1008 / Nov '95 / Les Disques Du Crepuscule

☐ **ANTONIA'S LINE (Metropole Orchestra Of The Netherlands)**
Sekacz, Ilona *c*
Bakker, D. *con*
FILMCD 183 / Oct '96 / Silva Screen

☐ **ANTONY AND CLEOPATRA (Berlin Radio Symphony Choir/Orchestra)**
Scott, John *c*
Scott, John *con*
JSCD 114 / Jan '93 / JOS

☐ **ANYTHING GOES (1989 London Cast)**
Porter, Cole *c*
Prelude / There's no cure like travel / You're the top / I want to row on the crew / Friendship / Anything goes / Public enemy No.1 / Goodbye little dream goodbye / All through the night / Buddie beware / I get a kick out of you / Bon voyage / Easy to love / Sailor's chantey / It's de-lovely / Entr'acte / Blow Gabriel blow / Be like the bluebird / Gypsy in me
OCRCD 6038 / Oct '95 / First Night

☐ **ANYTHING GOES (1969 London Cast)**
Porter, Cole *c*
CDTER 1219 / Jan '94 / TER

☐ **ANYTHING GOES (Criswell, Kim & Cris Groenendaal/Jack Gilford/Frederica VonStade/Ambrosian Chorus/London Symphony Orchestra)**
Porter, Cole *c*
Overture / I get a kick out of you / Bon voyage / All through the night / There'll always be a lady fair / Where are the men / You're the top / You're the top (encore) / There'll always be a lady fair (reprise) / Anything goes (finale) / Entr'acte / Public enemy No.1 / What a joy to be young / Blow Gabriel blow / Be like the bluebird / Buddie beware / Gypsy in me / Finale ultimo / Kate the great / Waltz down the aisle
CDC 7498482 / Oct '89 / EMI Classics

☐ **ANYTHING GOES (Luker, Rebecca)**
Porter, Cole *c*
VSD 5647 / Jun '96 / Varese Sarabande

☐ **ANYWHERE I WANDER (Cast Recording)**
Loesser, Frank *c*
VSD 5434 / Oct '93 / Varese Sarabande

☐ **APOCALYPSE NOW**
Coppola, Carmine *c*
End / End part 2 / Terminate / Delta / PBR / Dossier / Colonel Kilgore / Orange light / Ride of the Valkyries / Napalm in the morning / Pre-tiger / Dossier II / Suzie Q / Dossier III / 75 klicks / Ning river / Do Lung Bridge / Letters from home / Clean's death / Chief's death / Strange voyage / Kurtz' compound / Errand boy / Chief's head / Hollow men / Horror / Even the jungle wanted him dead / End: *Doors*
7559606892 / Apr '96 / Elektra

☐ **APOLLO 13**
Horner, James *c*
Horner, James *con*
Night train: *Brown, James* / Groovin': *Young Rascals* / Somebody to love: *Jefferson Airplane* / I can see for miles: *Who* / Purple haze: *Hendrix, Jimi* / Spirit in the sky: *Greebaum, Norman* / Honky tonkin': *Williams, Hank* / Blue moon: *Mavericks* / Main title / One small step / Launch control / All systems go / Welcome to Apollo 13 / House cleaning / Houston we have a problem / Master Alarm / What's going on / Into the LEM / Out of time / Shut her down / Dark side of the moon / Failure is not an option / Waiting for disaster / Privelege / Re-entry and splashdown / End titles
MCD 11241 / 8 Sep '97 / MCA

☐ **APOSTLE, THE**
RTD 53058 / 8 Jun '98 / Radioactive

☐ **APPLE TREE, THE (Broadway Cast)**
Bock, Jerry *c*
Harnick, Sheldon *l*
Lawrence, Elliot *con*
SK 48209 / Dec '91 / Sony Broadway

☐ **ARE YOU LONESOME TONIGHT (1985 London Cast)**
Peace in the valley / Heartbreak hotel / That's alright mama / I don't care if the sun don't shine / Loving you / Blue suede shoes / Hound dog / If I can dream / All my trials / NBC-TV special 1968 / You gave me a mountain / I was the one / If we never meet again / Are you lonesome tonight
OCRCD 6027 / Dec '95 / First Night

☐ **ARISTOCATS, THE**
Sherman, Richard & Robert *c*
WD 742502 / Mar '96 / Disney Music & Stories

☐ **ARMAGEDDON**
I don't want to miss a thing: *Aerosmith* / Remember me: *Journey* / What kind of love are you on: *Aerosmith* / La grange: *ZZ Top* / Roll me away: *Seger, Bob & The Silver Bullet Band* / When the rainbow comes: *Colvin, Shawn* / Sweet emotion: *Aerosmith* / Mr. Big Time: *Bon Jovi, Jon* / Come together: *Aerosmith* / Wish I were you: *Smyth, Patty* / Starseed: *Our Lady Peace* / Leaving on a jet plane: *Kreviazuk, Chantal* / Theme from Armageddon: *Rabin, Trevor* / Animal crackers: *Tyler, Steven*
4913842 / 29 Jun '98 / Columbia

☐ **ARRIVAL, THE**
Band, Richard c
MAF 7032D / Nov '92 / Intrada

☐ **ARRIVAL, THE (Score) (Northwest Sinfonia)**
Kempel, Arthur c
Kempel, Arthur con
FILMCD 182 / Oct '96 / Silva Screen

☐ **AS GOOD AS IT GETS**
As good as it gets: Zimmer, Hans / Better man: Zimmer, Hans / Humanity: Zimmer, Hans / Too much reality: Zimmer, Hans / 12345: Zimmer, Hans / Greatest woman on Earth: Zimmer, Hans / Everything my heart desires: Brisebois, Danielle / My only: Brisebois, Danielle / Under stars: Roy, Phil / For sentimental reasons: Cole, Nat 'King' / Hand on my heart: Owen, Judith / Climb on (a back that's strong): Colvin, Shawn / Always look on the bright side of life: Garfunkel, Art
4895022 / 2 Mar '98 / Columbia

☐ **ASCENSEUR POUR L'ECHAFAUD (Lift To The Scaffold) (Davis, Miles)**
Davis, Miles c
Nuit sur Les Champs-Elysee / Assassinat / Motel / Final / Le petit bal / Sequence voiture / Generique / L'assassinat de Carala / Sur l'autoroute / Julien dans l'ascenseur / Florence dans l'ascenseur / Florence sur Les Champs-Elysee / Diner au motel / Evasion de Julien / Visite du vigile / Au bar du petit bac / Chez le photographe du motel
8363052 / Mar '94 / Fontana

☐ **ASPECTS OF LOVE (London Cast)**
Lloyd Webber, Andrew c
Love changes everything / Seeing is believing / Chason d'enfante / She's far better off without you / Leading lady / There's more to love / First man you remember / Falling / Anything but lonely / Cafe / Memory of a happy moment / Everybody loves a hero / Stop wait please / Other pleasures / Mermaid song / Journey of a lifetime / Hand me the wine and the dice
8411262 / Aug '89 / Really Useful

☐ **ASPECTS OF LOVE/CATS (Cast Recording)**
Lloyd Webber, Andrew c
340832 / Oct '95 / Koch

☐ **ASSASSINS (1991 Broadway Cast)**
Sondheim, Stephen c
Everybody's got the right / Ballad of Booth / How I saved Roosevelt / Gun song / Ballad of Czolgosz / Unworthy of your love / Ballad of Guiteau / Another national anthem / November 22 1963 / Final sequence - You can close the New York Stock Exchange / Everybody's got the right (reprise)
RD 60737 / '91 / RCA Victor

☐ **ASSOCIATE, THE**
5307472 / Apr '97 / Polydor

☐ **ASTERIX IN BRITAIN/CAESAR'S GIFT**
Cosma, Vladimir c
951292 / Nov '97 / Pomme

☐ **ASTRONOMERS, THE**
Redford, J.A.C. c
MAF 7018D / Jan '93 / Intrada

☐ **AT PLAY IN THE FIELDS OF THE LORD (Polish Radio Grand Symphony Orchestra)**
Preisner, Zbigniew c
Wit, Antoni con
FCD 210072 / Jan '93 / Fantasy

☐ **AT THE MOVIES**
Someday (I'm coming back): Stansfield, Lisa / This city never sleeps: Eurythmics / You don't own me: Eurythmics / Crash: Primitives / Get together: Youngbloods / Ghostbusters: Parker, Ray Jnr. / Nothing's gonna stop us now: Parker, Ray Jnr. / Everybody's talkin': Nilsson, Harry / Theme from Harry's Game: Clannad / Natural thing: M People / Roadhouse blues: Healey, Jeff Band / I will always love you: Parton, Dolly / Jumping Jack Flash: Franklin, Aretha / Neutron dance: Pointer Sisters / Let the river run: Simon, Carly / Sentimental journey: Esquivel & His Orchestra
74321412732 / Feb '97 / RCA

☐ **ATHENIAN TOUCH (Off Broadway Cast)**
AEICD 010 / May '98 / AEI

☐ **ATLANTIC CITY**
Legrand, Michel c
Casta diva / Slot machine baby / Bellini rock / Atlantic city / My old friend / Balcon / Piano blackjack / Steel pier / Song of India / Roadmap for a free jazz group / No gambling allowed / AC/DC / Trio jazz
CDRG 6104 / Jan '89 / DRG
119072 / Jan '97 / Musidisc

☐ **ATLANTIS**
Serra, Eric c
Creation / Secret life of angels / Visions of the underways / Snake / Iguana dance / Down to the unknown world / Magic forest / In the kingdom of spirits / Legend of Manatees / Time to get your lovin' / Shark attack / Realms of ice
30867 / Jan '93 / Silva Screen

☐ **ATTACK AND RETREAT/THE CAMP FOLLOWERS (Italiani Brava Gente/Le Soldatesse)**
Trovajoli, Armando/Mario Nascimbene c
OST 112 / Apr '92 / Milano Dischi

☐ **AUSTIN POWERS**
1621122 / Sep '97 / Polydor

☐ **AVENGERS, THE**
Avengers: Devries, Marius / Storm: Jones, Grace / Many weathers apart: Merz / Karma: Ashtar Command / Bad twin: Baby Bird / Mama: Lennox, Annie / Flash: Stereo MC's / Tecknowlegy: Utah Saints & Iggy Pop / Blow them away: Verve Pipe / Burning dog: Sugar Ray / I am: Suggs / Truth serum: Dish Wallah / Visiting angels: Roni Size / Summer's end: O'Connor, Sinead
7567831182 / 3 Aug '98 / Atlantic

☐ **AVENGERS, THE/THE NEW AVENGERS/THE PROFESSIONALS (London Studio Orchestra)**
Johnson, Laurie c
VCD 47270 / Jan '89 / Varese Sarabande

B

☐ **BABE**
Bernstein, Elmer c
VSD 5661 / Oct '95 / Varese Sarabande

☐ **BABES IN ARMS (Film Cast)**
Rodgers, Richard c
Hart, Lorenz l
NW 3862 / Aug '92 / New World

☐ **BABES IN TOYLAND (Cast Recording)**
Herbert, Victor c
AEICD 044 / May '98 / AEI

☐ **BABY (Broadway Cast)**
Shire, David c
Maltby, Richard Jr. l
Opening / We start today / What could be better / Plaza song / Baby baby baby / I want it all / At night she comes home to me / Fatherhood blues / Romance / I chose right / Story goes on / Ladies singing their song / Patterns / Romance 2 / Easier to love / Romance 3 / Two people in love / With you / And what if we had loved like that / Birth / Finale
CDTER 1089 / Mar '84 / TER

☐ **BABY OF MACON, THE**
March / Batille and comet / Opening part one / Opening part two / Morning hymn / Evening hymn / Suscepit Israel / Cia cona / Selling of the child's fluids / Dance one / Dance two / Lamentations / Ave Maria Stella / Dismemberment of the child / Improvisation of batille and drums / Cantor
340142 / Sep '93 / Koch

☐ **BABYLON 5/FACE OF THE ENEMY (Franke, Christopher)**
Franke, Christopher c
SI 0417 / 21 Apr '98 / Sonic Images

☐ **BABYLON 5/FALL OF NIGHT (Franke, Christopher)**
Franke, Christopher c
SI 0222 / 21 Apr '98 / Sonic Images

☐ **BABYLON 5/INTERLUDES AND EXAMINATIONS (Franke, Christopher)**
Franke, Christopher c
SI 0315 / 21 Apr '98 / Sonic Images

☐ **BABYLON 5/INTO THE FIRE (Franke, Christopher)**
Franke, Christopher c
SI 0406 / 21 Apr '98 / Sonic Images

☐ **BABYLON 5/LATE DELIVERY FROM AVALON (Franke, Christopher)**
Franke, Christopher c
SI 0312 / 1 Dec '97 / Sonic Images

☐ **BABYLON 5/MESSAGES FROM EARTH (Franke, Christopher)**
Franke, Christopher c
SI 8602 / 1 Dec '97 / Sonic Images

☐ **BABYLON 5/NO SURRENDER NO RETREAT (Franke, Christopher)**
Franke, Christopher c
SI 0415 / 21 Apr '98 / Sonic Images

☐ **BABYLON 5/RAGGED EDGE (Franke, Christopher)**
Franke, Christopher c
SI 0513 / 21 Apr '98 / Sonic Images

☐ **BABYLON 5/SEVERED DREAMS (Franke, Christopher)**
Franke, Christopher c
SI 0310 / 1 Dec '97 / Sonic Images

☐ **BABYLON 5/SHADOW DANCING (Franke, Christopher)**
Franke, Christopher c
SI 0321 / 1 Dec '97 / Sonic Images

☐ **BABYLON 5/WALKABOUT (Franke, Christopher)**
Franke, Christopher c
SI 0318 / 1 Dec '97 / Sonic Images

☐ **BABYLON 5/Z'HA'DUM (Franke, Christopher)**
Franke, Christopher c
SI 0322 / 1 Dec '97 / Sonic Images

☐ **BACK TO THE FUTURE**
Johnny B Goode: McFly, Marty & the Starlighters / Power of love: Lewis, Huey & The News / Time bomb town: Buckingham, Lindsey / Back to the future: Silvestri, Alan / Heaven is one step away: Clapton, Eric / Back in time: Lewis, Huey & The News / Back to the future overture: Silvestri, Alan / Wallflower (dance with me Henry): James, Etta / Night train: Berry, Marvin & the Starlighters / Earth angel: Berry, Marvin & the Starlighters
MCLD 19151 / Apr '93 / MCA

☐ **BACK TO THE FUTURE III**
Silvestri, Alan c
Main title / It's Clara / Train / Hill Valley / Hanging / At first sight / Indians / Goodbye Clara / Doc returns / Point of no return / Future isn't written / Showdown / Doc to the rescue / Kiss / We're out of gas / Wake up juice / Science experiment / Doubleback: ZZ Top / End credits
VSD 5272 / Sep '90 / Varese Sarabande

☐ **BACKBEAT (Backbeat Band)**
Money / Long tall Sally / Bad boy / Twist and shout / Please Mr. Postman / C'mon everybody / Rock 'n' roll music / Slow down / Roadrunner / Carol / Good golly Miss Molly / Twenty flight rock
CDV 2729 / Apr '94 / Virgin

☐ **BACKBEAT (Score)**
Was, Don c
You asked I came / Darkroom / What do they call this drink / He's wearing my bathrobe / Just read the poems / You asked I came / He's wearing my bathrobe
CDV 2740 / Apr '94 / Virgin

☐ **BACKDRAFT**
Zimmer, Hans c
Set me in motion: Hornsby, Bruce & The Range / Fighting 17th / Brothers / Arsonist's waltz / 335 / Burn it all / You go we go / Fahrenheit 451 / Show me your firetruck / Show goes on
262023 / Jan '95 / Milan

☐ **BAD BOYS**
Shy guy: King, Diana / So many ways: Warren G. / Five o'five o'(here they come): 69 / Boom boom boom: Juster / Me against the world: 2Pac / Someone to love: Jon B / I've got a little something for you: MN8 / Never find someone like you: Martin, Keith / Theme from Bad Boys: Mancina, Mark / Bad boys reply: Inner Circle / Juke joint jezebel: K.M.F.D.M. / Cloud of smoke: Call O'da Wild / Work me slow: Xscape / Da B side: Da Brat / Call the police: Kamoze, Ini
4804532 / Jun '95 / Columbia

☐ **BAD CHANNELS**
Demons kiss: Blue Oyster Cult / Horsemen arrive: Blue Oyster Cult / That's how it is: Joker / Jane Jane (the hurricane): Joker / Somewhere in the night: Fair Game / Blind faith: Fair Game / Manic Depresso: Sykotik Synfoney / Mr. Cool: Sykotik Synfoney / Myth of freedom: DMT / Touching myself again: DMT / Little old lady polka: Ukelaliens
IRSCD 993018 / Oct '96 / Blueprint

☐ **BAD SEED, THE**
North, Alex c
TSU 0124 / Jan '95 / Tsunami

☐ **BAD TASTE**
QDKCD 002 / Sep '94 / QDK Media

☐ **BAGDAD CAFE**
Calling you: Steele, Jevetta / Zwifach: Blasmusik, Deihinger / C major prelude: Flagg, Darron / Blues harp: Galison, William / Brenda Brenda: Steele, Jevetta / Calliope: Telson, Bob
IMCD 102 / Feb '90 / Island

☐ **BAJOUR (Broadway Cast)**
Marks, Walter c
Engel, Lehman con
SK 48208 / Dec '91 / Sony Broadway

☐ **BAKER'S WIFE, THE (London Cast)**
Schwartz, Stephen c
CDTER 1175 / Jul '90 / TER

☐ **BALANCING ACT (Original New York Cast)**
Goggin, Dan c
Life is a balancing act / Next stop: New York City / Home sweet home / Play away the blues / Tough town / I left you there / Twist of fate / Fifth from the right / You heard it here first / Long long way / Women of the century / Welcome bienvenue / Where is the rainbow / I am yours / That kid's gonna make it / Chew chew chow / Hollywood 'n' vinyl / California suite / I knew the music
DRGCD 19004 / Jan '95 / DRG

☐ **BALLAD OF LITTLE JOE (Mansfield, David & Kate/Anne McGarrigle)**
Mansfield, David c
MAF 7053D / Jan '93 / Intrada

☐ **BALLAD OF LITTLE MIKEY, THE (Cast Recording)**
Savage, Mark c
AEICD 021 / May '98 / AEI

☐ **BALLAD OF THE IRISH HORSE, THE (Chieftains)**
Moloney, Paddy c
Ballad of the Irish horse / Green pastures / Birth of the foals / Lady Hemphill / Horses of Ireland - part 1 / Chasing the fox / Going to the fair / Galway races / Story of the horse / Boyne hunt/Mullingar races/ Five-mile chase / Horses of Ireland - part 2
CCF 15CD / May '93 / Claddagh

☐ **BALLROOM (Broadway Cast)**
Goldenberg, Billy c
Jennings, Don con
SK 35762 / Jan '93 / Sony Broadway

☐ **BALLYKISSANGEL (Davey, Shaun)**
Davey, Shaun c
Ballykissangel theme / Siobahn and Brendan / Maura's confession / Peter's parish / Earthmovers / Dogs and poker / Death of a mountainy man / Graves and terminators / Tripe casserole / Niamh and Ambrose / Jenny's farewell / Our lady of Bonanza / Yellow bus crusade / Quigley's rosary / Peter and Assumpta / Rolling packing case
VTCD 117 / Jan '97 / Virgin

☐ **BAND WAGON, THE/THE BELLE OF NEW YORK (Astaire, Fred & Cast)**
Schwartz, Arthur/Harry Warren c
BMCD 7011 / Nov '96 / Blue Moon

☐ **BANDIT QUEEN (Khan, Nusrat Fateh Ali)**
Khan, Nusrat Fateh Ali & Roger White c
74321378112 / Oct '96 / Milan

☐ **BANDOLERO**
Goldsmith, Jerry c
Trap / El jefe / Bait / Ambushed / Sabinas / Dee's proposal / Across the river / Bad day for a hanging / Better way
TCS 10012 / Jan '90 / Edel

☐ **BAPS**
74321486842 / Aug '97 / Milan

☐ **BARB WIRE**
Welcome to planet boom: Lee, Tommy & Pamela Anderson Lee / She's so free: Napolitano, Johnette / Spill the wine: Hutchence, Michael / Word up: Gun / Don't call me Babe: Shampoo / Hot child in the city: Hagfish / Let's all go together: Marion / Dancing barefoot: Die Cheerleader / Scum: Meat Puppets In Vapourspace / Ca plane pour moi: Mr. Ed Jumps The Gun / None of your business: Salt 'N' Pepa
8287462 / Mar '96 / London

☐ **BARBARIANS, THE**
Donaggio, Pino c
MAF 7008D / Jan '93 / Intrada

☐ **BARCELONA**
Suozzo, Mark c
Americans abroad / Cathedral / Theme of Ted / Aurora reverie / Aftermath (USO) / Americans in peril / Elegy / Theme of Ted (hospital) / Reconciliation / Lake / Everybody limbo / Barcelona merengue / Una lacrima sul viso / L'home dibuixat / Night on the town (Cava bar) / You've got what it takes / Breakin' up / Me voy pal pueblo / Suenos de amor / Vinyl Hampton / Ligia elena
237942 / Jan '95 / Milan

☐ **BAREFOOT CONTESSA, THE/ROOM AT THE TOP/THE QUIET AMERICAN (The Film Music Of Mario Nascimbene/ 3 Complete Soundtracks)**
Nascimbene, Mario c
Main titles / Recalling at the graveyard / Harry meets Maria Vargas / Gypsy bolero / Guitar for Maria / Nocturne Bolero / Death of Maria/Finale / Main titles/ Alice and Joe at the pub / Alice's beguine / Alice and Joe at home / Alice and Joe / Alice alone / Joe Alice is dead / Joe and the prostitute / Joe after the fight/ Finale / Main titles/City streets / Cathedral / Morgue / Psychological and passionate / Search for Tuong/ Finale
DRGCD 32961 / Aug '96 / DRG

☐ **BARMITZVAH BOY (1978 London Cast)**
Styne, Jule c
Black, Don l
Faris, Alexander con
Overture / Why / If only a little bit sticks / Bar mitzvah of Elliot Green / This time tomorrow / Thou shalt not / Harolds of this world / We've done alright / Simchas / You wouldn't be you / Rita's request / Sun shines out of your eyes / Where is the music coming from / I've just begun
SMK 53498 / Nov '92 / Sony West End

☐ **BARRY LYNDON**
Moloney, Paddy c
Sarabande (main title) / Women of Ireland / Piper's maggot jig / Seamaiden / Tin whistle / British Grenadiers / Hohenfriedberger march / Lilliburlero / March: Idomeneo / Sarabande-duel / German dance no.1 in C major / Il barbiere di siviglia / Cello concerto / Concerto for two harpsichords and orchestra in / Piano trio in E flat / Sarabande (end title)
7599259842 / Jan '95 / Warner Bros.

☐ **BASHVILLE (1983 London Cast)**
King, Denis c
Green, Benny l
Prelude / Fancy Free / Lydia / 8-9-10 / One pair of hands / Gentleman's true to his code / Because I love her / Take the road to the ring / Entr'acte / Hymn to law and order / Blackman's burden / He is my son / Bashville / Boats are burned / Finale
CDTER 1072 / Aug '95 / TER

☐ **BASIC INSTINCT**
Goldsmith, Jerry c
Goldsmith, Jerry con
Main title / Crossed legs / Night life / Kitchen help / Pillow talk / Morning after / Games are over / Catherine's sorrow / Roxy loses / Unending story
VSD 5360 / Mar '92 / Varese Sarabande

☐ **BASIL THE GREAT MOUSE DETECTIVE**
Mancini, Henry c
VSD 5359 / Feb '92 / Varese Sarabande

☐ **BASKET CASE II/FRANKENHOOKER (Renzetti, Joe)**
Renzetti, Joe *c*
I'm pregnant I'm dead / Granny at freak tent / Barbecue / Original main titles / Out of hospital / Out of window / Big escape / Room of memories / In the attic / Granny meeting / In love / Frankenhooker / Lookin' for hookers / Jeffrey and parts / Creation / Eyeball / Happy day / Jeffrey fixes Elizabeth / Zoro killing
FILMCD 073 / '89 / Silva Screen

☐ **BASKETBALL DIARIES**
Catholic boy: Carroll, Jim & Pearl Jam / Devil's toe: *Revell, Graeme & Jim Carroll* / Down by the water: *PJ Harvey* / What a life: *Rockers Hi Fi* / I am alone: *Revell, Graeme & Jim Carroll* / People who died: *Carroll, Jim Band* / Riders on the storm: *Doors* / Dizzy: *Green Apple Quickstep* / It's been hard: *Revell, Graeme & Jim Carroll* / Coming right along: *Posies* / Strawberry wine: *Massive Internal Complications* / Star: *Cult* / Dream massacre: *Revell, Graeme* / I've been down: *Flea* / Blind dogs: *Soundgarden*
5240934 / Jul '95 / Island

☐ **BASQUIAT**
Van Gough boat / Public image: *Public Image Ltd* / It's all over now baby blue: *Them* / Suicide hotline: *Taylor, Nick Marion* / I'm not in love: *Toadies* / Is that all there is: *Parish, John & Polly Jean Harvey* / White lines (don't do it): *Grandmaster Flash & Melle Mel* / Rise: *Tripping Daisy* / These days: *Joy Division* / She's dancing: *Kelly, Brian* / Tom Traubert's blues: *Waits, Tom* / Small plot of land: *Bowie, David* / Summer in Siam: *Pogues* / Last song I'll ever sing: *Friday, Gavin* / Hallelujah: *Cale, John*
5242602 / Mar '97 / Island

☐ **BAT 21**
VSD 5202 / Dec '88 / Varese Sarabande

☐ **BATHING BEAUTY/HERE COME THE WAVES/THIS GUN FOR HIRE**
Bim bam boom / Munequita linda / Trumpet blues and cantabile / By the waters of Minnetonka / Tico tico / Loch Lomond / I'll take the high note / Alma llanera / Nutcracker / Hora staccato / I cried for you / Finale (I'll take the high note) / Here come the waves / That old black magic / Let's take the long way home / Accentuate the positive / I promise you / This gun for hire / Now you see it now you don't
CD 60001 / Apr '97 / Great Movie Themes

☐ **BATMAN (Score) (Sinfonia Of London)**
Elfman, Danny *c*
Walker, S. *con*
Batman theme / First confrontation / Clown attack / Roasted dude / Descent into mystery / Joker's poem / Charge of the Batmobile / Up the cathedral / Final confrontation / Roof fight / Flowers / Batman to the rescue / Photos / Beautiful dreamer / Bat cave / Love theme / Attack of the batwing / Waltz to the death / Finale
9259772 / Aug '89 / WEA

☐ **BATMAN (Prince)**
Prince *c*
Future / Electric chair / Arms of Orion / Partyman / Vicki waiting / Trust / Lemon crush / Scandalous / Batdance
9259362 / Feb '95 / WEA

☐ **BATMAN (Original Score Of The 20th Century Fox TV Series & 19 Hefti Bat Songs) (Hefti, Neal Orchestra/Chorus)**
Hefti, Neal *c*
RE 2153 / Aug '97 / Razor & Tie

☐ **BATMAN AND ROBIN**
End is the beginning is the end: *Smashing Pumpkins* / Beginning is the end is the beginning: *Smashing Pumpkins* / Look into my eyes: *Bone Thugs n' Harmony* / Foolish games: *Jewel* / Lazy eye: *Goo Goo Dolls* / Moaner: *Underworld* / Bug: *Soul Coughing* / Poison ivy: *Ndegeocello, Me'shell* / Fun for me: *Moloko* / House on fire: *Arkarna* / Breed: *Christy, Lauren* / Gotham City Overture: *Goldenthal, Elliot* / Revolution: *REM* / Gotham city: *R. Kelly*
9362466202 / Jun '97 / Warner Bros.

☐ **BATMAN FOREVER**
Hold me thrill me kill me: *U2* / One time too many: *PJ Harvey* / Where are you now: *Brandy* / Kiss from a rose: *Seal* / Hunter gets captured by the game: *Massive Attack & Tracey Thorn* / Nobody lives without love: *Reader, Eddie* / Tell me now: *Mazzy Star* / Smash it up: *Offspring* / There is a light: *Cave, Nick* / Riddler: *Method Man* / Passenger: *Hutchence, Michael* / Crossing the river: *Devlins* / 8: *Sunny Day Real Estate* / Bad days: *Flaming Lips*
7567827592 / Jun '95 / Warner Bros.

☐ **BATMAN FOREVER (Score)**
Main title fanfare / Perils of Gotham / Fledermausmarchmusik / Nygma variations (an ode to science) / Spank me / Chase blanc / Two Face three step / Mr. E's dance card / Under the top / Gotham City boogie / Mouth to mouth nocturne / Pull of regret / Batterdammerung / Holy rusted metal / Descent / Chase noir / Perpetuum mobile
7567827762 / Jun '95 / Warner Bros.

☐ **BATMAN RETURNS**
Elfman, Danny *c*
Birth of Penguin / Lair / Selina transforms / Cemetary / Cat suite / Batman Vs The Circus / Rise and fall from grace / Sore spots / Rooftops / Wild ride / Children's hour / Final confrontation / Finale / End credits / Face to face: *Siouxsie & the Banshees*
7599269722 / Jun '92 / Warner Bros.

☐ **BATMAN TRILOGY, THE (Themes From Batman, Batman Returns And Batman Forever)**
VSD 5766 / Jul '97 / Varese Sarabande

☐ **BATTLE OF ALGIERS/MASSACRE IN ROME**
Pontecorvo, Gillo *c*
OST 105 / Jan '93 / Milano Dischi

☐ **BATTLE OF STALINGRAD/OTHELLO (Bratislava Symphony Orchestra)**
Khachaturian, Aram *c*
Adriano *con*
8223314 / Jul '94 / Marco Polo

☐ **BEACHES (Midler, Bette)**
Under the boardwalk / I've still got my health / Otto Titsling / Glory of love / Oh industry / Wind beneath my wings / I think it's going to rain today / I know you by heart / Baby mine / Friendship theme
7819332 / Feb '95 / WEA

☐ **BEAN**
Picture of you: *Boyzone* / I get around: *Beach Boys* / Walking on sunshine: *Katrina & The Waves* / Yesterday: *Wet Wet Wet* / Running back for more: *Louise* / That kinda guy: *Jules-Stock, Thomas* / Give me a little more time: *Gabrielle* / I love LA: *OMC* / He's a rebel: *Alisha's Attic* / Stuck in the middle with you: *Hoffs, Susanna* / Art for art's sake: *10cc* / Have fun go mad: *Blair* / Can we talk: *Code Red* / Bean theme: *Goodall, Howard* / Elected: *Mr. Bean & Smear Campaign*
5537742 / Aug '97 / Mercury

☐ **BEAST (Original TV Soundtrack)**
VSD 5731 / Jul '96 / Varese Sarabande

☐ **BEASTMASTER II**
MAF 7019D / Mar '92 / Intrada

☐ **BEAT GIRL/STRINGBEAT (Barry, John Seven & Orchestra)**
Barry, John *c*
PLAY 001 / Jan '93 / Play It Again

☐ **BEAUTIFUL THING (Mamas & The Papas)**
Altman, John *c*
It's getting better
MCD 60013 / Jun '96 / MCA

☐ **BEAUTY AND THE BEAST**
MBOCD 1 / Dec '95 / MBO

☐ **BEAUTY AND THE BEAST**
Menken, Alan *c*
Ashman, Howard *l*
WD 713602 / Mar '96 / Disney Music & Stories

☐ **BEAUTY AND THE BEAST (Singalong)**
WD 713824 / Nov '96 / Disney Music & Stories

☐ **BEAUTY AND THE BEAST (The Musical)**
Menken, Alan *c*
Ashman, Howard *l*
Prologue / Belle / No matter what / No matter what/ Wolf chase / Me / Home / Gaston / Gaston / How long must this go on / Be our guest / If I can't love her / Entr'acte/Wolf chase / Something there / Human again / Maison des lunes / Beauty and the beast / If I can't love her / Mob song / Battle / Transformation / Beauty and the beast
WD 6086112 / Oct '97 / Disney Music & Stories

☐ **BEAVIS & BUTTHEAD DO AMERICA (Score)**
Frizzell, John *c*
74321475362 / May '97 / Milan

☐ **BECAUSE OF YOU (Hamar, Jeff)**
Hold me thrill me kiss me/You send me / Young at heart / It's not for me to say / Quizas (perhaps) / Little white cloud that cried / Secret love / Fever / Smile/ Cry / Nature boy / Cabin in the sky/Stranger in paradise/Angel / Because of you / Unchained melody
VSD 5831 / 16 Feb '98 / Varese Sarabande

☐ **BED AND SOFA (Cast Recording)**
VSD 5729 / Sep '96 / Varese Sarabande

☐ **BED OF ROSES**
Convertino, Michael *c*
Kane, A. *con*
74321348632 / Feb '96 / Milan

☐ **BEETLEJUICE (Elfman, Danny)**
Elfman, Danny *c*
Banana boat song (Day O): *Belafonte, Harry* / Jump in the line: *Belafonte, Harry* / Main title / Travel music / Book / Enter... the family/Sand worm planet / Fly / Lydia discovers / In the model / Juno's theme / Beetle-snake / Sold / Flyer / Incantation / Lydia strikes a bargain / Showtime / Laughs / Wedding / Aftermath / End credits
GFLD 19296 / Oct '95 / Geffen

☐ **BEIDERBECKE CONNECTION, THE (Ricotti, Frank All Stars)**
Connection / Viva le van / Morgans mystery / Tulips for Chris / Barney's walk / Boys in blue / Hobson's chase / Tiger jive / Scouting ahead / Jennie's tune / Live at the Limping Whippet / Russian over / Dormouse delights / Crying all day
DMCD 20 / Dec '88 / Dormouse

☐ **BEING HUMAN**
Gibbs, Michael *c*
Snell, David *con*
Story of a story / Mine mine / Blow in my ear / Free man / Am I really a priest / You're bewitching me / Sun on my back / That's it / Hanging's fine / It's eggs for supper / Give the chickens a break / Best moment of your life / Have a great time
VSD 5479 / May '94 / Varese Sarabande

☐ **BELLE EPOQUE**
Duhamel, Antoine *c*
74321279312 / Jun '97 / Milan

☐ **BELLY OF AN ARCHITECT (London Sinfonietta)**
Mertens, Wim & Glen Branca *c*
Augustus / Birds for the mind / Aural trick / Struggle for pleasure / Tourtour / Four mains / Close cover / Time passing / Tourtour / And with them / Andria Doria / Galba / Caracalla / Hadrian
NORMAL 63CD / Jun '96 / Normal

☐ **BEN FRANKLIN IN PARIS (1964 Broadway Cast)**
Sandrich, Mark *c*
Michaels, Sidney *l*
ZDM 5651342 / Apr '94 / EMI Classics

☐ **BEN HUR (New Score For 1925 Silent Movie) (Royal Liverpool Philharmonic Orchestra)**
Davis, Carl *c*
Davis, Carl *con*
Opening titles / Nativity / Esther and the young prince / Roman march and disaster / Galley slave / Pirate battle / Iras the Egyptian / Chariot race / Ben Hur's return / Via Dolorosa / Earthquake and new dawn
FILMCD 043 / Nov '89 / Silva Screen

☐ **BEN HUR**
Rozsa, Miklos *c*
Rozsa, Miklos *con*
Overture / Of Bethlehem / Adoration of magic / Prelude / Marcia Romana / Salute for gratus / Gratus entry to Jerusalem / Desert / Exhaustion / Prince of peace / Roman gallery / Battle preperations / Pirate fleet / Attack / Ramming speed / Rescue / Victory parade / Arrius party / Nostalgia / Farewell to Rome / Return / Promise / Sorrow and intermission / Fanfare for circus parade / Circus parade / Valley of the lepers / Search / Procession to Calvary / Bearing of the cross / Recognition / Miracle / Finale
CDODEON 18 / Jul '96 / Premier/EMI

☐ **BERLIN '39**
Trovajoli, Armando *c*
SPALAX 14987 / Oct '96 / Spalax

☐ **BERLIN IS MINE (Lincoln Center Theater Cast)**
AEICD 030 / May '98 / AEI

☐ **BEST FOOT FORWARD (Revival Cast)**
Martin, Hugh & Ralph Blane *c*
Wish I may / Three men on a date / Hollywood story / Three B's / Ev'ry time / Alive and kicking/The guy who bought me / Shady lady bird / Buckle down Winsocki / You're lucky / What do you think I am / Raving beauty / Just a little joint with a juke box / You are for loving / Finale: Buckle down Winsocki
DRGCD 15003 / Sep '93 / DRG

☐ **BEST LITTLE WHOREHOUSE GOES PUBLIC, THE (Broadway Cast)**
Hall, Carol *c*
VSD 5542 / Jan '95 / Varese Sarabande

☐ **BEST MR. MEN ALBUM IN THE WORLD...EVER, THE**
Mr. Men theme / It's a happy place / Mr. Jelly is a scaredy cat / Everything is possible / Like a rolling pin / Daydreaming / Poor old Mr. Grumble / Cleverest person ever / Dizzy dizzy / Bump crash smash tickle / So very tall / Mr. Gnorw / As big as a pin / Mr. Uppity's party / Hello hello / Very very slow / Talking always talking / Mr. Quiet's special day / Banging crashing snoring sneezing / Lucky Mr. Sneeze / He's so funny / Mr. Perfect's perfect day / Topsy turvy land / Always busy / Tickly tickly tickly scream / I really have to get away / Bouncing / Inspection time / Peeking / Mr. Brave's dance / I'm very very mean / Mr. Strong saves the day / Wake up wake up / Happy happy Mr. Cheerful / Grass is blue / Mischief is his game / Eat all night eat all day / Nonsense song / He just can't remember / Clean Mr. Messy / Grumpy by name grumpy by nature / Son don't worry / When is up down / He's so clumsy / Mr. Men theme (reprise)
VTCD 166
VTCDX 166 / 10 Nov '97 / Virgin

☐ **BETTY BLUE (Yared, Gabriel)**
Yared, Gabriel *c*
Betty et Zorg / Des orages pour la nuit / Cargo voyage / La poubelle cuisine / Humecter la monture / Le petit Nicolas / Gyneco zebre / Comme les deux doigts de la main / Zorg et Betty / Chili con carne / C'est le vent Betty / Un coucher de soleil accroche dans les arbres / Lisa rock / Le coeur en skai mauve / Bungalow zen / 37-2 le matin / Maudits maneges
CDV 2396 / Sep '86 / Virgin

☐ **BEVERLY HILLBILLIES, THE**
663132 / Jan '93 / Silva Screen

☐ **BEVERLY HILLS 90210**
Bend time back around: *Abdul, Paula* / Got 2 have U: *Color Me Badd* / Right kind of love: *Jordan, Jeremy* / Love is: *Williams, Vanessa & Brian McKnight* / Just wanna be your friend: *Puck & Natty* / Let me be your baby: *Williams, Geoffrey* / Saving forever for you: *Shanice* / All the way to heaven: *Watley, Jody* / Why: *Dennis, Cathy & D-Mob* / Time to be lovers: *McDonald, Michael & Chaka Khan* / Action speaks louder than words: Kemp, Tara / Beverly Hills 90210: *Davis, John*
74321147982 / 11 May '98 / Giant

☐ **BEVERLY HILLS 90210 - THE COLLEGE YEARS**
Make it right: *Stansfield, Lisa* / Not one more time: *Piersa, Stacey* / Every day of the week: *Jade* / Not enough hours in the...: *After 7* / SOS: *Dennis, Cathy* / No intermission: *5th Power* / Cantaloop (Flip fantasia): *US 3* / Moving on up: *M People* / Saturday: *Omar* / Touch my light: *Big Mountain* / I'll love you anyway: *Neville, Aaron* / What your love means to me: *Hi-Five* / Forever yours: *Moten, Wendy*
74321203032 / Nov '94 / Giant

☐ **BEVERLY HILLS COP**
New attitude: *Labelle, Patti* / Don't get stopped in Beverly Hills: *Shalamar* / Do you really want my love: *Giscombe, Junior* / Emergency: *Robbins, Rockie* / Neutron dance: *Pointer Sisters* / Heat is on: *Frey, Glenn* / Gratitude: *Elfman, Danny* / Stir it up: *Labelle, Patti* / Rock 'n' roll me again: *System* / Axel F: *Faltermeyer, Harold*
MCLD 19087 / Sep '92 / MCA

☐ **BEYOND RANGOON**
Waters of Irrawaddy / Memories of the dead / I dreamt I woke up / Freedom from fear / Brother morphine / Our ways will part / Village under siege / Beyond Rangoon
286652 / Jul '95 / Milan

☐ **BEYOND THE CLOUDS/PURSUING THE CLOUDS (Fenton, George)**
Fenton, George *c*
CDWM 109 / Sep '94 / Westmoor

☐ **BEYOND THE LAW/DAY OF ANGER**
Ortolani, Riz *c*
OST 110 / Jan '93 / Milano Dischi

☐ **BEYOND THE VALLEY OF THE DOLLS/ GROUPIE GIRL**
SGLDCD 0010 / Jun '97 / Screen Gold

☐ **BIBLE, THE (La Bibbia)**
Mayuzumi, Toshiro *c*
Ferrara, Franco *con*
OST 115 / '94 / Milano Dischi

☐ **BIG BATTALIONS, THE**
Gunning, Christopher *c*
Big Battalions / Yared in exile / Yousef's faith awakens / Gil and Susan / Intafada / Yousef's resignation / Edward denied bishopric / Libera me / Goodbye Susan / Mecca / Alan dies / Edward's remorse / Welcome to Jordan / Gil with his sick father / Edward in Ethiopia / Military preparations in Jerusalem / Ethiopian trek / Gil shoots Yousef / Yousef buried / Yared counsels Edward / Yared leads Martha to safety / Family soul searching / Yousef's father in mourning / Gil visits Susan and confesses / New beginnings / Return to Ethiopia / Closing sequence
AHLCD 6 / Nov '92 / Hit

☐ **BIG BLUE I, THE**
Serra, Eric *c*
Big Blue overture / Rescue in a wreck / Huacracocha / Remembering a heart beat / Homo delphinus / Virgin Island / For Enzo / My lady blue / Deep blue dream / In raya / Between the sky scrapers / Let them try / Synchronised instant / Monastery of Amorgos / Leaving the world behind
CDV 2541 / Nov '88 / Virgin

☐ **BIG BLUE I, THE (Complete)**
Serra, Eric *c*
30193 / Jan '93 / Silva Screen

☐ **BIG BLUE II, THE**
Serra, Eric *c*
30667 / Jan '93 / Silva Screen

☐ **BIG BLUE II, THE/THE MISSION/ BETTY BLUE**
TPAK 33 / Jan '95 / Virgin

☐ **BIG CITY RHYTHM (The Songs Of Barry Kleinbort) (Original Cast)**
Kleinbort, Barry *c*
Big city rhythm / I get around / Milwaukee / Love me love me / Sondheim song / Love me love me / Leading lady Valentine / When ya gonna learn / To be wanted/Everybody needs someone / What would you say/I'm waiting / Lost movie themes / Skyline / I belong / Voices / When / Big city rhythm
HCD 1401 / 23 Mar '98 / Harbinger

☐ **BIG COUNTRY, THE (Philharmonia Orchestra)**
Moross, Jerome *c*
Bremner, Tony *con*
Main title / Julie's house / Welcoming / Courtin' time / Old thunder / Raid/Capture / Major Terrill's party: Dance/Waltz/Polka / McKay's ride/McKay is missing/Old house / Waiting / Big muddy / McKay alone/Night at Ladder Ranch/The fight / Cattle at the river / War party gathers/McKay in Blanco Canyon/ Major alone / Duel/Death of Buck Hannassey / End title
FILMCD 030 / Nov '95 / Silva Screen

☐ **BIG EASY, THE**
Iko iko: *Dixie Cups* / Tipitina: *Professor Longhair* / Ma 'tit fille: *Buckwheat Zydeco* / Colinda: *Newman, Jimmy C.* / Tell it like it is: *Neville, Aaron & The Neville Brothers* / Zydeco gris gris: *Beausoleil* / Oh yeah: *Simien, T. & The Mallet Playboys* / Hey hey: *Wild Tchoupitoulas* / Closer to you: *Quaid, Dennis* / Savour pass...: *Swan Silvertones*
5511592 / Sep '95 / Spectrum

☐ **BIG JAKE/THE SHOOTIST/CAHILL US MARSHALL (Music From John Wayne Westerns Vol. 2)**
Bernstein, Elmer *c*
Shootist / Ride / In the fire / Necktie party / Nocturne / Riders / Reunion / All Jake / Buzzards / Going home
VCD 47264 / Jan '89 / Varese Sarabande

☐ **BIG LEBOWSKI, THE**
Her eyes are a blue million miles: *Captain Beefheart* / Just dropped in: *Rogers, Kenny & The First Edition* / Hotel California: *Gipsy Kings* / Traffic boom: *Piccioni, Piero* / Lujon: *Mancini, Henry* / I got it bad and that ain't good: *Simone, Nina* / Ataypura: *Sumac, Yma* / Dead flowers: *Van Zandt, Townes* / Walking song: *Monk, Meredith* / Man in me: *Dylan, Bob* / My mood swings: *Costello, Elvis* / Gluck das mir verblieb: *Korngold, Erich* / Technopop: *Burwell, Carter* / Stamping ground: *Moondog & Orchestra*
5369032 / 9 Mar '98 / Mercury

☐ **BIG NIGHT**
Stornelli amorisi: *Villa, Claudio* / Il pescivendolo: *Salvatore, Matteo* / La trada del bosco: *Villa, Claudio* / Art of art / Oh Marie: *Prima, Louis* / Mambo Italiano: *Clooney, Rosemary* / Love of my life: *Prima, Louis & Keely Smith* / Dinner / Tic ti tic ta: *Villa, Claudio* / Five months two weeks two days: *Prima, Louis & The Witnesses* / Don't take your love from me: *Smith, Keely* / Buona sera: *Prima, Louis* / Angular dissent / Mo ve'la bella mia da la muntagna: *Salvatore, Matteo* / Pascal's waltz / Big night theme
0022782CIN / Jul '97 / Edel

☐ **BIG SWAP, THE**
OCD 11 / 22 Jun '98 / Ocean Deep

☐ **BIG TROUBLE IN LITTLE CHINA**
Carpenter, John *c*
Big trouble in little China: *Coup De Villes* / Pork chop express / Alley / Here come the storms / Lo Pan's domain / Escape from Wing Kong / Into the spirit path / Great arcade / Final escape
DSCD 2 / Aug '91 / Demon

☐ **BILL AND TED'S BOGUS JOURNEY**
Shout it out: *Slaughter* / Battle stations: *Winger* / God gave rock 'n' roll to you II: *Kiss* / Drinking again: *Neverland* / Dream of a new day: *Kotzen, Richie* / Reaper: *Vai, Steve* / Perfect crime: *Faith No More* / Go to hell: *Megadeth* / Tommy the cat: *Primus* / Junior's gone wild: *Kings X* / Showdown: *Love on Ice* / Reaper rap: *Vai, Steve*
IND 91725 / 8 Sep '97 / Interscope

☐ **BILLY BARNES IN LA (Cast Recording)**
Barnes, Billy *c*
AEICD 013 / May '98 / AEI

☐ **BILLY BARNES SINGS MOVIE STAR (Cast Recording)**
Barnes, Billy *c*
AEICD 029 / May '98 / AEI

☐ **BILLY CONNOLLY'S MUSICAL TOUR OF SCOTLAND**
5298162 / Dec '95 / PolyGram TV

☐ **BING BOYS ARE HERE (Cast Recording)**
Ayer, Nat D. *c*
Grey, Clifford *l*
Orchestral selection: *Orchestra* / In other words: *Robey, George* / If you were the only girl in the world: *Robey, George & Violet Loraine* / Whistler: *Intermezzo* / Another little drink: *Robey, George & Violet Loraine* / Shoeblack's dance: *Orchestra* / Right side of Bond Street: *Morrison, Jack* / Kipling walk: *Orchestra* / Lady of a thousand charms: *Lester, Alfred & Violet Loraine* / Kiss trot dance: *Orchestra* / Dear old Shepherd's Bush: *Lester, Alfred* / I start my day over again: *Morrison, Jack* / Languid melody: *Orchestra* / I stopped I looked and I listened: *Robey, George* / Ragging the dog: *Orchestra* / Vocal gems: *Columbia Revue Company* / Orchestral finale: *Orchestra*
PASTCD 9716 / '90 / Flapper

☐ **BIOGRAPH GIRL, THE (1980 London Cast)**
Heneker, David *c*
Heneker, David & Warner Brown *l*
Reed, Michael *con*
CDTER 1003 / May '92 / TER

☐ **BIRD WITH THE CRYSTAL PLUMAGE, THE/FOUR FLIES ON GREY VELVET/ CAT O'NINE TAILS**
Morricone, Ennio *c*
DRGCD 32911 / Sep '95 / DRG

☐ **BIRDCAGE, THE**
22572 MCM / May '96 / Edel

☐ **BIRDMAN OF ALCATRAZ, THE**
Bernstein, Elmer *c*
TSU 0126 / Jan '95 / Tsunami

☐ **BIRDS OF PARADISE (Off-Broadway Cast)**
Evans, David *c*
Holzman, Winnie *l*
CDTER 1196 / Apr '93 / TER

☐ **BIRDY (Gabriel, Peter)**
Gabriel, Peter *c*
At night / Floating dogs / Quiet and alone / Close up / Slow water / Dressing the wound / Birdy's flight / Slow marimbas / Heat / Sketchpad with trumpet and voice / Under lock and key / Powerhouse at the foot of the mountain / dfasf: *bish*
CASCD 1167 / Mar '85 / Charisma

☐ **BITTER SWEET (1988 London Cast)**
Coward, Sir Noel *c*
Reed, Michael *con*
Opening / That wonderful melody / Call of life / If you could only come with me / I'll see you again / Polka / What is love / Last dance / Finale / Opening chorus (Life in the morning) / Ladies of the town / If love were all / Dear little cafe / Bittersweet waltz / Officer's chorus (we wish to order wine) / Tokay / Bonne nuit merci / Kiss me / Ta-ra-ra-boom-de-ay / Alas the time is past / We all wear a green carnation / Zigeuner
CDTER2 1160 / Nov '97 / TER

☐ **BITTER SWEET (Highlights) (1988 London Cast)**
Coward, Sir Noel *c*
Reed, Michael *con*
CDTEO 1001 / Nov '89 / TER

☐ **BIX (Beiderbecke, Bix)**
Idolizing / Dardanella / Singing the blues (till my dad) / My pretty girl / Maple leaf rag / Riverboat shuffle 2 / Since my best gal turned me down / Jazz me blues / Somebody stole my gal / Stardust / I'll be a friend with pleasure / In a mist / Tin roof blues / Riverboat shuffle / I'm coming Virginia / Davenport blues / Singing the blues (till my dad) / Bix
PD 74766 / Aug '91 / RCA

☐ **BLACK AND BLUE (Broadway Cast)**
DRG 19001 / Jan '95 / DRG

☐ **BLACK AND WHITE MINSTREL SHOW, THE (Stars From...) (Black & White Minstrels)**
URCD 105 / Apr '91 / Upbeat

☐ **BLACK CAULDRON, THE**
Bernstein, Elmer *c*
VCD 47241 / Jan '89 / Varese Sarabande

☐ **BLACK RAIN (Zimmer, Hans)**
Zimmer, Hans *c*
Livin' on the edge of the night: *Iggy Pop* / Way you do the things you do: *UB40* / Back to life: *Soul II Soul* / Laser man: *Sakamoto, Ryuichi* / Singing in the shower: *Les Rita Mitsouko & The Sparks* / I'll be holding on: *Allman, Gregg* / Sato / Charlie loses his head / Sugai / Nick and Masa
CDV 2607 / Feb '90 / Virgin

☐ **BLACKOUT (Schoolly D & Joe Delia)**
Player: *Schoolly D* / Miami: *U2* / Live and die / Beatrice theme: *Delia, Joe* / Murder 1: *Schoolly D* / Cold blooded: *Redd, Heather* / 2 to tango: *Mol, Gretchen* / Blacked out / Babyheart: *Delia, Joe* / Muy fregado: *Delia, Joe* / Inside straight: *Delia, Joe* / Sleepless in south beach: *Delia, Joe* / Breathless: *Wolfe, Jim* / What was gonna be your name: *Simon, Harper*
5378542 / 16 Feb '98 / Polydor

☐ **BLADE**
TVT 82102 / 3 Aug '98 / TVT

☐ **BLADERUNNER (Vangelis)**
Vangelis *c*
Main title / Blush response / Wait for me / Rachel's song / Love theme / One more kiss Dear / Bladerunner blues / Memories of green / Tales of the future / Damask rose / End titles / Tears in rain
4509965742 / May '94 / Warner Bros.

☐ **BLESS THE BRIDE (1947 London Cast)**
Ellis, Vivian *c*
AEICD 015 / May '98 / AEI

☐ **BLISS**
VSD 5836 / May '97 / Varese Sarabande

☐ **BLONDEL (1983 London Cast)**
Oliver, Stephen *c*
Rice, Tim *l*
Monk's introduction / Blondel and Fiona / Ministry of Reudal affairs / Last of my troubles / Lionheart / No rhyme for Richard / Trio / Assassins song / Running back for more / Blondel in Europe / Saladin days / I can't wait to be King / Inn at Salzburg / Blondel's search / Duke of Austria's quarters / Cell / Westminster Abbey / I'm a monarchist
MCD 11486 / Aug '96 / MCA

☐ **BLOOD BROTHERS (1983 London Cast)**
Russell, Willy *c*
Narration / Marilyn Monroe / My child / Devil's got your number / Easy terms / Just a game / Sunday afternoon / My friend / Bright new day / One summer narration / Saying a word / Miss Jones (sign of the times) / Prison song / Light romance / There's a madman / Tell me it's not true
CLACD 270 / May '93 / Castle

☐ **BLOOD BROTHERS (1988 London Cast)**
Russell, Willy *c*
09026616892 / Jul '91 / RCA Victor

☐ **BLOOD BROTHERS (International Cast)**
Russell, Willy *c*
CASTCD 50 / Nov '95 / First Night

☐ **BLOOD BROTHERS (1995 London Cast)**
Russell, Willy *c*
CASTCD 49 / Jul '95 / First Night

☐ **BLOOD IN BLOOD OUT**
Conti, Bill *c*
VSD 5396 / Mar '93 / Varese Sarabande

☐ **BLOOD OF HEROES, THE**
Boekelheide, Todd *c*
Adler, M. *con*
MAF 7060D / May '95 / Intrada

☐ **BLOW IN (Including Music From The Film Guiltrip) (Power, Brendan)**
Power, Brendan *c*
HBCD 0008 / Apr '96 / Hummingbird

☐ **BLOW UP (Hancock, Herbie)**
Hancock, Herbie *c*
Blow up / Verushka / Naked camera / Bring down the birds / Jane's theme / Thief / Kiss / Curiosity / Thomas studies photos / Bed / Stroll on: *Yardbirds* / Am I glad to see you: *Tomorrow* / Blow up: *Tomorrow* / Blow up
CDODEON 15 / Jun '96 / Soundtracks

☐ **BLUE COLLAR (Nitzsche, Jack)**
Nitzsche, Jack *c*
Hard workin' man: *Captain Beefheart* / Zeke Jerry and Smokie / Satin sheets: *Pruett, Jeanne* / Party / Wang dang doodle / Coke machine / Quittin' time / Easy listening / FBI / Goodbye so long: *Turner, Ike & Tina* / Saturday night: *Lynyrd Skynyrd*
EDCD 435 / Aug '95 / Edsel

☐ **BLUE HAWAII (Presley, Elvis)**
Blue Hawaii / Almost always true / Aloha oe / No more / Can't help falling in love / Rock-a-hula baby / Moonlight swim / Ku-u-i-pu / Ito eats / Slicin' sand / Hawaiian sunset / Beach boy blues / Island of love / Hawaiian wedding song / Steppin' out of line / Can't help falling in love / Slicin' sand / No more / Rock-a-hula baby / Beach boy blues / Blue Hawaii
07863674592 / Apr '97 / RCA
07863669592 / 2 Feb '98 / RCA

☐ **BLUE IN THE FACE**
9362460132 / Jan '96 / WEA

☐ **BLUE MAX, THE**
Goldsmith, Jerry *c*
Dream machine / Sing song blues / Bad bad amigo / Hangman / Need your love / Flying to Moscow / Paid assassin / Camera camera / Photographing gold / Murder at the movies / I know you're there / Wait for the new one
VCD 47238 / Jan '89 / Varese Sarabande

☐ **BLUE SKIES/RHYTHM ON THE RIVER**
Blue skies overture / Pretty girl is like a melody / I've got my captain working for me now / You'd be surprised / All by myself / Serenade to an old fashioned girl / Puttin' on the Ritz / I'll be seeing you in CUBA / Couple of song and dance men / You keep coming back like a song / Blue skies / Everybody step / Getting nowhere / Heat wave / Any bonds today/This is the army Mrs.Jones/White Christmas / You keep coming back like a song / What would Shakespear have said / That's for me / Only forever / When the moon comes up over Madison Square Gardens / Rhythm on the river / Ain't it a shame about Mame / I don't want to cry anymore / Only forever
CD 60025 / Nov '97 / Great Movie Themes

☐ **BLUES BROTHERS 2000**
UND 53116 / 16 Feb '98 / Universal

☐ **BLUES BROTHERS, THE (Blues Brothers)**
Shake a tailfeather: *Charles, Ray* / Think: *Franklin, Aretha* / Minnie the moocher: *Calloway, Cab* / Rawhide / Jailhouse rock / She caught the Katy / Gimme some lovin' / Old landmark / Sweet home Chicago / Peter Gunn / Everybody needs somebody to love
7567827872 / Nov '95 / Atlantic

☐ **BLUES BROTHERS, THE (A Tribute To The Blues Brothers) (1991 Cast)**
CASTCD 25 / '94 / First Night

☐ **BLUES BROTHERS, THE (Christopher/ Emery Company)**
She caught the Katy / Peter Gunn theme / Gimme some lovin' / Shake your tail feather / Everybody needs somebody to love / Think / Minnie the moocher / Sweet home Chicago / Jailhouse rock / Shotgun blues / Soul man / Hey bartender
QED 202 / Nov '96 / Tring

☐ **BLUES IN THE NIGHT (1987 London Cast)**
Epps, Sheldon *c*
OCRCD 6029 / Oct '95 / First Night

☐ **BOCCACCIO '70**
Rota, Nino/Armando Trovailo/Piero Umiliani *c*
OST 116 / Jan '93 / Milano Dischi

☐ **BODY BAGS**
Carpenter, John & Jim Lang *c*
VSD 5448 / Feb '94 / Varese Sarabande

☐ **BODY HEAT**
Barry, John *c*
VSD 5951 / 10 Aug '98 / Varese Sarabande

☐ **BODY LOVE (Schulze, Klaus)**
Schulze, Klaus *c*
Stardancer / Blanche / PTO
CDTB 123 / Jan '92 / Thunderbolt

☐ **BODY OF EVIDENCE**
Revell, Graeme *c*
Main title / Passion theme / Funeral / Houseboat / Hot wax and champagne / Fight / Handcuffs / Parking garage / Waiting for the jury / Confrontation / Karma / End credits
127202 / Feb '94 / Milan

☐ **BODY PARTS**
Dikker, Loek *c*
VSD 5337 / Aug '91 / Varese Sarabande

☐ **BODY, THE (Waters, Roger & Ron Geesin)**
Our song / Sea shell and stone / Red stuff writhe / Gentle breeze through life / Lick your partners / Bridge passage for three plastic teeth / Chain of life / Womb bit / Embryo thought / March past of the embryos / More than seven dwarfs in Penis-land / Dance of the red corpuscles / Body transport / Hand dance - full evening dress / Breathe / Old folks ascension / Bedtime dream climb / Piddle in perspex / Embryonic womb walk / Mrs. Throat goes walking / Sea shell and soft stone / Give birth to a smile
CZ 178 / Feb '96 / Premier/EMI

☐ **BODYGUARD, THE**
I will always love you: *Houston, Whitney* / I have nothing: *Houston, Whitney* / I'm every woman: *Houston, Whitney* / Run to you: *Houston, Whitney* / Queen of the night: *Houston, Whitney* / Jesus loves me: *Houston, Whitney* / Even if my heart would break: *Kenny G. & Aaron Neville* / Someday (I'm coming back): *Stansfield, Lisa* / It's gonna be a lovely day: *S.O.U.L. System & Michelle Visage* / Peace love and understanding: *Stigers, Curtis* / Waiting for you: *Kenny G.* / Trust in me: *Cocker, Joe*
07822186992 / Jan '93 / Arista

☐ **BODYWORK**
Stilgoe, Richard *c*
CASTCD 15 / Oct '88 / First Night

☐ **BOLERO**
Bernstein, Peter *c*
PCD 124 / Mar '93 / Prometheus

☐ **BONANZA (Bonanza Cast)**
Bonanza / Sourwood mountain / Sky ball paint / Early one morning / Ponderosa / Careless love / Skip to my Lou / In the pines / Happy birthday / My sons my sons / Hangin' blues / Shenandoah / Miss Cindy / Hark the herald angels sing / Deck the halls with boughs of holly / New born King / First Christmas trees / Oh fir tree dear / Christmas is a comin' / O come all ye faithful (Adeste Fidelis) / Jingle bells / Santa got lost in Texas / Stuck in the chimney / Why we light candles on the Christmas tree / Merry Christmas neighbour / Merry Christmas and goodnight / Intro / Alamo: *Greene, Lorne* / Pony Express: *Greene, Lorne* / Ol' tin cup: *Greene, Lorne* / Endless prairie: *Greene, Lorne* / Ghost riders in the sky: *Greene, Lorne* / Ringo: *Greene, Lorne* / Blue guitar: *Greene, Lorne* / Sand: *Greene, Lorne* / Saga of the Ponderosa: *Greene, Lorne* / Five card stud: *Greene, Lorne* / Cool water: *Greene, Lorne* / Devil's grin: *Greene, Lorne* / Pretty horses: *Greene, Lorne* / Devil cat: *Greene, Lorne* / Ol' Chisholm trail: *Greene, Lorne* / Wagon wheels: *Greene, Lorne* / Frightened town: *Greene, Lorne* / Shadow of the cactus: *Greene, Lorne* / Tumbling tumbleweeds: *Greene, Lorne* / Gold: *Greene, Lorne* / Whoopee ti yi yo: *Greene, Lorne* / Search: *Greene, Lorne* / Dig dig dig dig (there's no more water...): *Greene, Lorne* / Ol' cyclone: *Greene, Lorne* / Twilight on the trail: *Greene, Lorne* / Geronimo: *Greene, Lorne* / Mule train: *Greene, Lorne* / I'm a gun: *Greene, Lorne* / Gunslinger's prayer: *Greene, Lorne* / Nellie Cole: *Greene, Lorne* / Home on the range: *Greene, Lorne* / Virginia town: *Greene, Lorne* / Place where I worship: *Greene, Lorne* / Pop goes the hammer: *Greene, Lorne* / End of the track: *Greene, Lorne* / Nine pound hammer: *Greene, Lorne* / Bring on the dancin' girls: *Greene, Lorne* / Oh what a town: *Greene, Lorne* / Fourteen men: *Greene, Lorne* / Destiny: *Greene, Lorne* / Sixteen tons: *Greene, Lorne* / Trouble row: *Greene, Lorne* / Chickasaw mountain: *Greene, Lorne* / Darling my darling: *Greene, Lorne* / Man: *Greene, Lorne* / Ringo (French): *Greene, Lorne* / Du sable: *Greene, Lorne* / Bold soldier: *Roberts, Pernell* / Mary Ann: *Roberts, Pernell* / They call the wind Maria: *Roberts, Pernell* / Sylvie: *Roberts, Pernell* / Lily of the west: *Roberts, Pernell* / Water is wide: *Roberts, Pernell* / Rake and the rambling boy: *Roberts, Pernell* / Quiet girl: *Roberts, Pernell* / Shady grove: *Roberts, Pernell* / Alberta: *Roberts, Pernell* / Empty pocket blues: *Roberts, Pernell* / Come all ye fair and tender ladies: *Roberts, Pernell* / Springfield mountain: *Blocker, Dan & John Mitchum* / Roll out heave that cotton: *Blocker, Dan & John Mitchum* / Battle hymn of the Republic: *Blocker, Dan & John Mitchum* / Erie canal: *Blocker, Dan & John Mitchum* / Paiute sunrise chant: *Blocker, Dan & John Mitchum* / Charles steal away: *Blocker, Dan & John Mitchum* / He never said a mumblin': *Blocker, Dan & John Mitchum*
BCD 15684 / May '93 / Bear Family

☐ **BOOGIE NIGHTS**
Intro (feel the heat): *Reilly, John C. & Mark Wahlberg* / Best of my love: *Emotions* / Jungle fever: *Chakachas* / Brand new key: *Burdon, Eric & War* / Spill the wine: *Burdon, Eric & War* / Got to give it up (part 1): *Gaye, Marvin* / Machine gun: *Commodores* / Magnet and steel: *Egan, Walter* / Ain't no stoppin us now: *McFadden & Whitehead* / Sister Christian: *Night Ranger* / Livin' thing: *ELO* / God only knows: *Beach Boys* / Big top: *Penn, Michael*
8556312 / 12 Jan '98 / Premier/EMI

☐ **BOOGIE NIGHTS VOL.2**
Mama told me not to come: *Three Dog Night* / Fooled around and fell in love: *Bishop, Elvin* / You sexy thing: *Hot Chocolate* / Boogie shoes: *KC & The Sunshine Band* / Do your thing: *Wright, Charles & The Watts 103rd Street Rhythm Band* / Driver's seat: *Sniff N' The Tears* / Feel too good: *Move* / Jessie's girl: *Springfield, Rick* / JP Walker: *Sound Experience* / I want to be free: *Ohio Players* / Joy: *Apollo 100*
4930762 / 9 Mar '98 / Premier/EMI

☐ **BOOMERANG**
Give U my heart: *Babyface & Tony Braxton* / It's gonna be alright: *Hall, Aaron & Charlie Wilson* / Tonight is right: *Washington, Keith* / I'd die without you: *P.M. Dawn* / Seven day weekend: *Jones, Grace* / End of the road: *Boyz II Men* / Reversal of a dog: *LaFace Cartel* / Love shoulda brought you home: *Braxton, Toni* / There you go: *Gill, Johnny* / Don't wanna love you: *Shanice* / Feels like heaven: *Vaughan, Kenny & The Art Of Love* / Hot sex: *Tribe Called Quest*
73008260062 / Feb '97 / Arista

☐ **BOOTY CALL**
Can we: *SWV* / Don't wanna be a playa: *Joe* / Baby baby baby...: *R. Kelly* / Fire and desire: *Gill, Johnny & Coko* / Don't stop don't quit: *1 Accord* / Feel good: *Silk* / Hold that thought: *Levert, Gerald* / Let me see you squirrel: *Squirrel* / If you stay: *Backstreet Boys* / Call me: *Too Short & Lil' Kim* / Don't blame it on me: *E-40 & B-Legit Aka 40 Fonzarelli & The Savage* / (I'll be you') huckleberry: *D-Shot* / Plan up you family: *KRS-1* / Chocolate: *LA Ganz* / Looking for love: *Whitey Don* / When I rise: *Crooked*
CHIP 182 / Mar '97 / Jive

☐ **BORDELLO OF BLOOD**
Boardman, Chris *c*
VSD 5728 / Sep '96 / Varese Sarabande

☐ **BORGIAS**
Delerue, Georges *c*
PCD 109 / Jan '93 / Prometheus

☐ BOSTON KICKOUT
Kickout: Whiteout / Love will tear us apart: Joy Division / Fools gold: Stone Roses / Symposium of sickness: Carcass / Last chance: China Drum / Gangsta: Livingstone / Neat neat neat: Damned / I wanna be adored: Stone Roses / Adieu Ted: Hartshorne, Robert / Loaded: Primal Scream / Last time: Paradise Lost / Resiliant little muscle: Solar Race / Bakery: Hartshorne, Robert / New rose: Damned / European son: Velvet Underground
ORECD 543 / Oct '96 / Silvertone

☐ BOUGHT AND SOLD (Dull Bang, Gushing Sound, Human Shriek) (Previte, Bobby)
Previte, Bobby c
378212 / Aug '96 / Koch Jazz

☐ BOY MEETS BOY (Los Angeles Cast)
AEICD 009 / May '98 / AEI

☐ BOY WHO GREW TOO FAST, THE (1986 Royal Opera House Cast)
Menotti, Gian Carlo c
CDTER 1125 / Jan '93 / TER

☐ BOYFRIEND, THE (1954 Broadway Cast)
Wilson, Sandy c
Overture / Perfect young ladies / Boyfriend / Won't you Charleston with me / Fancy forgetting / I could be happy with you / Sur la plage / Room in Bloomsbury / You-don't-want-to-play-with-me blues / Safety in numbers / Riviera / It's never too late to fall in love / Carnival tango / Poor little Pierrette / Finale
GD 60056 / Oct '89 / RCA Victor

☐ BOYFRIEND, THE (1984 London Cast)
Wilson, Sandy c
Overture / Perfect young ladies / Boyfriend / Won't you Charleston with me / Fancy forgetting / I could be happy with you / Sur la plage / Room in Bloomsbury / It's nicer in Nice / You-don't-want-to-play-with-me blues / Safety in numbers / Riviera / It's never too late too fall in love / Poor little Pierrette / Finale
CDTER 1095 / Nov '97 / TER

☐ BOYFRIEND, THE (CC Productions)
Wilson, Sandy c
Perfect young ladies / Boyfriend / Won't you charleston with me / I could be happy with you / Sur la plage / Room in Bloomsbury / It's nicer in Nice / You don't want to play with me blues / Safety in numbers / Boyfriend / Riviera / It's never too late to fall in love / Poor little pierrette
QED 214 / Nov '96 / Tring

☐ BOYFRIEND, THE (London Cast)
Wilson, Sandy c
Perfect young ladies / Boyfriend / Won't you charleston with me / Fancy forgetting / I could be happy with you / Room in Bloomsbury / It's nicer in Nice / You don't-want-to-play-with-me blues / Safety in numbers / Riviera / It's never too late to fall in love / Poor little Pierrette
SHOWCD 027 / Oct '96 / Showtime

☐ BOYFRIEND, THE/ME AND MY GIRL (Cast Recording)
Wilson, Sandy c
340802 / Oct '95 / Koch

☐ BOYS
She's not there: Cruel Sea / Alright: Cast / Gotta know right now: Smoking Popes / Honeysimple: Scarce / Wild wood: Weller, Paul / Coloured water: Orbit / Sad and beautiful world: Sparklehorse / Fading fast: Willis, Kelly / Tell her this: Del Amitri / If I didn't love you: Squeeze / Inside: Slider / Wait for the sun: Supergrass / Belly laugh: Compulsion / Begging you: Stone Roses / Evade chums: Copeland, Stewart
5404892 / Jun '96 / A&M

☐ BOYS FROM SYRACUSE, THE (1953 Studio Cast)
Rodgers, Richard c
Hart, Lorenz l
Engel, Lehman con
SK 53329 / Nov '94 / Sony Broadway

☐ BOYS FROM SYRACUSE, THE (Off-Broadway Cast)
Rodgers, Richard c
Hart, Lorenz l
ZDM 7646952 / Apr '93 / EMI Classics

☐ BOYS FROM SYRACUSE, THE (Original Cast)
Rodgers, Richard c
Hart, Lorenz l
Falling in love with love / Sing for your supper / This can't be love / What can you do with a man / You have cast your shadow on the sea / I had twins / Dear old Syracuse / Shortest day of the year / Let antiphouls in / Ladies of the evening / He and she / Come with me / Oh diogenes
DRGCD 94767 / Sep '97 / DRG

☐ BOYS ON THE SIDE
You got it: Raitt, Bonnie / I take you with me: Etheridge, Melissa / Keep on growing: Crow, Sheryl / Power of two: Indigo Girls / Somebody stand by me: Nicks, Stevie / Everyday is like Sunday: Pretenders / Dreams: Cranberries / Why: Lennox, Annie / Ol' 55: McLachlan, Sarah / Willow: Armatrading, Joan / Crossroads: Mosser, Jonell
07822187482 / Feb '97 / Arista

☐ BOYZ N THE HOOD
How to survive in South Central: Ice Cube / Just ask me to: Campbell, Tevin / Mama don't take no mess: Yo Yo / Growin' up in the hood: Compton's Most Wanted / Just a friendly game of baseball: Main Source / Me and you: Tony Toni Tone / Work it out: Love, Monie / Every single weekend: Kam / Too young: Hi-Five / Hangin' out: 2 Live Crew / It's your life: Too Short / Spirit: Force One Network / Setembro: Jones, Quincy / Black on black crime
7599266432 / Aug '91 / WEA

☐ BRAINDEAD
QDKCD 006 / Sep '94 / QDK Media

☐ BRANQUIGNOL (Music & Dialogue From Branquignol/Allez France/Le Petit Baigneur/Vous Gueles Les Muettes)
K 1511 / Mar '97 / Auvidis Travelling

☐ BRASSED OFF (Jones, Trevor & Grimethorpe Colliery Band)
Death or glory / Sad old day / Floral dance / Aforementioned essential items / Concerto de Aranjuez / Years of coal / March of the cobblers / There's more important things in life / Cross of honour / Jerusalem / Florentia march / Danny boy / We'll find a way / Clog dance / Colonel Bogey / Honest decent human beings / Land of hope and glory
09026687572 / Nov '96 / RCA Victor

☐ BRAVEHEART (London Symphony Orchestra)
Horner, James c
Horner, James con
Main title / Gift of a thistle / Wallace courts Murron / Secret wedding / Attack on Murron / Revenge / Murron's burial / Making plans/Gathering the clans / Sons of Scotland / Battle of Stirling / For the love of a Princess / Falkirk / Betrayal and desolation / Mornay's dream / Legend spreads / Princess pleads for Wallace's life / Freedom/Execution Bannockburn / End credits
4482952 / Sep '95 / London

☐ BREAKFAST AT TIFFANY'S/BALLET ETUDES
PB 00155 / Jun '98 / Power Bros.

☐ BREAKFAST CLUB, THE
Don't you forget about me: Simple Minds / Fire in the twilight: Wang Chung / We are not alone: De Vito, Karla / Heart too hot to hold: Johnson, Jesse / Waiting: Daly, Elizabeth / Didn't I tell you: Kennedy, Joyce / I'm the dude: Forsey, Keith / Dream montage: Forsey, Keith / Reggae: Forsey, Keith / Love theme: Forsey, Keith
CDMID 179 / Jan '94 / A&M

☐ BREAKING GLASS (O'Connor, Hazel)
Writing on the wall / Monsters in disguise / Come into the air / Big brother / Who needs it / Will you / Eighth day / Top of the wheel / Calls the tune / Blackman / Give me an inch / If only
5513562 / Sep '95 / Spectrum

☐ BREAKING THE RULES
VSD 5386 / Sep '92 / Varese Sarabande

☐ BRIDE OF FRANKENSTEIN, THE (Westminster Philharmonic Orchestra)
Waxman, Franz c
Alwyn, Kenneth con
Main title / Prologue - Menuetto and storm / Monster entrance / Processional march / Strange apparition/ Pretorius' entrance/You will need a coat / Bottle sequence / Female monster music/Pastorale/ Village/Chase / Crucifixion/Monster breaks out / Fire in the hut/Graveyard / Dance macabre / Creation / Tower explodes/Finale / Invisible ray suite
FILMCD 135 / Mar '94 / Silva Screen

☐ BRIDESHEAD REVISITED
Burgon, Geoffrey c
Brideshead revisited / Going to Brideshead / First visit / Venice nocturne / Sebastian's summer / Hunt / Sebastian against the world / Julia in love / Julia / Rain in Venice / General strike / Fading light / Julia's theme / Sebastian alone / Orphans of the storm / Finale
CDMFP 6172 / Sep '95 / Music For Pleasure

☐ BRIDGE, THE
Mitchell, Richard G. c
Opening titles / Quay house / Arriving in Suffolk / Storm / Reginald and Isobel return to London / Sitting / Walberswick fete / Fireworks / France / Kiss / Love theme / Reginald's proposition / Mrs. Todd's release / What did you see Emma / Garden / Leaving without saying goodbye / We've come to an arrangement / End titles
DSCD 5 / Feb '92 / Demon

☐ BRIGADOON (1988 London Cast)
Loewe, Frederick c
Lerner, Alan Jay l
OCRCD 6022 / Oct '95 / First Night

☐ BRIGADOON (Studio Cast & Ambrosian Chorus/London Sinfonietta)
Loewe, Frederick c
Lerner, Alan Jay l
McGlinn, John con
CDC 7544812 / Apr '93 / EMI Classics

☐ BRIGADOON (Cast Recording)
Loewe, Frederick c
Lerner, Alan Jay l
CDTER2 1218 / Aug '95 / TER

☐ BRIGADOON (Kelly, Gene & Film Cast)
Loewe, Frederick c
Lerner, Alan Jay l
Main title / Once in the Highlands / Brigadoon / Down on MacConnachy Square / Waitin' for my dearie / I'll go home with bonnie Jean / Come to me bend to me / Heather on the hill / Almost like being in love / Talk to Dominie / Til the end of our days / There but for you I go / Two hundred years later / Gathering of the clans / Wedding dance / Chase / Fiona's search / From this day on / Heather on the hill / Heather on the hill / Waitin' for my dearie / Even miracles / Finale/End credits / Dinna ye know / Tommy
CDODEON 16 / Aug '96 / Soundtracks

☐ BRIGADOON
SHOWCD 056 / 18 May '98 / Showtime

☐ BRIGHT ANGEL (Utah Symphony Orchestra)
MAF 7014D / Mar '92 / Intrada

☐ BRINGING IT ALL BACK HOME
HBCD 0010 / Feb '97 / Hummingbird

☐ BROADWAY SCANDALS OF 1928 (Cast Recording)
AEICD 037 / May '98 / AEI

☐ BROKEN ARROW
Zimmer, Hans c
74321348652 / Mar '96 / Milan

☐ BRONX TALE, A
Streets of the bronx: Cool Change / I wonder why: Dion & The Belmonts / Little girl of mine: Cleftones / Don't you know: Reese, Della / For your precious love: Butler, Jerry / Ain't that a kick in the head: Cool Change / Father and son: Cool Change / Beautiful morning: Rascals / Tell it like it is: Neville, Aaron / Bus talk: Watson, Bobby / I only have eyes for you: Niewood, Gerry Quartet / Ninety nine and a half (won't do): Pickett, Wilson / Nights in white satin: Moody Blues / Baby I need your loving: Four Tops / Regrets: Barbella, Butch / All along the watchtower: Hendrix, Jimi Experience / I'm so proud: Impressions / It's a man's man's man's world: Brown, James / Christo redemptor: Byrd, Donald
4748062 / Mar '94 / Epic

☐ BROTHER FROM ANOTHER PLANET, THE
DRCD 1007 / Feb '96 / Daring

☐ BROTHERS MCMULLEN, THE
Egan, Seamus c
I will remember you: McLachlan, Sarah / Week in January / Slip jigs / Intro no.1/Reel Beatrice / Fermoy lasses / When Juniper sleeps / Eamon Coyne's/ Longford collector / Once upon a time / Cape Breton set / Lark / Dark slender boy / Weep not for the memories
07822188032 / Dec '95 / Arista

☐ BROWNING VERSION, THE (St. Mary's School Choir/London Metropolitan Orchestra)
Isham, Mark c
Kugler, Ken con
In Founder's court / Taplow / Cromwells / Agamemnon / Art of learning is to conceal learning / Hitler of the lower fifth / In the village / Just good friends / God from afar looks graciously upon a gentle master / Defiant creature / Secrets of a marriage / Night crawlers / Toujours la politesse / Goodbye / Noblest calling / To forgive myself / Prize giving / Browning version
213012 / Oct '94 / Milan

☐ BUBBLING BROWN SUGAR (1977 London Cast)
Harlem '70 / Bubbling Brown Sugar / That's what Harlem is to me: Delmar, Elaine / Bill Robinson speciality: Augins, Charles / Harlem sweet Harlem / Nobody: Daniels, Billy / Goin' back in time: Augins, Charles / Some of these days: Lawrence, Stephanie / Moving Uptown: Augins, Charles / Strolling: Cameron, David & others / I'm gonna tell God all my troubles: Taylor, Mel / His eye is on the sparrow/ Swing low sweet chariot: Brown, Miquel & Company / Sweet Georgia Brown: Gelzer, Helen/Newton Winters/David Cameron / Honeysuckle Rose: Delmar, Elaine/Billy Daniels / Stormy Monday blues: Brown, Miquel / Sophisticated lady: Peters, Clarke / In honeysuckle time when Emaline said she'd be mine: Satton, Lon/Billy Daniels / Rosetta: Collins, Ray/David Cameron/Newton Winters / Solitude: Gelzer, Helen/Newton Winters/Ray Collins/David Cameron / C'mon up to Jive Time: Augins, Charles / Stompin' at the Savoy/Take the 'A' train / Harlem-time: Augins, Charles / Bubbling Brown Sugar II: Peters, Clarke/Amii Stewart / Ain't misbehavin': Daniels, Billy / Pray for the lights to go out: Satton, Lon / I got it bad: Stewart, Amii / Harlem makes me feel: Sharpe, Bernard / Jim jam jumpin' jive: Augins, Charles/Newton Winters/Ray Collins / There'll be some changes made: Delmar, Elaine / Memories of you: Daniels, Billy / God bless the child: Gelzer, Helen / It don't mean a thing: Peters, Clarke & Company / Bubbling Brown Sugar (reprise)
CDSBL 13106 / Oct '92 / DRG

☐ BUCCANEER, THE
Bernstein, Elmer c
VSD 5214 / Feb '90 / Varese Sarabande

☐ BUDDY (London Cast)
Holly, Buddy c
CASTCD 55 / Apr '96 / First Night

☐ BUDDY (CC Productions)
Holly, Buddy c
Ready Teddy / Rock around the Ollie Vee / Changing all those changes / That'll be the day / Blue days black nights / Everyday / Not fade away / Peggy Sue / Words of love / Oh boy / True love ways / Chantilly lace / Maybe baby / Heartbeat / La bamba / Raining in my heart / It doesn't matter anymore / Rave on
QED 204 / Nov '96 / Tring

☐ BUDDY (Cast Recording)
Holly, Buddy c
VSD 5829 / Jul '97 / Varese Sarabande

☐ BUGSY MALONE (National Youth Music Theatre)
Williams, Paul c
Overture / Bugsy Malone / Fat Sam's grand slam / That's why they call him Dandy / Tomorrow / Show business / Bad guys / Double chorus / You give a little love / Finale Act 1 / My name is Tallulah / I'm feeling fine / So you wanna be a boxer / Ordinary fool / Down and out / Finale act 2 / Exit music
CDTER 1246 / Jan '98 / TER

☐ BUIO OMEGA (Goblin)
Simonetti, Claudio c
CDMF 304 / 1 May '98 / Cinevox

☐ BULLETPROOF
MCAD 11498 / Sep '96 / MCA

☐ BULLETPROOF (Score)
Bernstein, Elmer c
VSD 5757 / Oct '96 / Varese Sarabande

☐ BULLETS OVER BROADWAY
SK 66822 / May '95 / Sony Classical

☐ BULLITT
Schifrin, Lalo c
Schifrin, Lalo con
Bullitt theme / Room 26 / Hotel Daniels / Aftermath of love / Music to interrogate by / On the way to San Mateo / Ice Pick Mike / Song for Cathy / Shifting gears / Cantata for combo / First snowfall / Bullitt
9362450082 / Aug '97 / Warner Bros.

☐ BUSTER
Two hearts: Collins, Phil / Just one look: Hollies / Big noise: Collins, Phil / Robbery: Dudley, Anne / I got you babe: Sonny & Cher / Keep on running: Davis, Spencer Group / Loco in Acapulco: Four Tops / How do you do it: Gerry & The Pacemakers / I just don't know what to do with myself: Springfield, Dusty / Sweets for my sweet: Searchers / Will you still be waiting: Dudley, Anne / Groovy kind of love: Collins, Phil
CDV 2544 / Apr '92 / Virgin

☐ BUTCH CASSIDY AND THE SUNDANCE KID (Bacharach, Burt)
Bacharach, Burt c
Sundance kid / Raindrops keep fallin' on my head / Not goin' home anymore / South American getaway / Old fun city / Come touch the sun / On a bicycle built for joy
5514332 / Aug '95 / Spectrum

☐ BUTCHER BOY, THE
Goldenthal, Elliot c
Francie Brady Show: Goldenthal, Elliot / Blood of the apache: Goldenthal, Elliot / Tune for da: Goldenthal, Elliot / Mack the knife: Santo & Johnny / Pur fur Elise: Santo & Johnny / No one knows: Dion & The Belmonts / My ole pal: Goldenthal, Elliot / Blessed mothers carnival night: Goldenthal, Elliot / Funeral and Ava Maria: Goldenthal, Elliot / Oh mein Papa: Galvert, Eddie / Francie Brady not our lady: Goldenthal, Elliot / Nut rocker: B Bumble & The STingers / Sweet heart of Jesus: Nathan, Regina / Butcher boy: O'Connor, Sinead
0022892CIN / 30 Mar '98 / Edel/ Cinerama

☐ BUTTERFLY
Morricone, Ennio c
PCD 108 / Jan '93 / Prometheus

☐ BY JEEVES (Highlights) (1996 London Cast)
Lloyd Webber, Andrew c
Ayckbourn, Alan l
False start / Code of the Woosters / Travel hopefully / That was nearly us / Deadlier than the male / Hallo song / By Jeeves / When love arrives / What have you got to say Jeeves / Half a moment / It's a pig / Banjo boy / Wizard rainbow
5317232 / Jul '96 / Really Useful

☐ BY JEEVES (1996 London Cast)
Lloyd Webber, Andrew c
Ayckbourn, Alan l
Some introductory chat / Code of the Woosters / Plot thickens / Travel hopefully / Curious hedgehog incident / Travel hopefully (continued) / In which my character is tested / That was nearly us / Days of jams and mazes / Love's maze / Wooster thinks on his feet / Hallo song / Identity crisis (or two) / By Jeeves / Wooster nobly intercedes / When love arrives / I am let down (badly) / What have you got to say Jeeves / I answer the call of the code / Half a moment / I risk my neck to save the bacon / It's a pig / Satisfactory outcome / Banjo boy / Wizard rainbow / In conclusion
5331872 / Jul '96 / Really Useful

☐ BY THE BEAUTIFUL SEA (Broadway Cast)
ZDM 7648892 / Apr '93 / EMI Classics

C

☐ CABARET (Film Cast)
Kander, John c
Ebb, Fred l
Wilkommen / Mein herr / Two ladies / Maybe this time / Sitting pretty / Tiller girls / Money money / Heiraten / If you could see her / Tomorrow belongs to me / Cabaret / Finale
MCLD 19088 / Apr '97 / MCA

☐ CABARET (1986 London Cast)
Kander, John *c*
Ebb, Fred *l*
Wilkommen / So what / Don't tell mama / Perfectly marvellous / Two ladies / It couldn't please me more / Why should I wake up / Money money money / Married / Meeskite / Tomorrow belongs to me / If you could see her / Maybe this time / What would you do / Cabaret / Auf wiedersehen
OCRCD 6010 / Mar '93 / First Night

☐ CABARET (Highlights) (Cast Recording)
Kander, John *c*
Ebb, Fred *l*
Wilkommen / Don't tell Mama / Telephone song / Perfectly marvellous / Two ladies / Tomorrow belongs to me / Why should I wake up / Maybe this time / Sitting pretty / Money money / If you could see her / Cabaret
SHOWCD 021 / Feb '95 / Showtime

☐ CABARET (Gray, Joel & Lotte Lenya/Jill Hayworth/1966 Broadway Cast)
Kander, John *c*
Ebb, Fred *l*
SK 60533 / Jul '98 / Columbia Broadway Masterworks

☐ CABARET (1968 London Cast)
Kander, John *c*
Ebb, Fred *l*
Davies, Gareth *con*
SMK 53494 / Jan '93 / Sony West End

☐ CABARET (Cast Recording)
Kander, John *c*
Ebb, Fred *l*
Wilkommen / So what / Don't tell Mama / Telephone dance / Perfectly marvellous / Two ladies / It could not please me more / Tomorrow belongs to me / Why should I wake up / Sitting pretty / Married / Fruit shop dance / Meeskite / Tomorrow belongs to me / Entr'acte / Kick line / Married / If you could see her / What would you do / Sally's revolt / Cabaret / Break up / Finale ultimo / Curtain calls / Exit music / Money / Don't go / I don't care much / Mein Herr / Maybe this time / Money money / Tiller girls
CDTER2 1210 / Jan '98 / TER

☐ CABARET (Willcox, Toyah & Nigel Planer/Cast)
Kander, John *c*
Ebb, Fred *l*
Overture / Wilkommen / Sitting pretty / Mein herr / Two ladies / Money money / Tomorrow belongs to me / Cabaret / Don't tell Mama / If you could see her / Married / Maybe this time / Finale
3036200392 / Jul '97 / Shows Collection

☐ CABARET (Cast Recording)
Kander, John *c*
Ebb, Fred *l*
Wilkommen / So what / Don't tell mama / I don't care much / Perfectly marvellous / Sitting pretty / It couldn't please me more / Two ladies / Don't go / If you could see her / Married / Maybe this time / What would you do / Cabaret
VSD 5945 / 17 Aug '98 / Varese Sarabande

☐ CABIN IN THE SKY (Broadway Cast)
Duke, Vernon *c*
Latouche, John *l*
ZDM 7648922 / Aug '93 / EMI Classics

☐ CABIN IN THE SKY (Film Cast)
Duke, Vernon *c*
Latouche, John *l*
Main title / Foreword / Li'l black sheep/Old ship of Zion / But the flesh is weak / Prayer / First revelation / Saint Petunia / Happiness is a thing called Joe / Dat suits me / Beside the still waters / Cabin in the sky / Ain't it the truth / Takin' a chance on love / Meek and mild / Life's full of consequence / Petunia in the wilderness / Things ain't what they used to be / Going up / Down at Jim Henry's / Shine / Honey in the honeycomb / Love me tomorrow / Third revelation / Little Joe throws snake eyes / Amen
CDODEON 31 / 15 Sep '97 / Soundtracks

☐ CABIN IN THE SKY/PORGY AND BESS/CARIB SONG (Broadway Cast)
AEICD 017 / May '98 / AEI

☐ CABINET OF DR. CALIGARI, THE (Bravura String Quartet)
Brock, Timothy *c*
KOC 04 / Jan '97 / K

☐ CAL (Knopfler, Mark)
Knopfler, Mark *c*
Irish boy / Road / Waiting for her / Irish love / Secret place / Father and son / Meeting at the trees / Potato picking / In a secret place / Fear and hatred / Love and guilt / Long road
8227692 / Mar '97 / Vertigo

☐ CALAMITY JANE (Cast Recording)
Fain, Sammy *c*
Webster, Paul Francis *l*
Overture / Deadwood stage / Careless with the truth / Adelaide / Ev'ryone complains about the weather / Men / Can can / Hive full of honey / I can do without you / Tis Harry I'm planning to marry / Just blew in from the windy city / Keep it under your hat / Ent'racte / Woman's touch / Higher than a hawk / Black hills of Dakota / Love you dearly / Fianletto / Secret love / Play out music
CDTER 1215 / Nov '97 / TER

☐ CALAMITY JANE (Craven, Gemma & 1996 London Cast)
Fain, Sammy *c*
Webster, Paul Francis *l*
Secret love / Deadwood stage / Hive full of honey / I can do without you / It's Harry I'm planning to marry / Windy city / Keep it under your hat / Woman's touch / Higher than a hawk / Black hills of Dakota / Love you dearly
3036200302 / Jul '96 / Carlton

☐ CALAMITY JANE (Cast Recording/ National Symphony Orchestra)
Fain, Sammy *c*
Webster, Paul Francis *l*
Edwards, John Owen *con*
Overture / Deadwood stage / Hive full of honey / I can do without you / It's Harry I'm planning to marry / Just blew in from the Windy City / Keep it under your hat / Woman's touch / Higher than a hawk deeper than a well / Black hills of Dakota / Secret love / Finale
SHOWCD 036 / Oct '96 / Showtime

☐ CALIFORNIA DREAMS
This time / Castles on quicksand / Everybody's got someone / It's gonna be rain / Let me be the one / If only you knew / One world / If you lean on me / If it wasn't for you / Love is not like this / Heart don't lie / California dreams theme
MCLD 19301 / Oct '95 / MCA

☐ CALL ME MADAM (Revival Cast)
Berlin, Irving *c*
DRGCD 94761 / Jun '95 / DRG

☐ CAMELOT (Film Cast)
Loewe, Frederick *c*
Lerner, Alan Jay *l*
Overture / I wonder what the king is doing tonight / Simple joys of maidenhood / Camelot and the wedding ceremony / C'est moi / Lusty month of May / Follow me / How to handle a woman / Take me to the fair / If ever I would leave you / What do the simple folk do / I loved you once in silence / Guenevere / Finale
7599273252 / Mar '94 / Warner Bros.

☐ CAMELOT (1982 London Cast)
Loewe, Frederick *c*
Lerner, Alan Jay *l*
Overture / Camelot / Simple joys of maidenhood / I wonder what the king is doing tonight / C'est moi / Follow me / Joust / Lusty month of May / Resolution / Then you may take me to the fair / How to handle a woman / Entracle madrigal / Before I gaze at you again / If ever I would leave you
CDTER 1030 / Nov '97 / TER

☐ CAMELOT (Highlights) (1982 London Cast)
Loewe, Frederick *c*
Lerner, Alan Jay *l*
Overture / I wonder what the king is doing tonight / Simple joys of maidenhood / Camelot / Follow me / C'est moi / Lusty month of May / How to handle a woman / Before I gaze at you again / If ever I would leave you / What do the simple folk do / I loved you once in silence
SHOWCD 013 / Feb '95 / Showtime

☐ CAMELOT (Burton, Richard & Julie Andrews/Robert Goulet/Broadway Cast)
Loewe, Frederick *c*
Lerner, Alan Jay *l*
SK 60542 / Jul '98 / Columbia Broadway Masterworks

☐ CAMELOT/MY FAIR LADY (Cast Recording)
Loewe, Frederick *c*
Lerner, Alan Jay *l*
340792 / Oct '95 / Koch

☐ CAMILLE 2000
Piccioni, Piero *c*
ET 905CD / 14 Apr '98 / Easy Tempo

☐ CAN-CAN (1953 Broadway Cast)
Porter, Cole *c*
ZDM 7646642 / Apr '93 / EMI Classics

☐ CANDIDE (1988 Scottish Opera)
Bernstein, Leonard *c*
Wilbur, Richard *l*
Brown, Justin *con*
Overture / Best of all possible worlds / O happy we / Candide begins his travels / It must be so / Candide's lament / Ring around a rosy / Paris waltz / Glitter and be gay / You were dead you know / I am easily assimilated / My love / Introduction to Eldorado / Ballad of Eldorado / Words words words / Bon voyage / King's barcarolle / We are women / What's the use / Venice gavotte / Nothing more than this / Finale
CDTER 1156 / 15 Jun '98 / TER

☐ CANDIDE (1956 Broadway Cast)
Bernstein, Leonard *c*
Wilbur, Richard *l*
Krachmalnick, Samuel *con*
Overture / Best of all possible worlds / What's the use / It must be so / Glitter and be gay / Oh happy me / Mazurka / You were dead you know / My love / I am easily assimilated / Eldorado / Quiet / Bon Voyage / Gavotte / Make our garden grow
SK 48017 / Dec '91 / Sony Broadway

☐ CANDIDE (1982 New York Opera Cast)
Bernstein, Leonard *c*
Wilbur, Richard *l*
Fanfare/Life is happiness indeed / Best of all possible worlds / Happy instrumental/Oh happy we / Candide begins his travels / It must be so / Westphalian fanfare/Chorale/Battle music / Entrance of the Jew / Glitter and be gay / Earthquake music/Dear boy / Auto da fe / Candide's lament / You were dead you know / Travel(to the stables)/I am easily assimilated / Quartet finale / Entr'acte / Ballad of the new world / My love / Barcarolle / Alleluia / Eldorado / Sheep song / Governor's waltz / Bon voyage / Quiet / Constantinople/What's the use / Finale: Make our garden grow
NWCD 3401 / Oct '86 / New World

☐ CANDIDE (& West Side Story) (Hadley, Jerry & June Anderson/London Symphony Orchestra/Chorus)
Bernstein, Leonard *c*
Wilbur, Richard *l*
Bernstein, Leonard *con*
4297342 / Aug '91 / Deutsche Grammophon

☐ CANDIDE (Highlights) (1988 Scottish Opera)
Bernstein, Leonard *c*
Wilbur, Richard *l*
CDTEO 1006 / Jul '88 / TER

☐ CANDIDE (Hadley, Jerry & June Anderson/London Symphony Orchestra/Chorus)
Bernstein, Leonard *c*
Wilbur, Richard *l*
Bernstein, Leonard *con*
4479582 / May '96 / Deutsche Grammophon

☐ CANDIDE (1997 New Broadway Cast)
Bernstein, Leonard *c*
Wilbur, Richard *l*
Overture / Life is happiness indeed / Old lady's face entrance / Best of all possible worlds / Oh happy we / It must be so / Glitter and be gay / Old lady's second false entrance / Auto da fe / Candide's lament / You were dead you know / I am easily assimilated / Quartet finale to Act I / Entr'acte / Ballad of the new world / I am easily assimilated / My love / Eldorado / Sheep song / Governor's waltz / Bon voyage / Quiet / What's the use / Make our garden grow
09026688352 / Aug '97 / RCA Victor

☐ CANNONBALL FEVER
Wheatley, David *c*
CST 348042 / Feb '90 / Varese Sarabande

☐ CAPEMAN (Simon, Paul)
Simon, Paul *c*
Adios Hermanos / Born in Puerto Rico / Satin summer nights / Bernadette / Vampires / Quality / Can I forgive him / Sunday afternoon / Killer wants to go to college / Time is an ocean / Virgil / Killer wants to go to college / Trailways bus
9362468142 / 24 Nov '97 / Warner Bros.

☐ CAPTAIN FROM CASTILE
Newman, Alfred *c*
FCD 8103 / Mar '84 / Fantasy

☐ CAPTAIN FUTURE
Bruhn, Christian *c*
CST 8051 / Mar '96 / Colosseum

☐ CAPTIVE (Edge)
Edge *c*
Rowena's theme / Heroine / One foot in heaven / Strange party / Hiro's theme / Drift / Dream theme / Djinn / Island / Hiro's theme 2
CDV 2401 / Sep '86 / Virgin

☐ CAR WASH
Carwash / 6 O'clock DJ (Let's rock) / I wanna get next to you / Put your money where your mouth is / Zig Zag / You're on my mind / Mid day DJ Theme / Born to love you / Daddy rich / You gotta believe / I'm going down / Yo yo / Sunrise / Righteous rhythm / Water / Crying / Doin' what comes naturally / Keep on keepin' on
MCD 11502 / Mar '97 / MCA

☐ CARAVAGGIO 1610 (Fisher-Turner, Simon)
Fisher-Turner, Simon *c*
Hills of Abruzzi / Dog star / All paths lead to Rome / Fantasia childhood memories / How blue sky was / Light and dark (From Missa Lux Et Orrigo) / Umber wastes / Cafe of the moors / Timeout and mind / In the still of the night / Michele of the shadows / Waters of forgetfullness / Running running / Frescobaldi the greatest organist of our time / Hourglass / I love you more than my eyes
DSCD 10 / Jul '95 / Demon

☐ CARD, THE (1994 London Cast)
Hatch, Tony *c*
Trent, Jackie *l*
Typical machin / Another time another place / You'll do / How do / Nobody thought of it / Rents / Moving on / Time to spend (beside the sea) / Lock stock and barrell / Is it just me / Typical machin (Reprise) / That's the way the money grows / If only / Countess of chell / Card / Opposite your smile / If only (Reprise) / Moving on (Reprise) / Finale the company
OCRCD 6045 / Apr '97 / First Night

☐ CARLA'S SONG
Fenton, George *c*
CDDEB 1005 / Apr '97 / Debonair

☐ CARLITO'S WAY
I love music: *Rozalla* / Rock the boat: *Hues Corporation* / Rock your baby: *Terry, Ed* / Perece mentira: *Anthony, Mark* / Backstabbers: *O'Jays* / Sound of Philadelphia: *MFSB* / Got to be real: *Lynn, Cheryl* / Lady Marmalade: *Labelle* / Pillow talk: *Sinoa* / El watusi: *Barretto, Ray* / Oye como va: *Santana* / You are so beautiful: *Preston, Billy*
4749942 / Jan '94 / Columbia

☐ CARLITO'S WAY (Score)
Doyle, Patrick *c*
Carlito's way / Carlito and Gail / Cafe / Laline / You're over man / Where's my cheesecake / Buoy / Elevator / There's an angel here / Grand central / Remember me
VSD 5463 / Jan '94 / Varese Sarabande

☐ CARMEN JONES (London Cast)
Bizet, Georges *c*
Hammerstein II, Oscar *l*
Lewis, Henry *con*
CDC 7543512 / Apr '93 / EMI Classics

☐ CAROUSEL (Film Cast)
Rodgers, Richard *c*
Hammerstein II, Oscar *l*
Carousel waltz / You're a queer one Julie Jordan / Mr. Snow / If I loved you / When the children are asleep / June is bustin' out all over / Soliloquy / Blow high blow low / Real nice clambake / Stonecutters cut it on stone / What's the use of wonderin' / You'll never walk alone
ZDM 7646922 / Apr '93 / EMI Classics

☐ CAROUSEL (1993 London Cast)
Rodgers, Richard *c*
Hammerstein II, Oscar *l*
Prologue / Mister Snow / If I loved you / June is bustin' out all over / Mister Snow (reprise) / When the children are asleep / Blow high blow low / Soliloquy / Real nice clambake / Geraniums in the winder / Stonecutters cut it on stone / What's the use of wond'rin' / You'll never walk alone / Ballet / If I loved you (reprise) / You'll never walk alone (reprise)
OCRCD 6042 / Apr '96 / First Night

☐ CAROUSEL (Highlights - The Shows Collection) (Cast Recording)
Rodgers, Richard *c*
Hammerstein II, Oscar *l*
If I loved you / You're a queer one Julie Jordan / Mr. Snow / June is bustin' out all over / Soliloquy / Blow high blow low / When the children are asleep / Real nice clambake / Stonecutters cut it on stone / What's the use of wonderin' / Highest judge of all / You'll never walk alone
PWKS 4144 / Oct '93 / Carlton

☐ CARRIE
Donaggio, Pino *c*
Donaggio, Pino *con*
Theme / I never dreamed someone like you could love someone like me / Telekenisis / And God made Eve / Raven was called sin / At the prom / Contest winners / Born to have it all / Bucket of blood / They're all going to laugh at you / School in flames / Mother at the top of the stairs / For the last time we'll pray / Devil has come home / Collapse of Carrie's home / Sue's dream / Powers / Theme
RCD 10701 / 3 Nov '97 / Rykodisc

☐ CARRINGTON (Nyman, Michael Band)
Nyman, Michael *c*
Nyman, Michael *con*
4448732 / Sep '95 / Argo

☐ CASABLANCA
Medley / It had to be you / Shine / Konck on wood / Rick and Renault / Arrival of Ilsa and Victor at Ricka / Play it again sam / Of all the gin joints / Paris montage / Medley / Medley / Airport finale / Medley / Dat's what Noah done / Knock on wood / Medley / Medley / As time goes by
8235022 / 3 Nov '97 / Premier/EMI

☐ CASINO
Contempt/Theme de Camille: *Delerue, Georges* / Angelina zooma zooma medley: *Prima, Louis* / Hoochie coochie man: *Waters, Muddy* / I'll take you there: *Staple Singers* / Nights in white satin: *Moody Blues* / How high the moon: *Paul, Les & Mary Ford* / Hurt: *Yuro, Timi* / Ain't got no home: *Henry, Clarence 'Frogman'* / Without you: *Nilsson, Harry* / Love is the drug: *Roxy Music* / I'm sorry: *Lee, Brenda* / Go your own way: *Fleetwood Mac* / Thrill is gone: *King, B.B.* / Love is strange: *Mickey & Sylvia* / In crowd: *Lewis, Ramsey* / Stardust: *Carmichael, Hoagy* / Fa fa fa fa fa (Sad song): *Redding, Otis* / I ain't superstitious: *Beck, Jeff/Rod Stewart* / Glory of love: *Velvetones* / Satisfaction: *Devo* / What a difference a day makes: *Washington, Dinah* / Working in a coalmine: *Dorsey, Lee* / House of the rising sun: *Burdon, Eric* / Those were the days: *Cream* / Who can I turn to (When nobody needs me): *Bennett, Tony* / Slippin' and slidin': *Little Richard* / You're nobody till somebody loves you: *Martin, Dean* / Compared to what: *McCann, Les & Eddie Harris* / Basin Street blues: *Prima, Louis* / When it's sleepy time down South: *Prima, Louis* / Matthaus passion: *Chicago Symphony Orchestra/Sir George Solti*
MCD 11389 / Feb '96 / MCA

☐ CASINO ROYALE
Bacharach, Burt *c*
Casino Royale theme: *Alpert, Herb* / Money penny goes for broke / Home James and don't spare the horses / Look of love / Little French boy / Venerable Sir James Bond / Big cowboys and indians / Le chiffre's torture of ... / Sir James' trip to find ... / Hi there Miss Good Thighs / Flying saucer / Dream on James
VSD 5265 / Nov '90 / Varese Sarabande

☐ CASPER (Score)
Horner, James *c*
Horner, James *con*
No sign of ghosts / Carrigan and Dibs / Strangers in the house / First haunting / Swordfight / March of the exorcists / Lighthouse / Casper makes breakfast / Fond memories / Dying to be a ghost / Casper's lullaby / Descent to Lazarus / One last wish / Remember me this way / Casper the friendly ghost / Uncle's swing / End credits
MCD 11240 / Jul '95 / MCA

☐ **CASPER (A Spirited Beginning)**
Casper: *KC & The Sunshine Band/Kool & The Gang* / Love sensation: *911* / Back to where we started: *World's Apart* / Delicious: *Shampoo* / Mansize rooster: *Supergrass* / Best friend: *CTFG* / I'm not alone: *CTFG* / Kandy pop: *CTFG* / I wanna be with you: *Backstreet Boys* / Spooky madness: *Big Bad Voodoo Daddy* / No one lives forever: *Oingo Boingo* / Big bomb bomb: *Oingo Boingo* / Don't worry be happy: *McFerrin, Bobby* / You're in trouble: *CTFG*
8213452 / 27 Oct '97 / Premier/EMI

☐ **CAST OF THOUSANDS (Gillet, Eric Michael)**
Carnelia, Craig *c*
Cast of thousands / Old movies / She was KC / Look in my eyes / Apartment 1F / Give me a nickel / You can have the TV / Things I learned in High School / Kid inside / What you'd call a dream / Kid inside/ Magellan / Come on snow / What the song should say/Fran and Janie / Mason / Just a housewife / For them / Flight / Life on Earth / Minute
HCD 1504 / 27 Jul '98 / DRG

☐ **CASTLE FREAK**
Band, Richard *c*
Band, Richard *con*
MAF 7065 / Feb '96 / Intrada

☐ **CATHERINE WHEEL (Complete Score) (Byrne, David)**
Byrne, David *c*
7599274182 / May '89 / Sire

☐ **CATS (1981 London Cast)**
Lloyd Webber, Andrew *c*
Eliot, T.S./Trevor Nunn/Richard Stilgoe *l*
Jellicle songs for jellicle cats / Old gumbie cat / Naming of cats / Rum rum tugger / Grizabella / Bustopher Jones / Memory / Mungojerrie and Rumpleteazer / Old Deuteronomy / Moments of happiness / Gus the theatre cat / Overture/Prologue / Invitation to the Jellicle ball / Jellicle ball / Journey to the heavy side / Ad - dressing of cats / Growltiger's last stand / Ballad of Billy McCaw's Skimbleshanks / Macavity / Mr. Mistoffelees
8178102 / Jun '84 / Really Useful

☐ **CATS (Highlights) (1981 London Cast)**
Lloyd Webber, Andrew *c*
Eliot, T.S./Trevor Nunn/Richard Stilgoe *l*
Prologue: Jellicle songs for jellicle cats / Solo dance / Old gumbie cat / Rum tum tugger / Mungojerrie and rumpelteazer / Old deuteronomy / Jellicle ball / Grizabella the glamour cat / Gus the theatre cat / Shimbleshanks: The railway cat / Macavity / Mr. Mistoffelees / Memory / Journey to the heaviside layer / Ad - dressing of cats
8394152 / Aug '88 / Really Useful

☐ **CAUGHT (Botti, Chris)**
Botti, Chris *c*
5330952 / Nov '96 / Verve

☐ **CAUGHT UP**
CDVUS 139 / 2 Mar '98 / Noo Trybe

☐ **CAVALCADE (1931 London Cast)**
Coward, Sir Noel *c*
AEICD 033 / May '98 / AEI

☐ **CB4**
Thirteenth message: *Public Enemy* / Livin' in a zoo: *Public Enemy* / Black cop: *Boogie Down Productions* / May Day on the front line: *M.C. Ren* / Stick em up: *Hurricane & Beastie Boys* / Lifeline: *Parental Advisory* / Nocturnal is in the house: *P.M. Dawn* / Baby be mine: *Blackstreet & Teddy Riley* / It's alright: *Spencer, Tracie* / Straight out of Locash: *CB4* / Rapper's delight: *CB4* / Sweat of my balls: *CB4* / Creepin' up on ya: *Fu-Schnickens*
MCD 10758 / Apr '93 / MCA

☐ **CEMETERY CLUB, THE**
Bernstein, Elmer *c*
VSD 5412 / Mar '93 / Varese Sarabande

☐ **CENTURY/CLOSE MY EYES (Gibbs, Michael)**
Gibbs, Michael *c*
IONIC 10CD / Jan '94 / The Fine Line

☐ **CHAIN REACTION**
Goldsmith, Jerry *c*
VSD 5746 / Sep '96 / Varese Sarabande

☐ **CHAMANKA**
Korzynski, Andrzej *c*
SMC 35707 / Jun '97 / Sergent M

☐ **CHAMBER**
Burwell, Carter *c*
VSD 5758 / Nov '96 / Varese Sarabande

☐ **CHAPLIN**
Barry, John *c*
Barry, John *con*
Main theme / Early days in London/Honeysuckle and the Bee / Charlie proposes / To California/The cutting room / Discovering the tramp/The wedding chase / Chaplin's studio opening / Salt Lake City episode / Roll dance / News of Hetty's death / Smile / From London to LA / John Barry trouble/Oona arrives / Remembering Hetty / Roll dance (reprise)
4726022 / Dec '96 / Epic

☐ **CHARIOTS OF FIRE (Vangelis)**
Vangelis *c*
Titles / Five circles / Abraham's theme / Eric's theme / 100 metres / Jerusalem / Chariots of fire
8000202 / May '84 / Polydor

☐ **CHARLIE CHALK**
CDHARL 1 / Aug '89 / Redrock

☐ **CHARLIE GIRL (1986 London Cast)**
Heneker, David & John Taylor *c*
McMillan, I. *con*
Overture / Most ancestral home of all / Bells will ring / I love him I love him / What would I get from being married / Let's do a deal / My favourite occupation / What's the magic / When I hear music I dance / I 'ates money / Charlie Girl waltz / Party of a lifetime / Like love / That's it / Washington / Fish and chips / Society twist / You never know what you can do / Finale
OCRCD 6009 / Feb '96 / First Night

☐ **CHARLOTTE SWEET (Cast Recording)**
At the music hall / Forever / Liverpool sunset / Layers of underwaer / Quartet agonistes / Circus of voices / Keep it low / Bubbles in me bonnet / Vegetable Reggie / My baby and me / A-weaving / Your high note / Kantika / Darkness / You see me in a bobby / Christmas buche / Letter / Volley of indecision/Good things come / It could only happen in the theatre / Lonely canary / Queenly comments / Farewell to auld lang syne/Finale
DRGCD 6300 / Jan '95 / DRG

☐ **CHASE, THE**
Barry, John *c*
VSD 5229 / Feb '90 / Varese Sarabande

☐ **CHASING THE DEER**
6043881242 / 19 May '98 / BPT

☐ **CHERCHEZ L'IDOLE**
174902 / Nov '97 / Musidisc

☐ **CHERRY, HARRY AND RAQUEL (& Mondo Topless/Good Morning...& Goodbye)**
QDKCD 014 / Sep '97 / QDK Media

☐ **CHESS (1984 London Cast)**
Ulvaeus, Bjorn & Benny Andersson *c*
Rice, Tim *l*
Merano / Russian and Molokov / Where I want to be / Opening ceremony / Quartet / American and Florence / Nobody's side / Chess / Mountain duet / Florence quits / Embassy lament / Anthem / Bangkok / One night in Bangkok / Heaven help my heart / Argument / I know him so well / Deal (no deal) / Pity the child / Endgame / Epilogue - You and I / Story of Chess
8474452 / Feb '96 / Polydor

☐ **CHESS (CC Productions)**
Ulvaeus, Bjorn & Benny Andersson *c*
Rice, Tim *l*
Merano / Arbiter / Nobody's side / Chess / Embassy lament / Anthem / One night in Bangkok / Heaven help my heart / I know him so well / Pity the child / You and I / Story of chess
QED 210 / Nov '96 / Tring

☐ **CHICAGO (Broadway Cast)**
Kander, John *c*
Ebb, Fred *l*
Overture / All that jazz / Funny honey / Cell block tango / When you're good to Mama / All I care about / Little bit of good / We both reached for the gun / Roxie / I can't do it alone / My own best friend / Me and my baby / Mr. Cellophane / When Velma takes the stand / Razzle dazzle / Class / Nowadays / All that jazz (reprise)
07822189522 / 2 Feb '98 / Arista

☐ **CHICAGO (The Musical) (Reinking, Ann & Bebe Neuwirth/James Naughton/ Joel Gray/Broadway Cast)**
Kander, John *c*
Ebb, Fred *l*
Overture / All that jazz / Funny honey / Cell block tango / When you're good to Mama / All I care about / Little bit of good to Mama / All I care about / Little bit of good / We both reached for the gun / Roxie / I can't do it alone / My own best friend / Entr'acte / I know a girl / Me and my baby / Mr. Cellophane / When Velma takes the stand / Razzle dazzle / Class / Nowadays / Hot honey rag / Finale
09026687272 / 17 Nov '97 / RCA Victor

☐ **CHICAGO (London Cast)**
Intro and overture / All that jazz / Funny honey / Cell block tango / When you're good to mama / All I care about / Little bit of good / We both reached for the gun / Roxie's / Roxie's / I cannot do it alone / My own best friend / Finale act 1 / Entr'acte / I know a girl / Me and my baby / Mister Cellophane / When Velma takes the stand / Razzle dazzle / Class / Nowadays / Hot honey rag / Finale
09026631552 / Jul '98 / RCA Victor

☐ **CHICAGO HOPE**
Rona, Jeff & Mark Isham *c*
SI 8702 / 1 Dec '97 / Sonic Images

☐ **CHILDREN OF A LESSER GOD**
Convertino, Michael *c*
Silence and sound / Sarah sleeping / Rain pool / Underwater love / On the ferry / James and Sarah / Goodnight / Boomerang
GNPD 8007 / Jan '89 / GNP Crescendo

☐ **CHILDREN OF EDEN (Cast Recording)**
Schwartz, Stephen *c*
Let there be: *Page, Ken & Company* / Naming: *Smith, Martin & Shezwae Powell* / Spark of creation: *Powell, Shezwae* / In pursuit of excellence: *Lloyd King, Richard & Snake* / World without you: *Smith, Martin* / Wasteland / Lost in the wilderness / Close to home / Children of Eden: *Powell, Shezwae & Company* / Generations: *Shell, Ray & Company* / Civilised society: *Colson, Kevin & Company* / Shipshape / Return of the animals / Stranger to the rain: *Ruffelle, Frances* / In whatever time we have: *Barclay, Anthony & Frances Ruffelle* / Degenerations: *Page, Ken* / Dove song: *Ruffelle, Frances* / Hardest part of love: *Colson, Kevin* / Ain't it good: *Dubois, Jacqui & Company* / In the beginning
8282342 / Apr '91 / London

☐ **CHILDREN OF NATURE (Hilmarsson, Hilmar Orn)**
Hilmarsson, Hilmar Orn *c*
T 33.14 / Oct '95 / Touch

☐ **CHILDREN'S THIEF, THE/ON MY OWN**
Piersanti, Franco *c*
OST 117 / Jul '93 / Milano Dischi

☐ **CHILLER (Cincinnati Pops Orchestra)**
Kunzel, Erich *c*
CD 80189 / Aug '90 / Telarc

☐ **CHINA 9 LIBERTY 37**
Donaggio, Pino *c*
PCD 117 / Jan '93 / Prometheus

☐ **CHINATOWN**
Goldsmith, Jerry *c*
Goldsmith, Jerry/U. Rasey *con*
VSD 5677 / Feb '96 / Varese Sarabande

☐ **CHITTY CHITTY BANG BANG**
Kostal, Irwin *c*
Sherman, Richard & Robert *l*
RCD 10702 / 13 Oct '97 / Rykodisc

☐ **CHORUS LINE, A (1975 Broadway Cast)**
Hamlisch, Marvin *c*
Kleban, Edward *l*
Pippin, Donald *con*
I hope I get it / I can do that / At the ballet / Sing / Hello twelve hello thirteen hello love / Nothing / Music and the mirror / Dance ten looks three / One / What I did for love / One / Chorus line
SK 65282 / Jul '98 / Columbia Broadway Masterworks

☐ **CHORUS LINE, A**
Hamlisch, Marvin *c*
Kleban, Edward *l*
BGOCD 360 / 26 Sep '97 / Beat Goes On

☐ **CHRISTINE (Score)**
Carpenter, John *c*
Arnie's love theme / Obsessed with the car / Football run / Kill your kids / Rape / Discovery / Show me / Moochie's death / Junkins / Buddie's death / Nobody's home / Restored / Car obsession reprise / Christine attacks (Plymouth fury) / Talk on the couch / Regeneration / Darnell's tonight / Undented / Moochie mix four
VSD 5240 / Jan '90 / Varese Sarabande

☐ **CHRISTOPHER COLUMBUS (The Discovery)**
Eidelman, Cliff *c*
VSD 5389 / Sep '92 / Varese Sarabande

☐ **CHRYSANTHEMUM (1956 London Cast)**
Stewart, Robb *c*
Phillips, Neville & Robin Chancellor *l*
AEICD 018 / May '98 / AEI

☐ **CHU CHIN CHOW (1959 London Cast)**
Norton, Frederic *c*
Asche, Oscar *l*
Prelude: *Orchestra* / Here be oysters stewed in honey: *Te Wiata, Inia* / I am Chu Chin Chow: *Te Wiata, Inia* / Cleopatra's Nile: *Bryan, Julie* / When a pullet is plump: *Te Wiata, Inia* / Serenade / Mahbubah: *Chorus* / I'll sing and dance / I long for the sun: *Leigh, Barbara* / Robber's chorus: *Te Wiata, Inia* / I love thee so: *Bryan, Julie* / Behold: *Te Wiata, Inia* / Anytime's kissing time: *Bryan, Julie & Inia Te Wiata* / Cobbler's song: *Te Wiata, Inia* / I built a fairy palace in the sky: *Connors, Ursula* / We bring ye fruits: *Williams Singers* / Finale: *Chorus*
CDANGEL 5 / Apr '94 / Angel

☐ **CHULAS FRONTERAS/DEL MERO CORAZON**
ARHCD 425 / Sep '95 / Arhoolie

☐ **CINDERELLA (Broadway Cast)**
Rodgers, Richard *c*
Hart, Lorenz *l*
Green, John *con*
SK 53538 / Dec '91 / Sony Broadway

☐ **CINDERELLA**
Overture / In my own little corner / Spread a little happiness / Dream is a wish that your heart makes / Raise a ruckus / Impossible / Ball / Whay has love got to do with getting married / Lovely night/Ten minutes ago / Do I love you because you're so beautiful / Midnight / On the steps of the palace / Once I was loved / If the shoe fits / Tell him anything / Stepsister's lament / Finale
VSD 5875 / 26 May '98 / Varese Sarabande

☐ **CINEMA PARADISO**
Morricone, Ennio *c*
Cinema Paradiso / Maturity / While thinking about her again / Childhood and manhood / Cinema on fire / Love theme / After the destruction / First youth / Love theme for Nata / Visit to the cinema / Four interludes / Runaway search and return / Projection for two / From American sex appeal to the first Fellini / Toto and Alfredo / For Elena
DRGCD 12598 / Jul '93 / DRG

☐ **CIRCLE OF FRIENDS**
You're the one / Ireland 1949 / Cottage (Sonatina) / Dublin / Knock Glen / Bo Weevil / Sean / Benny and Jack / Fathers death / Love is a many splendored thing / You're the one
0630109572 / Jun '95 / East West

☐ **CIRQUE DU SOLEIL (Alegria) (Cirque Du Soleil)**
Dupere, Rene & Benoit Jutras *c*
Overture / Bulgares / Boule 4 / Tango / Trapeze cadres / Fil de fer / Bicyclettes / Boules 1 a 3 / Les chaises / Entracte / Pingouins
09026627012 / Mar '98 / RCA Victor

☐ **CITIZEN X**
Edelman, Randy *c*
VSD 5601 / Mar '95 / Varese Sarabande

☐ **CITY HALL**
Goldsmith, Jerry *c*
Goldsmith, Jerry *con*
VSD 5699 / Mar '96 / Varese Sarabande

☐ **CITY LIGHTS (City Lights Orchestra)**
Chaplin, Charlie *c*
Davis, Carl *con*
Overture/Unveiling the statue / Flower girl (Violetera) / Evening/Meeting the millionaire / At the millionaire's home / Nightclub / Limousine / Sober dawn / Party and the morning after / Eviction/The road sweeper/At the girl's home / Boxing match / Burglars / Reunited
FILMCD 078 / Jan '93 / Silva Screen

☐ **CITY OF ANGELS (1993 London Cast)**
Coleman, Cy *c*
Zippel, David *l*
Blakemore, M. *con*
Prelude / Double talk / What you don't know about women / Ya gotta look after yourself / Buddy system / With every breath I take / Tennis song / Everybody's gotta be somewhere / Lost and found / All ya have to do is wait / You're nothing without me / Stay with me / You can always count on me / It needs work / With every breath I take (Reprise) / Funny
OCRCD 6034 / Mar '96 / First Night

☐ **CITY OF ANGELS**
If God will send his angels: *U2* / Univited: *Morissette, Alanis* / Red house: *Hendrix, Jimi* / Feelin' love: *Cole, Paula* / Mama you got a daughter: *Hooker, John Lee* / Angel: *McLachlan, Sarah* / Iris: *Goo Goo Dolls* / I grieve: *Gabriel, Peter* / I know: *Jude* / Further on up the road: *Clapton, Eric* / Angel falls: *Yared, Gabriel* / Unfeeling kiss: *Yared, Gabriel* / Spreading wings: *Yared, Gabriel* / City of angels: *Yared, Gabriel*
9362468672 / 4 May '98 / Warner Sunset/Reprise

☐ **CITY OF FEAR**
Goldsmith, Jerry *c*
W 9104 / 14 Apr '98 / Taran

☐ **CITY OF INDUSTRY**
Three: *Massive Attack* / Last night: *Lush* / Overcome: *Tricky* / Bug powder dust: *Bomb The Bass & Justin Warfield* / Rocco: *Death In Vegas* / Walking through water: *Palmskin Productions* / Call a cab: *Lionrock* / Degobrah: *Butter 08* / Hidden camera: *Photek* / Mr. Jones: *Red*
5243082 / Jul '97 / Quango

☐ **CITY OF VIOLENCE (CITTA VIOLENTA) (& Svegliati E Uccidi)**
Morricone, Ennio *c*
OST 127 / May '95 / Milano Dischi

☐ **CITY SLICKERS**
Shaiman, Marc *c*
VSD 5321 / Sep '91 / Varese Sarabande

☐ **CIVIL WAR, THE**
Burns, Ken *c*
Drums of war / Oliver Wendell Holmes / Ashokan farewell / Battle cry of freedom / We are climbing Jacob's ladder / Dixie / Bonnie blue flag / Cheer boys cheer / Angel band / Johnny has gone for a soldier / Lorena / Parade / Hail Columbia / Kingdom coming / Battle hymn of the republic / All quiet on the Potomac / Yankee doodle / Palmyra Schottische / When Johnny comes marching home / Shenandoah / Marching through Georgia / Sullivan Ballou letter
7559792562 / Mar '91 / Nonesuch

☐ **CLERKS**
Clerks: *Love Among Freaks* / Kill the sexplayer: *Girls Against Boys* / Got me wrong: *Alice In Chains* / Making me sick: *Bash & Pop* / Chewbacca: *Super Nova* / Panic in Cicero: *Jesus Lizard* / Shooting star: *Golden Smog* / Leaders and followers: *Bad Religion* / Violent moodswings: *Stabbing Westward* / Berserker: *Love Among Freaks* / Big problems: *Corrosion Of Conformity* / Go your own way: *Seaweed* / Can't even tell: *Soul Asylum*
4778022 / Dec '96 / Columbia

☐ **CLIFFHANGER (London Philharmonic Orchestra)**
Jones, Trevor *c*
Snell, David *con*
Cliffhanger theme / Sarah's farewell / Sarah falls / Gabe returns / I understand / Sunset searching / Tolerated help / Base jump / Bats / Two man job / Kynette is impaled / Fireside chat / Frank's demise / Rabbit hole / Icy stream / Jessie's release / Helicopter flight / End credits
5144552 / Jun '94 / Polydor

☐ **CLOCKERS**
People in search of a life: *Dorsey, Marc* / Love me still: *Khan, Chaka* / Silent hero: *Des'ree* / Bird of freedom: *Seal* / Return of the Crooklyn Dodgers: *Crooklyn Dodgers* / Changes: *Dorsey, Marc* / Reality: *Brooklynytes* / Sex soldier: *Rebelz Of Authority* / Illa killa: *Strictly Difficult* / Reality check: *Buckshot LeFonque* / Blast of the iron: *Rebelz Of Authority* / Bad boy no go a jail: *Mega Banton*
MCD 11304 / 8 Sep '97 / MCA

☐ CLOCKWORK ORANGE, A
Carlos, Walter/Rossini/Beethoven/Elgar/Rimsky-Korsakov *c*
Clockwork orange / Thieving magpie (La gazza ladra) / Symphony no. 9 / March: Clockwork Orange / William Tell / Pomp and circumstance / Timesteps (excerpt) / Overture to the sun / I want to marry a lighthouse keeper / Suicide Scherzo / Singin' In The Rain: *Astaire, Fred*
246127 / Oct '93 / WEA

☐ CLUELESS
Kids in America: Muffs / Shake some action: *Cracker* / Ghost in you: *Counting Crows* / Here: *Luscious Jackson* / All the young dudes: *World Party* / Fake plastic trees: *Radiohead* / Change: *Lightning Seeds* / Need you around: *Smoking Popes* / Mullet head: *Beastie Boys* / Where'd you go: *Mighty Mighty Bosstones* / Rollin' with my homies: *Coolio* / Alright: *Supergrass* / My Forgotten favourite: *Velocity Girl* / Supermodel: *Sobule, Jill*
CDEST 2267 / Sep '95 / Capitol

☐ COBB
Goldenthal, Elliot *c*
SK 66923 / Jan '95 / Sony Classical

☐ COCKTAIL
Wild again: *Starship* / Powerful stuff: *Fabulous Thunderbirds* / Since when: *Nevil, Robbie* / Don't worry be happy: *McFerrin, Bobby* / Hippy hippy shake: *Georgia Satellites* / Kokomo: *Beach Boys* / Rave on: *Mellencamp, John* / All shook up: *Cooder, Ry* / Oh I love you so: *Smith, Preston* / Tutti frutti: *Little Richard*
9608062 / Oct '88 / Elektra

☐ COCOON: THE RETURN
Horner, James *c*
VSD 5211 / Feb '90 / Varese Sarabande

☐ COLD FEET
Bahler, Tom *c*
Afternoon roundup / Shoot the doc / Just remember / Watch my lips / Cowboy reggae / Monty shows off infidel / Maureen and Kenny on the road / Survival camp / Infidel's and inspiration / Isometrics / Monty stole the horse / It's a sham/ Workin' man / Sheriff's a preacher / Lizard boots size 100 / Good morning / Maureen's monologue / Sceered fitless / Monty hides infidel / Have a Turkish fig / Chasin' Monty / Kenny's in the vat / Happy now and forever
VSD 5231 / Feb '90 / Varese Sarabande

☐ COLD ROOM, THE
Nyman, Michael *c*
FILMCD 157 / Jan '95 / Silva Screen

☐ COLLETTE COLLAGE (1993 Studio Cast)
VSD 5473 / Jun '94 / Varese Sarabande

☐ COLOURS OF BRAZIL
233872 / Mar '95 / Milan

☐ COLUMBUS & THE AGE OF DISCOVERY
Mirowitz, Sheldon *c*
Overture / Idea takes shape / Crossing / Worlds found / Worlds lost / In search of Columbus
CD 6002 / Jun '92 / Narada

☐ COMMANCHEROS/TRUE GRIT
Bernstein, Elmer *c*
VCD 47236 / Jan '89 / Varese Sarabande

☐ COMMITMENTS VOL.1, THE
Mustang Sally / Take me to the river / Chain of fools / Dark end of the street / Destination anywhere / I can't stand the rain / Try a little tenderness / Treat her right / Do right woman do right man / Mr. Pitiful / I never loved a man / In the midnight hour / Bye bye baby / Slip away
MCAD 10286 / Aug '91 / MCA

☐ COMMITMENTS VOL.2, THE
Hard to handle / Grits ain't groceries / I thank you / That's the way love is / Show me / Saved / Too many fish in the sea / Fa fa fa fa fa (sad song) / Land of the 1000 dances / Nowhere to run / Bring it on home to me
MCLD 19312 / Oct '95 / MCA

☐ COMPANY (1972 London Cast)
Sondheim, Stephen *c*
Hastings, Harold *con*
SMK 53496 / Nov '93 / Sony West End

☐ COMPANY (In Jazz) (Trotter Trio)
Sondheim, Stephen *c*
VSD 5673 / Nov '95 / Varese Sarabande

☐ COMPANY (London Cast)
Sondheim, Stephen *c*
Valentine, G. *con*
CASTCD 57 / Apr '96 / First Night

☐ CON AIR
Rabin, Trevor *c*
162099 / Jul '97 / Hollywood

☐ CONAN
Fox, Charles *c*
78282788012 / 24 Mar '98 / Sonic Images

☐ CONAN THE BARBARIAN (American Score)
Poledouris, Basil *c*
VSD 5390 / Jan '93 / Varese Sarabande

☐ CONEHEADS
Magic carpet ride: *Slash* / Tainted love: *Soft Cell* / No more tears (enough is enough): *Lang, k.d. & Andy Bell* / Kodachrome: *Simon, Paul* / Can't take my eyes off you: *Harket, Morten* / It's a free world baby: *REM* / Soul to squeeze: *Red Hot Chili Peppers* / Fight the power: *Barenaked Ladies* / Little Renee: *Digable Planets* / Chale jao: *Babble* / Conehead love: *Beldar*
9362453452 / Jul '93 / Warner Bros.

☐ CONFESSIONS OF A POLICE CAPTAIN/IN THE GRIP OF THE SPIDER
Ortolani, Riz *c*
OST 114 / Jul '93 / Milano Dischi

☐ CONNECTICUT YANKEE, A (1943 Revival Cast)
Rodgers, Richard *c*
Hart, Lorenz *l*
Introduction/Prologue / Toast / This is my night to howl / Thou swell / At the round table / On a desert island with thee / To keep my love alive / Ye lunchtime follies / Can't you do a friend a favour / I feel at home with you / You always love the same girl / Entertainment / Camelot samba / My heart stood still
AEICD 043 / May '98 / AEI

☐ CONNECTION, THE (Redd, Freddie/Howard McGhee/Tina Brooks/Milt Hinton)
Redd, Freddie *c*
Who killed cock robin / Music forever / Wigglin' / OD / Jim Dunn's dilemma / Time to smile / Sister salvation
CDBOP 019 / Jul '95 / Boplicity

☐ CONSPIRACY THEORY
Burwell, Carter *c*
SNACD 805 / 2 Mar '98 / Snapper

☐ CONTACT
Silvestri, Alan *c*
Awful waste of space / Ellie's bogey / Primer / Really confused / Test run bomber / Heart attack / Media event / Button me up / Good to go / No words / Small moves / I believe her / End credits
9362468112 / 20 Oct '97 / Warner Bros.

☐ COOK, THE THIEF, HIS WIFE AND HER LOVER, THE (Nyman, Michael Band)
Nyman, Michael *c*
Nyman, Michael *con*
Memorial / Misere paraphase: Nyman, Michael & Alexander Balanescu / Miserere: *London Voices* / Coupling / Book depository
CDVE 53 / May '90 / Virgin

☐ COOL RUNNINGS
Wild wild life: *Wailing Souls* / I can see clearly now: *Cliff, Jimmy* / Stir it up: *King, Diana* / Cool me down: *Tiger* / Picky picky head: *Wailing Souls* / Jamaican bobsledding chant: *Worl-A-Girl* / Sweet Jamaica: *Tony Rebel* / Dolly my baby: *Super Cat* / Love you want: *Wailing Souls* / Countrylypso: *Zimmer, Hans* / Walk home: *Zimmer, Hans*
4748402 / Dec '96 / Columbia

☐ COOL WORLD, THE (& Dizzy Goes Hollywood) (Gillespie, Dizzy)
Gillespie, Dizzy *c*
5312302 / Jul '96 / Verve

☐ COPACABANA (1994 London Cast)
Manilow, Barry *c*
Overture / Copacabana (opening sequence) / Just arrived / Dancin' fool / Night on the town / Man wanted / Lola / Who needs to dream / Ay caramba / Balero de amor / Sweet heaven / Who am I kidding / This can't be real / Welcome to Havana / Mermaids tale / Bravo / Who needs to dream (reprise) / Copacabana (finale)
OCRCD 6047 / Apr '97 / First Night

☐ COPLAND
74321531282 / 8 Nov '97 / RCA

☐ COPYCAT
Young, Christopher *c*
Anthony, Pete *con*
74321337422 / Mar '96 / Milan

☐ CORNBREAD, EARL AND ME (Blackbyrds)
Cornbread / One eye two step / Mother Son theme / Heavy town / One gun salute / Gym fight / Riot / Soulful source / Mother Son talk / At the carnival / Candy store dilemma / Wilford's gone / Mother Son bedroom talk / Courtroom emotions / Cornbread
CDBGPM 094 / May '95 / Beat Goes Public

☐ COSI COME SEI (Stay The Way You Are)
Morricone, Ennio *c*
PCD 115 / Mar '92 / Prometheus

☐ COTTON CLUB, THE
Mooche / Cotton Club stomp no.2 / Drop me off in Harlem / Creole love call / Ring dem bells / East St. Louis toodle-oo / Truckin' / Ill wind / Cotton Club stomp / Mood indigo / Minnie the moocher / Copper coloured gal / Dixie kidnaps Vera / Depression hits / Best beats sandman / Daybreak Express medley
GED 24062 / 2 Feb '98 / Geffen

☐ COUNT DRACULA (Il Conte Dracula)
Nicolai, Bruno *c*
PAN 2502 / May '95 / Silva Screen

☐ COUNT OF LUXEMBOURG, THE (Highlights In English) (New Sadler's Wells Opera Chorus/Orchestra)
Lehar, Franz *c*
Maschwitz, Eric *l*
Introduction/Carnival march / Attic for two / Feast of Mardi Gras / I'm so in love / Cheque on the safest of banks / I'm to be a bride today / Tell me can this be love/Finale act 1 / Hail Angele / Love's a dream / Lip to lip cheek to cheek / Why surely this is love / Razzle dazzle Basil / Angel you're my heart's delight / Perfume of blossom's in May / Finale act 3
CDTER 1050 / Mar '98 / TER

☐ COUNT OF LUXEMBOURG, THE (Highlights) (New Sadler's Wells Opera Chorus/Orchestra)
Lehar, Franz *c*
Maschwitz, Eric *l*
CDTEO 1004 / May '89 / TER

☐ COUNT OF MONTE CRISTO, THE/THE MAN IN THE IRON MASK (London Studio Symphony Orchestra)
Ferguson, Allyn *c*
Ferguson, Allyn *con*
PCD 130 / Oct '94 / Prometheus

☐ COUNTESS MARITZA (Highlights In English) (New Sadler's Wells Opera Chorus/Orchestra)
Kalman, Emmerich *c*
Douglas, Nigel *l*
Overture / Luck is a golden dream / How do you do / Vienne mine / Set the gypsy music laying / Childhood memories / Let's go to Varasdin / Play gipsy/Finale act 1 / When I start dreaming / Corks are popping / Be mine be love be mine / Finale act 2 / Nut brown maiden from the praire / Finale act 3/Waltz our worries away
CDTER 1051 / Mar '98 / TER

☐ COUNTESS MARITZA (Highlights) (New Sadler's Wells Opera Chorus/Orchestra)
Kalman, Emmerich *c*
Douglas, Nigel *l*
CDTEO 1007 / May '89 / TER

☐ COUNTRYMAN
Natural mystic: *Marley, Bob* / Rastaman chant: *Marley, Bob* / Theme from Countryman: *Badarou, Wally* / Rat race: *Marley, Bob* / Jah live: *Marley, Bob* / Three o'clock roadblock: *Marley, Bob* / Ramble: *Rico* / Sound system: *Steel Pulse* / Mosman skank: *Aswad* / Small axe: *Marley, Bob* / Sitting and watching: *Brown, Dennis*
RRCD 44 / May '94 / Reggae Refreshers

☐ COUSTEAU'S AMAZON VOL.1 (The River)
Scott, John *c*
Scott, John *con*
JSCD 104 / Jan '95 / JOS

☐ COUSTEAU'S AMAZON VOL.2 (The Indians)
Scott, John *c*
Scott, John *con*
JSCD 105 / Jan '95 / JOS

☐ COUSTEAU'S CAPE HORN & THE CHANNEL ISLANDS (Royal Philharmonic Orchestra/Berlin Radio Concert Orchestra)
Scott, John *c*
Scott, John *con*
JSCD 103 / Jan '93 / JOS

☐ COUSTEAU'S FIRST 75 YEARS/THE WARM BLOODED SEA
Scott, John *c*
Scott, John *con*
JSCD 108 / Jan '95 / JOS

☐ COUSTEAU'S PAPUA NEW GUINEA JOURNEY
Scott, John *c*
Scott, John *con*
JSCD 112 / Jan '93 / JOS

☐ COUSTEAU'S PARC OCEANIQUE (Purbrook, Colin & Royal Philharmonic Orchestra)
Scott, John *c*
Scott, John *con*
JSCD 106 / Jan '95 / JOS

☐ COUSTEAU'S ST. LAWRENCE/AUSTRALIA
Scott, John *c*
Scott, John *con*
JSCD 107 / Jan '95 / JOS

☐ COWBOYS, THE
Williams, John *c*
Williams, John *con*
VSD 5540 / Jul '95 / Varese Sarabande

☐ COWGIRLS (Cast Recording)
Murfitt, Mary *c*
Murfitt, Mary *l*
VSD 5740 / Oct '96 / Varese Sarabande

☐ CRADLE WILL ROCK, THE (1985 London Cast)
Blitzstein, Marc *c*
Moll's song / I'll show you guys / Solicitin' / Hard times/The sermon / Croon spoon / Freedom of the press / Let's do something / Honolulu / Summer weather / Love duet (Gus and Sadie) / Don't let me keep you / Ask us again / Art for art's sake / Nickel under your foot / Cradle will rock / Joe worker / Cradle will rock (Final scene)
CDTER 1105 / Oct '85 / TER

☐ CRAFT, THE (Score)
Revell, Graeme *c*
Simonec, T. *con*
VSD 5732 / Jul '96 / Varese Sarabande

☐ CRAFT, THE
Tomorrow never knows: *Our Lady Peace* / I have the touch: *Nova, Heather* / All this and nothing: *Sponge* / Dangerous type: *Letters To Cleo* / How soon is now: *Love Spit Love* / Dark secret: *Sweet, Matthew* / Witches song: *Hatfield, Juliana* / Jump into the fire: *Tripping Daisy* / Under the water: *Jewel* / Warning: *All Too Much* / Spastica: *Elastica* / Horror: *Spacehog* / Bells books and candles: *Revell, Graeme*
4841522 / Nov '96 / Columbia

☐ CRASH AND BURN (Band, Richard)
Band, Richard *c*
MAF 7033D / Nov '92 / Intrada

☐ CRAZY FOR YOU (1993 London Cast)
Gershwin, George *c*
Gershwin, Ira *l*
CASTCD 37 / Oct '93 / First Night

☐ CRAZY FOR YOU (Broadway Cast)
Gershwin, George *c*
Gershwin, Ira *l*
CDC 7546182 / Apr '93 / EMI Classics

☐ CRIMES OF PASSION (Wakeman, Rick)
Wakeman, Rick *c*
RWCDP 3 / Nov '93 / President

☐ CRIMETIME (Stewart, David A.)
Stewart, David A. *c*
POLLYPREM 002 / Dec '96 / Pollyanna

☐ CRIMINAL LAW
Goldsmith, Jerry *c*
VSD 5210 / Dec '88 / Varese Sarabande

☐ CRISS CROSS
Jones, Trevor *c*
MAF 7021D / Sep '92 / Intrada

☐ CRITTERS II (The Main Course)
Pike, Nicholas *c*
MAF 7045D / Jul '93 / Intrada

☐ CROCODILE DUNDEE (Best, Peter)
Best, Peter *c*
Mick and his mate / Cyril / Walkabout bounce / Goodnight Walter / In the truck / Buffalo / In the boat / Never never land / Death roll / Sunset / Nice one Skippy / Walk in the bush / Would you mind / Mick meets New York / G'day / Yessir / Mad bad and dangerous / Pimp / Stone the crows / That's not a knife / Oh Richard / Pimp returns / Crocodile Dundee
FILMCD 009 / Dec '86 / Silva Screen

☐ CROCODILE SHOES II (Nail, Jimmy)
0630169352 / Nov '96 / East West

☐ CROSSING DELANCEY
Chihara, Paul *c*
VSD 5201 / Dec '88 / Varese Sarabande

☐ CROW I, THE
Burn: *Cure* / Golgotha tenement blues: *Machines Of Loving Grace* / Big empty: *Stone Temple Pilots* / Dead souls: *Nine Inch Nails* / Darkness: *Rage Against The Machine* / Color me once: *Violent Femmes* / Ghost rider: *Rollins, Henry* / Milktoast: *Helmet* / Badge: *Pantera* / Slip slide melting: *For Love Not Lisa* / After the flesh: *My Life With The Thrill Kill Kult* / Snakedriver: *Jesus & Mary Chain* / Time baby II: *Medicine* / It can't rain all the time: *Siberry, Jane*
7567825192 / Mar '94 / WEA

☐ CROW I, THE (Score)
Revell, Graeme *c*
Birth of the legend / Resurrection / Crow descends / Remembrance / Rain forever / Her eyes...so innocent / Tracking the prey / Pain and retribution / Believe in angels / Captive child / Devil's night / On hallowed ground / Inferno / Return to the grave / Last rites
VSD 5499 / Jun '94 / Varese Sarabande

☐ CROW II, THE
5331472 / Nov '96 / Polydor

☐ CROW III, THE
1620472 / Jul '96 / Polydor

☐ CRUCIBLE, THE (Fenton, George)
Fenton, George *c*
Salem 1692 / Witch-hunt begins / Accusation / Resolution
09026686662 / Feb '97 / RCA Victor

☐ CRUMB
Boeddinghaus, David & Craig Ventresco *c*
Ragtime nightingale / Sensation rag / Harlem strut / Abraham Jefferson / Washington Lee / Belle of the Philippines / Last kind word blues / Radiator cap blues / Gabby glide medley / Frog-I-more Reg / Cocaine / Won't you fondle me medley / Pass the jug / Skinny leg blues / Buffalo rag / 35th Street blues / Mabel's dream / Wall Street rag / Hateful blues / Real slow drag / Comic montage stomp / Someday sweetheart / Rag pickings / Black diamond rag
RCD 10322 / Jul '95 / Rykodisc

☐ **CRY BABY**
King cry baby: *Intveld, James* / Doin' time: *Intveld, James* / Please Mr. Jailer: *Sweet, Rachel* / Teardrops are falling: *Intveld, James* / Mr. Sandman: *Baldwin & The Whiffles* / Bad boy: *Jive Bombers* / I'm so young: *Students* / I'm a bad bad girl: *Phillips, Esther* / Cherry: *Jive Bombers* / Sh-boom: *Baldwin & The Whiffles* / Teenage prayer: *Sweet, Rachel* / Cry baby: *Honey Sisters* / Nosey Joe: *Jackson, Bull Moose* / High school hellcats: *Intveld, James* / Flirt: *Shirley & Lee* / My heart goes: *Brown, Nappy* / Jungle drums: *Bostic, Earl* / Rubber biscuit: *Chips*
MCLD 19260 / Jun '94 / MCA

☐ **CRYING GAME, THE**
Crying game / Soldier's wife / Live for today (gospel) / It's in my nature / March to the execution / Let the music play / I'm thinking of your man / Dies irae / Live for today / White cliffs of Dover / Transformation / Live for today (orchestral) / Assassination / Crying game / Soldier's tale
5170242 / Jan '93 / Polydor

☐ **CURDLED**
Cumbia del sol: *Blazers* / El talisman: *Rosana* / Obsession confession: *Slash* / El punal y Corazon: *Cafe Tacuba* / Cumbia de Surf: *Gonzalez, Joseph Julian* / Cunbia del Monte: *Laza, Pedro* / Lunas rotas: *Rosana* / Guajira de Gabriela: *Gonzalez, Joseph Julian* / Cumbia Colombiana: *La Intergracion* / Mambo de Muerte: *Gonzalez, Joseph Julian* / Ritmo de Tambo: *La Sonora Dinamita* / Danza macabra suite: *Gonzalez, Joseph Julian* / Te Llevare: *Zuloaga, Tulio* / Buscandote: *Latin Brothers* / Jardin de amor: *Los Destellos* / Obsession: *Slash & Marta Sanchez*
GED 25103 / Feb '97 / Geffen

☐ **CURE, THE (Grusin, Dave)**
Grusin, Dave *c*
First visit / Battleship / Shopping cart ride / Soon as they find a cure / Candy montage / Gathering leaves / Bedtime/Big changes / Mississippi montage / Make mine a T-bone / Million light years / Found money / Chase and confrontation / Going home / We call it a miracle / Rain/Realization / Requiem / Last visit / Down the river/End credits
GRP 98282 / Jun '95 / GRP

☐ **CUTTHROAT ISLAND (London Symphony Orchestra)**
Debney, John *c*
FILMCD 178 / Apr '96 / Silva Screen

☐ **CYBERCITY 808**
DSCD 8 / Jan '95 / Demon

☐ **CYCLO**
Tiet, Ton-That *c*
74321301082 / May '96 / Milan

☐ **CYRANO DE BERGERAC**
Petit, Jean Claude *c*
Cyrano / Chandeliers / Magic lantern / Duel / Gate of Nesle / Roxane / No thank you / Letters / Count's visit / Marriage / Lute / Affected young ladies / Cyrano's declaration / Mad man / File / Arrival of Roxane / Spaniard's mass / Death of Christian / Song of the nuns / Revelation / Death of Cyrano
DRGCD 12602 / Jan '95 / DRG

☐ **CYRANO DE BERGERAC (Paris Opera Orchestra)**
Petit, Jean Claude *c*
Petit, Jean Claude *con*
Cyrano / Die leuchter / Die magische laterne / Das duell / Das tor von Nesle / Roxane / Nein danke / Die briefe / Der besuch des grafen / Die hochzeit / Die laute / Die damen der gesellschaft / Cyranos erklarung / Die verzweiflung / Der pfeifer / Roxanes ankunft / Die messe der spanier / Christians tod / Nonnengesang / Das gestandnis / Cyranos tod / Finale
CST 348046 / Jul '90 / Colosseum

D

☐ **DALLE ARDENNE ALL'INFERNO/IL SORRISO DEL GRANDE TENTATORE**
Morricone, Ennio *c*
CDCR 18 / Apr '97 / Silva Screen

☐ **DALLE ARDENNE ALL'INTERNO**
Morricone, Ennio *c*
SPALAX 14983 / Oct '96 / Spalax

☐ **DAMAGE**
Preisner, Zbigniew *c*
Introduction / Last time / Stephen / Anna / At the beginning / Cafe Royal / Anna II / Intimacy / Brussels - Paris / Lutecia hotel / Memories / In the country / Night / Dramatic departure / Late thought / Stephen II / Last time II / Fatal exit / Memories are made for this / Damage / End titles
VSD 5406 / Feb '93 / Varese Sarabande

☐ **DAMES AT SEA (1989 Touring Cast)**
Wise, Jim *c*
Haimsohn, George & Robin Miller *l*
Wall Street / It's you / Broadway baby / That mister man of mine / Choo choo honeymoon / Sailor of my dreams / Singapore Sue / Broadway baby (reprise) / Good times are here to stay / Entr'acte / Dames at sea / Beguine / Raining in my heart / There's something about you / Echo waltz / Star tar / Let's have a simple wedding / Dames at sea (overture)
CDTER 1169 / Jul '89 / TER

☐ **DAMES AT SEA (1968 Broadway Cast)**
Wise, Jim *c*
Haimsohn, George & Robin Miller *l*
Leonard, Richard J. *con*
SK 48214 / Nov '92 / Sony Broadway

☐ **DAMES/SAN FRANCISCO/SUZY**
Dames overture / When you were a smile on your mother's lips / I only have eyes for you / Try to see it my way / Girl at the ironing board / I only have eyes for you / Dames / Try to see it my way / San Francisco overture / Heart that's free / Holy city / Would you / Faust / Faust / Sempre libera degg'io / San Francisco / Nearer to thee / Did I remember
CD 60022 / Nov '97 / Great Movie Themes

☐ **DAMNED, THE/A SEASON IN HELL/ FOR THOSE I LOVED**
Jarre, Maurice *c*
DRGCD 32906 / Jul '95 / DRG

☐ **DANCE A LITTLE CLOSER (1983 Broadway Cast)**
Strouse, Charles *c*
Lerner, Alan Jay *l*
CDTER 1174 / Jul '90 / TER

☐ **DANCE TO THE MUSIC OF TIME**
20th century blues / Masculine woman and feminine men / Oxford / Huntercombe ball / My heart stood still / Blue room / Mountain greenery / Jean / It had to be you / Affair begins / End titles / My heart stood still / Ghosts / Moreland's piano quintet / Anything goes / It's a lovely day tomorrow / Kiss me goodnight / Whitehall / Thanks Mr. Roosevelt / Waltz of my heart / Someday I'll find you / Death of the novelist / Abduction from the Seraglio / Honours / Death of Widmerpool
MPRCD 002 / Nov '97 / MCI Music

☐ **DANCEHALL QUEEN**
Dancehall Queen: *Franklyn, Chevelle & Beenie Man* / Badman sonata: *Buccaneer* / What's the move: *Chaka Demus & Pliers* / Unbelievable: *Marley Girls* / My Jamaican guy: *Jones, Grace & Bounty Killer* / Tune in: *Bounty Killer & Sugar Minott* / Satisfaction guaranteed: *Franklyn, Chevelle & Red Dragon* / Nuff gal: *Beenie Man* / Joyride: *Wayne Wonder & Babycham*
5243962 / Sep '97 / Island Jamaica

☐ **DANCES WITH WOLVES**
Barry, John *c*
Barry, John *con*
Main title / Looks like a suicide / John Dunbar / Journey to Fort Sedgewick / Ride to Fort Hays / Death of Timmons / Two Socks - the wolf theme / Pawnee Attack / Kicking Bird's gift / Journey to the buffalo killing ground / Buffalo hunt / Stands with a fist / Remembers / Love theme / John Dunbar theme / Two Socks at play / Death of Cisco / Rescue of Dances With Wolves / Loss of the journal and the return to winter camp / Farewell and end title
ZK 66817 / Nov '95 / Mastersound

☐ **DANCING THRU THE DARK**
Paradise / Power and the glory / Jam it jam / Dancin' thru the dark / Shoe shine / I'm livin' a life of love / Caribbean queen (no more love on the run) / Get busy / People all around the world / So many people / Once in a lifetime
CHIP 92 / Mar '90 / Jive

☐ **DANGEROUS GROUND**
CHIP 181 / Mar '97 / Jive

☐ **DANGEROUS LIAISONS (Fenton, George)**
Fenton, George *c*
Dangerous liasons / O Malheureuse iphigenie / Beneath the surface / Her eyes are closing / Tourvel's flight / Concerto in A minor for 4 harpsichords / Success / Madame de Tourvel / Valmont's first move / Staircase / Key / Ombra mau fu / Ombra mai fu reprise / the mirror / Beyond my control
CDV 2583 / Mar '89 / Virgin

☐ **DANGEROUS MINDS**
Gangsta's paradise: *Coolio* / Curiosity: *Hall, Aaron* / Havin' thangs: *Big Mike* / Problems: *Rappin' 4-Tay* / True OG: *Mr. Dalvin & Static* / Put ya back into it: *Tre Black* / Don't go there: *Rappin' 4-Tay* / Feel the funk: *Immature* / It's alright: *Sista* / Message for your mind: *Rappin' 4-Tay* / Gin and juice: *Devante* / This is the life: *Wendy & Lisa*
MCD 11228 / Oct '95 / MCA

☐ **DANTE'S PEAK**
Frizzell, John *c*
VSD 5793 / Mar '97 / Varese Sarabande

☐ **DANZON**
Black tears / Traveller / To love and to live / Blue / Schubert's serenade / Magic flute / Long distance telephone / Perjured woman / Moorish woman
DRGCD 12605 / Jan '95 / DRG

☐ **DARK CITY**
Jones, Trevor *c*
Sway: *Kelsey, Anita* / Information: *Course Of Empire* / Just a touch away: *Echo & The Bunnymen* / Dark: *Numan, Gary* / Sleep now: *Hall, Hughes* / Night has a thousand eyes: *Kelsey, Anita* / Into the city / No more Mr. Quick / Emma / Strangers are tuning / Memories of shell beach / Wall / Living an illusion / You have the power
SMACD 810 / 26 May '98 / Madfish Movies

☐ **DARK EYES**
Lai, Francis *c*
For the love of your dark eyes / Great waltz / Gardens of the villa / Sonate en si bermol no.17 / Blue danube / Una voce poco fa / First night / Gallant night / Travelling to St Petersburg / Tzigane 2 / Transaltion of the letter / Chivalry / Governor / Ninna nanna / Ford / Liuli liuli / Dark eyes / HAdful
CDSBL 12592 / 23 Mar '98 / DRG

☐ **DARK HALF, THE (Munich Symphony Orchestra)**
Young, Christopher *c*
Young, Christopher *con*
VSD 5340 / Apr '93 / Varese Sarabande

☐ **DARK SHADOWS**
VSD 5702 / Sep '96 / Varese Sarabande

☐ **DARK STAR**
Carpenter, John *c*
VSD 5327 / Nov '92 / Varese Sarabande

☐ **DARLING BUDS OF MAY, THE (English Light Concert Orchestra)**
Guard, Barry *c*
Perfick / Pop's rolls royce / Home farm / Strawberry time / Devil's gallop / Calling all workers / Breath of French air / Gore Court march / One the river / Dinner in the shade / Hop picker's hop / Puffin' Billy / In a party mood / Girl in yellow / Gymkhana / Darling buds of May
CDMFP 6128 / Jul '94 / EMI

☐ **DAS BARBECU (1995 US Cast)**
VSD 5593 / Aug '95 / Varese Sarabande

☐ **DAY IN HOLLYWOOD, A NIGHT IN THE UKRAINE, A (1980 Broadway Cast)**
Lazarus, Frank *c*
Vosburgh, Dick *l*
Just go to the movies / Famous feet / I love a film cliche / Nelson / It all comes out of the piano / Best in the world / Doin' the production code / Night in the Ukraine / Samovar the lawyer
DRGCD 12580 / Mar '92 / DRG

☐ **DAY THE EARTH STOOD STILL, THE**
Herrmann, Bernard *c*
07822110102 / Apr '94 / Fox Film Scores

☐ **DAY THE FISH CAME, THE (Theodorakis, Mikis)**
Theodorakis, Mikis *c*
SR 50088 / May '94 / Varese Sarabande

☐ **DAYLIGHT**
Daylight / Latura's theme / Searching for a miracle / Survival / Kit's plan / Community is formed / Leaving George / Rats / Tunnel claims its own / Power / Short swim under water / Sandhog's chapel / Light at the end / Madelyne's fate / Whenever there is love / Don't go out with your friends tonite
UND 53024 / Dec '96 / Universal

☐ **DAYS OF HOPE (1991 London Cast)**
Goodall, Howard *c*
CDTER 1183 / Sep '91 / TER

☐ **DAZED AND CONFUSED**
74321166752 / 11 May '98 / Giant

☐ **DEAD AGAIN**
Doyle, Patrick *c*
Headlines / Final request / Walk down death row / Woman with no name / Winter 1948 / Two halves of the same person / It never rains in LA / I'm not Roman / Inga's secret / Hightower House / Fate happens / Death of a mad son / Door is closed / Dead again
D5339 / Aug '91 / Varese Sarabande

☐ **DEAD MAN (Young, Neil)**
Young, Neil *c*
9362461712 / Feb '96 / Reprise

☐ **DEAD MAN WALKING**
Dead man walkin': *Springsteen, Bruce* / In your mind: *Cash, Johnny* / Woman on the tier (I'll see you through): *Vega, Suzanne* / Promises: *Lovett, Lyle* / Face of love: *Khan, Nusrat Fateh Ali & Eddie Vedder* / Fall of Troy: *Waits, Tom* / Quality of mercy: *Shocked, Michelle* / Dead man walking (a dream like this): *Carpenter, Mary-Chapin* / Walk away: *Waits, Tom* / Ellis Unit One: *Earle, Steve* / Walkin' blind: *Smith, Patti* / Long road: *Khan, Nusrat Fateh Ali & Eddie Vedder*
4835342 / Apr '96 / Columbia

☐ **DEAD MEN DON'T WEAR PLAID**
Rozsa, Miklos *c*
Holdridge, Lee *con*
PCD 126 / Jan '93 / Prometheus

☐ **DEAD PRESIDENTS VOL.1**
If you want me to stay: *Sly & The Family Stone* / Walk on by: *Hayes, Isaac* / Payback: *Brown, James* / I'll be around: *Spinners* / Never gonna give you up: *White, Barry* / I miss you: *Melvin, Harold & The Bluenotes* / Get up and get down: *Dramatics* / If there's hell below: *Mayfield, Curtis* / Do right woman do right man: *Franklin, Aretha* / Where is the love: *Jesse & Trina* / Tired of being alone: *Green, Al* / Love train: *O'Jays* / Look of love: *Hayes, Isaac* / Dead Presidents theme: *Elfman, Danny*
PRDCD 4 / May '96 / Premier/EMI

☐ **DEAD PRESIDENTS VOL.2**
I got the feeling: *Brown, James* / Keep on pushing: *Impressions* / Smiling faces sometimes: *Undisputed Truth* / Right on for darkness: *Mayfield, Curtis* / Just my imagination: *Temptations* / Cowboys to girls: *Intruders* / Never gonna give you up: *Butler, Jerry* / I was made to love her: *Wonder, Stevie* / (Man oh man) I want to go back: *Impressions* / When something is wrong with my baby: *Sam & Dave* / We people darker than blue: *Mayfield, Curtis* / Ain't that a groove: *Mayfield, Curtis*
PRMDCD 5 / Sep '96 / Soundtracks

☐ **DEAD SOLID PERFECT (Tangerine Dream)**
Tangerine Dream *c*
Theme / In the pond / Beverly leaves / Of cads and caddies / Tournament montage / Whore in one / Sand trap / In the rough / Nine iron / US Open / My name is bad hair / In the hospital room / Welcome to Bushwood/Golfus interruptus / Deja vu (I've heard this before) / Birdie / Divot / Kenny and Donny montage / Off to see Beverly / Phone to Beverly / Nice shots / Sinking putts / Kenny's winning shot
FILMCD 079 / Mar '91 / Silva Screen

☐ **DEAD, THE**
North, Alex *c*
VCD 47341 / Jan '89 / Varese Sarabande

☐ **DEADLY CARE (Tangerine Dream)**
Tangerine Dream *c*
Deadly care / Paddles / Stolen pills / Strong drink / Bad morning / Wasted and sick / Hope for future / Hospital / In bed / Annie and father / More pills / In the Head Nurse's office / At the father's grave / Clean and sober
FILMCD 121 / Nov '92 / Silva Screen

☐ **DEAR DIARY**
Piovani, Nicola *c*
210542 / Nov '94 / Milan

☐ **DEAR WORLD (1969 Broadway Cast)**
Herman, Jerry *c*
Pippin, Donald *con*
SK 48220 / Nov '92 / Sony Broadway

☐ **DEAREST ENEMY (Jeffreys, Anne & Robert Sterling/Cast)**
Rodgers, Richard *c*
Hart, Lorenz *l*
AEICD 042 / May '98 / AEI

☐ **DEATH BECOMES HER**
Silvestri, Alan *c*
VSD 5375 / Aug '92 / Varese Sarabande

☐ **DEATH RIDES A HORSE/A PISTOL FOR RINGO**
Morricone, Ennio *c*
OST 107 / Jan '93 / Milano Dischi

☐ **DEEP COVER**
Deep cover: *Snoop Doggy Dogg* / Love or lust: *Jewell* / Down with my nigga: *Paradise* / Sex is on: *Po', Broke & Lonely* / Way (is in the house): *Calloway* / Minute you fall in love: *3RD Avenue* / John and Betty's theme: *Colombier, Michel* / Mr. Loverman: *Shabba Ranks* / I see ya Jay: *Ragtime* / Nickel slick nigga: *Ko-Kane* / Typical relationship: *Times 3* / Digits: *Deele* / Sound of one hand clapping: *Calloway* / Why you frontin' on me: *Emmage*
4716692 / Feb '93 / Epic

☐ **DEEP IMPACT**
Horner, James *c*
Horner, James *con*
Distant discovery / Crucial rendezvous / Our best hope / Comet's sunrise / National lottery / Wedding / Long return home / Sad news / Leo's decision / President's speech / Drawing straws / Goodbye and Godspeed
SK 60690 / Jun '98 / Sony Classical

☐ **DEEP IN THE HEART (OF TEXAS)**
Just a wave not the water: *Gilmore, Jimmie Dale* / Just on elove: *Nelson, Willie & Kimmie Rhodes* / Deep in the West: *Jennings, Waylon & Jesse Coulter* / Panhandle Jane: *Dayton, Jesse* / Rolling stone from Texas: *Walser, Don* / Hill country hillbilly gal: *Hancock, Wayne* / Boxcars: *Flores, Rosie* / Voodoo man: *White, Lavelle* / Stop these teardrops: *Barton, Lou Ann* / Lone star shootout: *Hunter, Long John* / La ti da: *Ball, Marcia* / This time Lucille: *Hyatt, Walter* / Last call: *Hyatt, Walter*
SHANCD 6033 / Jul '98 / Shanachie

☐ **DEEP RISING**
Goldsmith, Jerry *c*
162120 / 26 Jan '98 / Hollywood

☐ **DEF CON 4**
Young, Christopher *c*
MAF 7010D / Jan '94 / Intrada

☐ **DELIVERANCE (Weissberg, Eric & Steve Mandell)**
Weissberg, Eric *c*
Duellin' banjos / Little Maggie / Shuckin' the corn / Pony Express / Old Joe Clark / Eight more miles to Louisville / Farewell blues / Earl's breakdown / End of a dream / Buffalo gals / Reuben's train / Riding the waves / Fire on the mountain / Eighth of January / Bugle call rag / Hard ain't it hard / Mountain dew / Rawhide
246214 / Sep '88 / WEA

☐ **DELORES CLAIBORNE (Elfman, Danny)**
Elfman, Danny *c*
VSD 5602 / Mar '95 / Varese Sarabande

☐ **DELTA FORCE II (European Symphony Orchestra)**
Talgorn, Frederic *c*
A 8921 / Feb '92 / Alhambra

☐ **DELUSION (Adamson, Barry)**
Adamson, Barry *c*
IONIC 4CD / Aug '91 / The Fine Line

☐ **DEMOLITION MAN**
Goldenthal, Elliot *c*
Sheffer, Jonathan/A.Kane *con*
Dies irae / Fire fight / Guilty as charged / Action guns fun / Machine waltz / Defrosting / Confronting the Chief / Museum duel / Subterranean slugfest / Meeting Cocteau / Tracking Simon Phoenix / Obligatory car chase / Flawless pearl / Final confrontation / Code 187 / Silver screen kiss
VSD 5447 / Nov '93 / Varese Sarabande

☐ DES FEMMES DISPARAISSENT/LES TRICHEURS (Blakey, Art & The Jazz Messengers)
Generique Pierre et Beatrice / Nasol / Tom poursuite dans la ruelle / Ne chucote pas / Mambo dans la voiture / Merlin juste pour eux seuls / Blues pour doudou / Blues pour Marcel / Blues pour Vava / Pasquier / Quaglio / La divorce de Leo Fall / Suspense Tom et Nasol / Des femmes disparaissent / Final pour Pierre et Beatrice / Les tricheurs / Clo's blues / Phil's tune / Mic's jump / Crazy Hamp
8347522 / Mar '94 / Fontana

☐ DESERT SONG/THE NEW MOON/THE BLUE TRAIN (Cast Recording)
GEMMCD 9100 / May '94 / Pearl

☐ DESPERADO
Cancion del Mariachi: *Los Lobos & Antonio Banderas* / Six blade knife: *Dire Straits* / Jack the ripper: *Wray, Link & The Waymen* / Manifold de amor: *Latin Playboys* / Forever night shade Mary: *Latin Playboys* / Pass the hatchet: *Roger & The Gypsies* / Bar fight: *Los Lobos* / Strange face of love: *Tito & Tarantula* / Bucho's gragias/Navajas attacks: *Los Lobos* / Bulletproof: *Los Lobos* / Bella: *Santana* / Quedate aqui: *Hayek, Salma* / Rooftop action: *Los Lobos* / Phone call: *Los Lobos* / White train: *Tito & Tarantula* / Back to the house that love built: *Tito & Tarantula* / Let love reign: *Los Lobos* / Mariachi suite: *Los Lobos*
4809442 / Jan '96 / Epic

☐ DESPERATE HOURS
Mansfield, David *c*
Chase / Nancy slashes the jaguar / Jailbreak / Tim leaves with Zeck / Too many bad memories / Into the lake / Tim meets Bosworth / Nancy's apartment / May meets Bosworth / Tim stabbed / Tim and Nora's theme / Albert leaves / Dumping the body / I'll be back / Albert persued / Give me the Gun / Tim and Nora / Bosworth and the FBI / Stadium / Aftermath / End credits
VSD 5284 / Oct '90 / Varese Sarabande

☐ DESPERATE REMEDIES
Scholes, Peter *c*
887938 / May '94 / Milan

☐ DESPERATELY SEEKING SUSAN
Newman, Thomas *c*
Leave Atlantic City / Port Authority by night / New York by day / Through the viewscope / St. Mark's place / Key and a picture of Battery Park / Amnesia / Jail / Port Authority by day / Rain / Running with birds in cages / Trouble almost / Chemtek promo video / Ulysses' escape / Night visit / Frankie's drive / Ulysses / In the lab / Sondra and Jeff / Mr. Right / Wedding reception / Parting glance
VSD 47291 / Feb '90 / Varese Sarabande

☐ DESPERATELY SEEKING SUSAN/ MAKING MR RIGHT
Newman, Thomas *c*
VCD 47291 / Aug '91 / Varese Sarabande

☐ DESTRY RIDES AGAIN (1979 London Cast)
Rome, Harold *c*
Bottle neck / Ladies / Hoop-de-dingle / Tomorrow morning / Ballad of gun / I know your kind / I hate him / Anyone would love you / Every once in a while / Destry rides again: Finale act I / Are you ready Gyp Watson / Not guilty / Only time will tell / That ring on the finger / I say hello / Destry rides again: Finale act II / Curtain call
CDTER 1034 / Dec '94 / TER

☐ DEVIL IN A BLUE DRESS
West side baby: *Walker, T-Bone* / Ain't nobody's business: *Witherspoon, Jimmy* / Ellington duke / Hy-ah Su: *Ellington, Duke* / Hop skip and jump: *Milton, Roy* / Good rockin' tonight: *Harris, Wynonie* / Blues after hours: *Crayton, Pee Wee* / I can't go on without you: *Jackson, Bull Moose* / Round midnight: *Monk, Thelonius* / Chicken shack boogie: *Milburn, Amos* / Messin' around: *Memphis Slim* / Chica boo: *Glenn, Lloyd* / Theme from Devil In A Blue Dress: *Bernstein, Elmer* / Malibu chase: *Bernstein, Elmer*
4813792 / Dec '95 / Columbia

☐ DEVIL'S OWN, THE
Horner, James *c*
Horner, James *con*
Main title / God be with you / Ambush / Irish Republican Navy / New world / Launching the boat / Secrets untold / Pool hall / Rory's arrest/Diaz is killed / Quiet goodbyes / Rooftop escape / Mortal blow / Going home
TBCD 1204 / Apr '97 / Tommy Boy

☐ DI QUESTO NON SI PARLA
Piovani, Nicola *c*
887865 / Jan '95 / Milan

☐ DIABOLIQUE
0022582CIN / Jul '96 / Edel

☐ DIAMONDS ARE FOREVER
Barry, John *c*
Diamonds are forever: *Bassey, Shirley* / Moon buggy ride / Bond meets Bambi and Thumper / Circus circus / Death at the Whyte house / Bond smells a rat / Tiffany case / 007 and counting / Q's trick / To hell with blofeld
CZ 554 / Dec '95 / Premier/EMI

☐ DIARY OF ANNE FRANK, THE
Newman, Alfred *c*
Newman, Alfred *con*
TSU 0122 / May '95 / Tsunami

☐ DIDIER
Chany, Philippe *c*
LBS 10970102 / Aug '97 / XIII Bis

☐ DIE HARD II (Kamen, Michael)
Kamen, Michael *c*
Colonel Stuart / General Esperanza / Church / Runaway / Icicle / Terminal / Baggage handling / Annexe skywalk / Doll / In the plane / Snowmobiles / Finlandia
VSD 5273 / Jul '90 / Varese Sarabande

☐ DIE HARD WITH A VENGEANCE
Kamen, Michael *c*
Summer in the city: *Lovin' Spoonful* / Goodbye Bonwits: *Kamen, Michael* / John and Zeus: *Kamen, Michael* / Papaya King: *Kamen, Michael* / Take another train: *Kamen, Michael* / Waltz of the bankers: *Kamen, Michael* / Gold vault: *Kamen, Michael* / Surfing in the aquaduct: *Kamen, Michael* / Got it covered: *Fu-Schnickens* / In front of the kids: *Extra Prolific* / Iron foundry: *Mosolov*
09026683062 / 11 May '98 / RCA

☐ DIE ZWEITE HEIMAT
Mamangakis, Nikos *c*
BM 3018 / Jan '96 / Bella Musica

☐ DIFFERENT FOR GIRLS
OCD 010 / 13 Apr '98 / Ocean Deep

☐ DINER
Brody, Bruce *c*
ASTCD 4004 / Nov '96 / Astrion Audio

☐ DIRTY DANCING
I've had the time of my life: *Medley, Bill & Jennifer Warnes* / Be my baby: *Ronettes* / She's like the wind: *Swayze, Patrick & Wendy Fraser* / Hungry eyes: *Carmen, Eric* / Stay: *Williams, Maurice & The Zodiacs* / Yes: *Clayton, Merry* / You don't own me: *Blow Monkeys* / Hey baby: *Channel, Bruce* / Overload: *Zappacosta* / Love is strange: *Mickey & Sylvia* / Where are you tonight: *Johnston, Tom* / In the still of the nite: *Five Satins*
BD 86408 / Oct '87 / RCA

☐ DIRTY DANCING - MORE DIRTY DANCING
I've had the time of my life: *Morris, John Orchestra* / Big girls don't cry: *Four Seasons* / Merengue: *Lloyd, Michael & Le Disc* / Some kind of wonderful: *Drifters* / Johnny's mambo: *Lloyd, Michael & Le Disc* / Do you love me: *Contours* / Love man: *Redding, Otis* / Wipeout: *Surfaris* / These arms of mine: *Redding, Otis* / De todo un poco: *Lloyd, Michael & Le Disc* / Cry to me: *Burke, Solomon* / Trot the fox: *Lloyd, Michael & Le Disc* / Will you still love me tomorrow: *Shirelles* / Kellerman's anthem: *Emile Bergstein Chorale*
74321369152 / Jun '96 / RCA

☐ DISCLOSURE
Morricone, Ennio *c*
Serene family / Unusual approach / With energy and decision / Virtual reality / Preparation and victory / Disclosure / Sad family / Unemployed / Sex and computers / Computers and work / Sex and power / First passacaglia / Second passacaglia / Third passacaglia / Sex power and computers
CDVMM 16 / Feb '95 / Virgin

☐ DIVINE MADNESS (Midler, Bette)
7567814762 / Feb '92 / Atlantic

☐ DIVORCE ME DARLING (1965 London Cast)
Wilson, Sandy *c*
Wilson, Sandy *l*
Overture / Here we are in Nice again / Someone to dance with / Whatever happened to love / Lights! Music / On the loose / Maisie / Paradise hotel / No harm done / Together again / Divorce me darling / Here am I (but where's the guy) / Out of step / You're absolutely me / Back where we started / Blondes for danger / Swing time is here to stay / Finale
CDTER 1245 / Nov '97 / TER

☐ DO I HEAR A WALTZ (Broadway Cast)
Rodgers, Richard *c*
Sondheim, Stephen *l*
Dvonch, Frederick *con*
SK 48206 / Jan '93 / Sony Broadway

☐ DOA
Jankel, Chas *c*
VCD 70461 / Aug '91 / Varese Sarabande

☐ DOCTEUR CHANCE
3035632 / 24 Apr '98 / Arcade

☐ DOCTOR DOLITTLE (Harrison, Rex & Samantha Eggar/Anthony Newley & 1967 Film Cast)
Bricusse, Leslie *c*
Bricusse, Leslie *l*
Newman, Lionel *con*
Overture / My friend the doctor / Vegetarian / Talk to the animals / At the crossroads / I've never seen anything like it / Beautiful things / When I look in your eyes / Like animals / After today / Fabulous places / Where are the worlds / I think I like you / Doctor Dolittle / Something in your smile / My friend the Doctor
5545272 / Jul '98 / Spectrum

☐ DOCTOR DOLITTLE
That's the way I lie: *Ray J* / Let's ride: *Jordan, Montell & Shaunta* / Are you that somebody: *Aaliyah* / Same ol' g: *Ginuwine* / Lady marmalade: *All Saints* / Da funk: *Timberland* / Do little things: *Changing Faces & Ivan Matias* / Woof woof: *69 Boys* / Rocksteady: *Robinson, Dawn* / In your world: *Twista & Speed Knot Mobsters* / Loving you so: *Watley, Jody* / Your dress: *Palya* / Dance: *Robin S & Mary Mary* / Push 'em up: *Kane, Eddie & Deville* / Ain't nothin' but a party: *Sugarhill Gang*
7567831131 / 13 Jul '98 / Atlantic

☐ DOCTOR DOLITTLE (Highlights)
78067472042 / 14 Jul '98 / Drive Archive

☐ DOCTOR JEKYLL AND MR. HYDE
McKenzie, Mark *c*
MAF 7063D / Apr '96 / Intrada

☐ DOCTOR NO
Norman, Monty *c*
Norman, Monty *con*
James Bond / Kingston calypso / Island speaks / Under the mango tree / Jump up / Dr. No's fantasy / Boy chase / Love at last / Jamaican rock / Audio bongo / Twisting with James / Jamaica jazz
CZ 558 / Dec '95 / Premier/EMI

☐ DOCTOR QUINN MEDICINE WOMAN
SI 8804 / 12 May '98 / Sonic Images

☐ DOCTOR WHO: EARTHSHOCK (Classic Music From The BBC Radiophonic Workshop I) (BBC Radiophonic Workshop)
Tardis / Sea devils / Meglos / Keeper of Traken / Four to doomsday / Leisure hive / Arc of infinity / Warrior's gate / Earthshock
FILMCD 709 / Nov '92 / Silva Screen

☐ DOCTOR WHO: EVOLUTION
McCulloch, Keff & Ron Grainger/Dominic Green *c*
Tardis / Dr. Who / Gavrok's search / Child's return / Towers el paradiso / Burton's escape / Drinksmat dawning / Future pleasure / Newsreel past / Sting / Dr. Who / Dr. Who / 8891 royale / White flag / Guards of silence / Making of pex / Cemetery chase / Brain / Here's to the future / Goodbye Doctor
RDSGP 0320 / May '97 / Prestige

☐ DOCTOR WHO: GHOSTLIGHT (Ayres, Mark)
Ayres, Mark *c*
Madhouse / Redvers I presume / Uncharted territory / Heart of the interior / Enter Josiah Indoor lightning / Nimrod observed / Time to emerge / Burnt toast / Ace's adventures underground / Where's is Mamma / Way to the zoo / Memory teller / Lighting the touchpaper / Homo victorianus ineptus / Light enlightened / Tropic of Perivale / Tricks of the light / Judgement in stone / Requiem / Passing thoughts
FILMCD 133 / Jun '93 / Silva Screen

☐ DOCTOR WHO: MYTHS AND OTHER LEGENDS
Ayres, Mark *c*
FILMCD 088 / '94 / Silva Screen

☐ DOCTOR WHO: PYRAMIDS OF MARS (Blair, Heathcliff)
Simpson, Dudley *c*
Ark in space / Planet of evil / Brain of Morbius / Genesis of the Daleks / Pyramids of Mars
FILMCD 134 / '94 / Silva Screen

☐ DOCTOR WHO: THE CURSE OF FENRIC (Ayres, Mark)
Ayres, Mark *c*
Introduction: Doctor Who / Boats / Beach-head and rat-trap / Sealed orders / Eyes watching / Commander Milington / Viking graves / Maidens' point / Translations / Audrey and Milington's office / Curse of Fenric / High stakes / Crypt / Ambush / Well of Vergelmir / Ultima machine / Dangerous undercurrents / Seduction of Prozorov / Half-time score / Exit Miss Hardaker/The vicar and the vampires / Stop the machine / Haemovores / Battle for St. Jude's / Mineshaft / Sealing the hatch / House guests / Telegram / Evil from the dawn of time / Storm breaks / Ancient enemies / Shadow dimensions / Chemical grenade / Great serpent / Pawns in the game / Kathleen's escape / Wolves of Fenric / Black wins Time Lord / Final battle / Epilogue: Doctor Who
FILMCD 087 / Apr '94 / Silva Screen

☐ DOCTOR WHO: THE FIVE DOCTORS (Classic Music From The BBC Radiophonic Workshop II) (BBC Radiophonic Workshop)
Five doctors / King's demons / Enlightenment / Warriors of the deep / Awakening / Resurrection of the Daleks / Planet of fire / Caves of Androzani
FILMCD 710 / Nov '92 / Silva Screen

☐ DOCTOR WHO: THE GREATEST SHOW IN THE GALAXY (Ayres, Mark)
Ayres, Mark *c*
Introduction: Doctor Who / Psychic rap / Invitation to segonax / Bellboy and flowerchild / Warning / Fellow explorers / Robot attacks / Something sinister / Welcome one and all / Circus ring / Deadbeat / Eavesdropping / Let me entertain you/Stone archway / Well / Powers on the move / Sifting dreams / Survival of the fittest / Bellboy's sacrifice / Plans / Werewolf/Request stop / Gods of Ragnarok / Playing for time / Entry of the psychic clowns / Liberty who / Psychic carnival / Coda: Kingpin's new circus / Epilogue: Doctor Who
FILMCD 114 / Feb '92 / Silva Screen

☐ DOCTOR WHO: THE TOMB OF THE CYBERMEN
VSATASTRA 3967 / Jul '97 / Via Satellite

☐ DOCTOR WHO: THE WORLDS OF DOCTOR WHO (Music Sampler)
Doctor Who / Tardis / World of Doctor Who / Sea devils / Ark in space / Pyramids of Mars / Brain of Morbius / Doctor Who themes / Meglos / Five Doctors / Caves of Androzani / Myth Makers theme / Doctor Who - Terror Vision / Terror in Trotter's Lane / Greatest show in the galaxy / Ghost light / Curse of Fenric / Return to Devil's End
FILMCD 715 / Apr '94 / Silva Screen

☐ DOCTOR WHO: VARIATIONS ON A THEME
Doctor Who - Mood version: *Ayres, Mark* / Doctor Who - Terror version: *Glynn, Dominic* / Doctor Who - Latin version: *McCulloch, Keff* / Panopticon eight: *Ayres, Mark*
FILMCD 706 / '94 / Silva Screen

☐ DOCTOR ZHIVAGO
Jarre, Maurice *c*
Jarre, Maurice *con*
Overture / Main title / Kontakion/Funeral song / Lara is charming / Internationale / Lara and Komarovsky dancing up a storm / Komarovsky with Lara in the hotel / Interior student cafe / Sventitsky's waltz/After the shooting / Military parade / They began to go home / After deserters killed the Colonel / At the hospital / Lara says goodbye to Yuri / Tonya greets Yuri / Stove's out / Yevgraf snaps his fingers / Evening bells - Moscow Station / Flags flying over the train / Yuri gazing through a tiny open hatch / Door is banged open / Intermission / Yuri follows the sound of the waterfall / Tonya and Yuri arrive at Varykino / They didn't lock the cottage / Varykino cottage winter snow / Yuri and the daffodils / On a Yuriatin street / In Lara's bedroom / Yuri rides to Yuriatin / Yuri is taken prisoner by the Red Partisans / For as long as we need you / Yuri is escaping / Yuri approaches Lara's apartment / Yuri looks into the mirror / Lara and Yuri arriving at Varykino / Yuri is trying to write / Yuri frightens the wolves away / Lara reads her poem / Yuri frightens the wolves away pt.2 / Yuri works on / Then it's a gift / Lara's theme
CDODEON 1 / Feb '96 / Premier/EMI

☐ DOMINICK AND EUGENE
Jones, Trevor *c*
VCD 70454 / Jan '89 / Varese Sarabande

☐ DON JUAN DEMARCO (London Metropolitan Orchestra)
Kamen, Michael *c*
Kamen, Michael *con*
Have you ever really loved a woman: *Adams, Bryan* / Habanera: *Kamen, Michael* / Don Juan: *Kamen, Michael* / I was born in Mexico: *Kamen, Michael* / Love at first sight (mother and father): *Kamen, Michael* / Dona Julia: *Kamen, Michael* / Don Alfonso: *Kamen, Michael* / Arabia: *Kamen, Michael* / Don Octavia del Flores: *Kamen, Michael* / Dona Ana: *Kamen, Michael*
5403572 / Jan '95 / A&M

☐ DONNIE BRASCO
1621022 / May '97 / Polydor

☐ DON'T BE A MENACE TO SOUTH CENTRAL (While Drinking Your Juice In The Hood)
5241462 / Feb '96 / Island

☐ DOOM GENERATION, THE (Teen Is A Four Letter Word)
Intro: *Blue, Amy* / On the wheel: *Curve* / This heaven: *Love & Rockets* / Summerblink: *Cocteau Twins* / Christianity: *Wolfgang Press* / Paradise now: *Meat Beat Manifesto* / Already there: *Verve* / Penetration: *Jesus & Mary Chain* / But if you go: *MC 900 ft Jesus* / Undertow: *Lush* / Double coupon: *Babyland* / Slut: *Medicine* / Groovy is my name: *Pizzicato Five* / Violator: *Extra Fancy* / Blue skied an' clear: *Slowdive*
74321318722 / Sep '96 / American

☐ DOORS, THE (Doors)
Movie / Riders on the storm / Love street / Break on through / End / Light my fire / Ghost song / Roadhouse blues / Heroin / Carmina burana / Stoned immaculate / When the music's over / Severed garden / LA Woman
7559610472 / Mar '91 / WEA

☐ DOUBLE IMPACT
Kempel, Arthur *c*
FILMCD 110 / '91 / Silva Screen

☐ DOUBLE INDEMNITY (& The Killers/ Lost Weekend) (New Zealand Symphony Orchestra)
Rozsa, Miklos *c*
Sedares, James *con*
373752 / Apr '97 / Koch International

☐ DOWN BY LAW/VARIETY
Lurie, John *c*
What do you know about music you're not a lawyer / Strangers in the day / Promenade du maquereau / Invasion of Poland / Please come to my house / Are you warm enough / Swamp / Swamp (part 2) / Are you warm enough again / King of Thailand the Queen of Stairs / Hundred miles from Harry / Nicoletta can't cook / Fork in road / Variety theme / Porno booth / Porno booth II / Car / Million dollar walk / Anders leaps in / Garter belt / End titles
MTM 14 / Apr '96 / Made To Measure

☐ DOWNTIME
Levine, Ian *c*
FILMCD 717 / Nov '95 / Silva Screen

☐ DRACULA (1992 Version)
Kilar, Wojciech *c*
Dracula / Beginning / Vampire hunters / Mina's photo / Lucy's party / Brides / Storm / Love remembered / Hunt builds / Hunter's prelude / Green mist / Mina/Dracula / Ring of fire / Love eternal / Ascension / End credits / Love song for a vampire: *Lennox, Annie*
4727462 / Sep '96 / Columbia

☐ DRACULA (Hammer Presents) (Lee, Christopher & Hammer City Orchestra)
Bernard, James *c*
Dracula / Four faces of evil
BGOCD 240 / Mar '95 / Beat Goes On

☐ DRAGONHEART
Edelman, Randy *c*
World of the heart - Main title / To the stars / Wonders of an ancient glory / Einon / Last dragon slayer / Bowen's ride / Mexican standoff / Draco / Refreshing swim / Re-baptism / Bowen's decoy / Kyle the wheat boy / Connection / Flight to Avalon / Finale
MCD 11449 / Oct '96 / MCA

☐ DRAT THE CAT (Studio Cast)
Schafer, Milton *c*
VSD 5721 / 15 Sep '97 / Varese Sarabande

☐ DRAUGHTSMAN'S CONTRACT, THE
Nyman, Michael *c*
Queen of the night / Disposition of the linen / Watery death / Garden is becoming a robe room / Chasing sheep is best left to shepherds / Eye for optical theory / Bravura in the face of grief
CASCD 1158 / Aug '95 / Charisma

☐ DRAW/RED RIVER (National Philharmonic Orchestra/Little Mountain Studio Symphony Orchestra)
Wannberg, Ken *c*
Wannberg, Ken *con*
PCD 129 / Oct '94 / Prometheus

☐ DREAM LOVER
Young, Christopher *c*
Anthony, Pete *con*
387002 / Dec '94 / Koch

☐ DREAM WITH THE FISHES
SNACD 811 / 13 Jul '98 / Snapper

☐ DRESSED TO KILL
Donaggio, Pino *c*
VCD 47148 / Jan '89 / Varese Sarabande

☐ DRIFTWOOD
OCD 03 / Mar '97 / Ocean Deep

☐ DRIVING MISS DAISY
Zimmer, Hans *c*
VSD 5246 / Feb '90 / Varese Sarabande

☐ DROP ZONE
Zimmer, Hans *c*
Drop Zone / Hyphopera / Hijack / Terry's dropped out / Flashback and fries / Miami jump / Too many notes not enough rests / After the dub
VSD 5581 / Dec '94 / Varese Sarabande

☐ DROWNING BY NUMBERS (Nyman, Michael Band)
Nyman, Michael *c*
Trysting fields / Sheep and tides / Great death game / Drowning by number 3 / Wheelbarrow walk / Dead man's catch / Drowning by number 2 / Bees in trees / Fish beach / Wedding tango / Crematorium conspiracy / Knowing the ropes / End game
CDVE 23 / Aug '88 / Venture

☐ DU BARRY WAS A LADY/THE SKY'S THE LIMIT/42ND STREET
Du Barry was a lady / Well git it / Do I love you: *Kelly, Gene* / Salome: *O'Brien, Virginia* / I love an esquire girl: *Skelton, Red & Dick Haymes* / Katie went to Haiti / Madame I loev your crepes suzettes: *Skelton, Red* / Friendship / My shining hour: *Leslie, Joan* / My shining hour: *Astaire, Fred & Joan Leslie* / I've got a lot in common with you: *Astaire, Fred & Joan Leslie* / My shining hour: *Slack, Freddie Orchestra* / One for my baby: *Astaire, Fred* / 42nd street overture: *Astaire, Fred* / You're getting to be a habit with me: *Astaire, Fred* / Shuffle off to Buffalo / Young and healthy: *Powell, Dick* / 42nd street: *Powell, Dick & Ruby Keeler*
CD 60010 / Jun '97 / Great Movie Themes

☐ DUBARRY, THE/MADAME POMPADOUR (London Cast)
Millocker, Carl/Leo Fall *c*
Leigh, Rowland/Harry Graham *l*
GEMMCD 9068 / Nov '93 / Pearl

☐ DUE SOUTH VOL.1 (Music From The TV Series)
62428400042 / Nov '96 / Nettwerk

☐ DUE SOUTH VOL.2
400072 / 1 Jun '98 / Nettwerk

☐ DUEL AT DIABLO/HORSE SOLDIERS
Hefti, Neal *c*
W 9105 / 14 Apr '98 / Taran

☐ DUSTY SPRINGFIELD STORY, THE (Original Cast)
OCD 015 / 29 Jun '98 / Ocean Deep

☐ DUTCH
D5336 / Aug '91 / Varese Sarabande

☐ DUTCH HARBOR
ALP 85CD / Feb '97 / Atavistic

☐ DYING YOUNG
Howard, James Newton *c*
Dying young: *Kenny G.* / Driving North/Moving in/ The Clock/Love montage/The Maze: *Kenny G & James Newton Howard* / All the way: *Osborne, Jeffrey* / Hillary's theme/Victor teaches art/The bluff/ San Francisco/V: *Kenny G & James Newton Howard* / All the way: *King Curtis* / I'll never leave you: *Kenny G & James Newton Howard*
261952 / 1 Sep '97 / Arista

E

☐ EARTHQUAKE
Williams, John *c*
VSD 5262 / Apr '91 / Varese Sarabande

☐ EASTER PARADE (1948 Film Cast)
Berlin, Irving *c*
Green, Johnny *con*
Main title / Happy Easter / Drum crazy / It only happens when I dance with you / Happy Easter (reprise 1) / Everybody's doin' it now / I want to go back to Michigan (down on the farm) / Happy Easter (reprise 2) / Making faces / Beautiful faces need beautiful clothes / This is the life (Dog act) / Along came Ruth / Call me up some rainy afternoon / Fella with an umbrella / Vaudeville montage / I love a piano / Snookey ookums / Ragtime violin / When the midnight choo-choo leaves for Alabam / Mixed greens / That international rag / Shakin' the blues away / It only happens when I dance with you / Fanfare and montage - Globe Theatre / Steppin' out with my baby / Mr. Monotony / Couple of swells / Roof garden (drum crazy reprise) / Girl on the magazine cover / New Amsterdam roof / Better luck next time / End title
CDODEON 4 / Feb '96 / Premier/EMI

☐ EASY COME, EASY GO/SPEEDWAY (Presley, Elvis)
Easy come easy go / Love machine / Yoga is as yoga does / You gotta stop / Sing you children / I'll take love / She's a machine / Love machine (alternate take) / Sing you children (alternate take) / She's a machine (alternate take 13) / Suppose (alternate mater) / Speedway / There ain't nothing like a song / Your time hasn't come yet baby / Who are you who am I / He's your uncle not your dad / Let yourself go / Five sleepy heads / Suppose / Your groovy self
07863665582 / Mar '95 / RCA

☐ EASY RIDER
Pusher: *Steppenwolf* / Born to be wild: *Steppenwolf* / Weight: *Band* / I wasn't born to follow: *Byrds* / If you want to be a bird: *Holy Modal Rounders* / Don't Bogart me: *Fraternity of Man* / If six was nine: *Hendrix, Jimi Experience* / Kyrie Eleison Mardi Gras: *Electric Prunes* / It's alright Ma (I'm only bleeding): *McGuinn, Roger* / Ballad of Easy Rider: *McGuinn, Roger*
MCLD 19153 / Nov '92 / MCA

☐ EASY RIDER (Songs From & Inspired By The Film)
NTRCD 027 / Sep '94 / Quality

☐ EDDIE
5242432 / 15 Sep '97 / Island

☐ EDGE, THE
Goldsmith, Jerry *c*
Goldsmith, Jerry *con*
Lost in the wild / Ravine / Birds / Mighty hunter / Bitter coffee / Stalking / Deadfall / River / Rescued / Edge
09026689502 / 23 Feb '98 / RCA Victor

☐ ED'S NEXT MOVE
Golson, Benny *c*
Tea and symphony: *Comedians* / Manhattan bound: *Golson, Benny* / Looking for a home: *Golson, Benny* / Look away: *Stubborn All Stars* / City walking: *Golson, Benny* / Spoken word: *Ed's Redeeming Qualities* / Morning groove: *Golson, Benny* / Something there: *Golson, Benny* / Planet Robin: *Trouble Dolls* / She ate the fly: *Ed's Redeeming Qualities* / I'm just feeling it now: *Williams, Jane Kelly* / Rough at first: *Golson, Benny* / Lonesome bus: *Mr. Henry* / Buck tempo: *Ed's Redeeming Qualities* / Another turn in the road: *Golson, Benny* / More bad times: *Ed's Redeeming Qualities*
74321413362 / Jul '97 / Milan

☐ EDUCATING RITA (Hentschel, David)
Hentschel, David *c*
Educating Rita / Franks theme Pt. 1 (A dead good poet) / Franks theme Pt. 2 / Variations on Frank and Rita (Innocence and experience) / Educating Rita (reprise) / Thought for Rita Pt. 1 / University challenge / Burning books / Franks theme pt. 3 (Virginia Charlotte Jane or Emily) / Thought for Rita Pt. 2 / Educated woman / Macbeth
C5CD 587 / Mar '98 / See For Miles

☐ EDWARD SCISSORHANDS (Elfman, Danny)
Elfman, Danny *c*
Main title / Story time / Castle on the hill / Cookie factory / Edwardo the barber / Etiquette lesson / Ballet de suburbia (suite) / Death / Final confrontation / Finale / Farewell / Ice dance / Home sweet home / Esmerelda / Helst / Rampage / Plot unfolds / End credits / Beautiful new world / With these sands
MCLD 19303 / Oct '95 / MCA

☐ EDWARD THE II (Fisher-Turner, Simon)
Fisher-Turner, Simon *c*
IONIC 8CD / Nov '91 / The Fine Line

☐ EIGER SANCTION, THE
Williams, John *c*
Williams, John *con*
VSD 5277 / Mar '91 / Varese Sarabande

☐ EIGHT HEADS IN A DUFFLEBAG
VSD 5835 / May '97 / Varese Sarabande

☐ EL CID (New Zealand Youth Choir)
Rozsa, Miklos *c*
Sedares, James *con*
373402 / Mar '96 / Koch International

☐ EL GRECO/GIORDANO BRUNO
Morricone, Ennio *c*
OST 111 / Mar '92 / Milano Dischi

☐ ELECTRA
Theodorakis, Mikis *c*
SR 50090 / May '94 / Varese Sarabande

☐ ELECTRIC DREAMS
Moroder, Giorgio *c*
Electric dreams: *Arnold, P.P.* / Video: *Lynne, Jeff* / Dream: *Culture Club* / Duel: *Moroder, Giorgio* / Now you are mine: *Terry, Helen* / Love is love: *Culture Club* / Chase runner: *Heaven 17* / Let it run: *Lynne, Jeff* / Madeline's theme: *Moroder, Giorgio* / Together in electric dreams: *Moroder, Giorgio & Philip Oakey*
CDVIP 127 / Oct '94 / Virgin

☐ ELEGIES (1993 London Cast)
Hood, Janet *c*
Russell, Bill *l*
Angels punks and raging queens / I'm holding onto you / And the rain keeps falling down / I don't do that anymore / I don't know how to help you / Celebrate / Heroes all round / Spend it while you can / My brother lived San Francisco / Learning to let go
OCRCD 6035 / Mar '96 / First Night

☐ EMERALD FOREST, THE
Homrich, Junior & Brian Gascoigne *c*
VCD 47251 / Jan '89 / Varese Sarabande

☐ EMPIRE OF THE SUN
Williams, John *c*
Williams, John *con*
Suo Gan / Cadillac of the skies / Jim's new life / Lost in the crowd / Imaginary air battle / Liberation: exsultate justi / Return of the city / British Grenadiers / Toy planes home and hearth / Streets of Shangai / Pheasant hunt / No road home/seeing the bomb / Exsultate justi
7599256682 / Feb '91 / WEA

☐ EMPIRE RECORDS
Til I hear it from you: *Gin Blossoms* / Liar: *Cranberries* / Girl like you: *Collins, Edwyn* / Free: *Martinis* / Crazy life: *Toad The Wet Sprocket* / Bright as yellow: *Innocence mission* / Circle of friends: *Better Than Ezra* / I don't want to live today: *Ape Hangers* / Whole lotta trouble: *Ape Hangers* / Ready steady go: *Meices* / What you are: *Drill* / Nice overalls: *Lustre* / Here it comes again: *Lustre* / Ballad of El Goodo: *Dando, Evan* / Sugarhigh: *Coyote Shivers* / Honeymoon is over: *Cruel Sea*
5404372 / 23 Feb '98 / A&M

☐ EMPIRE STRIKES BACK, THE (The Star Wars Trilogy Special Edition)
Williams, John *c*
Williams, John *con*
09026687472
09026687732 / Mar '97 / RCA Victor

☐ ENCHANTED ISLAND, THE (The Music For A Restoration 'Tempest') (Musicians Of The Globe)
Pickett, Philip *con*
4565052 / 18 May '98 / Philips

☐ END OF VIOLENCE, THE (Cooder, Ry)
Cooder, Ry *c*
OPD 30007 / 15 Sep '97 / Outpost

☐ ENEMIES (A Love Story)
Jarre, Maurice *c*
Herman / Tamara / In the wood / Masha / Third wife / Kertchmar Country Club / Rumba / Baby Masha
VSD 5253 / May '90 / Varese Sarabande

☐ ENGLAND, MY ENGLAND (The Story Of Henry Purcell) (Monteverdi Choir & English Baroque Soloists)
Purcell, Henry *c*
Gardiner, John Eliot *con*
0630107002 / Jan '96 / Erato

☐ ENGLISH PATIENT, THE (Academy Of St. Martin In The Fields)
Yared, Gabriel *c*
English patient / Retreat / Rupert bear / What else do you love / Why picton / Cheek to cheek: *Astaire, Fred* / Kip's lights / Hana's curse / I'll always go back to the church / Black nights / Swoon I'll catch you / Am I K in your book / Let me come in / Wang wang blues: *Goodman, Benny* / Convento di sant'ana / Herodotus / Szerelem szerelem: *Muzsikas & Marta Sebestyen* / Ask your saint who he's killed / One o'clock jump: *Goodman, Benny* / I'll be back / Let me tell you about winds / Read me to sleep / Cave of swimmers / Where or when: *Shepheard's Hotel Jazz Orchestra* / Aria from the Goldberg variations: *Steinberg, Julie* / Cheek to cheek: *Fitzgerald, Ella* / As far as Florence
FCD 16001 / Jun '97 / Fantasy

☐ EQUINOX
Mystery man: *Rypdal, Terje* / Milonga del angel: *Piazzolla, Astor* / Al Bine: *Toure, Ali Farke* / Left alone: *Shepp, Archie* / Mirage: *Rypdal, Terje* / Istoria ne Edna Lyubov: *Paposov, Ivo* / Symphonic dances: *Paposov, Ivo* / Once upon a time: *Rypdal, Terje*
VSD 5424 / May '93 / Varese Sarabande

☐ EQUUS
Bennett, Richard Rodney *c*
RCD 10726 / 20 Jul '98 / Rykodisc

☐ ER
Howard, James Newton *c*
7567829424 / Jan '97 / East West

☐ ESCAPE FROM LA (Score)
Carpenter, John & Shirley Walker *c*
74321409512 / Sep '96 / Milan

☐ ESCAPE FROM LA
7567927142 / Oct '96 / Atlantic

☐ ET
Williams, John *c*
Three million light years from home / Abandoned and pursued / ET's halloween / Flying / ET phone home / Over the moon / Adventure on Earth
MCLD 19021 / Apr '92 / MCA

☐ ETOILE/THE VISITOR
Knieper, Jurgen/Franco Micalizzi *c*
OST 108 / Jul '93 / Milano Dischi

☐ EUROPEANS
CDQ 5551022 / Apr '94 / EMI

☐ EVEN COWGIRLS GET THE BLUES (Lang, k.d.)
Lang, k.d./Ben Mink *c*
Just keep me moving / Much finer place / Or was I / Hush sweet lover / Myth / Apogee / Virtual vortex / Lifted by love / Overture / Kundalini yoga waltz / In perfect dreams / Curious soul astray / Ride of Bonanza Jellybean / Don't be a lemming polka / Sweet Cherokee / Cowgirl pride
9362454332 / Oct '93 / WEA

☐ EVENT HORIZON (Orbital)
8289392 / 1 Sep '97 / Internal

☐ EVEREST
ELDCD 003 / 30 Mar '98 / Eldorado

☐ EVERYBODY'S ALL AMERICAN
C 21Z91184 / '89 / Silva Screen

☐ EVERYONE SAYS I LOVE YOU (Alda, Alan & Woody Allen/Goldie Hawn/Julia Roberts/Tim Roth/Dick Hyman & New York Studio Players)
Allen, Woody *c*
Allen, Woody *l*
Just you just me / Everyone says I love you / My baby just cares for me / I'm a dreamer aren't we all / I'm thru with love / Just say I love her / Venetian scene / Recurrence / All my life / Cuddle up a little closer / Looking at you / No lover no friend (that's the end) / I can't believe that you're in love with me / What a little moonlight can do / Chinatown my Chinatown / Cocktails for two / Chiquita banana / Mimi / Louise / You brought a new kind of love to me / Hooray for Captain Spaulding
09026687562 / Apr '97 / RCA Victor

☐ EVIL DEAD I (Loduca, Joseph)
Loduca, Joseph *c*
Introduction / Eye games / Charm / Bridge out / Rape of the vines / Ascent / Inflection / Automatic writing / Skin / Give her the ax / Love never dies / Kandanian dagger / Book burning / Dawn of the evil dead / Not the shower curtain / Check on you / Pencil you in / Get the lantern / Book of the dead / Down / Incantation / Shotgun / Games / Cabin / Wounded melody
VSD 5362 / Jun '93 / Varese Sarabande

☐ EVIL DEAD III (Army Of Darkness)
Loduca, Joseph *c*
VSD 5411 / Mar '93 / Varese Sarabande

☐ EVITA (1976 Studio Cast)
Lloyd Webber, Andrew *c*
Rice, Tim *l*
Cinema in Buenos Aires 26 July 1952 / Requiem for Evita/Oh what a circus / On this night of a thousand stars / Buenos Aires / Goodnight and thank you / Lady's got potential / Charity concert/I'd be surprisingly good for you / Another suitcase in another hall / Dangerous Jade / New Argentina / On the balcony of the Casa Rosada / High flying adored / Rainbow high / Rainbow tour / Actress hasn't learned the lines (you'd like to hear) / And the money kept rolling in (and out) / Santa Evita / Waltz for Eva and Che / She is a diamond / Dice are rolling/Eva's sonnet / Eva's final broadcast / Montage / Lament
RMCX 503 / Dec '96 / MCA

☐ EVITA (1978 London Cast)
Lloyd Webber, Andrew *c*
Rice, Tim *l*
Requiem for Evita / Oh what a circus / On this night of a thousand stars / Eva and Magaldi / Eva beware of the city / Buenos Aires / Goodnight and thank you / Lady's got potential / Charity concert / I'd be surprisingly good for you / Another suitcase in another hall / Dangerous Jade / New Argentina / On the balcony of the Casa Rosada / Don't cry for me Argentina / High flying adored / Rainbow high / Rainbow tour / Actress hasn't learned the lines (you'd like to hear) / And the money kept rolling in (And out) / Santa Evita / Waltz for Eva and Che / She is a diamond / Dice are rolling / Eva's sonnet / Eva's final broadcast / Montage / Lament / Cinema in Buenos Aires 26 July 1952 / Art of the possible / Peron's latest flame
DMCG 3527 / Jul '85 / MCA

☐ EVITA (Webb, Marti)
Lloyd Webber, Andrew *c*
Rice, Tim *l*
PWKS 4233 / Feb '95 / Carlton

☐ EVITA (Sung In Korean) (Korean Cast)
Lloyd Webber, Andrew *c*
Rice, Tim *l*
DRGCD 13104 / Jan '95 / DRG

☐ EVITA (Film Cast)
Lloyd Webber, Andrew *c*
Rice, Tim *l*
9362464322
9362463462 / Nov '96 / Warner Bros.

☐ EVITA (Cast Recording)
Lloyd Webber, Andrew *c*
Rice, Tim *l*
GFS 086 / Nov '97 / Going For A Song

☐ **EXECUTIVE DECISION**
Goldsmith, Jerry *c*
Goldsmith, Jerry *con*
VSD 5714 / May '96 / Varese Sarabande

☐ **EXIT (Tangerine Dream)**
Tangerine Dream *c*
Kiew mission / Pilots of purple twilight / Choronzon / Exit / Network 23 / Remote viewing
TAND 13 / Jul '95 / Virgin

☐ **EXIT TO EDEN**
Doyle, Patrick *c*
VSD 5553 / Jun '95 / Varese Sarabande

☐ **EXODUS/JUDITH**
Gold, Ernest/Sol Kaplan *c*
TSU 0115 / Jan '95 / Tsunami

☐ **EXOTICA**
Danha, Mychael *c*
Exotica / Something hidden / Dilko tamay huay / Pagan song / Kiss / Inside me / My angel / Little touch / Field 3 / Snake dance / Field 4 / Mujay yaad / Ride home
VSD 5543 / Mar '95 / Varese Sarabande

☐ **EXPERIENCE (Original Soundtrack To The Movie Experience) (Hendrix, Jimi Experience)**
CDGR 246 / 1 Jun '98 / Charly

☐ **EXPRESSO BONGO (1958 London Cast)**
Heneker, David & Monty Norman *c*
Norman, Monty & David Heneker/Julian More *l*
AEICD 020 / May '98 / AEI

☐ **EXTREME MEASURES**
Elfman, Danny *c*
VSD 5767 / Nov '96 / Varese Sarabande

☐ **EYE SPY EARS ONLY (Neumann, Drew)**
Neumann, Drew *c*
TCCD 97242 / 27 Oct '97 / Tone Casualties

F

☐ **FABULOUS BAKER BOYS, THE**
Main title: *Grusin, Dave* / Welcome to the road: *Grusin, Dave* / Makin' whoopee: *Pfeiffer, Michelle* / Suzie and Jack: *Grusin, Dave* / Shop till you bop: *Grusin, Dave* / Soft on me: *Grusin, Dave* / Do nothin' 'til you hear from me: *Ellington, Duke Orchestra* / Moment of truth: *Grusin, Dave* / Moonglow: *Goodman, Benny* / Lullaby of birdland: *Palmer, Earl Trio* / My funny valentine: *Pfeiffer, Michelle*
RRP 20022 / 25 May '98 / GRP

☐ **FACE**
CID 8061 / 27 Oct '97 / Island

☐ **FACE TO FACE/THE BIG GUNDOWN (Faccia A Faccia/La Resa Dei Conti)**
Morricone, Ennio *c*
MASK MK701 / May '95 / Silva Screen

☐ **FACE/OFF (Powell, John)**
Powell, John *c*
1621252 / 7 Nov '97 / Philips

☐ **FALL OF THE ROMAN EMPIRE**
Tiomkin, Dimitri *c*
Tiomkin, Dimitri *con*
VSD 5228 / Feb '90 / Varese Sarabande

☐ **FALL OF THE ROMAN EMPIRE (More Music From The Film)**
Tiomkin, Dimitri *c*
Tiomkin, Dimitri *con*
ACN 7016 / Sep '91 / Cloud Nine

☐ **FALSETTOLAND (Cast Recording)**
Finn, William *c*
Finn, William & James Lapine *l*
Falsettoland / About time / Year of the child / Miracle of Judaism / Baseball game / Day in falsettoland / Round tables square tables / Everyone hates his parents / What more can I say / Something bad is happening / More racquetball / Holding to the ground / Days like this / Cancelling the Barmitzvah / Unlikely lovers
DRGCD 12601 / Mar '92 / DRG

☐ **FAME (1995 London Cast)**
Margoshes, Steve *c*
Levy, Jacques *l*
Hard work / I want to make magic / Can't keep it down / Tyrone's rap / There she goes/Fame / Let's play a love scene / Teacher's argument / Hard work (reprise) / I want to make magic (reprise) / Mabel's prayer / Think of Meryl Streep / Dancin' on the sidewalk / These are my children / In LA / Let's play a love scene (reprise) / Bring on tomorrow / Fame
5291092 / Aug '95 / Really Useful

☐ **FAME (CC Productions)**
Margoshes, Steve *c*
Levy, Jacques *l*
Fame / Out here on my own / Hot lunch jam / Dogs in the yard / Red light / Is it OK to call you mine / Never alone / Ralph and Monty / I sing the body electric
QED 203 / Nov '96 / Tring

☐ **FAMILY THING**
0022602CIN / Jul '96 / Edel

☐ **FAN**
Zimmer, Hans *c*
SNACD 806 / 2 Mar '98 / Snapper

☐ **FANTASTICKS (1960 Broadway Cast)**
Schmidt, Harvey *c*
Jones, Tom *l*
Try to remember / Much much more / Metaphor / Never say no / It depends on what you pay / You wonder how these things begin / Soon it's gonna rain / Rape ballet / Happy ending / This plum is too ripe / I can see it / Plant a radish / Round and round / There is a curious paradox / They were you / Try to remember (reprise)
CDTER 1099 / Aug '90 / TER

☐ **FANTASTICKS (Japan Tour Cast)**
Schmidt, Harvey *c*
Jones, Tom *l*
Overture / Try to remember / Much more / Metaphor / Never say no / It depends on what you pay / Soon it's gonna rain / Abduction ballet / Happy ending / This plum is too ripe / I can see it / Plant a radish / Round and round / They were you
DRGCD 19005 / Jun '93 / DRG

☐ **FAR FROM HOME: THE ADVENTURES OF YELLOW DOG (Score)**
Scott, John *c*
JSCD 118 / Oct '96 / JOS

☐ **FAR NORTH (Red Clay Ramblers)**
Far north / Blue duluth / Amy's theme (Kitchen)/ Gourd part 1 / Amy's theme (Field) / Roll on Buddy/ Montage / Gangar / Big ships / Katie's ride / Train through the big woods / Night harps / Run sister run / Camptown races/Amy's theme / Amy's theme (Over the hill) / Gourd part 2
SHCD 8502 / Jan '97 / Sugar Hill

☐ **FARAWAY, SO CLOSE**
Faraway so close: *Cave, Nick* / Stay (faraway so close): *U2* / Why can't I be good: *Reed, Lou* / Chaos: *Gronemeyer, Herbert* / Travellin' on: *Bonney, Simon* / Wanderer: *U2* / Cassiel's song: *Cave, Nick* / Slow tango: *Siberry, Jane* / Call me: *House Of Love* / All God's children: *Bonney, Simon* / Tightrope: *Anderson, Laurie* / Speak my language: *Anderson, Laurie*
CDEMC 3660 / Sep '93 / EMI

☐ **FARENHEIT 451 (Seattle Symphony Orchestra)**
Herrmann, Bernard *c*
McNeely, Joel *con*
VSD 5551 / Jul '95 / Varese Sarabande

☐ **FAREWELL TO ARMS, A/SONS AND LOVERS**
Nascimbene, Mario *c*
Ferrara, Franco *con*
DRGCD 32962 / Oct '96 / DRG

☐ **FAREWELL TO ARMS, A/THE BAREFOOT CONTESSA**
Nascimbene, Mario *c*
LEGENDCD 11 / Sep '93 / Legend

☐ **FARGO/BARTON FINK**
Burwell, Carter *c*
SNACD 808 / 2 Mar '98 / Snapper

☐ **FARINELLI**
K 1005 / Oct '95 / Auvidis Travelling

☐ **FAST CHEAP AND OUT OF CONTROL (Sampson, Caleb)**
AC 5027 / 1 Dec '97 / Accurate

☐ **FATAL FLAMES**
Festo, Al *c*
VCDS 7022 / Oct '96 / Varese Sarabande

☐ **FATHER CHRISTMAS (Phoenix Chamber Orchestra)**
Hewer, Mike *c*
Bigg, Julian *con*
4694752 / Nov '95 / Columbia

☐ **FAUST**
Newman, Randy *c*
9362456722 / Sep '95 / Warner Bros.

☐ **FAUST (Score) (Olympia Chamber Orchestra)**
Brock, Timothy *c*
KOC 03 / Jan '97 / K

☐ **FAUST ARGENTIN**
Arias, Alfredo *c*
LBS 10970401 / Aug '97 / XIII Bis

☐ **FEAR AND LOATHING IN LAS VEGAS**
GED 25218 / 15 Jun '98 / Geffen

☐ **FEDS (Edelman, Randy)**
Edelman, Randy *c*
GNPD 8014 / Jan '95 / GNP Crescendo

☐ **FEVER PITCH (A Match Made In Heaven)**
There she goes: *La's* / Liquidator: *Harry J All Stars* / Fiesta: *Pogues* / Cafe '68: *MacColl, Neil & Boo Hewerdine* / Baba O'Riley: *Who* / How can we hang on to a dream: *Hardin, Tim* / Good thing: *Fine Young Cannibals* / All around the world: *Stansfield, Lisa* / Bright side of the road: *Morrison, Van* / Goin' back: *Pretenders* / Fever pitch: *Pretenders*
0630184532 / Mar '97 / Warner Bros.

☐ **FIDDLER ON THE ROOF (1971 Film Cast)**
Bock, Jerry *c*
Harnick, Sheldon *l*
Williams, John *con*
Prologue/Tradition/Main title / If I were a rich man / Sabbath prayer / To life / Miracle of miracles / Tevye's dream / Sunrise sunset / Wedding celebration and the bottle dance / Do you love me / Far from the home I love / Chava ballet sequence / Anatevka / Finale / Matchmaker matchmaker / Bottle dance / Now I have everything
CDP 7460912 / Jul '94 / EMI

☐ **FIDDLER ON THE ROOF (1964 Broadway Cast)**
Bock, Jerry *c*
Harnick, Sheldon *l*
Greene, Milton *con*
Prologue - Tradition / Matchmaker matchmaker / If I were a rich man / Sabbath prayer / To life / Miracle of miracles / Dream / Sunrise sunset / Wedding dance / Now I have everything / Do you love me / Rumour / Far from the home I love / Anatevka
RD 87060 / Aug '90 / RCA Victor

☐ **FIDDLER ON THE ROOF (London Cast)**
Bock, Jerry *c*
Harnick, Sheldon *l*
Robbins, Jerome *con*
SMK 53499 / Jul '94 / Sony Classical

☐ **FIDDLER ON THE ROOF (Merrill, Robert & Molly Picon/London Festival Orchestra/Chorus)**
Bock, Jerry *c*
Harnick, Sheldon *l*
Black, Stanley *con*
4489492 / Aug '96 / Phase 4

☐ **FIDDLER ON THE ROOF (CC Productions)**
Bock, Jerry *c*
Harnick, Sheldon *l*
Tradition/matchmaker / If I were a rich man / Sabbath prayer / To life / Sunrise sunset / Bottle dance / Now I have everything / Do you love me / Far from the home I love / Anatevka
QED 209 / Nov '96 / Tring

☐ **FIELDS OF AMBROSIA (1995 London Cast)**
Silvestri, Martin *c*
Higgins, Joel *l*
Warman, M. *con*
CASTCD 58 / Jul '96 / First Night

☐ **FIERCE CREATURES**
Goldsmith, Jerry *c*
VSD 5792 / Feb '97 / Varese Sarabande

☐ **FIFTH ELEMENT, THE (London Session Orchestra)**
Serra, Eric *c*
Little light of love / Mondoshawan / Timecrash / Korben Dallas / Koolen / Akta / Leeloo / Five millenia later / Plavalaguna / Ruby Rap / Heat / Badaboom / Mangalores / Lucia di Lammermoor / Diva dance / Leeloominai / Bomb in the hotel / Mina Hinoo / No cash no trash / Radiowaves / Human nature / Pictures of war / Lakta Ligunai / Protect life / Little light of love / Aknot wot
CDVIR 63 / Jun '97 / Virgin

☐ **FILM WORKS VOL.7 (Cynical Hysterie Hour) (Zorn, John)**
TZA 7315 / Jul '97 / Tzadik

☐ **FIORELLO (Broadway Cast)**
Bock, Jerry *c*
Harnick, Sheldon *l*
ZDM 5650232 / Dec '93 / EMI Classics

☐ **FIORILE**
Piovani, Nicola *c*
873148 / May '95 / Milan

☐ **FIRE**
CST 348068 / 10 Nov '97 / Colosseum

☐ **FIRE IN THE SKY**
Isham, Mark *c*
White Mountains Arizona / Travis Walton / Fire in the sky / Return / Man on display / Evil spirits from the sky / They didn't like me - a case unsolved
VSD 5417 / Apr '93 / Varese Sarabande

☐ **FIRELIGHT**
Gunning, Christopher *c*
Gunning, Christopher *con*
FILMCD 198 / 1 Jun '98 / Silva Screen

☐ **FIRESTARTER (Tangerine Dream)**
Tangerine Dream *c*
Crystal voice / Testlab / Escaping point / Burning force / Shop territory / Out of the heat / Run / Charly the kid / Rainbirds move / Between realities / Flash final
VSD 5251 / '90 / Varese Sarabande

☐ **FIRM, THE (Grusin, Dave)**
Grusin, Dave *c*
Firm / Stars on the water / Mitch and Abby / Money / Memphis stomp / Never mind / Ray's blues / Dance class / Plan / Blues: The death of love and trust / Start it up / Mud island chase / How could you lose me
GRLD 19358 / Apr '97 / MCA

☐ **FIRST KNIGHT**
Goldsmith, Jerry *c*
Arthur's fanfare / Promise me / Camelot / Raid on Leonesse / New life / To Leonesse / Night battle / Village ruins / Arthur's farewell / Camelot lives
4809372 / Jul '95 / Epic

☐ **FIRST MEN IN THE MOON, THE**
Johnson, Laurie *c*
Johnson, Laurie *con*
Prelude / Modern moon landing / Newscasters/ Union Jack/Journey to Dymchurch / Cherry cottage/ Kate and Bedford / Arguments / Cavor's experiments / Sphere / Love theme / To the moon / Lunar landing/Moonscpae/Weightlessness/ Planting the Union Ja / Lens pit/Shadows / Battle with the Selenites / Search for the sphere/Kate in peril / Moon beast / Lens complex/Dismantling the sphere/Cocooning Selenites/The / End of the eclipse/The grand lunar / Bedford shoots at the grand lunar / Pursuit and escape from the moon/End title
ACN 7015 / Jul '91 / Cloud Nine

☐ **FIRST STRIKE**
74321477342 / 8 Nov '97 / RCA

☐ **FIRST WIVES CLUB, THE**
Wives and lovers: *Warwick, Dionne* / Beautiful morning: *Rascals* / Over and over: *Johnson, Puff* / Piece of my heart: *King, Diana* / Game of love: *Brownstone* / Love is on the way: *Porter, Billy* / Sisters are doin' it for themselves: *Eurythmics* / Think: *Franklin, Aretha* / Heartbreak Road: *Ferris, Dionne* / I will survive: *Savage, Chantay* / Movin' on up: *M People* / I'm still standing: *Wash, Martha* / You don't own me: *Midler, Bette & Goldie Hawn/Diane Keaton*
4853962 / Nov '96 / Columbia

☐ **FIRST WIVES CLUB, THE (Score)**
Shaiman, Marc *c*
VSD 5781 / Jan '97 / Varese Sarabande

☐ **FITZCARRALDO (Popul Vuh)**
Popul Vuh *c*
14876 / Sep '96 / Spalax

☐ **FIVE CORNERS**
Howard, James Newton *c*
VCD 47354 / Jan '89 / Varese Sarabande

☐ **FIVE GUYS NAMED MOE (1991 London Cast)**
Jordan, Louis *c*
Five guys named Moe / Early in the morning / Brother beware / I like em fat like that / Messy Bessy / Pettin' and pokin' / Life is so peculiar / I know what I've got / Azure te / Safe sane and single / Push ka pi shee pie / Saturday night fish fry / What's the use of gettin' sober / Band played out / Is you is ir is you ain't my baby / Hurry home / Choo choo ch'boogie / Look out sister / Don't let the sun catch you crying / There ain't nobody here but us chickens / Cal'donia / Let the good times roll / Cabaret
OCRCD 6050 / Apr '97 / First Night

☐ **FIVE HEARTBEATS, THE**
Heart Is A House For Love: *Dells* / We haven't finished yet: *Labelle, Patti & Thomas, Tressa* / Nights Like This: *After 7* / Bring Back The Days: *U.S. Male* / Baby stop running around: *Bird & The Midnight Falcons* / In The Middle: *Flash & The Five Heartbeats* / Nothing but Love: *Five Heartbeats* / Are you ready for me: *Flash & The Ebony Sparks* / Stay in my corner: *Dells* / I feel like going on: *Eddie, Baby Doll & The LA Mass Choir/Billy Valentine*
CDVMM 4 / Sep '92 / Virgin

☐ **FIVE MAN ARMY/THE LINK**
Morricone, Ennio *c*
CDE 76 / Apr '96 / Silva Screen

☐ **FIVE SUMMER STORIES (Honk)**
Honk *c*
Creation / Blue of your backdrop / Brad and David's theme / High in the middle / Hum drums / Bear's country / Made my statement (Love you baby) / Don't let your goodbye stand / Lopez / Blue of your backdrop (instrumental) / Tunnel of love
GNPD 8027 / Jan '91 / GNP Crescendo

☐ **FIX (Original Cast)**
CASTCD 62 / 29 Sep '97 / First Night

☐ **FLAHOOLEY (Broadway Cast)**
Lane, Burton *c*
Harburg, E.Y. 'Yip' *l*
ZDM 7647642 / Apr '93 / EMI Classics

☐ **FLAMING STAR/WILD IN THE COUNTRY/FOLLOW THAT DREAM (Presley, Elvis)**
Flaming star / Summer kisses winter tears / Britches a cane and a high starched collar / Black star / Flaming star (end title version) / Wild in the country / I slipped I stumbled I fell / Lonely man / In my way / Forget me never / Lonely man (solo) / I slipped I stumbled I fell (Alternate master) / Follow that dream / Angel / What a wonderful life / I'm not the marrying kind / Whistling tune / Sound advice
07863665572 / Mar '95 / RCA

☐ **FLAMINGO KID**
Breakaway / Heatwave / He's so fine / One fine day / Stranger on the shore / Runaround Sue / Good golly Miss Molly / Money (Thats what I want) / It's alright / Finger poppin' time / Get a job / Boys will be boys
5515392 / Aug '95 / Spectrum

☐ **FLASH FEARLESS**
I'm Flash: *Cooper, Alice* / Space pirates: *Cooper, Alice* / Trapped: *Brooks, Elkie* / Sacrifice: *Brooks, Elkie* / Country cookin: *Dandy, Jim* / Blast off: *Dandy, Jim* / What's happening: *Trower, Robin* / Let's go to the chop: *Entwistle, John* / All around my hat: *Prior, Maddy* / Georgia syncopator: *Prior, Maddy*
RPM 148 / Mar '95 / RPM

☐ FLASH GORDON (Queen)
Flash's theme / In the space capsule / Ming's theme (in the court of Ming the merciless) / Ring / Football fight / In the death cell / Execution of Flash / Kiss / Arboria (planet of the tree men) / Escape from the swamp / Flash to the rescue / Vultan's theme (attack of the hawk men) / Battle theme / Wedding march / Marriage of Dale and Ming (and Flash approaching) / Crash dive on Mingo city / Flash's theme reprise (victory celebrations) / Hero
CDPCSD 137 / Apr '94 / Parlophone

☐ FLASHDANCE
Moroder, Giorgio c
Flashdance (what a feeling): *Cara, Irene* / He's a dream: *Shandi* / Flashdance love theme: *St. John, Helen* / Manhunt: *Kamon, Karen* / Lady lady lady: *Esposito, Joe* / Imagination: *Branigan, Laura* / Romeo: *Summer, Donna* / Seduce me tonight: *Cycle V* / I'll be here where the heart is: *Carnes, Kim* / Maniac: *Sembello, Michael*
8114922 / Dec '83 / Casablanca

☐ FLINTSTONES, THE (Stone Age Project)
Meet the Flintstones / Human Being (Bedrock Steady) / Hit and run holiday / Prehistoric daze / Rock with the caveman / I showed a caveman how to rock / Bedrock twitch / I wanna be a flintstone / In the days of the caveman / Anarchy in the UK / Walk the dinosaur / Bedrock anthem / Mesozoic music
AAOHP 93552 / Oct '94 / Start

☐ FLIRTING WITH DISASTER
Anything but love: *Dr. John & Angela McCluskey* / Somebody else's body: *Urge Overkill* / Outasight: *G-Love & The Philly Cartel* / You're not a slut: *Southern Culture On The Skids* / Camel walk: *Southern Culture On The Skids* / Lend me your comb: *Perkins, Carl* / Acid propaganda: *Cake* / You part the waters: *Cake* / Lonnie cooks quail: *Southern Culture On The Skids* / Red beans 'n' reverb: *Southern Culture On The Skids* / Flirting with disaster: *Dr. John & Angela McCluskey* / Hypospadia: *Dr. John & Angela McCluskey* / Melodie d'amour: *Martin, Dean* / For duty and humanity: *Inch* / Flirting suite: *Endelman, Stephen*
GED 24970 / Feb '97 / Geffen

☐ FLORA, THE RED MENACE (1987 Off-Broadway Cast)
Kander, John c
Ebb, Fred l
Prologue/Unafraid / Street song I / Kid herself / All I need is one good break / Not every day of the week / Street song II / Sign here / Street song III / Quiet thing / Flame / Not every day of the week (reprise) / Street song IV / Dear love / Keepin' it hot / Street song V / Express yourself / Where did everybody go / Street song VI / You are you / Joke / Quiet thing (reprise) / Sing happy / Closing scene
CDTER 1159 / May '89 / TER

☐ FLORA, THE RED MENACE (1965 Broadway Cast)
Kander, John c
Ebb, Fred l
Hastings, Harold con
Overture / Prologue/Unafraid / All I need (is one good break) / Not every day of the week / Sign here / Flame / Palomino pal / Quiet thing / Hello waves / Dera love / Express yourself / Knock knock / Sing happy / You are you
GD 60821 / Dec '92 / RCA Victor

☐ FLOWER DRUM SONG (1960 London Cast)
Rodgers, Richard c
Hammerstein II, Oscar l
Lowe, R. con
Overture / You are beautiful / Hundred million miracles / I enjoy being a girl / I am going to like it here / Like a god / Chop suey / Don't marry me / Grant Avenue / Love look away / Fan tan Fannie / Gliding through my memoree / Other generation / Sunday / Finale
CDANGEL 7 / Apr '94 / Angel

☐ FLOWER DRUM SONG (1958 Broadway Cast)
Rodgers, Richard c
Hammerstein II, Oscar l
Dell'Isola, Salvatore con
SK 53536 / Nov '93 / Sony Broadway

☐ FLOWERS IN THE ATTIC
Young, Christopher c
MAF 7009D / Jul '92 / Intrada

☐ FLOYD COLLINS (Off Broadway Cast)
Guettel, Adam c
7559794342 / May '97 / Nonesuch

☐ FLUBBER
WD 775662 / Mar '98 / Disney Music & Stories

☐ FLY I, THE (London Philharmonic Orchestra)
Shore, Howard c
Main title / Last visit / Phone call / Ronnie calls back / Particle magazine / Ronnie's visit / Fingernails / Creature / Maggot The/Fly graphic / Ultimate family / Plasma pool / Stathis entera / Seth goes through / Jump / Armwrestle / Stairs / Baboon teleportation / Steak montage / Success with baboon / Finale
VCD 47272 / Jan '89 / Varese Sarabande

☐ FLY I, THE/THE OMEN III (THE FINAL CONFLICT)
VSD 47272 / Feb '90 / Varese Sarabande

☐ FLY II, THE
Young, Christopher c
Fly II / Fly variations / Spider and the fly / Fly march / Bay 17 mysteries / What's the magic word / Come fly with me / Musica domestica metastasis / More is coming / Accelerated Brundle disease / Bartok barbaro / Dad
VSD 5220 / May '89 / Varese Sarabande

☐ FLYING DOWN TO RIO/HOLLYWOOD HOTEL
Theme / I know why / In the mood / It happend in sun valley / Chattanooga choo choo / Flying down to Rio / Orchids in the moonlight / Carioca / Music makes me / Sing you son of a gun / Dark eyes / Silhouttes in the moonlight / Sing sing sing / Let that be a lesson to you / I'm like a fish out of water
CD 60008 / Apr '97 / Great Movie Themes

☐ FOG, THE
Carpenter, John c
Carpenter, John con
VCD 47267 / Jan '89 / Varese Sarabande

☐ FOLLIES (1985 Lincoln Center Revival Cast)
Sondheim, Stephen c
Overture / Beautiful girls / Don't look at me / Waiting for the girls upstairs / Rain on the roof / Ah Paree / Broadway baby / Road you didn't take / In Buddy's eyes / Who's that woman / I'm still here / Too many mornings / Right girl / One more kiss / Could I leave you / Loveland / You're gonna love tomorrow/Love will see us through / Buddy's blues / Losing my mind / Story of Lucy and Jessie / Live laugh love / Finale
RD 87128 / Aug '90 / RCA Victor

☐ FOLLIES (1987 London Cast)
Sondheim, Stephen c
OCRCD 6019 / Oct '95 / First Night

☐ FOLLIES (1971 Broadway Cast)
Sondheim, Stephen c
ZDM 7646662 / Apr '93 / EMI Classics

☐ FOLLIES (Trotter Trio)
Sondheim, Stephen c
Opening / Waiting for the girl upstairs / Too many mornings / I'm still here / Broadway baby / Could I leave you / In Buddy's eyes / Who's that woman / Loveland / Buddy's blues / Losing my mind / Live laugh love
VSD 5934 / 3 Aug '98 / Varese Sarabande

☐ FOLLOW THE BOYS/STAR DUST/ WATERLOO BRIDGE/TO HAVE AND HAVE N
Follow the boys overture / Is everybody happy goodnight / Dance routine / Bigger the army the navy / Beer barrel polka / Swing low sweet chariot / Kittens with their mittens laced / Beyond the blue horizon / I'll walk alone / Liebstraum / Besame mucho / I'll get by / Is you or is you not my baby / Sweet Georgia brown / Dance routine / I'll see you in my dreams / House I live in / Shoo shoo baby / Better day is coming / Satr dust overture / Secrets in the moonlight / Star dust / Don't let it get you down / Waterloo overture / Auld lang syne / Closing theme / Am I blue
CD 60032 / Nov '97 / Great Movie Themes

☐ FOOTLOOSE
Footloose: *Loggins, Kenny* / Let's hear it for the boy: *Williams, Deniece* / Almost paradise: *Wilson, Ann & Mike Reno* / Holding out for a hero: *Tyler, Bonnie* / Dancing in the street: *Shalamar* / I'm free (heaven helps the man): *Loggins, Kenny* / Somebody's eyes: *Bonoff, Karla* / Girl gets around: *Hagar, Sammy* / Never: *Moving Pictures*
4630002 / Nov '88 / CBS

☐ FOR ME AND MY GAL (Film Cast)
Main title / Vaudeville routine / Doll shop (pt.1) / Oh you beautiful doll / Doll shop (pt.1 cont.) / Don't leave me Daddy / Oh you beautiful doll (reprise) / Doll shop (pt.2) / By the beautiful sea / Darktown strutters ball / For me and my gal / Confession / When you wore a tulip / Don't bite the hand that's feeding you / Do I love you / It started with Eve / Woman's perogative / After you've gone / Spell of the waltz / Love song / Dream crashes / I'm sorry I made you cry / Tell me / Till we meet again / We don't want the bacon what we want is a piece of the Rhin / Ballin' the Jack / Small time / What are you going to do about the boys / How ya gonna keep 'em down on the farm / There's a long long trail / Where do we go from here / Over there / It's a long way to Tipperary / Goodbye Broadway hello France / Yankee doodle / Smiles / Hinky dinky parlay voo / Oh Frenchy / Pack up your troubles in your old kit bag and smile smile / When Johnny comes marching home / Finale / Main title / Dear old pal of mine / Smiles (outtake) / Three cheers for the yanks / For me and my gal (outtake)
CDODEON 12 / Apr '96 / Soundtracks

☐ FOR RICHER OR POORER
VSD 5891 / 12 Jan '98 / Varese Sarabande

☐ FOR ROSEANNA (Roseanna's Grave) (London Symphony Orchestra)
Jones, Trevor c
Ingman, Nick con
Roseanna's theme / Luna Rossa / Marcello / Hospital visitor / Doing the rounds / At Marcelina's grave / Her dying wish / Torna a surriento / Last rites / I don't want you to be lonely / Confession / Another funeral / My darling wife / Roseanna's funeral / Journey to the station / We'll be dining on the plane
09026688362 / Aug '97 / RCA Victor

☐ FOR THE BOYS (Midler, Bette)
Billy-a-dick / Stuff like that there / PS I love you / Girlfriend of the whirling dervish / I remember you / Dixie's dream / Baby it's cold outside / Dreamland / Vickie and Mr. Valves / For all we know / Come rain or come shine / In my life / Every road leads back to you
7567823292 / Feb '92 / Atlantic

☐ FORBIDDEN BROADWAY I (Unoriginal Cast)
Alessandrini, Gerard l
DRGCD 12585 / Mar '92 / DRG

☐ FORBIDDEN BROADWAY II (Unoriginal Cast)
Alessandrini, Gerard l
CDSBL 12599 / Mar '92 / DRG

☐ FORBIDDEN BROADWAY III (Unoriginal Cast)
Alessandrini, Gerard l
Carol Channing sequence / Forbidden Broadway III / Ya got troubles / Guys And Dolls sequence / Topol / Anna Karenina: the musical / Julie Andrews / Grim hotel / Barbara: The Broadway album / Dustin Hoffman / Return to Merman and Martin / Ms. Saigon / Michael Crawford sequence / Robert Goulet sequence / Mess of the spider woman / Back to Barbara / Mug brothers / Who's Tommy / Finale
DRGCD 12609 / Apr '94 / DRG

☐ FORBIDDEN BROADWAY IV (Unoriginal Cast)
DRGCD 12614 / Feb '97 / DRG

☐ FORBIDDEN HOLLYWOOD (Cast Recording)
VSD 5669 / Nov '95 / Varese Sarabande

☐ FORBIDDEN PLANET
Barron, Louis & Bebe c
PRD 001 / 16 Feb '98 / Small Planet

☐ FOREVER AMBER
Raskin, David c
VSD 5857 / 13 Apr '98 / Varese Sarabande

☐ FOREVER KNIGHT
Molin, Fred c
GNPD 8043 / Apr '96 / GNP Crescendo

☐ FOREVER PLAID (1993 London Cast)
Three coins in the fountain / Gotta be this or that undecided / Moments to remember / Crazy about ya baby / Not too much / Perfidia / Cry / Sixteen tons/ Chain gang / Tribute to Mr. C / Caribbean plaid / Heart and soul / Lady of Spain / Scotland the brave / Shangri-la/Rags to riches / Love is a many splendoured thing
CASTCD 33 / Jul '93 / First Night

☐ FOREVER WILD
Whalen, Michael c
Dark and the light / American fields / Magnolia / Canyon wind / Shelter / Winding to infinity / Pathway to Waterrock / Peril in the timberland / Magic forest / Rain / Secret garden / Song of the Everglades / Through the parched land: Desert flower / Puritan's dream / Times of change / Stormlight: Dawn / Kingdom of the sun / Monongahela / Muir's paradise / By the sea / Hudson Valley / Survival / Windows and walls / Great highway / Karen's song / Wilderness of the East / Storyteller sleeps / Theme to Forever Wild
ND 63926 / Nov '96 / Narada

☐ FOREVER YOUNG
Goldsmith, Jerry c
Love theme / Test flight / Experiment / Tree house / Kitchen aid / Diner / Air show / She's alive / Let's go / Reunited / Very thought of you: *Holiday, Billie*
WA 244822 / '93 / Silva Screen

☐ FORREST GUMP
Hound dog: *Presley, Elvis* / Rebel rouser: *Eddy, Duane* / But I do: *Henry, Clarence 'Frogman'* / Walk right in: *Rooftop Singers* / Land of 1000 dances: *Pickett, Wilson* / Blowin' in the wind: *Baez, Joan* / Fortunate son: *Creedence Clearwater Revival* / I can't help myself: *Four Tops* / Respect: *Franklin, Aretha* / Rainy day women 12/35: *Dylan, Bob* / Sloop John B: *Beach Boys* / California dreamin': *Mamas & The Papas* / For what it's worth: *Buffalo Springfield* / What the world needs now is love: *De Shannon, Jackie* / Break on through (to the other side): *Doors* / Mrs. Robinson: *Simon & Garfunkel* / Volunteers: *Jefferson Airplane* / Let's get together: *Youngbloods* / San Francisco: *McKenzie, Scott* / Turn turn turn: *Byrds* / Aquarius (let the sunshine in): *5th Dimension* / Everybody's talkin': *Nilsson, Harry* / Joy to the world: *Three Dog Night* / Stoned love: *Supremes* / Raindrops keep falling on my head: *Thomas, B.J.* / Mr. President (Have pity on the working man): *Newman, Randy* / Sweet home Alabama: *Lynyrd Skynyrd* / It keeps you runnin': *Doobie Brothers* / I've got to use my imagination: *Knight, Gladys & The Pips* / Against the wind: *Nelson, Willie* / Suite from Forrest Gump: *Silvestri, Alan*
4769412 / Oct '94 / Epic

☐ FORREST GUMP (Score) (Silvestri, Alan)
Silvestri, Alan c
I'm Forrest... Forrest Gump / You're no different / You can't sit here / Run Forrest run / Pray with me / Crimson Gump / They're sendingme to Vietnam / I ran and ran / I had a destiny / Washington reunion / Jesus on the mainline / That's my boat / I never thanked you / Jenny returns / Crusade / Forrest meets Forrest / Wedding guest / Where heaven ends / Jenny's grave / I'll be right here / Suite from Forrest Gump
4773692 / Oct '94 / Epic

☐ FORTUNELLA/LA GRAN GUERRA/IL MAESTRO DI VIGEVANO
Rota, Nino c
LEGENDCD 24 / Apr '96 / Silva Screen

☐ FORTY FIVE MINUTES FROM BROADWAY (Cast Recording)
Cohen, George M. c
AEICD 026 / May '98 / AEI

☐ FOUR WEDDINGS AND A FUNERAL
Love is all around: *Wet Wet Wet* / But not for me: *Wet Wet Wet* / You're the first my last my everything: *White, Barry* / Smoke gets in your eyes: *Nu Colours* / I will survive: *Gaynor, Gloria* / La la (means I love you): *Swing Out Sister* / Crocodile rock: *John, Elton* / Right time: *I to I* / It should have been me: *Knight, Gladys* / Loving you tonight: *Squeeze* / Can't smile without you: *Fiagbe, Lena* / Four weddings and a funeral/ Funeral blues / Secret marriage: *Sting* / Chapel of love: *John, Elton*
5167512 / Jun '94 / Vertigo

☐ FRANCIS OF ASSISI/DOCTOR FAUSTUS
Nascimbene, Mario c
DRGCD 32965 / Mar '97 / DRG

☐ FRANKENSTEIN - THE CREATION (Original Cast)
Joyce, Paul c
Ice overture / I am become death / Offertium / Creation / In paradisum / Trinity / Frankenstein - The creation
PKJCD 001 / May '97 / Creation

☐ FRANKIE AND JOHNNY/PARADISE, HAWAIIAN STYLE (Presley, Elvis)
Frankie and Johnny / Come along / Petunia the gardener's daughter / Chesay / What every woman lives for / Look out Broadway / Beginner's luck / Down by the riverside/When the saints go marching in / Shout it out / Hard luck / Please don't stop loving me / Everybody come aboard / Paradise Hawaiian style / Queenie Wahine's papaya / Scratch my back / Drums of the islands / Datin' / Dog's life / House of sand / Stop where you are / This is my heaven / Sand castles
07863663602 / Jun '94 / RCA

☐ FRANKIE STARLIGHT
Bernstein, Elmer c
VSD 5679 / Nov '95 / Varese Sarabande

☐ FREE WILLY III
Eidelman, Cliff c
VSD 5830 / 13 Oct '97 / Varese Sarabande

☐ FREEBIRD THE MOVIE (Lynyrd Skynyrd)
Lynyrd Skynyrd c
Workin' for MCA / I ain't the one / Saturday night special / Whiskey rock-a-roller / Travellin' man / Searching / What's your name / That smell / Gimme three steps / Call me the breeze / T for Texas (blue yodel no.1) / Sweet home Alabama / Free bird / Dixie
MCD 11472 / Aug '96 / MCA

☐ FRENCH KISS
Someone like you: *Morrison, Van* / La vie en rose: *Armstrong, Louis* / Dream a little dream: *Beautiful South* / Via con me: *Conte, Paolo* / I love Paris: *Thielemans, Toots* / La mer: *Kline, Kevin* / I love Paris: *Fitzgerald, Ella* / Verlaine: *Trenet, Charles* / C'est trop beau: *Rossi, Tino* / Les yeux ouverts: *Beautiful South* / I want you: *Howard, James Newton* / Les yeux de ton pere: *Les Negresses Vertes*
5283212 / Jun '95 / Mercury

☐ FRENCH LIEUTENANT'S WOMAN, THE
Davis, Carl c
Sarah's walk / Proposal / Period research / Her story / Decision taken / Towards love / Location lunch / Together / Domestic scene / Resurrection / House in Windermere / End of shoot party / Happy ending
DRGCD 6106 / '88 / DRG

☐ FRIDAY
Friday: *Ice Cube* / Keep their heads ringin': *Dr. Dre* / Friday night: *Scarface* / Lettin' niggas know: *Threat* / Roll it up light it up smoke it up: *Cypress Hill* / Take a hit: *Mack 10* / Tryin' to see another day: *Isley Brothers* / You got me wide open: *Collins, Bootsy & Bernie Worrell* / Mary Jane: *James, Rick* / I wanna get next to you: *Rose Royce* / Superhoes: *Funkdoobiest* / Coast II coast: *Alkaholiks* / Blast if I have to: *E-A-Ski* / Hoochie mama: *2 Live Crew* / I heard it through the grapevine: *Roger*
CDPTY 117 / Apr '95 / Priority/Virgin

☐ FRIDAY THE 13TH (The TV Series) (Molin, Fred)
Molin, Fred c
GNPD 8018 / Jan '90 / GNP Crescendo

☐ FRIENDLY PERSUASION
Tiomkin, Dimitri c
Tiomkin, Dimitri con
MSCD 402 / Jan '93 / Movie Sound
VSD 5828 / 10 Nov '97 / Varese Sarabande

☐ FRIENDS (Music From The TV Series)
I'll be there for you: *Rembrandts* / I go blind: *Hootie & The Blowfish* / Good intentions: *Toad The Wet Sprocket* / You'll know you were loved: *Reed, Lou* / Sexuality: *Lang, k.d.* / Shoebox: *Barenaked Ladies* / Free world: *REM* / Sunshine: *Westerberg, Paul* / Angel of the morning: *Pretenders* / In my room: *Grant Lee Buffalo* / Big yellow taxi: *Mitchell, Joni* / Stain yer blood: *Westerberg, Paul* / I'll be there for you: *Rembrandts*
9362460082 / Apr '97 / Warner Bros.

☐ FRIGHTENERS, THE
Elfman, Danny c
Intro / Lads / Poltergeists / Victim number 38 / Who's next / Garden / Chilly / Time / Patty's palce / Flashbacks / Patty attack / Frank's wife / Doom / Heaven / Don't fear the reaper: *Mutton Birds*
MCAD 11469 / Feb '97 / MCA

☐ **FRITZ THE CAT**
FCD 4532 / Jan '94 / Fantasy

☐ **FRITZ THE CAT/HEAVY TRAFFIC**
Black talk / Duke's theme / Fritz the cat / Mambllues / Bo Diddley: *Diddley, Bo* / Bertha's theme / Winston / House rock / Synagogue / Yesterdays: *Holiday, Billie* / Love light of mine: *Watson Sisters* / Riot / You're the only girl (I ever really loved) / Scarborough Fair: *Mendes, Sergio & Brazil '66* / Scarborough Street Fair / Twist and shout: *Isley Brothers* / Angie's theme / Take five: *Brubeck, Dave* / Carol's theme / Heavy traffic / What you sow / Maybellene: *Berry, Chuck* / Michael's Scarborough fair / Ballroom beauties / Ballroom dancers / Cartoon time / Ten cent philosophy
FCD 24745 / Nov '96 / Fantasy

☐ **FROG PRINCE, THE**
Train to Paris / First day / Mack the knife / Let it be me / With Jean-Phillipe / Jenny / Reflections / Frog Prince / Dreams / Kiss / Sweet Georgia Brown / Georgia on my mind / Kiss by the fountain / Jenny and Roz / Les flon-flons du bal / Epilogue
5510992 / Jun '95 / Spectrum

☐ **FROM DAWN TILL DUSK**
Everybody be cool: *Blasters* / Dark night: *Blasters* / Mexican blackbird: *ZZ Top* / Texas funeral: *Wayne, Jon* / Foolish heart: *Mavericks* / Would you do me a favour: *Vaughan, Jimmy* / Dengue woman blues: *Vaughan, Jimmy* / Torquay: *ZZ Top* / Leftovers: *ZZ Top* / She's just killing me: *ZZ Top* / Chet's speech: *Tito & Tarantula* / Angry cockroaches: *Tito & Tarantula* / Mary had a little lamb: *Vaughan, Stevie Ray & Double Trouble* / After dark: *Vaughan, Stevie Ray & Double Trouble* / Willie the wimp (and his cadillac coffin): *Revell, Graeme* / Kill the band: *Revell, Graeme* / Mexican standoff: *Revell, Graeme* / Sex machine attacks: *Revell, Graeme*
4836172 / Mar '96 / Epic

☐ **FROM RUSSIA WITH LOVE**
Barry, John *c*
Opening titles / James Bond is back/From Russia with love/James Bond theme / Tania meets Klebb / Meeting in St. Sophia / Golden horn / Girl trouble / Bond meets Tania / 007 / Gypsy camp / Death of Grant / Spectre island / Guitar lament / Man overboard - SMERSH in action / James Bond with bongos / Stalking / Leila dances / Death of Kerim / 007 takes the lektor
CZ 550 / Dec '95 / Premier/EMI

☐ **FUGITIVE, THE**
Howard, James Newton *c*
Howard, James Newton *con*
Main title / Storm drain / Kimble dyes his hair / Helicopter chase / Fugitive theme / Subway fight / Kimble returns / No press / Stairway chase / Sykes' apt / It's over
7559615922 / Dec '96 / Elektra

☐ **FULL CIRCLE (The Haunting Of Julia)**
Towns, Colin *c*
Towns, Colin *con*
387032 / Apr '95 / Koch

☐ **FULL METAL JACKET**
Mead, Abigail *c*
Full metal jacket / Hello Vietnam / Chapel of love / Wooly bully / I like it like that / These boots are made for walking / Surfin' bird / Marines' hymn / Transition / Parris Island / Ruins / Leonard / Attack / Time suspended / Sniper
9256132 / Sep '87 / WEA

☐ **FULL MONTY, THE**
You sexy thing: *Hot Chocolate* / You can leave your hat on: *Jones, Tom* / Moving on up: *M People* / Je t'aime...moi non plus: *Gainsbourg, Serge* / Zodiac: *Lindup, David* / (Come up and see me) make me smile: *Harley, Steve & The Cockney Rebel* / Rock 'n' roll: *Glitter, Gary* / Land of a 1000 dances: *Pickett, Wilson* / Full monty: *Dudley, Anne* / Flash dance: *Cara, Irene* / Hot stuff: *Summer, Donna* / We are family: *Sister Sledge* / Stripper: *Loss, Joe Orchestra*
09026689042 / Aug '97 / RCA Victor

☐ **FUNNY FACE (Astaire, Fred)**
Gershwin, George *c*
Gershwin, Ira *l*
5312312 / May '96 / Verve

☐ **FUNNY GIRL**
Styne, Jule *c*
Merrill, Bob *l*
Funny girl overture / I'm the greatest star / If a girl isn't pretty / Roller skate rag / I'd rather be blue over you (than happy with somebody else) / His love makes me beautiful / People / You are woman / Don't rain on my parade / Sadie Sadie / Swan / Funny girl / My man (mon homme) / Finale
4625452 / Apr '94 / Columbia

☐ **FUNNY GIRL (1964 Broadway Cast)**
Styne, Jule *c*
Merrill, Bob *l*
Rosenstock, Milton *con*
Overture / If a girl isn't pretty / I'm the greatest star / Cornet man / Who taught her everything / His love makes me beautiful / I want to be seen with you tonight / Henry Street / People / You are woman / Don't rain on my parade / Sadie Sadie / Find yourself a man / Rat-tat-tat-tat / Who are you now / Music that makes me dance / Finale
ZDM 7646612 / Apr '93 / EMI Classics

☐ **FUNNY THING HAPPENED ON THE WAY TO THE FORUM (1962 Broadway Cast)**
Sondheim, Stephen *c*
ZDM 7647702 / Apr '93 / EMI Classics

☐ **FUNNY THING HAPPENED ON THE WAY TO THE FORUM (1963 London Cast)**
Sondheim, Stephen *c*
CDANGEL 3 / Apr '93 / Angel

☐ **FUNNY THING HAPPENED ON THE WAY TO THE FORUM (In Jazz) (Trotter Trio)**
Sondheim, Stephen *c*
VSD 5707 / Jun '96 / Varese Sarabande

☐ **FUNNY THING HAPPENED ON THE WAY TO THE FORUM (1966 Film Cast)**
Sondheim, Stephen *c*
Sondheim, Stephen *l*
Thorne, Ken *con*
RCD 10727 / 20 Jul '98 / Rykodisc

G

☐ **GAMBLE, THE**
Donaggio, Pino *c*
OST 106 / Jul '93 / Milano Dischi

☐ **GAMBLER, THE**
724354531224 / 7 Nov '97 / Virgin Classics

☐ **GAME OF DEATH/NIGHT GAMES**
Barry, John *c*
FILMCD 123 / Jan '93 / Silva Screen

☐ **GAME, THE**
Shore, Howard *c*
4585562 / 13 Oct '97 / Decca

☐ **GANG RELATED**
CDPTY 149 / 10 Aug '98 / Priority/Virgin

☐ **GARDEN OF THE FINZI-CONTINIS, THE**
De Sica, Manuel *c*
Micol's theme / Tennis match / Giorgio and Micol (love theme) / Persecution / Garden of the Finzi-Continis / Meeting at Easter / Declaration of war / Leaving for Genoble / Giorgio's delusion / Villa / Childhood memories / Finale / Micol's theme (reprise)
OST 125 / Aug '94 / Milano Dischi

☐ **GARDEN, THE (Fisher-Turner, Simon)**
Fisher-Turner, Simon *c*
IONIC 5CD / Jan '91 / Mute

☐ **GAS FOOD LODGING**
Mascis, J. & Barry Adamson *c*
IONIC 9CD / Oct '92 / The Fine Line

☐ **GATTACA (Nyman, Michael)**
Nyman, Michael *c*
Morrow / God's hands / One moment / Traces / Arrival / Becoming Jerome / Call me Eugene / Borrowed ladder / Further and further / Not the only one / Second morrow / Impromptu for 12 fingers / Crossing / It must be the light / Only a matter of time / I thought you wanted to dance / Irene's theme / Yourself for the day / Up stairs / Now that you're here / Truth / Other side / Departure / Irene and the morrow
CDVE 936 / 9 Mar '98 / Venture

☐ **GAY 90'S**
Gay 90's / Couplets / Sweet dreams / Simply love / 976 number / Mirror image / John and Fred / Lookin' at me / Desmond Sam and Ellen / Well spoken woman / My superman / Any once upon a time / All the good men are gay / Mirror image / Bisexual tango / Jonathon Wesley Oliver / Ship sails on / In this moment
VSD 5867 / 9 Mar '98 / Varese Sarabande

☐ **GAY LIFE, THE (Broadway Cast)**
Schwartz, Arthur *c*
Dietz, Howard *l*
ZDM 7647632 / Apr '93 / EMI Classics

☐ **GAZON MAUDIT**
CDVIR 49 / Apr '96 / Virgin

☐ **GBH (Costello, Elvis & Richard Harvey)**
Costello, Elvis & Richard Harvey *c*
Life and times of Michael Murray / It wasn't me / Men of alloy / Lambs to the slaughter / Bubbles / Goldilocks theme / Perfume the odour of money / Assassin: *Douglas, Barbara* / Pursuit suite / Roaring boy: *Prufrock Quartet* / So I used five / Love from a cold land / In a cemetery garden / Smack 'im / Woodlands - Oh joy / It's cold up there / Going home service / Grave music / Puppet masters' work / He's so easy / Another time another place / Closing titles
DSCD 4 / Jul '91 / Demon

☐ **GENERAL WITH THE COCKEYED ID, THE**
Goldsmith, Jerry *c*
W 9103 / 14 Apr '98 / Taran

☐ **GENERAL, THE**
HBCD 0015 / 13 Jul '98 / Hummingbird

☐ **GENOCIDE (Royal Philharmonic Orchestra)**
Bernstein, Elmer *c*
Bernstein, Elmer *con*
FMT 8007D / Jan '93 / Intrada

☐ **GENTLEMEN PREFER BLONDES (inc. Unreleased Songs/Never Before And Never Again) (Monroe, Marilyn)**
Styne, Jule *c*
Robin, Leo *l*
Gentlemen prefer blondes / Diamonds are a girl's best friend / Little girl from Little Rock / Ain't there anyone here for love / When love goes wrong / Bye bye baby / Do it again / Kiss / You'd be surprised / Fine romance / She acts like a woman should / Heatwave / Happy birthday Mr. President
DRGCD 15005 / Jan '95 / DRG

☐ **GENTLEMEN PREFER BLONDES (1949 Broadway Cast)**
Styne, Jule *c*
Robin, Leo *l*
Rosenstock, Milton *con*
SK 48013 / Dec '91 / Sony Broadway

☐ **GENTLEMEN PREFER BLONDES (Monroe, Marilyn)**
Styne, Jule *c*
Robin, Leo *l*
DRGCD 94762 / Jun '95 / DRG

☐ **GERMINAL**
Roques, Jean-Louis *c*
Germinal (Generique debut) / Les machines / La descente a la mine / Catherine et etienne / Une piece de cent sous... / La remonte / Montsou l'ete / Bal du bon joyeux / Le voreux occupe / Catherine n'est pas rentree / En bas... / La greve / Catherine et chaval / Saccage a jean bart / Le viol / La revolte / Mort de maheu / Apres l'ecroulement de voreux / Germinal (Generique fin)
CDVIR 28 / Jun '94 / Virgin

☐ **GET CARTER**
Budd, Roy *c*
ESSCD 656 / 7 Sep '98 / Essential

☐ **GET ON THE BUS**
Shabooyah: *Bus Crew* / Destiny is calling: *Guru* / Tonite's the night: *Doug E Fresh* / Remedy: *Tribe Called Quest* / Girl you need a change of mind: *D'Angelo* / Redemption song: *Wonder, Stevie* / New world order: *Mayfield, Curtis* / Over a million strong: *Neville Brothers* / My life is in your hands: *God's Property & Kirk Franklin* / I love my woman: *Davis, Marvin* / Cruisin': *Earth, Wind & Fire* / Welcome: *Dorsey, Marc* / Coming home to you: *Blackstreet* / Ayinde's speech: *Jean-Baptiste, Ayinde*
IND 90089 / Jul '97 / Interscope

☐ **GET SHORTY**
5293102 / Mar '96 / Verve

☐ **GHOST (Extended Version)**
Jarre, Maurice *c*
Jarre, Maurice *con*
74321342782 / Mar '96 / Milan

☐ **GHOST AND MRS. MUIR, THE**
Herrmann, Bernard *c*
Bernstein, Elmer *con*
VSD 5850 / 20 Oct '97 / Varese Sarabande

☐ **GHOST DANCE (Cunningham, David & Jamie Muir/Michael Giles)**
Cunningham, David & Jamie Muir/Michael Giles *c*
PIANO 052 / Mar '96 / Piano

☐ **GHOST STORY**
Sarde, Philippe *c*
VSD 5259 / Apr '91 / Varese Sarabande

☐ **GHOST TOWN/SLAUGHTER ON TENTH AVENUE/LA PRINCESSE ZENOBIA**
Rodgers, Richard *c*
CDTER 1114 / '88 / TER

☐ **GHOSTS OF THE CIVIL DEAD (Cave, Nick & The Bad Seeds)**
Cave, Nick *c*
CDIONIC 3 / Apr '89 / The Fine Line

☐ **GI BLUES (Presley, Elvis)**
Tonight is so right for love / What's she really like / Frankfurt special / Wooden heart / GI blues / Pocketful of rainbows / Shopping around / Big boots / Didja ever / Blue suede shoes / Doin' the best I can / Big boots / Shoppin' around / Frankfurt special / Pocketful of rainbows / Didja ever / Big boots / What's she really like / Doin' the best I can
07863674602 / Apr '97 / RCA
07863669602 / 2 Feb '98 / RCA

☐ **GI JANE**
1621092 / 17 Nov '97 / Polydor

☐ **GIANT**
Tiomkin, Dimitri *c*
TSU 0106 / Jan '94 / Tsunami

☐ **GIGI (1985 London Cast)**
Loewe, Frederick *c*
Lerner, Alan Jay *l*
Paris is Paris again / It's a bore / Earth and other minor things / Thank heaven for little girls / She's not thinking of me / Night they invented champagne / I remember it well / Gigi / Entr'acte / Contract / I'm glad I'm not young anymore / Wide wide world / Finale
OCRCD 6007 / Feb '96 / First Night

☐ **GIGI (Film Cast)**
Loewe, Frederick *c*
Lerner, Alan Jay *l*
Main title / Opening / Interlude / And there is the future / Thank heaven for little girls / Meet Gigi / Gaston's house / Armenonville / It's a bore (prelude) / It's a bore / After it's a bore / Aunt Alicia / Parisians introduction / Parisians / Ice skating sequence / Dissolve maxim's / Gossip / Introduction to Maxim's / Waltz at Maxim's / It's a bore (reprise) / To the inn / Goodbye madame / Bore montage / Night they invented champagne / Trouville / I remember it well / Panting Grandma / Lessons / Upset / Gaston's souloquy / Gigi / Gaston with flowers / You never told me / I'm glad I'm not young anymore / I'm glad I'm not young anymore (reprise) / Aunt Alicia's march / Bracelet / Say a prayer for me tonight / Gigi's big moment / Second gossip / Waltz at Maxim's (dance version) / Gaston's decision / Change of heartland / End title / Parisians (outtake) / Night they invented champagne (outtake)
CDODEON 10 / Apr '96 / Soundtracks

☐ **GIGI (Cast Recording)**
Loewe, Frederick *c*
Lerner, Alan Jay *l*
Overture: *Cast* / Thank heaven for little girls: *Cast* / It's a bore: *Cast* / Waltz at Maxim's: *Cast* / She's not thinking of me: *Cast* / Night they invented champagne: *Cast* / I remeber it well: *Cast* / Say a prayer for me tonight: *Cast* / Gigi: *Cast* / In this wide wide world: *Cast* / I'm glad I'm not young anymore: *Cast* / Finale: *Cast*
SHOWCD 052 / Apr '97 / Showtime

☐ **GINGER ALE AFTERNOON (Dixon, Willie)**
Dixon, Willie *c*
VSD 5234 / Oct '89 / Varese Sarabande

☐ **GIOVANNI FALCONE**
Donaggio, Pino *c*
LEGENDCD 12 / Jan '93 / Legend

☐ **GIRL 6 (Prince)**
Prince *c*
9362462392 / Mar '96 / Warner Bros.

☐ **GIRL CRAZY (Cast Recording)**
Gershwin, George *c*
Gershwin, Ira *l*
Mauceri, John *con*
7559792502 / Feb '91 / Nonesuch

☐ **GIRL CRAZY (Garland, Judy & Mickey Rooney/Tommy Dorsey Orchestra/ Film Cast)**
Gershwin, George *c*
Gershwin, Ira *l*
Main title/Montage / Sam and Delilah / Treat me rough / Bidin' my time / Could you use me / Ginger dear / Happy birthday to you / Embraceable you / Walking in the garden / Barbary Coast / Fascinating rhythm / Bronco busters / Boy what has love done to me / Embraceable you / But not for me / I got rhythm / End title
CDODEON 30 / 15 Sep '97 / Soundtracks

☐ **GIRL ON A MOTORCYCLE**
Reed, Les *c*
Girl on a motorcycle / Dream / Holiday with Raymond / Daniel / Au revoir Daniel / Souvenirs of Raymond / Sweet souvenirs of Raymond / Surrender to a stranger / Take me to your lover / Dawn idyll / Journey of love / Big bare beat / Summer house / Don't ask me
RPM 171 / Nov '96 / RPM

☐ **GIRL WHO CAME TO SUPPER, THE (Noel Coward Sings His Score) (Coward, Sir Noel)**
Coward, Sir Noel *c*
DRGCD 5178 / Oct '95 / DRG

☐ **GIRL WHO CAME TO SUPPER, THE (1963 Broadway Cast)**
Coward, Sir Noel *c*
Blackton, Jay *con*
SK 48210 / Nov '93 / Sony Broadway

☐ **GIRL WITH THE BRAINS IN HER FEET**
VVR 1002652 / 15 Jun '98 / V2

☐ **GIRLFRIEND, THE (1987 Colchester Cast)**
Rodgers, Richard *c*
Hart, Lorenz *l*
CDTER 1148 / Aug '95 / TER

☐ **GIVE MY REGARDS TO BROAD STREET (McCartney, Paul)**
McCartney, Paul *c*
No more lonely nights / Good day sunshine / Corridor music / Yesterday / Here there and everywhere / Wanderlust / Ballroom dancing / Silly love songs / Silly love songs (reprise) / Not such a bad boy / So bad / No values / No more lonely nights (reprise) / For no one / Eleanor Rigby / Eleanor's dream / Long and winding road / No more lonely nights (version) / Goodnight princess
CDP 7892682 / Aug '93 / Parlophone

☐ **GLADIATORS - THE ALBUM**
Main theme: *Gladiators* / Everything about you: *Ugly Kid Joe* / Holding out for a hero: *Tyler, Bonnie* / Final Countdown: *Europe* / Bat out of hell: *Meat Loaf* / Since you've been gone: *Rainbow* / Burning heart: *Survivor* / Hold the line: *Toto* / More than a feeling: *Boston* / All right now: *Free* / Power: *Snap* / War: *Starr, Edwin* / Wild thing: *Troggs* / You ain't seen nothin' yet: *Bachman-Turner Overdrive* / Gladiator's entrance: *Storm* / Medley mix: *Warren's world* / Duel: *Storm* / Eliminator: *Storm* / Wall: *Storm* / Atlaspheres: *Storm* / You're a winner: *Storm* / Danger zone: *Storm* / Hang tough: *Storm* / Swingshot: *Storm* / There are no losers: *Storm*
515 877-2 / Nov '92 / PolyGram TV

☐ GLAM METAL DETECTIVES
650103392 / Apr '95 / Warner Bros.

☐ GLINT OF SILVER, A (Silly Wizard)
GLCD 1070 / Mar '87 / Green Linnet

☐ GLORY (Harlem Boys Choir)
Horner, James *c*
Horner, James *con*
Call to arms / After antietam / Lonely Christmas / Forming the regiment / Whipping / Burning the town of darien / Brave words / Braver deeds / Year of jubilee / Preparations for battle / Charging for Wagner / Epitaph / Closing credits
CDV 2614 / '90 / Virgin

☐ GLORY DAZE
Theme from Glory Daze: Vandals / It's a fact: Vandals / Change the world with my hockey stick: *Vandals* / Here we go: *Bouncing Souls* / Joe lies: *Bouncing Souls* / I just wanna do it with you: *Mr T. Experience* / Fucking my mom: *NOFX* / Even Hitler had a girlfriend: *Mr T. Experience* / Brain dead: *Assorted Jelly Beans* / Sports pack: *Epoxy* / Country time: *Hepcat* / Crying jag: *Tilt* / Baby: *Billy Nayer Show* / Runnin' on go: *New Bomb Turks* / Moron brothers: *NOFX* / Berkeley pier: *Tilt* / We're only gonna die: *Sublime*
787612 / 29 Jun '98 / Kung Fu

☐ GO WEST (New Jazz Score For Buster Keaton Film)
Frisell, Bill *c*
7559793502 / Jan '95 / Elektra

☐ GOBLIN MARKET (1985 Off-Broadway Cast)
Pen, Polly *c*
Rosetti, Christine *l*
CDTER 1144 / Mar '90 / TER

☐ GODFATHER I, THE
Rota, Nino *c*
Godfather waltz / I have but one heart / Pick-up / Connie's wedding / Halls of fear / Sicilian pastorale / Godfather (love theme) / Appollonia / New godfather / Baptism / Godfather finale
MCLD 19022 / Apr '92 / MCA

☐ GODFATHER II, THE
Rota, Nino/Carmine Coppola *c*
MCAD 10232 / 19 Jan '98 / MCA

☐ GODFATHER III, THE
Rota, Nino/Carmine Coppola *c*
Godfather part III main title / Godfather waltz / Marcia Religioso / Michael's letter / Immigrant / Godfather part III love theme / Godfather waltz / To each his own / Vincent's theme / Altobella / Godfather intermezzo / Sicilian medley / Promise me you'll remember (love theme) / Preludio and Siciliano / A case amiche / Preghiera / Godfather finale / Coda: The Godfather finale
4678132 / Mar '91 / Epic

☐ GODFATHER SUITE, THE (Music Featured In The Godfather Trilogy) (Milan Philharmonia Orchestra)
Rota, Nino/Carmine Coppola/Francesco Pennino *c*
Coppola, Carmine *con*
Love theme / Godfather's tarantella / Godfather's mazurka / Every time I look in your eyes / Godfather's waltz / Michael's theme / Godfather's fox-trot / Senza mamma / Napule ve salute / Marcia religiosa / Festa march / Kay's theme / New carpet / Immigrant
FILMCD 077 / Mar '91 / Silva Screen

☐ GODMONEY
VVR 1000602 / Aug '97 / V2

☐ GODSPELL (Cast Recording)
Schwartz, Stephen *c*
Prepare ye the way of the Lord / Save the people / Day by day / Learn your lessons well/Bless the lord / All for the best / All good gifts / Turn back old man / Alas for you / By my side / We beseech thee / On the willow / Finale
SHOWCD 012 / Feb '95 / Showtime

☐ GODSPELL (Cast Recording)
Schwartz, Stephen *c*
Prologue / Prepare ye the way of the Lord / Save the GospelSave the people / Day by day / Learn your lesson well / Bless the Lord / All for the best / All good gifts / Light of the world / Turn back old man / Alas for you / By my side / We beseech thee / On the willows / Beautiful city / Finale
CDTER 1204 / Nov '97 / TER

☐ GODSPELL (CC Productions)
Schwartz, Stephen *c*
Prepare ye the way of the Lord / Save the people / Day by day / Learn your lesson well / O bless the Lord my soul / All of the best / All good gifts / Light of the world / Turn back o man / By my side / We beseech thee / On the willows / Godspell
QED 211 / Nov '96 / Tring

☐ GODSPELL/JESUS CHRIST SUPERSTAR (Highlights - The Songs Collection) (Cast Recording)
Schwartz, Stephen/Andrew Lloyd Webber *c*
Schwartz, Stephen/Tim Rice *l*
PWKS 4220 / Nov '94 / Carlton

☐ GODZILLA
Heroes: Wallflowers / Come with me: *Puff Daddy & Jimmy Page* / Deeper underground: *Jamiroquai* / No shelter: *Rage Against The Machine* / Air: *Folds, Ben Five* / Running knees: *Days Of The New* / May day parade: *Penn, Michael* / Walk the sky: *Fuel* / A320: *Foo Fighters* / Brain stew: *Green Day* / Untitled: *Silverchair* / Out there: *Fuzz Bubble* / Undercover: *Joey Deluxe* / Opening titles: *Arnold, David* / Looking for clues: *Arnold, David*
4896102 / 18 May '98 / Epic

☐ GOING ALL THE WAY
White sport coat / Bess boogie / Mighty mighty man / Rocket 88 / Big heavy / Sunday kind of love / Gonna hoot and holler Saturday night / Skokiaan / Tangled and tempted / Mopsticks / You've changed / Sexy man / Why was I born / Farther along / Goofball
5379082 / Oct '97 / Verve

☐ GOLD DIGGERS (Cooper, Lindsay)
McNeely, Joel *c*
VSD 5633 / Nov '95 / Varese Sarabande

☐ GOLD RUSH, THE (Tak, Max Orchestra)
Chaplin, Charlie *c*
Far North - the great gold rush / Eating well-prepared shoes / Hungry hallucination - the chicken / Mock fight with a bear / Georgia the dancehall girl / Heart full of lost dreams / Waltzing the dog / Beans smelled fine the coffee was piping hot / Flock of pretty maidens / New year's eve / Dance of the rolls / Excluded from the festivities / Message / Cabin at the abyss / And so they were millionaires / Happy end
BASTA 309050 / Sep '97 / Basta

☐ GOLDEN APPLE, THE (Original Broadway Cast)
Moross, Jerome *c*
Latouche, John *l*
Overture / My love is on the way / Heroes come home / It was a glad adventure / Come along boys / It's the going home together / Mother Hare's prophecy / Helen is always willing / Judgment of Paris / Lazy afternoon / Departure for Rhododendron / My picture in the papers / Hector's song / Windflowers / Store bought suit / Big spree / Calypso / Scylla and Charybdis / Goona-goona / Doomed doomed doomed / Circe / Ulysses' soliloquy / Sewing bee / Tirade / Finale/Coming home together
09026689342 / 12 Jan '98 / RCA Victor

☐ GOLDEN BOY (1959 Broadway Cast)
Strouse, Charles *c*
Adams, Lee *l*
ZDM 5650242 / Nov '93 / EMI Classics

☐ GOLDEN GATE
Goldenthal, Elliot *c*
VSD 5470 / Aug '94 / Varese Sarabande

☐ GOLDENEYE
Serra, Eric *c*
Goldeneye: *Turner, Tina* / Goldeneye overture / Ladies first / We share the same passions / Little surprise for you / Severnaya suite / Our lady of Smolensk / Whispering statues / Run shoot and jump / Pleasant drive in St. Petersburg / Fatal weakness / That's what keeps you alone / Dish out of water / Scale to hell / For ever James / Experience of love
CDVUSX 100 / Nov '95 / Virgin

☐ GOLDFINGER
Barry, John *c*
Teasing the Korean / Main title / Alpine drive / Auric's factory / Oddjob's pressing engagement / Bond back in action again / Gassing the gangsters / Goldfinger (instrumental version) / Dawn raid on Fort Knox / Arrival of the bomb and countdown / Death of Goldfinger / End titles
CZ 557 / Dec '95 / Premier/EMI

☐ GOLDILOCKS (1958 Broadway Cast)
Anderson, Leroy *c*
Ford, Joan/Jean & Walter Kerr *l*
Engel, Lehman *con*
SK 48222 / Nov '92 / Sony Broadway

☐ GOLEM, THE (How He Came Into The World - 1977 Score) (Berlin Symphony Orchestra)
Sasse, Karl-Ernst *c*
Keuschnig, Peter *con*
10467 / Apr '96 / Capriccio

☐ GONDOLIERS, THE (D'Oyly Carte Opera Chorus/New Symphony Orchestra)
Sullivan, Sir Arthur *c*
Gilbert, W.S. *l*
Godfrey, I. *con*
4251772 / Jan '90 / Decca

☐ GONDOLIERS, THE (Evans, Geraint & Alexander Young/Glyndebourne Festival Choir/Pro Arte Orchestra)
Sullivan, Sir Arthur *c*
Gilbert, W.S. *l*
Sargent, Sir Malcolm *con*
CMS 7643942 / Apr '94 / EMI Classics

☐ GONDOLIERS, THE (D'Oyly Carte Opera Chorus/Orchestra)
Sullivan, Sir Arthur *c*
Gilbert, W.S. *l*
Pryce Jones, J. *con*
Overture / Opening act 1 / From the sunny Spanish store / In the enterprise of martial kind / O rapture when alone together / Therew was a time a time forever gone / I stole the prince and brought him here / But bless my heart / Try we life long / Bridegroom and bride / When a merry maiden marries / Fianle act 1 / Oh happiness in the very pith in Barataria / Rising early in the morning / Take a pair of sparkling eyes / Here we are at the risk of our lives / Dance a cachucha / There live a king / Ina contemplative fashion / With ducal pomp and ducal pride / On the day when I was wedded / To help unhappy commoners / I am a courtier brave and serious / Finale act 2 / Di ballo overture / To help unhappy customers / I am a courtier grave and serious
CDTER2 1187 / Nov '97 / TER

☐ GONDOLIERS, THE/PATIENCE (D'Oyly Carte Opera Chorus/New Symphony Orchestra)
Sullivan, Sir Arthur *c*
Gilbert, W.S. *l*
Sargent, Sir Malcolm *con*
Z 80952 / Jul '89 / Arabesque

☐ GONDOLIERS, THE/TRIAL BY JURY (D'Oyly Carte Opera Chorus/ Orchestra)
Sullivan, Sir Arthur *c*
Gilbert, W.S. *l*
Sargent, Malcolm/H. Norris *con*
GEMMCDS 9961 / Sep '93 / Pearl

☐ GONE WITH THE WIND (National Philharmonic Orchestra)
Steiner, Max *c*
Gerhardt, Charles *con*
Selznick international trademark/Main title / Opening sequence / Driving home / Dance montage - Charleston heel and toe polka / Grazioso/Love theme / Civil war/Fall of the South/Scarlett walks among the wounded / True love/Ashley returns to Tara from the war/Tara in ruins / Belle Watling / Reconstruction/Nightmare/Tara rebuilt/Bonnie/The accident / Mammy and Melanie on the staircase/ Rhett's sorrow / Apotheosis - Melanie's death/ Scarlett and Rhett/Tara
GD 80452 / Mar '90 / RCA Victor

☐ GONE WITH THE WIND (London Sinfonietta)
Steiner, Max *c*
12436 / Jun '95 / Laserlight

☐ GONE WITH THE WIND
Steiner, Max *c*
BMCD 7009 / Jul '96 / Blue Moon

☐ GONE WITH THE WIND (Film Cast)
Steiner, Max *c*
Main title / Tara / O'Hara family / Scarlett prepares for the barbecue / Twelve oaks / Barbecue / Afternoon nap / Charles Hamilton challenges Rhett / In the library / War is declared/The death of Charles / At the bazaar / Maryland my Maryland / Dances / Gettysburg / Outside the Examiner newspaper office / At the depot / Christmas at Aunt Pitty's / Melanie and Scarlett tend the wounded / Scarlett's promise / Train depot / Melanie in labour / Rhett returns / Escape from Atlanta / Soldiers in retreat / Rhett and Scarlett on McDonough Road / Twelve oaks in ruin/ Scarlett comes home / I'll never be hungry again / Alternate entr'acte / Battle montage / Deserter / Melanie and Scarlett / It's over / Frank Kennedy asks for Sue Ellen's hand / Paddock scene / Gerald's death / Old folks at home / New store / Scarlett in shantytown / Ashley and Dr. Mede/Frank's death / Belle waiting and Melanie / Scarlett gets tipsy / New Orleans honeymoon / Can can / Scarlett's new wardrobe / Scarlett's nightmare / Bonnie's birth / Twenty inches / Lumber mill / After the party / London / Rhett and Scarlett's fight / Death of Bonnie / Melanie and Mammy / Death of Melanie / Scarlett in the mist/Rhett leaves / Flashback/Finale
CDODEON 27 / Jan '97 / Soundtracks

☐ GOOD COMPANIONS, THE (1974 London Cast)
Previn, Andre *c*
Mercer, Johnny *l*
Camaraderie / Pools / Footloose / Pleasure of your company / Stage struck / Dance of life / Slippin' around the corner / Good companions / Little travelling music / And points beyond / Darkest before the dawn / Susie for everybody / Ta luv / I'll tell the world / Stage door John
DRGCD 15020 / Jan '95 / DRG

☐ GOOD MORNING VIETNAM
Nowhere to run: *Reeves, Martha* / I get around: *Beach Boys* / Game of love: *Fontana, Wayne & The Mindbenders* / Sugar and spice: *Searchers* / Liar liar: *Castaways* / Warmth of the sun: *Beach Boys* / I got you (I feel good): *Brown, James* / Baby please don't go: *Them* / Danger heartbreak dead ahead: *Marvelettes* / Five o'clock world: *Vogues* / California sun: *Rivieras* / What a wonderful world: *Armstrong, Louis*
CDMID 163 / Oct '92 / A&M

☐ GOOD NEWS (1994 American Cast)
Henderson, Ray *c*
De Sylva, B.G. & Lew Brown *l*
Overture/Students are we / Good news / He's a ladies man / Football drill / Button up your overcoat / Together / My lucky star / On the campus / Best things in life are free / You're the cream in my coffee / Varsity drag / Lucky in love / Today's the day / Girl of the Pi Beta Phi / Never swat a fly / Tait song / Just imagine / Keep your sunny side up / Life is just a bowl of cherries / Fianle
CDTER 1230 / Nov '97 / TER

☐ GOOD ROCKIN' TONITE (1992 London Cast)
Rock around the clock / R-O-C-K rock / Razzle dazzle / Six-five special / Freight train / That is rock'n'roll / Rock Island line / Singing the blues / Book of love / Rock with the caveman / Fabulous / Green door / Keepa knockin' / Ma he's making eyes at me / Giddy up a ding dong / Get a job / Trouble / Rock'n'roll is here to stay / Runaround Sue / At the hop / High school confidential / Donna / Move it / Let the good times roll / Happy Jack / La bamba / Baby I don't care / Rip it up / Down the line / Maybe tomorrow / Willie and the hand jive / Stupid cupid / Hey hey hey / Wondrous place / That's love / Don't knock upon my door / Baby blue / Be bop a lula / Dance in the street / Summertime blues / C'mon everybody / Something else / Twenty flight rock / I was born to rock'n'roll / Surfin' USA / Fun fun fun / I get around / Johnny B Goode / Respect / I'm a woman / Good rockin' tonite / What'd I say / Saved
OCRCD 6026 / Apr '96 / First Night

☐ GOOD, THE BAD AND THE UGLY, THE
Morricone, Ennio *c*
Good the bad and the ugly / Sundown / Strong / Desert / Carriage of the spirits / Marcia / Story of a soldier / Marcia without hope / Death of a soldier / Ecstasy of gold / Trio
CDP 7484082 / Sep '88 / EMI Manhattan

☐ GOOD WILL HUNTING
Between the bars (Orch): *Smith, Elliott* / As the rain: *Nichols, Jeb Loy* / Angeles: *Smith, Elliott* / No name number three: *Smith, Elliott* / Fisherman's blues: *Waterboys* / Why do I lie: *Jackson, Luscious* / Will hunting (main titles): *Jackson, Luscious* / Between the bars: *Smith, Elliott* / Say yes: *Smith, Elliott* / Baker street: *Rafferty, Gerry* / Somebody's baby: *Donalds, Andru* / Boys better: *Dandy Worhols* / How can you mend a broken heart: *Heart* / Miss mystery: *Elfman, Danny* / Weepy donuts: *Elfman, Danny*
8233382 / 2 Mar '98 / Premier/EMI

☐ GOODBYE GIRL (London Cast)
Hamlisch, Marvin *c*
SCORECD 44 / Apr '97 / First Night
CASTCD 63 / 26 Jan '98 / First Night

☐ GOODBYE MR. CHIPS (1982 Chichester Festival Cast)
Bricusse, Leslie *c*
Edwards, John Owen *con*
Roll call / Fill the world with love / Would I had lived my life then / Schooldays / That's a boy / Where did my childhood go / Boring / Take a chance / Walk through the world / When I am older / Miracle / Day has a hundred pockets / You and I / What a lot of flowers / When I was younger / Goodbye Mr Chips
CDTER 1025 / Aug '98 / TER

☐ GOODFELLAS
Rags to riches: *Bennett, Tony* / Sincerely: *Moonglows* / Speedo: *Cadillacs* / Stardust: *Ward, Billy* / Look in my eyes: *Chantels* / Life is but a dream: *Harptones* / Remember (walkin' in the sand): *Shangri-Las* / Baby I love you: *Franklin, Aretha* / Beyond the sea: *Darin, Bobby* / Sunshine of your love: *Cream* / Mannish boy: *Waters, Muddy* / Layla: *Derek & The Dominoes*
7567821522 / Nov '90 / Atlantic

☐ GOODTIME CHARLEY (Original Broadway Cast)
Grossman, Larry *c*
Hackady, Hal *l*
Overture/History / Goodtime Charley / Voices and visions / Bits and pieces / To make the boy a man / Why can't we all be nice / Born lover / I am going to love (the man you're going to be) / Castles of the Loire / You still have a long way to go / Merci bon dieu / Confessional / One little year / I leave the world / Finale/History (reprise)
09026689352 / 12 Jan '98 / RCA Victor

☐ GOOFY MOVIE, THE
WD 764002 / Oct '96 / Disney Music & Stories

☐ GORKY PARK
Horner, James *c*
Horner, James *con*
Main title / Following Kirwill / Irina's theme / Following KGB / Chase through the park / Arkady and Irina / Faceless bodies / Irina's chase / Sable shed / Airport farewell / Releasing the sables/ End title
VCD 47260 / Jan '89 / Varese Sarabande

☐ GOSPEL AT COLONUS, THE (Broadway Cast)
Live where you can / Stop do not go on / How shall I see you through my tears / Voice foretold prayer / Never drive you away / Numberless are the world's wonders / Lift me up (like a dove) / Sunlight of no light / Eternal sleep / Lift him up / Now let the weeping cease
7559791912 / Jan '95 / Nonesuch

☐ GOTHIC (Dolby, Thomas)
Dolby, Thomas *c*
Fantasmagoria / Byronic love / Shelleymania / Mary's theme / Party games / Gypsy girl / Crucifix / Fundamental source / Sin and buggery / Impalement / Leech juice / Restless sleep 1 2 and 3 / It's his / Coitus per stigmata / Once we vowed eternal love / Riddled with guilt / Metamorphosis / Hangman / Beast in the crypt / Final seance / Funeral by the lake / No ghosts in daylight / To the grave / Devil is an Englishman / Skull pulse / Trickle of blood
CDV 2417 / Feb '87 / Virgin

☐ GOTHIC DRAMAS (Original Cast)
Kaiserstrasse / La strada dell follia / Follia nella strada / Fuori dalla realta / Pioggia / Ma non e un vampiro / Citta' ferita / Suoni dissociati / E'una vampira / Il vampiro / La casa delle streghe / Viole nella nebbia / Tra sospiri e lamenti / Ricordo di dino asciolla / Diario di un pazzo / Phantavox / Elegia per violino e pianoforte
DRGCD 32916 / Jun '96 / DRG

☐ GRACE OF MY HEART
God give me strength: *Bacharach, Burt & Elvis Costello* / Love doesn't ever fail us: *Williams Brothers* / Take a run at the sun: *Mascis, J.* / I do: *For Real* / Between two worlds: *Colvin, Shawn* / My secret love: *Banquette, Miss Lily* / Man from Mars: *Vigard, Kristen* / Born to love that boy: *For Real* / Truth is you lied: *Sobule, Jill* / Unwanted number: *For Real* / Groovin' on you: *Juned* / In another world: *Portrait* / Don't you think it's time: *Mascis, J.* / Absence makes the heart grow fonder: *Anders, Tiffany & Boyd Rice* / Boat on the sea: *Vigard, Kristen*
MCD 11554 / Feb '97 / MCA

☐ GRADUATE, THE (Simon & Garfunkel)
Simon, Paul *c*
Sound of silence / Jungleman party foxtrot / Mrs. Robinson / Sunporch cha-cha-cha / Scarborough Fair / On the strip / April come she will / Great effect / Big bright green pleasure machine
CD 32359 / Feb '94 / CBS

☐ **GRAFFITI BRIDGE (Prince)**
Prince *c*
Can't stop this feeling I got / Question of U / Round and round: *Campbell, Tevin* / Joy in repetition / Tick tick bang / Thieves in the temple / Melody cool / Graffiti bridge / Release it: *Time* / Elephants and flowers / We can funk / Love machine / Shake: *Time* / Latest fashion / Still would stand all time / New power generation
7599274932 / Aug '90 / WEA

☐ **GRAND CANYON**
Howard, James Newton *c*
Main title / Claire returns the baby / My sister lives around here / Those rocks / Bloodstain / Baby / Don't work late / Mack's flashback / Don't want out / Searching for a heart / Mack and Claire's dream / Dee in Brentwood / Otis runs / You white / Keep the baby / Doesn't matter / Grand Canyon fanfare / End titles
262493 / Feb '94 / Milan

☐ **GRAND DUKE, THE (D'Oyly Carte Opera Chorus/Royal Philharmonic Orchestra)**
Sullivan, Sir Arthur *c*
Gilbert, W.S. *l*
Nash, R. *con*
4368132 / Jun '92 / London

☐ **GRAND HOTEL (1992 Broadway Cast)**
Forrest, George *c*
Forrest, George & Robert Wright *l*
Lee, Jack *con*
Grand parade/Some have some have not/As it should be / Look at him / At the Grand Hotel/Table with a view / Maybe my baby loves me / Fire and ice/ Twenty-two years/Villa on a hill / I want to go to Hollywood / Sorry to report / Crooked path/Some have some have not/As it should be / Who couldn't dance with you / So tell me Baron / Love can't happen / What you need / Bonjour amour / Happy/ We'll take a glass together / I waltz alone / No creature on this planet / Bolero / How can I tell her / Final scene / Grand waltz
09026613272 / Jul '92 / RCA Victor

☐ **GRAND NIGHT FOR SINGING, A (Cast Recording)**
VSD 5516 / Dec '94 / Varese Sarabande

☐ **GRAND, THE**
75605522912 / 2 Mar '98 / Happy Days

☐ **GRAND TOUR/LONDON MORNING (The Ballet Music Of Noel Coward) (City Of Prague Philharmonic Orchestra)**
Coward, Sir Noel *c*
SILKD 6007 / Sep '95 / Silva Classics

☐ **GREASE (Film Cast)**
Grease: *Valli, Frankie* / Summer nights: *Travolta, John & Olivia Newton John* / Hopelessly devoted to you: *Newton-John, Olivia* / Sandy: *Travolta, John* / Look at me I'm Sandra Dee: *Channing, Stockard* / Greased lightnin': *Travolta, John* / It's raining on prom night: *Bullens, Cindy* / You're the one that I want: *Travolta, John & Olivia Newton John* / Beauty school dropout: *Avalon, Frankie* / Alone at the drive-in movie: *Watts, Ernie* / Blue moon: *Sha Na Na* / Rock 'n' roll is here to stay: *Sha Na Na* / Those magic changes: *Sha Na Na* / Hound dog: *Sha Na Na* / Born to hand jive: *Sha Na Na* / Tears on my pillow: *Sha Na Na* / Mooning: *Bullens, Cindy* / Freddy my love: *Bullens, Cindy* / Rock 'n' roll party queen: *St. Louis, Louis* / There are worse things I could do: *Channing, Stockard* / Look at me I'm Sandra Dee (reprise): *Newton-John, Olivia* / We go together: *Travolta, John & Olivia Newton John* / Love is a many splendoured thing: *Studio Orchestra* / Grease (reprise): *Valli, Frankie*
8179982 / Feb '91 / Polydor
0440412 / 6 Jul '98 / Polydor

☐ **GREASE (1993 London Cast)**
Radio WAXX jingle / Vince Fontaine / Sandy (opening) / Grease / Summer nights / Those magic changes / Freddie my love / Look at me I'm Sandra Dee / Greased lightnin' / Rydell fight song / Mooning / We go together / Shakin' at the high school hop / It's raining on prom night / Born to hand jive / Hopelessly devoted to you / Beauty school dropout / Sandy / Rock 'n' roll party queen / There are worse things I could do / Look at me I'm Sandra Dee (reprise) / You're the one that I want / Finale (medley)
4746322 / Sep '93 / Epic

☐ **GREASE (Highlights - The Shows Collection) (1993 Studio Cast)**
Grease / Summer nights / You're the one that I want / Sandy / Beauty school dropout / Greased lightnin' / Blue moon / Rock 'n' roll is here to stay / Hound dog / Tears on my pillow / Hopelessly devoted to you / Look at me I'm Sandra Dee / Freddy my love / It's raining on prom night
PWKS 4176 / Oct '93 / Carlton

☐ **GREASE (New Broadway Cast)**
Alma Mater / We go together / Summer nights / Those magic changes / Freddy my love / Greased lightnin' / Greased lightnin' (Reprise) / Rydell fight song / Mooning / Look at me I'm Sandra Dee / Since I don't have you / We go together (Reprise) / Shakin' at the High School Hop / It's raining on Prom night / Born to hand jive / Beauty school dropout / Alone at a drive-in movie / Rock 'n' roll party Queen / There are worse things I could do / Look at me I'm Sandra Dee (reprise) / Finale
09026627032 / Sep '94 / RCA

☐ **GREASE (1994 Studio Cast)**
Jacobs, Jim & Warren Casey *c*
Yates, Martin *con*
Grease / Rydell Alma mater / Rydell parody / Summer nights / Those magic changes / Freddy my love / Greased lightnin' / Mooning / Look at me I'm Sandra Dee / Hopelessly devoted to you / We go together / Shakin at the high school hop / It's raining on prom night / Alone at the drive in movie / Born to hand jive / Beauty school drop out / Sandy / Rock n roll queen / Therer are worse things I could do / All choked up / You're the one that I want / We go together
CDTER 1220 / Nov '97 / TER

☐ **GREASE (Cast Recording)**
Grease / Summer nights / Freddy my love / Greased lightnin' / Look at me I'm Sandra Dee / Hopelessly devoted to you / We go together / Shakin' at the high school hop / Beauty school dropout / There are worse things I could do / Sandy / You're the one that I want
SHOWCD 007 / Feb '95 / Showtime

☐ **GREASE (Pink Bruce Production)**
Grease / Summer nights / Hopelessly devoted to you / You're the one that I want / Sandy / Beauty school dropout / Look at me I'm Sandra Dee / Greased lightning / It's raining on prom night / Alone at the drive-in movie / Blue moon / Rock 'n' roll is here to stay / Those magic changes / Hound dog / Born to hand jive / Tears on my pillow / Mooning / Freddy my love / Rock 'n' roll party queen / There are worse things I could do / Look at me I'm Sandra Dee / We go together / Love is a many splendoured thing / Grease
GRF 274 / Apr '93 / Tring

☐ **GREASE (Highlights) (Cast Recording)**
Grease / Summer nights / You're the one that I want / Look at me I'm Sandra Dee / Hopelessly devoted to you / Beauty school drop out / Sandy / Hound dog / Born to hand jive / There are worse things I could do / Greased lightning / We go together
CD 6088 / 29 Sep '97 / Music

☐ **GREASE II**
Back to school again: *Four Tops* / Cool rider: *Pfeiffer, Michelle* / Score tonight: *T-Birds & Pink Ladies* / Girl for all seasons: *Teefy, Maureen/Lorna Luft/Alison Price/Michelle Pfeiffer* / Do it for our country: *Frechette, Peter* / Who's that guy: *Cast* / Prowlin': *T-Birds* / Reproduction: *Hunter, Tab* / Charades: *Caulfield, Maxwell* / Turn back the hands of time: *Caulfield, Maxwell & Michelle Pfeiffer* / Rock-a-hula: *Cast* / We'll be together: *Caulfield, Maxwell*
8250962 / Apr '94 / Polydor

☐ **GREAT AMERICAN BACKSTAGE MUSICAL, THE**
AEICD 011 / May '98 / AEI

☐ **GREAT ESCAPE, THE**
Bernstein, Elmer *c*
Bernstein, Elmer *con*
Main title / Premature plans / Cooler and Mole / Blythe / Discovery / Various troubles / On the road / Betrayal / Hendley's risk / Road's end / More action / Chase / Finale
MAF 7025D / Jul '92 / Intrada
RCD 10711 / 12 Jan '98 / Rykodisc

☐ **GREAT EXPECTATIONS (1993 Clwyd Cast)**
CDTER 1209 / Mar '94 / TER

☐ **GREAT EXPECTATIONS**
Finn runs: *Amos, Tori* / Siren: *Amos, Tori* / Life in mono: *Mono* / Sunshower: *Cornell, Chris* / Resignation: *Reef* / Like a friend: *Reef* / Wishful thinking: *Shiek, Duncan* / Today: *Poe* / Lady your roof brings me down: *Weiland, Scott* / Her ornament: *Verve Pipe* / Walk this earth alone: *Christy, Lauren* / Breakable: *Fisher* / Success: *Iggy Pop* / Slave: *Garza, David* / Uncle John's band: *Grateful Dead* / Besame mucho: *Evora, Cesaria*
7567830582 / 13 Apr '98 / East West

☐ **GREAT MUPPET CAPER, THE (Muppets)**
Main title / Hey a movie / Big red bus / Happiness hotel / Lady Holiday / Steppin' out with a star / Apartment / Night life / First time it happens / Couldn't we ride / Piggy's fantasy / Great muppet caper / Homeward bound / Finale
74321 18246-2 / Jan '94 / BMG Kidz

☐ **GREAT ROCK 'N' ROLL SWINDLE, THE (Sex Pistols)**
God save the Queen (Symphony) / Johnny B Goode / Roadrunner / Anarchy in the UK / Don't give me no lip child / Stepping stone / L'anarchie pour le UK / Silly thing / My way / I wanna be me / Something else / (We're gonna) Rock around the clock: *Tenpole Tudor* / Lonely boy / EMI / Great rock 'n' roll swindle / Friggin' in the riggin' / You need hands: *McLaren, Malcolm* / Who killed Bambi: *Tenpole Tudor* / Belsen was a gas (live) / Black arabs: *Black Arabs* / Substitute / No one is innocent: *Biggs, Ronnie* / C'mon everybody / Belsen was a gas: *Biggs, Ronnie*
CDVDX 2510 / Jan '95 / Virgin

☐ **GREAT WAR & THE SHAPING OF THE 20TH CENTURY, THE**
Daring, Mason *c*
DARINGCD 3029 / Nov '96 / Daring

☐ **GREED IN THE SUN/PAUL GAUGIN**
Delerue, Georges *c*
PCD 101 / Jan '89 / Prometheus

☐ **GREEN CARD**
Zimmer, Hans *c*
Subway drums: *Wright, Larry* / Instinct / Restless elephants / Cafe Afrika / Greenhouse / Moonlight / 9am Central Park / Clarinet concerto in A major / Silence / Instinct II / Asking you / Pour Bronte / Eyes on the prize
VSD 5309 / Apr '91 / Varese Sarabande

☐ **GREENWILLOW (1960 Broadway Cast)**
Loesser, Frank *c*
DRGCD 19006 / Jun '95 / DRG

☐ **GREMLINS**
Goldsmith, Jerry *c*
Gremlins mega madness / Make it shine / Out out: *Gabriel, Peter* / Gift / Gizmo / Mrs. Deagle / Gremlin rag
GED 24044 / Oct '89 / Geffen

☐ **GREMLINS II (The New Batch)**
Goldsmith, Jerry *c*
Just you wait / Gizmo escapes / Leaky faucet / Cute / Pot luck / Visitors / Teenage mutant gremlins / Keep it quiet / No rats / Gremlin pudding / New trends / Gremlin credits
VSD 5269 / Aug '90 / Varese Sarabande

☐ **GREY FOX, THE (Chieftains)**
Moloney, Paddy *c*
Main title / Oyster bed sequence / Country store sequence / Ride to Kamloops / Meeting tram at Ducks Siding / Chase / End titles / Sweet Betsy from Pike: *Farnsworth, Richard*
DRGCD 9515 / Jan '95 / DRG

☐ **GRIDLOCK'D**
Wanted dead or alive: *2Pac & Snoop Doggy Dog/Dat Niggaz Daz/Roger Troutman* / Sho shot: *Lady Of Rage* / It's over now: *Babyface* / Don't try to play me homey: *Dat Nigga Daz* / Never had a friend like me: *2Pac & Johnny Jackson* / Why: *Nate Dogg* / Out the moon (boom boom boom): *LBC Crew* / I can't get enough: *Thomas, Damon & Rodney Day* / Tonight it's on: *Jones, Char & BGOTI* / Off the hook: *Snoop Doggy Dogg & Charlie Wilson/Val Young* / Lady heroine: *Flex, J & The Lady Of Rage/Sean Thomas* / Will I rise: *Storm & Val Young/Char Jones* / Body and soul / Life is a traffic jam: *Medusa & 2Pac/Vondie Curtis Hall* / Deliberation: *Chestnutt, Cody*
5346842 / Feb '97 / Def Jam

☐ **GRIFTERS, THE**
Bernstein, Elmer *c*
VSD 5290 / Dec '90 / Varese Sarabande

☐ **GRIND (1985 Broadway Cast)**
Grossman, Larry *c*
Fitzhugh, Ellen *l*
This must be the place / Cadava / Sweet thing like me / I get myself out / My daddy always taught me to share / All things to one man / Line / Katie my love / Grind / Yes ma'am / Why mama why / This crazy place / From the ankles down / Who is he / Never put it in writing / I talk you talk / Timing / These eyes of mine / New man / Down / Century of progress / Finale
CDTER 1103 / Sep '85 / TER

☐ **GROSSE POINTE BLANK**
Blister in the sun: *Violent Femmes* / Rudie can't fail: *Clash* / Mirror in the bathroom: *Beat* / Under pressure: *Beat* / I can see clearly now: *Nash, Johnny* / Live and let die: *Guns N' Roses* / We care a lot: *Faith No More* / Pressure drop: *Specials* / Absolute beginners: *Jam* / Armagideon time: *Clash* / Los fabulosos cadillacs el matador / Let my love open the door / Blister 2000
8288672 / Aug '97 / London

☐ **GRUMPIER OLD MEN**
(I'll be glad when you're dead) you rascal you: *Armstrong, Louis & Louis Jordan* / Hit the road Jack: *Poindexter, Buster* / That's amore: *Martin, Dean* / Understand your man: *Cash, Johnny* / Venus: *Shocking Blue* / Jump in the line (Shake Senora): *Belafonte, Harry* / Stayin' alive: *Bee Gees* / Chicken dance: *Olsen, Wally Band* / 'S wonderful: *Brown, Les Orchestra/Doris Day* / Almost like being in love: *Cole, Nat 'King'* / I hear bells (wedding bells): *Del-Vikings* / What the heck: *Silvestri, Alan* / End title: *Silvestri, Alan*
5354822 / May '96 / London

☐ **GUILTY BY SUSPICION**
Howard, James Newton *c*
VSD 5310 / Apr '91 / Varese Sarabande

☐ **GUMMO**
Gold torques of Ulaid: *BSU* / Serving time in the middle of nowhere: *Eyehategod* / Dwsob: *Electric Hellfire Club* / Gummo love theme: *Spazz* / Rundgang um die tranz: *Bethlehem* / Schuld uns'res knoch: *Barzum* / Equimanthon: *Bathory* / Smokin' husks: *Dark Noerd* / Dragonaut: *Sleep* / Matando gueros 97: *Brujeria* / Medicined man: *Namanx* / Hellish blasphemy: *Nifelheim* / Skin peeler: *Mortician* / Give the humen devil his due: *Mystefier* / Mom's and dad's pussy: *Destroy All Monsters* / Verschleirete irrelgiosität: *Bethlehem* / Suite no.2 for solo cello in D minor: *Maisky, Mischa* / Some grass: *Sleep* / Jesus loves me: *Shepherd, Rose & Ellen M. Smith*
WIGCD 052 / 29 Jun '98 / Domino

☐ **GUNS OF NAVARONE, THE**
Tiomkin, Dimitri *c*
VSD 5236 / Feb '90 / Varese Sarabande

☐ **GUYS AND DOLLS (1982 London Cast)**
Loesser, Frank *c*
Runyon Land / Fugue for tinhorns / Follow the fold / Oldest established craps game in New York / I'll know / Bushel and a peck / Adelaide's lament / Guys and dolls / If I were a belle / My time of day / I've never been in love before / Take back your mink / Adelaide's lament (reprise) / More I cannot wish you / Craps shooter's ballet / Luck be a lady / Sue me / Sit down you're rockin' the boat / Marry the man today / Guys and dolls (reprise)
CDMFP 5978 / 12 Jan '98 / Music For Pleasure

☐ **GUYS AND DOLLS (1991 Broadway Cast)**
Loesser, Frank *c*
09026613172 / Oct '92 / RCA Victor

☐ **GUYS AND DOLLS (Original Broadway Cast)**
Loesser, Frank *c*
MCLD 19155 / Jan '93 / MCA

☐ **GUYS AND DOLLS (Cast Recording)**
Loesser, Frank *c*
Colonel Buffalo Bill / I'm a bad bad man / Doin' what comes naturally / Girl that I marry / You can't get a man with a gun / Gun fantasy / There's no business like showbusiness / They say it's wonderful / Moonshine lullaby / Wild west ballet / My defences are down / Motorcycle / Indian dance / I'm an Indian too / Finale act one / I got lost in his arms / Ballroom / I got the sun in the morning / Old fashioned wedding / Anything you can do / I'll share it with you / Who do you love I hope
CDTER2 1228 / Nov '97 / TER

☐ **GUYS AND DOLLS (CC Productions)**
Loesser, Frank *c*
Runyon land / Fugue for tinhorns / Follow the fold / I'll know / Bushel and a peck / My time of day / Adelaide's lament / Guys and dolls / If I were a bell / I've never been in love before / Take your mink / Luck be a lady / Sit down you're rocking the boat
QED 174 / Nov '96 / Tring

☐ **GUYS AND DOLLS (Cast Recording/ National Symphony Orchestra)**
Loesser, Frank *c*
Edwards, John Owen *con*
Fugue for tinhorns / Oldest established craps game in New York / I'll know / Pet me Poppa / Adelaide's lament / Guys and dolls / Adelaide / Woman in love / If I were a bell / Take back your mink / Luck be a lady / Sit down you're rockin' the boat
SHOWCD 034 / Oct '96 / Showtime

☐ **GUYS AND DOLLS (The Best Of Guys And Dolls)**
EMPRCD 802 / 18 May '98 / Emporio

☐ **GUYS AND DOLLS (Reprise Musical Repertory Theatre)**
Loesser, Frank *c*
9362450142 / May '98 / Reprise

☐ **GYPSY (Ross, Annie & Buddy Bregman Band)**
Styne, Jule *c*
Sondheim, Stephen *l*
CDP 8335742 / Jan '96 / Pacific Jazz

H

☐ **HACKERS**
22562 CIN / May '96 / Edel

☐ **HAIR (1968 Broadway Cast)**
MacDermot, Galt *c*
Ragni, Jerome & James Rado *l*
Aquarius / Donna / Hashish / Sodomy / Coloured spade / Manchester England / I'm black / Ain't got no air / Initials / I got life / Hair / My conviction / Don't put it down / Frank Mills / Be in / Where do I go / Black boys / White boys / Easy to be hard / Walking in space / Abie baby / Three five zero zero / What a piece of work is man / Good morning starshine / Let the sunshine in
74321289852 / Aug '95 / RCA Victor

☐ **HAIR (1968 London Cast)**
MacDermot, Galt *c*
Ragni, Jerome & James Rado *l*
Aquarius: *Edward, Vince & The Company* / Donna: *Tobias, Oliver & The Company* / Sodomy: *Feast, Michael & The Company* / Coloured spade: *Straker, Peter & The Company* / Ain't got no: *Feast, Michael/ Peter Straker/Joanne White/The Company* / Air: *Kendrick, Linda & The Company* / I got life: *Nicholas, Paul & The Company* / Hair: *Nicholas, Paul/Oliver Tobias/The Company* / My conviction: *Forray, Andy* / Easy to be hard: *Leventon, Annabel* / Frank Mills: *Kristina, Sonja* / Where do I go: *Nicholas, Paul & The Company* / Electric blues: *Gulliver, John/Rohan McCullough/Andy Forray/Jimmy Winston* / Black boys: *Kelly, Colette/Rohan McCullough/Lucy Fenwick* / White boys: *Hunt, Marsha/Ethel Coley/ Joanne White* / Walking in space / Able baby: *Straker, Peter/Limbert Spencer/Leighton Robinson* / Three five zero zero / What a piece of work is man: *Edward, Vince & Leighton Robinson* / Good morning starshine / Bed / Let the sunshine in
5199732 / Sep '93 / Polydor

☐ **HAIR (1993 London Cast)**
MacDermot, Galt *c*
Ragni, Jerome & James Rado *l*
Aquarius / Donna/Hashish / Holy orgy / Coloured spade / Manchester England / I'm black / Ain't got no / Dead end / I believe in love / Ain't got / Air / I got life / Initials / Going down / Hair / My conviction / Easy to be hard / Frank Mills / Hare Krishna / Where do I go / Electric blues / White boys / Walking in space / Yes it's finished / Abie baby / All you have to do / Three five zero zero / What a piece of work is man / Bed / Good morning starshine / Let the sunshine in
CDEMC 3663 / Nov '93 / EMI

☐ **HAIR (CC Productions)**
MacDermot, Galt *c*
Ragni, Jerome & James Rado *l*
Aquarius / Dead end / Easy to be hard / Good morning starshine / Be in (Hare Krishna) / Walking in space / Where do I go / Aquarius / Let the sunshine in / Donna / Frank Mills / Hair / I got life / What a piece of work is man
QED 205 / Nov '96 / Tring

☐ **HAIR**
SHOWCD 055 / 18 May '98 / Showtime

☐ **HALF COCKED**
Dragnalus: *Unwound* / Time expired: *Slant 6* / Tron: *Rodan* / CB: *Sleepyhead* / Dusty: *Ruby Falls* / Drunk friend: *Freakwater* / Be-9: *Versus* / Can I ride: *Polvo* / (We got) Flowers in our hair: *Big Heifer* / Invertebrate: *Boondoggle* / Hey cops: *Crain* / Magic box: *Helium* / Man went out: *Dungbeetle* / Truckstop theme: *Dungbeetle* / Want: *Grifters* / Thirty seven push-ups: *Smog* / Star 60: *2 Dollar Guitar* / Satellite: *Kicking Giant* / Crazy man: *Freakwater*
OLE 1522 / Aug '95 / Matador

☐ HALLELUJAH, BABY (1967 Broadway Cast)
Styne, Jule *c*
Comden, Betty & Adolph Green *l*
Davis, Buster *con*
SK 48218 / Nov '92 / Sony Broadway

☐ HALLOWEEN I
Carpenter, John *c*
Halloween theme / Laurie's theme / Shape escapes / Meyers' house / Michael kills Judith / Loomis and Shape's car / Haunted House / Shape lurks / Laurie knows / Better check the kids / Shape stalks
VCD 47230 / Jan '89 / Varese Sarabande

☐ HALLOWEEN II
Carpenter, John & Alan Howarth *c*
Halloween theme / Laurie's theme / He knows where she is / Laurie and Jimmy / Still he kills (murder montage) / Shape enters Laurie's room / Mrs. Alves / Flats in the parking lot / Michael's sister / Shape stalks again / In the operating room / Mr. Sandman: *Chordettes*
VCD 47152 / Jan '89 / Varese Sarabande

☐ HALLOWEEN III (Season Of The Witch)
Carpenter, John & Alan Howarth *c*
VSD 5243 / Feb '90 / Varese Sarabande

☐ HALLOWEEN IV (The Return Of Michael Myers)
Howarth, Alan *c*
VSD 5205 / Dec '88 / Varese Sarabande

☐ HALLOWEEN V (The Revenge Of Michael Myers)
Howarth, Alan *c*
Romeo Romeo: *Becca* / Dancin' on Churchill: *Churchill* / Sporting woman: *Diggy/Chosak/Clark* / Shape also rises / First victim / Tower farm / Trapped / Jailbreak / Anything for money: *DVB* / Second time around: *Rhythm Tribe* / Halloween 5 - the revenge / Evil child must die / Stranger in the house / Stop the rage / Attic / Halloween finale
VSD 5239 / Dec '89 / Varese Sarabande

☐ HALLOWEEN VI (The Curse Of Michael Myers)
Howarth, Alan *c*
VSD 5678 / Nov '95 / Varese Sarabande

☐ HAMLET
Doyle, Patrick *c*
SK 62857 / Feb '97 / Sony Classical

☐ HAMLET (& Richard III/Julius Caesar - Orchestral Suites) (National Philharmonic Orchestra)
Herrmann, Bernard *con*
4551562 / Aug '97 / Decca

☐ HANDFUL OF DUST, A
Fenton, George *c*
Handful of Dust / Cafe de Paris / Talking pips / Weekend episodes / Moving over / Memories / Fans
DRGCD 6110 / 23 Mar '98 / DRG

☐ HANDMAID'S TALE, THE (Sakamoto, Ryuichi)
Sakamoto, Ryuichi *c*
GNPD 8020 / Dec '90 / GNP Crescendo

☐ HANGED MAN, THE (Bullet)
Tew, Alan *c*
Contract man / GBH / Road runner / Heist / Duluth blues / Spic / Hanged man / Blue panther / Killer hill / Smokey Joe the dreamer / Gentle in the night / Peterman / Funky bear / Hanged man
DC 015CD / 10 Aug '98 / DC Recordings

☐ HANGING GARDEN, THE
CDVIR 72 / May '98 / Virgin

☐ HANNAH...1939 (Off-Broadway Cast)
Merrill, Bob *c*
CDTER 1192 / Jan '93 / TER

☐ HANS ANDERSON (Original Cast)
Overture / Thumbelina / This town / Dare to take a chance / Truly loved / For Hans tonight / Jenny kissed me / Inchworm / Ecclesiasticus / Anywhere I wander / Wonderful Copenhagen / I'm Hans Christian Anderson / Happy days / Have I stayed away too long / Ugly duckling / No two people / King's new clothes
DRGCD 13116 / Jun '96 / DRG

☐ HANS CHRISTIAN ANDERSON/THE COURT JESTER (Kaye, Danny)
I'm Hans Christian Anderson / Anywhere I wander / Ugly duckling / Inchworm / Thumbelina / No two people / King's new clothes / Wonderful Copenhagen / Overture / Life could not better be / Outfox the fox / I'll take you dreaming / My heart knows a lovely song / I live to love / Willow willow Waley / Pass the basket / Maladjusted jester / Where walks my true love / Life could not better be
VSD 5498 / Jun '94 / Varese Sarabande

☐ HAPPY END (Cologne Pro Musica/ Konig Ensemble)
Weill, Kurt *c*
Brecht, Bertolt *l*
Latham Konig, Jan *con*
600151 / Jun '90 / Capriccio

☐ HAPPY END/THE SEVEN DEADLY SINS (Lenya, Lotte & Chorus/ Orchestra)
Weill, Kurt *c*
Brecht, Bertolt *l*
Bruckner-Ruggenberg, Wilhelm *con*
CD 45886 / Apr '91 / CBS

☐ HARD DAY'S NIGHT, A (Beatles)
Beatles *c*
I should have known better / If I fell / I'm happy just to dance with you / And I love her / Tell me why / Can't buy me love / Hard day's night / Anytime at all / I'll cry instead / Things we said today / When I get home / You can't do that / I'll be back
CDP 7464372 / Feb '87 / Parlophone

☐ HARD RAIN
74321564252 / 28 Feb '98 / RCA Victor

☐ HARD TARGET (Kodo Japanese Drum Ensemble)
Revell, Graeme *c*
Simonec, T. *con*
VSD 5445 / Oct '93 / Varese Sarabande

☐ HARD TO KILL/ABOVE THE LAW/OUT FOR JUSTICE (Music From The Films Of Steven Seagal)
Frank, David Michael *c*
GNPD 8028 / May '92 / GNP Crescendo

☐ HARD WAY, THE
Rubinstein, Arthur *c*
VSD 5315 / Apr '91 / Varese Sarabande

☐ HARDBOILED (Gibbs, Michael)
Gibbs, Michael *c*
IONIC 11CD / Jul '93 / The Fine Line

☐ HARDER THEY COME, THE
You can get it if you really want: *Cliff, Jimmy* / Many rivers to cross: *Cliff, Jimmy* / Harder they come: *Cliff, Jimmy* / Sitting in limbo: *Cliff, Jimmy* / Draw your brakes: *Scotty* / Rivers of Babylon: *Melodians* / Sweet and Dandy: *Toots & The Maytals* / Pressure drop: *Toots & The Maytals* / Johnny too bad: *Slickers* / Shanty town: *Dekker, Desmond*
RRCD 11 / Sep '90 / Reggae Refreshers

☐ HARUM SCARUM/GIRL HAPPY (Presley, Elvis)
Harem holiday / My desert serenade / Go eat young man / Mirage / Kismet / Shake that tambourine / Hey little girl / Golden coins / So close yet so far / Animal instinct / Wisdom of the ages / Girl happy / Spring fever / Fort Lauderdale chamber of commerce / Startin' tonight / Wolf call / Do not disturb / Cross my heart and hope to die / Meanest girl in town / Do the clam / Puppet on a string / I've got to find my baby
74321 13433-2 / Mar '93 / RCA

☐ HARVEY GIRLS, THE (Film Cast)
Main title / In the valley (where the evening sun goes down) / Wait and see / On the Atchinsom Topeka and Santa Fe / Training montage (The train must be fed) / Oh you kid / Jusy get the meat / Honky tonk / Wait and see (reprise) / It's a great big world / Wild wild west / Judy goes to the valley / My intuition / Wait and see (reprise 2) / Judy's fight / Ray Bolger dance / Swing your partner round and round / March of the Doagies / In the valley (where the evening sun goes down) (reprise) / Fire / Morning after / New end title / In the valley (where the evening sun goes down) / March of the doagies (reprise) / Hayride / End title
CDODEON 11 / Apr '96 / Soundtracks

☐ HAUNTED (Wiseman, Debbie & Andrew Bottrill)
Wiseman, Debbie *c*
Wiseman, Debbie *con*
TRXCD 2002 / Nov '95 / Silva Screen

☐ HAUNTED SUMMER (Young, Christopher)
Young, Christopher *c*
Haunted summer / Menage / Villa diodati / Night was made for loving / Polidori's potions / Ariel / Confreres / Geneva / Alby / Unquiet dream / Hauntings
FILMCD 037 / Jan '89 / Silva Screen

☐ HAV PLENTY
Fire: *Babyface & Des'ree* / Heat: *Absoulute* / Keep it real: *Jon B & Coko* / I can't help it: *Shya* / I can't get you out of my mind: *Blackstreet* / Tears away: *Faith* / What the hell do you want: *Az Yet* / Rock the body: *Queen Pen & Tracey Lee* / Wanna be where you are: *SWV* / Whatcha gonna do: *Jayo Felony* / Any other night: *DeBarge, Chico* / What I've been missing: *Changing Faces* / Ye yo: *Badu, Erykah*
4910042 / 15 Jun '98 / Sony Music

☐ HE GOT GAME (Public Enemy)
Resurrection: *Public Enemy & Masta Killa* / He got game / Unstoppable: *Public Enemy & KRS One* / Shake your booty / Is your God a dog / House of the Rising Sun / Revelation 33 1/3 Revolutions / Game face / Politics of the sneaker pimps / Waht you need is Jesus / Super agent / Go cat go / Sudden death
5581302 / 20 Apr '98 / Def Jam

☐ HEART OF MIDNIGHT (Yanni)
Yanni *c*
Overture Carol's theme / Welcome to "Midnight" / Carol through the rooms / Oh Daddy / Carol sees Fletcher/Rathead on ice / Carol's theme - soft interlude / Rape (parts I and II) / Aftermath / Carol talks to Maria / Sharpe no.2 dies/Carol's nightmare / Carol's theme - sadness of the heart / Library of porn / Cabinet falls / Carol out in the street / Dinner and downstairs in the club / S and M room / End sequence / Final confrontation / Carol's theme - sisters in pain / Sonny's death / Finale - Carol's theme
FILMCD 119 / Apr '92 / Silva Screen

☐ HEARTBEAT (40 Number One Love Songs Of The Sixties - The Official Heartbeat Album)
You've lost that lovin' feeling: *Righteous Brothers* / (There's) always something there to remind me: *Shaw, Sandie* / World without love: *Peter & Gordon* / I'm into something good: *Herman's Hermits* / I got you babe: *Sonny & Cher* / (Sittin' on the) dock of the bay: *Redding, Otis* / When a man loves a woman: *Sledge, Percy* / Release me: *Humperdinck, Engelbert* / Green green grass of home: *Jones, Tom* / Distant drums: *Reeves, Jim* / Can't help falling in love: *Presley, Elvis* / Minute your gone: *Richard, Cliff* / Make it easy on yourself: *Walker Brothers* / How do you do it: *Gerry & The Pacemakers* / Something's gotten hold of my heart: *Pitney, Gene* / Poetry in motion: *Tillotson, Johnny* / Breaking up is hard to do: *Sedaka, Neil* / Will you still love me tomorrow: *Shirelles* / Johnny remember me: *Leyton, Johnny* / Cathy's clown: *Everly Brothers* / Love is all around: *Troggs* / What becomes of the broken hearted: *Ruffin, Jimmy* / Heartbeat: *Holly, Buddy* / Don't throw your love away: *Searchers* / Silence is golden: *Tremeloes* / Baby come back: *Equals* / Go now: *Moody Blues* / Whiter shade of pale: *Procul Harum* / I'm a believer: *Monkees* / Out of time: *Farlowe, Chris* / You don't have to say you love me: *Springfield, Dusty* / What a wonderful world: *Armstrong, Louis* / I'll never find another you: *Seekers* / (If paradise is) half as nice: *Amen Corner* / Baby now that I've found you: *Foundations* / Anyone who had a heart: *Black, Cilla* / You really got me: *Kinks* / With a little help from my friends: *Cocker, Joe* / Sweets for my sweet: *Searchers* / Letter: *Box Tops* / Bad to me: *Kramer, Billy J.* / Where do you go my lovely: *Starstedt, Peter* / Time in a bottle: *Croce, Jim* / Fruit tree: *Drake, Nick*
RADCD 46 / Oct '96 / Global TV

☐ HEARTBEAT (Love Me Tender)
Always on my mind: *Presley, Elvis* / True love ways: *Holly, Buddy* / You're all I need to get by: *Gaye, Marvin & Tammi Terrell* / I say a little prayer: *Franklin, Aretha* / Let there be love: *Cole, Nat 'King'* / Can't take my eyes off you: *Williams, Andy* / Love letters: *Lester, Ketty* / Only the lonely: *Orbison, Roy* / Then I kissed her: *Beach Boys* / Will you love me tomorrow: *Shirelles* / Till I kissed you: *Everly Brothers* / Don't throw your love away: *Searchers* / First cut is the deepest: *Arnold, P.P.* / (Take a little) Piece of my heart: *Franklin, Erma* / Stand by me: *King, Ben E.* / I second that emotion: *Ross, Diana & The Supremes/ Temptations* / I just want to make love to you: *James, Etta* / My girl: *Redding, Otis* / Make it with you: *Bread* / Walk on by: *Warwick, Dionne* / I believe: *Bachelors* / More than I can say: *Vee, Bobby* / It's a man's man's man's world: *Brown, James* / Love me tender: *Presley, Elvis* / Chapel of love: *Dixie Cups* / Band of gold: *Payne, Freda* / Third finger left hand: *Reeves, Martha & The Vandellas* / There's a kind of hush: *Herman's Hermits* / Just like a woman: *Manfred Mann* / Waterloo sunset: *Kinks* / Lay lady lay: *Dylan, Bob* / Private number: *Clay, Judy & William Bell* / She's not there: *Zombies* / Everybody's talkin': *Nilsson, Harry* / Look of love: *Springfield, Dusty* / Smoke gets in your eyes: *Platters* / Rhythm of the rain: *Cascades* / I love you because: *Reeves, Jim* / Stranger on the shore: *Bilk, Acker* / Mad about the boy: *Washington, Dinah* / (I left my heart in) San Francisco: *Bennett, Tony* / I guess I'll always love you: *Isley Brothers* / Come see about me: *Ross, Diana & The Supremes* / (If paradise is) Half as nice: *Amen Corner* / Everyone's gone to the moon: *King, Jonathan* / Hey Jude: *Pickett, Wilson* / Man of the world: *Fleetwood Mac* / Twelfth of never: *Richard, Cliff*
RADCD 72 / Nov '97 / Global TV

☐ HEARTBEAT - THE BEST OF HEARTBEAT
Heartbeat: *Holly, Buddy* / Just one look: *Hollies* / Do you love me: *Poole, Brian & The Tremeloes* / I like it: *Gerry & The Pacemakers* / Night has a thousand eyes: *Vee, Bobby* / In dreams: *Orbison, Roy* / Tired of waiting: *Kinks* / Flowers in the rain: *Move* / First cut is the deepest: *Arnold, P.P.* / Sloop John B: *Beach Boys* / Apache: *Shadows* / Do wah diddy diddy: *Manfred Mann* / Rescue me: *Bass, Fontella* / Got to get you into my life: *Bennet, Cliff & The Rebel Rousers* / Two kinds of teardrops: *Shannon, Del* / Monday Monday: *Mamas & The Papas* / Hello little girl: *Fourmost* / Out of time: *Farlowe, Chris* / Last night was made for love: *Fury, Billy* / Bad to me: *Kramer, Billy J.* / Wipeout: *Surfaris* / Yesterday man: *Andrews, Chris* / I only want to be with you: *Springfield, Dusty* / Letter: *Box Tops* / Wheel's on fire: *Driscoll, Julie* / Hippy hippy shake: *Swinging Blue Jeans* / Sun ain't gonna shine anymore: *Walker Brothers* / Wild thing: *Troggs* / Diamonds: *Harris, Jet* / Need your love so bad: *Fleetwood Mac* / Clapping song: *Ellis, Shirley* / Can't get used to losing you: *Williams, Andy* / (Dance with the) Guitar man: *Eddy, Duane* / Judy's turn to cry: *Gore, Lesley* / Picture of you: *Gore, Lesley* / Keep your hands off my baby: *Little Eva* / Don't throw your love away: *Searchers* / Do you believe in magic: *Lovin' Spoonful* / Sweet talkin' guy: *Chiffons* / Keep on running: *Davis, Spencer Group* / Crying game: *Berry, Dave* / It's not unusual: *Jones, Tom*
MOODCD 37 / Sep '96 / Columbia

☐ HEARTBEAT II
Look through any window: *Hollies* / Go now: *Moody Blues* / Tired of waiting for you: *Kinks* / Bend me shape me: *Amen Corner* / Sunny: *Fame, Georgie* / FBI: *Shadows* / Itchycoo Park: *Small Faces* / Crying game: *Berry, Dave* / You were made for me: *Freddie & The Dreamers* / Heartbeat: *Berry, Nick* / Hi ho silver lining: *Beck, Jeff* / Do you love me: *Poole, Brian & The Tremeloes* / Bad to me: *Kramer, Billy J. & The Dakotas* / You've got your troubles: *Fortunes* / When you walk in the room: *Searchers* / Gimme some lovin': *Davis, Spencer Group* / Mighty Quinn: *Manfred Mann* / Catch the wind: *Donovan* / Let it be: *Cocker, Joe* / Daydream believer: *Berry, Nick*
4755292 / Nov '93 / Columbia

☐ HEARTBREAK HIGH
Helping hand / Satisfy the groove / Don't be shy / Rockin' for myself / 4-letter word / Greedy people / Testify / Steppin' on / Less than a feeling / Breathe in / Lonely / Hip hop holiday / Forever and ever / Don't tell me what to do / More wine waiter please / Outside these walls / Easy / Alone like me
4509999382 / May '95 / Warner Bros.

☐ HEARTBREAKERS (Tangerine Dream)
Tangerine Dream *c*
FILMCD 163 / Jun '95 / Silva Screen

☐ HEAT
Goldenthal, Elliot *c*
9362461442 / Jan '96 / Warner Bros.

☐ HEAT AND DUST
Robbins, Richard *c*
CDQ 5551012 / Apr '94 / EMI

☐ HEATHCLIFF (Songs From The Show) (Richard, Cliff)
Misunderstood man / Sleep of the good / Gypsy bundle / Had to be: *Richard, Cliff & Olivia Newton-John* / When you thought of me / Dream tomorrow: *Richard, Cliff & Olivia Newton-John* / I do not love you Isabella: *Richard, Cliff/Olivia Newton-John/ Kristina Nichols* / Choosing (when it's too late): *Richard, Cliff & Olivia Newton-John* / Marked with death: *Richard, Cliff & Olivia Newton-John* / Be with me always
CDEMD 1091 / Oct '95 / EMI

☐ HEATHCLIFF (Heathcliff Live) (Richard, Cliff & 1996 London Cast)
Richard, Cliff *c*
Overture / Misunderstood man / Funeral cortege / Sleep of the good / Grange waltz / Each to his own / Had to be / Mrs Edgar Linton / Journey / India Africa China / When you thought of me (reprise) / Dream tomorrow / Isabella (bridge) / Gambling song / I do not love you Isabella / Isabella (reprise) / Choosing when it's too late / Madness of Cathy / Marked with death / Be with me always / Funeral cortege (reprise) / Nightmare / Be with me always (reprise) / Finale / Music for curtain calls
CDEMD 1099 / Nov '96 / EMI

☐ HEAVEN AND EARTH (Kitaro)
Kitaro *c*
Heaven and earth (land theme) / Sau dau tree / Ahn and Le Ly love theme / Saigon reunion / Arvn / Sau nightmare / VC Bonfire / Trong com / Ahn's house / Destiny / Last phone call / Child without a father / Village attack/The arrest / Walk to the village / Steve's ghosts / Return to Vietnam / End titles
GED 24614 / Jan '94 / Geffen

☐ HEAVY
022642CIN / Dec '96 / Edel

☐ HEAVY METAL
Heavy metal: *Hagar, Sammy* / Heartbeat: *Hagar, Sammy* / Working in the coalmine: *Devo* / Veteran of the psychic wars: *Devo* / Reach out: *Cheap Trick* / Heavy metal (takin' a ride): *Felder, Don* / Crazy (a suitable case for treatment): *Nazareth* / Radar rider: *Riggs* / Open arms: *Journey* / Queen Bee: *Grand Funk Railroad* / I must be dreamin': *Cheap Trick* / Mob rules: *Black Sabbath* / All of you: *Felder, Don* / Prefabricated: *Trust* / Blue lamp: *Nicks, Stevie*
4867492 / Apr '97 / Columbia

☐ HELL CAN BE HEAVEN (1983 London Cast)
Kaye, Hereward *c*
CDTER 1068 / Aug '95 / TER

☐ HELLO AGAIN
Goldstein, William *c*
Hello again / Lucy's reflection / Kevin and Lucy / In the beginning / Zelda visits the beyond / Dinner party / Transfiguration / Jason's remorse / Second thoughts / Lucy despairs / Kimmy pie / Grand finale
7956760052 / 7 Apr '98 / Multimedia

☐ HELLO DOLLY (1967 Broadway Cast)
Herman, Jerry *c*
Overture / I put my hand in / It takes a woman / Put on your Sunday clothes / Ribbons down my back / Motherhood / Dancing / Before the parade passes by / Elegance / Hello Dolly / It only takes a moment / So long dearie / Finale
GD 81147 / Aug '91 / RCA Victor

☐ HELLO DOLLY (1994 Studio Cast)
Herman, Jerry *c*
VSD 5557 / Jan '95 / Varese Sarabande

☐ HELLO DOLLY (1964 Broadway Cast)
Herman, Jerry *c*
Lang, P.J. *con*
Prologue / I put my hand in / It takes a woman / Put on your Sunday clothes / Ribbons down my back / Motherhood / Dancing / Before the parade passes by / Elegance / Hello Dolly / It only takes a moment / So long dearie / Finale
GD 83814 / Oct '89 / RCA Victor

☐ HELLO DOLLY (Songs From The Show) (Cast Recording)
Herman, Jerry *c*
Hello Dolly: *Vaughan, Frankie* / Put on your Sunday clothes: *Collier, Tracy* / It takes a woman: *Vaughan, Frankie* / Ribbons down my back: *Collier, Tracy* / It only takes a moment: *Collier, Tracy* / Elegance: *Collier, Tracy* / Dancing: *Madoc, Ruth* / Before the parade: *Madoc, Ruth* / So long Dearie: *Madoc, Ruth*
3036200032 / Apr '96 / Carlton

☐ HELLRAISER I (Young, Christopher)
Young, Christopher *c*
Resurrection / Hellbound heart / Lament configuration / Reunion / Quick death / Seduction and pursuit / In love's name / Cenobites / Rat slice quartet / Re-resurrection / Uncle Frank / Brought on by night / Another puzzle
FILMCD 021 / Nov '87 / Silva Screen

☐ HELLRAISER II (Hellbound) (Graunke Symphony Orchestra)
Young, Christopher *c*
Young, Christopher *con*
Hellbound / Second sight seance / Looking through a woman / Something to think about / Skin her alive / Stringing the puppet / Hall of mirrors / Dead or living / Leviathan / Sketch with fire
GNPD 8015 / Jan '89 / GNP Crescendo

☐ HELLRAISER III (Score) (Mosfilm State Orchestra & Choir)
Miller, Randy *c*
GNPD 8033 / Nov '92 / GNP Crescendo

☐ HELLRAISER IV (Northwest Sinfonia)
Licht, Daniel *c*
Anthony, Pete *con*
FILMCD 179 / Apr '96 / Silva Screen

☐ **HELP (Beatles)**
Beatles *c*
Help / Night before / You've got to hide your love away / I need you / Another girl / You're going to lose that girl / Ticket to ride / Act naturally / It's only love / You like me too much / Tell me what you see / I've just seen a face / Yesterday / Dizzy Miss Lizzy
CDP 7464392 / Apr '87 / Parlophone

☐ **HENRY (Portrait Of A Serial Killer)**
QDKCD 004 / Sep '94 / QDK Media

☐ **HENRY AND JUNE (Splet, Alan)**
Splet, Alan *c*
VSD 5294 / Apr '91 / Varese Sarabande

☐ **HENRY V (& As You Like It/ Arrangements For Chamber Ensemble) (Nettles, John & Lorna Rushton/English Serenata)**
Walton, Sir William *c*
Wolfenden, Guy *con*
CDE 84349 / 8 Jan '98 / Meridian

☐ **HERCULES**
Menken, Alan *c*
Zippel, David *l*
Shooting star: Boyzone / Go the distance: *Bolton, Michael* / Star is born: *Brown, Jocelyn* / Gospel truth: *Brown, Jocelyn* / I won't say (I'm in love): *Carlisle, Belinda* / No importa la distancia: *Martin, Ricky* / Long ago / Gospel truth I-III / Oh mighty Zeus / Go the distance / One last hope / Zero to hero / I won't say (I'm in love) / Star is born / Big olive / Prophecy / Destruction of the Agora / Phil's island / Rodeo / Speak of the devil / Hydra battle / Meg's garden / Hercules' villa / All time chunp / Cutting the thread / True hero / Star is born
WD 608642 / Oct '97 / Disney Music & Stories

☐ **HERCULES - THE LEGENDARY JOURNEYS VOL.1 (TV Soundtrack)**
Loduca, Joseph *c*
VSD 5660 / Jun '96 / Varese Sarabande

☐ **HERCULES - THE LEGENDARY JOURNEYS VOL.2 (Loduca, Joseph)**
Main title / Argonauts / Barrel o' monkeys / Dance of the demons / Summoning skeletons / To heroes / Wedding gift / Waiters and serpents / Monster fights / Cute harpies / Enforcer / Fight with pyro / Raiders of the lost tomb / Festival of ghouls / That was perfect / Anakit's chambers / That's better / Inside the harem / Ritual of daggers / Footprints / Broken man / Lolus dies / Where memories dwell / Surfing lolus / 50 Daughters of Thespius / Lava lamp land / Grape crushing / Ringer / Love birds / Temple of Ares / Disguised demon / Cure for loneliness / Dream fulfilled / Good and simple
VSD 5884 / 23 Feb '98 / Varese Sarabande

☐ **HERE WE GO ROUND THE MULBERRY BUSH**
Here we go round the mulberry bush: *Traffic* / Taking out time: *Davis, Spencer Group* / Every little thing: *Davis, Spencer Group* / Virginals dream: *Davis, Spencer Group* / Utterly simple: *Traffic* / It's been a long time: *Ellison, Andy* / Looking back: *Davis, Spencer Group* / Picture of her: *Davis, Spencer Group* / Just like me: *Davis, Spencer Group* / Waltz for Caroline: *Davis, Spencer Group* / Posession: *Davis, Spencer Group* / Am I what I was or was I what I am: *Traffic* / Taking out time: *Davis, Spencer Group* / Picture of her: *Davis, Spencer Group* / Just like me: *Davis, Spencer Group* / Posession: *Davis, Spencer Group*
RCD 10717 / 6 Apr '98 / Rykodisc

☐ **HERE'S LOVE (1963 Broadway Cast)**
Willson, Meredith *c*
Lawrence, Elliot *con*
SK 48204 / Dec '91 / Sony Broadway

☐ **HERITAGE: CIVILISATION AND THE JEWS (Symphonic Dances) (Royal Philharmonic Orchestra)**
Bernstein, Leonard/John Duffy *c*
Williams, Richard *con*
On the Town / Heritage symphonic dances / Heritage fanfare and chorale / Heritage suite for orchestra
CDDCA 630 / Oct '88 / ASV

☐ **HERO AND THE TERROR**
Frank, David Michael *c*
Two can be one / Obsession / Workout / Terror / Hero's seduction / San Pedro bust / Ladies room / Breakout / Birthday wishes / Discovery / Showtime / Angela / Subterranean terror / Simon's lair / Search / Living nightmare / Love and obsession
EDL 25082 / Jan '90 / Edel

☐ **HIDDEN, THE**
Convertino, Michael *c*
VCD 47349 / Jan '89 / Varese Sarabande

☐ **HIDEAWAY**
IONIC 12CD / Jun '95 / The Fine Line

☐ **HIDER IN THE HOUSE**
Young, Christopher *c*
MAF 7007D / Jan '94 / Intrada

☐ **HIGH SCHOOL HIGH**
7567927092 / Oct '96 / Atlantic

☐ **HIGH SIGN, THE (New Jazz Score For Buster Keaton Film) (Frisell, Bill)**
Frisell, Bill *c*
7559793512 / Jan '95 / Elektra

☐ **HIGH SOCIETY (Film Cast)**
Porter, Cole *c*
Overture / Calypso / Little one / You're sensational / I love you Samantha / Now you has jazz / Well did you evah / Mind if I make love to you
CDP 7937872 / Apr '95 / Capitol

☐ **HIGH SOCIETY (Highlights - The Shows Collection) (1994 Studio Cast)**
Porter, Cole *c*
Orchestra medley / High Society calypso / Litle one / Who wants to be a millionaire / True love / Now you has jazz / You're sensational / I love you Samantha / Well did you evah / Mind if I make love to you / I love you Samantha / True love (reprise)
PWKS 4193 / Mar '94 / Carlton

☐ **HIGH SOCIETY (Cast Recording)**
Porter, Cole *c*
PBHSCD 1 / Oct '96 / Playback

☐ **HIGH SOCIETY (CC Productions)**
Porter, Cole *c*
High Society overture / High Society calypso / Little one / Who wants to be a millionaire / True love / You're sensational / I love you Samantha / Now you has jazz / Well did you evah / Mind if I make love to you
QED 208 / Nov '96 / Tring

☐ **HIGH SPIRITS (Fenton, George)**
Fenton, George *c*
Overture / Castle Plunkett / Plunkett's lament / Ghost bus tours / Ghostly reflections / She is from the far land / Bumps in the knight / Mary appears
GNPD 8016 / '88 / GNP Crescendo

☐ **HIGH SPIRITS (inc. Four Bonus Songs Performed By Noel Coward) (1964 London Cast)**
Martin, Hugh & Timothy Gray *c*
Overture / Was she prettier than I / Bicycle song / You'd better love me / Where is the man I married / Go into your trance / Forever and a day / Something tells me / I know your heart / Faster than sound / If I gave you / Talking to you / Home sweet heaven / Something is coming to tea / What in the world did you want / Faster than sound (reprise) / High spirits / Something to tell me
CDSBL 13107 / Oct '92 / DRG

☐ **HIGHER AND HIGHER/STEP LIVELY**
It's a most important affair / Today I'm a debutante / I couldn't sleep a wink last night / Music stopped / I saw you first / Lovely way to spend an evening / You're on your own / Minuet in boogie / Finale / Step / As long as there's music / Ask the madame / Why must there be an opening song / Some other time / Where does love begin
CD 60004 / Apr '97 / Great Movie Themes

☐ **HIGHLANDER (MELT)**
FLIPCD 1 / 27 Feb '98 / Whampire

☐ **HIGHLANDER - THE FINAL DIMENSION (The Best Of The Highlander Scores)**
Kamen, Michael/Stewart Copeland/ J.Peter Robinson *c*
EDL 28892 / Sep '97 / Edel

☐ **HIGHLANDER III**
Honest Joe: *James* / Immortality: *Fall* / Yalili ya aini: *Jah Wobble's Invaders Of The Heart* / High in your face: *House Of Love* / Cry mercy judge: *Verlaine, Tom* / Jam J: *James* / Sept Marins/Hanter Dro: *Whirling Pope Joan* / Bonny Portmore: *McKennitt, Loreena* / Quiet mind - for Joe: *Ruby Blue* / Ce he mise le ulaingt: *McKennitt, Loreena* / Two trees: *McKennitt, Loreena* / Little muscle: *Catherine Wheel* / Dummy crusher: *Kerbdog* / Becoming more like God: *Jah Wobble's Invaders Of The Heart* / Bluebeard: *Cocteau Twins*
5267472 / Mar '95 / Mercury

☐ **HIRED MAN, THE (1992 London Cast)**
Goodall, Howard *c*
Song of the hired men / Scene: the Tallentire boys / Fill it to the top / Now for the first time / Narration / Work song: It's all right for you / Narration II / Who will you marry then / Scene: Jackson and Emily / Get up and go lad / I wouldn't be the first / Scene: Emily did you get the message / Fade away / Hear your voice / What a fool I've been / If I could / Narration III / You never see the sun / Scene: Jackson meets May / Scene: Harry you're not going down the pit / What would you say to your son / Union song: Men of stone / Narration IV / Farewell song / War song: So tell your children / Narration V / No choir of angels / Scene: the mining disaster / Scene: John and Seth / Re-hiring
CDTER2 1189 / May '92 / TER

☐ **HITCHER, THE**
Isham, Mark *c*
FILMCD 118 / Mar '92 / Silva Screen

☐ **HMS PINAFORE (New Sadler's Wells Opera Chorus/Orchestra)**
Sullivan, Sir Arthur *c*
Gilbert, W.S. *l*
Phipps, S. *con*
Overture / We sail the ocean blue / Hail maen o' wars men / I'm called little buttercup / But tell me who's the youth / Nightingale wherefore / Maiden fair to see / My gallant crew information / I am the captain of the Pinafore / Sir you are sad / Sorry her lot / Over the bright blue sea / Sir Josephs barge is seen / Now give three cheers / I am the monarch of the sea / When I was a lad / For I hold that on the seas / British star / Refrain audacious tar / Finale act 1 / Can I survive this overbearing / Mess mates ahoy / Shall they submit / My friends / Ah stay your hand / Oh joy oh rapture unforeseen / This very night with bated breath / Forbear or carry out the scene / En'tracte / Fair moon to thee I sing / Things are seldom what they seem / Hours creep on apace / Never mind the why and wherefore / Kind captain I've important / Carefully in tiptoe stealing / Hold pretty daughter of mine / He is an Englishman / In uttering reprobation / My pain and my distress / Farewell my own / Many years ago / Here take her Sir / Finale act 2
CDTER2 1150 / Nov '97 / TER

☐ **HMS PINAFORE (D'Oyly Carte Opera Chorus/New Symphony Orchestra)**
Sullivan, Sir Arthur *c*
Gilbert, W.S. *l*
Godfrey, I. *con*
4142832 / Jan '90 / Decca

☐ **HMS PINAFORE (Welsh National Opera Choir/Orchestra)**
Sullivan, Sir Arthur *c*
Gilbert, W.S. *l*
Mackerras, Sir Charles *con*
CD 80374 / Jan '95 / Telarc

☐ **HMS PINAFORE (New Sadler's Wells Opera/Chorus)**
Sullivan, Sir Arthur *c*
Gilbert, W.S. *l*
Overture / We sail the ocean blue / I'm called little buttercup / My gallant crew/I am the Captain of The Pinafore / Over the bright blue sea / I've got three cheers/I am the monarch of the sea / When I was a lad/For I hold that on the seas / British tar / Things are seldom what they seem / Never mind the why and wherefore / Farewell my own / Here take her Sir/Oh joy oh rapture unforseen
SHOWCD 022 / Oct '96 / Showtime

☐ **HMS PINAFORE (& Excerpts From The Pirates Of Penzance/Ruddigore/The Mikado) (D'Oyly Carte Opera Company/Royal Philharmonic Orchestra)**
Sullivan, Sir Arthur *c*
Gilbert, W.S. *l*
Walker, James *con*
4551602 / Aug '97 / Decca

☐ **HMS PINAFORE/THE MIKADO (D'Oyly Carte Opera Chorus/New Symphony Orchestra)**
Sullivan, Sir Arthur *c*
Gilbert, W.S. *l*
Sargent, Sir Malcolm *con*
CDHD 253/4 / Jan '94 / Happy Days

☐ **HMS PINAFORE/TRIAL BY JURY (Baker, George & John Cameron/ Glyndebourne Festival Choir/Pro Arte Orchestra)**
Sullivan, Sir Arthur *c*
Gilbert, W.S. *l*
Sargent, Sir Malcolm *con*
CMS 7643972 / Apr '94 / EMI Classics

☐ **HOFFA**
Newman, David *c*
07822110012 / Jan '94 / Fox Film Scores

☐ **HOLLOW REED (Dudley, Anne/Michala Petri)**
Dudley, Anne *c*
Main title / Oliver's theme / Upside down world / Family life / Questioning / Mother and son / Silent witness / Waking nightmare / Resolution / It will never happen again / Seeds of doubt / Unnatural practices / White lies / Decision / No hiding place / In a child's mind / Meditations / I shall be released: *Weller, Paul*
09026686302 / Sep '96 / RCA Victor

☐ **HOLLYWOOD CANTEEN**
Hollywood canteen / One o'clock jump / What are you doin' the rest of your life / General jumped at dawn / We're having a baby / Tumblin' tumbleweeds / Don't fence me in / Gettin' corns for my country / You can always tell a Yank / Sweet dreams sweetheart / Ballet in jive / Bee / Voodoo moon / Gypsy dance / My dancing lady / Rhythm of the day / Lulu's back in town / Too marvellous for words / You must have been a beautiful baby / With plenty of money and you
CD 60024 / Nov '97 / Great Movie Themes

☐ **HOLOCAUST 2000/SEX IN A CONFESSIONAL**
Morricone, Ennio *c*
SPALAX 14986 / Oct '96 / Spalax

☐ **HOME ALONE I**
Williams, John *c*
Williams, John *con*
MK 46595 / Jan '94 / Sony Classical

☐ **HOME ALONE II (Score)**
Williams, John *c*
07822110002 / Dec '92 / Fox Film Scores

☐ **HOME ALONE II**
All alone on Christmas: *Love, Darlene* / Holly jolly Christmas: *Jackson, Alan* / Somewhere in my memory: *Midler, Bette* / My Christmas tree: *Home Alone Children's Choir* / Sombras de otros tiempos: *Belen, Ana* / Merry Christmas Merry Christmas: *Williams, John* / Cool jerk: *Capitols* / It's beginning to look a lot like Christmas: *Mathis, Johnny* / Christmas star: *Williams, John* / O come all ye faithful: *Fischer, Lisa*
74321165162 / Oct '93 / Arista

☐ **HOME FOR THE HOLIDAYS**
Evil ways: *Rusted Root* / Holiday blues: *Isham, Mark* / Candy: *Cole, Nat 'King'* / It's not unusual: *Jones, Tom* / Blue nights: *Isham, Mark* / Birth of the cool whip: *Isham, Mark* / Trouble in mind: *Washington, Dinah* / Late night blues: *Isham, Mark* / Very thought of you: *Isham, Mark* / Very thought of you: *Cole, Nat 'King'* / Piece of my heart: *Joplin, Janis*
5288712 / 15 Sep '97 / Mercury

☐ **HOMEGROWN**
78016336522 / 7 Apr '98 / Will

☐ **HOMEWARD BOUND**
Broughton, Bruce *c*
MAF 7041D / Jan '94 / Intrada

☐ **HONEY, I BLEW UP THE KIDS**
Broughton, Bruce *c*
Broughton, Bruce *con*
MAF 7030D / Sep '92 / Intrada

☐ **HOODLUM**
INTD 90131 / 17 Nov '97 / Interscope

☐ **HOPE AND GLORY**
Martin, Peter *c*
VCD 47290 / Jan '89 / Varese Sarabande

☐ **HOPE FLOATS**
To make you feel my love: *Brooks, Garth* / In need: *Crow, Sheryl* / Honest I do: *Rolling Stones* / Chances are: *Seger, Bob & Martina McBride* / All I get: *Mavericks* / Paper wings: *Welch, Gillian* / Stop in the name of love: *Mosser, Jonell* / Wither I'm a flower: *Whiskeytown* / What makes you stay: *Carter, Deanne* / To get me to love you: *McCann, Lila* / Smile: *Lovett, Lyle* / When you love someone: *Adams, Bryan* / To make you feel my love: *Yearwood, Trisha*
4934022 / 13 Jul '98 / Premier/EMI

☐ **HORSE WHISPERER, THE (Score)**
Newman, Thomas *c*
1621372 / 24 Aug '98 / Philips Classics

☐ **HORSE WHISPERER, THE**
UMD 80503 / 24 Aug '98 / Universal

☐ **HOT MIKADO (London Cast)**
Overture / We are gentlemen of japan / Wand'ring minstrel 1 / Drums will crash / Behold the lord high executioner / I've got a little list / Three little maids / Playout / Finale / Beauty in the bellow / Tit-willow / Alone and yet alive / Mikado song / Here's a howdy-do / Swing a merry madrigal / Sun and I / Braid the raven hair / Entr'acte / Act one / Let the thong our joy advance / I am so proud / Katisha's entrance / For he's gonna marry yum-yum / Hour of gladness
OCRCD 6048 / Apr '97 / First Night

☐ **HOT SHOE SHUFFLE (1993 Australian Cast)**
Overture / Telegram Sam / I've got to be a rugcutter / Where was I when they passed out luck / Long ago and far away / Ain't misbehavin' / Handful of keys / This joint is jumpin' / Ac-cent-tchu-ate the positive / Fifteen minute intermission / Entr'acte / I get along without you very well / When I get my name in lights / Act / Hot shoe shuffle / Puttin' on the ritz / How lucky can you get / Song and dance man / Big band tap melody / Little brown jug / Pennyslyvania 6-5000 / Mood indigo / Tiger rag
OCRCD 6046 / Apr '97 / First Night

☐ **HOT SHOE SHUFFLE (Cast Recording)**
FLHSSCD 1 / Dec '95 / JVO

☐ **HOT SHOTS**
Levay, Sylvester *c*
VSD 5338 / Sep '91 / Varese Sarabande

☐ **HOUSE OF AMERICA**
I'm waiting for the man: *Cale, John* / Girls and boys: *Blur* / Green green grass of home: *Jones, Tom* / Your love is the place where I come from: *Teenage Fanclub* / She's so loose: *Supergrass* / Dream on: *Catatonia* / Stars: *Dubstar* / Superglider: *Drugstore* / Voodoo people: *Prodigy* / All tomorrow's people: *Linoleum* / Picture the scene: *Cale, John* / Motorcycle emptiness: *Manic Street Preachers*
PRMDCD 29 / 6 Oct '97 / Premier/EMI

☐ **HOUSE OF ELIOT**
Parker, Jim *c*
House of Eliot / Tango De La Luna / Shopping spree / Evie's tune / Eliott rag / Manhattan blues / Brooklands / Highgate memories / Jack's blues / Fashion parade / Tiger moth / Paris morning / Wedding / Paris by night / Hermitage (A new ballet) / Beatrice and Jack / New apartment / Paraquay / Funny man blues / Charity waltz / Reunion blues / Leaving for America
CDSTM 5 / Jul '93 / Soundtrack Music

☐ **HOUSE OF FRANKENSTEIN (Moscow Symphony Orchestra)**
Salter, Hans *c*
Stromberg, William T. *con*
8223748 / Mar '96 / Marco Polo

☐ **HOUSE OF FRANKENSTEIN/GHOST OF FRANKENSTEIN (RTE Concert Orchestra)**
Salter, Hans *c*
Penny, Andrew *con*
8223477 / Aug '94 / Marco Polo

☐ **HOUSE ON SORORITY ROW, THE/THE ALCHEMIST (London Philharmonic Orchestra)**
Band, Richard *c*
Band, Richard *con*
MAF 7046D / '93 / Intrada

☐ **HOUSE PARTY II**
Announcement of pajama jammi jam / House party (Don't know what you come to do) / Christopher Robinson scholarship fund / Ready or not / Kid 'n' play wreck shop / Ain't gonna hurt nobody / I like your style / Kid and Sydney break up candelight and you / I lust 4 U / Bilal gets off / Let me know something / Yo baby yo / FFF Rap what's on your mind / Big ol' jazz / You gotta pay what you owe / It's so hard to say goodbye to yesterday / Confidence / It's so hard to say goodbye to yesterday (Acapella) / Kid's goodbye thanks to Pope
MCLD 19246 / Apr '94 / MCA

☐ **HOUSE/HOUSE II**
Manfredini, Harry *c*
VCD 47295 / Jan '89 / Varese Sarabande

☐ **HOUSEKEEPING (Gibbs, Michael)**
Gibbs, Michael *c*
VCD 47308 / Jan '89 / Varese Sarabande

☐ **HOW GREEN WAS MY VALLEY**
Newman, Alfred *c*
07822110082 / Apr '94 / Fox Film Scores

☐ **HOW TO BE A PLAYER**
Big bad mamma: Brown, Foxxy / Hard to get: *James, Rick* / I gotta know: *Playa* / Young casanovas: *Junior MAFIA* / Down wit us: *Redman* / Usual suspects: *Mic Geronimo* / How to be a player: *Master P* / It's a cold day: *Too Short & George Clinton* / Street 2 street: *Jayo Felony* / In the wind: *Eightball* / Never seen before: *EPMD* / Never wanna let you go: *Absolute* / When the players live: *Crucial Conflict* / Troublesome: *2Pac* / Say what: *Dymon* / If u stay ready: *Suga Free* / Don't ever: *Chill*
5379732 / 1 Sep '97 / Def Jam

☐ **HOW TO STEAL A MILLION**
Williams, John *c*
TSU 0109 / Jan '93 / Tsunami

☐ **HOW TO SUCCEED IN BUSINESS WITHOUT REALLY TRYING (Film Cast)**
Loesser, Frank *c*
Loesser, Frank *l*
RCD 10728 / 20 Jul '98 / Rykodisc

☐ **HOWARD'S END**
Robbins, Richard *c*
NI 5339 / Apr '92 / Nimbus

☐ **HUDSON HAWK**
Kamen, Michael *c*
Hudson Hawk theme: *Dr. John* / Swinging on a star: *Willis, Bruce & Danny Aiello* / Side by side: *Willis, Bruce & Danny Aiello* / Leonardo / Welcome to Rome / Reading the codex / Igg and Ook / Cartoon fight / Gold room / Hawk swing: *Kraft, Robert* / Hudson Hawk: *Kraft, Robert*
VSD 5323 / Jul '91 / Varese Sarabande

☐ **HUMANOID, THE/NIGHTMARE CASTLE**
Morricone, Ennio *c*
OST 118 / Jan '93 / Milano Dischi

☐ **HUNCHBACK OF NOTRE DAME, THE**
WD 771902 / Jul '96 / Disney Music & Stories

☐ **HUNDRA, THE**
Morricone, Ennio *c*
PCD 107 / Jan '93 / Prometheus

☐ **HUNGER, THE**
Rubini, Michael & Denny Jaeger *c*
Trio in E flat Op100 / Beach house: *Spruill, Stefany* / Suite 1 for solo cello in G / Waiting room / Flashbacks / Sarah's panic / Arisen / Gavotte en Rondeau / Lakme / Sarah's transformation / Final death
VSD 47261 / Oct '94 / Varese Sarabande

☐ **HUNT FOR RED OCTOBER, THE**
Poledouris, Basil *c*
Hymn to Red October / Nuclear scam / Putin's demise / Course two-five-zero / Ancestral aid / Chopper / Two wives / Red route 1 / Plane crash / Kaboom
MCLD 19306 / Oct '95 / MCA

☐ **HUNTERS, THE (Residents)**
311692 / Dec '95 / Milan

☐ **HUNTING OF THE SNARK (1991 London Cast)**
Batt, Mike *c*
CASTCD 24 / Nov '91 / First Night

☐ **HURRICANE STREETS**
5570672 / 8 Jun '98 / Polydor

☐ **HYPERSPACE (Inc. Symphonic Suite From Beauty & The Beast)**
Davis, Don *c*
PCD 120 / Jan '93 / Prometheus

I

☐ **I AND ALBERT (1972 London Cast)**
Strouse, Charles *c*
Adams, Lee *l*
Draw the blinds / I and Albert / Leave it alone / I've 'eard the bloody 'indoos
CDTER 1004 / Aug '95 / TER

☐ **I DO I DO (Cast Recording)**
VSD 5730 / Aug '96 / Varese Sarabande

☐ **I KNOW WHAT YOU DID LAST SUMMER**
Hush: *Kula Shaker* / Summer breeze: *Type O Negative* / DUI: *Offspring* / Step kid: *Green Apple Quick* / This ain't the summer of love: *L7* / Losin' it: *Soul Asylum* / Hey bulldog: *Toad The Wet Sprocket* / My baby's got the strangest ways: *Southern Culture On The Skids* / Waterfall: *Din Pedals* / Clumsy: *Our Lady Peace* / Flick: *Clumsy* / Great life: *Goatboy* / 2 Wicky: *Hooverphonic* / Don't mean anything: *Cohen, Adam* / Proud: *Korn*
4886632 / 1 Dec '97 / Columbia

☐ **I LOVE MY WIFE (Broadway Cast)**
Coleman, Cy *c*
Stewart, Michael *l*
We're still friends / Monica / By threes / Love revolution / Mover's life / Someone wonderful I missed / Sexually free / Hey there / Good times / By the way if you are free tonight / Lovers on Christmas Eve / Scream / Ev'rybody today is turning on / Married couple seeks married couple / I love my wife / In conclusion
DRGCD 6109 / Jan '89 / DRG

☐ **I LOVE YOU PERFECT (Yanni)**
Yanni *c*
Theme / Lovers quarrel / Allan fired / Chair shower and court room montage / Testing the horse free / Lovers make up / Clarinet quintet K581 - allegretto: *Camerata Academica Salzburg* / Marry me / I'll be by your side / Temper tantrum / But I have some good days / Hospital montage / Christina dies / I love you perfect (reprise)
FILMCD 122 / Jun '93 / Silva Screen

☐ **I LOVE YOU, YOU'RE PERFECT, NOW CHANGE (Cast Recording)**
VSD 5771 / Mar '97 / Varese Sarabande

☐ **I MARRIED AN ANGEL (Broadway Cast)**
Rodgers, Richard *c*
Hart, Lorenz *l*
AEICD 002 / May '98 / AEI

☐ **I NEVER TOLD YOU**
Hersch, Fred *c*
VSD 5547 / Jul '95 / Varese Sarabande

☐ **I REMEMBER MAMA (1985 Studio Cast)**
Rodgers, Richard *c*
Charnin, Martin *l*
I remember Mama / Little bit more / Writer writes at night / Ev'ry day (comes something beautiful) / You could not please me more / Most disagreeable man/ Uncle Chris / Lullaby / Easy come easy go / It's not the end of the world / Entr'acte / Mama always makes it better / When / Fair trade / I write you read (fair trade) / It's going to be good to be gone / Time / Finale
CDTER 1102 / Oct '85 / TER

☐ **I SHOT ANDY WARHOL**
7567926902 / May '96 / Warner Bros.

☐ **I WENT DOWN**
OCD 008 / 9 Feb '98 / Ocean Deep
64565150152 / 14 Jul '98 / PRPH

☐ **ICE STORM**
VEL 797132 / 9 Feb '98 / Velvel

☐ **IDIOT BOX**
4321451782 / Feb '97 / Roo Art

☐ **IL GRANDE SILENCIO/UN BELLISSIMO NOVEMBRE**
Morricone, Ennio *c*
CDCR 27 / Apr '97 / Silva Screen

☐ **IL MERCENARIO (The Professional Gun)**
Morricone, Ennio *c*
VCDS 7018 / Apr '96 / Varese Sarabande

☐ **IL PREFETTO DI FERRO/IL MOSTRO**
Morricone, Ennio *c*
SPALAX 14985 / Oct '96 / Spalax

☐ **IL TRONO DI FUOCO**
Nicolai, Bruno *c*
EFA 043692 / 6 Apr '98 / Lucertola

☐ **I'LL DO ANYTHING**
Zimmer, Hans *c*
Glennie-Smith, Nick *con*
VSD 5474 / '94 / Varese Sarabande

☐ **ILLUSTRATED MAN**
Goldsmith, Jerry *c*
W 9102 / 14 Apr '98 / Taran

☐ **I'M GETTING MY ACT TOGETHER AND TAKING IT ON THE ROAD (1981 London Cast)**
Ford, Nancy *c*
Cryer, Gretchen *l*
Natural high / Smile / In a simple way / Miss Africa / Strong woman number / Dear Tom / Old friend / Put in a package and sold / If only things were different / Feel the love / Lonely lady / Happy birthday
CDTER 1006 / May '89 / TER

☐ **IM KAMPF MIT DEM BERGE**
Hindemith, Paul *c*
Imig, Helmut *con*
317722 / May '98 / Koch Schwann

☐ **IMMORTAL BELOVED**
Beethoven, Ludvig Van *c*
Solti, George *con*
SK 66301 / Mar '95 / Sony Classical

☐ **IMMORTAL BELOVED - MORE IMMORTAL BELOVED (More Music From The Film & Other Great Beethoven Classics) (Perahia, Murray/ Carlo Maria Giulini/Emmanuel Ax/ Michael Tilson-Thomas)**
Beethoven, Ludvig Van *c*
SK 62616 / Jun '96 / Sony Classical

☐ **IMPOSSIBLE HOLIDAYS (Schmidt, Irmin)**
Schmidt, Irmin *c*
IRMIN 2CD / Nov '92 / The Fine Line

☐ **IN AND OUT**
I will survive: *Ross, Diana* / Wedding preparations / Everything's coming up roses: *Merman, Ethel* / To serve and protect / Howard is outed / Morning after / Bachelor party / Interviews with townsfolk / Homosecton / I don't / Mom and Dad / Cameron and Emily / Teacher of the year/People/Wedding / Crazy: *Cline, Patsy* / Macho man: *Village People*
5308412 / 2 Feb '98 / Polydor

☐ **IN CUSTODY**
CDQ 5550972 / Apr '94 / EMI

☐ **IN LIKE FLINT/OUR MAN FLINT**
Goldsmith, Jerry *c*
Where the bad guys are gals / Golf lesson / Get Flint / Ahh your father's Bob lip / Uninvited guest / Mince and cook until tender / Ballet music / Odin dva tri kick / Deep freeze / Ladies will kindly remove their hats / Your Zowie face / Westward ho / Lost in space / Flint is alive / End titles / Our man Flint / Quest / Man does not live by bread alone / New York skyline / Bit of research / Tell me more about that volcano / Take some risks Mr Flint / In like Flint / Boilermaker / Never mind you'd love it / You're a foolish man Mr Flint / It's gotta be a world's record
VSD 5935 / 17 Aug '98 / Varese Sarabande

☐ **IN LOVE AND WAR (Fenton, George)**
Fenton, George *c*
In love and war / Battle / Private Hemingway reporting for duty / Bullet / You're in love with me / Drive with Domenico / Aggie with the kid / Receiving the medal / Roberto e morto / Lake / Jimmy's death / Jimmy's letter / Field hospital / Brothel / Weekend in Venice / No news from Italy / Domenico's proposal / Hardest letter to write / Most beautiful waltz / Kid grew up / In love and war
09026687252 / Feb '97 / RCA Victor

☐ **IN SEARCH OF ANGELS**
In search of angels: *Story, Tim* / Angel of the elegies: *Story, Tim* / Voices in the liquid air: *Story, Tim* / Angelos: *Story, Tim* / Woman at the well: *Story, Tim* / Theme reprise: *Story, Tim* / Calling all angels: *Siberry, Jane & K D Lang* / Requiem in paradisum: *Trinity Boys Choir* / Close cover: *Mertens, Wim* / Assumpta est Maria in coelum: *Schroeder-Sheker, Terese* / Star in the east: *St. Olaf Choir* / Good thing (angels running): *Larkin, Patty* / Love's ash dissolves: *Isham, Mark* / Oh of pleasure: *Sevag, Oystein* / Jesus Christ the apple tree: *American Boys' Choir*
01934111532 / Nov '94 / Windham Hill

☐ **IN STURM UND EIS (Deutsches Symphonie Orchester)**
Hindemith, Paul *c*
Russell Davies, Dennis *con*
09026681472 / Nov '96 / RCA Victor

☐ **IN THE ARMY NOW (Sinfonia Of London)**
Folk, Robert *c*
MAF 7058D / Sep '94 / Intrada

☐ **IN THE BLOOD**
RCD 20174 / Aug '91 / Rykodisc

☐ **IN THE CABINET OF DR. CALIGARI (In The Nursery)**
CORP 015CD / Nov '96 / ITN Corporation

☐ **IN THE HEAT OF THE NIGHT**
Jones, Quincy & Ray Charles *c*
W 9106 / 14 Apr '98 / Taran

☐ **IN THE HEAT OF THE NIGHT/THEY CALL ME MR. TIBBS**
Jones, Quincy *c*
RCD 10712 / 12 Jan '98 / Rykodisc

☐ **IN THE MOUTH OF MADNESS (Carpenter, John & Jim Lang)**
Carpenter, John & Jim Lang *c*
In the mouth of madness / Robby's office / Axe man / Bookstore creep / Alley nightmare / Trent makes the map / Boy and his bike / Don't look down / Hobb's end / Pickman Hotel / Picture changes / Black church / You're wrong Trent / Mommy's day / Do you like my ending / I'm losing me / Main street / Hobb's end escape / Portal opens / Old ones return / Book comes back / Madness outside / Just a bedtime story
DRGCD 12611 / Mar '95 / DRG

☐ **IN THE NAME OF THE FATHER**
Jones, Trevor *c*
In the name of the Father: *Bono & Gavin Friday* / Voodoo chile: *Hendrix, Jimi* / Billy Boola: *Bono & Gavin Friday* / Dedicated follower of fashion: *Kinks* / Interrogation: *Jones, Trevor* / Is this love: *Marley, Bob* / Walking the circle: *Jones, Trevor* / Whiskey in the jar: *Thin Lizzy* / Passage of time: *Jones, Trevor* / You made me the thief of your heart: *O'Connor, Sinead*
IMCD 208 / Apr '95 / Island

☐ **IN WITH THE OLD (1986 BBC Radio 2 Cast)**
Prelude / Music goes round and around / I want to be happy / Did you ever see a dream walking / Stompin' at the Savoy / I'm putting all my eggs in one basket / Only a glass of champagne / Ten cents a dance / Goody goody / Zing went the strings of my heart / Lulu's back in town / Pretty baby / Where are the songs we sung / Storm / And her mother came too / With plenty of money and you / Playout
CDTER 1122 / Aug '95 / TER

☐ **INCOGNITO**
Ottman, John *c*
Opening titles / Tricks of the trade / Dealers / Creation / Rubbing it in / On the run again / Tokens of Rembrandt / Note / Re-creation / Police search / Harry's gift / Reveal / Forgive me / Eyes / To catch a train / Truth / Interlude / Front page news / Murder / Bad deal / Changer of fortune / Reprise
09026689712 / 10 Nov '97 / RCA Victor

☐ **INCUBO (City Of The Walking Dead/ Nightmare City/Grossangriff Der Zombies) (Cipriani, Stelvio)**
EFA 043622 / 2 Mar '98 / Lucertola

☐ **INDAGINE SU UN CITTADINO AL SI SOPRA DI OGNI (Morricone, Ennio)**
Morricone, Ennio *c*
CDMDF 311 / 27 Apr '98 / Cinevox

☐ **INDEPENDENCE DAY**
Arnold, David *c*
1969 / We came in peace / SETI / Radio signal / Darkest day / Cancelled leave / Evacuation / Fire storm / Aftermath / Base attack / El toro destroyed / International code / President's speech / Day we fight back / Jolly Roger / End titles
09026685642 / Aug '96 / RCA Victor

☐ **INDIAN IN THE CUPBOARD, THE**
Edelman, Randy *c*
Edelman, Randy *con*
SK 68475 / Feb '96 / Sony Classical

☐ **INDIANA JONES AND THE LAST CRUSADE**
Williams, John *c*
Williams, John *con*
Indy's very first adventure / X marks the spot / Scherzo for motorcycle and orchestra / Ah rats / Escape from Venice / No ticket / Keeper of the grail / Keeping up with the Joneses / Brother of the cruciform sword / Belly of the steel beast / Canyon of the crescent moon / Penitent man will pass / End credits (raiders march)
K 9258832 / Jun '89 / WEA

☐ **INDOCHINA**
Doyle, Patrick *c*
VSD 5397 / Jan '93 / Varese Sarabande

☐ **INFERNO (Emerson, Keith)**
Emerson, Keith *c*
Inferno / Rose's descent into the cellar / Taxi ride / Library / Sarah in the library vaults / Bookbinder's delight / Rose leaves the apartment / Rose gets it / Elisa's story / Cat attic attack / Kazanians tarantella / Mark's discovery / Mater tenebrarum / Inferno (finals) / Cigarettes ices etc
CDMF 3060 / 16 Feb '98 / Cinevox

☐ **INKWELL, THE**
Dancing machine: *Jade* / Let's get it on: *Jade* / On and on: *Knight, Gladys & The Pips* / Lets get it on: *Gaye, Marvin* / Fire: *Ohio Players* / Do you like it: *B.T. Express* / This house is smokin': *B.T. Express* / Do it (till you're satisfied): *B.T. Express* / Everything good to you: *B.T. Express* / Jam: *Graham Central Station* / I don't know what it is but it sure is funky: *Graham Central Station*
74321 21568-2 / Jul '94 / Giant

☐ **INNOCENT SLEEP, THE (Chamber Orchestra Of London)**
Ayres, Mark *c*
Raine, Nic *con*
FILMCD 167 / Jan '96 / Silva Screen

☐ **INNOCENT, THE**
Gouriet, Gerald *c*
164622 / Jan '95 / Milan

☐ **INSIDE OUT**
Russ, Adryan *c*
DRGCD 19007 / Feb '97 / DRG

☐ **INSPECTOR MORSE (The Essential Collection) (Pheloung, Barrington)**
Pheloung, Barrington *c*
Inspector Morse / Evolving mystery / Andantino / Lewis and Morse / Mi tradi quell alma ingrata / Student's death / Eirl theme / Dark suspicion / Adieu notre petite table / Worrying dilemma / La fille aux cheveux de lin / Sad discovery / Senza mamma / Sad echoes / Terzettino - soave sia il vento / Morse's remorse / String quartet in C minor d703 - Quartettsatz / Inspector Morse theme
VTCD 62 / Nov '95 / Virgin

☐ **INSPECTOR MORSE I (Pheloung, Barrington)**
Pheloung, Barrington *c*
Main theme / Oxfordshire country home / Overture from Die Zauberflote / K 620 / Student's death / Morse's optimism / O Isis and Osiris / Potential murder / Morse on the case / Macabre pursuit / Sad discovery / Senza mama / Hunt / Oxford college / Lewis / Gothic ritual / Closing credits
VTCDX 2 / Nov '96 / Virgin TV

☐ **INSPECTOR MORSE II (Pheloung, Barrington)**
Pheloung, Barrington *c*
Main theme / Warmer side of Morse / Che faro senza Eurydice / Gently sinister revelation / Concerto for 2 mandolini in G / Sad echoes / Mitradi quell alma ingrata / Gentle loving / Andante / Lewis and Morse / Chorale 'er kenne mich mein huter' / Morse's sympathetic ear / Adagio quintet in C / Tenderness / Tersettino 'soave sia il vento' / Morse's second chance / Signore Ascolta
CDVIP 154 / Oct '96 / Virgin VIP

☐ **INSPECTOR MORSE III (Pheloung, Barrington)**
Pheloung, Barrington *c*
Eirl theme / Oxford / Duet: Bei Mannern - Welche Liebe Fuhlen / Cryptic contemplation / Adante from string sextet No 1 in BB OP 18 / Reflections / Traume from wesendonk-lieder / Generic Morse theme / Dark suspicion / Adagio from piano concert K488 in A / Apprension - confession - resolution / Promised land / Hab'mir's gelbot from der rosenkavalier / Painful admissions / Adieu notre petite from manon / Quiet awakening / Brunnhilde's immolation from gotterdammerung / Main theme
CDVIP 178 / Apr '97 / Virgin

☐ **INSPECTOR MORSE VOLS I-III (Pheloung, Barrington)**
Pheloung, Barrington *c*
TPAK 27 / Jan '95 / Virgin

☐ **INSTRUMENT OF WAR (Celtic Legends)**
Instrument of war theme / Celtic melodies / Rebellion / Great warpipe of the north / Irish traditional / New world / Bretons / On active service / Silent cinema / Great war
RECD 507 / Jun '98 / REL

☐ **INTERVIEW WITH THE VAMPIRE**
Goldenthal, Elliot *c*
Sheffer, Jonathan *con*
Libera me / Born to darkness / Lestat's tarantella / Madeleine's lament / Claudia's allegro agitato / Escape to Paris / Marche funebre / Lestat's recitative / Santiago's waltz / Theatre des vampires / Armand's seduction / Plantation pyre / Forgotten lore / Scent of death / Abduction and absolution / Armand rescues Louis / Louis revenge / Born to darkness part II / Sympathy for the devil: *Guns N' Roses*
GED 24719 / 8 Sep '97 / Geffen

☐ **INTO THE WOODS (Broadway Cast)**
Sondheim, Stephen *c*
Prologue - Into the woods / Cinderella at the grave / Hello little girl / I guess this is goodbye / Maybe they're magic / I know things now / Very nice prince / First midnight / Giants in the sky / Agony / It takes two / Stay with me / On the steps of the palace / Ever after / Act 2 Prologue - So happy / Agony / Lament / Any moment / Moments in the woods / Your fault / Last midnight / No more / No one is alone / Finale - Children will listen
07863567962 / Jun '94 / RCA Victor

☐ **INTO THE WOODS (1990 London Cast)**
Sondheim, Stephen *c*
Prologue - Once upon a time / Cinderella at the grave / Hello little girl / I guess this is goodbye / Maybe they're magic / Our little world / I know things now / Very nice Prince / First midnight / Giants in the sky / Agony / It takes two / Stay with me / On the steps of the palace / Finale - Ever after / Act 2 Prologue - So happy / Agony / Lament / Any moment / Moments in the woods / Your fault / Last midnight / No more / No one is alone / Finale - Children will listen
RD 60752 / Jun '93 / RCA Victor

☐ **INTOLERANCE**
Davis, Carl *c*
PCD 105 / Jan '93 / Prometheus

☐ **INVADE MY PRIVACY (1993 London Cast)**
Landesman, Frans *l*
Brown, D. *con*
CDTER 1202 / Sep '93 / TER

☐ **INVASION: EARTH**
Mitchell, Richard G. *c*
Invasion Earth / Fast moving target moving in from the North East / Symbol / Echoes / Military machines / Terrell's return / Love theme / ND implants / Echo in the emergency room / Kirkhaven Water / Story so far / Amanda's arm / She's been found / Fighting back / Last battle / End titles / Armageddon
MPRCD 009 / 15 Jun '98 / MCI Music

☐ **INVENTING THE ABBOTTS**
CST 348062 / May '97 / Colosseum

☐ **IOLANTHE (Baker, George & Ian Wallace/Glyndebourne Festival Choir/ ProArte Orchestra)**
Sullivan, Sir Arthur *c*
Gilbert, W.S. *l*
Sargent, Sir Malcolm *con*
CMS 7644002 / Apr '94 / EMI Classics

☐ **IOLANTHE (D'Oyly Carte Opera Chorus/New Symphony Orchestra/ Grenadier Guards Band)**
Sullivan, Sir Arthur *c*
Gilbert, W.S. *l*
Godfrey, I. *con*
4141452 / Jan '90 / Decca

☐ **IOLANTHE (D'Oyly Carte Opera Chorus/Orchestra)**
Sullivan, Sir Arthur *c*
Gilbert, W.S. *l*
Pryce Jones, J. *con*
Overture / When a maiden loves she sits and sighs / Tower warders under orders / When our gallant Norman foes / Alas I waver to and fro / Is life a boon / Here's a man of jollity / I ahve a song to sing o / How say you maiden will you wed / I've jibe and joke and quip and crank / Tis done I am a bride / Were I thy bride / Oh sergeant Meryll is it true / Did thou not O Leonard Meryll / To thy fraternall care / Prisoner comes to meet his doom / Night has spread her pall once more / Oh a private buffoon is a light hearted loon / Hereupon we're both agreed / Free from his fetters grim / Strange adventure / Hark what was that sir / Man who would woo a fair maid / When a wooer goes a wooing / Hark / What was that Sir
CDTER2 1188 / Nov '97 / TER

☐ **IPHIGENIA**
Theodorakis, Mikis *c*
SR 50089 / May '94 / Varese Sarabande

☐ **IRENE (Broadway Cast)**
Tierney, Harry *c*
Lee, Jack *con*
SK 32266 / Dec '91 / Sony Broadway

☐ **IRISH AND HOW THEY GOT THAT WAY, THE**
Opening/Butterfly / Butterfly / Musicmakers / Irish medley / Digression / Mrs. McGrath / Mother Machree / Rare old times / Fields of Athenry / Skibbereen / Shores of Amerikay / Anchor's aweigh / No Irish need apply/Irish washerwomen / Letter / Erie canal / Presenting the Cohans / Moonshiner / Danny boy / Who threw the overalls in Mrs. Murphy's chowder / Finnegan's wake / Dear old Ireland / Ghost of Molly Maguire / George M. Cohan medley / Johnny I hardly knew ye / I still haven't found what I'm looking for
VSD 5916 / 18 May '98 / Varese Sarabande

☐ **IRMA LA DOUCE (1960 Broadway Cast)**
Monnot, Marguerite *c*
Breffort, Alexandre *l*
Lebowsky, Stanley *con*
SK 48018 / Dec '91 / Sony Broadway

☐ **IRMA LA DOUCE (Broadway Cast)**
Monnot, Marguerite *c*
Breffort, Alexandre *l*
MCAD 6178 / Jan '89 / MCA

☐ **IRMA LA DOUCE (Film Cast)**
Previn, Andre *c*
RCD 10729 / 20 Jul '98 / Rykodisc

☐ **IRON AND SILK (Gibbs, Michael)**
Gibbs, Michael *c*
IONIC 7CD / Nov '91 / The Fine Line

☐ **IRON EAGLE III (Aces) (Utah Symphony Orchestra)**
Manfredini, Harry *c*
MAF 7022D / Mar '92 / Intrada

☐ **IRON WILL**
McNeely, Joel *c*
McNeely, Joel *con*
VSD 5467 / Aug '94 / Varese Sarabande

☐ **IS PARIS BURNING**
Jarre, Maurice *c*
VSD 5222 / Feb '90 / Varese Sarabande

☐ **ISLAND OF DR. MOREAU, THE**
Chang, Gary *c*
74321409552 / Nov '96 / Milan

☐ **ISLANDS IN THE STREAM (Hungarian State Symphony Orchestra)**
Goldsmith, Jerry *c*
Goldsmith, Jerry *con*
Island / Boys arrive / Pillow fight / Is ten too old / Night attack / Marlin / Boys leave / Letter / How long can you stay / I can't have him / Refugees / Eddie's death / Is it all true
RVF 6003D / Jan '89 / Intrada

☐ **IT HAPPENED AT THE WORLD'S FAIR/ FUN IN ACAPULCO (Presley, Elvis)**
Beyond the bend / Relax / Take me to the fair / They remind me too much of you / One broken heart for sale (Film version) / I'm falling in love tonight / Cotton candy land / World of our own / How would you like to be / Happy ending / One broken heart for sale / Fun in Acapulco / Vino dinero y amor / Mexico / El toro / Marguerita / Bullfighter was a lady / No room to rhumba in a sports car / I think I'm gonna like it here / Bossa nova baby / You can't say no in Acapulco / Guadalajara
74321134312 / Mar '93 / RCA

☐ **IT'S A BIRD, IT'S A PLANE, IT'S SUPERMAN (1966 Broadway Cast)**
Strouse, Charles *c*
Adams, Lee *l*
Hastings, Harold *con*
SK 48207 / Nov '92 / Sony Broadway

☐ **IT'S A MAD MAD MAD MAD WORLD**
Gold, Ernest *c*
David, Mack *l*
Gold, Ernest *con*
Overture / It's a fact / Main title / Every man for himself / Follow the leader / Away we go / Oh I couldn't / Gullible Otto Meyer / What's wrong with America / Living end / You satisfy my soul / Only way to fly / Thirty one flavours / You're bugging me / Adios Santa Rosita / Instant chase / At the big W / Big W / Great pursuit / Retribution / It's a mad mad mad mad world / Desserts / Interview with Ernest Gold/ Stanley Kramer
RCD 10704 / 3 Nov '97 / Rykodisc

☐ **IT'S ALIVE II**
Herrmann, Bernard *c*
Johnson, Laurie *con*
Main title / Birth traumas / Evil evolving / Savage trilogy / Nightmares / Beautiful and bizarre / Revulsion / Basement nursery / Lamentation / Living with fear / Stalking the infants / Climax
FILMCD 074 / Jan '91 / Silva Screen

☐ **IT'S MY PARTY**
Poledouris, Basil *c*
Poledouris, Basil *con*
VSD 5701 / Mar '96 / Varese Sarabande

☐ **IVAN THE TERRIBLE (Frankfurt Radio Symphony Orchestra)**
Prokofiev, Sergei *c*
Kitaenko, Dmitri *con*
09026619542 / Nov '95 / RCA Victor

☐ **IVAN THE TERRIBLE (Philharmonia Orchestra & Chorus)**
Prokofiev, Sergei *c*
Jarvi, Neeme *con*
CHAN 8977 / Jan '95 / Chandos

☐ **IVANHOE (Sinfonia Of London)**
Rozsa, Miklos *c*
Broughton, Bruce *con*
MAF 7055D / Jan '95 / Intrada

J

☐ **JACKAL**
MCD 11688 / 3 Nov '97 / MCA

☐ **JACKIE BROWN**
Across 110th street: Womack, Bobby / Beaumont's lament / Strawberry letter 23: *Brothers Johnson* / WHo is he and what is he to you: *Withers, Bill* / Tennessee stud: *Cash, Johnny* / Natural high: *Bloodstone* / Longtime woman: *Grier, Pam* / Letter to the firm: *Brown, Foxxy* / Street life: *Crawford, Randy* / Didn't I blow you're mind: *Delfonics* / Midnight confessions: *Grass Roots* / Inside your love: *Ripperton, Minnie* / Lions and the cucumber: *Vampiros Sound Incorporation* / Monte Carlo Nights: *Vampiros Sound Incorporation*
9362468412 / 16 Mar '98 / Warner Bros.

☐ **JACOB'S LADDER**
Jarre, Maurice *c*
Jacob's ladder / High fever / Descent to inferno / Sarah / Ladder / Sonny boy: *Jolson, Al*
VSD 5291 / Dec '90 / Varese Sarabande

☐ **JACQUES BREL IS ALIVE AND WELL AND LIVING IN PARIS (London Cast)**
Brel, Jacques *c*
Overture / Marathon / Alone / Madeleine / I loved / Mathilde / Batchelor's dance / Timid Frieda / My death / Girls and dogs / Jackie / Statue / Desperate ones / Sons of... / Amsterdam / Bulls / Old folks / Marieke / Brussels / Fanette / Funeral tango / Middle class / You're not alone / Next / Carousel / If we only have love
CDTEM2 1231 / Jan '98 / TER

☐ **JAILHOUSE ROCK (Presley, Elvis)**
Jailhouse rock / Treat me nice / I want to be free / Don't leave me now / Young and beautiful / (You're so square) baby I don't care / Jailhouse rock / Treat me nice / I want to be free / Young and beautiful / Love me tender / Let me / Poor boy / We're gonna move / Don't leave me now / Treat me nice / Let me / We're gonna move / Poor boy / Love me tender
07863674532 / 2 Feb '98 / RCA

☐ **JAKE'S PROGRESS (Costello, Elvis & Richard Harvey)**
Costello, Elvis & Richard Harvey *c*
DSCD 14 / Nov '95 / Demon

☐ **JAMES AND THE GIANT PEACH**
WD 681202 / Oct '96 / Disney Music & Stories

☐ **JANE EYRE (Bratislava Symphony Orchestra)**
Herrmann, Bernard *c*
8223535 / Nov '93 / Marco Polo

☐ **JANE EYRE/LAURA**
Herrmann, Bernard/David Raskin *c*
07822110062 / Jul '92 / Fox Film Scores

☐ **JASON'S LYRIC**
U will know: *BMU* / Forget I was a G: *Whitehead Brothers* / Candyman: *LL Cool J* / If trouble was money: *Mint Condition* / Just like my Papa: *Tony Toni Tone* / If you think you're lonely now: *Jodeci* / Rodeo: *Jamecia* / Up and down: *J-Quest* / Walk away: *Five Footer Crew* / Love is the key: *LSD* / No more love: *DRS* / Crazy love: *McKnight, Brian* / That's how it is: *Ahmad* / First round draft pick: *Twinz* / Brothas and Sistas: *Jayo Felony* / This city needs help: *Guy, Buddy* / Nigga sings the blues: *Spice* / Jesse James: *Scarface* / Love is still enough: *Sovory* / Many rivers to cross: *Adams, Oleta*
5229152 / Mar '95 / Mercury

☐ **JAWS**
Williams, John *c*
Main title / Chrissie's death / Promenade / Out to sea / Indianapolis story / Sea attack no. 1 / One barrel chase / Preparing the cage / Night search / Underwater siege / Hand to hand combat / End titles
MCLD 19281 / Jun '95 / MCA

☐ **JAZZ SINGER, THE (Diamond, Neil)**
Diamond, Neil *c*
America / Adorn o lume / You baby / Love on the rocks / Amazed and confused / Robert E Lee / Summer love / Hello again / Acapulco / Hey Louise / Songs of life / Jerusalem / Kol nidre / My name is Yussel / America (reprise)
4839272 / 27 Jul '98 / Columbia

☐ **JEANNE LA PUCELLE (Hesperon XX)**
Dufay, Guillaume/Jordi Savall *c*
K 1006 / Oct '95 / Auvidis Travelling

☐ **JEFFREY**
Endelman, Stephen *c*
VSD 5649 / Mar '96 / Varese Sarabande

☐ **JERRY MAGUIRE**
Shelter from the storm: *Dylan, Bob* / Sandy: *Wilson, Nancy* / Momma Miss America: *McCartney, Paul* / Wise up: *Mann, Aimee* / Singalong junk: *McCartney, Paul* / Secret garden: *Springsteen, Bruce* / Horses: *Jones, Rickie Lee* / We meet again: *Wilson, Nancy* / World on a string: *Young, Neil* / Pocketful of rainbows: *Presley, Elvis* / Magic bus: *Who* / Gettin' in tune: *Who* / Sitting still moving still staring outlooking: *Who*
4869812 / Mar '97 / Epic

☐ **JERRY'S GIRLS (1984 Broadway Cast)**
Herman, Jerry *c*
Jerry's girls / Put on your Sunday clothes / It only takes a moment / Wherever he ain't / We need a little Christmas / I won't send roses / Tap your troubles away / Two a day / Bosom buddies / Man in the moon / So long dearie / Take it all off / Shalom / Milk and honey / Showtum / If he walked into my life / Hello Dolly / Nelson / Just go to the movies / Movies were movies / Look what happened to Mabel / Time heals everything / It's today / Mame / Kiss her now / That's how young I feel / Gooch's song / Before the parade passes by / I don't want to know / La cage aux folles / Song on the sand / I am what I am / Best of times / Jerry's turn
CDTER2 1093 / Mar '85 / TER

☐ **JESUS CHRIST SUPERSTAR (The 20th Anniversary Recording) (1992 London Cast)**
Lloyd Webber, Andrew *c*
Rice, Tim *l*
09026614342 / Jan '93 / RCA Victor

☐ **JESUS CHRIST SUPERSTAR (Highlights From The 20th Anniversary Recording) (1992 London Cast)**
Lloyd Webber, Andrew *c*
Rice, Tim *l*
OCRCD 6031 / Dec '95 / First Night

☐ **JESUS CHRIST SUPERSTAR (Cast Recording)**
Lloyd Webber, Andrew *c*
Rice, Tim *l*
CDTER2 1216 / Aug '95 / TER

☐ **JESUS CHRIST SUPERSTAR (Cast Recording)**
Lloyd Webber, Andrew *c*
Rice, Tim *l*
Overture / Heaven on their minds / What's the buzz/ Strange thing mystifying / Everything's alright / This Jesus must die / Hosanna / Simon zealots/Poor Jerusalem / Pilate's dream / Temple / Everything's alright / I don't know how to love him / Damned for all time/Blood money / Last supper / Gethsemane (I only want to say) / Arrest / Peter's denial / Pilate and Christ / King Herod's song / Could we start again please / Judas' death / Trial before Pilate / Superstar / Crucifixion / John 1941
5337952
5337352 / Nov '96 / Really Useful

☐ **JESUS CHRIST SUPERSTAR (Cast Recording)**
Lloyd Webber, Andrew *c*
Rice, Tim *l*
Heaven on their minds / Everything's alright / This Jesus must die / Hosanna / Pilate's dream / I don't know how to love him / Gethsemane / King Herod's song / Trial before Pilate / Superstar / John 1941
SHOWCD 026 / Oct '96 / Showtime

☐ **JESUS CHRIST SUPERSTAR (Highlights) (Cast Recording)**
Lloyd Webber, Andrew *c*
Rice, Tim *l*
Overture / Heaven on their minds / What's the buzz/ Stange thing mystifying / Everything's alright / Hosanna / Simon zealotes/Poor Jerusalem / Pilate's dream / Temple / I don't know how to love him / Last supper / Gethsemane (I only want to say) / King Herod's song / Could we start again please / Judas's death / Trial by Pilate / Superstar / Crucifixion / John 1941
5376862 / May '97 / Really Useful

☐ JESUS CHRIST SUPERSTAR (National Symphony Orchestra)
Lloyd Webber, Andrew c
Rice, Tim l
Heaven on their minds / What's the buzz / Strange thing mystifying / Everything's alright / This Jesus must die / Hosanna / Simon Zealots / Poor Jerusalem / Pilate's dream / Temple / I don't know how to love him / Damned for all time / Blood money / Last supper / Gethsemane / Arrest / Peter's denial / Pilate and Christ / Herod's song / Judas death / Trial by Pilate / Superstar / Crucifixion / John / Could we start again please
CDTER 9026 / Nov '97 / TER

☐ JOHN & JEN
VSD 5688 / Apr '96 / Varese Sarabande

☐ JOHNNY AND THE DEAD
Girandet, Stefan c
CDWEEK 106 / Jul '95 / Weekend

☐ JOHNNY GUITAR
Young, Victor c
Young, Victor con
VSD 5377 / May '93 / Varese Sarabande

☐ JOHNNY HANDSOME (Cooder, Ry)
Cooder, Ry c
Main theme / I can't walk this time - the prestige / Angola / Clip joint rhumba / Sad story / Fountain walk / Cajun metal / First week at work / Greasy oysters / Smells like money / Sunny's tune / I like your eyes / Adios Donna / Cruising with Rafe / How's my face / End theme
9259962 / Sep '89 / WEA

☐ JOHNNY JOHNSON (Music For Johnny Johnson) (Boston Camerata)
Weill, Kurt c
Cohen, Joel con
0630178702 / 20 Oct '97 / Erato

☐ JOHNS
VSD 5778 / Feb '97 / Varese Sarabande

☐ JOLSON (Conley, Brian/London Cast)
Jolson, Al c
Evans, J. con
CASTCD 56 / May '96 / First Night

☐ JOSEPH AND THE AMAZING TECHNICOLOUR DREAMCOAT (1973 London Cast)
Lloyd Webber, Andrew c
Rice, Tim l
Jacob and sons / Joseph's coat / Joseph's dreams / Poor poor Joseph / One more angel in heaven / Potiphar / Close every door / Go go go Joseph / Pharaoh story / Poor poor Pharaoh / Song of the king / Pharaoh's dreams explained / Stone the crows / Those Canaan days / Brothers come to Egypt / Grovel grovel / Who's the thief / Benjamin calypso / Joseph all the time / Jacob in Egypt / Any dream will do
MCLD 19023 / Apr '92 / MCA

☐ JOSEPH AND THE AMAZING TECHNICOLOUR DREAMCOAT (1991 London Cast)
Lloyd Webber, Andrew c
Rice, Tim l
5111302 / Sep '91 / Really Useful

☐ JOSEPH MCCARTHY IS ALIVE AND LIVING IN DADE COUNTY (Cast Recording)
Scantlin, Ray c
AEICD 025 / May '98 / AEI

☐ JOURNEY TO THE CENTER OF THE EARTH
VSD 5849 / 20 Oct '97 / Varese Sarabande

☐ JUBILEE
Deutscher girls: *Adam & The Ants* / Plastic surgery: *Adam & The Ants* / Paranoia blues: *County, Wayne & The Electric Chairs* / Right to work: *Chelsea* / Nine to five: *Maneaters* / Rule Britannia: *Pinns, Suzi* / Jerusalem: *Pinns, Suzi* / Wargasm in pornotopia: *Amilcar* / Slow water: *Eno, Brian* / Dover beach: *Eno, Brian*
EGCD 34 / Jul '96 / EG
1112 / Sep '97 / Caroline

☐ JUDE
Johnston, Adrian c
5341162 / Oct '96 / Philips

☐ JUDGEMENT AT NUREMBURG
Gold, Ernest c
RCD 10723 / 8 Jun '98 / Rykodisc

☐ JUDGEMENT NIGHT
I love you Mary Jane: *Cypress Hill & Sonic Youth* / Judgement night: *Onyx & Biohazard* / Just another victim: *House Of Pain & Helmet* / Me myself and my microphone: *Run DMC & Living Colour* / Disorder: *Ice-T & Slayer* / Missing link: *Del Tha Funky Homosapien & Dinosaur Jr* / Fallin': *De La Soul & Teenage Fanclub* / Freak momma: *Sir Mix-A-Lot & Mudhoney* / Another body murdered: *Boo-Yaa T.R.I.B.E. & Faith No More* / Come and die: *Fatal & Therapy* / Real thing: *Cypress Hill & Pearl Jam*
4741832 / Oct '93 / Epic

☐ JUICE
MCLD 19308 / Oct '95 / MCA

☐ JULES ET JIM/LA CLOCHE TIBETAINE
Delerue, Georges c
PCD 103 / Feb '90 / Prometheus

☐ JULIA AND JULIA
Jarre, Maurice c
VCD 47327 / Jan '89 / Varese Sarabande

☐ JUMANJI
Horner, James c
Prologue and main title / First move / Monkey mayhem / New world / It's Sarah's move / Hunter / Rampage through town / Alan Parrish / Stampede / Pelican steals the game / Monsoon / Jumanji / End titles
4815612 / Feb '96 / Epic

☐ JUNGLE BOOK, THE
WD 704002 / Mar '96 / Disney Music & Stories

☐ JUNGLE BOOK, THE/THE THIEF OF BAGHDAD
Rozsa, Miklos c
CST 348044 / Sep '90 / Colosseum

☐ JURASSIC PARK - THE LOST WORLD
Williams, John c
Williams, John con
Lost World / Island prologue / Malcolm's journey / Hunt / Trek / Finding camp Jurassic / Rescuing Sarah / Hammond's plan / Raptors appear / Compys dine / Stegosaurus / Ludlow's demise / Visitor in San Diego / Finale/Jurassic Park theme
MCD 11628 / Jun '97 / MCA

☐ JUST CAUSE
Howard, James Newton c
VSD 5596 / Feb '95 / Varese Sarabande

☐ JUST IN TIME
Kuhn, Judy c
VSD 5472 / Feb '95 / Varese Sarabande

☐ JUST LIKE A WOMAN
Return to sender: *Presley, Elvis* / Wife's return / (You're the) devil in disguise: *Presley, Elvis* / Transformation / Big girls don't cry: *Pasdar, Adrian* / La senorita: *Latin Touch* / Sisters are doin' it for themselves: *Eurythmics & Aretha Franklin* / Geraldine / Love letters: *Presley, Elvis* / Waltz / End titles / Politics of love: *Blunstone, Colin*
74321110702 / Sep '92 / RCA

☐ JUSTINE
Goldsmith, Jerry c
TSU 0119 / May '95 / Tsunami

☐ JUTE CITY (Stewart, David A.)
Stewart, David A. c
Jute City / Dead planets / Last love / In Duncan's arms / Black wedding / Jute City revisited / Contaminated / See no evil / Jigula / Lords theme / Hats off to Hector / Deep waters / Dark wells
ZD 75187 / Nov '91 / RCA

K

☐ K2
Zimmer, Hans c
VSD 5354 / Sep '91 / Varese Sarabande

☐ KAMA SUTRA
Danna, Mychael c
CST 348063 / Jul '97 / Colosseum

☐ KANSAS CITY
5295542 / Aug '96 / Verve

☐ KANSAS CITY (More Music From & Inspired By The Film)
5373222 / Aug '97 / Verve

☐ KARA BEN NEMSI EFFENDI
Bottcher, Martin c
FICSP 10002 / 14 Apr '98 / Taran

☐ KARAOKE/COLD LAZARUS (London Symphony Orchestra)
Gunning, Christopher c
FILMCD 181 / Apr '96 / Silva Screen

☐ KARATE KID
Moment of truth: *Survivor* / On the beach: *Flirts & Jan & Dean* Bop Bop / No shelter: *Broken Edge* / It takes two to tango: *Davis, Paul* / Tough love: *Shandi* / Rhythm man: *St. Regis* / Feel the night: *Robertson, Baxter* / Desire: *Gang Of Four* / You're the best: *Esposito, Joe*
5511362 / Sep '95 / Spectrum

☐ KAT AND THE KINGS (Cast Recording)
Kramfr, David c
CASTCD 64 / 26 Jan '98 / First Night

☐ KAVANAGH QC (Dudley, Anne & John Keene)
Main title / Heartland / Private prosecution / Motherlove / Happy trails / Family affair / Unconditional love / Custody / Boat / Nothing but the truth / Sweetest thing / Preparation for the trial / Scarifice / Aldermartin's romance / Reconciliation / Asphalt jungle / Funeral / Aldermartin's triumph / Sam Wicks goes too far / Selfless courage / Flagship victory / Farewell / Family rejection / Kavanagh
VTDCD 134 / Apr '97 / Virgin

☐ KAZAAM
I am Kazaam: *O'Neal, Shaq* / I'll make your dreams come true: *Subway* / I swear I'm in love: *Usher* / Wishes: *Morris, Nathan* / All out on my own: *Shyheim* / No tighter wish: *Tangi & Lisa 'Left Eye' Lopes* / Lay light (one for the money): *Almighty Arrogant* / Show me your love: *Immature* / We genie: *O'Neal, Shaq & Wade Robson* / Dance wit' me: *Weaver, Jason* / If you believe: *Spinderella* / Key to my heart: *Choice* / I get lifted: *Barrio Boyzz* / Get down: *YBTO* / Boys will be boys: *Backstreet Boys* / Best of me: *Jamecia* / Mr. Material: *O'Neal, Shaq*
5490272 / Aug '96 / A&M

☐ KEEP THE ASPIDISTRA FLYING (Royal Philharmonic Orchestra)
Batt, Mike c
Tiger in the night / Theme from Keep the Aspidistra flying / Booking at Modigliani's / Bower made for us / Aspidistra waltz / Call off the search / Orchestral suite
CDC 5566132 / 19 Jan '98 / EMI Classics

☐ KEEP, THE (Tangerine Dream)
Tangerine Dream c
TCI 0616 / Apr '96 / Tsunami

☐ KEEPER OF THE CITY (Utah Symphony Orchestra)
Rosenman, Leonard c
MAF 7024D / Apr '92 / Intrada

☐ KERN GOES TO HOLLYWOOD (1985 London Cast)
Kern, Jerome c
Song is you/I've told every little star / I'll be hard to handle / Smoke gets in your eyes / Yesterdays / I won't dance / I'm old fashioned / Dearly beloved / Pick yourself up / She didn't say yes / Folks who live on the hill / Long ago and far away / Lovely to look at/ Just let me look at you / Remind me / Last time I saw Paris / Ol' man river / Why was I born / Can't help lovin' dat man / All the things you are/They didn't believe me
OCRCD 6014 / Mar '96 / First Night

☐ KEY TO REBECCA, THE
Redford, J.A.C. c
PCD 123 / Mar '93 / Prometheus

☐ KEYS OF THE KINGDOM, THE
Newman, Alfred c
TSU 0134 / Oct '96 / Tsunami

☐ KID GALAHAD/GIRLS GIRLS GIRLS (Presley, Elvis)
King of the whole wide world / This is living / Riding the rainbow / Home is where the heart is / I got lucky / Whistling tune / Girls girls girls - girls girls girls / I don't wanna be tied / Where do you come from / I don't want to / We'll be together / Boy like me a girl like you / Return to sender / Because of love / Thanks to the rolling sea / Song of the shrimp / Walls have ears / We're coming in loaded / Mama / Plantation rock / Dainty little moonbeams / Girls girls girls
74321 13430-2 / Mar '93 / RCA

☐ KIDS
Casper: *Johnston, Daniel* / Daddy never understood: *Folk Implosion* / Nothing gonna stop: *Folk Implosion* / Jenny's theme: *Folk Implosion* / Simean groove: *Folk Implosion* / Casper the friendly ghost: *Johnston, Daniel* / Natural one: *Folk Implosion* / Spoiled: *Sebadoh* / Crash: *Folk Implosion* / Wet stuff: *Folk Implosion* / Mad fright night: *Folk Implosion* / Raise the bell: *Folk Implosion* / Good morning captain: *Slint*
4286402 / Apr '96 / London

☐ KIDS IN THE HALL: BRAIN CANDY
Some days it's dark: *Death Lurks* / Painted soldiers: *Pavement* / Happiness: *Sweet, Matthew* / Happiness pie: *Death Lurks* / Sex dick pimp: *Phair, Liz* / Spiralling shape: *They Might Be Giants* / Swoon: *Pell Mell* / Birthday cake: *Cibo Matto* / Butts wigglin': *Tragically Hip* / Postal blowfish: *Guided By Voices* / Pablo and Andrea: *Yo La Tengo* / How to play your internal organs overnight: *Stereolab* / Nata di Marzo: *Pizzicato Five* / Eat my brain: *Odds* / Long dark twenties: *Bellini, Paul* / Having an average weekend: *Shadowy Men On A Shadowy Planet*
OLE 1832 / Dec '96 / Matador

☐ KILL THE MOONLIGHT
SFTR 1482CD / May '97 / Sympathy For The Record Industry

☐ KILLER TONGUE, THE
0022692CIN / 26 May '98 / Cinerama

☐ KILLING FIELDS, THE (Oldfield, Mike)
Oldfield, Mike c
Pran's theme / Requiem for a city / Evacuation / Capture / Execution / Bad news / Pran's departure / Work site / Year zero / Blood sucking / Pran's escape / Trek / Boy's burial The/Pran sees the red cross / Good news / Etude / Pran's theme - 2 / Year zero
CDV 2328 / Nov '84 / Virgin

☐ KINDERGARTEN COP
Edelman, Randy c
Astoria school theme / Children's montage / Love theme (Joyce) / Stalking Crisp / Dominic's theme / Rough day / Line up / Fireside chat / Rain ride / Kindergarten cop / Poor Cindy / Gettysburg address / Dinner invitation / Love theme (reprise) / Magic place / Kimball reveals the truth / Tower
VSD 5305 / Jan '91 / Varese Sarabande

☐ KING AND I, THE (Film Cast)
Rodgers, Richard c
Hammerstein II, Oscar l
Newman, Alfred con
I whistle a happy tune / My lord and master / Hello young lovers / March of the Siamese children / Puzzlement / Getting to know you / We kiss in a shadow / I have dreamed / Shall I tell you what I think of you / Something wonderful / Song of the King / Shall we dance
ZDM 7646932 / Apr '93 / EMI Classics

☐ KING AND I, THE (1977 Broadway Cast)
Rodgers, Richard c
Hammerstein II, Oscar l
Overture / Arrival at Bangkok/I whistle a happy tune / My lord and master / Hello young lovers / March of the Siamese children / Children sing priests chant / Puzzlement / Royal Bangkok Academy / Getting to know you / So big a world / We kiss in a shadow / Puzzlement (reprise) / Shall I tell you what I think of you / Something wonderful / Finale (Act 1) / Western people funny / Dance of Anna and Sir Edward / I have dreamed / Song of the king / Shall we dance / Finale
RD 82610 / Aug '90 / RCA Victor

☐ KING AND I, THE (New Broadway Cast)
Hammerstein II, Oscar c
Rodgers, Richard l
VSD 5763 / Oct '96 / Varese Sarabande

☐ KING AND I, THE (Cast Recording)
Rodgers, Richard c
Hammerstein II, Oscar l
Overture / I whistle a happy tune / My lord and my master / Hello young lovers / March of the Siamese children / Puzzlement / Getting to know you / We kiss in a shadow / Something wonderful / I have dreamed / Shall we dance / Finale
SHOWCD 024 / Oct '96 / Showtime

☐ KING AND I, THE (& The Sound Of Music/South Pacific - Aspects Of Broadway Vol.1) (Orchestra Of The Americas)
Rodgers, Richard c
Hammerstein II, Oscar l
Freeman, Paul con
I whistle a happy tune / Hello young lovers / March of the Siamese children / I have dreamed / Getting to know you / We kiss in a shadow / Shall we dance / Sound of music / How can love survive / Lonely goat herd / My favourite things / Sixteen going on seventeen / So long farewell / Do re mi / Edelweiss / Ordinary couple / No way to stop it / Maria / Climb every mountain / Dites-moi / Cock-eyed optimist / Some enchanted evening / Bloody Mary / There's nothing like a dame / Bali ha'i / I'm gonna wash that man right out of my hair / Wonderful guy / Younger than Springtime / Happy talk / Honeybun / This nearly was mine
SION 18301 / Jul '97 / Sion

☐ KING AND I, THE
Rodgers, Richard c
Hammerstein II, Oscar l
I whistle a happy tune / My Lord and master / Hello young lovers / March of the Siamese children / Puzzlement / Getting to know you / We kiss in the shadow / Something wonderful / Western people funny / I have dreamed / Song of the King / Shall I tell you what I think of you / Shall we dance
3036200412 / 15 Sep '97 / Carlton

☐ KING AND I, THE (Modern Jazz Rendition) (Wiggins, Gerald Trio)
Rodgers, Richard c
Hammerstein II, Oscar l
FSRCD 53 / Jan '98 / Fresh Sound

☐ KING AND I, THE (1996 Broadway Cast/ National Symphony Orchestra)
Rodgers, Richard c
Hammerstein II, Oscar l
Edwards, John Owen con
Overture / Opening act 1 / I whistle a happy tune / Vignettes and dance / My lord and master / Hello young lovers / March of the Siamese children / Postlude/Scene before curtain / Puzzlement / School room scene / Getting to know you / We kiss in the shadows / Puzzlement / Shall I tell you what I think of you / Something wonderful / Finale act 1 / Entr'acte / Western people funny / Dance of Anna and Sir Edward / We kiss in the shadows / I have dreamed / Hello young lovers / Small house of Uncle Thomas / Song of the king / Shall we dance / Melos / Processional / Something wonderful / Polka doloroso / I whistle a happy tune / Finale ultimo / Exit music
CDTER2 1214 / Mar '98 / TER

☐ KING AND I, THE/OKLAHOMA (Cast Recording)
Rodgers, Richard c
Hammerstein II, Oscar l
340772 / Oct '95 / Koch

☐ KING CREOLE (Presley, Elvis)
King Creole / As long as I have you / Hard headed woman / Trouble / Dixieland rock / Don't ask me why / Lover doll / Crawfish / Young dreams / Steadfast loyal and true / New Orleans / King Creole / As long as I have you / Danny / Lover doll / Steadfast loyal and true / As long as I have you / King Creole
07863674542 / 2 Feb '98 / RCA

☐ KING KONG (1976)
Barry, John c
MK 702 / Apr '96 / Silva Screen

☐ KING KONG (The All African Jazz Opera) (Masakela, Hugh/Miriam Makeba/Original Cast)
Matshikizia, Todd c
Williams, Pat l
668902 / Apr '96 / Melodie

☐ KING KONG (1933 Film Score Reconstructed By John Morgan) (Moscow Symphony Orchestra)
Steiner, Max c
Stromberg, William T. con
8223763 / Feb '98 / Marco Polo

☐ KING OF THE WIND
Scott, John c
Scott, John con
JSCD 109 / Jan '95 / JOS

☐ KING SOLOMON'S MINES (Hungarian State Opera Orchestra)
Goldsmith, Jerry c
Goldsmith, Jerry con
FMT 8005D / Mar '92 / Intrada

☐ KINGS ROW (National Philharmonic Orchestra)
Korngold, Erich c
Gerhardt, Charles con
Main title / Children (Parris and Cassie) / Parris and grandmother / Cassie's party / Icehouse / Operation / Cassie's farewell / Parris goes to Dr. Tower / Winter / Grandmother's last will / Seduction / All is quiet / Grandmother dies / Sunset / Parris leaves Kings Row / Flirtation / Vienna and Happy New Year 1900 / Randy and Drake / Financial ruin / Accident and amputation / Drake awakens / Vienna/Cable/Randy and Drake / Letters across the ocean / Parris comes back / Kings Row / Elise / Parris' decision / Finale
VCD 47203 / Jan '89 / Varese Sarabande

☐ KISMET (Cast Recording)
Forrest, George & Robert Wright c
Overture/Sands of time / Rhymes have I / Fate / Not since nineveh / Baubles bangles and beads / Stranger in paradise / Gesticulate / Night of my nights / Was I wazir / Rahadakum / This is my beloved / Olive tree
SHOWCD 014 / Feb '95 / Showtime

☐ KISMET (Ambrosian Singers/New York Concert Chorale/London Symphony Orchestra)
Forrest, George & Robert Wright c
Gemignani, Paul con
SK 46438 / Mar '92 / Sony Broadway

☐ KISMET (Film Cast)
Forrest, George & Robert Wright c
Main title / Rhymes have I / Fate / Bazaar of caravans / Not since Ninevah / Dabba / Baubles bangles and beads / I am a gardener / Stranger in paradise / Gesticulate / Bored / Fate / Night of my nights / Olive tree / Rhadalakum / Marsinah arrives at the castle/ I'm in love/Certain young wom / And this is my beloved / Innocent amusement / Diwan dances / Drowning scene/Sentence / Sands of time/End title
CDODEON 23 / 12 Jan '98 / Soundtracks

☐ KISMET/TIMBUKTU (1990 Studio Cast/ Ambrosian Chorus/Philharmonia Orchestra)
Forrest, George & Robert Wright c
Edwards, John Owen con
Overture / Sands of time / Rhymes have I / Fate / Hand of fate / Bazaar of the caravans / Entrance of lalume / Not since nineveh / Stolen oranges / Baubles bangles beads / Paradise garden / Stranger in paradise / He's in love / Gesticulate / And this is my beloved / Poets meet / Olive tree / Zubbediya / Finale act 2 / Night of my lights / Sands of time / Bored / In the beginning woman / Golden land golden life / My magic lamp / Power
CDTER2 1170 / Nov '97 / TER

☐ KISS ME KATE (1987 Royal Shakespeare Cast)
Porter, Cole c
OCRCD 6020 / Oct '95 / First Night

☐ KISS ME KATE (Broadway Cast)
Porter, Cole c
ZDM 7647602 / Apr '93 / EMI Classics

☐ KISS ME KATE (Barstow, Josephine & Thomas Hampson/Kim Criswell/ Ambrosian Chorus/London Sinfonietta)
Porter, Cole c
McGlinn, John con
CDS 7540332 / Apr '93 / EMI Classics

☐ KISS ME KATE (Cast Recording)
Porter, Cole c
Overture / Another op'nin / Why can't you behave / Wunderbar / So in love / We open in Venice / Tom Dick or Harry / Rose dance / I've come to live it wealthily in Padua / I hate men / Were thine that special face / I sign of love / Dance / Finalle act one / Entr'acte / Too darn hot / Where is the life that late I led / Always true to you in my fashion / Biance / Brush up your Shakespeare / Pavane / I am ashamed that women are so simple / Shrew / Can can overture / Jubilee overture / Out of this world overture
CDTER2 1212 / Nov '97 / TER

☐ KISS ME KATE (Film Cast)
Porter, Cole c
Overture medley / Main title / So in love / Too darn hot / Why can't you behave / Electric sign / Lili's cork / Wunderbar / So in love / We open in Venice / Tom Dick or Harry / I've come to wive it wealthily in Padua / I hate men / Were thine that special face / Finale / And so to wed / I've come to wive it wealthily in Padua / Where is the life that late I led / Bianca / Why can't you behave / Were thine that special face / Always true to you in my fashion / Brush up your Shakespeare / Bianca's wedding / From this moment on / Down on Kate / Finale
CDODEON 25 / Jan '97 / Soundtracks

☐ KISS ME KATE (Cast Recording/ National Symphony Orchestra)
Porter, Cole c
Edwards, John Owen con
Overture / Another op'nin' another show / Why can't you behave / Wunderbar / So in love / We open in Venice / I've come to wive it wealthily in Padua / I hate men / Too darn hot / Where is the life that late I led / Brush up your Shakespeare
SHOWCD 032 / Oct '96 / Showtime

☐ KISS ME KATE (Drake, Alfred & Patricia Morison/Lisa Kirk/Harold Lang/Broadway Cast)
Porter, Cole c
SK 60536 / Jul '98 / Columbia Broadway Masterworks

☐ KISS OF DEATH
Back in my life: Roberts, Joe / Spaceman: Rosemarys / Feeling free: Liquid City / Porque no unirnos: Liquid City / Kiss of death / Jimmy's dilemma / Illegal convoy / Calvin's revenge / Rosie and Corinna / Junior suspects / Corinna is kidnapped / Junior's arrest / Jimmy's resolve / End credits
280282 / Jun '95 / Milan

☐ KISS OF THE SPIDER WOMAN (1992 London Cast)
Kander, John c
Ebb, Fred l
OCRCD 6030 / Oct '95 / First Night

☐ KISSIN' COUSINS/CLAMBAKE/STAY AWAY, JOE (Presley, Elvis)
Kissin' cousins / Smoky mountain bay / There's gold in the mountains / One boy two little girls / Catchin' on fast / Tender feeling / Anyone (could fall in love with you) / Barefoot ballad / Once is enough / Kissin' cousins / Clambake / Who needs money / House that has everything / Confidence / Hey hey hey / You don't know me / Girl I never loved / How can you lose what you never had / Clambake (Reprise) / Stay away Joe / Dominic / All I needed was the rain / Goin' home / Stay away
07863663622 / Jun '94 / RCA

☐ KISSING A FOOL
Vitarelli, Joseph c
VSD 5922 / 5 May '98 / Varese Sarabande

☐ KNACK, THE
Barry, John c
RCD 10718 / 6 Apr '98 / Rykodisc

☐ KNICKERBOCKER HOLIDAY (Broadway Cast)
Weill, Kurt c
AEICD 007 / May '98 / AEI

☐ KNIGHTS OF THE ROUND TABLE
Rozsa, Miklos c
VCD 47269 / Jan '89 / Varese Sarabande

☐ KOLYA (Prague City Philharmonic Players/The Stern Quartet)
Svarovsky, Leos/Olga Ceskova con
4564322 / May '97 / Philips

☐ KUFFS (Faltermeyer, Harold)
Faltermeyer, Harold c
Kuffs theme / Stake out / Craze in the district / Night drive / Visitor / George gets Sam / Happy family / Need for speed / At the laundry / Ave Maria / Confrontation / So sad / Kuffs theme (reprise)
101512 / Jan '94 / Milan

☐ KULL THE CONQUEROR
Goldsmith, Jerry c
VSD 5862 / 22 Sep '97 / Varese Sarabande

☐ KUNDUN
Glass, Philip c
7559794602 / 9 Mar '98 / Nonesuch

☐ KUNG FU - THE LEGEND CONTINUES (Danna, Jeff)
Danna, Jeff c
From out of the past / Theme from Kung Fu / Place of light and song / Promise / Longest night / Omeishan / Reunion / Yellow flower in her hair / Tomb/Searching for Tan / Dragon's eye / Posse / Father and son / Emperor
ND 66008 / May '94 / Narada

☐ KWAMINA (Broadway Cast)
ZDM 7648912 / Aug '93 / EMI Classics

L

☐ LA BELLE ET LA BETE (Moscow Symphony Orchestra)
Auric, Georges c
Adriano con
8223765 / May '96 / Marco Polo

☐ LA BELLE HISTOIRE
Lai, Francis c
800442 / Jan '97 / Melodie

☐ LA BOUM I/LA BOUM II
Cosma, Vladimir c
950192 / Nov '97 / Pomme

☐ LA CALIFFA
Morricone, Ennio c
A 8928 / Feb '92 / Alhambra

☐ LA CLASSE OPERAIA VA IN PARADISO
Morricone, Ennio c
OST 122 / Jul '92 / Milano Dischi

☐ LA CONFIDENTIAL
Badge of honour: Goldsmith, Jerry / Ac-cent-tchu-ate the positive: Mercer, Johnny / Christmas blues: Martin, Dean / Look for the silver lining: Baker, Chet / Makin' whoopee': Mulligan, Gerry Quartet & Chet Barker / Hit the road to dreamland: Hutton, Betty / Oh look at me now: Wiley, Lee / Lady is a tramp: Mulligan, Gerry Quartet / Wheel of fortune: Starr, Kay / But not for me: Gleason, Jackie / Looking at you: Wiley, Lee / Powder our face with sunshine: Martin, Dean / LA confidential: Goldsmith, Jerry
74321525962 / 27 Oct '97 / RCA

☐ LA CONFIDENTIAL (Score)
Goldsmith, Jerry c
Bloody christmas / Cafe / Questions / Susan Lefferts / Out of the rain / Rollo Tomasi / Photos / Keys / Shootout / Good lad / Victor
VSD 5885 / 8 Dec '97 / Varese Sarabande

☐ LA DONNA DELLA DOMENICA/LA MOGLIE PIU BELLA
Morricone, Ennio c
PCD 119 / Apr '92 / Prometheus

☐ LA DOUBLE VIE DE VERONIQUE
Preisner, Zbigniew c
DPI 01 / Mar '96 / DPI

☐ LA FEMME NIKITA
TVT 81702 / 3 Aug '98 / TVT

☐ LA GLORIE DE MON PERE...
Cosma, Vladimir c
950652 / Nov '97 / Pomme

☐ LA HAINE
Intro / Sacrifice de poulets: Ministere Amer / Le vent tourne: Sens Unik / La 25eme image: Nuttea, Iam & Daddy / Dealer pour survivre: Expression Direkt / C'est la meme histoire: Ste Strausz / Requiem: La Cliqua / Comme dance un film: M.C. Solaar / La vague a l'arme: FF / Sors avec ton gun: Raggasonic / Bons baisers du poste: Les Sages Poetes De La Rue / L'etat assassine: Assassin
CDVIR 45 / Nov '95 / Virgin

☐ LA MACHINE
Portal, Michel c
4447892 / Sep '95 / London

☐ LA MOME SINGE
Tibi, Jean-Pierre c
SMC 35717 / Aug '97 / Sergent M

☐ LA PASSIONE (Rea, Chris/Shirley Bassey)
Rea, Chris c
0630166952 / May '97 / East West

☐ LA REINE MARGOT
Begovic, Goran c
5226552 / Jan '95 / Silva Screen

☐ LA REVOLUTION FRANCAISE
Schonberg, Claude-Michel c
Boublil, Alain l
OCRCD 6006 / Dec '95 / First Night

☐ LA STRADA/NIGHTS OF CABIRIA
Rota, Nino c
LEGENDCD 7 / Apr '92 / Legend

☐ LA YELLOW 357
YP 010ACD / Jul '96 / Yellow

☐ LABYRINTH (Bowie, David)
Bowie, David c
Underground / Into the labyrinth / Magic dance / Sarah / Chilly down / Hallucination / As the world falls down / Goblin battle / Within you / Thirteen o'clock / Home at last / Underground (reprise)
CDFA 3322 / Jul '95 / Fame

☐ LACOMBE LUCIEN (Music & Dialogue From Louis Malle's Lacombe Lucien/ Le Souffle Au Coeur/Milou En Mail/ Zazie Dans Le Metro)
K 1512 / Mar '97 / Auvidis Travelling

☐ LADY AND THE TRAMP
Main title/Wag of a dog's tail / Peace / It has a ribbon/ Lady to bed/A few mornings later / Sunday/The rat/ Morning paper / New collar/Jock and Trusty/It's Jim Dear / What a day / Warning/Breakout/Snob hill/A wee bairn / Countdown to b-day / Baby's first morning/What is a baby/La la la / Going away/Aunt Sarah / Siamese cat song/What's going on down there / Muzzle/Wrong side of the tracks / You poor kid/He's not my dog / Through the zoo/A log puller / Footloose and collarfree/Bella notte / It's morning/ Ever chase chickens/Caught / Home sweet home / Pound / What a dog/He's a tramp / In the doghouse / Finale
WD 6021328 / Oct '97 / Disney Music & Stories

☐ LADY BE GOOD (Cast Recording)
Gershwin, George c
Gershwin, Ira l
Stern, Eric con
7559793082 / Jul '93 / Nonesuch

☐ LADY IN THE DARK, THE (Abravanel, Kaye)
Weill, Kurt c
Gershwin, Ira l
MHK 62869 / Jun '97 / Masterworks Heritage

☐ LADY IN THE DARK, THE (London Cast)
Weill, Kurt c
Gershwin, Ira l
Glamour dream / Wedding dream / Circus dream / Childhood dream
CDTER 1244 / 15 Jun '98 / TER

☐ LADY IN THE DARK, THE (Lawrence, Gertrude & Audrey Christie/Cast)
Weill, Kurt c
Gershwin, Ira l
AEICD 003 / May '98 / AEI

☐ LADY IN THE DARK, THE (Sothern, Ann & Carleton Carpenter/Cast)
Weill, Kurt c
Gershwin, Ira l
Hobo dance / Jenny / Oh fabulous one / One life to give / Girl of the moment / It looks like Liza / Wedding dream ballet / Mapleton High chorale / This is new / Woman at the altar / Greatest show on Earth / Best years of his life / Tchaikowsky / Finaletto / Two step / My ship / Princess of pure delight
AEICD 041 / May '98 / AEI

☐ LADY IN WHITE
Laloggia, Frank c
VCD 47530 / Jan '89 / Varese Sarabande

☐ LADY SINGS THE BLUES (Ross, Diana)
Lady sings the blues / Baltimore brothel / Billie sneaks into Dean and Dean's / Swinging uptown / T'ain't nobody's business if I do / Big Ben / CC rider / All of me / Man I love / Them there eyes / Gardenias from Louis / Cafe Manhattan / Had you been around / Love theme / Country tune / I cried for you / Billy and Harry / Mean to me / Fine and mellow / What a little moonlight can do / Louis visits Billie on tour / Persuasion / Agent's office / Love is here to stay / Lover man / You've changed / Gimme a pigfoot and a bottle of beer / Good morning heartache / My man (mon homme) / Don't explain / Strange fruit / God bless the child / Closing theme
5301352 / Jan '93 / Motown

☐ LADY SINGS THE BLUES (1989 Musical Cast)
BEARCD 33 / Oct '90 / Big Bear

☐ LADYHAWKE (Philharmonia Orchestra)
GNPD 8042 / May '96 / GNP Crescendo

☐ L'AMANT (Yared, Gabriel)
Yared, Gabriel c
CDVMM 9 / Jan '95 / Virgin

☐ LAND BEFORE TIME, THE (Songs From The Film)
UMD 80388 / Jul '97 / Universal

☐ LAND GIRLS, THE
Lock, Brian c
Firman, David con
FILMCD 300 / 1 Sep '98 / Silva Screen

☐ LAND OF SMILE, THE (Tauber, Richard & Margit Suchy/Hella Kurty/Willy Stettner)
Lehar, Franz c
Dessau, Paul con
313732 / Aug '98 / Koch Schwann

☐ LAND OF THE PHAROAHS
Tiomkin, Dimitri c
TCI 0608 / May '95 / Tsunami

☐ LANDRAIDERS, THE
Nicolai, Bruno c
PCD 128 / Jul '93 / Prometheus

☐ L'ANGE NOIR
Musy, Jean c
682369 / Feb '97 / Playtime

☐ L'ANTICHRISTO/SEPOLTA VIVA
Morricone, Ennio c
SPALAX 14984 / Oct '96 / Spalax

☐ LARGER THAN LIFE (Goodman, Miles)
Goodman, Miles c
Goodman, Miles con
74321442822 / Apr '97 / Milan

☐ L'ASSOLUTO NATUTALE
Morricone, Ennio c
CDMF 310 / 14 Apr '98 / Cinevox

☐ LAST COMMAND
Steiner, Max c
W 9109 / 14 Apr '98 / Taran

☐ LAST DAYS OF CHEZ NOUS, THE (Grabowsky, Paul)
Grabowsky, Paul c
Last days of chez nous / Last days / Inversions / Warm hands / Conversations / New life / New lives / Big car people / Small car people / Two hands / Lover man / Donna Lee / Day's end
DRGCD 12607 / Jun '93 / DRG

☐ LAST EXIT TO BROOKLYN (Knopfler, Mark)
Knopfler, Mark c
Last exit to Brooklyn / Victims / Think fast / Love idea / Tralala / Riot / Reckoning / As low as it gets / Finale
8387252 / Mar '97 / Vertigo

☐ LAST KLEZMER, THE (Kozlowski, Leopold)
GVCD 168 / Nov '94 / Global Village

☐ **LAST MAN STANDING (Score)**
Bernstein, Elmer *c*
VSD 5755 / Nov '96 / Varese Sarabande

☐ **LAST MAN STANDING (Cooder, Ry)**
Cooder, Ry *c*
5334152 / Oct '96 / Verve

☐ **LAST OF ENGLAND, THE**
Fisher-Turner, Simon *c*
CDIONIC 1 / Oct '87 / The Fine Line

☐ **LAST OF THE HIGH KINGS, THE**
Last of the high kings: *Convertino, Michael* / Boys are back in town: *Thin Lizzy* / Ever fallen in love: *Buzzcocks* / Watching the detectives: *Costello, Elvis* / Milk and alcohol: *Dr. Feelgood* / 2-4-6-8 motorway: *Robinson, Tom Band* / All the young dudes: *Mott The Hoople* / Thunder: *Convertino, Michael* / Oh yeah: *Ash* / Spanish stroll: *Mink Deville* / Heart on my sleeve: *Gallagher & Lyle* / Can't take my eyes off this place for one minute: *Convertino, Michael* / Dancing in the moonlight: *Thin Lizzy* / How long: *Ace*
PRMDCD 26 / Dec '96 / Premier/EMI

☐ **LAST TANGO IN PARIS**
Barbieri, Gato *c*
Last tango in Paris / Jeanne / Girl in black / Last tango in Paris / Fake Ophelia / Picture in the rain / Return / It's over / Goodbye (un largo adios) / Why did she choose you / Last tango in Paris
RCD 10724 / 8 Jun '98 / Rykodisc

☐ **LAST TIME I COMMITTED SUICIDE, THE**
Better get it in your soul: *Mingus, Charles* / Straight no chaser: *Roach, Max* / Move: *Davis, Miles* / It's a metaphor: *Reeves, Dianne* / Shaw nuff right back where I started: *Parker, Charlie & Dizzy Gillespie* / A tisket a tasket: *Fitzgerald, Ella* / Sixteen: *Monk, Thelonius* / Thin man: *Blakey, Art & The Jazz Messengers* / Country girl: *Wilson, Cassandra* / He may be your man: *Andrews Sisters* / Wild stuff: *Reeves, Dianne* / Budism: *Terrasson, Jacky* / Suicide suite: *Red Fish Blue Fish* / Carry on my brother: *Red Fish Blue Fish* / Ride my heart who is this: *Pet*
CDP 8367362 / 1 Jun '98 / Blue Note

☐ **LAST WALTZ, THE (Band)**
Last waltz / Up on Cripple Creek / Who do you love / Helpless / Stage fright / Coyote / Dry your eyes / It makes no difference / Such a night / Night they drove old Dixie down / Mystery train / Mannish boy / Further on up the road / Shape I'm in / Down South in New Orleans / Ophelia / Tura lura larai (That's an Irish lullaby) / Caravan / Life is a carnival / Baby let me follow you down / I don't believe you (she acts like we never have met) / Forever young / I shall be released / Last waltz suite / Well / Evangeline / Out of the blue / Weight
266076 / Mar '88 / WEA

☐ **LAURA/JANE EYRE**
Herrmann, Bernard *c*
07822110062 / Apr '94 / RCA

☐ **L'AVVENTURIERO/OCEANO**
Morricone, Ennio *c*
OST 120 / Jan '93 / Milano Dischi

☐ **LAWNMOWER MAN II (Beyond Cyberspace) (Sinfonia Of London)**
Folk, Robert *c*
Folk, Robert *con*
VSD 5698 / Mar '96 / Varese Sarabande

☐ **LAWRENCE OF ARABIA (London Philharmonic Orchestra)**
Jarre, Maurice *c*
Overture / Main title / Miracle / Nefud mirage / Rescue of Gasim / Bringing Gasim into camp / Arrival at Auda's camp / Voice of the guns / Continuation of the miracle / Sun's anvil / Lawrence and his bodyguard / That is the desert / End titles
VSD 5263 / Apr '91 / Varese Sarabande
CLACD 271 / '92 / Castle

☐ **LAWRENCE OF ARABIA (Philharmonia Orchestra)**
Jarre, Maurice *c*
Bremner, Tony *con*
Overture/Main titles / First entrance to the desert - night and stars / Lawrence and Tafas / Miracle / That is the desert / Nefud mirage/Sun's anvil / Rescue of Gasim/Bringing Gasim into camp / Arrival at Auda's camp / On to Akaba/The beach at night / Sinai desert / Voice at the guns / Horse stampede - Ali rescues Lawrence / Lawrence and his bodyguard / End/ Playoff music
FILMCD 036 / Jan '89 / Silva Screen

☐ **LE CRIME DE MONSIEUR LANGE (& La Grande Illusion/La Bete Humaine/Une Partie De Campagne - The Film Music Of Jean Renoir)**
K 1510 / Dec '96 / Travelling

☐ **LE DECALOGUE**
Preisner, Zbigniew *c*
AMP 709 / Mar '96 / Amplitude

☐ **LE DESTIN**
LBSA 970032 / Nov '97 / XIII Bis

☐ **LE GRAND BLOND/LE RETOUR**
Cosma, Vladimir *c*
950312 / Nov '97 / Pomme

☐ **LE HUITIEME JOUR**
5327132 / Nov '96 / Mercury

☐ **LE HUSSARD SUR LE TOIT (Orchestre National De France)**
Petit, Jean Claude *c*
Petit, Jean Claude *con*
K 10106 / Dec '95 / Auvidis Travelling

☐ **LE NOUVELLE VAGUE**
887825 / Jun '95 / Milan

☐ **LE PLUS BEAU METIER DU MONDE**
Cosma, Vladimir *c*
951982 / Nov '97 / Pomme

☐ **LEAVE IT TO BEAVER**
VSD 5838 / 15 Sep '97 / Varese Sarabande

☐ **LEAVE IT TO JANE (1959 Off Broadway Cast)**
Kern, Jerome *c*
Wodehouse, P.G. *l*
AEICD 038 / May '98 / AEI

☐ **LEAVE IT TO JANE/OH KAY (Broadway Cast)**
Kern, Jerome/George Gershwin *c*
Wodehouse, P.G./Ira Gershwin *l*
Just you watch my step / Leave it to Jane / Siren's song / Cleopatterer / Crickets are calling / Sun shines brighter / Sir Galahad / Wait 'til tomorrow / I'm going to find a girl / Godd old atwater / There it is again / Poor prune / Finale / Overture / Woman's touch / Twenties are here to stay / Home / Stiff upper lip / Maybe / Pophams / Do do do / Clap yo' hands
DRGCD 15017 / Apr '91 / DRG

☐ **LEAVING LAS VEGAS**
Figgis, Mike *c*
Intro / Angel eyes: *Sting* / Are you desirable / Ben and Bill / Leaving Las Vegas / Sera's dark side / Mara / Burlesque / On the street / Bossa Vega / Ben pawns his Rolex/Sera talks to her schrink / My one and only love: *Sting* / Sera invites Ben to stay / Come rain or shine: *Henley, Don* / Ben and Sera theme / Ridiculous: *Cage, Nicolas* / Biker bar / Ben's hell / It's a lonesome old town: *Sting* / Blues for Ben / Get out / Reunited / Sera talks to the cab driver / She really loved him / I won't be going south for a while: *Palladinos*
5404762 / Mar '96 / A&M

☐ **LEGEND (American Score) (Tangerine Dream)**
Tangerine Dream *c*
VSD 5645 / Sep '95 / Varese Sarabande

☐ **LEGEND (National Philharmonic Orchestra)**
Goldsmith, Jerry *c*
Goldsmith, Jerry *con*
Main title/Goblins / My true love's eyes/Cottage / Unicorns / Living river/Bumps and hollows/Freeze / Faeries/Riddle / Sing the wee / Forgive me / Faerie dance / Armour / Oona/Jewels / Dress waltz / Darkness fails / Ring / Re-united
FILMCD 045 / Jan '90 / Silva Screen

☐ **LEGENDS OF THE FALL**
Horner, James *c*
Legends of the fall / Ludlows / Off to war / To the boys / Samuel's death / Alfred moves to Helena / Farewell/ Descent into madness / Changing seasons / Wild horses / Tristan's return / Wedding / Isabel's murder / Recollections of Samuel / Revenge / Goodbyes / Alfred / Tristan / Colonel / Legend
4785112 / May '95 / Epic

☐ **LEGS DIAMOND (Broadway Cast)**
Allen, Peter *c*
79832 / Feb '90 / Silva Screen

☐ **LENNY**
Burns, Ralph *c*
Opening / Lament / We're all the same / Nan's dream / Intro by Dustin Hoffman / Honeycomb / To come / Time does it again / Niggers / Aurenthology / Dirty / It never entered my mind / We're all the same / Myrtle's tune / Blah blah / Flic flac / Lenny
RCD 10707 / 12 Jan '98 / Rykodisc

☐ **LEON (Serra, Eric)**
Serra, Eric *c*
Noon / Cute name / Ballad for Mathilde / What's happening out there / Bird in New York / She is dead / Fatman / Leon the cleaner / Can I have a word with you / Game is over / Feel the breath / Room 4602 / Very special delivery / When Leon does his beast / Back on the crime scene / Bird of storm / Thony the IBM / How do you know this it's love / Fight / Two ways / Out hey little angel
4783232 / Feb '95 / Columbia

☐ **LEON THE PIG FARMER**
Murphy, John & David Hughes *c*
I fell in love with the moon / Feels so right / Mon dieu / Jump out of your skin (Instrumental) / Siman Tov / Asher Bara / Feelings / Gallery / Every valley shall be exalted / Nothing ever goes to plan / Yorkshire theme / Jewish transformation / Leon's theme (Instrumental) / Jump out of your skin / Leon chase / Hava nagila / If I'd never known you / Mess around
CDSTY 1 / May '94 / Soundtrack Music

☐ **LES ADVENTURES DE RABBI JACOB**
Cosma, Vladimir *c*
950242 / Nov '97 / Pomme

☐ **LES LIAISONS DANGEREUSES (Blakey, Art & The Jazz Messengers/ Barney Wilen)**
No problem / No hay problema / Prelude in blue / Valmontana / Miguel's party / Weehawken mad pad
8120172 / Mar '94 / Fontana

☐ **LES MISERABLES (Highlights) (International Cast)**
Schonberg, Claude-Michel *c*
Kretzmer, Herbert *l*
CASTCD 20 / Oct '91 / First Night

☐ **LES MISERABLES (1985 London Cast)**
Schonberg, Claude-Michel *c*
Kretzmer, Herbert *l*
Koch, Martin *con*
At the end of the day / I dreamed a dream / Lovely ladies / Who am I / Come to me / Confrontation / Castle on a cloud / Master of the house / Stars / Look down / Little people / Red and black / Do you hear the people sing / I saw him once / In my life / Heart full of love / One day more / On my own / Attack / Little fall of rain / Drink with me to days gone by / Bring him home / Dog eats dog / Soliloquy / Empty chairs at empty tables / Wedding chorale / Beggars at the feast / Finale
ENCORECD 1 / Dec '85 / First Night

☐ **LES MISERABLES (Cast Recording)**
Schonberg, Claude-Michel *c*
Kretzmer, Herbert *l*
WMCD 5672 / Feb '93 / Woodford Music

☐ **LES MISERABLES (Cast Recording)**
Schonberg, Claude-Michel *c*
Kretzmer, Herbert *l*
GRF 197 / Jan '93 / Tring

☐ **LES MISERABLES (Highlights - The Shows Collection) (1993 Studio Cast)**
Schonberg, Claude-Michel *c*
Kretzmer, Herbert *l*
At the end of the day / I dreamed a dream / Master of the house / Stars / Do you hear the people sing / In my life / Heart full of love / On my own / Little fall of rain / Drink with me / Bring him home / Empty chairs at empty tables
PWKS 4175 / Oct '93 / Carlton

☐ **LES MISERABLES (Complete Symphonic Score) (International Cast)**
Schonberg, Claude-Michel *c*
Kretzmer, Herbert *l*
MIZCD 1 / Dec '88 / First Night

☐ **LES MISERABLES (Five Outstanding Performances From The Symphonic Score) (International Cast)**
Schonberg, Claude-Michel *c*
Kretzmer, Herbert *l*
Empty chairs at empty tables / Stars / One day more / I dreamed a dream / On my own
SCORECD 17 / Apr '89 / First Night

☐ **LES MISERABLES (The Original French Concept Album) (Cast Recording)**
Schonberg, Claude-Michel *c*
DOCRCD 1 / '94 / First Night

☐ **LES MISERABLES (Wilkinson, Colm & P. Quast/R. Henshall/10th Anniversary Cast/Royal Philharmonic Orchestra)**
Schonberg, Claude-Michel *c*
Kretzmer, Herbert *l*
Abell, D.C. *con*
ENCORECD 8 / Mar '96 / First Night

☐ **LES MISERABLES (Complete Score) (Czech-Slovak Radio Symphony Orchestra)**
Honegger, Arthur *c*
Adriano *con*
8223181 / Jan '95 / Marco Polo

☐ **LES MISERABLES/LA ROUE/ MERMOZ/MAPOLEON (Czech-Slovak Radio Symphony Orchestra)**
Honegger, Arthur *c*
Adriano *con*
8223134 / Jan '95 / Marco Polo

☐ **LES PALMES DE M. SCHUTZ**
Cosma, Vladimir *c*
952122 / Jul '97 / Pomme

☐ **LES PASSIONS AMOREUSES**
887974 / Jun '95 / Milan

☐ **LES SILENCES DU PALAIS**
Amal hayeti / Lecon de oud / Lessa faker / Bachraf mazmoum / Elegie (chant patriotique version radio) / Danse 1 / Fogue achajera / Notes / Taalila / Vocalises cris de douleurs / Danse II / Ghanili cheoui cheoui / Bachraf / Elegie (chant patriotique) / Theme alia
CDVIR 35 / Apr '95 / Virgin

☐ **LETHAL WEAPON III (Kamen, Michael)**
Kamen, Michael *c*
It's probably me: *Sting* / Runaway train: *John, Elton & Eric Clapton* / Grab the cat / Leo Getz goes to the hockey game / Darryl dies / Riggs and Roger / Roger's boat / Armour piercing bullets / God judges us by our scars / Lorna - a quiet evening by the fire
7599269892 / Jun '92 / WEA

☐ **L'ETUDIANTE**
Cosma, Vladimir *c*
950202 / Nov '97 / Pomme

☐ **LEVIATHAN**
Goldsmith, Jerry *c*
VSD 5226 / Feb '90 / Varese Sarabande

☐ **LEXX: THE DARK ZONE STORIES**
Cluster anthem / Prisoner transport/Snake chase / Welcome to the dark zone/Battle of the universe / Planet cruise / Poet man/Cryochamber / Love muscle / Gigashadow march / YO-A-O (Fight song of the brunnen-G) / Lexx escape / Zev's shower / Cleric theme / Kai collapse / Shadows and prophets / Feppo's party / Milk fed boys / Brunnis / Fantasy dance / Moth ride
CST 348064 / 1 Dec '97 / Colosseum

☐ **LIAR LIAR**
Debney, John *c*
Debney, John *con*
My Dad's a liar / To court / Pen is blue / I'm a bad Father / Pulled over / Unwish / Bathroom folly / I love my Son / Airport chase / It's Fletcher / Together / Claw returns / End credits / Out-take montage
MCD 11618 / Jun '97 / MCA

☐ **LIE OF THE MIND, A (Red Clay Ramblers)**
SHCD 8501 / Jan '97 / Sugar Hill

☐ **LIFE IS FOR LIVING/A MAN AND A WOMAN**
Lelouch, Claude & Francis Lai *c*
101292 / Aug '90 / Musidisc

☐ **LIFE LESS ORDINARY, A**
Deadweight: *Beck* / Love is here: *Luscious Jackson* / Life Less Ordinary: *Ash* / Velvet divorce: *Sneaker Pimps* / Kingdom of lies: *Folk Implosion* / Leave: *REM* / Don't leave: *Faithless* / Oh: *Underworld* / It's war: *Cardigans* / Always on my mind: *Presley, Elvis* / Peace in the valley: *Alabama 3 & Errol Thompson* / Beyond the sea: *Darin, Bobby* / Put a lid on it: *Squirrel Nut Zippers* / Deeper river: *Dusted* / Full throttle: *Prodigy*
5408372 / 13 Oct '97 / A&M

☐ **LIFETIMES (To Live)**
Jiping, Zhao *c*
Lifetimes / Fugui performs puppetry / Jiazhen leaves Fugui / Fugui leaves his old home / Wounded soldiers / Fugui performs for the army / Jiazhen returns / Fengxia dies / Fugui takes his son to school / Fugui returns from the war / Erxi fixes the house / Fugui performs at the steelworks / 1950's / Fengxia leaves her parents / Closing credits / Puppet performance
210532 / Oct '94 / Milan

☐ **LILIES**
Danna, Mychael *c*
VSD 5868 / 17 Nov '97 / Varese Sarabande

☐ **LILLIES OF THE FIELD**
Goldsmith, Jerry *c*
TSU 0101 / Sep '93 / Tsunami

☐ **LINGUINI INCIDENT, THE**
Newman, Thomas *c*
VSD 5372 / Jun '93 / Varese Sarabande

☐ **LINK**
Goldsmith, Jerry *c*
VCD 47276 / Jan '89 / Varese Sarabande

☐ **L'INTEGRALE COMPLETE**
887988 / Jun '95 / Milan

☐ **LION IN WINTER, THE**
Barry, John *c*
VSD 5217 / Feb '90 / Varese Sarabande

☐ **LION KING, THE (John, Elton)**
John, Elton *c*
Rice, Tim *l*
Circle of life: *Twillie, Carmen* / I just can't wait to be King: *Weaver, Jason* / Be prepared: *Irons, Jeremy* / Hakuna matata: *Lane, Nathan & Ernie Sabella* / Can you feel the love tonight: *Williams, Joseph & Sally Dworsky* / This land: *Zimmer, Hans* / To die for / Under the stars / King of Pride Rock / Circle of life / I just can't wait to be King / Can you feel the love tonight
5226902 / Jun '94 / Rocket

☐ **LION KING, THE (Rumble In The Jungle - A Tribute To The Music Of The Lion King)**
Circle of life / I just can't wait to be king / Be prepared / Hakuna matata / Can you feel the love tonight / This land / To die for / Under the stars / King of the pride rock / Circle of life / I just can't wait to be king / Can you feel the love tonight / Lion king of the jungle
CDMFP 6225 / May '96 / Music For Pleasure

☐ **LION KING, THE (Singalong)**
WD 706824 / Nov '96 / Disney Music & Stories

☐ **LION KING, THE (Cast Recording)**
WD 608022 / 6 Apr '98 / Disney Music & Stories

☐ **LIONHEART (AWOL)**
Scott, John *c*
Scott, John *con*
MAF 7011D / Jan '93 / Intrada

☐ **LIONHEART VOL.1**
Goldsmith, Jerry *c*
Ceremony / Failed knight / Robert and Blanche / Children in bondage / Banner / Lake / Mathilda / Wrong flag / King Richard
VSD 5484 / Apr '94 / Varese Sarabande

☐ **LIONHEART VOL.2**
Goldsmith, Jerry *c*
Castle / Circus / Gates of Paris / Plague / Final fight / Road from Paris / Dress / Forest hunt / Paris underground / Bring him back / Future
VCD 47288 / Jan '89 / Varese Sarabande

☐ **LIQUID SKY**
VCD 47181 / Jan '89 / Varese Sarabande

☐ LISA
Mertens, Wim c
TW 11032 / Feb '97 / Crepuscule

☐ LITANIES OF SATAN (Galas, Diamanda)
Galas, Diamanda c
CDISO 1 / May '89 / The Fine Line

☐ LITTLE BOY BLUE
78282788102 / 14 Jul '98 / Sonic Images

☐ LITTLE BUDDHA/RAISE THE RED LANTERN/CYCLO (Music From The Orient)
Sakamoto, Ryuichi & Zhao Jipzing/Ton-That Tiet c
7432132O312 / May '96 / Milan

☐ LITTLE MARY SUNSHINE (1962 London Cast)
Besoyan, Rick c
Overture / Forest rangers / Little Mary Sunshine / Look for a sky of blue / You're the fairest flower / Swingin' - how do you do / Colorado love call / What has happened / Tell a handsome stranger / Once in a blue moon / Every little nothing / Such a merry party / Say Uncle / Heap big Injun / Mata Hari / Do you ever dream of Vienna / Coo coo / Finale
CDSBL 13108 / Nov '92 / DRG

☐ LITTLE MARY SUNSHINE (Broadway Cast)
Besoyan, Rick c
ZDM 7647742 / Apr '93 / EMI Classics

☐ LITTLE ME (London Cast)
Coleman, Cy c
Leigh, Carolyn l
Overture / Truth / On the other side of the tracks / Rich kids rag / I love you / Deep down inside / To be a performer / Le grand boom-boom / I've got your number / Real live girl / Poor little Hollywood star / Little me / Goodbye / Here's to us
CDSBL 13111 / Aug '93 / DRG

☐ LITTLE ME (1962 Broadway Cast)
Coleman, Cy c
Leigh, Carolyn l
09026614822 / Jul '93 / RCA Victor

☐ LITTLE MERMAID, THE
Menken, Alan c
Ashman, Howard l
Fathoms below / Fanfare / Daughters of Triton / Part of your world / Poor unfortunate souls / Les poissons / Kiss the girl / Firework / Jig / Storm / Destruction of the grotto / Flotsam and Jetsam / Tour of the kingdom / Bedtime / Wedding announcement / Eric to the rescue / Happy ending
WD 609462 / 15 Jun '98 / Disney Music & Stories

☐ LITTLE MERMAID, THE (Shell We Dance)
Menken, Alan c
Ashman, Howard l
WD 606282 / 11 May '98 / Disney Music & Stories

☐ LITTLE MERMAID, THE (Sing Along)
WD 775840 / 15 Jun '98 / Disney Music & Stories

☐ LITTLE NIGHT MUSIC, A (1975 London Cast)
Sondheim, Stephen c
Wheller, H. l
Overture and night waltz / Now later soon / Glamorous life / Remember / You must meet my wife / Liaisons / In praise of women / Every day a little death / Weekend in the country / Sun won't set / It would have been wonderful / Perpetual anticipation / Send in the clowns / Miller's son / Finale
GD 85090 / Apr '90 / RCA Victor

☐ LITTLE NIGHT MUSIC, A (Cast Recording)
Sondheim, Stephen c
Wheller, H. l
Edwards, John Owen con
Overture / Night waltz / Now / Later / Soon / Glamourous life / Remember / You must meet my wife / Liaisons / In praise ofw om / Every day a little death / Weekend in the country / It would have been wonderful / Perpetual anticipation / Send in the clowns / Miller's son / Last waltz
CDTER 1179 / Nov '97 / TER

☐ LITTLE NIGHT MUSIC, A
Sondheim, Stephen c
Wheller, H. l
Overture / Now / Later / Soon / Glamorous life / You must meet my wife / Liaisons / Weekend in the country / It would have been wonderful / Send in the clowns / Miller's son / Last waltz
SHOWCD 042 / Jan '97 / Showtime

☐ LITTLE NIGHT MUSIC, A (Trotter, Terry)
Sondheim, Stephen c
Wheller, H. l
VSD 5819 / 1 Dec '97 / Varese Sarabande

☐ LITTLE PRINCESS
Doyle, Patrick c
VSD 5628 / Feb '96 / Varese Sarabande

☐ LITTLE RED RIDING HOOD (London Philharmonic Orchestra)
Patterson, Paul c
Dahl, Roald l
Weiser-Most, Franz con
CDC 5555532 / Nov '95 / EMI Classics

☐ LITTLE ROMANCE, A
Delerue, Georges c
Delerue, Georges con
VSD 5367 / Nov '92 / Varese Sarabande

☐ LITTLE SHOP OF HORRORS (1987 Film Cast)
Menken, Alan c
Ashman, Howard l
Prologue / Da doo / Grow for me / Somewhere that's green / Some fun now / Dentist / Feed me / Suddenly Seymour / Suppertime / Meek shall inherit / Mean green mother from outer space / Finale / Skid Row (downtown)
GFLD 19289 / Oct '95 / Geffen

☐ LITTLE SHOP OF HORRORS (Cast Recording)
Menken, Alan c
Ashman, Howard l
Prologue / Skid row / Da doo / Grow for me / Somewhere that's green / Be a dentist / Mushnik and son / Git it (feed me) / Suddenly Seymour / Suppertime / Finale / Megamix
LS 94CD01 / Apr '94 / Dreamtime

☐ LITTLE WOMEN
Newman, Thomas c
Newman, Thomas con
SK 66922 / Mar '95 / Sony Classical

☐ LIVE A LITTLE.../TROUBLE WITH GIRLS/CHANGE OF HEART/CHARRO (Presley, Elvis)
Almost in love / Little less conversation / Wonderful world / Edge of reality / Little less conversation (album version) / Charro / Let's forget about the stars / Clean up your own backyard / Swing low sweet chariot / Swing low sweet chariot / Signs of the zodiac / Almost / Whiffenpoof song / Violet / Clean up your own backyard (undubbed version) / Almost (undubbed version) / Have a happy / Let's be friends / Change of habit / Let us pray / Rubberneckin'
07863665592 / Mar '95 / RCA

☐ LIVE AND LET DIE
Martin, George c
Live and let die: *McCartney, Paul & Wings* / Just a closer walk with thee / New second line: *Dejan, Harold A. 'Duke' & The Olympia Brass Band* / Bond meets Solitaire / Whisper who dares / Snakes alive / Baron Samedi's dance of death / San Monique / Fillet of soul / Bond drops in / If he finds it kill him / Trespassers will be eaten / Solitaire gets her cards / Sacrifice / James Bond
CZ 553 / Dec '95 / Premier/EMI

☐ LIVE FLESH
Iglesias, Alberto c
Christmas 1970 / Madrid / Call / Circular 1 / Circular 2 / First time / David spies / Rehearsel for a crime / Lovestruck / La ventilla / Ti sono molto vicino / El fontanar / Cannon fodder / That's why he shot you / Fire / Love theme / Clara and Sancho / Letter / Dragging myself along / Christmas 1996 / Somos
74321542732 / 15 May '98 / RCA Victor

☐ LIVE FROM A QUARRY (Joyce, Paul)
Joyce, Paul c
Space overture / Invasion / Alien / Contact / Chaos / Universal / Music for mars
PKJCD 002 / 6 Oct '97 / PKJ

☐ LIVES OF JESUS, THE
Sanctus / Yad vashem / One sacred voice / Kamakami / Desert dance / Ex templo / Jericho / In cathedra / Transfiguratas est / Via dolorosa / Lives of Jesus (titles)
RCD 60030 / Dec '96 / MCA

☐ LOADED
OCD 1 / 13 Apr '98 / Ocean Deep

☐ LOCAL HERO (Knopfler, Mark)
Knopfler, Mark c
Rocks and the water / Wild theme / Freeway flyer / Boomtown / Way it always starts / Rocks and the thunder / Ceilidh and the Northern lights / Mist covered mountain / Ceilidh / Louis favourite Billy tune / Whistle / Smooching / Stargazer / Going home
8110382 / Mar '97 / Vertigo

☐ LOCK STOCK AND TWO SMOKING BARRELS
CID 8077 / 31 Aug '98 / Island

☐ LODOSS WAR I
Hagita, Matsuo c
AM 3 / Nov '96 / Animanga

☐ LODOSS WAR II
Hagita, Matsuo c
AM 4 / Nov '96 / Animanga

☐ LODOSS WAR III
Hagita, Matsuo c
AM 8 / Nov '96 / Animanga

☐ LOLITA
Love theme from Lolita / Guilty / Guilty as charged: *Mason, James & Peter Sellers* / Ramsdale / Cherry pies: *Winters, Shelley & James Mason* / Lolita ya ya / Hula hoop / There's no you / Quilty's caper / Lovely lilting lyrical name: *Sellers, Peter & Shelley Winters* / Put your dreams away: *Sellers, Peter & Shelley Winters* / Shelley Winters cha cha / Music to eat by / Diary entry / Last martini / Charlotte is dead / Instant music / Don't smudge your toenails / Strange call / Mrs Schiller / Twenty five paces / End title
8219782 / 13 Oct '97 / Premier/EMI

☐ LOLITA
Morricone, Ennio c
74321523182 / 11 May '98 / RCA

☐ LONE WOLF MCQUADE
De Masi, Francesco c
VSD 5573 / Nov '95 / Varese Sarabande

☐ LONELY ARE THE BRAVE
Goldsmith, Jerry c
NR 9104 / 6 Jul '98 / Delphi

☐ LONESTAR
DARINGCD 3023 / Jun '96 / Daring

☐ LONG GOOD FRIDAY, THE (Monkman, Francis)
Monkman, Francis c
Long good Friday / Overture / Scene is set / At the pool / Discovery / Icehouse / Talking to the police / Guitar interludes / Realization / Fury / Taken
FILMCD 020 / Jan '89 / Silva Screen

☐ LONG KISS GOODNIGHT, THE
Woman: *Cherry, Neneh* / Bring it on home to me: *Redding, Otis & Carla Thomas* / Stubborn kind of fellow: *Gaye, Marvin* / FNT: *Semisonic* / Keep this party bouncin': *LA Ganz* / Funny how time slips away: *Hinton, Joe* / Tomorrow man: *Gus* / She's not there: *Santana* / Next time you see to me: *Parker, Junior* / Mannish boy: *Waters, Muddy* / Many rivers too cross: *Tom Tom Club* / Chair: *Jars Of Clay* / Main title: *Silvestri, Alan* / Lady marmalade: *Labelle*
MCD 11526 / Nov '96 / MCA

☐ LONG RIDERS, THE (Cooder, Ry)
Cooder, Ry c
Long riders / I'm a good old rebel / Seneca square dance / Archie's funeral (hold to God's unchanging hand) / I always knew that you were the one / Rally round the flag / Wildwood boys / Better things to think about / My grandfather / Cole Younger / Escape from Northfield / Leaving Missouri / Jesse James
7599234482 / Jan '96 / WEA

☐ LONG WALK HOME, THE (Fenton, George)
Fenton, George c
VSD 5304 / Apr '91 / Varese Sarabande

☐ LORD JIM
Kaper, Bronislaw c
W 9108 / 14 Apr '98 / Taran

☐ LORD OF ILLUSIONS
Boswell, Simon c
Lord of Illusion / Detective / God's eyes / Flesh is a trap / Magic moments / Swann's last act / Dorothea and d'amour / While the blood runs warm in your veins / Resurrection / Origami man / What are you looking at / Born to murder the world / Magic sets us free / Laura / Dancing in the dark
IONIC 13CD / Jul '95 / The Fine Line

☐ LORD OF THE FLIES (London Symphony Orchestra)
Sarde, Philippe c
Lord of the flies / Island / Demons / Fire on the mountain / Cry of the hunters / Last hope / Savages / After the storm / Bacchanalia / Lord Of The Flies (finale)
FILMCD 067 / Jun '90 / Silva Screen

☐ LORD OF THE RINGS
Rosenman, Leonard c
Rosenman, Leonard con
FMT 8003D / Apr '92 / Intrada

☐ LORNA (& Vixen/Faster Pussycat)
QDKCD 008 / Sep '97 / QDK Media

☐ LOST BOYS, THE
To the shock of Miss Louise: *Newman, Thomas* / Good times: *INXS & Jimmy Barnes* / Lost in the shadows: *Gramm, Lou* / Don't let the sun go down on me: *Daltrey, Roger* / Laying down the law: *INXS & Jimmy Barnes* / People are strange: *Echo & The Bunnymen* / Cry little sister: *McMann, Gerard* / Power play: *Eddie & The Tide* / I still believe: *Cappello, Tim* / Beauty has her way: *Mummy Calls*
7817672 / Aug '87 / Atlantic

☐ LOST EMPIRES
Hilton, Derek c
Lost empires theme / Army of today's alright / Your king and country / Pure white rose / Somewhere / Oh Flo / They didn't believe me / Wedding glide / Cigar girl / Honeysuckle and the bee / Mother Machree / Alexander's ragtime band / Land of hope and glory / Rule Britannia / I don't want to play in your yard / Yankee doodle boy / Shine on harvest moon / Love's old sweet song / Trombone song / Take me on the flip flap / Nobody knows nobody cares / Mr. Knick Knock / Poor little Dolly / Waiting for the Robert E Lee / Catari catari / Nightingale and the star / Julia's theme
CDTER 1119 / Nov '86 / TER

☐ LOST HIGHWAY
I'm deranged (Edit): *Bowie, David* / I'm deranged (Reprise): *Bowie, David* / Videodrones: *Reznor, Trent* / Questions: *Reznor, Trent* / Perfect drug: *Nine Inch Nails* / Red bats with teeth: *Badalamenti, Angelo* / Haunting and heartbreaking: *Badalamenti, Angelo* / Dub driving: *Badalamenti, Angelo* / Fred and Renee make love: *Badalamenti, Angelo* / Fats revisited: *Badalamenti, Angelo* / Fred's world: *Badalamenti, Angelo* / Police: *Badalamenti, Angelo* / Driver down: *Reznor, Trent* / Eye: *Smashing Pumpkins* / Mr. Eddy's theme 1: *Adamson, Barry* / Something wicked this way comes: *Adamson, Barry* / Hollywood sunset: *Adamson, Barry* / Hierate mich: *Rammstein* / Rammstein (Edit): *Rammstein* / I put a spell on you: *Manson, Marilyn* / This magic moment: *Reed, Lou* / Mr. Eddy's theme 2: *Adamson, Barry* / Apple of sodom: *Manson, Marilyn* / Insensatez: *Jobin, Antonio Carlos*
IND 90090 / Feb '97 / Interscope

☐ LOST IN SPACE
Lost in space: *Apollo 440* / I'm here another planet: *Juno Reactor & The Creatures* / Busy child: *Crystal Method* / Bang on: *Propellerheads* / Everybody needs a 303: *Fatboy Slim* / Will and Penny's theme: *Apollo 440* / Song for Penny: *Death In Vegas* / Lost in space: *Space* / Original motion picture score: *Broughton, Bruce*
1658181802 / 31 Mar '98 / TVT
4913032 / 25 May '98 / Epic

☐ LOST WEEKEND/BLOOD ON THE RUN
Rozsa, Miklos c
TSU 0132 / Apr '96 / Tsunami

☐ LOUISIANA PURCHASE
Berlin, Irving c
DRGCD 94766 / Dec '96 / DRG

☐ LOUISIANA STORY (New London Orchestra)
Thomson, Virgil c
Corp, R. con
Power among men / Louisiana story / Acadian songs and dances / Plow that broke the plains
CDA 66576 / Feb '92 / Hyperion

☐ LOVE AND DEATH ON LONG ISLAND
OCD 014 / 13 Jul '98 / Ocean Deep

☐ LOVE JONES
Brother to the night (a blues for Nina): *Tate, Larenz* / Hopeless: *Farris, Dionne* / Sweetest thing: *Refugee Camp All-Stars & Lauryn Hill* / I got a love Jones for you: *Refugee Camp All-Stars & Melky & Day* / Sumthin' sumthin': *Maxwell* / Never enough: *Groove Theory* / Inside my love: *Broussard, Tina* / In the rain: *Xscape* / You move me: *Wilson, Cassandra* / Rush over: *Miller, Marcus & Me'Shell Ndegeocello* / I like it: *Brand New Heavies* / Girl Cassie: *Lattimore, Kenny* / Can't get enough: *Lattimore, Kenny* / Jelly jelly: *Lincoln Centre Jazz Orchestra* / In a sentimental mood: *Ellington, Duke & John Coltrane* / I am looking at music: *Long, Nia*
4872302 / Mar '97 / Columbia

☐ LOVE ME TENDER (Presley, Elvis)
295 052 / May '95 / RCA

☐ LOVE STORY
Lai, Francis c
Love story / Snow frolic / Sonata No.12 in F major / I love you Phil / Christmas tree / Search for Jenny / Bozo Barrett / Skating in Central Park / Long walk home / Concerto No.3 in D Major / Love story (finale)
MCLD 19157 / Jan '93 / MCA

☐ LOVE VALOUR COMPASSION
Wheeler, Harold c
4556442 / Aug '97 / Decca

☐ LOVED UP
Smoke belch II: *Sabres Of Paradise* / Crystal clear: *Grid* / Prologue: *10th Chapter* / Two full moons and a trout: *Union Jack* / Little bullet: *Spooky* / Gut drum mix: *Funtopia* / Plastic dream: *Jaydee* / Break and enter: *Prodigy* / Acperience: *Hardfloor* / Surjestive: *Advances* / Melt: *Leftfield*
PRIMACD 002 / Oct '95 / Prima Vera

☐ LOVING YOU (Presley, Elvis)
Mean woman blues / Teddy bear / Got a lot of livin' to do / Lonesome cowboy / Hot dog / Party / Blueberry Hill / True love / Don't leave me now / Have I told you lately that I love you / One night of sin / Loving you / Tell me why / Is it so strange / When it rains it really pours / I beg of you / Loving you / Party / Got a lot of livin' to do
07863674522 / 2 Feb '98 / RCA

☐ LOVING YOU
Herman, Jerry c
VSD 5586 / Aug '95 / Varese Sarabande

☐ LOW DOWN DIRTY SHAME, A
Down 4 whateva: *Nuttin' NYC* / Shame: *Zhane* / I can go deep: *Silk* / Homie lover friend: *R. Kelly* / Turn it up: *Raja-Nee* / Stroke you up: *Changing Faces* / Thing I like: *Aaliyah* / Gotta get yo groove on: *Campbell, Tevin* / Birthday girl: *Hi-Five* / Get the girl grab the money and run: *Souls Of Mischief* / Cray-Z: *Fu-Schnickens* / Later on: *Casual* / How's that: *Murray, Keith* / Let's organize: *Organized Konfusion* / Ghetto style: *Smooth* / Front back and side to side: *UGK's* / In front of the kids: *Extra Prolific* / U rong 4 that: *Mz Kilo*
CHIP 156 / Apr '95 / Jive

☐ LUBITSCH TOUCH, THE (& Die Austernprinzessin/Die Puppe - Music For Silent Movies) (Film Orchestra Babelsberg)
Sasse, Karl-Ernst c
Rosenberg, Manfred con
09026626562 / Nov '95 / RCA Victor

☐ LUCIFER RISING
Beausoleil, Bobby c
DIGUST 2 / Feb '94 / Masters Of Disgust

☐ LUCKY STIFF
Flaherty, Stephen c
Something funny's going on / Mr. Witherspoon's friday night / Uncle's last request / Good to be alive / Rita's confession / Lucky / Dogs versus you / Phone call / Monte Carlo / Speaking French / Times like this / Fancy meeting you here / Him them it her / Nice / Welcome back Mr. Witherspoon / Confession no.2 / Finale: Good to be alive
VSD 5461 / Apr '94 / Varese Sarabande

☐ LUNCH (The Studio Recording)
Dorff, Steve c
Bettis, John l
Lunch / He'll never know / I never danced with you / Requiem for a lightweight / Man like me / Skyline / Time stands still / I'm no angel / Why fall at all / Perfectly alone / Lunch concerto
DRGCD 12610 / Mar '95 / DRG

M

☐ **M. BUTTERFLY**
Shore, Howard *c*
Shore, Howard *con*
M Butterfly / Concubine / Entrance of Butterfly / Drunken beauty / Dragonfly / Great wall / Even the softest skin / Shi jia bang / Bonfire of the vanities / Cultural rèvolution / He was the perfect father / Are you my butterfly / Only time I ever really existed / What I loved was the lie / Everything has been destroyed / Un bel di / My name is Rene Gallimard
VSD 5435 / Oct '93 / Varese Sarabande

☐ **MA 6T VA CRACK-ER**
PIAS 085104120CD / 25 Aug '97 / Play It Again Sam

☐ **MACARTHUR (The Rebel General)**
Goldsmith, Jerry *c*
VSD 5260 / Oct '90 / Varese Sarabande

☐ **MACBETH/KING ARTHUR/MERRY WIVES OF WINDSOR (Incidental Music To The Shakespearean Plays) (MacDonald, Margaret & RTE Chamber Choir/Concert Orchestra)**
Sullivan, Sir Arthur *c*
Penny, Andrew *con*
8223635 / Sep '95 / Marco Polo

☐ **MACHINE GUN MCCAIN**
Morricone, Ennio *c*
Morricone, Ennio *con*
A 8922 / Feb '92 / Alhambra

☐ **MACK AND MABEL (1974 Broadway Cast)**
Herman, Jerry *c*
Overture: Orchestra / Movies were movies: *Preston, Robert* / Look what happened to Mabel: *Mack & Mabel* / Big time: *Kirk, Lisa* / I won't send roses: *Preston, Robert* / I wanna make the world laugh: *Preston, Robert* / Wherever he ain't: *Peters, Bernadette* / Hundreds of girls: *Preston, Robert & The Bathing Beauties* / When Mabel comes in the room: *Simmonds, Stanley* / My heart leaps up: *Preston, Robert* / Time heals everything: *Peters, Bernadette* / Tap your troubles away: *Kirk, Lisa* / I promise you a happy ending: *Preston, Robert*
MCLD 19089 / Oct '92 / MCA

☐ **MACK AND MABEL (In Concert) (1988 London Cast)**
Herman, Jerry *c*
Overture / Introduction / When movies were movies / Look what happened to Mabel / Big time / I won't send roses / I wanna make the world laugh / Wherever he ain't / Hundreds of girls / Entr'acte / When Mabel comes in the room / Hit 'em on the head / Time heals everything / Tap your troubles away / I promise you a happy ending / I won't send roses (reprise)
OCRCD 6015 / Oct '95 / First Night

☐ **MACK AND MABEL (1995 London Cast)**
Herman, Jerry *c*
CDEMC 3734 / Dec '95 / Premier/EMI

☐ **MACROSS PLUS VOL.1**
National anthem of Macross / Fly up in the air - tension / After in the dark - torch song / Myung theme / Bees and honey / In captivity / More than 3cm / Voices / Break out - cantabile / Very little wishes / Santi-U
DSCD 12 / May '95 / Demon

☐ **MACROSS PLUS VOL.2**
DSCD 13 / 27 Oct '97 / Demon

☐ **MCVICAR**
Bitter and twisted / Escape / Free me: *Daltrey, Roger* / Just a dream away / McVicar / My time is gonna come / Waiting for a friend / White City lights / Without your love: *Daltrey, Roger*
5273412 / Jan '94 / Polydor

☐ **MAD CITY**
Newman, Thomas *c*
Channel / Max goes out / He's sunk / Mic tap / Sole demand / Max back in / Max goes out / Wrong bullet / Meanwhile / Pizza man / Hollander report / Feds fly in / See the crowd / Good tease / Massive complications / Caffish corner / Mic tap / Big John / Softball questions / Shove Ms. Banks / Rolling / Max goes out / Unfavourable light
VSD 5887 / 6 Apr '98 / Varese Sarabande

☐ **MAD DOG AND GLORY**
Bernstein, Elmer *c*
Bernstein, Elmer *con*
VSD 5415 / Mar '93 / Varese Sarabande

☐ **MAD MAX I**
May, Brian *c*
Main title / Max the hunter / Max decides on vengeance / Final chase / Terrible death of Jim Goose / We'll give 'em back their heroes / Pain and triumph / Dazed Goose / Foreboding in the vast landscape / Declaration of war / Flight from the evil Toecutter / Pursuit and tragedy / Jesse alone uneasy and exhausted / Beach house / Nightriders race / Jesse searches for her child / Rampage of the toecutter / Crazing of Johnny the boy / Outtakes suite
VCD 47144 / Jan '89 / Varese Sarabande

☐ **MAD MAX II (The Road Warrior)**
May, Brian *c*
Opening titles / Montage / Confrontation / Marauder's massacre / Max enters compound / Feral boy strikes / Gyro saves Max / Gyro flight / Breakout / Chase continues / Journey over the mountain / Finale and largo / End title
VCD 47262 / Jan '89 / Varese Sarabande

☐ **MAD MAX III (Beyond The Thunderdome) (Royal Philharmonic Orchestra)**
Jarre, Maurice *c*
We don't need another hero: *Turner, Tina* / One of the living: *Turner, Tina* / We don't need another hero (instrumental) / Bartertown / Children / Coming home
GNPD 8037 / Sep '92 / GNP Crescendo

☐ **MADAME SOUSATZKA**
Gouriet, Gerald *c*
VSD 5204 / Dec '88 / Varese Sarabande

☐ **MADDIE (Cast Recording)**
Keeling, Stephen *c*
McKenna, Shaun *l*
DRESSCD 003 / 24 Mar '98 / Dress Circle

☐ **MADE IN AMERICA**
Go Away: *Estefan, Gloria* / Does he do it good: *Sweat, Keith* / Made in America: *Del Tha Funky Homosapien* / Colours of love: *Fischer, Lisa* / What is this: *Mendes, Sergio* / Made in Love: *Isham, Mark* / I know I don't walk on water: *Satterfield, Laura & Ephraim Lewis* / Dance or die: *D.J. Jazzy Jeff & The Fresh Prince* / Smoke on the water: *Deep Purple* / If you need a miracle: *King, Ben E.* / Stand: *Y.T Style*
7559614982 / Dec '96 / WEA

☐ **MADNESS OF KING GEORGE, THE**
Fenton, George *c*
Opening the Houses of Parliament / Prelude/Front titles / Smile it's what you're paid for / King goes riding / Family matter / Cricket match / King wakes up early / Do it England / Concert / We have no time / He will be restrained / London is flooding / Going to Kew / Starting to recover / Chancellor drives to London / Prince Regent / Mr. and Mrs. King / End credits
4784772 / Apr '95 / Epic

☐ **MADWOMAN OF CENTRAL PARK WEST, THE (Broadway Cast)**
DRGCD 5212 / Jan '95 / DRG

☐ **MAGDALENE (Munich Symphony Orchestra)**
Eidelman, Cliff *c*
Eidelman, Cliff *con*
MAF 7029D / Sep '92 / Intrada

☐ **MAGIC SWORD, THE (Quest For Camelot)**
Looking through your eyes: *Rimes, LeeAnn* / I stand alone: *Perry, Steve* / Prayer: *Dion, Celine* / United we stand: *Perry, Steve* / On my Father's wings: *Corrs* / Looking through your eyes: *Corrs & Brian White* / Ruber: *Oldman, Gary* / I stand alone: *White, Brian* / If I didn't have you: *Idle, Eric & Don Rickles* / Dragon attack/Forbidden forest: *Doyle, Patrick* / Battle: *Doyle, Patrick* / Looking through your eyes: *Foster, David* / Prayer: *Bocelli, Andrea*
7567831122 / 1 Jun '98 / Warner Bros.

☐ **MAGNIFICENT SEVEN, THE/THE HALLELUJAH TRAIL (Arizona State University Choir/Phoenix Symphony Orchestra)**
Bernstein, Elmer *c*
Sedares, James *con*
372222 / Jan '95 / Koch International

☐ **MAIN EVENT**
Melvoin, Michael *c*
Main event / Fight / Body shop / Copeland meets the Coasters / Get a job / Big girls don't cry / It's your foot again / Angry eyes / I'd clean a fish for you
4749062 / '95 / Columbia

☐ **MAJOR DUNDEE**
Amfitheatrof, Daniele *c*
TSU 0111 / Jan '95 / Tsunami

☐ **MAJOR LEAGUE II**
Boom bapa boom: *Vaughan, Jimmy* / (Everything I do) Got to be funky: *Vaughan, Jimmy* / Wild thing '94: *X* / Shake me up: *Little Feat* / Rude mood: *Vaughan, Stevie Ray* / All my love is gone: *Lovett, Lyle* / Born under a bad sign: *King, Albert* / House is rockin': *Vaughan, Stevie Ray & Double Trouble* / Wild thing: *X*
523245-2 / Jun '94 / Morgan Creek

☐ **MALICE**
Goldsmith, Jerry *c*
Goldsmith, Jerry *con*
Main title / Lift home / No friends / With malice / Handyman / Clues / No choice / Body
VSD 5442 / Jan '94 / Varese Sarabande

☐ **MAMA, I WANT TO SING (London Cast)**
Treasure of love / On Christ / Solid rock / You are my child / Faith can move a mountain / I know who hold tomorrow / He'll be your strength / Gifted is / This bitter earth / Stormy weather / In my solitude / God bless the child / Mama I want to sing / I'll do anything / What do you win when you win / Take my hand (precious Lord) / His eye is on the sparrow / Take my hand (precious Lord) / Know when to leave the party / Just one look / One who will love me
CDEMC 3709 / May '95 / EMI

☐ **MAMBO KINGS, THE**
La dicha mia / Ran kan kan / Cuban Pete / Mambo caliente / Quiereme mucho / Sunny ray / Melao da cana (moo la lah) / Para los rumberos / Perfidia / Guantanamera / Tea for two / Accidental mambo / Come fue / Tanga / Rumba afro cubana / Beautiful Maria of my soul
7559612402 / May '92 / Elektra

☐ **MAN AND A WOMAN, A/LIVE FOR LIFE**
Lai, Francis *c*
Man and a woman / Samba saravah / Today it's you / Stronger than us / In our shadow / 124 Miles an hour / Live for life / Theme to Catherine / Theme to Candice / Now you want to be loved / Theme to Robert / All at once it's love / Zoom
DRGCD 12612 / May '96 / DRG

☐ **MAN CALLED MOON, A**
Bacalov, Luis Enriquez *c*
A 8935 / Jan '93 / Silva Screen

☐ **MAN FROM 42ND STREET, THE (Powell, Dick)**
You've got something there / This year's kisses / I know now / In a moment of weakness / You can't run away from love tonight / Have you got any castles baby / Lulu's back in town / Love is in the air tonight / Stein song / 'Cause my baby says it's so / Moonlight on the campus / Song of the marines / I've got my love to keep me warm / I'm like a fish out of water / Mr. and Mrs. is the name / By a waterfall / I'm going shopping with you / Thanks a million / Lullaby of Broadway / I'll string along with you / Why do I dream those dreams / Fair and warmer
PASTCD 7079 / Mar '96 / Flapper

☐ **MAN FROM SNOWY RIVER, THE**
Rowland, Bruce *c*
VCD 47217 / Jan '89 / Varese Sarabande

☐ **MAN FROM UNCLE, THE**
Montenegro, Hugo *c*
Montenegro, Hugo *con*
Man from UNCLE / Meet Mr. Solo / Martini built for two / Wild bike / Solo on a raft / Fiddlesticks / Man from THRUSH / Illya / Invaders / Solo's samba / Bye bye Jill / Watch out / Sandals only / Solo busanova / Off and running / Boo-bam-boo baby / Slink / Run spy run / Jungle beat / Wiggely pig walk / Lament for a trapped spy / There they go / Jo Jo's torch thing / Dance of the flaming swords
74321241792 / Jan '95 / RCA

☐ **MAN FROM UNCLE, THE (The Original Soundtrack Affair)**
RE 2133 / Aug '97 / Razor & Tie

☐ **MAN OF LA MANCHA**
Leigh, Mitch *c*
Darion, Joe *l*
RCD 10730 / 20 Jul '98 / Rykodisc

☐ **MAN ON FIRE (Graunke Symphony Orchestra)**
Scott, John *c*
VCD 47314 / Jan '89 / Varese Sarabande

☐ **MAN WHO KNEW TOO LITTLE, THE**
VSD 5886 / 11 May '98 / Varese Sarabande

☐ **MAN WITH THE GOLDEN GUN, THE**
Barry, John *c*
Man with the golden gun: *Lulu* / Scaramanga's fun house / Chew mee in Grisly land / Man with the golden gun (jazz instrumental) / Getting the bullet / Goodnight goodnight / Let's go get em / Hip's trip / Kung fu fight / In search of Scaramanga's island / Return to Scaramanga's fun house / Man with the golden gun (reprise): *Lulu*
CZ 552 / Dec '95 / Premier/EMI

☐ **MANDELA**
CIDM 1116 / Mar '97 / Mango

☐ **MANGALA, THE INDIAN GIRL**
AAA 121 / Feb '96 / Club Du Disque Arabe

☐ **MANNAJA/TE DEUM**
De Angelis, G. & M. *c*
OST 121 / Jul '94 / Milano Dischi

☐ **MARCH OF THE FALSETTOS (1981 Off-Broadway Cast)**
Finn, William *c*
Finn, William *l*
Four Jews in a room bitching / Tight-knit family / Love is blind / Thrill of first love / Marvin at the psychiatrist / My Father's a homo / Everyone tells Jason to see a psychiatrist / This had better come to a stop / Please come to my house / Jason's therapy / Marriage proposal / Trina's song / March of the falsettos / Chess game / Making a home
DRGCD 12581 / Mar '92 / DRG

☐ **MARCH OF THE FALSETTOS/ FALSETTOLAND (Cast Recording)**
Finn, William *c*
Finn, William & James Lapine *l*
DRGCD 22600 / Jan '95 / DRG

☐ **MARKED FOR DEATH**
I wanna do something freaky to you: *Kenyatta* / I joke but I don't play: *Tone Loc* / Roots and culture: *Shabba Ranks* / Put the funk back in it: *Brand New Heavies* / Welcome to my groove: *Mellow Man Ace* / Quiet passion: *Davenport, N'Dea* / Domino: *Masters Of Reality* / Shadow of death: *Def Jef & Papa Juggy* / Ya gets none: *Body & Soul* / Rats chase cats: *Attic Black* / Pick up the pace: *Young MC* / Weapons montage: *Howard, James Newton* / John Crow: *Cliff, Jimmy* / Steppin' razor: *Tosh, Peter* / No justice: *Cliff, Jimmy* / Rebel in me: *Cliff, Jimmy*
BRCD 561 / Jan '94 / 4th & Broadway

☐ **MARLENE (Cast Recording)**
RBMARCD 1 / Apr '97 / Playback

☐ **MARNIE**
Herrmann, Bernard *c*
TCI 0601 / Jan '95 / Tsunami

☐ **MARS ATTACKS**
Elfman, Danny *c*
Introduction / Main titles / First sighting / Landing / Ungodly experiments / State address / Martian madame / Martian lounge / Return message / Destructo x / Loving heads / Pursuit / War room / Airfield dilema / New world / Ritchie's speech / End credits / Indian love call: *Whitman, Slim* / It's not unusual: *Jones, Tom*
7567829922 / Feb '97 / East West

☐ **MARTHA MEET FRANK DANIEL AND LAURENCE**
I only want to be with you: *Springfield, Dusty* / Halo: *Texas* / Please fall in love with me: *Booth, Tim* / I think I was meant to come to London: *Shearmur, Ed* / Fools like us: *Echo & The Bunnymen* / This is the best pick up joint in London: *Shearmur, Ed* / If you can't do it when you're young when can you do it: *Theaudience* / Step into my world: *Hurricane No.1* / Moment I saw him she knew: *Shearmur, Ed* / Brown paper bag: *Roni Size* / Tape loop: *Morcheeba* / Iceland huh: *Shearmur, Ed* / Back in the shadow: *Serious Jones*
5583962 / 11 May '98 / Mercury

☐ **MARTIN GUERRE (London Cast)**
CASTCD 59 / Nov '96 / First Night

☐ **MARY POPPINS**
Sherman, Richard & Robert *c*
Overture / Sister Suffragette / Life I lead / Perfect nanny / Spoonful of sugar / Pavement artist (chim chim cher-ee) / Jolly holiday / Supercalifragilisticexpialidocious / Stay awake / I love to laugh / British bank (the life I lead) / Feed the birds (tuppence a bag) / Fidelity diduciary bank / Chim chim cheree / Step in time / Man has dreams / Let's go and fly a kite
WD 775722 / 23 Mar '98 / Disney Music & Stories

☐ **MARY REILLY**
Fenton, George *c*
SK 62259 / May '96 / Sony Music

☐ **MASK AND GOWN (1957 Broadway Cast)**
AEICD 040 / May '98 / AEI

☐ **MASK OF ZORRO (Horner, James)**
Horner, James *c*
Horner, James *con*
Plaza of execution: / Elena and Esperanza / Ride / Elena's truth / Fencing lesson / Tornado in the barracks / Confession / Zorro's theme / Mine / Stealing the map / Leave no witnesses / Diego's goodbye / I want to spend my lifetime loving you
SK 60627 / 13 Jul '98 / Sony Classical

☐ **MATCH GIRLS, THE (1966 London Cast)**
Russell, Tony *c*
Owen, Bill *l*
AEICD 019 / May '98 / AEI

☐ **MATEWAN**
DARING 1011CD / Feb '95 / Daring

☐ **MAVERICK**
Newman, Randy *c*
Renegades rebels and rogues / Good run of bad luck / Maverick / Ophelia / Something already gone / Dream on Texas ladies / Ladies love outlaws / Solitary travelers / Rainbow down the road / You don't mess around with me / Ride gambler ride / Amazing grace
7567825952 / Jul '94 / Warner Bros.

☐ **MAXIMUM OVERDRIVE (Who Made Who) (AC/DC)**
Who made who / You shook me all night long / DT / Sink the pink / Ride on / Hell's bells / Shake your foundations / Chase the ace / For those about to rock (we salute you)
7816502 / May '86 / Atlantic

☐ **MAXIMUM RISK**
Folk, Robert *c*
VSD 5756 / Oct '96 / Varese Sarabande

☐ **MAXIMUM SPEED**
VTDCD 173 / 1 Dec '97 / Virgin

☐ **ME AND MY GIRL (1985 London Cast)**
Gay, Noel *c*
Furber, Douglas & L. Arthur Rose *l*
Overture / Weekend at Hareford / Thinking of no one but me / Family solicitor / Me and my girl / English gentleman / You would if you could / Lambeth walk / Sun has got his hat on / Once you lose your heart / Take it on the chin / Song of Hareford / Love makes the world go round / Leaning on a lamp-post / If only you cared for me / Finale
CDP 7463932 / Jun '92 / EMI

☐ **ME AND MY GIRL (Highlights - The Shows Collection) (Cast Recording)**
Gay, Noel *c*
Furber, Douglas & L. Arthur Rose *l*
PWKS 4143 / Jan '95 / Carlton

☐ **ME AND MY GIRL (1987 Broadway Cast)**
Gay, Noel *c*
Furber, Douglas & L. Arthur Rose *l*
CDTER 1145 / Nov '97 / TER

☐ MEDAL OF HONOUR
Stone, Richard *c*
PCD 106 / Jul '94 / Prometheus

☐ MEDICINE MAN
Goldsmith, Jerry *c*
Goldsmith, Jerry *con*
Rae's arrival / First morning / Campbell and the children / Trees / Harvest / Mocara / Mountain high / Without a net / Finger painting / What's wrong / Injection / Sugar / Fire / Meal and a bath
VSD 5350 / Mar '92 / Varese Sarabande

☐ MEET ME IN ST. LOUIS (1989 Broadway Cast)
Martin, Hugh & Ralph Blane *c*
DRGCD 19002 / Jan '95 / DRG

☐ MEET ME IN ST. LOUIS (1944 Film Cast)
Main title / Meet me in St. Louis Louis / Boy next door / Meet me in St. Louis Louis / Getting ready for the party / Skip to my Lou / Under the bamboo tree / Saying goodnight / Over the bannister / Trolley song / Boys and girls like you and me / All Hallow's Eve / Most horrible one / You and I / Winter in St. Louis / I hate basketball / Under the Anheuser Bush / Esther accepts / Tootie's music box / Have yourself a merry little Christmas / Toutie's grief / Finale
CDODEON 2 / Feb '96 / Premier/EMI

☐ MEET THE FEEBLES
QDKCD 003 / Sep '94 / QDK Media

☐ MEGAZONE 23
Eden the last city / Sleepless beauty in the woods / Eiji / Netjacker / Ryo / G form / Artifact / Wall of Eden / Another story of megazone / Tragedy of an idol / Wang dai / Netpolice / Bahamoud / Cyberspace force / Project heaven / Pandora's boat / Mother Earth
DSCD 9 / May '95 / Demon

☐ MELROSE PLACE
That's just what you are: Mann, Aimee / Back on me: *Urge Overkill* / Baby I can't please you: *Phillips, Sam* / Blah: *Dinosaur Jnr* / Ordinary angels: *Frente* / Precious: *Lennox, Annie* / I'm jealous: *Divinyls* / Kids this is fabulous: *Seed* / Here and now: *Letters To Cleo* / How was it for you: *James* / Star is bored: *Westerberg, Paul*
74321226082 / Nov '94 / Giant

☐ MEMORIES
Kanno, Yoko & Jun Miyake/Hiroyuki Nagashika/Takkyu Ishino *c*
AM 7 / Nov '96 / Animanga

☐ MEMPHIS BELLE
Fenton, George *c*
Fenton, George *con*
Londonderry air/Front titles / Green eyes / Flying home / Steel lady / Prepare for take-off / Final mission / With deep regret... / I know why and so do you / Bomb run / Limping home / Crippled Belle: The landing / Resolution / End title suite / Danny Boy
VSD 5293 / Nov '90 / Varese Sarabande

☐ MEN IN BLACK
Men in black: *Smith, Will* / We just wanna party with you: *Snoop Doggy Dogg* / I'm feeling for you: *Ginuwine* / Dah dee dah: *Keys, Alicia* / Notic: *D'Angelo & The Roots* / Make you happy: *Lorenz, Trey* / Escobar: *Nas* / Erotic City: *Emoja* / Same ol' thang: *Tribe Called Quest* / Killing time: *Destiny's Child* / Waiting for love: *3T* / Channel no. fever: *De la soul* / Cowfonge: *Buck Shot* / Score
4881222 / Jun '97 / Columbia

☐ MENACE 2 SOCIETY
CHIP 137 / Jun '93 / Jive

☐ MEPHISTO WALTZ
Goldsmith, Jerry *c*
VSD 5851 / 20 Oct '97 / Varese Sarabande

☐ MER DE CHINE (Coe, Tony)
Coe, Tony *c*
Binh a la sortie de l'ecole / Le secretaire / Conversation sous la pluie / Troop long temps / La famille de binh / Sans cesse / La criee / Le departe de la famille / Le bus / L'arrestation de l'oncle / La mission / Vers le refuge / La fuite / La mort de la mere / Le delta / Boat people / La rencontre des boats / Pirates / Mer a boire / Enfin / Les eaux internationales / Marine de la nuit / I never held one before / Marine de jour / Nuit de boat / Les visages / Le bateau de binh / Sur le point / La seperation / L'arrivee / Binh et joy / La bicyclette / Mer de chine
626506 / Aug '91 / Nato

☐ MERCURY RISING
Barry, John *c*
VSD 5925 / 5 May '98 / Varese Sarabande

☐ MERLIN
Jones, Trevor *c*
VSD 5929 / 24 Aug '98 / Varese Sarabande

☐ MERRILY WE ROLL ALONG (1994 Cast)
Sondheim, Stephen *c*
VSD 5548 / Jan '95 / Varese Sarabande

☐ MERRILY WE ROLL ALONG (1993 Leicester Haymarket Theatre Cast)
Sondheim, Stephen *c*
Kelly, Julian *con*
Overture / Merrily we roll along / That frank / Transition / Old friends / Franklin Shepard inc. / Transition / Old friends / Growing up / Transition / Not a day goes by / Now you know / Entr'acte / Act 2 opening / It's a hit / Transition / Blob / Growing up / Good thing going / Blob / Transition / Bobbie and Jackie and Jack / Not a day goes by / Transition / Opening doors / Our time
CDTER 1225 / 15 Jun '98 / TER

☐ MERRILY WE ROLL ALONG (Cast Recording)
Sondheim, Stephen *c*
CDTEM 21203 / Jan '93 / TER

☐ MERRY WIDOW, THE (1986 London Cast/New Sadler's Wells Opera Choir/ Orchestra)
Lehar, Franz *c*
Wordsworth, Barry *con*
Opening act 1 / ALone at last / Well my gallant friends / Hanna's entrance / O fatherland I must protest / Off to old Maxim's / Finale act / Opening act 2 / Dance vilja / Maiden look a soldier boy / Oh the women / Just as the sun awakens / Finale act 2 / Cake walk / Grisette's song / Words forbidden / Finale act 3
CDTER 1111 / Nov '97 / TER

☐ MERRY WIDOW, THE (Highlights) (1986 London Cast/New Sadler's Wells Opera Choir/Orchestra)
Lehar, Franz *c*
Wordsworth, Barry *con*
CDTEO 1003 / Sep '86 / TER

☐ MERRY WIDOW, THE (Studer, Cheryl & Monteverdi Choir/Wiener Philharmoniker)
Lehar, Franz *c*
Gardiner, John Eliot *con*
4399112 / Jan '95 / Deutsche Grammophon

☐ MERRY WIDOW, THE (Harwood, Elizabeth & Teresa Stratas/Berliner Philharmoniker)
Lehar, Franz *c*
Von Karajan, Herbert *con*
4357122 / Jan '95 / Deutsche Grammophon

☐ MERRY WIDOW, THE (New Sadler's Wells Opera)
Lehar, Franz *c*
Opening act one / Alone at last / Well my gallant friends/Hanna's entrance / O Fatherland I must protest/Off to old Maxim's / Finale act one / Vilja / Maiden look a soldier boy / Oh the women / Just as the sun awakens / Grisette's song / Words forbidden / Finale act three
SHOWCD 037 / Oct '96 / Showtime

☐ MESSAGE, THE/LION OF THE DESERT (The Epic Film Music Of Maurice Jarre) (Royal Philharmonic Orchestra/ London Symphony Orchestra)
Jarre, Maurice *c*
Jarre, Maurice *con*
Message: *Royal Philharmonic Orchestra* / Lion of the desert: *London Symphony Orchestra*
FILMCD 060 / Feb '90 / Silva Screen

☐ METROLAND
Metroland: *Knopfler, Mark* / Annick: *Knopfler, Mark* / Tous les garcons et les filles: *Hardy, Francoise* / Brats: *Knopfler, Mark* / Blues chair: *Reinhardt, Django* / Down day: *Knopfler, Mark* / Walk in Paris: *Knopfler, Mark* / She's gone: *Knopfler, Mark* / Minor swing: *Reinhardt, Django* / Peaches: *Stranglers* / Sultans of swing: *Dire Straits* / So you win again: *Hot Chocolate* / Alison: *Costello, Elvis*
5369122 / 11 May '98 / Mercury

☐ METROPOLIS (1988 London Cast)
Brooks, Joe *c*
Brooks, Joe & Dusty Hughes *l*
Marman, Mark *con*
Opening/101.11/Look the sun Maria / Hold back the night / Machines are beautiful / He's distant from me now / Elitist dance / Oh my what a beautiful city / This is the vision we're forbidden / Children of Metropolis / 50,000 pounds of power / One more morning / It's only love / Bring on the night / Pressure chant / Day after day / When Maria comes / You are the light / Girl is a witch / It's only love / Sun / Almost done / I don't need help from you / There's a girl down below / Futura/End of act 1 / I've seen a nightmare / This is life / Look at this girl who stands before you / Futura's dance / Where do you think she's gone your precious Maria / If that was love / Listen to me / Learning song / Old friends / When Maria wakes / Futura's promise / Maria's insane / Perfect face / Haven't you finished with me / Let's watch the world go to the devil / One of those nights / Requiem / Metropolis / Finale / Nothing really matters / It's only love / Bring on the night / One of those nights
CDTER2 1168 / 15 Jun '98 / TER

☐ METTI UNA SERA CENA (Morricone, Ennio)
Morricone, Ennio *c*
CDMDF 309 / 8 Dec '97 / Cinevox

☐ MIAMI VICE (Hammer, Jan)
Hammer, Jan *c*
Miami Vice / Smuggler's blues: *Frey, Glenn* / Own the night: *Khan, Chaka* / You belong to the city: *Frey, Glenn* / In the air tonight: *Collins, Phil* / Vice / Better be good to me: *Turner, Tina* / Flashback / Chase / Evan
MCLD 19024 / Apr '92 / MCA

☐ MICHAEL
Through your hands: *Henley, Don* / I don't care if you love me anymore: *Mavericks* / Chain of fools: *Franklin, Aretha* / Bright side of the road: *Morrison, Van* / Heaven is my home: *Newman, Randy & Valerie Carter* / Spider and the fly: *Shepherd, Kenny Wayne & James Cotton* / Feels like home: *Raitt, Bonnie / Willie Nelson*: *Nelson, Willie* / Love God (and everyone else): *Green, Al* / Sittin' by the side of the road: *MacDowell, Andie* / Spirit in the sky: *Greenbaum, Norman*
74321418802 / Feb '97 / Revolution

☐ MICHAEL COLLINS
Fire and arms / Football match / Defiance and arrest / Boland returns / Boland's death / His majesty's finest / Macushla / Funeral coda / She moved through the fair / Anthem deferred / Collins' proposal / Civil war / Home to cork / Train to granard / On cats feet / Elegy for a sunday / Easter rebellion / Winter raid / Train station farewell
7567829602 / Jan '97 / Atlantic

☐ MICHAEL FLATELY'S LORD OF THE DANCE
Hardiman, Ronan *c*
Cry of the Celts / Suil a ruin / Celtic dream / Warriors / Gypsy / Breakout / Lord of the dance / Cry of the Celts / Spirit of the new world / Firey nights / Lament / Siamsa / Our wedding day / Stolen kiss / Nightmare / Victory / Lord of the dance
5337572 / Oct '96 / PolyGram TV

☐ MICHEL STROGOFF
Cosma, Vladimir *c*
950272 / Nov '97 / Pomme

☐ MICROCOSMOS (Coulais, Bruno)
Coulais, Bruno *c*
K 1028 / Jan '97 / Travelling

☐ MIDNIGHT COWBOY
Barry, John *c*
Everybody's talkin' / Joe Buck rides again / Famous myth / Fun City / He quit me man / Jungle gym at the zoo / Midnight cowboy / Old man Willow / Florida fantasy / Tears and joys / Science fiction
PRMCD 6 / Jun '96 / Soundtracks

☐ MIDNIGHT EXPRESS
Moroder, Giorgio *c*
Chase / Love's theme / Midnight express / Istanbul blues / Wheel / Istanbul opening / Cacaphoney / Billy's theme
8242062 / Apr '85 / Phonogram

☐ MIDNIGHT IN THE GARDEN OF GOOD AND EVIL
Skylark: *Lang, k.d.* / Too marvelous for words: *Williams, Joe* / Autumn leaves: *Cole, Paula* / Fools rush in: *Clooney, Rosemary* / Dream: *Mehldau, Brad* / Days of wine and roses: *Wilson, Cassandra* / That old black magic: *Spacey, Kevin* / Come rain or come shine: *Eastwood, Clint* / This time the dream's on me: *Krauss, Alison* / Laura: *Mahogany, Kevin* / Midnight sun: *Krall, Diana* / I'm old cowhand: *Redman, Joshua* / I wanna be around: *Bennett, Tony*
9362468292 / 9 Mar '98 / Malpaso/ Warner

☐ MIDNIGHT STING (Diggstown)
Howard, James Newton *c*
VSD 5379 / Sep '92 / Varese Sarabande

☐ MIDSOMER MURDERS (Parker, Jim)
Parker, Jim *c*
OCD 013 / 13 Apr '98 / Ocean Deep

☐ MIGHTY APHRODITE
Neo minore / Horos tou sakena / I've found a new baby / Whispering / Manhattan / When your lover is gone / Li'l darlin' / Take five / Penthouse serenade (When we're alone) / I hadn't anyone till you / In crowd / You do something to me / When you're smiling (the whole world smiles with you)
SK 62253 / Apr '96 / Sony Classical

☐ MIGHTY MORPHIN' POWER RANGERS (Score)
Revell, Graeme *c*
VSD 5672 / Nov '95 / Varese Sarabande

☐ MIKADO, THE (Highlights) (English National Opera)
Sullivan, Sir Arthur *c*
Gilbert, W.S. *l*
If you want to know who we are / Wandering minstrel I / Our great Mikado / Young man/Despair / Behold the Lord/High executioner / I've got a little list / Three little maids / Braid with raven hair / Sun whose rays / Flowers that bloom in the spring / On a tree by a river (tit' willow) / There is a beauty in the bellow of the blast
SHOWCD 005 / Feb '95 / Showtime

☐ MIKADO, THE (Brannigan, Owen & Richard Lewis/Glyndebourne Festival Choir/Pro Arte Orchestra)
Sullivan, Sir Arthur *c*
Gilbert, W.S. *l*
Sargent, Sir Malcolm *con*
CMS 7644032 / Apr '94 / EMI Classics

☐ MIKADO, THE (D'Oyly Carte Opera Chorus/Royal Philharmonic Orchestra)
Sullivan, Sir Arthur *c*
Gilbert, W.S. *l*
Nash, R. *con*
4251902 / Jan '90 / London

☐ MIKADO, THE (D'Oyly Carte Opera Chorus/Orchestra)
Sullivan, Sir Arthur *c*
Gilbert, W.S. *l*
Pryce Jones, J. *con*
CDTER2 1178 / Nov '97 / TER

☐ MIKADO, THE (Welsh National Opera Choir/Orchestra)
Sullivan, Sir Arthur *c*
Gilbert, W.S. *l*
Mackerras, Sir Charles *con*
CD 80284 / May '92 / Telarc

☐ MIKADO, THE (Sadler's Wells Opera Chorus/Orchestra)
Sullivan, Sir Arthur *c*
Gilbert, W.S. *l*
Faris, Alexander *con*
CDCFPD 4730 / Apr '94 / Classics For Pleasure

☐ MIKADO, THE (Highlights) (English National Opera)
Sullivan, Sir Arthur *c*
Gilbert, W.S. *l*
If you want to know who we are / Wandering minstrel I / Our great Mikado / Young man despair / Behold the Lord high executioner / I've got a little list / Comes a train of little ladies / Three little maids / So please you sir / Were you not to KO-ko plighted / Finale act 1 / Braid the raven hair / Sun whosr rays here's a how de do / More humane Mikado / Flowers that nloom in the spring / Alone and yet alive / On a tree by a river it willow / There is a beauty in a bellow of a blast
CDTER 1121 / Nov '97 / TER

☐ MILLENIUM (Tribal Wisdom & The Modern World) (Mancina, Mark)
Zimmer, Hans *c*
Shaman's song / Stories for a thousand years / Journey begins / Stone drag / Courting song/Love in the Himalayas / Inventing reality / Fiddlers/ Pilgrimage to Wirikuta / Shock of the other / Race of the initiates / Art of living / Geerewol celebrations / Song for the dead / Pilgrims' chant/In the land of the ancestors / Ecology of mind / Well song/A desert home / Initiation chant/Rites of passage / Journey continues / Millenium theme
CD 6001 / May '92 / Narada

☐ MILLION TO JUAN
RMD 813052 / 12 May '98 / RMM

☐ MIMIC (Dixon, Dillon)
Beltrami, Marco *c*
Main title / Race to the subway / Time to seperate / Chuy steps out / Manny searches for his son / Slow tango / Chased by a bug / Susan meets Chuy / Faulty scaffolding / Manny's tango / Evil among us / Confronting terror / Lucistic's alive / Reunited / End credits / La cucaracha
VSD 5863 / 15 Jun '98 / Varese Sarabande

☐ MIRACLE MILE (Tangerine Dream)
Tangerine Dream *c*
Teetering scales / One for the book / After the call / On the spur of the moment / All of a dither / Final statement
260016 / Feb '96 / Private Music

☐ MIRACLE ON 34TH STREET
Jingle bells: *Cole, Natalie* / It's beginning to look like Christmas: *Warwick, Dionne* / Have yourself a merry little Christmas: *Kenny G.* / Santa Claus is coming to town: *Charles, Ray* / Joy to the world: *Franklin, Aretha* / Santa Claus is back in town: *Presley, Elvis* / Singing: *McLachlan, Sarah* / Bellevue carol: *McLachlan, Sarah* / Song for a winter's night: *McLachlan, Sarah*
07822110222 / Nov '94 / Arista

☐ MIRROR HAS TWO FACES, THE
Main title/Inquesta reggia / Got any Scotch / Ad / In a sentimental mood / Rose sees Greg / Dating montage / My intentions / You picked me / Funny kind of proposal / Picnic in the park / Greg falls for Rose / Try a little tenderness: *Sanborn, David* / Mirror / Going back to Mom / Rocking in the chair / Power inside me: *Marx, Richard* / Rose leaves Greg / Ruby / Rose dumps Alex / Apology/Nessun dorma: *Pavarotti, Luciano* / I finally found someone: *Streisand, Barbra & Bryan Adams* / All of my life: *Streisand, Barbra*
4853952 / Dec '96 / Columbia

☐ MISFITS, THE
North, Alex *c*
TCI 0609 / May '95 / Tsunami

☐ MISHIMA
Glass, Philip *c*
Opening / Morning 1934 / Grandmother and Kimitake / Temple of the golden pavillion / Osamu's theme / Kyoko's house / 1937 / St. Sebastian / November 25th / Ichigaya / 1957 / Award montage / Runaway horses / 1962 / Bodybuilding / Last day / F 104 / Epilogue from sun and steel / Closing
7559791132 / Nov '85 / Nonesuch

☐ MISS LIBERTY (1949 Broadway Cast)
Berlin, Irving *c*
Blackton, Jay *con*
Overture / What do I have to do to get my picture took / Most expensive statue in the world / Little fish in a big pond / Let's take an old fashioned walk / Homework / Paris wakes and smiles / Only for Americans / Just one way to say I love you / You can have him / Policemen's ball / Falling out of love can be fun / Give me your tired your poor
SK 48015 / Dec '91 / Sony Broadway

☐ MISS SAIGON (Highlights) (1989 London Cast)
Schonberg, Claude-Michel *c*
Maltby, Richard Jnr. & Alain Boublil *l*
CASTCD 38 / Oct '93 / First Night

☐ MISS SAIGON (Music From The Show) (Criswell & Wayne)
Schonberg, Claude-Michel *c*
PWKS 4229 / Nov '94 / Carlton

☐ MISS SAIGON (Complete Symphonic Suite) (1989 London Cast)
Schonberg, Claude-Michel *c*
KIMCD 1 / Jul '95 / First Night

☐ **MISS SAIGON (Highlights From The Complete Recording)**
Schonberg, Claude-Michel c
Overture/Backstage dreamland / Heat is on in Saigon / Movie in my mind / Why God why / Sun and moon / Last night of the world / I still believe / Thuy's death/You will not touch him / I'd give my life for you / Bui doi / Kim's nightmare / Now that I've seen her / American dream / Finale
CASTCD 60 / Jun '97 / First Night

☐ **MISS SAIGON/LES MISERABLES (Symphonic Suites) (Bournemouth Symphony Orchestra)**
Schonberg, Claude-Michel c
Overture / Heat is on is Saigon / Sun and moon / Why God why / Morning of the dragon / Last night of the world / If you want to die in bed / I'd give my life for you / Bio doi / Fall of Saigon / American dream / This is the hour / Prologue (Look down) / At the end of the day / I dreamed a dream / Lovely ladies / Who am I / Master of the house / Stars / Red and black / Heartful of love / Waltz of treachery / Do you hear the people sing / Bring him home / Red and black (reprise) / Attack / Drink with me / On my own / Heart full of love
OCRCD 6049 / Apr '97 / First Night

☐ **MISSION IMPOSSIBLE**
Schifrin, Lalo c
GNPD 8029 / Nov '92 / GNP Crescendo

☐ **MISSION IMPOSSIBLE (Music From & Inspired By Mission Impossible)**
MUMCD 9603 / Jun '96 / Mother

☐ **MISSION IMPOSSIBLE**
Elfman, Danny c
Kane, A. con
4545252 / Jul '96 / Point Music

☐ **MISSION IMPOSSIBLE**
MCLD 19320 / Aug '96 / MCA

☐ **MISSION, THE (London Philharmonic Orchestra)**
Morricone, Ennio c
On earth as it is in Heaven / Mission / Falls / River / Gabriel's oboe / Ave Maria Guarani / Te Deum Guarani / Brothers / Refusal / Carlotta / Asuncion / Vita nostra / Alone / Climb / Guarani / Remorse / Sword / Penance / Miserere
CDV 2402 / Oct '86 / Virgin

☐ **MISSISSIPPI BURNING**
Jones, Trevor c
Take my hand precious Lord: *Jackson, Mahalia* / Murder in Mississippi (Part 1) / Some things are worth dying for / Murder in Mississippi (Part 2) / Anderson and Mrs Pell / When we all get to Heaven: *Choral* / Try Jesus: *Williams, Vesta* / Abduction / You live it you breathe it you marry it / Murder in Mississippi (Part 3) / Requiem for three young men / Burning cross / Justice in Mississippi / Walk by faith: *McBride, Lannie* / Walk on by faith: *McBride, Lannie*
5511002 / Sep '95 / Spectrum

☐ **MO' MONEY**
Mo' money groove: *Mo' Money Allstars* / Best things in life are free: *Vandross, Luther & Janet Jackson* / Ice cream dream: *M.C. Lyte* / Let's just run away: *M.C. Lyte* / I adore you: *Wheeler, Caron* / Get off my back: *Public Enemy & Flavor Flav* / Forever love: *Color Me Badd* / Money can't buy you love: *Tresvant, Ralph* / Let's get together (so groovy now): *Krush* / Joy: *Sounds Of Blackness* / New style: *Jam & Lewis* / Job ain't nuthin' but work: *Big Daddy Kane & Lo-Key* / My dear: *Mint Condition* / Brother Will: *Harlem Yacht Club*
3610042 / Apr '95 / A&M

☐ **MOBY DICK (1992 London Cast)**
Kaye, Hereward c
Longden, Robert l
DICKCD 1 / Nov '92 / First Night

☐ **MOBY DICK (Highlights) (1992 London Cast)**
Kaye, Hereward c
Longden, Robert l
SCORECD 35 / '92 / First Night

☐ **MOBY DICK**
Gordon, Christopher c
Call me Ishmael / Queequeg / Silhouettes / Nantucket docks / Pequod / Harpooner / Jonah and the whale / Farewell / Voyage begins / Devoured it was / Crow's nest / Ahab / This gold ounce / Indissoluble league / God fugitive / I am the prophet / Beware the blasphemer's end / There she blows / Devil himself / Midnight sea / Man overboard / Ye hairy hearted ghouls / Bad magic / Onward to nowhere / Ice / Ye shall will it / Queequeg's prophecy / Captain Pip / Shadow of a knife / Apparition / At the helm / St. Elmo's fire / Forty years / Lower the boats / Pilot / Fate's lieutenant / Eternal rest / Queequeg's death / Pequod burns / Orphan of the sea / Moby Dick theme
VSD 5921 / 26 May '98 / Varese Sarabande

☐ **MODERNS, THE (Isham, Mark)**
Isham, Mark c
Les modernes / Cafe Selavy / Paris la nuit / Really the blues / Madame Valentin / Dada je suis / Parlez-moi d'amour / La valse moderne / Les peintres / Death of Irving Fagelman / Je ne veux pas de tes chocolats / Selavy
CDV 2530 / May '88 / Virgin

☐ **MOJO**
Christo redentor: *Byrd, Donald* / Crazy crazy Momma: *Lewis, Little* / Ooh ma liddi: *Jackson, JJ & The Jackaels* / Please: *St. Etienne* / Big hurt: *Cave, Nick & Gallon Drunk* / Stone cold stroll: *Stone Cold Strollers* / Listen to loving you: *Matheson, Hans* / Sequins and stars: *Almond, Marc* / Write my name: *Warm Jets* / Constantly: *St. Etienne* / Ooh my soul: *Stone Cold Strollers* / Since I don't have you: *Skyliners* / I put a spell on you: *McAlmont, David* / Don't make me wait: *Lewis, Little* / I love how you love me: *Orton, Beth* / One night of sin: *Almond, Marc* / Mojo: *Cave, Nick*
8217182 / 6 Jul '98 / Premier/EMI

☐ **MOLL FLANDERS (1993 London Cast)**
Stiles, George & Paul Leigh c
Let us tell a tale / Lullaby / Baby / Moll's prayer / Portrait song / Seduction / Her love made her rich / Masque / Mint / Life of a sailor / Lapdogs / Sailing to Virginia / Never look back / Bath promenade / Frail man beware / Frail man rejoice / Mr. Honest / Fits and starts / Ride / Hour is late / Mr. Honest / Honest's death / Damn damn damn / Stolen / I shall work alone / Hang hang hang / Child of Newgate / Hour was late
OCRCD 6036 / Dec '95 / First Night

☐ **MOLL FLANDERS**
Mancina, Mark c
4524852 / May '97 / Decca

☐ **MONEY TALKS**
Avenues: *Refugee Camp All-Stars & Lauryn Hill* / My everything: *White, Barry & Faith Evans* / No way out: *Puff Daddy* / Dream: *Blige, Mary J.* / Money talks: *Lil' Kim* / Penetration: *Naughty By Nature* / Tell me how you want it: *SWV* / Every day: *Stone, Angie & Devox* / Keep it bubblin': *Brand Nubian* / Teaching: *Ndegeocello, Me'shell* / Back in you again: *James, Rick* / Real thing: *Stansfield, Lisa* / Feel so good: *Mase* / You're the first the last my everything: *White, Barry*
7822189752 / 1 Sep '97 / RCA

☐ **MONEY TRAIN**
Train is coming: *Shaggy & Ken Boothe* / Top of the stairs: *Skee Lo* / Do you know: *Total* / Show you the way to go: *Men Of Vision* / Hiding place: *Assorted Phlavors & Patra* / Making love: *112* / Thrill I'm in: *Vandross, Luther* / Still not over you: *Lorenz, Trey* / It's alright: *Terri & Monica* / Oh baby: *4.0* / Merry go round: *UBU* / Hold on I'm coming: *Neville Brothers* / Money train suite: *Mancina, Mark*
4815622 / Jan '96 / Epic

☐ **MONK DAWSON**
Jensen, Mark c
Jensen, Mark con
DWPCD 01 / 1 Sep '98 / Silva Productions

☐ **MOONRAKER**
Barry, John c
Main title / Space laser battle / Miss Goodhead meets Bond / Cable car and snake fight / Bond lured to pyramid / Flight into space / Bond arrives in Rio / Boat chase / Centrifuge and Corrine put down / Bond smells a rat / End title
CZ 551 / Dec '95 / Premier/EMI

☐ **MORITURI - THE SABOTEUR (& Music From In Harm's Way)**
Goldsmith, Jerry c
TCI 0604 / Jan '95 / Tsunami

☐ **MORTAL KOMBAT**
Taste of things to come: *Clinton, George* / Goodbye: *Gravity Kills* / Juke joint Jezebel: *KMFDM* / Unlearn: *Psykosonik* / Control: *Lords, Traci* / Halcyon + on + on: *Orbital* / Utah Saints take on the theme from Mortal Kombat: *Utah Saints* / Invisible: *G/Z/R* / Zero signal: *Fear Factory* / Burn: *Sister Machine Gun* / Blood and fire: *Type O Negative* / I reject: *Bile* / Twist the knife (slowly): *Napalm Death* / What u see/We all bleed red: *Mutha's Day Out* / Techno syndrome: *Immortals* / Goro Vs. art: *Clinton, George*
8288972 / Oct '95 / London

☐ **MORTAL KOMBAT (Score)**
Clinton, George c
Taste of things to come / Liu vs. Sub-Zero / It has begun / Garden / Goro vs. Art / Banquet / Liu vs. Katana / Liu's dream / Liu vs. Reptile / Stairway / Goro Goro / Kidnapped / Zooom / Johnny vs. Scorpion / Hand and shadow / Scorpion and Sub-Zero / Soul snatchin' / On the beach / Johnny Cage / Goro chase / Evening bells / Monks / Friends / Flawless victory / Farewell / Kids
8287152 / Jan '96 / London

☐ **MORTAL KOMBAT - ANNIHILATION**
8289992 / 9 Feb '98 / London

☐ **MORTAL KOMBAT - MORE MORTAL KOMBAT**
TVT 80302 / Nov '96 / TVT
0022672CIN / Feb '97 / Edel

☐ **MOSES THE LAWGIVER**
Morricone, Ennio c
OST 113 / Jan '93 / Milano Dischi

☐ **MOSQUITO COAST, THE**
Jarre, Maurice c
Jarre, Maurice con
Mosquito Coast / Goodbye America / Gimme soca: *Lee, Byron & The Dragonaires* / Up the river / Geronimo / Fat boy / Destruction / Storm / Allie's theme
FCD 210052 / Jan '89 / Fantasy

☐ **MOST HAPPY FELLA, THE (1956 Broadway Cast)**
Loesser, Frank c
Greene, Herbert con
SK 48010 / Dec '91 / Sony Broadway

☐ **MOST WANTED**
74321563352 / 5 May '98 / Milan

☐ **MOTHER NIGHT**
Convertino, Michael c
VSD 5780 / Dec '96 / Varese Sarabande

☐ **MOUSE HUNT**
Silvestri, Alan c
Main title / Funeral prologue / Chez Ernie / Dying wish / Charles Lyle Larue / What are you doing / Nail gun / Hot toboggan / Cherry catapault / Ernie finds the contract / Silent movie / Caesar's big drag / Shotgun chase / Insufficient postage / Flaming doo / String cheese / End credits
VSD 5892 / 30 Mar '98 / Varese Sarabande

☐ **MOUTARDE ME MONTE AU NEZ**
Cosma, Vladimir c
951322 / Nov '97 / Pomme

☐ **MOUVEMENTS DU DESIR**
Preisner, Zbigniew c
SMC 35715 / Jun '97 / Sergent M

☐ **MR. AND MRS. BRIDGE**
Robbins, Richard c
Opening title / Boogie woogie: *Dorsey, Tommy Orchestra* / Painting class / String of pearls: *Miller, Glenn Orchestra* / Little brown jug: *Miller, Glenn Orchestra* / Rhumba jumps: *Miller, Glenn Orchestra* / Ruth's journey / Jeepers creepers: *Waters, Ethel & Edward Mallory* / Blues in the night: *Shore, Dinah* / Stormy weather: *Horne, Lena, Lou Bring & His Orchestra* / She was my best friend / Take me I'm yours / Choo choo conga / Down on the farm / Locking up / Closing credits
PD 83100 / Mar '91 / Novus

☐ **MR. CINDERS (1983 London Cast)**
Ellis, Vivian & Richard Myers c
Grey, Clifford & Greatrex Newman l
Reed, Michael con
Tennis / Blue blood / True to two / I want the world to know / One man girl / On with the dance / At the ball / Spread a little happiness / Entr'acte / Eighteenth century dance / She's my lovely / Please Mr. Cinders / On the Amazon / Every little moment / I've got you you've got me / Honeymoon for four / Finale
CDTER 1069 / Aug '98 / TER

☐ **MR. DESTINY (Newman, David)**
Newman, David c
VSD 5299 / '90 / Varese Sarabande

☐ **MR. HOLLAND'S OPUS**
5295082 / Mar '96 / PolyGram

☐ **MR. HOLLAND'S OPUS (Score) (Seattle Symphony Orchestra/London Metropolitan Orchestra)**
Kamen, Michael c
Kamen, Michael con
4520652 / May '96 / Decca

☐ **MR. PRESIDENT (1962 Broadway Cast)**
Berlin, Irving c
Blackton, Jay con
SK 48212 / Nov '92 / Sony Broadway

☐ **MR. RELIABLE**
Flightless bird: *Judd, Philip* / Summer in the city: *Lovin' Spoonful* / Strange brew: *Cream* / Gimme some lovin': *Davis, Spencer Group* / Summer of '68: *Judd, Philip* / Something in the air: *Thunderclap Newman* / Nature: *Muttonbirds* / Summertime blues: *Who* / I'm a fan: *Judd, Philip* / Loved ones: *INXS* / Itchycoo park: *Small Faces* / I close my eyes and count to ten: *Springfield, Dusty* / Bloody circus: *Judd, Philip* / Only one woman: *Marbles* / For what it's worth: *Clouds* / Mongrels: *Judd, Philip* / Eloise: *Ryan, Barry* / With a little help from my friends: *Cocker, Joe* / To love somebody: *Bee Gees* / Bronto V: *Judd, Philip*
5168202 / Nov '96 / Polydor

☐ **MR. SATURDAY NIGHT**
Shaiman, Marc c
124682 / Feb '94 / Milan

☐ **MRS. BROWN**
Warbeck, Stephen c
74321510722 / 1 Sep '97 / Milan

☐ **MRS. DALLOWAY**
74321572312 / 6 Apr '98 / Milan

☐ **MRS. DOUBTFIRE**
Horner, James c
Mrs. Doubtfire / Divorce / My name is Elsa Immelman / Meeting Mrs. Doubtfire / Tea time with Mrs Sellner / Dinner is served / Daniel and the kids / Cable cars / Bridges restaurant / Show's over / Kids need you / Figaro/Papa's got a brand new bag
07822110152 / Jan '94 / Arista

☐ **MRS. PARKER AND THE VICIOUS CIRCLE**
Isham, Mark c
Into love / Algonquin bounce / Vanity blues / Observation / Smart set stomp / If you and I were one / Daydreams / Park bench / Two volume novel / Into love and out again / Benchley's blues / Ballad of Dorothy Parker / Lady's reward / Vicious blues / Well worn story / He didn't love back / Two wives' blues / Algonquin smart set / ...And out again
VSD 5471 / Jan '95 / Varese Sarabande

☐ **MRS. WINTERBOURNE (Doyle, Patrick)**
Doyle, Patrick c
Walters, M. con
VSD 5720 / Jul '96 / Varese Sarabande

☐ **MUCH ADO ABOUT NOTHING**
Doyle, Patrick c
Snell, David con
Picnic / Overture / Sweetest lady / Conspirators / Masked ball / Prince woos hero / Star danced / Rich she shall be / Sigh no more ladies / Gulling of Benedick / It must be required / Gulling of Beatrice / Contempt farewell / Lady is disloyal / Hero's wedding / Take her back again / Die to live / You have killed a sweet lady / Choose your revenge / Pardon Goddess of the night / Did I not tell you / Hero revealed / Benedick the married man / Strike up pipers
MOODCD 30 / Sep '93 / Epic

☐ **MUDHONEY (& Motor Psycho/Finders Keepers)**
QDKCD 011 / Sep '97 / QDK Media

☐ **MUHAMMAD ALI - THE GREATEST**
Masser, Michael c
Masser, Michael l
RE 2139 / 29 Jun '98 / Razor & Tie

☐ **MULHOLLAND FALLS**
0022592CIN / Jul '96 / Edel

☐ **MUPPET CHRISTMAS CAROL, THE (Muppets)**
Overture / Scrooge / Room in your heart / Good king Wenceslas / One more sleep till Christmas / Marley and Marley / Christmas past / Chairman of the board / Fozziwigs party / When love is gone / It feels like Christmas / Christmas scat / Bless us all / Christmas future / Christmas morning / Thankful heart / Finale
7432112194-2 / Nov '93 / Arista

☐ **MUPPET MOVIE, THE (Muppets)**
Rainbow connection / Movin' right along / Never before never again / I hope that something better comes along / Can you picture that / I'm going to go back there someday / God bless America / Come back animal / Magic stone
74321182472 / Jan '94 / BMG Kidz

☐ **MUPPET TREASURE ISLAND (Muppets)**
Treasure Island / Shiver my timbers / Something better / Sailing for adventure / Cabin fever / Professional pirate / Boom shakalaka / Love led us here / Map / Captain Smollet / Land ho / Compass / Long John / Rescue / Honest brave and true / Love power / Love led us here
PRMCD 5 / May '96 / Premier/EMI

☐ **MURDER ON THE ORIENT EXPRESS/ DEATH ON THE NILE**
Bennett, Richard Rodney/Nino Rota c
CNS 5007 / Aug '93 / Cloud Nine

☐ **MURDER WAS THE CASE**
Murder was the case: *Snoop Doggy Dogg* / Natural born killaz: *Dr. Dre & Ice Cube* / What would you do: *Dogg Pound* / 21 Jumpstreet: *Snoop Doggy Dogg & Tray Deee* / One more day: *Dogg, Nate* / Harvest for the world: *Jewell* / Who got some gangsta shit: *Snoop Doggy Dogg & Tha Dogg Pound* / Come when I call: *Boy, Danny* / U better recognise: *Sneed, Sam & Dr. Dre* / Come up to my room: *Jodeci & Tha Dogg Pound* / Woman to woman: *Jewell* / Dollars and sense: *D.J. Quik* / Eulogy: *Capone, Slip & CPO* / Horny: *Rezell, B* / East side west side: *Young Soldierz*
IND 92484 / Feb '97 / Interscope

☐ **MURIEL'S WEDDING**
Bridal dancing queen: *Wedding Band & Blazey Best* / Sugar baby love: *Rubettes* / We've only just begun: *Carpenters* / Lonely hearts: *Wedding Band* / Tide is high: *Blondie* / Waterloo: *Abba* / I go to Rio: *Allen, Peter* / Bean bag: *Wedding Band* / T-shirt and jeans: *Razorbrain* / I just don't know what to do with myself: *Springfield, Dusty* / I do I do I do I do I do: *Abba* / Happy together: *Turtles* / Muriel's wedding: *Wedding Band* / Dancing queen: *Abba*
5274932 / May '95 / Polydor

☐ **MUSIC BRUT-INSECT**
Revell, Graeme c
BRUT 1CD / Jul '94 / Grey Area

☐ **MUSIC IN THE AIR (1952 London Cast)**
Kern, Jerome c
Hammerstein II, Oscar l
AEICD 024 / May '98 / AEI

☐ **MUSIC MAN, THE (1957 Broadway Cast)**
Willson, Meredith c
Overture/Rock island / Iowa stubborn / Ya got trouble / Piano lesson / Goodnight my someone / Seventy six trombones / Sincere / Sadder but wiser girl for me / Pick-a-little take-a-little/Goodnight ladies / Marian the librarian / My white knight / Wells Fargo wagon / It's you / Shipoopi / Lida Rose/Will I ever tell you / Gary Indiana / Till there was you / Finale
ZDM 7646632 / Nov '93 / EMI Classics

☐ **MUSIC MAN, THE (Original London Cast)**
Willson, Meredith c
Overture/Rock Island / Ya got trouble / Goodnight my someone / Seventy six trombones / Pick a little talk a little / Goodnight ladies / Marian the librarian / Wells Fargo wagon / It's you / Lida Rose / Will I ever tell you / Gary Indiana / Till there was you / Finale
12447 / Mar '97 / Laserlight

☐ **MUSIC TEACHER (LE MAITRE DE MUSIQUE)**
Cortigiani vil razza dannata / Alcandro lo confessa...non so d'onde viene / Waltz / Das lied von der erde / Symphony no. 4 in g major / Deh vieni alla finestra / Wohl denk ich oft / Du meine seele du mein herz / Stille tranen / Sorgio o padre / An die musik d547 / Caro nome / Tanton duol / Ich bin der welt abhanden
PCOM 1109 / Nov '90 / President

☐ **MUSK AT DAWN (Schmidt, Irmin)**
Schmidt, Irmin c
IRMIN 1CD / Nov '92 / The Fine Line

☐ **MUTANT (National Philharmonic Orchestra)**
Band, Richard c
MAF 7052D / Jan '93 / Intrada

☐ **MY COUSIN VINNY (Edelman, Randy)**
Edelman, Randy *c*
VSD 5364 / Apr '92 / Varese Sarabande

☐ **MY FAIR LADY (Film Cast)**
Loewe, Frederick *c*
Lerner, Alan Jay *l*
Previn, Andre *con*
Overture / Why can't the English / Wouldn't it be loverly / I'm just an ordinary man / With a little bit of luck / Just you wait / Rain in Spain / I could have danced all night / Ascot gavotte / On the street where you live / You did it / Show me / Get me to the church on time / Hymn to him / Without you / I've grown accustomed to her face
CD 70000 / Dec '85 / CBS

☐ **MY FAIR LADY (Harrison, Rex & Julie Andrews/Stanley Holloway/1959 London Cast)**
Loewe, Frederick *c*
Lerner, Alan Jay *l*
Overture / Why can't the English / Wouldn't it be loverly / With a little bit of luck / I'm just an ordinary man / Just you wait / Rain in Spain / I could have danced all night / Ascot gavotte / On the street where you live / You did it / Show me / Get me to the church on time / Hymn to him / Without you / I've grown accustomed to her face
SK 60539 / Jul '98 / Columbia Broadway Masterworks

☐ **MY FAIR LADY (Highlights - The Shows Collection) (Cast Recording)**
Loewe, Frederick *c*
Lerner, Alan Jay *l*
Why can't the English / Wouldn't it be loverly / With a little bit of luck / I'm just an ordinary man / Just you wait / Rain in Spain / I could have danced all night / On the street where you live / Show me / Get me to the church on time / Hymn to him / Without you / I've grown accustomed to her face
PWKS 4174 / Oct '93 / Carlton

☐ **MY FAIR LADY (Cast Recording)**
Loewe, Frederick *c*
Lerner, Alan Jay *l*
Overture / Why can't the English / Wouldn't it be loverly / With a little bit of luck / I'm an ordinary man / Just you wait / Poor Professor Higgins / Rain in spain / I could have danced all night / Ascot gavotte / On the street where you live / Eliza's entrance / Proemnade / Embassy waltz / En'tracte / You did it / Show me / Flower market / Get me to the church on time / Hymn to him / Without you / I've grown accustomed to her face / Fianl scene / Curtain calls / Come to the ball
CDTER2 1211 / Nov '97 / TER

☐ **MY FAIR LADY (Includes Previously Unavailable Music) (Film Cast)**
Loewe, Frederick *c*
Lerner, Alan Jay *l*
Previn, Andre *con*
SK 66711 / May '95 / Sony Broadway

☐ **MY FAIR LADY (Starlight Orchestra/ Singers)**
Loewe, Frederick *c*
Lerner, Alan Jay *l*
My fair lady / I'm an ordinary man / On the street where you live / I could have danced all night / With a little bit of luck / You did it / Rain in Spain / Show me / I've grown accustomed to her face / Wouldn't it be loverly / Without you / Why can't the English / Just you wait / Get me to the church on time / Hymn to him
QED 102 / Nov '96 / Tring

☐ **MY FAIR LADY (CC Productions)**
Loewe, Frederick *c*
Lerner, Alan Jay *l*
Why can't be the English / Wouldn't it be loverly / With a little bit of luck / I'm an ordinary man / Just you wait / Rain in Spain / I could have danced all night / Ascot Gavotte / On the street where you live / Show me / Get me to the church on time / Hymn to him / I've grown accustomed to her face
QED 212 / Nov '96 / Tring

☐ **MY FAIR LADY (& Camelot/Gigi/ Brigadoon - Aspects Of Broadway Vol.6) (Orchestra Of The Americas)**
Loewe, Frederick *c*
Lerner, Alan Jay *l*
Freeman, Paul *con*
I could have danced all night / On the street where you live / Wouldn't it be loverly / Show me / Embassy waltz / Get me to the church on time / I've grown accustomed to her face / With a little bit of luck / I wonder what the king is doing tonight / March to welcome Guenevere / Where are the simple joys of maidenhood / Camelot / If ever I would leave you / Fie on goodness / How to handle a woman / Follow me / Loved you once in silence / Entry of the knights / Lusty month of May / Guenevere / Night they invented champagne / Gigi / Waltz at Maxim's / I'm glad I'm not young anymore / Parisians / Say a prayer for me tonight / Thank Heaven for little girls / Gigi / Brigadoon / Down on MacConnachy Square / Heather on the hill / I'll go home with Bonnie Jean / Come to me bend to me / Almost like being in love
SION 18306 / Jul '97 / Sion

☐ **MY FATHER'S GLORY/MY MOTHER'S CASTLE**
Cosma, Vladimir *c*
Cosma, Vladimir *con*
DRGCD 12604 / Jan '95 / DRG

☐ **MY FELLOW AMERICANS**
SNACD 807 / 2 Mar '98 / Snapper

☐ **MY NAME IS NOBODY**
Morricone, Ennio *c*
Morricone, Ennio *con*
A 8918 / Feb '92 / Alhambra

☐ **MY SO CALLED LIFE**
Make it home: *Hatfield, Juliana* / Soda jerk: *Buffalo Tom* / Genetic: *Sonic Youth* / Petty core: *Further* / Drop a bomb: *Madder Rose* / Fountain and Fairfax: *Afghan Whigs* / South Carolina: *Archers Of Loaf* / Dawn can't decide: *Lemonheads* / Book song: *Frente* / Come see me tonight: *Johnston, Daniel* / My so called life theme
7567827212 / Jan '95 / Warner Bros.

☐ **MY SON THE FANATIC**
Little Britain: *Dreadzone* / Joe Le Taxi: *Boodram, Sharlene* / That's a rockin' good way: *Benton, Brook & Dinah Washington* / Bad talk: *Levy, Barrington* / You're in my corner: *Cornershop* / Ain't goin' to Goa: *Alabama 3* / Into my world: *Audioweb* / Tum bin jaya: *Sagoo, Bally* / Please send me someone to love: *Mayfield, Percy* / John B. Calypso: *Mensah, E.T.* / Back o' town blues: *Armstrong, Louis* / Making music: *Hussein, Zakir*
MPRCD 010 / 15 Jun '98 / MCI Music

☐ **MY STEPMOTHER IS AN ALIEN**
Pump up the volume: *M/A/R/R/S* / Room to move: *Animotion* / Be the one: *Jackson, Jackie* / One good lover: *Siren* / Klystron / Not just another girl: *Neville, Ivan* / I like the world: *Cameo* / Hot wives: *Aykroyd, Dan* / Enjoy / Celeste
5511352 / Sep '95 / Spectrum

☐ **MYSTERIOUS ISLAND (London Symphony Orchestra)**
Herrmann, Bernard *c*
ACN 7017 / Mar '93 / Cloud Nine

☐ **MYSTERY OF EDWIN DROOD (Broadway Cast)**
Holmes, Rupert *c*
There you are / Man could go quite mad / Two kinsmen / Moonfall / Wages of sin / Ceylon / Both sides of the coin / Perfect strangers / No good can come from bad / Never the luck / Name of love / Setting up the score / Off to the races / Don't quit while you're ahead / Garden path to hell / Out on a limerick / Jasper's confession / Puffer's confession / Writing on the wall
VSD 5597 / Oct '95 / Varese Sarabande

☐ **MYTH OF FINGERPRINTS, THE**
Hal sings / Myth / I like it like this / Verandah / Le roi d'ys / Don't be that way / Low / Mia cries / le roi d'ys / Bad person / Underneath / Tenderfly / Super 8 / Fingerprints / Banks of the Wabash
VEL 797052 / 16 Feb '98 / Velvel

N

☐ **NAILS**
Conti, Bill *c*
VSD 5384 / Sep '92 / Varese Sarabande

☐ **NAKED GUN 2 1/2, THE (The Smell Of Fear)**
Newborn, Ira *c*
VSD 5331 / Aug '91 / Varese Sarabande

☐ **NAKED LUNCH, THE (London Philharmonic Orchestra)**
Shore, Howard/Ornette Coleman *c*
262732 / Feb '94 / Milan

☐ **NAPOLEON (New Score For 1927 Silent Film) (Wren Orchestra)**
Davis, Carl *c*
Davis, Carl *con*
Eagle of destiny / Teaching the Marseillaise / Reunion in Corsica / Pursued / Double storm / Drums of the 6th Regiment / Victor of Toulon / Gigue / Fan / Tambourin / Acting lesson / Ghosts / Peroration / Strange conductor in the sky
FILMCD 149 / Mar '94 / Silva Screen

☐ **NATURE: GREAT AFRICAN MOMENTS (Whalen, Michael)**
Whalen, Michael *c*
Elephants / Night on the Serengeti / Fire and ice / Killer instinct / Rain the rain / Lost on the plains / After the rain / Cheetah hunt / Jacana and the fish eagle / Hyena and the melons / Chimps / Journey of the thousands / Mountain gorillas / Wild pups / Meerkats / Flamingoes / African sunset / Vultures / Slowpake club / Cycles of life
ND 66066 / Apr '94 / Narada

☐ **NATURE: PHANTOM OF THE FOREST (Whalen, Michael)**
Whalen, Michael *c*
Spirits / Sea of trees / Hawk appears / Killing to survive / Wood cock / Open spaces / New forests / Building a nest / Feather / Life in the nest / Catherdral of the woods / Sunrise dance / Night creatures / Forest edge / Brink of extinction / Quite beauty / Winter rain / Predators of the predators / Woodland lullaby / Soliloquy
ND 66007 / Apr '94 / Narada

☐ **NAVIGATOR, THE**
Tabrizi, Davood A. *c*
CDSBL 12596 / Apr '96 / DRG

☐ **NEAR DARK (Tangerine Dream)**
Tangerine Dream *c*
Caleb's blues / Pick up at high noon / Rain in the third house / Bus station / Good times / She's my sister / Mae comes back / Father and son / Severin dies / Flight at dawn / Mae's transformation
FILMCD 026 / Jun '90 / Silva Screen

☐ **NED KELLY**
Silverstein, Shel *c*
Ned Kelly / Wild colonial boy / Son of a scoundrel / Shadow of the gallows / Lonigan's widow / Stoney cold ground / Kelly's keep comin' / Ranchin' in the evenin' / Blame it on the Kellys / Pictures of a Sunday afternoon / Hey Ned
RCD 10708 / 12 Jan '98 / Rykodisc

☐ **NEEDFUL THINGS**
Doyle, Patrick *c*
Snell, David *con*
VSD 5438 / Jul '93 / Varese Sarabande

☐ **NENETTE ET BONI (Tindersticks)**
Ma souer / La passerelle / Les gateaux / Camions / Nenette est la / Petites chiennes / Nosterfrau / Petites gouttes d'eau / Les cannes a peche / La mort de Felix / Nenette s'en va / Les bebes / Rumba
5243002 / Oct '96 / This Way Up

☐ **NET, THE (Isham, Mark)**
Isham, Mark *c*
VSD 5662 / Oct '95 / Varese Sarabande

☐ **NEVADA SMITH**
Newman, Alfred *c*
TSU 0113 / Jan '95 / Tsunami

☐ **NEVER ON SUNDAY**
Hadjidakis, Manos *c*
RCD 10722 / 8 Jun '98 / Rykodisc
MM 209 / 12 May '98 / Musurgia Graeca

☐ **NEVER SAY NEVER AGAIN**
Legrand, Michel *c*
Legrand, Michel *con*
Bond back in action / Never say never again: *Hall, Lani* / Prologue - enter 007 / Fatima Bush/A very bad lady / Dinner with 007 / Bahama Island / Bond smells a rat/Nurse Blush / Plunder of a nuclear missile / Big band death of Jack Petachi / Bond and Domino / Fight to death with the tiger sharks / Une Chanson d'amour / Video duel/Victory / Nuclear nightmare / Tango to the death / Bond returns home / Death of Nicole / Chase her / Felix and James exit / Jealousy / Largo's waltz / Bond to the rescue / Big escape / Tears of Allah / Underwater cave / Fight to the death / Bond in retirement / End title - Never say never again: *Hall, Lani*
FILMCD 145 / Apr '95 / Silva Screen

☐ **NEW JACK CITY**
New jack hustler: *Ice-T* / I'm dreaming: *Williams, Christopher* / I wanna sex you up: *Color Me Badd* / I'm still waiting: *Gill, Johnny* / (There you go) tellin' me no again: *Sweat, Keith* / Facts of life: *Madden, Danny* / For the love of money/Living for the city (medley): *Troop/Levert* / Lyrics 2 the rhythm: *Essence* / Get it together (black is a force): *Black Is A Force* / In the dust: *2 Live Crew* / New jack city: *Guy*
74321151042 / 1 Sep '97 / Giant

☐ **NEW JERSEY DRIVE VOL.1**
TBCD 1114 / Mar '95 / Tommy Boy

☐ **NEW JERSEY DRIVE VOL.2**
TBCD 1130 / Apr '95 / Tommy Boy

☐ **NEW ORLEANS (Holiday, Billie & Louis Armstrong)**
Free as a bird / When the saints go marching in / Westend blues / Do you know what it means to miss New Orleans / Brahms lullaby / Tiger rag / Buddy Bolden's blues / Basin Street blues / Raymond Street blues / Melenberg joys / Where the blues was born in New Orleans / Farewell to Storyville / Beale Street stomp / Dippermouth blues / Shimme sha wobble / Ballin' the Jack / King Porter stomp / Mahogany Hall stomp / Endie / Blues are brewin'
GOJCD 1025 / Jan '95 / Giants Of Jazz

☐ **NEW YORK ROCK (Cast Recording)**
Ono, Yoko *c*
It happened / I'll always be with you / Speck of dust / Midsummer New York / What a bastard the world is / Loneliness / Give me something / Light on the other side / Tomorrow may never come / Don't be scared / Growing pains / Warzone / Never say goodbye / O'sanity / I want my love to rest tonight / I felt like smashing my face in a clear glass window / Now or never / We're all water / Yes I'm your angel / Where do we go from here / Sleepless night / No no no / Even when you're far away / Hell in paradise / Toyboat / Story of an oak tree / Goodbye sadness
CDP 8298432 / Aug '95 / Capitol

☐ **NEXT GENERATIONS**
EDL 27202 / Jul '97 / Edel

☐ **NEXT OF KIN**
Brother to brother / Hillbilly heart / Paralysed / My sweet baby's gone / Brothers / On a Spanish Highway (revised) / Hey backwoods / Straight and narrow / Yard sale / Pyramids of cans / Wailing sax
4662402 / May '90 / Epic

☐ **NIAGARA NIAGARA**
6381270142 / 7 Apr '98 / VTW

☐ **NICK AND NORA (1991 Broadway Cast)**
Strouse, Charles *c*
Maltby, Richard Jr. *l*
CDTER 1191 / Sep '92 / TER

☐ **NIGHT CROSSING (National Philharmonic Orchestra)**
Goldsmith, Jerry *c*
Goldsmith, Jerry *con*
Main title / All in vain / Picnic / Plans / Success / First flight / Patches / Tomorrow we go / No time to wait / Final flight / In the West
RVF 6004D / Jan '89 / Intrada

☐ **NIGHT OF THE GENERALS**
Jarre, Maurice *c*
Jarre, Maurice *con*
FMT 8004D / Mar '92 / Intrada

☐ **NIGHT OF THE HUNTER, THE**
Introduction / Story begins / Ben Harper's downfall / Ben's prison companion / Preacher's plot / Uncle Birdie / John hates the preacher / John will never tell / Preacher strikes / Children hide / Children flee / Pearl's dream / Hunted / Rachel Cooper / Ruby / Rachel defends her changes / Christmas, the conclusion
BCD 16263 / Jul '98 / Bear Family

☐ **NIGHT VISION**
ICH 4574 / 29 Jun '98 / Ichiban

☐ **NIGHTINGALE (1982 London Cast)**
Strouse, Charles *c*
Prologue / Perfect harmony / Why am I so happy / Take us to the forest / Who are these people / Never speak directly to an Emperor / Nightingale / Emperor is a man / I was lost / Entr'acte / Charming / Singer must be free / Mechanical bird / Please don't make me hear that song again / Rivers cannot flow upwards / Death duet / We are China / Finale
CDTER2 1031 / Aug '95 / TER

☐ **NIGHTMARE CAFE**
Robinson, J. Peter *c*
VSD 5363 / Jul '92 / Varese Sarabande

☐ **NIGHTMARE ON ELM STREET - THE BEST OF NIGHTMARE ON ELM STREET (Freddy's Favourites)**
Young, Christopher *c*
VSD 5427 / Nov '93 / Varese Sarabande

☐ **NIGHTMARE ON ELM STREET I & II**
VCD 47255 / Jan '89 / Varese Sarabande

☐ **NIGHTMARE ON ELM STREET III (Dream Warriors) (Badalamenti, Angelo)**
Badalamenti, Angelo *c*
VCD 47293 / Jan '89 / Varese Sarabande

☐ **NIGHTMARE ON ELM STREET IV (The Dream Master/Score) (Safan, Craig)**
Safan, Craig *c*
VCD 5203 / Jan '89 / Varese Sarabande

☐ **NIGHTMARE ON ELM STREET V (Dream Child/Score) (Ferguson, Jay)**
Ferguson, Jay *c*
VSD 5238 / Oct '89 / Varese Sarabande

☐ **NIGHTMARE ON ELM STREET VI (Freddy's Dead: The Final Nightmare/ Score)**
May, Brian *c*
VSD 5333 / Sep '91 / Varese Sarabande

☐ **NIKITA (Serra, Eric)**
Serra, Eric *c*
Rico's gang suicide / Playing on saucepans / As cold as ice / Sentence / Paradise / Failed escape / Leaning time / Smile / Fancy face / First night out / Tpokmop / Last time I kiss you / Free side / I am on duty / Josephine and the big dealer / Mission in Venice / Fall / Let's welcome Victor / Last mission / We will miss you / Dark side of time
CDVMM 2 / Nov '90 / Virgin

☐ **NINE (1992 London Cast)**
Yeston, Maury *c*
Higgs, Timothy *con*
CDTER 1193 / Oct '92 / TER

☐ **NINE (Australian Cast)**
Yeston, Maury *c*
CDTER 1190 / May '93 / TER

☐ **NINE AND A HALF WEEKS**
I do what I do: *Taylor, John* / Best is yet to come: *Luba* / Slave to love: *Ferry, Bryan* / Black on black: *Dalbello* / Eurasian eyes: *Hart, Corey* / You can leave your hat on: *Cocker, Joe* / Bread and butter: *Devo* / This city never sleeps: *Eurythmics* / Cannes: *Copeland, Stewart* / Let it go: *Luba*
CDEST 2003 / Sep '94 / EMI

☐ **NO BANANAS**
Yes we have no banans / Boom / Who's in love / Run rabbit run / Mad about the boy / Cheek to cheek / Down by the seaside / Love for sale / Lambeth walk / One I love belongs to somebody else / Who's sorry now / Jingle bells / Falling in love again / All over the place / S'later / Jeepers creepers / Lord and Lady Whoozis / Panic / Blue skies around the corner / Tiggerty Boo / Swing out
CDVIP 176 / Apr '97 / Virgin VIP

☐ **NO FOR AN ANSWER (1941 US Cast)**
Blitzstein, Marc *c*
AEICD 031 / May '98 / AEI

☐ **NO MAN'S LAND**
Poledouris, Basil *c*
Jewel movement / Medusa's refrain / Spark from the infinite / Return of the dream collector / Jaipur local / Blue anthem
VCD 47352 / Jan '89 / Varese Sarabande

☐ **NO NO NANETTE (London Cast)**
Youmans, Vincent *c*
Harbach, Otto & Irving Caesar *l*
SMK 66173 / Jul '94 / Sony West End

☐ **NO RETREAT, NO SURRENDER**
Gilreath, Paul *c*
Gilreath, Paul *con*
FILMCD 150 / Mar '94 / Silva Screen

☐ **NO STRINGS (Broadway Cast)**
Rodgers, Richard *c*
ZDM 7646942 / Apr '93 / EMI Classics

☐ **NOBLE HOUSE**
Chihara, Paul *c*
VCD 47360 / Jan '89 / Varese Sarabande

☐ **NOEL AND GERTIE (1986 London Cast)**
Coward, Sir Noel *c*
Overture / Some day I'll find you / Mrs. Worthington / Touring days / Parisian pierrot / Dance little lady / Play orchestra play / We were dancing / Man about town / I travel alone / Sail away / Why must the show go on / Come the wild wild weather / I'll remember her / I'll see you again / Curtain music
CDTER 1117 / Aug '95 / TER

☐ **NORMA JEAN & MARILYN**
Young, Christopher *c*
Anthony, P. *con*
MAF 7070 / Oct '96 / Intrada

☐ **NORTH AND SOUTH/THE RIGHT STUFF (London Symphony Orchestra)**
Conti, Bill *c*
Conti, Bill *con*
VCD 47250 / Jan '89 / Varese Sarabande

☐ **NORTH BY NORTHWEST (London Studio Symphony Orchestra)**
Herrmann, Bernard *c*
VCD 47205 / '90 / Varese Sarabande

☐ **NORTH BY NORTHWEST**
Herrmann, Bernard *c*
Herrmann, Bernard *con*
Overture / Streets / It's a most unusual day / Kidnapped / Door / Cheers / Wild ride / Car crash / Return / Two dollars / Rosalie / In the still of the night / Elevator / UN / Information desk / Knife / Fashion show / Interlude / Detectives / Conversation piece / Duo / Station / Phone booth / Farewell / Crash / Hotel lobby / Reunion / Goodbye / Question / Pad and pencil / Auction / Police / Airport / Cafeteria / Shooting / Forest / Flight / Ledge / House / Balcony / Match box / Message / TV / Airplane / Gates / Stone faces / Ridge / On the rocks / Cliff / Finale
CDODEON 6 / Feb '96 / Premier/EMI

☐ **NORTHERN EXPOSURE**
Northern Exposure: *Schwartz, David* / Jolie Louise: *Lanois, Daniel* / Hip hug-her: *Booker T & The MG's* / At last: *James, Etta* / Everybody be yourself: *Chic Street Man* / Alaskan nights: *Schwartz, David* / Don Quichotte: *Magazine 60* / When I grow too old to dream: *Cole, Nat 'King'* / Emabhaceni: *Makeba, Miriam* / Gimme three steps: *Lynyrd Skynyrd* / Bailero: *Von Stade, Frederica & The Royal Philharmonic Orchestra* / Medley: *Schwartz, David*
MCD 10685 / 8 Sep '97 / MCA

☐ **NORTHERN EXPOSURE - MORE MUSIC FROM NORTHERN EXPOSURE**
Ojibway square dance (love song) / Theme from Northern Exposure / Stir it up / Mambo baby / Someone loves you / Ladder / If you take me back / Un marriage casse (A broken marriage) / There I go again / Lay my love / Wrap your troubles in dreams (and dream your troubles away) / Mooseburger stomp / I may want a man
MCLD 19350 / Oct '96 / MCA

☐ **NOSFERATU (A Symphony In Horror) (Brandenburg Philharmonic Orchestra)**
Erdmann, Hans *c*
Anderson, Gillian *con*
9026681432 / Nov '95 / RCA Victor

☐ **NOSFERATU (City Of Prague Philharmonic Orchestra)**
Bernard, James *c*
Raine, Nic *con*
FILMCD 192 / Nov '97 / Silva Screen

☐ **NOSTROMO**
Morricone, Ennio *c*
5336582 / Feb '97 / Polydor

☐ **NOTHING TO LOSE**
Nothin' to lose: *Naughty By Nature* / Not tonight: *Lil' Kim & Left Eye/Da Brat/Missy Elliot/Angie Martinez* / C U when you get there: *Coolio & 40 Thevz* / Put the money in it: *Dat Nigga Daz & Soopafly* / Thug paradise: *Capone & Noreaga/Tragedy* / Way 2 saucy: *Mac & AK/Mac Mall* / Get down with me: *Amari & Buckshot* / Poppin' that fly: *Jones, 'Oran' Juice & Stu Large/Camp Lo* / QuRoute: *Quad City DJ'S* / Hit 'em up: *Master P & Tru/Mercedez* / OuEverlasting: *Outkast* / 9Ina magazine: *911 & Queen Pen* / It's alright: *Queen Latifah* / What's going on: *Black Ceasar* / Stesa I: *Stetsasonic* / Crazy maze: *Des'ree*
TBCD 1169 / Jul '97 / Tommy Boy

☐ **N'OUBLIE PAS QUE TU VAS MOURIR (Cale, John)**
Cale, John *c*
Cale, John *l*
TWI 1028 / Mar '96 / Les Disques Du Crepuscule

☐ **NOUVELLE VAGUE**
Eicher, Manfred *c*
4498912 / Jun '97 / ECM

☐ **NOW AND THEN**
Eidelman, Cliff *c*
VSD 5675 / Jun '96 / Varese Sarabande

☐ **NOW AND THEN**
Sugar sugar: *Archies* / Knock three times: *Orlando, Tony & Dawn* / I want you back: *Jackson 5* / Signed sealed delivered I'm yours: *Wonder, Stevie* / Band of gold: *Payne, Freda* / Daydream beliver: *Monkees* / No matter what: *Badfinger* / Hitchin' a ride: *Vanity Fare* / All right now: *Free* / I'm gonna make you love me: *Ross, Diana* / I'll be there: *Jackson 5* / Now and then: *Hoffs, Susanna*
4816062 / Jun '96 / Columbia

☐ **NOWHERE**
Freak out: *311* / How can you be sure: *Radiohead* / In the city: *Elastica* / Dicknail: *Hole* / Life is sweet: *Chemical Brothers* / Daydreaming: *Massive Attack* / Killing time: *Coco & The Bean* / Intravenous: *Catherine Wheel* / Nowhere: *Curve* / I have the moon: *Lush* / Flippin' the bird: *Ruby* / Thursday treatments: *James* / Generation wrekked: *Chuck D* / Kiddie grinder: *Manson, Marilyn* / Trash: *Suede*
5345222 / Apr '97 / Mercury

☐ **NUNSENSE I (1986 Off-Broadway Cast)**
Goggin, Dan *c*
Nunsense is habit forming / Difficult transition / Benedicte/Biggest ain't best: *Hubert & Leo* / Playing second fiddle: *Anne, Robert* / So you want to be a Nun: *Amnesia, Mary* / Turn up the spotlight: *Cardelia, Mary* / Lilacs bring back memories / Tackle that temptation with a time-step: *Hubert & Cast* / Growing up Catholic: *Anne, Robert & Cast* / Drive-in: *St. Andrew's Sister* / I could've gone to Nashville: *Amnesia, Mary* / Holier than thou: *Hubert & Cast* / Finale
CDSBL 12589 / Apr '87 / DRG

☐ **NUNSENSE II (The Second Coming) (Cast Recording)**
Goggin, Dan *c*
Jubilate deo/Nunsense - The magic word / Winning is just the beginning / Prima ballerina / Biggest still ain't the best / I've got pizazz / Country nun / Look Ma I made it / Padre polka / Classic Queens / Hat and cane song / Angeline / We're the nuns to come to / What would Elvis do / Yes we can / I am here to stay / No one cared like you / There's only one way to end your prayers / Nunsense - The magic word (Reprise)
DRGCD 12608 / Jun '93 / DRG

☐ **NUTTY PROFESSOR, THE**
Touch me tease me: *Case & Foxy Brown* / I like: *Jordan, Montell & Slick Rick* / My crew can't go for that: *Trigger Tha Gambler* / Ain't nobody: *Monica & Naughty By Nature* / Pillow: *Richie Rich* / Last night: *Az Yet* / Come around: *Dos Of Soul* / We want yo hands up: *Warren G.* / Ain't no N-G-A: *Jay Z & Foxy Brown* / Breaker 1 breaker 2: *Def Squad* / Doin' it again: *LL Cool J* / Nasty immigrants: *12 O'Clock* / Love you down: *Da Bassment*
5319112 / Oct '96 / Def Jam

O

☐ **O CAN YOU SEE (Cast Recording)**
AEICD 034 / May '98 / AEI

☐ **O LUCKY MAN (Price, Alan)**
O Lucky man / Poor people / Sell sell / Pastoral / Arrival / Look over your shoulder / Justice / My home town / Changes
9362461372 / Oct '96 / Warner Bros.

☐ **O PIONEERS**
Broughton, Bruce *c*
Broughton, Bruce *con*
MAF 7023D / Apr '92 / Intrada

☐ **OASIS (Tangerine Dream)**
Flashflood / Zion / Reflections / Cliff dwellers / Waterborne / Cedar breaks / Summer storm / Hopi mesa heart
TD 1007CD / Jun '97 / TDI

☐ **OBJECT OF MY AFFECTION**
Fenton, George *c*
1868100272 / 24 Mar '98 / Ark 21

☐ **OBSESSION (Includes Welles Raises Kane/The Devil and Daniel Webster) (National Philharmonic Orchestra)**
Herrmann, Bernard *c*
Herrmann, Bernard *con*
UKCD 2065 / Nov '94 / Unicorn-Kanchana

☐ **OCTOPUS/ALL ABOUT THE MAFIA**
Morricone, Ennio *c*
EDL 25492 / Jan '93 / Edel

☐ **OCTOPUSSY**
Barry, John *c*
RCD 10705 / 13 Oct '97 / Rykodisc

☐ **ODNA (Katchur, Svetlana & Vladimir Kazatchouk/Rundfunk Sinfonie)**
Shostakovich, Dmitry *c*
Jurowski, Michail *con*
10562 / Sep '96 / Capriccio

☐ **ODYSSEY INTO THE MIND'S EYE (Livgren, Kerry)**
Livgren, Kerry *c*
RMED 0004CD / 9 Mar '98 / Renaissance

☐ **OF THEE I SING**
Kaufman, George S. & Morrie Ryskind *c*
ZDM 5650252 / Feb '94 / EMI Classics

☐ **OFF LIMITS (aka Saigon)**
Howard, James Newton *c*
VCD 70445 / Jan '89 / Varese Sarabande

☐ **OFF THE WALL (1991 Cast)**
Stephens, Geoff *c*
Black, Don *l*
Off the wall / Bums on seats / He looks fine / Good music won't always be here / Spin of the wheel / Jazz mad / You know who I mean / Rosie Miller / I won't be doing that tonight / Life goes on / Only the dreamer can change the dream
OCRCD 6051 / Apr '97 / First Night

☐ **OFFICER AND A GENTLEMAN, AN**
Officer and a gentleman: *Ritenour, Lee* / Up where we belong: *Cocker, Joe & Jennifer Warnes* / Hungry for your love: *Morrison, Van* / Tush: *ZZ Top* / Treat me right: *Benatar, Pat* / Be real: *Sir Douglas Quintet* / Tunnel of love: *Dire Straits*
IMCD 77 / Jan '93 / Island

☐ **OH, KAY (Upshaw, Dawn & Orchestra Of St. Luke's)**
Gershwin, George *c*
Gershwin, Ira *l*
Stern, Eric *con*
7559793612 / May '95 / Nonesuch

☐ **OIL CITY SYMPHONY (Broadway Cast)**
Ohio afternoon / Beaver ball / Dear Miss Reaves / Old Kentucky rock 'n' roll home / Bus ride / Beehive polka / In a gaddada vida / Baby it's cold outside / Exodus song / Getting acquainted / End of the world / Dizzy fingers
CDSBL 12594 / Jan '89 / DRG

☐ **OKLAHOMA (Film Cast)**
Rodgers, Richard *c*
Hammerstein II, Oscar *l*
Blackton, Jay *con*
Overture / Oh what a beautiful morning / Surrey with the fringe on top / Kansas City / I cain't say no / Many a new day / People will say we're in love / Poor Jud is dead / Out of my dreams / Farmer and the cowman / All er nothin' / Oklahoma
ZDM 7646912 / Apr '93 / EMI Classics

☐ **OKLAHOMA (1980 London Cast)**
Rodgers, Richard *c*
Hammerstein II, Oscar *l*
CDTER 1208 / 1 Sep '98 / TER

☐ **OKLAHOMA (1980 London Cast)**
Rodgers, Richard *c*
Hammerstein II, Oscar *l*
Overture / OH what a beautiful morning / Surrey with the fringe on top / Kansas City / I cain't say no / Many a new day / People will say we're in love / Pore Jud is daid / Out of my dreams / Farmer and the cowman / All er nothin' / Oaklahoma
SHOWCD 001 / Feb '95 / Showtime

☐ **OKLAHOMA (1952 Broadway Cast)**
Rodgers, Richard *c*
Hammerstein II, Oscar *l*
Engel, Lehman *con*
SK 53326 / Nov '93 / Sony Broadway

☐ **OKLAHOMA (CC Productions)**
Rodgers, Richard *c*
Hammerstein II, Oscar *l*
Oh what a beautiful morning / Surrey with a fringe on top / Kansas City / I can't say no / Many a new day / People will say we're in love / Pore Jud is daid / Out of my dreams / All er nothin' / Oklahoma / Finale
QED 216 / Nov '96 / Tring

☐ **OKLAHOMA/SHOW BOAT (Broadway Cast)**
Overture / Ol man river / You are love / Make believe / Bill / Can't help lovin' dat man / Why do I love you / Lonesome road / It still suits me / Oh what a beautiful morning / Surrey with a fringe on top / Kansas City / I cain't say no / Many a new day / People will say we're in love / Pore Jud is daid / Out of my dreams / All er nothin' / Oklahoma / Finale
CDAJA 5198 / May '96 / Living Era

☐ **OLD GRINGO**
Holdridge, Lee *c*
Ride to the hacienda / Battle / Harriet's theme / Bitter's last ride / Mirrors / Nightime / Bell tower / Sigh / Battle (resolution) / Bitter's destiny / Finale
GNPD 8017 / Nov '89 / GNP Crescendo

☐ **OLD MAN AND THE SEA, THE**
Tiomkin, Dimitri *c*
VSD 5232 / Feb '90 / Varese Sarabande

☐ **OLD MAN AND THE SEA, THE (TV Version)**
Broughton, Bruce *c*
RVF 6008D / Jul '93 / Intrada

☐ **OLD MAN AND THE SEA, THE**
SHANTY 1001 / Nov '97 / Shanty

☐ **OLIVER (1963 Broadway Cast)**
Bart, Lionel *c*
Food glorious food / Oliver / I shall scream / Boy for sale / Where is love / Consider yourself / You've got to pick a pocket or two / It's a fine life / I'd do anything / Be back soon / Oom-pah-pah / My name / As long as he needs me / Who will buy / Reviewing the situation / As long as he needs me (reprise) / Reviewing the situation (reprise) / Finale
GD 84113 / Oct '89 / RCA Victor

☐ **OLIVER (1960 London Cast)**
Bart, Lionel *c*
8205902 / Jan '95 / London

☐ **OLIVER (Film Cast)**
Bart, Lionel *c*
Overture / Food glorious food / Boy for sale / Where is love / You've got to pick a pocket or two / Consider yourself / I'd do anything / Be back soon / As long as he needs me / Who will buy / It's a fine life / Reviewing the situation / Oom pah pah / Finale
ND 90311 / Mar '89 / RCA

☐ **OLIVER (Highlights - The Shows Collection) (1994 Studio Cast)**
Bart, Lionel *c*
PWKS 4194 / Mar '94 / Carlton

☐ **OLIVER (1966 Studio Cast)**
Bart, Lionel *c*
Food glorious food / Oliver / I shall scream / Where is love / Consider yourself / Pick a pocket or two / It's a fine life / Be back soon / I'd do anything / Oom pah pah / My name / As long as he needs me / Who will buy this wonderful morning / Reviewing the situation
CC 8253 / Oct '94 / Music For Pleasure

☐ **OLIVER (1994 London Cast)**
Bart, Lionel *c*
CASTCD 47 / Mar '95 / First Night

☐ **OLIVER (Cast Recording)**
Bart, Lionel *c*
Overture/Food glorious food / Oliver / Where is love / Consider yourself / You've got to pick a pocket or two / It's a fine life / I'd do anything / Be back soon / Oom-pah-pah / As long as he needs me / Who will buy / Reviewing the situation
SHOWCD 004 / Feb '95 / Showtime

☐ **OLIVER (Holloway, Stanley & Alma Cogan/Tony Osborne Orchestra)**
Bart, Lionel *c*
ZDM 7648902 / Aug '93 / EMI Classics

☐ **OLIVER (1991 Cast)**
Bart, Lionel *c*
Overture / Food glorious food / Oliver / I shall scream / Boy for sale / That's your sale / Where is love / Consider yourselfPick a pocket or two / It's fine life / I'd do anything / Be back soon / Oom-pah pah / My name / As long as he needs me / WHo will buy / Reviewing the situation / Finale
CDTER 1182 / Nov '97 / TER

☐ **OLIVER AND COMPANY**
Once upon a time in New York City: *Lewis, Huey* / Why should I worry: *Joel, Billy* / Streets of gold: *Pointer, Ruth* / Perfect isn't easy: *Midler, Bette* / Good company: *Tran, Myhanh* / Sykes / Bedtime story / Rescue / Pursuit through the subway / Buscando guayaba: *Blades, Ruben* / End title
WD 608902 / Oct '97 / Disney Music & Stories

☐ **OLIVIER OLIVIER/EUROPA EUROPA**
Preisner, Zbigniew *c*
Main title / Affection et amour / Arrivee au cafe / Elizabeth S'evancuit / Olivier / Exode / Attaque aerienne / Bataille / Troubles / Hitler Staline
DRGCD 12606 / Jun '93 / DRG
PSB 890 / Mar '96 / PSB

☐ **OLYMPUS ON MY MIND (1986 US Cast)**
Sturiale, Grant *c*
Harman, Barry *l*
Welcome to Greece: *Chorus* / Heaven on earth: *Jupiter, Alchmene* / Gods on tap: *Delores, Jupiter* / Surprise: *Sosia & Mercury* / Love - what...: *Jupiter, Mercury & Dolores* / Enter the husband: *Chorus* / I know my wife: *Amphitryon* / It was me: *Sosia & Amphitryon* / Back so soon: *Amphitryon, Sosia & Orchestra* / Wonderful: *Alchmene* / At liberty...: *Charis & The Chorus* / Jupiter slept here: *Jupiter & All* / Something of yourself: *Mercury* / Star is born: *Delores & all* / Final sequence: *Amphitryon, alchmene*
CDTER 1131 / Aug '95 / TER

☐ **OMEN I, THE**
Goldsmith, Jerry *c*
Goldsmith, Jerry *con*
VSD 5281 / '91 / Varese Sarabande

☐ **OMEN II, THE (Damien) (National Philharmonic Orchestra)**
Goldsmith, Jerry *c*
Newman, Lionel *con*
Main title / Runaway train / Claws / Thoughtful night / Broken ice / Fallen temple / I love you Mark / Shafted / Knife / All the power
FILMCD 002 / Nov '89 / Silva Screen

☐ **OMEN III, THE (The Final Conflict)**
Goldsmith, Jerry *c*
Goldsmith, Jerry *con*
VCD 47242 / Sep '86 / Varese Sarabande

☐ **OMEN IV, THE**
Sheffer, Jonathan *c*
VSD 5318 / Jul '91 / Varese Sarabande

☐ **ON A CLEAR DAY YOU CAN SEE FOREVER (1970 Film Cast)**
Lane, Burton *c*
Lerner, Alan Jay *l*
Hurry it's lovely up here / On a clear day (you can see forever) / Love with all the trimmings / Melinda / Go to sleep / He isn't you / What did I have that I don't have / Come back to me
4749072 / '95 / Columbia

☐ **ON A CLEAR DAY YOU CAN SEE FOREVER (1965 Broadway Cast)**
Lane, Burton *c*
Lerner, Alan Jay *l*
09026608202 / Jan '90 / RCA Victor

☐ **ON DEADLY GROUND**
Poledouris, Basil *c*
Poledouris, Basil *con*
VSD 5468 / Mar '94 / Varese Sarabande

☐ **ON HER MAJESTY'S SECRET SERVICE**
Barry, John *c*
We have all the time in the world / This never happened to the other fella / Try / Ski chase / Do you know how Christmas trees are grown / Main theme / Journey to Blofeld's hideaway / Over and out / Battle at Piz Gloria / We have all the time in the world/James Bond theme
CZ 549 / Dec '95 / Premier/EMI

☐ **ON THE BIG HILL (Croker, Brendan & Guy Fletcher)**
Opening shot / Best laid plans / Mountain madness / Thru the window / Try not to fall / Higher ground / There are times / Things look different / Take a short walk / Some people get hurt / Long walk / Across the bridge / Dougie's march / Each night you die a little / In the back of your mind / Home Dougie home
ORECD 501 / Mar '94 / Silvertone

☐ **ON THE TOWN (Von Stade, Frederica & Thomas Hampson/London Voices/ London Symphony Orchestra)**
Bernstein, Leonard *c*
Comden, Betty & Adolph Green *l*
Tilson Thomas, Michael *con*
4375162 / Oct '93 / Deutsche Grammophon

☐ **ON THE TOWN (Cast Recording)**
Bernstein, Leonard *c*
Comden, Betty & Adolph Green *l*
Overture / New York new York / Miss Turnstiles / Come up to my place / Carried away / Lonely town / High school girls / Carnegie Hall Pavane / I can cook too / Lucky to be me / Times square / Finale act one / So long baby / I wish I was dead / Ya got me / Slam bang blues / Pitkin's song / Subway ride / Imaginary coney island / Great lover display himself / Some other time / Real coney island / Finale act 2 / Gabey's cming
CDTER 1217 / Nov '97 / TER

☐ **ON THE WATERFRONT (1995 Broadway Cast)**
Amran, David *c*
Schulberg, Bud *l*
VSD 5638 / Aug '95 / Varese Sarabande

☐ **ON YOUR TOES (1983 Broadway Cast)**
Rodgers, Richard *c*
Hart, Lorenz *l*
Mauceri, John *con*
Overture / Two a day for Keith / It's got to be love / Too good for the average man / There's a small hotel / Heart is quicker than the eye / Quite night / Questions and answers / Glad to be unhappy / On your toes / Princess Zenobia ballet / Slaughter on 10th Avenue
CDTER 1063 / Aug '98 / TER

☐ **ON YOUR TOES/PAL JOEY (Cast Recording)**
Rodgers, Richard *c*
Hart, Lorenz *l*
340822 / Oct '95 / Koch

☐ **ONCE AROUND**
Horner, James *c*
Horner, James *con*
VSD 5308 / Apr '91 / Varese Sarabande

☐ **ONCE ON THIS ISLAND (Broadway Cast)**
Ahrens, Lynn *c*
CDTER 1224 / Nov '94 / TER

☐ **ONCE UPON A MATTRESS (Parker, Sarah Jessica & Broadway Cast)**
Overture / Many moons ago / In a little while / On a stormy night... / Shy / Minstrel jester and I / Sensitivity / Swamps of home / Normandy / Spanish panic / Song of love / Entr'acte / Quiet / Goodnight sweet Princess / Happily ever after / Man to man talk / Very soft shoes / Yesterday I loved you / Lullaby / Finale
09026687282 / Apr '97 / RCA Victor

☐ **ONCE WERE WARRIORS**
74321249022 / May '96 / Milan

☐ **ONE AGAINST THE WIND**
Holdridge, Lee *c*
MAF 7039D / Jul '93 / Intrada

☐ **ONE EYED JACKS**
Friedhofer, Hugo *c*
TSU 0114 / Jan '95 / Tsunami

☐ **ONE FINE DAY**
4869102 / Feb '97 / Sony Music

☐ **ONE FLEW OVER THE CUCKOO'S NEST**
Nitzsche, Jack *c*
FCD 4531 / Jan '96 / Fantasy

☐ **ONE FROM THE HEART (Waits, Tom & Crystal Gayle)**
Waits, Tom *c*
Opening montage / Tom's piano / Once upon a town / Wages of love / Is there any way out of this dream / Presents / Picking up after you / Old boy friends / Broken bicycles / I beg your pardon / Little boy blue / Instrumental montage / Tango / Circus girl / You can't unring a bell / This one's from the heart / Take me home
4676092 / Dec '90 / CBS

☐ **ONE MILLION YEARS BC (& When Dinosaurs Ruled The Earth/The Creatures The World Forgot)**
Nascimbene, Mario *c*
LEGENDCD 13 / Jun '94 / Legend

☐ **ONE NIGHT STAND**
Figgis, Mike *c*
One night stand / Angel no.2 / Max and Karen / Organ grinder's swing / Liberty / Exactly like you / Mugging / I'd like you to stay / Air on a G string / San Vicente / Question for Charles / Heart noir / Life is an orange / Maxwerk / Graveyard shift / Karen and Max / Angel no.3 / Cavatina / Opus 130
5390252 / 10 Nov '97 / Verve

☐ **ONE TRICK PONY (Simon, Paul)**
Simon, Paul *c*
Late in the evening / That's why God made the movies / One-trick pony / How the heart approaches what it yearns / Oh Marion / Ace in the hole / Nobody / Jonah / God bless the absentee / Long long day
256846 / Feb '94 / WEA

☐ **ONE WEEK (New Jazz Score For Buster Keaton Film)**
Frisell, Bill *c*
7559793522 / Jan '95 / Elektra

☐ **ONLY THE LONELY**
Jarre, Maurice *c*
VSD 5324 / Jul '91 / Varese Sarabande

☐ **ONLY THE LONELY (The Roy Orbison Story) (London Cast)**
CASTCD 51 / Aug '95 / First Night

☐ **OPERATION DUMBO DROP**
Newman, David *c*
1620322 / Feb '96 / Hollywood

☐ **ORCA - KILLER WHALE**
Morricone, Ennio *c*
LEGENDCD 10 / Jul '93 / Legend

☐ **ORIGINAL GANGSTAS**
Inner city blues: *Ideal* / World is a ghetto: *Geto Boys* / XO: *Luniz* / On the grind: *Click* / White chalk part II: *Junior MAFIA* / How many: *N.O. Joe* / Flowmatic 9: *3X Crazy* / Ain't no fun: *Dino* / Rivals: *Face Mob* / War's on: *Almighty RSo* / Who wanna be the villain: *M.C. Ren* / Slugs: *Spice 1* / How does it feel: *Ice-T* / Good stuff: *Smooth*
CDVUS 104 / Apr '96 / Virgin

☐ **ORLANDO**
Motton, David & Sally Potter *c*
VSD 5413 / Mar '93 / Varese Sarabande

☐ **ORPHEUS IN THE UNDERWORLD (English National Opera)**
Offenbach, Jacques *c*
Wilson, Snoo & David Pountney *l*
Elder, Mark *con*
Prelude / Hello I'm public opinion / Eurydice is all a-flutter / So that's the game / I feel a cool intoxication / We the watchdogs of the people / Tzing tzing tzing tzing / Night on the town / Remember what you did to Leda / Look out look out move over there / He is coming oh how boring / Oh oh look at that look he's giving me / Though I was King of all Beotia / We can tell she's in hell / My little spies uncover / There you are you look so neat / It's strange but a touch seemed to wake / Do not look back or all will be lost / ...He is the only God / Infernal gallop
CDTER 1134 / 15 Jun '98 / TER

☐ **ORPHEUS IN THE UNDERWORLD (Highlights) (English National Opera)**
Offenbach, Jacques *c*
Wilson, Snoo & David Pountney *l*
CDTEO 1008 / May '89 / TER

☐ **ORSON WELLES' OTHELLO**
Lavagnino, Angelo Francesco *c*
VSD 5420 / Feb '94 / Varese Sarabande

☐ **OSCAR**
Bernstein, Elmer *c*
VSD 5313 / Apr '91 / Varese Sarabande

☐ **OTHELLO**
Mole, Charlie *c*
VSD 5689 / Feb '96 / Varese Sarabande

☐ **OTHELLO**
Goldenthal, Elliot *c*
VSD 5942 / 20 Jul '98 / Varese Sarabande

☐ **OUR FRIENDS IN THE NORTH**
Times they are a-changin': *Dylan, Bob* / House of the rising sun: *Animals* / You really got me: *Kinks* / Eve of destruction: *McGuire, Barry* / Wild thing: *Troggs* / All or nothing: *Small Faces* / Substitute: *Who* / See my friend: *Kinks* / We gotta get out of this place: *Animals* / Goodbye yellow brick road: *John, Elton* / Le freak: *Chic* / Can you feel the force: *Real Thing* / Denis: *Blondie* / Babylon's burning: *Ruts* / English civil war: *Clash* / My perfect cousin: *Undertones* / Karma chameleon: *Culture Club* / What difference does it make: *Smiths* / When tomorrow comes: *Eurythmics* / Common people: *Pulp*
TTVCD 2922 / Jul '97 / Telstar TV

☐ **OUR PRIVATE WORLD**
Mayes, Sally *c*
VSD 5529 / Mar '95 / Varese Sarabande

☐ **OUT FOR JUSTICE (Score/Songs)**
Frank, David Michael *c*
Don't stand in my way: *Allman, Gregg* / Shake the firm: *Cool J.T.* / Temptation: *Belmont James, Teresa* / When the night comes down: *Smallwood, Todd* / One good man: *Armstrong, Kymberli* / Puerto Riqueno: *Jimenez, Michael* / Bad side of town: *Ball, Sherwood* / Bigger they are: *Cool J.T.*
VSD 5317 / Aug '91 / Varese Sarabande

☐ **OUT OF AFRICA**
Barry, John *c*
Barry, John *con*
I had a farm in Africa / I'm better at hello (Karen's theme I) / Have you got a story for me / Concerto for clarinet in A / Safari / Karen's journey / Siyawe / Flying over Africa / I had a compass from Denys (Karen's theme II) / Alone on the farm / Let the rest of the world go by / If I know a song from Africa (Karen's theme III) / You are Karen (end theme) / Music of goodbye
MCLD 19092 / Oct '92 / MCA
VSD 5816 / 26 Jan '98 / Varese Sarabande

☐ **OUT OF THIS WORLD (1950 Broadway Cast)**
Porter, Cole *c*
Davenport, Pembroke *con*
SK 48223 / Nov '92 / Sony Broadway

☐ **OUT OF THIS WORLD (1995 New York Cast)**
Porter, Cole *c*
Overture / Prologue / I jupiter I Rex / Use your imagination / Entrance of night / Hail hail hail / I got beauty / Maiden fair / Where oh where / They couldn't compare to you / From this moment on / What do you think about men / Dance of the long night / You don't remind me / I sleep easier now / I am loved / Climb up the mountain / Dawn / No lover / Cherry pies ought to be you / Hark to the song of the night / Nobody's chasing me / Finale
DRGCD 94764 / Apr '96 / DRG

☐ **OUTBREAK**
Howard, James Newton *c*
VSD 5599 / Mar '95 / Varese Sarabande

☐ **OUTER LIMITS (The Man Who Was Never Born/100 Days Of the Dragon/ Nightmare)**
Frontiere, Dominic *c*
Frontiere, Dominic *con*
GNPD 8032 / Apr '93 / GNP Crescendo

☐ **OUTER LIMITS, THE**
Van Tongeren, John *c*
SI 8604 / Jan '98 / Sonic Images

☐ **OUTLAND/CAPRICORN ONE**
Goldsmith, Jerry *c*
Goldsmith, Jerry *con*
GNPD 8035 / Nov '93 / GNP Crescendo

☐ **OUTSIDE EDGE**
LBWCD 1 / Feb '95 / Echo

☐ **OVER HERE (Broadway Cast)**
Sherman, Richard & Robert *c*
Klein, Joseph *con*
SK 32961 / Nov '92 / Sony Broadway

☐ **OZ**
AM 2 / Nov '96 / Animanga

P

☐ **PACIFIC HEIGHTS**
Zimmer, Hans *c*
Zimmer, Hans *con*
VSD 5286 / Feb '91 / Varese Sarabande

☐ **PACIFIC OVERTURES (Complete) (London Cast/English National Opera)**
Sondheim, Stephen *c*
Weidman, J. *l*
Holmes, James *con*
Prologue / Advantages of floating in the middle of the sea / Even in a land... / Prisoner's name / Underscore / What did the councillors say / There is no other way / Four black dragons / They come from a land... / Please I am here / Why do they laugh / Please I must speak / Disaster / Chrysanthemum tea / Americans have not left / My Lord Governer of Kanagawa / Americans insisted / From the personal journal / March to the Treaty House / No one knows what was said / Someone in a tree / Whatever happened... / Lion dance / Spiritual heart / Americans did not come / Please hello / Admiral's exeunt / Americans did not come / Tale of the courageous King / Intriguing performance / Two men whose fortunes / Bowler hat / Kenjitsu an ancient art / Pretty lady / Murder of these English / You are sure that the indemnity / Death to all traitors / In the name of the Emperor / Next
CDTER2 1152 / 15 Jun '98 / TER

☐ **PAGEMASTER, THE**
Horner, James *c*
Dream away: *Stansfield, Lisa & Babyface* / Whatever you imagine: *Moten, Wendy* / Main title / Stormy ride to the library / Pagemaster / Dr. Jekyll and Mr. Hyde / Narrow escape / Towards the open sea / Pirates / Loneliness / Flying dragon / Swallowed alive / Wonder in books / New courage / Magic of imagination
07822110192 / Nov '94 / RCA

☐ **PAINT YOUR WAGON (Film Cast)**
Loewe, Frederick *c*
Lerner, Alan Jay *l*
I'm on my way / I still see Elisa / First thing you know / Hand me down that can o' beans / They call the wind Maria / Million miles away behind the door / There's a coach comin' in / Whoop-ti-ay (shivaree) / I talk to the trees / Gospel of no name city / Best things / Wandering star / Gold fever / Finale
MCLD 19310 / Oct '95 / MCA

☐ **PAINT YOUR WAGON (1951 Broadway Cast)**
Loewe, Frederick *c*
Lerner, Alan Jay *l*
Allers, Franz *con*
I'm on my way / Rumson / What's goin' on here / I talk to the trees / They call the wind Maria / I still see Elsa / How can I wait / In between / Whoop-ti-ay / Carino mio / There's a coach comin' in / Hand me down that can o' beans / Another autumn / All for him / Wandrin' star
GD 60243 / Jan '90 / RCA Victor

☐ **PAJAMA GAME, THE (Cast Recording)**
Overture / Pyjama game / Racing with the clock / New town is a blue town / I'm not at all in love / I'll never be jealous again / Hey there / Sleep tite / Once a year day / Small talk / There once was a man / Think of the time I save / Factory music / Finale act 1 / Steam heat / Hernando's hideaway / Seven and a half cents / Exit music
CDTER2 1232 / 1 Sep '98 / TER

☐ **PAL JOEY (1980 London Cast)**
Rodgers, Richard *c*
Hart, Lorenz *l*
Fiske, John *con*
Overture / You mustn't kick it around / I could write a book / Chicago / That terrific rainbow / What is a man / Happy hunting horn / Bewitched bothered and bewildered / Pal Joey / Flower garden of my heart / Zip / Plant you now dig you later / In our little den / Do it the hard way / Take him / Bewitched bothered and bewildered
CDTER 1005 / Aug '98 / TER

☐ **PAL JOEY (Highlights) (London Cast)**
Rodgers, Richard *c*
Hart, Lorenz *l*
You mustn't kick it around / I could write a book / That terrific rainbow / What is a man / Happy hunting horn / Bewitched bothered and bewildered / Flower garden of my heart / Zip / Plant you now dig you later / In our little den / Do it the hard way / Take him
SHOWCD 008 / Feb '95 / Showtime

☐ **PAL JOEY (Broadway Cast)**
Rodgers, Richard *c*
Hart, Lorenz *l*
ZDM 7646962 / Apr '93 / EMI Classics

☐ **PAL JOEY**
Rodgers, Richard *c*
Hart, Lorenz *l*
DRGCD 94763 / Oct '95 / DRG

☐ **PALERMO MILANO - SOLO ANDATA**
Donaggio, Pino *c*
VCDS 7017 / Apr '96 / Varese Sarabande

☐ **PANAMERICANA (A Film Music Journey From Alaska To Tierra Del Fuego) (Berlin Radio Symphony Orchestra)**
Zillig, Winfried *c*
Fritzsch, Georg *con*
9026626592 / Jun '96 / RCA Victor

☐ **PAPER, THE**
Newman, Randy *c*
Newman, Randy *con*
Opening / Clocks / Henry goes to work / Sun / Bernie calls deanne / Busting the guys / Marty and Henry / Newsroom 700 PM / More clocks / Henry leaves with McDougal / Bernie finds Deanne / Bernie / Stop the presses / Henry's fired / Marty / Marty's in trouble / To the hospital / Little polenta is born / New day / 7.00 A.M. / Make up your mind
9362456162 / Feb '94 / WEA

☐ **PAPILLON**
Goldsmith, Jerry *c*
Goldsmith, Jerry *con*
Papillon / Camp / Reunion / New friend / Freedom / Gift from the sea / Antonio's death / Cruel sea / Hospital / Survival
FILMCD 029 / Sep '88 / Silva Screen

☐ **PARADISE BEACH**
Elated / Holiday / Laughing (on the outside) / Train of thought / Freedom / Satisfy me / Under the sun / R U sexin' me / It's the love / This isn't love / 747 / Break in the weather / We got it goin' on / Juliette / Weekend / Faith in love / Choir girl / Boy
4509934472 / Apr '93 / East West

☐ **PARDON MY ENGLISH (Cast Recording)**
Gershwin, George *c*
Gershwin, Ira *l*
Stern, Eric *con*
7559793382 / Nov '94 / Nonesuch

☐ **PARIS BLUES**
Ellington, Duke *c*
RCD 10713 / 12 Jan '98 / Rykodisc

☐ **PARIS S'EVEILLE (Cale, John)**
Cale, John *c*
TWI 9522 / Mar '96 / Les Disques Du Crepuscule

☐ **PARIS S'EVEILLE (Suivi D'Autres Compositions) (Cale, John)**
Cale, John *c*
YMCD 006 / Nov '95 / Yellow Moon

☐ **PARIS, TEXAS (Cooder, Ry)**
Cooder, Ry *c*
Paris Texas / Brothers / Nothing out there / Cancion mixteca / No safety zone / Houston in two seconds / She's leaving the bank / On the couch / I knew these two people / Dark was the night
9252702 / Feb '92 / WEA

☐ **PARK IS MINE, THE (Tangerine Dream)**
Tangerine Dream *c*
FILMCD 080 / Oct '91 / Silva Screen

☐ **PART OF YOUR WORLD**
Shapiro, Debbie *c*
VSD 5452 / Jun '94 / Varese Sarabande

☐ **PARTY PARTY**
Party party: *Costello, Elvis* / Run Rudolph run: *Edmunds, Dave* / No woman no cry: *Black, Pauline* / Yakety yak: *Bad Manners* / Elizabethan reggae: *Bad Manners* / Tutti frutti: *Sting* / Need your love so bad: *Sting* / No feelings: *Bananarama* / Band of gold: *Modern Romance* / Little town flirt: *Altered Images* / Man who sold the world: *Ure, Midge* / Auld lang syne: *Chas & Dave*
5514402 / Aug '95 / Spectrum

☐ **PASSION (London Cast)**
Sondheim, Stephen *c*
CASTCD 61 / 6 Oct '97 / First Night

☐ **PASSION FISH**
DR 3008 / Apr '93 / Daring

☐ **PASSION FLOWER HOTEL (1965 London Cast)**
Barry, John *c*
Peacock, Trevor *l*
Holmes, Richard *con*
SMK 66175 / Jul '94 / Sony West End

☐ **PASSION IN JAZZ**
Sondheim, Stephen *c*
VSD 5556 / Nov '94 / Varese Sarabande

☐ **PATIENCE (D'Oyly Carte Opera Chorus/New Symphony Orchestra)**
Sullivan, Sir Arthur *c*
Gilbert, W.S. *l*
Godfrey, I. *con*
Overture / Twenty love sick maidens we / Still brooding on their mad infatuation / I cannot tell what this love may be / Soldiers of our queen / In a doleful train / When I first put this unifrom on / Am I alone and unodserved / Long years ago / Prithee pretty maiden / Though to marry you would really selfish be / Let the merry symbols sound / Now tell us we pray you / Heatt broken at my patience barbarity / Stay we implore you / Your maiden's heart / Come walk up and purchase with avidity / And are you going a ticket for to buy / Hold stay your hand / True love must singlehearted be / I hear the soft note / Oh list while we love a confess / On such eyes as ravens cherish / Sad is that a woman's lot / Silver'd is the raven hair / Turn oh turn in this direction / Magnet hung in a hardware shop / Love is a plaintive song / So go to him and say to him / It's clear that medieval art / If Saphir I choose to marry / When I go out of door / I'm a Waterloo house young man / Finale act 2 / After much debate internal / Duke's song / Sorcerer overture / Utopia ltd / Ruggigore overture
4251932 / Jan '90 / London

☐ **PATIENCE (D'Oyly Carte Opera Chorus)**
Sullivan, Sir Arthur *c*
Gilbert, W.S. *l*
CDTER2 1213 / Nov '97 / TER

☐ **PATIENCE/PRINCESS IDA (Oldham, Derek & George Baker/Sir Henry Lytton/D'Oyly Carte Opera Chorus & Symphony Orchestra)**
Sullivan, Sir Arthur *c*
Gilbert, W.S. *l*
Sargent, Sir Malcolm *con*
75605522732 / Aug '96 / Happy Days

☐ **PATLABOR II**
DSCD 15 / Jun '96 / Demon

☐ **PATTON/TORA TORA TORA**
VSD 5796 / 20 Oct '97 / Varese Sarabande

☐ **PAULIE**
Debney, John *c*
Pauline medley / Ivy and Paulie head out / Cancion del mariachi: *Bandidos De Amor* / Bungled burglar / Misha's memory / New discoveries/Paulie and cat / Estoy loco: *Bandidos De Amor* / Paulie's big flight: *Bandidos De Amor* / Reunion with Marie: *Alvorado, Trini*
VSD 5936 / 20 Jul '98 / Varese Sarabande

☐ **PAWNBROKER, THE/THE DEADLY AFFAIR (Jones, Quincy Orchestra)**
Jones, Quincy *c*
Jones, Quincy *con*
5312332 / Jun '96 / Verve

☐ **PEAU D'ANE (& Other Masterworks)**
Legrand, Michel *c*
302256 / Feb '97 / Playtime

☐ **PEE WEE'S BIG ADVENTURE/BACK TO SCHOOL**
Elfman, Danny *c*
VCD 47281 / Jan '89 / Varese Sarabande

☐ **PEG (1984 London Cast)**
Heneker, David *c*
CDTER 1024 / Dec '94 / TER

☐ **PENITENT**
VCD 47299 / '87 / Varese Sarabande

☐ **PENNIES FROM HEAVEN**
POTTCD 300 / May '93 / Connoisseur Collection

☐ **PEOPLE'S CENTURY, THE**
Up in the air / Age of Hope: Paris 1990 / March of the Women-Plymouth Music Festival Choir / Cry of the Africans: *Soweto Teachers Choir* / Killing Fields: Lambs to the Slaughter / What a life: *Latymer Upper School Boys* / Oui oui Marie: *Fields, Arthur & Orchestra* / Killing fields: Mud: *Fields, Arthur & Orchestra* / My kuznetsky: *Fields, Arthur & Orchestra* / Red flag: *Fields, Arthur & Orchestra* / Lost Peace: New Nations: *Fields, Arthur & Orchestra* / Badenviller: *Fields, Arthur & Orchestra* / Lost peace: Lost Hopes / On the line / Great escape: celluloid dreams / Take your girlie to the movies: *Murray, Billy & The Orchestra* / Toot toot tootsie goodbye: *Jolson, Al & Vibraphone Orchestra* / Great Escape: end of an era: *Jolson, Al & Vibraphone Orchestra* / Panic is on: *Jenkins, Hazekiah* / Breadline: walking the streets: *Jenkins, Hazekiah* / I ain't got no home anymore: *Guthrie, Woody* / Breadline : a new deal: *Guthrie, Woody* / Babe Ruth: *Pasadena Roof Orchestra* / I do like to see a game of football: *Kyte, Sydney* / Sporting fever: *Kyte, Sydney* / Master race: factory street and farm / Verkirte nacht op 4 / Total war / Symphony no.7 in c / Flying home: *Miller, Glenn & The Army Air Force Band* / Barbed wire: *Miller, Glenn & The Army Air Force Band* / Va-voom time: *Miller, Glenn & The Army Air Force Band* / Boom time: *Miller, Glenn & The Army Air Force Band* / Independence day: *Miller, Glenn & The Army Air Force Band* / Freedom now:Independence day: *Miller, Glenn & The Army Air Force Band* / Ghana freedom: *Mensah, E.T. Tempos Dance Band* / Sweat of their labours: *Mensah, E.T. Tempos Dance Band*
CDVIP 177 / Apr '97 / Virgin VIP

☐ **PERCY (Kinks)**
Davies, Ray *c*
God's children / Lola / Way love used to be / Completely / Running round town / Moments / Animals in the zoo / Just friends / Whip lady / Dreams / Helga / Willesden Green / End titles
CLACD 164 / Dec '89 / Castle

☐ **PERFECT MURDER**
Howard, James Newton *c*
VSD 5946 / 20 Jul '98 / Varese Sarabande

☐ **PERFORMANCE**
Nitzsche, Jack *c*
Gone dead train: *Jagger, Mick* / Performance / Get away / Powis Square / Rolls Royce / Dyed dead red / Harry Flowers / Memo from Turner: *Jagger, Mick* / Hashishin / Wake up niggers / Poor white hound dog / Natural magic / Turner's murder
7599264002 / Oct '93 / WEA

☐ **PET SEMATARY (Goldenthal, Elliot)**
Goldenthal, Elliot *c*
VSD 5227 / Jul '89 / Varese Sarabande

☐ **PETER AND THE WOLF (A Musical Tale For Children & Orchestral Underscore) (RCA Symphony Orchestra)**
Prokofiev, Sergei/Cameron Patrick *c*
Daugherty, George *con*
Introduction / Peter and the meadow / Peter and the bird / Duck / Cat / Grandfather / Wolf / Cat was the first one in the meadow to notice the wolf / Here's how things stood in the meadow / Peter tugged on the rope / Hunters / Duck ballet / Peter takes charge / Grandfather reappears / Grand parade / Main title / Grandfather's morning / Reunion / Taxi driver / Peter and Grandfather / Meadow / Familiar ring / Story / I am Peter / Little yellow suit / Grandfather's memories / Peter's adventure/Finale
74321318692 / Sep '96 / RCA Victor

☐ **PETER PAN (Film Cast)**
Wallace, Oliver & Paul Smith *c*
Main title / Second star to the right / You can fly / Pirate's life / Following the leader / What made the red man red / Your mother and mine / Elegant Captain Hook / Never smile at a crocodile / Finale
WD 775832 / Mar '98 / Disney Music & Stories

☐ **PETER PAN (1994 London Cast)**
CASTCD 46 / Dec '94 / First Night

☐ **PETER PAN (Film Cast)**
Wallace, Oliver & Paul Smith *c*
VSD 5722 / Nov '96 / Varese Sarabande

☐ **PETER'S FRIENDS**
Everybody wants to rule the world: *Tears For Fears* / My baby just cares for me: *Simone, Nina* / You're my best friend: *Queen* / Girls just wanna have fun: *Lauper, Cyndi* / If you let me stay: *D'Arby, Terence Trent* / Hungry heart: *Springsteen, Bruce* / Don't get me wrong: *Pretenders* / King of rock 'n' roll: *Prefab Sprout* / What's love got to do with it: *Turner, Tina* / Give me strength: *Clapton, Eric* / Love and regret: *Deacon Blue* / Let's stay together: *Pasadenas* / Rio: *Nesmith, Michael* / Wherever I lay my hat: *Young, Paul* / I guess that's why they call it the blues: *John, Elton* / As the days go by: *Braithwaite, Daryl*
MOODCD 27 / Nov '92 / Epic

☐ **PHAEDRA**
Theodorakis, Mikis *c*
Love theme from Phaedra / Rendezvous / Ship to shore / London's fog / One more time / Agapimou / Only you / Fling / Candlelight / Rodostimo / Love theme: *Mercouri, Melina* / Goodbye John Sebastian
SR 50060 / Oct '93 / Sakkaris

☐ **PHANTOM (1993 Broadway Cast)**
Yeston, Maury *c*
09026616602 / May '93 / RCA Victor

☐ **PHANTOM OF THE OPERA (Budapest Studio Symphony Orchestra)**
Segal, Misha *c*
Segal, Misha *con*
Phantom of the opera - main title / Don Juan triumphant/Travel through time / Phantom's lair/ Hellbound (Freddy at the opera)/Maddie / Young Phantom's piano etude / You are him/Into the lair / Phantom on fire/The Phantom's face / Salon talk / Jewel song / Music of the knife/Killing Joseph / Graveyard violin/Pact with the devil/Richard gets killed / Ride to the cemetery/The cursed manuscript/ What's in the clo / Wedding/The intruder from Springwood/Christine's decision / Mott stalks the Phantom/Davis' death/Phantom's fiery death / Finale/End title
FILMCD 069 / Jun '90 / Silva Screen

☐ **PHANTOM OF THE OPERA (1986 London Cast)**
Lloyd Webber, Andrew *c*
Hart, Charles *l*
Overture / Think of me / Angel of music / Little Lotte / Mirror / Phantom of the opera / Music of the night / I remember / Stranger than you dreamt it / Magical lasso / Prima donna / Poor fool he makes me laugh / All I ask of you / Entr'acte / Masquerade / Why so silent / Twisted every way / Wishing you were somehow here again / Wandering child / Point of no return / Down once more / Phantom of the opera (finale)
8312732 / Feb '87 / Polydor

☐ **PHANTOM OF THE OPERA (Highlights) (Cast Recording)**
Lloyd Webber, Andrew *c*
Hart, Charles *l*
Think of me / Phantom of the opera / Music of the night / Prima donna / All I ask of you / En'tracte / Masquerade / Wishing you were somewhere here again / Point of no return
CDTER 1207 / Nov '97 / TER

☐ **PHANTOM OF THE OPERA (On Ice - Music & Songs)**
Lloyd Webber, Andrew *c*
Hart, Charles *l*
PZA 008CD / Apr '96 / Plaza

☐ **PHANTOM OF THE OPERA (& Jesus Christ Superstar/Cats/Evita - Aspects Of Broadway Vol.2) (Orchestra Of The Americas)**
Lloyd Webber, Andrew *c*
Freeman, Paul *con*
Phantom / Think of me / Angel of music / Phantom of the opera / All I ask of you / Masquerade / Music of the night / Superstar / Everything is alright / King Herod's song / I don't know how to love him / Overture / Jellicle songs for jellicle cats / Old gumbie cat / Macavity: the mystery cat / Shimbleshanks: the railway cats / Memory / Buenos Aires / High flying adored / Don't cry for me Argentina / She is a diamond / Another suitcase another hall / Finale
SION 18302 / Jul '97 / Sion

☐ **PHANTOM OF THE OPERA (Carl Davis' New 1925 Score) (City Of Prague Philharmonic Orchestra)**
Davis, Carl *c*
Davis, Carl *con*
FILMCD 193 / Nov '97 / Silva Screen

☐ **PHANTOM OF THE OPERA/ASPECTS OF LOVE (Highlights - The Shows Collection) (Cast Recording)**
Lloyd Webber, Andrew *c*
Hart, Charles/Don Black *l*
Phantom of the Opera / All I ask of you / Wishing you were somehow here again / Think of me / Music of the night / Love changes everything / There is more to love / First man you remember / Chanson d'enfance / Anything but lonely / Seeing is believing / Journey of a lifetime
PWKS 4164 / Oct '93 / Carlton

☐ **PHANTOM OF THE OPERA/CATS (Cast Recording)**
Lloyd Webber, Andrew *c*
Hart, Charles *l*
340782 / Oct '95 / Koch

☐ **PHANTOM, THE**
Newman, David *c*
Newman, David *con*
74321393252 / Feb '97 / Milan

☐ **PHENOMENA (Goblin)**
Simonetti, Claudio *c*
DCMDF 303 / Sep '97 / Cinevox

☐ **PHILADELPHIA (Songs)**
Streets of Philadelphia: *Springsteen, Bruce* / Love town: *Gabriel, Peter* / It's in your eyes: *Washington, Pauletta* / Ibo Lele (dreams come true): *Ram* / Please send me someone to love: *Sade* / Have you ever seen the rain: *Spin Doctors* / I don't want to talk about it: *Indigo Girls* / La mamma morta: *Callas, Maria* / Philadelphia: *Young, Neil* / Precedent: *Shore, Howard*
4749982 / Mar '94 / Epic

☐ **PHILADELPHIA EXPERIMENT/ MOTHER LODE (National Philharmonic Orchestra)**
Wannberg, Ken *c*
Wannberg, Ken *con*
PCD 121 / Mar '93 / Prometheus

☐ **PIANO, THE (Munich Philharmonic Orchestra)**
Nyman, Michael *c*
Nyman, Michael *con*
To the edge of the earth / Big my secret / Wild and distant shore / Heart asks pleasure first / Here to there / Promise / Bed of ferns / Fling / Scent of love / Deep in the forest / Mood that passes through you / Lost and found / Embrace / Little impulse / Sacrifice / I clipped your wing / Wounded / All imperfect things / Dreams of a journey / Heart asks pleasure first/The promise
CDVEX 919 / May '94 / Venture

☐ **PICKWICK (1993 London Cast)**
Ornadel, Cyril *c*
Bricusse, Leslie *l*
Prologue/Business is booming/Debtor's lament / Talk / That's what I'd like for Christmas / Pickwickians / Bit of a character / There's something about you / You've never met a fella like me / Look into your heart / Hell of an election / If I ruled the world / Do as you would be done by
SHOWCD 023 / Oct '96 / Showtime

☐ **PICKWICK/SCROOGE (Cast Recording)**
Bricusse, Leslie *c*
340812 / Oct '95 / Koch

☐ **PICTURE BRIDE**
Eidelman, Cliff *c*
VSD 5651 / Jul '95 / Varese Sarabande

☐ **PILLOW TALK**
DeVol, Frank *c*
Pillow talk: *Day, Doris* / Inspiration to Eileen: *Hudson, Rock* / Tabasco sauce for Alma's hangover / Inspiration to Yvette: *Hudson, Rock* / Alma's second hangover / Telephone inspector's visit / Alma's third hangover / Jan and Alma's discussion / Bedroom problems / Jonathan's proposal / Alma's eavesdropping on Brad / Jonathan's visit to Brad's pad / Brad's 'tree' theory on bachelorhood / Jan's refusal to Brad's attempt for date / Inspiration to Marie: Hudson, Rock / Jonathan's offer to drive Jan home / Theme / Copra Del Rio mambo / Jan and Jonathan's dance / First appearance as Rex / Sending Jonathan's taxi home / Brad squeezing into Jonathan's car / Brad's legs dangling over the car door / Brad's efforts to get out of the car / Taxi ride / At Jan's apartment door / Theme / Like a potbelly stove on a frosty morning / Jonathan's evasion to meet Brad's cousin Moose / Jan and Brad do the town / Jan you can't live in... / Jonathan objection / Roly poly: *Day, Doris & Rock Hudson/Perry Blackwell* / I wonder if I can get the recipe / Brad setting the trap for Jan / Is that all it is withus friendship / Jan falling right into it / I need no atmosphere: *Blackwell, Perry* / You lied: *Blackwell, Perry* / Jan packing and telephoning to inform Brad how wrong he was / Jonathan sending Brad on his way / Possess me: *Day, Doris* / Romantic scene in front of a fireplace / Brad trying to hide the music for inspiration / Jan's first suspicion / Jan ready to leave / Jonathan rushing to expose Rex / New York 80 miles / You got an apartment / She decorates apartments / Right right Alma's advice / Jan's business visit to Brad's apartment / Brad bidding goodbye to all former girlfriends / Jan ordering strange objects for her projects / Newly finished Chamber of Horrors / Brad in Jan's bedroom / They'll never believe this in Wichita Falls / Brad carrying Jan back to the scene of her crime / Inspiration / Brad kidnapped by an obstetrician and his nurse / Pillow talk: *Day, Doris* / Pillow talk: *Hudson, Rock* / Inspiration: *Hudson, Rock* / Roly poly: *Hudson, Rock* / Introduction: *Day, Doris* / Pillow talk: *Day, Doris* / Inspiration: *Hudson, Rock* / Roly poly: *Day, Doris & Rock Hudson* / Possess me: *Day, Doris* / Pillow talk: *Day, Doris* / Inspiration: *Day, Doris* / Roly poly: *Day, Doris* / Possess me: *Day, Doris* / Pillow talk: *Day, Doris* / Doris Day introduces movie dialogue segments: *Day, Doris* / Rock Hudson introduces movie dialogue segments: *Hudson, Rock*
BCD 15913 / Oct '96 / Bear Family

☐ **PILLOWBOOK, THE**
LBS 197101 / Jan '97 / XIII Bis

☐ **PINOCCHIO (The Adventures Of Pinocchio)**
Wonder, Stevie & Brina May/Rachel Portman *c*
4527402 / Oct '96 / Decca

☐ **PINOCCHIO**
WD 754302 / Mar '96 / Disney Music & Stories

☐ **PIRATES OF PENZANCE, THE (Highlights) (D'Oyly Carte Opera Chorus)**
Sullivan, Sir Arthur *c*
Gilbert, W.S. *l*
Overture / When Fred'ric was a little lad / Oh better far to live and die / Oh is there not one maiden breast / Poor wandering one / I am the very model / Oh dry the glistening tear / When the foreman bares his steel / When you had left our pirates fold / When a felon's not engaged in his employment / With cat-like tread / Finale
SHOWCD 010 / Feb '95 / Showtime

☐ **PIRATES OF PENZANCE, THE (D'Oyly Carte Opera Chorus/Royal Philharmonic Orchestra)**
Sullivan, Sir Arthur *c*
Gilbert, W.S. *l*
Godfrey, I. *con*
4251962 / Jan '90 / Decca

□ **PIRATES OF PENZANCE, THE (Glyndebourne Festival Choir/Pro Arte Orchestra)**
Sullivan, Sir Arthur *c*
Gilbert, W.S. *l*
Sargent, Sir Malcolm *con*
CMS 7644092 / Apr '94 / EMI Classics

□ **PIRATES OF PENZANCE, THE (D'Oyly Carte Opera Chorus/Orchestra)**
Sullivan, Sir Arthur *c*
Gilbert, W.S. *l*
Pryce Jones, J. *con*
CDTER2 1177 / Nov '97 / TER

□ **PIRATES OF PENZANCE, THE (Welsh National Opera Choir/Orchestra)**
Sullivan, Sir Arthur *c*
Gilbert, W.S. *l*
Mackerras, Sir Charles *con*
CD 80353 / Nov '93 / Telarc

□ **PIRATES OF PENZANCE, THE/HMS PINAFORE (Complete 1929/1930 Recordings) (D'Oyly Carte Opera Chorus & Orchestra/London Symphony Orchestra)**
Sullivan, Sir Arthur *c*
Gilbert, W.S. *l*
Sargent, Sir Malcolm *con*
890022 / May '96 / Romophone

□ **PIRATES OF PENZANCE, THE/THE SORCERER (D'Oyly Carte Opera Chorus/New Symphony Orchestra)**
Sullivan, Sir Arthur *c*
Gilbert, W.S. *l*
Sargent, Sir Malcolm *con*
Z 80682 / Nov '87 / Arabesque

□ **PLAIN AND FANCY (Broadway Cast)**
Hague, Albert *c*
Horwitt, Arnold *l*
ZDM 7647622 / Apr '93 / EMI Classics

□ **PLANET OF THE APES (Remastered With Extra Music)**
Goldsmith, Jerry *c*
Goldsmith, Jerry *con*
FMT 8006D / Dec '92 / Intrada

□ **PLANET OF THE APES**
Goldsmith, Jerry *c*
Goldsmith, Jerry *con*
VSD 5848 / 20 Oct '97 / Varese Sarabande

□ **PLATOON**
Village: *Vancouver Symphony Orchestra* / Tracks of my tears: *Robinson, Smokey* / Okie from Muskogee: *Haggard, Merle* / Hello I love you: *Doors* / White rabbit: *Jefferson Airplane* / Barnes shoots Elias: *Vancouver Symphony Orchestra* / Respect: *Franklin, Aretha* / (Sittin' on) the dock of the bay: *Redding, Otis* / When a man loves a woman: *Sledge, Percy* / Groovin': *Rascals* / Adagio for strings: *Vancouver Symphony Orchestra*
7817422 / Jun '87 / Atlantic

□ **PLATOON LEADER**
Clinton, George *c*
GNPD 8013 / Jan '89 / GNP Crescendo

□ **PLAY ON (Original Broadway Cast)**
Ellington, Duke *c*
VSD 5837 / Jul '97 / Varese Sarabande

□ **PLAYER, THE**
Newman, Thomas *c*
VSD 5366 / May '92 / Varese Sarabande

□ **PLAYER'S CLUB, THE**
5408862 / 6 Apr '98 / A&M

□ **PLEASE SAVE MY EARTH**
Kanno, Yoko *c*
AM 6 / Nov '96 / Animanga

□ **POCAHONTAS**
WDR 75462 / Oct '96 / Disney Music & Stories

□ **POCAHONTAS (Singalong)**
WD 481424 / Nov '96 / Disney Music & Stories

□ **POINT BREAK**
Nobody rides for free: *Ratt* / Over the edge: *L.A. Guns* / I will not fall: *Wiretrain* / I want you: *Concrete Blonde* / 7 and 7 is: *Liquid Jesus* / Smoke on the water: *Loudhouse* / My city: *Shark Island* / Criminal: *Public Image Ltd* / So long cowboy: *Westworld* / Hundreds of tears: *Crow, Sheryl*
MCLD 19327 / Sep '96 / MCA

□ **POLTERGEIST**
Goldsmith, Jerry *c*
Star Spangled Banner / Calling / Neighbourhood / Tree / Clown / They're here / Broken glass / TV people / Twisted abduction / Contacting the other side / Light / Night visitor / No complaints / It knows what scares you / Rebirth / Night of the beast / Escape from surburbia
8219752 / 13 Oct '97 / Premier/EMI

□ **POLTERGEIST (The Legacy)**
SI 8701 / 1 Dec '97 / Sonic Images

□ **POLTERGEIST II**
Goldsmith, Jerry *c*
Power / Late call / Smoke / Worm / Reaching out
VCD 47266 / Jan '89 / Varese Sarabande
CDTER 1116 / Jan '92 / TER

□ **POLTERGEIST III**
Renzetti, Joe *c*
VCD 70462 / Jan '89 / Varese Sarabande

□ **PONDICHERY**
Meer, Stephane *c*
SMC 35705 / Jun '97 / Sergent M

□ **POPPIE NONGENA (1983 Cast)**
Mgcina, Sophie *c*
Kotze, Sandra & Elsa Joubert *l*
Amen / Taru bawo / Wenzeni na / U Jehovah / Uzubale / Makoti / Lalasana / Jerusalem / Nkosi Sikela l'Afrika / Zisana abantwane / Bantwena besikolo / Liza Lisi Dinga / Mampondo mse
HNCD 1351 / Jan '87 / Hannibal

□ **PORGY AND BESS (Film Cast)**
Gershwin, George *c*
Gershwin, Ira & DuBose Heyward *l*
Previn, Andre *con*
SMK 64314 / Nov '93 / Sony Classical

□ **PORGY AND BESS (1942 Broadway Cast)**
Gershwin, George *c*
Gershwin, Ira & DuBose Heyward *l*
Overture/Summertime / Woman is a sometime thing / My man's gone now / It takes a long pull to get there / I got plenty o' nuttin' / Buzzard song / Bess you is my woman now / It ain't necessarily so / What you want wid Bess / Strawberry woman's call - crab man's call / I loves you Porgy / Requiem / There's a boat dat's leavin' soon for New York / Porgy's lament/Finale
MCLD 19158 / Jan '94 / MCA

□ **PORGY AND BESS (Scenes) (Price, Leontyne)**
Gershwin, George *c*
Gershwin, Ira & DuBose Heyward *l*
GD 85234 / Mar '95 / RCA

□ **PORGY AND BESS (Highlights) (Houston Grand Opera)**
Gershwin, George *c*
Gershwin, Ira & DuBose Heyward *l*
DeMain, J. *con*
RD 84680 / '88 / RCA Victor

□ **PORGY AND BESS (White, Willard & Cynthia Haymon/Glyndebourne Festival OperaCast/London Philharmonic Orchestra)**
Gershwin, George *c*
Gershwin, Ira & DuBose Heyward *l*
Rattle, Simon *con*
CDS 5562202 / Aug '97 / EMI Classics

□ **PORGY AND BESS (Highlights) (White, Willard & Cynthia Haymon/Glyndebourne Festival OperaCast/London Philharmonic Orchestra)**
Gershwin, George *c*
Gershwin, Ira & DuBose Heyward *l*
Rattle, Simon *con*
CDC 7543252 / Apr '93 / EMI Classics

□ **PORGY AND BESS (Suite From Porgy & Bess) (Houdini's & Nieuw Sinfonietta, Amsterdam)**
Gershwin, George *c*
Gershwin, Ira & DuBose Heyward *l*
CCS 8395 / Nov '95 / Channel Classics

□ **PORGY AND BESS (Torme, Mel/Frances Faye/Duke Ellington Orchestra/Russ Garcia Orchestra)**
Gershwin, George *c*
Gershwin, Ira & DuBose Heyward *l*
BET 6028 / Jan '95 / Bethlehem

□ **PORGY AND BESS (Highlights) (White, Willard & Leona Mitchell/McHenry Boatwright/Barbara Hendricks/Cleveland Orchestra)**
Gershwin, George *c*
Gershwin, Ira & DuBose Heyward *l*
Maazel, L. *con*
4363062 / May '97 / Argo

□ **PORGY AND BESS (Henderson, Joe)**
Gershwin, George *c*
Gershwin, Ira & DuBose Heyward *l*
Intro/Jasbo Brown blues / Summertime: *Henderson, Joe & Chaka Khan* / Here come de honeyman/They pass by singin' / My man's gone now / I got plenty o' nuttin' / Bess you is my woman now / T'ain't necessarily so: *Henderson, Joe & Sting* / I loves you Porgy / There's a boat dat's leavin' soon for New York / Oh Bess where's my Bess / Summertime
5390482 / Oct '97 / Verve

□ **PORGY AND BESS (1951 Studio Recording)**
Gershwin, George *c*
Gershwin, Ira & DuBose Heyward *l*
Engel, Lehman *con*
MH2K 63322 / Jun '98 / Masterworks Heritage

□ **PORGY AND BESS/BLUE MONDAY**
Gershwin, George *c*
CD 80434 / 6 Jul '98 / Telarc

□ **POSTMAN, THE**
Howard, James Newton *c*
Main titles / Shelter in the storm / Belly of the beast / General Bethlehem / Abby comes calling / Restored united states / Postman / Almost home: *Manson, Jono* / Next big thing: *Manson, Jono* / This perfect world: *Manson, Jono* / Once this was the promised land: *Coinman, John* / I miss my radio: *Manson, Jono & John Coinman* / Come and get your lvoe: *Coinman, John* / You didn't have to be so nice: *Grant, Amy & Kevin Costner*
9362468422 / 9 Mar '98 / Warner Bros.

□ **POUR RIRE**
Del Fra, Ricardo *c*
SMC 35701 / Apr '97 / Sergent M

□ **POWAQQATSI**
Glass, Philip *c*
Riesman, Michael *con*
755991922 / Aug '88 / Nonesuch

□ **POWER OF ONE, THE**
Zimmer, Hans *c*
Rainmaker / Mother Africa / Of death and dying / Limpopo river song / Power of one / Woza Mfana / Southland concerto / Senzenina / Penny whistle song / Funeral song / Wangal unozipho / Mother Africa (reprise)
7559613352 / Oct '92 / Elektra

□ **PRAYER FOR THE DYING, A (Graunke Symphony Orchestra)**
Scott, John *c*
Scott, John *con*
JSCD 1202 / Jan '88 / JOS

□ **PREACHER'S WIFE, THE (Houston, Whitney)**
I believe in you and me / Step by step / Joy / Hold on help is on the way / Go to the rock / I love the Lord / Who'd imagine a king / Lord is my shepherd / Somebody bigger than you and I / My heart is calling / You were loved / I believe in you and me / Step by step / Joy to the world
07822189512
74321441252 / Dec '96 / Arista

□ **PREACHING TO THE PERVERTED**
Welcome to the house of Thwax: *Fiennes, Magnus & Maya* / Evil queen: *Shimmon & Woolfson* / Journey into hell: *Fiennes, Magnus & Maya* / Sycophantasy: *Rejuvination* / Postman always rings Thwice: *Fiennes, Magnus & Maya* / Alien spoke: *Broom, Mark* / In zebra suspension: *Fiennes, Magnus & Maya* / Mind: *Aloof* / Ajare: *Way Out West* / Enlightenment: *Fiennes, Magnus & Maya* / Goodmorning mistress: *Fiennes, Magnus & Maya* / Wastelands: *Fiennes, Magnus & Maya* / Who are you: *Omni Trio* / Aerobix: *Percy X* / Futura: *Amethyst* / Grind transubmission: *Fiennes, Magnus & Maya* / House of Thwax reprised: *Fiennes, Magnus & Maya*
PERVCDLIM 001 / 8 Dec '97 / Naked
PERVCDLP 001 / Jul '97 / Naked

□ **PREDATOR II**
Silvestri, Alan *c*
VSD 5302 / Jan '91 / Varese Sarabande

□ **PRELUDE TO A KISS**
Shore, Howard *c*
111252 / May '94 / Milan

□ **PRESUMED INNOCENT**
Williams, John *c*
VSD 5280 / Oct '90 / Varese Sarabande

□ **PRET-A-PORTER**
Here comes the hotstepper: *Kamoze, Ini* / My girl Josephine: *Super Cat* / Here we come: *Salt 'N' Pepa* / Natural thing: *M People* / 70's love groove: *Jackson, Janet* / Jump on top of me: *Rolling Stones* / These boots were made for walkin': *Phillips, Sam* / Pretty: *Cranberries* / Martha: *Deep Forest* / Close to you: *Brand New Heavies* / Keep givin' me your love: *Peniston, Ce Ce* / Get wild: *New Power Generation* / Supermodel sandwich: *D'Arby, Terence Trent* / Lemon: *U2*
4782262 / Dec '96 / Columbia

□ **PRETTY WOMAN**
Wild women do: *Cole, Natalie* / Fame '90: *Bowie, David* / King of wishful thinking: *Go West* / Tangled: *Wiedlin, Jane* / It must have been love: *Roxette* / Life in detail: *Palmer, Robert* / No explanation: *Cetera, Peter* / Real wild child: *Otcasek, Christopher* / Fallen: *Wood, Lauren* / Oh pretty woman: *Orbison, Roy* / Show me your soul: *Red Hot Chili Peppers*
CDMTL 1052 / Apr '90 / EMI Manhattan

□ **PRETTYBELLE (Broadway Cast)**
VSD 5439 / Sep '93 / Varese Sarabande

□ **PRIDE AND PREJUDICE**
Davis, Carl *c*
Davis, Carl *con*
Pride and prejudice / Netherfield ball montage / Elizabeth observed / Piano summary / Canon Collins / Gardeners / Winter into Spring / Parting / Rosings / Telling the truth / Farewell to the regiment / Darcy returns / Thinking about Lizzie / Lydia's elopement / Return of Bingley / Double wedding
CDEMC 3726 / Aug '97 / EMI

□ **PRIEST OF LOVE**
Lawrence / English hotel trio / Variations / Mabel's tango / Frieda's theme (part 1) / Frieda's theme (part 2) / Italy / Cornwall / Fugue / Lawrence's death / Priest of love (finale) / Way we get it together
DSCD 1003 / Nov '85 / D-Sharp

□ **PRINCE OF DARKNESS**
Carpenter, John *c*
VCD 47310 / Jan '89 / Varese Sarabande

□ **PRINCESS BRIDE, THE (Knopfler, Mark)**
Knopfler, Mark *c*
Once upon a time...storybook love / I will never love again / Florin dance / Morning ride / Friends' song / Cliffs of insanity / Sword fight / Guide my sword / Fire swamp and the rodents of unusual size / Revenge / Happy ending / Storybook love
8328642 / Mar '97 / Vertigo

□ **PRINCESS CARABOO**
Hartley, Richard *c*
VSD 5544 / Dec '94 / Varese Sarabande

□ **PRINCESS IDA/PINEAPPLE POLL (D'Oyly Carte Opera Chorus/Royal Philharmonic Orchestra/Philharmonia Orchestra)**
Sullivan, Sir Arthur *c*
Gilbert, W.S. *l*
Sargent, Malcolm/C. Mackerras *con*
4368102 / Jan '90 / London

□ **PRISONER VOL.1, THE**
Grainer, Ron/Wilfred Josephs/Albert Elms *c*
Arrival / A B and C / Free For All / General / Fall Out / Many Happy Returns / Dance Of The Dead / Checkmate / Hammer Into Anvil / Girl Who Was Death / Once Upon A Time
FILMCD 042 / Nov '89 / Silva Screen

□ **PRISONER VOL.2, THE**
Grainer, Ron/Wilfred Josephs/Albert Elms *c*
Arrival / Chimes of Big Ben / A B And C / Many happy returns / Checkmate / Dance of the dead / Do not forsake me oh my darling / Girl who was death / Fall out
FILMCD 084 / Jun '92 / Silva Screen

□ **PRISONER VOL.3, THE**
Grainer, Ron/Wilfred Josephs/Albert Elms *c*
Arrival / Chimes of Big Ben / A B and C / Free for all / General / Dance of the dead / Hammer into anvil / Change of mind / Do not forsake me oh my darling / Girl who was death / Fall out
FILMCD 126 / Nov '92 / Silva Screen

□ **PRIVATE LIVES OF ELIZABETH AND ESSEX, THE (Munich Symphony Orchestra)**
Korngold, Erich *c*
Davis, Carl *con*
Suite one / Suite two / Suite three / Suite four / Suite five / Suite six
VSD 5696 / 29 Jun '98 / Varese Sarabande

□ **PRIVATE PARTS - HOWARD STERN**
Pig virus / Great American nightmare: *Zombie, Rob & Howard Stern* / Mama look a boo boo / I make my own rules: *LL Cool J & Flea/Dave Navarro/Chad Smith* / Match game / Hard charger: *Porno For Pyros* / Moti / Suck for your solution: *Marilyn Manson* / Lance eluction / Pictures of matchstick men: *Osbourne, Ozzy & Type O Negative* / Contest / Tired of waiting for you: *Green Day* / WRNW / Pinhead: *Ramones* / Oh Howard / Ben Stern megamix / Howard Stern experience / Smoke on the water: *Deep Purple* / WCCC / I want you to help me: *Cheap Trick* / Antichrist / Cat scratch fever: *Nugent, Ted* / WNBC / Jamie's cryin': *Van Halen* / Crackhead Bob / You shook me all night long: *AC/DC* / Howard you stink / Ladies and gentlemen / Totured man: *Stern, Howard & The Dust Brothers*
9362464772 / Mar '97 / Warner Bros.

□ **PRIVATE PARTS/RICHTHOFEN AND BROWN (Graunke Symphony Orchestra)**
Friedhofer, Hugo *c*
Graunke, K. *con*
FE 8105 / Mar '94 / Facet

□ **PRODUCERS, THE (Music & Dialogue)**
Morris, John *c*
Morris, John *con*
Titles / Plot / Biallystock seduces bloom / World's worst play / Franz Liebkind / Little old ladyland / Ulla/ That's a toy / Producers / World's worst director / Auditioning 100 Hitlers / Love power / Opening night/Lobby overture / Springtime for Hitler / Background music / Disaster/Bar / Where did I go right / Courtroom / Prisoners of love
RE 2147 / Aug '97 / Razor & Tie

□ **PROFUNDO ROSSO (Goblin)**
Simonetti, Claudio *c*
CDMF 301 / 1 May '98 / Cinevox

□ **PROOF (Not Drowning, Waving)**
Not Drowning, Waving *c*
A 8927 / Jan '92 / Alhambra

□ **PROSPERO'S BOOKS (Leonard, Sarah/Marie Angel/Ute Lemper/Deborah Conway/Michael Nyman Band)**
Nyman, Michael *c*
Nyman, Michael *con*
4252242 / Nov '91 / Decca

□ **PROVIDENCE**
Rozsa, Miklos *c*
CDSL 9502 / Jul '92 / DRG

□ **PSYCHO (National Philharmonic Orchestra)**
Herrmann, Bernard *c*
Herrmann, Bernard *con*
UKCD 2021 / Nov '94 / Unicorn-Kanchana

☐ PSYCHO
Herrmann, Bernard c
VSD 5765 / 20 Oct '97 / Varese Sarabande

☐ PUBLIC EYE, THE
Isham, Mark c
VSD 5374 / Nov '92 / Varese Sarabande

☐ PULP FICTION
Miserlou: *Dale, Dick & His Del-Tones* / Jungle boogie: *Kool & The Gang* / Let's stay together: *Green, Al* / Bustin' surfboards: *Tornadoes* / Lonesome town: *Nelson, Ricky* / Son of a preacher man: *Springfield, Dusty* / Bullwinkle (part 2): *Centurions* / You never can tell: *Berry, Chuck* / Girl you'll be a woman soon: *Urge Overkill* / If love is a red dress (hang me in rags): *McKee, Maria* / Comanche: *Revels* / Flowers on the wall: *Statler Brothers* / Surf rider: *Lively Ones*
MCD 11103 / Sep '94 / MCA

☐ PUMP UP THE VOLUME
Everybody knows: *Concrete Blonde* / Why can't I fall in love: *Neville, Ivan* / Stand: *Liquid Jesus* / Wave of mutilation: *Pixies* / I've got a secret minature camera: *Murphy, Peter* / Kick out the jams: *Bad Brains & Henry Rollins* / Freedom of speech: *Above The Law* / Heretic: *Soundgarden* / Titanium expose: *Sonic Youth* / Me and the Devil blues: *Cowboy Junkies*
MCD 06121 / 8 Sep '97 / MCA

☐ PURE LUCK
Sheffer, Jonathan c
VSD 5330 / Aug '91 / Varese Sarabande

☐ PURPLE RAIN (Prince & The Revolution)
Prince c
Let's go crazy / Take me with U / Beautiful ones / Computer blue / Darling Nikki / When doves cry / I would die 4 U / Baby I'm a star / Purple rain
9251102 / Feb '95 / WEA

☐ PUSHER
MCD 85013 / 3 Oct '97 / MCA

☐ PUTTING IT TOGETHER (1993 US Cast)
Sondheim, Stephen c
Invocation and instructions to the audience / Putting it together / Rich and happy / Merrily we roll along / Everybody ought to have a maid / Sooner or later / Ah but underneath / Hello little girl / My husband the pig / Every day a little death / Have I got a girl for you / Pretty women / Now / Bang / Country house / Could I leave you / Back in business / Night waltzes / Love takes time / Remember / In praise of women / Perpetual anticipation / Sun won't set / Game sequence / What would we do without you / Gun song / Little priest / Miller's son / Live alone and like it / Sorry / Grateful / Sweet Polly Plunket / I could drive a person crazy / Marry me a little / Getting married today / Being alive / Like it was / Old friends
09026617292 / Jan '94 / RCA Victor

☐ PYROMANIACS LOVE STORY
Portman, Rachel c
VSD 5620 / Jun '95 / Varese Sarabande

Q

☐ QB VII
Goldsmith, Jerry c
Goldsmith, Jerry con
MAF 7061D / Jan '95 / Intrada

☐ QUADROPHENIA (Who)
I am the sea / Real me / I'm one / 5.15 / I've had enough / Love reign o'er me / Bell boy / Helpless dancer / Dr. Jimmy / Four faces / Get out and stay out / Joker James / Punk and the Godfather / Louie Louie: *Kingsmen* / Zoot suit: *High Numbers* / Hi-heel sneakers: *Cross Section* / Night train: *Brown, James* / Green onions: *Booker T & The MG's* / He's so fine: *Chiffons* / Rhythm of the rain: *Cascades* / Be my baby: *Ronettes* / Da doo ron ron: *Crystals*
5319712 / 6 Apr '98 / Polydor

☐ QUANTUM LEAP
Post, Mike c
GNPD 8036 / Nov '93 / GNP Crescendo

☐ QUARTET
CDQ 5551002 / Apr '94 / EMI

☐ QUEIMADA (Burn)
Morricone, Ennio c
VCDS 7020 / Oct '96 / Varese Sarabande

☐ QUEL MALEDETTO GIORNO DI FUOCO/ATTENTO GRINGO/LO CHIAMAVANO
Piccioni, Piero/Manuel De Sica c
CDCR 31 / Apr '96 / Silva Screen

☐ QUEST
Edelman, Randy c
VSD 5716 / May '96 / Varese Sarabande

☐ QUEST FOR FIRE
Sarde, Philippe c
CDFMC 1 / Jan '89 / Silva Screen

☐ QUICK AND THE DEAD, THE
Silvestri, Alan c
Redemption / Gunfight montage / Couldn't tell us apart / John Herod / Ellen's first round / Lady's the winner / Dinner tonight / Cort's story / Ellen vs. Dred / Kid vs. Herod / I don't wanna die / Big day / Ellen returns / Law's come back to town / Quick and the dead (End credits)
VSD 5595 / Oct '95 / Varese Sarabande

☐ QUIEN SABE
Bacalov, Luis Enriquez c
A 8932 / Jan '93 / Alhambra

☐ QUIET DAYS IN CLICHY
VMD 79303 / 27 Apr '98 / Vanguard

☐ QUIET MAN, THE (Dublin Screen Orchestra)
Young, Victor c
Alwyn, Kenneth con
SFC 1501 / Nov '97 / Silva Screen

☐ QUIET MAN, THE/SAMSON AND DELILAH
Young, Victor c
Young, Victor con
VSD 5497 / Jun '94 / Varese Sarabande

☐ QUIGLEY DOWN UNDER
Poledouris, Basil c
MAF 7006D / Jan '93 / Intrada

☐ QUILLER MEMORANDUM,THE
Barry, John c
VSD 5218 / Feb '90 / Varese Sarabande

R

☐ RADIO GALS (Cast Recording)
VSD 5604 / Jul '95 / Varese Sarabande

☐ RAGTIME (Broadway Cast)
Prologue-Ragtime / Goodbye my love / journey on / Crime of the century / What kind of woman / A shtetl iz Amereke / Success / Definition of ragtime / Getting ready rag / Henry Ford / Nothing like the city / Your daddy's son / Coalhouse arrives / New music / Wheels of a dream / Night that Goldman spoke at Union Square / Gliding / Trashing of the car / justice / President / Till we reach that day / Entr'acte / Harry Houdini / Master escapist / Coalhouse's soliloquy / Coalhouse demands / What a game / Fire in the city / Atlantic city / Buffalo nickel photoplay / Our children / Harlem sequence-Pas dedeux / Sarah brown eyes / He wanted to say / Back to before / Look what you've done / Make them hear you / Epilogue-Ragtime / Wheels of a dream
09026631672 / 6 Apr '98 / RCA Victor

☐ RAGTIME (Themes From The Musical)
Ragtime / Crime of the century / Your daddy's son / Gettin' ready rag / New music / Goodbye my love / Sarah Brown eyes / I have a feeling / Till we reach that day / Henry Ford / Back to before / What a game / Make them hear you / Ragtime
VSD 5880 / 18 May '98 / Varese Sarabande

☐ RAIDERS OF THE LOST ARK (Digitally Remastered) (London Symphony Orchestra)
Williams, John c
Williams, John con
RAIDERS 001 / Nov '95 / Silva Screen

☐ RAILWAY CHILDREN, THE (Jeffries, Lionel & Cast)
CDMFP 6373 / Apr '97 / Music For Pleasure

☐ RAINMAKER, THE
North, Alex c
TSU 0120 / Jan '95 / Tsunami

☐ RAINMAKER, THE
Bernstein, Elmer c
Bernstein, Elmer con
1621412 / 13 Feb '98 / Philips

☐ RAISE THE RED LANTERN
Jiping, Zhao c
887952 / Jan '95 / Milan

☐ RAISIN (Broadway Cast)
Woldin, Judd c
Roberts, Howard A. con
SK 32754 / Jan '95 / Sony Broadway

☐ RAMBO I
Goldsmith, Jerry c
FMT 8001D / Jan '89 / Intrada

☐ RAMBO II
Goldsmith, Jerry c
Main title / Preperation / Jump / Snake / Stories / Cage / Betrayed / Peace in our life / Escape from torture / Ambush / Revenge / Bowed down / Pilot over / Home flight / Day by day
VSD 47234 / Feb '90 / Varese Sarabande

☐ RAMBO III (Score) (Hungarian State Opera Orchestra)
Goldsmith, Jerry c
Goldsmith, Jerry con
RVF 6006D / Jan '90 / Intrada

☐ RANCHO DELUXE
Buffett, Jimmy c
Rancho Deluxe / Christmas bonus / Ridin' in style / Left me with a nail to drive / Rustlers that's us / Cattle truckin' / Countin' the cows ev'ry day / Wrangler / Rancho Deluxe / Livingston Saturday night / Dork / Some gothic ranch action / Wonder why you ever go home / Hood ornament / Fifteen gears / Can't remember when I last slept / Rancho Deluxe
RCD 10709 / 12 Jan '98 / Rykodisc

☐ RANSOM (AKA The Terrorist & The Chairman)
Goldsmith, Jerry c
Goldsmith, Jerry con
FILMCD 081 / Jul '91 / Silva Screen

☐ RANSOM
1620862 / Jan '97 / Polydor

☐ RAP MASTER RONNIE
Swados Satirical Revue c
Trudeau, Garry l
AEICD 012 / May '98 / AEI

☐ RAPA NUI
Copeland, Stewart c
214402 / Nov '94 / Milan

☐ RAPID FIRE
Young, Christopher c
VSD 5388 / Sep '92 / Varese Sarabande

☐ RAW DEAL
Bahler, Tom c
VSD 47286 / Feb '93 / Varese Sarabande

☐ RE-ANIMATOR/BRIDE OF THE RE-ANIMATOR
Band, Richard c
FILMCD 082 / '92 / Silva Screen

☐ RE-JOYCE (Lipman, Maureen)
Addinsell, Richard c
SCENECD 21 / '94 / First Night

☐ REAL MCCOY, THE
Fiedel, Brad c
Walker, S. con
VSD 5450 / Oct '93 / Varese Sarabande

☐ REALITY BITES
My Sharona: *Knack* / Spin the bottle: *Hatfield, Juliana* / Bed of roses: *Indians* / When you come back to me: *World Party* / Going going gone: *Posies* / Stay: *Loeb, Lisa & Nine Stories* / All I want is you: *U2* / Locked out: *Crowded House* / Spinning around after you: *Kravitz, Lenny* / I'm nuthin': *Hawke, Ethan* / Turnip farm: *Dinosaur Jnr* / Revival: *Me Phi Me* / Tempted (94): *Squeeze* / Baby I love your way: *Big Mountain*
07863663642 / Aug '96 / RCA

☐ REBECCA (& Alfred Newman's Selznick International Pictures Fanfare) (Bratislava Symphony Orchestra)
Waxman, Franz c
Adriano con
8223399 / Oct '92 / Marco Polo

☐ RED CORNER
Newman, Thomas c
0022882CIN / 26 May '98 / Cinerama

☐ RED DAWN
Poledouris, Basil c
Invasion / Drive-in / Let it turn / Woverines / Flowers / Eulogy / Robert's end / Death and freedom / End titles
RVF 6001D / Jan '89 / Intrada

☐ RED HOT AND BLUE/STARS IN YOUR EYES (Broadway Cast)
Porter, Cole c
AEICD 001 / May '98 / AEI

☐ RED KNIGHT, WHITE KNIGHT
Scott, John c
MAF 7016D / Jan '93 / Intrada

☐ RED SCORPION (Chattaway, Jay)
Chattaway, Jay c
VSD 5230 / Sep '89 / Varese Sarabande

☐ RED TENT, THE
Morricone, Ennio c
Love theme / Do dreams go on / Death at the Pole / Love like the snow / Message from Rome / They're alive / Farewell / Others who will follow us
LEGENDCD 15 / Aug '94 / Legend

☐ REIVERS, THE
Williams, John c
Williams, John con
CK 66130 / Apr '95 / Columbia

☐ REMAINS OF THE DAY, THE
Robbins, Richard c
Rabinowitz, H. con
CDQ 5550292 / Aug '94 / Angel

☐ RENAISSANCE MAN
Zimmer, Hans c
VSD 5502 / Aug '94 / Varese Sarabande

☐ RENT
DRD 50003 / 11 May '98 / Dreamworks

☐ REPLACEMENT KILLERS, THE (Gregson-Williams, Harry)
Gregson-Williams, Harry c
John's theme / Stalked / Temple / He means business / Kill or be replaced / We have visitors / John reflects / Surreal shoot-out / John traps his man / Race against time / Heavies arrive / Final confrontation
VSD 5915 / 8 Jun '98 / Varese Sarabande

☐ RESERVOIR DOGS
Little green bag: *Baker, George Selection* / Hooked on a feeling: *Blue Swede* / I gotcha: *Tex, Joe* / Magic carpet ride: *Bedlam* / Fool for love: *Rogers, Sandy* / Stuck in the middle with you: *Stealer's Wheel* / Harvest moon: *Bedlam* / Coconut: *Nilsson, Harry*
MCD 10793 / 27 Apr '98 / MCA

☐ RESPECTABLE TRADE, A
Nott, Julian c
3984232472 / 20 Apr '98 / Warner ESP

☐ RETURN OF THE JEDI (National Philharmonic Orchestra)
Williams, John c
Gerhardt, Charles con
Approaching the Death Star / Parade of the Ewoks / Luke and Leia / Jabba the Hutt / Return of the Jedi / Ewok battle / Han Solo returns / Into the trap / Heroic Ewok / Battle in the forest / Finale
GD 60767 / Jun '91 / RCA Victor

☐ RETURN OF THE JEDI (The Star Wars Trilogy Special Edition)
Williams, John c
Williams, John con
09026687742
09026687482 / Mar '97 / RCA Victor

☐ RETURN OF THE LIVING DEAD I
Surfin' dead: *Cramps* / Party time (Zombie version): *45 Grave* / Nothing for you: *T.S.O.L.* / Eyes without a face: *Flesh Eaters* / Burn the flames: *Erickson, Roky* / Dead beat dance: *Damned* / Take a walk: *Tall Boys* / Love under will: *Jet Black Berries* / Tonight (we'll make love until we die): *SSQ* / Trash's theme: *SSQ*
CDWIK 38 / Jun '88 / Big Beat

☐ RETURN OF THE MAGNIFICENT SEVEN
Berstein, Elmer c
RCD 10714 / 12 Jan '98 / Rykodisc

☐ RETURN TO SNOWY RIVER
Rowland, Bruce c
VCD 70451 / Jan '89 / Varese Sarabande

☐ RETURN TO THE FORBIDDEN PLANET (CC Productions)
Wipe out / It's a man's man's man's world / Great balls of fire / Don't let me be misunderstood / Good vibrations / Teenage in love / Young girl / She's not there / All shook up / Who's sorry now / Robot man / Shake rattle and roll / Go now / Only the lonely / Young ones / We gotta get out of this place / Wipe out / Mr. Spaceman / Monster mash / Great balls of fire
QED 213 / Nov '96 / Tring

☐ REVENGE
Nitzsche, Jack c
Love theme / Friendship / Miryea / Betrayal / Jeep ride / On the beach / Illicit love / Tibey's revenge / Whorehouse and healing / Dead Texan / Confrontation / Miryea's death
FILMCD 065 / Aug '90 / Silva Screen

☐ REVENGE OF MR. MOPOJI, THE (Jackson, Mike & The Soul Providers)
Jackson, Mike c
Submarine / Unstoppable oldsmobile / Saturday in the park / Out the door / Chicken (catch it) / Mopoji strikes back / Disco party / Wisdom of Master Shen / King of the impossible / Angry mob / Gambling at the capri / Eye for an eye
ST 5918CD / 6 Apr '98 / Desco

☐ REVOLVER
Morricone, Ennio c
A 8919 / Feb '92 / Alhambra

☐ REX (Original Broadway Cast)
Rogers, Richard c
Harnick, Sheldon l
Overture and Te Deum / No song more pleasing / Field of cloth and gold / Where is my son / As once I loved you / Chase / Away from you / Elizabeth / Why / So much you loved me / Christmas at Hampton Court / Wee golden warrior / From afar / In time / Finale/Te Deum
09026689332 / 12 Jan '98 / RCA Victor

☐ RHAPSODY IN BLUE
Gershwin, George c
Gershwin, Ira l
Rhapsody in blue overture / Swanee / Swanee / 'S wonderful / Somebody loves me / Blue Monday blues / Rhapsody in blue / Man I love / Embraceable you / American in Paris / Cuban overture / Delicious / Summertime / Piano concerto in F 1 and 2 / Rhapsody in blue
CD 60028 / Nov '97 / Great Movie Themes

☐ RICHARD III
Richard III theme / Monarchy / People and the passion / Flower in Winter / Queen Elizabeth tango / Lady Ann's lament / Sitting on top of the world / Come be my love
8287192 / Apr '96 / London

☐ RICHIE RICH (Silver Screen Orchestra)
Silvestri, Alan *c*
VSD 5582 / Mar '95 / Varese Sarabande

☐ RIDER ON THE RAIN
Lai, Francis *c*
A 8926 / Mar '92 / Alhambra

☐ RIGHT AS THE RAIN (Cast Recording)
Previn, Andre *c*
Price, Leontyne *l*
Right as rain / Sunrise sunset / It's good to have you near again / It never entered my mind / Nobody's heart / My melancholy baby / Sleepin' bee / They didn't believe me / Hello young lovers / Love walked in / Where I wonder
GD 82983 / Apr '90 / RCA

☐ RINGO IL CAVALIERE SOLITARIO/UNA COLT IN PUGNO AL DIAVOLO/ L'LUTIMO MERCENARIO
De Masi, Francesco/Reverberi/Bruno Nicolai *c*
CDCR 32 / Apr '96 / Silva Screen

☐ RINK, THE (1983 Broadway Cast)
Kander, John *c*
Ebb, Fred *l*
Colored lights / Chief cook and bottle washer / Don't ah ma me / Blue crystal / Under the roller coaster / Not enough magic / Here's to the rink / We can make it / After all these years / Angel's rink... / What... / Marry me / Mrs. A / Rink / Wallflower / All the children / Coda
CDTER 1091 / Nov '97 / TER

☐ RINK, THE (1988 London Cast)
Kander, John *c*
Ebb, Fred *l*
CDTERS 1155 / Jan '90 / TER

☐ RIO CONCHOS (& The Artist Who Did Not Want To Paint/Prelude From Agony & The Ecstasy) (London Symphony Orchestra)
Goldsmith, Jerry *c*
Goldsmith, Jerry *con*
RVF 6007D / Feb '90 / Intrada

☐ RIO GRANDE (Sons Of The Pioneers)
Young, Victor *c*
I'll take you home again Kathleen / Cattle call / Erie canal / Yellow stripes / My gal is purple / Down by the glenside / Footstore cavalry
VSD 5378 / Aug '93 / Varese Sarabande

☐ RIOT ON SUNSET STRIP (& Standells Rarities)
Riot on Sunset Strip: *Standells* / Sunset Sally: *Mugwumps* / Sunset theme: *Sidewalk Sounds* / Old country: *Travis, Debra* / Don't need your lovin': *Chocolate Watch Band* / Children of the night: *Mom's Boys* / Make the music pretty: *Sidewalk Sounds* / Get away from here: *Standells* / Like my baby: *Drew* / Sitting there standing: *Chocolate Watch Band* / Love me: *Standells* / Batman: *Standells* / Our candidate: *Standells* / Boy who is lost: *Standells* / It's all in your mind: *Standells* / School girl: *Standells* / I hate to leave you: *Standells* / Looking at tomorrow: *Standells* / Don't say nothing at all: *Standells* / Try it: *Standells* / Rari: *Standells*
CDWIKD 113 / Jun '93 / Big Beat

☐ RISING SUN (Tanaka, Seiichi & San Francisco Taiko Dojo Drums)
Takemitsu, Toru *c*
Iwaki, Hiroyuki *con*
07822110032 / Feb '94 / Arista

☐ RISKY BUSINESS
Old time rock 'n' roll: *Seger, Bob* / Dream is always the same: *Tangerine Dream* / No future: *Tangerine Dream* / Mannish boy: *Waters, Muddy* / Pump: *Beck, Jeff* / DMSR: *Prince* / After the fall: *Journey* / In the air tonight: *Collins, Phil* / Love on a real train: *Tangerine Dream* / Guido the killer pimp: *Tangerine Dream* / Lana: *Tangerine Dream*
CDV 2302 / May '87 / Virgin

☐ RIVER, THE
Williams, John *c*
VSD 5298 / May '91 / Varese Sarabande

☐ RIVERDANCE (This Land - Inspired By Riverdance) (Kennedy, Fiona & Dun Carmel Band/Irish Dancers)
CDMFP 6237 / Aug '96 / Music For Pleasure

☐ RIVERDANCE (Music From The Show)
Whelan, Bill *c*
Reel around the sun / Heart's cry / Countess Cathleen/Women of the Sidhe / Caoineadh cu chulainn (lament) / Shivna / Firedance / Slip into Spring / Riverdance / American wake (the Nova Scotia set) / Lift the wings / Macedonian morning / Marta's dance/The Russian dervish / Andulucia / Home and the heartland / Harvest / Riverdance
UND 53076 / Jun '97 / Celtic Heartbeat

☐ RIVERDANCE (Whelan, Bill)
UND 53106 / 3 Oct '97 / Universal

☐ RIVERDANCE (Highlights From Riverdance And Lord Of The Dance) (Voices of Ireland)
Riverdance / Lord of the dance / Heart's cry / Our wedding / Suil a run / Star of the County Down / Medley / Cockles and mussels (Molly Malone) / Miss Murphy / Medley / Dusty miller / Boys of Belfast/Girls of Belfast / Lament of the three Mary's / Lord of the dance (reprise) / Riverdance (reprise)
ECD 3396 / 23 Feb '98 / K-Tel

☐ RIVERDANCE DISTILLED (Brendan Power Plays Music From Riverdance) (Power, Brendan)
Countess Cathleen / Reel around the sun / Slip into Spring / American wake / Lift the wings / Riverdance / Caoineadh chu chulainn / Firedance/Andalucia / Riverdance/Women of Sidhe / Marta's dance/ Russian dervish
CDTRAX 135 / Jun '97 / Greentrax

☐ ROAD TO WELLVILLE
Portman, Rachel *c*
Snell, David *con*
VSD 5512 / Jan '95 / Varese Sarabande

☐ ROB ROY
CDVMM 18 / May '95 / Virgin

☐ ROBBERY UNDER ARMS
IMICD 1013 / Jan '93 / Silva Screen

☐ ROBE, THE
Newman, Alfred *c*
Newman, Alfred *con*
Farewell to Diana / Palm Sunday / Carriage of the cross / Marcellus returns to Capri / Village of Cana / Redemption of Marcellus / Miriam / Catacombs / Rescue of Demetrius / Better kingdom
07822110112 / Apr '94 / Fox Film Scores

☐ ROBERT AND ELIZABETH (1987 Chichester Festival Cast)
Grainer, Ron *c*
Millar, Ronald *l*
Here on the corner of Wimpole Street / Family Moulton-Barrett / World outside / Moon in my pocket / I said love / You only to love me / Real thing / In a simple way / I know now / Escape me never / Soliloquy / Pass the eau de cologne / I'm the master here / Hate me please / Girls that boys dream about / Long ago I loved you / What the world calls love / Woman and man / Frustration
OCRCD 6032 / Oct '95 / First Night

☐ ROBERT ET ROBERT
Lai, Francis *c*
MANTRA 053 / Jan '93 / Silva Screen

☐ ROBIN HOOD
Burgon, Geoffrey *c*
Burgon, Geoffrey *con*
FILMCD 083 / May '91 / Silva Screen

☐ ROBIN HOOD (US Cast)
De Koven, Reginald *c*
AEICD 032 / May '98 / AEI

☐ ROBIN HOOD - MEN IN TIGHTS
Mann, Hummie *c*
Brooks, Mel *l*
Mann, Hummie *con*
176392 / Feb '94 / Milan

☐ ROBOCOP (A Future To This Life) (Walsh, Joe)
ESMCD 491 / Apr '97 / Essential

☐ ROBOCOP I
Poledouris, Basil *c*
Poledouris, Basil *con*
Main title / Van chase / Murphy's death / Rock shop / Home / Robo vs. ED-209 / Dream / Across the board / Betrayal / Clarence frags Bob / Drive to Jones' office / We killed you / Directive IV / Robo tips his hat / Showdown
VSD 47298 / Apr '91 / Varese Sarabande

☐ ROBOCOP II
Rosenman, Leonard *c*
Rosenman, Leonard *con*
Overture / City mayhem / Happier days / Robo cruiser / Robo memories / Robo and Nuke / Robo fanfare / Robo and Cain chase / Creating the monster / Robo I vs Robo II
VSD 5271 / Aug '90 / Varese Sarabande

☐ ROBOCOP III
Poledouris, Basil *c*
Poledouris, Basil/M. Boddicker *con*
VSD 5416 / Nov '93 / Varese Sarabande

☐ ROBOTJOX
Talgorn, Frederic *c*
PCD 125 / Jan '93 / Prometheus

☐ ROCKERS
We 'a' rockers: *Inner Circle* / Money worries: *Maytones* / Police and thieves: *Murvin, Junior* / Book of rules: *Heptones* / Stepping razor: *Tosh, Peter* / Tenement yard: *Miller, Jacob* / Fade away: *Byles, Junior* / Rockers: *Wailer, Bunny* / Slave master: *Isaacs, Gregory* / Dread lion: *Perry, Lee 'Scratch' & The Upsetters* / Graduation in Zion: *Kiddus 1* / Jah no dead: *Burning Spear* / Satta a masagana: *Third World* / Natty takes over: *Hinds, Justin & The Dominoes* / Driving me backwards: *Eno, Brian* / Baby's on fire: *Eno, Brian* / Heartbreak hotel: *Cale, J.J.* / Standing in a buketful of blues: *Ayers, Roy* / Stranger in blue suede shoes: *Ayers, Roy* / Everybody's sometime and some people's all the time blues: *Ayers, Roy* / Two goes into four: *Ayers, Roy*
RRCD 45 / May '94 / Reggae Refreshers

☐ ROCKY HORROR COLLECTION, THE
ROKCD 103 / 26 Jan '98 / Essential

☐ ROCKY HORROR INTERNATIONAL
O'Brien, Richard *c*
ROCKY 1 / 24 Nov '97 / Essential

☐ ROCKY HORROR PICTURE SHOW, THE (1990 London Cast)
O'Brien, Richard *c*
Science fiction / Dammit Janet / Over at the Frankenstein place / Time warp / Sweet transvestite / Rocky's birth/Sword of Damocles / I can make you a man / Hot patootie - Bless my soul / I can make you a man (reprise) / Touch-a-touch-a-touch-a-touch me / Once in a while / Eddie's teddy / Planet Schmanet / Floor show - Rose tint my world / Fanfare - Don't dream it / Wild and untamed thing / I'm going home / Super heroes / Science fiction (reprise)
CDMFP 5977 / Dec '92 / Music For Pleasure

☐ ROCKY HORROR PICTURE SHOW, THE (Cast Recording)
O'Brien, Richard *c*
ESSCD 286 / Apr '95 / Essential

☐ ROCKY HORROR PICTURE SHOW, THE (Cast Recording)
O'Brien, Richard *c*
GRF 231 / Aug '93 / Tring

☐ ROCKY HORROR SHOW, THE (Cast Recording)
O'Brien, Richard *c*
RDTER 1221 / Nov '97 / TER

☐ ROCKY HORROR SHOW, THE (Original Cast)
OCRCD 6040 / May '96 / First Night

☐ ROCKY HORROR SHOW, THE (CC Productions)
O'Brien, Richard *c*
Science fiction double feature / Damn it Janet / Over at the Frankenstein's place / Time warp / Sweet transvestite / I can make you a man / Hot patootie bless my soul / I can make you a man / Touch-a-touch-a-touch-a-touch me / Eddie's teddy / Medley
QED 201 / Nov '96 / Tring

☐ ROCKY HORROR SHOW, THE (Cast Recording)
O'Brien, Richard *c*
Yates, Martin *con*
Science fiction / Damn it Janet / Over at Frankenstein's place / Sweet transvestite / Time warp / Touch a-touch a-touch me / Once in a while / Eddie's teddy / Rose tint my world / Hot patootie / I'm going home / Super heroes
SHOWCD 025 / Oct '96 / Showtime

☐ ROCKY HORROR SHOW, THE (Cast Recording)
O'Brien, Richard *c*
O'Brien, Richard *l*
Yates, Martin *con*
CDTER 1221 / 1 Sep '98 / TER

☐ RODGERS AND HAMMERSTEIN'S STATE FAIR (Original Broadway Cast)
Rodgers, Richard *c*
Hammerstein II, Oscar *l*
Overture / Opening / It might as well be spring / Driving at night / Our state fair / That's for me / More than just a friend / Isn't it kinda fun / You never had it so good / Reprise: It might as be spring / When I go out walking wiht my baby / So far / It's a grand night for singing / Entr'acte / Man I used to be / All I owe loway / That's the way it happens / Boys and girls like you and me / Next time it happens / Finale ultimo
DRGCD 94765 / Aug '96 / DRG

☐ ROLLER (Goblin)
CDMDF 307 / 16 Feb '98 / Cinevox

☐ ROM (Kypourgos, Nikos)
Karamaghiolis, Menelaos *c*
MS 89015 / 12 May '98 / Musurgia Graeca

☐ ROMA (Rota, Nino)
Rota, Nino *c*
Savina, Carlos *con*
CDST 311 / 27 Apr '98 / Screen Trax

☐ ROMANCE ROMANCE (1988 Broadway Cast)
Herrmann, Keith & Barry Harman *c*
Little comedy / Goodbye Emily / I'll always remember the song / Night it had to end / Think of the odds / Let's not talk about it / Through a window / Small craft warnings / So glad I married her / Letters / It's not too late / Oh what a performance / Women of Vienna / Summer share / Plans A and B / Words he doesn't say / Romantic notions / Romance romance
CDTER 1161 / Feb '89 / TER

☐ ROMEO AND JULIET
Eidelman, Cliff *c*
VSD 5752 / Mar '97 / Varese Sarabande

☐ ROMEO AND JULIET
Rota, Nino *c*
Rota, Nino *con*
FILMCD 200 / 6 Apr '98 / Silva Screen

☐ ROMEO AND JULIET VOL.1
Crush: *Garbage* / Local God: *Everclear* / Pretty piece of flesh: *One Inch Punch* / Kissing you: *Des'ree* / Whatever: *Butthole Surfers* / Lovefool: *Cardigans* / Young hearts run free: *Mazelle, Kym* / Everybody'd free: *Traver, Quindon* / To you I bestow: *Mundy* / Talk show host: *Mundy* / Little star: *Nordenstam, Stina* / You and me song: *Wannadies*
PRMDCD 28 / Aug '97 / Premier/EMI

☐ ROMEO AND JULIET VOL.2
Prologue / O Verona / Montague boys / Gas station / O Verona / Introduction to Romeo / Queen mab scene / Young hearts run free / Kissing you / Balcony scene / When dove's cry / Challenge / Tybalt arrives / Fight scene / Mercutio's death / Drive of death / Slow movement / Morning breaks / Juliet's requiem / Mantua / Escape from Mantua / Death scene / Liebestod / Epilogue
PRMDCD 34 / Jan '98 / Premier/EMI

☐ ROMEO IS BLEEDING (Isham, Mark)
Isham, Mark *c*
Romeo is bleeding / Bird alone / Romeo is moving / Romeo and Juliette / Nightmare on Marple Street / I know better now / Romeo is searching / Romeo and Natalie / Mona / Take two toes / Back street driving / Mona lends a helping hand / Dance of death / Empty chambers / Romeo is dreaming / Romeo alone
5212312 / Jan '94 / Verve

☐ ROMPER STOMPER
PTR 002 / Jun '97 / Picture This

☐ ROMY AND MICHELLE'S HIGH SCHOOL REUNION
1620962 / Aug '97 / Polydor

☐ ROSE AND THE GUN, THE
Johnson, Laurie *c*
FLYCD 103 / Aug '95 / Fly

☐ ROSE OF WASHINGTON SQUARE/ GOLDDIGGERS OF 1933/DOLLY SISTERS
Pretty baby: *Jolson, Al* / Rock-a-bye your baby with a dixie melody: *Jolson, Al* / California here I come: *Jolson, Al* / I never knew heaven could speak: *Jolson, Al* / Rose of Washington square: *Jolson, Al* / My mammy: *Jolson, Al* / My man: *Faye, Alice* / We're in the money: *Rogers, Ginger* / Shadow waltz: *Powell, Dick* / Pettin' in the park: *Powell, Dick* / Remember my forgotten man: *Blondell, Joan & Etta Moten* / I'm always chasing rainbows: *Blondell, Joan & Etta Moten* / We've been around / Carolina in the morning / Don't be too old fashioned / Powder lipstick and rouge / I'm always chasing rainbows / Darktown strutter's ball / I'm always chasing rainbow / I can't begin to tell you / Sidewalks of New York
CD 60009 / Jun '97 / Great Movie Themes

☐ ROSE, THE (Midler, Bette)
Midnight in Memphis / Concert monologue / When a man loves a woman / Sold my soul to rock'n'roll / Keep on rockin' / Love me with a feeling / Camellia / Homecoming monologue / Stay with me / Let me call you sweetheart / Rose / Whose side are you on
7567827782 / Nov '95 / East West

☐ ROSEMARY'S BABY
Komeda, Krzysztof *c*
TSU 0116 / Jan '95 / Tsunami
PIG 02 / 14 Apr '98 / Discmedi

☐ ROTHSCHILD'S VIOLIN (Leiferkus, Sergei & Ilya Levinsky/Konstantin Pluzhnikov/Marina Shaguch)
Fleischmann, Benjamin/Dmitri Shostakovich *c*
Rozhdestvensky, Gennadi *con*
Wedding band / What are you playing / This small town is worse than a village / Band music / Do you remember Iakov do you recall / God had given us a little girl / Band music/Make that trumpet merrier / Down here on earth everything flies so fast / Rothschild runs away / Loss-one coffin for Marfa Ivanova / If they could live without hatred or evil / It's better to die / Be kind to me don't hit me / Rothschild plays the violin
09026684342 / Nov '96 / RCA Victor

☐ ROTHSCHILDS, THE (Cast Recording)
Bock, Jerry *c*
Harnick, Sheldon *l*
Greene, Milton *con*
SK 30337 / Nov '92 / Sony Broadway

☐ ROULA HIDDEN SECRETS
Schleip, Dieter *c*
CST 8056 / Nov '96 / Colosseum

☐ ROUND MIDNIGHT
Hancock, Herbie *c*
Round Midnight / Body and soul / Berangere's nightmare / Fair weather / Una noche con Francis / Peacocks / How long has this been going on / Rhythm-a-ning / Still time / Minuit aux Champs Elysees / Chan's song
4867992 / Dec '96 / Columbia

☐ ROUND MIDNIGHT - THE OTHER SIDE OF ROUND MIDNIGHT (Gordon, Dexter)
7463972 / 1 Jun '98 / Blue Note

☐ RUBY
Scott, John *c*
MAF 7026D / Jan '93 / Intrada

☐ RUDDIGORE (Light Opera Company)
Sullivan, Sir Arthur *c*
Gilbert, W.S. *l*
CDHD 255 / May '95 / Happy Days

☐ RUDDIGORE (New Sadler's Wells Opera Chorus/Orchestra)
Sullivan, Sir Arthur *c*
Gilbert, W.S. *l*
Phipps, S. *con*
CDTER2 1128 / Nov '97 / TER

☐ **RUDDIGORE (Baker, George & Richard Lewis/Glyndebourne Festival Choir/ Pro Arte Orchestra)**
Sullivan, Sir Arthur *c*
Gilbert, W.S. *l*
Godfrey, I. *con*
CMS 7644122 / Apr '94 / EMI Classics

☐ **RUDDIGORE/COX AND BOX (D'Oyly Carte Opera Chorus/Orchestra Of The Royal Opera House)**
Sullivan, Sir Arthur *c*
Gilbert, W.S. *l*
Godfrey, I. *con*
4173552 / Jan '90 / London

☐ **RUNAWAY**
Goldsmith, Jerry *c*
VCD 47221 / Jan '89 / Varese Sarabande

☐ **RUNNING MAN, THE (Faltermeyer, Harold)**
Faltermeyer, Harold *c*
VCD 47356 / Jan '89 / Varese Sarabande

☐ **RUSH (Clapton, Eric)**
Clapton, Eric *c*
New recruit / Tracks and lines / Realization / Kristen and Jim / Preludin fugue / Cold turkey / Will gaines / Help me up / Don't know which way to go / Tears in heaven
7599267942 / Oct '94 / WEA

☐ **RUTH RENDELL MYSTERIES, THE (Bennett, Brian)**
Bennett, Brian *c*
Ruth Rendell Mysteries / Wexford in LA / Put on by cunning / Search for Mina / Love from Doon / Castle / Kissing the gunner's daughter / New lease of death / Let me believe / Letters from the past / Cry from the tomb / Strange confessions / Corsica / Day in Provence / Achilles heel / Mouse in the corner / Mother and daughter / Means of evil / Premonition / Speaker of Mandarin
CDSTM 2 / May '94 / Soundtrack Music

☐ **RUTHLESS - THE MUSICAL (Los Angeles Cast)**
VSD 5476 / Oct '94 / Varese Sarabande

S

☐ **SAFE (Tomney, Ed)**
Tomney, Ed *c*
IONIC 14CD / Aug '95 / The Fine Line

☐ **SAHARA**
Morricone, Ennio *c*
Morricone, Ennio *con*
MAF 7047D / Mar '93 / Intrada

☐ **SAIL AWAY (Broadway Cast)**
Coward, Sir Noel *c*
ZDM 7647592 / Apr '94 / EMI Classics

☐ **SAINT, THE**
Saint theme: *Orbital* / 6 underground: *Sneaker Pimps* / Oil 1: *Moby* / Atom bomb: *Fluke* / Roses fade: *Luscious Jackson* / Setting sun: *Chemical Brothers* / Pearl's girl: *Underworld* / Out of my mind: *Duran Duran* / Da funk: *Daft Punk* / Little wonder: *Bowie, David* / Pollaroid millenium: *Superior* / Dream without a dream: *Dreadzone* / In the absence of sun: *Sheik, Duncan* / Before today: *Everything But The Girl*
CDVUS 126 / Apr '97 / Virgin

☐ **SALAAM BOMBAY (Subramaniam, L.)**
Subramaniam, L. *c*
Subramaniam, L. *con*
DRGCD 12595 / Jan '95 / DRG
119052 / Sep '96 / Musidisc

☐ **SALAD DAYS (1982 London Cast)**
Slade, Julian *c*
Slade, Julian & Dorothy Reynolds *l*
Things that are done by a Don / We said we wouldn't look back / Find yourself something to do / I sit in the sun / Oh look at me / Hush-hush / Out of breath / Cleopatra / Sand in my eyes / It's easy to sing / We're looking for a piano / I've had the time of my life / Saucer song / We don't understand our children
CDTER 1018 / Nov '97 / TER

☐ **SALAD DAYS (Highlights) (London Cast)**
Slade, Julian *c*
Slade, Julian & Dorothy Reynolds *l*
Things that are done by a Don / We said we wouldn't look back / Find yourself something to do / I sit in the sun / Oh look at me / Hush-hush / Cleopatra / Sand in my eyes / It's easy to sing / We're looking for a piano / I've had the time of my life / We don't understand our children
SHOWCD 009 / Feb '95 / Showtime

☐ **SALAD DAYS (London Cast)**
Slade, Julian *c*
Slade, Julian & Dorothy Reynolds *l*
SMK 66176 / Jul '94 / Sony West End

☐ **SALAD DAYS (40th Anniversary Production) (London Cast)**
Slade, Julian *c*
Slade, Julian & Dorothy Reynolds *l*
Hutchinson, S. *con*
SCORECD 43 / Apr '96 / First Night

☐ **SAND PEBBLES, THE (Royal Scottish National Orchestra)**
Goldsmith, Jerry *c*
Goldsmith, Jerry *con*
Overture / Main title / Getting acquainted / Repel boarders / Changsha dock / Death of a thousand cuts / My secret / Jake and Shirley / Wedding / Frenchy's death / Maily's death / Final mission / Almost home
TSU 0107 / Jan '93 / Tsunami
VSD 5795 / 26 Jan '98 / Varese Sarabande

☐ **SANDPIPER, THE**
Mandel, Johnny *c*
5312292 / Jun '96 / Verve

☐ **SANTA CLAUSE, THE**
Convertino, Michael *c*
323642 / Nov '95 / RCA Victor

☐ **SARAFINA (Broadway Cast)**
Ngema, Mbongeni *c*
Zibuyille emasisweni / Sarafina / Lord's prayer / Yes mistress it's a pity / Give us power / Afunani amaphoyisa e Soweto / Nkois sikeleli Afrika / Freedom is coming tomorrow / Entr'acte / Meeting tonight / Stand and fight / Uyamemeza ungoma / Iswe lami / Wawungalelani / Mama Sechaba / Isizwe (the nation is dying) / Goodbye / Kilimanjaro / Africa is burning in the sun / Olyaithi (It's all right) / Bring back Nelson Mandela / Freedom is coming tomorrow (reprise)
RD 89307 / Jul '89 / RCA Victor

☐ **SARAFINA (The Sound Of Freedom)**
Myers, Stanley *c*
Sarafina / Lord's prayer / Nkonyane kandaba / Freedom is coming tomorrow / Sabela / Sechaba / Safa saphel' isizwe / Thank you mama / Vuma dlozi lami / Lizobuya / One more time
9362450602 / Jan '91 / Warner Bros.

☐ **SATURDAY NIGHT (Cast Recording)**
CASTCD 65 / 8 Jun '98 / First Night

☐ **SATURDAY NIGHT FEVER**
Stayin' alive: *Bee Gees* / How deep is your love: *Bee Gees* / Night fever: *Bee Gees* / More than a woman: *Bee Gees* / Jive talkin': *Bee Gees* / You should be dancing: *Bee Gees* / Calypso breakdown: *Donaldson, Ralph* / If I can't have you: *Elliman, Yvonne* / Fifth of Beethoven: *Murphy, Walter* / Open sesame: *Kool & The Gang* / Boogie shoes: *K.C. & The Sunshine Band* / MFSB: *K.C. & The Sunshine Band* / K Jee: *K.C. & The Sunshine Band* / Disco inferno: *Tramps* / Manhattan skyline: *Tramps* / Night on disco mountain: *Tramps* / Salsation: *Tramps*
8253892 / Oct '95 / Polydor

☐ **SATURDAY NIGHT FEVER (Original London Cast)**
5579322 / 3 Aug '98 / Polydor

☐ **SAVAGE (Super Soul Soundtrack) (Julian, Don)**
Julian, Don *c*
Savage: *Julian, Don & Arthur G. Wright* / Lay it on your head / Where I'm coming from / It's a sad song: *Wright, Arthur G.* / My favourite beer joint / Janitizio / Just kiss me
CDSEWM 114 / Apr '97 / Southbound

☐ **SAVING PRIVATE RYAN**
DRD 50046 / 27 Jul '98 / Dreamworks

☐ **SAY AMEN, SOMEBODY**
Dorsey, Thomas A. *c*
Highway to heaven / Singing in my soul / What manner of man is this / When I've done my best / Take my hand precious Lord / I'm his child / He chose me / No ways tired / Jesus dropped the charges / I'll never turn back / Storm is passing over / It's gonna rain / He brought us / Canaan
DRGCD 12584 / Jan '95 / DRG

☐ **SCARFACE**
MCD 06126 / 25 May '98 / MCA

☐ **SCARLET LETTER**
Barry, John *c*
Theme / Arrival / Search for home / Hester rides to town / Bird / Swimmer / Very exhilarating read / I'm not the man I seem / Agnus dei / I can see what others cannot / Love scene / Are you with child / Small act of contrition / Birth / I baptise this child / Pearl / She will not speak / Dr. Roger Prynne / Hester walks through town / Poor fatherless child / Attempt at rape / Savages have killed him / Round up / I am the father of her child / Indians attack / Letter has served a purpose / End title
4835772 / Jan '96 / Epic

☐ **SCARLETT (Sung In Japanese) (Japanese Cast)**
Rome, Harold *c*
He loves me / We belong to you / Two of a kind / Blissful Christmas / My soldier / Goodbye my honey / Lonely stranger / Time for love / What is love / Gambling man / Which way is home / Bonnie blue flag / O'Hara / Newlywed's song / Strange and wonderful / Blueberry eyes / Little wonder / Bonnie gone
DRGCD 13105 / Jan '95 / DRG

☐ **SCENT OF GREEN PAPAYA**
Tiet, Ton-That *c*
887794 / May '94 / Milan

☐ **SCHINDLER'S LIST (Boston Symphony Orchestra with Itzhak Perlman)**
Williams, John *c*
Williams, John *con*
Theme / Jewish town / Immolation / Remembrances / Schindler's workforce / Oyf'n pripetshok / And nacht aktion / I could have done more / Auschwitz-Birkenau / Stolen memories / Making the list / Give me your names / Yeroushalaim chel zahav / Theme (reprise)
MCD 10969 / Feb '94 / MCA

☐ **SCRAMBLED FEET (Broadway Cast)**
Driver, John & Jeffrey Haddow *c*
DRGCD 6105 / Jan '95 / DRG

☐ **SCREAM I**
Youth of America: *Birdbrain* / Whisper: *Catherine* / Red right hand: *Cave, Nick & The Bad Seeds* / Don't fear the reaper: *Cave, Nick & The Bad Seeds* / Artificial world: *Cruise, Julee & The Flow* / Better than me: *Sister Machine Gun* / Whisper to a scream: *Soho* / Schools out: *Last Hard Men* / Drop dead gorgeous: *Republica* / Trouble in Woodboro/Sidney's lament: *Beltrami, Marco*
0022822CIN / Jul '97 / Edel
TVT 8080 / Jun '97 / TVT

☐ **SCREAM I/SCREAM II**
Beltrami, Marco *c*
VSD 5959 / 24 Aug '98 / Varese Sarabande

☐ **SCREAM II**
Scream: *Master P. & Silkk The Shocker* / Surburban life: *Kottonmouth Kings* / Rivers: *Sugar Ray* / She's always in my hair: *D'Angelo* / Help myself: *Matthews, Dave Band* / She said: *Collective Soul* / Right place at the wrong time: *Spencer, Jon Blues Explosion* / Dear lover: *Foo Fighters* / Eyes of sand: *Tonic* / Swing: *Everclear* / I think I love you: *Less Than Jake* / Your lucky day: *Eels* / Red right hand: *Cave, Nick & The Bad Seeds* / One more chance: *Kelly* / Race: *Ear2000*
8219112 / 27 Apr '98 / Premier/EMI

☐ **SCROOGE (1992 Cast)**
Bricusse, Leslie *c*
Pedlar, Stuart *con*
Christmas carol / No better life / Christmas children / I hate Christmas / Father Christmas / Make the most of this world / It's not my fault / December the twenty fifth / Happiness / You you / Entr'acte / Good times / Beautiful day / Minister's cat / Better life / Thank you very much / I like life / I'll begin again / Father Christmas / Thank you very much / I'll begin again / Better life
CDTER 1194 / Aug '98 / TER

☐ **SCROOGED**
Put a little love in your heart: *Green, Al & Annie Lennox* / Wonderful life: *Lennon, Julian* / Sweetest thing: *New Voices Of Freedom* / Love you take: *Hartman, Dan & Denise Lopez* / Get up 'n' dance: *Kool Moe Dee* / We three kings of Orient are: *Davis, Miles & Larry Carlton* / Christmas must be tonight: *Robertson, Robbie* / Brown eyed girl: *Poindexter, Buster* / Christmas song: *Cole, Natalie*
5513202 / Sep '95 / Spectrum

☐ **SEA HAWK, THE (Utah Symphony Orchestra)**
Korngold, Erich *c*
VCD 47304 / Jan '89 / Varese Sarabande

☐ **SEA HAWK, THE**
Korngold, Erich *c*
CDTER 1164 / Jan '91 / TER

☐ **SEA OF LOVE**
Jones, Trevor *c*
Sea of love: *Phillips, Phil & Twilights* / Poetic killing / Cocktails and fingerprints / Fear and passion / Helen's 45 / Is she or isn't she / Sea of love Reprise
5501302 / Oct '93 / Spectrum

☐ **SEA POWER (Whalen, Michael)**
Whalen, Michael *c*
ND 66005 / Nov '93 / Narada

☐ **SEAFORTH**
Petit, Jean Claude *c*
Seaforth / Light / Bri / In a public house / First kiss / Love / I can do anything / Tension / Obsession / Bob's family / Petite fugue / Waiting / Diana / Don't call here / Diana drama / Paula and Bob / Suspense / Melancholly / In private / Paula / End
DSHCD 7016 / Oct '94 / D-Sharp

☐ **SEAQUEST DSV**
Debney, John *c*
Debney, John *con*
VSD 5565 / Jul '95 / Varese Sarabande

☐ **SEASON IN HELL, A**
Jarre, Maurice *c*
CDA 8923 / Jan '95 / Tsunami

☐ **SECRET GARDEN, THE (Cracow Boys Choir/Sinfonia Varsovia)**
Preisner, Zbigniew *c*
Michniewski, W. *con*
VSD 5443 / Sep '93 / Varese Sarabande

☐ **SECRET GARDEN, THE (Cast Recording)**
VSD 5451 / Oct '94 / Varese Sarabande

☐ **SECRET OF NIMH, THE**
Goldsmith, Jerry *c*
Goldsmith, Jerry *con*
VSD 5541 / Mar '95 / Varese Sarabande

☐ **SECRET OF ROAN INISH, THE**
DARING 3015CD / Sep '95 / Daring

☐ **SECRET OF THE SAHARA**
Morricone, Ennio *c*
Secret of the Sahara / Red ghosts / Sholomon / Mountain / Kerim / Hawk / Golden door / Myth and the adventure / Anthea and the desert / Farewell Orso / Death of Tamameth / Saharan dram / Miriam and Philip / Second dedication / First dedication
74321342262 / Jun '96 / RCA

☐ **SECRET POLICEMAN'S CONCERT, THE (Cast Recording)**
CCSCD 351 / Nov '92 / Castle

☐ **SEESAW (1973 Broadway Cast)**
Coleman, Cy *c*
Fields, Dorothy *l*
Seesaw / My city / Nobody does it like me / In tune / Spanglish / Welcome to Holiday Inn / You're a loveable lunatic / He's good for me / Ride out the storm / Entr'acte / We've got it / Poor everybody else / Chapter 54 Number 1909 / Seesaw ballet / It's not where you start / I'm way ahead and seesaw / It's not where you start (bows)
DRGCD 6108 / Jun '92 / DRG

☐ **SELFISH GIANT, THE (1993 Cast)**
Jenkins, Michael *c*
Williams, Nigel *l*
CDTER 1206 / Nov '93 / TER

☐ **SENSE AND SENSIBILITY**
Doyle, Patrick *c*
Eaglen, J./R. Ziegler *con*
SK 62258 / Nov '96 / Sony Classical

☐ **SENSELESS**
GEE 1001362 / 6 Apr '98 / Gee Street

☐ **SEPOLTA VIVA/THE ANTICHRIST**
Morricone, Ennio *c*
CDCR 17 / Jul '94 / Silva Screen

☐ **SEQUEL, THE (It Ain't Over) (Jackson, Millie & Cast)**
ICH 15042 / Mar '97 / Ichiban

☐ **SERPENT AND THE RAINBOW, THE**
Fiedel, Brad *c*
VCD 47362 / Jan '89 / Varese Sarabande

☐ **SERPICO**
Theodorakis, Mikis *c*
SR 50061 / Oct '93 / Sakkaris

☐ **SET IT OFF**
Angel / From yo blind side / Heist / Let it go / Come on / Angelic wars / Name callin' / Missing you / Don't let go (Love) / Days of our lives / Sex is on my mind / Live to regret / Set it off / Hey Joe
7559619952 / Oct '96 / East West

☐ **SET IT OFF (Score)**
Young, Christopher *c*
VSD 5779 / Dec '96 / Varese Sarabande

☐ **SEVEN**
0022432CIN / Jan '96 / Edel

☐ **SEVEN BRIDES FOR SEVEN BROTHERS (1986 London Cast)**
De Paul, Gene *c*
Mercer, Johnny *l*
Yates, Martin *con*
Overture / Bless your beautiful hide / Wonderful wonderful day / One man / Goin' courtin' / Love never goes away / Sobbin' women / Townsfolk's lament / Woman ought to know her place / We gotta make it through the winter / We gotta make it through the winter (Reprise) / Spring spring spring / Woman ought to know her place (Reprise) / Glad that you were born / Wedding dance / Goin' courtin/ Wonderful wonderful day
OCRCD 6008 / Oct '95 / First Night

☐ **SEVEN BRIDES FOR SEVEN BROTHERS**
De Paul, Gene *c*
Mercer, Johnny *l*
Bless your beautiful hide / Spring spring spring / Wonderful wonderful day / When you're in love / Goin' cotin / Hoedown / Lonesome polecat / Sobbin' women / June bride
PWKS 4209 / Jul '94 / Carlton

☐ **SEVEN BRIDES FOR SEVEN BROTHERS (Film Cast)**
De Paul, Gene *c*
Mercer, Johnny *l*
Main title / Bless yore beautiful hide / Do unto udders / Bless yore beautiful hide / Wonderful wonderful day / Adam in treetop / When you're in love / Goin' co'tin' / Barn dance / Barn raising/fight / When you're in love / Brothers advice/Lonesome Winter / Lament / Lovesick / Sobbin' women / Kidnapped and chase / June bride / June bride / Spring Spring Spring / When you're in love / Girls girls girls/End title / Bless yore beautiful hide / Lament / Goin' co'tin' / Queen of the May / When you're in love / Spring Spring Spring
CDODEON 17 / Aug '96 / Soundtracks

☐ **SEVEN BRIDES FOR SEVEN BROTHERS (Cast Recording)**
De Paul, Gene *c*
Mercer, Johnny *l*
Overture: *Cast* / Bless your beautiful hide: *Cast* / Wonderful wonderful day: *Cast* / Goin' courtin': *Cast* / Love never goes away: *Cast* / Sobbin' women: *Cast* / Women ought to know her place: *Cast* / We've gotta make it through the winter: *Cast* / Lonesome polecat: *Cast* / Spring spring spring: *Cast* / Glad that you were born: *Cast* / Finale: *Cast*
SHOWCD 051 / Apr '97 / Showtime

☐ **SEVEN DEADLY SINS (& Little Threepenny Music: Songs of Kurt Weill) (Johnson, Julia Migenes/London Symphony Orchestra)**
Weill, Kurt c
Tilson Thomas, Michael con
MK 44529 / Jan '89 / Masterworks

☐ **SEVEN DEADLY SINS (Van Otter, A./ North German Symphony Orchestra)**
Weill, Kurt c
Brecht, Bertolt l
Gardiner, John Eliot con
4398942 / Dec '94 / Deutsche Grammophon

☐ **SEVEN DEADLY SINS (Lemper, Ute/ Cast & Berlin RIAS Sinfonietta)**
Weill, Kurt c
Brecht, Bertolt l
Mauceri, John con
4301682 / Apr '91 / Decca

☐ **SEVEN DEADLY SINS (May, Gisela & Peter Schreier/Hans Joachim Rotzsch/ Leipzig Rundfunk Sinfonie Orchestra)**
Weill, Kurt c
Brecht, Bertolt l
Kegel, Herbert & Heinz Roger/Henry Krtschill con
0020692BC / Sep '96 / Berlin Classics

☐ **SEVEN DEADLY SINS (Stratas, Teresa & Orchestre De L'Opera National De Lyon)**
Weill, Kurt c
Nagano, Kurt con
0630170682 / May '97 / Erato

☐ **SEVEN DEADLY SINS/HAPPY END (Lenya, Lotte)**
Weill, Kurt c
Brecht, Bertolt l
Bruckner-Ruggenberg, Wilhelm con
MPK 45886 / Jan '93 / Masterworks

☐ **SEVEN MURDERS FOR SCOTLAND YARD/7 HYDE PARK: LA CASA MALEDET**
Piccioni, Piero/Francesco De Masi c
CDCR 29 / Apr '96 / Silva Screen

☐ **SEVENTH SIGN**
Nitzsche, Jack c
Opening fish desert wrath 1st seal / Nightmare / David's apartment / Abby follows David to the synagogue / World in trouble / Parchment 229 / Stabbing / Attempted suicide / Lucci revealed / Last martyr / Walk to the gas chamber / Birth / Abby's death / End credits
EDL 25062 / Jan '89 / Edel

☐ **SEVENTH VOYAGE OF SINBAD, THE**
Herrmann, Bernard c
VCD 47256 / Jan '89 / Varese Sarabande

☐ **SHADOW, THE (Score/Songs)**
Goldsmith, Jerry c
Goldsmith, Jerry con
07822187632 / Sep '94 / Arista

☐ **SHADOWLANDS (London Symphony Orchestra)**
Fenton, George c
CDQ 5550932 / Mar '94 / Angel

☐ **SHAFT (Hayes, Isaac)**
Hayes, Isaac c
Shaft / Bumpy's lament / Walk from Regio's / Ellie's love theme / Shaft's cab ride / Cafe Regio's / Early Sunday morning / Be yourself / Friend's place / Soulsville / No name bar / Bumpy's blues / Shaft strikes again / Do your thing / End theme
CDSXD 021 / Oct '89 / Stax

☐ **SHAKEDOWN**
Ayres, Mark c
FILMCD 718 / Jan '96 / Silva Screen

☐ **SHAKESPEARE ODE ON THE WITCHES AND FAIRIES, A (Music From A Midsummer Night's Dream/The Tempest/Macbeth) (Musicians Of The Globe)**
Linley, Thomas c
Pickett, Philip con
4466892 / 18 May '98 / Philips

☐ **SHALLOW GRAVE**
Boswell, Simon c
Shallow grave: *Leftfield* / Shallow grave theme / My baby just cares for me: *Simone, Nina* / Laugh not riot / Release the dubs: *Leftfield* / Strips the willo: *Carmichael, John & His Band* / Loft conversion / Spade we need a spade / Shallow grave deep depression / Hugo's last trip / Happy heart: *Williams, Andy*
CDEMC 3699 / Feb '95 / EMI

☐ **SHANGHAI TRIAD**
Guangtian, Zhang c
Beddy-bye beddy-bye over Grandma's bridge / Main theme / Go away / Bright moon / Bijou cries / Lilac menuet / Murder on a rainy night / Express train / Garden / Tree under the bright moon / Shui Sheng climbs the stairs / False pretenses / Umbrella / Game (Mah Jong) / Russian hills / Shuisheng and bijou / Escape from Shanghai / Eyes of Shui Sheng / Bright moon (instrumental) / Conversation at night / Main theme (reprise) / Beddy-bye beddy-bye over Grandma's bridge (reprise)
CDVIR 44 / Nov '95 / Virgin

☐ **SHARE MY LETTUCE (Smith, Maggie & Kenneth Williams/Roderick Cook/1957 London Cast)**
Statham, Keith & Patrick Gowers c
Gascoigne, Bamber l
AEICD 016 / May '98 / AEI

☐ **SHARPE - OVER THE HILLS AND FAR AWAY (Music From The TV Series)**
Overture: *Moscow Symphony Orchestra* / Sharpe's theme: *Moscow Symphony Orchestra* / I'm 95: *Band Of The Light Division* / Over the hills and far away: *Tams, John* / Spanish sword: *Muldowney, Dominic* / Rogue's march: *Tams, John* / Collier recruit: *Rusby, Kate* / Bird in the bush: *Tams, John* / Colours: *Muldowney, Dominic* / Shilling: *Muldowney, Dominic* / Spanish bride: *Tams, John* / Gentleman soldier: *Tams, John* / Bugle call - Moneymusk: *Band Of The Light Division* / Broken hearted I will wander: *Rusby, Kate* / Badajoz: *Muldowney, Dominic* / Rambling soldier: *Tams, John & Barry Coope* / Huntsman's chorus: *Tams, John & Barry Coope* / Italian song: *Tams, John & Barry Coope* / Johnny is gone for a soldier: *Tams, John* / Forlorn hope: *Muldowney, Dominic* / Love farewell: *Tams, John* / Sunset: *Band Of The Light Division* / Sharpe's song: *Tams, John*
VTCD 81 / Apr '96 / Virgin

☐ **SHAWSHANK REDEMPTION, THE**
Newman, Thomas c
May / Shawshank prison (stoic theme) / New fish / Rock hammer / Inch of his life / If I didn't care: *Ink Spots* / Brooks was here / His judgement cometh / Suds on the roof/Workfield / Shawshank redemption / Lovesick blues: *Williams, Hank* / Elmo blatch / Sisters Zihuatanejo / Marriage of Figaro: *Deutsch Opera Berlin/Karl Bohm* / Lovely Raquel / And that right soon / Compass and guns / So was red / End titles
4783322 / Feb '95 / Epic

☐ **SHE LOVES ME (1963 Broadway Cast)**
Bock, Jerry c
Harnick, Sheldon l
Loud, D. con
VSD 5464 / Jun '94 / Varese Sarabande

☐ **SHE LOVES ME (1994 London Cast)**
Bock, Jerry c
Harnick, Sheldon l
Scott, R. con
Overture / Good morning good day / Sounds while selling / Days gone by / No more candy / Three letters / Tonight at eight / Perspective / I don't know his name / Goodbye George / Will he like me / Ilona / I resolve / Romantic atmosphere / Tango tragique / Mr Nowack will you / Dear friend / Entr'acte / Try me / Where's my shoe / Vanilla ice cream / She loves me / Trip to the library / Grand knowing you / Twelve days to Christmas / Finale
OCRCD 6052 / May '97 / First Night

☐ **SHE LOVES ME (1964 London Cast)**
Bock, Jerry c
Harnick, Sheldon l
Ainsworth, A. con
Overture/Good morning good day / Sounds while selling / No more chocolates / Letters / Tonight at eight / Perspective / Ilona / Heads I win / Romantic atmosphere / Dear friend / Try me / Ice cream / She loves me / Trip to the library / Grand knowing you / Twelve days of Christmas / Ice cream (reprise)
CDANGEL 6 / Apr '94 / Angel

☐ **SHELTERING SKY, THE**
Sakamoto, Ryuichi c
Sacred koran / Sheltering sky / Belly / Port's composition / On the bed (dream) / Loneliness / On the hill / Kyoto / Cemetry / Dying / Market / Grand Hotel / Louange au prophet houria aaichi flute / Je chante / Midnight sun / Fever ride / Chantavec citare / Marnia's tent / Goula lima / Happy bus ride / Night train / Guedra
CDV 2652 / Nov '90 / Virgin

☐ **SHERLOCK HOLMES (The Sign of Four/The Adventures of.../The Return of...)**
Gowers, Patrick c
Gowers, Patrick con
CDTER 1136 / Mar '90 / TER

☐ **SHERLOCK HOLMES (London Cast)**
Bricusse, Leslie c
Sherlock Holmes / Without him there can be no me / London is London / Vendetta / Anything you want to know / Her face / Men like you / Lousy life / I shall find her / No reason / Halcyon days / Without him there can be no me (reprise) / Down the apples 'n' pears / He's back / Million years ago or was it yesterday / Best of you the best of me / Sherlock Holmes (reprise)
BD 74145 / Jun '89 / RCA

☐ **SHERLOCK HOLMES (1993 Cast)**
Bricusse, Leslie c
CDTER 1198 / Jan '94 / TER

☐ **SHE'S THE ONE (Petty, Tom)**
9362462852 / Aug '96 / Warner Bros.

☐ **SHILOH**
Goldsmith, Joel c
VSD 5893 / 12 Jan '98 / Varese Sarabande

☐ **SHINE**
4547102 / Aug '97 / Philips

☐ **SHIPHUNTERS**
Morricone, Ennio c
OST 109 / Jan '93 / Milano Dischi

☐ **SHIRLEY VALENTINE (Russell, Willy & George Hatzinassios)**
Russell, Willy & George Hatzinassios c
Girl who used to be me: *Austin, Patti* / Shirley Valentine / Affection / Crumbling resolve / Dreams / Costas / Coming to Greece / Nocturne / Arrival in Mykonos
FILMCD 062 / Nov '89 / Silva Screen

☐ **SHOES OF THE FISHERMAN, THE**
North, Alex c
GAD 94009 / Jan '95 / Tsunami

☐ **SHOGUN MAYEDA (Utah Symphony Orchestra)**
Scott, John c
MAF 7017D / Mar '92 / Intrada

☐ **SHOOTING FISH**
Me and you vs the world: *Space* / Beautiful alone: *Strangelove* / Day before yesterday's man: *Supernaturals* / Golden skin: *Silver Sun* / Twist: *Symposium* / Neighborhood: *Space* / Waht the world need now is love: *De Shannon, Jackie* / I'm a better man: *McAlmont, David* / Body medusa: *Supereal* / Friends: *Wannadies* / Bluetonic: *Bluetones* / Do you know the way to San Jose: *Warwick, Dionne* / In charge: *Dubstar* / To be the one: *Passion Star* / In pursuit of happiness: *Divine Comedy* / Shooting fish: *Syrewicz, Stanislas*
PRMDCD 35 / 13 Oct '97 / Premier/EMI

☐ **SHOOTING PARTY, THE/BIRDS AND PLANES (Royal Philharmonic Orchestra)**
Scott, John c
Scott, John con
JSCD 113 / Jan '93 / JOS

☐ **SHORT CUTS**
Open on helicopters / Coversation on a barstool / To hell with love / Punishing kiss / Cello concerto in B minor / Blue / Evil California / Bercuese / Thousand years / Cello concerto no.2 opus 30 / Imitation of a kiss / Full moon / I don't know you / Nothing can stop me know / Prisoner of life/I'm gonna go fishin' / How does she do it so quickly
IMACD 23013 / Jul '98 / Imago

☐ **SHORT EYES (Mayfield, Curtis)**
Mayfield, Curtis c
Doo wop is strong in here / Back against the wall / Need someone to love / Heavy dude / Short eyes / Break it down / Another fool in love / Father confessor
CPCD 8183 / Jun '96 / Charly

☐ **SHOW AND TELL**
WHI 666CD / May '97 / Which

☐ **SHOW BOAT (Highlights - The Shows Collection) (Cast Recording)**
Kern, Jerome c
Hammerstein II, Oscar l
Ol' man river / Where's the mate for me / Make believe / Can't help lovin' dat man / I might fall back on you / Life upon the wicked stage / You are love / Why do I love you / Bill / Goodbye my lady love / After the ball / Ol' man river (reprise)
PWKS 4161 / Sep '93 / Carlton

☐ **SHOW BOAT (1946 Broadway Revival Version) (1993 Studio Cast)**
Kern, Jerome c
Hammerstein II, Oscar l
Edwards, John Owen con
Overture / OPening act 1 / Where's the mate for me / Make believe / Orchestral interlude / Ol' man river / Can't help lovin' dat man / Life upon the the wicked stage / Queenie's ballyhoo / Villain's dance / You are love / Finale act 1 / En'tracte / Opening act 2 / Why do I love you / Dahomey / Letter interlude / Bill / St Agatha's convent / Washington post march / Goodbye my love / Happy new year / Finale
CDTER 1199 / Nov '97 / TER

☐ **SHOW BOAT (1987 Studio Cast & Ambrosian Chorus/London Sinfonietta)**
Kern, Jerome c
Hammerstein II, Oscar l
McGlinn, John con
CDRIVER 1 / Sep '88 / EMI Classics

☐ **SHOW BOAT (Cast Recording)**
Kern, Jerome c
Hammerstein II, Oscar l
Overture / Where's the mate for me / Make believe / Ol' man river / Can't help lovin' dat man / Life on the wicked stage / Queenie's ballyhoo / You are love / Why do I love you / Bill / Goodbye my lady love / After the ball
SHOWCD 011 / Feb '95 / Showtime

☐ **SHOW BOAT (Highlights) (1987 Studio Cast & Ambrosian Chorus/London Sinfonietta)**
Kern, Jerome c
Hammerstein II, Oscar l
McGlinn, John con
Overture / Cotton blossom / Where's the mate for me / Make believe / Ol' man river / Can't help lovin' dat man / Life on the wicked stage / Till good luck comes my way / I might fall back on you / Queenie's ballyhoo / You are love / Showboat / At the fair / Why do I love you / Bill / Goodbye my Lady love / After the ball / Hey feller / Finale ultimo
CDC 7498472 / Oct '89 / EMI Classics

☐ **SHOW BOAT (Previn, Andre & Mundell Lowe/Ray Brown/Grady Tate)**
Kern, Jerome c
Hammerstein II, Oscar l
Make believe / Can't help lovin' dat man / Ol' man river / Bill / Life on the wicked stage / Why do I love you / I might fall back on you / Nobody else but me
4476392 / Jan '95 / Deutsche Grammophon

☐ **SHOW BOAT (1951 Film Cast)**
Kern, Jerome c
Hammerstein II, Oscar l
Main title / Cap'n Andy's calliope / Natchez / Cap'n Andy's presentation / Cap'n Andy's ballyhoo / Encore on dock / Where's the mate for me (Gambler's song) / Young romance / Make believe / Can't help lovin' dat man / Can't help lovin' dat man (reprise 1) / I might fall back on you / Julie leaves the boat / Ol' man river / Ol' man river (reprise) / You are love / Why do I love you / Ravenal is gone / Bill / Can't help lovin' dat man (reprise 2) / Life on the wicked stage / After the ball / Packet boat / Natchez dock / Make believe (reprise) / Reunion / Ol' man river (Finale ultimo) / Can't help lovin' dat man (outtake) / Bill (outtake)
CDODEON 5 / Feb '96 / Premier/EMI

☐ **SHOW BOAT (Broadway Cast)**
Kern, Jerome c
Hammerstein II, Oscar l
McArthur, Edwin con
SK 53330 / Jan '93 / Sony Broadway

☐ **SHOW BOAT (Original London Cast)**
Kern, Jerome c
Hammerstein II, Oscar l
Cotton blossom / Make believe / Can't help lovin' dat man / I might fall back on you / Ol' man river / How'd you like to spoon with me / You are love / I still suits me (no matter what you say) / Nobody else but me / Life upon the wicked stage / Bill / After the ball/Ol' man river / Why do I love you
12446 / Mar '97 / Laserlight

☐ **SHOW BOAT (1998 London Cast)**
Kern, Jerome c
Hammerstein II, Oscar l
Overture (opening act 1) / Where's the mate for me / Orchestral interlude / Can't help lovin' dat man / Queenie's ballhoo / You are love / Opening act 2 / Dahomey / Bill / Washington post march / After the ball / You are love / Make believe / Ol' man river / Life upon the wicked stage / Villain's dance / Finale act 1 (entr'acte) / Why do I love you / Letter interlude / St. Agatha's convent / Goodbye my lady love / Happy new year / Finale
CDTER2 1199 / May '98 / TER

☐ **SHOW OF FORCE, A**
Delerue, Georges c
Delerue, Georges con
XCD 1005 / Apr '91 / Varese Sarabande

☐ **SHOW, THE**
5290212 / Aug '95 / Def Jam

☐ **SHOWGIRLS**
6544926612 / Jan '96 / Atlantic

☐ **SHVITZ, THE**
KFWCD 144 / Feb '95 / Knitting Factory

☐ **SICILIAN CHECKMATE/A BRIEF SEASON (La Violenza: Quinto Potere/ Una Breve Stagione)**
Morricone, Ennio c
LEGENDCD 26 / Oct '96 / Legend

☐ **SILKWOOD**
Delerue, Georges c
Drew's theme / Ride to Texas / Ride from Texas / Largo / Karen is contaminated / Legato / Karen and Drew on the porch / Down the highway / Love theme / Down the highway (reprise) / Drew leaves Karen / Karen looks trhough files / Pretty little horses lullaby / Karen has a car accident / After stripping Karen's house of her possessions / Drew walks through the empty house / Largo desolato / Amazing grace / Epilogue and end titles
DRGCD 6107 / Jun '95 / DRG

☐ **SILVERADO**
Broughton, Bruce c
MAF 7035D / Feb '93 / Intrada

☐ **SIMPLE MAN, A (English Chamber Orchestra)**
Davis, Carl c
White on white / Characters appear / Organ grinder / Sitting / Death of mother / Going to work / Coming from the hill / Waiting / Golden room / Three Anns / Seascape / Man with red eyes / Clogs / Homage
OCRCD 6039 / Feb '96 / First Night

☐ **SIMPLE TWIST OF FATE, A**
Eidelman, Cliff c
VSD 5538 / Jul '95 / Varese Sarabande

☐ **SIMPSONS - SONGS IN THE KEY OF SPRINGFIELD, THE (Original Music/ Dialogue From Seven Seasons Of Simpsons Episodes)**
Simpsons main title theme / We do (The Stonecutters Song): *Marge & Homer* / Dancin' Homer: *Simpsons* / Crosstown bridge: *Simpsons* / Capital city: *Bennett, Tony & Simpsons* / Who needs the kwik-E-mart: *Apu & The Simpsons* / Whoo needs the kwik-e-mart: *Marge & Homer* / Round springfield(medley): *Marge & Homer* / Bleeding gums blues: *Cast & Lisa* / Four-headed king: *Bleeding Gums Murphy* / There she sits brokenhearted: *Lisa & Bleeding Gums Murphy* / Jazzman: *Lisa & Bleeding Gums Murphy* / Oh streetcar/White hot grease fires: *Director & Cast* / Long before the superdrome: *Chief Wiggum* / New Orleans: *Cast* / I thought my life would be a mardi gras: *Marge, Apu & Cast* / I am just a simple paper boy: *Apu* / Stella: *Flanders, Ned* / She flies: *Marge & Cast* / Kindness of strangers: *Marge & Cast* / Jingle bells: *Goulet, Robert, Bart, Smithers, Mr. Burns & Nelson* / Springfield (medley) / Itchy and scratchy main title theme / Itchy and scratchy end credits theme / Day the violence died (medley): *Krusty The Clown* / Amendment song: *Sheldon, Jack, Kid, Bart, Lisa & Cast* / Senor Burns: *Puente, Tito & His Latin Jazz Ensemble* / Simpsons end credits theme: *Puente, Tito & His Latin Jazz Ensemble* / Your wife don't understand you: *D'Angelo, Beverley & Homer* / Kamp Krusty (medley): *Merlino, Gene* / South of the border: *Merlino, Gene* / Simpsons end credits theme / Simpsons end credits theme / Simpsons end

credits theme / Treehouse of horror 5 (medley): *Bart & Homer* / Controlling the transmission (prologue): *Simpsons* / Halloween special main title theme: *Simpsons* / Honey roasted peanuts: *Marge & Homer* / Boy scouts n the hood (medley): *Simpsons* / Saved by the bell: *Simpsons* / Jackpot: *Bart & Millhouse* / Springfield (parts 1 and 2): *Springfield* / Remember this: *Bart & Lisa* / Another Edwardian morning: *Simpsons* / Two dozen and one greyhounds (medley): *Mr. Burns & Lisa* / Pick of the litter: *Mr. Burns & Lisa* / See my vest: *Simpsons* / Eye on springfield theme: *Brockman, Kent & Homer* / Flaming moes: *Lennon, Kip & Cast* / Homer's barbershop quartet (medley): *Principal Skinner & Apu* / One last call: *Principal Skinner & Apu* / Baby on board: *Be Sharps & Cast* / TV sucks: *Bart & Homer* / Fish called Selma (medley): *Agent MacArthur Parker & Troy McClure* / Stop the planet of the apes: *Simpsons & Troy McClure* / Chimpan A to chimpan Z: *McClure, Troy & Cast* / Send in the clowns: *Krusty The Clown & Sideshow Mel* / Monorail song: *Lanley, Lyle & Cast* / In search of an out of body vibe: *Grampa & Mrs. Bouvier* / Bagged me a homer: *D'Angelo, Beverley, Recording Studio Guy & The Simpsons* / It was a very good beer: *Homer* / Bart sells his soul (medley): *Bart* / From God's brain to your mouth: *Bart* / In-a-gadda-da-vidda: *Reverend Lovejoy & The Simpsons* / Happy Birthday Lisa: *Lennon, Kip & Cast* / Simpsons Halloween special end credits theme: *Lennon, Kip & Cast* / Who shot Mr. Burns (medley) / Simpsons end credits theme / Simpsons end credits theme
8122727232 / Jun '97 / Rhino

☐ **SIMPSONS SING THE BLUES, THE (Simpsons)**
Do the bartman / School day / Born under a bad sign / Moanin' Lisa blues / Deep deep trouble / God bless the child / I love to see you smile / Springfield soul stew / Look at those idiots / Sibling rivalry
GED 24308 / Nov '96 / Geffen

☐ **SINATRA (Sinatra, Frank)**
9362450912 / May '98 / Reprise

☐ **SINGIN' IN THE RAIN (Kelly, Gene & Film Cast)**
Freed, Arthur *c*
Brown, Nacio Herb *l*
Main title / Fit as a fiddle and ready for love / Stunt montage / First silent picture / Tango / All I do is dream of you / Gene dreams of Kathy / All I do is dream of you / Make 'em laugh / Mood music / Beautiful girl montage / Beautiful girl / Have lunch with me / Stage is set / You were meant for me / You are my lucky star / Moses / Good morning / Goodnight Kathy / Singin' in the rain / From duelling to dancing / Would you / Broadway Melody Ballet / Would you (reprise) / Singin' in the rain in A-flat / Finale
CDODEON 14 / Jun '96 / Soundtracks

☐ **SINGIN' IN THE RAIN (1983 London Cast)**
Freed, Arthur *c*
Brown, Nacio Herb *l*
Reed, Michael *con*
Overture / Fit as a fiddle / Temptation / I can't give you anything but love / Be a clown / Too marvellous for words / You are my lucky star / Moses / Good morning / Singin' in the rain / Would you / Fascinating rhythm / Finale
OCRCD 6013 / Oct '93 / First Night

☐ **SINGING DETECTIVE, THE/OTHER SIDE OF THE SINGING DETECTIVE**
Umbrella man: *Kaye, Sammy Orchestra* / Copenhagen: *Ambrose & His Orchestra* / I'll just close my eyes: *Shelton, Anne* / Old Moses put Pharoah in his place: *Waring, Fred & His Pennsylvanians* / Stop crying: *Oliver, King Orchestra* / Three caballeros: *Crosby, Bing & Andrews Sisters* / That's for me: *Haymes, Dick* / I'll be around: *Mills Brothers* / Sing nightingale sing: *Anderson, Lale* / There's something wrong with the weather: *Stone, Lew & His Band* / Java jive: *Ink Spots* / There's a fellow waiting in Poughkeepsie: *Crosby, Bing & Andrews Sisters* / Till then: *Mills Brothers* / Chinatown my Chinatown: *Jolson, Al* / Let the people sing: *Payne, Jack & His Orchestra* / I'm making believe: *Ink Spots & Ella Fitzgerald* / Little Dutch mill: *Noble, Ray & His Orchestra & Al Bowlly* / Hush hush hush here comes the bogeyman: *Hall, Henry Orchestra* / Later on: *Lynn, Vera* / Birdsong at Eventide: *Ronalde, Ronnie & Robert Farnon Orchestra*
POTTCD 200 / May '93 / Connoisseur Collection

☐ **SINGLES**
Would: *Alice In Chains* / Breath: *Pearl Jam* / Seasons: *Cornell, Chris* / Dyslexic heart: *Westerberg, Paul* / Battle of Evermore: *Lovemongers* / Chloe dancer/Crown of thorns: *Mother Love Bone* / Birth ritual: *Soundgarden* / State of love and trust: *Pearl Jam* / Overblown: *Mudhoney* / Waiting for somebody: *Westerberg, Paul* / May this be love: *Hendrix, Jimi* / Nearly lost you: *Screaming Trees* / Drown: *Smashing Pumpkins*
4714382 / Jul '92 / Epic

☐ **SIRENS**
Portman, Rachel *c*
213022 / Jul '94 / Milan

☐ **SKYBOUND**
Skybound: *Seymour, Pat* / Skybound (no limits): *Irma* / (No more) fear of flying: *Brooker, Gary* / I'll fly for you: *Spandau Ballet* / Looking up: *Seymour, Pat* / Wouldn't it be good: *Kershaw, Nik* / To fly: *De Bel, Piet Jan* / Year of the cat: *Stewart, Al* / Above and beyond: *De Bel, Piet Jan* / Reaching higher: *De Bel, Piet Jan* / Kayleigh: *Marillion* / Living in another world: *Talk Talk* / Bon voyage: *Carnes, Kim* / Baker Street: *Rafferty, Gerry* / Air that I breathe: *Hollies* / Wings: *De Bel, Piet Jan* / Skybound (no limits): *De Bel, Piet Jan* / Skybound: *Seymour, Pat*
MSA 99004 / Sep '97 / Movies Select Audio

☐ **SKYSCRAPER (Cast Recording)**
Van Heusen, James *c*
Cahn, Sammy *l*
ZDM 5651322 / Apr '94 / EMI Classics

☐ **SLAB BOYS, THE**
Lucille: *Little Richard* / Dream lover: *Collins, Edwyn* / No particular place to go: *Proclaimers* / Let's jump the broomstick: *Lulu* / Maybe baby: *Proclaimers* / I'll be home: *Kane, Pat* / Ain't that a shame: *Proclaimers* / I thought of you last night: *Reader, Eddie* / Young love: *Kane, Pat* / True love: *Kane, Pat & Eddie Reader* / Love is strange: *Bruce, Jack & Edwyn Collins/Pat Kane*
OCD 006 / 15 Sep '97 / Ocean Deep

☐ **SLEEPING BEAUTY**
WDR 75622 / Oct '96 / Disney Music & Stories

☐ **SLEEPLESS IN SEATTLE**
As time goes by: *Durante, Jimmy* / Kiss to build a dream on: *Armstrong, Louis* / Stardust: *Cole, Nat 'King'* / Makin' whoopee: *Dr. John & Rickie Lee Jones* / In the wee small hours of the morning: *Simon, Carly* / Back in the saddle again: *Autry, Gene* / Bye bye blackbird: *Cocker, Joe* / Wink and a smile: *Connick, Harry Jr.* / Stand by your man: *Wynette, Tammy* / Affair to remember: *Durante, Jimmy* / Make someone happy: *Durante, Jimmy* / When I fall in love: *Dion, Celine & Clive Griffin*
4735942 / Dec '96 / Epic

☐ **SLEEPWALKERS**
Pike, Nicholas *c*
74321101322 / 24 Nov '97 / Milan

☐ **SLICE OF PYE (London Cast)**
DRGCD 13114 / Mar '96 / DRG

☐ **SLICE OF SATURDAY NIGHT, A (1989 London Cast)**
Heather Brothers *c*
OCRCD 6041 / Oct '95 / First Night

☐ **SLIDING DOORS**
MCD 11715 / 27 Apr '98 / MCA

☐ **SMALL SOLDIERS**
Goldsmith, Jerry *c*
VSD 5963 / 17 Aug '98 / Varese Sarabande

☐ **SMILLA'S SENSE OF SNOW**
Gregson-Williams, Harry & Hans Zimmer *c*
0630178722 / 17 Nov '97 / Teldec Classics

☐ **SMOKE**
1620242 / Apr '96 / Polydor

☐ **SMOKEY JOE'S CAFE**
7567827652 / Oct '96 / Atlantic

☐ **SNAKES AND LADDERS**
74321430112 / 18 May '98 / Milan

☐ **SNOOPY (1981 New York Cast)**
Grossman, Larry *c*
Hackady, Hal *l*
DRGCD 6103 / Jan '95 / DRG

☐ **SNOOPY (1982 London Cast)**
Grossman, Larry *c*
Hackady, Hal *l*
Overture: The world according to Snoopy / Edgar Allen Poe / Woodstock's theme / I know now / Vigil / Clouds / Where did that little dog go / Friend / Great writer (It was a dark and stormy night) / Poor sweet baby / Don't be anything less / Big wow-wow / Just one person
CDTER 1073 / Sep '93 / TER

☐ **SNOW WHITE AND THE SEVEN DWARFS**
Churchill, Frank E. *c*
WD 745402 / Oct '96 / Disney Music & Stories

☐ **SNOWMAN, THE (Blake, Howard)**
4071136 / Nov '95 / Columbia

☐ **SO I MARRIED AN AXE MURDERER**
Brother: *Toad The Wet Sprocket* / Break: *Soul Asylum* / Starve to death: *Whitley, Chris* / Rush: *Big Audio Dynamite II* / This poem sucks: *Myers, Mike* / Saturday night: *Ned's Atomic Dustbin* / Long day in the universe: *Darling Buds* / Two princes: *Spin Doctors* / My insatiable one: *Suede* / Maybe baby: *Sun 60* / There she goes: *La's*
4742732 / Nov '93 / Columbia

☐ **SOAPDISH**
Silvestri, Alan *c*
VSD 5322 / Aug '91 / Varese Sarabande

☐ **SOLO**
CHAN 8769 / Jul '89 / Chandos

☐ **SOME KIND OF WONDERFUL**
Do anything: *Shelley, Peter* / Brilliant mind: *Furniture* / Cry like this: *Blue Room* / I go crazy: *Flesh For Lulu* / She loves me: *Duffy, Stephen 'Tin Tin'* / Hardest walk: *Jesus & Mary Chain* / Shyest time: *Apartments* / Miss Amanda Jones: *March Violets* / Can't help falling in love: *Lick The Tins* / Turn to the sky: *March Violets* / Dr. Mabuse: *Propaganda*
BGOCD 178 / Feb '95 / Beat Goes On

☐ **SOME LIKE IT HOT**
Styne, Jule *c*
Merrill, Bob *l*
Running wild: *Monroe, Marilyn* / Sugar blues: *Deutsch, Adolph & His Orchestra* / Down among the sheltering palms: *Society Syncopators* / Randolph Street rag: *Deutsch, Adolph & His Orchestra* / I wanna be loved by you: *Monroe, Marilyn* / Park Avenue fantasy: *Deutsch, Adolph & His Orchestra* / La Cumparsita / I'm through with love: *Monroe, Marilyn* / Tell the whole darn world: *Deutsch, Adolph & His Orchestra* / Play it again Charlie: *Deutsch, Adolph & His Orchestra* / Sweet Georgia Brown: *Malneck, Matty & His Orchestra* / By the beautiful sea: *Society Syncopators* / Some like it hot: *Malneck, Matty & His Orchestra*
RCD 10715 / 12 Jan '98 / Rykodisc

☐ **SOME LIKE IT HOT (1992 London Cast)**
Styne, Jule *c*
Merrill, Bob *l*
OCRCD 6028 / Mar '96 / First Night

☐ **SOME MOTHER'S SON (Whelan, Bill)**
7567829562 / Jan '97 / Atlantic

☐ **SOMETHING FOR THE BOYS (Broadway Cast)**
Porter, Cole *c*
AEICD 004 / May '98 / AEI

☐ **SOMETHING TO TALK ABOUT**
Zimmer, Hans & Graham Preskett *c*
VSD 5664 / Nov '95 / Varese Sarabande

☐ **SOMETHING WILD**
Loco de amor: *David Y Celia* / Ever fallen in love: *Fine Young Cannibals* / Zero zero seven Charlie: *UB40* / Not my slave: *Oingo Boingo* / You don't have to cry: *Cliff, Jimmy* / With or without you: *Jones, Steve* / High life: *Okossun, Sonny* / Man with a gun: *Harrison, Jerry* / Temptation: *New Order* / Wild thing: *Sister Carol*
MCAD 6194 / Jan '89 / MCA

☐ **SOMEWHERE IN TIME**
Barry, John *c*
Somewhere in time / Old woman / Journey back in time / Day together / Rhapsody on a theme of Paganini / Is he the one / Man of my dreams / Return to the present
BGOCD 222 / Feb '95 / Beat Goes On

☐ **SOMMERSBY**
Elfman, Danny *c*
Sheffer, Jonathan/T. Pasatieri *con*
Main title / Homecoming / Welcoming / First love / At work / Alone / Return montage / Mortal sin / Homer / Going to nashville / Baby / Tea cups / Townsend's tale / Death / Finale / End credits
7559614912 / Dec '96 / WEA

☐ **SON OF THE MORNING STAR**
Safan, Craig *c*
MAF 7037D / Feb '93 / Intrada

☐ **SON OF THE PINK PANTHER**
Mancini, Henry *c*
164612 / Dec '94 / Milan

☐ **SONATINE**
293452 / Sep '95 / Milan

☐ **SONG OF NORWAY, THE (Broadway Cast & The Ambrosian Chorus/ Philharmonia Orchestra)**
Forrest, George & Robert Wright *c*
Edwards, John Owen *con*
Prelude / Legend / Nina appears / Hill of dreams / Entr'acte / Pillow dance ballet / Halling / Freddy and his fiddle / Louisa's appearance / Strange music / Louisa discovers Grieg / Midsummer's eve / Song for Nina / March for Trolgers / Edvard announces betrothal / Hymn of betrothal / Louisa changes her mind / Finale act 1 / Opening act 2 / Bon vivant / Three loves / Finaletto / Rikaars farewell / Entr'acte 3 / Waltz eternal Peer Gynt ballet / Solveig's song / Hall of the mountain king / Anitra's dance / Exit of Louisa / I love you / At Christmastime / Christmas postlude / Finale act 2
CDTER2 1173 / Aug '98 / TER

☐ **SONG OF SINGAPORE (Cast Recording)**
Song of Singapore / Inexpensive tango / I miss my home in Harlem / You gotta do what you gotta do / Rose of Rangoon / Necrology / Sunrise / Never pay musicians what they're worth / Harbour of love / I can't remember / I want to get offa this island / Harbour of love / Foolish geese / Serve it up / Fly away Rose / I remember / Shake shake shake / We're rich / Sunrise/Song of Singapore
DRGCD 19003 / Jan '95 / DRG

☐ **SONGBOOK (London Cast)**
Norman, Monty *c*
More, Julian *l*
Songbook / East river rhapsody / Talking picture show / Mr. Destiny / Your time is different to mine / Pretty face / Je vous aime milady / Les halles / Olympics song 1936 / Nazi party pooper / I'm gonna take him home to momma / Bumpity bump / Girl in the window / Victory V / April in Wisconsin / Happy hickory / Lovely Sunday morning / Rusty's dream ballet / Storm on my heart / Pokenhatchit / Public protest committee / I accuse / Messages / I found love / Don't play the love song any more / Golden oldie / Climbin' / Nostalgia
DRGCD 13117 / Mar '96 / DRG

☐ **SONGS FOR A NEW WORLD (Original Broadway Cast)**
Brown, Jason Robert *c*
Brown, Jason Robert *l*
Opening: The New World / On the deck of a Spanish sailing ship / Just one step / I'm not afraid of anything / River won't flow / Stars and moon / She cries / Steam train / World was dancing / Surabaya-Santa / Christmas lullaby / King of the world / I'd give it all for you / Flagmaker / Flying home / Hear my song
09026686312 / May '97 / RCA Victor

☐ **SOPHIE (US Cast)**
Allen, Steve & Libi Staiger *c*
AEICD 027 / May '98 / AEI

☐ **SORCERER, THE (Tangerine Dream)**
Tangerine Dream *c*
Search / Call / Creation / Vengeance / Journey / Grind / Rainforest / Abyss / Mountain road / Impressions of sorcerer / Betrayal
MCLD 19159 / May '93 / MCA

☐ **SORCERER, THE/THE ZOO (D'Oyly Carte Opera Chorus/Royal Philharmonic Orchestra)**
Sullivan, Sir Arthur *c*
Gilbert, W.S. *l*
Godfrey, I./R. Nash *con*
4368072 / Jan '90 / London

☐ **SOUL IN THE HOLE**
Game of life: *Deep Press* / Diesel: *Wu Tang Clan* / Against the grain: *Sauce Money* / Ride: *MOP* / You ain't a killer: *Big Punisher* / LA Times: *Xzibit* / Main aim\: *Dwellas* / Rare species: *Mobb Deep* / High expectations: *Common* / Child is born: *Brand Nubian* / Won on won: *Cocoa Brovaz* / Sole in a hole: *Wu All Stars* / Visions of blur: *Darc Mind* / Late night action: *Organised Konfusion* / Your life: *OC*
078636753126 / 24 Nov '97 / Loud

☐ **SOUL MUSIC (Hopwood, Keith & Phil Bush)**
Hopwood, Keith & Phil Bush *c*
Discworld main title theme / To the city / Gatherin' rhubarb / Big moon rising / Chrysophase / Cover girl / Death / She won't change her mind / Touchstone / Clete / Good lovin' / Pathway to paradise / Unseen university / Stoni bod da / Messenger
RH 030746 / Nov '97 / Pluto

☐ **SOULFOOD**
73008260412 / 15 Sep '97 / RCA
74321523072 / 29 Jun '98 / RCA

☐ **SOUND BARRIER, THE (Royal Philharmonic Orchestra)**
Arnold, Sir Malcolm *c*
Alwyn, Kenneth *con*
CNS 5446 / Jan '89 / Cloud Nine

☐ **SOUND OF MUSIC, THE (1959 Broadway Cast)**
Rodgers, Richard *c*
Hammerstein II, Oscar *l*
Dvonch, Frederick *con*
SK 53537 / Nov '93 / Sony Broadway

☐ **SOUND OF MUSIC, THE (Film Cast)**
Rodgers, Richard *c*
Hammerstein II, Oscar *l*
Climb every mountain / So long farewell / Edelweiss / Maria / Processional / Something good / Do re mi / Sound of music / Lonely goatherd / My favourite things / Sixteen going on seventeen / Mornign hymn / Alleluia / I have confidence in me
07863665872 / Apr '95 / RCA

☐ **SOUND OF MUSIC, THE (Highlights - The Shows Collection) (Cast Recording)**
Rodgers, Richard *c*
Hammerstein II, Oscar *l*
PWKS 4145 / Jan '95 / Carlton

☐ **SOUND OF MUSIC, THE (Studio Cast/ May Fest Choir/Cincinnati Pops Orchestra)**
Rodgers, Richard *c*
Hammerstein II, Oscar *l*
Kunzel, Erich *con*
CD 80162 / Dec '88 / Telarc

☐ **SOUND OF MUSIC, THE (Original London Cast)**
Rodgers, Richard *c*
Hammerstein II, Oscar/Stephen Sondheim *l*
Sound of music / Maria / My favourite things / Do-re-mi / You are sixteen / So long farewell / Climb every mountain / Ordinary couple / Processional / Edelweiss / Finale/Climb every mountain
12448 / Mar '97 / Laserlight

☐ **SOUTH PACIFIC (1958 Film Cast)**
Rodgers, Richard *c*
Hammerstein II, Oscar *l*
Newman, Alfred *con*
South Pacific overture / Dites moi / Cock-eyed optimist / Twin soliloquies / Some enchanted evening / Bloody Mary / My girl back home / There is nothin' like a dame / Bali Ha'i / I'm gonna wash that man right outa my hair / I'm in love with a wonderful guy / Younger than Springtime / Happy talk / Honey bun / Carefully taught / This nearly was mine / Finale
ND 83681 / Feb '89 / RCA

☐ **SOUTH PACIFIC (1986 Studio Cast)**
Rodgers, Richard *c*
Hammerstein II, Oscar *l*
Overture / Dites moi / Cock-eyed optimist / Twin soliloquies / Some enchanted evening / Bloody Mary / There is nothin' like a dame / Bali Ha'i / I'm gonna wash that man right outa my hair / I'm in love with a wonderful guy / Younger than Springtime / This is how it feels / Entr'acte / Happy talk / Honey bun / Carefully taught / This nearly was mine / March / Take off / Communications established / Finale ultimo
CD 42205 / '86 / CBS

☐ **SOUTH PACIFIC (1988 London Cast)**
Rodgers, Richard *c*
Hammerstein II, Oscar *l*
OCRCD 6023 / Feb '96 / First Night

☐ **SOUTH PACIFIC (1949 Broadway Cast)**
Rodgers, Richard *c*
Hammerstein II, Oscar *l*
Dell'Isola, Salvatore *con*
SK 53327 / Nov '93 / Sony Broadway

☐ SOUTH PACIFIC (Highlights - The Shows Collection) (Cast Recording)
Rodgers, Richard c
Hammerstein II, Oscar l
Bali Ha'i / Twin soliloquys / Some enchanted evening / Bloody Mary / Cock-eyed optimist / There is nothin' like a dame / I'm gonna wash that man right outa my hair / Younger than springtime / Happy talk / Honey bun / Carefully taught / This nearly was mine / Dites moi / I'm in love with a wonderful guy
PWKS 4162 / Sep '93 / Carlton

☐ SOUTH PACIFIC (Te Kanawa, Dame Kiri & Jose Carreras/Sarah Vaughan/ Mandy Patinkin/Ambrosian Singers/ London Symphony Orchestra)
Rodgers, Richard c
Hammerstein II, Oscar l
Tunick, Jonathan con
MK 42205 / Dec '91 / Sony Classical

☐ SOUTH PACIFIC (Cast Recording)
Hammerstein II, Oscar c
Hammerstein II, Oscar l
Overtures / Dites moi / Cock eyed optimist / Twin soliloquies / Some enchanted evening / Finaletto / Bloody Mary / There is nothin' like a dame / Mary and Lootellan / Bali ha'i / Cable hears Bali Ha'i / Company street / I'm gonna wash that man right out of my hair / Wonderful guy / Younger than springtime / This is how it feels / Finale act one / En'tracte / Opening act two / Entrance of liat / Happy talk / Honey bun / You've got to be carefully taught / This nearly was mine / After Emile's solo / Communications discounted / Operation alligator / Finale ultimo / Exit music
CDTER2 1242 / Nov '97 / TER

☐ SOUTHERN MAID (1920 London Cast)
Fraser Simson, Harold c
Clayton Calthorp, Dion & Harry Graham l
GEMMCD 9115 / Jan '93 / Pearl

☐ SOUVENIRS DE VOYAGE
Herrmann, Bernard c
VSD 5559 / 17 Aug '98 / Varese Sarabande

☐ SPACE JAM (Score)
Howard, James Newton c
Main titles / Moron mountain / Back to earth / We seek bugs bunny / Charles / Toonland meeting / General bugs / Alien transformation / Hole in one / Michael in toonland / Spit shine / Monstars / Toons practice / Stealing the shorts / Ultimate game / Monstars locker room / Secret stuff / Second half / You got me / Crush 'em / You the duck / Winning shot / Gimme the ball / Not good at cheatin' / Michael Jordan returns
7567829792 / Mar '97 / Warner Sunset/ Atlantic Classics

☐ SPACE JAM
Fly like an eagle: *Seal* / Winner: *Coolio* / Space jam: *Quad City DJ'S* / I believe I can fly: *Kelly, R* / Hit 'em high: *B Real, Busta Rhymes, Coolio, LL Cool J & Method Man* / I found my smile again: *D'Angelo* / For you I will: *Monica* / Upside down: *Salt 'N' Pepa* / Givin' u all that I've got: *Robin S* / Basketball Jones: *White, Barry & Chris Rock* / I turn to you: *All 4 One* / All of my days: *Kelly, R & Changing Faces & Jay Z* / That's the way (I like it): *Spin Doctors & Biz Markie* / Buggin': *Bugs Bunny*
7567829612 / Mar '97 / Warner Bros.

☐ SPAWN
(Can't you) Trip like I do: *Filter & Crystal Method* / It's a long hard road out of hell: *Marilyn Manson & Sneaker Pimps* / Satan: *Orbital & Kirk Hammett* / Kick the pa: *Korn & Dust Brothers* / Tiny rubber band: *Butthole Surfers & Moby* / For whom the bell tolls (The irony of it all): *Metallica & Spooky* / Torn apart: *Stabbing Westward & Josh Wink* / Skin up pin up: *Mansun & 808 State* / One man army: *Prodigy & Tom Morello* / Spawn: *Silverchair Vitro* / T-4 strain: *Rollins, Henry & Goldie* / Familiar: *Incubus & Greyboy* / No remorse (I wanna die): *Slayer & Atari Teenage Riot* / Plane scraped its belly on a sooty yellow moon: *Soul Coughing & Roni Size*
4881182 / Jul '97 / Immortal

☐ SPEED I
Speed: *Idol, Billy* / Million miles away: *Plimsouls* / Soul deep: *Gin Blossoms* / Let's go for a ride: *Cracker* / Go outside and drive: *Blues Traveller* / Crash: *Ocasek, Ric* / Rescue me: *Benatar, Pat* / Hard road: *Stewart, Rod* / Cot: *Carnival Strippers* / Cars: *Numan, Gary* / Like a motorway: *St. Etienne* / Mr. Speed: *Kiss*
07822110182 / 1 Sep '97 / Arista

☐ SPEED II (Cruise Control)
Tell me is it true: *UB40* / My dream: *Shaggy* / Make love beautiful: *Tamia* / Crazy: *Morrison, Mark* / Speed TK: *TK* / Namoranda: *Brown, Carlinhos* / Tide is high: *Priest, Maxi* / I feel the earth move: *Andreone, Leah* / Never give up: *Common Sense* / You can get it if you really want: *Cliff, Jimmy* / Some people: *Rayvon* / Every breath you take: *Wright, Betty*
CDVUS 129 / 1 Sep '97 / Virgin

☐ SPHERE
Goldenthal, Elliot c
VSD 5913 / 23 Mar '98 / Varese Sarabande

☐ SPIES LIKE US
Bernstein, Elmer c
Ace tomato company / Off to spy / Russians in the desert / Pass in the tent / Escape / To the bus / Road to Russia / Rally 'round / WAMP / Martian act / Arrest / Recall / Winners
VCD 47246 / Jan '89 / Varese Sarabande

☐ SPINOUT/DOUBLE TROUBLE (Presley, Elvis)
Stop look and listen / Adam and evil / All that I am / Never say yes / Am I ready / Beach shack / Spinout / Smorgasbord / I'll be back / Double trouble / Baby if you'll give me all your love / Could I fall in love / Long legged girl with the short dress on / City by night / Old MacDonald / I love only one girl / There's so much world to see / It won't be long
07863663612 / Jun '94 / RCA

☐ SPIRIT OF ST. LOUIS, THE/RUTH (Shirley, George & Rundfunk Sinfonie Orchestra)
Waxman, Franz c
Foster, Lawrence con
Part 1 - Building the spirit / Part 2 - In flight / Part 3 - Arrival / I Boaz of Bethlehem / Prelude / Who is this woman / And the answer to this was yet only her song / Then as Naomi in time told it to me / Great dance of tribal time / Then Naomi in praise of Ruth told me / Boaz and Ruth sleepless nights / Oh only too well I knew / So I prepared / Marriage feast of Boaz and Ruth / And out of our loving union
10711 / Sep '96 / Capriccio

☐ SPITFIRE GRILL
Horner, James c
SK 62776 / Jun '97 / Sony Classical

☐ SPRUNG
9362465412 / 1 Sep '97 / Warner Bros.

☐ SPY WHO LOVED ME, THE
Hamlisch, Marvin c
Nobody does it better: *Simon, Carly* / Bond '77 / Ride to Atlantis / Mojave club / Anya / Tanker / Pyramids / Eastern lights / Conclusion / Spy who loved me The (end titles) / Bond 77
CZ 555 / Dec '95 / Premier/EMI

☐ ST. ELMO'S FIRE
St. Elmo's fire: *Parr, John* / Shake down: *Squier, Billy* / Young and innocent: *Elefante* / This time it was really right: *Anderson, Jon* / Saved my life: *Waybill, Fee* / Love theme: *Foster, David* / Georgetown: *Foster, David* / If I turn you away: *Moss, Vikki* / Stressed out (Close to the edge): *Airplay* / St. Elmo's fire (man in motion) / ehake down
7567812612 / Feb '95 / Atlantic

☐ ST. LOUIS WOMAN (Broadway Cast)
Arlen, Harold c
Mercer, Johnny l
ZDM 7646622 / Apr '93 / EMI Classics

☐ STAIRWAY TO THE STARS (1989 London Cast)
That's dancing / Who's sorry now / You stepped out of a dream / Fine romance / Three little words / Bye bye baby / Chattanooga choo choo / Rose's turn / Finale hooray for Hollywood / Ma belle Marguerite / 'S Wonderful / Not even nominated / Life upon the wicked stage / Buttons and bows / I got a gal in Kalamazoo / Lucky numbers / Bosom buddies
OCRCD 6021 / Dec '95 / First Night

☐ STAND AND DELIVER
Safan, Craig c
VCD 70459 / Jan '89 / Varese Sarabande

☐ STAND BY ME
Everyday: *Holly, Buddy* / Let the good times roll: *Shirley & Lee* / Come go with me: *Del-Vikings* / Whispering bells: *Del-Vikings* / Get a job: *Silhouettes* / Lollipop: *Chordettes* / Yakety yak: *Coasters* / Great balls of fire: *Lewis, Jerry Lee* / Mr. Lee: *Bobbettes* / Stand by me: *King, Ben E.*
7567816772 / Feb '94 / Atlantic

☐ STAND, THE (Walden, W.G. 'Snuffy')
Walden, W.G. 'Snuffy' c
VSD 5496 / Aug '94 / Varese Sarabande

☐ STANLEY AND IRIS
Williams, John c
Williams, John con
Stanley and Iris / Bicycle / Finding a family / Putting it all together / Letters / Reading lessons / Factory work / Stanley at work / Stanley and Iris end credits / Stanley's invention
VSD 5255 / May '90 / Varese Sarabande

☐ STAR (& Alfred Newman's 20th Century Fox Fanfare) (Andrews, Julie & Film Cast)
07822110092 / May '94 / Fox Film Scores

☐ STAR IS BORN, A (with Barbara Streisand) (1976 Film Cast)
Williams, Paul & Others c
Watch closely now / Queen Bee / Everything / Lost inside of you / Hellacious acres / Love theme (Evergreen) / Woman in the moon / I believe in love / Crippled crow / With one more look at you / Watch closely now / Reprise
4749052 / Apr '95 / Columbia

☐ STAR SPANGLED RHYTHM/ FOOTLIGHT PARADE
That old black magic / Hit the road to dreamland / On a swing shift / I'm doing it for defence / Sweater a sarong and a peek-a-boo bang / Sharp as a tack / Old glory / Overture / Sittin' on a backyard fence / Honeymoon hotel / By a waterfall / Shaghai lil'
CD 60013 / Jun '97 / Great Movie Themes

☐ STAR TREK - 30TH ANNIVERSARY EDITION
Trouble with tribbles / Heart of glory / Inner light / Visitor / Heroes and demons
GNPD 8053 / Dec '96 / GNP Crescendo

☐ STAR TREK - 30TH BIRTHDAY EDITION
VSD 57622 / Oct '96 / Varese Sarabande

☐ STAR TREK - FIRST CONTACT
GNPD 8052 / Dec '96 / GNP Crescendo

☐ STAR TREK - SYMPHONIC STAR TREK (& Star Trek Sound Effects/Bonus Star Trek PC Games CD-Rom) (Cincinnati Pops Orchestra)
Kunzel, Erich con
Star Trek / Menagerie / Star Trek I / Star Trek II/The Wrath Of Khan / Star Trek IV/The Voyage Home / Star trek V/Final frontier / Star Trek/The Next Generation / Deep space nine / Voyager / Star Trek III/In Search Of Spock / Star Trek VI/The Undiscovered Country / Star Trek VII/Generations
CD 80383C / Jun '96 / Telarc

☐ STAR TREK - VOL.1 (The Cage/Where No Man Has Gone Before) (Royal Philharmonic Orchestra)
Courage, Alexander c
Courage, Alexander con
GNPD 8006 / '88 / GNP Crescendo

☐ STAR TREK - VOL.2 (The Doomsday Machine/Amok Time) (Kaplan, Sol & Gerald Fried)
Kaplan, Sol & Gerald Fried c
GNPD 8025 / Sep '90 / GNP Crescendo

☐ STAR TREK - VOL.3 (Shore Leave/The Naked Time)
Fried, Gerald & Alexander Courage c
GNPD 8030 / Nov '92 / GNP Crescendo

☐ STAR TREK CLASSIC BOX SET
GNPBX 3006 / Sep '93 / GNP Crescendo

☐ STAR TREK II: THE WRATH OF KHAN
Horner, James c
Main title / Surprise attack / Spock / Kirk's explosive reply / Khan's pets / Enterprise clears moorings / Battle in the Mutara Nebula / Genesis countdown / Epilogue (End title)
GNPD 8022 / Jul '91 / GNP Crescendo

☐ STAR TREK III: THE SEARCH FOR SPOCK
Horner, James c
Horner, James con
Prologue and main title / Klingons / Stealing the Enterprise / Mind meld / Bird Of Prey decloaks / Returning to Vulcan / Katra ritual / End titles
FILMCD 070 / Aug '90 / Silva Screen

☐ STAR TREK VI: THE UNDISCOVERED COUNTRY
Eidelman, Cliff c
Eidelman, Cliff con
Overture / Incident / Clear all moorings / Assassination / Surrender for peace / Death of Gorkon / Rura Penthe / Dining on ashes / Battle for peace / Sign off / Star Trek VI suite
MCLD 19348 / Oct '96 / MCA

☐ STAR TREK VII: GENERATIONS
McCarthy, Dennis c
GNPD 8040 / Feb '95 / GNP Crescendo

☐ STAR TREK: DEEP SPACE NINE
McCarthy, Dennis c
McCarthy, Dennis con
GNPD 8034 / May '93 / GNP Crescendo

☐ STAR TREK: THE NEXT GENERATION VOL.1
McCarthy, Dennis c
GNPD 8012 / Jan '89 / GNP Crescendo

☐ STAR TREK: THE NEXT GENERATION VOL.1-3
GNPBX 3007 / Sep '93 / GNP Crescendo

☐ STAR TREK: THE NEXT GENERATION VOL.2
Jones, Ron c
GNPD 8026 / Sep '90 / GNP Crescendo

☐ STAR TREK: THE NEXT GENERATION VOL.3
McCarthy, Dennis c
GNPD 8031 / Nov '92 / GNP Crescendo

☐ STAR TREK: TV SERIES VOL.1 (Royal Philharmonic Orchestra)
VCD 47235 / Jan '89 / Varese Sarabande

☐ STAR TREK: TV SERIES VOL.2 (Royal Philharmonic Orchestra)
Empath / Trouble with the Tribbles / Mirror mirror / By any other name
VSD 47240 / Jan '90 / Varese Sarabande

☐ STAR TREK: VOYAGER
Chattaway, Jay c
GNPD 8041 / Jun '95 / GNP Crescendo

☐ STAR WARS (A New Hope/The Star Wars Trilogy Special Edition)
Williams, John c
Williams, John con
09026687462
09026687722 / Mar '97 / RCA Victor

☐ STAR WARS - MUSIC FROM THE STAR WARS TRILOGY (Boston Pops Orchestra)
Williams, John c
Williams, John con
Main theme / Princess Leia / Asteroid field / Yoda's theme / Imperial march / Parade of the ewoks / Luke and Leia / Jabba the hutt / Forest battle / March / Love theme / Adventures on Earth / Flying theme / Suite
4320502 / May '97 / Philips

☐ STAR WARS - SKETCHES OF STAR WARS
VSD 5794 / Apr '97 / Varese Sarabande

☐ STAR WARS TRILOGY (Music From The Films) (Utah Symphony Orchestra)
Williams, John c
Kojian, Varujan con
Star Wars main title / Princess Leia's theme / Here they come / Asteroid field / Yoda's theme / Imperial march / Parade of the Ewoks / Luke and Leia / Fight with tie fighters / Jabba the Hutt / Darth Vader's death / Forest battle / Star Wars
VCD 47201 / Jan '89 / Varese Sarabande

☐ STAR WARS TRILOGY (John Williams Conducts John Williams) (Skywalker Symphony Orchestra)
Williams, John c
Williams, John con
SK 45947 / Jan '95 / Sony Classical

☐ STAR WARS: SHADOWS OF THE EMPIRE (Royal Scottish National Orchestra)
McNeely, Joel c
McNeely, Joel con
VSD 5700 / Aug '96 / Varese Sarabande

☐ STARGATE (Score) (Sinfonia Of London)
Arnold, David c
Dodd, Nicholas con
Stargate overture / Giza 1928 / Unstable / Coverstones / Orion / Stargate opens / You're on the team / Entering the Stargate / Other side / Mastadge drag / Mining pit / King of the slaves / Caravan to Nagado / Daniel and Shauri / Symbol discovery / Sarcophagus opens / Daniel's mastadge / Leaving Nagada / Ra - The Sun God / Destruction of Nagada / Myth faith belief / Procession / Slave rebellion / Seventh symbol / Quartz shipment / Battle at the pyramid / We don't want to die / Surrender / Kasuf returns / Going home
74321249012 / Oct '96 / Milan

☐ STARLIGHT EXPRESS (1984 London Cast)
Lloyd Webber, Andrew c
Stilgoe, Richard l
Overture / Rolling stock / Call me Rusty / Lotta locomotion / Pumping iron / Freight / AC/DC / Hitching and switching / He whistled at me / Race - heat one / There's me / Blues / Belle / Race - heat two / Race - heat three / Starlight Express / Rap / Uncoupled / Rolling stock (reprise) / CB / Race - uphill final / Right place right time / Race - downhill final / No comeback / One rock 'n' roll too many / Only He / Only you / Light at the end of the tunnel
8215972 / Jun '84 / Polydor

☐ STARLIGHT EXPRESS (1993 London Cast)
Lloyd Webber, Andrew c
Stilgoe, Richard l
5190412 / Apr '93 / Really Useful

☐ STARLIGHT EXPRESS/CATS (Highlights - The Shows Collection) (Cast Recording)
Lloyd Webber, Andrew c
Stilgoe, Richard l
Starlight express / Rolling stock / UNCOUPLED / Crazy / Pumping iron / One rock'n' roll too many / Next time we fall in love / Light at the end of the tunnel / Memory / Grizabella / Gus / Mr. Mistoffelees / Old deuteronomy / Macavity / Memory (Reprise)
PWKS 4192 / Jul '94 / Carlton

☐ STARMAN
Nitzsche, Jack c
VCD 47220 / Jan '89 / Varese Sarabande

☐ STARSHIP TROOPERS
VSD 5877 / 8 Dec '97 / Varese Sarabande

☐ STARTING HERE, STARTING NOW (London Cast)
Shire, David c
Maltby, Richard Jr. l
CDTER 1200 / Jan '93 / TER

☐ STATE OF SIEGE
Theodorakis, Mikis c
SR 50063 / Oct '93 / Sakkaris

☐ STEAL BIG, STEAL LITTLE (Lopez, Israel 'Cachao' & Albita/Andy Garcia)
Olvis, William c
74321327222 / Sep '96 / Milan

☐ STEEL PIER (Broadway Cast)
Overture/Prelude / Willing to ride / Everybody dance / Second chance / Powerful thing / Dance with me/ The last girl / Shag / Everybody's girl / Two step / Wet / Harmonica speciality / Lovebird / Sprints / Entr'acte / Leave the world behind / Somebody older / Running in place / Two little words / First you dream / Steel pier / Steel pier / Final dance
09026688782 / Aug '97 / RCA Victor

☐ STEINER II (The Iron Cross Breakthrough)
Thomas, Peter *c*
FICSP 10003 / 14 Apr '98 / Taran

☐ STEPPING OUT (Minnelli, Liza)
Kander, John *c*
Ebb, Fred *l*
Matz, Peter *con*
262062 / Feb '94 / Milan

☐ STEPPING OUT (Original London Cast)
One night a week / Quite / Don't ask me / Love to / What do men think / Too much / Never feel the same again / Definitely you / One night a week / Not quite / Just the same / What I want / Once more / Loving him / Stepping out
SCENECD 24 / 3 Aug '98 / First Night

☐ STILL BREATHING
78016336492 / 5 May '98 / Will

☐ STING, THE
Hamlisch, Marvin & Scott Joplin *c*
Solace / Entertainer / Easy winners / Pineapple rag / Gladiolus rag / Merry go round music / Listen to the mockingbird / Darling Nellie Gray / Turkey in the straw / Ragtime dance / Hooker's hooker / Luther / Glove / Little girl
MCLD 19027 / Apr '92 / MCA

☐ STONE KILLER, THE
Budd, Roy *c*
LEGENDCD 6 / Jan '94 / Legend

☐ STOP IN THE NAME OF LOVE (With The Fabulous Singlettes) (1988 London Cast)
Do wah diddy diddy / Da doo ron ron / My guy / Be my baby / It's in his kiss (Shoop shoop song) / Needle in a haystack / Walk in the room / Time is on my side / Dum dum ditty / Leader of the pack / It's my party / Maybe / Born too late / I only want to be with you / You don't own me / Will you still love me tomorrow / Dancing in the streets / Supremes medley / Thank you and good night
OCRCD 6017 / Feb '96 / First Night

☐ STOP THE WORLD I WANT TO GET OFF (1961 London Cast)
Newley, Anthony & Leslie Bricusse *c*
ABC / I wanna be rich / Typically English / Lumbered / Gonna build a mountain / Glorious Russia / Mellinki Meilchick / Typiache Deutsche / Nag nag nag / All American / Once in a lifetime / Mumbo jumbo / Someone nice like you / What kind of fool am I
CDTER 1226 / Aug '95 / TER

☐ STORIES FROM MY CHILDHOOD
Chase, Tom & Steve Rucker/Mark Mothersbaugh *c*
78282788052 / 7 Apr '98 / Sonic Images

☐ STORYVILLE
Burwell, Carter *c*
VSD 5347 / Sep '92 / Varese Sarabande

☐ STRAIGHT TO HELL
Good the bad and the ugly: *Pogues* / Rake at the gates of hell: *Pogues* / If I should fall from grace with God: *Pogues* / Rabinga: *Pogues* / Danny boy: *Pogues* / Evil darling: *Strummer, Joe* / Ambush or mystery rock: *Strummer, Joe* / Money guns and coffee: Pray For Rain / Killers: *Pray For Rain* / Salsa y ketchup: *Zander Schloss* / Big nothing: *MacManus Gang*
REP 4224-WY / Aug '91 / Repertoire

☐ STRANGE DAYS
Selling Jesus: *Skunk Anansie* / Real thing: *Lords Of Acid* / Overcome: *Tricky* / Coral lounge: *Deep Forest* / No white clouds: *Strange Fruit* / Hardly wait: *Lewis, Juliette* / Here we come: *Me Phi Me & Jeriko One* / Feed: *Skunk Anansie* / Strange days: *Prong & Ray Manzarek* / Walk in freedom: *Satchel* / Dance me to the end of love: *Hate Gibson* / Fall in the night: *Carson, Lori & Graeme Revell* / While the earth sleeps: *Deep Forest*
4809842 / Jan '96 / Epic

☐ STRANGER THAN PARADISE/THE RESURRECTION OF ALBERT AYLER (Lurie, John)
Lurie, John *c*
Bella by barlight / Car Cleveland / Sad trees / Lampposts are mine / Car Florida / Eva and Willie's room / Beer for boys / Eva packing / Good and happy army / Woman can take you to another universe / Sometimes she just leaves you there / Sixties avant-garde / Sex with monster / You owe me money / Resurrection
MTM 7 / Apr '96 / Made To Measure

☐ STRANGER, THE/THE INNOCENT (Two Legendary Films By Luchino Visconti)
Piccioni, Piero/Franco Mannino *c*
Nicolai, Bruno *con*
DRGCD 32922 / 27 Oct '97 / DRG

☐ STRATAGEM (Big Head Todd & The Monsters)
Kensington line / Stratagem / Wearing only flowers / Neckbreaker / Magdalena / Angel leads me on / In the morning / Candle / Ninety nine / Greyhound / Poor miss / Shadowlands
74321229042 / Oct '94 / Giant

☐ STREET FIGHTER (Revell, Graeme)
Revell, Graeme *c*
VSD 5560 / May '95 / Varese Sarabande

☐ STREET FIGHTER
Street fighter: *Ice Cube* / Come widdit: *Ahmad & Ras Kass/Saafir* / One on one: *Nas* / Pandemonium: *Pharcyde* / Street soldier: *Paris* / Something kinda funky: *Rally Ral* / It's a street fight: *B.U.M.S.* / Life as...: *L.L. Cool J* / Do you have what it takes: *Mack, Craig* / Straight to my feet: *Hammer & Deion Sanders* / Rumbo n da jungo: *Public Enemy & Wreck League* / Rap commando: *Anotha Level* / Worth fighting for: *Kidjo, Angelique* / Something there: *Chage & Aska*
CDPTY 114 / Dec '94 / Priority/Virgin

☐ STREET IS WATCHING, THE
5581322 / 15 Jun '98 / Def Jam

☐ STREET SCENE (1991 London Cast)
Weill, Kurt *c*
Hughes, Langston *l*
Intro / Ain't it awful / I've got a marble and a star / Get a load of that / When a woman has a baby / She shouldn't be staying out nights / Somehow I never could believe / Ice cream sextet / Let the things like they always was / Wrapped in a ribbon and a bow / Lonely house / Wouldn't you be on Broadway / What good would that moon be / Moon faced starry eyed / Dance / Remember that I care / Fianletto / Intro act II / cATCH me if you can / There'll be trouble / I tried to be a good wife to him / Boy like you / We'll go away together / MurderWoman who lived up there / Interlude / Fianle / Ain't it awful the heat / MurderMurder / murder
CDTER2 1185 / Nov '97 / TER

☐ STREETCAR NAMED DESIRE, A (National Philharmonic Orchestra)
North, Alex *c*
Goldsmith, Jerry *con*
VSD 5500 / Oct '95 / Varese Sarabande

☐ STREETS OF FIRE
Steinman, Jim *c*
Nowhere fast: *Fire Inc.* / Sorcerer: *Martin, Marilyn* / Deeper and deeper: *Fixx* / Countdown to love: *Phillinganes, Greg* / One bad stud: *Blasters* / Tonight is what it means to be young: *Fire Inc.* / Never be you: *McKee, Maria* / I can dream about you: *Hartman, Dan* / Hold that snake: *Cooder, Ry* / Blue shadows: *Blasters*
BGOCD 220 / Feb '95 / Beat Goes On

☐ STREETS OF NEW YORK, THE (1963 Off Broadway Cast)
AEICD 023 / May '98 / AEI

☐ STRICTLY BALLROOM
Love is in the air: *Young, John Paul* / Perhaps perhaps perhaps: *Day, Doris* / La cumparsita: *Hirschfelder, David & The Bogo Pogo Orchestra* / Tango please: *Hirschfelder, David & The Bogo Pogo Orchestra* / Tequila: *Hirschfelder, David & The Bogo Pogo Orchestra* / Sinful samba: *Hirschfelder, David & The Bogo Pogo Orchestra* / Rumba de burros: *Jones, Ignatius* / Doug's tearful waltz/First kiss: *Hirschfelder, David & The Bogo Pogo Orchestra* / Time after time: *Williams, Mark & Morice, Tara* / Standing in the rain: *Young, John Paul* / Scott's sinful solo: *Hirschfelder, David & The Bogo Pogo Orchestra* / Blue Danube: *Hirschfelder, David & The Bogo Pogo Orchestra* / Scott and Fran's paso doble: *Hirschfelder, David & The Bogo Pogo Orchestra* / Yesterday's hero: *Jones, Ignatius*
4723002 / Dec '96 / Columbia

☐ STRIKE UP THE BAND (Cast Recording)
Gershwin, George *c*
Gershwin, Ira *l*
Mauceri, John *con*
7559792732 / Jan '92 / Nonesuch

☐ STUDENT PRINCE, THE (Lanza, Mario)
Brodszky, Nicholas *c*
Callinicos, C. *con*
Overture / Serenade / Golden days / Drink drink drink / Summertime in Heidelberg / I'll walk with God / Thoughts will come back to me / Student life / Just we two / Beloved / Gaudeamus igitur / Deep in my heart
GD 60048 / Sep '89 / RCA

☐ STUDENT PRINCE, THE (1990 Studio Cast/Ambrosian Chorus/Philharmonia Orchestra)
Romberg, Sigmund *c*
Donnelly, Dorothy *l*
Edwards, John Owen *con*
Overture / Prologue / Golden days / Garlands bright / To the inn we're marching / Drinking song / Entrance of Kathie / Come boys let's all be gay boys / Entrance of Prince and Engel / Gaudeamus igitur / Exit of students / Golden days / Deep in my heart dear / Finale act 1 part 1 / Serenade / Carnival of springtime / Finale act 1 conclusion / Act 2 introduction / Student life / Finale act 2 / We're off to Paris city of joy / Finale act 2 conclusion / Act 2 opening / Ballet / Waltz / Just we two / Flag that flies above us / Gavotte / Finale act 3 / Act 4 opening chorus / Let us sing a song / Finale act 4
CDTER2 1172 / 15 Jun '98 / TER

☐ STUDENT PRINCE, THE (Highlights) (1990 Studio Cast/Ambrosian Chorus/ Philharmonia Orchestra)
Romberg, Sigmund *c*
Donnelly, Dorothy *l*
Edwards, John Owen *con*
CDTEO 1005 / Mar '91 / TER

☐ STUDENT PRINCE, THE (London Cast & Ambrosian Chorus/Philharmonic Orchestra)
Romberg, Sigmund *c*
Donnelly, Dorothy *l*
Edwards, John Owen *con*
Overture / Golden days / To the inn we're marching / Drinking song / Come boys let's all be gay boys / Gaudeamus igitur / Deep in my heart dear / Serenade / Student life / Thoughts will come to me of days / Just we two / Finale
SHOWCD 033 / Oct '96 / Showtime

☐ SUDDEN DEATH
Debney, John *c*
VSD 5663 / Apr '96 / Varese Sarabande

☐ SUGAR BABIES (The Burlesque Musical) (Broadway Cast)
McHugh, Jimmy *c*
Sugar babies overture / Good old burlesque show / Welcome to the Gaiety - Intro / Let me be your sugar baby / In Louisiana / I feel a song coming on / Going back to New Orleans / Broken Arms Hotel / Sally / Don't blame me / Immigration rose / Little red house / Sugar baby bounce / Introduction Mme Rentz / Down at the Gaiety Burlesque / Mr. Banjo man / When my sugar walks down the street / Candy butcher / Entr'Acte / I'm keeping myself available for you / Exactly like you / I'm in the mood for love / I'm just a song and dance man / Warm and willing / Father dear father dear / Boss upstairs / Cuban love song / Every week another town / I can't give you anything but love / I'm shooting high / When you and I were young Maggie / On the sunny side of the street / You can't blame your Uncle Sammy
VSD 5453 / Dec '93 / Varese Sarabande

☐ SUGAR HILL
07822110162 / Jun '94 / Arista

☐ SULEYMAN THE MAGNIFICENT
CDCEL 023 / Feb '88 / Celestial Harmonies

☐ SULT: SPIRIT OF THE MUSIC
Sult theme: *Sult House Band* / St Dominic's preview: *Morrison, Van* / Oro: *Brennan, Oro* / Causeway: *Casey, Nollaig* / On Raglan road: *Knopfler, Mark* / Murphy tunes: *Shannon, Sharon & Laoise Kelly* / Rocks of Bawn: *Brady, Paul* / Liquid sunshine: *O'Connor, Martin* / Siuil a ruin: *Ni Dhomhnail, Maighread* / Rollicking boys of Tandagree: *Nomos* / Parting of friends: *Moloy, Matt* / Mystic slip jigs: *Breatnach, Maire* / Crazy love: *Kennedy, Brian & Anuna* / Sweet Biddy Daly far from home: *Cooney, Stephen & Seamus Begley* / Rinn na mara: *Spillane, John* / Brown haired girl: *O'Flynn, Liam*
HBCD 0009 / Mar '97 / Hummingbird

☐ SUMMER HOLIDAY (Richard, Cliff & The Shadows)
Seven days to a holiday / Summer holiday / Let us take you for a ride / Les girls / Foot tapper / Round and round / Stranger in town / Orlando's mime / Bachelor boy / Swingin' affair / Really waltzing / All at once / Dancing shoes / Yugoslav wedding / Next time / Big news
CDMFP 6021 / Apr '88 / Music For Pleasure

☐ SUN VALLEY SERENADE/ ORCHESTRA WIVES (Miller, Glenn)
Opening / Kiss the polka / Theme / I know why / In the mood / It happened in sun valley / Chattanooga choo choo / Kiss polka / It happend / People like you and me / At last / Bugle call rag / Serenade in blue / I've got a girl in Kalamazoo
CD 60002 / Apr '97 / Great Movie Themes

☐ SUNDOWN (The Vampire In Retreat) (Graunke Symphony Orchestra)
Stone, Richard *c*
Wilson, Allan *con*
FILMCD 044 / Jan '90 / Silva Screen

☐ SUNNY/SHOW BOAT/LIDO LADY (Cast Recording)
Kern, Jerome & Richard Rodgers *c*
Harbach, Otto & Oscar Hammerstein II *l*
GEMMCD 9105 / May '94 / Pearl

☐ SUNSET BOULEVARD (1993 London Cast)
Lloyd Webber, Andrew *c*
Black, Don & Christopher Hampton *l*
White, D. *con*
Prologue / Let's have lunch / Sheldrake's office / On the road / Surrender / With one look / Salome / Greatest star of all / Let's have lunch (reprise)/Girl meets boy / House on Sunset / New ways to dream / Lady's paying / Perfect year / Artie Green's apartment / This time next year / Sunset Boulevard / Perfect year (reprise) / Journey to Paramount / As if we never said goodbye / Girl meets boy (reprise) / Eternal youth / Too much in love to care / Sunset Boulevard (reprise) / Greatest star of all (reprise)
5197672 / Aug '93 / Really Useful

☐ SUNSET BOULEVARD (1994 US Cast)
Lloyd Webber, Andrew *c*
Black, Don & Christopher Hampton *l*
Bogaev, P. *con*
Overture/I guess it was 5am / Let's have lunch / Every movie's a circus / Car chase / At the house on Sunset / Surrender / With one look / Salome / Greatest star of all / Every movie's a circus (reprise) / Girl meets boy / Back at the house on Sunset / New ways to dream / Completion of the script / Lady's paying / New Year's Eve / Perfect year / This time next year / New Year's Eve (Back at the house on Sunset) / Entr'acte / Sunset Boulevard / There's been a call/Journey to Paramount / As if we never said goodbye / Paramount conversations/Surrender / Girl meets boy (reprise) / Eternal youth is worth a little suffering / Who's Betty Schaefer / Betty's office at Paramount / Too much love to care / New ways to dream (reprise) / Phone call / Final Scene
5235072 / Oct '94 / Really Useful

☐ SUPERCOP
Kung Fu fighting: *Jones, Tom & Ruby* / What's love got to do with it: *Warren G & Adina Howard* / Harry the dog: *Black Grape* / Head like a hole: *Devo* / Made niggaz: *2Pac & The Outlawz* / Caged in a rage: *Dimebag Darrell* / On a rope: *Rocket From the Crypt* / Stayin' alive: *Lynch, Siobhan* / I'll do it: *Tha Dogg Pound & Kausion* / Great life: *Goatboy* / Open the gate: *No Doubt* / Pubstar: *Pur* / Scorched youth policy: *Polara* / Supercop: *Devo* / Main title: *McNeely, Joel*
IND 90088 / Nov '96 / Interscope

☐ SUPERFLY (Mayfield, Curtis)
Little child runnin' wild / Freddie's dead / Give me your love (Love song) / No thing on me (cocaine song) / Superfly / Pusherman / Junkie chase (Instrumental) / Eddie you should know better / Think (Instrumental)
MPG 74028 / Nov '93 / Movieplay Gold
CPCD 8039 / Jun '94 / Charly

☐ SUPERFLY (Mayfield, Curtis)
Mayfield, Curtis *c*
CDNEW 1302 / 29 Jun '98 / Charly

☐ SUPERFLY/SHORT EYES (Mayfield, Curtis)
Little child runnin' wild / Pusherman / Freddie's dead / Junkie chase / Give me your love / Eddie you should know better / No thing on me / Think / Superfly / Do do wap is strong in here / Back against the wall / Need someone to love / Heavy dude / Short eyes / Freak freak free free free / Break it down / Another fool in love / Father confessor
NEMCD 964 / 1 Jun '98 / Sequel

☐ SUPERGIRL (National Philharmonic Orchestra)
Goldsmith, Jerry *c*
Goldsmith, Jerry *con*
Overture / Main title and Argo city / Argo city / Butterfly / Journey begins / Arrival on earth / Flying ballet / Chicago light / Street attack / Superman / New school / Spellbound / Monster tractor / Map / Bracelet / First kiss / Monster storm / Where is she / Monster bumper cars / Flying bumper car / Where's Linda / Black magic / Phantom zone / Vortex / End of Zaltar / Final showdown and victory / End title
FILMCD 132 / May '93 / Silva Screen

☐ SUPERMAN (Lois & Clark - The Adventures Of Superman)
Gruska, Jay *c*
SI 8703 / 1 Dec '97 / Sonic Images

☐ SURRENDER
Colombier, Michel *c*
VCD 47312 / Jan '89 / Varese Sarabande

☐ SURVIVAL (The Music Of Nature)
Survival theme / Citizens of the Coral / Valley beneath the sea / Dwellers of the deep / Suite for silver shoals / Dreams of mermaids / Sonata for the seal / Creatures of the ocean / Glide with a manatee / Song of the river / Empire of the elephant / Rhythm of Hell's Gate / In the heart of Africa / Animal outback / Empire of the plains / East of Eden / Amazonian market day / Apalachian heights / Madagascar - land of hope / Mountains of the snow leopard / Tarantula's reach / Amazonian journey / Web of the spider monkey / Dragons at play / Andes landscape / Night raiders / Queen of the beasts / Red in tooth and claw / Leaders of the pack / Gorilla's shattered kingdom / Wings over the world / Hummingbird calypso / Flight of the snow geese / Fly to the stars / Angels of the Orient / Mysterious skies / Sumatra dawn / Through the eye of an eagle
VTDCD 148 / Aug '97 / Virgin

☐ SUSPECT
Kamen, Michael *c*
VCD 47315 / Jan '89 / Varese Sarabande

☐ SUSPENDED STEP OF THE STORK, THE
Karaindrou, Eleni *c*
Refugee's theme/variations / Train-car neighbourhood/variations / Suspended step / Hassaposerviko / Waltz of the bride / Finale
5115142 / Jul '94 / ECM

☐ SUSPIRIA (Goblin)
CDMDF 305 / Nov '97 / Pick Up

☐ SWAN DOWN GLOVES, THE (1982 London Cast)
Hess, Nigel *c*
Hess, Nigel & Bille Brown *l*
Overture / With the sun arise / Everything's going to be fine / Catastrophe / Let's be friends / Make your own world / How's the way / Going into town / Stuck in a muddle / Best foot forward / Demewer but dangerous / Muck / Any old rose / Firedown / Finale
CDTER 1017 / Aug '95 / TER

☐ SWAN PRINCESS, THE
Prologue / This is my idea / Practice practice practice / Far longer than forever / No fear / No more Mr. Nice Guy / Princess on parade / Enchanted castle / It's not what it seems / Derek finds Odette / Gator aid / Odette flies / Derek gallops / End credits / Eternity
4837722 / Jul '96 / Sony Wonder

☐ SWEDEN, HEAVEN AND HELL (Umiliani, Piero)
Umiliani, Piero *c*
You tried to warn me / Le ragazza dell'arcipelago / Stoccolma my dear / Man na mah na / Essere Donna / Notte di mezza estate / Sequenza psichedelica / Violenza / Fotomodelle / La signora cameriera / Solitidine / Free in monore / Piano bossa nova / Nel cosmo / Topless party / Eva svedese / Hippies / Hippies 2 / L'uorno integrato / Samba mah na / Organo e chitarroni / Beer vermouth e gin / Sleep now little one
ET 901CD / Apr '97 / Easy Tempo

☐ SWEENEY TODD (Jazz Version) (Cast Recording)
Sondheim, Stephen *c*
VSD 5603 / Jul '95 / Varese Sarabande

☐ SWEET CHARITY (Cast Recording)
Coleman, Cy *c*
Fields, Dorothy *l*
CDTER2 1222 / Aug '95 / TER

☐ SWEET CHARITY (1967 London Cast)
Coleman, Cy c
Fields, Dorothy l
SMK 66172 / Jul '94 / Sony West End

☐ SWEET CHARITY (Cast Recording/ National Symphony Orchestra)
Coleman, Cy c
Fields, Dorothy l
Edwards, John Owen con
Overture / My personal property / Big spender / Rich man's frug / If my friends could see me now / There's gotta be something better than this / It's a nice face / Rhythm of life / Sweet charity / Where am I going / I'm a brass band / I love to cry at weddings
SHOWCD 035 / Oct '96 / Showtime

☐ SWEET HEREAFTER, THE
Sweet hereafter / Procession / One more colour / Bus / Bus stop / Courage / It's important that we talk / Dog track drizzle / Thin ice / It was a wonderful time in our lives / Pied piper / Huge wave / Boy / Why I lied / Different town
CDVIR 68 / 27 Oct '97 / Virgin

☐ SWEET SWEETBACK'S BAADASSS SONG (Earth, Wind & Fire)
Van Peebles, Melvin c
Sweetback losing his cherry / Sweetback getting it uptight... / Come on feet / Sweetback's theme / Hoppin' John / Voices / Mojo woman / Sanra Z / Voices / Reggin hanging on in there as best they can / Voices / Man tries running his usual game but...
CDSXE 103 / Apr '97 / Stax

☐ SWEPT FROM THE SEA (English Chamber Orchestra)
Barry, John c
Barry, John con
4587932 / 20 Apr '98 / Decca

T

☐ TAFFETAS, THE (1988 Off-Broadway Cast)
Lewis, Rick c
Sh-boom / Mr. Sandman / Three bells / I'm sorry / Ricochet / I cried / Cry / Smile / Achoo cha-cha / Mockin' Bird Hill / Tonight you belong to me / Happy wanderer / Constantinople / My little grass shack / C'est si bon / Sweet song of India / Arrivederci Roma / See the USA in your Chevrolet / Allegheny moon / Tennessee waltz / Old Cape Cod / Fly me to the moon / Nel blue de pinto di blue / Around the world / Music music music / You're just in love / Love letters in the sand / LOVE / I-M-4-U / Rag mop / You you you / Puppy love / (How much is that) doggie in the window / Hot canary / Tweedlee dee / Lollipop / Sincerely / Johnny Angel / Mr. Lee / Dedicated to the one I love / Where the boys are / I'll think of you / Little darlin' / Spotlight on the music
CDTER 1167 / Jun '89 / TER

☐ TAI PAN
Jarre, Maurice c
VCD 47274 / Jan '89 / Varese Sarabande

☐ TALES FROM THE CRYPT
Cemetery gates / Diadems / Hey man nice shot / My misery / Fall guy / Policia / 1-800-suicide / Tonight we murder / Beaten / Instant larry
7567827252 / Jan '95 / Warner Bros.

☐ TALES FROM THE DARKSIDE
GNPD 8021 / Jan '95 / GNP Crescendo

☐ TALES OF BEATRIX POTTER
Lanchberry, John c
Lanchberry, John con
CDCFP 6074 / 4 May '98 / Classics For Pleasure

☐ TALK RADIO/WALL STREET
Copeland, Stewart c
Unpredictable: Kent / We know where you live: Tick / He has a heart: Trend / Bud's scam: Copeland, Stewart / Trading begins: Copeland, Stewart / Break up: Copeland, Stewart / End titles: Copeland, Stewart / Just come right in here please: Dietz / We feel too much: Tick / Are you with me: Copeland, Stewart / Tall weeds: Copeland, Stewart / Anacott steel: Copeland, Stewart
VSD 5215 / Feb '90 / Varese Sarabande

☐ TANK GIRL
Ripper sole / Army of me / Girl u want / Mockingbird girl / Drown soda / Roads / Bomb / Big gun / Aurora / Thief / Let's do it / Shove
7559617602 / Apr '95 / Warner Bros.

☐ TAP DANCE KID, THE (1984 Broadway Cast)
Krieger, Henry c
Lorick, Robert l
Overture / Another day / Four strikes against me / Class act / They never hear what I say / Dancing is everything / Fabulous feet / I could get used to him / Man in the moon / Like him / My luck is changing / Someday / I remember how it was / Tap tap / Dance if it makes you happy / William's song / Finale
CDTER 1096 / Mar '85 / TER

☐ TARAS BULBA
Waxman, Franz c
Bernstein, Elmer con
09026626572 / Nov '95 / RCA

☐ TARAS BULBA
Waxman, Franz c
W 9107 / 14 Apr '98 / Taran

☐ TAXI DRIVER
Herrmann, Bernard c
Theme / I work the whole city / Betsy in a white dress / Days do not end / All the animals come out at night / 44 Magnum is a monster / Sport and Iris / Theme from Taxi Driver
258774 / Feb '97 / Arista

☐ TEARS OF STONE (Iceland Symphony Orchestra)
Leifs, Jon c
Sakari, P./S. Wilkinson con
ITM 605 / Feb '96 / ITM

☐ TEENAGE OPERA, A
Wirtz, Mark c
RPM 165 / May '96 / RPM

☐ TELEVOID
Rockenfield, Scott & Paul Speer c
9008230972 / 24 Mar '98 / Miramar

☐ TELL ME ON A SUNDAY (Webb, Marti)
Lloyd Webber, Andrew c
Black, Don l
Capped teeth and Caesar salad / Come back with the same look in your eyes / I'm very you you're very me / It's not the end of the world / If he's married if he's younger if I lose him / Let me finish / Let's talk about you / Letter home to England / Nothing like you've ever known / Second letter home / Sheldon bloom / Take that look off your face / Tell me on a Sunday / You made me think you were in love
8334472 / Jun '90 / Polydor

☐ TENANT OF WILDFELL HALL, THE
Mitchell, Richard G. c
KCCD 4 / Nov '96 / NMC

☐ TENDERLOIN (Broadway Cast)
Bock, Jerry c
Harnick, Sheldon l
ZDM 5650222 / Dec '93 / EMI Classics

☐ TERMINATOR II (Judgement Day)
Fiedel, Brad c
VSD 5335 / Aug '91 / Varese Sarabande

☐ TERMINATOR II (Special)
VSD 5861 / 26 Aug '97 / Varese Sarabande

☐ TERMINATOR, THE
Fiedel, Brad c
Theme from Terminator / Terminator main title / Terminator's arrival / Reese chased / Sarah on her motorbike / Gun shop/Reese in alley / Sarah in the bar / Tech noir/Alley chase / Garage chase / Arm and eye surgery / Police station/Escape from police station / Future flashback/Terminator infiltration / Coversation by the window/Love scene / Tunnel chase / Death by fire/Terminator gets up / Factory chase / Reese's death/Terminator sits up/You're terminated / Sarah's destiny/Coming storm / Theme from The Terminator
0022082CIN / 26 May '98 / Cinerama

☐ THANK YOUR LUCKY STARS
TEST1 / 11 Jul '98 / EMI

☐ THAT THING YOU DO
Lovin' you lots and lots: Wooster, Norm Singers / That thing you do: Wonders / Little wild one: Wonders / Dance with me tonight: Wonders / All my only dreams: Wonders / I need you (that thing you do): Wonders / She knows it: Heardsmen / Mr. Downtown: Fredrickson, Freddy / Hold my hand hold my heart: Chantrelles / Voyage around the moon: Saturn 5 / My world is over: Dane, Diane / Drive faster: Vickburgs / Shrimp shack: Cap 'N' Geech & The Shrimp Shack Shooters / Time to blow: Paxton, Del / That thing you do: Wonders
4865512 / Jan '97 / Play Tone

☐ THAT'S THE WAY IT IS (Presley, Elvis)
I just can't help believin' / Twenty days and twenty nights / How the web was woven / Patch it up / Mary in the morning / You don't have to say you love me / You've lost that lovin' feelin' / I've lost you / Just pretend / Stranger in the crowd / Next step is love / Bridge over troubled water
7432114690-2 / Jul '93 / RCA

☐ THELMA AND LOUISE
Zimmer, Hans c
MCLD 19313 / Oct '95 / MCA

☐ THEY LIVE (Carpenter, John)
Carpenter, John & Alan Howarth c
Coming to LA / Message / Siege of Justiceville / Return to church / All out of bubblegum / Back to the street / Kidnapped / Transient hotel / Underground / Wake up
DSCD 1 / Oct '90 / Demon

☐ THEY WANTED MEAT SO THEY ATE THE FLOWER CHILDREN
SFTRI 338CD / Apr '97 / Sympathy For The Record Industry

☐ THEY'RE PLAYING OUR SONG (1980 London Cast)
Hamlisch, Marvin c
Bayer Sager, Carole l
Hossack, Grant con
Overture / Fallin' / If he really knew me / Workin' it out / They're playing my song / If she really knew me / Right / Entr'acte / Just for tonight / When you're in my arms / Fill in the words / They're playing our song (finale)
CDTER 1035 / May '89 / TER

☐ THEY'RE PLAYING OUR SONG (London Cast)
Hamlisch, Marvin c
Bayer Sager, Carole l
Overture / Fallin' / Workin' it out / If he really knew me / They're playing my song / Right / Just for tonight / When you're in my arms / I still believe in love / Fill in the words / They're playing our song
SHOWCD 031 / Oct '96 / Showtime

☐ THIBEAUD THE CRUSADER
Delerue, Georges c
PCD 114 / Jan '93 / Prometheus

☐ THIEF (Tangerine Dream)
Tangerine Dream c
Beach theme / Dr. Destructo / Diamond diary / Burning bar / Beach scene / Scrap yard / Trap feeling / Igneous
TAND 12 / Jul '95 / Virgin

☐ THIN BLUE LINE, THE (Glass, Philip Ensemble)
Glass, Philip c
Riesman, Michael con
Opening credits / Interrogation / Turko (part one) / Vidor / Adam's story / Defense attorney's / Judge / Trial (part two) / Mystery eyewitness (part two) / Thin blue line / Defense attorney's II / Hell on earth / Confession / Prologue / Interrogation (part two) / Turko (part two) / Harris' story / Comets and Vegas / Harris' crimes / Trial (part one) / Mystery eyewitness (part one) / Mystery eyewitness (part three) / Electric chair / Harris' testimony / Mystery eyewitness (part five) / Harris' childhood / End credits
7559792092 / Apr '89 / Nonesuch

☐ THIN LINE BETWEEN LOVE AND HATE, THE
Beware of my crew: LBC Crew / Thin line between love and hate: H-Town / Damned if I do: Somethin' For The People / Freak tonight: R. Kelly / I don't hang: Soopafly / Love got my mind trippin': Ganjah K / Ring my bell: Luniz / Play fo real: Dra Down / Chocolate city: Troutman, Roger & Shirley Murdock / Thin line: Drawz / Ladies night at chocolate city: Dark Complexion / Knocks me off my feet: Campbell, Tevin / Let's stay together: Beret, Eric / Cover over: St. Victor, Sandra / Way back when: Smooth
9362461342 / Feb '96 / WEA

☐ THING, THE
Morricone, Ennio c
Morricone, Ennio con
VSD 5278 / Aug '91 / Varese Sarabande

☐ THINGS TO DO IN DENVER WHEN YOU'RE DEAD
Jockey full of bourbon: Waits, Tom / Mile high: Morphine / On the way out: Johnston, Freddy / Born under a bad sign: Neville Brothers / Thrill is gone: Dishwalla / Bittersweet: Big Head Todd & The Monsters / Get out of Denver: Blues Traveller / This is my life: Ape Hangers / She's a superstar: Guy, Buddy / Take out some insurance on me baby: Reed, Jimmy / Folsom prison blues: Cash, Johnny / You're nobody till somebody loves you: Martin, Dean / Things to do in Denver when you're dead: Zevon, Warren
5404242 / May '96 / A&M

☐ THINNER
Licht, Daniel c
VSD 5761 / Dec '96 / Varese Sarabande

☐ THIRST
May, Brian c
IMICD 1003 / Jan '93 / Silva Screen

☐ THIS IS MY LIFE (Simon, Carly)
Simon, Carly c
Love of my life / Back the way (Dottie's point of view) / Moving day / Easy on the eyes / Walking and kissing / Show must go on / Back the way (girls' point of view) / Little troupers / Night before christmas / This is my life suite / Love of my life (drive to the city)
7599269012 / May '92 / Qwest

☐ THIS IS SPINAL TAP (Spinal Tap)
8178462 / Aug '90 / Polydor

☐ THIS WORLD THEN THE FIREWORKS
VSD 5860 / 15 Sep '97 / Varese Sarabande

☐ THOMAS AND THE KING (1975 London Cast)
Williams, John c
Harbert, James l
Spencer, Herbert con
Processional / Look around you / Am I beautiful / Man of love / Question / What choice have I / We shall do it / Improbable as spring / Power / Question / New way to turn / Tis love / Sincerity / Test / Replay the game / Will no one rid me / So many other worlds
CDTER 1009 / 1 Sep '98 / TER

☐ THOMAS CROWN AFFAIR, THE
Legrand, Michel c
Legrand, Michel con
RCD 10719 / 6 Apr '98 / Rykodisc

☐ THORN BIRDS II, THE
VSD 5712 / Mar '96 / Varese Sarabande

☐ THREE GUYS NAKED FROM THE WAIST DOWN (1985 Off-Broadway Cast)
Rupert, Michael & Jerry Colker c
Overture / Promise of greatness / Angry guy/Lovely day / Don't wanna be no superstar / Operator / Screaming clocks (The dummies song) / History of stand-up comedy / Dreams of heaven / Kamikaze kaberaet / American dream / What a ride / Hello fellas TV special world tour / Father now / Three guys naked from the waist down / I don't believe in heroes anymore / Finale
CDTER 1100 / May '93 / TER

☐ THREE MUSKETEERS
Kamen, Michael c
All for love: Adams, Bryan & Rod Stewart/Sting / Cavern of Cardinal Richelieu / D'Artagnan / Athos Porthos and Aramis / Sword fight / King Louis XIII Queen Anne and Constance / Cardinal's coach / Cannonballs / M'lady de winter / Fourth musketeer
5401902 / Apr '95 / A&M

☐ THREE O'CLOCK HIGH (Tangerine Dream)
Tangerine Dream c
VCD 47307 / Jan '89 / Varese Sarabande

☐ THREE STEPS TO HEAVEN
DBG 53034 / Sep '94 / Double Gold

☐ THREE WISHES FOR JAMIE (Broadway Cast)
Moloney, Paddy c
ZDM 7648882 / Apr '93 / EMI Classics

☐ THREE WORLDS OF GULLIVER, THE
Herrmann, Bernard c
ACN 7018 / Apr '95 / Cloud Nine

☐ THREEPENNY OPERA, THE (1954 Broadway Cast)
Weill, Kurt c
Brecht, Bertolt l
Matlowsky, Samuel con
Overture / Ballad of Mack the Knife / Morning anthem / Instead-of-song / Wedding song / Pirate Jenny / Army song / Love song / Ballad of dependency / Melodrama/Polly's song / Ballad of the easy life / World is mean / Barbara's song / Tango ballad / Jealousy duet / How to survive / Useless song / Solomon song / Call from the grave / Death message / Finale
CDTER 1101 / 15 Jun '98 / TER

☐ THREEPENNY OPERA, THE (1995 London Cast)
Weill, Kurt c
Brecht, Bertolt l
Overture / Peachum's morning song / Kids today / Gang song / Pirate Jenny / Squaddies song / Love duet / Barbara song / Life's a bitch / Melodrama/ Polly's song / Ballad of sexual imperative / Knocking song tango / Flick knife song / Easy life / ¡EJealousy duet / What keeps a man alive / What's the point / Socrates song / Call from the grave / Act III FINALE
CDTER 1227 / Nov '97 / TER

☐ THREEPENNY OPERA, THE (Lenya, Lotte/Marlene Dietrich)
Weill, Kurt c
Brecht, Bertolt l
9031720252 / Jan '95 / Teldec Classics

☐ THREEPENNY OPERA, THE (Berlin RIAS Chamber Choir/Sinfonietta)
Weill, Kurt c
Brecht, Bertolt l
Mauceri, John con
4300752 / Mar '90 / Decca

☐ THREEPENNY OPERA, THE (Bulgarian TV/Radio Mixed Choir/Symphony Orchestra)
Weill, Kurt c
Brecht, Bertolt l
370062 / Feb '91 / Koch

☐ THREEPENNY OPERA, THE (Lenya, Lotte)
Weill, Kurt c
Brecht, Bertolt l
Bruckner-Ruggenberg, Wilhelm con
MK 42637 / Jan '94 / Masterworks

☐ THREEPENNY OPERA, THE (Cast & The Konig Ensemble)
Weill, Kurt c
Brecht, Bertolt l
Latham Konig, Jan con
Ouverture / Moritat von Mackie Messer / Morgenchoral / Anstatt dass song / Hochzeitslied / Seerauber Jenny / Kanonen song / Liebeslied / Barbara song / Erstes dreigroschen finale / Melodram / Pollys lied / Ballade von der sexuellen horigkeit / Zuhalter ballade / Ballade vom angenehmen leben / Eifersuchts duett / Arie der Lucy / Zweites dreigroschen finale / Lied von der unzulanglichkeit menschlichen strebens / Salomon song / Ruf aus der gruft / Grabschrift / Drittes dreigroschen finale
600581 / Sep '97 / Capriccio

☐ THUNDER ON THE BORDERLINE
Thomas, Peter c
FICSP 10001 / 14 Apr '98 / Taran

☐ THUNDERBALL
Barry, John c
Thunderball: Jones, Tom / Chateau fight / Electrocution - searching Lippe's room / Switching the body / Vulcan crash landing - loading bombs into disc / Cape Martinique - Mr. Kiss Kiss Bang Bang / Thunderball / Death of Fiona / Bond below Disco Volante / Search for vulcan / 007 / Mr. Kiss Kiss Bang Bang
CZ 556 / Dec '95 / Premier/EMI

☐ THUNDERHEART
Horner, James c
MAF 7027D / Jan '93 / Intrada

☐ TIETA DO BRASIL
Velos, Caetano c
74321466122 / Jun '97 / Milan

☐ TILL WE MEET AGAIN
XCD 1003 / Apr '91 / Varese Sarabande

☐ TIME MACHINE, THE
Garcia, Russell *c*
London 1900 / Time machine model / Time machine / Quick trip into the future / All the time in the world / Beautiful forest / Great hall / Fear / Weena / Rescue
GNPD 8008 / Jan '89 / GNP Crescendo

☐ TIME OF DESTINY, A
Morricone, Ennio *c*
7909382 / Jan '89 / Silva Screen

☐ TIMECOP (Isham, Mark)
Isham, Mark *c*
VSD 5532 / Nov '94 / Varese Sarabande

☐ TINTYPES (Broadway Cast)
CDXP 5196 / Jan '89 / DRG

☐ TIRE A PART
Goude, Jean Philippe *c*
SMC 35703 / Apr '97 / Sergent M

☐ TITANIC (Broadway Cast)
Overture/Prologue - to every age / How did they build Titanic / There she is / I must get on that ship / First class poster / Godspeed Titanic / Barrett's song / To be a captain / Lady's maid / What a remarkable age this is / Proposal/Night was alive / Hymn/Doing the latest rag / I have danced / No moon / Autumn/Finale / Dressed in your pyjamas in the Grand Salon / Blame / To the lifeboats / We'll meet tomorrow / Still / To be a captain / Mr. Andrew's vision / Epilogue - In every age
09026688342 / Aug '97 / RCA Victor

☐ TITANIC
Horner, James *c*
Horner, James *con*
Never an absolution / Distant memories / Southampton / Take her to sea Mr.Murdoch / Hard to starboard / Unable to stay / Unwilling to leave / Sinking / Death of the Titanic / Promise kept / Life so changed / Ocean of memories / My heart will go on / Hymn to the sea
SK 63213 / 19 Jan '98 / Sony Classical

☐ TITANIC (Symphonic Themes From The Film, TV Series & Show)
VSD 5926 / 26 May '98 / Varese Sarabande

☐ TITO
Theodorakis, Mikis *c*
SR 50087 / May '94 / Varese Sarabande

☐ TO DIE FOR
Elfman, Danny *c*
VSD 5646 / Nov '95 / Varese Sarabande

☐ TO DIE FOR II - SON OF DARKNESS (To Die For II)
McKenzie, Mark *c*
PCD 110 / Jan '93 / Prometheus

☐ TO HAVE AND TO HOLD (Bargeld, Blixa & Nick Cave/Mick Harvey)
To have and to hold / Jungle of love / Candlelit bedroom / Luther / House in the jungle / Delerium / River at night / Mourning song / Romantic theme / Snow vision / Rose / Clouds / Noah's funeral / Flight / Kate leaves / We're coming/riot / Murder / Red Dress / Threw it all away / Gangster bone
CDIONIC 015 / 10 Aug '98 / Mute

☐ TO KILL A MOCKINGBIRD
Bernstein, Elmer *c*
VSD 5754 / 20 Oct '97 / Varese Sarabande

☐ TO LIVE AND DIE IN LA (Wang Chung)
Wang Chung *c*
To live and die in LA / Lullaby / Wake up stop dreaming / Wait / City of the angels / Red stare / Black-blue-white / Every big city / Dance hall days
GED 24081 / Nov '96 / Geffen

☐ TO THE ENDS OF THE EARTH
Scott, John *c*
Scott, John *con*
PCD 102 / Jan '89 / Prometheus

☐ TO WONG FOO, THANKS FOR EVERYTHING JULIE NEWMAR
I am the body beautiful: *Salt 'N' Pepa* / Free yourself: *Khan, Chaka* / Who taught you how: *Waters, Crystal* / Turn it out: *Labelle* / She's a lady: *Jones, Tom* / Brick house: *Commodores* / Nobody's body: *Monifah* / Do what you wanna do: *Arrington, Charisse* / Hey now (girls just wanna have fun): *Lauper, Cyndi* / Over the rainbow: *Labelle, Patti* / Too wong foo suite: *Portman, Rachel*
MCD 11231 / Jan '96 / MCA

☐ TOGETHER WITH MUSIC (Archive Recording Of The Television Event) (Martin, Mary & Noel Coward)
Together with music / Uncle Harry / Nina / Mad dogs and Englishmen / Dites moi / Cockeyed optimist / Some enchanted evening / Wash that man right out of my hair / Wonderful guy / My heart belongs to Daddy
DRGCD 1103 / Jan '95 / DRG

☐ TOM AND VIV (For Better, For Worse, Forever) (Palm Court Theatre Orchestra)
Wiseman, Debbie *c*
Wiseman, Debbie *con*
SK 64381 / Nov '94 / Sony Classical

☐ TOM JONES
Parker, Jim *c*
Betjeman, John *l*
OCD 012 / 8 Dec '97 / Ocean Deep

☐ TOMBSTONE
Broughton, Bruce *c*
MAF 7038D / Jan '93 / Intrada

☐ TOMMY (Cast Recording)
Townshend, Pete *c*
CCSCD 408 / Nov '94 / Castle

☐ TOMMY (1993 Broadway Cast)
Townshend, Pete *c*
09026618742 / '93 / RCA Victor

☐ TOMMY
Townshend, Pete *c*
Overture from Tommy / Prologue / Captain Walker/ It's a boy / Bernie's holiday camp 1951/What about the boy / Amazing journey / Christmas / Eyesight to the blind / Acid Queen / Do you think it's alright / Cousin Kevin / Do you think it's alright / Fiddle about / Do you think it's alright / Sparks / Extra extra extra / Pinball wizard / Champagne / There's a doctor / Go to the mirror / Tommy can you hear me / Smash the mirror / I'm free / Mother and son / Sensation / Miracle cure / Sally Simpson / Welcome TV studio / Tommy's holiday camp / We're not gonna take it / Listening to you/See you feel me
8411212 / Jan '94 / Polydor

☐ TOMMY (London Symphony Orchestra)
Townshend, Pete *c*
ESMCD 404 / Jun '96 / Essential

☐ TOMMY (CC Productions)
Townshend, Pete *c*
1921 / Amazing journey / Eyesight to the blind / Christmas / Cousin Kevin / Acid queen / Pinball wizard / Go to the mirror / I'm free / Sally Simpson / Sensation / We're not gonna take it
QED 207 / Nov '96 / Tring

☐ TOMMY BOY
Superstar / My hallucination / I love it loud / Wait for the blackout / Call on me / My lucky day / Eres tu / It's the end of the world as we know it (and I fee / Come on eileen / Is chicago is not chicago / Air / Silver naked ladies
9362459042 / Aug '95 / Warner Bros.

☐ TOMORROW NEVER DIES
5408302 / 24 Nov '97 / A&M

☐ TONITE LET'S ALL MAKE LOVE IN LONDON (1967 Film Cast)
SEECD 258 / '90 / See For Miles

☐ TOP BANANA (Broadway Cast)
Mercer, Johnny *c*
ZDM 7647722 / Apr '93 / EMI Classics

☐ TOP GUN
Danger zone: *Loggins, Kenny* / Mighty wings: *Cheap Trick* / Playing with the boys: *Loggins, Kenny* / Lead me on: *Marie, Teena* / Take my breath away: *Berlin* / Hot summer nights: *Miami Sound Machine* / Heaven in your eyes: *Loverboy* / Through the fire: *Greene, Larry* / Destination unknown: *Marietta* / Top Gun anthem: *Faltermeyer, Harold & Steve Stevens*
CD 70296 / Sep '86 / CBS

☐ TOP HAT (Follow The Fleet/Swing Time/Carefree - Let's Swing & Dance With Fred Astaire 1935-1938) (Astaire, Fred)
Cheek to cheek / No strings / Isn't this a lovely day / Top hat white tie and tails / Piccolino / Let's face the music and dance / I'm putting all my eggs in one basket / We saw the sea / Let yourself go / I'd rather lead a band / I'm building up to an awful let down / Fine romance / Way you look tonight / Never gonna dance / Pick yourself up / Bojangles of Harlem / Waltz in swing time / Change partners / I used to be colourblind / Yam / Yam steps
CD 60015 / Sep '97 / Great Movie Themes

☐ TORN CURTAIN (National Philharmonic Orchestra)
Herrmann, Bernard *c*
Prelude / Ship / Radiogram / Hotel / Phone / Bookstore / Book / Valse lente / Travel desk / Blurring / Hotel Berlin / Sarah / Dawn / Gromek / Farmhouse / Killing / Body / Street / Toast / Photos / Sausage / Fall / Cab driver / Hill / Search / Discovery / Blackboard / Formula / Corridor / Bicycles / Bus
VSD 5817 / 27 Jul '98 / Varese Sarabande

☐ TOTAL ECLIPSE (Wilanow St. Quartet & Warsaw Symphony Orchestra/Marta Boberska)
Kaczmarek, Jan A.P. *c*
SK 62037 / Mar '97 / Sony Classical

☐ TOTAL RECALL
Goldsmith, Jerry *c*
Goldsmith, Jerry *con*
Dream / Hologram / Big jump / Mutant / Cleaver girl / First meeting / Treatment / Where am I / End of a dream / New life
VSD 5267 / Aug '90 / Varese Sarabande

☐ TOTALLY LOVED UP
Crystal clear: *Grid* / For what you dream of: *Bedrock* / Gut drum mix: *Funtopia* / Acperience: *Hardfloor* / Two full moons and a trout: *Union Jack* / Attached: *Union Jack* / Make it funky: *Rebound* / Advances: *Surjestive* / Little bullet part 1: *Spooky* / Melt: *Leftfield* / Oneski: *Kirk, Richard* / Prologue: *10th Chapter* / Texas cowboys: *Grid* / Lollipop man: *Union Jack* / Full throttle: *Prodigy* / Calling the people: *A Zone* / Souffie: *Banco De Gaia* / Plastic dream: *Jaydee* / Song of life: *Leftfield* / Forever: *Orbital* / Smoke belch 11: *Sabres Of Paradise*
PRIMAXCD 3 / Jun '97 / Prima Vera

☐ TOUCH (Grohl, Dave)
Grohl, Dave *c*
Bill Hill theme / August Murray theme / How do you do / Rickie Baker's miracle / Making popcorn / Outrage / Saints in love / Spinning newspaper / Remission my ass / Scene 6 / This loving thing / Final miracle / Touch
8556322 / 8 Jun '98 / Roswell

☐ TOUCH OF CLASS, A
Cameron, John *c*
All that love went to waste / Steve's theme / Vickie's theme / Love theme / Touch of class / Amor / Mrs Allessio's rock and roll band / I alwasy knew (love theme) / Bullfight theme / Golf theme / Steve's thme / Antonio's restaurant / She told me so last night / Nudge me every morning
DRGCD 13115 / May '96 / DRG

☐ TOUCH OF EVIL, A
Mancini, Henry *c*
Mancini, Henry *con*
VSD 5414 / Jul '93 / Varese Sarabande

☐ TOUGH GUYS/TRUCK TURNER (Hayes, Isaac)
Title theme / Randolph and Dearborn / Red rooster / Joe Bell / Hung up on my baby / Kidnapped / Run Fay run / Buns o'plenty / End theme / Main title: Truck Turner / House of beauty / Blue's crib / Driving in the sun / Breakthrough / Now we're one / Duke / Dorinda's party / Persuit of the pimpmobile / We need each other girl / House full of girls / Hospital shootout / You're in my arms again / Give it to me / Drinking / Insurance company
CDSXE 2095 / Jul '93 / Stax

☐ TOUS LES MATINS DU MONDE
AUE 004640 / Feb '93 / Auvidis/Ethnic

☐ TOVARICH (Broadway Cast)
ZDM 7648932 / Aug '93 / EMI Classics

☐ TOWN FOX, THE (And Other Musical Tales) (Royal Liverpool Philharmonic Orchestra)
Davis, Carl *con*
SCENECD 19 / '94 / First Night

☐ TOY SOLDIERS
Folk, Robert *c*
MAF 7015D / Jan '93 / Intrada

☐ TOY STORY
WD 771302 / Mar '96 / Disney Music & Stories

☐ TOY STORY (Singalong)
WD 771424 / Oct '96 / Disney Music & Stories

☐ TOYS
Tchaikovsky's Symphony No.1 (excerpt) / Closing of the year: *Wendy & Lisa/Cast* / Ebudae: *Enya* / Happy worker: *Amos, Tori* / Alsatia's lullaby: *Migenes, Julia & Hans Zimmer* / Workers: *Cast of Toys* / Let joy and innocence prevail: *Metheny, Pat* / General: *Gambon, Michael & Hans Zimmer* / Mirror song: *Dolby, Thomas & Robin Williams/John Cusack* / Battle introduction: *Williams, Robin* / Welcome to the pleasure dome: *Frankie Goes To Hollywood* / Let joy and innocence prevail: *Jones, Grace* / Closing of the year/Happy Workers (Reprise): *Siberry, Jane*
450991603-2 / Mar '93 / ZTT

☐ TRAINSPOTTING VOL.1
Lust for life: *Iggy Pop* / Deep blue day: *Eno, Brian* / Trainspotting: *Primal Scream* / Atomic: *Sleeper* / Temptation: *New Order* / Nightclubbing: *Iggy Pop* / Sing: *Blur* / Perfect day: *Reed, Lou* / Mile End: *Pulp* / For what you dream of: *Bedrock feat. KYO* / 2:1: *Elastica* / Final hit: *Leftfield* / Born slippy: *Underworld* / Closet romantic: *Albarn, Damon*
CDEMC 3739 / Feb '96 / Premier/EMI

☐ TRAINSPOTTING VOL.2
Choose life: *PF Project* / Passenger: *Iggy Pop* / Dark and long: *Underworld* / Habenera: *Underworld* / Statuesque: *Sleeper* / Golden years: *Bowie, David* / Think about the way: *Ice MC* / Final hit: *Leftfield* / Temptation: *Heaven 17* / Nightclubbing: *Iggy Pop* / Our lips are sealed: *Fun Boy Three* / Come together: *Primal Scream* / Atmosphere: *Joy Division* / Inner city life: *Goldie* / Born slippy/NUXX: *Underworld*
PRMDCD 36 / 15 Sep '97 / Soundtracks

☐ TRAVELLER
King of the road: *Travis, Randy* / If youy've got the money: *Gilmore, Jimmie Dale* / I've love you a thousand ways: *Gilmore, Jimmie Dale* / Seven lonely days: *Lang, k.d.* / Rockin' Robin: *White, Bryan* / Please help me I'm falling: *McCann, Lila* / Blues stay away from me: *Shiver, Thrasher* / Sweet nothin's: *Tina And The B-Side Movement* / Searching: *Barnett, Mandy* / Gonna find me a bluebird: *Royal Wade Kimes* / Don't rob another man's castle: *Royal Wade Kimes* / I'm thinking tonight of my blue eyes: *Cox Family* / Sweeter than the flowers: *Cox Family* / Love and happiness: *Green, Al* / Dark moon: *Barnett, Mandy* / Young love: *Sharp, Kevin*
7559620302 / Jun '97 / Elektra

☐ TRAVELLING MAN (Browne, Duncan & Sebastian Graham Jones)
CDSGP 0114 / Sep '95 / Prestige

☐ TREASURE OF SIERRA MADRE, THE (& The Charge Of The Light Brigade/ Suites) (Slovak State Philharmonic Orchestra)
Steiner, Max *c*
Kolman, Barry *con*
CRC 2367 / 15 Jun '98 / Centaur

☐ TREE GROWS IN BROOKLYN, A (1951 Broadway Cast)
Schwartz, Arthur *c*
Fields, Dorothy *l*
Goberman, Max *con*
SK 48014 / Dec '91 / Sony Broadway

☐ TREES LOUNGE
You always hurt the one you love: *Lee, Brenda* / I never had a dream come true: *Ink Spots* / I've been hurt: *Deal, Bill & The Rhondels* / That woman got me drinking: *MacGowan, Shane & The Popes* / Tellin' the dice how to roll: *Tuzzolino, Patrick* / Mudslide: *Ross, Craig* / I don't know enough about you: *Mills Brothers* / I understand (Just how you feel): *Ink Spots* / Trees lounge: *Hayden* / Tommy blues: *Lurie, Evan* / Color of your eyes: *Balint, Eszter & Smokey Hormel*
MCD 11539 / Feb '97 / MCA

☐ TRESPASS
Trespass: *Ice-T & Ice Cube* / Gotta do what I gotta do: *Public Enemy* / Depths of hell: *Ice-T* / I check my bank: *Sir Mix-a-Lot* / I'm a playa (bitch): *Penthouse Players Clique* / On the wall: *Black Sheep* / Don't be a 304: *AMG* / Gotta get over (taking loot): *Gang Starr* / You know what I'm about: *Lord Finesse* / I'm gonna smoke him: *Donald D* / Quick way out: *W.C. & the Maad Circle* / King of the street: *Cooder, Ry*
7599269782 / Feb '93 / Sire

☐ TRESPASS (Score) (Cooder, Ry)
Cooder, Ry *c*
9362452202 / Jan '94 / Warner Bros.

☐ TRIAL, THE
Davis, Carl *c*
873150 / Feb '94 / Milan

☐ TRIUMPH OF THE SPIRIT
Eidelman, Cliff *c*
Main title / Dark tunnel to Aushwitz / Answer us / Avram refuses to work / Hard felt rest / Elena's false dreams / Begging for bread / Slaughter / Hunger / Salamo desperately finds Allegra / New assignment / Epilogue / Love in wedlock / There was a time / Mi dyo mi / Longing for home / Hell realization / There was a memory / Mourning / It was a month before we left / Mercy on to us / Allegra's punishment / Death march
VSD 5254 / Apr '90 / Varese Sarabande

☐ TROIS COULEURS - BLEU (Preisner, Zbigniew)
Preisner, Zbigniew *c*
Chant pour l'unification d'Europe / Van den budenmayer - musique funebre / Julie - images d'enterrement / Memento - premiere apparition / Lutte de carnaval contre le careme / Memento - Julie avec Olivier / Ellipse 1 / Premiere flute / Julie - dans son nouvel appartement / Memento - Julie dans l'escalier / Deuxieme flute / Ellipse 2 / Lutte de carnaval contre le careme II / Memento - flute / Ellipse 3 / Theme d'Olivier - piano / Olivier et Julie - essai de composition / Theme d'Olivier - version finale / Bolero - annonce du film "Rouge" / Chant pour l'unification d'Europe - version de Julie / Generique de fin / Memento - orgue / Bolero - film "Rouge"
CDVMM 12 / Oct '93 / Virgin

☐ TROIS COULEURS - BLEU, BLANC, ROUGE (Preisner, Zbigniew)
Preisner, Zbigniew *c*
CDVMMX 15 / Nov '94 / Virgin

☐ TROIS COULEURS - ROUGE (Preisner, Zbigniew)
Preisner, Zbigniew *c*
Fashion show / Meeting the judge / Tapped conversation / Leaving the judge / Psychoanalysis / Today is my birthday / Do not take another man's wife / Treason / Fashion show / Conversation at the theatre / Rest of the conversation at the theatre / Do not take another man's wife / Catastrophe / Finale
CDVMM 14 / Nov '94 / Virgin

☐ TROMEO AND JULIET
42907 / Sep '97 / Troma

☐ TROUBLE MAN (Gaye, Marvin)
Gaye, Marvin *c*
Trouble man main theme / T plays it cool / Poor Abbey Walsh / Break in (police shoot big) / Cleo's apartment / Trouble man / Trouble man / T stands for trouble / Trouble man main theme / Life is a gamble / Deep in it / Don't mess with Mr. T / There goes mister 'T'
5300972 / Jan '92 / Motown

☐ TROUBLESOME CREEK - A MIDWESTERN (Mirowitz, Sheldon & Duke Levine)
Mirowitz, Sheldon & Duke Levine *c*
Sunday dusk / Summer montage / Titles / Downtown summer storm / Farm crisis / Family history / Thanksgiving / Cemetry / Driving to Rolfe / Last cow feed / Cattle auction Winter / Fall turns to Winter / Auction ends / Leaving Iowa / Combining / Quilt / Credit roll
DARINGCD 3024 / Sep '96 / Daring

☐ TRUE BLUE
Syrewicz, Stanislas *c*
4520122 / Nov '96 / Decca

☐ TRUE GRIT/COMANCHEROS (Music From John Wayne Westerns Vol. 1)
Bernstein, Elmer *c*
VSD 47236 / Jan '89 / Varese Sarabande

☐ TRUSTING BEATRICE/COLD HEAVEN
Myers, Stanley *c*
MAF 7048D / Mar '93 / Intrada

☐ **TRUTH ABOUT CATS AND DOGS, THE**
For once in my life: *Farris, Dionne* / Caramel: *Vega, Suzanne* / Bed's too big without you: *Sting* / Angel mine: *Cowboy Junkies* / This road: *Squeeze* / Give it everything: *Green, Al* / I can't imagine: *Neville, Aaron* / Run around: *Blues Traveller* / Well I lied: *Cray, Robert Band* / Where do I begin: *Sobule, Jill* / You do something to me: *Weller, Paul* / World keeps spinning: *Brand New Heavies* / Bad idea: *Folds, Ben Five* / Cats and dogs: *Shore, Howard*
5405072 / May '96 / A&M

☐ **TRYOUT (Songs From Where Do We Go From Here/One Touch Of Venus) (Weill, Kurt & Ira Gershwin)**
DRGCD 904 / Jan '95 / DRG

☐ **TUSITALA, TELLER OF TALES (Music From BBC's Stevenson's Tales) (Stevenson, Savourna)**
ECLCD 9412 / Jan '95 / Eclectic

☐ **TWELFTH NIGHT (Score)**
Davey, Shaun *c*
FILMCD 186 / Oct '96 / Silva Screen

☐ **TWICE A WOMAN (Breuker, Willem)**
Breuker, Willem *c*
BVHAASTCD 9708 / Apr '98 / Bvhaast

☐ **TWILIGHT**
Bernstein, Elmer *c*
Swimmer / Discovery / Betrayal / Pier music / Anger / Verna / Suspicians / Kiss / Ranch / Bye bye mucho / Troubles / Consequences / End credits / Jubilation
0022902CIN / 1 Jun '98 / Edel

☐ **TWILIGHT ZONE VOL.1, THE (Music From The TV Series)**
Invaders / Where is everybody / I sing the body electric / Jazz themes / Nervous man in a four dollar room / Walking distance / Main title / End titles
VCD 47233 / Jan '89 / Varese Sarabande

☐ **TWILIGHT ZONE VOL.2, THE (Music From The TV Series)**
Main theme / Back there / And when the sky was opened / Passerby / Lonely / Two / End theme
VCD 47247 / Jan '89 / Varese Sarabande

☐ **TWILIGHT'S LAST GLEAMING (Graunke Symphony Orchestra)**
Goldsmith, Jerry *c*
Goldsmith, Jerry *con*
Silo 3 / Takeover begins / General Mackenzie arrives / He has launch control / Special forces arrive / Bubble / Nuclear nightmare / Reflective interlude / After you Mr President / Heading for home / President falls / Taking of silo 3 / Operation gold begins / Watching and waiting / Tanks / Down the elevator shaft / Gold bomb / Gold team enters silo 3 / Final betrayal
FILMCD 111 / Apr '92 / Silva Screen

☐ **TWIN PEAKS (Badalamenti, Angelo)**
Badalamenti, Angelo *c*
Twin Peaks / Laura Palmer's theme / Audrey's dance / Nightingale / Freshly squeezed / Bookhouse boys / Into the night / Night life in Twin Peaks / Dance of the dream man / Love theme from Twin Peaks / Falling: *Cruise, Julee*
7599263162 / Nov '90 / Warner Bros.

☐ **TWIN PEAKS - FIRE WALK WITH ME (Badalamenti, Angelo)**
Badalamenti, Angelo *c*
Twin Peaks - fire walk with me / Pine float / Sycamore trees / Don't do anything (I wouldn't do) / Real indication / Questions in a world of blue / Pink room / Black dog runs at night / Best friends / Moving through time / Montage from Twin Peaks
9362450192 / Feb '95 / WEA

☐ **TWINTOWN**
Other man's grass is always greener: *Clark, Petula* / Metronomic underground: *Stereolab* / In the summertime: *Mungo Jerry* / Good enough: *Dodgy* / Downtown: *Clark, Petula* / Bad behaviour: *Super Furry Animals* / Butterfly 747: *Moloko* / You've got a lot to answer for: *Catatonia* / Motown junk: *Manic Street Preachers* / Stem: *DJ Shadow*
5407182 / Apr '97 / A&M

☐ **TWISTER**
9362462542 / May '96 / East West

☐ **TWO BY TWO (Broadway Cast)**
Rodgers, Richard *c*
Blackton, Jay *con*
SK 30338 / Dec '91 / Sony Broadway

☐ **TWO MOON JUNCTION**
Elias, Jonathan *c*
VSD 5518 / Oct '94 / Varese Sarabande

U

☐ **U BOATS: THE WOLF PACK**
Young, Christopher *c*
CEUR 0214 / Jan '93 / Silva Screen

☐ **U-TURN**
It's a good day: *Lee, Peggy* / Help me make it through the night: *Smith, Sammi* / More and more: *Pierce, Webb* / La mujer que amas: *Fernandez, Pedro* / I wish you love: *Lynne, Gloria* / Honky tonk girl: *Cash, Johnny* / Your cheatin' heart: *Cline, Patsy* / Ring of fire: *Cash, Johnny* / Lonesome town: *Nelson, Ricky* / Speaking of happiness: *Nelson, Ricky* / Original score: *Morricone, Ennio*
4890032 / 30 Mar '98 / Epic

☐ **UCCELLACCI/LE STREGHE/ TEOREMA (Music From The Films Of Pier Paolo Pasolini)**
Morricone, Ennio *c*
OST 130 / Apr '96 / Milano Dischi

☐ **ULYSSES**
Cicognini, Alessandro *c*
LEGENDCD 8 / Apr '92 / Legend

☐ **ULYSSES' GAZE**
Karaindrou, Eleni *c*
4491532 / Oct '95 / ECM

☐ **UN COEUR EN HIVER**
Ravel, Maurice/Philippe Sarde *c*
4509924082 / Jan '95 / WEA

☐ **UN EROE BORGHESE**
Donaggio, Pino *c*
LEGENDCD 19 / May '95 / Legend

☐ **UN INVERNO FREDDO FREDDO**
Cimpanelli, Claudio *c*
LIFE 3301 / 14 Apr '98 / Life

☐ **UNBEARABLE LIGHTNESS OF BEING, THE**
Janacek, Leos *c*
Fairytale III / Holy Virgin of Frydek / In the mists / Hey Jude / Joy joy joy / String quartet no. 2 / Sonata for violin and piano / Bird of ill omen lingers on / On the overgrown path set 2 / String quartet no. 3 / Blow away leaf / Goodnight / Idyll for string orchestra II
FCD 21006 / Jan '89 / Fantasy

☐ **UNDER SIEGE (Chang, Gary)**
Chang, Gary *c*
VSD 5409 / Feb '93 / Varese Sarabande

☐ **UNDER SIEGE II**
Poledouris, Basil *c*
VSD 5648 / Oct '95 / Varese Sarabande

☐ **UNDERNEATH**
Martinez, Cliff *c*
VSD 5587 / Mar '95 / Varese Sarabande

☐ **UNDERNEATH THE ARCHES (1982 London Cast)**
Old Bull and Bush / Just for laughs / Underneath the arches / Maybe it's because I'm a Londoner / Home town / Umbrella man / Strollin' / Siegfried line
CDTER 1015 / 20 Apr '98 / MCI/TER

☐ **UNFORGIVEN**
Niehaus, Lennie *c*
VSD 5380 / Sep '92 / Varese Sarabande

☐ **UNFORGIVEN, THE**
Tiomkin, Dimitri *c*
TSU 0108 / Jan '95 / Tsunami

☐ **UNINVITED, THE (Kiszko, Martin)**
Kiszko, Martin *c*
OCD 007 / 6 Oct '97 / Ocean Deep

☐ **UNIVERSAL SOLDIER**
Franke, Christopher *c*
VSD 5373 / Nov '92 / Varese Sarabande

☐ **UNLAWFUL ENTRY**
Horner, James *c*
MAF 7031D / Dec '92 / Intrada

☐ **UNSINKABLE MOLLY BROWN, THE (Broadway Cast)**
Willson, Meredith *c*
ZDM 7647612 / Apr '93 / EMI Classics

☐ **UNTAMED HEART**
Eidelman, Cliff *c*
VSD 5404 / Mar '93 / Varese Sarabande

☐ **UNTIL THE END OF THE WORLD**
Opening titles / Sax and violins: *Talking Heads* / Summer kisses winter tears / Move with me / Adversary / What's good: *Reed, Lou* / Last night sleep / Fretless: *REM* / Days / Claire's theme / Till the end of the world / It takes time / Death's door / Love theme / Calling all angels: *Siberry, Jane* / Humans from earth / Sleeping in the devil's bed / Until the end of the world: *U2*
7599267072 / Dec '91 / WEA

☐ **UP (& Mega Vixens/Beneath the Valley of the Ultravixens)**
QDKCD 009 / Sep '97 / QDK Media

☐ **UP CLOSE & PERSONAL**
1620532 / Jun '96 / Polydor

☐ **UP 'N' UNDER**
Steam: *East 17* / Turn on tune in cop out: *Freakpower* / Keep on burning: *Collins, Edwyn* / Walk away: *Cast* / On and on: *Longpigs* / So good: *Boyzone* / Like I do: *Monorail* / On standby: *Shed Seven* / I said hey: *Drayton, Luce* / Tomorrow: *James* / You're the only one: *Varney, Paul* / Give to me: *Coade*
0022872CIN / 16 Feb '98 / Edel

☐ **UP ON THE ROOF**
OCD 009 / 3 Nov '97 / Ocean Deep

☐ **UPTIGHT (Booker T & The MG's)**
Johnny I love you / Cleveland now / Children don't get weary / Tank's lament / Blues in the gutter / We've got Johnny Wells / Down at Ralph's joint / Deadwood Dick / Run tank run / Time is tight
CDSXE 024 / Jan '90 / Stax

☐ **US MARSHALLS**
Goldsmith, Jerry *c*
Goldsmith, Jerry *con*
VSD 5914 / 27 Apr '98 / Varese Sarabande

☐ **UTILIZER, THE**
McCarthy, Dennis *c*
McCarthy, Dennis *con*
MAF 7067 / Mar '96 / Intrada

☐ **UTOPIA LIMITED (D'Oyly Carte Opera Chorus/Royal Philharmonic Orchestra)**
Sullivan, Sir Arthur *c*
Gilbert, W.S. *l*
Nash, R. *con*
4368162 / Jan '90 / London

V

☐ **VAGRANT, THE**
Young, Christopher *c*
Young, Christopher *con*
MAF 7028D / Sep '92 / Intrada

☐ **VALLEY OF THE DOLLS**
Previn, Andre *c*
3145368762 / 2 Feb '98 / Philips

☐ **VALMOUTH (1982 Chichester Festival Cast)**
Wilson, Sandy *c*
Valmouth / Magic fingers / Mustapha / I loved a man / All the girls were pretty / What do I want with love / Just once more / Lady of de manor / Big best shoes / Niri Esther / Cry of the peacock
CDTER 1019 / May '89 / TER

☐ **VALMOUTH (1958 London Cast)**
Wilson, Sandy *c*
Valmouth / Magic fingers / Mustapha / I love a man / All the girls were pretty / What do I want with love / Just one more / Lady of de manor / Big best shoes / Niri Esther / Cry of the peacock / Little girl baby / Cathedral of Clemenza / Only a passing phase / Where the trees are green with parrots / My talking day / I will miss you / Finale
CDSBL 13109 / Nov '92 / DRG

☐ **VERTIGO (Royal Scottish National Orchestra)**
Herrmann, Bernard *c*
McNeely, Joel *con*
VSD 5600 / May '96 / Varese Sarabande

☐ **VERTIGO**
Herrmann, Bernard *c*
VSD 5759 / Feb '97 / Varese Sarabande

☐ **VERY GOOD EDDIE (1975 Broadway Cast)**
Kern, Jerome *c*
Greene, Schuyler *l*
Overture / We're on our way / Some sort of somebody / Thirteen collar / Bungalow in Quogue / Isn't it great to be married / Good night boat / Left all alone again / Hot dot / If you're a friend of mine / Wedding bells are calling me / Honeymoon Inn / I've got to dance / Moon of love / Old boy neutral / Babes in the wood / Katy D / Nodding roses / Finale
DRGCD 6100 / '88 / DRG

☐ **VERY WARM FOR MAY (Cast Recording)**
Kern, Jerome *c*
Hammerstein II, Oscar *l*
AEICD 008 / May '98 / AEI

☐ **VICTOR VICTORIA**
Mancini, Henry *c*
You and me / Shady dame from Seville / Alone in Paris / King's can can / Le jazz hot / Crazy world / Chicago Illinois / Cat and mouse / Gay Paree / Finale
GNPD 8038 / Sep '94 / GNP Crescendo

☐ **VICTOR VICTORIA (1995 Broadway Cast)**
Mancini, Henry *c*
Bricusse, Leslie *l*
Fraser, I. *con*
4469192 / Jan '96 / Philips

☐ **VICTORIA PLUMS (Steafel, Shelia)**
Somebody else's baby / For her good name/Don't say I did it Jack / Little 'un / Twiddley bits / When is my birthday daddy / She is beautiful to me / Newsboy's debt / Girl and the baloon / Had she listened to her mother / Sad sad story / Kate O'Farrell / Grandma's last amen / Blessing of old Zachariah / Bunny at the bunshop / Come inside / Percy / Story the violets told / Mesmerize Magee / Under the shadow of St. Pauls / There'll be no wedding here today / You can't punch my ticket / Soldier boy / Only a dear old bugle / Peter Peter/Won't you come over and play croquet/Liza / Father's grave
5572092 / 27 Apr '98 / Redial

☐ **VICTORY AT SEA (Cincinnati Pops Orchestra)**
Rodgers, Richard *c*
Kunzel, Erich *con*
CD 80175 / Aug '90 / Telarc

☐ **VICTORY AT SEA (RCA Victor Symphony Orchestra)**
Rodgers, Richard *c*
Bennett, Robert Russell *con*
Song of the high seas / Pacific boils over / Guadalcanal march / D-Day / Hard work and horseplay / Theme of the fast carriers / Beneath the Southern Cross / Mare nostrum / Victory at sea / Fire on the waters / Danger down deep / Mediterranean mosaic / Magnetic North
09026609632 / '90 / RCA Victor

☐ **VICTORY AT SEA (More Victory At Sea) (RCA Victor Symphony Orchestra)**
Rodgers, Richard *c*
Bennett, Robert Russell *con*
Allies on the march / Voyage into fate / Peleliu / Sound of victory / Rings around Rabaul / Full fathom five / Turkey shoot / Ships that pass / Two if by sea / Turning point / Symphonic scenario
09026609642 / '90 / RCA Victor

☐ **VIDEO GIRL AI VOL.1**
AM 1 / Nov '96 / Animanga

☐ **VIDEO GIRL AI VOL.2**
AM 9 / Nov '96 / Animanga

☐ **VIKINGS, THE/SOLOMON & SHEBA**
Nascimbene, Mario *c*
LEGENDCD 9 / Jan '93 / Legend

☐ **VILLAGE OF THE DAMNED**
Carpenter, John *c*
VSD 5629 / Jun '95 / Varese Sarabande

☐ **VIRTUOSITY**
RAD 11295 / Nov '95 / Radioactive

☐ **VIVA LAS VEGAS/ROUSTABOUT (Presley, Elvis)**
Viva Las Vegas / If you think I don't need you / If you need somebody to lean on / You're the boss / What I'd say / Do the Vega / C'mon everybody / Lady love me (With Ann Margaret) / Night life / Today tomorrow and forever / Yellow rose of Texas/The eyes of Texas / Santa Lucia / Roustabout / Little Egypt / Poison ivy league / Hard knocks / It's a wonderful world / Big love big heartache / One track heart / It's carnival time / Carmy town / There's a brand new day on the horizon / Wheels on my heels
74321 13432-2 / Mar '93 / RCA

☐ **VIVA ZAPATA**
North, Alex *c*
Goldsmith, Jerry *con*
Foreword / Main title / Zapata / Zapata's love and children episode / Innocente's death / Gathering forces / Huerta / Pablo / Conscience / Morelos / Eufemio / Josefa's love / Josefa / End title and cast
VSD 5900 / 11 Apr '98 / Varese Sarabande

☐ **VIXEN**
Loose, William *c*
12922 / 24 Nov '97 / Laserlight

☐ **VOICES**
I will always wait for you / Rose Marie's theme / Disco if you want to / Children's song / Family theme / Anything that's rock 'n' roll / I will always wait for you (instrumental) / On a stage / Across the river / Bubbles in my beer / Rose Marie and drew / Drunk as a punk / Children's song (instrumental) / Rose Marie's dance
DINTVCD 44 / Sep '92 / Dino

☐ **VOLCANO**
VSD 5833 / 6 Oct '97 / Varese Sarabande

☐ **VON RYAN'S EXPRESS/OUR MAN FLINT/IN LIKE FLINT**
Goldsmith, Jerry *c*
TCI 0602 / Jan '95 / Tsunami

☐ **VOYAGE OF TERROR (The Achille Lauro Affair)**
Morricone, Ennio *c*
OST 101 / Jan '93 / Milano Dischi

☐ **VOYAGES (Silvestri, Alan)**
Silvestri, Alan *c*
VSD 5641 / Oct '95 / Varese Sarabande

W

☐ **WAG THE DOG (Knopfler, Mark)**
Knopfler, Mark *c*
5368642 / 19 Jan '98 / Mercury

☐ **WAITING TO EXHALE**
Babyface *c*
Exhale: *Houston, Whitney* / Count on me: *Houston, Whitney* / Let it flow: *Braxton, Toni* / This is how it works: *TLC* / Sittin' in my room: *Brandy* / Not gonna try: *Blige, Mary J.* / All night long: *SWV* / Kissing you: *Evans, Faith* / My funny valentine: *Khan, Chaka* / My love sweet love: *Labelle, Patti* / Hurts like hell: *Franklin, Aretha* / Wey U: *Moore, Chante* / How could you call her baby: *Shanna* / Love will be waiting at home: *For Real* / And I give you love: *Marie, Sonja*
07822187962 / Nov '95 / Arista

☐ **WALK IN THE CLOUDS, A**
Jarre, Maurice *c*
74321286662 / 22 Nov '97 / RCA Victor

☐ **WALKING HAPPY (1966 Broadway Cast)**
Van Heusen, James *c*
Cahn, Sammy *l*
ZDM 5651332 / Apr '94 / EMI Classics

☐ **WALKING THUNDER (Munich Symphony Orchestra)**
Scott, John *c*
JSCD 117 / Oct '96 / JOS

☐ **WANDERERS, THE**
You really got a hold on me: *Miracles* / Shout: *Isley Brothers* / Big girls don't cry: *Four Seasons* / Ya ya: *Dorsey, Lee* / My boyfriend's back: *Angels* / Soldier boy: *Shirelles* / Pipeline: *Chantays* / Do you love me: *Contours* / Wipeout: *Surfaris* / Wanderer: *Dion* / Stand by me: *King, Ben E.* / Tequila: *Champs*
NEMCD 765 / Oct '95 / Sequel

☐ **WAR AND PEACE (Ovchinnikov, Vyacheslav)**
Ovchinnikov, Vyacheslav *c*
VSD 5225 / Feb '90 / Varese Sarabande

☐ **WAR LORD, THE**
Moross, Jerome *c*
VSD 5536 / Apr '95 / Varese Sarabande

☐ **WAR LORD, THE/THE CARDINAL**
Moross, Jerome *c*
TSU 0117 / Jan '95 / Tsunami

☐ **WAR OF THE BUTTONS**
Portman, Rachel *c*
VSD 5554 / Oct '94 / Varese Sarabande

☐ **WARLOCK II - THE ARMAGEDDON**
McKenzie, Mark *c*
MAF 7049D / Jan '93 / Intrada

☐ **WARRIORS**
In the city: *Walsh, Joe* / Warriors theme: *De Vorzon, Barry* / Baseball furies chase: *De Vorzon, Barry* / Fight: *De Vorzon, Barry* / Echoes in my mind: *Mandrill* / Nowhere to run: *McCuller, Arnold* / In Havana: *Vance, Kenny & Ismael Miranda* / Love is a fire: *Ravan, Genya* / You're movin' too slow: *Vastano, Johnny* / Last of an ancient breed: *Child, Desmond*
5511692 / Sep '95 / Spectrum

☐ **WARRIORS OF VIRTUE**
Beautiful morning: *Speech* / You can fly: *Hubbard, Wade* / Forces of nature: *Clannad* / Inside of you: *Havens, Richie* / Tennessee plates: *Sexton, Charlie* / In a dream: *Judyjudyjudy* / When you go: *Ultraglide* / Alembic: *Hart, Mickey & Bakithi Kumalo* / Song of the seas: *Vangelis* / Underscore: *Colorado Symphony Orchestra*
8122726402 / Jul '97 / Kid Rhino

☐ **WASHINGTON SQUARE**
Washington square / Catherine in the window / Catherine and Morris / Una vita / First kiss / That must be love / Lavinia / No to Morris / No to Catherine / Catherine and the mirror / Catherine's nocturne / Romance quartet / Please wait for me / L'absence / Lavinia and Morris / Alps / Reunion / Unfinished nocturne / Despair / Lullaby / Father is dying / Tale of the string / Please don't come here again / Chiami una vita / End credits / L'absence again
VSD 5869 / 25 May '98 / Varese Sarabande

☐ **WATERWAYS**
Hardiman, Ronan *c*
HBCD 0005 / Oct '94 / Hummingbird

☐ **WATTSTAX**
Oh la de da: *Staple Singers* / I like the things about you: *Staple Singers* / Respect yourself: *Staple Singers* / I'll take you there: *Staple Singers* / Knock on wood: *Floyd, Eddie* / Lay your loving on me: *Floyd, Eddie* / I like what you're doing (to me): *Thomas, Carla* / Gee Whiz: *Thomas, Carla* / I have a God who loves: *Thomas, Carla* / Do the breakdown: *Thomas, Rufus* / Do the funky chicken: *Thomas, Rufus* / Do the funky penguin: *Thomas, Rufus* / Son of Shaft: *Bar-Kays* / Feel it: *Bar-Kays* / I can't turn you loose: *Bar-Kays* / Killing floor: *King, Albert* / I'll play the blues for you: *King, Albert* / Angel of mercy: *King, Albert* / I don't know what this world is coming to: *Soul Children* / Hearsay: *Soul Children* / Ain't no sunshine: *Hayes, Isaac*
CDSXE2 079 / Nov '92 / Stax

☐ **WAY WE WERE, THE (Streisand, Barbra)**
Hamlisch, Marvin *c*
Bergman, Marilyn *l*
Being at war with each other / Something so right / Best thing you've ever done / Way we were / All in love is fair / What are you doing the rest of your life / Summer me Winter me / Pieces of dreams / I've never been a woman before / My buddy / How about me
4749112 / Jan '94 / Columbia

☐ **WAYNE'S WORLD I**
Bohemian rhapsody: *Queen* / Hot and bothered: *Cinderella* / Rock candy: *Bulletboys* / Dream weaver: *Wright, Gary* / Silkamikanico: *Red Hot Chili Peppers* / Time machine: *Black Sabbath* / Wayne's world theme: *Myers, Mike* / Ballroom blitz: *Carrere, Tia* / Foxy lady: *Hendrix, Jimi* / Feed my Frankenstein: *Cooper, Alice* / Why you wanna break my heart: *Carrere, Tia*
7599268052 / Feb '95 / Reprise

☐ **WAYNE'S WORLD II**
Dude (looks like a lady): *Aerosmith* / Shut up and dance: *Aerosmith* / Louie Louie: *Plant, Robert* / Superstar: *Superfan* / Frankenstein: *Winter, Edgar* / Radar love: *Golden Earring* / Spirit in the sky: *Greenbaum, Norman* / Can't get enough: *Bad Company* / Out there: *Dinosaur Jnr* / Idiot summer: *Gin Blossoms* / Mary's house: *4 Non Blondes* / YMCA: *Village People*
9362454852 / Feb '94 / Warner Bros.

☐ **WE BEGIN (Isham, Mark & Art Lande)**
Isham, Mark *c*
Melancholy of departure / Ceremony in starlight / We begin / Lord Ananea / Surface and symbol / Sweet circle / Fanfare
8316212 / Jul '87 / ECM

☐ **WEDDING BANQUET, THE**
LDM 1093 / Mar '96 / LDM

☐ **WEDDING BELL BLUES**
VSD 5853 / Aug '97 / Varese Sarabande

☐ **WEDDING SINGER VOL.1, THE**
Video killed the radio star: *Presidents of the USA* / Do you really want to hurt me: *Culture Club* / Every little thing she does is magic: *Police* / How soon is now: *Smiths* / Love my way: *Thompson Twins* / Everyday I write the book: *Costello, Elvis* / White wedding: *Idol, Billy* / China girl: *Bowie, David* / Blue Monday: *New Order* / Pass the dutchie: *Musical Youth* / Have you written anything lately / Somebody kill me: *Sandler, Adam* / Rapper's delight: *Dow, Ellen*
9362468402 / 8 Jun '98 / Warner Bros.

☐ **WEDDING SINGER VOL.2, THE**
Too shy: *Kajagoogoo* / It's all I can do: *Cars* / True: *Spandau Ballet* / Space age love song: *Spandau Ballet* / Private Idaho: *B-52's* / Money (that's what I want): *Flying Lizards* / You spin me round: *Dead Or Alive* / Just can't get enough: *Depeche Mode* / Love stinks: *J. Geils Band* / You make my dreams: *Hall & Oates* / Holiday: *Madonna* / Grow old with you: *Sandler, Adam*
9362469842 / 10 Aug '98 / Warner Bros.

☐ **WEEDS**
Badalamenti, Angelo *c*
VCD 47313 / Jan '89 / Varese Sarabande

☐ **WELCOME TO SARAJEVO**
Way young lovers do: *Morrison, Van* / I wanna be adored: *Stone Roses* / Shine on: *House Of Love* / Don't worry be happy: *McFerrin, Bobby* / Emira: *London Chamber Orchestra* / Donovan: *Happy Mondays* / It's a bad world: *Teenage Fanclub* / MOR: *Blur* / Adagio in G minor: *London Chamber Orchestra*
4930142 / 1 Dec '97 / Premier/EMI

☐ **WES CRAVEN'S NEW NIGHTMARE**
Robinson, J. Peter *c*
235152 / Jan '95 / Milan

☐ **WEST SIDE STORY (1961 Film Cast)**
Bernstein, Leonard *c*
Sondheim, Stephen *l*
Green, John *con*
Jet song / Something's coming / dance at the gym / America / Maria / Tonight / Gee officer Krupke / I feel pretty / One hand one heart / Quintet / Rumble / Cool / Boy like that / I have a love / Somewhere
SK 48211 / Aug '93 / Sony Music

☐ **WEST SIDE STORY (Highlights) (Te Kanawa, Dame Kiri & Jose Carreras/ 1984 Studio Cast)**
Bernstein, Leonard *c*
Sondheim, Stephen *l*
Bernstein, Leonard *con*
Jet song / Something's coming / Maria / Tonight / America / Cool / One hand one heart / I feel pretty / Somewhere / Gee Officer Krupke / Boy like that / I have a love / Taunting scene / Finale
4159632 / May '85 / Deutsche Grammophon

☐ **WEST SIDE STORY (Te Kanawa, Dame Kiri & Jose Carreras/1984 Studio Cast)**
Bernstein, Leonard *c*
Sondheim, Stephen *l*
Bernstein, Leonard *con*
Prologue/Jet song / Something's coming / Dance at the gym / Maria / Tonight / Rumble / I feel pretty / Somewhere / Gee Officer Krupke / Boy like that / I have a love / Finale
4152532 / May '85 / Deutsche Grammophon

☐ **WEST SIDE STORY (1993 Studio Cast)**
Bernstein, Leonard *c*
Sondheim, Stephen *l*
Wordsworth, Barry *con*
Prologue / Jet Song / Something's coming / Blues / Promenade / Mambo / Cha cha / Meeting scene / Jump / Maria / Balcony scene (Tonight) / America / Cool / One hand one heart / Tonight / Rumble / I feel pretty / Scherzo / Somewhere / Procession/Adagio / Gee Officer Krupke / Boy like that / I have a love / Taunting scene / Finale
IMGCD 1801 / Mar '93 / IMG

☐ **WEST SIDE STORY (London Cast)**
Bernstein, Leonard *c*
Sondheim, Stephen *l*
Jet song / Something's coming / Maria / America / Cool / One hand one heart / Quintet (tonight) / I feel pretty / Somewhere / Gee officer Krupke / Boy like that / I have a love
SHOWCD 006 / Feb '95 / Showtime

☐ **WEST SIDE STORY (Broadway Cast)**
Bernstein, Leonard *c*
Sondheim, Stephen *l*
Prologue / Jet song / Something's coming / Dance at the gym / Maria / Tonight / America / Cool / One hand one heart / Rumble / I feel pretty / Somewhere / Gee Officer Krupke / Boy like that / I have a love / Finale
CK 64419 / Feb '95 / Mastersound

☐ **WEST SIDE STORY (Chorus & National Symphony Orchestra)**
Bernstein, Leonard *c*
Sondheim, Stephen *l*
Edwards, John Owen *con*
Overture / Jet song / Something's coming / Dance at the gym / Maria / Balcony scene / Tonight / America / One hand one heart / Cool / Rumble / En'tarcate / Ballet sequence / Gee officer Krupte / Boy like that / Ihave a love / Taunting scene / Finale
CDTER2 1197 / Nov '97 / TER

☐ **WEST SIDE STORY (The Songs Of West Side Story)**
Bernstein, Leonard *c*
Sondheim, Stephen *l*
Something's coming: *All 4 One* / Boy like that: *Selena* / Maria: *McDonald, Michael/James Ingram/David Pack* / Prologue/Jet song: *Setzer, Brian* / Tonight: *Loggins, Kenny & Wynonna* / Cool: *Austin, Patti/Mervyn Warren/Bruce Hornsby* / Somewhere: *Franklin, Aretha* / America: *Cole, Natalie/Patti Labelle/Sheila E* / I feel pretty: *Little Richard* / One hand one heart: *Campbell, Tevin* / Gee officer Krupke: *Salt 'N' Pepa/Def Jef/Lisa Lopez/Jerky Boys/Paul Rodriguez* / I have a love: *Yearwood, Trisha* / Prelude to the rumble: *Corea, Chick* / Rumble: *Corea, Chick & Steve Vai* / Prelude to somewhere / Somewhere: *Collins, Phil*
09026627072 / May '96 / RCA Victor

☐ **WEST SIDE STORY (Symphonic Dances & On The Waterfront Suite/ Candide Overture) (Los Angeles Philharmonic/Israel Philharmonic/ Vienna Philharmonic Orchestra)**
Bernstein, Leonard *c*
Sondheim, Stephen *l*
Bernstein, Leonard *con*
4479522 / May '96 / Deutsche Grammophon

☐ **WEST SIDE STORY (& Candide) (Te Kanawa, Kiri & Jose Carreras/Marilyn Horne/London Symphony Orchestra & Chorus)**
Bernstein, Leonard *c*
Sondheim, Stephen *l*
Bernstein, Leonard *con*
4479582 / May '96 / Deutsche Grammophon

☐ **WEST SIDE STORY (Starlight Orchestra/Singers)**
Bernstein, Leonard *c*
Sondheim, Stephen *l*
America / Something's coming / Maria / Tonight / I feel pretty / One hand one heart / Rumble / Cool / Boy like that / Somewhere / Finale
QED 088 / Nov '96 / Tring

☐ **WEST SIDE STORY (Symphonic Dances & Fancy Free/Candide) (Baltimore Symphony Orchestra)**
Bernstein, Leonard *c*
Sondheim, Stephen *l*
Zinman, David *con*
4529162 / May '97 / Decca

☐ **WEST SIDE STORY (Arranged By Dave Grusin)**
Bernstein, Leonard *c*
Prologue / Something's coming / Jet song / Maria / Tonight / I feel pretty / One hand one heart / Somewhere / America
N2KD 10021 / 13 Oct '97 / N2K

☐ **WEST SIDE STORY (Te Kanawa, Kiri & Jose Carreras/Tatiana Troyanos)**
Bernstein, Leonard *c*
Bernstein, Leonard *con*
4571992 / Jul '98 / Deutsche Grammophon

☐ **WEST SIDE STORY/MY FAIR LADY (Previn, Andre/Shelly Manne/Leroy Vinnegar)**
Bernstein, Leonard/Frederick Loewe *c*
Sondheim, Stephen/Alan Jay Lerner *l*
CDCOPD 942 / Aug '94 / Contemporary

☐ **WHALES OF AUGUST, THE**
Price, Alan *c*
VCD 47311 / Jan '89 / Varese Sarabande

☐ **WHAT A FEELING (The Rock 'n' Pop Musicals In Concert) (Sonia & Luke Goss/Sinitta/Carl Anthony/Cast)**
Fame / Aquarius / See me feel me/Pinball wizard / Mustang Sally / I finally found someone / I'm every woman / Footloose / Out here on my own / Everything's alright/Jesus Christ Superstar/I don't know how / Summer nights/Greased lightnin'/ Grease/You're the one that I / Kiss from a rose / Maniac / Run to you / Night fever/Jive talking/ Staying alive/You should be dancing / What a feeling
MCCD 287 / 8 Sep '97 / Music Club

☐ **WHAT ABOUT LUV (1990 Cast)**
Marren, Howard *c*
Birkenhead, Susan *l*
CDTER 1171 / Jul '90 / TER

☐ **WHEN SATURDAY COMES**
When Saturday comes: *Elliott, Joe* / Beginning: *Dudley, Anne* / Throwing it all away: *Big Wide World* / Build me up: *Hadley, Tony* / You'll never walk alone: *Gerry & The Pacemakers* / Eyes of blue: *Carrack, Paul* / Born to lose: *Big Wide World* / Seven day weekend: *Gregory, Glenn & Martin Fry* / I've been drinking: *Beck, Jeff & Rod Stewart* / Turning point: *Dudley, Anne* / Nessun Dorma: *Pavarotti* / Boys are back in town: *Thin Lizzy* / Jimmy Jimmy: *Undertones* / If the kids are united: *Sham 69* / Annie's theme: *Dudley, Anne* / Hi ho silver lining: *Beck, Jeff* / Back on my feet again: *Carrack, Paul* / World in motion: *New Order* / Penalty: *Dudley, Anne* / Jimmy's theme: *Elliott, Joe*
5323072 / Mar '96 / Polystar

☐ **WHEN THE WIND BLOWS (Waters, Roger)**
When the wind blows: *Bowie, David* / Facts and figures: *Cornwell, Hugh* / Brazilian: *Genesis* / What have they done: *Squeeze* / Shuffle: *Hardcastle, Paul* / Towers of faith / Russian missile / Hilda's dream / American bomber / Anderson shelter / British submarine / Attack / Fallout / Hilda's hair / Folded flags
CDVIP 132 / Apr '95 / Virgin VIP

☐ **WHEN WE WERE KINGS**
5344622 / Feb '97 / Mercury

☐ **WHERE THE RIVER RUNS BLACK**
Horner, James *c*
VCD 47273 / Jan '89 / Varese Sarabande

☐ **WHILE YOU WERE SLEEPING**
Edelman, Randy *c*
VSD 5627 / Jun '95 / Varese Sarabande

☐ **WHISPERERS, THE**
Barry, John *c*
RCD 10720 / 6 Apr '98 / Rykodisc

☐ **WHISPERS IN THE DARK**
Newman, Thomas *c*
VSD 5387 / Sep '92 / Varese Sarabande

☐ **WHITE PALACE**
Fenton, George *c*
VSD 5289 / Nov '90 / Varese Sarabande

☐ **WHITE SQUALL**
1620402 / Mar '96 / Polydor

☐ **WHO'S AFRAID OF VIRGINIA WOOLF**
North, Alex *c*
TSU 0112 / Jan '95 / Tsunami

☐ **WHO'S AFRAID OF VIRGINIA WOOLF**
North, Alex *c*
VSD 5800 / 20 Oct '97 / Varese Sarabande

☐ **WHO'S THAT GIRL**
Who's that girl: *Madonna* / Causing a commotion: *Madonna* / Look of love: *Madonna* / Twenty four hours / Turn it up / Best thing ever / Can't stop: *Madonna* / El loco loco
9256112 / Feb '95 / Sire

☐ **WICKER MAN, THE (Giovanni, Paul & Magnet)**
BARKED 4CD / 1 Jun '98 / Trunk

☐ **WILD BOYS**
REP 4120-WZ / Aug '91 / Repertoire

☐ **WILD IS THE WIND**
Tiomkin, Dimitri *c*
TSU 0110 / Jan '95 / Tsunami

☐ **WILD THINGS**
Clinton, George *c*
Main title / Gator tango / I had my chance / Outside / Lizard road / Gremlin / After tonight / DFMO / Dom Peridontal / Dead Kelly / Good shooting / Murders for the money / End credits
VSD 5924 / 26 May '98 / Varese Sarabande

☐ **WILD WEST**
Nowhere road: *Earle, Steve* / I ain't ever satisfied: *Honky Tonk Cowboys & Steve Earle* / River: *Honky Tonk Cowboys* / Fearless heart: *Earle, Steve* / No. 29: *Honky Tonk Cowboys & Steve Earle* / Love wore a halo: *Honky Tonk Cowboys & Nanci Griffiths* / Anyone can be somebody's fool: *Honky Tonk Cowboys & Nanci Griffiths* / Akhan naz akhan: *Anaara* / Wild west: *Honky Tonk Cowboys* / Guitars and cadillacs: *Yoakam, Dwight*
COOKCD 056 / May '93 / Cooking Vinyl

☐ **WILDE**
Wiseman, Debbie *c*
Wilde / Wild West / I do need an audience / Almost as beautiful as his mother / Nothing should reveal the body but the body / He loves / Gates thrown open / Love goes round / I will kiss thy mouth Jokanaan / Wounds of love / Constant Constance / Selfish giant

/ Mr. Wilde you must go / Cast into outer darkness / Don't ever change your love / What is the love that dare not speak it's name / Angel at my side / Who has dared to wound thee / De profundis / So wildly worshipped and so madly kissed / Age of silver
MPRCD 001 / Nov '97 / MCI Music

□ WILDSTYLE
Military cut / MC Battle-Busy Bee and Rodney Cee / Basketball throwdown / Fantastic freaks at the Dixie / Subway theme / Coldcrush at the dixie / Busy Bee's limo rap / Cuckoo clocking / Stool rap / Double trouble at the Amphitheatre / Bronx subway rap / Street rap by Busy Bee / Busy Bee at the Amphtheatre / Fantastic freaks at the Amphitheatre / Gangbusters / Rammellzee and Shockdell at the Amphitheatre / Down by law
BEGOCD 001 / 8 Jun '98 / Beyongolia

□ WILLIAM THE CONQUEROR
Scott, John *c*
Scott, John *con*
JSCD 110 / Jan '95 / JOS

□ WILLOW (London Symphony Orchestra/King's College Choir)
Horner, James *c*
Horner, James *con*
Elora Danan / Escape from the tavern / Canyon of mazes / Tir asleen / Willow's theme / Willow's journey begins / Bavmorda's spell is cast / Willow the sorcerer
CDV 2538 / Nov '88 / Virgin

□ WIND AND THE LION, THE
Goldsmith, Jerry *c*
Goldsmith, Jerry *con*
RVF 7005D / Feb '90 / Intrada

□ WINDY CITY (1982 London Cast)
Macaulay, Tony *c*
Vosburgh, Dick *l*
Bowles, A. *con*
Overture: *Orchestra* / Hey hallelujah: *Waterman, Dennis & Company* / Wait till I get you on your own: *Redman, Amanda & Dennis Waterman* / Waltz for Mollie: *Langton, Diane & Reporters* / Saturday: *Allen, Arhlene/Terese Stevens/Tracey Booth & Reporters* / Long night again tonight / No one walks out on me: *Rodgers, Anton* / Saturday (reprise): *Waterman, Dennis/Anton Rodgers/Leonard Lowe* / Windy city: *Waterman, Dennis & Reporters* / Round in circles / I can just imagine it: *Waterman, Dennis & Anton Rodgers* / I can talk to you: *Langton, Diane* / Perfect casting: *Redman, Amanda* / Besinger's poem: *Spinetti, Victor* / Water under the bridge: *Waterman, Dennis* / Windy city (reprise) / Shake the city: *Waterman, Dennis*
CDANGEL 8 / Apr '94 / Angel

□ WINGS OF DESIRE, THE
CDIONIC 2 / Aug '88 / The Fine Line

□ WINGS OF THE DOVE, THE
74321558812 / 7 Jan '98 / Milan

□ WINNER, THE
Main title: *Licht, Daniel* / Meet Joey: *Licht, Daniel* / At the strip joint: *Licht, Daniel* / On the steps/You're going to lose: *Licht, Daniel* / Visiting Liberace: *Licht, Daniel* / Wolf's daddy: *Licht, Daniel* / Pina colada: *Licht, Daniel* / You gotta trust someone: *Licht, Daniel* / Let's go bury dad/I'm cold/Louise returns: *Licht, Daniel* / Louise dies: *Licht, Daniel* / End credits: *Licht, Daniel* / Cha cha no.69: *Altruda, Joey & Cocktail Crew* / Tropical espionage: *Altruda, Joey & Cocktail Crew* / I've been working on you: *Feminine Complex*
RCD 10392 / Jul '97 / Rykodisc

□ WINNIE THE POOH (Singalong)
WD 695324 / Jun '96 / Disney Music & Stories

□ WINTER GUEST
Kamen, Michael *c*
VSD 5895 / 9 Feb '98 / Varese Sarabande

□ WINTER PEOPLE/PRAYER FOR THE DYING (Graunke Symphony Orchestra)
Scott, John *c*
Scott, John *con*
JSCD 102 / Jan '95 / JOS

□ WIRED (Score/Songs)
Poledouris, Basil *c*
I'm a king bee / Soul man / Raven's theme / Two thousand pounds / Still looking for a way / You are so beautiful / I can't turn you loose / You don't know like I know / Choice / Bee / Angel of death
VSD 5237 / Oct '89 / Varese Sarabande

□ WISDOM
Elfman, Danny *c*
VSD 5209 / Jan '89 / Varese Sarabande

□ WIZARD OF OZ, THE (1988 Royal Shakespeare Cast)
Arlen, Harold *c*
Harburg, E.Y. 'Yip' *l*
Edwards, John Owen *con*
Overture / Over the rainbow / Twister / Munchkinland / Munchkinland / If I only had a brain / We're off to see the wizard / If I only had a heart / We're off to see the wizard / If I only had the nerve / We're off to see the wizard / Poppies / Entr'acte / Merry old land of Oz / If I were the King of the forest / Courage / Jitterbug / Winkies' march / Over the rainbow / Ding dong the witch is dead / Finale act 2
CDTER 1165 / 15 Jun '98 / TER

□ WIZARD OF OZ, THE (Highlights) (London Cast)
Arlen, Harold *c*
Harburg, E.Y. 'Yip' *l*
Overture / Over the rainbow / Munchkinland / If only I had a brain / We're off to see the Wizard / If I only had a heart / We're off to see the Wizard (reprise) / If I only had the nerve / Merry old land of Oz / If I were the King of the forest/Courage / Jitterbug / Finale
SHOWCD 003 / Feb '95 / Showtime

□ WIZARD OF OZ, THE (1939 Film Cast)
Arlen, Harold *c*
Harburg, E.Y. 'Yip' *l*
Main title: *MGM Studio Orchestra & Chorus* / Over the rainbow: *Garland, Judy* / Cyclone: *MGM Studio Orchestra* / Come out come out: *Burke, Billie & The Munchkins* / It really was no miracle: *Garland, Judy/Billy Bletcher/The Munchkins* / We thank you very sweetly: *Koziel, Joseph/Frank Cucksey* / Ding-dong the witch is dead: *Munchkins* / As mayor of the Munchkin City: *Bletcher, Billy/Pinto Colveg/J.D. Jewkes* / As coroner I must aver: *Stanton, Harry* / Ding-dong the witch is dead (reprise): *Munchkins* / Lullaby league: *Bridges, Lorraine/Betty Rome/Carol Tevis* / Lollipop Guild: *Bletcher, Billy/Pinto Colveg/Harry Stanton* / We welcome you to Munchkinland: *Munchkins* / Follow the Yellow Brick Road/You're off to see the Wizard: *Garland, Judy/The Munchkins* / If I only had a brain: *Bolger, Ray/Judy Garland* / We're off to see the Wizard (Duo): *Bolger, Ray/Judy Garland* / If I only had a heart: *Haley, Jack* / We're off to see the wizard (Trio): *Garland, Judy/Ray Bolger/Buddy Ebsen* / If I only had the nerve: *Lahr, Bert/Ray Bolger/Jack Haley/Judy Garland* / We're off to see the wizard (Quartet): *Garland, Judy/Ray Bolger/Buddy Ebsen/Bert Lahr* / Optimistic voices: *MGM Studio Orchestra/The Debutantes/The Rhythmettes* / Merry old land of Oz: *Morgan, Frank/Judy Garland/Ray Bolger/Jack Haley/Bert Lahr/T* / If I were King of the Forest: *Lahr, Bert/Judy Garland/Ray Bolger/Jack Haley/Buddy Ebsen* / Jitterbug: *Lahr, Bert/Judy Garland/Ray Bolger/Jack Haley/Buddy Ebsen* / Ding dong Emerald City: *Dalby, Ken/The MGM Studio Chorus* / Delirious escape: *MGM Studio Orchestra* / Delirious escape continued: *MGM Studio Orchestra* / End title: *MGM Studio Orchestra*
CDODEON 7 / Feb '96 / Premier/EMI

□ WOMAN IN RED, THE (Wonder, Stevie)
Wonder, Stevie *c*
Woman in red / It's you: *Wonder, Stevie & Dionne Warwick* / It's more than you / I just called to say I love you / Love light in flight / Moments aren't moments / Weakness: *Wonder, Stevie & Dionne Warwick* / Don't drive drunk
5300302 / Jan '93 / Motown

□ WOMAN OF THE YEAR (Bacall, Lauren & The Original Broadway Cast)
Kander, John *c*
Ebb, Fred *l*
RE 21462 / Sep '97 / Razor & Tie

□ WONDERFUL COUNTRY
North, Alex *c*
TSU 0118 / Jan '95 / Tsunami

□ WONDERFUL TOWN (1953 Broadway Cast)
Bernstein, Leonard *c*
Comden, Betty & Adolph Green *l*
Ferber, Mel *con*
Christopher Street / Ohio / Hundred ways to lose a man / What a waste / Little bit in love / Pass the football / Conversation piece / Quiet girl / Conga / My darlin' Eileen / Swing / Ohio (reprise) / It's love / Vortex ballet / Wrong note rag / It's love (reprise)
SK 48021 / Dec '91 / Sony Broadway

□ WONDERFUL TOWN (1986 London Cast)
Bernstein, Leonard *c*
Comden, Betty & Adolph Green *l*
Overture / Christopher Street / Ohio / Hundred ways to lose a man / What a waste / Little bit in love / Pass the football / Conversation piece / Quiet girl / Conga / My darlin' Eileen / Swing / It's love / Vortex ballet / Wrong note rag / Finale
OCRCD 6011 / Apr '96 / First Night

□ WONDERFUL TOWN (Cast Recording)
Bernstein, Leonard *c*
Comden, Betty & Adolph Green *l*
CDTER2 1223 / Aug '95 / TER

□ WOO
Woo woo (freak out): *MC Lyte* / Money: *Baltimore, Charli* / Bouncin': *Lost Boyz* / Nobody does it better: *Nate Dogg & Warren G* / Get'n it on: *Mona Lisa* / If you love me: *Mint Condition* / T-shirt and panties: *Howard, Adina* / Niggas dun started sumthin': *Howard, Adina* / 357: *Cam'ron* / Let it be: *Allure* / Take a ride: *Heavy D* / I will: *Hines, Simone* / Superman: *DeBarge, Chico* / Searching (for your love): *Brownstone* / Drama in me: *Eightball* / I know you love her: *Too Short*
4911212 / 11 May '98 / Epic

□ WOODLANDERS, THE
Fenton, George *c*
CDDEB 1007 / 2 Feb '98 / Debonair

□ WORKING GIRL
Let the river run: *Simon, Carly* / In love: *Simon, Carly* / Man that got away: *Mounsey, Rob/George Young/Chip Jackson/Grady Tate* / Scar: *Simon, Carly* / Lady in red: *De Burgh, Chris* / Carlotta's heart: *Simon, Carly* / Looking through Katherine's house: *Simon, Carly* / Poor butterfly: *Rollins, Sonny* / I'm so excited: *Pointer Sisters* / Let the river run: *Thomas Choir of Men & Boys*
259767 / Feb '97 / Arista

□ WUTHERING HEIGHTS (The Musical) (Cast/Philharmonic Orchestra & Chorus)
Taylor, Bernard J. *c*
Raine, Nic *con*
Prelude / Wuthering Heights / Cathy / They say he's a gypsy / You were my first love / I see a change in you / One rules my heart / I have no time for them / He's gone / Let her live/I will have my vengeance / Gypsy waltz / I belong to the earth / Coming home to you / Pleasure of your company / If only / Heathcliff's lament / Up here with you
SONGCD 904 / Jul '92 / Silva Classics

X

□ X-FILES (Snow, Mark)
Snow, Mark *c*
9362460792 / Mar '96 / Warner Bros.

□ X-FILES (The Truth & The Lies - Music From The X-Files) (Snow, Mark)
Snow, Mark *c*
9362464482 / Sep '96 / Warner Bros.

□ X-FILES (Fight The Future)
X-Files theme: *Oldfield, Mike* / One: *Filter* / Flowerman: *Tonic* / Walking after you: *Foo Fighters* / Beacon light: *Ween* / Invisible sun: *Aswad & Sting* / Deuce: *Cardigans* / One more murder: *Better Than Ezra* / More than this: *Cure* / Hunter: *Bjork* / 16 horses: *Soul Coughing* / Crystal ship: *X* / Black: *McLachlan, Sarah* / Teotihuscan: *Gallagher, Noel* / X-Files theme: *Dust Brothers*
7559622662 / 8 Jun '98 / Elektra

□ X-FILES (Score) (Snow, Mark)
Snow, Mark *c*
7559622172 / 15 Jun '98 / Elektra

□ XENA - WARRIOR PRINCESS BITTER SUITE
Loduca, Joseph *c*
Sweat hut/Slapped out of it/Xena's in town / Horrible drag/On the edge/Song of the fool / What's still unwritten... / War and peace/Gab is stabbed / Melt into me/Let's go / Dead/Hearts are hurting / Deliverer / Hate is the star (song of torment)/Hearts are hurting / Way out/Love of your love/Passing through
VSD 5918 / 18 May '98 / Varese Sarabande

□ XENA - WARRIOR PRINCESS VOL.1
Le Duca, Joseph *c*
VSD 5750 / Jan '97 / Varese Sarabande

□ XENA - WARRIOR PRINCESS VOL.2
Loduca, Joseph *c*
Main title / At mother's tomb / Xena kicks bacchae butt / Pop goes Xena / Quicksand / Squeal / Sword play / Homeland / Capoiera fight / Many winters ago / Stowaway / You really believe that / Rarrr / Friend / Crucifixion of Xena / To the rescue / Fighting destiny / Talk with Solan / Ballad of Joxer the mighty / Solstice night / First fate / Where as me / More fun and games / Hard core fishing / River wild / Xena is bitten / Restoration / Caught in the current / Callisto becomes a god / Swamp creatures
VSD 5883 / 23 Feb '98 / Varese Sarabande

Y

□ YEAR OF LIVING DANGEROUSLY, THE
Jarre, Maurice *c*
VCD 47222 / '85 / Varese Sarabande

□ YEAR OF THE COMET
Mann, Hummie *c*
VSD 5365 / Nov '92 / Varese Sarabande

□ YELLOW SUBMARINE (Beatles)
Beatles *c*
Yellow submarine / Only a northern song / All you need is love / Hey bulldog / It's all too much / All together now / Pepperland / Sea of time / Sea of holes / Sea of monsters / March of the meanies / Pepperland laid to waste / Yellow submarine in Pepperland
CDPCS 7070 / Aug '87 / Parlophone

□ YEOMAN OF THE GUARD (Dowling, Denis & Richard Lewis/Glyndebourne Festival Choir/Pro Arte Orchestra)
Sullivan, Sir Arthur *c*
Gilbert, W.S. *l*
Sargent, Sir Malcolm *con*
CMS 7644152 / Jan '95 / EMI Classics

□ YEOMAN OF THE GUARD (D'Oyly Carte Opera Chorus/Orchestra)
Sullivan, Sir Arthur *c*
Gilbert, W.S. *l*
Edwards, John Owen *con*
Overture / When a maiden loves she sits and sighs / Tower warders under offer / When our gallant Norman foes / Alas I waver to and fro / Is life a boon / Here's a man of jollity / I have a song to sing o / How say you maiden will you wed / I've jibe and joke and quip and crank / Tis done I am a bride / Were I thy bride / O Sergeant Meryll is it true / Didst thou not o Sergeant Meryll / To thy frraternal care / Prisoner comes to meet his doom / Night has spread her pall once more / Oh a private buffoon is a light hearted loon / Here upon we are both agreed / Free from his fetters grim / Strange adventure / Hark what was that Sir / Man who would woo a fair maid / When a wooer goes a wooing / Rapture rapture / Comes the pretty young guard / Laughing boy / Jealous torment
CDTER2 1195 / Nov '97 / TER

□ YEOMAN OF THE GUARD/TRIAL BY JURY (D'Oyly Carte Opera Chorus/Royal Philharmonic Orchestra/Orchestra Of The Royal Opera House)
Sullivan, Sir Arthur *c*
Gilbert, W.S. *l*
Sargent, Malcolm/I. Godfrey *con*
4173582 / Jan '90 / Decca

□ YEOMAN OF THE GUARD/TRIAL BY JURY (Welsh National Opera Choir/Orchestra)
Sullivan, Sir Arthur *c*
Gilbert, W.S. *l*
Mackerras, Sir Charles *con*
CD 804804 / Feb '96 / Telarc

□ YOU CAN'T HAVE EVERYTHING (& Go Into Your Dance/You'll Never Get Rich/Melody For Two)
You can't have everything: *Faye, Alice* / Long underwear: *Ritz Brothers* / Loveliness of you: *Martin, Tony* / Danger love at work: *Faye, Alice & Louis Prima Orchestra* / You can't have everything: *Ritz Brothers & Louis Primaa* / Afraid to dream: *Faye, Alice & Tony Martin/Don Ameche* / Please pardon us we're in love: *Faye, Alice & Ritz Brothers/Tony Martin/Charles Winniger/Don* / Mammy I'll sing about you: *Jolson, Al* / About a quarter to nine: *Jolson, Al* / Casino de Paris: *Jolson, Al* / She's a latin from Manhattan: *Jolson, Al* / Go into your dance: *Jolson, Al* / September in the rain: *Melton, James* / Shooting the work for Uncle Sam: *Astaire, Fred* / Astairable rag: *Astaire, Fred* / So near and yet so far: *Astaire, Fred* / Wedding cake walk: *Hayworth, Rita*
CD 60014 / Sep '97 / Great Movie Themes

□ YOU GOTTA WALK IT LIKE YOU TALK IT (Becker, Walter & Donald Fagen)
You gotta walk it like you talk it / Flotsam and jetsam / War and peace / Roll back the meaning / You gotta walk it like you talk it / Dog eat dog / Red giant/White dwarf / If it rains
SEECD 357 / Jun '97 / See For Miles

□ YOU ONLY LIVE TWICE
Barry, John *c*
You only live twice: *Sinatra, Nancy* / Capsule in space / Fight at Kobe Dock / Halga / Tanaka's world / Drop in the ocean / Death of Aki / Mountains and sunsets / Wedding / James Bond astronout / Countdown for Blofeld / Bond averts World War III / Twice is the only way to live
CZ 559 / Dec '95 / Premier/EMI

□ YOUNG AMERICANS
Cathode ray: *Sheep On Drugs* / Gave up: *Nine Inch Nails* / Opening titles: *Arnold, David* / Don't let up: *Stereo MC's* / Explosion: *Arnold, David* / Uberman: *Sheep On Drugs* / He's watching me: *Arnold, David* / Hypocrisy is the greatest luxury: *Disposable Heroes Of Hiphoprisy* / Christian's requiem: *Arnold, David* / Stop the confusion: *Le Blanc, Keith & Tim Simenon* / 15 minutes of fame: *Sheep On Drugs* / Leaving London: *Arnold, David* / Play dead: *Arnold, David & Bjork*
IMCD 220 / Mar '96 / Island

□ YOUNG BESS
Rozsa, Miklos *c*
Rozsa, Miklos *con*
PCD 133 / Jan '95 / Prometheus

□ YOUNG GUNS II (Blaze Of Glory) (Bon Jovi, Jon)
Billy get your guns / Blaze of glory / Santa Fe / Never say die / Bang a drum / Guano City / Miracle / Blood money / Justice in the barrel / You really got me now / Dyin' ain't much of a livin'
8464732 / Aug '90 / Vertigo

□ YOUNG INDIANA JONES CHRONICLES I, THE (Paris, 1916/Verdun, 1916) (Munich Symphony Orchestra)
McNeely, Joel *c*
McNeely, Joel *con*
VSD 5381 / May '93 / Varese Sarabande

□ YOUNG INDIANA JONES CHRONICLES II, THE (German East Africa, 1916/London, 1916/The Congo, 1917) (Munich Symphony Orchestra)
McNeely, Joel *c*
McNeely, Joel *con*
VSD 5391 / Sep '93 / Varese Sarabande

□ YOUNG INDIANA JONES CHRONICLES III, THE (The Mystery Of The Blues/The Scandal Of 1920)
McNeely, Joel *c*
McNeely, Joel *con*
Rhapsody in blue / Swanee / Somebody loves me / Sounds like perfection / Scandal walk / Sweetie Dear / My handyman / 12th Street rag / Blue horizon / Tiger rag / I can't believe that you're in love with me / Twinkle Dixie
VSD 5401 / Jun '93 / Varese Sarabande

☐ YOUNG INDIANA JONES
CHRONICLES IV, THE (Ireland 1916/
Northern Italy 1918) (Munich
Philharmonic Film Orchestra/West
Australian Philharmonic Orchestra)
Rosenthal, Laurence/Joel McNeely c
Rosenthal, Laurence/Joel McNeely con
VSD 5421 / Jan '95 / Varese Sarabande

☐ YOUNG LIONS, THE/THE EARTH IS
MINE
Friedhofer, Hugo c
Friedhofer, Hugo con
VSD 25403 / Jun '93 / Varese Sarabande

☐ YOUNG POISONERS'S HANDBOOK,
THE
8444292 / Jan '96 / Deram

☐ YOUNG SOUL REBELS
BLRCD 10 / Sep '91 / Big Life

☐ YOU'RE UNDER ARREST
Tani, Kow c
AM 5 / Nov '96 / Animanga

☐ ZABRISKIE POINT
Heart beat pig meat: Pink Floyd / Brother Mary:
Kaleidoscope / Dark star (excerpt): Grateful Dead /
Crumbling land: Pink Floyd / Tennessee waltz: Page,
Patti / Sugar babe: Youngbloods / Love scene:
Garcia, Jerry / I wish I were a single girl again:
Holcomb, Roscoe / Mickey's tune: Kaleidoscope /
Dance of death: Fahey, John / Come in Number 51
your time is up: Pink Floyd / Outtakes
R233642 / 20 Oct '97 / Premier/EMI

☐ ZED AND TWO NOUGHTS, A (Zoo
Orchestra)
Nyman, Michael c
Nyman, Michael con
Angelfish decay / Car crash / Time lapse / Prawn
watching / Bisocosis populi / Swan rot / Delft waltz /
Up for crabs / Vermeer's wife / Venus de Milo / Lady
in the red hat / L'escargot
CDVE 54 / Feb '90 / Virgin

☐ ZELLY AND ME
Donaggio, Pino c
VCD 70422 / Jan '89 / Varese
Sarabande

☐ ZERO PATIENCE
Schellenberg, Glenn c
887971 / Jan '95 / Milan

☐ ZIEGFELD FOLLIES (1946 Film Cast)
Main title / Here's to the girls / Bring on those
wonderful men / We will meet again in Honolulu / Liza
(all the clouds'll roll away) / Libiamo / Heart of mine /
Love / If swing goes I go too / Limehouse blues /
Interview / Babbitt and the bromide / There's beauty
everywhere
CDODEON 3 / Feb '96 / Premier/EMI

☐ ZIEGFELD FOLLIES OF 1934 (Cast
Recording)
AEICD 039 / May '98 / AEI

☐ ZORBA (Broadway Cast)
Kander, John c
Ebb, Fred l
ZDM 7646652 / Apr '93 / EMI Classics

☐ ZOYA/THE YOUNG GUARD (Suites
From The Film Scores) (Minsk Chamber
Choir/Byelorussian Radio & TV
Symphony Orchestra)
Shostakovich, Dmitry c
Mnatsakanov, Walter con
RDCD 10002 / Jul '96 / Russian Disc

☐ ZULU (& Other Themes)
Barry, John c
Barry, John con
Istanchiwania / News of the massacre / First Zulu /
Wagons over / Durnford's horses arrive and depart /
Zulu's final appearance and salute / VC roll/Men of
Harlech / Elizabeth theme / From Russia with love /
Four in the morning
FILMCD 022 / Nov '89 / Silva Screen

☐ ZULU DAWN (Royal Philharmonic
Orchestra)
Bernstein, Elmer c
CD 0201 / Jan '89 / Silva Screen

Collections

☐ **007 CLASSICS (London Symphony Orchestra)**
James Bond / Thunderball / Goldfinger / From Russia With Love / Diamonds Are Forever / You Only Live Twice / Look of love / On Her Majesty's Secret Service / Man With The Golden Gun
EDL 25132 / Dec '89 / Edel

☐ **18 WONDERFUL FILM THEMES**
Arthur's theme (the best you can do) / She's out of my life / Hill street blues / Nights in white satin / Bolero / Woman / Only he has the power to move me / Chariots of fire / Thorn birds - love theme / Way he makes me feel / Cacharpaya / Derry air / Winds of war / Educating Rita / Country diary of an Edwardian lady / Jewel in the crown / Terms of endearment / Good the bad and the ugly
EMPRCD 516 / Jul '94 / Emporio

☐ **20 CLASSIC SCI-FI THEMES (Channel X)**
X-Files / Close Encounters Of The Third Kind / Star Wars / ET / Twilight Zone / Doctor Who / Tomorrow People / Blakes 7 / Eve of the war / Dune / Alien / Bladerunner / Star Trek / Quantum Leap / Red Dwarf / Space 1999 / Lost In Space / Time Tunnel / UFO / 2001: A Space Odyssey
SUMCD 4098 / Feb '97 / Summit

☐ **20 GREAT WESTERN THEMES**
EMPRCD 514 / Jul '94 / Emporio

☐ **32 MOVIE & TV HITS**
24005 / Mar '95 / Music

☐ **40 FAMOUS SONGS FROM THE MUSICALS (Sinatra, Frank)**
You'll never walk alone / Girl that I marry / Begin the beguine / September song / Oh what a beautiful mornin' / People will say we're in love / Song is you / You're lonely and I'm lonely / It's a lovely day tomorrow / Without a song / I'll be seeing you / World is in my arms / Just one of those things / You do something to me / Ol' man river / Night and day / You are love / They didn't believe me / Love me or leave me / There's no business like show business / 'S wonderful / Embraceable you / Kiss me again / Where or when / All the things you are / If I loved you / Someone to watch over me / These foolish things / Why shouldn't I / Bess oh where's my Bess / They say it's wonderful / Soliloquy / Lost in the stars / Falling in love with love / You make me feel so young / I'll string along with you / I've got my love to keep me warm / On the sunny side of the street / Who told you I cared / I don't know why (I just do)
DBG 53057 / Jul '97 / Double Gold

☐ **40 YEARS OF BBC TV THEMES (Paramor, Norrie)**
Television march / Ordinary copper / March from a little suite / Today's tonight / Maigret theme / Watermill / Marching strings / Music from the movies / Calypso / Ciccolino / Moonlight and roses / Snowdrops and raindrops / Last of the summer wine theme / Come dancing theme
EMPRCD 633 / Jun '96 / Emporio

☐ **50 BROADWAY SHOWSTOPPERS**
Night they invented champagne / Gigi / As long as he needs me / If ever I would leave you / Bali hai / Wouldn't it be lovely / Superstar / You're just in love / How to handle a woman / Rain in Spain / Tonight / Some enchanted evening / Aquarius / People / I have dreamed / It's a lovely day today / Mame / So in love / Don' what comes naturally / My favourite things / Oh what a beautiful morning / Matchmaker matchmaker / Camelot / Climb every mountain / If I were a rich man / Hello young lovers / Thank heaven for little girls / I don't know how to love him / Get me to the church on time / Tradition / Big spender / Something wonderful / Food glorious food / Somewhere / Maria / Wonderful guy / Wunderbar / I feel pretty / June is bustin' out all over / Shall we dance / Flash bang wallop / Half a sixpence / I love Paris / Out of my dreams / Anything you can do / Day by day / C'est magnifique / Good morning starshine / Surrey with a fringe on top
330442 / Mar '97 / Hallmark

☐ **50 CLASSIC TV THEMES**
Bonanza / Wagon Train / Alias Smith and Jones / Emergency Ward 10 / Angels / Mission Impossible / Johnny Staccato / Colditz / Warship / Dad's Army / Saint / Persuaders / Department S / Onedin Line / Poldark / Pallisers / No Honestly / Liverbirds / Likely Lads / Ironside / Kojak / Columbo / Protectors / Brothers / Seven Faces Of A Woman / Hawaii Five-O / McCloud / Owen MD / Dr. Kildare / Dr. Finlay's Casebook / Today / On The Move / Nationwide / Virginian / Deputy / Rawhide / Coronation Street / Crossroads / Avengers / Callan / Van Der Valk / Thunderbirds / Star Trek / Upstairs Downstairs / Duchess Of Duke Street / When The Boat Comes In / Softly Softly / Sweeney / Dixon Of Dock Green / Z Cars
330432 / Mar '97 / Hallmark

☐ **50 FAMOUS SONGS FROM THE MOVIES (Sinatra, Frank)**
Too romantic / Say it / This is the beginning of the end / April played the fiddle / I haven't time to be a millionaire / Call of the canyon / I could make you care / Our love affair / I'd know you anywhere / Do you know why / Not so long ago / You lucky people / It's always you / Dolores / I'll never let a day pass by / Love me as I am / How about you / Poor you / I'll take Tallulah / Last call for love / Be careful it's my heart / You'll never know / Night and day / You make me feel so young / I'm in the mood for love / Sunday Monday or always / If you please / I couldn't sleep a wink last night / Lovely way to spend an evening / Music stopped / White Christmas / I begged her / What makes the sunset / I fall in love too easily / Stormy weather / Charm of you / Embraceable you / I should care / Friend of yours / Over the rainbow / House I live in / You are too beautiful / I only have eyes for you / Paradise / All through the day / Two hearts are better than one / That old black magic / Somewhere in the night / Five minutes more / Somebody loves me
DBG 53056 / Jul '97 / Double Gold

☐ **50 YEARS OF CLASSIC HORROR FILM MUSIC**
Omen / She / Rosemary's Baby / Dr. Jekyll And Mr. Hyde / King Kong / Vampire Lovers / Fear In The Night / Exorcist 2 / Hellraiser / Dr. Jekyll And Sister Hyde
FILMCD 017 / Nov '89 / Silva Screen

☐ **100 YEARS OF CINEMA GOLD**
D2CD 4025 / Jun '95 / Deja Vu

☐ **100 YEARS OF FILM MUSIC**
09026683162 / Jan '96 / RCA Victor

☐ **100 YEARS OF THE MOVIES (BBC Concert Orchestra)**
ASTCD 4001 / Nov '96 / Astrion Audio

A

☐ **A-Z OF BRITISH TV THEMES VOL.1 (1960's/70's)**
Avengers: *Johnson, Laurie* / Captain Scarlet: *Gray, Barry* / Catweazle: *Dicks, Ted* / Champions: *Hatch, Tony* / Crossroads: *Hatch, Tony* / Dad's Army: *Taverner, Perry* / Danger Man / Department S / Doctor In The House / Dr. Who: *Grainer, Ron* / Emmerdale Farm: *Hatch, Tony* / Fireball XL5 / Forsyth Saga / Hadleigh: *Hatch, Tony* / Hancock: *Scott, Derek* / Maigret: *Grainer, Ron* / Man In A Suitcase: *Grainer, Ron* / No Hiding Place: *Johnson, Laurie* / Please Sir: *Fonteyn, Sam* / Power Game / Return Of The Saint: *Dee, Martin* / Saint / Sportsnight: *Hatch, Tony* / Steptoe And Son: *Grainer, Ron* / Stingray: *Gray, Barry* / Thank Your Lucky Stars: *Knight, Peter* / Thunderbirds: *Gray, Barry* / Top Secret / Z Cars
PLAY 004 / Oct '92 / Play It Again

☐ **A-Z OF BRITISH TV THEMES VOL.2**
All Creatures Great And Small / Angels / Bergerac / Animal Magic / Bread / BBC Cricket / Auf Wiedersehen Pet / Doctor Who / Grandstand / Four Feather Falls / Juke Box Jury / Liver Birds / Man About The House / New Avengers / Persuaders / Supercar / Tales Of The Unexpected / Van Der Valk / Upstairs Downstairs / Whatever Happened To The Likely Lads
PLAY 006 / Jul '94 / Play It Again

☐ **A-Z OF BRITISH TV THEMES VOL.3**
Blake's 7 / Blott / Dangerfield / Lovejoy / Dempsey and Makepeace / Doctor Finlay's casebook / Emergency Ward 10 / Just William / Terry and June / Newcomers / Poirot / Professionals / Ruth Rendell mysteries / Shoestring / Sexton Blake / This is your life / When the boat comes in / Ski Sunday / World of sport / Wycliffe
PLAY 010 / Apr '96 / Play It Again

☐ **A-Z OF BRITISH TV THEMES VOL.4**
PLAY 009 / Nov '97 / Play It Again Sam

☐ **ACADEMY AWARD WINNERS & NOMINATIONS (London Theatre Orchestra)**
Gould, Alec *con*
West Side Story medley / Hello Dolly medley / Music Man medley / Jesus Christ Superstar medley / Paint Your Wagon medley / Boy Friend medley / Fiddler On The Roof medley / Sound Of Music medley
3036000402 / Feb '97 / Carlton

☐ **ACTION COLLECTION - JEAN CLAUDE VAN DAMME**
VSD 5691 / Nov '96 / Varese Sarabande

☐ **ACTION MOVIE THEME COLLECTION, THE (Montague Orchestra)**
MACCD 369 / 30 Mar '98 / Autograph

☐ **ACTION MOVIE THEMES**
We don't need another hero / I can dream about you / Delta force theme / Take my breath away / Ride of the Valkyries / Brains and trains / It's a long road / Eye of the tiger / Love theme / Glory of love / When the going get tough the tough get going / One vision / Voice of America's son's
22527 / Dec '95 / Music

☐ **ACTION THEMES (Power Pack Orchestra)**
Cagney and Lacey / Rocky 3 / Magnum PI / Great escape / Superman / Crazy like a fox / 633 Squadron / Hill Street Blues / Reamington Steele / Hunter / Operation crossbow / Sweeney / Mike Hammer / Miami Vice / Longest day / Bond theme / Hawaii Five-O / New avengers / Bergerac / Bill / Starsky and Hutch / A-Team / TJ Hooker / Shoestring / Dempsey and Makepeace / Knots landing / Scarecrow and Mrs. King / Hart to Hart / Where eagles dare / Indiana Jones
CC 8247 / Nov '94 / EMI

☐ **AIN'T IT THE TRUTH (Lena Horne At MGM - Soundtrack Anthology) (Horne, Lena)**
Just one of those things / Spring / Ain't it the truth / Life's full of consequence / Honey in the honeycomb / Honeysuckle rose / You're so indiff'rent / Jericho / Brazilian boogie / Somebody loves me / Tete a tete at tea time / Potato salad / Paper doll / Trembling leaf / Love / Can't help loving dat man / Why was I born / Bill / Where or when / Lady is a tramp / Baby come out of the clouds / If you can dream / You got looks
CDODEON 32 / 15 Sep '97 / Soundtracks

☐ **ALICE FAYE (Faye, Alice)**
Got my mind on music / I could use a dream / Halfmoon on the hudson / Think twice / This is where I came in / Carry me back to ol'Virginny / I've taken a fancy to you / Alexander's ragtime band / Remember / Blue skies / Are you in the mood for mischief / Go in and out the window / I'm just wild about Harry / I'm sorry I made you cry / I'm always chasing rainbows / I'll see you in my dreams / I never knew heaven could speak / There'll be other nights / Get out and get under / Chica chica boom chic / It's all in a lifetime / Where you are / Tropical magic / Romance and rhumba / Man with the lollypop song
CD 60011 / Jun '97 / Great Movie Themes

☐ **ALL MY LOVE**
Flower duet from Lakme: *Garrett, Lesley* / Time to say goodbye: *Brightman, Sarah & Andrea Bocelli* / Pie Jesu: *Brightman, Sarah & Jose Carreras* / Phantom of the opera: *Brightman, Sarah & Jose Carreras* / Amigos para sempre: *Brightman, Sarah & Jose Carreras* / Miss Sarajevo: *Pavarotti & U2/Brian Eno* / Barcelona: *Mercury, Freddie & Montserrat Caballe* / Miserere: *Zucchero & Pavarotti* / Wild horses: *John, Elton & Luciano Pavarotti* / Love changes everything: *Ball, Michael* / Music of the night: *Streisand, Barbra & Michael Crawford* / Abide with me: *Inspirational Choir* / En aranjuez con tu amor: *Carreras, Jose* / Nessun dorma: *3 Tenors* / Amazing Grace: *Collins, Judy* / Don't cry for me Argentina: *Covington, Julie & Madonna/Elaine Paige* / O mi babbino caro: *Covington, Julie & Madonna/ Elaine Paige* / Somewhere: *Te Kanawa, Dame Kiri* / Show me how to love you: *Cura, Jose & Sarah Brightman* / Ave Maria: *Paige, Elaine*
9548359482 / 20 Oct '97 / Warner Bros.

☐ **ALL THAT JAZZ (The Best Of Ute Lemper) (Lemper, Ute)**
4589312 / 9 Feb '98 / Decca

☐ **ALWAYS CHASING RAINBOWS (The Young Judy Garland) (Garland, Judy)**
All God's chillun got rhythm / Buds won't bud / Cry baby cry / Embraceable you / End of the rainbow / Everybody sing / FDR Jones / I'm always chasing rainbows / I'm just wild about Harry / I'm nobody's baby / In between / It never rains but it pours / Oceans apart / Our love affair / Over the rainbow / Sleep my baby sleep / Stompin' at the Savoy / Sweet sixteen / Swing Mister Charlie / Ten pins in the sky / You can't have everything / Zing went the strings of my heart
CD AJA 5093 / Jul '92 / Living Era

☐ **AMERICAN TELEVISION THEMES VOL. 1**
Caine, Daniel *con*
Midnight caller / LA Law / Twin Peaks / Star Trek: the next generation / North and South / Hooperman / Murder she wrote / Spenser for hire / 21 Jump Street / Newhart / Hunter / Bronx Zoo / Sonny Spoon
TVPMCD 400 / Mar '91 / Primetime

☐ **AMERICAN TELEVISION THEMES VOL. 2**
Caine, Daniel *con*
Thirtysomething / Falcon Crest / Doogie Howser MD / Highway to Heaven / Quantum Leap / McGyver / Slap Maxwell Story / Head of the class / Alf / Wiseguy / Nutt House / Remington Steele / Men / Bring 'em back alive
TVPMCD 401 / Mar '91 / Primetime

☐ **AMERICAN TELEVISION THEMES VOL. 3**
Caine, Daniel *con*
Law and order / Capital News / Sledgehammer / China Beach / BL Stryker / Days and Nights of Molly Dodd / Parker Lewis Can't Lose / Young Riders / Night Court / Stingray / Houston Knights / Over My Dead Body / Buck James / Top of the Hill
TVPMCD 404 / Oct '91 / Primetime

☐ **AMERICAN TELEVISION'S GREATEST HITS**
A-Team / Airwolf / Barnaby Jones / Battlestar Galactica / Baywatch / Cheers / Beverly Hills 90210 / Cagney and Lacey / Cosby Show / Falcon Crest / Knight Rider / Quantum leap / Roseanne / Twin Peaks / Incredible Hulk / Waltons / Equalizer / Hunter / Little house on the prairie / Melrose Place / North and South / Taxi / V
TVPMCD 804 / Aug '94 / Primetime

☐ **ANOTHER OPENIN', ANOTHER SHOW - BROADWAY'S OVERTURES**
Engel, Lehman *con*
SK 53540 / Jul '94 / Sony Classical

☐ **APOCALYPSE NAM (The 10,000 Day War)**
Apocalypse Now / Vietnam Texas / Deer Hunter / Airwolf / Platoon Leader / First Blood / Purple Hearts / Missing in Action / Missing in Action III / Platoon
CIN 22042 / Jan '95 / Silva Screen

☐ **ARGENTO VIVO I**
MAF 170D / Jan '93 / Intrada

☐ **ARGENTO VIVO II**
MAF 185D / Jan '92 / Intrada

☐ **ARNOLD (Great Music From The films Of Arnold Schwarzenegger)**
VSD 5398 / Jul '93 / Varese Sarabande

☐ **AROUND THE MUSICAL WORLD**
SHOWCD 057 / 18 May '98 / Showtime

☐ **AS TIME GOES BY (Classic Movie Love Songs) (Mancini, Henry & Mancini Pops Orchestra)**
RD 60974 / Jul '92 / RCA

☐ **ASPECTS OF BROADWAY VOL.3 (Orchestra Of The Americas)**
Freeman, Paul *con*
I feel pretty / Maria / Something's coming / Tonight / One hand one heart / Cool / America / Overture / Send in the clowns / Cotton blossom / Make believe / Valon's theme / Ol' man river / Misery / Can't help lovin' dat man / You are love / Why do I love you / Hey fellah / Ol' man river / Clara / Woman is a sometime thing / Summertime / I got plenty o' nuttin' / Bess you is my woman / Oh I can't sit down / There's a boat dat's leavin' soon for New York / It ain't necessarily so / Oh Lord I'm on my way
SION 18303 / Jul '97 / Sion

☐ **ASPECTS OF BROADWAY VOL.4 (Orchestra Of The Americas)**
Freeman, Paul *con*
Tomorrow / It's the hard knock life / Maybe / Let's go to the movies / Easy street / I don't need anything but you / We got Annie / Finale - Tomorrow / I hope I get it / At the ballet / One / What I did for love / At the end of the day / I dreamed a dream / Master of the house / On my own / Do you hear the people sing / La cafes aux follies / We are what we are / With you on my arm / Song on the sand / Best of times / They're playing my song / Just for tonight / If he really knew me / Right / 42nd Street / Some people / Everything's coming up roses / Let me entertain you / You'll never get away from me / Together wherever we go / Small world / Mr. Goldstone / All I need is the girl
SION 18304 / Jul '97 / Sion

☐ **ASPECTS OF BROADWAY VOL.5 (Orchestra Of The Americas)**
Freeman, Paul *con*
Fiddler on the roof / Matchmaker / If I were a rich man / Sunrise sunset / Wedding dance / To life / Tradition / People / Don't rain on my parade / Who are you now / Music makes me dance / You are woman I am man / People / Yankee doodle / Harrigan / Mary's a grand old name / You're a grand old flag / Mame / My best girl / Open a new window / If he walked into my life / We need a little Christman / Man of La Mancha / Dulcinea / Little bird little bird / Little gossip / Quest / Impossible dream / Oliver / Where is love / I'd do anything / As long as he needs me / Consider yourself / Wunderbar / Why can't you behave / Another op'nin' another show / Always true to you in fashion / Were thine that special face / I sing of love / So in love
SION 18305 / Jul '97 / Sion

☐ **ASPECTS OF BROADWAY VOL.7 (Orchestra Of The Americas)**
Freeman, Paul *con*
Farmer and the cowman / Oklahoma / People will say we're in love / Out of my dreams / Oh what a beautiful morning / Pore Jud is daid / Surrey with the fringe on top / Many a new day / Kansas City / Farmer dance / I can't say no / Carousel waltz / June is bustin' out all over / You'll never walk alone / Mr. Snow / If I loved you / Real nice clambake / What's the use wond'rin' / If I loved you / You are beautiful / Grant Avenue / Love look away / Chop suey / I am going to like it here / Like a God / Don't marry me / I enjoy being a girl / Sunday / Grand night for singing / It might as well be Spring / That's for me / All I owe loway / With a song in my heart
SION 18307 / Jul '97 / Sion

☐ **ASPECTS OF BROADWAY VOL.8 (Orchestra Of The Americas)**
Freeman, Paul *con*
Luck be a lady / Fugue for tinhorns / Guys and dolls / I've never been in love before / Bushel and a peck / Sit down you're rockin' the boat / Caravan / Solitude / Do nothin' 'til you hear from me / Mood indigo / Sophisticated lady / I don't mean a thing / Stranger in paradise / Baubles bangles and beads / He's in love / Before the parade passes by / Dancing / Ribbons down my back / Hello dolly / Take a little one-step / I want to be happy / Too many rings around Rosie / No no Nanette / Tea for two / Peach on the beach / Can can / I love Paris / Never give anything away / C'est magnifique / Come along with me / It's alright with me / Allez vous-en Montmart / Silk stockings / Satin and silk / All of you / Hail Bibinski
SION 18308 / Jul '97 / Sion

☐ **ASTERIX AU CINEMA**
3017682 / Jan '97 / Wotre Music

☐ **ASTRAL MEDITATION**
74321329622 / May '96 / Milan

☐ **AT THE FLICKS (Formby, George)**
I could make a good living at that / Baby / It's in the air / They can't fool me / Goodnight litte fellow goodnight / Pardon me / I'm making headway now / I could not let the stable down / I wish I was back on the farm / Count your blessings and smile / Oh don't the wind blow cold / Emperor of Lancashire / You're everything to me / You can't go wrong in these / I

AT THE FLICKS
COLLECTIONS
R.E.D. CD CATALOGUE

played on my Spanish guitar / I'd do it with a smile / Barmaid at the Rose and Crown / Get crackin' / Home Guard blues / Bell bottom George / Serves you right / Got to get your photo in the press / Hillbilly Willie / Unconditional surrender
PLCD 554 / Nov '96 / President

☐ **AT THE MOVIES**
11816 / Jul '95 / Music

☐ **AT THE THEATRE (Mantovani)**
CDSIV 6108 / Jul '95 / Horatio Nelson

☐ **AUDREY HEPBURN - FAIR LADY OF THE SCREEN (Dobson, Rudi)**
Audrey Hepburn - Fair lady of the screen / Belgian rock / Fight for time / Dark city / Broadway melody / Little dog called "Mr Famouse" / Sister Audrey / Moon river / Breakfast at Tiffany's / Charade / My fair lady (Medley) / Desert anthem / Lac Genieve (Lake Geneva) / Moon river (Requiem)
PCOM 1136 / Aug '94 / President

☐ **AUSTRALIAN TV'S GREATEST HITS**
Neighbours / Prisoner Cell Block H / Sullivans / Sons and daughters / Anzacs / Skippy / Paul Hogan show / Young Doctors / Chopper Squad / Country Practice / Carson's Law
FILMCD 028 / Nov '88 / Silva Screen

B

☐ **BACHELOR IN PARADISE (Cocktail Classics From MGM Films)**
Bachelor In Paradise Theme / Bossa Nova Bessie / Over the rainbow / Sunday in New York Theme / Ol' man river / How about you / Love is oh so easy / Aruba Liberace / I've got you under my skin / I've got rhythm / Temptation / Girl From Ipanema / Fashion Show / Wonderful World Of The Brothers Grimm Theme / Appreciation / Dancing in the dark / Coffee time
8219632 / 13 Oct '97 / Premier/EMI

☐ **BACK TO BROADWAY (Streisand, Barbra)**
Some enchanted evening / Everybody says don't / Music of the night / Speak low / As if we never said goodbye / Children will listen / I have a love / I've never been in love before / Luck be a lady / With one look / Man I love / Move on
4738802 / Jun '93 / Columbia

☐ **BADMUTHAS (18 Original Black Movie Hits)**
Trouble man: Gaye, Marvin / Shaft: *Hayes, Isaac* / Are you man enough: *Four Tops* / Love doctor: *Jackson, Millie* / Sweet Sweetback's Theme: *Earth, Wind & Fire* / Foxy Brown: *Hutch, Willie* / Superfly: *Mayfield, Curtis* / Cleopatra Jones: *Simon, Joe & The Mainstreeters* / Mack: *Hutch, Willie* / Slaughter: *Brown, James* / Time is tight: *Booker T & The MG's* / Across 10th Street: *Womack, Bobby & Peace* / Pusherman: *Mayfield, Curtis* / Cornbread: *Blackbyrds* / Black enough: *Moore, Melba* / Down and out in New York City: *Brown, James* / Truck Turner: *Hayes, Isaac* / Savage: *Julian, Don*
MUSCD 039 / 6 Oct '97 / MCI Music

☐ **BATMAN/TV THEMES (Ventures)**
Batman Theme / Zocko / Cape / Get Smart Theme / Man from UNCLE / Hot Line / Joker's Wild / Up Up And Away / Green Hornet 1966 / 00-711 / Vampcamp / Secret Agent Man / Charlie's Angels / Medical Centre / Star Trek / Streets Of San Francisco / Starsky and Hutch / Baretta's Theme / Hawaii Five-0 / SWAT / Police Story / MASH / Policewoman / Nadia's Theme (The Young And The Restless)
C5HCD 653 / Jun '97 / See For Miles

☐ **BATMANIA (Songs Inspired By The Batman TV Series)**
Batman theme: *Hefti, Neal* / Story of Batman: *West, Adam* / Capture: *Meredith, Burgess* / Batman to the rescue: *Baker, LaVern* / Batman theme: *Hirt, Al* / Ratman and Bobin in the clipper caper: *Bros Four* / Batman a go go: *Combo Kings* / Miranda: *West, Adam* / That man: *Lee, Peggy* / Batman theme: *Allan, Dave & The Arrows* / Joker is wild: *Jan & Dean* / Riddler: *Gorshin, Frank* / Escape: *Meredith, Burgess* / Batman and Robin: *West, Adam* / Batman theme: *Royal Scottish National Orchestra*
VSD 5821 / 20 Apr '98 / Varese Sarabande

☐ **BBC RADIO TOP TUNES (Paramor, Norrie Radio Orchestra)**
Sweet and gentle / Sky at night / Archers / Sleepy shores / Midweek / Medley / Onedin Line / Film '74 / I wish I knew how it would feel to be free / Forsythe Saga / Lotus Eaters / Softly Softly / Medley / Match Of The Day
EMPRCD 660 / Oct '96 / Emporio

☐ **BEAT AT CINECITTA VOL.1 (1960/70s Italian Erotic Film Score Music)**
EFA 043822 / Jun '97 / Crippled Dick Hot Wax

☐ **BEAT AT CINECITTA VOL.2 (1960/1970s Italian Erotic Film Score Music)**
Mr. Dante Fontana / Babylon I'm coming / Per le strade di Roma / Doppia Faccia / Shake per un divorzio / Soho / Bada Caterina / Easy dreamer / Love war call / London streets / Sensi / Party al piper / Supercoipo shake / Abigaille / Kiss kiss bang bang / Notti caldi
EFA 043852 / 20 Oct '97 / Crippled Dick Hot Wax

☐ **BEAUTIFUL HOLLYWOOD (Cincinnati Pops Orchestra)**
Kunzel, Erich *con*
Forrest Gump / River Runs Through It / Robert and Mary / Jerry Maguire / Ludlows / You must love me / Bridges Of Madison County / Colours of the wind / On Earth as it is in Heaven / Free Willy / Forever Young / Cinema Paradiso / Rudy / Chaplin / Grumpier Old Men / Act of faith / Schindler's List / Gettysburg
CD 80440 / 6 Oct '97 / Telarc

☐ **BEST OF ARNOLD SCHWARZENEGGER, THE (City Of Prague Philharmonic Orchestra)**
Conan the Barbarian / Conan the Destroyer / Predator / Terminator / Terminator II / Kindergarten Cop / Twins / Junior / Running Man / Commando / Red Heat / Raw Deal / Total Recall
FILMCD 164 / Oct '95 / Silva Screen

☐ **BEST OF BOND, THE**
Goldeneye / James Bond Theme From Dr No / View To A Kill / Man With The Golden Gun / Never Say Never Again / Live And Let Die / All Time High / Thunderball / From Russsia With Love / License To Kill / Living Daylights / For Your Eyes Only / Theme From Casino Royale / Moonraker / You Only Live Twice / Mr Kiss Kiss Bang Bang / Diamonds Are Forever / Goldfinger
CD 6070 / Apr '97 / Music

☐ **BEST OF BRITISH TV MUSIC, THE**
London's burning / Forever green / Professionals / Agatha Christie's Poirot / To have and to hold / Upstairs downstairs / Thomas and Sarah / Gentle touch / Bouquet of barbed wire / Partners in crime / Budgie / Wish me luck as you wave me goodbye / Love for Lydia / Lillie / Black beauty / Dempsey and Makepeace
CDSTM 3 / May '94 / Soundtrack Music

☐ **BEST OF BROADWAY MUSICALS, THE**
Best things in life are free / I've grown accustomed to her face / Anything you can do / Try to remember / Time heals everything / Sit down you're rockin' the boat / People will say we're in love / Impossible dream / People / I get a kick out of you / Younger than springtime / Before the parade passes by
SHOWCD 043 / Jan '97 / Showtime

☐ **BEST OF BROADWAY, THE (The Revues)**
Ain't misbehavin' / Doin' the new low down/I must have that man / You're lucky to me / Heat wave / Easter parade / Harlem on my mind / Shakin' the blues away / Oh how I hate to get up in the morning / I left my heart at the stage door canteen / Something I dreamed last night / Exactly like you / My man / Second hand rose / Pretty girl is like a melody / Always / This is the Missus / Something to remember you by / Sweet music / That's the kind of baby for me / South American way / Anatole of Paris
PASTCD 7813 / 24 Nov '97 / Flapper

☐ **BEST OF CABARET, THE**
You're never fully dressed without a smile: *Graae, Jason* / Manhattan: *Haran, Mary Cleere* / Little bit in love: *Mayes, Sally* / Who are you now: *Kuhn, Judy* / If I were a belle: *Callaway, Liz* / There but for you go I: *Beechman, Laurie* / Too late now: *Gravitte, Debbie Shapiro* / There's a change in me: *Graff, Randy* / Time heals everything: *O'Hara, Paige* / Don't like goodbyes: *Kaye, Judy*
VSD 5854 / 2 Feb '98 / Varese Sarabande

☐ **BEST OF CHINESE FILM MUSIC, THE**
VSD 5455 / Jan '95 / Varese Sarabande

☐ **BEST OF GENE KELLY, THE (Kelly, Gene)**
Singin' in the rain / You were meant for me / All I do is dream / Moses / Broadway ballet / You are my lucky star / I like myself / Blue Danube / Almost like being in love / Heather on the hill / Les girls / Why am I so gone about that gal / You're just too too / Nina / You wonderful you / Heavenly music / I got rhythm / Love is here to stay / 'S wonderful
CDODEON 9 / Jun '96 / Soundtracks

☐ **BEST OF GODZILLA VOL.1 1954-1995, THE**
FILMCD 201 / 29 Jun '98 / Silva Screen

☐ **BEST OF GODZILLA VOL.2, THE**
FILMCD 202 / 29 Jun '98 / Silva Screen

☐ **BEST OF HOLLYWOOD MUSICALS, THE (Songs From the Timeless Silver Screen Classics)**
New York New York: *Freeman, Ethan & Gregg Edelman/Tim Flavin* / Deadwood stage: *Company* / Woman in love: *Loesser, Emily & Company* / I'm a brass band: *Dankworth, Jacqueline* / Over the rainbow: *Bevan, Gillian* / With a little bit of luck: *Moody, Ron* / Night they invented champagne: *Hamilton, Lindsay & Graham Bickley/Sian Phillips* / Money money: *Pryce, Jonathan & Maria Friedman* / I feel pretty: *Olafimihan, Tinuke & Elinor Stephenson/Julie Paton/Nicole Carty* / I talk to the trees: *Freeman, Ethan* / Tomorrow: *French, Sarah & Girls* / Grease: *Barrowman, John & Girls*
SHOWCD 044 / Jan '97 / Showtime

☐ **BEST OF JAMES BOND, THE (30th Anniversary Collection)**
James Bond: *Norman, Monty & Studio Orchestra* / Goldfinger: *Bassey, Shirley* / Nobody does it better: *Simon, Carly* / View to a kill: *Duran Duran* / Mr. Kiss Kiss Bang Bang: *Warwick, Dionne* / For your eyes only: *Easton, Sheena* / We have all the time in the world: *Armstrong, Louis* / Live and let die: *McCartney, Paul* / All time high: *Coolidge, Rita* / Living daylights: *A-Ha* / Licence to kill: *Knight, Gladys* / From Russia with love: *Monro, Matt* / Thunderball: *Jones, Tom* / You only live twice: *Sinatra, Nancy* / Moonraker: *Bassey, Shirley* / On her Majesty's Secret Service: *Barry, John & Studio Orchestra* / Man with the golden gun / Diamonds are forever / 007: *Barry, John & Studio Orchestra*
CDBOND 007 / Dec '95 / EMI

☐ **BEST OF OFF BROADWAY, THE**
Born to entertain: *Ridgeway, Lindsay* / County fair: *Mayes, Sally* / So much in common: *Grupper, Adam & Marguerite Macintyre/Alix Korey* / Times like this: *Blazer, Judy* / Dear Mr. Gershwin: *Blackhurst, Klea* / Back and forth: *Klausner, Terri & Michael X. Martin/Jason Workman* / I will be loved tonight: *Simard, Jennifer* / That was my way/Every goodbye is hello: *Carmello, Carolee & James Ludwig* / Loves sorrow/Looking for a miracle: *Cast Recording* / Rose: *Cast Recording*
VSD 5856 / 2 Feb '98 / Varese Sarabande

☐ **BEST OF THE BROADWAY DIVAS, THE**
Belle: *Nicastro, Michelle* / No one is alone: *Beechman, Laurie* / You'll never get away from me: *Kuhn, Judy* / Learn to be lonely/My own morning: *Mayes, Sally* / Love: *Gravitte, Debbie Shapiro* / Where is the warmth: *Kaye, Judy* / Wherever he ain't: *O'Hara, Paige* / Night and day: *Luker, Rebecca* / Codependency duet: *Graff, Randy* / Story goes on: *Callaway, Liz*
VSD 5855 / 2 Feb '98 / Varese Sarabande

☐ **BEST OF THE HOLLYWOOD MUSICALS, THE**
PWKS 4213 / Nov '94 / Carlton

☐ **BEST OF THE WEST, THE (MGM Soundtracks Presents Great Western Movie Themes)**
Big Country / Unforgiven / Wonderful Country / Scalphunters / Return Of A Man Called Horse / Hallelujah Trail / Hour Of The Gun / Young Billy Young / Hang 'Em High / Horse Soldiers / Return Of The Magnificent Seven
RCD 10721 / 18 May '98 / Rykodisc

☐ **BEST OF WEST END MUSICALS, THE**
Consider yourself / All I ask of you / I don't know how to love him / Spread a little happiness / I could be happy with you / Thank you very much / Leaning on a lamp-post / Reviewing the situation / If I ruled the world / Ta-ra-ra-boom-de-ay / Wishing you were somehow here again / Oh look at me
SHOWCD 019 / Feb '95 / Showtime

☐ **BIG BAND THEME TUNES**
MACCD 358 / 24 Nov '97 / Autograph

☐ **BIG SCORE, THE (A Soundtrack To The Black Films Of The Seventies)**
Call me Mr.Tibbs: *Jones, Quincy* / Superfly: *Mayfield, Curtis* / Theme from Cleopatra Jones: *Simon, Joe* / Brothers gonna work it out: *Hutch, Willie* / Across 110th Street: *Womack, Bobby* / Freddie's dead: *Mayfield, Curtis* / Easing in: *Starr, Edwin* / People get up and drive your funky soul: *Brown, James* / Mama feel good: *Collins, Lyn* / Shaft: *Hayes, Isaac* / Sweetback's theme: *Van Peebles, Melvin* / Final comedown: *Green, Grant* / Are you man enough: *Four Tops* / Coffy is the colour: *Ayers, Roy* / Together brother: *White, Barry* / Flying machine: *War* / car wash: *Rose Royce*
4936292 / 30 Mar '98 / EMI

☐ **BIG SCREEN ADVENTURE**
EMPRCD 710 / Mar '97 / Emporio

☐ **BING CROSBY AT THE MOVIES 1934-1945 (Crosby, Bing)**
I've got a pocketful of dreams / On the sentimental side / Sing a song of moonbeams / Swingin' on a star / Accentuate the positive / Only forever / Pessimistic character (with the crab apple face) / Sweet Leilani / Pennies from heaven / Moonburn / Moon got in my eyes / Love is just around the corner / Down by the river / Please / Bells of St. Mary's / I wished on the moon / If I had my way / White Christmas / Going my way / Road to Morocco
CD 60017 / Sep '97 / Great Movie Themes

☐ **BIT OF A SHOWMAN, A (Hobbs, Jeremy)**
Applause / Mascara / I promise you a happy ending / Time heals eveything / I won't send roses / Movies were movies / Maybe this time / And yet and yet / Hurt / My way / Ballad of the sad young men / I am what I am / Look over there
CDGRS 1285 / Jan '96 / Grosvenor

☐ **BLACK EMMANUELLE'S GROOVE**
RED 1012 / 15 Jun '98 / Dagored

☐ **BLACK TO BROADWAY (Kent, Monroe III)**
Don't get around much anymore / Stick around / Knock me a kiss / When I first saw you / God bless the child / What would I do if I could feel / In my day / It's not over / Talking to yourself / I'm just a lucky so and so (blues in the night) / Nobody knows you when you're down and out / Down home / I got it bad and that ain't good / Azure te / Do nothing till you hear from me / Satin doll / Jitterbug waltz
3036000302 / Mar '96 / Carlton

☐ **BLADE RUNNER (Synthesizer Soundtracks)**
Hitcher / Big trouble in Little China / Haunted summer / Revenge / Lock up / Halloween / Blade runner
SILVAD 3008 / Aug '94 / Silva Treasury

☐ **BLAXPLOITATION VOL.1 (Soul Funk & Jazz From The Inner City)**
RADCD 43 / Sep '96 / Global TV

☐ **BLAXPLOITATION VOL.2**
RADCD 54 / Feb '97 / Global TV

☐ **BLAXPLOITATION VOL.3**
RADCD 76 / 1 Nov '97 / Global TV

☐ **BLAXPLOITATION VOL.4 (Harlem Hustle)**
Law of the land: *Temptations* / Am I black enough for you: *Paul, Billy* / Death wish: *Hancock, Herbie* / (Don't worry) if there's a hell below we're gonna go: *Mayfield, Curtis* / September 13th: *Deodato* / Grandma's hands: *Scott-Heron, Gil* / Who is he and what is he to you: *Withers, Bill* / Truck turner: *Hayes, Isaac* / Son of shaft: *Bar-Kays* / Mister magic: *Washington, Grover JR* / Theme from Cleopatra Jones: *Simon, Joe & The Mainstreeters* / Flying machine: *War* / Sweet sweetback's theme: *Earth, Wind & Fire* / I want you: *Gaye, Marvin* / Theme from savage: *Julian, Don* / For the love of money: *O'Jays* / Strawberry letter 23: *Brothers Johnson* / Natural high: *Bloodstone* / Inside my love: *Ripperton, Minnie* / One gun salute: *Byrd, Donald* / Always there: *Laws, Ronnie* / God made me funky: *Headhunters* / Get up I feel like being a sex machine: *Brown, James* / Harlem shuffle: *Bob & Earl* / Didn't I (blow your mind this time): *Delfonics*
RADCD 92 / 4 May '98 / Global TV

☐ **BLOOD AND THUNDER**
Ben Hur / Captain from Castile / Cleopatra / Wind and the lion / North by northwest / Ten commandments / Taras bulba / Mutiny on the bounty
VSD 5561 / May '95 / Varese Sarabande

☐ **BLUE MOVIES (Scoring For The Studio)**
I wish I knew how: *Taylor, Billy* / James Bond theme: *Holmes, Leroy* / Kojak: *Bobo, Willie* / Bullit: *Felder, Wilton* / From Russia with love: *Basie, Count* / Shadow of your smile: *Donaldson, Lou* / Down here on the ground: *Green, Grant* / Blow up: *Hutcherson, Bobby* / Star Trek: *Three Sounds* / Mission impossible: *May, Billy* / Alfie's theme: *Patton, 'Big' John* / Midnight cowboy: *Morgan, Lee* / Last tango in Paris: *Shaw, Marlena* / Moon river: *Wilson, Nancy* / Love story: *Holmes, Richard 'Groove'* / MASH: *Hutcherson, Bobby* / Windmills of your mind: *Shank, Bud*
CDP 8577482 / Sep '97 / Blue Note

☐ **BOND AND BEYOND (Cincinnati Pops Orchestra)**
Kunzel, Erich *con*
CD 80251 / May '92 / Telarc

☐ **BOND COLLECTION, THE (The 30th Anniversary) (Bassey, Shirley)**
View to a kill / Nobody does it better / From Russia with love / We have all the time in the world / You only live twice / Diamonds are forever / Live and let die / Moonraker / For your eyes only / All time high / Thunderball / Goldfinger
ICOCD 007 / Mar '93 / Icon

☐ **BORN ON THE FOURTH OF JULY (Music From The Films Of Tom Cruise)**
Born On The Fourth Of July / Risky Business / Days Of Thunder / Color of Money / Outsiders / Legend / Top Gun / Rain Man / Cocktail / Firm / Few Good Men / Far And Away
FILMCD 152 / Sep '94 / Silva Screen

☐ **BRITISH FILM MUSIC (From The 1940s & 1950s)**
Way to the stars / Blithe spirit (Prelude and waltz) / Night has eyes / Western approaches (Seascape) / Passionate friends (Film theme) / Man between / Sound barrier (Rhapsody Op38) / Matter of life and death (Prelude) / Kid for two farthings / Hungry hill / Rake's progress (Calypso music) / Wanted for murder (A voice in the night) / Ha'penny breeze (Film theme) / Scott of the Antartic / Christmas (Intermezzo) / Pony march penguins climbing the glacier final music
CDGO 2059 / May '94 / EMI

☐ **BROADWAY BOUND**
VSD 5676 / Aug '96 / Varese Sarabande

☐ **BROADWAY CHRISTMAS**
Be a Santa / Chtistmas eve / Pine cones and holly berries / Turkey lurkey time / Christmas gifts / That man over there / Hard candy Christmas / Christmas child / I thank you for your love / I don't remember Christmas / We need a little Christmas / Greenwillow Christmas / Lovers on Christmas eve / Happy New Year blues / Have yourself a merry little Christmas
VSD 5517 / Oct '94 / Varese Sarabande

☐ **BROADWAY GOLD**
TRTCD 213 / Feb '96 / TrueTrax

☐ **BROADWAY HITS**
CDCD 1231 / Jun '95 / Charly

☐ **BROADWAY MUSICAL 1918-1929**
CIN 025 / 1 Jan '98 / IMP

☐ **BROADWAY MUSICAL 1918-1946**
CIN 028 / 1 Jan '98 / IMP

☐ **BROADWAY MUSICAL 1930-1938**
CIN 026 / 1 Jan '98 / IMP

☐ **BROADWAY MUSICAL 1939-1946**
CIN 027 / 1 Jan '98 / IMP

☐ **BROADWAY SHOWSTOPPERS (Casts & Ambrosian Chorus/London Sinfonietta)**
CDC 7545862 / Apr '93 / EMI Classics

☐ **BROADWAY SHOWSTOPPERS**
CDTEZ 7002 / Jan '95 / TER

☐ **BROADWAY TO HOLLYWOOD (Philharmonic Pops Orchestra)**
MBSCD 444 / Jul '96 / Castle

☐ **BROADWAY'S BIGGEST HITS 1997-1998**
VSD 5923 / 26 May '98 / Varese Sarabande

☐ **BUGS BUNNY ON BROADWAY (New Recordings Of Music From Bugs Bunny Cartoons)**
9264942 / Sep '93 / Silva Screen

☐ **BUSBY BERKELY ALBUM, THE (Barrett, Brent & Judy Blazer/Ann Morrison/London Sinfonietta & Chorus)**
CDC 5551892 / Apr '93 / EMI Classics

☐ **BUSTS UP LAS VEGAS (Mansfield, Jayne)**
MISS 005 / 1 May '98 / Missing/Marginal

C

☐ **CAPTAIN BLOOD - VINTAGE HOLLYWOOD ADVENTURE SCORES (Captain Blood/Scaramouche/Three Musketeers/King's Thief) (Brandenburg Philharmonic Orchestra)**
Kaufman, Richard *con*
8223607 / Feb '96 / Marco Polo

☐ **CAROUSEL WALTZ (Philharmonia/ National Symphony/D'Oyly Carte Opera/New Sadler's Wells/Scottish Opera Orchestras)**
Edwards, John Owen/J. Pryce Jones/M. Reed/G. Hossack *con*
CDVIR 8315 / Oct '91 / TER

☐ **CASABLANCA (Classic Film Scores For Humphrey Bogart) (National Philharmonic Orchestra)**
Gerhardt, Charles *con*
Casablanca / Passage to Marseille / Treasure of the Sierra Madre / Big Sleep / Two Mrs Carrolls / Caine Mutiny / To Have and Have Not / Sabrina / Virginia City / Key Largo / Left Hand of God / Sahara
GD 80422 / '90 / RCA Victor

☐ **CBS - THE FIRST 50 YEARS**
1658115502 / 19 May '98 / TVT

☐ **CELEBRATE BROADWAY VOL.1 - SING HAPPY**
Sing happy: *Minnelli, Liza* / Blow Gabriel blow: *Lupone, Patti* / Freedom: *Theodore, Donna & Chip Ford* / Consider yourself: *Goodman, Michael* / I've gotta crow: *Martin, Mary & Kathy Nolan* / Good morning starshine: *Kellogg, Lyn* / Born again: *Martin, Mary* / Our time: *Walton, Jim* / Hey look me over: *Ball, Lucille* / Before the parade passes by: *Channing, Carol* / I got love: *Moore, Melba* / To life: *Mostel, Zero* / Certain girl: *Wayne, David* / Little me: *Andrews, Nancy* / H-A-P-P-Y/We'll take a glass together: *Jackson, David* / Best of times: *Hearn, George*
09026619872 / Apr '94 / RCA

☐ **CELEBRATE BROADWAY VOL.10 - BEST MUSICALS**
Overture / If I were a rich man / Song on the sand / Honeysuckle rose / Hello Dolly / Kiss Of The Spiderwoman / Stranger in paradise / Little priest / Look who's in love / Send in the clowns / Shall we dance / Bring him home / Brotherhood of man / Music of the night
09026680372 / May '96 / RCA Victor

☐ **CELEBRATE BROADWAY VOL.2 - YOU GOTTA HAVE A GIMMICK**
I've got your number: *Swenson, Swen* / Step to the rear: *Roberts, Anthony & Charlotte Jones* / I can't say no: *Ebersole, Christine* / Mama will provide: *Lewis, Kecia* / Carribean plaid (medley): Kingston market/Matilda Matilda: *Chandler, Stan* / Dream: *Mostel, Zero* / Lizzie Borden: *Lautner, Joe* / Arthur in the afternoon: *Ziemba, karn* / Your feet's too big: *Page, Ken* / Crossword puzzle: *Ackerman, Loni* / Well known fact: *Preston, Robert* / Shuffle off to Buffalo: *Prunczik, Karen* / Siberia: *Lascoe, Henry* / Another wedding song: *Barrett, Brent* / So long dearie: *Bailey, Pearl* / Little more mascara: *Hearn, George* / You gotta have a gimmick: *Shapiro, Debbie*
09026619882 / Apr '94 / RCA

☐ **CELEBRATE BROADWAY VOL.3 - LULLABY OF BROADWAY**
Lullaby of Broadway / Broadway baby / Be a performer / All I need is the girl / Opening doors / One step / Hello Dolly / Life upon the wicked stage / I want to go to Hollywood / Stereophonic sound / Comedy tonight / La Cage Aux Folles / Cabaret / There's no business like showbusiness
09026619892 / Feb '96 / RCA Victor

☐ **CELEBRATE BROADWAY VOL.4 - OVERTURES**
Carousel / Finian's Rainbow / Follies / Roar of the Greasepaint (The Smell of the Crowd) / Hello Dolly / Boyfriend / Peter Pan / On a Clear Day You Can See Forever / Merrily We Roll Along / King and I / Mack and Mabel / Gypsy
09026619902 / Feb '96 / RCA Victor

☐ **CELEBRATE BROADWAY VOL.5 - HELLO YOUNG LOVERS**
King and I / Showboat / Once On This Island / I do I do / Closer Than Ever / Roar Of The Greasepaint / Grand Hotel / High Button Shoes / Merrily We Roll Along / Gypsy / Follies / Chess / Hair / And the world goes 'round / Phantom
09026619912 / Mar '96 / RCA Victor

☐ **CELEBRATE BROADWAY VOL.6 - BEAUTIFUL GIRLS**
Follies / Annie Get Your Gun / Flora The Red Menace / I do I do / Sunday In The Park With George / Ain't misbehavin' / 110 In The Shade / Company / Broadway / New Faces Of 1952 / Oliver / On A Clear Day / Putting It Together / Gypsy
09026619922 / Mar '96 / RCA Victor

☐ **CELEBRATE BROADWAY VOL.7 - KIDS**
Bye Bye Birdie / Peter Pan / King and I / Flora The Red Menace / Oliver / Once On This Island / Funny Thing Happened On The Way To The Forum / Carousel / Hair / Forever plaid / Annie Get Your Gun / Wildcat / Bye bye birdie / Follies
09026680342 / Mar '96 / RCA Victor

☐ **CELEBRATE BROADWAY VOL.8 - DUETS**
Anything Goes / Oklahoma / Annie Get Your Gun / Assassins / Gigi / Jekyll and Hyde / Chess / Roar Of The Greasepaint / My Favourite Year / Fiddler On The Roof / Guys And Dolls / Phantom / I do I do / Kismet
09026680352 / Apr '96 / RCA Victor

☐ **CELEBRATE BROADWAY VOL.9 - GOTTA DANCE**
Dancing / Charleston / Pick-pocket tango / We're in the money / Who couldn't dance with you / Secretary is not a toy / Who's that woman / We dance / Joint is jumpin' / One night in Bangkok / On the SS Bernard Cohn / Dance at the gym/Somewhere
09026680362 / May '96 / RCA Victor

☐ **CELEBRATING THE MUSICALS**
76 Trombones / Till there was you / Shipoopi / Not since Ninevah / Stranger in paradise / He's in love / And this is my beloved / Hostess with the mostess / It's a lovely day today / You're just in love / How are things in Glocca Morra / You must meet my wife / Miller's son / Send in the clowns / Weekend in the country / Adelaides lament / Luck be a lady / My time of life/I've never been in love before / Sit down you're rockin' the boat
WMEV 00202 / 17 Aug '98 / BBC Audio

☐ **CENTENARY (Etting, Ruth)**
Nothing else to do / I'm nobody's baby / After you've gone / Keep sweeping the cobwebs off the moon / Love me or leave me / My blackbirds are bluebirds / Place to call home / Ain't misbehavin' / Crying for the Carolines / More than you know / Button up your overcoat / I'll get by / Mean to me / I'll be blue / Ten cents a dance / Just a little closer / If I could be with you / All of me / Guilty / Hey young fella / Were your ears burning baby / It's been so long / Take my heart / There's a lull in my life
CDGSE 785074 / Nov '97 / Claremont

☐ **CENTRE STAGE (Warlow, Anthony)**
Music of the night / Easy to love / Luck be a lady / Somewhere / This nearly was mine / I am what I am / Anthem / Bring him home / You're nothing without me / Impossible dream / Johanna / Colours of my life / Soliloquy
5112232 / Nov '91 / London

☐ **CHANSONS DE FILMS 1936-1961 (Piaf, Edith)**
175112 / Nov '97 / Musidisc

☐ **CHANSONS DE FILMS 1937-1943 (Trenet, Charles)**
175102 / 21 Aug '97 / Musidisc

☐ **CHANSONS POUR FELLINI**
CDCH 330 / Feb '94 / Milan

☐ **CHRISTMAS WITH DISNEY**
WD 724602 / Nov '96 / Disney Music & Stories

☐ **CINE CHANTANT VOL.1 1931-1960**
175092 / Aug '97 / Musidisc

☐ **CINE CHANTANT VOL.2 1931-1961**
175122 / Aug '97 / Musidisc

☐ **CINE STARS 1929-1939**
FA 063 / Jun '97 / Fremeaux

☐ **CINEMA CENTURY (A Musical Celebration Of 100 Years Of Cinema/58 Classic Themes)**
20th Century Fox Fanfare / City lights / Bride of Frankenstein / Gone with the wind / Stagecoach / Citizen Kane / Casablanca / Oliver Twist / Quo vadis / Quiet man / High and the mighty / Searchers / Bridge on the River Kwai / Big country / North by Northwest / Ben Hur / Psycho / La dolce vita / Magnificent seven / Alamo / Pink panther / Lawrence of Arabia / Great escape / 633 squadron / Zulu / Zorba the Greek / Doctor Zhivago / Born free / Lion in Winter / Once upon a time in America / Where eagles dare / Midnight cowboy / Wild bunch / Godfather / Jaws / Rocky / Taxi driver / Star wars / Diva / Raiders of the lost ark / Chariots of fire / Conan the barbarian / ET / Once upon a time in the West / Terminator / Witness / Out of Africa / Passage to India / Mission / Room with a view / Cinema paradiso / Ghost / Dances with wolves / 1492 Conquest of paradise / Unforgiven / Fugitive / Jurassic park / Schindler's list
FILMCD 180 / Apr '96 / Silva Screen

☐ **CINEMA CHORAL CLASSICS (Crouch End Festival Chorus)**
Temple, David *con*
Jesus Of Nazareth / Abyss / First Knight / Lion In Winter / Conan The Barbarian / Mission / Henry V / 1492 - Conquest Of Paradise / Agnus Dei / Carmina Burana
SILKD 6015 / Mar '97 / Silva Screen

☐ **CINEMA CLASSICS**
Blue Danube / William Tell overture / Fruhlingsstimmen / Pamina's aria from The Magic Flute / Mad scene from Lucia Di Lammermoor / Pathetique sonata adagio cantabile / Air / Nocturne in F minor / O mio babbino caro / March from piano sonata no.2 / Hebrides overture
8551182 / Apr '98 / Naxos

☐ **CINEMA CLASSICS 1997**
8551181 / Jul '97 / Naxos

☐ **CINEMA CLASSICS VOL.2**
Rachmanivov piano conc no.3 / Yared / Delibes / Kissing You / Sorcerer's apprentice / Mon coeur s'ouvre a ta vois / Un coueve en hiver / Harpsichord concerto no.5 / Love theme / Il dolce suono / Horn concerto no.2 / Somewhere in time / Richard Duke Of York / Henry V / Nessun dorma / Goldberg variation / Eine kleine nachtmusik / La forza del destino overture
CMS 5666472 / 3 Nov '97 / EMI Classics

☐ **CINEMA DU MONDE (18 Film Soundtrack Masterpieces)**
MCCD 127 / Sep '93 / Music Club

☐ **CINEMA MOODS**
Heart asks pleasure first/The promise: *Nyman, Michael* / Sheltering sky theme: *Sakamoto, Ryuichi* / Dangerous liasons / On earth as it is in heaven: *Morricone, Ennio* / Veni sancte spiritus: *Fenton, George* / Jean De Florette: *Petit, Jean Claude* / Darlington Hall: *Robbins, Richard* / Germinal: *Roques, Jean-Louis* / Betty et Zorg: *Yared, Gabriel* / Last emperor: *Byrne, David* / Etude: *Tarrega, Francisco* / Chasing sheep is best left to shepherds: *Nyman, Michael* / Age of innocence: *Bernstein, Leonard* / Hamlet: *Morricone, Ennio* / Pensione Bertollini: *Robbins, Richard* / Cinema paradiso: *Morricone, Ennio* / Adagio for strings / Big Blue overture: *Serra, Eric*
CDV 2774 / Mar '95 / Virgin

☐ **CINEMA SOUNDTRACK COLLECTION VOL.3**
VSD 5709 / Mar '96 / Varese Sarabande

☐ **CINEMA'S CLASSIC ROMANCES (City Of Prague Philharmonic Orchestra)**
Alwyn, Kenneth *con*
Sense and Sensibility / Much Ado About Nothing / Hamlet / Hamlet / Wuthering Heights / Romeo and Juliet / Last Of The Mohicans / Twelfth Night / Tess / Pride and Prejudice / Little Women / Far From The Madding Crowd / Mrs. Dalloway
SILKD 6018 / Mar '98 / Silva Classics

☐ **CINEMATIC PIANO - SOLO PIANO MUSIC FROM THE MOVIES (Chertock, M.)**
CD 80357 / Jul '94 / Telarc

☐ **CINEMOTIONS (The Best Film Music Ever)**
VSD 5624 / Apr '96 / Varese Sarabande

☐ **CLASSIC FILM SCORES FOR BETTE DAVIS (National Philharmonic Orchestra)**
Gerhardt, Charles *con*
Now Voyager / Dark Victory / Stolen Life / Private Lives of Elizabeth and Essex / Mr. Skeffington / In This Our Life / All About Eve / Jezebel / Beyond the Forest / Juarez / Letter / All This and Heaven Too
GD 80183 / '89 / RCA Victor

☐ **CLASSIC FILM THEMES (Carter, Gaylord)**
King's row / Bad and the beautiful / How green was my valley / High noon / Uninvited / Exodus / Gone with the wind / Best years of our lives / Spellbound / Place in the sun / Raintree county
FA 8102 / May '94 / Facet

☐ **CLASSIC FILM THEMES**
TRTCD 202 / Jun '95 / TrueTrax

☐ **CLASSIC FILM THEMES**
PBXCD 514 / Nov '96 / Pulse

☐ **CLASSIC FILM THEMES**
TSS 108 / 9 Mar '98 / BMG

☐ **CLASSIC GREEK FILM MUSIC (City Of Prague Philharmonic Orchestra)**
Zorba the Greek / 300 Spartans / Topkapi / Never on a Sunday / Chariots of Fire / 1492 (Conquest of Paradise) / Z / Phaedra / Honeymoon / State of Siege / Blue / Serpico / Shirley Valentine / Missing
FILMCD 165 / Oct '95 / Silva Screen

☐ **CLASSIC HOLLYWOOD (New World Philharmonic)**
FMICD 1 / Feb '95 / FMI

☐ **CLASSIC ITALIAN SOUNDTRACKS (The Horror Film Collection)**
Deep red / Night of the devils / Nightmare crypt / Planet of the vampires / Monk / Throne of fire / Seven notes in black / Mysterious island of Dr Nemo / Deadly steps lost in the dark
DRGCD 32903 / Jun '95 / DRG

☐ **CLASSIC ITALIAN SPAGHETTI WESTERN THEMES**
DRGCD 32909 / Oct '95 / DRG

☐ **CLASSIC MOVIE SONGS OF THE 40'S (Haran, Mary Cleere)**
VSD 5482 / Oct '94 / Varese Sarabande

☐ **CLASSIC MUSICALS (Performed On Pan Pipes)**
Love changes everything / First man you remember / I dreamed a dream / Bring him home / Come to me / Empty chairs at empty tables / With one look / Perfect year / Wishing you were somehow here again / All I ask of you / Memory / I know him so well / I don't know how to love him / Don't cry for me Argentina / Any dream will do
SUMCD 4092 / Jan '97 / Sound & Media

☐ **CLASSIC WAR MOVIE THEMES (London Theatre Orchestra)**
Dambusters / Bridge Too Far / Lawrence Of Arabia / Ride Of The Valkyries / Hamburger Hill / 633 Squadron / Reach For The Sky / Adagio for strings / Eagle Has Landed / Green Berets / Battle Of Britain / Guns Of Navarone / Longest Day / Great Escape / Cavatina / Where Eagles Dare
EMPRCD 751 / Nov '97 / Music Club

☐ **CLASSICAL FILM THEMES**
MBSCD 421 / Nov '93 / Castle

☐ **CLASSICS AT THE MOVIES**
2001 - A Space Odyssey / Sleeping With The Enemy / Raging Bull/The Godfather Part III / Breaking Away / Manhattan / Witches Of Eastwick / Kramer Vs. Kramer / Who Framed Roger Rabbit / Heat And Dust / Mrs Doubtfire / Silence Of The Lambs / Hannah And Her Sisters / Amadeus / Fantasia / Last Emperor / Untouchables / Clockwork Orange / Great Dictator / Love Story / Midsummer Night's Sex Comedy / Age Of Innocence / Dead Poets Society / Atlantic City / Parent Trap / Moonstruck / Seven Year Itch/Brief Encounter / Fatal Attraction / Platoon/Elephant Man / Strictly Ballroom / Excalibur / Out Of Africa / Nijinsky / Children Of A Lesser God / Wall Street / Apocalypse Now / Short Cuts / Rollerball / French Lieutenant's Woman / Die Hard 2 / Ordinary People
TFP 046 / Apr '95 / Tring

☐ **CLASSICS AT THE MOVIES**
Eine kliene nachtmusik-allegro / Canon in D major / Bolero / Reveries from symphonie fantastique / Clarinet concerto in A major / Also sprach zarathustra / Adagietto from symphony No.5 in c sharp major / O fortuna / Piano trio No.2 D 929 / Adagio for strings in G minor
DC 880882 / May '97 / Disky

☐ **CLASSICS AT THE MOVIES**
GFS 083 / Nov '97 / Going For A Song

☐ **CLASSICS AT THE MOVIES**
Adagio for strings / Eine kleine nachtmusik / Finlandia / Vesti la giubba / Symphony no.5 in C# minor / Un bel di Vedremo (Madame Butterfly) / Symphony no.3 Poco allegretto / Nutcracker/Dance of the sugar plum fairy / 1812 overture / For Elise
302152 / Feb '98 / Hallmark

☐ **CLASSICS FROM THE MOVIES**
QUAD 015 / Nov '96 / Tring

☐ **CLASSICS OF CINEMA**
BM 515 / Feb '97 / Blue Moon

☐ **CLASSICS OF THE SILVER SCREEN (Kunzel, Erich & Cincinnati Pops Orchestra)**
CD 80221 / Aug '90 / Telarc

☐ **CLASSICS TO BROADWAY (Paratore, A. & J.)**
310115 / Oct '92 / Koch

☐ **CLIFF RICHARD AT THE MOVIES 1959-1974 (Richard, Cliff)**
No turning back / Living doll / Mad about you / Love / Voices in the wilderness / Shrine on the second floor / Friday night / Got a funny feeling / Nothing is impossible / Young ones / Lessons in love / When the girl in your arms / We say yeah (It's wonderful to be young) / Outsider / Seven days to a holiday / Summer holiday / Let us take you for a ride / Stranger in town / Bachelor boy / Swingin' affair / Dancing shoes / Next time / Big news / Wonderful life / Girl in every port / Little imagination / On the beach / Do you remember / Look don't touch / In the stars / What've I gotta do / Matter of moments / Shooting star / Finders keepers / Time drags by / Washerwoman / La la la song / Oh senorita / This day / Paella / Two a penny / Twist and shout / I'll love you forever today / Questions / It's only money / Midnight blue / Game / Brumburger duet / Take me high / Anti-brotherhood of man / Winning
CDEMD 1096 / Jul '96 / EMI

☐ **CLIFFHANGERS (Action & Adventure In The Movies) (City Of Prague Philharmonic Orchestra)**
Motzing, William *con*
Bear Island / Flight of the Intruder / Duellists / Shoot to Kill / Riddle of the Sands / Remo / Savage Islands / Jaws IV / Last of the Mohicans / Arachnophobia / First Blood / King Solomon's Mines / Farewell to the King / Young Indiana Jones / 1492 (Conquest of Paradise) / Cliffhanger
FILMCD 155 / Sep '94 / Silva Screen

☐ **CLIFFHANGERS (Music From The Classic Republic Serials) (Cinema Sound Orchestra)**
King, J. *con*
Perils Of Nyoka / Adventures Of Captain Marvel / Dick Tracy's G-Men / Zorro's Fighting Legion / Fighting Devil Dogs / King Of The Royal Mounted / Daredevils Of The Red Circle / Mysterious Dr. Satan / Hawk Of The Wilderness / Drums Of Fu Manchu / Adventures Of Red Ryder
VSD 5658 / May '96 / Varese Sarabande

☐ **CLINT EASTWOOD MOVIE THEMES**
Good The Bad And The Ugly / Every Which Way But Loose / Fistful Of Dollars / For A Few Dollars More / Misty / Sudden Impact / Any Which Way You Can / Claudia's theme / Dead Pool / Doe eyes / Two Mules For Sister Sara / High Plains Drifter / Hang 'Em High / Outlaw Josey Wales / Joe Kidd / Pale Rider / Enforcer / Tightrope / Magnum Force / City Heat
ECD 3319 / May '97 / K-Tel

☐ **COCKTAILS ON THE BEACH**
I put a spell on you: *Kenyon, Carol* / I'll be seeing you: *Harrison, Deirdre* / Unchained melody / Sorrow: *Schumann, Mort* / As time goes by: *Bolling, Claude Big Band* / Water of Irrawaddy / Adios nonino: *Tirao, Cachao* / Always and forever: *Carsen, Nathalie* / Passion theme: *Hill, Warren* / Body double: *Donaggio, Pino* / Over the wall: *Migenes, Julia* / Two different worlds: *Loggins, Kenny* / Man I love: *Holiday, Billie* / Shattered / Looking back: *Q Rose*
74321395942 / Aug '96 / Milan

☐ **COLLECTION (Monroe, Marilyn)**
COL 042 / Mar '95 / Collection

☐ **COLLECTION: MARILYN MONROE (20 Golden Greats) (Monroe, Marilyn)**
Diamonds are a girl's best friend / River of no return / Heatwave / Do it again / Kiss / My heart belongs to daddy / I'm gonna file my claim / This is a fine romance / Little girl from Little Rock / Happy birthday Mr. President / After you get what you want you don't want it / You'd be surprised / She acts like a woman should / Lazy / When love goes wrong nothing goes right / One silver dollar / When I fall in love / Things / Bye bye duet / Bye bye baby
DVCD 2001 / Jul '87 / Deja Vu

☐ **COLLECTORS GEMS FROM MGM FILMS (Garland, Judy)**
Waltz with a swing/Americana / Opera vs. Jazz / Everybody sing / Yours and mine / Your Broadway and my Broadway / Got a pair of new shoes / Sun showers / Down on melody farm / Why because / Ever since the world began/Shall I sing a melody / It between / It never rains but what it pours / Bei mir bist du schoen / Meet the beat of my heart / Zing went the strings of my heart / On the bumpy road to love / Ten pins in the sky / I'm nobody's baby / All I do is dream of you / Alone / It's a great day for the Irish / Danny boy / Pretty girl milking her cow / Singin' in the rain / Easy to love / We must have music / I'm always chasing rainbows / Minnie from Trinidad / Every little minute has a meaning of its own / Tom Tom the piper's son / When I look at you / Paging Mr. Greenback / Where's the music / Joint is really jumpin' / Down at Carnegie Hall / D'ya love me / Mack the knife / Love of my life / Voodooo / You can't get a man with a gun / There's no business like showbusiness / They say it's wonderful / Girl that I marry / I've got the sun in the morning / Let's go West again / Anything you can do / There's no business like showbusiness
CDODEON 22 / Jan '97 / Soundtracks

☐ **COMEDIES MUSICALES AMERICAINES**
3017062 / Jul '97 / IMP

☐ **COMEDIES MUSICALES AMERICAINES**
3017072 / Jul '97 / IMP

☐ **COMMERCIAL BREAK (Old Tunes From The New Ads)**
Jeepers creepers: *Warren, Mercer* / Happy feet: *Hylton, Jack* / Bottleneck blues: *Weaver, Sylvester* / Jungle jamboree: *Ellington, Duke Orchestra* / Sweet and lovely: *Bowlly, Al* / Won't you get off it please: *Waller, Fats* / Egyptian Ella: *Lewis, Ted* / Sun has got his hat on: *Browne, Sam* / Love is the sweetest thing: *Bowlly, Al* / Teddy bear's picnic: *Hall, Henry Orchestra* / Let's face the music and dance: *Astaire, Fred & Johnny Green Orchestra* / Stompin' at the Savoy: *Goodman, Benny Orchestra* / Very thought of you: *Bowlly, Al* / Pennies from heaven: *Langford, Frances & Louis Armstrong/Bing Crosby* / Oriental shuffle: *Grapelli, Stephane & Django Reinhardt* / Boum: *Trenet, Charles* / In the mood: *Miller, Glenn Orchestra* / La cumparsita: *Shore, Dinah* / When you wish upon a star: *Edwards, Cliff* / Grasshoppers' dance: *Campoli, Alfredo* / Yes sir that's my baby: *Cantor, Eddie* / Tico tico: *Andrews Sisters* / Sentimental journey: *Day, Doris & Les Brown Orchestra* / Zip a de doo dah: *Mercer, Johnny* / As time goes by: *Wilson, Dooley*
CDAJA 5281 / 2 Jun '98 / Living Era

☐ **COMPLETE CINEMA CLASSICS COLLECTION, THE**
Piano / Shadowlands / Schindler's List / Remains of the Day / Philadelphia / Diva / Apocalypse Now / Platoon / My Left Foot / Fatal Attraction / Room With A View / Immortal Beloved / Jefferson in Paris / Sleeping With The Enemy / Madness of King George / Out of Africa / Driving Miss Daisy / Raging Bull / Untouchables / Gallipoli / Amadeus / Pretty Woman / Brief Encounter / Moonstruck / True Romance / Children of a Lesser God / Dead Poets Society
CDEMTVD 106 / Oct '95 / EMI

☐ **COMPOSERS OF FRENCH MUSIC**
Andante pour violon et orchestre: *Delerue, Georges* / Danse paysanne: *Portal, Michel* / Vendredi ou la vie sauvage: *Jarre, Maurice* / Les poneys sauvages: *Louisier, Jaques* / Le chandelier: *Delerue, Georges* / Le premier cercle: *Yared, Gabriel* / La vallee des espoirs: *Senia, Marie* / Brouillard au point de tolbiac: *Gaubert, Christian* / Catherine il suffit d'un armour: *Viger, Robert* / Couer tzigane: *Delerue, Georges* / Les joiles de la famille pinelli: *Alessandrini, Gerard* / La vie devant soi: *Sarde, Philippe* / Touch'n die: *Petit, Jean Claude* / L'entrage monsieur duvallier: *Bolling, Claude* / Look back: *Legrand, Michel* / Nous les beaux dimanches: *Franklin, Serge* / Catherine et julien: *Garvarentz, Georges* / La valse de juliette recaimer: *Duhamel, Antoine*
FE 953 / Apr '97 / Fremeaux

☐ **COPS (26 Themes From The Right Side Of The Law) (Brooks, Paul)**
Medley / Inspector Morse / Mission: Impossible / Avengers / Miss Marple / Kojak / Sweeney / A-Team / Rockford Files / Charlie's Angels / Magnum PI / Perry Mason / Man From UNCLE / Medley
ECD 3369 / Jul '97 / K-Tel

☐ **COPS ON THE BOX (Montague Orchestra)**
MACCD 367 / 30 Mar '98 / Autograph

☐ **COPS ON THE BOX UK (London Theatre Orchestra)**
EMPRCD 788 / 16 Mar '98 / Emporio

☐ **COPS ON THE BOX USA**
Hawaii 5-0 / Starsky and Hutch / Streets of San Francisco / Kojak / NYPD blue / Miami vice / Columbo / Cagney and Lacey / Dragnet / Police woman / Due South / Perry Mason / Ironside / TJ Hooker / Highway patrol / Hill St. Blues
EMPRCD 711 / Apr '97 / Emporio

☐ **CORONATION STREET ALBUM, THE**
Devoted to you: *Richard, Cliff & Denise Black* / Blue eyes: *Tarmey, Bill* / He ain't heavy he's my brother: *Hollies & Coronation Street Cast* / I remember it well: *Barlow, Thelma & Peter Baldwin* / Life on the street: *Deuce featuring Sherrie Hewson* / Tra la la la la: *Waddington, Bill* / Something stupid: *Barrie, Amanda & Johnny Briggs* / Baby's in black: *Kennedy, Kevin* / Didn't we: *Ball, Michael & Barbara Knox* / Teardrops: *Griffin, Angela & Chloe Newsome* / I'll string along with you: *Nicholls, Sue* / Always look on the bright side of life: *Coronation Street Cast featuring Bill Waddington*
CDCOROTV 1 / Nov '95 / Premier/EMI

☐ **CULT FILES VOL.1, THE (40 Classic Themes) (Royal Philharmonic Orchestra/City Of Prague Philharmonic Orchestra/Mark Ayres)**
Townend, Mark/Nic Raine *con*
X files / Prisoner / Saint / Dangerman / Randall and Hopkirk (Deceased) / Avengers / Jason King / Persuaders / Blake's seven / Red Dwarf / Doctor Who / Adventures Of Robinson Crusoe / Alfred Hitchcock Presents / Hawaii 5-0 / Perry Mason / (A Man Called) Ironside / Kojak / Mission Impossible / Star Trek / Seaquest DSV / Babylon 5 / X files / 2001: A Space Odyssey / Excalibur / Alien / Mad Max beyond The Thunderdrome / Body Heat / Omen / Halloween / Assault On Precinct 13 / Blade Runner / Batman / Superman / Shadow / Rocketeer / Heaven's Gate / Legend / Somewhere In Time / Taxi Driver / Pink Panther / Blues Brothers
FILMXCD 184 / Oct '96 / Silva Screen

☐ **CULT FILES VOL.2, THE (Re-Opened)**
Xena The Warrior Princess / Battlestar Galactica / Hitchhikers Guide To The Galaxy / Space Above And Beyond / Twilight Zone / Outer Limits / Fireball XL5 / Stingray / Stingray / Captain Scarlet / Joe 90 / Police Squad / Burke's Law / Fugutive / Kojak / Miami Vice / Streets Of San Francisco / Beauty And The Beast / Superman / Edward Scissorhands / Beetlejuice / UFO / Space 1999 / Space 1999 / Batman / Time Tunnel / Lost In Space / Voyage To The Bottom Of The Sea / Land Of The Giants / Hercules / Stingray / Young Frankenstein / Midnight Express / Suspiria / Merry Christmas Mr. Lawrence / Withnail and I / Clockwork Orange / Wild Wild West / Addams Family / MASH / Monty Python's Flying Circus
FILMXCD 191 / Oct '97 / Silva Screen

☐ **CULT THEMES FROM THE 1970'S VOL.1**
FLEG 8CD / Mar '97 / Future Legend

☐ **CULT TV (London Theatre Orchestra)**
EMPRCD 783 / 18 May '98 / Emporio

☐ **CURTAIN UP**
I feel pretty: *Kesselman, Maria* / Bless your beautiful hide: *Hockridge, Edmund* / I've grown accustomed to her face: *Quilley, Denis* / Me and my girl: *Quilley, Denis* / Don't cry for me Argentina: *Hendley, Fiona* / We're a couple of swells: *Craven, Gemma & Edmund Hockridge* / Younger than springtime: *Curtis, Nick* / Climb every mountain: *Hibberd, Linda* / My funny Valentine: *Willetts, Dave* / From this moment on: *Jefferson, Jackie* / Secret love: *Craven, Gemma* / As if we never said goodbye: *Kesselman, Maria & John Dulieu*
307752 / Aug '97 / Hallmark

D

☐ **DANGER GIRL (Page, Betty)**
QDKCD 012 / 26 Jan '98 / QDK Media

☐ **DEVIL RIDES OUT, THE (Music For Hammer Horror, Romance & Adventure) (Westminster Philharmonic/City Of Prague Philharmonic)**
Bateman, Paul/Nic Raine *con*
She / Kiss of the vampire / Frankenstein created woman / Scars of Dracula / Quatermass / Devil rides out
FILMCD 174 / Jul '96 / Silva Screen

☐ **DIAMOND COLLECTION, THE (Monroe, Marilyn)**
WWRCD 6002 / Jun '95 / Wienerworld

☐ **DIGITAL SPACE (London Symphony Orchestra)**
Star Wars / Tribute to a bad man / Lady Hamilton / Airport / Things to come / Windjammer / Big Country / Red pony / 49th Parallel / Spitfire prelude and fugue
VCD 47229 / Jan '89 / Varese Sarabande

☐ **DIGITAL THEMES SPECTACULAR VOL.1**
Dallas / My name is Bond / Rocky medley / Chariots of Fire / Knots landing / Raiders of the Lost Ark / Falcon Crest / Only love / Where no man has gone before / Chi Mai / Dynasty / Those Magificent Men in their Flying Machine / Rockford files / Eastenders / Warship / Barwick Green / Dambusters march / Longest Day / Concert march- Cockleshell Heroes
BNA 5011 / Feb '88 / Bandleader

☐ **DIGITAL THEMES SPECTACULAR VOL.2**
2001 / Superman / Hill Street Blues / Kojak / Cagney and Lacey / Dempsey and makepeace / Dad's Army / TV Sports themes / Cavatina / 633 Squadron / Swing march / Trap / Howard's Way / Last starfighter / Masterpiece / Nobilmente / Things to come / Bridge Too Far / Squadron / In party mood / Liberty bell / Black Hole / Lawrence of Arabia / Elizabeth Tudor / Battle of Britain
BNA 5031 / Aug '89 / Bandleader

☐ **DISNEY FAVOURITES**
WD 685624 / Nov '96 / Disney Music & Stories

☐ **DISNEY HITS**
When you wish upon a star: *Sammes, Mike Singers* / Thomas O'Malley cat: *Hilton, Ronnie* / Give a little whistle: *Sammes, Mike Singers* / When I see an elephant fly: *Peterson, Clive* / Who's afraid of the big bad wolf: *Sammes, Mike Singers* / Ugly bug ball: *Hilton, Ronnie* / Whistle while you work / Winnie the Pooh / Heigh ho / Siamese cat song: *Sammes, Mike Singers* / Bare necessities: *Sammes, Mike Singers* / Supercalifragilisticexpialidocious / Colonel Hathi's march: *Sammes, Mike Singers* / Trust in me: *Curtis, Nick* / That's what friends are for: *Sammes, Mike Singers* / I wanna be like you: *Sammes, Mike Singers* / Never smile at a crocodile: *Peterson, Clive* / Feed the birds: *Dawn, Julie* / Aristocats: *Hilton, Ronnie* / Hi diddle dee dee: *Sammes, Mike Singers* / Everybody wants to be a cat: *Hilton, Ronnie* / My own home: *Heard, Enid* / I've got no strings: *Sammes, Mike Singers*
CC 262 / Oct '90 / Music For Pleasure

☐ **DISNEY MODERN CLASSICS**
WD 699902 / Nov '96 / Disney Music & Stories

☐ **DISNEY MOVIE FAVOURITES (BBC Concert Orchestra)**
Brooker, Stephen *con*
I wanna be like you / Can you feel the love tonight / Whole new world / Some day / Cruella de Ville / Beauty and the beast / Colours of the wind / When I see an elephant fly / Circle of life / Dream is a wish that your heart makes / Everybody wants to be a cat / Bobbidy bodiddy boo / Alice in wonderland / You can fly / Under the sea / When you wish upon a star
11022 / Oct '97 / BBC Concert Orchestra

☐ **DISNEY ORIGINAL CLASSICS**
WD 699802 / Nov '96 / Disney Music & Stories

☐ **DISNEY SPECTACULAR, A (Cincinnati Pops Orchestra)**
When you wish upon a star / It's a small world / Alice in Wonderland / March of the cards / Mary Poppins / Cinderella / Jungle book / Who's afraid of the big bad wolf / Snow White and the seven dwarfs / Mickey Mouse march / Baroque hoedown / Disney fantasy medley
CD 80196 / '89 / Telarc

☐ **DISNEY TUNES IN THE STYLE OF THE GREAT COMPOSERS VOL.1 (Heigh Ho Mozart)**
DE 3186 / Nov '97 / Delos

☐ **DISNEY TUNES IN THE STYLE OF THE GREAT COMPOSERS VOL.2 (Bibbidi Bobbidi Bach)**
DE 3195 / Nov '97 / Delos

☐ **DISNEY'S HIT SINGLES AND MORE**
Circle of life: *John, Elton* / Shooting star: *Boyzone* / Someday: *Eternal* / Beauty and the beast: *Dion, Celine & Peabo Bryson* / Colours of the wind: *Williams, Vanessa* / You've got a friend in me: *Newman, Randy* / Cruella De Vil: *Dr. John* / He's a tramp: *Lee, Peggy* / Bibbidi bobbidi boo: *Armstrong, Louis* / Ev'rybody wants to be a cat / Zip a dee doo dah / Chim chim cheree / Jungle book groove / Whistle while you work / Hakuna matata / Star is born: *Brown, Jocelyn* / Part of your world: *Newton-John, Olivia* / Whole new world: *Bryson, Peabo & Regina Belle* / Can you feel the love tonight: *John, Elton* / When you wish upon a star: *Armstrong, Louis*
WD 115632 / Oct '97 / Disney Music & Stories

☐ **DIVA - SOPRANO AT THE MOVIES (Garrett, Lesley)**
SONGCD 903 / Jan '94 / Silva Classics

☐ **DIVA BY DIVA (Kaye, Judy)**
VSD 5589 / Nov '95 / Varese Sarabande

☐ **DIVAS OF THE SILVER SCREEN (Monroe, Marilyn/Judy Garland/ Marlene Dietrich)**
MCBX 016 / Dec '94 / Music Club

☐ **DON'T ASK FOR THE MOON, WE HAVE THE STARS**
Way you look tonight / Let there be love / Boy next door / September song / She's funny that way / You're a sweetheart / I'm making believe / Amor amor / I'm knee deep in daisies / How do I know it's real / That old feeling / Too marvellous for words / That old black magic / Sweet Lorraine / It can't be wrong / Let's do it / Never took a lesson in my life / Let's get away from it all / Long ago and far away / Only forever / Dinah / I've got a heart filled with love / Very thought of you / Boy what love has done to me / I remember you / Now voyager
UCD 400 / Jan '96 / Happy Days

☐ **DRACULA (Classic Scores From Hammer Horror) (Philharmonia Orchestra)**
Richardson, Neil *con*
Dracula / Dracula has risen from the grave / Taste the blood of Dracula / Vampire circus / Hands of the ripper / Dracula prince of darkness
FILMCD 714 / May '93 / Silva Screen

E

☐ **EARFUL OF MERMAN, AN (Merman, Ethel)**
I got rhythm / Sam and Delilah / Shake well / Eadie was a lady / Animal in me / Spanish custom / He reminds me of you / Earful of music / Shake it off with rhythm / You're the top / Shanghai-de-ho / Riding high / It's de-lovely / Hot and happy / You are the music to the words in my heart / Heatwave / Marching along with time / This is it / I'll pay the check / Friendship / Make it another old-fashioned please / Let's be buddies
CMSCD 015 / May '94 / Movie Stars

☐ **EARLY MOVIE HITS (Chevalier, Maurice)**
Louise / Wait 'til you see ma cherie / Mimi / All I want is just one girl / (Up on top of a rainbow) sweepin' the clouds away / Livin' in the sunlight lovin' in the moonlight / You brought a new kind of love to me / Personne ne s'en sert maintenant / Mon cocktail d'amour / Paris stay the same / Mon ideal / Quand on tient le coup / Qu' auriez-vous fait / Oh cette Mitzi
DRGCD 5575 / 27 Jul '98 / DRG

☐ **EASY PROJECT VOL.3, THE (The Very Best Of The Tony Hatch Orchestra) (Hatch, Tony Orchestra)**
Naked City / Joanna / Dick Powell / Soul coaxing / Mondo Kane / Music to watch girls by / Crossroads / Downtown / Man Alive / Doctors / Sportsnight / Sounds Of The Seventies / Memories of summer / Occasional Man / Champions / Call me / Emmerdale Farm / Birds / Hadleigh / Maori / Mr. and Mrs. / While The City Sleeps / Willow waltz / Best in football / Devil's herd / Surrey with the fringe on top / La paloma / World At War / Man And A Woman / Out Of This World
NEMCD 920 / Jan '97 / Sequel

☐ **EASY TEMPO VOL.1**
RTCL 813CD / Jul '96 / Right Tempo

☐ **EASY TEMPO VOL.3 (A Further Cinematic Easy Listening Experience)**
Saudade / Nago / I cavalli / Bob E Hellen / North Pole penguin / Frenesia / La bikina / Il Libanese / Lady Magnolia / Diamond bossa nova / Amanda's train / Beryl's tune / La seduzione / Easy lovers / Flute sequence / Beryl's tune / Soul samba / Casa di moda / Honey rhythm and butter / Danza citar free / Esquetando os tambourinos e cuica
ET 904CD / Jun '97 / Easy Tempo

☐ **EASY TEMPO VOL.4 (A Kaleidospic Collection Of Exciting And Diverse Cinematic Themes)**
So / Citta viva / Masquerade / Pedro come / Ore / Tremendous stars / Dreaming / Tropical club / Side sleep / Realta'n No.5 / Under drama / Little shakie girl / Meeti una sera a cena / Roma bene / Flirt a Rio / Paranagua / Robert's theme / Israelities
ET 907CD / 9 Nov '97 / Easy Tempo

☐ **EASY TEMPO VOL.6 (Cinematic Jazz Experience)**
ET 912CD / 6 Jul '98 / Easy Tempo

☐ **EASY TEMPO VOL.7 (Bikini Beat)**
ET 915CD / 6 Jul '98 / Easy Tempo

☐ **EMBRACEABLE YOU - BROADWAY IN LOVE (Broadway Casts)**
SK 53542 / Jul '94 / Sony Broadway

☐ **EMPIRE MOVIE MUSIC COLLECTION**
On Earth as it is in heaven: *London Philharmonic Orchestra* / Last Emperor (main title): *Byrne, David* / Merry Christmas Mr. Lawrence: *Sakamoto, Ryuichi* / Black rain suite: *Zimmer, Hans* / Looks like a tablecloth: *Martinez, Cliff* / Homeboy: *Clapton, Eric* / C'est le vent Betty: *Yared, Gabriel* / Key: *Fenton, George* / Etude: *Oldfield, Mike* / Call to arms: *Horner, James* / Les modernes: *Krause, Steven*
CDVMM 1 / Nov '90 / Virgin

☐ **ENCORE, ENCORE (Hits From The West End Stage Show) (London Theatre Orchestra & Singers)**
Only He / Memory / Maria / Another suitcase in another hall / I know him so well / Aquarius / Edelweiss / One night in Bangkok / She's so beautiful / Tomorrow / Grease / Hey there / Prepare the way of the Lord / People / Don't cry for me Argentina / I don't know how to love him / Impossible dream / Day by day / Sound of music / Till there was you
OP 0002 / Apr '87 / MCI Music

☐ **EPIC FILM SCORES**
King of Kings / Nativity / Miracles of Christ / Salome's dance / Way of the cross / Resurrection and finale / Ben Hur / Victory parade / Miracle and finale / El Cid overture / Palace music / Legend and epilogue
VCD 47268 / '88 / Varese Sarabande

☐ **EROTIC CINEMA**
12167 / Sep '93 / Laserlight

☐ **ESSENTIAL JAMES BOND, THE (City Of Prague Philharmonic Orchestra)**
Raine, Nic *con*
Dr. No / From Russia With Love / 007 / Goldfinger / Thunderball / You Only Live Twice / On Her Majesty's Secret Service / Diamonds Are Forever / Man With the Golden Gun / Spy Who Loved Me / Moonraker / For Your Eyes Only / Octopussy / Living Daylights / View to a Kill / Licence to Kill
FILMCD 007 / Dec '97 / Silva Screen

☐ **ETHEL MERMAN'S BROADWAY (Merman, Ethel)**
VSD 5665 / Nov '95 / Varese Sarabande

☐ **EVENING WITH DOROTHY FIELDS, AN (Fields, Dorothy)**
DRGCD 5167 / 27 Jul '98 / DRG

☐ **EVERYBODY SING (Great Songs From The Hollywood Musicals)**
Everybody sing: Garland, Judy / If it's you: Martin, Tony / When I love I love: Miranda, Carmen / Bojangles of Harlem: Astaire, Fred / Ain't it a shame about Mame: Martin, Mary / When my ship comes in: Cantor, Eddie / I'm no angel: West, Mae / Treat me rough: Rooney, Mickey / Let yourself go: Rogers, Ginger / With plenty of money and you: Powell, Dick / Easy to love: Langford, Frances / Two sleepy people: Hope, Bob & Shirley Ross / Sand in my shoes: Boswell, Connie / Ol' man river: Robeson, Paul / Never in a million years: Faye, Alice / Sweet little headache: Crosby, Bing / Moon of Manakoora: Lamour, Dorothy / You are too beautiful: Jolson, Al / It's raining sunbeams: Durbin, Deanna / Lovely way to spend an evening: Sinatra, Frank
PPCD 78113 / Feb '95 / Past Perfect

F

☐ **FAMOUS THEMES (Radio/TV/ Newsreel Themes From 1940's/50's) (Queens Hall Light Orchestra)**
Portrait of a flirt/Willo the wisp/Jumping bean / Journey into melody / Sapphires and sables / Invitation waltz / By the sleepy lagoon / Puffin' Billy / Coronation Scot / Rhythm on rails / Music everywhere / Horse guards Whitehall / Devil's gallop / Destruction by fire / On a spring note / All sports march / Cavalcade of youth / Drum majorette / Girls in grey / Elizabethan serenade / Melody on the move / Alpine pastures / Young ballerina / Horse feathers / Sportsmaster
GRCD 10 / May '86 / Grasmere

☐ **FANTASTIC JOURNEY (Kunzel, Erich & Cincinnati Pops Orchestra)**
CD 8023 / Aug '90 / Telarc

☐ **FANTASTIC TELEVISION THEMES**
Caine, Daniel *con*
Quantum Leap / V the series / Freddy's Nightmares / Star Trek - The Next Generation / Knight Rider / Highway to Heaven / Streethawk / Battlestar Galactica / Airwolf / Buck Rogers in the 25th Century / North Star / Bring 'Em Back Alive / Return of the Man From UNCLE / Tales of the Gold Monkey
TVPMCD 402 / May '91 / Primetime

☐ **FANTASTIC VOYAGE (A Journey Through Classic Fantasy Film Music) (City Of Prague Philharmonic Orchestra)**
Motzing, William *con*
Alien / Terminator / My Stepmother Is An Alien / Dead Zone / Gremlins 2: The New Batch / Countdown / 2010 / Seconds / Ghostbusters / Flash Gordon / V For Victory / Mad Max 2 / Fantastic Voyage / Explorers / Fortress / Philadelphia Experiment / Illustrated Man / Battle For The Planet Of The Apes / Total Recall / Batman
FILMCD 146 / Jan '94 / Silva Screen

☐ **FANTASTIC WORLD OF SPAGHETTI WESTERNS, THE**
VCDS 7016 / Apr '96 / Varese Sarabande

☐ **FANTASY MOVIE THEMES (London Symphony Orchestra)**
HRM 7002 / Jan '86 / Hermes

☐ **FANTASY WORLDS OF IRWIN ALLEN, THE (& Bonus Disc Of Alt. Cues/Sound Effects/Cast Interviews)**
Lost in space I / Lost in space II / Voyage to the bottom of the sea / Time tunnel / Land of the giants
GNPD 8044/9 / Apr '96 / GNP Crescendo

☐ **FASCINATING RHYTHM (Astaire, Fred)**
Shall we dance / Fascinating rhythm / Night and day / Crazy feet / Puttin' on the ritz / My one and only / Babbitt and the bromide / I've got you on my mind / Foggy day / Let's call the whole thing off / New sun in the sky / High hat / Hang on to me / Funny face / They can't take that away from me / Nice work if you can get it
HADCD 163 / May '94 / Javelin

☐ **FAVOURITE MOVIE CLASSICS**
CDCFP 4606 / Jan '95 / Classics For Pleasure

☐ **FAVOURITE TV CLASSICS VOL.1**
CDCFP 4613 / Jan '95 / Classics For Pleasure

☐ **FAVOURITE TV CLASSICS VOL.2**
CDCFP 4626 / Jan '95 / Classics For Pleasure

☐ **FAVOURITE TV THEMES**
Inspector Morse / Ruth Rendell mysteries / Upstairs and downstairs / She / Agatha Christie's Poirot / Woman of substance / The unexpected / Professionals / Match / Avengers / Forever green / New adventures of Black Beauty / Chimera / London's burning / Dr. Who / Saylon Dola / World Cup '90 / Hundred acres / On the line / Wish me luck as you wave me goodbye / Summer's lease (Carmina Valles) / ITV Athletics / Good guys / Classic adventures
MCCD 069 / Jun '92 / Music Club

☐ **FAVOURITE TV THEMES**
Coronation Street / Eastenders / Prisoner Cell Block H / Dallas / Dynasty / Brookside / Dr.Who / Star Trek / Batman / Man from UNCLE / Avengers / Fugitive / Saint / Dr.Kildare / Thunderbirds / Crossroads / Emmerdale / Neighbours / Home and Away / Country Practice
CD 6112 / Jan '98 / Music

☐ **FELLINI FILM THEMES**
Amarcord / Juliet of the spirits / 8-1/2 / La dolce vita / Satyricon Roma / White sheik / I vitteloni / Il bidone / Nights of Cabiria / La strada
HNCD 9301 / Jan '87 / Hannibal

☐ **FILM AND MUSICAL FAVOURITES (Keel, Howard)**
15093 / May '94 / Laserlight

☐ **FILM COLLECTION, THE**
11818 / Aug '95 / Music

☐ **FILM FANTASY (National Philharmonic Orchestra)**
Journey to the Centre of the Earth / Seventh voyage of Sinbad / Day the earth stood still / Fahrenheit
4212662 / '88 / Decca

☐ **FILM FAVOURITES (Mancini, Henry)**
Love story / Pink panther / Windmills of your mind / Moon river / Raindrops keep falling on my head
295469 / Aug '95 / Ariola Express

☐ **FILM FAVOURITES (Mantovani & His Orchestra)**
Love story / Big country / Secret love / Wand'rin' star / Tammy / Never on a Sunday / When you wish upon a star / Born free / Que sera sera / Alfie / High Noon / Trolley song / Moon river / Windmills of your mind / Moulin Rouge theme / Chim chim cher-ee / As time goes by / My foolish heart
5516012 / Nov '95 / Spectrum

☐ **FILM MUSIC OF CHARLES CHAPLIN, THE (German Symphony Orchestra)**
Davis, Carl *con*
Gold rush / Kid / Circus / City lights / Modern times
9026682712 / Jun '96 / RCA Victor

☐ **FILM MUSIC OF HUGO FRIEDHOFER, THE (Richthofen & Brown Symphonic Suite)**
8105 / May '97 / Facet

☐ **FILM MUSIC VOL.2**
La force du destin: *New Philharmonia Orchestra* / Intermezzo en un diese mineur: *Rudy, Mikhail* / Heart asks pleasure first: *Erdbeer, Johannes* / La Mamma morta: *Callas, Maria/Philharmonia Orchestra* / Concerto pour clarinette/orchestre en la majeur K622: *Meyer, Sabine/Staatskapelle Dresden* / La traviata: *Scotto, Renato/Philharmonia Orchestra* / Marche hongroise: *Orchestre De La Societe Des Concerts Du Conservatoire* / Requiem K626: *Pace, Patrizia/Choeur De Chambre De Stockholm* / Adagia pour cordes: *Philadelphia Orchestra* / Casta diva: *Callas, Maria/Choeurs & Orchestre Du Theatre De La Scala DeMilan* / Sonate pour violin en re mineur Op.5 no.12/La follia: *Kurosaki, Hiro/Emmanuel Balsa/William Christie* / Sonate pour piano no.14/Clair de lune: *Hiedsieck, Eric* / O mio babbino caro: *De Los Angeles, Victoria/Orchestre Du Theatre De L'Opera DeRome* / Main theme: *Little, Tasmin/New World Philharmonic* / Romance: *Laniau, Pierre* / Symphonie no.9: *Morris, James/Westminster Choir & Philadelphia Orchestra* / Funeral music: *Ensemble* / Barcarolle en sol mineur Op.37 no.6: *Laval, Danielle* / Zadok The Priest: *Ambrosian Singers/Menuhin Festival Orchestra* / Recitar vesti la giubba: *Carreras, Jose/Philharmonia Orchestra* / Sonate pour piano en si bemol majeur: *Naoumoff, Emile* / Un bel de vedremo: *Caballe, Montserrat/London Symphony Orchestra* / Trio pour piano violon and violoncelle: *Trio Chung* / Le patre sur le rocher: *Ludwig, Christa/Gervase De Peyer/Gerald Moore* / Duo des fleurs: *Mesple, Mady/Danielle Millet/Orchestre Du Theatre National De L'Opera De Paris* / Concerto pour piano et orchestre no.3: *Tacchino, Gabriel/Orchestre Philharmonique De Berlin*
CZS 5693142 / Feb '97 / Rouge Et Noir

☐ **FILM NOIR (Concert Suites To The Series Film Noir) (Brandenburg Philharmonic Orchestra)**
Stromberg, William T. *con*
Maltese Falcon / All through the night / Verdict / Dark passage / White heat
09026681452 / Nov '96 / RCA Victor

☐ **FILM STAR PARADE**
I wanna be loved by you: *Kane, Helen* / Please: *Crosby, Bing* / Ich bin von kopf bis fuss auf liebe eingestellt: *Dietrich, Marlene* / My wife is on a diet: *Cantor, Eddie* / You're always in my arms (but only in my dreams): *Daniels, Bebe* / Living in clover: *Buchanan, Jack* / Let me sing and I'm happy: *Jolson, Al* / What'll I do: *Pidgeon, Walter* / Dance of the cuckoos: *Laurel & Hardy* / Eadie was a lady: *Merman, Ethel* / All I need is just one girl: *MacMurray, Fred* / Love your magic spell is everywhere: *Swanson, Gloria* / Sweet music: *Astaire, Fred & Adele* / I could make a good living at that: *Formby, George* / Don't tell him what's happened to me: *Bankhead, Tallulah* / My rock-a-bye baby: *Moore, Grace* / (I'd like to be) A bee in your boudoir: *Rogers, Charles 'Buddy'* / Love me tonight: *MacDonald, Jeanette & Maurice Chevalier* / Goodnight Vienna: *Buchanan, Jack*
CDAJA 5020 / Jul '89 / Living Era

☐ **FILM THEMES (Mantovani)**
CDSIV 6105 / Jul '95 / Horatio Nelson

☐ **FILM THEMES (Synthonic 2000)**
RCACD 208 / Jun '96 / RCA

☐ **FILM WORKS 1986-1990 (Zorn, John)**
7559792702 / Jan '95 / Nonesuch
TZA 7314 / Jul '97 / Tzadik

☐ **FILM WORKS VOL.5 (Zorn, John)**
TZ 7307 / Oct '96 / Tzadik

☐ **FILM WORKS VOL.6 (Zorn, John)**
TZ 7308 / Oct '96 / Tzadik

☐ **FORBIDDEN BROADWAY VOL.1-4**
DRGCD 12987 / 20 Apr '98 / DRG

☐ **FRANK SINATRA REMEMBERS THE MOVIES 1943-1946 (Sinatra, Frank)**
Three little words / Where or when / That old black magic / If I had my way / My ideal / Till the end of time / Make believe / I only have eyes for you / Somebody loves me / Empty saddles / That's for me / It's been a long long time / White Christmas / You'll never know / As time goes by / Easy to love/You've got you under my skin / On the Atchinson Topeka and Santa Fe / People will say we're in love / Don't fence me in / With a song in my heart / Hot time in the town of Berlin / I'll remember April / There goes that song again
CD 60016 / Sep '97 / Great Movie Themes

☐ **FRED ASTAIRE AT MGM (Astaire, Fred)**
Heigh ho the gang's all here / Please don't monkey with Broadway / I've got my eyes on you / Here's to the girls / If the swing goes I go to / Yolanda / Steppin' out with my baby / It only happens when I dance with you / Couple of swells / You'd be hard to replace / Shoes with wings on / Weekend in the country / They can't take that away from me / Manhattan downbeat / Where do you get that girl / So long ooh long / Nevertheless / Medley / Every night at seven / How could you believe me when I said I love you... / You're all the world to me / I left my hat in Haiti / Bachelor dinner song / Oops / Seeing is believing / Baby doll / I wanna be a dancin' man / By myself / Shine on your shoes / That's entertainment / Got a brand new suit / Triplets / I guess I'll have to change my plan / Paris loves lovers / All of you / Fated to be mated / Rotz rock and roll
8218752 / 13 Oct '97 / Premier/EMI

☐ **FRED ASTAIRE IN HOLLYWOOD (Astaire, Fred)**
AMSC 570 / Jun '96 / Avid

☐ **FROM THE BIG SCREEN (Band Of The Life Guards)**
Jurassic Park / Medley from The Lion King / ET / Robin Hood Prince of Thieves / Medley from Indiana Jones and the Temple of Doom / Medley: an Aladdin fantasy / Star Trek / Medley from The Bodyguard / Evening at tops
BNA 5116 / Jul '95 / Bandleader

☐ **FURRY FRIENDS**
WD 695102 / Nov '96 / Disney Music & Stories

G

☐ **GALA CONCERT FOR HAL PRINCE, A (Willetts, Dave & L. Cariou/R. Jones/C. Sunnerstam/Munich Radio Orchestra)**
Prince, C. *con*
DOCRCD 2 / Apr '96 / First Night

☐ **GARY WILMOT - THE ALBUM (Wilmot, Gary & The London Symphony Orchestra)**
Luck be a lady / I've never been in love before / We're off to see the wizard / Somewhere over the rainbow / If I only had a brain / Younger than springtime / Bali ha'i / Night they invented champagne / Gigi / Where is love / Consider yourself / Who will buy / Stan' up and fight / Beat out dat rhythm on a drum / Perfect year / Sunset Boulevard
3036000092 / Oct '95 / Carlton

☐ **GHOST (Classic Fantasy Film Music Vol.2) (City Of Prague Philharmonic Orchestra)**
Motzing, William *con*
Conan The Barbarian / Highlander / Addams Family / Demolition Man / Excalibur / Ladyhawke / Witches Of Eastwick / Rocketeer / Island Of Dr. Moreau / Super Mario Brothers / Short Circuit / Monkey Shines / Wolfen / Ghost
FILMCD 156 / Sep '94 / Silva Screen

☐ **GLORY OF BROADWAY, THE**
Waltz suite/June is bustin' out all over / September song / I'm a stranger here myself/Speak low / Papa won't you dance with me/I still got jealous / Tchaikovsky/Sea of Jenny/My ship / Eagle and me / Come rain or come shine / You're the top / I wanna be loved by you / Fellow needs a girl/Gentleman is a dope / My heart belongs to daddy / How are things in Giocca Morra / Taking a chance on love / What do you think I am / Mountain high valley low / Surrey with a fringe on top/Oklahoma
MPMCD 005 / 20 Apr '98 / MCI Music

☐ **GLORY OF HELEN MORGAN, THE (The Original Torch Singer 1920's-1930's) (Morgan, Helen)**
Me and my shadow / When I discover my man / Just like a butterfly (that's caught in the rain) / You remind me of a naughty springtime cuckoo / Possibly / Lazy weather / Maybe / Do-do-do / Who cares what you have been / Mean to me / What wouldn't I do for that man / More than you know / Why was I born / Don't ever leave me / Body and soul / Something to remember you by / Bill / Can't help lovin' dat man / Frankie and Johnnie / Winter overnight / I see two lovers / Little things you used to do / I was taken by storm
MPMCD 003 / May '98 / MCI Music

☐ **GLORY OF HOLLYWOOD, THE**
Hooray for Hollywood / We're in the money / I only have eyes for you / As time goes by / Lullaby of Broadway / Swanee / I've got my love to keep me warm / Donkey serenade / It had to be you / Doctor lawyer Indian chief / One night of love / Thanks for the memory / Two sleepy people / Happiness is a thing called Joe / Inka-dinka-doo / Till the clouds roll by medley / Stormy weather / Lovely to look at / Sand in my shoes / Moon over Burma / I'll walk alone / Swinging on a star
MPMCD 006 / 20 Apr '98 / MCI Music

☐ **GLORY OF THE MOVIE SONGS, THE**
Amor: *Russell, Andy* / Trolley song: *Pied Pipers* / Golden earrings: *Lee, Peggy* / To each his own: *Howard, Eddy* / Beside you: *Hope, Bob & Dorothy Lamour* / Laura: *Haymes, Dick* / Jingle jangle jingle: *Merry Macs* / I should care: *Tilton, Martha* / ON the Atchinson Topeka and Santa Fe: *Mercer, Johnny* / I can't begin to tell you: *Crosby, Bing* / All through the day: *Whiting, Margaret* / Amapola: *O'Connell, Helen & Bob Eberly* / You'll never know: *Sinatra, Frank* / Till the end of time: *Como, Perry* / I'll be with you in apple blossom time: *Andrews Sisters* / Anniversary song: *Shore, Dinah*
MPMCD 008 / Jul '98 / MCI Music

☐ **GLORY OF THE WEST END, THE**
Lambeth Walk: *Lane, Lupino & Teddie St. Denis* / We'll gather lilacs: *Barron, Muriel & Olive Gilbert* / This is my lovely day: *Guetary, Georges & Lizbeth Webb* / Mignon polonaise: *Andrews, Julie* / Little white room: *Mills, John & Frances Day* / Most gentlemen don't like love: *Kirkwood, Pat* / Waltz of my heart: *Ellis, Mary* / Spread a little happiness: *Hale, Binnie* / Someday I'll find you: *Lawrence, Gertrude* / Lover come back to me: *Laye, Evelyn* / I'll see you again: *Wood, Peggy & George Metaxa* / My heart stood still: *Matthews, Jessie* / Run rabbit run: *Flanagan & Allen* / Music in May: *Dickson, Dorothy*
MPMCD 007 / Jul '98 / MCI Music

☐ **GODFATHER, THE (& Other Movie Themes) (London Symphony Orchestra/Philadelphia Orchestra Pops)**
Mancini, Henry *con*
09026614782 / Jan '90 / RCA Victor

☐ **GODZILLA (Classic Themes From The Classic Films)**
King Kong vs. Godzilla / Godzilla vs. Mothra / Godzilla vs. Biolante / Godzilla vs. King Ghidorah / Godzilla vs. Space Godzilla / Destroy all monsters / Godzilla vs. Destroyer / Godzilla / Godzilla / Godzilla vs. Mechagodzilla / Godzilla vs. The Seamonster / Son of Godzilla
VSD 5920 / 22 Jun '98 / Varese Sarabande

☐ **GODZILLA VS. KING KONG (Monster Movie Music Album)**
FILMCD 196 / 1 Jun '98 / Silva Screen

☐ **GOING HOLLYWOOD (Crosby, Bing)**
JASCD 1089 / 6 Apr '98 / Jasmine

☐ **GOLD COLLECTION, THE (Monroe, Marilyn)**
R2CD 4035 / 13 Apr '98 / Deja Vu

☐ **GOLDEN FILM AND TV THEMES (Hollywood Film Festival Orchestra)**
13830162 / Oct '97 / Galaxy

☐ **GOLDEN VOICES FROM THE SILVER SCREEN VOL.1**
Jaadugar kaatil: *Bhosle, Asha* / Dil cheez kya hai: *Bhosle, Asha* / Aplam chaplam: *Mangeshkar, Lata & Usha* / Toote hue khwabon ne: *Rafi, Mohammed* / Chahe koi mujhe: *Rafi, Mohammed* / Bechain dil khoi si nazar: *Mangeshkar, Lata & Geeta Dutt* / Sari sari raat: *Mangeshkar, Lata* / Inhi logon ne: *Mangeshkar, Lata* / Na to karavankitalash hai / Yeh hai ishq ishq / Aaj phir jeene ki: *Mangeshkar, Lata* / Yashomati maiya se bole nandlala: *Mangeshkar, Lata & Manna Dey*
CDORBD 054 / Mar '90 / Globestyle

☐ **GOLDEN VOICES FROM THE SILVER SCREEN VOL.2**
Daiya re daiya: *Bhosle, Asha* / O megha re bole: *Rafi, Mohammed* / Babuji dheere chalna: *Dutt, Geeta* / Na jao saiyan: *Dutt, Geeta* / Chhalia mera naam: *Mukesh* / O hasina zulfonwai: *Bhosle, Asha & Mohammed Rafi* / Sar pe topi laal: *Bhosle, Asha & Mohammed Rafi* / Chalte chalte: *Mangeshkar, Lata* / Tere bina aag yeh chandini: *Mangeshkar, Lata & Manna Dey* / Ghar aaya mera pardesi: *Mangeshkar, Lata*
CDORBD 056 / Apr '90 / Globestyle

☐ **GOLDEN VOICES FROM THE SILVER SCREEN VOL.3**
Dhoondo dhoondo re: *Mangeshkar, Lata* / Saqiya aaj mujhe: *Bhosle & Chorus, Asha* / Satyam shivam (part 1): *Mangeshkar, Lata* / Ab reat guzarne vali: *Mangeshkar, Lata* / Leke pahla ahla pyar: *Bhosle/Begum/Rafi* / Hondton pe aisi: *Mangeshkar/Bupinder* / Salam e ishq: *Mangeshkar, Lata* / Aaj ki raat: *Bhosle & Chorus, Asha* / Satyam shivam (part 2): *Mangeshkar, Lata* / Jean Pehchaan no: *Rafi, Mohammed* / Toote na dil toote na: *Mukesh*
CDORBD 059 / May '90 / Globestyle

☐ **GREAT AMERICAN SONGWRITERS (Te Kanawa, Dame Kiri & Thomas Hampson/Frederica Von Stade/Bruce Hubbard)**
CDM 7646702 / Apr '93 / EMI Classics

☐ **GREAT BRITISH EXPERIENCE**
Devil gallop / Special agent / Music while you work / Westminster waltz / Puffin' Billy / Down your way / In party mood / Housewive's choice / By the sleepy lagoon / Desert island discs / Girls in grey / Silks and satins / Emergency ward 10 / March from a little suite / Dr Finlays casebook / Barwick green / Archers / Runaway rocking horse / Girl from Corsica / Non stop tv theme / Skyscraper fantasy / Headless horsemen / On a spring note / Sea songs / Billy Bunters of Greyfriars school / PC 49 theme / Changing moods / Canadian in Mayfair / Dancer at the fair / Las Vegas / Animal magic / Starlight roof waltz / Knightsbridge march / In town tonight / Marching strings / Top of the form / Coronation Scot / Jumping bean / Send for shiner / Sound and vision / TV opening march / Young ballerina / Potter's wheel / Parisian mode / What's my line / Horse feathers /

Portrait of a flirt / Calvacade of youth / Barlows of Beddington / Running off the rail / Radio 4 late night shipping forecast / Winter sunshine / Parakeets and peacocks / Melody on the move / High heels / Haunted ballroom / All strings and fancy free / Saphires and sables / Dance of an ostracized imp / Smile of a latin / Beachcomber / Dreaming / Quiet stroll / Farming

CDGB 50 / 3 Nov '97 / EMI Classics

☐ **GREAT BRITISH FILM MUSIC (National Philharmonic Orchestra)**
Herrmann, Bernard con
Richard III / Anna Karenina / Oliver Twist / Escape me never / 49th Parallel / Things to come

4489542 / Aug '96 / Phase 4

☐ **GREAT CLASSIC MOVIE THEMES**
TCD 2880 / Dec '96 / Telstar

☐ **GREAT CLASSICAL THEMES (Mantovani)**
MU 5011 / Oct '92 / Musketeer

☐ **GREAT FILM MUSICALS, THE**
Lullaby of Broadway / Lulu's back in town / Jeepers creepers / Moonlight becomes you / Over the rainbow / Singin' in the rain / Love walked in / Boogie woogie bugle boy / Chattanooga choo-choo / Thanks for the memory / Isn't this a lovely day / I yi yi yi like you very much / Smoke gets in your eyes / Let yourself go / Keep young and beautiful / Road to Morocco / Puttin' on the Ritz / Wake up and live / Lover come back to me / I'm in the mood for love / Dearly beloved / I've got you under my skin / Yankee doodle boy / Hooray for Hollywood

CDMOIR 514 / Jan '96 / Memoir

☐ **GREAT FILM THEMES**
TFP 024 / Nov '92 / Tring

☐ **GREAT FILMS AND SHOWS (Sinatra, Frank)**
Night and day / I wish I were in love again / I got plenty o' nuttin' / I guess I'll have to change my plan / Nice work if you can get it / I won't dance / You'd be so nice to come home to / I got it bad and that ain't good / From this moment on / Blue moon / September in the rain / It's only a paper moon / You do something to me / Taking a chance on love / Get happy / Just one of those things / I love Paris / Chicago / High hopes / I believe / Lady is a tramp / Let's do it / C'est magnifique / Tender trap / Three coins in the fountain / Young at heart / Ain't next door / They can't take that away from me / Someone to watch over me / Little girl blue / Like someone in love / Foggy day / I get a kick out of you / My funny valentine / Embraceable you / That old feeling / I've got a crush on you / Dream / September song / I'll see you again / All the time / Dancing in the dark / Too close for comfort / I could have danced all night / Cheek to cheek / Song is you / Baubles bangles and beads / Almost like being in love / Lover / On the sunny side of the street / That old black magic / I've heard that song before / You make me feel so young / Too marvellous for words / It happened in Monterrey / I've got you under my skin / How about you / Pennies from heaven / You're getting to be a habit with me / You brought a new kind of love to me / Love is here to stay / Old devil moon / Makin' whoopee / Anything goes / What is this thing called love / Glad to be unhappy / I get along without you very well / Dancing on the ceiling / Can't we be friends / All the way / To love and be loved / All my tomorrows / I couldn't sleep a wink last night / Spring is here / One for my baby / Time after time / It's all right with me / It's the same old dream / Johnny Concho theme (wait for me) / Wait till you see her / Where are you / Lonely town / Where or when / I concentrate on you / Love and marriage

CDFS 1 / Apr '89 / Capitol

☐ **GREAT FRENCH FILM MUSIC COMPOSERS VOL.2, THE**
La conquete du ciel: Alessandrini, Gerard / En survolant son amega: Legrand, Michel / La fin du drame: Alessandrini, Gerard / Le temps: Jarre, Maurice / Des chambs et des bataille: Delerue, Georges / Salzburg: Boiling, Claude / L'enfant au violoncelle: Viger, Robert / Jeanne: Lousier, Jacques / Battling le tenebreux: Portal, Michel / Madame Rosa: Sarde, Philippe / Des jours et des nuit: Duhamel, Antoine / Scene d'amour: Delerue, Georges / Amitie: Jarre, Maurice

FE 954 / Nov '97 / Fremeaux

☐ **GREAT MGM HOLLYWOOD MUSICALS**
CD 023 / Jan '89 / Silva Screen

☐ **GREAT MOVIE THEMES (London Philharmonic Orchestra)**
Exodus / Chariots Of Fire / I will wait for you / Zorbas' dance / Star Wars / Tara's theme / Lawrence Of Arabia / Colonel Bogey / Moulin Rouge / Third Man / Shenandoah / Godfather / Midnight Cowboy / Lara's theme

DC 880652 / May '97 / Disky

☐ **GREAT MUSICAL STANDARDS**
HCD 327 / Jun '95 / Hindsight

☐ **GREAT MUSICALS**
Oklahoma suite / My Fair Lady Suite / Annie Get Your Gun Suite / King and I Suite / Sound Of Music Suite / West Side Story suite / Porgy And Bess Suite / South Pacific Suite / Guys And Dolls Suite / Carousel Suite

PC 612 / 10 Nov '97 / Start

☐ **GREAT OVERTURES FROM THE MUSICALS**
CDVIR 8324 / Aug '95 / TER

☐ **GREAT OVERTURES FROM THE MUSICALS (Popular Opening Orchestral Themes From 12 Legendary Shows)**
My Fair Lady: National Symphony Orchestra / Oklahoma: Munich Symphony Orchestra / Candide: Scottish Opera Orchestra / Can can: National Symphony Orchestra / King and I: Philharmonic Orchestra / Sweet Charity: National Symphony Orchestra / Phantom Of The Opera: Munich Symphony Orchestra / Kiss Me Kate: National Symphony Orchestra / West Side Story: National Symphony Orchestra / Funny Girl: National Symphony Orchestra / Cats: National Symphony Orchestra / Gypsy: National Symphony Orchestra

SHOWCD 030 / Oct '96 / Showtime

☐ **GREAT SCIENCE FICTION THEMES (Once Upon A Time At The Movies) (Silver Screen Orchestra)**
Close Encounters Of The Third Kind / Star Wars / Superman / Battlestar Galactica / Alien / X-Files / Star Trek / Empire Strikes Back / Bladerunner / Black Hole / Twilight Zone / ET / Dune / Eve of the war

DC 880682 / May '97 / Disky

☐ **GREAT SCREEN LOVERS COLLECTION**
Who is there among...: Nicholson, Jack / Chattanooga choo choo: Power, Tyrone / Louise: Chevalier, Maurice / Manhattan: Rooney, Mickey / Let's do it: Coward, Sir Noel / Foolish pride: Mitchum, Robert / Puttin' on the Ritz: Gable, Clark / Two of us: Curtis, Tony & Gloria De Haven / Let's make love: Montand, Yves / Day after day: Stewart, James / Did I remember: Grant, Cary / Kashmiri love song: Valentino, Rudolph / Pillow talk: Hudson, Rock / Mary's a grand old name: Cagney, James / Woman in love: Brando, Marlon & Jean Simmons / As long as there is music: Sinatra, Frank / Chico's choo choo: Wagner, Robert & Debbie Reynolds / Lover come back to me / All I do is dream of you: Reynolds, Gene / Gotta bran' new suit: Astaire, Fred & Nanette Fabray

DVCD 2117 / Dec '87 / Deja Vu

☐ **GREAT SHAKESPEARE FILMS (National Philharmonic Orchestra & London Festival Orchestra)**
4212682 / '88 / Decca

☐ **GREAT SONGS FROM THE MOVIES**
GALE 427 / 20 Apr '98 / Gallerie

☐ **GREAT SONGS FROM THE MUSICALS**
MCCD 162 / Jul '94 / MCI Music

☐ **GREAT SONGS FROM THE MUSICALS - 1930'S/1940'S**
Lambeth walk: Kernan, David / My funny valentine: Ellie / You made me love you: Craven, Gemma / Putting on the ritz: Newley, Anthony / Leaning on a lampost: Kernan, David / Dancing in the dark: Hockridge, Edmund / Ol' man river: Martin, James / Me and my girl: Kernan, David / That's entertainment: London Symphony Orchestra / Pretty girl is like a melody: Hockridge, Edmund / Our love is here to stay: Willetts, David / Nice work if you can get it: Hockridge, Edmund / Oh what a beautiful mornin': Malton, Richard / When the children are asleep: Pollard, Su & Ian Wallace / Trolley song: Craven, Gemma / You'll never walk alone: Kimm, Fiona / June is bustin' out all over: Hibberd, Linda / People will say we're in love: Perry, Lynette & Richard Malton

330082 / Jul '96 / Hallmark

☐ **GREAT SONGS FROM THE MUSICALS - 1950'S/1960'S**
Who wants to be a millionaire: Wayne, Carl & Tracy Collier / I could have danced all night: Ellie, Fiona / Thank Heaven for little girls: Newley, Anthony / Bless your beautiful hide: Hockridge, Edmund / True love: Lotis, Dennis & Tracy Collier / Summertime: Samantha: Willetts, Dave / Make 'em laugh: Newley, Anthony / There is nothing like a dame: Master Singers / Some enchanted evening: Kernan, David / Baubles bangles and beads: Craven, Gemma / I've grown accustomed to her face: Quilley, Denis / I'm gonna wash that man right out of my hair: Perry, Lynette / Hello Dolly: Green, Simon / Food glorious food: Boys Chorus / Don't rain on my parade: London Symphony Orchestra / If I were a rich man: Greene, Brian / Sunrise sunset: Kimm, Fiona & Brian Greene / My favourite things: Robertson, Liz / People, people, Ellie / Impossible dream: Willetts, Dave / As long as he needs me: Langford, Bonnie / Consider yourself: Boys Chorus / Climb every mountain: Kimm, Fiona / Edelweiss: Quilley, Denis

330092 / Jul '96 / Hallmark

☐ **GREAT SONGS FROM THE MUSICALS - 1970'S/1980'S**
Superstar: London Symphony Orchestra / Day by day: Wayne, Carl / On this night of a thousand stars: Wayne, Carl / Overture: Mack and Mabel: London Symphony Orchestra / Any dream will do: Quilley, Denis / You're the one that I want: Wayne, Carl & Michaela Strachan / Another suitcase in another hall: Lawrence, Stephanie / Hopelessly devoted to you: Strachan, Michaela / Cabaret: Perry, Lynette / I don't know how to love him: Hendley, Fiona / Memory: Hendley, Fiona / I dreamed a dream: Malton, Claire / Tell me on a Sunday: Wayne, Carl / Heat's on in Saigon: Wayne, Carl / Pumping iron: Conrad, Jess / Take that look of your face: Hendley, Fiona / Sun and moon: Stephanie & David Smith / Empty chairs at empty tables: Willetts, Dave / Love changes everything: Skellern, Peter / Movie in your mind: Crisswell, Kim

330102 / Jul '96 / Hallmark

☐ **GREAT SONGS FROM THE SILVER SCREEN**
Dames / Good morning / If I only had a brain / Spring spring spring / Begin the beguine / Secret love / best things in life are free / I love you / Woman in love / It's a nice face / New York New York

SHOWCD 054 / Apr '97 / Showtime

☐ **GREAT SPORTING EXPERIENCE, THE**
CDGOAL 1 / 8 Jun '98 / EMI Classics

☐ **GREAT SPORTS THEMES (London Theatre Orchestra)**
Match Of The Day / BBC Cricket theme / BBC Grandstand / Grand Prix / 5 Live Sports Report / BBC Golf theme / Pot Black / Wimbledon / ITV Big Match / Rugby Special / ITV World Of Sport / BBC Horse Of The Year / Ski Sunday / Sportsnight / BBC Snooker / Question Of Sport

EMPRCD 715 / Jun '97 / Emporio

☐ **GREAT STAGE MUSICALS 1924-1941, THE**
CDMOIR 501 / Jul '97 / Memoir

☐ **GREAT TV THEMES**
TFP 029 / Nov '92 / Tring

☐ **GREAT WAR MOVIE THEMES (Silver Screen Orchestra)**
Das Boot / Adagio for strings Op11 / River Kwai march / Ride of the Valyries / Ballad Of The Green Berets / Guns Of Navarone / Battle hymn of the republic / Longest Day / Paris brule-t-il / Cavatina / Schindler's List / Lawrence Of Arabia / Bridge Too Far / In the mood

DC 880692 / May '97 / Disky

☐ **GREAT WAR THEMES**
Dam Busters / Longest Day / Bridge Too Far / Colditz march / High On A Hill / Colonel Bogey / Top Gun / Aces High / Great Escape / Lawrence Of Arabia / Cockleshell Heroes / MASH (Suicide is painless) / Road To Vera / Raiders march and Imperial march / Cavalry of the clouds / Cavatina / Berliner luft / Normandy veterans / Battle Of Britain march

309222 / 13 Jul '98 / Hallmark

☐ **GREAT WESTERN FILM THEMES**
Rio bravo / Man with the harmonica / Fistful of dollars / Magnificent seven / Once upon a time in the west / My name is nobody / High noon / Ballad of the Alamo / Johnny guitar / Comancheros / Shane / Vera cruz / Virginian / Bonanza / Riders in the sky

22526 / Dec '95 / Music

☐ **GREAT WESTERN MOVIE AND TV SOUNDTRACKS VOL.1 (My Rifle, My Pony And Me)**
My rifle my pony and me: Martin, Dean & Ricky Nelson / Legend of Shenandoah: Stewart, James / Montana/The searchers/Wagons west/Song of the wagonmaster: Sons Of The Pioneers / Nevada Smith: Kilgore, Merle / Ballad of the Alamo/ The hanging tree: Robbins, Marty / Ballad of Paladin: Western, Johnny / Sons of katie Elder/Rebel Johnny Yuma: Cash, Johnny / Rawhide/Gunfight at the OK Corral: Laine, Frankie / Ballad of Davy Crockett: Parker, Fess / Rio Bravo: Martin, Dean / Last roundup / North to Alaska: Horton, Johnny / Runaway: Hunter, Tab / Bonanza: Greene, Lorne / Tex / And the moon grew brighter: Douglas, Kirk / Pecos Bill: Rogers, Roy & Sons Of The Pioneers / Yellow rose of Texas/The Roll on Texas moon/Don't fence me: Rogers, Roy / Cowboy: Hall, Dickson

BCD 15625 / Mar '93 / Bear Family

☐ **GREAT WESTERN MOVIE AND TV SOUNDTRACKS VOL.2 (From Alamo To El Dorado)**
Ballad of Cat Ballou: Cole, Nat 'King' & Stubby Kaye / High Chapparal: Rose, David / Lonely man: Ford, Tennessee' Ernie / Man from Laramie: Martino, Al / El Dorado: Alexander, George & Mellowmen / Man with True Grit: Campbell, Glen / Fury: Prairie Chiefs / Wichita: Ritter, Tex / Old Turkey Buzzard: Feliciano, Jose / Bronco: Gregory, Johnny / Love in the country: Limelighters / Sugarfoot: Sons Of The Pioneers / Stagecoach to Cheyenne: Newton, Wayne / Green leaves of summer: Bros Four / Marmalade molasses and honey: Williams, Andy & Dick Powell / Over The Rainbow: Garland, Judy / Sonny Boy: Jolson, Al / Sunny Side Up: Endor, Chick / Pick yourself Up: Astaire, Fred / Lulu's Back In Town: Powell, Dick / Sun Valley Jump: Miller, Glenn Orchestra / Yours And Mine: Powell, Eleanor / My Man: Brice, Fanny / Easy To Love: Stewart, James & Eleanor Powell / Fine Romance: Astaire, Fred & Ginger Rogers / (Dear Mr Gable) You Made Me Love You: Garland, Judy / Goodnight My Love: Faye, Alice

BCD 15983 / May '97 / Bear Family

☐ **GREAT WESTERN THEMES (Pioneer Orchestra)**
Bonanaza / Once Upon A Time In The West / Good The Bad And The Ugly / Magnificent Seven / Green Leaves Of Summer / High Noon / Fistful Of Dollars / Hondo / Man With The Harmonica / Professional Gun / Return Of The Seven / Wand'rin Star / Hang 'Em High / Man From Laramie / How The West Was Won / Ballad Of The Alamo / Comancheros / True Grit

QED 105 / Nov '96 / Tring

☐ **GREAT WESTERN THEMES (Silver Screen Orchestra)**
For A Few Dollars More / Gambler / Good The Bad And The Ugly / Hang 'Em High / High Noon / How The West Was Won / My Name Is Nobody / Man With The harmonica / True Grit / Magnificent Seven / Fistful Of Dollars / Claudia's theme / Alamo / Streets Of Laredo

DC 880672 / May '97 / Disky

☐ **GREATEST COP THEMES IN THE WORLD, THE**
Mission Impossible / Professionals / Hawaii 5-0 / Charlie's Angels / Starsky and Hutch / Sweeney / Dempsey and Makepeace / 77 Sunset Strip / NYPD Blue / Kojak / Murder She Wrote / Quincy / Moonlighting / Bill / Miss Marple / Poirot / Ruth Rendell / Inspector Morse / Law And Order / Taggart / Miami Vice / NYPD Blue / Adam-12 / A-Team / Crockett's Theme / Hill Street Blues / Columbo / Juliet Bravo / Bergerac / Between The Lines / Z Cars / Prisoner / Avengers / Saint / Man From UNCLE / Untouchables / X-Files

SUDCD 4505 / Nov '98 / Summit

☐ **GREATEST HOLLYWOOD THEMES VOL.1 (The 1990's) (Lu, Stephen & The Hollywood Sessions Orchestra)**
ICHCD 4572 / 29 Jun '98 / Ichiban

☐ **GREATEST LOVE SONGS FROM THE MUSICALS, THE**
Love changes everything / Hello young lovers / As the street where you live / As long as he needs me / All I ask of you / Human heart / Hopelessly devoted to you / I don't know how to love him / If ever I would leave you / You are love / Stranger in paradise / So in love

SHOWCD 020 / Feb '95 / Showtime

☐ **GREATEST MOVIE THEMES**
Jaws / Godfather / Deerhunter (Cavatina) / Star wars / Gone with the wind (Tara's theme) / Lawrence of Arabia / Apocalypse now (Ride of the valkyries) / Raiders of the lost ark / Magnificent seven / Longest day / Bridge too far / Good the bad and the ugly / ET / Butch Cassidy and The Sundance Kid (Raindrops are falling on / Dr. Zhivago / Love story / 10 Ravels bolero / Close encounters of the third kind

CDMFP 6236 / Jul '96 / Music For Pleasure

☐ **GREATEST SCIENCE FICTION HITS, VOL 1 (Norman, Neil & his Orchestra)**
Alien / Moonraker / Star Wars / Superman / 2001 / Battlestar Galactica / Space 1999 / Star trek / Black hole

GNPD 2128 / Jan '89 / GNP Crescendo

☐ **GREATEST SCIENCE FICTION HITS, VOL 2 (Norman, Neil & his Orchestra)**
Empire strikes back / Twilight zone / Buck Rogers / Time tunnel / Dr. Who / Voyage to the bottom of the sea / Dark star / Sinbad and the eye of the tiger

GNPD 2133 / Jan '89 / GNP Crescendo

☐ **GREATEST SCIENCE FICTION HITS, VOL 3 (Norman, Neil & his Orchestra)**
War Of the worlds / Lost in space / Bladerunner / Flash Gordon / Thing / Prisoner / Land of giants / Space 1999 / Angry red planet / Capricorn one / Raiders of the Lost Ark / Invaders / UFO / Vena's dance / Return of the jedi

GNPD 2163 / Jan '89 / GNP Crescendo

☐ **GREATEST SHOW THEMES**
Overture / Memories / Oliver / Where is love / I'd do anything / As long as he needs me / Consider yourself / I feel pretty / Maria / Tonight / America / Farmer and the cowman / Oklahoma / People will say we're in love / Oh what a beautiful morning / Poor Judd is dead / Surrey with the fringe on top / Many a new day / Kansas city / I can't say no / Buenos aires / High flying / Adored / Don't cry for me Argentina / She is a diamond / Another suitcase in another hall / I could have danced all night / On the street where you live / Wouldn't it be lovely / Show me / Embassy waltz / Get me to the church on time / I've grown accustomed to your face / With a little bit of luck / Sound of music / How can love survive / Lonely goatherd / My favourite things / Sixteen going on seventeen / Climb every mountain / No way to stop it / Ordinary couple / Edelweiss / So long farewell

CDMFP 6235 / Jul '96 / Music For Pleasure

☐ **GREATEST TV THEMES**
London's Burning / Forever Green / Professionals / Agatha Christie's Poirot / To Have and To Hold / Upstairs Downstairs / Thomas and Sarah / Good Guys / Gentle Touch / Bouget Of Barbed Wire / Partners In Crime / Budgie / Wish Me Luck / Love For Lydia / Lillie / Black Beauty / Dempsey and Makepiece

CDMFP 6234 / Jul '96 / Music For Pleasure

☐ **GUYS N' GIRLS**
I'm A Yankee Doodle Dandy: Cagney, James / Lullaby Of Broadway: Powell, Dick / Pennies From Heaven: Crosby, Bing / Three Little Words: Ellington, Duke & The Rhythm Boys / On The Good Ship Lollipop: Temple, Shirley / It's Only A Paper Moon: Edwards, Cliff / Let's Face The Music And Dance: Astaire, Fred & Ginger Rogers / 42nd Street: Keeler, Ruby & Dick Powell / Over The Rainbow: Garland, Judy / Sonny Boy: Jolson, Al / Sunny Side Up: Endor, Chick / Pick yourself up

ONEC 005 / Apr '96 / Tring

☐ **HARK, HARK THE LARK (Music For Shakespeare's Company)**
CDA 66836 / Jan '98 / Hyperion

☐ **HEART TO HEART (Classic Duets From The Great Shows)**
They say it's wonderful: Craven, Gemma & Edmund Hockridge / I've never been in love before: Robertson, Liz & Keith Michell / Summer nights: Newley, Anthony & Linda Hibberd / Summer nights: Grant, Carl & Michaela Strachan / Last night of the world: Criswell, Kim & Carl Wayne / People will say we're in love: Jones, Paul & Fiona Hendley / True love: Collier, Tracy Buddington / As long as he needs me: Stringer, Mike & love/As long as he needs me: Stringer, Gareth & Bonnie Langford / I might fall back on you: Craven, Gemma & David Kernan / Where is love/As long as he needs me: Robertson, Liz & Tracy Miller / Twin soliloquys: Craven, Gemma & David Kernan / Something good: Robertson, Liz & Denis Quilley / First man you remember: Lawrence, Stephanie & Dave Willetts /

Rain in Spain: *Robertson, Liz & Denis Quilley* / At the end of the day: *Willetts, Dave & Claire Moore* / Who wants to be a millionaire: *Wayne, Carl & Tracy Collier* / You're the one that I want: *Wayne, Carl & Michaela Strachan* / Anything you can do: *Hockridge, Edmund & Gemma Craven* / Sunset sunset: *Newley, Anthony & Linda Hibberd*
3036200372 / Feb '97 / Carlton

☐ **HELLO CHILDREN EVERYWHERE**
Bertha: *Daly, Bryan* / Barnacle Bill: *Torch, Sidney* / Camberwick: *Phillips, Freddie* / Chigley: *Phillips, Freddie* / Puffin' Billy / Fireman Sam / Heads and Tails / Henry's Cat / Jim'll Fix It / Acrobat: *Brighouse & Rastrick Band* / Magic Roundabout: *Legrand, Alain* / Mop and Smiff: *Amatt, Mike* / Play Away / Postman Pat: *Daly, Bryan* / Ragtime / Record Breakers / Rhubarb and Custard / Rubovia: *Phillips, Freddie* / Superted / Swap Shop: *Batt, Mike* / Parade of the toy soldiers: *New Light Symphony Orchestra* / Trumpton: *Phillips, Freddie* / Willo The Wisp
336362 / 24 Nov '97 / Koch International

☐ **HER FAVOURITE MOVIE SONGS (Marjane, Leo)**
995702 / Sep '96 / EPM

☐ **HISTORICAL ROMANCES (Juarez/ Devotion/Gunga Din/Charge Of The Light Brigade) (Brandenburg Philharmonic Orchestra)**
Kaufman, Richard *con*
8223608 / Feb '96 / Marco Polo

☐ **HISTORY OF HITCHCOCK VOL.1, A (Dial M For Murder) (City Of Prague Philharmonic Orchestra)**
Bateman, Paul *con*
Psycho / North by Northwest / Rebecca / Spellbound / Under Capricorn / Vertigo / Topaz / Marnie / Frenzy / Suspicion / Dial M for murder
FILMCD 137 / Sep '93 / Silva Screen

☐ **HISTORY OF HITCHCOCK VOL.2, A (To Catch A Thief) (City Of Prague Philharmonic Orchestra)**
Bateman, Paul *con*
Thirty Nine Steps / Lady Vanishes / Stagefright / Rope / Lifeboat / To Catch a Thief / Vertigo / Torn Curtain / Family Plot / North by Northwest / Strangers on a Train / Trouble with Harry / Rear Window
FILMCD 159 / Apr '95 / Silva Screen

☐ **HISTORY OF THE WESTERN FILM SCORE VOL.1, THE (How The West Was Won) (City Of Prague Philharmonic Orchestra)**
Raine, Nic/Paul Bateman *con*
How the West was won / Wild bunch / Buffalo girls / Professionals / Magnificent seven / Gettysburg / Wild rovers / High plains drifter
FILMCD 173 / Apr '96 / Silva Screen

☐ **HISTORY OF THE WESTERN FILM SCORE VOL.2, THE (Lonesome Dove) (City Of Prague Philharmonic Orchestra)**
Bateman, Paul/D. Wadsworth/N. Raine *con*
Red river / Old gringo / Proud rebel / El condor / Sons of Katie Elder / Outlaw Josie Wales / Hang 'em high / Heaven's gate / Lonesome dove / Red sun / She wore a yellow ribbon
FILMCD 176 / Jul '96 / Silva Screen

☐ **HIT SONGS FROM BROADWAY**
Oh what a beautiful morning / Surrey with a fringe on top / People will say we're in love / If I loved you / When the children are asleep / What's the use of wond'rin / To keep my love alive / Johnny one note / Ten cents a dance / I love Louisa / Triplets / You and the night and music / Got a bran' new suit / This is it / After you who / Ridin' high / Harlem on my mind / I left my heart at the stage door canteen / This is the army Mr. Jones / Speak low / That's him / I'm alone...the song is you / Heaven in my arms / All the things we are
CDMOIR 519 / Jun '97 / Memoir

☐ **HIT SONGS FROM THE WESTERN MUSICALS**
Bless your beautiful hide / Is it really me / Oh waht a beautiful morning / I say hello / I talk to the trees / 76 Trombones / I will always love you / Anything you can do / Just blew in from the windy city / Indian love call / Ol' man river / It's a grand night for singing
SHOWCD 053 / Apr '97 / Showtime

☐ **HITCHCOCK - MASTER OF MAYHEM (San Diego Symphony Pops)**
Schifrin, Lalo *con*
Invisible Third / Alfred Hitchcock theme / Vertigo / Marnie / Psycho / Rebecca / Rear Window / Rollercoaster / Bullitt / Mannix / Dirty Harry / Mission Impossible
SION 18170 / Jul '97 / Sion

☐ **HITS & MOVIES**
11817 / Aug '95 / Music

☐ **HITS FROM THE MOVIES**
Crying game / Heat is on / Axel F / Power of love / Nothing has been proved / More than a woman / Call me / Born to be wild / Sisters are doin' it for themselves / Everybody's talkin' / Midnight cowboy / Joy to the world / Warmth of the sun / Woodstock / Gonna fly now (Rocky theme)
CDMFP 6138 / Jun '95 / Music For Pleasure

☐ **HITS FROM THE MOVIES**
CDCD 1230 / Jun '95 / Charly

☐ **HITS FROM THE MOVIES**
La bamba / Good golly Miss Molly / When I'm walkin' / Will you love me tomorrow / Raindrops keep falling on my head / Emmanuelle / As time goes by / Tell it like it is / England swings / Man whos hot Liberty Valance / Get a job / Tequila / Louie Louie / Whole lotta shakin' going on / Yesterday's hero / Sweet Gene Vincent
12608 / Apr '96 / Laserlight

☐ **HITS FROM THE MUSICALS (Starlight Orchestra/Singers)**
West side story overture / C'est magnifique / Anything you can do / I got plenty o' nuttin' / Gigi / I've grown accustomed to her face / Cheek to cheek / Hello young lovers / Oklahoma / Somewhere / Almost like being in love / Summertime / True love / On the street where you live / Oh what a beautiful mornin' / Maria / Begin the beguine / With a little bit of luck / You'll never walk alone / Bali ha'i / They say it's wonderful / There's no business like showbusiness
QED 110 / Nov '96 / Tring

☐ **HOBSON'S CHOICE (Hobson, Helen)**
On my way to you / Don't rain on my parade / Merry go round / With every breath I take / Show me / Day I stop loving you / If ever I would leave you: *Hobson, Helen & Cliff Richard* / If I've let you down / You've got to give me room / Minute waltz / What's new/ Since you stayed here / Anything but lonely: *Hobson, Helen & Graham Bickley* / Girls of Summer / And I am telling you / Wedding song: *Hobson, Helen & Cliff Richard* / Is it really me
URCD 124 / Oct '96 / Upbeat

☐ **HOLLYWOOD (London Festival Orchestra)**
Man and a woman / Il silenzio / Love story / Affair to remember / Hello young lovers / Sound of music / Moon river / La ronde / Tara's theme / Three coins in the fountain / Shane / Anything goes / Dancing in the dark / Days of wine and roses / Love is a many splendoured thing / Tammy / Pennies from Heaven / It's magic / Magnificent seven / High noon
OP 0004 / Apr '87 / MCI Music

☐ **HOLLYWOOD (San Diego Symphony Pops)**
Schifrin, Lalo *con*
Superman / Raiders Of The Lost Ark / Bridge Over The River Kwai / Captain From Castille / Great Escape / Patton / Return Of The Jedi / Music Man / What did you do in the war Daddy / Statue Of Liberty march / Apocalypse Now / Armed Forces medley / Hunt For Red October / Cinerama march / Dirty Dozen / Great waldo pepper / Stars and stripes forever
SION 18150 / Jul '97 / Sion

☐ **HOLLYWOOD '94 (McNeely, Joel & Seattle Symphony Orchestra)**
VSD 5531 / Jan '95 / Varese Sarabande

☐ **HOLLYWOOD '95 (McNeely, Joel & Seattle Symphony Orchestra)**
VSD 5671 / Nov '95 / Varese Sarabande

☐ **HOLLYWOOD '96**
VSD 5764 / Mar '97 / Varese Sarabande

☐ **HOLLYWOOD A LA HAMMOND**
Time for us / Shadow of your smile / Autumn leaves / Love is a many splendoured thing / People / Georgy girl / James Bond theme / Certain smile / Ballad of Bonnie and Clyde / What are you doing the rest of your life / Singin' in the rain / If I were a rich man / Speak softly love / Theme from MASH / Theme from Love Story / Jesus Christ superstar / Goldfinger / Man and a woman / Mrs. Robinson / Windmills of your mind / Diamonds are forever / Day by day / Lara's theme / Raindrops keep falling on my head
303942 / Jun '97 / Hallmark

☐ **HOLLYWOOD BACKLOT VOL.3**
VSD 5361 / Dec '92 / Varese Sarabande

☐ **HOLLYWOOD BOWL ON BROADWAY, THE (Hollywood Bowl Symphony Orchestra)**
Mauceri, John *con*
June is bustin' out all over / When the children are asleep / Blow high blow low / If I loved you / Real nice clambreak / Stonecutters cut it on stone / What's the use of wond'rin / You'll never walk alone / Any place I hang my hat is home / I had myself a true love / One for my baby (and one more for the road) / Come rain or come shine / Mack the knife / Surabaya Johnny / Bilbao song / J'attends un navire / Train to Johannesburg / Lost in the stars / My ship / September song / Ol' man river / Can't help lovin' that man / You are love / Why do I love you
4464042 / Mar '97 / Philips

☐ **HOLLYWOOD CHRISTMAS, A**
VSD 5621 / Nov '96 / Varese Sarabande

☐ **HOLLYWOOD CHRONICLE - GREAT MOVIE CLASSICS VOL. 1**
VSD 5351 / Nov '92 / Varese Sarabande

☐ **HOLLYWOOD COLLECTION**
Singin' in the rain: *Kelly, Gene* / Over the rainbow: *Garland, Judy* / Entertainer: *Joplin, Scott* / Cheek to cheek: *Astaire, Fred* / Mammy: *Jolson, Al* / Let's face the music and dance: *Rogers, Ginger* / Couple of swells: *Astaire, Fred* / Diamonds are a girl's best friend: *Monroe, Marilyn* / Night and day: *Sinatra, Frank* / In the mood: *Miller, Glenn* / Trail of the lonesome pine: *Laurel & Hardy* / Ol' man river: *Robeson, Paul* / I'm in the mood for love: *Hutton, Betty* / Hello Dolly: *Armstrong, Louis* / Zip: *Hayworth, Rita* / I've got my love to keep me warm: *Bogart, Humphrey* / Gentlemen prefer blondes: *Russell, Jane & Marilyn Monroe* / Hi lili hi lo: *Caron, Leslie & Mel Ferrer* / Who's sorry now: *De Haven, Gloria* / It had to be you: *Lamour, Dorothy*
DVCD 2054 / May '86 / Deja Vu

☐ **HOLLYWOOD DREAMS (Hollywood Bowl Symphony Orchestra)**
Mauceri, John *con*
4321092 / Sep '91 / Philips

☐ **HOLLYWOOD GOLDEN CLASSICS (Carreras, Jose)**
9031737932 / Jul '93 / WEA

☐ **HOLLYWOOD GOLDEN YEARS (Garland, Judy)**
BMCD 7010 / Nov '96 / Blue Moon

☐ **HOLLYWOOD GOLDEN YEARS (Kelly, Gene)**
BM 99908 / Jan '97 / Blue Moon

☐ **HOLLYWOOD HEROES**
Great Escape / Dances With Wolves / Raiders Of The Lost Ark / High Road To China / Mad Max III / Alamo / Born On The 4th Of July / El Cid / Zulu / Out Of Africa / War is over / Torn Curtain / Robin And Marion / Cliffhanger
SILVAD 3501 / Nov '97 / Silva Treasury

☐ **HOLLYWOOD HITS**
Serene family/Disclosure / Conquest of paradise / Lily was here / Emmanuelle / Basic Instinct / Gayle's theme / Age Of Innocence / Everything has it's price / Pelican Brief / My big secret / Claudia's theme / Good The Bad And The Ugly / Silence Of The Lambs / Dances With Wolves / Desert landing / Firm / Only You / Jurrasic Park
301562 / Feb '98 / Hallmark

☐ **HOLLYWOOD IN LOVE (Greatest Love Songs From The Movies) (Hollywood Bowl Symphony Orchestra)**
Mauceri, John *con*
Love is a many splendoured thing / Unchained melody / Cathie's theme / Love theme / Peyton Place / Oh mio babbino caro / Eternal love / Age of innocence / Cinema paradiso / Somewhere in time / Love for love / Conversation piece / Four weddings and a funeral / Laura / Now voyager / Affair to remember
4546472 / Aug '96 / Philips

☐ **HOLLYWOOD LADIES SING (I'm Ready For My Close Up)**
85972 / Feb '90 / Silva Screen

☐ **HOLLYWOOD MUSICALS**
Mammy: *Jolson, Al* / Cheek to cheek: *Astaire, Fred* / Over the rainbow: *Garland, Judy* / Yankee doodle boy: *Cagney, James* / Road to Morocco: *Hope, Bob/ Bing Crosby/Judy Garland* / Put the blame on mame: *Hayworth, Rita* / White Christmas: *Crosby, Bing* / Best things in life are free: *Allyson, June & Peter Lawford* / Johnny one note: *Garland, Judy* / Couple of swells: *Garland, Judy & Fred Astaire* / Who's sorry now: *De Haven, Gloria* / 'S Wonderful: *Kelly, Gene* / diamonds are a girl's best friend: *Monroe, Marilyn* / Bye bye baby: *Monroe, Marilyn & Jane Russell* / Too darn hot: *Miller, Arthur* / Hi lili hi lo: *Caron, Leslie & Mel Ferrer* / Indian love call: *Blyth, Ann & Fernando Lamas* / Rose Marie: *Keel, Howard* / Stranger in paradise: *Blyth, Ann & Vic Damone* / Thank heavens for little girls: *Chevalier, Maurice* / Hello Dolly: *Armstrong, Louis* / There's no business like show business: *Merman, Ethel* / Move over darling: *Day, Doris* / Oh what a beautiful morning: *McRae, Gordon*
DVRECD 26 / '89 / Deja Vu

☐ **HOLLYWOOD MUSICALS, THE**
CIN 020 / Oct '96 / IMP

☐ **HOLLYWOOD SINGS (Stars Of The Silver Screen)**
Happy feet: *Whiteman, Paul & Rhythm Boys* / Toot toot Tootsie goodbye: *Jolson, Al* / Johnny: *Dietrich, Marlene* / Day after day: *Stewart, James* / Can Broadway do without me: *Clayton, Jackson & Durante* / If you haven't got love: *Swanson, Gloria* / Doin' the new low down: *Robinson, Bill 'Bojangles'* / Keep your sunny side up: *Gaynor, Janet* / Kashmiri love song: *Valentino, Rudolph* / Broadway melody: *King, Charles* / Puttin' on the ritz: *Richman, Harry* / How long will it last: *Crawford, Joan* / Hooray for Captain Spaulding: *Marx, Groucho & Zeppo* / Just like a butterfly: *Morgan, Helen* / I love Louisa: *Astaire, Fred* / Can't get along: *Rogers, Ginger* / You've got that thing: *Chevalier, Maurice* / Beyond the blue horizon: *MacDonald, Jeanette* / White dove: *Tibbett, Lawrence* / Yes yes (my baby says yes): *Cantor, Eddie*
CD AJA 5011 / Feb '87 / Living Era

☐ **HOLLYWOOD SINGS - THE GIRLS**
It's foolish but it's fun: *Durbin, Deanna* / Waltzing in the clouds: *Durbin, Deanna* / When the roses bloom again: *Durbin, Deanna* / Body and soul: *Langford, Frances* / Someone to watch over me: *Langford, Frances* / I've got you under my skin: *Langford, Frances* / Lovely to look at: *Dunne, Irene* / Jitterbug: *Garland, Judy* / Over the rainbow: *Garland, Judy* / It never rains but it pours: *Garland, Judy* / Mister five by five: *Andrews Sisters* / Ferryboat serenade: *Andrews Sisters* / Say 'si si': *Andrews Sisters* / Mayor of Kaunakakai: *Andrews Sisters* / Kiss the boys goodbye: *Martin, Mary* / Katie went to Haiti: *Martin, Mary* / On the lollipop song: *Miranda, Carmen* / One I love: *Fitzgerald, Ella* / Falling in love again: *Dietrich, Marlene* / Moon song: *Smith, Kate*
304112 / Jun '97 / Hallmark

☐ **HOLLYWOOD SINGS - THE GUYS**
Moonlight becomes you: *Crosby, Bing* / I'm thinking tonight of my blue eyes: *Crosby, Bing* / I have eyes: *Crosby, Bing* / Moon and the willow tree: *Crosby, Bing* / I haven't time to be a millionaire: *Crosby, Bing* / Always in my heart: *Baker, Kenny* / There are two rivers to cross: *Baker, Kenny* / Love walked in: *Baker, Kenny* / Blue Tahitian moon: *Baker, Kenny* / Farming: *Kaye, Danny* / Fairy pipers: *Kaye, Danny* / Tchaikovsky (and other Russians): *Kaye, Danny* / Antole of Paris: *Kaye, Danny* / Rock-a-bye your baby with a Dixie melody: *Jolson, Al* / April showers: *Jolson, Al* / Stein song: *Powell, Dick* / In a moment of weakness: *Powell, Dick* / 'Tis Autumn: *Martin, Tony* / Cancel the flowers: *Martin, Tony* / Indian summer: *Martin, Tony*
304102 / Jun '97 / Hallmark

☐ **HOLLYWOOD SOUND, THE (John Williams Conducts The Academy Awards Best Scores) (London Symphony Orchestra)**
Williams, John *con*
Out Of Africa / Dances With Wolves / ET / Star Wars / Jaws / Place In The Sun: *London Symphony Orchestra & Grover Washington Jr.* / Last Emperor / Spellbound / Godfather II / Beauty And The Beast / Pocahontas / Robin Hood / Lawrence Of Arabia / Wizard Of Oz
SK 62788 / Mar '97 / Sony Classical

☐ **HOLLYWOOD SOUNDSTAGE VOL.1**
VSD 5301 / Jul '91 / Varese Sarabande

☐ **HOLLYWOOD STARS GO TO WAR**
VJC 1048 / Jul '93 / Vintage Jazz Classics

☐ **HOLLYWOOD TOUGH GUYS**
Terminator / Blade Runner / Big Trouble In Little China / Spartacus / Redemption / March of the villians / Villa Rides / Cape Fear / Good times are coming / Man with the harmonica / Professionals / Taras Bulba / Licence To Kill / Serpico / Horror
SILVAD 3506 / Oct '97 / Silva Treasury

☐ **HOLLYWOOD'S GREATEST HITS**
GRF 192 / Jan '93 / Tring

☐ **HOLLYWOOD'S GREATEST HITS (Tritt, W./Cincinnati Pops Orchestra)**
Kunzel, Erich *con*
CD 80168 / Sep '88 / Telarc

☐ **HOLLYWOOD'S GREATEST HITS, VOL 2 (Cincinnati Pops Orchestra)**
CD 80319 / Aug '93 / Telarc

☐ **HOMAGE A MARCEL CARNE (Musique De Films) (Orchestre Du Capitole De Toulouse)**
Plasson, Michel *con*
CDC 75477642 / Apr '94 / EMI Classics

☐ **HOOKED ON MOVIES (Brooks, Paul)**
Oklahoma / Maria / Over The Rainbow / Secret Love / Singin' In The Rain / On The Street Where You Live / Hello Dolly / Wand'rin' Star / Shall We Dance / Sound Of Music / 633 Squadron / Colonel Bogey / Great Escape / Where Eagles Dare / Dam Busters / Also Sprach Zarathustra / Star Wars / Close Encounters Of The Third Kind / Eve Of The War / Superman / Ghostbusters / Doctor Who / Star Trek / ET - The Extra Terrestrial / Batman / Piano / Everybody's Talkin' / Chariots Of Fire / Rocky / Zorba The Greek / Jaws / Entertainer / Lawrence Of Arabia / Godfather / Cavatina / Tara's Theme / I Will Always Love You / Theme From Love Story / Days Of Wine And Roses / Theme From A Summer Place / Unchained Melody / Love Is All Around / Somewhere My Love / Moon River / Big Country / Hang 'Em High / Good The Bad And The Ugly / High Noon / Man Who Shot Liberty Valance / Magnificent Seven
ECD 3313 / Apr '97 / K-Tel

☐ **HOORAY FOR HOLLYWOOD**
Hooray for Hollywood: *MGM Studio Orchestra* / Shall we dance: *Astaire, Fred* / Good morning: *Garland, Judy & Mickey Rooney* / My mammy: *Jolson, Al* / Puttin' on the Ritz: *Jolson, Al* / Fine romance: *Jolson, Al* / They're either too young or too old: *Davis, Bette* / Sweet Leilani: *Crosby, Bing* / Put the blame on mame: *Hayworth, Rita* / 42nd street: *MGM Studio Orchestra* / When you wish upon a star: *Edwards, Cliff* / Like a guy that takes his time: *West, Mae* / White Christmas: *Crosby, Bing* / California here I come: *Jolson, Al* / Meet me in St. Louis: *Garland, Judy* / Biys in the backroom: *Dietrich, Marlene* / Pick yourself up: *Astaire, Fred & Ginger Rogers* / Lullaby of Broadway: *MGM Studio Orchestra* / As time goes by: *Wilson, Dooley* / Swinging on a star: *Crosby, Bing* / Over the rainbow: *Garland, Judy* / We're off to see the wizard: *Garland, Judy & Ray Bolger/Bert Lahr/ Buddy Ebson* / Cheek to cheek: *Astaire, Fred* / They call me sister honky tonk: *West, Mae* / We're in the money: *Rogers, Ginger* / Let's call the whole thing off: *Jolson, Al & Sonny Boy/Fred Astaire/Ginger Rogers* / You excite me: *Hayworth, Rita* / I fall in love too easily: *Sinatra, Frank* / Dames: *Warner Brothers Studio Orchestra* / Babbit and the bromide: *Astaire, Fred & Ginger Rogers* / My own: *Durbin, Deanna* / I'm just wild about Harry: *Astaire, Fred & Ginger Rogers/ Mickney Rooney* / If I only had a brain: *Garland, Judy & Ray Bolger* / I'm putting all my eggs in one basket: *Astaire, Fred & Ginger Rogers* / Boogie woogie bugle boy: *Andrews Sisters* / Let me sing and I'm happy: *Jolson, Al* / Thanks for the memory: *Hope, Bob & Shirley Ross*
PC 619 / 10 Nov '97 / Start

☐ **HORROR (The 1950/1960's Horror Film Music Album) (Westminster Philharmonic Orchestra)**
Alwyn, Kenneth *con*
Night of the demon / Corridors of blood / Haunting / Abominable snowman / Witchfinder general / Curse of the Mummy's tomb / Konga / Fiend without a face / Devil rides out / Horrors of the black museum / Curse of the werewolf
FILMCD 175 / Apr '96 / Silva Screen

☐ **HORROR (Monsters Witches & Vampires)**
Ave Satan / Bride Of Frankenstein theme / Dracula theme / Taste the blood of Dracula / Horrors of the black museum overture / Halloween theme / Prince Of Darkness theme / They Live theme / Witchfinder General / Power Of Evil / Flower duet / Curse Of The Werewolf theme / Vampire circus theme
SILVAD 3507 / Nov '97 / Silva Treasury

☐ **HORROR THEMES**
Fly / Thing / Fog / Carrie / Psycho / Poltergeist 3 / Exorcist / Hellraiser / Halloween / Amityville Horror / Friday The 13th / Vertigo / Silence Of The Lambs / Rosemary's Baby
SUMCD 4122 / May '97 / Sound & Media

☐ **HORRORVISIONS**
EDL 25722 / Jan '92 / Edel

☐ HOT MOVIE THEMES
24030 / Mar '95 / Music

I

☐ I WANTS TO BE A ACTOR LADY (Cincinnati Uni Singers/Orchestra)
Rivers, E. *con*
802212 / Apr '94 / New World

☐ I WISH IT SO (Songs By Sondheim/ Bernstein/Weill/Blitzstein) (Upshaw, Dawn)
Stern, Eric *con*
7559793452 / Dec '94 / Nonesuch

☐ IF I LOVED YOU (Love Duets From The Musicals) (Allen, Thomas & Valerie Masterson/Philharmonia Orchestra)
Edwards, John Owen *con*
All I ask of you / Heather on the hill / They say it's wonderful / Til there was you / My time of day / I've never been in love before / People will say we're in love / Tonight / I have dreamed / Make believe / Indian love call / I f I loved you / Hello young lovers / Some enchanted evning
CDVIR 8317 / Nov '97 / TER

☐ I'M NO ANGEL (The Original Commercial Recordings/The Film Soundtracks) (West, Mae)
I like a guy who takes his time / Easy rider / I'm no angel / I found a new way to go to town / I want you I need you / They call me Sister Honky Tonk / Willie of the valley / I like a guy who takes his time / Easy rider / Frankie and Johnny / They call me Sister Honky Tonk / That Dallas man / I fond a new way to get to town / I want you I need you / I'm no angel / When St. Louis woman comes down to New Orleans / My old flame / Memphis blues / Troubled waters / He's a bad bad man / Mon coeur s'ouvre a ta voix / I'm an Occidental woman in an Oriental mood for love / Mister Deep Blue Sea / Little Bar Butterfly / On a typical tropical night / I was saying to the moon / Fifi / Now I'm a lady
JASCD 102 / Oct '96 / Jasmine

☐ IN CONCERT (Welch, Elizabeth)
OCRCD 6016 / Apr '96 / First Night

☐ IN LOVE IN HOLLYWOOD (Jones, Salena)
CDVIR 8328 / Jan '95 / TER

☐ IN LOVE ON BROADWAY (Jones, Salena)
Only love / I still believe in love / Hello young lovers / I only miss him when you think of him / Embraceable you / Quiet thing / My heart stood still / Time heals everything / Young and foolish / Taking a chance on love / Who can I turn to / But not for me / Old friend / Fascinating rhythm
CDVIR 8327 / Nov '97 / TER

☐ IN THE REAL WORLD (Hadley, Jerry & American Theatre Orchestra)
Gemignani, Paul *con*
09026619372 / Apr '94 / RCA Victor

☐ IN TOWN TONIGHT (25 Nostalgic Theatre & Cabaret Songs)
London pride: *Coward, Sir Noel* / Someday I'll find you: *Lawrence, Gertrude* / Home town: *Flanagan & Allen* / Walter Walter: *Bowlly, Al* / Mad about the boy: *Lillie, Beatrice* / Everything's in rhythm with my heart: *Matthews, Jessie* / Mae time: *Desmond, Florence* / Dancing in the dark: *Hutchinson, Leslie 'Hutch'* / Mad dogs and Englishmen: *Coward, Sir Noel* / Auf weidersehen sweetheart: *Bowlly, Al* / Sophisticated lady: *Hall, Adelaide* / Broadway melody: *Layton & Johnstone* / Free: *Flanagan & Allen* / Little Betty Bouncer: *Flotsam & Jetsam* / My sweet Virginia: *Bowlly, Al* / Shirts: *Lane, Lupino* / Little silkworm: *Matthews, Jessie* / My sweet: *Lawrence, Gertrude* / When I grow too old to dream: *Fields, Gracie* / You were meant for me: *Layton & Johnstone* / I wanna be loved: *Hall, Adelaide* / Rain on the roof: *Bowlly, Al* / Simon the bootlegger: *Flotsam & Jetsam* / You're blase: *Hutchinson, Leslie 'Hutch'*
PLATCD 172 / Mar '96 / Prism

☐ INDIANA JONES (Music From The Films Of Harrison Ford) (City Of Prague Philharmonic Orchestra)
Bateman, Paul *con*
Witness / Regarding Henry / Mosquito coast / Patriot games / Fugitive / Blade runner / Presumed innocent / Star Wars / Empire strikes back / Return of the Jedi / Raiders of the Lost Ark / Indiana Jones and the temple of doom / Indiana Jones and the last crusade / Hanover Street
FILMCD 154 / Oct '94 / Silva Screen

☐ IS IT REALLY ME (Philharmonia/ Symphony/Scottish Opera/New Sadler's Wells Opera Orchestras)
CDVIR 8314 / Oct '91 / TER

J

☐ JAMES BOND THEMES, THE (London Theatre Orchestra)
James Bond Theme / Licence To Kill / Living Daylights / Never Say Never Again / Man With The Golden Gun / View To A Kill / All Time High / Casino Royale / For Your Eyes Only / Live And Let Die / From Russia With Love / Diamonds Are Forever / You Only Live Twice / Nobody Does It Better / Thunderball / Moonraker / Mr. Kiss Kiss Bang Bang / Goldfinger / Goldeneye
QED 057 / Nov '96 / Tring

☐ JAMES BOND THEMES, THE (14 Classic Movie Themes) (London Theatre Orchestra)
James Bond Theme / Live And Let Die / Licence To Kill / From Russia With love / Nobody Does It Better / View To A Kill / For Your Eyes Only / On Her Majesty's Secret Service / Diamonds Are Forever / All time high / Thunderball / Goldfinger / Man With The Golden Gun / Moonraker / James Bond Theme
EMPRCD 576 / Jul '95 / Emporio

☐ JAMES BOND THEMES, THE
James Bond Theme / Live And Let Die / Licence TO Kill / From Russia With Love / Nobody does it better / View To A Kill / For Your Eyes Only / On Her Majesty's Secret Service / Diamond's Are Forever / All Time High / Thunderball / Goldfinger / Man With The Golden Gun / Moonraker / Golden Eye
SUMCD 4126 / Jun '97 / Sound & Media

☐ JAZZ AT THE CINEMA
Don't cry for me Argentina: *Getz, Stan* / Autumn leaves: *Baker, Chet* / Laura: *Bryant, Ray* / Something's coming: *Hi-Lo's* / It ain't necessarily so: *Franklin, Aretha* / Get me to the church on time: *Previn, Andre Quartet* / As time goes by: *Supersax & LA Voices* / Blues de la plume: *Grappelli, Stephane* / Exodus song: *Williams, Marion* / Tonight: *Bryant, Ray*
4874602 / 29 Sep '97 / Sony Jazz

☐ JAZZ GOES TO HOLLYWOOD (Karlin, Fred)
VSD 5639 / Nov '95 / Varese Sarabande

☐ JEAN GABIN VOL.2
302254 / Feb '97 / Playtime

☐ JEAN-PIERRE MOCKY - FINEST MUSIC OF HIS FILMS
302614 / Feb '97 / Playtime

☐ JOHN TRAVOLTA (Travolta, John)
EMPRCD 524 / Sep '94 / Empress

☐ JOHN WILLIAMS PLAYS THE MOVIES (& The World Of John Williams) (Williams, John)
Kiss from a rose / Everything I do / Unchained melody / Love is all around / Godfather / Moon river / Somewhere over the rainbow / Mission / Cavatina / As tme goes by / Les Parapluies De Cherbourg / It had to be you / Bagdad Cafe / Entertainer / Il Postino / Once Upon A Time In America / Once Upon A Time In The West / Schindler's List
S2K 62784 / Oct '96 / Sony Classical

☐ JOLSON SONGBOOK, THE (Minstrel Singers)
Rock-a-bye your baby / Swanee / My Mammy / April showers / California here I come / Toot toot tootsie / Sonny boy / Let me sing and I'm happy / You made me love you / Back in your own backyard / There's a rainbow 'round my shoulder / I'm sitting on top of the world / Waiting for the Robert E Lee / Me and my shadow / Carolina in the morning / Baby face / Give my regards to Broadway / Pretty baby / Bye bye blackbird / For me and my girl
3036200292 / Feb '97 / Carlton

☐ JOSE CARRERAS SINGS MUSICALS (Carreras, Jose)
4169732 / Jan '88 / Philips

☐ JOURNEY TO THE STARS
4464032 / Feb '96 / Philips

☐ JUNGLE BOOGIE
Bare necessities / Hakuna matata / I just can't wait to be king / Yummy yummy yummy / I wan'na be like you / Circle of life / Take your sweet sweet time / Alone together / Colonel Hathi's march / Stand by me / Can you feel the love tonight / Wharthog rhapsody / Bare necessities / Jungle book groove
WD 608615 / Oct '97 / Disney Music & Stories

☐ JUNGLE GIRL (Page, Betty)
QDKCD 017 / 26 Jan '98 / QDK Media

K

☐ KIRI ON BROADWAY (Te Kanawa, Dame Kiri)
My fair lady / One touch of Venus / Too many girls / Carousel / Kiss me Kate / West Side Story / Sound of music
4402802 / Jan '94 / Decca

☐ KISS (Monroe, Marilyn)
You'd be surprised / River of no return / I wanna be loved by you / When I fall in love / Bye bye baby / Diamonds are a girl's best friend / One silver dollar / I'm gonna file my claim / When love goes wrong nothing goes right / After you get what you want you don't want it / Runnin' wild / Specialisation / My heart belongs to Daddy / Two little girls from Little Rock / Heat wave / Kiss
CD 3555 / Nov '95 / Cameo

L

☐ LADIES OF THE 20TH CENTURY, THE (Monroe, Marilyn)
Kiss / Do it again / She acts like a woman should / Little girl from Little Rock / Bye bye bye / Diamonds are a girl's best friend / When love goes wrong / Fine romance / River of no return / Down in the meadow / After you get what you want you don't want it / Heatwave
JD 1238 / Aug '93 / Jazz Door

☐ LADYKILLER, THE (Music From Those Glorious Ealing Films) (Royal Ballet Sinfonia)
Alwyn, Kenneth *con*
FILMCD 177 / Feb '98 / Silva Screen

☐ LAST ACTION HEROES, THE (Starlight Orchestra/Singers)
Gonna fly now / Terminator II / Living in America / Big gun / Fugitive / Peace in our lives / Raiders of the lost ark / Eye of the tiger / Still cruisin' / Shaft / He ain't heavy he's my brother / Robocop II / Philadelphia morning / It's a long road / Runaway train / Can't stop the fire / Anything goes / You could be mine
GRF 287 / Apr '95 / Tring

☐ LAUREL AND HARDY'S MUSIC BOX VOL.1 (New Recordings Of Laurel & Hardy Scores)
Ku-ku / On to the show / Bells / Dash and dot / We're out for fun / Drunk / Rockin' chairs / Give us a hand / Riding along / Gangway Charlie / Here we go / Moon and you / You are the one I love / Beautiful lady / Look at him now / Funny faces / On a sunny afternoon / Sons of the Desert
LH 10012 / Nov '89 / Silva Screen

☐ LAUREL AND HARDY'S MUSIC BOX VOL.2
LH 10022 / Nov '89 / Silva Screen

☐ LE CINEMA (Kremer, Gidon)
Improvviso / Nostalghia / Tamti anni prima / Rag-i-con-time / Absalom's death/Tango / Ovad / Le boef sur le toit / Fantasy / Smile
0630172222 / 16 Mar '98 / Teldec Classics

☐ LE CINEMA QUI CHANTE VOL.1
3007492 / Feb '97 / Orphee/Cinestars

☐ LE CINEMA QUI CHANTE VOL.2
3007502 / Feb '97 / Orphee/Cinestars

☐ LE CINEMA QUI CHANTE VOL.3
3007512 / Feb '97 / Orphee/Cinestars

☐ LE CINEMA QUI CHANTE VOL.4
3007522 / Feb '97 / Orphee/Cinestars

☐ LE CINEMA QUI CHANTE VOL.5
3007532 / Feb '97 / Orphee/Cinestars

☐ LE CINEMA QUI CHANTE VOL.6
3007542 / Feb '97 / Orphee/Cinestars

☐ LEADING LADIES
Broadway baby theme / Music and the mirror: *Harris, Anita* / Broadway baby: *Langford, Bonnie* / Don't rain on my parade: *Moore, Claire* / I get along without you very well: *Kesselman, Maria* / It's better with a band: *Harris, Anita* / Once you lose your heart: *Langford, Bonnie* / Birth of the blues: *Moore, Claire* / City lights: *Harris, Anita* / I enjoy being a girl: *Kesselman, Maria* / Tell me it's not true: *Langford, Bonnie* / Move over darling: *Moore, Claire* / How are things in Glocca Morra: *Moore, Claire* / My secret love: *Langford, Bonnie* / Bewitched: *Kesselman, Maria* / Hello young lovers: *Kesselman, Maria* / Perfect year: *Harris, Anita*
3036200342 / Mar '97 / Carlton

☐ LEGENDARY PERFORMERS 1930/ 1941 (MacDonald, Jeanette & Nelson Eddy)
Indian love call / Rose-Marie / Song of love / Waltz / I'm falling in love with someone / Italian street song / Tramp tramp tramp along the highway / Ah the mystery of life (dream melody) / Little love a little kiss / Drink to me only with thine eyes / Kerry dance / Smilin' through / Lover come back to me / One kiss / Who are we to say (obey your heart) / Isn't romantic / Beyond the blue horizon / Will you rember / Farewell to dreams / Sweethearts waltz
CD 60012 / Jun '97 / Great Movie Themes

☐ LEGENDARY SONG STYLIST (Merman, Ethel)
MACCD 361 / 24 Nov '97 / Autograph

☐ LES FILMS NOIR
887976 / Jun '95 / Milan

☐ LES MUSIQUES DES PALMES D'OR
Harry Lime theme / Manha de carnaval / La Dolce Vita / Il gattapardo / Les Parapluies De Cherbourg / Un Homme Et Une Femme / MASH / Go-Between / Ride of the valkyries / Concerto in G / Paris Texas / Gabriel's oboe / Big my secret / Bullwinkle
DC 880702 / May '97 / Disky

☐ LET ME SING AND I'M HAPPY (Al Jolson At Warner Bros. 1926-1936) (Jolson, Al)
April showers / Rock-a-bye your baby with a dixie melody / Dirty hands dirty face / Toot toot tootsie / Blue skies / Mother of mine I still have you / My Mammy / It all depends on you / I'm sitting on top of the world / Spaniard that blighted my life / There's a rainbow 'round my shoulder / Golden gate / Sonny boy / Back in your own back yard / Used to you / I'm in seventh Heaven / Let me sing and I'm happy / (Across the breakfast table) looking at you / Why do they all take the night boat to Albany / Liza Lee / Little sunshine / About a quarter to nine / I love to sing
CDODEON 24 / Jan '97 / Soundtracks

☐ LET'S FACE THE MUSIC (Astaire, Fred)
Let's face the music and dance / Fine romance / Foggy day / Change partners / I'm old fashioned / They can't take that away from me / Flying down to Rio / Let yourself go / Fascinating rhythm / They all laughed / Pick yourself up / Nice work if you can get it / Isn't this a lovely day / Dearly beloved / Way you look tonight / Let's call the whole thing off / Cheek to cheek / Funny face / Bojangles of Harlem / Shall we dance / Love of my life / Top hat white tie and tails / I'm putting all my eggs in one basket / I used to be colour blind / Dream dancing
AVC 537 / Oct '95 / Avid

☐ LET'S FACE THE MUSIC (Astaire, Fred)
Let's face the music and dance / Things are looking up / Way you look tonight / Nice work if you can get it / Poor Mr. Chisolm / Let's call the whole thing off / They all laughed / Shall we dance / My one and only / I'm putting all my eggs in one basket / Piccolino / Pick yourself up / They can't take that away from me / Isn't this a lovely day / No strings I'm fancy free / Fascinating rhythm
SUMCD 4049 / Nov '96 / Summit

☐ LET'S FACE THE MUSIC (A Tribute To Fred Astaire Live) (BBC Concert Orchestra)
Top hat selection / I'm putting alll my eggs in one basket / Smoke gets in your eyes / I won't dance / Fine romance / Continental / Night and day / Couple of swells / I've got my eyes on you / Overture / S'Wonderful / Be careful it's my heart / Nice work if you can get it / Theme to Finians Rainbow / Puttin' on the ritz / Way you look tonight / Change partners / Let's call the whole thing off / That's entertainment
11212 / Oct '97 / BBC Concert Orçhestra

☐ LET'S FACE THE MUSIC AND DANCE (Astaire, Fred)
Change partners / Cheek to cheek / I used to be colour blind / I'm putting all my eggs in one basket / Let's face the music and dance / No strings / Top hat white tie and tails / Yam / Foggy day / I can't be bothered now / I've got beginner's luck / Let's call the whole thing off / Nice work if you can get it / Shall we dance / Slap that bass / They all laughed / They can't take that away from me / Things are looking up / Poor Mr. Chisholm / Dearly Beloved / Fine romance / I'm old fashioned / Never gonna dance / Pick yourself up / Way you look tonight / You were never lovelier / Since I kissed my baby goodbye
CDAJA 5123 / Mar '94 / Living Era

☐ LET'S FACE THE MUSIC AND DANCE (All His Greatest Songs) (Astaire, Fred)
They can't take that away from me / Isn't this a lovely day / I'm putting all my eggs in one basket / They all laughed / Let's call the whole thing off / Shall we dance / Way you look tonight / Nice work if you can get it / Poor Mr. Chisholm / Let's face the music and dance / Piccolino / I used to be colour blind / Foggy day / My one and only / Pick yourself up / Yam / Let yourself go / Things are looking up / No strings (I'm fancy free) / Fascinating rhythm
305512 / Oct '96 / Hallmark

☐ LET'S GO ON WITH THE SHOW (Hits From The West End & Broadway)
America / If my friends could see me now / Send in the clowns / Wilkommen / I am what I am / Wunderbar / OH what a beautiful morning / Shall we dance / You'll never walk alone / Camelot / Get me to the church on time / Stranger in Paradise
SHOWCD 016 / Feb '95 / Showtime

☐ LET'S HAVE A LAUGH (16 Great British Comedy Themes) (London Theatre Orchestra)
Hancock's Half Hour / Happy Harry / Up to date / Men Behaving Badly / 2 Point 4 Children / Liberty bell / Some Mothers Do 'Ave 'Em / Fawlty Towers / Blackadder / Porridge / Rising Damp / Dick Emery Show / Old Ned / Bell hop / Good Life / Bond Street parade
EMPRCD 750 / 8 Sep '97 / Emporio

☐ LITTLE LIGHT MUSIC, A (A Showbiz Compilation Filled With Humour & Melody) (Singers Unlimited)
Old friends / Let's face the music and dance / Can that boy foxtrot / There are bad times just around the corner / Anyone can whistle / Broadway baby / It's bound to be right on the night / Why must the show go on / I've got a crush on you / Boy like that / I hate men / Why can't you behave/I got lost in his arms/ You're just in I / Losing my mind / Parisian Pierrot/ Last time I saw Paris/Ah Paris / Send in the clowns / Prelude No.2 / Maybe this time / We're gonna be alright
URCD 123 / Jun '96 / Upbeat

☐ LIVING DAYLIGHTS, THE (18 James Bond Themes)
RCD 10725 / 8 Jun '98 / Rykodisc

☐ LONDON PRIDE (Twiggy)
VSD 5715 / Nov '96 / Varese Sarabande

□ **LONGEST DAY, THE (Music From The Classic War Films) (City Of Prague Philharmonic Orchestra)**
Bateman, Paul *con*
Longest Day / 633 Squadron / Guns Of Navarone / Dambusters / Battle Of Britian / MacArthur/Patton / Night Of The Generals / Bridge On The River Kwai / Where Eagles Dare / Das Boot (The Boat) / Great Escape / Battle Of Midway / Battle Of The Bulge / Force 10 From Navarone / In Harm's Way / Sink The Bismark / Bridge At Remagen / Bridge Too Far / 1941 / Is Paris Burning
FILMCD 151 / '94 / Silva Screen

□ **LORDS OF THE MUSICAL (London Symphony Orchestra)**
FMI 201CD / Mar '97 / Focus

□ **LORELEI, THE (Songs By Gershwin, Porter & Berlin) (Criswell, Kim & Ambrosian Chorus/London Sinfonietta)**
McGlinn, John *con*
CDC 7548022 / Apr '94 / EMI Classics

□ **LOST IN BOSTON VOL.1**
VSD 5475 / Aug '94 / Varese Sarabande

□ **LOST IN BOSTON VOL.2**
VSD 5485 / Mar '95 / Varese Sarabande

□ **LOST IN BOSTON VOL.3 (Lost Gems From The Greatest Shows & Composers)**
VSD 5563 / Aug '95 / Varese Sarabande

□ **LOST IN BOSTON VOL.4**
VSD 5768 / Apr '97 / Varese Sarabande

□ **LOVE AT THE MOVIES...THE ALBUM**
Kiss from a rose: *Seal* / It must have been love: *Roxette* / In all the right places: *Stansfield, Lisa* / Crying game: *Boy George* / Absolute beginner: *Bowie, David* / No more lonely nights: *McCartney, Paul* / Nothing has been proved: *Springfield, Dusty* / I got you babe: *Sonny & Cher* / I will survive: *Savage, Chantay* / Goldeneye: *Turner, Tina* / Slave to love: *Ferry, Bryan* / Misty blue: *Moore, Dorothy* / Glory of love: *Cetera, Peter* / Sea of love: *Phillips, Phil* / Stardust: *Cole, Nat 'King'* / Beauty and the beast: *Bryson, Peabo & Celine Dion* / Falling: *Cruise, Julee* / I will find you: *Clannad* / Someday: *Eternal* / Love song for a vampire: *Lennox, Annie* / Show me Heaven: *McKee, Maria* / Take my breath away: *Berlin* / Up where we belong: *Cocker, Joe & Jennifer Warnes* / Unchained melody: *Righteous Brothers* / Blue velvet: *Vinton, Bobby* / Brown eyed girl: *Morrison, Van* / My girl: *Temptations* / Shy guy: *King, Diana* / It's in his kiss (shoop shoop song): *Cher* / Kokomo: *Beach Boys* / Coming round again: *Simon, Carly* / Give me the reason: *Vandross, Luther* / Against all odds: *Collins, Phil* / I don't wanna talk about it: *Indigo Girls* / Arthur's theme: *Cross, Christopher* / 500 miles: *Proclaimers* / Let me into your heart: *Carpenter, Mary-Chapin*
CDEMTVD 144 / Nov '96 / EMI

□ **LOVE AT THE THEATRE**
PMCD 7006 / Nov '94 / Pure Music

□ **LOVE AT THE THEATRE (Starlight Orchestra/Singers)**
Perfect year / All I ask of you / What I did for love / On the street where you live / People / She's so beautiful / Maria / I know him so well / Send in the clowns / I don't know how to love him / With one look / Love changes everything / Almost like being in love / Some enchanted evening / Memory
QED 118 / Nov '96 / Tring

□ **LOVE IN THE CINEMA (A Collection Of Romantic Movie Music)**
191892 / Jan '95 / Milan

□ **LOVE IS HERE TO STAY (Henshall, Ruthie)**
Love is here to stay / Somebody loves me / Someone to watch over me / Nice work if you can get it / Lady be good / 'S wonderful / But not for me / Summertime / Man I love / Embraceable you / Boy what love has done to me / They all laughed / Swanee / Love walked in
BRCD 6000 / Mar '94 / Bravo

□ **LOVE MOVIE THEMES**
22510 / Dec '95 / Music

□ **LOVE SONGS AT THE MOVIES (Starlight Orchestra/Singers)**
I will always love you / Streets of Philadelphia / What's love got to do with it / I can see clearly now / Book of days / Greatest love of all / Whole new world / Stand by me / Hello again / My girl / Nothing's gonna stop us now / Long and winding road / Rose / For all we know / Up where we belong / Try a little tenderness / First time ever I saw your face / You gotta love someone / Wind beneath my wings / (Everything I do) I do it for you / No ordinary love / All night long / Do you know where you're going to / Mona Lisa / Somewhere out there / Unchained melody / Arthur's theme (The best that you can get) / Way we were / It must have been love / He ain't heavy he's my brother / Power of love / Let the river run / Hopelessly devoted to you / Nobody does it better / Bright eyes / Suddenly / Love song for a vampire / Yesterday / Take my breath away / Will you be there / When I fall in love / I just called to say I love you / Love is in the air / Against all odds / Beauty and the Beast / Run to you / Tracks of my tears / King of wishful thinking / I don't wanna fight / If we hold on together / Again / Say you say me / Places that belong to you / Are you lonesome tonight / Sorry seems to be the hardest word / What becomes of the broken hearted / You light up my life / All for love / Someday I'm coming back / With you I'm born again / How deep is your love / Glory of love / Love on the rocks / (I've had) The time of my life / Endless love / All time high / Crying game / I can't help falling in love / Just the way you are / We may never love like this again / Shoop shoop song (It's in his kiss) / This used to be my playground / As time goes by / It's probably me / Sandy / Under the Boardwalk
QUAD 011 / Nov '96 / Tring

□ **LOVE SONGS FROM THE MOVIES**
(Everything I do) I do it for you / Unchained melody / It must have been love / I will always love you / Try a little tenderness / What becomes of the broken hearted / When I fall in love / No ordinary love / Can you feel the love tonight / Streets of Philadelphia / Big my secret / Love is all around / Deeper love / Wind beneath my wings / Take my breath away / (I've had) the time of my life
EMPRCD 902 / Jan '97 / Emporio

□ **LOVE THEMES FROM THE MOVIES**
I will always love you / Rose / Do you know where you're going to / Greatest love of all / It must have been love / Nobody loves it better / Hard to say I'm sorry / Hopelessly devoted to you / Wind beneath my wings / Beauty and the beast / Take my breath away / First time ever I saw your face / Up where we belong / Endless love / Way we were / Love touch / Evergreen / My own true love
ECD 3132 / Jan '95 / K-Tel

□ **LULLABY OF BROADWAY (The Best Of Busby Berkeley At Warner Bros.)**
Young and healthy / Shuffle off to Buffalo / 42nd Street / We're in the money / I've got to sing a torch song / Shadow waltz / Remember my forgotten man / Honeymoon Hotel / By a waterfall / Shanghai Lil / Don't say goodnight / Fashions of 1934 / Spin a little web of dreams / Girl at the ironing board / I only have eyes for you / Dames / Words are in my heart / Lullaby of Broadway / Lady in red / All's fair in love and war / Hooray for Hollywood
CDODEON 8 / Feb '96 / Premier/EMI

M

□ **MAD WORLD OF SOUNDTRACKS, THE**
5534992 / Apr '97 / Motor Collector

□ **MAGIC FROM THE MUSICALS**
Only you: *Blessed, Brian* / Good morning starshine: *Clark, Petula* / If I were a rich man: *Topol* / Luck be a lady: *Jones, Paul* / Memory: *Clark, Petula* / Send in the clowns: *Webb, Marti* / Impossible dream: *Blessed, Brian* / Bless your beautiful hide: *Keel, Howard* / Thank heavens for little girls: *Topol* / Lullaby of Broadway: *Jones, Paul* / If he walked into my life: *Webb, Marti* / Annie get your gun medley: *Keel, Howard* / I don't know how to love him: *Webb, Marti* / I've grown accustomed to her face: *Jones, Paul*
MCCD 012 / Feb '91 / Music Club

□ **MAGIC OF THE BRITISH MUSICALS, THE**
CDTEZ 7003 / Jan '95 / TER

□ **MAGIC OF THE MUSICALS, THE (40 Hits From 40 Great Musicals Of Stage & Screen)**
There's no business like show business: *Silver Screen Orchestra* / Couple of swells: *Silver Screen Orchestra* / It's a lovely day today: *Silver Screen Orchestra* / Let's face the music and dance: *Silver Screen Orchestra* / Cheek to cheek: *Silver Screen Orchestra* / Pretty girl is like a melody: *Silver Screen Orchestra* / Play a simple melody: *Silver Screen Orchestra* / Heatwave: *Silver Screen Orchestra* / I love a piano: *Silver Screen Orchestra* / Stepping out with my baby: *Silver Screen Orchestra* / Change partners and dance: *Silver Screen Orchestra* / Everything's coming up roses: *Bassey, Shirley* / People: *Bassey, Shirley* / Tonight: *Bassey, Shirley* / Lady is a tramp: *Bassey, Shirley* / I get a kick out of you: *Bassey, Shirley* / It might as well be spring: *Bassey, Shirley* / As long as he needs me: *Bassey, Shirley* / I've never been in love before: *Bassey, Shirley* / Any dream will do: *Jones, Paul* / Take it on the chin: *O'Hara, Mary* / Unusual way: *O'Hara, Mary* / How to handle a woman: *Young, Robert* / Love changes everything: *Keel, Howard* / Music of the night: *Keel, Howard* / O what a beautiful morning: *Keel, Howard* / Hello young lovers: *Monro, Matt* / Who can I turn to: *Monro, Matt* / I can give you the starlight: *Hill, Vince* / Someday my heart will awake: *Hill, Vince* / Edelweiss: *Hill, Vince* / Shine through my dreams: *Hill, Vince* / Sunrise sunset: *Dodd, Ken* / This is my lovely day: *Wallace, Ian* / Mr. Mistoffelees: *Morriston Orpheus Choir* / Starlight Express: *Morriston Orpheus Choir* / Don't cry for me Argentina: *Morriston Orpheus Choir & Margaret Williams* / Day by day: *Laine, Cleo* / Prepare ye the way of the Lord: *Laine, Cleo* / All I do is dream of you: *Cogan, Alma* / I've got my love to keep me warm: *Berlin, Irving*
CDDL 1227 / Apr '92 / Music For Pleasure

□ **MAGIC OF THE MUSICALS, THE (Webb, Marti & Mark Rattray)**
Lullaby of broadway / I got rhythm / I get a kick out of you / It ain't necessarily so / Got plenty of nothing / There's a boat dat's leavin' soon for New York / Porgy I's your woman now / Summertime / Blow Gabriel blow / Losing my mind / Not while I'm around / Send in the clowns / Do you hear the people sing / Empty chairs at empty tables / I dreamed a dream / Last night of the world / Bui-doi / Don't cry for me Argentina / Jesus Christ superstar / Mama a rainbow / Take that look off your face / In one of my weaker moments / Anthem / You and I / Tell me it's not true / Only he / Love changes everything / Music of the night / Memory
MCCD 149 / Feb '94 / Music Club

□ **MAGIC OF THE MUSICALS, THE**
MCBX 014 / Dec '94 / Music Club

□ **MAGICAL MOVIE MUSIC**
Can you feel the love tonight / Beauty and the beast / Whole new world / Circle of life / Be our guest / I just can't wait to be king / Prince Ali / Hakuna Matata / Arabian nights / Gaston / I've got no strings / Part of your world / Some day my prince will come / When you wish upon a star
CDMFP 6224 / May '96 / Music For Pleasure

□ **MAGICAL MUSIC OF DISNEY, THE (Cincinnati Pops Orchestra)**
Circle of life / I just can't wait to be king / Hakuna matara / Be prepared / Can you feel the love tonight / Arabian nights / One jump ahead / Whole new world / Prince Ali / Part of your world / Under the sea / Poor unfortunate souls / Le poissons / Kiss the girl / Happy ending / She's a funny girl / That Belle / Be our guest / Gaston / Beauty and the beast
CD 80381 / Jun '95 / Telarc

□ **MAMMY (The Jolson Story)**
Let me sing and I'm happy / Ma blushin' Rosie / I want a girl / My Mammy / I'm sitting on top of the world / You made me love you / Swanee / Spaniard that blighted my life / April showers / California here I come / Liza / There's a rainbow 'round my shoulder / She's a latin from Manhattan / About a quarter to nine / Anniversary song / Waiting for the Robert E Lee / Rock a bye baby with a dixie melody / April showers / Who paid the rent for Mrs. Rip Van Winkle / Yes we have no bananas / Looking at you / Why do they all take the night boat to Albany / Let me sing and I'm happy / To my Mammy / Let me sing and I'm happy
CD 60021 / Nov '97 / Great Movie Themes

□ **MANTOVANI AT THE MOVIES (Mantovani)**
CDMOIR 506 / Oct '93 / Memoir

□ **MANY SONGS OF WINNIE THE POOH, THE**
Wonderful thing about tiggers / Up down and touch the ground / Winnie the Pooh / Rumbly in my tummy / Rather blustery day / Heffalumps and woozles / Hip hip ooh-ray / Little black rain cloud / It's so much more friendly with pooh / Rain rain rain come down down down / Pooh Pooh the birthday bear / It really was a woozle yes it was / Forever and ever / Adventure is a wonderful thing / If it says so / Wherever you are / Everything is right / Kangaroo hop
WD 115642 / Oct '97 / Disney Music & Stories

□ **MARCHING DOWN BROADWAY (Australian Marching Band)**
MBPCD 7005 / 11 May '98 / Quantum Mobius

□ **MARCOVICCI SINGS MOVIES (Marcovicci, Andrea)**
As time goes by / It might be you / On such a night as this / Folks who live on the hill / Two for the road / Happy endings / Don't ever leave me / Here lies love / Let's not talk about love / Girl medley / Someone to love / Mad about the boy / World War II medley / Too late now / Love is here to stay
DRGCD 91405 / Mar '92 / DRG

□ **MARILYN MONROE (Monroe, Marilyn)**
I wanna be loved by you / Two little girls from Little Rock: *Monroe, Marilyn & Jane Russell* / I'm gonna file my claim / My heart belongs to Daddy / Runnin' wild / Fine romance / You'd be surprised / Diamonds are a girl's best friend / Bye bye baby / I'm through with love / Specialisation: *Monroe, Marilyn & Frankie Vaughan* / Heatwave / Do it again / When love goes wrong nothing goes right: *Monroe, Marilyn & Jane Russell* / After you get what you want you don't want it / River of no return / Lazy / Kiss / When I fall in love / Happy birthday Mr. President
399534 / May '97 / Koch Presents

□ **MARILYN SINGS (Monroe, Marilyn)**
CDCD 1195 / Sep '94 / Charly

□ **MARLENE DIETRICH (Dietrich, Marlene)**
Lili Marlene / La vie en rose / Lola / Boys in the backroom / I may never go home anymore / Another Spring another love / Go away from my window / Honeysuckle rose / Such trying times / Near you / Allein / Johnny / I can't give you anything but love / Laziest gal in town / Frag nicht warum ich gere / I wish you love / I will come back again (maybe I'll come back) / Illusions / Falling in love again / Shir hatan / You go to my head
399536 / May '97 / Koch Presents

□ **MARLENE DIETRICH COLLECTION (20 Golden Greats) (Dietrich, Marlene)**
Lili Marlene / Boys in the backroom / Lola / Illusions / Johnny / I've been in love before / Black market / Lazy afternoon / Another spring another love / Symphonie / You do something to me / Falling in love again / You go to my head / You've got that look / If he swings by the string / This world of ours / Near you / Candles glowing / Kisses sweeter than wine / Such trying times
DVCD 2098 / Jan '87 / Deja Vu

□ **MEDICS (Great TV Drama Themes)**
Casualty / Angels / MASH / Marcus Welby MD / Country Practice / General Hospital / Dr. Finlay's Casebook / Owen MD / Chicago Hope / ER / St. Elsewhere / Shortland Street / Where The Heart Is / Quincy / Dr. Kildare / Children's Hospital / Dangerfield / Peak Practice
308682 / 20 Apr '98 / Hallmark

□ **MGM ALBUM, THE (Gravitte, Debbie Shapiro)**
Get happy / Love / Treat me rough / Where the boys are / Tico Tico / I love a piano / Everybody loves my baby / Too late now / Theme from 2001: A Space Odyssey / Smoke gets in your eyes / Nevertheless (I'm in love with you) / Little Girl Blue/My romance / Love me or leave me / By myself
VSD 5742 / Jun '97 / Varese Sarabande

□ **MISS SAIGON AND OTHER SHOWS**
HM 021 / Jun '97 / Harmony

□ **MISS SHOW BUSINESS (Garland, Judy)**
Over the rainbow / Foggy day (in London Town) / Make someone happy / When the sun come sout / Smile / I'm always chasing rainbows / How about me / That's all / That's entertainment / Almost like being in love / This can't be love / Love of my life / Chicago / Fly me to the moon / Boy next door / Stormy weather / Man that got away / For me and my gal / Trolley song / Swanee / I'm nobody's baby / Alexander's ragtime band / I feel a song comin' on / Rock-a-bye your baby with a dixie melody / Battle hymn of the Republic
QED 132 / Nov '96 / Tring

□ **MISS SHOWBUSINESS (Garland, Judy)**
Zing went the strings of my heart / Stompin' at the savoy / All God's chillun got rhythm / Everybody sing / You made me love you / Over the rainbow / Sweet sixteen / Embraceable you / (Can this be) The end of the rainbow / I'm nobody's baby / Pretty girl milking her cow / It's a great day for the Irish / Sunny side of the street / For me and my gal / That old black magic / When you wore a tulip
HADCD 156 / May '94 / Javelin

□ **MISSION IMPOSSIBLE & OTHER TV THEMES (Gregory, John Orchestra)**
Mission impossible / Rockford files / Cannon / Softly softly / Columbo / M Squad / Man called Ironside / Griff / Untouchables / Mannix / Route 66 / McMillan and Wife / Harry-O / Streets of San Francisco / Six million dollar man / Hawaii 5-O / It takes a thief / Theme from SWAT / I spy / McCloud / Perry Mason / Name of the game / Banacek / Johnny Staccato / Policewoman / Sweeney / Avengers / Kojak
5329862 / Jul '96 / Mercury

□ **MONSTROUS MOVIE MUSIC VOL.1**
MMM 1950 / Oct '97 / Mmm

□ **MONSTROUS MOVIE MUSIC VOL.2**
MMM 1951 / Oct '97 / Mmm

□ **MOODS**
Hercule Poirot: *Belgian Detective* / Rowena's theme: *Edge* / Another green world: *Eno, Brian* / Blow the wind/Pie Jesu: *Pook, Jocelyn* / Father of eternal life: *Divine Works* / Brideshead revisited: *Burgon, Geoffrey* / Salva nos: *Mediaeval Baebes* / Peoples century / Theme from the mission: *Morricone, Ennio* / Through the blue: *Eno, Roger* / Tubular bells: *Oldfield, Mike* / Schindler's List: *Little, Tasmin/New World Philharmonic* / Adiemus: *Adiemus* / Inspector Morse: *Pheloung, Barrington* / Heart asks pleasure first/Promise / Tor-cheney-nahana: *Sacred Spirit*
CDVIP 200 / 13 Apr '98 / Virgin

□ **MOONSTRUCK (Edwardian Theatre Music) (Hill-Smith, Marilyn & The Southern Festival Orchestra)**
White, Robin *con*
Two Parisian sketches / Montmartre / O who shall say that love is cruel / Grashoppers' dance / Sail my ships / Nell Gwyn dances / Destiny / Moonstruck / Pink lady / Pipes of pan / In the shadows / Soldiers in the park / Nights of gladness
FBCD 2005 / 17 Jun '98 / Flyback

□ **MOVIE CLASSICS**
CDZ 76772542 / Apr '93 / EMI Classics

□ **MOVIE CLASSICS**
CES 5690952 / Feb '96 / EMI Classics

□ **MOVIE CLASSICS (20 Classic Film Themes)**
4527232 / Jan '97 / Decca

□ **MOVIE CLASSICS (Performed On Pan Pipes)**
Don't cry for me Argentina / (Everything I do) I do it for you / Groovy kind of love / Cavatina / Moon river / Somewhere out there / Take my breath away / Chariots of fire / Whole new world / Way we were / Wind beneath my wings / Up where we belong / Can you feel the love tonight / My girl / Love is all around
SUMCD 4095 / Jan '97 / Sound & Media

□ **MOVIE HITS**
12196 / Apr '95 / Laserlight

□ **MOVIE HITS IN BRASS (Brassband Burgermusik Luzern)**
Indiana Jones / Batman / Jurassic Park / Star Wars / James Bond / 633 Squadron / Everything I do I do it for you / Onedin Line / Can you read my mind / Schindler's List / Start Trek - The Voyage Home / Love Story
340842 / Apr '96 / Koch

□ **MOVIE HITS, THE (Crosby, Bing)**
Apple for the teacher / Man and his dream / If I had my way / Too romantic / I haven't time to be a millionaire / Meet the sun halfway / My heart is taking lessons / Funny old hills / I have eyes / Still the bluebird sings / Moonburn / Love thy neighbour / Waiter and the porter and the upstairs maid / Small fry / Moon got in my eyes / Smarty / Without a word of warning / My heart and I / Let's call a heart a heart / Go fly a kite / Empty saddles / Birth of the blues
PASTCD 9784 / Mar '92 / Flapper

□ **MOVIE KILLERS**
TCD 2836 / Jun '96 / Telstar

□ **MOVIE LOVE SONGS (Philadelphia Orchestra)**
Ormandy, Eugene *con*
Love Story / Elvira Madigan: *Wild, Earl* / Yesterday / Thomas Crown Affair / Romeo and Juliet / Heart is a Lonely Hunter / West Side Story / Tristan and Isolde / Now Voyager
09026609652 / Jan '92 / RCA Victor

□ **MOVIE LOVE THEMES (Tritt, W./A. Romero/Cincinnati Pops Orchestra)**
Kunzel, Erich *con*
CD 80243 / Feb '91 / Telarc

□ **MOVIE LOVERS**
Brown eyed girl: *Morrison, Van* / Perfect day: *Reed, Lou* / Girl you'll be a woman soon: *Urge Overkill* / In dreams: *Orbison, Roy* / Blue Spanish sky: *Isaak, Chris* / Venus as a boy: *Bjork* / Love song for a vampire: *Lennox, Annie* / I've never been to me: *Charlene* / Sea of love: *Wilde, Marty* / Love letters: *Lester, Ketty* / Everybody's talkin': *Nilsson, Harry* /

When a man loves a woman: *Sledge, Percy* / You've really got a hold on me: *Robinson, Smokey & The Miracles* / Soul on fire: *Baker, LaVern* / Gimme your love: *Mayfield, Curtis* / Baby I love you: *Franklin, Aretha* / Falling: *Cruise, Julee* / Love and happiness: *Green, Al* / Tell it like it is: *Neville, Aaron* / Fa-fa-fa-fa-fa (sad song): *Redding, Otis*
TCD 2876 / Nov '96 / Telstar

☐ **MOVIE MEMORIES (Music From The Greatest Films) (Nuremberg Symphony Orchestra)**
Kaufman, Richard *con*
CST 348052 / Nov '95 / Colosseum

☐ **MOVIE MUSIC**
PCD 887 / '88 / Prometheus

☐ **MOVIE SONG ALBUM, THE (Bennett, Tony)**
Maybe September / Girl talk / Gentle rain / Emily / Pawnbroker / Samba de orfeu / Shadow of your smile / Smile / Second time around / Days of wine and roses / Never too late / Trolley song
4879472 / Jul '97 / Columbia

☐ **MOVIE SONGS 1929-1930 (Ingham-Grosz Cosmpolites)**
SOSCD 1323 / Feb '98 / Stomp Off

☐ **MOVIE'S GREATEST LOVE SONGS**
Play dead: *Arnold, David & Bjork* / Love song for a vampire: *Lennox, Annie* / No ordinary love: *Sade* / Unchained melody: *Righteous Brothers* / Licence to kill: *Knight, Gladys* / Show me heaven: *McKee, Maria* / Falling: *Cruise, Julee* / Forbidden colours: *Sakamoto, Ryuichi & David Sylvian* / Going home: *Knopfler, Mark* / Book of days: *Enya* / Take my breath away: *Berlin* / Glory of love: *Cetera, Peter* / Up where we belong: *Cocker, Joe & Jennifer Warnes* / Nothing has been proved: *Springfield, Dusty* / I guess that's why they call it the blues: *John, Elton* / Arthur's theme: *Cross, Christopher* / Love is in the air: *Young, John Paul* / My girl: *Temptations* / Try a little tenderness: *Commitments* / Brown eyed girl: *Morrison, Van*
516651-2 / Feb '94 / PolyGram TV

☐ **MOVIES, THE (BBC Concert Orchestra)**
Big Country / Star Wars / Casablanca / Dambusters / Moon river / Bridge Over the River Kwai / Chariots Of Fire / James Bond medley / Dr. Zhivago / Rocky / Love Story / Great Escape / Godfather / Sting / Alamo / Magnificent Seven / Gone With The Wind
10682 / Oct '97 / BBC Concert Orchestra

☐ **MOZART TV (Favourite TV Tunes In The Style Of Great Composers) (Hollywood Chamber Symphony)**
Gershon, Grant *con*
Friends / X-Files / Brady Bunch / MASH / Hill Street Blues / Mary Tyler Moore Show / Cheers / Mr. Ed / Bewitched / Jeopardy / Star Trek: Voyager / Taxi / I Love Lucy / Green Acres / Jetsons
DE 3222 / Nov '97 / Delos

☐ **MUSIC FOR FILMS**
ASCD 04 / Jun '92 / All Saints

☐ **MUSIC FOR STAGE AND SCREEN (Williams, John & The Boston Pops Orchestra)**
Born on the fourth of July / Revivers / Red pony / Quiet city
SK 64147 / Jan '95 / Sony Classical

☐ **MUSIC FOR THE SILENT MOVIES**
Silent movie drama / Pianola rag / High hat and tap / Chaplin crying / Palm court / Charlie chase / Bowler hat and a piano / Borsalino theme / Tramp / Keaton laughing / Gypsy rosalee / Wash rag / Laurel and Hardy / Mack Sennett / Cartoon rag / Policeman / Bootleggers and co / Old crock rag / Chico Marx and brothers / Tender waltz for a tough guy / Curtain down the show is over
304682 / Jun '97 / Hallmark

☐ **MUSIC FOR TV DINNERS**
SCP 97212 / Sep '97 / Scamp

☐ **MUSIC FROM DEANNA DURBIN FILMS, THE**
My heart is singing / It's raining sunbeams / Heart that's free / Libiamo / Chapel bells / I love to whistle / Serenade to the stars / You're as pretty as a picture / My own / Je veux vivre / Last rose of summer / Love is all / Loch Lomond / Ave Maria / When April sings / When I sing / Goin' home / Mighty lak' a rose / Begin the beguine / Say a prayer for the boys over there / Kashmiri song / In the spirit of the moment / When you're away / Russian melody / None shall sleep
CMSCD 013 / Aug '94 / Movie Stars

☐ **MUSIC FROM GREAT AUSTRALIAN FILMS (Australian Broadcasting Commission Philharmonic Orchestra)**
Motzing, William *con*
Newsfront / Gallipoli / My brillant career / Tall timbers / Cathy's child / Eliza Frazer / Breaker morant / Chant of Jimmy Blacksmith / Picture show man / Picnic at Hanging Rock / Mango tree / Dimboola / Caddie
DRGCD 12582 / Jan '95 / DRG

☐ **MUSIC FROM HIS MOVIES (Sinatra, Frank)**
GO 3805 / 1 Dec '97 / Golden Options

☐ **MUSIC FROM JACQUES TATI FILMS**
8369832 / Feb '90 / Silva Screen

☐ **MUSIC FROM THE FILMS OF AUDREY HEPBURN**
9245032 / Jan '93 / Silva Screen

☐ **MUSIC FROM THE FILMS OF CLINT EASTWOOD (City Of Prague Philharmonic Orchestra)**
Wadsworth, Derek *con*
Where Eagles Dare / Outlaw Josey Wales / Good the Bad and the Ugly / Fistful Of Dollars / For A Few Dollars More / Play Misty For Me / Hang 'Em High / In The Line Of Fire / Rawhide / Dirty Harry / Sudden Impact / Magnum Force / Two Mules For Sister Sara / Unforgiven
FILMCD 138 / '93 / Silva Screen

☐ **MUSIC FROM THE FILMS OF JEAN-PIERRE MOCKY**
MANTRA 033 / Jan '93 / Silva Screen

☐ **MUSIC FROM THE FILMS OF KEVIN COSTNER**
Dances With Wolves / Revenge / No Way Out / JFK: *City Of Prague Philharmonic Orchestra* / Field of dreams / Untouchables: *City Of Prague Philharmonic Orchestra* / Fandango / Silverado: *City Of Prague Philharmonic Orchestra* / Robin Hood Prince Of Thieves
FILMCD 194 / 30 Mar '98 / Silva Screen

☐ **MUSIC FROM THE FILMS OF MEL GIBSON**
FILMCD 195 / 30 Mar '98 / Silva Screen

☐ **MUSIC FROM THE FILMS OF SEAN CONNERY (City Of Prague Philharmonic Orchestra)**
Dr. No / Medicine Man / From Russia With Love / Untouchables / Highlander / Goldfinger / Name Of The Rose / Thunderball / Presidio / You Only Live Twice / Russia House / Diamonds Are Forever / Marnie / Never Say Never Again: *Hall, Lani* / Robin And Marian
FILMCD 189 / 30 Mar '98 / Silva Screen

☐ **MUSIC FROM THE GOLDEN AGE**
20th Century Fox fanfare / Prince Valiant / Seven year itch / Razor's edge / Love is a many splendored thing / Captain from Castille / Leave her to heaven / All about Eve / Song of Bernadette / Best of everthing / President's lady / Man called Peter / Beneath the 12 mile reef / Ghost and Mrs. Muir / Journey to the centre of the Earth / Anna and the King of Siam / Prince of players / Man in the grey flannel suit / Garden of evil / Rains of Ranchipur / Violent Saturday / Viva Zapata / Will sucess spoil Rock Hunter / Daddy long legs / Tall men / Stripper / Rio Conchos / Patton
VSD 5937 / 24 Aug '98 / Varese Sarabande

☐ **MUSIC FROM THE HAMMER FILMS (Philharmonia Orchestra)**
Dracula suite / Dracula Prince of Darkness suite / Hands of the Ripper suite / Taste the blood of Dracula suite / Vampire Circus suite
FILMCD 066 / Jan '90 / Silva Screen

☐ **MUSIC FROM THE MOVIES**
CDMFP 5915 / '91 / Music For Pleasure

☐ **MUSIC FROM THE MOVIES (Levy, Louis)**
Strike up the band / It's love again / It's love again / Swing time / Swing time / Broadway melody of 1938 / Broadway melody of 1938 / Gangway / Gangway / Pennies from Heaven / Pennies from Heaven / Gone with the wind / Gone with the wind / Pinocchio / Pinocchio / Alexander's ragtime band / Alexander's ragtime band / Limelight / Limelight / Shall we dance / Shall we dance / Joy of living / Music from the movies march
RAJCD 884 / Sep '96 / Empress

☐ **MUSIC FROM THE MOVIES (London Philharmonic Orchestra)**
Chariots Of Fire / Five Circles / Abraham's theme / Eric's theme / Bladerunner / Ride of the Valkyries / Also Sprach Zarathustra / Battle Of The Planets / Imperial attack / Jaws / Longest Day / Bridge Too Far / Battle of Bordino / Good The Bad And The Ugly / Raiders Of The Lost Ark
DC 880662 / May '97 / Disky

☐ **MUSIC FROM THE NEW YORK STAGE VOL.1 (1890-1908)**
GEMMCDS 90502 / Aug '93 / Pearl

☐ **MUSIC FROM THE NEW YORK STAGE VOL.2 (1908-1913)**
GEMMCDS 90535 / Nov '93 / Pearl

☐ **MUSIC FROM THE NEW YORK STAGE VOL.3 (1913-1917)**
GEMMCDS 90568 / Nov '93 / Pearl

☐ **MUSIC FROM THE NEW YORK STAGE VOL.4 (1917-1920)**
GEMMCDS 905961 / Nov '93 / Pearl

☐ **MUSIC FROM THE OSCAR WINNERS (Silver Screen Orchestra)**
Everybody's talking / French Connection / Entertainer / One Flew Over The Cuckoo's Nest / Cavatina / Mandoline concerto in C major / Chariots Of Fire / For all mankind / Terms Of Endearment / Last Emperor / Rain Man / Dances With Wolves / Silence Of The Lambs / Schindler's List / Braveheart / Claudia's theme
DC 880712 / May '97 / Disky

☐ **MUSIC FROM THE SILVER SCREEN**
ACCD 1001 / Apr '96 / Silva Screen

☐ **MUSIC OF THE MOVIES**
GRF 241 / Aug '93 / Tring

☐ **MUSIC OF THE MOVIES (The Love Songs) (Starlight Orchestra/Singers)**
I will always love you / Streets of Philadelphia / What's love got to do with it / I can see clearly now / Book of days / Greatest love of all / Whole new world / Stand by me / Hello again / My girl / Nothing's gonna stop us now / Long and winding road / Rose / For all we know / Up where we belong / Try a little tenderness / What a wonderful world / First time ever I saw your face / You gotta love someone / Wind beneath my wings / (Everything I do) I do it for you / No ordinary love / All night long / Do you know where you're going to / Mona Lisa / Somewhere out there / Unchained melody / Arthur's theme / Way we were / It must have been love / He ain't heavy he's my brother / Power of love / All you need is love / Let the river run / Hopelessly devoted to you / Nobody does it better / Bright eyes / Suddenly / Love song for a vampire / Yesterday / Take my breath away / Will you be there / When I fall in love / I just called to say I love you / Love is in the air / Against all odds / Beauty and the beast / Run to you / Tracks of my tears / King of wishful thinking / I don't want to fight / If we hold on together / Again / Groovy kind of love / Say you say me / Places that belong to you / Are you lonesome tonight / Sorry seems to be the hardest word / What becomes of the broken hearted / You light up my life / All for love / Someday I'm coming back / With you I'm born again / Bohemian rhapsody / How deep is your love / Glory of love / Love on the rocks / (I've had) the time of my life / Endless love / All time high / Crying game / Can't help falling in love / Just the way you are / We may never love like this again / Shoop shoop song (It's in his kiss) / This used to be my playground / As time goes by / It's probably me / Sandy / Under the boardwalk
TFP 042 / Apr '95 / Tring

☐ **MUSIC OF THE MOVIES (The Love Songs) (Starlight Orchestra/Singers)**
Take my breath away / He ain't heavy he's my brother / Glory of love / Up where we belong / I just called to say I love you / Time of my life / Say you say me / Against all odds / Way we were / Stand by me / Almost paradise / Endless love / You light up my life / Groovy kind of love / Let the river run / Unchained melody / It must have been love
QED 013 / Nov '96 / Tring

☐ **MUSIC OF THE NIGHT (Pops On Broadway 1990) (Williams, John & The Boston Pops Orchestra)**
Williams, John *con*
SK 45567 / Jan '95 / Sony Classical

☐ **MUSICAL**
15 400 / Jan '93 / Laserlight

☐ **MUSICAL HIGHLIGHTS**
22536 / Jul '95 / Music

☐ **MUSICAL MAGIC**
TREB 5019 / May '96 / Scratch

☐ **MUSICAL SELECTIONS FROM THE RIDICULOUS THEATRICAL COMPANY (The 25th Anniversary) (Original Casts)**
Reverse psychology / Heterosexual Heidi / Conquerer / Sophisticated love / Humanity / Thank God he made me a drag queen / Artificial jungle overture / Eddie's swing / Illusory thing is love / You've changed / Dutch elm disease / Strange way song / Valkyrie dance and song / Yah yah yah - The music has me so confused
DRGCD 6301 / Jan '95 / DRG

☐ **MUSICAL WORLD HITS**
15086 / Dec '94 / Laserlight

☐ **MUSICALS (Ambrosian Chorus & London Sinfonietta)**
McGlinn, John *c*
Cafe song / Empty chairs at empty tables / Maria / It must be so / Gigi / How to handle a woman / There but for you go I / Never will I marry / Way you look tonight / Fine romance / Love song / Johanna / Finishing the hat / Silly people / Alone together / You do something to me / Gay divorcee / Night and day
CDC 7497922 / Aug '93 / EMI Classics

☐ **MUSICALS AFTER DARK, THE (Classic Late Night Love Songs From The Shows)**
Some enchanted evening: *Allen, Thomas* / Bill: *Welch, Elizabeth* / Only love: *Jones, Salena* / If love were all: *Ashe, Rosemary* / I still believe in love: *Craven, Gemma* / Send in the clowns: *Phillips, Sian* / Glad to be unhappy: *Andreas, Christine* / I'm in the mood for love: *Shore, Julia* / Smoke gets in your eyes: *Welch, Elizabeth* / Maybe this time: *Friedman, Maria* / Tell me on a Sunday: *Robertson, Liz* / Old friend: *Langton, Diane*
SHOWCD 028 / Oct '96 / Showtime

☐ **MUSICALS COLLECTION, THE (London Theatre Orchestra & Singers)**
Perfect year / I still believe / Summer nights / I dreamed a dream / Losing my mind / Anything goes / If I were a rich man / I enjoy being a girl / Everything's alright / One night only / Don't cry for me Argentina / Hello Dolly / One night in Bangkok / Skid row / I could have danced all night / On this night / Some enchanted evening / Day by day / Somewhere / Close every door / Memory / Big spender / Cabaret / What I did for love / Love changes everything / Tahiti / Another suitcase in another hall / My blue Heaven / Everything's coming up roses / Everyday / All I ask of you / When I marry Mr. Snow / Starlight express / What kind of fool am I / Bewitched bothered and bewildered / On the street where you live / Honeysuckle rose / One more angel in Heaven / Maybe this time / Lullaby of Broadway / Phantom Of The Opera / I know him so well / Anything you can do I can do better / Mame / High flying adored / Bali ha'i / I don't know how to love him / Almost like being in love / Somewhere that's green / Two ladies / Time warp / People / That'll be the day / Getting to know you / Impossible dream / Movie in my mind / Trolley song / Send in the clowns / Tea for two / If ever I would leave you / Any dream will do / Maria / Money / I remember it well / Buenos Aires / Ol' man river / People will say we're in love / Diamond's are a girl's best friend / There's a small hotel / I'm still here / Do you hear the people sing / With one look / Overture / King Herod's song / Lucky to be me / Baubles bangles and beads / She's so beautiful / You're the one that I want / Sweet transvestite / There's no business like show business
TFP 044 / Jan '95 / Tring

☐ **MUSICALS OF THE NIGHT**
SHOWCD 058 / 18 May '98 / Showtime

☐ **MUSICALS VOL.1 (15 Hit Songs From Classic Musical Shows)**
CDC 7548352 / Apr '93 / EMI Classics

☐ **MUSICALS VOL.2 (Highlights From Porgy & Bess/Oklahoma/King And I/ West Side Story) (Royal Liverpool Philharmonic Orchestra)**
Davis, Carl *con*
CDCFP 4601 / Jan '95 / Classics For Pleasure

☐ **MUSICALS, THE (Ball, Michael)**
All I ask of you / Something's coming / Losing my mind / Memory / Don't rain on my parade / With one look / Show me / I dreamed a dream / You'll never walk alone / Easy terms / Last night of the world / Loving you / Anthem / Love changes everything / With one look
5338922 / Nov '96 / PolyGram TV

☐ **MUSICALS, THE (BBC Concert Orchestra)**
That's entertainment / Singin' in the rain / Carousel / Bali hali / Shall we dance / Don't cry for me Argentina / Cabaret / Disney medley / Thank heaven for little girls / I could have danced all night / If I were a rich man / 76 Trombones / Hello dolly / Food glorious food / Hey big spender / Sound of music
10692 / Oct '97 / BBC Concert Orchestra

☐ **MY DELICIOUS SPAGHETTI WESTERN**
RED 1022 / 15 Jun '98 / Dagored

☐ **MY KIND OF BROADWAY (Sinatra, Frank)**
7599270312 / May '98 / Reprise

N

☐ **NIGHT AT THE MOVIES, A (Essex, David)**
Girl you'll be a woman soon / Can you feel the love tonight / Crying game / Wind beneath my wings / Stardust / Together in electric dreams / Oh what a circus / Seperate lives / St. Elmo's fire / Kiss from a rose / Somewhere out there / Silver dream machine / Sea of love / If I had words (anthem)
5376082 / May '97 / PolyGram TV

☐ **NIGHT AT THE MOVIES, A (London Philharmonic Orchestra)**
Bolero / Love Story / French Lieutenant's Woman / Cavatina / Love Is A Many Splendoured Thing / Man and a woman / On Golden Pond / Windmills of your mind / Somewhere In Time / Kramer vs. Kramer / Fantasia / Evita / Madigan / Clockwork Orange / 20,000 Leagues Under The Sea
DC 880642 / May '97 / Disky

☐ **NO.1 SCI-FI ALBUM, THE**
Star Wars: *Williams, John & The Boston Pops Orchestra* / Independence Day: *City Of Prague Philharmonic Orchestra* / Abyss: *City Of Prague Philharmonic Orchestra* / Empire Strikes Back: *Williams, John & The Boston Pops Orchestra* / Superman: *Williams, John & The Boston Pops Orchestra* / ET: *Williams, John & The Boston Pops Orchestra* / Blade Runner: *Ayres, Mark* / Return Of The Jedi: *Williams, John & The Boston Pops Orchestra* / Apollo 13: *City Of Prague Philharmonic Orchestra* / Eve of the war: *Wayne, Jeff* / Close Encounters Of The Third Kind: *Williams, John & The Boston Pops Orchestra* / Jurassic Park: *City Of Prague Philharmonic Orchestra* / Batman: *City Of Prague Philharmonic Orchestra* / Dune: *Eno, Brian* / Dark Star: *Caine, Daniel* / Capricorn One: *City Of Prague Philharmonic Orchestra* / Alien: *Williams, John & The Boston Pops Orchestra* / Black Hole: *City Of Prague Philharmonic Orchestra* / 2001: A Space Odyssey: *Williams, John & The Boston Pops Orchestra* / X Files: *Ayres, Mark* / Star Trek: The Next Generation: *Goldsmith, Jerry & Alexander Courage* / Dark Skies: *Hoenig, Michael* / Buck Roger's In The 25th Century: *Philips, Stu* / Battlestar Galactica: *Williams, John & The Boston Pops Orchestra* / Twilight Zone: *Williams, John & The Boston Pops Orchestra* / Star Trek: Voyager: *City Of Prague Philharmonic Orchestra* / Babylon 5: *Ayres, Mark* / Dr. Who: *Grainer, Ron* / Red Dwarf: *Hunte, Diane & Mark Lambert/Ian Hu* / Hitch-Hiker's Guide To The Galaxy: *Lambert, Mark & Ian Hu* / Thunderbirds: *Gray, Barry Orchestra* / Sting Ray: *Gray, Barry Orchestra & The Gary Miller Orchestra* / Fireball XL5: *Gray, Barry* / Captain Scarlet: *Gray, Barry Orchestra* / Joe 90: *Gray, Barry Orchestra* / Blake's Seven: *Ayres, Mark* / Lost In Space I and II: *Williams, John* / Time Tunnel: *Williams, John*
5533602 / Mar '97 / PolyGram TV

☐ **NOUVEAU CINEMA - NOUVELLES MUSIQUES**
74321413922 / Nov '96 / Milan

O

☐ **OLIVER STONE CONNECTION**
UMD 80481 / 29 Jun '98 / Universal

☐ **ON AND OFF STAGE (Willetts, Dave)**
SONGCD 902 / Jan '95 / Silva Screen

☐ **ON BROADWAY**
CD 12236 / Apr '94 / BR Music

☐ **ON MY OWN (Nicastro, Michelle)**
Dancing all the time / Sun and moon / Waiting for life / Someone else's story / On my own / Second chance / Loving you / Last night of the world / Come back with the same look in your eyes / Unexpected song / This is the moment / Human heart / All I ask of you / I dreamed a dream / Seasons of love
VSD 5810 / 16 Feb '98 / Varese Sarabande

☐ **ON THE BOARDS (Songs From The Victorian Music Halls) (Down East Band)**
Whatcher 'Rai / When these old clothes were new / All through sticking to a soldier / Man that broke the bank at Monte Carlo / By the sad sea waves / That is love / Oh Mr. Porter / Ballad of Sam Hall / Stroke of the pen / McDermott's great war song / Boy I love is up in the gallery / I'm very unkind to my wife / For he was her only son / Mad butcher / Doing the academy / East and West / Leo Leo Leo / Hampstead is the place to ruralise
SAMHSCD 204 / Jun '96 / Soundalive

☐ **ONE FROM THE HEART - SAX AT THE MOVIES (Jazz At The Movies Band)**
This one's from the heart / Can you read my mind / Last tango in Paris / How do you keep the music playing / Places that belong to you / Take my breath away / Love theme from Pretty Woman / Flight over Africa / Endless love / Way we were
77015 / Feb '95 / Discovery

☐ **OPERA AT THE MOVIES**
Con onor muore / Un'aura amorosa / Intermezzo sinfonico / Overture / Overture no.2 / Nessun dorma / Che gelida manina / Figaro / Vesta la giubba / Questa o quella / Ride of the valkyries
DC 880872 / May '97 / Disky

☐ **ORIGINAL HOLLYWOOD HITS**
Pennies from Heaven: *Crosby, Bing* / For me and my gal: *Garland, Judy & Gene Kelly* / Tangerine: *Dorsey, Jimmy Orchestra* / Sand in my shoes: *Boswell, Connie* / Love in bloom: *Crosby, Bing* / I'm old fashioned: *Astaire, Fred* / This year's kisses: *Faye, Alice* / Trolley song: *Garland, Judy* / Jeepers creepers: *Armstrong, Louis* / I had the craziest dream: *James, Harry Orchestra* / Chattanooga choo choo: *Miller, Glenn Orchestra* / Last time I saw Paris: *Martin, Tony* / Blues in the night: *Shore, Dinah* / I'll sing along with you: *Powell, Dick* / Two sleepy people: *Waller, Fats & His Rhythm* / I don't want to walk without you: *Rhodes, Betty Jane* / Take the 'A' train: *Ellington, Duke Orchestra* / Be careful it's my heart: *Sinatra, Frank* / Rhumboogie: *Andrews Sisters* / My own: *Durbin, Deanna*
306182 / Jan '97 / Hallmark

☐ **ORIGINAL LAUREL & HARDY MUSIC VOL.1, THE (Beau Hunks)**
MSA 99003 / Sep '97 / Movies Select Audio

☐ **ORIGINAL LAUREL & HARDY MUSIC VOL.2, THE (Beau Hunks)**
MSA 99025 / Sep '97 / Movies Select Audio

☐ **ORIGINAL LAUREL & HARDY MUSIC, THE (Beau Hunks)**
MSA 99026 / Sep '97 / Movies Select Audio

☐ **OVER THE RAINBOW (Garland, Judy)**
Over the rainbow / Stompin' at the Savoy / Swing Mr. Charlie / Zing went the strings of my heart / All God's chillun got rhythm / Everybody sing/You made me love you / It never rains but it pours / In-between / Sweet sixteen / Embraceable you / (Can this be) the end of the rainbow / I'm nobody's baby / Wearing Of The Green / Friendship / I'm always chasing rainbows / Pretty girl milking her cow / It's a great day for the Irish
CD 406 / Oct '96 / Entertainers

☐ **OVER THE RAINBOW (Garland, Judy)**
Do it again / Too late now / When you're smiling / Rock-a-bye your baby / Johnny one note / Friendly star / They can't take that away from me / You belong to me / It's all for me / I'd like to hate myself in the morning / Give my regards to Broadway / Alexander's ragtime band / You go to my head / Over the rainbow
100732 / May '97 / A-Play Collection

P

☐ **PALACE OF THE WIND (Piano At The Movies) (Chertock, Michael)**
Feather theme / Heaven's light / Ashokan farewell / With God's help / Prelude in C sharp minor op.3/2 / Piano concerto no.3 / Prelude no.15 / Round midnight / Il Postino / Bodyguard / English Patient / Immortal Beloved / Doe eyes / Don't cry for me Argentina / X-Files / Claudia's theme / Summer of '42
CD 80477 / Sep '97 / Telarc

☐ **PARTY'S OVER (Broadway Sings The Blues) (Broadway Casts)**
SK 53543 / Jul '94 / Sony Classical

☐ **PERFORMANCE (Webb, Marti & The Philharmonia Orchestra)**
OCRCD 6033 / Dec '95 / First Night

☐ **PERFORMANCE (Paige, Elaine)**
I have dreamed / Anything goes / Heart don't change my mind / Another suitcase in another hall / Rose / Love hurts / What'll I do/Who / I only have eyes for you / He's out of my life / I know him so well / Don't cry for me Argentina / Memory
74321446802 / Feb '97 / Camden

☐ **PHANTOM OF THE OPERA (& Other Broadway Hits) (Florida Symphony Pops Orchestra)**
Cacavas, John *con*
Phantom Of The Opera / Broadway Babies / Carousel / All That Jazz / Les Miserables / Kiss Me Kate overture / Porgy And Bess fantasy / Annie Get Your Gun medley
SION 18160 / Jul '97 / Sion

☐ **PLAY SAM PLAY...AS TIME GOES BY**
As time goes by: *Bergman, Ingrid & Dooley Wilson* / I can't give you anything but love: *Armstrong, Louis* / Stormy weather: *Horne, Lena* / Hong Kong blues: *Carmichael, Hoagy* / Falling in love again: *Dietrich, Marlene* / Inka dinka doo: *Durante, Jimmy* / Over the rainbow: *Garland, Judy* / Thanks for the memory: *Hope, Bob & Shirley Ross* / Chica chica boom chic: *Miranda, Carmen* / Night and day: *Astaire, Fred* / Moon of Manakoora: *Lamour, Dorothy* / Temptation: *Crosby, Bing* / Rumboogie: *Andrews Sisters* / Lobby numbers: *Kaye, Danny* / Song is you: *Johnstone, Johnnie & Kathryn Grayson* / For me and my gal: *Garland, Judy & Gene Kelly/George Murphy* / I'll see you in my dreams: *Faye, Alice* / Dinah: *Crosby, Bing & Mills Brothers* / Let yourself go: *Rogers, Ginger* / Hooray for Hollywood
CD 60018 / Sep '97 / Great Movie Themes

☐ **PLAYS THE HITS FROM BROADWAY (BBC Concert Orchestra)**
Arnold, David *con*
Jellicle ball / Tonight / Don't rain on my parade / Sunset boulevard / Send in the clowns / All I ask of you / Carousel waltz / What I did for love / Why God why / Come follow the band / Bring him home / Guys and dolls / As if we never said goodbye / Crazy for you
11242 / Oct '97 / BBC Concert Orchestra

☐ **POPULAR SONGS FROM 1940'S SPANISH CINEMA**
BMCD 20252 / 24 Apr '98 / Blue Moon

☐ **PORTRAIT OF BROADWAY, A (Pierce, Joshua & Dorothy Jonas)**
CDPC 5003 / Aug '90 / Prestige

☐ **PORTRAIT OF JUDY GARLAND, A (Garland, Judy)**
GALE 407 / May '97 / Gallerie

☐ **PRIME TIME MUSICALS**
VSD 5858 / 9 Mar '98 / Varese Sarabande

☐ **PRINCE AND THE PAUPER, THE (& Other Film Music) (National Philharmonic Orchestra)**
Gerhardt, Charles *con*
Revivers / Jane Eyre / Lost weekend / Between two worlds / Constant nymph / Prince and the pauper / Escape me never / Spectre of the rose / Madwoman of Chaillot / Cleopatra / Julie / Who's afraid of Virginia Woolf / Anne of the 1000 days / Henry V / Henry V suite
VSD 5207 / '90 / Varese Sarabande

☐ **PRINCESS COLLECTION**
WD 695002 / Nov '96 / Disney Music & Stories

☐ **PUBLIC TV'S GREATEST HITS**
604702 / Jul '92 / Silva Screen

☐ **PUTTIN' ON THE RITZ (Cincinnati Pops Orchestra)**
CD 80356 / Nov '95 / Telarc

R

☐ **ROMANCING THE FILM (Rochester Pops Orchestra)**
Schifrin, Lalo *con*
Tara's theme / Over the rainbow / As time goes by / Moon river / Lawrence Of Arabia / Lara's theme / Symphonic sketches / Love theme / Space medley / Time of my life / Medley / Around The World In 80 Days
SION 18210 / Jul '97 / Sion

☐ **ROMANTIC MOVIE THEMES (Mancini, Henry)**
Romeo and Juliet / Cinema Paradiso / Breakfast at Tiffany's / As time goes by / Once Upon A Time In America / Midnight Cowboy / Thorn Birds / Love Story / Godfather / Misty / Windmills of your mind / Adventurers / Evergreen / Medley / Shadow of your smile / Secret love / Raindrops keep falling on my head / Sweetheart tree / Mission/Gabriel's oboe / Untouchables
74321400602 / Sep '96 / Camden

☐ **RON GOODWIN CONDUCTS FILM AND TV THEMES (Bournemouth Symphony Orchestra)**
Goodwin, Ron *con*
London Marathon / Here where you are / Medley / Here's that rainy day / Tribute to Miklos Rozsa / Trolley song / Disneytime selection / Caravan / Girl from Corsica / Stephen Foster suite / Beauty And The Beast / Festival time / Candleshoe / Force 10 from Navarone / Minuet in blue / Spaceman and King Arthur / Girl with the misty eyes / Amazing grace
FBCD 2004 / 19 Nov '97 / Chandos

☐ **ROYAL PHILHARMONIC ORCHESTRA VISITS MAGICAL MOVIELAND (Royal Philharmonic Orchestra)**
When you wish upon a star / I wanna be like you / Can you feel the love tonight / Whole new world / Someday / Cruella De Vil / Beauty And the Beast / Colours of the wind / When I see an elephant fly / Circle of life / Dream is a wish your heart makes / Ev'rybody wants to be a cat
MCCD 313 / 8 Sep '97 / Music Club

☐ **RUTHIE HENSHALL ALBUM (Henshall, Ruthie)**
TRING 0022 / Nov '96 / Tring

S

☐ **SATCHMO AT THE CINEMA (Armstrong, Louis)**
3035900062 / '95 / Carlton

☐ **SATURDAY MORNING CARTOONS**
MCD 11348 / Jun '96 / MCA

☐ **SAX AND VIOLENCE**
VSD 5562 / Apr '95 / Varese Sarabande

☐ **SAX AT THE MOVIES**
Unchained melody / Love is all around / Show me heaven / Because you loved me / How deep is your love / Kiss from a rose / Can you feel the love tonight / Somewhere out there / Everything I do (I do it for you) / Glory of love / Arthur's theme / (I've had) The time of my life / Up where we belong / When a man loves a woman / My funny valentine / I will always love you / Take my breath away / It must have been love / Waiting for a star to fall / Gangsta's paradise
CDVIP 181 / Apr '97 / Virgin

☐ **SCHWARZENEGGER - SUPER HERO**
True Lies / Last Action Hero / Predator / Terminator / Kindergarten Cop / Conan The Barbarian / Twins / Total Recall / Raw Deal / Red Sonja / Commando / Conan The Destroyer / Red Heat / Running Man / Last Action Hero / Terminator II: Judgement Day
0022232CIN / 26 May '98 / Cinerama

☐ **SCI-FI**
Star Wars: *Williams, John* / Empire Strikes Back: *Williams, John* / Return Of The Jedi: *Williams, John* / Total Recall: *Goldsmith, Jerry* / Predator: *Silvestri, Alan* / Dark Star: *Carpenter, John* / Starman: *Nitzsche, Jack* / Gremlins II: *Goldsmith, Jerry* / Terminator II: *Fiedel, Brad* / Thing: *Morricone, Ennio* / Apollo 13: *Horner, James* / Star Trek: *Goldsmith, Jerry* / Deep Space Nine: *McCarthy, Dennis* / Star Trek Generations: *McCarthy, Dennis*
SILVAD 3508 / Oct '97 / Silva Treasury

☐ **SCI-FI COLLECTION (Montague Orchestra)**
MACCD 368 / 30 Mar '98 / Autograph

☐ **SCI-FI MOVIE THEMES**
15153 / Mar '95 / Laserlight

☐ **SCI-FI THEMES (16 Science Fiction Screen Hits) (London Theatre Orchestra)**
Star Wars / X-Files / Close encounters of the third kind / 2001 A space odyssesy / Star Trek / Battlestar Galactica / Space 1999 / Blake 7 / Dune / Stargate / Blade Runner / Total Recall / War of the world's / Tomorrow people / Doctor Who / ET: The Extra Terrestrial
EMPRCD 655 / Jun '96 / Emporio

☐ **SCIENCE FICTION AND FANTASY (TV Soundtracks)**
Welcome to the darkzone from Lexx / Suite from Robocop / Main title / First season / Preparing for battle / Main title / Preparing for battle / Lexx escape from Lexx / Warrior princess / To adventures bold / Main title / Power Rangers triumph / Main title / Main theme / Main title / Main theme / Bridge to Eternity / Project Blue/Dream begins
VSD 5865 / 2 Mar '98 / Varese Sarabande

☐ **SCIENCE FICTION THEMES**
Star Trek / X files / Close encounters of the third kind / ET / Star wars / Twilight zone / Robocop 2 / Superman / Timecop / Battleship galactica / Dune / Batdance / Stark Trek 3 / Flash / Blade runner / Terminator 2 / Empire strikes back / Star trek: The next generation
ECD 3225 / Jan '95 / K-Tel

☐ **SCREEN ACTION (Power Pack Orchestra)**
Superman / Miami Vice / Magnum PI / Hunter / Professionals / Starsky and Hutch / Shoestring / Hawaii Five-O / Dempsey and Makepeace / Indiana Jones and the Temple of Doom / TJ Hooker / James Bond / New Avengers theme / Rockford files / Street hawk / Good the bad and the ugly / A-Team / Knight rider / Crazy like a fox / Mike Hammer theme / Fall guy / Sweeney / Chinese detective / Highway patrol / Airwolf
CDMFP 6017 / Apr '88 / Music For Pleasure

☐ **SCREEN DANCE MANIA (Worsley, John)**
Doctor Who / X Files / Star Wars / Hawaii five-O / Kojak / Mission Impossible / Prisoner / Batman / Close encounters of the third kind / Starsky and Hutch / Star Trek / Dallas / James Bond theme / Baywatch
3036000802 / Mar '97 / Carlton

☐ **SCREEN EXTRAVAGANZA**
MPRCDM 2004 / 16 Mar '98 / Music Club

☐ **SCREEN HITS (40 Orchestral TV & Film Themes)**
DEMPCD 014 / Mar '96 / Emporio

☐ **SCREEN SINATRA (Sinatra, Frank)**
From here to eternity / Three coins in the fountain / Young at heart / Just one of those things / Someone to watch over me / Not as a stranger / Tender trap / Wait for me (Johnny Concho theme) / All the way / Chicago / Monique-Song from Kings Go Forth / They came to Cordura / To love and be loved / High hopes / All my tomorrows / It's all right with me / C'est magnifique / Dream
4939822 / 16 Mar '98 / EMI Gold

☐ **SCREEN THEMES (Royal Philharmonic Orchestra)**
Scott, John *con*
Die Hard / Big / Who Framed Roger Rabbit / Milagro Beanfield War / Beetlejuice / Crossing Delancey / Cocoon - the Return / Madame Sousatzka / Criminal Law / Nightmare on Elm Street IV / Betrayed / Coming to America / Masquerade / Da
VSD 5208 / Dec '88 / Varese Sarabande

☐ **SCREEN THEMES '93 (Garson, Michael)**
Jurassic park / Schindler's list / Indecent proposal / Fugitive / Age of innocence / Shadowlands / Pelican brief / Piano (Heart asks for pleasure) / Bleu / Heaven and earth / Firm / MrdDoubtfire (Snow's over) / Philadelphia (Streets of Philadelphia) / Sleepless in Seattle
77009 / Jun '94 / Discovery

☐ **SECRET AGENT FILE (Norman, Neil & his Orchestra)**
Reilly ace of spies / Octopussy / I spy / Rockford files / Man from UNCLE / Casino Royale / Ipcress file / Get smart / Thunderball / Spy who came in from the cold
GNPD 2166 / Jan '89 / GNP Crescendo

☐ **SHAKEN AND STIRRED (The David Arnold 007 Project) (Arnold, David)**
Diamonds are forever: *Arnold, David & David McAlmont* / 007 theme: *Arnold, David & LTJ Bukem* / Spy who loved me: *Arnold, David & Aimee Mann* / All time high: *Arnold, David & Pulp* / Space march: *Arnold, David & Leftfield* / Live and let die: *Arnold, David & Chrissie Hynde* / Moonraker: *Arnold, David & Shara Nelson* / Thunderball: *Arnold, David & ABC* / From Russia with love: *Arnold, David & Natacha Atlas* / You only live twice: *Arnold, David & Candi Staton* / On her majesty's secret service: *Arnold, David & Propellerheads* / All the time in the world: *Arnold, David & Iggy Pop*
3984207382 / 20 Oct '97 / East West

☐ **SHAKESPEARE ON BROADWAY**
VSD 5622 / Jul '96 / Varese Sarabande

☐ **SHAKESPEARE'S MUSICK (Songs & Dances From Shakespeare's Plays) (Musicians Of The Globe)**
Pickett, Philip *con*
Hollis berrie / Daphne / My robin is to the greenwood gone / Tickle my toe / It was a lover and his lasse / Kemp's jig / Take o take those lips away / Bonny sweet Robin / Farewell dear love / Tarletones riserrectione / Hold lingel hold / How should I your true love know / Walsingham / Get your hense for I must go / La coranto / La coranto / Hark hark the lark / La volta / La volta / Willow song (the poor soul sat sighing) / Robin / O mistress mine / O mistress myne / Full fathom five / Where the bee sucks / Can she excuse / Frog galliard / Go from my window
4466872 / Jun '97 / Philips

☐ **SHALL WE DANCE (Classic Dance Hits From The West End & Broadway)**
Can can: *English National Opera Company* / Shall we dance: *Lee, Christopher & Valerie Masterson* / I could have danced all night: *Olafimihan, Tinuke & Company* / Oh look at me: *Matthews, Christina* / I got rhythm: *Shore, Julia* / Too darn hot: *Collis, Paul & Company* / Won't you charleston with me: *Newent, Bob & Linda-Mae Brewer* / Dance a little closer: *Robertson, Liz* / Lambeth walk: *Lindsay, Robert & Mary Ann Plankctt/Company* / Dance at the gym: *National Symphony Orchestra* / On your toes: *Andreas, Christine* / Varsity drag: *Morrison, Ann & Company*
SHOWCD 029 / Oct '96 / Showtime

☐ **SHERLOCK HOLMES (Classic Themes From 221B Baker Street)**
Sherlock Holmes / Seven percent solution / Adventures of Sherlock Holmes / Study in terror / Universal Holmes / Young Sherlock Holmes / I never do anything twice / Masks of death / Hound of the Baskervilles / Dressed to kill / Private life of Sherlock Holmes / Without a clue
VSD 5692 / Aug '96 / Varese Sarabande

☐ **SHOOT 'EM UPS**
VSD 5666 / May '96 / Varese Sarabande

☐ SHOW BOAT (& Other Classic Broadway Shows)
3036600022 / Jun '98 / Hallmark

☐ SHOW STOPPERS
95902 / Feb '90 / Silva Screen

☐ SHOW STOPPERS (18 Unforgettable Songs...18 Unforgettable Shows) (Starsound Singers & Orchestra)
Music of the night / Memory / If ever I would leave you / Send in the clowns / Anemone / If I were a rich man / I enjoy being a girl / Some enchanted evening / If my friends could see me now / Cabaret / Good morning starshine / I don't know how to love him / Stranger in paradise / I could have danced all night / Sound of music / Hello young lovers / I can't give you anything but love / There's no business like show business
ECD 3133 / Jan '95 / K-Tel

☐ SHOW STOPPERS - TIMELESS HITS FROM THE MUSICALS
Big spender / Consider yourself / Cabaret / Somewhere / You're the one that I want / Send in the clowns / Ol' man river / Oklahoma / Windy city / I won't send roses / I could write a book / Memory
SHOWCD 018 / Feb '95 / Showtime

☐ SHOWSTOPPERS (The Greatest Show Songs)
DINCD 118 / Nov '95 / Dino

☐ SHOWSTOPPERS (Hits From The Musicals)
I don't know how to love him / Summer nights / Send in the clowns / All that jazz / What I did for love / Don't cry for me Argentina / Take that look off your face / Any dream will do / Memory / I am what I am / Only he / I know him so well / Music of the night / Love changes everything / On my own / Last night of the world
11983 / Feb '96 / Music

☐ SHOWSTOPPERS (BBC Big Band)
BBB 004 / Nov '96 / BBC Big Band

☐ SHOWSTOPPERS
Macavity: Bassey, Shirley / You do something to me: Cogan, Alma & Frank Cordell Orchestra / My dearest dear: Ellis, Mary & Ivor Nordello / Love changes everything: Keel, Howard / Who can I turn to: Monro, Matt / I can give you starlight: Hill, Vince / Me and my girl: Lindsay, Robert & Emma Thompson / Close every door: West End Theatre Orchestra / Don't cry for me Argentina: Williams, Margaret & The Morriston Opheus Choir / Superstar: West End Theatre Orchestra / Any dream will do: Jones, Paul / Everything's coming up roses: Bassey, Shirley / Singin' in the rain: Monro, Matt / How to handle a woman: Treorchy Male Choir / Day by day: Laine, Cleo / Prepare ye the way of the Lord: Laine, Cleo / There's no business like show business: Bassey, Shirley / Bless your beautiful hide: Keel, Howard / One more angel in heaven: Sammes, Mike Singers / As long as he needs me: Bassey, Shirley / Climb every mountain: Treorchy Male Choir / Lambeth walk: Lindsay, Robert & Emma Thompson / O what a beautiful morning: Keel, Howard / I don't know how to love him: Bassey, Shirley / Edelweiss: Hill, Vince / Hello young lovers: Monro, Matt / Tell me on a Sunday: West End Theatre Orchestra / Sunrise sunset: Dodd, Ken / There is nothing like a dame: Hallmark Of Harmony / People: Bassey, Shirley / Drinking song: Locke, Josef / Bring him home: Keel, Howard / Rose Marie: Lawrence, Syd & His Orchestra / True love: Martin, Dean / I love you Samntha: Ball, Kenny & His Jazzmen / sOmeday my heart will wake: Hill, Vince / Starlight express: Warlow, David
CDTRBOX 328 / 6 Oct '97 / EMI Gold

☐ SHOWTIME
CDPK 417 / Oct '93 / Charly

☐ SHOWTIME (London Theatre Orchestra)
Young lovers / March of the Siamese children / Of my dreams / Anything goes / You're just in love / I get a kick out of you / People will say we're in love / Kansas city / Lovely day today / Best thing for you / Shall we dance / Getting to know you / Whistle a happy tune / Surrey with a fringe on top / Do what I do what comes naturally / Can't get a man with a gun / Make believe / Ol' man river / On the street where you live / I could have danced all night / I could write a book / My defences are down / Girl that I marry / Why do I love you / Rain in Spain / Wouldn't it be lovely / I've grown accustomed to her face / Bewitched / Bill / Can't help lovin' that man / Ascot Gavotte / They say it's wonderful / I got the sun in the morning / June is bustin' out all over / Carousel Waltz / If this isn't love / I got plenty of nuthin' / I'm gonna wash that man right out of my hair / Cockeyed optimist / Hernando's hideaway / You'll never walk alone / Some enchanted evening / Hey there / When the children are asleep / If I loved you / Sound Of Music / Climb every mountain / Lady is a tramp / My funny Valentine / I wish I were in love again / So In Love / Wunderbar / Another opening another show / Woman in love / Bushel and a peck / Slaughter on 10th Avenue / Where or when / Edelweiss / If I were a cad / I've never been in love before / Heatwave / Easter parade
391292 / Aug '97 / Hallmark

☐ SILENTS, THE (Contemporary Scores For Classic Films) (Alloy Orchestra)
Plain Crazy / Lost World / Nosferatu / Metropolis / Unknown
RC 5026 / Nov '97 / Accurate

☐ SING SOMETHING SIMPLE FROM THE SHOWS (Adams, Cliff Singers)
PWKS 4148 / '95 / Carlton

☐ SINGS (Travolta, John)
VSD 5682 / 6 Apr '98 / Varese Sarabande

☐ SLAUGHTER ON TENTH AVENUE (Fiedler, Arthur & The Boston Pops Orchestra)
Slaughter on Tenth Avenue / Interplay / Fancy free / El sombrero de tres picos / Golden age / Rodeo / Estancia / Gayaneh
09026685502 / 6 Apr '98 / RCA Victor

☐ SMASH HITS OF BROADWAY
CDTEZ 7005 / Jan '95 / TER

☐ SOME LIKE IT HOT (Monroe, Marilyn)
Diamonds are a girl's best friend / Man chases a girl / Every baby needs a da da daddy / Happy birthday Mr. President / Incurably romantic / Down in the meadow / Some like it hot / I found a dream / Anyone can see I love you / Specialization / Heatwave / Ladies of the chorus / When I fall in love / Let's make it meadow / Bye bye baby / Fine romance / One silver dollar / That old black magic / There's no business like show business / I wanna be loved by you
HADCD 153 / May '94 / Javelin

☐ SONGS FROM SIX FILMS (Garland, Judy)
CIN 016 / Sep '96 / IMP

☐ SONGS FROM THE MOVIES (Astaire, Fred)
No strings / Isn't this a lovely day (to be caught in the rain) / Top hat white tie and tails / Cheek to cheek / Piccolino / We saw the sea / Let yourself go / I'd rather be nice / Something's coming up roses / Bojangles of Harlem / Never gonna dance / Beginner's luck / Slap that bass / They all laughed / Let's call the whole thing off / They can't take that away from me / Shall we dance / I can't be bothered now / Things are looking up / Foggy day / Nice work if you can get it
PPCD 78115 / Feb '95 / Past Perfect

☐ SONGS FROM THE MOVIES (Crosby, Bing)
You belong to my heart / Gal in Calico / Ain't got a dime to my name / On the Atcheson Topeka and Santa Fe / September song / Aren't you glad you're you / I can't begin to tell you / Baia / I'd rather be me / Oh but I do / As long as I'm dreaming / Swinging on a star / Birds of St. Mary's / It could happen to you / Blue skies / If you please / Count your blessings / Moonlight becomes you / Dream / More and more / It's anybody's spring / People will say we're in love / Sunday Monday or always / Out of this world / Going my way
RAJCD 895 / 6 Apr '98 / Empress

☐ SONGS FROM THE MUSICALS
Grease / Summer nights / Hopelessly devoted to you / You're the one that I want / Beauty school dropout / Look at me I'm Sandra Dee / Greased lightning / It's raining on Prom night / Alone at the Drive-In movie / Blue moon / Rock 'n' roll is here to stay / Those magic changes / Hound dog / Born to hand jive / Tears on my pillow / Mooning / Freddy my love / Rock 'n' roll party Queen / There are worse things I could do / Look at me I'm Sandra Dee (reprise) / We go together / Witch Doctor / Who put the bomp / Grease (reprise) / Ready Teddy / Rock around with Ollie Vee / Changing all those changes / That'll be the day / Blue days / Everyday / Not fade away / Peggy Sue / Words of love / Oh boy / True love ways / Chantilly lace / Maybe baby / Heartbeat / La bamba / Raining in my heart / It doesn't matter anymore / Rave on / Fame / Out here on my own / Hot lunch jam / Dogs in the yard / Red light / It's OK to call you mine / Never alone / Flashdance / What a feeling / Maniac / I love rock and roll / Gloria / Seventeen / Hungry eyes / Time of my life / Bad reputation
SUMCD 4128 / Jun '97 / Sound & Media

☐ SONGS FROM THE SHOWS (Treorchy Male Choir)
CDMFP 6364 / May '97 / Music For Pleasure

☐ SONGS FROM THE SILVER SCREEN (Kaye, Judy)
Wonderful day / Everything / Craziest dream / Milkman keep those bottles quiet / Folks who live on the hill / Carmen Miranda medley / Secret love / Thanks a lot but no thanks / You'll never know / Shakin' the blues away / Falling in love again / On the good ship lollipop / Ginger and Fred medley / You and I
VSD 5894 / 9 Mar '98 / Varese Sarabande

☐ SONGS FROM THE STAGE & SCREEN (Garland, Judy)
MCCD 101 / May '93 / MCI Music

☐ SONGS FROM THEIR FILMS (Robeson, Paul & Elisabeth Welch)
I still suits me/Emperor Jones/Water boy / Lazy lady / Canoe song/Congo lullaby / Medley from Show Boat / Medley from Song of freedom / Nightfall / Medley from Big fella / Ho ho (the wagon song)/Climbin' up (the mountain song) / My way/Deep desert / Red hot / Annabelle / Medley from Proud Valley
CMSCD 011 / Mar '98 / Movie Stars

☐ SONGS OF ALMODOVAR, THE
One year of love: Luz / Thinks of me: Luz / Suck it to me: Almodovar & MacNamara / Great gangs: Almodovar & MacNamara / It was written: Bell, Monna / Chained: Gatica, Lucho / I left because I left: Feliciano, Cheo / Wait for me in heaven: Mina / Oh my love: De Nieve, Bola / In the last sip: Vargas, Chavela / I'm unhappy: Beltran, Lola / Pure theatre: La Lupe / I will resist: Duo Dinamico / I'm going to be a mother: Almodovar & MacNamara / Satanasa: Almodovar & MacNamara / If you go away: Almodovar & MacNamara / Susan get down: Almodovar & MacNamara / I doubt it: Los Panchos / Let me remember: De Nieve, Bola / Well paid one: De Molina, Miguel / Moonlight: Vargas, Chavela / Our love was broken: Vargas, Chavela
4946742 / 18 May '98 / Premier/EMI

☐ SONGS OF SHIRLEY TEMPLE'S FILMS, THE (Temple, Shirley)
CIN 024 / Nov '97 / IMP

☐ SONGS OF THE MUSICALS
Phantom of the opera/Music of the night / Memory / Don't cry for me Argentina / Cabaret / Tonight / Angel of music / If I were a rich man / I could have danced all night / Last night of the world / You'll never walk alone / I dreamed a dream / Some enchanted evening / Big spender / What I did for love / Almost like being in love / There's no business like showbusiness
EMPRCD 901 / Jan '97 / Emporio

☐ SOPRANO IN HOLLYWOOD (Garrett, Lesley & BBC Concert Orchestra)
Bateman, Paul con
Lover / Danny boy / Love is where you find it / Smoke gets in your eyes / With a song in my heart / Long ago and far away / One kiss / Man I love / Love is here to stay / Love walked in
SILKTVCD 2 / Oct '96 / Silva Classics

☐ SOUND OF HOLLYWOOD, THE (Hollywood Bowl Symphony Orchestra)
Mauceri, John con
4464992 / Feb '96 / Philips

☐ SOUND OF MUSICALS, THE (Piano Selections From The Greatest Shows) (Laurence, Paul)
Sound Of Music medley / West Side story medley / Fiddler On The Roof medley / My Fair Lady medley / Guys and Dolls medley / South Pacific medley
305812 / Oct '96 / Hallmark

☐ SOUNDS ORCHESTRAL MEETS JAMES BOND (Sounds Orchestral)
Thunderball / Solitaire / Goldfinger / Mr. Kiss Kiss Bang Bang / Blues for pussy / Mr. Oddjob / Moonshot / James Bond theme / Spectre / From Russia With Love / Kissy Suzuki / 007 theme
NEBCD 908 / Sep '96 / Sequel

☐ SPACE AND BEYOND VOL.1 (The Ultimate Sci-Fi Movie Themes Album)
2001: A Space Odyssey / Apollo 13 / Right Stuff / Species / Lifeforce / Alien / Capricorn One / Cocoon / Black Hole / Star Wars/Empire Strikes Back / Enemy / Close Encounters Of The Third Kind / Star Trek I / Star Trek II: The Wrath Of Kahn / Star Trek IV: The Voyage Home / Star Trek V: The Final Frontier / Star Trek VI: The Undiscovered Country / Star Trek: Deep Space Nine/Star Trek Generations / Star Trek: The Next Generation / Star Trek: Voyager / Star Trek
FILMXCD 185 / Feb '97 / Silva Screen

☐ SPACE AND BEYOND VOL.2 (Alien Invasion)
FILMXCD 190 / 2 Feb '97 / Silva Screen

☐ SPACE MOVIE THEMES (Star Wars/ Empire Strikes Back/Return Of The Jedi/etc) (London Symphony Orchestra)
HRM 7001 / Jan '86 / Hermes

☐ SPACE THEMES (Starlight Orchestra)
ET / Close Encounters Of The Third Kind / Star Trek / Empire Strikes Back / Star Wars / Flash / Return Of The Jedi / Star Trek II / Cantina band / Star beyond / time / Conversation / Star Trek III / Prophecy theme / Eve of the war / Star Trek / Yoda's theme
QED 169 / Nov '96 / Tring

☐ SPAGHETTI WESTERNS VOL.1
DRGCD 32905 / Jun '95 / DRG

☐ SPECTACULAR MUSIC FROM THE SILVER SCREEN
Mars Attacks / Body Heat / Rock / Wyatt Earp / False Mask III / Total Recall / Lion In Winter / Taras Bulba / El Cid / Captain Blood / Cinema Paradiso / English Patient / Capricorn One / James Bond Theme
ACCD 1002 / 1 Jun '98 / Silva Screen

☐ SPECTACULAR WORLD OF CLASSIC FILM SCORES (National Philharmonic Orchestra)
Gerhardt, Charles con
Studio fanfares / Star Wars / Captain Blood / Now Voyager / Gone With the Wind / Elizabeth and Essex / Peyton Place / Citizen Kane / Caine Mutiny / Knights of the Round Table / Objective Burma / Guns of Navarone / Julius Caesar / Thing from Another World / King of the Khyber Rifles / Jailbreak
GD 82792 / '92 / RCA Victor

☐ SPIELBERG CONNECTION, THE (Fantasia)
Jaws / Arachnophobia / Back To The Future / Indiana Jones And The Temple Of Doom / Always / Close Encounters Of The Third Kind / Hook / Schindler's List / Raiders Of The Lost Ark / Color Purple / Casper / ET / 1941 / Empire Of The Sun / Indiana Jones And The Last Crusade / Jurassic Park
307632 / Jul '97 / Hallmark

☐ STALLONE (Music From The Films Of Sylvester Stallone)
Rocky: London Screen Orchestra / FIST: City Of Prague Philharmonic Orchestra / Paradise Alley: London Screen Orchestra / Rocky II: London Screen Orchestra / Nighthawks: London Screen Orchestra / Rocky III / First Blood: City Of Prague Philharmonic Orchestra / Rambo - First Blood II: City Of Prague Philharmonic Orchestra / Cobra: Ayres, Mark / Over The Top: Ayres, Mark / Rambo III: City Of Prague Philharmonic Orchestra / Lock Up: Ayres, Mark / Cliffhanger: City Of Prague Philharmonic Orchestra
FILMCD 139 / Nov '93 / Silva Screen

☐ STANDING ROOM ONLY (Broadway Favourites) (Hadley, Jerry & American Theatre Orchestra)
Gemignani, Paul con
09026613702 / Jul '93 / RCA Victor

☐ STAR TRACKS (Silver Screen Orchestra)
Star Wars / Empire strikes back / Imperial march / Luke and Leia / March of the Jedi Knights / Yoda's theme / Cantina band / Star Trek / Wrath of Kahn / Search for Spock star beyond time / Battlestar Galactica / Cylon trap / Destruction of peace / Red nova / Let's go home
DC 881572 / Aug '97 / Disky

☐ STAR TREK EXPERIENCE, THE (Silver Screen Orchestra)
Star Trek / Star Trek Generations / Wrath Of Khan / Star Trek Voyager / Search For Spock / Star Trek Deep Space Nine / Voyage Home / Undiscovered Country / Star Trek The Final Frontier / Star Trek : The Next Generation / Star Trek Generations / Star Trek
3036001172 / 13 Oct '97 / Carlton

☐ STAR WARS/CLOSE ENCOUNTERS OF THE THIRD KIND (& Other Space Themes/Disco Galactic Themes) (Love, Geoff & His Orchestra)
Star Wars / UFO / Star Trek / Barbarella / Space 1999 / Also sprach zarathustra / Things To Come / Thunderbirds / Star Wars / Dr. Who / Buzz / Empire of war / Close Encounters of The Third Kind / Logan's Run / Flight Fantastic / Time Machine / Star Wars / Blake Seven / Omega Man
CDMFP 6395 / Jun '97 / Music For Pleasure

☐ STARRING FRED ASTAIRE (Astaire, Fred)
Top hat white tie and tails / Cheek to cheek / Piccolino / No strings / Pick yourself up / Way you look tonight / Fine romance / Let's call the whole thing off / Let's face the music and dance / Nice work if you can get it / Let yourself go / Let's face the music and dance / Fascinating rhythm / Night and day / I used to be colour blind / Change partners
CD 405 / Oct '96 / Entertainers

☐ STARS OF STAGE AND SCREEN, THE
Donkey serenade: Jones, Allan / You've done something to my heart: Laye, Evelyn / Night and day: Astaire, Fred / Indian love call: Astaire, Fred / My heart belongs to daddy: Martin, Mary / Louise: Chevalier, Maurice / Amapola: Durbin, Deanna / Goodnight vienna: Buchanan, Jack / Let yourself go: Rogers, Ginger / One night of love: Moore, Grace / Little whiteroom: Eddy, Nelson & John Mills / Inka-dinka-doo: Durante, Jimmy / Lovely to look at: Dunne, Irene / I'll see you again: Oliver, Vic / Falling in love again: Dietrich, Marlene / I'll get by: Haymes, Dick / I can give you the starlight: Ellis, Mary / Experiment: Lawrence, Gertrude / Solomon: Welch, Elizabeth / Thanks for the memory: Hope, Bob & Shirley Ross / Dancing on the ceiling: Matthews, Jessie / I get a kick out of you: Merman, Ethel
PASTCD 7016 / Mar '97 / Flapper

☐ STARS OF THE MUSICAL STAGE, THE (Stars Of The West End & Broadway Perform Hit Songs From The Hit Shows)
Willkommen: Pryce, Jonathan & Company / Any dream will do: Barrowman, John / If I ruled the world / Secombe, Harry / I'm getting married in the morning: Hoskins, Bob / Don't cry for me Argentina: Friedman, Maria / Coloured lights: Minnelli, Liza / How to handle a woman: Harris, Richard / I don't believe in heroes anymore: Ball, Michael / Science fiction: Dobson, Anita / Send in the clowns: Phillips, Sam / Unusual way: Paige, Elaine
SHOWCD 040 / Oct '96 / Showtime

☐ STEREO ULTRA
Ok chicago: Resonance / Le crocodile porte cle: Gerard, Bernard / Nues dans l'eau: Garvarentz, Georges / Petrol pop: Magne, Michel & Jean Yanne / Kidnapping: Shaffer, Karl-Heinz / Ten and medor: Goraqeur, Alain / Batacuda: Delerue, Georges / Hashisch party: Garvarentz, Georges / Full speed: Bolling, Claude / Seropols: Mirouze, Jean Pierre / La theme d'Olivier: Lai, Francis / La course d'auto: Dumont, Charles / Take one: Golden Port / Grand theme walka: Magne, Michel
FR 364CD / 30 Mar '98 / Big Cheese

☐ STORY GOES ON, THE (Callaway, Liz)
VSD 5585 / Oct '95 / Varese Sarabande

☐ SUPPLY AND DEMAND (Songs by Brecht, Weill & Eisler) (Krause, Dagmar)
HNCD 1317 / Mar '86 / Hannibal

☐ **SWASHBUCKLERS (Swordsmen Of The Silver Screen) (City Of Prague Philharmonic Orchestra)**
Bateman, Paul con
Captain Blood / Private Lives Of Elizabeth And Essex / Hook / Crimson Pirate / Willow's theme / Robin Hood / Robin Hood / Robin And Marian / Adventures Of Robin Hood / Sea Hawk / Mark Of Zorro / Duellists / Buccaneer / Adventures Of Don Juan / Crimson Permanent Assurance / Seventh Voyage Of Sinbad / Golden Voyage Of Sinbad / Swordsmen Of Siena / Cutthroat Island
FILMXCD 188 / Oct '97 / Silva Screen

☐ **SWEET SWAN OF AVON (Music From Productions At Stratford-Upon-Avon) (English Serenata)**
CDE 84301 / 8 Jan '98 / Meridian

☐ **SYMPHONIC SUITE OF THE ANIMATED CLASSICS (Kingston Symphony)**
MACD 2501 / Mar '95 / Hindsight

☐ **SYNTHESIZER AT THE MOVIES**
Also sprach Zarathustra / Raiders march / Claudia's theme / Chase / (Everything I do) I do it for you / Love is all around / Close Encounters Of The Third Kind / Goldeneye / John Dunbar theme / Mission / Deerhunter / Streets of Philadelphia / Jaws / Tubular bells / ET / Star Wars / Silence Of The Lambs / Love theme / Mission Impossible / Bladerunner / Missing / Cockeye's song / Rain man / 1492 Conquest Of Paradise / I will always love you / It must have been love / Chariots of fire / Axel F / Heart asks pleasure first/The Promise / Out Of Africa / Second time / Mutiny On The Bounty / Take my breath away / Unchained melody / Star Trek / Gonna fly now
330292 / Mar '97 / Hallmark

☐ **SYNTHESIZER HITS (TV Themes)**
MU 5006 / Oct '92 / Musketeer

☐ **SYNTHESIZER HITS (Film Themes)**
MU 5003 / Oct '92 / Musketeer

☐ **SYNTHESIZER HITS (James Bond Themes)**
MU 5004 / Oct '92 / Musketeer

☐ **SYNTHESIZER HITS OF CINEMA AND TV**
22528 / Jul '95 / Music

☐ **SYNTHESIZER THEMES**
Elsewhere / Magic Fly / Popcorn / Miami Vice / Oxygene / Pulstar / Battlestar Galactica / Crocket's Theme / Pepper Box / Chase / Maid Of Orleans / Axel F / Onyx / Chi Mai / Rotations Logic / Italian Song
EMPRCD 651 / Nov '97 / Emporio

T

☐ **TARANTINO CONNECTION, THE**
Interview (Spoken word): Tarantino, Quentin / Miserlou: Dale, Dick & His Del-Tones / Dark night: Blasters / Little green bag: Baker, George Selection / Graceland: Sexton, Charlie / Girl you'll be a woman soon: Urge Overkill / Waiting for the miracle: Cohen, Leonard / Little bitty tear: Ives, Burl / Interview (2) (Spoken word): Tarantino, Quentin / Stuck in the middle with you: Stealer's Wheel / You never can tell: Berry, Chuck / Love is (the tender trap): Palmer, Robert / Sweet Jane: Cowboy Junkies / Six blade knife: Dire Straits / Foolish heart: Mavericks / Vertigo: Combustible Edison
MCD 80325 / Oct '96 / MCA

☐ **TASTE OF MUSIC, A (Music From The BBC TV Series)**
Rick Stein: A taste of the sea / Carluccio's: Italian Feast / Far Flung Floyd / Floyd on Italy / Floyd On Africa
V 1021 / Apr '97 / Voyager

☐ **TEENAGE TV (Countdown Rock Band)**
We will rock you / Another one bites the dust / We are the champions / Beverly Hills 90210 / Baywatch / Simpsons / I'll be there for you / Heartbreak High / Power Rangers / Holding out for a hero / Action speaks louder than words / All the way to Heaven / Happy Days / Due South / Brady Bunch / Roseanne / Star Trek: The Next Generation / Lois and Clark / Gladiators / On the inside
QED 078 / Nov '96 / Tring

☐ **TELEVISION'S GREATEST HITS**
GRF 198 / Jan '93 / Tring

☐ **TELEVISION'S GREATEST HITS VOL.1 (TV Themes From The 1950's And 1960's)**
0022702CIN / May '97 / Edel

☐ **TELEVISION'S GREATEST HITS VOL.2 (TV Themes From The 1970's And 1980's)**
0022712CIN / May '97 / Edel

☐ **TELEVISION'S GREATEST HITS VOL.3**
Muppet Show / Scooby Doo / Sesame Street / Cheers / Waltons / Mash / Hill Street Blues / Rockford Files / Starsky and Hutch
0022722CIN / 26 Aug '97 / Edel

☐ **TELEVISION'S GREATEST HITS VOL.4**
Lassie / Untouchables / Laurel and Hardy / Real McCoys / Roger Ramjet
0022732CIN / 26 Aug '97 / Edel/ Cinerama

☐ **TELEVISION'S GREATEST HITS VOL.5 (In Living Colour)**
0022742CIN / 10 Nov '97 / Edel

☐ **TELEVISION'S GREATEST HITS VOL.6 (Remote Control)**
0022752CIN / 10 Nov '97 / Edel

☐ **TELEVISION'S GREATEST HITS VOL.7 (Cable Ready)**
0022762CIN / 10 Nov '97 / Edel

☐ **TELEVISION'S GREATEST THEMES (Starlight Orchestra/Singers)**
Miami Vice / LA Law / MASH / Cheers / Fame / Dynasty / Happy Days / Dallas / Star Trek / Quincy / Rockford Files / Magnum / Moonlighting / Reilly Ace Of Spies / Superman / Kojak / Mah Na Mah Na / Hawaii 5-O / High Chaparral / Bonanza / Hill Street Blues / A-Team / Charlie's Angels
QED 066 / Nov '96 / Tring

☐ **TEST CARD CLASSICS VOL.1 (The Girl, The Doll, The Music)**
FBCD 2000 / Aug '96 / Flyback

☐ **TEST CARD CLASSICS VOL.2 (Big Band Width)**
Fings ain't what they used to be: Brandenburg Philharmonic Orchestra / Smiling fortune: Martin, Alexander Orchestra / Story of my life: Winters, George Orchestra / Lucky bounce: Skymasters / Here in a smokey room: Keller, Otto Band / Waltz express: Scott, Joe Orchestra / Slinky: Basshoppers / Carry me back to Old Virginny: Haensch, Delle Band / Beat in: Pleyer, Frank & His Orchestra / Alamo: Palmer, Joe / Small town: Gardner, William Orchestra / Take off: Monza, Henry Orchestra / Meet me on the bridge: Skymasters / Happy walk: Pleyer, Frank & His Orchestra / Charleston-time: Pleyer, Frank & His Orchestra / Apron strings: Hatter, Hans & His Orchestra / Scotch broth: Brandenburg Philharmonic Orchestra / Tele-vision: Haensch, Delle Band / Concerto grosso '67: Landy, Eric / High ball: Keller, Otto Band / Hallelujah honey: Valdor, Frank Orchester / Soho swing: Peters, Walt / Daisy: Peters, Walt / Walking on the shore: Taormina, Franco / Hello Lissy: Palmer, Joe / Craig Hill surprise: Keller, Otto Band / Post haste: Brasshoppers / Swingin' affair: Brandenburg Philharmonic Orchestra / Jeff's special: Haskey, Jeff / Indian boots: Winters, George Orchestra
FBCD 2001 / May '97 / Flyback

☐ **THAT'S ENTERTAINMENT (The Best Of The MGM Musicals)**
That's entertainment: Astaire, Fred & Jack Buchanan / Get happy: Garland, Judy / From this moment on: Miller, Ann/Bobby Van/Tommy Rall/ Bob Fosse / Over the rainbow: Garland, Judy / Ol' man river: Warfield, William / Singin' in the rain: Kelly, Gene / Trolley song: Garland, Judy / Varsity drag: Allyson, June & Peter Lawford / Easter parade: Garland, Judy & Fred Astaire / All of you: Astaire, Fred / On the Atchison Topeka and the Santa Fe: Garland, Judy / Honeysuckle rose: Horne, Lena / I like myself: Astaire, Fred / Hallelujah: Martin, Tony/ Vic Damone/Russ Tamblyn/Jubilaires / There's no business like showbusiness: Hutton, Betty & Howard Keel
CDODEON 21 / Sep '96 / Soundtracks

☐ **THAT'S MUSICAL**
12554 / Jun '95 / Laserlight

☐ **THEATRE ORGAN FAVOURITES**
Cabaret / Exodus / Mack the knife / Mister Sandman / That old black magic / Georgy girl / All the way / Somewhere my love / Man and a woman / Never on a Sunday / Impossible dream / Everybody loves someone
HADCD 216 / Jun '97 / Spotlight On

☐ **THEATRE ROYAL DRURY LANE**
Rose Marie / Door of my dreams / Desert song / One alone / Can't help lovin' dat man / Ol' man river / Why do I love you / Lover come back to me / Wanting you / March of the musketeers / You are my heart's delight / Keep smiling / Hand in hand / Fold your wings / Shine through my dreams / Music in May / Why is there ever goodbye / Rose of England / River God / Waltz of my heart / I can give you the starlight
CDHD 233 / Sep '95 / Happy Days

☐ **THEMES AND INSTRUMENTALS**
Albatross: Fleetwood Mac / Baby elephant walk: Mancini, Henry / Good The Bad And The Ugly: Montenegro, Hugo / Peter Gunn: Mancini, Henry / James Bond: Barry, John / Stranger on the shore: Bilk, Acker / Entertainer: Hamlisch, Marvin / Light flight: Pentangle / Harry's game: Clannad / Rocket to the moon: Brickman, Jim / Inspector Morse / Crocket's theme: Hammer, Jan / Miami Vice: Hammer, Jan / Scarborough Fair: Intune / La serenissima: Veneziano, Rondo / Mon amour: Thore, Frank / Petite fleur: Barber, Chris & Monty Sunshine / Summer Place: Faith, Percy / Cherry ppink and apple blossom white: Prado, Parez / Pink Panther: Mancini, Henry / Light my fire: Booker T & The MG's / Between the lines: Lindes, Hal / Aria: Bilk, Acker / Sheperd's lament: Zamphir, Georgi / Thorn Birds: Burgon, Geoffrey / From Russia With Love: Barry, John / Snowflakes are dancing: Tomita / Windmills of your mind: Legrand, Michel / Midnight in Moscow: Ball, Kenny / Hang 'Em High: Montenegro, Hugo / Sukiyaki: Ball, Kenny
RCACD 220 / Jul '97 / RCA

☐ **THEMES FROM ACADEMY AWARD WINNERS**
Gerhardt, Charles/Arthur Fiedler/Henry Mancini/David Raksin con
Star Wars / Tom Jones / Casablanca / Ben Hur / Breakfast at Tiffany's / Exodus / West Side Story / Airport / High Noon / Laura / Lawrence of Arabia / Doctor Zhivago / Gone With the Wind
09026609662 / Jan '92 / RCA Victor

☐ **THEMES FROM THE SIXTIES VOL. 3**
FLEG 5CD / Sep '95 / Future Legend

☐ **THEMES FROM THE SIXTIES VOL.1**
Avengers: Grave / To Sir with love: Studio 68 / On her Majesty's secret sevice: Editors / Prisoner: Kitch / Man in a suitcase: Ministry of Defiance / Up the junction: Eleanor Rigby / You only live twice: Eleanor Rigby / Man from UNCLE: Grave / Mission impossible: Ministry of Defiance / Captain Zeppo: Beatboy / Stingray: C.B.U. / Addams family: Perestroika / Batman: Waterloo Sunset Allstars
FLEG 1CD / Mar '93 / Future Legend

☐ **THEMES FROM THE SIXTIES VOL.2**
FLEGCD 2 / Mar '94 / Future Legend

☐ **THEMES OF HORROR (14 Spine Chillers)**
Fly / Thing / Fog / Carrie / Psycho / Poltergeist III / Exorcist / Hell Raiser / Halloween / Amityville Horror / Friday The 13th / Vertigo / Silence Of The Lambs / Rosemary's Baby
EMPRCD 628 / Jun '96 / Emporio

☐ **THEMES UNLIMITED**
EMTBX 309 / Aug '97 / Emporio

☐ **THERE'S NO BUSINESS LIKE SHOW BUSINESS**
There's no business like show business / When the midnight choo choo leaves for Alabam' / Play a simple melody / After you get what you want you don't want it if you believe / Man chases a girl / Lazy / Heat way / Sailor's not a sailor ('til a sailor's been tattooed) / Alexander's ragtime band
VSD 5912 / 13 Apr '98 / Varese Sarabande

☐ **THERE'S NO BUSINESS LIKE SHOW BUSINESS (Broadway Showstoppers) (Original Broadway/London/Film Casts)**
SK 53541 / Jul '94 / Sony Broadway

☐ **THERE'S NO BUSINESS LIKE SHOW BUSINESS (Songs From The Hit Musicals)**
There's no business like show business / If I were a rich man / We're in the money / Send in the clowns / Boy like that / Guys and dolls / I know him so well / Hello Dolly / Food glorious food / Pick a pocket or two / Pinball wizard / See me feel me / Age of Aquarius / Wash that man right out of my hair / Some enchanted evening / There ain't nothing like a dame / Wanderin' star / Do re mi / Prelude and the Sound Of Music / Greased lightning / We go together / Summer holiday / Summer holiday
74321479662 / Jun '97 / RCA

☐ **THERE'S NO BUSINESS LIKE SHOW BUSINESS (Merman, Ethel)**
RE 21442 / Sep '97 / Razor & Tie

☐ **THERE'S NOTHIN' LIKE A DAME - BROADWAY'S BROADS (Broadway Casts)**
SK 53539 / Jul '94 / Sony Broadway

☐ **THIS IS CULT FICTION**
Little green bag: Baker, George Selection / Misirlou: Dale, Dick & His Del-Tones / Mission impossible: Schifrin, Lalo / Shaft: Hayes, Isaac / Jungle boogie: Kool & The Gang / Man from UNCLE: Montenegro, Hugo / Everybody's talkin': Nilsson, Harry / Stuck in the middle with you: Stealer's Wheel / Blue velvet: Vinton, Bobby / Touch of evil: Mancini, Henry / We have all the time in the world: Armstrong, Louis / James Bond: Barry, John Seven / Joe 90: Gray, Barry Orchestra / Harder they come: Cliff, Jimmy / Here comes the hotstepper: Kamoze, Ini / Guaglione: Prado, Perez 'Prez' / Play dead: Arnold, David & Bjork / Avengers: Johnson, Laurie Orchestra / You never can tell: Berry, Chuck / Rumble: Wray, Link / Saint: Reed, Les / Hawaii five o: Ventures / Streets of San Francisco: Gregory, John / Long good Friday: Monkman, Francis / Sweeney: Power Pack Orchestra / Dangerman: Leaper, Bob Orchestra / Twin peaks: Baladamenti, Angelo / All the animals come out at night: Herrmann, Bernard
VTCD 59 / Aug '95 / Virgin

☐ **THIS IS CULT FICTION - CULT FICTION ROYALE**
Bullitt / Persuaders / EVA / Prisoner / Space 1999 / Dirty Harry / Sweeney / Man In A Suitcase / James Bond / Get Carter / Whodunnit / Champions / Joe 90 / Avenues and Alleyways: Protectors / Randall and Hopkirk Deceased / Van Der Valk / Avengers / Saint / Dempsey and Makepeace / Jason King / Sapphire and Steele / UFO / Baron / Professionals / Missiom Impossible / Department S / Man From UNCLE / Return Of The Saint / Stingray / Danger Man / 007 / Fireball XL5 / Thunderbirds / Strange Report / New Avengers / Captain Scarlet / Supercar / Tiswas / Magic Roundabout / Tales Of The Unexpected / Aqua Marina / Crown Court / Hill Street Blues / Twin Peaks / Blade Runner
VTDCD 151 / 8 Sep '97 / Virgin

☐ **THIS IS CULT FICTION - THIS IS SON OF CULT FICTION**
Real me: Who / Whole lotta love: CCS / All right now: Free / Lust for life: Iggy Pop / Theme from the "A" Team: Post, Mike / Born to be wild: Steppenwolf / Smoke on the water: Deep Purple / People are strange: Echo & The Bunnymen / Werewolves of London: Zevon, Warren / Lions and the cucumbers: Vampiros Sound Incorporation / Porpoise song (theme from "Head"): Monkees / White rabbit: Jefferson Airplane / Venus in furs: Velvet Underground / Girl you'll be a woman soon: Urge Overkill / Be bop a lula: Vincent, Gene / Green onions: Booker T & The MG's / Louie Louie: Kingsmen / Bring down the birds: Hancock, Herbie / Theme from Northern Exposure: Swchwartz, David / Duelling banjos: Weissberg, Eric & Steve Mandell / Suicide is painless: Mandel, Jamie / Calling you: Steele, Jevetta / Cavatina: Williams, John
VTCD 114 / Feb '97 / Virgin TV

☐ **THIS IS CULT FICTION - THIS IS THE RETURN OF CULT FICTION**
Professionals / Enter The Dragon / Gotcha / Six Million Dollar Man / Charlie's Angels / Wonderwoman / Dr. Who / Chase Scene / Detectives / Magnum PI / Get Smart / Dave Allen At Large / Kojak / Tales Of The Unexpected / Angela / Fly Me To The Moon / Gallery / Last Tango In Paris / Hill Street Blues / North By North West / Once Upon A Time In America / Budgie / Taxi Driver / White Horses / Park Avenue Beat / Saint Orchestra / I Dream Of Jeannie / Man About The House / On The Buses / World Of Sport / Bewitched / Minder / Please Sir / Grange Hill / Ski Sunday / Roobarb And Custard
VTCD 112 / Sep '96 / Virgin

☐ **THOSE FABULOUS BUSBY BERKELEY MUSICALS (Radio Versions From The Thirties)**
CDMR 1161 / Jan '91 / Radiola

☐ **THOSE SENSATIONAL SWINGING SIRENS OF THE SILVER SCREEN**
VJC 1002-2 / Aug '90 / Victorious Discs

☐ **THRILLER MEMORANDUM, THE**
Mexican flyer: Woodman, Ken Piccadilly Brass / Main chance: Schroeder, John / Yes and no: Des Champ / Party: Mamanqakis, Nicos / Fly by night: Marxhall, Brain Orchestra / Ghost Squad: Hatch, Tony Orchestra / Silencers: Seymour, Pat / Fade out: Shakespeare, John Orchestra / Le train fou: Denjean, Jaques / Live and let die: Lloyd, David London Orchestra / Kissy Suzuki: Sounds Orchestral / Twelve by two: Woodman, Ken Piccadilly Brass / Night with Naki: Marshall, Brian Orchestra / Saint: Reed, Les Brass / Sharp sharks: Hoffman, Ingried / Mission impossible: Hurst, Mike Orchestra / Adventure: Wirtz, Mark Orchestra/ Chorus / Wednesday's child: Hurst, Mike Orchestra / Hustle: Kirchen, Basil / Big M: Des Champ / Interception: Whittaker, David Orchestra / Man In A Suitacse: Grainer, Ron Orchestra / Penthouse: Hawksworth, Johnny Orchestra
RPM 173 / Dec '96 / RPM

☐ **THRILLERS**
North By Northwest / Electronic battlefield / Untouchables / It's over / Wednesday's child / Nighthawks / In The Line Of Fire / Firm / Man alone / Magnum Force / Mission Impossile / Presumed Innocent / Il sonno innocente / Building the barn
SILVAD 3504 / Nov '97 / Silva Treasury

☐ **THUNDERBIRDS ARE GO (20 TV Favourites)**
Thunderbirds: Gray, Barry Orchestra / Joe 90: Gray, Barry Orchestra / Champions: Hatch, Tony Orchestra / Avengers: Johnson, Laurie Orchestra / Stingray: Gray, Barry Orchestra / Mysterons: Gray, Barry Orchestra / Dangerman: Leaper, Bob Orchestra / Crossroads: Hatch, Tony Orchestra / Maigret: Eagles / Emmerdale Farm: Hatch, Tony Orchestra / Who do you think you are kidding Mr. Hitler: Flanagan, Bud / Old Ned: Grainer, Ron Orchestra / Aqua Marina: Gray, Barry Orchestra / Parker well done: Gray, Barry Orchestra / Z-Cars: Keating, Johnny / Fugitive: Schroeder, John Orchestra / Hi-jacked: Gray, Barry Orchestra / Man in a suitcase: Grainer, Ron Orchestra / Return Of The Saint: Saint Orchestra
SUMCD 4104 / Nov '96 / Summit

☐ **TIMELESS TV THEMES**
Thunderbirds: Gray, Barry Orchestra / Avengers: Johnson, Laurie Orchestra / Man in a suitcase: Grainer, Ron Orchestra / Z-cars: Keating, Johnny & The Z Men / Captain Scarlet: Gray, Barry Orchestra / Champions: Hatch, Tony Orchestra / Fugitive: Schroeder, John Orchestra / Emmerdale Farm: Hatch, Tony Orchestra / Danger man: Leaper, Bob Orchestra / Stranger on the shore: Bilk, Acker / Maigret: Eagles / Stingray: Gray, Barry Orchestra & The Gary Miller Orchestra / Crossroads: Hatch, Tony Orchestra / Forsyte saga (Elizabeth Tudor): Stapleton, Cyril & Orchestra / Mysterons theme: Gray, Barry Orchestra / Return of the Saint: Saint Orchestra / Dr. Who: Winstone, Eric & His Orchestra / Fireball: Flee-Rekkers / Steptoe And Son (Old Ned): Grainer, Ron Orchestra
TRTCD 122 / Oct '94 / TrueTrax

☐ **TOP HAT (Music From The Films Of Astaire & Rogers) (Mancini Pops Orchestra)**
Mancini, Henry con
Roberta / Flying Down to Rio / Gay Divorcee / Follow the Fleet / Shall We Dance / Swing Time
09026607952 / Nov '92 / RCA Victor

☐ **TOP OF THE BILL (Over 60 Of Their Greatest Successes)**
PASTCD 9753 / Apr '92 / Flapper

☐ **TOP TV & MOVIE THEMES**
Star trek / High noon / 2001 / Shaft / Howard's Way / Eastenders
2802 / Jan '89 / Sound

☐ **TOP TV SOAP THEMES (London Theatre Orchestra)**
Eastenders / Coronation Street / Neighbours / Home and Away / Prisoner Cell Block H / Sons and Daughters / Brookside / Waltons / Emmerdale / Young Doctors / Soap / Falcon Crest / Crossroads / Peyton Place / Flying Doctors / Sullivans
EMPRCD 662 / Oct '96 / Emporio

☐ **TOP TV THEMES**
MACCD 152 / Aug '96 / Autograph

☐ **TRACKSPOTTING**
Saint: Orbital / Theme from Mission: Impossible: Clayton, Adam & Larry Mullen / Lovefool (Tee's club radio): Cardigans / Shallow grave: Leftfield / Born slippy: Underworld / Papau New Guinea: Future Sound Of London / Crash and carry: Orbital / Slid: Fluke / Wake up: Stereo MC's / Wildwood: Weller, Paul / This is not America: Bowie, David & Pat Metheny Group / Downtown: Cole, Lloyd / Wait for the sun: Supergrass / Natural one: Folk Implosion / Gone: Holmes, David & Sarah Cracknell / Play dead: Bjork & David Arnold / Small plot of land: Bowie, David / Forbidden colours: Sylvian, David / Falling: Cruise, Julee / Hold me thrill me kiss me kill me: U2 /

36 degrees: *Placebo* / Sunshine shakers: *Reef* / Begging you: *Stone Roses* / Let's all go together: *Marion* / I spy: *Pulp* / There she goes: *La's* / You and me song: *Wannadies* / Bad behaviour: *Super Furry Animals* / Lust for life: *Iggy Pop* / That woman's got me drinking: *MacGowan, Shane & The Popes* / Perfect crime: *Faith No More* / Sugar ray: *Jesus & Mary Chain* / Misirlou: *Dale, Dick & His Del-Tones* / 5:15: *Who* / Pet semetary: *Ramones* / Pretty in pink: *Psychedelic Furs* / Girl you'll be a woman soon: *Urge Overkill* / Left of centre: *Vega, Suzanne* / Stuck in the middle with you: *Stealer's Wheel* / How can we hang on to a dream: *Hardin, Tim*
5534302 / May '97 / PolyGram TV

☐ **TREASURY OF EARLY MUSICAL COMEDY, A**
AEICD 014 / May '98 / AEI

☐ **TRUE GRIT (Music From The Classic Films Of John Wayne) (City Of Prague Philharmonic Orchestra)**
Bateman, Paul *con*
Stagecoach / She Wore a Yellow Ribbon / Quiet Man / Searchers / Alamo / True Grit / Cowboys / How the West Was Won / High and the Mighty / In Harm's Way
FILMCD 153 / Jul '94 / Silva Screen

☐ **TRUFFAUT FILM MUSIC**
887790 / Jan '95 / Milan

☐ **TUBE 2 (TV's Greatest Bass)**
5429189172 / 5 May '98 / Pandisc

☐ **TUNES FROM THE TOONS (The Best Of Hanna Barbera)**
MCCD 279 / Dec '96 / Music Club

☐ **TV AND FILM THEMES**
SUMBX 4011 / Jan '98 / Summit

☐ **TV CLASSICS**
MBSCD 412 / Feb '93 / Castle

☐ **TV SOAP THEMES**
Eastenders / Falcon Crest / Eldorado / Emmerdale / Prisoner Cell Block H / Melrose Place / Crossroads / Neighbours / Country Practice / Coronation Street / Beverley Hills 90210 / Brookside / Young Doctors / Dallas / Dynasty / Sons and Daughters / Peyton Place / Home and Away
306242 / Jan '97 / Hallmark

☐ **TV TERROR**
Felix The Cat: *Collide* / Mr. Rogers' Neighbourhood: *Numb* / Laverne and Shirley: *Alien Faktor* / Mary Tyler Moore: *Institute Of Technology* / Happy Days: *Christ Analogue* / Love Boat: *16 Volt* / Addams Family: *29 Died* / Charles In Charge: *Electric Hellfire Club* / One Day At A Time: *Kervorkian Death Cycle* / X-Files: *Battery* / Facts Of Life: *Hate Dept.* / Magnum PI: *Society Burning* / Three's Company: *Terminal 46* / Dark Shadows: *Oneiroid Psychosis* / Brady Bunch: *Idiot Stare* / Dukes Of Hazzard: *Pinchpoint* / WKRP In Cincinnati: *Apolitiq* / Speed Racer: *Sweat Engine* / Twin Peaks: *Liquid Sex Decay* / Jeffersons: *Cut Rate Box* / Scooby Doo: *Loretta's Doll* / Welcome Back Cotter: *Kill Switch Klick* / Batman: *Alien Sex Fiend* / Fat Albert: *Haloblack* / Creature Feature: *Stone 588* / Ballad Of Gilligan's Island: *Ikon* / Baretta: *Ex-Voto* / Star Trek: *Lick* / Spiderman: *Wreckage* / Outer Limits: *Coin Of The Realm* / Dynasty: *Triple Point* / Knight Rider: *Dystopia One* / And Then There's Maude: *Thessalonian Dope Gods* / Mary Hartman Mary Hartman: *Sullen* / Muppet Show: *My Glass Beside Yours* / Josie and The Pussycats: *Sofia Run*
CDREC 032 / 22 Sep '97 / Re-Constriction

☐ **TV THEMES AMERICA**
Dallas / Perfect Strangers / Knots Landing / Midnight Caller / Head of the Class / Mission Impossible / McGyver / Cagney and Lacey / Dynasty / Odd Couple / High Chapparal / MASH (Suicide is painless) / Bonanza / Taxi / Rockford Files / Dr. Kildare
EMPRCD 556 / Mar '95 / Emporio

☐ **TV TIMES (Name That Theme) (Montague Orchestra)**
MACCD 366 / 30 Mar '98 / Autograph

☐ **TV'S GREATEST HITS VOL.1**
TVT 1100 / Sep '97 / TVT

☐ **TV'S GREATEST HITS VOL.2**
TVT 1200 / Sep '97 / TVT

☐ **TV'S GREATEST HITS VOL.3 (The 1970/1980s)**
TVT 1300 / Sep '97 / TVT

☐ **TV'S GREATEST HITS VOL.4**
TVT 16002 / Sep '97 / TVT

☐ **TV'S GREATEST HITS VOL.5**
TVT 17002 / Sep '97 / TVT

☐ **TV'S GREATEST HITS VOL.6**
TVT 18002 / Sep '97 / TVT

☐ **TV'S GREATEST HITS VOL.7**
TVT 19002 / Sep '97 / TVT

U

☐ **ULTIMATE MOVIE KILLERS**
TTVCD 2949 / 25 May '98 / Telstar TV

☐ **ULTIMATE MUSICALS ALBUM, THE**
UMD 80358 / 17 Nov '97 / Universal

☐ **ULTIMATE SHOW COLLECTION, THE (CC Productions)**
Heat is on in Saigon / I dreamed a dream / Time warp / Peter Gunn / Day by day / One night in Bangkok / Marilyn Monroe / American dream / I'm free / Pinball wizard / I don't know how to love him / Empty chairs at empty tables / Another suitacse in another hall / Memory / Phantom of the opera / Oh boy / Fame / Grease / Old deuteronomy / Science fiction
QED 081 / Nov '96 / Tring

☐ **UNFORGETTABLE (Boston Pops Orchestra)**
Williams, John *con*
SK 53380 / Jan '94 / Sony Classical

☐ **UNFORGETTABLE CLASSICS**
CDCFP 4696 / Apr '96 / Classics For Pleasure

☐ **UNSUNG MUSICALS VOL.1**
Fay, T. *con*
Smile / Postcards / Will we ever know each other / Ragtime Romeo / Starfish / Silverware / Her laughter in my life / In the name of love / There are days and there are days / In our hands / Sherry / She's roses / At my side / Disneyland / New words
VSD 5462 / Apr '94 / Varese Sarabande

☐ **UNSUNG MUSICALS VOL.2**
VSD 5564 / Jun '95 / Varese Sarabande

☐ **UNSUNG MUSICALS VOL.3**
VSD 5769 / Jul '97 / Varese Sarabande

V

☐ **VAMPIRE CIRCUS (The Essential Vampire Theme Collection)**
Return of Dracula / Vampire circus / Fright night / Transylvania twist / Vamp / Children of the night / Thirst / Transylvania / Forever knight / To die for / Son of darkness: To die for II / Sundown: The vampire in retreat / Hunger
FILMCD 127 / Mar '93 / Silva Screen

☐ **VERY BEST OF THE BOSTON POPS, THE (Boston Pops Orchestra)**
Williams, John *con*
4328022 / Dec '92 / Philips

☐ **VISIONS**
Flying / Harry's Game / MASH (Suicide is painless) / Hill Street Blues / Chariots of fire / Brideshead revisited / Arthur's theme / I don't know how to love him / Don't cry for me Argentina / Eve of the war / Star Wars / Fame / For your eyes only / Dallas / Shoestring / Chain / Angela / Take that look off your face
MCCD 190 / Nov '94 / Music Club

☐ **VISIONS (Stoltzman, Richard)**
Promise/A bed of ferns / O mio babbino caro / La Strada / Manha da carnaval / When I fall in love / Singin' in the rain / With this love / Can you feel the love tonight / Adagio from Mozart clarinet concerto / Love theme from Sophie's Choice/I'll never leave you / Somewhere / Spartacus love theme / Once Upon a Time in America / Calling you / Schindler's List theme / Philadelphia
09026680722 / Feb '96 / RCA Victor

W

☐ **WAR**
Where Eagles Dare / Battle Of The Bulge / Casualties Of War / 633 Squadron / Sink The Bismarck / Bridge At Remagen / Generals suite / Das Boot / Night Of The Generals / Guns Of Navarone / Longest Day / Battle Of Midway / In Harm's Way / Is Paris Burning
SILVAD 3502 / Oct '97 / Silva Treasury

☐ **WAR FILM THEMES**
MACCD 278 / Aug '96 / Autograph

☐ **WARRIORS OF THE SILVER SCREEN (The Ultimate Epic Movie Themes Album) (City Of Prague Philharmonic Orchestra)**
Bateman, Paul *con*
Braveheart / Thief Of Bagdad / Taras Bulba / Anthony And Cleopatra / First Knight / Henry V / El Cid / Prince Valiant / Ben Hur / Vikings / Rob Roy / Spartacus / 300 Spartans / War Lord / Last Valley / Conan The Barbarian / Jason And The Argonauts
FILMXCD 187 / May '97 / Silva Screen

☐ **WATCHING THE DETECTIVES (Starshine Orchestra)**
Inspector Morse / LA Law / Bill / Poirot / Sweeney / Law and Order / Bergerac / Juliet Bravo / Magnum PI / Miami Vice / Miss Marple / Ruth Rendell Mysteries / Starsky and Hutch / Taggart / Hill Street Blues / NYPD Blue / Cagney and Lacey / Kojak
307262 / Jun '97 / Hallmark

☐ **WESTERN MOVIE THEMES**
15 492 / Jan '93 / Laserlight

☐ **WESTERN MOVIE THEMES**
MACCD 243 / Aug '96 / Autograph

☐ **WESTERNS**
Big Country / Wild Rovers / Claudia's theme / Distant Trumpet / Once Upon A Time In The West / Ran with the harmonica / How The West Was Won / John Dunbar theme / Magnificent Seven / Fistful Of Dollars / Stagecoach / True grit / Two Mules For Sister Sara / Sons Of Katie Elder
SILVAD 3503 / Oct '97 / Silva Treasury

☐ **WHEN I GROW TOO OLD TO DREAM (Her Greatest Musical Comedy Successes) (Laye, Evelyn)**
Lover come back to me / Girl on the prowl / One kiss / You've done something to my heart / Let the people sing / Night is young / When I grow too old to dream / Glass of golden baubles / Butterfly song / Brave hearts / Near and yet so far / Princess is awakening / Love is a song / Ensa / Zigeuner / I'll see you again / All thro' a glass of champagne / If you look into her eyes
PASTCD 9717 / Mar '91 / Flapper

☐ **WHEN YOU WISH UPON A STAR (Barbara Hendricks Sings Disney) (Hendricks, Barbara)**
Tunick, Jonathan *con*
Some day my Prince will come / When you wish upon a star / Bibbidi-bobbidi-boo / In the golden afternoon / Part of your world / With a smile and a song / Very good advice / Bella notte / Zip-a-dee-doo-dah / Cruella de ville / Dream is a wish your heart makes / I'm late / Circle of life / Feed the birds / Chim chim cher-ee / Beauty and the beast / Whistle while you work
CDC 5561772 / Nov '96 / EMI Classics

☐ **WHITE HEAT - FILM NOIR (Jazz At The Movies Band)**
This gun for hire / Bad and the beautiful / White heat / Double indemnity / Touch of evil / Key largo / Laura / Lost weekend / Postman always rings twice / Asphalt jungle / Big sleep / Strange love of Martha Ivers / Naked city
77008 / Jun '94 / Discovery

☐ **WHY EVER DID THEY (Hollywood Stars At The Microphone)**
Kashmiri love song: *Valentino, Rudolph* / El relicario: *Valentino, Rudolph* / Long ago in Alcala: *Novarro, Ramon* / Two white arms: *Menjou, Adolphe* / Not for all the rice in China: *Webb, Clifton* / One little drink: *Beery, Noah* / Whip: *Beery, Noah* / Where the lighthouse shines: *Veidt, Conrad* / Tout la-bas: *Boyer, Charles* / Salue la lune: *Boyer, Charles* / Matrosenlied: *Albers, Hans* / Where is the song of songs for me: *Velez, Lupe* / Mi amado: *Velez, Lupe* / Ramona: *Del Rio, Dolores* / Ya va cayendo: *Del Rio, Dolores* / Come to me: *Swanson, Gloria* / Ich liebe dich my dear: *Swanson, Gloria* / What do I care: *Bankhead, Tallulah* / Don't tell him: *Bankhead, Tallulah* / It's all so new to me: *Crawford, Joan* / I'm in love with the Honourable Mr. So and So: *Crawford, Joan* / Little bit bad: *Brody, Estelle* / Lorna's song: *Hopper, Victoria*
PASTCD 9735 / Mar '91 / Flapper

☐ **WILD BUNCH, THE (The Best Of The West) (Czech Symphony Orchestra)**
Motzing, William *con*
Sons of Katie Elder / Dances with wolves / Silverado / High noon / Once upon a time in the west / Magnificent seven / Alamo / Lonesome dove / Blue and the grey / Fistful of dynamite / TV Western themes / Ballad of Cable Hogue / Young guns II / Return of a man called horse / Gunfight at the OK Corral / Wild bunch / Big country
FILMCD 136 / Jun '93 / Silva Screen

☐ **WILD, WILD WEST, THE (16 Great Western Tracks)**
Good the bad and the ugly / Ghost riders in the sky / Fistful of dollars / Man who shot Liberty Valance / Hanging tree / Streets of Loredo / Hang 'em high / High noon / High chaparal / Bonanza / For a few dollars more / Big country / Magnificent seven / Shenandoah / Red river valley / Once upon a time in the West
ECD 3043 / Jan '95 / K-Tel

☐ **WISDOM OF A FOOL, THE (Wisdom, Norman)**
Don't laugh at me / Wisdom of a fool / Dream for sale / Up in the world / Narcissus: *Wisdom, Norman & Joyce Grenfell* / Beware / Me and my imagination / Skylark / Who can I turn to / Boy meets girl: *Wisdom, Norman & Ruby Murray* / You must have been a beautiful baby / Heart of a clown / I don't arf love you: *Wisdom, Norman & Joyce Grenfell* / By the fireside / Joker / Impossible / You're getting to be a habit with me / Happy ending / Make a miracle: *Wisdom, Norman & Pip Hinton* / Once in love with Amy / My darling my darling / Leaning on a lampost / For me and my girl / Lambeth walk
SEECD 477 / May '97 / See For Miles

☐ **WONDERFUL WEST END**
MACCD 130 / Aug '96 / Autograph

☐ **WOODY ALLEN CLASSICS**
SK 53549 / Jul '94 / Sony Classical

☐ **WORKING IN A COALMINE (Songs From TV Commercials)**
SMP 850007 / Jan '94 / Movieplay

☐ **WORLD OF HORROR, THE**
ZYX 110902 / 1 Sep '97 / ZYX

☐ **WORLD OF JAMES BOND, THE (Shaw, Roland Orchestra)**
James Bond theme / Diamonds are forever / You only live twice / Wedding / Goldfinger / Dawn raid on Fort Knox / Arrival of the bomb and countdown / Pussy Galore's flying circus / From Russia with love / Thunderball / Bond below Disco Volante / Chateau flight / Casino Royale / Look of love / Let the love come through / Jump up / Dr. No's fantasy / Twisting with James / Girl trouble / Mr. Kiss Kiss Bang Bang / On Her Majesty's Secret Service / 007 theme
8445862 / Oct '96 / Deram

☐ **WORLD OF SCIENCE FICTION, THE**
ZYX 110912 / 1 Sep '97 / ZYX

☐ **WORLD OF SOUND (Favourite Themes From BBC TV)**
999: *Bolton, Rodger* / Somebody stole my gal: *Cotton, Billy Band* / Casualty: *Freeman, Ken* / Children's hospital: *Wiseman, Debbie* / By the sleepy lagoon: *Coates, Eric* / Dr.Who: *Grainer, Ron & the Radiophonic Workshop* / Eastenders: *May, Simon* / Fawlty Towers: *May, Simon* / I wish I knew how it feels to be free: *Taylor, Billy Trio* / Going Straight: *Barker, Ronnie* / Have I got news for you: *Big George Webley & Sons* / Hetty Wainthropp: *Hess, Nigel* / In party mood: *Strachey, Jack* / Howard's Way: *May, Simon* / Knightsbridge march: *Coates, Eric* / Hit and miss: *Barry, John Seven* / Bring me sunshine: *Coates, Eric* / Calling all workers: *Coates, Eric* / Michael's theme: *Stoneham, Harry Five* / At the sign of the swinging cymbal: *Stoneham, Harry Five* / Mars the bringer of war: *Holst, Gustav* / Imperial echoes: *Band Of The Royal Air Force* / Rhodes: *Parker, Alan* / On a mountain stood a lady: *Scaffold* / Marching strings: *Martin, Ray & His Orchestra*
336352 / 24 Nov '97 / Koch International

☐ **WORLD OF VARIETY, A**
Bee song: *Askey, Arthur* / Have a bit of pity on the crooner: *Askey, Arthur* / Put a penny underneath your pillow: *Waters, Elsie & Doris* / Here's to the mums and dads: *Waters, Elsie & Doris* / Eels: *Warner, Jack* / Littul gel: *Warner, Jack* / Neath the shanty town moon: *Warner, Jack* / Are you havin any fun with Sonny: *Warner, Jack* / Nobody loves a fairy when she's forty: *O'Shea, Tessie* / Good girl and the bad girl: *O'Shea, Tessie* / Don't kiss her in the daylight: *O'Shea, Tessie* / Thirsty thirsty throats: *O'Shea, Tessie* / I go twice a week to the pictures: *O'Shea, Tessie* / You're at Blackpool by the sea: *O'Shea, Tessie* / Grandfathers clock: *Harris, Doreen* / Talks to Gerry: *Harris, Doreen* / Button up your shoes and dance: *Wall, Max* / Dears of St Windermere/Vamp of Baghdad: *Chester, Charlie* / Sing a happy-go-lucky song: *Tinder, Tommy* / What was that that you said: *Wall, Max*
EMPRCD 778 / Nov '97 / Emporio

☐ **WORLD SO WIDE, THE (Upshaw, Dawn)**
Once I thought...(Laurie's song) / What a movie / This is prophetic / Willow song / Oh Yemanja / Give me some music / Godfather death / Lonely house / Ain't it a pretty night
7559794582 / 1 Jun '98 / Nonesuch

☐ **WORLD WAR II FILM THEMES (Royal Military School Of Music)**
Dambusters march / Where eagles dare / Bridge too far / 633 Squadron / Battle of the river plate / Great escape march / Reach for the sky / Aces high / Operation crossbow / Longest day / Cockleshell heroes / River Kwai march / Battle of Britain
CDPR 131 / Apr '95 / Premier/MFP

☐ **WORLD WAR II FILM THEMES**
Dambusters march / Where eagles dare / Bridge too far / 633 Squadron / Battle of the River Plate / Great escape march / Reach for the sky / Aces high (From The Battle of Britain) / Operation crossbow / Longest day / Cockleshell heroes / Battle of Britain / St Louis blues (From "The Glenn Miller story") / River Kwai march / Guns of Navarone
CDMFP 6199 / Jul '96 / Music For Pleasure

☐ **WORLD'S GREATEST MUSICALS, THE**
MU 5064 / Oct '92 / Musketeer

X

☐ **X-MUSIC (The Sound Of Mysteries) (Mysteries Sound Orchestra)**
Stonehenge sunrise / Mystic dance / Twin Peaks / Ocean thunderstorm / Lost island / Mystic energy / Crow -burn / Gate to the past / Grave of silence / Pharoah visions / Mystic procession / Atramchasis epos / River of shadows / X files / Start to infinity / Cosmic lights / Spirit of darkness / Comet dance / Daybreak communion / Stonewall faces / Main title and storm sequence / Madness eyes / dance of sacrifice / Grave of silence / Poltergeist / Witches procession / Dance on the clouds / Close the book of mystics
CD 24357 / Nov '97 / Laserlight

Y

☐ **YOU MUST REMEMBER THIS - CLASSIC THEMES FROM TV & RADIO**
By the sleepy lagoon: *Coates, Eric Symphony Orchestra* / Trout Quintet: *Schnabel, Artur & Pro Arte Quartet/Claude Hobday* / Barwick Green: *New Concert Orchestra/Jay Wilbur* / Won't you get off it please: *Waller, Fats & His Buddies* / Grasshoppers' dance: *Hylton, Jack Orchestra* / Oh what a beautiful mornin': *Miller, Glenn Army Air Forces Training Command Orchestra & Johnny Desmond/Crew Chiefs* / Coronation Scot: *Queen's Hall Light Orchestra/Charles Williams* / My ship: *Lawrence, Gertrude* / Oriental shuffle: *Reinhardt, Django Quintet Of The Hot Club Of France & Stephane Grappelli* / Waltz of the flowers: *Philadelphia Orchestra/Leopold Stokowski* / New world symphony: *Czech Philharmonic Orchestra/Georg Szel* / ITMA signature tune: *BBC Variety Orchestra/Charles Shadwell* / Devil's gallop: *Queen's Hall Light Orchestra/Charles Williams* / Nessun dorma: *Bjorling, Jussi* / Makin' whoopee: *Cantor, Eddie* / Air on a G string: *London Symphony Orchestra/Sir Henry Wood* / Roses from the South: *Sandler, Albert Palm Court Orchestra*
75605522712 / Feb '97 / Happy Days

☐ **YOU MUST REMEMBER THIS - GREAT FILM SONGS**

Am I blue: Waters, Ethel / Falling in love again: Dietrich, Marlene / Bench in the park: Whiteman, Paul Orchestra & The Rhythm Boys/Brox Sisters / Goodnight Vienna: Buchanan, Jack / Tinkle tinkle tinkle/Over my shoulder: Matthews, Jessie / One night of love: Moore, Grace / Okay toots: Cantor, Eddie / Smoke gets in your eyes: Dunne, Irene / Lullaby of Broadway: Shaw, Winifred / Love is everywhere: Fields, Gracie & Tommy / Top hat white tie and tails: Astaire, Fred / Isn't this a lovely day: Rogers, Ginger / I've got a feelin' you're foolin':

Powell, Eleanor / When did you leave Heaven: Martin, Tony / This year's kisses: Faye, Alice / I've got my love to keep me warm: Powell, Dick / Will you remember: MacDonald, Jeanette & Nelson Eddy / Jeepers creepers: Armstrong, Louis / I go for that: Lamour, Dorothy / It's foolish but it's fun: Durbin, Deanna / Chattanooga choo choo: Miller, Glenn Orchestra & Tex Beneke/The Modernaires/Paula Kelly / I yi yi yi yi (I like you very much): Miranda, Carmen / Moonlight becomes you: Crosby, Bing / Trolley song: Garland, Judy / More I see you: Haymes, Dick / Out of nowhere: Forrest, Helen

75605522832 / Feb '97 / Happy Days

☐ **YOU MUST REMEMBER THIS - THEATRE SONGS**

Swanee: Jolson, Al / Fascinating rhythm: Astaire, Fred & Adele / Who: Hale, Binnie & Jack Buchanan / Where's that rainbow: Dickson, Dorothy / Miss Annabelle Lee: Smith, 'Whispering' Jack / Ol' man river: Robeson, Paul / Dance little lady: Coward, Sir Noel / I'll see you again: Melaxa, George & Peggy Wood / Dancing on the ceiling: Matthews, Jessie / Got a date with an angel: Howes, Bobby / She didn't say yes: Wood, Peggy / I've told ev'ry little star: Ellis, Mary / Heat wave: Waters, Ethel / Physician: Lawrence, Gertrude / You're the top: Merman, Ethel

/ Dancing with a ghost: Day, Frances / Girl I knew: Welch, Elizabeth / Family solicitor: Lupinn, Wallace / Me and my girl: Lane, Lupino & Teddie St. Denis / Take it on the chin: St. Denis, Teddle / Lambeth walk: Lane, Lupino / Only a glass of champagne: Laye, Evelyn / Saga of Jenny: Lawrence, Gertrude / Surrey with the fringe on top: Drake, Alfred / Never say goodbye: Burke, Patricia / Pedro the fisherman: Tildsley, Vincent Mastersingers / We'll gather lilacs: Baron, Muriel & Olive Gilbert

75605522842 / Feb '97 / Happy Days

Composer Collections

Addinsell, Richard

☐ FILM MUSIC (BBC Concert Orchestra)
Alwyn, Kenneth *con*
Goodbye Mr. Chips / Prince and the showgirl / Tom Brown's schooldays / Fire over England / Tale of two cities
8223732 / Jul '94 / Marco Polo

☐ WARSAW CONCERTO, THE
Blithe Spirit / Dangerous Moonlight / Day Will Dawn / Greengage Summer / Highly Dangerous / Invocation / Lion Has Wings / March of the United Nations / Out Of The Clouds / Passionate Friends / Sea Devils / Under Capricorn
CDWHL 2108 / 13 Jul '98 / White Cloud

Alwyn, William

☐ ALWYN: FILM MUSIC (London Symphony Orchestra)
Hickox, Richard *con*
Rake's progress / Odd man out / Fallen idol / History of Mr. Polly
CHAN 9243 / Mar '94 / Chandos

Arlen, Harold

☐ MUSIC OF HAROLD ARLEN, THE (Arlen, Harold)
Love a New Yorker / My shining hour / Come rain or come shine / Let's take a walk around the block / Wonder what became of me / Can I leave off wearin' my shoes / I had myself a true love / Fun to be fooled / Happiness is a thing called Joe / Halloween / Right as the rain / One for my baby / Hit the road to Dreamland / Moanin' in the mornin' / Minuet / You're the cure for what ails me / It's a new world / Buds won't bud / I never has seen snow / Last night when we were young / T'morra t'morra / House of flowers waltz / Hooray for love
HCD 1505 / 27 Jul '98 / DRG

☐ SINGS THE HAROLD ARLEN SONGBOOK (Wilson, Julie)
Blues in the night / Man that got away / Fun to be fooled / This time / Dream's on me / Buds won't bud / Last night when we were young / One for my baby / Lydia the tattooed the lady / Out of this world
DRG 5211 / Jan '95 / DRG

☐ SONGWRITER SERIES VOL.4 (Over The Rainbow)
(You got me in between) the devil and the deep blue sea / I've got the world on a string / I gotta right to sing the blues / Public melody no.1 / When the sun comes out / Hittin' the bottle / Let's fall in love / Let's put our heads together / Now I know / As long as I live / Raisin' the rent / Blues in the night / Down with love / Over the rainbow / It's only a paper moon / Buds won't bud / One for my baby (and one more for the road) / Stormy weather / Kickin' the gong around / Two blind loves / That old black magic / Accentuate the positive / Ill wind / Get happy
PASTCD 7095 / 27 Oct '97 / Flapper

☐ THAT OLD BLACK MAGIC
5375732 / Jul '97 / Verve

Arnold, Sir Malcolm

☐ ARNOLD: FILM MUSIC (London Symphony Orchestra)
Hickox, Richard *con*
Bridge on the River Kwai / Inn of the sixth happiness / Hobson's choice / Whistle down the wind / Sound barrier
CHAN 9100 / Feb '93 / Chandos

Bacalov, Luis Enriquez

☐ ITALIAN WESTERN SCORES OF LUIS ENRIQUEZ BACALOV, THE
VCDS 7015 / Apr '96 / Varese Sarabande

Bacharach, Burt

☐ BURT BACHARACH ALBUM, THE (Broadway Sings The Best Of Bacharach)
VSD 5889 / 29 Jun '98 / Varese Sarabande

Baird, Tadeusz

☐ TADEUSZ BAIRD: FILM MUSIC (Polish Symphony Orchestra)
Baird, Tadeusz *con*
Room for one / Warsaw in Canaletto paintings / Visit at the kings / Year one / Passenger / Manhunter / Panic on a train / April / Rugged creativeness / When love was a crime
OCD 604 / Aug '94 / Olympia

☐ TADEUSZ BAIRD: FILM MUSIC II (Polish Symphony Orchestra)
Baird, Tadeusz *con*
Between the shores / Burning mountains / Every day / Sky of stone / Those who are late / Samson
OCD 607 / Aug '94 / Olympia

Baldan Bembo, Alberto

☐ IO E MARA (Baldan Bembo, Alberto)
ET 910CD / 6 Jul '98 / Easy Tempo

Barry, John

☐ 007 AND OTHER GREAT SOUNDTRACK THEMES
CDCD 1225 / Jun '95 / Charly

☐ CLASSIC JOHN BARRY VOL.1, THE (City Of Prague Philharmonic Orchestra)
Raine, Nic *con*
Zulu / Out Of Africa / Midnight Cowboy / Last Valley / Eleanor And Franklin / Hanover Street / Born Free / Chaplin / Dances With Wolves / Raise The Titanic / Indecent Proposal / Persuaders / Robin And Marian / Body Heat / Somewhere In Time / Lion In Winter
FILMCD 141 / Oct '93 / Silva Screen

☐ CLASSIC JOHN BARRY VOL.2, THE (City Of Prague Philharmonic Orchestra)
Ipcress File / Scarlet Letter / Mary Queen Of Scots / High Road To China / Quiller Memorandum / Knack / Dove / Monte Walsh / Black Hole / Wrong Box / Walkabout / Appointment
FILMCD 169 / Feb '96 / Silva Screen

☐ EMBER YEARS VOL.2, THE (16 John Barry Themes) (Barry, John)
PLAY 003 / Mar '92 / Play It Again

☐ EMI YEARS VOL.3, THE (1962-1964) (Barry, John Seven & Orchestra)
James Bond theme / Blacksmith blues / Cutty Sark / Lost patrol / Roman Spring of Mrs Stone: *Loewe, Frederick* / Tears: *Loewe, Frederick* / Blueberry Hill: *Barry, John Orchestra* / Cherry pink and apple blossom white: *Barry, John Orchestra* / Smokey Joe: *Barry, John* / Unchained melody: *Barry, John Orchestra* / Party's over / Lolly theme / March of the Mandarins / Human jungle / Big safari: *1989 Broadway Cast* / Mouse on the moon: *1989 Broadway Cast* / Twangin' cheek / I'll be with you in apple blossom time: *Barry, John Orchestra* / Volare: *Barry, John Orchestra* / Human jungle / Onward Christian spacemen / Seven faces / Twenty four hours ago: *Stone, Richard* / Jolly Bad Fellow: *Belen, Ana* / Oublie ca: *Barry, John Orchestra* / Seance on a Wet Afternoon: *Barry, John* / That fatal kiss: *Barry, John*
CDEMS 1555 / Sep '95 / EMI

☐ HITS AND THE MISSES, THE (Barry, John)
PLAY 007 / Nov '97 / Play It Again Sam

☐ JOHN BARRY EXPERIENCE, THE
007 / From Russia with love / Loneliness of autumn / Four in the morning / River walk / Lover's tension / First reconciliation / Judi comes home / Elizabeth in London / London theme / Elizabeth theme / Lovers / Aliki / Zulu / First Zulu appearance and assault / Zulu stamp / Teltha leyanto / Monkey feathers / Fancy dance / Christine X
3036000812 / Apr '97 / Carlton

☐ MOVIOLA
Out of Africa / Midnight cowboy / Body heat / Somewhere in time / Mary Queen of Scots / Born free / Dances With Wolves / Chaplin / Cotton club / Walkabout / Frances / We have all the time in the world / Moviola
4724902 / Dec '96 / Epic

☐ SOUNDSCAPE
Persuaders / Midnight Cowboy / Ipcress File / Knack / Wednesday's Child / Space March (Capsule In Space) / Girl with the sun in her hair / Vendetta / Danny Scipio / James Bond theme / Goldfinger / Diamonds are forever / From Russia with love / You only live twice / Thunderball / On her Majesty's secret service / 007 / Walk don't run / Beat for beatniks / Hit and miss / Born Free
4885822 / 8 Sep '97 / Columbia

☐ THEMEOLOGY (Barry, John)
Persuaders / Midnight Cowboy / Ipcress File / Knack / Wednesday's Child / Space March (Capsule In Space) / Girl With THe Sun In Her Hair / Vendetta / Danny Scipio / James Bond / Goldfinger / Diamonds are forever / From Russia With Love / You Only Live Twice / Thunderball / On Her Majesty's Secret Service / 007 / Walk Don't Run / Beat For Beatniks / Hit And Miss / Born Free / I had a farm in Africa / Dances With Wolves
4885829 / 13 Jul '98 / Columbia

☐ ZULU (The Film Themes Of John Barry)
MACCD 221 / Aug '96 / Autograph

Bart, Lionel

☐ SONGS OF LIONEL BART, THE
MCCD 176 / Sep '94 / MCI Music

Berlin, Irving

☐ BERLIN ALWAYS (The Songs Of Irving Berlin)
Cheek to cheek: *Astaire, Fred* / Let yourself go: *Astaire, Fred* / This year's kisses: *Faye, Alice* / Alexander's ragtime band: *Goodman, Benny Orchestra* / Always: *Goodman, Benny Orchestra* / Slummin' on Park Avenue: *Lunceford, Jimmy* / I'm putting all my eggs in one basket: *Armstrong, Louis* / Waiting at the end of the road: *Waters, Ethel* / Harlem on my mind: *Waters, Ethel* / Isn't this a lovely day: *Ambrose & His Orchestra* / Shakin' the blues away: *Etting, Ruth* / When I lost you: *Crosby, Bing* / How deep is the ocean: *Crosby, Bing* / He ain't got rhythm: *Holiday, Billie* / I've got my love to keep me warm: *Tatum, Art* / Blue skies: *Dorsey, Tommy Orchestra* / When the midnight choo-choo leaves for Alabam': *Dorsey, Tommy Orchestra* / I want to be in Dixie: *American Ragtime Octette* / How's chances: *Hall, Henry Orchestra* / Russian lullaby: *Berigan, Bunny* / Now it can be told: *Bowlly, Al*
AVC 517 / Apr '95 / Avid

☐ BERLIN AND GERSHWIN GOLD
D2CD 4024 / Jun '95 / Deja Vu

☐ BERLIN, GERSHWIN & PORTER
R2CD 4024 / 13 Apr '98 / Deja Vu

☐ BLUE SKIES (The Irving Berlin Songbook)
5316362 / Jul '96 / Verve

☐ COMPLETE IRVING BERLIN SONGBOOKS, THE (Cheek To Cheek/ Blue Skies/How Deep Is The Ocean)
5394422 / 10 Nov '97 / Verve

☐ ELIZABETH WELCH SINGS IRVING BERLIN (Welch, Elizabeth)
CDVIR 8305 / Jan '89 / TER

☐ HOW DEEP IS THE OCEAN (The Irving Berlin Songbook)
5377012 / Aug '97 / Verve

☐ IRVING BERLIN SHOWCASE, THE
Follow the fleet: *Anton & The Paramount Theatre Orchestra* / I can't remember: *Wood, Scott & His Orchestra* / Puttin' on the Ritz: *Alfredo & His Band* / Reaching for the moon: *Da Costa, Raie* / Piccolino: *Mantovani & His Tipica Orchestra* / With you: *Marvin, Johnny* / Berlin waltz medley: *Coventry Hippodrome Orchestra* / Say it isn't so: *Vallee, Rudy & His Connecticut Yankees* / I miss you in the evening: *Davidson, Harry* / My bird of paradise: *Hilo Hawaiian Orchestra* / Cocoanuts: *Light Opera Company* / Russian lullaby: *Savoy Orpheans* / Mammy: *Bidgood, Harry & His Broadcasters* / Because I love you: *Fillis, Len* / I never had a chance: *Leader, Harry & His Band* / Top hat: *Arnold, Doris & Harry S. Pepper* / I'm playing with fire: *Rabin, Oscar & His Band* / How many times: *Brox Sisters* / Just a little longer: *Spitalny, Philip & His Orchestra* / Song is ended (but the melody lingers on): *Richardson, Foster* / On the Avenue: *Levy, Louis & His Gaumont British Symphony Orchestra*
PASTCD 9733 / Feb '91 / Flapper

☐ KIRI SINGS BERLIN (Te Kanawa, Dame Kiri)
Always / It only happens when I dance with you / Cheek to cheek / Easter parade / How deep is the ocean / I've got my love to keep me warm / It's a lovely day today / Let's face the music and dance / Say it isn't so / Song is ended / They say it's wonderful / What'll I do / Isn't this a lovely day / I got the sun in the morning / Blue Skies
CDC 5564152 / 3 Nov '97 / EMI Classics

☐ NOTHING BUT BLUE SKIES (The Irving Berlin Songbook) (Swingle Singers)
Top hat white tie and tails / How deep is the ocean / Isn't it a lovely day / Blue skies / Always / They say it's wonderful / No strings / Song is ended / Steppin' out with my baby / Let yourself go / Cheek to cheek / Let's face the music and dance / Marrying for love / Girl that I marry / What'll I do / Puttin' on the Ritz / Abraham / Change partners / Heatwave / I've got my love to keep me warm / Count your blessings / White Christmas
SUMCD 4054 / Nov '96 / Summit

☐ SONG IS...IRVING BERLIN, THE
I'm putting all my eggs in one basket: *Boswell Sisters* / Let yourself go: *Bowlly, Al & the Ray Noble Orchestra* / Marie: *Bowlly, Al & the Ray Noble Orchestra* / Cheek to cheek: *Browne, Sam & Lew Stone* / Pretty girl is like a melody: *Dennis, Denny & Roy Fox* / Top hat white tie and tails: *Dorsey Brothers* / Heat wave: *Farnon, Robert* / Slumming on Park Avenue: *Farnon, Robert* / Alexander's ragtime band: *Geraldo & His Orchestra* / White Christmas: *Geraldo & His Orchestra* / He ain't got rhythm: *Gonella, Nat* / Blue skies: *Goodman, Benny* / This year's kisses: *Gibbons, Carroll* / You keep coming back like a song: *James, Dick* / Let me sing and I'm happy: *Jolson, Al* / I never had a chance: *Joyce, Teddy & Jimmy Mesene* / I've got my love to keep me warm: *Melachrino, George & Carroll Gibbons* / Let's face the music and dance: *Roy, Harry & His Orchestra* / Piccolino: *Roy, Harry & His Orchestra* / We saw the sea: *Roy, Harry & His Orchestra* / All alone: *Shaw, Artie Orchestra* / Because I love you: *Shaw, Artie Orchestra*
CDAJA 5068 / Oct '95 / Living Era

☐ SONGS OF IRVING BERLIN, THE
MCCD 188 / Nov '94 / Music Club

☐ SPOTLIGHT ON IRVING BERLIN
Cheek to cheek / Anything you can do / Top hat white tie and tails / Let's face the music and dance / Easter parade / There's no business like show business / You're just in love / Girl that I marry / Always / White Christmas / They say it's wonderful
HADCD 137 / Feb '94 / Javelin

☐ STARS SALUTE IRVING BERLIN, THE
CDCD 1247 / Jun '95 / Charly

☐ TRIBUTE TO IRVING BERLIN, A
CDDL 1248 / Jan '94 / Music For Pleasure

☐ UNSUNG IRVING BERLIN (31 Hidden Treasures)
VSD 5770 / Apr '97 / Varese Sarabande

Bernstein, Leonard

☐ BERNSTEIN CONDUCTS BERNSTEIN (New York Philharmonic Orchestra)
Bernstein, Leonard *con*
West Side Story / Candide / Rhapsody in blue / American in Paris
SMK 47529 / Nov '92 / Sony Classical

☐ BERNSTEIN CONDUCTS BERNSTEIN (New York Philharmonic Orchestra)
Bernstein, Leonard *con*
On the Waterfront / On the Town / Fancy Free
SMK 47530 / Nov '92 / Sony Classical

☐ BERNSTEIN ON BROADWAY (Highlights - West Side Story/Candide/ On The Town) (Casts/London Symphony Chorus & Orchestra)
Bernstein, Leonard/Michael Tilson Thomas *con*
4478982 / Jan '95 / Deutsche Grammophon

☐ NEW YORK (Upshaw, Dawn & Mandy Patinkin/Donna Murphy/Orchestra Of St.Luke's)
Stern, Eric *con*
Balcony scene / Somewhere / Ballet sequence / One hand one heart / Little bit in love / Ballet at the Village Vortex / Wrong note rag / Quiet girl / What a waste / Story of my life / New York New York / Ya got me / Come up to my place / Some other time / Lonely town / Lonely town pas de deux / Ain't got no tears left / Danzon variation / Cab and bedroom
7559794002 / Feb '97 / Nonesuch

☐ THEATRE WORKS (ON THE TOWN/ FANCY FREE/TROUBLE IN TAHITI) (& Candide/West Side Story/On The Waterfront Excerpts)
Bernstein, Leonard *con*
SM3K 47154 / May '92 / Sony Classical

☐ UNFORGETTABLE CLASSICS
Overture / Chichester psalms / Simple song / Seena / Symphonic dances / Prelude Fugue and riffs
CDCFP 6062 / 6 Apr '98 / Classics For Pleasure

Black, Don

☐ BORN FREE (The Don Black Songbook)
Born free: *Monro, Matt* / To sir with love: *Lulu* / Girl with the sun in her hair: *Clinton, Davy* / True grit: *Street, Danny* / On days like these: *Monro, Matt* / This way Mary: *Monro, Matt* / Wish now was then: *Monro, Matt* / Curiouser and curiouser: *Monro, Matt* / Me I never knew: *Monro, Matt* / Billy: *Martell, Lena* / Lady from LA: *Crawford, Michael* / I missed the last rainbow: *Crawford, Michael* / Play it again: *Reading, Wilma* / I'll put you together again: *Hot Chocolate* / Tell me on a Sunday: *Webb, Marti* / Last man in my life: *Webb, Marti* / Anyone can fall in love: *Webb, Marti* / Always there: *Webb, Marti* / There is love and there is love: *Faith, Adam* / In one of my weaker moments: *Dobson, Anita* / Anything but lonely: *Webb, Marti* / Love changes everything: *Webb, Marti*
PLAY 005 / Sep '93 / Play It Again

Bliss, Arthur

☐ BLISS - FILM MUSIC (Slovak Philharmonic Choir/Bratislava Symphony Orchestra)
Capova, S. *con*
8223315 / Dec '91 / Marco Polo

☐ BLISS CONDUCTS BLISS (London Symphony Orchestra/National Symphony Orchestra)
Bliss, Arthur *con*
Introduction/Allegro / Things to come / Men of two worlds
CDLXT 2051 / Jan '95 / Dutton Laboratories

Bolling, Claude

☐ BOLLING FILMS (Bolling, Claude)
111982 / Nov '94 / Musidisc

☐ LUCKY LUKE AU CINEMA
3020842 / Jun '97 / Arcade

Breuker, Willem

☐ MUSIC FOR THE FILMS OF JOHAN VEN DER KEUKEN 1967-1994, THE (Breuker, Willem)
BVHAASTCD 9709/10 / Apr '98 / Bvhaast

Burgon, Geoffrey

☐ **BRIDESHEAD REVISITED (The Television Scores Of Geoffrey Burgon) (Philharmonia Orchestra)**
Burgon, Geoffrey *con*
Brideshead Revisited / Julia / Julia's theme / Hunt / Fading light / Farewell to Brideshead / Testament of youth / Intimations of war / Elegy / Finale / Bleak house / Streets of London / Dedlock versus Boythorn / Lady Dedlock's quest / Finale / Opening music / Nunc Dimittis / Aslan's theme / Great battle / Mr. Tumnus' tune / Storm at sea / Aslan sacrificed / Journey to Harlang / Farewell to Narnia
FILMCD 117 / Mar '98 / Silva Screen

Caesar, Irving

☐ **GREAT ONES, THE**
PASTCD 7075 / Nov '95 / Flapper

Cahn, Sammy

☐ **EVENING WITH SAMMY CAHN, AN (Cahn, Sammy & Bobbi Baird/Shirley Lemmon/Jon Peck)**
DRG 5172 / Jun '93 / DRG

Carmichael, Hoagy

☐ **SONG IS...HOAGY CARMICHAEL, THE**
Ev'ntide: *Armstrong, Louis* / Lazy river: *Armstrong, Louis* / Lyin' to myself: *Armstrong, Louis* / Rockin' chair: *Armstrong, Louis* / Judy in the morning: *Bowlly, Al* / One morning in May: *Bowlly, Al* / Two sleepy people: *Bowlly, Al* / Heart and soul: *Carless, Dorothy & Billy Mayerl* / Doctor lawyer Indian chief: *Carr, Carole* / Nearness of you: *Carr, Carole* / Blue orchids: *Dennis, Denny & Jack Hylton* / Little old lady: *Dennis, Denny & Jack Hylton* / Sing me a swing song: *Fitzgerald, Ella* / Down 't Uncle Bill's: *Gonella, Nat* / Jubilee: *Gonella, Nat* / Moon country: *Gonella, Nat* / Small fry: *Gonella, Nat* / I get along without you very well: *Layton, Turner* / Georgia on my mind: *Mills Brothers* / Stardust: *Mills Brothers* / Sing it way down low: *Prima, Louis* / Snowball: *Roy, Harry & His Orchestra* / Lazybones: *Stone, Lew & His Band*
CDAJA 5074 / Oct '95 / Living Era

☐ **SONGS OF HOAGY CARMICHAEL, THE**
GRF 094 / '93 / Tring

Carpenter, John

☐ **BEST OF HALLOWEEN, THE (Carpenter, John)**
VSD 5773 / Nov '96 / Varese Sarabande

☐ **HALLOWEEN (The Best Of John Carpenter)**
Halloween / Fog / Christine / Thing / They live / Prince of Darkness / Starman / Escape from New York / Dark Star / Big trouble in Little China / Assault on Precinct 13
FILMCD 113 / Sep '93 / Silva Screen

☐ **JOHN CARPENTER'S GREATEST HITS VOL.1**
VSD 5266 / Nov '92 / Varese Sarabande

☐ **JOHN CARPENTER'S GREATEST HITS VOL.2**
VSCD 345336 / Jul '93 / Varese Sarabande

Cary, Tristram

☐ **QUATERMASS AND THE PIT (The Film Music Of Tristram Cary Vol.1)**
Quatermass and the pit / Sammy going south / Twist of sand / Flesh is weak / Tread softly stranger
CNS 5009 / Jul '96 / Cloud Nine

Chaplin, Charlie

☐ **CHARLIE (Music From The Films Of Charlie Chaplin) (Munich Symphony Orchestra)**
Shaw, Francis *con*
Limelight / Modern times / King in New York / City lights / Great dictator / Countess from Hong Kong
FILMCD 711 / Jan '93 / Silva Screen

☐ **CHARLIE CHAPLIN (Music Of His Films) (Villard, Michel)**
Modern times / City lights / It's a dog's life / Smile / King in New York / Loving mandolin / Greater dictator / Marching tune / Prelude to Lohengrin / 5th Hungarian dance / Limelight / Two little ballet shoes / Pilgrim / Sqaure dance / Little buns on forks polka / Encounter with Georgia / Gold miners / Gold rush / You my love
74321141452 / Jun '96 / RCA

☐ **MUSIC OF CHARLIE CHAPLIN, THE (Bavarian Symphony Orchestra)**
PLSCD 275 / 2 Mar '98 / Pulse

☐ **OH THAT CELLO (Chaplin, Charlie)**
63301444022 / 27 Apr '98 / Zebra

☐ **ORIGINAL MUSIC FROM HIS MOVIES, THE**
Day's pleasure / Pay day / Gold rush / Circus / City lights / Modern times / Great dictator / Limelight
BM 99903/4 / Jul '96 / Blue Moon

Cirque Du Soleil

☐ **MYSTERE (Cirque Du Soleil)**
Egypte / Rumeurs / Birimbau / Kunya sobe / En ville / Ulysse / Tondo / Caravena / Kalimando
09026626862 / Jan '96 / RCA Victor

☐ **NOUVELLE EXPERIENCE (Cirque Du Soleil)**
Fanfare / Meandres / Bolero / Bascule / Fixe / Ballant / Baleines / Havi vahli / Suite chinoise / Eclipse / L'oiseau / Azimut / Sanza / Grosse femme
09026615312 / Jan '96 / RCA Victor

☐ **SALTIMBANCO (Cirque Du Soleil)**
Kumbalawe / Barock / Kaze / Amazonia / Norweg / Urgence / Polinoi / Saltimbanco / Il sogno di volare / Horere ukunde / Rideau
74321257072 / Jan '96 / RCA Victor

Comden & Green

☐ **BETTY COMDEN & ADOLPH GREEN PERFORM THEIR OWN SONGS (Comden, Betty & Adolph Green)**
New York New York/Lonely town / Taxi song / Some other time / Carried away / Bad timing / Broadway blossom / French lesson / If / How will he know / Catch our act at the Met / Distant melody / Hook's waltz / Never never land / Mysterious lady / Ohio/It's love/Quiet girl / Wrong note rag / March march / Stillman's gym / Time for parting / Thanks a lot but no thanks / I said good mornin' / I like myself / Love is nothing but a racket / Once upon a time
DRGCD 5247 / 20 Apr '98 / DRG

☐ **COMDEN AND GREEN SONGBOOK, THE (Broadway Casts)**
SK 48202 / Feb '93 / Sony Broadway

☐ **PARTY WITH BETTY COMDEN AND ADOLPH GREEN (Comden, Betty & Adolph Green)**
ZDM 7647732 / Apr '93 / EMI Classics

Cosma, Vladimir

☐ **LES PLUS BELLES CHANSONS CINEMA/TV**
951592 / Nov '97 / Pomme

☐ **LES PLUS BELLES CHANSONS FILM/TV**
951582 / Nov '97 / Pomme

☐ **LES PLUS BELLES MUSIQUES DE FILMS VOL.1**
951632 / Nov '97 / Pomme

☐ **LES PLUS BELLES MUSIQUES DE FILMS VOL.2**
951642 / Nov '97 / Pomme

☐ **VERY BEST OF VLADIMIR COSMA, THE**
DRGCD 32900 / Jan '95 / DRG

Coward, Sir Noel

☐ **20TH CENTURY BLUES (The Songs Of Sir Noel Coward)**
Intro / Parisian Pierott: *Texas* / I've been to a marvellous party: *Divine Comedy* / MRoom with a view: *McCartney, Paul* / Sail away: *Pet Shop Boys* / Someday I'll find you: *Ama, Shola & Craig Armstrong* / There are bad times just around the vcorner: *Williams, Robbie* / I'll see you again: *Ferry, Bryan* / Mad about the boy: *Faithfull, Marianne* / Mad dogs and englishmen: *Space* / Poor little rich girl: *Suede & Raissa* / I'll follow my heart: *Sting* / London pride: *Albarn, Damon & Michael Nyman* / Mrs Worthington: *Reeves, Vic* / 20th century blues: *John, Elton*
4946312 / 13 Apr '98 / EMI

☐ **GREAT BRITISH DANCE BANDS PLAY NOEL COWARD**
PASTCD 9758 / Aug '91 / Flapper

☐ **TALENT TO AMUSE, A (The Songs Of Noel Coward) (Greenwell, Peter)**
Sail away / I travel alone / Mad dogs and Englishmen / Room with a view / Sigh no more / Bar on the piccola marina / Mrs. Worthington
SILVAD 3009 / Sep '95 / Silva Treasury

Cunningham, David

☐ **WATER (Cunningham, David)**
Stars: *Cunningham, David & Robert Fripp* / Next day / Once removed / Fourth sea / White blue and grey / Shade creek / Short winter's day / Blue river / Beneath the vines / Yellow river / Low sun / Only shadows: *Cunningham, David & Peter Gordon* / Liquid hand / Dark ocean / Same day
MTM 31 / Jun '96 / Made To Measure

De Masi, Francesco

☐ **FILM MUSIC OF FRANCESCO DE MASI, THE**
VCDS 7007 / May '95 / Varese Sarabande

Delerue, Georges

☐ **LONDON SESSIONS VOL 1, THE**
Rich and famous / Platoon / Beaches
VSD 5241 / Apr '90 / Varese Sarabande

☐ **LONDON SESSIONS VOL 2, THE (Hommage A Francois Truffaut)**
VSD 5245 / Sep '90 / Varese Sarabande

☐ **LONDON SESSIONS VOL 3, THE**
VSD 5256 / Jul '91 / Varese Sarabande

☐ **NONESUCH FILM MUSIC SERIES (London Sinfonietta)**
Wolff, Hugo *con*
7559794052 / Aug '97 / Nonesuch

☐ **TRUFFAUT AND DELERUE ON THE SCREEN**
Confidentially yours / Beautiful girl like me / Day for night / Last metro / Woman next door
DRGCD 32902 / Sep '93 / DRG

Dessau, Paul

☐ **FOUR ALICE COMEDIES (Music For Silent Films Directed By Walt Disney/ The Magic Clock) (RIAS Sinfonietta)**
Zimmer, Hans *con*
Alice in the wooly west / Alice and the firefighter / Magic clock / Enchanted forest / Alice's monkey business / Alice helps the romance
09026681442 / Nov '96 / RCA Victor

Devreesse, Frederic

☐ **DEVREESE - FILM MUSIC (Belgian Radio & TV Orchestra)**
Devreese, Frederic *con*
8223681 / Nov '94 / Marco Polo

Elfman, Danny

☐ **MUSIC FROM A DARKENED THEATRE**
Pee Wee's Big Adventure / Batman / Dick Tracy / Beetlejuice / Nightbreed / Darkman / Back to school / Midnight Run / Wisdom / Hot to Trot / Big Top Pee Wee / Simpsons / Alfred Hitchcock Presents / Tales From the Crypt / Face like a frog / Forbidden zone / Scrooged
MCD 10065 / 8 Sep '97 / MCA

Ellis, Vivian

☐ **SPREAD A LITTLE HAPPINESS**
PASTCD 7076 / Nov '95 / Flapper

☐ **SPREAD A LITTLE HAPPINESS**
CDHD 2578 / Oct '95 / Happy Days

Erskine, Peter

☐ **BIG THEATRE (Scores Based On 12th Night/Richard III/Midsummer Night's Dream) (Cast Recording)**
AHUM 004 / Jul '90 / Ah-Um

Ferguson, David

☐ **VIEW FROM NOW, THE (Ferguson, David)**
Wilderness and west / Flowers on the road / To be a somebody / Me or the sculpture / La peste / Long run / Graveyard suite / I didn't ask you to fight / Luminists and railways / Big crunch / Two welcomes / Rabbit's foot / Gentle kidnap / Objects trouvees / Maggie's baby / Not waving / Marilyn / Eden's debt
CHAN 9679 / 20 Aug '98 / Chandos

Fisher-Turner, Simon

☐ **MANY MOODS OF SIMON FISHER-TURNER, THE (Fisher-Turner, Simon)**
Isles of spice / Exotic hats / Esperanza / Caravaggio 1986 / Sloane Square / Gourmet's love song / Colours of my life / Violet crumble
MONDE 14CD / 16 Mar '98 / Richmond

Forrest & Wright

☐ **CLASSICS FROM HOLLYWOOD TO BROADWAY (Holliday, Melanie & Steven Kimborough/Frankfurt Radio Orchestra)**
Falk, Peter *con*
310642 / Dec '95 / Koch Schwann

Friml, Rudolf

☐ **ROMANTIC WORLD OF RUDOLF FRIML, THE**
Song of the vagabonds / Only a rose / Blue kitten / Indian love call / One kiss / Rose Marie / Love me tonight / Three musketeers / Huguette waltz / Ma belle / Totem Tom / Twelve o'clock girl in a nine o'clock town / Sympathy waltz / Love everlasting / Vagabond King
PASTCD 9764 / Jul '92 / Flapper

Garvarentz, Georges

☐ **MUSIQUE DE FILMS**
3017692 / Jun '97 / Arcade

Gay, Noel

☐ **LEANING ON A LAMP POST (The Music Of Noel Gay)**
Run rabbit run: *Flanagan & Allen* / Oh buddy I'm in love: *Gibbons, Carroll* / Let the people sing: *Geraldo & His Orchestra* / Lambeth walk: *Lane, Lupino* / There's something about a soldier: *Courtneidge, Cicely* / Love makes the world go round: *Browne, Sam* / I don't want to go to bed: *Browne, Sam* / Sun has got his hat on: *Browne, Sam* / You've done something to my heart: *Geraldo & His Orchestra* / All over the place: *Trinder, Tommy* / Fleet's in port again: *Breeze, Alan* / La di da di da: *Noble, Ray* / Bless you for being an angel: *Ink Spots* / Leaning on a lampost: *Formby, George* / Me and my girl: *Munro, Ronnie* / I took my harp to a party: *Cotton, Billy* / Hold my hand: *Bowlly, Al*
306372 / Jan '97 / Hallmark

☐ **SONG IS...NOEL GAY, THE**
Sun has got his hat on: *Ambrose & His Orchestra* / Hold my hand: *Bowlly, Al* / Girl who loves a soldier: *Cotton, Billy & His Band* / I took my harp to a party: *Cotton, Billy & His Band* / That started it: *Cotton, Billy & His Band* / There's something about a soldier: *Courtneidge, Cicely* / Run rabbit run: *Flanagan & Allen* / Leaning on a lamp post: *Formby, George* / All over the place: *Geraldo & His Orchestra* / Who's been polishing the sun: *Hulbert, Jack* / Love makes the world go round: *Hutch* / Melody maker: *Hylton, Jack* / Lambeth walk: *Lane, Lupino* / Let the people sing: *Laye, Evelyn* / You've done something to my heart: *Laye, Evelyn* / Oh what a wonderful night: *Laye, Evelyn* / Who's little what's-it are you: *London Piano Accordion Band* / Me and my girl: *Munro, Ronnie* / Fleet's in port again: *Payne, Jack & His Orchestra* / Moonlight Avenue: *Silvester, Victor*
CDAJA 5081 / Oct '95 / Living Era

Gershwin, George

☐ **BY GEORGE**
3036701297 / Jun '98 / Hallmark

☐ **CENTURY OF GLORY, A**
FA 152 / 24 Apr '98 / Fremeaux

☐ **CRAZY FOR GERSHWIN**
Someone to watch over me: *Fitzgerald, Ella* / Love is here to stay: *Jones, Jack* / But not for me: *Crosby, Bing* / Embraceable you: *Garland, Judy* / Nice work if you can get it: *Fitzgerald, Ella* / I got plenty o' nuttin': *Crosby, Bing* / Swanee: *Jolson, Al* / How long has this been going on: *Fitzgerald, Ella* / They can't take that away from me: *Lee, Peggy* / Mine: *Garland, Judy & Bing Crosby* / Oh lady be good: *Fitzgerald, Ella* / I got rhythm: *Garland, Judy* / I loves you Porgy: *Holiday, Billie* / Love walked in: *Crosby, Bing* / Liza (all the clouds'll roll away): *Jolson, Al* / I've got a crush on you: *Fitzgerald, Ella*
CDMOIR 502 / Jul '93 / Memoir

☐ **GENIUS OF GEORGE GERSHWIN, THE (Starlight Orchestra)**
But not for me / Embraceable you / Fascinating rhythm / Foggy day / I got rhythm / It ain't necessarily so / Let's call the whole thing off / Liza / Man I love / Nice work if you can get it / Shall we dance / Someone to watch over me / 'S wonderful / They can't take that away from me / Who cares / Long ago and far away / Summertime / There's a boat dat's leaving soon for New York / Oh I can't sit down / Somebody loves me
QED 109 / Nov '96 / Tring

☐ **GEORGE & IRA GERSHWIN SONGBOOK, THE (Fitzgerald, Ella)**
Riddle, Nelson *con*
5397592 / 26 May '98 / Verve Master Edition

☐ **GEORGE AND IRA GERSHWIN IN HOLLYWOOD (A Soundtrack Anthology)**
Overture/Rhapsody In Blue medley / Swannee: *Jolson, Al* / Somebody loves me: *Horne, Lena* / I can't be bothered now: *Astaire, Fred* / (I'll build a) stairway to paradise: *Guetary, Georges* / They can't take that away from me: *Astaire, Fred* / Fascinating rhythm: *Dorsey, Tommy Orchestra* / Love is here to stay: *Kelly, Gene* / They all laughed: *Rogers, Ginger* / Embraceable you: *Garland, Judy* / 135th street blues: *Hughes, John B.* / Summertime: *Brown, Anne* / Let's call the whole thing off: *Astaire, Fred & Ginger Rogers* / But not for me: *Fitzgerald, Ella* / Nice work if you can get it: *Astaire, Fred* / Liza: *Long, Avon* / I've got a crush on you: *Kelly, Gene* / Third prelude: *Levant, Oscar* / Strike up the band: *Garland, Judy & Mickey Rooney* / Boy what love has done to me: *Dorsey, Tommy Orchestra* / Slap that bass: *Astaire, Fred* / Aren't you kind of glad we did: *Haymes, Dick & Betty Grable* / Man I love: *La Centra, Peg* / Treat me rough: *Allyson, June & Mickey Rooney* / Foggy day: *Astaire, Fred* / You've got what gets me: *Quillan, Eddie & Dixie Lee/Mitzi Green* / Oh lady be good: *Shaw, Artie Orchestra* / He loves and she loves: *Astaire, Fred* / I was doing alright: *Logan, Ella* / Love walked in: *Verril, Virginia* / Promenade: *RKO Radio Studio Orchestra* / (I've got) beginner's luck: *Astaire, Fred* / 'S wonderful: *Kelly, Gene & Georges Guetary* / Things are looking up: *Astaire, Fred & Stafford Sisters* / Delishious: *Sweetland, Sally* / Shall we dance: *Astaire, Fred* / I got rhythm: *Garland, Judy* / You'd be hard to replace: *Astaire, Fred* / In our united state: *Frosse, Bob* / For you for me for everyone: *Haymes, Dick & Betty Grable*
CDODEON 29 / 15 Sep '97 / Soundtracks

☐ **GEORGE GERSHWIN COLLECTION, THE (McVay, Ray)**
HMNCD 020 / 3 Nov '97 / Half Moon

☐ **GEORGE GERSHWIN SONGBOOK, THE (18 Gershwin Songs With Gershwin's Own Piano Improvisations) (Hill, Julie & Craig Bohmler)**
Man I love / Swanee / Nobody like you / I'll build a stairway to paradise / Do it again / Fascinating rhythm / Oh lady be good / Somebody loves me / Sweet and low down / Clap yo' hands / Do do do / My one and only / 'S wonderful / Strike up the band / I got rhythm / Who cares / That certain feeling / Liza
CRC 2322 / 15 Jun '98 / Centaur

☐ **GERSHWIN**
Rhapsody in blue: *Miller, Glenn* / When do we dance: *Gershwin, George* / But not for me: *Garland, Judy* / Someone to watch over me: *Gershwin, George* / Man I love: *Shaw, Artie* / Maybe: *Gershwin, George* / I was doing alright: *Fitzgerald, Ella* / Clap yo hands: *Gershwin, George* / Somebody loves me: *Carter, Benny* / I was young you were so beautiful: *Gershwin, George* / Fascinating rhythm: *Lee, Buddy & The Gilt-Edged Four* / They all laughed: *Astaire, Fred* / That certain feeling: *Gershwin, George* / Oh lady be good: *Shaw, Artie Orchestra* / Prelude no.1: *Gershwin, George* / How long has this been going on: *Lee, Peggy* / Nice work if you can get it: *Dorsey, Tommy* / Summertime: *Holiday, Billie* / Long ago and far away: *Como, Perry* / Swanee: *Jolson, Al* / So am I: *Gershwin, George* / Love walked in: *Armstrong, Louis* / Rhaposody in blue: *Gershwin, George* / Do do do: *Gershwin, George* / Embraceable you: *Garland, Judy* / Te oodle um bum bo: *Gershwin, George* / Foggy day: *Granthan, Cyril* / Kickin' the clouds away: *Gershwin, George* / Shall we dance: *Astaire, Fred* / Sweet and low down: *Gershwin, George* / Drifting along with the tide: *Gershwin,*

GERSHWIN, GEORGE COMPOSER COLLECTIONS R.E.D. CD CATALOGUE

George / I've got a crush on you: *Wiley, Lee* / Looking for a boy: *Gershwin, George* / My one and only: *Waller, Fats & Lee Wiley* / They can't take that away from me: *McCrae, Carmen* / I got rhythm: *Waller, Fats & His Orchestra*
PC 611 / 10 Nov '97 / Start

☐ **GERSHWIN ARRANGEMENTS (Andre, Maurice & Nicolas Andre/Beatrice Andre)**
Carradot, Andre *con*
CDC 5556202 / Jun '96 / EMI Classics

☐ **GERSHWIN CENTENARY ALBUM, THE (Petters, John Broadway Melodists)**
RRCD 1013 / May '98 / Rose

☐ **GERSHWIN PLAYS HIS GREATEST HITS (Gershwin, George)**
1509537072 / 27 Apr '98 / Intersound

☐ **GERSHWIN SONGBOOK, A (Marshall, Wayne)**
Fascinating rhythm / I love you Porgy / Can't take that away / Summertime / Oh lady be good / Let's call the whole thing off / Embraceable you / Someone to watch over me / Love walked in / By Strauss / Our love is here to stay / Porgy trio / Clara Clara / I got rhythm
VC 5452982 / 6 Oct '97 / Virgin Classics

☐ **GERSHWIN TRIBUTE**
Strike up the band / Embraceable you / Fascinating rhythm / Rhapsody in blue / But not for me / Bidin' my time / Foggy day / They can't take that away from me / Oh lady be good / How long has this been going on / Man I love / Prelude no.2 / Somebody loves me / S'wonderful
HCD 266 / Jan '98 / Hindsight

☐ **GLORY OF GERSHWIN, THE**
Summertime: *Gabriel, Peter* / Do what you do: *De Burgh, Chris* / Nice work if you can get it: *Sting* / They can't take that away from me: *Stansfield, Lisa* / Someone to watch over me: *John, Elton* / Our love is here to stay: *John, Elton* / I've got a crush on you: *Simon, Carly* / But not for me: *Costello, Elvis* / It ain't necessarily so: *Cher* / Man I love: *Bush, Kate* / How long has this been going on: *Bon Jovi, Jon* / Bidin' my time: *White, Willard* / My man's gone now: *O'Connor, Sinead* / I got rhythm: *Palmer, Robert* / Somebody loves me: *Meat Loaf* / Stairway to paradise: *Van Randwyck, Issy* / Rhapsody in blue: *Adler, Larry*
5227272 / Jul '94 / Mercury

☐ **GREAT AMERICAN GERSHWIN (Pennario, Leonard & Hollywood Bowl Orchestra)**
Slatkin, Felix/Alfred Newman *con*
Rhapsody in blue / American in Paris / Porgy And Bess / I got rhythm / Cuban overture / Second rhapsody
CDM 5660862 / Jun '97 / Angel

☐ **KIRI SINGS GERSHWIN (Te Kanawa, Dame Kiri & The New Princess Theater Orchestra)**
McGlinn, John *con*
CDC 7474542 / Apr '93 / EMI Classics

☐ **MARNI NIXON SINGS GERSHWIN (Nixon, Marni)**
RR 19 / Sep '91 / Reference Recordings

☐ **PLAY GERSHWIN'S POPULAR WORKS (Boston Pops Orchestra)**
Fiedler, Arthur *con*
Girl crazy suite / Wintergreen for president / Three preludes / Second rhapsody / Overtures from Oh Kay / Funny face / Let 'em eat cake / Of thee I sing
4439002 / Feb '96 / Decca

☐ **S'MARVELLOUS**
5216582 / Feb '94 / Verve

☐ **SONG IS...GEORGE GERSHWIN, THE**
Half of it dearie blues: *Astaire, Fred* / I found a four leaf clover: *Audrey, Irene & Charles Hart* / Fascinating rhythm: *Edwards, Cliff* / When do we dance: *Gershwin, George* / My one and only: *Gershwin, George* / Little jazz bird: *Hylton, Jack* / Oh lady be good: *Hylton, Jack* / Liza (all the clouds'll roll away): *Jolson, Al* / Someone to watch over me: *Lawrence, Gertrude* / Do what you do: *O'Neal, Zelma* / Sweet and low down: *Selvin, Ben* / That certain feeling: *Selvin, Ben* / Funny face: *Smith, Jack* / I got plenty o' nuttin': *Tibbett, Lawrence* / I got rhythm: *Waller, Fats* / Nashville nightingale: *Waring, Fred & His Pennsylvanians* / Man I love: *Welch, Elizabeth* / I'll build a stairway to paradise: *Whiteman, Paul & Rhythm Boys* / S'wonderful: *Winter, Marius B. & His Dance Band*
CDAJA 5048 / Oct '95 / Living Era

☐ **SONGBOOK**
Let's call the whole thing off: *Holiday, Billie* / Summertime: *Parker, Charlie* / S'wonderful: *Basie, Count & Joe Williams* / Oh lady be good: *Goodman, Benny* / It ain't necessarily so: *Armstrong, Louis & Ella Fitzgerald* / How long has this been going on: *Hawkins, Coleman* / There's a boat dat's leavin' soon for New York: *Anderson, Ernestine* / Our love is here to stay: *Cleveland, Jimmy* / I was doing alright: *Armstrong, Louis* / I got rhythm: *Peterson, Oscar Trio* / They all laughed: *Astaire, Fred* / I've got a crush on you: *Washington, Dinah* / Foggy day: *Carter, Benny* / Things are looking up: *Fitzgerald, Ella* / Someone to watch over me: *Kirk, Roland* / Strike up the band: *Garner, Erroll* / Embraceable you: *Vaughan, Sarah*
5526462 / Mar '97 / Spectrum

☐ **SONGS & DUETS (Kaye, J./W. Sharp/S. Blier)**
370282 / Jul '91 / Koch

☐ **SPOTLIGHT ON GEORGE GERSHWIN**
Fascinating rhythm / 'S wonderful / Summertime / Embraceable you / Foggy day / It ain't necessarily so / Nice work / Man I love / Somebody loves me / They can't take that away from me / I got rhythm
HADCD 139 / Feb '94 / Javelin

☐ **S'WONDERFUL (The Songs Of George & Ira Gershwin)**
Swanee: *Jolson, Al* / I got plenty o' nuttin': *Tibbett, Lawrence* / Love walked in: *Armstrong, Louis* / Embraceable you: *Garland, Judy* / Liza (all the clouds'll roll away): *Webb, Chick* / How long has this been going on: *Lee, Peggy* / Nice work if you can get it: *Dorsey, Tommy Orchestra* / Funny face: *Smith, Jack* / Oh lady be good: *Hawkins, Coleman* / Somebody loves me: *Carter, Benny* / Someone to watch over me: *Gershwin, George* / I've got a crush on you: *Wiley, Lee* / S'Wonderful: *Goodman, Benny* / I'll build a stairway to paradise: *Whiteman, Paul & Rhythm Boys* / I got rhythm: *Waller, Fats* / Man I love: *Forrest, Helen* / They all laughed: *Astaire, Fred* / Summertime: *Robeson, Paul* / I was doing alright: *Fitzgerald, Ella* / Fascinating rhythm: *Lee, Buddy* / They can't take that away from me: *Holiday, Billie*
AVC 520 / Apr '95 / Avid

☐ **S'WONDERFUL (The Songs Of George Gershwin)**
Nice work if you can get it: *Astaire, Fred* / Someone to watch over me: *Lawrence, Gertrude* / Looking for a boy: *Dickson, Dorothy* / Liza (all the clouds'll roll away): *Jolson, Al* / Foggy day: *Astaire, Fred* / S'wonderful: *Astaire, Adele & Bernard Clifton* / Lady be good: *Lee, Buddy & The Gilt-Edged Four* / Do do do: *Lawrence, Gertrude & Harold French* / Somebody loves me: *Crosby, Bing* / I got rhythm: *Webb, Chick & His Little Chicks* / I'll build a stairway to Paradise: *Whiteman, Paul & His Orchestra* / They can't take that away from me: *Astaire, Fred* / Funny face: *Astaire, Fred & Adele* / Fascinating rhythm: *Edwards, Cliff* / They all laughed: *Astaire, Fred* / That certain feeling: *Dickson, Dorothy & Allen Kearns* / Maybe: *Lawrence, Gertrude & Harold French* / My one and only: *Astaire, Fred* / Summertime: *Jamison, Anne* / Swanee: *Jolson, Al* / Let's call the whole thing off: *Astaire, Fred* / I got plenty o' nuttin': *Tibbett, Lawrence*
PASTCD 9777 / Dec '92 / Flapper

☐ **TRIBUTE TO GEORGE GERSHWIN, A**
CDDL 1278 / Nov '94 / EMI

☐ **TRIBUTE TO GEORGE GERSHWIN, A**
ENTCD 13053 / Apr '94 / Entertainers

☐ **ULTIMATE GERSHWIN, THE**
PBXCD 407 / 20 Apr '98 / Pulse

☐ **UNFORGETTABLE CLASSICS**
Rhapsody In Blue / Bess you is my woman now / Bidin' my time / American In Paris / Symphonic picture
CDCFP 6064 / 6 Apr '98 / Classics For Pleasure

☐ **WE LIKE A GERSHWIN TUNE (Whyte, Ronny & Travis Hudson)**
ACD 54 / May '98 / Audiophile

Gesner, Clark

☐ **JELLO IS ALWAYS RED, THE (The Cabaret Songs Of Clark Gesner) (Original Cast)**
Jello is always red / Hey there let's have all have a little fun / Your the one I'm for / Resolution / Reflection / Everything I buy was made in China / There is always more toothpaste / In the tube / By the sea / It's very warm in here / If I could / Peanut butter affair / Hey buckaroo / Chickens / Bird's song / Beautiful song / I'm no sure / You are / I love a lad / Cool / Chipmunk / Bird in a cage / Dog outside a store / Alligators / Ending
HCD 1502 / 23 Mar '98 / Harbinger

Gilbert & Sullivan

☐ **ARIAS AND DUETS (The Best Of Gilbert & Sullivan)**
Three little maids / When a felon's not engaged in his employment / Poor wandering one / Loudly let the trumpet bray / Take a pair of sparkling eyes / I have a song to sing / I know a youth / I'm called little buttercup / On a tree by a river / If somebody there chanced to be / Wandering minstrel / When the foreman bares his steel
SHOWCD 017 / Feb '95 / Showtime

☐ **ARIAS AND DUETS OF GILBERT & SULLIVAN**
CDVIR 8325 / Aug '95 / TER

☐ **BEST OF GILBERT & SULLIVAN LIVE, THE (BBC Concert Orchestra)**
Wordsworth, Barry *con*
Trial by jury / HMS Pinafore overture / I'm called a little buttercup / Maiden fair to see / I am the captain of the Pinafore / Medley / Pirates of Penzance / Major General's song / Paradox trio / Medley / Iolanthe / None shall part us / O foolish play / Mikado overture / Wanderin' minstrel I / Sun whose rays are all ablaze / Tit willow / There is beauty in the bellow / Ruddigore / Welcome gentry / Gondoliers / Medley / Grand duke / Finale
11222 / Oct '97 / BBC Concert Orchestra

☐ **BEST OF GILBERT & SULLIVAN, THE**
CDTEZ 7004 / Jan '95 / TER

☐ **BEST OF GILBERT & SULLIVAN, THE**
Sargent, Sir Malcolm *con*
CDZ 7625312 / Apr '93 / EMI Classics

☐ **GILBERT & SULLIVAN - EXCERPTS (Soloists & Glyndebourne Festival Choir/Pro Arte Orchestra)**
Sargent, Sir Malcolm *con*
CDCFP 4238 / Jan '95 / Classics For Pleasure

☐ **GILBERT & SULLIVAN CLASSICS VOL.1 (Selections From The Mikado/ Pirates Of Penzance/The Gondoliers/ HMS Pinafore)**
Alwyn, Kenneth/Richard Hickox *con*
HMV 58 / Jan '95 / HMV

☐ **GILBERT & SULLIVAN CLASSICS VOL.2**
Sargent, Sir Malcolm *con*
HMV 102 / Jan '95 / HMV

☐ **GILBERT & SULLIVAN HIGHLIGHTS (Welsh National Opera Choir/ Orchestra)**
Mackerras, Sir Charles *con*
Mikado / HMS Pinafore / Pirates Of Penzance / Yeoman Of The Gaurd / Trial By Jury
CD 80431 / Mar '96 / Telarc

☐ **GILBERT & SULLIVAN OVERTURES (Pro Arte Orchestra)**
Sargent, Sir Malcolm *con*
CDCFP 4529 / Jan '95 / Classics For Pleasure

☐ **OPERAS THAT GOT AWAY, THE**
Steadman, David *con*
CDTER 1248 / 1 Sep '98 / TER

☐ **OVERTURES (New Sadler's Wells/ D'Oyly Carte Opera Orchestra)**
Pryce Jones, J./S. Phipps/John Owen Edwards *con*
HMS Pinafore / Pirates Of Penzance / Patience / Iolanthe / Princess Ida / Mikado / Ruddigore / Yeoman Of The Guard / Gondoliers / Di Ballo overture
CDVIR 8316 / 1 Sep '98 / TER

☐ **OVERTURES (Pro Arte Orchestra/ Vienna Philharmonic Orchestra)**
Sargent, Sir Malcolm *con*
Mikado / Gondoliers / Yeoman of the guard / HMS Pinafore / Iolanthe / Sorcerer / Cox and box / Princes Ida / Ruddigore / Patience
CES 5691372 / Feb '96 / EMI Classics

☐ **UNFORGETTABLE CLASSICS**
CDCFP 4695 / Apr '96 / Classics For Pleasure

☐ **VERY BEST OF GILBERT & SULLIVAN, THE**
CDMOIR 413 / Aug '93 / Memoir

☐ **WORLD OF GILBERT & SULLIVAN VOL.1, THE**
HMS Pinafore / Mikado / Yeoman of the guard / Pirates of Penzance / Iolanthe / Gondoliers
4300952 / Jun '91 / Decca

☐ **WORLD OF GILBERT & SULLIVAN VOL.2, THE**
HMS Pinafore / Mikado / Patience / Iolanthe / Gondoliers / Ruddigore / Sorcerer / Yeoman of the guard / Princess Ida / Pirates of Penzance
4338682 / Feb '93 / Decca

Glass, Philip

☐ **FILM WORKS (Anima Mundi/Mishima/ Powaqattsi/The Thin Blue Line) (Glass, Philip Ensemble/Kronos Quartet)**
7559793772 / Jan '95 / Nonesuch

Goldsmith, Jerry

☐ **JERRY GOLDSMITH FRONTIERS (Royal Scottish National Orchestra)**
End title from Star Trek First Contact / Overture from Twilight Zone / Main title from Capricorn One / Monument from Logan's Run / End of the city from Logan's Run / Main title from the Illustrated Man / Enterprise from Star Trek / Main title from Total Recall / Main title from Damnation Alley / End title from Damnation Alley / Main title from Star Trek Voyager / End title from Alien
VSD 5871 / 26 Jan '98 / Varese Sarabande

Grainer, Ron

☐ **DOCTOR WHO (& Other Classic Ron Grainer TV Themes)**
Maigret / Steptoe and son / Some people / Man in a suitcase / Prisoner / Assassination bureau / Only when I larf / Paul Temple / Tales of the unexpected / Edward and Mrs. Simpson / Dr. Who
PLAY 008 / Oct '96 / Play It Again

Gray, Barry

☐ **FAB (Music From The Gerry Anderson TV Shows) (Royal Philharmonic Orchestra)**
Pavlov, Konstantin *con*
Thunderbirds / Space 1999 / Joe 90 / Stingray / UFO / Captain Scarlet
FILMCD 124 / Nov '92 / Silva Screen

☐ **NO STRINGS ATTACHED (Gray, Barry Orchestra)**
Thunderbirds / Captain Scarlet / Hijacked / Aqua Marina / Stingray / Mysterons / Joe 90 / Parker - well done
CLACD 204 / Oct '90 / Castle

Hammerstein II, Oscar

☐ **OSCAR & STEVE (Patinkin, Mandy)**
Showboat / Passion / Follies / Pacific overtures / Anyone can whistle / Merrily we roll along / Into the woods / Little night music / Carousel / Flower drum song / South Pacific / Sound of music / Kiss to build a dream on / Carmen Jones / Night is young
7559793922 / Apr '96 / Nonesuch

Harburg, E.Y.'Yip'

☐ **YIP SINGS HARBURG (Harburg, E.Y. 'Yip')**
373862 / Jun '97 / Koch International

Harnick, Sheldon

☐ **EVENING WITH SHELDON HARNICK, AN (Harnick, Sheldon & Margery Gray/ Mary Louise)**
Suave young man / How could I / Merry little minuet / Boston beguine / At the Basilica of St. Anne / Garbage / Worlds apart / Little tin box / Till tomorrow / Picture of happiness / She loves me / Dear friend / Sunrise sunset / Do you love me / When Messiah comes / How much richer could one man be / If I were a rich man / In my own lifetime
DRG 5174 / Jun '93 / DRG

Harvey, Richard

☐ **SHROUD FOR A NIGHTINGALE (The Television & Film Music Of Richard Harvey)**
Doctor Finlay / Game set and match / Defence of the realm / Assam garden / Hostages / Doomsday gun / Small dance / To each his own / Shape of the world / Wimbledon poisoner / Deadly advice / Shroud for a nightingale / Inspector Dalgleish investigates / GBH / Jake's progress
FILMCD 172 / Jul '96 / Silva Screen

Herbert, Victor

☐ **VICTOR HERBERT SHOWCASE, A**
PASTCD 9798 / Oct '92 / Flapper

Herman, Jerry

☐ **EVENING WITH JERRY HERMAN, AN (Herman, Jerry & Lisa Kirk/Joe Masiell/ Carol Dorian)**
Salome salome / Just leave everything to me / Put on your Sunday clothes / Ribbons down my back / Before the parade passes by / It only takes a moment / It's today / Open a new window / Man in the moon / Hooch's song / We need a little Christmas / Bosom buddies / If he walked into my life / I don't want to know / And I was beautiful
CDSL 5173 / Jan '93 / DRG

☐ **JERRY HERMAN SONGBOOK, THE (Feinstein, Micahel & Jerry Herman)**
7559793152 / Jan '95 / Nonesuch

Herrmann, Bernard

☐ **CITIZEN KANE (Classic Film Scores Of Bernard Herrmann) (National Philharmonic Orchestra)**
Gerhardt, Charles *con*
Citizen Kane / On Dangerous Ground / Beneath the 12-Mile Reef / Hangover Square / White Witch Doctor
GD 80707 / Jun '91 / RCA Victor

☐ **CLASSIC FANTASY FILM SCORES**
Three Worlds Of Gulliver / Mysterious Island / Seventh Voyage Of Sinbad / Jason And The Argonauts
ACN 7014 / Jun '88 / Cloud Nine

☐ **FILM SCORES, THE (Salonen, Esa-Pekka & Los Angeles Philharmonic Orchestra)**
Man who knew too much / Psycho / Marnie / North by North West / Vertigo / Torn curtain / Farenheit 451 / Taxi driver
RK 62700 / Dec '96 / Sony Classical

☐ **GREAT FILM MUSIC OF BERNARD HERRMANN, THE**
4438992 / Feb '96 / London

☐ **MUSIC FROM GREAT HITCHCOCK THRILLERS, THE (London Philharmonic Orchestra)**
Herrmann, Bernard *con*
Psycho narrative / Marnie / North by North West / Vertigo / Trouble with Harry
4438952 / Mar '96 / London

☐ **MUSIC FROM THE GREAT FILM CLASSICS**
Herrmann, Bernard *con*
Citizen Kane: *London Philharmonic Orchestra* / Jane Eyre: *London Philharmonic Orchestra* / Mysterious Island: *National Philharmonic Orchestra* / Devil and Daniel Webster: *London Philharmonic Orchestra* / Snows of Kilimanjaro: *London Philharmonic Orchestra* / Jason and the Argonauts: *National Philharmonic Orchestra*
4489482 / Aug '96 / Phase 4

☐ PARTNERSHIP IN TERROR, A (City Of Prague Philharmonic Orchestra)
Bateman, Paul *con*
Psycho / North by North West / Marnie / Man who knew too much / Trouble with Harry / Vertigo / Torn curtain
SILVAD 3010 / Oct '96 / Silva Screen

☐ TORN CURTAIN (Classic Film Music Of Bernard Herrmann) (City Of Prague Philharmonic Orchestra)
Bateman, Paul *con*
Citizen Kane / Cape Fear / Psycho / Ghost and Mrs. Muir / Obsession / Snows of Kilimanjaro / Taxi driver / On dangerous ground / Man who knew too much / Ray Harryhausen fantasy film suite
FILMCD 162 / Sep '95 / Silva Screen

Holdridge, Lee

☐ FILM MUSIC OF LEE HOLDRIDGE, THE (London Symphony Orchestra)
Gerhardt, Charles *con*
Wizards and warriors / Splash / Great Whales / Hemingway play - Parisian sketch / Going home / Journey / Beastmaster suite / Music for strings / East of Eden (suite)
VCD 47244 / Jan '89 / Varese Sarabande

Honegger, Arthur

☐ HONEGGER: FILM MUSIC (Bratislava Symphony Orchestra)
Crime et chatiment suite / Deserteur fragment / Farinet suite / Grand barrage image / Idee
8223466 / Jun '94 / Marco Polo

☐ HONEGGER: FILM SCORES (Slovak Philharmonic Choir/Bratislava Symphony Orchestra)
Mayering / Regain / Demons d'Himalaya
8223467 / Jun '94 / Marco Polo

Horner, James

☐ ESSENTIAL JAMES HORNER, THE (Film Music Collection)
Raine, Nic *con*
FILMXCD 197 / 3 Aug '98 / Silva Screen

I Gres

☐ EXOTIC THEMES FOR FILM TV AND RADIO (I Gres)
PL 004CD / 27 Apr '98 / Plastic

Ibert, Jacques

☐ IBERT - FILM MUSIC (Bratislava Symphony Orchestra)
Macbeth suite / Golgotha suite / Don Quichotte / Chansons de Don Quichotte
8223287 / Mar '91 / Marco Polo

Jacobs, Dick

☐ THEMES FROM CLASSIC SCIENCE FICTION, FANTASY & HORROR FILMS
VSD 5407 / Feb '93 / Varese Sarabande

Jarre, Maurice

☐ DOCTOR ZHIVAGO (The Classic Film Music Of Maurice Jarre) (City Of Prague Philharmonic Orchestra)
Bateman, Paul *con*
Dr. Zhivago / Passage to India / Ryan's daughter / Lawrence of Arabia / Ghost / Witness / Is Paris Burning / Night of the Generals / Man Who Would Be King / Villa Rides / Fatal Attraction / El Condor / Fixer / Jesus of Nazareth
FILMCD 158 / May '95 / Silva Screen

☐ FILM MUSIC OF MAURICE JARRE, THE
MCCD 277 / Dec '96 / Music Club

☐ MAURICE JARRE AT ABBEY ROAD (Royal Philharmonic Orchestra)
Jarre, Maurice *con*
262321 / Sep '93 / Milan

☐ MAURICE JARRE AT THE ROYAL FESTIVAL HALL (Jarre, Maurice)
74321433572 / Feb '97 / Milan

☐ THEATRE NATIONAL POPULAIRE
74321468322 / Jul '97 / Milan

☐ THEATRE NATIONAL POPULAIRE (The Complete Works)
74321468312 / Jul '97 / Milan

Johnson, Laurie

☐ EASY PROJECT VOL.4, THE (...With A Vengeance) (Johnson, Laurie Orchestra)
Avengers / Top Secret / Dr. Strangelove / No Hiding Place / Beauty Jungle / Doin' the raccoon / Echo Four Two / M1 / Soho / City / Limehouse / West End / Latin Quarter / Grand Central / Times Square / South Beach / Seventh Avenue / Stick or twist / Drum crazy / Minor bossa nova / Dear friend / Heat wave / Twango / Winter wonderland / Hoe down / Deputy / Spring spring spring / Chaka / Sabre dance
NEMCD 935 / 24 Nov '97 / Sequel

☐ MUSICAL WORLD OF LAURIE JOHNSON VOL.2, THE (Johnson, Laurie)
5578192 / 3 Aug '98 / Redial

☐ PROFESSIONAL, THE (Johnson, Laurie)
Avengers / Doctor Strangelove / This is your life / When the kissing had to stop / Tiger bay / Shirley's world / Caeser Smith / Hot millions / Professionals / Jason King / New Avengers / Avengers tag scene / Lady and the highwayman / Hazard of hearts / Duel of hearts / Ghost in Monte Carlo / Four Musketeers / First men in the moon/Romance / I aim at the stars / Animal magic / Freewheelers / Bolero / Avengers
5572102 / 27 Jul '98 / Redial

Johnston, Philip

☐ MUSIC FOR FILMS (Johnston, Philip)
TZA 7510 / 1 Jun '98 / Tzadik

Kalthoum, Oum

☐ SOUNDTRACK CUTS 1936-1946 (Kalthoum, Oum)
829412 / Jun '97 / BUDA

Kamen, Michael

☐ MICHAEL KAMEN SOUNDTRACK ALBUM, THE
4589122 / 18 May '98 / Decca

Kancheli, G.A.

☐ FILM MUSIC (Georgia State Symphony Orchestra/USSR Cinema Symphony Orchestra)
Kakhidze, D./S. Skripka *con*
Don't grieve / Day of wrath / Kin-dza-dza / Passport
OCD 608 / Mar '96 / Olympia

Kander & Ebb

☐ CELEBRATING KANDER & EBB
Broadway my street / Coloured lights / Coffee in a cardboard cup / Ragtime from blue skies / Caberet / Steel pier duet / City lights / Chicago overture/All that jazz / Willkommen / Maybe this time / Sometimes a day goes by/I don't remember you / Arthur in the afternoon / Kiss of the spiderwoman / Sing happy / My own space / New York New York
WMEV 00172 / 17 Aug '98 / BBC Audio

☐ EVENING WITH KANDER & EBB, AN (Kander, John & Fred Ebb)
Sara Lee / Liza with a 'z' / My colouring book / Ring them bells / Life is / Cabaret / Quiet thing / Money money money / Maybe this time / Tomorrow morning / Please stay / All that jazz / Roxie / Yes
DRG 5171 / Jan '95 / DRG

Kaper, Bronislaw

☐ FILM MUSIC OF BRONISLAW KAPER, THE
Mutiny on the bounty / Lilli / Glass slipper / Butterfield 8 / Auntie Mame / Chocolate soldier / Invitation / Brother Karamazov / Green Dolphin Street / Swan / Lord Jim / San Francisco
FA 8101 / May '94 / Facet

Karaindrou, Eleni

☐ MUSIC FOR FILMS
Farewell theme / Elegy for Rosa / Fairytale / Parade / Return / Wandering in Alexandria / Journey / Scream / Adagio / Fairytale / Parade / Elegy for Rosa / Rosa's song / Improvisation on farewell and waltz / Wandering in Alexandria / Song / Farewell theme
8476092 / Jul '94 / ECM

Kazanecki, Waldemar

☐ WALDEMAR KAZANECKI: FILM MUSIC (Polish Symphony Orchestra)
Kazanecki, Waldemar *con*
Night and days / House / Love will forgive you everything / By journey / Eva's madness / Boat to Sweden / Dark haired man / Gypsy Autumn / Harbours / Pacific 88
OCD 603 / Aug '94 / Olympia

Kern, Jerome

☐ ALL THE THINGS YOU ARE (The Jerome Kern Songbook)
5299072 / Mar '96 / Verve

☐ CAN'T HELP SINGING (New Choral Arrangements Of Jerome Kern Classics) (Voices Of Ascension)
Keene, Dennis *con*
DE 3224 / 2 Apr '98 / Delos

☐ CLASSIC MOVIE AND BROADWAY SHOW TUNES FROM RARE PIANO ROLLS
Look for the silver lining: *Cook, J. Lawrence* / Who: *Arden, Victor* / Smoke gets in your eyes: *Cook, J. Lawrence* / Fine romance: *Cook, J. Lawrence* / Way you look tonight: *Jouard, Paul* / All the things you are: *Cook, J. Lawrence* / Last time I saw Paris: *Cook, J. Lawrence* / Show Boat medley: *Watson, Dick*
BCD 142 / Jun '97 / Biograph

☐ COMPLETE JEROME KERN SONGBOOKS, THE (All The Things You Are/A Fine Romance/Yesterdays)
5394412 / 10 Nov '97 / Verve

☐ ELIZABETH WELCH SINGS JEROME KERN (Welch, Elizabeth)
CDVIR 8310 / Jan '90 / TER

☐ FINE ROMANCE, A (The Jerome Kern Songbook)
5238272 / Jan '95 / Verve

☐ INCOMPARABLE JEROME KERN, THE (Chacksfield, Frank Orchestra/Chorus)
Last time I saw Paris / All the things you are / Folks who live on the hill / Look for the silver lining / She didn't say yes / Smoke gets in your eyes / I won't dance / Long ago (and far away) / Who / Yesterdays / Show Boat medley
4551532 / Aug '97 / Decca

☐ JEROME KERN SHOWCASE, A
Back to the heather / D'ye love me / Showboat / Who / Try to forget / Song is you / I might grow fond of you / Cabaret girl / Look for the silver lining / Do I do wrong / Fine romance / Cat and the fiddle / I've told every little star / Sunny / Reckless / Sweet Adeline / High wide and handsome / Waltz / New love is old / Sally
PASTCD 9767 / Nov '91 / Flapper

☐ JEROME KERN TREASURY (London Sinfonietta)
McGlinn, John *con*
CDC 7548832 / Apr '94 / EMI Classics

☐ KERN/PORTER FAVOURITES (Gould, Morton & His Orchestra)
Night and day / Jockey on the carousel / I've got you under my skin / Can I forget you / All the things you are / What is this thing called love / I get a kick out of you / I dream too much / Smoke gets in your eyes / Way you look tonight / Yesterdays
09026648782 / 6 Apr '98 / RCA Victor

☐ KIRI SINGS KERN (Te Kanawa, Dame Kiri & London Sinfonietta)
Tunick, Jonathan *con*
CDC 7545272 / Apr '93 / EMI Classics

☐ MARNI NIXON SINGS CLASSIC KERN (Nixon, Marni)
RR 28 / '90 / Reference Recordings

☐ MUSIC OF JEROME KERN, THE (Auletta, Ted Orchestra & Reid Shelton)
ACD 45 / May '98 / Audiophile

☐ SHOW BOAT (& Other Classics) (Stride, Fred Orchestra)
Stride, Fred *con*
Showboat medley / Last time I saw Paris / I won't dance / I'm old fashioned / Roberta / Folks who live on the hill / Who / Way you look tonight / I've told every little star / All the things you are / Song is you
MVCD 1099 / Nov '96 / CBC

☐ SILVER LININGS (Songs Of Jerome Kern) (Morris, Joan & William Bolcom)
Z 6515 / Nov '85 / Arabesque

☐ SONG IS...JEROME KERN, THE
She didn't say yes: *Ambrose & His Orchestra* / They didn't believe me: *Ambrose & His Orchestra* / Song is you: *BBC Dance Orchestra* / I'll be hard to handle: *Coleman, Emil* / Let's begin: *Coleman, Emil* / Make believe: *Crosby, Bing & Paul Whiteman* / I've told ev'ry little star: *Ellis, Mary* / Who: *Hopkins, Claude* / Look for the silver lining: *Hopkins, Claude* / Bill: *Morgan, Helen* / Can't help lovin' dat man: *Morgan, Helen* / Ol' man river: *Robeson, Paul* / Hand in hand: *Stone, Lew & Al Bowlly* / Sunny: *Ipana Troubadours* / Smoke gets in your eyes: *Whiteman, Paul & Rhythm Boys* / Something had to happen: *Whiteman, Paul & Rhythm Boys*
CDAJA 5036 / Oct '95 / Living Era

☐ SONGS OF JEROME KERN
MCCD 187 / Nov '94 / Music Club

☐ SURE THING, A (The Jerome Kern Songbook)
4421292 / Dec '94 / Philips

☐ SURE THING, A (Song Arrangements) (Bennett, Richard Rodney & Barry Tuckwell)
Richardson, Neil *con*
CDEMX 2270 / Apr '96 / Eminence

☐ TRIBUTE TO JEROME KERN, A
CDDL 1290 / Jun '95 / EMI

☐ YESTERDAYS (The Unforgettable Music Of Jerome Kern)
Pick yourself up: *Astaire, Fred* / Never gonna dance: *Astaire, Fred* / Look for the silver lining: *Matthews, Jessie* / Song is you: *BBC Dance Orchestra* / Smoke gets in your eyes: *Robins, Phyllis* / Last time I saw Paris: *Shelton, Anne* / I've told ev'ry little star: *Ellis, Mary* / She didn't say yes: *Wood, Peggy* / Make believe: *Goodman, Benny* / Yesterdays: *Holiday, Billie* / Why was I born: *Holiday, Billie* / Whose baby are you: *Gershwin, George* / Why do I love you: *Beiderbecke, Bix* / Can't help lovin' dat man: *Morgan, Helen* / I might grow fonder of you: *Randolph, Elsie* / It'll be hard to handle: *Coleman, Emil* / They didn't believe me: *Stone, Lew & Al Bowlly* / Something had to happen: *Whiteman, Paul & Rhythm Boys* / Ol' man river: *Robeson, Paul* / Folks who live on the hill: *Crosby, Bing*
AVC 519 / Apr '95 / Avid

☐ YESTERDAYS (The Jerome Kern Songbook)
5333312 / May '97 / Verve

Khachaturian, Aram

☐ FILM MUSIC (Armenian Philharmonic Orchestra)
Tjeknavorian, Loris *con*
Pepo / Undying Flame / Secret Mission / Admiral Ushakov / Prisoner No. 217
CDDCA 966 / Jun '97 / ASV

Kilar, Wojciech

☐ COLLECTION
176382 / Jul '93 / Milan

☐ FILM MUSIC (Polish Symphony Orchestra)
Kilar, Wojciech *con*
Land of promise / Balance / Hypothesis / Polaniecki family / Silence / Taste of black earth / Pearl in the crown / Salto / Jealousy and medicine / Leper
OCD 602 / Aug '94 / Olympia

☐ WARSAW TO HOLLYWOOD
Chronique des Evenements Amoureux / La ligne d'Ombre / La Terre de la Grande Promesse / Bram Stoker's Dracula / Death and the maiden / Full gallop / Bilan Trimestriel / Contrat / L'Annee du Soleil Calme / Wherever you are / Father Kolbe / Life for life / Hasard / Jalousie et Medecine / La Lepreuse
74321459722 / Mar '97 / Milan

Koechlin, Charles

☐ SEVEN STARS' SYMPHONY, THE (& Four Interludes/L'Andalouse Dans Barcelone) (German Symphony Orchestra)
Judd, James *con*
9026681462 / Jun '96 / RCA Victor

Korngold, Erich

☐ ELIZABETH AND ESSEX (The Classic Film Scores Of Erich Wolfgang Korngold) (National Philharmonic Orchestra)
Gerhardt, Charles *con*
Private Lives of Elizabeth and Essex / Prince and the Pauper / Sea Wolf / Deception / Of Human Bondage / Anthony Adverse / Another Dawn
GD 80185 / Jun '91 / RCA Victor

☐ WARNER BROS. YEARS, THE (Korngold, Erich)
Captain Blood / Green Pastures / Anthony Adverse / Prince and the pauper / Adventures of Robin Hood / Juarez / Private lives of Elizabeth and Essex / Sea hawk / Sea wolf / Kings row / Constant nymph / Devotion / Between two worlds / Of human bondage / Escape me never / Deception
CDODEON 13 / Apr '96 / Soundtracks

Korzynski, Andrzej

☐ FILM MUSIC
Korzynski, Andrzej *con*
Man of iron / Man of marble / Birchwood / Hunting flies
OCD 601 / Aug '94 / Olympia

Kunzel, Erich

☐ BIG PICTURE, THE (Cincinnati Pops Orchestra)
Kunzel, Erich *con*
Mission Impossible / Batman Forever / Re-entry and splashdown / Express bus to LA / Speed / Roll tide / Into the battle / Independence Day / Braveheart / Cutthroat island / Tornado terror / House visit / Last Of The Mohicans / Dragon Heart / Remora / Going home / Library stampede / Gettysburg / Bovine Barnstorm / Jumanji
CD 80437 / Jun '97 / Telarc

☐ VERY BEST OF ERICH KUNZEL, THE (Laine, F./R. Leech/Central St. Uni. Choir/Cincinnati Pops Orchestra)
Kunzel, Erich *con*
Round up / Star Trek / Sing sing sing / Tara's theme (Gone with the wind) / Unchained melody / Nessun dorma / Little fugue in G minor / Star Wars / Batman / Grand Canyon suite / From Russia with love / Olympic fanfare / Opening sequence from Chiller / Overture to the Phantom Of The Opera / Godfather / Pink Panther / O mio babbino caro / Non-stop fast polka / Op 112 / Honor honor do lord / Cybergenesis / Terminator / Jurassic lunch
CD 80401 / Sep '94 / Telarc

Kurylewicz, Andrzej

☐ ANDRZEJ KURYLEWICZ: FILM MUSIC (Warsaw National Philharmonic/Lodz Philharmonic Orchestras)
Kurylewicz, Andrzej *con*
Polish roads / On the Niemen river / Doll / Pan Tudeusz
OCD 605 / Aug '94 / Olympia

Lai, Francis

☐ 30 YEARS OF FILM MUSIC VOL.1 & 2
Les Etoiles Du Cinema / Un Homme Et Une Femme / Vivre Pour Vivre / 13 Jours En France / Mayerling / Le Passger De La Pluie / Love Story / Smic Smac Smoc / La Course Du Lievre A Travers Les Champs / Un Amour De Pluie / Mariage / La Babysitter / Emmanuelle II / Le Corps De Mon Ennemi / Bilitis / Un Autre Homme Une Autre Chance / Un Autre Homme Une Autre Choice / Robert Et Robert / International Velvet / Les Borsalinis / Indian Summer / Les Uns Et les Autres / Madam Claude II / Edith Et Marcel / Canicule / Les Ripoux / Mary A True Story / Un Homme Et Une Femme Vingt Ans Deja / Les Yeux Noirs / Itineraire D'Un Enfant Gate / Les Pyramids

Bleus / Il Y A Des Jours Et Des Lunes / Ripoux Contre Ripoux / Les Cles Du Paradis / La Belle Histoire / Le Provincial / Tolgi Il Disturbo / L'Inconnu Dans La Maison / Tout Ca Pour Ca / Les Miserables / Instrumental theme: La valse du XXeme siecle
SION 18602 / Jul '97 / Sion

☐ **FRANCIS LAI**
HM 012 / Jun '97 / Harmony

☐ **ROMANTIC MUSIC OF FRANCIS LAI, THE**
Love story / Man and a woman / Love in the rain / Live for life / Seduction / Emotion / Solitude / Les unes et les autres / La ronde / African summer / Par le sang des autres / Intimate moments / Whitechapel / Smic smac smoc / Blue rose / Bilitis / Sur notre etoile / Happy new year
EMPRCD 722 / Jun '97 / Emporio

Legrand, Michel

☐ **LA VIE DE CHATEAU/LE SAUVAGE/ LES MARTES**
3003992 / Feb '97 / Playtime

☐ **TRAVELLING MUSIC & CINEMA SERIES (Harp/Orchestra Arrangements Of Legrand Film Sores)**
K 1020 / Feb '96 / Travelling Music & Cinema Series

Lerner & Lowe

☐ **LERNER & LOEWE SONGBOOK (Cincinnati Pops Orchestra)**
CD 80375 / Jan '94 / Telarc

☐ **SPOTLIGHT ON LERNER & LOWE**
I've grown accustomed to her face / Gigi / Wouldn't it be lovely / Almost like being in love / I talk to the trees / They call the wind Maria / On the street where you live / Waltz at Maxim's / Get me to the church on time / If ever I would leave you / Rain in Spain / Thank heaven for little girls
HADCD 138 / Feb '94 / Javelin

Lerner, Alan Jay

☐ **ALAN JAY LERNER PERFORMS HIS OWN SONGS (Lerner, Alan Jay)**
Almost like being in love / Love song / Jug of wine / Economics / There but for you go I / Love of my life / Here I'll stay / Wanderin' star / Green up time / Progress / Susan's dream / Heather on the hill / I talk to the trees / Mr.Right / I ain't never felt so good before / Huckleberry Finn / World full of suckers / When you grow up you'll know / Headin' for New Orleans / Pittsburgh blue
DRGCD 5246 / 20 Apr '98 / DRG

☐ **EVENING WITH ALAN JAY LERNER, AN**
OCRCD 6012 / Apr '96 / First Night

☐ **EVENING WITH ALAN JAY LERNER, AN (Lerner, Alan Jay & Bobbi Baird/J.T. Cromwell/Barbara Williams)**
How to handle a woman / Why can't a woman / I talk to the trees / Wouldn't it be loverly / Oh come to the ball / On the street where you live / Come back to me / What did I have that I don't have / I'm glad I'm not young anymore / I loved you in silence / Gigi / Camelot / On a clear day / I've grown accustomed to her face
DRG 5175 / Jan '95 / DRG

☐ **LERNER LOEWE LANE AND FRIENDS**
Overture / Applause applause / Almost like being in love / Heather on the hill / When the idle poor become the idle rich / Everything I have is yours / With a little bit of luck / Wouldn't it be lovely / Ascot gavotte / From this day on / Little prince / In our united state / Dance a little closer / Moments like this / When you grow up you'll know / How could you believe me when I said I love you when I've be / How far is the next town / Economics / C'est moi / There but for you go I / Take care of this house / You're all the world to me / Follow me/On a clear day you can see forever / They call the wind Maria / She wasn't you / How to handle a woman / Seven deadly virtues / Before I gaze at you again / In the broken promise land of fifteen / Old devil moon / I've grown accustomed to her face / Come back to me / Don't let it get you down (love is a lovely thing) / On the street where you live / I could have danced all night / Too late now / How about you / What did I have that I don't have / If ever I would leave you / Here I'll stay
VSD 5917 / 26 May '98 / Varese Sarabande

Lesiman

☐ **FUTURE SOUND OF LESIMAN, THE (Lesiman)**
ET 920CD / 6 Jul '98 / Easy Tempo

Lloyd Webber, Andrew

☐ **ANDREW LLOYD WEBBER ALBUM, THE (Beechman, Laurie)**
VSD 5583 / Aug '95 / Varese Sarabande

☐ **ANDREW LLOYD WEBBER COLLECTION, THE**
Starlight express: *Wayne, Carl* / Unexpected song: *Jones, Paul* / Macavity: *Lawrence, Stephanie* / Memory: *Lawrence, Stephanie* / Gus the theatre cat: *Jones, Paul* / Pumping iron: *Conrad, Jess* / Tell me on a Sunday: *Wayne, Carl* / I don't know how to love him: *Hendley, Fiona* / Any dream will do: *Conrad, Jess* / Love changes everything: *Lawrence, Stephanie* / All I ask of you: *Lawrence, Stephanie* / Oh what a circus: *Conrad, Jess* / Wishing you were somehow here again: *Lawrence, Stephanie*
PWKS 4065 / Aug '91 / Carlton

☐ **ANDREW LLOYD WEBBER COLLECTION, THE (Clayderman, Richard)**
Phantom Of The Opera / Music of the night / Love changes everything / High flying adored / Seeing is believing / All I ask of you / Don't cry for me Argentina / Another suitcase in another hall / Tell me on a Sunday / I don't know how to love him / Memory / Take that look off your face
30012 / Oct '97 / Go On Deluxe

☐ **ANDREW LLOYD WEBBER COLLECTION, THE (Brightman, Sarah)**
Phantom Of The Opera / Unexpected song / Chanson d'enfance / All I ask of you / Don't cry for me Argentina / Another suitcase in another hall / Love changes everything / Amigos para siempre / Memory / Gus the theatre act / Anything but lonely / Macavity the mystery cat / Tell me on a Sunday / Wishing you were somehow here again / Pie Jesu / Music of the night
5393302 / 1 Dec '97 / Polydor

☐ **ANDREW LLOYD WEBBER'S GREATEST HITS**
CDTEZ 7001 / Jan '95 / TER

☐ **ASPECTS OF ANDREW LLOYD WEBBER (BBC Concert Orchestra)**
Music of the night / Memory / Variations / Don't cry for me Argentina / Anything but lonely / Tell me on a Sunday / Jellicle ball / Love changes everything / I only want to say / Pie Jesu / Close every door / Buenos Aires / I don't know how to love him / Aspects of Andrew
PLACD 246 / 27 Oct '97 / Pulse

☐ **BEST OF ANDREW LLOYD WEBBER, THE**
Journey of a lifetime / Last man in my life / Rolling stock / Another suitcase in another hall / Close every door / Everything's alright / Gethsemane / There is more to love / Old deuteronomy / High flying adored / Don't cry for me Argentina / First man you remember / Pie jesu / Starlight express / Uexpected song / Memory / Macavity / Gus the theatre cat / Pumping iron / Tell me on a Sunday / I don't how to love him / Any dream will do / Love changes everything / All I ask of you / Oh what a circus / Wishing you were here again / Superstar / Chanson d'enfance / Mr. Mistoffeelees / One more angel in heaven / Anything but lonely / Half a moment / Take that look off your face / On this night of a thousand stars / Seeing is believing / Think of me / Music of the night / Phantom of the opera
BOXD 39T / Oct '94 / Carlton

☐ **CLASSIC SONGS (Featuring Lesley Garrett) (Royal Philharmonic Concert Orchestra)**
Bateman, Paul *con*
SONGCD 909 / Sep '93 / Silva Classics

☐ **ESSENTIALS VOL.1**
Memory: *Friedman, Maria* / Any dream will do: *Barrowman, John* / Think of me: *Moore, Claire & John Barrowman* / Don't cry for me Argentina: *Friedman, Maria* / There's me: *Carter, Clive* / All I ask of you: *Moore, Claire & John Barrowman* / Another suitcase in another hall: *Renihan, Grania* / Mr. Mistoffelees: *Carter, Clive* / Tell me on a Sunday: *Robertson, Liz* / High flying adored: *Barrowman, John & Maria Friedman* / I don't know how to love him: *Friedman, Maria* / Only you: *Renihan, Grania* / Music of the night: *Dietrich, John* / Seeing is believing: *Barrowman, John & Janis Kelly* / Close every door: *Carter, Clive* / Wishing you were somehow here again: *Moore, Claire* / Love changes everything: *Barrowman, John*
322634 / Mar '92 / Koch

☐ **ESSENTIALS VOL.2 (The Ultimate Andrew Lloyd Webber Collection)**
340132 / May '97 / Koch International

☐ **ESSENTIALS VOL.3 (The Ultimate Andrew Lloyd Webber Collection)**
340892 / May '97 / Koch International

☐ **GREATEST HITS (Lloyd Webber, Andrew)**
Perfect year / Music of the night / Memory / Friends for life / Starlight express / Jesus Christ Superstar / Don't cry for me Argentina / Love changes everything / Any dream will do / Take that look off your face / I don't know how to love him / Only he (has the power to move me) / As if we never said goodbye / Another suitcase in another hall / All I ask of you / Pie Jesu / Magical Mr. Mistoffelees
11956 / Dec '95 / Music

☐ **GREATEST SONGS, THE**
Bateman, Paul *con*
Superstar / I don't know how to love him / Everything's alright / Close every door / High flying adored / Another suitcase in another hall / Oh what a circus / Don't cry for me Argentina / Tell me on a Sunday / Take that look off your face / Unexpected song / Macavity / Mystery cat / Memory / Starlight express / Next time you fall in love / Only you / Pie Jesu / Phantom of the opera / Wishing you were here again / Music of me / Angel of music / Point of no return / All I ask of you / Seeing is believing / Love changes everything / Sunset boulevard / Perfect year / With one look / Too much in love to care / As if we never say goodbye
SONGCD 911 / Apr '95 / Silva Classics

☐ **HIT SONGS OF ANDREW LLOYD WEBBER, THE**
Music of the night / I don't know how to love him / Any dream will do / Don't cry for me Argentina / Wishing you were somehow here again / Mr. Mistoffelees / Another suitcase in another hall / Memory / Only you / Take that look off your face / Love changes everything / Superstar
SHOWCD 015 / Feb '95 / Showtime

☐ **LOVE SONGS (Garrett, Lesley & Dave Willets/Royal Philharmonic Pops Orchestra)**
Bateman, Paul *con*
SONGCD 908 / 2 Feb '98 / Silva Classics

☐ **LOVE SONGS OF ANDREW LLOYD WEBBER, THE**
OCRCD 6044 / Nov '96 / First Night

☐ **LOVE SONGS OF ANDREW LLOYD WEBBER, THE**
Love changes everything: *Barrowman, John* / All I ask of you: *Barrowman, John & Claire Moore* / I don't know how to love him: *Friedman, Maria* / Too much in love to care: *Newey, Andrew & Katrina Murphy* / Another suitcase in another hall: *Renihan, Grania* / Half a moment: *Lindsay, Shona* / Only you: *Langton, Diane* / Anything but lonely: *Kelly, Janis* / Wishing you were somehow here again: *Moore, Claire* / Last man in my life: *Robertson, Liz* / There's me: *Carter, Clive* / There is more to love: *Lindsay, Shona*
SHOWCD 038 / Oct '96 / Showtime

☐ **MAGIC OF ANDREW LLOYD WEBBER, THE**
PWKS 4110 / Jan '95 / Carlton

☐ **MORE - THE MUSIC OF ANDREW LLOYD WEBBER**
Old gumbie cat: *Skellern, Peter* / With one look: *Kesselman, Maria* / Sunset Boulevard: *Dulieu, John* / Make up my heart: *Moore, Claire* / Love changes everything: *Skellern, Peter* / Angel of music: *Kesselman, Maria & John Dulieu* / Skimbleshanks: *Dulieu, John* / He'll whistle at me: *Moore, Claire* / Other pleasures: *Skellern, Peter* / Point of no return: *Kesselman, Maria & John Dulieu* / As if we never said goodbye: *Kesselman, Maria* / Perfect year: *Skellern, Peter*
3036200242 / Mar '96 / Carlton

☐ **MUSIC OF ANDREW LLOYD WEBBER, THE (Royal Philharmonic Orchestra)**
Reed, Michael *con*
Music of the night / Memory / Jesus Christ superstar / Take that look off your face / Don't cry for me Argentina / All I ask of you
LLOYDCD 1 / Sep '88 / First Night

☐ **MUSIC OF ANDREW LLOYD WEBBER, THE**
TFP 030 / Nov '92 / Tring

☐ **MUSIC OF ANDREW LLOYD WEBBER, THE (Cincinnati Pops Orchestra)**
Kunzel, Erich *con*
Phantom Of The Opera / Music of the night / Here again / All I ask of you / Angel of music / As if we never said goodbye / Memory / I don't know / Don't cry for me Argentina / Starlight Express / Any dream will do
CD 80405 / Mar '96 / Telarc

☐ **MUSIC OF ANDREW LLOYD WEBBER, THE (Starlight Orchestra/Singers)**
Music of the night / Take that look off your face / Another suitcase in another hall / I don't know how to love him / Any dream will do / Don't cry for me Argentina / Old deuteronomy / All I ask of you / Pumping iron / King Herod's song / One more angel in Heaven / Love changes everything / Jesus Christ superstar / Phantom of the opera / Tell me on a Sunday / Starlight express / Memory / Mister Mistoffelees
QED 009 / Nov '96 / Tring

☐ **MUSIC OF ANDREW LLOYD WEBBER, THE (Greatest Hits From The Musicals)**
I don't know how to love him / Perfect year / Poppa's blues / Sunset boulevard / Phantom of the opera / What's the buzz / Think of me / Light at the end of the tunnel / Macavity / Tell me on Sunday / As if we never said goodbye / Nothing like you've ever known / Invitation to the Jellicle ball / Tell me on a sunday / Pumping iron / King Herod's song / Any dream will do / All I ask of you / Don't cry for me Argentina / Music of the night / Go go go Joseph / Jesus Christ superstar / Magical Mister moistoffelees / Last supper / With one look / Amigos para siempre (Friends for life) / Blood money / Love changes everything / High flying adored / Memory / Pie Jesu / Arrest / Close every door / Prelude from phantom of the opera / Take that look off your face / Chanson d'enfance / Angel of music / Old deuteronomy / Pilate's dream / Another suitcase in another hall / Starlight express / Damned for all time / Heaven on their mind / Only he / Last man in my life / Everything's alright
55171 / Apr '97 / Music

☐ **MUSIC OF THE NIGHT (Gratz, Wayne)**
Think of me / With one look / Don't cry for me Argentina / As if we never said goodbye / Music of the night / Memory / Love changes everything / I don't know how to love him / Pie Jesu / Another suitcase in another hall / All I ask of you
ND 62810 / Aug '97 / Narada

☐ **MUSICAL THEATRE GREATS**
CDVIR 8320 / Aug '95 / TER

☐ **OVATION (The Best Of Andrew Lloyd Webber)**
Don't cry for me Argentina: *Dickson, Barbara* / Another suitcase in another hall: *Dickson, Barbara* / I don't know how to love him / Take that look off your face / Tell me on a Sunday: *Storm, Rebecca* / King Herod's song / One more angel in heaven / Pumping iron / Starlight express / Pie Jesu: *New Scottish Concert Choir* / Old deuteronomy: *Quilley, Denis* / Introduction: variations
CLACD 298 / '92 / Castle

☐ **OVATION (A Musical Tribute To Andrew Lloyd Webber)**
Take that look off your face / Phantom of the opera / Don't cry for me Argentina / Close every door / Only he has the power to move me / Jesus Christ superstar / Sunset boulevard / Mr. Mistoffelees / Music of the night / Memory / All I ask of you / I don't know how to love him / Pie Jesu / Love changes everything / Another suitcase in another hall / Tell me on a Sunday / Joseph's coat / Starlight express
ECD 3062 / Jan '95 / K-Tel

☐ **PERFORMS RICE AND LLOYD WEBBER (London Symphony Orchestra)**
VISCD 4 / Oct '94 / Vision

☐ **PREMIERE COLLECTION (The Best Of Andrew Lloyd Webber)**
Phantom of the opera: *Harley, Steve & Sarah Brightman* / Take that look off your face: *Webb, Marti* / All I ask of you: *Richard, Cliff & Sarah Brightman* / Don't cry for me Argentina: *Covington, Julie* / Mr. Mistoffelees: *Nicholas, Paul* / Variations 1-4: *LLoyd Webber, Julian* / Superstar: *Head, Murray* / Memory: *Paige, Elaine* / Starlight express: *Shell, Ray* / Tell me on a Sunday: *Webb, Marti* / Music of the night: *Crawford, Michael* / Another suitcase in another hall: *Dickson, Barbara* / I don't know how to love him: *Elliman, Yvonne* / Pie Jesu: *Brightman, Sarah & Paul Miles Kingston*
8372822 / Oct '88 / Really Useful

☐ **SHADOWS PLAY ANDREW LLOYD WEBBER AND TIM RICE, THE (Shadows)**
Whole new world / Phantom Of The Opera / Memory / Tell me on a Sunday / I know him so well / Starlight Express suite / I'd be surprisingly good for you / Don't cry for me Argentina / Can you feel the love tonight / Love changes everything / Oh what a circus / Music of the night / Take that look off your face / All I ask of you / Another suitcase in another hall / One night in Bangkok
5394792 / 10 Nov '97 / PolyGram TV

☐ **SONGS OF ANDREW LLOYD WEBBER, THE (Lloyd Webber, Andrew)**
SHOWCD 915 / Mar '95 / Showtime

☐ **SONGS OF ANDREW LLOYD WEBBER, THE**
MCCD 210 / Jul '95 / MCI Music

☐ **SONGS OF ANDREW LLOYD WEBBER, THE (Footlights Orchestra/Chorus)**
Phantom of the opera / As if we never said goodbye / Don't cry for me Argentina / Another suitcase in another hall / Memory / Everything's alright / I don't know how to love him / Jesus Christ superstar / With one look / Starlight express / Only he (has the power to move me) / Any dream will do / Love changes everything / Angel of music / All I ask of you / Magical Mr. Mistoffelees
EMPRCD 904 / Jan '97 / Emporio

☐ **SPOTLIGHT ON ANDREW LLOYD WEBBER**
Starlight Express: *Wayne, Carl* / Another suitcase another hall: *Webb, Marti* / First man to remember: *Lawrence, Stephanie & Dave Willetts* / I don't know how to love him: *Hendley, Fiona* / Any dream will do: *Conrad, Jess* / Phantom of the opera: *Hendley, Fiona & Paul Jones* / Memory: *Hendley, Fiona* / Close every door: *Willetts, Dave* / Mr. Mistoffelees: *Jones, Paul* / Chanson D'enface: *Lawrence, Stephanie & Jack Emblow* / Tell me on a Sunday: *Wayne, Carl* / Oh what a circus: *Conrad, Jess*
300002 / Feb '98 / Hallmark

☐ **STAGES (Hollywood Studio Orchestra)**
Phantom medley / Don't cry for me Argentina / I don't know how to love him / Memory / Any dream will do / Amigos para siempre (Friends for life) / Seeing is believing / Starlight Express / Love medley / Take that look off your face / Pie Jesu / Tell me on a Sunday / Close every door to me / With one look / Perfect year / Oh what a circus
ECD 3264 / Jan '97 / K-Tel

☐ **SURRENDER (The Unexpected Songs) (Brightman, Sarah)**
Surrender / Unexpected song / Chanson d'enfrance / Tell me on a Sunday / Nothing like you've ever known / Macavity the mysterious cat / Gus the theatre cat / Piano / Everything's alright / Last man in my life / Pie Jesu / Amigos parasiempre (Friends for life) / No llores por mi Argentina (Don't cry for me Argentina) / Guardami (With one look) / There is more to love / Wishing you were somehow here again / Music of the night
5277022 / Oct '95 / Polydor

☐ **SYMPHONIC LLOYD WEBBER, THE (Phantom Of The Opera/Cats/Evita/ Aspects Of Love) (Royal Philharmonic Orchestra)**
Stratta, Ettore *con*
9031737422 / Jan '95 / Teldec Classics

☐ **TRIBUTE TO ANDREW LLOYD WEBBER, A (Starlight Orchestra/ Singers)**
Oh what a circus / On this night of a thousand stars / Another suitcase in another hall / Don't cry for me Argentina / High flying adored / Angel of music / Phantom of the opera / Music of the night / All I ask of you / Wishing you were somehow here again / Overture / What's the buzz / Everything's alright / I don't know how to love him / King Herod's song / Jesus Christ superstar / Love changes everything / Seeing is believing / Everyone loves a hero / Cafe / Anything but lonely / Take that look off your face / Tell me on a Sunday / Unexpected song / Last man in my life / Nothing like you've ever known / Rolling stock / AC/DC / Make up my heart / Starlight Express / Next time you fall in love / Light at the end of the tunnel / Any dream will do / One more angel in heaven / Close every door / Joseph's dreams / Song of the King / Poor poor Joseph / Memories / Mr. Mistoffelees / Old Deuteronomy / Gus the theatre cat / McCavity the mystery cat / Odessa anthem
QUAD 010 / Nov '96 / Tring

☐ **VERY BEST OF ANDREW LLOYD WEBBER, THE (Lloyd Webber, Andrew)**
Memory: *Paige, Elaine* / Music of the night: *Crawford, Michael* / Take that look off your face: *Webb, Marti* / Any dream will do: *Donovan, Jason* / Don't cry for me Argentina: *Brightman, Sarah* / Love changes everything: *Ball, Michael* / I don't know how to love him: *Brightman, Sarah* / Perfect year: *Carroll, Dina* / Phantom of the opera: *Harley, Steve* / Oh what a circus: *Essex, David* / Tell me on a Sunday: *Webb, Marti* / Close every door: *Schofield, Philip* / With one look: *Streisand, Barbra* / All I ask of you: *Richard,*

Cliff & Sarah Brightman / Sunset Boulevard: *Ball, Michael* / As if we never said goodbye: *Close, Glenn* / Next time you fall in love: *Rice, Reva & Greg Ellis* / Amigos Para Siempra: *Carreras, Jose & Sarah Brightman*
5238602 / Oct '94 / Really Useful

Loesser, Frank

☐ EVENING WITH FRANK LOESSER, AN (Performing Songs From His Great Shows) (Loesser, Frank)
Fugue from tinhorns / I'll know / Luck be a lady / I've never been in love before / Sit down you're rockin' the boat / Sue me / Traveling light / Adelaide / Happy to keep his dinner warm / Organization man / Secretary is not a toy / Been a long day / Grand old Ivy / Paris original / Rosemary / Love from a heart of gold / I believe in you / Ooh my feet / Love letter / Wanting to be wanted / House and garden
DRGCD 5169 / Jan '95 / DRG

☐ FRANK SINGS LOESSER (Loesser, Frank)
372512 / Nov '95 / Koch International

☐ LOESSER BY LOESSER (A Salute To Frank Loesser) (Loesser, Jo Sullivan & Emily/Don Stephenson)
Romoff, Colin *con*
DRGCD 5170 / Jan '95 / DRG

Mackeben, Theo

☐ THEO MACKEBEN (Cologne Radio Orchestra)
Smola, Emmerich *con*
10705 / Feb '96 / Capriccio

Malek, Ahmed

☐ ALGERIAN FILM MUSIC (Malek, Ahmed)
AAA 122 / Feb '96 / Club Du Disque Arabe

Mancini, Henry

☐ IN THE PINK (Mancini, Henry & His Orchestra)
Pink Panther theme / Moon river / Days of wine and roses / Baby elephant walk / Hatari / Charade / Thorn Birds / Blue satin / Two for the road / Mr. Lucky / Molly Maguires / Moment to moment / As time goes by / Shot in the dark / Misty / Love Story / Pennywhistle jig / Everything I do (I do it for you) / Moonlight sonata / Tender is the night / Mommie Dearest / Raindrops keep falling on my head / Crazy world / Mona Lisa / Peter Gunn / Unchained melody / Summer knows / Experiment in terror / Windmills of your mind / Till there was you / Speedy Gonzales / Sweetheart tree / Romeo and Juliet / Dream a little dream of me / Lonesome / Pie in the face polka / Love is a many splendored thing / By the time I get to Phoenix / Dear heart / Charade (opening titles) / Shadow of your smile / One for my baby / Breakfast at Tiffany's / That old black magic / Evergreen / Midnight cowboy
74321242832 / Nov '95 / RCA Victor

☐ MUSIC OF MANCINI, THE (Starshine Orchestra)
Moon river / Thornbirds theme / Crazy world / Dear heart / Baby elephant walk / Romeo and Juliet Theme / Charade / Pink Panther Theme / Days of wine and roses / How soon / Shot in the dark / Peter Gunn Theme / Jazz Hot / Mr. Lucky / Hatari / Love Story
307762 / 25 Aug '97 / Hallmark

☐ ORANJ SYMPHONETTE PLAYS MANCINI (Oranj Symphonette)
Shot in the dark / Experiment in terror / Pink Panther / Lujon / Inspector Clouseau / Moon river / Charade / Days of wine and roses / Mr. Yunioshi / Mr. Lucky / March of the cue balls / Baby elephant gun
GCD 79515 / Oct '96 / Gramavision

☐ PINK PANTHER, MOON RIVER, BABY ELEPHANT WALK AND OTHER HITS (Mancini, Henry & His Orchestra)
Pink Panther / Royal blue / Champagne and quail / Lonely princess / It had better be tonight / Charade (with chorus) / Megeve / Latin snowfall / Bateau mouche / Bistro / Hatari / Baby elephant walk / Night side / Your father's feathers / Sounds of Hatari / Breakfast at Tiffany's / Something for the cat / Sally's tomato / Holly / Latin golightly / Moon river
RD 85938 / Feb '92 / RCA Victor

☐ RARE MANCINI, THE
12430 / May '95 / Laserlight

☐ SINGS THE MANCINI SONGBOOK (Vaughan, Sarah)
5584012 / 3 Aug '98 / Verve

☐ TWO FOR THE ROAD (A Tribute To Henry Mancini) (Grusin, Dave)
Peter Gunn / Dreamsville / Mr. Lucky / Moment to moment / Baby elephant walk / Two for the road / Days of wine and roses / Hatari / Whistling away the dark / Soldier in the rain
GRP 98652 / Apr '97 / GRP

Martin & Blane

☐ SING MARTIN & BLANE (Martin, Hugh & Ralph Blane)
Wish I may wish I might / Every time / That's how I love the blues / Buckle down winsocki / Have yourself a merry little christmas / Love / Trolley song / Boy next door / Pass that peace pipe / Connecticut / Occasional man / Venezia
DRGCD 5168 / Apr '94 / DRG

Martin, Hugh

☐ HUGH MARTIN SONGBOOK, THE (Feinstein, Michael)
7559793142 / Jan '95 / Nonesuch

Menken, Alan

☐ ALAN MENKEN ALBUM (Gravitte, Debbie Shapiro)
VSD 5741 / Jan '97 / Varese Sarabande

Mercer, Johnny

☐ BLUES IN THE NIGHT
BMCD 3041 / Jul '97 / Blue Moon

☐ EVENING WITH JOHNNY MERCER, AN (Mercer, Johnny & Margaret Whiting/ Robert Sands)
I'm old fashioned / And the angels sing / Out of this world / Glow worm / Hit the road to dreamland / Lazy bones / Jeepers creepers / Satin doll / That old black magic / Fools rush in / Come rain or come shine / Hooray for Hollywood / Laura / Skylark / Autumn leaves / Moon river / Days of wine and roses
DRG 5176 / Jan '95 / DRG

☐ PORTRAIT OF JOHNNY MERCER, A (Syms, Sylvia)
DRG 91433 / Feb '95 / DRG

☐ SONGWRITER SERIES VOL.3 (That Old Black Magic)
PASTCD 7094 / Jun '96 / Flapper

☐ STARS SALUTE JOHNNY MERCER, THE
CDCD 1238 / Jun '95 / Charly

☐ TOO MARVELLOUS FOR WORDS (The Johnny Mercer Songbook)
5571402 / 26 May '98 / Verve

Mercouri, Melina

☐ GREATEST GREEK SINGERS (Mercouri, Melina)
ML 0031 / 12 May '98 / Musurgia Graeca

Meyers, Lanny

☐ ONCE UPON A TIME IN THE CINEMA
VSD 5630 / Mar '96 / Varese Sarabande

Moross, Jerome

☐ VALLEY OF GWANGI, THE (Film Scores Of Jerome Moross) (City Of Prague Philharmonic Orchestra)
Adventures of Huckleberry Finn / Sharkfighters / Mountain Road / Rachel Rachel / War lord / Valley of the Gwangi / Five finger exercise / Wagon train
FILMCD 161 / Sep '95 / Silva Screen

Morricone, Ennio

☐ BELMONDO MORRICONE
3020832 / Jun '97 / Arcade

☐ BEST OF ENNIO MORRICONE, THE
For a few dollars more / Fistful of dollars / Sacco and Vanzetti / Moses the lawgiver / Metello / God with us / Once upon a time in the west / 1900 / Death rides a horse / Life's tough isn't it / Cirbiribin / Scetate
74321289842 / Aug '95 / RCA

☐ BIG GUNDOWN, THE (The Music Of Ennio Morricone) (Zorn, John)
7559791392 / Jan '95 / Nonesuch

☐ CANTO MORRICONE VOL.1 (The Sixties)
Ho messo gli: *Dino* / Thrilling: *Monico, Rita* / Se telefonando: *Mina* / Il disco rotto: *Mina* / Sapore di sale: *Paoli, Gino* / Quattro vestiti: *Milva* / Fruscio di foglie verdi: *Trio Junior* / Una stanza vuota: *Moffo, anna* / Nuddu: *Cigliano, Fausto* / Cantata basilisca: *Cigliano, Fausto* / Questi vent'anni miei: *Spaak, Catherine* / Penso a te: *Spaak, Catherine* / Tra tante gente: *Tenco, Luigi* / Quello che conta: *Tenco, Luigi* / Deep down: *Christy* / Je changerais d'avis (se telefonando): *Hardy, Francoise* / Funny world: *Colman, Ken* / Hurry to me: *Sandpipers* / funny world: *Gilberto, Astrid* / Scetate: *Martino, Miranda*
BCD 16244 / Jul '98 / Bear Family

☐ CANTO MORRICONE VOL.2 (Western Songs & Ballads)
Messico que vorrei: *Christy* / Corri uomo corri: *Christy* / Death rides a horse: *Raoul* / Vamos a mattar: *Studio choir* / Gringo like me: *Tevis, Peter* / Lonesome Billy: *Tevis, Peter* / Per un pugno di dollari: *Tevis, Peter* / Angel face: *Graf, Zio* / Return of Ringo: *Graf, Zio* / Eye for an eye: *Graf, Zio* / Ballad of Hank McCain: *Lynton, Jackie* / Faith: *Roberts, Rocky* / La Canzone della liberta: *Endrigo, Sergio* / Ballad of Sacco and Vanzetti: *Baez, Joan* / Here's to you: *Baez, Joan* / Ballad of Sacco and Vanzetti: *Walker, Scott* / Le marche de Sacco and Vanzetti: *Moustaki, Georges*
BCD 16245 / Jul '98 / Bear Family

☐ CINEMA ITALIANO (Music Of Ennio Morricone/Nino Rota) (Mancini Pops Orchestra)
Mancini, Henry *con*
Cinema Paradiso / Boccaccio 70 / Once Upon a Time in the West / Once Upon a Time in America / Godfather
RD 60706 / Apr '91 / RCA Victor

☐ ENNIO MORRICONE ANTHOLOGY, AN
La cage aux folles III / Professional / This kind of love / Serpent / Without apparent motive / What am I doing in the middle of this revolution
DRGCD 32908 / Sep '95 / DRG

☐ ENNIO MORRICONE WESTERN QUINTET, AN
Fistful of dynamite / My name is nobody / Fist goes west / Blood and guns / Companeros
DRGCD 32907 / Aug '95 / DRG

☐ FILM HITS
Once upon a time in the West / For a few dollars more / Moses theme / Bye bye Colonel / Fistful of dollars / Gun for Ringo / Ballad of Sacco and Vanzetti / Here's to you / Vice of killing / Paying off scores: *Morricone, Ennio* / Adventurer / What have you done to Solange / Violent city / Mertello
ND 70091 / May '90 / RCA

☐ GOLDEN FILM THEMES
175132 / Aug '97 / Musidisc

☐ GREATEST FILM THEMES
402222 / Aug '90 / Musidisc

☐ GREATEST MOVIE THEMES
139220 / '86 / Accord

☐ MAGIC FILM WORLD OF ENNIO MORRICONE, THE
VCDS 7014 / Apr '96 / Varese Sarabande

☐ MAIN TITLES 1965-1995
DRGCD 32920 / Dec '96 / DRG

☐ MISSION, THE (The Classic Film Music Of Ennio Morricone) (Crouch End Festival Choir/Prague City Philharmonic Orchestra)
Bateman, Paul/D. Wadsworth/N. Raine *con*
Mission / Untouchables / Once upon a time in America / Novecento / Casualties of war / Two mules for sister Sara / In the line of fire / Thing / Chi mai / Marco Polo / Once upon a time in the West / Good the bad the ugly / Fistful of dollars / For a few dollars more / Cinema paradiso
FILMCD 171 / Mar '96 / Silva Screen

☐ MONDO MORRICONE VOL.1
CST 348057 / Nov '96 / Colosseum

☐ MONDO MORRICONE VOL.2
CST 348058 / Feb '97 / Colosseum

☐ MOVIE CLASSICS
Good the bad and the ugly / Fistful Of Dollars / For A Few Dollars More / Bye Bye Colonel / Ballad Of Sacco and Vanzetti / Vice Of Killing / Paying Off Scores / Adventurer / Once Upon A Time In The West / Gun For Ringo / Metello / Man from UNCLE / Sixty Seconds To What / Battle Of Algiers
74321446792 / Feb '97 / Camden

☐ MUSIC OF ENNIO MORRICONE, THE (London Studio Orchestra)
North, Nicky *con*
For A Few Dollars More / Man with the harmonica / Cockeye's song / Good The Bad and The Ugly / Once Upon A Time in the West / Once Upon A Time in America / El mercenario / My Name is Nobody / Il etait une fois la revolution / Chi mai / Here's to you / Exorcist II / La libertad / Fistful of Dollars / Square dance / Fistful of Dynamite / Apres l'explosion
CD 3509 / Nov '95 / Cameo

☐ SINGLES COLLECTION, THE (47 Themes From 25 Movies 1969-1981) (Morricone, Ennio)
DRGCD 32921 / Sep '97 / DRG

☐ SPAGHETTI WESTERN
Gun for Ringo / Grotesque suspense / Heroic Mexico / Wait / Slaughter / Angel face / At times life is very hard isn't that fate / McGregor's march / Santa Fe express / Gringo like me / Lonesome Billy / Indians / Young girl and the sheriff / Bullets don't argue / Woman for the McGregors / Death rides a horse / Mystic and severe / Guitar and nocturne / Anger and sorrow / We'll be back isn't that fate / Mouth to mouth / Gallop / Return of Ringo / Disguise / Fuentes / Funeral / Wedding and the revenge / Peace comes in Mimbres
74321264952 / May '95 / RCA

☐ TIME FOR ADVENTURE, A
74321315512 / Feb '96 / RCA

☐ TIME FOR SUSPENSE, A
VCDS 7013 / Apr '96 / Varese Sarabande

☐ TV FILM MUSIC
74321315522 / Feb '96 / RCA

☐ VERY BEST OF ENNIO MORRICONE, THE
323122 / Feb '94 / Koch

Nascimbene, Mario

☐ MARIO NASCIMBENE ANTHOLOGY, THE (Main Titles/Vocals/Rare Tracks/ Outtakes)
Farewell to arms / Quiet American / One million years BC / Francis of Assissi / When dinosaurs ruled the earth / Alexander The Great / Where the spies are / Romanoff and Juliet / Barefoot contessa / Room at the top / Solomon and Sheba / Vikings / Creatures the world forget / Siege of Leningrad / Scent of mystery / Sons and lovers / Light in the piazza / Barabbas / Doctor Faustus / Joseph and his brethren / Vengeance of she / Jessica
DRGCD 32960 / Aug '96 / DRG

Newman, Alfred

☐ CAPTAIN FROM CASTILE (Classic Film Scores Of Alfred Newman) (National Philharmonic Orchestra)
Gerhardt, Charles *con*
Captain from Castile / How to Marry a Millionaire / Wuthering Heights / Down to the Sea in Ships / Bravados / Anastasia / Best of Everything / Airport / Song of Bernadette / Robe / Map of Jerusalem
GD 80184 / Oct '90 / RCA Victor

☐ NEWMAN (Moscow Symphony Orchestra)
Stromberg, William T. *con*
8223750 / Jan '98 / Marco Polo

Nicastro, Michelle

☐ REEL IMAGINATION
VSD 5537 / Jun '95 / Varese Sarabande

North, Alex

☐ NONESUCH FILM MUSIC SERIES (London Symphony Orchestra)
Stern, Eric *con*
7559794462 / Aug '97 / Nonesuch

Novello, Ivor

☐ IVOR NOVELLO - CENTENARY CELEBRATION
GEMMCD 9062 / Nov '93 / Pearl

☐ MARILYN HILL-SMITH SINGS IVOR NOVELLO (Hill-Smith, Marilyn & The Chandos Concert Orchestra)
Barry, Stuart *con*
Some day my heart will awake / Primrose / Love is my reason / Dark music / Little damozel / When the gypsy played / On such a night as this / Fly home little heart / Keep the home fires burning (til the boys come home) / Music in May / Violin began to play / Spring of the year / My dearest dear / Finder please return / Look in my heart / When I curtsied to the King / We'll gather lilacs / Fairy laughter / Glamorous night / Why is there ever goodbye
FBCD 2006 / 18 Mar '98 / Flyback

Petit, Jean Claude

☐ CYRANO/JEAN DE FLORETTE
302330 / Feb '97 / Playtime

Porter, Cole

☐ CENTENARY TRIBUTE TO COLE PORTER, A
Let's do it / What is this thing called love / You do something to me / You've got that thing / Miss Otis regrets / My heart belongs to Daddy
DOLD 15 / Apr '91 / Old Bean

☐ CENTENARY TRIBUTE TO COLE PORTER, THE
You're the top / Anything goes / Solomon / Jubilee selections / What is this thing called love / My heart belongs to Daddy / Swingin' the jinx away / Goodbye little dream goodbye / Gypsy in me / I've got you under my skin / Let's do it (Let's fall in love) / Something for the boys selections / There'll always be a lady fair / Nymph errant / Thank you so much / Mrs. Lownsborough-Goodby / All through the night / Night and day / Rap tap on wood / How could we be so wrong / Begin the beguine
PASTCD 9751 / Feb '91 / Flapper

☐ CENTENNIAL GALA CONCERT
9031752772 / Jan '95 / Teldec Classics

☐ CLASSIC MOVIE AND BROADWAY SHOW TUNES FROM RARE PIANO ROLLS
You do something to me: *Henderson, Douglas* / What is this thing called love: *Cook, J. Lawrence* / Night and day: *Cook, J. Lawrence* / I get a kick out of you: *Kortlander, Max* / Anything goes: *Redding, Walter* / Begin the beguine: *Kortlander, Max* / Just one of those things: *Cook, J. Lawrence* / In the still of the night: *Watson, Dick* / It's de-lovely: *Cook, J. Lawrence* / Rosalie: *Cook, J. Lawrence* / My heart belongs to Daddy: *Cook, J. Lawrence* / Wunderbar: *Baxter, Ted* / I love Paris: *Cook, J. Lawrence* / C'est magnifique: *Scott, Harold*
BCD 143 / Jun '97 / Biograph

☐ COLE PORTER ALBUM, THE (Moonlight Serenaders)
Who wants to be a millionaire / Anything goes / It's de lovely / Lets' do it lets fall in love / Love for sale / All of you / I love Paris / Everytime we say goodbye / Begin the beguine / I got you under my skin / I get a kick out of you / What is this thing called love / I concentrate on you / Easy to love / Did you ever / Just one of those things / From this moment on
307772 / Aug '97 / Hallmark

☐ COLE PORTER COLLECTION, A
JCD 632 / Jan '92 / Jass

☐ COLE PORTER SONGBOOK, THE
I've got you under my skin: *Sinatra, Frank* / I get a kick out of you: *Merman, Ethel* / Anything goes: *Bennett, Tony* / You'd be so nice to come home to: *Crosby, Bing* / My heart belongs to daddy: *Fitzgerald, Ella* / Let's do it: *Holiday, Billie* / You do something to me: *Sinatra, Frank* / True love: *Cole, Nat 'King'* / Just one of those things: *Sinatra, Frank* / You do something to me: *Dietrich, Marlene* / Miss Otis regrets: *Mills Brothers* / Love of my life: *Garland, Judy* / Rosalie: *Eddy, Nelson* / At long last love: *Sinatra, Frank* / How could we be wrong: *Bowlly, Al* / I'm a gigolo: *Porter, Cole* / They all fall in love: *Hylton, Jack Orchestra* / Love for sale: *Holman, Libby* / All through the night: *Ambrose & His Orchestra* / Don't fence me in: *Laine, Frankie* / You'd be so easy to love: *Damone, Vic* / I love you: *Crosby, Bing* / Night

and day: *Holiday, Billie* / Begin the beguine: *Sinatra, Frank* / At long last love: *Horne, Lena* / You're the top: *Merman, Ethel* / Thank you so much Mrs. Lowsborough goodbye: *Porter, Cole* / Blow Gabriel blow: *Gonella, Nat* / Most gentlemen don't like love: *Hylton, Jack Orchestra* / Banjo: *Hylton, Jack Orchestra* / Who knows: *Ternent, Billy* / Goodbye little dream goodbye: *Hylton, Jack Orchestra* / In the still of the night: *Silvester, Victor* / I've got my eyes on you: *Geraldo & His Orchestra* / Swingin' the jinx away: *Gonella, Nat* / It's bad for me: *Noble, Ray & His Orchestra & Al Bowlly* / It's d'lovely: *Gibbons, Carroll* / I'm in love again: *Hylton, Jack Orchestra* / Experiment: *Noble, Ray & His Orchestra & Al Bowlly* / Hey good lookin': *Geraldo & His Orchestra*

PC 622 / 1 Jun '98 / Start

☐ **GEORGE FEYER PLAYS COLE PORTER (Feyer, George)**

Feyer, George *con*

Anything goes / Leave it to me / Miss Otis regrets / Jubilee / Red hot and blue / Fifty million Frenchman / Gay divorce / Rosalie / Born to dance / New Yorkers / Can can / Let's face it / Don't fence me in / Broadway medley / Mexican hayride / Kiss me Kate / Where oh where / Seven lively arts / Silk stockings / High society / From this moment on

08601471 / Jun '91 / Vanguard Classics

☐ **KIRI SINGS PORTER (Te Kanawa, Dame Kiri & New World Philharmonic Orchestra)**

Matz, Peter *con*

CDC 5550502 / Apr '93 / EMI Classics

☐ **LOVE FOR SALE (Moonlight Serenaders)**

PWKM 4060 / Feb '96 / Carlton

☐ **MUSICAL TOAST, A (Porter, Cole)**

VSD 25826 / 8 Dec '97 / Varese Sarabande

☐ **NIGHT AND DAY (Sings Cole Porter) (Hampson, Thomas & Ambrosian Chorus/London Symphony Orchestra)**

McGlinn, John *con*

CDC 7542032 / Apr '93 / EMI Classics

☐ **OVERTURES (London Sinfonietta)**

McGlinn, John *con*

CDC 7543002 / Apr '93 / EMI Classics

☐ **PLAYS THE COLE PORTER SONGBOOK, THE (Peterson, Oscar Trio)**

8219872 / Jul '97 / Verve

☐ **SINGS THE COLE PORTER SONGBOOK (Wilson, Julie)**

Most gentlemen don't like love / My heart belongs to Daddy / Easy to love / All of you / You'd be so nice to come home to / Experiment / Dream dancing / Queen of Terre Haute / You've got that thing

DRG 5208 / Jan '95 / DRG

☐ **SONG IS...COLE PORTER, THE**

All through the night: *Ambrose & His Orchestra* / Lady Fair: *Anything Goes Foursome* / Night and day: *Astaire, Fred* / I'm in love again: *Bernie, Ben* / How could we be wrong: *Bowlly, Al* / Miss Otis regrets: *Byng, Douglas* / Let's do it: *Crosby, Bing* / Just one of those things: *Himber, Richard* / Love for sale: *Holman, Libby* / They all fall in love: *Hylton, Jack* / Experiment: *Lawrence, Gertrude* / I get a kick out of you: *Merman, Ethel* / Anything goes: *Porter, Cole* / Be like the bluebird: *Porter, Cole* / I'm a gigolo: *Porter, Cole* / Thank you so much Mrs. Lowsborough-Goodby: *Porter, Cole* / You're the top: *Porter, Cole* / What is this thing called love: *Reisman, Leo*

CDAJA 5044 / Oct '95 / Living Era

☐ **SONGBOOK**

Too darn hot: *Torme, Mel* / Easy to love: *Parker, Charlie* / It's delovely: *O'Day, Anita* / I've got you under my skin: *Evans, Bill & Jim Hall* / You'd be so nice to come home to: *Eckstine, Billy & Helen Merrill* / What is this thing called love: *Brown, Clifford & Max Roach* / Love for sale: *Holiday, Billie* / Begin the beguine: *Tatum, Art* / You're the top: *Armstrong, Louis* / Get out of town: *Kirk, Roland* / Just one of those things: *Fitzgerald, Ella* / I get a kick out of you: *Carter, Benny* / All of you: *Vaughan, Sarah* / Rosalie: *Garner, Erroll* / Let's do it: *Washington, Dinah* / Night and day: *Getz, Stan & Bill Evans*

5526452 / Mar '97 / Spectrum

☐ **SONGS OF COLE PORTER, THE**

MCCD 175 / Sep '94 / MCI Music

☐ **SPOTLIGHT ON COLE PORTER**

I love Paris / What is this thing called love / Begin the beguine / Can can / My heart belongs to daddy / Night and day / So in love / C'est magnifique / From this moment on / It's alright with me / Wunderbar / True love

HADCD 136 / Feb '94 / Javelin

☐ **YOU'RE THE TOPS (The Songs Of Cole Porter)**

Begin the beguine: *Shaw, Artie Orchestra* / My heart belongs to Daddy: *Humes, Helen* / Let's do it: *Crosby, Bing* / In the still of the night: *Reinhardt, Django* / Love for sale: *Holman, Libby* / What is this thing called love: *Johnson, James P.* / Experiment: *Bowlly, Al* / Easy to love: *Holiday, Billie* / I get a kick out of you: *BBC Dance Orchestra* / Miss Otis regrets: *Mills Brothers* / Night and day: *Dorsey, Tommy Orchestra* / Anything goes: *Stone, Lew & His Band* / Vous faites partie de moi: *Baker, Josephine* / Soloman: *Welch, Elizabeth* / Physician: *Lawrence, Gertrude* / Just one of those things: *Himber, Richard* / I'm a gigolo: *Porter, Cole* / All through the night: *Ambrose & His Orchestra* / It's D'Lovely: *Day, Frances* / You're the top: *Aubert, Jeanne & Jack Whiting* / Night and day: *Astaire, Fred*

AVC 518 / Apr '95 / Avid

☐ **YOU'RE THE TOPS (Music & Songs Of Cole Porter)**

CDHD 181 / Mar '92 / Happy Days

☐ **YOU'RE THE TOPS**

VN 180 / Mar '96 / Viper's Nest

Post, Mike

☐ **INVENTIONS FROM THE BLUE LINE (Post, Mike)**

NYPD Blue / One five open for business / Blue line / Rough wolf / Song for Rudy / Has the heart of a lion / Law and order / Silk stockings / Theme from Renegade / Cop files

AGCD 450 / May '94 / American Gramophone

Raben, Peer

☐ **MUSIC FROM FASSBINDER FILMS, THE**

Berlin Alexanderplatz / Wedding Of Maria Braun / Mother Kuster's Trip To Heaven / Niklashauser Journey / Stationmaster's Wife / Fox And His Friends / Despair / Whity / I Only Want You To Love Me / Third Generation / Satan's Brew / Chinese Roulette / Fear Eats The Soul / Merchant Of Four Seasons / Gods Of The Plague / Querelle / Lili Marleen / Lola / In A Year With 13 Moons / Schatten Der Engel

74321450582 / Mar '97 / Milan

Rachmaninoff, Sergey

☐ **RACHMANINOFF GOES TO THE CINEMA (Famous Works As Featured In Films) (Graffman, Gary & Andre Watts/Seiji Ozawa/Leonard Bernstein/N)**

SFK 63032 / Apr '97 / Sony Classical

Rice, Tim

☐ **I KNOW THEM SO WELL (The Best Of Tim Rice)**

Golden boy: *Mercury, Freddie & Montserrat Caballe* / Oh what a circus: *Essex, David* / I know him so well: *Paige, Elaine & Barbara Dickson* / Don't cry for me Argentina: *Covington, Julie* / Everything's alright: *Elliman, Yvonne & Ian Gillan* / I don't know how to love him: *Elliman, Yvonne* / Ziggy: *Dion, Celine* / All time high: *Coolidge, Rita* / World is stone: *Lauper, Cyndi* / One night in Bangkok: *Head, Murray* / Another suitcase in another hall: *Dickson, Barbara* / Any dream will do: *Donovan, Jason* / Second time: *Paige, Elaine* / Least of my troubles: *Nicholas, Paul* / Close every door: *Schofield, Philip* / Song of the king: *Daltrey, Dave* / Winter's tale: *Essex, David* / Legal boys: *John, Elton* / Only the very best: *Kingsberry, Peter* / Superstar: *Head, Murray* / Whole new world: *Bryson, Peabo*

5166502 / Mar '94 / PolyGram TV

☐ **TIM RICE COLLECTION, THE**

I know him so well: *Moore, Claire & Gemma Craven* / Can you feel the love tonight: *Skellern, Peter* / Circle of life: *Wayne, Carl* / One night in Bangkok: *Wayne, Carl* / Anthem / Whole new world: *Lawrence, Stephanie & Monroe Kent III* / Winter's tale: *Skellern, Peter* / Another suitcase in another hall: *Lawrence, Stephanie* / Close every door: *Willetts, Dave* / Everything's alright: *Hendley, Fiona & Paul Jones* / Gethsemane: *Willetts, Dave* / I don't know how to love him: *Moore, Claire* / Any dream will od: *Conrad, Jess* / Don't cry for me Argentina: *Webb, Marti* / I'd be surprisingly good for you: *Webb, Marti & Carl Wayne* / Buenos Aires: *Webb, Marti* / Rainbow high: *Webb, Marti* / On this night of a thousand stars: *Wayne, Carl* / One more angel in heaven: *Conrad, Jess* / Superstar: *Wayne, Carl* / Oh what a circus: *Conrad, Jess* / Any dream will do: *Conrad, Jess*

3036000322 / Apr '96 / Carlton

Rodgers & Hammerstein

☐ **PLATINUM COLLECTION, THE**

Getting to know you / I whistle a happy tune / My lord and master / Shall we dance / Something wonderful / We kiss in a shadow / I have dreamed / Hello young lovers / All or nothing / I can't say no / Many a new day / Oklahoma / Oh what a beautiful morning / Cockeyed optimist / Happy talk / I'm gonna wash that man right out of my hair / I'm in love with a wonderful guy / Some enchanted evening / This nearly was mine / Bloody Mary / Dites-moi / Honey bun / Younger than springtime / Bali ha'i / Soliloquy / June is busting out all over / When the children are asleep / What's the use of wond'rin' / When I marry Mr. Snow / You'll never walk alone / Carousel waltz / My favourite things / Climb ev'ry mountain / Do-re-mi / Edelweiss / Sound of music / So far / I enjoy being a girl / It might as well be spring / It's a grand night for singing

PC 626 / 29 Jun '98 / Start

☐ **RODGERS AND HAMMERSTEIN SONGBOOK, THE**

SK 53331 / Dec '93 / Sony Broadway

☐ **SOMETHING WONDERFUL (The Songs Of Rodgers & Hammerstein) (Terfel, Bryn & Chorus Of Opera North/English Northern Philharmonia)**

Daniel, Paul *con*

Fellow needs a girl / What a lovely day for a wedding / Come home / So far / No other love / Surrey with the fringe on top / Oh what a beautiful morning / If I loved you / You'll never walk alone / Soliloquy / June is bustin' out all over / Some enchanted evening / This nearly was mine / Younger than Springtime / Bali ha'i / There is nothing like a dame / It might as well be Spring / Edelweiss / I have dreamed / Something wonderful

4491632 / Oct '96 / Deutsche Grammophon

☐ **SPOTLIGHT ON RODGERS AND HAMMERSTEIN**

Hello young lovers / Oh what a beautiful morning / Carousel waltz / Climb every mountain / It might as well be spring / Oklahoma / If I loved you / Bali Ha'i / Shall we dance / You'll never walk alone / Sound of music

HADCD 135 / Feb '94 / Javelin

☐ **TIMELESS SONGS OF RODGERS & HAMMERSTEIN, THE**

Climb every mountain: *Dickinson, Muriel* / Getting to know you: *Masterson, Valerie & Chorus* / Some enchanted evening: *Allen, Thomas* / Surrey with the fringe on top: *Diedrich, John & Madge Ryan/ Rosamund Shelley* / Carousel waltz: *National Symphony Orchestra* / Sound of music: *Lindsay, Shona* / Hello young lovers: *Masterson, Valerie* / Younger than Springtime: *Bickley, Graham* / Do re mi: *Lindsay, Shona & Children* / You'll never walk alone: *Dickinson, Muriel*

SHOWCD 039 / Oct '96 / Showtime

Rodgers & Hart

☐ **DAWN UPSHAW SINGS RODGERS & HART (Upshaw, Dawn & Fred Hersch/ Audra McDonald/David Garrison/ Orchestra Of St. Luke's)**

Stern, Eric *con*

He was too good to me / Manhattan / You're nearer / Sing for your supper / Nobody's heart/Little girl blue / Thou swell / I didn't know what time it was / Twinkle in your eye / I could write a book / Why can't I / Ev'ry Sunday afternoon / Mountain greenery / Ship without a sail / Dancing on the ceiling / It never entered my mind

7559794062 / Jun '96 / Nonesuch

☐ **HITS OF RODGERS & HART, THE**

There's a small hotel / Little girl blue / My romance / On your toes / You took advantage of me / My heart stood still / This can't be love / My man is on the make / Atlantic blues / Where's that rainbow / Isn't it romantic / It never entered my mind / Where or when / Sing for your supper / Blue moon a tree in the park / With a song in my heart / Girl friend / Ten cents a dance / Lover / You are too beautiful / Lady is a tramp / Slaughter on 10th Avenue

PASTCD 9794 / Dec '92 / Flapper

☐ **MUSIC AND SONGS OF RODGERS & HART**

Manhattan / Here in my arms / Girlfriend / Mountain greenery / Blue room / Where's the rainbow / My heart stood still / Thou swell / You took advantage of me / With a song in my heart / Ten cents a dance / I've got five dollars / Isn't it romantic / Dancing on the ceiling / You are too beautiful / That's the rhythm of the day / Fly away to Iowa / That's love / Bad in every man / Blue moon / Soon / There's a small hotel / On your toes / Lady is a tramp / This can't be love / Sing for your supper / I didn't know what time it was / Bewitched bothered and bewildered

CDHD 223 / Jul '94 / Happy Days

☐ **MY FUNNY VALENTINE (Sings Rodgers & Hart) (Von Stade, Frederica & Ambrosian Chorus/London Symphony Orchestra)**

McGlinn, John *con*

CDC 7540712 / Apr '93 / EMI Classics

☐ **MY FUNNY VALENTINE (The Rodgers & Hart Songbook)**

5264482 / Mar '95 / PolyGram Jazz

☐ **RODGERS AND HART - WITH A SONG IN THEIR HEARTS**

With a song in my heart: *Hutch* / Ten cents a dance: *Etting, Ruth* / Manhattan: *Todd, Dick* / There's a small hotel: *Thornhill, Claude* / Ship without a sail: *Wiley, Lee* / Glad to be unhappy: *Wiley, Lee* / Maybe it's me: *Hylton, Jack* / Where or when: *Horne, Lena* / Give her a kiss: *Coslow, Sam* / Dancing on the ceiling: *Matthews, Jessie* / It's easy to remember: *Crosby, Bing* / On your toes: *Whiting, Jack* / Spring is here: *Sullivan, Maxine* / Blue moon: *Trumbauer, Frankie* / Lady is a tramp: *Dickson, Dorothy* / Where's that rainbow: *Dickson, Dorothy* / Thou swell: *Waller, Fats* / My heart stood still: *Baker, Edith* / I didn't know what time it was: *Shaw, Artie Orchestra* / Sing for your supper: *Basie, Count* / You took advantage of me: *Mole, Miff* / Blue room: *Dorsey Brothers* / C'est un nid Charmant: *Baker, Josephine* / This can't be love: *Langford, Frances*

AVC 538 / May '94 / Avid

☐ **SONG IS...RODGERS & HART, THE**

We'll be the same: *Arden, Victor* / Thou swell: *Beiderbecke, Bix* / Give her a kiss: *Coslow, Sam* / It's easy to remember: *Crosby, Bing* / Little things you do: *Hutch* / With a song in my heart: *Hutch* / Maybe it's me: *Hylton, Jack* / Little birdie told me so: *Kahn, Roger Wolfe* / Girlfriend: *Light Opera Company* / Mountain greenery: *Light Opera Company* / Step on the blues: *Light Opera Company* / What's the use of talking: *Light Opera Company* / Hello: *Light Opera Company* / Where's that rainbow: *Light Opera Company* / Tree in the park: *Light Opera Company* / Dancing on the ceiling: *Matthews, Jessie* / My heart stood still: *Matthews, Jessie* / Yours sincerely: *Reisman, Leo* / Who do you suppose: *Ross & Sargent* / Blue room: *Savoy Orpheans*

CDAJA 5041 / Oct '95 / Living Era

☐ **SONGBOOK**

I could write a book: *Washington, Dinah* / Lover: *Parker, Charlie* / It's got to be love: *Vaughan, Sarah* / With a song in my heart: *Carter, Benny* / Ten cents a dance: *O'Day, Anita* / Dancing on the ceiling: *Garner, Erroll* / Little girl blue: *Armstrong, Louis* / There's a small hotel: *Baker, Chet* / I wish I were in love again: *Fitzgerald, Ella* / Lady is tramp: *Peterson, Oscar Trio* / I didn't know what time it was: *Holiday, Billie* / You took advantage of me: *Tatum, Art* / Thou swell: *Williams, Joe & Count Basie* / It never entered my mind: *Hawkins, Coleman & Ben Webster* / Falling in love with love: *Merrill, Helen* / Ev'rything I've got: *Farlow, Tal* / Nobody's heart: *Torme, Mel*

5526372 / Mar '97 / Spectrum

☐ **STARS SALUTE RODGERS AND HART, THE (Tributes To The Songwriting Legends)**

This can't be love / Isn't it romantic: *Torme, Mel* / My funny valentine: *Vaughan, Sarah* / Lover: *Armstrong, Louis* / It never entered my mind: *Goodman, Benny* / Where or when: *Haymes, Dick* / Falling in love with love: *Horne, Lena* / Thou swell: *Beiderbecke, Bix* / Bewitched: *Goodman, Benny* / Little girl blue: *Simone, Nina* / I didn't know what time it was: *Greco, Buddy* / You took advantage of me: *Tatum, Art* / There's a small hotel: *Fitzgerald, Ella* / My romance: *Webster, Ben* / I could write a book: *McRae, Carmen* / Manhattan: *Torme, Mel* / Spring is here: *Sullivan, Maxine* / Lady is a tramp: *Greco, Buddy*

305852 / Oct '96 / Hallmark

Rodgers, Mary

☐ **HEY LOVE (The Songs Of Mary Rodgers)**

I'm looking for someone / Opening for a Princess / Shy / Oh mistress mine / Show me / Nebraska/ Normandy / Boy from... / Once I had a friend / At the same time / Hey love / Happily ever after / Love is on parade / Don't take my word for it / Medley / Double or nothing / Who knows/I know / Something known / Like love

VSD 5772 / Jun '97 / Varese Sarabande

Rodgers, Richard

☐ **MUSICAL THEATRE GREATS**

CDVIR 8321 / Aug '95 / TER

☐ **TRIBUTE TO RICHARD RODGERS, A**

CDDL 1287 / Jun '94 / EMI

Roger, Roger

☐ **GRANDS TRAVAUX (Roger, Roger)**

Stulen, Jan *con*

387082 / Jun '96 / Koch Screen

Romberg, Sigmund

☐ **GOLDEN DAYS (The Songs Of Romberg, Friml & Herbert) (Hadley, Jerry)**

Song of the vagabonds / Stout hearted men / I'm falling in love with someone / Streets of New York / Neapolitan love song / Desert song / One alone / Every day is ladies day with me / Donkey serenade / Softly as in a morning sunrise / Drining song / When you're away / I love to go swimmin' with wimmin / I might be your once in a while / Marianne / Serenade / Indian summer / Gypsy love song / Golden days

09026626812 / Nov '94 / RCA Victor

☐ **GREAT HITS FROM SIGMUND ROMBERG**

It / Who are we to say / Gaucho march / Waltz / Song of love / In old Granada / Farewell to dreams / Your smiles / Marienne / Softly as in a morning sunrise / My first love my last love / I bring a love song / When I grow to old to dream

PASTCD 9761 / Feb '92 / Flapper

Rosenman, Leonard

☐ **NONESUCH FILM MUSIC SERIES (London Sinfonietta)**

Adams, John *con*

7559794022 / Aug '97 / Nonesuch

Rota, Nino

☐ **SYMPHONIC FELLINI/ROTA, THE (Nino Rota's Music From The Films Of Frederico Fellini) (Czech Symphony Orchestra)**

Wadsworth, Derek *con*

White Sheikh / I vitelloni / La strada / Swindle (il bidone) / La notti di cabiria / La dolce vita / 8/1/2 / Juliet of the spirits / Toby Dammit - The clowns / Satyricon Roma / Amarcord / Il casanova (o venezia venaga) / Il casanova (pin penin) / Orchestra rehearsal

FILMCD 129 / Apr '93 / Silva Screen

Rozsa, Miklos

☐ **CLASSIC MIKLOS ROZSA FILM THEMES, THE**

CDTER 1135 / May '89 / TER

☐ **EPIC FILM MUSIC OF MIKLOS ROZSA, THE (Crouch End Festival Choir/ Prague City Philharmonic Orchestra)**

Alwyn, Kenneth *con*

Golden voyage of Sinbad / King of kings / El Cid / Sodom and Gomorrah / Quo vadis suite / Beau Brummell / Ben Hur / All the brothers were valiant / Madame Bovary

FILMCD 170 / Mar '96 / Silva Screen

☐ **FILM MUSIC**

PASTCD 7093 / Apr '96 / Flapper

☐ **FILM MUSIC FOR PIANO VOL.1 (Knight Without Armour)**

Robbins, D. *con*

Knight without armour / Lydia / Man in half moon street / Because of him / Strange love of Martha Ivers / Killers / Macomber affair / Time out of mind / Other love / Woman's vengeance / Kiss the blood off my hands / Fedora

MAF 7057D / Jan '94 / Intrada

☐ **FILM MUSIC FOR PIANO VOL.2**

MAF 7064D / Feb '96 / Intrada

Salter, Hans

☐ **MONSTER MUSIC OF HANS SALTER & FRANK SKINNER (Moscow Symphony Orchestra)**

Stromberg, William T. *con*

Son of Frankenstein / Wolf man / Invisible man returns / Universal Picture fanfare

8223747 / Mar '96 / Marco Polo

Schmidt, Irmin

☐ SOUNDTRACKS 1978-1993 (Schmidt, Irmin)
SPOONCD 32/33/34 / Oct '94 / The Fine Line

Schnittke, Alfred

☐ ALFRED SCHNITTKE: FILM MUSIC (USSR Cinema Symphony Orchestra)
Khachaturian, E. *con*
Story of an unknown actor / Sport sport sport / Agony / Music for an imaginary play
OCD 606 / Aug '94 / Olympia

Scott, John

☐ JOHN SCOTT CONDUCTS HIS OWN FAVOURITE FILM SCORES (Royal Philharmonic Orchestra/Berlin Radio Concert Orchestra)
Scott, John *con*
Final countdown / Shooting party / North Dallas forty / England made me / People that time time forgot / Cousteau's Amazon / Outback / Greystoke / Antony and Cleopatra
JSCD 111 / Jan '93 / JOS

Serra, Eric

☐ BEST OF ERIC SERRA, THE
Big Blue overture / La raya / Let them try / My lady blue / Alcool / Ruines (part 2) / Masquerade / It's only mystery / Procession in the Shakuashi temple / Edge of madness / Rico's gang suicide / Free side / Dark side of time / Snake / Time to get your lovin' / Noon / Hey little angel / That's what keeps you alone / Experience of love
CDVIR 56 / Jan '97 / Virgin

Sharp, Elliot

☐ FIGURE GROUND (Four Complete Scores) (Sharp, Elliot)
TZA 7505 / Feb '97 / Tzadik

Shore, Howard

☐ DEAD RINGERS (Symphonic Suites From The Films Of David Cronenberg) (Shore, Howard)
Shore, Howard *con*
Scanners / Brood / Dead ringers: *London Philharmonic Orchestra*
FILMCD 115 / Jul '92 / Silva Screen

Shostakovich, Dmitry

☐ MOVIE MADNESS (Katchur, Swetlana & Jelena Zaremba/Wladimir Kazatchouk/Rundfunk Sinfonie/Radio Symphonie Orchester)
Jurowski, Michail & James Judd/Leonid Grin *con*
Prelude / Fair / In the garden / Waltz / Song of Cordelia / Ball at the castle / Prologue / Waltz / Galop / Tempo di Marcia / Introduction / Galop / In the garden / Liberated Dresden / Romance / Storming of the Seelov Heights
10822 / Sep '97 / Capriccio

Simonetti, Claudio

☐ MYSTERY, MAGIC & MADNESS (Simonetti Project)
Profondo rosso / Tenebre / Phenomena / Suspiria / Opera / Crows / I'll take the night / Searching / Albinoni in rock / Carmina burana / Days of confusion / Demon
PCOM 1137 / Aug '94 / President

☐ ORIGINAL SOUNDTRACKS VOL.1 1975-1989 (Rare Tracks/Out-Takes) (Goblin)
DRGCD 32904 / Jun '95 / DRG

☐ ORIGINAL SOUNDTRACKS VOL.2 1975-1980 (Goblin)
Amo non amo / Night of the zombies / Zombi / Il fantastico viaggo del bagarozzo mark / Vampire / Cherry five / Squadra anti gangster / Phenomena / Il risveglio del serpente / Shock
DRGCD 32923 / 26 May '98 / DRG

Slusser, David

☐ DELIGHT AT THE END OF THE TUNNEL (Slusser, David)
TZA 7024 / Jul '97 / Tzadik

Sondheim, Stephen

☐ CELEBRATING SONDHEIM
Merrily we roll along / Me and my town / Sunday in the park with George / Joanna / You could drive a person crazy / Being alive / Comedy tonight / Not while I'm around / Everybody loves Louis / In Buddy's eyes / Franklin Shepherd inc / I remember / Too many mornings / Buddy's blues / Move on / Our time / Old friends
WMEV 00182 / 17 Aug '98 / BBC Audio

☐ MUSICAL THEATRE GREATS
CDVIR 8322 / Aug '95 / TER

☐ SINGS THE STEPHEN SONDHEIM SONGBOOK (Wilson, Julie)
Can that boy foxtrot / Good thing going / Not a day goes by / Love I hear / I do like you / Not while I'm around / I never do anything twice / With so little to be sure of / Too many mornings / Beautiful girls
DRG 5206 / Jan '95 / DRG

☐ SONDHEIM (A Celebration At Carnegie Hall)
09026614842 / '93 / RCA Victor

☐ SONDHEIM (A Celebration At Carnegie Hall - Highlights)
09026615162 / '93 / RCA Victor

☐ SONDHEIM - A CELEBRATION (McKenzie, Julia & David Kernan/ Millicent Martin)
Old friends / Comedy tonight / Back in business / Losing my mind / In Buddy's eyes / Not while I'm around / By the sea / It takes two / Could I leave you / Buddy's blues / Send in the clowns / Liaisons / Ladies who lunch / Broadway baby / Uptown downtown / Being alive / Side by side by side
3036200382 / Jun '97 / Carlton

☐ SONDHEIM - A CELEBRATION
VSD 25820 / 8 Dec '97 / Varese Sarabande

☐ SONDHEIM AT THE MOVIES
VSD 5805 / 1 Dec '97 / Varese Sarabande

☐ SONDHEIM SONGBOOK, THE (Broadway Casts)
SK 48201 / Feb '93 / Sony Broadway

☐ STEPHEN SONDHEIM SONGBOOK, THE (Turner, Geraldine)
Like it was / Old friends / Losing my mind / Not while I'm around / Could I leave you / With so much to be sure of / Miller's son / Buddy's blues / I remember / Parade in town / There won't be trumpets / Being alive / Anyone can whistle / Another hundred people / Goodbye for now
SILVAD 3011 / '95 / Silva Treasury

☐ UNSUNG SONDHEIM
Saturday Night / Love's a bond: *Willison, Walter* / All for you: *Gaines, Davis* / In the movies: *Cooper, Marilyn* / What can you lose: *Kuhn, Judy* / Invitation to a march / That old piano roll: *Groener, Harry & Lynette Perry* / They asked me why I believed in you: *Luker, Rebecca* / No Mary Ann: *Grace, Jason* / Truly contest: *Kaye, Judy* / Water under the bridge: *Gravitte, Debbie Shapiro* / Enclave / There's always a woman: *Ballard, Kaye & Sally Mayes* / Two of you: *Moore, Christa* / Multitudes of Amys: *Rupert, Michael* / Goodbye for now: *Callaway, Liz*
VSD 5433 / Sep '93 / Varese Sarabande

Stein, Ronald

☐ NOT OF THIS EARTH (The Film Music Of Ronald Stein)
Attack of the 50 foot woman / Attack of the crab monsters / Spider baby / Not of this earth
VSD 5634 / Oct '95 / Varese Sarabande

Steiner, Max

☐ FLAME AND THE ARROW, THE (The Classic Film Music Of Max Steiner) (City Of Prague Philharmonic Orchestra)
Alwyn, Kenneth *con*
Spencer's Mountain / Dark At The Top Of The Stairs / Mildred Pierce / Ice Palace / Life With Father / Now Voyager / FBI Story / Sergeant York / Hanging Tree / Parrish / Johnny Belinda / Flame And The Arrow
SFC 1502 / May '98 / Silva Screen

☐ GONE WITH THE WIND (The Classic Max Steiner) (Westminster Philharmonic Orchestra)
Alwyn, Kenneth *con*
Adventures of Mark Twain / Distant Trumpet / Casablanca / Summer Place / Treasure of the Sierra Madre / Helen of Troy / Caine Mutiny / Gone With the Wind
FILMCD 144 / Mar '94 / Silva Screen

☐ NOW VOYAGER (Classic Film Scores Of Max Steiner) (National Philharmonic Orchestra)
Gerhardt, Charles *con*
Now Voyager / King Kong / Saratoga Trunk / Charge of the Light Brigade / Four Wives / Big Sleep / Johnny Belinda / Since You Went Away / Informer / Fountainhead
GD 80136 / Oct '90 / RCA Victor

Styne, Jule

☐ CELEBRATES THE MUSIC OF JULE STYNE (Tompkins, Ross)
PCD 7103 / Nov '95 / Progressive

☐ CELEBRATING JULE STYNE
Overture / Let me entertain you / I'm the greatest star / Some people / You are woman I am man / Small world / Cornet man / Guess I'll hang my tears out / Just in time / Everything's coming up roses / Gypsy overture / All I need is the girl / If you hadn't but you did / Red shoes ballet / Never never land / People / Rose's turn / Together
WMEV 00192 / 17 Aug '98 / BBC Audio

☐ OVERTURES VOL.1 (Everything's Coming Up Roses) (National Symphony Orchestra)
Everly, Jack *con*
CDVIR 8318 / May '94 / TER

☐ OVERTURES VOL.2 (National Symphony Orchestra)
Everly, Jack *con*
CDVIR 8319 / May '94 / TER

Takemitsu, Toru

☐ NONESUCH FILM MUSIC SERIES
7559794042 / Aug '97 / Nonesuch

Tangerine Dream

☐ DREAM MUSIC VOL.1 (The Movie Music Of Tangerine Dream) (Tangerine Dream)
Park Is Mine / Deadly Care / Dead Solid Perfect
FILMCD 125 / Feb '93 / Silva Screen

☐ DREAM MUSIC VOL.2 (Tangerine Dream)
FILMCD 166 / Nov '95 / Silva Screen

Theodorakis, Mikis

☐ GOLD
MMB 10674 / 12 May '98 / Musurgia Graeca

☐ LAS MEJORES BANDAS SONORAS ORIGINALES
32544 / 14 Apr '98 / Divusca

☐ MEJORES BANDAS SONORAS ORIGINALES VOL.1
32545 / 14 Apr '98 / Divusca

☐ MEJORES BANDAS SONORAS ORIGINALES VOL.2
32546 / 14 Apr '98 / Divusca

☐ MEJORES BANDAS SONORAS ORIGINALES VOL.3
32547 / 14 Apr '98 / Divusca

☐ MEJORES BANDAS SONORAS ORIGINALES VOL.4
32548 / 14 Apr '98 / Divusca

☐ MEJORES BANDAS SONORAS ORIGINALES VOL.5
32549 / 14 Apr '98 / Divusca

☐ MIKIS THEODORAKIS ON THE SCREEN (4 Complete Soundtracks - Z/ Serpico/Phaedra/State Of Siege)
Z / Serpico / Phaedra / State of siege
DRGCD 32901 / Sep '93 / DRG

Thomas, Peter

☐ BEST OF THE JERRY COTTON FILMS, THE
EFA 043662 / 20 Oct '97 / Crippled Dick Hot Wax

Tiomkin, Dimitri

☐ GREAT EPIC FILM SCORES (Music From The Samuel Bronston Productions)
Tiomkin, Dimitri/Miklos Rozsa *con*
Overture / Main title / Thirteen knights / Pride and sorrow / Scene d'amour / El Cid march / Falcon and the dove / Overture / Prelude / Murder of the German ambassador / Orphan and the Major / Attack on the French legation / Intermezzo: So little time / Fanfares and flourishes / Prelude / Livius' arrival / Old acqaintances / Decoy patrol / Battle in the forest / Reinforcements / Intermezzo: Livius and Lucilla / New God / John Wayne march / Main title 'Circus World' / Buffalo gal / Toni and Giovanna / In old Vienna / Exit music 'Circus World'
CNS 5006 / Nov '92 / Cloud Nine

☐ ORIGINAL FILM SCORES (Berlin Radio Symphony Orchestra)
Foster, Lawrence *con*
Cyrnao de Bergerac / High noon / Alamo / 55 days at Peking
09026656582 / Nov '95 / RCA Victor

☐ TIOMKIN - FILM MUSIC (Royal College Of Music Orchestra)
Willcocks, D./D. King *con*
Fall of the Roman empire / President's country / Guns of Navarone / Wild is the wind / Rhapsody of steel
UKCD 2079 / May '96 / Unicorn-Kanchana

☐ WESTERN FILM WORLD OF DIMITRI TIOMKIN, THE (London Studio Symphony Orchestra)
Johnson, Laurie *con*
Giant / Red River / Duel in the Sun / High Noon / Night Passage / Rio Bravo
UKCD 2011 / Jan '89 / Unicorn-Kanchana

Trovajoli, Armando

☐ FILM MUSIC OF ARMANDO TROVAJOLI, THE
VCDS 7005 / May '95 / Varese Sarabande

Vangelis

☐ THEMES (Vangelis)
Bladerunner / Missing / L'Enfant / Chung kuo (the long march) / Hymn / Tao of love / Antarctica / Bladerunner love theme / Mutiny on the Bounty / Memories of green / La petite fille de la mer / Chariots of Fire / Five circles
8395182 / Jul '89 / Polydor

Vasconcelos, Nana

☐ FRAGMENTS: MODERN TRADITION (Vasconcelos, Nana)
TZA 7506 / Jul '97 / Tzadik

Vaughan Williams

☐ FILM MUSIC (RTE Concert Orchestra)
Penny, Andrew *con*
49th parallel / Story of a Flemish farm / Coastal command / England of Elizabeth
8223665 / Jan '95 / Marco Polo

Ventura, Lina

☐ FILM MUSIC OF LINA VENTURA, THE
3025992 / Nov '97 / Arcade

Walton, Sir William

☐ WALTON: FILM MUSIC VOL.1 (Academy Of St. Martin In The Fields)
Marriner, Neville *con*
Hamlet / As you like it
CHAN 8842 / Jun '90 / Chandos

☐ WALTON: FILM MUSIC VOL.2 (Academy Of St. Martin In The Fields)
Marriner, Neville *con*
Battle of Britain / Spitfire prelude and fugue / Escape me never / Three sisters / Wartime sketchbook
CHAN 8870 / Dec '90 / Chandos

☐ WALTON: FILM MUSIC VOL.3 (Westminster Cathedral Choir/ Academy Of St. Martin In The Fields)
Marriner, Neville *con*
Henry V / Rosa solis / Watkin's ale / Chants d'Auvergne
CHAN 8892 / Apr '91 / Chandos

☐ WALTON: FILM MUSIC VOL.4 (Academy Of St. Martin In The Fields)
Marriner, Neville *con*
Richard III / Macbeth / Major Barbara
CHAN 8841 / May '91 / Chandos

Warren, Harry

☐ LULLABY OF BROADWAY (The Music Of Harry Warren)
Pasadena / I found a million dollar baby / Lullaby of Broadway / Love is where you find it / You're my everything / I yi yi yi / You're getting to be a habit with me / September in the rain / Shadow waltz / Keep young and beautiful / Nagasaki / You must have been a beautiful baby / With plenty of money and you / Jeepers creepers / I only have eyes for you / I've got to sing a torch song / About a quarter to nine / Lulu's back in time / Man with the lollipop / Boulevard of broken dreams / I'll string along with you / She's a latin from Manhattan / By a waterfall / 42nd Street / Medley
PASTCD 9795 / Jul '93 / Flapper

☐ PLAY THE HARRY WARREN SONGBOOK (Sharon, Ralph Trio)
That's amore / You're getting to be a habit with me / September in the rain / This heart of mine / My heart tells me / You must have been a beautiful baby / Spring isn't everything / Serenade in blue / At last / More I see you / Shuffle off to Buffalo / You'll never know / Jeepers creepers / I only have eyes for you / Affair to remember / I've got a gal in Kalamazoo / Lullaby of broadway / Harry's minor lament
DRGCD 5245 / 27 Oct '97 / DRG

☐ SONG IS...HARRY WARREN, THE
Love is where you find it: *Andrews Sisters* / 42nd Street: *Boswell Sisters & Dorsey Brothers* / Shuffle off to Buffalo: *Boswell Sisters & Dorsey Brothers* / I'll string along with you: *Bowlly, Al & the Ray Noble Orchestra* / Shadow waltz: *Browne, Sam* / You're my everything: *Carlisle, Elsie* / You must have been a beautiful baby: *Crosby, Bing* / Young and healthy: *Crosby, Bing* / Ooh that kiss: *Day, Frances* / Keep young and beautiful: *Dennis, Denny & Roy Fox* / I only have eyes for you: *Duchin, Eddie* / You're getting to be a habit with me: *Four Musketeers* / You'll never know: *Haymes, Dick* / Nagasaki: *Henderson, Fletcher* / I've got to sing a torch song: *Hutch* / September in the rain: *Hutch* / Serenade in blue: *Langford, Frances* / I found a million dollar baby: *Langford, Frances* / At last: *Miller, Glenn* / Chattanooga choo choo: *Miller, Glenn* / Jeepers creepers: *Mills Brothers* / I yi yi yi yi (I like you very much): *Miranda, Carmen* / Lullaby of Broadway: *Roy, Harry & His Orchestra* / Lulu's back in town: *Roy, Harry & His Orchestra* / Would you like to take a walk: *Sanderson, Julia & Frank Crumit*
CDAJA 5139 / Apr '95 / Living Era

Waxman, Franz

☐ LEGENDS OF HOLLYWOOD VOL.1
VSD 5242 / Apr '90 / Varese Sarabande

☐ LEGENDS OF HOLLYWOOD VOL.3
VSD 5480 / Jun '94 / Varese Sarabande

WAXMAN, FRANZ

☐ LEGENDS OF HOLLYWOOD VOL.4 (Queensland Symphony Orchestra) Mills, R. con
Untamed / On Borrowed Time / My Geisha / Devil Doll / My Cousin Rachel / Story Of Ruth / Dark City / Christmas Carol
VSD 5713 / Nov '96 / Varese Sarabande

☐ PARADINE CASE, THE (Film Music Composed By Franz Waxman, Bernard Herrmann & Alex North) (Beuchner, David/New Zealand Symphony Orchestra)
Sedares, James con
CD 372252 / Aug '96 / Koch International

☐ SAYONARA (The Film Music Of Franz Waxman) (Berlin Radio Symphony Orchestra)
Bernstein, Elmer con
Taras bulba suite / Place in the sun scenario / Hemingway suite / Sayonara suite
09026626572 / Nov '95 / RCA Victor

Webb, Roy

☐ CURSE OF THE CAT PEOPLE, THE (The Film Music Of Roy Webb)
Out of the past / Crossfire / Bedlam / Sinbad the sailor / Dick Tracy / Ghost ship / Mighty Joe Young / Notorious / Locket / Cornered / Curse of the cat people
CNS 5008 / May '95 / Cloud Nine

Weill, Kurt

☐ BARBARA SONG (Arranged For Saxophone & String Quartet) (Thompson, Barbara & The Medici String Quartet)
Je te n'aime pas / Barbara song / Mack the Knife / Zuhalterballade / It never was you / Speak low / Surabaya / Johnny / September song / Bilbao song / Nanas lied / My ship
VC 5451672 / Nov '95 / Virgin Classics

☐ BERLIN AND AMERICAN THEATRE SONGS (Songs Of Kurt Weill) (Lenya, Lotte)
MK 42658 / Jan '89 / Masterworks

☐ FROM BERLIN TO BROADWAY VOL.1
GEMMCDS 9189 / Feb '96 / Pearl

☐ FROM BERLIN TO BROADWAY VOL.2
GEMMCDS 9294 / Sep '97 / Pearl

☐ KURT WEILL - A MUSICAL PORTRAIT (Wust, Stefanie)
AS 20102 / Jun '96 / Al Segno

☐ KURT WEILL EDITION - HIGHLIGHTS
Die silbersee / Aufstieg und fall der stadt mahogonny / Der kuhhandel / Down in the valley / Gisela may singt Kurt Weill / Der zar lasst sich photographieren / Der jasager / Kurt Weill. - historische originalaufnahmen / Derlindberghflug / Happy end
14854 / Feb '96 / Capriccio

☐ KURT WEILL ON BROADWAY (Hampson, Thomas & Jerry Hadley/ London Sinfonietta & Chorus)
McGlinn, John con
CDC 5555632 / Oct '96 / EMI Classics

☐ KURT WEILL ON BROADWAY
You do what you have to do / Rhyme for Angela / There'll be life / Love and laughter / This is the life / Here I'll stay / Moriate of Dr. Crippen / Westwind / Who am I / Bachelor song / Westpointer / Cowboy song
314162 / Jun '97 / Koch Schwann

☐ SEPTEMBER SONGS (The Music Of Kurt Weill)
Mack the knife: Cave, Nick / Soldier's wife: Harvey, P.J. / Alabama song: Johansen, David / Youkali tango: Stratas, Teresa / Lost in the stars: Costello, Elvis & The Brodsky Quartet / Pirate Jenny: Lenya, Lotte / Speak low: Haden, Charlie / O Heavenly salvation: Persuasions / Lonely house: Carter, Betty / Surabaya Johny: Stratas, Teresa / Don't be afraid: O'Hara, Mary Margaret / September song: Reed, Lou / Mack the knife: Brecht, Bertolt / What keep mankind alive: Burroughs, William
SK 63046 / 1 Sep '97 / Sony Classical

☐ SINGS THE KURT WEILL SONGBOOK (Wilson, Julie)
One touch of venus / That's him / September song / There's nowhere to go but up / Surabaya Johnny / Sing me not a ballad / Foolish heart / This is new / Speak low / Trouble man / Stay well / Jenny
DRG 5207 / Jan '95 / DRG

☐ STRATAS SINGS WEILL (Stratas, Teresa & Chamber Symphony)
Schwarz, Gerard con
75597913172 / Jan '95 / Nonesuch

☐ UNKNOWN KURT WEILL (Stratas, Teresa)
Woitach, Richard con
7559790192 / Jan '95 / Nonesuch

☐ UTE LEMPER SINGS KURT WEILL VOL.1 (Lemper, Ute & Berlin Radio Ensemble)
Mauceri, John/W. Meyer/K. Rautenberg con
4252042 / Mar '89 / Decca

☐ UTE LEMPER SINGS KURT WEILL VOL.2 (Lemper, Ute/J. Cohen/London Voices/Berlin RIAS Sinfonietta)
Mauceri, John con
Happy end / Marie Galante / Lady in the dark / Youkali
4364172 / Jul '93 / Decca

Wilden, Gert

☐ I TOLD YOU NOT TO CRY (Swinging Themes From Thrilling German Crime Films 1966-1972) (Wilden, Gert)
EFA 043802 / Jan '97 / Crippled Dick Hot Wax

Williams, John

☐ FILM WORKS
Jurassic park - end credits / Jurassic park - My friend the brachiosaurus / Always - follow me / Always - Dorinda solo flight / Earthquake / Jaws - out to sea / Jaws II - end title/cast / Eiger sanction / Midway - / Schindler's list / ET The extra terrestrial - Over the moon / ET The extra terrestrial - Flying / River / Far and away - County Galway June 1982 / Far and away - End credits
MCD 32877 / Jun '95 / MCA

☐ FILMWORKS (Williams, John)
UMD 80417 / 25 May '98 / Universal

☐ GREAT MUSIC OF JOHN WILLIAMS
873044 / Jan '95 / Milan

☐ SCHINDLER'S LIST (The Classic Film Music Of John Williams) (City Of Prague Philharmonic Orchestra)
Bateman, Paul con
FILMCD 160 / Apr '95 / Silva Screen

☐ SPIELBERG/WILLIAMS COLLABORATION, THE (John Williams Conducts His Classic Scores For The Films Of Steven Spielberg) (Boston Pops Orchestra)
Williams, John con
Always / ET / Sugarland express / Jaws / Empire of the sun / 1941 / Indiana Jones and the temple of doom / Indiana Jones and the last crusade
SK 45997 / Nov '91 / Sony Classical

☐ STAR TRACKS (Cincinnati Pops Orchestra)
Kunzel, Erich con
CD 80094 / May '85 / Telarc

☐ STAR WARS/CLOSE ENCOUNTERS (Classic Film Scores Of John Williams) (National Philharmonic Orchestra)
Gerhardt, Charles con
Star Wars / Close Encounters of the Third Kind
GD 82698 / Sep '91 / RCA Victor

☐ WILLIAMS ON WILLIAMS: CLASSIC SPIELBERG SCORES (Boston Pops Orchestra)
Williams, John con
Jurassic Park / Schindler's list / Hook / Jaws / Empire of the sun / Close encounters of the third kind / Raiders of the lost ark
SK 68419 / Feb '96 / Sony Classical

Young, Victor

☐ SHANE (A Tribute To Victor Young) (New Zealand Symphony Orchestra)
Kaufman, Richard con
Shane / For whom the bell tolls / Quiet man / Around the world in eighty days / Samson and Delilah
373652 / Nov '96 / Koch International